Waterlow's
Solicitors' & Barristers' Directory 2012

168th Edition

WATERLOW

W

Established 1844

Publisher
Paula Pusey

Editor
Keya Pereira

Assistant Editor
Jacqui Smith

Senior Display Sales Manager
Gino De Antonis

Senior Classified Sales Manager
Emma Regester

Sales Executives
Sheena Amin
Luke Roberts
Mike Taylor

Director of Publishing Systems
Bethan Cater

Head of Production
Jamie Beer

Production Team
Alex Wheelhouse
Oliver Davitt

Marketing
Katherine Stott
Robert Shearwood

Editorial and Advertising
Tel: 020 7490 0049
Fax: 020 7253 1308
DX: 122030 Finsbury 3

Customer Services Department
6-14 Underwood Street
London N1 7JQ

Solicitors' & Barristers' Directory 2012
ISBN 978-1-85783-179-5

a division of Waterlow Legal and Regulatory
19-23 Christopher Street
London EC2A 2BS

Tel: 020 7490 0049
Fax: 020 7253 1308
DX: 122030 Finsbury 3
E-mail: editorial@waterlow.com
http://www.waterlowlegal.com

PLEASE NOTE: DO NOT USE THE INFORMATION IN THIS DIRECTORY TO COMPILE MAILING LISTS AS YOU WILL BE LIABLE TO PROSECUTION.

INTRODUCTION

Welcome to the 2012 edition of the Waterlow's Solicitors' and Barristers' Directory – now in our 168th year!

The Directory

Contained in the Directory are details of over 12,000 Solicitors' firms, and 70,000 individual Solicitors, Barristers and Ilex qualified individuals. This information is presented in an easy to use format, allowing you to quickly and simply find the information you are looking for. The Directory also has sections covering a wide range of specialised services: Agency Commissions, Charities, Expert Witnesses, International Law Firms and also Legal Services. Details of Professional, Education and Regulatory bodies are also provided, along with a general reference section.

'Waterlow's Directory gives me - instantly - what it would take me hours to source even via the internet. Everything I need to know about local firms is there, in an easy to use format. I would never use any other source.'
Elizabeth A Hodder, Solicitor and Collaborative Lawyer, Gross & Co, Bury St Edmunds

The Websites

Our website **www.waterlowlegal.com,** which complements the Directory, continues to go from strength to strength. We also have a public facing version of the online directory at **www.search4solicitors.com** – Members of the public can use this to quickly and easily locate Solicitors firms in their area, with the particular expertise they require. Please visit our websites and let us know what you think!

We are constantly looking to the legal profession and attempt to reflect its developments within the Directory. If you would like to suggest any changes to the directory content, or notify us of any changes or developments in the legal profession, we would be very grateful to hear from you.

Waterlow would like to thank all the organisations whose contributions make the directory possible.

USER'S GUIDE

The directory is compiled from research, responses to questionnaires mailed to entrants twice a year and from information submitted by professional and regulatory bodies. The greatest detail is given throughout in the main "company" entries – be they Solicitors' firms, Barristers Chambers, companies or other institutions. Personal and corporate name entries, which occur in the later indices of the directory, all give the page number for the position of the main entry.

The majority of entries in the main body of the directory are free of charge regardless of their length. Logos preceding an entry, expanded entries and bold entries all lend greater prominence to a listing and are available for a charge. Facing the start of each new section there is a contents page preceded by a guide to various work categories. These same categories provide the headings for the "Firms Specialisation Index" and "Counsel's Chambers Specialisation Index".

CONTENTS

SOLICITORS

Lists firms across London alphabetically by the name of the firm.

The information may include:

- Indication of Principal office
- Full contact details including DX addresses
- Partner List
- Work categories – firms may list any number of applicable categories free of charge
- Provision of particular services – Agency, Advocacy etc.
- List of solicitors in attendance, showing Partners (or alternatively Members or Directors), Associates, Assistants and Consultants and giving details of qualifications and dates of admission.

Lists information for a range of non-legal organisations employing solicitors.

Provides the same information as for London firms but ordered alphabetically by town.

Lists all firms in Section 1 and Section 2 alphabetically by name of firm giving the location of the office, the page number where the main entry occurs in sections 1 and 2 and the telephone number of each office. Firms who have chosen to pay for greater prominence in the listings have their entries produced here in bold type.

England & Wales firms by Work Specialisation

In this section firms may choose to be placed under three headings free of charge. Additional entries under further headings are chargeable. Each entry gives the following information:

- Name of firm
- Town
- Telephone number
- Page number where main entry occurs.

Publicly Funded Legal Services lists, by type of franchise, firms in England and Wales who hold these. The data is updated from responses to the Directory & Diary mailings. The entries give:

- Firm name
- Telephone number
- Page number where the firm's main entry occurs.

Lists solicitors in private practice and in employment alphabetically by surname. Solicitors not falling into either of these categories are not listed, but basic details are kept on the database. To be certain of maintaining a listing in the directory solicitors changing their employment status should contact the editorial department. Solicitors may specify up to fifteen work categories free of charge. Each entry gives the following information:

- Name
- Work categories undertaken by the individual
- Firm/Company
- Town
- Telephone number
- Page number where the employer's main entry occurs.

This list presents firms alphabetically by town heading: Each entry may list:

- Firm name
- Address
- Telephone and Fax numbers
- DX address.

BARRISTERS

continued on page xi

ABBREVIATIONS

Asoc=	Associate	♦	Higher Rights of Audience, Civil	Ptr=	Partner	Mem=	Member
Ast=	Assistant	★	Higher Rights of Audience, Criminal	SPr=	Sole Practitioner	*	Member of Law Society
Con=	Consultant	●	Higher Rights of Audience, all	Sol=	Solicitor	‡	Principal Offices
Dx=	Document Exchange			†	Member of Notaries Society	§	Solicitors' Benevolent Association
Est=	Year Established						
NSP -	Non-Solicitor Partner						

Work categories for firms and solicitors

Main categories

A1 Agricultural law, holdings and property
A2 Animals, farming, forestry
A3 Arbitration and mediation
B1 Bankruptcy
B2 Fraud
B3 Accounting standards
C1 Commercial and company law
C2 Mergers and acquisitions
C3 Competition law
D1 Child care and wardship
D2 Adoption
E Commercial property
F1 Consumer law - agreements, credit, licensing, sale of goods
F2 Consumer protection - advertising, trade descriptions, trading standards, product liability
G Crime – general
H Crime – juvenile
I Computer law
J1 Employment law
J2 Health and safety at work
K1 Family law
K2 Family mediation
K3 Divorce and matrimonial
K4 Elderly
L Housing, landlord and tenant
M1 European Community law
M2 International law
M3 Air law
M4 Islamic law
N Litigation - accidents, injury compensation, personal injury
O Litigation - commercial
P Environmental liability
Q Litigation - general
R1 Planning, compulsory purchase, lands tribunal
R2 Property - finance, development
S1 Residential conveyancing
S2 Commercial conveyancing
T1 Taxation – business
T2 Taxation – personal
U1 Communications and telecommunications
U2 Internet and e-commerce
V Welfare benefits
W Wills, trusts and probate
X Education law
Za Admiralty
Zb Banking law
Zc Building law, building contracts
Zd Charity law
Ze Copyright, patents, trade marks and intellectual property
Zf Entertainment, artists and performers
Zg Human rights and civil liberties
Zh Housing association law
Zi Immigration and nationality
Zj Insurance law
Zk Libel, slander and defamation
Zl Liquor, betting and gaming licensing
Zm Mental health
Zn Mines, minerals, oil and gas
Zo Pensions, investments and financial services
Zp Race and sex discrimination
Zq Professional negligence
Zr Clinical negligence
Zs Rating law
Zt Road haulage licensing
Zu Local government
Zv Regulated by the FSA in the conduct of investment Business
Zw Sports Law
Zx Ecclesiastical law
Zy Food and drugs law
Zz Printing and publishing
ZZa Data Protection

The Above scheme provides the headings for the Firms Specialisation Index

Work categories for Chambers and Barristers

Main categories

1 Administrative Law, Constitutional Law and Public Law
2 Farming and Agriculture
3 Arbitration including International Trade
4 Aviation
5 Banking
6 Bankruptcy
7 Building
8 Chancery, General
9 Charities
10 Children
11 Commercial Law
12 Common Law, General
13 Intellectual Property
14 Court of Protection
15 Criminal Work - General
16 Defamation and Slander
17 Ecclesiastical Courts
18 Employment Law
19 European Community Law
20 Family Law
21 International Law
22 Housing and Social Welfare
23 Immigration
24 Insurance
25 Licensing
26 Local Government and Public Sector
27 Medical Law
28 Parliamentary Law
29 Partnerships and Business Arrangements
30 Personal Injury
31 Planning & Rating
32 Probate
33 Public International Law
34 Revenue
35 Shipping and Admiralty
36 Tribunals and Inquiries
37 Wills & Trusts
38 Insolvency
39 Food and Drugs Law
40 Professional Negligence
41 Arbitration
42 Military Law
43 Communications and Telecommunications
44 Competition Law
45 Information Technology
46 Environment
47 Consumer Law - Agreements, Credit, Licensing, Sale of Goods
48 Consumer Protection - Advertising, Trade Descriptions, Trading Standards, Product Liability
49 Alternative Dispute Resolution (ADR)
50 Entertainment, Artists and Performers
51 Human Rights and Civil Liberties
52 Media
53 Clinical Negligence
54 Mines and Minerals
55 Discrimination
56 Sports Law
57 Taxation – Business
58 Taxation – Personal
59 Tourism and Travel
60 Transport
61 Utilities - Electric, Gas, Water
62 Fraud
63 Mental Health
64 Islamic Law
65 Accountancy
66 Agency
67 Contract Law
68 Coroner
69 Corporate Finance
70 Criminal Work - Police & Prisons
71 Criminal Work - International
72 Criminal Work - Criminal Procedures
73 Data Protection
74 Construction
75 E-Commerce
76 Education
77 Elder Law & Elder care
78 Energy
79 Offshore
80 Evidence
81 Financial Services
82 Firearms
83 Gaming & Lotteries
84 Health & Safety at Work
85 Healthcare Law
86 Private Client
87 Internet Law
88 Landlord & Tenant
89 Litigation
91 Military Law & Courts Martial
92 Pensions
93 Property
94 Road Traffic Law
95 Terrorism
96 Mediation
97 Company Law

The above scheme provides the headings for the Counsel's Chambers Specialisation Index.

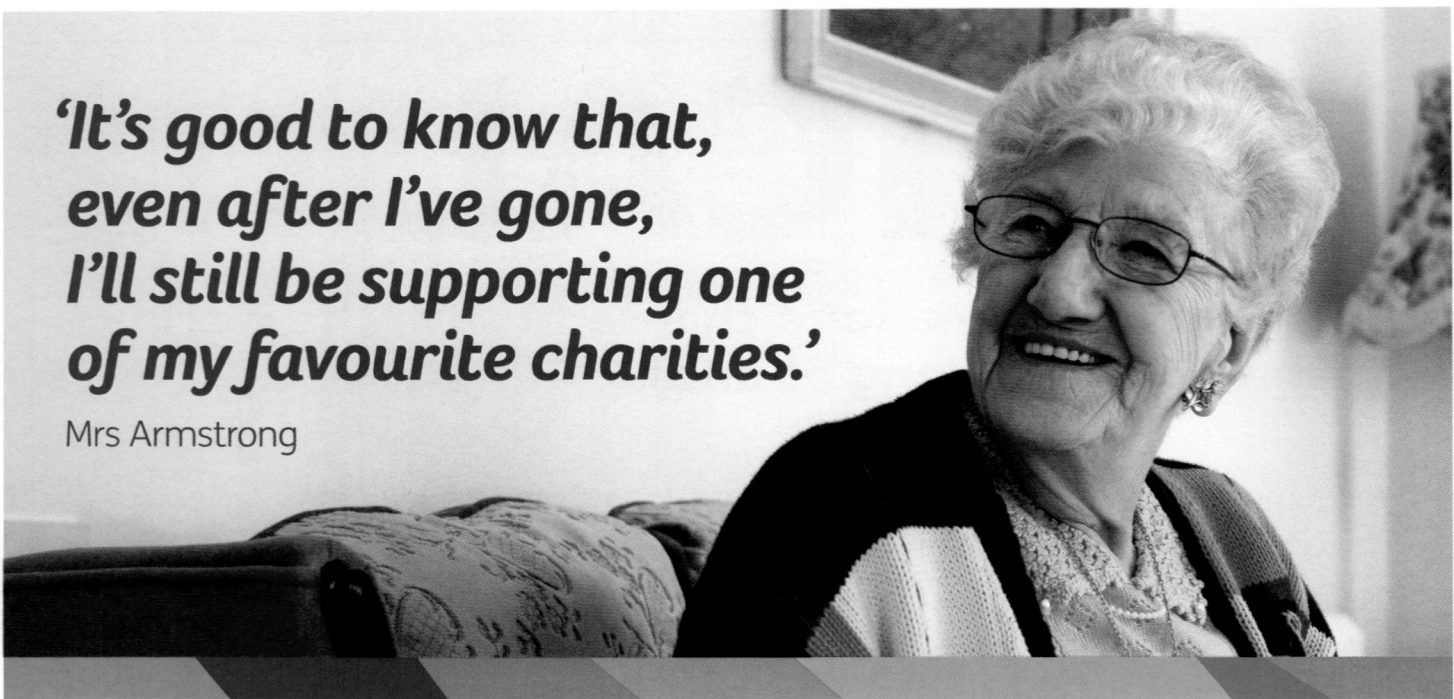

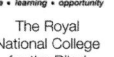

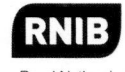

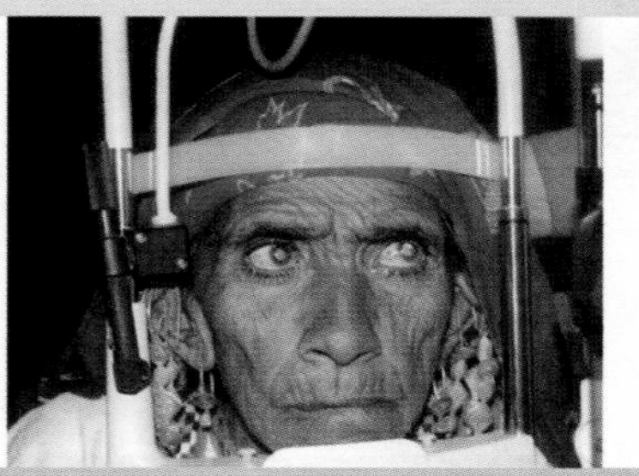

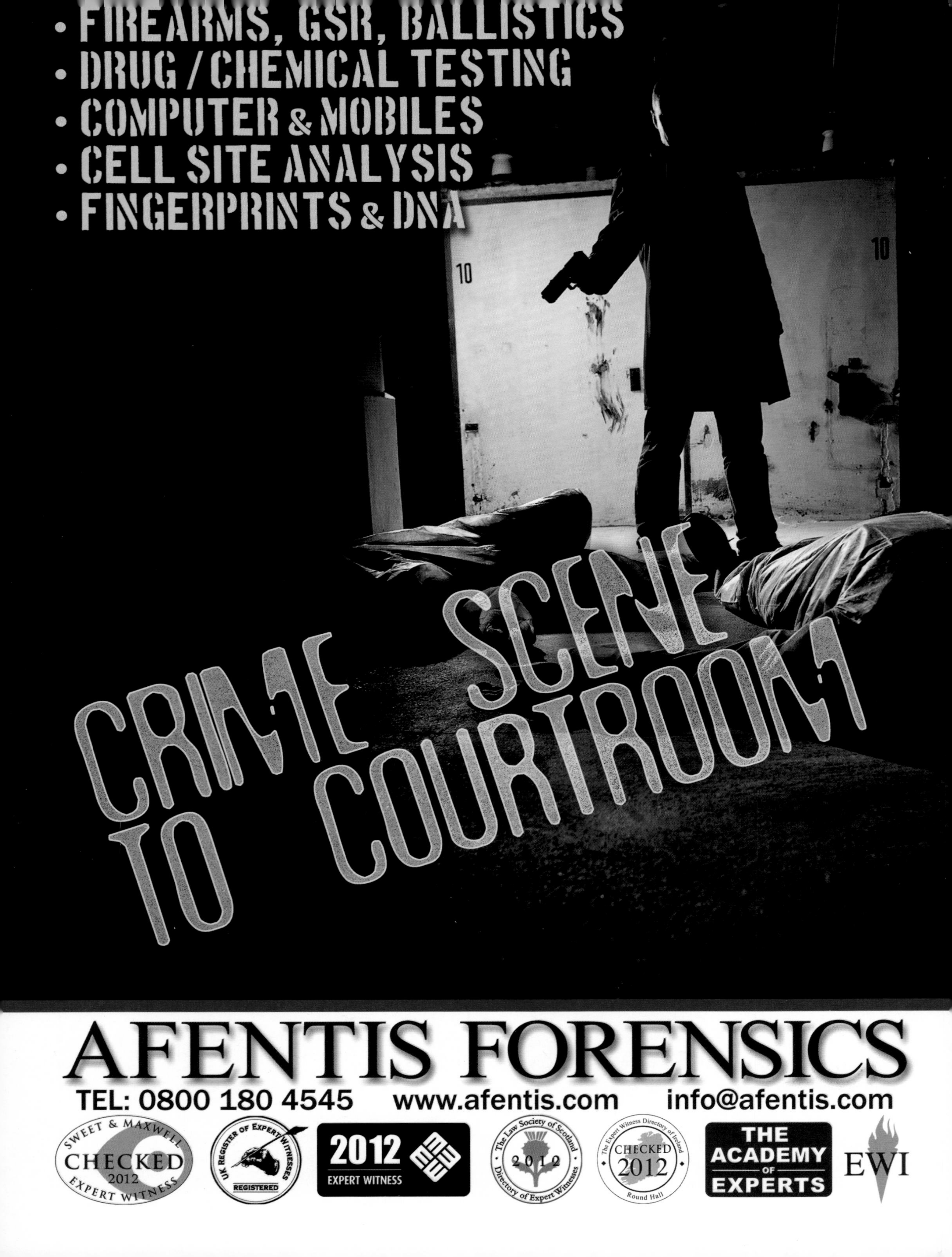

SWEET & MAXWELL
CHECKED
2012
EXPERT WITNESS

UK REGISTER OF EXPERT WITNESSES
REGISTERED

2012
EXPERT WITNESS

The Law Society of Scotland
2012
Directory of Expert Witnesses

The Expert Witness Directory of Ireland
CHECKED
2012
Round Hall

THE
ACADEMY
OF
EXPERTS

EWI

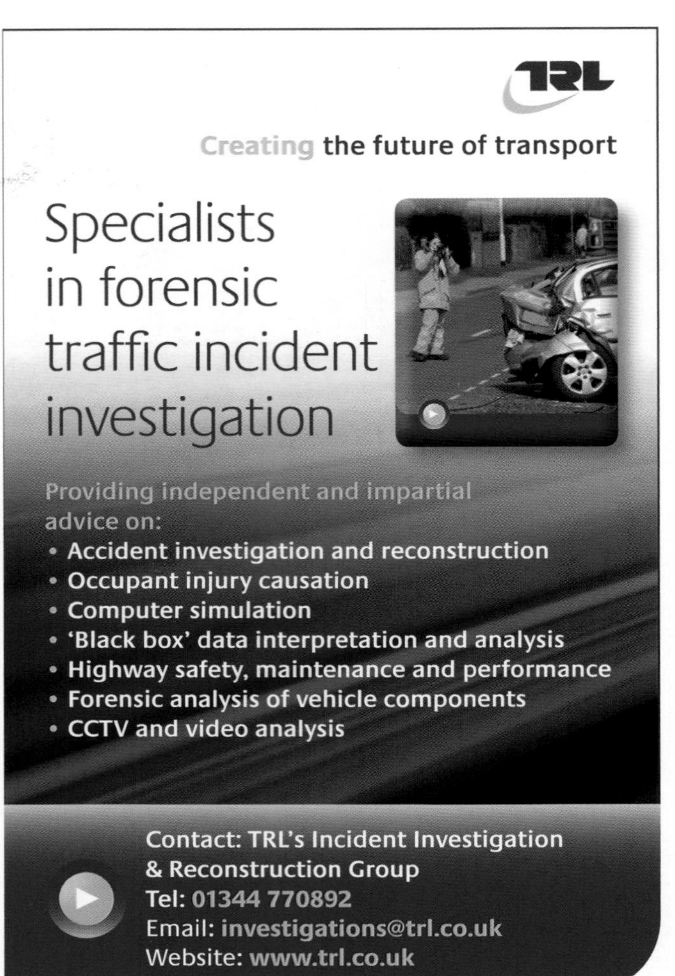

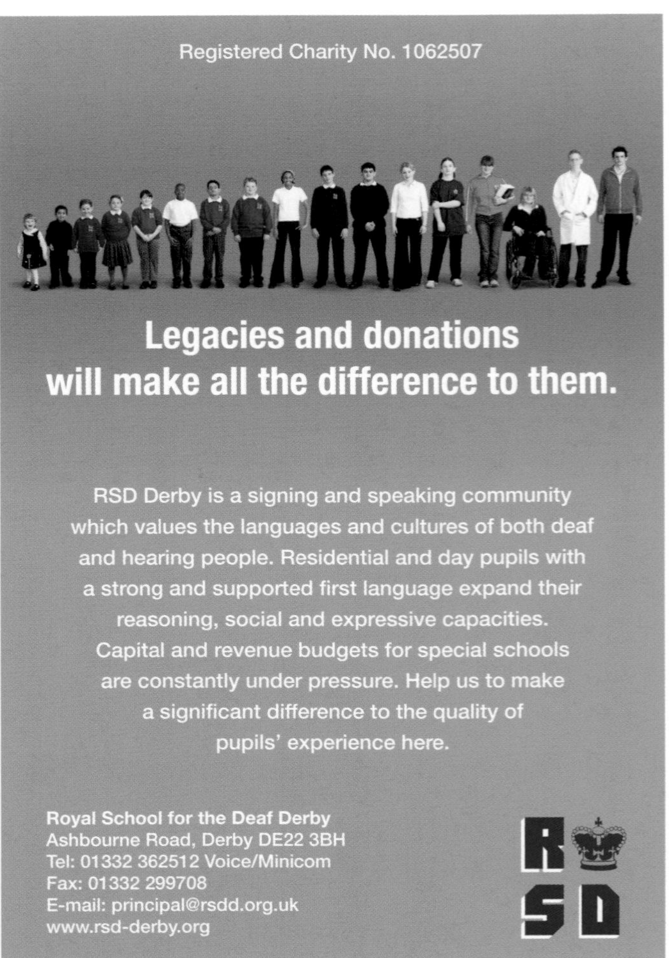

Stroke is the third biggest killer and the leading cause of severe disability in the UK

To find out more telephone our Legacy Department on 020 7566 1505 or email legacy@stroke.org.uk

The Stroke Association, Stroke House, 240 City Road, London EC1V 2PR

Registered Charity No. 211015

Stroke helpline
0845 3033 100

Website
www.stroke.org.uk

SECTION 1

SOLICITORS

LONDON

CONTENTS

Work Categories for Solicitors Firms

A1 Agricultural Law, Holdings & Property
A2 Animals, Farming, Forestry
A3 Arbitration & Mediation
B1 Bankruptcy
B2 Fraud
B3 Accounting Standards
C1 Commercial & Company Law
C2 Mergers & Acquisitions
C3 Competition Law
D1 Child Care & Wardship
D2 Adoption
E Commercial Property
F1 Consumer Law – Agreements, Credit, Licensing, Sale of Goods
F2 Consumer Protection – Advertising, Trade Descriptions, Trading Standards, Product Liability
G Crime – General
H Crime – Juvenile
I Computer Law
J1 Employment Law
J2 Health & Safety at Work
K1 Family Law
K2 Family Mediation
K3 Divorce & Matrimonial
K4 Elderly
L Housing, Landlord & Tenant
M1 European Community Law
M2 International Law
M3 Air Law
M4 Islamic Law
N Litigation, Accidents, Injury, Criminal Injury Compensation, Personal Injury
O Litigation, Commercial
P Environmental Liability
Q Litigation, General
R1 Planning, Compulsory Purchase, Lands Tribunal
R2 Property – Finance, Development
S1 Residential Conveyancing
S2 Commercial Conveyancing
T1 Taxation – Business
T2 Taxation – Personal
U1 Communications & Telecommunications
U2 Internet & e-commerce
V Welfare Benefits
W Wills, Trusts & Probate
X Education Law
Za Admiralty
Zb Banking Law
Zc Building Law, Building Contracts
Zd Charity Law
Ze Copyright, Patents, Trade Marks & Intellectual Property
Zf Entertainment, Artists & Performers
Zg Human Rights & Civil Liberties
Zh Housing Association Law
Zi Immigration & Nationality
Zj Insurance Law
Zk Libel, Slander & Defamation
Zl Liquor, Betting & Gaming Licensing
Zm Mental Health
Zn Mines, Minerals, Oil & Gas
Zo Pensions, Investments & Financial Services
Zp Race & Sex Descrimination
Zq Professional Negligence
Zr Clinical Negligence
Zs Rating Law
Zt Road Haulage Licensing
Zu Local Government
Zv Regulated by the FSA for Investment Business
Zw Sports Law
Zx Ecclesiastical Law
Zy Food & Drugs
Zz Printing & Publishing
Zza Data Protection

Key to symbols

Asoc = Associate
Ast = Assistant
Con = Consultant
Dir = Director
Dx = Document Exchange
E-mail = Electronic mail box
Est = Year Established
Fax = Facsimile number
Mem = Member
NSP = Non Solicitor Partner
Ptr = Partner
Sol = Solicitor
SPr = Sole Practitioner
Tel = Telephone number
Higher Rights of Audience – ♦ = Civil
Higher Rights of Audience – ★ = Criminal
Higher Rights of Audience – ● = All
† = Member of Notaries Society
* = Law Society member
‡ = Principal office
§ = Solicitors Benevolent Association

LONDON FIRMS – A-Z

A-Z LAW SOLICITORS ‡
198-200 Balham High Road Wandsworth London SW12 9BP
Tel: 020 8355 0830 *Fax:* 020 8355 0831 *Dx:* 41616 BALHAM
Emergency telephone 07787527112
E-mail: info@a-zlawsolicitors.co.uk
List of partners: E A M Hamlin, M Z Z Khan, A Yussuf
Languages: Arabic, Bengali, French, Hindi, Punjabi, Sinhalese, Somali, Spanish, Tamil, Urdu
Work: D1 G H J1 K1 K3 L N Q S1 S2 W Z(g,i)
Ptr: Hamlin, Mr Errol A M BA . . . . *May 1989
Khan, Mr Mohammad Ziaullah Zaki . . . . Jun 1997
Yussuf, Mr Abdi . . . . Jan 2005

AA & CO SOLICITORS ‡
60a Plumstead High Street London SE18 1SL
Tel: 020 8317 3333 *Fax:* 020 8317 3333
E-mail: aa@aasolicitors.com

A CITY LAW FIRM LLP ‡
2 Devonshire Square London EC2M 4UJ
Tel: 020 7426 0382 *Fax:* 020 7426 0180
E-mail: enquiries@acitylawfirm.com

ADH LAW ‡
1a Turnpike Parade Green Lane London N15 3LA
Tel: 020 3240 1010 *Fax:* 020 3240 1011 *Dx:* 35652 WOOD GREEN 2

AJA SOLICITORS ‡
Unit 94-96 555 White Hart Lane London N17 7RN
Tel: 020 8888 2142 *Fax:* 020 8888 6355
E-mail: ajasolicitors@btconnect.com

AKP SOLICITORS LTD ‡
19 Plashet Grove Upton Park London E6 1AD
Tel: 020 8472 4462 *Fax:* 020 8471 9731 *Dx:* 133010 UPTON PARK 2
E-mail: info@akp-london.com
Languages: Bengali, Gujarati, Hindi, Punjabi, Urdu
Work: C1 D1 E F1 K1 L N O Q R1 T2 W Z(e)
Emergency Action, Agency, Advocacy and Legal Aid undertaken

AK SOLICITORS ‡
241a Whitechapel Road Tower Hamlets London E1 1DB
Tel: 020 7377 9366 *Fax:* 020 7247 4251
E-mail: aksolicitors@netscape.net
Languages: Arabic, Bengali, Hindi, Urdu
Work: J1 K3 L M4 S2 W Z(d,i)

A KAY PIETRON & PALUCH ‡
371 Uxbridge Road Ealing London W3 9RH
Tel: 020 8992 9997 *Fax:* 020 8993 5698 *Dx:* 80251 ACTON
E-mail: info@akpp.co.uk
List of partners: R M Paluch, I M Pietron
Languages: French, Gujarati, Kiswahili, Polish, Punjabi, Spanish, Urdu
Work: K1 K3 L Q S1 S2 W Z(i)
Fixed Fee Interview undertaken
Ptr: Paluch, Ms Romualda M BA . . . . *Oct 1987
Pietron, Ms Irma M BA . . . . *Jan 1984
Ast: Pluss, Mr Harold LLB . . . . Dec 1980

ALMT LEGAL ‡
20 St Dunstans Hill London EC3R 8HY
Tel: 020 7645 9190 *Fax:* 020 7645 9194
E-mail: sagarwal@almtlegal.com
List of partners: S Aganwal, S Khaitan
Languages: German, Gujarati, Hindi
Work: A3 B1 C1 C2 D1 I J1 K1 K3 M2 M3 O Q T1 T2 U1 U2 W Z(b,d,e,i,j,r,za)
Agency and Advocacy undertaken
Ptr: Aganwal, Ms Shalini . . . . Aug 1995
Khaitan, Mr Sakate . . . . Sep 2003

AM LEGAL CONSULTANTS CO LTD ‡
61 Brook Road Neasden London NW2 7DR

AMZ LAW ‡
1st Floor 412 Edgware Road Marble Arch London W2 1ED
Tel: 020 7724 7888 *Fax:* 020 7724 8887
E-mail: ashwaq@amzlaw.co.uk

APD SOLICITORS ‡
1st Floor 22 Wardour Street London W1D 6QJ
Tel: 020 7287 7880

AQSA LAW CHAMBERS ‡
26 Green Street London E7 8BZ
Tel: 020 8552 5833 *Fax:* 020 8548 9871

AR LEGAL SOLICITORS ‡
68-70 Turnham Green Terrace Chiswick London W4 1QN
Tel: 020 8747 9090 *Fax:* 020 8747 9555 *Dx:* 80309 CHISWICK
E-mail: info@arlegal.co.uk
List of partners: A Rashid
Languages: Arabic, French
Work: A3 C1 E G I J1 K1 K2 K3 L N O Q S1 S2 W Z(i,l,q)
Emergency Action, Agency, Advocacy, Fixed Fee Interview undertaken and Member of Accident Line
SPr: Rashid, Aseel BSc; LLB. . . . . May 1998
Ast: Al Rawi, Mr Ziad LLB(Hons). . . . . *Nov 2004
Shakkour, Miss Sawsan LLB; MA . . . . Feb 2006

ATE SOLICITORS ‡
Unit F 24 (b) Waterfront Studios 1 Dock Road London E16 1AH
Tel: 020 7476 8739 *Fax:* 020 7476 8491
E-mail: enawtaken@hotmail.com

AZRIGHTS SOLICITORS ‡
81 Essex Road Islington Green Islington London N1 2SF
Tel: 020 7700 1414 *Fax:* 0870 622 0367
E-mail: shireen@ip-brands.com
List of partners: S Smith
Languages: French
Work: I U2 Z(e,w)
SPr: Smith, Shireen LLM. . . . . Jan 1985

AARONSON & CO ‡
197a Kensington High Street London W8 6BA
Tel: 020 7376 9124 *Fax:* 020 7376 9125
Dx: 400750 KENSINGTON HIGH STREET 5
List of partners: F J Aaronson, L F Aaronson
Work: D1 D2 J1 K1 K2 L N O S1 S2 V W Z(g,i,l)
Emergency Action, Agency, Advocacy and Legal Aid Franchise
Ptr: Aaronson, Mr Francis J LLB. . . . . *Sep 1978
Aaronson, Ms Linda F BA; Dr Jur; LLM(Lond). . . . . *Nov 1992

AASKELLS SOLICITORS & ADVOCATES ‡
Urban House 43-45 Chase Side Southgate London N14 5BP
Tel: 020 8920 2400 *Fax:* 020 8920 2450
E-mail: info@aaskellsolicitors.com
List of partners: K Mensah
Ptr: Mensah, Kobbie. Jul 2006

ABBISS CADRES LLP ‡
15 Old Baily London EC4M 7EF
Tel: 020 3051 5711 *Fax:* 020 3051 5712

ABBOT BERESFORD ‡
4 Bloomsbury Square London WC1A 2RP
Tel: 020 7405 5529 *Fax:* 020 7405 5530
E-mail: mel@abbotberesford.com

ABBOTT CRESSWELL LLP ‡
179 Upper Richmond Road West East Sheen London SW14 8DU
Tel: 020 8876 4478 *Fax:* 020 8878 5686 *Dx:* 36353 EAST SHEEN
List of partners: R J Cooles, C R W Delves, C P Pinnell
Work: C1 E K3 S1 W Z(x)
Ptr: Cooles, Mr Robert J. . . . . *Dec 1971
Delves, Mr Clive R W . . . . *Jan 1982
Pinnell, Mr Colin P. . . . . *Jul 1969

ABBOTT FAHLBUSCH ‡
(in association with Zimmers Solicitors)
5 Water Lane London NW1 8NZ
Tel: 020 7284 6970 *Fax:* 020 7284 6980
E-mail: jeanette.fahlbusch@zimmerslaw.com

ABBOTT LAW LLP ‡
The Workplace 105 Ladbroke Grove London W11 1PG
Tel: 020 7616 8442 *Fax:* 020 7616 8443
E-mail: caroline@abbottlaw.co.uk

SIMON ABBOTT ‡
3 Maguire Street London SE1 2JE
Tel: 020 3283 4230
E-mail: mail@abbottsolicitors.co.uk

ABBOUSHI ASSOCIATES ‡
18 Oakdene Park Finchley London N3 1EU
Tel: 020 8343 4045 *Fax:* 020 8343 1375
List of partners: R Abboushi
Languages: Arabic, French, Urdu
Work: E F2 N O Q S1 S2 W Z(e,k,r)
Legal Aid undertaken
SPr: Abboushi, Miss Rabia BA . . . . *May 1981

ABILOYE & CO ‡
4 Station Road Manor Park London E12 5BC
Tel: 020 8478 5678 *Fax:* 020 8534 9143
Emergency telephone 07717 558747
E-mail: info@abilawyers.com
List of partners: A O Abiloye, P M Chipatiso
Languages: Creole, French, Igbo, Krio, Mandigo, Ndebele, Shona, Spanish, Wobe, Wolof, Yoruba
Work: E G J1 K1 K3 Q S2 V Z(i)
Agency undertaken
Ptr: Abiloye, Mr Alexander O LLB(Hons). . . . . *Mar 1997
Chipatiso, P M . . . . Jan 2000

ABLE SOLICITORS ‡
51 Blackbird Hill Kingsbury London NW9 8RS
Tel: 020 8358 3580 *Fax:* 020 8358 3581 *Dx:* 99353 KINGSBURY 2
List of partners: B A Kpogho
Work: C1 D1 E J1 K1 K3 L O Q S2 W Z(i)
Ptr: Kpogho, Mr Ben Amaju LLB(Hons); LLM(Lond) . . . . *Mar 1998

ABLETT & STEBBING ‡
Caparo House 101-103 Baker Street London W1U 6FQ
Tel: 020 7935 7720 *Fax:* 020 7935 7790
E-mail: info@absteb.co.uk
Work: Z(e)

ABLITTS ‡
24 Metro Business Centre Kangley Bridge Road Bromley London SE26 5BW
Tel: 020 8776 8783 *Fax:* 020 8776 5867
E-mail: mail@ablitts-solicitors.co.uk
List of partners: R H Ablitt
Work: C1 E J1 K4 L N O Q R1 S1 S2 W Z(c,d,h)
SPr: Ablitt, Mr Richard H BA Notary Public . . . . *Sep 1981
Ast: Wilkinson, Mr Martin . . . . Jun 1974

D ABRAHAM & CO ‡
21-22 Grosvenor Street London W1K 4QJ
Tel: 020 7989 0501
E-mail: david.abraham@dabraham.co.uk

ABRAHAMS DRESDEN ‡
111 Charterhouse Street London EC1M 6AW
Tel: 020 7251 3663 *Fax:* 020 7251 3773 *Dx:* 53334 CLERKENWELL
Emergency telephone 020 8959 5711
E-mail: law@ad-solicitors.co.uk
List of partners: R M Abrahams, S A Glockler, G D McGonagle, I M Robertson
Work: B1 C1 C2 C3 D1 E F1 I J1 L N O Q S1 W Z(e,f,k,p)
Agency undertaken
Ptr: Abrahams, Mr Russell Mark BA(Kent). . . . . *Oct 1986
Glockler, Miss Sarah Anne . . . . Oct 2002
McGonagle, Mr Gary Daniel LLB(Hons) . . . . Jul 2001
Robertson, Mr Ian Massey . . . . *Apr 2001
Con: De La Fuente, Ms Hollie LLB . . . . Sep 2006
Joseph, Mr David LLB. . . . . *Sep 2001
Tolan, Miss Leah LLB(Hons) . . . . Sep 2000

ABRAHAMSON & ASSOCIATES ‡
(incorporating Francis & Solomons)
10 North End Road Golders Green London NW11 7PH
Tel: 020 8458 1100 *Fax:* 020 8458 1588
E-mail: postoffice@abrahamsons.co.uk
List of partners: B S Abrahamson
Work: B1 C1 E J1 L N O Q S1 S2 W Z(i,q,r)
Agency undertaken
Ptr: Abrahamson, Mr Barry Selvin BSc(Econ) . . . . . . *§Dec 1974
Asoc: Nathan, Mr Trevor G BA . . . . *Apr 1978
Con: Abrahamson, Mr D Elkan LLB(Jerusalem); LLM(Lond) *Feb 1983
Blank, Mr John Allan BA(Oxon) . . . . *Apr 1971

ABSOLUTE LAW LTD ‡
15 Broadway Market Bethnal Green London E8 4PH
Tel: 020 7812 9222

ABSOLUTELY LEGAL ‡
255a Sheen Lane Richmond upon Thames London SW14 8RN
Tel: 020 8487 1000 *Fax:* 020 8876 2320
List of partners: R Knott
Languages: French, Italian
Work: C2 K1 T2
Advocacy undertaken

ACHILLEA & CO ‡
113 Station Road Chingford Waltham Forest London E4 7BU
Tel: 020 8529 8555 *Fax:* 020 8529 8383 *Dx:* 37852 CHINGFORD 2
E-mail: aki@achillealaw.net

ACHOM & PARTNERS ‡
92 Stroud Green Road Finsbury Park London N4 3EN
Tel: 020 7281 7222 *Fax:* 020 7272 7324
Dx: 57478 FINSBURY PARK

JOSEPH ACKERMAN ‡
UK House 11-20 Sentinel Square London NW4 2EL
Tel: 020 8457 6700 *Fax:* 020 8588 0495
List of partners: J Ackerman
Office: London NW4
SPr: Ackerman, Mr Joseph. . . . . Jul 1965

JOSEPH ACKERMAN
113 Brent Street London NW4 2DX
Office: London NW4

ADAMS & REMERS
Dukes Court 32 Duke Street St James's London SW1Y 6DF
Tel: 020 7024 3600 *Fax:* 020 7839 5244
E-mail: london@adams-remers.co.uk
Office: Lewes
Work: E S1 W

MARK ADAMS LLB ‡
Malta House 36-38 Piccadilly London W1J 0DP
Tel: 020 7494 4441 / 07976 478562
E-mail: mark@markadamsllb.com

ADAMS SOLICITORS ‡
Adams House 129 Mile End Road London E1 4BG
Tel: 020 7790 2000 *Fax:* 020 7791 1113
Dx: 300705 TOWER HAMLETS
E-mail: info@adamslaw.co.uk
List of partners: R Alom, M K Chima, S S Chima
Office: London SW6, London W1
Work: B1 C1 D1 E J1 K1 L N O P Q R1 S1 W Z(c,i,l)
Agency and Advocacy undertaken
Ptr: Alom, Mr Ruhel LLB(Hons) . . . . . Jul 2002
Chima, Mrs Mohinder K BA . . . . . *Jan 1987
Chima, Mr Santokh S BA . . . . . *Jul 1987
Ast: Greany, Mr David . . . . . *Feb 1991

ADAMS SOLICITORS
33 Cavendish Square London W1G 0PW
Tel: 020 7182 4500 *Fax:* 0845 021 1500
E-mail: info@adamslaw.co.uk
Office: London E1, London SW6

ADAMS SOLICITORS
Mulberry House 583 Fulham Road London SW6 5UA
Tel: 020 7471 1744 *Fax:* 020 7471 1847
E-mail: info@adamslaw.co.uk
Office: London E1, London W1

ADDIE & CO ‡
6th Floor Waterman House 41 Kingsway London WC2B 6TP
Tel: 020 7395 3740 *Fax:* 020 7395 3750
List of partners: A K Gbaja, A Nkontchou, T Oshunniyi
Languages: French
Work: C1 E F1 J1 L O Q S1 S2 W Z(e,g,i,q)
Fixed Fee Interview undertaken
Ptr: Gbaja, Mrs Abimbola Kehinde LLB; LLM; BL . . . . . *Oct 1996
Nkontchou, Mrs Adebimpe LLB; LLM; BL . . . . . *Aug 1997
Oshunniyi, Mrs Taiwo . . . . . Dec 2007

ADDLESHAW GODDARD ‡
(in association with Klein Goddard(Paris); Theodore Goddard(Jersey))
Milton Gate 60 Chiswell Street London EC1Y 4AG
Tel: 020 7606 8855 *Fax:* 020 7606 4390 *Dx:* 47 LONDON/CITY
E-mail: info@addleshawgoddard.co.uk
List of partners: L S Ahmed, A D Aldred, J R Allison, J E Amphlett, M Amsden, G Anderson, A Bailey, G A Barnes, M Barnett, T J M Bee, G A Bennett, P J Bentham, A Beresford, A B Besser, A Bever, R S Bhaskaran, M J Birchall, A Blower, G M Briggs, N M A Burch, S A Butt, A J Carpenter, M Carter, A M J Chamberlain, S P Chater, M Clough, R A Cockram, A P Collins, P Conroy, D T Copley, H Corner, J Cromack, J W Davey, R Davies, J Dawson, J Delroy, P Devitt, P M Dillon, M F Duggan, A S Duncan, I Edwards, G Elliot, N Elphicke, J Emerton, D J Engel, D F Evans, J A Fawcett, R G Fleetwood, H J Garety, S M Garrett, J K Gatenby, M Gilbert, M S Gill, A Goldthorp, R Goodfellow, P Goodstone, J A Gosling, A C Gray, M J Green, S Griffiths, R Guit, T G Hamilton, D Handy, P J Hardy, I Hargreaves, G R Harries, M Harris, R Hart, D P Hartley, M A Harvey, I A W Hastings, R W Hayes, M B Haywood, D G Heffron, M W Hilton, M Hinchliffe, J J Hiscock, J Hollinshead, S Houston, P J Howell, S A Humphrey, M P Isaacs, L I Jackson, C E Jagger, W K James, N Jansen, C W Jenkins, E G Jenkins, T K Johnston, D M Jones, J G Joyce, S P Kamstra, P Kaur, J R Kelleher, N Kelsall, R A Kempner, P J Kershaw, B Kilpatrick, J Langley White, A J Leake, P A Lee, R N F Lee, R J Leedham, M A Leftley, G I F Leigh, B R Lightbody, R D Linsell, C S Lippell, J C Lovatt, M Lowry, R J MacCarthy, P M Marino, A S L Maskill, C McAllister, P McDonnell, N J McGuire, I W McIntosh, M A McQuillan, J A Middlemass, J Murray, L Newcomb, M G O'Connor, P H O'Loughlin, M D O'Shea, S D Palmer, R N Papworth, M T Park, C D S Penney, E Peters, A Petry, A Pettinger, J D Pike, M J Pike, S M Pilling, E B Pitt, C Porter, A B Price, N C Proctor, C Rattray, R M Rawnsley, D M Redstone, M A Reevey, J Richard, R Riley, F J Ritson, E M Robertson, A J Rosling, J Salford, P A Salsbury, I C Sampson, P W Sayer, Y Seedat, L Shankland, D Shaw, N J Shaw, J A Shellard, C S Sheppard, A M Shufflebotham, D Sian, A J Simpson, P Slater, R A Smith, R E Snell, J F Stone, A D Sturrock, L F Sturrock, J Tattersall, C Thomas, R Thomas, M Tofalides, D N Tolley, J T Toon, J M Tully, C J Tweedie, S C H Twigden, W Wastie, R A Wheeldon, Q J Whittaker, D M Wilson, N T Woolhouse, D P K Woolley, R Yeomans
Office: Leeds, Manchester
Languages: Cantonese, French, German, Hebrew, Italian, Japanese, Russian, Spanish
Work: A3 B1 B2 C1 C2 C3 E F1 F2 G I J1 J2 L M1 M2 M3 N O P Q R1 R2 S1 T1 T2 U1 W Z(b,c,d,e,f,g,i,j,k,l,n,o,p,q,r,s,t,u,w,y,z)
Fixed Fee Interview undertaken and Member of Accident Line
Ptr: Ahmed, Ms Leona Shireen . . . . . Feb 1996
Aldred, Mr Adam David LLM(Cantab); DipLaw(SAB). . Nov 1990
Allison, Mr John Robert BA(Oxon); LSF . . . . . *Nov 1993
Amphlett, Ms Jane Elizabeth LLB; LSF . . . . . *Jan 1994
Bailey, Mr Andrew LLB . . . . . Nov 1990
Barnett, Mr Michael . . . . . Jan 1994
Bee, Mr Tim J M . . . . . Jan 1988
Besser, Mr Andrew B LLB. . . . . *Oct 1987
Blower, Mr Andrew . . . . . Nov 1993
Burch, Ms N Monica A BA(Hons)(Oxon)(Jurisprudence)Jun 1990
Carpenter, Dr Andrew J BSc; PhD East Midlands Law Society Prize . . . . . *Oct 1991
Carter, Mr Michael . . . . . Nov 1992
Chater, Mr Stephen P MA(Oxon) . . . . . *Jun 1981
Clough, Mr Mark ● . . . . . Dec 1995
Collins, Mr Adrian P LLB . . . . . *Apr 1992
Dawson, Mr James . . . . . Dec 1996
Duggan, Mr Michael Francis BA(Dunelm); DipLS . . *Sep 1996
Duncan, Mr Alan Stuart BA(Law) . . . . . Sep 1998
Edwards, Mr Ivor . . . . . Nov 1999
Elphicke, Ms Natalie . . . . . Aug 1999
Engel, Mr David Jonathan MA. . . . . *Oct 1995
Evans, Mr Douglas F LLB(Soton) . . . . . Mar 1978
Garety, Mr Hugh J LLB(Lond) . . . . . *Dec 1972
Gilbert, Mr Mark LLB . . . . . *Oct 1978
Gill, Mr Mark S LLB(Lond). . . . . *§Jun 1977
Goldthorp, Ms Alison . . . . . Oct 1990
Green, Mr Michael J LLB . . . . . *Mar 1991
Griffiths, Mr Simon BA . . . . . Jul 1988
Guit, Mr Richard . . . . . Sep 1999
Hardy, Mr Peter Justin BA(Cantab) . . . . . *Oct 1991
Hargreaves, Mr Ian BA . . . . . Nov 1994
Harries, Mr Geraint Rhys BA . . . . . *Mar 1997
Hartley, Mr David P LLM(Lond) . . . . . Nov 1991
Hinchliffe, Mr Mike . . . . . Apr 1999
Hollinshead, Miss Jane LLB. . . . . Jan 1993
Jackson, Leslie I BCom(Rand); MBA(Columbia); BA(Oxon) . . . . . *Jun 1977
James, Mr William K . . . . . Oct 1989
Jenkins, Mr Clive W LLB . . . . . *Nov 1983
Kelleher, Mr John R LLB . . . . . *Nov 1978
Kilpatrick, Mr Bruce . . . . . Nov 2000
Langley White, Mrs Jacqui . . . . . *Jan 1983
Leedham, Mr Richard J LLB. . . . . *Nov 1992
Leftley, Mr Michael A LLB(Warw); LLM . . . . . *Nov 1993
Leigh, Mr Guy I F BA; JD(Penn); Dip(Int Law)(Cantab) . . . . . *§Nov 1974
Linsell, Mr Richard D MA(Cantab). . . . . *§Dec 1972
Lovatt, Mr J Clive MA(Cantab) . . . . . *Nov 1984
McAllister, Ms Catherine . . . . . Mar 1997
MacCarthy, Mr Rory J MA; LLB(Lond); Dip(Air Law) . *Jun 1981
McQuillan, Mr Mark Andrew LLB . . . . . Sep 1996
Marino, Mr Pietro M LLB(Durham). . . . . May 1992
Newcomb, Ms Lucy. . . . . Nov 1998
Penney, Mr Charles D StJ MA(Cantab) . . . . . *Nov 1984
Peters, Mr Emmett . . . . . Aug 2005
Petry, Mr Andrew . . . . . Apr 1992
Pitt, Mr Edward B MA(Oxon) . . . . . *Jan 1976
Rattray, Mr Craig . . . . . Nov 2001
Redstone, Mr Daniel Morris BSc . . . . . Dec 1995
Richard, Mr Jonathon. . . . . Nov 1993
Ritson, Mr Fraser J LLB. . . . . *§Jul 1998
Robertson, Ms Elizabeth Mary LLB . . . . . *Nov 1995
Rosling, Mr Andrew John BA(Hons). . . . . *Nov 1995
Salford, Mr James. . . . . Oct 1999
Salsbury, Mr Paul A LLB . . . . . *Dec 1982
Sayer, Mr Peter William MA; ATII . . . . . *Apr 1988
Shellard, Ms Jeanette A BA(Dunelm) . . . . . *Oct 1982
Sheppard, Ms Claire S BSc. . . . . *Dec 1991
Shufflebotham, Mr Andrew Michael LLB(Hons) . . . Nov 1988
Sian, Ms Dee . . . . . Mar 1998
Simpson, Mr Alasdair J LLB(Lond) . . . . . *Dec 1967
Slater, Mr Phillip. . . . . Sep 1997
Smith, Mr Raymond Anthony BJuris(Hons); LLB. . . May 1991
Sturrock, Miss Lucy Francesca BA; CPE; LSF. . . . *Oct 1995
Thomas, Miss Clare LLB . . . . . Sep 2000
Thomas, Mr Mark. . . . . Dec 1998
Tofalides, Mrs Margaret MA; LLB . . . . . *Feb 1986
Twigden, Mr Simon C H MA(Cantab) . . . . . *Mar 1988
Wastie, Mr William . . . . . Apr 2007
Wilson, Mr David M LLB(Edin) Keith Berrigdale Prize; Muirhead Prize . . . . . Sep 1988
Yeomans, Mr Richard. . . . . Sep 1997

ADESEMOWO & CO ‡
Unit 15 Blackheath Business Centre 78b Blackheath Hill London SE10 8BA
Tel: 020 8692 9700 *Fax:* 020 8692 1130 *Dx:* 144363 SOUTHWARK 4
E-mail: solicitors@adelaw.com

ADILSONS ‡
139 Cricklewood Broadway London NW2 3HY
Tel: 020 8452 3793 *Fax:* 020 8208 4460
List of partners: R J Bernstein
Ptr: Bernstein, Mr Raymond J. . . . . May 1964

ADLEX SOLICITORS ‡
76a Belsize Park Lane London NW3 5BJ
Tel: 020 7317 8404 *Fax:* 020 7317 8405
E-mail: adamt@adlexsolicitors.co.uk

ADRIAN & CO ‡
293-299 Kentish Town Road Kentish Town London NW5 2TJ
Tel: 020 7485 8450 / 7267 1240 *Fax:* 020 7485 7826
Dx: 46453 KENTISH TOWN
List of partners: A I Brodkin, D B Brodkin
Work: E K3 L N S1 W Z(i)
Ptr: Brodkin, Mr Adrian I LLB(Leeds) . . . . . *Jul 1972
Brodkin, Mrs Diane B LLB(Leeds). . . . . *Apr 1972

ADVISA SOLICITORS ‡
4th Floor 33 Cavendish Square London W1G 0PW
Tel: 0845 388 9623 *Fax:* 020 7883 3403
E-mail: enquiries@advisasolicitors.co.uk

AEQUITAS LAW LLP ‡
(in association with Singapore; West Malaysia)
43 Berkeley Square Mayfair London W1J 5AP
Tel: 020 7495 2776 *Fax:* 020 7495 1005
List of partners: P Kay Kanagaratnam
Languages: Bahasa, Mandarin, Tamil
Work: B1 C1 M2 N O Q Z(a,f)
Agency undertaken
SPr: Kay Kanagaratnam, Mr Puvanesan LLB(Hons)(Lond) *Mar 1996
Ast: Afzal, Mr Mohammed . . . . . *Sep 1997

AFRIFA & PARTNERS ‡
36-38 Clapham Road London SW9 0JQ
Tel: 020 7820 9177 *Fax:* 020 7820 9266
Emergency telephone 07956 584106
List of partners: K Afrifa-Yamoah, D Owusu-Yaw
Languages: Creole, Ga, Twi
Work: G J1 K1 L Z(g,i)
Fixed Fee Interview, Legal Aid undertaken and Legal Aid Franchise
Ptr: Afrifa-Yamoah, Mr Kwaku LLB(Hons) . . . . . Jul 1994
Owusu-Yaw, Mr Daniel . . . . . *Mar 1997

AHMADS SOLICITORS ‡
Suite 31 329-339 Putney Bridge Road London SW15 2PG
Tel: 020 8788 1234 *Fax:* 020 8788 1284
E-mail: mashood@ahmads-solicitors.com

AHMED & CO ‡
67a Camden High Street Camden London NW1 7JL
Tel: 020 7383 2243 *Fax:* 020 7383 2166
Dx: 121903 KENTISH TOWN 3
Emergency telephone 07798 526586
E-mail: mail@ahmedco.com
List of partners: I Ahmed, N Saleem
Languages: Arabic, Punjabi, Turkish, Urdu
Work: G H J1 L Q V Z(h,i)
Emergency Action, Fixed Fee Interview, Legal Aid undertaken and Legal Aid Franchise
Ptr: Ahmed, Mr Iqbal BSc . . . . . *Jun 1988
Saleem, Ms Nosheen LLB(Hons) . . . . . *Jan 1996
Ast: Akram, Ms Ghazala LLB(Hons) . . . . . *Oct 1996
Goldman, Ms Sally BA(Hons); CPE . . . . . *Sep 2001
Hayre, Ms Manjit Kaur BA(Hons) . . . . . *Aug 1999

AITCHISON & CO ‡
2 Ching Court 53 Monmouth Street London WC2H 9EY
Tel: 020 7240 0020 *Fax:* 020 7240 0030
E-mail: mail@aitchisonco.co.uk
List of partners: P W Aitchison
Languages: French, Spanish
Work: D1 J1 K1 Q S1 X Z(m)
Emergency Action, Agency, Advocacy, Legal Aid undertaken and Legal Aid Franchise
SPr: Aitchison, Mr Paul W BA(Lond) . . . . . *Oct 1987

AITKEN ASSOCIATES ‡
144 Liverpool Road Islington London N1 1LA
Tel: 020 7700 6006 *Fax:* 020 7700 0247
Dx: 122236 UPPER ISLINGTON
E-mail: info@aitkenassociates.co.uk
List of partners: H E MacDonald, K Wild, M Wray
Work: D1 D2 K1 K2 W
Emergency Action, Agency, Advocacy, Fixed Fee Interview, Legal Aid undertaken and Legal Aid Franchise
Ptr: MacDonald, Ms Helen Elizabeth LLB . . . . . *Aug 1999
Wild, Ms Kelly LLB(Hons) . . . . . *Aug 2001
Wray, Mr Martin BA . . . . . *Nov 1990
Ast: Khela, Mrs Pavinder BA. . . . . *May 2003
Rogers, Mrs Heather Lynn BSocSc . . . . . Oct 1992
Straub, Ms Kathleen . . . . . *May 1997

AKIN & LAW LLP ‡
3 Angel Gate 326 City Road London EC1V 2PT
Tel: 020 7878 2800 *Fax:* 020 7278 6700 *Dx:* 400212 FINSBURY 2
E-mail: law@akinlaw.co.uk

AKIN GUMP STRAUSS HAUER & FELD ‡
Eighth Floor Ten Bishops Square London E1 6EG
Tel: 020 7012 9600 *Fax:* 020 7012 9601
E-mail: londoninfo@akingump.com
List of partners: J R Drew
Ptr: Drew, Mr Jeffery R BA(Oxon) . . . . . *Mar 1980
Asoc: Crouchman, Mr Andrew C MA(Cantab) . . . . . Jun 1991
Rice, Mr Sebastian BA . . . . . Sep 1998

AKODU & CO SOLICITORS ‡
1b Fentiman Road London SW8 1LD
Tel: 020 7587 1111 *Fax:* 020 7587 1075 *Dx:* 37056 STOCKWELL
E-mail: info@akodulaw.co.uk

ALAGA & CO ‡
305 Northborough Road London SW16 4TR
Tel: 020 8764 7073 *Fax:* 020 8764 7729
List of partners: S Alagarajah
Languages: Malay, Tamil
Work: K1 L Z(i)
Legal Aid undertaken
Ptr: Alagarajah, Sasheecala. . . . . Aug 1991

ALBAN GOULD BAKER & CO ‡
405-407 Holloway Road Islington London N7 6HG
Tel: 020 7607 5085 *Fax:* 020 7700 5631 *Dx:* 38654 HOLLOWAY
List of partners: P J Baker, C M Brown
Work: E F1 K1 L N O Q S1 S2 W
Legal Aid undertaken
Ptr: Baker, Mr Paul John . . . . . *Dec 1992
Brown, Mr Christopher M BA . . . . . *Jul 1978
Ast: Lawrence, Mr Martin D S . . . . . *Jul 1979

ALBERTO PEREZ CEDILLO SPANISH LAWYERS AND SOLICITORS ‡
2nd Floor 1 New Square London WC2A 3SA
Tel: 020 3077 0000 *Fax:* 020 7404 7821

ALBION GEE & CO ‡
12 Chiswick Lane Chiswick London W4 2JE
Tel: 020 8742 7600 *Fax:* 020 8742 7666
List of partners: A G J Gee
Languages: French
Work: C1 M2 W Z(e,f)
Agency undertaken
SPr: Gee, Mr Albion Gerald Joseph . . . . . *Jun 1974

E J C ALBUM ‡
Exchange Tower 1 Harbour Exchange Square London E14 9GE
Tel: 020 7971 5667 *Fax:* 020 7971 5668
Emergency telephone 020 7431 2942
E-mail: ejcalbum@miuk.co.uk
List of partners: E J C Album
Languages: French
Work: A3 C1 C2 E J1 M2 O Z(a,b)
Advocacy undertaken and Member of Accident Line
Ptr: Album, Mr Edward Jonathan Corcos MA(Oxon). . . . *Jan 1964

ALEN-BUCKLEY & CO ‡
2-4 Bennet Court 1 Bellevue Road Wandsworth Common Wandsworth London SW17 7EG
Tel: 020 8767 8336 *Fax:* 020 8767 1241 *Dx:* 38104 CLAPHAM 2
E-mail: general@alen-buckley.co.uk
List of partners: O M D P Alen-Buckley, I A Conner, G C Hast, J G Polsue
Work: A1 B1 C1 C2 D1 E F1 J1 K1 L N O Q S1 S2 T1 T2 W Z(c,k,l,m,n,q,r)
Agency undertaken and Member of Accident Line
Ptr: Alen-Buckley, Miss Oonagh M D P BA(Hons) . . . . . *Jan 1981
Hast, Mr Greville C BA; LLB. . . . . *Mar 1996
Polsue, Mr John Gwavas BA(Cantab). . . . . *May 1979
Mem: Conner, Ms Ingrid Anne LLB(Hons) . . . . . Jul 2004

See p2 for the Key to Work Categories & other symbols

ALEXANDER & PARTNERS ‡
28 Craven Park Road Harlesden Brent London NW10 4AB
Tel: 020 8965 7121 *Fax:* 020 8965 1524 *Dx:* 141580 HARLESDEN 3
Emergency telephone 07659 115745
E-mail: mail.alexander@btconnect.com
List of partners: M E Boyd, M R Fanthorpe, S K Pollard
Languages: French, Punjabi, Spanish
Work: B2 D1 D2 G H K1 N Z(i)
Emergency Action, Agency, Advocacy, Fixed Fee Interview, Legal Aid undertaken and Member of Accident Line
Ptr: Boyd, Mr Michael E MA . . . . Dec 1979
Fanthorpe, Mr Mark R MA . . . . Feb 1985
Pollard, Mr Simon K LLB . . . . *Jun 1970
Ast: Berrange, Ms Bo LLB . . . . *Dec 1989
Bhinder, Rupinder LLB; LPC Middlesex Law Society Prize . . . . Mar 2006
Chalcraft, Mr David James LLB . . . . Jul 1985

ALEXANDER JLO ‡
138-148 Cambridge Heath Road London E1 5QJ
Tel: 020 7791 3600
List of partners: P C Johnson, J Lewis
Office: London E14

ALEXANDER JLO
11 Lanark Square Glengall Bridge London E14 9RE
Tel: 020 7537 7000 *Fax:* 020 7538 2442 *Dx:* 42653 ISLE OF DOGS
Office: London E1
Work: B1 C1 C2 E F1 G J1 K1 L O Q R1 S1 W Z(c,e,f,j,k)
Emergency Action, Agency, Advocacy, Fixed Fee Interview, Legal Aid undertaken and Member of Accident Line
Ptr: Johnson, Mr Peter C MA(Cantab) . . . . *Apr 1975
Lewis, Mr Jeremy LLB . . . . *Nov 1982
Ast: Horton, Ms Tracey Breta LLB(Hons)(Law) . . . . . . Sep 1994

ALEXANDER JLO ‡
7a The Broadway Highams Park London E4 9LQ
Tel: 020 8527 3401 *Fax:* 020 8527 6196 *Dx:* 42653 ISLE OF DOGS
E-mail: info@london-law.co.uk

ALEXANDER JLO ‡
2nd Floor Northern & Shell Tower 4 Selsdon Way London E14 9GL
Tel: 020 7531 8820 *Fax:* 020 7531 8830 *Dx:* 42653 ISLE OF DOGS

ALEXANDER JOHNSON ‡
246 Bethnal Green Road Bethnal Green London E2 0AA
Tel: 020 7739 1563 *Fax:* 020 7729 9326
Dx: 40904 BETHNAL GREEN
E-mail: tony@alexander-johnson.co.uk

ALEXANDER LAWYERS LLP
Regent House 24-25 Nutford Place London W1H 5YN
Tel: 01245 216050 *Fax:* 020 7725 7086
E-mail: info@alexanderlawyersllp.com
Office: Chelmsford
Work: C1 E J1 O P Q S1 T1 T2 W Z(h,i)
Ptr: Puri, Miss Ratika . . . . Sep 2001

ALEXANDER MARKS LLP ‡
55 Queen Anne Street Westminster London W1G 9JR
Tel: 020 7317 1166 *Fax:* 020 7224 1474
Dx: 53815 OXFORD CIRCUS NORTH
E-mail: cavi@amlaw.co.uk
List of partners: A J Marks
Work: B1 B2 C1 E F1 G J1 K1 K3 L M3 O Q S1 S2 W Z(b,c,d,e,j,k,l)
Legal Aid undertaken
Ptr: Marks, Mr Alexander John BA(Hons) . . . . *Dec 1980

ALEXANDER SOLICITORS ‡
3 Fleet Street London EC4Y 1DP
Tel: 020 3384 1000 *Fax:* 020 7936 4473
Dx: 398 LONDON/CHANCERY LN
E-mail: legal@alexandersolicitors.co.uk
Office: Luton

ALEXEN AVOCATS ‡
7 Savoy Court The Strand London WC2R 0ER
Tel: 020 7497 8034 *Fax:* 020 7836 9481

ALEXIOU FISHER PHILIPPS ‡
106-108 Wigmore Street London W1U 3LR
Tel: 020 7409 1222 *Fax:* 020 7409 7222
Dx: 42720 OXFORD CIRCUS NORTH
E-mail: administrator@afp-law.co.uk
List of partners: D A Alexiou, J J Fisher, S Hannell, E K Harte, S Philipps
Work: D1 K1 K2 K3
Agency undertaken
Ptr: Alexiou, Douglas A LLB(Lond) . . . . *§Dec 1970
Fisher, Mr Jeremy J BA(Dunelm) . . . . *May 1988
Hannell, Ms Sara BA . . . . *Nov 1995
Harte, Mrs Emma K LLB . . . . *Nov 1993
Philipps, Mrs Susan LLB . . . . *§May 1984
Ast: Amin, Sejal . . . . Nov 2003

S ALI & COMPANY SOLICITORS ‡
133a City Road London EC1V 1JB
Tel: 020 7608 2005 *Fax:* 020 7117 3670
E-mail: info@salicolaw.com
List of partners: S Ali, G Unuefa
Office: London N8

S ALI & COMPANY SOLICITORS
19a Turnpike Lane Haringey London N8 0EP
Tel: 020 8340 5544 *Fax:* 020 8340 2255 *Dx:* 34705 WOOD GREEN 2
Office: London EC1
Work: E G J1 L N S1 S2 W Z(i,l,p)
Legal Aid undertaken
Ptr: Ali, Shoaib MA . . . . *§Jan 1986
Unuefa, Mr Godwin . . . . May 2002

ALLAN JAY PAINE & CO ‡
(incorporating C J Saunders & Co)
273 Green Lanes Palmers Green Enfield London N13 4XE
Tel: 020 8886 1404 *Fax:* 020 8882 9452
Dx: 57857 PALMERS GREEN
E-mail: info@allanjaypaine.co.uk
List of partners: C J Saunders, J M Saunders
Work: E K1 S1 T2 W
Ptr: Saunders, Mr Christopher John LLB(Lond) . . . . . . *Jun 1976
Saunders, Mrs Jeanette Margaret LLB . . . . *Nov 2000
Ast: Bird, Mrs Mandy Louise LLB(Hons) . . . . Apr 1989

ALLEN & OVERY LLP ‡
One Bishops Square London E1 6AO
Tel: 020 3088 0000 *Fax:* 020 3088 0088 *Dx:* 73 LONDON/CITY
E-mail: information@allenovery.com
List of partners: P Akhtar, C Andrew, I A Annetts, T Arnheim, A H Asher, A E Baldock, A Bamber, R S W Barry, A M Beardsley, P H D Bedford, D M Benton, G G Beringer, J E M Bevan, N M H Bird, V K Blackmore, T J Borthwick, P Bowden, M R Brailsford, J L F Brayne, F M Bridgeman, R M Brown, J M Brownson, C D Burnett, A E Buscall, B Capeci, W A Castle, S P Chater, A J C Clark, A A Cleal, A H Clist, B A Coleman, S T Connell, L Cook, R W L Cranfield, P Crook, R J C De Basto, B K Desai, M Dighero, D P Doble, A Drake-Brockman, A J Duncan, M G Duncan, I F Elder, J Evans, R Fairley, I J A Ferguson, S Fiamma, I T Field, E J E P Finlayson-Brown, P T Flanagan, M E Florent, M W Friend, G W Fuller, C M Gardner, M G P Gearing, N Gibbon, J A E Gill, A S Gillespie, J Golden, E D C Gorrie, J Gould, S A Haddock, A C M Haines, S M Harray, J P Harris, B W Harrison, P A Harrison, H M Harrison-Hall, M P Hartley, R H Harvey, S A Hazeldine, G Henderson, S G V Hill, J D J Hitchin, P B Hockless, G A Holgate, C J Hopper, R I Hough, T J House, S D Howard, D C Hughes, D S Hughes, A R Humphrey, J D Hunt, R J Hunter, M Jacovides, S Jagusch, T Jones, A L Joyce, A C Keal, C A Keck, E Kelliher, S Kensell, D S Krischer, M Krone, A Kupitz, C J B Lambie, J L Lang, D P Lee, D E Lewis, A Lindsay, D Lines, G P Link, O Lomas, I D Lopez, D L Mackie, M J Mansell, Y Manuelides, S F Martin, C M Maurice, H McCallum, P H McCarthy, M McDonald, D M McGown, D M McKimm, G C McLean, P M Mears, J S T Mellor, S M Miller, P N Monk, D H Morley, D T J Murray, E Murray, S A Myers, M S Nathoo, J G T O'Conor, M B O'Neill, J M Page, J Parr, G M Parry, A D Paul, C J Pearson, A M Pease, P Phillips, T Polglase, N J Pritchard, J M Quinn, A F Rae Smith, S Roberts, R A P Rowland, C Rushton, R Sallustio, J A Salt, M P Scargill, A Schoorlemmer, P F Schulz, K E Seward, T Shilling, D J Shurman, Y E M Siew, D S Sloan, R M Slynn, C M Smith, D M W Smith, G R E Smith, R J Smith, P J W Speller, K M Spooner, I G Stanley, G C Stewart, C Thornes, R P Tredgett, J A Tucker, R W C Turnor, M B A Vaswani, G D Vinter, C J Walker, M S J Walker, M H Walton, P M Watson, S B Watts, A R Wedderburn-Day, R Weeks, B S Wells, T Werlen, D L Williams, N Williams, A Wilson, M A Wippell, D H Wootton, J P Wotton
Office: London E14
Languages: Afrikaans, Arabic, Bengali, Cantonese, Danish, Dutch, Farsi, Finnish, French, German, Greek, Gujarati, Hebrew, Hindi, Hungarian, Italian, Japanese, Malay, Mandarin, Punjabi, Russian, Spanish, Urdu
Work: A1 A3 B1 B2 C1 C2 C3 E F1 I J1 J2 L M1 M2 N O P Q R1 R2 S1 T1 T2 U1 U2 W Z(b,c,d,e,f,i,j,k,l,n,o,w)
Ptr: Akhtar, Pervez . . . . Nov 1992
Andrew, Mr Christopher . . . . Sep 1994
Annetts, Mr Ian A . . . . *Nov 1987
Arnheim, Mr Timothy . . . . Dec 1989
Asher, Mr Alistair H LLB(Soton) . . . . *Jun 1981
Baldock, Ms Anne E LLB . . . . *Apr 1984
Bamber, Mr Andrew . . . . Nov 1984
Barry, Mr Robert S W BPharm . . . . *Dec 1989
Beardsley, Ms Alison M BA(Oxon) . . . . *Oct 1983
Bedford, Mr Paul H D LLB . . . . *Sep 1982
Benton, Mr David M . . . . Sep 1990
Beringer, Mr Guy G MA . . . . *§Aug 1980
Bevan, Mr Jonathan E M . . . . Sep 1993
Bird, Mr Nicholas M H MA . . . . *§Dec 1975
Blackmore, Ms Vanessa K . . . . Feb 1989
Borthwick, Mr Trevor J . . . . Sep 1989
Bowden, Mr Philip . . . . Apr 1999
Brailsford, Mr Mark R . . . . Sep 1989
Brayne, Mr Jonathan L F MA(Cantab) . . . . §Oct 1980
Bridgeman, Mr Francis M . . . . Sep 1993
Brown, Mr Roderick M BA(Oxon) . . . . *§Dec 1975
Brownson, Mr Jonathan M . . . . Sep 1993
Burnett, Mr Calum D . . . . Sep 1992
Buscall, Miss Anna E LLB; LLM Andrews Medal & English Law Prize . . . . *Oct 1988
Capeci, Mr Bart . . . . Jun 1987
Castle, Mr W Andrew . . . . Mar 1991
Chater, Mr Stephen P MA(Oxon) . . . . *Jun 1981
Clark, Mr Andrew J C MA(Cantab) . . . . *§Jan 1980
Cleal, Mr Adam A LLB . . . . *Feb 1982
Clist, Miss Angela H . . . . Nov 1992
Coleman, Miss Brenda A LLB; AKC(Lond) . . . . *Nov 1984
Connell, Ms Sheila T . . . . Dec 1990
Cook, Miss Lucinda LLB . . . . *Sep 1986
Cranfield, Mr Richard W L MA(Cantab) . . . . *§Jul 1980
Crook, Mr Paul MA; LLB(Cantab) . . . . *§Jun 1978
De Basto, Mr Richard Jeremy Charles . . . . Jul 1994
Desai, Bimal K LLB(Bris); LLM(Cantab) . . . . *Jan 1992
Dighero, Mr Mark . . . . Nov 1994
Doble, Mr David P LLB . . . . *Apr 1988
Drake-Brockman, Mr Anthony . . . . Sep 1992
Duncan, Mr Angus J . . . . *Feb 1989
Duncan, Mr Michael G BA(Cantab) . . . . *§Jun 1981
Elder, Mr Ian F MA(St Andrews); LLB(Edin) . . . . *Apr 1984
Evans, Ms Jacqueline . . . . Sep 1992
Fairley, Mr Ross . . . . Sep 1993
Ferguson, Mr Ian J A LLB(Soton) Sir Winston Churchill Memorial Prize . . . . *Oct 1985
Fiamma, Mr Stephen . . . . Jan 1979
Field, Mr Ian T . . . . Nov 1992
Finlayson-Brown, Ms Evelyn J E P . . . . Sep 1994
Flanagan, Mr Paul T . . . . Nov 1995
Florent, Mr Marc E LLB . . . . Nov 1992
Friend, Mr Mark W MA(Cantab); Licence en Droit Europeen(Brussels) . . . . *Oct 1982
Fuller, Mr Geoffrey William MA(Oxon) . . . . Sep 1986
Gardner, Mrs Ceris M BA(Lond) . . . . Nov 1988
Gearing, Mr Mark G P MA(Oxon) . . . . *Dec 1985
Gibbon, Mr Nick . . . . Jan 1988
Gill, Mrs Judith A E MA(Oxon) ♦ . . . . *Oct 1985
Gillespie, Mr A Stephen MA(Oxon) . . . . Nov 1987
Golden, Mr Jeffrey . . . . Jan 1978
Gorrie, Mr Euan D C . . . . Nov 1989
Gould, Mr Jonathan LLB . . . . *§Jun 1976
Haddock, Mr Simon A LLB . . . . Apr 1986
Haines, Miss Alexandra C M BA(Lond); LLM . . . . *Oct 1992
Harray, Mr Stuart M . . . . Aug 1993
Harris, Mr Julian P . . . . *Apr 1988
Harrison, Mr Brian W LLB . . . . *§Sep 1985
Harrison, Miss Pauline A . . . . Sep 1987
Harrison-Hall, Mrs Helen M MA(Oxon) . . . . *Oct 1984
Hartley, Mr Matthew Peter LLB(Hons) . . . . *Dec 1993
Harvey, Mr Robin H . . . . Oct 1992
Hazeldine, Ms Susan A . . . . Apr 1992
Henderson, Mr Guy BA(Cantab) . . . . *Oct 1982
Hill, Mr Simon G V . . . . Mar 1993
Hitchin, Mr Jonathan D J BA . . . . Jul 1990
Hockless, Mr Peter B MA(Cantab) . . . . *Jun 1981
Holgate, Ms Gillian A LLB . . . . Sep 1987
Hopper, Ms Carol J BA . . . . *Apr 1989
Hough, Mr Richard I . . . . Mar 1992
House, Mr Timothy J LLB . . . . *Mar 1986
Howard, Ms Susan D BA(Oxon) . . . . *Sep 1987
Hughes, Mr David C LLB(Lond) . . . . *§Jun 1979
Hughes, Mr David S . . . . Dec 1994
Humphrey, Mr Anthony R BA(Dunelm) . . . . *§Dec 1975
Hunt, Mr Jeremy D . . . . Oct 1990
Hunter, Mr Robert J MA; LLM . . . . *Oct 1984
Jacovides, Mr Mario LLB . . . . Sep 1989
Jagusch, Mr Stephen . . . . Aug 1998
Jones, Mr Thomas . . . . Jan 1994
Joyce, Mr Andrew L BA(Oxon) . . . . *Sep 1988
Keal, Mr Anthony C BA(Oxon) . . . . *§Jun 1974
Keck, Ms Colleen A BA; LLB; LLM . . . . *Jul 1988
Kelliher, Miss Eileen . . . . Sep 1997
Kensell, Mr Stephen . . . . Nov 1994
Krischer, Mr David Sherwin LLB(Oxon) . . . . Mar 1992
Krone, Morgan . . . . Sep 1993
Kupitz, Mr Adam . . . . Jan 1991
Lambie, Mr Christian J B . . . . Jun 1997
Lang, Mr Jonathan L BA . . . . *Sep 1986
Lee, Mr David P . . . . May 1992
Lewis, Mr David E LLB . . . . *§Jun 1976
Lindsay, Mr Alistair . . . . Mar 2001
Lines, Mr David . . . . Nov 1995
Link, Mr George P . . . . Nov 1991
Lomas, Mr Owen . . . . *Mar 1980
Lopez, Mr Ian D . . . . Dec 1993
McCallum, Ms Heather . . . . Mar 1991
McCarthy, Mr Paul H BA(Oxon) . . . . *Nov 1987
McDonald, Mr Michael . . . . Aug 1997
McGown, Mr Donald M LLB(Soton) . . . . *Apr 1983
Mackie, Mr David L MA(Oxon) ● . . . . *§Jun 1971
McKimm, Mr Daniel M . . . . Oct 1990
McLean, Mr Gary C MA(Cantab) . . . . *May 1988
Mansell, Mr Mark J LLB . . . . *Nov 1985
Manuelides, Mr Yannis . . . . Mar 1991
Martin, Mr Stefan Ferdinand LLB . . . . *Mar 1992
Maurice, Ms Clare M LLB . . . . *§Oct 1978
Mears, Mr Patrick M LLB(Lond) . . . . *Oct 1982
Mellor, Mr Jonathan S T LLB . . . . Sep 1986
Miller, Mr Stephen M . . . . Jan 1992
Monk, Mr Paul N MA(Oxon) . . . . *§Apr 1974
Morley, Mr David H MA(Cantab) . . . . *Oct 1982
Murray, Mr David T J MA(Cantab) . . . . Oct 1983
Murray, Mr Edward . . . . Jan 1986
Myers, Mr Sidney A BA(Oxon) . . . . *Oct 1984
Nathoo, Mr M Salim LLB . . . . *Oct 1992
O'Conor, Mr John G T . . . . Mar 1990
O'Neill, Mr Mark B . . . . Sep 1995
Page, Ms Joanna M MA(Cantab) . . . . *Apr 1988
Parr, Mr Jeremy . . . . Dec 1989
Parry, Mr G Mervyn MA(Cantab) . . . . *§May 1975
Paul, Mr Alan D BA; MA(Oxon) . . . . *§Jun 1980
Pearson, Mr Colin J BA; LLB; LLM . . . . *Jul 1993
Pease, Mr Alexander M MA(Oxon) . . . . *Nov 1981
Phillips, Mr Paul LLB . . . . *Sep 1987
Polglase, Mr Timothy BA(Oxon) . . . . *Oct 1986
Pritchard, Mr Nigel J . . . . Sep 1990
Quinn, Ms Julie M . . . . Sep 1994
Rae Smith, Mr Alan F MA(Cantab) . . . . May 1986
Roberts, Mr Simon . . . . Nov 1993
Rowland, Mr Richard A P MA; LLB(Cantab) . . . . *§Sep 1969
Rushton, Chris . . . . Jan 1984
Sallustio, Mr Riccardo . . . . Jan 1993
Salt, Ms Julia A BA(Oxon) . . . . *§Dec 1980
Scargill, Mr Michael P BA . . . . *Nov 1980
Schoorlemmer, Mr Andrew . . . . Mar 1993
Schulz, Mr Peter F MA(Cantab) . . . . *Oct 1983
Seward, Ms Karen E LLB . . . . *Sep 1990
Shilling, Mr Tim . . . . Mar 1992
Shurman, Mr Daniel J LLB(Nott'm) . . . . Oct 1990
Siew, Ms Yvonne E M . . . . Sep 1995
Sloan, Mr Derek S BA(Oxon) . . . . *§May 1973
Slynn, Mr Richard M MA(Cantab) . . . . *Jul 1988
Smith, Ms Catriona M MA(St Andrews) . . . . Apr 1982
Smith, Mr David M W BA(Oxon) . . . . *Oct 1984
Smith, Mr Graham R E BA(Law) . . . . *Oct 1982
Smith, Mr Richard J . . . . Sep 1994
Speller, Mr Patrick J W . . . . Nov 1989
Spooner, Ms Kerry M LLB . . . . *Apr 1990
Stanley, Mr Ian G BA(Cantab) . . . . *Apr 1984
Stewart, Mr Gordon C MA(Oxon) . . . . Oct 1980
Thornes, Mr Christopher . . . . Sep 1994
Tredgett, Mr Richard P . . . . Sep 1995
Tucker, Mr Julian A LLM . . . . Oct 1989
Turnor, Mr Richard W C BA . . . . *§Dec 1980
Vaswani, Ms Mona B A . . . . Sep 1993
Vinter, Mr Graham D BA(Oxon) . . . . *Oct 1982
Walker, Mr Calvin J . . . . Sep 1988
Walker, Mr Mark St J . . . . Mar 1991
Walton, Mr Miles H MA(Oxon); ATII . . . . *Nov 1980
Watson, Mr Peter M BA(Oxon) . . . . *§Nov 1981
Watts, Ms Sylvie Brigitte BA(Hons)(Cantab) . . . . *Nov 1988
Wedderburn-Day, Mr A Roger LLB(Lond) Richard Fitzgerald Prize (UCL) . . . . *Sep 1987
Weeks, Randal . . . . Sep 1999
Wells, Boyan S MA(Oxon) . . . . *Nov 1979
Werlen, Mr Thomas . . . . Jan 2001
Williams, Mr David L BSc . . . . *§Dec 1977
Williams, Mr Nicholas BA . . . . Oct 1985
Wilson, Mr Andrew LLB . . . . *Oct 1984
Wippell, Mr Mark A BA(Oxon); LLM . . . . *Oct 1983
Wootton, Mr David H BA . . . . *§May 1975
Wotton, Mr John P BA . . . . *§Jul 1978
Asoc: Barker, Mr David B BA(Oxon) . . . . Mar 1978
Calver, Ms Clare L . . . . Aug 1996
Staples, Miss Kate Tamzine . . . . Mar 1998
Wilson, Ms Lynda I . . . . Sep 1997
Wolinsky, Mr Jonathan LLB . . . . *Oct 1984
Woodall, Ms Lucy A MA(Cantab) . . . . *Apr 1991
Ast: Andrews, Mrs Helen Louise . . . . Sep 1996
Barnett, Mr Edward Guy BA(Hons); DipLaw . . . . *Sep 1998
Beahan, Ms Catherine Anne BA; LLB . . . . Aug 1994
Bickerton, Ms Phillipa J . . . . Sep 1997
Chakrabarti, Mr Arnondo Moy . . . . Sep 1997
Edwards, Mrs Amy Stella LLB(Cantab) . . . . Sep 1997

Hartley, Mr Matthew C T. . . . Mar 1993
Highnam, Mr Thomas Edmund BA(Hons) . . . Sep 1998
Johnson, Mr Nicholas Winston Thomas . . . Oct 1998
Mellor, Mr Adrian Michael MEng; CPE; LSF . . . Aug 1996
Owen, Mr Hugh Alexander . . . Mar 1996
Scales, Mr Timothy M C. . . . Sep 1995
Sulston, Mr Andrew BA(Hons); MA(Law) . . . Mar 1997
Con: Taylor, Miss Diana Folland . . . Nov 1970

ALLEN & OVERY LLP
40 Bank Street London E14 5DU
Tel: 020 3088 0000 *Fax:* 020 3088 0088
Office: London E1

ALLIED LAW CHAMBERS ‡
Office No210 Regent House 1 Thane Villas London N7 7PH
Tel: 020 7281 4924 *Fax:* 020 7263 8069
E-mail: alliedlaw@live.co.uk

DAVID ALTERMAN & CO ‡
PO Box 33387 London NW11 0XT
Tel: 020 8209 1234

ALTERMANS ‡
233 Regents Park Road London N3 3LF
Tel: 020 8346 1777 *Fax:* 020 8346 2776 *Dx:* 57257 FINCHLEY 2
E-mail: info@altermans.co.uk

ALTERNATIVE FAMILY LAW ‡
3 Southwark Street London SE1 1RQ
Tel: 020 7407 4007 *Fax:* 020 7407 4008
E-mail: andrea@alternativefamilylaw.co.uk
Languages: British Sign Language, German
Work: K1 K2

ALAN AMBRIDGE SOLICITOR ‡
45 Henry Tate Mews London SW16 3HA
Tel: 020 8835 8287
E-mail: alan@ambridge8287.fsnet.co.uk

AMBROSE APPELBE ‡
7 New Square Lincoln's Inn London WC2A 3RA
Tel: 020 7242 7000 *Fax:* 020 7242 0268
Dx: 467 LONDON/CHANCERY LN
E-mail: mailbox@ambrose.appelbe.co.uk
List of partners: H C E Bolgar-Smith, J Freemantle, L Sleeman, C Thomas
Work: A1 B1 D1 E J1 K1 K2 K3 K4 N O P R2 S1 S2 T1 W Z(d,e,l,q,r)
Agency and Fixed Fee Interview undertaken
Ptr: Bolgar-Smith, Mrs Henrietta C E BA. . . . *Jun 1980
Freemantle, Mr James . . . *Jan 2008
Sleeman, Mrs Lucie. . . . *Jul 2005
Thomas, Catherine . . . *Sep 2008
Con: Appelbe, Mr Felix BSc(Estate Management); FRSA . . *Oct 1972

AMER SARGENT & CO ‡
Argyll House 1a All Saints Passage London SW18 1EP
Tel: 0845 612 1006

AMPHLETT LISSIMORE ‡
Greystoke House 80-86 Westow Street Croydon London SE19 3AF
Tel: 020 8771 5254 *Fax:* 020 8771 9276
Dx: 34150 NORWOOD NORTH
E-mail: enquiries@amphlettlissimore.co.uk
List of partners: R M Bagshaw, C B Cook, E A Edwards, F H Lissimore, S G Pryse-Davies
Work: B2 D1 D2 E G H K1 K2 K3 K4 S1 S2 W
Emergency Action, Legal Aid undertaken and Legal Aid Franchise
Ptr: Bagshaw, Mr R Mark LLB ★. . . . *Oct 1982
Cook, Mr Christopher B LLM(Lond) . . . *Oct 1977
Edwards, Ms Elizabeth Ann BA . . . *Dec 1980
Lissimore, Mr Frank Howard BA. . . . *Dec 1980
Pryse-Davies, Ms Susan Gwen BA . . . *Nov 1992
Asoc: Cooke, Mr John Arthur Frederick MA; LLB . . . *Nov 1984
Ast: Antenen, Mrs Clare BA ★ . . . May 1999
Brown, Ms Estella May . . . Oct 2006
Dhanda, Ms Bawita . . . Jan 2003
Graziani, Mr Marcus Rex BA . . . *Oct 1987
Ilori, Mrs Margaret Abimbola LLB . . . *Sep 1997
Judson, Mr Christopher LLB ★ . . . *Apr 1998
Pickering, Mrs Ann Judith MSc . . . *Feb 2004
Salaman, Mrs Catherine Muriel MA . . . *Oct 1983
Seeboruth, Jaysen ★ . . . Jan 2004
Valimahomed, Mr Asan . . . Oct 1998
Con: Keall, Mr David John Holmes . . . *Jan 1971

AMWELLS ‡
205 Aberdeen House 22-24 Highbury Grove London N5 2EA
Tel: 0845 130 9792 *Fax:* 020 7000 1343
Dx: 122231 UPPER ISLINGTON
E-mail: amccallion@amwells.co.uk

AMY & CO ‡
1st Floor Fleur de Lis Court 112 Houndsditch London EC3A 7BD
Tel: 020 7539 3535 *Fax:* 020 7539 3544 *Dx:* 851 LONDON/CITY
E-mail: mail@amyandco.com
List of partners: A Patel
Languages: French, Gujarati, Hindi, Italian, Punjabi
Work: B2 C1 E F1 G J1 K1 K3 L N O Q R2 S1 S2 V W Z(d,e,f,h,i,l,q)
Fixed Fee Interview and Legal Aid undertaken
SPr: Patel, Ms Amita LLB . . . *§Apr 1989

ANA KANELLOS FURLONG SOLICITOR ‡
29 Lansdowne Gardens London SW8 2EQ
Tel: 020 7627 8131 *Fax:* 020 7627 8131
E-mail: anakanellos@me.com

ANAYSSE-JACOBS SOLICITORS ‡
1st Floor 33-35 Powis Street London SE18 6HZ
Tel: 020 8316 5000 *Fax:* 020 8316 5001 *Dx:* 33324 WOOLWICH
E-mail: nicole@anaysse-jacobs.co.uk
List of partners: N Anaysse-Jacobs
Work: K3 S1 S2 W Z(i)
Ptr: Anaysse-Jacobs, Mrs Nicole LLB; LPC . . . Aug 2001

ANDERSON CASTLE & CO LIMITED ‡
13-14 Old Square Lincoln's Inn London WC2A 3UE
Tel: 020 7831 4445 *Fax:* 020 7841 5825
Dx: 52 LONDON/CHANCERY LN
E-mail: janiecastle@13oldsquare.com

R W ANDERSON & CO ‡
(in association with M C Greenleaf & Co)
18 Great Portland Street Westminster London W1W 8QR
Tel: 020 7323 4520 *Fax:* 020 7323 4521
E-mail: rwanderson010@aol.com
List of partners: R W Anderson
Languages: Arabic
Work: E K1 L O Q S1 W Z(i,l)
Ptr: Anderson, Mr Roy William. . . . May 1985

S C ANDREW LLP ‡
Hillgate House 26 Old Bailey London EC4M 7HW
Tel: 020 7183 1701 *Fax:* 020 7183 1702
Dx: 248 LONDON/CHANCERY LN
E-mail: pamela.pillay@scandrew.com

GEORGE ANTHONY ANDREWS SOLICITORS ‡
The Old Bank 6 Western Avenue London W3 7UD
Tel: 020 8746 0550 *Fax:* 020 8746 0330 *Dx:* 153660 ACTON 7
E-mail: george@gaasolicitors.com
List of partners: G Sa'id
Languages: Arabic, French
Work: B1 D1 D2 E F1 G I J1 K1 L N O Q S1 S2 W Z(g,i,k,q,r)
Emergency Action and Fixed Fee Interview undertaken
SPr: Sa'id, Mr George LLB. . . . *Aug 1997
Ast: Hawkins, Mr Derek Malcolm. . . . Feb 1982
Pankhania, Shetal. . . . Oct 2005

ANGEL & CO ‡
1 Green Street Mayfair Westminster London W1K 6RG
Tel: 020 7495 0555 *Fax:* 020 7495 7550
E-mail: mail@legalangel-uk.com
List of partners: N P Angel
Work: B1 C1 E J1 K1 L N O Q S1 S2 W Z(e,f,k,z)
Ptr: Angel, Mr Nigel Philip LLB. . . . *Jun 1978

ANGEL LAW ‡
12 Chapel Market Islington London N1 9EZ
Tel: 020 7837 7877 *Fax:* 020 7689 1570
E-mail: info@angel-law.co.uk

JONATHAN ANGELL & CO ‡
26 Farringdon Street London EC4A 4AB
Tel: 020 7947 3366

ANKAMAH GUNN LTD ‡
118-119 Piccadilly London W1J 7NW
Tel: 020 7355 5109 *Fax:* 020 7355 5109 *Dx:* 82999 MAYFAIR
E-mail: kaa@ankamahandgunn.com

CHARLES ANNON & CO ‡
Lower Ground Floor 84 Shepherd Bush Road London W6 7PD
Tel: 020 7603 5539 *Fax:* 020 7603 7756
Dx: 32755 HAMMERSMITH 2
E-mail: info@charlesannon.co.uk
List of partners: C Appiah
SPr: Appiah, Mr Charles . . . Oct 2000

ANOOMA & HEGODA ‡
First Floor 2 Queens Parade London N8 0RD
Tel: 020 8348 7772 *Fax:* 020 8348 8100
E-mail: norma5000@gmail.com
List of partners: A N D Hegoda, R A K Hegoda
Languages: French, Polish, Sinhalese
Work: K1 Z(i)
Emergency Action undertaken
Ptr: Hegoda, Anoma Nelum Devi . . . Jul 1985
Hegoda, Ranasinghearatchige Anura K . . . *Jul 1989

ANSAH SOLICITORS ‡
2h Chatsworth Way Lambeth London SE27 9HR
Tel: 020 8761 5271 *Fax:* 020 8761 4512
Emergency telephone 07939 026876
E-mail: hilda9954@hotmail.com
List of partners: H Amoo-Gottfried
Languages: Akan, Twi
Work: B2 E G H S1 S2
Emergency Action, Advocacy and Legal Aid undertaken
SPr: Amoo-Gottfried, Mrs Hilda LLB ★. . . . *Jun 1982

ANTELL & CO ‡
PO Box 28835 London SW13 9WZ
Tel: 020 8563 0793 *Fax:* 020 8741 0952
Emergency telephone 07973 233333
List of partners: S Antell
Work: Z(m)
Emergency Action, Agency, Advocacy and Legal Aid undertaken
SPr: Antell, Ms Susan LLB(B'ham) . . . *Mar 1988

ANTHONY GOLD ‡
The Counting House 53 Tooley Street London Bridge City London SE1 2QN
Tel: 020 7940 4000 *Fax:* 020 7378 8025
Dx: 39915 LONDON BRIDGE SOUTH
E-mail: mail@anthonygold.co.uk
Web: www.anthonygold.co.uk
List of partners: R Ahmad, K Beatson, S Bibi, A J Brookes, E Chapman, M Cornish, C Fusco, N J Gunn, M Hatwood, C Kelly, J Kennedy, H A Lerman, A Malsher, P D K Mantell, D T Marshall, I Mitchell, J C Nicholson, J G Nokes, S K Prior, J P Spinks, C Tibber, T Waitt, D E Wedgwood, S R Whitaker, D Wilson
Office: London SE17, London SW16
Languages: Bengali, French, German, Gujarati, Italian, Polish
Work: A3 C1 E J1 K1 K2 K3 K4 L N O Q R2 S1 S2 T1 T2 W Z(e,g,h,p,q,r)
Emergency Action, Agency, Advocacy, Fixed Fee Interview, Legal Aid undertaken, Legal Aid Franchise and Member of Accident Line
Ptr: Beatson, Miss Kim LLB . . . *Feb 1984
Bibi, Ms Sana LLB . . . *Dec 2001
Chapman, Mrs Ellie LLB(Hons) . . . *Jan 1972
Cornish, Mr Mark BA(Hons). . . . *Mar 2002
Fusco, Ms Camilla LLB . . . *Jan 1988
Hatwood, Ms Margaret . . . *Feb 1983
Kelly, Ms Clare MA; LLB . . . *Oct 2005
Kennedy, Ms Jenny. . . . *May 1996
Lerman, Mr Howard A. . . . *Jan 1973
Malsher, Ms Ali BA; MA; RGN. . . . *Mar 1998
Marshall, Mr David T MA(Oxon) Civil Justice Council *Sep 1987
Nicholson, Mr Jonathan C BA(Oxon) Paton Studentship . . . *Nov 1991
Nokes, Mr Jonathan G LLB . . . *Jun 1975
Prior, Miss Stephanie Kathryn. . . . *Sep 1997
Spinks, Ms Jacqueline P LLB(Hons). . . . *Oct 1996
Tibber, Mr Clifford. . . . *Nov 1984
Wedgwood, Mr David Egerton DipLaw; DipASP; BA; LLM ♦ Notary Public . . . *Nov 1993
Ahmad, Mr Rafiq FCCA. . . . NSP
Ast: Anderson, Ms Katherine. . . . Sep 2009
Bourke, Miss Caroline. . . . *Jan 2010
Byrka, Ms Monika. . . . *Sep 2010
Cumbers, Mrs Shelley. . . . *Sep 2007
De Souza, Miss Sandra LLB . . . *Mar 2009
Hopkins, Miss Amanda LLB(Hons) . . . *Sep 2004
Hughes, Miss Sarah. . . . *Sep 2008
Katira, Ms Jaymini . . . *Mar 2009
Knipe, Mrs Alexandra . . . *Sep 2009
McNeill, Mr Christopher R BA; ATII; TEP . . . *May 1981
Niranjanan, Miss Roseane . . . *Apr 2008
Peters, Mr Ian. . . . *Mar 2008
Walne, Ms Victoria . . . *Sep 2009
Wright, Ms Kim . . . *Jul 2005

Other offices in London SE17 , London SW16. Holders of Franchise for Clinical Negligence, Housing. We conduct business in Bengali, French, German, Gujarati, Italian, Polish.

ANTHONY GOLD
169 Walworth Road London SE17 1RW
Tel: 020 7940 4000 *Fax:* 020 7708 3133 *Dx:* 34905 WALWORTH
E-mail: mail@anthonygold.co.uk
Office: London SE1, London SW16
Languages: Bengali, French, German, Gujarati, Hindi, Italian, Polish, Urdu
Work: A3 B1 C1 E F1 J1 K1 K2 K3 K4 L N O Q R2 S1 S2 T1 T2 W Z(e,g,h,k,p,q,r)
Emergency Action, Agency, Advocacy, Fixed Fee Interview, Legal Aid undertaken and Member of Accident Line
Ptr: Brookes, Mr Andrew James. . . . *Nov 1994
Mantell, Mr Peter D K BA(Hons). . . . *Nov 1999
Waitt, Mr Timothy . . . *Jul 2003
Ast: Collins, Ms Charlotte . . . Sep 2005
Peaker, Mr Giles . . . *Nov 2008
Stephens, Ms Sara . . . *Mar 2009

We conduct business in Bengali, French, German, Gujarati, Hindi, Italian, Polish, Urdu. We specialise in the following areas of work Housing, Landlord and Tenant, Residential Conveyancing, Commercial Conveyancing, Wills and Probate.

ANTHONY GOLD
Lloyds Bank Chambers 186 Streatham High Road London SW16 1BG
Tel: 020 7940 4000 *Fax:* 020 8664 6484 *Dx:* 58604 STREATHAM
E-mail: mail@anthonygold.co.uk
Web: www.anthonygold.co.uk
Office: London SE1, London SE17
Languages: Bengali, French, German, Gujarati, Italian, Polish
Work: A3 C1 E J1 K1 K2 K3 K4 L N O Q R2 S1 S2 T1 T2 W Z(e,g,h,p,q,r)
Emergency Action, Agency, Advocacy, Fixed Fee Interview, Legal Aid undertaken, Legal Aid Franchise and Member of Accident Line
Ptr: Gunn, Miss Nicola Jane LLB; LPC. . . . *Sep 1998
Mitchell, Mr Ian . . . *Jul 2004
Whitaker, Mr Stephen R LLB(Hons) . . . *Mar 1984
Wilson, Ms Debra BA(Hons); LLM. . . . *Apr 1992
Ast: Smith, Mr David LLB . . . *Feb 2011
Con: Bowden, Mrs Caroline LLB . . . *Apr 1992
Hamilton, Mr John. . . . Feb 1973
Wallace, Mr Philip Notary Public. . . . *Nov 1978

Holders of Franchise for Clinical Negligence, Housing. We conduct business in Bengali, French, German, Gujarati, Italian, Polish.

ANTHONY HOLDEN CROFTS & CO
Orion Park Northfield Avenue Ealing London W13 9SJ
Tel: 020 8840 7878 *Fax:* 020 8840 7073 *Dx:* 5111 EALING
E-mail: m.cosstick@anthony-holden-crofts.co.uk
Office: Brentford
Work: E K4 S1 S2 W Z(d)
Ptr: Cosstick, Mr Mark LLB . . . *Oct 1981

ANTHONY SOLICITORS ‡
933 Green Lanes Winchmore Hill Enfield London N21 2PB
Tel: 020 8360 4333 *Fax:* 020 8360 5444
List of partners: A Demetriou
Languages: Greek
Work: J1 K1 K3 L N O Q S1 W
SPr: Demetriou, Mr Anthony BA(Hons). . . . Apr 1991

GEORGE A ANTONIADES ‡
72 Queens Drive Finsbury Park London N4 2HW
Tel: 020 8800 4146 *Fax:* 020 8809 1764
List of partners: G A Antoniades
Languages: Greek
Work: E F1 S1 S2 W
SPr: Antoniades, Mr George A MA(Oxon) . . . Dec 1975

ANTONS ‡
14 Wordsworth House Wordworth Parade London N8 0SJ
Tel: 020 8888 6211 *Fax:* 020 8888 1403 *Dx:* 57763 HARRINGAY
List of partners: K A R Bulathwela, R M S Bulathwela
Languages: Bengali, Hindi, Punjabi, Russian, Sinhalese, Somali, Tamil, Turkish
Work: G H J1 K1 L N Q S1 S2 V Z(i,l)
Fixed Fee Interview and Legal Aid undertaken
Ptr: Bulathwela, Mr Kumar Anton Rohitha LLB. . . . *Jul 1991
Bulathwela, Mrs Rani M S. . . . May 1991

APEX SOLICITORS ‡
163 Ray Lane London SE15 4TL
Tel: 020 7635 6160 *Fax:* 020 7639 1305
E-mail: admin@apexsolicitors.co.uk

See p2 for the Key to Work Categories & other symbols

APPLEBY ‡
4th Floor 2 Royal Exchange Buildings London EC3V 3LF
Tel: 020 7283 6061 *Fax:* 020 7469 0540
E-mail: wcabral@applebyglobal.com

ARAVINDANS ‡
216a High Street North Newham London E6 2JA
Tel: 020 8503 5034 *Fax:* 020 8471 7307 *Dx:* 4721 EAST HAM
E-mail: aravindans@tiscali.co.uk
List of partners: R Aravindan, S Aravindan
Languages: Sinhalese, Tamil
Work: S1 S2 Z(i,l)
Ptr: Aravindan, Mrs Renuka . . . . Jun 1986
Aravindan, Selvadurai. . . . . Jun 1986

ARBIS LLP ‡
Marble Quay St Kathrine's Dock London E1W 1UH
Tel: 020 7481 2188 *Fax:* 020 7481 4622
E-mail: london@arbisllp.com

ARC PROPERTY SOLICITORS LLP
3rd Floor 207 Regent Street London W1B 3HH
Tel: 0800 612 9097 *Fax:* 0845 260 0777
E-mail: info@arcpropertysolicitors.com
Office: Harrogate

ARCHON SOLICITORS ‡
Martin House 5 Martin Lane London EC4R 0DP
Tel: 020 7397 9650 *Fax:* 020 7929 6316 *Dx:* 706 LONDON/CITY
E-mail: n.ralph@archonlaw.co.uk
List of partners: C Aldridge, R McCreath, N J Ralph, J Scott, J A G Williams
Work: J1 Z(p)
Advocacy and Fixed Fee Interview undertaken
Ptr: Aldridge, Ms Corinne . . . . Sep 1987
McCreath, Mr Robert . . . . Jan 1989
Ralph, Mr Nicholas J . . . . Jan 1988
Scott, Mrs Jill LLB; LLM. . . . . Apr 1991
Mem: Williams, Mr James Alistair Goronwy LLB; LLM . . . . Sep 2000

ARDEN SOLICITORS (IMMIGRATION SPECIALIST) ‡
Ealing House 33 Hanger Lane North Ealing London W5 3HJ
Tel: 020 8997 8885
Emergency telephone 07508 257657
E-mail: info@ardensolicitors.com

GRANT ARGENT & CO ‡
(incorporating Frederick Bauer & Co)
Bank House 59-61 The Broadway Cricklewood Brent London NW2 3JX
Tel: 020 8452 7651 *Fax:* 020 8450 9903 *Dx:* 35350 CRICKLEWOOD
E-mail: post@grantargent.com
List of partners: G M Argent, P J Hallinan
Work: B1 C1 E L N O Q R1 S1 S2 W Z(c,l)
Ptr: Argent, Mr Grant M MA; LLB . . . . *Dec 1965
Hallinan, Mr Patrick J . . . . *May 1981
Ast: Anderson, Mr Timothy MA. . . . . Aug 2009
Gilbride, Ms Caroline BSc. . . . . Dec 2006

E G ARGHYRAKIS & CO ‡
11 Bouverie Street London EC4Y 8DP
Tel: 020 7353 2302 *Fax:* 020 7353 2295
Emergency telephone 020 7353 2302
E-mail: office@egalegal.com
List of partners: E G Arghyrakis, S L Glover
Languages: French, Greek, Spanish
Work: A3 O Z(a,j)
Ptr: Arghyrakis, Mr Epaminondas George . . . . May 1994
Glover, Ms Susan Louise LLB. . . . . *Mar 1982

ARION LAW ‡
41 Lothbury London EC2R 7HG
Tel: 020 3178 3944 *Fax:* 020 3170 8701
E-mail: tao@arionlaw.com

ARLINGTON CROWN SOLICITORS ‡
Suite 1 596 Green Lanes Winchmore Hill London N13 5RY
Tel: 020 8882 1166

ARLINGTON SOLICITORS ‡
350 Walworth Road London SE17 2NA
Tel: 020 7703 4002 *Fax:* 020 7703 4126

ARLINGTONS SHARMAS SOLICITORS ‡
6 Arlington Street London SW1A 1RE
Tel: 020 7299 8999

ARMSTRONG & CO ‡
2 Dartmouth Road Forest Hill London SE23 3XU
Tel: 020 8699 3477 *Fax:* 020 8291 3645 *Dx:* 34400 FOREST HILL
List of partners: J L Burrows, S G Heiman, A S Pimstone
Work: B1 C1 E K1 L O Q S1 S2 W Z(q)
Ptr: Burrows, Miss Jane L BA . . . . *Nov 1983
Heiman, Mr S Gerald LLB(Sydney) . . . . *Jul 1965
Pimstone, Mr Anton S BA. . . . . *§Sep 1975

ARMSTRONG LAW LLP ‡
600 Lea Bridge Road Leyton London E1 7DN
Tel: 020 8556 7090

ARMSTRONGS ‡
167b Kingston Road London SW19 1LJ
Tel: 020 8543 6800 *Fax:* 020 8543 6812
E-mail: simon@armstrongslaw.co.uk

ARNOLD & PORTER LLP ‡
Tower 42 25 Old Broad Street London EC2N 1HQ
Tel: 020 7786 6100 *Fax:* 020 7786 6299 *Dx:* 42622 CHEAPSIDE
List of partners: A F Brown
Ptr: Brown, Ms Alison F LLB(Bris) . . . . *Nov 1990
Ast: Casey, Mr Stuart BSc(Bris) . . . . Sep 1997

ARNOLD FOOKS CHADWICK LLP ‡
15 Bolton Street London W1J 8AR
Tel: 020 7499 3007 *Fax:* 020 7499 3863
E-mail: info@afclaw.co.uk
List of partners: J E N Bates, R G Millman, T C O'Callaghan
Languages: French
Work: A3 B1 B3 C1 C2 C3 E I J1 K4 L M2 N O P Q R1 R2 S1 S2 T1 T2 U1 U2 W X Z(c,d,e,f,j,q,r,w,za)
Emergency Action, Agency, Advocacy undertaken and Member of Accident Line
Ptr: Bates, Mr Jonathan E N BA. . . . . *Jun 1980
Millman, Mr Roger G BSc. . . . . *Nov 1974
O'Callaghan, Mr Timothy C LLB. . . . . *Aug 2002
Asoc: Varma, Miss Nina LLB. . . . . *Apr 1989
Con: Young, Mr David B S BA . . . . *Oct 1986

K A ARNOLD & CO ‡
One Canonbury Place London N1 2NG
Tel: 020 7354 4926 *Fax:* 020 7354 5148 *Dx:* 51852 HIGHBURY
E-mail: kenneth@kaarnold.com
List of partners: K A Arnold
Work: B1 C1 E G J1 K1 L M1 M2 N O P Q S1 W Z(c,e,i,k)
Emergency Action, Agency and Legal Aid undertaken
Ptr: Arnold, Mr Kenneth Alan ACIArb Deputy District Judge *Jun 1972

ARONA SARWAR LLP ‡
250c Hoe Street Walthamstow London E17 3AX
Tel: 020 8520 5170 *Fax:* 020 8520 2197 *Dx:* 32018 WALTHAMSTOW
E-mail: info@aronasarwar.co.uk
Languages: Punjabi, Urdu
Work: B1 C1 E F1 F2 J1 K1 K3 O Q S1 S2 W Z(e,f,i,za)
Fixed Fee Interview undertaken

ARORA LODHI HEATH ‡
170 High Street London W3 6QZ
Tel: 020 8993 9995 *Fax:* 020 8992 2628 *Dx:* 80258 ACTON
Emergency telephone 07956 565819 / 900667
E-mail: alh@lawyer.com
List of partners: R S Arora, R A Lodhi, T Mahmood, N Patel
Office: London NW5
Languages: Arabic, French, Gujarati, Polish, Punjabi, Spanish, Urdu
Work: B2 D1 D2 F1 G H I J1 K1 K2 K3 N O Q S1 V W Z(g,i,r)
Emergency Action, Agency, Advocacy, Fixed Fee Interview, Legal Aid undertaken and Legal Aid Franchise
Ptr: Arora, Raghwinder Singh ★. . . . . Mar 1994
Lodhi, Roohul Ameen ★. . . . . Apr 1993
Mahmood, Mr Tahir . . . . Jun 2000
Patel, Miss Nimisha ★. . . . . Nov 1997
Ast: Aldeiri, Mr Malik LLB . . . . Jan 2006

ARORA LODHI HEATH
Office 6 19 Greenwood Place Kentish Town London NW5 1LB
Tel: 020 7267 3281 *Fax:* 020 7424 9627 *Dx:* 80258 ACTON
Emergency telephone 07930 560724
E-mail: alh@lawyer.com
Office: London W3
Work: B2 G H
Emergency Action, Agency, Advocacy, Fixed Fee Interview and Legal Aid undertaken

ARORA SOLICITORS ‡
12 Green Street Forest Gate London E7 8BZ
Tel: 020 8472 6869 *Fax:* 020 8472 6853 *Dx:* 52111 FOREST GATE

ARUAN CONSULTING LIMITED ‡
51 Montpelier Walk London SW7 1JH
Tel: 020 7225 2696
E-mail: cchia123@hotmail.com

ASH NORTON SOLICITORS ‡
7th Floor Westgate House London W5 1YY
Tel: 020 8991 3330 / 8991 3331 *Fax:* 020 8991 3332
E-mail: enquiries@ashnorton-solicitors.com
Languages: Gujarati, Hindi, Kurdish
Work: D2 M1 Z(g,i)
Agency and Fixed Fee Interview undertaken

ASHBY COHEN SOLICITORS LIMITED
1 Creed Court 5 Ludgate Hill London EC4M 7AA
Tel: 020 3201 0062 *Fax:* 020 7434 3925
E-mail: infosp@ashbycohen.co.uk
Office: London W1

ASHBY COHEN SOLICITORS LTD ‡
18 Hanover Street London W1S 1YN
Tel: 020 7408 1338 *Fax:* 020 7491 0414
E-mail: info@ashbycohen.co.uk
Office: London EC4
Work: J1

ASHFORDS LLP
41 Dover Street London W1S 4NS
Tel: 020 3581 8970 *Fax:* 020 3581 8971
E-mail: info@ashfords.co.uk
Office: Bristol, Exeter, Plymouth, Taunton, Tiverton
Work: C1 E O
Agency undertaken

ALAN ASHLEY & CO ‡
36 Whitefriars Street London EC4Y 8BQ
Tel: 020 7822 7482 *Fax:* 020 7583 3433
Dx: 329 LONDON/CHANCERY LN
E-mail: mail@ashlaw.co.uk
List of partners: A J Ashley
Work: A1 C1 C2 E J2 L M1 O P Q R1 R2 S2 Z(c,q,s,u)
SPr: Ashley, Mr Alan J LLB. . . . . *Jun 1973

ASHURST LLP ‡
Broadwalk House 5 Appold Street London EC2A 2HA
Tel: 020 7638 1111 *Fax:* 020 7638 1112 *Dx:* 639 LONDON/CITY
E-mail: enquiries@ashurst.com
List of partners: B A R Allen, P J Allen, N B Avery, J Bell, R Beven, G D Boothman, S Bromwich, N Bryans, A T Burnett-Scott, H C Burton, D Bushner, C J Carter, D Carter, A Clare, A S Clark, J Coiley, S T Cookson, C Coulter, A G T Curnow, A A A Dear, A Delgado, J C Drake, C Easter, L Eccleston, M P Elsey, M C Elvy, D J Evans, G G Fernandez, R J Finbow, J Fissenden, C S H Geffen, C K Georgiou, G S Green, R S Gubbins, E Handling, M C Hanson, B J Hanton, R Harris, S M Harris, J Hogben, N Holmes, M Hughes, S Hull, M C Johns, I L Johnson, D N Jones, M Jordan, G V Kelly, R Kendall, R C King, A W N Kitchin, J Levy, D J M Liddell, S Lloyd, M Logie, H J E Loose, M A Lubbock, H Lumby, M Madden, L Mair, L McDonald, M McDonald, A McDougall, A McMillan, R E Ogilvy Watson, D W Page, R C S Palmer, N Parr, A Pearson, J H Perry, G Picton-Turbervill, P N Randall, T M C Reid, M G Robins, M C Rogers, S Roy, J Sanders, E Saunders, J Sharrock, J B Sheldon, J N Sheldon, C Smith, M Smith, M J Smith, E C A Sparrow, N J Stacey, I C Starr, D R Stiles, E Stuart, J A Sultoon, H C Thomas, J A Thomas, P Thomson, W H Thorburn, S Thrower, B J C Tidswell, P W Vernon, R D Vernon, M H Vickers, C Vigrass, D Von Sauckon, G C Ward, N T Ward, S Watkinson, G Watson, J G Watson, C Whiteley, N C Williamson, F Wood, M C E Wright
Languages: Afrikaans, Arabic, Bengali, Cantonese, Chinese, Czech, Danish, French, German, Greek, Gujarati, Hebrew, Hindi, Hungarian, Icelandic, Italian, Japanese, Korean, Latin, Latvian, Mandarin, Norwegian, Portuguese, Punjabi, Russian, Spanish, Turkish, Welsh
Work: A3 B1 C1 C2 C3 E F2 I J1 J2 L M1 M2 N O P Q R1 R2 S1 S2 T1 U1 Z(b,c,e,j,n,o,p,u,w)
Ptr: Allen, Miss Barbara A R MA(Cantab) . . . . Oct 1983
Allen, Ms Patricia J BA . . . . Jun 1992
Avery, Mr Nicholas B LLB(Leics) . . . . Jan 1990
Bell, Mr Jeremy . . . . Nov 1994
Beven, Mr Ray . . . . Jul 1990
Boothman, Mr Giles D. . . . . May 1993
Bromwich, Mr Simon . . . . Jan 1992
Bryans, Mr Nicholas. . . . . Oct 1996
Burnett-Scott, Mr Anthony T LLB . . . . *Apr 1990
Burton, Ms Helen C. . . . . Dec 1994
Bushner, Mr Daniel . . . . Oct 1996
Carter, Mrs Caroline J LLB Herbert Ruse Prize; Clabon Prize . . . . *§Apr 1990
Carter, Mr David . . . . *Nov 1993
Clare, Mr Anthony. . . . . May 1995
Clark, Mr Adrian S MA(Cantab) . . . . *Nov 1983
Coiley, Mr James . . . . Jan 1994
Cookson, Mr Simon T BA(Oxon) . . . . Oct 1984
Coulter, Mr Chris BA(Oxon); LPC . . . . *Dec 1992
Curnow, Mr Anthony G T LLB(Leics) . . . . *Apr 1979
Dear, Mr Adrian A A LLB(Lond) . . . . *Oct 1982
Delgado, Ms Anna . . . . Oct 1995
Drake, Mr Jonathan C LLB . . . . *Oct 1990
Easter, Ms Caroline LLB . . . . *Apr 1991
Eccleston, Ms Louise . . . . Mar 1993
Elsey, Mr Mark P LLB(Lond). . . . . Nov 1985
Elvy, Mr Mark C LLB(UNSW) . . . . Apr 1991
Evans, Mr David J LLB(Bris) . . . . Nov 1987
Fernandez, Mr Gonzalo G LLB; AKC . . . . May 1990
Finbow, Mr Roger J MA(Oxon) . . . . Oct 1977
Fissenden, Ms Jane. . . . . Dec 1991
Geffen, Mr Charles S H LLB(Leics) . . . . Oct 1984
Georgiou, Mr Christopher K. . . . . Nov 1991
Green, Mr Geoffrey S MA(Cantab) . . . . Dec 1975
Gubbins, Mr Richard S LLB(Wales) . . . . *Oct 1982
Handling, Ms Erica . . . . Jan 1996
Hanson, Mr Marc C BA(East Anglia) . . . . *Apr 1994
Hanton, Mr Bruce J LLB; LLM(Bris) . . . . Dec 1988
Harris, Ms Ruth. Oct 1997
Harris, Mr Stephen M BA(Oxon). . . . . Oct 1988
Hogben, Mr James . . . . Oct 1997
Holmes, Mr Nicholas . . . . Sep 1994
Hughes, Mat . . . . Jan 2003
Hull, Mr Steven . . . . Oct 1989
Johns, Mr Michael C BA(Oxon) New Inn Prize. . . . . *§Apr 1972
Johnson, Mr Ian L. . . . . Jul 1992
Jones, Mr David N LLB . . . . Nov 1994
Jordan, Ms Melanie . . . . Oct 1997
Kelly, Mr Gerald V. . . . . Jun 1993
Kendall, Mr Richard MA. . . . . *Oct 1985
King, Mr Ronald C BA(Cantab); LLM(Cantab) Simmons Scholar . . . . Oct 1986
Kitchin, Mr Alan W N BA(Cantab) . . . . *May 1978
Levy, Mr James. Apr 1996
Liddell, Mr Duncan J M . . . . Oct 1995
Lloyd, Mr Stephen BA(Cantab) . . . . *Nov 1994
Logie, Mr Michael. . . . . Apr 1999
Loose, Miss Helen Jane Elizabeth LLB . . . . *Aug 1992
Lubbock, Mr Mark A BA(Cantab) . . . . Sep 1984
Lumby, Mr Hugh . . . . Nov 1992
McDonald, Mr Lee . . . . Apr 1997
McDonald, Mr Matt . . . . Jan 1995
McDougall, Arundel MA(Oxon) . . . . *Dec 1978
McMillan, Mr Andrew . . . . Oct 1997
Madden, Mr Michael LLB(Lond). . . . . *Oct 1987
Mair, Mr Logan . . . . Jan 1995
Ogilvy Watson, Mr Robert Eric LLB . . . . Sep 1993
Page, Mr David W LLB(Leics). . . . . *Dec 1982
Palmer, Mr Richard C S MA(Cantab); LLM(Lond) . . . *Oct 1988
Parr, Mr Nigel LLB; LLM; PhD(Exon) . . . . Nov 1989
Pearson, Ms Angela . . . . Nov 1991
Perry, Mr James H BA . . . . Nov 1989
Picton-Turbervill, Mr Geoffrey BA(Cantab). . . . . . . Nov 1985
Randall, Mr Paul N LLB(Lond). . . . . *Oct 1984
Reid, Mr Timothy M C LLB(Bris). . . . . Nov 1987
Robins, Mr Michael G BA(Lond). . . . . Dec 1985
Rogers, Mr Martyn C BA . . . . Apr 1997
Roy, Ms Susan LLB; BA(Canberra) . . . . Jun 1989
Sanders, Mrs Janis LLB(Sheff) Sheffield & Marshall Strout Prize . . . . Oct 1984
Saunders, Eavan . . . . Mar 2003
Sharrock, Ms Judith LLB(Soton). . . . . Jun 1990
Sheldon, Mr Jeremy B LLB(Soton) . . . . Sep 1990
Sheldon, Mr Jeremy N BA(Leeds). . . . . Oct 1980
Smith, Mr Cameron . . . . Sep 1998
Smith, Mr Michael. . . . . Mar 1992
Smith, Mr Michael J. . . . . Mar 1992
Sparrow, Mr Edward C A MA(Oxon). . . . . Dec 1977
Stacey, Mr Nigel J LLB(Soton) . . . . *Jan 1992
Starr, Mr Ian C MA(Cantab) . . . . Apr 1979
Stiles, Mr Duncan R. . . . . Nov 1992
Stuart, Mr Eric . . . . Jan 1992
Sultoon, Mr Jeffrey A MA(Oxon). . . . . Jul 1978
Thomas, Mr Huw C . . . . Oct 1985
Thomas, Mr Jeremy A. . . . . Apr 1996
Thomson, Mr Phillip. . . . . Apr 1977
Thorburn, Mr Wilson H . . . . May 1993
Thrower, Mr Simon . . . . Jan 1991
Tidswell, Mr Benjamin James Cuthbert ♦ . . . . Jul 1994
Vernon, Mr Philip W MA(Oxon) . . . . Nov 1989
Vernon, Mr Richard D. . . . . Nov 1992
Vickers, Mr Mark H LLB(B'ham). . . . . *Oct 1982
Vigrass, Mr Christopher MA(Cantab) . . . . *Apr 1980
Von Sauckon, Mr David. . . . . Jul 2002
Ward, Mr Graeme C LLB(Lond) . . . . Nov 1988
Ward, Mr Nigel T BA(Oxon). . . . . Oct 1985
Watkinson, Ms Sarah . . . . Oct 1994
Watson, Mr Gary MA(Oxon). . . . . *Apr 1979
Watson, Mr John G MA(Cantab) . . . . Jan 1985
Whiteley, Chris . . . . Nov 1994
Williamson, Mr Nicholas C . . . . Oct 1996
Wood, Mr Fraser . . . . Jan 1977
Wright, Mr Martin C E LLB . . . . *Nov 1988
Asoc: Ostrovsky, Mr Sergei . . . . Oct 1999

Ast: Arends, Mr Gerald Sep 2005
Arnold, Mr David Sep 2000
Ashman, Mr Giles Sep 2002
Asser, Mr Carl Dec 1993
Atkinson, Mr Justin Sep 2004
Attrill, Mr Louis Sep 2004
Austin, Ms Miranda Mar 2002
Backhouse, Mr Theodore Sep 2005
Balasubramanian, Mr Anu Nov 2000
Barber, Ms Georgina Ann Sep 2002
Barwick, Mr Glynn Jan 2003
Batchelor, Mr Dominic Sep 2000
Bate, Ms Marianne Jun 2002
Bates, Mr Christopher Mar 2003
Bavinton, Mr Martin Oct 2000
Behrens, Mr Peter Sep 2004
Belcher, Mr William Sep 1999
Bell, Mr Graeme Sep 2003
Benham, Mr Nicholas Mar 2002
Bennett, Mr Edward Mar 2002
Biddulph, Ms Annabel Mar 2002
Biles, Ms Caroline Sep 2004
Bointon, Ms Sarah Sep 2001
Boulton, Ms Kim Nov 1994
Bowe, Ms Andrea Oct 2000
Boyle, Mr Patrick Sep 1998
Broadhurst, Mr Jamie Sep 2002
Broomfield, Mr Robert Dec 1975
Brozyniak-Siddiqui, Edyta Sep 2002
Buckland, Mr James Oct 1997
Burmeister, Mr Nikolaus Sep 2002
Cartwright, Mr Tom Sep 2000
Castagnino, Mr Peter Jul 2000
Cave, Mr David Sep 2003
Chamberlain, Mr Patrick Sep 2004
Chapman, Mr Jamie Jun 1997
Cheng, Ms Angelina Aug 2001
Cheshire, Mr Nick Sep 1998
Choi, Doos Sep 1999
Christoforou, Ms Joanna Sep 2000
Clark, Ms Emily Mar 2002
Clarke, Ms Emma Mar 2002
Clarke, Ms Paula Sep 1999
Cockerton, Ms Emma Sep 2002
Collins, Mr Niall Oct 2005
Colquhoun, Mr Ian Feb 1970
Conner, Mr Tom Sep 2004
Cottell, Ms Sarah Sep 2005
Cox, Mr Alexander Sep 1999
Criscuolo, Mr Luis Sep 2005
Crowther, Ms Julia Dec 1991
Cuninghame, Mr Neil Oct 1997
Dailly, Mr Andrew Sep 2003
Dare, Ms Jocelyn *Mar 1997
Davidson, Mr Ross Mar 2003
De Caulaincourt, Ms Catherine Dauger Mar 2002
Dinamani, Ms Karan Sep 2005
Dixon, Mr Christ BA(Hons); DipLaw Sep 1998
Dunphy, Shereagh Sep 2004
Earle, Mr Jon Mar 2000
Edey, Ms Kate Mar 2000
Edwards, Mr Mark Mar 2003
Ekanayake, Mr Joanna Mar 2002
Elliott, Mr Adrian Sep 2002
Epton, Mr Dom Sep 2000
Evans, Mr Alex Sep 2005
Eveleigh, Ms Kate Nov 1994
Fenech-Pisani, Mr Clinton Sep 2002
Ferguson, Mr Gordon Sep 2003
Filkin, Mr Matthew Sep 2003
Fisk, Ms Mary Sep 2005
Fletcher, Mr James Sep 2005
Foh, Ms Dione May 2005
Fry, Ms Monique Jan 2000
Futter, Mr David Sep 2004
Gardner, Mr Nicholas Sep 2003
Gatehouse, Ms Mary Sep 2002
Giaretta, Mr Ben Sep 2001
Gin, Ms Anita Sep 2002
Glynn, Mr Laurence Oct 2000
Goddard, Mr Nick Sep 2005
Gordon, Mr Gavin Sep 1999
Gordon-Orr, Mr Adair Sep 2004
Gori, Mr Luca Sep 2003
Griffin, Mr Chris Mar 2003
Gwilliams, Mr Ivor Sep 2000
Hagan, Mr Phil Apr 1998
Haines, Mr Jonathan Apr 1998
Hammon, Mr Charles Sep 1998
Hardy, Ms Nicola Feb 2003
Harvey, Mr Julian Sep 2003
Henderson, Ms Stephanie Sep 2005
Hendry, Ms Eva Sep 2000
Hetherington, Ms Louisa Sep 2001
Higgs, Mr Mark Sep 2005
Hoare, Mr Jonathan Oct 1986
Hoffman, Ms Camilla Sep 2004
Holland, Mr Alastair Sep 1999
Holmes, Mr Chris Sep 2004
Holness, Ms Kirsty Sep 2005
Hooper, Mr James Sep 2001
Hooton, Mr Matthew Sep 1998
Hoquee, Mr Steve Nov 1993
Hudson, Mr Andrew Apr 1977
Hurst, Mr Phillip Jul 1994
Huxley, Ms Kirsty Sep 1999
Iseries, Inbali Mar 2004
Jenner, Ms Jessica Sep 2003
Jones, Mr Marc *Apr 1999
Keane, Ms Louise Sep 1999
Ketteley, Jo Sep 2000
Ketteley, Mr Stephen Sep 2000
Kettle, Ms Sarah Oct 1998
King, Ms Claire Sep 2003
Krige, Mr Karen Feb 1999
Kyriakou, Mr Shane Nov 2003
Langat, Mr Ronald Jul 2002
Laver, Ms Sara Nov 1992
Lawford, Ms Louise Sep 2003
Lees, Mr Nicholas Sep 2002
Legge, Ms Anna Sep 2005
Leighton, Mr Dafydd Sep 2003
Levy, Mr Nick Sep 2004
Lewis, Mr Alex Mar 2004
Lewis, Ms Lucy Mar 2004
Lo, Ms Michelle Jul 2005
Lonsdale, Ms Annalisa Oct 1994
Ludiman, Ms Sarah Jun 2002
McGregor, Mr Andrew Sep 2003
Mackenzie, Mr Ross Mar 2002
McNeil, Ms Georgina Sep 2002
Mander, Ms Claire Mar 2001
Mantle, Mr Myles Dec 1995
Markanday, Mr Nikhil Mar 2004
Markey, Mr David Sep 2004
Marr, Ms Fiona Nov 2000
Marsh, Mr James Sep 2004
Matthews, Ms Caroline Sep 2000
May, Mr Richard Mar 2002
Mercer, Mr Tom Sep 2003
Miller, Mr Paul Sep 2000
Millers, Liga Mar 2003
Minott, Diala Sep 2000
Moss, Mr Henry Sep 2003
Murdoch, Mr Paul Mar 2003
Murphy, Mr Brian Jul 1976
Neuberger, Mr Jessica Sep 2005
O'Hare, Mr Robert Sep 2003
O'Neill, Mr Daniel Oct 2003
O'Neill, Ms Phillippa Sep 2000
Ornolfsson, Mr Jon Sep 2005
Osler, Mr Jeremy Sep 1999
Owen, Mr Dyfan Mar 2004
Page, Mr Martin Sep 2005
Parry, Mr Jonathan Sep 2002
Pawson, Mr Nicholas Sep 2003
Pearman, Mr Tom Sep 2005
Pirie, Ms Mia Forbes Dec 2002
Plenderleith, Mr Mark Sep 1999
Power, Ms Shona Sep 2002
Preston, Ms Diane Nov 1988
Purewal, Amarjit Sep 2003
Quirolo, Mr David Oct 2004
Race, Mr Mark Oct 1984
Rasaratnam, Pritheeva Mar 2002
Raven, Mr Anthony Sep 1999
Ravenscroft, Mr Stephen May 1998
Raynes, Mr Jonathan Oct 1993
Rayson, Ms Caroline Mar 2003
Reed, Mr Duncan Mar 2004
Reid, Mr Alexander Sep 2004
Rickard, Ms Tamsin Sep 2004
Ridley, Ms Kate Sep 2003
Robertson, Ms Sian Mar 2003
Robinson, Jo Sep 2005
Robley, Ms Liza Sep 2004
Roseveare, Mr Martin Sep 2004
Russell, Mr Jamie Sep 2005
Sami, Mr Fuat BA(Modern History) Sep 2004
Sandhu, Jaskiran Mar 2004
Sanichara, Mr Dhanesh Sep 1999
Schady, Ms Beatrice Sep 2000
Schulze, Ms Sandra Sep 2005
Scott, Mr Ian Feb 1968
Segall, Mr Mark Oct 2001
Senior, Mr Joe Nov 1993
Shearer, Ms Lucy Aug 1999
Shergill, Kiran Sep 2005
Simpson, Mr Tom Mar 2001
Sivyour, Ms Sarah Sep 2002
Sokhi, Rabinder Sep 1999
Sonneborn, Ms Katharine Sep 2005
Sperotto, Mr Mark Sep 1998
Squire, Mr Paul Mar 2004
Stalbow, Mr Nick Sep 1999
Staples, Ms Maria Sep 2003
Stephens, Mr Daniel Sep 2000
Stewart, Mr Paul Mar 2000
Stimson, Mr Matthew Sep 2002
Swann, Mr Simon Sep 2000
Tam, Ms Katie Mar 2004
Tan, Mr Gene Sep 2005
Tang, Mr Chris Apr 2002
Taylor, Mr Christopher Arthur LLB *Nov 1995
Thomas, Ms Lucy Sep 2002
Triscott, Ms Alana Nov 1995
Van Poortvliet, Mr Terry Mar 2003
Wade, Ms Patricia Dec 1990
Warburton, Mr Edward Piers MA Sep 1998
Warner, Mr Ian Sep 2000
Warren, Ms Georgina Mar 2004
Watson, Ms Sara A LLB(Leeds) Oct 1991
Whitehead, Ms Catherine Jun 2002
Willmott, Ms Anna Sep 2005
Withey, Mr Mark Sep 2001
Woodford, Crowley Mar 1998
Woodroffe, Mr Brad Mar 2002
Yow, Mr Edwin Oct 2003
Con: Beddow, Mr Simon D J LLB(Bris) Oct 1989
Burrows, Mr W Rupert Dec 1991
Collis, Mr James H R Sep 1998
De Cordova, Mr Paul BA *Mar 1985
Fox, Mr Steven May 1993

ASHWORTHS SOLICITORS ‡
The Old Exchange 12 Compton Road Wimbledon London SW19 3RU
Tel: 0845 370 1000 ***Fax:*** 0845 370 1001
Dx: 300112 WIMBLEDON CENTRAL
E-mail: astruthers@ashworths.co.uk
List of partners: B Dean, J A Howard, L Newton, A Struthers
Work: C1 E S1 S2
Ptr: Dean, Mr Brendan Dec 1997
Howard, Mr James Alexander LLB Apr 2000
Newton, Loveday Mar 1978
Struthers, Mr Andrew Jan 1979
Ast: Hook, Mrs Merryn BA; LLB *Oct 2003
McKendrick, Miss Rachel Sarah LLB(Hons) Aug 2004
Martin, Ms Joanna Elizabeth Oct 1987
Reed, Mr Nicholas Joseph Oct 2003

ASKBEG SOLICITORS ‡
Suite 111 4-16 Deptford Bridge Bilt Mansions London SE8 4HH
Tel: 020 8320 2272 ***Fax:*** 020 8320 2285
E-mail: admin@askbegsolicitors.com

ASLAN CHARLES KOUSETTA LLP ‡
Welbeck House 66-67 Wells Street London W1T 3PY
Tel: 020 3326 2280 ***Fax:*** 020 7582 9290
E-mail: s.charles@ackmedialaw.com

ASTON CLARK ‡
225-227 High Street Acton London W3 9BY
Tel: 020 8752 1122 ***Fax:*** 020 8752 1128 ***Dx:*** 80267 ACTON
Emergency telephone 07956 828314
E-mail: aston@clark1996.fsnet.co.uk
List of partners: Z D Hashmi
Languages: French, German, Italian, Polish, Punjabi, Spanish, Urdu
Work: B1 B2 D1 D2 F1 F2 G H J1 K1 L N O Q S1 V W Z(h,i,p)
Emergency Action, Agency, Advocacy, Fixed Fee Interview, Legal Aid undertaken, Legal Aid Franchise and Member of Accident Line
Ptr: Hashmi, Mr Zaki D BA(Oxon) *Mar 1995
Ast: Groombridge, Mr Julian LLB *Jul 1998
Raval, Miss Reena BA(Hons) Nov 1999

ATANDA SOLICITORS ‡
2nd Floor 59-61 Old Kent Road London SE1 4RF
Tel: 020 7231 3060 ***Fax:*** 020 7231 2230 ***Dx:*** 80722 BERMONDSEY

ATHURALIYAGE SOLICITORS ‡
257a White Chapel Road Tower Hamlets London E1 1DB
Tel: 020 7377 0144 ***Fax:*** 020 7377 0144
E-mail: a.thuraliyage@hotmail.co.uk
List of partners: S Athuraliyage
SPr: Athuraliyage, Sumanasean May 1992

C M ATIF & CO ‡
35 Upper Tooting Road Wandsworth London SW17 7TR
Tel: 020 8767 4913 ***Fax:*** 020 8682 0317
Dx: 58854 TOOTING SOUTH
E-mail: info@cmatif.com

ATLEE CHUNG & COMPANY ‡
1st Floor Havana Suite 13-14 Dean Street London W1D 3RS
Tel: 020 7287 9988 ***Fax:*** 020 7439 1353
Emergency telephone 020 8670 5036
List of partners: J D Atlee, S M Y Chung
Languages: Cantonese, French, German, Italian, Spanish
Work: B1 B2 C1 C3 D1 E F1 G H J1 J2 K1 L N Q R1 S1 W Z(g,i,j,k,m,p)
Emergency Action, Agency, Advocacy and Legal Aid undertaken
Ptr: Atlee, Mr Julian D MA *Nov 1973
Chung, Ms Susan M Y BA *Mar 1998

ATTI & CO ‡
15 New Cross Road London SE14 5DS
Tel: 020 7639 3636 ***Fax:*** 020 7639 3773 ***Dx:*** 80715 BERMONDSEY
Emergency telephone 07956 442209
Work: G J1 K1 L M1 Q V Z(g,i)

ATTIYAH LONE ‡
1st Floor 106-108 King Street Hammersmith London W6 0QP
Tel: 020 8735 9999 ***Fax:*** 020 8735 9988
E-mail: allaw2@aol.com

ATTWELLS SOLICITORS
88 St John's Wood High Street London NW8 7SH
Tel: 020 7722 9898 ***Fax:*** 020 7722 5612
Dx: 83411 ST JOHNS WOOD
E-mail: info@attwells.com
Office: Ipswich
Work: A1 B1 C1 C2 E J1 J2 L N O Q R1 R2 S1 S2 T1 T2 W Z(b,c,d,e,h,l,za)
Agency, Advocacy and Fixed Fee Interview undertaken

AUDU & CO ‡
176 Caledonian Road Islington London N1 0SQ
Tel: 020 7278 9340 ***Fax:*** 020 7278 9460 ***Dx:*** 130404 KINGS CROSS
E-mail: audulaw@hotmail.com
List of partners: M Audu
Languages: Bengali
Work: G K1 K3 L S1 Z(i)
Emergency Action, Agency, Advocacy and Legal Aid undertaken
SPr: Audu, Mr Musa LLB; BA; MA *Jun 1996

AUSTIN LAW SOLICITORS LLP ‡
2nd Floor 244 Edgware Road London W2 1DS
Tel: 020 7723 5171 ***Fax:*** 020 7723 5191 ***Dx:*** 38772 PADDINGTON
E-mail: mail@austin-law.co.uk

AUSTIN RYDER & CO ‡
Royal London House 349 Hertford Road Edmonton Enfield London N9 7BN
Tel: 020 8804 5111 ***Fax:*** 020 8804 9863 ***Dx:*** 36252 EDMONTON 2
E-mail: enquiries@austinryder.com
Web: www.austinryder.com
List of partners: G A Couling, B L Crabb, M Demetriou, C Dunn
Office: Cheshunt, London NW1
Languages: Greek
Work: C1 D1 E F1 G H K1 K3 L N Q S1 S2 W Z(l)
Emergency Action, Fixed Fee Interview and Legal Aid undertaken
Ptr: Couling, Mr Glenn Albert *Dec 1974
Crabb, Mr Bruce L *Jun 1973
Demetriou, Mrs Maria Jan 1997
Dunn, Mrs Claire Oct 2003

AUSTIN RYDER & CO
1 Euston Road London NW1 2SA
Tel: 020 7833 0882 ***Fax:*** 020 7843 4305 ***Dx:*** 37909 KINGS CROSS
E-mail: john.harris@arsolicitors.co.uk
Web: www.austinryder.com
Office: Cheshunt, London N9
Work: E S1 S2
Ptr: Dunn, Mrs Claire Oct 2003

AUSTINS SOLICITORS ‡
153 Chiswick High Road Chiswick London W4 2EA
Tel: 0800 377 7716 ***Fax:*** 0845 658 3635

AVADIS & CO ‡
169 Malden Road London NW5 4HT
Tel: 020 7267 4240 ***Fax:*** 020 7916 2553 ***Dx:*** 123980 BELSIZE PARK
E-mail: lavadis@aol.com
List of partners: L Avadis
Languages: French
Work: D1 D2 K1 K3 N O Q W Z(q)
Emergency Action, Advocacy, Fixed Fee Interview, Legal Aid undertaken and Member of Accident Line
Ptr: Avadis, Mr Laurie BA(Hons) *Nov 1985

See p2 for the Key to Work Categories & other symbols

AWTANI IMMIGRATION SOLICITORS ‡
Marble Arch Tower 55 Bryanston Street London W1H 7AA
Tel: 020 7868 2222 *Fax:* 020 7868 8600
E-mail: sushma@awtanimigration.com

AZAM & CO SOLICITORS ‡
1st Floor 6 Minories London EC3N 1BJ
Tel: 020 7709 0707 *Dx:* 534 LONDON
E-mail: azamsolicitors@btconnect.com

AZAR FREEDMAN & CO ‡
90-92 Islington High Street London N1 8EG
Tel: 020 7704 7500 *Fax:* 020 7704 7501 *Dx:* 146641 ISLINGTON 4

AZZOPARDI & CO ‡
12 Devereux Strand London WC2R 3JL
Tel: 020 7353 6060 *Dx:* 86 LONDON/CHANCERY LN

BCL BURTON COPELAND ‡
51 Lincoln's Inn Fields London WC2A 3LZ
Tel: 020 7430 2277 *Fax:* 020 7430 1101 *Dx:* 37981 KINGSWAY
Emergency telephone 020 7430 2277
E-mail: law@bcl.com
Web: www.bcl.com
List of partners: G R Bastable, R C Booth, I R Burton, J Cornwell, M J Drury, J Glass, M S C Haslam, R M Hubbard, S J Moore, P Morris, E T Peart, R Sallybanks, B Spiro, H A Travers
Languages: French, German, Italian, Spanish
Work: B2 G H I J2 O Z(za)
Ptr: Bastable, Mr Guy Robert . . . . . *Nov 2007
Booth, Mr Robin C BA(Hons) . . . . . *Nov 1973
Burton, Mr Ian R . . . . . *Jun 1971
Drury, Mr Michael John CMG . . . . . Dec 1996
Glass, Miss Jane BA(Hons) . . . . . *Nov 1996
Haslam, Mr Mark S C MA(Cantab) ★ . . . . . *Apr 1981
Hubbard, Ms Rachel M BA(Hons) . . . . . *Nov 1989
Moore, Miss Samantha Jane BA(Hons) . . . . . *Jun 1995
Morris, Mr Paul LLB(Hons) . . . . . *Jul 1998
Peart, Miss Ellen T LLB(Hons) . . . . . *Feb 2002
Sallybanks, Mr Richard LLB . . . . . *Nov 1992
Spiro, Mr Brian LLB(Hons) . . . . . *Nov 1984
Travers, Mr Harry A BCL; MA(Oxon) . . . . . *Feb 1990
Cornwell, Mr Jonathan . . . . . NSP
Ast: Binns, Mr John David LLB; MPhil . . . . . Oct 2000
Calnan, Miss Diane M. . . . . . *Dec 2008
Enstein, Miss Linda . . . . . May 2010
Hayes, Mr Julian . . . . . *Oct 2000
McCalister, Mr Aaron John Coulter LLB(Hons). . . . . Apr 2011
McNeill, Mr Thomas Andrew. . . . . Jan 2011
Mailer, Mr Gregory James. . . . . *Nov 2004
Raphael, Miss Hannah BA(Hons) . . . . . *Mar 2003

BKS SOLICITORS ‡
107 High Street Penge London SE20 7DT
Tel: 020 8776 9388 *Fax:* 020 8776 9517 *Dx:* 34863 PENGE
E-mail: penge@bkslegal.co.uk
List of partners: O Alli-Balogun, M Kirvan, V K Sharma
Ptr: Alli-Balogun, Mr Olayode LLB(Hons) . . . . . *Oct 1992
Kirvan, Mr Martin BA(Hons). . . . . *Jun 1981
Sharma, Vinod Kumar LLB . . . . . *Feb 1991

BPE SOLICITORS LLP
Bedford House John Street London WC1N 1DH
Tel: 020 7387 1437
E-mail: bpe@bpe.co.uk
Office: Cheltenham
Languages: French, German, Italian, Spanish, Welsh
Work: C1 C2 C3 Z(e)
Emergency Action, Agency, Fixed Fee Interview undertaken and Member of Accident Line
Ptr: Bretherton, Mr Richard J H . . . . . *§Dec 1969

BSB SOLICITORS ‡
5-7 Euston Road Kings Cross London NW1 2SA
Tel: 020 7837 3456 *Fax:* 020 7837 9696

BSG SOLICITORS LLP ‡
314 Regents Park Road London N3 2JX
Tel: 020 8343 4411 *Fax:* 020 8343 2773 *Dx:* 57277 FINCHLEY 2
E-mail: info@bsgsolicitors.com
List of partners: S M Courts, P J A Grant, A W Morris, J S Swerner
Office: Bushey
Languages: Farsi, French, Hebrew
Work: C1 C2 E F1 I J1 K1 L N O Q S1 W Z(d,e,i,k,l,o,p,q)
Emergency Action, Agency, Advocacy and Legal Aid undertaken
Ptr: Courts, Saul Michael . . . . . Aug 2002
Grant, Mr Paul Joseph Alexander LLB Honorary Solicitor to College of Osteopaths; Deputy District Judge . . . *Nov 1973
Morris, Alan Wayne . . . . . Jun 1972
Swerner, Mr Jeremy Spencer . . . . . *Jul 1979

BWF SOLICITORS ‡
529 Kingsland Road Dalston London E8 4AR
Tel: 020 7241 7180 *Fax:* 020 7241 7181 *Dx:* 48615 DALSTON
Emergency telephone 07712 761884
E-mail: admin@bwfsolicitors.com
List of partners: W N Boahene, B Owusu
Languages: Ga, Twi, Urdu
Work: C1 D1 D2 E J1 K1 K3 L N Q S1 S2 W Z(g,i)
Emergency Action, Fixed Fee Interview undertaken and Member of Accident Line
Ptr: Boahene, Mr William Ntow ♦ . . . . . *Sep 2003
Owusu, Bennard . . . . . *Aug 1999

WILLIAM BACHE SOLICITORS LIMITED
2nd Floor Rear Building 34-35 Hatton Garden London EC1N 8DX
Tel: 020 7831 1311 *Fax:* 020 7831 0373 *Dx:* 46152 AMESBURY
E-mail: enquiries@williambache.co.uk
Office: Salisbury

PETER BADHAM & CO ‡
6b Gwendwr Road London W14 9BG
Tel: 020 7603 9798 *Fax:* 020 7603 9700
List of partners: P F D Badham
Work: A1 C1 E L O Q R1 S1 S2 T2 W Z(d)
SPr: Badham, Mr Peter F D LLB . . . . . *Sep 1972

WILLIAM BAILEY ‡
150 Lordship Lane Dulwich Southwark London SE22 8HB
Tel: 020 8693 9615 *Fax:* 020 8299 2117 *Dx:* 32150 EAST DULWICH
E-mail: info@williambaileysolicitors.net
List of partners: D W Bailey, D J Coombs
Work: J1 K1 L Q S1 S2 W
Advocacy undertaken
Ptr: Bailey, Mr Donald W BA(Oxon) . . . . . *§Dec 1972
Coombs, Mr David J LLB(Lond) . . . . . *Jan 1979

BAINS COHEN LLP
Central House 1 Ballards Lane London N3 1LQ
Tel: 020 8252 7373 *Fax:* 020 8252 7793
E-mail: info@bainscohen.com
Office: Barking, London EC3, London N8

BAINS COHEN LLP
10 Fenchurch Avenue London EC3M 5BN
Tel: 020 8252 7373 *Fax:* 020 8252 7793
E-mail: info@bainscohen.com
Office: Barking, London N3, London N8

BAINS COHEN LLP
91 Weston Park Crouch End London N8 9PR
Tel: 020 8252 7373 *Fax:* 020 8252 7793
E-mail: info@bainscohen.com
Office: Barking, London EC3, London N3

A BAJWA & CO ‡
39 Gowers Walk London E1 8BS
Tel: 020 7423 0006 *Fax:* 020 7767 3410
E-mail: azfar.bajwa@btopenworld.com

FAROOQ BAJWA & CO ‡
45 Charles Street London W1J 5EH
Tel: 020 3174 0332 *Fax:* 020 7499 0868 *Dx:* 82969 MAYFAIR
E-mail: info@farooqbajwa.com

BAKER & MCKENZIE ‡
100 New Bridge Street London EC4V 6JA
Tel: 020 7919 1000 *Fax:* 020 7919 1999
Dx: 233 LONDON/CHANCERY LN
E-mail: london.info@bakernet.com
Languages: Afrikaans, Bulgarian, Cantonese, Czech, French, German, Greek, Hebrew, Hindi, Hungarian, Italian, Japanese, Kiswahili, Malay, Marathi, Polish, Portuguese, Punjabi, Russian, Spanish
Work: A3 B1 B2 C1 E F1 F2 I J1 J2 L M1 M2 O P Q R1 R2 T1 U1 V Z(b,c,e,f,h,i,j,n,o,p,w)

BAKER BOTTS LLP ‡
41 Lothbury London EC2R 7HF
Tel: 020 7726 3636 *Fax:* 020 7726 3637
Languages: Arabic, Cantonese, French, Hindi, Mandarin, Russian, Spanish, Urdu
Work: A3 B1 C1 C2 M2 O P Q R2 U1 Z(b,e,n)

BAKER SANFORD LLP ‡
1 Quality Court Chancery Lane London WC2A 1HR
Tel: 020 7061 6448 *Fax:* 020 7900 2786
E-mail: info@bakersanford.co.uk

BALA & CO ‡
101 Wakefield Road East Ham London E6 1NR
Tel: 020 8548 8808
List of partners: B Balaraman
Languages: Bengali, Sinhalese, Tamil
Work: G J1 K1 L N Q V W Z(h,i,l)
Agency, Advocacy and Legal Aid undertaken
SPr: Balaraman, Balasingham . . . . . Dec 1986

BALDWIN & CO ‡
236-238 Jamaica Road London SE16 4BE
Tel: 020 7237 3035 *Fax:* 020 7252 1630 *Dx:* 80708 BERMONDSEY
E-mail: baldwinandco@btconnect.com
List of partners: C F Baldwin
Languages: German
Work: C1 I J1 S1 S2 Z(e)
Ptr: Baldwin, Mr Christopher F. . . . . . *Jul 1980

BALHAM LAW PARTNERSHIP ‡
1-3 Hildreth Street Balham London SW12 9RO

BALINDA & CO ‡
246-250 Romford Road London E7 9HZ
Tel: 020 8221 4541 *Fax:* 020 8221 4503 *Dx:* 52113 FOREST GATE
E-mail: law@balindaandco.com

BALLANTYNE TAYLOR SOLICITORS ‡
11 Hickmore Walk London SW4 6EE

BALSARA & CO ‡
4th Floor Thavies Inn House 3-4 Holborn Circus London EC1N 2HA
Tel: 020 7797 6300 *Fax:* 020 7797 6301
Dx: 101 LONDON/CHANCERY LN
E-mail: info@balsara.co.uk
List of partners: A K Patel
Languages: Gujarati, Hindi
Ptr: Patel, Mr Ashok Kumar LLB. . . . . . *Jan 1982
Ast: Jandu, Mr Randeep. . . . . . Sep 2003
Con: Balsara, Mr Jal Shapurji LLB; BA ♦ . . . . . *Dec 1979

M H BANHARALLY & CO ‡
(in association with Karachi; Delhi; New Jersey; Singapore)
355a Green Street Upton Park London E13 9AR
Tel: 020 8471 7572 *Fax:* 020 8675 6566
List of partners: M H Banharally
Office: London SW17
Languages: Bengali, Chinese, French, Gujarati, Punjabi, Urdu
Work: B1 C1 D1 E G K1 L O Q S1 W Z(b,c,d,e,i,l,s)
Agency, Advocacy and Legal Aid undertaken

BANKS KELLY ‡
60 Cheapside London EC2V 6JS
Tel: 020 7248 4231 *Fax:* 020 7651 0270 *Dx:* 42600 CHEAPSIDE
E-mail: niallkelly@bankskelly.co.uk
List of partners: N C Kelly
Work: A1 B1 C1 C2 D1 E F1 G H J1 K1 L M2 N O P Q R1 S1 T1 T2 W Z(b,c,i,j,k,l,s)
Emergency Action and Advocacy undertaken
Ptr: Kelly, Mr Niall Clifford BA(Hons). . . . . . *Sep 1991
Asoc: Blythe, Mr Iain LLB . . . . . *Oct 2000
Nurcombe, Miss Sarah LLB(Hons) . . . . . *Aug 1998

BANKSIDE COMMERCIAL SOLICITORS ‡
58 Southwark Bridge Road Southwark London SE1 0AS
Tel: 020 7654 0200 *Fax:* 020 7654 0221 *Dx:* 44310 SOUTHWARK
E-mail: info@banksidecommercial.com
List of partners: S A Buttleman, P J Gould, F W Warburton
Languages: Chinese, French, German, Spanish
Work: B1 B2 C1 C2 D1 E G J1 K1 L M1 N O P Q R1 R2 S1 S2 Z(e,f,g,h,i,j,k,q,r)
Emergency Action, Agency and Legal Aid undertaken
Ptr: Buttleman, Ms Sarah A LLB. . . . . . *Nov 1984
Gould, Mr Peter J LLB . . . . . Dec 1983
Warburton, Mr Frederick W LLB. . . . . . *Jun 1980
Con: Compton, Mr Graham M LLB(Hons). . . . . . *Apr 1981

BANKSIDE LAW LTD ‡
Thrale House 44-46 Southwark Street London SE1 1UN
Tel: 0844 745 4000 *Fax:* 0844 745 4001
Dx: 132068 LONDON BRIDGE 4
Emergency telephone 07766 192327
E-mail: enquiries@banksidelaw.com
List of partners: J C Moreton, J Williams, W R Wilson
Work: B2 G
Legal Aid Franchise
Dir: Moreton, Mr James Clive BA . . . . . Nov 1990
Williams, Mr John LLB(Wales). . . . . . *Oct 1981
Wilson, Mr William Robert LLB(Hons) . . . . . *Oct 1995
Ast: Anodu, Mr Osondu . . . . . May 2007
Colhoun, Ms Aileen H LLB; MPhil . . . . . *Oct 1983
Da Costa, Mr Marcus . . . . . Sep 2004
Gupta, Mr Ravi . . . . . Jan 2006
Siddiqui, Saadia. . . . . . Jun 2002

BANKSIDE PROPERTY LIMITED ‡
58 Southwark Bridge Road Southwark London SE1 0AS
Tel: 020 7654 7500 *Fax:* 020 7928 3185
Dx: 132068 LONDON BRIDGE 4
E-mail: enquiries@banksideproperty.net

BARBER YOUNG BURTON & RIND ‡
Suite 5 Blandel Bridge House 56 Sloane Square Westminster London SW1W 8AX
Tel: 020 3376 6706 *Dx:* 130444 CHELSEA 3
List of partners: T H Burton, H J Rind
Languages: German
Work: D2 E K1 K3 L S1 S2 W
Ptr: Burton, Mr Trevor H. . . . . . *Nov 1971
Rind, Mr Howard J . . . . . *Nov 1973

BARCLAY TAYLOR ‡
3rd Floor 24 Martin Lane London EC4R 0DR
Tel: 0845 054 4069 *Fax:* 0845 054 4079
Dx: 38156 KNIGHTSBRIDGE

BARGATE MURRAY ‡
Morrell House 98 Curtain Road London EC2A 3AF
Tel: 020 7729 7778

J E BARING & CO ‡
First Floor 63-66 Hatton Garden London EC1N 8LE
Tel: 020 7242 8966 *Fax:* 020 7404 5316
Dx: 151 LONDON/CHANCERY LN
List of partners: B K Bloom, A J Hooper
Work: B1 O Q S1 S2 W
Agency and Fixed Fee Interview undertaken
Ptr: Bloom, Mr Bradley K FILEx . . . . . Jan 2000
Hooper, Mr Allan James FILEx . . . . . *Jan 1999

BARK & CO ‡
Bridewell Court 14 New Bridge Street London EC4V 6AG
Tel: 020 7353 1990 *Fax:* 020 7353 1880
Dx: 447 LONDON/CHANCERY LN
Emergency telephone 07788 742888
E-mail: office@barkco.com
List of partners: A G Bark-Jones
Languages: French, Greek, Gujarati, Hindi, Italian, Latin, Punjabi, Spanish, Urdu
Work: A3 B2 G J1 N O Q Z(g)
Fixed Fee Interview and Legal Aid undertaken
Ptr: Bark-Jones, Mr Antony Giles . . . . . Mar 1996

BARKER AUSTIN ‡
28 Hanbury Street Tower Hamlets London E1 6QR
Tel: 020 7377 1933 *Fax:* 020 7247 0262 *Dx:* 887 LONDON/CITY
E-mail: mail@barker-austin.co.uk
List of partners: G W Austin, J V Barker, N E Coates
Languages: French, German, Spanish
Work: B1 C1 C2 C3 E F1 G H J1 K1 M1 M2 N P S1 T1 T2 W Z(a,b,e,f,k,n)
Emergency Action, Agency, Advocacy, Fixed Fee Interview, Legal Aid undertaken and Member of Accident Line
Ptr: Austin, Mr Gary W MA; ACIArb . . . . . *Feb 1984
Barker, Mr John V BA(Cantab) . . . . . Sep 1979
Coates, Mr Nicholas E BA(Lond) . . . . . *Jun 1981

BARKER GILLETTE ‡
11-12 Wigmore Place London W1U 2LU
Tel: 020 7636 0555 *Fax:* 020 7323 3950 *Dx:* 9033 WEST END
List of partners: S J Barker, M H Davies, A M Deal, N B Forsyth, J F Gillette, M Q Khanzada, F M R Ryan, I R Searle, V K Verma
Languages: Italian, Urdu
Work: B1 B2 C1 E G J1 L N O Q S1 S2 Z(q)
Emergency Action and Legal Aid undertaken
Ptr: Barker, Mr Steven J LLB; Dip European Law (Amsterdam) . . . . . *Feb 1986
Davies, Mr Michael Haydn LLB . . . . . *Dec 1976
Deal, Mr Alexander Marc . . . . . Mar 2001
Forsyth, Mr Nigel B MA(Cantab). . . . . . *Mar 1979
Gillette, Mr John F LLB . . . . . *Nov 1980
Khanzada, Mr M Qaiser BSocSc Deputy Chairman of the ACCA Disciplinary Committee . . . . . *Jan 1984
Searle, Mr Ian Richard LLB; JIEB . . . . . *Oct 1984
Verma, Vinay Kumar LLB . . . . . *Sep 1996
Mem: Ryan, Mr Francis M R. . . . . . *Oct 1983

BARKER GOOCH & SWAILES
(incorporating A J Davey & Co)
Woodside House 37 The Green Winchmore Hill London N21 1HT
Tel: 020 8886 5928 / 8886 5734 *Fax:* 020 8882 5607
Dx: 36955 WINCHMORE HILL
Office: Enfield
Work: E G J1 K1 L N O Q S1 S2 W Z(y)
Ptr: Roer, Mr Colin F M MA(Cantab). . . . . . *Jun 1978

Ast: McBride, Miss Odette Marie-Chantal BA(Hons) *Nov 1999
McGarry, Mr Kevin Michael BA *Oct 1977
Taebi, Mrs Vanessa *Oct 1995

BARLOW LYDE & GILBERT LLP ‡
The merged firm of Barlow Lyde & Gilbert and Clyde & Co
The St Botolph Building 138 Houndsditch London EC3A 7AR
Est: 1841
Tel: 020 7876 5000 *Fax:* 020 7876 5111 *Dx:* 160030 LIME STREET 5
List of partners: D M Abbott, P Allen, K J Bitmead, R Black, A D Blair, C Brett, J D Bright, G C Brown, S Browning, J P Butchart, F A Cathie, S A Chumas, A S Clover, P T Coles, J E Cooper, S J Cooper, J W Dadge, N A H Dent, H Donegan, S P Donegan, K P Finnigan, J D Flaherty, P J Flint, P W Foss, S Gamblin, R J Gimblett, J Goodman, S Hall, J Hanson, R J Harrison, L D H Hassett, M O Hifzi, J R Hill, P A R Hinton, A J Horrocks, M J Howard, A V Howell, D I Howie, N M L Hughes, D S James, N D Jamieson, C Jojo, M A Karali, G W C Kavanagh, R Keady, F J Kean, M C Kenton, D R W Knapp, S N Konsta, A D Lambert, J Lambert, I J Mason, R C McLauchlan, D Moon, H K Mullins, M J Munro, C Murray, A R Nurse-Marsh, C P O'Connell, J S Parker, T N Parsons, P I Perry, R G Pike, J J Randall, J Roberts, M Rogerson, A J Scott, J Shebson, D Singer, R A Smith, D G Smyth, D I Strang, T S Strong, T Taylor, A J Thomson, P Walmsley, C V Walsh, D T Whelan, L M Williams, K Wilson, M J D Wing, J Yorke, C S Zavos
Office: Manchester, Oxford
Work: A3 C1 C2 C3 E F1 I J1 M1 M2 N O P Q R2 T1 U1 U2 Z(b,c,e,j,o,q,r)
Ptr: Abbott, Mr David Michael Jul 2003
Allen, Mr Peter LLB *May 1997
Bitmead, Mr Kevin James BA Jan 1987
Black, Mr Richard Dec 1977
Blair, Mr Andrew David LLB(Hull) *Oct 1987
Brett, Mr Clive MA(Oxon) *Nov 1997
Bright, Mr Jason David *Sep 1994
Brown, Mr Geoffrey Charles Oct 2006
Browning, Mr Stephen LLB(CNAA) *Nov 1988
Cathie, Mr Fergal Austin BA(Hons) *Oct 1994
Chumas, Mr Simon Andre LLB Aug 1980
Clover, Mrs Anne Sarah *Oct 1983
Coles, Mr Peter Timothy BA *Sep 1996
Cooper, Mr James Edward LLB Sep 1996
Cooper, Mr Simon Jeremy MA; DipLaw *Aug 1990
Dent, Mr Nicholas Andrew Hazard BA Sep 1996
Donegan, Ms Heida Oct 1995
Donegan, Mr Seamus Patrick Aug 1992
Flaherty, Mr John David LLB *Nov 1993
Flint, Mr Peter Jeremy BA(Oxon) Jan 1984
Foss, Mr Patrick William LLB; LLM *Oct 1989
Gamblin, Mr Simon Nov 1994
Gimblett, Mr Richard Jeremy BA(Hons)(Oxon) *Mar 1990
Goodman, Mr John Nov 1992
Hall, Mr Stuart MA(Cantab) *May 1975
Hanson, Mr John MA(Oxon) *Apr 1977
Harrison, Mr Richard James LLB Mar 1989
Hassett, Miss Lynn Denise Helen LLB(Lond) May 1982
Hifzi, Mert O LLB *Oct 1997
Hill, Mr John Robert Jan 1992
Hinton, Mr Paul Anthony Rooke Sep 2001
Horrocks, Mr Andrew John BA(Oxon) Nov 1988
Howard, Mr Mark Justin Sep 1998
Howell, Mr Andrew Valentine BA *Nov 1997
Howie, Mr Douglas Ian MA(Cantab) *Apr 1980
Hughes, Mr Nicholas Maxwell Lloyd BA(Law); MRaeS*§Apr 1981
James, Mr Drew Scott Nov 1987
Jamieson, Mr Neil Douglas BA(Oxon)(Jurisprudence) *Nov 1986
Jojo, Ms Camille LLB *Dec 1980
Karali, Mrs Miranda Antigoni LLB; LLM *Aug 1993
Kavanagh, Mr Giles Wilfred Conor Mar 1999
Keady, Mr Richard Apr 1997
Kean, Mr Francis Jonathan LLB *Nov 1985
Kenton, Mr Maurice Cyril BA; LLB Oct 1997
Knapp, Mr David Richard William LLB Oct 1986
Konsta, Mr Simon Nicholas Feb 1991
Lambert, Mr Adam David Oct 1996
Lambert, Ms Janet LLB *Apr 1980
McLauchlan, Mr Roderic Charles LLB; BCL Wilson Entrance Scholarship 1991 Mar 2004
Mason, Mr Ian James MA(Cantab) Dec 1991
Munro, Mr Michael John BA(Oxon) *Sep 1993
Nurse-Marsh, Mr Anthony Roger Sep 1990
O'Connell, Mr Clive Patrick LLB(Lond) Sep 1982
Parker, Mr James Stuart Sep 1999
Parsons, Mr Timothy Norman LLB(Hons) *Sep 1992
Perry, Mr Patrick Ian LLB *Oct 1996
Pike, Mr Richard Gordon LLB Oct 1987
Randall, Mr Julian James MA(Oxon)(Jurisprudence) *Dec 1986
Roberts, Mr James Mar 2007
Rogerson, Mr Malcolm MA(Cantab) *Apr 1981
Scott, Mr Andrew John BA; LLM *Jan 1985
Shebson, Mr Jeremy LLB(Lond) *Nov 1991
Singer, Ms Danielle LLB *Nov 1993
Smith, Mr Ray Anthony Aug 1991
Smyth, Mr David Gordon BA(Law) *Jan 1985
Strang, Mr David Ivor BA(Hons)(Oxon); DES Marseille; Lic Spec Brussels *Sep 1982
Strong, Mr Timothy Simon LLB(Euro) *Oct 1994
Taylor, Mr Timothy LLB *Apr 1978
Thomson, Mr Aidan John Sep 1993
Walsh, Ms Carmel Veronica LLB Sep 2001
Whelan, Mr Denis Timothy BA(Oxon) Oct 1996
Williams, Mr Leigh Michael Sep 1996
Wilson, Mrs Katy-Marie LLB; Barrister Solicitor Advocate ♦ *Mar 1996
Wing, Mr Mark John David BA(Hons) Sep 2001
Yorke, Mr Jonathan LLB *Oct 1986
Zavos, Mr Christopher Spyros LLB *Oct 1991
Asoc: Albino, Mr Fernando Jul 2002
Alexander, Mr Leon Stephen Sep 2007
Anderson, Ms Tracey Denise Oct 2001
Arazi, Mr Joseph Ezer BA Sep 2000
Austin, Mr Kevin Jul 2005
Baird, Ms Katie Louise Sep 2001
Ball, Ms Jennifer Margaret BA(Hons)(Cantab); CPE; LPC *Aug 1999
Ballantyne, Ms Jane Margaret Quentin BA(Oxon) Sep 1993
Batchelor, Mr Gawaine James Michael Nov 1997
Bathurst, Mr Nicholas Charles Stuart Oct 1996
Batistich, Mr Mark Edward Mar 2001
Bell, Mr Andrew Jonathan Sep 2005
Benguigui, Mr Michael Sep 2004
Benson, Ms Emily Mary Caroline LLB(Lond) *Oct 1986
Biagi, Ms Inez Gabriella Mar 1988
Blomfield, Ms Nina Marie Mar 2004
Brader-Smith, Ms Caroline Sep 2006
Breslin, Ms Kathryn Sep 2007
Broadmore, Mr David Thomas Mar 2005
Bromley, Mr Elliot Martin Mar 2006
Brumpton, Ms Stephanie Lorna May 2006
Butler-Smith, Ms Lyndsey Jane Apr 1992
Cantlon, Ms Zoe Michele Oct 2001
Caton, Mr Matthew Aug 2001
Cawley, Mr Anthony Sep 2002
Charter, Mr Paul Andrew Nov 1994
Chipperfield, Ms Rosalyn Flora Jane Sep 2005
Chu, Ms Kwung Shien Jul 2007
Clulow, Mr Jeb Anthony BA; LLB; LLM Jul 2001
Collier, Ms Tina Samantha Sep 2007
Cooke, Ms Laura Anne BA(Hons)(History); PGDipLaw; LPC Sep 2003
Cope, Ms Emily Jane Sep 2004
Cornish, Mrs Susannah Caroline BA Mar 1994
Cottam, Mr Adrian Mark Sep 1991
Crook, Mr Benjamin Charles Mar 2005
Crowther, Ms Sarah Louise Sep 2000
Cubbon, Miss Sophie Emily LLB Sep 2003
Cundy, Mr Jack Patrick Sep 2004
Deeny, Ms Lorna Bea Sep 2007
Dennis, Mr James Anthony John Sep 1997
Desai, Miss Neila Dipty ILEX; CPE; LPC Nov 2002
Dixon, Ms Anna Louise Sep 2004
Dobson, Ms Michelle Karen Apr 2001
Doyle, Mr John Mar 2004
Dunbar, Mr Benjamin James Sep 2006
Dunlop, Mr Christopher Michael Sep 2003
Durkin, Mr Simon Hugh Sep 2002
Edwards, Mr Richard James BA Nov 1995
Ellis, Mr Simon David Mar 2008
Evans, Ms Caroline Elizabeth Sep 2007
Fisher, Ms Sian Louise Dec 1996
Forsyth, Mr Andrew John Scott BA *Nov 1994
Foster, Mrs Shao Inn LLB Feb 2002
French, Ms Karen Michelle Sep 2004
Gardiner, Mr Gordon Ashley Wynne Sep 1998
Gilberg, Mr Steven James Sep 2005
Given, Ms Tracey Jane Jan 1992
Golding, Ms Natasha Sep 2007
Goodman, Ms Sherry Oct 2005
Graham, Ms Natalie Eyamede Sep 2001
Ham, Mr Richard Gibson BA(Oxon) *Nov 1983
Hamill, Mr Kieran Nov 2007
Hammond, Ms Zoe Karen Sep 2001
Harris, Miss Corinna BA; MA Oct 1998
Harwood, Ms Emily Catherine Sep 2003
Herman, Ms Dorothy Ann Jan 2005
Heslehurst, Ms Rachel Elizabeth Sep 2003
Hession, Ms Rita Ann LLB(Hons) *Jan 1992
Hickson, Lyall Mar 2004
Hill, Mr Christopher Michael Sep 2007
Hodgkiss, Ms Kate Sep 2004
Holme, Mr Christopher Robert Sep 2002
Horovitz, Ms Laura Sylvia Mar 2006
Ions, Mr Jonathan Alexis LLB(Hons) Sep 2001
Isaacs, Mr Jonathan Andrew BA(Cantab) Sep 2003
Jackson, Mr Simon Timothy Sep 2006
James, Ms Hazel Dorothy Nov 1999
James, Miss Madeleine Catherine BA(Hons) *Oct 1998
Jenkins, Mr Peter Llewellyn Dec 2005
Jenkins, Ms Veronica Jane Sep 2005
Jones, Mr Paul Edward Sep 2007
Jones, Mr Rhys Jarman Sep 2006
Kaiser, Ms Gabrielle Teresa Mar 1999
Kearney, Ms Catherine Miriam Apr 2005
Keogh, Ms Karen Enid Aug 2002
Kershaw, Mr Alexander James Sep 2002
Killin, Mr Julian Renton Sep 2001
Kish, Mr Marc BA; MA(Oxon) *Sep 2003
Large, Ms Fay Kirsty Sep 2005
Le Gouellec De Schwarz, Tanguy Francois Marie Sep 2001
LLoyd-Lewis, Mr Edward Eurof LLB(Wales) *Dec 1993
Loweth, Mr Jonathan Craig May 1997
Lulic, Chris Oct 2004
Lyttleton, Ms Natalia Alexandra Oct 2007
McConway, Ms Marlene Mar 1994
McCormack, Mr Clifford Nov 1993
McEwen, Mr Gregory Andrew Sep 1999
McGonigal, Mr Patric Jun 2000
Mcintosh, Mr Warren Leslie LLB(Hons) Feb 2001
McNamara, Ms Rachael Jane Sep 2007
McQuillen, Mr Jason Paul Sep 2004
Major, Mr James David Sep 2002
Malik, Marriam Soriya Sep 2001
Mallorie, Ms Charlotte Jane Sep 2007
Manson, Ms Catherine Elizabeth Jul 2007
Martin, Mr Simon Mar 2007
Millington-Jones, Ms Zoe Virginia Sep 1998
Moloney, Mr Peter Henry Sep 2003
Norris, Mr William Sep 2007
Oliver, Mrs Samantha Jayne BA(Hons) *Sep 2001
Orr, Ms Patricia Ann Sep 1997
Petts, Miss Claire Louise LLB Sep 1999
Phiri, Niya Msewa Sep 2005
Pierce, Ms Hannah Mary Mar 2006
Plumley, Mr Ian James Sep 2002
Proctor, Mr Richard Mar 2004
Protheroe, Ms Christianne Sep 2007
Reddick, Ms Susannah Mar 2002
Robinson, Ms Natalie Victoria Sep 2006
Robson, Ms Marianne LLB(Manc) *Nov 1994
Sana, Ms Amber Sep 2003
Saverymuttu, Ms Claire Louise Sep 2006
Schooling, Mr Simon BA(Hons)(Oxon); DipLaw Jul 1999
Scragg, Mr Jonathan Kilby Jul 2007
Sharp, Ms Sarah Jane Apr 2002
Shaw, Ms Caroline Josephine Sep 2006
Sheikh, Ms Yasmin Oct 2003
Shepherd, Mr Timothy David Sep 2005
Sheppard, Mr Andrew Joseph BSc *Oct 1994
Shepperson, Ms Laura Joan Sep 2003
Sherratt, Ms Victoria Jane MA(Bris) *Sep 1999
Skaanild, Ms Laura Danielle Sep 2002
Small, Ms Lilian Alexandra Sep 2006
Smith, Mr Christopher Adam Sep 2007
Smith, Mr Daniel John MA; BCL Henry Henriques Prize 1998 Sep 2000
Speake, Mr Andrew Charles BA *Sep 1996
Spencer, Mr Edward Paul Gerald Sep 1999
Spikes, Mr Dion Richard Oct 2007
Suchak, Sonali Sep 2005
Taylor, Mr James Harrison MA *Sep 1994
Taylor, Mr James Scott Sep 2001
Teather, Ms Joanne Carolyn Oct 2004
Thomas, Ms Chloe Louise Jan 2008
Tolaini, Mrs Lisa Katherine LLB; LPC Jan 2000
Tormey, Ms Sheila Sep 2000
Traxler, Miss Michelle Jeanne LLB *Oct 1993
Turnbull, Ilona Nicole Jul 2007
Tuson, Mr Andrew Frederick Lance Feb 2006
Vannelli, Ms Elizabeth Aug 2006
Walshaw, Mr Tom Christian BA(Hons) Nov 1994
Ward, Ms Joanna Claire LLB Sep 2004
Waters, Mr Mark Jonathan Jan 2008
White, Mr Thomas Henry Sep 2005
Whyld, Miss Joanne Mary LLB(Hons) *Nov 1997
Wild, Ms Elizabeth Sep 2005
Wilkinson, Mr Ivan Joshua Mar 1994
Wilson, Ms Lorraine Mary Oct 1996
Wilson, Ms Rebecca Hannah Sep 2007
Winterton, Mr Stephen John LLB *Jun 1984
Woods, Ms Jane Marian Sep 2005
Con: Southey, Mr Verner George BA(Cape Town); LLB(Lond) *Jan 1977
Thorp, Mr Clive BSc(Hull)(Econ) *Dec 1975

BARNES & PARTNERS ‡
60 Fore Street Edmonton London N18 2TT
Tel: 020 8884 2277 *Fax:* 020 8807 0614 *Dx:* 36200 EDMONTON 1
E-mail: people@barnesandpartners.com
Office: Cheshunt, Enfield, Harlow, London E4, London N15, London N16, London N8, Pinner, Ware
Work: D1 E K1 L N Q S1 S2 W Z(r)

BARNES & PARTNERS
30 Broadway Parade Tottenham Lane Haringey London N8 9DB
Tel: 020 8340 6697 *Fax:* 020 8340 4494 *Dx:* 35956 CROUCH END
E-mail: people@barnesandpartners.com
Office: Cheshunt, Enfield, Harlow, London E4, London N15, London N16, London N18, Pinner, Ware
Work: D1 E K1 L N O Q S1 W

BARNES & PARTNERS
45-47 Old Church Road Chingford London E4 6SJ
Tel: 020 8524 9222 *Fax:* 020 8524 9888
Dx: 35404 CHINGFORD SOUTH
E-mail: people@barnesandpartners.com
Office: Cheshunt, Enfield, Harlow, London N15, London N16, London N18, London N8, Pinner, Ware
Work: E K1 L N Q S1 S2 W

BARNES & PARTNERS
187 Philip Lane Tottenham Haringey London N15 4HQ
Tel: 020 8801 0085 *Fax:* 020 8365 0957
Dx: 55606 SOUTH TOTTENHAM
E-mail: people@barnesandpartners.com
Office: Cheshunt, Enfield, Harlow, London E4, London N16, London N18, London N8, Pinner, Ware
Work: C1 D1 E F1 J1 K1 L N O P Q R1 S1 S2 W

BARNES & PARTNERS
50 Church Street Stoke Newington Hackney London N16 0NB
Tel: 020 7241 5577 *Fax:* 020 7254 8757
Dx: 58055 STOKE NEWINGTON
E-mail: people@barnesandpartners.com
Office: Cheshunt, Enfield, Harlow, London E4, London N15, London N18, London N8, Pinner, Ware

ARTHUR BARNES & CO ‡
1st Floor 364 City Road London EC1V 2PY
Tel: 020 7278 3046 *Fax:* 020 7812 1446
E-mail: ajab@arthurbarnes.co.uk

JAMES E BARNES ‡
Access House Manor Road Ealing London W13 0AS
Tel: 020 8810 7100 *Fax:* 020 8810 5163 *Dx:* 5163 EALING
E-mail: info@jamesebarnes.co.uk
List of partners: J E Barnes
Work: S1 Z(h)
SPr: Barnes, Mr James E LLB *Jul 1979

KERVIN BARNES LIMITED ‡
99 Cowley Road Mortlake London SW14 8QD
Tel: 020 7887 6296
E-mail: gk31@hotmail.co.uk

BARNET SOLICITORS ‡
Unit 1c Haggerston Studios 284-288 Kingsland Road London E8 4DN
Tel: 020 7249 2668 *Fax:* 020 7249 2699

BARNETT ALEXANDER CONWAY INGRAM ‡
Sovereign House 1 Albert Place Ballards Lane London N3 1QB
Tel: 020 8349 7680 *Fax:* 020 8346 8245 *Dx:* 57288 FINCHLEY 2
Emergency telephone 020 8203 6744
E-mail: mail@bacisolicitors.co.uk
List of partners: J D Chart, D R Cumway, J M Ingram, C A Isenberg, N J Shestopal
Languages: German, Hebrew, Polish
Work: C1 C3 E F1 G H I J1 K1 L M1 M2 N O P Q S1 S2 U1 W Z(i,l,p,q)
Emergency Action, Agency and Advocacy undertaken
Ptr: Chart, Mr John D LLB *Dec 1968
Cumway, Mr David R LLB *§Jun 1980
Ingram, Mr Jonathan M LLB *Aug 1986
Isenberg, Mr Colin A LLM; LLB *May 1974
Shestopal, Mr Neil J LLB Jun 1970

BARNETT ALEXANDER CONWAY INGRAM LLP ‡
Caldew House 92-94 King Street London W6 0QW
Tel: 020 8741 7272 *Fax:* 020 8741 7273 *Dx:* 46768 HAMMERSMITH
E-mail: info@bacisolicitors.co.uk

MARCUS BARNETT ‡
16 Whaddon House William Mews London SW1X 9HG
Tel: 020 7235 9215 *Fax:* 020 7235 2429
E-mail: jd@marbar.demon.co.uk
List of partners: J Dowell
Languages: French
Work: L
Ptr: Dowell, Miss Jane BA *Nov 1981
Con: Sullivan, Mr Barry J LLB *Jun 1976

See p2 for the Key to Work Categories & other symbols

NORMAN H BARNETT & CO ‡
397 Barking Road East Ham London E6 2JT
Tel: 020 8471 2112 ***Fax:*** 020 8472 8560 ***Dx:*** 4704 EAST HAM
Emergency telephone 020 8852 9291
List of partners: N F Heslop, C Holt, P Rosen, I Sher
Languages: French
Work: B1 C1 D1 E F1 G H J1 K1 L M1 N P R1 S1 S2 T1 V W Z(b,c,f,h,i,j,k,l,m,p,t)
Emergency Action, Agency, Advocacy, Fixed Fee Interview, Legal Aid undertaken and Member of Accident Line
Ptr: Heslop, Mr Nicholas Frank LLB(Hons)(Warw) . . . . . Oct 1982
Holt, Mr Christopher. . . . . Jan 1999
Rosen, Mr Paul LLB(Hons) . . . . *Mar 1974
Sher, Mr Imran LLB . . . . Jul 2001

ROBIN BARON COMMERCIAL LAWYERS ‡
40 Laurier Road Camden London NW5 1SJ
Tel: 020 7485 4477 ***Fax:*** 020 7117 4800
E-mail: enquiries@robinbaron.com
List of partners: R M Baron
Work: C1 C2 F1 F2 I J1 U2 Z(e,za)
SPr: Baron, Mr Robin Michael LLB; LLM . . . . Mar 1973

BARRETTS ‡
107 Gray's Inn Road London WC1X 8TZ
Tel: 020 7248 0551 ***Fax:*** 020 7236 2789
List of partners: J C Adler, M D Barrett
Work: E L S1 S2
Ptr: Adler, Mr John C LLB(B'ham) . . . . *Apr 1977
Barrett, Mr Michael D LLB. . . . . Apr 1975

BARRINGTON CHARLES EDWARDS & CO ‡
77 High Street Penge London SE20 7HW
Tel: 020 8659 7228 / 8659 7227 ***Fax:*** 020 8659 6889
List of partners: B C Edwards, G A Scott
Office: London SE25
Work: D1 F1 G H J1 K1 L M1 N P W
Emergency Action, Fixed Fee Interview and Legal Aid undertaken
Ptr: Edwards, Mr Barrington C. . . . . Jun 1976

BARRINGTON CHARLES EDWARDS & CO
226 Portland Road South Norwood London SE25 4SL
Tel: 020 8656 8318 / 8656 8319 ***Fax:*** 020 8656 2020
Dx: 48650 SHIRLEY CROYDON
Office: London SE20
Work: D1 F1 K1 Q S1 S2 W
Emergency Action, Agency, Advocacy, Fixed Fee Interview, Legal Aid undertaken and Member of Accident Line
Ptr: Scott, Mr Gerard A BA . . . . *Nov 1982

BARRYS ‡
Central Court 25 Southampton Buildings London WC2A 1AL
Tel: 020 7645 8270 ***Fax:*** 020 3170 7396

BARTLETTS ‡
38 Willoughby Road Turnpike Lane Haringey London N8 0JQ
Tel: 020 8340 2202 / 8340 2203 ***Fax:*** 020 8340 5488
E-mail: mail@turnpikelane.co.uk
List of partners: S Kaya, J H Martin
Languages: Turkish
Work: C1 E S1 S2 W Z(i)
Ptr: Kaya, Selda LLB . . . . Apr 2006
Martin, Mr John H. . . . . *Dec 1972

ANTHONY BARTON ‡
42 Gibson Square Islington London N1 0RB
Tel: 020 7700 7348 ***Fax:*** 020 7700 7379
Work: N

BARTRAM & CO ‡
210 Northfield Avenue Ealing London W13 9SJ
Tel: 020 8840 0444 ***Fax:*** 020 8840 0555
E-mail: info@bartramsolicitors.co.uk
List of partners: P S Bartram
Languages: French, Spanish
Work: Z(i)
Legal Aid undertaken
Ptr: Bartram, Mr Peter S LLB(Bris); MA(Brunel) . . . . . . *Oct 1981

GRAHAM BASH & CO ‡
26 Wattisfield Road Hackney London E5 9QH
Tel: 020 8985 8892 ***Fax:*** 020 8985 6785
E-mail: grahambash@gn.apc.org
List of partners: G L Bash
Work: J1 L N Q
Agency, Legal Aid undertaken, Legal Aid Franchise and Member of Accident Line
SPr: Bash, Mr Graham L LLB . . . . Dec 1975

BASKIN ROSS & CO ‡
628 Finchley Road London NW11 7RS
Tel: 020 8458 5688 ***Fax:*** 020 8455 2296
E-mail: simonlaz1@btconnect.com
List of partners: S Lazarus
Work: B1 C1 E F1 G H J1 K1 L N O Q S1 V W Z(h,i,j,l)
Emergency Action, Agency, Advocacy and Legal Aid undertaken
Ptr: Lazarus, Mr Simon BA . . . . *Oct 1985

BATCHELORS SOLICITORS
6 Gray's Inn Square Gray's Inn London WC1R 5AX
Tel: 020 7269 9027 ***Fax:*** 020 7269 9029
E-mail: batchelors@batchelors.co.uk
Office: Bromley
Work: A3 C1 C2 E J1 K1 K3 K4 L O Q R1 R2 S1 S2 T1 T2 W Z(c,h,m,p,q)
Agency and Fixed Fee Interview undertaken

JANIE BATCHFORD SOLICITORS ‡
4th Floor Suit 401 Davina House London EC1V 7ET
Tel: 020 7060 3089 ***Fax:*** 0871 528 9087
E-mail: janie_batchford@yahoo.co.uk

BATES N V H ‡
(incorporating Brunel)
44 Essex Street London WC2R 3JF
Tel: 020 7936 2930 ***Fax:*** 020 7583 0532
Dx: 48 LONDON/CHANCERY LN
E-mail: receptionlondon@batesnvh.co.uk
List of partners: A W H Barnes, G D Gibbons, J V Hardy, C A C Hodgson, G Jones, D C Knudsen, I N MacDonald, R E Wasem
Office: Fleet, Hook (3 offices), Leigh-on-Sea
Work: A1 C1 C2 C3 D1 E F1 G I J1 K1 L M1 M2 N O P Q R1 S1 T1 T2 W Z(c,d,e,o,q,w)
Advocacy, Legal Aid Franchise and Member of Accident Line
Ptr: Barnes, Ashley W H LLB . . . . *Oct 1990
Hardy, Miss Jane V BA . . . . *Jan 1988
Jones, Miss Gwyneth LLB(Exon) . . . . *Oct 1983
MacDonald, Mr Ian N LLB(Bris) . . . . *Apr 1971

BATES WELLS & BRAITHWAITE LONDON LLP ‡
2-6 Cannon Street London EC4M 6YH
Tel: 020 7551 7777 ***Fax:*** 020 7551 7800 ***Dx:*** 42609 CHEAPSIDE 1
E-mail: mail@bwbllp.com
List of partners: J A Blake, P Bohm, M C Bunch, A C G Cartmell, R L Earle, S W D Egan, W M M Garnett, M J Gunson, N C Ivey, P D J Kirkpatrick, S T Lloyd, T Longley, R McCarthy, L McLynn, R Oakley, L A Robinson, M P Robson, A Rumbold, L Simanowitz, M D Townley, M Traynor, P D A Trott, J M Trotter, D Tuck
Languages: Arabic, Bengali, Cantonese, Czech, French, German, Gujarati, Hakka, Hindi, Italian, Japanese, Kiswahili, Mandarin, Portuguese, Punjabi, Slovak, Spanish, Turkish, Urdu, Welsh
Work: A1 A3 C1 C2 C3 E J1 J2 L M1 M2 N O P Q R1 R2 S1 S2 T1 T2 W X Z(d,e,f,g,h,i,j,k,p,q,u,w,za)
Emergency Action, Agency and Advocacy undertaken
Ptr: Blake, Mr Julian A BA(Oxon) . . . . *Nov 1991
Bohm, Mr Peter MA(Cantab) . . . . *Apr 1976
Bunch, Mr Martin C BSc . . . . *Oct 1987
Cartmell, Mr Anthony C G BA. . . . . Feb 1983
Earle, Mr Rupert L . . . . Oct 1988
Egan, Mr Sean W D BA(Cantab) . . . . *Apr 1988
Garnett, Mr William M M BA. . . . . *Feb 1986
Gunson, Mr Martin J . . . . *Nov 1981
Ivey, Mr Nicholas C BA; LLB . . . . *Aug 1981
Kirkpatrick, Mr Philip Duncan John . . . . *Dec 1995
Lloyd, Mr Stephen T BA. . . . . *Oct 1977
Longley, Ms Thea . . . . Oct 2001
McCarthy, Ms Rosamund . . . . Nov 1993
McLynn, Ms Lucy . . . . Nov 2002
Oakley, Mr Robert. . . . . Oct 1999
Robinson, Miss Lesley A LLB . . . . Nov 1990
Robson, Mr Malcolm P LLB(Hons)(B'ham) . . . . . *§Apr 1981
Rumbold, Ms Abbie. . . . . Oct 2001
Simanowitz, Lawrie . . . . Sep 2000
Townley, Mr Michael D BA . . . . *Sep 1988
Traynor, Mr Mark . . . . Sep 2000
Trott, Mr Philip D A LLB. . . . . *May 1979
Trotter, Mr John M LLB . . . . Dec 1973
Tuck, Miss Dinah BA . . . . Dec 1990
Ast: Anderton, Ms Jennie . . . . Oct 2006
Andrews, Ms Joy . . . . Sep 2004
Biden, Ms Stephanie . . . . Oct 2005
Bull, Ms Sarah . . . . Mar 2003
Craig, Mr John Hugh BA . . . . *May 1965
Curran, Mr John. May 2006
De Jongh, Mr Alex . . . . Sep 2002
Dean, Ms Tara . . . . Oct 2005
English, Mr Jon . . . . Nov 2006
Faraoni, Mr Duccio . . . . Sep 2000
Faure Walker, Ms Alice . . . . May 1993
Fletcher, Mr Luke . . . . Mar 2007
Gecaga, Soiya . . . . Mar 2003
Gravestock, Mrs Anne E BA. . . . . Nov 1995
Groom, Mrs Mary BSc; CPE; LPC. . . . . *Nov 1998
Huard, Mr Jamie . . . . Sep 2007
Kramer, Mr Martin C . . . . *§Jul 1969
Lewis, Mr Arwel I LLB(Hons); LLM . . . . Dec 1997
Lloyd, Ms Kathryn. . . . . Nov 2001
Lowe-Petraske, Ms Alana. . . . . Oct 2007
McCartney, Miss Louise BA(Hons); PGDipLaw . . . . *Oct 2001
McGoay, Ms Siobhan . . . . Dec 2005
McHugh, Ms Leona . . . . Sep 2002
Maitland, Mr Ben . . . . Oct 2006
O'Reilly, Mairead . . . . Sep 2006
Petch, Ms Elizabeth. . . . . Oct 2006
Phelps, Miss Rosemary J C LLB . . . . *Apr 1979
Pratt, Mr Tom . . . . Oct 2006
Randall, Mr Christopher W BA . . . . *Nov 1987
Rigby, Ms Christine M LLB(Cantab) . . . . *Apr 1991
Seath, Mr Paul . . . . Sep 1999
Soley, Ms Laura. Mar 1999
Woolhouse, Ms Tamsin . . . . Sep 2008
Con: Phillips, Mr Andrew W BA(Cantab) . . . . *§Jul 1964

H BATRA & CO ‡
1st Floor 100 Pall Mall London SW1Y 5HP
Tel: 0845 017 5588 ***Fax:*** 0845 017 5522 ***Dx:*** 99201 PICCADILLY
E-mail: himanshu@hbatralaw.com
Work: B1 C1 E J1 N O Q R1 S1 Z(i,q)
Advocacy and Fixed Fee Interview undertaken
Ast: Holden, Mrs Karen BA(Hons)(Law); MPhil(Cantab)(Criminology) . . . . Sep 2005

BAXTER BROWN MCARTHUR ‡
150a Falcon Road Clapham Junction London SW11 2LW
Tel: 020 7924 8130 ***Fax:*** 020 7924 8131
Dx: 58558 CLAPHAM JUNCTION
Emergency telephone 07790 101631
E-mail: office@bbmlaw.co.uk
List of partners: N Baxter, R Brown, A McArthur
Languages: French
Work: B2 G H V
Advocacy, Fixed Fee Interview and Legal Aid undertaken
Ptr: Baxter, Mr Neil . . . . Sep 1995
Brown, Mr Richard . . . . Nov 2002
McArthur, Mr Andrew BA(Hons). . . . . *Jul 2003

JOHN BAYS & CO ‡
(in association with Denis Mann Bays & Co)
240a High Road Wood Green Haringey London N22 8HH
Tel: 020 8881 3609 ***Fax:*** 020 8889 2855 ***Dx:*** 35653 WOOD GREEN 1
E-mail: johnbayslawyer@btconnect.com
List of partners: J D Bays, R A McDoom
Office: London N17
Work: E L N Q S1 W Z(l)
Ptr: Bays, Mr John D BA(Hons)(Dunelm) . . . . *Jun 1973
McDoom, Mr Riyad Ally LLB . . . . Sep 2004

BAZEER & CO ‡
150 Merton Road London SW19 1EH
Tel: 020 8543 6600 ***Fax:*** 020 8543 3198
Emergency telephone 07939 095467
E-mail: bazeerandco@gmail.com
List of partners: S M Bazeer
Languages: Hindi, Urdu
Work: F1 G K1 L Z(g,i)
Emergency Action and Fixed Fee Interview undertaken
Ptr: Bazeer, Mr Seyed Mohamed BA . . . . *Apr 1993
Asoc: Qayyum, Mr Abdul LLB . . . . *Aug 1996

MARTIN BEACH (HOUSE OWNERS CONVEYANCERS LTD) ‡
109 Cricklewood Broadway London NW2 3GJ
Tel: 020 8452 6622

BEACHROFTS ‡
Gunnery House 9 Gunnery Terrace Royal Arsenal London SE18 6SW
Tel: 020 8301 8183 ***Fax:*** 020 8301 8185
E-mail: enquiry@beachcrofts.co.uk

BEALE AND COMPANY SOLICITORS LLP ‡
Garrick House 27-32 King Street Covent Garden London WC2E 8JB
Tel: 020 7240 3474 ***Fax:*** 020 7240 9111
Dx: 51632 COVENT GARDEN
E-mail: reception@beale-law.com
List of partners: M E Anderson, M J Archer, D R Barnes, S Chessher, J D Henderson, R Howell, M A John, H J Kapadia, S Lal-Sood, P W L Redfern, D L Richards, A Smith, J J Ward
Office: Bristol
Languages: French, Gujarati, Hindi, Italian, Kiswahili, Punjabi
Work: A1 A3 B1 C1 C2 C3 E F1 I J1 J2 L M1 M2 N O P Q R1 S1 S2 T1 U1 W Z(b,c,d,e,f,i,j,k,o,q)
Ptr: Anderson, Mr Michael Edward LLB . . . . *Oct 1995
Archer, Mr Michael J BA . . . . *Oct 1985
Barnes, Mrs Diana R LLB. . . . . *Jun 1975
Chessher, Mr Stephen BA. . . . . Apr 2000
Henderson, Mr John D LLB . . . . May 1991
Howell, Miss Rhian . . . . Jan 1996
John, Mr Martin Andrew MA. . . . . *Apr 1988
Kapadia, Mrs Heidi Joanne BA; MA . . . . *Oct 2000
Lal-Sood, Ms Sheena LLB Sweet & Maxwell Law Prize*Sep 1992
Redfern, Mr Paul W L LLB(Exon) . . . . Apr 1978
Richards, Mr David Lydon BA(Hons) . . . . *Oct 1993
Smith, Mr Antony LLB. . . . . *Oct 1983
Ward, Mr John J LLB . . . . *Apr 1975
Asoc: De Freitas, Mr Mark Andrew BA. . . . . *Jan 1999
Eizenberg, Mr Joseph BSc . . . . *Jul 2004
Gillies, Mr Nicholas Peter LLB(Hons); BCom . . . . . *Aug 2007
Hutchinson, Mr James Philip LLB; PGDip(LPC); FRSA Lord Lloyd of Kilgerran Prize . . . . *Apr 2003
Sell, Mr Keith Matthew BSc . . . . Sep 1999
Vernon, Mr James Peter BA(Hons); PGDipLaw; LPC . Sep 2005
Ast: Bristow, Ms Sarah Madelaine BA; MSc; CPE; LPC . . *Apr 2005
Cuskin, Ms Catherine Anne BA; CPE; LPC . . . . . . Sep 2002
Eastman, Miss Elizabeth BA . . . . Sep 2008
Gardiner, Ms Eimear Therese LLB . . . . *Jul 2008
Johnstone, Miss Lesley LLB(Hons) . . . . *Sep 2006
Jones, Mr Marc Islwyn LLB . . . . *Sep 2008
Masser, Mr Ian Urquhart LLB . . . . *Sep 2007
Modell, Mr Nathan Richard LLB. . . . . *Sep 2007
Rutter, Miss Joanna BA; CPE; LPC. . . . . *Mar 2006
Tan, Ms Estee BCom; LLB . . . . Sep 2008
Con: Harrington, Mr Keith G LLB(Hons). . . . . *Nov 1973
Sayani, Noorali R . . . . *Nov 1973

BEARING SACHS SOLICITORS LLP ‡
59a Broadway Stratford London E15 4BQ
Tel: 020 8555 4552

MARK BEATTIE ‡
16 Hadley Gardens London W4 4NX
Tel: 020 8742 7319 ***Fax:*** 020 8742 7319
E-mail: markbeattie1@montc.fsnet.co.uk

BEAUCHAMPS ‡
53 Clarewood Court Crawford Street Westminster London W1H 2NW
Tel: 020 7724 7724 ***Fax:*** 020 7724 7734 ***Dx:*** 94262 MARYLEBONE 2
E-mail: law@beauchamps.co.uk
List of partners: F C Katz, M S Reis
Work: E R2 S1 S2
Ptr: Katz, Mr Francis C LLB. . . . . *Oct 1982
Reis, Mr Mark S BA. . . . . *Feb 1991

S M BECK SOLICITORS ‡
1st Floor 144 Buckingham Palace Road London SW1W 9TR
Tel: 020 7730 8401 ***Fax:*** 020 7730 9749
E-mail: susan.beck@smbeck.com

DAVID W BEECH ‡
Foxglove House 166 Piccadilly Westminster London W1J 9EF
Tel: 020 7493 4932 ***Fax:*** 020 7493 4938
E-mail: peterbryanco@btinternet.com
List of partners: D W Beech
Work: T2 W
SPr: Beech, Mr David William LLB(Hons). . . . . *Apr 1975

BEGUM & CO ‡
93 East Hill London SW18 2QD
Tel: 020 8877 0242

NORMAN BEIGEL & CO ‡
57 Princes Park Avenue London NW11 0JR
Tel: 020 8455 8183 ***Fax:*** 020 8455 0435
List of partners: N N Beigel
Work: E L
Ptr: Beigel, Mr Norman N . . . . *Jun 1976

BELMONT & LOWE ‡
Priory House 18-25 St Johns Lane London EC1M 4HD
Tel: 020 7608 4600 ***Fax:*** 020 7608 4601 ***Dx:*** 53320 CLERKENWELL
E-mail: enquries@belmontandlowe.co.uk
List of partners: B J Hornsby-Cox, M J Loudon, M J Whaley
Work: A1 B1 C1 C2 C3 E F1 I J1 K1 K3 L O P Q S1 S2 T2 W Z(e)
Ptr: Hornsby-Cox, Ms Belinda J . . . . *Oct 1989
Loudon, Mr Michael J BA(Oxon). . . . . *Nov 1983
Whaley, Mr Martyn John LLB(Lond) . . . . *Mar 1981
Ast: Carlton, Miss C Angela BA . . . . *Dec 1980
Ho, Mrs Florence W S BSc(Hons). . . . . *Oct 1987
Leota, Mrs Susana . . . . Jul 2009
Con: Bardswell, Mr Charles N MA(Oxon) . . . . *Dec 1966
Wood, Mr John LLB(Lond) . . . . *Feb 1969

BELSHAW & CURTIN ‡
23a Camberwell Green London SE5 7AA
Tel: 020 7708 3311 ***Fax:*** 020 7708 3300
Dx: 35316 CAMBERWELL GREEN 1

E-mail: solicitors@belshawandcurtin.co.uk
List of partners: A J Curtin
Work: E L N S1 W
Emergency Action, Advocacy, Fixed Fee Interview and Legal Aid undertaken
Ptr: Curtin, Mr Andrew John BA(Hons). . . . . *Dec 1990

BELVEDERES ‡
(incorporating S Farren & Co)
6-9 Quality Court Chancery Lane London WC2A 1HP
Tel: 020 7404 5262 / 7405 0046 *Fax:* 020 7405 0788
Dx: 455 LONDON/CHANCERY LN
E-mail: access@belvederes.co.uk
List of partners: R T Trebacz, B S Wereszczynski
Languages: French, German, Polish
Work: B1 C1 E F2 J1 K1 L N O Q S1 S2 T1 T2 W Z(b,c,d,e,f,k,l,q)
Ptr: Trebacz, Mr Ryszard Tomasz . . . . May 1979
Wereszczynski, Boguslaw S. . . . . *Aug 1972

BENEDEK JOELS SOLICITORS ‡
133 Hampstead Way London NW11 7JN
Tel: 020 8458 0005 *Fax:* 020 8455 4803
Ast: Benedek, Mr Simon Peter. . . . . Nov 1996

BENN CAMERON SOLICITORS ‡
8 Glenburnie Road London SW17 7PJ
Tel: 020 8672 8306
E-mail: admin@benncameron.co.uk

ANN C BENNETT ‡
Shelley House 1 Chelsea Embankment Chelsea London SW3 4LG
Tel: 020 7352 7494 *Fax:* 020 7351 0051
E-mail: acbsol@aol.com
List of partners: A C Bennett
Languages: Spanish
Work: J1 W X Z(d,i)
SPr: Bennett, Miss Ann C BA . . . . *Jun 1974

BENNETT WELCH & CO ‡
Bank Chambers Westow Hill Upper Norwood London SE19 1TY
Tel: 020 8670 6141 *Fax:* 020 8670 8149
Dx: 34152 NORWOOD NORTH
List of partners: G R Crews, M R Foot, A C Gillan, G A Harding, D S F Troup
Work: C1 E J1 K1 M1 N O P Q R1 S1 T1 W Z(c,g,j,k,l)
Legal Aid undertaken and Member of Accident Line
Ptr: Crews, Mr Glyn R BA(Hons) . . . . *§Oct 1979
Foot, Mr Michael R . . . . *§Jan 1972
Gillan, Mr Adrian C . . . . *Dec 1988
Harding, Mr Geoffrey A LLB. . . . . *§Jul 1972
Troup, Mr Douglas S F BA Notary Public . . . . . . *§Sep 1980
Ast: Danher, Ms Susan C LLB . . . . Jan 1992

J BENSON SOLICITORS ‡
Suite 324 158 Belsize Road London NW6 4BT
Tel: 020 7316 1884 *Fax:* 020 7624 3629 *Dx:* 37706 KILBURN
E-mail: info@jbensonsolicitors.com

BENSON MAZURE LLP ‡
3rd Floor 66-70 Baker Street Westminster London W1U 7DJ
Tel: 020 7486 8091 *Fax:* 020 7299 9618 *Dx:* 9007 WEST END
E-mail: info@bensonmazure.co.uk
List of partners: A M Levy, S I Marcovitch, M A Zuckerman
Languages: French
Work: B1 C1 C2 C3 E F1 G J1 K1 L M1 M2 N O Q R1 R2 S1 S2 T1 T2 W Z(b)
Emergency Action, Agency, Advocacy and Legal Aid undertaken
Ptr: Levy, Mr Anthony M LLB . . . . *Jun 1969
Marcovitch, Mr Steven I LLB . . . . *Sep 1997
Zuckerman, Mr Michael A LLB(Lond); MBA . . . . . . *Jul 1977

BENTLEYS ‡
Saxon House 182 Hoe Street Walthamstow Waltham Forest London E17 4QH
Tel: 020 8521 8751 *Fax:* 020 8520 5069
Dx: 32004 WALTHAMSTOW
E-mail: e17law@aol.com
List of partners: R A Bentley
Languages: French
Work: B1 C1 D1 E F1 G H K1 L M1 N P R1 S1 T1 W Z(f,k,l,o)
Emergency Action, Agency, Advocacy, Fixed Fee Interview, Legal Aid undertaken and Member of Accident Line
Ptr: Bentley, Mr Robert A . . . . Jun 1980

BENTLEYS STOKES & LOWLESS ‡
International House 1 St Katharine's Way Tower Hamlets London E1W 1YL
Tel: 020 7782 0990 *Fax:* 020 7481 7978
E-mail: law@bentleys.co.uk
List of partners: W J Chetwood, O De Sybel, P M Gregson, P S Griffiths, M W Moon, J E Quain, V E Sewell, J M Steele, S R Tatham, N S R Wilson
Languages: French, Greek, Italian, Japanese, Spanish
Work: M2 N O Q Z(a,b,c,j)
Emergency Action, Agency and Advocacy undertaken
Ptr: Chetwood, Mr William J LLB . . . . *Nov 1979
De Sybel, Mr Oswald . . . . Feb 1991
Gregson, Mr Philip Michael . . . . Oct 1995
Griffiths, Mr Paul S LLB. . . . . *Dec 1979
Moon, Mr Michael William BA; LLB(Rhodes, S Africa) *Feb 1999
Quain, Mr Joseph Edwin LLB(Hons). . . . . Oct 1995
Sewell, Mr Vernon E MA . . . . *Apr 1982
Steele, Ms Joanna M . . . . May 1992
Tatham, Mr Simon Ralph LLB . . . . *Oct 1980
Wilson, Mr Nicholas Stuart Ross . . . . Dec 1991
Ast: Clarke, Mr Andrew . . . . *Apr 1990
Kennedy, Mr Hugh . . . . Sep 1997
Sheen, Mr Roderick John BA . . . . *Aug 1994

BERKELEY LAW LIMTED ‡
19 Berkeley Street London W1J 8ED
Tel: 020 7399 0930
E-mail: info@berkeley-law.com

DANIEL BERMAN & CO ‡
4th Floor Linton House 39-51 Highgate Road London NW5 1RS
Tel: 020 7428 7798 *Fax:* 020 7428 7799 *Dx:* 46455 KENTISH TOWN
Emergency telephone 07855 525494
E-mail: djb@danielberman.co.uk
List of partners: D J Berman, E Perry
Work: B2 G H
Advocacy and Legal Aid undertaken
Ptr: Berman, Mr Daniel James ★ . . . . *Jul 1994
Perry, Mr Elliot BA; MA; DipLaw ★. . . . . Mar 2002

DANIEL BERNSTEIN & CO ‡
8 Rosemont Road London NW3 6NE
Tel: 020 7435 8921 *Fax:* 020 7435 8448
E-mail: post@danielbernstein.co.uk

BERRY SMITH LLP
1 Northumberland Avenue Trafalgar Square London WC2N 5BW
Tel: 0845 603 8337 *Fax:* 0845 603 4524
E-mail: london@berrysmith.com
Office: Bridgend, Bristol, Cardiff

BERRYMANS LACE MAWER ‡
Salisbury House London Wall London EC2M 5QN
Tel: 020 7638 2811 *Fax:* 020 7920 0361
Dx: 33861 FINSBURY SQUARE
E-mail: info@blm-law.com
Office: Birmingham, Bristol, Cardiff, Leeds, Liverpool, Manchester, Southampton, Stockton-on-Tees
Languages: French, German, Italian, Spanish
Work: A3 D1 F2 J1 J2 K1 M1 M2 N O P Q R1 X Z(c,e,g,h,j,k,q,r,t)

BERWIN LEIGHTON PAISNER LLP ‡
Adelaide House London Bridge London EC4R 9HA
Tel: 020 7760 1000 *Fax:* 020 7760 1111 *Dx:* 92 LONDON
E-mail: info@blplaw.com
Languages: Afrikaans, Dutch, French, German, Greek, Hebrew, Italian, Japanese, Kiswahili, Polish, Russian, Spanish
Work: A3 B1 C1 C2 C3 E J1 M1 O P Q R1 R2 S1 S2 T1 U1 U2 W Z(b,c,e,o,q,u)

BEST & SOAMES LIMITED ‡
Clerkenwell Workshops 27-31 Clerkenwell Close London EC1R 0AT
Tel: 020 7014 3525

SIMON BETHEL SOLICITORS ‡
58-60 Lewisham High Street London SE13 5JH
Tel: 020 8297 7933 *Fax:* 020 8297 4180
E-mail: info@simonbethel.co.uk

BEULAH SOLICITORS ‡
Suite 1 6 Teasel Crescent London SE28 0LP
Tel: 020 8331 0305

BEVAN BRITTAN LLP
Fleet Place House 2 Fleet Place Holborn Viaduct London EC4M 7RF
Tel: 0870 194 1000 *Fax:* 0870 194 7800
Dx: 1058 LONDON/CHANCERY LN
E-mail: info@bevanbrittan.com
Office: Birmingham, Bristol
Languages: French, German, Russian
Work: B2 C1 C2 E I J1 J2 L M1 O P Q R1 S2 Z(b,c,e,j,m,p,q,r,u)
Emergency Action, Agency, Advocacy, Fixed Fee Interview, ADVOC and Member of Accident Line
Ptr: Atkins, Mr Graham G MA(Oxon). . . . . *Jun 1972
Caplan, Mr Ian . . . . Mar 1997
Chapman, Mr John T LLB. . . . . *Apr 1983
Coetzee, Mr Hugo. . . . . Feb 2000
Cooksley, Ms Karen. . . . . Oct 1989
Duthie, Mr Adam L BEc; LLB(Hons); BCL(Hons) Butterworths Prize; Commonwealth Scholarship . . . . *Apr 1992
Easterbrook, Ms Joanne Louise. . . . . Nov 1988
Fogarty, Mr Timothy Michael . . . . Apr 1991
Grant, Mr Neil Andrew BA(Oxon) . . . . *Oct 1992
Miller, Mr Iain G. Oct 1988
Moody, Mr Peter Herbert Charles . . . . Oct 1984
Proddow, Mr Charlie W N. . . . . May 1996
Sinclair, Ms Jodie N BA . . . . *Apr 2000
Tobin, Mr Andrew C. . . . . Nov 1993
Trinder, Mr Matthew S J LLB(Hons) . . . . *Oct 1996
Westell, Ms Sherree LLB(Bris) . . . . *Oct 1992
Widdowson, Mr David G LLB(B'ham) . . . . *§Jan 1986

BEVAN KIDWELL ‡
113-117 Farringdon Road London EC1R 3BX
Tel: 020 7843 1820 *Fax:* 020 7278 4685 *Dx:* 53343 CLERKENWELL
E-mail: bk@bevankidwell.com
List of partners: J R Bevan, J A Bevan, V J Haynes, L M T Inzani, M F Wheatley
Languages: Italian
Work: B1 C1 C2 E I J1 J2 K3 L N O Q R1 S1 S2 W Z(e,f,k,l,p,q)
Agency and Fixed Fee Interview undertaken
Ptr: Bevan, Mr John Arthur BSc(Econ). . . . . *Jul 1987
Bevan, Miss Jean R LLB(L'pool). . . . . *Jul 1990
Haynes, Ms Vivienne J BA . . . . Nov 1987
Inzani, Miss Lisa M T LLB(Hons) . . . . *Nov 1990
Wheatley, Ms Marianne F BA(Leics). . . . . *Oct 1989
Ast: Pead, Mr Nick BA(Hons) . . . . Sep 2001

BEVANS
46 Essex Street The Strand London WC2R 3JF
Tel: 020 7353 9995 *Fax:* 020 7353 9994
Dx: 413 LONDON/CHANCERY LN
E-mail: thestrand@bevans.co.uk
Office: Bristol
Languages: French, German, Italian
Ast: Fawcett, Ms Philippa M MA(Cantab). . . . . *Jan 1979
Freeman, Mr David LLB. . . . . *Apr 1974
Walker, Mr Stephen M BA(Oxon); FCIArb . . . . *Oct 1978
Xavier, Mr Lee Andrew LLB . . . . *Nov 1994

BEYNONS NICHOLLS ‡
7 Hind Court 147 Fleet Street London EC4A 2BU
Tel: 020 7353 5860 *Fax:* 020 7353 1111
List of partners: R W Beynon, N S Boucher
Work: B1 C1 E F1 G H J1 K1 L M1 N P R1 S1 T1 W
Emergency Action, Agency, Advocacy, Legal Aid undertaken and Member of Accident Line
Ptr: Beynon, Mr Richard W LLB . . . . *Jan 1975
Boucher, Mr Nicholas S LLB . . . . Jul 1977

BHATT MURPHY ‡
27 Hoxton Square Hackney London N1 6NN
Tel: 020 7729 1115 *Fax:* 020 7729 1117 *Dx:* 36626 FINSBURY
List of partners: R Bhatt, S R Creighton, F Murphy, M Scott
Languages: Gujarati, Hindi
Work: Z(g)
Legal Aid undertaken
Ptr: Bhatt, Rajendra BA(Oxon). . . . . Nov 1988
Creighton, Mr Simon Randal . . . . Oct 1991
Murphy, Ms Fiona. . . . . Mar 1993
Scott, Mr Mark BSc . . . . Oct 1993

BIBI GADWAH SOLICITORS ‡
Ground Floor Snowdon House Meridian Gate London E14 9PG
Tel: 020 7377 6102 *Fax:* 020 7068 5773 *Dx:* 42652 ISLE OF DOGS
E-mail: bgadwah@aol.com
List of partners: B A Gadwah
Languages: Arabic, Bengali
Work: D1 K1
Fixed Fee Interview, Legal Aid undertaken and Legal Aid Franchise
Ptr: Gadwah, Ms Bibi A BA Notary Public . . . . *Dec 1990

BIGNALLS ‡
5th Floor 9-10 Market Place Westminster London W1W 8AQ
Tel: 020 7637 3071 *Fax:* 020 7637 5516
E-mail: bignalls@dial.pipex.com
List of partners: J Bignall, N Bignall
Languages: French, German
Work: C1 C2 C3 E J1 O P T1 T2 Z(c,e)
Ptr: Bignall, Mr John LLB(Lond) . . . . *Jun 1968
Bignall, Mrs Nancy BA(Lond) . . . . *Mar 1976

BILBEISI & CO SOLICITORS ‡
5 Oakleigh Mews Oakleigh Road North Barnet London N20 9HQ
Tel: 020 8446 7262 *Fax:* 0560 075 4869
E-mail: alilbeisi@onetel.com
List of partners: A M Bilbeisi
Languages: Arabic
Work: D1 K1 K3 L V W Z(i)
Fixed Fee Interview undertaken
SPr: Bilbeisi, Amer Munther BA(Hons) . . . . Jul 2001

BILMES LLP ‡
218 Strand London WC2R 1AT
Tel: 020 7490 9656 *Dx:* 272 LONDON/CHANCERY LN
E-mail: law@bilmesllp.com
Office: Brighton

BILSON HENAKU SOLICITORS ‡
6 Devonshire Road London SE23 3JT
Tel: 020 8291 1043

BINDMANS LLP ‡
275 Gray's Inn Road London WC1X 8QB
Tel: 020 7833 4433 *Fax:* 020 7837 9792 *Dx:* 37904 KINGS CROSS
Emergency telephone 07659 136205 (PAGER)
E-mail: info@bindmans.com
List of partners: T D Allen, S Chahal, J M Crocker, K E Gieve, S E Grosz, J Halford, S Kelly, L Knowles, N D O'May, S Qureshi, M Rackstraw, P Ridge, M Schwarz, A J Stanley, K Wheatley
Languages: French, German, Gujarati, Hindi, Punjabi, Spanish
Work: B2 D1 G H J1 J2 K1 K3 L M1 M2 N P Q V Z(d,e,g,h,i,k,m,p,r,za)
Emergency Action, Agency, Advocacy, Legal Aid undertaken, Legal Aid Franchise and Member of Accident Line
Ptr: Allen, Ms Tamsin D . . . . Jun 1998
Chahal, Saimo . . . . Jun 1990
Crocker, Mr Jonathan Maurice BA(Hons) . . . . . . *Oct 1992
Gieve, Ms Katherine E BA(Oxon) . . . . *Jun 1978
Grosz, Mr Stephen E MA(Cantab); Licence en Droit Europeen(Brussels). . . . . *Oct 1978
Halford, Mr John . . . . Mar 1996
Kelly, Miss Siobhan LLB. . . . . *Oct 2001
Knowles, Ms Lynn. . . . . Sep 1996
O'May, Mr Neil D BSc. . . . . *Oct 1986
Qureshi, Shah. . . . . Aug 2002
Rackstraw, Mr Martin BA; MA . . . . *Nov 1995
Ridge, Mr Paul BSc Law Society Prize . . . . *Aug 1998
Schwarz, Mr Michael . . . . Nov 1992
Stanley, Ms Alison J BA. . . . . May 1985
Wheatley, Ms Katie . . . . *Jul 1991
Asoc: Barratt, Ms Liz BA; CPE. . . . . Sep 2001
Cole, Miss Emilie LLB(Law & French) . . . . Mar 2006
Cotton, Ms Chez LLB . . . . *May 2000
Coubrough, Ms Louise . . . . Nov 1986
Friedman, Ms Rhona . . . . *Nov 1999
Goold, Ms Kate BA . . . . Nov 1996
Murphy, Ms Alla Catherine Mary BA(Hons); CPE; LSF *Nov 1992
Ast: Broadley, Ms Janet BA(Hons) . . . . Jan 1999
Budhani, Salima. Mar 2010
Carson, Ms Pearl Mae-Ying BA(Contemporary History); GDL; LPC. . . . . Mar 2010
Cohen, Ms Emma BA(Hispanic Studies); CPE. . . . . *Oct 1995
Fitzgerald, Ms Rosalind MA(Cantab) . . . . Feb 2008
Fry, Mr Nicholas BA(Hons); MRes; LLB; LPC . . . . . Mar 2011
Haslam, Ms Roberta . . . . Mar 2010
Haworth-Hird, Ms Charlotte BSocSci; GDL, LPC . . . Jul 2008
Higgs, Laura . . . . Sep 2004
Jackson, Ms Catherine . . . . Nov 2008
Macken, Ms Kathryn BSc(Social Psychology); PGDL; LPC . . . . *Sep 2007
Morgan, Ms Gwendolen LLB; MA Law Soc Excellence Awards 2009. Finalist in the 2008 Legal Aid Lawyer of the Year awards in Young Solicitor category. Trinity College Dublin Entrance Exhibition Scholarship & Results Prize 2000. . . . . Nov 2006
Rowe, Amy . . . . Mar 2010
Skinns, Ms Jessica . . . . Sep 2005
Smith, Mr Stephan LLB . . . . Mar 2011
Con: Bindman, Sir Geoffrey L QC BCL; MA(Oxon) . . . . *Nov 1959

BINGHAM MCCUTCHEN (LONDON) LLP ‡
41 Lothbury London EC2R 7HF
Tel: 020 7661 5300 *Fax:* 020 7661 5400
E-mail: info@bingham.com
List of partners: E Baltay, T Bannister, P A Bibby, V Chapman, J Clark, N Harrison, H Marshall, S D E Peppiatt, J H D Roome, B Russell, J Terry
Work: B1 C2 O Z(b,o)
Ptr: Baltay, Ms Elisabeth. . . . . Jan 1998
Bannister, Mr Tom. . . . . Jan 2005
Bibby, Mr Peter A LLB; LSF. . . . . Oct 1989
Chapman, Mr Vance . . . . Jan 1997
Clark, Mr John . . . . Jan 1986
Harrison, Ms Natasha. . . . . Jan 2004
Marshall, Ms Helen . . . . Jan 1987
Peppiatt, Mr Stephen D E LLB . . . . May 1987
Roome, Mr James H D LLB. . . . . *Oct 1984

See p2 for the Key to Work Categories & other symbols

Russell, Mr Barry . . . . Jan 2000
Terry, Mr James. Jan 1997

BIRCHAM DYSON BELL ‡
(incorporating Dyson Bell Martin; Stoneham Langton & Passmore)
50 Broadway Westminster London SW1H 0BL
Tel: 020 7227 7000 *Fax:* 020 7222 3480 *Dx:* 2317 VICTORIA
E-mail: reception@bdb-law.co.uk
List of partners: I R Adamson, J Bracken, E N W Brown, P J Chapman, G A Couch, J E Darnton, D J Darvill, N M Emerson, C D Findley, P W Goodwin, C M Hand, D G Humphreys, P T Jacobsen, C J A Johnston, S M Jones, G H Josselyn, S R Lewin, C A Martin, I H McCulloch, D Mundy, R J V Owen, M A Parker, R A Perrin, A M Smith, G S Smith, J M Stephenson, S A Stowell, P H Thompson, J C Turnbull, G W Vincent, P M G Voller, S P Weil, M D Wood
Languages: Danish, French, German, Italian, Spanish
Work: A1 A2 B1 C2 C3 D1 D2 E F1 J1 K1 L N O P Q R1 S1 T1 T2 W Z(c,d,e,g,i,l,n,o,u)
Agency undertaken and Member of Accident Line
Ptr: Adamson, Mr Ian R MA; PhD(Cantab); DipLaw . . . *§Nov 1983
Bracken, Mr Jonathan. . . . . *Aug 1999
Brown, Mr E Nicholas W MA(Oxon) Clerk to General Commissioners of Taxes . . . . *§Jan 1983
Chapman, Miss Penelope J BA(Oxon). . . . . Nov 1986
Couch, Mr Graeme A MA(Oxon) . . . . *§May 1979
Darnton, Mr John E LLB. . . . . *§Mar 1985
Darvill, Mr David J LLB . . . . *Mar 1985
Emerson, Mr Neil Mark MA(Cantab). . . . . *Nov 1993
Findley, Mr Christopher D LLB(Lond) . . . . *Jun 1979
Goodwin, Mr Peter W BA(Oxon). . . . . *§Jun 1968
Hand, Mrs Catherine M . . . . *Apr 1978
Humphreys, Mr David Gordon MA(Cantab) . . . . . *Mar 1969
Jacobsen, Mr Peter T BSc . . . . *§Apr 1976
Johnston, Mr Charles James Andrew MA . . . . . . *Dec 1986
Jones, Ms Sian M LLB . . . . *Oct 1992
Josselyn, Mr George H . . . . *§Jun 1977
Lewin, Mr Stephen R LLB(B'ham). . . . . *Jun 1977
McCulloch, Mr Ian H LLB . . . . *§Apr 1976
Martin, Ms Carol A LLB(Wales) . . . . *Oct 1988
Mundy, Mr David BA . . . . *Dec 1990
Owen, Mr Robert J V BA . . . . *Dec 1989
Parker, Mr Michael A LLB(Soton) . . . . *§Dec 1980
Perrin, Mr Robert A MA(Cantab) . . . . *§Apr 1981
Smith, Mr Andrew Macdonald LLB . . . . *Dec 1990
Smith, Mr George S. . . . . *Jul 1965
Stephenson, Mr John M MA(Oxon) . . . . *§Oct 1983
Stowell, Miss Sarah A MA(Oxon) . . . . *Dec 1978
Thompson, Mr Paul H LLB . . . . *Dec 1990
Turnbull, Mr John C MA(Oxon) . . . . *§Jun 1977
Vincent, Mr Guy W BA . . . . *§Mar 1981
Voller, Mr Paul M G BA . . . . *Apr 1981
Weil, Mr Simon P MA(Cantab) . . . . *§May 1980
Wood, Mr Michael D . . . . *Jun 1996
Asoc: Alton, Ms Nicola. . . . . *Jan 1995
Cabot, Mrs Janet BA(Cantab). . . . . *Feb 1985
Christensen, Mr Jesper . . . . *Oct 1998
Millar, Miss Judith BA(Hons)(Cantab) . . . . *Nov 1993
Painter, Mr Simon. . . . . *Dec 1994
Smith, Ms Jenny . . . . *May 1996
Ast: Yusuf, Ms Salma LLB(Hons); LLM. . . . . *Feb 1993
Con: Davies, Mr Peter R . . . . *Apr 1962
Foster, Mr John G. . . . . *§Jan 1968
Goodman, Mr David R LLB(Lond) . . . . *Jun 1964
Venables, Mr Robert C . . . . *Jun 1962

BIRCHLEY TITMUS COMMERCIAL SOLICITORS ‡
16 Hanover Square London W1S 1HT
Tel: 020 7408 9427 *Fax:* 020 7408 9417
E-mail: info@birchleytitmus.com

BIRD & BIRD LLP ‡
15 Fetter Lane London EC4A 1JP
Tel: 020 7415 6000 *Fax:* 020 7415 6111
Dx: 119 LONDON/CHANCERY LN
E-mail: info@twobirds.com
List of partners: E Alder, C Aldridge, G M Andrews, T R D Asserson, D H Ayers, C Barrett, R M Bickerstaff, N S P Blundell, R J Boardman, L C Brazell, P R Brownlow, R H Butterworth, D W Byam-Cook, G E Camps, P J Christie, D C J Cook, T M Cook, V S A Crook, P C Dally, G Defries, M J Dennis, I C Evans, R W Fawcett, H J Grant, J Gyngell, D Harriss, I D Hunter, B M Israel, N T Jenkins, D Kerr, M P Lindsay, M Macdonald, N K Maguire, J M Mutimear, M J O'Conor, H E Pearson, N J Perry, G Powell, P D Quinan, F A Reeve, H J Rubin, A J Sanderson, H R Sandison, R N Scott, J R Sharman, G J H Smith, P Smith, J Stannard, K J Stephens, A J Stobbart, T C G Tether, S K Topping, J R C Walkey, R J Ward, J Wilkinson, D L Wilson
Languages: Dutch, French, German, Hebrew, Italian, Mandarin, Spanish
Work: A3 B1 C1 C2 C3 E I J1 M1 O R2 T1 U1 U2 Z(a,b,e,f,i,k,u,w,z)
Emergency Action, Agency and Advocacy undertaken
Ptr: Alder, Mr Edward MA(Cantab)(Law). . . . . *Jul 1991
Aldridge, Ms Corinne LLB(Hons) . . . . *Sep 1987
Andrews, Ms Gill M BA(Oxon). . . . . Apr 1990
Asserson, Mr Trevor Richard David BA(Hons)(Oxon) . *Nov 1984
Ayers, Mr David H BA(Durham) . . . . *Nov 1987
Barrett, Mr Chris BCom; LLB(UNSW) . . . . *May 1991
Bickerstaff, Mr Roger M MA(Cantab); MPhil. . . . . *Sep 1990
Blundell, Mr Neil S P LLM(Cantab) . . . . *Nov 1988
Boardman, Mrs Ruth Jane BA(Hons)(Oxon) Sheffield Prize; Syrett Prize. . . . . *Nov 1995
Brazell, Ms Lorna C LLM(Lond) . . . . *May 1994
Brownlow, Mr Peter R LLB(Leeds). . . . . *May 1991
Butterworth, Mr Roger H MA(Cantab). . . . . *Apr 1979
Byam-Cook, Mr David W BA(Hons)(Kent). . . . . . . *Jun 1976
Camps, Mr Graham E. . . . . *§Nov 1970
Christie, Ms Penelope J MA(Cantab) . . . . *Jun 1977
Cook, Mr Dominic C J LLB(Hons) . . . . *Oct 1992
Cook, Mr Trevor M BSc(Soton) . . . . *§Dec 1977
Crook, Mrs Vivien S A LLB(Hons). . . . . *Oct 1990
Dally, Mr Peter C LLB. . . . . *Aug 1980
Defries, Mr Graham BA. . . . . *Oct 1994
Dennis, Mr Matthew J LLB(Soton). . . . . Sep 1990
Evans, Mrs Isabel C LLB(Hons)(Manc) . . . . *May 1986
Fawcett, Mr Richard W LLB(Hons) . . . . *Nov 1991
Grant, Miss Hazel J MA(Cantab) . . . . *Oct 1992
Gyngell, Mr Julian LLB(Sydney); Dip IPL(Lond) . . . *May 1991
Harriss, Mr David MA(Cantab). . . . . *Oct 1977
Hunter, Mr Ian D BA(Hons) . . . . *May 1989
Israel, Mr Brett M LLB(Warw) . . . . Sep 1990
Jenkins, Mr Neil T BSc(Bris) . . . . *Nov 1988
Kerr, Mr David MA(Cantab) . . . . *Oct 1985
Lindsay, Mr Matthew Paul LLB(Cantab) . . . . *Mar 1992
Macdonald, Ms Morag MA(Cantab) . . . . *Dec 1988
Maguire, Ms Nicola Kay LLB(Manc) . . . . *Sep 1988
Mutimear, Ms Jane M LLB(Sheff) . . . . *Nov 1990
O'Conor, Mr Mark J BA(Hons). . . . . *Dec 1994
Pearson, Ms Hilary E MA(Oxon); LLB(Lond) Chrystal Macmillan Memorial Prize 1976 . . . . *Jul 1995
Perry, Mr Nicholas J MA(Cantab) . . . . *Oct 1994
Powell, Mr Grant LLB(Bris) . . . . *Feb 1990
Quinan, Mr P Duncan LLB(Soton). . . . . *Jan 1981
Reeve, Miss Felicity A BA(Hons)(Oxon). . . . . . . *Nov 1993
Rubin, Mr Howard J. . . . . *May 1981
Sanderson, Mr Allan J BA(Leics) . . . . *Dec 1977
Sandison, Mr Hamish R MA(Cantab); LLM(Berkeley) . Nov 1991
Scott, Mr Robert N LLB(Bris) . . . . *May 1974
Sharman, Mr Jeremy R LLB. . . . . *Jul 1987
Smith, Mr Graham J H LLB(Bris) . . . . *Nov 1978
Smith, Miss Pauline LLB(Sheff); TEP . . . . *Jun 1974
Stannard, Ms Joanne LLB. . . . . *May 1990
Stephens, Mrs Katharine J MEng(Brunel) . . . . . . *Sep 1992
Stobbart, Mr Andrew J BA(Cantab) . . . . *Nov 1995
Tether, Mr Trystan C G BA(Oxon). . . . . *Nov 1985
Topping, Mr Simon K BA(Oxon); MA(German Law); MA(Euro Law) . . . . *Apr 1995
Walkey, Mr Justin R C BA(Hons) . . . . *Mar 1984
Ward, Mr Richard J BA(Oxon). . . . . *Nov 1985
Wilkinson, Mr John BSc(Lond) . . . . *Jan 1995
Wilson, Mr David Lawrence BSc(Lond) . . . . *Aug 1999
Ast: Abbott, Ms Madeleine. . . . . *Sep 1997
Chapman, Mr Peter BA(Leeds) . . . . Mar 1998
Chapman, Ms Ruth BA(Hons). . . . . Mar 1999
Courtney-Stubbs, Mr Julian BA(Leeds) . . . . Nov 1996
Drake, Ms Alexandra V L BA(Durham) . . . . *Apr 1989
Dugan, Ms Samantha LLB(Warw) . . . . *Sep 1993
Con: Chalton, Mr Simon N L LLB . . . . *§Dec 1958
Dann, Mr Phillip J MA; LLB(Cantab). . . . . Mar 1991
Gaythwaite, Dr D Miles BSc(Glasgow); PhD(Cantab) . *Mar 1978

A J BIRD & CO ‡
1 Warwick Row London SW1E 5ER
Tel: 020 7808 7908 *Fax:* 020 7808 7909
E-mail: info@ajbird.com

ERNEST BIRD & SONS ‡
9a Craven Hill Westminster London W2 3EN
Tel: 020 7262 3814 *Fax:* 020 7402 3628
List of partners: I Dean
Languages: French, German
Work: C1 C2 E P S1 S2 T1 T2 W Z(c,u)

BIRDS SOLICITORS ‡
1 Garratt Lane Wandsworth London SW18 2PT
Tel: 020 8874 7433 *Fax:* 020 8870 4770
Dx: 59062 WANDSWORTH NORTH
Emergency telephone 07966 234994
E-mail: info@birds.eu.com
List of partners: S D Bird, R B Locke
Work: B2 G H
Emergency Action, Agency, Advocacy and Legal Aid undertaken
Ptr: Bird, Mr Steven D LLM ★. . . . . *Dec 1990
Locke, Mr Richard Brian BA(Cantab) ★. . . . . *Jun 1994

BIRIYOK SHOW SOLICITORS ‡
12 The Dock Offices Surrey Quay Road London SE16 2XU
Tel: 020 7237 4646 *Fax:* 020 7394 8273
Emergency telephone 07973 689232
E-mail: birisho@aol.com
List of partners: L Biriyok
Work: F1 G J1 K1 Q S1 S2 W Z(i)
Agency undertaken
SPr: Biriyok, Mrs Lawumi BSc; LLB(Hons)(Lond). . . . . . *Dec 1995

BIRNBERG PEIRCE & PARTNERS ‡
14 Inverness Street Camden London NW1 7HJ
Tel: 020 7911 0166 *Fax:* 020 7911 0170 *Dx:* 57059 CAMDEN TOWN
Emergency telephone 020 7911 0166
List of partners: N Leskin, G Peirce, M Willis Stewart
Work: G H N Z(g,i)
Fixed Fee Interview and Legal Aid undertaken
Ptr: Leskin, Mr Nigel. . . . . Apr 1983
Peirce, Mrs Gareth LLB(Lond). . . . . Dec 1978
Willis Stewart, Ms Marcia . . . . Mar 1999
Asoc: Graham, Mr Ronald John Christopher MA(Hons)(Anthropology); CPE; BVC; QLTT Diplock Prize; Bristow Scholarship . . . . Oct 2008
Graham Wood, Miss Camilla . . . . *Oct 2011
Ast: Croft, Mr Benjamin Victor LLB(Law with French); DipLP Oct 2005
Dasgupta, Ms Debaleena BA(Hons); PGDL; LPC . . . Jun 2007
Despicht, Miss Rachael LLB; LPC. . . . . Oct 2000
Foot, Mr Matthew . . . . May 2000
Guedalla, Mr Daniel Roger BA(Hons)(Politics); CPE; LPC . . . . Mar 2001
Kellas, Ms Sarah . . . . Apr 2008
Lyon, Mr Alastair BA(Hons) . . . . Jan 2001
Malik, Ms Sajida . . . . Mar 2005
Middleton, Miss Sally LLB; BA(History) . . . . *Oct 2005
Miller, Mr Henry. . . . . Sep 2003
Nembhard, Ms Irene . . . . Nov 1998
O'Connor, Mr Liam . . . . Nov 2007
Routledge, Ms Sonia . . . . Aug 2003
Wistrich, Ms Harriet BA . . . . Dec 1997

BIROL & CO SOLICITORS ‡
71b Stoke Newington Road London N16 8AD
Tel: 020 7923 4065

BISHOP & SEWELL LLP ‡
59-60 Russell Square London WC1B 4HP
Est: 1979
Tel: 020 7631 4141 *Fax:* 020 7636 5369
Dx: 278 LONDON/CHANCERY LN
E-mail: info@bishopandsewell.co.uk
Web: www.bishopandsewell.co.uk
List of partners: S C Bishop, K L Bright, M Chick, G M Fairfax, M J Gillman, D A Martin, A R E T Murray, N F Potter, A D Swaine
Languages: French, German, Gujarati, Punjabi
Work: A3 B1 C1 C2 C3 E J1 K1 K2 K3 L M2 O Q R1 R2 S1 S2 T1 T2 W Z(b,c,i,k,p)
Emergency Action, Agency and Advocacy undertaken
Mem: Bishop, Mr Stephen C LLB . . . . *Nov 1976
Bright, Ms Karen Linda BA(Hons) . . . . Apr 2002
Chick, Mr Mark BSc. . . . . *Sep 2001
Fairfax, Mrs Gina Margaret LLB; AKC(Lond). . . . . *§Dec 1988
Gillman, Mr Michael J BA(Law) • Deputy District Judge . . . . *Aug 1979
Martin, Mr David Andrew MA(Cantab). . . . . Dec 1972
Murray, Mr Andrew Raymond Edward Teyhatyr LLB. . Mar 1986
Potter, Mr Nicholas F LLB. . . . . Oct 1984
Swaine, Mr Andrew D LLB; HND . . . . *Sep 1991
Asoc: Barry, Ms Nessa Catherine BCL; LLB; LLM . . . . . Apr 2005
Bhatt, Mr Chandresh LLB . . . . *Oct 1983
Coffey, Mrs Julienne LLB . . . . Sep 2003
Pirani, Mrs Monika Luise LLB . . . . Oct 1995
Ast: Hales, Ms Lauren Josephine Ironmonger LLB . . . . Jan 2008
Humphrey, Mr Andrew. . . . . Apr 2003
Patel, Ms Senal BA(Hons). . . . . Sep 2007
Pope, Mr Ian . . . . Sep 1975
Stallard, Mr Nicholas Charles Maxwell BA(Hons) . . . Apr 2010
Studd, Mr Simon George BA(Hons). . . . . Apr 1981
Uphill, Louise . . . . Aug 2009

Company and Commercial Law; Banking; Landlord & Tenant; Commercial & Residential Property; Insolvency; Litigation; Matrimonial; Wills, Trust and Probate.

BISHOP LLOYD & JACKSON ‡
111 Uxbridge Road Ealing London W5 5LB
Tel: 020 8832 1162 *Fax:* 020 8832 1161 *Dx:* 5115 EALING
E-mail: info@bljlaw.co.uk

BIVONAS LIMITED SOLICITORS ‡
24 Cornhill London EC3V 3ND
Tel: 020 7337 2600 *Fax:* 020 7337 2601 *Dx:* 42613 CHEAPSIDE
Emergency telephone 020 7337 2600
E-mail: info@bivonas.com
List of partners: J F Bechelet
Work: B2 G O Q S2 Z(j)
Fixed Fee Interview and Legal Aid undertaken
Ptr: Bechelet, Mr John F BA(Law). . . . . *Sep 1983
Ast: Sharp, Mr Stephen Richard LLB(Hons) . . . . *Mar 1985

BLACK GRAF & CO ‡
14-15 College Crescent Swiss Cottage London NW3 5LL
Tel: 020 7586 1141 *Fax:* 020 7586 3721
Dx: 38853 SWISS COTTAGE
List of partners: D Aarons, P Dyar, R A S Graf, P H McKee, A J Wheldon
Languages: Spanish
Work: B1 C1 E F1 J1 K1 N O P Q S1 S2 W Z(c,i,l,q,r)
Ptr: Aarons, Mr Derek LLB . . . . *Mar 1973
Dyar, Mr Patrick BA; LLM . . . . *Jan 1991
Graf, Mr Robin Anthony Scott. . . . . *Oct 1975
McKee, Mr Paul H BA. . . . . *Aug 1997
Wheldon, Mr Andrew J LLB . . . . *Feb 1985
Ast: Brett, Mr Michael P LLB. . . . . *Jan 1985
Scott, Mr Peter LLB. . . . . *Jun 1980
Sutton, Mr Michael Philip BA . . . . *Sep 1997
Yeo, Miss Belinda. . . . . *Nov 1992

BLACK STONE SOLICITORS ‡
The Courtyard 7 Francis Grove Wimbledon London SW19 4DW

BLACKFORDS LLP
2nd Floor Lamb Building Temple London EC4Y 7AS
Tel: 020 8686 6232 *Fax:* 020 8681 5078
Emergency telephone 07876 081080
E-mail: london@blackfords.com
Office: Cardiff, Croydon, Woking

BLACKWELL SANDERS PEPER MARTIN LLP ‡
150 Aldersgate Street London EC1A 4EJ
Tel: 020 7788 5073 *Fax:* 020 7788 5090

BLACKWHITE SOLICITORS ‡
Suite 112 Queensway House 275-285 High Street London E15 2TF
Tel: 020 8522 4150 *Fax:* 020 8534 2136
E-mail: info@blackwhitesolicitors.com

BLAKE CASSELS & GRAYDON LLP ‡
5th Floor 23 College Hill London EC4R 2RP
Tel: 020 7429 3550 *Fax:* 020 7429 3560
E-mail: karim.mahmud@blakes.com

CHARLOTTE BLAKE ‡
10 Glenhurst Avenue London NW5 1PS
Tel: 020 7485 4010
E-mail: charlotte@charlotteblake.co.uk
List of partners: C M Blake
Languages: French
Work: C1 J1 Z(c)
SPr: Blake, Ms Charlotte M LLB . . . . *Jun 1980

BLAKE LAPTHORN
Watchmaker Court 33 St John's Lane London EC1M 4DB
Tel: 020 7405 2000 *Fax:* 020 7814 9421 *Dx:* 53323 CLERKENWELL
E-mail: info@bllaw.co.uk
Office: Chandlers Ford, Oxford, Portsmouth
Ptr: Arnold, Mr Nicholas J LLB. . . . . *Oct 1983
Barrow, Mr Kevin M MA(Oxon) . . . . *Nov 1990
Brandman, Mr Michael A . . . . *Apr 1968
Couldrick, Mr Timothy David BA(English); LSF. . . . . *Nov 1993
Diamond, Mr Philip D BA . . . . *May 1977
Foot, Mr Warren Douglas BA(Hons). . . . . *Nov 1995
Guttridge, Mr Richard James . . . . *§Nov 1970
McEwen, Mr Nigel A BA. . . . . *Apr 1978
Martin, Mr Maurice LLB(Lond). . . . . *Jun 1973
Mawhood, Mr John N BA(Cantab). . . . . *Mar 1986
Meadon, Mr Simon John BA(Hons) . . . . *Feb 1983
Moody, Mr Peter H C LLB(B'ham) . . . . *Oct 1984
Munson, Mr Stanley H MA(Cantab) . . . . *Jun 1975
Pennal, Mr Patrick J LLB(Bris) . . . . *Dec 1989
Phillips, Mr Lawrence S LLB(Lond) . . . . *Jun 1986
Smith, Mr Douglas J LLB(Warw). . . . . *Aug 1991
Southern, Mr Timothy R LLB . . . . *Dec 1980

Stokes, Mr Simon Jeremy MA(Oxon); MSc(MIT); LLM *Nov 1992
Taylor, Mr Jeremy F MA . . . *Nov 1986
Wilson, Mr Peter C BA(Warw) . . . *Nov 1991
Ast: Andersen, Mr Warwick John BIT; LLB; LLM . . . *Jul 2000
Brosnan, Miss Lucy Katherine BA(Hons) . . . *Jan 1999
Candey, Ashkhan Darius LLB . . . *Sep 1999
Cochrane, Miss Leanne . . . *Sep 2001
Cotterill, Miss Sarah E BA(Hons) . . . *Nov 2000
Fox, Miss Claire . . . *Oct 2001
Gentles, Ms Sandra . . . *Feb 2000
Haslam, Mrs Katherine Elizabeth MA(Hons)(Cantab) . *Oct 1995
Lewis, Ms Frances . . . *Sep 1999
McGregor, Miss Lindsay H LLB(Nott'm) Hill Prize in Law; Maxwell Law Prize; Cooper Exhibition . . . *Oct 1986
Molloy, Mr William John LLB(Hons) . . . *Sep 1996
Rowan, Miss Sara . . . *Jul 2001
Simons, Mr Mark . . . *Nov 2001
Slanickova, Ms Stephanie LLB(Hons); LPC . . . *Jun 2000
Stader, Mr Richard W LLB . . . *Oct 1992
Stockdale, Ms Emma LLB(Hons) . . . *Sep 1993
Stokes, Mr Andrew Michael PGDipLaw; PGDipLP . . Sep 1998
Thompson, Dr Guy . . . Sep 1999
Tom, Mr Matthew N BA(Hons); CPE; LPC . . . *Mar 2000
Walmsley, Mr James Benjamin LLB; DipLaw . . . *Sep 1997
Wood, Ms Bridget E BA(Hons); CPE; LSF . . . *Nov 1997
Con: Jennings, Mr Charles J BA(Dunelm) . . . *Jan 1980

BLAKE-TURNER & CO ‡
128-129 Minories London EC3N 1PB
Tel: 020 7480 6655 *Fax:* 020 7481 4837 *Dx:* 598 LONDON/CITY
E-mail: rupert.farr@blaketurner.com
Languages: French, Polish
Work: A3 B1 B2 C1 C2 C3 J1 L N O Q Z(e,f,i,q)

WILLIAM BLAKENEY ‡
Garrick House 26-27 Southampton Street Westminster London WC2E 7RS
Tel: 020 7717 8510
List of partners: W Blakeney
Work: E L Q S1 W
Ptr: Blakeney, Mr William . . . *May 1966

BLANDFORDS ‡
46 Blandford Street London W1U 7HT
Tel: 020 7935 7373 *Fax:* 020 7935 7272
E-mail: reception@blandfords.com
List of partners: C Waller, J Waller
Work: B1 C1 E F1 J1 K1 K2 K3 L O Q S1 S2 T1 T2 W Z(i,o,p,q)
Ptr: Waller, Mr Clive MA(Oxon) . . . *Jun 1977
Waller, Mrs Juliet BA(Hons) . . . *Feb 1995

BLAVO & CO SOLICITORS ‡
19 John Street London WC1N 2DL
Tel: 020 7025 2020 *Fax:* 020 7404 1650
Dx: 273 LONDON/CHANCERY LN
E-mail: enquiries@legalblavo.co.uk
List of partners: J Blavo
Office: Enfield, Guildford, London EC2, London N3, St Albans, Uxbridge
Work: B2 G H J1 S1 Z(i,m,p,w)
Ptr: Blavo, Mr John . . . Jan 1997

BLAVO & CO SOLICITORS
Rivington House Office 201 82 Great Eastern Street London EC2A 3JF
Tel: 020 7729 9286 *Fax:* 020 7613 0197 *Dx:* 273 CHANCERY LANE
E-mail: enquiries@legalblavo.co.uk
Office: Enfield, Guildford, London N3, London WC1, St Albans, Uxbridge

BLAVO & CO SOLICITORS
Central House 1 Ballards Lane London N3 1LQ
Tel: 020 8349 8020 *Fax:* 020 8349 8630 *Dx:* 273 CHANCERY LANE
E-mail: enquiries@legalblavo.co.uk
Office: Enfield, Guildford, London EC2, London WC1, St Albans, Uxbridge

BLICK & CO ‡
6 Artillery Passage Bishopsgate Tower Hamlets London E1 7LJ
Tel: 020 7247 9696 *Fax:* 020 7247 9740
Dx: 33876 FINSBURY SQUARE
E-mail: info@blickco.com
List of partners: A J Blick, R D Blick
Languages: French
Work: C2 D1 E G H J1 K1 K2 K3 M2 M3 O Q R1 S1 W Z(a,f,i,l)
Emergency Action undertaken
Ptr: Blick, Mrs Abigail J LLB . . . *Aug 1981
Blick, Mr Robert D LLB; MA; ACIArb; MBIM . . . *§Jun 1980
Con: Timmis, Mr Richard BA(Dunelm) . . . Jun 1979
Wicks, Miss Judith A R BA(Legal Studies) . . . *Oct 1976

BLOKH SOLICITORS ‡
83 Baker Street London W1U 6AG
Tel: 020 7034 7055 *Fax:* 020 7074 7165
E-mail: info@blokh.co.uk

LEONARD BLOMSTRAND ‡
32 Versailles Road London SE20 8AX
Tel: 020 8776 7707 *Fax:* 020 8402 7345
Emergency telephone 020 8249 1947
E-mail: blomlaw@cwcom.net
List of partners: L E Blomstrand
Work: E L Q S1 W Z(l)
Agency undertaken
SPr: Blomstrand, Mr Leonard E . . . *Feb 1988

BLUESTONE & CO ‡
124 Upton Lane Forest Gate London E7 9LW
Tel: 020 8470 2266
List of partners: S M Bluestone
Ptr: Bluestone, Mr Stephen M . . . *Jan 1980

BLUETTS SOLICITORS ‡
Park House 111 Uxbridge Road Ealing London W5 5LB
Tel: 0800 157 7574 *Fax:* 020 8832 3778
E-mail: bluettssolicitors@hotmail.co.uk
Work: N S1 S2 W

ANDREW C BLUNDY SOLICITORS ‡
13 Nelson Road Greenwich London SE10 9JB
Tel: 020 8293 3633 *Fax:* 020 8853 2050 *Dx:* 35215 GREENWICH 2
E-mail: administration@andrewcblundy.co.uk
List of partners: A C Blundy, A Hamzavi
Languages: Farsi
Work: C1 E J1 K1 L N O Q R1 S1 S2 W Z(i,l)
Ptr: Blundy, Mr Andrew C BA . . . Oct 1983
Hamzavi, Amir MA . . . Apr 2000

BOKHARI & CO ‡
244b Edgware Road Marble Arch London W2 1DS
Tel: 020 7724 7010 *Fax:* 020 7724 2007 *Dx:* 38759 PADDINGTON
E-mail: bokhari_co@hotmail.com
Languages: Arabic, French, Hindi, Persian, Polish, Punjabi, Urdu
Work: B3 C1 E G H K1 K3 L M2 M4 N O Q S1 S2 W Z(g,i,j,l)

BOLT BURDON ‡
Providence House Providence Place Islington London N1 0QX
Tel: 020 7288 4700 *Fax:* 020 7288 4701
Dx: 122237 UPPER ISLINGTON
E-mail: info@boltburdon.co.uk
List of partners: G S Balchin, R K Bolt, L C Burdon, J Chapman, S P Gillings, S D Hill, C M Klage, H F Matthews, M D Miller, D N J Poole, R H D Rhodes-Kemp, R G Smith, J R Wheeler
Languages: French, Gujarati, Hindi, Italian, Polish, Punjabi, Spanish
Work: B1 C1 C2 C3 D1 E I J1 J2 K1 K3 M1 N O P Q R1 R2 S1 S2 T1 T2 W Z(c,d,e,f,h,l,o,p,za)
Ptr: Balchin, Mr Graham Stewart LLB . . . *Dec 1992
Bolt, Mr Roger K Law Society Assessor . . . *Feb 1977
Burdon, Ms Lynne C BSc(Lond) . . . *§May 1980
Chapman, Ms Joanna BA . . . *Nov 1990
Gillings, Mr Stuart P BA(Kent) . . . *Nov 1982
Hill, Mr Stephen Denys . . . *Sep 1999
Klage, Miss Caroline Mary LLM Cavendish Prize 1997; FH Lawson Prize 1997 . . . Sep 2001
Matthews, Mrs Helen Frances . . . *Dec 1992
Miller, Mr Matthew David . . . *Sep 1999
Poole, Dr David Norman John MA; BD; Dr Theol; FRGS; MIL . . . *Oct 1995
Rhodes-Kemp, Mrs Rosamund Henrietta Duncan . . *Oct 1992
Smith, Mr Roderick Graham . . . Nov 1998
Wheeler, Mr Jonathan Robert LLB(Hons) . . . *Oct 1993
Ast: Abrahams, Miss Cheryl . . . *May 2003
Antoni, Miss Marilene . . . Aug 2003
Cumberland, Miss Juanita . . . *Aug 2000
Dumolo, Miss Karen . . . *Dec 2005
Graham, Ms Jo-Anne . . . Dec 2002
Greenup, Mr Adam LLB . . . *Aug 2006
Hilder, Miss Marrion Carol BA; PGDipLaw . . . *Oct 2003
Kerr, Ms Caroline . . . May 2002
Lam, Ms Pauline . . . *Mar 2004
McGuinness, Mrs Sophie . . . *Aug 2001
Mowat, Mr Ryan Paul . . . *Sep 2002
Tatham, Miss Sacha Chelsea . . . *Mar 2005
Tuckman, Ms Philippa . . . *Apr 1991
Wilson, Miss Emma . . . *Sep 2004
Young, Mr Ed . . . *Nov 2006

J BON SOLICITORS ‡
541 Barking Road London E6 2LW
Tel: 020 8471 8822 *Fax:* 020 8503 5568
E-mail: info@jbonsolicitors.com

P R M BOND & CO ‡
61 Gray's Inn Road London WC1X 8TH
Tel: 020 7242 0058
E-mail: prmbondandco@btconnect.com

BOND PEARCE LLP
8th Floor New London House 6 London Street London EC3R 7LP
Tel: 0845 415 0000 *Fax:* 0845 415 6200 *Dx:* 645 LONDON/CITY
E-mail: info@bondpearce.com
Office: Bristol, Plymouth, Southampton
Work: A1 A3 B1 C1 C2 C3 E F1 F2 I J1 J2 L M3 N O P Q R1 R2 S1 S2 T1 T2 U1 U2 W X Z(b,c,e,j,l,o,p,q,r,u)
Ptr: Chester, Ms Jane E . . . Dec 1985
Jones, Ms Melissa LLB(Hons) . . . *Oct 1995
McGoldrick, Mr Paul Alexander . . . Oct 1989
Morrish, Miss Karen Jane LLB(Hons) . . . Sep 1996
Ross, Miss Hilary A LLB(Glasgow) . . . *Jul 1994
Trayhurn, Mr Neil M LLB . . . *§Oct 1989

BOND SOLICITORS ‡
62a Belgrave Court 36 Westferry Circus London E14 8RL
Tel: 020 7513 1113

BONELLI EREDE PAPPALARDO LLP ‡
30 Cannon Street London EC4M 6XH
Tel: 020 7776 3488 *Fax:* 020 7776 3468

PETER BONNER & CO ‡
8-12 Lee High Road Lewisham London SE13 5LQ
Tel: 020 8297 1727 *Fax:* 020 8297 9097 *Dx:* 200953 LEWISHAM 2
Emergency telephone 020 8297 1727
E-mail: pbonner@netway.co.uk
List of partners: P L Bonner
Languages: French, Spanish
Work: D1 G H
Emergency Action, Agency, Advocacy, Legal Aid undertaken and Legal Aid Franchise
SPr: Bonner, Mr Peter Lloyd BA . . . *Feb 1988
Ast: Davis, Mr Royston James . . . *Mar 1997

BOODLE HATFIELD ‡
89 New Bond Street Westminster London W1S 1DA
Tel: 020 7629 7411 *Fax:* 020 7629 2621
Dx: 53 LONDON/CHANCERY LN
E-mail: bh@boodlehatfield.com
List of partners: K M Black, J Brand, H E Devas, S J Fitzpatrick, F Graham, V C Hardy, N J D Hassall, D Johnson, S P Kerrigan, C F King, J S Littlejohn, S Maccallum, T J C Manning, K N Mason, R D C Maughan, R M Moyse, S Rylatt, B M Simpson, N P Stone, H Streeton, T E F Sutherland, G Todd, K J B Turton, A Wilmot-Smith, M Wood, C J Young
Office: Oxford
Languages: French, German
Work: A1 B1 C1 C2 C3 E F1 I J1 K1 K3 L O Q R1 R2 S1 S2 T1 T2 U2 W Z(b,c,d,i,j,p)
Ptr: Black, Miss Karen M LLB(Hons); LPC . . . *Sep 1998
Brand, Mr James . . . Sep 1996
Devas, Mr Hugh E MA(Oxon) . . . *Dec 1975
Fitzpatrick, Mr Simon J LLB(Soton) . . . *Nov 1991
Graham, Ms Fiona . . . Mar 1997
Hardy, Ms Vivian C . . . Jan 1992
Johnson, Mr David . . . Apr 1981
Kerrigan, Mr Simon P LLB; LPC . . . *Oct 1996
King, Miss Caroline F LLB(B'ham) . . . *Oct 1989
Littlejohn, Miss Jane S MA(Cantab) . . . *Oct 1984
Maccallum, Mrs Sara LLB(Manc) . . . *Oct 1991
Manning, Mr Timothy J C BA(Oxon) . . . *§Oct 1973
Mason, Miss Karen N BA(Oxford Brookes) . . . *Apr 1986
Maughan, Mr Richard D C BSc . . . *Jun 1975
Moyse, Mr Richard M BA(Oxon) . . . *§Jul 1970
Rylatt, Mr Simon LLB(Hons) . . . *Sep 1999
Stone, Mr Nigel P MA(Oxon) . . . *Nov 1985
Streeton, Ms Helen . . . Sep 1992
Sutherland, Mr T Edward F . . . *§Nov 1972
Todd, Mr Geoffrey . . . Jan 1995
Turton, Mr K Jonathan B MA(Cantab) Slaughter & May Prize . . . *§Oct 1985
Wilmot-Smith, Mr Andrew . . . Mar 1999
Wood, Mr Michael . . . May 1967
Young, Mr Colin James LLB(Bris) . . . *Sep 1995
Asoc: Haley, Ms Emma Jayne BA(Hull) . . . *Dec 1993
Hindle, Mr Andrew J BA(Oxon) . . . *§Nov 1979
Symons, Ms Kate LLB(Soton) . . . *Oct 1995
Symons, Miss Victoria J BA; LLM . . . *Sep 1999
Williams, Mr Simon . . . Jan 1998
Ast: Arkell, Ms Helen . . . *Sep 2002
Arthur, Ms Saskia . . . Sep 1998
Bickford, Mr Dean Justin BA . . . *§Sep 1999
Blair, Mr Benjamin . . . Jan 2003
Chappell, Ms Annelie . . . Oct 2003
Christou, Miss Christina . . . Sep 2004
Darlow, Ms Tara . . . Mar 2003
Dracoulis, Mr Andreas . . . Oct 2004
Dutton, Ms Mary . . . *Nov 1973
Edwards, Ms Amanda . . . Oct 1999
Hall, Ms Sarah . . . Sep 2003
Hankins, Miss Caroline . . . Sep 2004
Hourihan, Ms Natalie . . . Sep 2001
Ions, Mrs Kirsty . . . Sep 2001
Kengington, Ms Sharon . . . Oct 1993
Litt, Mr Jamie . . . Jun 2000
Love, Ms Emma . . . *Sep 2002
McRobert, Ms Cerys . . . Oct 2001
Malhotra, Ms Surbhi . . . Jan 2004
Mei Man, Yue . . . Mar 2004
Middleton, Ms Elizabeth LLB; MSc . . . *Apr 2000
Nair, Ms Reeta . . . Sep 2002
Negyal, Ms Jessica . . . Oct 2002
Nisar, Mr Faisal . . . Mar 2000
Noble, Miss Sally . . . Jan 2002
Pennant, Ms Jessica . . . *Oct 2002
Potter, Ms Jane . . . Sep 2002
Shaw, Mr Simon . . . *Sep 2002
Tarry, Ms Catherine . . . Sep 2001
Thomas, Ms Anne . . . Sep 2000
Wigham, Ms Chloe . . . Sep 2002
Wilson-Smith, Ms Jenny . . . Jun 2000
Winkley, Mr Graham . . . Sep 2004
Wright, Ms Caroline . . . *Oct 2002
Con: Feeny, Miss Maeve N M . . . *§Nov 1980

S BOOTH & CO ‡
84 Islington High Street Islington London N1 8EG
Tel: 020 7226 3366 *Fax:* 020 7226 0833 *Dx:* 146643 ISLINGTON 4
E-mail: law@sbooth.co.uk
List of partners: S J Booth
Work: E O Q S1 S2 W
Agency and Advocacy undertaken
Ptr: Booth, Mr Stewart James . . . *Feb 1983

BOOTHROYDS ‡
(in association with Stoffel & Co)
1 Station Buildings Catford Road London SE6 4HJ
Tel: 020 8690 4848 *Fax:* 020 8690 9802 *Dx:* 34361 CATFORD
Emergency telephone 020 8690 4848
List of partners: N D Sinclaire
Work: D1 G H K1 Z(m)
Emergency Action, Agency, Advocacy, Fixed Fee Interview and Legal Aid undertaken
SPr: Sinclaire, Mr Nigel D LLB . . . *Jun 1979
Ast: Dilloway, Ms Helen J . . . Apr 1989
Con: Boothroyd, Mr Christopher D . . . *Feb 1969

BOUCHARD & ASSOCIATES ‡
117a Munster Road London SW6 6DH
Tel: 020 7736 1823 *Fax:* 020 7736 4512
E-mail: pbouchard@bouchardsolicitors.co.uk
List of partners: P H M Dahan-Bouchard
Languages: French, Spanish
Work: C1 S1 T1 T2 W
Ptr: Dahan-Bouchard, Miss Patricia H M-J LLB; AKC . . . *Jul 1976

BOULTER & COMPANY ‡
1st Floor 11-19 Park Road London N8 8TE
Tel: 020 8340 0222 *Fax:* 020 8340 7771 *Dx:* 35966 CROUCH END
E-mail: boulter@boulterandco.com
List of partners: M Boulter, A A Joannides
Office: Waltham Cross
Languages: Greek, Italian
Work: L N Q S1 S2 W
Fixed Fee Interview, Legal Aid undertaken and Member of Accident Line
Ptr: Boulter, Mrs Maria . . . *Dec 1990
Joannides, Mr Andrew Anthony . . . Nov 1998

HENRY BOUSTRED & SONS ‡
(incorporating D J Davies)
18 Highgate High Street Highgate London N6 5JG
Tel: 020 8348 5223 *Fax:* 020 8348 4922 *Dx:* 51900 HIGHGATE
E-mail: peter@boustreds.co.uk
List of partners: C N Boustred, P F Boustred, R K W Boustred
Languages: French
Work: E J1 K1 L N O Q S1 S2 T2 W
Agency and Advocacy undertaken
Ptr: Boustred, Mr Christopher N BA(Lond) . . . *Jun 1985
Boustred, Mr Peter F LLB(Lond) . . . *Nov 1977
Boustred, Mr Roger K W BA . . . *Apr 1980
Ast: Cramer, Mrs Jacalyn . . . Jan 1999

BOWEN MUSCATT ‡
111 Baker Street London W1U 6SG
Tel: 020 7908 3800 *Fax:* 020 7486 3081
Dx: 42702 OXFORD CIRCUS NORTH
E-mail: nigelbowen@aol.com
List of partners: N Bowen, S Muscatt
Languages: French

 See p2 for the Key to Work Categories & other symbols

Work: B2 C1 C2 E F1 F2 G I J1 J2 L M3 N O Q R1 R2 S1 S2 T1 T2 W X Z(c,e,f,k,l,p,q,w)
Ptr: Bowen, Mr Nigel LLB(Hons). . . . . Oct 1986
Muscatt, Mr Stephen BSc . . . . *Mar 1990

BOWER COTTON KHAITAN ‡
36 Whitefriars Street London EC4Y 8BQ
Est: 1818
Tel: 020 7353 1313 *Fax:* 020 7353 3535
Dx: 94 LONDON/CHANCERY LN
E-mail: rogerxharris@bcklaw.co.uk
List of partners: R Harris, A Khaitan
Work: A3 B1 B2 C1 C2 E F1 F2 J1 K1 K2 L M2 M3 O Q R1 R2 S1 S2 W Z(b,c,d,e,i)
Emergency Action, Agency, Advocacy and Fixed Fee Interview undertaken
Ptr: Harris, Mr Roger . . . . *Oct 1981
Khaitan, Mr Abhishek LLB(Hons) . . . . Apr 2004
Asoc: Marmion, Miss Katharine E BSocSc. . . . . *May 1985

JOHN BOWER ‡
15 Golders Green Crescent Golders Green London NW11 8LA
Tel: 020 8455 8366 *Fax:* 020 8455 8366
List of partners: J G Bower
Work: W

BOWERS ‡
172-174 Granville Road London NW2 2LD
Tel: 020 8455 9881 *Fax:* 020 8455 6658
Dx: 33800 GOLDERS GREEN
E-mail: raymond@bowers-solicitors.com
List of partners: R H Esdaile
Languages: French, German
Work: C1 E L S1 T1 T2 W
Ptr: Esdaile, Mr Raymond H. . . . . *Oct 1972
Con: Hyman, Mr Lewis Leslie LLB . . . . *Oct 1968

BOWLING & CO ‡
62 Broadway Stratford London E15 1NG
Tel: 020 8221 8000 *Fax:* 020 8519 5504 *Dx:* 5405 STRATFORD
E-mail: info@bowlinglaw.co.uk
List of partners: J P Barker, P Bhogal, P Holland, H E Huseyin, P S Laskey, J Lewis, D D Raja, M Real, H Youssouf
Languages: Gujarati, Kiswahili, Punjabi, Turkish, Urdu, Yiddish
Work: A3 B1 C1 C2 D1 E J1 J2 K1 K2 K3 L O Q R1 R2 S1 S2 U2 W Z(c,i,k,l,p,q,y)
Emergency Action, Agency, Advocacy and Legal Aid undertaken
Ptr: Barker, Mr Justin Piers . . . . *Jul 2004
Bhogal, Mr Parmjit . . . . *Jan 2003
Holland, Mr Peter . . . . *Mar 1987
Huseyin, Mr Huseyin Enver BA(Hons). . . . . *Aug 1991
Laskey, Mr Peter S MA(Cantab) . . . . *Oct 1982
Lewis, Mr Jeremy LLB . . . . *Nov 1982
Raja, Dinesh D LLB. . . . . *Oct 1985
Real, Mr Martin . . . . *Feb 1999
Youssouf, Mr Huseyin. . . . . *Jan 1998
Asoc: Patel, Ms Jyoti LLB . . . . *May 1982
Seenath, Miss Urmilla. . . . . Sep 1990
Ast: Karia, Ms Leena . . . . *Jul 2005
Con: Ebrahim, Mr Ali . . . . *Jan 2007
Hirschfield, Mr Graham A LLB. . . . . *Jul 1976
Hoque, Mr Roger . . . . *Jan 2000
Maton, Miss Jane Elizabeth . . . . *Dec 1988
Mayor, Mr Andrew D . . . . *Mar 1983
Pinidiya, Mr Thejaka . . . . *Jan 2002

BRACEWELL & GIULIANI LLP ‡
15 Old Bailey London EC4M 7EF
Tel: 020 3159 4220 *Fax:* 020 3159 4221
E-mail: adam.mozel@bgllp.com

BRACHER RAWLINS LLP ‡
(incorporating Bazley White & Co)
6th Floor Fox Court 14 Gray's Inn Road London WC1X 8HN
Tel: 020 7404 9400 *Fax:* 020 7404 9401
Dx: 168 LONDON/CHANCERY LN
E-mail: brlaw@bracherrawlins.co.uk
List of partners: A R Bracher, P A Craig, A Cromby, J M Gaymer, S R Rawlins, T Wilkinson, P G Williams
Languages: French, Gujarati, Hindi, Italian, Spanish
Work: A3 B1 C1 C2 C3 E F1 F2 I J1 J2 L M1 M2 N O Q R1 R2 S1 S2 T1 U1 U2 W Z(c,d,e,j,l,n,p,q,r,s,w)
Emergency Action, Agency and Advocacy undertaken
Ptr: Bracher, Mr Alan R MA(Cantab). . . . . *Jul 1971
Craig, Mr Paul A LLB(Exon). . . . . *Dec 1974
Cromby, Mr Andrew. . . . . Nov 1992
Gaymer, Mr John M BA(Oxon) . . . . *Oct 1972
Rawlins, Mr Simon R BA . . . . *Sep 1980
Wilkinson, Mr Thom MA(Hons); Jurisprudence(Oxon) . Sep 2000
Williams, Mr Patrick G LLB(Nott'm) . . . . *Oct 1975
Ast: Caldwell, Miss Emma . . . . Oct 2005
Gabbie, Mr Lee . . . . Jan 2001
Holden-Shah, Miss Emma. . . . . *Sep 2000
Park, Mr Christopher . . . . Oct 2009
Tsui, Alice. . . . . Sep 2008
Turner, Ms Caroline. . . . . *Sep 1999

J PATRICK F BRADLEY ‡
98 Abinger Road London W4 1EX
Tel: 020 7024 3624

BRADY EASTWOOD PIERCE & STEWART ‡
Noah's Ark 229 Deptford High Street Lewisham London SE8 3NT
Tel: 020 8692 8181 *Fax:* 020 8692 8585 *Dx:* 56703 DEPTFORD
Emergency telephone 020 8692 8181
E-mail: justinpierce@bepssolicitors.co.uk
List of partners: P Brady, S Eastwood, J Pierce
Office: Dartford
Languages: Bengali, Cantonese, Yoruba
Work: B2 G H
Advocacy and Legal Aid undertaken
Ptr: Brady, Mr Peter . . . . *May 1985
Eastwood, Mr Simon ★ . . . . *May 1981
Pierce, Mr Justin . . . . *Jun 1984
Ast: Chan, Wing Yang . . . . *Nov 2003
Ghosh, Mr Robin . . . . *May 2003
Rowe, Ms Aisling BA ★ . . . . *Jan 2007

MARK BRADY LAW LLP ‡
Aurora House 5-6 Carlos Place London W1K 3AS
Tel: 020 7099 5936 *Fax:* 020 7099 5937

KENNETH BRAND & CO ‡
39 Vivian Avenue Hendon London NW4 3UX
Tel: 020 8202 6751 *Fax:* 020 8202 1283 *Dx:* 59333 HENDON
List of partners: K Brand, H H Elias
Work: E L N O Q S1 S2 W
Agency, Fixed Fee Interview and Legal Aid undertaken
Ptr: Brand, Mr Kenneth LLB(Lond). . . . . *Jun 1975
Elias, Mr Harold H LLB(Lond) . . . . *Dec 1976

ROBERT BRAND & CO ‡
17 Bentinck Street Westminster London W1U 2ES
Tel: 020 7935 2408 *Fax:* 020 7935 6334
Dx: 53801 OXFORD CIRCUS NORTH
E-mail: info@robertbrand.com
List of partners: R S Brand, P D Neidle
Work: B1 C1 C2 C3 E F1 G J1 L O Q S1 S2 W Z(f,h,l)
Agency undertaken
Ptr: Brand, Mr Robert Simon BA. . . . . *Apr 1980
Neidle, Mr Peter D BSc(Econ). . . . . *Jun 1975
Con: Drukker, Mr Timothy J BSc . . . . Mar 1990

HENRI BRANDMAN & CO ‡
71 Wimpole Street London W1G 8AY
Tel: 020 7224 0616 *Fax:* 020 7487 5617
E-mail: hblaw@henribrandman.co.uk
List of partners: H Brandman
Languages: French, German
Work: C1 F2 G J1 K1 K3 N O Q Z(e,f,k,p,w,z)
Ptr: Brandman, Mr Henri. . . . . *May 1980

BRANDSWORTH ‡
28 Gillespie Road London N5 1LN
Tel: 07919 575020

BRAY & KRAIS SOLICITORS ‡
Suite 10 Fulham Business Exchange The Boulevard London SW6 2TL
Tel: 020 7384 3050 *Fax:* 020 7384 3051
E-mail: bandk@brayandkrais.com
List of partners: R M Bray, M J Krais
Work: C1 J1 Z(e,f)
Ptr: Bray, Mr Richard M Travers Smith Scholarship; Clements Inn Prize; Ruse & Claborn prize. . . . . *Apr 1989
Krais, Mr Mark Justin BA(Hons)(Oxon) . . . . *Nov 1993
Ast: Siddall, Mr Ben BA; PGDipLaw . . . . Apr 2005

RICHARD BRAY & CO ‡
8 Exchange Court Covent Garden London WC2R 0JH
Tel: 020 7497 3561 *Fax:* 020 7497 5383
E-mail: richardbraymail@tiscali.co.uk
List of partners: R M Bray
Languages: French
Work: B1 C1 C2 E G J1 K1 L N O Q S1 W Z(c,e,f,i,l)
Agency undertaken
SPr: Bray, Mr Richard M . . . . *Jun 1981

FRANK BRAZELL & PARTNERS ‡
97 White Lion Street London N1 9PF
Tel: 020 7689 8989 *Dx:* 58272 ISLINGTON
E-mail: reception@frankbrazell.co.uk

BRECHER ‡
Heron Place 3 George Street London W1U 3QG
Tel: 020 7563 1000 *Fax:* 020 7486 7796
Dx: 42701 OXFORD CIRCUS NORTH
E-mail: admin@brecher.com
List of partners: J A Abram, M M B Bennett, A J Brecher, V Z Brecher, R Byrne, D M Grossbard, J M Harris, D H Hershkorn, D T Merson, N Richmond, S T Ross
Languages: French, German, Hebrew
Work: B1 C1 C2 E F1 L O P Q R1 R2 S1 S2 Z(b,c,u)
Ptr: Abram, Mr Jeremy Alexander BA . . . . May 1987
Bennett, Mr Martin M B MA(Cantab). . . . . *Jun 1976
Brecher, Mr Andrew J LLB(Lond) . . . . *Nov 1989
Brecher, Ms Valerie Z BA . . . . *Apr 1979
Byrne, Redmond . . . . Apr 1996
Grossbard, Mr David Marc BA(Hons) . . . . *Sep 1996
Harris, Mr Jeremy Marc BA(Econ). . . . . *Nov 1994
Hershkorn, Mr David Howard LLB. . . . . Sep 1997
Merson, Mr David Todd BA; JD . . . . Apr 2004
Richmond, Nicky . . . . *Oct 1988
Ross, Mr Steven T LLB(Hons). . . . . Sep 2000
Asoc: Selwyn, Mr Clive . . . . Oct 2003
Ast: Glassberg, Ms Emma Louise LLB. . . . . Oct 2002
Lee, Mr Bradley. Oct 1998
Saade, Mr George BA . . . . Jul 2002
Con: Brecher, Mr David J MA(Cantab) . . . . *§Dec 1952
Brecher, Mr Henry A . . . . *Oct 1954
Broughton, Mr Michael BA(Bris). . . . . *§Dec 1978

BREEDY HANDERSON LLP ‡
52 Brook Street London W1K 5DS
Tel: 020 7268 2260
E-mail: rosalynbreedy@breedyhenderson.com

BREEDY HENDERSON LLP ‡
45 Upper Park Road London NW3 2UL
Tel: 020 7419 4135 / 07841 094160
E-mail: rosalynbreedy@aol.com

M M E BRENNINKMEYER ‡
212 Piccadilly London W1J 9HG
Tel: 020 7917 1897 *Fax:* 020 7245 6980
E-mail: millie@wenstan.com
List of partners: M Brenninkmeyer
Languages: Dutch
Work: W
SPr: Brenninkmeyer, Ms Millie BA(Cantab) . . . . Nov 1991

ALASTAIR J BRETT ‡
18 Edenhurst Avenue London SW6 3EP
Tel: 020 7736 0071
E-mail: alastair@bretts.org.uk

BRETT WILSON LLP ‡
Challoner House 19 Clerkenwell Close Clerkenwell London EC1R 0RR
Tel: 020 7183 8950 *Fax:* 020 7183 8951 *Dx:* 53341 CLERKENWELL
E-mail: law@brettwilsonllp.co.uk

BRICE DROOGLEEVER & CO ‡
(incorporating Smith Braithwaite)
3 Queripel House 1 Duke of York Square Kings Road Kensington & Chelsea London SW3 4LY
Tel: 020 7730 9925 / 7730 7231 *Fax:* 020 7730 6609
Dx: 130443 CHELSEA 3
E-mail: mail@bdlegal.co.uk
List of partners: J P Braithwaite, J J Brice, R M Paterson-Morgan
Languages: French
Work: E L Q S1 S2 W
Ptr: Braithwaite, Mr Jonathan Paul BA. . . . . Dec 1976
Brice, Mr John J. *Nov 1971
Paterson-Morgan, Mrs Rosalind M . . . . *Nov 1980

BRIDGEHOUSE PARTNERS LLP ‡
Suite 426 Linen Hall 162-168 Regent Street London W1B 5TE
Tel: 020 7851 7160 *Fax:* 0845 644 5163
Office: Birmingham

BRIFFA ‡
Business Design Centre Upper Street Islington London N1 0QH
Tel: 020 7288 6003 *Fax:* 020 7288 6004
E-mail: briffa@briffa.com
List of partners: M Briffa, R Wehrle
Languages: French
Work: O Z(e,f)
Emergency Action, Agency, Advocacy, Fixed Fee Interview and Legal Aid undertaken
Ptr: Briffa, Ms Margaret LLM(Lond) . . . . *Nov 1987
Wehrle, Mr Ralph . . . . *Apr 1992
Ast: Brown, Mr Silas Augustine John BA(Law & Politics) . . *Mar 2003
Cochrane, Mr Craig LLB . . . . Jul 2007
Farnell, Mr James MA(Hons)(Philosophy); PGDipLaw; LPC . . . . Aug 2007
Mason, Mr Peter LLB . . . . Nov 2007
Papakyriacou, Mr Alexander Angelo LLB . . . . Dec 2005
Triantafillou, Miss Maria LLB . . . . *Jan 2003

DAVID BRIGGS & CO ‡
111a Walton Street Chelsea London SW3 2HP
Tel: 020 7823 9040 *Fax:* 020 7823 7664
E-mail: mail@davidbriggs.co.uk
List of partners: D H Briggs
Work: A1 E L S1 S2 W
Emergency Action and Agency undertaken
Ptr: Briggs, Mr David H . . . . *Jun 1973

BRIGHTWAY SOLICITORS ‡
2nd Floor Office 14-16 Powis Street Woolwich London SE18 6LF
Tel: 020 8309 8808 *Fax:* 020 8855 1057

BRION & CO ‡
1 Southampton Place Holborn London WC1A 2DA
Tel: 020 7831 5556 *Fax:* 020 7831 5557
Languages: Cantonese, Mandarin, Urdu
Work: K1 K3 S1 S2 Z(i)
Fixed Fee Interview undertaken

BRISTOWS ‡
100 Victoria Embankment London EC4Y 0DH
Tel: 020 7400 8000 *Fax:* 020 7400 8050
Dx: 269 LONDON/CHANCERY LN
E-mail: info@bristows.com
List of partners: J P M Allcock, L J Anderson, K E Appleton, S Ayrton, D J C Brown, R Burnett, M C Cass, Q G P Cooke, R Cox, L R Farrell, S A Field, P X Gilbert, M R Hawes, C Hore, A Johnson, J D Lace, A R G Lethbridge, A N Lykiardopoulos, A J McCulloch, E J Nodder, T Powell, M J Rowles, P M Treacy, P A Walsh, M M Warren, J J S Watts, P G Westmacott, D C Wilkinson
Languages: Dutch, French, German, Greek, Italian, Polish, Punjabi, Spanish
Work: C1 C2 C3 E F1 F2 I J1 L M1 O P R1 R2 S1 T1 T2 U1 U2 W Z(d,e,f,k,l,z)
Advocacy undertaken
Ptr: Allcock, Mr John P M BSc; MSc. . . . . *Nov 1977
Anderson, Miss Laura Jane BA . . . . *Nov 1993
Appleton, Mr Kevin E . . . . *Oct 1983
Ayrton, Mr Simon MA(Cantab); DipLaw(Bris) . . . . *Nov 1993
Brown, Mr David J C . . . . *§Mar 1973
Burnett, Miss Rachel BA(Hons); AIL; FBCS; FIMIS . . Feb 1980
Cass, Miss Miranda Caroline MA(Cantab). . . . . . . Apr 1990
Cooke, Mr Q G Paul City of London Solicitors Co Prize*Dec 1972
Cox, Mr Ralph BA(Oxon); DipLaw(De Montford). . . . Nov 1994
Farrell, Mrs Linda R BA . . . . *Jul 1990
Field, Miss Sally A BA(Dunelm) . . . . *Sep 1981
Gilbert, Dr Penny X MA; DPhil(Oxon); DipLaw(Bris) . . *Jul 1991
Hawes, Mr Mark R LLB(Lond). . . . . *Oct 1986
Hore, Ms Christine MA(Cantab); DipLaw(Bris). . . . Nov 1993
Johnson, Mr Alan MA(Oxon) . . . . *Nov 1983
Lace, Mr John D . . . . *§Dec 1973
Lethbridge, Mrs Alexandra R G BA(Dunelm). . . . . *Oct 1984
Lykiardopoulos, Mr Andrew Nicolas BA . . . . *Nov 1994
McCulloch, Mr Alastair John MA(Cantab) . . . . . . *Nov 1994
Nodder, Mr Edward J MA(Cantab). . . . . *Oct 1980
Powell, Mr Tim MA(Cantab); DipLaw(Bris). . . . . . *Oct 1990
Rowles, Mr Michael J MA(Cantab) . . . . *Mar 1974
Treacy, Miss Patricia M MA(Cantab). . . . . *Nov 1986
Walsh, Mr Paul A BA(Oxon). . . . . *Mar 1983
Warren, Mr Matthew M BSc(Lond); DipLaw(Bris) . . . *Jun 1991
Watts, Dr Jerome Justin Sebastian BA; MA; PhD(Cantab); AMIEE; ATII. . . . . *Sep 1994
Westmacott, Mr Philip G BA(Cantab) . . . . *Dec 1978
Wilkinson, Mr David Clifford LLB(QUB) Maxwell Law Prize . . . . Sep 1992
Asoc: Hughes Scholes, Miss Charlotte BSc . . . . Mar 1999
Ast: Anderton, Mrs Clare MA; CPE; LPC Law Society LPC Prize . . . . *Sep 1999
Baigent, Dr Derek BSc; PhD . . . . Sep 1999
Batteson, Mr Alexander BSc(Hons)(Physics) . . . . . *Jan 1999
Bowler, Mr Andrew BA(Hons); CPE; LPC . . . . . . *Sep 1999
Bradshaw, Ms Kate LLB(Hons); BSc(Hons) . . . . . . Apr 2002
Burfitt, Ms Rachel K BA(Hons) . . . . *Oct 1995
Burton, Mr Ian BA. . . . . Sep 1998
Butler, Miss Zoe Marianne BA(Hons)(Cantab) Legal Practice Course National Prize 1994. . . . . *Sep 1996
Chaudri, Ms Abida LLB(Hons). . . . . Oct 1992
Clark, Mrs Victoria C BA(Human Sciences); CPE; LPC Sep 1997
Clarke, Ms Madeleine Mary BSc; MSc. . . . . *Dec 1989
Cordery, Mr Brian Douglas BA(Oxon) Norton Rose Prize . . . . *Sep 1996
Coulson, Mr Neil Kenneth Lindsay BA(Oxon) . . . . . *Oct 1997
Delafaille, Mr Oliver Martin BA(Hons) . . . . *Oct 2000
Edmund, Mrs Teresa LLB . . . . *Oct 1986

Fitt, Mr Robert MBiochem . . . . . *Sep 2001
Goodman, Ms Clare Louise BA(Hons)(Oxon); LSF . . . Oct 1997
Gorst-Williams, Ms Henrietta H A LLB; LPC; PSC . . . Sep 2000
Hall, Miss Sarah BA . . . . . Sep 1998
Hill, Ms Julie Ann BA(Cantab) . . . . . *Oct 2000
Hollingsworth, Ms Alison J BA(Hons); CPE; LPC . . . Sep 1996
Jelf, Dr Peter Myles BEng; PhD; PGDipLaw; PGDipLP Sep 1997
Kearney, Ms Charlotte Elizabeth LLB . . . . . *Sep 1998
Lawrence, Ms Rebecca Amy BA(Oxon); CPE; LPC . . Jan 2000
Miller, Ms Diane BA(Hons) . . . . . *Sep 1999
Moore, Mr George MChem . . . . . *Jul 2001
Moss, Mr Aliastair Micheal MA(Oxon) . . . . . Sep 1998
Obhi, Dr Harjinder Singh BSc; PhD(Cantab) . . . . . Oct 1997
Payne, Miss Sara . . . . . Sep 1998
Phillips, Miss Liz . . . . . Sep 2001
Plaskitt, Miss Polly BA(Hons) . . . . . Sep 2001
Redford, Mr Iain P BA(Oxon); LSF . . . . . Jan 1996
Reynolds, Mrs Laura M MA(Cantab); DipLaw(Bris) . *Sep 1992
Roy, Mr Bratin BSc; CPE; LPC . . . . . *Sep 2000
Rumboll, Mr Antony MA; PGDipLaw; LPC . . . . . Sep 2001
Sloper, Miss Kristie BA(Hons)(Natural Sciences) . . . Jan 2000
Von Schmieder, Mr Charlie BA . . . . . Mar 2000
Wilson, Mr Alex . . . . . Apr 1996
Wilson, Mr Alexander John Diebler BSc(Lond) . . . . . Apr 1996
Con: Burnett-Hall, Mr Richard H MA(Cantab) . . . . . *§Jun 1974
Judge, Mr Ian M MA(Cantab) . . . . . *§May 1967
Loughran, Ms Elizabeth M LLB . . . . . *Jun 1988

BROADGATE LEGAL ‡
4 Broadgate London EC2M 2QS
Tel: 020 7856 2406

BROADWAY SOLICTORS ‡
1st Floor Offices 40 Tooting High Street Tooting Broadway Wandsworth London SW17 0RG
Tel: 020 8767 7718 *Fax:* 020 8767 7719
Dx: 58886 TOOTING SOUTH
Emergency telephone 07957 322868
E-mail: admin@broadwaysolicitors.com
List of partners: B Desai
Languages: Gujarati
Work: D1 E K1 K3 S1 S2 W
Emergency Action, Agency, Fixed Fee Interview, Legal Aid undertaken and Legal Aid Franchise
Ptr: Desai, Bhavna . . . . . Nov 1995

BROCKLESBY & CO ‡
13 Sandbourne Avenue London SW19 3EW
Tel: 020 8540 9966 *Fax:* 020 8540 9966

BROADBRIDGE GRIMES & SOLICITORS ‡
110 Morden Road London SW19 3BP
Tel: 020 8545 1480 *Fax:* 020 8545 1499
Dx: 300012 SOUTH WIMBLEDON
E-mail: brian@broadbridgegrimes.co.uk

BROMPTONS ‡
219 Kensington High Street London W8 6BD
Tel: 020 7937 0005 *Fax:* 020 7937 3533
Dx: 714178 KENSINGTON HIGH STREET
E-mail: info@bromptons.net
List of partners: M A Suleman
Languages: Gujarati, Hindi, Urdu
Work: B1 C1 E J1 O Q S1 S2 Z(q)
SPr: Suleman, Mr Mohamed Azim BA(Hons) . . . . . *Nov 1991
Con: Omar, Harun LLB ♦ . . . . . Jul 1978

BROOK MARTIN & CO ‡
29 York Street Westminster London W1H 1EZ
Tel: 020 7935 8520 *Fax:* 020 7486 6180 *Dx:* 41745 MARYLEBONE 2
E-mail: sb@brookmartin.co.uk
List of partners: S O Brook, M M Martin
Languages: French, German
Work: B2 C1 E G K1 L N O Q R1 S1 W Z(c,e)
Agency undertaken
Ptr: Brook, Mr Stephen O LLB . . . . . *Oct 1975
Martin, Mr Michael M LLB . . . . . *Jul 1977

BROOKE NORTH LLP
1st Floor Heron Place 3 George Street London W1V 3QG
Tel: 0870 120 8336 *Fax:* 0870 120 8337
Dx: 713100 LEEDS PARK SQUARE
Office: Leeds

BROOKES & CO ‡
4 Brabant Court London EC3M 8AD
Tel: 020 7621 0067 *Fax:* 020 7621 0360
E-mail: mail@brookes-and-co.co.uk
List of partners: M Brookes, J Lewis
Languages: German, Greek
Work: C1 O Q Z(a,j)
Ptr: Brookes, Mrs Marianne BSc(Econ) . . . . . Apr 1989
Lewis, Ms Johanah LLB(Hons) . . . . . Feb 2000
Ast: Hunt, Miss Sophie-Jane Victoria LLB(Hons) . . . . . Apr 2005

BROOKMAN ‡
18-19 Jockey's Fields London WC1R 4LP
Tel: 020 7430 8470 *Fax:* 020 7242 8294
E-mail: henry@brookman.co.uk
Work: K1

BROOKS & CO
89 Judd Street London WC1H 9NE
Tel: 020 7887 1437
Office: Fetcham

BROOME PALMER SOLICITORS ‡
Eldon Park House 43 Church Road London SW19 5DQ
Tel: 020 8944 0343

BROSS BENNETT ‡
Stable House 64a Highgate High Street London N6 5HX
Tel: 020 8340 0444 *Fax:* 020 8341 9100 *Dx:* 51909 HIGHGATE
E-mail: gen@brossbennett.co.uk
List of partners: S R Bennett, R V Bross, C D Falkus
Languages: French, German, Hebrew
Work: K1 K2 W
Emergency Action and Agency undertaken
Ptr: Bennett, Ms Sharon R BA(Hons) Deputy District Judge . . . . . *Nov 1987
Bross, Ms Ruth Vivian LLB(Bris) . . . . . *Apr 1982
Falkus, Ms Caroline Deborah LLB . . . . . *Nov 1988
Ast: Bortnik, Miss Jayne Anne LLB(Hons) . . . . . Oct 2003
Tyfield, Ms Karen Sarah LLB(Hons) . . . . . Mar 2004
Con: Harris, Mrs Lea . . . . . *May 1980

ANNE BROWN SOLICITORS ‡
811 Green Lanes Winchmore Hill London N21 2RX
Tel: 020 8364 2121 *Fax:* 020 8364 1900
E-mail: absolicitors@aol.com
List of partners: A M Brown
Work: C1 F1 F2 J1 L O Q S1 W
Agency and Fixed Fee Interview undertaken
SPr: Brown, Mrs Anne M BA(Hons)(Law) . . . . . *Oct 1988

LAURENCE BROWN SOLICITOR ‡
27 Southerland Place London W2 5BZ
Tel: 020 7792 9727
E-mail: lb@laurencewbrown.com

PHILIP BROWN & CO ‡
45a Upper Berkeley Street London W1H 7QE
Tel: 020 7935 7235 / 7935 7270 *Fax:* 020 7935 3933
E-mail: pbrownco@googlemail.com
List of partners: P O Brown
Languages: French, Swedish
Work: C1 C2 E F1 G J1 K1 L M2 R2 S1 S2 T2 W Z(c,e,f,i,l,n,y)
SPr: Brown, Mr Philip Owen MA(Cantab) . . . . . *Nov 1962
Con: Waller, Mr Clive MA(Oxon) . . . . . *Jun 1977
Waller, Mrs Juliet BA(Hons) . . . . . *Feb 1995

BROWN RUDNICK BERLACK ISRAELS LLP ‡
8 Clifford Street London W1S 2LQ
Tel: 020 7851 6000

YVONNE BROWN & CO ‡
PO Box 56933 Muswell Hill London N10 1UW
Tel: 020 8444 7254 / 8171 *Fax:* 020 8444 7254
Dx: 36015 MUSWELL HILL
E-mail: yb@yblaw.net

BROWNE JACOBSON LLP
(in association with DS Paris)
6th Floor 77 Gracechurch Street London EC3V 0AS
Tel: 020 7539 4900 *Fax:* 020 7836 3882
Dx: 142420 LONDON/GRACECHURCH STREET
E-mail: lon@brownejacobson.com
Office: Birmingham, Nottingham
Languages: French, Italian, Spanish
Work: B1 C1 C2 C3 E J1 M1 M2 N O P Q R1 S1 T1 T2 Z(e,g,i,j,m,o,q,r,w)
Agency undertaken
Ptr: Silverstein, Mr Raymond M LLB . . . . . *Oct 1988
Ast: Clark, Miss Faye E LLB(Hons) . . . . . *Jan 1997
Davis, Mr Neil LLB . . . . . *Oct 1996
Hughes, Mr Mark R LLB(Dunelm) . . . . . *Sep 1999
Maggs, Mr David William LLB(Nott'm) . . . . . *Oct 1990
Con: Back, Miss Fidelma J E LLB . . . . . *Oct 1986

BUDE NATHAN IWANIER ‡
1-2 Temple Fortune Parade Bridge Lane Golders Green London NW11 0QN
Tel: 020 8458 5656 *Fax:* 020 8458 5065
Dx: 92006 TEMPLE FORTUNE
List of partners: A E Bude, N N Iwanier, V N Vernick
Work: B1 C1 E L O Q S1 S2 W Z(i)
Ptr: Bude, Mr Aron E LLB . . . . . *Oct 1983
Iwanier, Mr Nathan N BA . . . . . *May 1978
Vernick, Mr Vivian N BA . . . . . *Nov 1988
Ast: Bernstein, Mr Bernard LLB(Lond) . . . . . *Jul 1974
Con: Kandler, Mr Jonathan Barry BA(Law) . . . . . *May 1983

BUDE STORZ ‡
220 Stamford Hill Hackney London N16 6RD
Tel: 020 8800 2800 *Fax:* 020 8800 4800
Dx: 37653 STAMFORD HILL
List of partners: R Bude
Work: E S1
Ptr: Bude, Mr Raphael . . . . . Oct 1992

VINCENT BUFFONI & CO ‡
13 Provost Street Islington London N1 2NH
Tel: 020 7251 8484 *Fax:* 020 7251 6262
E-mail: enquiry@vincentbuffoni.co.uk
List of partners: V P Buffoni
Ptr: Buffoni, Mr Vincent P BA(Oxon) . . . . . *Oct 1989

BULCRAIGS ‡
2 Replingham Road Southfields Wandsworth London SW18 5LS
Tel: 020 8870 2207 / 8877 0531 *Fax:* 020 8877 0020
Dx: 58953 WANDSWORTH SOUTH
E-mail: bulcraigs@bulcraigs.co.uk
List of partners: B A Spear
Work: C1 E L R2 S1 S2 T1 T2 W Z(c)
SPr: Spear, Mr Brian Anthony ACIS Herbert Ruse Prize Notary Public . . . . . *§Mar 1969
Con: Sealy-Jones, Mr Dennis Charles LLM(Lond); TEP . . *Dec 1945
Particular areas of work include: Commercial and Company Law, Commercial Property, Housing, Landlord and Tenant, Property - Finance, Development, Residential Conveyancing.

BULLIVANT & PARTNERS ‡
15 Great St Thomas Apostle London EC4V 2BJ
Tel: 020 7332 8250 *Fax:* 020 7332 8260 *Dx:* 98932 CHEAPSIDE 2
E-mail: mail@bullivant.uk.net
List of partners: A S Bhatoa
Languages: Hindi, Punjabi
Work: G H
Agency, Advocacy, Legal Aid undertaken and Legal Aid Franchise
Ptr: Bhatoa, Avtar Singh ● . . . . . Aug 1994
Ast: Craig, Mr Andrew LLB . . . . . Oct 1987
Wolfson, Mr Daniel . . . . . Feb 1979
Con: Burton, Mr Peter Harman ★ . . . . . Jun 1970

DAVID BURCHER & CO ‡
43 St Gabriels Road London NW2 4DT
Tel: 020 8452 4127 *Fax:* 020 8450 6995
List of partners: D Burcher
Languages: French
Work: N S1
Ptr: Burcher, Mr David BA(Hons)(Oxon) . . . . . *Jul 1967

BURNLEY-JONES BATE & CO ‡
The Manor House 120 Kingston Road Wimbledon London SW19 1LY
Tel: 020 8542 8101 *Fax:* 020 8540 1636
Dx: 300016 WIMBLEDON SOUTH
E-mail: gerald.bate@bjbsolicitors.co.uk
List of partners: A Adoki, D H G Bate, C L Burnley-Jones, O S U Kadri
Languages: Spanish, Urdu
Work: G H S1 S2
Emergency Action, Agency, Advocacy, Fixed Fee Interview, Legal Aid undertaken and Legal Aid Franchise
Ptr: Adoki, Mr Alaibi . . . . . *Dec 1989
Bate, Mr David H Gerald LLB(Soton) . . . . . *Jun 1974
Burnley-Jones, Mr Christopher L . . . . . *Feb 1989
Kadri, Ovais S U BSc(Lond)(Econ) . . . . . *Jan 1986
Ast: Clarke, Mr Ian Aidan BA(Hons); LLM . . . . . *Feb 2007
Con: Nicholson, Mr Michael . . . . . *Oct 1995
Pritchard, Ms Karen . . . . . *Oct 1991
Tadeusz, Mrs Caryn . . . . . *Jan 2005

BURT STAPLES & MANER LLP ‡
Suite 105-106 Hamilton House 1 Temple Avenue London EC4Y 0HA
Tel: 020 7353 4722 *Fax:* 020 7353 4723
Work: M2

C R BURTON & CO ‡
192 High Street Penge London SE20 7QB
Tel: 020 8778 4455 / 8659 5775 *Fax:* 020 8676 0501
Dx: 34852 PENGE
Emergency telephone 020 8778 4455
E-mail: enquiries@crburton.co.uk
List of partners: A Burton, C R Burton
Work: D1 G H K1 K3 Q S1 W Z(l)
Emergency Action, Agency, Advocacy, Fixed Fee Interview, Legal Aid undertaken and Legal Aid Franchise
Ptr: Burton, Mr Anthony LLB(Hons) . . . . . Jul 2008
Burton, Mr Colin R . . . . . *Sep 1979
Ast: Beckett, Miss Christine Anne LLB(Lond) . . . . . *Oct 1992
Cross, Mr Robin Falcon RD . . . . . *Jul 1969
Con: Young, Mr Hamish LLB . . . . . Oct 1980

BURTON WOOLF & TURK ‡
22-24 Ely Place London EC1N 6TE
Tel: 020 7831 6478 *Fax:* 020 7405 4181
Dx: 0004 LONDON/CHANCERY LN
List of partners: C S Bharj, S E Simon
Work: B1 C1 D2 E F1 F2 G J1 K1 K3 L N O Q R2 S1 S2 T1 T2 U2 W X Z(c,d,e,h,i,l,q,r)
Agency and Advocacy undertaken
Ptr: Bharj, Mr Charanjit S LLB(Hons) . . . . . *Mar 1999
Simon, Mrs Sara Elizabeth . . . . . *May 1976
Ast: Cornell, Mr Keith Peter LLB(Hons) . . . . . *Nov 2007

BURTONWOODS ‡
Museum House 25 Museum Street London WC1A 1JT
Tel: 020 7636 2448 *Dx:* 35735 BLOOMSBURY
E-mail: queries@burtonwoods.com
List of partners: J A Burton, S P Woods
Work: C1 D2 E K1 K3 S1 S2 W Z(f)
Ptr: Burton, Ms Judith Ann BA . . . . . *Jan 1983
Woods, Mr Simon P BA . . . . . *Feb 1986
Con: Butler, Ms Gillian A BSc(Econ) . . . . . *Jan 1979

BUTCHER BURNS LLP ‡
Beaumont House 47 Mount Pleasant London WC1X 0AE
Tel: 020 7713 7100 *Fax:* 020 7713 6121
Dx: 350 LONDON/CHANCERY LN
E-mail: advice@bblaw.co.uk
List of partners: V Cassidy, M J McKeever, S I Rifkin, C Rollo
Languages: French, Spanish
Work: B1 C1 E F1 F2 J1 K1 K3 L M1 N O P Q R1 S1 S2 T1 W Z(e,f,k,l,q)
Agency undertaken
Ptr: Cassidy, Miss Vanessa LLB(Hons) . . . . . *Jan 2005
McKeever, Mr Michael James . . . . . *Nov 1992
Rifkin, Sacha I . . . . . *Nov 1998
Rollo, Ms Claire BA(Law) . . . . . *Feb 1993
Asoc: Thomas, Lucy . . . . . Oct 1991
Ast: Donoghue, Mr Lee . . . . . Nov 2006
Moreira, Bianca . . . . . Sep 2006
Con: Canning, Mr Malcolm Frank . . . . . *Jun 1974
Engelsman, Mr Simon Marc BA . . . . . *Oct 1983
Krestin, Mr Jonathan M . . . . . *Jul 1976
Levinger, Mr Peter D . . . . . *Jun 1975
Winfield, Mr Roger H . . . . . *Jan 1970

CLIVE BUTLER ‡
30 Strokenchurch Street London SW6 3TR
Tel: 020 7731 2281

BYRNE & PARTNERS ‡
1 Plough Place London EC4A 1DE
Tel: 020 7842 1616 *Fax:* 020 7842 1617
Dx: 392 LONDON/CHANCERY LN
E-mail: info@byrneandpartners.com
List of partners: A Benson, N Boulton, D K Byrne, M P Frankland, B O'Sullivan, M Potts, E Seborg
Work: B2 G O
Legal Aid undertaken and Legal Aid Franchise
Ptr: Benson, Mr Andrew . . . . . *Dec 1996
Boulton, Miss Nicola BA(Oxon) . . . . . *Nov 1994
Byrne, Mr David K BA(Law); LLM(Lond) Sweet & Maxwell Law Prize . . . . . *Oct 1978
Frankland, Mr Matthew Paul LLB . . . . . *Sep 1991
O'Sullivan, Mr Bernard LLB . . . . . Dec 1992
Potts, Mr Michael . . . . . *Nov 1997
Seborg, Elizabeth BA(California, Berkely); CPE; LPC . Oct 2002
Ast: Pacifico, Ms Joanna . . . . . *Nov 1998

BYRT & CO SOLICITORS ‡
25 Floral Street London WC2E 9DS
Tel: 020 7745 7337

C A LEGAL
(in association with Marriott Davies Yapp)
18 Westminster Palace Gardens 1-7 Artillery Row London SW1P 1RR
Office: Sutton

See p2 for the Key to Work Categories & other symbols

CAS LAW LIMITED ‡
H72 Du Cane Court Balham High Road Balham London SW17 7JT
Tel: 07786 272579
E-mail: carionas@yahoo.co.uk

CB LEGAL ‡
Dilke House 1 Malet Street Camden London WC1E 7JN
Tel: 020 7323 9192 *Fax:* 020 7323 9394
E-mail: keithcox@cb-legal.com
List of partners: K A Cox, S P Willson
Work: B2 C1 J1 T1 T2 W Z(b)
Ptr: Cox, Mr Keith Alan . . . . *§Jun 1976
Willson, Mr Samuel Peter LLB(Hons) . . . . *Feb 2003

CFB PARTNERSHIP ‡
7 High Street London E11 2AA
Tel: 020 8532 9911

CIPIT SOLICITORS ‡
127 Hampstead House 176 Finchley Road London NW3 6CT
Tel: 020 8457 7457 *Fax:* 020 8731 7795
List of partners: A Spencer
Work: C1 E I J1 S2 U2 Z(e,z)
Fixed Fee Interview undertaken
SPr: Spencer, Dr Ann BSc; PhD . . . . *Oct 1979

CJ ASSOCIATES ‡
26 Upper Brook Street London W1K 7QE

CKFT ‡
25-26 Hampstead High Street London NW3 1QA
Est: 1992
Tel: 020 7431 7262 *Fax:* 020 7431 7261 *Dx:* 155120 HAMPSTEAD 5
E-mail: law@ckft.com
List of partners: R A Barnett, A B Blain, D Fireman, L M Katz, G S Kaye, J E Leigh, B C Lester, G Locke, I G Roden, A W Taylor, S O M Taylor, F C Turner, N Waldman
Work: B1 C1 C2 D1 D2 E J1 K1 N O Q R1 R2 S1 S2 U2 W Z(c,j,k,q,r)
Emergency Action and Advocacy undertaken
Ptr: Barnett, Mr Richard A BA(Warw) . . . . Jun 1977
Blain, Mr Adam B MA . . . . *Nov 1996
Fireman, Mr Daniel . . . . *Oct 1988
Katz, Mr Laurence Michael . . . . Nov 1991
Kaye, Mr Graham S BA . . . . *Sep 1988
Leigh, Mr Joel E LLB . . . . *Jul 1993
Lester, Belinda Catherine . . . . Sep 1999
Locke, Ms Gillian . . . . Dec 1992
Roden, Mr Iain G LLB. . . . . *Oct 1989
Taylor, Mr Adam W LLB(Bris) . . . . *Oct 1991
Taylor, Mr Simon O M LLB . . . . *Oct 1987
Turner, Miss Fiona Clare . . . . Nov 1995
Waldman, Ms Nicola BA(Hons) . . . . *Jun 1989
Asoc: Brown, Michelle. . . . . Sep 2003
Louis, Ms Julie LLB . . . . *Oct 1988
Nyman, Lara . . . . Sep 1999
Patel, Jay. . . . . Mar 1993
Ast: Aftab, Farooq . . . . Jan 2007
Cooper, Mr Phillip. Sep 2005
Fakhrai, Miss Bibi. Jul 2004
Kay, Joanna. . . . . Oct 2004
Lockhart, Mr Duncan . . . . Oct 2009
May, Jessica . . . . Jan 2004
Salim, Miss Ayesha . . . . Feb 2001
Shmuel, Georgie . . . . Sep 2005
Vecerova, Vendula . . . . Jan 2007
Waters, Mrs Alison . . . . Sep 2005
Con: Collis, Miss Pamela C N LLB . . . . *§May 1981
Tash, Mr Selwyn LLB . . . . Oct 1976

C K SOLICITORS ‡
717 High Road Leytonstone London E11 4RD
Tel: 020 8536 9911 *Fax:* 020 8536 9922 *Dx:* 58216 LEYTONSTONE
Office: Ilford

CLS SERVICES ‡
1 Harbour Exchange Square London E14 9GE

CMS CAMERON MCKENNA LLP ‡
Mitre House 160 Aldersgate Street Tower Hamlets London EC1A 4DD
Tel: 020 7367 3000 *Fax:* 020 7367 2000 *Dx:* 135316 BARBICAN 2
E-mail: info@cmck.com
List of partners: N S D Agar, P D Aldred, J S Armstrong, M Atkinson, S Badham, M F Baker, M J Bartholomew, S C Barty, I C Batty, J P Beckitt, I P Bendell, E C Benzecry, G Billington, A Blach, D L Bresnick, N A Brown, T Butcher, W Carr, R A D Croker, C J Cummins, M E Cupitt, R Curd, T J Davies, D C Day, C J Delaney, R S Derry-Evans, A R Doughty, M G Draper, S F Dufficy, P Edmondson, N Eller, A L R Fincham, M P Fox, M S Grant, A M S Green, G M Green, K V Gregory, D H F Griston, N M Hadley, J E Hall, S H Hallam, K Ham, J C Hammond, S P Hankey, M C Hanson, J Harding, T P F Hardy, B H Hearnden, S C Hegarty, M R Heighton, P L Hewes, R W Hickmott, A J Hobkinson, C J S Hodges, T Ingham, A S Ivison, S J Johnston, M Jones, P J Karia, E K Kelleher, A B Kitson, I Kovari, A L Kozlowski, R C Lane, E M Layton, R A Lowe, P Maguire, A L Marks, D R Marks, N S McAlister, H A McDowell, M C Mendelssohn, S Millar, N C Moore, S J Morris, M M Moseley, J R Naccarato, S J Netherway, M B Nichols, L O'Connell, J A Ogley, J E Onslow-Cole, G Ormai, R Palmer, N W Paul, V M Peckett, M D Pennell, R J Phillips, S M Pilcher, R S Price, S K Rafferty, M W Rich, D J E Roberts, C D A Romney, B A Schofield, A Seaton, A J Sheach, P F Sheridan, H C Sherman, S D Shone, A Smith, P N Smith, C Southorn, C P Spragge, C St John-Smith, P Stallebrass, A Symons, R J J Taylor, R M Temple, S K Tester, M L Tyler, R H Tyler, J T Uwins, H C K Waddell, A L Walker, L H Wallace, S P Warne, S M Watson, D J Weston, V A Wheatley, S K Whybrow, C J C Williams, P R Wiltshire, C F Woolf, N A E Zervos
Office: Bristol, London EC3
Languages: Cantonese, Czech, French, German, Greek, Hungarian, Italian, Japanese, Mandarin, Polish, Russian, Slovak, Spanish
Work: A3 B1 B2 C1 C2 C3 E F1 F2 I J1 J2 M1 M2 N O P Q R1 R2 S2 T1 U1 Z(a,b,c,d,e,g,i,j,k,n,o,q,s,y)
Advocacy undertaken
Ptr: Aldred, Mr P Duncan LLB. . . . . *Oct 1982
Armstrong, Mr John S LLB(Soton). . . . . *Nov 1984
Atkinson, Mr Mark BA(Cantab) . . . . Sep 1993
Baker, Mr Michael F LLB(Hons) . . . . *Apr 1977
Bartholomew, Mr Mark J BA(Canterbury) . . . . *Oct 1986
Barty, Miss Susan C LLB(Bris) . . . . *Feb 1985
Batty, Mr Iain Charles LLB(Hons)(Cardiff) . . . . Nov 1991
Beckitt, Mr Jonathan P LLB(Bris) . . . . *Nov 1984
Bendell, Mr Ian P BA(Oxon). . . . . *Dec 1987
Benzecry, Mr Edward C LLB . . . . *Jan 1988
Billington, Mr Guy MA(Cantab) . . . . *§Apr 1971
Blach, Mr Andrzej. . . . . Jun 1993
Bresnick, Mr David L . . . . Nov 1992
Brown, Mr Nicholas A BA(Bris) . . . . *§Dec 1974
Butcher, Mr Trevor LLB(Leics). . . . . *Dec 1986
Carr, Mr William LLB(Lond); Maitrise en Droit . . . . . *Apr 1993
Croker, Mr Richard A D BA(Dunelm) . . . . *Dec 1989
Cummins, Ms Caroline J BA(Oxon) . . . . *Oct 1989
Cupitt, Miss Maxine E BA . . . . Nov 1988
Curd, Mr Richard LLB(Lond) . . . . *Oct 1987
Davies, Mr T Jason LLB; MA(Lond) . . . . *Nov 1994
Day, Mr David Christopher BA(Hons) . . . . Nov 1989
Delaney, Ms Caroline Julia . . . . Oct 1993
Derry-Evans, Mr Robert S MA(Oxon) . . . . Dec 1977
Doughty, Mr Alexander Robert . . . . Nov 1993
Draper, Mr Michael G . . . . Oct 1984
Dufficy, Mr S Frank BA; DipLL. . . . . *Oct 1983
Edmondson, Mr Paul . . . . *Nov 1994
Eller, Ms Nancy LLM(Lond); Member New York State Bar . . . . *Aug 1995
Fincham, Mr Anthony L R MA(Oxon) . . . . *Nov 1980
Fox, Mr Martin P LLB . . . . *Oct 1990
Grant, Mr Mark S BA(Oxon). . . . . *Feb 1997
Green, Mr Alexander Michael Stuart. . . . . Dec 1993
Green, Mr Gary M LLB(Bris) . . . . *Oct 1986
Gregory, Mr Keith V MA(Oxon) . . . . *Oct 1980
Griston, Mr David H F LLB(Exon) . . . . Oct 1994
Hadley, Mr Nicholas M LLB; PhD(Law)(B'ham) . . . . *§Dec 1979
Hall, Mr John E MA(Cantab) . . . . *Oct 1980
Hallam, Mr Stephen H. . . . . *Feb 1974
Ham, Mr Keith . . . . May 1987
Hammond, Mr John C BA(Oxon) . . . . *Dec 1987
Hankey, Ms Susan Patricia BA . . . . Nov 1989
Hanson, Mr Marc C BA(East Anglia) . . . . *Apr 1994
Harding, Mr Jason . . . . May 1996
Hardy, Mr Timothy P F . . . . *Dec 1977
Hearnden, Mr Barney H MA(Cantab) . . . . *Nov 1988
Heighton, Mr Mark R LLB(Sheff) . . . . Oct 1988
Hewes, Mr Peter L BA(Oxon). . . . . *§Apr 1972
Hickmott, Mr Robert W LLB. . . . . *Apr 1991
Hobkinson, Mr Anthony J LLB. . . . . *Oct 1985
Hodges, Mr Christopher J S MA(Oxon) . . . . *§Dec 1979
Ingham, Mr Tim LLB . . . . Oct 1990
Ivison, Mr Andrew S MA(Cantab) . . . . *Apr 1980
Johnston, Mr Simon James BA(Exon). . . . . *Aug 1995
Jones, Mr Michael BA(Hons)(Law) . . . . Oct 1987
Karia, Mr Pranai J LLB(Hons) . . . . Oct 1989
Kelleher, Mrs E Kate MA(Oxon). . . . . *Apr 1980
Kitson, Mr Antony B LLB(Warw). . . . . *Dec 1975
Kovari, Istvan . . . . Jul 1992
Kozlowski, Mr Andrew L. . . . . Nov 1989
Lane, Mr Robert C LLB(Lond). . . . . *Oct 1982
Layton, Miss Eleanor Mary BA . . . . *Mar 1996
Lowe, Ms Rita A . . . . Mar 1992
McAlister, Mr Niall S LLB(Bris) . . . . *Oct 1989
McDowell, Ms Hilary A BA(Leics) . . . . *Apr 1994
Maguire, Mr Peter BA. *Nov 1984
Marks, Mr Anthony L LLB(Bris) . . . . *Jun 1975
Marks, Mr David R LLB(L'pool); LLM(Exon) . . . . *Jul 1983
Mendelssohn, Mr Martin C LLB(Bris) . . . . *Nov 1982
Millar, Mr Stephen. . . . . Oct 1996
Moore, Mr Nigel C LLB(Warw); MA(Lond) . . . . *Nov 1986
Morris, Mr Simon J MA(Cantab). . . . . *Nov 1982
Moseley, Mr Mark M . . . . Mar 1998
Naccarato, Mr John R LLB(Soton). . . . . *May 1984
Netherway, Mr Stephen J LLB. . . . . *Oct 1987
Nichols, Mr Mark B LLB(Lond) . . . . Feb 1990
O'Connell, Mr Liam . . . . Sep 1992
Ogley, Mr Julian A BA(Oxon) . . . . *§Apr 1973
Onslow-Cole, Ms Julia E LLB Chairman of the Migration & Nationality Commission of the International Bar Association . . . . *Oct 1984
Ormai, Ms Gabriella. . . . . Oct 1978
Palmer, Mr Robert MA(Hons)(Cantab). . . . . *May 1987
Paul, Mr Nicholas W LLB . . . . *Oct 1981
Peckett, Miss Victoria Mary BA(Cantab). . . . . Sep 1994
Pennell, Mr Martin D BA(Dunelm) . . . . Nov 1988
Phillips, Mr Robert J. Jan 1971
Pilcher, Mr Simon M. Sep 1996
Price, Mr Richard S BA; LLB(Leeds) . . . . *Apr 1977
Rafferty, Ms Sandra K BA(Durham) . . . . *Dec 1993
Rich, Mr Michael W MA(Cantab) . . . . *Apr 1971
Roberts, Mr David J E. . . . . Sep 1986
Romney, Mr Charles D A LLB. . . . . *Nov 1973
Schofield, Miss Belinda A LLB(Leics); LLM(Lond) . . . *Jun 1980
Seaton, Ms Amanda . . . . Feb 1992
Sheach, Mr Andrew J MA . . . . Oct 1987
Sheridan, Mr Paul F LLB(Hons)(Soton) . . . . Nov 1985
Sherman, Mr Henry C BA(Oxon) . . . . *Jan 1978
Shone, Mr Stephen D LLB . . . . *Mar 1982
Smith, Mr Ashley . . . . §Oct 1996
Smith, Mr Peter N LLB(Bris). . . . . *Apr 1980
Southorn, Mr Christopher . . . . Nov 1992
Spragge, Mr Charles P BA(Lancs). . . . . Nov 1990
St John-Smith, Mr Christopher BA(Oxon) . . . . Jan 1981
Stallebrass, Mr Paul. Sep 1991
Symons, Mr Andrew BSc(Hons). . . . . *Nov 1991
Taylor, Mr Richard J J MA(Oxon) . . . . *§Dec 1969
Temple, Mr Richard M BA; LLM . . . . *Sep 1989
Tester, Mr Stephen K MA(Cantab). . . . . *Nov 1981
Tyler, Mr Mark L MA(Oxon); LLM(Lond) . . . . *Nov 1986
Tyler, Mr Richard H MA(Cantab). . . . . *Nov 1985
Uwins, Mr John T MA(Cantab); BA(Cantab) . . . . *Apr 1981
Waddell, Mr H Charles K LLB(Bris) . . . . *Sep 1988
Walker, Mr Andrew L BA(Hons) . . . . *Oct 1986
Wallace, Ms Louise H LLB(Lond) . . . . Nov 1990
Warne, Mrs S Penelope LLB(Bris). . . . . *Apr 1981
Watson, Mr Sean M LLB(Manc). . . . . *§Apr 1972
Weston, Mr Duncan J BA(Keele); LLM . . . . Sep 1990
Wheatley, Mr Vere A LLB(Bris) . . . . *Nov 1982
Whybrow, Mr Stephen K MA; LLB(Cantab) . . . . *Nov 1971
Williams, Mr Christopher J C MA(Cantab). . . . . Jun 1991
Wiltshire, Mr Peter R BA . . . . *Dec 1990
Woolf, Mrs C Fiona BA(Keele) . . . . *Jun 1973
Zervos, Mr Nicholas A E LLB . . . . Apr 1988
Ast: Baggs, Mrs Eleanor L LLB . . . . Nov 1985
Winterbourne, Mr Neil LLB(Hons) . . . . *Aug 1995
Woodward, Mr Nicholas LLB . . . . *Nov 1994
Woollam, Mr Edmund Victor. . . . . *Jan 1996

CMS CAMERON MCKENNA LLP
100 Leadenhall Street London EC3A 3BP
Tel: 020 7367 3000 *Fax:* 020 7367 2000
Office: Bristol, London EC1

CVS SOLICITORS ‡
17 Albemarle Street London W1S 4HP
Tel: 020 7493 2903 *Fax:* 020 7493 3877 *Dx:* 82980 MAYFAIR
E-mail: gce@cvs-law.co.uk
List of partners: G P Courtenay-Evans, C A Housby, A H McClean, A M Shah, N Van der Borgh
Languages: French, Gujarati, Hindi
Work: A1 A3 B1 C1 C2 C3 E F1 F2 G I J1 K1 L M1 N O Q R1 R2 S1 S2 T1 T2 W Z(b,c,d,e,f,l,o,p,q,w,z)
Agency undertaken
Ptr: Courtenay-Evans, Mr Giles P . . . . *Nov 1966
Housby, Ms Christine A LLB; BA(Hons) . . . . *Mar 1991
McClean, Mr Alistair Hugh BA(Hons)(Durham) . . . . Nov 1989
Shah, Mr Anup M LLB(Hons) . . . . *Oct 1986
Van der Borgh, Mr Nicholas . . . . *Jun 1966
Asoc: O'Shea, Mr Michael P LLB(Manc). . . . . *§May 1979
Rutter, Mrs Sharon Avril LLB . . . . *Oct 1987
Ast: Bond, Mr Robert Edward Rolland LLB. . . . . Oct 2001
Machray, Mr Mark BSc; DipLaw. . . . . Sep 2000
Williams, Mr Matthew Oliver LLB(Europe with French); Diplome en Droit. . . . . Sep 2002
Con: Lloyd, Mr Christopher E. . . . . *Jul 1966

JOHN F S CABOT ‡
54 Perrymead Street London SW6 3SP
Tel: 020 7384 9583 *Fax:* 020 7384 9587
E-mail: john@jfscabot.eclipse.co.uk
Work: B1 G J1 K1 K3 N O Q Z(c,j,k,q,r,w)

CADWALADER WICKERSHAM & TAFT ‡
265 The Strand London WC2R 1BH
Tel: 020 7170 8700 *Dx:* 238 LONDON/CHANCERY LN
List of partners: P D Biggs
Work: C2 E O R2 U1 U2 Z(b,j)
Ptr: Biggs, Mr Paul David LLB(Hons)(Manc). . . . . Oct 1990
Asoc: Croucher, Ms Yvette LLB . . . . Dec 1994
Ast: Bennet, Mr I Douglas BSc(Bris) . . . . Apr 1996
Woodcroft, Ms Paula U . . . . Apr 1996

CAHILL DE FONSEKA SOLICITORS ‡
89a The Broadway London SW19 1QE
Tel: 020 7998 3488 *Fax:* 020 7998 3488
E-mail: info@cdfsolicitors.com

CAHILL GORDON & REINDEL ‡
Augustine House 6a Austin Friars London EC2N 2HA
Tel: 020 7920 9800 *Fax:* 020 7920 9825
E-mail: info@cahill.com

CAINS ADVOCATES LIMITED ‡
1 Love Lane London EC2V 7JN
Tel: 020 7367 0030 *Fax:* 020 7367 0031
E-mail: london@cains.com

CALADASHINS ‡
222 Northfield Avenue Ealing London W13 9SJ
Tel: 020 8832 9000 *Fax:* 020 8832 9009
List of partners: B Bluett
Work: N Q R1
Member of Accident Line
Ptr: Bluett, Mr Brian . . . . Jan 2001

CALE SOLICITORS ‡
Suite One 80a Blackhealth Road Greenwich London SE10 8DA
Tel: 020 8694 2269 *Fax:* 020 8694 0399
E-mail: louise@calesolicitors.com

CALISKAN CARTER SOLICITORS ‡
338 City Road London EC1V 2PY
Tel: 020 7239 8291 *Fax:* 020 7239 8284
E-mail: info@caliskancarter.co.uk

CALLAGHAN & CO ‡
113 Gloucester Place Westminster London W1U 6JR
Tel: 020 7486 8173 *Fax:* 020 7224 1406
E-mail: pmc@calllaw.lawlite.net
List of partners: P M Callaghan
Work: B1 C1 E L S1 S2 W Z(l)
Advocacy undertaken
SPr: Callaghan, Mr Peter M . . . . *Dec 1975

CALLISTES ‡
146 Acre Lane Lambeth London SW2 5UT
Tel: 020 7501 8388 *Fax:* 020 7924 0794
Emergency telephone 07939 026876
E-mail: callistes@btconnect.com
Office: London EC4, London W1
Work: G H K1 S1 Z(i)
Fixed Fee Interview, Legal Aid undertaken and Legal Aid Franchise

CALLISTES
107-111 Fleet Street London EC4A 2AB
Tel: 020 7936 9033 *Fax:* 020 7936 9100
E-mail: callistes@btconnect.com
Office: London SW2, London W1

CALLISTES
1 Berkeley Street Mayfair London W1J 8DJ
Tel: 020 3402 2139 *Fax:* 020 7016 9100
E-mail: callistes@btconnect.com
Office: London EC4, London SW2

JOHN B CALVER & CO ‡
(in association with E H Seager Winn & Co)
56 Queensway Westminster London W2 3RY
Tel: 020 7221 9181 *Fax:* 020 7221 4979
List of partners: J B Calver
Work: B1 C1 D1 E F1 F2 G H K1 L M1 N P Q R1 S1 S2 V W
Emergency Action, Agency, Advocacy and Legal Aid undertaken
Ptr: Calver, Mr John B. *Jul 1974

CALVERT SOLICITORS ‡
77 Weston Street Southwark London SE1 3RS
Tel: 020 7234 0707 *Fax:* 020 7234 0909
E-mail: mail@calvertsolicitors.co.uk

List of partners: M W Hartley
Work: C1 C2 E F1 J1 L O Q R1 R2 S1 S2 U1 U2 Z(e,f,h,k,l,w,z)
Fixed Fee Interview and Legal Aid undertaken
Ptr: Hartley, Mr Michael W. *Mar 1980

CALYON ‡
Broadwalk House 5 Appold Street London EC2A 2DA
Tel: 020 7214 5000 ***Fax:*** 020 7214 5999

CAMERON DEACON LLP ‡
9 Botolph Alley Monument London EC3R 8DR
Tel: 020 7621 2214

CAMERON TAYLOR ‡
Shand House 14-20 Shand Street London SE1 2ES

CAMERONS SOLICITORS LLP ‡
Fourth Floor 27 Gloucester Road London W1U 8HU
Tel: 020 7866 6010

CAMILLA BALDWIN ‡
7 Lanark Road London W9 1DD
Tel: 020 7286 5189

CAMPBELL CHAMBERS ‡
25 Hatton Garden London EC1N 8BQ
Tel: 020 7691 8777 ***Fax:*** 020 7691 8778 ***Dx:*** 53310 CLERKENWELL
E-mail: info@campbellchambers.com
List of partners: A L Campbell, E B Chambers
Work: B2 D1 D2 G H K1 K2 Z(i)
Emergency Action, Agency, Advocacy, Fixed Fee Interview and Legal Aid undertaken
Ptr: Campbell, Ms Angela L FILEx. May 1993
Chambers, Mr Earl B Sep 1998

CAMPBELL COMMERCIAL LAW ‡
Third Floor 35-37 Ludgate Hill London EC4M 7JN
Tel: 020 7489 7771

FIONA CAMPBELL ‡
27a Pembridge Villas Kensington & Chelsea London W11 3EP
Tel: 020 7243 1982 ***Fax:*** 020 7221 2736
Dx: 94212 NOTTING HILL GATE
E-mail: fionacampbell@fcampbell.co.uk

CAMPBELL-TAYLOR SOLICITORS ‡
Office D1 3 Bradbury Street Hackney London N16 8JN
Tel: 0845 567 2457 ***Fax:*** 020 7923 0055
Emergency telephone 07976 854479
E-mail: admin@rhctlegal.co.uk
List of partners: R H Campbell-Taylor
Office: London W10
Languages: Italian
Work: K4 W Z(g,m)
Fixed Fee Interview, Legal Aid undertaken and Legal Aid Franchise
SPr: Campbell-Taylor, Mr Roderick H ♦. Apr 1995

CAMPBELL-TAYLOR SOLICITORS
Canalot Studios 222 Kensal Road London W10 5BN
Tel: 0845 567 2457
E-mail: admin@rhctlegal.co.uk
Office: London N16

CANDEY LLP ‡
8 Stone Buildings Lincoln's Inn London WC2A 3TA
Tel: 020 3370 8888 ***Fax:*** 020 3328 7778

CANNINGS CONNOLLY ‡
16 St Martin's-le-Grand London EC1A 4EE
Tel: 020 7329 9000 ***Fax:*** 020 7329 5000
Dx: 50 LONDON/CHANCERY LN
E-mail: email@cclaw.co.uk
List of partners: T I Barwick, J J Connolly, D M Golten, W S Pearce, J R Roberts, M Sillett
Work: B1 C1 C2 E I J1 N O Q R2 S2 U2 Z(b,c,e)
Ptr: Barwick, Mr Timothy I. *Dec 1991
Connolly, Mr John James *Nov 1980
Golten, Mr David Martin. *Nov 1994
Pearce, Mr William Steven *Dec 1985
Roberts, Mrs Jill R *Oct 1979
Sillett, Mr Matthew LLB(Business Law) *Apr 1992
Ast: Bates, Ms Vicky. *Sep 2003
Bradley, Mr Paul John BA; PGDipLaw; LPC. *Sep 2006
Budge, Mr Simon Alexander Courtney BSc(Hons); CPE *Oct 2009
Lusher, Mr Robert. *Oct 2002
Saville, Mr Nicholas P LLB(Hons) *Oct 1998
Tinker, Miss Jessica Emma *Sep 2007

CAPITAL LAW LLP
99 City Road London EC1Y 1AX
Tel: 0333 240 0489 ***Fax:*** 0333 240 0487
E-mail: info@capitallaw.co.uk
Office: Cardiff

CAPITAL SOLICITORS LLP ‡
Unit 2 41 Vallance Road London E1 5AB
Tel: 020 7377 0847 ***Fax:*** 020 7788 9674
Dx: 155242 TOWER HAMLETS 1
E-mail: info@capitalsolicitors.co.uk

IRVING CAPLIN & CO ‡
1 College Mews St Ann's Hill Wandsworth London SW18 2SJ
Tel: 020 8874 7633 ***Fax:*** 020 8870 1650 ***Dx:*** 82150 EARLSFIELD
E-mail: irvingcaplin@btconnect.com
List of partners: I D Caplin
Work: S1 W
SPr: Caplin, Mr Irving David LLB(Lond). *Dec 1974

CAPSTICKS SOLICITORS LLP ‡
1 St Georges Road Wimbledon London SW19 4DR
Tel: 020 8780 2211 ***Fax:*** 020 8780 1141
Dx: 300118 WIMBLEDON CENTRAL
E-mail: info@capstick.co.uk
List of partners: H Blackwell, S L Bloom, C J Brophy, P W Brown, J B Capstick, S Durey, P J Edwards, D M A Firth, L M Gee, M W Hamilton, L Hardman, P J Hatherall, K E Hay, T Hayes, C Long, C E Lynch, P B Marquand, D Mason, T W Mawer, M Paget Skelin, I Pickering, D W R Purcell, J D B Reynolds, T Richards, J A Smith, S L Stanton, R Wilson, J N E Witt
Office: Birmingham
Work: A1 B2 C1 C2 D1 E I J1 L M1 N O P Q R1 R2 S2 Z(c,d,g,h,k,m,p,r,u)
Ptr: Blackwell, Mrs Hilary LLB. *Oct 1986
Bloom, Ms Suzanne L BJuris; LLB; Dip CL; Barrister & Solicitor Victoria Australia Supreme Court Prize *Jan 1983
Brophy, Mr Christopher J LLB(Hons) *Oct 1987
Brown, Mr Philip W BA *Nov 1988
Capstick, Mr J Brian MA *Jul 1977
Durey, Ms Suzanne LLB(Manc) *Oct 1988
Edwards, Mr Peter J BA(Hons)(Oxon). *Jan 1991
Firth, Mr David M A BA(Hons); MA *Nov 1995
Gee, Miss Lindsay M BA(Hons)(Oxon); DPhil *Mar 1990
Hamilton, Mr Martin William BA(Hons)(Oxon) *Sep 1996
Hardman, Ms Lorna LLB(Oxon) *Dec 1993
Hatherall, Mr Philip John LLB(Hons). *Nov 1995
Hay, Mrs Katharine E BA *Oct 1988
Hayes, Mr Tom BA(Hons). Sep 1998
Long, Ms Camilla MA(Hons). *Aug 1998
Lynch, Mr Colin E LLB(Hons) *Oct 1988
Marquand, Dr Peter Blondel BSc; MBBS; MRCP(UK) *Sep 1996
Mason, Mr David MA(Oxon); DipLaw(City) *Jun 1990
Mawer, Mr Trevor W LLB(Hons). *Nov 1994
Paget Skelin, Mr Mark LLB(Hons). *Apr 1996
Pickering, Mr Iain BA(Hons). *May 1993
Purcell, Mr Daniel William Robert LLB. *Sep 1996
Reynolds, Mr James D B LLB. *Apr 1991
Richards, Ms Tania BA *Oct 1995
Smith, Miss Janice A LLB(Hons) *Oct 1985
Stanton, Mrs Sarah Louise LLB(Hons). *Oct 1993
Wilson, Mr Robert BA(Oxon) *Oct 1995
Witt, Mr John N E BA(Hons)(Dunelm) *Apr 1988
Ast: Adedapo, Mr Ade LPC *Sep 2001
Barker, Ms Jane LLB Sep 2000
Bhogal, Ms Harjit LLB(Hons) *Oct 1999
Box, Mr Cassius BA(Econ) *Oct 1998
Bzowska, Miss Mary E *Nov 1984
Chaudary, Miss Shahliza LLB(Hons); PGDip. *Nov 2000
Clarke, Mr David BA; CPE Oct 2002
Conlan, Ms Sasha LLB(Hons). *Sep 1996
Culpan, Ms Veronica BA; LLB; IPLS. Feb 1997
Daboh, Ms Eva Ayo LLB; LPC *Sep 2000
Danziger, Ms Verity H LLB Sep 1997
Davis, Mrs Serena Julie Elinor MA *Mar 1996
De Graeve, Mr Michael J A MA(Cantab); BA *Dec 1980
Dix, Ms Belinda BA(Hons). *Sep 1999
Edmunds, Miss Sarah Elizabeth LLB *Oct 1997
Elliott, Mrs Tina Helen LLB *Nov 1984
Evans, Ms Esther Ann BSc(Hons); MSc. *Sep 2001
Everson, Miss Juliet C BA(Hons)(Oxon). *Sep 1998
Ford, Ms Julie LLB(Hons) *Oct 2000
Froome, Mr David. *Sep 2001
Harle, Miss Kathryn Jean LLB; PGDipLaw. Nov 2002
Hill, Miss Susie BA Nov 2002
Johnston, Mr Andrew BA Nov 2002
Jones, Miss Rosamund C BA(Exon). *Nov 1988
Kingsley, Mr Paul BA(Hons). *Nov 1995
Kinsella, Ms Marie RMN; RGN *Oct 1998
Kohler, Mrs Jessica Ruth BA; LLB. Mar 2001
Lynch, Miss Jane BA(Hons); PGDipLaw. Nov 2002
Moore, Ms Louisa Anne BA; AKCL; DipLaw Nov 2002
Norriss, Ms Clare Louise LLB(Hons); MA *Sep 2001
Pearson, Ms Sophie Anne BA(Hons); CPE *Sep 1996
Pedley, Ms Jennie Christina LLB *Sep 2001
Peters, Ms Katy J LLB(Hons) Sep 2000
Reuvecamp, Ms Iris LLB; BA *Mar 2002
Rowland, Mr Andrew John BA(Hons)(Law) *Sep 1998
Sekhon, Mrs Kirandeep Kaur LLB. *Sep 2001
Vickery, Ms Catherine M J BA(Hons) Annual Law Society Prize for Outstanding Performance(98/99 LPC); Burges Salmon Prize(98/99 LPC) *Sep 2001
Whitting, Mr Mark Howard BA(Hons) *Sep 2001
Worth, Ms Anna L BA(Hons)(Cantab) *Oct 1998
Wyatt, Ms Vashti LLB(Law with French Law) Oct 2002
Con: Morley, Ms Alison FILEx. Jan 1991

CARDINAL SOLICITORS ‡
Prosper House Prosper Business Centre London NW6 4JD
Tel: 020 7691 4501

CAREY OLSEN ‡
20 King Street London EC2V 8EG
Tel: 020 7796 3911 ***Fax:*** 020 7796 4025

CARLSONS ‡
Whetstone House 1-3 Oakleigh Road North Whetstone London N20 9HE
Tel: 020 8445 3331 / 8445 5752 ***Fax:*** 020 8446 2809
Dx: 37102 WHETSTONE
E-mail: admin@carlsonsolicitors.com
List of partners: I J N Robins, D M Russell
Work: A3 B1 B2 C1 D1 D2 E F1 F2 G J1 K1 K3 K4 L M1 N O P Q R2 S1 S2 W X Z(c,e,f,i,j,k,l,p,q,r,s)
Agency undertaken
Ptr: Robins, Mr Ian J N MA(Cantab) *Jun 1976
Russell, Mr Daniel Michael LLB(Hons). *Oct 1992

CARNGIE BROWN LIMITED ‡
5 Doria Road London SW6 4UF
Tel: 020 8906 6731 ***Fax:*** 020 7127 5061
E-mail: info@carnegiebrown.com

CARPENTERS ROSE ‡
26 The Broadway Mill Hill London NW7 3NL
Tel: 020 8906 0088 ***Fax:*** 020 8959 1281 ***Dx:*** 51350 MILL HILL
E-mail: carpenters.rose@btinternet.com
List of partners: A P Rose
Languages: French, German
Work: C1 C2 S2 T1 T2 W Z(d,m,o)
Ptr: Rose, Mr Alan Peter MA(Cantab) Notary Public *§Nov 1975
Ast: Royston, Mrs Michelle A LLB(Hons). *Jun 1984
Con: Carpenter, Mr Philip G *§Jan 1970

CARR & KAYE SOLICITORS ‡
No3 8 Frognal Hampstead London NW3 6AJ
Tel: 0333 900 0770 ***Fax:*** 020 7681 2421
E-mail: djcarr@btinternet.com
Office: Welwyn Garden City
Work: W

S A CARR & CO ‡
416 Mare Street Hackney London E8 1HP
Tel: 020 8986 5438 ***Fax:*** 020 8986 0216 ***Dx:*** 35456 HACKNEY
E-mail: office@sacco.co.uk
List of partners: S A Carr, B M Osbaldeston
Work: D1 K1 L N O Q S1 W Z(h,i,q)
Emergency Action, Agency, Advocacy, Fixed Fee Interview and Legal Aid undertaken
Ptr: Carr, Mr Stephen A LLB. *Jul 1981
Osbaldeston, Mrs Beatrice M BSc. *Oct 1982

CARRINGTON & ASSOCIATES ‡
2nd Floor Fleet House 8-12 New Bridge Street London EC4V 6AL
Tel: 020 7822 1855 ***Fax:*** 020 7822 1856
Emergency telephone 01428 683417
E-mail: lawyers@carringtonlaw.com
List of partners: A R W Carrington
Languages: French, Spanish
Work: B1 B2 C1 C2 C3 F1 F2 I J1 M2 N O P U1 U2 Z(b,e,j)
SPr: Carrington, Mr Andrew R W Rylands Brothers Prize. *Dec 1968

CARRITT & CO LLP ‡
1 Duchess Street London W1W 6AN
Tel: 020 7323 2765 ***Fax:*** 020 7636 1672
Dx: 42726 OXFORD STREET NORTH
E-mail: info@carritt.co.uk
List of partners: D M Carritt, J J Orlebar-Reid
Languages: French
Work: C1 E K1 K2 K3 L O Q R2 S1 S2
Ptr: Carritt, Miss Denise Melanie LLB *Oct 1986
Orlebar-Reid, Miss Joanna J BA *Mar 1985

MICHAEL CARROLL & CO ‡
798 High Road Tottenham London N17 0DH
Tel: 020 8365 9900 ***Fax:*** 020 8365 0500

CARSON & CO (SOLICITORS) LIMITED ‡
59 Shooters Hill Road Blackheath London SE3 7HS
Tel: 0845 455 0055 ***Fax:*** 0845 527 6272
E-mail: enquiries@carson-solicitors.com

CARTER AND COMPANY ‡
93-95 Borough High Street London SE1 1NL
Tel: 020 8295 2984 ***Fax:*** 020 8295 2894
E-mail: cc@carterandcompany.co.uk

GEORGE CARTER ‡
11-13 Breams Buildings London EC4A 1DT
Tel: 020 7440 8800 ***Fax:*** 020 7440 8801

CARTER LEMON CAMERONS ‡
10 Aldersgate Street London EC1A 4HJ
Tel: 020 7406 1000 ***Fax:*** 020 7406 1010
Dx: 25 LONDON/CHANCERY LN
List of partners: R T Ballaster, J S Brennan, J F Cumberlege, A J L Firman, L Ginesi, C E Picardo, J S S Smyth, D M Tuft, I R West
Languages: Chinese, Danish, French, German, Hungarian, Italian, Spanish
Work: C1 C2 C3 E J1 K4 L O P Q R1 R2 S1 T1 T2 W Z(b,c,d,e,h,i,k,l)
Agency, Advocacy and Fixed Fee Interview undertaken
Ptr: Ballaster, Mr Rufus T BA(Oxon). Oct 1988
Cumberlege, The Hon Justin F BA(Hons) *Apr 1991
Firman, Mr Andrew J L LLB; LLM R G Lawson Prize for Law & Medicine *§Sep 1995
Ginesi, Mrs Lisa LLB *Nov 1992
Picardo, Mr Christopher Edward. *Sep 1999
Smyth, Mr James S S BA; LLB(Wits); LLM(Lond) *Jun 1977
Tuft, Mr Duncan M *Dec 1976
West, Mr Ian Richard LLB. *Sep 1981
Mem: Brennan, Mr James S LLB *Oct 1973
Ast: Crippin, Mr Stuart. *Aug 2005
Lawrence, Miss Audrey Mennelli LLB(Hons). *Mar 1996
Lee, Ms Su-Fern *Jul 2007
Orosz, Mr Nicholas Endre. *May 1995
Shahim, Mrs Asma *Oct 2006
Con: Newth, Mr John F MA(Oxon) *§Dec 1956
Scott, Mr Laurence R ♦ Notary Public *Jan 1969

CARTER MOORE SOLICITORS
15 Old Bailey London EC4M 7EF
Tel: 0845 873 7333 ***Fax:*** 0845 873 7334
E-mail: info@cartermoore.com
Office: Manchester (2 offices)

CARTER PERRY BAILEY LLP ‡
10 Lloyd's Avenue London EC3N 3AJ
Tel: 020 7863 6600 ***Fax:*** 020 7863 6711
E-mail: info@cpblaw.com

CARTER-RUCK ‡
6 St Andrew Street London EC4A 3AE
Tel: 020 7353 5005 ***Fax:*** 020 7353 5553
Dx: 333 LONDON/CHANCERY LN
Emergency telephone 020 7353 5005
E-mail: lawyers@carter-ruck.com
Web: www.carter-ruck.com
List of partners: M Boyd, R E Collard, C S Doley, C F Gill, I J Hudson, G F N Martin, A G T Pepper, A J Stephenson, N G T M Tait, A Tudor
Languages: French, Italian
Work: J1 M2 O Q Z(e,f,g,k,q,w,z)
Emergency Action undertaken
Ptr: Boyd, Mr Magnus BA; MA; LLB ♦ *Oct 2001
Collard, Miss Ruth E MA(Cantab) *Oct 1990
Doley, Mr Cameron S MA(Oxon) ♦ *Oct 1992
Gill, Mrs Claire Frances LLB(Exon) ♦ *Sep 1996
Hudson, Miss Isabel Jennifer BA(Cantab) ♦ Glanville Williams Prize *Sep 2003
Martin, Mr Guy F N MA(Cantab) ♦. *Nov 1985

See p2 for the Key to Work Categories & other symbols

Pepper, Mr Alasdair G T ♦. . . . . *Jun 1984
Stephenson, Mr Andrew J LLB . . . . *Jul 1983
Tait, Mr Nigel G T M BA ♦. . . . . *Oct 1988
Tudor, Mr Adam BA(Oxon) ♦ . . . . *Jun 1997
Asoc: Staiano, Mr Luke Alessandro BA; PGDipLaw; PGDipLPSep 2005
Ast: Foster, Miss Antonia Clare ♦ . . . . *Oct 2001
Garner, Mr Dominic James BA(Hons) . . . . Jun 2011
Loughrey, Mr Stephen LLB . . . . *Jan 2008
Middleton, Miss Lucy Catherine BA(Jt Hons)(French & Italian) . . . . *Sep 2007
Spearing, Miss Laura Jane BA(Oxon)(Jurisprudence) . Mar 2008
Toman, Miss Rebecca Danielle LLB. . . . . May 2010
Yell, Mr Edward BA(Hons)(Politics); GDL; BVC; QLTT Queen Mother Scholar . . . . *Nov 2008

CARTERS ‡
26 Dover Street London W1S 4LY
Tel: 020 7763 7130 *Fax:* 020 7763 7101
E-mail: info@carterssolicitors.org.uk
Emergency Action, Agency and Legal Aid undertaken

CARTIER & CO ‡
Queens House 55-56 Lincoln's Inn Fields London WC2A 3LJ
Tel: 020 7405 7777
List of partners: L Cartier
Languages: French, Hebrew
Work: A3 B2 C1 E N O Q S1 S2 Z(b,e,g,k,q,r)
SPr: Cartier, Mr Lawrence . . . . Jan 1971

CARTWRIGHT ADAMS SOLICITORS LIMITED ‡
16 Old Bond Street Mayfair London W1S 4PS
Tel: 020 7408 9270 *Fax:* 020 7791 2929
E-mail: info@cartwrightadams.co.uk

CARTWRIGHT CUNNINGHAM HASELGROVE & CO ‡
282-284 Hoe Street Walthamstow Waltham Forest London E17 9PL
Tel: 020 8520 1021 *Fax:* 020 8520 5107 *Dx:* 32007 WALTHAMSTOW
List of partners: G I Gayer, B Klingher, J Mayo, N P Smith
Office: Woodford Green
Work: A1 A3 B2 C1 C2 C3 D1 D2 E F1 F2 G H J1 K1 L M1 M2 N O P Q R1 R2 S1 S2 T1 T2 W Z(b,c,d,e,f,h,i,j,k,l,m,o,p,q,r,s)
Emergency Action, Agency, Advocacy, Legal Aid undertaken, Legal Aid Franchise and Member of Accident Line
Ptr: Klingher, Mr Bernard . . . . Aug 1997
Mayo, Mr John . . . . Mar 1986
Smith, Mr Nigel P . . . . *Jan 1983
Ast: Choudhury, Mr Asif . . . . Oct 2006

CAULKER & CO ‡
Suite 25 Millmead Business Centre Millmead Road London N17 9QU
Tel: 020 8801 9020 *Fax:* 020 8885 2536
E-mail: caulkerco@aol.com

CAULKER & OZKUTAN ‡
Meridan Centre Unit 17 London E8 4DG
Tel: 020 7241 0759

BRYAN CAVE ‡
88 Wood Street London EC2V 7AJ
Tel: 020 7207 1100 *Fax:* 020 7207 1881
List of partners: D M Arboneaux, C H Attlee, R J Cowper, A Esslinger, A N Fiducia, P E Hauser, S Linton, R J Stewart, R Wieder
Work: A3 B1 B3 C1 C2 C3 E F1 F2 I J1 M1 M2 N O Q R2 S2 T1 T2 U1 U2 W Z(b,c,d,e,f,i,j,k,l,o,p,y,za)
Ptr: Arboneaux, Mrs Dyke Morris JD. . . . . *Aug 1995
Attlee, Mr Charles H . . . . *§Jul 1981
Cowper, Mr Roderick J MA(Cantab) TSB Articled Clerk Award . . . . *Sep 1984
Esslinger, Ms Anita JD; BSFS. . . . . *Jan 2003
Fiducia, Mr Anthony N BA(Hons) . . . . *Nov 1978
Hauser, Mr Paul Edward . . . . *Jan 1995
Linton, Ms Sarah BA . . . . *Sep 1994
Stewart, Mr Richard Jason BA(Hons)(Kent) . . . . . . *Dec 1980
Wieder, Mr Robert LLB(Hons); MCIArb . . . . Nov 1981
Asoc: Ashman, Ms Amy BA . . . . *Mar 2005
Assi, Gupinder LLB . . . . *Mar 1999
Cherryman, Ms Tracey SD; BA . . . . Apr 2002
Cox, Ms Johanne BSc; MSc; CPE; LPC; PGDip; ICA . *Jun 2005
Dougans, Mr Robert BA(Hons)(Oxon)(History) . . . . *Sep 2007
Hart, Mr Andrew LLB(Hons). . . . . *Sep 2001
Hodgins, Ms Neelam LLB . . . . *Mar 2002
Pepper, Ms Charlotte LPC; CPE; MA . . . . *Sep 2004
Unsworth, Ms Estelle Leona LLB . . . . *Nov 1996
Wanambwa, Mr Edward. . . . . Oct 2003
Ast: Saideman, Mr Jeremy BA; MA(Cantab) . . . . *Apr 1994
Con: Crawley, Miss Fiona LLB(Leics); LLM(Cantab). . . . *§Oct 1980
Gorst, Mr Jonathan LLB. . . . . *Apr 1980
Marlow, Mr Edward MA . . . . *Apr 1980
Slaters, Mr Michael CPE; BA . . . . *Aug 1996

CAVELL SOLICITORS LLP ‡
10-12 Whitechapel Road Tower Hamlets London E1 1EW
Tel: 020 7426 5520 *Fax:* 020 7539 1972
Dx: 40912 BETHNAL GREEN
E-mail: admin@covellsolicitors.co.uk
Languages: Arabic, Bengali, Hindi, Punjabi, Spanish, Urdu
Work: B1 G J1 K1 K3 M4 S1 V W Z(i)
Emergency Action and Fixed Fee Interview undertaken

CAVENDISH LAW ‡
52 Berkeley Square Mayfair London W1J 5BT
Tel: 020 7495 2188 *Fax:* 020 3174 0509
E-mail: remi@cavendish-law.com

CAVENDISH LAW ‡
9 Devonshire Square London EC2M 4YF
Tel: 020 7147 9974
E-mail: cwalker@cavendishlaw.co.uk

CAYTON & CO ‡
150 Minories London EC3N 1LS
Tel: 020 7264 2242 *Fax:* 020 7264 2243
E-mail: cayton@caytonslaw.com

CEDARS & CO ‡
99 Eltham High Street Eltham Greenwich London SE9 1TD
Tel: 020 8331 6161 *Fax:* 020 8850 7822 *Dx:* 32512 ELTHAM
E-mail: info@cedarsandcosolicitors.com
List of partners: P Kobi-Fordah, S V Koranteng
Languages: Fanti, Twi
Work: S1 S2
Ptr: Kobi-Fordah, Mr Paul . . . . *Mar 2000
Koranteng, Mr Samuel Victor LLB. . . . . *Sep 1997

CENTRAL LAW PRACTICE ‡
4-6 Staple Inn Holborn Bars London WC1V 7QH
Tel: 020 3051 2187 *Fax:* 020 3051 2188
E-mail: info@clpsolicitors.com
Ast: Shafeeque, Mr Muhammad . . . . .Jul 2005

CHABRA CASS & CO ‡
149 Cricklewood Broadway Brent London NW2 3HY
Tel: 020 8450 9833 / 8452 2200 *Fax:* 020 8452 6749
Dx: 35363 CRICKLEWOOD
Emergency telephone 020 8480 9833
E-mail: chabracass@dsl.pipex.com
List of partners: S Cass, A Chabra
Languages: French
Work: G H
Emergency Action, Agency, Advocacy and Legal Aid undertaken
Ptr: Cass, Mr Stephen MA(Oxon) . . . . *Jul 1969
Chabra, Ashley . . . . *Jun 1980
Con: Daly, Mr John M. *Jan 1979

CHADBOURNE & PARKE ‡
Regis House 45 King William Street London EC4R 9AN
Tel: 020 7337 8000
List of partners: A J Congdon
Ptr: Congdon, Mr Adrian John. . . . . Mar 1990

CHADWYCK-HEALEY & CO ‡
244-249 Temple Chambers Temple Avenue London EC4Y 0DT
Tel: 020 7353 6900 *Fax:* 020 7353 6911
Emergency telephone 020 7353 6900
E-mail: mail@chadwyckhealey.co.uk
List of partners: N G Chadwyck-Healey
Languages: Cantonese, French, Mandarin
Work: B2 G H
Agency, Legal Aid undertaken and Legal Aid Franchise
SPr: Chadwyck-Healey, Mr Nicholas Gerald . . . . Nov 1982
Asoc: Moreton, Mr James BA . . . . *Oct 1990
Ast: Arunachalam, Miss Ailimarie . . . . Oct 1996
Conley, Mr Richard David LLB. . . . . *Sep 2000
Crome, Mr Paul LLB . . . . *Nov 1997
de Sousa, Miss Shazmeen LLM. . . . . Sep 1999

CHAMBERS RUTLAND & CRAUFORD ‡
845d High Road Finchley London N12 8PT
Tel: 020 8446 2777 *Fax:* 020 8446 3223 *Dx:* 152742 FINCHLEY 3
E-mail: legal@chambersrutland.co.uk
List of partners: D M Dunn, B J Thorne
Work: D1 E K1 L Q S1 W
Emergency Action, Agency, Advocacy, Legal Aid undertaken and Legal Aid Franchise
Ptr: Dunn, Mr David M. . . . . *Dec 1978
Thorne, Miss Barbara J LLB(Lond) . . . . *May 1981
Con: Wilton, Mr Robert C LLB(Lond) . . . . *Dec 1970

JAMES CHAN & CO ‡
First Floor 107-111 Fleet Street London EC4A 2AB
Tel: 0844 848 9988 *Fax:* 0844 991 1189
E-mail: law@chanlegal.com
List of partners: J C P Chan
Languages: Mandarin
Work: C1 C2 E J1 O
Agency and Fixed Fee Interview undertaken
SPr: Chan, Mr James C P LLB ♦ Privy Council Agent. . . *Nov 1991

CHAN NEILL SOLICITORS ‡
107 Charterhouse Street London EC1M 6PT
Tel: 020 7253 7781 *Fax:* 020 7253 7785
Dx: 138788 CLERKENWELL
E-mail: enquiries@cnsolicitors.com

CHANCERY CS SOLICITORS ‡
1a Landor Road Clapham Common London SW9 9RX
Tel: 020 7737 6379 *Fax:* 020 7274 0009
Dx: 53253 CLAPHAM COMMON

THE CHANCERY PARTNERSHIP SOLICITORS ‡
Lower Ground 4 Kings Bench Walk Temple London EC4Y 7DL
Tel: 020 7822 8840 *Fax:* 020 7822 8841
Dx: 409 LONDON/CHANCERY LN
E-mail: contact@tcplegal.com

CHANCERY SOLICITORS ‡
The Chandlery 50 Westminster Bridge Road London SE1 7QY
Tel: 020 7754 5455 *Fax:* 020 7900 6500
E-mail: info@chancerysolicitors.com

CHAPEL COURT SOLICITORS ‡
1 Chapel Court London SE1 1HH
Tel: 020 7378 8726 *Fax:* 020 7407 8835
E-mail: info@chapelcourtsolicitor.com

CHARLES RUSSELL LLP ‡
5 Fleet Place London EC4M 7RD
Tel: 020 7203 5000 *Fax:* 020 7203 0200
Dx: 19 LONDON/CHANCERY LN
E-mail: enquiries@charlesrussell.co.uk
List of partners: H E Adlard, S T Anticoni, N Armstrong, M P Bennett, D H Berry, R H Blower, M Bradshaw, H S Brooks, I J Brothwood, R W Bynoe, S L Carter, L Y Clark, A Clason, S Code, P A E Coles, R Collins, I J Cooke, M Cover, S J Cozens, E D Craig, P A Critchley, A L Crowe, T R Cullen, D M Davidson, S A Davies, M M Davis, C A Drew, G L Duncan, P M Elliott, D W Elson, J H Fletcher, R P H Fordyce, T W Galloway, P Gearon, S A Gilbert, P Glynn, K Gordon, D J S Green, W P Harriman, S Hey, S D Higgins, R Highmore, J D Holder, C Hopewell, D J Horner, G Howell, N S Hurley, T Jenkins, G W Jordan, A Keepin, T S Lall, D Lamont, V Lanni, E Lecchi, P D M Levaggi, W F Longrigg, S J Marriott, A G A Mayer, S J McMenemy, M A C Moncreiffe, N J Morton, R W F Norton, J Owers, C J Page, S Pallister, B Palmer, R Partridge, B G Peerless, W J Perry, N J Pidgeon, J J Pierce, R T W Pierce, L J Povey, K M Powell, M Powner, D H Reissner, T Roberts, F R S Rundall, C P Russell, P J Russell, J A Saiban, D Savage, P D Scandrett, J M E Scott, E A Shelton, A K Slatter, A Solomon, G Sparks, A Stevens, M C B Syed, J R H Sykes, G Tombolis, M A Tyson, R A Vallance, K Weber
Office: Cambridge, Cheltenham, Guildford, Oxford
Work: A1 A3 B1 C1 C2 C3 D1 E I J1 K1 K2 K3 L M1 M2 N O P Q R1 R2 S1 T1 T2 U1 U2 W Z(b,c,d,e,f,h,i,j,k,l,n,o,p,q,r,w,z,za)
Agency undertaken
Ptr: Anticoni, Ms Sarah T LLB. . . . . *Feb 1988
Armstrong, Mr Nick . . . . *Dec 1986
Bennett, Mr Michael P LLB . . . . *§Jun 1974
Berry, Mr David H LLB . . . . *Nov 1985
Blower, Mr Robert H LLB; MA. . . . . *Dec 1991
Bradshaw, Mr Micheal LLB(Hons). . . . . *Oct 1998
Brooks, Miss Helen Sarah LLB . . . . *Nov 1996
Bynoe, Mr Robin W BA(Oxon). . . . . *§Jul 1973
Carter, Mr Stephen L BA(Dunelm); ACIArb . . . . . . *Apr 1980
Clark, Miss Louise Y BA. . . . . *Oct 1986
Clason, Mr Andrew MA(Cantab). . . . . Nov 1997
Code, Ms Stephanie LLB . . . . *Dec 1990
Coles, Mr Peter A E BA. . . . . *Jun 1976
Collins, Mr Richard BA(Hons); CPE; LPC . . . . *Sep 1996
Cooke, Mr Ian James MA . . . . *Apr 1993
Cover, Mr Michael LLB; Accredited CEO Mediator (CEDR); FCIArb . . . . Dec 1988
Cozens, Ms Susan J BA . . . . *Nov 1990
Craig, Mr Edward D. . . . . *Nov 1998
Crowe, Miss Amanda L LLB. . . . . *Apr 1978
Cullen, Mr Timothy R . . . . *Nov 1970
Davidson, Mr David M LLB(Edin) . . . . *Nov 1972
Davies, Mr Simon Alan . . . . *Apr 1995
Duncan, Mr George L MA(Oxon); PhD(Lond); ATII . . *Oct 1984
Fletcher, Mr John Holisey . . . . Sep 1997
Galloway, Mr Timothy William . . . . Nov 1996
Gilbert, Mr Simon A MA(Oxon) . . . . *Sep 1983
Glynn, Ms Philippa . . . . *Mar 1994
Gordon, Mr Keir. . . . . Aug 1991
Green, Mr David J S LLB(Lond). . . . . *Mar 1978
Harriman, Mr W Paul BA; LLB(Dublin). . . . . *§Dec 1973
Hey, Mr Stewart. *Oct 1995
Higgins, Ms Sarah D BA(Oxon); CPE . . . . *§Oct 1988
Highmore, Mr Robert MA(Cantab). . . . . *Oct 1982
Holder, Mr James D MA(Cantab) . . . . *Nov 1978
Hopewell, Mr Clive BA(Hons) . . . . *Nov 1994
Horner, Mr David J LLB . . . . *Jul 1975
Howell, Mr Grant LLB; MBA(Legal Practice). . . . . . *Jun 1980
Hurley, Mr Nicholas Simon BA . . . . *Oct 1995
Keepin, Mr Alexander LLB(Hons) . . . . Sep 1998
Lall, Mr Tarlochan S LLB(Hons); LLM; FTII . . . . . . *Aug 1990
Lamont, Mr Duncan MA(Cantab); Dip International Copyright Law. . . . . *Aug 1990
Lanni, Mr Vincenzo BA(Hons). . . . . *Jan 1998
Lecchi, Ms Emanuela MA; LLM; MSc . . . . *Sep 1997
Longrigg, Mr William F BA . . . . *Oct 1987
Marriott, Mrs Suzanne Jane BA(Hons); AKC. . . . . . *Nov 1996
Moncreiffe, Mr Mark A C MA(Cantab); Licence en Droit Europeen(Brussels). . . . . *Apr 1978
Owers, Ms Joanne BSc(Hons); LLM. . . . . *Sep 1995
Palmer, Mr Brian . . . . *Oct 1990
Partridge, Mr Robert LLB . . . . *May 1978
Peerless, Mr Bartholomew Guy BA(Hons). . . . . . . *Jun 1995
Perry, Mr William John PhD; MA(Oxon); FRSA; MCIArb; MCMI; MACTAPS . . . . *Dec 1977
Pierce, Ms Jennifer J BA . . . . *Mar 1987
Povey, Miss Lynn J LLB(Nott'm). . . . . *§Oct 1985
Powell, Mr Keith M . . . . *§May 1978
Powner, Mr Michael LLB(Hons) . . . . *Apr 1996
Reissner, Mr David H LLB. . . . . *Dec 1978
Roberts, Ms Tanya LLB. . . . . *Nov 1991
Russell, Mr Patrick J BA(Oxon) . . . . *May 1979
Saiban, Mr Jason A LLB; DipLP. . . . . *Feb 1998
Scott, Mr J Michael E MA(Oxon) . . . . *Dec 1978
Shelton, Ms Erica A BA . . . . *Apr 1984
Slatter, Mr Andrew Kenneth LLB . . . . *Jan 1992
Solomon, Mrs Amanda LLB(Hons) . . . . *Sep 1990
Syed, Miss Mary Catriona Balfour. . . . . *Mar 1989
Sykes, Mr John R H BA. . . . . *Sep 1989
Tombolis, Mr Glafkos LLB(Hons) . . . . Nov 1993
Vallance, Mr Richard A . . . . *Jun 1970
Weber, Mr Kris BA(Law & Accountancy). . . . . *Sep 1995
Asoc: Ahmed, Mr Pervaze LLB; MSc; LPC. . . . . Oct 1998
Bailey, Ms Bernadette. . . . . Nov 1998
Brett, Miss Victoria J LLB . . . . *Oct 1998
Butcher, Mr Tobey G . . . . *Dec 1990
Cameron, Mr Andrew W BA(Oxon) . . . . *Sep 2000
Dowden, Mr Malcolm . . . . *Dec 1994
Gandhi, Mrs Sonal LLB(Hons). . . . . *Dec 2000
Janaway, Mr Stuart BA(Hons). . . . . *Sep 1999
Rawson, Ms Edwina LLB; LLM(IP) . . . . *Sep 1999
Whitten, Miss Sarah Katharine BA(Hons) . . . . *Nov 1996
Wort, Ms Joanna . . . . *Nov 1994
Ast: Duncan, Mr Matthew Neil Richard LLB(Hons) . . . . *Sep 1998
Handley, Mr William J LLB(Sheff) . . . . *Feb 1980
Hodgson, Ms Sian . . . . *Sep 1997
Hunneyball, Ms Susan Judith BSc(Hons) . . . . *Nov 1994
Staines, Ms Julia . . . . *Oct 1997
Williams, Ms Margaret Ruth LLB(Lond) . . . . *Apr 1977
Con: Carey, Mr Peter W LLB; LLM(Masters); LSF. . . . . . *Sep 1990
Chapman, Mr Colin . . . . *Sep 1991
Crouch, Mr Richard G LLB . . . . *§Dec 1963
Fisher, Mr Ian M LLB(L'pool) . . . . Mar 1971
George, Mr Peter M C. . . . . *§Mar 1962
Lockhart, Mr Ian S MA(Cantab) . . . . *§Jun 1967
Long, Mr David E MA(Oxon) . . . . *Jul 1973
Macfadyen, Mr Michael Robert . . . . *Jun 1966
Watt, Mr Laurence J. . . . . *§Nov 1970
Wethered, Mr Simon R BA(Hons)(Oxon) . . . . *Oct 1970

CHARTWELL & SADLERS ‡
111 Asylum Road London SE15 2LB
Tel: 020 7635 5255 *Fax:* 020 7635 1616 *Dx:* 34255 PECKHAM

CHASE SOLICITORS ‡
90-92 George Lane South Woodford London E18 1JJ
Tel: 020 8989 9956 *Fax:* 020 8989 9899

CHAUNCY & CO ‡
Peek House 20 Eastcheap London EC3M 1EB
Tel: 020 7929 0330 *Fax:* 020 7929 0440
E-mail: law@chauncy.co.uk
Languages: Norwegian
Work: A3 C1 C3 F1 F2 I J1 J2 M1 M2 N O Q S1 S2 U1 U2 W Z(a,e,j,k,q,za)

CHERITH SOLICITORS LLP ‡
Ground Floor 176a Victoria Park Road London E9 7HD
Tel: 020 8986 2882

CHESHAM & CO ‡
5 Varley Parade The Hyde Barnet London NW9 6SN
Tel: 020 8205 3656
List of partners: R Goldwater, E R Shulman
Languages: Hebrew
Work: D1 E F1 G H J1 K1 L M1 P S1 W Z(i,l)
Emergency Action, Agency, Advocacy, Fixed Fee Interview, Legal Aid undertaken and Member of Accident Line
Ptr: Shulman, Mr Errol R LLB . . . . . Feb 1973

CHILD & CHILD ‡
(incorporating Pettman Smith)
14 Grosvenor Crescent Knightsbridge London SW1X 7EE
Tel: 020 7235 8000 *Fax:* 020 7235 9447
Dx: 38155 KNIGHTSBRIDGE
E-mail: info@childandchild.co.uk
List of partners: C L Allan, J A Beat, D M Briffa, G A Jones, D W McNair, M Newton, K Patel, A D K Pitcairn, K Sharif, A C Smith
Work: A3 B1 C1 C2 C3 E F1 F2 J1 J2 K1 K2 K3 L N O P Q R1 R2 S1 S2 T1 T2 W Z(b,c,e,i,k,l,p,q,r)
Emergency Action, Agency, Advocacy and Fixed Fee Interview undertaken
Ptr: Allan, Miss Claire Louise BA(Hons) . . . . . Mar 2005
Beat, Mr James Allan LLB. . . . . Jan 2007
Briffa, Mr David M. . . . . *Jun 1982
Jones, Mr Graham A LLB ♦ . . . . . *§Dec 1977
McNair, Mr Duncan William LLB(Bris) Knight of the Holy Sepulchre. . . . . *Jan 1983
Newton, Ms Marie-Garrard LLB . . . . . *Jul 1971
Patel, Mr Ketan . . . . . Sep 1997
Pitcairn, Mr Andrew Duncan Kilvert MA(Cantab). . . . Dec 1990
Sharif, Mr Khalid LLB . . . . . Jul 2005
Smith, Mr Andrew Cormac ♦ . . . . . *Jun 1977
Con: Chubb, Mr Allen Howard TEP ♦ . . . . . *§Dec 1969
Glaves-Smith, Miss Ann L LLB; BCL . . . . . Jun 1979
Leigh, Miss Mary Deborah . . . . . *Oct 1966

CHILD & CHILD ‡
79 Knightsbridge London SW1X 7RB
Tel: 020 7235 1288 *Fax:* 020 7235 9447
Dx: 38168 KNIGHTSBRIDGE

CHILDREN & FAMILIES LAW FIRM ‡
1-3 Brixton Road London SW9 6DE
Tel: 020 7582 6002 *Fax:* 020 7793 0538 *Dx:* 33256 KENNINGTON
E-mail: mail@childrenandfamilies.co.uk
List of partners: E A Bower
Languages: French, Spanish, Urdu
Work: D1 D2 H K1 K3
Emergency Action, Agency, Advocacy, Fixed Fee Interview, Legal Aid undertaken and Legal Aid Franchise
SPr: Bower, Ms Elizabeth A LLM(Public Law). . . . . *Feb 1976
Ast: Gayle, Ms Claira LLB . . . . . *Apr 2005
Con: McKiernan, Ms Fiona LLB. . . . . *Jul 1990
Newton, Ms Jennifer LLB . . . . . *Jun 1991
Thatcher, Mrs Viviane A L M T LLB . . . . . *Jan 1970

CHIPATISO & CO SOLICITORS ‡
612 Romford Road Manor Park London E12 5AF
Tel: 020 8514 9870

CHIU & BENSON ‡
23 Haymarket London SW1Y 4DG
Tel: 020 7930 1133 *Fax:* 020 7930 1188
Dx: 138416 CHARING CROSS
List of partners: M P C Chiu
Work: B1 C1 E J1 O Q Z(j,k,p)
Ptr: Chiu, Mr Michael P C . . . . . *Jun 1972

ZAMAN CHOUDHURY & CO ‡
6 Havergal Villas 538 West Green Road London N15 3DX
Tel: 020 8881 4511 *Fax:* 020 8881 5184
E-mail: zaman-choudhury@btconnect.com
List of partners: R Z Choudhury
Languages: Bengali, Hindi, Turkish, Urdu
Work: K1 M4 Q S1 S2 Z(g,i)
SPr: Choudhury, Mr Rahat Zaman BA(Hons); MA ●. . . . . Jun 1980

CHOWDHURY & CO ‡
57a Mile End Road Tower Hamlets London E1 4TT
Tel: 020 7790 6991

CHRIS SOLICITORS ‡
7-9 Woolwich New Road Greenwich London SE18 6EX
Tel: 020 8855 0903

CHRISTOFI WELLS & CO ‡
708 High Road Leytonstone London E11 3AJ
Tel: 020 8539 3123 *Fax:* 020 8556 9743 *Dx:* 58210 LEYTONSTONE
E-mail: info@cwells-law.co.uk

C P CHRISTOU LLP ‡
767 High Road North Finchley London N12 8LQ
Tel: 020 8446 6777 *Fax:* 020 8446 5774 *Dx:* 57355 FINCHLEY 1
E-mail: costas@cpchristou.com
List of partners: C P Christou, M Pavlou
Languages: French, German, Greek
Work: B1 C1 E F1 G J1 J2 K1 K2 K3 L M1 N O Q S1 S2 W Z(c,e,g,i,l,p,q)
Agency undertaken
Ptr: Christou, Mr Costas Peter LLB(B'ham) . . . . . Nov 1983
Pavlou, Miss Maria LLB(Lond). . . . . *Feb 1983
Asoc: Appell, Ms Belinda Fleur LLB(Hons). . . . . Aug 1999

CHUA'S SOLICITORS ‡
6 Breams Buildings London EC4A 1QL
Tel: 020 7242 6789 *Fax:* 020 7242 6790
Emergency telephone 07979 905839
E-mail: e.mail@chuas.co.uk
List of partners: B B Y Chua, G D Stubbert
Languages: French
Work: J1 K3 O Q S1 S2 W Z(e,f)
Agency, Advocacy and Fixed Fee Interview undertaken
Ptr: Chua, Ms Bebe B Y BA(Hons) Justice of the Peace . *Feb 1995
Stubbert, Mr Gerard D LLB(Hons) ♦. . . . . *Jun 1981
Con: Dickins, Mr Edward LLB. . . . . *Oct 1967

CHURCH & CO ‡
63a Cumberland Street London SW1V 4LY
Tel: 020 7828 4194

CHURCH LANE SOLICITORS LIMITED ‡
Office 11 Church Lane Chambers 11-12 Church Lane London E11 1HG
Tel: 020 8539 2022 *Fax:* 020 8539 8829 *Dx:* 58206 LEYTONSTONE
E-mail: info@churchlanesolicitors.co.uk

CHURCHILLS SOLICITORS ‡
Churchills House 137 Brent Street London NW4 4DJ
Tel: 020 8457 2981

CHURCHWARD & CO ‡
Lloyds Building Gallery 4 12 Leadenhall Street London EC3V 1LP
Tel: 020 7816 5442 *Fax:* 020 7068 7775
E-mail: abchurchward@dial.pipex.com

CITY LAW FINANCIAL LLP ‡
1 Kings Arms Yard London EC2R 7AF
Tel: 020 7367 0100 *Fax:* 020 7022 1592
E-mail: info@city-law.net

CITY NET LAW ‡
10 Lloyd's Avenue London EC3N 3AJ
Tel: 020 7863 6635 *Fax:* 020 7863 6797
E-mail: hughbohling@citynetlaw.com

CITYGATE SOLICITORS ‡
3a Old Montague Street London E1 5NL
Tel: 020 7375 2930 *Fax:* 020 7377 1454
Dx: 155248 TOWER HAMLETS 2
E-mail: info@citygatesolicitors.co.uk

CLAPHAM & CO ‡
799 Wandsworth Road London SW8 3JH
Tel: 020 7622 9747

GUY CLAPHAM & CO ‡
51-55 Weymouth Street London W1G 8NH
Tel: 020 7935 1095 *Fax:* 020 7935 9127 *Dx:* 83300 WEST END 2
E-mail: gc@guyclapham.com
List of partners: G R C Clapham, A M Veitch
Work: A1 B1 C1 E F1 G J1 K1 K3 K4 L N O Q R1 S1 S2 T1 W Z(c,d,e,f,i,j,k,l,p,q,r)
Emergency Action, Agency, Advocacy and Fixed Fee Interview undertaken
Ptr: Clapham, Mr Guy R C. . . . . *Jun 1979
Veitch, Mr Andrew Muir LLB; MA . . . . . *Nov 2000

CLAPHAM LAW CHAMBERS ‡
11 Bedford Road London SW4 7SH
Tel: 020 7207 1913

CLAREMONT RICHARDS ‡
12 Bridewell Place London EC4V 6AP
Tel: 020 7353 3030 *Fax:* 020 7353 9055
Dx: 375 LONDON/CHANCERY LN
E-mail: hrichards@claremontrichards.com
List of partners: S P Levine, H J Richards, V H J Yeend
Languages: Arabic, French, German, Hebrew
Work: C1 E J1 L P R1 R2 S1 S2 T1 T2 W Z(d,i,u)
Ptr: Levine, Mr Simon P LLB(Hons); LSF; TEP. . . . . *Nov 1990
Richards, Mr Howard J LLB(Soton) . . . . . *Mar 1980
Yeend, Mrs Virginia Helen Juliana BA(Hons) . . . . . *Oct 1976
Con: Harris, Mr Robert L LLB; LLM Rupert Bremner Medal *Nov 1962
Ross, Mr Howard Allen BA(Hons) . . . . . *Nov 1985

DAVID CLARK & CO ‡
38 Heath Street Hampstead London NW3 6TE
Tel: 020 7433 1562 *Fax:* 020 7433 1625
E-mail: office@davidclarkandco.co.uk
List of partners: D A Clark, D J Williamson
Languages: Afrikaans
Work: D1 G H K1 K2 S1 W
Emergency Action, Agency and Legal Aid undertaken
Ptr: Clark, Mr David A. . . . . *Jan 1975
Williamson, Mr Daniel James BA(Hons) . . . . . *Dec 1994

CLARK RICKETTS LLP ‡
Waterman House 41 Kingsway London WC2B 6TP
Tel: 020 7240 6767 *Fax:* 020 7836 0699
E-mail: aviationlaw@clarkricketts.com
List of partners: I F Clark, R A Ricketts
Work: C1 M3
Ptr: Clark, Mr Ian F LLB(Lond). . . . . *§Oct 1985
Ricketts, Mr Robert Anthony LLB; MRAeS. . . . . *Nov 1987
Ast: Chase, Mr Gordon James LLB . . . . . *Jan 2004
Crossley, Mr Robert Vaughan BCom; LLM. . . . . *Mar 2001
Hamandi, Thamer MA(Lond) . . . . . *Nov 1994

CLARKE WILLMOTT
10 Furnival Street Holborn London EC4A 1YH
Tel: 0845 209 1000 / 0117 305 6000 *Fax:* 0845 209 2514
Dx: 427 LONDON/CHANCERY LN
Office: Birmingham, Bristol, Manchester, Southampton, Taunton
Work: A1 A2 A3 B1 C1 C2 C3 E F1 F2 I J1 J2 K1 K3 L M2 N O P Q R1 R2 S1 S2 T1 T2 U2 W X Z(b,c,d,e,h,j,k,l,o,p,q,r,t,u,w,za)

CLARKSLEGAL LLP
12 Henrietta Street Covent Garden London WC2E 8LH
Tel: 020 7539 8000 *Fax:* 020 7539 8001
Dx: 138415 CHARING CROSS
E-mail: contact@clarkslegal.com
Office: Cardiff, Reading, Swansea
Work: A3 C1 C2 E J1 J2 L O P R1 R2 S1 U2 W Z(e,u)
Advocacy undertaken
Ptr: Krol, Mrs Rachel Susan LLB(Hons) Maxwell Law Prize 1976 . . . . . Apr 1980
Mem: Lapthorne, Mr Simon . . . . . *Dec 1999
Stevens, Mr Peter John LLB . . . . . *Mar 1973
Asoc: Baynton, Mr George William LLB(Leics). . . . . *Apr 1977
Ast: Dusad, Mishail . . . . . *Jan 2007
Fuller, Ms Rachel Elizabeth BA . . . . . *Apr 2001

Mackenzie Hill, Ms Rebecca . . . . . Jan 2006
Mishra, Miss Anita Jayanti LLB . . . . . *Apr 2006
Thurlow, Mr Rebecca Sarah LLB(Hons) . . . . . Sep 2004
Titchener, Jessie May. . . . . *Dec 2007

CLAUDE HORNBY & COX ‡
3rd Floor 15 Great St Thomas Apostle London EC4V 2BJ
Tel: 020 7332 8269 *Fax:* 020 7332 8270 / 7332 8271
Dx: 37211 PICCADILLY
Emergency telephone 07623 407846
E-mail: law@claudiahornbycox.fsnet.co.uk
List of partners: R S Hallam, A Moxon
Languages: French
Work: B2 G H
Emergency Action, Agency, Advocacy, Fixed Fee Interview, Legal Aid undertaken and Legal Aid Franchise
Ptr: Hallam, Mr Richard S BA(Oxon). . . . . *Oct 1986
Moxon, Mr Andrew BA; LLB; LSF . . . . . *§Nov 1994
Ast: Corcoran, Mr Dermot LLB. . . . . *Sep 2003

CLAUDINE MEYRAND ‡
89 Onslow Square London SW7 3LT
Tel: 020 7589 6468
E-mail: claudinemeyrand@googlemail.com

CLAUSEN MILLER LLP ‡
41 Eastcheap London EC3M 1DT
Tel: 020 7645 7970 *Fax:* 020 7645 7971
E-mail: jbeacham@clausen.com
List of partners: J H Beacham, N D Plant, J P Startin
Languages: German, Portuguese, Spanish
Work: A3 O Z(j,q)
Ptr: Beacham, Ms Jane H BA . . . . . Nov 1991
Plant, Mr Nigel D LLB. . . . . Apr 1981
Startin, Mr John P BA(Oxon) . . . . . Jul 1977

CLEARY GOTTLIEB STEEN & HAMILTON ‡
Level 5 City Place House 55 Basinghall Street London EC2V 5EH
Est: 1946
Tel: 020 7614 2200 *Fax:* 020 7600 1698
Work: B1 C1 C2 C3 O T1 Z(b,e)

CLEGG MANUEL ‡
26-27 Great Sutton Street Islington London EC1V 0DS
Tel: 020 7847 5600 *Fax:* 020 7608 0015 *Dx:* 53337 CLERKENWELL
E-mail: mail@cleggmanuel.co.uk
List of partners: R H M Clegg, S Manuel
Languages: Bengali, Gujarati, Hindi
Work: C1 C2 E J1 R2 S1 S2
Ptr: Clegg, Mr Richard H M MA . . . . . *Oct 1987
Manuel, Mr Simon LLB . . . . . *Oct 1987
Ast: Holden-Shah, Miss Emma. . . . . *Sep 2000
Nadarajah, Ms Pamela . . . . . Aug 2002
Uddin, Ms Roshonara LLB . . . . . *Jan 2001
Wood, Mr Simon Jonathan LLB . . . . . *Jan 2004

TIM CLEMENT-JONES ‡
10 Northbourne Road London SW4 7DJ
Tel: 020 7622 4205 *Fax:* 020 7976 1833

C L CLEMO & CO ‡
88 Copse Hill Wimbledon Common London SW20 0EF
Tel: 020 8944 1017 *Fax:* 020 8879 7027 *Dx:* 36560 RAYNES PARK
E-mail: clc@clclemo.co.uk
List of partners: C L Clemo
Work: C1 E G J1 K1 M1 M2 N O S1 W Z(c,d,f,g,i,l)
Emergency Action, Agency, Advocacy and Legal Aid undertaken
Ptr: Clemo, Mr Charles Lyn BA; LLM . . . . . *Dec 1979

F J CLEVELAND ‡
40-43 Chancery Lane London WC2A 1JQ
Tel: 020 7405 5875 *Fax:* 020 7831 0749
E-mail: mail@fjcleveland.co.uk
Languages: French, German

CLEVELAND SOLICITORS ‡
2nd-3rd Floor 234 Whitechapel Road Tower Hamlets London E1 1BJ
Tel: 020 7377 8866 *Fax:* 020 7377 8844
List of partners: M S J Davies
Ptr: Davies, Mr Marcus St J MA(Oxon) . . . . . *Sep 1981

CLIFFORD CHANCE ‡
10 Upper Bank Street London E14 5JJ
Tel: 020 7006 1000 *Fax:* 020 7006 5555
Dx: 149120 CANARY WHARF 3
List of partners: G M Abbott, R M B Baggallay, I P Bagshaw, J W Baird, A H M Bankes-Jones, J M Barlow, C J Bates, M D Bates, S Baylin, J R Beastall, J Beechey, R S M Best, D J Bickerton, P M W Blake, E L Bradley, M P Bray, O W Bretz, A M Briam, M J Brosnahan, I C Brown, K J Brunicki, M Bryceland, N E Buchan, R N Burley, J A Bush, M P Cahill, M Campbell, A J Carnegie, C S Carpenter, M J Carroll, A Cartwright, E Cavett-Dunsby, P J Charlton, D R Childs, I R F Clark, J M Clarke, S R Clinton, K A Coates, A J N Coats, C Cochrane, A L Cohen, J A Connick, J Connolly, P C E Cornell, L Cullinane, J J Curran, S M Curtis, C J D Davies, S W Davis, D Dey, S Dunlop, D Dunnigan, A J Dyson, D T Eatough, A N L Edgar, M J Edwards, A Elias, P J Elliott, J A Elman, H Evenett, N M Fletcher, J Fleury, A J Forryan, A D French, K Gibbons, C P Goodwill, M R Gossling, A T Grenville, D H Griffiths, B Hall, N J A Hamilton, D Harkness, N H Harvey, N R Hatfield, R B Hedley, D C Hepburn, P L Hertz, E M Hiester, J P Hill, K D Hodson, K T Honeywood, J R Hornby, K A Howles, N W Howorth, G O Hughes, R Hunjan, I Hunter, M R Hyde, D K Hyman, A J Inglis, K P Ingram, S T James, L A Johansen, J Johnson, S Jones, D A Jones-Parry, M G Judd, C D Jury, R Kelly, G Khehar, J P Kosky, D J Kossoff, R I Lambert, M R Layton, R H G Lee, R G Leese, A J M Levy, S P A Lew, D M Lewis, R MacVicar, R P Margree, V G Marsland, C J McAuley, M R McGillivray, P E McGowan, R P McIlwee, M McMahon, D S J Metzger, R W Moore, E R A Morony, A T Morris, M W E Morrison, H N Motani, I R Moulding, N C Munday, J Myers, M Newick, G T D Norman, R M North, A R M Nourry, G N D O'Neill, T O'Neill, C H A Oakley, J W Osborne, C C Osman, T A C Page, P A Palmer, A Panayides, D Pantelia, R Parkash, D R Pearson, C C Perrin, D N Perry, R J Pettit, B G Phillips, J F Pickston, G T Plews, S G Popham, R M Poulton, A Price, D J Pudge, N M Rees-Jones, S C Reisbach, H Robinson, R P

See p2 for the Key to Work Categories & other symbols

Rocher, A J Rolfe, S E Rose, I D Roxborough, D A Sandelson, J V Sandelson, M Saunders, R Sharples, S E Shea, A W Sheppard, N A Sherwin, R N T Short, A Signy, S Sinclair, R E Smith, M T Smyth, J D Solomon, S J Squires, T M St Clair, T R Steadman, D J Steinberg, R Stevenson, M R O Stewart, L E Stuart, S J Surgeoner, R H Sutherland, R G Sutton-Mattocks, M J Sweeting, C Swirski, P C Taylor, P D Taylor, G J Teague, B M Thomas, M R Thomas, K G Thompson, S Tinkler, R Trefny, R T Tremaine, J D Turing, P A Turner, P G Voisey, D J Walker, J Walter, N Wherity, G M White, M J Wistow, E K W Wong, C J Wyman, A S Yianni, E J Young, J M Ziff
Languages: French, German, Italian, Spanish
Work: B1 C1 C2 C3 E I J1 L M1 M2 P S2 T1 Z(b,c,e,g,h,j,o)
Member of Accident Line
Ptr: Abbott, Mrs Gabrielle M BA(Reading) Samuel Herbert Easterbrook Prize; Maurice Norden Prize; Reginald Pilkington Prize . . . *Sep 1980
Baggallay, Mr Roger M B MA(Oxon) . . . *Apr 1978
Bagshaw, Mr Ian P . . . Nov 1996
Baird, Mr James W LLB(Glasgow) Notary Public . . . Sep 1988
Bankes-Jones, Mr Anthony H M BA(Oxon) . . . *Apr 1976
Barlow, Mr James M LLB(Nott'm) . . . *Jul 1967
Bates, Mr Christopher J MA(Oxon); LLM(Columbia) . . . *Oct 1982
Bates, Mr Michael David . . . Dec 1993
Baylin, Mr Spencer . . . Oct 1995
Beastall, Mr Jonathan R LLB(B'ham) . . . *Nov 1985
Beechey, Mr John MA(Oxon) . . . *Nov 1977
Best, Mr Roger S M BA(Dunelm) . . . *Oct 1980
Bickerton, Mr David J BA(Cantab) . . . *Oct 1989
Blake, Mr Peter M W LLB(Lond) . . . *Jan 1980
Bradley, Mr Edward L MA(Cantab) . . . Oct 1983
Bray, Mr Michael P LLB(L'pool) . . . *Aug 1972
Bretz, Mr Oliver Werner . . . Oct 1996
Briam, Mr Anthony M MA(Cantab) . . . *Apr 1974
Brosnahan, Mr Michael John . . . Mar 2001
Brown, Mr I Claude BA . . . *Aug 1993
Brunicki, Kazimierz J LLB(Lond) . . . *May 1977
Bryceland, Mr Michael . . . Sep 1998
Buchan, Ms Nina Elizabeth BA(Dunelm) . . . *Nov 1992
Burley, Mr Robert N LLB(Wales) Sir Samuel Evans Memorial Prize . . . *Mar 1983
Bush, Miss Jane A LLB(Exon) . . . Sep 1982
Cahill, Mr Matthew Patrick . . . Dec 1992
Campbell, Mr Mark MA(Oxon) . . . *Oct 1984
Carnegie, Mr Andrew J LLB(Newc) . . . *Dec 1983
Carpenter, Mr Clive S BCL; MA(Oxon) . . . *Sep 1981
Carroll, Mr Mark J LLB . . . Oct 1986
Cartwright, Mr Adrian . . . Nov 1992
Cavett-Dunsby, Ms Esther BA . . . *Oct 1993
Charlton, Mr Peter J LLB(Lond) . . . *Apr 1981
Childs, Mr David R LLM(Lond) Daniel Reardon Prize; Reginald Pilkington Prize . . . *Oct 1976
Clark, Ms Imogen Rebecca Frances . . . Jan 1992
Clarke, Miss Julia M MA(Oxon) . . . May 1989
Clinton, Mr Simon R LLB(Exon) . . . Jan 1991
Coates, Mrs Katherine A BA(Oxon) . . . *Nov 1983
Coats, Mr Andrew J N BA(Oxon) . . . Apr 1990
Cochrane, Mr Charles . . . Nov 1995
Cohen, Mr Adrian L . . . Jun 1996
Connick, Mr Jeremy A LLB . . . *Nov 1988
Connolly, Mr John . . . May 1999
Cornell, Mr Peter C E BA(Exon) . . . Oct 1978
Cullinane, Mr Lee LLB(Lond) . . . *Oct 1988
Curran, Mr John Joseph . . . May 1991
Curtis, Mr Stephen Marc . . . Apr 1993
Davies, Mr Christopher J D LLB(Leics) . . . Oct 1991
Davis, Mr Simon W MA . . . Nov 1984
Dey, Debashis . . . Mar 1998
Dunlop, Mr Stewart . . . Sep 1991
Dunnigan, Mr David LLB(Nott'm) . . . *Oct 1986
Dyson, Mr Arthur John . . . Nov 1988
Eatough, Mr David T . . . Apr 1993
Edgar, Mr Andrew N L LLB(Lond) . . . *Jan 1981
Edwards, Mr Michael J LLB(Hull) . . . *Nov 1983
Elias, Mr Alan LLB(Lond) . . . *Jul 1980
Elliott, Mr Peter J Charles Steele Prize . . . *Dec 1975
Elman, Mr Jonathan A BA(Nott'm); ATII . . . Apr 1987
Evenett, Mrs Hilary BA(Oxon) . . . Sep 1990
Fletcher, Mr Nicholas M LLB(Bris) ♦ . . . *Apr 1987
Fleury, Mr Joachim . . . Jan 1985
Forryan, Mr Andrew J MA(Cantab) . . . Feb 1986
French, Mr A Douglas BA(Oxon); ATII . . . Apr 1981
Gibbons, Ms Kate LLB(Lond) . . . Oct 1983
Goodwill, Mr Christopher P LLB(Lancs); LLM(Cantab) Sweet & Maxwell Law Prize (University of Lancaster) . . . *Oct 1988
Gossling, Ms Margaret R BA(Oxon) . . . Oct 1986
Grenville, Mr Andrew T MA(Cantab) . . . Dec 1986
Griffiths, Mr David Hugh . . . May 1983
Hall, Mr Brian LLB; DMA; ACIS(Lond) . . . *Apr 1980
Hamilton, Mr Nigel J A LLB(Soton) . . . *Oct 1983
Harkness, Mr David LLB(Sheff) . . . Apr 1985
Harvey, Mr Neil H MA(Cantab) . . . *Apr 1977
Hatfield, Mr Nigel Royston . . . Apr 1994
Hedley, Mr R Bruce BSc(Econ); LLM(Lond) . . . *Oct 1988
Hepburn, Mr Daniel C BA(Oxon) . . . Dec 1992
Hertz, Mr Philip Lee . . . Oct 1993
Hiester, Mrs Elizabeth M LLB(Manc); Dip European Integration(Amsterdam) . . . *Apr 1982
Hill, Mr J Philip BA(Oxon) . . . Aug 1991
Hodson, Miss Karen D BSc(Nott'm) . . . Oct 1989
Honeywood, Miss Kathleen T LLB(Lond) . . . *Oct 1989
Hornby, Mr John R BSc(Cantab) ♦ . . . Dec 1989
Howles, Ms Katharine A BA(Oxon) Charles Steele Prize; Travers Smith Scholarship . . . Apr 1980
Howorth, Mr Nigel William . . . May 1996
Hughes, Mr Geraint Owen . . . Oct 1991
Hunjan, Ranbir . . . Nov 1992
Hunter, Mr Iain BA . . . May 1992
Hyde, Mr Mark R LLB(B'ham) . . . *Mar 1984
Hyman, Mr D Keith MA(Cantab) . . . *Nov 1988
Inglis, Mr Alan J LLB(B'ham) . . . Dec 1985
Ingram, Mr Kevin P . . . Nov 1991
James, Mr Simon T BA(Oxon) . . . *Oct 1983
Johansen, Mrs Lynn A MA(Cantab) . . . *Dec 1985
Johnson, Mr James . . . Nov 1987
Jones, Mr Sarah . . . Nov 1994
Jones-Parry, Mr David A LLB(Bris) . . . Feb 1979
Judd, Mr Matthew Geoffrey . . . Jun 1994
Jury, Ms Caroline Denise . . . Dec 1990
Kelly, Mrs Rachael LLB . . . *Feb 1987
Khehar, Miss Geeta LLB(Leics) . . . Nov 1990
Kosky, Mr Jeremy Paul . . . Oct 1992
Kossoff, Mr Daniel J BA(Dunelm)(Econ) . . . *Nov 1982
Lambert, Mr Robert I BA(Oxon) . . . *Nov 1989
Layton, Mr Matthew R LLB(Leeds) . . . Feb 1986
Lee, Mr Robert H G LLB(Exon) . . . Apr 1990
Leese, Mr Roger G LLB(Oxon) . . . Oct 1990
Levy, Mr Adrian Joseph Morris . . . May 1995
Lew, Mr Simon P A BA(Cantab) . . . Oct 1986
Lewis, Mr David Mark . . . Apr 1996
McAuley, Mr Clifford J BA; BCL . . . *Nov 1987
McGillivray, Mr M Roderick BA(Cantab) . . . *Oct 1984
McGowan, Mr Peter E . . . Aug 1992
McIlwee, Mr Richard P LLB(Lond) . . . Dec 1989
McMahon, Ms Maryann . . . Jul 1994
MacVicar, Mr Robert LLB(Oxon) . . . Apr 1979
Margree, Mr Richard Paul . . . Dec 1990
Marsland, Miss Vanessa G MA(Cantab) . . . Nov 1981
Metzger, Mr David S J MA(Cantab) . . . *Sep 1992
Moore, Mr Roger W LLM(Lond) . . . *Oct 1979
Morony, Ms Elizabeth Rachel Anne . . . Oct 1989
Morris, Mr A Timothy MA(Oxon) . . . *Nov 1982
Morrison, Mr Mark W E LLB; BCL(Oxon) . . . *Nov 1983
Motani, Habib N MA(Cantab) . . . *Oct 1980
Moulding, Mr Ian R BA . . . Nov 1989
Munday, Mr Nicholas C BA . . . *Dec 1985
Myers, Mr Jonny . . . Sep 1988
Newick, Mr Matthew ♦ . . . Jan 1993
Norman, Mr Guy T D BSc(Lond) . . . Dec 1991
North, Mr R Murray MA(Oxon) . . . *Dec 1987
Nourry, Ms Alexandre R M LLB(Hull); LLM(Exon) . . . *Nov 1984
O'Neill, Mr Gerald Nicholas Doyle . . . Dec 1990
O'Neill, Mr Terry ♦ . . . Jan 1978
Oakley, Mr Christopher H A BA(Oxon) . . . *Mar 1983
Osborne, Mr John W LLB(Bris); LLM(LSE) . . . *Nov 1973
Osman, Mr Christopher C LLB(Soton) . . . *Jun 1976
Page, Mr Timothy A C LLB . . . *Apr 1989
Palmer, Mr Phillip A BA . . . *Nov 1984
Panayides, Mr Alexandros . . . Nov 1995
Pantelia, Ms Despina . . . Nov 1987
Parkash, Rajiv MA(Cantab) . . . *Oct 1982
Pearson, Mr David R BA(Cantab) . . . *Nov 1986
Perrin, Chris C BA(Oxon) . . . *Dec 1982
Perry, Mr Damian N . . . Aug 1991
Pettit, Mr Richard J LLB(Bris) . . . §Mar 1971
Phillips, Bleddyn G . . . Oct 1998
Pickston, Mr John F BA . . . Apr 1983
Plews, Mr George Timothy MA(Cantab) . . . *Jan 1988
Popham, Mr Stuart G LLB(Soton) . . . *§Apr 1978
Poulton, Mr R Mark LLB(Nott'm) . . . Mar 1990
Price, Ms Alison MA(Cantab) . . . *Nov 1983
Pudge, Mr David J LLB(Oxon) . . . May 1990
Rees-Jones, Mr N Mark MA; LLB(Cantab) . . . *Nov 1981
Reisbach, Mr Stephen C MA(Cantab) . . . *Apr 1978
Robinson, Mr Hywel . . . Sep 1996
Rocher, Mr R Philip LLB(B'ham) . . . *§Apr 1981
Rolfe, Mr Andrew J LLB(Nott'm) . . . Feb 1980
Rose, Ms Susan Elizabeth . . . Oct 1993
Roxborough, Mr Iain D LLB(Lond); LLM(Cantab) ♦ . . . *Jul 1986
Sandelson, Mr Daniel A BA(Oxon) . . . *Oct 1984
Sandelson, Mr Jeremy V MA(Cantab) . . . Apr 1981
Saunders, Mr Martin . . . Apr 1991
Sharples, Mr Richard . . . Sep 1992
Shea, Mr Stephen E BA(Oxon) . . . Apr 1985
Sheppard, Audley W LLB; LLM . . . *Jan 1990
Sherwin, Mr Nicholas A MA(Cantab); LLM; ATII Maxwell Law Prize . . . Nov 1986
Short, Mr Rodney N T MBA . . . *Dec 1970
Signy, Mr Adam BA(Sussex) . . . *Apr 1982
Sinclair, Mr Simon . . . Oct 1993
Smith, Mr Robert E . . . *Nov 1976
Smyth, Mr Michael T MA(Cantab) . . . *Oct 1982
Solomon, Mr Jonathan D LLB(Warw) . . . *Jan 1987
Squires, Ms Sarah J LLB(Nott'm) . . . *Nov 1991
St Clair, Ms Teresa Moss . . . Jan 2000
Steadman, Mr Timothy R BA(Oxon) . . . *§Apr 1978
Steinberg, Mr David J BA . . . *Nov 1988
Stevenson, Ms Ruth . . . Nov 1992
Stewart, Mr Mark R O LLB(Bris) . . . Oct 1983
Stuart, Ms Laura Elizabeth . . . Aug 1998
Surgeoner, Mr Stephen John . . . Oct 1994
Sutherland, Ms Rosemary Helen . . . *Feb 1994
Sutton-Mattocks, Mr Richard G BA(Oxon) . . . *Sep 1985
Sweeting, Mr Malcolm J BA(Lond) . . . *Oct 1981
Swirski, Ms Clare BSc(Hons); PhD; LSF(Hons) . . . *Nov 1994
Taylor, Mr Peter C LLB(Bris) . . . *Apr 1980
Taylor, Mr Peter D LLB(B'ham) . . . Nov 1984
Teague, Mr Gavin J BA; MA . . . Oct 1989
Thomas, Mr Barry M BA(Warw) . . . *Jun 1976
Thomas, Miss Marian R MA(Oxon) . . . *Apr 1977
Thompson, Mr Kevin G . . . Apr 1992
Tinkler, Mr Simon . . . Jan 1993
Trefny, Mr Robert . . . Aug 1999
Tremaine, Mr Robin T MA(Cantab) . . . *Jan 1987
Turing, Mr J Dermot MA(Cantab); PhD(Oxon) . . . Jul 1991
Turner, Mr Paul A MA(Cantab); Former Barrister . . . *Jan 1987
Voisey, Mr Peter G MA(Cantab) . . . Apr 1987
Walker, Mr David James . . . Oct 1993
Walter, Mr Jeremy . . . Apr 1991
Wherity, Ms Nicola . . . Oct 1994
White, Mr Geoffrey M LLM; LLB; BComm(Melbourne) . . . *Jan 1977
Wistow, Mr Michael J LLB(Manc) . . . Sep 1990
Wong, Etienne K W LLB(Bris) . . . Jan 1991
Wyman, Mr Christopher J MA(Cantab) . . . *Apr 1981
Yianni, Mr Andrew S BSc(Bris); MA(Toronto) . . . *Oct 1986
Young, Mrs Elizabeth J BA(Cantab) . . . *Oct 1982
Ziff, Mr Joel Meade BA . . . *Dec 1993
Ast: Anderson, Mr James . . . Sep 1996
Butters, Mr James Sebastian . . . Oct 1993
Cheong Tung Sing, Ms Jane Christina . . . Aug 1998
Crosse, Ms Katrina Louise . . . Mar 1996
Davies, Mr Robert Leighton . . . Nov 1995
Grigg, Mr Matthew . . . Apr 1998
Howell, Mr Roderick James . . . Apr 2003
Khan, Mr Faizal . . . Sep 1999
McCormick, Kari . . . Jul 2001
Stewart, Mr Anthony Peter . . . Sep 1997

CLIFFORD HARRIS & CO ‡

PO Box 4UA 51 Welbeck Street London W1A 4UA
Tel: 020 7486 0031 *Fax:* 020 7486 3333
E-mail: sv@cliffordharris.co.uk
List of partners: J A Crighton, D Dionissiou, M F Selwood, S Varma
Languages: French, German, Greek, Italian, Spanish
Work: B1 C1 C2 J1 K1 K3 L M1 M2 N O P Q R2 S1 T1 W Z(i,k,l,q)
Emergency Action and Agency undertaken
Ptr: Crighton, Mr James Alexander LLB(Hons) . . . Oct 2002
Dionissiou, Mr Demetris LLB(Hons) . . . Oct 2000
Selwood, Mr Martin F . . . *Nov 1984
Varma, Sunil . . . *Dec 1983

CLINTON DAVIS PALLIS ‡

47a Tottenham Lane London N8 9BD
Tel: 020 8880 5000 *Fax:* 020 8806 9089 *Dx:* 35952 CROUCH END
Emergency telephone 07767 497423
E-mail: howardpallis@clintondavispallis.co.uk
Work: G H L N Q R1 S1 W Z(i,l)

CLINTONS ‡

55 Drury Lane Covent Garden London WC2B 5RZ
Tel: 020 7379 6080 *Fax:* 020 7240 9310
Dx: 40021 COVENT GARDEN 1
E-mail: info@clintons.co.uk
Languages: French, Hebrew, Italian
Work: B1 C1 D1 E F1 G J1 K1 K2 L M1 N P R1 S1 T1 W Z(b,c,d,e,f,g,i,j,k,o,w)

CLORE & CO ‡

Hamilton House Mabledon Place London WC1H 9BB
Tel: 020 8922 0563 *Fax:* 020 8248 2663
Dx: 33803 GOLDERS GREEN

CLYDE & CO LLP ‡

See entry for Barlow Lyde & Gilbert

ERIC COATES ‡

6-8 Cole Street London SE1 4YH
Tel: 020 7720 3278

GARTH COATES SOLICITORS ‡

Gainsborough House 81 Oxford Street London W1D 2EN
Tel: 020 7993 6299
E-mail: garth@garthcoates.com

COBBETTS LLP

70 Gray's Inn Road London WC1X 8BT
Tel: 0845 404 2404 *Fax:* 0845 404 4144
E-mail: enquiries@cobbetts.com
Office: Birmingham, Leeds, Manchester

COBHAM SOLICITORS ‡

5 Hillgate Street Notting Hill Gate London W8 7SP

COFFEY GRAHAM LLP ‡

1-6 Yarmouth Place London W1J 7BU
Tel: 020 3145 1170
E-mail: info@coffeygraham.com

DANIELLE COHEN SOLICITORS ‡

Unit 4 Stucley Place London NW1 8NS
Tel: 020 7267 4133

DAVID COHEN & CO ‡

17 Mayfield Gardens London NW4 2PY
Tel: 020 8202 8937 *Fax:* 020 8202 8937

JULIAN COHEN ‡

67 Athenaeum Road London N20 9AL
Tel: 020 3016 3935
E-mail: julian@juliancohen.co.uk

LIZ COHEN SOLICITOR ‡

23 Midhurst Avenue London N10 3EP
Tel: 020 8444 4003

COLDHAM SHIELD & MACE ‡

123-127 Station Road Chingford London E4 6AG
Tel: 020 8524 6323 *Fax:* 020 8529 8390 *Dx:* 37850 CHINGFORD 2
E-mail: info@csmlaw.co.uk
List of partners: L E Ashworth, R C Ellis, T R I Lindop
Work: C1 E J1 K1 K2 L N O Q S1 S2 W
Legal Aid Franchise and Member of Accident Line
Ptr: Ellis, Mr Richard C . . . *Dec 1977
Lindop, Mrs Tessa R I . . . Feb 1983
Ast: Blatcher, Ms Paula LLB . . . *May 1994
Kayani, Mr Jan . . . Nov 2001
Stride, Mrs Susan Rosemary . . . Sep 2001
Wright, Mr Neil LLB . . . *May 1982

COLE ASSOCIATES ‡

3 Grosvenor Street London W1K 4PU
Tel: 020 7958 9370

COLLINS BENSON GOLDHILL LLP ‡

26-28 Great Portland Street Westminster London W1W 8QT
Tel: 020 7436 5151 *Fax:* 020 7436 6122 *Dx:* 82973 MAYFAIR
E-mail: cbg@cbglaw.co.uk
List of partners: S Hsu, N Rajani, J W Roberts, P W Ruchniewicz, J F Thorby
Work: B1 C1 J1 O S2 W Z(w)
Ptr: Hsu, Sammi . . . *May 1999
Rajani, Miss Nina LLB(Lond) . . . *Nov 2001
Roberts, Mr Jeffrey William BA; MSPI . . . *Mar 1983
Ruchniewicz, Mr Peter Waclaw LLB(Lond) . . . *Dec 1979
Thorby, Mr James Frederick BA . . . Oct 1999
Ast: Evans, Mr Richard BA(Hons); LLM . . . Dec 2004
Gant, Miss Philippa . . . Jun 2005
Harris-Hughes, Mr Edward . . . May 2007
Con: Messer, Mr Laurence BA(Hons) . . . *Jun 1974

COLLINS LONG ‡

24 Pepper Street Southwark London SE1 0EB
Tel: 020 7401 9800 *Fax:* 020 7401 9850
E-mail: info@collinslong.com
List of partners: J Collins, S A Long, S Waddington
Work: C1 O Q Z(e,f)
Emergency Action and Fixed Fee Interview undertaken
Ptr: Collins, Mr James LLB(Hons) . . . *Apr 1993
Long, Mr Simon A BA . . . *Apr 1981
Waddington, Miss Sarah LLB(Hons) . . . *Dec 1995
Ast: Whitington, Mr Dan LLB(Hons) . . . Jan 2000
Con: Benedict, Mr John C LLB; FRSA . . . *May 1979

COLLIS & CO ‡
19c Tooting High Street Tooting Wandsworth London SW17 0SN
Tel: 020 8767 3332 *Fax:* 020 8767 9333
Dx: 58852 TOOTING SOUTH
E-mail: info@collisf.plus.com
List of partners: F Collis
Work: E S1 W
Ptr: Collis, Ms Frances BA . . . . *Nov 1983

JOHN COLLIS SOLICITORS ‡
64 Clifton Street London EC2A 4HB
Tel: 020 7539 6690 *Fax:* 020 7539 6620 *Dx:* 515 LONDON/CITY

COLLYER BRISTOW LLP ‡
4 Bedford Row London WC1R 4DF
Tel: 020 7242 7363 *Fax:* 020 7405 0555
Dx: 163 LONDON/CHANCERY LN
E-mail: cblaw@collyerbristow.com
List of partners: C Algar, J C Armstrong-Fox, J Cohen, J M Czyzowski, A Dixon, M J Drake, O Drennan, S Fazio, D A P Giacon, T Goodman, E Graham, V Greig, S Heffer, J P Kennedy, S F Loble, G Locke, A Marco, M W B Marsh, C M Parr, H I Ricklow, G Rivers, S A Rosen, G M Rutter, P A Rutter, J D Saner, P J Sillis, D Simon, P J Wheeler, G Withey, I R Woolfe, T W Yerburgh
Languages: Arabic, French, German, Italian, Polish, Portuguese, Spanish
Work: A1 A3 B1 B2 C1 C2 D1 E F1 J1 K1 K2 L M1 M3 N O P Q R1 S1 S2 T1 U2 W Z(a,b,c,d,e,f,g,i,j,k,o,p,s,w)
Agency undertaken
Ptr: Algar, Ms Clare MA(Cantab) Holborn Law Prize . . . . Jan 2000
Armstrong-Fox, Mrs Janet C BA. . . . . . . *Feb 1991
Cohen, Mr Joseph . . . . *Jan 1980
Czyzowski, Mr Jack M BA(Law). . . . . . . Apr 1984
Dixon, Mr Andrew. . . . . . . *May 1971
Drake, Mr Michael J MA(Cantab) . . . . *§Nov 1971
Drennan, Mr Oliver . . . . Sep 1993
Fazio, Miss Silvia . . . . Aug 2002
Giacon, Mr Dominic A P LLB . . . . *§Apr 1976
Goodman, Ms Tania LLB . . . . *Oct 1993
Graham, Mrs Eileen. . . . . . . *Nov 1974
Greig, Ms Victoria. . . . . . . *Oct 2001
Heffer, Mr Steven ● . . . . Dec 1985
Kennedy, Miss Joanna P BA(TCD) . . . . Aug 1976
Loble, Mr Steven F MA(Cantab). . . . . . . Mar 1984
Locke, Ms Gillian LLB. . . . . . . Oct 1992
Marco, Mr Alan LLB(Lond) Deputy District Judge at the Principal Registry of the Family Division . . . . *Jan 1965
Marsh, Mr Matthew W B BA. . . . . . . *May 1977
Parr, Mr Christopher M . . . . Oct 1987
Ricklow, Mr Howard I BA(Hons). . . . . . . *Jan 1987
Rivers, Ms Gillian . . . . Nov 1995
Rosen, Mr Stephen A LLB. . . . . . . Jun 1970
Rutter, Mr Philip Alec LLB. . . . . . . *Nov 1992
Saner, Mr John D MA(Oxon) . . . . *§Oct 1979
Sillis, Mr Paul J MA(Cantab) . . . . *Apr 1980
Simon, Mr Daniel BSc(Hons) . . . . Sep 1993
Wheeler, Mr Patrick John MA(Cantab). . . . . . . *Oct 1982
Withey, Mr Gary. . . . . . . Oct 1991
Woolfe, Mr Ian R MA; LLM(Cantab) . . . . *§Aug 1970
Yerburgh, Mr Toby W BA(Hons). . . . . . . Nov 1992
Asoc: Harries, Miss Nicola J LLB . . . . *May 1995
Horner, Mr Ian R LLB(Lond). . . . . . . *Dec 1972
Ross, Miss Catherine BA(Hons). . . . . . . Nov 1999
Simmons, Mr John Alexander LLB . . . . *Oct 1994
Con: Burdon-Cooper, Mr Alan R MA; LLB(Cantab) . . . . . *§Jul 1968

COLMAN COYLE LLP ‡
Wells House 80 Upper Street Islington London N1 0NU
Tel: 020 7354 3000 *Fax:* 020 7354 2244 *Dx:* 147080 ISLINGTON 5
E-mail: enquiries@colmancoyle.com
Web: www.colmancoyle.com
List of partners: H Anand, H Colman, R W Coyle, N Curbison, A P Flint, G S Kyriacou, D Malamatenios
Languages: Bengali, French, Greek, Hindi, Italian, Portuguese, Punjabi, Spanish, Urdu
Work: A3 B1 C1 E J1 N O Q R2 S1 S2 W Z(q)
Ptr: Anand, Ms Hema . . . . *Apr 2002
Colman, Mr Howard. . . . . . . *Jan 1979
Coyle, Mr Robert W BA(Hons) . . . . *Dec 1979
Curbison, Mr Neil . . . . *Apr 2006
Flint, Mr Andrew P BA(Hons) . . . . *May 1988
Kyriacou, Ms Georgina Socrates BA(Hons) . . . . . *Mar 1990
Malamatenios, Mr David BA(Hons) . . . . *Oct 1992
Asoc: Ali, Mr Tafozzul LLB(Hons) . . . . *Sep 2001
Chambers, Ms Samantha T LLB . . . . *Oct 1988
Makin, Mr Colin . . . . *Aug 1999
Martins, Miss Sandra Fernandes . . . . *Sep 2001
Morillas-Paredes, Mr Ignacio . . . . Mar 2005
Porter, Mr Simon John . . . . Oct 1990
Quinn, Ms Linda Marie MA . . . . *Jul 2001
Santra, Ms Krishna . . . . Oct 1999
Scally, Ms Lydia. . . . . . . *Nov 2008
Smith, Mr Matt . . . . *Apr 2008
Ast: Tennant, Mr Simon . . . . *Nov 2009

C E P COLOMBOTTI ‡
15 Hanover Square London W1S 1HY
Tel: 020 7569 1054 *Fax:* 020 7569 1002
E-mail: carlo@colombotti.com
Languages: Italian
Work: C1 E M2 R2 S2 T1 T2 Z(b)

COLVIN & PARTNERS ‡
23 Craven Terrace London W2 3QH
Tel: 020 7402 4222

COMMUNITY LAW CLINIC SOLICITORS LTD ‡
101 Chamberlayne Road Kensal Rise London NW10 3NP

COMPTONS ‡
90-92 Parkway Regents Park Camden London NW1 7AN
Tel: 020 7485 0888 *Fax:* 020 7485 1145 *Dx:* 57057 CAMDEN TOWN
E-mail: advice@comptons.co.uk
List of partners: S J Compton, N A Goldreich, J A Midgley, A L Neale, J Sheldrick
Languages: French, Hebrew
Work: B1 C1 C2 C3 E F1 J1 L N O P Q R1 R2 S1 S2 W Z(c,e,f,k,l,q,r)
Emergency Action, Agency, Advocacy, Legal Aid undertaken and Member of Accident Line
Ptr: Compton, Mr Stephen J. . . . . Jan 1980
Goldreich, Mr Nicholas A BA . . . . *Feb 1983
Midgley, Mr John A LLB. . . . . . . *Nov 1992
Neale, Ms Angela L. . . . . . . *May 2000
Sheldrick, Mr John . . . . *Aug 1990

CONINGHAMS SOLICITORS ‡
Grosvenor Gardens House 35/37 Grosvenor Gardens London SW1W 0BS
Tel: 020 8296 1957 *Fax:* 020 8296 1854 *Dx:* 2304 VICTORIA
Emergency telephone 07699 728623
E-mail: law@coninghams.co.uk
List of partners: J P Coningham
Languages: French, German, Punjabi
Work: A3 B2 C1 G H K3 N O Q W Z(f,g,i,p,za)
Emergency Action, Agency, Advocacy, Legal Aid undertaken and Legal Aid Franchise
SPr: Coningham, Mr Julian Paul ● . . . . *Jan 1990

MICHAEL B CONN ‡
845 Finchley Road London NW11 8NA
Tel: 020 8455 1111 *Fax:* 020 8455 9191

CONTEGO INTELLECTUAL PROPERTY ‡
90 Long Acre Covent Garden London WC2E 9RZ
Tel: 020 7849 3430 *Fax:* 020 8686 0453
E-mail: contego@contegoip.co.uk

CONYBEARE SOLICITORS ‡
Clearwater House 4-7 Manchester Street London W1V 3AE
Tel: 0870 753 0925 *Fax:* 0870 762 7925
E-mail: law@conybeare.com
Languages: French, Hungarian
Work: C1 C2 J1 U2 Z(e)

CONYERS DILL & PEARMAN ‡
34 Threadneedle Street London EC2R 8AY
Tel: 020 7374 2444 *Fax:* 020 7374 2445

RICHARD COOK SOLICITORS ‡
Lowood House Partingdale Lane London NW7 1NS
Tel: 020 8371 3490 *Fax:* 020 8371 3489
E-mail: rcook2005@gmail.com

COOK TAYLOR ‡
3 Thomas Street Woolwich Greenwich London SE18 6HR
Tel: 020 8854 1166 *Fax:* 020 8317 0093 *Dx:* 33300 WOOLWICH
E-mail: kt@cooktaylor.com
List of partners: K Tallon, A Thompson
Work: D1 D2 G K1 S1
Emergency Action, Agency, Advocacy, Fixed Fee Interview, Legal Aid undertaken and Legal Aid Franchise
Ptr: Tallon, Mr Keith . . . . *Sep 1973
Thompson, Mr Alan LLB . . . . *Feb 1963
Ast: Klein, Miss Victoria Nancy LLB . . . . *Jan 2008
Thompson, Mr Alexander Aiden. . . . . . . *Feb 2003

COOK TAYLOR WOODHOUSE ‡
68-70 Eltham High Street London SE9 1BZ
Tel: 020 8859 0936 *Fax:* 020 8850 3866 *Dx:* 32503 ELTHAM
E-mail: nwoodhouse@ctwsolicitors.co.uk
List of partners: J E Goodman, N J Woodhouse
Office: Dartford
Work: E K1 L S1 S2 W Z(o)
Ptr: Goodman, Mr John E. . . . . Dec 1990
Woodhouse, Mr Neil J LLB . . . . *Dec 1980

COOKE YOUNG & KEIDAN LLP ‡
Candlewick House 120 Cannon Street London EC4N 6AS
Tel: 020 7148 7800 *Fax:* 020 7283 1499
E-mail: india.goodwin@cyklaw.com

DAVID COOPER & CO ‡
Fleet House 8-12 New Bridge Street London EC4V 6AL
Tel: 020 7583 8338 *Fax:* 020 7583 5600

J COOPER ‡
53 Mile End Road Tower Hamlets London E1 4TT
Tel: 020 7790 0441 *Fax:* 020 7790 8998
Dx: 300707 TOWER HAMLETS
E-mail: jc@jcoopersolicitors.org.uk
List of partners: J Cooper
SPr: Cooper, Ms Julia . . . . Nov 1993

SHEILA COOPER LLB ‡
6 Naseby Close London NW6 4EY
Tel: 020 7372 0510 *Fax:* 020 7372 0510
Emergency telephone 07737 250316
E-mail: sl.cooper@tiscali.co.uk
List of partners: S L Cooper
Work: G H L W
Agency, Advocacy, Fixed Fee Interview and Legal Aid undertaken
SPr: Cooper, Mrs Sheila L LLB(Hons)(Lond) ★. . . . . . . Mar 1979

THOMAS COOPER ‡
Ibex House 42-47 Minories London EC3N 1HA
Tel: 020 7481 8851 *Fax:* 020 7480 6097 *Dx:* 548 LONDON/CITY
E-mail: info@thomascooperlaw.com
List of partners: J Alegre Climent, P F Barfield, D W Bateson, D P Brown, R I Crumplin, G R Eldred, T J R Goode, N H Green, G Harris, K E Harrison, T M Kelleher, D Kennard, A Liversedge, E A Marsden, R Morris, M Sachs, T Scorer, R J Strange, S J Swabey, C R G Williams
Languages: Bahasa, Dutch, French, German, Greek, Italian, Mandarin, Portuguese, Russian, Spanish
Work: A3 B1 C1 E J1 K1 K3 L M1 M3 N O P Q R1 R2 S1 T1 W Z(a,b,c,e,j)
Emergency Action undertaken
Ptr: Alegre Climent, Mr Juan LLM . . . . *Jul 1993
Barfield, Mr Paul F . . . . *§Jun 1980
Bateson, Mr Douglas W BA . . . . *Oct 1985
Brown, Mr David Phillip BA . . . . Oct 1998
Crumplin, Mr Russell Iain LLB. . . . . . . *Jun 1993
Eldred, Mr Grant R LLB . . . . *Oct 1991
Goode, Mr Timothy J R MA(Cantab). . . . . . . *§Apr 1975
Green, Mr Nicholas H MA(Oxon) . . . . *Mar 1978
Harris, Mr Graham . . . . Oct 1981
Harrison, Ms Kate E LLB . . . . *Feb 1987
Kelleher, Mr Timothy M MA(Oxon). . . . . . . Mar 1985
Kennard, Mr Darryl LLB . . . . *Oct 1994
Liversedge, Miss Anne LLB(Hons); LLM(Soton) . . . . *Nov 1994
Marsden, Ms E Ann LLB . . . . *Oct 1988
Morris, Mr Richard . . . . Sep 2004
Sachs, Mr Mark. . . . . . . Nov 1987
Scorer, Mr Tim . . . . Jul 1966
Strange, Mr R John LLB. . . . . . . *Apr 1980
Swabey, Mr Stephen J BA(Nott'm) . . . . *§Nov 1972
Williams, Mr Charles R G LLB(B'ham). . . . . . . *Jul 1979
Ast: Glen, Miss Rachel BSc; PGDipLaw; LPC . . . . Sep 2004
Vitta, Ioanna LLB(Athens); LLM(Soton) . . . . Sep 2002
Vouvoussiras, Ms Kelly . . . . Sep 2002

COOPER WHITEMAN ‡
34 Bloomsbury Way London WC1A 2SA
Tel: 020 7831 5222 *Fax:* 020 7831 4194 *Dx:* 35714 BLOOMSBURY
E-mail: law@cooperwhiteman.co.uk
List of partners: M L Cooper, D F Whiteman
Work: C1 E J1 K1 N O Q S1 S2 W Z(k,l,q,r)
Member of Accident Line
Ptr: Cooper, Mr Michael Laurence LLB(Lond) . . . . *Jul 1976
Whiteman, Mr David F LLB(Lond). . . . . . . Jun 1977
Ast: Brodkin, Mrs Bella LLB . . . . Dec 1976
Con: McDevitt, Mr Jonathan F LLB . . . . May 1982

R T COOPERS SOLICITORS ‡
Telfords Yard 6-8 The Highway London E1W 2BS
Tel: 020 7488 9947 *Fax:* 020 7488 2102
E-mail: enquiries@rtcoopers.com
List of partners: R Cooper
Work: C1 C2 C3 E F1 F2 I J1 M1 M2 O Q X Z(e,f,p,q,w,z,za)
Ptr: Cooper, Dr Rosanna BSc(Hons); CChem; FRSC; Dip IPJan 1993

COPITCH ‡
303a Muswell Hill Broadway Haringey London N10 1DA
Tel: 020 8883 9831 *Fax:* 020 8883 4720 *Dx:* 36001 MUSWELL HILL
List of partners: M H Copitch, K Levy
Work: C1 D1 E F1 J1 K1 L N O Q S1 S2 W Z(l)
Emergency Action, Agency, Advocacy, Fixed Fee Interview, Legal Aid undertaken and Legal Aid Franchise
Ptr: Copitch, Mr Michael H LLB(B'ham) . . . . *Oct 1981
Levy, Ms Kate LLB(Hons) . . . . *Nov 1995

COPPER STONE SOLICITORS ‡
32-38 Lenham Street London E1 8EW
Tel: 020 7173 6175

CORBAIN SOLICITORS ‡
51 The Hale Tottenham Hale London N17 9JZ
Tel: 020 8801 3737 *Fax:* 020 8801 9002
E-mail: info@corbansolicitors.co.uk

CORBIN & HASSAN ‡
First Floor 49 Raven Road Tower Hamlets London E1 2EG
Tel: 020 7247 6518 *Fax:* 020 7247 0554
Dx: 300703 TOWER HAMLETS
E-mail: info@corbinhassan.co.uk
List of partners: S H A Hassan
Languages: Portuguese, Sinhalese, Tamil, Twi
Work: V Z(i)
Emergency Action, Advocacy, Fixed Fee Interview, Legal Aid undertaken and Legal Aid Franchise
Ptr: Hassan, Mr Shahul Hameed Abul LLB. . . . . . . *May 1986
Ast: Amaning, Kwarteng LLB. . . . . . . *Jul 2001
Khaled, Mr Muhammad Saif Uddin LLM. . . . . . . Jan 2010
Nazeem, Mr Mansoor LLB . . . . *Feb 2005

BERNARD CORDELL ‡
Flat 3 3 Tasker Road London NW3 2YR
Tel: 020 8209 3752 *Fax:* 020 8209 3753
E-mail: bernard.cordell@virgin.net
List of partners: B Cordell
Work: C1 E J1 K1 L O S1
Agency and Advocacy undertaken
SPr: Cordell, Mr Bernard . . . . *Jan 1982

CORFORD INTERNATIONAL LLP ‡
25 Beech Hall Crescent London E4 9NW
Tel: 020 8527 6217

CORKER BINNING SOLICITORS ‡
12 Devereux Court Strand London WC2R 3JJ
Tel: 020 7353 6000 *Fax:* 020 7353 6008
Dx: 363 LONDON/CHANCERY LN
Emergency telephone 07771 683378
E-mail: law@corkerbinning.co.uk
List of partners: P Binning, D T Corker, N Finnerty
Languages: French, German, Italian, Spanish
Work: B2 G
Agency, Advocacy and Legal Aid undertaken
Ptr: Binning, Mr Peter LLB Member of the Council of Justice . . . . *Feb 1992
Corker, Mr David T BA; MA(Oxon) . . . . *Nov 1990
Finnerty, Miss Nicola LLB(Hons). . . . . . . *Oct 1996
Con: Brown, Mr Robert T J MA(Cantab) . . . . *Oct 1983

CORMACT CAWLEY & CO ‡
21 Lime Close London E1W 2QP
Tel: 020 7702 2654 *Fax:* 020 7481 1486
E-mail: cormaccawley@yahoo.co.uk

CORNELIAN LAWYERS AND MEDIATORS ‡
Ludgate House 107-111 Fleet Street London EC4A 2AB
Tel: 0845 009 1377 *Fax:* 020 7936 9226
E-mail: contact@cornelian.com

CORNERSTONEKING ‡
185 New Cross Road London SE14 5DG
Tel: 020 7635 6033 *Fax:* 020 7639 0196

CORNERSTONES ‡
Unit 12 The Hiltongrove Business Centre London E17 4QP
Tel: 020 8520 6330 *Fax:* 020 8509 6930

CORPER SOLICITORS ‡
308-310 High Street Stratford London E15 1AJ
Tel: 020 8555 6006 *Fax:* 020 8503 1271
E-mail: enquiries@corpersolicitors.co.uk

CORREN TROEN ‡
4 Buckingham Place London SW1E 6HR
Tel: 020 7798 9344 *Fax:* 020 7798 9349

COST ADVOCATES LIMITED ‡
4th Floor Dukes House 32-38 Dukes Place London EC3A 7LP
Tel: 0870 402 7871

COUCHMANS LLP ‡
20-22 Bedford Row London WC1R 4EB
Tel: 020 7611 9660 *Fax:* 020 7611 9661
E-mail: enquiries@couchmansllp.com
List of partners: N Couchman, D Harrington, S Khandke, F Reid, M Whitehead
Work: A3 C1 C2 C3 I M1 O Q U1 U2 Z(e,f,k,l,w,za)
Fixed Fee Interview undertaken
Ptr: Couchman, Mr Nic . . . Jun 1990
Harrington, Mr Dan . . . Mar 2000
Khandke, Satish . . . Nov 2005
Reid, Mr Fraser . . . Oct 1992
Whitehead, Mr Mark . . . Oct 1995

COURTYARD SOLICITORS LLP ‡
2 St Marks Place Wimbledon London SW19 7ND
Tel: 020 8946 9466 *Fax:* 020 8946 9480
Dx: 300111 WIMBLEDON CENTRAL
List of partners: S F Vitty, S White
Languages: French
Work: C1 D2 E F1 K1 K3 K4 L O Q S1 S2 W Z(g,i,l)
Agency undertaken
Mem: Vitty, Mr Samuel Frederick . . . *Jan 2010
White, Mr Sean . . . *Apr 1984

COVENT GARDEN FAMILY LAW ‡
17 Shorts Gardens Camden London WC2H 9AT
Tel: 020 7257 6130 *Fax:* 020 7836 3656
Dx: 40002 COVENT GARDEN
E-mail: k.mcgowan@cgfamilylaw.co.uk
List of partners: A Burt, H Sundram
Languages: French, Malay
Work: D1 D2 K1 K3 W
Emergency Action, Agency, Advocacy, Legal Aid undertaken and Legal Aid Franchise
Ptr: Burt, Ms Alison BA(Hons)(Cantab) . . . *Sep 1993
Sundram, Ms Haema LLB(Hons) . . . *Oct 1992
Con: Gaff, Ms Angela LLB ♦ . . . *Dec 1986

COVINGTON & BURLING LLP ‡
265 Strand London WC2R 1BH
Tel: 020 7067 2000 *Fax:* 020 7067 2222
Languages: French, German, Gujarati, Hindi, Italian, Portuguese, Spanish
Work: A3 B2 C1 C2 J1 O T1 U1 U2 Z(e,w,za)

COWARD AND SAHDEV SOLICITORS ‡
16-19 Southampton Place London WC1A 1AJ
Tel: 020 7745 7220 *Fax:* 020 7745 7222
E-mail: sureetasadev@hotmail.com

LEONIE COWEN & ASSOCIATES ‡
3a Loveridge Mews London NW6 2DP
Tel: 020 7604 5870 *Fax:* 020 7604 5871
E-mail: admin@lcowen.co.uk
List of partners: L E Cowen
Work: C1 E J1 S2 X Z(d,h,u)
Ptr: Cowen, Miss Leonie E LLB . . . *Apr 1974
Con: Riddell, Mr Andrew J S LLB . . . *Dec 1975

COWEN ROSS SOLICITORS ‡
First Floor 27 Downham Road London N1 5AA
Tel: 020 7241 1140

COWLES ‡
Lloyds Bank Chambers 1433a London Road Norbury Croydon London SW16 4AF
Tel: 020 8679 1811 *Fax:* 020 8765 8570
List of partners: R A Cowles, J A Thompson
Work: E K4 S1 S2 W
Ptr: Cowles, Mr Roderick A . . . *May 1984
Thompson, Miss Judith A LLB . . . *Jan 1980

COX RODERICK LLP ‡
16 Old Town London SW4 0JY
Tel: 020 7819 4262 *Fax:* 020 8082 5028
E-mail: london@coxroderick.com
List of partners: M Cox

COYLE WHITE DEVINE
Central Court 25 Southampton Buildings London WC2A 1AL
Tel: 0845 094 5945 *Fax:* 0845 094 5995
Office: Amersham

COZEN O'CONNOR LLP ‡
9th Floor Fountain House 130 Fenchurch Street London EC3M 5DJ
Tel: 020 7864 2000 *Fax:* 020 7864 2013

CRAIGEN WILDERS & SORRELL ‡
23 Turnpike Lane London N8 0EP
Tel: 020 8888 2255 *Fax:* 020 8881 5080 *Dx:* 34700 WOOD GREEN 2
E-mail: info@cwssolicitors.co.uk
List of partners: A D M Sorrell, A G Sorrell, J R Sorrell
Languages: French
Work: A1 B1 C1 D1 E F1 G H J1 K1 L M1 N P R1 S1 T1 V W Z(c,d,h,j,k,l,m,p,s)
Emergency Action, Agency, Advocacy and Legal Aid undertaken
Ptr: Sorrell, Mrs Andrea G LLB . . . *Apr 1978
Sorrell, Mr Jeremy R . . . *Dec 1977

CRAMER PELMONT ‡
33 Cavendish Square London W1G 0PW
Tel: 020 7016 3016 *Fax:* 020 7016 3026
Dx: 42704 OXFORD CIRCUS NORTH
E-mail: ggligorevic@cramerpelmont.co.uk
List of partners: P I Cramer, N Pelmont
Office: London N8

CRAMER PELMONT
8 Middle Lane Crouch End London N8 8PL
Tel: 020 8340 0091 *Fax:* 020 8341 5552 *Dx:* 35951 CROUCH END
E-mail: areid-nelson@cramerpelmont.co.uk
Office: London W1
Work: L Q S1 S2 W Z(l)
Ptr: Cramer, Mr Paul I . . . *Oct 1988
Pelmont, Mr Nicholas . . . *Aug 1996

CRAVATH SWAINE & MOORE LLP ‡
Citypoint 1 Ropemaker Street London EC2Y 9HR
Tel: 020 7453 1000 *Fax:* 020 7860 1150

CRAWFORD ‡
1 Northumberland Avenue Trafalgar Square London WC2N 5BW
Tel: 020 7872 5495
E-mail: acrawford@crawfordlaw.co.uk

CRAWFORD SOLICITORS ‡
Lower Ground Floor 20-24 Kirby Street London EC1N 8TS
Tel: 020 7831 3343

CRAWFORD SOLICITORS ‡
Arando House 128-134 Cleveland Street London W1T 6PH
Tel: 0845 000 9500 *Fax:* 0845 345 6699
E-mail: cec@crawfordsolicitors.com

T H R CRAWLEY ‡
12 Cavendish Road London W4 3UH
Tel: 020 8994 8643 *Fax:* 0870 161 5800

CREE GODFREY & WOOD ‡
28 High Road East Finchley London N2 9PJ
Tel: 020 8883 9414 *Fax:* 020 8444 5414 *Dx:* 52050 EAST FINCHLEY
E-mail: admin@creegodfreyandwood.co.uk
List of partners: G E Nosworthy, S G Nosworthy
Languages: French
Work: C1 E J1 K1 K3 K4 L N O Q R2 S1 S2 W
Ptr: Nosworthy, Mr George E Commissioner for Oaths. . . *Jul 1965
Nosworthy, Mr Simon George BA(Econ & Social History) . . . *Aug 2001
Ast: Taylor, Mr Paul Michael LLB(Hons) . . . Apr 2010

CREED LANE LAW GROUP ‡
8 Creed Lane London EC4V 5BR
Tel: 020 7248 6817

CREIGHTON & PARTNERS ‡
24 Bedford Square Bloomsbury London WC1B 3HN
Tel: 020 7976 2233 *Fax:* 020 7636 4753
Dx: 134209 TOTTENHAM COURT ROAD 2
E-mail: louise.creighton@creighton.co.uk
List of partners: T G Chester, L Creighton, D Taylor
Office: Staines
Languages: French
Work: D1 D2 K1 K2 Z(u)
Legal Aid undertaken
Ptr: Chester, Ms Tracy G BA . . . *Nov 1996
Creighton, Ms Louise BA . . . *Jan 1984
Taylor, Mr Douglas BA . . . *Dec 1991
Ast: Wilson, Miss Dawn . . . *Oct 1996

CRESCO LEGAL SOLICITORS ‡
12 Melcombe Place Marylebone London NW1 6JJ
Tel: 020 3356 4938 *Fax:* 020 3356 4938
Office: Oxford

CRESSWELL & CO ‡
Lloyds Bank Chambers 308/312 Chiswick High Road Chiswick London W4 1NP
Tel: 020 8742 0070 *Fax:* 020 8742 0080
E-mail: acresswell@cresswell-law.co.uk
List of partners: A J Cresswell, S Russell
Languages: French, German, Greek
Work: B1 C1 C3 E F1 I J1 K1 K2 L M1 O Q R1 S1 S2 U2 W Z(c,e)
Emergency Action, Agency and Advocacy undertaken
Ptr: Cresswell, Mr Andrew John LLB(Cardiff) . . . *Jan 1987
Russell, Ms Susanna . . . Oct 1989

CRIMINAL DEFENCE SOLICITORS ‡
227-228 Strand Westminster London WC2R 1BE
Tel: 020 7353 7000 *Fax:* 020 7353 7111
Dx: 442 LONDON/CHANCERY LN
Emergency telephone 0800 015 1015
List of partners: N Lodhi, J Navani
Languages: Afrikaans, Bosnian, Farsi, French, German, Gujarati, Turkish, Urdu
Work: B2 G H
Agency, Advocacy and Legal Aid undertaken
Ptr: Lodhi, Mr Noor LLB(Hons) . . . Jan 1997
Navani, Mr John LLB(Hons) . . . *Jan 1996
Ast: Chirag, Patel LLB(Hons) . . . Sep 2003
Fottrell, Miss Catherine MA(Hons) . . . Aug 2007
Panasar, Miss Jatinder BA(Hons) . . . Mar 2002
Sevin, Mrs Isil LLB(Hons) . . . Apr 2004
Con: Jamil, Mr Shakeel LLB ★ . . . Jul 2002
Williams, Mr Timothy LLB(Hons) ★ . . . Feb 2002

CRIPPS HARRIES HALL LLP
53 Chandos Place Covent Garden London WC2N 4HS
Tel: 020 7930 7879 *Fax:* 020 7839 9224
Dx: 3954 TUNBRIDGE WELLS
E-mail: reception@crippslaw.com
Office: Tunbridge Wells
Work: A1 A2 B1 B2 C1 C2 C3 D1 E F1 F2 I J1 J2 K1 L M1 N O P Q R1 R2 S1 S2 T1 T2 U1 U2 W Z(b,c,d,e,f,h,j,k,l,m,n,p,q,s,t,u)
Emergency Action, Agency, Advocacy undertaken and Member of Accident Line

CRISP & CO SOLICITORS
37th Floor One Canada Square Canary Wharf London E14 5AP
Tel: 0844 800 6863 *Fax:* 0844 800 6864
E-mail: info@crispandco.com
Office: Guildford, Kingston upon Thames

CROMWELLS LAW LIMITED ‡
Berkeley Square House Berkeley Square London W1J 6BD
Tel: 020 7887 6474 *Fax:* 020 7887 6001

CROSSMANS MTA
5 Bream's Buildings London EC4A 1EA
E-mail: rachel.dunne@crossmansmta.com
Office: Cambridge, Manchester

CROWELL & MORING ‡
11 Pilgrim Street London EC4V 6RN
Est: 1995
Tel: 020 7413 0011 *Fax:* 020 7413 0333
Dx: 91 LONDON/CHANCERY LN
List of partners: A Ali, W Berg, T De Meese, M DeFeo, A Gourley, E Gybels, P Kiernan, T Leeson, R Maclean, R Murray, G Owen, F Petillion, K Roox, N R Sharma, J P Wheeler
Languages: French, German, Hindi, Punjabi, Spanish, Urdu, Welsh
Work: A3 B2 C1 C2 C3 E F1 F2 G I J1 J2 M1 M2 N O P Q S2 U1 U2 Z(b,e,j,k,p,q,w,y,za)
Ptr: Ali, Arif . . . *Nov 1992
Berg, Mr Werner . . . *Oct 1997
De Meese, Mr Thomas . . . *Jan 1993
DeFeo, Mr Morris . . . *Jan 1988
Gourley, Mr Alan . . . Dec 1981
Gybels, Mr Emmanual . . . *Jan 1988
Kiernan, Mr Peter LLB; LLM. . . . *Sep 1988
Leeson, Mr Timothy LLM . . . *Mar 1998
Maclean, Mr Robert . . . *Feb 1994
Murray, Mr Rob BA(Jurisprudence); LLM(Intl & Comparative Law)(Brussels) . . . *Jan 1989
Owen, Mr Gerallt BA(Hons) . . . *Nov 1995
Petillion, Flip . . . *Jan 1992
Roox, Kirstof . . . *Oct 1994
Sharma, Nilam R . . . *Nov 1992
Wheeler, Mr Joel Patrick MA(Philosophy, Politics & Economics); CPE; LPC. . . . Jan 1998
Ast: Addison Smith, Ms Kirsten . . . *Sep 2008
Austin, Mr Gareth . . . *Sep 2006
Davies, Ms Ann Caroline LLB . . . Jan 1991
Donovan, Mr Matthew James LLB(Hons); LPC . . . *Mar 2005
Haste, Miss Michelle BA; LLM. . . . *Dec 1991
Khan, Aabida . . . *Feb 2008
Kostenko, Mr Maksim LLM; LLB. . . . *May 2007
Simpson, Ms Fiona Anne BA(French & Linguistics) . . . May 1994
Wessel, Ms Jane BA; JD . . . *Sep 1996
Zainab, Charchafchi. . . . *Oct 2006

CROWTHER SOLICITORS ‡
14 Greville Street London EC1N 8SB
Tel: 020 7785 6944 / 6945 *Fax:* 020 7785 6946
Dx: 53330 CLERKENWELL
E-mail: info@crowthersolicitors.co.uk

A S CROXSON ‡
216 Sheen Lane London SW14 8LB
Tel: 020 8998 3097 *Fax:* 020 8998 3097
E-mail: tony@croxson.com

A S CROXSON SOLICITORS ‡
45 Gordon Road London W5 2AP

CRUICKSHANKS SOLICITORS ‡
(in association with Beijing; Auckland; Sydney; Kuala Lumpur)
10 Bentinck Street London W1U 2EN
Tel: 020 7487 4468 *Fax:* 020 7487 5466
Dx: 42723 OXFORD CIRCUS NORTH
E-mail: email@lawco.co.uk
List of partners: J M Cruickshank, X Zhu-Cruickshank
Languages: Cantonese, Mandarin
Work: C1 E J1 K1 K3 O Q S1 S2 W Z(b,e,i)
Advocacy, Fixed Fee Interview undertaken and Member of Accident Line
Ptr: Cruickshank, Mr John M LLB(NZ) ● . . . *Feb 1990
Zhu-Cruickshank, Dr Xiaojiu PhD ♦ . . . *Sep 2001
Ast: Tang, Miss Ching Yee LLB . . . *Nov 2008

CRUMPLINS ‡
142 Gloucester Avenue Primrose Hill Camden London NW1 8JA
Tel: 020 7483 0282 *Fax:* 020 7483 0257 *Dx:* 96858 PRIMROSE HILL
E-mail: paul@crumplinsolicitors.fsnet.co.uk
List of partners: P R Crumplin
Languages: French, German, Greek, Spanish, Urdu
Work: B1 E F1 G J1 K1 L N O Q R1 S1 W Z(e,i,l,p)
Agency, Fixed Fee Interview and Legal Aid undertaken
Ptr: Crumplin, Mr Paul Robert . . . Aug 1987

CRYSTAL PARTNERS SOLICITORS ‡
8a Turnpike Lane London N8 0PT
Tel: 0845 500 0240 *Fax:* 0845 500 0241 *Dx:* 35663 WOOD GREEN
E-mail: info@crystalpartners.co.uk

CUBISM LIMITED ‡
116-118 Chancery Lane London WC2A 1PP
Tel: 020 7831 0101 *Fax:* 020 7831 0001
Dx: 477 LONDON/CHANCERY LN
E-mail: contact@cubismlaw.com
List of partners: D L P Salamons, R J R Taylor
Ptr: Salamons, Mr David L P BA. . . . Apr 1981
Taylor, Mr Robert J R BComm; LLB; Attorney South Africa . . . Jan 1996

CUMBERLAND ELLIS PEIRS ‡
Atrum Court 15-17 Jockeys Field London WC1R 4QR
Tel: 020 7242 0422 *Fax:* 020 7831 9081
Dx: 250 LONDON/CHANCERY LN
E-mail: cep@cep-law.co.uk
List of partners: C D'Souza, S C de Galleani, T A Edwards, S Eva, S P J Howell, J Lamont, A Lucy, D K Martin, C R Sels, A F Stanyer, N E Turner, H K Wright
Languages: French
Work: A1 A3 B1 C1 C2 C3 D1 E F1 I J1 K1 K2 K3 L M1 M2 N O P Q R1 S1 S2 T2 U2 W Z(d,e,f,h,i,m,p,s,w)
Agency undertaken
Ptr: D'Souza, Ms Chandrika LLB(Hons) . . . *Nov 1989
de Galleani, Mr Simon C . . . *Nov 1977
Edwards, Mr Thomas A BA(Hons); DipLaw . . . *Nov 1998
Eva, Ms Suzanne BA; MA(Oxon) . . . *Sep 1988
Howell, Mr Simon P J. . . . Nov 1971
Lamont, Mr James BA; DipLaw . . . *Jun 2000
Lucy, Miss Angela. . . . *Aug 1997
Martin, Mr David K MA(Cantab) . . . *Jun 1969
Sels, Mr Colin R LLB(Lond) . . . *Oct 1976
Stanyer, Miss Ann F Notary Public . . . *Apr 1987
Turner, Mr Neil E LLB . . . *Mar 1972
Wright, Ms Hazel K MA(Cantab) . . . *May 1981
Asoc: Collier-Wright, Mr Richard G MA(Oxon) . . . *§Feb 1973
Fritsche, Miss Susan E M . . . *Dec 1999
Jones, Miss Eleri S BA(Hons); LSF . . . Nov 1993
Ast: Hammon, Mr William Arthur LLB(B'ham) . . . *Oct 2003
James, Miss Madeleine Catherine BA(Hons) . . . *Oct 1998
Ries, Ms Emma R BA(Hons); DipLaw; LPC . . . *Oct 1998
Satterly, Mrs Emma J BA(Oxon) . . . *Dec 1989
Smith, Mrs Sarah LLB(Hons) . . . *Sep 1996
Con: Bartlett, Mr Timothy J LLB(Lond) . . . *§Mar 1975
Lester, Mr Richard C . . . *§Jul 1975

CUMMINGS ‡
88 Bramfield Road London SW11 6PY
Tel: 020 7585 1406 *Fax:* 020 7585 1389
E-mail: claire.cummings@cummingslaw.com

CUNNINGHAM BLAKE ‡
(in association with Stephen Mackenzie & Co of Dublin)
Spencer House 3 Tranquil Vale Blackheath London SE3 0BU
Tel: 020 8463 0071 *Fax:* 020 8852 5115 *Dx:* 50908 BLACKHEATH
List of partners: K M C Cunningham
Office: London SE13
Languages: Burmese, French, German, Spanish
Work: C1 D1 E F1 G H J1 K1 L M1 N P S1 V W
Emergency Action, Agency, Advocacy, Fixed Fee Interview and Legal Aid undertaken
Ptr: Cunningham, Mr Kenneth M C LLB(Leeds) . . . . . . *Jan 1980

CUNNINGHAM BLAKE
81 Lewisham High Street Lewisham London SE13 5JX
Tel: 020 8463 9800 *Fax:* 020 8463 9808 *Dx:* 200955 LEWISHAM 2
Office: London SE3

CURREY & CO ‡
21 Buckingham Gate Westminster London SW1E 6LS
Tel: 020 7802 2700 *Fax:* 020 7828 5049 *Dx:* 2300 VICTORIA
List of partners: S J Atkinson, M F Black, P A Bostock, V M S Goodlad, J V Naunton Davies, E R H Perks, W L G Swan
Work: A1 E S1 T2 W Z(d)
Ptr: Atkinson, Mr Simon Jonathon BA(Hons). . . . . . . *Nov 1995
Black, Mrs Mary Felicity LLB . . . . *Apr 1995
Bostock, Mr Peter A MA; LLB(Cantab) . . . . *§Dec 1977
Goodlad, Mrs Victoria Mary Sophia MA . . . . *Mar 2001
Naunton Davies, Mr John V MA(Cantab) . . . . *Mar 1985
Perks, Mr Edward R H . . . . *Jun 1987
Swan, Mr William L G. . . . . *Nov 1988
Asoc: Curtis, Mr Malcolm Geoffrey. . . . . *Aug 1977
Gee, Mr William Geoffrey Foster . . . . *§Oct 1985
Ast: Holladay, Miss Anna Francesca BA(Hons). . . . . . *Sep 2003
Con: Powell, Mr Nicholas R D MA(Cantab) . . . . *§Jun 1969
Smith, Mr Nicholas W BA(Cantab). . . . . *Feb 1964

STELLA CURRIE ‡
3 Brandon Mews Barbican London EC2Y 8BE
Tel: 020 7638 9979 *Fax:* 020 7628 4846 *Dx:* 46616 BARBICAN
E-mail: stella.currie@cityoflondon.gov.uk
List of partners: S E M Currie
Work: E S1 W

CURRY POPECK ‡
87 Wimpole Street London W1G 9RL
Tel: 020 7224 6633 *Fax:* 020 7935 4042 *Dx:* 9082 WEST END
E-mail: cpinfo@currypopeck.com
List of partners: L G Curry, J J Lemon, P I Popeck
Office: Kenton
Languages: French, German
Work: A3 B1 C1 C2 D1 E I J1 K1 K3 L M1 M2 N O P Q R1 R2 S1 S2 T1 U2 W Z(b,c,d,e,f,i,q,w)
Ptr: Curry, Mr Lionel G. . . . . *Jun 1978
Asoc: Dargan, Mrs Tracey Anne. . . . . *Nov 1999
Lester, Mr Jamie . . . . *Sep 2001
Sond, Mrs Amritpal Kaur . . . . Sep 2001
Ast: Swimer, Mr Daniel. . . . . Sep 2006
Whiteley, Mr James Mark LLB(Hons) . . . . Nov 1999
Con: Harris, Mr Clifford LLB(Lond) . . . . *Jan 1955
Webber, Mrs Diane LLB(Hons); Former Barrister . . *Dec 1980

CURTIS MALLET-PREVOST COLT & MOSLE LLP ‡
99 Gresham Street London EC2V 7NG
Tel: 020 7710 9800 *Fax:* 020 7710 9801

CURTIS TURNER & DRUKKER LTD ‡
Mitre House 44-46 Fleet Street London EC4Y 1BN
Tel: 020 7353 1770 *Fax:* 020 7353 1771
Emergency telephone 07831 693692
E-mail: admin@ctdlaw.co.uk
List of partners: N J B Drukker, D Wheeler
Languages: French, Italian
Work: B1 C1 C2 C3 E F1 F2 J1 K3 N O R1 S1 S2 W Z(a,b,c,e,j,l)
Emergency Action and Agency undertaken
Ptr: Drukker, Mr Nicholas J B . . . . *Jul 1975
Wheeler, Mr David . . . . Jul 1997
Ast: Griffin, Miss Kathryn . . . . Jan 2008
Lyon, Mr Mark. Nov 1989

DAC BEACHCROFT ‡
100 Fetter Lane London EC4A 1BN
Tel: 020 7242 1011 *Fax:* 020 7831 6630
Dx: 45 LONDON/CHANCERY LN
List of partners: E J Adams, W H Allison, K Archer, M P Austwick, D L Bear, R J G Beaty, N Bhan, M A Blake, H L M Bothamley, A P Boulton, J Brogden, G C Brothwood, N J Butcher, M C Butterworth, J M Campbell, M J Cannon, L M Carolan, T K Chamberlain, A J Cherry, A J S Chesser, N J Chronias, V E Clegg, P M Cole, T G Corrigan, A Crofts, M E Darling, A R Dewar, R M Dineley, J C Doran, H Durston-Hillyer, C Dye, D R Esam, R C Evans, H L Faulkner, K M R Forsyth, R H P Fry, N C Gibbon, F M A Gill, J A Gizzi, M L Goldberg, D R Gowan, D M Greenwood, D Hallatt, E M Hava, R Heenan, D Hely, R I Highley, P Hill, G M Hindle, S Hocking, S J Hodson, W Hopkins, L A Hughes, D J F Hunt, P Jefferson, S A Jenkins, T G Johnson, A M Key, N Knapman, G A C Knight, H C Larter, P J Lee, R J Lee, P Leighton, J M Levinson, E Lewis, A Lock, J A MacNish Porter, L P Markham, A C M Marsh, S E May, A L McAdams, B G McCarthy, J P McCartney, I F McConkey, M J McGrath, K S McKenzie, S J Metcalfe, J Miller, N Montgomery, I C Moore, J S Morris, R J Moss, P C Murray, P J Murrin, C H Newman, J L Ormond, P F Parke, A J C Parker, S J Pearl, J C Phelps, D E Pollitt, L Porter, A J Pratt, D S Preddy, J B Ralston, S A Ramsden, C A Rees, O J Rees, J E Richards, R Richards, W D A Roach, R Roberts-Jenkins, S Roff, J J Roper, D S Rutter, A W H Scott, M Shaya, R Sheikh Collins, C F S Sherwood, H Simpson, C L Sinker, T Sless, C Slingo, H C Staines, A M Stokes, H Stevens, F I Suttie, G Taylor, N Taylor, S J Thompson, M S Thomson, B Thornycroft, S Tombolis, A C Tomlinson, R F Viney, A Wallbank, L M Walsh, D P C Wells, S Wharton, Z Wigan, C J Wilkes, J B A Williams, F M Willis, R Winterbottom, N M Young, S E Yuill
Office: Birmingham, Bristol, Leeds, London EC3 (3 offices), London EC4, Manchester (2 offices), Newcastle upon Tyne, Newport, Winchester
Languages: French, Italian, Spanish
Work: A3 B1 B2 B3 C1 C2 C3 E F1 F2 G I J1 J2 L M1 N O P Q R1 R2 S1 S2 T1 T2 U1 U2 W X Z(c,d,e,h,j,l,n,o,p,q,r,s,u,w,y,z)
Emergency Action, Agency, Advocacy undertaken and Member of Accident Line
Ptr: Adams, Ms Elizabeth J BA . . . . *Oct 1980
Bhan, Mr Neil. Sep 1998
Blake, Ms Monica A BA. . . . . *Nov 1974
Chesser, Mr Andrew J S LLB(Exon). . . . . *Oct 1987
Chronias, Mr Nicholas John. . . . . Mar 2003
Crofts, Ms Anne. . . . . *Nov 1992
Darling, Mr Matthew E BA. . . . . Aug 1994
Dineley, Ms Rachel Margaret LLB(Exon) University of Exeter Scholar . . . . *Apr 1983
Fry, Mr Robin H P LLB(Exon) . . . . *Oct 1980
Gibbon, Mr Nicholas C MA(Cantab). . . . . *Oct 1988
Gizzi, Mr Julian A MA(Cantab) . . . . *Apr 1981
Hocking, Mr Stephen . . . . Feb 2002
Hodson, Mr Simon James LLB . . . . *§Apr 1981
Hunt, Mr David J F MBE LLB(Bris) . . . . Jul 1968
Jefferson, Ms Paula. . . . . Nov 1994
MacNish Porter, Mr James Alexander LLB(Exon) . . *Dec 1988
Markham, Mr Laurence P LLB(Lond) . . . . *Apr 1981
Newman, Mr Charles H MA(Cantab) . . . . *May 1992
Parker, Mr Andrew J C MA(Cantab). . . . . *Oct 1983
Phelps, Mr John Christopher LLB . . . . Oct 1978
Ramsden, Mr Steven Anthony BA(Law). . . . . *Oct 1988
Richards, Ms Jean E LLB(Warw) . . . . *Nov 1975
Sless, Ms Tania BA . . . . *Jan 1991
Tombolis, Sakis . . . . Dec 1997
Wells, Mr David P C LLB(Lond). . . . . *Jul 1976
Wigan, Ms Zoe . . . . Nov 1998
Con: Baxter, Ms Patricia A LLB. . . . . *Nov 1991
Child, Mr Anthony A LLB(Hons) Solicitor to the Audit Commission. *Oct 1971
Cox, Mr Christopher C A BCL; MA(Oxon) . . . . *Apr 1970
Heslett, Mr Robert A . . . . *Jun 1970

DAC BEACHCROFT
6-8 Bouverie Street London EC4Y 8DD
Tel: 020 7936 2222 *Fax:* 020 7936 2020
Dx: 172 LONDON/CHANCERY LN
Office: Birmingham, Bristol, Leeds, London EC3 (3 offices), London EC4, Manchester (2 offices), Newcastle upon Tyne, Newport, Winchester
Languages: Afrikaans, Arabic, Catalan, Danish, Dutch, French, German, Greek, Gujarati, Hebrew, Hindi, Irish, Italian, Japanese, Latin, Norwegian, Portuguese, Punjabi, Russian, Spanish, Swedish, Welsh
Work: A1 A3 B1 B2 C2 C3 E F1 I J1 J2 L M1 N O P Q R1 R2 S2 U2 Z(a,b,c,f,h,j,r,u,w,y)
Emergency Action, Fixed Fee Interview undertaken and Member of Accident Line
Ptr: Allison, Mr William Henry LLB(East Anglia) . . . . . . Nov 1992
Bear, Mr David Laurence BA . . . . *Oct 1988
Boulton, Mr Andrew Peter. . . . . Sep 1996
Brogden, Mr Jonathan. . . . . Mar 2000
Butterworth, Mr Martin Chris LLB(Hons)(Manc) . . . . *Apr 1978
Dewar, Mr Ashley Robert . . . . Oct 1998
Gill, Ms Fiona Mary Ann LLB . . . . Apr 1992
Goldberg, Mr Michael Louis. . . . . Oct 1995
Gowan, Mr Daniel Robert LLB; FCIArb . . . . *Jan 1983
Hava, Ms Evi Melanie LLB . . . . *Sep 2000
Highley, Mr Richard Ian LLB. . . . . *Oct 1988
Johnson, Mr Timothy Guy. . . . . *Oct 1990
Knight, Mr Guy Adrian Charles BA(Oxon) . . . . *Nov 1991
Lee, Mr Robert James LLB . . . . *Oct 1984
Lewis, Mr Elliot LLB(Lond) . . . . *Jun 1993
McAdams, Miss Alison Louise BA(Hons)(Oxon); LLM(Hons)(Cantab). . . . . *Nov 1991
McCartney, Mr John Paul . . . . Oct 1989
McKenzie, Mr Kenneth Stevenson LLB . . . . *Feb 1978
Murrin, Mr Philip James LLB(Hons)(Exon); LSF . . . . Oct 1995
Pearl, Mr Simon Jeremy LLB . . . . *Apr 1977
Rees, Mr Christopher Anthony LLB . . . . *Dec 1979
Shaya, Mr Mark BSc(Hons)(Econ) Legal Adviser Waterloo Legal Advice Service . . . . *Nov 1995
Taylor, Mr Nicholas LLB; LLM . . . . *Oct 1995
Tomlinson, Mr Anthony Crispin . . . . Sep 1997
Viney, Mr Robert Frederick BA . . . . *Oct 1987
Walsh, Mrs Lucinda Mary LLB. . . . . *Oct 1983
Young, Mr Nicholas Michael LLB . . . . *Oct 1990
Asoc: Hunter, Ms Sharon . . . . Mar 1997
Massey-Crow, Miss Helen Valerie LLB . . . . Sep 2001
Ast: Coomber, Mr Gareth BA. . . . . *Nov 1992
Pritchard, Ms Kelly-Anne . . . . Mar 2002
Con: Dobias, Mr Michael Philip LLB. . . . . *Oct 1975
Goodman, Mr John Austen BA; LLB. . . . . *Nov 1990
Lee, Mr Anthony N BA . . . . *Sep 1979
Martin, Mr Richard J LLB . . . . *§Nov 1982
Roberts, Mr David Mclachlan LLB. . . . . *Jun 1973
Smith, Mr John David. . . . . *Dec 1976
Smith, Mr Kenneth C LLB. . . . . *Mar 1980
Wood, Mr Jonathan G. . . . . *Jul 1968

DAC BEACHCROFT
6th Floor 40 Lime Street London EC3M 7AW
Tel: 020 7894 6960 *Fax:* 020 7894 6968 *Dx:* 753 LONDON/CITY
Office: Birmingham, Bristol, Leeds, London EC3 (2 offices), London EC4 (2 offices), Manchester (2 offices), Newcastle upon Tyne, Newport, Winchester

DAC BEACHCROFT
30 Eastcheap London EC3M 1HD
Tel: 020 7208 6800 *Fax:* 020 7208 6801 *Dx:* 753 LONDON/CITY
Office: Birmingham, Bristol, Leeds, London EC3 (2 offices), London EC4 (2 offices), Manchester (2 offices), Newcastle upon Tyne, Newport, Winchester
Languages: French, German, Spanish
Work: A3 B1 B2 B3 C1 C2 C3 E F1 F2 I J1 J2 L M1 N O P Q R1 R2 S2 T1 T2 U1 U2 W X Z(c,d,e,h,j,l,n,o,p,q,r,s,t,u,w,y,z)
Ptr: Beaty, Mr Richard J G LLB . . . . *Mar 1990
Chamberlain, Mr Trevor K BA. . . . . *Jun 1981
Doran, Mr James Christopher. . . . . Apr 1998
Dye, Mr Campbell. . . . . Sep 1999
Evans, Mr Richard C LLB(Lond). . . . . §Apr 1976
Forsyth, Mr Kenneth M R BA . . . . Oct 1985
Hill, Mr Patrick . . . . Sep 1997
Hopkins, Ms Wendy BA(Cantab) . . . . *Nov 1994
McCarthy, Mr Brendan Gerard BCL . . . . *Jan 1991
Miller, Mr Julian LLB(Lond) . . . . *Apr 1987
Strevens, Miss Harriet LLB . . . . *Mar 1990
Wilkes, Mr Christopher J BA . . . . *Oct 1983

DAC BEACHCROFT
85 Gracechurch Street London EC3V 0AA
Tel: 020 7936 2222 *Fax:* 020 7936 2020
Dx: 172 LONDON/CHANCERY LN
Office: Birmingham, Bristol, Leeds, London EC3 (2 offices), London EC4 (2 offices), Manchester (2 offices), Newcastle upon Tyne, Newport, Winchester

DBP LAW SOLICITORS ‡
Kingsbury House 468 Church Lane Kingsbury London NW9 8UA
Tel: 020 8200 2356 *Fax:* 020 8200 2359
E-mail: info@dbplaw.co.uk

D E T CHILD ‡
5a Sheridan Road London SW19 3HW
Tel: 020 8540 3087 *Fax:* 020 8542 2460

DF SOLICITORS ‡
791 Sidcup Road London SE9 3SB
Tel: 020 3223 1061

DG LAW ‡
31 Rashness Road London SW11 6RY
Tel: 0845 634 6253 *Fax:* 020 7806 8211
Work: C1 C2 E S1 S2 Z(b)

DH LAW SOLICITORS LLP ‡
142 Uxbridge Road London W7 3SL
Tel: 020 8840 8008 *Fax:* 020 8567 4550 *Dx:* 39508 HANWELL
E-mail: ealing@dhlaw.org.uk
Office: Hayes, London SW1

DH LAW SOLICITORS LLP
83 Victoria Street London SW1H 0HW
Tel: 020 8840 8008 *Fax:* 020 8567 4550 *Dx:* 2303 VICTORIA
E-mail: westminster@dhlaw.org.uk
Office: Hayes, London W7

DKLM SOLICITORS ‡
City House 3 Cranwood Street London EC1V 9PE
Tel: 020 7549 7888 *Fax:* 020 7549 7889 *Dx:* 36601 FINSBURY
E-mail: p.li@dklm.co.uk
Work: A3 B1 C1 E J1 L O Q S1 S2 Z(q)

DLA PIPER UK LLP ‡
(incorporating Bird Semple)
(in association with Price & Partners)
3 Noble Street London EC2V 7EE
Tel: 0870 011 1111 *Fax:* 020 7796 6666
Dx: 33866 FINSBURY SQUARE
Emergency telephone 0870 011 1111
E-mail: catherine.usher@dlapiper.com
List of partners: J Ahern, I Alexopoulos, D Allen, P M Anson, R W H Arnison, V Arora, C W Arrand, C I Ashford, N Bamford, D Barbour, T Barker, H R Barraclough, H Bassford, M Beardmore, M P Beardwood, R G Beckett, S Bell, P Bennett, B Bentley, P Billing, T H Birch Reynardson, B Bishop, S G Blacksell, R A Bointon, R Bonnar, S D Boon, S Bottley, C G Bowes, N D Bowker, I W Bowler, D J Bradley, G Bradley, D J Breakell, E Bremner, I Brierley, L D Brierley, P Brook, H Brunt, T D Buckingham, C Burden, M L Burgess, P A Burnley, M J Burton, P M Butler, D H Cadwallader, D Calow, J Cameron, J Campion, A Chalmers, J R Chandler, M A Chidley, P Chong, M Christmas, J N Clark, A Clarke, M F Clarke, P H Coleman, R G Collier, C Cook, E Cooke, S Coucher, L Cowell, M J Cowley, C Craig, M Crichard, P J Crichton, D G Crosse, M R Crossfield, N A Crossley, S V Croxon, A J Da Costa, A D Darwin, F P Davie, A Davies, C Davis, H Davison, G C Day, S J Day, K R Dearsley, A B Dell, S Devlin, H Dolphin, P W Dowle, N J Drew, P Duffy, A Dury, H F Dyer, A Dyson, J M Eatough, M C Elsenaar, H C Evans, J Exten-Wright, S E Fanning, J G Fenton, M J Fiddy, T F Field, P N Firth, T Fisher, N Fitzpatrick, P J Fleming, H Foster, K E Francis, M B Franklin, K E Friebe, K T Fung, G Gallen, M E Gay, D N Gerrard, D Gillespie, D Glover, L Gluyas, M Glynn, G W Godar, M Goodwin, C A Gordon, R Gough, S G Gough, A J Gowman, R Gowrley, D J Gray, T R Green, A Griffith, E Griffiths, H Hall, K Hall, S Halladay, M C Hallam, S M Haller, C Hanson, A D Harris, J J Harris, W A Harrison, A Hartley, N Haywood, E Heffernan, M Hemsted, A Herring, T Heylen, M V Hirst, T C Hitchcock, M Holland, A Holt, N E Howard, R Hoy, W J A Hyde, A J Ibrahim, N P Iliff, M Illingworth, A S Jacobs, S James, M Javaid, P Jayson, J Jeffreys, S P Jennings, N Jew, A Jones, S H Jones, S R Jordan, A Kamerling, M C Keates, J Kenworthy, S Kenyon, J E Kerrigan, M Kim, J Kittle, N G Knowles, G M Lamb, J C Lavery, M Leach, K A Lee, J Legrand, S R Levine, T Littler, M J Lonergan, A Low, M Lynch, K Macpherson, Y Maka, N Maltby, S Marais, T T Marshall, E Martin, V Massarano, V F Mather, J Matthews, R May, R J McGrane, M Mckee, D W R McKie, N M McLean, M F McMorrow, A Mehta, P J Michau, D Miles, H Miles, B Miller, A L Mills, A Monk, E Montorio, E F Mooney, M J Morgan, A Morris, G Morris, C Morrison, J Morrissy, D P Mosley, A Moss, A Mott, A J W Muriel, D P Murphy, R M Muttock, S A Neilson-Clark, M Newell, A Noon, R Norman, R J Norris, S R O'Brien, M J O'Conor, M O'Hanlon, R C Obank, J A Ogley, G W E Orchison, R P Orme, S Osuntokun, P Owen, G Paddison, A Page, A E Pattinson, K Payne, L J Peasland, P G Perry, M D Phillips, D Pickering, J C Pickworth, J Pinsent, J S F Plant, M J Pollen, S Porter, M J Prince, J Procter, M R Pullen, D Raff, B Ramsay, A R Randle, C D Rawstron, M H Rees, J Richards, M F Ridley, P Rimmer, A Roberts, P J Rooney, W D Rosen, P J Rout, A Samad, H Samaha, M D Saunders, H R Scheiwiller, R Seiger, C Severs, K Sharma, S M Sharma, N P Shepherd, M S J Sims, N D Slater, S Sly, M R Smith, R Smyth, P A N Somekh, J Stait, C Staton, P B Stone, J Stout, J C P Sullivan, L Sweeney, S Sweeney, M R Swindell, M Swynnerton, A Tamlyn, M Taylor, P Taylor, E Thomas, D Thompson, P K Thompson, M D Tinker, R Tozer, C T Tulley, G C Tyler, C F Usher, J Vickery, A Videon, M R A Vipan, S Wallace, J Watkins, W A Watson, P B Wayte, A Weightman, A S Weightman, N W West, R Whittaker, R Wilkinson, C J Wilson, B Woolcock, R Woolich, D Wright
Office: Birmingham, Leeds, Liverpool, Manchester, Sheffield
Languages: French, German, Russian
Work: A1 B1 C1 C2 C3 D1 E F1 F2 J1 J2 L M1 M2 N O P Q R1 S1 T1 T2 W Z(a,b,c,d,e,f,h,i,j,k,l,n,o,p,q,u)
Emergency Action, Agency undertaken and Member of Accident Line
Ptr: Ahern, Mr John . . . . Jun 1995
Alexopoulos, Ioannis BA(Cantab & Athens); Dip(Cantab) . . . . *Oct 1992
Allen, Mr Daren BA . . . . *Oct 1990
Arora, Ms Vinita. . . . . Sep 1999
Barbour, Ms Debbie. . . . . Aug 2000

See p2 for the Key to Work Categories & other symbols

Barker, Mr Toby BA Sep 1997
Bassford, Mr Howard Sep 1997
Bennett, Ms Philipa Nov 1994
Birch Reynardson, Mr Thomas H MA(Oxon). *Apr 1983
Bishop, Mr Bob Sep 1995
Boon, Mr Simon D BA. *Nov 1981
Breakell, Mr David J MA(Oxon) *Oct 1977
Bremner, Ms Elisabeth Oct 1996
Brierley, Mr Ian Oct 1994
Burden, Mr Christopher Dec 1993
Burton, Mr Michael J BA(Dunelm) *Apr 1979
Butler, Mr Philip M BA(Lond) Nov 1992
Calow, Mr Duncan Oct 1994
Cameron, Mr James Apr 1997
Chandler, Mr John R *Dec 1989
Chong, Mr Philip Oct 1992
Clark, Mr John N Nov 1983
Coleman, Mr Peter H Nov 1975
Cooke, Mr Ed. Sep 2000
Coucher, Ms Sarah Nov 1991
Cowley, Mr Michael J BA(Oxon) *Mar 1984
Crichard, Mr Mark LLB(B'ham) *Nov 1992
Crichton, Mr Peter James BA *Nov 1994
Crossfield, Mr Mark Richard LLB *Feb 1988
Croxon, Miss Sian V BA. Sep 1977
Da Costa, Mr Alastair John LLB. *Oct 1990
Darwin, Mr Andrew D MA Clements Inn Prize; Stokes Memorial Prize *Oct 1983
Davis, Ms Cecily Nov 1993
Day, Mr Gordon C MA(Oxon) *§Jun 1978
Dearsley, Mr Kenneth R MA(Cantab) *Dec 1974
Dell, Mr Alex B LLB. *Oct 1995
Drew, Mr Nigel J MA(Cantab) *Nov 1983
Dyer, Ms Helen F LLB. Nov 1990
Elsenaar, Mr Marnix Christiaan LLB(Hons)(Exon) *Nov 1995
Exten-Wright, Mr Jonathan MA *Oct 1990
Fanning, Miss Susan Elizabeth BA(Oxon)(History); CPE; LSF *Nov 1992
Fenton, Mr Jonathan G MA(Oxon). Dec 1983
Fiddy, Mr Michael Jonathan BA(Hons); LSF Chairman of SPI Students Committee Feb 1994
Fisher, Ms Tracy Nov 1993
Fitzpatrick, Mr Nicholas Nov 1993
Fleming, Mr Paul Joseph BA *Dec 1992
Foster, Mr Hartley. Feb 2007
Francis, Ms Kate E BA(Oxon). *Dec 1995
Franklin, Mr Mark Bernard LLB(Hons) International Lawyer of the Year 98-99; Miami Law Review *Oct 1984
Friebe, Miss Karen E LLB(Hons) *Feb 1983
Fung, Mr King Tak Aug 1997
Gay, Mr Mark E BA(Oxon) *Jan 1989
Gerrard, Mr D Neil LLB(Hons). *Oct 1991
Gillespie, Mr Duncan Sep 1998
Gluyas, Mr Lee Nov 1994
Glynn, Mr Matthew Sep 2001
Godar, Mr George W MA(Cantab) Herbert Ruse Prize; Clements Inn Prize; Sheffield Prize; Edmund Thos Childs Prize; John Marshall Prize. *Jun 1974
Gordon, Mr Charles A BA(Oxon) *Jun 1981
Gough, Mr Simon G LLB Sep 1990
Gowman, Miss Alison J BA(Dunelm) Member of the Court of Common Council *Oct 1980
Green, Mr Terry Roy LLB(Hons); LLM(Hons) *Sep 1985
Griffith, Mr Alexander Sep 1999
Griffiths, Mr Edward. Sep 1999
Halladay, Mr Stephen LLB. *Nov 1991
Haller, Mr Stephen M BSc(Lond) *§Dec 1977
Hanson, Mr Christopher. Dec 1991
Heffernan, Ms Eva Nov 2004
Holt, Mr Andrew. Oct 1984
Hoy, Ms Ruth Sep 1998
Illingworth, Mr Matthew Sep 1997
Javaid, Mr Makbool Nov 1988
Jayson, Mr Paul. Sep 1997
Jordan, Mr Stuart R BA(Hons). *Dec 1992
Kamerling, Alix Mar 1993
Kim, Mr Michael Bng; MSc; LLB. Sep 1998
Knowles, Mr Nigel G LLB Jun 1980
Legrand, Ms Janet MA(Cantab) *Nov 1983
Levine, Mr Simon R MA(Cantab) Nov 1990
Low, Mr Adrian May 1998
McGrane, Mr Richard J BComm; LLB(Hons)(Auckland); BCL(Oxon) ♦ Jan 1990
Mckee, Mr Michael LLB; LLM(Cantab). Apr 1990
McKie, Mr David William Roberts BA(Hons) *May 1996
Marais, Mr Stephen Sep 1996
Marshall, Mr Timothy T LLB. *Feb 1989
Martin, Mr Edwin Sep 1995
Matthews, Mr Julian. Oct 1996
Mehta, Anil Mar 1997
Michau, Mr Peter J BA; LLB. *Mar 1975
Miles, Mr David Oct 1996
Monk, Mr Alex Sep 1997
Morrison, Mr Charles BA *Oct 1987
Muriel, Mr Andrew J W LLB *Feb 1988
Murphy, Mr David P BA(Kent) *Mar 1989
Neilson-Clark, Mr Simon A BSc *Oct 1989
Newell, Mr Michael Sep 1998
O'Brien, Mr Stephen R LLB Sep 1990
O'Conor, Mr Mark J BA(Hons). *Dec 1994
Ogley, Mr Julian A BA(Oxon) *§Apr 1973
Osuntokun, Segun BA Oct 1993
Paddison, Mr Gary LLB(Hull) Nov 1993
Peasland, Ms Lorinda J LLB. Oct 1987
Perry, Mr Philip G BA Jun 1975
Phillips, Mr Mark David Aug 1991
Pickering, Mr Duncan Sep 1997
Pickworth, Mr Jonathan Charles. Dec 1990
Pollen, Mr Michael J *Nov 1979
Porter, Ms Sarah May 2005
Pullen, Mr Michael Rhodes Nov 1994
Raff, Mr David LLB(Lond) *Oct 1983
Ramsay, Bonella Sep 1992
Rees, Mr Martin H MA(Oxon) Oct 1976
Richards, Mr Jonathan Nov 1995
Ridley, Mr Michael F BA. Apr 1980
Rosen, Mr William David BA(Hons) *Nov 1994
Samad, Askandar Dec 1991
Samaha, Ms Helena Sep 1996
Saunders, Mr Matthew David BA(Oxon) *Nov 1991
Severs, Mr Charles LLB(Bris) *Mar 1994
Sharma, Mr Kiran Sep 1999
Sharma, Siddharth M *Sep 1998
Sims, Mr Melvyn S J LLB *Nov 1982
Stait, Mr Julian Jul 1992
Swindell, Mr Mark R LSF Oct 1985
Swynnerton, Mr Matthew Sep 1998
Tamlyn, Mr Alexander LLB Sep 1996
Taylor, Mr Mark Nov 1988
Thomas, Ms Elinor Sep 2007
Tyler, Mr Graham Craig LLB(Hons) *Nov 1990
Usher, Mrs Catherine F *§Jun 1975
Videon, Ms Alicia Nov 2004
Watson, Miss Wendy A LLB. *Oct 1990
Wayte, Mr Peter B LLB Jun 1974
West, Mr Nicholas W Oct 1985
Whittaker, Mr Roger. *Apr 1969
Wilkinson, Mr Richard. Mar 1998
Wilson, Mr Colin John LLB *Apr 1995
Woolich, Mr Richard MA(Cantab); ATII; AITP *Dec 1989
Dir: Brunt, Mr Harry Oct 1996
Gowrley, Mr Rupert Apr 2003

DL LEGAL LLP ‡
Fitzroy House London WC1E 7EY
Tel: 0845 456 9800

DMH STALLARD LLP
6 New Street Square New Fetter Lane London EC4A 3BF
Tel: 020 7822 1500 ***Fax:*** 020 7842 2333 ***Dx:*** 344 CHANCERY LANE
E-mail: enquiries@dmhstallard.com
Office: Brighton, Crawley
Languages: Dutch, French, German, Italian, Spanish
Work: A1 A3 B1 B2 C1 C2 C3 D1 D2 E F1 F2 G H I J1 K1 K3 K4 L M1 N O P Q R1 R2 S1 S2 T1 T2 U2 V W X Z(b,c,d,e,f,g,h,k,l,m,o,p,q,r,s,t,u,w,x,z,za)

DPNA SOLICITORS ‡
374 Brockley Road London SE4 2BY
Tel: 020 8177 7199 ***Fax:*** 020 8314 1313

DWF
Capital House 85 King William Street London EC4N 7BL
Tel: 020 7645 9500 ***Fax:*** 020 7645 9501
E-mail: enquiries@dwf.co.uk
Office: Leeds, Liverpool, Manchester, Newcastle upon Tyne, Preston

DWFM BECKMAN ‡
33 Welbeck Street Westminster London W1G 8LX
Tel: 020 7872 0023 ***Fax:*** 020 7872 0024 ***Dx:*** 9031 WEST END 1
E-mail: enquiries@dfmbeckman.com
List of partners: B C Beckman, N I Beckman, P Beckman, M Boccali-Vine, D G Bray, P J Bridson, I S David, C Jaque, S L Killen, A Y Mead, A Simmons, V Wineman
Languages: French, Greek, Hebrew
Work: A1 A3 B1 C1 C2 E F1 F2 J1 L M2 N O Q R1 R2 S1 S2 T1 T2 U2 W Z(c,d,e,k,p,q,r)
Fixed Fee Interview undertaken
Ptr: Beckman, Mr Brian C LLB(Lond) *Jan 1965
Beckman, Mr Norman I MA(Oxon). Nov 1956
Beckman, Mr Philip MA(Oxon) John Mackrell Prize; Clifford's Inn Prize; Maurice Nordon Prize *Apr 1959
Boccali-Vine, Mrs Maria LLB *Oct 1986
Bray, Mr David Graham LLB(B'ham). *Nov 1972
Bridson, Mr Peter J LLB(Lond) *Dec 1978
David, Mr Irving S LLB(Lond) May 1972
Jaque, Mr Colin. *Jan 2001
Killen, Mr Stuart L LLB(Hons) Chairman of Area Legal Aid Committee *Dec 1967
Mead, Mr Anthony Y *§Nov 1975
Simmons, Mr Anthony. *Jan 2005
Wineman, Mr Vivian MA(Cantab) *Nov 1975
Asoc: Calligas, Ms Louisa MA. *Jan 2000
Ast: Balli, Ergin BA(Hons); CPE; LPC Mar 1998
Con: Brahams, Mr Malcolm H MA(Oxon) *Jan 1966
Davis, Mr Malcolm M *Nov 1957
Frankel, Montague D LLB. *Nov 1971
Raybould, Mr Martin Howard LLB; MBA. *May 1977

GORDON DADDS ‡
80 Brook Street Mayfair London W1K 5DD
Tel: 020 7493 6151 ***Dx:*** 131 LONDON/CHANCERY LN
E-mail: info@gordondadds.com
List of partners: S H Bland, E Box, H Elder, A Ellis, K Peat, R M Peters, D Ruck, M Tussaud, A H Wagstaff, A Whittaker
Languages: French, German, Italian, Spanish
Work: A3 C1 C2 E J1 K1 K2 K3 N O R2 S1 S2 T1 T2 W Z(b,d,n)
Ptr: Bland, Miss Susan H LLB. *Dec 1982
Box, Ms Emma BA(Hons). Feb 1997
Elder, Mr Hugh Feb 1976
Ellis, Miss Anne-Marie LLB(Hons). Mar 1993
Peat, Mrs Kathryn LLB Recorder Mar 1980
Peters, Mr Roger M. Oct 1973
Ruck, Mr David MA *§Mar 1987
Tussaud, Mr Michael FCA. *§Dec 1978
Wagstaff, Miss Anna Heather LLB(Hons) *Nov 1995
Whittaker, Mr Andrew *Feb 1979
Ast: Bhula, Mr Dharmesh BA; LLB. *Jan 2005
Kelly, Miss Lauren Elizabeth. Oct 2006
Nottage, Ms Victoria Elizabeth LLB *Sep 2002
O'Farrell, Miss Louise Mary LLB(Hons) Feb 1981
Rees, Mrs Catrin Ann BA(Hons)(English); PGDipLaw; LPC Oct 2000

DALE-STEVENS LLP ‡
St Mary Abchurch House 123 Cannon Street London EC4N 5AU
Tel: 020 7929 2247 / 7929 3897 ***Fax:*** 020 7929 3170
E-mail: law@dalestevens.com
List of partners: M Dale
Office: Felixstowe

DALTON BARRETT SOLICITORS ‡
33 Milligan Street London E14 8AT
Tel: 020 7537 7904
E-mail: barrett582@btinternet.com

DALTON HOLMES GRAY ‡
7a D'arblay Street London W1F 8DF
Tel: 020 7025 7878 ***Fax:*** 020 7025 7877 ***Dx:*** 37237 PICCADILLY
Emergency telephone 07973 214337
E-mail: enquiries@daltonholmesgray.co.uk

DANIEL AND HARRIS ‡
338 Kilburn High Road Camden London NW6 2QN
Tel: 020 7625 0202 ***Fax:*** 020 7372 5029 ***Dx:*** 123861 KILBURN 2
E-mail: mail@danielandharris.co.uk
List of partners: M N H Leiper, M E Ross
Work: D1 E K1 K2 S1 S2 V W
Emergency Action, Legal Aid undertaken and Legal Aid Franchise
Ptr: Leiper, Ms Margaret N H BA *Oct 1984
Ross, Mr Martin E BA. *Nov 1986
Asoc: Walia, Mrs Kiran LLB Aug 2001
Ast: Huynh, Mr Quang Chuong LLB *Aug 2001
Con: Daniel, Mr Timothy P C LLB(Bris) *Sep 1968
Lavelle, Ms Felicity BA *Oct 1980

DANOBEITIA & FORSTER ‡
125 Gorriano Avenue London NW5 2RX
Tel: 020 8876 4733 / 7267 2286

ADAM DARCY ‡
Hyde House The Hyde Colindale London NW9 6LH

DARE EMMANUEL SOLICITORS ‡
Suite 2.34 75 Whitechapel Road London E1 1DU
Tel: 020 7392 9566 ***Dx:*** 591 LONDON/CITY

DASS SOLICITORS
Millbank Tower 21-24 Millbank London SW1P 4QP
Tel: 020 7802 5040 ***Fax:*** 020 7802 5044 ***Dx:*** 149245 VICTORIA 13
Office: Birmingham

DAVENPORT LYONS ‡
30 Old Burlington Street London W1S 3NL
Tel: 020 7468 2600 ***Fax:*** 020 7437 8216
List of partners: J E Ayres, M D Bateman, K J Bays, F D Bloom, J Burrell, J D Cohen, P I Conway, L Courtney, N Davies, A J Domb, M Elstow, R Ferguson, T S Flatau, D J Gore, J M Gregson, S L Haggard, M Hatchwell, N R Kelsey, J A Killip, J D Lass, J Lockyer, D L Marchese, B L Miller, R L Moxon, T O'Maoileoin, L J Powell, T P R Sears, R H L Shaw, S Tatton-Brown, M Themistocli, A R Thomas, P A Toolan, M S Van der Zyl, P Weiss
Languages: Flemish, French, German, Italian, Spanish
Work: B1 B2 C1 C2 C3 E F1 I J1 K1 K2 K3 L M1 N O P Q R1 S1 T1 T2 U1 U2 W Z(b,c,d,e,f,g,i,j,k,l,o,p,w,z,za)
Emergency Action, Agency, Legal Aid undertaken and Member of Accident Line
Ptr: Ayres, Ms Janet Elizabeth LLB(Hons) Jan 1978
Bateman, Mr Mark D LLB *Mar 1996
Bays, Mr Kevin J LLB *Apr 1979
Bloom, Mr Fraser D BA(Cantab). *Jul 1997
Burrell, Mr John BA(Nott'm) *Dec 1977
Cohen, Mr Jeffrey D LLB(Lond); MA. *Feb 1986
Conway, Mr Philip I *May 1984
Courtney, Linda. Jan 1994
Davies, Mr Nigel Jan 1986
Domb, Mr Alon J BA(Hons) *Nov 1988
Elstow, Ms Marilyn MSc; BA(Hons) Jan 1987
Ferguson, Ms Rebecca LLB(Hons)(Manc). *Nov 1999
Flatau, Mr Thomas Sebastian LLB Sep 1995
Gore, Mr David J BA *Jul 1978
Gregson, Miss Jeanette M BA. *Jun 1990
Haggard, Ms Susan L BA(Cantab) *Nov 1985
Hatchwell, Mr Michael BA. *May 1988
Kelsey, Mr N Richard *Jul 1966
Killip, Miss Julie A LLB(Hons) *Apr 1984
Lass, Mr Jonathan D MA(Cantab). *Nov 1972
Lockyer, Mrs Jane BA(Hons); CPE; LSF(Hons) *Nov 1995
Marchese, Mr David L MA(Oxon) *Jul 1976
Miller, Mr Brian L MA *Oct 1992
Moxon, Mr Richard L LLB(B'ham) *Jun 1975
O'Maoileoin, Mr Thomas Jul 2001
Powell, Leslie J. *§Sep 1972
Sears, Mr Trevor P R *Jan 1972
Shaw, Mr Robin H L. *Dec 1983
Tatton-Brown, Sam BA(Hons)(Durham) *Sep 1998
Themistocli, Mino BA *Oct 1982
Thomas, Mr Alun Richard. *May 1999
Toolan, Mr Paul Anthony BA; MA Oct 2000
Van der Zyl, Mrs Marie S LLB. *§Nov 1991
Weiss, Mr Peter BA. *Mar 2000
Asoc: Brown, Ms Michelle BA(Cantab). *Sep 1997
Calcara, Ms Vincenza. Nov 1991
Constable, Mrs Jenny LLB *Mar 1997
Davis, Ms Elizabeth. Mar 1999
Feldman, Ms Deborah LLB *Apr 1980
Gill, Ms Amandeep *Nov 2000
Isaac, Ms Fleur Samantha Sep 2000
Mustafa, Mr Paul LLB. Oct 2002
Sprawson, Mr Rupert BA(Hons). *Dec 1998
Ast: Baker, Ms Catherine Sep 1998
Elliott, Mr Richard. Oct 2004
Etheridge, Ms Alexa. Sep 2001
Gilroy, Mr Nigel LLB. *Sep 2001
Hugill, Mr Adam Scott LLB(Hons) *Oct 2004
Robertson, Mr Bryn *Apr 1998
Tandy, Miss Sarah BSc *Oct 2002
Con: Charlton, Mr Robert BA(Witwatersrand). Feb 1998
McCombie, Mr Paul J LLB(Lond) *Nov 1971
Morgan, Mr Leon R. *Jul 1964
Selig, Ms Yael LLB(Hons) *Aug 1997

AUBREY DAVID ‡
40 Manchester Street Westminster London W1U 7LL
Tel: 020 7224 4410 ***Fax:*** 020 7935 2410 ***Dx:*** 41738 MARYLEBONE 2
E-mail: dfreedman@aubreydavid.com
List of partners: M Adler, G V Bayliss, D Freedman, A A Marks
Work: B1 C1 C2 E J1 L O Q R2 S1 S2 T1 T2 W Z(q)
Agency, Advocacy and Fixed Fee Interview undertaken
Ptr: Adler, Mr Malcolm LLB(Hons) *Apr 1977
Bayliss, Mr Glen V Outstanding Achievement (Law Soc LPC) 1998 *Nov 1998
Freedman, Mr David LLB *Jul 1987
Marks, Mr Adrian A. *Apr 1974
Ast: Kirby, Ms Fiona BA(Hons). Jul 2003
Singh, Mr Rajwinder LLB; LLM *Oct 1993

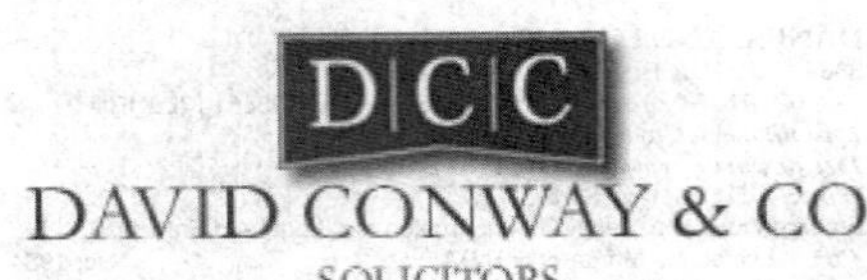

DAVID CONWAY & CO ‡
1 Great Cumberland Place Marble Arch London W1H 7AL
Tel: 020 7258 3000 *Fax:* 020 7258 3390 *Dx:* 41704 MARYLEBONE 2
E-mail: dconway@conwaylaw.co.uk
List of partners: D P Conway
Work: C1 C2 E J1 L O Q R1 S1 S2 W Z(e,l,w)
Ptr: Conway, Mr David Peter. . . . . *Sep 1970
Ast: Barnes, Mr Rupert Alexander Howard LLB(Hons) . . . Nov 1992

PAUL DAVID CONSULTING LIMITED ‡
22 Danescroft Brent Street London NW4 2QH
Tel: 07715 420980
E-mail: paul.friedman@hotmail.co.uk

DAVIDSON MERALI & CO ‡
Vicarage House 58/60 Kensington Church Street London W8 4DB
Tel: 020 7937 2525 *Fax:* 020 7937 1915
List of partners: J J S Davidson, S H J Merali
Emergency Action, Agency, Advocacy and Legal Aid undertaken
Ptr: Davidson, Mr John J S MA(Cantab). . . . . *Jun 1964
Merali, Shahin H J . . . . *Oct 1983
Con: Merali, Mr Abu-Talib H J. . . . . *Nov 1982

DAVIDSON MORRIS SOLICITORS ‡
33 Soho Square London W1D 3QU
Tel: 0845 413 7000 *Fax:* 0845 413 7001
E-mail: info@davidsonmorris.com
Work: Z(i)

W A G DAVIDSON & CO ‡
33 Horn Lane Acton London W3 9NJ
Tel: 020 8992 4884 *Fax:* 020 8992 5783 *Dx:* 80252 ACTON
E-mail: wagdavidson@aol.com
List of partners: C R Benjamin, R L Grey, G A G Speechly
Languages: French
Work: C1 D1 E F1 G J1 K1 L M1 N P S1 T1 V W Z(l)
Emergency Action, Agency and Legal Aid undertaken
Ptr: Benjamin, Mr Clive R LLB. . . . . *Nov 1975
Grey, Mr Robin L . . . . *Jun 1977
Speechly, Mr Guy A G LLB(Lond) . . . . *Feb 1955
Ast: Sumner, Ms M Ellen LLB(Hull) . . . . *Apr 1981

DAVIES & DAVIES ASSOCIATES LIMITED ‡
14 Anning Street London EC2A 3LQ
Tel: 0800 840 4025 *Fax:* 0800 840 4026
E-mail: enquiries@daviesanddavies.net
Office: Banbury

DAVIES BATTERSBY LTD ‡
St Michaels Rectory St Michael's Alley London EC3V 9DS
Tel: 020 7621 1090 *Fax:* 020 7621 1040
Emergency telephone 07785 737636
E-mail: patrick@daviesbattersby.com
List of partners: P Battersby, G Davies
Work: A3 B1 B2 C1 C2 J1 L M2 M3 N O Q Z(a,c,j)
Fixed Fee Interview undertaken
Ptr: Battersby, Mr Patrick BA; LLB. . . . . *Dec 1990
Davies, Mr Guy LLB. . . . . *Nov 1991
Ast: Nash, Ms Melanie BA ♦. . . . . *Oct 1986
Con: Clark, Mr Mark Colin Charles BSc(Economic & Social History) . . . . Oct 1989

DAVIES BAYS & CO T/A WINDSOR & CO
(in association with John Bays & Co)
670 High Road Tottenham Haringey London N17 0AH
Tel: 020 8808 3237 *Fax:* 020 8365 0849 *Dx:* 52201 TOTTENHAM 2
Office: London N22
Work: B1 C1 D1 E K1 L N Q S1 T1 T2 W Z(l)
Ptr: Bays, Mr John D BA(Hons)(Dunelm) . . . . *Jun 1973
McDoom, Mr Riyad Ally LLB . . . . Sep 2004

JEREMY DAVIES & CO ‡
30 Thurloe Street South Kensington London SW7 2LT
Tel: 020 7589 4999 *Fax:* 020 7589 4990
E-mail: jdavies@chelseaman.com
List of partners: J H Davies
Work: E L O Q R2 S1 S2 W
Agency, Advocacy and Fixed Fee Interview undertaken
Ptr: Davies, Mr Jeremy Hugh . . . . *Oct 1982

LAWRENCE DAVIES & CO ‡
90 Lillie Road Fulham Hammersmith & Fulham London SW6 7SR
Tel: 020 7381 1171 *Fax:* 020 7381 2232
Dx: 132856 WEST KENSINGTON 3
Emergency telephone 07775 538 702
E-mail: mail@lawrence-davies.com
List of partners: E P Davies, C K Holland
Languages: Welsh
Work: D1 D2 G H K1 K3
Emergency Action, Agency, Advocacy, Fixed Fee Interview, Legal Aid undertaken and Legal Aid Franchise
Ptr: Davies, Elen P BA . . . . *Oct 1985
Holland, Ms Claire Kathleen. . . . . *Oct 1991
Ast: Daly, Ms Melrose LLB. . . . . *Jan 2001
Jones, Mr David. *Jun 2006
Olanrewaju, Ms Olawumi LLB. . . . . *Jan 2003

DAVIES MORGANTE LAW LIMITED ‡
10 The Broadway Wimbledon London SW19 1RF
Tel: 020 8944 7700 *Fax:* 020 8947 6717
Dx: 300114 WIMBLEDON CENTRAL
E-mail: clerks@dmlaw.co.uk

DAVIS & CO ‡
St Michael's Rectory St Michael's Alley Cornhill London EC3V 9DS
Tel: 020 7621 1091 *Fax:* 020 7626 5174
Emergency telephone 07940 913232
E-mail: trevor.davis@davis-solicitors.com
List of partners: T A Davis
Languages: French, German, Spanish, Vietnamese
Work: M2 O Q Z(a,e,j,n)
Emergency Action, Agency, Advocacy and Fixed Fee Interview undertaken
SPr: Davis, Mr Trevor Andes LLB(Hons); LLM . . . . . . *Nov 1986
Ast: Elsey, Mr Steven Keith LLB(Hons). . . . . *Nov 2005
Tran, Miss Cac Cam Thi LLB(Hons). . . . . *May 2004

DAVIS & CO (SOLICITORS) LIMITED ‡
27 Old Gloucester Street London WC1N 3XX
Tel: 020 8123 6373
E-mail: mail@davis-solicitors.co.uk

IAN DAVIS ‡
54 Winchmore Hill Road London N14 6PX
Tel: 020 8886 1830 *Fax:* 020 8882 0994
E-mail: imdavies8@aol.com

LEIGH DAVIS ‡
17 Gosfield Street London W1W 6HE
Tel: 020 7631 0302 *Fax:* 020 7631 1101
Dx: 42728 OXFORD CIRCUS NORTH
E-mail: info@leighdavis.co.uk
List of partners: A Davis, R D Leigh, A Tankel
Work: A3 C1 C2 E F1 J1 K1 K3 L N O Q R2 S1 S2 U2 W Z(e,f,i,k,l,p,q,w)
Ptr: Davis, Mr Antony BA . . . . *Oct 1982
Leigh, Mr Robin D BA. . . . . *Sep 1982
Tankel, Mrs Andrea BA(Law) . . . . *Oct 1982
Asoc: Morris, Mr Richard BA. . . . . *Sep 2002

RALPH DAVIS ‡
1-2 Faulkner's Alley Cowcross Street Islington London EC1M 6DD
Tel: 020 7253 7200 *Fax:* 020 7253 7279 *Dx:* 53307 CLERKENWELL
E-mail: ralph.davis@ralphdavis.co.uk
List of partners: R G Davis, P A Nixon
Languages: French
Work: J1 L N O Q S1 S2 Z(k,q)
Emergency Action undertaken
Ptr: Davis, Mr Ralph G BA. . . . . *§Jan 1983
Nixon, Ms Penelope Ann LLB. . . . . Jan 1979

DAVIS SOLICITORS ‡
26 Mallard House Station Court London SW6 2BF
Tel: 020 7930 6996

DAVITT & CO ‡
193 Chatsworth Road Willesden Green London NW2 5QS
Tel: 020 7566 8244
List of partners: O Davitt
Ptr: Davitt, Mr O. . . . . Sep 1998

DAWSON CORNWELL ‡
15 Red Lion Square London WC1R 4QT
Tel: 020 7242 2556 *Fax:* 020 7831 0478
Dx: 181 LONDON/CHANCERY LN
E-mail: mail@dawsoncornwell.com
List of partners: J F Abraham, K C Allen, M P Beard, R J Bywater, J R Cornwell, S R Harker, A Hutchinson, H S Kings, R K Lewis, C Marin Pedreno, L Marks
Languages: Arabic, French, German, Greek, Gujarati, Hindi, Italian, Polish, Portuguese, Spanish
Work: D1 D2 E K1 K2 K3 L Q S1 S2 T1 T2 W Z(d,o)
Emergency Action, Agency, Advocacy and Legal Aid undertaken
Ptr: Abraham, Mr Jeremy F BA . . . . Mar 1983
Allen, Miss Katherine C BA(Econ); CPE; LPC . . . . . Dec 1998
Beard, Mr Martin P BA(Cantab) . . . . *Jun 1978
Bywater, Mr Russell J LLB(Brunel) . . . . *Oct 1985
Cornwell, Mr John R LLB(Bris) Deputy District Judge of the Family Division of the High Court . . . . *Jan 1969
Harker, Mr Stephen R LLB(Brunel) . . . . *Mar 1987
Hutchinson, Ms Anne-Marie OBE BA . . . . *Feb 1985
Kings, Ms Helen S LLB(Hons). . . . . Mar 1991
Lewis, Ms Rhiannon K BA. . . . . *Nov 1981
Marin Pedreno, Carolina . . . . Oct 2006
Marks, Ms Lucy MA; CPE; LPC . . . . Sep 2001
Ast: Benhadj, Ms Sarah BA . . . . Feb 2011
Connor, Ms Charlotte LLB. . . . . Mar 2005
Dupre, Ms Lisette LLB . . . . Mar 2008
Rogerson, Mr Colin LLB. . . . . Jul 2011

DAYBELLS LLP ‡
43-45 Broadway Stratford London E15 4BL
Tel: 020 8555 4321 *Fax:* 020 8555 4545 *Dx:* 5402 STRATFORD
List of partners: F M Ahmed, D T Gowlet, P W Riley, F R Sheikh
Work: C1 C2 E F1 K1 K3 L N O P Q S1 S2 T1 T2 W Z(c,i,l,q,r)
Emergency Action, Agency, Advocacy, Fixed Fee Interview, Legal Aid undertaken, Legal Aid Franchise and Member of Accident Line
Ptr: Ahmed, Mr Farhat Mahmood . . . . Jun 2006
Gowlet, Mr David T . . . . *Dec 1984
Riley, Mr Peter W . . . . *Jan 1969
Sheikh, Mr Feisal R LLB; LLM(Hons) . . . . Nov 2000
Ast: Choudhury, Mr Habib LLB(Hons) . . . . Dec 2006

DAYSPARKES ‡
Ground Floor (West) 9 Gray's Inn Square London WC1R 5JQ
Tel: 020 7242 8018 *Fax:* 020 3441 1345

DE BRAUW BLACKSTONES WESTBROEK ‡
5th Floor East Wing 10 King William Street London EC4N 7TW
Tel: 020 7337 3510 *Fax:* 020 7337 3520

DE CRUZ SOLICITORS ‡
38 North Audley Street London W1K 6ZN
Tel: 020 7493 4265

DE SOYZA & FERNANDO ‡
68 Alleyn Park London SE21 8SF
Tel: 020 8670 9918 *Fax:* 020 8766 7805
Dx: 34164 NORWOOD NORTH
Emergency telephone 07956 497773
E-mail: upali@desoyzaandfernando.co.uk
List of partners: U De Soyza
Languages: Arabic, French, German, Italian, Mandarin, Sinhalese
Work: B2 B3 D1 G H J1 K1 S1 S2 T1 T2 Z(i)
Emergency Action, Agency, Advocacy, Fixed Fee Interview, Legal Aid undertaken, Legal Aid Franchise and Member of Accident Line
SPr: De Soyza, Upali FCCA; ACMA . . . . *Nov 1995

INES DE VECCHI ‡
18 Holmside Road London SW12 8RJ
Tel: 020 8675 0152 *Fax:* 020 8675 0152
List of partners: I M T De Vecchi
Languages: Italian
Work: C1 J1 L S1 W
SPr: De Vecchi, Ines M T LLB . . . . Nov 1989

DEBEVOISE & PLIMPTON ‡
Tower 42 14 Old Broad Street London EC2N 1HQ
Tel: 020 7786 9000 *Fax:* 020 7588 4180
List of partners: A L Marriott
Ptr: Marriott, Mr Arthur L ♦. . . . . *Jul 1966

DEBIDINS ‡
6 Broadway West Ealing Ealing London W13 0SR
Tel: 020 8567 1381 / 8567 6343 *Fax:* 020 8579 7494
Dx: 39500 HANWELL
Emergency telephone 07956 361775
E-mail: info@debidins.co.uk
List of partners: D D P Debidin, D S Debidin
Languages: Hindi, Punjabi
Work: B1 D1 E F1 G H J1 K1 L N Q S1 S2 W Z(i,k)
Emergency Action, Agency, Advocacy undertaken and Member of Accident Line
Ptr: Debidin, Mr Daniel D P . . . . *Jan 1976
Debidin, Ms Davina Soshma LLB(Hons)(Lond) . . . . *Jun 2006
Ast: Bal, Mr Kanwar Punjab Singh . . . . Apr 2008

DEBRIDGE SOLICITORS ‡
52 Lower Clapton Road Hackney London E5 0RN
Tel: 020 8986 2581 *Fax:* 020 7923 9644 *Dx:* 46811 DALSTON
List of partners: R M Archer, L M White
Work: B2 G H
Advocacy and Legal Aid undertaken
Ptr: Archer, Ms Rachael M. . . . . Jan 1990
White, Ms Lorna M . . . . Jan 1990

DECHERT ‡
(in association with Dechert Price & Rhoads(USA); Paris; Brussels)
160 Queen Victoria Street London EC4V 4QQ
Tel: 020 7184 7000 *Fax:* 020 7184 7001
Dx: 30 LONDON/CHANCERY LN
E-mail: marketing@titmuss-dechert.com
List of partners: K Anderberg, P D Astleford, J Butwick, B J Caulfield, P R Crockford, J Crook, G Defries, P Draper, S A Fogel, R Frase, W A Fryzer, S F Geraghty, J Gordon, J Grose, D O A Gubbay, A E T Hearn, A M Hougie, A Hutchinson, A Kamalpour, P A Kavanagh, E Kling, A Levin, S A Martin, W Rapozo, M A Stapleton, M R Steinfeld, B J Thorne, D N Vogel, D G Wallis, G M Walters, C A Wynn-Evans
Languages: French, German, Italian
Work: A1 A3 B1 B2 C1 C2 C3 E F1 F2 I J1 L M1 M2 M4 O P Q R1 R2 S2 T1 U1 U2 Z(b,c,d,e,g,i,j,k,o,p,q,s,u,z,za)
Ptr: Anderberg, Ms Karen BA . . . . Jan 1992
Astleford, Mr Peter D LLB. . . . . *Oct 1986
Butwick, Mr Jason. . . . . Nov 1994
Caulfield, Mr Bernard J BSc(Hull)(Econ). . . . . . . *§Jul 1981
Crockford, Mr Peter R LLB(Lond) . . . . *Oct 1978
Crook, Mr James BCom; LLB . . . . Sep 1979
Defries, Mr Graham. . . . . Oct 1994
Draper, Mr Peter LLB . . . . Nov 1976
Fogel, Mr Steven A LLB; LLM(Lond) . . . . *§Dec 1976
Frase, Mr Richard BA(Oxon) . . . . Feb 1981
Fryzer, Mr William A LLB(Exon) . . . . *Apr 1983
Geraghty, Mr Sean Francis BA . . . . Nov 1995
Gordon, Mr John BA . . . . Dec 1989
Grose, Mr Jeremy LLB; AKC(Lond) . . . . *§Jul 1977
Gubbay, Mr David O A BA(Oxon)(Rhodes); LLB. . . *Nov 1991
Hearn, Mr Andrew E T BA(Oxon) . . . . *Nov 1982
Hougie, Mr Andrew M MA. . . . . Oct 1986
Hutchinson, Mr Andrew BA(Law) . . . . *Nov 1986
Kamalpour, Abradat BA(Hons) . . . . Aug 2004
Kavanagh, Mr Paul A LLB. . . . . *Feb 1989
Kling, Mr Edward MA; MA; BA; Member of the California Bar . . . . Nov 1974
Levin, Mr Adam BA . . . . Nov 1989
Martin, Mr Stuart A BA(Manc). . . . . *Oct 1985
Rapozo, Mr Wayne BA . . . . Jan 1991
Stapleton, Mr Mark A LLB. . . . . *Oct 1988
Steinfeld, Mr Michael R BA(Oxon). . . . . *§Nov 1970
Thorne, Mr Barry J . . . . §Dec 1970
Vogel, Mr David N LLM(Lond). . . . . *§Apr 1973
Wallis, Mr David G BA . . . . *Mar 1989
Walters, Mr Geoffrey M LLB(Leics) Leicester Law Society Prize . . . . Jun 1975
Wynn-Evans, Mr Charles A LLB(Bris); BCL(Oxon). . *Nov 1992

DECIMUS FEARON ‡
186 Sloane Street London SW1X 9PR
Tel: 020 7823 0450 *Fax:* 020 7823 0451
Dx: 38150 KNIGHTSBRIDGE
E-mail: enquiries@decimusfearon.com

DEIGHTON GUEDALLA ‡
382 City Road London EC1V 2QA
Tel: 020 7713 9434 *Dx:* 146640 ISLINGTON 4

DEL & CO SOLICITORS ‡
2nd Floor Suite 77 Millmead Business Centre London N17 9QU
Tel: 020 8880 9393

CLAUDIO DEL GIUDICE ‡
Rivington House 82 Great Eastern Street London EC2A 3JF
Tel: 020 7613 2788 *Fax:* 020 7613 2799
E-mail: claudio@italy-uk-law.com
List of partners: C Del Giudice
Languages: Italian
Work: C1 M2 O
Agency undertaken
Ptr: Del Giudice, Dr Claudio MA; Italian Lawyer . . . . . *Sep 1986

MICHAEL DEMIDECKI ‡
Taxi House 11 Woodfield Road London W9 2BA
Tel: 020 7266 3607 *Fax:* 020 7266 4050
List of partners: M R Demidecki-Demidowicz
Work: G Q
SPr: Demidecki-Demidowicz, Mr Michael R MSc . . . . . *Jan 1980

DENNING SOLICITORS ‡
320b Romford Road London E7 8BD
Tel: 020 8519 2999 *Fax:* 020 8519 2229
E-mail: info@denningsolicitors.com

See p2 for the Key to Work Categories & other symbols

DENNISS MATTHEWS ‡
145 Anerley Road London SE20 8EG
Tel: 020 8778 7301 / 8778 7631 *Fax:* 020 8778 6782
Dx: 141820 PENGE 2
E-mail: dm@denniss-mathews.co.uk
List of partners: G P Fairless, N S Matthews, P N R Nathan, R K Sims, G C Sofaer
Languages: French, German
Work: C1 E K1 N O Q S1 W
Emergency Action, Legal Aid undertaken and Legal Aid Franchise
Ptr: Fairless, Miss Gillian P BA . . . . *Oct 1989
Matthews, Mr Nigel Stephen MA . . . . Nov 2001
Nathan, Mr Paul N R LLB(Lond). . . . . *Jan 1983
Sims, Mr Richard K LLB. . . . . *§Mar 1983
Sofaer, Mr G Clive Deputy District Judge . . . . . . *§Nov 1971
Asoc: Harman, Miss Virginia A BSc(Soton) Herbert Ruse Prize . . . . Nov 1980
Spence, Mrs Catherine E MA(Oxon). . . . . *Jun 1981
Ast: Barber, Mrs Jeannette M . . . . Jan 1980
Con: Dennies, Olwer . . . . Jan 1979
Leete, Mr Michael Charles LLB(Lond) Clerk to Commissioner . . . . *Jun 1963

DENT ABRAMS SOLICITORS ‡
7th Floor 3 Shortlands Hammersmith London W6 8DA
Tel: 0845 833 2318 *Fax:* 0845 833 2319
E-mail: info@dentabramslondon.co.uk
Office: Southampton

DENTON SOLICITORS ‡
Enterprise House 113 George Lane South Woodford London E18 1AB
Tel: 020 8989 7477 *Fax:* 020 8989 9022

DEVASSEY LEGAL
33 Cavendish Square London W1G 0PW
Tel: 020 7182 4226
E-mail: philip@devasseyleagal.co.uk
Office: Nottingham

DEVEREAUX SOLICITORS ‡
Oldebourne House 46-47 Chancery Lane London WC2A 1JE
Tel: 020 7242 7766 *Fax:* 020 7242 8879 *Dx:* 370 CHANCERY LANE

LAURA DEVINE SOLICITORS ‡
11 Old Jewry London EC2R 8DU
Tel: 020 7710 0700 *Fax:* 020 7710 0719

DEVONSHIRES ‡
30 Finsbury Circus London EC2M 7DT
Tel: 020 7628 7576 *Fax:* 020 7256 7318
Dx: 33856 FINSBURY SQUARE
E-mail: info@devonshires.co.uk
List of partners: P T Barden, J G M Barker, C N Billingham, J Bradley, D E Brown, P A Buckland, A Casstles, D I Clifford, A J Cowan, A J Crawford, J H R Dunn, J R Ebsworth, N G Grant, G N Hall, S Hall, A L Harvey, A J Hudson, J R Hulley, S Kirkham, M London, J C Mogollon, J Passman, N Philp, A Power, P J Skelton, A L Thompson
Languages: French, German, Spanish
Work: A3 B1 B2 C1 C2 D1 E G I J1 J2 K1 K3 L N O Q R1 R2 S1 S2 T1 U2 W Z(b,c,d,e,g,h,p,q,r,u,x)
Fixed Fee Interview undertaken
Ptr: Barden, Mr Philip T LLB(Leics) Inner Temple Student Mooting Competition Winner 1982. . . . . *Nov 1986
Barker, Mr Julian G M CPE; LPC . . . . Sep 1996
Billingham, Mr Charles Nicholas BA ♦. . . . . *Oct 1992
Bradley, Mrs Julie LLB(Hons)(Bris) . . . . *Jan 1987
Brown, Mr Duncan E BSc(Econ) Maurice Norden Prize*Dec 1974
Buckland, Mr Paul Andrew LLB(Hons)(Exon); MSc(Oxon) . . . . *Aug 1998
Casstles, Mr Andrew MA(Hons). . . . . Oct 1997
Clifford, Mr Daniel Ian LLB(Hons)(Leeds) . . . . *Sep 1993
Cowan, Mr Andrew J LLB(Hons) . . . . *Apr 1990
Crawford, Mr Andrew J LLB. . . . . *Dec 1982
Dunn, Mr James Henry Roberts BA(Hons)(Accountancy) . . . . Aug 1999
Ebsworth, Mr Jonathan R LLB(Hons) . . . . *Jan 1991
Grant, Mr Nicholas Grenville BA(Hons) . . . . Sep 1999
Hall, Mr Gareth N MA(Oxon) . . . . *Oct 1984
Hall, Ms Susan LLB(Hons) . . . . *Jan 1976
Harvey, Ms Amanda Leigh LLB(Hons). . . . . *Dec 1994
Hudson, Mr Allan James BA(Durham) Butterworth Prize . . . . *Dec 1978
Hulley, Mr Jonathan Roger BA; LLB. . . . . *Feb 2003
Kirkham, Mrs Sharon CPE; LPC Law Society Prize for Outstanding Performance on LPC. . . . . Oct 1998
London, Mr Mark LLB . . . . Jan 2001
Mogollon, Ms Jane C BA(Hons). . . . . *May 1992
Passman, Mr Jonathan LLB. . . . . Mar 1985
Philp, Miss Nicola LLB . . . . Apr 2000
Power, Mr Antony LLB(Hons) . . . . *Nov 1998
Skelton, Mr Paul Jonathan BA; CPSE; LPC . . . . . . Sep 1998
Thompson, Mr Andrew Leslie BComm; LLB(Hons) . . Jan 1996

DEWAR HOGAN ‡
7 Ludgate Broadway London EC4V 6DX
Tel: 020 7634 9550 *Fax:* 020 7634 9551 *Dx:* 98939 CHEAPSIDE 2
E-mail: info@dewarhogan.co.uk
List of partners: J J Cox, R D Hogan
Work: A3 L O Q Z(q)
Ptr: Cox, Mr John James BA(Oxon) . . . . *Jan 1990
Hogan, Mr Ronald Dewar . . . . *Jun 1979
Ast: Jones, Miss Siobhan Catherine . . . . *Oct 2002

DEWEY & LEBOEUF ‡
1 Minster Court Mincing Lane London EC3R 7YL
Tel: 020 7459 5000 *Fax:* 020 7459 5099

DEWEY BALLANTINE ‡
The Library Dewey Ballantine One London Wall London EC2Y 5EZ
Tel: 020 7456 6000 *Fax:* 020 7456 6001
Work: C1 C2 M2 T1 Z(b)

DEXTER HENRY & CO ‡
227b Streatham High Road London SW16 6EN
Tel: 020 8769 5550 *Fax:* 020 8769 0061 *Dx:* 58452 NORBURY
E-mail: dexterhenry@aol.com

DHILLON & CO ‡
Dever House 764 Barking Road London E13 9PJ
Tel: 020 8471 7884 *Fax:* 020 8470 3881
Emergency telephone 020 8470 6000
Office: Southend-on-Sea
Languages: Albanian, Creole, French, Malay, Mende, Punjabi, Russian, Urdu, Yoruba
Work: G H J1 K1 L Q X Z(g,i,m)
Emergency Action, Agency, Legal Aid undertaken and Legal Aid Franchise

DIAMOND SOLICITORS LIMITED ‡
2nd Floor 108a Whitechapel Road London E1 1JE
Tel: 020 7247 0707 *Fax:* 020 7375 2958
E-mail: info@diamondsolicitors.co.uk

DIAS SOLICITORS ‡
Garden Studios 11-15 Betterton Street Covent Garden London WC2H 9BP
Tel: 020 7866 8110
E-mail: info@diassolicitors.co.uk
Office: London W1

DIAS SOLICITORS
130 Shaftesbury Avenue London W1D 5EU
Tel: 020 7031 1117 *Fax:* 020 7031 1116
Office: London WC2

HECTOR DIAZ & CO ‡
14 Old Square Lincoln's Inn London WC1A 3UB
Tel: 020 7404 9349 *Fax:* 020 7404 9348

DICKINSON DEES
Gate House 1 Farringdon Street London EC4M 7LG
Tel: 0844 984 1500 *Fax:* 0844 984 1501
E-mail: law@dickinson-dees.com
Office: Newcastle upon Tyne (2 offices), Stockton-on-Tees, York

DICKINSON SOLICITORS LIMITED ‡
100 Bridge House 18 St George Wharf London SW8 2LQ
Tel: 020 7820 1669 *Fax:* 020 7990 8330
E-mail: mail@cmdlaw.co.uk

DICKSON MINTO WS ‡
Broadgate Tower 20 Primrose Street London EC2A 2EW
Tel: 020 7628 4455 *Fax:* 020 7628 0027

DIVORCE SOLICITORS ONLINE ‡
145-157 St Johns Street London EC1V 4PY
Tel: 020 7870 6263

DAVID DOBLE ‡
6-7 Bedford Row London WC1R 4BS
Tel: 020 7831 1516

VINCENT DOCHERTY & CO ‡
1 Park Road Camden London NW1 6XN
Tel: 020 7723 1284 *Fax:* 020 7723 1489

DOCKLAND SOLICITORS LLP ‡
1-2 Beatty House Admirals Way London E14 9UF
Tel: 020 7531 2990

DODD LEWIS SOLICITORS ‡
18 Tranquil Vale Blackheath London SE3 0AZ
Tel: 020 8852 1255 *Fax:* 020 8852 7531 *Dx:* 50901 BLACKHEATH
E-mail: info@dodd-lewis.co.uk
List of partners: C G L Dodd, J McLarney, R A Rowe, R A H Webster
Languages: Punjabi, Urdu
Work: E J1 K1 K2 K3 O Q S1 S2 W
Ptr: Dodd, Mr C Graham L . . . . *Jun 1963
McLarney, Mr John LLB. . . . . *Nov 1978
Rowe, Mr Richard Anthony BA John Mackrell Prize; Charles Steele Prize. *Dec 1975
Webster, Mrs Rosalind Anita Harvey BA. . . . . *Oct 1989
Asoc: Edinboro-Wright, Mrs Tracey . . . . Sep 1999
Shaw, Ms Mary V MA . . . . *Oct 1982
Ast: Chaudry, Nasreen. . . . . *Apr 2005
Evans, Mr Stephen LLB(Hons)(Business Law). . . . . *Aug 2008
Grewal, Miss Parminder Kaur BA(Hons)(Law). . . . . Mar 2010
MacPherson, Mr Hamish Grant BA(Hons); MA . . . . Mar 2008
Parkinson, Miss Gemma BA(Hons)(History); PGDL; LPC . . . . *Jul 2008

We conduct business in Punjabi & Urdu. We specialise in Commercial Property, Residential Conveyancing, Landlord & Tenant, Wills & Probate, Family Law and Dispute Resolution

THE DOFFMAN ISAACS PARTNERSHIP ‡
29 Charles Lane St John's Wood London NW8 7SB
Tel: 020 7722 0999 *Fax:* 020 7722 0998
E-mail: gsd3215477@aol.com

DOLPHINE SOLICITORS ‡
Unit 150 Camberwell Business Centre 99-103 Lomond Grove London SE5 7HN
Tel: 020 7358 6160 *Fax:* 020 7358 6170

DORMAN JOSEPH WACHTEL ‡
57 Mansell Street Tower Hamlets London E1 8AN
Tel: 020 7680 6300 *Fax:* 020 7680 6301
List of partners: P S V Joseph, M Wachtel
Work: A3 C1 C2 E J1 L O Q S1 S2 W Z(b)
Emergency Action and Agency undertaken
Ptr: Joseph, Mr Paul Simon Victor LLB(Hons)(Bris) . . . . *Oct 1984
Wachtel, Mr Michael LLB(Leics). . . . . *Feb 1984
Con: Hart-Leverton, Mr Derek A LLB . . . . *Oct 1955

DORSEY & WHITNEY ‡
21 Wilson Street London EC2M 2TD
Tel: 020 7588 0800 *Fax:* 020 7588 0555 *Dx:* 33890 FINSBURY
E-mail: london@dorsey.com
List of partners: J R Byrne
Ptr: Byrne, Mr John R LLB; LLM. . . . . Oct 1985
Ast: Khan, Mr Nadeem A LLB(Kent) . . . . *Nov 1987

DOTCOM SOLICITORS ‡
560-568 High Road London N17 9TA
Tel: 020 8880 9000 *Fax:* 020 8885 4555
E-mail: advice@dotcomsolicitors.com

THEODORE DOUGAN SOLICITORS ‡
Southbank House Black Prince Road London SE1 7SJ
Tel: 020 7463 2111 *Fax:* 020 7793 4029
E-mail: info@tdsolicitors.co.uk

CHARLES DOUGLAS SOLICITORS ‡
17 Albermarle Street London W1S 4HP
Tel: 020 7866 6190

DOUGLASS SIMON
2 Kenway Road Earls Court London SW5 0RR
Tel: 020 7373 4429 *Fax:* 020 7370 6738
E-mail: info@douglass-simon.com
Office: Brentford

DOVES SOLICITORS ‡
209 Old Kent Road London SE1 5MA
Tel: 020 7232 5100 *Fax:* 020 7232 5101 *Dx:* 80730 BERMONDSEY
List of partners: F Olaide, A Seun
Languages: Arabic, Igbo, Yoruba
Ptr: Olaide, Fatai . . . . Dec 2000
Seun, Mr Ajayl LLB(Hons). . . . . *Nov 2001

PETER DOVEY AND CO ‡
105 Ladbroke Grove London W11 1PG
Tel: 020 7616 8424 *Fax:* 020 7616 8425
E-mail: peterdovey@pdcosol.co.uk

DOWSE & CO ‡
23-25 Dalston Lane Dalston Hackney London E8 3DF
Tel: 020 7254 6205 *Fax:* 020 7923 1497 *Dx:* 46800 DALSTON
Emergency telephone 020 8345 6789
E-mail: dowse@dowse.co.uk
List of partners: J A Armstrong, F H M Hickey, J Nilsen, W A Parry-Davies, P Spence
Languages: Farsi
Work: D1 D2 J1 J2 K1 K3 L N Q Z(g,h,p,q)
Emergency Action, Agency, Advocacy, Legal Aid undertaken, Legal Aid Franchise and Member of Accident Line
Ptr: Armstrong, Ms Julie Ann BSc(Hons); MSc. . . . . . . Sep 1988
Hickey, Mr Francis H Myles LLB(Lond) . . . . *Jun 1979
Nilsen, Mr John-Olav LLB(Hons) . . . . Jun 2004
Parry-Davies, Mr William A LLB. . . . . *Mar 1982
Spence, Mr Patrick BSc(Hons) . . . . *Sep 2001
Ast: Mohammed, Mr Jamille LLB; LPC. . . . . .Jul 2007

DOWSE BAXTER ‡
79a High Street Wimbledon Village London SW19 5EG
Tel: 020 8946 9110 *Fax:* 020 8946 9296
Dx: 35067 WIMBLEDON VILLAGE
E-mail: info@dowsebaxter.co.uk
List of partners: C N A Baxter
Work: B2 C1 E J1 K1 N O Q
SPr: Baxter, Mr Christopher N A . . . . *Jun 1977

DOYLE CLAYTON SOLICITORS LIMITED ‡
One Crown Court Cheapside London EC2V 6LR
Tel: 020 7329 9090 *Fax:* 020 7329 5050 *Dx:* 42611 CHEAPSIDE
E-mail: info@doyleclayton.co.uk
List of partners: D F Clayton, J Corsi, P De Maria, P C Doyle, P J Leigh-Pollitt, J Nicol, T Wisener
Office: London E14, Reading
Work: J1 Z(i,p)
Ptr: Corsi, Ms Jessica MA(Cantab)(Law). . . . . *Oct 1996
De Maria, Mr Peter LLB. . . . . *Mar 1999
Nicol, Ms Jennifer LLB(Hons) . . . . *Dec 1996
Dir: Clayton, Mr Darren F BA(Hons)(Law) . . . . *Nov 1990
Doyle, Mr Peter C BA. . . . . *May 1985
Asoc: Gingell, Mr Matthew LLB(Hons) . . . . *Jul 1999
Smith, Ms Melanie BA(Hons) . . . . *Sep 2004
Sulkowski, Mr Daniel LPC; PSC; LLB . . . . *Oct 2007
Ast: Jennings, Ms Eleanor BA(Hons); PGDipLaw. . . . . . *Sep 2007
Jones, Mr Owen LLB . . . . *Sep 2002
Liddington, Mr Jamie BSc(Geological Sciences)(Oxford Brookes) . . . . *Sep 2007
Littner, Ms Amanda Lee BA(Hons) . . . . *Sep 2007

DOYLE CLAYTON SOLICITORS LIMITED
Level 33 25 Canada Square Canary Wharf London E14 5LQ
Tel: 020 7038 8051 *Fax:* 020 7038 8151
E-mail: info@doyleclayton.co.uk
Office: London EC2, Reading
Dir: Clayton, Mr Darren F BA(Hons)(Law) . . . . *Nov 1990
Asoc: Smith, Ms Melanie BA(Hons) . . . . *Sep 2004
Ast: Liddington, Mr Jamie BSc(Geological Sciences)(Oxford Brookes) . . . . *Sep 2007

DOZIE & CO ‡
Rachel House 214-218 High Road Tottenham Haringey London N15 4NP
Tel: 020 8808 2244 *Fax:* 020 8808 2266
Dx: 55607 SOUTH TOTTENHAM
Emergency telephone 07742 981 432
E-mail: info@dozieand.co.uk
Languages: Igbo, Russian, Turkish
Work: G Z(m)
Legal Aid Franchise

DRIVING DEFENCES LLP ‡
Gainsborough House 81 Oxford Street London W1D 2EU
Tel: 020 7903 5144 *Fax:* 020 7903 5333
E-mail: info@drivingdefences.com

DRUCES LLP ‡
Salisbury House London Wall London EC2M 5PS
Tel: 020 7638 9271 *Fax:* 020 7628 7525
Dx: 33862 FINSBURY SQUARE
E-mail: info@druces.com
List of partners: T Bignell, N J Brent, P R Campbell, K E Chapman, S J Gilchrist, P J S Goward, C J Hamer, P L R Mitchell, R E Monkcom, J S Redding, I R Searle, R M Sherrin, I C Shrago, C T Stroh, J E G Toth, S J Whittaker
Languages: Dutch, French, German, Hebrew, Italian, Portuguese, Spanish
Work: A1 A3 B1 B3 C1 C2 C3 E F1 I J1 J2 L M1 M2 O P Q R1 R2 S1 S2 T1 T2 W Z(b,c,d,e,f,i,j,k,l,o,p,q,s,y)
Agency, Advocacy and Fixed Fee Interview undertaken
Ptr: Bignell, Mr Timothy . . . . *Dec 1985
Brent, Mr Nicholas J LLB(Manc). . . . . Dec 1980
Campbell, Mr P Roy. . . . . *§Jul 1980
Chapman, Ms Karen E BA . . . . *Nov 1990

Gilchrist, Mr Simeon James LLB(Law & French). . . *Nov 1992
Goward, Mr Paul J S LLB . . . . *§Nov 1986
Hamer, Mr Christopher J MA(Cantab) . . . . *§May 1974
Mitchell, Mr Philip L R LLB(Lond) . . . . *Jul 1980
Monkcom, Mr Richard E BA(CNAA); LLM(Cantab) . *§Sep 1983
Redding, Mr Jon S LLB(Nott'm) . . . . *Apr 1979
Searle, Mr Ian Richard LLB; JIEB . . . . *Oct 1984
Sherrin, Mr Richard M BA. . . . . *§Jan 1980
Shrago, Mr Ivor Colin . . . . *Jun 1966
Stroh, Mr C Toby BA . . . . *§Apr 1981
Toth, Mr John Edward Gerald BA Notary Public . . . *Nov 1985
Whittaker, Mr Stephen J BA. . . . . *Dec 1988
Asoc: Harman, Ms Louise A BA . . . . *Mar 1984
Middleton Lindsley, Ms Suzanne . . . . Jan 1987
Ast: Arnott, Mr Ian BA(Hons). . . . . Apr 2006
Croft, Mr Alistair Charles BA(Hons)(Politics). . . . . Oct 2004
Day, Ms Suzanne Elizabeth BA . . . . *Nov 1994
Lomer, Mr Benjamin Charles Richard BSc; PGDipLaw; CPE . . . . Nov 2004
MacDonald, Mr Benjamin BSc. . . . . Mar 2005
Perry, Ms Susan . . . . Apr 2002
Schwarz, Mr Danny. . . . . Jan 2001
Williams, Miss Charlotte Eliza BA(Law & Society) . . . Apr 2005
Con: Bowles, Mr G Anthony J BA(Sussex) . . . . *§Jun 1973
Edwardes Jones, Mr John R MA(Cantab). . . . . . *§Mar 1963
Kirk, Mr Graeme Donald BA(Hons) Clerk to General Commissioners for Tax . . . . *Apr 1981

DAVID DU PRE & CO ‡
23 Bedford Row Holborn London WC1R 4EB
Tel: 020 7430 1950 *Fax:* 020 7430 1968
Dx: 117 LONDON/CHANCERY LN
E-mail: info@davidduprе.co.uk
List of partners: D R K du Pre
Work: K1
Ptr: du Pre, Mr David R K LLB(Lond) . . . . *Jan 1980
Asoc: Osborne, Miss Rosalind Gaye MA(Cantab) . . . . . . *Jun 1982

DUANE MORRIS ‡
2nd Floor 10 Chiswell Street London EC1Y 4UQ
Tel: 020 7786 2100 *Fax:* 020 7786 2101
Dx: 33885 FINSBURY SQUARE
List of partners: J P Armstrong, J S Cohen, A M Geisler, M G Hartley, S A Laws, D M Maislish, M A Patel, J V Rodwell, R B Smyth
Languages: French
Work: A3 B1 C1 C2 C3 E F1 F2 I J1 J2 M1 M2 O P Q R1 R2 S1 S2 U1 U2 W Z(b,c,e,f,i,j,k,o,w,za)
Ptr: Armstrong, Mr Jonathan Philip LLB; FCIM. . . . . . . Oct 1991
Cohen, Mr Jonathan S MA(Oxon). . . . . *Nov 1993
Geisler, Mr Alexander M LLB . . . . *Sep 1984
Hartley, Mr Mark G BA . . . . May 1980
Laws, Ms Susan A MBA; LLB. . . . . *Dec 1980
Maislish, Mr David Michael LLB . . . . Sep 1972
Patel, Milan A LLB . . . . Mar 1996
Rodwell, Mr Jeffrey Vivian LLB; MHA; BSW. . . . . . Apr 2004
Smyth, Mr Raymond B BA(Hons) . . . . *Nov 1983

MUSA DUDHIA & CO ‡
36 Upper Brook Street London W1K 7QJ
Tel: 020 7499 5353 *Fax:* 020 7493 9335 *Dx:* 44440 MARBLE ARCH
E-mail: law@musadudhia.com
List of partners: M I M Dudhia
Work: C1 C2 E L O Q S1 S2 W Z(l)
SPr: Dudhia, Mr Musa I M . . . . *Feb 1969

DUNDAS & WILSON CS LLP ‡
Northwest Wing Bush House Aldwych London WC2B 4EZ
Tel: 020 7240 2401 *Fax:* 020 7240 2448 *Dx:* 127 LDE
Work: A3 B1 B2 C1 C2 C3 E I J1 J2 L M1 M2 O P Q R1 R2 T1 U1 U2 X Z(b,c,e,f,h,i,j,n,o,p,q,r,u,w,za)

DUNNING & CO ‡
64-70 Denmark Hill London SE5 8RZ
Tel: 020 7733 6217 *Fax:* 020 7708 1535
Dx: 35302 CAMBERWELL GREEN
Emergency telephone 020 7317 7233
E-mail: rosdunning@freeuk.com
List of partners: R D K Dunning, S C Jackson
Languages: French, Italian
Work: D1 G H K1 N S1 V W Z(i,l,m)
Emergency Action, Agency, Advocacy, Legal Aid undertaken and Legal Aid Franchise
Ptr: Dunning, Ms Rosalind D K BA(Oxon) . . . . *Oct 1980
Jackson, Ms Susan Charlotte BA . . . . *Sep 1990
Ast: Dawkins, Miss Andrea Loren LLB(Hons); LLM(Hons) *Sep 1998

UMA DURAISINGAM ‡
First Floor 92 Forrest Road Walthamstow Waltham Forest London E17 6JQ
Tel: 020 8521 1314 *Fax:* 020 8521 9671
E-mail: ooma.durai@hotmail.com

DUVAL VASSILIADES SOLICITORS ‡
85 Gracechurch Street London EC3V 0AA
Tel: 020 7623 8580 *Fax:* 020 7623 9932
E-mail: info@duvass.com

DYLAN CONRAD KREOLLE ‡
Stirling House Breasy Place 9 Burroughs Gardens London NW4 4AU
Tel: 020 8359 1123 *Fax:* 020 8359 1224
E-mail: info@dcksolicitors.co.uk

E&A LAW ‡
42 Brook Street London W1K 5DB
Tel: 020 3178 7918 *Fax:* 020 7691 7707
E-mail: office@ealaw.eu

EBR ATTRIDGE LLP ‡
Kings House 436 High Road Tottenham London N17 9JB
Tel: 020 8808 0774 *Fax:* 020 8885 1462 *Dx:* 58500 TOTTENHAM
Emergency telephone 07831 418400
E-mail: warrenbrazier@ebrattridge.com
List of partners: D W Attridge, F J Flanagan
Office: London NW10, London SE16, London SW11, London WC1
Work: B1 D1 G H J1 K1 L N O P Q W Z(i,l)
Emergency Action, Agency, Advocacy, Fixed Fee Interview, Legal Aid undertaken and Member of Accident Line
Ptr: Attridge, Mr Derek W . . . . *§Mar 1979
Ast: May, Mr Dennis A LLB . . . . *Sep 1988
Townsend, Miss Melanie Jane BSocSc(Hons). . . . *Feb 1997

EBR ATTRIDGE LLP
23 Southampton Place London WC1A 2BP
Tel: 020 7842 8600 *Fax:* 020 7242 9489
Office: London N17, London NW10, London SE16, London SW11

EBR ATTRIDGE LLP
The Colleen Bawn 196 Southwark Park Road Bermondsey London SE16 3RP
Tel: 020 7231 5166 *Fax:* 020 7231 6014 *Dx:* 80713 BERMONDSEY
Emergency telephone 07836 595619
E-mail: bernieduke@ebrattridge.com
Office: London N17, London NW10, London SW11, London WC1
Work: B2 C1 D1 G H I K1 L M1 N Q W Z(i,l)
Emergency Action, Agency, Advocacy, Fixed Fee Interview and Legal Aid undertaken
Ast: Lee, Mr Martin BA. . . . . Jul 1990

EBR ATTRIDGE LLP
17-19 High Street London NW10 4NE
Tel: 020 8961 5146 *Fax:* 020 8961 0442 *Dx:* 141583 HARLESDEN 3
Office: London N17, London SE16, London SW11, London WC1

EBR ATTRIDGE LLP
(incorporating Jeffrey Gordon & Co; Mildred & Beaumont)
1 Lavender Sweep (Off Lavender Hill) Battersea London SW11 1DY
Tel: 020 7228 7050 *Fax:* 020 7223 8241
Dx: 58557 CLAPHAM JUNCTION
Emergency telephone 020 8789 0944 / 0589 051613
E-mail: vincereveglia@ebrattridge.com
Office: London N17, London NW10, London SE16, London WC1
Languages: French, Turkish
Work: B2 G H I K1 L Z(i)
Emergency Action, Agency, Advocacy and Legal Aid undertaken
Ptr: Attridge, Mr Derek W . . . . *§Mar 1979
Flanagan, Mr Finbar J LLB(Hons) . . . . *Apr 1998

E G LAW ‡
73 Abingdon Villas London W8 6XB
Tel: 020 7937 5594
E-mail: emma.gibson@eg-law.co.uk

ELC SOLICITORS ‡
Westgate House Westgate Road Ealing London W5 1YY
Tel: 020 8566 4045 *Fax:* 020 8566 4046 *Dx:* 155870 EALING 4
E-mail: enquiries@elcsolicitors.com
List of partners: K K Pathmanathan
Languages: Punjabi, Tamil, Urdu
Work: B1 C1 E F1 J1 K1 L O Q S1 S2 W Z(i)
Ptr: Pathmanathan, Mr Kanthia K . . . . Nov 1987

ELS INTERNATIONAL LAWYERS LLP ‡
12 Burleigh Street London WC2E 7PX
Tel: 020 7212 9000 *Fax:* 020 7212 9001
Dx: 40008 COVENT GARDEN
E-mail: london@elslegal.com

EMW
7th Floor 88 Kingsway London WC2B 6AA
Tel: 0845 070 6000 *Fax:* 0845 074 2501
Dx: 157030 BLOOMSBURY 4
E-mail: enquiries@emwllp.com
Office: Milton Keynes
Work: A3 B1 C1 C2 C3 E F1 I J1 L M1 N O Q R1 R2 S1 S2 U1 U2 W Z(b,e,g,i,q,w)
Ptr: Hessel, Mr Mark LLB . . . . Jun 2000
Rondel, Mr Mark Richard de Chastelai LLB(Hons). . . *Jan 1989
Ast: Marzec, Mr Jan Mikolaj BA . . . . Oct 2000
Con: Bustos Molinero, Mrs Sonia . . . . Dec 2007
Davidian, Mr Greg. . . . . Mar 1996
Davis, Mr Jason Alistair LLB(Hons)(Business Law); LLM(Corporate Law) . . . . Mar 2000

EOS LAW ‡
Amadeus House Floral Street Covent Garden London WC2E 9DP
Tel: 020 3402 2800 *Fax:* 020 3014 8700
E-mail: info@eos-law.com

E-BUSINESS LEGAL ‡
38 Elmore Street London N1 3AL
Tel: 020 7704 0253

EAGLE SOLICITORS ‡
163 Kennington Lane London SE11 4EZ
Tel: 020 7840 0671 *Fax:* 020 3242 0001
E-mail: info@eaglesolicitors.co.uk

EAGLES SOLICITORS ‡
26 Abbey Parade Merton High Street London SW19 1DG
Tel: 020 8543 3938 *Fax:* 020 8543 3903
E-mail: info@eagleslaw.co.uk

EARLE & WALLER ‡
45 Green Lanes Palmers Green London N13 4TB
Tel: 020 8888 7866 *Fax:* 020 8889 5608
List of partners: M F Harding, M G Waller
Work: C1 C2 E J1 O S1 S2 W Z(l)
Ptr: Harding, Mr Michael F. . . . . *Jun 1974
Waller, Mr Michael G LLB(Exon). . . . . *Mar 1968

GERALDINE EAST SOLICITOR ‡
39a Belsize Avenue London NW3 4BN
Tel: 020 7794 9884
E-mail: geraldine@geraldineast.com

EASTWOODS SOLICITORS ‡
16-18 New Bridge Street London EC4V 6AG
Tel: 020 3137 4800 *Fax:* 020 3137 4821 *Dx:* 366 LDE
E-mail: info@eastwoodslaw.co.uk
List of partners: S Eastwood
Work: G J1 N Q Z(j,r,w)
Ptr: Eastwood, Mr Simon LLB(Hons); LLM. . . . . *May 1984
Ast: Dubb, Mr Surjit Singh LLB. . . . . *Dec 2000
Smith, Mr Adam Fraser LLB(Hons) . . . . *Oct 1999

EBURY HOUSE SOLICITORS ‡
17 Grosvenor Street London W1K 4QG
Tel: 020 7355 7050
E-mail: eburyhouse@btconnect.com

DAVID EDE SOLICITORS ‡
2nd Floor Room 223 Island Business Centre London SE18 6PF
Tel: 020 8316 4758
Emergency telephone 07855 955840
List of partners: E Arnold, D Ede
Languages: French, German
Work: K4 L X Z(h,m,u,za)
Ptr: Arnold, Miss Elizabeth BA. . . . . *Mar 1990
Ede, Mr David BA(Law) . . . . *Feb 1983

EDELL JONES & LESSERS ‡
1 Ron Leighton Way East Ham London E6 1JA
Tel: 020 8548 5700 *Fax:* 020 8548 5720 *Dx:* 4701 EAST HAM
E-mail: eje@aol.com
List of partners: G C Hanson, C J Twyman
Work: D1 E F1 K1 L N Q S1 V W Z(l)
Fixed Fee Interview, Legal Aid undertaken and Member of Accident Line
Ptr: Hanson, Mr Grahame Clive BA . . . . Feb 1979
Twyman, Mr Christopher J BA. . . . . *May 1985
Con: Bell, Mr David W . . . . *May 1973

ALAN EDWARDS & CO ‡
Campden Hill House 192-196 Campden Hill Road Kensington & Chelsea London W8 7TH
Tel: 020 7221 7644 *Fax:* 020 7243 1076
Dx: 94205 NOTTING HILL GATE
Emergency telephone 07693 365094 (PAGER)
E-mail: reception@aelaw.co.uk
Web: www.aelaw.co.uk
List of partners: S Anand, A Edwards, G A French, G Glover, M A John, M Rubens
Languages: French, German, Gujarati, Hindi, Italian, Spanish, Urdu
Work: E G H J1 L O Q S1 S2 W Z(g,h,q,u,w)
Emergency Action, Agency, Advocacy, Legal Aid undertaken and Legal Aid Franchise
Ptr: Anand, Ms Susan BA(Hons) Notary Public . . . . . *Nov 2000
Edwards, Mr Alan. . . . . *Jan 1969
French, Mr Graham A BA; MPhil(Cantab) Deputy District Judge . . . . *Jan 1984
Glover, Ms Gusta LLB(Hons) . . . . *Oct 1994
John, Mr Morris A LLB . . . . *Oct 1996
Rubens, Ms Matilda BA; LLM ♦. . . . . *May 2000
Asoc: Lewis, Ms Amy BA(Hons); CPE; LPC . . . . *Mar 2006
Marrs, Gemma . . . . Oct 2010
Turner, Miss Natalie LLB(Hons); PGDipLaw; LPC . . *Oct 2010
Con: Hinde, Miss Jane A BSc(Hons)(Sociology); LPC. . . *Nov 1983
Thomas, Miss Mary Kathleen BA(Law) . . . . *Jun 1980

Holders of Franchise for Housing. We conduct business in French, German, Gujarati, Hindi, Italian, Spanish, Urdu. We specialise in the following areas of work Housing, Landlord and Tenant, Commercial & Residential Conveyancing, Leasehold Enfranchisement, Public Law, Commercial & General Litigation, Crime (Not legally aided)

EDWARDS ANGELL PALMER & DODGE ‡
Dashwood 69 Old Broad Street London EC2M 1QS
Tel: 020 7583 4055 *Fax:* 020 7353 7377
Dx: 103 LONDON/CHANCERY LN
List of partners: N K Adams, H Clark, D Cory-Wright, T H Daniel, M C Everiss, L Harris, R M Hopley, D Johnson, C S Joseph, D R Kendall, A K Kochhar, L C Metcalfe, M D Meyer, A M Perry, K J Perry, A Robson, A Salamat, R J Spiller, V M Tyrell, S J Williams, A J Woodhouse
Languages: Chinese, French, German, Greek, Hebrew, Italian, Mandarin, Portuguese, Spanish
Work: A3 B1 B2 C1 C2 E J1 L M1 M2 N O P Q R1 T1 Z(b,c,e,f,g,h,i,j,k,n,o,q,u)
Ptr: Adams, Mr Neil Kenneth LLB(Hons). . . . . *§Oct 1993
Clark, Ms Helen. . . . . Nov 1993
Cory-Wright, Ms Dorothy . . . . *May 1991
Daniel, Mr Timothy H BA . . . . *Jan 1976
Everiss, Mr Mark C LLB. . . . . *Jan 1991
Harris, Mr Laurence. . . . . *Nov 1990
Hopley, Mr Richard M LLB . . . . *Nov 1986
Johnson, Mr David . . . . Apr 1981
Joseph, Mr Colin S BA(Oxon). . . . . *Apr 1971
Kendall, Mr David R MA; LLB; AIL. . . . . *May 1981
Kochhar, Ashwani K BA. . . . . *Nov 1988
Metcalfe, Ms Lee Catherine. . . . . Oct 1996
Meyer, Mr Mark David LLB . . . . *Nov 1992
Perry, The Hon Alan M MA(Oxon) Harmsworth Major Scholarship . . . . *Jun 1982
Perry, Mr Kevin J LLB. . . . . Nov 1985
Robson, Mrs Ann LLB(Hons) . . . . Jan 1990
Salamat, Ms Ambereen LLB. . . . . Jan 1997
Spiller, Mr Richard John MA; LLB . . . . *May 1980
Tyrell, Mrs Vivien M BA(Oxon) . . . . *Sep 1980
Williams, Mr Simon James BSc(Hons). . . . . Oct 1997
Woodhouse, Mr Antony J BA(Hons). . . . . Oct 1996
Ast: Allen, Miss Catherine J LLB. . . . . Sep 1999
Anderson, Ms Victoria. . . . . Sep 2000
Andrew, Ms Catherine Mary LLB . . . . Sep 2000
Beale, Mr Edmund Charles BA(Hons); PGDipLaw. . . Jan 2003
Buttrey, Miss Katherine BA . . . . Sep 1998
Cairns, Ms Alana LLB. . . . . Jan 2002
Chaudhuri, Ms Alexandra Anouska BA(Hons); CPE; LPC . . . . Jan 2003
Clipston, Mrs Hannah LLB . . . . Jan 2003
Costello, Miss Clare Louise BSc. . . . . Sep 2005
Depree, Mrs Helen LLB(Hons) . . . . Jan 2003
Dimitriou, Mr Alexi George MSc. . . . . Sep 2005
Downes, Ms Carol-Ann . . . . Sep 2001
Fawell, Mr Simon James Kirtley LLB . . . . Jan 2002
Griffiths, Mr Joseph Lyndon BA(Hons). . . . . *Sep 1997
Hardie, Miss Alexandra Margaret BA . . . . Sep 2005
Hardy, Ms Imogen BA(Hons) . . . . Jan 2004
Hartley, Miss Rebecca Bonnel BA. . . . . Sep 2005
Hills, Ms Sarah Jane . . . . Sep 1998
Hughes, Ms Jane. . . . . Dec 1994
Maton, Mr James BA . . . . Oct 1998
Mingay, Mr George Frederick BA(Hons). . . . . . . Jan 2003
Moore, Miss Erica Jane LLB(Hons); CPE; LPC . . . . Jan 2003
Nagel, Mr Daniel . . . . Sep 2005
Paydon, Mr Robert BA . . . . Oct 1998
Peatfield, Ms Lisa BA. . . . . Jan 1999
Pitt, Mr Steven MA . . . . Oct 1998
Roberts, Ms Melissa J. . . . . Sep 2001
Sage, Mr Christopher John LLB(Hons) . . . . Jan 2003
Seddiki, Miss Louisa MA; LLB. . . . . Sep 2005
Stern, Mr Nicholas . . . . Sep 2001

See p2 for the Key to Work Categories & other symbols

Street, Ms Abby BSc(Hons) . . . . Jan 2004
Suarez-Martinez, Mr Antonio Vincente LLB . . . . . . Jan 2002
Teacher, Mr Jonathan Saul . . . . Sep 2000
Tornari, Ms Katie . . . . Sep 2001

EDWARDS DUTHIE
585 Barking Road Plaistow London E13 9EZ
Tel: 020 8514 9000 *Fax:* 020 8548 5471 *Dx:* 152320 PLAISTOW 3
Emergency telephone 020 8471 8115
E-mail: allinfo@edwardsduthie.com
Office: Ilford, London E6
Work: D1 D2 G H K1 Q W Z(m,q)
Emergency Action, Agency, Advocacy, Fixed Fee Interview, Legal Aid undertaken, Legal Aid Franchise and Member of Accident Line
Ptr: Garvey, Ms Rajinder Kaur BA(Hons) . . . . Feb 1995
Huber, Mr Bernard LLB . . . . *Jun 1980
Life, Ms Joanna E LLB(Warw) . . . . *Jun 1989
Murphy, Mr Shaun P LLB Crown Court Recorder . . . *Mar 1980
Ast: Ahmed, Mr Shabaz . . . . Nov 2007
Blackman, Mr Gavin . . . . Aug 2007
King, Mr Timothy . . . . Aug 2005
May, Mr Simon Daniel . . . . *Jan 2002
Middleton, Mrs Elizabeth Anne . . . . *Jan 2002
Neal, Miss Elizabeth Anne . . . . *Nov 1990
Orpwood, Ms Anna . . . . May 2006
Parker, Mr Alistair Dawood LLB . . . . *Aug 2004
Shields, Mrs Marcia R BA(Law) . . . . *Feb 1986
Styles, Ms Karley . . . . Feb 2008

EDWARDS DUTHIE
292-294 Plashet Grove East Ham London E6 1EE
Tel: 020 8514 9000 *Fax:* 020 8552 1864 *Dx:* 4702 EAST HAM
Emergency telephone 020 8471 8115
E-mail: allinfo@edwardsduthie.com
Office: Ilford, London E13
Languages: French, German, Gujarati, Hindi, Punjabi, Urdu
Work: D1 D2 F1 G H J1 K1 L N S1 S2 V W X Z(g,h,i,m,p,t)
Emergency Action, Agency, Advocacy, Fixed Fee Interview, Legal Aid undertaken, Legal Aid Franchise and Lawnet
Ptr: Harrison, Mr James Richard . . . . *Jan 2002
Reeves, Miss Doreen PGDipLaw . . . . *Jun 1997
Ast: McGhee, Mrs Ola . . . . Jun 2008
Malik, Mr Attiq . . . . Jul 2007
Martinez, Mr David . . . . Oct 2006
Oliver, Ms Jennifer . . . . Jul 2007
Roberts, Mrs Rebecca . . . . Jul 2006
Wentworth, Ms Charlotte . . . . Mar 2008
Withers, Ms Sinead . . . . *May 2003
Yousaf, Miss Naheed LLB Achievement Excellence LPC . . . . *Feb 1999

EDWIN COE LLP ‡
2 Stone Buildings Lincoln's Inn London WC2A 3TH
Tel: 020 7691 4000 *Fax:* 020 7691 4111
Dx: 191 LONDON/CHANCERY LN
E-mail: law@edwincoe.com
List of partners: C R Berry, P J Boursnell, S J Brower, A S Carn, G J A Clark, V N Davies, R T Franklin, S J Gilchrist, N P Giles, I A Gilmour, D R Goepel, J R Gore, D M Greene, J L Griffiths, R J Harrap, V J Hawrych, R E Hickling, D P Kinch, E P O Mercer, A J Merkel, S J Miles, N Neocleous, J H A Osborne, R C Shear, I C Shrago, L Trott, C M West, M Whitton, N Williams, A Zaidi
Languages: Cantonese, French, German, Greek, Gujarati, Hebrew, Italian, Mandarin, Polish, Russian, Spanish
Work: A3 B1 B2 C1 C2 C3 E F1 F2 I J1 L M1 M2 N O P Q R2 S1 S2 T2 U2 W Z(b,c,d,e,f,g,j,k,q,w,z)
Agency undertaken
Ptr: Berry, Mr Christopher Robin FCIArb Recorder; Chartered Arbitrator; Licensed Insolvency Practitioner . . . *§Nov 1969
Brower, Mr Stephen J BA(Kent) . . . . *Oct 1984
Clark, Mr Graham J A BA . . . . *Jun 1973
Davies, Ms Vivien Nayef BA(Hons)(Law & Politics) . *Apr 1999
Franklin, Mr Roger T BA(Hons) . . . . *Nov 1999
Gilchrist, Mr Simeon James LLB(Law & French) . . . *Nov 1992
Giles, Mr Nicholas P LLB(Hons)(B'ham) . . . . *Jul 1978
Gilmour, Mr Ian A LLB(Hons) . . . . *Nov 1986
Goepel, Mr David Robert MA(Hons) . . . . Sep 2000
Gore, Mr Julian Robert . . . . *§Oct 1975
Greene, Mr David Michael MSc; FCIArb; CEDR Accredited Mediator Member of the Civil Procedure Rules Committee; Member of the Civil Justice Council . . . . . . *§Dec 1980
Griffiths, Mr Joseph Lyndon BA(Hons) . . . . *Sep 1997
Harrap, Miss Rachel J LLB(Hons); Admitted to the Gibraltar Bar . . . . *Oct 1980
Hawrych, Mr Victor J BA(Hons) . . . . *Oct 1984
Hickling, Miss Ruth Elizabeth LLB . . . . Apr 1988
Kinch, Mr David P BA(Hons)(Bris) . . . . *Oct 1986
Mercer, Mr Edward Peter Opgard MA(Cantab) . . . . Dec 1980
Merkel, Mr Alan Joseph BA(Oxon) . . . . *Jun 1976
Miles, Mr Simon Justin LLM(Commercial Law); LLB(Hons) . . . . Oct 1995
Neocleous, Mr Nick LLB; LLM . . . . Jan 1985
Osborne, Mrs Joanna H A LLB(Hons) . . . . *Dec 1989
Shear, Mr Russel Charles LLB(Hons) Conflict of Laws (Manchester University) . . . . *§Nov 1987
Shrago, Mr Ivor Colin . . . . *Jun 1966
Trott, Miss Linky LLB(Hons) . . . . *Sep 1993
West, Mrs Carolyn Mary . . . . Nov 1981
Whitton, Mr Michael MA(Hons)(Cantab) . . . . *Nov 1986
Williams, Mr Nicholas MA(Cantab) . . . . *Sep 1984
Zaidi, Mr Ali LLB; LSF . . . . *Nov 1992
Mem: Boursnell, Mr Philip John LLB(Sheff) . . . . Jan 1978
Carn, Miss Alexandra Sophia BA; CPE; LPC . . . . . *Sep 2001
Ast: Black, Ms Lisa Ellen LLB . . . . Sep 2005
Butt, Ms Zahira LLB; LPC . . . . Oct 2008
Calverley, Mr Jim BA(Hons); GDL . . . . Oct 2008
Davies, Mr John Nicholas Cameron LLB(Law & French)Sep 2005
de Bono, Mr Dominic MA(Hons) . . . . Jul 2000
Elliott, Mr James Oliver LLB; BA; PGDip . . . . Sep 2011
Hardcastle, Ms Lowri BA(Hons) . . . . *Sep 2006
Jackson, Ms Katrina Emma BSc(Hons); LSF . . . . . *Dec 1995
Lee, Miss Karen LLB; PGDip . . . . Sep 2011
Macleod, Ms Katherine Jane BA; LLB . . . . Sep 2003
Overton, Mr Matthew Alexander BA . . . . *Sep 2007
Pandelis, Ms Myri BA(Hons); GDL; LPC . . . . Sep 2008
Russell, Ms Marina BA(Hons) . . . . Sep 2006
Su, Mr Pey Kan LLB(Hons); LLM(Lond); MSc(Lond); FCIArb . . . . *Apr 1991
White, Mr Charles James Henry LLB; PGDip Commercial Law Prize 2006 . . . . Sep 2010
Con: Loose, Mr Peter MA(Oxon) Cecil Karuth Prize . . . . *§Nov 1960

THOMAS EGGAR LLP
(in association with Avrio; The Bridge Group; Lexcel)
76 Shoe Lane London EC4A 3JB
Tel: 020 7842 0000 *Fax:* 020 7842 3900
Dx: 183 LONDON/CHANCERY LN
E-mail: london@thomaseggar.com
Office: Chichester, Crawley, Newbury, Southampton, Worthing
Work: A1 C1 C2 C3 D2 E F1 J1 K1 K2 K3 K4 L M1 M2 M3 N O P Q R1 S2 T1 T2 U2 W X Z(c,d,e,j,k,o,q,w)

EGMONT SOLICITORS & NOTARY PUBLIC ‡
Suite 6 Egmont House 116 Shaftesbury Avenue London W1D 5EW
Tel: 020 7494 3885 *Fax:* 020 7788 9688
E-mail: info@egmontsolicitors.co.uk

EGOROV PUGINSKY AFANASIEV & PARTNERS LLP ‡
3 Gough Square London EC4A 3DE
Tel: 020 7822 7060 *Fax:* 020 7353 5905

A A EHRENZWEIG & CO ‡
65 Avondale Avenue North Finchley London N12 8ER
Tel: 020 7584 1516 *Fax:* 020 7225 2286
Languages: French, German
Work: E L S1 S2

MARK EISENTHAL & CO ‡
44 Wellington Street Covent Garden London WC2E 7BD
Tel: 020 7379 3475 *Fax:* 020 7379 0664
Dx: 40042 COVENT GARDEN
Emergency telephone 07775 782 015
E-mail: markeisenthal@btconnect.com
List of partners: M M Eisenthal, J R Jones
Work: B1 C1 E J1 K1 L P R1 R2 S1 S2 T2 W Z(d,e,f,i,k,l,q)
Agency undertaken
Ptr: Eisenthal, Mr Mark Montague LLB . . . . *Jun 1968
Jones, Mr Joseph Roland LLB . . . . *Nov 1990
Ast: Collier, Mrs Jane Caroline BA; MSc . . . . *Dec 1992

ELBORNE MITCHELL LLP ‡
One America Square Crosswall London EC3N 2PR
Tel: 020 7320 9000 *Fax:* 020 7320 9111 *Dx:* 1063 LONDON/CITY
E-mail: lawyers@elbornes.com
List of partners: T A Akeroyd, A J Booth, T W B Brentnall, M Clark, T J Goodger, R H Jones, K C Payne, J Sleightholme, E A E Stanley, P J Tribe
Languages: French, German, Italian, Spanish
Work: A3 B1 C1 C2 F1 J1 M1 M2 N O Q S2 T1 U2 Z(a,c,k,o,q,w)
Ptr: Akeroyd, Mr Timothy A . . . . Dec 1971
Booth, Miss Alexandra Jane BA(Hons) . . . . Sep 1996
Brentnall, Mr Timothy W B . . . . Dec 1979
Clark, Mr Matthew . . . . Feb 1991
Goodger, Mr Timothy J LLB(Hons) . . . . *§Jun 1992
Jones, Mrs Rosalind H LLB(Hons) . . . . Dec 1989
Payne, Miss Katherine Clare BSc . . . . *Nov 1995
Sleightholme, Mr James MA(Cantab) . . . . May 1981
Stanley, Mr Edmund A E MA(Oxon) . . . . Oct 1984
Tribe, Mr Peter J . . . . Jul 1989

ELDER RAHIMI LIMITED ‡
Norvin House 45-55 Commercial Street London E1 6BD
Tel: 020 7377 6600 *Fax:* 020 7377 8800 *Dx:* 579 BISHOPGATE
E-mail: office@elderrahimi.co.uk
Office: Folkestone

ELLICOTTS ‡
1278 High Road Whetstone London N20 9RS
Tel: 020 8445 5257 / 8445 2880 *Fax:* 020 8446 7928
Dx: 37101 WHETSTONE
E-mail: info@ellicotts.co.uk
List of partners: M C Ellicott, A V B Henderson
Work: C1 E F1 J1 K1 L S1 W
Ptr: Ellicott, Mr Malcolm C . . . . *Jul 1961
Henderson, Mr Andrew V B BA . . . . *Apr 1976
Ast: Ziman, Mr Peter D LLB . . . . *§Jan 1969

ELLIOTS BOND & BANBURY ‡
Bank Chambers 53 The Broadway Ealing London W5 5JT
Tel: 020 8567 0176 *Fax:* 020 8579 3940 *Dx:* 5154 EALING
E-mail: johnferg@eb-b.co.uk
Languages: French, German
Work: C1 C2 D1 E G H J1 K1 L N O Q S1 W X Z(q)
Emergency Action, Agency, Advocacy and Legal Aid undertaken

ELLIOTT & WILLIAMS ‡
3c Church Lane Hornsey London N8 7BU
Tel: 020 7566 8244
List of partners: C Elliott
SPr: Elliott, C. . . . . May 2006

ELLIS TAYLOR LAW LLP ‡
44/45 Chancery Lane London WC2A 1JB
Tel: 020 7405 0206 *Fax:* 020 7404 1191
Dx: 499 LONDON/CHANCERY LN
E-mail: info@ellistaylor.com
List of partners: N Desai, J S Tasselli, P E Taylor
Languages: French, Gujarati, Hindi, Tamil, Urdu
Work: A3 B1 C1 E J1 O Q S2 Z(c,i,k,q)
Fixed Fee Interview undertaken
Mem: Desai, Naynesh . . . . *Apr 1986
Tasselli, Mr John Stephen LLB(Wales) . . . . *Apr 1981
Taylor, Mr Peter E BSc(Hons) . . . . *Nov 1982
Ast: Moghul, Mr Jayhangir . . . . Nov 2007

W A ELLIS ‡
174 Brompton Row London SW3 1HP

ELLUM LLP ‡
34 Alie Street Tower Hamlets London E1 8DA
Tel: 020 7481 0977 *Fax:* 020 7481 0886
E-mail: patrick@ellum.co.uk
List of partners: P R A Ellum, M E Lesser
Languages: French
Work: A3 C1 C3 F1 F2 I J1 M2 O Q Z(c,e,j)
Advocacy undertaken
Ptr: Ellum, Mr Patrick R A LLB ● . . . . *Oct 1978
Lesser, Mr Maxwell E LLB . . . . *Sep 1990
Ast: Irish, Mrs Tina LLB; LLM . . . . *Jun 2000

ELSTON GERMAIN DAVIDSON ‡
1 Kentish Building Borough High Street London SE1 1NP
Tel: 020 3195 7272 *Fax:* 020 3195 7273
E-mail: peter.germain@egdlaw.com

ELTHORN SOLICITORS ‡
14 South Ealing Road South Ealing London W5 4QA
Tel: 020 8579 3838 *Fax:* 020 8567 0700 *Dx:* 5114 EALING
E-mail: info@elthornesolicitors.com

ELTON & CO ‡
2-4 Kelly Street Camden London NW1 8PH
Tel: 020 7267 7373 *Fax:* 020 7284 0414
Dx: 119326 KENTISH TOWN
E-mail: mail@eltonsolicitors.co.uk
Work: E J1 K1 L N O S1 S2 W

EMERLY HALIL AND BROWN SOLICITORS ‡
596 Kingsland Road London E8 4AH
Tel: 020 7241 4433 / 8519 5500 *Fax:* 020 7241 6633
Dx: 48617 DALSTON
E-mail: info@emeryhalil.co.uk

EMIN READ SOLICITORS ‡
236 Railton Road London SE24 0JT
Tel: 020 7733 9898 *Fax:* 020 8929 8083
E-mail: enquiries@eminread.co.uk

EMIN READ SOLICITORS ‡
33 Montpelier Vale London SE3 0TJ
Tel: 020 8218 1773
E-mail: enquiries@eminread.co.uk

H EMIR & CO ‡
2b Stanford Hill London N16 6XZ
Tel: 020 8806 8480 *Fax:* 020 8806 0287
Dx: 58060 STOKE NEWINGTON 1
E-mail: h.emir@btconnect.com

EMPLOYEE SOLICITORS ‡
352-352 Camberwell New Road London SE5 0RW
Tel: 0870 730 8880

EMPLOYMENT SOLICITORS LONDON LIMITED ‡
2 Devonshire Square London EC2M 4UJ
Tel: 020 7426 0382 *Fax:* 020 7247 3582
E-mail: karen@acitylawfirm.com

ENGLAND PALMER ‡
3 Angel Gate 326 City Road Islington London EC1V 2QA
Tel: 020 7278 2800 *Fax:* 020 7278 6700 *Dx:* 400212 FINSBURY 2
E-mail: guildford@englandpalmer.co.uk
Office: Guildford
Work: B1 C1 E J1 K3 O Q S2 W Z(p,q)

ENNON & CO SOLICITORS ‡
Unit 6 Wells House 5-7 Wells Terrace London N4 3JU
Tel: 020 7281 2123 *Fax:* 020 7281 2220
Dx: 57485 FINSBURY PARK
E-mail: info@ennonsolicitors.co.uk
Languages: Fanti, French, Thai, Vietnamese, Yoruba
Work: B2 G H K1 K3 Z(g,i,l)
Emergency Action, Agency, Advocacy, Fixed Fee Interview and Legal Aid undertaken

EQUAL JUSTICE LTD ‡
15 Southampton Place London WC1A 2AJ
Tel: 020 7405 5292 *Fax:* 020 7405 5296
E-mail: enquiries@equaljustice.co.uk

EQUITABLE SOLICITORS ‡
Unit 9 & 10 289 Kennington Lane London SE11 5QY
Tel: 020 7820 8236 *Fax:* 020 7820 9743
E-mail: equitablesols@aol.com

ERICA PEAT & DIABLE ‡
314 Mare Street London E8 1HA
Tel: 020 8533 7999 *Fax:* 020 8533 9777 *Dx:* 35454 HACKNEY
E-mail: erica.peat@criminaldefencelondon.co.uk

ERNEST & CO SOLICITORS ‡
14 Stoke Newington High Street London N16 7PL
Tel: 020 7254 2244 *Fax:* 020 7254 2212
E-mail: ernestandandco@yahoo.com

ERNEST & COMPANY ‡
511 Seven Sisters Road London N15 6EP
Tel: 020 8880 2222 *Fax:* 020 8880 2200

ERSAN & CO SOLICITORS LIMITED ‡
7 Willoughby Road London N8 0HR
Tel: 020 8342 7070 *Fax:* 020 8342 7071 *Dx:* 57755 HARINGEY
E-mail: info@erans.co.uk

ESHAGIAN & CO ‡
Savant House 63-65 Camden High Street London NW1 7JL
Tel: 020 7388 5599 *Fax:* 020 7388 7733
E-mail: aecds1@gmail.com

ESKINAZI & CO ‡
3 Castle Mews Castle Road London N12 9EH
Tel: 020 8445 7707 *Fax:* 020 8445 7750 *Dx:* 57388 FINCHLEY
E-mail: family@eskinazi.co.uk

CHARLES ETE & CO ‡
168 Camberwell New Road London SE5 0RR
Tel: 020 7820 9818 *Fax:* 020 7091 0432
Dx: 35301 CAMBERWELL GREEN
E-mail: enquiry@charlesete.co.uk
List of partners: C Ete
Languages: Efik, Gujarati, Igbo, Spanish, Urdu, Yoruba
Work: C1 E G H K1 K3 S1 S2 Z(i,w)
Advocacy, Fixed Fee Interview and Legal Aid undertaken
Ptr: Ete, Mr Charles LLB(Hons); BL Professional Person of the Year 1998 . . . . Mar 1997

ETERNAL ALLIANCES ‡
91 Belmont Hill London SE13 5AX
Tel: 0845 271 2828
E-mail: info@eternalalliances.com

EUROPEAN BUSINESS LAWYERS LIMITED ‡
Third Floor Essex Hall 1-6 Essex Street London WC2R 3HU
Tel: 0807 395 2180 *Fax:* 020 7395 2181
E-mail: hugh.barrett@orrlitchfield.com

EVANS BISSETT SOLICITORS ‡
Suite 3-4 19 Greenwood Place London NW5 1LB
Tel: 020 7428 6090 *Fax:* 020 7428 6091 *Dx:* 46469 KENTISH TOWN
E-mail: pevans@evansbissett.co.uk

EVANS DODD LLP ‡
5 Balfour Place London W1K 2AU
Tel: 020 7491 4729 *Fax:* 020 7499 2297 *Dx:* 44644 MAYFAIR
E-mail: mail@evansdodd.co.uk
List of partners: M H Ahmed, G S Dodd, D L Manghnani, J R Stott
Languages: French
Work: B1 C1 C2 C3 E F1 J1 L O Q R2 S1 S2 T1 T2 W Z(b,c,e,i,j,l)
Ptr: Ahmed, Mahmood H MA(Oxon); MBA. . . . . *Nov 1980
Dodd, Mr Geoffrey S Alfred Syrett Prize . . . . *Oct 1968
Manghnani, Mr Deepak L BA . . . . *Nov 1982
Stott, Mr James R. . . . . *Dec 1977
Ast: Alleear, Mr Dave . . . . *Jan 2010
Patel, Miss Neelam LLB(Hons) . . . . Nov 2008

J E EVANS-JACKSON & CO ‡
Parchment House 13 Northburgh Street London EC1V 0AH
Tel: 020 7608 3098 *Fax:* 020 7608 2934

EVANS LONDON SOLICITORS ‡
Suite 406 19-21 Crawford Street London W1H 1PJ
Tel: 020 8144 8001 *Fax:* 020 7900 1717
E-mail: evanslondon@btinternet.com

N K EVANS & CO ‡
40 Stockwell Street Greenwich London SE10 8EY
Tel: 020 8853 1414 *Fax:* 020 8853 8079 *Dx:* 35210 GREENWICH 2
E-mail: law@nkevans.co.uk
Work: C1 J1 S1 S2 T2 W Z(j)

EVANS WALLACE SOLICITORS ‡
57-61 Mortimer Street London W1W 8HS
Tel: 0845 838 2984 *Fax:* 0845 838 2986
E-mail: info@evanswallace..com

EVERGREEN SOLICITORS ‡
2 London Wall Buildings London Wall London EC2M 5UU
Tel: 020 7448 5151 *Fax:* 020 7448 5048
Dx: 33865 FINSBURY SQUARE
E-mail: contact@evergreensolicitors.com

EVERSFIELD & CO ‡
8 West Street London WC2H 9NG
Tel: 020 7836 5547 *Fax:* 020 7240 2712
E-mail: eversfieldco@talk21.com
List of partners: R D Eversfield
Work: A1 B1 C1 C2 E F1 J1 K1 L N O P Q R1 S1 S2 T1 T2 W X Z(c,d,e,f,j,k,m,s)
Agency undertaken
Ptr: Eversfield, Ms Rosemary D LLB(Lond) . . . . *§Jun 1967

EVERSHEDS LLP ‡
(incorporating Frere Cholmeley Bischoff)
1 Wood Street London EC2V 7WS
Tel: 0845 497 9797 *Fax:* 0845 497 4919 *Dx:* 154280 CHEAPSIDE 8
Office: Birmingham, Cambridge, Cardiff, Ipswich, Leeds, Manchester, Newcastle upon Tyne, Nottingham
Languages: French, German, Hindi, Italian, Polish, Punjabi, Spanish
Work: A1 B1 C1 C2 C3 D1 E F1 J1 K1 L M1 M2 N O P Q R1 T1 T2 V W Z(b,c,d,e,f,g,h,i,j,k,l,m,o,p,s,t)

EVERSLEY & CO ‡
Percy House 363 Liverpool Road Islington London N1 1NL
Tel: 020 7607 0001 *Fax:* 020 7700 5999 *Dx:* 51857 HIGHBURY
E-mail: stuartappleman@eversleys.co.uk
List of partners: S H Appleman
Languages: French, German
Work: A1 B1 C1 C2 C3 E F1 J1 L N O Q S1 W Z(c,e,h,k,l)
Emergency Action, Agency, Advocacy and Legal Aid undertaken
Ptr: Appleman, Mr Stuart H Deputy District Judge . . . . *Dec 1969

EWART PRICE & PRIMHAK
(in association with Ewart Price)
First Floor 1 Heathgate Place 75-87 Agincourt Road London NW3 2NU
Tel: 020 7267 7344 *Fax:* 020 7267 3074
E-mail: inter.price@btconnect.com
Office: Welwyn Garden City
Work: E J1 K1 L M1 N P S1 T1 W Z(c,j,k)
Emergency Action, Agency and Advocacy undertaken

EWINGS & CO ‡
148 High Street Penge London SE20 7EU
Tel: 020 8778 1126 *Fax:* 020 8676 9662 *Dx:* 34851 PENGE
Emergency telephone 07956 388093
E-mail: enquiry@ewings.uk.com
List of partners: S J Brown, P G P Cartin, D M Ewings, P I Ewings, N D Riley
Languages: French, Italian
Work: C1 C2 D1 D2 F1 G H J1 K1 L N Q S1 V W Z(m)
Emergency Action, Agency, Advocacy, Fixed Fee Interview, Legal Aid undertaken and Legal Aid Franchise
Ptr: Brown, Mr Simon J LLB. . . . . *Dec 1982
Cartin, Mr Philip G P BA Pro Bono High Street Lawyer of Year 2001 . . . . *Aug 1998
Ewings, Mrs Dympna M BA. . . . . *Mar 1988
Ewings, Mr Paul I BA . . . . *May 1980
Riley, Mr Nigel D BA . . . . *Mar 1983
Asoc: McGinty, Mr Eoin LLB. . . . . *Jan 2001
Ast: Barry, Mr Gerald David St Clair BCL; LLB; LLM Clerk to West Brixton Tax Commissioner. . . . . *Jul 1981
Keane, Mr John LLB . . . . *Aug 1997
Lloyd, Ms Helen Winifred Pauline LLB; AKC. . . . . *Dec 1974
Parkinson, Mr Paul M. . . . . *Dec 1980
Styring, Ms Jennifer M P LLB . . . . *Nov 1973

EXCEL SOLICITORS ‡
8 Bridge House Defence Close London SE28 0NR
Tel: 020 8854 1201 *Fax:* 020 8854 1201
E-mail: obifather@hotmail.com

F&L LEGAL LLP ‡
8 Lincoln's Inn Fields London WC2A 3BP
Tel: 020 7404 4140
E-mail: info@fitzgeraldandlaw.com

FLK SOLICITORS ‡
310 High Road Leyton London E10 5PW
Tel: 020 8558 9699 *Fax:* 020 8539 9678
Dx: 32026 WALTHAMSTOW
E-mail: fareeda57@hotmail.com

FABMELIA MANUEL ‡
15 Borough High Street London SE1 9SE
Tel: 020 7378 9593 *Fax:* 020 7373 9540
Dx: 144366 SOUTHWARK 4

FADIGA & CO SOLICITORS ‡
257 Balham High Road Wandsworth London SW17 7BW
Tel: 020 8672 8779 *Fax:* 020 8675 5958
Dx: 34005 TOOTING NORTH
E-mail: admin@fadiga.co.uk
Office: London E7
Languages: Arabic, French, Hakka, Italian, Russian, Sinhalese, Somali, Tamil
Work: Z(i)
Legal Aid undertaken and Legal Aid Franchise

FADIGA & CO SOLICITORS
458 Romford Road London E7 8DF
Tel: 020 8470 5656 *Fax:* 020 8470 5561 *Dx:* 117353 UPTON PARK
E-mail: info@hardingslaw.com
Office: London SW17

FAEGRE & BENSON LLP ‡
7 Pilgrim Street London EC4V 6LB
Tel: 020 7450 4500 *Fax:* 020 7450 4545
Dx: 401 LONDON/CHANCERY LN
E-mail: fharrington@faegre.com
List of partners: R Campbell, A Denny, J Enstone, P Finlan, G Laitner, D J Stewart, M Wadsworth
Languages: Bengali, Cantonese, Farsi, French, German, Hindi, Portuguese, Punjabi, Spanish
Work: A3 B1 C1 C2 C3 E F1 F2 I J1 L M1 M2 O P Q R1 S2 U1 U2 Z(b,c,e,i,k,l,n,p,q,z,za)
Ptr: Campbell, Mr Robert LLB(Hons). . . . . *Feb 1994
Denny, Mr Alexander BA . . . . *Nov 1997
Enstone, Mr John LLB . . . . *Jul 1998
Finlan, Mr Paul LLB(Hons) . . . . *Jun 1977
Laitner, Mr Gary LLB(Hons). . . . . *Oct 1982
Stewart, Mr Donald J LLB. . . . . *Dec 1990
Wadsworth, Ms Melanie BSc(Hons). . . . . *Oct 1998
Asoc: Byford, Ms Anna BA . . . . Sep 2011
Castell, Mr John LLB . . . . *Jun 1977
Crow, Ms Linda J LLB(Hons) Chairman of the Quoted Companies Alliance Legal Committee. . . . . . . *Sep 1989
Curtin, Mr Richard C LLB(Hons). . . . . *Oct 1986
Dowsett, Ms Kathryn BA(Hons). . . . . *Nov 2005
James, Mr Scott M . . . . *Jan 1975
Jennett, Ms Catrin BSc(Hons). . . . . *Oct 1992
Jennings, Mr Nicholas LLB(Hons). . . . . *Oct 2006
Llewellyn, Mr Stephen Paul BA . . . . *Oct 1993
McLennan, Ms Sarah BA . . . . *Sep 2000
Pengelly, Ms Victoria . . . . *Sep 2006
Peters, Ms Jennifer LLB(Hons) . . . . Oct 2009
Sheibani, Ms Sherry BSc(Hons). . . . . *Oct 2010
Shields, Ms Mary LLB(Hons) . . . . *Oct 2003

FAHRI JACOB ‡
147 Crouch Hill London N8 9QH
Tel: 020 8347 4070 *Fax:* 020 8347 4071 *Dx:* 35953 CROUCH END
E-mail: info@fahrijacob.co.uk
Office: Hatfield
Work: D1 D2 K1 K2 K3 L N O Q S1 S2 V
Agency and Legal Aid undertaken

EDWARD FAIL BRADSHAW & WATERSON ‡
402 Commercial Road Tower Hamlets London E1 0LG
Tel: 020 7790 4032 *Fax:* 020 7790 2739
Dx: 300701 TOWER HAMLETS
Emergency telephone 07841 454170
E-mail: main@efbw.co.uk
List of partners: P S Harris, S Keshvari, K M Monighan, E A Preston
Office: London EC3
Work: B2 G H
Emergency Action, Agency, Advocacy, Legal Aid undertaken and Legal Aid Franchise
Ptr: Harris, Mr Paul Simon LLB ★ President of London Criminal Courts Solicitors Association . . . . *§Sep 1992
Keshvari, Ms Shila LLB(Hons) ★ . . . . *Feb 2002
Monighan, Miss Kirsty Moyra LLB ★. . . . . *Sep 2001
Preston, Mr Edward A BA; LLM ★. . . . . *Jul 1981
Ast: Anderson, Ms Kate LLB ★. . . . . *Sep 2002
Chahal, Miss Kirandeep Kaur BA(Hons); MA(Law). . . *Oct 2008
Fallen, Mr Peter Dennis ★. . . . . *Sep 1997
Gondhia, Miss Shreeta LLB(Hons) . . . . *Dec 2007
Meadowcroft, Mrs Hilary LLB(Hons). . . . . *Sep 2003
Nicol, Ms Alexia Grace BA(Hons)(Law & Criminology) ★ . . . . *Dec 2003
Raphael, Miss Natalie Claire BA(Hons)(Law & Politics) ★ . . . . *Nov 2008

EDWARD FAIL BRADSHAW & WATERSON
Suite G04 150 Minories Tower Hamlets London EC3N 1LS
Tel: 020 7264 2016 *Fax:* 020 7790 2739
Dx: 300701 TOWER HAMLETS
Emergency telephone 07841 454170
E-mail: main@efbw.co.uk
Office: London E1
Work: B2 G H
Emergency Action, Agency, Advocacy, Legal Aid undertaken and Legal Aid Franchise
Ptr: Harris, Mr Paul Simon LLB ★ President of London Criminal Courts Solicitors Association . . . . *§Sep 1992
Ast: Anderson, Ms Kate LLB ★. . . . . *Sep 2002
Fallen, Mr Peter Dennis ★. . . . . *Sep 1997
Nicol, Ms Alexia Grace BA(Hons)(Law & Criminology) ★ . . . . *Dec 2003
Raphael, Miss Natalie Claire BA(Hons)(Law & Politics) ★ . . . . *Nov 2008

FAIRBAIRN SMITH & CO ‡
Barclays Bank Chambers 549 High Road Tottenham London N17 6SF
Tel: 020 8808 4901 *Fax:* 020 8808 4905 *Dx:* 52202 TOTTENHAM 2
E-mail: enquiries@fairbairnsmith.co.uk
List of partners: R H Burton, D H Smith
Work: K1 N Q S1 S2 W
Ptr: Burton, Mr Russell Hilary LLB(Hons) . . . . *Jul 1979
Smith, Mr David H Deputy District Judge . . . . . . *§Jun 1975

FAIRCHILD GREIG ‡
(in association with Fairchild Dobbs)
Bank Chambers 199 High Street Acton London W3 9DD
Tel: 020 8993 6886 *Fax:* 020 8992 1164 *Dx:* 80254 ACTON
E-mail: enquiries@fairchildgreig.co.uk
List of partners: D N Halliday
Work: E J1 L N O Q R1 S1 S2 W Z(d,q)
Fixed Fee Interview undertaken
Ptr: Halliday, Mr Duncan Neil . . . . *Dec 1978
Con: Hutson, Mr Christopher LLB. . . . . *Jun 1972

FAIRLAW SOLICITORS ‡
39 Sandbrook Road London N16 0SH
Tel: 0845 459 0271 *Fax:* 020 7254 4213
E-mail: info@fairlaw.co.uk

R M FALVEY & CO ‡
26 Ives Street London SW3 2ND
Tel: 020 7100 3414 *Fax:* 020 7100 3415
E-mail: law@falvey.eu
List of partners: R M Falvey
Languages: French
Work: G
SPr: Falvey, Mr Robin M . . . . Jul 1979

FAMILY LAW ASSOCIATES LLP ‡
1 The Courtyard Lynton Road Haringey London N8 8SL
Tel: 020 8342 7760 *Fax:* 020 8347 4227 *Dx:* 35965 CROUCH END
E-mail: mail@familylawassociates.co.uk
List of partners: J A Goodman, D K McHardy
Work: K1 K2 K3
Ptr: Goodman, Miss Judith A LLB Deputy District Judge . . *Jun 1980
McHardy, Mr David K LLB Deputy District Judge . . . *Jul 1978
Ast: Barnes, Ms Melanie. . . . . Jul 2007
Granby, Mrs Jennifer LLM; LLB(Hons). . . . . Feb 2006
Sparks, Ms Lucy BA(Hons) . . . . Apr 2008

FAMILY LAW IN PARTNERSHIP LLP ‡
1 Neal Street Covent Garden London WC2H 9QL
Tel: 020 7420 5000 *Fax:* 020 7420 5005
Dx: 40012 COVENT GARDEN
E-mail: info@flip.co.uk
List of partners: D N Allison, G F Bishop, D A D Coombes, N Hackett, J M Pirrie, B J Williams
Languages: French, German
Work: A3 D1 D2 K1 K2 K3
Emergency Action, Agency and Advocacy undertaken
Ptr: Allison, Mr David Neil DipLP. . . . . *Sep 1995
Bishop, Ms Gillian F LLB(Lond) . . . . *Nov 1982
Coombes, Mr Daniel Andres Dalmedo LLB(Hons). . . *Nov 1998
Hackett, Ms Nicole . . . . *Jan 1979
Pirrie, Mr James M LLB. . . . . *Oct 1985
Williams, Mr Bradley John LLB; DipLP. . . . . *May 2004
Ast: Ditz, Mrs Carla BSc; LLB . . . . *Oct 2010
Fletcher, Ms Elizabeth MA(Hons); CPE; LPC . . . . *Sep 2006
Greenfield, Ms Helen Louise LLB . . . . Dec 2006
Peirse, Miss Rachel Anne MA(Arts); PGDipLaw; LPC . *Jan 2003

THE FAMILY LAW PRACTICE ‡
549-551 Cable Street London E1W 3EN
Tel: 020 7791 0432 *Fax:* 020 7791 0440
Dx: 300709 TOWER HAMLETS
E-mail: abeale@famlawpractice.co.uk

FARADAYS LAW LIMITED ‡
40 Devonshire Drive London SE10 8JZ
Tel: 020 8432 9473
E-mail: ed@faradayslaw.co.uk

FARADAYS SOLICITORS LTD ‡
144a Seven Sisters Road Finsbury Park London N7 7NS
Tel: 020 7281 1001 *Fax:* 020 7281 1021 *Dx:* 89204 HORNSEY
E-mail: enquiries@faradayssolicitors.co.uk
Languages: French, Greek, Indonesian, Marathi, Turkish, Ukrainian
Work: D1 G H K1 K3 N Q Z(i,q)
Emergency Action, Fixed Fee Interview and Legal Aid undertaken

FARANI TAYLOR ‡
Verulam House 60 Grays Inn Road London WC1X 8LU
Tel: 020 7242 1666 *Fax:* 020 7242 7306
Dx: 499 LONDON/CHANCERY LN
E-mail: info@faranitaylor.com

DEBORAH FARQUHAR-SNAITH FAMILY LAW SOLICITOR ‡
180 Langton Way Blackheath London SE3 7JR
Tel: 020 8858 6562 *Fax:* 020 8858 6562
E-mail: deborah.snaith@btconnect.com

FARRELL MARTIN NEE ‡
158-160 Battersea Park Road London SW11 4ND
Tel: 020 7819 2320 *Fax:* 020 7819 2329

FARRELL MATTHEWS & WEIR ‡
Broadway Chambers 20 Hammersmith Broadway London W6 7AF
Tel: 020 8746 3771 *Fax:* 020 8748 7033
Dx: 46758 HAMMERSMITH 3
Emergency telephone 07659 108932
E-mail: info@fmwlaw.co.uk
List of partners: K L Dawson, N G Gray, C J H Matthews, P J McGovern
Office: London W6
Languages: Danish, Italian, Maltese
Work: D1 D2 E G H K1 K3 S1
Emergency Action, Agency, Advocacy, Legal Aid undertaken and Legal Aid Franchise
Ptr: Dawson, Ms Kandy L LLB(Hons)(Warw). . . . . *Nov 1988

See p2 for the Key to Work Categories & other symbols

Matthews, Mr Clive J H LLB(Leeds) ● . . . . *May 1981
Ast: Hammond, Mr Robert Scott LLB. . . . . *Aug 1995
Henderson, Ms Helen Catriona MA; MSc . . . . *Jul 1998
Houghton, Ms Catherine Jonquil BA(Hons) . . . . . . *Mar 1994
Hudson, Mrs Primrose Pearl BA(Hons) . . . . *Dec 1990
Levitt, Mrs Alison M BA(Hons). . . . . *Oct 1986
Con: Weir, Mr Iain T MA(Aberdeen). . . . . *Jul 1973

FARRELL MATTHEWS & WEIR
30-38 Hammersmith Broadway London W6 7AB
Tel: 020 8741 1482 *Fax:* 020 8741 0739
Dx: 46758 HAMMERSMITH 3
Emergency telephone 07659 108932
E-mail: partners@fmw-law.co.uk
Office: London W6
Languages: Finnish, French, Polish
Work: D1 E G H K1 S1
Emergency Action, Agency, Advocacy, Legal Aid undertaken and Legal Aid Franchise
Ptr: Dawson, Ms Kandy L LLB(Hons)(Warw). . . . . *Nov 1988
Gray, Mr Neville G LLB(Sheff). . . . . *Feb 1986
McGovern, Mr Peter John MBA . . . . *Nov 1995
Ast: Carter, Mr J Stephen LLB . . . . *Aug 1984
Caute, Mr Edward BA. . . . . *Aug 1995
Haddadi, Lona . . . . Jul 2001
Pieros, Ms Louise. . . . . *Sep 2001
Podolska, Ms Anna MA . . . . *Feb 1997
Ponting, Ms Anna. Apr 1990
Con: Lynch, Ms Maura LLB. . . . . *Mar 1990

FARRER & CO LLP ‡
66 Lincoln's Inn Fields London WC2A 3LH
Tel: 020 3375 7000 *Fax:* 020 3375 7001
Dx: 32 LONDON/CHANCERY LN
E-mail: enquiries@farrer.co.uk
List of partners: G J Acheson, C R A Anderson, G Baird, J Bal, J Bayliss, B Beabey, C Belcher, S Blair, M T Bridges, S J Bruce, H Bryant, J Carleton, J D P Carrell, M J Chantler, R Cohen, J Coleman, D E Davidson, W Dawson, P J Downy, J Edmondson, A W C Edwards, J Eley, C Faller, M T Fenton, E Fetherston-Dilke, D Fletcher, J Furber, C Gordon, J Gordon, H H J Goulding, S Graham, T Graham, A Gregory, S M A Hedley-Dent, D Hunt, S T Kingston, C A Kirby, P Krafft, K E Lancaster, R T C Lane, R Lewis, S H Macdonald, W Massey, C M McAleavey, A Misquitta, A C Parkhouse, R W J Parry, J Pike, A Piper, J Posnansky, R A Powles, J Price, S J Pring, G W Richards, H J Sainty, R A Shillito, D C Smellie, J A V Smith, A J Springett, J Thorne, J Tizzard, W P Twidale, S von Schmidt, A Walker, P Wienand
Languages: French, German
Work: A1 A2 A3 B1 B2 B3 C1 C2 C3 E F1 F2 I J1 J2 K1 K2 K3 L M1 O Q R1 R2 S1 S2 T1 T2 U1 U2 W X Z(b,c,d,e,f,j,k,n,o,p,q,w,z,za)
Ptr: Acheson, Mr Gavin J BA(Oxon) . . . . *Nov 1990
Anderson, Mr Charles R A MA(Oxon) . . . . *Dec 1985
Baird, Miss Grania BA(Oxon) . . . . *Nov 1996
Bal, Jai . . . . Nov 1996
Bayliss, Mr Jonathan . . . . *Apr 1988
Beabey, Mr Ben BA(Oxon) . . . . *Nov 1999
Belcher, Mr Christopher BA(Hons)(Cantab) . . . . . *Sep 1999
Blair, Mr Stephen . . . . Dec 1979
Bridges, The Hon Mark T MA(Cantab). . . . . *Apr 1980
Bruce, Mr Simon J MA(Oxon). . . . . *Nov 1986
Bryant, Ms Helen MA(Cantab). . . . . *Apr 1980
Carleton, Mr James BA(Cantab). . . . . *Dec 1996
Carrell, Mr John D P MA(Oxon) . . . . *Dec 1981
Chantler, Mr Michael J BA(Oxon) . . . . *Apr 1981
Cohen, Mr Rusell . . . . Nov 2000
Coleman, Ms Joanne . . . . *Sep 1998
Davidson, Ms Diana E BA(Dunelm) . . . . *Oct 1990
Dawson, Mr William. . . . . Oct 1980
Downy, Mr Peter J LLB(Lond) . . . . *Jul 1975
Edmondson, Mr Jim. . . . . Apr 1973
Edwards, Mr Anthony W C . . . . *§Jul 1969
Eley, Mr Jonathan MA(Cantab) . . . . *Sep 2001
Faller, Ms Carrie . . . . Nov 1984
Fenton, Mr Mark T . . . . Oct 1990
Fetherston-Dilke, Mr Edmund BA(Cantab). . . . . . . *Nov 1996
Fletcher, Mr David. . . . . Sep 2000
Furber, Mr James. . . . . Jun 1979
Gordon, Ms Claire BA(Oxon) . . . . *Sep 2000
Gordon, Mr Jeremy . . . . Nov 1991
Goulding, Mr Henry H J MA(Edin). . . . . Nov 1995
Graham, Mr Simon . . . . Sep 2000
Graham, Mr Toby . . . . Feb 1992
Gregory, Ms Anna BA(Cantab) . . . . *Nov 1999
Hedley-Dent, Ms Serena M A BA(Oxon). . . . . *Sep 1998
Hunt, Mr David . . . . *Sep 2001
Kingston, Mr Simon T. . . . . *§May 1973
Kirby, Miss Caroline A MA(Oxon) . . . . *Oct 1977
Krafft, Mr Paul LLB(Bris) . . . . *Nov 1999
Lancaster, Mrs Katie E BA(Cantab) . . . . *Nov 1997
Lane, Mr Richard Thomas Christopher BA. . . . . . . *Nov 1995
Lewis, Miss Rachel BA(Oxon). . . . . *Nov 1996
McAleavey, Miss Catherine M BA(Sussex) . . . . . . *Nov 1985
Macdonald, Mr Samuel H BA . . . . *Nov 1997
Massey, Mr William . . . . Jan 1991
Misquitta, Mr Anthony LLB(Lond) . . . . *Nov 1999
Parkhouse, Mr Adrian C BA(Oxon) . . . . *Sep 1984
Parry, Mr Richard W J BA(Oxon)(Law) . . . . *Oct 1976
Pike, Mr Julian . . . . Oct 1992
Piper, Ms Anne-Marie LLB . . . . *Jun 1988
Posnansky, Mr Jeremy . . . . Nov 2007
Powles, Mr Richard A MA(Oxon) . . . . *§Jun 1971
Price, Mr James LLB(Dunelm). . . . . *Nov 1997
Pring, Mr Simon J MA(Cantab) . . . . *Oct 1988
Richards, Mr Geoffrey W MA(Oxon). . . . . *May 1972
Sainty, Mr Henry J BA(Oxon) . . . . *Nov 1995
Shillito, Mr Richard A MA(Oxon). . . . . *Dec 1976
Smellie, Mr David C BA(Cantab) . . . . *Jan 1990
Smith, Mr Julian A V BA(Cantab) . . . . *Oct 1994
Springett, Miss Alison J MA(St Andrews) . . . . . . *Dec 1990
Thorne, Mr James. . . . . Mar 1978
Tizzard, Mr Jeremy . . . . Nov 1999
Twidale, Mr William P LLB(Cantab) . . . . *Nov 1994
von Schmidt, Ms Sarah BA(Oxon). . . . . *Nov 1997
Walker, Mr Adrian. . . . . Oct 1991
Wienand, Mr Peter . . . . Oct 1988

FARRER & CO TRUST CORPORATION LIMITED ‡
65-66 Lincoln's Inn Fields London WC2A 3LH
Tel: 020 7242 2022 *Fax:* 020 7242 9899 *Dx:* 32 CHANCERY LANE
E-mail: enquiries@farrer.co.uk

FARRINGDONS ‡
61 Gray's Inn Road London WC1X 8TL
Tel: 020 7242 0949 *Fax:* 020 7242 0956
E-mail: info@farringdonssolicitors.co.uk
List of partners: M K Choudhury
Work: A3 B1 C2 D2 E G K1 M2 S2 Z(a,i)
Ptr: Choudhury, Manof Kumar. . . . . Apr 1994

FASKEN MARTINEAU LLP ‡
17 Hanover Square London W1S 1HU
Tel: 020 7917 8500 *Fax:* 020 7917 8555 *Dx:* 82984 MAYFAIR
E-mail: london@fasken.com
List of partners: M J Ackland, A P Booth, D A Connick, N R Gordon, R E Hickling, G R Howes, N S Kravitz, R J Loosley, J M Paddock, D Smith, P D Yerbury, N J Ziman
Languages: German, Greek, Hebrew, Russian
Work: B1 C1 C2 C3 E F1 I J1 L O P Q R1 R2 S1 S2 T1 T2 U2 W Z(b,c,e,f,l,n,o,s,y,z)
Ptr: Ackland, Mr Martin J BA(Oxon) . . . . *Dec 1979
Booth, Mr Allistair P LLB; BCom. . . . . Jul 1992
Connick, Mr David A . . . . *May 1982
Gordon, Mr Nigel Raymond BA . . . . *Oct 1987
Hickling, Miss Ruth Elizabeth LLB. . . . . Apr 1988
Howes, Mr Gary Russell LLB . . . . *Aug 1992
Kravitz, Nicola S LLB . . . . *Oct 1991
Loosley, Mr Roger John Notary Public. . . . . *Oct 1971
Paddock, Ms June Mary BA(Hons) . . . . *Oct 1980
Smith, Mr David BA(Oxon) . . . . Oct 1981
Yerbury, Mr Paul D MA; BSc(Oxon) . . . . *Jan 1991
Ziman, Mr Norman J LLB; MBA. . . . . *Dec 1969
Asoc: Rosenburg, Mr Robert Bernard LLB(Hons) . . . . . . Sep 2002
Ast: Chrysanthou, Chris . . . . Sep 2001
Liu, Ms Mun-Ling BA(Hons). . . . . Sep 1999
Richards, Mr Stuart David LLB; DipLP; DipEC Comp . Sep 1998

JEREMY FEAR & CO ‡
25 Warwick Road London N11 2SB
Tel: 020 8361 7915 *Fax:* 020 8361 7916

FEARNLEY & CO ‡
7 Springbridge Mews Ealing London W5 2AB
Tel: 020 8579 9898 *Fax:* 020 8579 7575 *Dx:* 5120 EALING
E-mail: enquiries@fearnleyandco.com
List of partners: A A Fearnley
Languages: Hebrew, Spanish
Work: C1 L M2 R1 S1 T1 T2 W
Fixed Fee Interview undertaken
SPr: Fearnley, Mr A Andrew LLB(Hons) . . . . *Jun 1989

FELLOWES SOLICITORS ‡
21 Church Hill London E17 3AD
Tel: 020 8520 7392 *Fax:* 020 8509 0759
E-mail: info@fellowes.org
List of partners: M Butler, S R J Fellowes, G Rance, M Woolf
Ptr: Butler, Mrs Marielyne BA(Hons) . . . . *Apr 2003
Fellowes, Mr Stephen R J LLB(Lond) . . . . *Oct 1990
Rance, Mr Gregory LLB(Hons) . . . . *Mar 2004
Woolf, Mr Michael BA(Hons) . . . . *Sep 1998
Ast: Anderson, Miss Natasha LLB(Hons). . . . . Dec 2007

R FELSTEAD SOLICITORS ‡
2 Akehurst Street London SW15 5DR
Tel: 020 8789 3856 *Fax:* 020 8789 3856
E-mail: rachel@rfelstead6.wanadoo.co.uk

FELTONS ‡
5 Raleigh House Admirals Way Canary Wharf London E14 9SN
Tel: 0870 751 5600 *Fax:* 0870 751 6066
E-mail: info@canarywharflaw.com

FENCHURCH LAW LLP ‡
Warnford Court 29 Throgmorton Street London EC2N 2AT
Tel: 020 7337 6116
E-mail: info@fenchurchlaw.co.uk

FENTONS SOLICITORS LLP ‡
22 Chancery Lane London WC2A 1LS
Tel: 020 7580 0143 / 0845 026 4749 *Fax:* 020 7291 6599
E-mail: info@fentons.co.uk

FENWICK ELLIOTT ‡
Aldwych House 71-91 Aldwych London WC2B 4HN
Tel: 020 7421 1986 *Fax:* 020 7421 1987
Dx: 178 LONDON/CHANCERY LN
Emergency telephone 020 7421 1986
E-mail: nelliot@fenwickelliott.co.uk
List of partners: P Collie, G H J Critchlow, N L Elliot, A W Francis, K Gidwani, F Gillion, J R Glover, N Gould, E Lowery, T Randle, D Robertson, V E Russell, R Smellie, J Stagg, S J A Tolson
Languages: French, German
Work: A3 O P Q R2 Z(c,h,j)
Emergency Action, Agency and Advocacy undertaken
Ptr: Critchlow, Mr Geoffrey H J MSc(Lond); FCIArb; LLB. . *Oct 1984
Francis, Mr Anthony W LLB. . . . . *Dec 1987
Gidwani, Ms Karen . . . . Jan 1999
Gillion, Mr Frederic LLB; MSc(Construction Law & Arbitration); FCIArb . . . . *Nov 2002
Glover, Mr Jeremy R BA . . . . *Nov 1992
Gould, Mr Nicholas . . . . *Nov 1999
Lowery, Mr Edward LLB. . . . . *Jun 1997
Randle, Mr Toby. Jan 1998
Robertson, Mr David . . . . May 2007
Russell, Miss Victoria E LLB(Exon); FCIArb . . . . . *Aug 1981
Smellie, Mr Richard BA; LLB . . . . *Aug 1991
Stagg, Ms Julie . . . . Oct 1997
Tolson, Mr Simon J A BA; FFB; ACIArb . . . . *Feb 1987
Collie, Peter. . . . . NSP
Elliot, Mr Neil L . . . . NSP

FERGUSON SOLICITORS ‡
11 Gough Square London EC4A 3DE
Tel: 020 7822 2999 *Fax:* 020 7822 2950
E-mail: admin@fergusonsolicitors.co.uk
List of partners: J C C Ferguson
Work: A3 B1 C1 F1 J1 L N O Q Z(b,c,e,j,k,q)
SPr: Ferguson, Mr J Charles C. . . . . *Apr 1971
Ast: MacDonald, Miss Fiona Mary MA(Oxon); MMus BPP Dissertation Prize 2000 . . . . Oct 2003
Murray, Mr Justin James MA(Cantab) . . . . Sep 2001
Con: Puxon, Mr Paul Benidict. . . . . *Jan 1985

FERNANDO & CO ‡
15 Trinity Road Tooting Bec Wandsworth London SW17 7SD
Tel: 020 8767 4611 *Fax:* 020 8682 4422
E-mail: reseba@aol.com
List of partners: H S Fernando
Languages: Sinhalese, Tamil
Work: D1 E F1 K1 S1 W Z(l)
Fixed Fee Interview undertaken
Ptr: Fernando, Harilal S . . . . *Nov 1975

FERNANDO SCORNIK GERSTEIN SOLICITORS ‡
Holborn Hall 193-197 High Holborn London WC1V 7BD
Tel: 020 7404 8400 *Fax:* 020 7404 8500
E-mail: london@scornik-gerstein.co.uk

FERNS ‡
112 Clapham High Street London SW4 7UJ
Tel: 020 7498 9537 *Fax:* 020 7720 7736
Dx: 53260 CLAPHAM COMMON
E-mail: ferns@property-solicitors.com
List of partners: D D Narayan, D Patel
Ptr: Narayan, Mr Douglas D. . . . . Mar 1989
Patel, Mr Dipak . . . . *Jun 1995

FIDEX LAW ‡
Ground Floor North Southeland House 70-78 West Handson Broadway London NW9 7BT
Tel: 020 8457 3258 *Fax:* 020 8457 3251
E-mail: stephen@fidexgroup.com

STEPHEN FIDLER & CO ‡
5 Dyers Buildings London EC1N 2JT
Tel: 020 7353 8999 *Fax:* 020 7353 9032
Dx: 8 LONDON/CHANCERY LN
Emergency telephone 07974 429835
E-mail: sfidler@stephenfidler.co.uk
List of partners: S M Fidler
Languages: Arabic, French, Hebrew
Work: D1 F1 G H I K1 L M1 N P Q
Emergency Action, Agency, Advocacy, Fixed Fee Interview, Legal Aid undertaken and Member of Accident Line
Ptr: Fidler, Mr Stephen M LLB; MA ★ . . . . *Jun 1984
Ast: Fidler, Mr Adam P BA. . . . . *Dec 1988
Fidler, Mr Mark D . . . . Dec 1992
Thorpe-Anderson, Ms Joan . . . . Oct 1996

FIELD & CO ‡
36 Great Saint Helens Bishopsgate London EC3A 6AP
Tel: 020 7329 8615 *Fax:* 020 7236 6683

FIELD FISHER WATERHOUSE LLP ‡
35 Vine Street London EC3N 2AA
Tel: 020 7861 4000 *Fax:* 020 7488 0084 *Dx:* 823 LONDON/CITY
E-mail: info@ffw.com
List of partners: P M Abell, K M Baillie, R Banga, E Bannister, I S Barnard, J M Barrett, P D Barton, N C Beecham, B Benney, A M Blankfield, A L Brockbank, L Bruce, S T Chamberlain, M P Chissick, J Chrystie, F H Coffell, R P Cooke, T J Davies, M A Davis, J C Elkins, S Ellson, A G Evans, J K Fife, M Frochot, D Gallagher, S N Gibbs, M A C Gilmour, D R S Gurney-Champion, M Holah, W P Houston, D J G Hunt, C J Jackson, T Kato, R J Kenyon, D M G Knight, A Lafferty, M Lewis, M Lohn, D M Lowe, A Lucas, B Marzheuser-Wood, K A Maxwell, C McArthur, P McNeil, E Miller, S J Moore, A G Morgan, R M Nelson-Jones, N R Noble, G J Nuttall, J R Olsen, N Palmer, A Poulter, T M O Redgrave, A T B Rider, N P Rose, R J P Sargologo, M Sellers, M Smith, P J R Stewart, N Taylor, N P Thompsell, M Timms, G Usher, R P Webber, C R Whiddington, N D Wildish, D L Wilkinson, P Williams
Languages: Danish, French, German, Italian, Japanese, Korean, Mandarin, Norwegian, Spanish, Swedish
Work: A1 B1 C1 C2 C3 D1 E F1 I J1 L M1 M2 N O P R1 S1 T1 T2 W Z(a,b,c,d,e,f,g,h,i,j,k,l,m,n,o,p,s,t)
Emergency Action, Agency, Advocacy undertaken and Member of Accident Line
Ptr: Abell, Mr Philip M LLB. . . . . *Dec 1984
Baillie, Ms Kirstene M MA(Oxon) . . . . *Nov 1987
Banga, Ramatu . . . . Nov 1994
Barnard, Mr Ian S. Nov 1984
Barrett, Mr J Martin LLB. . . . . *Oct 1984
Barton, Mr Paul D LLB . . . . Nov 1991
Beecham, Mr Nicholas C BSc. . . . . *Oct 1986
Benney, Miss Belinda LLB(Bris) . . . . *Apr 1981
Blankfield, Mr Andrew M MA(Cantab) City of London Solicitors Company Prize . . . . *Nov 1987
Brockbank, Mr Anthony L MA(Oxon) . . . . *§Oct 1986
Bruce, Mr Lawrence LLB . . . . *Nov 1982
Chamberlain, Mr Simon T. . . . . *May 1977
Chissick, Mr Michael P LLB . . . . *Sep 1989
Chrystie, Miss Judith . . . . Oct 1997
Coffell, Mr F Howard MA(Oxon). . . . . *§Jan 1975
Cooke, Mr Robert P MA(Oxon) . . . . *Oct 1985
Davies, Mr Timothy J LLB. . . . . *Jun 1979
Davis, Mrs Margaret Ann LLB(Lond); BA Non-Executive Director of the Health Trust . . . . *Oct 1983
Elkins, Miss Jayne C LLB; AKC . . . . *Nov 1983
Ellson, Ms Sarah . . . . Sep 1997
Evans, Mr Andrew G . . . . *Dec 1977
Fife, Mr Jonathan K MA(Oxon) . . . . *§Jun 1973
Frochot, Ms Marie-Caroline Maitrise en Droit(Hons); LLM(Hons) . . . . Aug 1991
Gallagher, Mr David. . . . . Feb 2001
Gibbs, Mr Stephen N MA(Cantab). . . . . *Apr 1979
Gilmour, Ms Moira A C MA; LLB. . . . . *Jun 1987
Gurney-Champion, Mr Dominic R S LLB . . . . Oct 1994
Holah, Mr Mark . . . . Oct 1996
Houston, Mr W Paul LLB; DipLP. . . . . *Aug 1991
Hunt, Mr D Jasper G MA(Oxon). . . . . May 1972
Jackson, Mr Christopher J LLB(Lond) . . . . *Jul 1975
Kato, Teruo BA . . . . *Nov 1997
Kenyon, Mr Richard J . . . . Dec 1992
Knight, Mr David M G BSc(Hons); BEng; CEng; MIEE. Aug 1992
Lafferty, Mr Andrew . . . . Dec 1992
Lewis, Mr Mark . . . . Nov 1986
Lohn, Mr Matthew. . . . . Sep 1996
Lowe, Mr D Mark BA(Kent) . . . . Dec 1974
Lucas, Mr Andrew. . . . . Sep 1997
McArthur, Mr Colin BA(Cantab) . . . . *§Oct 1969
McNeil, Mr Paul LLB . . . . *§Nov 1983
Marzheuser-Wood, Ms Babette . . . . Mar 1993
Maxwell, Mr Kenneth A MA(Cantab). . . . . *Oct 1984
Miller, Edward. . . . . Oct 1996

Moore, Mr Simon J LLB . . . Mar 1985
Morgan, Mr Andrew G LLB; MSc . . . Jan 1993
Nelson-Jones, Mr Rodney M BA(Oxon) Herbert Ruse Prize . . . *Nov 1975
Noble, Mr Nicholas R . . . *Oct 1979
Nuttall, Mr Graeme J MA(Cantab); ATII . . . *Oct 1984
Olsen, Mr John Raymond BA; BSc . . . *Nov 1992
Palmer, Mr Neil . . . Nov 1994
Poulter, Mr Allan . . . Dec 1992
Redgrave, Mr Toby Michael Ormsby . . . *Jul 1993
Rider, Mr A Thomas B LLB . . . *§Oct 1982
Rose, Mr Nicholas P LLB . . . *Nov 1983
Sargologo, Mr Roger J P LLB(Hons) . . . *Mar 1985
Sellers, Mr Mark LLB . . . May 1988
Smith, Mr Martin . . . Jan 1999
Stewart, Mr Peter J R . . . Mar 1982
Taylor, Mr Nigel . . . Sep 1993
Thompsell, Mr Nicholas P LLB; AKC . . . *Nov 1985
Timms, Miss Mary MA(Oxon) . . . Nov 1991
Usher, Mr Guy . . . Nov 1990
Webber, Mr Richard P DMS . . . *Oct 1973
Whiddington, Mr Charles R LLB(Cardiff); Member of New York Bar . . . Oct 1982
Wildish, Mr Nigel D BA(Cantab) . . . *§May 1972
Wilkinson, Mr David L LLB . . . Oct 1992
Williams, Mr Peter . . . Nov 1993
Ast: Albertini, Miss Louisa . . . Sep 1996
Allan, Ms Janet J . . . Apr 1992
Banton, Ms Lisa . . . Sep 1998
Barsey, Dr Hilary BSc; MBBS . . . *Sep 1996
Batchelor, Mr Gawaine James Michael . . . Nov 1997
Beresford, Mr Nicholas . . . Sep 1999
Bond, Mr David . . . Sep 1998
Brown, Miss Victoria . . . Sep 1996
Buchanan, Ms Nichola . . . Sep 1998
Cassidy, Mrs Sarah L BA . . . *Apr 1985
Chrystie, Miss Judith . . . Oct 1997
Coskery, Ms Siobhan . . . Sep 1994
Cross, Ms Fiona M . . . Oct 1997
Danielian, Mr Mark . . . Jan 2000
Daniels, Ms Samantha J . . . Nov 1995
Davenport, Ms Kate . . . Oct 1995
Dennis, Mr James Anthony John . . . Sep 1997
Elkins, Ms Jane LLB(Hons) . . . Jan 1999
Farnell, Ms Clare . . . Sep 1999
Fishley, Mr Barry . . . Jun 1990
Fuff, Mrs Heather BA(Law); TEP . . . *Dec 1987
Gibson, Mr Colin . . . Sep 1999
Gorczac, Ms Jan . . . Sep 1999
Greenbury, Mr Simon C LLB . . . *Apr 1977
Hackelsberger, Mr Roman . . . Sep 1996
Hamilton, Mr Grant . . . Aug 1995
Harris, Ms Kelly Anne . . . Nov 1997
Hart, Ms Annabel . . . Mar 1997
Helmer, Mr Michael BSc; LLB . . . Apr 1997
King, Ms Christine P . . . Sep 1990
Laffery, Mr Andrew N BA . . . *Dec 1992
Lindop, Ms Jane . . . Jul 1996
Liu, Yamin . . . Sep 1999
Lumb, Mr E Laurence . . . Sep 1997
Mcnamara, Ms Jackie . . . Sep 1998
May, Ms Elizabeth J O . . . Oct 1997
Miller, Edward . . . Oct 1996
Mitchiner, Mr James . . . Mar 1999
Munro, Ms Joanne . . . Sep 1998
Murphy, Ms Emma . . . Sep 1995
Nadler, Ms Shelley . . . *Sep 1993
Newcombe, Ms Catherine . . . Nov 1989
Osborne, Mr Michael Fraser CPE; LSF; BA(Hons) . . . *Oct 1991
Parris, Ms Emily . . . Sep 1996
Pickard, Mr Gary . . . Sep 1998
Pimlott, Mr Nicholas . . . Sep 1997
Pinfold, Ms Caroline E BA . . . *Jun 1983
Riley, Ms Nadine . . . Sep 1999
Rowan, Ms Jane LLB . . . Oct 1994
Sexton, Ms Denise . . . Sep 1999
Sidiqui, Saida . . . Jun 1988
Smith, Mr Daniel LLB . . . Sep 1999
Sondermann, Ms Annett . . . Apr 1997
Stallard, Miss Hayley . . . Nov 1990
Timmings, Ms Claire . . . Nov 1991
Timms, Miss Mary MA(Oxon) . . . Nov 1991
Tormann, Ms Kathy . . . Mar 1996
Turle, Mr Marcus . . . Apr 1999
Turner, Mr Paul . . . Sep 1999
Varoujian, Raffi . . . Sep 1999
Vartoukian, Miss Rita . . . Sep 1997
Veysey, Mr Guy . . . Sep 1999
Walton, Mr Brian . . . May 1979
Weakley, Ms Jane . . . Sep 1994
Wotton, Miss Penelope A BSc(York) . . . *Oct 1988

FIGUEIREDO & BOWMAN ‡
Rivington House 82 Great Eastern Street Hackney London EC2A 3JF
Tel: 020 7739 5599 *Fax:* 020 7739 6399 *Dx:* 137776 FINSBURY 5
Emergency telephone 07956 914814 / 07725 582872
E-mail: enquiries@fbsolicitors.co.uk
List of partners: M A Bowman, A X D R Figueiredo
Languages: Portuguese, Spanish
Work: K1 K3 O Q S1 S2 W Z(i)
Fixed Fee Interview, Legal Aid undertaken and Legal Aid Franchise
Mem: Bowman, Mr Mark A MA(Hons); PGDipLaw . . . §Mar 2008
Figueiredo, Anacleto Xavier Dos Remedios LLB; LLM; MA; BCom; MSc; BSc(Hon) Psych (OU) Notary Public §Sep 1994

FILATOV GOLDBERG MUSATOV LLP ‡
20 Hanover Square London W1S 1JY
Tel: 020 3178 5769 *Fax:* 020 3178 2456
E-mail: enquiry@fgmlaw.co.uk

FINERS STEPHENS INNOCENT LLP ‡
179 Great Portland Street London W1W 5LS
Tel: 020 7323 4000 *Fax:* 020 7580 7069
Dx: 42739 OXFORD CIRCUS NORTH
Emergency telephone 020 8421 3376
E-mail: marketing@fsilaw.co.uk
List of partners: C A Brown, P A Carter, R D Craig, G P Eder, H J Goulden, J P Hindmarsh, A Kaufman, R C Lands, M H Lewis, S W Lewis, E Mailer, S Malkiel, A L McNeil, P M Millett, E A Palmer, A J Reeback, P D Rubens, J Sellors, B Slater, M H Stephens, S Thackeray, S J Wax
Languages: French, German, Hebrew, Italian, Spanish
Work: A3 B1 C1 C2 E F1 F2 I J1 K1 K2 L M1 M2 N O Q R1 R2 S1 S2 T1 T2 U2 W X Z(c,e,f,g,k,l,p,q,r,w,z)
Emergency Action and Advocacy undertaken
Ptr: Brown, Miss Carolyn A LLB . . . *Oct 1983
Carter, Mr Peter A BA . . . *§Apr 1974
Craig, Mr Robert D LLM; AKC John Mackrell Prize . . . *Mar 1971
Eder, Mr G Philip LLB(Lond); LLM(Brussels) . . . *Apr 1976
Goulden, Mr Howard J LLB(Lond) . . . Oct 1989
Hindmarsh, Mr Julian Paul LLB . . . *Oct 1987
Kaufman, Mr Alan MA(Cantab) . . . *§May 1971
Lands, Mr Robert Clifford BA . . . Sep 1999
Lewis, Mr Michael H . . . *§Jun 1972
Lewis, Mr Stephen W LLB . . . *Nov 1988
Mailer, Emily . . . Apr 1999
Malkiel, Mr Simon . . . Sep 2001
Millett, Mr Paul M LLB . . . Sep 1986
Palmer, Ms Elizabeth A BA; ATT; ATII . . . *Sep 1996
Reeback, Ashley J BSc . . . Sep 1994
Rubens, Mr Philip D LLB . . . *Mar 1986
Sellors, Mr Jonathan . . . Apr 2000
Stephens, Mr Mark H BA . . . *Jul 1982
Wax, Ms Sara Jean LLB . . . Sep 1999
Mem: McNeil, Ms Amanda Louise LLB . . . *Nov 1991
Thackeray, Ms Sue . . . Dec 1997
Ast: Aggarwal, Nisha . . . Sep 2009
Annetts, Mr John BA(Hons) . . . Sep 2000
Christie, Lydia . . . Sep 2004
Dayal, Amrita . . . May 2003
Hallows, Mr Jonathan . . . Sep 2009
Maclean, Ms Imogen LLB . . . Sep 2000
Morley, Mr Guy . . . Sep 2009
Con: Hewitt, Mr John E . . . *§Jan 1979
Kutner, Mr Michael D . . . *Dec 1973
Miller, Ms Katherine M . . . Oct 1988
Nathan, Mr Michael J . . . *§Dec 1968
Orton, Mr Melvyn D LLB(Lond) . . . *Nov 1970
Silman, Mr Geoffrey N LLB(B'ham) . . . *§Jun 1973

FIRST CONVEYANCING ‡
3 Century Yard London SE23 3XT
Tel: 020 8291 5427

FISCHER & CO ‡
56 Linkside Barnet London N12 7LG
Tel: 020 8346 7036 / 8922 0689 *Fax:* 020 8922 0689
Emergency telephone 020 8346 7036
E-mail: pfischer1948@yahoo.co.uk
List of partners: R B Fischer
Work: E L S1 W
Fixed Fee Interview undertaken
SPr: Fischer, Mrs Rita Barbara LLB(Hons) . . . *Nov 1973

FISHBURNS ‡
60 Fenchurch Street London EC3M 4AD
Tel: 020 7280 8888 *Fax:* 020 7280 8899 *Dx:* 584 LONDON/CITY
E-mail: wood@fishburnslaw.com
List of partners: P D Campion, A T Davis, P A Heartfield, M S Klimt, R S Lloyd, A L Marsh, S D Mason, P B Sewell, A Wilson, S M Wood
Languages: French, German, Portuguese, Russian, Spanish
Work: A3 B2 C1 M2 N O P Q Z(c,j,q)
Agency undertaken
Ptr: Campion, Mr Peter D LLB . . . *Oct 1990
Davis, Mr Andrew T LLB . . . *Apr 1980
Heartfield, Mr Philip A BA . . . *Oct 1989
Klimt, Mr Mark S BA(Oxon) . . . *Feb 1986
Lloyd, Mr Robert S . . . *Dec 1993
Marsh, Mr Anthony L LLB . . . *Oct 1990
Mason, Mr Simon Dane LLB . . . *Dec 1991
Sewell, Mr Peter B . . . *Jan 1995
Wilson, Mr Angus . . . *Dec 1985
Wood, Ms Sheona Mary BA(Oxon) . . . *Dec 1988
Ast: Bodenstein, Mr Chris . . . Jul 2002
Eaton, Ms Sara-Jane BA(Hons) . . . *Nov 1995
Fisher, Mr Richard . . . *Mar 2000
Guest, Ms Sam . . . Jul 2002
Hazelton, Mr Gary A . . . *Nov 1990
Hernandez, Mr Gavin . . . Sep 2003
Knight, Mr Michael Thomas BA; ACII; FILEx . . . *Nov 1993
Lambert, Mr Robin Charles LLB(Hons) . . . Oct 2002
Mace, Ms Kirsteen . . . *Sep 1996
Moss, Mr Jonathan Charles . . . Oct 1996
O'Reilly, Miss Louise . . . Sep 2003
Oldham, Ms Helen . . . *Oct 1989
Rogers, Mr Steve . . . Sep 2003
Sheldon, Mr Tim BA; ACII . . . *Nov 1993
Silver, Miss Samantha . . . *Jul 1999
Varco, Ms Philippa BSc(Hons) . . . *Jan 1991
Varcoe, Ms Philippa . . . Jan 1991
Ward-Smith, Miss Clare . . . *Sep 2000
Whibley, Mr Jack . . . Sep 2004
Williams, Miss Janet L LLB(Bris) . . . *Oct 1991
Con: Dagonnot, Mr Pierre . . . Jan 1999

FISHER LEVINE & CO ‡
27 Leicester Road East Finchley London N2 9DY
List of partners: M Levine
Ptr: Levine, Ms M BA(Hons) . . . Jun 1985

FISHER MEREDITH ‡
Blue Sky House 405 Kennington Road Lambeth London SE11 4PT
Tel: 020 7091 2700 *Fax:* 020 7091 2800 *Dx:* 37050 KENNINGTON 3
Emergency telephone 07836 780109
E-mail: info@fishermeredith.co.uk
List of partners: S W D Banks, J A Bishton, F J Dunkley, L S Hawkes, S F Hewitt, E E Jones, E M Pembridge, S V Ruis
Office: Richmond upon Thames
Languages: Cantonese, French, German, Hakka, Hokkien, Italian, Mandarin, Russian, Spanish
Work: B2 C1 D1 D2 E G H J1 K1 K3 L M1 O P Q S1 S2 X Z(e,g,i,k,m,p,q,za)
Emergency Action, Agency, Advocacy, Fixed Fee Interview, Legal Aid undertaken and Legal Aid Franchise
Ptr: Banks, Mr Stephen William Desmond MA(Cantab) . . . *Apr 1973
Bishton, Mrs Judith A BA(Hons) . . . *Dec 1990
Dunkley, Ms Fiona J LLB ★ . . . *Jan 1992
Hawkes, Mrs Linda S LLB . . . *Oct 1980
Hewitt, Mr Stephen F LLB . . . *Oct 1980
Jones, Miss Elizabeth Eirwen LLB . . . Feb 1991
Pembridge, Ms Eileen M BA(Cantab) Law Society Council Member . . . *Dec 1975
Ruis, Mr Stefano V BA(Hons) . . . *Aug 1997
Ast: Arnold, Mr Noel LLB . . . Apr 2006
Arthur, Mr Andrew LLB . . . May 1999
Barretto, Mrs Moira Louise BCom; LLB . . . Apr 2003
Blain, Mr Simon BA; PGDipLaw . . . Nov 2002
Bourdages, Mr Michael . . . Nov 2003
Burke, Mr John LLB . . . Jan 1999
Cornes, Ms Julia BA(Hons) . . . Nov 1999
Cuming, Ms Fiona BA; MSc; CPE; LSF . . . Oct 1995
Dutta, Mr Shamik BSc(Politics); PGDip; LPC . . . Oct 2005
Halberstam, Mr Jason BSc(Hons); PGDipLaw . . . *Sep 1997
Higbee, Mr James Henry LLB(Hons) . . . *Apr 2005
Kanani, Mr Ashok BA(Hons)(Econ); PGDipLaw; LPC . Aug 2005
Loveday, Mr Brett LLB . . . *Sep 1997
Mouls, Ms Hazel S LLB . . . *May 1993
Palmer, Mr Patrick G BA(Lond) . . . *Nov 1981
Patel, Mr Dighayu LLB; LLM . . . Jan 2003
Pitts, Ms Lisa Miranda Jane BA(Hons); PGDipLaw; LPC . . . Sep 2005
Robinson, Miss Catherine LLB . . . Apr 2006
Singh, Mr Thakur Rakesh LLB(Hons) . . . Oct 2000
Stirling, Ms Jacqueline Jamima BA(Hons)(Law & Society) . . . *Aug 2001
Twaite, Ms Alice BA; MSc . . . Nov 2002
Vnuk, Mr Stefan Chad LLB(Hons); BSc(Jurisprudence) . . . *Aug 1996

OLIVER FISHER ‡
2nd Floor Astley House 33 Notting Hill Gate London W11 3JQ
Tel: 020 3219 0145 *Fax:* 020 3219 0175
Dx: 94204 NOTTING HILL GATE
E-mail: advice@oliverfisher.co.uk
List of partners: R B Conway
Languages: French, German
Work: E F1 G H J1 K1 L M1 N P R1 S1 W Z(h,l)
Emergency Action, Agency, Advocacy, Fixed Fee Interview, Legal Aid undertaken and Member of Accident Line
Ptr: Conway, Mr Russell B LLB . . . *Jun 1981
Ast: Barran, Mrs Veronica T BA(Oxon); Dip Crim(Cantab) . Mar 1981
Shortland, Ms Joanne L LLB . . . Feb 1988

FISHER SCOGGINS WATERS LLP ‡
Hamilton House 1 Temple Avenue London EC4Y 0HA
Tel: 020 7489 2035 *Fax:* 020 7183 8211
E-mail: waters@fisherscogginswaters.co.uk
List of partners: A Fisher, M Scoggins, C Waters
Work: A3 J2 N P Q Z(j)
Emergency Action, Advocacy and Fixed Fee Interview undertaken
Ptr: Fisher, Mr Alan BA ♦ . . . Jun 1978
Scoggins, Mr Mark BA; MA(Cantab) • . . . Apr 1993
Waters, Miss Charlotte BA • . . . Apr 2001

FISHERS ‡
71 Leonard Street London EC2A 4QX
Tel: 020 7613 8111 *Fax:* 020 7613 8112
E-mail: info@fishcity.co.uk

FISHMAN & CO SOLICITORS ‡
131 Baker Street London W1U 6SE
Tel: 020 7935 3500 *Fax:* 020 7935 9111
Dx: 53807 OXFORD CIRCUS NORTH
E-mail: info@fishmanlaw.co.uk
List of partners: I M D Fishman, C D Sellar-Elliott
Work: B1 C1 C2 E J1 L N O Q R2 S1 S2 W Z(e)
Ptr: Fishman, Mr Ian Maxwell David LLB . . . *Nov 1973
Sellar-Elliott, Ms Claire Dawn BA(Hons) . . . Jan 2000
Con: Timms, Mr Howard LLB(Hons) . . . Mar 1998

DAVID FISHWICK ‡
32 Kensington Park Road London W11 3BU
Tel: 020 7792 8811 *Fax:* 020 7792 8586

FITZPATRICK & CO ‡
Unit A 446 New Cross Road London SE14 6TY
Tel: 020 8691 5112 *Fax:* 020 8469 2891

FLACK & CO ‡
Gardiner House 3-9 Broomhill Road Wandsworth London SW18 4JQ
Tel: 020 8875 1888 *Fax:* 020 8870 8139

FLADGATE LLP ‡
16 Great Queen Street London WC2B 5DG
Tel: 020 3036 7000 *Fax:* 020 3036 7600 *Dx:* 37971 KINGSWAY
E-mail: fladgate@fladgate.com
List of partners: P Bohm, A J R Brandes, S A Brew, J M Buckley, E J Cannon, A Cohen, N Cohen, B A Eilon, S J Ekins, A D Erwin, N D A Greenstone, C A Jamieson, K Jamieson, A C Kaufman, R Kaufman, J A Keeley, A Kelman, P Leese, A N McKenzie, A J Mould, R W Muir, I A Narbeth, D P Robinson, H M Smith, R H Stanton, J A S Vaughan, C D Wander
Languages: French, German, Hebrew, Italian, Spanish, Thai, Yiddish
Work: A1 A3 B1 C1 C2 C3 E F1 I J1 K1 L M1 M2 N O P Q R1 R2 S1 S2 T1 W Z(b,c,d,e,f,h,i,j,k,l,o,q,w)
Agency undertaken
Ptr: Bohm, Mr Peter MA(Cantab) . . . *Apr 1976
Brandes, Mrs Antonia Jane Rebecca LLB(Hons)(Lond) . . . *Mar 1979
Brew, Mr Simon Andrew LLB(Reading) . . . *Nov 1992
Buckley, Mr J Mark BA . . . *Feb 1985
Cannon, Mr Eamonn John LLB(Hons) . . . *Dec 1968
Cohen, Mr Allen BA . . . Dec 1979
Cohen, Mr Norman LLB(Hons) . . . *May 1976
Eilon, Mrs Barbara A BA . . . Jan 1985
Ekins, Mr Simon Jeremy BSc . . . Mar 1987
Erwin, Mr Alan D BA(Hons) . . . Aug 1989
Greenstone, Mr Nicolas D A BA(Oxon) Herbert Ruse Prize . . . *Jun 1972
Jamieson, Mrs Catherine A BA(Oxon) . . . Nov 1986
Jamieson, Ms Kate . . . Oct 1986
Kaufman, Mr Andrew C MA(Oxon) . . . §Dec 1971
Kaufman, Mr Richard BA . . . *§Mar 1985
Keeley, Ms Janet A LLB . . . *Oct 1984
Kelman, Avram . . . Mar 1993
Leese, Mr Paul LLB . . . *Nov 1973
McKenzie, Mr Andrew N MA(Cantab) . . . *Apr 1971
Mould, Miss Alison J LLB . . . *Nov 1989
Muir, Mr Robert W LLB(Lond) . . . *Apr 1979
Narbeth, Mr Ian A MA(Cantab) . . . Nov 1985
Robinson, Mr David Paul BA; MA . . . *Apr 1995
Smith, Mr Harold M . . . Jun 1970
Stanton, Mr Richard H . . . *Dec 1967
Vaughan, Mr J Anthony S BA(UEA); DipLaw . . . *Dec 1979
Wander, Mr Charles D LLB . . . *Dec 1979
Ast: Adams, Mr Jeremy A J BA(Hons) . . . Sep 1994
Blowers, Miss Margaret BA(Hons) . . . Sep 1996
Bonsignore, Miss Samantha BA(Hons) . . . Feb 2000

See p2 for the Key to Work Categories & other symbols

Brassey, Mr Lewis Mark BA(Hons) . . . . *Nov 1996
Daneshmand, Mrs Natasha LLB(Hons); LPC . . . . . Apr 2000
Dayle, Mr Richard MA(Cantab) . . . . *Oct 1998
Edwards, Mrs Amanda M Catherine Barker Prize . . . *Oct 1999
Farr, Miss Helen J LLB . . . . *Nov 1993
Handscombe, Miss Sarah Elizabeth LLB . . . . *Nov 1995
Haworth, Miss Diane M LLB. . . . . *Oct 1992
Hetherington, Mr David John BA(Cantab) . . . . Oct 1975
Jeram, Miss Nistha LLB(Hons); LLM(Lond) . . . . . . *Mar 1997
Montlake, Mr Matthew L LLB(Law & Politics) . . . . . Oct 1999
Oxburgh, Ms Maria BA(Hons)(Oriental Studies); MA. . *Sep 1996
Patel, Amit . . . . *Feb 1998
Rumbelow, Mr Matthew N. . . . . *Sep 1999
Scharfer, Mr Julian J LLB(Hons). . . . . *Dec 1997
Turner, Mr Philip Daniel LLB(Hons)(Lond) . . . . . . *Nov 1996
Con: Kaufman, Mr Herbert LLB. . . . . Feb 1955
Lane, Mr Martin S. . . . . Dec 1965

FLETCHER DERVISH ‡
582-584 Green Lanes Haringey London N8 0RP
Tel: 020 8800 4615 *Fax:* 020 8802 2273 *Dx:* 57753 HARRINGAY
Emergency telephone 07831 894858
E-mail: e.isil@fletcherdervish.co.uk
List of partners: D Dervish
Languages: Bengali, French, Greek, Hindi, Igbo, Italian, Kurdish, Punjabi, Turkish, Urdu, Yoruba
Work: B1 B2 C1 D1 E F1 G H J1 K1 K3 L N O Q R1 S1 S2 V W Z(c,g,h,i,j,l,m,p,q,s)
Emergency Action, Agency, Advocacy, Fixed Fee Interview, Legal Aid undertaken, Legal Aid Franchise and Member of Accident Line
SPr: Dervish, Djemal BSc . . . . *§Dec 1974
Ast: Benson, Mr Theo MA; MSc; BA(Hons) ● . . . . *Jan 2006
Njindou, Mr Charles Paulin LLB . . . . *Nov 2001
Orgev, Mr Emin LLB . . . . *Jan 2010
Ryan, Ms Carol FILEx. . . . . *May 1991
Seaka, Mr Marius LLB(Hons) . . . . *Jan 2008

J P FLETCHER & CO ‡
8 Newburgh Street London W1F 7RJ
Tel: 020 7494 4700

RONALD FLETCHER & CO ‡
243 Elgin Avenue Maida Vale London W9 1NJ
Tel: 020 7624 0041 *Fax:* 020 7328 4144 *Dx:* 46252 MAIDA VALE
E-mail: derek@rfclaw.co.uk
List of partners: D S Rosenblatt
Work: D1 D2 J2 K1 K2 K3 K4 L N O Q W Z(q,r)
Emergency Action, Agency, Advocacy, Fixed Fee Interview, Legal Aid undertaken, Legal Aid Franchise and Member of Accident Line
Ptr: Rosenblatt, Mr Derek S LLB Honorary Legal Advisor to Paddington CAB . . . . *Jul 1979
Con: Johnson, Mr John. . . . . *Nov 1993

P A FLEURY ‡
First Floor 5 London Wall Building Finsbury Circus London EC2M 5NS
Tel: 020 7374 4434 *Fax:* 020 7638 6130
E-mail: philipafleury@aol.com

P A FLEURY & CO ‡
79 Carter Lane London EC4V 5EP
Tel: 020 7329 3405 *Fax:* 020 7489 7363
Emergency telephone 07977 572689
E-mail: philipafleury@aol.com
List of partners: P A Fleury
Languages: French, German
Work: A1 B1 C1 E J1 L Q S1 S2 T1 T2 W Z(d,e,i,l)
Agency, Advocacy and Legal Aid undertaken
SPr: Fleury, Mr Philip Amoret LLB(Lond) . . . . *Jul 1971

FORBES ANDERSON FREE ‡
7th Floor 60 Charlotte Street London W1T 2NU
Tel: 020 7291 3500 *Fax:* 020 7791 3511
E-mail: aforbes@forbesanderson.com

FORBES HALL LLP (in association with Forbes Wheater)
New City House 71 Rivington Street London EC2A 3AY
Tel: 020 7729 9111 *Fax:* 020 7729 9050 *Dx:* 137787 FINSBURY 5
E-mail: info@forbeshall.co.uk
Office: Woodford Green
Languages: Italian
Work: B1 C1 C2 E F1 J1 K3 K4 L N O Q R1 S1 S2 T2 W Z(b,c,l,m,p,r)
Ptr: Carroll, Mr John D MA(Cantab) . . . . *Nov 1983
Paganuzzi, Renzo D P BA . . . . *Jan 1985
Wheater, Mr Phillip T LLB. . . . . *Mar 1978
Ast: Paganuzzi, Ms Sandra D BA(Hons) . . . . *Dec 1984
Thomson, Mr Paulus Anthony Adrian . . . . Dec 1980
Con: Hall, Mr Brian William LLB(Hons) . . . . *Jan 1968

JOHN FORD SOLICITORS ‡
3a Blackstock Road London N4 2JF
Tel: 020 8800 6464 *Fax:* 020 8800 6066
Dx: 57470 FINSBURY PARK
E-mail: admin@johnfordsolicitors.co.uk
List of partners: J Ford
Languages: French, German
Work: Q R1 X Z(e,g,p,q,u,za)
Emergency Action, Fixed Fee Interview and Legal Aid undertaken
SPr: Ford, Mr John BSc(Hons) ♦ . . . . *Dec 1975
Asoc: May, Miss Karen Julia LLB(Hons) ♦ . . . . Apr 1997
Shaughnessy, Ms Marian BA(Hons)(History) ♦ . . . . Nov 1990
Ast: Gill, Ms Helen LLB(Hons); LLM . . . . Sep 2004

FOREST SOLICITORS ‡
Unit 3 California Building Deals Gateway London SE13 7SB
Tel: 020 8534 1025 *Fax:* 020 8534 1089

FORESTERS SOLICITORS ‡
155 Hoe Street Walthamstow London E17 3AL
Tel: 020 8521 5999 *Fax:* 020 8521 5996 *Dx:* 32016 WALTHAMSTOW
E-mail: joemwnsah@forresterssolicitors.co.uk

FRANK FORNEY & PARTNERS LLP ‡
Cleveden House 455 High Road Wood Green Haringey London N22 8JD
Tel: 020 8889 1971 / 8888 5481 *Fax:* 020 8888 2391
Dx: 56953 BOWES PARK
E-mail: ajayshah@forneys.co.uk
List of partners: A G Shah, V Ved
Languages: Gujarati
Work: C1 C2 E F1 R1 S1 W
Mem: Shah, Mr Ajay Govindji LLB. . . . . *Mar 1985
Ved, Vijaykumar. . . . . *Mar 1981

J A FORREST & CO ‡
10 Buckingham Palace Road Westminster London SW1W 0QP
Tel: 020 7233 9140 *Fax:* 0845 833 1075 *Dx:* 2378 VICTORIA
E-mail: jaf@jaforrest.com
List of partners: J A Forrest
Languages: French, Hindi, Japanese, Punjabi, Urdu
Work: B1 C1 E F1 J1 K1 M1 N Q R1 S1 W Z(d,i,j,k,l)
Agency and Advocacy undertaken
Ptr: Forrest, Mr Jeffrey Allan LLB . . . . *§Dec 1975
Ast: Butt, Ms Yumna Merium LLB . . . . *May 2006
Con: Takeuchi, Hiroko . . . . Feb 2001

FORSTERS LLP ‡
31 Hill Street Westminster London W1J 5LS
Tel: 020 7863 8333 *Fax:* 020 7863 8444 *Dx:* 82988 MAYFAIR
E-mail: mail@forsters.co.uk
List of partners: S Alexander, C A Bassett, C A E Cook, S Cook, A R Crabbie, G S Dunn, S Edwards, V M Edwards, P A H Elliott, E J Exton, H F Gill, P J Golden, M Halling, S C Hamilton, P F Harney, M J Hassett, A J Head, M G Jordan, A H Lane, E McMahon, R T Mead, S E P Mulroney, P J Neville, K Noel-Smith, A E Northover, S A Pass, C A Pearson, C L Pike, N Rees, P A Roberts, D J R Robinson, J M H Ross, E A F P Small, F A Smith, M P Swainston, T J J Taylor
Work: A1 C1 C2 E J1 K1 L O Q R1 R2 S1 S2 T1 T2 W Z(c,d,e,f,j,q)
Ptr: Alexander, Ms Shona LLB. . . . . *Sep 1996
Bassett, Mrs Caroline Anne BA . . . . *Oct 1985
Cook, Ms Carole Ann Elizabeth LLB. . . . . *Oct 1987
Cook, Ms Sarah MA. . . . . *Nov 1996
Crabbie, Mr Andrew Robert LLB. . . . . *Oct 1993
Dunn, Mr Glenn Stuart LLB . . . . *Oct 1995
Edwards, Mrs Smita LLB . . . . *Dec 1985
Edwards, Mrs Victoria Mary LLB . . . . *Sep 2001
Elliott, Ms Penelope Ann Hylton MA(Cantab) . . . . . *Nov 1985
Exton, Ms Emily Joan BA(Oxon) . . . . *Nov 1995
Gill, Mr Howard Frederick BA . . . . *Nov 1989
Golden, Mr Peter John LLB . . . . Sep 2004
Halling, Mr Martin BA; MPhil . . . . *Nov 1988
Hamilton, Ms Sophie Charlotte BA(Cantab) . . . . . . *Jun 1979
Harney, Mr Patrick Francis BSc . . . . *Jan 2004
Hassett, Mr Magnus J LLB . . . . *Mar 2000
Head, Mr Andrew J MA . . . . *Nov 1991
Jordan, Mr M Guy BA. . . . . Jul 1980
Lane, Mr Andrew Herbert MA . . . . Dec 1993
McMahon, Mr Eugene LLB . . . . *Sep 1996
Mead, Mr Rupert T MA . . . . *Sep 2003
Mulroney, Miss Sharon Elizabeth Peterson BA; LLM(Cantab) . . . . *Oct 1986
Neville, Mr Paul Justin LLB . . . . *Feb 1987
Noel-Smith, Ms Kelly BA . . . . Nov 1992
Northover, Ms Ann Elizabeth BA . . . . *Nov 1992
Pass, Ms Sarah Anne LLB . . . . *Dec 1990
Pearson, Ms Craigie Anne LLB . . . . Feb 2001
Pike, Mr Charles L MA(Cantab) . . . . *Jun 1974
Rees, Miss Natasha BSc . . . . *Nov 1995
Roberts, Mr Paul Anthony MA(Oxon) . . . . *Dec 1981
Robinson, Mr David James Roper MA(Cantab) . . . . . *Nov 1981
Ross, Mr Jonathan M H BA(Kent) . . . . *Sep 1983
Small, Miss Elizabeth Anne Francesca Pascale LLB; CIOT . . . . Mar 2003
Smith, Miss Fiona A BA; MA Notary Public . . . . . . *Oct 1988
Swainston, Mr Matthew Peter BA . . . . *Nov 1996
Taylor, Mr Timothy Jacob John BA; MRICS . . . . . . *Sep 2004
Ast: Abrahams, Mr Guy . . . . Sep 2008
Andrews, Miss Poornima Grace BA . . . . *Jun 2002
Atkins, Ms Ruth LLB . . . . Sep 2006
Atkinson, Miss Harriet Francesca BSc. . . . . *Sep 2005
Baker, Ms Lianne BA . . . . *Aug 2005
Baker, Miss Stephanie J BA. . . . . *Sep 2001
Barber, Miss Lucy J LLB . . . . *Sep 2004
Bottaro, Ms Amanda Leigh BA; LLB. . . . . Sep 2003
Brayford, Mr Ben BA . . . . Sep 2007
Brown, Ms Laura Margaret Zoe BA . . . . Sep 2003
Carey, Mr Niall John LLB . . . . Oct 2005
Carter, Mrs Caroline A LLB . . . . *Mar 1978
Clarke, Mr Spencer BA . . . . *Sep 2005
Clayton, Mr James Ian BA . . . . Sep 2007
Cosby, Ms Antonia . . . . Sep 2010
Cullis, Ms Rosalind S E LLB. . . . . *Sep 1988
Davies, Ms Alexandra LLB . . . . Sep 2009
Doran, Ms Katherine LLB . . . . Sep 2008
Druiff, Ms Naomi Deborah Jessel LLB. . . . . May 1978
Ekers, Ms Katherine Angela LLB STEP Prize for Private Client Work; College of Law Prize - Highest Average LPC Mark; Nigel Asquith Prize for Best Overall Mark Nationwide in Business Law & Practice; Law Prize for Best Performance in Business Law & Practice and in Advanced Property Law . . . . *Sep 2011
Fagan, Mr Paul William MA . . . . *Jul 2003
Fisher, Miss Nicola Maria BA . . . . *Oct 2007
Fleming, Ms Hannah Jane BA. . . . . Sep 2010
France, Ms Amy BA. . . . . Sep 2010
Golding, Mrs Rachel LLB . . . . *Mar 2007
Gosling, Ms Emma Sophie LLB . . . . Sep 2009
Harcus, Mrs Gail Alexandra LLB . . . . Apr 1977
Harper, Ms Katherine Louise MA . . . . Sep 2009
Harrison, Mr Thomas BA . . . . *Sep 2011
Hayllar, Ms Linda BA . . . . Sep 2002
Heathcote, Ms Tina BA . . . . Sep 2010
Holdstock, Ms Emily Jane BA. . . . . Sep 2010
Jackson, Mr Christopher J BA. . . . . *Sep 2003
Jones, Ms Holly Alexandra Jane BSc . . . . Sep 2011
Kanani, Miss Zahra Abdulaziz LLB . . . . Sep 2009
Kent, Ms Catherine Elizabeth Georgina LLB. . . . . . *Oct 1986
Laird Craig, Mr Robert Joseph MA . . . . Sep 2010
Ledwidge, Mr Ronan BA . . . . *Sep 2000
Mastrominas, Mr George MA . . . . *Apr 2001
Myers, Mr Christopher Owen BSc. . . . . *Sep 2004
Nicholas, Mr Xavier Joseph BA . . . . Nov 2007
Nicolet, Mrs Laura Felicity BA. . . . . *Oct 2005
Nixon, Mr Matthew BSc. . . . . *Oct 2011
Noble, Mr James BA . . . . *Sep 2006
Osborne, Mr Simon Christopher MA. . . . . Sep 2008
Paravicini, Mr Jack Vincent Rudolph BA. . . . . *Sep 2007
Parker, Mr Andrew Simon LLB . . . . Oct 2003
Penny, Mr Andrew Hugh MA(Oxon) . . . . *Feb 1983
Pickard, Ms Helen Marie MA . . . . Sep 2011
Ralphs, Mr Simon James Thomas LLB . . . . *Sep 2002
Reeve, Miss Polly Llewellyn BSc . . . . Nov 2009
Ribet, Mr Dominic Pierre Lartigue BSc . . . . *Sep 2008
Ross, Mrs Charlotte Antonia Ruth BSc . . . . *Sep 2008
Sandham, Ms Rachel Louise MA . . . . *Sep 2011
Selwyn, Mr Peter Raymond BA . . . . Sep 2007
Seymour, Mrs Rachel Louise LLB. . . . . *Sep 2007
Shacklady, Mr Bryan Robert LLM; MA. . . . . Oct 2006
Short, Mrs Anna Marie BA . . . . *Sep 2007
Showan, Mr Richard Neil LLB. . . . . *Sep 2011
Thomson, Miss Alison Lesley LLB. . . . . Sep 2009
Towers, Mrs Victoria Elizabeth LLB . . . . *Oct 2003
Trinh, Ms Naomi LLB . . . . Nov 2004
Wheeler, Ms Jane Emma BA . . . . Sep 2004
White, Ms Emma Jane LLB . . . . *Oct 2011
Wigg, Mr Philip BA . . . . Sep 2006
Williamson, Mrs Laura Elisabeth Garrett BA. . . . . . *Sep 2008
Wright, Mr Oliver Thomas Irwim MA. . . . . *Mar 2008
Con: Cole, Mr Robin Andrew BMus. . . . . *Oct 1984
Cunliffe, Mr Michael D BA. . . . . *Jun 1974
Digby-Bell, Mr Christopher Harvey. . . . . *Dec 1972
Drewitt, Mr John Leslie . . . . *Apr 1962
Hill, Ms Catherine Ross MA . . . . Oct 1996
Mellor, Miss Eliza G MA. . . . . *May 1974
Rodgers, Miss Hilary A LLB . . . . *Oct 1987

FORSYTH SIMPSON ‡
7 Cavendish Square London W1G 0PE
Tel: 020 7612 7615 *Fax:* 020 7612 7602
E-mail: campbell@forsythsimpson.com

FORTUNE LAW ‡
Second Floor 10 Argyll Street London W1F 7TQ
Tel: 020 7440 2540 *Fax:* 020 7440 2543
E-mail: skassam@fortunelaw.com
Work: A3 C1 C2 E F1 J1 O Q S2 U2 Z(e,i,q,za)

FOX ‡
78 Cornhill London EC3V 3QQ
Tel: 020 7618 2400 *Fax:* 020 7618 2409
E-mail: info@foxlawyers.com

FOX HARTLEY
Room 773 Lloyd's 1 Lime Street London EC3M 7DQ
Tel: 0117 917 7210 *Fax:* 0117 917 7211
Office: Bristol

FOX WILLIAMS ‡
Ten Dominion Street London EC2M 2EE
Tel: 020 7628 2000 *Fax:* 020 7628 2100
Dx: 33873 FINSBURY SQUARE
E-mail: mail@foxwilliams.com
List of partners: P Aldrich, T N L Custance, G Foggo, R D Fox, J E Greager, J E Mann, N Miller, E A Nicholson, P L Osborne, D Preece, S L Sidkin, H E Streeton, M M B J Tasker, M A Watson, C J Williams
Languages: French, German, Italian
Work: B1 C1 C2 C3 E F1 F2 I J1 J2 L M1 M2 O P Q R2 S2 T1 Z(b,c,e,f,i,j,o,p,q)
Emergency Action and Agency undertaken
Ptr: Aldrich, Ms Philippa BA(Hons)(Oxon) . . . . *Jan 1990
Custance, Mr Thomas N L BA(Hons) ♦ . . . . *Oct 1989
Foggo, Mr Gavin BA(Dunelm). . . . . *Feb 1992
Fox, Mr Ronald D MA(Oxon) . . . . *§Jun 1972
Greager, Mr John Eriksen LLB; BCA . . . . May 1993
Mann, Ms Jane E MA(Cantab) . . . . *Dec 1981
Miller, Mr Nigel LLB(Manc) . . . . *§Dec 1983
Nicholson, Ms E Anne BA(Oxon) . . . . *Sep 1996
Osborne, Mr Paul L LLB(Warw) . . . . *§Oct 1983
Preece, Mr Douglas. . . . . *Dec 1989
Sidkin, Mr Stephen L LLB(Lond); MA . . . . *§Oct 1981
Streeton, Ms Helen Elizabeth LLB. . . . . *Oct 1992
Tasker, Mr Mark M B J LLB(Hons). . . . . *Nov 1989
Watson, Mr Mark A MA(Cantab). . . . . *§Oct 1981
Williams, Mrs Christine J MA(Oxon). . . . . *§Dec 1977
Asoc: Barnett, Mr Steven P MA(Cantab). . . . . *Nov 1995
Besch, Miss Helen Clare BA(Hons)(Law) . . . . *Nov 1996
Chatterton, Mrs Joanna Kate BA(Oxon)(Litorae Humaniores) . . . . *Mar 1997
Davies, Mr Matthew MA. . . . . *Nov 1997
Dykins, Mr Roderick BA; LLB . . . . *Sep 2000
McEney, Ms Elizabeth Christina BA(Hons)(History) . . Jun 2004
Monson, Ms Helen Louise LLB; LLM . . . . *Sep 1999
Pereira, Mr Miguel . . . . Feb 2000
Richards, Mr Carl Eliot LLB; LPC . . . . Sep 1999
Talpade, Mr Archin BSc; MSc . . . . *Sep 1998
Underwood, Ms Rachel L LLB. . . . . *Sep 1996
Ast: Elliot, Ms Jane Laura . . . . Sep 2000
Hughes, Mr Robert Anthony BA(Hons)(History) . . . . Sep 2002
Kellman, Ms Elaine . . . . Oct 2004
Levin, Ms Michelle . . . . Sep 2000
McTavish, Ms Caroline . . . . Sep 2002
Martyn, Mr Charis. . . . . Sep 2003
Padmore, Ms Suzanne . . . . Apr 2003
Pooley, Miss Sarah Laverne LLB(Hons). . . . . Oct 2002
Pope, Mr Aron BA(Hons)(History). . . . . Dec 2004
Spread, Ms Sophie . . . . Mar 2001
Stone, Kolvin Foster. . . . . *Mar 2000
Tierney, Mr Patrick Damian BA(Civil Law) . . . . Jan 2004
Tostivin, Miss Meena BA(Hons); DipLaw; LLS; LLM . . . Oct 1999
Vickerman, Mr James Robert BSc(Hons)(Econ) . . . . . Jun 2004
Vinsen, Miss Joanne LLB; BA. . . . . Jun 1997
Williams, Mr Andrew . . . . Sep 2003
Williams, Ms Cerys . . . . Sep 2000
Winter, Ms Hannah . . . . Sep 2001
Winterton, Miss Katherine C BA; DipLaw . . . . *Sep 1999
Con: Coles, Mrs Anne M BA . . . . *Jun 1978

FOYEN & CO ‡
30 Aylesbury Street London EC1R 0ER
Tel: 020 7490 6336 *Fax:* 020 7490 6334

FRAGOMEN LLP ‡
4th Floor Holborn Gate 326-330 High Holborn London WC1V 7QY
Tel: 020 3077 5000 *Fax:* 020 3077 5001
E-mail: apatarson@fragomen.com

ANN FRANCIS & CO SOLICITORS ‡
Unit 31-32 Eurolink Business Centre London SW2 1BZ
Tel: 020 7326 7266

FRANCIS WILKS & JONES LLP ‡
6 Coldbath Square London EC1R 5NA
Tel: 020 7841 0390 *Fax:* 0845 402 5477
Dx: 138787 CLERKENWELL
E-mail: info@franciswilksandjones.co.uk

FRANK & CO ‡
28 Dorset Street London W1U 8AS
Tel: 020 7224 3837 *Fax:* 020 7242 3841 *Dx:* 41747 MARYLEBONE 2
List of partners: G M Frank, S Frank
Work: E O Q R1 S1 S2 W
Ptr: Frank, Mr George M . . . . . Jul 1992
Frank, Ms Suzan . . . . . Mar 1990

FRANKLANDS SOLICITORS ‡
231a Kentish Town Road Kentish Town London NW5 2JT
Tel: 020 7485 0300 *Fax:* 020 7267 9893
E-mail: peterfrankland@franklandssolicitors.co.uk

FRANKS & CO ‡
9-13 Cursitor Street London EC4A 1LL
Tel: 020 7242 8008 *Fax:* 020 7404 0323
Dx: 96 LONDON/CHANCERY LN
Emergency telephone 020 7242 8008
List of partners: R A Franks
Work: B1 C1 E F1 J1 K1 K3 L N O Q S1 S2 W Z(b,c,k,l,q)
Emergency Action, Agency and Advocacy undertaken
Ptr: Franks, Mr Raymond A BA(Lancs) . . . . . *Dec 1976

LESLIE FRANKS SOLICITORS ‡
Linton House 39-51 Highgate Road London NW5 1RS
Tel: 020 7428 7787

FRANKS SOLICITORS ‡
313 Mare Street Hackney London E8 1EJ
Tel: 020 8533 4477 *Fax:* 020 8533 4488 *Dx:* 35467 HACKNEY
Emergency telephone 07956 467201
E-mail: info@frankssolicitors.co.uk
Languages: Yoruba

FREEDMAN GREEN DHOKIA ‡
105 Boundary Road Camden London NW8 0RG
Tel: 020 7625 6003 *Fax:* 020 7372 3861
Dx: 38860 SWISS COTTAGE
List of partners: R Dhokia, J M Freedman, A G Green
Office: London NW8 (2 offices)

FREEDMAN GREEN DHOKIA
109 Boundary Road Camden London NW8 0RG
Tel: 020 7624 2981 *Fax:* 020 7372 3861
Dx: 38860 SWISS COTTAGE
Office: London NW8 (2 offices)
Languages: French, Italian
Work: K1 K3 K4 T2 W
Ptr: Freedman, Mr Jeremy Michael MA(Cantab); BPhil; LLB; CQSW . . . . . *Oct 1985
Asoc: Silverman, Mr Trevor . . . . . Nov 2009
Snowdon, Miss Fiona LLB. . . . . . Apr 2008

FREEDMAN GREEN DHOKIA
104 Boundary Road Camden London NW8 0RH
Tel: 020 7625 6003 *Fax:* 020 7372 3861
Dx: 38860 SWISS COTTAGE
Office: London NW8 (2 offices)
Languages: Gujarati
Work: B1 C1 C2 E F1 F2 J1 L N O Q R1 S1 S2 Z(e,j,p,q)
Ptr: Dhokia, Mr Rajendra LLB . . . . . Sep 1991
Green, Mr Alan Gary BA . . . . . *Mar 1984
Con: Fine, Mr Martin . . . . . Nov 1992
Grossman, Mr Dean J BA(Hons) . . . . . *Oct 1984

FREEDMANS ‡
Oak Cottage Chiswick Mall London W4 2PR
Tel: 020 8987 9155 *Fax:* 020 8995 0046
List of partners: C C E M Freedman, S Freedman
Work: A3 C1 O Q Z(c,f)
Ptr: Freedman, Mr Conrad C E M FCIArb . . . . . Jul 1959
Freedman, Ms Sylvia MA(Cantab); MA(Lond) . . . . . Apr 1961

FREEDMANS LAW ‡
42 Brook Street London W1K 5DB
Tel: 020 3170 7155 *Fax:* 020 3170 7156
E-mail: danielfreedman@freedmanslaw.com

FREEMAN & PARTNERS ‡
58 Bell Street Westminster London NW1 6ST
Tel: 020 7724 5855 *Fax:* 020 7724 3488 *Dx:* 38771 PADDINGTON
E-mail: freemansolicitors@hotmail.com
Languages: Arabic, Urdu
Work: J1 K1 N S1 V Z(i)

FREEMAN BOX ‡
8 Bentinck Street London W1U 2BJ
Tel: 020 7486 9041 *Fax:* 020 7486 2552 *Dx:* 9045 WEST END
List of partners: T Box, R J Davis, J Freeman, H S Granville, M Lester
Work: E G J1 K1 K2 K3 L N P S1 W Z(i,l)
Agency undertaken
Ptr: Box, Mr Trevor LLB(Soton) . . . . . *Nov 1977
Davis, Mr Robert J DL MA(Cantab) . . . . . *Oct 1983
Freeman, Mr Jeremy . . . . . *Jun 1977
Granville, Mr Howard S LLB. . . . . . *Nov 1988
Lester, Mr Miles. . . . . . Jan 2006
Ast: Abrahams, Sam LLB . . . . . Nov 2006
Con: Dhanota-Jones, Mrs Teena BA(Hons) . . . . . Feb 1999
Greenwood, Mrs Naomi LLB . . . . . Feb 1993

FREEMAN HARRIS ‡
Flat 1 4 Alaska Buildings 61 Grange Road London SE1 3BA
Tel: 020 7231 7150 *Fax:* 020 7064 1140 *Dx:* 80702 BERMONDSY
E-mail: info@freemanharris.co.uk

RICHARD FREEMAN & CO ‡
13 Radnor Walk Chelsea Kensington & Chelsea London SW3 4BP
Tel: 020 7351 5151 *Fax:* 020 7351 1697 *Dx:* 35111 CHELSEA
E-mail: tcope@richardfreemanandco.com
List of partners: T J Cope, M A Da Costa, S M Mazzier, X Pollard-Levron
Languages: French
Work: A1 B1 C1 C2 C3 E F1 J1 L M1 M2 N O P Q R1 R2 S1 S2 T1 T2 W Z(e,f)
Ptr: Cope, Mr Timothy J LLB . . . . . *Oct 1972
Da Costa, Mr Marc A BA . . . . . *Jan 1999
Mazzier, Mr Stephen M MA . . . . . *Apr 1980
Pollard-Levron, Ms Xuan . . . . . *Sep 1996

FREEMANS SOLICITORS ‡
35 Duke Street London W1U 1LH
Tel: 020 7935 3522 *Fax:* 020 7535 1335
Dx: 42719 OXFORD CIRCUS NORTH
E-mail: yp@freemansolicitors.net
List of partners: G K Bhudia, M C Field, H Freeman, N L Hansen, K D Kotecha-Pau, N J Moran, S J Nelken, O A A Osibona, Y K Patel, N A D Woodward
Languages: French, Urdu, Yoruba
Work: B1 B2 C1 D1 D2 E F1 G H J1 K1 K3 L O Q R2 S1 S2 W Z(b,i,q)
Emergency Action, Agency, Advocacy and Legal Aid undertaken
Ptr: Bhudia, Mr Gopal Karsan . . . . . Dec 2001
Field, Mr Michael C ★. . . . . . *Oct 1997
Freeman, Mr Howard LLB(Hons) . . . . . *Oct 1985
Hansen, Ms Nina Lind BSc(Hons)(Econ) . . . . . *Dec 1987
Kotecha-Pau, Ms Kishoree D LLB. . . . . . *May 1986
Moran, Mr Nicholas James LLB(Hons) . . . . . Sep 2002
Nelken, Mr Stephen Jonathan BA(Hons) . . . . . May 1981
Osibona, Oluwole A A. . . . . . *Aug 1998
Patel, Mr Yogesh K LLB(Hons) . . . . . *Mar 1986
Woodward, Mr Nathan Alexander David. . . . . . Apr 2004
Asoc: Chadha, Ms Karan Kaur. . . . . . Nov 2004
Hogg, Ms Deborah Jane BA(Hons) ★. . . . . . Dec 1994
Ast: Cheung, Ms Caroline Jane . . . . . Oct 2003
Coyle, Ms Laura Bernadette. . . . . . Jan 2007
Loughlin, Mr Joseph BA. . . . . . Dec 1998
Oguejiofor, Ms Chinelo . . . . . Jul 2004
Orrett, Mr Lynton James Roy LLB. . . . . . Mar 1999
Con: Shah, Mr Vadana Matank . . . . . Oct 1984

THE FRENCH LAW PRACTICE ‡
28 Eton Court Eton Avenue London NW3 3HJ
Tel: 07971 616893
E-mail: carolinecohen2@yahoo.co.uk

FRESHFIELDS BRUCKHAUS DERINGER LLP ‡
65 Fleet Street London EC4Y 1HS
Tel: 020 7936 4000 *Fax:* 020 7832 7001
Dx: 23 LONDON/CHANCERY LN
E-mail: enquiries@freshfields.com
Work: B1 C1 C2 C3 E J1 M1 M2 O P T1 Z(b,e,j,n,o)

FRIDAYS PROPERTY LAWYERS ‡
8-16 Cromer Street London WC1H 8LH
Tel: 0845 644 0337 *Fax:* 020 7278 5486

FRIED FRANK HARRIS SHRIVER & JACOBSON LLP ‡
99 City Road London EC1Y 1AX
Tel: 020 7972 9600 *Fax:* 020 7972 9602

FRISBY & CO
9 Carmelite Street London EC4Y 0DR
Tel: 020 7936 6399 *Fax:* 01785 251508 *Dx:* 226 CHANCERY LANE
E-mail: enquiries@frisbysolicitors.co.uk
Office: Stafford (2 offices)

C FROM & CO ‡
(in association with Tovell & Co (London))
5 South Parade Chiswick London W4 1JU
Tel: 020 8995 6153 *Fax:* 020 8995 5590
E-mail: inmail@cfromco.com
List of partners: C D A From
Languages: French, German, Italian
Work: B1 E L N O Q S1 W Z(b,c,h)
Ptr: From, Miss Claire Dorothy Ann LLB. . . . . . *Apr 1980

FRORIEP RENGGLI ‡
17 Godliman Street London EC4V 5BD
Tel: 020 7236 6000 *Fax:* 020 7248 0209
E-mail: london@froriep.ch

R J FROST & CO ‡
3rd Floor 69 Lonsdale Road Barnes London SW13 9JR
Tel: 020 8563 1453 *Fax:* 020 8563 1453
E-mail: rjf@frostandcompany.eu

J HOWARD FRY SOLICITOR ‡
1b Russell Road Wimbledon London SW19 1QN
Tel: 020 8543 7700

FUGLERS ‡
(in association with David Berens & Co)
70 Charlotte Street London W1T 4QG
Tel: 020 7323 6450 *Fax:* 020 7323 6451 *Dx:* 89256 SOHO SQUARE
E-mail: admin@fuglers.co.uk
List of partners: D A Berens, M S Jacob, K Sallangou, M I Stowe
Languages: French, Greek, Hebrew, Malay, Spanish
Work: A3 B1 C1 C2 C3 D1 E F1 I J1 J2 K1 L M1 N O P Q R1 R2 S1 S2 T1 T2 U1 U2 W Z(b,c,d,e,f,i,j,k,l,m,n,o,p,s,w,z)
Fixed Fee Interview undertaken
Ptr: Berens, Mr David A BA(Hons)(Dunelm) . . . . . Mar 1988
Jacob, Mr Mark Selas BA(Hons) . . . . . Oct 1992
Sallangou, Mr Kiryacos LLB(Hons) . . . . . Jun 1994
Stowe, Mr Michael Ian . . . . . Jan 1965
Ast: Crolla, Ms Colette. . . . . . May 2003
D'Aubney-Abdullah, Miss Faye Miriam BA(Hons); CPE; LPC . . . . . Sep 2002
Greenberg, Talya Kim LLB(Hons) . . . . . *Feb 2004
Michael, Mr Antonios LLB. . . . . . Oct 2005
Phillips, Miss Emma Fiona LLB(Hons). . . . . . *Aug 2000
Con: Fugler, Mr Bryan M . . . . . *Dec 1970

FUJIOKA COMPANY LIMITED ‡
Level 4 City Tower 40 Basinghall Street London EC2V 5DE
Tel: 020 7614 5806
E-mail: fujioka@fujiokalaw.co.uk

FULBRIGHT & JAWORSKI LLP ‡
85 Fleet Street London EC4Y 1AE
Tel: 020 7832 3600 *Fax:* 020 7832 3699
E-mail: lcannon@fulbright.com

FULCRUM LAW LLP ‡
MacMillan House Paddington Station London W2 1FT
Tel: 020 7043 7534 *Fax:* 020 7681 2208
Dx: 115757 PADDINGTON 3
E-mail: law@fulcrumlaw.co.uk

FURLEY PAGE LLP
Lloyds Building Gallery 4 12 Leadenhall Street London EC3V 1LP
Tel: 020 7816 3642 *Fax:* 0870 368 1620
E-mail: info@furleypage.co.uk
Office: Canterbury, Chatham, Whitstable

CHARLES FUSSELL & CO ‡
Adam House 7-10 Adam Street London WC2N 6AA
Tel: 020 7520 9323 *Fax:* 020 7520 9324

GH CORNISH LLP
3rd Floor Temple Chambers 3-7 Temple Avenue London EC4Y 0HP
Tel: 020 8090 0800 *Fax:* 020 8090 1234
E-mail: info@ghcornish.com
Office: Ilford

GMG ‡
241 Barking Road London E13 8EQ
Tel: 020 7511 3771 *Fax:* 020 7511 3772

GQ EMPLOYMENT LAW ‡
88 Wood Street London EC2V 7RS
Tel: 020 3375 0330 *Fax:* 020 3375 0332
E-mail: gq@gqemploymentlaw.com
Office: Reading

GSC SOLICITORS ‡
31-32 Ely Place London EC1N 6TD
Tel: 020 7822 2222 *Fax:* 020 7822 2211
Dx: 462 LONDON/CHANCERY LN
E-mail: info@gscsolicitors.com
List of partners: P L Belcher, A D Dickman, C J S Halperin, M P Phillips, H D Posener, S R Sheikh
Languages: French, German, Gujarati, Hebrew, Kiswahili, Punjabi, Urdu
Work: A3 B1 C1 C2 C3 D1 E F1 F2 I J1 K1 L M1 M2 N O Q R1 R2 S1 S2 U2 W Z(b,c,e,f,k,p,q)
Agency undertaken
Ptr: Belcher, Mr Peter L LLB. . . . . . *Dec 1985
Dickman, Mr Adam Dickman BA . . . . . *Oct 1996
Halperin, Mr Clive J S BPharm . . . . . *Oct 1994
Phillips, Mr Matthew P LLB . . . . . *Nov 1995
Posener, Mr Harvey D LLB . . . . . Oct 1985
Sheikh, Mr Saleem R LLB; ACIArb . . . . . *Oct 1983
Ast: Benjamin, Mr John M LLB; LLM. . . . . . *Nov 1999
Hayes, Mr Nicholas D LLB(Hons) . . . . . Sep 1999
Ioannou, Mr John LLB; LLM(Wales) . . . . . *Nov 1987
Sheikh, Mr Feisal R LLB; LLM(Hons) . . . . . Nov 2000
Con: Hamilton Barns, Mr Julian Martin BA(Hons) . . . . . Mar 1985

GT STEWART SOLICITORS ‡
15 Bell Yard Mews 159 Bermondsey Street London SE1 3TY
Tel: 020 7089 0600 *Fax:* 020 7378 0455 *Dx:* 15432 BLACKFRIARS
E-mail: info@gtstewart.co.uk

GT STEWART SOLICITORS ‡
42 Tower Bridge Road London SE1 4TR
Tel: 020 7394 7488 *Fax:* 020 7394 7407 *Dx:* 154324 BLACKFAIRS 6
E-mail: info@gtstewart.co.uk

GABRIEL BASIL SOLICITORS ‡
Suite W58 Grove Business Centre 560-568 High Road London N17 9TA
Tel: 020 8801 0289 *Fax:* 020 8885 4658

ANGELA GAFF ‡
47 Arbour Square London E1 0PS
Tel: 020 7265 8710 *Fax:* 020 7423 9975
E-mail: mail@angelagaff.co.uk

GALBRAITH BRANLEY ‡
736 High Road North Finchley London N12 9QD
Tel: 020 8446 8474 *Fax:* 020 8446 4254 *Dx:* 57357 FINCHLEY 1
Emergency telephone 07831 166462
E-mail: solicitors@galbraithbranley.com
List of partners: A Branley, D Onuma
Languages: French, Gujarati
Work: B2 D1 D2 G H K1 K3 Z(g)
Emergency Action, Agency, Advocacy, Fixed Fee Interview, Legal Aid undertaken and Legal Aid Franchise
Ptr: Branley, Mr Anthony LLB ★. . . . . . *Oct 1984
Onuma, Mr David ★. . . . . . *Sep 1993
Ast: Appleton, Mr James LLB . . . . . May 2007
Brar, Mr Tajinder Singh LLB(Hons) . . . . . Sep 2004
Csemiczky, Mr Peter . . . . . Nov 2009
Davis, Jessica. . . . . . Nov 2009
Harrison, Mr William. . . . . . Feb 2010
Houghton, Ms Andrea LLB; MA . . . . . Jul 2006
Johnson, Mr Ross LLB ★ . . . . . *Jan 2002
Newman, Rachel . . . . . Oct 2009
Shah, Mr Rumit . . . . . Nov 2007
Westell, Abby. . . . . . Mar 2010
Con: Dewis, Ms Samantha BA(Hons) ♦. . . . . . *Oct 1985

DONALD GALBRAITH & CO ‡
No3 Archgate Business Centre 823-825 High Road North Finchley London N12 8UB
Tel: 020 8492 2700
Work: K1 K3 L Q
Emergency Action, Agency, Fixed Fee Interview, Legal Aid undertaken and Legal Aid Franchise
Ast: Bywater, Ms Melanie Jane LLB . . . . . Jun 2001
Con: Watson, Mr Robert Geoffrey LLB(Hons). . . . . . Jan 1998

GALLANT MACMILLAN LLP ‡
3 Greek Street Soho London W1D 4DA
Tel: 020 7758 4720 *Fax:* 020 7758 4721
E-mail: enquiries@gmlegal.co.uk

GANDECHA & PAU ‡
1st Floor 508 Kingsbury Road Kingsbury Barnet London NW9 9HE
Tel: 020 8905 0900 *Fax:* 020 8905 0041 *Dx:* 42804 KINGSBURY
E-mail: p.gandecha@gaplaw.com
List of partners: P Gandecha, A C Pau
Languages: Gujarati, Hindi

See p2 for the Key to Work Categories & other symbols

Work: B1 C1 D1 E F1 G J1 K1 L N O Q R1 S1 W Z(b,c,d,i,l)
Emergency Action, Agency, Advocacy and Fixed Fee Interview undertaken
Ptr: Gandecha, Prakash BA . . . . *Dec 1982
Pau, Ajaykumar C LLB . . . . *Feb 1985

GANI & CO ‡
496 Brixton Road Brixton Lambeth London SW9 8EQ
Tel: 020 7733 8169 *Fax:* 020 7924 0524 *Dx:* 132675 BRIXTON 2
Emergency telephone 07831 863224
E-mail: zarina@ganisol.freeserve.co.uk
List of partners: Z Gani
Languages: Bengali, German, Urdu
Work: B2 G H
Agency, Advocacy, Fixed Fee Interview and Legal Aid undertaken
SPr: Gani, Ms Zarina LLB; LLM . . . . *Nov 1991

GANNONS LIMITED ‡
20-21 Jockeys Fields Camden London WC1R 4BW
Tel: 020 7438 1060 *Fax:* 020 7430 9545
E-mail: clientservices@gannons.co.uk
List of partners: C Gannon
Languages: Czech, French, German, Greek, Italian, Slovak
Work: C1 C2 J1 O T1 Z(p)
Dir: Gannon, Miss Catherine. . . . . Jan 2000
Asoc: Kleanthous, Mr Alexander. . . . . Nov 1989

GANPATE ‡
21 Vivian Avenue London NW4 3UX
Tel: 020 8202 5092 *Fax:* 020 8202 0018
E-mail: ganpateuk@yahoo.co.uk
List of partners: H A Patel
Languages: French, Gujarati, Hindi, Swedish
Work: B1 C1 E F1 L N O Q S1 W Z(b,c,i,l,o,p)
Advocacy and Fixed Fee Interview undertaken
Ptr: Patel, Mr Harihar Ashabhai MA(Stockholm) ♦ . . . . . *Apr 1990

GANS & CO SOLICITORS LLP ‡
214-216 Rye Lane Peckham London SE15 4NF
Tel: 020 7469 7010 *Fax:* 020 7469 7011 *Dx:* 15264 PECKHAM 3
E-mail: info@ganssolicitors.com
Office: London SE8 (2 offices)

GANS & CO SOLICITORS LLP
Unit 10a Evelyn Court Grinstead Road London SE8 5AD
Tel: 020 8691 4464 *Fax:* 020 8469 8282
E-mail: info@ganssolicitors.com
Office: London SE15, London SE8

GANS & CO SOLICITORS LLP
Unit 10b Evelyn Court Grinstead Road London SE8 5AD
Tel: 020 7820 8222 *Fax:* 020 8469 8282
E-mail: info@ganssolicitors.com
Office: London SE15, London SE8

GANTS HILL SOLICITORS ‡
186 Cann Hall Road Walthamstow London E11 3NH
Tel: 0845 359 0058 *Fax:* 020 8519 5655 *Dx:* 58201 LEYTONSTONE
E-mail: info@gantshillsolicitors.com

GARCHA & CO ‡
88a Whitechapel High Street Tower Hamlets London E1 7QX
Tel: 020 7375 1888 *Fax:* 020 7375 1999
Emergency telephone 07958 279211
List of partners: G S Garcha
Languages: Bengali, Hindi, Punjabi, Urdu
Work: B2 E F1 F2 G H J1 L N O Q S1 S2 V W Z(g,i,l,p)
Emergency Action, Agency, Advocacy, Legal Aid undertaken and Legal Aid Franchise
SPr: Garcha, Mr Gurpreet Singh LLB(Hons); LLM . . . . . *Nov 1990

GARDINER & CO ‡
6 Aldred Road London NW6 1AN
Tel: 020 7435 0810 *Fax:* 0870 458 4993
E-mail: george.gardiner@gardinerlaw.co.uk

GARDINERS SOLICITORS
19-20 North End Road West Kensington London W14 8ST
Tel: 020 7603 7245 *Fax:* 020 7381 4456
Dx: 47208 KENSINGTON HIGH STREET
Emergency telephone 07850 130540
E-mail: pauldgardiner@gardinerssolicitors.co.uk
Office: London W6
Languages: Farsi, Greek, Hindi, Polish, Punjabi, Spanish
Work: G H S1 S2 Z(l)
Agency and Advocacy undertaken
SPr: Gardiner, Mr Paul D LLB(Lond) . . . . *Jun 1983
Ast: Newey, Ms Katherine J LLB(Hons) . . . . *May 1997

GARDNER AUSTIN ‡
King Scholar's House 230 Vauxhall Bridge Road Westminster London SW1V 1AU
Tel: 020 7831 2600 *Fax:* 020 7630 5851 *Dx:* 2322 VICTORIA
E-mail: gardneraustinlaw@gardneraustin.com
List of partners: T M A Austin, S W Gardner
Languages: French, German, Italian
Work: A3 B1 C1 C2 E J1 O Q R1 R2 S1 S2 W Z(j,l,q)
Advocacy undertaken
Ptr: Austin, Miss Tania M A LLB(Hons) . . . . *Nov 1984
Gardner, Mr Steven Walter . . . . *Dec 1970

F S GARFORD ‡
26 Fairfax Place London NW6 4EH
Tel: 020 7604 4554 *Fax:* 0870 288 7570
E-mail: stephen@garford.org

GARNER HUTCHINGS ‡
28 Eccleston Square Victoria Westminster London SW1V 1NS
Tel: 020 7932 2400 *Fax:* 020 7932 2401
E-mail: mh@number28.co.uk
List of partners: K Garner, J M H Hutchings
Languages: French
Work: B1 C1 C2 C3 E L S1 S2 U1
Ptr: Garner, Miss Karen LLB; Former Barrister; Admitted in Australia 1988 . . . . *Sep 1987
Hutchings, Mr John Merlin Hinton BA(Econ). . . . . . *Jan 1983

GARSTANGS
227-228 Strand London WC2R 1BA
Tel: 020 7427 5678 *Fax:* 020 7427 5679
Dx: 496 LONDON/CHANCERY LN
Emergency telephone 07778 030783
E-mail: admin@garstangs.com
Office: Bolton
Languages: French, German, Greek, Italian, Spanish
Work: B2 G H I O Q
Emergency Action, Agency, Advocacy, Legal Aid undertaken and Legal Aid Franchise
Ptr: Cornthwaite, Mr Richard Barrington BA(Hons). . . . . *Dec 1977
Harris, Mr Anthony J H BA . . . . *Jul 1979
Ingram, Mr Roger . . . . *Nov 1996
Ast: Grover, Aneka . . . . Jun 2007
Henry, Mr Glen LLB. . . . . Nov 1996
McQuinn, Matthew . . . . Nov 2008
Sophocleous, Mr Michael . . . . *Jan 2002

E MICHAEL GARSTON ‡
97 Abbotsbury Road Holland Park London W14 8EP
Tel: 020 7603 2903 *Fax:* 020 7602 0881
E-mail: michaelgarston@hotmail.com

GATELEY LLP
Fleet Place House 2 Fleet Place Holborn Viaduct London EC4M 7RF
Tel: 020 7653 1600 *Fax:* 020 7653 1601 *Dx:* 824 LONDON/CITY
E-mail: info@gateleyuk.com
Office: Birmingham, Leicester, Manchester, Nottingham
Work: C2 E Z(a)
Ptr: Coles, Mr Richard Michael Fenning TD LLB(Hull) . . . §Jun 1972
Hardingham, Mr Adrian C MA(Oxon) . . . . *§Apr 1978
Hobbs, Ms Jane MA(Oxon) . . . . *Nov 1991
Knight, Mr Timothy A K BA . . . . *Sep 1988
Messent, Mr Andrew D MA(Cantab). . . . . *Apr 1975
Richards, Mr Stephen LLB . . . . Nov 1997
Walser, Mr Nicholas M MA(Cantab). . . . . *Apr 1977
Asoc: Cradick, Mr James Stephen BA; DipLaw . . . . Jul 2004
Davies, Miss Sarah E LLB. . . . . Oct 2002
Kershaw, Mr Graham Paul BA. . . . . *Sep 2001
Large, Mr Andrew BA . . . . *Oct 1986
Con: Padovan, Mr David C A BA(Lond) Clifford's Inn Prize . *Nov 1972

GATES AND PARTNERS ‡
20 Saint Mary At Hill London EC3R 8EE
Tel: 020 7220 5950 *Fax:* 020 7220 5951
List of partners: P Freeman, S Gates, J Korzeniowski, A O'Sullivan, D B Soffin
Languages: Arabic, Bahasa, Cantonese, Croatian, French, German, Greek, Hebrew, Mandarin, Russian, Spanish
Work: C1 C2 C3 F1 F2 J1 M1 M2 M3 N O Q U2 Z(i,j,k,p)
Ptr: Freeman, Mr Paul. . . . . Jan 1987
Gates, Mr Sean. . . . . Jan 1972
Korzeniowski, Mr John . . . . Jan 2000
O'Sullivan, Aoife . . . . Jan 1998
Soffin, Mr Daniel Bruce . . . . *Jan 1994

GATTAS DENFIELD SOLICITORS ‡
The White House 301a Kingsbury Road Kingsbury London NW9 9PE
Est: 1965
Tel: 020 8204 7181 *Fax:* 020 8206 1016 *Dx:* 42800 KINGSBURY
Emergency telephone 07767 684399
E-mail: info1@gattas.co.uk
List of partners: J J N Gattas
Office: Harrow
Work: C1 E F1 G J1 L O P Q R2 S1 S2 W
Emergency Action, Agency, Advocacy, Legal Aid undertaken and Member of Accident Line
Ptr: Gattas, Mr Julian J N BA . . . . *May 1982
Ast: Patel, Miss Bijal BSc(Hons) . . . . *Aug 2005

GAVINS SOLICITORS ‡ (incorporating Nathoo & Co)
473 Archway Road London N6 4HX
Tel: 020 8374 4459 *Fax:* 020 8374 0236
List of partners: H D Nathoo
Languages: Gujarati, Hindi, Kiswahili
Work: E L S1 W Z(i)
SPr: Nathoo, Mr Husein D . . . . *Jul 1977

GAWOR & CO ‡
New Crane Wharf New Crane Place Wapping London E1W 3TS
Tel: 020 7481 8888 *Fax:* 020 7481 4444
Dx: 124912 WAPPING (GUN COURT)
Emergency telephone 07973 838898
E-mail: info@gawor.com
List of partners: R Bozier, M A Gawor, J R Ham
Work: E R2 S1 S2 Z(c)
Ptr: Bozier, Mrs Rebecca LLB . . . . Sep 1997
Gawor, Mr Mark A. . . . . Jun 1984
Ham, Mr Jason Roger LLB(Hons). . . . . Oct 1994
Ast: Sembi, Mrs Neeru LLB; LPC . . . . Jan 2006
Yousuf, Mr Sameer BA; LPC . . . . *Dec 2004
Con: Cocks, Miss Valerie S BA . . . . *Nov 1986
Leasor, Mr Jeremy J BA(Law). . . . . Dec 1978

GELBERGS LLP ‡
188 Upper Street Islington London N1 1RQ
Tel: 020 7226 0570 *Fax:* 020 7359 7194
Dx: 122233 UPPER ISLINGTON
E-mail: enquiries@gelbergs.co.uk
List of partners: S Henry, R H Shapiro, G H Taylor
Work: B1 C1 E F1 J1 K1 L N O Q R1 S1 S2 T1 T2 W Z(b,d,e,j,k,l,p,q,r)
Agency undertaken
Mem: Henry, Mr Sheldon LLB . . . . *Apr 1999
Shapiro, Mr Russell H LLB . . . . *Nov 1984
Taylor, Mr Graeme H BA; M Inst D; TEP. . . . . . . *Oct 1984
Ast: Manville, Miss Jane LLB . . . . *Sep 2010
Taylor-Moran, Ms Emma-Jane LLB . . . . *Sep 2006

GELSON HAYLOR ‡
61 Roupell Street Southwark London SE1 8TB
Tel: 020 7928 0675
List of partners: N A G Haylor
Ptr: Haylor, Mr Nicholas A G MA(Oxon) . . . . *Jul 1971

P GEORGE & CO ‡
42 Elder Avenue Crouch End Haringey London N8 8PS
Tel: 020 8341 9080 *Fax:* 020 8341 9394 *Dx:* 35960 CROUCH END
E-mail: info@pgeorgesolicitors.co.uk
List of partners: P Demosthenous
Languages: Greek
Work: N S1 Z(l)
Legal Aid undertaken
SPr: Demosthenous, Mr Panikos LLB(Hons) . . . . *Oct 1991

KAY GEORGIOU ‡
1 Dyer's Buildings London EC1N 2JT
Tel: 020 7831 3685 *Fax:* 020 7404 0456

ROULLA GEORGIOU ‡
74 Friars Walk Barnet London N14 5LN
Tel: 020 8368 0220 *Fax:* 020 8368 0440
E-mail: roullageorgiousolicitor@hotmail.com
List of partners: R Georgiou
Languages: Greek
Work: E L S1 S2 W Z(l)
SPr: Georgiou, Mrs Roulla . . . . *Oct 1993

GHERSON & CO ‡
1 Great Cumberland Place London W1H 7AL
Tel: 020 7724 4488 *Fax:* 020 7724 4888

GIAMBRONE LAW ‡
88-90 Hatton Garden London EC1N 9PN
Tel: 020 7183 9482 *Fax:* 020 8853 8143

GIANNI ORIGONI & PARTNERS ‡
6-8 Tokenhouse Yard London EC2R 7AS
Tel: 020 7397 1700 *Fax:* 020 7397 1701

GIBSON DUNN & CRUTCHER LLP ‡
Telephone House 2-4 Temple Avenue London EC4Y 0HB
Tel: 020 7071 4000 *Fax:* 020 7071 4244
Dx: 217 LONDON/CHANCERY LN

GIBSON YOUNG ‡
58-60 St John's Road Clapham Junction London SW11 2QS
Tel: 020 7228 2211 / 7228 2213 *Fax:* 020 7924 1686
Dx: 58551 CLAPHAM JUNCTION
E-mail: badgeholt@badgeholt.demon.co.uk
List of partners: C M Young
Languages: Bulgarian, French, Russian
Work: C1 C2 C3 E L R1 S1 T1 T2 W
Agency and Fixed Fee Interview undertaken
Ptr: Young, Mr Christopher M . . . . *Jun 1972

GIDE LOYRETTE NOUEL LLP ‡
125 Old Broad Street London EC2N 1AR
Tel: 020 7382 5500 *Fax:* 020 7382 5501
E-mail: gln.london@gide.com

GILBERT TURNER COOMBER ‡
188-190 Hoe Street Walthamstow Waltham Forest London E17 4QN
Tel: 020 8520 5886 *Fax:* 020 8520 4670 *Dx:* 32012 WALTHAMSTOW
Emergency telephone 07973 266746
E-mail: gilturcomb@aol.com
List of partners: M C Conroy, H H Freeman, D Turner, R W West
Languages: French
Work: C1 D1 E F1 G J1 K1 L N O P Q S1 W Z(h,j,m,p)
Agency, Advocacy, Legal Aid undertaken and Legal Aid Franchise
Ptr: Conroy, Mr Matthew Charles . . . . *Mar 1996
Freeman, Mr H Howard. . . . . Dec 1984
Turner, Mr David . . . . *Mar 1984
West, Mr Richard W. . . . . Mar 1969

GILCHRIST SOLICITORS ‡
Charles House 18b Charles Street Mayfair London W1J 5DU
Tel: 020 7667 6868 *Fax:* 020 7667 6468 *Dx:* 82959 MAYFAIR
E-mail: info@markgilchrist.co.uk

GILL JENNINGS & EVERY ‡
Broadgate House 7 Eldon Street London EC2M 7LH
Tel: 020 7377 1377 *Fax:* 020 7377 1310

GILLHAMS SOLICITORS LLP ‡
Second Floor 47 Fleet Street London EC4Y 1BJ
Tel: 020 7353 2732 *Fax:* 020 7353 2733 *Dx:* 174 CHANCERY LANE
E-mail: solicitors@gillhams.com
List of partners: R A Caller, A S Krikler, M H Williams
Office: London NW10

GILLHAMS SOLICITORS LLP
Rowan House 9-31 Victoria Road Park Royal London NW10 6DP
Tel: 020 8965 4266 *Fax:* 020 8965 0229 *Dx:* 57657 HARLESDEN
E-mail: solicitors@gillhams.com
Office: London EC4
Languages: French, Hebrew
Work: C1 C2 E F1 J1 N O Q S1 S2 W Z(c,q)
Advocacy, Fixed Fee Interview undertaken and Member of Accident Line
Ptr: Caller, Mr Russell A LLB . . . . *§Oct 1983
Krikler, Mr Anthony S . . . . *§Feb 1985
Williams, Mr Mark H LLB . . . . Jul 1977
Ast: Raizon, Mrs Melanie C LLB . . . . Oct 1981
Tailor, Mrs Hina LLB. . . . . Mar 1989

GLADE LAW LIMITED ‡
88 Wood Street London EC2V 7RS
Tel: 020 7156 5199 *Fax:* 020 7156 5001
E-mail: sdar@gladelaw.co.uk

RUTH GLADWIN SOLICITOR ‡
89 Winston Road London N16 9LN
Tel: 020 7241 1685 *Fax:* 020 7241 1767

GLASS LAW ‡
Suite 1 7 Chalcot Road London NW1 8LH
Tel: 0870 066 1953

GLAZER DELMAR ‡
27-31 North Cross Road East Dulwich London SE22 9ET
Tel: 020 8299 0021 *Fax:* 020 8299 1588 *Dx:* 32152 EAST DULWICH
E-mail: enquiries@glazerdelmar.com
List of partners: A D Barron, M H Glazer, C A Sherry
Languages: Cantonese, Creole, French, Ganda, Hindi, Spanish, Urdu
Work: E K1 K3 K4 L N R2 S1 S2 W Z(h,i)
Fixed Fee Interview undertaken
Ptr: Glazer, Mr Michael H LLB. . . . . *Oct 1981
Sherry, Ms Caroline Anne BSc . . . . *Nov 1991
Barron, Mr Andrew David FILEx. . . . . NSP
Ast: Allen, Ms Kate Ellenor. . . . . *Mar 2010

Aslam, Ms Norien . . . *Nov 2009
Aveling, Mr Nicholas Edward Hamilton . . . *Apr 2003
Chetouani, Ms Imane . . . *Mar 2001
Cornish, Ms Tara Jayne LLB(Hons) . . . *Sep 2006
Crawford, Mr Fraser Anthony . . . *Jun 2008
Day, Ms Suzanne Elizabeth BA(Hons) . . . *Nov 1994
Lewis, Ms Joy Genevieve LLB(Hons) . . . *Aug 1995
Martynski, Mr Mark A BA(Hons) . . . *Jan 1988
Olaniyan, Mr Oluseye Olawale LLB(Hons) . . . *Nov 2001
Phillips, Ms Helen M BA; CPE . . . *Nov 1993
Sumputh, Ms Vijaya Kumaree BA(Hons) . . . *Feb 2001
Wong, Ms Tsiu-Fun LLB(Hons) . . . *Aug 2006

GLINERT DAVIS ‡
Suite A Cumberland Court Great Cumberland Place Westminster London W1H 7DP
Tel: 020 7724 4442 *Fax:* 020 7724 8488 *Dx:* 83312 WEST END 2
E-mail: glinertdavis@btinternet.com
List of partners: R A Davis, D A Glinert, I G Hibberd
Work: B1 C1 E J1 L O Q R2 S1 Z(b,f,i,w)
Ptr: Davis, Mr R Adam LLB . . . Oct 1992
Glinert, Mr Daniel A LLB(Hons) . . . *Oct 1987
Hibberd, Ms Inez G LLB(Hons) . . . Mar 1988

GLOBAL LAWYER LLP ‡
58 Arcadia Road St Johns Wood London NW8 6AE

GLOVERS SOLICITORS LLP ‡
6 York Street London W1U 6QD
Tel: 020 7935 8882 *Fax:* 020 7486 7666 *Dx:* 44438 MARBLE ARCH
E-mail: central@glovers.co.uk
List of partners: S Andela, J D Barber, C Connolley, P J Eyre, K Friday, R Gilchrist, P Gilks, L Lam-Kee, A K Nicklinson, A J Parker, P F Pitt, P Shotter, E G Vaughan
Languages: French, German
Work: A3 B1 C1 E J1 J2 L N O R1 R2 S1 S2 Z(b,c,j,k,l,q)
Ptr: Andela, Miss Sikin BA; MA(Cantab) . . . *Oct 1995
Barber, Mr John D BA(Manc) . . . *§Oct 1982
Connolley, Mrs Catherine BA(Sheff) . . . *Nov 1990
Eyre, Mr Philip J LLB(Hons)(Westminster) . . . *Nov 1998
Friday, Mr Kenny . . . Sep 2004
Gilchrist, Mr Richard . . . Mar 1998
Gilks, Mr Paul . . . Oct 1979
Lam-Kee, Miss Liza . . . *Sep 2002
Nicklinson, Mr Andrew K LLB(Sheff) . . . *Nov 1991
Parker, Mr Andrew J BA(Hons) . . . Feb 1982
Pitt, Mr Peter F LLB(Bris) . . . *§Feb 1981
Shotter, Mr Phillip LLB(Hons)(Soton) . . . *May 1996
Vaughan, Mr Edward Geoffrey LLB(Exon) . . . *§Oct 1983
Asoc: Waller, Mrs Helen J BA(Hons)(Manc) . . . Sep 2001
Ast: Francis, Mr Peter . . . Feb 2010
Nelson, Mr Christopher Laird LLB(Hons)(Newc) . . . Jan 2007
Seaton, Ms Caroline . . . Sep 2006
Con: Cava, Miss Catherine Rosa . . . Jul 1983

MATHEW GOLD & COMPANY ‡
2nd Floor Winston House 2 Dollis Park London N3 1HE
Tel: 020 8343 3678 *Fax:* 020 8383 4843 *Dx:* 57266 FINCHLEY 2
E-mail: mg@mathewgold.co.uk

MEL GOLDBERG LAW ‡
Media House 4 Stratford Place London W1C 1AT
Tel: 020 7355 0310 *Fax:* 020 7355 0325
Dx: 42729 OXFORD CIRCUS NORTH
E-mail: enquiries@mgplaw.co.uk

GOLDEN LEAVER LLP ‡
16 Old Queen Street London SW1H 9HP
Tel: 020 3159 5160 *Fax:* 020 3292 1501

GOLDEN SOLICITORS ‡
85-87 Bayham Street London NW1 0AG
Tel: 020 7424 7898 *Fax:* 020 7424 7899
E-mail: admin@goldensolicitors.com

GOLDFIELDS SOLICITORS ‡
QSG Business Centre 54 Plumstead High Street London SE18 1SL
Tel: 020 8316 0511 *Fax:* 020 8316 8708

GOLDKORN MATHIAS GENTLE PAGE LLP ‡
6 Coptic Street Bloomsbury London WC1A 1NW
Tel: 020 7631 1811 *Fax:* 020 7631 0431 *Dx:* 35705 BLOOMSBURY
E-mail: enquiries@gmgplegal.com
List of partners: D B Gentle, G Goldkorn, T M Hassan, R Mathias, R A Page
Languages: Turkish
Work: B1 C1 D1 E G J1 K1 L M1 N O P Q S1 S2 W Z(c,e,g,h,i,k,l,o,q)
Emergency Action, Agency, Advocacy, Legal Aid undertaken and Legal Aid Franchise
Mem: Gentle, Mr David B LLB . . . *Jan 1969
Goldkorn, Mr Geoffrey MA(Cantab) ♦ . . . *Jun 1970
Hassan, Mr Tarkan Mustafa LLB(Hons) . . . Feb 2001
Mathias, Mr Roy LLB ♦ Deputy District Judge . . . *Jul 1967
Page, Mr Robert Adam LLB(Hons) . . . *Jan 1994
Con: Adair, Mr Carl W BA . . . Apr 1984

GOLDKORN SOLICITORS ‡
62 Camberwell Road London SE5 0EN
Tel: 020 7703 1144 *Fax:* 020 7703 2241
Dx: 35313 CAMBERWELL GREEN
Emergency telephone 020 7703 1144
List of partners: G Goldkorn
Work: G H K3 Z(f)
Emergency Action, Agency and Advocacy undertaken
Ptr: Goldkorn, Mr Geoffrey MA(Cantab) ♦ . . . *Jun 1970

GOLDMAN BAILEY SOLICITORS ‡
Savant House 63-65 Camden High Street London NW1 7JL
Tel: 020 3326 2585 *Fax:* 020 3006 8500 *Dx:* 57050 CAMDEN TOWN
E-mail: info@goldmanbaileysolicitors.co.uk

J J GOLDSTEIN & CO ‡
77a Brent Street London NW4 2EA
Tel: 020 8202 1899 *Fax:* 020 8202 1416 *Dx:* 59311 LONDON
E-mail: jjgsol@aol.com
List of partners: J J Goldstein
Work: C1 E L S1 W
Ptr: Goldstein, Mr Jonathan J LLB(Lond) . . . *Mar 1979

RICHARD S GOLDSTEIN ‡
1st Floor 96a Mount Street London W1K 2TB
Tel: 020 7499 8200 *Fax:* 020 7499 8300
E-mail: lawoffices@goldsteinvisa.com

GOLDSWORTH SOLICITORS ‡
Unit 3 Nice Business Park 19-35 Sylvan Grove London SE15 1PD
Tel: 020 7358 8150 *Fax:* 020 7732 3190
E-mail: info2goldsworthsolicitors@yahoo.com

GOLDSWORTH SOLICITORS ‡
189 Angel Place Fore Street London N18 2UD
Tel: 020 8887 1350 *Fax:* 020 8887 1351

GOMEZ ACEBO & POMBO ‡
Five Kings House 1 Queen Street Place London EC4R 1QS
Tel: 020 7329 5407 *Fax:* 020 7489 7466
E-mail: rmohial@gomezacebo-pombo.com

GOODGE LAW ‡
15 Goodge Place London W1T 4SQ
Tel: 020 7636 9222 *Fax:* 020 7637 3553
Dx: 134204 TOTTENHAM COURT ROAD 2
E-mail: email@goodgelaw.com
List of partners: R Kalia, S Kalia
Languages: Arabic, Bengali, Greek, Hindi, Punjabi, Russian
Work: A3 B1 C1 F1 J1 L N O Q S1 S2 W Z(q,r)
Agency undertaken
Ptr: Kalia, Rajesh . . . Sep 1994
Kalia, Mrs Sangeeta . . . Nov 1993
Ast: Greenstein, Mr Michael Barry LLB . . . Sep 1998

GOODGERS ‡
7-10 Adam Street London WC2N 6AA
Tel: 020 7520 9012 *Fax:* 020 7520 9013
E-mail: legalteam@goodgers.com

DAVID GOODMAN ‡
81 College Road Kensal Green London NW10 5ES
Tel: 020 8969 0646 / 8969 0966 *Fax:* 020 8969 0631
Dx: 53951 KENSAL RISE
Work: E S1 S2

DAVID GOODMAN & CO ‡
34-35 Newman Street Westminster London W1T 1PZ
Tel: 020 7323 3369 *Fax:* 020 7636 7368
E-mail: dgoodmanandco@aol.com
List of partners: D M Goodman
Languages: French
Work: B1 C1 C2 C3 E G I J1 L M1 M2 N O P Q R1 R2 S1 S2 T1 T2 U2 W Z(b,c,e,f,j,l,q,s)
Emergency Action, Agency, Fixed Fee Interview and Legal Aid undertaken
Ptr: Goodman, Mr David M LLB(Lond) . . . *Nov 1981

GOODMAN DERRICK LLP ‡
90 Fetter Lane London EC4A 1PT
Tel: 020 7404 0606 *Fax:* 020 7831 6407
Dx: 122 LONDON/CHANCERY LN
List of partners: N D Armstrong, M J Collins, B D Copland, A J Crumley, N Deans, D P Edwards, M G Emmison, G E Hamlen, P T Herbert, M W Kendrick, P J D Langford, T J Langton, J J Maunsell, I Montrose, D M Rawstron, J T P Roberts, T Shillingford, P L J Swaffer, C G Walker, P D R Webb, S C White
Languages: French, German, Gujarati, Hindi, Italian, Kiswahili, Turkish, Welsh
Work: B1 C1 E F1 J1 M1 N O P Q R1 T1 W Z(b,c,d,e,f,i,k)
Agency undertaken
Ptr: Armstrong, Mr Nicholas D MA(Cantab) . . . *Dec 1986
Collins, Mr Michael J . . . *May 1985
Copland, Miss Belinda D BA(Cantab) . . . *Nov 1991
Crumley, Miss Annabel J LLB . . . *Nov 1988
Deans, Mr Noel BA . . . Jul 1999
Edwards, Mr David P . . . Oct 1986
Emmison, Mr Martin G MA(Cantab) . . . *May 1971
Hamlen, Mr Gregor E BA(Oxon) . . . *Oct 1981
Herbert, Mr Paul T LLB . . . *Nov 1985
Kendrick, Mr Mark W BA . . . *Oct 1986
Langford, Mr Philip J D LLB . . . *§Dec 1969
Langton, Mr Timothy J BA(Exon) . . . *Dec 1978
Maunsell, Mr Jeffery J . . . §Feb 1962
Montrose, Mr Ian MA(Oxon) . . . §Oct 1974
Rawstron, Mrs Diana M LLB Clifford's Inn; Clabon & Travers-Smith Prize . . . *Dec 1972
Roberts, Mr John T P LLB . . . *§Aug 1968
Shillingford, Ms Tanya . . . Oct 1993
Swaffer, Mr Patrick L J LLB . . . *§May 1976
Walker, Mr Craig G LLB . . . *Nov 1991
Webb, Mr Paul D R BA . . . *Nov 1986
White, Miss Susan C BA(Oxon) . . . *Oct 1988
Ast: Adams, Mr Nigel LLB . . . Sep 1999
Barrett, Mr Michael . . . *Mar 1999
Beadman, Ms Sarah LLB . . . Sep 2000
Bradshaw, Mr Ian G P LLB . . . *Sep 1990
Hoare, Ashley BSc . . . Sep 1999
Wanford, Mr Matthew LLB . . . Sep 2000
Whittle, Mr Stewart BA . . . Sep 2000
Wyatt, Ms Helen Jane LLB(Hons) . . . Dec 1997
Con: Bigmore, Mr David BA(Oxon) Sole Practitioner of the Year - Welsh Law Awards November 2004 . . . *Apr 1972
Strain, Mr Andrew J . . . *Sep 1974

GOODMAN RAY ‡
5 Cranwood Street Old Street Hackney London EC1V 9SR
Tel: 020 7608 1227 *Fax:* 020 7250 1786 *Dx:* 36614 FINSBURY
E-mail: mail@goodmanray.com
List of partners: J Dally, T Featherstone, P R Ray, V L Wasserberg, G L Williams
Office: London EC2
Work: D1 D2 K1 K3
Emergency Action, Agency, Advocacy, Fixed Fee Interview, Legal Aid undertaken and Legal Aid Franchise
Ptr: Dally, Jemma . . . Aug 2004
Featherstone, Miss Trudi BA(Hons) . . . *Sep 1995
Ray, Ms Peggy R BA; LLB . . . *Sep 1980
Wasserberg, Mr Victor Lewis BA(Hons) . . . *Oct 1993
Williams, Ms Gwen L BA(Hons) . . . *Oct 1994
Ast: Beeharry, Kiran . . . Oct 2007
Con: Bosanquet, Ms Joanna C MA . . . *Nov 1990
Bourdages, Mr Michael . . . Nov 2003

GOODMAN RAY
No1 Liverpool Street London EC2M 7QD
Tel: 020 7608 1227 *Fax:* 020 7250 1786 *Dx:* 36614 FINSBURY
E-mail: mail@goodmanray.com
Office: London EC1

GOODSELLS ‡
18 Old Town London SW4 0LB
Tel: 020 7622 2221 *Fax:* 020 7622 0286
Dx: 53264 CLAPHAM COMMON
E-mail: enquiries@goodsellssolicitors.co.uk

GOODWIN & CO ‡
22 Sunnyhill Road Streatham London SW16 2UH
Tel: 020 8677 9554 *Fax:* 020 8677 4475
List of partners: D P Goodwin
Work: S1
Ptr: Goodwin, Mr David P LLB . . . *Oct 1982

GOPAL GUPTA SOLICITORS ‡
99 High Street London NW10 4TS
Tel: 020 8838 0008 *Fax:* 020 8838 5544
E-mail: gopalgupta@london.com

GORDON & CO ‡
25 James Street London W1U 1DU
Tel: 020 7486 9150

GORDONS ‡
22 Great James Street London WC1N 3ES
Tel: 020 7421 9421 *Fax:* 020 7421 9422
Dx: 107 LONDON/CHANCERY LN
E-mail: sols@gordonsols.co.uk
List of partners: J S Austin, H D Ferguson, J D S Gordon, P D Hole, B R Turner
Office: Guildford
Languages: French
Work: A3 B1 C1 C2 C3 E F1 I J1 L M1 M2 O Q R2 S1 S2 U2 X Z(a,b,e,f,i,k,p)
Agency, Fixed Fee Interview and Legal Aid undertaken
Ptr: Ferguson, Mr Hamish Dempster BA(Hons)(Law) . . . *Nov 1985
Gordon, Mr James D S MA . . . *Nov 1988
Hole, Mr Patrick David MA(Oxon)(Modern Languages); LSF . . . *Nov 1994
Turner, Mr Brian R BSc(Bris); IPA(Assoc) . . . *Oct 1984

GORE LEGAL ‡
Acacia House 21 St Mary's Road Ealing London W5 5RA
Tel: 020 8810 1652 *Fax:* 020 8810 1653
E-mail: shally@girn.biz
List of partners: H Kaur
Work: G J1 Z(p)
SPr: Kaur, Miss Harvinder LLB Sweet & Maxwell Law Prize Apr 1991

GOUGH & CO SOLICITORS ‡
84 Grove Green Road London E11 4EL
Tel: 020 8926 3080

J S L GOULDEN ‡
1a Oakhill Avenue London NW3 7RD
Tel: 020 7435 8887
List of partners: J S L Goulden
SPr: Goulden, Ms Judith S L Justice of the Peace . . . *Dec 1966

GOWLINGS (UK) LLP ‡
1st Floor 3 America Square London EC3N 2LR
Tel: 020 3004 3500 *Fax:* 020 7480 5367

GRACE & CO ‡
(in association with Brian Harris & Co; Heydons)
15 Thayer Street London W1U 3JT
Tel: 020 7935 7938 *Fax:* 020 7935 6935
List of partners: C D Grace
Languages: French
Work: E L R2 S1 S2 W Z(d,h)
SPr: Grace, Ms Caroline D LLB . . . *Nov 1979

GRACELAND SOLICITORS ‡
315 Lewisham High Street London SE13 6NL

GRACELAND SOLICITORS ‡
15 Beresford Square Woolwich London SE18 6AY
Tel: 020 8836 9350 *Fax:* 020 8836 9351 *Dx:* 56605 LEWISHAM
E-mail: admin@gracelandsolicitors.co.uk

GRAMDAN SOLICITORS ‡
15 Old Oak Common Lane London W3 7EL
Tel: 020 8749 7282 *Fax:* 020 8749 7252 *Dx:* 99634 ACTON 2
E-mail: london@gramdansolicitors.co.uk

GRANGE & CASTLE ‡
209-210 Grange Road London SE1 3AA
Tel: 020 7967 7070 *Fax:* 020 7967 7077 *Dx:* 80714 BERMONDSEY
E-mail: post@grangeandcastlesolicitors.com

ANDRE GRANT & CO ‡
56 High Road Haringey London N15 6JU
Tel: 020 8800 8802 *Fax:* 020 8800 0386
E-mail: info@aglaw.co.uk
List of partners: A C M Grant
Work: E S1 S2 W Z(l)
Fixed Fee Interview undertaken
SPr: Grant, Mr Andre Charles McGregor BA(Hons)(Law) . *Dec 1982

GRANT SAW SOLICITORS LLP ‡
1st Floor Norman House 110-114 Norman Road Greenwich London SE10 9EH
Tel: 020 8858 6971 *Fax:* 020 8858 5796 *Dx:* 35202 GREENWICH 2
E-mail: enquiries@grantsaw.co.uk
List of partners: A J Blackburn, R J Chichester, M Clary, R H Crudgington, M Lati
Languages: French, Greek, Igbo
Work: C1 C2 E F1 J1 K1 K3 K4 L N O Q S1 S2 T2 W Z(d,i,l,p,q)
Advocacy undertaken
Ptr: Blackburn, Mr Andrew J MA . . . *May 1975
Chichester, Mr Rupert Jolyon MA(Oxon) . . . *Mar 1985
Clary, Mr Michael LLB(Hons) . . . *Jun 2000
Crudgington, Mr Raymond H LLB . . . *Oct 1991
Lati, Ms Maria LLB(Hons) . . . Mar 1999
Ast: Clair, Miss Mandeep K LLB . . . *Apr 2000

See p2 for the Key to Work Categories & other symbols

Hetherington, Mr David John BA(Cantab) . . . . Oct 1975
King, Ms Virginia Carmel BSc; CPE; LSF . . . . *Apr 1996
O'Connor, Mr Damien. . . . . *Sep 1999
Okeke, Miss Chiamaka LLB. . . . . *Sep 2001
Pinnington, Mrs Michelle LLB . . . . *May 2003
Savvides, Mr Mario LLB(Hons) . . . . Sep 2009
Con: Greenhalgh, Mrs A Mary MA(Cantab) . . . . *Jul 1972
Jordan, Mrs Gillian L LLB(Lond). . . . . *Jun 1971
Meakin, Mr William J B MA; LLM(Cantab) . . . . *Nov 1971
Templeton, Mr John D BA(Cantab) . . . . *Jul 1968

GRAZING HILL LAW PARTNERS ‡
67a Halliford Street London N1 3HF
Tel: 020 7354 1444 *Fax:* 0560 116 2015
E-mail: info@grazinghill.com

IAN GREEN CONSULTING ‡
Apartment E April House 45 Maresfield Gardens London NW3 5TE
Tel: 07860 539360 *Fax:* 020 7443 5942
E-mail: idgreen@compuserve.com
Work: C1

GREENBERG TRAURIG MAHER LLP ‡
31st Floor 30 St Mary Axe London EC3A 8EP
Tel: 020 3349 8700 *Fax:* 020 7900 3632 *Dx:* 616 LONDON/CITY

GREENFIELDS SOLICITORS ‡
6 Market Parade Winchester Road Edmonton London N9 9HF
Tel: 020 8884 1166 *Fax:* 020 8884 1144
E-mail: info@greenfieldsolicitors.com

GREENHOUSE STIRTON & CO ‡
1-2 Faulkner's Alley Cowcross Street London EC1M 6DD
Tel: 020 7490 3456 *Fax:* 020 7490 3242 *Dx:* 53309 CLERKENWELL
E-mail: greenhousestirton@mediationlawyers.co.uk
List of partners: G I Greenhouse, M J Stirton
Work: A3 K2 K4 T2 W Z(d)
Ptr: Greenhouse, Mr Geoffrey I LLB; LLM(Lond); FRSA; TEP . . . . *Jul 1977
Stirton, Mr Michael J LLB; FCIArb. . . . . *Jun 1974

GREENLAND SOLICITORS ‡
Camden High Street Camden Town Camden London NW1 0NE
Tel: 020 7428 0777 *Dx:* 57073 CAMDEN TOWN

GREENWOOD & CO ‡
Premier House 12-13 Hatton Garden London EC1N 8AN
Tel: 020 7831 8386 *Fax:* 020 7404 0523
E-mail: greenwoodco@btinternet.com
List of partners: R S Friend, J H Greenwood
Languages: German, Hebrew, Yiddish
Work: B1 C1 C2 C3 E F1 J1 L M2 N O P Q R1 S1 S2 T1 U1 W Z(b,c,e,f,j,l)
Ptr: Friend, Mr Ronald S. . . . . *Jan 1985
Greenwood, Mr Jonathan H LLB . . . . *Mar 1979

GREENWOODS ‡
77 Gracechurch Street London EC3V 0AS
Tel: 020 7220 7818 *Fax:* 020 7469 6289
E-mail: contact@greenwoods-solicitors.com
List of partners: C R J Ashmore, M Guy, K Mann, T Neuhoff, P T S Parsons
Office: Bristol, Fareham, London WC1, Manchester, Milton Keynes
Work: N O Q Z(c,j)
Ptr: Ashmore, Mr Charles Robert James LLB . . . . . . *§Nov 1992
Asoc: Gellert, Ms Marise S LLB(Hons). . . . . Oct 1990
Howcroft, Mr Stephen BA(Hons) . . . . *Dec 1991
O'Shea, Mr John . . . . Mar 2005

GREENWOODS
18 Bedford Square London WC1B 3JA
Tel: 020 7323 4632 *Fax:* 020 7631 3142
E-mail: contact@greenwoods-solicitors.com
Office: Bristol, Fareham, London EC3, Manchester, Milton Keynes
Ptr: Mann, Miss Karen FILEx; LPC(Dip) . . . . *Nov 1998
Asoc: Khalid, Ghazala . . . . Jun 2003

GREGORIAN EMERSON FAMILY LAW SOLICITORS ‡
3 The Fountain Centre Lensbury Avenue Imperial Wharf London SW6 2TW
Tel: 01483 898076 *Fax:* 01483 891829
E-mail: enquiries@gelaw.co.uk

GREGORY ABRAMS DAVIDSON LLP
Pearl House 746 Finchley Road Golders Green London NW11 7TH
Tel: 020 8209 0166 / 8458 9322 *Fax:* 020 8209 0409
Dx: 92005 TEMPLE FORTUNE
E-mail: david.sichel@rjrlaw.co.uk
Office: Liverpool (3 offices)
Languages: French, Hebrew
Work: B1 C1 C2 E F1 J1 K1 L M1 N O Q R1 S1 T1 T2 W Z(c,l,p,q)
Ptr: Joseph, Mr Peter J LLB. . . . . *Jun 1979
Rumke, Mr Charles M BSc . . . . Jun 1977

CHARLES GREGORY ASSOCIATES ‡
Connaught House 144 Harrow Road London E11 3PX
Tel: 020 8988 1118

GREGORY ROWCLIFFE MILNERS ‡
1 Bedford Row London WC1R 4BZ
Tel: 020 7242 0631 *Fax:* 020 7242 6652
Dx: 95 LONDON/CHANCERY LN
E-mail: law@grm.co.uk
List of partners: C K Bannister, W R Bennett, I Bowyer, P A R Carter, J A Fitzgerald, C J Harper, J K Hoppe, J Laidler, T J Moloney, M E O Palmer, T J Sharpe, N R Spurrier
Languages: French, German, Italian, Korean, Maltese, Spanish
Work: A1 A2 A3 B1 C1 C2 C3 D1 D2 E F1 F2 I J1 J2 K1 K2 K3 L M1 M2 M3 N O P Q R1 R2 S1 S2 T1 T2 U1 U2 V W X Z(b,c,d,e,f,g,h,i,j,k,l,m,n,o,p,q,r,s,w,x,y,z,za)
Emergency Action, Agency, Advocacy undertaken and Member of Accident Line
Ptr: Bannister, Mr Christopher K. . . . . Oct 1992
Bennett, Mr William R. . . . . *May 1971
Carter, Mr Philip A R LLB . . . . *Jan 1986
Fitzgerald, Ms Jacqueline Angela . . . . Oct 1989
Harper, Mr Christopher J LLB(Lond). . . . . *§Apr 1976
Hoppe, Mr Jan Klaus . . . . *Jul 2000
Laidler, Mrs Jane LLB. . . . . *Jun 1977
Moloney, Mr Timothy J LLB(Manc) . . . . *May 1979
Palmer, Mr Michael E O LLB(Soton). . . . . *§Oct 1974
Sharpe, Mr Thomas J. . . . . *Dec 1969
Spurrier, Mr Neil R BA . . . . *§Dec 1979
Bowyer, Mr Ian FILEx. . . . . NSP
Asoc: Barber, Mr Christopher C . . . . *§Jun 1979
Iodice, Ms Caterina . . . . *Mar 2008
Ast: Cooper, Ms Olivia BSc; MA . . . . Nov 2007
Jallow, Ms Muna LLB . . . . Oct 2008
Ko, Mrs Caroline BA . . . . Sep 2003
Moore, Mr Thomas . . . . Oct 2008
Riaz, Mrs Sarah. . . . . Oct 2009
Ross, Ms Helena BA . . . . Dec 2007
Con: Holloway, Mr Paul A LLB . . . . *§Dec 1968
Mezzetti, Mr Adrian J LLB(Bris) . . . . *Jun 1968
Parnell-King, Mr Michael . . . . Jan 1979
Pendlebury Cox, Mrs Lesley P BSocSc . . . . *Jun 1976
Poole, Mr Richard N L MA(Cantab) . . . . *Jun 1972

We conduct business in French, German, Italian, Spanish, Korean. We specialise in the following areas of work Commercial and Company Law, Mergers and Acquisitions, Competition Law.

GREGSONS ‡
St Christophers House 19 Tabor Grove Wimbledon London SW19 4EX
Tel: 020 8946 1173 *Fax:* 020 8946 6182
Dx: 300108 WIMBLEDON CENTRAL
Emergency telephone 020 8879 4400
E-mail: info@gregsons.co.uk
List of partners: A A Adam, M G Creamore, M Jones, E A Middlehurst
Languages: German, Spanish
Work: B1 C1 C2 C3 E F1 G H I J1 L M1 M2 N O P Q R1 S1 T2 V W Z(a,c,d,e,h,k,l,p)
Emergency Action, Agency, Advocacy, Legal Aid undertaken, Legal Aid Franchise and Member of Accident Line
Ptr: Adam, Ms Alexandra A . . . . *Nov 1984
Creamore, Mr Michael Gary. . . . . Sep 1994
Jones, Mr Michael LLB . . . . *Oct 1991
Middlehurst, Mr Edmund A BA . . . . Mar 1977
Ast: Hagopian, Ms Sylvia N . . . . Sep 1990
Con: Ward, Mr Michael V Notary Public. . . . . Jun 1970

GRIER OLUBI SOLICITORS ‡
65 London Wall London EC2M 5TU
Tel: 020 7256 7770 *Fax:* 020 7256 6660
E-mail: lawyers@grierolubi.co.uk
List of partners: O A Adejobi
SPr: Adejobi, Olubi A LLB . . . . Jun 1992

GRINDALL & HANNA SOLICITORS ‡
58 Underhill Road Southwark London SE22 0QT
Tel: 020 8299 3801 *Fax:* 020 8299 3756
E-mail: mail@grindallandhanna.co.uk
List of partners: D J Grindall, S M E Hanna
Work: C1 J1
Ptr: Grindall, Mr David J LLB(Lond) . . . . *Dec 1976
Hanna, Ms Sara M E LLB(Warw) . . . . *Apr 1988

PAUL GROMETT & CO ‡
95 Mortimer Street London W1W 7ST
Tel: 020 7631 2066 *Fax:* 020 7631 2088
List of partners: P Gromett
Work: B1 C1 D1 E F1 G H J1 K1 L M1 N P R1 S1 T1 W Z(k)
Agency and Advocacy undertaken
Ptr: Gromett, Mr Paul . . . . *Dec 1972

GROMYKO AMEDU SOLICITORS ‡
Lower Ground Floor Office 276-278 Brixton Hill London SW2 1HP
Tel: 020 8678 8996 *Fax:* 020 8678 0664
E-mail: gromykoamedu@yahoo.com

GROVE SOLICITORS ‡
98 Mountgrove Road London N5 2LT
Tel: 020 7226 2226 *Fax:* 020 7226 5226

GROVES & CO ‡
58 Croftdown Road London NW5 1EN

GROWER FREEMAN ‡
Ivor House 25 Ivor Place London NW1 6HR
Tel: 020 7723 3040 *Fax:* 020 7723 9015 *Dx:* 44433 MARBLE ARCH
E-mail: sportslaw@gfg-law.co.uk
Languages: French, Gujarati, Hindi, Kiswahili, Urdu
Work: B1 C1 E J1 K1 L N O Q S1 S2 W Z(c,j,k,l,w)

M C GRUMBRIDGE ‡
The Hogarth Group 1a Airedale Avenue London W4 2NW
Tel: 020 8994 0929 *Fax:* 020 8995 1373
Dx: 32774 HAMMERSMITH 2
E-mail: mcg@thehogarth.co.uk
List of partners: M C Grumbridge
SPr: Grumbridge, Mr Malcolm C BA . . . . *§Apr 1978

WESLEY GRYK ‡
140 Lower Marsh Lambeth London SE1 7AE
Tel: 020 7401 6887 *Fax:* 020 7261 9985 *Dx:* 36517 LAMBETH
E-mail: enquiries@gryklaw.com
List of partners: W C Gryk
Languages: Arabic, French, German, Polish
Work: Z(g,i)
Agency and Legal Aid undertaken
SPr: Gryk, Mr Wesley C BA; JD; LPC Law Society Council Member . . . . *Nov 1990
Ast: Barnden, Mr Tim BA . . . . Aug 1998
Coll, Ms Barbara A LLB(Hons); LPC; LLM. . . . . . . *Oct 1996
Hunter, Ms Alison LLB; MA; LPC . . . . *Nov 1997
Kerr, Ms Carolyn Jane BA; LPC. . . . . Apr 2007
O'Leary, Mr Barry Antone BA; LPC . . . . *Dec 1997

GUDSONS SOLICITORS ‡
230 Regents Park Road London N3 3HP
Tel: 020 8371 8389 *Fax:* 020 8371 8390
E-mail: gudsons@london.com
List of partners: S Shah
Work: C1 E J1 L Q R1 S1 S2 W Z(l)
Fixed Fee Interview undertaken
SPr: Shah, Mrs Smita LLB . . . . Nov 1990

ALIDA GUEST ‡
24 Lonsdale Road London W11 2DE
Tel: 020 7727 6273 *Fax:* 020 7727 5296
E-mail: alidaguest@aguest.fsbusiness.co.uk
List of partners: A F Guest
Languages: French
Work: M1 Z(g,i)
Emergency Action and Fixed Fee Interview undertaken
SPr: Guest, Mrs Alida F LLB . . . . *Feb 1982

GUILE NICHOLAS ‡
43 Lodge Lane North Finchley London N12 8JG
Tel: 020 8492 2290 *Fax:* 020 8445 5376 *Dx:* 57351 FINCHLEY 1
E-mail: sols@gnlaw.co.uk
List of partners: A Stokoe
Office: Kingston upon Thames

GUISE SOLICITORS ‡
1 Alie Street London E1 8DE
Tel: 020 7264 0350 *Fax:* 020 7264 0351 *Dx:* 522 LONDON/CITY
E-mail: info@guisesolicitors.co.uk

GULAY MEHMET ‡
Sixth Floor London WC1X 8HN
Tel: 020 7400 1565

GULBENKIAN ANDONIAN SOLICITORS ‡
2nd Floor Sicilian House Sicilian Avenue London WC1A 2QH
Est: 1987
Tel: 020 7269 9590 *Fax:* 020 7404 7624
Dx: 437 LONDON/CHANCERY LN
E-mail: paulg@gulbenkian.co.uk
List of partners: B Andonian, B P Gulbenkian
Languages: Armenian, Farsi, French
Work: K1 Z(i)
Emergency Action and Fixed Fee Interview undertaken
Ptr: Andonian, Mr Bernard MA(Intellectual Property) ♦ Part time Immigration Judge . . . . *Jun 1985
Gulbenkian, Mr Basil Paul LLB(Lond) ♦ Recorder; Immigration Judge; Assistant Commissioner to Boundary Commission . . . . *§Jan 1965

GULSEN & CO SOLICITORS ‡
89 Silver Street London N18 1RP
Tel: 020 8803 4196 *Fax:* 020 8807 6393
E-mail: info@gulsen.co.uk

GUNEY CLARK & RYAN ‡
60 Green Lanes London N16 9NH
Tel: 020 7275 7788 *Fax:* 020 7923 2554
Dx: 142580 STOKE NEWINGTON 3
E-mail: info@guneyclarkryan.com

HOWARD GURPINER ‡
Unit 4f N17 Studios 784-788 Tottenham High Road London N17 0DA
Tel: 020 8885 3337

H2O LAW LLP ‡
1st Floor 20-21 Took's Court London EC4A 1LB
Tel: 020 7405 4700 *Fax:* 020 7061 9461
E-mail: enquiries@h2o-law.com
List of partners: P F J E Fox, D M Greenhalgh, J D McCue
Languages: French, German, Italian, Spanish
Work: D1 G J1 K1 N O Q U2 W Z(e,f,g,k,p,w,z)
Advocacy undertaken
Mem: Fox, Mr Paul Francis Joseph Edmund LLB(Hons) ♦ . . *Oct 1986
Greenhalgh, Mr David Mark LLB(Hons)(Lond). . . . . *Oct 1994
McCue, Mr Jason Daniel LLB(Hons). . . . . Oct 1993
Ast: Jury, Mr Matthew David. . . . . May 2009
Con: Penhaligan, Ms Lee. . . . . *Dec 1990

HCLS LLP ‡
4th Floor 31 Davies Street London W1K 4LP
Tel: 020 7499 4779 *Fax:* 020 7629 4948 *Dx:* 44645 MAYFAIR
E-mail: info@hamblelaw.com

HGF LAW
40-43 Chancery Lane London WC2A 1JA
Tel: 020 7440 8900 *Fax:* 020 7440 8901
E-mail: law@hgf-law.com
Office: Leeds
Languages: German, Spanish

HRO GRANT DAWE LLP ‡
First Floor Block 6 Thames Wharf Studios London W6 9HA
Tel: 020 7386 2240 *Fax:* 020 3010 3054

HSR SOLICITORS ‡
Victoria House 526 Commercial Road London E1 0HY
Tel: 020 7791 1111 *Fax:* 020 7791 2222
Dx: 300715 TOWER HAMLETS
Emergency telephone 07958 375376
E-mail: info@hsrsolicitors.com
List of partners: H S Rana, J M Rufai, S Walia
Languages: Bengali, Hindi, Punjabi, Russian, Urdu, Yoruba
Work: E G H J1 S1 S2 Z(i,l)
Ptr: Rana, Harsharan S LLB(Hons) . . . . Aug 1998
Rufai, Mr Jubril Mobolaji LLB(Hons). . . . . May 2002
Walia, Ms Sarika BA(Hons) . . . . May 2003
Con: Bahra, Mrs Avneet Anne Kaur LLB(Hons) . . . . Oct 1999

HAFEZIS SOLICITORS ‡
73-74 London Fruit Exchange Brushfield Street London E1 6EP
Tel: 020 7377 0600

HAFIZ & HAQUE SOLICITORS ‡
511 Hackney Road London E2 9ED
Tel: 020 7729 1911

HAIDER KENNEDY LEGAL SERVICES LTD ‡
25 Station Road South Norwood London SE25 5AH
Tel: 020 8771 2323 *Fax:* 020 8771 2424
Dx: 37805 SOUTH NORWOOD
E-mail: haiderkennedy@haider_kennedy.co.uk
List of partners: S Haider
Work: D1 K1 K3 O Q Z(f)
Legal Aid undertaken
SPr: Haider, Shuja . . . . Feb 1999

HALDANES
(in association with Haldanes(Hong Kong))
40 Gerrard Street London W1D 5QE
Tel: 020 7437 5629 *Fax:* 020 7437 5628
Dx: 40028 COVENT GARDEN

E-mail: info@haldanes.net
Office: Stevenage
Work: A3 B1 C1 E F1 J1 L N O Q S1 W Z(k,l,q)
Ptr: Miles, Mr Geoffrey R . . . . *Jun 1972

HALEBURY VENTURES LIMITED ‡
3 Wigmore Place Cavendish Square London W1U 2LN
Tel: 020 7127 2500 *Fax:* 020 7990 9200
E-mail: info@halebury.com

HALL & CO ‡
Chelco House 39 Camberwell Church Street London SE5 8TR

R C HALL SOLICITORS ‡
Gibson House 800 High Road London N17 0DH
Tel: 020 8801 2345 *Fax:* 020 8801 2555 *Dx:* 36205 EDMONTON
E-mail: rchallegal@yahoo.co.uk

HALLAM-PEEL & CO ‡
218 Strand London WC2R 1AT
Tel: 020 3006 1661 *Fax:* 0808 280 0130
Dx: 232 LONDON/CHANCERY LN
E-mail: dhp@hallam-peel.co.uk
List of partners: D A Hallam-Peel, J D Sewell, A Tribe
Work: F1 J2 K1 L N O Q Z(q,r)
Emergency Action, Agency, Advocacy, Fixed Fee Interview, Legal Aid undertaken, Legal Aid Franchise and Member of Accident Line
Ptr: Hallam-Peel, Mr David A LLB . . . . *Oct 1986
Sewell, Mr Jonathan Daniel BA; LLB . . . . *Dec 1998
Tribe, Miss Alexandra BSc(Hons) . . . . *May 2004
Ast: Patez, Mrs Jayshree . . . . Jun 2003

GRAHAM HALLIDAY & CO ‡
5 Sandringham Gardens North Finchley London N12 0NY
Tel: 020 8445 4071 *Fax:* 020 8343 7495 *Dx:* 57386 FINCHLEY 1
List of partners: G P Halliday
Work: K1 L N
Ptr: Halliday, Mr Graham P . . . . Jun 1980

HALLINAN BLACKBURN GITTINGS & NOTT ‡
Suite 22 Westminster Palace Gardens Artillery Row Westminster London SW1P 1RR
Tel: 020 7233 3999 *Fax:* 020 7233 3888
Emergency telephone 07831 406242
List of partners: C R Nott, C S Williams
Work: B2 G H
Emergency Action, Agency, Advocacy, Fixed Fee Interview, Legal Aid undertaken, Legal Aid Franchise and Member of Accident Line
Ptr: Nott, Mr Colin R LLB ★ . . . . *Dec 1978
Williams, Miss C Sian LLB ★ . . . . *Oct 1987
Ast: Lowry-Mullins, Mr Kevin LLB(Hons) ★. . . . . *Oct 1999
McDonald, Mr Stuart M LLB(Hons) ★ . . . . *Jul 1991

HALPINS ‡
1 Bridge Place London SW1V 1QA
Tel: 020 3286 6041 *Fax:* 020 7900 2440
E-mail: halpins@btinternet.com
List of partners: B A Haplin
Ptr: Haplin, Mr Bernard Anthony. . . . . Jun 1975

HAMEED & CO ‡
(in association with Desmond Fernado P C 26 Charles)
147 High Road Willesden London NW10 2SJ
Tel: 020 8830 1335 *Fax:* 020 8830 1556
Emergency telephone 07930 377442
E-mail: info@hameed.co.uk
List of partners: R Hameed
Languages: Dutch, German, Sinhalese, Tamil
Work: D1 E F1 G H J1 K1 K2 L M1 M2 O Q S1 S2 V W Z(g,i,l)
Emergency Action, Agency, Advocacy, Fixed Fee Interview, Legal Aid undertaken and Legal Aid Franchise
Ptr: Hameed, Dr Reeza LLM(Harv); PhD(Lond); Attorney(New York) . . . . *Sep 1990
Ast: Van Der Weit, Mrs Elisabeth LLM(Lond, Leiden). . . . *Oct 1995

HAMILTON & CO ADVOKATBYRA ‡
St James' House 13 Kensington Square London W8 5HD
Tel: 020 7795 4775 *Fax:* 020 7795 4776

HAMILTON DOWNING QUINN ‡
Ruskin House 40-41 Museum Street London WC1A 1LT
Est: 1985
Tel: 020 7831 8939 *Fax:* 020 7831 8798 *Dx:* 35717 BLOOMSBURY
E-mail: law@hamd.co.uk
List of partners: J E M Davis, W L Eddlestone, P Hamilton, C J P Iliff
Languages: French, Polish, Russian
Work: A1 A3 B1 C1 C2 C3 E F1 F2 J1 J2 K1 K2 K3 K4 L M1 N O P Q R1 R2 S1 S2 T1 T2 U1 U2 W Z(b,c,d,e,f,j,k,l,p,q,w,z)
Emergency Action, Agency and Legal Aid undertaken
Ptr: Davis, Mr James E M LLB. . . . . *Oct 1991
Eddlestone, Mr Walton L MA(Oxon); ACIArb . . . . . *Jun 1979
Hamilton, Mr Philip . . . . *Jun 1977
Iliff, Mr Charles J P MA(Cantab). . . . . *Dec 1977
Asoc: Taylor, Mr Alan David . . . . Jun 1963
Con: Jerrard, Mr Warner Leigh . . . . Jun 1968
Pinkerfield, Mr Howard A . . . . *Dec 1978
Shone, Mr Michael J MA(Hons)(Cantab); FCIArb Notary Public . . . . *§Jun 1982

HAMILTON GERARD SOLICITORS ‡
1a Blackheath Hill Greenwich London SE10 8BP
Tel: 020 8692 1492 *Fax:* 020 8692 1061

hamlins
SOLICITORS

HAMLINS LLP ‡
Roxburghe House 273-287 Regent Street London W1B 2AD
Tel: 020 7355 6000 *Fax:* 020 7518 9100
Dx: 53803 OXFORD CIRCUS NORTH
Emergency telephone 020 7355 6000
E-mail: admin@hamlins.co.uk
Web: www.hamlins.co.uk
List of partners: D M Bellau, M A Copping, I K Down, D J Featherstonhaugh, L Gilmore, A F J Gordon, L Harcombe, P A Herbert, M Hurst, B D Kilshaw, D L Lewis, N C Mason, G C Oliver, A D Perlmutter, K Roffey, P M Spacey, V E Stanborough
Work: B1 C1 C2 C3 E J1 L O Q R2 S1 S2 T1 Z(b,c,e,f,g,j,k,l,o,w,za)
Fixed Fee Interview undertaken
Ptr: Bellau, Mr Daniel M. . . . . Mar 1999
Copping, Mr Mark A BA(Oxon) . . . . *Sep 1984
Down, Mr Ian K BA . . . . *May 1988
Featherstonhaugh, Ms Diana J BA(Law). . . . . . . *Nov 1981
Gilmore, Mr Laurence BA; LLM(Cantab). . . . . . . *Apr 1986
Gordon, Alban F J MA(Oxon) . . . . *Apr 1981
Harcombe, Mrs Laura. . . . . Apr 2011
Herbert, Mr Philip A LLB . . . . *Nov 1991
Hurst, Mr Mark . . . . Jan 1997
Kilshaw, Mr Benjamin Daniel LLB . . . . Nov 1999
Lewis, Mr David L LLB . . . . *§May 1993
Mason, Mr Nigel C BA . . . . *Oct 1985
Oliver, Mr Gordon C LLB . . . . *Apr 1976
Perlmutter, Mr Antony David LLB(Hons); DipLP . . . . May 1998
Roffey, Mr Keith LLB Sweet & Maxwell Law Prize 1985 . . . . *Sep 1988
Spacey, Mr Paul M LLB. . . . . *Mar 1987
Stanborough, Ms Victoria Elizabeth LLB(Hons) . . . *Nov 1995
Asoc: Raymond, Miss Yvonne Marina . . . . *Nov 1993
Ast: Hawkyard, Mr Peter M LLB; DMS. . . . . *Jun 1970
Maxwell, Mr Charles LLB . . . . Aug 2006
Schmittzehe, Mrs Naazneen LLB(Hons). . . . . *Aug 1995

We specialise in the following areas of work: Commercial Property, Commercial Litigation, Intellectual Property, Brands and Rights, Media and Entertainment, Debt Management, Property-Finance.

HAMMOND BALE ‡
27 New Bond Street London W1S 2RH
Tel: 020 7499 7624 *Fax:* 020 7493 7412 *Dx:* 82952 MAYFAIR
E-mail: mail@hammondbale.com
List of partners: M D E Bale, M C Gebhard, C J Hammond
Languages: French, German, Italian, Spanish
Work: B1 C1 C2 C3 E F1 J1 K1 L M1 M2 N O P Q S1 S2 T1 T2 W Z(c,e,f,i,k,w)
Agency and Advocacy undertaken
Ptr: Bale, Mr Martin D E BA. . . . . *May 1982
Gebhard, Mr Mark Christian LLB . . . . *Sep 1995
Hammond, Mr Christopher J . . . . *Nov 1977
Ast: Booth, Mr Richard James LLB. . . . . Sep 2003
Kershaw, Ms Heather LLB; LLM. . . . . Feb 2001

PAUL HAMPTON ‡
28 Eccleston Square London SW1V 1NZ
Tel: 020 7932 2450 *Fax:* 0870 751 8338
E-mail: phampton@number28.co.uk
Asoc: Hampton, Mr Paul ●. . . . . Dec 1987

HAMPTONS SOLICITORS ‡
3rd Floor Office 38 William IV Street London WC2N 4DD
Tel: 020 7395 6050 *Fax:* 020 7240 6373
Dx: 40017 COVENT GARDEN
E-mail: jude@hamptonslaw.co.uk

HANNAH & MOULD ‡
2 Eaton Gate London SW1W 9BJ
Tel: 020 7384 9527 *Fax:* 020 7834 5156
E-mail: jhannah@hannahmould.com
Work: A3 C1 J1 O Q Z(c)

HANNE & CO ‡
St Johns Chambers 1c St Johns Hill Clapham Junction London SW11 1TN
Est: 1898
Tel: 020 7228 0017 *Fax:* 020 7326 8300
Dx: 58550 CLAPHAM JUNCTION
Emergency telephone 07710 454125
E-mail: info@hanne.co.uk
List of partners: M F G Cardew, E A Francis, S M Harlow, N E Jones, M J A Meadows, D Taylor
Languages: French, German
Work: D1 D2 E G H J1 K1 K3 L S1 S2 W Z(h,p)
Emergency Action, Agency, Advocacy, Fixed Fee Interview, Legal Aid undertaken, Legal Aid Franchise and Member of Accident Line
Ptr: Cardew, Mr Mark F G BA . . . . *§Jun 1980
Francis, Ms Elizabeth A BA . . . . *Oct 1984
Harlow, Ms Susan M LLB . . . . §May 1979
Jones, Ms Nia E BA(Dunelm); MA(B'ham). . . . . . . Apr 1980
Meadows, Mr Martyn J A LLB. . . . . *Dec 1978
Taylor, Mr David BA. . . . . *Sep 1994
Asoc: Brierley, Mr Michael. . . . . Jan 2009
Carr, Mr Paul . . . . Jan 2009
Cook, Samantha . . . . Jan 2008
Dronfield, Mr Harry . . . . Jan 2009
Dunn, Mr James . . . . Jan 2002
Feeny, Elinor . . . . Jan 2009
Field, Ms Hannah . . . . Jan 2007
Gowen, Anna . . . . Jan 2004
Martin, Claire . . . . Jan 2006
Paget, Clare BA(Hons) . . . . Apr 1999
West, Lorna. . . . . Jan 2007
Ast: Butler, Mr Ian Andrew LLB . . . . *Jul 1997
Cservenka, Miss Lorna LLB. . . . . Jan 1997
Fahy, Grainne LLB . . . . Jan 2005
Pearce, Ms Jacqueline Mary MA . . . . *Dec 1995
Ricks, Miss Helen Fiona BA(Hons) . . . . *Mar 1999
Wiles, Ms Claire LLB . . . . Mar 2001
Con: Burdett, Mr Michael F BA(Nott'm) . . . . *§Jun 1970
Little, Ms Caroline LLB . . . . Feb 1980
Widgery, Ms Rosalind L P BA. . . . . *Jun 1977

HANOVER SOLICITORS ‡
14 Basil Street Knightsbridge London SW3 1AJ
Tel: 0870 383 1974 *Fax:* 020 7117 1591
E-mail: info@hanoversolicitors.co.uk
List of partners: L Greg, C Joseph
Work: S1 S2 Z(e,f)
Ptr: Greg, Ms Lindsay. . . . . Aug 2003
Joseph, Ms Caroline LLB(Hons). . . . . Jun 2001

HANSEL HENSON LLP ‡
3rd Floor 22 Newman Street London W1T 1PH
Tel: 020 7307 5145 *Fax:* 020 7504 8717
E-mail: tmh@hanselhenson.com

HANSEN PALOMARES ‡
153 Kennington Road Lambeth London SE11 6SF
Est: 1995
Tel: 020 7640 4600 *Fax:* 020 7640 4610 *Dx:* 33260 KENNINGTON
E-mail: mailto@hansenpalomares.co.uk
List of partners: O L Hansen, M M Palomares
Languages: Danish, French, Portuguese, Spanish
Work: L N V Z(q)
Emergency Action, Advocacy, Fixed Fee Interview, Legal Aid undertaken and Legal Aid Franchise
Ptr: Hansen, Ole L MA . . . . *Sep 1971
Palomares, Ms Maria Mercedes CQSW. . . . . *Jul 1996
Asoc: Cade, Ms Natasha Veronique LLB. . . . . *Aug 2005
Hansen, Mr Christian BSc. . . . . *Jan 2003
Clarkson, Ms Zorina Nadine LLB ♦ . . . . *Feb 2004
Ten Caten, Ms Lara. . . . . *Jun 2004

HANWELL CHAMBERS ‡
110a Grove Avenue Hanwell London W7 3ES
Tel: 020 8840 8555 *Fax:* 020 8280 1091 *Dx:* 5104 EALING

HAQ HAMILTON HUGHES ‡
577a Lea Bridge Road London E10 6AJ
Tel: 020 8503 7228 *Fax:* 020 8503 7255
Dx: 32028 WALTHAMSTOW
E-mail: enquiries@hhhsolicitors.com

HARAZI ‡
Unit 14 Euro Link Business Centre 49 Effra Road London SW2 1BZ
Tel: 020 7733 4099 / 4165 *Fax:* 020 7733 4165
E-mail: leagal-harazi@tiscali.co.uk

HARBOTTLE & LEWIS LLP ‡
Hanover House 14 Hanover Square London W1S 1HP
Est: 1955
Tel: 020 7667 5000 *Fax:* 020 7667 5100 *Dx:* 44617 MAYFAIR
E-mail: info@harbottle.com
List of partners: N Adleman, T M Amlot, G Atchison, T Ballard, P Cairns, M A Derham, C M Howes, H Hymanson, M Jones, P Jones, R Llewellyn, L N Marino, A L Millmore, C R Mitchell, M W Owen, T C Parker, A J Payne, S Peermohamed, M D Phillips, R K Reilly, S L Simons, C F Turner, G Tyrrell, A R Wilds
Languages: French, German, Italian, Spanish
Work: B1 C1 C2 C3 E F1 F2 I J1 J2 K1 K2 K3 L M1 M2 M3 N O Q R1 R2 S1 S2 T1 T2 U1 U2 W Z(b,c,d,e,f,g,h,i,j,k,l,o,p,w,z)
Fixed Fee Interview undertaken
Ptr: Adleman, Mr Neil . . . . *Oct 1997
Amlot, Mr Thomas M BA . . . . *Sep 1999
Atchison, Mr Glen BA(Oxon) . . . . *Nov 1995
Ballard, Mr Tony MA(Cantab) . . . . *May 1974
Cairns, Mr Paul . . . . May 1996
Derham, Ms Marian A LLB(Lond) . . . . *Oct 1984
Howes, Mr Colin M MA(Oxon). . . . . *Oct 1981
Hymanson, Mr Howard . . . . Jun 1993
Jones, Medwyn LLB. . . . . *Apr 1980
Jones, Mr Paul . . . . *Nov 1992
Llewellyn, Mr Rhys LLB(Leeds) . . . . *Sep 2001
Marino, Mr Leonardo Natale. . . . . *Apr 1999
Millmore, Mr Andrew L MA(Cantab) . . . . *§Oct 1985
Mitchell, Mr Charles Robert LLB. . . . . *Oct 1992
Owen, Mr Mark W LLB(Lond) . . . . *Sep 1989
Parker, Mr Timothy C MA(Cantab); CPE; LPC. . . . . *Nov 1996
Payne, Miss Abigail Jane BA(Hons). . . . . *Dec 1996
Peermohamed, Ms Shireen MA(Oxon) . . . . Oct 1989
Phillips, Mr Mark D LLB(Lond). . . . . *Apr 1986
Reilly, Mr Robert K LLB(Bris) . . . . *Mar 1985
Simons, Mrs Sandi Linda LLB. . . . . *Jun 1996
Turner, Miss Caroline F LLB(Bris) . . . . *Mar 1998
Tyrrell, Mr Gerrard LLB(Bris) . . . . *Apr 1981
Wilds, Miss Alison R BA(History); CPE . . . . *Mar 1988
Asoc: Benson, Ms Melanie . . . . Oct 1999
Bridge, Ms Sarah Jayne LLB(Hons); PGDip . . . . . *Sep 2001
Bull, Linzi . . . . Dec 2002
Bye, Mr Benjamin BA; PGDipLaw . . . . *Mar 2003
Castellani, Mr Louis LLB . . . . *May 2000
Leveque, Mr Charles . . . . Feb 2004
Littner, Mr Anthony . . . . *Mar 2003
Manita, Ms Cassandra Maria LLB . . . . *Jan 2001
Mitton, Mr Adam . . . . *Jan 2003
Prince, Miss Louise LLB(Hons); LPC . . . . *Sep 2000
Sanders-Key, Ms Joanne . . . . Oct 2003
Scott, Mr David . . . . *Jan 2000
Ast: Bamford, Mr Tim . . . . *Sep 2005
Brink, Mr John . . . . Jul 2008
Davies, Miss Victoria . . . . *Sep 2005
Edgar, Mr Justin. . . . . Mar 2006
Erskine-Naylor, Ms Fiona . . . . *Mar 2005
Greaves, Mr Lee . . . . Sep 2005
Groves, Mr Paul. . . . . *Jan 2006
Hart, Ms Melanie . . . . Sep 2006
Leverton, Mr Matthew. . . . . Sep 2007
Lewis, Alys . . . . Apr 2008
Lister, Mr Michael. . . . . Mar 2009
Longmate, Ms Katie. . . . . Oct 2007
McGurk, Ms Alexandra . . . . Sep 2007
Matharu, Anil . . . . Mar 2006
Moss, Mr Alan . . . . Oct 2004
Payne, Ms Cordelia. . . . . Sep 2007
Phillips, Amal . . . . *Sep 2001
Pritty, Miss Emily . . . . *Jan 2005
Scholey, Ms Eleanor . . . . Sep 2005
Siklos, Ms Tabatha . . . . Mar 2005
Tager, Ms Nicola . . . . Sep 2007
Wright, Ms Chloe MA(Hons)(Oxon)(Jurisprudence) . *Feb 2004
Con: Patten, Mr Alan J LLB(Manc) . . . . *Jan 1969
Porter, Mr Robert MA(Cantab). . . . . *Jul 1992
Storer, Mr Robert A LLB(Lond) . . . . *May 1971

HARCUS SINCLAIR ‡
3 Lincoln's Inn Fields London WC2A 3AA
Tel: 020 7242 9700 *Fax:* 020 7539 4701
Dx: 340 LONDON/CHANCERY LN
E-mail: mail@harcus-sinclair.co.uk
List of partners: K J Bruce-Smith, R B Cobden-Ramsay, J L Gibson, A F Meek, D J Parker, K Peat
Work: B2 K1 K3 Q T2 W Z(q)
Ptr: Bruce-Smith, Mr Keith James TD MA(Hons)(Oxon) . *§Dec 1978
Cobden-Ramsay, Mr Roger Bawtree . . . . *Mar 1975
Gibson, Miss J Lucy BA(Hons) . . . . *Sep 1997
Meek, Ms Alison Fiona BA(Hons). . . . . *Sep 1986
Parker, Mr Damon J MA(Hons); DipLaw. . . . . *Sep 1997
Peat, Mrs Kathryn LLB Recorder . . . . Mar 1980
Ast: Beresford, Mr Jon LLB . . . . *Sep 2000

See p2 for the Key to Work Categories & other symbols

Bray, Miss Tessa Louise LLB(Hons); PGDip . . . *Sep 2001
Casey, Mrs Georgina Rose BA . . . *Sep 2007
Hickman, Mr Henry BA(Hons) . . . Sep 2004
Moorcroft, Mr Christopher LLB . . . *Mar 2009
Southon, Miss Hannah Lucy BA(Hons); MSc; MA(Oxon); PGDipLaw . . . Sep 2006
Walsh, Miss Eleanor C BA(Hons); GDL; LPC . . . *Oct 2008
Con: Harcus, Mr James B LLB . . . *Dec 1974

PAUL HARDEN & CO ‡
34 Ascott Avenue London W5 5QB
Tel: 0800 756 1436 ***Fax:*** 0800 756 9416
E-mail: ph@hardenlaw.co.uk

HARMAN & HARMAN ‡
Unit 32 Eurolink Business Centre 49 Effra Road London SW2 1BZ
Tel: 01227 452977 ***Fax:*** 01227 762481
List of partners: N Fairweather, S M Harman, K Miller, L M Payne, D P Tamplin
Work: C1 D1 D2 F1 G H J1 K1 M1 P S1 V W X Z(g,m,q,r)
Emergency Action, Agency, Advocacy, Fixed Fee Interview, Legal Aid undertaken and Legal Aid Franchise
Ptr: Fairweather, Mr Nicholas LLB . . . *Dec 1991
Harman, Ms Sarah M BA(Kent) ♦ . . . *Mar 1979
Miller, Mrs Kate MA(Glasgow) . . . *Oct 1994
Payne, Mrs Lesley Marie . . . *Oct 2003
Tamplin, Mr Darren Phillip LLB . . . *Jun 2004
Ast: Tengroth, Mr Alex James LLB . . . *Dec 2004

HARNEY WESTWOOD & RIEGELS ‡
5th Floor 5 New Street Square London EC4A 3BF
Tel: 020 7842 6080 ***Fax:*** 020 7353 0487

HARPER & ODELL ‡
111-113 St John Street Clerkenwell Islington London EC1V 4JA
Tel: 020 7490 0500 ***Fax:*** 020 7490 8040 ***Dx:*** 53319 CLERKENWELL
E-mail: law@harperandodell.co.uk
List of partners: M R Hussein, M C Odell
Languages: Turkish
Work: B1 E K1 L N O Q S1 S2 W Z(j,l,q,r)
Ptr: Hussein, Mr Mehmet R LLB . . . *Apr 1991
Odell, Mr Melvyn C . . . *Nov 1960

HARPERS ‡
75 Gray's Inn Road Holborn Camden London WC1X 8US
Tel: 020 7405 8888 ***Fax:*** 020 7242 7777
Dx: 243 LONDON/CHANCERY LN
List of partners: S Harpalani
Languages: Hindi, Sindhi, Urdu
Work: A3 B1 F1 J1 L O Q S2 Z(c)
Agency and Advocacy undertaken
Ptr: Harpalani, Mr Satish . . . Oct 1994

HARRIS & CO ‡
Sovereign House 1 Albert Place Finchley Central London N3 1QB
Tel: 020 3330 7289 ***Fax:*** 020 8346 1113 ***Dx:*** 57281 FINCHLEY 2
E-mail: enquiries@harrisandco.co.uk
List of partners: C D Harris
Office: London W1
Languages: Ilocano, Tagalog
Work: B1 C1 E J1 K1 K3 K4 N Q S1 S2 W Z(g,i)
Agency and Fixed Fee Interview undertaken
SPr: Harris, Mr Colin David LLB(Hons) Notary Public . . . *Apr 1989

HARRIS & CO
55 Bryanston Street Marble Arch London W1H 7AJ
Office: London N3

BRIAN HARRIS & CO ‡
87 Wimpole Street London W1G 9RL
Tel: 020 7935 5541 ***Fax:*** 020 7935 6638
E-mail: mail@brianharrislaw.com
List of partners: B B Harris, J S Harris
Languages: French, German, Hebrew, Italian
Work: A1 B2 C1 E G J1 K1 L M1 M3 N O Q S1 T1 W Z(b,c,e,i,k,l)
Ptr: Harris, Mr Brian B . . . *Jul 1971
Harris, Mr Jeremy Saul BA(Hons)(Law); DipLP . . . *Jan 1996
Con: Grace, Ms Caroline D LLB . . . *Nov 1979
Heydon, Mr Gordon Howard . . . *Jun 1968
Sutton, Mr Stephen D BA; LLM(Cantab) . . . *Nov 1988

HARRIS CARTIER LLP
Queens House 55-56 Lincoln's Inn Fields London WC2A 3LJ
Tel: 020 7405 7100 ***Fax:*** 020 7405 7772 ***Dx:*** 37953 KINGSWAY
E-mail: info@hclaw.co.uk
Office: Slough
Languages: French, Greek, Hebrew, Italian
Work: B1 B2 C1 C2 C3 E I J1 K1 K3 M2 O Q S2 U2 W Z(q,w)
Ptr: Cartier, Mr Lawrence I MA; LLB(Cantab) . . . *Jun 1971
Fuller, Mr Stephen J . . . *§May 1977
McDonagh, Mr Gregory Aiden LLB(Hons) . . . Sep 1999
Nicholls, Mr Dean Christian LLB(Hons) . . . *Oct 1995
Pattinson, Kent BA . . . *§Jan 1988
Asoc: Tuff, Mr Matthew A . . . Dec 1999
Ast: Cassidy, Mr Jake . . . Jan 2006
Olivelle, Miss Rosheana Sryanthi LLB . . . Oct 2008
Patter, Mrs Jaspreet . . . Sep 2007
Wilkie, Miss Toni Loretta LLB . . . Sep 2009
Williamson, Mr Thomas David LLB . . . Sep 2009

D HARRIS & CO INTERNATIONAL ‡
83 Baker Street London W1U 6LA
Tel: 020 7600 5600

HARRIS DA SILVA ‡
355 City Road Islington London EC1V 1LR
Tel: 020 7713 0700 ***Fax:*** 020 7713 0731 ***Dx:*** 400208 FINSBURY 2
E-mail: harrisdasilva@harsil.demon.co.uk
List of partners: C J L da Silva, H D Harris
Languages: Greek, Portuguese, Spanish
Work: B1 B2 C1 E F1 G H J1 K1 L N O Q S1 W Z(c,i,l,p,q)
Emergency Action, Agency, Advocacy and Legal Aid undertaken
Ptr: da Silva, Mr Charles J L BA . . . *Jun 1989
Ast: Christodoulou, Mr Andrew LLB(Hons) . . . *Apr 1995

GABRIEL HARRIS ‡
44 Chessington Avenue Barnet London N3 3DP
Tel: 020 8343 1355 ***Fax:*** 020 8343 2690
E-mail: g.harris@gabrielharris.co.uk
List of partners: G Harris
Work: C1 E Q S1 S2 W Z(k)
SPr: Harris, Mr Gabriel LLB . . . *Dec 1977

HARRIS HAGAN ‡
6 Snow Hill London EC1A 2AY
Tel: 020 7002 7636 ***Fax:*** 020 7002 7788
E-mail: info@harrishagan.com
List of partners: J A Hagan, J A Harris
Work: Z(l)
Ptr: Hagan, Mr John A BCL(Dublin) . . . Dec 1993
Harris, Mr Julian Anthony . . . Apr 1980

HARRIS TEMPERLEY ‡
271-273 King Street Hammersmith London W6 9LZ
Tel: 020 8233 2989 ***Fax:*** 020 8233 2988
Dx: 46755 HAMMERSMITH 3
E-mail: partners@harristemperley.com
List of partners: P Harris
Work: D1
Agency undertaken
Ptr: Harris, Mr Peter . . . Feb 1989

HARRIS-BARRINGTON & CO SOLICITOR ‡
Deptford Broadway London SE8 4PA
Tel: 020 8469 3880

HARRISON GRANT ‡
15 Wosley Mews London NW5 2DX
Tel: 020 7267 6727

HARRISON MORGAN ‡
7 More Street London E8 4RP

DAVID HARRISONS SOLICITORS ‡
208 High Road Leytonstone Waltham Forest London E11 3HU
Tel: 020 8522 4907 ***Fax:*** 020 8522 4806
Dx: 5409 STRATFORD (LONDON)
Languages: Fanti, French, Ga, Shona, Twi
Work: K1 K3 S1 Z(b,g,i)
Advocacy undertaken

HARRISONS SOLICITORS ‡
15 Old Bailey London EC4M 7EF
Tel: 020 3008 8245 ***Fax:*** 020 3008 8246

HART BROWN SOLICITORS
(incorporating Ponsford Devenish)
58 High Street Wimbledon Village London SW19 5EE
Tel: 0800 068 8177 ***Fax:*** 020 8879 7352
Dx: 35050 WIMBLEDON VILLAGE
E-mail: lawyers@hartbrown.co.uk
Office: Cobham, Cranleigh, Godalming, Guildford, Woking
Languages: French
Work: C1 C2 E J1 L N R1 S1 S2 T1 T2 W Z(b,c,d,j)
Advocacy undertaken
Con: Ross, Mr Frederick B . . . Dec 1972

J H HART & CO ‡
(incorporating Pearce & Davis)
15 Plashet Grove Upton Park London E6 1AQ
Tel: 020 8472 2652 ***Fax:*** 020 8471 8031 ***Dx:*** 133015 UPTON PARK 2
E-mail: jhh@jh-hart.co.uk
List of partners: V D Bharakhda, J H Hart
Languages: Gujarati, Hindi
Work: C1 E L N O Q R1 S1 S2 W Z(i,l)
Advocacy and Fixed Fee Interview undertaken
SPr: Hart, Mr Julian H BA . . . *Oct 1977
Ptr: Bharakhda, Mr Vikesh Dinoo LLB . . . *Jun 2007

HARTER & LOVELESS ‡
325 Caledonian Road Islington London N1 1DR
Tel: 020 7688 2900 ***Fax:*** 020 7688 2031
Dx: 132191 LOWER HOLLOWAY
E-mail: solicitors@harterloveless.co.uk
List of partners: J Guest, H F Purkiss
Work: L S1 S2 W Z(g)
Emergency Action, Advocacy, Fixed Fee Interview and Legal Aid undertaken
Ptr: Guest, Ms Jacqueline ♦ . . . *Nov 1990
Purkiss, Mr Hugh F ♦ . . . *Dec 1984
Ast: Tully, Ms Georgina BA(Leeds)(History) . . . Aug 2005
Con: Garfinkel, Mr David I LLB(Leeds) . . . Jul 1975

DAVID HARTER ‡
12 Thornhill Square London N1 1BQ
Tel: 020 7607 1163

HARTERS ‡
398 Caledonian Road Islington London N1 1DN
Tel: 020 7607 5768 ***Fax:*** 020 7700 5695
Dx: 132196 LOWER HOLOWAY
E-mail: info@harters.co.uk

HARTNELLS ‡
2 Camberwell Church Street London SE5 8QU
Tel: 020 7703 9222 ***Fax:*** 020 7701 2219
Dx: 35304 CAMBERWELL GREEN
Emergency telephone 07956 610171
E-mail: office@hartnells.com
Languages: French
Work: B2 G H S1 S2 V W Z(g,l)
Emergency Action, Agency, Advocacy and Legal Aid undertaken
Ast: Finnis, Jane . . . Jan 2004
Pavitt, Ms Abigail E LLB(Exon) . . . *Oct 1991

HARTWIG NOTARY CHAMBERS
1 Heddon Street London W1B 4BD
Tel: 020 7470 7131 ***Fax:*** 020 7470 7132
E-mail: mk@hartwiglondon.eu
Office: Croydon, London SW1

HARTWIG NOTARY CHAMBERS
15 William Mews London SW1X 9HF
Tel: 020 7235 1504
Office: Croydon, London W1
Languages: French, German, Italian, Spanish
Work: A1 B1 C1 D1 E J1 K1 M1 N P R1 S1 T1 W Z(b,d,e,f,j)
Legal Aid undertaken

HARVEY CAMFORD LLP ‡
New Liverpool House 15 Eldon Street London EC2M 7LD
Tel: 0844 879 4137

HARVEY SON & FILBY
19 Garrick Street London WC2E 9AX
Tel: 020 3159 4235 ***Fax:*** 020 3159 4236
Dx: 40016 COVENT GARDEN
E-mail: richard.kong@harveysf.co.uk
Office: Birmingham, Ipswich
Languages: Chinese
Work: K3 Z(i)
Ptr: Kong, Mr Richard LLB; LLM . . . Nov 2005
Kong, Mr Stephen LLB; LLM . . . Jan 2006

HASELTINE LAKE & CO
5th Floor Lincoln House 300 High Holborn London WC1B 7JH
Tel: 020 7611 7900 ***Fax:*** 020 7611 7901
Office: Leeds

HASLAM & PAYNE ‡
14-15 Lower Grosvenor Place London SW1W 0EX
Tel: 020 7828 8725 ***Fax:*** 020 7821 8936 ***Dx:*** 99927 VICTORIA 3
List of partners: M S Lewis, W R S Payne
Work: E F1 J1 J2 K1 K3 L N O Q R2 S1 S2 W Z(h,r)
Agency undertaken and Member of Accident Line
Ptr: Lewis, Mr Mark S LLB . . . *Jun 1979
Payne, Mr William Richard Sulby LLB . . . *Aug 1979

HASLAW & CO LLP ‡
45 Station Road London E12 5BP
Tel: 020 8514 5551 ***Fax:*** 020 8478 7188
E-mail: info@haslaw.co.uk

HATRICK & CO ‡
6a-6c Vanburgh Terrace London SE3 7AP
Tel: 020 8293 7070

HAUSFELD & CO LLP ‡
2nd Floor 12 Gough Square London EC4A 3DW
Tel: 020 7665 5000 ***Fax:*** 020 7665 5001
E-mail: info@hausfeldllp.com

C H HAUSMANN & CO ‡
5 De Walden Court 85 New Cavendish Street London W1W 6XD
Tel: 020 7436 6333 ***Fax:*** 020 7436 6337 ***Dx:*** 82977 MAYFAIR
E-mail: gordon@chhausmann.co.uk
List of partners: G B S Hausmann
Languages: French, Hebrew, Hungarian
Work: A3 B1 C1 C2 E J1 L M2 M3 O Q R1 R2 S1 S2 T2 W Z(b,c,d,f,i,k)
Ptr: Hausmann, Mr Gordon B S LLB . . . *Dec 1977
Asoc: Trager-Lewis, Mr Alexander Joseph LLB . . . Apr 2004

HAW & CO ‡
245 Camberwell New Road Camberwell London SE5 0TH

EDWARD HAYES LLP
Blackwell House Guildhall Yard London EC2V 5AE
Tel: 020 7353 0011 ***Fax:*** 020 7427 7391
Dx: 432 LONDON/CHANCERY LN
Office: Bognor Regis, Chichester (2 offices), Havant, Littlehampton, London EC4, Worthing

EDWARD HAYES LLP
Temple Bar House 23-28 Fleet Street London EC4Y 1AA
Tel: 020 7353 0011 ***Fax:*** 020 7427 7391
Dx: 432 LONDON/CHANCERY LN
Emergency telephone 0845 602 3043
E-mail: info@edwardhayes.co.uk
Office: Bognor Regis, Chichester (2 offices), Havant, Littlehampton, London EC2, Worthing
Work: B2 D1 D2 G H J1 K1 K2 K3 M2 N Q S2 Z(l,q,r,w)
Emergency Action, Agency, Advocacy and Legal Aid Franchise
Ptr: Ambridge, Mr Grant ★ . . . *Dec 2002
French, Mr Mark Sean BA(Hons) ★ . . . *Jun 1999
Hayes, Mr Christopher Charles Edward LLB(Hons) ★ . *Dec 1991
Long, Mr Charles Ian LLB ★ . . . *Jun 2003
Patel, Yogesh BSc(Hons) ★ . . . Apr 1992
Ast: Dew, Mrs Stephanie LLB(Hons) . . . Sep 2009
Hitschmann, Miss Ruth . . . Oct 2006
Shaffron, Miss Amy . . . May 2011

HAYES LAW LLP
1 Lyric Square London W6 0NB
Tel: 020 3159 4248 ***Fax:*** 020 3159 4091
Dx: 46767 HAMMERSMITH 3
E-mail: info@hayeslaw.co.uk
Office: Eastleigh

HAYNES & CO ‡
10 Barley Mow Passage London W4 4PH
Tel: 020 8987 6076 ***Fax:*** 020 8994 1533
E-mail: info@haynesco.net
List of partners: M A Haynes
Work: B1 C1 K1 O Q W
SPr: Haynes, Mr Michael A LLB(Bris) . . . *Jul 1975

HAYNES ORME ‡
3 Bolt Court London EC4A 3DQ
Tel: 020 7356 0990 ***Fax:*** 020 7936 2237
Dx: 423 LONDON/CHANCERY LN
E-mail: enquiries@haynesorme.com

HAZELWOODS ‡
4th Floor Temple Chambers 3-7 Temple Avenue London EC4Y 0DT
Tel: 020 7936 4844 ***Fax:*** 020 7183 5272
Dx: 266 LONDON/CHANCERY LN

HEADD SOLICITORS ‡
84 Chester Road Tottenham London N17 6BZ
Tel: 020 7566 8244
List of partners: B Headd
SPr: Headd, Mr B . . . Sep 2010

HEALYS LLP ‡
76 Shoe Lane London EC4A 3JB
Tel: 020 7822 4000 ***Fax:*** 020 7822 4100 ***Dx:*** 1021 CHANCERY LANE

List of partners: J D Austen-Jones, C Christofi, M S Davies, N Evans, C Green, J A Healy, J Jacobs, R Johnson, K Papantoniou, M K Pattihis, D E Skinner, N J Taylor
Office: Brighton
Ptr: Christofi, Mr Christopher BA(Law) *Jun 1992
Davies, Mr Mark S BA *Feb 1990
Evans, Mr Nicholas BA(Hons)(Law) *Apr 1993
Green, Mr Charles *Aug 2004
Jacobs, Mr James-Guy LLB *Dec 1993
Johnson, Mr Robert *Mar 1990
Papantoniou, Mr Kyri *Sep 2004
Pattihis, Marios K *Nov 1980
Asoc: Wilson, Miss Carolyn Marie LLB; LPC *Oct 2002
Ast: Islam-Syed, Mrs Nazneen Farah LLB(Hons) Jun 2007
McLean, Miss Kerry LLB Jan 2010
Milne, Mr James David Paul *Sep 2008
Winslow, Mr Daniel Oct 2010
Con: D'Costa, Mr Savio BA(Hons)(Law) *Jun 1986
Stirling, Ms Julia BA Aug 1999
Ward, Mr Gary David Jul 2001

WILLIAM J HEARD ‡
1-3 College Hill London EC4R 2RA
Tel: 020 7329 7370 ***Fax:*** 020 7329 7380
E-mail: wjh@williamjheard.com

WILLIAM HEATH & CO ‡
16 Sale Place Sussex Gardens Westminster London W2 1PX
Tel: 020 7402 3151 ***Fax:*** 020 7402 0373 ***Dx:*** 38750 PADDINGTON
List of partners: F R Abbott, D M Fleming, D M Fleming, G Lack, E R Lee, H S Sangha, J A Sidnick, J Willsher
Office: London SW11
Languages: Arabic, French, German, Hindi, Punjabi, Serbo-Croat
Work: A1 B1 C1 C2 E F1 J1 K1 L N O Q R1 R2 S1 T1 T2 W Z(c,k,l,q)
Ptr: Fleming, Mr David M BA(Oxon) *Sep 1982
Lee, Mr Edwin R LLB *§Sep 1973
Sangha, Harbinder S LLB *Apr 1989
Sidnick, Mr Justin A LLB R G Lawson Prize *Nov 1997

WILLIAM HEATH & CO
77-79 St Johns Road Clapham Junction London SW11 1QZ
Tel: 020 7350 1068 ***Fax:*** 020 7228 5178 ***Dx:*** 38107 CLAPHAM 2
Office: London W2
Ptr: Abbott, Mr Francis R BA(Oxon) Mar 1975
Fleming, Mr David M BA(Oxon) Oct 1980
Lack, Miss Gaia Feb 2005
Willsher, Mr Jonathan Oct 2004
Ast: Sabaa, Fayruz Jan 2007

HEATHER MAINS & CO ‡
Daws House 33-35 Daws Lane Mill Hill London NW7 4SD
Tel: 020 8906 6660 ***Fax:*** 020 8906 6612 ***Dx:*** 51373 MILL HILL
E-mail: bela@hmains.co.uk
List of partners: B Patel
Languages: Bengali, Gujarati
Work: C1 E F1 J1 K1 L O Q R1 S1 S2 W Z(e,l)
Emergency Action, Agency and Fixed Fee Interview undertaken
Ptr: Patel, Mrs Bela LLB(Hons) *Jan 1989
Con: Mukherjee, Ms Debjani BSc(Hons); MSc *Oct 1992

HEATHER THOMAS CONSULTING ‡
5 Lambert Jones Mews Barbican London EC2Y 8DP
Tel: 020 7588 0686 ***Fax:*** 020 7638 4368
E-mail: ht@ht-consulting.co.uk

HEMPSONS ‡
40 Villiers Street Westminster London WC2N 6NJ
Tel: 020 7839 0278 ***Fax:*** 020 7839 8212
Dx: 138411 CHARING CROSS 1
E-mail: enquiries@hempsons.co.uk
List of partners: L M Abbess, C J Alderson, J E Austin, A P Ball, J C Barber, S B Bennett, K E Blohm, J Bullbrook, A Callaghan, A E D'Arcy, J D Dollimore, P Donaldson, J Donnison, S P Evans, C Farrer, F A Harrison, A K Hartrick, C J Z Harvey, I D Hempseed, J C Holmes, M L Holroyd, C Hugh-Jones, R Kneale, I A Lazonby, G J Lea, W A Leason, M A M S Leigh, W J M Lovel, A Meadowcroft, C D N Morris, R Morris, A B Parker, D Roberts, M A Shaw, M Taylor, F Wilson, K J Wilson
Office: Harrogate, Manchester, Newcastle upon Tyne
Languages: French, German, Spanish
Work: B1 B2 C1 D1 E F1 I J1 L N P Q R2 S2 W Z(c,d,e,h,j,k,m,p,q,r)
Emergency Action, Agency and Advocacy undertaken
Ptr: Abbess, Miss Lynne M BA *Nov 1982
Austin, Miss Julie E BSc(Soton) *Mar 1985
Barber, Mrs Janice C BA *Nov 1983
Dollimore, Ms Jean Diana Nov 1972
Farrer, Mr Charles Jan 1974
Harvey, Miss C J Zoe LLB *Apr 1979
Hempseed, Mr Ian Drysdale BA(Oxon) *Dec 1985
Holmes, Mr John C LLB ♦ *Nov 1984
Kneale, Ms Rachel LLB(with French Law) Oct 1995
Lea, Mr Graham John LLB Nov 1987
Leigh, Mr Mark A M S BA *§Jun 1976
Morris, Mr Christopher D N BDS; LLM *Nov 1993
Shaw, Mr Mark A LLB ♦ *Oct 1989
Wilson, Miss Fiona BA(Hons)(French) *Nov 1990
Ast: Ball, Mr Matthew Keneric James BSc(Hons); CPE; LPC Nov 1999
Donoghue, Mr Martin D LLB(Hons) *Oct 1990
East, Mr Nathan LLB; LLM Sweet & Maxwell Law Prize 1998; Clyde & Co Prize 1997 Mar 2002
Hynes, Miss Susan A MA(Oxon) *Dec 1993
Michie, Ms Isobel Jane BSc Sep 1994
Wolferstan, Miss Nadya LLB; MA *Oct 2000
Con: King, Miss Hilary J BSocSc *Oct 1987

HENNEBERRY & CO ‡
206a Willesden Lane London NW6 7PR
Tel: 020 8830 1907
List of partners: G A Craig
Work: C1 E F1 G J1 K1 L N P S1 W Z(i)
Emergency Action, Agency and Advocacy undertaken
Ptr: Craig, Mr Glenn Alexander BA; DMS ● *May 1994

HENRY HUGHES & HUGHES ‡
The Beehive Coffee Tavern 496 High Road Streatham London SW16 3QB
Tel: 020 8765 2700 ***Fax:*** 020 8765 2727 ***Dx:*** 58464 NORBURY
E-mail: law@henry-hughes.co.uk
List of partners: M J Blackburn, B K Hughes, M Q H Hughes
Languages: French, German, Greek, Spanish, Welsh
Work: C1 E L R1 S1 T1 W Z(b,d,h,l,m)
Ptr: Blackburn, Miss Melanie J LLB Jan 1990
Hughes, Mr Benedict K BA(Nott'm) *§Mar 1987
Hughes, Mr Mark Q H LLB(Nott'm) *§Dec 1979
Ast: Duncan, Ms Claire LLM May 2002
Janalli-Brown, Ms Esther LLB Sep 2003
Le Riche, Ms Christina LLB Nov 2004
Con: Edwards, Mr Christopher John LLB Jul 1980
McGuire, Mr Spencer Paul Oct 1996

HENSCOTT SOLICITORS ‡
413 Chingford Road London E17 5AF
Tel: 0870 880 0007 ***Fax:*** 0870 880 0006
Dx: 32049 WALTHAMSTOW
Emergency telephone 0870 880 0007
E-mail: solicitor@henscott.co.uk
List of partners: H Benson, E Umenyilora
Work: G H
Agency, Advocacy and Legal Aid undertaken
Ptr: Benson, Ms Harriet LLB(Hons) *May 1999
Umenyilora, Miss Emi LLB(Hons) *May 1999
Ast: Naidu, Mr Gokeda LLB(Hons) *Mar 2002

HEPBURNS ‡
Unit 1 Blackwater Court 17-21 Blackwater Street London SE22 8SD
Tel: 020 8299 3376 ***Fax:*** 020 8693 8673 ***Dx:*** 32158 EAST DULWICH
List of partners: N J Harper, M J Harrison, G Hunter
Agency, Advocacy and Legal Aid undertaken
Ptr: Harper, Mr Nicholas J BA(Law); MA *Oct 1980
Harrison, Mr Malcolm J LLB(Leics) *§Jan 1981
Hunter, Mr Gary BA Jun 1984

HERBERT REEVES & CO ‡
44 Great Eastern Street London EC2A 3EP
Tel: 020 7739 6660 ***Fax:*** 020 7739 1052 ***Dx:*** 36617 FINSBURY
E-mail: kerri.blake@herbert-reeves.co.uk
List of partners: K N Jay, M Kennedy, P E Summers
Work: E J1 K1 L S2 W Z(e,f,w)
Ptr: Summers, Mr Paul Edward Oct 2000
Jay, Mr Kieran Nicholas LLB *Oct 1996
Kennedy, Mr Michael *Jun 1966

HERBERT SMITH LLP ‡
Exchange House Primrose Street London EC2A 2HS
Tel: 020 7374 8000 ***Fax:*** 020 7374 0888 ***Dx:*** 28 LONDON/CITY
E-mail: enquiries@herbertsmith.com
List of partners: D M Albagli, M C Asmar, A Bafi, J Baily, M J Bakes, C Band, C D Barnard, J C Barnes, S E Black, M Bonye, A M Brown, A Brown, D Brynmor-Thomas, P Burrell, S J Bushell, D Byrne-Hill, A J Calderwood, P M Carrington, S Chadney, A Cheng, S Clarke, A J Clough, S Cochrane, J Copeman, I J Cox, J J G D'Agostino, J H Davey, G Davies, M E Davis, M J Dawbney, A M Deeth, A D R Dempster, N P Downing, A S Dymond, P D Ellerman, L Elliott, N Elverston, G A Fairfield, C J Fanner, J R Farr, N J Farr, J T H Farrell, E Fergusson, C Fielding, R J H Fleck, R Forsdyke, C Foster, J J Fox, L Freestone, P J Frost, S Gale, N J Gardner, I T Gault, M Geday, J A Geraghty, H Gething, D L Gold, C M H Goodall, E P Greeno, P J Griffin, A Hale, S C Hancock, C Haynes, D Hill, M Hitching, P Hodges, G Hommel, M J Hopper, C B P Howarth, M Howie, D Hudson, M A Ife, J Jackaman, A M Johnson, A Kay, C I Kehoe, A E Levin, A J Levitt, P Lewis, R M Lewis, R Lewis, S V Leydecker, A W Lidbetter, K F Lloyd, A M Lloyd-Williams, T London, P W Long, A D Macaulay, G C Maddock, R Martin, D W Mayhew, S McKibbin, E S McKnight, J Milne, G Milner-Moore, N P Mitchell, A Moir, A Montgomery, D M J Moore, S Moore, R Morton, G Mulley, H Murray, S Murray, H Nahal, A Newbery, M Newbery, A Oddy, J S Ogilvie, J E Palmer, T C Parkes, C J H Parsons, D S Paterson, S Paterson, N Peacock, W Pearce, A C Pertoldi, B S Phillips, J Pollock, A Pretorius, S J Price, K Pullen, J Pyke, J M Quinney, H B Raine, C W Rees, D C Reston, A M T Rich, G J Roberts, K Roberts, V Roberts, P C Robinson, D Rosen, I A Rothnie, D Rowlands, J W Scott, M D Shaw, M R Shillito, C M Shutkever, J B Smith, T J Steadman, A Taggart, P S Talboys, C Tevendale, N P Tott, T Tun, M M Turner, N Turner, T W Turtle, C Wake, J Walden, M Walter, B M Ward, N Warriner, H J Watson, A T Watts, M Weiniger, J Wickenden, S C Wilkinson, D A Willis, C A Wilson, S Wisking, D A Wyles, S Youdale, I Zailer, N Zar
Languages: Afrikaans, Arabic, Cantonese, Chinese, Danish, Dutch, Farsi, French, German, Greek, Gujarati, Hebrew, Hindi, Italian, Japanese, Malay, Mandarin, Norwegian, Polish, Portuguese, Punjabi, Russian, Spanish, Swedish, Turkish, Urdu
Work: A3 B1 B2 B3 C1 C2 C3 E F1 F2 I J1 L M1 M2 N O P Q R1 R2 S1 S2 T1 U1 W Z(b,c,d,e,f,h,j,k,n,o,p,q,r,s,u,w)
Emergency Action, Agency, Advocacy and Fixed Fee Interview undertaken
Ptr: Albagli, Miss Dina M LLB(Lond); Maitrise en Droit(Paris) Sep 1987
Asmar, Ms Martina C LLB(B'ham) *Sep 1988
Bafi, Mr Alexander Oct 1994
Baily, Mr James Mar 2000
Bakes, Mr Martin J MA(Cantab) *Apr 1980
Band, Ms Christa BCL(Oxon); MA(Cantab) ● *May 1993
Barnard, Mr Clive D MA(Cantab) *Oct 1984
Barnes, Mr James C LLB(Belfast) *Nov 1980
Black, Ms Susan E LLB(Exon) *Oct 1990
Bonye, Mr Matthew BA(Bris) ♦ *Nov 1994
Brown, Mr Andrew BA(Oxon) *May 1992
Brown, Miss Alison M LLB(Lond) Sep 1993
Brynmor-Thomas, Mr David MB; ChB(Edin) *Oct 1993
Burrell, Mr Peter BA(Cantab) *Oct 1993
Bushell, Mr Simon J LLB(B'ham) *Nov 1989
Byrne-Hill, Mr Damien LLB(Cantab) *Oct 1993
Calderwood, Mr Andrew J BA; LLB *Feb 1983
Carrington, Mr Philip M LLB(Bris) *Oct 1982
Chadney, Mr Simon Sep 1997
Cheng, Mr Adrian Jul 1996
Clarke, Mr Simon BA(Oxon) Mar 1998
Clough, Mr Adrian J MA(Oxon) *Oct 1988
Cochrane, Mr Scott BA(Hons) Dec 1995
Copeman, Mr Julian BA(Cantab) Nov 1994
Cox, Mr Ian J LLB(Exon) *Sep 1989
D'Agostino, Mr Justin John Gaetano Sep 2000
Davey, Mr J Henry MA(Cantab) Nov 1988
Davies, Mr Gavin BA(Cantab) *Nov 1994
Davis, Mr Michael E BA(Lond) *Dec 1977
Dawbney, Mr Martin J LLB(Glasgow) *Jun 1984
Deeth, Ms Alison Maree Mar 2001
Dempster, Mr Anthony D R LLB(Lond) *Oct 1988
Downing, Mr Nicholas P LLB *Oct 1986
Dymond, Mr Anthony Simon Feb 2004
Ellerman, Mr Paul D *Feb 1993
Elliott, Mr Laurence Oct 1993
Elverston, Mr Nick Nov 1993
Fairfield, Ms Gillian Amanda Mar 1999
Fanner, Mr Christopher J BA(Cantab); MA Scholarship Cambridge University *Jul 1990
Farr, Mr John R LLB(Lond) *May 1974
Farr, Mr Nigel J MA(Cantab) *Oct 1987
Farrell, Mr James Thomas Hugh MA Oct 1992
Fergusson, Mr Ewen BA(Oxon) *Dec 1993
Fielding, Ms Clare Nov 2000
Fleck, Mr Richard J H LLB(Soton) *Jul 1973
Forsdyke, Mr Richard BA(Cantab) Mar 1994
Foster, Mr Christopher LLB(Lond) *May 1995
Fox, Mr Jason J LLB(Lond) *Nov 1987
Freestone, Ms Louise Oct 1994
Frost, Mr Peter J MA(Cantab) *Oct 1985
Gale, Mr Stephen LLB *Oct 1982
Gardner, Mr Nicholas J LLB(Nott'm) ♦ *Nov 1988
Gault, Mr Ian T BA(Cantab) *Mar 1977
Geday, Mr Mark LLB(Manc) *Nov 1993
Geraghty, Mr John Andrew Sep 2001
Gething, Miss Heather BA(L'pool) *Mar 1983
Gold, Mr David L LLB(Lond) *Dec 1975
Goodall, Miss Caroline M H MA(Cantab) *Apr 1980
Greeno, Mr Edward P LLB(Lond) *Nov 1983
Griffin, Mr Paul J LLB *Nov 1981
Hale, Amanda Apr 1995
Hancock, Mr Stephen C LLB(Sheff) *Oct 1980
Haynes, Mr Christopher Sep 1995
Hill, Mr Derek Nov 1997
Hitching, Mr Malcolm *Oct 1998
Hodges, Ms Paula MA(Cantab) *Nov 1989
Hommel, Mr Gary LLB(Bris) *Nov 1993
Hopper, Mr Martyn John Nov 2004
Howarth, Mr Charles Bernard Paul Nov 1992
Howie, Ms Michelle BA(Cantab) *Apr 1993
Hudson, Mr Daniel Jul 2004
Ife, Mr Mark Andrew Sep 2000
Jackaman, Mr Jake Mar 1994
Johnson, Mr Adam M MA(Cantab) *Oct 1990
Kay, Mr Alexander Sep 1997
Kehoe, Mrs Caroline I LLB(Manc) *Oct 1985
Levin, Mrs Ann E LLB(Leeds) *Oct 1982
Levitt, Mr Adam J MA(Oxon) Apr 1991
Lewis, Mr Paul LLB *Mar 1994
Lewis, Mr Rupert Sep 2001
Lewis, Mr Richard M MA(Oxon) *Nov 1989
Leydecker, Miss Sonya V BA(Manc) *Mar 1984
Lidbetter, Mr Andrew W BCL; MA(Oxon) *Oct 1990
Lloyd, Mr Kevin F LLB(Lond); LLM(Cantab) *Apr 1980
Lloyd-Williams, Mr A Mark MA(Cantab) Nov 1982
London, Ms Tracey Feb 2001
Long, Mr Peter W MA(Cantab) *Mar 1985
Macaulay, Mr Anthony D BA(Oxon) Charles Steele; City of London Solicitors' Co Prizes *Dec 1974
McKibbin, Ms Shelagh LLB(B'ham) *Nov 1984
McKnight, Ms Elizabeth S BA; LLB(Oxon) *Feb 1988
Maddock, Mr Geoffrey C MA(Cantab) *Oct 1990
Martin, Mr Roderick Nov 1995
Mayhew, Mr David W BA; LLB(Otago) ♦ *Sep 1983
Milne, Mr James BA(Cantab) Mar 1997
Milner-Moore, Mr Gary LLM(Harv) Sep 1997
Mitchell, Mr N Patrick BA(Cantab) *Nov 1988
Moir, Mr Andrew Mar 2003
Montgomery, Mr Alan Sep 1998
Moore, Mr David Matthew John MA Dec 1992
Moore, Mr Sebastian Sep 1999
Morton, Mr Roderick Nov 1995
Mulley, Mr Gregory Mar 1999
Murray, Mr Howard BA(Cantab); MA Oct 1993
Murray, Mr Stephen Oct 1993
Nahal, Hardeep BA; LLM(Cantab) ♦ Nov 1994
Newbery, Mr Andrew Jun 1994
Newbery, Mr Mark LLB(Nott'm) *Oct 1982
Oddy, Mr Alex BA(Cantab) Mar 1997
Ogilvie, Mr John S BA(Kent) *Oct 1986
Palmer, Mr James Edwin MA(Cantab) *Oct 1988
Parkes, Mr Timothy C BA(Oxon) *Mar 1980
Parsons, Mr Christopher J H LLB(Cardiff) *Oct 1986
Paterson, Mr David Scott BA(Oxon) *Oct 1988
Paterson, Mr Stuart Mar 2000
Peacock, Mr Nicholas Sep 1999
Pearce, Mr William Sep 1998
Pertoldi, Miss Anna C LLB(Bris) *Nov 1988
Phillips, Mr Bradley Spencer LLB(Soton); LLM(Lond) *Nov 1991
Pollock, Mr Julian BA(Dunelm) Oct 1996
Pretorius, Mr Andrew Mar 2003
Price, Mr Simon James Sep 1998
Pullen, Mr Kevin LLB Oct 1990
Pyke, Ms Julia BA(Cantab) *Apr 1994
Quinney, Mr James Matthew BA(Oxon) May 1993
Raine, Mr Henry B BA(Oxon) *Oct 1984
Rees, Mr Christopher W MA(Cantab) Herbert Ruse Prize Apr 1979
Reston, Mr David C LLB(B'ham) Judge Jellinek Prize *Oct 1983
Rich, Mr Andrew M T BSc(L'pool) *Oct 1989
Roberts, Mr Gareth J MA(Cantab) *Oct 1985
Roberts, Ms Kristen Sep 1999
Roberts, Ms Veronica May 1997
Robinson, Mr Patrick C LLB Legal Associate of the Royal Town Planning Institute *Feb 1989
Rosen, Mr David Sep 2002
Rothnie, Mr Iain A MA(Cantab) *Oct 1981
Rowlands, Mr Donald Apr 1996
Scott, Mr Jonathan W MA(Cantab) Sep 1981
Shaw, Mr Michael D BA(Cantab) *May 1990
Shillito, Mr Mark Robert LLB(Lond) *Oct 1989
Shutkever, Ms Carol M BA(Cantab) *Oct 1987
Smith, Mr Joel Benjamin LLB(Cantab) Nov 1996
Steadman, Mr Timothy James LLB(Nott'm) *Nov 1986
Taggart, Mr Andrew BA Nov 1995
Talboys, Mr Philip S BA(Oxon) *Apr 1992
Tevendale, Mr Craig Sep 2001
Tott, Mr Nicholas Peter LLB(Edin) *Aug 1991
Tun, Thiha Oct 1997
Turner, Mr Mark McDougall BA(Oxon) Exhibitioner University College *Apr 1983
Turner, Mr Nicholas BA(Oxon) Nov 1996
Turtle, Mr Trevor W BA; LLB(Cantab) *Apr 1978
Wake, Cecile Apr 2003
Walden, Mr Jeremy LLB(Lond) *Nov 1994
Walter, Mr Michael MA(Cantab) *Oct 1981
Ward, Mr Benjamin M BA(Cantab) *Jun 1992
Warriner, Mr Neil MA(Oxon) *Oct 1987

See p2 for the Key to Work Categories & other symbols

Watson, Mr Howard J LLB(Nott'm) . . . *Oct 1991
Watts, Mr Alan T LLB(Lond). . . . *Dec 1990
Weiniger, Mr Matthew BA(Cantab) . . . Nov 1996
Wickenden, Mr James . . . Jan 1990
Wilkinson, Mr Stephen C BA; LLB(Durham) . . . *Nov 1989
Willis, Mr David A BA(Oxon) . . . *Oct 1983
Wilson, Miss Clare A LLB(Manc) . . . *Nov 1989
Wisking, Mr Stephen ♦ . . . Dec 1990
Wyles, Mr David A LLB(Lond). . . . *Oct 1989
Youdale, Mr Simon BA(York) . . . Nov 1996
Zailer, Mr Isaac. . . . Oct 1997
Zar, Nusrat . . . Oct 1997

HEREFORDS SOLICITORS LIMITED ‡
Floor 1 26 Hereford Road London W2 4AA
Tel: 020 7221 3180 *Fax:* 020 7221 3180
E-mail: enquiries@herefordssolicitors.co.uk

HEREWARD & FOSTER ‡
145 Barking Road Canning Town London E16 4HQ
Tel: 020 7476 6600 *Fax:* 020 7476 2032
Dx: 52400 CANNING TOWN
List of partners: D G Adler, S Lerner, C J Wilson
Languages: French, Urdu
Work: B1 D1 E F1 G H J1 K1 L M1 P R1 S1 V W Z(c,d,i,k,l,m,p,s)
Emergency Action, Agency, Advocacy, Legal Aid undertaken, Legal Aid Franchise and Member of Accident Line
Ptr: Adler, Ms Deborah G BA . . . *Feb 1986
Lerner, Ms Sarah BSc. . . . *Jan 1983
Wilson, Mr Christopher J . . . Dec 1987

HERSI & CO SOLICITORS ‡
Trafalgar House Grenville Place Mill Hill London NW7 3SA
Tel: 020 8906 7795

G M HEWETT SOLICITOR ‡
PO Box 62458 London E16 9AH
Tel: 020 7476 2544 *Fax:* 020 7511 7813
E-mail: info@gmhewettsolicitor.com

HEXTALLS ‡
(in association with Clousen Miller(USA); La Giroudiere Larroze & Associes(France))
33 Throgmorton Street London EC2N 2BR
Tel: 020 7382 0700 *Fax:* 020 7382 0729
E-mail: info@hextalls.com
List of partners: A P Cornforth, A R W Deans, D W Hadfield, D R Haydon, A C Nathan, A R Sita-Lumsden, S G White
Languages: French, German, Portuguese
Work: A3 C1 E J1 J2 K1 L M1 M2 N O P Q S1 S2 T1 T2 W Z(c,j,p,q,w)
Agency undertaken
Ptr: Cornforth, Mr Alastair P LLB(Hons)(Lond). . . . *Oct 1977
Deans, Mr Andrew R W LLB(Bris). . . . *Oct 1980
Hadfield, Mr David W MA; PhD . . . *§Dec 1988
Haydon, Mrs Davina R LLB . . . *§Nov 1990
Nathan, Mr Andrew C. . . . *§Dec 1984
Sita-Lumsden, Mrs Anne R BEd(Lond) . . . *Nov 1989
White, Mr Stuart G MA(Oxon). . . . *§Feb 1984

HEXTALLS LIMITED ‡
28 Leman Street London E1 8ER
Tel: 020 7488 1224 *Fax:* 020 7481 0232 *Dx:* 562 CITY

HICKMAN & ROSE ‡
214 High Road London N15 4NP
Tel: 020 7700 2211 *Fax:* 020 7253 1367
Emergency telephone 07659 138106
E-mail: mail@hickmanandrose.co.uk
Languages: Hebrew
Work: G H Z(g,i,m)
Emergency Action, Agency, Advocacy, Legal Aid undertaken and Legal Aid Franchise

KATHRYN HICKMOTT ‡
39 Duke Avenue London W4 2AA
Tel: 020 8995 6194

HIERONS ‡
2 Chester Row London SW1W 9JH
Tel: 020 3328 4510 *Fax:* 020 7730 5214
E-mail: rh@hieronslaw.com

HIGHGATE HILL SOLICITORS ‡
98 Dresdon Road London N19 3BQ
Tel: 020 8804 9412

CHARLES HILL & CO SOLICITORS ‡
7-13 Camberwell Road London SE5 0EX
Tel: 020 7525 6630

HILL DICKINSON LLP
Irongate House 22-30 Duke's Place London EC3A 7HX
Tel: 020 7283 9033 *Fax:* 020 7283 1144 *Dx:* 550 LONDON/CITY
E-mail: law@hilldickinson.com
Office: Chester, Liverpool, Manchester, Sheffield
Languages: Cantonese, Danish, French, German, Italian, Latin, Norwegian, Portuguese, Spanish, Swedish, Welsh
Work: A1 A3 B1 B2 B3 C1 C2 C3 D1 D2 E F1 F2 G H I J1 J2 K1 K2 L M1 M2 M3 N O P Q R1 R2 S1 S2 T1 T2 U1 U2 V W X Z(a,b,c,d,e,f,g,h,i,j,k,l,m,o,p,q,r,t,u,w,x,y,z)
Emergency Action, Agency, Advocacy, Fixed Fee Interview, Legal Aid undertaken, Legal Aid Franchise and Member of Accident Line
Ptr: Allen, Mr Anthony C LLB; Cert Higher European Studies(Bruges) . . . *Jan 1985
Armstrong, Mr Stuart A LLB(Soton) . . . *Jan 1983
Ayres, Miss Kate E . . . *Oct 1996
Baucher, Mrs Heather A LLB . . . *Nov 1986
Caddies, Mr Andrew J LLB . . . *Oct 1990
Cheyney, Mr Edwin Charles LLB . . . *Oct 1985
Clift, Mr N Rhys LLB; Desu (Aix-Marseille) Alfred Syrett Prize . . . *Oct 1983
D'Costa, Mr Phillip BA(Hons)(Law) . . . Jan 1997
Entwistle, Mr Malcolm G LLB . . . *Apr 1979
Gardner, Mr Russell St J MA(Oxon). . . . Oct 1984
Godfrey, Mr David N LLB(Bris) . . . *Jun 1968
Goldsmith, Mr Anthony James LLB . . . *Nov 1995
Haddon, Mr Philip. . . . Sep 2001
Hawkins, Mr Patrick H MA(Cantab) Liverpool Law Society Prize 1985 . . . *Dec 1987
Heanley, Mr Robert B. . . . *Nov 1975
Horne, Ms Angela. . . . Nov 1985
Hoyes, Mr David Michael LLB. . . . *Mar 1995
Humphreys, Mr Nicholas . . . Sep 1999
Isaacs, Mr Jeffrey E BA(Cantab) . . . *Oct 1983
Johnson, Mr Andrew BA . . . *§Mar 1984
Lawson, Mr James Edward Stewart LLB . . . *Nov 1995
Mallin, Mr Michael F BSc . . . *Jan 1985
Mavroghonis, Mr Peter Christopher . . . Oct 1997
Monck-Mason, Mr Jamie B R BA(Hons). . . . *Sep 1997
Palmer, Mr Roderick James BA . . . *Nov 1992
Panayotopoulou, Electra . . . Oct 1998
Penny, Mr Martin BA; LLB. . . . Apr 1997
Phillips, Mr D Nicholas . . . *Nov 1977
Pitlarge, Mr David C. . . . Nov 1989
Pittordis, Ms Maria LLB . . . *Dec 1989
Pople, Mr John N LLB(Exon) . . . *§Jun 1975
Pourgourides, Mr Panos Kyriacou. . . . Apr 1996
Speed, Mr Alan W. . . . Oct 1998
Stephenson, Mr Timothy Charles LLB. . . . *§Aug 1990
Taylor, Mr Malcolm R LLB(Leics) . . . *Oct 1982
Taylor, Mr Richard M LLB . . . *Mar 1983
Wallis, Mr Robert H LLB. . . . Dec 1975
Mem: Konynenburg, Mr Fred BA. . . . *Nov 1997
Lucas, Mr C David LLB(Bris) . . . *Nov 1972
Meads, Mr Andrew . . . *Nov 1998
Rabagliati, Mr David McLaren LLB(Wales). . . . *Dec 1975
Asoc: McDonach, Mr Anthony Robert . . . Aug 2000
Marshall, Mr Trevor J LLB. . . . *Dec 1972
Moisidou, Mrs Maria. . . . Mar 1996
Vernon, Mrs Hilary BA. . . . *Jul 1979
Ast: Gay, Mr Robert J BA; MA. . . . *Aug 1998
Lee, Mr Andrew David Robert. . . . May 1989
O'Brien, Mr Paul James LLB . . . *Aug 1999
Prentice, Miss Mary Louise . . . Sep 2004
Con: Hann, Mr Patrick LLB(Lond). . . . Dec 1980

JOSEPH HILL & CO ‡
Bank Chambers 220/224 High Road Tottenham London N15 4AJ
Tel: 020 8880 3535 *Fax:* 020 8801 8404
Dx: 55603 SOUTH TOTTENHAM
Emergency telephone 07831 800401 / 07956 506718
E-mail: josephhillsols@yahoo.co.uk
List of partners: J Hill
Languages: Greek, Mandarin, Punjabi, Urdu
Work: D1 G H K1 N Q Z(i)
Emergency Action, Agency, Advocacy and Legal Aid undertaken
SPr: Hill, Mr Joseph LLB(Hons) . . . Nov 1983
Ast: Georgiou, Mr Phaedon LLB(Hons). . . . Jan 2002
Hayre, Miss Sukhwinder LLB(Hons). . . . *Nov 1995
Jean-Baptiste, Ms Marianne LLB(Hons). . . . Nov 1996
Lymbourides, Miss Constantina LLB. . . . Dec 2001

HILMI + PARTNERS LLP ‡
Audley House 9 North Audley Street London W1K 6ZD
Tel: 020 7659 0340 *Fax:* 020 7659 0341
Dx: 42713 OXFORD CIRCUS NORTH
E-mail: info@hilmipartners.com

HINDLEY & CO ‡
1st Floor Suite 3 Drayton Park London N5 1NU
Tel: 020 7609 1161 *Fax:* 020 7609 1152
E-mail: philip@hindleyimmigration.com
List of partners: P J Hindley
Work: Z(i)
Agency undertaken
SPr: Hindley, Mr Philip Jack BA . . . *Oct 1989

HINDLEY PARSONS KAPOOR ‡
19 Fortis Green London N2 9JN
Tel: 020 8883 0313

S HIRSCH & CO ‡
314 Regents Park Road London N3 2JX
Tel: 020 8371 3284 *Fax:* 020 8346 1036
E-mail: j.stern@shlaw.org.uk

C HOARE & CO ‡
37 Fleet Street London EC4P 4DQ
Tel: 020 7353 4522

HOCKFIELD & CO ‡
41 Reedworth Street Kennington Road Lambeth London SE11 4PQ
Tel: 020 7582 8784 *Fax:* 020 7820 1707 *Dx:* 33252 KENNINGTON
E-mail: mail@hockfield.co.uk
List of partners: J W Garvey, L A Jackson, S E Mossop
Languages: French, German
Work: E L N O Q S1 W Z(h,q)
Emergency Action, Advocacy undertaken and Member of Accident Line
Ptr: Garvey, Mr James W MA . . . *Jan 1983
Jackson, Ms Lucy A BA. . . . *Oct 1983
Mossop, Mrs Sarah Elizabeth MA(Hons)(Cantab); DipLP . . . *Nov 1996
Asoc: McCrone, Mr Michael MA . . . Oct 2004

A predominantly civil litigation practice with considerable experience in the areas of Personal Injury, Professional Negligence and Housing & Landlord & Tenant.

HODDERS ‡
PO Box 344 11 Station Road Harlesden London NW10 4UD
Tel: 020 8965 9862 *Fax:* 020 8965 5803 *Dx:* 57651 HARLESDEN
E-mail: enquiries@hodders.co.uk
List of partners: C Kwaw, K G Rieveley, A S Silva, J M Tompkins
Office: High Wycombe, London NW10, London SW11, Wembley
Languages: Dutch, French, German, Greek, Gujarati, Hindi, Italian, Kanada, Polish, Punjabi, Sinhalese, Spanish
Work: B1 C1 C2 C3 E F1 J1 M1 M2 O P Q R1 S1 S2 T1 T2 W Z(c,e,f,k,l,q)
Emergency Action, Agency, Advocacy, Legal Aid undertaken and Legal Aid Franchise
Ptr: Silva, Mrs Aminta Sherine LLB . . . *Oct 1994
Ast: Kulczykowska, Mrs Dagmara . . . Oct 2004
Con: Hill, Mr Stephen J. . . . *§May 1979
Stokes, Miss Rosemary A LLB . . . *§Oct 1983

HODDERS
50 Station Road Harlesden London NW10 4UA
Tel: 020 8838 1537 *Fax:* 020 8965 7104 *Dx:* 57651 HARLESDEN
E-mail: enquiries@hodders.co.uk
Office: High Wycombe, London NW10, London SW11, Wembley
Languages: Dutch, French, German, Greek, Gujarati, Hindi, Italian, Kanada, Polish, Punjabi, Sinhalese, Spanish
Work: A3 B1 C3 D1 D2 F1 F2 J1 O Q Z(c,f,h)
Emergency Action, Agency and Advocacy undertaken
Ptr: Kwaw, Ms Christina. . . . Oct 1998
Tompkins, Mr James M BA . . . *Nov 1993
Ast: Mitchell, Mr Ian . . . *Jul 2004
Yeowart, Mr Simon . . . Oct 2005
Con: Ward, Mr Robert G BA . . . *Feb 1982

HODDERS
The Old Bank 24 Battersea Park Road Battersea London SW11 4HY
Tel: 020 7720 1647 *Fax:* 020 7498 0571 *Dx:* 121054 BATTERSEA
E-mail: enquiries@hodders.co.uk
Office: High Wycombe, London NW10 (2 offices), Wembley
Languages: Danish, Dutch, French, German, Greek, Gujarati, Hindi, Italian, Kanada, Polish, Punjabi, Sinhalese, Spanish
Work: C1 E L O Q R1 S1 S2 Z(l)
Ptr: Rieveley, Ms Karen G. . . . *Nov 1992
Ast: Brown, Ms Rachael. . . . Dec 2004

HODDERS ‡
186 High Street London NW10 4ST
Tel: 020 8965 9878 *Fax:* 020 8961 5164 *Dx:* 57651 HARLESDEN
E-mail: enquiries@hodders.co.uk

HODGE JONES & ALLEN LLP ‡
180 North Gower Street London NW1 2NB
Tel: 020 7874 8300 *Fax:* 020 7388 2106 *Dx:* 2101 EUSTON
Emergency telephone 07659 111192
E-mail: hja@hja.net
Web: www.hja.net
List of partners: N Ali, P J H Allen, S C Breen, S Caulfield, R Chada, F Chowdhury, J Cockburn, S K Cooper, I Greenidge, F Grossman, T Hales, E L Hall, R C Harris, S Hooke, J Kunwardia, S L Labinjoh, H D Modha, S Noor-Khan, S P O'Loughlin, S Parsloe, V Patel, S Paul, P Reddy, N J Richardson, N Rudston, J Say, P Todd, M Williams
Languages: Arabic, Bengali, Dutch, French, German, Greek, Hindi, Polish, Punjabi, Russian, Spanish, Turkish, Urdu
Work: A3 B2 D1 D2 F2 G H K1 K2 K3 L N O Q W Z(g,p,q,r)
Emergency Action, Agency, Advocacy, Fixed Fee Interview, Legal Aid undertaken, Legal Aid Franchise and Member of Accident Line
Ptr: Ali, Naheed. . . . *Jul 2002
Allen, Mr Patrick J H BA(Oxon) . . . *Dec 1977
Breen, Susan Colette LLB(Hons) . . . *Sep 1991
Caulfield, Mr Sean LPC ★. . . . Sep 2005
Chada, Mr Raj Councillor for the London Borough Camden . . . Oct 1998
Chowdhury, Mrs Farzana LLB; LPC. . . . Jul 2001
Cockburn, Ms Jocelyn BA(Hons); LLM . . . *Jan 1997
Cooper, Sarah Kathryn . . . *Feb 2001
Greenidge, Mr Ian LLB(Hons)(Law & Sociology). . . . Oct 1997
Grossman, Ms Flora BA(Hons) . . . *Nov 1996
Hales, Mr Toby . . . *Jan 2001
Hall, Ms Emma Louise . . . *Aug 1998
Harris, Miss Ruth Caroline ★ . . . Sep 2000
Hooke, Ms Samantha. . . . Sep 2001
Kunwardia, Mr Jayesh LLB(Hons). . . . Aug 2000
Labinjoh, Ms Susie Leonora BSc; DipLaw; LPC MJSS Advisory Board Member . . . Sep 1999
Modha, Miss Hina Dhirajlal LLB. . . . *Aug 2001
Noor-Khan, Mrs Samira BSc(Hons) . . . Sep 2000
O'Loughlin, Mr Simon Patrick . . . Jul 2002
Parsloe, Ms Sally . . . Nov 1987
Patel, Vandana . . . Jul 2003
Paul, Ms Sandra BSc(Hons); CPE; PGDipLaw ★ . . . Sep 2003
Reddy, Miss Pamela LLB . . . Nov 1997
Richardson, Mr Nigel J MA ★. . . . *Nov 1987
Say, Julie ♦. . . . *Jan 1990
Todd, Mr Peter BSc(Hons) Member of the Legal Services Commission Funding Review Committee (London Region) . . . *Oct 1994
Williams, Miss Melanie LLB; LSF . . . *Oct 1995
Rudston, Neville. . . . NSP
Asoc: Fitzpatrick, Mr Daniel . . . Jan 2001
Gadsby, Ms Juliette Karen . . . Oct 1992
Godden, Mr Daniel . . . Mar 2005
Greaves, Mr Timothy Robert ★ . . . Nov 2005
Johnson, Ms Deborah. . . . Sep 2004
Rattan, Anita Devi. . . . Nov 1999
Sahota, Ms Satvir LLB(Hons) . . . *Oct 2005
Sellars, Ms Hannah ♦. . . . Sep 2007
Treloar, Dawn Anne. . . . Oct 2008
Truong, Ms Chun LLB. . . . Oct 2005
Ast: Arunachalam, Miss Ailimarie . . . Oct 1996
Barton, Sasha Victoria . . . May 2009
Bell, Miss Sophie LLB. . . . Oct 2005
Brennan, Sabrina . . . Jul 2011
Britz, Hannah. . . . Sep 2010
Brosnan, Caroline. . . . Sep 2011
Clinch, Lucie . . . Sep 2010
Clyne, Helen . . . Sep 2011
Collins, Caroline. . . . Mar 2011
Davis, Jessica. . . . Nov 2009
Dhanoa, Amoldeep Kaur . . . Nov 2006
Fazaluddin, Siddiq Mohiuddin Mohammed. . . . Oct 2003
Forrest, Mr Lewis . . . Mar 2010
Fry, Joanne Claire. . . . Jul 2008
Gallagher, Claire Maria . . . Feb 2009
Hamann, Ruth . . . Sep 2011
Hilder, Clair. . . . Sep 2011
Ison-Jacques, Leticia Arletta . . . Sep 2009
Jackman, Mr Myles . . . Mar 2008
Jennings, Melissa. . . . Sep 2010
Jones, Mr Edward Daniel Elwyn. . . . Oct 2006
Kainth, Gursharon. . . . Sep 2009
Kirton-Darling, Mr Edward Ingram. . . . Sep 2009
Malik, Perveen Razia . . . Mar 2010
Martin, Mr Leo Charles . . . May 2008
Milligan, Sarah Margaret . . . Mar 2009
Nash, Emma . . . Sep 2008
Roddy, Ms Rosie . . . Sep 2003
Rought-Brooks, Amy Claire . . . Sep 2009
Scott, Alexandra . . . Sep 2011
Sedacca, Natalie . . . Sep 2010
Serwanga, Mrs Grace. . . . Jan 2002
Shariff, Tumana. . . . Jan 2009
Sharma, Miss Angela LLB; LPC. . . . Sep 2008
Smart, Jennifer Anna ★. . . . Sep 2010
Staple, Ms Dawn . . . Jan 2001
Taylor, Tayo. . . . Dec 2002
Thwaites, Ms Anna . . . Sep 2006
Upton, Sara Catherine . . . Sep 2006

Usewicz, Ms Agata BA(Hons) . . . . Sep 2006
Vaughan, Alison . . . . Mar 2010
Wray, Emma . . . . Mar 2009
Wright, Mr Joseph . . . . Jul 2007
Yamin, Shazia . . . . Dec 2010

Established: 1977; Hours: 9:30-5:30. Range of funding: Legal Aid, No Win No Fee, Private. Accreditations include Lexcel, Investor in People, Assoc. of Personal Injury Lawyers, Criminal Defence Service.

HOFFMAN-BOKAEI SOLICITORS ‡
Lithos House 307 Finchley Road London NW3 6EH
Tel: 020 7433 2380 *Fax:* 020 7433 2381
Dx: 38863 SWISS COTTAGE
E-mail: lawyers@hoffman-bokaei.co.uk
Office: London NW7

HOFFMAN-BOKAEI SOLICITORS
Suite 107 Churchill House 120 Bunns Lane London NW7 2AP
Tel: 020 3114 2117 *Fax:* 020 3114 2105
Dx: 38863 SWISS COTTAGE
Office: London NW3

HOGAN & HARTSON ‡
Juxon House 100 St Paul's Churchyard London EC4M 8BU
Tel: 020 7367 0200 *Fax:* 020 7367 0220 *Dx:* 98940 CHEAPSIDE 2

HOGAN LISLE ‡
115 Gloucester Place Westminster London W1U 6JS
Tel: 020 7224 3300 *Fax:* 020 7224 1523 *Dx:* 41730 MARYLEBONE 2
E-mail: hoganlisle@cwcom.net
Work: E I J1 Z(e,i,t)

HOGAN LOVELLS INTERNATIONAL LLP ‡
Atlantic House Holborn Viaduct London EC1A 2FG
Tel: 020 7296 2000 *Fax:* 020 7296 2001
Dx: 57 LONDON/CHANCERY LN
E-mail: enquiry@lovells.com
List of partners: L M Ainsworth, R J Anderson, M Andrews, P Angell, L Angus, Q D R Archer, K S Ashman, C Ashworth, N M Atkins, K Banks, J Bannister, S Bennett, K Booth, H Brannigan, A Briggs, S Bright, J Brittenden, P Brown, R M Brown, S Bryan, D I Buchanan, L Caisley, A P D Carey, C N Cheffings, J N Cole, A N Cooke, J Cooper, M J Cottis, J Craughan, L A Crowley, P A Dacam, M D Davison, A M Dimsdale Gill, M Donald, R Downey, J Doyle, C Dutch, A B Edgar, N Evans, N Feinstein, V Fornasier, S Foster, R Freeman, A Gallagher, M Gallimore, A Gamble, P D Gershuny, J M Gerszt, F P A Giacon, T Goggin, R M Grant, A E Greenough, D A Gregory, C K Grierson, R L Hallam, C Hardman, P Harle, D A Harper, D A Harris, N Heaton, D Hill, S Hill, J R Holland, N Holman, D G T Hudd, K E Hughes, R M Huleatt-James, G P K Huntley, T Ijaz, S Ito, E Jamieson, S Keen, R Kent, R J Kidby, C Kochberg, D Lane, D A Latham, F C Le Grys, R Lewis, H Lyons, N R Macfarlane, T Marshall, M S Matheou, J McDonald, G McGreevy, P McLoughlin, J McMichael, G J McQuater, J L Meltzer, N Mirchandani, A Monks, M Morrison, D J Moss, S Mottershead, K Mulhern, P Mullen, S Nesbitt, J A Newstead, D Norris, C J Norton, P A Oldman, D M C Panambalana, N B Parden, P Parish, A Pearson, C W Rapinet, N P L Read, E H Reid, C Rix, P Robb, C R Robson, J M Samsworth, A W Sanders, M J Seymour, P P Sherrington, G J Sinfield, A D Skipper, E T Slattery, R Spencer, M F Stancombe, D J Sullivan, V Sutcliffe, R Sydenham, A Taylor, M Taylor, P L Taylor, G B Thomas, J G Trotter, R C Tyler, R Tym, R M Ufland, A J Walker, C D Ward, K Watts, P D Watts, A C Welbourn, R Welfare, E C J Wells, T A Whelan, L L Whitewright, A Wood, G B B Yeowart, J T Young, L Zafer
Work: A1 A3 B1 B2 C1 C2 C3 E F1 F2 I J1 J2 M1 M2 M3 M4 N O P Q R1 R2 S2 T1 T2 U1 U2 Z(a,b,c,e,f,g,i,j,k,n,o,p,q,u,w,y,z,za)
Emergency Action undertaken
Ptr: Ainsworth, Miss Lesley M MA(Oxon) . . . . *Oct 1981
Anderson, Mr Robert J BSc(Edin) . . . . *§Dec 1972
Andrews, Mr Matthew . . . . Sep 2000
Angell, Ms Penny BA(Hons) . . . . Oct 1995
Angus, Luci . . . . Mar 2000
Archer, Mr Quentin D R MA; LLM(Cantab) . . . . *Apr 1981
Ashman, Mr Kevin S BA . . . . *§Nov 1983
Ashworth, Mr Christopher LLB(Soton) . . . . *Sep 1979
Atkins, Mr Nicholas M LLB . . . . *Oct 1986
Banks, Ms Katie BA(Hons) . . . . Nov 1994
Bannister, Mr Joe BA; MA . . . . Oct 1987
Bennett, Mr Stephen LLB . . . . Apr 1995
Booth, Ms Kay LLB . . . . Nov 1987
Brannigan, Ms Helen . . . . Dec 1993
Briggs, Mr Andrew MA . . . . Nov 1995
Bright, Miss Suzanne LLB . . . . *§Nov 1994
Brittenden, Mr Jeremy LLB(Hons); BCom . . . . Apr 2000
Brown, Mr Philip . . . . Oct 1993
Brown, Mr Richard Michael MA(Hons) . . . . *Apr 1994
Bryan, Mr Steven BA . . . . Oct 1988
Buchanan, Mr Duncan I LLB . . . . Oct 1990
Caisley, Mr Lawson LLB(Hons) . . . . Apr 1995
Carey, Mr Andrew P D . . . . May 1992
Cheffings, Mr C Nicholas LLB . . . . *Sep 1983
Cole, Mr Jeremy N LLB . . . . Nov 1985
Cooke, Mr Adam N BSc(Dunelm); FRGS . . . . *May 1986
Cooper, Mr John MA(Cantab); ARCM New Inn Prize . *Apr 1979
Cottis, Mr Matthew J BA(Oxon) . . . . *Nov 1987
Craughan, Mr Julian . . . . Sep 2000
Crowley, Mr Laurence A BA(Oxon)(Jurisprudence) . *Oct 1983
Dacam, Mr Paul A LLB . . . . Dec 1988
Davison, Mr Michael D BA(Oxon) . . . . *Sep 1988
Dimsdale Gill, Miss Angela M BA . . . . *Sep 1981
Donald, Mr Mark LLB(Hons) . . . . Sep 1999
Downey, Ms Roberta MA(Hons); MSc . . . . Nov 1994
Doyle, Mr James . . . . Sep 2000
Dutch, Ms Claire . . . . Jul 1998
Edgar, Ailbhe Baranie BA . . . . Nov 1992
Evans, Ms Nicola . . . . May 2001
Feinstein, Ms Naomi LLB . . . . *Oct 1987
Fornasier, Mr Victor LLB; MA . . . . Apr 2000
Foster, Mr Stephen MA . . . . Dec 1989
Freeman, Mr Rod BA; MA . . . . Apr 2001
Gallagher, Mr Andrew LLB . . . . Apr 1996
Gallimore, Mr Michael MA(Cantab) . . . . *Oct 1983
Gamble, Mr Andrew BA . . . . Apr 1978
Gershuny, Mr Philip D BA . . . . *Apr 1985
Gerszt, Mr John M BJuris; LLB(Monash); LLM(Lond) . Oct 1988
Giacon, Mr Francis P A LLB; AKC . . . . *Oct 1982
Goggin, Mr Tim BA . . . . Apr 1996
Grant, Miss Ruth M LLB Samuel Herbert Easterbrook Prize; City of London Solicitors Co Prize; Charles Steele Prize . . . . *Oct 1983
Greenough, Mr Alan E LLB . . . . Oct 1973
Gregory, Mrs Deborah A LLB . . . . Mar 1984
Grierson, Mr Christopher K BA(Dunelm) . . . . *May 1996
Hallam, Mr Robin L MA(Cantab) . . . . Feb 1980
Hardman, Mr Chris LLB(Hons) . . . . Oct 1996
Harle, Mr Philip . . . . Mar 2001
Harper, Mr David A BA(Oxon) . . . . *Oct 1978
Harris, Mr David A LLB(Lond) . . . . *Nov 1979
Heaton, Mr Nicholas BSc . . . . Jan 1996
Hill, Mr Dominic . . . . Mar 1997
Hill, Mr Stuart BA(Hons) . . . . Nov 1993
Holland, Mr Jonathan R LLB(Exon) . . . . *Nov 1988
Holman, Mr Nicholas LLB . . . . Sep 1998
Hudd, Mr David G T BA(Oxon) . . . . Nov 1983
Hughes, Ms Karen E LLB; MPhil(Manc) . . . . *Dec 1991
Huleatt-James, Mr R Mark BA(Rhodes) . . . . *Dec 1976
Huntley, Mr Graham P K BA . . . . *Nov 1986
Ijaz, Tauhid LLB . . . . Apr 1992
Ito, Mr Stephen . . . . Mar 1992
Jamieson, Mr Erik . . . . Mar 2001
Keen, Ms Stephanie BA; MA . . . . Apr 1998
Kent, Ms Rachel . . . . Aug 1997
Kidby, Mr Robert J LLB(Lond) . . . . *Dec 1977
Kochberg, Ms Cary BA ♦ . . . . Apr 1992
Lane, Mr David MA(Cantab) . . . . *Oct 1983
Latham, Mr David A MA; LLM . . . . *Jun 1980
Le Grys, Ms Frances C BA(Oxon) . . . . *Dec 1989
Lewis, Mr Richard BSc(Hons) . . . . Apr 1994
Lyons, Mr Hugh LLB . . . . Sep 1997
McDonald, Mr James LLB(Lond) . . . . *Dec 1993
Macfarlane, Mr Nicholas R BA . . . . *Dec 1977
McGreevy, Ms Gillian LLB . . . . Nov 1994
McLoughlin, Mr Paul . . . . Sep 1999
McMichael, Ms Jessica LLB . . . . Oct 1990
McQuater, Mr Gavin J MA(Cantab) . . . . *Apr 1979
Marshall, Mr Tony MA . . . . Mar 1984
Matheou, Mr Michael S LLB . . . . Nov 1983
Meltzer, Mr John L . . . . Sep 1991
Mirchandani, Mr Neil BA(Oxon) . . . . *Nov 1989
Monks, Ms Andrea . . . . Jan 2003
Morrison, Ms Maegan . . . . Feb 2004
Moss, Mr David J MA(Cantab) . . . . *Apr 1981
Mottershead, Ms Shelley . . . . May 1997
Mulhern, Ms Katherine BA . . . . Sep 2002
Mullen, Mr Paul LLB(Hons) . . . . Mar 1997
Nesbitt, Mr Simon MA . . . . Dec 1994
Newstead, Miss Jacqueline A BA . . . . *Nov 1986
Norris, Mr Daniel . . . . Mar 2000
Norton, Mr Christopher John BA(L'pool) . . . . *Mar 1981
Oldman, Mr Paul A LLB . . . . Apr 1982
Panambalana, Mr Dion M C LLB . . . . *Oct 1986
Parden, Mr Nicholas B LLB(Hons) . . . . Oct 1992
Parish, Mr Philip LLB . . . . Aug 1988
Pearson, Mr Andrew BA . . . . *Sep 1989
Rapinet, Mr Crispin W BA(Hons) . . . . Oct 1990
Read, Mr Nigel P L . . . . Nov 1984
Reid, Miss Emily H BA(Lond) . . . . *Oct 1984
Rix, Mr Charles MA . . . . Nov 1992
Robb, Mr Phillip LLB . . . . Sep 1991
Robson, Mr Charles R . . . . Dec 1989
Samsworth, Mrs Jane M BA . . . . *Dec 1978
Sanders, Mr Andrew W LLB; LLM Associated Law Societies of Wales Prize 1978 . . . . *Dec 1978
Seymour, Mr Michael J LLB(Exon) . . . . *§Oct 1974
Sherrington, Mr Patrick P LLM(Exon) . . . . *Apr 1980
Sinfield, Mr Gregory J MA(Cantab) . . . . *Jul 1989
Skipper, Mr Andrew D BA(Oxon) . . . . Oct 1987
Slattery, Miss Elizabeth T LLB . . . . *Oct 1983
Spencer, Mr Robin . . . . May 1991
Stancombe, Mr Michael F LLB(Lond) . . . . *Mar 1979
Sullivan, Mr David J LLB . . . . Aug 1991
Sutcliffe, Ms Victoria LLB . . . . Nov 1995
Sydenham, Mr Rupert . . . . Nov 1995
Taylor, Mr Andrew . . . . Dec 1995
Taylor, Mr Mark . . . . Mar 1999
Taylor, Mr Peter L MA(Cantab); Barrister of Law . . *May 1989
Thomas, Ms Gillian B . . . . Nov 1992
Trotter, Mr John G BA(Oxon) . . . . *§Aug 1977
Tyler, Mr Richard C MA . . . . Nov 1991
Tym, Mr Roger BA(Hons) . . . . *Mar 1984
Ufland, Mr Richard M MA(Cantab) . . . . *May 1981
Walker, Mr Adrian J . . . . Feb 1992
Ward, Mr Conor Davitt . . . . Sep 1994
Watts, Ms Katherine LLB . . . . *Jul 1988
Watts, Mr Peter D BA . . . . *Oct 1989
Welbourn, Mr Andrew Crompton LLB . . . . *Jan 1994
Welfare, Mr Richard BA . . . . Dec 1996
Wells, Mr E Christian J BA . . . . *Dec 1980
Whelan, Mr Thomas A . . . . Nov 1993
Whitewright, Miss Louise L MA(Oxon); Jurisprudence *Nov 1986
Wood, Mr Alexander . . . . Sep 1999
Yeowart, Mr Geoffrey B B LLB(Soton); LLM(Lond) . . *Apr 1975
Young, Mr John T MA(Cantab) . . . . *Apr 1981
Zafer, Ms Louise LLB(Hons) . . . . Sep 1997

HOLDEN HAIE ‡
Second Floor 71 Burdett Road London E3 4TN
Tel: 020 8983 4130 *Fax:* 020 8983 0386 *Dx:* 55652 BOW
E-mail: holdenhaie@live.co.uk

HOLDING PARSONS ‡
5th Floor Sun Alliance House 2-3 Cursitor Street London EC4A 1NE
Tel: 020 7430 9474

HOLLINGWORTH BISSELL ‡
49 Queen Victoria Street London EC4N 4SA
Tel: 020 7653 1994 *Fax:* 020 7653 1954

HOLMAN COPELAND ‡
112 Hither Green Lane Lewisham London SE13 6QA
Tel: 020 8852 1162 / 8852 2632 *Fax:* 020 8318 9882
Dx: 34359 CATFORD
E-mail: copelandsolicitor@hotmail.com
List of partners: H Copeland
Work: B1 E G H J1 K1 L M1 N P S1 W
Emergency Action, Agency and Advocacy undertaken
Ptr: Copeland, Mr Holman . . . . *Jun 1974

HOLMAN FENWICK WILLAN ‡
Friary Court 65 Crutched Friars London EC3N 2AE
Tel: 020 7264 8000 *Fax:* 020 7264 8888 *Dx:* 1069 LONDON/CITY
Emergency telephone 020 7264 8000
E-mail: holmans@hfw.co.uk
List of partners: R Allcoat, R E Baines, R Balson, A Bandurka, S Blows, M Bowman, D Brookes, H Brown, J Campbell, N Campbell, J Cashman, A Chamberlain, J Clark, S Congdon, R Crump, M Dalby, E Dautlich, P Dean, A Dekany, K Dhir, S Drury, G Eddings, A Feeney, J E Forrester, D France, C Frangeskides, R C A Gogarty, J Gosling, G Gray, G Hardaker, D Honey, R Hopkirk, N Hutton, M Illingworth, A Johnston, A Leir, H Livingstone, C Lowe, R Mabane, J Mackay, A Mackie, M Morrison, C Neame, R Osborne, S Paull, B S Perrott, J Pierce, V Pitroff, D Relf, A Ridings, S Roberts, D Robinson, O Sefton, A Shire, P Smith, T Stephens, C Swart, C Taylor, S Taylor, J Tooker, M Wandless, J Webb, N Wick, R Wilson, A Woolich, P Wordley
Languages: Afrikaans, Arabic, Bengali, Cantonese, Castillian, Czech, Dutch, Farsi, Flemish, French, German, Greek, Hebrew, Hindi, Hungarian, Indonesian, Italian, Japanese, Malay, Mandarin, Norwegian, Polish, Portuguese, Punjabi, Russian, Sinhalese, Spanish, Swedish, Urdu
Work: A3 B1 B2 C1 C2 C3 E I J1 L M1 M2 M3 N O P Q R1 T1 T2 U1 Z(a,b,c,e,j,n,q,s)
Advocacy undertaken
Ptr: Allcoat, Ms Ruth LLB . . . . Nov 1992
Baines, Mr Richard E BA . . . . *Jun 1982
Balson, Mr Roger . . . . Nov 1978
Bandurka, Mr Andrew . . . . Dec 1989
Blows, Mr Simon . . . . Oct 1981
Bowman, Mr Marcus . . . . Dec 1990
Brookes, Mr David . . . . Jan 1997
Brown, Mr Hugh . . . . Jun 1973
Campbell, Mr Jonathan . . . . Feb 1992
Campbell, Mr Noel . . . . Apr 1976
Cashman, Mr James . . . . Sep 1996
Chamberlain, Mr Andrew . . . . Oct 1994
Clark, Mr Julian . . . . Feb 2002
Congdon, Mr Simon . . . . Nov 1987
Crump, Mr Richard . . . . May 1981
Dalby, Mr Martin . . . . Jan 2005
Dautlich, Ms Elinor . . . . Oct 1996
Dean, Mr Paul . . . . Feb 1991
Dekany, Mr Andrew . . . . Dec 1989
Dhir, Kapil . . . . Aug 1994
Drury, Mr Stephen . . . . Nov 1980
Eddings, Mr George . . . . Oct 1983
Feeney, Mr Alistair . . . . Sep 2002
Forrester, Mr John E LLB . . . . Nov 1989
France, Ms Diana MA . . . . *Oct 1988
Frangeskides, Mr Costas . . . . Dec 1994
Gogarty, Mr Rory C A LLM(Lond) . . . . Jun 1992
Gosling, Mr James . . . . May 1980
Gray, Mr Gregory . . . . May 1978
Hardaker, Mr Guy . . . . Oct 1982
Honey, Mr Damian . . . . Nov 1996
Hopkirk, Ms Rebecca . . . . Dec 1992
Hutton, Mr Nicholas . . . . Oct 1981
Illingworth, Mr Matthew . . . . Sep 1997
Johnston, Mr Alistair . . . . Oct 1994
Leir, Mr Andrew . . . . Mar 1993
Livingstone, Mr Hugh . . . . Dec 1985
Lowe, Mr Charles . . . . Nov 1971
Mabane, Mr Richard . . . . May 1995
Mackay, Mr James . . . . Aug 1991
Mackie, Mr Alistair . . . . Aug 1991
Morrison, Mr Mark . . . . Jan 1983
Neame, Mr Craig . . . . Nov 1998
Osborne, Mr Robin . . . . Oct 1979
Paull, Mr Steven . . . . May 1980
Perrott, Mr Brian Sean LLB . . . . Oct 1991
Pierce, Mr Julian . . . . Nov 1980
Pitroff, Ms Vivienne . . . . Dec 1988
Relf, Mr David LLB . . . . Apr 1977
Ridings, Mr Andrew LLB; LLM . . . . *Dec 1993
Roberts, Miss Samantha . . . . Sep 1997
Robinson, Mr David . . . . May 1979
Sefton, Ottilie . . . . Oct 1981
Shire, Mr Adam LLB . . . . Sep 1991
Smith, Mr Peter . . . . Jan 1986
Stephens, Mr Toby . . . . Jun 1999
Swart, Mr Christopher . . . . Dec 1991
Taylor, Mr Christian . . . . Jan 2002
Taylor, Ms Sarah . . . . Sep 1997
Tooker, Jay . . . . Mar 1989
Wandless, Mr Mark . . . . Jan 1986
Webb, Mr Jonathan . . . . Aug 1997
Wick, Mr Nigel . . . . Nov 1993
Wilson, Mr Robert . . . . May 1977
Woolich, Mr Anthony MA(Cantab) . . . . Oct 1987
Wordley, Mr Paul . . . . May 1994

HOLME ROBERTS & OWEN ‡
9th Floor 12-20 Camomile Street London EC3A 7PJ
Tel: 020 7015 0520

HOPKIN MURRAY BESKINE ‡
Tower House 149 Fonthill Road London N4 3HF
Tel: 020 7272 1234 *Fax:* 020 7272 4050
Dx: 57474 FINSBURY PARK
List of partners: S J M Beskine, B T Chataway, L Curtis, B J Hopkin, V M Murray, A Thompson
Work: D1 D2 K1 K2 L
Emergency Action, Agency, Advocacy, Legal Aid undertaken and Legal Aid Franchise
Ptr: Beskine, Ms Sarah J M BSc . . . . *Nov 1989
Chataway, Mr Ben T BA(Hons); Barrister . . . . *Aug 1998
Curtis, Lesley . . . . Dec 1989
Hopkin, Ms Barbara J BA . . . . *Jan 1983
Murray, Ms Valerie M MA(Oxon); DPhil(Oxon); MA(Lond) . . . . *Nov 1981
Thompson, Ms Anne LLB(Hons) . . . . Sep 1993
Ast: Boatswain, Celene . . . . Nov 2003
Roots, Mr Lee Robert . . . . Sep 2000
Sarma, Ms Abarna . . . . Dec 2001
Sherrington, Ms Emma BA(Hons) . . . . Aug 1999
Yao, Ms Sandra Akosua LLB(Hons) . . . . Jun 2001
Zentner, Heike . . . . Jul 2007

HOPKINS & CO ‡
67 Warwick Square London SW1V 2AR
Tel: 020 7808 7744 / 7233 8686 *Fax:* 020 7233 9595
E-mail: bruce@hopkinslaw.co.uk

See p2 for the Key to Work Categories & other symbols

PETER HORADA ‡
81 Cricklewood Broadway Cricklewood London NW2 3JR
Tel: 020 8450 0737 *Fax:* 020 8452 7507 *Dx:* 35356 CRICKLEWOOD
Languages: Portuguese
Work: B1 F1 G H J1 K1 L M1 M2 O Q V W Z(i)
Fixed Fee Interview undertaken
Con: Horada, Mr Peter D. . . . . *Dec 1981

HORN & CO ‡
Gallery 4 The Lloyds Building 12 Leadenhall Street London EC3V 1LP
Tel: 020 7816 5960 *Fax:* 020 7816 5900
E-mail: ben@hornandco.co.uk

HORNBY & LEVY ‡
411a Brixton Road London SW9 7DG
Tel: 020 7737 0909 *Fax:* 020 7274 0886 *Dx:* 58755 BRIXTON
Emergency telephone 020 7737 2382
List of partners: S D Gibbs, S V Isaacs, S K Kumar, L Verity
Languages: French, German, Italian, Punjabi, Urdu
Work: D1 D2 K1
Emergency Action, Agency, Advocacy, Legal Aid undertaken and Legal Aid Franchise
Ptr: Gibbs, Miss Sonya Dianne . . . . *Aug 1994
Isaacs, Miss Sephona V LLB . . . . *Jul 1989
Kumar, Santosh K LLB . . . . *Sep 1990
Verity, Miss Lucy . . . . *Oct 1995
Con: Hornby, Mrs Simonetta G A Dr Jur(Palermo) . . . . . *Sep 1977
Sadd, Ms Corraine MA(Oxon). . . . . *Jun 1978

HORSEY LIGHTLY
Devon House 12-15 Dartmouth Street Queen Anne's Gate Westminster London SW1H 9BL
Tel: 020 7222 8844 *Fax:* 020 7222 4123 *Dx:* 2311 VICTORIA 1
Emergency telephone 020 7732 6000
E-mail: lon@horseylightly.com
Office: Newbury
Languages: French, German, Italian, Polish, Spanish
Work: A1 B1 C1 C2 D1 D2 E F1 F2 J1 K1 L M1 N O P Q R1 R2 S1 S2 T1 T2 V W X Z(d,e,j,l,n,p,q,r)
Emergency Action, Agency, Advocacy undertaken and Member of Accident Line
Ptr: Brooks, Mr Peter . . . . *Jul 1974
Devlin, Mr Anthony J M LLB. . . . . *Jun 1980
Fitzgibbon, Mr Jeremy. . . . . Jan 1988
Popham, Mr Christopher F J LLB(Soton) . . . . . . *§Jun 1976
Reed, Mr Simon. . . . . Jan 1974
Asoc: Larke, Mr James . . . . Jan 2001
Ast: Farndon, Miss Claudie Joelle Carrington LLB . . . . . May 2010
Con: Fletcher, Miss Vicky. . . . . *Jan 1997
Fox, Mr John A . . . . *§Nov 1973
Meyer, Mr Alan . . . . Jan 1959
Plaut, Mr Nicholas David Forbes . . . . §Jun 1974

HORWICH COHEN COGHLAN
1 Creed Court 5 Ludgate Hill London EC4M 7AA
Tel: 020 7332 2230 *Fax:* 020 7332 2248
E-mail: law@hccsolicitors.com
Office: Manchester
Work: D1 E G H J1 J2 K3 L N O R1 R2 S1 S2 W Z(o,p)
Ptr: Coghlan, Mr Brian. . . . . Nov 1995
Cohen, Mr Simon E LLB . . . . Jun 1977
Horwich, Mr David J BA(L'pool)(Law) . . . . *Oct 1987

HOSHI & CO SOLICITORS ‡
Unit 8 Archway Business Centre 19-23 Wedmore Street London N19 4RZ
Tel: 020 7485 5180

HOUSEMANS
60 Lombard Street London EC3V 9EA
Tel: 020 3170 6000 *Fax:* 020 3170 6001 *Dx:* 42628 CHEAPSIDE
Office: Newcastle upon Tyne
Work: A3 B1 B2 C1 E F1 F2 J2 L N O Q S1 S2 W Z(j,r,za)
Fixed Fee Interview undertaken
Ptr: Appleby, Mr Michael Ronald James BSc. . . . . Oct 1989
Davison, Mr Gary ♦ . . . . Jun 1984
Ast: Flynn, Ms Brenda . . . . Oct 1993

HOUSING & PROPERTY LAW PARTNERSHIP ‡
99 Charterhouse Street Islington London EC1M 6HR
Tel: 020 7553 9000 *Fax:* 020 7553 9001 *Dx:* 53338 CLERKENWELL
Emergency telephone 020 7553 9000
E-mail: info@housingandproperty.co.uk
List of partners: R J S Duff, M Eaton, A Oberoi
Languages: French, German, Spanish
Work: B1 E L O Q R1 R2 S1 S2 Z(c,h,l)
Agency, Advocacy and Fixed Fee Interview undertaken
Ptr: Duff, Mr Richmond J S BA(Hons) . . . . *Jun 1988
Eaton, Mr Mark . . . . *Apr 1994
Oberoi, Mr Aashu LLB(Hons) . . . . *Jan 1995
Asoc: Allan, Miss Claire Louise BA(Hons) . . . . Mar 2005
Ast: Blackwood, Miss Ruth Hannah MA . . . . *Oct 2008
Cantor, Miss Chiara LLB . . . . *Nov 2002

HOUTHOFF BURMA ‡
33 Sun Street London EC2M 2PY
Tel: 020 7422 5050 *Fax:* 020 7422 5055

HOWARD & COMPANY ‡
43 Wimpole Street Westminster London W1G 8AE
Tel: 020 7486 6610 *Fax:* 020 7486 6620 *Dx:* 83308 WEST END 2
Emergency telephone 07831 822778
E-mail: wimpole@howard-howard.co.uk
List of partners: B R Howard
Work: C1 E J1 S1 S2 Z(l,r)
SPr: Howard, Mr Barry R LLB . . . . Jan 1982

FIONA M HOWARD ‡
99 Darwin Court Gloucester Avenue London NW1 7BH
Tel: 020 7482 2705
List of partners: F M Howard
Work: C2 E L S1 W X Z(d,i)
SPr: Howard, Mrs Fiona M. . . . . *Feb 1979

RICHARD HOWARD & CO LLP ‡
Central Court 25 Southampton Buildings London WC2A 1AL
Tel: 020 7831 4511 *Fax:* 020 7831 4512
Dx: 9 LONDON/CHANCERY LN
E-mail: richard.howard@richardhoward.co.uk
List of partners: H P Howard, R V Howard
Office: Aylesbury
Languages: French
Work: A3 C1 C2 E I J1 K1 K2 M1 R2 S2 T1 U1 Z(e,f,k,w,z)
Ptr: Howard, Ms Helen P LLB(Hons). . . . . *May 1983
Howard, Mr Richard V LLB(Hons) . . . . *§Jun 1981

HOWARD STONE ‡
Sophia House 32-35 Featherstone Street London EC1Y 8TW
Tel: 020 7490 5900 *Fax:* 020 7251 8597 *Dx:* 46647 BARBICAN
Emergency telephone 07768 667043
E-mail: hvs@hstonesolrs.co.uk
Web: www.hstonesolrs.co.uk
List of partners: H V Stone
Languages: French
Work: A3 B1 C1 E F1 J1 K1 K3 K4 M2 O Q S1 S2 W Z(q)
Emergency Action and Advocacy undertaken
SPr: Stone, Mr Howard Victor ACIArb . . . . *§Nov 1978
Founded in 1996 by Howard Stone. Howard Stone Solicitors offers a business and private law service to Clients who expect City standards but at a realistic cost. Principal Howard Stone provides direct personal expertise in those fields of law which impact most upon SMEs and private clients.

HOWARDS ‡
(incorporating Spilsbury & Co)
358 Kilburn High Road London NW6 2QH
Tel: 020 7328 1947 *Fax:* 020 7328 5211 *Dx:* 123860 KILBURN 2
Emergency telephone 020 8640 0994
E-mail: howard358@aol.com
List of partners: M J Hallam
Work: C1 E G H L S1 S2 W Z(i,l)
Emergency Action and Fixed Fee Interview undertaken
Ptr: Hallam, Mr Michael J LLB. . . . . *Jan 1964

HOWE & CO ‡
40 Uxbridge Road Ealing London W5 2BS
Tel: 020 8840 4688 *Fax:* 020 8840 7209 *Dx:* 5142 EALING
E-mail: law@howe.co.uk
List of partners: M J Howe, K O'Rourke
Languages: Hebrew, Kurdish, Polish, Spanish, Turkish
Work: N S1 Z(g)
Emergency Action, Fixed Fee Interview, Legal Aid undertaken, Legal Aid Franchise and Member of Accident Line
Ptr: Howe, Mr Martin J BA(Law). . . . . *Dec 1983
O'Rourke, Mr Kieron LLB . . . . *Apr 1990

NICK HOWE SOLICITORS ‡
St Martins House 16 St Martin's Le Grand London EC1A 4EN
Tel: 020 7397 8430 *Fax:* 020 7397 8433
E-mail: andrew.keates@howe-keates.co.uk
Work: A3 C1 O Z(a,j)

HOWELL & CO ‡
Citygate House 246-250 Romford Road London E7 9HZ
Tel: 020 8221 4536 *Fax:* 020 8221 4537

HOWELL-JONES LLP
218 The Strand London WC2R 1AT
Tel: 020 7183 0919 *Fax:* 020 8549 3383
E-mail: london@howell-jones.com
Office: Cheam, Kingston upon Thames, Leatherhead, London SW20, Walton-on-Thames

HOWELL-JONES LLP
22 Coombe Lane Raynes Park London SW20 8ND
Tel: 020 8947 7991 *Fax:* 020 8947 8725 *Dx:* 36555 RAYNES PARK
E-mail: raynespark@howell-jones.com
Office: Cheam, Kingston upon Thames, Leatherhead, London WC2, Walton-on-Thames
Work: E S1 S2 W
Member of Accident Line
Mem: Robertson, Mr Ian Charles LLB(Hons). . . . . Aug 1977

HOWES PERCIVAL LLP
Fourth Floor 160/161 Drury Lane London WC2B 5PN
Tel: 020 3040 0200 *Fax:* 020 7242 6522 *Dx:* 37976 KINGSWAY
E-mail: law@howespercival.com
Office: Leicester, Manchester, Milton Keynes, Northampton, Norwich

HOXTONS SOLICITORS ‡
First Floor Offices 331a Old Street Islington London EC1V 9LE
Tel: 020 7729 9229 *Fax:* 020 7729 7489 *Dx:* 137774 FINSBURY 5
E-mail: mail@hoxtons.com
Languages: French, Gujarati
Work: B1 E J1 K1 L N O Q S1 S2 W Z(i,l,p)
Emergency Action, Agency, Advocacy, Fixed Fee Interview and Legal Aid undertaken

HUBBARD PEGMAN & WITNEY ‡
7 King Street Cloisters Clifton Walk King Street London W6 0GY
Tel: 020 8735 9770 *Fax:* 020 8735 9780
Dx: 32773 HAMMERSMITH 2

HUDGELL & PARTNERS ‡
35-36 Market Street Woolwich Greenwich London SE18 6QP
Tel: 020 8854 1331 *Fax:* 020 8317 0760 *Dx:* 33302 WOOLWICH
E-mail: nh@hudgellpartners.co.uk
List of partners: G N W Hart, A T Simpson, N W Simpson, P M Wilkins
Languages: French
Work: C1 D1 D2 E K1 K2 L S1 S2 W
Emergency Action, Agency, Advocacy, Legal Aid undertaken and Legal Aid Franchise
Ptr: Hart, Mr Gerard N W BSc. . . . . *Dec 1982
Simpson, Mrs Angela T . . . . *Oct 1982
Simpson, Mr Nicholas W . . . . *Apr 1976
Wilkins, Mr Philip M BA . . . . *Nov 1983
Ast: Berry, Mr William LLB. . . . . *Apr 1974

HUDSON & CO ‡
2nd Floor Gray's Inn Chambers Gray's Inn London WC1R 5JA
Tel: 020 7405 4812 / 7831 3282 *Fax:* 020 7831 6552
E-mail: hudsonco@globalnet.co.uk
List of partners: D G V Hudson
Languages: French, Thai
Work: C1 C2 C3 E J1 L M2 S1 T1 W X Z(d,e,i,l,n)
Agency undertaken
Ptr: Hudson, Mr David G V LLB; Barrister & Solicitor of Supreme Court of Victoria (Aus). . . . . *Feb 1985
Con: Robson, Mr Lancelot W G LLB(Newc); CESF(Aosta); ACIArb Senior Lecturer in Law; Rents Assessment Panellist . . . . *Apr 1978

HUDSON BROWN ‡
Devlin House 36 St George Street London W1S 2FW
Tel: 020 7518 0370 *Fax:* 020 7518 0302
E-mail: info@hudsonbrownsolicitors.co.uk

HUDSON MCCONAGHUGH SOLICITORS ‡
5 Charnwood Drive Southwoodford London E18 1PD
Tel: 020 8530 2005 *Fax:* 020 8530 2005
E-mail: s.limbada@hudsonmcconaghugh.co.uk

HUDSONS ‡
63 Walnut Tree Walk Kennington London SE11 6DN
Tel: 020 7793 8740
List of partners: A D Hudson
Work: A1 B1 C1 E J1 K1 S1 T1 W Z(c,d,e,f,j,k,n)
Agency undertaken
SPr: Hudson, Miss Angela D BA . . . . Dec 1978

HUGGINS & LEWIS FOSKETT ‡
(incorporating Denis Tye & Co)
5-6 The Shrubberies George Lane South Woodford Redbridge London E18 1BG
Est: 1921
Tel: 020 8989 3000 *Fax:* 020 8989 9000 *Dx:* 90703 WOODFORD
E-mail: law@huggins-law.co.uk
List of partners: S Alam, B K Battu, J S Carmichael, S C Huggins, M Legister
Languages: Hindi, Punjabi
Work: A1 B1 B2 C1 C2 C3 D1 D2 E F1 F2 J1 K1 K2 K3 L N O Q R1 R2 S1 S2 T1 T2 W Z(b,c,e,f,g,h,i,k,l,p,q,r,u)
Agency, Advocacy, Fixed Fee Interview, Legal Aid undertaken and Legal Aid Franchise
Ptr: Alam, Ms Saika LLB(Hons) . . . . *Feb 1993
Battu, Mr Baldev K LLB Notary Public. . . . . *Jun 1989
Carmichael, Mr James S LLB . . . . *Jul 1979
Huggins, Mr Simon C . . . . *Aug 1992
Legister, Mr Michael Notary Public . . . . *Apr 1990
Ast: Menikou, Miss Joanna LLB . . . . *Sep 2004
West, Miss Helen . . . . Sep 2006
Con: Baldwin, Mr Andrew P de F. . . . . *Jul 1969
Huggins, Mr Adrian P S LLB . . . . *Nov 1967

HUGH CARTWRIGHT & AMIN ‡
12 John Street London WC1N 2EB
Tel: 020 7632 4200 *Fax:* 020 7831 8171
Dx: 356 LONDON/CHANCERY LN
E-mail: hca@hcasols.com
List of partners: A S Amin, R H S Moser, A Tennent
Work: E F1 J1 L N O Q R1 R2 S1 S2 W Z(q)
Ptr: Amin, Atul S BSc . . . . *Oct 1978
Moser, Mr Robert H S MA(Cantab) . . . . *Jan 1982
Tennent, Mr Andrew BA. . . . . *Dec 1978

HUGH JAMES
Level 33 25 Canada Square Canary Wharf London E14 5LQ
Tel: 020 7038 8301 *Fax:* 020 7038 8110
Office: Cardiff

HUGH JONES & CO ‡
137 Ballards Lane Church End Finchley London N3 1LJ
Tel: 020 8346 2236 *Fax:* 020 8349 2910 *Dx:* 57253 FINCHLEY 2
E-mail: enquiries@hugh-jones.co.uk
List of partners: E N Dervish, P N A King
Languages: Italian, Turkish
Work: C1 E G H J1 K4 L N O Q R1 R2 S1 S2 W Z(i,j,l,m,p,q)
Ptr: Dervish, Mr Erdogan Nesset . . . . Jun 1994
King, Mr Peter Nigel A LLB(Soton) . . . . *§Mar 1972
Asoc: White, Miss Michelle Giulia LLB(Hons); LPC. . . . . . Nov 2001

HUGHES & DORMAN ‡
60 Cannon Street London EC4N 6NP
Tel: 020 3402 2325 *Fax:* 020 7002 1100
E-mail: law@hughesdorman.com

A L HUGHES & CO ‡
340 Streatham High Road London SW16 6HH
Tel: 020 8769 7100 *Fax:* 020 8677 6644 *Dx:* 58457 NORBURY
E-mail: mail@alhughes.co.uk
List of partners: F A Holton, L N Mann, N D Mann
Languages: French, German
Work: C1 C2 C3 E F1 J1 L P R1 S1 S2 T1 T2 W Z(d,e)
Ptr: Holton, Ms Frances Anne . . . . *Mar 1983
Mann, Mr Laurence N LLB(Lond) Councillor. . . . . . *Jun 1984
Mann, Mr Norman D . . . . *§Dec 1969

HUGHES FOWLER CARRUTHERS ‡
Academy Court 94 Chancery Lane London WC2A 1DT
Tel: 020 7421 8383 *Fax:* 020 7421 8384
Dx: 251 LONDON/CHANCERY LN
E-mail: mail@hfclaw.com
List of partners: A S Carruthers, P J Fowler, F M T Hughes, A M Ison, R Labi, J Nicholson, J Vaitilingam
Work: D1 K1 K2 K3
Ptr: Carruthers, Mr Alexander Stevens MA(Cantab) . . . . *Nov 1994
Fowler, Ms Pauline J BA . . . . *Dec 1983
Hughes, Ms Frances M T MA(Oxon) . . . . *Nov 1981
Ison, Ms Ann Michelle LLB(Hons). . . . . *Mar 1981
Labi, Mr Renato BA(Hons) . . . . *Sep 1997
Nicholson, Mr John MA(Oxon). . . . . Mar 1998
Vaitilingam, Mr Joseph BA(Hons) . . . . *Nov 1996

HUGHES WILLSON SOLICITORS ‡
29 Weymouth Street London W1G 7DA
Tel: 020 7631 0131

HUGHES-NARBOROUGH & THOMAS ‡
83-85 Powis Street Greenwich London SE18 6JX
Tel: 020 8854 1291 *Fax:* 020 8854 9563 *Dx:* 33307 WOOLWICH 1
E-mail: info@hntsolicitors.co.uk
List of partners: B Harris
Work: D1 D2 E J1 K1 K3 L Q S1 S2 W Z(l)
Emergency Action, Agency, Advocacy and Fixed Fee Interview undertaken
SPr: Harris, Ms Barbara LLB(Lond); MA . . . . *Jun 1977

HUGHMANS ‡
1st Floor 32 Farringdon Street London EC4A 4HJ
Tel: 020 7246 6560 *Fax:* 020 7236 7896 *Dx:* 53321 CLERKENWELL
Emergency telephone 020 7246 6560
E-mail: hughmans@hughmans.co.uk
List of partners: P M Black, P G Hughman, M Jenkins
Work: B1 B2 C1 E G H J1 K1 K2 K3 L N O Q R2 S1 S2 W Z(j,q,r)
Advocacy, Fixed Fee Interview and Legal Aid undertaken
Ptr: Black, Mr Peter Michael BA . . . Nov 1977
Hughman, Mr Peter Graham . . . Dec 1971
Jenkins, Mr Matthew . . . Feb 2002
Ast: Adams, Mr Lee . . . Feb 2008
Johar, Ms Sofia . . . Oct 2004
Lipscombe, Ms Emma . . . Oct 2002

HUKA & CO ‡
Argo House Kilburn Park Road London NW6 5LF
Tel: 020 7624 9341 *Fax:* 020 7644 0600
List of partners: A Huka
SPr: Huka, Mr Anton . . . Jan 1999

HUMAN LAW ‡
911 Green Lanes London N21 2QP
Tel: 0844 800 3249 *Fax:* 020 8364 3414
E-mail: justin@human-law.co.uk

ANN L HUMPHREY ‡
The Boathouse Office 57a Gainsford Street London SE1 2NB
Tel: 020 7378 9370 *Fax:* 020 7378 9360
E-mail: annhumphrey@dial.pipex.com

MARK HUMPHRIES LEGAL ‡
One Fetter Lane London EC4A 1BR
Tel: 020 3440 5490
E-mail: mh@markhumphries.co.uk

HUNT & LISNERS
69 Holders Hill Drive London NW4 1NN
Tel: 020 8202 3746 *Fax:* 020 8457 9036 *Dx:* 59314 HENDON
Emergency telephone 07710 271347
E-mail: johnlisners@btinternet.com
Office: Northampton
Languages: French, German, Latvian
Ptr: Lisners, Mr John LLB(Hons) Pattinson Brewer Prize in Employment Law . . . *Jan 2004

DAVID C HUNT ‡
8 Indus Road London SE7 7DE
Tel: 020 8856 6350
List of partners: D C Hunt
SPr: Hunt, Mr David C LLB . . . *§Jul 1984

KAREN HUNTE & CO SOLICITORS ‡
12 Evesham Road London N11 2RP
Tel: 020 8361 6277

P M HUNTER & CO ‡
145 Dulwich Road Herne Hill London SE24 0NG
Tel: 020 7737 7725 *Dx:* 96300 HERNE HILL
List of partners: M B A Fitzpatrick
Work: C1 C2 E F1 L S1 S2 T1 W Z(l)
SPr: Fitzpatrick, Mr Mark B A . . . *Jul 1978

HUNTERS

HUNTERS ‡
9 New Square Lincoln's Inn London WC2A 3QN
Tel: 020 7412 0050 *Fax:* 020 7412 0049
Dx: 61 LONDON/CHANCERY LN
E-mail: info@hunters-solicitors.co.uk
Web: www.hunters-solicitors.co.uk
List of partners: P A Almy, L Barton, J M Clements, H Gleave, J R Godwin-Austen, H L A Hood, R C Kershaw, E C A Martineau, A L Melvin, G T Moran, J S Morrall, R D O'Halloran, G D Ogilvie, J H Owen, J C Richardson, P Robinson, P A Sykes, L J Tite, J C Vernor-Miles, J C Vernor-Miles, W E Vernor-Miles, L Walker
Office: Towcester
Work: A1 C1 E J1 K1 K2 K3 K4 L N O Q R1 S1 S2 T2 W Z(b,d,h,p,q,r)
Agency undertaken
Ptr: Almy, Mr Paul A LLB . . . *§Feb 1982
Barton, Mrs Lara BA . . . *Oct 2002
Clements, Ms Jacqueline M MA(Oxon) . . . *§Dec 1976
Gleave, Ms Hetty LLB . . . *§May 1996
Godwin-Austen, Mr Jonathan R MA . . . *§Mar 1991
Hood, Mr Henry L A MA . . . *§Apr 1987
Kershaw, Mr Richard C BA . . . *Sep 1997
Martineau, Mr Edward C A MA(Cantab) . . . *Nov 1976
Melvin, Mr Andrew L MSc . . . *Dec 1976
Moran, Mr Gerald T LLB . . . *Apr 1974
Morrall, Mr John Stephen LLB; LLM . . . Oct 1978
O'Halloran, Mr Richard D LLB . . . *§Nov 1973
Ogilvie, Mr Graham D MA . . . *Apr 1976
Owen, Mr John H MA . . . *Apr 1976
Richardson, Mr Joseph C BA . . . *Jan 1975
Robinson, Mr Peter LLB . . . *Mar 1987
Sykes, Ms Patricia A . . . *§Nov 1976
Tite, Ms Lucinda J LLB . . . *§Nov 1984
Vernor-Miles, Mr John Crosfield MA . . . Jan 1964
Vernor-Miles, Mr James Crosfield BA; CPD . . . Aug 1997
Vernor-Miles, Mr Wilfrid Edward LLB . . . *Oct 1999
Walker, Mrs Louise LLB . . . *Oct 2003
Asoc: Carr-West, Ms Joanna BA . . . *Oct 2004
Ho, Mr Ivan LLB . . . Nov 2006
Lingham, Mr David BA . . . *Sep 2004
Mainwaring-Taylor, Miss Rachel MA(Oxon) . . . *Sep 2002
Martin, Ms Katherine BA . . . *Oct 1998
Parry, Mr Andrew BA(Hons) . . . *Sep 2003
Roiser, Mrs Anna Rachel BA(Hons); MA(Cantab); LLM*Sep 2008
Yates, Mr Matthew James BA . . . *Sep 2004
Ast: Draisey, Mr David James BA(Hons) . . . *Mar 2009
Hawkins, Mr John Rowland . . . *Jun 1981
Lecoutre, Mr Robin BA(Hons); FILEx . . . *Sep 2009
Mabey, Mr James . . . Sep 2010
Maddocks, Ms Rhiannon BA . . . *Mar 2008
Richardson, Mr Charles Edward BA(Hons) . . . Sep 2011
Vernon, Miss Chloe Frances LLB(Hons); MA(Hons) Cavendish Publishing Prize 2005 . . . *Sep 2009
Wright, Miss Katie Victoria BA(Hons); MA(Hons) . . . *Sep 2009
Con: Daldorph, Mr Martyn J MA . . . *§Jul 1971
Robertson, Mr Nicolas MA . . . *Jun 1972

Private Clients; Business Affairs; Charity Law, Employment, Family, Matrimonial, Civil Litigation, Partnerships, Property, Agricultural, Conveyancing, Landlord and Tenant, Personal Taxation, Wills, Trusts & Probate, Banking, Security work.

HUNTERS ‡
30 Lincoln's Inn Fields London WC2A 3PD
Tel: 020 7412 0050 *Fax:* 020 7412 0049
E-mail: info@hunters-solicitors.co.uk

HUNTLEY LEGAL ‡
45 Antrobus Road Chiswick London W4 5HZ
Tel: 0844 873 2881
E-mail: mhuntley@huntleylegal.co.uk

HUNTON & WILLIAMS ‡
30 St Mary Axe London EC3A 8EP
Tel: 020 7220 5700 *Fax:* 020 7220 5772
E-mail: info@hunton.com

DOROTHY A HURRELL ‡
69 Kensington Church Street Kensington London W8 4BG
Tel: 020 7938 5355 *Fax:* 020 7938 4871
Dx: 84004 KENSINGTON HIGH STREET 2
E-mail: dhurrell@kensingtonlaw.co.uk
List of partners: D A Hurrell
Languages: French, Portuguese
Work: E K1 L S1 S2 W
SPr: Hurrell, Miss Dorothy A MA(Oxon) . . . Nov 1978

ROBERT A HURST ‡
73 Southway London NW11 6SB
Tel: 020 8209 1733 *Fax:* 020 8209 1733
E-mail: robert_a_hurst@hotmail.com
List of partners: R A Hurst
Languages: French, German
Work: A3 B1 M1 M2 O Q Z(e,q)
SPr: Hurst, Mr Robert Alfred LLB(Bris) . . . *Jun 1975

HUTCHINS & CO ‡
85 Lower Clapton Road Hackney London E5 0NP
Tel: 020 8986 3911 *Fax:* 020 8986 8252 *Dx:* 35452 HACKNEY
E-mail: info@hutchinsandcosolicitors.co.uk
List of partners: P W Gilbert, T Moloney
Languages: French
Work: D1 D2 E K1 L N R1 S1 V W Z(l,r)
Emergency Action, Legal Aid undertaken, Legal Aid Franchise and Member of Accident Line
Ptr: Gilbert, Mr Paul W BA . . . *Nov 1986
Moloney, Ms Tessa LLB . . . *Jun 1980

HUTCHINSON MAINPRICE ‡
45 Lower Belgrave Street Belgravia Westminster London SW1W 0LS
Tel: 020 7259 0121 *Fax:* 020 7259 0051
List of partners: A S Hutchinson
Languages: French
Work: C1 E L S1
Ptr: Hutchinson, Mr Alastair S LLB . . . *Jan 1984

HYAM LEHRER ‡
51 South Audley Street London W1K 2AA
Tel: 020 7499 0104

HYDE LAW ‡
70 Conduit Street London W1S 2GF
Tel: 020 7022 0058 *Fax:* 020 7022 0059

HOWARD HYMAN & CO ‡
Lord Chambers 1a Friern Park London N12 9DE
Tel: 020 8446 5511 *Fax:* 020 8446 8180 *Dx:* 57372 FINCHLEY
E-mail: info@howardhyman.com
List of partners: H S Hyman
Work: D1 E K1 N S1 W
Legal Aid Franchise
SPr: Hyman, Mr Howard S BSc(Econ) . . . *Jun 1979

IA SOLICITORS ‡
85a Watford Way London NW4 4RS
Tel: 020 8201 7728

IEC SOLICITORS ‡
282 High Road Willesden London NW10 2EY
Tel: 020 8830 2784 *Fax:* 020 8830 2786
E-mail: iecsolicitors@yahoo.co.uk

IDEAL SOLICITORS ‡
311 High Street North Manor Park London E12 6SL
Tel: 020 8552 8624

IGNATIOU-FAKHOURI & CO SOLICITORS ‡
Oxford House Derbyshire Street London E2 6HG
Tel: 020 7739 8454

IGOR & CO ‡
London House 100 New Kings Road Hammersmith & Fulham London SW6 4LX
Tel: 020 7384 7580
E-mail: info@igorandco.co.uk

IKIE SOLICITORS LLP ‡
153 Lewisham High Street London SE13 6AA
Tel: 020 8463 0808
E-mail: ikiesolicitors@aol.com

ILAW LEGAL SERVICES LTD ‡
Hamilton House 1 Temple Avenue London EC4Y 0HA
Tel: 020 7489 2059 *Fax:* 020 7117 4737

IMMANUEL & CO ‡
Burgon House 2 Burgon Street London EC4V 5DR
Tel: 020 7213 9901 *Fax:* 020 7213 9902
Emergency telephone 020 7213 9901
List of partners: H L Immanuel
Work: J1 N Z(g,q)
Advocacy, Fixed Fee Interview and Legal Aid undertaken
Ptr: Immanuel, Mr Harold Leon BA(Manc); MSc(Lond) . . . *Jun 1990

INAL & CO ‡
Terra House 25 Newington Green Road Islington London N1 4QT
Tel: 020 7354 5272
List of partners: Y R Inal
Languages: Turkish
Legal Aid undertaken
Ptr: Inal, Youksel R . . . *Dec 1981

INCE & CO SERVICES LTD ‡
International House 1 St Katharine's Way London E1W 1AY
Est: 1870
Tel: 020 7481 0010 *Fax:* 020 7481 4968 *Dx:* 1070 LONDON/CITY
List of partners: S M Askins, R Axe, D J B Baker, R Barbier-Emery, G S Belsham, J Biggs, N D Burgess, I A Chetwood, K Cooper, I T Cranston, C E Davies, C M de la Rue, C Dwyer, J Ewen, J R Farr, S C Fox, T Garrood, F Gavin, A D G George, J Goldfarb, N S B Gould, E J Graham, S Hems, A M Hepworth, P R Herring, J Heuvels, S Jarvis, C J Q Jefferis, C J Kidd, A G N Levy, M Linderman, C Lockwood, J S Lux, W Marshall, D J McInnes, P Measures, D Norton, J O'Keeffe, B Ogden, A A Ottley, F Peermohamed, P J H Rogan, D R Rutherford, C Searle, S W Shepherd, D W Steward, M D Stockwood, J S Todd, M Volikas, A H M Weir, O A R Weiss, J R K Wilson, E Woodruff
Languages: Dutch, French, German, Greek, Hindi, Italian, Mandarin, Norwegian, Portuguese, Russian, Spanish, Welsh
Work: B1 C1 E J1 M1 N O P S1 T1 W Z(a,b,c,j,o)
Emergency Action undertaken
Ptr: Askins, Mr Stephen M LLB . . . Dec 1993
Axe, Ms Rebecca . . . Sep 1997
Baker, Mr David J B BA . . . Mar 1985
Barbier-Emery, Mr Renaud . . . Feb 2002
Belsham, Miss Gillian S BA(Oxon) . . . *Apr 1985
Biggs, Mr Jeremy . . . Sep 2003
Burgess, Mr Nicholas Daniel BA(Hons) . . . *Oct 1996
Chetwood, Mr Ian A LLB(Soton) . . . *Oct 1980
Cooper, Mr Kevin . . . Nov 2004
Cranston, Mr Ian Trevor LLB; LSF . . . *Jun 1993
Davies, Miss Charlotte E LLB(Lond) . . . *Oct 1985
de la Rue, Mr Colin M BA(Cantab) . . . *Dec 1980
Dwyer, Mr Christian . . . Sep 1999
Ewen, Ms Johanna . . . Sep 2000
Farr, Mr Jeremy R BSc(Surrey) . . . *Oct 1987
Fox, Mr Steven C BA(Oxon) . . . Dec 1983
Garrood, Mr Trevor . . . Oct 1983
Gavin, Fionna . . . Sep 1997
George, Mr Anthony D G MA(Oxon) . . . *Feb 1971
Goldfarb, Jonathan . . . Jan 2001
Gould, Mr Nicholas S B LLB(Leics) . . . *Feb 1981
Graham, Mr Edward James . . . *Oct 1996
Hems, Simon . . . Sep 2001
Hepworth, Mr Allan M LLB(Law with French) . . . *Nov 1988
Herring, Mr Paul R LLB(Leics) . . . *Aug 1981
Heuvels, Mr Jan BA(Oxon) . . . *Nov 1995
Jarvis, Mr Stephen . . . Aug 1997
Jefferis, Mr Christopher J Q MA(Cantab) . . . *Nov 1984
Kidd, Mr Christopher J MA(Cantab) . . . Oct 1986
Levy, Mr Albert G N MA(Cantab) . . . *Apr 1978
Linderman, Ms Michelle . . . Sep 1999
Lockwood, Mr Charles . . . Sep 1999
Lux, Mr Jonathan S LLB(Nott'm) University Exhibition Prize . . . *Jun 1977
McInnes, Mr David James . . . Oct 1996
Marshall, Mr Will . . . Sep 2000
Measures, Mr Peter . . . Dec 1980
Norton, Mr Dean . . . Oct 1993
O'Keeffe, Mr Joseph . . . Nov 1993
Ogden, Mr Ben MA . . . May 1993
Ottley, Mr Andrew A LLB(Lond) . . . *May 1980
Peermohamed, Faz . . . Jun 1998
Rogan, Mr Peter J H BComm; LLB(Stellenbosch); LLM(Lond) . . . *Jul 1979
Rutherford, Mr David R LLB(Lond) . . . Jun 1983
Searle, Carol . . . Jan 1997
Shepherd, Mr Stuart W LLB(Wales) . . . *Oct 1984
Steward, Mr David W MA(Cantab) . . . *Jan 1983
Stockwood, Mr Michael D BA(Cantab) . . . *Oct 1981
Todd, Mr John Simon BA(L'pool)(Law) . . . *Oct 1986
Volikas, Mr Michael . . . Nov 1991
Weir, Mr Alan H M BA(Cantab) . . . Nov 1984
Weiss, Mr Oliver A R MA(Cantab) . . . *§May 1976
Wilson, Mr James R K MA(Cantab) . . . Oct 1985
Woodruff, Mr Elliot . . . Feb 1993
Asoc: Collett, Deborah LLB(Hons) . . . Apr 1978
Conway, Mr Ben . . . Feb 1998
Dimitrellou, Simonie . . . Aug 1996
Gold, Mr Damian . . . Sep 2003
Grantham, Mr David . . . Sep 2002
Kempkens, Clare . . . Sep 2000
Maclean, Mr Ian . . . Jul 2002
Moon, Mr Ben . . . Sep 1999
Morgan, Mr Jeff MA(Cantab) . . . Oct 1980
Morris, Mr Richard BA . . . *Sep 2002
Nam, Kijong . . . Sep 2004
Patel, Ms Mona . . . Jun 2001
Plotnek, Mr Stuart G LLB(Lond) . . . *Oct 1990
Tadros, Rania . . . Sep 2000
Urwin, Amanda . . . Sep 2002
Ast: Angell, Carrie . . . Apr 2007
Blagbrough, Mr William . . . Sep 2009
Boden, Mr Daniel . . . Sep 2009
Brown, Joanna . . . Apr 2007
Cadywould, Anna . . . Sep 2008
Carr, Ms Kathryn Juliet MA(Cantab) . . . *Aug 1996
Clifford, Heloise . . . Oct 2008
Cruft, Mr Bill . . . Sep 2004
Devereaux, Anna . . . Sep 2007
Duffy, Mette . . . Sep 2008
Farmer, Mr Chris . . . Apr 2006
Fernandes, Lorraine . . . Sep 2007
Fitzgerald, Jane . . . Sep 2007
Fomina, Anna . . . Sep 2008
Gilbertson, Mr James . . . Sep 2005
Hawkings, Genelle . . . Mar 2003
Henwood, Scarlett . . . Sep 2009
Hickland, Mr James . . . Sep 2007
Howard, Mr Liam . . . Sep 2008
Hughes, Jennifer . . . Mar 2007
Iyer, Milena . . . Jan 2003
Jackson, Antonia . . . Sep 2009
Jama, Mansour . . . May 2009

See p2 for the Key to Work Categories & other symbols

Johnson, Mr Tim . . . . Sep 2008
Jones, Mr Roderic. . . . . Sep 2009
Karunakaran, Devandran . . . . Sep 2006
Keville, Alex. Sep 2005
Kirby, Mr Shawn . . . . Mar 2007
Lescure, Alison BA(Hons); CPE; LPC . . . . Oct 1997
Leslie, Camilla . . . . Sep 2007
McDonald, Louise. . . . . Sep 2009
Marsh, Mr William BA(Cantab) . . . . *Nov 1992
Martin, Rachel . . . . Oct 2005
Munro, Mr Stewart . . . . Oct 2006
Murray, Olivia . . . . Sep 2004
Nickel, Eva . . . . Aug 2006
Olubajo, Tolu . . . . Sep 2006
Pattard, Estelle . . . . Sep 2006
Peatfield, Lisa. . . . . Apr 2006
Potter, Tera . . . . Sep 2008
Pounds, Fiona . . . . Sep 2009
Richards, Mr David . . . . Sep 2007
Robinson, Mr David. . . . . Sep 2008
Rochester, Vanessa. . . . . Sep 2008
Rodgers, Kate. . . . . Sep 2008
Sacha, Mr Christopher . . . . Sep 2004
Seymour, Mr Peter . . . . Sep 2005
Sierra, Mr Juan . . . . Oct 2004
Smith, Zoe . . . . Sep 2009
Stephens, Jo . . . . Apr 2007
Stetzel, Charlotte . . . . Sep 2008
Tudor, Philippa . . . . Sep 2009
Turner, Mr William. . . . . Apr 2007
Waite, Victoria . . . . Sep 2008
Walker, Mr Carl . . . . Nov 2008
Watson, Natalie. . . . . Sep 1999
Con: Arditti, Mr E Paul . . . . *Apr 1974
Fitzsimmons, Mr Anthony J E MA(Cantab); AMIEE; MRHES . . . . *Jul 1980
Foster, Mr Charles . . . . Jun 1972
Griggs, Mr Patrick J S. . . . . §Jul 1963
Kennedy, Mr George R LLB. . . . . *Dec 1969
Loftus, Mr S Jonathan BA(Oxon) . . . . *Oct 1985
Scorer, Mr Tim . . . . Jan 1965
Suchy, Mr Anthony R S LLB(Leeds). . . . . *Aug 1972
Walsh, Chris . . . . Nov 1978
Williams, Mr Richard . . . . Dec 1973

INDEPENDENT PENSION TRUSTEE LIMITED ‡
Beaufort House 15 St Botolph Street London EC3A 7EE
Tel: 020 7247 6555

DARRYL INGRAM & CO ‡
1-3 Heriot Road Hendon London NW4 2EG
Tel: 020 8202 0843 *Fax:* 020 8202 1485 *Dx:* 59315 HENDON
Emergency telephone 07976 813824
List of partners: D E Ingram
Work: D1 D2 G H K1 L N Q S1 W
Emergency Action, Agency, Advocacy, Fixed Fee Interview, Legal Aid undertaken, Legal Aid Franchise and Member of Accident Line
Ptr: Ingram, Darryl E LLB . . . . *Jun 1977

INGRAM WINTER GREEN ‡
Bedford House 21a John Street Camden London WC1N 2BF
Tel: 020 7845 7400 *Fax:* 020 7845 7401
Dx: 1055 LONDON/CHANCERY LN
E-mail: info@iwg.co.uk
Languages: Arabic, Bengali, French, Gujarati, Hebrew, Hindi, Punjabi, Urdu
Work: A3 B1 C1 C2 C3 E F1 G I J1 L M1 M2 M3 N O P Q R2 S1 S2 T1 T2 U1 U2 W Z(a,b,c,d,e,f,j,k,l,n,q,za)

WILLIAM INNES ‡
56 Crescent Lane London SW4 9PU
Tel: 020 7622 4893 *Fax:* 020 7622 4893
E-mail: williaminnes@btinternet.com

INNSTEP (NOMINEES) LIMITED ‡
Woodbridge House 30 Aylesbury Street London EC1R 0ER
Tel: 020 7490 4000 *Fax:* 020 7490 2545

INTERNATIONAL FAMILY LAW CHAMBERS ‡
218 Strand London WC2R 1AP
Tel: 020 7583 5040 *Fax:* 020 7583 5151
Dx: 252 LONDON/CHANCERY LN
E-mail: mail@internationalfamilylaw.com
List of partners: L Samuels, D Truex
Languages: French, German, Swedish
Work: K1 K3 M1 M2
Emergency Action, Agency, Advocacy and Fixed Fee Interview undertaken
Ptr: Samuels, Ms Lorna LLB(Hons) . . . . *Oct 1987
Truex, Mr David LLB; Dip Fam Law; LLM; Admitted in Australia . . . . *Jul 1990

THE INTERNATIONAL FAMILY LAW GROUP ‡
Hudson House 8 Tavistock Street London WC2E 7PP
Tel: 020 3178 5668 *Fax:* 020 3178 5669
Dx: 40000 COVENT GARDEN
Emergency telephone 07973 890648
E-mail: enquiries@iflg.uk.com
List of partners: H J Blackburn, P Denley, L D A Greenwood, A Thomas, A C Usher
Languages: French, Punjabi, Urdu
Work: A3 D1 K1 K2 K3 M2
Emergency Action and Agency undertaken
Ptr: Blackburn, Miss Helen Jane LLB . . . . Sep 1998
Denley, Mrs Punam LLB(Hons) . . . . *§Dec 1995
Greenwood, Ms Lucy Dorothy Anne BSc(Hons); DipLaw . . . . *Oct 1995
Thomas, Ms Ann . . . . *Jan 1993
Usher, Mrs A Carolynn BA . . . . Dec 1975
Ast: Dhami, Miss Mandeep . . . . *Feb 2008
Donaldson, Miss Jenny . . . . *Sep 2008
Con: Hodson, Mr David M LLB Deputy District Judge . . . . *Jun 1978

THE INTERNATIONAL PROPERTY LAW CENTRE LLP ‡
4th Floor Frazer House 32-38 Leman Street London E1 8EW
Tel: 020 7173 6180 *Fax:* 01482 240192
E-mail: stefanol@iplc.co.uk

INYAMA & CO ‡
Gordon House 6 Lissenden Gardens London NW5 1LX
Tel: 020 7482 8863

JOHN IRELAND & CO ‡
57 Elgin Crescent London W11 2JU
Tel: 020 7792 1666

IRVINE & PARTNERS ‡
1 & 2 Charterhouse Mews London EC1M 6BB
Tel: 020 3176 0300 *Fax:* 020 3176 0301 *Dx:* 53301 CLERKENWELL

MARIEL IRVINE ‡
Alto House 29-30 Newbury Street London EC1A 7HZ
Tel: 020 7606 0517 *Fax:* 020 7796 3017 *Dx:* 13878 CLERKENWELL
E-mail: irvine@marielirvine.com

IRVINE THANVI NATAS ‡
Queensway House Suite 208 London E15 2TF
Tel: 020 8522 7707

IRVING & CO ‡
152-156 Kentish Town Road Camden London NW1 9QB
Tel: 020 7428 9600 *Fax:* 020 7428 9601
Dx: 46466 KENTISH TOWN 1
E-mail: mail@irvinglegal.co.uk
Office: Brighton
Work: Z(g,i)
Fixed Fee Interview, Legal Aid undertaken and Legal Aid Franchise

IRWIN MITCHELL LLP
40 Holborn Viaduct London EC1N 2PZ
Tel: 0870 150 0100 *Fax:* 020 7404 0208 *Dx:* 87 CHANCERY LANE
Office: Birmingham, Bristol, Leeds, Manchester, Newcastle upon Tyne, Sheffield
Languages: French, Spanish
Work: J1 M1 M2 N Q Z(j)
Agency undertaken
Ptr: De Lorenzo, Mr Jose-Maria Spanish Abogado. . . . . Jun 1993
Eddy, Ms Alison M BA. . . . . *Oct 1980
Ettinger, Mr Colin B LLB. . . . . *Jun 1978
Robinson, Mr Kevin . . . . *Jun 1972
Wylde, Mr Peter R BA(Law). . . . . *Mar 1983
Zurbrugg, Mr Michael R W BA; MA . . . . *Sep 1981
Ast: Aykroyd, Mrs Victoria L BA(Hons). . . . . *Apr 1999
Cheetham, Ms Anne BA(Hons) . . . . *Nov 1995
Darlaston, Mr Guy W E LLB. . . . . *Oct 1995
Dickinson, Mr Christopher Michael LLB . . . . *Jul 1995
Dinsmore, Mr Andrew Derek William BA; LPC. . . . . *Sep 1996
Dolman, Ms Dominique J . . . . *Oct 1995
Kerr, Ms Louise A BA; PGDipLaw. . . . . *Sep 1997
Parry, Ms Justine Sian BA(Hons) . . . . *Sep 1996
Rea, Ms Morag . . . . *Feb 1998
Walace, Miss Sarah CTA . . . . *Nov 1999
Con: Lomas, Ms Julia Carole BA(Hons); FIMgt Public Trustee & Accountant General of the Supreme Court . . . . *Feb 1980

ISADORE GOLDMAN SOLICITORS ‡
12 Bridewell Place London EC4V 6AP
Tel: 020 7353 1000 *Fax:* 020 7353 9055
Dx: 124 LONDON/CHANCERY LN
E-mail: cguy@isadoregoldman.com
List of partners: F Brumby, D J Buckoke, A J Cary, S Loome, K Mitchell, M M Mollaghan, D M Schaffer
Languages: Arabic, Armenian, Danish, Farsi, French, German
Work: B1 C1 C2 C3 J1 O Q S2
Emergency Action undertaken
Ptr: Brumby, Mr Frank LLB(Hons)(Hull); BA(Hons); LPC(Notts) . . . . *Sep 1998
Buckoke, Mr Denis J BA . . . . *Jan 1986
Cary, Ms Alison Jane BA(Hons). . . . . *Jan 1993
Loome, Mr Simon LLB(Hons)(Kingston). . . . . *Nov 1995
Mollaghan, Miss Mary Michelle . . . . *Jan 1999
Schaffer, Mr Daniel M LLB(B'ham) Deputy Bankruptcy Registrar (High Court). . . . . *§Apr 1975
Mitchell, Mr Kevin. . . . . NSP
Asoc: Parrett, Mr Craig Geoffrey James LLB. . . . . . . Feb 2009
Ast: Stuart, Miss Fiona LLB(Law & Criminology)(Sheff). . . Sep 2011

THE ISLAMIC WILLS COMPANY LTD ‡
8 Howden Close London SE28 8HD
Tel: 0845 813 2323
E-mail: contact@islamwills.com

ISRAEL STRANGE & CONLON ‡
384 City Road Islington London EC1V 2QA
Tel: 020 7833 8453 *Fax:* 020 7833 8454 *Dx:* 400205 FINSBURY 2
List of partners: M A Conlon, A S Israel, I R Strange
Languages: French
Work: C1 C2 E K4 S1 S2 T2 W
Ptr: Conlon, Mr Michael A LLB. . . . . *Jun 1978
Israel, Mr Arnold S LLB . . . . *Mar 1971
Strange, Mr Ian R. . . . . *Jun 1966
Ast: Fendt, Ms Anne. . . . . *Oct 1989

ISSAT & CO SOLICITORS ‡
175-177 Borough High Street London SE1 1HR
Tel: 020 7939 9900 *Fax:* 020 7939 9954
E-mail: info@issatsolicitors.co.uk

JOHN ITSAGWEDE & CO ‡
1-3 Atwell Road London SE15 4TW
Tel: 020 7732 8750 *Fax:* 020 7732 0362 *Dx:* 152641 PECKHAM 3
E-mail: info@itsagwede.co.uk

IYAMA SOLICITORS ‡
85-87 Borough High Street Southwark London SE1 1NH
Tel: 020 7357 0709 *Fax:* 020 7357 0762 *Dx:* 144362 SOUTHWARK 4
Emergency telephone 07958 930851
E-mail: info@iyamasolicitors.co.uk
List of partners: I Iyama
Languages: French, Igbo, Kiswahili, Lingala, Yoruba
Ptr: Iyama, Ms Isabella BA; LLB; LLM Notary Public. . . . Sep 1996

IZOD EVANS ‡
The Hop Exchange 24 Southwark Street London SE1 1TY
Tel: 020 7015 1850 *Fax:* 020 7015 1851
E-mail: mail@izodevans.co.uk

J D LAW LLP ‡
Fourth Floor Temple Bar House 23-28 Fleet Street London EC4Y 1AA
Tel: 020 7438 0990 *Fax:* 020 7438 0999
Dx: 381 LONDON/CHANCERY LN
E-mail: info@jd-law.co.uk

JDS SOLICITORS ‡
12 Church Street Stratford London E15 3HX
Tel: 020 8221 0233 *Fax:* 020 8555 9431
E-mail: info@jds.co.uk

JEH ‡
Fleet House 8-12 New Bridge Street London EC4V 6AL
Tel: 020 7583 8853 *Fax:* 020 7583 8852
E-mail: jeh@humelaw.com

JF LAW SOLICITORS ‡
Unit 54 Camberwell Business Centre London SE5 7HN
Tel: 020 7277 0444

JGE SOLICITORS ‡
Unit W/41 Grove Business Centre 560-568 High Road London N17 9TA
Tel: 020 8885 6477 *Fax:* 020 8885 1424 *Dx:* 58507 TOTTENHAM

JPS LAW SOLICITORS ‡
45 Weymouth Street Westminster London W1G 8BY
Tel: 020 7935 9955 *Fax:* 020 7486 8304
E-mail: jpslaw@btconnect.com
List of partners: S J Robinson, J P Sue-Patt
Work: B1 C1 E J1 K1 L O Q S1 S2 W
Ptr: Robinson, Ms Sonia Josline. . . . . *May 2007
Sue-Patt, Ms Jassette Patricia . . . . *Mar 1998

JVA LAW ‡
57 Holland Park London W11 3RS
Tel: 020 3220 0070 *Fax:* 020 3031 1194
Dx: 94203 NOTTING HILL GATE
E-mail: admin@jvalaw.co.uk

ANGELA JACKSON ‡
1 Lonsdale Square London N1 1EN
Tel: 020 7609 5615 *Fax:* 020 7609 8684
E-mail: aj@angela-jackson.co.uk

JAMES JACKSON SOLICITOR ‡
21 Woodland Gardens London N10 3UE
Tel: 020 8245 2365

JACKSON PARTON ‡
4th Floor 1 Alie Street Tower Hamlets London E1 8DE
Tel: 020 7702 0085 *Fax:* 020 7702 0858
E-mail: mail@jacksonparton.com
List of partners: J D Clyne, N F Dahl-Nielsen, R C Fielden, M V A Gerakaris, D A Hughes, N G Parton, A R Patrinos, B J Roberts
Languages: French, Greek
Work: A3 O Z(a,j)
Ptr: Clyne, Mr Jonathan David. . . . . *Aug 1998
Dahl-Nielsen, Nils F BA(Hons) . . . . *Nov 1985
Fielden, Mr Robert C MA(Oxon). . . . . *Jun 1978
Gerakaris, Ms Maria Vasso Aspasia LLB(Hons) . . . . *Nov 1997
Hughes, Mr David A BA. . . . . *Jun 1977
Parton, Mr Nicholas G BA. . . . . *Nov 1979
Patrinos, Mr Andrew R . . . . *Jan 1994
Roberts, Mr Brian J MA; BTech . . . . *Jun 1977

JACKSONS SOLICITORS ‡
26 Grosvenor Street Mayfair London W1K 4QW
Tel: 020 3058 0512 *Fax:* 020 7493 5024
Emergency telephone 07765 256128
E-mail: nigel@jacksonslegal.com
List of partners: N S Jackson
Languages: French, German, Russian
Work: B1 C1 C2 C3 E I J1 K1 K3 N O Q S1 U1 U2 W Z(d,e,f,i,k,z)
SPr: Jackson, Mr Nigel S. . . . . Jul 1981

JACOBS ALLEN HAMMOND ‡
3 Fitzhardinge Street Manchester Square London W1H 6EF
Tel: 020 7299 9800 *Fax:* 020 7299 9801
Dx: 42734 OXFORD CIRCUS NORTH
E-mail: info@jahlaw.co.uk
List of partners: C J G Allen, P W Jacobs, J H Sykes
Ptr: Allen, Mr Christopher James Girton BA(Oxon). . . . *Dec 1972
Jacobs, Mr Peter W LLB . . . . *Dec 1974
Sykes, Mr John H LLB . . . . §Oct 1965
Asoc: Hussein-Doru, Lale . . . . Nov 2006

D H K JACOBS & CO ‡
730 Romford Road Manor Park London E12 6BT
Tel: 020 8514 7466 *Fax:* 020 8514 7461

JACOBS FORBES SOLICITORS ‡
Suite 341 Lee Valley Techno Park Ashley Road London N17 9LN
Tel: 020 8880 4154
List of partners: J Ekokobe, C A Parillon
Work: J1 K1 O Q S1 S2 Z(i,p)
Fixed Fee Interview undertaken
Ptr: Ekokobe, Miss Jacqueline LLB; LLM . . . . *Sep 2001
Parillon, Miss Cleo Anne-Marie LLB(Hons) . . . . . . *Nov 2000

GARY JACOBS & CO ‡
137 George Lane South Woodford London E18 1AN
Tel: 020 8536 4050 *Fax:* 020 8936 3440 *Dx:* 90704 WOODFORD
E-mail: pj@gjlaw.co.uk
List of partners: D A J Jacobs
Languages: French, Punjabi, Spanish, Urdu
Work: D1 K1 K3
Emergency Action, Agency, Advocacy, Fixed Fee Interview, Legal Aid undertaken and Member of Accident Line
Ptr: Jacobs, Miss Deborah A J ♦. . . . . *Sep 1988
Ast: Ali, Mr Kazi F Riasheed. . . . . Jul 2004
Sehmi, Mr Davinder Singh . . . . Aug 2003

JACOBS SOLICITORS ‡
451 Barking Road London E6 2JX
Tel: 020 8821 9222 *Fax:* 020 8472 2227 *Dx:* 4708 EAST HAM
E-mail: frontdesk@jacobs-solicitors.com

STANLEY JACOBS ‡
40 Oakdene Park Finchley Central Barnet London N3 1EU
Tel: 020 8349 4241 *Fax:* 020 8349 4245 *Dx:* 57268 FINCHLEY 2
E-mail: stan@sjacobs.u-net.com
List of partners: S G Jacobs
Work: E L O Q S1 S2 W
Emergency Action and Agency undertaken
SPr: Jacobs, Mr Stanley Geoffrey LLB(Hons). . . . . *Apr 1980

JACOBSEN & CO ‡
6 Stephendale Yard Stephendale Road London SW6 2LR
Tel: 020 7736 6277 *Fax:* 020 7610 6664
Dx: 83803 FULHAM BROADWAY
E-mail: mail@jacobsenlegal.com
List of partners: H V Jacobsen
Languages: Danish
Work: C1 E L S1 W Z(f)
SPr: Jacobsen, Mrs Helle V LLB . . . . *Sep 1974

JACOBSENS ‡
41 Tabernacle Street London EC2A 4AA
Tel: 020 7608 2568 *Fax:* 020 7608 2751
E-mail: colin.sturge@jacobsens.co.uk
List of partners: N L Jacobsen
Work: A3 C1 C2 C3 E J1 O Q R2 S2 Z(b,c)
Ptr: Jacobsen, Mr Neil L LLB(Lond) . . . . *Nov 1971
Ast: Buck, Charlotte . . . . Jan 2009

JAFFE PORTER CROSSICK ‡
Omni House 252 Belsize Road London NW6 4BT
Tel: 020 7625 4424 *Fax:* 020 7328 5840 *Dx:* 37702 KILBURN
E-mail: enquiries@jpclaw.co.uk
List of partners: K A Cohen, S Cohen, S P Crossick, G M Ditz, G N Jaffe, K P Maynard, D A J Payne, S N Porter, C Prince
Languages: French, Gujarati, Hebrew, Polish, Punjabi, Russian, Spanish
Work: B1 C1 D1 E F1 J1 K1 K3 L M1 M2 O Q R1 S1 S2 T1 T2 W Z(d,h,l)
Ptr: Cohen, Miss Katie Alexandra . . . . *Sep 2007
Cohen, Miss Surina BA; CPE; PGDL; LPC Law Society Prize for Outstanding Performance on LPC 2003. . . . . *Aug 2005
Crossick, Mr Stephen Philip LLB(Lond) . . . . *Jun 1972
Ditz, Mr Geoffrey Michael . . . . *Aug 1998
Jaffe, Mr Graham N LLB Commissioner for Oaths for New Zealand. . . . . *May 1990
Maynard, Mr Keith Philip . . . . *Dec 1979
Payne, Mr Derek Anthony James . . . . *Jan 2000
Porter, Mr Steven N. . . . . *Dec 1979
Prince, Miss Claire BA(Hons); PGDipLaw; CPE; LPC *Feb 2002
Ast: Chauhan, Mr Niten . . . . *Jan 2006
Gomes, Miss Natacha Amado Santiago . . . . *Aug 2008
Manski, Mr Paul Laurence. . . . . *Nov 1979
Mead, Mr John Michael . . . . *Feb 1985
Con: Atkin, Mr Peter Stuart Richard. . . . . *Jun 1973
Cohen, Mr Michael . . . . *Nov 1960
Shaw, Mr Kenneth Robert. . . . . *Jul 1969

CHARLES JAMES & CO ‡
45 Portman Square London W1H 6HN
Tel: 020 7969 2740 *Fax:* 020 7060 2742 *Dx:* 44608 MAYFAIR
E-mail: enquiries@jlaw.co.uk

JULIAN JAMES ‡
101 Bartholomew Road London NW5 2AR
Tel: 020 7448 5200 / 07801 140980 *Fax:* 020 7485 2383

MARGARET JAMES ‡
11 Eccleston Square Westminster London SW1V 1NP
Tel: 020 7834 3447 *Fax:* 020 7834 2112
E-mail: margaretjames26@hotmail.com
List of partners: M A James
Work: S1
SPr: James, Ms Margaret A LLB . . . . *Oct 1977

JAMES SOLICITORS ‡
3rd Floor 18-36 Wellington Street London SE18 6PF
Tel: 020 8555 9545 *Fax:* 020 8855 7462 *Dx:* 33314 WOOLWICH
E-mail: info@jamessolicitors.co.uk

JAMES WARE BAXTER SCHOENFELD LLP ‡
6 Gray's Inn Square Gray's Inn London WC1R 5AX
Tel: 020 7269 9025 *Fax:* 020 7404 7275

JANES ‡
17 Waterloo Place Pall Mall London SW1Y 4AR
Tel: 020 7930 5100 *Fax:* 020 7839 2208 *Dx:* 140544 PICCADILLY 5
Emergency telephone 07789 622430
E-mail: office@janes-solicitors.co.uk
List of partners: S Barker, R L Berg, R S Cannon, D K Janes, J Mullion
Languages: Hebrew
Work: B2 G H
Advocacy, Legal Aid undertaken and Legal Aid Franchise
Ptr: Barker, Mr Simon LLB. . . . . Sep 2000
Berg, Mr Robert L ★ . . . . *Jun 1978
Cannon, Mr Richard Simon . . . . Oct 1993
Janes, Mr David K . . . . *§Jun 1975
Mullion, Mr James BA. . . . . Sep 2005
Ast: Gilmore, Mr Andrew. . . . . Jun 2008
O'Donnell, Miss Caroline BA . . . . Sep 2005
Con: Lee, Mr Julian Andrew BA. . . . . *May 1975

JASWAL JOHNSTON BOYLE ‡
51 Welbeck Street London W1A 4UA
Tel: 020 7317 1540 *Fax:* 020 7935 5969
E-mail: sj@jaswaljohnston.co.uk
List of partners: S S Jaswal, A F Johnston
Languages: French, German
Work: B1 C1 C2 E J1 N O Q R2 S1 S2 W Z(b,f,i,l)
Agency undertaken
Ptr: Jaswal, Sandeep Singh LLB(Hons) . . . . *Nov 1990
Johnston, Mr Anthony Francis LLB(Hons) . . . . . . *Sep 1993
Asoc: Smee, Mr Christopher Archdale BA(Hons). . . . . . *Sep 2001

ANTHONY JAYES LLP ‡
Universal House 251 Tottenham Court Road London W1T 7JY
Tel: 020 7291 9110 *Fax:* 020 7291 9120

JEFFREY GREEN RUSSELL ‡
Waverley House 7-12 Noel Street London W1F 8GQ
Tel: 020 7339 7000 *Fax:* 020 7339 7001 *Dx:* 44627 MAYFAIR
E-mail: jgr@jgrlaw.co.uk
List of partners: P G Cohen, A R Coles, D A Connick, T Halliwell, P N Harris, S A Jarvis, P W Johnson, R S Krol, R B Lincoln, D T Mills, J R O'Connell, F R Price, S C Rees-Howell, M P Reynolds, M T Saunders, J M Skeens, P A Spencer, M R Spragg, P J Stevens, R K Vala, R Webster, C Whitfield-Jones
Languages: French, German, Gujarati, Italian, Japanese, Kiswahili, Spanish
Work: B1 C1 C2 C3 E F1 I J1 K1 L M1 M2 N P R1 S1 T1 T2 W Z(b,c,d,e,j,k,l,o,s)
Member of Accident Line
Ptr: Cohen, Mr Philip G MA(Cantab). . . . . *Mar 1979
Coles, Mr Anthony R City of London Solicitors Co Grotius Prize . . . . *§Jul 1969
Connick, Mr David A . . . . *May 1982
Halliwell, Ms Tilly LLB(Manc) . . . . *Jan 1971
Harris, Mr Phillip N LLB . . . . *Jul 1970
Jarvis, Mrs Susan A LLB(Lond); MBA . . . . *Mar 1983
Johnson, Mr Peter W BSc. . . . . *Jun 1978
Krol, Mrs Rachel Susan LLB(Hons) Maxwell Law Prize 1976 . . . . Apr 1980
Lincoln, Mr R Bryan MA. . . . . *Dec 1962
Mills, Miss Deborah T LLB . . . . Oct 1989
O'Connell, Mr John Richard BA . . . . Nov 1988
Price, Mr Franklin R LLB . . . . *Oct 1984
Rees-Howell, Mr Simon Christopher. . . . . *Mar 1978
Reynolds, Mr Michael P FCIArb. . . . . *Jan 1980
Saunders, Mr Mark T LLB. . . . . Nov 1985
Skeens, Mr Julian M LLB . . . . *Nov 1980
Spencer, Ms Penelope A BA . . . . *Oct 1983
Spragg, Mr Mark R BA . . . . *Oct 1982
Stevens, Mr Peter John LLB . . . . *Mar 1973
Vala, Ramesh K LLB . . . . *May 1979
Webster, Mr Robert LLB. . . . . *Sep 1991
Whitfield-Jones, Mr Clive BA(Hons) . . . . *Apr 1975
Ast: Baynton, Mr George William LLB(Leics). . . . . . . *Apr 1977
Brothers, Mr Nicholas S LLB(Hons) . . . . *Nov 1992
Gerada, Mr Charles BA(Hons)(Politics & Law); DipLP *Sep 1999
Greig, Mr David Paul Lyle BA; LLB . . . . *Dec 1995
Hilmi, Merter Dervish BA(Hons). . . . . Nov 1999
Horne, Ms Nichola LLB . . . . *Oct 1996
Lee-Nichols, Ms Rayda P. . . . . §Feb 1995
Lewis, Miss Melanie A BA. . . . . *Oct 1987
Nuttall, Mr Stuart Phillip LLB(Hons) . . . . *Apr 1997
Prashant, Mr Dave LLB(Hons). . . . . Feb 2000
Wilson, Mr Kenneth George Hamilton . . . . *Dec 1965
Woodcraft, Mr Jeremy. . . . . *Oct 1993

JEIN SOLICITORS ‡
9a Lee High Road Lewisham London SE13 5LD
Tel: 020 8852 5214 *Fax:* 020 8852 2465
E-mail: jeinsolicitors@yahoo.co.uk

JENKINS LAW ‡
384 Garratt Lane London SW18 4HP
Tel: 020 8879 0656 *Fax:* 020 8879 1382 *Dx:* 82151 EARLSFIELD
E-mail: benbarth@jobsols.co.uk

RICHARD JENKINS ‡
25b Walton Street London SW3 2HU
Tel: 01794 388596
E-mail: rj@richardjenkins.co.uk

WALTER JENNINGS & SONS ‡
259-263 Kentish Town Road London NW5 2JT
Tel: 020 7485 8626 *Fax:* 020 7485 8426 *Dx:* 46454 KENTISH TOWN
List of partners: R D Smith
Work: C1 E O Q S1 S2
SPr: Smith, Mr Rodney David LLB . . . . *May 1981

JENS HILLS SOLICITORS LLP ‡
Northburgh House 10 Northburgh Street London EC1V 0AT
Tel: 020 7490 8160 *Fax:* 020 7490 7140 *Dx:* 53317 CLERKENWELL

JEYA & CO ‡
322 High Street North Manor Park Newham London E12 6SA
Tel: 020 8552 1999 *Fax:* 020 8552 9933 *Dx:* 4733 EAST HAM
Emergency telephone 07818 022841
E-mail: info@jeyaandco.co.uk
List of partners: M Jeyanantham, K Ponnampalam
Languages: Bengali, Punjabi, Sinhalese, Tamil, Urdu
Work: E K3 L Q S1 S2 Z(i)
Legal Aid Franchise
Ptr: Jeyanantham, Mrs Malathy . . . . *Sep 1994
Ponnampalam, Mrs Kavina LLB. . . . . *Nov 1998
Con: Bari, Mr Mustak LLB . . . . *Mar 2007
Kanagasingham, Mr Jeyaraj. . . . . *Oct 2010

JIREHOUSE CAPITAL ‡
8 John Street London WC1N 2ES
Tel: 020 8906 6662 *Fax:* 020 8906 6678
E-mail: stephendavid.jones@jirehouse.com

JIVA SOLICITORS ‡
16-17 Little Portland Street London W1W 8HH
Tel: 020 7290 0400 *Fax:* 020 7290 0450 *Dx:* 44406 MARBLE ARCH
Languages: French, Hindi, Punjabi, Urdu
Work: N
Member of Accident Line

JO & CO SOLICITORS ‡
10 Ironmonger Lane Poultry London EC2V 8EY
Tel: 020 7778 0715 *Fax:* 020 8539 7776
E-mail: info@joandcosolicitors.co.uk

JOELSON WILSON LLP ‡
30 Portland Place Westminster London W1B 1LZ
Tel: 020 7580 5721 *Fax:* 020 7580 2251
E-mail: info@joelsonwilson.com
List of partners: P A Chiappe, D R G Clifton, S A Cordell, S C Davies, J E Gregory, P Hails-Smith, J G W Hussey, N M McCann
Languages: French, Italian, Spanish
Work: C1 C2 C3 E F1 F2 I J1 J2 L M2 O P Q R1 R2 S1 S2 T1 U1 U2 Z(b,e,f,i,k,l,n,p,s,w,y,z,za)
Ptr: Chiappe, Mr Paul A LLB(Leeds); LLM(Essex) . . . . Mar 1997
Clifton, Mr David R G LLB(Reading). . . . . *May 1981
Cordell, Mr Sheldon A LLB(Bris); MSc(Lond)(Econ) . *Sep 1980
Davies, Ms Suzanne C BA(Manc). . . . . *Nov 1991
Gregory, Ms Joanne Elaine BA(Hons). . . . . *Oct 1996
Hails-Smith, Mr Phillipe LLB(UWE) . . . . *Nov 2000
Hussey, Mr John Gerard Wylie BA(Hons); PGDL . . *Sep 1997
McCann, Mr Niall Michael. . . . . *Oct 2003
Ast: Cross, Miss Hayley Louise LLB(Hons); DipLaw . . . . Nov 2010
Gold, The Hon Alexander Neil Michael LLB; DipLaw. . Mar 2011
Hood, Miss Elizabeth Claire BA; GDL; LPC . . . . . . Nov 2009
Koe, Mr Digby Michael MA(Hons). . . . . Oct 2006
Maxwell-Harris, Miss Jennifer Marian BA . . . . Mar 2002
Sturt, Miss Philippa Bethany BA; MA . . . . Oct 2002
Con: Harper, Mr Dean LLB . . . . *Nov 1991

JOHN & CO ‡
1st Floor Suite G, H & I 135-143 Stockwell Road London SW9 9TN
Tel: 020 7737 4141

PAUL JOHN ‡
115a The Grove London E15 1EN
Tel: 020 8215 1205

JOHNS & SAGGAR ‡
16 High Holborn London WC1V 6BX
Tel: 020 3490 1475 *Fax:* 020 3116 6402
Dx: 179 LONDON/CHANCERY LN
E-mail: info@johnandsaggar.co.uk
List of partners: S Saggar, K M Sofi
Languages: Albanian, Farsi, French, Greek, Gujarati, Hindi, Urdu
Work: B1 B2 C1 D1 D2 E F1 G H J1 J2 K1 K3 L M1 O Q S1 S2 W Z(c,d,e,g,i,p,q,w)
Emergency Action, Agency, Advocacy, Fixed Fee Interview and Legal Aid undertaken
Ptr: Saggar, Sunil ♦ . . . . *Jan 1986
Sofi, Mr Khalid Muzafar LLB(Hons); LLM ♦ . . . . . *Aug 1996
Asoc: Etuk, Mr Jonathan. . . . . *Jan 2007
Holdridge, Ms Justine Ann BSc; PGDipLaw . . . . . . Jun 2006
Nawrozzadeh, Mr Abbas GDL. . . . . *Jan 2010
Peters, Mrs Christina LLB(Hons) . . . . Nov 1997
Rexhepaj, Ms Belerta LLB; LPC. . . . . Jun 2010

JOHNSON & CO ‡
402 Harrow Road London W9 2HU
Tel: 020 7266 9977

JOHNSON CRILLY SOLICITORS LLP ‡
33 Kingston Road London SW19 1JX
Tel: 020 8544 1412 *Fax:* 020 8542 7156
E-mail: info@johnsoncrilly.co.uk

TIM JOHNSON-LAW ‡
7 Ludgate Broadway London EC4V 6DX
Tel: 020 7036 9120 *Fax:* 020 7036 9121
E-mail: contact@timjohnson-law.com

C J JONES SOLICITORS ‡
9 Mallow Street London EC1Y 8RQ
Tel: 020 7253 7419 *Fax:* 020 7490 7908 *Dx:* 36611 FINSBURY
Emergency telephone 07929 028873
E-mail: chris.jones@cjjlaw.co.uk
Work: B1 I J1 O Q U2 Z(e,j,p,q)
Agency and Advocacy undertaken

JONES DAY ‡
21 Tudor Street London EC4Y 0DJ
Tel: 020 7039 5959 *Fax:* 020 7039 5999
Dx: 67 LONDON/CHANCERY LN
E-mail: london@jonesday.com
List of partners: M E Angulo, R Anyamene, A D Barker, E Borrini, V Brophy, M Brown, S Brown, D Bushner, L Coffey, R Connor, N Cotter, G Elliott, L Ferera, N Ferguson, T Flood, A Galledari, J Goold, A G Grant, A C S Greaves, V Irani, H Lal, J R Little, I F Lupson, B Marin-Curtoud, A J McCulloch, A D W Millar, K Morley, F Murphy, E Nalbantian, M Pabst, C Papanicolaou, J Phillips, S Richards, D A Roberts, A Rotenberg, J Runnicles, M Rutstein, C L Sallabank, W Saunders, S N Seaton, C C Shuttleworth, D Smith, E Stuart, B Stueck, M Taylor, M B Thorneycroft, S F Walter
Languages: French, German, Greek, Italian, Russian, Spanish, Welsh
Work: A3 B1 B2 C1 C2 C3 E F2 I J1 M1 M2 O P Q R1 R2 S2 T1 T2 U1 U2 W Z(b,e,i,j,k,n,o)
Ptr: Angulo, Ms Marie Elena. . . . . Feb 1996
Anyamene, Mr Richard . . . . Nov 1995
Barker, Mr Andrew D . . . . Jan 1998
Borrini, Mr Edwin . . . . Jan 1999
Brophy, Mr Vincent . . . . Jan 1996
Brown, Mr Michael . . . . Jan 1993
Brown, Mr Stephen . . . . Jan 1991
Bushner, Mr Daniel . . . . Jan 1983
Coffey, Mr Lee LLB(Warw) . . . . Sep 1993
Connor, Ms Rosalind BA(Hons) . . . . *Nov 1998
Cotter, Mr Nicholas . . . . *Oct 1997
Elliott, Mr Giles BA(Hons). . . . . *Nov 1997
Ferera, Mr Leon BA. . . . . *Nov 1997
Ferguson, Mr Neil BA(Hons) . . . . *Nov 1998
Flood, Mr Timothy LLB(Hons) . . . . *Sep 1998
Galledari, Arman . . . . Oct 1992
Goold, Mr James BA(Hons). . . . . *Nov 1996
Grant, Mr Alistair G LLB. . . . . *Sep 2000
Greaves, Mr Adam C S MA(Cantab) . . . . *Oct 1982
Irani, Miss Vica LLB. . . . . *Oct 2000
Lal, Mr Hamish . . . . Sep 2001
Little, Mr Jonathon Ralph BA(Oxon). . . . . *Nov 1993
Lupson, Mr Ian F MA(Oxon). . . . . *Nov 1985
McCulloch, Mr Alastair John MA(Cantab) . . . . . . *Nov 1994
Marin-Curtoud, Mr Blaise LLB(Kent). . . . . *Sep 1994
Millar, Mr Alexander David Wharton MA(Cantab); LLM. Apr 2003
Morley, Ms Kay . . . . Jan 2002
Murphy, Frances . . . . Jan 1987
Pabst, Mr Michael. . . . . Feb 1998
Papanicolaou, Mr Christopher LLB(B'ham) . . . . . *Nov 1982
Phillips, Mr John MA(Cantab) . . . . *Nov 1988
Richards, Mr Sion LLB(Hons) . . . . *Nov 1996
Roberts, Mr David A LLB(B'ham) . . . . *Nov 1989
Rotenberg, Mr Andrew . . . . Jan 2002

See p2 for the Key to Work Categories & other symbols

Runnicles, Mr Julian LLM . . . *Sep 2000
Rutstein, Mr Michael . . . Jan 1989
Sallabank, Ms Charlotte L BSc; AKC; ATII. . . . *Sep 1985
Saunders, Mr William MA . . . *Mar 1986
Seaton, Mr S Neil MA(Cantab) . . . *Apr 1980
Shuttleworth, Mr Craig C BA(Oxon) . . . *Nov 1989
Smith, Mr David LLB(Hons) . . . *Dec 1994
Stueck, Mr Barnaby . . . Sep 2001
Taylor, Mr Mark . . . Jan 1979
Thorneycroft, Mr Max B BA(Oxon) . . . *Apr 1975
Walter, Mr Stephen F LLB(Sheff) . . . *Feb 1990
Nalbantian, Edward . . . NSP
Stuart, Eric . . . NSP
Asoc: Adams, Mr Richard LLB(Hons) . . . Jan 2003
Bainbridge, Mr Tom . . . Jan 2005
Barden, Mr Gregory . . . Oct 2010
Batley, Miss Sarah . . . Sep 2009
Billington, Miss Jessica . . . Apr 2011
Boast, Mr James . . . Sep 2008
Bonamy, Mr Liam . . . Sep 2008
Brown, Mr Adam . . . Sep 2005
Busby, Miss Emily . . . Mar 2006
Cartwright, Ms Anna . . . Mar 2005
Chakravortty, Ms Satarupa . . . Aug 2006
Conway, Ms Alice . . . Mar 2007
Davies, Ms Christine . . . Jan 1999
Davies, Mr Nicholas . . . Sep 2007
Druce, Ms Georgina . . . Apr 2011
Felce, Mr Jonathan . . . Jan 2006
Fendick, Miss Lauren . . . Apr 2010
Ferguson, Ms Victoria . . . Jan 2004
Ferrera, Mr Philip . . . Sep 2004
Firn, Ms Emily . . . Sep 2007
Fricker, Mr David . . . Sep 2005
Galbraith, Miss Ciara . . . Apr 2011
Harding, Mr David . . . Sep 2005
Harvey, Mr Luke . . . Apr 2008
Haywood, Miss Laura . . . Sep 2009
Hindhaugh, Mr Iain . . . Jan 2003
Hornblow, Mr Dominic J BA(Hons) . . . *Oct 2001
Hughes, Mr Eilian . . . Apr 2011
Hussey, Mr Thomas . . . Mar 2009
Kelly, Miss Claire . . . Apr 2011
Kiff, Mr Simon . . . Sep 2005
Leslie, Mr Simon . . . Sep 2005
Liberatore, Mr Francesco . . . Jan 2003
McDonald, Mr William . . . Mar 2009
McKay, Mr Tom . . . Sep 2008
Mehta, Ms Hannah . . . Jan 2004
Metcalf, Mr Peter . . . Apr 2009
Moore, Mr Lucas . . . Jan 2004
Olarou, Mr Denis . . . Apr 2011
Ormerod, Ms Lavina . . . Sep 2007
Orton, Mr Sebastian . . . Jan 2003
Phelps, Mr Rhys . . . Apr 2008
Purushothaman, Mr Deepak . . . Jan 2004
Rasool, Miss Zarah . . . Sep 2010
Roberts, Mr Nick . . . Sep 2005
Rogerson, Ms Kirsty . . . Jan 2005
Sandler, Ms Nicole . . . Apr 2001
Stafford, Mr Guillaume . . . Mar 2009
Stafford, Mr Patrick . . . Jan 2003
Storrs, Mr Nick . . . Apr 2010
Thomas, Mr Rhys E BA(Law) . . . Jan 2003
Travers, Mr Daniel . . . Sep 2009
Walton, Mr Benedict . . . Jan 2004
Ward, Mr Ben . . . Mar 2007
Weare, Mr Justin . . . Sep 2005
West, Ms Kathryn . . . Jan 2006
Witherall, Mr Jonathon Ben . . . Oct 2010
Zahn, Miss Lynette . . . Sep 2002
Ast: Basran, Miss Sukhvir . . . Jan 2000
Chana, Miss Jaskie LLB . . . Sep 2000
Coulson, Mr Neil Kenneth Lindsay BA(Oxon) . . . *Oct 1997
Davis, Ms Suzanne BA . . . *Nov 1996
Emerson, Mr Mark LLB(Soton) . . . *Jul 1993
Evans, Mr Matt . . . Mar 2000
Gumpert, Mr Andrew LLB(B'ham) . . . *Nov 1988
Kho, Ms Amy . . . Jan 2002
Mitchell, Mr John F MA(Cantab) . . . *Dec 1979
Papadakis, Mr John J BA(Sussex) . . . *Nov 1987
Robertson, Ms Liz . . . Jan 1997
Saxton, Ms Elizabeth LLB(Oxon); BA; BCL Vinerian Scholarship 1992 . . . *Sep 1994
Scarrott, Mr Adam . . . Sep 1997
Territt, Ms Harriet LLB(Hons) . . . *Nov 1998

J R JONES ‡
58 Uxbridge Road London W5 2ST
Tel: 020 8566 2595 *Fax:* 020 8579 4288 *Dx:* 5134 EALING
E-mail: solicitors@jrjones.co.uk

W T JONES ‡
71 Grays Inn Road Holborn London WC1X 8TR
Tel: 020 7405 4631 / 7242 7767 *Fax:* 020 7242 4337
List of partners: P C Hambleton
Work: C1 E L O Q S1 S2 W
Ptr: Hambleton, Mr Peter C LLB. . . . *Apr 1977

JOSEPH & CO SOLICITORS ‡
40 New Park Road London SW2 4UN
Tel: 020 8671 1149 *Fax:* 020 8678 9491 *Dx:* 132673 BRIXTON 2
E-mail: j.ameyawkyeremeh@yahoo.com

JOSIAH LAKE GARDINER LLP ‡
River House 143-145 Farringdon Road London EC1R 3AB
Tel: 020 7713 7011 *Fax:* 020 7713 7018 *Dx:* 5330 CLERKENWELL

JOSIAH-LAKE SOLICITORS ‡
3rd Floor 47 Dean Street Soho London W1D 5BE
Tel: 020 7439 2900

JOVES SOLICITORS ‡
312 Lewisham Road London SE13 7PA
Tel: 020 8852 4544

JOY & CO ‡
845 Romford Road London E12 5JY
Tel: 020 8514 8188 *Fax:* 020 8514 8303
E-mail: admin@joyandco.net

JUDGE SYKES FRIXOU ‡
York House 23 Kingsway London WC2B 6YF
Tel: 020 7379 5114 *Fax:* 020 7836 4974
Dx: 419 LONDON/CHANCERY LN
List of partners: D N Cockle, S Fothergill, B Frixou, J Kischland, N D Melin, K J Perryman-Best, S S Savani
Languages: French, Greek, Spanish
Work: A1 A3 B1 B2 C1 C2 C3 D1 E F1 J1 J2 K1 L M1 M2 N O P Q R1 R2 S1 S2 T1 T2 W Z(b,c,d,e,f,g,h,i,j,k,l,o,p,q,r,w)
Emergency Action, Advocacy undertaken and Member of Accident Line
Ptr: Cockle, Mr Derek N LLB(Hons) . . . *Dec 1988
Fothergill, Mr Simon . . . Jan 2001
Frixou, Ms Belinda LLB . . . *§Jun 1979
Kischland, Mr Jonathan . . . Jan 1991
Melin, Mr Nicholas D . . . Apr 2001
Perryman-Best, Ms Kirsty J . . . Apr 2002
Savani, Mr Shilpen S LLM; LLB . . . Nov 1997

JULIUS & CO SOLICITORS ‡
Countrywide House High Street Wanstead London E11 1QQ
Tel: 020 8989 2929 *Fax:* 020 8989 2974
E-mail: mail@juliusandcosolicitors.com

JULIUS CEASAR SOLICITORS ‡
174 Old Kent Road London SE1 5TY
Tel: 020 7708 8888

JUST COSTS SOLICITORS
Central Court 25 Southampton Buildings London WC2A 1AL
Tel: 020 7758 2155 *Fax:* 020 7758 2156 *Dx:* 426 LDE
E-mail: info@justcosts.com
Office: Chesterfield, Leeds, Manchester (2 offices)

K&L GATES LLP ‡
One New Change London EC4M 9AF
Tel: 020 7648 9000 *Fax:* 020 7648 9001
Dx: 58 LONDON/CHANCERY LN
E-mail: london@klng.com
List of partners: C M Barbor, N Baylis, R Boothroyd, D Bray, C G Causer, J P Coleman, C A E Cook, S D Cox, M B Curtis, J N Elgar, K J Greene, A Griffiths, R V Hadley, R Hardwick, V J Harte-Lovelace, R G W Herbert, J J S Hudson, M S M Johns, L A Kent, H D Kleiman, J J Landau, J D Magnin, A T McCarthy, P J Morgan, W L Phelops, D W Race, R J E Smith, W Smith
Languages: Arabic, French, German, Hebrew, Italian, Spanish
Work: A3 B1 C1 C2 C3 E F1 F2 I J1 L M1 M2 N O P Q R1 R2 S1 S2 T1 T2 U1 W Z(b,c,d,e,f,i,j,k,l,n,o,p,q,s,u,w,y,z)
Agency undertaken
Ptr: Barbor, Mrs Cynthia M LLB . . . *Jul 1976
Baylis, Mr Neil MA(Law) . . . Mar 1994
Boothroyd, Miss Rachel MA . . . *Mar 1996
Bray, Mr Dominic BA . . . *Oct 1995
Causer, Mr Christopher George . . . *Dec 1993
Coleman, Mr J Piers LLB(Lond) . . . *Apr 1978
Cook, Ms Carole A E LLB . . . *Oct 1987
Cox, Mr Steven D BA(Oxon) . . . *Dec 1988
Curtis, Ms Melanie B LLB . . . *Oct 1982
Elgar, Mr John N BA(Oxon) . . . *Oct 1982
Greene, Mr Kevin J LLB . . . *Nov 1984
Griffiths, Mr Antony LLB . . . *May 1989
Hadley, Mr Robert V LLB . . . *Nov 1985
Hardwick, Mr Richard LLB . . . *Dec 1994
Harte-Lovelace, Miss V Jane LLB . . . *Oct 1983
Herbert, Mr Richard G W LLB(Nott'm) . . . *Apr 1979
Hudson, Mr James Jeremy S LLB . . . *Dec 1977
Johns, Mr Michael S M . . . *Jun 1968
Kent, Ms Linda A LLB(Soton) . . . *Oct 1986
Kleiman, Mr Howard D LLB . . . *Oct 1985
Landau, Mr Jeremy J MEng(Leeds); MA(City); DipLaw(LSE) . . . *Oct 1996
McCarthy, Miss Anne T BSc(Econ) . . . *Feb 1983
Magnin, Mr John D LLB(Lond) . . . *Nov 1987
Morgan, Mr Philip J BA(Oxon) Martin Wronker Prize - Best Administrative Law Paper; SI & May Prize for Best Contract Paper . . . *Nov 1995
Phelops, Mr Warren L LLB . . . *Mar 1992
Race, Mr David W LLB . . . *Jun 1974
Smith, Mr Richard J E BA(Cantab) . . . *Nov 1976
Smith, Mr Wayne BA; LLB . . . *Nov 1988
Ast: Amzallag, Mr David . . . Sep 2001
Atkinson, Mr James . . . Sep 2002
Banyard-Smith, Mr Edward . . . Sep 2002
Booth, Miss Susan MA . . . Mar 1998
Borrie, Mr A J Stuart MA(Oxon) . . . *Oct 1995
Brosinovich, Ms Pia . . . Sep 2001
Brousson, Mr Richard . . . Sep 1997
Callegari, Mr Paul LLB . . . *Nov 1998
Davies, Mr James Charles . . . Sep 2001
Dillabough, Ms Elizabeth Rachael . . . Sep 2001
Down, Mr Simon . . . Sep 2002
Eady, Ms Caroline Sarah LLB . . . *Sep 2000
Gibson, Mr Alex Robert James LLB . . . Sep 2000
Hurle, Mr Brynley E LLB(Hons)(Bris) . . . *Oct 1998
Leaney, Miss Inga K BEc(Hons); LLB . . . Oct 1997
McIntosh, Mr Milton . . . Dec 2002
Mackereth, Mr Edward BA(Hons) . . . *Oct 1997
Mahmood, Mr Yassir Bin BA(Oxon) . . . Sep 2001
Major, Mr Christian Thomas BA(Hons)(History) . . . Sep 1999
Morallee, Mr Adam Omar . . . Sep 2001
Morton, Mr Peter BSc . . . *Oct 1997
Otterwell, Ms Lucy . . . Sep 2002
Papworth, Ms Karen . . . Sep 2002
Pegrum, Ms Victoria Anneli BA(Hons); CPE . . . Sep 2000
Pilkington, Mr Oliver . . . Sep 2002
Reid, Ms Eleanor . . . Sep 2002
Smith, Mr Matthew Edward BSc(Hons) . . . Nov 1995
Stone, Ms Sarah . . . *Jun 1998
Tanner, Ms Rebecca Clare . . . *Sep 1998
Taylor, Ms Sarah R . . . Sep 2002
Turner, Mr Robert E LLB(Hons) . . . *Sep 1999
Wargent, Mr Nicholas . . . *Sep 1998
Williamson, Mr Richard E F BC; CPE; LPC . . . Nov 1998
Woodward, Mr Stephen . . . Sep 2002

K&S @ LAW SOLICITORS ‡
133 Plumstead High Street Plumstead London SE18 1SL
Tel: 020 8331 0505

KC LAW CHAMBERS SOLICITORS ‡
62 Beechwood Road London E8 3DY
Tel: 020 7254 3353 *Fax:* 020 7249 5152
E-mail: info@kclawchambers.com

KD LAW LIMITED ‡
Warnford Court 29 Throgmorton Street London EC2N 2AT
Tel: 020 7947 4027
E-mail: info@kd-law.co.uk

KK SOLICITORS ‡
The Club House 16 Kenver Avenue London N12 0PG
Tel: 020 8446 3240 *Fax:* 020 8446 3240
E-mail: info@kksolicitors.com

KLS LAW
49 Britton Street London EC1M 5UL
Tel: 020 7553 7923
Office: Warrington

KPM SOLICITORS ‡
116-118 Chancery Lane London WC2A 1PP
Tel: 020 7404 1995 *Fax:* 020 7404 2335 *Dx:* 105 LDE
E-mail: chancery@kpmlegal.co.uk
List of partners: K T South, M S Stubbs
Work: C1 F1 J1 K1 K3 L N O Q S1 S2 W Z(g)
Legal Aid Franchise
Ptr: South, Ms Karen T LLM. . . . *§Jun 1990
Stubbs, Mr Matthew S LLB(Hons) . . . *May 1995

KAGAN & CO ‡
245a Lewisham Way London SE4 1XF
Tel: 020 8694 9969 *Fax:* 020 8694 9667
List of partners: K Kagan
Languages: Turkish
Work: E F1 G H J1 K1 S1
Fixed Fee Interview and Legal Aid undertaken
Ptr: Kagan, Kerim LLM; BA . . . *Feb 1988

KAIM TODNER LTD ‡
11 Bolt Court London EC4A 3DQ
Tel: 020 7353 6660 *Fax:* 020 7353 6661
Dx: 265 LONDON/CHANCERY LN
Emergency telephone 020 7353 6660
E-mail: solicitors@kaimtodner.com
List of partners: H Ali, C M Anderson, S H Garland, R J Kaim, H A Leaney, B M Quearney, R D Quinn, K E Todner
Office: Ashford, London N1, London SE17
Languages: French, Hebrew, Italian, Spanish, Urdu
Work: B2 D1 G H K1 Z(m)
Emergency Action, Agency, Advocacy, Fixed Fee Interview and Legal Aid undertaken
Dir: Ali, Mr Hulusi ★ . . . Feb 1999
Anderson, Miss Claire M LLB . . . Oct 1989
Kaim, Mr Robert John BSc ★ . . . Jun 1977
Leaney, Ms Heidi Ann . . . Jan 2002
Quearney, Ms Brenda Mary . . . Sep 1996
Todner, Ms Karen Elizabeth . . . *May 1987
Ast: Ballato, Ms Leanne . . . Apr 2009
Barun, Ms Joanna . . . Jul 2009
Dinkeldein, Mr David . . . Mar 2010
Evans, Ms Claire . . . Oct 1981
Evans, Mr Michael BA(Hons) . . . Sep 2009
Hearty, Mr Niall . . . Mar 2006
Jappie, Mr Robert LLB(Hons) . . . Apr 2008
Jerome, Mr Daniel Paul ★ . . . *Feb 1991
Katz, Mr Robert Simon . . . Mar 2005
Pandit, Mr Deepesh . . . Jul 2002

KAIM TODNER LTD
195 Walworth Road London SE17 1RW
Tel: 020 7701 4747 *Fax:* 020 7703 8698
Dx: 265 LONDON/CHANCERY LN
Emergency telephone 020 7353 6660
E-mail: solicitors@kaimtodner.com
Office: Ashford, London EC4, London N1
Languages: Bengali, French, Turkish
Work: D1 G H K1 M1 V Z(i,m)
Emergency Action, Agency, Advocacy, Fixed Fee Interview and Legal Aid undertaken
Ast: Bhuller, Mr Tejpal Singh . . . Sep 2004
Cleanthous, Ms Lucy LLB(Hons) . . . May 2005
Jeyasselan, Ms Apiramy . . . Apr 2010
Snodgrass, Mr Cameron John Adam Ingus . . . Aug 2002
Wilson, Mr Jonathon Henry Clarke . . . Nov 2004
Wilson, Ms Sarah . . . Mar 2010

KAIM TODNER LTD
5 The Ivories 6-8 Northampton Street Islington London N1 2HY
Tel: 020 7700 0070 *Fax:* 020 7619 9222
Dx: 265 LONDON/CHANCERY LN
Emergency telephone 020 7353 6660
E-mail: solicitors@kaimtodner.com
Office: Ashford, London EC4, London SE17
Work: D1 G H K1 K2 K3 Z(m)
Agency undertaken
Dir: Garland, Mr Stephen Henry . . . Apr 2002
Ast: Bloom, Mr David LLB(Hons) . . . Nov 2010
Corcoran, Mr John Joseph . . . Aug 2003
Ennis-Gayle, Mr Darrell . . . Aug 2010
Jackson, Ms Caroline . . . Jun 1996
Jordan, Ms Nandipha . . . Apr 2008
Katz, Mr Robert Simon . . . Mar 2005
Lusingu, Ms Linda . . . Jul 2010
McGonigal, Ms Rachel . . . Mar 1998
Narsi, Ms Miriam . . . Aug 2008
Pandit, Mr Deepesh . . . Jul 2002

KAJ & CO ‡
406 Holloway Road London N7 6PZ
Tel: 020 7700 7826

KALAM SOLICITORS ‡
1st Floor 128 Whitechapel Road London E1 1JE
Tel: 020 7247 4884 *Fax:* 020 7377 9915
Dx: 155245 TOWER HAMLETS 2
E-mail: info@kalamsolicitors.co.uk

KALBER STRUCKLEY & CO ‡
3rd Floor 2 New Burlington Street London W1S 2JE
Tel: 020 7734 1102 *Fax:* 020 7434 2497 *Dx:* 44728 SOHO SQUARE
Emergency telephone 020 8203 3822
E-mail: office@kalber-struckley.co.uk
List of partners: T M Kalber, K Struckley
Work: G H
Emergency Action, Agency and Legal Aid undertaken

Ptr: Kalber, Mr Thomas M . . . Jun 1977
Struckley, Ms Karen FILEx . . . Nov 1993

KALRA & CO ‡
304 High Road Leyton Waltham Forest London E10 5PW
Tel: 020 8539 0123 ***Fax:*** 020 8558 4243
List of partners: K Kalra
Languages: Hindi, Punjabi
Work: K1 K3 L S1 Z(i)
SPr: Kalra, Kasturi MA; LLB . . . Apr 1997

KALTONS ‡
Suite 302 Spitfire Studios 63-71 Collier Street London N1 9BE
Tel: 020 7278 1817

KAMBERLEY SOLICITORS ‡
First Floor 100a Chase Side London N14 5PH
Tel: 020 8886 9718

KANAGA SOLICITORS ‡
108 High Street Colliers Wood London SW19 2BT
Tel: 020 8544 1100

PETER KANDLER & CO ‡
60 Goldborne Road London W10 5PR
Tel: 020 8960 9222 ***Fax:*** 020 8960 0777 ***Dx:*** 46658 MAIDA HILL
Emergency telephone 07623 498618
E-mail: enquiries@peterkandler.com
List of partners: D B Martin
Languages: French, Russian
Work: G H
Ptr: Martin, Mr David B BA . . . Jan 1976

KANGS SOLICITORS
9 Carmelite Street London EC4Y 0DR
Tel: 020 7936 6396
E-mail: enquiries@kangssolicitors.co.uk
Office: Birmingham (2 offices), Manchester

KAPADIA STUART SOLICITORS ‡
5 Underwood Street London N1 7LY
Tel: 0871 575 0522

STUART KARATAS SOLICITORS ‡
First Floor 83 Kingsland High Street London E8 2PB
Tel: 020 7923 8600 ***Fax:*** 020 7254 1197
E-mail: info@sk-solicitors.com

STUART KARATAS SOLICITORS ‡
1st Floor 285 Fore Street London N9 0PD
Tel: 020 8887 1360 ***Fax:*** 020 8887 1370 ***Dx:*** 36210 EDMONTON
E-mail: info@sk-solicitors.com

P KARMA & CO ‡
346-348a Kilburn High Road London NW6 2QJ
Tel: 020 7624 8814 ***Fax:*** 020 7624 8813 ***Dx:*** 123864 KILBURN 2
E-mail: para@krama.fsnet.co.uk

KASLERS SOLICITORS LLP
29th Floor 1 Canada Square Canary Wharf London E14 5DY
Tel: 020 7712 1751
E-mail: info@docklandssolicitors.co.uk
Office: West Malling

KATTENMUCHINROSENMANCORNISH LLP ‡
1-3 Fredrick's Place Old Jewry London EC2R 8AE
Tel: 020 7776 7620 ***Fax:*** 020 7776 7621
Languages: Afrikaans, Cantonese, French, Hebrew
Work: R2 Z(b)

KAURA & CO ‡
23 Offham Slope Woodside Park London N12 7BZ
Tel: 020 8445 4069 ***Fax:*** 020 8445 4370
List of partners: R Kaura
Languages: Gujarati, Hindi, Punjabi, Urdu
Work: C1 E L S1 S2 W
Agency undertaken
SPr: Kaura, Mrs Rita BA . . . *§Jan 1979

LEON KAYE SOLICITORS ‡
12 Ivory House Clove Hitch Quay Plantation Wharf London SW11 3TN
Tel: 020 7228 2020 ***Fax:*** 020 7228 6484
Dx: 155220 CLAPHAM WHARF
E-mail: info@leonkaye.co.uk
List of partners: J M Berry, L J Kaye
Languages: French, German, Italian, Spanish
Work: C1 C2 C3 E J1 M1 O P Q S1 S2 W
Ptr: Berry, Mr Jamie Marc . . . May 2003
Kaye, Mr Leon J LLB(Lond) . . . *§Jun 1970

KEELYS LLP
30-34 Curtain Road London EC2A 3NZ
Tel: 020 7422 8686 ***Dx:*** 36609 FINSBURY
E-mail: office@keelys.co.uk
Office: Lichfield
Asoc: Clifford, Mr Eamonn Patrick . . . *Nov 2003
Con: Burrell, Mr Derek Raymond . . . *Dec 1990

ANDREW KEEN & CO ‡
10 The Shrubberies George Lane South Woodford London E18 1BG
Tel: 020 8989 3123 ***Fax:*** 020 8989 3223 ***Dx:*** 90717 WOODFORD
E-mail: andrewkeenco@aol.com
List of partners: A S Keen
Work: D2 K1 K3 L Q W Z(g,r)
Emergency Action, Advocacy and Fixed Fee Interview undertaken
Ptr: Keen, Mr Andrew S LLB(Soton) . . . *Dec 1984

ANDREW KEENAN & CO ‡
Nickleby House Charles Dickens Terrace Maple Road London SE20 8RE
Tel: 020 8659 0332 ***Fax:*** 020 8659 3689 ***Dx:*** 34860 PENGE
Emergency telephone 020 8659 0332
E-mail: law@andrewkeenan.co.uk
List of partners: A C Keenan
Work: B2 G H
Emergency Action, Agency, Advocacy, Fixed Fee Interview, Legal Aid undertaken and Legal Aid Franchise
SPr: Keenan, Mr Andrew C OBE . . . *Mar 1966
Ast: Crossley, Ms Gemma BA; LLM . . . *Jan 2002
Goodger, Mr Steven William . . . *Oct 2007

McGrath, Mr Gerard Alan CQSW; BA(Hons) ★ . . . *Feb 2008
Con: Musters, Mr Patrick Havelock Auchmuty ★ . . . Jun 1978

DAVID KELTIE ASSOCIATES ‡
Fleet Place House 2 Fleet Place London EC4M 7ET
Tel: 020 7329 8888 ***Fax:*** 020 7329 1111
E-mail: mailbox@keltie.com

KEMI LAW CHAMBERS ‡
Unit 37 Design Works Park Parade London NW10 4HT
Tel: 020 8965 6000 ***Fax:*** 020 8965 6066
E-mail: kemilawchambers@yahoo.co.uk

J A KEMP & CO ‡
14 South Square Gray's Inn London WC1R 5JJ
Tel: 020 7405 3292 ***Fax:*** 020 7242 8932
List of partners: S Ali, M A Ayers, J Benson, A Bentham, P Campbell, T Cresswell, T Duckworth, J Fish, W Geoffrey, C Keen, J Leeming, G McCluskie, C Merryweather, M Nicholls, S Roques, A Senior, J Sexton, S Smith, R Srinivasan, R Tyson, A Webb, S Wright
Work: Z(e)
Ptr: Ali, Suleman . . . Jan 2000
Ayers, Mr Martyn Ayers . . . Jan 1978
Benson, Mr John . . . Jan 1980
Bentham, Mr Andrew . . . Jan 1997
Campbell, Mr Patrick . . . Jan 1995
Cresswell, Mr Thomas . . . Jan 1981
Duckworth, Mr Timothy . . . Jan 1993
Fish, Mr James . . . Jan 1996
Geoffrey, Woods . . . Jan 1980
Keen, Ms Celia . . . Jan 1992
Leeming, Mr John . . . Jan 1993
McCluskie, Ms Gail . . . Jan 1992
Merryweather, Mr Colin . . . Jan 1996
Nicholls, Mr Michael . . . Jan 1990
Roques, Ms Sarah . . . Jan 1995
Senior, Mr Alan . . . Jan 1972
Sexton, Ms Jane . . . Jan 1988
Smith, Mr Samuel . . . Jan 1994
Srinivasan, Ravi . . . Jan 1998
Tyson, Mr Robin . . . Jan 1998
Webb, Mr Andrew . . . Jan 1984
Wright, Mr Simon . . . Jan 1992

KEMP LITTLE LLP ‡
Cheapside House 138 Cheapside London EC2V 6BJ
Tel: 020 7600 8080 ***Fax:*** 020 7600 7878
List of partners: C H Claisse, M Conradi, P Garland, P Hinton, A J R Joint, R H Kemp, S J McElhinney, C Middleton, A Moseby, C G Murray, P O'Hare, S Sheppard, L K Vernall, D Williams
Work: C1 C2 C3 F1 F2 I J1 M1 O Q U1 U2 Z(b,e,f,z,za)
Ptr: Claisse, Mr Charles Henry LLB; LLM; MA . . . *Aug 1998
Conradi, Mr Michael BA; PGDL; LPC . . . *Oct 1998
Garland, Mr Paul . . . *Apr 1997
Hinton, Mr Paul BA(Hons) . . . *Sep 2001
Joint, Mr Andrew James Reid LLB . . . *Aug 2002
Kemp, Mr Richard Harry MA(Cantab); Licence Specialise en Droit Europeen(Brussels); ULB . . . *§Sep 1980
McElhinney, Miss Siobhan Johanna LLB . . . *Sep 1998
Middleton, Mr Chris . . . *Jan 2000
Moseby, Mr Andy LLB . . . *Sep 1999
Murray, Mr Calum G LLB(Hons); DipLP; MPhil(Cantab) Notary Public . . . *Oct 1999
O'Hare, Mr Paul LLB Legal Director of the National Outsourcing Association . . . *Sep 1998
Sheppard, Miss Susannah MA(Oxon); Maitrise(ULB) *Nov 2001
Vernall, Mrs Lucy Kate BA(Law) Cambridge University Prize for Contract Law 1991 . . . *Sep 1996
Williams, Mr David LLB R G Lawson Prize . . . *Sep 1996

KEN'D SOLICITORS ‡
Unit 53 Millennium Business Centre 3 Humber Trading Estate London NW2 6DW
Tel: 020 8438 6666 ***Fax:*** 020 8438 6666
E-mail: kensolicitors@yahoo.co.uk

KENNARDS WELLS ‡
718 High Road Leytonstone London E11 3AJ
Tel: 020 8539 8338 ***Fax:*** 020 8556 3234 ***Dx:*** 58200 LEYTONSTONE
Emergency telephone 07939 559152
List of partners: R H Cohen, S J Redpath, A J Yeshin
Office: Epping, Redbridge
Languages: Bengali, Hindi, Urdu
Work: B1 B2 C1 D1 E F1 G H J1 J2 K1 K2 K3 K4 L N O P Q R2 S1 S2 V W Z(l,p,q,r)
Emergency Action, Agency, Advocacy, Fixed Fee Interview, Legal Aid undertaken and Legal Aid Franchise
Ptr: Redpath, Mr Stephen J LLB . . . *§Jan 1982
Yeshin, Ms Anne Judith . . . Oct 1983
Asoc: Collier, Ms Inez Lorraine LLB(Hons) . . . Apr 2002
Ast: London, Ms Katrina . . . Feb 2008

HOWARD KENNEDY LLP ‡
(incorporating Malkins; Peter T James & Co)
(in association with Camilotti Ceccou Polettini Padua(Italy); Siaoweng & Leung(Hong Kong))
19 Cavendish Square London W1A 2AW
Tel: 020 7636 1616 ***Fax:*** 020 7499 2899
Dx: 42748 OXFORD CIRCUS NORTH
E-mail: enquiries@howardkennedy.com
List of partners: P F G Amandini, S A Aslan, H Azmi, A L Banes, L Begner, K D Bichard, R Bindshedler, P Birkett, D J E Blakeman, R A Bryk, J J F Butler, M J Chapelow, S Charles, S Clinning, A W Collins, D Collinson, A G Coyne, G H Craig, G Dabby-Joory, D M Davies, C Donnison, B Eagles, D J Eldridge, C A Emden, N Emerson, C A Gooding, E M Gummers, I M Harris, M L Harris, S M Haworth, S Heinemann, B Higgins, D Hill, A J Hunt, S M Johnson, P S Kornbluth, H Kousetta, C Langan, C R Langford, K Lassman, P H Leacock, A S Levene, J J Levinson, J G R Lewis, L Lloyd, P J Miller, D L Mills, M Morgan, S N Morris, H Mozzi, I P Mulkis, T J A Newey, P Paschalis, D Philips, A Pike, S Pullen, R M Roseman, D R Seaton, R B Sigurdsson, E S Smith, P R Springall, J Stephenson, J Stewart, N Stewart, J Summers, D Swanwick, S P Taylor, C Thompson, N J Treppass, J M Weider, C M Woodgate, A Woolf
Languages: Dutch, French, German, Greek, Hebrew, Hindi, Italian, Russian, Spanish, Swedish
Work: B1 C1 C2 C3 D1 E F1 I J1 K1 K3 L M2 N O Q R1 R2 S1 T1 T2 W Z(b,c,d,e,f,i,j,k,l,n,r,w)
Emergency Action, Agency and Advocacy undertaken
Ptr: Amandini, Mr Paul F G LLB Cecil Karuth Prize . . . *Apr 1979

Aslan, Ms Susan A BA(English Lit) . . . Oct 1985
Azmi, Hardani LLB(Hons) . . . Feb 1998
Banes, Mr Alan L MSI . . . *Jan 1970
Begner, Mr Laurence . . . Mar 1976
Bichard, Mr Kevin D MA(Cantab) . . . *Apr 1977
Bindshedler, Mr Roger BSc; LLB(Hons) . . . Feb 1998
Birkett, Mr Peter BA; LLB(Hons) . . . Dec 1989
Blakeman, Mr David J E LLB(Lond) . . . *Oct 1984
Bryk, Mr Raymond A . . . *Nov 1973
Butler, Mr Jeremy J F BA(Lond) . . . *Dec 1977
Chapelow, Mr Michael J LLB . . . *Jul 1978
Charles, Ms Susan LLB(Hons) . . . Nov 1988
Clinning, Mr Steve BA(Hons) . . . Mar 2002
Collins, Mr Andrew W BA . . . *Oct 1987
Collinson, Mr Derek LLB . . . Jul 1969
Coyne, Mr Anthony G LLB . . . *Sep 1988
Craig, Mr Graham H LLB . . . *Dec 1964
Dabby-Joory, Mr Gideon LLB; LLM . . . *Dec 1998
Davies, Mr D Martin LLB(Lond) . . . *Dec 1983
Donnison, Mr Christopher BA . . . Feb 1983
Eagles, Mr Brian LLB; ACIArb . . . *May 1960
Eldridge, Mr David J Commissioner for Oaths . . . *Oct 1956
Emden, Mr Craig A LLB . . . *Dec 1985
Emerson, Mr Nigel MA(Cantab) . . . *Oct 1981
Gooding, Mr Christopher A LLB(Brunel) . . . *Apr 1981
Gummers, Mr Eric Michael BA(Hons)(Cantab) Legal Adviser at Pimlico CAB . . . *Nov 1985
Harris, Mr Iain M . . . *Oct 1977
Harris, Mr Michael L BA(Oxon); MSI . . . *Jul 1979
Haworth, Miss Susan M LLB . . . *Oct 1992
Heinemann, Mr Stephen BSc(Econ) . . . *Sep 1999
Higgins, Bronwyn BA . . . Sep 1986
Hill, Mr David . . . Sep 2001
Hunt, Mr Anthony J LLB . . . *Oct 1989
Johnson, Miss Susan M LLB . . . *Oct 1985
Kornbluth, Mr Philip Stanley MA(Cantab) . . . *Nov 1982
Kousetta, Hakan BA; LPC; LLW . . . *Sep 1999
Langan, Mr Christopher BA(Hons) . . . Dec 1988
Langford, Mr Christopher Robin . . . *Aug 1975
Lassman, Mr Keith LLB; MSI . . . *Oct 1983
Leacock, Mr Philip Henry . . . *Jul 1967
Levene, Mr Allen S . . . *Jan 1971
Levinson, Mr Jonathan James BA . . . Nov 1989
Lewis, Mr Jason G R BA; LLB(Hons) . . . *Apr 1992
Lloyd, Leighton BA; CPE; LPC . . . *Sep 1999
Miller, Mr Paul J BA(Hons)(Manc)(Econ) . . . *Sep 1997
Mills, Mrs Deborah Louise LLB . . . *Jan 1990
Morgan, Mr Matthew BA(Hons) . . . Oct 1997
Morris, Mr Steven N MA; LLB(Cantab) . . . *Apr 1981
Mozzi, Mr Humbert BA(Hons) . . . Sep 2002
Mulkis, Mr Ian P BSc . . . Oct 1988
Newey, Mr Trevor J A . . . *Jun 1971
Paschalis, Mr Peter LLB; PGDip . . . *Nov 1997
Philips, Mr David . . . *Sep 1996
Pike, Mr Andrew . . . Nov 2001
Pullen, Mr Simon BA(Oxon) . . . Feb 1980
Roseman, Mr Rolfe M LLB . . . Dec 1968
Seaton, Mr D Roger MA(Cantab) . . . Dec 1967
Sigurdsson, Mr Robert B BA . . . *Oct 1985
Smith, Mrs Elizabeth S LLB(Lond) . . . *May 1990
Springall, Mr Paul R LLB . . . *Oct 1984
Stephenson, Mr Justin BA(Hons) . . . Nov 1990
Stewart, Mr James LLB(Hons) . . . *Oct 1994
Stewart, Nicky . . . Nov 1998
Summers, Jo LLB . . . Nov 1995
Swanwick, Ms Deborah LLB(Hons) . . . Nov 1994
Taylor, Miss Susan P LLB . . . *Apr 1981
Thompson, Mr Craig LLB(Hons) . . . Dec 1994
Treppass, Mr Nicholas J LLB . . . *Apr 1977
Weider, Mr Julian Michael . . . *Dec 1974
Woodgate, Ms Catherine Mary BSc . . . Nov 1995
Woolf, Mr Andrew LLB . . . Sep 1994
Asoc: Rambard, Ms Samantha LLB . . . Sep 2003
Ast: Amin, Miss Beena BA; LLB(Hons) . . . Nov 1989
Bailey, Ms Elizabeth BA(Hons) . . . Mar 2006
Birchall, Mr Gavin LLB(Hons); LLM(Tax) . . . Sep 2001
Bishop, Mr Guy B M BA(Hons); MA; DipLP . . . *Sep 1997
Brice, Ms Rachel LLB . . . Sep 2006
Brook, Mr Simon BA . . . Jan 2006
Catterall, Mr Paul BA; LLB(Hons) . . . Sep 2001
D'este-Hoare, Chris LLB . . . Sep 2006
Dhillon, Miss Sukina BA . . . Sep 2001
Dubignon, Ms Christine BA; LLB(Hons) . . . May 2006
Foley, Mr Rupert BA . . . Sep 2004
Frey, Ms Sharon BA(Hons); MA . . . May 2003
Goldspink, Mr Graham BA(Hons) . . . Sep 2001
Goldstein, Mr Scott BA(Hons); MA . . . Sep 2002
Greenby, Mr Barry H BA; LLB(Sussex) . . . *Jun 1976
Hanspaul, Ms Sandy LLB . . . Oct 2002
Hargreaves, Ms Sarah LLB . . . Nov 2003
Herbert, Mrs Rosemary LLB(Manc) . . . Apr 1976
Hernandez-Garcia, Ms Maria LLB . . . Jun 2006
Hewitson, Mr Nigel LLB . . . Dec 1988
Hook, Ms Samantha ACIB . . . Sep 2003
Howard, Ms Jane Anna LLB . . . *Aug 1999
Hylton, Mr Ian LLB(Hons) . . . Mar 2006
Johns, Ms Kathryn LLB(Hons) . . . Mar 2005
Joseph, Ms Rosaleen LLB . . . *Nov 1994
Kaler, Sukhi BA . . . *Oct 1992
Kaye, Mr Gregory BSc(Jt Hons) . . . Oct 1999
Langford, Mr David LLB . . . Sep 2002
Levy, Mr Myles LLB; BSc . . . Mar 1997
Liu, Ms Michelle LLB(Hons) . . . Apr 2003
Lofts, Mr Hugo . . . Jul 2002
McCarthy, Ms Claire LLB(Hons) . . . Sep 2000
McGill, Ms Nessa BA; LLB(Hons) . . . Sep 2001
March-Taylor, Ms Rebecca BA; LLB(Hons) . . . May 2001
Mendelson, Ms Tessa BA; LLB(Hons) . . . Apr 2006
Miller, Mr Nick BA . . . Aug 2001
Mills, Ms Diane E LLB(Hons) . . . Nov 1991
Miranda, Mrs Susana Notary Public . . . Aug 1996
Mitchell, Miss Nicola LLB(Hons) . . . Sep 2001
Mocatta, Ms Gabrielle BA . . . *Sep 2000
Needof, Mr Marc BA(Hons) . . . Mar 2006
Perera, Ms Emma BA(Hons) . . . Sep 1999
Presland, Mr Mark LLB . . . Sep 2003
Rambaud, Ms Samantha LLB . . . Sep 2003
Rumens, Mr Ian BSc(Hons) . . . Oct 2002
Scott, Mr Ian BA . . . May 1998
Siddle, Mr Paul BA(Hons) . . . Sep 2003
Singleton, Mr James Hew LLB . . . Sep 1999
Spear, Ms Katie BA . . . Sep 2004
Tennant, Ms Sharron . . . Sep 2004
Thompson, Mr Angus MA . . . Sep 2000
Yasutake, Ms Naoko BSc(Hons) . . . Sep 2003

See p2 for the Key to Work Categories & other symbols

Con: Duval, Mr Mark S . . . . *Apr 1966
Philips, Mr Martin J M BA Grotius Prize (City of London Solicitor) . . . . *Oct 1967
Shebson, Mr Victor Lionel LLB . . . . *Dec 1960
Slingsby, Mr Charles Anthony MA(Oxon) . . . . *Apr 1969
Smithson, Mr Peter D . . . . *Oct 1958

JOHN KENNEDY & CO
35 Great Peter Street Westminster London SW1P 3LR
Tel: 020 7222 0441 *Fax:* 020 7222 1064 *Dx:* 2312 VICTORIA
Office: London SE1, Oxford

KENNEDYS ‡
25 Fenchurch Avenue London EC3M 5AD
Tel: 020 7667 9667 *Fax:* 020 7667 9777 *Dx:* 766 LONDON/CITY
List of partners: C D K Abbott, M Andrews, S E Antram, P Barlow, S Basha, R A Bates, C W Berens, N Bowman, C W Brewer, M Burton, S M Cantle, P Carter, A S Coates, S T Craig, T J E Davies, R Dawbarn, R A Dubbins, K Dwyer, P W J Ellingham, S J Gibson, A F Gilbert, L N Gilford, J Graham, A L Greenwood, J K Harris, R S Harris, P J Hartley, J C H Harvey, T L Head, A J Hunn, S D R Jack, R A H Jones, A Kershaw, J D Lapraik, M K Lawrence, G A Lord, C MacGregor, C Malla, I N d C McCracken, D McShee, I A G Morrison, C Oldfield, B Paganuzzi, J Palmer, J A Penrose-Stevens, D Philip, J L Raw, C Ritchie, J Sayers, S Sayers, C S K Sharrock, J W Shaw, J Shrimpton, M Skinner, P A Spibey, D J Sullivan, C E Sumner, M J Sutton, D P J Thomas, N P G Thomas, H S Tilley, R Tobin, C A Vernon, M F J Walker, M J Wells, K L West, P F C West, R P West, N D Williams, T J Wilson, R Wotherspoon, J D Yates
Office: Belfast, Birmingham, Cambridge, Chelmsford, Maidstone, Manchester, Sheffield, Taunton
Ptr: Andrews, Mr Matthew LLB . . . . Jan 1998
Antram, Ms Sally E BA(Oxon) . . . . *Oct 1993
Basha, Miss Sumiya LLB(Bris) . . . . Oct 1993
Bates, Mr Richard A . . . . *Oct 1989
Burton, Mr Mark . . . . Sep 1999
Cantle, Mr Stephen M . . . . *Jun 1978
Carter, Mr Paul LLB . . . . *Oct 1995
Coates, Mr Andrew Stuart LLB; ACIArb . . . . *Oct 1987
Davies, Mr Trevor J E LLB . . . . *Oct 1980
Dubbins, Mr Roger A LLB . . . . *Nov 1971
Dwyer, Ms Kathleen FILEx . . . . *Nov 1996
Ellingham, Mr Peter W J LLB . . . . *Nov 1990
Gibson, Mr Simon J LLB . . . . Oct 1984
Gilbert, Mr Andrew F LLB . . . . Dec 1993
Gilford, Mr Laurence N LLB(B'ham) . . . . *Nov 1973
Graham, Mr John LLB . . . . *Dec 1980
Greenwood, Mr Anthony L BA(Law) . . . . *§Oct 1982
Harris, Mr Richard S LLB . . . . *§Dec 1968
Hartley, Mr Philip J LLB . . . . *Nov 1990
Harvey, Mr John C H LLB; LLM . . . . *Oct 1987
Head, Ms Tracy L LLB(Hons) . . . . *Jan 1989
Hunn, Mr Andrew J MA(Oxon); ACII . . . . Apr 1981
Jack, Mr Stephen D R LLB(Hons) . . . . *§Mar 1992
Jones, Mr Roger A H BA . . . . *Aug 1992
Lawrence, Mr Michael K LLB(Lond) . . . . *Apr 1975
Lord, Mr Geoffrey A LLB(Lond) . . . . *§Jun 1972
McCracken, Mr Ivan N de C MA(Oxon); ACIArb . . . . *§Jul 1967
MacGregor, Ms Christina BA . . . . Sep 1991
McShee, Mr Daniel . . . . Mar 1997
Malla, Mr Christopher LLB; LLM . . . . Sep 1997
Morrison, Mr Iain A G MA(Oxon) . . . . *Dec 1978
Paganuzzi, Bernadino LLB . . . . Oct 1988
Palmer, Mr Jeremy . . . . Apr 1981
Philip, Mr David BSc . . . . Oct 1994
Raw, Ms Jillian Lee BA; LLB; LLM . . . . Sep 2004
Sayers, Mrs Janet BA(Law) . . . . *May 1981
Sayers, Mr Shane BA . . . . *Oct 1981
Sharrock, Mr Christopher S K MA(Cantab) . . . . . . *Oct 1981
Shaw, Mr James W MA(Oxon) . . . . Dec 1979
Shrimpton, Mr James LLB . . . . *Oct 1996
Skinner, Mr Mark . . . . Nov 1993
Spibey, Mr Paul A LLB(Bris) . . . . *Nov 1991
Sullivan, Mr David J BA(Law) . . . . *Jun 1976
Sumner, Mr C Eric MA(Cantab) . . . . *Jan 1977
Thomas, Mr Dominic Peter Jocelyn BA(Hons)(Law) . . Nov 1993
Thomas, Mr Nicholas P G LLB; FCIArb . . . . Jun 1980
Tilley, Ms Helen S LLB(Hons) . . . . *Sep 1992
Vernon, Miss Carole A LLB . . . . *Oct 1989
Walker, Mr Michael F J BA(Oxon) . . . . *Aug 1977
Wells, Mr Michael J LLB . . . . Oct 1989
West, Mr Philip F C LLB . . . . *Nov 1983
Williams, Mr Nicholas D LLB . . . . Nov 1980
Wilson, Mr Timothy J LLB . . . . *Jun 1979
Wotherspoon, Mr Robert . . . . Oct 1988
Mem: Berens, Ms Caroline Wendy LLB . . . . *Dec 1991
Dawbarn, Mr Robert . . . . Apr 1994
Tobin, Mr Robert . . . . Sep 2003
Asoc: Palmer, Miss Alison G FILEx ♦ . . . . *Sep 1997
Rouse, Mr Nicholas LLB(Hons) . . . . *Nov 1993
Ast: Acheson, Miss Elizabeth S BA(Hons); CPE; LPC; PSC Sep 1999
Avery, Kathleen . . . . Dec 1990
Bell, Ms Victoria . . . . Sep 2001
Blake, Mr Peter John LLB . . . . Sep 2005
Blocker, Almut . . . . *Oct 1994
Boldon, Ms Jennifer LLB . . . . Sep 1998
Brown, Mr William BA . . . . *Sep 1999
Cha, Ms Susan LLB . . . . Mar 1998
Charlwood, Ms Denise BA(Hons) . . . . Sep 2001
Chesher, Mr Martin LLB . . . . Jan 1998
Cheung, Ms Ching-Ching LLB . . . . Nov 1999
Clark, Miss Janine . . . . Feb 2008
Craigie, Mrs Caroline A BA(Hons); DipLaw . . . . . . Jul 1997
Deaville, Mr Matthew . . . . Sep 2005
Dowding, Miss Sarah . . . . Mar 2005
Falloon, Ms Katherine . . . . *Sep 1994
Farrell, Mr John BA . . . . Oct 1993
Froome, Mr David . . . . *Sep 2001
Goodchild, Ms Emma LLB . . . . Sep 1998
Hannon, Mr D Anthony LLB . . . . *Mar 1998
Hanson, Mr Craig Peter LLB . . . . Oct 1995
Hopkins, Miss Clair . . . . Sep 2004
Jasani, Karishma . . . . Jun 2006
Kelly, Joanne . . . . May 2004
Kemp, Miss Samantha Rose LLB . . . . Jul 2001
Kettle, Miss Teresa LLB(Hons) . . . . *Sep 1995
Lennon, Natalie . . . . Sep 2006
MacGeogh, Ms Sushma LLB . . . . Feb 1993
Mandel, Ms Claire . . . . Sep 1999
Mason, Ms Janine LLB . . . . Sep 2001
Morgan, Fiona . . . . Sep 2005
Morris, Mr Paul Derek LLB(Hons) . . . . *Dec 1998
Nightingdale, Mr Scott LLB . . . . Jan 1998
Obertelli, Miss Carla BA . . . . Oct 1993
Plumridge, Mr Dean . . . . Dec 2006
Saunders, Mr Craig BSc; LLB . . . . Jan 1997
Silver, Miss Samantha . . . . *Jul 1999
Smyth, Nathalie . . . . Nov 2005
Stapleton, Mr Thomas BSc . . . . Sep 1998
Taggart, Mrs Alison J LLB; LLM(Lond) . . . . Nov 1995
Taylor, Ms Irene SRN; DipNur; LLB(Hons) . . . . . . *Nov 1999
Vickers, Mrs Nicola M LLB . . . . *Oct 1992
Weston, Miss Jill BA(Hons) . . . . *Sep 1997
Winckler, Mr Barnaby . . . . Jun 2006
Woodland, Ms Kerry . . . . Sep 1994
Con: Harris, Ms Sandra . . . . Jun 1968
Thompson, Mr Peter Derek ♦ . . . . *Jun 1993
Watson, Mrs Gina C LLB . . . . *Oct 1987

KENSINGTON LAW CHAMBERS ‡
186 North End Road London W14 9NX
Tel: 020 7739 1032 *Fax:* 020 7739 1032

KENSINGTON SOLICITORS ‡
34 Roehampton Vale London SW15 3RY
Tel: 020 8488 5798 *Fax:* 020 8488 9875
E-mail: kensingtonsolicitor@yahoo.co.uk

KENSINGTON SOLICITORS ‡
252 High Holborn London WC1V 7EN
Tel: 07931 820928 *Fax:* 020 8488 9875

KENT SOLICITORS ‡
206 Hertford Road London N9 7HH
Tel: 020 8805 9735 *Fax:* 020 8805 5718 *Dx:* 36259 EDMONTON 2
E-mail: info@kentsolicitorslondom.co.uk

KENWRIGHT & LYNCH ‡
The Plaza Professional Chambers 2 Mitcham Road Tooting Broadway Wandsworth London SW17 0TF
Tel: 020 8767 1211 *Fax:* 020 8767 7509
Dx: 58851 TOOTING SOUTH
List of partners: J S F Hales, R M Lynch
Languages: French, Italian
Work: C1 E L S1 W Z(c,h,l)
Legal Aid undertaken and Member of Accident Line
Ptr: Hales, Mr John S F BA(Oxon) . . . . *Jun 1978
Lynch, Robyn M . . . . Nov 1982
Asoc: Chambers, Mr Martin David BA(Hons)(Law) . . . . . *Feb 1984

A PATRICK KEOGH ‡
335 Muswell Hill Broadway London N10 1BW
Tel: 020 8883 4412 *Fax:* 020 8883 6278 *Dx:* 36007 MUSWELL HILL
E-mail: kgraham@apattrickkeogh.co.uk

KERMAN & CO LLP ‡
200 Strand London WC2R 1DJ
Tel: 020 7539 7272 *Fax:* 020 7240 5780
Dx: 99 LONDON/CHANCERY LN
E-mail: cag@kermanco.com
List of partners: P G Babb, M L Bennett, P D Dempsey, K R Dempster, J K Evans, C A Gorman, S Gorman, A D Kerman, J B Martin, D G O'Connell, D A Oakland, I S Ogus, J S Yu
Languages: French, German, Irish, Russian, Serbo-Croat
Work: A1 A3 B1 C1 C2 C3 D1 E F1 I J1 K1 K3 L O P Q R1 S1 S2 T1 T2 U2 W Z(b,d,e,f,i,k,l,n)
Ptr: Dempsey, Mr Peter David . . . . Mar 2005
Dempster, Mr Keith Richard LLB(Hons); MBA . . . . *Nov 1993
Evans, Mr John Kingsley . . . . *Aug 1998
Gorman, Mr Charles A LLB(Hons) . . . . *Nov 1997
Gorman, Mr Seymour . . . . *Dec 1963
Oakland, Mr Daniel Alan . . . . Nov 1990
Yu, Ms Joan Shu-Pui . . . . Oct 2002
Mem: Babb, Mr Peter George LLB . . . . *Apr 1974
Bennett, Mr Michael Louis . . . . *Jul 2001
Kerman, Mr Anthony David LLB . . . . *§Jan 1971
Martin, Ms Janice Barbara LLB; DipLP Notary Public . *Aug 1992
O'Connell, Mr Daniel Gerard BCL . . . . *Jan 1991
Ogus, Mr Ian Simeon . . . . *Jul 1973
Asoc: Blachford, Mr Michael K BA . . . . *Apr 1984
Robinson, Mr Carl M A . . . . Nov 2000
Ast: Bates, Mr Roger Philip . . . . Mar 2000
Bird, Ms Helen . . . . Sep 2002
Corcoran, Mr Michael . . . . Sep 2005
Deretic, Ms Una . . . . Nov 2005
Devlin, Mr Sebastian . . . . Oct 2008
Donaghey, Ms Yvonne . . . . Feb 2006
Lloyd, Mr Cormac W . . . . Mar 2003
Sekhon, Mr Jaspal . . . . Nov 2008
Towner, Ms Emily Jane . . . . Oct 2007

KEY2LAW LLP
18-19 Jockey's Fields London WC1R 4BW
Tel: 020 7404 2121 *Fax:* 020 7404 2323
Dx: 44 LONDON/CHANCERY LN
E-mail: info@key2law.co.uk
Office: Ewell

KEYSTONE LAW ‡
Matrix Studios 91 Peterborough Road London SW6 3BU
Tel: 020 7152 6550 *Fax:* 0845 458 9398

KHAN & PARTNERS ‡
311a High Street North Manor Park London E12 6SL
Tel: 020 8470 6969

AZAM KHAN & CO SOLICITORS ‡
61 Leigham Court Road Streatham Hill London SW16 2NJ
Tel: 020 8769 3320 *Fax:* 020 8677 9754

CHRISTIAN KHAN SOLICITORS ‡
5 Gower Street Bloomsbury London WC1E 6HA
Tel: 020 7631 9500 *Fax:* 020 7636 6852 *Dx:* 35737 BLOOMSBURY
Emergency telephone 020 7659 1052
E-mail: info@christiankhan.co.uk
List of partners: L H Christian, M Gordon, S McSherry, H Shah
Languages: French, Punjabi, Turkish, Urdu
Work: G H J1 N Z(g,p,r)
Agency, Advocacy, Legal Aid undertaken and Legal Aid Franchise
Ptr: Christian, Ms Louise H MA(Oxon) . . . . *Jan 1978
Gordon, Ms Margaret BA . . . . *May 1992
McSherry, Sarah . . . . *Sep 2004
Shah, Haroon . . . . *Feb 1999
Ast: Ahmad, Amer . . . . *Jan 2007
Craig, Katherine . . . . *Oct 2008
McNelis, Fiona . . . . *Feb 2001
Robinson, Josie . . . . Jan 2002

IMRAN KHAN & PARTNERS ‡
47 Theobalds Road London WC1X 8SP
Tel: 020 7404 3004 *Dx:* 35711 BLOOMSBURY

THE KHAN PARTNERSHIP LLP ‡
48-49 Russell Square London WC1B 4JY
Tel: 020 7612 2530

KHATRY SOLICITORS ‡
1 Berkeley Street Mayfair London W1J 8DJ
Tel: 020 7016 8860

KHATTAK SOLICITORS ‡
82 Uxbridge Road London W7 3SU
Tel: 020 8579 7976 *Fax:* 020 8579 7595

KHINDRIA & CO ‡
40 Doughty Street London WC1N 2LF
Tel: 020 7430 0556 *Fax:* 020 7430 0540
E-mail: t.khindria@khindria.com

KIDD RAPINET ‡
14-15 Craven Street London WC2N 5AD
Tel: 020 7205 2115 *Fax:* 020 7925 0334
Dx: 2 LONDON/CHANCERY LN
E-mail: ptaylor@kiddrapinet.co.uk
List of partners: P J G Astles, J M Aylwin, C S Banks, A I Baptist, G F W Bellenger, R L Benz, M A G S Bugg, C M L P Butler, P J S Bysshe, C M Comley, K A Coyle, R E M Hallifax, K N Haycock, C A M Henniker, J R J Lett, E McMahon, S Meakins, J F O'Shea, J P Ralph, C J Rawlings, C Rhodes, T Richardson, G Sehra, P D Taylor, R P Tymkiw, J White, P R Wild, T J Williams, P S Wood
Office: Aylesbury, Farnham, High Wycombe, Maidenhead, Reading, Slough
Languages: French, Gujarati, Hindi
Work: A1 B1 C1 C2 C3 D1 E F1 G H J1 K1 L M1 M2 N O P Q R1 S1 T1 T2 V W Z(a,c,d,e,f,g,h,i,j,k,l,m,n,p,s)
Emergency Action, Agency, Advocacy, Fixed Fee Interview, Legal Aid undertaken and Member of Accident Line
Ptr: Baptist, Mr Anthony I . . . . *Dec 1978
Bellenger, Mr Graeme F W LLB(Hons) . . . . *Jun 1997
Butler, Mr Colin Michael L P BA(Hons) . . . . *Nov 1995
Hallifax, Ms Rosalind E M BA . . . . *Jan 1985
Henniker, Mr Christopher A M . . . . *Jan 1978
Ralph, Mr John P . . . . *Nov 1977
Taylor, Mr Paul D BA . . . . *Jun 1980
Tymkiw, Mr Richard P LLB . . . . *Jun 1979
Wild, Mr Philip R MA(Cantab) . . . . *May 1984
Con: Cruickshank, Mr Richard Ian Sarell LLB . . . . . . *Jan 1978
Miller, Mr David Jacob . . . . *Jul 1961
Robeson, Mr Simon Paul Toby LLB(Hons) . . . . *Oct 1987

KIDSON BRAY & LAWSON
Albert Yard 7 Glasshouse Walk London SE11 5ES
Tel: 020 7582 0111 *Fax:* 020 7582 3727 *Dx:* 33259 KENNINGTON
E-mail: mail@kidsonandco.com
Office: Hindhead
Work: C1 E J1 L S1 T2 W
Ptr: Kidson, Mr Nigel David Learmonth . . . . *Jun 1970

KIERS & CO ‡
BM Box 3678 27 Gloucester Street London WC1N 3XX
Tel: 020 7729 9497

KILIC HAS & ONAY LLP ‡
121 Stoke Newington Road London N16 8BT
Tel: 020 7254 7111 *Fax:* 020 7254 7999
Dx: 58056 STOKE NEWINGTON
E-mail: info@khosolicitors.co.uk

KIMBERLY WAYNE & DIAMOND SOLICITORS ‡
24 Willrose Crescent London SE2 0LQ
Tel: 020 8310 0738 *Fax:* 020 3259 0024
E-mail: mail@kwdsolicitors.co.uk
Office: London SE18

KIMBERLY WAYNE & DIAMOND SOLICITORS
2nd Floor Room 207 Island Business Centre London SE18 6PF
Tel: 020 8317 0896 *Fax:* 020 8317 1392
E-mail: mail@kwdsolicitors.co.uk
Office: London SE2

KINAS SOLICITORS ‡
Metropolitan Business Centre Suite A3 359 Kingsland Road London N1 5AZ
Tel: 020 7249 0907 *Fax:* 020 7249 0937 *Dx:* 46803 DALSON
E-mail: info@kinas.co.uk

KING & SPALDING INTERNATIONAL LLP ‡
125 Old Broad Street London EC2N 1AR
Tel: 020 7551 7500 *Fax:* 020 7551 7575
E-mail: kingspalding@kslaw.com
List of partners: C Alexander, J Ali, S Beck
Work: A3 C1 C2 C3 M4 O Q T1 Z(b,n)
Ptr: Alexander, Mr Charles . . . . Jan 1989
Ali, Mr Jawad . . . . Jan 1995
Beck, Ms Susan . . . . Jan 1982

KING PARTNERS SOLICITORS ‡
7th Floor Suite 4 Ockway House London N16 5SR
Tel: 020 8802 9592 *Fax:* 020 8080 1511
Dx: 58054 STOKE NEWINGTON
E-mail: enquiry@kingpartnerssolicitors.com

KINGFIELDS SOLICITORS ‡
2nd Floor 38 Poland Street London W1F 7LY
Tel: 0845 459 0007 *Fax:* 020 7681 3293 *Dx:* 44618 MAYFAIR
E-mail: zalauddin@kingfields.co.uk

KINGSCOURT SOLICITORS ‡
117 Catford Hill London SW6 4PR
Tel: 020 8690 5999 *Fax:* 020 8690 5469 *Dx:* 34357 CATFORD
E-mail: info@kingscourtsolicitors.com

KINGSLEY NAPLEY ‡
Knights Quarter 14 St John's Lane London EC1M 4AJ
Tel: 020 7814 1200 *Fax:* 020 7490 2288
Dx: 22 LONDON/CHANCERY LN
Emergency telephone 020 7814 1202
E-mail: mail@kingsleynapley.co.uk
List of partners: S Adams, M F J Baker, C Ballard Scott, P H Belchak, D G Benjamin, C K Bradley, M G Caplan, T J Donovan, R J Foss, R M Fox, S Gentle, E H Guild, P Harbour, J C Harding, L Hodges, M S J Janney, K J Keir, K M Laws, A K McBride, L McDonald, A J Moore, D P Moss, C M Murray, S B Pollard, S R Purkis, K L Rohde, N W Rollason, A Sacker, B R Samuels, D Smythe, D M Speker, P W Tilley, D Walsh, F A Weaver, L Woolley
Languages: French, German, Spanish, Welsh
Work: A1 A3 B1 B2 C1 C2 E G H J1 K1 K2 K3 L N O Q R1 R2 S2 T1 W Z(c,d,f,i,j,k,l,p,q,r,w,z)
Emergency Action, Agency, Advocacy, Fixed Fee Interview, Legal Aid undertaken and Member of Accident Line
Ptr: Adams, Miss Sally BA(Hons); LLM . . . . . *Nov 1997
Baker, Ms Miranda F J MA(Cantab) . . . . . *Oct 1981
Ballard Scott, Mrs Charlotte LLB . . . . . *Oct 1999
Belchak, Miss Patricia H LLB; LLM . . . . . *Sep 1984
Benjamin, Ms Diana G . . . . . *§Jan 1966
Bradley, Miss Charlotte Kate BSc(Hons); DipLaw; CPE . . . . . *Nov 1995
Caplan, Mr Michael G QC LLB; AKC ★ . . . . . *§Apr 1977
Donovan, Mr Terrence J BA . . . . . *Nov 1988
Foss, Mr Richard James LLB . . . . . *Oct 1991
Fox, Mr Richard M LLB . . . . . *Oct 1986
Gentle, Mr Stephen BA . . . . . *Nov 1995
Guild, Prof Elspeth H Member of the Council of Justice *Oct 1989
Harbour, Mr Paul LLB . . . . . *Nov 1995
Harding, Mr John C LLB . . . . . *Oct 1988
Hodges, Ms Louise . . . . . *Sep 1999
Janney, Mr Michael S J BA(Nott'm) . . . . . *Apr 1981
Keir, Miss Katherine J LLB . . . . . *Dec 1987
Laws, Mr Keith M LLB(Leeds) . . . . . *Oct 1975
McBride, Mr Angus K BA . . . . . *Nov 1991
McDonald, Ms Linzi . . . . . *Apr 1995
Moore, Mrs Alison Jane BA(Hons) . . . . . *Nov 1994
Moss, Mr David Parker LLB . . . . . *Oct 1985
Murray, Mr Christopher M LLB(Lond) . . . . . *§Oct 1972
Pollard, Mr Stephen B BA(Oxon) . . . . . *Feb 1985
Purkis, Miss Sophia Rowena BA(Hons) . . . . . *Sep 1998
Rohde, Miss Katherine L LLB . . . . . *Oct 1989
Rollason, Mr Nicolas William BA(Oxon) . . . . . *May 1996
Sacker, Mr Anthony . . . . . *§Jun 1963
Samuels, Mr Barry R LLB(Manc) Serjeants Inn Prize . *Apr 1972
Smythe, Mr David LLB . . . . . *Oct 1988
Speker, Mr David M LLB(Dunelm) . . . . . *§Jan 1969
Tilley, Mr Paul W TD; BA . . . . . *§Apr 1965
Walsh, Mr David LLB(Leeds) . . . . . *§May 1960
Weaver, Mr Francis A . . . . . *§Mar 1968
Woolley, Ms Linda BA . . . . . *Sep 1992
Ast: Barrett, Mr Michael . . . . . *Mar 1999
Beardsworth, Mr Mark LLB . . . . . *Sep 2000
Blakemore, Ms Claire . . . . . *Jan 2000
Bloom, Mrs Gilly MA(Oxon) . . . . . *Mar 1988
Boddington, Ms Lucia F BA . . . . . *Feb 1996
Brain, Mr Ross LLB . . . . . *May 1999
Chiko-Radomski, Mrs Miri LLM . . . . . *Jul 2002
Cohen, Mr Julian . . . . . *§Dec 1975
Dom Paul, Ms Angelicka . . . . . *Oct 1997
Giles, Ms Eve LLB . . . . . *Jan 2001
Gooch, Mr John . . . . . *Nov 1995
Grimes, Mr Jonathan BA(Hons) . . . . . *Jan 2002
Heyes, Ms Caron BA(Hons) . . . . . *Oct 1997
Hostick, Ms Karen LLB(Hons) . . . . . *Sep 2001
Jenvey, Ms Nicola Louise LLB . . . . . *Jun 1996
Marlow, Miss Tara LLB(Hons) . . . . . *Mar 2000
Melchior, Miss Jasmin . . . . . *Jun 1999
Nadel, Miss Deborah BA . . . . . *Sep 1995
Price, Ms Debbie A . . . . . Sep 1999
Ranton, Mr Duncan LLB . . . . . *Sep 2000
Russell, Miss Samantha LLB(Hons) . . . . . *Oct 1996
Stinton, Ms Marnee J . . . . . *Nov 1999

KINGSTONS SOLICITORS ‡
251a Haydons Road London SW19 8TY
Tel: 020 8540 0468

KIRBY & CO ‡
3 Cobden Mews The Broadway Wimbledon London SW19 1RH
Tel: 020 8545 7171 *Fax:* 020 8545 7177
Dx: 30006 WIMBLEDON SOUTH
E-mail: clare.kirby@kirbyandco.co.uk
List of partners: C D Kirby
Languages: Danish, German
Work: K1 Q
Legal Aid undertaken
SPr: Kirby, Ms Clare D BA(Dunelm) . . . . . *Apr 1983
Ast: Wilson, Mrs Alexandra BA(Hons)(Politics) . . . . . Sep 2005

CHARLES KIRIT & CO ‡
Unit 4 2 Broadway Chambers Stratford London E15 4QS
Tel: 020 8221 0827 *Fax:* 020 8221 0828 *Dx:* 92230 STRATFORD

KIRK & PARTNERS ‡
25-27 Passey Place Eltham London SE9 5DF
Tel: 020 8850 2484 *Fax:* 020 8850 1529 *Dx:* 32500 ELTHAM
E-mail: info@kirkandpartners.co.uk
List of partners: S Bhandari, H A Lewis
Work: A1 E J1 K1 K3 K4 L P Q R1 S1 S2 T1 T2 W Z(p)
Fixed Fee Interview undertaken
Ptr: Bhandari, Mr Soheel LLB . . . . . Jan 1982
Lewis, Mr Hugh A LLB(B'ham) . . . . . *Nov 1979

KIRKLAND & ELLIS INTERNATIONAL LLP ‡
30 St Mary Axe London EC3A 8AF
Tel: 020 7469 2000 *Fax:* 020 7469 2001

M C KIRTON & CO ‡
83 St Albans Avenue Chiswick London W4 5JS
Tel: 020 8987 8880 *Fax:* 020 8932 7908
E-mail: mckirton@netscapsonline.co.uk
Work: Z(e,f)

KLEIN SOLICITORS ‡
42 Brook Street Mayfair London W1K 5DB
Tel: 020 7958 9080 *Fax:* 020 7900 6375
E-mail: info@kleinsolicitors.com

KLIMT & CO ‡
49 Welbeck Street Westminster London W1G 9XN
Tel: 020 7486 4432 *Fax:* 020 7486 2127
Dx: 42743 OXFORD CIRCUS NORTH
E-mail: eklimt@klimt.co.uk
List of partners: R D Charon, A H M Griffiths, L E Klimt
Work: C1 E L S1
Ptr: Charon, Mr Robert D MA; LLB . . . . . *Oct 1981
Griffiths, Mr Aled Huw Mason LLB(Lond) . . . . . *Feb 1984
Klimt, Mrs Lorna E LLB(Lond) . . . . . *Jul 1972

KNIGHT-WEBB SOLICITORS ‡
47 Beckwith Road London SE24 9LQ
Tel: 020 7207 6195

KNIGHTS ‡
498-500 Harrow Road Paddington London W9 3QA
Tel: 020 8964 1212 *Fax:* 020 8964 4554 *Dx:* 46652 MAIDA HILL

KNOWLES SOLICITORS ‡
The Outer Temple 222 Strand London WC2R 1BA
Tel: 0870 753 0852

LUKE KORE SOLICITORS ‡
2nd Floor 350 Walworth Road London SE17 2NA
Tel: 020 7277 3880 *Fax:* 020 7277 3888
List of partners: M de-Souza
Ptr: de-Souza, Mr Martin . . . . . Dec 2002

KOSTICK HANAN HERSKOVIC LLP ‡
1 Egerton Road London N16 6UE
Tel: 020 8800 8866 *Fax:* 020 8800 8086
Dx: 37652 STAMFORD HILL
E-mail: offica@khhlaw.co.uk

LESLIE KOVACS ‡
Unit 2 8-9 Clerkenwell Green London EC1R 0DE
Tel: 020 7251 8529 *Fax:* 020 7251 8530

KRAMER & CO ‡
162 Regents Park Road London N3 3HT
Tel: 020 8346 8070 *Fax:* 020 8346 2767

KRIS SEN SOLICITORS ‡
62 Pendle Road London SW16 6RU
Tel: 020 8769 7125
E-mail: kris.sen@kssolicitors.com
Languages: French, German, Italian
Work: A3 C1 C2 E I J1 M2 O Q S2 U2 W Z(e,f,w,za)

KROMANN REUMERT ‡
42 New Broad Street London EC2M 1JD
Tel: 020 7920 3030

KUDDUS SOLICITORS ‡
2 White Chapel Road London E1 1EW
Tel: 020 7247 5476

KUDDUS SOLICITORS (UK) LTD ‡
Unit 102 21-23 Shacklewell Lane London E8 2DA
Tel: 020 7241 0560 *Fax:* 020 7993 5343
E-mail: ak@kuddussolicitors.com

KYRIAKIDES & BRAIER ‡
37 Queen Anne Street London W1G 9JB
Tel: 020 7637 3289 *Fax:* 020 7636 3013
List of partners: R A F Kyriakides
Languages: French
Work: B1 C1 E F1 G J1 K1 L M1 N O P R1 S1 T1 W Z(c,d,e,f,i,j,l)
Emergency Action and Advocacy undertaken
Ptr: Kyriakides, Mr Robert A F LLB; TEP . . . . . *Jun 1974

ADONIS KYRIAKIDES & CO ‡
56 Queensway Westminster London W2 3RY
Tel: 020 7229 3800 *Fax:* 020 7727 2668
List of partners: A K Kyriakides
Ptr: Kyriakides, Mr Adonis K . . . . . *May 1976

LB & CO SOLICITORS ‡
91 Whitechapel High Street London E1 7RA
Tel: 020 7655 4941 *Fax:* 020 7655 4942 *Dx:* 576 LONDON/CITY

LG LAWYERS ‡
4 More London Riverside London SE1 2AU
Tel: 020 7379 0000 *Fax:* 020 7379 6854
Dx: 132076 LONDON BRIDGE 4
E-mail: info@lg-legal.com
List of partners: L S Ahmed, T D Blaney, P Borrie, N S Bradley, D M K Breslin, P J E Bryan, J M Bussell, R S Chaggar, C J Diggle, A C Dobson, M J Duffy, J L Edgell, A W Elliott, R W Elphick, J G Elway, L J Feaver, N J Fisher, J Foster, J Fox-Edwards, P J L Francis, Y Gallagher, L O Gowman, D P Hayward, N R Heather, C M Jackson, N D G Jacob, S S Kakkad, M P Kiely, P F Lester, M Lewis, J E Lloyd, S J Malcolm, M G Mankabady, T R Marshall, H P Maule, R J Miles, M B Murphy, T D Nicholls, T R Pullan, T J Railton, B W D Richards, J J A Riley, R J Smith, J Spiers, M G F Stacey, S R Stephens, W J Sturge, R G Thom, A I Thompson, L A M Thompson, C C Tite, S H Turnball, N S Turner, J R Verrill, A G Wade, S E Wilson, A Witts, A H Young, V M Younghusband
Languages: Danish, Filipino, French, German, Hindi, Italian, Polish, Portuguese, Punjabi, Russian, Spanish
Work: A1 A3 B1 C1 C2 C3 D1 E F1 F2 G I J1 J2 K1 L M1 M2 N O P Q R1 R2 S1 S2 T1 T2 U1 W Z(a,b,c,d,e,f,g,h,i,j,k,l,n,o,p,q,r,s,u,w,y,z)
Agency undertaken
Ptr: Ahmed, Ms Leona Shireen . . . . . Feb 1996
Blaney, Mr Trevor D BSc; MSc(Lond) . . . . . *Jun 1977
Borrie, Mr Peter LLB . . . . . *May 1988
Bradley, Mr Nicholas Stanley . . . . . May 1986
Breslin, Mrs David Michael Kenneth . . . . . Sep 1990
Bryan, Mrs Pam J E LLB . . . . . *Nov 1982
Bussell, Ms Joanna Margaret . . . . . May 1995
Chaggar, Rabinder S LLB . . . . . *Jun 1985
Diggle, Ms Catherine J BA . . . . . *Sep 1980
Dobson, Mr Andrew C MA(Cantab) . . . . . *Nov 1980
Duffy, Mr Michael J . . . . . *Dec 1977
Edgell, Mr Jonathan Lee . . . . . Mar 1996
Elliott, Mr Anthony William . . . . . Jun 1976
Elphick, Mr Richard W . . . . . Jan 1984
Elway, Mr Jeffrey G LLB(Soton) . . . . . *Oct 1985
Feaver, Mr Lance John . . . . . Jun 1981
Fisher, Mr Norman J LLB(Lond) . . . . . *§Jun 1974
Foster, Mr James . . . . . May 1981
Fox-Edwards, Ms Jane MA(Cantab) . . . . . *Oct 1988
Francis, Mrs Penelope J L LLB(Bris) . . . . . *Jun 1984
Gallagher, Miss Yvonne . . . . . Oct 1987
Gowman, Ms Louise Olivia . . . . . Jan 1992
Hayward, Mr David P MA(Cantab) . . . . . *Oct 1978
Heather, Mr Nicholas R . . . . . Mar 1986
Jackson, Ms Christine M . . . . . *Mar 1987
Jacob, Mr Nicholas David Grenville . . . . . Oct 1982
Kakkad, Sunil Shantilal . . . . . Oct 1984
Kiely, Mr Myles P BA Edis Conveyancing & Real Property Prizes . . . . . Dec 1987
Lester, Mr Paul Francis . . . . . Sep 1988
Lewis, Mr Mark . . . . . May 1991
Lloyd, Mr Jonathan Edwin . . . . . *Oct 1988
Malcolm, Mr Simon John . . . . . Oct 1986
Mankabady, Mr Martin Graff . . . . . Feb 1995
Marshall, Ms Thelma Rose . . . . . May 1994
Maule, Mr Hugh P . . . . . Oct 1991
Miles, Mr Richard John . . . . . Oct 1990
Murphy, Mr Michael B LLB . . . . . Nov 1987
Nicholls, Mr Tom David . . . . . Sep 1996
Pullan, Mr Timothy Roger . . . . . Jul 1998
Railton, Mr Timothy John . . . . . May 1973
Richards, Mr B William D BA . . . . . *Jun 1976
Riley, Mr Jonathan J A . . . . . Oct 1985
Smith, Mr Robert J BA(Oxon); APMI . . . . . *May 1977
Spiers, Ms Jane . . . . . Oct 1995
Stacey, Mr Martin G F LLB . . . . . *Nov 1989
Stephens, Mr Stephen R BCom; LLB . . . . . *Feb 1985
Sturge, Mr William John . . . . . Nov 1984
Thom, Mr Ronald Geoffrey . . . . . Apr 1974
Thompson, Mr Anthony I BSc . . . . . *§Oct 1985
Thompson, Ms Lisa Ann Morgan . . . . . Dec 1994
Tite, Mr Christopher Charles . . . . . May 1985
Turnball, Mr Stephen Hollings . . . . . Oct 1984
Turner, Mr Nicholas S . . . . . Jan 1989
Verrill, Mr John R LLB(Lond) Licensed Insolvency Practitioner . . . . . *Jun 1981
Wade, Mr Andrew G MA(Cantab) . . . . . *§Apr 1979
Wilson, Ms Susan Edith . . . . . Dec 1992
Witts, Mr Andrew . . . . . Nov 1990
Young, Mr Andrew H MA(Oxon) . . . . . *Nov 1986
Younghusband, Ms Victoria M LLB Maxwell Law Prize . *Oct 1984
Ast: Adam, Mr Robert Thomas . . . . . Sep 1998
Ali, Fahmida . . . . . Sep 2005
Ali, Iftikhar . . . . . Sep 2004
Ashby, Ms Elizabeth Jane . . . . . Sep 1999
Aubin-Parvu, Ms Nicole Louise . . . . . Nov 1996
Bailes, Ms Rebecca Elizabeth . . . . . Mar 2004
Bailey, Ms Sarah . . . . . Sep 2005
Banks, Ms Danica Mair Anne . . . . . Sep 2005
Barel, Ms Susannah Emma . . . . . Sep 1999
Bearn, Ms Katherine Mary . . . . . Sep 2004
Beeson, Ms Susanna Caroline . . . . . Oct 2000
Bell, Ms Catherine Anne BSc(Econ) . . . . . *Oct 1989
Bishop, Ms Fiona Jane . . . . . Sep 1999
Bradley, Mr Adam . . . . . Sep 2001
Broomfield, Ms Kathryn Sarah Elizabeth . . . . . Sep 1999
Choueka, Ms Rosemary Sara . . . . . May 2002
Cohen, Mr Russell Andrew . . . . . Nov 2000
Coombes, Ms Victoria . . . . . Sep 2003
Crampton, Mr Tom . . . . . Sep 2003
Dalley, Mr Ian Christopher . . . . . Oct 2002
De Froberville, Ms Vanessa . . . . . Sep 2002
Deacon, Ms Melissa . . . . . Jul 2003
Elliott, Ms Carol Ann . . . . . Feb 2002
Evans, Mr Richard Alistair . . . . . Sep 2000
Fleming, Ms Phillipa . . . . . Oct 1994
Fraser, Mr William . . . . . Sep 2003
Gavens, Ms Christianne Mara . . . . . Sep 2002
Geaney, Ms Sinead BA(Hons)(Modern History & Politics); PGDipLaw; LPC . . . . . Sep 2004
Gordon, Ms Rebecca . . . . . Sep 2005
Gouriet, Mr Geoffrey Costerton . . . . . Sep 1999
Gravell, Devreaux . . . . . Sep 2001
Green, Mr James . . . . . Sep 2005
Groves, Ms Gemma Leigh . . . . . Sep 2003
Gwilliam, Mr Daniel John . . . . . Sep 1999
Haigh, Ms Carolyn . . . . . Sep 2003
Hawkins, Mr John Rowland . . . . . *Jun 1981
Hayes, Miss Angela MA(Oxon) . . . . . Nov 1993
Hind, Ms Sarah Louise . . . . . Sep 1999
Hommel, Ms Lisa Fiona . . . . . Nov 1991
Huckle, Ms Catrin . . . . . Sep 2005
Hudson, Karima A . . . . . Oct 1995
Hussain, Shabnum . . . . . Sep 2001
Joseph, Mr Vinod George . . . . . Jan 2004
King, Mr Simon Gareth . . . . . Sep 1999
Kitchen, Ms Charlotte . . . . . Sep 2002
Lacey, Mr Michael R A LLB . . . . . *May 1991
Larkin, Ms Marie Isobel . . . . . Sep 2001
Lea, Mr Jonathan Edward . . . . . Sep 2003
Legg, Mr Jonathan Charles . . . . . Oct 2001
Lent, Mr Jonathan David . . . . . Sep 2005
Lewis, Mr Edward Tudor . . . . . May 1993
Lok, Xanthe . . . . . Sep 2005
Long, Ms Rachel Elizabeth . . . . . Sep 2004
Lundie, Mr Alex John . . . . . Sep 1997
McCarthy, Ms Gillian . . . . . Sep 2005
Mackay, Ms Clare . . . . . Sep 1998
Maclaurin, Mr Duncan . . . . . Sep 2000
Mander, Bhaljinder Singh . . . . . Sep 2003
Mardon, Ms Caroline . . . . . Nov 1986
Martin, Ms Angela Kay . . . . . Aug 1999
Matthams, Ms Kate . . . . . Mar 2004
Mills, Ms Rachel . . . . . Oct 2001
Moghadam, Farhod . . . . . Sep 2003
Morley, Ms Kate Helen . . . . . Sep 2000
Myers, Mr David Daniel . . . . . Sep 2001
Noon, Ms Sonia Jayne . . . . . Nov 1993
Northey, Mr Jonathan David . . . . . Sep 2000
Nystrom, Mr John Stefan . . . . . Sep 2001
O'Higgins, Ms Naomi Grace . . . . . Sep 2003
Olley, Ms Hayley . . . . . Apr 2001
Pathmanathan, Janani . . . . . Sep 1998
Pearson, Ms Catherine . . . . . Sep 2003
Peters, Ms Alison Alexandra . . . . . Sep 2000
Pritchard, Mr Timothy Paul . . . . . Sep 2002
Pugh, Ms Caroline Sarah . . . . . Nov 1994
Redden, Ms Kate . . . . . Sep 2003
Reed, Mr John Charles . . . . . Sep 2001

See p2 for the Key to Work Categories & other symbols

Reynolds, Ms Frances Mary. . . . . Oct 1996
Richardson, Mr Anthony Edward Forster . . . . Sep 2002
Riddy, Mr Jack Edward . . . . Sep 2003
Riley, Mr Oliver James Daniel. . . . . Sep 2000
Rucker, Mr Nicholas Patrick Hamilton . . . . Sep 1997
Ruffel, Ms Alexandra Marguerite . . . . Sep 2001
Satterthwaite, Ms Philippa. . . . . Sep 1996
Scott, Mr Stewart Crosbie. . . . . Sep 2003
Shiramba, Mr Charles. . . . . Oct 1995
Shire, Ms Phillippa J . . . . Sep 2003
Shutler, Ms Kelly Anne . . . . Mar 2005
Singh-Dalal, Ms Sunita . . . . Sep 1999
Slack, Mr Adrian . . . . Sep 2005
Soomro, Mr Naveed. . . . . Feb 2000
Stanley, Ms Lucy . . . . Nov 2001
Steel, Ms Claire. . . . . Mar 2002
Suneja, Anju . . . . Sep 2000
Thomson, Mr Richard John . . . . Dec 1978
Thorp, Ms Victoria Jane. . . . . Mar 1999
Tideswell, Ms Lucinda Clare. . . . . Sep 1997
Walker, Ms Caroline Elizabeth. . . . . Sep 2004
Watson, Ms Eluned Sally . . . . Sep 2005
Weil, Ms Nicola Jane . . . . Feb 1987
Wilkinson, Ms Kate Mary . . . . Mar 2001
Williams, Ms Emma Ann . . . . Sep 1999
Willis, Mr Benjamin George . . . . Oct 2001
Wingfield, Mr James Richard . . . . Sep 2000
Withyman, Mr Thomas Anthony MA(Cantab) . . . . . Apr 1992

LH LEGAL LIMITED ‡
9 The Ridgeway London NW11 8TD
Tel: 020 8458 4415
E-mail: leahhurst@mac.com

LK BALTICA SOLICITORS ‡
9 Mandeville Place London W1U 3AU
Tel: 020 7935 2960

LKNY LAW ‡
Britannia House 11 Glenthorne Road London W6 0LH
Tel: 07931 516912 / 020 8735 6500
E-mail: lknylaw-pk@fsmail.net

LLC LAW ‡
4 Bramber Court Bramber Road London W14 9PW
Tel: 020 7471 0371

LL LAW LLP ‡
Unit 12 Indescon Court 20 Millharbour London E14 9TN
Tel: 020 7987 7198 *Fax:* 020 7987 8137
E-mail: tom@lllaw.co.uk

LSG SOLICITORS ‡
4th Floor 35 Piccadilly London W1J 0LP
Tel: 020 7851 0100 *Fax:* 020 7851 0136 *Dx:* 37225 PICCADILLY 1
E-mail: dp@lsg.co.uk
List of partners: H Branch, S R Daultrey, D Pollacchi, N M Salt, M Zysblat
Languages: Czech, French, German, Hungarian, Polish, Russian, Slovenian
Work: B1 C1 C2 E I J1 K1 K2 K3 L N O Q R1 R2 S1 S2 T1 Z(b,e,q,r,z)
Ptr: Branch, Mr Hal BA(Modern History). . . . . *Nov 2001
Daultrey, Mr Steven Richard LLB(Hons) . . . . Apr 1977
Pollacchi, Mr David LLB(Hons) . . . . *§Dec 1990
Salt, Mr Nigel M. . . . . *Jan 1972
Zysblat, Mr Michael. . . . . *Dec 1968
Ast: Norris, Mr Timothy John LLB(Hons); LLM . . . . . . May 2010
Con: Garvin, Mr Michael S P LLB. . . . . *Jul 1969
Gregory, Miss Rosamund BA(Hons). . . . . *Nov 1980
Salamon, Mr Thomas MA. . . . . *Mar 1985

LT LAW ‡
18 Soho Square London W1D 3QL
Tel: 020 7025 8332 *Fax:* 020 7025 8132
E-mail: office@ltlaw.co.uk

LADAS & PARRY ‡
1-2 Bolt Court London EC4A 4DQ
Tel: 020 7242 5566

B D LADDIE ‡
16-18 Denbigh Street Westminster London SW1V 2ER
Tel: 020 7963 8585 *Fax:* 020 7963 8586 *Dx:* 152240 VICTORIA 14
E-mail: post@bdladdie.co.uk
List of partners: S Fiaca, H P Freeman, N S Russell
Languages: Greek
Work: D1 E J1 K1 K3 L O Q R2 S1 S2 W Z(p)
Emergency Action undertaken
Ptr: Fiaca, Savvakis LLB . . . . *Apr 1987
Freeman, Mr Howard P LLB. . . . . *Feb 1989
Russell, Mr Neil S LLB . . . . *Feb 1990
Ast: Morris, Miss Mary LLB(Hons) . . . . Feb 2008
Theodosiou, Mr Christopher LLB(Hons). . . . . *Oct 2003

LADERMAN & CO ‡
4 The Shrubberies George Lane South Woodford Redbridge London E18 1BD
Tel: 020 8530 7319 *Fax:* 020 8530 6805
Dx: 90705 SOUTH WOODFORD
E-mail: mail@laderman.co.uk
List of partners: D C Laderman, R E Laderman
Languages: French, Punjabi, Turkish, Urdu
Work: B1 C1 C2 C3 E F1 G J1 J2 K1 K3 K4 L M1 M2 N O P Q R1 R2 S1 T1 T2 W Z(c,f,k,l,p,q,w)
Emergency Action, Agency and Advocacy undertaken
Ptr: Laderman, Mr Daniel C LLB; TEP. . . . . *Jul 1981
Laderman, Mr Robert E BA . . . . *Dec 1981
Ast: Anwar, Ms Sadia LLB . . . . Jun 2002
Smith, Leslie BA(Hons) . . . . *Nov 1994
West, Mr Matthew James BA; LLB . . . . Dec 2010

LADERMANS ‡
17 Brinsdale Road London NW4 1TB
Tel: 020 8203 6136
List of partners: D A Laderman, H Laderman
Work: C1 C2 E F1 L S1 W Z(h,j)
Ptr: Laderman, Mr David Alan LLB(Wales). . . . . *Apr 1987
Laderman, Mr Howard LLB(B'ham) . . . . *Nov 1986

LAHIFF & CO ‡
2nd Floor Thames House Wellington Street Greenwich London SE18 6NZ
Tel: 020 8855 5656 *Fax:* 020 8317 3294
Emergency telephone 020 8378 2599
List of partners: P F Lahiff
Work: G H
Emergency Action, Advocacy and Legal Aid undertaken
Ptr: Lahiff, Mr Paul Francis BA ★ . . . . *May 1985

LAING & CO ‡
1 Langbourne Avenue Highgate London N6 6AJ
Tel: 020 8341 1147

LAKE JACKSON ‡
Gun Court 70 Wapping Lane London E1W 2RF
Tel: 020 7490 3356
Office: Norwich

LAKHANI & CO ‡
521 Kingsbury Road Kingsbury Brent London NW9 9EG
Tel: 020 8204 7100 *Fax:* 020 8204 6100
E-mail: info@lakhanilaw.com
List of partners: N Lakhani
Languages: Gujarati
Work: B1 C1 I J1 K1 K3 L O Q U2 W Z(e,i,q)
Fixed Fee Interview undertaken
SPr: Lakhani, Ms Nita LLB(Hons). . . . . *Sep 1994

LAMB & KAVANAGH ‡
PO Box 20295 Camden London NW1 7GB
Tel: 020 7209 2481 *Fax:* 020 7419 9507
List of partners: S Kavanagh, A D Lamb
Work: D1 K1
Agency, Advocacy and Legal Aid undertaken
Ptr: Kavanagh, Ms Sheila LLB. . . . . *Nov 1989
Lamb, Ms Alison Dorothy MA; BA; CPE; LSF . . . . . *Nov 1987

STEPHEN J LAMB ‡
6 Sunray Avenue Herne Hill Southwark London SE24 9PY
Tel: 020 7738 6838 *Fax:* 020 7738 6536
Emergency telephone 020 7738 5747
E-mail: stephen.lamb@btinternet.com
List of partners: S J Lamb
Work: T1 T2
Fixed Fee Interview undertaken
SPr: Lamb, Mr Stephen J BSc; FCA; ATII . . . . *Apr 1978

LAMPIER & CO ‡
Salisbury Square House 8 Salisbury Square London EC4Y 8BB
Tel: 020 7694 8666
E-mail: sfl@lampierco.com

LANCASTERS ‡
486 Chiswick High Road London W4 5TT
Tel: 020 8742 1314 *Fax:* 020 8742 1574 *Dx:* 80315 CHISWICK
E-mail: lawyers@lancasters-solicitors.com
List of partners: A D Lancaster
Languages: Afrikaans, Armenian, French, Greek, Punjabi, Turkish, Urdu
Work: C1 E G J1 K1 L N O Q S1 V W Z(c,i,j,k,l)
Emergency Action, Agency, Advocacy, Fixed Fee Interview, Legal Aid undertaken and Member of Accident Line
Ptr: Lancaster, Mr Anthony D BA . . . . *Jun 1980
Ast: Matthews, Miss Joanne LLB(Hons) . . . . *Jul 1994
Con: Matossian, Mr John BA; LLM(Kent) . . . . *Jan 1982

LANDAU ZEFFERTT WEIR ‡
10 Bickles Yard 151-153 Bermondsey Street London Bridge London SE1 3HA
Tel: 020 7357 9494 *Fax:* 020 7357 9696
Dx: 132075 LONDON BRIDGE 4
E-mail: info@lzwlaw.co.uk
List of partners: S Awtani, P S Landau, A F Weir, A D M Zeffertt
Languages: Hindi, Italian, Punjabi, Urdu
Work: B1 C1 C2 C3 E F1 J1 K1 L N O Q R1 S1 W Z(b,c,e,i,j,k,l,o,p,q)
Agency, Advocacy, Fixed Fee Interview undertaken and Member of Accident Line
Ptr: Awtani, Sushma LLB . . . . *Oct 1999
Landau, Mr Philip S LLB . . . . *Apr 1990
Weir, Mr Andrew F BA(Hons) . . . . *Oct 1990
Zeffertt, Mr Alan D M LLB. . . . . *Jan 1978

LANE GRAHAM SOLICITORS ‡
29th Floor 1 Canada Square Canary Wharf London E14 5DY
Tel: 020 7712 1715
E-mail: enquiries@lanegraham.co.uk

JON LANG ‡
68 Lombard Street London EC3V 9LJ
Tel: 020 7868 1685

DALE LANGLEY & CO ‡
60 Lombard Street London EC3V 9EA
Tel: 020 7464 8433 *Fax:* 020 7464 8659
E-mail: info@dalelangley.co.uk
Office: London E14

DALE LANGLEY & CO
Floor 29 1 Canada Square Canary Wharf London E14 5DY
Tel: 020 7464 8433 *Fax:* 020 7464 8659
E-mail: info@dalelangley.co.uk
Office: London EC3

LANSBURY WORTHINGTON ‡
5 King Street Cloisters Clifton Walk King Street London W6 0GY
Tel: 020 8563 9797 *Fax:* 020 8563 9798
Dx: 32756 HAMMERSMITH 2
Emergency telephone 07802 725778
E-mail: info@lansbury-worthington.co.uk
List of partners: P D Gardiner, R B Gowthorpe, B J Lansbury, C Worthington
Office: London W14
Languages: Spanish
Work: B2 G H J1 N Z(l,q)
Emergency Action, Agency, Advocacy, Fixed Fee Interview, Legal Aid undertaken, Legal Aid Franchise and Member of Accident Line
Ptr: Gowthorpe, Mr Richard Bruce LLB ★ . . . . *Mar 1994
Lansbury, Mr Benjamin J BA(Law) ★ . . . . *Feb 1981
Worthington, Mr Charles BA. . . . . *Jan 1992

Asoc: James, Mr Martin A C LLB ★ . . . . *Apr 1980
Newey, Ms Katherine J LLB(Hons) . . . . *May 1997
Ast: Al Jarrah, Ms Farah LLB . . . . *Sep 2002
Alcendor, Ms Naomi LLB . . . . *Nov 2006
O'Mara, Ms Katy BA; DipLaw . . . . *Sep 2004
Palfrey, Mr James. . . . . *Sep 2005

LANSDOWNE SOLICITORS ‡
83 Sotheby Road London N5 2UT
Tel: 020 7226 7825 *Fax:* 020 7226 3924
Work: R1 Z(d,u)

LATHAM & WATKINS LLP ‡
99 Bishopsgate London EC2M 3XF
Tel: 020 7710 1000 *Fax:* 020 7374 4460
List of partners: M A Bond, W N Campion-Smith, J D H Chesterman, D Miles
Work: A3 B1 C1 C2 C3 J1 M2 O R2 T1 U1 Z(b,n)
Ptr: Bond, Mr Michael A LLB . . . . Nov 1992
Campion-Smith, Mr W Nigel MA(Cantab) . . . . . . *§Apr 1978
Chesterman, Mr James D H BA(Cantab) . . . . Oct 1987
Miles, Mr David BA; LLB(Nott'm) . . . . Apr 1980
Asoc: Allen, Mr Christopher . . . . May 1995
Ast: Cline, Mr Nicholas Andrew Falsen BSc(Hons); CPE; LPC . . . . *Sep 1996
Colahan, Mr John. . . . . Aug 1992

LATTEY & DAWE ‡
21 Liverpool Street London EC2M 7RD
Tel: 020 7623 2345 *Fax:* 020 7220 7624 *Dx:* 547 LONDON/CITY
E-mail: dominic.filleul@lattey.co.uk
List of partners: P G Watson, R A Watson
Languages: French, Gujarati
Work: B1 C1 E F1 J1 L N O Q S1 S2 T2 W Z(b,e,k,q)
Agency undertaken
Ptr: Watson, Mr Peter G Grotius Prize. . . . . *§Mar 1975
Watson, Mr Richard A LLB . . . . *Mar 1987
Ast: Collins, Mrs Chi Yuen LLB. . . . . Nov 1992

LAUREL & CO ‡
25-27 Passey Place Eltham London SE9 5DF
Tel: 020 8331 6655 *Fax:* 020 8331 6654

L G LAURELLA ‡
95 Delamere Road Ealing London W5 3JP
Tel: 020 8840 5761 *Fax:* 020 8579 8206
List of partners: L G Laurella
Languages: French, Italian
Work: S1 S2
SPr: Laurella, Ms Lillian G . . . . *Dec 1980

LAVEN LEGAL SERVICES LIMITED ‡
8 Cromwell Place London SW7 2JN
Tel: 020 7594 4973 *Fax:* 020 7838 0884
E-mail: jerome@lavenlegal.com

LAVERY HAYNES ‡
1 Heath Street Hampstead London NW3 6TP
Tel: 020 7435 7441
E-mail: law@laveryhaynes.com
List of partners: D A Douglas, A D Lavery
Work: E K1 K2 K4 L O Q R2 S1 S2 W
Ptr: Douglas, Miss Deirdre A LLB(Hons); MA; DipLPC. . . May 2002
Lavery, Mr Andrew D . . . . *Oct 1989
Con: Bluston, Mr Derek LLB . . . . *Oct 1959

LAW & LAWYERS ‡
349 High Street North London E12 6PQ
Tel: 07793 452184 / 020 8586 5657 *Fax:* 020 8586 0290
Dx: 4700 EAST HAM
E-mail: awandlawyers@yahoo.co.uk

THE LAW DEPARTMENT ‡
7a Wellington Road London NW10 5LJ
Tel: 020 7898 0585
E-mail: info@lawdepartment.co.uk

LAW FIRM LTD ‡
Second Floor Suite 12 Queens House London W1T 7PD
Tel: 020 7907 1460 *Fax:* 020 7907 1463
List of partners: S S Aronsohn
Languages: French, German, Russian
Work: A3 E R1 S1 S2 Z(i,s)
SPr: Aronsohn, Mr Simon S . . . . *Jun 1996

THE LAW OFFICE OF RICHARD STEPHENS ‡
11-15 Betterton Street Covent Garden London WC2H 9BP
Tel: 020 7470 8767
E-mail: richard.stephens@lorsonline.com

LAW PARTNERS SOLICITORS LTD ‡
St John's Chambers Klaco House 28-30 St John's Square London EC1M 4DN
Tel: 0870 600 9444 *Fax:* 0870 600 9555 *Dx:* 53331 CLERKENWELL
Emergency telephone 07831 403631
E-mail: info@lawpartners-solicitors.com
List of partners: H S Brown, A M Goldstone, L J Heinl, B M Jobling
Languages: German, Hebrew
Work: B2 G N O Z(g,p)
Emergency Action, Agency, Fixed Fee Interview and Legal Aid undertaken
Ptr: Brown, Mr Howard S LLB ● . . . . *Mar 1984
Goldstone, Mr Adrian M LLB(Hons) . . . . *Nov 1988
Heinl, Mr Leo J . . . . *Oct 2000
Jobling, Mr Bruce M ● . . . . *Nov 1972

LAW WORKS LEAGAL SERVICES LIMITED ‡
14 Upper Tachbrook Street Westminster London SW1V 1SH
Tel: 020 7233 7566 *Fax:* 020 7233 7504
E-mail: mjreilly2007@yahoo.co.uk

LAWANA & CO SOLICITORS ‡
274 Hither Green Lane London SE13 6TT
Tel: 020 8461 0700 *Fax:* 020 8695 0507
E-mail: g.lawana@btconnect.com

LAWFORD DAVIES DENOON ‡
14a Clerkenwell Green London EC1R 0DP
Tel: 020 8616 1887 *Fax:* 020 3441 0908

LAWRENCE & ASSOCIATES ‡
2nd Floor Daily Times House Cold Harbour Lane London SE5 9NR
Tel: 020 7326 3941 *Fax:* 020 7326 4092
E-mail: lawrence_associates2002@yahoo.com
Languages: Spanish
Work: Z(i)

LAWRENCE & CO ‡
404 Harrow Road London W9 2HU
Tel: 020 7266 4333 *Fax:* 020 7289 3161 *Dx:* 148160 MAIDA HILL 2
Emergency telephone 07961 460770
E-mail: info@lawsol.co.uk
List of partners: J E Kelman, L B Lederman
Work: D1 E G H J1 K1 L M1 M2 N O P Q S1 V W X Z(i,m,p)
Emergency Action, Agency, Advocacy, Fixed Fee Interview, Legal Aid undertaken, Legal Aid Franchise and Member of Accident Line
Ptr: Kelman, Ms Judith E LLB ★ . . . *§Sep 1990
Lederman, Mr Lawrence B LLB . . . *Jun 1978
Asoc: Daoud, Fadi J BA . . . *Sep 1997

H LAWRENCE & CO ‡
West Hill House 6 Swains Lane Highgate London N6 6QS
Tel: 020 7482 2613 / 7482 4212 *Fax:* 020 7284 2388
Dx: 51905 HIGHGATE
E-mail: hlawrence@londonweb.net
List of partners: B A S Lawrence, H V H P Lawrence
Languages: French, Polish, Spanish
Work: C1 E F1 J1 K1 L N O Q S1 S2 W
Ptr: Lawrence, Mrs Barbara A S BA(Law & Politics) . . . *Jan 1980
Lawrence, Mr Herbert Victor Hugh Parker BA(Law & Econ) . . . *Jan 1987

LAWRENCE LAW ‡
Network Business Centre 329 Putney Bridge Road London SW15 2PG
Tel: 020 8788 0055 *Fax:* 020 8788 6683 *Dx:* 59454 PUTNEY
Emergency telephone 07956 307861
E-mail: js@lawrencelaw.co.uk
List of partners: J Savitt
Work: D1 G H J1 K1 N S1 W Z(p)
Emergency Action, Agency, Advocacy, Fixed Fee Interview, Legal Aid undertaken, Legal Aid Franchise and Member of Accident Line
Ptr: Savitt, Mr Jonathan MA; LLB . . . *Nov 1979
Ast: Flack, Mr William LLB . . . *Apr 1991
Kearney, Mr Frank LLB . . . May 1995

LAWSON GEORGE ‡
2nd Floor South Point House 321 Chase Road London N14 6JT
Tel: 020 8920 3131 *Fax:* 020 8886 6618
E-mail: info@lawsongeorge.com

LAWSON TURNER & GILBERT ‡
395 Suffolk Park London SE16 2JH
Tel: 020 7394 1311 *Fax:* 020 7394 0335 *Dx:* 85457 ROTHERHITHE
Emergency telephone 020 7934 0131
E-mail: enq@ltglaw.co.uk
Office: Dover
Languages: French, Ganda, Kiswahili, Portuguese, Ruganda, Somali, Yoruba
Work: B1 C1 D1 E F1 G H J1 K1 L N O Q S1 V Z(i,j,l,p)

LAWSON-CRUTTENDEN & CO ‡
10-11 Gray's Inn Square London WC1R 5JD
Tel: 020 7405 0833 *Fax:* 020 7405 0866
Dx: 268 LONDON/CHANCERY LN
E-mail: info@lawson-cruttenden.co.uk
List of partners: A T Lawson-Cruttenden
Work: B1 K1 L N Q S1 S2 W Z(b,g,r)
Emergency Action and Advocacy undertaken
SPr: Lawson-Cruttenden, Mr A Timothy TD MA(Cantab) • Chairman of Law Reform; Legal Adviser to Blues & Royals *May 1979

LAX & CO LLP ‡
78 Cornhill London EC3V 3QQ
Tel: 020 7623 9432 *Fax:* 020 7623 9431

ROBERT LAYTON & CO ‡
324 Uxbridge Road London W3 9QP
Tel: 020 8993 5208 *Fax:* 020 8993 4154 *Dx:* 80264 ACTON
E-mail: mail@robertlayton.co.uk

LAYTONS ‡
(in association with Libralex; Gesica)
Carmelite 50 Victoria Embankment Blackfriars London EC4Y 0LS
Tel: 020 7842 8000 *Fax:* 020 7842 8080
Dx: 253 LONDON/CHANCERY LN
E-mail: london@laytons.com
List of partners: N A Andrews, B N Bannister, C E Barker, J M S Beesley, N J Bucknell, I A Burman, S J Chapman, A S Collins, I A Cook, J W R Davies, S J Emmerson, J V Gavan, B J C Hall, R M Harrison, P R N Kelly, R J Kennett, D Knight, P L Lochner, Z K Melville-Harris, G I Mendelsohn, J Morley, J B Quibell, D W Sefton, M B Selby, W A J L Slater, P Spencer, C A Sturge, C B Sunter, G D Thomas
Office: Guildford, Manchester
Languages: Afrikaans, Cantonese, Chinese, Dutch, French, German, Gujarati, Hakka, Italian, Japanese, Kiswahili, Malay, Mandarin, Spanish, Welsh
Work: A3 B1 C1 C2 C3 D1 D2 E F1 F2 I J1 K1 K2 L M1 M2 N O P Q R1 R2 S1 S2 T1 T2 U1 W X Z(a,b,c,d,e,f,i,j,k,l,n,o,p,q,r,t,y,z)
Emergency Action undertaken
Ptr: Andrews, Mr Neale Alan . . . Oct 1988
Beesley, Mr Jonathan Michael Sherman BMus(Hons) *May 1986
Burman, Mr Ian Anthony LLB(Lond) . . . *Oct 1985
Collins, Mr Andrew Seymour TD LLB General Commissioner of Income Tax . . . *Jan 1969
Davies, Mr James William Rhys BA . . . *Sep 1992
Hall, Mr Brendan J C LLB; TEP; ACTAPS . . . *Sep 1984
Harrison, Mr Richard Mark LLB . . . *Oct 1983
Kelly, Mr Patrick Richard N BA . . . *Apr 1978
Kennett, Mr Richard John MA; LLM(Cantab) . . . *Oct 1970
Selby, Mr Marc Brian LLB(Lond); ATII; AIIT . . . *Nov 1979
Slater, Mr William Arthur John Leslie LLB . . . *Jul 1995
Sunter, Mr Cameron Beresford BA(Oxon) . . . *Nov 1983
Thomas, Mr Geraint David LLB . . . *Feb 1993
Asoc: Cates, Mr Stephen Andrew MA . . . *Sep 1996
McLean, Ms Lisa Caroline LLB; Diplome d'Etudes Juridiques Francaises . . . *Oct 1997
Oldfield, Mr Daniel James LLB(Hons) . . . *Oct 1997
Ast: Beard, Mr Russell James LLB . . . *Sep 2001
Crewe, Mr Justin LLB . . . *Sep 1999
Davies, Mr Timothy John BA(Hons); PGDipLaw . . . *Sep 2001
Goodwin, Mr Michael Charles Anthony LLB . . . *Oct 2000
Gunaratnam, Mrs Esther MEng . . . *Oct 1998
Lee, Miss Sui Ping LLB; ATT . . . Feb 2002
Leech, Mr Gary Paul . . . *Oct 1998
Simpson, Mr Graeme John . . . Mar 1997
Woolhouse, Miss Helen Elizabeth LLB . . . *Jul 1978
Con: Hillyer, Mr David Michael . . . *Jul 1965

LAYZELLS ‡
255 Muswell Hill Broadway Muswell Hill London N10 1DG
Tel: 020 8444 0202 *Fax:* 020 8883 2181 *Dx:* 36000 MUSWELL HILL
E-mail: info@layzellssolicitors.co.uk
List of partners: I E Cohen, N J Hall, J M Levy, A McMorrough
Work: C1 E J1 R1 R2 S1 S2 W Z(l,w)
Agency undertaken
Ptr: Cohen, Mr Ian Elliot LLB . . . Jan 1977
Hall, Mr Nicholas J BA . . . *Apr 1979
Levy, Mr Jack M . . . *Jan 1969
McMorrough, Ms Anna BSc(Econ); MSc(Econ) . . . *Oct 1983
Con: Bayes, Mr Alan M . . . Jul 1971

J S LAZAR ‡
723a Romford Road Manor Park London E12 5AW
Tel: 020 8553 5301 *Fax:* 020 8553 3501

KARINA LEAPMAN & CO ‡
215 West End Lane West Hampstead London NW6 1XJ
Tel: 020 7794 7741 *Fax:* 020 7794 0001 *Dx:* 38 SWISS COTTAGE
E-mail: kl@karina-leapman.co.uk
List of partners: K Leapman
Languages: French, Italian, Serbo-Croat
Work: D1 K1 K3 L N O Q
Legal Aid undertaken
SPr: Leapman, Miss Karina LLB(Exon) . . . *Dec 1980
Ast: De Sica, Mr Giuseppe CPE; LLM . . . *May 2004

LEARMOND CRIQUI SOKEL ‡
28b Hampstead High Street London NW3 1QA
Tel: 020 7431 0707

LECOTE SOLICITORS ‡
Accurist House 44 Baker Street London W1U 7AL
Tel: 07870 164686
E-mail: andrewsparrow@lecotelondon.com

LEDGISTERS ‡
1 The Lanchesters Hammersmith London W6 9ER
Tel: 020 8746 1122
Emergency telephone 07950 399583
Work: B2 G H Z(g)
Agency and Advocacy undertaken

LEE & KAN ‡
1st Floor National House 60-66 Wardour Street London W1F 0TA
Tel: 020 7287 8888 *Fax:* 020 7287 2600 *Dx:* 44725 SOHO SQUARE
List of partners: T Y C Kan, D K W Lee
Languages: Chinese
Work: A1 C1 C2 C3 D1 E F1 G H J1 K1 L M1 M2 N O P Q R1 S1 T1 T2 W Z(b,c,e,i,j,k,l,t)
Agency, Advocacy and Legal Aid undertaken
Ptr: Kan, Mr Timothy Y C LLB(Lond) . . . *Dec 1977
Lee, Mr Dominic K W MA . . . *Jun 1980
Ast: Gibbons, Mr Hsaio Mei . . . Mar 2003

LEE & THOMPSON ‡
Green Garden House 15-22 St Christophers Place London W1U 1NL
Tel: 020 7935 4665 *Fax:* 020 7563 4949
E-mail: mail@leeandthompson.com
List of partners: R M Antoniades, J A T Gawade, R J C Horsfall, R W Lee, N C Parfitt, Z V Reynolds, A J Thompson
Work: C1 J1 O Q Z(e,f,k,w)
Fixed Fee Interview undertaken
Ptr: Antoniades, Mr Renos Michael LLB(Leics) . . . *Oct 1991
Gawade, Mr Jeremy A T BA(Hons)(Oxon) . . . *Jan 1982
Horsfall, Mr Robert J C LLB(Hons) . . . *Mar 1982
Lee, Mr Robert W LLB(Bris) . . . *Dec 1970
Parfitt, Ms Nicola Clair MA(Cantab) . . . *Sep 1993
Reynolds, Miss Zoe Virginia LLB . . . *Sep 1992
Thompson, Mr Andrew J LLB . . . *Nov 1977
Ast: Ashelford, Mr Mark BA . . . *Oct 1997
Brookes, Mr Michael Andrew LLM . . . *Nov 1995
Carmen-Davis, Ms Nicole BA(Hons); CPE; LPC . . . *Sep 2001
Diwan, Miss Tushar Sonia MA(Cantab) . . . *Aug 1997
Facer, Miss Sarah-Jane LLB(Hons); DipLP . . . *Apr 2001
Lever, Mr Richard Charles Jeremy BA(Hons) . . . *Apr 1996
Robb, Miss Sophia Mary MA(Cantab) . . . *Sep 1996
Stone, Mr Lee LLB(English & French Law) . . . *Sep 1998

LEE ASSOCIATES
30 Tooting Beck Road Tooting Wandsworth London SW17 8BD
Tel: 020 8682 9797 *Fax:* 020 8682 9884 *Dx:* 133356 BALHAM
E-mail: lee_associates@btconnect.com
Office: London E13
Ptr: Banharally, Mr Mohammad Haref LLB . . . *Jun 1990

LEE BOLTON MONIER-WILLIAMS ‡
1 The Sanctuary Westminster London SW1P 3JT
Tel: 020 7222 5381 *Fax:* 020 7799 2781
Dx: 145940 WESTMINSTER 4
E-mail: enquiries@lbmw.com
List of partners: P F B Beesley, R D Cooper, R Cottingham, H Dellar, M J G Fletcher, C K Hargreaves, D M Higgs, C V Hughes, E J Macey-Dare, J P G Randel, S Z Reisman, J P Sergeant, N D Urwin, K E W Wallace
Work: A1 B1 C1 C2 C3 D1 E J1 K1 L M1 M2 N O P Q R1 R2 S1 S2 T1 T2 W X Z(c,d,e,h,i,k,q,r,s,x)
Emergency Action, Agency, Advocacy and S.I.G
Ptr: Beesley, Mr Peter F B LLB(Exon) Registrar of the Faculty Office of the Archbishop of Canterbury Diocese; Registrar of Ely Guildford and Hereford . . . *§Jun 1967
Cooper, Mr Robin D . . . *Mar 1972
Cottingham, Mr Robert BA . . . *Jan 1989
Dellar, Mr Howard . . . *Feb 1999
Fletcher, Mr Michael J G MA(Cantab) Clerk to the Worshipful Company of Musicians . . . *Dec 1982
Hargreaves, Mr Colin K . . . *Nov 1972
Higgs, Mr David Mark LLB . . . *Jan 1997
Hughes, Mr Christopher V MA(Cantab) Clerk to the Worshipful Company of Distillers . . . *Oct 1982
Macey-Dare, Mr Edward J BA(Dunelm) . . . Sep 1996
Randel, Mr John P G BA(Cantab) Gropius Prize . . . *Jun 1971
Reisman, Mr Seymour Z LLB(B'ham) . . . *§Jun 1968
Sergeant, Mr J Philip MA(Cantab) . . . *Jun 1976
Urwin, Mr Nigel D MA(Oxon) . . . *Jul 1976
Wallace, Mr Keith Edward William . . . *Nov 1994
Ast: Clarke, Mr Bruce . . . Sep 2008
Morgan, Ms Claire . . . Sep 2008
Reed, Mr Joseph . . . Sep 2003
Sherbrooke, Mr Archie . . . Sep 2008
Vlahos, Mr David LLB; RSADip; TEP . . . *Jan 2006
Ward, Mr James . . . Sep 2006
Con: Dunn, Mr Michael . . . *§Jul 1961
Sills, Mr David G LLB . . . *Jan 1970

CHRISTINE LEE & CO (SOLICITORS) LTD
171 Wardour Street London W1F 8WS
Tel: 020 7287 6233 *Fax:* 020 7287 2263 *Dx:* 37214 PICCADILLY
Office: Birmingham
Languages: Cantonese, Chinese, Malay, Mandarin, Punjabi
Work: E K1 K3 L O Q R2 S1 S2 W Z(g,i,p)
Fixed Fee Interview undertaken
Ptr: Ho, Mr David Tat Wai . . . Nov 2003
Lee, Ms Christine C K LLB . . . Feb 2002
Wilkes, Mr Martin F LLB . . . May 1977
Asoc: Lai, Ms Sharon Yee-Mei LLB(Hons) . . . Mar 2006

STEWART LEE ‡
58 Mountfield Road London N3 3NP
Tel: 020 8346 2769 *Fax:* 020 8343 4870
E-mail: sleekennington@yahoo.co.uk
List of partners: S J Lee
Work: E L S1 S2
SPr: Lee, Mr Stewart Jonathan . . . *Dec 1971

LEELANES SOLICITORS LLP ‡
(incorporating S B Gilinsky & Co)
6th Floor 28-30 Cornhill London EC3V 3NF
Tel: 020 7220 9410 *Fax:* 020 7220 9411
E-mail: info@leelanes.com
List of partners: J M Jacob
Work: B1 C1 C2 C3 E F1 J1 K1 L M1 M2 N P S1 T1 T2 W Z(b,d,e,i,k,m)
Agency undertaken
Ptr: Jacob, Mr Jonathan M LLB(B'ham) . . . *Jun 1981
Con: Mayes, Mr Charles S . . . *Jul 1961
Sloan, Mr George J D LLB(Lond) . . . *Jun 1966

LEGAL CITY ‡
35 Lansdowne Road Finchley London N3 1ET
Tel: 020 8922 3282

LEGAL HOBBIT ‡
New Broad Street House 35 New Broad Street London EC2M 1NH
Tel: 020 7194 8400 *Fax:* 0845 658 6313
E-mail: katherine@legalhobbit.com
List of partners: K Evans
Ptr: Evans, Mrs Katherine . . . Sep 1995

LEGITIMUS SOLICITORS ‡
5th Floor 133 Houndsditch London EC3A 7BX
Tel: 020 3402 6009 *Fax:* 020 8711 5300 *Dx:* 733 LONDON/CITY
E-mail: info@legitimus.co.uk

LEHMAN BROTHERS ‡
25 Bank Street London E14 5LE
Tel: 020 7102 1000

LEIGH DAY & CO ‡
Priory House 25 St John's Lane London EC1M 4LB
Est: 1987
Tel: 020 7650 1200 *Fax:* 020 7253 4433 *Dx:* 53326 CLERKENWELL
E-mail: postbox@leighday.co.uk
Web: www.leighday.co.uk
List of partners: C Benson, S Campbell, M J Day, R H Dyson, D Easton, C Fazan, S Humber, P Knight, R A Levy, O Lewin, S Malik, G Matthews, R B Meeran, B Michalowska-Howells, A Millar, S C Moore, S J Nicholes, C Palmer, J Paterson, S Srinivasan, R Stein, F M Swaine, N Wainwright, S White, A H Winyard
Languages: Arabic, Finnish, French, German, Greek, Gujarati, Hindi, Italian, Malay, Polish, Spanish, Tamil, Urdu
Work: J1 N P R1 X Z(g,r)
Agency, Fixed Fee Interview, Legal Aid undertaken, Legal Aid Franchise and Member of Accident Line
Ptr: Benson, Mr Chris BA; PGDipLaw; CPC; MA . . . Jan 2003
Campbell, Ms Sarah . . . Jan 1999
Day, Mr Martyn J . . . *Apr 1981
Dyson, Mr R Henry . . . Nov 1989
Easton, Mr Daniel . . . Sep 2003
Fazan, Ms Claire LLB . . . *Dec 1985
Humber, Mr Sean . . . Sep 1996
Knight, Miss Penny BSc . . . Nov 1995
Levy, Mr Russell A BA; LLB Maxwell Law Prize . . . *Oct 1984
Lewin, Miss Olive BSc; CPE . . . *Sep 1990
Malik, Ms Sapna BSc; LLM Litigation Team of the Year - The Lawyer 2003 . . . Nov 1998
Matthews, Gene LLB . . . Jan 2003
Meeran, Mr Richard B . . . Apr 1988
Michalowska-Howells, Bozena . . . Apr 1995
Millar, Ms Alison . . . Jul 2000
Moore, Ms Sally C . . . Nov 1989
Nicholes, Ms Sally Jean BA(Leeds) . . . *Dec 1990
Palmer, Ms Camilla LLB . . . Jan 1983
Paterson, Jill . . . Oct 2003
Srinivasan, Ms Shubhaa . . . Nov 2003
Stein, Mr Richard LLM; BA(Hons) . . . *Apr 1994
Swaine, Miss Frances Mary BA(Hons); MA(UCL) . . . *Oct 1990
Wainwright, Ms Nicola . . . Nov 1997
White, Suzanne LLB; MA . . . Jan 1999
Winyard, Ms Anne H MA(Oxon) . . . *Dec 1977

Holders of Franchise for Clinical Negligence, Personal Injury. We conduct business in Dutch, Greek, Malay, Polish, Tamil.

DAVID LEMCO & CO ‡
287 Green Lanes Palmers Green London N13 4XS
Tel: 020 8882 1074 *Fax:* 020 8886 8024
Dx: 57858 PALMERS GREEN
E-mail: davidlemco@aol.com
List of partners: M D Lemco
Languages: French
Work: B1 C1 E J1 K1 L N S1 S2 T1 T2 W Z(l)
Fixed Fee Interview undertaken
Ptr: Lemco, Mr Malcolm David. . . . . *Dec 1976

LENNOX BYWATER ‡
9 Limes Avenue Mill Hill London NW7 3NY
Tel: 020 8906 1206 *Fax:* 020 8906 3898
List of partners: C L Bywater
Languages: French, German, Spanish
Work: C1 C2 C3 M1 M2 Z(e,f,w,y)
Ptr: Bywater, Mr Colin L BA . . . . *Jun 1967

LEONARD LOWY & CO ‡
85-87 Bayham Street London NW1 0AG
Tel: 020 7788 4333 *Fax:* 0870 880 9435
E-mail: lowy@leonardlowy.co.uk

EDWARD LEONARDS SOLICITORS ‡
245 Walworth Road Walworth London SE17 1WT
Tel: 020 7252 7676 *Fax:* 020 7252 5800 *Dx:* 34912 WALWORTH
Emergency telephone 07956 467921
E-mail: edward.leonards@yahoo.co.uk
List of partners: E Obioha
Ptr: Obioha, Mr Edward BSc(Hons); LLB(Hons); PGDipLP; LLM . . . . .Jul 2003

LAW OFFICES OF JOAN LEOPOLD ‡
Flat 36 Ashton Court 254-256 Camden Road London NW1 9HF
Tel: 020 7485 5540 *Fax:* 020 9218 3427

LESLIEOWEN ‡
108 Lambton Road London SW20 0TJ
Tel: 07711 047549 *Fax:* 020 8879 9821
E-mail: saraleslie44@hotmail.com

LESTER ALDRIDGE LLP
(incorporating Park Nelson)
70 Chancery Lane London WC2A 1AF
Tel: 0844 967 0785
E-mail: info@la-law.com
Office: Bournemouth (2 offices), Southampton
Languages: French, German
Work: A1 B1 C1 C2 C3 D1 E F1 J1 K1 L M1 M2 N O P Q R1 S1 T1 T2 W Z(b,c,d,e,j,k)
Agency and Legal Aid undertaken
Ptr: Deehan, Ms Ruth H LLB(Hons) . . . . *Apr 1994
Fairbairn, Mr Richard M LLB . . . . *§Jul 1978
Flood, Mr Colm Thomas LLB . . . . *Jul 1979
Ford, Mr Timothy G. . . . . *§Jun 1969
Galloway, Mr Robert A H LLB . . . . *Apr 1975
Herbert, Mr David M LLB . . . . *Apr 1981
Kings, Mr John C . . . . *§Jan 1969
O'Keeffe, Mr Eugene A LLB. . . . . *§Jun 1975
Rickard, Mr W Jocelyn LLB(Lond); LLM . . . . *Apr 1979
Skelding, Mr Barry Howard . . . . *Jan 1970
Stone, Mr Simon N . . . . *§Mar 1973
Ast: Dosanjh, Mr Sarbjeet Paul Singh BA(Hons) . . . . . . Aug 1997
Newson, Mr Stephen Thomas LLB . . . . .Jul 2001
Page, Mr David R S LLB(Hull). . . . . *Jul 1973
Thomas, Miss Gaenor Rebecca Morgana BA . . . . . .Jul 2001
Con: Ireland, Mr Richard H . . . . *Jun 1978

LESTER DOMINIC SOLICITORS ‡
Upper Floors 85-87 Ballards Lane Finchley Central London N3 1XT
Tel: 020 8371 7400 *Fax:* 020 8346 7685 *Dx:* 57276 FINCHLEY 2
E-mail: reception@lesterdominic.com
Languages: Cantonese, Mandarin, Punjabi, Urdu
Work: C1 E K1 K3 L Q S2 T1 T2 W Z(i)
Asoc: Bhatti, Ms Sangeet Kaur LLB(Hons). . . . . *Sep 2007

LEVENES EMPLOYMENT ‡
Cromwell House 14 Filwood Place London WC1V 6HZ
Tel: 020 7148 7850 *Fax:* 020 7831 5959
E-mail: employment@levenes.co.uk

LEVENES SOLICITORS ‡
Ashley House 235-239 High Road Wood Green Haringey London N22 8HF
Tel: 020 8881 7777 / 8881 6764 *Fax:* 020 8889 6395
Dx: 135576 WOOD GREEN 4
Emergency telephone 07699 753011
E-mail: info@levenes.co.uk
List of partners: S Allsop, P I K Baria, T J Beasley, M R Clingman, D Levene, J Lynn, R O Mainwaring, D V Nicolls, K M O'Sullivan, A Onwukwe, D E Ruebain
Office: Birmingham
Languages: Arabic, Bengali, Greek, Gujarati, Italian, Lithuanian, Polish, Punjabi, Russian, Tamil, Turkish, Urdu
Work: B2 G H J1 N O Q X Z(j,p)
Emergency Action, Agency, Advocacy, Fixed Fee Interview, Legal Aid undertaken, Legal Aid Franchise and Member of Accident Line
Ptr: Allsop, Ms Sadiye LLB . . . . May 2001
Baria, Ms Pinky Inderjit Kaur LLB . . . . *Nov 1995
Beasley, Mr Timothy John LLB(Hons); LPC . . . . . . *Oct 1992
Clingman, Mr Mark R BA; LLM . . . . Feb 1990
Levene, Mr David LLB(Warw) . . . . *Oct 1981
Lynn, Mr Jonathan BA(Hons); CPE . . . . *Jan 2004
Mainwaring, Mr Richard O BA. . . . . *Nov 1988
Nicolls, Mr David V BA(Hons) . . . . *Oct 1988
O'Sullivan, Mr Kevin M BA(Hons); CPE . . . . *Jan 1999
Onwukwe, Ms Audrey BSc; CPE . . . . *Sep 1994
Ruebain, Mr David E BA(Hons) Trustee of Disability Law Service . . . . *May 1989

LEVETTS ‡
Unit 27 Cannon Wharf Business Centre 35 Evelyn Street London SE8 5RT
Tel: 020 7237 7771 *Fax:* 020 7394 8988 *Dx:* 56707 DEPTFORD
List of partners: P G Corbett
Work: C1 E F1 J1 K1 L N O Q S1 W Z(l)
Emergency Action and Fixed Fee Interview undertaken
SPr: Corbett, Mr Peter G LLB . . . . *Jun 1977

LEVI SOLICITORS LLP ‡
31 Threadneedle Street London EC2R 8AY
Tel: 020 7763 6407 *Fax:* 0113 297 1872 *Dx:* 42602 CHEAPSIDE
E-mail: info@levisolicitors.co.uk

MARSHALL F LEVINE & ASSOCIATES ‡
81 Haverstock Hill London NW3 4SL
Tel: 020 7586 7149 *Fax:* 020 7586 7149
E-mail: info@marshalllevineassociates.com

LEVISON MELTZER PIGOTT ‡
45 Ludgate Hill London EC4M 7JU
Tel: 020 7556 2400 *Fax:* 020 7556 2401
Dx: 200 LONDON/CHANCERY LN
E-mail: enquiries@lmplaw.co.uk
List of partners: N Fletcher, A Hayes, J I Levison, S C Pigott, J Ribet
Work: K1 K2 K3
Ptr: Fletcher, Miss Nicola BA(Hons)(Psychology) . . . . . Sep 1997
Hayes, Ms Alison BA(Hons). . . . . Oct 1994
Levison, Mr Jeremy Ian . . . . Oct 1976
Pigott, Mr Simon C BSc. . . . . Jan 1983
Ribet, Mr Julian . . . . Jun 1999
Ast: Billingsley, Miss Elisabeth MA(Oxon) . . . . Sep 2008
Myles, Mr Alistair BA(Hons) . . . . Oct 2008
Schmidt, Mrs Alison BA(Hons) . . . . Apr 2005
Sutherland, Miss Natalie Louise LLB(Hons) . . . . . . .Jul 2006

JANE LEVY SOLICITORS ‡
85-87 Bayham Street London NW1 0AG
Tel: 020 7788 4288 *Fax:* 020 7788 4289 *Dx:* 57065 CAMDEN TOWN
E-mail: jls@janelevy.co.uk
Languages: French
Work: S1

P S LEVY & CO ‡
48 Welbeck Street London W1G 9XL
Tel: 020 7486 7717 *Fax:* 020 7486 6484 *Dx:* 41715 MARYLEBONE 2
E-mail: info@pslevylaw.com
List of partners: P S Levy
Work: E J1 L N O Q S1 S2 W Z(f)
Ptr: Levy, Mr Peter Stephen. . . . . *Jun 1966

LEWIS & CO ‡
21 Green Walk Hendon London NW4 2AL
Tel: 020 8202 4343 *Fax:* 020 8202 9117 *Dx:* 59336 HENDON
Emergency telephone 07956 679019
E-mail: lewisandcosolicitors@hotmail.com
List of partners: J S Lewis
Work: B1 C1 E F1 L N S1 S2 U2 W Z(b,k)
Agency and Fixed Fee Interview undertaken
SPr: Lewis, Mr Jonathan Simon BA(Hons)(Law) . . . . . *May 1985

BRIAN LEWIS & CO ‡
17 Pemberton House 7 Pemberton Row London EC4A 3AB
Tel: 020 7583 9900

LEWIS CUTNER & CO ‡
Barkat House Suite 2 116-118 Finchley Road London NW3 5HT
Tel: 020 7433 2552 *Fax:* 020 7794 5595
E-mail: lewis@cutner.wanadoo.co.uk
List of partners: L Cutner
Work: B1 C1 E J1 K3 N O Q S1 S2 Z(k,p,q)
Fixed Fee Interview undertaken and Member of Accident Line

DUNCAN LEWIS & CO ‡
1a Kingsland High Street Hackney London E8 2JS
Tel: 020 7923 4020 *Fax:* 020 7923 3320
Emergency telephone 07768 934333
E-mail: admin@duncanlewis.com
List of partners: A S Gupta, N Joshi
Office: Harrow, London SE14, London SW17, London W12, Romford
Work: B1 B2 D1 D2 E F1 G H J1 J2 K1 L M1 O Q R2 S1 S2 T1 T2 V W X Z(b,d,e,g,h,j,k,l,p,q,z)
Emergency Action, Agency, Advocacy, Fixed Fee Interview and Legal Aid undertaken
Ptr: Gupta, Mr Amarpal S ● . . . . Dec 1996
Joshi, Ms Nina ● . . . . Feb 1998
Ast: Appalakondiah, Mr Vanketaramana LLB(Hons) . . . . *Feb 1996
Dhaliwal, Mr Hardeep Singh ●. . . . . Nov 1997
Rahman, Ms Henna ●. . . . . May 2001
Sumputh, Ms Vijaya. . . . . Mar 2001
Tyers, Ms Emma Jane . . . . Oct 2001
Con: Rafique, Syed T H MA(Cantab) . . . . *Jun 1970

DUNCAN LEWIS & CO
54 Goldhawk Road Shepherd's Bush London W12 8HA
Tel: 020 7923 4020 *Fax:* 020 7923 3320
Dx: 58704 SHEPHERDS BUSH
E-mail: admin@duncanlewis.com
Office: Harrow, London E8, London SE14, London SW17, Romford
Work: A1 D1 E K1 K3 L O Q S1 S2 W Z(e,f,g,i,l)
Emergency Action, Legal Aid undertaken and Legal Aid Franchise
Asoc: Montgomery, Mrs Shelia. . . . . *Jan 1997
Ast: Hendry, Mr Jonathan Bruce LLB. . . . . Jan 2007
Hussain, Saqib LLB . . . . *Oct 1998
Javed, Mr Irfan MA; LLB; LLM. . . . . .Jul 2004
Sarandou, Ms Georgia LLM. . . . . *Aug 1998
Seelhoff, Mr Adrian Charles LLM; BA(Criminal Law). . Sep 2005
Tear, Mr Adam Michael . . . . *Apr 2004

DUNCAN LEWIS & CO
3rd Floor Offices 40 Tooting High Street London SW17 0RG
Tel: 020 7923 4020 *Fax:* 020 7923 3320
E-mail: admin@duncanlewis.com
Office: Harrow, London E8, London SE14, London W12, Romford

DUNCAN LEWIS & CO
182 New Cross Road New Cross Gate London SE14 5AA
Tel: 020 7923 4020 *Fax:* 020 7923 3320
E-mail: admin@duncanlewis.co.uk
Office: Harrow, London E8, London SW17, London W12, Romford

LEWIS GREEN & CO SOLICITORS ‡
57 Duke Street London W1K 5NR
Tel: 0845 094 8044 *Fax:* 0845 094 8055
E-mail: lg@lpgreen.co.uk

LEWIS NEDAS & CO ‡
24 Camden High Street Camden London NW1 0JH
Tel: 020 7387 2032 *Fax:* 020 7388 6575 *Dx:* 57056 CAMDEN TOWN
Emergency telephone 020 7387 2032
E-mail: conveyancing@lewisnedas.co.uk
List of partners: M R Herman, J Lamb, J A Lewis, A Meisels, P S Muir, S E K Nedas, K J Wood
Work: B2 D1 E G H K1 L S1 S2 W Z(h,l)
Emergency Action, Agency, Advocacy, Fixed Fee Interview, Legal Aid undertaken and Legal Aid Franchise
Ptr: Herman, Mr Miles R LLB Notary Public . . . . *Nov 1992
Lamb, Ms Julia LLB. . . . . *Jan 1991
Lewis, Mr Jeffrey A BSc(Econ) . . . . *Mar 1978
Meisels, Mr Anthony. . . . . *Nov 2000
Muir, Ms Penelope Susan. . . . . *Sep 1987
Nedas, Ms Stephanie E K. . . . . *Oct 1971
Wood, Mr Keith James BA . . . . *Sep 1996
Ast: Abrahams, Ms Prudence A LLB. . . . . *Oct 1992
Bailey, Ms Rhean . . . . Jun 2000
Corcoran, Miss Samantha BA(Hons) . . . . *Nov 2003
Rasool, Ms Leila . . . . Jan 2000

LEWIS SIDHU SOLICITORS ‡
Northumberland House 11 The Pavement London W5 4NG
Tel: 020 8832 7321

LEWIS SILKIN LLP ‡
5 Chancery Lane Clifford's Inn London EC4A 1BL
Tel: 020 7074 8000 *Fax:* 020 7864 1200
Dx: 182 LONDON/CHANCERY LN
E-mail: info@lewissilkin.com
List of partners: R M Alexander, D Appleton, G M Bastow, G Brahams, R A P Brimelow, M Burd, J P Carr, H Cavanagh, T J Coates, S Cohen, L Convery, G Cordall, G Crown, R E Dadak, J B Davies, B J C Dresden, N M Edwards, S R Entwistle, J Evans, D C Farnsworth, C G Fluet, P E J Foster, N Goode, V Goode, L I Goodrich, C I Greenwood, I R Jeffery, S Johnson, B M G Kilcoyne, P R Lamb, J Levy, S Lorber, A Lorenzo, H Oliver, K F Payne, C L Reddy, J B Reuben, N A Toner, T J Watkins
Office: Oxford
Languages: French, German, Italian, Spanish
Work: A3 B1 C1 C2 C3 E F1 F2 I J1 J2 L M1 M2 O P Q R1 R2 S2 T1 U1 U2 Z(b,c,d,e,f,g,h,i,j,k,n,p,q,s,u,w,z)
Advocacy undertaken
Ptr: Alexander, Mr Roger M . . . . *§Jul 1965
Appleton, Mr David BA . . . . *Nov 1994
Bastow, Ms Gillian M MA(Oxon); LLM(Leics) . . . . *§May 1981
Brahams, Mr Gareth LLB(Hons). . . . . *Nov 1995
Burd, Mr Michael BA(Columbia); MPhil(Cantab) . . . *§Oct 1986
Cavanagh, Miss Helen LLB; LPC . . . . Mar 1997
Coates, Mr Thomas J BA . . . . *§Oct 1979
Cohen, Ms Sara. . . . . Dec 1981
Convery, Mrs Linda LLB. . . . . Nov 1985
Cordall, Ms Gillian BA(Hons) . . . . *§Feb 1993
Crown, Mr Giles MA(Law). . . . . Oct 2000
Dadak, Mr Roderick E LLB(Hons) . . . . *Nov 1972
Davies, Mr James B LLB; Dip d'Etudes Juridiques Francaises . . . . *§Dec 1988
Dresden, Mr Brinsley Julian Caspar LLB(Hons) . . . . *Nov 1991
Edwards, Mr Nigel Martin LLB. . . . . *Nov 1991
Entwistle, Mr Simon Robert LLB. . . . . *Oct 1988
Evans, Ms Joanne BA(Hons) . . . . *Nov 1995
Farnsworth, Mr Dominic Clark LLM . . . . *Sep 1995
Fluet, Mr Clifford Gary. . . . . Oct 1996
Foster, Mr Philip E J BA(Dublin); MPhil(Lond) . . . . *§Mar 1980
Goode, Ms Naomi MA; MSc. . . . . *Nov 1990
Goode, Ms Victoria . . . . Dec 1992
Goodrich, Mr Leonard I LLB. . . . . *§Apr 1982
Greenwood, Mr Clive I . . . . *Nov 1989
Jeffery, Mr Ian Richard LLB . . . . Nov 1992
Johnson, Ms Sally. . . . . *Nov 1990
Kilcoyne, Mr Brian Michael Gerard . . . . Mar 1992
Lamb, Mr Philip R. . . . . *Oct 1988
Levy, Mr John LLB . . . . *§Apr 1971
Lorber, Mr Steven. . . . . *Apr 1978
Lorenzo, Mr Antonio BA(Hons) . . . . *Nov 1995
Oliver, Ms Hazel MA(Oxon); BCL; LLM(Toronto). . . . Nov 1997
Payne, Mr K Fergus LLB . . . . *§May 1981
Reddy, Ms Clare L LLB(Hons). . . . . Sep 1998
Reuben, Mr Jonathan B LLB . . . . *§Sep 1985
Toner, Mr Neil A BA. . . . . Dec 1992
Watkins, Mr Trevor J BSc(Wales) . . . . *§Apr 1979
Ast: Appleton, Mrs Nicola LLB(Hons) Law Society Prize (Newcastle) . . . . Sep 1999
Ashley, Mr Sean LLB(Hons). . . . . Oct 1998
Bagg, Mr Simon J BA. . . . . *Sep 1995
Barnard, Mr Jamie . . . . Sep 2002
Barr, Ms Louise. . . . . Mar 1995
Barry, Ms Paula E BA(Kent). . . . . *Nov 1989
Baxter, Ms Karen Elizabeth . . . . Sep 2003
Briggs, Mrs Tessa LLB . . . . Sep 1996
Carney, Ms Bethan M CPU in Law Conversion . . . . . Oct 1997
Carter, Ms Lucy LLB; Dip Sports LA. . . . . Mar 2002
Casey, Ms Laura LPC. . . . . Sep 2001
Daneshku, Sohrab BA; CPE; LSF; ULB(Brussels). . *May 1995
Davenport, Ms Barbara Mary . . . . Sep 2002
Davis, Mr Spencer . . . . Dec 2002
Dempsey, Mr Sean Francis . . . . Sep 2001
Dore, MIss Pauline BCL; LLM(Cantab); Dip IT Law . . Sep 1999
Dunbar, Mr Matthew. . . . . Sep 1999
Eastwood, Mr Owen LLB; BA . . . . Feb 2001
Ely, Mr Jonathan LLB(Hons). . . . . Jun 2000
Ewing, Ms Helen Christa . . . . Oct 2004
Farmer, Ms Jo . . . . Sep 1999
Godfrey, Miss Nicola BA(Law); LPC. . . . . Oct 1996
Grant, Mr Thomas R BA . . . . *Sep 2001
Halevy, Ms Tamar LLB; LLM; MPhil . . . . Oct 1996
Halsey, Mr Benjamin . . . . Sep 2004
Horne, Ms Tracey. . . . . Nov 1995
Hurren, Ms Sharon . . . . May 1996
Illingworth-Law, Mr Neville E H LLB; LP . . . . Sep 1998
James, Mr Philip Edwin Francis . . . . Sep 2001
Kendon, Mr Colin . . . . Jan 1990
Khanna, Ms Shalina. . . . . Sep 2004
Kilcoyne, Miss Elizabeth Anne LLB . . . . Sep 1998
Kuness, Mr Alexander Patrick. . . . . Oct 2004
Leigh, Ms Emma Louise. . . . . Sep 2002
Levy, Mr James. . . . . *Nov 1993
Lim, Mr Mark . . . . Sep 2001
Miskella, Mr Richard . . . . .Jul 2001
Morrisey, Mr Simon BA . . . . Oct 1996
Mortimer-Tracey, Ms Jane. . . . . Oct 2004
O'Reilly, Ms Sarah Louise. . . . . Mar 2005
Perera, Ms Emma Dheemati . . . . Sep 2003
Phillips, Ms Vivenne Lucy. . . . . Oct 2004
Poulter, Ms Julia Anne . . . . Oct 2003
Pratt, Ms Elaine LLB . . . . Sep 2000
Rajput, Mr Paul. . . . . Oct 2002

Regnard-Weinrabe, Ms Sophie Delphine . . . Sep 2003
Ross, Mr Jonathan LLB(Hons); LPC. . . . Sep 2001
Rousell, Ms Michelle . . . Dec 1993
Scott, Ms Emma Jane. . . . Sep 2003
Shah, Sanjeev Hasmukhrai LLB(Hons) . . . Oct 1997
Silverman, Ms Kate . . . Nov 1999
Soakell, Mrs Carolyn LLB . . . Sep 1999
Stern, Ms Charlotte Kathryn. . . . Sep 2004
Townsend, Mr Peter BA(Hons); CPE; LCP. . . . Aug 1999
Wilder, Ms Kate Sara . . . Sep 2004
Williams, Mr Owen Thomas Godfrey. . . . Sep 2004
Wright, Ms Rachel . . . Sep 2000
Con: Davies, Mr Geoffrey R LLB; AKC . . . *Oct 1972

LEWIS TERRANCE ROSE SOLICITORS ‡
2nd Floor Southgate Office Village Block F 288 Chase Road London N14 6HF
Tel: 020 8920 9970

LEX LAW ‡
4 Middle Temple Lane Temple London EC4Y 9AA
Tel: 020 7183 0529 *Fax:* 020 7183 0539
E-mail: maa@lexlaw.co.uk

LEXICA LAW ‡
131-151 Great Titchfield Street London W1W 5BB
Tel: 020 7158 0031 *Fax:* 0870 745 6266 *Dx:* 2109 EUSTON
List of partners: G Calliste, S Gurr, N A Hutchings, J J Sharratt
Office: Canterbury

LEXICON INSURANCE SERVICES ‡
7 Glasshill Street London SE1 0QR
Tel: 020 7981 9888

LEXIS LAW SOLICITORS ‡
52 High Street Colliers Wood London SW19 2BY

LI & CO SOLICITOR ‡
Unit 3b Kensal Town Telegraph Works 14 Conlan Street Kensington & Chelsea London W10 5AR
Tel: 020 8964 8525 *Fax:* 020 8964 8525
List of partners: M Li
Languages: Hakka
Work: Z(i)
Fixed Fee Interview undertaken
Ptr: Li, Miss Mannwey BA(Hons) . . . *Dec 1997

LIBERTY & CO SOLICITORS ‡
149 Plumstead Road London SE18 7DY
Tel: 020 8331 0660 *Fax:* 020 8331 4385 *Dx:* 33308 WOOLWICH
E-mail: info@libertysolicitors.co.uk

LIGHTFOOT O'BRIEN WESTCOTT
34 South Molton Street Mayfair London W1Y 2BP
Tel: 01394 386336 *Fax:* 01394 380098 *Dx:* 41402 WOODBRIDGE
E-mail: mail@lightfoot-obrien.co.uk
Office: Woodbridge
Work: A1 B1 C1 D1 D2 E F1 J1 K1 K3 L N O Q S1 S2 T2 W Z(c,l)
Fixed Fee Interview undertaken
Ptr: Lightfoot, Mr James C E MA(Oxon) . . . *Jan 1979
O'Brien, Mr B Rory MA(Cantab). . . . *Jun 1985

C S LIMA & CO ‡
42 Manchester Street London W1U 7LW
Tel: 020 7935 1881

LINCOLN'S CHAMBERS SOLICITORS ‡
1st Floor 108a Whitechapel Road London E1 1JE
Tel: 020 7375 0062 *Fax:* 020 7247 9541
E-mail: lc.solicitors@yahoo.co.uk

LINCOLNS SOLICITORS ‡
383b Green Street Upton Park London E13 9AU
Tel: 020 8471 6328 *Fax:* 020 8503 6545
E-mail: llincolnsolicitors@yahoo.co.uk

LINDSAY & JOCKELSON ‡
169a Walworth Road London SE17 1RW
Tel: 020 7701 9898

LINK2LAW ‡
2 London Wall Buildings London Wall London EC2M 5UU
Tel: 020 8448 5091 *Fax:* 020 7448 5161 *Dx:* 42612 CHEAPSIDE
E-mail: info@link-2-law.co.uk
Office: London W1

LINK2LAW
6 Porter Street London W1U 6DD
Tel: 020 7989 5091 *Fax:* 020 7989 5161
E-mail: info@link-2-law.co.uk
Office: London EC2

LINKLATERS LLP ‡
One Silk Street London EC2Y 8HQ
Tel: 020 7456 2000 *Fax:* 020 7456 2222
Dx: 10 LONDON/CHANCERY LN
List of partners: C Ahlborn, W Allan, I M G Andrews, P A Ashall, H J Baker, D E O Barber, D A Barnes, R P Barron, S Bedford, B Bell, E A Bennett, M J Bennett, P Bevan, B Bird, A W Black, S M Blackshaw, M Bland, M Blyth, I J Bowler, K J Bradford, G C H Brannan, J A Brown, M Brown, A J Bruce, W D M Buckley, A Bugg, M C Burgess-Smith, A L Burn, R Bussell, A D Byrne, M W Canby, A J Carmichael, E Chan, G Chapman, D W Cheyne, C E M Clark, S H T Clark, E Clarke, O H Clay, R Cleaver, R M Cohen, A I Comiskey, J Conder, E Conway, C B Coombe, J Cooper, T E Cox, J Crozier, R J Cumbley, M J Cutting, A Davies, J E J Davies, S Davies, J De Lance-Holmes, J Dickson, M Didizian, S Dogra, E J Doran, J Douglass, B Dulieu, H C H Dunn, N W Eastwell, S R R Edlmann, M J H Elliott, R J Elliott, D P Ereira, C P Evans, J M Evans, J A A Evans, P S Farren, I W Fenn, L C Fergusson, S N Firth, M Fletcher, S Fletcher, I France, N Franks, A Freeman, R Fugard, J Gewirtz, R W Godden, R J Goldman, D F Good, S G Griffin, S Griffin, S Gwynne, J Harbach, M J Hardwick, N Harnby, V Havard-williams, C Hayes, J Hayes, E Hickman, F Hobbs, A Hoe, R C T Holden, N Hopkins, A Hughes, M J Humphries, M Ijaz, J Inglis, J S Innes-Taylor, C Jacobs, B James, R Jarvis, A Jones, N H Jones, N Kar, I Karet, S S Katwala, E Keats, M Keats, M Kent, M A Kingstone, R Knowles, J Knox, F J Kucera, A Kurdian, J Lane, C Lawson, R Levy, P Lewis, T Lidstrom, J Lovett, S Lucas, K E Ludlow, M Lynchehan, J Martin, N Mayo, O McKendrick, D N McMenamin, M S Middleditch, M Middleton, C Miller Smith, A Minogue, G Moore, M Moran, C Morgan, A L Morris, C Moulder, P M Nelson, Y Ng, J G Parr, C B Petheram, O Petrovic, J Pickett, P G A Plant, N Porter, C B Ransome, N W Rees, G Reid, N W Reid, B Rentoul, J J E Rice, J Richards, P Riedel, G Robert, A P Roberts, P Robinson, S Rowson, N Rumsby, Y R Rupal, S R Salt, V Samani, V R Sander, D Sanders, M Sanders, T Schwarz, T J M Shipton, D Sitlani, C Smith, E Smith, P Spittal, M A Stamp, J J Stokeld, C Stonehill, C J D Style, M A Sullivan, N Swann, R Z Swift, N Syson, L Taylor, S A Thierbach, S Thomas, K J Thomson, J C Tucker, J W Turnbull, M Van Kesteren, M R M Voisin, L Walkington, W A Walls, D W Watkins, C L Watson, T Wells, C J Welsh, B B White, S M Wiggins, J Windsor, D Winter, J Woolf, N Xanthopol, R Youle
Work: B1 C1 C2 C3 E J1 M1 O P Q R1 R2 T1 U1 Z(n,o,q)
Member of Accident Line
Ptr: Ahlborn, Mr Christian . . . Jul 1996
Allan, Mr William LLB; LLM; BA Dennis Ramsden Prize . . . *§May 1976
Andrews, Mr Ian M G . . . Oct 1989
Ashall, Ms Pauline A MA; BCL . . . *Jun 1987
Baker, Mr Huw J MA(Cantab) . . . *Nov 1987
Barber, Mr Duncan E O LLB. . . . *Mar 1993
Barnes, Mr David A MA(Cantab) . . . *§Apr 1977
Barron, Mr Roger Paul LLB . . . *Oct 1993
Bedford, Mr Stuart . . . Mar 1996
Bell, Mr Bruce. . . . Aug 1998
Bennett, Mrs Elizabeth A MA(Cantab). . . . *§Jun 1976
Bennett, Mr Michael J LLB . . . *Dec 1991
Bevan, Mr Peter. . . . Nov 1996
Bird, Mr Benedict MA . . . *Oct 1993
Black, Mr Alan W LLB. . . . *§Apr 1976
Blackshaw, Mr Stephen M LLB(European). . . . *Apr 1989
Bland, Mr Matthew . . . Jan 2000
Blyth, Mr Mark LLB . . . *Sep 1990
Bowler, Mr Ian J BA(Oxon) Norton Rose Company Law Prize - Oxford University 1988; Wills Probate & Administration Prize 1989 . . . *Nov 1991
Bradford, Ms Katie Jane LLB . . . *Sep 1982
Brannan, Mr Guy C H MA(Cantab); LLM(Virginia) . . . *§Feb 1981
Brown, Ms Jane A MA . . . *Apr 1986
Brown, Mr Mark. . . . Oct 1990
Bruce, Mr Andrew J LLB . . . Nov 1994
Buckley, Mr William Donald McLean BA. . . . *Apr 1982
Bugg, Mr Anthony BA(Law) . . . *May 1981
Burgess-Smith, Mr Mark C LLB . . . *Apr 1988
Burn, Mr A Lachlan LLB(Bris) . . . *§Mar 1976
Bussell, Mr Richard LLB. . . . Oct 1993
Byrne, Mrs Anne D LLB. . . . *Nov 1991
Canby, Mr Michael William MA; LLB(Cantab) Clifford's Inn Prize; Harry Strouts Prize; Alfred Syrett Prize . . . *§Apr 1980
Carmichael, Mr Andrew J MA(Cantab). . . . *§Apr 1981
Chan, Mr Edward BA(Oxon); LLM(Lond) . . . *Nov 1996
Chapman, Ms Gillian LLB. . . . *Sep 1989
Cheyne, Mr David W BA(Cantab) . . . *§Mar 1974
Clark, Mr Charles E M MA(Cantab) . . . *§Oct 1982
Clark, Mr Simon H T BA(Cantab) . . . *§Oct 1981
Clarke, Mr Euan. . . . Oct 1997
Clay, Mr Owen Harvey . . . *Apr 1993
Cleaver, Mr Robert . . . Sep 1998
Cohen, Mr Raymond M BA(Oxon). . . . *Oct 1985
Comiskey, Aedamar Ita LLB. . . . Dec 1994
Conder, Mr Joseph BA(Hons) . . . Oct 1997
Conway, Ms Elizabeth. . . . Nov 1996
Coombe, Mr Christopher B MA(Oxon). . . . *§Apr 1977
Cooper, Miss Janet LLB. . . . *Oct 1984
Cox, Mr Timothy E BA; BCL. . . . *Nov 1987
Crozier, Mr John . . . Feb 2000
Cumbley, Mr Richard J BA . . . Sep 1998
Cutting, Mr Michael J MA(Cantab). . . . *Nov 1988
Davies, Mr Alan BA; LLM . . . *Jan 1988
Davies, Mr Julian Edward Joseph BA(Cantab). . . . *§Dec 1987
Davies, Mr Simon BA . . . *Nov 1992
De Lance-Holmes, Mr Jonathan. . . . Dec 1987
Dickson, Mr James . . . Feb 1990
Didizian, Miss Marly. . . . Jun 1996
Dogra, Mr Satindar . . . Nov 1996
Doran, Mr Eamonn J BA(Oxon). . . . *Dec 1988
Douglass, Mr James . . . Aug 1995
Dulieu, Mr Ben . . . Sep 1997
Dunn, Mr H Charles H BA. . . . *Nov 1988
Eastwell, Mr Nicholas W MA(Cantab) . . . *§Jan 1983
Edlmann, Mr Stephen R R MA(Cantab) . . . *§Mar 1979
Elliott, Mr Martin J H BA(Oxon) . . . *§Apr 1979
Elliott, Mr Robert J LLB(Lond). . . . *§Apr 1976
Ereira, Mr David P LLB(Manc). . . . *Jun 1981
Evans, Mr Carlton P BA. . . . *Oct 1989
Evans, Jasper Adie Ashley BA . . . *Jan 1987
Evans, Mr J Mark LLB. . . . *Oct 1985
Farren, Mr Peter S LLB(Lond). . . . *§Jun 1969
Fenn, Mr Iain William BA . . . *Nov 1992
Fergusson, Ms Lucy C MA . . . *Jan 1988
Firth, Mr Simon N BA . . . *Sep 1989
Fletcher, Mr Mark . . . Nov 1992
Fletcher, Mr Stephen . . . Nov 1996
France, Ms Isabel. . . . Sep 1998
Franks, Ms Nemone. . . . Jan 2000
Freeman, Mr Adam . . . Nov 1996
Fugard, Mr Robert . . . Nov 1989
Gewirtz, Mr Jeremy . . . Dec 1991
Godden, Mr Richard W MA(Cantab) Sheffield Prize . . . *Sep 1982
Goldman, Ms Ruth J BA(Oxon); MA(Warw) . . . *Oct 1985
Good, Mrs Diana Frances BA(Oxon) . . . *§Feb 1982
Griffin, Mr Stephen . . . Sep 1998
Griffin, Mr Shane Gerard BA; LLB; LLM(Cantab) . . . *§Oct 1986
Gwynne, Mr Simon . . . Feb 1996
Harbach, Mr James . . . Nov 1991
Hardwick, Mr Michael J MA(Oxon); LLM(Cantab) . . . *Oct 1984
Harnby, Mr Neil . . . Nov 1995
Havard-Williams, Miss Vanessa. . . . Nov 1990
Hayes, Miss Clodagh LLB. . . . *Oct 1993
Hayes, Mr Jonathan LLB . . . *Nov 1993
Hickman, Mr Edward BA . . . Nov 1994
Hobbs, Ms Fiona LLB. . . . *Sep 1989
Hoe, Ms Anne LLM(Lond). . . . Jan 1994
Holden, Mr Richard C T BA(Cantab). . . . *§Oct 1982
Hopkins, Mr Nicola . . . Jan 2000
Hughes, Mr Andrew. . . . Nov 1994
Humphries, Mr Mark J MA ♦. . . . *Oct 1986
Ijaz, Mr Manzer . . . Jan 1990
Inglis, Mr James . . . Nov 1996
Innes-Taylor, Mr Julian S LLB; AKC(Lond). . . . *Oct 1986
Jacobs, Mr Charles . . . Nov 1992
James, Mr Benedict. . . . Nov 1993
Jarvis, Miss Rebecca . . . Mar 1993
Jones, Mr Andrew. . . . Dec 1994
Jones, Mr Nigel H BA(Oxon) . . . *Nov 1988
Kar, Ms Nicole . . . Sep 2001
Karet, Mr Ian BA . . . *Sep 1989
Katwala, Mr Sandeep Shashikant BA . . . *Jun 1993
Keats, Ms Elaine . . . Nov 1996
Keats, Mr Matthew . . . Mar 1997
Kent, Mr Michael . . . Oct 1986
Kingstone, Mr Mark A BA; BCL . . . *Dec 1988
Knowles, Ms Rosalind. . . . Nov 1993
Knox, Mr James. . . . Oct 1987
Kucera, Ms Francis J LLB(Warw) . . . Nov 1991
Kurdian, Ms Annette . . . Feb 2002
Lane, Mr John LLB . . . *Nov 1993
Lawson, Mr Casper . . . Dec 1987
Levy, Mr Richard LLB . . . Nov 1994
Lewis, Mr Paul . . . Sep 1999
Lidstrom, Mr Thomas . . . Mar 1996
Lovett, Ms Jean. . . . Jun 1991
Lucas, Mr Stephen . . . Sep 1996
Ludlow, Ms Kathryn E BA Maxwell Law Prize; Sir Samuel Evans Prize; Calcott Pryce Prize; Heather Meredydd Parry Prize . . . *Nov 1988
Lynchehan, Mr Martin. . . . Nov 1989
McKendrick, Ms Olivia . . . Feb 1996
McMenamin, Mr Derek Neil MA(Cantab). . . . *§Oct 1982
Martin, Mr James . . . Feb 1998
Mayo, Ms Nicola . . . Sep 1998
Middleditch, Mr Matthew S MA(Cantab) . . . *Oct 1982
Middleton, Mr Mark . . . Jan 1997
Miller Smith, Ms Caroline . . . May 1995
Minogue, Ms Ann . . . Apr 1980
Moore, Mr Gideon. . . . May 1991
Moran, Ms Mary. . . . Nov 1994
Morgan, Ms Charlotte. . . . Apr 2005
Morris, Mr Anthony L LLB(Lond); LLM(Cantab) . . . *§Apr 1976
Moulder, Ms Clare. . . . Oct 1984
Nelson, Mr Paul Maurice MA(Cantab). . . . *§Apr 1981
Ng, Mr Yushan . . . Apr 2001
Parr, Mr Jeremy G BA(Cantab) . . . *Oct 1986
Petheram, Ms Claire Bridget LLB . . . *Mar 1989
Petrovic, Ms Olga. . . . Sep 2002
Pickett, Mr John. . . . Apr 1997
Plant, Mr Patrick G A LLB. . . . *Nov 1986
Porter, Mr Nick . . . Nov 2000
Ransome, Mr Clive B BA; LLB . . . *Oct 1985
Rees, Mr Nicholas Wyn MA. . . . *§Dec 1987
Reid, Mr Greg LLB . . . Oct 1985
Reid, Mr Nigel W MA(Oxon). . . . *§Apr 1980
Rentoul, Ms Brigid . . . Nov 1994
Rice, Mr James J E MA(Oxon) . . . *§Oct 1982
Richards, Mr Jonathan . . . Sep 1997
Riedel, Ms Paula . . . Jun 1996
Robert, Mr Gavin BA . . . *Nov 1992
Roberts, Mr Andrew P. . . . Apr 1988
Robinson, Mr Patrick . . . Nov 2000
Rowson, Mr Stuart . . . Nov 1992
Rumsby, Mr Nick . . . Feb 1999
Rupal, Yashpal R BA . . . *Nov 1988
Salt, Mr Stuart R LLB . . . *Nov 1985
Samani, Mr Vinay. . . . Dec 1994
Sander, Ms Victoria R. . . . Sep 1997
Sanders, Mr Dominic . . . Apr 1991
Sanders, Mr Michael . . . Jan 2002
Schwarz, Mr Tim . . . Oct 1989
Shipton, Mr Timothy J M MA(Cantab) . . . *§Apr 1980
Sitlani, Mr Deepak . . . Sep 2000
Smith, Ms Catrina. . . . Oct 1995
Smith, Mr Edward. . . . Sep 1999
Spittal, Mr Philip. . . . Jan 1992
Stamp, Mr Mark A LLB(Soton); LLM(Wisc); LLM(Cantab) . . . *Nov 1985
Stokeld, Mr Jeremy John LLB. . . . *§Nov 1986
Stonehill, Mr Christopher BA . . . Dec 1995
Style, Mr Christopher J D MA(Cantab). . . . *§Feb 1979
Sullivan, Mr Michael Andrew LLB(Lond); AKC Alfred Syrett Prize . . . *Sep 1987
Swann, Ms Nadia . . . Sep 1996
Swift, Mr Robert Z LLB(Lond) . . . *§Dec 1967
Syson, Mr Nick . . . Nov 1987
Taylor, Mr Lee. . . . Sep 1989
Thierbach, Mr Stephen Alfred. . . . Jan 1988
Thomas, Mr Stuart . . . Dec 1995
Thomson, Mr Keith J BA(Dunelm); LLB(Cantab). . . . *§May 1979
Tucker, Mr John C . . . *Sep 1988
Turnbull, Mr John W LLB . . . *§Dec 1982
Van Kesteren, Ms Mirthe . . . Nov 1999
Voisin, Mr Michael R M BA . . . *Jul 1987
Walkington, Ms Lynne. . . . Jan 1997
Walls, Mr William A MA(Cantab). . . . *§Apr 1981
Watkins, Mr David W . . . Oct 1985
Watson, Ms Claire L LLB . . . *Apr 1992
Wells, Mr Tom. . . . Mar 1992
Welsh, Mr Carson Joseph LLB . . . *Nov 1993
White, Mr Bruce Balfour LLB . . . *Feb 1990
Wiggins, Ms Sarah Maria BA . . . *Nov 1992
Windsor, Mr Joe BA. . . . *Oct 1990
Winter, Ms Dominic . . . Nov 1997
Woolf, Ms Julia . . . Oct 1990
Xanthopol, Ms Nicole . . . Sep 1999
Youle, Mr Richard. . . . Sep 1998

LINKSIDE SOLICITORS ‡
6 Bittacy Business Centre Bittacy Hill London NW7 1BA
Tel: 020 8371 8445 *Fax:* 020 8371 8446

LITA GALE ‡
Suite 4 202 Kensington Church Street Notting Hill London W8 4DX
Tel: 020 7404 2899 *Fax:* 020 7404 2966
Dx: 51 LONDON/CHANCERY LN
E-mail: info@litagale.com
Languages: French, Portuguese, Spanish
Work: B1 E F1 G J1 K1 M1 M2 N Q S1 T1 T2 V W Z(b,c,i,l)

S G LITCHFIELD ‡
32 Abbey Road London NW8 9AX
Tel: 020 7624 2103 *Fax:* 020 7624 2103
E-mail: stephen.litchfield@btconnect.com
List of partners: S G Litchfield
Work: E L S1
Ptr: Litchfield, Mr Stephen G LLB . . . Jan 1965

See p2 for the Key to Work Categories & other symbols

LITHMAN & CO ‡
72 Wimpole Street Westminster London W1G 9RP
Tel: 020 7935 2212 *Fax:* 020 7487 4657
E-mail: ihl@lithman.freeserve.co.uk
List of partners: I H Lithman
Languages: French
Work: E N O Q S1 S2 W Z(a,q)
SPr: Lithman, Mr Ian H Council & Committee Member of the Law Society Sole Practitioners Group . . . . *Jun 1959

GUY LITTLER ‡
98 Warwick Road Kensington & Chelsea London W14 8PT
Tel: 020 7373 3700 *Fax:* 020 7373 3565
List of partners: G C Littler
Work: E K1 K3 R1 R2 S1 S2 W
SPr: Littler, Mr Guy C LLB . . . . *Jul 1980

LITTONS ‡
Number 9 3 Kings Yard London W1K 4JR
Tel: 020 7495 0518 *Fax:* 020 7499 7141

HOWARD LIVINGSTONE SOLICITOR ‡
37 Trinity Road London N2 8JJ
Tel: 020 8365 2962

LLOYD & ASSOCIATES ‡
35 Thurloe Street London SW7 2LQ
Tel: 020 7589 9599 *Fax:* 020 7589 9589
Dx: 35759 SOUTH KENSINGTON
E-mail: info@lloyd-law.co.uk
Languages: French, German
Work: A1 B1 C1 C2 C3 D1 E F1 G H I J1 K1 K2 L M1 M2 N O P Q R1 R2 S1 S2 T1 T2 V W X Z(a,b,c,d,e,f,g,h,i,j,k,l,m,n,o,p,q,t)
Emergency Action, Agency, Advocacy, Fixed Fee Interview, Legal Aid undertaken, Legal Aid Franchise and Member of Accident Line
Con: Dorman, Mr Benjamin H BA; Member of the California Bar . . . . *Sep 1995
Lodge, Ms Jane E BA; LSF . . . . *Nov 1991

LLOYD PLATT & CO ‡
Third Floor Elscot House Arcadia Avenue London N3 2JU
Tel: 020 8343 2998 *Fax:* 020 8343 4950 *Dx:* 57274 FINCHLEY 2
E-mail: lloydplatt@divorcesolicitors.com
List of partners: V Lloyd Platt
Work: D1 K1 K3
Agency undertaken
Ptr: Lloyd Platt, Mrs Vanessa LLB(Hons)(Lond) . . . . . . *Jun 1979
Ast: Abrahams, Mrs Joanna BA(Hons)(Russian); CPE; LPC . . . . *Sep 2000
Hassett, Ms Sharan MA. . . . . *Apr 1998
Jones, Mr Kristian LLB(Hons) . . . . Jul 2004
Wolman, Mr Simon LLM; LLB(Hons) . . . . Jan 2007

LLOYD REHMAN & CO ‡
32 Farringdon Street London EC4A 4HJ
Tel: 020 7778 7550 *Fax:* 020 7778 7558
Dx: 336 LONDON/CHANCERY LN
E-mail: nigel@lloydco.plus.com
List of partners: N G Lloyd
Languages: French, German, Greek, Italian, Spanish
Work: B1 B2 C1 E G L N O Q S1 W Z(c,e,j)
Advocacy and Legal Aid undertaken
Ptr: Lloyd, Mr Nigel George MA . . . . *Oct 1989

LLOYDLAW LLP ‡
Wigglesworth House 69 Southwark Bridge Road London SE1 9HH
Tel: 020 7403 5050 *Fax:* 020 7403 5057
E-mail: info@lloydlaw.co.uk
List of partners: P Froggatt, M D Lloyd
Work: C1 I U1 U2 Z(e,w,za)
Ptr: Froggatt, Miss Penny BSc. . . . . Oct 1991
Lloyd, Mr Mark David LLB. . . . . Nov 1990

LLOYDS PR SOLICITORS ‡
11 Station Road Harlesden London NW10 4UJ
Tel: 020 8963 1050 *Fax:* 020 8963 1975 *Dx:* 57654 HARLESDEN
Emergency telephone 07973 178828
E-mail: info@lloydspr.com
Office: Watford
Languages: Chinese, Gujarati, Malay, Tamil
Work: E G H K1 S1 W
Emergency Action, Agency, Advocacy, Fixed Fee Interview and Legal Aid undertaken

LOBLE SOLICITORS ‡
The Grain Store 70 Weston Street London SE1 3QH
Tel: 020 7939 9100

LOCH ASSOCIATES ‡
1 East Poultry Avenue London EC1A 9PT
Tel: 020 3301 5357 *Fax:* 020 7504 3790
E-mail: info@lochassociates.co.uk
Office: Tunbridge Wells

LOCK & MARLBOROUGH ‡
3 The Broadway Gunnersbury Lane London W3 8HR
Tel: 020 8993 7231 *Fax:* 020 8992 5165 *Dx:* 80256 ACTON
E-mail: elock@lockandmarlborough.co.uk
List of partners: E H S Lock, S Marlborough
Languages: Cantonese, French, German, Italian
Work: A1 B1 C1 C3 D1 E F1 J1 K1 O S1 T1 T2 W Z(b,c,e,q)
Emergency Action, Agency, Advocacy, Legal Aid undertaken and Legal Aid Franchise
Ptr: Lock, Mr Edward H S BA . . . . *Apr 1979
Marlborough, Mr Simon LLB. . . . . *Apr 1985
Ast: Hurst, Mr Ian LLB(Hons) . . . . Aug 1999
Pope, Miss Linda Lucille LLB(Hons); Grad CIPD . . . Mar 2003

LOCKHARTS SOLICITORS ‡
Tavistock House South Tavistock Square London WC1H 9LS
Tel: 020 7383 7111 *Fax:* 020 7383 7117
Dx: 122015 TAVISTOCK SQUARE 2
E-mail: csd@lockharts.co.uk
List of partners: A R Lockhart-Mirams, R A Parkin, V A Pattni
Languages: French, Gujarati, Spanish
Work: A3 C1 C2 E J1 O Q W Z(d,e,k,p,za)
Ptr: Lockhart-Mirams, Mr Andrew R FCIArb . . . . Jul 1965
Parkin, Ms Rosalind A LLB(Exon). . . . . Mar 1986
Pattni, Ms Varsha A BA . . . . Mar 1986

LOGOS UK LIMITED ‡
42 New Broad Street London EC2M 1JD
Tel: 020 7920 3020 *Fax:* 020 7920 3099

LOMAX LLOYD-JONES & CO ‡
204 Old Kent Road Southwark London SE1 5TY
Tel: 020 7703 6461 *Fax:* 020 7708 5319 *Dx:* 34904 WALWORTH
Emergency telephone 020 7703 6461
List of partners: E Lloyd-Jones
Languages: French
Work: D1 G H J1 K1 L M1 M2 P S1 V W X Z(i)
Emergency Action, Agency, Advocacy, Fixed Fee Interview, Legal Aid undertaken and Member of Accident Line
Ptr: Lloyd-Jones, Mr Edward LLB . . . . *Oct 1978
Asoc: Sinha, Ms Ajanta BA(Hons)(Law) . . . . *May 1994

LONDON LAW FIRM ‡
298 High Road Leyton Leyton London E10 5PW
Tel: 020 8539 9869 *Fax:* 020 8539 4170
E-mail: farzana.akbar@btinternet.com

LONDON SOLICITORS LLP ‡
Office 1 Horn House Hale Wharf London N17 9NF
Tel: 020 8808 1285 *Fax:* 020 8808 4216 *Dx:* 58510 TOTTENHAM
E-mail: info@thelondonsolicitors.co.uk

JUDITH M LONG ‡
76 Empire Square East Long Lane Southwark London SE1 4NB
Tel: 020 7403 3337 *Fax:* 020 7407 1982 *Dx:* 144364 SOUTHWARK 4
E-mail: judithmlong@msn.com
List of partners: J M Long
Languages: French, German
Work: C1 E J1 O Q S2 Z(e,k,za)
SPr: Long, Miss Judith M BA. . . . . *Jul 1982

LORD BISSELL & BROOK ‡
Suite 785 1 Lime Street Lloyds Buildings London EC3M 7DQ
Tel: 020 7327 4534 *Fax:* 020 7929 2250

E D C LORD & CO
Unit 4 & 5 Rossknoll House Orion Park Ealing London W13 9SJ
Tel: 020 8579 9292 *Fax:* 020 8810 0600
Office: Hayes, Potters Bar
Languages: French, Spanish
Work: C1 E L
Agency, Advocacy undertaken and Member of Accident Line
Ptr: Urwin, Mr Paul B . . . . *§Jul 1980
Ast: Rees, Mr Michael E. . . . . Dec 1975

LORIMER & CO ‡
2 Upper Tachbrook Street London SW1V 1SH
Tel: 020 7592 7660

LORRELLS LLP ‡
(incorporating Heath & Co)
25 Ely Place Holborn London EC1N 6TD
Tel: 020 7681 8888 *Fax:* 020 7539 4599
Languages: Greek, Hindi
Work: B1 C1 E F1 J1 L M1 N P S1 T1 W Z(a,c,f,i,k,l)
Emergency Action, Agency, Advocacy, Legal Aid undertaken and Member of Accident Line
Con: Georgiou, Mr George C. . . . . *May 1985

LOSANAA & CO SOLICITORS ‡
165a First Floor Office High Street North East Ham London E6 1JB
Tel: 020 8503 4409 *Fax:* 020 8503 4470

ANTHONY LOUCA SOLICITORS ‡
24 Lisson Grove Marylebone Westminster London NW1 6TT
Tel: 020 7723 9889 *Fax:* 020 7723 6009 *Dx:* 38762 PADDINGTON
E-mail: anthony@anthonylouca.com
List of partners: F A Argyrou, L Louca
Languages: Arabic, Greek
Work: B1 D1 D2 E F1 J1 K1 L N O Q R2 S1 S2 V W Z(c,f,g,i,l,q,r)
Emergency Action, Agency, Advocacy, Fixed Fee Interview, Legal Aid undertaken and Legal Aid Franchise
Ptr: Argyrou, Mr Floros Antonios LLB(Hons) ♦. . . . . . . *Dec 1993
Louca, Ms Lucy LLB(Hons) . . . . *Aug 1993
Ast: Galvin, Michelle. Jan 2008

LOUDOUNS ‡
15 Old Bailey London EC4M 7EF
Tel: 020 3178 4136 *Fax:* 020 3178 4137
E-mail: wlc@loudouns.com

LOUGHRAN & CO INTERNATIONAL LAWYERS ‡
38 Hertford Street London W1J 7SE
Tel: 020 7355 2051

A LOUIS & CO IMMIGRATION LAW PRACTICE ‡
36 Brewery Road London SE18 7PT

LOUND MULRENAN & JEFFERIES SOLICITORS ‡
Southbank House Black Prince Road Southwark London SE1 7SJ
Tel: 020 7793 4012 *Fax:* 020 7793 4264
Emergency telephone 07659 142337
E-mail: imj@imj-solicitors.co.uk
List of partners: R J Jefferies, M M Lound, A W Mulrenan
Work: G H
Emergency Action, Agency, Advocacy and Legal Aid undertaken
Ptr: Jefferies, Mr Richard James LLB ★ . . . . *Dec 1989
Lound, Ms Margot Mary BA ★. . . . . *Sep 1991
Mulrenan, Mr Anthony William BA ★. . . . . *Jan 1992

LOVATT & CO ‡
Norvin House 45-55 Commercial Street Tower Hamlets London E1 6BD
Tel: 020 7247 9336
List of partners: J M Lovatt
Ptr: Lovatt, Mr John M LLB(Lond) . . . . *Apr 1981

CLIVE LOVATT SOLICITOR ‡
41 Howards Lane London SW15 6NX
Tel: 020 8788 9716 *Fax:* 020 8788 9716
E-mail: clive.lovatt@yahoo.co.uk

LOVELL SON & PITFIELD ‡
9 Gray's Inn Square Gray's Inn Camden London WC1R 5JT
Tel: 020 7242 7883 *Fax:* 020 7404 0165
Dx: 346 LONDON/CHANCERY LN
E-mail: lopit@msn.com

List of partners: A H MacWilliam, C D Noyce
Work: K1 Q S1 S2 W
Ptr: MacWilliam, Mr Alasdair Hamish . . . . *§Nov 1972
Noyce, Mr Christopher D MA(Hons)(Oxon) . . . . . *§Nov 1983
Ast: Richmond, Miss Mary Jane BA(Kingston) . . . . *Apr 1981

SETH LOVIS & CO ‡
33 Henrietta Street Covent Garden London WC2E 8NH
Tel: 020 7240 7020 *Fax:* 020 7240 7029
Dx: 40015 COVENT GARDEN
E-mail: enquiry@sethlovis.co.uk
Languages: German
Work: F1 F2 J1 L N O Q S1 W Z(j,r)
Agency, Fixed Fee Interview undertaken and Member of Accident Line

LEONARD LOWY ‡
500 Chiswick High Road London W4 5RG
Tel: 020 8956 2785

LOXFORD SOLICITORS ‡
168 High Street North East Ham London E6 2JA
Tel: 020 8548 1155 *Fax:* 020 8548 1166 *Dx:* 4717 EAST HAM

LUCAS LAW LIMITED ‡
21 Dalston Lane London E8 3DF
Tel: 020 7812 9067 *Fax:* 020 7812 9065
Emergency telephone 0800 136795
E-mail: stuart.lucas@lucas-law.org
List of partners: S Lucas, S J Powell
Work: N
Member of Accident Line
Ptr: Lucas, Mr Stuart LLB . . . . *Feb 1990
Powell, Mr Simon J BA(Hons). . . . . *Mar 1984
Ast: Talabi, Mrs Abiola LLB(Hons) . . . . *Jun 1996

LUQMANI THOMPSON & PARTNERS ‡
77-79 High Road London N22 6BB
Tel: 020 8365 7800

LYNDALES SOLICITORS ‡
Lynton House 7-12 Tavistock Square London WC1H 9LT
Tel: 020 7391 1000 *Fax:* 020 7383 3494
Dx: 122014 TAVISTOCK SQUARE 2
E-mail: mail@lyndales.co.uk
Work: B1 C1 E J1 K1 K3 L N P S1 S2 W Z(c,d,f,k,l)

MICHAEL LYNN & CO ‡
8a Cheval Place Knightsbridge London SW7 1ES
Tel: 020 7225 3681 *Fax:* 020 7584 5056
E-mail: michaelmxl@aol.com
List of partners: M Lynn
Work: E F1 J1 L Q S1 W Z(f,l)
Ptr: Lynn, Mr Michael LLB. . . . . Apr 1985

NIGEL LYNN ASSOCIATES ‡
1st Floor 30-31 Furnival Street London EC4A 1JQ

TREVOR LYTTLETON MBE ‡
23 Bryanston Court George Street Westminster London W1H 7HA
Tel: 020 7402 4810 *Fax:* 020 7262 4296
E-mail: trevor.lyttleton@btinternet.com
List of partners: T M Lyttleton
Languages: French, German, Spanish
Work: C1 W Z(d,e,f,m)
Agency undertaken
SPr: Lyttleton, Mr Trevor Michael MBE MA; LLM(Cantab) Founder & Chairman of Contact the Elderly. . . . . *Feb 1961

MA LAW (SOLICITORS) LLP ‡
72-74 Edgware Road London W2 2EG
Tel: 020 7723 1311 *Fax:* 020 7724 2738
E-mail: info@ma-law.co.uk

MHLAW ‡
First Floor 5 London Wall Building Finsbury Circus London EC2M 5NS
Tel: 020 7628 7757 *Fax:* 020 7628 8181

M H SOLICITORS LIMITED ‡
2 Portland Road South Norwood London SE25 4PF
Tel: 020 8656 7845 / 07092 807422

MK LAW ‡
74 Bellingham Road London SE6 2PT

MK LAW ‡
24 Deptford Broadway London SE8 4PA
Tel: 020 8692 2694 *Fax:* 020 8691 9659 *Dx:* 56712 DEPTFORD
E-mail: info@mk-law.co.uk

MKM SOLICITORS ‡
2nd Floor Green Street Forest Gate London E7 8LL
Tel: 020 8548 9490 *Fax:* 020 8470 7970 *Dx:* 4713 EAST HAM
E-mail: allinfo@mkmsolicitors.co.uk

M LAW ‡
42 Brook Street London W1K 5DB
Tel: 020 7927 6240 *Fax:* 020 7927 6259
E-mail: info@mlaw.co.uk
Office: London W1
Languages: German, Spanish

M LAW
3 Charlotte Mews London W1T 4DZ
Tel: 020 7927 6240 *Fax:* 020 7927 6259
E-mail: info@mlaw.co.uk
Office: London W1

MMS LAW ‡
64 Great Eastern Street London EC2A 3QR
Tel: 020 7749 4199 *Fax:* 020 7749 4198 *Dx:* 13778 FINSBURY 5
E-mail: info@mmslaw.co.uk

M R SOLICITORS ‡
490 Larkshall Road Highams Park London E4 9HH
Tel: 020 8518 1956 *Fax:* 020 8518 4896
E-mail: info@m-rsolicitors.co.uk

MS-LEGAL SOLICITORS ‡
88 Kingsway London WC2B 6AA
Tel: 020 7726 7380 *Fax:* 020 7726 7336
E-mail: info@ms-legal.co.uk

MTC LAW LIMITED ‡
Floors 3 & 4 17 Bentinck Street London W1U 2ES
Tel: 020 7486 7708 *Fax:* 0870 130 7818
Dx: 42718 OXFORD CIRCUS NORTH
E-mail: mtc1@mtclaw.co.uk

GERALDINE MCALEESE & CO ‡
82 Grove Park Terrace London W4 3JJ
Tel: 020 8987 8381 *Fax:* 020 8987 8363 *Dx:* 80329 CHISWICK
E-mail: mgm@gmcaleese.com
List of partners: G McAleese
Work: S1 S2 W
SPr: McAleese, Ms Geraldine BA(Hons) . . . . *Jul 1981

MCALLISTER OLIVARIUS ‡
Thames Wharf Studios Rainville Road London W6 9HA
Tel: 020 7386 1047 *Fax:* 020 7386 5626
E-mail: gclavert-lee@mcolaw.com

MACARTAN & CO ‡
24 Nelson Road Greenwich London SE10 9JB
Tel: 020 8269 0057 *Fax:* 020 8269 0058
E-mail: solicitors@macartan.co.uk

MACAULEY SMITH & CO ‡
93-95 Deptford High Street London SE8 4AA
Tel: 020 8692 4088 *Fax:* 020 8692 0565 *Dx:* 56710 DEPTFORD
E-mail: info@macauleysmith.co.uk
List of partners: P D Macauley
Work: D1 G H
Emergency Action, Agency, Advocacy, Legal Aid undertaken and Member of Accident Line
Ptr: Macauley, Mr Paul D ★ . . . . *Dec 1979

MCBRIDE WILSON & CO ‡
The Courtyard Queens House 55-56 Lincolns Inn Fields London WC2A 3LJ
Tel: 020 7242 1300 *Fax:* 020 7831 7097 *Dx:* 37961 KINGSWAY
List of partners: S H Krywald
Work: B1 C1 C2 E F1 J1 K1 L N O Q R1 R2 S1 S2 W Z(c,e,f,k,l,q)
Agency and Advocacy undertaken
SPr: Krywald, Ms Sandra H LLB . . . . *Sep 1981
Ast: Barton, Mr Patrick J LLB . . . . *Jan 1983
Malyali, Chetin M BA . . . . *Dec 1985

DAVID MCCARTHY ‡
20 Barclay Square London W1J 6HF
Tel: 020 7569 1500

MCCARTHY TETRAULT ‡
2nd Floor 5 Old Bailey London EC4M 7BA
Tel: 020 7489 5700 *Fax:* 020 7489 5777
Work: C1 C2 J1 P Z(n)

MCCAULEY-SLOWE SOLICITORS ‡
2 Gleneagle Mews London SW16 6AE
Tel: 020 8696 7253 *Fax:* 020 8696 7356 *Dx:* 58606 STREATHAM

MCCLURE NAISMITH ‡
Equitable House 47 King William Street London EC4R 9AF
Tel: 020 7623 9155 *Fax:* 020 7623 9154 *Dx:* 764 LONDON/CITY
E-mail: london@mcclurenaismith.com
List of partners: J W R Mackie, P A Sewell
Languages: French, German, Japanese
Work: B1 B2 C1 C2 C3 E F1 F2 I J1 J2 L M1 M2 N O Q R2 S1 S2 T1 T2 U2 Z(b,d,e,f,j,k,n,q)
Emergency Action, Agency, Advocacy, Fixed Fee Interview, Legal Aid undertaken and Member of Accident Line
Ptr: Mackie, Mr James W R LLB. . . . . Jun 1980
Sewell, Mr Philip A LLB . . . . *Jan 1992
Ast: Coxon, Ms Charlotte LLB . . . . Sep 1997
De Verneuil-Smith, Mr Bryan . . . . Sep 2003
Gordon, Mr Paul Dean LLB . . . . *Sep 1999
Hall, Miss Stella. . . . . Sep 1998
Southgate, Mr Scott. . . . . Sep 2000
Con: Fieldhouse, Mr Jeremy . . . . *Dec 1974

MCCORMACKS ‡
122 Mile End Road Stepney Tower Hamlets London E1 4UN
Tel: 020 7791 2000 *Fax:* 020 7790 5846
Dx: 300704 TOWER HAMLETS
Emergency telephone 020 7791 2000
E-mail: messages@mccormacks.co.uk
List of partners: L Cuthbert, H Mullan, A Palazzo, U R Palazzo, L Rahman
Office: Basildon, London E15, London EC1
Languages: British Sign Language, Cantonese, French, German, Italian, Punjabi, Turkish, Urdu
Work: B2 D1 D2 E G H I K1 L R1 S1 S2 V W Z(g,l,m)
Emergency Action, Agency, Advocacy, Legal Aid undertaken and Legal Aid Franchise
Ptr: Mullan, Mr Hugh ★ . . . . *Oct 1995
Palazzo, Mr Andrew BSc . . . . *Apr 1987
Asoc: Brereton, Mr Malcolm A. . . . . *Mar 1984
McCabe, Mr Stephen BA . . . . *Jun 1991
Ast: Donovan, Miss Ellen Mary Geraldine BA(Hons); MA. *Aug 1998
Liu, Ms Jenny Chen-Yiu. . . . . *Jul 1997
Malik, Mr Adnan BA. . . . . *Sep 1997

MCCORMACKS
85 Long Lane Tower Hamlets London EC1A 9ET
Tel: 020 7791 2000 *Fax:* 020 7600 4488
Dx: 300704 TOWER HAMLETS
Emergency telephone 020 7791 2000
E-mail: messages@mccormacks.co.uk
Office: Basildon, London E1, London E15
Languages: British Sign Language, French, German, Italian, Punjabi, Urdu
Work: B2 G H I
Emergency Action, Advocacy, Legal Aid undertaken and Legal Aid Franchise
Ptr: Palazzo, Ugo R BSc; MA . . . . *Dec 1986

MCCORMACKS
Security House 2 Romford Road Tower Hamlets London E15 4BX
Tel: 020 7791 2000
Emergency telephone 020 7265 8331
E-mail: messages@mccormacks.co.uk
Office: Basildon, London E1, London EC1
Languages: Bengali, British Sign Language, Italian, Punjabi
Work: D1 D2 H K1 Z(i,m)
Emergency Action, Agency, Advocacy, Legal Aid undertaken and Legal Aid Franchise
Ptr: Rahman, Mr Lutfur . . . . Apr 1997
Con: McCormack, Mr Michael E LLB(Hons). . . . . *Jul 1975

MCDERMOTT WILL & EMERY UK LLP ‡
7 Bishopsgate London EC2N 3AR
Tel: 020 7577 6900 *Fax:* 020 7577 6950 *Dx:* 42619 CHEAPSIDE
List of partners: N J Azis, A Bell, S Black, J S Blanch, R Britain, C Brockie, A Caunt, W F Charnley, K Clark, L Cohen, A Croxford, D Curley, D I Dalgarno, C Forrest, D J Garrod, R Harding-Hill, J Hill, K Larsen, K Learoyd, M McFall, S Megregian, R Mitchell, P M W Nias, N J Purcell, G Quenby, P Rebus, G W H Rowbotham, D Ryder, N C Terras, A A Watson, A C Wetherfield, W J G R Yonge, F R Younson
Work: A3 C1 C2 C3 I J1 M1 M2 O Q T1 U1 Z(b,e,n,o,za)
Ptr: Azis, Mr Nicholas Julian BA(Hons); LLB. . . . . . . *Jan 1994
Bell, Mr Alasdair. . . . . Jan 1995
Black, Mr Steven . . . . Jan 1995
Blanch, Ms Juliet S LLB(Exon) . . . . *Apr 1988
Britain, Mr Richard LLB . . . . *Jan 1993
Brockie, Cam . . . . Jan 2002
Caunt, Mr Andrew LLB . . . . Oct 1995
Charnley, Mr William Francis LLB; ACIS. . . . . . . *Oct 1987
Clark, Mrs Katherine . . . . *Apr 1998
Cohen, Mr Larry MA . . . . *Oct 1976
Croxford, Mr Andrew LLB . . . . *Sep 1996
Curley, Mr Duncan PhD; BSc . . . . *Jan 1995
Dalgarno, Mr David I LLB(Warw) . . . . *Jun 1988
Forrest, Mr Christopher LLB. . . . . *Aug 1991
Garrod, Mr Davina Jane LLB . . . . *Mar 1999
Harding-Hill, Ms Rebecca MA(Oxon); BA . . . . . . *Oct 1995
Hill, Dr Justin . . . . Jun 1999
Larsen, Kari. Jan 1998
Learoyd, Ms Kate. . . . . Jan 1998
McFall, Mr Michael . . . . Oct 1992
Megregian, Mr Scott BA; JD. . . . . Jun 1999
Mitchell, Mr Richard BA; JD. . . . . Jul 1987
Nias, Mr Peter M W LLB . . . . *May 1979
Purcell, Ms Nicola Jane . . . . *Sep 1996
Quenby, Ms Georgia . . . . Jan 1995
Rebus, Mr Paul-Micheal. . . . . Jan 2001
Rowbotham, Mr Graham W H MA(Oxon)(Jurisprudence) . . . . *Jan 1973
Ryder, Mr David. . . . . Jan 1994
Terras, Mr Nicholas Charles. . . . . *Sep 2002
Watson, Mr Andrew A. . . . . *Mar 1994
Wetherfield, Ms Alison C BA; LLM Trinity Hall Law Scholarship; Cambridge University Scholar 1983. . . . . *Jan 2001
Yonge, Mr William James George Rowley. . . . . . . *Apr 1999
Younson, Mr Fraser R. . . . . *Jun 1987
Ast: Tsang, Mr Danny . . . . Nov 1994

MCDONALD & CO ‡
40 Rivermill 151 Grosvenor Road Westminster London SW1V 3JN
Tel: 020 7834 2679 *Fax:* 020 7592 9790
Emergency telephone 020 7834 2679
E-mail: wmcdsol@aol.com
List of partners: W McDonald
Work: E G H J1 K1 K3 L N O Q S1 S2 W Z(l)
Emergency Action, Agency, Advocacy, Fixed Fee Interview and Legal Aid undertaken
SPr: McDonald, Mr William LLB(Lond) . . . . *Sep 1980

MACDONALD CHAPMAN ‡
4-6 Staple Inn High Holborn London WC1V 7QH
Tel: 020 7404 9005 *Fax:* 020 7900 2945

MCEVEDYS ‡
96 Westbourne Park Road London W2 5PL
Tel: 020 7243 6122 *Fax:* 020 7022 1721
E-mail: victoria@mcevedy.eu

MCEWEN PARKINSON ‡
83 Wimpole Street Westminster London W1G 9RQ
Tel: 020 7487 4361 *Fax:* 020 7935 8373 *Dx:* 9010 WEST END
E-mail: gregory.mcewen@mcewenparkinson.co.uk
List of partners: G Cselko, G P McEwen, T J Parkinson
Work: B1 C1 E F1 J1 K1 K3 L O Q S1 S2 T1 T2 W X Z(c,d,e,q)
Agency and Advocacy undertaken
Ptr: Cselko, Mr George BA(Hons); Non-Practising Barrister ♦ . . . . *Jul 1997
McEwen, Mr Gregory Paul . . . . *§Nov 1972
Parkinson, Mr Timothy James BA(Cantab) . . . . . *Jun 1972

MACEY & CO ‡
91 Shooters Hill Road Greenwich London SE3 7HU
Tel: 020 8853 2710 *Fax:* 020 8858 2283
List of partners: T J Macey
Work: E N O Q R1 Z(j,l,q)
Ptr: Macey, Mr Terence James LLB(Bris); LLM(Lond) . . *Mar 1973

MCFADDENS LLP ‡
City Tower 40 Basinghall Street London EC2V 5DE
Tel: 020 7588 9080 *Fax:* 020 7588 8988 *Dx:* 42601 CHEAPSIDE
E-mail: reception@mcfaddenslaw.co.uk
List of partners: T D L Eppel, A M MacLaren, J H McFadden, G K Pilkington
Office: Birmingham
Languages: French, German
Work: A3 B1 B2 C1 C2 E F1 F2 G I J1 K1 L M1 M2 O Q R2 S1 S2 T1 T2 W X Z(b,c,d,e,f,g,i,o,z)
Emergency Action, Fixed Fee Interview and Legal Aid undertaken
Ptr: Eppel, Mr Timothy David Lewis . . . . *Sep 1975
McFadden, Mr John H . . . . *Mar 1995
MacLaren, Mr Andrew M MA(Cantab) . . . . *Apr 1969
Pilkington, Mr Gregory K . . . . Jan 1997
Asoc: Hauer, Mr Marc Harris LLB . . . . Dec 1995
Con: Berwin, Mr Harold Brian. . . . . *Jun 1974

B J MACFARLANE & CO ‡
4 Lombard Street London EC3V 9HD
Tel: 020 7190 2988 *Fax:* 020 7190 2989
Emergency telephone 07765 364043
E-mail: b.macfarlane@bjm-co.com
Languages: Arabic, French, German, Italian
Work: A3 O Z(a,j,q)
Fixed Fee Interview undertaken

MACFARLANES ‡
20 Cursitor Street London EC4A 1LT
Tel: 020 7831 9222 *Fax:* 020 7831 9607
Dx: 138 LONDON/CHANCERY LN
List of partners: H G Arthur, M Baldwin, B C Barker, A J M Blackler, M J Blows, R M Booth, R Boyle, T R Bridgford, B G O Clutton, A J Conder, T C Cornick, D J Courtenay-Stamp, J R S Dodsworth, N J L Doran, S R Drewitt, C M Field, M A Furman, D A Greenbank, M A Hayes, S N Hillson, P D Holmes, J H Hornby, C P Horsfield, J F Howard, A G W Jackson, C Lampard, M D S Lavin, M H Leth, T J Lewis, C A Lloyd, I H Mackie, O MacSherry, J H R Manners, C D Z Martin, I C Martin, S R Martin, C H Meek, S N Nurney, C P Phippen, M D Pintus, S N Pitchford, R M E Reuben, J G Rhodes, N Richards, S C Robinson, D I Sanders, D R Shugar, J M Skelton, T D Steele, G Steward, R H Sutton, A G Thompson, K D Tuffnell, J Tyler, T R Vos, A E Whitfield, R J Whittaker
Languages: French, German, Hungarian, Italian, Japanese, Spanish
Work: A1 A3 B1 B2 C1 C2 C3 E F1 G I J1 L M1 M2 O P Q R1 R2 S1 T1 T2 U1 W Z(b,c,d,e,f,h,i,j,k,l,n,o,q,s,w,y,z)
Emergency Action and Advocacy undertaken
Ptr: Arthur, Mr Hugh Gilbert MA(Cantab). . . . . *§Feb 1980
Baldwin, Mr Mark BA(Dunelm) Marshall & Strouts Prize; Child & Pilkington Prize; Daniel Reardon Prize; Travers Smith Scholar . . . . Nov 1987
Barker, Miss Bridget C LLB(Soton) Winston Churchill Memorial Prize . . . . *§Jun 1983
Blackler, Mr Anthony J M BA; LLB; ACIArb . . . . . *§Jul 1967
Blows, Dr Matthew J PhD(Lond). . . . . Nov 1994
Booth, Ms Rachel M BA(Oxon) . . . . Mar 1994
Boyle, Mr Robert BA(Cantab) . . . . Oct 1993
Bridgford, Mr Tom R LLB(Sheff) . . . . Nov 1994
Clutton, Mr B G Owen BA; LLB; BCL; ATII . . . . . *§May 1980
Conder, Mr Andrew J BA(Dunelm)(Law). . . . . *Oct 1986
Cornick, Mr Timothy C BA(Oxon) . . . . *Oct 1982
Courtenay-Stamp, Mr D Jeremy LLB(Lond) . . . . . *Nov 1986
Dodsworth, Mr John R S BA(Dunelm) . . . . Nov 1991
Doran, Mr Nigel J L BA(Oxon); ATII . . . . *§Nov 1984
Drewitt, Mr Stephen R LLB(Leeds) . . . . Apr 1995
Field, Mr Christopher M MA(Oxon) . . . . *§Apr 1977
Furman, Mr Mark A MA(Oxon) . . . . Oct 1983
Greenbank, Mr D Ashley MA(Cantab); BCL(Oxon) . . Oct 1988
Hayes, Mr Michael A MA(Oxon). . . . . *§Dec 1968
Hillson, Mr Simon N MA; LLM(Cantab) . . . . *§Nov 1985
Holmes, Mr Patrick Duncan LLB(Lond) . . . . *Nov 1992
Hornby, Mr John H BSc(Exon) . . . . *§Jan 1982
Horsfield, Mr Charles P LLB(Oxon) . . . . *Nov 1989
Howard, Mr Julian F LLB(Exon). . . . . *§Jun 1986
Jackson, Mr Andrew G W MA(Oxon) . . . . *§Mar 1979
Lampard, Mr Clive MA . . . . *§Nov 1985
Lavin, Mr M D Sean BA(Oxon) . . . . May 1992
Leth, Miss Mary H. . . . . *Nov 1988
Lewis, Mr Timothy J BA(Oxon) . . . . Feb 1989
Lloyd, Mr Charles A LLB(Exon) . . . . May 1992
Mackie, Mr Iain H BA(Oxon). . . . . *Nov 1992
MacSherry, Ms Orla BA(Hons) . . . . Nov 1994
Manners, The Hon John H R . . . . *Dec 1980
Martin, Mr Charles D Z LLB(Bris) . . . . *Oct 1985
Martin, Mr Ian C BA(York). . . . . Nov 1992
Martin, Mr Simon R MA(Oxon) . . . . *Feb 1987
Meek, Mr Charles H BA(Lond) . . . . *Apr 1987
Nurney, Mr Simon N LLB(Nott'm) . . . . *Nov 1992
Phippen, Mr C Paul LLB(Exon) . . . . *§Oct 1982
Pintus, Mr Matthew D BA . . . . *Oct 1982
Pitchford, Mr Steven Neil BA(Cantab) . . . . *May 1990
Reuben, Mr Richard M E BA(Oxon). . . . . *Nov 1982
Rhodes, Mr John G MA(Cantab) . . . . *§Mar 1970
Richards, Miss Nicola MA(Cantab) . . . . *Dec 1988
Robinson, Mr Steven C LLB(Hons) . . . . *Aug 1997
Sanders, Mr David Ian LLB . . . . *May 1993
Shugar, Mr Douglas R MA(Oxon) . . . . *Nov 1986
Skelton, Mr John M BA(Oxon). . . . . *§Dec 1977
Steele, Mr Timothy D BA(Oxon). . . . . *Mar 1988
Steward, Mr Geoffrey LLB(Nott'm). . . . . *Nov 1995
Sutton, Mr Robert H BA(Oxon) . . . . *Apr 1979
Thompson, Mr Anthony G MA(Cantab) . . . . *§Jun 1976
Tuffnell, Mr Kevin D MA(Cantab) . . . . *Dec 1984
Tyler, Ms Jane LLB . . . . Apr 1993
Vos, Mr T Robin LLB(Soton) . . . . *Apr 1990
Whitfield, Ms Ann E LLB(Warw). . . . . Nov 1992
Whittaker, Miss R Jane LLB. . . . . *§Jun 1978
Asoc: Wilson, Miss Emma Jane . . . . *§Sep 2001

MCGLENNONS ‡
Park House 158-160 Arthur Road Wimbledon Park Merton London SW19 8AQ
Tel: 020 8946 6015 *Fax:* 020 8946 8803
E-mail: mail@mcglennons.co.uk
List of partners: W A Essex
Work: Q S1 W
SPr: Essex, William Allan BA. . . . . Mar 2006

MCGRIGORS LLP ‡
5 Old Bailey London EC4M 7BA
Tel: 020 7054 2500 *Fax:* 020 7054 2501
Dx: 227 LONDON/CHANCERY LN
Emergency telephone 020 7694 2500
E-mail: emma.conway@mcgrigors.com
List of partners: P W Blackmore, J F Bullock, P A Burroughs, P A Cashmore, R J A Collins, K M Davies, K A Fielding, M G Finnegan, A Forge, G J Freer, S F Gill, W Grieg, S M Howlett, M MacLean, P T Martin, A McAlister, L F Miotte, S C Nash, A O'Connor, N Ogden, A D Reason, A B Rippon, R Shiers, P R Sutton, D J White
Office: Belfast, Manchester
Work: A3 B2 C1 C2 C3 E F1 F2 I J1 J2 L M1 M2 O P Q R1 R2 S2 U1 U2 Z(b,c,e,g,l,o,p,u)
Ptr: Blackmore, Mr Peter W . . . . Jun 1993
Bullock, Mr James Francis MA(Cantab) . . . . Nov 1992
Burroughs, Mr Philip A LLB(Bris) . . . . *Mar 1980
Cashmore, Mr Peter Atherton . . . . Mar 1994
Collins, Mr Robert Jason Alexi LLB . . . . Jan 1999
Davies, Ms Katharine Margaret . . . . *Oct 1982
Finnegan, Mr Martin Gerald BA(Hons)(Law). . . . . . Sep 1996
Forge, Mrs Anna BA(Hons)(Law) . . . . *Apr 1982
Freer, Mr Gary John. . . . . Sep 1986
Gill, Ms Suzanne Fiona BA(Hons); BA(Cantab) . . . . Sep 1994
Grieg, Mr William . . . . Feb 1997
Howlett, Mrs Sarah Marina LLB . . . . Oct 1997

See p2 for the Key to Work Categories & other symbols

MacLean, Mr Murdo LLB; LLM . . . . Apr 1982
Martin, Mr Patrick Tyson LLB(Hons)(Soton) . . . . . . Oct 1988
Nash, Mr Stuart Clarke BA; JD . . . . *Apr 1996
O'Connor, Mr Alexander. . . . . *Apr 1993
Reason, Mr Allan David. . . . . *Oct 1987
Rippon, Mr Allan B BA . . . . Nov 1987
Shiers, Mr Rupert MA; BCL Foundation Scholar (Queen's College Cambridge) 1994. . . . . *Oct 1998
Sutton, Mr Paul Richard. . . . . Mar 1994
Dir: Fielding, Miss Karen Anne BA(Hons) . . . . *Nov 1995
Miotte, Mr Luke F. . . . . Sep 1998
White, Mr David John BSc; LLB. . . . . Jan 2001
Asoc: Anderson, Mr David. . . . . Sep 1999
Bowman, Ms Claire Alexandra LLB . . . . Oct 2002
Bryan, Ms Sarah Louise. . . . . Sep 1998
Elwen, Mr James D. . . . . May 2003
Gillham, Mr George E A. . . . . Mar 2007
Hack, Ms Kelly . . . . Sep 2003
Johnson, Mrs Susan E BA(Lond) . . . . *Jul 1979
Kiwana S M, Ms Nakato LLB . . . . *Oct 1995
McNeill, Mr Stuart LLB; DipLP. . . . . *Aug 1996
Menzies, Mr Angus . . . . Sep 2000
Nuttall, Miss Laura . . . . Oct 2000
Perera, Miss Nirosha LLB(Hons); DipLS. . . . . Oct 2002
Scott, Ms Kerry . . . . Sep 2002
Watkins, Mrs Rachael. . . . . Nov 2000
Ast: Blackwell, Mrs Anna. . . . . Sep 2005
Blackwell, Mr Michael. . . . . Mar 2006
Boyd, Miss Clara M. . . . . Sep 2007
Boyle, Miss Nicola A LLB; LLM . . . . Oct 2000
Broadhead, Miss Kerry . . . . Sep 2005
Carroll, Mr Alexander Joseph . . . . Sep 2006
Collett, Mrs Lynda J. . . . . Oct 2003
Crawford, Miss Gemma K. . . . . Sep 2007
Cunnane, Mrs Fiona . . . . Sep 2002
Davies, Mr Sam Jacob . . . . Dec 2001
Desai, Mr Devang. . . . . Sep 2006
Desai, Ms Manisha . . . . Sep 1999
Dixon, Ms Sophie Murray . . . . Oct 2006
Ellis, Miss Sophie Claire. . . . . Sep 2003
Emslie, Miss Jane R . . . . Sep 2007
Fairhead, Mr Benjamin Allen . . . . Mar 2004
Giles, Mr Brendon. . . . . Dec 2001
Gould, Ms Katrin Jane . . . . Oct 2006
Gray, Miss Susannah . . . . Sep 2005
Haq, Sohela. Sep 2006
Jackson, Mr Andrew. . . . . Sep 2004
John, Ms Francesca Rose. . . . . Sep 2006
Johnson, Mr Robert. . . . . Sep 2004
Kubba, Juman . . . . Sep 2006
Liu, Ms Michelle LLB(Hons) . . . . Apr 2003
Macpherson, Mr Rory. . . . . Sep 2004
Nagler, Mrs Elizabeth . . . . Sep 2003
Noon, Ms Jacqueline A . . . . Oct 1999
Nordmann, Mrs Bernadine . . . . Oct 2002
Ohbi, Miss Kirinpal . . . . Sep 2007
Patel, Miss Apicksha M . . . . Sep 2006
Piggin, Ms Maria Meredith. . . . . May 2003
Price, Miss Helen E. . . . . Sep 2007
Riordan, Ms Sarah C . . . . Oct 2005
Shah, Mr Anil M. . . . . Sep 2001
Shields, Miss Debra Mary. . . . . Sep 2005
Skinner, Mr Mark E . . . . Sep 2007
Soares, Mr Robert Anthony Trevor . . . . Sep 2004
Walsh, Mr Stuart James. . . . . Sep 2000
Warburton, Ms Louisa Mary. . . . . Sep 2006
Webb, Ms Helen Lisa . . . . Mar 2005

MCGUIREWOODS LONDON LLP ‡
11 Pilgrim Street London EC4V 6RN
Tel: 020 7632 1600 *Fax:* 020 7632 1638
Dx: 249 LONDON/CHANCERY LN
E-mail: london@mcguirewoods.com
List of partners: A O V Grundberg, B S Mocatta, S K Porter, R B Rakison, M O Tackley, L M M von Finckenhagen
Languages: Afrikaans, Dutch, Finnish, Gujarati, Hindi, Marathi, Punjabi, Russian, Spanish
Work: B1 C1 C2 C3 E F2 I J1 K1 K2 K3 L M1 M2 N O Q R1 R2 S1 S2 T1 T2 U1 U2 W Z(b,e,j,n,o,w,z)
Agency and Advocacy undertaken
Ptr: Grundberg, Anders O V. . . . . *§Jun 1977
Mocatta, Mr Bernard S MA(Oxon). . . . . *Oct 1978
Porter, Mr Simon K MA(Oxon). . . . . *Apr 1970
Rakison, Mr Robert B LLB(Hons) . . . . *Dec 1974
Tackley, Mr Michael O. . . . . *Jun 1976
von Finckenhagen, Mrs L M M . . . . *Oct 2000

JOHN T P MCGUIRK ‡
Flat 21 Elm Park Gardens London SW10 9QG
Tel: 020 7376 8175 *Fax:* 020 7376 8175
E-mail: mcguirk24@yahoo.co.uk

MCILHATTON & DE BRÚS ‡
Colman House Empire Square London SE20 7EX
Tel: 020 8676 7896 *Fax:* 020 8676 7960

AUSTIN MCKEE ‡
The Studio 16a Spencer Hill London SW19 4NY
Tel: 020 8946 6265

MCKENNA DONNELLY & CO ‡
21 Horsley Court Montaigne Close Westminster London SW1P 4BF
Tel: 020 7821 9927
List of partners: E S M McKenna-Donnelly
Languages: French, Gaelic
SPr: McKenna-Donnelly, Ms Erna S M BA . . . . *Nov 1981

MCKENZIE BRACKMAN ‡
22 Bloomsbury Street London WC1B 3QJ
Tel: 020 7580 8111 *Fax:* 020 7580 8777
Dx: 35718 THE BLOOMSBURY EXCHANGE
E-mail: mckb@mckenziebrackman.com
Languages: Spanish, Yoruba
Work: B1 B2 C1 C2 D2 E K1 L N O Q R2 S1 S2 W Z(c,i)

MCKENZIES ‡
20 Church Street Edmonton London N9 9DU
Tel: 020 8350 4114 *Fax:* 020 8350 4044 *Dx:* 36264 EDMONTON 2
Emergency telephone 020 8350 1451
E-mail: enquiries@mckenzies-solicitors.co.uk
List of partners: N Niyazi, N J E Purser
Office: Hertford
Languages: French, Gujarati, Japanese, Turkish, Urdu
Work: D1 D2 E G H J1 K1 K3 L Q S1 S2 W Z(p)
Emergency Action, Agency, Advocacy, Fixed Fee Interview, Legal Aid undertaken and Legal Aid Franchise
Ptr: Niyazi, Mr Nevzat LLB(Hons)(Law) . . . . Oct 1999
Purser, Mr Nicholas John Edward LLB(Hons)(Law) . . Nov 1998
Ast: Fernando, Christine. . . . . Jan 2006
Henwood, Miss Felicity LLB(Hons) . . . . Apr 2010
Hunt, Ms Debbie . . . . Aug 1986
Pugh, Mr Richard . . . . *Feb 1987
Shah, Mrs Kailash LLB(Hons). . . . . Jan 1996
Shah, Rukhsana . . . . Jan 2000
Con: Smyth, Mr Steven. . . . . Jun 1996

MACKESYS ‡
207 New Cross Road London SE14 5UH
Tel: 020 7639 0888 *Fax:* 020 7358 0007
Emergency telephone 020 7732 6793
E-mail: geoff@mackesyscrime.co.uk
List of partners: G M C Wordsworth
Work: D1 E G H M1 S1
Emergency Action, Agency, Advocacy, Fixed Fee Interview and Legal Aid undertaken
Ptr: Wordsworth, Mr Geoffrey M C LLB(Lond) . . . . *Oct 1980
Ast: Connolly, Ms Mary E BA . . . . *Oct 1986
Pearson, Mr Mark J. . . . . Jan 1988
Reid, Mr Michael A . . . . Apr 1986

MACKINTOSH DUNCAN ‡
103 Borough High Street Southwark London SE1 1NL
Tel: 020 7357 6464 *Fax:* 020 7357 8448 *Dx:* 144367 SOUTHWARK 4
E-mail: info@macklaw.co.uk
List of partners: I L Duncan, N A Mackintosh
Work: A1 J1 Q S1 S2 W Z(g,m)
Legal Aid Franchise
Ptr: Duncan, Mr Ian L BA ♦ . . . . *Dec 1975
Mackintosh, Ms Nicola Ann BA(Oxon)(Law Psychology); LSF . . . . Jun 1992

MACKRELL TURNER GARRETT ‡
(in association with Mackrell International)
Inigo Place 31 Bedford Street London WC2E 9EY
Tel: 020 7240 0521 *Fax:* 020 7240 9457
Dx: 40037 COVENT GARDEN
E-mail: partners@mackrell.com
List of partners: M G Adkin, C J Appleyard, D Cox, C J Croxton, M W Cummins, N J Davies, J A Dudley, M A John, A D Kent, P A Parrott, K J Provins, N Rowley, M Y Saviker, M A Slorick
Office: Addlestone, Woking (2 offices)
Languages: French, German, Italian, Russian, Spanish, Urdu
Work: A1 A3 B1 B2 C1 C2 C3 D1 D2 E F1 F2 G I J1 K1 K2 L M1 M2 M3 N O P Q R1 R2 S1 S2 T1 T2 W Z(b,c,d,e,f,h,i,j,k,l,m,n,o,r,w)
Agency, Fixed Fee Interview, Legal Aid undertaken and Member of Accident Line
Ptr: Croxton, Mr Christopher J. . . . . *Dec 1966
Davies, Mr Nicholas John LLB(Hons) . . . . Apr 1989
John, Mr Martin Andrew MA. . . . . *Apr 1988
Kent, Mr Anthony D BA(Hons)(Law & Econ). . . . . . . Jun 1983
Provins, Mr Keith John LLB(Hons). . . . . Nov 1992
Rowley, Mr Nigel LLB . . . . *Nov 1988
Asoc: Green, Miss Alison J LLB . . . . *Sep 1991
Ast: Jones, Miss Eloise LLB; LSF . . . . Oct 1996
Taylor, Miss Donna BA(Hons) . . . . *Aug 2000

MCLARTY & CO ‡
30-38 Fatherly Mews Walthamstow London E17 4QP

MACLAY & CO ‡
156 New Kent Road London SE1 4YS
Tel: 020 7701 8827

MACLAY MURRAY & SPENS LLP
One London Wall London EC2Y 5AB
Tel: 020 7002 8500 *Fax:* 020 7002 8501
Dx: 123 LONDON/CHANCERY LN
E-mail: lawyer@mms.co.uk
Work: C1 C2 E J1 J2 L O Q R1 T1 Z(b,h,o,za)
Ptr: Brooks, Mr Jonathan LLB . . . . Oct 1988
Cooke, Mr David BA(Mod) . . . . Oct 1986
Cordall, Ms Gillan BA(Hons). . . . . Feb 1993
Cullen, Mr Gary BA(Hons); LLM. . . . . Oct 1988
Davidson, Mr Graeme Walter Irving LLB(Hons); DipLP. Oct 1984
Higton, Mrs Joanna BSc . . . . *Oct 1988
Leckie, Mr David LLB(Hons); DipLP. . . . . Jan 1992
Norfolk, Mr Guy LLB; BA(Hons) . . . . Jan 2001
Skerrett, Mr Philip Edward. . . . . *Jul 1971
Smith, Mr Chris BSc(Econ) . . . . Dec 1978
Vause, Mr Christopher Manning. . . . . Feb 2004
Wilks, Ms Wendy . . . . Oct 1995
Woodruff, Mr Christopher L BA . . . . *Oct 1981

MCLEE & CO SOLICITORS ‡
Regent House 24-25 Nutford Place London W1H 5YN
Tel: 020 7569 3103 *Fax:* 020 7569 3102
E-mail: info@mcleeandco.com

MACLEISH LITTLESTONE COWAN ‡
11 Station Parade Snaresbrook Redbridge London E11 1QF
Tel: 020 8514 3000 *Fax:* 020 8530 3104 *Dx:* 52557 WANSTEAD
List of partners: P Bhambra, B Cowan, S G Lewis, R P Littlestone
Office: Barking, Ilford, Sawbridgeworth
Languages: Gujarati, Punjabi, Turkish
Work: A3 B1 C1 C2 D1 D2 E F1 G H J1 J2 K1 K2 L N O Q R1 S1 S2 V W Z(b,c,e,i,j,l,p,q,r)
Emergency Action, Agency, Advocacy, Fixed Fee Interview, Legal Aid undertaken, Legal Aid Franchise and Member of Accident Line
Ptr: Lewis, Mr Spencer Gordon . . . . *Jun 1999
Ast: Griffiths, Miss Emma . . . . Sep 2009
Con: Bean, Mr Ashley . . . . Oct 1990
Kemal, Mrs Aylin . . . . Oct 2004

MCLOUGHLIN & COMPANY LLP
Central Court 25 Southampton Buildings London WC2A 1AL
Tel: 020 7183 6025 *Fax:* 020 7183 2329
Office: Shrewsbury
Work: A3 B1 O Q Z(c,j,q)

HAMISH M MCMILLAN ‡
Sun Alliance House 2-3 Cursitor Street London EC4A 1NE
Tel: 020 7430 1789 *Fax:* 020 7430 1788
Dx: 274 LONDON/CHANCERY LN
Emergency telephone 020 7794 1523
E-mail: hamishmcmillan@o2.co.uk
List of partners: H M McMillan
Work: B1 E K4 O Q S1 S2 W Z(d,k,q)
SPr: McMillan, Mr Hamish M LLB . . . . *Jan 1961

MACMILLAN LTD ‡
The Macmillan Building 4 Crinan Street London N1 9XW

MCMILLEN HAMILTON MCCARTHY ‡
67 Burdett Road Bow London E3 4TN
Tel: 020 8980 6060 *Fax:* 020 8981 1345 *Dx:* 55650 BOW
Emergency telephone 020 8980 6060
E-mail: mail@mhm-solicitors.co.uk
List of partners: M M Hamilton, P A McCarthy, K Stubbs
Languages: French
Work: B2 D1 D2 G H K1 K3
Emergency Action, Agency, Advocacy, Fixed Fee Interview, Legal Aid undertaken and Legal Aid Franchise
Ptr: Hamilton, Ms Maria M LLB(Hons) . . . . *Feb 1989
McCarthy, Ms Patricia A LLB . . . . Feb 1986
Stubbs, Ms Karen BA(Hons) . . . . *Sep 1999
Ast: Fearn, Madeline. . . . . Jul 2010
Jamieson, Ms Sarah Louise BA(Hons) . . . . *§Mar 1994

MCNAIR & CO ‡
EBC House Ranelagh Gardens Hammersmith & Fulham London SW6 3PA
Tel: 020 7371 7896 *Fax:* 020 7371 7988
List of partners: H L McNair
Languages: French, Spanish
Work: C1 E I Q S1 S2 T2 W Z(e,k,z)
SPr: McNair, Mr Hamish L Former Chairman of LSSPGC. . *Mar 1982

MCPHERSONS ‡
32 Milford Road Ealing London W13 9HZ
Tel: 020 8840 9017 *Fax:* 020 8840 7560
E-mail: dsmcpherson_@hotmail.com
List of partners: D S McPherson
Work: E L S1 S2 W
SPr: McPherson, Mr David Samuel BA. . . . . *Jul 1980
Ast: McPherson, Mrs Susan Margaret BA . . . . *Jul 1978

MACRAE & CO LLP ‡
59 Lafone Street Southwark London SE1 2LX
Tel: 020 7378 7716 *Fax:* 020 7407 4318
E-mail: office@macraeco.com
List of partners: R G Gaskell, K R Goonesena, J A Turnbull
Work: A3 B1 C1 C2 C3 E I J1 L M1 M2 O Q R2 S1 S2 T1 U2 W Z(b,e,j,o)
Ptr: Gaskell, Mr Robert George BSc. . . . . *Aug 2006
Goonesena, K Ravindra BA. . . . . *Feb 1988
Turnbull, Mr Julian A MA . . . . *Dec 1989

MACS LAW ‡
93 Colwith Road London W6 9EZ
Tel: 020 8748 8431

MAGRATH LLP ‡
(in association with Gibney Anthony & Flaherty; David Hole Rechtsanwalt & Solicitors)
66-67 Newman Street London W1T 3EQ
Est: 1990
Tel: 020 7495 3003 *Fax:* 020 7317 6766 *Dx:* 44624 MAYFAIR
Emergency telephone 07775 902010
E-mail: magrath@magrath.co.uk
List of partners: S Beckett, N K Goldstone, J M Hershkorn, D A Little, C W M Magrath, A K Martins, S Mehta, S Pattison, B Sheldrick, S Thompson
Languages: Afrikaans, French, Italian
Work: A2 B1 B2 C1 C3 E F1 I J1 N O Q S1 S2 U1 U2 W Z(d,e,f,g,i,k,p,q,w,z,za)
Emergency Action, Fixed Fee Interview and Legal Aid Franchise
Ptr: Beckett, Mr Stanley BA(Hons). . . . . *Oct 1987
Goldstone, Mr Nicholas K BA(Hons)(Oxon) . . . . . . *Nov 1987
Hershkorn, Mr Jeremy M LLB . . . . Oct 1982
Little, Mr David Anthony. . . . . *Oct 1994
Magrath, Mr Christopher William Morrison BA; Admitted to the state Bar of New York Dec 1986 . . . . *Dec 1975
Martins, Mrs Adele Katherine LLB(Hons) . . . . *Aug 1996
Mehta, Miss Sharmila LLB(Hons) . . . . *Nov 1992
Pattison, Mr Stephen . . . . Nov 1978
Sheldrick, Mr Benjamin . . . . *Aug 1999
Thompson, Ms Susan. . . . . Nov 1993
Asoc: Dervin, Ms Delphine BSc . . . . *Jan 2005
Ast: Bhaijee, Ms Zulaykha LLB. . . . . Mar 2006
Blay, Mr Robin A LLB(Hons). . . . . Sep 2000
Chisholm, Miss Kate Alexandra BA(Jurisprudence); LLB . . . . Nov 2007
Joubert, Mrs Alfreda LLB; B Juris . . . . Jul 2005
Laroya, Ms Avinder . . . . *Jan 2005
Le Vay, Mr Joshua Noel BA; CPE; LPC . . . . Sep 2004
Oyetti, Mr Omotilewa Tilly LLM; LLB. . . . . Jan 2007
Roberson, Mr Adam LLB . . . . Nov 2005
Sparks, Mr Robert Edward LLB(Hons). . . . . Sep 2001
Thorpe, Mr Kevin G M LLB(Hons). . . . . *Oct 1998
Con: Grower, Mr Alexis H. . . . . *Jul 1971

MAGWELLS ‡
6 Angel Gate City Road Islington London EC1V 2PB
Tel: 020 7833 2244 *Fax:* 020 7833 8078 *Dx:* 400203 FINSBURY 2
E-mail: law@magwells.co.uk
Languages: Gujarati, Hindi, Kiswahili, Punjabi
Work: B1 C1 D1 E F1 G H J1 K1 L N O P Q R1 S1 T1 W Z(b,c,d,i,l,p)
Emergency Action, Agency, Advocacy and Legal Aid undertaken
Ast: Chohan, Paresh K LLB . . . . *Oct 1988
Nolan, Miss Lee V M . . . . *May 1976
Patel, Prakash LLB . . . . *May 1987

MAHESEN & CO ‡
30 Mellison Road Tooting Broadway Wandsworth London SW17 9AY
Tel: 020 8682 2846 *Fax:* 020 8682 2846

H H MAINPRICE ‡
80 Ebury Street Westminster London SW1W 9QD
Tel: 020 7730 8705 *Fax:* 020 7730 8706

MAISTO E ASSOCIATI ‡
5th Floor 2 Throgmorton Avenue London EC2N 2DG
Tel: 020 7374 0299

MAITLAND ‡
Berkshire House 168-173 High Holborn London WC1V 7AA
Tel: 020 3077 1234 *Fax:* 020 3077 1222

MAITLAND HUDSON & CO LLP ‡
Temple Chambers 3-7 Temple Avenue London EC4Y 0DA
Tel: 020 7832 0460 *Fax:* 020 7936 3518
Dx: 264 LONDON/CHANCERY LN
E-mail: london@maitlandhudson.com

MAKANDA & CO ‡
Paul Anthony House 724 Holloway Road London N19 3JD
Tel: 020 7272 8844 *Fax:* 020 7281 4115
List of partners: R C Makanda
Languages: Ndebele, Shona
Work: G H J1 N V Z(i,p)
Ptr: Makanda, Rangarirai C LLB(Lond) . . . . Jun 1974

MAKANDA BART ‡
78-82 Kirkton Road Tottenham London N15 5EY
Tel: 020 8802 0034 *Fax:* 020 8880 1507
Dx: 55602 SOUTH TOTTENHAM
Emergency telephone 020 8440 2125
List of partners: G O Bart
Work: D1 G H K1 Z(i)
Emergency Action, Agency, Fixed Fee Interview and Legal Aid undertaken
Ptr: Bart, Mrs Gwendolyn O LLB. . . . . *Dec 1981

MAKKA SOLICITORS LTD ‡
70 Upper Tooting Road London SW17 7PB
Tel: 020 8767 9090 *Fax:* 020 8767 9095
Dx: 58875 TOOTHING SOUTH
E-mail: makkaltd@hotmail.com

MAKWANA SOLICITORS ‡
449-451 High Road Willesden London NW10 2JJ
Tel: 020 8451 1999 *Fax:* 020 8451 0999 *Dx:* 57652 HARLESDEN
E-mail: info@makwanas.co.uk

MALCOLM & CO SOLICITORS ‡
4 Warner Place London E2 7DA
Tel: 020 7613 4300 *Fax:* 020 7613 4325
E-mail: donovan.malcolm@malcolmandco.co.uk

MALIK & MALIK SOLICITORS ‡
232 High Road Brent London NW10 2NX
Tel: 020 8830 3050 *Fax:* 020 8830 3051
List of partners: M M Nazeer, M M Saleem
Languages: Hindi, Punjabi, Urdu
Work: B2 G H N S1 Z(i)
Fixed Fee Interview, Legal Aid undertaken and Legal Aid Franchise
Ptr: Nazeer, Mr Malik Mohammed LLB(Hons) . . . . Apr 1997
Saleem, Mr Malik Mohammed LLB(Hons) . . . . Aug 1997

MALIK & MICHAEL ‡
(incorporating Malik & Co)
243a Whitechapel Road Tower Hamlets London E1 1DB
Tel: 020 7247 8458 *Fax:* 020 7426 0633
E-mail: law@malik-michael.com
Languages: Arabic, Bengali, Hindi, Urdu
Work: C1 E G J1 K1 L O Q S1 S2 W Z(g,i)

MALIK & MICHAEL ‡
31 Daventry Street London NW10 6TD
Tel: 020 7724 2223

MALLESONS STEPHEN JAQUES ‡
6th Floor Alder Castle 10 Noble Street London EC2V 7JX
Tel: 020 7778 7170 *Fax:* 020 7778 7199
E-mail: lon@mallesons.com
Work: C1 C2 T1 Z(b)

MALLETTS SOLICITORS
3 Field Court Gray's Inn London WC1R 5EP
Tel: 020 7061 3760 *Fax:* 020 7430 9760
Dx: 129 LONDON/CHANCERY LN
E-mail: info@malletts.com
Office: King's Lynn
Work: B2 C1 G H K1 O W Z(b)
Advocacy, Fixed Fee Interview, Legal Aid undertaken and Legal Aid Franchise
Dir: Mallett, Mr Richard . . . . *Nov 2000
Asoc: Hartley, Mr John . . . . *Mar 2008
Ast: Dehghan, Ms Juliet LLB(Hons) . . . . *Sep 1994

MANCHES LLP ‡
Aldwych House 81 Aldwych London WC2B 4RP
Tel: 020 7404 4433 *Fax:* 020 7430 1133
Dx: 76 LONDON/CHANCERY LN
Emergency telephone 020 7487 5260
E-mail: manches@manches.com
List of partners: G G Atkins, P C M Baddeley, N Benson, C Blackburn, J Bond, A Carter-Silk, D J Chism, G Clifford, J I Craig, R Dickinson, J Edwards, A P S Fox, S B Goldstraw, R Grove, S Johnson, F A Jones, S G Kelly, J Kinner Nilson, S E Levinson, S A Maier, L S Manches, M H J Martin, J Maude, J S Mitchell, P Northwood, R A B Oakes, C M Owen, M Pedro, C Reid, D Richardson, R N Sax, D K Schollenberger, A J Shaw, R M Shaw, C J G Shelley, J J Simpson, P A Smith, R A Smith, L R Spitz, J M A Taylor, D P Tighe, H M Ward, A V Worwood, C H Zietman
Office: Oxford, Reading
Work: A3 B1 C1 C2 C3 D1 E F1 I J1 K1 K2 L M1 O P Q R1 R2 S1 S2 T1 W Z(b,c,e,f,h,k,z)
Ptr: Atkins, Mr Graham G MA(Oxon). . . . . *Jun 1972
Benson, Mr Neil LLB(Hons)(B'ham) Chairman of the Property Association Training Committee. . . . . Nov 1995
Carter-Silk, Mr Alexander . . . . Aug 1988
Chism, Ms Debbie J BA(Oxon) . . . . *Oct 1993
Craig, Mrs Jane I LLB Seymour J Gubb Prize . . . . . . *Oct 1982
Dickinson, Mr Richard BSc(Hons)(Biochemistry). . . . *Sep 1996
Edwards, Ms Joanne MA . . . . Sep 1998
Fox, Mr Alexander Paul Simon BA(Hons)(Econ). . . . Sep 1998
Goldstraw, Mr Stephen B BA . . . . *Oct 1983
Grove, Mr Robin LLB . . . . Apr 1996
Johnson, Miss Sarah BA(Hons) . . . . Oct 1995
Jones, Ms Felicity A BA. . . . . *Sep 1985
Kelly, Mr Sloan Garfield LLB(NZ) . . . . Mar 1993
Levinson, Mr Stephen E LLB(Leics); FCIArb. . . . . . *§Jun 1976
Manches, Mr Louis S MA(Oxon). . . . . *Dec 1979
Martin, Mr Matthew H J LLB. . . . . *Oct 1991
Maude, Mr Jonathan LLB . . . . Oct 1993
Oakes, Mr Robert Alan Bedford BA; MA(Cantab) . . . *Jul 1978
Owen, Mr Christopher M LLB(Cardiff) . . . . *Mar 1984
Pedro, Mr Melvin BA(Dunelm). . . . . *Oct 1983
Sax, Mr Richard N MA(Oxon) . . . . *§Dec 1967
Schollenberger, Mr David Kennon BA; MBA; JD. . . . *Aug 1996
Shaw, Mr Andrew J ★. . . . . *§Jan 1981
Simpson, Mrs J Jane LLB(Lond) . . . . *§Dec 1967
Smith, Mr Peter A LLB(Hons); MSc . . . . *Nov 1986
Spitz, Mrs Louise R MA; LLB . . . . *Oct 1989
Ward, Lady Helen M LLB . . . . *§Nov 1978
Worwood, Mrs Anna V LLB . . . . Sep 1998
Zietman, Mr Clive H LLB(Manc) Manchester University Industrial Law Prize 1982 . . . . *Nov 1985
Ast: Alexian, Ms Katie . . . . *Sep 2005
Arthurs, Mrs Clare MA(Cantab)(German & French); CPE; LPC . . . . Sep 2003
Bell, Mr Andrew. *Sep 2005
Butcher, Mr James LLB(Euro). . . . . Sep 1999
Cockcroft, Miss Rebecca BA(Hons) . . . . Nov 2000
Cox, Miss Maxine BA . . . . Sep 2001
Dziobon, Mrs Rebecca BA; PGDipLaw; LPC . . . . . Sep 2005
Hay, Miss Nicola Marie MA(Oxon). . . . . *Sep 2002
Hyams, Mr Jamie . . . . Sep 2004
Jewitt, Miss Hester BA(Hons); CPE . . . . Nov 2001
Jones, Mr Edward Owen LLB . . . . Dec 1998
kay, Miss Nicola MA(Cantab) . . . . Sep 2004
Kingsbury, Miss Esra Victoria S A BA(Hons)(History with French) . . . . Sep 2001
Leiws, Miss Alison LLB . . . . *Nov 2001
Loblowitz, Mr Daniel Siegmund Henry BA; PGDipLaw; PGDipLP . . . . *Jan 2004
Mashall, Mr Jake LLB; Dip IP Law & Practice . . . . *Mar 2002
Middleton, Miss Joanne LLB; DipLP. . . . . Oct 2002
Modgil, Kush BA; MA . . . . Sep 2002
Nickolds, Ms Claire BSc(Econ) . . . . Aug 2002
Rizvi, Mr Raza Queen Mother Scholar 2000. . . . . . Sep 2004
Ross, Mr James BA(Hons) . . . . Jan 2002
Sentongo, Miss Lena BA(Hons). . . . . *Sep 1999
Seton, Mr Alex BA . . . . *May 2004
Shori, Mr Rajan LLB(Hons) Warner Cranston Tort Prize Oct 1999
Suergiu, Mr Gicrdanc LLB. . . . . Sep 2003
Taylaur, Mr Kevin . . . . *Sep 2004
Thomas, Mr Keith MEng(Electronic Systems Engineering) . . . . Mar 1996
Watt, Mr Alex PGDipLaw . . . . Sep 2005
Welch, Miss Heidi BA . . . . Sep 1999

MANDEL CORPORATE ‡
The Boat House Crabtree Lane London SW6 6TY
Tel: 020 7386 6651
E-mail: david@mandellcorporate.com

MANDEL KATZ & BROSNAN LLP ‡
4th Floor Genesis House 17 Godliman Street London EC4V 5BD
Tel: 020 7653 5678

MANDY PETERS SOLICITORS ‡
345 Lee High Road London SE12 8RU
Tel: 020 8297 4000 *Fax:* 020 8297 4090
E-mail: mandypeterssol@aol.com

MANG & CO ‡
Gibson House 800 High Road Tottenham London N17 0DH
Tel: 020 8808 5898 *Fax:* 020 8808 4674
E-mail: mang@mangsolicitors.co.uk

MANGALA & KALUM SOLICITORS ‡
307a Romford Road Forest Gate London E7 9HA
Tel: 020 8519 0261 *Fax:* 020 8503 1441
Emergency telephone 020 8295 2083
Languages: Bengali, French, Gujarati, Hindi, Malayalam, Punjabi, Sinhalese, Spanish, Tamil, Urdu
Work: G H Z(i)
Legal Aid undertaken

MANOGARAN & CO ‡
24 Hoe Street Walthamstow Waltham Forest London E17 4PH
Tel: 020 8521 5757 *Fax:* 020 8521 8202

THOMAS MANSFIELD LLP
35 Artillery Lane London E1 7LP
Tel: 0845 601 7756
E-mail: info@thomasmansfield.com
Office: Birmingham, Croydon, Manchester

DEAN MANSON SOLICITORS ‡
243-245 Mitcham Road London SW17 9JQ
Tel: 020 8767 5000

MANUEL MARTIN & ASSOCIATES ‡
92 New Cavendish Street London W1W 6XJ
Tel: 020 7631 5161 *Fax:* 020 7631 5147
E-mail: info@mmlawyers.co.uk

MANUEL SWADEN ‡
340 West End Lane West Hampstead London NW6 1LN
Tel: 020 7431 4999 *Fax:* 020 7794 9900
Dx: 53654 WEST HAMPSTEAD
List of partners: J H Manuel, M F Swaden
Work: B1 E J1 L O Q S1 W Z(d)
Ptr: Manuel, Mr Jeremy H LLB. . . . . *Apr 1984
Swaden, Mr Michael F LLB . . . . *Nov 1981
Ast: Sakran, Ms Seena LLB; PGDipLPC . . . . Aug 2000
Con: Golker, Mr Howard . . . . *Jul 1964
Lee, Miss Janet A LLB . . . . *May 1983

MAPLES TEESDALE ‡
21 Lincoln's Inn Fields London WC2A 3DU
Tel: 020 7831 6501 *Fax:* 020 7405 3867 *Dx:* 192 LONDON
E-mail: enq@mapleteesdale.co.uk

MAPLES TEESDALE LLP ‡
30 King Street London EC2V 8EE
Tel: 020 7600 3800 *Fax:* 020 3465 4400 *Dx:* 138754 CHEAPSIDE
E-mail: enq@maplesteesdale.co.uk
List of partners: M R Bryan, P S Burke, S R Dolasa, P W Matcham, D R Power, N Sagoo, D Stevens, J R C Thornton, K Watts, C J Wilkinson
Work: C1 E O Q R1 R2 S1 S2 Z(c)
Ptr: Bryan, Mr Mark R LLB(Newc) . . . . *Oct 1984
Burke, Mr Paul S . . . . Nov 1994
Dolasa, Ms Shehrnaz Rustom. . . . . *Oct 1996
Matcham, Mr Paul W . . . . *§Dec 1976
Power, Mr Declan R. . . . . *Nov 1989
Sagoo, Mr Neil LLB . . . . Oct 1996
Stevens, Mr David LLB . . . . *Jan 1990
Thornton, Mr J Roger C MA(Cantab) . . . . *Nov 1990
Watts, Ms Katherine LLB . . . . *Jul 1988
Wilkinson, Mr Christopher J BA . . . . *§Oct 1990
Ast: Atkins, Miss Claire Louise BSc; PGDipLaw; LPC . . *Sep 2006
Barnett, Mr James Roderick William BA(Hons); PGDipLaw; LPC . . . . *Sep 2008
Bereza, Miss Katherine Emily BA; LLB . . . . Sep 2010
Biedul, Mr Richard LLB(Business Law) . . . . Mar 2010
Bird, Mr Edward Rafe Wesson MA(Hons)(Classics); LLB . . . . Sep 2011
Gallagher, Mrs Kate Louise LLB; LPC. . . . . *Sep 2004
Harryman, Mr Mark Alexander MA(Cantab) . . . . . . Sep 2008
Kilner, Mr Michael Alexander LLB . . . . Sep 2005
Klein, Mrs Anastasia LLB; LPC . . . . *Mar 2005
Kotecha, Miss Shilpa LLB; LPC . . . . *Sep 2011
Lambert, Ms Rose Elizabeth May LLB(Hons) . . . . . Sep 2010
Lee, Miss Christina BSc(Jt Hons) . . . . Sep 2008
Monniot, Mr Edward. . . . . Oct 2006
Ottal, Amanpreet LLB; LPC . . . . Sep 2006
Parrett, Miss Claire Valerie Ellen LLB . . . . Sep 2009
Rahman, Mr Kamran . . . . *Sep 1995
Sainsbury, Mrs Laura Emily MA(Cantab); LPC. . . . . *Oct 2004
Sivill, Miss Clare Elizabeth BA. . . . . Apr 2009
Willmott, Mrs Erika Raine BA(Hons); GDL; LPC . . . . Sep 2007
Xitsas, Mr Christopher. . . . . Aug 2009
Yates, Mrs Rachel Marie BA(Hons) . . . . *Oct 2003

MAPLETOFT & CO ‡
192 Upper Richmond Road London SW15 2SH
Tel: 020 8785 2414 *Fax:* 020 8788 7707 *Dx:* 59458 PUTNEY
E-mail: nm@mapletoft.co.uk
List of partners: N Mapletoft, D S O'Sullivan
Work: A1 B1 C1 D1 E F1 G H J1 K1 L M1 N P R1 S1 T1 V
Emergency Action, Agency, Advocacy and Legal Aid undertaken
Ptr: Mapletoft, Mr Nigel . . . . *May 1980
O'Sullivan, Mr Donal S BCL. . . . . *Feb 1991

SAUL MARINE & CO ‡
Trafalgar House Grenville Place Mill Hill London NW7 3SA
Tel: 020 8959 3611 *Fax:* 020 8906 8167 *Dx:* 51362 MILL HILL
Emergency telephone 07740 656513
E-mail: saul@saulmarine.com
List of partners: S Marine
Languages: Hebrew
Work: E J1 L O Q S1 S2 W
Emergency Action, Agency, Advocacy, Fixed Fee Interview and Legal Aid undertaken
SPr: Marine, Mr Saul LLB ♦ . . . . *Mar 1984

STELLA MARIS SOLICITORS LLP ‡
78 York Street London W1H 1DP
Tel: 0800 098 8388 *Fax:* 020 7785 6818
E-mail: info@stellamarissolicitors.co.uk

MARK & CO ‡
133 Hammersmith Road London W14 0QL
Tel: 020 7603 3710 / 7602 6942
List of partners: M G Mark
Languages: French
Emergency Action, Fixed Fee Interview and Legal Aid undertaken
Ptr: Mark, Miss Marilyn G BA . . . . Jul 1978
Ast: Baxter, Mr Neil John LLB(Hons). . . . . *Sep 1995
Scott, Mr John P R LLB. . . . . Jan 1981

MARK & CO ‡
452 Green Lanes Palmers Green London N13 5XD
Tel: 020 8920 9999 *Fax:* 020 8447 9078
Emergency telephone 0845 456 0248
E-mail: mark@markandcolawyers.co.uk
List of partners: M Periklis
Languages: Greek
Work: E F1 L S1 S2 T1 T2 W
Fixed Fee Interview undertaken
SPr: Periklis, Mr Mark BA(Hons); LPC; MA. . . . . Oct 1997

MARKAND & CO ‡
(incorporating A C Sanders & Co)
275 Green Street Forest Gate London E7 8LJ
Tel: 020 8470 1422 *Dx:* 117350 UPTON PARK
List of partners: M Upadhyaya
Languages: Arabic, French, Gujarati, Hindi
Work: C1 D1 E G H J1 K1 M1 P R1 S1 W Z(c,i,l)
Emergency Action, Agency, Advocacy, Fixed Fee Interview and Legal Aid undertaken
Ptr: Upadhyaya, Markand LLB(Lond) . . . . *§Jul 1977
Ast: Pilling, Mr John N BA(Cantab). . . . . *Dec 1963
Con: Sanders, Mr Alan C. . . . . *Jun 1960

MARKS & CLERK ‡
90 Long Acre London WC2E 9RA
Tel: 020 7420 0250 *Fax:* 020 7420 0255
E-mail: solicitors@marks-clerk.com
Office: Birmingham, Cheltenham, Leeds, Leicester, Liverpool, Manchester, Oxford

O M MARKS & CO ‡
31 Fairholme Gardens Finchley Barnet London N3 3ED
Tel: 020 8371 6689 *Fax:* 020 7371 9493
E-mail: lawmarks.mayfair@virgin.net
List of partners: O M Marks
Work: C1 C2 E L M2 R1 R2 S1 S2 W Z(a,f)
SPr: Marks, Mr Omek Marian. . . . . *Jan 1970

JEREMY MAROZZI ‡
19 Merton Road Wimbledon London SW19 1EE
Tel: 020 8544 2800

MARRACHE & CO ‡
15 Hanover Square London W1S 1HS
Tel: 020 7569 1000 *Fax:* 020 7569 1001

MARRIOTT HARRISON ‡
Staple Court 11 Staple Inn Buildings London WC1V 7QH
Tel: 020 7209 2000 *Fax:* 020 7209 2001
Dx: 0001 LONDON/CHANCERY LN
E-mail: email@marriottharrison.co.uk
Languages: French, German, Italian, Portuguese, Spanish, Welsh
Work: A3 C1 C2 C3 E I J1 O U2 Z(b,e,f,k,w)

LAURENCE MARRON SOLICITORS ‡
68 Lambard Street London EC3V 9LJ
Tel: 020 8382 3770 *Fax:* 020 8382 3792
E-mail: lm@laurencemarron.com

MARSH BROWN & CO ‡
31 Lewisham High Street Lewisham London SE13 5AF
Tel: 020 8852 0052 *Fax:* 020 8463 9869 *Dx:* 56615 LEWISHAM
E-mail: mh@marshbrownsolicitors.co.uk
List of partners: M P Brown, C J Marsh
Work: D1 E F1 J1 J2 K1 L N O Q Z(p,q)
Agency undertaken
Ptr: Brown, Miss Mary P LLB(B'ham) . . . . *Oct 1985
Marsh, Mr Colin J BSc(Soc Sc); MA. . . . . *Jan 1983
Asoc: Harley, Ms Lori E BA . . . . *Jul 1987

MARSHALL & MASON SOLICITORS ‡
Suite 5 63 The Broadway London E15 4BQ
Tel: 020 8555 3999 *Fax:* 020 8555 3666

MARSHALL HATCHICK
Lower Ground Floor 44 Welbeck Street London W1G 8DY
Tel: 020 7935 3272 *Fax:* 020 3581 3235
Office: Woodbridge

MARTIN-SIMMS SOLICITORS ‡
11 Green Street Forest Gate London E7 8DA
Tel: 020 8552 7042 *Fax:* 020 8548 0700
Emergency telephone 020 8552 7042
E-mail: info@mcmartinandco.com
List of partners: M C Martin
Work: C1 E G H L R1 S1 W Z(l)
Agency and Legal Aid undertaken
SPr: Martin, Miss Merylin Cynthia . . . . *Nov 1988

MARTINE ALAN ‡
271 Regent Street London W1B 2ES
Tel: 020 3089 4086
E-mail: martine@martinealan.co.uk

MARTYNSROSE SOLICITORS
456 Kingsland Road London E8 4AE
E-mail: martynsrosesolicitors@yahoo.co.uk
Office: Hounslow

MARZIANO KHATRY MAK SOLICITORS ‡
108-110 High Street North East Ham London E6 2HT

B C MASCARENHAS ‡
678 Lordship Lane Wood Green Haringey London N22 5JN
Tel: 020 8889 6246
List of partners: B C Mascarenhas
Languages: Kiswahili
Work: E G S1 Z(i)
Fixed Fee Interview and Legal Aid undertaken
Ptr: Mascarenhas, Mr Bernard C . . . . *Dec 1974

MASON HAYES
Garrick House 26-27 Southampton Street London WC2E 7RS
Tel: 020 7717 8493 *Fax:* 020 7717 8401
Dx: 28111 HOLMES CHAPEL
E-mail: info@masonhayes.co.uk
Office: Manchester

MASSEYS LLP ‡
Hillgate House 26 Old Bailey London EC4M 7QH
Tel: 020 7634 9595 *Fax:* 020 7329 4057
E-mail: seanupson@masseyslaw.co.uk

MASTERS LEGAL SERVICES LIMITED ‡
8 Buckingham Place London SW1E 6HX
Tel: 020 7198 8024 *Fax:* 020 7198 8025
E-mail: colin@materstax.co.uk

MASTROVITO & ASSOCIATES ‡
Rapier House 40-46 Lamb's Conduit Street London WC1N 2NW
Tel: 020 7025 2375 *Fax:* 020 7025 2377

MATCH SOLICITORS ‡
3 Bolt Court Fleet Street London EC4A 3DQ
Tel: 020 7353 6881 *Fax:* 020 7353 6882
Dx: 133 LONDON/CHANCERY LN

MATHESON ORMSBY PRENTICE ‡
Pinnacle House 23-26 St Dunstan's Hill London EC3R 8HN
Tel: 020 7618 6750 *Fax:* 020 7618 6790

MATHYS & SQUIRE ‡
120 Holborn London EC1N 2SQ
Tel: 020 7830 0000 *Fax:* 020 7830 0001

MATINI MONTECRISTO ‡
34 South Molton Street London W1K 5RG
Tel: 0845 299 7866 *Fax:* 020 7691 7744
E-mail: law@matini-montercristo.co.uk

MATTHEW ARNOLD & BALDWIN LLP
85 Fleet Street London EC4Y 1AE
Tel: 020 7936 4600 *Fax:* 020 7842 3300 *Dx:* 448 CHANCERY LANE
E-mail: info@mablaw.com
Office: Milton Keynes, Watford
Ptr: Phillips, Mr Richard A LLB. . . . . *Apr 1989
Mem: Brittain, Mr Timothy LLB; Dip LP. . . . . Dec 1990

W H MATTHEWS & CO ‡
109 Old Street Islington London EC1V 9JR
Tel: 020 7251 4942 *Fax:* 020 7608 1371 *Dx:* 36619 FINSBURY
List of partners: D Bristow, P A Freely, D J Guy, C J Howard, I K Lanceley, I K Lanceley, R Lawrence, B Lesler, K M Lovering, E M Lowry, D M A Mangnall, R D Perriman, N J Quinney, A Tribick
Office: Kingston upon Thames, Staines, Sutton
Languages: French, German
Work: C1 C2 D1 E F1 G H J1 K1 K3 K4 L M1 M2 N O P Q R1 R2 S1 S2 T1 T2 V W X Z(c,e,i,j,k,l,q,r,t,w)
Agency undertaken
Ptr: Bristow, Mr David . . . . *Nov 1984
Freely, Mr Patrick A LLB . . . . *Oct 1985
Lanceley, Mr Ian K . . . . *Feb 1971
Lesler, Mr Barry LLB . . . . *Nov 1989
Ast: Pirinen, Tero . . . . *Jan 2006

MAUNSELL BOWER ‡
169 Borough High Street Wandsworth London SE1 1HR
Tel: 020 7378 9592 *Fax:* 020 8617 9436
E-mail: enquiries@maunsell-bower.com
List of partners: C B Maunsell Bower
Languages: French
Work: C1 E K1 K3 L O Q S1 S2 W
Advocacy undertaken
Ptr: Maunsell Bower, Mrs Catherine Bridgid LLB. . . . . . *Jun 1994

JUDITH MAURICE SOLICITORS ‡
Unit 59 Grove Business Centre 560-568 High Road London N17 9TA
Tel: 020 8808 8018 *Fax:* 020 8365 1869
E-mail: judithmaurice_solicitors@yahoo.co.uk

MAURICE NADEEM & ATIF ‡
64 Great Cumberland Place London W1H 7TT
Tel: 020 7723 3424 *Fax:* 020 7724 6024
E-mail: mauricenadeem@email.com
List of partners: M C Atif
Languages: Punjabi, Urdu
Work: E L Q S1 S2 W Z(i)
Ptr: Atif, Mr Mohammed C BA; LLB; LLM . . . . *Jun 1980

MAURICE TURNOR GARDNER LLP ‡
1 Threadneedle Street London EC2R 8AY
Tel: 020 7012 8610 *Fax:* 020 7012 8620

MAUS SOLICITORS ‡
Global House 228 Brownhill Road London SE6 1AT
Tel: 020 8695 0000 *Fax:* 020 8695 0022 *Dx:* 34355 CATFORD
E-mail: info@maussolicitors.com

MAX BITEL GREENE LLP ‡
1 Canonbury Place Islington London N1 2NG
Tel: 020 7354 2767 *Fax:* 020 7226 1210 *Dx:* 51852 HIGHBURY
E-mail: office@mbg.co.uk
List of partners: N A Bitel, R G Butler, C J Ledward, E M Reid, Y L Roberts, S Trimmer
Work: B1 C1 C2 C3 E F1 F2 I J1 K1 K3 L M1 M2 O Q R1 S1 S2 U2 W Z(e,f,k,l,w,za)
Fixed Fee Interview undertaken
Ptr: Bitel, Mr Nicholas A LLB . . . . *§Aug 1983
Butler, Mr Roger G . . . . *Jul 1976
Ledward, Mr Colin J. . . . . *§Dec 1975
Reid, Mr Ean M. . . . . *Jul 1964
Roberts, Ms Yvette Louise BSc(Hons). . . . . *Jul 2004
Trimmer, Mrs Sharon LLB. . . . . *May 2002
Asoc: Proctor, Ms Suzanne Elizabeth LLB(Hons) . . . . . . *Nov 2008
Shihab, Mr Zane LLB . . . . Oct 2009

Particular areas of work include: Bankruptcy, Commercial and Company Law, Mergers and Acquisitions, Competition Law, Sports Law.

RICHARD MAX & CO SOLICITORS ‡
87 Chancery Lane London WC2A 1ET
Tel: 020 7240 2400 *Fax:* 020 7240 7499
E-mail: info@richardmax.co.uk
Work: E P R1

MAXWELL ALVES ‡
44 Gray's Inn Road London WC1X 8LR
Tel: 020 7632 6950 *Fax:* 020 7632 6959
E-mail: j.soucek@maxwellalves.com

MAXWELL ALVES SOLICITORS ‡
28 Gray's Inn Road London WC1X 8HR
Tel: 020 7269 6470 *Fax:* 020 7269 6479
Dx: 443 LONDON/CHANCERY LN
E-mail: london@maxwellalves.com

MAXWELL WINWARD LLP ‡
100 Ludgate Hill London EC4M 7RE
Tel: 020 7651 0000 *Fax:* 020 7651 4800
Dx: 190 LONDON/CHANCERY LN
E-mail: info@maxwellwinward.com
List of partners: S C Ashworth, M J Bartholomew, J Bremen, L Calderwood, J R A Cox, H Crossman, M D Giess, R J Levine, C A Levontine, A P S Luto, S H Marks, F R McColl, I W R McIntyre, L Millar, C F J North, O O'Sullivan, W G B Parker, M G Sergeant, N J Stafford, M M Wieliczko, N C B Wilson
Languages: Arabic, French
Work: A3 B1 C1 C2 C3 E F1 J1 L M2 N O P Q R1 R2 S1 S2 T1 T2 U1 U2 W Z(c,e,h,i)
Emergency Action and Advocacy undertaken
Mem: Ashworth, Miss Sally Caroline LLB . . . . Sep 1998
Bartholomew, Mr Mark James BA(Law) . . . . Oct 1986
Bremen, Mr James BA . . . . Jul 2004
Calderwood, Ms Lisa MA(Hons). . . . . Mar 1998
Cox, Mr Julian Richard Alan BA. . . . . Oct 1997
Crossman, Mr Howard . . . . Feb 1988
Giess, Mr Michael David BA(Hons) . . . . Oct 1997
Levine, Mr Raymond J MA(Oxon) . . . . *§Jun 1972
Levontine, Mr Clive A LLB. . . . . *Apr 1988
Luto, Mr Adrian P S MA; LLB . . . . *Oct 1983
McColl, Mr Fraser R. . . . . §Oct 1973
McIntyre, Mr Ian W R BA(Oxon). . . . . *§Apr 1972
Marks, Mr Stephen Henry BA; MA(Jurisprudence). . . . Nov 1995
Millar, Ms Lindsay BA(Oxon); LLM(Lond) . . . . *Oct 1988
North, Mr Christopher F J LLB. . . . . *§Oct 1986
O'Sullivan, Mrs Orla BCL . . . . *Mar 1991
Parker, Mr William George Benjamin LLB . . . . Sep 1997
Sergeant, Mr Michael G LLB(Hons) . . . . *Nov 1995
Stafford, Mr Neil Jonathan. . . . . Nov 1993
Wieliczko, Mr Maximilian M LLB. . . . . *Nov 1987
Wilson, Mr Nigel C B BA . . . . *§Jun 1976
Ast: Abrahams, Mr Simon BA(Hons). . . . . Sep 2007
Booth, Mr Richard LLB . . . . Aug 2003
Corbett, Mr Adrian Charles LLB . . . . Sep 2000
Cordery, Mr David James BA(Hons). . . . . Oct 2008
Curry, Mr Kevin . . . . Oct 2006
Dellaway, Ms Lisa May BA(Hons); MA; LPC. . . . . . . Jul 2001
Dunmore, Mr William Michel BSc . . . . Apr 2004
Garcha, Mr Jatinder Singh BA; LLM. . . . . Sep 1988
Gauden, Ms Sara LLB(Hons) . . . . Sep 2001
Gradie, Mrs Elizabeth Claire BA(Hons); GDL . . . . . Oct 2008
Hennessey, Mr Justin . . . . Sep 2000
McNamara, Ms Una Cecilia LLB. . . . . Apr 2007
Pacey, Ms Giao Knanh . . . . Sep 2003
Rowswell, Mr Jonathan LLB. . . . . Mar 2006
Sear, Ms Emma Jane Maria. . . . . Aug 2006
Solomides, Mrs Joanna . . . . Oct 2006
Ubbey, Ms Mandeep Kaur BA; MA . . . . Nov 1999
Veitch, Mr Mark Howard. . . . . Aug 2006
Witt, Mr Jonathan Stafford LLB . . . . Oct 2004

MAY & CO ‡
257 Edgware Road Colindale Barnet London NW9 6NB
Tel: 020 8200 6116 *Fax:* 020 8905 9387
List of partners: D May
Work: E S1 W
Ptr: May, Mr David . . . . *Jan 1964

JOHN MAY LAW ‡
17 Kensington Place London W8 7PT
Tel: 020 7792 2900 *Fax:* 020 7792 2941
Dx: 47202 KENSINGTON HIGH STREET

MAY MAY & MERRIMANS ‡
12 South Square Gray's Inn London WC1R 5HH
Tel: 020 7405 8932 *Fax:* 020 7831 0011
Dx: 225 LONDON/CHANCERY LN
E-mail: mail@mmandm.co.uk
List of partners: M T Bermingham, S R Black, P A Camfield, M F Elliott, I F Layzell-Smith, R J E Milns, J L Richards, A A Sarkis, S Schofield, C P Simm, P Smith, D H Smyth, R L H Steen, R P Taylor, A H Togher
Work: A1 A3 C1 D1 E F1 J1 K1 K3 K4 L O P Q R1 S1 S2 T1 T2 W Z(d,k,n)
Agency undertaken
Ptr: Bermingham, Miss Marie Therese LLB . . . . *Oct 1985
Black, Miss Susan R LLB . . . . *Jun 1976
Camfield, Mr Paul A BA; TEP . . . . *Oct 1984
Elliott, Mrs Mary F LLB; TEP . . . . *Nov 1990
Layzell-Smith, Mr Ian Francis BA(Hons)(Dunelm) . . . *Nov 1992
Milns, Miss Rosemary J E LLB(Lond); TEP . . . . . . *Oct 1984
Richards, Miss Julia L BA(Hons) . . . . *Mar 1999
Sarkis, Miss Alexandra A BA(Dunelm); TEP. . . . . . *§Nov 1984
Schofield, Sandon LLB; LLM(Lond) . . . . *Sep 1974
Simm, Mrs Charlotte Patricia MA(Cantab); TEP . . . . *Oct 1993
Smith, Miss Pauline LLB(Sheff); TEP . . . . *Jun 1974
Smyth, Mr David H MA(Cantab); TEP . . . . *§Mar 1983
Steen, Mr Roderick L H MA(Oxon); TEP. . . . . *Apr 1975
Taylor, Mr Richard P BA(Oxon) . . . . *Jun 1982
Togher, Ms Angela Helen LLB(Hons) . . . . *Nov 1994
Ast: Reid, Mr Christopher BA(Hons); LLB(Hons) . . . . . *Oct 2010
Wright, Mr Robert William MA(Hons)(Cantab) . . . . . *Jan 2007

MAY MORRIS & CO ‡
9b Perry Vale London SE23 3NE
Tel: 020 8699 1000 *Fax:* 020 8699 1022

MAYER BROWN INTERNATIONAL LLP ‡
201 Bishopsgate London EC2M 3AF
Tel: 020 3130 3000 *Fax:* 020 3130 3001 *Dx:* 556 LONDON/CITY
E-mail: info@mayerbrown.com
List of partners: D M Allen, J P Anderson, M Bagnall, S Bates, J A Black, S J Bottomley, G A Bownes, S M Byrt, A J Carruthers, D M Chadwick, I Christie, J M L Clay, I Coles, S M Connolly, S A Davies, K S Desai, J M Dickins, P J G Dickinson, R M Evans, I Flowers, A Forge, M A M Freyne, W Glassey, K Hawken, I Hobbs, M P Hutchinson, D H Ive, P S James, T M John, A C Jones, M L Kidwell, D Levin, B Lewis, I J McDonald, J M Miles, F M Murphy, M Nicholaides, M Nicolaides, J E Nugent, J Oulton, M Pabst, R E Page, M A Prinsley, M D Regan, N R Robertson, A M Rogers, J W Roskill, P Rowell, D Salvest, E M Sautter, C Sharp, A P Sharples, D P Spenser Underhill, P Steiner, A K Stewart, C Taylor, I V Thomas, M Uhrynuk, M Walker, S J Walsh, A G White, N J White, S H K Williams, I C Wood, N A Wright
Office: London EC3
Languages: French, German, Italian, Spanish
Work: A1 A3 B1 C1 C2 C3 D1 E F1 I J1 K1 L M1 M2 N O P Q R1 R2 T1 T2 U1 U2 W Z(b,c,d,e,f,i,j,l,o,s,u)
Emergency Action and Member of Accident Line
Ptr: Allen, Mr David M LLB(Bris). . . . . *Nov 1984
Anderson, Ms Joanne P BSc . . . . Oct 1991
Bagnall, Ms Mary . . . . Nov 1997
Bates, Miss Stephanie LLB . . . . May 1985
Black, Mr James A . . . . *May 1977
Bottomley, Mr Stephen J BA(Hons) . . . . *Jun 1980
Bownes, Mr Gary A LLB . . . . Feb 1987
Byrt, Miss Sarah M LLB. . . . . Sep 1988
Carruthers, Mr Andrew J MA(Oxon); MCIArb . . . . . *Apr 1975
Chadwick, Mr David Michael LLB(Hons). . . . . *Oct 1989
Christie, Mr Ian BA(Leeds) . . . . *§Oct 1978
Clay, Mr Jeremy M L MA(Oxon); Jurisprudence . . . . *Oct 1985
Coles, Mr Ian . . . . Jan 2002
Connolly, Mr Sean M LLB . . . . *Oct 1984
Davies, Miss Sally Alexandra LLB(Hons) . . . . *Nov 1994
Desai, Kiran S . . . . Feb 1991
Dickins, Mrs Julie Mellinda LLB(Bris) Robert Innes & Geoffrey Howard-Watson Prizes 1980 . . . . *Oct 1982
Dickinson, Mr Peter J G LLB(Soton). . . . . *Oct 1986
Evans, Mr Richard Marshall BA; APMI . . . . Oct 1992
Flowers, Mr Ian LLB(Hons) . . . . Sep 1983
Forge, Mrs Anna BA(Hons)(Law) . . . . *Apr 1982
Freyne, Miss Michele A M MA(TCD) . . . . *§Jun 1978
Glassey, Mr William. . . . . Apr 2000
Hawken, Mr Kevin. . . . . Jan 2002
Hobbs, Ms Ingrid . . . . Jan 1995
Hutchinson, Mr Michael P BA . . . . Nov 1991
Ive, Mr David H LLB. . . . . *Jun 1974
James, Miss Philippa S LLB(Wales); FPMI . . . . . . *Apr 1980
John, Mr Trefor M BA(Hons)(Law). . . . . *Apr 1978
Jones, Miss Anita C LLB . . . . Oct 1991
Kidwell, Ms Marie Lisa LLB . . . . *Dec 1994
Levin, Mr David . . . . Apr 1981
Lewis, Ms Beverley . . . . Oct 1992
McDonald, Mr Ian James MA(Cantab). . . . . Jul 1992
Miles, Mr John M MA(Cantab). . . . . *§Jan 1982
Murphy, Ms Frances M BA(Hons); DipIP. . . . . Nov 1987
Nicholaides, Mr Mark . . . . Jan 2000
Nicolaides, Mr Mark. . . . . Jan 2002
Nugent, Mr Jonathan Edward LLB; MA . . . . May 1994

Oulton, Mr Jim . . . . Nov 1989
Pabst, Mr Michael. . . . . Feb 1998
Page, Mr Richard Edward LLB . . . . *Nov 1993
Prinsley, Mr Mark A BA(Oxon). . . . . *Oct 1981
Regan, Mr Michael D MA(Oxon). . . . . *Apr 1980
Robertson, Mr Nicholas R LLB . . . . Oct 1988
Rogers, Ms Anna M BA(Jurisprudence) . . . . *Oct 1985
Roskill, The Hon Julian W. . . . . *Nov 1974
Rowell, Mr Paul MA(Hons); APMI . . . . Oct 1993
Salvest, Ms Drew . . . . Oct 1987
Sautter, Mr Edmund M MA(Cantab) . . . . *Oct 1983
Sharp, Mrs Cate . . . . Oct 1993
Sharples, Mr Andrew P BA(Dunelm)(Econ History) . . Nov 1985
Spenser Underhill, Mr Dominic P . . . . Oct 1989
Steiner, Mr Peter BA(Hons)(Cantab). . . . . *Sep 1988
Stewart, Mr Andrew K LLB . . . . *Nov 1986
Taylor, Ms Caroline LLB(Reading). . . . . *Oct 1993
Thomas, Mr Iain V LLB . . . . Feb 1991
Uhrynuk, Mr Mark. . . . . Jan 1995
Walker, Mr Mark MA(Cantab) . . . . Aug 1989
Walsh, Mr Stephen J BA; BCL(Oxon) . . . . *Nov 1985
White, Mr Andrew G MA(Oxon) . . . . *§May 1974
White, Mr Nigel J LLB(Leics) . . . . Mar 1989
Williams, Mr Spencer H K. . . . . *§Jun 1971
Wood, Mr Ian C BSc; MSc(Dunelm). . . . . *§Apr 1977
Wright, Mr Nigel A LLB . . . . Nov 1987
Ast: Begner, Ms Sherry . . . . Sep 1999
Boran, Ms Ruth LLB(Hons) . . . . *Sep 1999
Brody, Ms Michelle . . . . Sep 1999
Brown, Mr Michael Paul BA(Cantab); CPE; LSF. . . . *Oct 1993
Cox, Ms Beverly A BA(Oxon) . . . . *Nov 1992
Craven, Mr Richard N BA(Oxon) . . . . Aug 1975
Dagnall, Ms Jane Elizabeth LLB. . . . . *§Nov 1994
Duff, Ms Catherine E LLB(Hons); BA . . . . Apr 1999
Henchie, Mr Nicholas David John LLB. . . . . Nov 1995
Jewitt, Mr William E LLB . . . . Oct 1991
Lewis, Ms Beverley J BSc(Hons)(Physics & Electronic Engineering) . . . . Dec 1992
Sharp, Ms Cathryn Frances BSc . . . . *Oct 1993

MAYER BROWN INTERNATIONAL LLP
Floor 29 30 St Mary Axe London EC3A 8EP
Tel: 020 3130 3000 *Dx:* 556 LONDON
Office: London EC2

MAYFAIR SOLICITORS ‡
8 Upper Brook Street Mayfair London W1K 6PA
Tel: 020 7493 0740 *Fax:* 020 7493 0741
Dx: 42707 OXFORD CIRCUS NORTH
E-mail: contact@mayfairsolicitors.co.uk

MAYS BROWN ‡
18b Ensign Street London E1 8JD
Tel: 020 7264 0600 *Fax:* 020 7264 0601
E-mail: mail@maysbrown.com

MEABY & CO ‡
2 Camberwell Church Street Camberwell Green London SE5 8QY
Tel: 020 7703 5034 *Fax:* 020 7708 3711
Dx: 35300 CAMBERWELL GREEN
E-mail: info@meaby.co.uk
List of partners: B W Meaby, R H Meaby
Office: Guildford
Languages: French
Work: C1 D1 E F1 G H J1 K1 L M1 N P R1 S1 W Z(l)
Emergency Action, Agency, Advocacy, Fixed Fee Interview and Legal Aid undertaken
Ptr: Meaby, Mr Brian W . . . . *Feb 1962
Meaby, Mr Robert H. . . . . *May 1963

MEADE & CO ‡
(in association with Stilemans)
45 Chase Side Southgate London N14 5BP
Tel: 020 8886 3643 *Fax:* 020 8882 8623 *Dx:* 34300 SOUTHGATE
List of partners: G J Jones, A Pallikarou
Work: E K4 S1 S2 W
Ptr: Jones, Mr Geoffrey J . . . . *§Jan 1969
Pallikarou, Miss Androulla BA. . . . . *§Jul 1983

MEDIA LAW CONSULTANCY LIMITED ‡
Studio 8 58 Chetwynd Road London NW5 1DJ
Tel: 020 7482 3011
E-mail: jan@jantomalin.com

MEDLICOTT & BENSON ‡
(incorporating Peter Sabel & Co)
(in association with Chiu & Benson)
23 Haymarket London SW1Y 4DG
Tel: 020 7839 2818 *Fax:* 020 7839 2818
List of partners: G N Benson, M P C Chiu
Languages: Chinese
Work: A1 B1 C1 C2 C3 E F1 G J1 K1 L M1 P R2 S1 S2 T1 T2 V W X Z(d,i)
Agency and Fixed Fee Interview undertaken
Ptr: Benson, Mr George N LLM; LLB; AKC . . . . *§May 1967
Chiu, Mr Michael P C . . . . *Jun 1972

MEDYCKYJ & CO ‡
12 Lauradale Road Haringey London N2 9LU
Tel: 020 8442 0000 *Fax:* 020 8442 0800
E-mail: mail@medyckyj.co.uk
List of partners: M M T Medyckyj
Work: A3 C3 M1 O Q Z(e,f)
Agency undertaken
SPr: Medyckyj, Ms Mary M T BSc(Manc). . . . . *Oct 1990

MEER & CO ‡
123 Erskine Hill London NW11 6HU
Tel: 020 8458 4554 *Fax:* 020 8458 4554
List of partners: S M Meer
Languages: Gujarati
Work: E S1 S2
SPr: Meer, Mr Siddiek M . . . . *Jun 1968

LAKSHMAN MEEWELLA ‡
6 Osten Mews Emperor's Gate Kensington London SW7 4HW
Tel: 020 7370 6595 *Fax:* 020 7370 1110
Emergency telephone 07956 547452
List of partners: L D Meewella
Languages: Bengali, Cantonese, French, Italian, Sinhalese, Tamil
Work: B2 D1 D2 F1 G H J1 K1 K2 L M2 N Q S1 S2 T2 V W X Z(g,i,k,l,o,p,q,r)
Emergency Action, Agency, Advocacy, Fixed Fee Interview, Legal Aid undertaken and Member of Accident Line
SPr: Meewella, Lakshman D Notary Public. . . . . *Jun 1977

MELANI & COMPANY SOLICITORS ‡
Link House 184 West Hendon Broadway London NW9 7EE
Tel: 020 8201 5976 *Fax:* 020 8201 6244
E-mail: inbo@melani.co.uk

JOSEPH MELCHIOR & CO ‡
16 Ulysses Road London NW6 1EE
Tel: 020 7435 7738 *Fax:* 020 7435 7411

MELLERSH & CO ‡
11 Ashby Street Islington London EC1V 0ED
Tel: 020 7251 2361 *Fax:* 0870 705 1252
E-mail: mfam@mellersh.uk.com
List of partners: M F A Mellersh
Work: A1 B1 C1 E J1 L S1 T1 W Z(b,f)
Emergency Action and Agency undertaken
SPr: Mellersh, Mr Michael F A . . . . *Mar 1970

MELROSE SOLICITORS ‡
33 Bream Close London N17 9DF
Tel: 020 8801 8919
E-mail: lizikirko@yahoo.com

MEMERY CRYSTAL ‡
44 Southampton Buildings London WC2A 1AP
Tel: 020 7242 5905 *Fax:* 020 7242 2058
Dx: 156 LONDON/CHANCERY LN
List of partners: L B Alexander, M V April, T C Crosley, P M Crystal, U M T Danagher, N L Davis, M Dawes, H R Deehan, C T Flood, L A Gregory, J K Hull, N S Kravitz, J Marsden, S G Milne, A M Moss, E A O'Keeffe, D H Rands, A Read, S E Rush, G P Scott, N Scott, B Taylor, A Titmas, D C Walker, P C Wilson
Languages: French, German, Italian, Spanish, Swedish
Work: A3 B1 C1 C2 C3 E F1 J1 K1 K2 K3 L M1 M2 O P Q R1 R2 S1 S2 T1 T2 W X Z(b,c,d,e,j,k,l,n,o,w,za)
Emergency Action, Advocacy and Fixed Fee Interview undertaken
Ptr: Alexander, Mrs Lindsey Brenda . . . . Oct 1985
April, Mrs Merrill V BA(Durham) . . . . *Oct 1987
Crosley, Mr Timothy Charles . . . . Sep 1996
Crystal, Mr Peter M MA(Oxon); LLM(McGill). . . . . *Oct 1973
Danagher, Ms Ursula Mary Teresa . . . . Feb 1993
Davis, Mr Nicholas Leon LLB(Hons). . . . . *Oct 1996
Dawes, Mr Michael LLB. . . . . Sep 1998
Deehan, Miss Helen Ruth. . . . . *Jan 1994
Flood, Mr Colm Thomas LLB . . . . *Jul 1979
Gregory, Ms Lesley A BA(Oxon). . . . . *Oct 1983
Hull, Mr John Kenneth . . . . Jan 1979
Kravitz, Nicola S LLB . . . . *Oct 1991
Marsden, Ms Jane BA(French & Spanish); CPE. . . . . *Jun 1994
Milne, Mr Stephen Graeme BA(Hons). . . . . *Oct 1998
Moss, Mr Aliastair Micheal MA(Oxon) . . . . Sep 1998
O'Keeffe, Mr Eugene Andrew LLB. . . . . *Jan 1975
Rands, Mr D Harvey BSc; ACIArb. . . . . *Jan 1976
Read, Mr Alex BA(Hons) . . . . Apr 1995
Rush, Mr Sean Edward . . . . Aug 1998
Scott, Mr Greg P LLB(Manc) Conflict of Laws University of Manchester 1985 . . . . *Oct 1988
Scott, Mr Nicholas. . . . . Sep 2003
Taylor, Ms Bree BA; LLB(Hons) . . . . Jan 2002
Titmas, Mr Andrew BA . . . . Oct 1996
Walker, Mr David Charles LLB. . . . . *Sep 2001
Wilson, Mr Peter C BA(Warw). . . . . *Nov 1991
Asoc: Alfille, Mr Nicholas Mark. . . . . Feb 1990
Brackenbury, Ms Lucie Marie . . . . Oct 2007
Evans, Mr Richard Duncan . . . . Nov 2004
Green, Mr Richard John. . . . . Oct 2000
Hinde-Smith, Ms Michelle . . . . Sep 1998
Jenkins, Ms Jennifer Anne . . . . May 2006
Mungovan, Mr James. . . . . Sep 2004
Nanji, Mr Rumit . . . . Sep 2007
Stone, Mr Kieran Peter . . . . Sep 2004
Ast: Barnett, Ms Marina Teresa . . . . May 2011
Basuta, Ms Minna. . . . . Sep 2010
Bell, Miss Fiona L LLB(Hons)(Lond); ATII; TEP . . . . *Oct 1985
Eriksson-Lee, Ms Abigail Jane . . . . Sep 2007
Gleeson, Mr Martin John . . . . Sep 2007
Hogan, Mark . . . . Jul 2007
Jory, Ms Melanie Anne Louise. . . . . Feb 2010
Lynch, Mr Ryan John . . . . Sep 2011
Malloy, Ms Caitlin Tara . . . . Oct 2008
Martin, Mr Gregory Mitford . . . . Sep 2009
Martin, Ms Sarah Elizabeth . . . . Sep 2009
Memery, Ms Joanna Vanessa Jane . . . . Sep 2009
Norris, Ms Joanna Clare . . . . Sep 2007
O'Dwyer, Mr David Stuart . . . . Oct 2007
Page, Mr David R S LLB(Hull). . . . . *Jul 1973
Pasquill, Ms Stephanie . . . . Sep 2008
Phillips, Ms Harriet Jane . . . . Sep 2007
Saunders, Ms Wendy Denise . . . . May 2009
Seal, Ms Kelly. Mar 2007
Webster, Mr Jeremy Nicolas. . . . . Sep 2009
Whitaker, Ms Charlotte Joanne . . . . Sep 2010
Yardley, Ms Michelle . . . . Oct 2011
Con: Davies, Mr Jonathan P MA(Oxon). . . . . *§Nov 1971

MENSONS & ASSOCIATES ‡
First Floor Left Side 99 Eltham High Street London SE9 1TD
Tel: 020 3145 3918 / 3917 *Fax:* 020 8331 6130
E-mail: mensonsassociates@googlemail.com

S MERALI SOLICITOR ADVOCATE ‡
27 Vincent Court Seymour Place Westminster London W1H 2ND
Tel: 020 7724 0508 *Fax:* 020 7723 4397
E-mail: shjmerali@btconnect.com
List of partners: S H J Merali
Languages: Gujarati, Kiswahili
Work: B1 C1 D1 E F1 J1 K1 K3 L N O P Q R1 S1 S2 W Z(f,g,i,p,q)
Agency and Advocacy undertaken
Ptr: Merali, Mr Salim H J BA ● . . . . *May 1981
Ast: Merali, Mr Aaron . . . . *Dec 2005

MERCHANT LEGAL LLP ‡
Aldermary House 10-15 Queen Street London EC4N 1TX
Tel: 020 7332 2251 *Fax:* 020 7681 2037
E-mail: info@merchantlegal.com
Office: New Malden

MERRIMAN WHITE ‡
(incorporating Messrs Wilson)
14 Tooks Court London EC4A 1LB
Tel: 020 7421 1900 *Fax:* 020 7421 1901
Dx: 1015 LONDON/CHANCERY LN
Languages: French, German
Work: C1 C2 C3 E F1 J1 K1 L M1 M2 N O P R1 S1 T1 T2 W Z(c,d,i,j,m)

CHARLES MIA LIMITED ‡
39-40 St James Place London SW1A 1NS
Tel: 020 7529 5848

MICHAEL & COMPANY ‡
75 Cottenham Park Road Merton London SW20 0DR
Tel: 020 8944 0877 *Fax:* 020 8947 0871
E-mail: michael@shpaizer.fsnet.co.uk
List of partners: M Shpaizer
Languages: French, Hebrew
Work: S1 S2 W
Ptr: Shpaizer, Mr Michael . . . . *Dec 1995

MICHAEL CONN GOLDSOBEL ‡
24 Queen Anne Street London W1G 9AX
Tel: 020 7580 8902 *Fax:* 020 7637 1074
Dx: 42725 OXFORD CIRCUS NORTH
E-mail: info@mcglex.co.uk
List of partners: S P Cohen, H Goldsobel, P J Levi, D Rose, J Waller
Languages: French, German, Hungarian
Work: A3 B1 C1 C2 E I J1 K1 K3 L N O Q R1 R2 S1 S2 T1 T2 W Z(c,e,q,s,za)
Agency and Advocacy undertaken
Ptr: Cohen, Mr Simon P MA(Oxon) . . . . *Nov 1983
Goldsobel, Mr Howard MBA. . . . . *May 1967
Levi, Mr Peter J. . . . . *Jun 1970
Rose, Mr David . . . . *Oct 1973
Waller, Mr Jamie BA . . . . *Dec 1997
Asoc: Gelb, Mr Sivan N MA; BSocSci . . . . *Sep 2006
Con: Goldenberg, Mr Philip MA(Oxon); FSALS Councillor for Woking Borough Council . . . . *Jun 1972

MICHAEL GERARD MCFALL ‡
37 Bennerley Road London SW11 6DR
Tel: 07801 413302 *Fax:* 020 7350 2070
E-mail: michaelgmcfall@aol.com

MICHEAL SEIFERT ‡
8-9 Frith Street London W1D 3JB
Tel: 020 3206 2700
E-mail: michaelseifertsolicitor@googlemail.com

MICHELMORES LLP
Clarges House 6-12 Clarges Street London W1J 8DH
Tel: 020 7659 7660 *Fax:* 020 7659 7661 *Dx:* 140549 PICCADILLY 5
E-mail: enquiries@michelmores.com
Office: Exeter, Sidmouth
Work: A3 B1 E L O Q R2 S1 S2 W Z(b)
Ptr: Elias, Mr Christopher Paul. . . . . *Nov 1977
Gribble, Mr Joe BA(Hons)(Econ); LPC; CPE. . . . . *Mar 1997
Maunder, Mr Charles LLB. . . . . *Oct 1995
Sigler, Mr Peter J BA(Hons)(Oxon) . . . . *Jun 1975
Whitfield, Mr Joseph BA(Hons) . . . . *Nov 1987

MILBANK TWEED HADLEY & MCCLOY ‡
10 Gresham Street London EC2V 7JD
Tel: 020 7615 3000 *Fax:* 020 7615 3100

MILES & PARTNERS ‡
88-90 Middlesex Street Tower Hamlets London E1 7EZ
Tel: 020 7426 0400 *Fax:* 020 7426 0100 *Dx:* 124407 LONDON/CITY
E-mail: office@milesandpartners.com
List of partners: H Al-Hassan, A Dench
Languages: Arabic, Bengali
Work: D1 D2 K1 K3 L Z(m)
Emergency Action, Agency, Advocacy and Legal Aid undertaken
Ptr: Al-Hassan, Mr Hayder. . . . . Sep 1991
Dench, Ms Amanda LLB . . . . Mar 1990
Ast: Bradley, Mrs Nova Jane LLB; BA . . . . *Nov 1990

ELIZABETH M MILLAR ‡
106 Highgate Hill London N6 5HE
Tel: 020 8348 3228 *Fax:* 020 8348 1614
List of partners: E M Millar
Languages: French, German, Russian
SPr: Millar, Ms Elizabeth M BA. . . . . *Jul 1978

MILLBANK SOLICITORS ‡
109-111 Farringdon Road London EC1R 3BW
Tel: 020 7100 1313 *Fax:* 020 7100 7029
E-mail: info@millbanksolicitors.co.uk

MILLER EVANS & CO ‡
1st Floor 19 Pepper Street Tower Hamlets London E14 9RP
Tel: 020 7987 2515 *Fax:* 020 7537 3573 *Dx:* 42654 ISLE OF DOGS
E-mail: askus@me-solicitors.co.uk
List of partners: C T Miller
Work: C1 E J1 Q R1 R2 S1 S2 W Z(l)
Fixed Fee Interview undertaken
SPr: Miller, Ms Charlotte Turnbull BA(Hons); CPE; LPC . *Nov 1986
Ast: Ifill, Miss Giselle LLB . . . . *Aug 2009
Khatun, Ms Minara . . . . *Nov 2010

MILLER LAW PRACTICE ‡
4a Topsfield Parade Crouch End Haringey London N8 8PR
Tel: 020 8340 2953 *Fax:* 020 8348 3494 *Dx:* 35957 CROUCH END
E-mail: info@millerlaw.co.uk
List of partners: G E P Miller
Languages: Czech
Work: C1 D1 E J1 K1 Q S1 S2 W
Advocacy, Fixed Fee Interview, Legal Aid undertaken and Legal Aid Franchise
SPr: Miller, Mr Geoffrey E P BSc; LLB; LLM . . . . *Dec 1977

PETER J MILLER ‡
53 Streathbourne Road Tooting Bec Wandsworth London SW17 8QZ
Tel: 0870 321 7561 *Fax:* 07010 707560
Emergency telephone 07010 707561
List of partners: P J Miller
Languages: French
Work: E L R1 R2 S1 S2 W Z(c,d)
SPr: Miller, Mr Peter John MA(Cantab) . . . . *§Jun 1975

See p2 for the Key to Work Categories & other symbols

MILLER ROSENFALCK ‡
Aylesbury House 17-18 Aylesbury Street London EC1R 0DB
Tel: 020 7553 9930 *Fax:* 020 7490 5060

STUART MILLER & CO ‡
247 High Road Wood Green Haringey London N22 8HF
Tel: 020 8888 5225 *Fax:* 020 8889 5871 *Dx:* 35654 WOOD GREEN 1
Emergency telephone 07980 000076
E-mail: stuartmiller@stuartmillersolicitors.co.uk
List of partners: G Kampanella, K Khushal, J Spicer, P Spicer
Languages: Greek
Work: G H Z(m)
Emergency Action, Agency, Advocacy, Legal Aid undertaken and Legal Aid Franchise
Ptr: Kampanella, Mr George. . . . . *Jan 2001
Khushal, Mr Kirit BA. . . . . Jan 2001
Spicer, Mr John . . . . Jan 2001
Spicer, Mr Philip LLB . . . . Jan 2001

ANDREW MILLET SOLICITOR ‡
24 Courthope Road London NW3 2LB
Tel: 020 7691 4327

MILLINGTON WALLACE & CO ‡
43 Chase Side Southgate London N14 5BP
Tel: 020 8882 1051 *Fax:* 020 8886 4232 *Dx:* 34303 SOUTHGATE
List of partners: R Barber, M E Palmer
Work: C1 E K1 L N S1 T1 W Z(o)
Agency, Advocacy undertaken and Member of Accident Line
Ptr: Barber, Mr Roger LLB. . . . . *Jun 1974
Palmer, Mrs Mary E. . . . . *Dec 1973
Asoc: Lawrence, Mr Ian R. . . . . *Feb 1976

MILLS & CO ‡
Westbourne House 14-16 Westbourne Grove London W2 5RH
Tel: 020 7313 5777 *Fax:* 020 7313 5788
E-mail: mail@millsandco.co.uk

MILLS & REEVE
Fountain House 130 Fenchurch Street London EC3M 5DJ
Tel: 020 7648 9220 *Fax:* 020 7648 9221 *Dx:* 152340 LIME STREET 4
Office: Birmingham, Cambridge, Leeds, Manchester, Norwich
Work: Z(j,q)
Ptr: Barrett, Mr Geoffrey S LLB(Lond) . . . . *Jan 1981
Driscoll, Mr Peter J LLB. . . . . *Sep 1982
Asoc: Davis, Mr Neil James Richard LLB . . . . Oct 1996
Ast: Graham, Miss Natalie BA(Law & Criminology). . . . . Sep 2001
Howes, Mr Neil LLB. . . . . Sep 1999
Stevenson, Mr Andrew BA(Hons)(History). . . . . . . Sep 1999

HENRY MILNER & CO ‡
County House 14 Hatton Garden London EC1N 8AT
Tel: 020 7831 9944 *Fax:* 020 7831 9941
Dx: 229 LONDON/CHANCERY LN
Emergency telephone 07774 671548 / 07850 494840
E-mail: law@henrymilner.co.uk
List of partners: H F Milner
Work: G H
Emergency Action, Advocacy and Legal Aid undertaken
Ptr: Milner, Mr Henry F LLB(Lond). . . . . *Jun 1975

MINAIDES ROBSON ‡
150 Fleet Street London EC4A 2DQ
Tel: 020 7831 7761 *Fax:* 020 7831 7485
List of partners: M G Minaides, K Onoufriou
Languages: Greek
Work: B1 C1 E F1 F2 J1 K1 L N O Q S1 S2 W Z(j,l)
Agency and Advocacy undertaken
Ptr: Minaides, Mr Marios G LLM. . . . . *Jun 1985
Onoufriou, Ms Kyriacou LLB(Hons) . . . . *Oct 1988

MINOGUE & CO ‡
6 Maldon Road London W3 6SU
Tel: 020 8752 0540 *Fax:* 020 8752 0540
Emergency telephone 07968 970101
E-mail: minogue@ukonline.co.uk
List of partners: M P Minogue
Work: B2 C1 F1 F2 G H Z(e)
Emergency Action undertaken
Ptr: Minogue, Mr Martin P LLB. . . . . *Jun 1990

MINTER ELLISON ‡
10 Dominion Street London EC2M 2EE
Tel: 020 7448 4800 *Fax:* 020 7448 4848
List of partners: N J Clark, S Farrands, M D Whalley
Work: C1 C2 C3 I J1 T1 T2 U2 Z(b)
Ptr: Clark, Mr Nigel Jeremy . . . . *Sep 1999
Farrands, Sam . . . . *Jul 1998
Whalley, Mr Michael Douglas LLB; BComm . . . . . *May 1979

MINTZ LEVIN COHN FERRIS GLOVSKY & POPEO LLP ‡
The Rectory 9 Ironmonger Lane London EC2V 8EY
Tel: 020 7726 4000 *Fax:* 020 7726 0055

MIRAMAR LEGAL ‡
Oakwood House 414-422 Hackney Road London E2 7SY
Tel: 020 3328 1600 *Fax:* 020 3328 1601
Dx: 40900 BETHNAL GREEN
E-mail: info@miramarlegal.co.uk

A A MIRSONS SOLICITORS LIMITED ‡
Ground Floor Temple Chambers Temple Avenue London EC4Y 0HP
Tel: 020 7822 2699 *Fax:* 0808 280 0990
E-mail: contact@aamirsons.com
Office: Leeds, London SE7

A A MIRSONS SOLICITORS LIMITED
1a The Village London SE7 8UG
Tel: 020 8856 5500 *Fax:* 020 8929 9880
Office: Leeds, London EC4

MIRZA & CO ‡
216a Hoe Street Walthamstow Waltham Forest London E17 3AY
Tel: 020 8520 4416 *Fax:* 020 8520 5617 *Dx:* 32038 WALTHAMSTOW
List of partners: M Y Mirza
Languages: Bengali, Pashto, Punjabi, Urdu
Work: G K1 V Z(i)
Agency, Advocacy, Legal Aid undertaken and Legal Aid Franchise
SPr: Mirza, Mr Mohammed Y. . . . . Jul 1992

MISHCON DE REYA ‡
Summit House 12 Red Lion Square London WC1R 4QD
Tel: 020 7440 7000 *Fax:* 020 7404 5982 *Dx:* 37954 KINGSWAY
E-mail: feedback@mishcon.co.uk
Languages: Afrikaans, Cantonese, Farsi, French, German, Hebrew, Hindi, Hungarian, Italian, Punjabi, Spanish
Work: B2 C1 C2 D2 E F2 J1 K1 L O Q R1 R2 S1 S2 T1 T2 U2 W Z(e,f,i,k,q,w)

CHRISTOPHER B MITCHELL ‡
9th Floor New Zealand House 80 Haymarket London SW1Y 4TQ
Tel: 020 7930 4944 *Fax:* 020 7930 4954
E-mail: christopher.michell@cbmitchell.co.uk

IAN MITCHELL SOLICITORS ‡
162 Stanstead Road Forest Hill London SE23 1BZ
Tel: 020 8291 9767

J P MITCHELL ‡
8 Sutton Court London W4 3JG
Tel: 020 8994 4565

P M MITCHELL ‡
5 Skipworth Road London E9 7JH
Tel: 020 8986 6934
E-mail: patmitchell@yahoo.com

MITCHELL SIMMONDS SOLICITORS ‡
Suite 3 80a Blackheath Road Greenwich London SE10 8DA
Tel: 020 8469 1441 *Fax:* 020 8469 1911
E-mail: info@mssolicitors.com

MITCHINERS ‡
31 Herne Hill London SE24 9NF
Tel: 020 8637 9165 *Fax:* 020 8637 9164
E-mail: info@mitchiners.com

MODSONS SOLICITORS ‡
City Business Centre 39 St Olav's Court Lower Road London SE16 2XB
Tel: 020 7237 4466 *Dx:* 85452 ROTHERHITHE

MOGHADASSI & ASSOCIATES ‡
18b Charles Street Mayfair London W1J 5DU
Tel: 020 7667 6555 *Fax:* 020 7691 9686
E-mail: london@moghadassi-associates.com

MOHABIRS ‡
11 Clapham Park Road Clapham London SW4 7EE
Tel: 020 7720 5742 / 7622 5495 *Fax:* 020 7498 0793
Dx: 53251 CLAPHAM COMMON
E-mail: info@mohabirs.com
List of partners: A H Mohabir, S S Mohabir, V R Salisbury
Languages: Armenian, Gujarati, Hindi, Russian, Urdu
Work: B2 D2 E G H K1 K3 S1 S2 W Z(l)
Emergency Action, Agency, Advocacy and Legal Aid undertaken
Ptr: Mohabir, Mr Annal H . . . . Nov 1987
Mohabir, Suneil S. . . . . May 1987
Salisbury, Ms Victoria R BA(Law) . . . . Mar 1985

M E MOLONEY & COMPANY ‡
Premier Business Centre 47-49 Park Royal Road Park Royal London NW10 7LQ
Tel: 020 8090 0449

M E MOLONEY & COMPANY ‡
Jubilee Business Centre Exeter Road London NW2 3UF
Tel: 020 7328 9521 *Fax:* 020 7625 1074
E-mail: memoloney@tiscali.co.uk

MONIORO LESS & CO ‡
4a The Works Bird In Hand Passage London SE23 3HJ
Tel: 020 8291 7657 *Fax:* 020 8291 7463 *Dx:* 34402 FOREST HILL
E-mail: eddie@monioroless.com

MONK & TURNER SOLICITORS LLP ‡
Unit 2 80a Ashfield Street London E1 2BJ
Tel: 020 7790 3772 *Fax:* 020 7790 0399
Dx: 155251 TOWER HAMLETS 2
E-mail: info@monkturner.co.uk

MONRO FISHER WASBROUGH LLP ‡
8 Great James Street Holborn London WC1N 3DF
Tel: 020 7404 7001 *Fax:* 020 7404 7002
Dx: 289 LONDON/CHANCERY LN
E-mail: law@monro-fisher.com
List of partners: N H Barlow, A J Clark, P N Hall, O G Meekin, D D C Monro, D Pow
Work: E J1 S1 T2 W Z(d)
Ptr: Barlow, Mr Nicholas H LLB(Exon); TEP . . . . *§Nov 1998
Clark, Ms Annabel J LLB . . . . *Dec 1986
Hall, Mr Paul N BA . . . . *§Dec 1975
Meekin, Miss Olivia Greer MA(Hons); TEP. . . . . . *Nov 2002
Monro, Mr David D C BA(Oxon). . . . . *Dec 1969
Pow, Mr David MA(Oxon) . . . . *§Dec 1974
Ast: Clapham, Mr Richard Alexander John PGDipLaw; LPC Nov 2007
Pickering, Mr Jeremy David PGDipLaw; LPC . . . . . Jun 2007
Con: Barrie Murray, Mr Gavin D BA; LLB(Cantab). . . . . *§Oct 1961
Evans, Mr Graham J LLB . . . . *§Jul 1970
Houghton, Mr J Adam C LLB . . . . *§Oct 1973
Turner, Mr Nicholas D MA(Cantab) . . . . *§Jun 1966
Wigmore, Mr Charles M BA(Exon). . . . . *§Nov 1971

MARY MONSON SOLICITORS LIMITED ‡
4th Floor 54 Fleet Street London EC4Y 1JU
Tel: 0161 794 0088 *Fax:* 020 7353 8233 *Dx:* 254 CHANCERY LANE
E-mail: info@marymonson.co.uk

MONTAGUE LAMBERT & CO ‡
37-38 Haven Green Ealing London W5 2NX
Tel: 020 8997 2288 *Fax:* 020 8991 9395 *Dx:* 5101 EALING
E-mail: mail@montaguelambert.com
List of partners: M D Cohen, R Cohen, T N Jenkins, C M Kidd, L A Thomas
Languages: French, Punjabi, Urdu
Work: B1 C1 D1 E F1 G H J1 K1 L N O P Q R1 R2 S1 S2 T1 U1 V W Z(c,d,e,h,i,k,l,m,o,p,r)
Agency, Advocacy, Fixed Fee Interview, Legal Aid undertaken and Member of Accident Line
Ptr: Cohen, Ms Marian D . . . . *Jan 1979
Cohen, Mr Robert. . . . . *Feb 1974
Jenkins, Mr Timothy N BA. . . . . *Oct 1980
Kidd, Mr C Michael . . . . *Jan 1969
Thomas, Miss Louise A . . . . *Feb 1991
Con: Arnold, Mr Simeon E LLB(Lond). . . . . *Jun 1958

MONTAGUE SOLICITORS ‡
201-202 Upper Street Islington London N1 1RQ
Tel: 020 7226 8238 *Fax:* 020 7226 6616
Dx: 122235 UPPER ISLINGTON
E-mail: info@montaguesolicitors.co.uk

MOORCROFT WILSON SOLICITORS ‡
9a Baynes Mews Hampstead London NW3 5BH
Tel: 020 7794 1771 *Fax:* 020 7794 2040
E-mail: info@moorcroftwilson.com

MOOREHOUSE SOLICITORS ‡
Sophia House 214-218 High Road Tottenham London N15 4NP
Tel: 020 8808 9212 *Fax:* 020 8808 5876
E-mail: mail@moorehouseslaw.co.uk

MOORHEAD JAMES LLP ‡
Kildare House 3 Dorset Rise London EC4Y 8EN
Tel: 020 7831 8888 *Fax:* 020 7936 3635
Dx: 288 LONDON/CHANCERY LN
E-mail: mail@moorheadjames.com
List of partners: J J H Bishop, C M Bowyer-Jones, D J James, B R K Moorhead, S A Simoes, E C L Wheen
Languages: Cantonese, French, German
Work: A3 B1 C1 C2 E J1 L O P Q R1 R2 S1 S2 Z(b,d,e,l,p,w,z,za)
Ptr: Bishop, Mr Julian J H . . . . *Dec 1979
Bowyer-Jones, Ms Christine M MA(Oxon). . . . . . . *Oct 1985
James, Mr David J LLB . . . . *Nov 1989
Moorhead, Mr Benedict R K BA. . . . . *Oct 1983
Simoes, Mr Stuart Anthony LLB(Hons) . . . . *Nov 1996
Wheen, Mr Edward C L BSc(Hons); DipL . . . . . . *Mar 1996
Asoc: Murray-Hinde, Miss Samantha Jane. . . . . *May 2008
Ast: Farrington, Ms Emma. . . . . *Aug 2009
Khan, Mr Raheel Badar. . . . . *Oct 2000
O'Maoileoin, Mr Michael Brendan BA; DipLaw. . . . . *Jan 2009
Con: Moorhead, Mrs Rachael W T BA(Law) . . . . *Oct 1982
Narraway, Mr Nicholas William . . . . *Oct 1982
Simon, Mr Richard Francis Jocelyn . . . . *Apr 1972
Sweet, Mr Robert LLM . . . . *Mar 1974

MORDI & CO SOLICITORS ‡
1st Floor 402 Holloway Road London N7 6PZ
Tel: 020 7619 9666 *Fax:* 020 7619 9676 *Dx:* 38655 HOLLOWAY
E-mail: info@mordiandco.com

MORE FISHER BROWN ‡
Fishmongers' Chambers 1 Fishmongers' Hall Wharf London EC4R 3AE
Tel: 020 7330 8000 *Fax:* 020 7256 6778
List of partners: A W Wright
Ptr: Wright, Mr Andrew W BA(Oxon). . . . . Dec 1988
Ast: Blaxell, Mr Stuart . . . . Jan 1994
Bruce, Miss Joanna LLB . . . . Nov 1992

MORELAND & CO SOLICITORS ‡
Moreland House 5 St Michael's Terrace Haringey London N22 7SJ
Tel: 020 8881 8833 *Fax:* 020 8881 7799
E-mail: dnd@morelandlaw.co.uk
List of partners: D Dionissiou, S Dionissiou
Languages: Greek
Work: B1 B2 C1 E G J1 K1 K3 L O Q S1 S2 W Z(i,p,q)
Agency undertaken
Ptr: Dionissiou, Mr Dionyssios. . . . . *Jan 2001
Dionissiou, Mrs Stavroulla BA(Hons) . . . . *Jan 2001
Ast: Karali, Miss Maria. . . . . *Feb 2008

MORGAN & MORGAN ‡
3rd Floor Meadows House 20 Queen Street London W1J 5PR
Tel: 020 7493 1978 *Fax:* 020 7493 1979
E-mail: morgan_morgan@btinternet.com
Languages: French, German, Italian, Japanese, Spanish
Work: M2 Z(a)

MORGAN BROWN & CAHILL SOLICITORS
Garrick House 26-27 Southampton Street Covent Garden London WC2E 7RS
Tel: 0845 303 7416
E-mail: info@mbcsolicitors.co.uk
Office: Manchester, Salford

L MORGAN & CO ‡
101 Tubbs Road Harlesden Brent London NW10 4QX
Tel: 020 8965 2850 *Fax:* 020 8965 2860 *Dx:* 57653 HARLESDEN
E-mail: lm@morgansols.com
List of partners: A O Fagade, L B Morgan
Work: L S1 S2
Ptr: Fagade, Mr A O. . . . . Mar 2000
Morgan, Ms Lorna B . . . . Apr 1997

MORGAN LEWIS & BOCKIUS ‡
Condor House 5-10 St Paul's Churchyard London EC4M 8AL
Tel: 020 3201 5000 *Fax:* 020 3201 5001
E-mail: info@morganlewis.com
List of partners: R Barratt, K Black, M Cashman, R Falkner, R A Goldspink, P Hardy, C Lubar, S Spencer, A Warnock-Smith
Languages: Afrikaans, French, German, Greek, Hindi, Italian, Kiswahili, Punjabi, Russian
Work: B1 B2 C1 C2 C3 E F1 F2 I J1 M1 M2 O P Q S1 T1 T2 Z(b,c,e,f,g,i,j,k,y,za)
Ptr: Barratt, Mr Richard . . . . *Jan 2004
Black, Mr Keith . . . . *Jan 2000
Cashman, Mr Michael BEc; LLB. . . . . *Sep 1991
Falkner, Mr Robert . . . . *Jan 2004
Goldspink, Mr Robert A . . . . *Jun 1975
Hardy, Mr Peter. . . . . *Jan 2004
Lubar, Mr Charles. . . . . Jan 1981
Spencer, Mr Simeon . . . . *Jan 1995
Warnock-Smith, Mr Anthony LLB(Hons). . . . . *Jun 1971

MORGAN REED SOLICITORS ‡
36 Spring Street Paddington London W2 1JA
Tel: 020 7402 9000 *Fax:* 020 7402 7888 *Dx:* 15717 PADDINGTON 9
E-mail: info@morganreed.co.uk

RICHARD C MORGAN ‡
10 Manor House Drive Brondesbury Park London NW6 7DF
Tel: 020 8459 0646 *Fax:* 020 8459 0646

E-mail: richardclivemorgan@hotmail.co.uk
List of partners: R C Morgan
Work: E S2 W
SPr: Morgan, Mr Richard Clive LLB . . . . *§Oct 1957

MORGAN ROSE SOLICITORS ‡
44-45 Chancery Lane London WC2A 1JB
Tel: 020 7242 2520 *Fax:* 020 7242 2530
Dx: 280 LONDON/CHANCERY LN

MORGAN WALKER ‡
115a Chancery Lane London WC2A 1PR
Tel: 020 7831 8333 *Fax:* 020 7831 9638
Dx: 424 LONDON/CHANCERY LN
E-mail: info@morganwalker.co.uk
List of partners: S Karmakar, A Sanchetti
Languages: Bengali, Burmese, Gujarati, Hindi, Japanese, Malayalam, Persian
Ptr: Karmakar, Mr Subir LLM . . . . *Jan 1991
Sanchetti, Ashok . . . . Feb 1999

MORGANS SOLICITORS ‡
108 Fenchurch Street London EC3M 5JR
Tel: 020 7481 1003 *Fax:* 020 7481 1004
E-mail: info@morgans-law.com

BEVERLEY MORRIS & CO ‡
35 Montpelier Vale Blackheath Village Lewisham London SE3 0TJ
Tel: 020 8852 4433 *Fax:* 020 8463 9494
E-mail: enquiries@beverleymorris.co.uk
List of partners: B M Morris, A M Stanton
Office: London EC4, London SE13
Ptr: Morris, Miss Beverley M LLB . . . . *Jul 1980
Stanton, Ms Angela M LLB . . . . *Mar 1980

BEVERLEY MORRIS & CO
Hamilton House 1 Temple Avenue London EC4Y 0HA
Tel: 020 8852 4433 *Fax:* 020 8463 9494
E-mail: enquiries@beverleymorris.co.uk
Office: London SE13, London SE3
Work: J1 O Q
Fixed Fee Interview undertaken

BEVERLEY MORRIS & CO (incorporating Peter Egan & Co)
62 High Street Lewisham London SE13 5JH
Tel: 020 8852 4433 *Fax:* 020 8463 9494
E-mail: enquiries@beverleymorris.co.uk
Office: London EC4, London SE3

MARK MORRIS SOLICITORS ‡
42-44 Bishopsgate London EC2N 4AJ
Tel: 020 7274 8155 *Fax:* 020 7374 6335
E-mail: mmorris@mark-morris.co.uk

N C MORRIS & CO ‡
1 Montpelier Street London SW7 1EX
Tel: 020 7584 8764 *Fax:* 020 7589 8342
Dx: 38176 KNIGHTSBRIDGE
E-mail: nick.morris@ncmorris.co.uk
List of partners: C R R Joly, F S Malan, N C Morris
Office: Salisbury
Work: E F1 L S1 S2 W
Agency undertaken
Ptr: Malan, Mr Francois S BCom; LLB(Cape Town) . . . . *Jul 1980
Morris, Mr Nicholas Charles MA(Oxon) . . . . *Nov 1972
Ast: Chen, Miss Shou Mung BSc(Hons); LLB(Hons) . . . . Jun 1998

NICHOLAS MORRIS ‡
24b Notting Hill Gate London W11 3JE
Tel: 020 7792 0890 *Fax:* 020 7792 0990
Dx: 94210 NOTTING HILL GATE
E-mail: mail@nicholasmorris.co.uk
List of partners: G d M Davies
Work: B1 E K1 O Q R1 S1 W Z(k)
SPr: Davies, Mr Geoffrey de M. . . . . *§Mar 1963

MORRISON & FOERSTER (UK) LLP ‡
Citypoint One Ropemaker Street London EC2Y 9AW
Tel: 020 7920 4000 *Fax:* 020 7496 8500
E-mail: info@mofo.com
List of partners: B Bates, A Bevitt, C Coulter, P J Green, E M Hahn, T James, J Jennings-Mares, D Leventhal, E Lukins, A Maughan, A Owens, K Roberts, J P Thurston, J Wheeler, K Wiggert
Languages: French, German, Irish, Italian, Portuguese, Russian, Spanish
Work: C1 C2 F1 I J1 M1 O T1 U1 U2 Z(b,e,f,p,za)
Ptr: Bates, Mr Brian JD(Notre Dame) . . . . Jan 1987
Bevitt, Ms Ann MA(Oxon) ♦ . . . . *Jul 2000
Coulter, Mr Chris BA(Oxon); LPC . . . . *Dec 1992
Green, Mr Peter J LLB(Leics) . . . . *Nov 1991
Hahn, Elana Maian . . . . Oct 2002
James, Mr Trevor LLB(Essex) Price Waterhouse International Tax Prize . . . . *Oct 1989
Jennings-Mares, Mr Jeremy LLB(Nott'm) . . . . . . *May 1993
Leventhal, Mr Daniel . . . . Oct 2010
Lukins, Mr Ed. . . . . *Jan 1992
Maughan, Mr Alistair LLB . . . . *Sep 1987
Owens, Mr Alan. . . . . *Jan 1997
Roberts, Mr Kevin. . . . . *Jan 1995
Thurston, Mr Julian P MA(Oxon) . . . . *May 1979
Wheeler, Mr Jonathan BA(Hons) . . . . *Nov 1994
Wiggert, Mr Kristian JD(Harv) . . . . *Nov 2000
Asoc: Adams, Mr John Robert LLB . . . . Sep 2004
Beirne, Keily Helen BA; LPC . . . . Sep 2007
Christie, Mr Nimesh BA . . . . Sep 2010
Crotty, Mr Andrew BA . . . . Sep 2007
Girgis, Sonia BBus; LLB. . . . . Mar 2009
Lee, Mr Lewis BSc(Hons) . . . . Sep 2005
Lloyd, James William BSc; LLB; GDL; LPC . . . . . . Dec 2009
McGrath, Miss Sophie BCom; LLB; GDL; QLTT . . . . *Jan 2004
McLean, Ms Susan LLB(Leeds); LPC . . . . *Sep 2000
Moynihan, Ms Deirdre BCL; LLM . . . . Nov 2007
Nagle, Mr Anthony LLB(TVU); LPC . . . . *Sep 1999
Reid, Mr Charlie BA(Newc); LPC . . . . *Sep 2003
Roughton, Mr Timothy James MEng(Oxon); LPC; CPE . . . . *Sep 1999
Ryan, Mr James BSc; PhD; GDL; LPC . . . . *Sep 2004
Stakim, Ms Caroline LLB(Hons). . . . . *Jan 2010
Stucchi, Mr Andrea LLM. . . . . *Nov 2007

MORRISON SPOWART ‡
191-193 Rushey Green Road Catford London SE6 4BD
Tel: 020 8698 9200 *Fax:* 020 8698 9290 *Dx:* 34382 CATFORD
Emergency telephone 020 8461 9016 (Crime only)
List of partners: J Morrison, A Spowart
Languages: French
Work: D1 D2 G H K1 K3 K4 L W Z(g,h,u)
Emergency Action, Fixed Fee Interview and Legal Aid undertaken
Ptr: Morrison, Ms Jennifer. . . . . Oct 1995
Spowart, Ms Anne . . . . Mar 1996

MORRISONS SOLICITORS LLP
5th Floor Sterling House 6-10 St Georges Road London SW19 4DP
Tel: 020 8971 1020 *Fax:* 020 8971 1021
Dx: 300102 WIMBLEDON CENTRAL
E-mail: info@morrlaw.com
Office: Camberley, Redhill, Woking
Languages: French
Work: B1 C1 C2 D1 E F1 G J1 K1 L M1 N P R1 S1 S2 W Z(b,i,m)
Ptr: Gravell, Mr Roger J B BA . . . . *Apr 1980
Harvey, Mr Paul A E LLB . . . . *Sep 1983
Martin, Mr Malcolm BA(Hons); MCIArb . . . . *Apr 1981
Asoc: Fisher, Mrs Rebecca . . . . *Sep 2005
Knights, Mr Michael. . . . . *Apr 2004
Williams-Jauvel, Mrs Kellie . . . . *Oct 2004
Con: Lavington, Mr Peregrine. . . . . *Feb 1989

MORTON FRASER LLP ‡
St Martins House 16 St Martin's Le Grand London EC1A 4EN
Tel: 020 7397 8621 *Fax:* 020 7397 8400
E-mail: infodesk@morton-fraser.com

MORTON PUGH WELCH ‡
65 London Wall London EC2M 5TU
Tel: 020 7374 4141 *Fax:* 020 7374 6161
Dx: 33877 FINSBURY SQUARE
E-mail: mpw@mpwlaw.co.uk
List of partners: D M Davies, C Pugh, M J Welch
Work: A3 B1 C1 C2 E F1 F2 G J1 J2 L N O Q S1 S2 W X Z(c,e,k,l,p,q,r)
Emergency Action and Agency undertaken
Ptr: Davies, Mr David Michael . . . . *Dec 1992
Pugh, Mr Crispin . . . . *Dec 1977
Welch, Mr Martin J . . . . *Dec 1987

MOSS & CO ‡
17 Lower Clapton Road Hackney London E5 0NS
Tel: 020 8986 8336 *Fax:* 020 8985 6608 *Dx:* 35460 HACKNEY
E-mail: info@mosslaw.co.uk
Languages: Punjabi
Work: B2 G H L Q V
Legal Aid undertaken

MOSS BEACHLEY MULLEM & COLEMAN ‡
37 Crawford Street Westminster London W1H 1HA
Tel: 020 7402 1401 / 7723 5783 *Fax:* 020 7224 8143
Dx: 141950 MARYLEBONE 5
List of partners: I K Beachley, A J Mullem
Languages: Arabic
Work: B1 C1 D1 E F1 G H J1 K1 L M1 M2 N P Q S1 V W Z(d,i,m,q,r)
Emergency Action, Agency, Advocacy, Fixed Fee Interview, Legal Aid undertaken and Legal Aid Franchise
Ptr: Beachley, Mr Ian K LLB(Melbourne); BSc(Lond). . . . *Jun 1971
Mullem, Mr Alan J BA. . . . . *Oct 1982
Ast: Penfold, Mr Stephen Denis LLB. . . . . Oct 1995

MOTOR INDUSTRY LEGAL SERVICES ‡
27b The Mansions 252 Old Brompton Road London SW5 9HW
Tel: 020 7244 6790 *Fax:* 020 7244 7139
Dx: 132857 WEST KENSINGTON 3
E-mail: legal@mils.co.uk
Office: Exeter

MOUNTAIN PARTNERSHIP ‡
143 New Cross Road Lewisham London SE14 5DJ
Tel: 020 7732 3737 *Fax:* 020 7732 6999 *Dx:* 34265 PECKHAM
Emergency telephone 07939 003259
E-mail: admin@mountainpartnership.co.uk
List of partners: O O Okenla, K Siaw
Languages: Arabic, Chinese, Igbo, Kurdish, Mandarin, Russian, Yoruba
Work: G H J1 L N Q S1 S2 V W Z(i)
Fixed Fee Interview, Legal Aid undertaken and Legal Aid Franchise
Ptr: Okenla, Olufemi O LLB(Hons). . . . . Jul 2000
Siaw, Kwame LLB. . . . . Sep 2002

MR LAWS SOLICITORS ‡
180 Mitcham Road Tooting Wandsworth London SW17 9NP
Tel: 020 8767 9717 / 8672 3447 *Fax:* 020 8767 9684
Dx: 58860 TOOTING SOUTH
E-mail: info@mrlaws-solicitors.com
List of partners: R Manoharan
Languages: Chinese, Polish, Sinhalese, Tamil
Work: B1 B2 F1 F2 G K1 K3 L N O Q S1 S2 Z(i,l)
Legal Aid undertaken and Legal Aid Franchise
Ptr: Manoharan, Rajadurai ★ . . . . Apr 1985

ELIZABETH MUIRHEAD SOLICITORS ‡
50 Essex Street London WC2R 3JF
Tel: 020 7936 4445 *Fax:* 020 7583 8586 *Dx:* 37952 KINGSWAY
E-mail: em@emulaw.com
List of partners: E M Muirhead
Languages: French
Work: K1 K2 K3
Agency and Advocacy undertaken
Ptr: Muirhead, Mrs Elizabeth Margaret LLB(Called to Bar in Australia; March 1967) . . . . *Jun 1971
Con: Bonnaillie-Valmorin, Mrs Francoise . . . . Apr 2009
Wells, Ms Stephanie BA; LLB; BVC . . . . *Jan 2001

MULBERRYS EMPLOYMENT LAW SOLICITORS ‡
1 Warwick Row London SW1E 5ER
Tel: 020 7808 7180 *Fax:* 020 7808 7100
E-mail: info@mulberryssolicitors.com
Office: Brighton

MUNRO SOLICITORS ‡
19 Woodgrange Road Forest Gate London E7 8BA
Tel: 020 8503 1718 *Fax:* 020 8503 0990 *Dx:* 52105 FOREST GATE
List of partners: A Farquhar, S Mahmood, E C Munro
Office: Woodford
Work: D1
Legal Aid undertaken
Ptr: Farquhar, Mr Alastair LLB ♦. . . . . *Jul 1996
Mahmood, Ms Sabina LLB ♦ . . . . *Oct 1994
Munro, Mr E Craig BA ♦. . . . . *Aug 1983

MURDOCHS ‡
45 High Street Wanstead Waltham Forest London E11 2AA
Tel: 020 8530 7291 *Fax:* 020 8530 8473 *Dx:* 52550 WANSTEAD
Emergency telephone 07626 260628
Work: B1 B2 B3 C1 E G J1 K1 L M3 N O Q S1 S2 W Z(l,q)

MURRAY ARMSTRONG SOLICITORS ‡
2nd Floor Berkeley Square House London W1X 6EA
Tel: 020 7887 6040 *Fax:* 020 7887 6460
E-mail: jmurray@ftech.co.uk

C M MURRAY ‡
Level 37 One Canada Square Canary Wharf London E14 5AA
Tel: 020 7718 0090 *Fax:* 020 7718 0091
E-mail: info@cm-murray.com

MURRAY HAY SOLICITORS ‡
159 High Street Putney London SW15 1RT
Tel: 020 8780 1225 *Fax:* 020 8780 1358 *Dx:* 59475 PUTNEY
E-mail: info@murrayhay.co.uk
List of partners: I D Hay, C P Murray
Work: C1 E J1 L S1 S2 W
Agency, Fixed Fee Interview and Legal Aid undertaken
Ptr: Hay, Mr Ian D. *Jan 1985
Murray, Mr Colum P LLB . . . . Apr 1979
Ast: Ash, Mrs Susan. . . . . Jan 1985
Con: Fox, Mr John Robert Crosby MA(Oxon) . . . . *Nov 1985

MURRAYS PARTNERSHIP ‡
94-96 Walworth Road Southwark London SE1 6SW
Tel: 020 7701 8653 *Fax:* 020 7708 1469 *Dx:* 133245 WALWORTH
Emergency telephone 020 7701 8653
E-mail: admin@murrayspartnership.co.uk
List of partners: A Guthberlet, G Heathcote
Work: G H
Legal Aid undertaken
Ptr: Guthberlet, Ms Annette . . . . *Nov 1990
Heathcote, Ms Gillian LLB. . . . . *Nov 1984
Ast: Burtwell, Mr Duncan Peter. . . . . Nov 2004
Rushby, Ms Rachel LLB(Hons) . . . . Apr 2004
Snell, Ms Helen LLB . . . . Mar 1993
Con: Balmain, Ms Louise A. . . . . Sep 1984

WARREN MURTON ‡
23 Bedford Row London WC1R 4EB
Tel: 020 7404 5511 *Fax:* 020 7404 1698
Dx: 925 LONDON/CHANCERY LN
E-mail: christopherlewis@warrenmurton.co.uk
List of partners: C J Lewis, C J G Lewis, R C Lewis
Work: B1 C1 C2 C3 E F1 F2 J1 L O Q S1 S2 T1 T2 W Z(c,d,e,f,i,k,l,m,p,t,w)
Agency and Advocacy undertaken
Ptr: Lewis, Mr Christopher J BA(Essex) . . . . *Oct 1990
Lewis, Mr Clive J G MA; LLM(Cantab) Clabon Prize. . *Oct 1959
Lewis, Mr Richard Clive BA(Surrey) . . . . *Jun 1994

MUSCATT WALKER HAYIM ‡
Speen House Porter Street London W1U 6WH
Tel: 020 7486 5131 *Fax:* 020 7935 8423 *Dx:* 41736 MARYLEBONE 2
E-mail: admin@muscattwalkerhayim.co.uk
List of partners: Y Addy, B Hayim, I J Pringle
Languages: Arabic, French, Hebrew, Italian, Mandarin
Work: A1 B1 C1 C2 E F1 G H J1 K1 L N O Q R1 S1 W Z(i,j,l)
Advocacy and Legal Aid undertaken
Ptr: Addy, Ms Yvonne LLB; LLM. . . . . *May 1996
Hayim, Mr Bruce LLB . . . . *Oct 1978
Pringle, Mr Ian J BA. . . . . *Nov 1989

MYERS FLETCHER & GORDON ‡
15 Cambridge Court 210 Shepherds Bush Road Hammersmith London W6 7NJ
Tel: 020 7610 4433 *Fax:* 020 7610 4455
Dx: 46761 HAMMERSMITH 3
E-mail: mfg@mfglon.co.uk
List of partners: J J Bayer, L J Crawford, G M Duke-Cohan, H Ebner, C J Edwards, B Levy, N Levy, D Pine-McLarty, M Toohig
Work: B1 C1 C2 E F1 J1 L M2 N O Q R2 S1 S2 T1 T2 W Z(b,e,f,i,j,k,l,p,q,w)
Emergency Action, Agency and Fixed Fee Interview undertaken
Ptr: Bayer, Mr John Jacob BA(Hons); CPE . . . . *Nov 1995
Crawford, Mr Lawson John LLB; LLM . . . . *Oct 2002
Duke-Cohan, Mr Gary M BA; Dip French Law. . . . *Nov 1988
Ebner, Mr Henry LLB . . . . *Oct 1961
Edwards, Mr Charles J LLB . . . . *Jul 1974
Levy, Mr Bruce LLB; LLM; Admitted in New York and Jamaica . . . . *Nov 1995
Levy, Mr Noel. *Nov 1979
Pine-McLarty, Mrs Dorothy . . . . *Dec 1995
Toohig, Mr Michael . . . . *Dec 1990
Asoc: Brooks, Ms Valda LLB. . . . . *Apr 1992
Grant, Mr Tyrone LLB. . . . . *Nov 1996
Harrison, Miss Merlene Lysia LLB(Hons) . . . . . . *Dec 2002
Hollins, Miss Lorraine . . . . *Feb 2006
Stylianou, Miss Helena LLB(Hons) . . . . *Sep 2005

JOSEPH MYNAH ‡
Unit 54 Grove Business Centre London N17 9TA
Tel: 020 8365 9940

JOSEPH MYNAH & CO SOLICITORS ‡
2nd Floor 73 Farringdon Road London EC1M 3JQ
Tel: 020 7430 9696

NCTM LLP ‡
St Michaels House 1 George Yard Lombard Street London EC3V 9DF
Tel: 020 7375 9900 *Fax:* 020 7929 6468
E-mail: infolondon@nctm.it

NUT SOLICITORS ‡
Hamilton House Mabledon Place London WC1H 9BD
Tel: 020 7380 4734 *Fax:* 020 7388 6226
List of partners: C O Romain
Dir: Romain, Mr Clive O. . . . . Mar 1985

See p2 for the Key to Work Categories & other symbols

Particular areas of work include: Employment Law, Accidents, Injury, Criminal Injury Com, Education Law, Pensions, Race and Sex Discrimination. In house solicitors for National Union of Teachers.

NWL SOLICITORS ‡
287-289 West End Lane London NW6 1RE
Tel: 020 7435 9624 *Fax:* 020 7431 5475
Dx: 53656 WEST HAMPSTEAD
E-mail: enquiries@nwlsolicitors.co.uk

NABARRO LLP ‡
(in association with Cabinet Lipworth France; Livasin & Co Hong Kong; Key & Dixon Dubai)
Lacon House 84 Theobalds Road London WC1X 8RW
Tel: 020 7524 6000 *Fax:* 020 7524 6524
Dx: 77 LONDON/CHANCERY LN
List of partners: J Blackwell, G Butera, M J Cant, R G Clarke, N J Collins, J Cumpson, J E Dakin, K L Denny, G C Dixon, C G Dray, S Fitzsimons, P C Ford, P E Godfrey, P Goodwill, M S Grabiner, M G Hales, D J Hawkins, G W Heath, A K Howard, K C B Hutcheson, A P Inkester, S Johnston, G W Jones, M J Kemp, D J Lloyd, G N Logan, M P Logan, G Lubega, C A Luck, J Marshall, S J McKenna, A P McLean, C K Mehta, P J Moore, G S Muir, I B Newman, P H Olmer, N E Paradise, D S Parry, N Pointon, K W Pugh, M Renger, J M Rickard, T J Shaw, J Snape, S A Staite, C Stanwell, K Stimpson, G D Taylor, I P H Travers, N Vergette, J D Warne, G Watkins, A Wigfall, R Williams, A Wright
Office: Sheffield
Languages: Afrikaans, Chinese, French, German, Hebrew, Italian, Polish, Portuguese, Russian
Work: A1 A3 B1 C1 C2 C3 E F1 F2 I J1 J2 L M1 M3 N O P Q R1 R2 S1 S2 T1 T2 U1 W Z(b,c,d,e,f,g,h,i,j,k,l,n,o,p,q,r,s,u,w)
Ptr: Butera, Gerlando BA(Oxon) . . . Nov 1982
Cant, Mr Michael J BA . . . *Jul 1984
Collins, Mr Nicholas J LLB . . . Jun 1989
Cumpson, Mr John . . . Oct 1991
Dakin, Mr James Edwin BA . . . *Sep 1992
Denny, Ms Karen L . . . Oct 1990
Dixon, Mr Giles C MA(Oxon) . . . *Jan 1968
Ford, Mr Peter C . . . Jun 1988
Godfrey, Miss Patricia E LLB . . . *§Oct 1986
Hales, Mr Michael G LLB(Lond) . . . Apr 1988
Hawkins, Mr David J LLB(Lond) . . . *Jul 1967
Heath, Mr Guy W LLB(Lond) . . . *Oct 1989
Howard, Ms Amanda K . . . *Oct 1988
Hutcheson, Mr Keith C B MA(Cantab) . . . Jan 1978
Inkester, Mr Andrew P LLB(Lond); ATII . . . *Apr 1980
Johnston, Mr Simon . . . *Oct 1989
Jones, Mr Gareth W MA(Cantab) . . . *Jun 1980
Kemp, Mrs Margaret J LLB(Bris) . . . *Apr 1968
Lloyd, Ms Deborah J BA(Manc) . . . *Nov 1985
Logan, Mr Michael P LLB . . . Oct 1986
Lubega, Mr George LLB(Cantab) . . . *Sep 1994
Luck, Mr Christopher A LLB . . . *Jan 1983
McLean, Mr Andrew P LLB . . . *Nov 1986
Marshall, Ms Joanna . . . May 1985
Mehta, Mr Cyrus K MA . . . *Dec 1985
Moore, Miss Penelope J LLB; MA . . . *Oct 1985
Muir, Mr Graham S BA(Cantab) . . . Nov 1988
Newman, Mr Iain B . . . Nov 1992
Olmer, Mr Philip H BA(Lond Poly) . . . *Dec 1985
Paradise, Miss Nicole E LLB(Lond) . . . *Jun 1983
Parry, Ms Deborah S BA . . . *Oct 1985
Rickard, Ms Jennifer M LLB . . . *Oct 1983
Snape, Mr James . . . Sep 2000
Staite, Mr Simon A BA(Oxon) . . . *Nov 1983
Stanwell, Mr Christopher . . . Oct 2001
Stimpson, Mr Kevin LLB . . . *Apr 1980
Taylor, Mr Glyn D MA(Oxon); LLB . . . *Oct 1987
Travers, Mr Iain P H BA . . . *Dec 1977
Vergette, Mr Nicholas . . . Oct 1989
Warne, Mr Jonathan D LLB(Reading) . . . *Oct 1987
Wigfall, Mr Andrew LLB; AKC . . . *Oct 1986
Wright, Miss Ann MA . . . Oct 1983
Asoc: Dad, Sima . . . Sep 2008
Lewis, Ms Janet . . . Sep 2003
Santer, Mr William . . . Jan 2004
Turner, Ms Claire . . . Sep 2006
Wood, Mr Nicholas LLB(Hons) . . . May 2003
Ast: Moore, Miss Penelope J LLB; MA . . . *Oct 1985

NAG & CO SOLICITORS ‡
Unit 3 Holles House Myatts Fields South London SW9 7JN
Tel: 020 7737 1211 *Fax:* 020 7737 1431 *Dx:* 58768 BRIXTON
Emergency telephone 07958 708570
List of partners: S Vilvaraj
Languages: French, Gujarati, Hindi, Konkani, Punjabi, Sinhalese, Spanish, Tamil
Work: B2 E F1 G J1 L S1 S2 T2 V Z(p)
Emergency Action, Fixed Fee Interview, Legal Aid undertaken and Legal Aid Franchise
SPr: Vilvaraj, Mrs Sushila . . . *Nov 1992

NAHLIS CHRISTOU ‡
243 Gray's Inn Road London WC1X 8RB
Tel: 020 7278 6888 *Fax:* 020 7278 1727 *Dx:* 37916 KINGS CROSS
E-mail: ncenquiries@aol.com
List of partners: C H Christou, A Nahlis
Languages: German, Greek
Work: C1 E L S1 W Z(l)
Ptr: Christou, Mr Christopher Herman LLB . . . *Oct 1991
Nahlis, Mr Andrew MA(Cantab) . . . *Nov 1974

NANDY & CO ‡
62 Woodgrange Road Forest Gate Newham London E7 0QH
Tel: 020 8536 1800 *Fax:* 020 8536 1900
E-mail: nandy@lineone.net
List of partners: N R Welivitigodage
Languages: Bengali, Gujarati, Punjabi, Sinhalese, Tamil
Work: D2 F1 F2 K1 K3 L O Q V Z(g,i,p)
Agency, Fixed Fee Interview, Legal Aid undertaken and Legal Aid Franchise
Ptr: Welivitigodage, Mrs Nanda R LLB ♦ . . . *Jun 1990
Asoc: Methuen, Samarasingher LLB; MSc ♦ . . . *§Jan 1985
Ast: Singh, Mr Gurmack ♦ . . . *Apr 2003

NASIM & CO SOLICITORS ‡
First Floor 52a Upton Lane Forest Gate London E7 9LN
Tel: 020 8552 8612 *Fax:* 020 8552 4445

NASIR & CO LAW FIRM ‡
Ground Floor South 14 Old Square Lincoln's Inn London WC2A 3UE
Tel: 020 7405 3818 *Fax:* 020 7831 1971
Dx: 153 LONDON/CHANCERY LN
E-mail: colinnasir@nasirlegal.co.uk
List of partners: C Nasir
Languages: Arabic, French
Work: A3 C1 E J1 M2 O S1 S2 Z(e)
SPr: Nasir, Mr Colin . . . *Apr 1997

NAT JEN SOYEGE SOLICITORS ‡
35 Waverley Road London E17 3LG
Tel: 020 8509 8543 *Fax:* 020 8509 8543
E-mail: adesoyegemnj@yahoo.com

NATADO SOLICITORS ‡
55 Deptford Broadway London SE8 4PH
Tel: 020 8691 9700 *Fax:* 020 8691 9701
E-mail: advice@natado.co.uk

NATHAN AARON SOLICITORS ‡
66 Brownhill Road Catford London SE6 2EW
Tel: 020 8695 0135 / 07940 356453 *Fax:* 020 8461 4118
E-mail: info@nathanaaronsolicitors.com

NATHAN & CO ‡
106 Kingston Road Wimbledon London SW19 1LX
Tel: 020 8542 1805 *Fax:* 020 8540 9773
Emergency telephone 020 8542 1805
E-mail: nathanandcosw19@gmail.com
List of partners: M Arunothayam, V S Shanmuganathan, S Sivadasan
Languages: German, Sinhalese, Tamil
Work: E G L P S1 Z(b)
Emergency Action, Advocacy, Fixed Fee Interview and Legal Aid undertaken
Ptr: Arunothayam, Mangayatkarasi LLB . . . Jun 1988
Shanmuganathan, V Sri . . . *May 1983
Sivadasan, Sivasamy . . . Apr 1988
Ast: Jayatilaka, Yoshan G . . . Nov 1986

NATHANIEL & CO ‡
422 Kingsland Road Hackney London E8 4AA
Tel: 020 7923 0500 *Fax:* 020 7249 2650 *Dx:* 48616 DALSTON

NATHENE & CO ‡
(in association with Maitre Hubert Couteau(Paris))
7 Redington Road Hampstead London NW3 7QX
Tel: 020 7431 5020 *Fax:* 020 7794 2942 *Dx:* 57556 HAMPSTEAD 1
E-mail: nathene@nathenesolicitors.co.uk
List of partners: N A Arnaoutis
Languages: Afrikaans, French, Greek, Italian
Work: E M1 M2 S1 S2 W Z(g,i)
SPr: Arnaoutis, Mrs Nathene Adele BA; BEd . . . *Oct 1979

NAUTADUTILH ‡
Bowman House 29 Wilson Street London EC2M 2SJ
Tel: 020 7786 9100 *Fax:* 020 7588 6888
E-mail: ndlondon@nautadutilh.com
Languages: Dutch, German
Work: B1 C1 Z(b)

NED NWOKO ‡
2 Beaufort Road Ealing London W5 3EA
Tel: 020 8997 6733 *Fax:* 020 8998 9334
Emergency telephone 07725 572584
E-mail: nednwoko@aol.com
List of partners: L Nwoko
Work: B1 C1 D1 D2 E F1 G H J1 K1 L N O Q R1 S1 S2 V W Z(i,j,l,p)
Emergency Action, Agency, Advocacy and Fixed Fee Interview undertaken
Ptr: Nwoko, Ms Lillian . . . Mar 1997

NEEDHAM POULIER & PARTNERS ‡
599 High Road London N17 6EW
Tel: 020 8808 6622 *Fax:* 020 8808 3311 *Dx:* 52205 TOTTENHAM 2
Emergency telephone 020 8808 6622
E-mail: lawyer@needhampoulier.co.uk
List of partners: L J Blizard, J M Chambers, N Hopkins, E L Needham, S S R Poulier
Work: G H Z(m)
Emergency Action, Agency, Advocacy, Legal Aid undertaken and Legal Aid Franchise
Ptr: Blizard, Ms Lindsey Jane LLB . . . *Oct 1998
Chambers, Ms Joanne Margaret LLB . . . *Mar 1996
Hopkins, Mr Nicholas BA(Oxon) . . . *Mar 1998
Needham, Ms Elaine L ★ . . . *Dec 1991
Poulier, Mr Sean S R ★ . . . *Sep 1992
Ast: Ali, Miss Leila CPE; LPC . . . Mar 2009
Evans, Ms Rachel LLB . . . Dec 2009
Hill, Miss Rebecca Louisa BA(Hons) . . . *Jan 2009
O'Brien, Miss Nijole LLB . . . Oct 2009
Patel, Miss Amita LLB . . . *Mar 2005
Sargeant, Ms Liz . . . *Feb 1992
Con: Barker, Miss Maxine C LLB(Hons) . . . *Oct 1986
Hydari, Mr Graeme BA(Hons)(Law) ★ . . . *Jun 1984

ALEXANDER NEIL ‡
359a Caledonian Road London N7 9DQ
Tel: 020 7609 8000 *Fax:* 020 7697 9000

NEIL WILLIAM BIGGS ‡
40 South Hill Park London NW3 2SJ
Tel: 020 7794 4659
E-mail: neilbiggsnotarial@googlemail.com

WILLIAM NELHAMS ‡
711 Finchley Road London NW2 5JN
Tel: 020 8458 8044

NELLEN ‡
19 Albemarle Street Westminster London W1S 4HS
Tel: 020 7499 8122 *Fax:* 020 7493 0146
E-mail: info@nellen.co.uk
List of partners: G A L Nellen
Languages: French
Work: C1 C2
Ptr: Nellen, Mr Gideon A L BA . . . *Oct 1978

NELSONS ‡
The Hub 9 Bell Yard Mews London SE1 3UY
Tel: 020 7403 4000 *Fax:* 020 7089 5000 *Dx:* 80703 BERMONDSEY
List of partners: R P Cowie, G Joseph
Languages: Spanish
Work: C1 C2 E J1 L N R1 S1 S2 Z(c)
Ptr: Cowie, Mr Roy P . . . Dec 1988
Joseph, Mr Gary . . . Jun 2001

NEUMANS LLP ‡
Ocean House 10-12 Little Trinity Lane London EC4V 2AR
Tel: 020 7429 3900 *Fax:* 020 7429 3901 *Dx:* 490 CHANCERY LANE
E-mail: mail@neumansllp.com

JOHN NEVILLE & CO ‡
135-143 Stockwell Road London SW9 9TN
Tel: 020 3372 4071 *Fax:* 020 7183 6858 *Dx:* 37055 KENNINGTON 3
List of partners: J N Singh
Work: B1 J1 K1 Q Z(p)
SPr: Singh, Mr John Neville LLB; FCCA; AMBIM . . . Nov 1981

NEW MEDIA LAW LLP ‡
102 Dean Street London W1D 3TQ
Tel: 020 7734 9777

ROBERT NEWEY & CO ‡
3 More London Riverside London SE1 2RE
Tel: 020 7407 9434 *Fax:* 020 3137 5525
E-mail: info@robertnewey.com
List of partners: R H J Newey
Languages: French, German
Work: C1 T1 T2
SPr: Newey, Mr Robert H J MA; LLB(Cantab) . . . *Oct 1982

NEWMAN LAW ‡
10 Hendon Lane Barnet London N3 1TR
Tel: 020 8349 2655 *Fax:* 020 8346 0270
E-mail: info@newmanlaw.co.uk
List of partners: S J Newman
Languages: French
Work: B1 C1 D1 E F1 G H J1 K1 L N O Q S1 W Z(c)
Agency and Legal Aid undertaken
Ptr: Newman, Miss Suzette J . . . *Dec 1978

NEWMANS ‡
52 Brook Street Mayfair London W1D 5DS
Tel: 020 3170 7045 *Fax:* 020 3170 7046
E-mail: law@ranewman.co.uk

NEWSHAMS LIMITED ‡
11-15 Betterton Street Covent Garden London WC2H 9BP
Tel: 020 7470 8820 *Fax:* 020 7379 0801
E-mail: enquiries@newshams.com

NEWTONS ‡
22 Fitzjohns Avenue Camden London NW3 5NB
Tel: 020 7794 9696 / 7435 5351 *Fax:* 020 7435 8881
E-mail: lawyers@newtonlaw.co.uk
List of partners: A Gelfer
Languages: French, German, Greek, Hebrew, Italian, Japanese, Punjabi, Russian, Spanish, Turkish, Urdu
Work: A3 C1 C2 C3 E G J1 K1 K2 K3 L M2 N O Q S1 S2 T1 T2 W Z(d,e,f,h,i,n,w)
Ptr: Gelfer, Mr Alan . . . Nov 1991
Con: Fraenkel, Miss Ellen Margaret . . . *Jun 1980
Selby, Mr Roger A MA(Hons)(Oxon) . . . *Jun 1969

NICHOLAS & CO ‡
18-22 Wigmore Street London W1U 2RG
Tel: 020 7323 4450 *Fax:* 020 7323 4401 *Dx:* 82985 MAYFAIR 1
E-mail: info@nicholassolicitors.com
List of partners: K Nicholas, N C K Nicholas, H Philippou, P Philippou, V S Sharron
Languages: Greek
Work: B1 C1 C2 C3 D1 E F1 G H J1 K1 L M1 M2 N O P Q R1 S1 T1 T2 W Z(d,e,i,k,l)
Emergency Action, Agency, Legal Aid undertaken and Member of Accident Line
Ptr: Nicholas, Kypros . . . *Jul 1969
Nicholas, Mr Nick C K . . . Sep 1998
Philippou, Ms Helen . . . *Dec 1984
Philippou, Mr Phillip . . . *Dec 1992
Sharron, Ms Valerie S BA . . . *Dec 1988
Ast: Nicholas, Ms Yiota Ann BA . . . *§Dec 1992
Con: Davis, Mr Donald D LLB . . . *Dec 1964
Davis, Mr Raymond R . . . *§Jan 1958
Emmott, Mr E Rodney . . . *Mar 1970
Levan, Mr Brian J . . . *Jul 1968

NICOS & CO ‡
17 Westbury Avenue Haringey London N22 6BS
Tel: 020 8888 1166 *Fax:* 020 8888 6444 *Dx:* 34708 WOOD GREEN 2
List of partners: A Papanicolaou
Languages: Greek
Work: K1 L S1 S2 W Z(l)
Ptr: Papanicolaou, Mr Andreas LLB(Hons) Lancaster & Morecambe District Law Society 1985 . . . *Jan 1990

NIMAN & CO ‡
10 Lockmead Road Haringey London N15 6BX
Tel: 020 8809 4923 *Fax:* 020 8211 7110 *Dx:* 37658 STAMFORD HILL
List of partners: G Niman
Languages: French, Hebrew, Yiddish
Work: E N S1 S2 W
SPr: Niman, Mr Geoffrey LLB . . . *Feb 1969

NIXON PEABODY INTERNATIONAL LLP ‡
Hill Gate House 26 Old Bailey London EC4M 7HQ
Tel: 020 7653 9760 *Fax:* 020 7248 6557
E-mail: rcgibson@nixonpeabody.com

NOORANI LAW ‡
6 Porter Street London W1U 6DD
Tel: 020 7486 1131 *Fax:* 020 7486 1141
Dx: 53806 OXFORD CIRCUS NORTH
E-mail: nooranilaw@btconnect.com
List of partners: A Noorani
Work: C1 E J1 L S1 S2 W
SPr: Noorani, Mr Altaf BA(Hons)(Law) . . . *Oct 1982

NORONHA ADVOGADOS ‡
4th Floor 193-195 Brompton Road London SW3 1NE
Tel: 020 7581 5040 *Fax:* 020 7581 8002

NORTHROP MCNAUGHTAN DELLER ‡
18c Pindock Mews Little Venice London W9 2PY
Tel: 020 7289 7300 *Fax:* 020 7286 9555
E-mail: nmd@nmdsolicitors.com
List of partners: M Deller, C McNaughtan, T Northrop
Work: O Q Z(e,f)
Ptr: Deller, Mr Martin . . . . . *Dec 1998
McNaughtan, Ms Christy . . . . . Nov 1996
Northrop, Mr Tim . . . . . *Feb 1990

NORTON ROSE LLP ‡
(in association with Lee & Lee; Athens & Piraeus)
3 More London Riverside London SE1 2AQ
Tel: 020 7283 6000 *Fax:* 020 7283 6500 *Dx:* 85 LONDON
Languages: Afrikaans, Arabic, Cantonese, Chinese, Czech, Danish, Dutch, French, German, Greek, Gujarati, Hebrew, Hindi, Irish, Italian, Japanese, Kiswahili, Malay, Maltese, Mandarin, Norwegian, Punjabi, Romanian, Russian, Shona, Spanish, Swedish, Urdu, Welsh
Work: A3 B1 B2 C1 C2 C3 E I J1 J2 L M1 M3 N O P R1 T1 U1 Z(a,b,c,e,i,j,l,n,o,s,u)

NOTABLE SERVICES LLP ‡
33 Wigmore Street London W1U 1AU
Tel: 020 7034 5204 *Fax:* 020 7486 0438
E-mail: info@notableservices.co.uk

NOTTAGE & CO ‡
Suite 10 Warren Court Euston Road London NW1 3AA

B M NYMAN & CO ‡
181 Creighton Avenue Haringey London N2 9BN
Tel: 020 8365 3060 *Fax:* 020 8883 5151
E-mail: info@bmnyman.co.uk
List of partners: B M Nyman
Work: I U2 Z(e,f,k,z)
SPr: Nyman, Mr Bernard M BA(Law) . . . . . *Mar 1979

O'CALLAGHAN & CO ‡
(in association with Tucker Turner Kingley Wood & Co)
18 Bedford Row London WC1R 4EQ
Tel: 020 7831 3455 *Fax:* 020 7831 3496
Dx: 220 LONDON/CHANCERY LN
E-mail: patrick@ocallaghanandco.co.uk
List of partners: P J O'Callaghan
Advocacy undertaken
Ptr: O'Callaghan, Mr Patrick J . . . . . *§Jan 1970

BRYAN O'CONNOR & CO ‡
18-20 Southwark Street Southwark London SE1 1TS
Tel: 020 7407 2643 *Fax:* 020 7407 0937
Dx: 149161 SOUTHWARK 9
List of partners: D G James, M J Maunsell, F J F O'Mahony
Ptr: James, Mr David G . . . . . *§Feb 1966
Maunsell, Mr Michael J LLB . . . . . *Nov 1987
O'Mahony, Mr Fergus J F LLB(Lond) . . . . . *Jan 1980

OGR STOCK DENTON ‡
Winston House 349 Regents Park Road Finchley London N3 1DH
Tel: 020 8349 0321 *Fax:* 020 8346 8605 *Dx:* 57254 FINCHLEY 2
E-mail: admin@ogr-law.com
List of partners: S Bernstein, P D Fraser, S S Goldberg, M A Kosmin-Barr, P D Martin, A Mays, S I Silverman, M R Stock, C A Woolhouse
Languages: French, Greek, Gujarati, Hebrew, Hindi, Spanish
Work: B1 C1 C2 D1 E F1 F2 G J1 J2 K1 K2 K3 K4 L M1 N O Q R1 S1 S2 T1 T2 W Z(b,c,d,e,f,j,k,l,o,p,q,r)
Emergency Action, Agency, Advocacy, Fixed Fee Interview, Legal Aid undertaken and Legal Aid Franchise
Ptr: Bernstein, Mrs Susan LLB(Lond) . . . . . Apr 1979
Fraser, Mr Peter David LLB . . . . . *May 1973
Goldberg, Mr Stephen S BCom(L'pool) . . . . . *Oct 1970
Kosmin-Barr, Mr Mark Andrew LLB(Hons) . . . . . *Jul 1997
Martin, Mr Peter D LLB . . . . . *Jul 1978
Mays, Mr Alan . . . . . *Dec 1976
Silverman, Mr Stephen I LLB . . . . . *Oct 1983
Stock, Mr Michael Raymond LLB . . . . . *Oct 1985
Woolhouse, Mrs Catharine A BA . . . . . *Feb 1986
Asoc: Amboaje, Ms Rebecca Victoria LLB . . . . . *Sep 2000
Gitlin, Miriam . . . . . Jul 2005
Masters, Mrs Francine Ruth . . . . . Jul 1979
Shah, Ms Priti LLB(Hons); CTA . . . . . *Apr 1992
Trovato, Mrs Hayley BA(Hons); PGDipLaw . . . . . *Nov 2005

ORR LITCHFIELD LLP ‡
3rd Floor Essex Hall 1-6 Essex Street London WC2R 3HY
Tel: 020 7395 2180 *Fax:* 020 7395 2181
E-mail: info@orrlitchfield.com

O'KEEFFE SOLICITORS ‡
1b Dyne Road Brent London NW6 7XG
Tel: 020 7644 8800 *Fax:* 020 7644 8801 *Dx:* 123869 KILBURN 2
Emergency telephone 0800 917 9172
E-mail: help@oksol.co.uk
List of partners: S Alessandrini, G Cummings, J A T O'Keeffe
Languages: Bengali, French, Hindi, Igbo, Italian, Punjabi, Turkish, Urdu
Work: B2 G H
Advocacy and Legal Aid undertaken
Ptr: Alessandrini, Miss Sara LLB . . . . . Apr 1999
Cummings, Mrs Gina LLB . . . . . Feb 1999
O'Keeffe, Mr James A T • . . . . . Oct 1994
Ast: Foggo, Mr Daniel . . . . . Dec 2001
Walker, Miss Carolyn . . . . . Feb 2005
Con: Spiteri, Mr Andrew John • . . . . . *Aug 2004

O'MELVENY & MYERS LLP ‡
Warwick Court 5 Paternoster Square London EC4M 7DX
Tel: 020 7088 0000 *Fax:* 020 7088 0001
E-mail: london@omm.com
List of partners: J Birtwell, J D Daghlian, S Hills, M D J Hudson, P Loynes, S Wifa
Languages: Cantonese, Danish, French, German, Gujarati, Hindi, Japanese, Mandarin, Mirpuri, Portuguese, Punjabi, Spanish, Turkish
Work: C2 J1 L R2 T1 T2 Z(b,e,h,o)
Ptr: Birtwell, Miss Janet . . . . . *Oct 1986
Daghlian, Mr John D . . . . . *Mar 1991
Hills, Mr Stuart . . . . . *Jan 1995
Hudson, Mr Matthew D J LLB . . . . . *Sep 1987
Loynes, Mr Paul . . . . . Jan 1998
Wifa, Mr Solomon . . . . . Jan 1999

CLIONA O'TUAMA ‡
Hamilton House 1 Temple Avenue London EC4Y 0HA
Tel: 020 7489 2015 *Fax:* 020 7489 2001
Dx: 135 LONDON/CHANCERY LN
E-mail: info@clionaotuama.com
List of partners: C M O'Tuama
Languages: French
Work: T2 W Z(d)
SPr: O'Tuama, Miss Cliona Mary BCL; AITI; TEP Irish Law Society Gold Medals for Oratory & Legal Debate President of Irish Solicitors Bar Association . . . . . *§Jan 1991

OAK SOLICITORS LIMITED ‡
10 Greycoat Place London SW1P 1SB
Tel: 020 7960 6043 *Fax:* 020 7960 6102

OAKLAND & CO ‡
27 Acacia Road London NW8 6AR
Tel: 020 7722 7257 *Fax:* 020 3318 0946
E-mail: mail@oaklandlaw.co.uk

THE OAKLEY SHEE PARTNERSHIP ‡
Studio 50 Soho Wharf 1 Clink Street London SE1 9DG
Tel: 020 7089 9066 *Fax:* 020 7357 6698
E-mail: ted@oakleyshee.com
List of partners: E A Oakley, F J Shee
Work: E L S1 W
Ptr: Oakley, Mr Edward Avery LLB(Hons) . . . . . *May 1988
Shee, Mr Frazer Jack LLB(Hons) . . . . . Mar 1991

OAKLEYS SOLICITORS ‡
2 Oakfield Street London SW10 9JB
Tel: 020 7351 1399 *Fax:* 020 7823 3834

OAKS SOLICITORS ‡
Argo Business Centre Kilburn Park Road London NW6 5LF
Tel: 020 7644 0203 *Fax:* 020 7644 0603
E-mail: k.behbahani@behbahani.co.uk

OBADIAH ROSE SOLICITORS ‡
Suite 10 225a Lewisham Way Oscar Street London SE4 1UY
Tel: 020 8691 0222 *Fax:* 020 8691 0220
E-mail: obadiahrose@hotmail.co.uk

OBASEKI SOLICITORS ‡
Unit 1 222 Kingsland Road London E2 8AX
Tel: 020 7739 7549

OBERMAN LAW ‡
15 Southampton Place Camden London WC1A 2AJ
Tel: 020 7242 6154 *Fax:* 020 7831 2593 *Dx:* 35707 BLOOMSBURY
E-mail: info@obermanlaw.co.uk
List of partners: M Feldmann, M Harris
Languages: French, German
Work: B1 C1 E L N O Q R1 R2 S1 S2 W Z(g,p,q,r)
Agency undertaken
Ptr: Feldmann, Mr Mark MA(Cantab) . . . . . *Mar 1970
Harris, Mr Mervyn LLB . . . . . *May 1970
Asoc: Harris, Mr Anthony Charles LLB(B'ham) . . . . . Jan 2003
Con: Torrance, Mr Ian Michael MA(Oxon) . . . . . *Jun 1970

DAVID A OBRART ‡
St Martins House 59 St Martin's Lane London WC2N 4JS
Tel: 020 7379 4441 *Fax:* 020 7240 3982
List of partners: D A Obrart
Languages: French, Hebrew, Spanish
Work: B1 C1 E L S1 T1 W Z(i)
Ptr: Obrart, Mr David A LLB . . . . . *Apr 1979

OGIER ‡
41 Lothbury London EC2R 7HF
Tel: 020 7160 5000 *Fax:* 020 7160 5099
E-mail: london@ogier.com

OGILVY RENAULT ‡
Bankside House 107 Leadenhall Street London EC3A 4AF
Tel: 020 7444 1910 *Fax:* 020 7444 1911
E-mail: a.hutchings@ogilvyrenault.com

ANTHONY OGUNFEIBO & CO ‡
352 Camberwell New Road London SE5 9HA
Tel: 020 7501 9898 *Fax:* 020 7274 9696
E-mail: info@anthonyogunfeibosolicitors.com

OLA LESLIE SOLICITORS ‡
11-15 Betterton Street London WC2H 9BP
Tel: 020 7183 0084 *Fax:* 0845 163 4208
E-mail: info@olaleslie.com

A OLDSCHOOL & CO ‡
116-118 Islington High Street London N1 8EG
Tel: 020 7359 8345 *Fax:* 020 7354 5477 *Dx:* 146644 ISLINGTON 4
E-mail: oldschool.uk@virgin.net

OLEPHANT SOLICITORS ‡
25 Southampton Buildings London WC2A 1AL
Tel: 020 7486 9627 *Fax:* 020 7486 6259
E-mail: mail@olephant.com

OLISAKWE VINCENT ONUEGBU ‡
372 Old Street London EC1V 9LT
Tel: 020 7613 1166 *Fax:* 020 7033 0110

OLSWANG LLP ‡
90 High Holborn London WC1V 6XX
Tel: 020 7067 3000 *Fax:* 020 7067 3999 *Dx:* 37972 KINGSWAY
E-mail: london@olswang.com
List of partners: J Akerman, M R W Barclay, A J A Bott, K B Butler, F A G Carpanini, H A Cartlidge, C L Cowen, M J Devereux, N I Fisch, D M Harris, C N F Hobson, A P E Inglis, M Joscelyne, H Kanter, J Q Kanter, S A Kanter, D H Kustow, G D Levy, P A Mendelsohn, M Michaelson, M A Needham, K A Nicholson, S M Olswang, J C Palca, S Potter, G A Proudler, P S Rapport, J Roodyn, L J G Savill, P A Stevens, V Timon, H J T Wilby, D C Zeffman
Office: Reading
Languages: French
Work: B1 C1 C2 C3 E F1 I J1 L M1 M2 N O Q S1 T1 T2 W Z(b,e,f,j,k,o)
Agency undertaken
Ptr: Akerman, Mr John . . . . . *Feb 1968
Barclay, Mr Marcus R W LLB . . . . . *Jul 1989
Bott, Mr Adrian J A LLB(Manc) . . . . . *Apr 1980
Butler, Ms Kay Beverly LLB; LLM(Tax) . . . . . *Nov 1987
Carpanini, Mr Fabrizio A G LLB Sweet & Maxwell Law Prize 1979 . . . . . *Oct 1984
Cartlidge, Mr Howard Arthur MA(Cantab) . . . . . *Nov 1991
Cowen, Mrs Christine L MA(Cantab) . . . . . *Nov 1987
Devereux, Mr Mark J LLB; Member of Supreme Court of California . . . . . *Apr 1981
Fisch, Mr Nigel I LLB . . . . . *Mar 1984
Harris, Miss Doreen M LLB(Lond) . . . . . *Apr 1976
Hobson, Mr Christopher N F . . . . . *§Dec 1981
Inglis, Mr Andrew P E LLB . . . . . *Apr 1990
Joscelyne, Mr Mark LLB(Lond) . . . . . *Apr 1981
Kanter, Mr Jeremy Quentin LLB(Hons) . . . . . *Sep 1993
Kanter, Mr Simon A LLB . . . . . *Nov 1985
Kustow, Mr David H . . . . . *Dec 1973
Levy, Mr Graeme David MA(Cantab) . . . . . Jan 1985
Mendelsohn, Mr Paul A LLB; ACIArb . . . . . *Oct 1986
Michaelson, Mrs Michele BA(Hons)(Manc) . . . . . *Nov 1981
Needham, Mr Martyn A BA(Hons) . . . . . *Sep 1989
Nicholson, Miss Kim A LLB(B'ham) . . . . . *Oct 1985
Olswang, Mr Simon M BA; Member of the State Bar of California . . . . . *Jun 1968
Palca, Miss Julia C BA(Dunelm) . . . . . *Apr 1980
Potter, Miss Selina BA . . . . . *Dec 1989
Proudler, Miss Geraldine Ann BA . . . . . *Sep 1980
Rapport, Mr Philip S LLB(B'ham) . . . . . *Apr 1975
Roodyn, Ms Jacqueline LLB(Lond) . . . . . *Jun 1975
Savill, Ms Lisbeth J G BA(UNSW); LLB(UNSW) Solicitor of the Supreme Court of NSW . . . . . *Jul 1987
Stevens, Mr Paul A BA; DipIP . . . . . *Oct 1990
Timon, Mr Victor BCL(Dublin) . . . . . Jan 1991
Wilby, Miss Heather J T LLB . . . . . Apr 1988
Zeffman, Mr David Charles MA(Oxon) . . . . . Oct 1983
Ast: Adams, Ms Penny BA(Hons) . . . . . *Oct 1996
Alexander, Ms Rosemarie S MA(Hons); CPE; ICSL . . . . . Mar 1997
Ashenhurst, Ms Deborah Jane MA . . . . . *May 1992
Ashton, Mr Keir LLB(Hons) . . . . . Sep 1995
Attfield, Mr David Vincent LLB(Hons)(Nott'm) . . . . . Oct 1993
Barry, Mr Joel A LLB(Hons) . . . . . Mar 1996
Bennett, Miss Emma D LLB . . . . . *Oct 1997
Blackmore, Mr Paul A BA(Hons); LSF . . . . . Sep 1994
Bouchier, Mr David I LLB(Exon); LLM(McGill) . . . . . Apr 1990
Brader, Mr Michael Hilton Charles MA(Cantab) . . . . . *Oct 1991
Briggs, Ms Karen BA; MA . . . . . *Nov 1991
Browne, Mr Darren LLB(Hons) . . . . . *Nov 1995
Browne, Mr David William LLB(Hons) . . . . . *Mar 1990
Buchan, Ms Ailsa BA(Hons); LLB . . . . . *Mar 1996
Chadwick, Ms Diane E MA(Hons)(Cantab) . . . . . *Nov 1996
Coburn, Miss Claire LLB(Hons); LSF . . . . . *Apr 1992
Cordran, Mr Robert . . . . . Sep 1998
Corney, Mr Steven T LLB . . . . . Sep 1998
Cottrill, Mr Stephen H BSc(Hons) . . . . . *Jul 1992
Cowan, Mr Matthew BSc; BA; LSF . . . . . *Dec 1993
Cowen, Mr Matthew BSc; BA . . . . . Dec 1993
Cronly-Dillon, Ms Maya BA; CPE; LPC . . . . . Oct 1997
Cushion, Miss Anita BA; CPE; LSF(Hons) . . . . . *Sep 1994
Dautlich, Mr Marc C MA(Oxon) . . . . . *Sep 1996
Davies, Mr Edward T BSc; MSc; CPE; LPC . . . . . *Sep 1997
Davies, Mr Martin Stuart MA(Cantab) . . . . . Apr 1994
Enser, Mr John BA(Hons) . . . . . *Sep 1989
Ford, Mr Stuart Anthony Luke BA(Hons)(Oxon) . . . . . *Oct 1994
Francis, Miss Linda J BSc; DipLaw . . . . . Oct 1997
Goobey, Miss Joanne FILEx; LPC . . . . . Nov 1996
Gringras, Mr Clive LLB; MA . . . . . *Sep 1997
Harvey, Miss Claire E LLB(Hons) . . . . . *Sep 1996
Hughes, Mr Stephen Robert LLB(Hons) . . . . . *Oct 1995
Ketley, Mr Miles BA . . . . . *Oct 1994
Knight, Mrs Heidi A BA(Hons); CPE; LPC . . . . . Sep 1997
Lockyer, Mrs Jane BA(Hons); CPE; LSF(Hons) . . . . . *Nov 1995
Meads, Mr Paul Graham LLB . . . . . Sep 2001
Miller, Mr Edward Charles Gerard BSc . . . . . *Sep 1994
Moore, Miss Jane . . . . . Oct 1993
Offenbach, Miss Deborah L LLB(Hons); LPC . . . . . *Nov 1996
Palmer, Mr Timothy Howard LLB . . . . . *Oct 1993
Punjabi, Ms Sheila Isabelle BA; LLM . . . . . *Apr 1996
Rogers, Ms Teresa A BA(Hons) . . . . . *Nov 1988
Rooney, Mr Paul Matthew Stuart BA(Hons)(Oxon) . . . . . *Sep 1996
Royde, Miss Melissa C LLB . . . . . Sep 1997
Russell, Mrs Melanie A H LLB(Hons) . . . . . *Nov 1993
Schroeder, Mrs Nicola Louise MA(Cantab) . . . . . *Sep 1994
Sharpe, Mr Gavin BSc Freeman of the City of London *Sep 1996
Taylor, Miss Catherine BA(Cantab) . . . . . Nov 1992
Thompson, Mr Craig LLB(Hons) . . . . . Dec 1994
Westwood, Mr Carl J LLB; DipLaw . . . . . Oct 1997
Whitehead, Ms Denise . . . . . *Nov 1995
Con: Remington, Mr Selwyn A LLB . . . . . *§Dec 1975

M OLUBI SOLICITORS ‡
Unit 4 2 Tunstall Road Brixton Lambeth London SW9 8BN
Tel: 020 7737 3400 / 07956 394567 *Fax:* 020 7737 3433
Emergency telephone 07799 444866
E-mail: info@m-olubi-law.com
List of partners: M Olubisose
Languages: Armenian, French, Gujarati, Igbo, Portuguese, Spanish, Yoruba
Work: G J1 K1 L Q Z(i)
Advocacy, Legal Aid undertaken and Legal Aid Franchise
SPr: Olubisose, Mr Moses . . . . . *May 1998

MARGARET OLUSEGUN ‡
3 The View Upper Abbey Wood London SE2 0DX
Tel: 01322 431807 / 07882 194223 *Fax:* 0871 714 8053
Dx: 31805 BEXLEYHEATH
E-mail: margaret@msegun.com

See p2 for the Key to Work Categories & other symbols

ON DEMAND LAWYERS ‡
41 Dacre Park London SE13 5SQ
Tel: 0800 234 3529 *Fax:* 0800 609 0361
E-mail: info@ondemandlawyers.co.uk

ONSIDE LAW ‡
23 Elysium Gate 126-128 New Kings Road London SW6 4LZ
Tel: 020 7384 6920 *Fax:* 020 7384 5175
E-mail: info@onsidelaw.co.uk
List of partners: O Hunt, J R C Singer, S Thorpe
Work: C1 O Z(e,f,k,w)
Ptr: Hunt, Mr Oliver . . . . Sep 1999
Singer, Mr Jamie R C BA(Hons); CPE; LPC . . . . . . Aug 1998
Thorpe, Mr Simon . . . . Sep 1999

ONYEMS & PARTNERS ‡
18 Wingfield Road Waltham Forest London E17 9NP
Tel: 020 8520 2500 *Fax:* 020 8279 9789 *Dx:* 32035 WALTHAMSTOW

MICHAEL OPPLER & CO ‡
10 Hood Avenue East Sheen London SW14 7LH
Tel: 020 8878 4195 / 8878 4180 *Fax:* 020 8392 8944
Dx: 36362 EAST SHEEN
Emergency telephone 020 8878 4195
List of partners: M D Oppler
Work: B1 E J1 K1 L O Q S1 W Z(c,k,q)
Agency and Advocacy undertaken
SPr: Oppler, Mr Michael David LLB(Soton) . . . . *Nov 1974

OPTIMUS LAW GROUP ‡
4/5 Park Place London SW1A 1LP
Tel: 020 3178 7958 *Fax:* 020 3070 0110

ORACLE SOLICITORS ‡
24-25 Nutford Place Marble Arch London W1H 5YN
Tel: 0870 752 1388 *Fax:* 0870 165 5235 *Dx:* 38770 PADDINGTON
E-mail: sas@oraclesolicitors.co.uk

ORIGIN LIMITED ‡
Twisden Works Twisden Road London NW5 1DN
Tel: 020 7424 1950 *Fax:* 020 7209 0643
E-mail: info@origin.co.uk

ORMERODS
(incorporating Gray Marshall & Campbell; The Heap Partnership; Quirke & Wombwell & Coningsbys)
1 Printers Yard 90a The Broadway Wimbledon London SW19 1RD
Tel: 020 8686 5000 *Fax:* 020 8542 9068
E-mail: enquiries@ormerods.co.uk
Office: Croydon, Reigate

ORRICK HERRINGTON & SUTCLIFFE LLP ‡
107 Cheapside London EC2V 6DN
Tel: 020 7862 4600 *Fax:* 020 7862 4800
List of partners: M Frangeskides
Ptr: Frangeskides, Ms Maria . . . . Nov 1991

ORTOLAN LEGAL LIMITED
81 Oxford Street London W1D 2EU
Tel: 020 7903 5074 *Fax:* 020 7903 5333
E-mail: info@ortolangroup.com
Office: Warrington

OSBORNE CLARKE
One London Wall London EC2Y 5EB
Tel: 020 7105 7000 *Fax:* 020 7105 7005
Dx: 466 LONDON/CHANCERY LN
E-mail: info@osborneclarke.com
Office: Bristol, Reading
Languages: Danish, French, German, Spanish
Work: A1 B1 C1 C2 C3 E F1 I J1 L M1 M2 N O P Q R1 S1 T1 T2 W X
Emergency Action, Agency, Advocacy, Fixed Fee Interview, Legal Aid undertaken and Member of Accident Line
Ptr: Almond, Mrs Kathryn L A LLB(Bris) . . . . *Nov 1991
Berg, Mr Raymond . . . . Sep 1992
Birt, Mr Timothy D BA . . . . *Nov 1988
Bott, Mr Adrian J A LLB(Manc) . . . . *Apr 1980
Cubitt, Mr David LLB . . . . *Oct 1991
Dyer, Mr Carl D BA(Hons) Anthoney London Law Prize *Jan 1997
Fielder, Mr Simon . . . . Dec 1994
Fongenie, Mr Wesley . . . . Nov 1981
Gait, Mr R Charles C MA(Cantab) . . . . *Apr 1980
Gardner, Mr Paul A LLB(Nott'm) . . . . Nov 1987
Groom, Mr Stephen . . . . Jan 1978
Johnson, Mr Nick . . . . Sep 1996
Kearney, Mr Colin F BA(Dunelm) . . . . *Dec 1978
Lifely, Mr Adrian M LLB . . . . *Mar 1986
Lougher, Miss Jane Alexandra LLB(Hons)(Exon) . . . *Oct 1984
Minto, Mr Henry C C BA(York) . . . . *§Oct 1980
Roma, Linton . . . . Jan 1998
Rutherford, Mr Brian . . . . Oct 1979
Saul, Mr Andrew J BA(Oxon) . . . . *Nov 1986
Savvides, Mr Theo A . . . . Sep 1994
Staunton, Ms Paula BSc . . . . *Oct 1991
Strahl, Miss Nadine R G LLB(Lond) . . . . *Oct 1984
Asoc: Badham, Mr Christopher LLB . . . . Jan 1994
Black, Ms Lisa . . . . Mar 1997
Brookes, Mr Timothy . . . . Dec 1994
Culbert, Mr Mark Christian LLB . . . . Nov 1995
Finn, Mr Mark A LLB(Soton) . . . . *Oct 1986
Fisher, Mr David MA(Cantab) . . . . *Dec 1993
Haines, Mr Adam . . . . Sep 1995
Hughes, Gawain Lewis . . . . Dec 1994
Parry, Mrs Victoria A LLB(Cardiff) . . . . *Nov 1994
Riley, Mr Frank W LLB . . . . *Apr 1979
Winton, Mr Ashley Peter BSc; MEng; AMIEE . . . . . *Sep 1995
Ast: Alberstat, Mr Philip . . . . *May 1990
Anderson, Mr Stewart . . . . Oct 2000
Baker, Mr Christopher . . . . Jul 2002
Bambury, Ms Hannah . . . . Sep 2002
Bradbury, Ms Christine . . . . Sep 2001
Clarke, Ms Lucy . . . . Sep 2001
Crawford, Ms Lisa . . . . Sep 1999
Davies, Ms Emelye . . . . Feb 2000
Dillon, Miss Eimear M LLB; MBA . . . . *Oct 1999
Evans, Ms Ashleigh MA(Cantab) . . . . Sep 2001
Farquharson, Mr David . . . . Sep 1999
Finnegan, Mr Angus J . . . . Jan 1998
Flower, Ms Helen . . . . Sep 2001
Foster, Ms Anna . . . . Sep 1998
Galea, Mr Vincent . . . . Nov 1998
Greenhaf, Ms Sarah . . . . Sep 2000
Gunston, Mr William . . . . Mar 1999
Heap, Ms Vanessa . . . . Feb 2002
Hodges, Ms Dawn . . . . Jun 2000
Hopkins, Mr Justin . . . . Aug 1999
Ingrey-Counter, Mr Miles LLB(Hons) . . . . *Sep 2000
Jansen, Lieve . . . . Apr 2000
Jennings, Mr Frank R . . . . Apr 1999
Johnston, Mr Jeffrey . . . . Sep 1996
Kanwar, Manoj . . . . Apr 2000
Kentsbeer, Ms Michelle J . . . . Apr 1998
King, Mr Christopher LLB(Hons) . . . . *Mar 1990
King, Mr Jonathan David . . . . Sep 1996
Lawrenson, Mr Gary . . . . Sep 2000
Leroy, Ms Lucy . . . . Sep 1999
Lewis, Ms Susan Elaine BSc . . . . *Jul 1980
Lindstrom, Ms Lucy . . . . Sep 1998
Marshall, Mr Dominic . . . . May 2000
Massy-Collier, Mr James P . . . . Jun 1981
Maughan, Mr Simon . . . . Sep 2002
Mirza, Miss Saira LLB . . . . *§Jan 1999
Mordecai, Ms Laura . . . . Mar 2000
Mullock, Mr James Justin . . . . Sep 1996
Nathan, Mr Ralph B LLB(Leics) . . . . *Apr 1986
Nelson, Ms Emma BA . . . . Jan 1996
North, Mr David L LLB(L'pool) . . . . Dec 1994
Perrin, Leslie C BA Secretary for Bristol Old Vic . . . *Nov 1985
Phillips, Ms Caroline . . . . Sep 2001
Pond, Mr James . . . . Jul 2001
Powell, Ms Victoria . . . . Sep 2001
Preston, Ms Emily . . . . Sep 1999
Scales, Mr Adrian H . . . . Feb 1998
Schroder, Mr Tom . . . . Mar 1996
Sinfield, Ms Olivia . . . . Oct 1998
Singh-Dalal, Ms Sunita . . . . Sep 1999
Walsh, Ms Patricia Mary . . . . Oct 1992
Wright, Mr David Alexander . . . . Sep 1995

OSBORNES ‡
Livery House 9 Pratt Street Camden London NW1 0AE
Tel: 020 7485 8811 *Fax:* 020 7485 5660 *Dx:* 57053 CAMDEN TOWN
E-mail: julianbeard@osbornes.net
Languages: French, Spanish
Work: D1 D2 E K1 K2 L N O Q S1 S2 T2 W Z(h,q)

OSIBANJO ETE & CO ‡
74 Camberwell Church Street London SE5 8QZ
Tel: 020 7708 0077 *Fax:* 020 7708 0770
Dx: 35320 CAMBERWELL GREEN
Languages: Hindi, Urdu
Work: D1 E F1 G H J1 K1 L N O Q S1 V W X Z(i,j,k,l,w)
Emergency Action, Fixed Fee Interview and Legal Aid undertaken

OSMOND & OSMOND ‡
55-57 Temple Chambers 3-7 Temple Avenue London EC4Y 0HP
Tel: 020 7583 3434 *Fax:* 020 7583 4242
Dx: 33 LONDON/CHANCERY LN
E-mail: ksmith@osmondandosmond.co.uk
List of partners: J G Osmond, W J G Osmond
Languages: French, Spanish
Work: A3 B1 C1 C2 C3 E F1 F2 J1 J2 K1 K2 K3 L M2 N O P Q R1 R2 S1 S2 U1 W Z(c,e,g,j,k,o,p,q,r)
Ptr: Osmond, Mr William J G LLB(Exon) . . . . Apr 1979
Ast: Hastie, Miss Sarah Marie LLB . . . . Mar 2005

PETER OTTO & CO SOLICITORS ‡
2nd Floor 151 Rye Lane London SE15 4TL
Tel: 020 7252 8278 *Fax:* 020 7639 6009
E-mail: peter@otto.uk.com

OURY CLARK ‡
10 John Street London WC1N 2EB
Tel: 020 7607 4300 *Fax:* 020 7607 4301
Dx: 84 LONDON/CHANCERY LN
E-mail: contact@ouryclarksolicitors.com
List of partners: J E Oury, J Oury, D Raingold, M Reid
Work: B3 C1 C2 E J1 M2 S2 T1 T2 U2 Z(e,g,i,p,q)
Legal Aid Franchise
Ptr: Oury, Juliet . . . . Oct 2000
Oury, Mr James E LLB; ACA Lawyer Awards - Pro Bono Activity of Year - 2nd Place . . . . *May 1996
Raingold, Mr Denis . . . . Dec 1973
Reid, Mr Martin . . . . *Jan 1994

OWEN & CO ‡
81a High Road Willesden London NW10 2SU
Tel: 020 8459 4836 / 8459 7263 *Fax:* 020 8451 1094
List of partners: M J Owen
Work: E L S1 S2 W
Ptr: Owen, Mr Martin J . . . . *Jun 1970

OWEN WHITE & CATLIN
174 King Street London W6 0RA
Tel: 020 8741 7171 *Fax:* 020 8741 7743
Dx: 32750 HAMMERSMITH 2
E-mail: hammersmith@owenwhitecatlin.co.uk
Office: Addlestone, Ashford, Feltham, Hounslow, London W4, Shepperton

OWEN WHITE & CATLIN
(incorporating Noel Barrett & Co)
181 Chiswick High Road Chiswick London W4 2DR
Tel: 020 8987 1400 *Fax:* 020 8987 1401 *Dx:* 80301 CHISWICK
E-mail: chiswick@owenwhitecatlin.co.uk
Office: Addlestone, Ashford, Feltham, Hounslow, London W6, Shepperton

OWENS STEVENS SOLICITORS ‡
PO Box 5741 152-156 Lower Clapton Road Hackney London E5 0QJ
Tel: 020 8986 7555 *Fax:* 020 8986 7444
E-mail: info@owensstevens.org.uk

OWOYELE DADA & CO ‡
Suite 336 Camberwell Business Centre 99-103 Lomond Grove London SE5 7HN
Tel: 020 7703 4145 *Fax:* 020 7252 6812

OZORAN TURKAN & CO ‡
203 Green Lanes London N16 9DJ
Tel: 020 7354 0802 *Fax:* 020 7704 9121
E-mail: ozoranturkan@aol.com
List of partners: D Ozoran
Ptr: Ozoran, Doudou . . . . Nov 1993

PCB LAWYERS LLP ‡
70 Baker Street London W1U 7DL
Tel: 020 7486 2566 *Fax:* 020 7486 3085 *Dx:* 9015 WEST END
E-mail: enquiries@pcblawyers.com
List of partners: M F Berwald, J C Fishman, D Fordham, J H Lobetta
Work: S1 S2 W
Member of Accident Line
Ptr: Berwald, Mr Melvin F BA . . . . *Jun 1976
Fishman, Ms Judith C LLB(LSE) . . . . *Oct 1986
Fordham, Mr Douglas . . . . *Feb 1989
Lobetta, Mr Julian H LLB . . . . *Oct 1986
Con: Gilmour, Mr Charles H D LLB . . . . *Feb 1961
Young, Mr Edward G . . . . *Jul 1969

PCB LITIGATION LLP ‡
150 Holborn London EC1N 2LR
Tel: 020 7831 2691 *Fax:* 020 7405 8629
Dx: 0038 LONDON/CHANCERY LN
Emergency telephone 07770 851381
E-mail: enquiries@pcblitigation.com
List of partners: T Mascarenhas, S N Philippsohn, A J Riem
Work: A3 B1 B2 C1 I J1 L M2 O U2 Z(b,c,q)
Agency undertaken
Ptr: Mascarenhas, Mr Trevor BA(Hons); LLB . . . . . . *Sep 2000
Philippsohn, Mr Steven N . . . . *Nov 1972
Riem, Mr Anthony J LLB . . . . *Apr 1990

PCM SOLICITORS LLP ‡
68 King William Street London EC4N 7DZ
Tel: 020 7959 2422 *Fax:* 020 7959 2421 *Dx:* 98947 CHEAPSIDE
E-mail: info@pcm-law.net

P G SOLICITORS ‡
Ground Floor 10 Station Parade London SW12 9AZ
Tel: 020 8675 2175 *Fax:* 020 8772 0522
E-mail: pgsolicitors@hotmail.co.uk

PADVA HASLAM-JONES & PARTNERS ‡
Hamilton House 1 Temple Avenue London EC4Y 0HA
Tel: 020 7353 5555 *Fax:* 020 7353 5557
E-mail: info@phjpartners.com

PAIL SOLICITORS ‡
10 Margaret Street London W1W 8RL
Tel: 020 7305 7491 *Fax:* 020 7305 7492
E-mail: support@pailsolicitors.co.uk

KUMARI PALANY & CO ‡
90 Long Acre Covent Garden London WC2E 9RZ
Tel: 020 7849 3420 *Fax:* 020 7849 3427
E-mail: info@kumarilawyers.com

PALIS SOLICITORS ‡
157 Kilburn High Road London NW6 7HU
Tel: 020 7604 3572 *Fax:* 020 7328 9232

PARAGON LAW
Suite 2a Princes House 38 Jermyn Street London SW1Y 6DN
Tel: 020 7494 3781 *Fax:* 020 7287 2131
Office: Nottingham

PARFITT CRESSWELL ‡
(incorporating Herbert Lord & Co; Carnt & Mudie & How Davey & Loxdale)
593-599 Fulham Road London SW6 5UA
Tel: 020 7381 8311 *Fax:* 020 7381 4044
Dx: 83800 FULHAM BROADWAY
E-mail: enquiry@parfittcresswell.com
List of partners: T J Payne, T W Wright
Office: London SE12
Languages: French, Italian
Work: B1 B2 B3 C1 C2 E J1 J2 K1 K2 K3 K4 L O Q R1 R2 S1 S2 T1 T2 W Z(b,c,d,e,g,o,p,q)
Ptr: Payne, Ms Teresa J LLB(Hons) . . . . *Jan 2004
Wright, Mr Thomas W LLB . . . . *Dec 1981
Asoc: Evans, Mr Robert T B BA . . . . *Mar 1988
Powell, Mr Bradley LLB(Hons); PGDipLaw . . . . . . *Sep 2002
Ast: Conlon, Mr James Michael LLB(Hons); LPC . . . . . *Nov 2002
Govinden, Mr Gavin LPC . . . . *Nov 2006
Con: Wilson, Mr David W LLB(Lond) . . . . *Nov 1971

PARFITT CRESSWELL
382 Lee High Road London SE12 8RW
Tel: 020 8297 9392 *Fax:* 020 8297 9492
Office: London SW6

PARFITT LAW ‡
Unit 2b 18-20 Hillgate Place Balham Hill London SW12 9EL

PARKER & CO ‡
28 Austin Friars London EC2N 2QQ
Tel: 020 7614 4030 *Fax:* 020 7614 4040
E-mail: helen.parker@parkerandcosolicitors.com

PARKER ARRENBERG ‡
37 Rushey Green Catford London SE6 4AS
Tel: 020 8695 2330 *Fax:* 020 8695 6370 *Dx:* 34365 CATFORD
List of partners: K F Arrenberg, R V Cobb, B Evans, S Gale, D Mahony, J B Parker
Work: C1 D1 E J1 K1 N O Q R1 S1 S2 W Z(c,d,l)
Legal Aid Franchise
Ptr: Arrenberg, Ms Kim F BSc . . . . *Dec 1979
Cobb, Mr Reginald V . . . . Dec 1967
Evans, Ms Beryl BSc . . . . Apr 1986
Gale, Mrs Sonya MA; DipLaw . . . . Jan 1988
Mahony, Mr Daniel LLB . . . . *Nov 1976
Parker, Mr John B LLB . . . . Jul 1969
Ast: Hullah, Mrs Aileen BA(Hons) . . . . Sep 1992

PARKER THOMAS ‡
Queens House 55-56 Lincoln's Inn Fields London WC2A 3LN
Tel: 020 7242 5462 *Fax:* 020 7405 2944 *Dx:* 279 CHANCERY LANE
E-mail: mail@parkerthomas.co.uk

PARLETT KENT ‡
Signet House 49-51 Farringdon Road London EC1M 3PP
Tel: 020 7430 0712 *Fax:* 020 7430 1796 *Dx:* 53308 CLERKENWELL
E-mail: enquiries@parlettkent.co.uk
List of partners: S Al-Sabbagh, C Hurrell, C H C Jenkins, J Nathwani, K Robins, J Say, J H Stevenson, M Wellington, M Young
Office: Exeter
Languages: French, German, Gujarati, Sinhalese
Work: N Z(q,r)
Legal Aid undertaken, Legal Aid Franchise and Member of Accident Line
Ptr: Al-Sabbagh, Ms Shurouk LLB . . . . Oct 1991
Jenkins, Ms Caroline H C BA ♦ . . . . *Nov 1980
Say, Ms Julie-Ann BA(Law) . . . . *Jan 1990
Stevenson, Mr James Henry LLB; LPC . . . . Apr 2009
Wellington, Mrs Manori LLB(Hons) . . . . *Jan 1997

O H PARSONS & PARTNERS ‡
3rd Floor Sovereign House 212-224 Shaftesbury Avenue London WC2H 8PR
Tel: 020 7379 7277 *Fax:* 020 7240 1577 *Dx:* 35703 BLOOMSBURY
E-mail: no1@ohparsons.co.uk
List of partners: K A Brough, M R Cartledge, P R Stanley, J S Tustian, N J Watkiss, N J Welsh, S M Wood
Office: Mansfield
Work: J1 N Z(p)
Member of Accident Line
Ptr: Brough, Mr Kenneth Andrew BA(Hons) . . . . *Sep 1999
Cartledge, Mr Matthew R BA(Econ) . . . . *Dec 1987
Stanley, Mr Paul R LLB . . . . *Nov 1972
Tustian, Miss Jayne Susannah LLB(Hons). . . . . . . Oct 1998
Watkiss, Miss Nicola J BSc(Hons). . . . . *Mar 1999
Welsh, Miss Natalie J LLB(Hons) . . . . *Jan 1998
Wood, Mr Spencer Mark LLB(Hons). . . . . *Sep 1995

PARTNERS & CO ‡
1st Floor Montague House 22 Montague Road London E11 3EX
Tel: 020 8988 9500 *Fax:* 020 8279 0551
E-mail: lperry@partnerssolicitors.co.uk

PARTNERS EMPLOYMENT LAWYERS ‡
65 London Wall London EC2M 5TU
Tel: 0844 800 9239 *Fax:* 020 7681 1857
E-mail: hina@partnerslaw.co.uk
Office: Epping
Work: J1

PASCALIDES & CO ‡
243 Gray's Inn Road London WC1X 8RB
Tel: 020 7837 0049 *Fax:* 020 7278 3387 *Dx:* 37914 KINGS CROSS
Emergency telephone 07836 331541
E-mail: info@pascalides.co.uk
List of partners: C C Pascalides, N Toffis
Languages: Greek
Work: B1 C1 D1 E F1 G H J1 K1 L M1 N P R1 S1 W Z(c,i,k,l,p)
Emergency Action, Agency, Advocacy and Legal Aid undertaken
Ptr: Pascalides, Mr Christopher C . . . . *Jun 1988
Toffis, Miss Natalie LLB . . . . May 1999

GEETA PATEL & COMPANY ‡
182 Bowes Road New Southgate London N11 2JG
Tel: 020 8365 7377 *Fax:* 020 8447 9033
E-mail: geeta.pa@virgin.net
List of partners: G Patel
Languages: Gujarati, Hindi, Kiswahili
Work: K1 V Z(i)
SPr: Patel, Mrs Geeta LLB(Hons) . . . . *Aug 1992

M M PATEL & CO ‡
26-28 Finchley Road St Johns Wood London NW8 6ES
Tel: 020 7722 7673
List of partners: H D M Pathirana
Work: E L S1 S2 W
Ptr: Pathirana, Hemani D M LLB. . . . . Jul 1990

PATON WALSH LAUNDY ‡
22-24 Worple Road London SW19 4DD
Tel: 020 8946 2229 *Fax:* 020 8944 6551
Dx: 300103 WIMBLEDON CENTRAL
E-mail: gn@patonwalsh.co.uk
List of partners: D J Laundy, G N E Needham
Work: B1 C1 C2 C3 E F1 J1 L O P Q R1 S1 W Z(c,l)
Ptr: Laundy, Mr David J LLB(Lond) . . . . *Jan 1973
Needham, Mr Grant N E LLB . . . . *Jun 1980

PATRICKS SOLICITORS ‡
453 High Street North Manor Park Newham London E12 6TJ
Tel: 020 8548 8844 *Fax:* 020 8548 8229 *Dx:* 4719 EAST HAM
E-mail: info@patricks.org.uk
Languages: Bengali, Hindi, Punjabi, Tamil, Urdu
Work: B1 D1 E F1 K1 K2 K3 L O Q S1 S2 W Z(i,l)
Agency, Fixed Fee Interview, Legal Aid undertaken and Legal Aid Franchise

PATTINSON & BREWER ‡
30 Great James Street London WC1N 3HA
Est: 1891
Tel: 020 7400 5100 *Fax:* 020 7400 5101
Dx: 394 LONDON/CHANCERY LN
E-mail: enquiries@pattinsonbrewer.co.uk
List of partners: G S Bansel, J M Davies, L R Levison, G Lightwood, F E McCarthy, N M O'Brady, C M Phelan, J Radcliffe, P M Statham, R Thompson, M Weatherby
Office: Bristol, York
Languages: French, Greek, Italian
Work: C1 C2 J1 M1 N Q S1 V W Z(g,k,p,r)
Legal Aid undertaken, Legal Aid Franchise and Member of Accident Line
Ptr: Bansel, Gurbinderpal Singh LLB Treasurer of ELA . *Nov 1995
Davies, Mr John M MA(Oxon) President of the City of Westminster & Holborn Law Society. . . . . . . *§Jan 1965
Levison, Miss Linda R LLB(Lond) . . . . *Jun 1980
Lightwood, Mr Gary. . . . . *Nov 1986
McCarthy, Miss Frances E LLB President of APIL . . *Jun 1981
O'Brady, Ms Niamh Mary BA; MA; LLB . . . . *Oct 1984
Phelan, Ms Caroline Mary LLB . . . . *Oct 1994
Radcliffe, Ms Jane LLB(Hons)(L'pool) . . . . *Feb 1990
Statham, Mr Paul M LLB . . . . *Nov 1985
Weatherby, Mr Marcus LLB . . . . *Sep 1996
Ast: Kilmister, Mr John William LLB . . . . *Nov 1994
Mehan, Mr Vijay LLB . . . . *Oct 2001
Smith, Ms Deborah LLB. . . . . *Oct 2000

PATTON MORENO & ASVAT ‡
4th Floor 22 Old Bond Street London W1S 4PY
Tel: 020 7491 9200 *Fax:* 020 7629 6933
E-mail: infolondon@pmalawpers.com

PAUL GUBBAY SOLICITORS ‡
7 Praed Street London W2 1NJ
Tel: 020 7262 7821 *Fax:* 020 7479 9635
E-mail: paul@pglegal.com

PAUL HASTINGS JANOFSKY & WALKER LLP ‡
10 Bishops Square London E1 6EG
Tel: 020 7710 2000 *Fax:* 020 7796 2233

PAYNE HICKS BEACH ‡
10 New Square Lincoln's Inn London WC2A 3QG
Tel: 020 7465 4300 *Fax:* 020 7465 4400
Dx: 40 LONDON/CHANCERY LN
E-mail: mail@phb.co.uk
Work: A1 B1 C1 C2 C3 D1 E F1 G J1 J2 K1 L O Q R1 R2 S1 S2 T1 T2 W X Z(b,c,d,e,i,k,o,p,q,w,z)

PAYTON'S SOLICITORS ‡
9-13 Cursitor Street London EC4A 1LL
Tel: 020 7405 1999 *Fax:* 020 7405 1991
Emergency telephone 07973 256529
E-mail: keima@payton.fg.co.uk
List of partners: K Payton
Work: G H
Advocacy and Legal Aid Franchise
Ptr: Payton, Miss Keima. . . . . Feb 1998

PEACE FARNELL LIMITED ‡
2 Welford Place Wimbledon London SW19 5AJ
Tel: 020 3086 8990
E-mail: nichola.peace@peacefarnell.com

PEACHEY & CO ‡
95 Aldwych London WC2B 4JF
Tel: 020 7316 5200 *Fax:* 020 7316 5222
Dx: 108 LONDON/CHANCERY LN
E-mail: email@peachey.co.uk
List of partners: N J Alun-Jones, H W Ashton, O M Lewis, D A Wilson, R C Wilson
Languages: French, German, Italian
Work: C1 C3 E J1
Ptr: Alun-Jones, Mr Nicholas Justin . . . . *Feb 1996
Ashton, Mr Hubert W BA(Exon) . . . . *§Oct 1983
Lewis, Mr Owen M BA . . . . *Dec 1978
Wilson, Mr David A LLB. . . . . *Nov 1985
Wilson, Mr Robert C LLB(Exon). . . . . *Apr 1981

PEACOCK & CO ‡
94 High Street Wimbledon London SW19 5EG
Tel: 020 8944 5290 *Fax:* 020 8944 5303
Dx: 35055 WIMBLEDON VILLAGE
E-mail: office@peacock-law.co.uk

PEARL & CO ‡
166 Station Road London NW4 3SP
Tel: 020 8202 6202 *Fax:* 020 8202 6205
E-mail: pearlaw@msn.com
List of partners: D Pearl
Office: London N15, Stanmore
Languages: French, German, Greek, Hebrew, Punjabi, Spanish
Work: B1 C1 C2 E F1 J1 K1 L M2 N Q S1 T1 T2 W Z(m,o)
Agency, Legal Aid undertaken and Member of Accident Line
Ptr: Pearl, Mr David BA; LLM(Lond) . . . . *Feb 1989

PEARL & CO
13 Ashmount Road London N15 4DD
Tel: 020 8808 4898 *Fax:* 020 8808 0221 *Dx:* 59334 HENDON
E-mail: pearlman@msn.com
Office: London NW4, Stanmore

J PEARLMAN ‡
Newman House Russell Parade Golders Green London NW11 9NN
Tel: 020 8458 9266 *Fax:* 020 8458 8529
Dx: 151121 HENDON WEST
E-mail: acb@bsnet.co.uk
List of partners: J Pearlman
Languages: Hebrew, Yiddish
Work: C1 E S1 S2 W Z(d)
Ptr: Pearlman, Mr Joseph MA; LLM(Cantab). . . . . *Jul 1971
Con: Becker, Mr Allan LLB . . . . *Sep 1999

RICHARD PEARLMAN & CO
29 Corsham Street London N1 6DR
Tel: 020 7490 7224
Office: London EC2

RICHARD PEARLMAN LLP ‡
27 Phipp Street London EC2A 4NP
Tel: 020 7739 6100 *Fax:* 020 7739 6300
Dx: 33867 FINSBURY SQUARE
E-mail: rkp@rpandco.com
List of partners: A H Bloom, A Draper, R K Pearlman
Office: London N1
Languages: Spanish
Work: B1 E F1 L O Q R1 S1 S2 W Z(l)
Ptr: Bloom, Mr Anthony H LLB(Hons) . . . . *Oct 1987
Draper, Mr Adam LLB(Hons) . . . . *Sep 1993
Pearlman, Mr Richard Keith BA Sweet & Maxwell Law Prize 1984 . . . . *Sep 1987
Ast: Atkinson, Miss Victoria Amanda LLB . . . . Feb 2003
Hado, Miss Amanda LLB . . . . Jan 2005
Taylor, Miss Donna Louise LLB . . . . Jun 2004

PEARLMANS SOLICITORS LLP ‡
39 Finchley Lane Hendon London NW4 1BX
Tel: 020 8201 6311 *Fax:* 020 8201 6344 *Dx:* 59347 HENDON
E-mail: info@pearlmans.co.uk
List of partners: S Franklin, D F Pearlman
Work: B1 C1 D1 E K1 K3 L S1 S2 W
Mem: Franklin, Mrs Sara LLB(Hons). . . . . Sep 1993
Pearlman, Mrs Denise F LLB(Hons). . . . . *Nov 1982
Ast: Landsberg, Ms Lesley. . . . . *Sep 2001

PEARSON LOWE ‡
48 Queen Anne Street Westminster London W1G 9JJ
Tel: 020 7224 0888 *Fax:* 020 7486 4220
E-mail: mail@pearsonlowe.co.uk
List of partners: G Dempsey, P T Hamlyn, J Pearson
Languages: French
Work: C1 C2 E L O Q R2 S1 S2 T1 T2 W Z(i)
Ptr: Dempsey, Ms Gillian LLB . . . . *Oct 1993
Hamlyn, Mr Peter T MA; LLB . . . . *§Nov 1961
Pearson, Mr James LLM . . . . *Oct 1970

PEARSONS SOLICITORS ‡
Broadway House 15-16 Deptford Broadway London SE8 4PA
Tel: 020 8694 6498 *Fax:* 020 8694 0402
E-mail: markjpearson@btinternet.com

PEGDEN & CO ‡
811 Green Lanes London N21 2RX
Tel: 020 8360 4715 *Fax:* 020 8364 1011
Dx: 36952 WINCHMORE HILL
List of partners: E Lombard
Work: E O S1 W
SPr: Lombard, Mr Enrico LLB . . . . Jan 1980

PEIRIS SOLICITORS ‡
89a High Road London N22 6BB
Tel: 020 8888 3616 *Fax:* 020 8888 3691

S C PELENTRIDES & CO ‡
2 Cambridge Terrace 419 Lordship Lane Tottenham London N17 6AG
Tel: 020 8365 1688 *Fax:* 020 8885 3677
E-mail: pelentrideslegal@aol.com
List of partners: S C Pelentrides
Languages: French, Greek
Work: B1 C1 D1 E F1 G H K1 L M1 N O P Q S1 S2 V W Z(c,g,i,k,q)
Fixed Fee Interview and Legal Aid undertaken
Ptr: Pelentrides, Savvas C LLB . . . . *Dec 1977

PEMBERTON GREENISH LLP ‡
45 Cadogan Gardens London SW3 2AQ
Tel: 020 7591 3333 *Fax:* 020 7591 3300 *Dx:* 35113 CHELSEA
E-mail: law@pglaw.co.uk
List of partners: R S Barham, L Blackwell, J D G Curtis, J W Eades, I W Gill, K D Glanville, J C Goodchild, D J W Greenish, J D McGeough, G E Pemberton, J D A Powell, A J F Stebbings
Languages: French, German, Hebrew, Italian, Welsh
Work: A1 C1 E L Q R1 S1 S2 T2 W Z(d)
Ptr: Barham, Mr Robert S LLB. . . . . *Oct 1990
Greenish, Mr Damian J W BA. . . . . Dec 1979
Mem: Blackwell, Ms Laura MA(Cantab) . . . . *Sep 1994
Curtis, Mr Jeremy David Godfrey BSc. . . . . Oct 1996
Eades, Mr Jason W LLB(Hons); DipLP; PSC . . . . *Nov 1997
Gill, Mr Ian William LLB . . . . Jan 1974
Glanville, Miss Kerry Denise LLB . . . . *Oct 1986
Goodchild, Mr John C LLB . . . . Oct 1985
McGeough, Mr John D LLB . . . . *Nov 1987
Pemberton, Mr Giles E LLB(Lond). . . . . *May 1978
Powell, Miss Janet D A BA(York) . . . . *Jun 1976
Stebbings, Mr Andrew J F MA(Oxon) . . . . *§Apr 1976
Ast: Checkley, Ms Laura LLB(Hons) . . . . Sep 2004
Doval, Miss Rosa Maria LLB(Hons). . . . . Jan 2002
Edwards, Mr William Michael Henry MA(Oxon) . . . . Sep 2004
Favre, Mrs Anna Bronwen LLB(Hons)(Lond) . . . . . Oct 2004
McCormick Paice, Mrs Rosemary BA(Hons)(Dunelm) . Sep 1996
Manderfield, Emma. . . . . Mar 2005
Mitchell, Miss Abigail Louise LLB(Hons). . . . . . . Nov 1994
Reeves, Mrs Susan Emma LLB(Hons) . . . . Mar 2002
Roberts, Mr Simon J . . . . *Nov 1985
Roskell, Mr Michael William LLB . . . . Nov 1988
Sales, Miss Elizabeth Jocelyn MA. . . . . Sep 2007
Simpson, Mrs Katherine Mary BA . . . . Nov 1993
Con: Drake, Mr Andrew MA(Oxon) . . . . *Dec 1976
Henry, Miss Jane Margaret Helen BA . . . . Apr 1976
King-Farlow, Mr Charles MA(Hons)(Oxon). . . . . . . *Jul 1965
Millett, Mr Andrew MA(Cantab) . . . . *Mar 1991

PEMBROKES SOLICITORS ‡
Rivington House 82 Great Eastern Street London EC2A 3JF
Tel: 0800 689 9163 *Fax:* 020 7112 8276
E-mail: post@pembrokesolicitors.com

PENNINGTONS ‡
Abacus House 33 Gutter Lane London EC2V 8AR
Tel: 020 7457 3000 *Fax:* 020 7457 3240 *Dx:* 42605 CHEAPSIDE
E-mail: info@penningtons.co.uk
List of partners: A M Appelboam-Meadows, C Archer, P Barth, S Bickerdike, D Bickford, P Bond, G Bosi, C M Brooks, J Burton, S Cardew, N Carter, M Cash, A Casstles, M Codd, M G Cole, T A Cole, N Curtis, L Dadswell, T Davies, R S Dubash, J Ewens, A Ezekiel, E Ezekiel, A C Frankum, J D Heuvel, G R F Hudson, R M Hunter, P Jansen, R Jarvis, D Kendall, J Klein, J Kyriacou, D Lambert, S Law, M Lee, C J Lintott, L J Lintott, P F B Luscombe, R Macro, A Madon, P Mander, P Massey, D C Masters, P D P McElligott, N A McMichael, N D Morris, J Nadin, D M Niven, T M Palmer, M Pearson, T S Rafter, D J Raine, C H Smith, L A Storey, D A Taylor, J Thackray, J W Thomas, R L Underwood, J Vengadesan, M A White, A R Whitwell, K Wingfield, G J Woodhead, J Yew
Office: Basingstoke, Godalming
Languages: Afrikaans, French, German, Gujarati, Italian, Punjabi, Russian, Spanish, Turkish, Urdu
Work: A1 B1 C1 C2 C3 D1 D2 E F1 G H I J1 J2 K1 K2 L M1 M2 N O P Q R1 R2 S1 S2 T1 T2 W Z(a,b,c,d,e,f,g,h,i,j,k,l,m,o,p,q,r,s,t,w,z)
Emergency Action, Agency, Advocacy and Fixed Fee Interview undertaken
Ptr: Archer, Miss Clare LLB(Hons). . . . . Oct 1994
Barth, Mr Philip MA(Cantab). . . . . *May 1982
Bond, Mr Peter . . . . Dec 1989
Carter, Ms Nichola LLB . . . . *May 1999
Casstles, Mr Andrew MA(Hons). . . . . Oct 1997
Codd, Mr Martin LLB . . . . *Feb 1989
Dubash, Rustam Soli LLB. . . . . *Nov 1984
Ezekiel, Mr Abraham BA(Hons); MA(Lond) . . . . . . *Dec 1990
Ezekiel, Mr Ellis LLB(Hons) . . . . *Nov 1989
Frankum, Ms Anna Catherine BA(Hons)(Oxon) . . . . *Nov 1995
Heuvel, Mr Jonathan Dominic BA(Hons)(Oxon) . . . . *Nov 1993
Hudson, Mr Geoffrey Robert Francois MA(Cantab) . . *Apr 1978
Hunter, Mr Richard Malcolm. . . . . *Nov 1972
Jansen, Mr Peter LLB(Hons) . . . . Oct 1981
Jarvis, Mr Russell BA . . . . *Jul 1989
Klein, Mr James. Sep 1998

See p2 for the Key to Work Categories & other symbols

Kyriacou, Mr John . . . Sep 1989
Lambert, Mr Donald BA(Oxon) . . . *Nov 1985
Lintott, Mr Christopher John MA(Oxon) . . . *Dec 1975
Lintott, Mrs Lesley Joan MA(Oxon) . . . *§Jun 1975
McElligott, Mr Peter David Patrick BA(Hons) . . . *Mar 1987
McMichael, Mr Noel Anderson BA . . . *Oct 1979
Macro, Mr Robert . . . Sep 2002
Madon, Ms Ava BSc(Hons) . . . Nov 1993
Mander, Mr Paul . . . Nov 1991
Massey, Mr Peter MEng(Hons) . . . Sep 2000
Masters, Mr David C BA . . . *Apr 1981
Morris, Mr Neil D LLB . . . *May 1977
Nadin, Mr James LLB(Hons) . . . Nov 1999
Niven, Mr David Matthew LLB(Lond) . . . *Nov 1985
Pearson, Mr Malcolm MA(Cantab); LLB(Lond) . . . *Oct 1987
Raine, Mr David John LLB(Hons) . . . *Dec 1986
Smith, Miss Catriona Helen MA(Cantab) . . . *§Jun 1978
Taylor, Mr Duncan Alexander BSc(Hons)(Econ) . . . *§Oct 1981
Thackray, Julia . . . Nov 1994
Thomas, J Wynne MA(Cantab) . . . *Apr 1979
White, Mr Michael A BA . . . *Jun 1980
Wingfield, Miss Katrina LLB(Exon) . . . Mar 1974
Woodhead, Mr Geoffrey John BA(Hons) . . . *§Oct 1980
Yew, Mr Julian . . . Apr 2000
Curtis, Nicole . . . NSP
Asoc: Basu, Saionton . . . Dec 2008
Godfrey, Mr Andrew . . . Mar 2004
Hammond, Mr Colin MA; LLB . . . Mar 1994
Haywood, Mr Andrew . . . Jul 2001
McVeigh, Maddie . . . Apr 2000
Reid, Jenny . . . Sep 2001
Saini, Pat . . . Nov 1998
Watmough, Miss Maria . . . *Apr 1998
Ast: Albayaty, Miss Asil LLB; LLM . . . Dec 2009
Barker, Katy . . . May 2010
Barnes, Ms Melanie . . . Jul 2007
Bruce-Smith, Anna . . . Sep 2008
Burke, Linda . . . Sep 2008
Burrows, Mr Mark . . . May 2005
Chin, Efun . . . Mar 2006
Dare, Hannah . . . Sep 2010
de Freitas, Gillian . . . Jun 2009
de Silva, Nicole . . . Sep 2007
El-Chamaa, Hazar . . . May 2006
Jameson, Mr Tom . . . Sep 2011
Kearsley, Mr David . . . Jun 2006
Le Roux, Hein . . . Nov 2009
Lyne, Alexandra . . . Nov 2009
McCann, Catherine . . . Sep 2009
McLardie, Lauren . . . Oct 2011
McNeilly, Mr James . . . Sep 2007
Matheson, Katherine . . . Sep 2008
Mistry, Pria . . . Sep 2008
Moorhouse, Ailsa . . . Nov 2009
O'Brien, David . . . Oct 2009
Peterson, Anne . . . Sep 2003
Pilgrim, Tarnya . . . Nov 1996
Rickman, Miss Denielle LLB(Hons) . . . Nov 2003
Roberts, Sophie . . . Sep 2011
Robinson, Ben . . . Oct 2008
Rogers, Fiona . . . Jun 2007
Scarfe, Rachael . . . Sep 2009
Sidhu, Sandip . . . Jul 2010
Suarez-Neves, Alicia . . . Sep 2010
Whitehouse, Lucy . . . Sep 2011
Wilks, Neil . . . Sep 2009
Con: Eaton, Mr Paul Gerard MA(Cantab) . . . *§Apr 1970
Frankel, Mr William H BA(Cape Town) . . . *Jun 1970
Grey, Mr Christopher . . . Dec 1971
Howard, Mr Peter MA(Cantab) . . . Mar 1976
Kidd, Mr Peter S . . . *Nov 1998
McBrien, Mr Howard Joseph . . . *§Mar 1970
Panizzo, Mrs Sarah E LLB . . . *§Dec 1976
Picton-Howell, Teja . . . Sep 1987
Ralph, Mr Stephen BA(Law); FCIArb; FSPI; MIPA; PGDip Licensed Insolvency Practitioner . . . Dec 1975

PEPI & CO ‡
2 Station Parade Southgate London N14 5BJ
Tel: 020 8886 0500 *Fax:* 020 8886 2899
List of partners: P Polycarpou
Languages: Greek
SPr: Polycarpou, Pepi . . . Feb 1992

PERCY SHORT & CUTHBERT ‡
(incorporating Montague Gardner & Selby)
Second Floor 402 Holloway Road Holloway Islington London N7 6PZ
Est: 1892
Tel: 020 7700 0265 *Fax:* 020 7607 2489 *Dx:* 38653 HOLLOWAY
Emergency telephone 07659 137891
E-mail: psc@percyshort.co.uk
List of partners: S M Friday, S Naik
Languages: Bengali, British Sign Language, Czech, French, German, Gujarati
Work: B2 D1 E G H K1 K3 L N O Q R2 S1 S2 W Z(c,q)
Emergency Action, Advocacy, Fixed Fee Interview, Legal Aid undertaken and Legal Aid Franchise
Ptr: Friday, Mr Stephen M LLB . . . *§Dec 1990
Naik, Mrs Shobha LLB(Hons); LLM(Cantab) . . . *Nov 1996
Ast: Matlib, Miss Naureen . . . *Jan 2005
Con: Boyes, Mr William O MA(Cantab) . . . *§Mar 1973
Selby, Mr John F BA . . . Jan 1976

PERERA & CO ‡
1st Floor 301 Romford Road Forest Gate London E7 9HA
Tel: 020 8503 0030 *Fax:* 020 8519 7093
Emergency telephone 07885 429910
E-mail: perera121@hotmail.com
List of partners: C Perera, M M D Perera
Languages: Sinhalese
Work: K1 V Z(i)
Emergency Action, Advocacy, Legal Aid undertaken and Legal Aid Franchise
Ptr: Perera, Ms Chandrika LLB ♦ . . . Jan 1990
Perera, Meegahage M D ♦ . . . *Nov 1987

PETER BLOXHAM ‡
Flat 3 Queen Alexandra Mansions 3 Grape Street London WC2H 8DX
Tel: 020 7240 0708 *Fax:* 020 7240 9108

PETERS & PETERS ‡
15 Fetter Lane London EC4A 1BW
Tel: 020 7629 7991 *Fax:* 020 7499 6792
Dx: 407 LONDON/CHANCERY LN
E-mail: law@petersandpeters.co.uk
List of partners: J M Balfour-Lynn, L M Delahunty, K Garbett, S L Hannam, C H Lipworth, H J McDowell, L J McMillan, K E Oliver, P M Raphael, J E Rickards, E M Robertson, J Tickner
Languages: French, German
Work: B1 B2 C1 C3 E F1 G H I J1 K1 L M1 M2 N O P Q R1 S1 S2 T1 T2 W Z(b,c,d,e,g,k,l,p)
Legal Aid undertaken and Legal Aid Franchise
Ptr: Balfour-Lynn, Mrs Julia M BA . . . *Oct 1984
Delahunty, Ms Louise M LLB . . . *Oct 1984
Garbett, Ms Kathryn LLB(Essex) . . . *Oct 1988
Hannam, Ms Sarah Lindsay MA(Oxon) . . . *Nov 1990
Lipworth, Ms Claire H LLB . . . Oct 1992
McDowell, Ms Helen Jane BA . . . Jan 1995
McMillan, Ms Lisa J LLB . . . Apr 1995
Oliver, Mr Keith E BA . . . *Jul 1980
Raphael, Mr P Monty LLB . . . *Mar 1962
Rickards, Ms Joanne E LLB . . . *Jan 1989
Robertson, Ms Elizabeth Mary LLB . . . *Nov 1995
Tickner, Mr Jonathan LLB . . . *Nov 1995
Ast: Doobay, Anand LLB(Hons); LLM . . . *Sep 1999
Friend, Mrs Clemency MA(Hons) . . . Sep 1998
McCann, Mr Stephen BSc . . . *Oct 1997
McCluskey, Mr David Robert . . . Jun 1998
O'Kane, Mr Michael Colin LLB(Hons) . . . Nov 1992
Smith, Mr Stephen Paul BA(Hons) . . . *Sep 2001
Swift, Mr Neil Thomas LLB(Hons) . . . *Jun 1999
Vaughan-Brown, Miss Janine Nicolle Gemini LLB . . . Mar 1996

PETROU & CO ‡
Block A Southgate Office Village 284 Chase Road London N14 6HF
Tel: 020 8920 5800 *Fax:* 020 8920 5805
E-mail: info@petrouandco.com
List of partners: A Costa-Petrou, A C Petrou
Languages: Greek
Work: B1 C1 E F1 J1 O Q R2 S1 S2 W Z(l)
Ptr: Costa-Petrou, Mrs Argiroulla BA(Hons) . . . *Jun 2000
Petrou, Mr Andros Christos LLB(Hons) . . . *Apr 1992

PETROU LAW PARTNERSHIP ‡
21 Grand Parade Green Lanes London N4 1LA
Tel: 020 8802 9393 *Fax:* 020 8802 9804 *Dx:* 57757 HARRINGAY
E-mail: mail@petrou-law.com
List of partners: P Petrou, S Petrou
Languages: Greek
Work: B1 C1 J1 K1 N O Q S2 W Z(l,q)
Fixed Fee Interview undertaken
Ptr: Petrou, Mr Petros . . . Sep 1990
Petrou, Stylianos . . . Oct 1997
Ast: Petrou, Mrs Doroulla . . . Nov 2000

PHIL SOLICITORS ‡
121 Bowes Road Palmers Green London N13 4SB
Tel: 020 8888 6199 *Fax:* 020 8888 9392

PHILCOX GRAY & CO ‡
(in association with Freemans)
61 Peckham High Street London SE15 5RU
Tel: 020 7703 2285 *Fax:* 020 7358 5660 *Dx:* 34253 PECKHAM
E-mail: postroom@philcoxgray.co.uk
List of partners: S S Donn, H Freeman, B King
Languages: Farsi, French, Spanish, Yoruba
Work: D1 D2 G H K1 L N S1 S2 V W Z(i)
Emergency Action, Agency, Advocacy, Fixed Fee Interview, Legal Aid undertaken and Legal Aid Franchise
Ptr: Donn, Ms Sheila S BSc(Econ) . . . *Feb 1992
Freeman, Mr Howard LLB(Hons) . . . *Oct 1985
King, Ms Beverley LLB . . . *Feb 1992
Ast: Akinwale, Mrs Josephine LLB(Hons) . . . *Jul 2001
Bishi, Mr Folarin LLB . . . *Jan 1999
Butler, Mr William J BA(Oxon) . . . *Jun 1981
Dawson-Asaam, Ms Eva LLB(Hons) . . . Dec 2001
Richards-Clarke, Ms Tonya . . . Nov 1994
Taylor, Mrs Sonya Jacqueline . . . *Oct 1993

PHILIPP & CO ‡
43 Lyttelton Court Lyttelton Road London N2 0EB
Tel: 020 7566 8244
List of partners: J Philipp
Ptr: Philipp, Ms J . . . Sep 2001

PHILIPPOU & CO ‡
Idalion House 273 Green Lanes Palmers Green London N13 4XE
Tel: 020 8882 4222 *Fax:* 020 8882 9993
E-mail: helen@philippousolicitors.com
Languages: Greek
Work: C1 D1 D2 E J1 K1 K3 L O Q S1 S2 W
Agency, Legal Aid undertaken and Legal Aid Franchise
Ast: Philippou, Ms Helen . . . *Jan 1985
Zavros, Mr Savvas LLB(Hons) . . . *Jan 2003

PHILLIPS & LEIGH ‡
5 Pemberton Row London EC4A 3BA
Tel: 020 7822 8888 *Fax:* 020 7822 8899

DAVID PHILLIPS & PARTNERS
72 Wimpole Street London W1G 9RP
Tel: 020 7486 5525 *Fax:* 020 7486 5526 *Dx:* 44642 MAYFAIR
E-mail: info@dpp-law.com
Office: Birmingham, Bootle (2 offices), Chadwell Heath, Leicester, Liverpool, London E1, London SE18, Manchester, Nelson, Wealdstone
Work: B2 G H

DAVID PHILLIPS & PARTNERS
219a Block P Island Business Centre 18-36 Wellington Street London SE18 5PF
Tel: 020 8597 5557 *Fax:* 020 8599 3435
E-mail: info@dpp.law.com
Office: Birmingham, Bootle (2 offices), Chadwell Heath, Leicester, Liverpool, London E1, London W1, Manchester, Nelson, Wealdstone

DAVID PHILLIPS & PARTNERS
408 Tower Bridge Business Centre 46-48 East Smithfield London E1W 1AW
Tel: 020 7709 3061 *Fax:* 020 7709 3062
E-mail: info@dpp.law.com
Office: Birmingham, Bootle (2 offices), Chadwell Heath, Leicester, Liverpool, London SE18, London W1, Manchester, Nelson, Wealdstone

FIONA PHILLIPS ‡
112 Wise Lane London NW7 2RB
Tel: 020 8959 9097 *Fax:* 020 8959 3341

PHOENIX LAW PARTNERSHIP ‡
86 Merton High Street South Wimbledon London SW19 1BE
Tel: 020 8543 9290 *Fax:* 020 8543 0843

PHOROS TRUSTEES (UK) LIMITED ‡
23 Austin Frairs London EC2N 2QP
Tel: 020 3178 4320 *Fax:* 020 3178 4321
E-mail: office@phorosgroup.com

PIERCE GLYNN ‡
8 Union Street Southwark London SE1 1SZ
Tel: 020 7407 0007 *Fax:* 020 7407 0444 *Dx:* 144360 SOUTHWARK 4
E-mail: mail@pierceglynn.co.uk
List of partners: D A Gellner, P Glynn, S E Pierce, J E L Thomson
Office: Bristol
Ptr: Gellner, Ms Deborah A . . . Nov 1989
Glynn, Ms Polly . . . *Sep 1993
Pierce, Mr Stephen E . . . *Jun 1990
Thomson, Ms Joanna Elizabeth Lee BA . . . Sep 1992

PIERCY & CO ‡
39 Carson Road London SE21 8HT

MYRIA PIERI & CO SOLICITORS ‡
13 Poplar Walk Herne Hill London SE24 0BX
Tel: 020 7274 8488 *Fax:* 020 7274 8488
E-mail: myria.pieri@ntlworld.com

PIERRE THOMAS & PARTNERS ‡
1 Cambridge Court 210 Shepherds Bush Road London W6 7NJ
Tel: 020 7602 0305 *Fax:* 020 7603 5062
Dx: 46770 HAMMERSMITH 3
E-mail: info@afa-ptp.co.uk
List of partners: S Ball, L S Mair, R Rataj
Languages: French, German, Spanish
Work: G M2 N O Q Z(j)
Member of Accident Line
Ptr: Ball, Mr Simon LLB(Hons); Diplome d'etudes Juridiques Francaises . . . *Apr 1991
Mair, Ms Lesley Susan MA(Hons) . . . *Sep 1978
Rataj, Mr Roman BA . . . Mar 2000
Asoc: Straughan, Ms Julie . . . Mar 2003
Ast: Waller, Ms Rebecca . . . Sep 2003
Con: Thomas, Mr Pierre Sydney LLB(Hons) . . . *Dec 1969

FRANCIS PIESSE ‡
The Dove Pier Lower Mall London W6 9DJ
Tel: 020 8748 0010
E-mail: francis.piesse@virgin.net
List of partners: F W R Piesse
Work: S1 S2
Fixed Fee Interview undertaken
SPr: Piesse, Mr Francis W R . . . *Jul 1971

PILLAI & JONES ‡
Lower Ground Floor 63 Broadway London E15 4BQ
Tel: 020 8555 3675 *Fax:* 020 8519 6436 *Dx:* 5416 STRATFORD
E-mail: pillaiandjones@btconnect.com

PILLSBURY WINTHROP SHAW PITTMAN LLP ‡
Level 23 Tower 42 25 Old Broad Street London EC2N 1HQ
Tel: 020 7847 9500 *Fax:* 020 7847 9501
List of partners: A Maughan, D A P Skinner, A M Smith
Ptr: Maughan, Mr Alistair LLB . . . *Sep 1987
Skinner, Mr David A P MA . . . *Sep 1995
Smith, Mr Andrew M LLB . . . *Sep 1985
Asoc: Kilbourne, Mrs Sandra Helen MA . . . *Feb 2000
McMahon, Miss Marie-Louise . . . Nov 1998
Nagle, Mr Anthony LLB(TVU); LPC . . . *Sep 1999
Roughton, Mr Timothy James MEng(Oxon); LPC; CPE*Sep 1999
Tarrant, Mrs Tracey BSc(Reading); CPE; LPC; PGDipIPLaw . . . *Sep 1999
Weir, Miss Elizabeth Anne MA . . . *Oct 1996
Wright, Mr Timothy Marcus BA; LLM; LSF . . . *Oct 1994
Young, Miss Alicia LLB . . . Aug 2003

PINDORIA SOLICITORS ‡
Level 7 Tower 42 25 Old Broad Street London EC2N 1HN
E-mail: info@pindorialaw.co.uk
Office: Stanmore

PINHORN BURNET ‡
591 Fulham Road Fulham Broadway Hammersmith & Fulham London SW6 5UB
Tel: 020 7385 6688
List of partners: D H Burnet
Work: W
SPr: Burnet, Mr David H . . . *Feb 1977

PINI FRANCO LLP ‡
22-24 Ely Place London EC1N 6TE
Tel: 020 7566 3140 *Fax:* 020 7566 3144
Dx: 487 LONDON/CHANCERY LN
E-mail: info@pinifranco.com
List of partners: N I F Bingham, R Franco, S Lavery, F Nolan, D A Pini
Languages: French, Italian, Polish, Spanish
Work: A3 B1 C1 C2 E J1 M2 O Q S1 S2 T1 U1 U2 W Z(b,e,j,l)
Ptr: Bingham, Mr Nicholas I F BA . . . *Mar 1990
Franco, Mr Rocco LLM(LSE); Italian Avvocato . . . *Apr 1994
Lavery, Mr Sandro LLB(Hons) . . . Jul 2000
Nolan, Ms Fionnuala LLB(Hons) . . . Sep 1997
Pini, Mr Domenic A MA(Cantab) . . . *Dec 1988

PINSENT MASONS LLP ‡
30 Crown Place Earl Street London EC2A 4ES
Est: 2004
Tel: 020 7418 7000 *Fax:* 020 7418 7050 *Dx:* 157620 BROADGATE 3
E-mail: enquiries@pinsentmasons.com
List of partners: A Aisbett, M Allan, G Alty, S Andrews, B Ang, P R Atkinson, K Ayre, M Baker, V K Bange, D Barker, I Barker, A P Barlow, G F Bell, C B Berkeley, N J Berry, S M Biddle, J Birch, J M Bishop, M Bishop, A J Black, M A Blanksby, M Blewett, N H Bogle, A J Bond, R S Booker, C D Booth, D S Bould, A Bowden, M P Boyd, J Brocklehurst, S V Brown, H W D Bruce-Watt, P C E Bullock, A W S Bunch, T J Burton, F Button, J L Castle, M O Cawthron, A Cha, H Chang, S J Chapman, J M S Christian, I H

Clark, P M Clayton, J Cleland, J Coane, J Cohen, J D Coley, M A Collingwood, S N Colvin, V Connor, J Crookes, S G Cross, L J Crow, R Daffern, E R Davies, L M Davies, A Davis, A Denton, W R Dixon, N Dobson, C M Dodsworth, N Dorman, J B Dye, G M Edwards, A Elliott, J Ellis, A C Farkas, H J Farr, J M Fell, J R Fenner, R J Fink, D Fischer, C A Fitton, T D Flanagan, B R Fleetwood, R E Foley, R Ford, J R Fortnam, B H Francis, J A French, L D Fryer, C P Garvie, H Gill, J Gill, V Goddard, P Goldsborough, E Goodwyn, S Gray, J A Greaves, M Griffith, S D V Gronow, J Hambury, M C Hann, P M Harkin, M J Harman, A P Harris, J Harris, M Harris, J Hart, N J Hart, K Hartley, R A Hartshorn, P Hawthorn, M Heaton, K H Hew, F J Heyes, A J Hibbert, M D Hopkins, A S Hornigold, J S Hoskin, J Howes, R Hutchings, I R Hyde, D Isaac, L Jacobs, R P Jay, J D Jeffries, M Job, L Johnson, T Johnson, L J Jones, N F Jones, S Joyston-Bechal, A M Jucker, C M Kelly, P C Kennedy, P Kent, A M Kerr, K Khangura, A Kilvington, V King, N E J Kissack, S B Laight, I Laing, D B Lancaster, M A Lane, D M Larder, R B G Laudy, J Lawson-King, T R Leman, S P Levy, A D Lewington, D Lewis, W Lewis, G Lougher, A M P Lovitt, G J Lowson, J MacKenzie, A M Masraf, A Masterson, R A McCallough, N P D McClea, F McMillan, R J S Mecrate-Butcher, A S Meeks, M C Membery, S J Miles, R Moir, J I Monaghan, C Mordue, E R Morgan, N Morris, A Morrison, C J Moss, M P Mullarkey, C P Mullen, S Mumford, P L Munro, D Nash, A J Norman, A Normington, I G Nurse-Marsh, J O'Shea, W H J Oliver, K Orviss, M R Owen, S Paciorek, L Parisi, C E Park, W M Parker, L Patmore, A J Paton, M P D Peeters, W Peter, D J Pett, J P Phillips, D J Philpot, S J Pigden, S Plunkett, A Quinlan, J A Reardon, K J Rees, P Rice, J H Richards, M D Richards, H E Ridge, J Riley, A Roberts, G Roberts, M C Roberts, C A Robins, M R Roe, V B Rowan, D P Ryan, M D Ryley, J Salmon, J Salway, S Sawicki, S Scholefield, C C Seddon, M Shaw, D W Shelley, H O P Stephens, D Stevenson, D Stroud, C Taylor, S J Thomas, J Timmins, J M J Tonks, J Trevethan, G P A Twist, J Tyerman, G R Tyler, K Valentine, C J Vickers, K Walker, C A L Wallace, G Warrington, R Watkinson, A J Watney, A M Watson, M Webster, A C Whetham, I R Whitaker, N C Whitaker, J White, A Whitton, R D Williams, A Winton, A K Wood, P Wood, C Workman, S S Wortley, C Wyn Davies, A P Yates, P Young

Office: Birmingham, Bristol, Leeds, Manchester

Work: A3 B1 B2 C1 C2 C3 E I J1 J2 M1 M2 O R1 R2 T1 U1 U2 X Z(b,e,j,o,p,q,u,za)

Emergency Action undertaken

Ptr: Allan, Mr Michael . . . Mar 2005
Andrews, Ms Susan . . . Aug 1991
Ang, Mr Bernard . . . Mar 1992
Ayre, Ms Kirsty . . . Feb 2003
Baker, Mr Matthew . . . Oct 1996
Barker, Mr David BA(Hons) . . . Sep 1997
Bell, Mr Gordon F LLB ♦ . . . *Sep 1990
Berkeley, Mr Christopher B BA; MA(Oxon) . . . *May 1980
Berry, Mr Nicholas J . . . Aug 1988
Biddle, Miss Susan Mary BA(Cantab) Stokes Memorial Prize 1988; Judge Jellinek Prize 1988 . . . *Nov 1990
Birch, Mr Jay . . . Nov 1994
Bishop, Mr John M . . . *Apr 1971
Bishop, Mr Martin . . . *Jan 1993
Black, Mr Andrew James . . . Nov 1997
Blanksby, Mr Mark A . . . *Nov 1991
Blewett, Mr Myles . . . *Oct 1994
Bogle, Mr Neil H . . . *Sep 1967
Booker, Mr Russell S . . . *Nov 1981
Bould, Ms Deborah S . . . Nov 1996
Bowden, Ms Anne . . . Sep 1998
Bruce-Watt, Mr Hugh William Douglas BA(Cantab); MA; LLB . . . Sep 1996
Bullock, Mr Peter C E . . . Nov 1988
Bunch, Mr Anthony W S . . . *Apr 1978
Burton, Mr Timothy J LLB . . . *Jan 1982
Button, Ms Fran LLB; MCs(Construction Law & Arbitration) . . . *Nov 1996
Castle, Miss Jacquetta Louise BA(Hons) . . . *Dec 1988
Cawthron, Mr Mark Owen LLB(Bris); ATII . . . *§May 1981
Cha, Ms Angela . . . *Jan 1990
Chang, Ms Helen . . . Jan 1994
Clark, Mr Ian Howard MA(Oxon) . . . *§Apr 1977
Coane, Mr Jonathan . . . Sep 1998
Cohen, Mr Julian . . . Aug 1994
Colvin, Mr Simon N . . . Sep 1996
Connor, Mr Vincent . . . May 1998
Crookes, Mr James . . . Nov 1996
Cross, Ms Siobhan G . . . Nov 1987
Davis, Mr Alan BCL(Dublin); Dip European Law . . . *Sep 1992
Dixon, Mr William Russell BA(Cantab) . . . *Dec 1985
Dodsworth, Mrs Catriona Margaret . . . *Dec 1991
Dorman, Ms Natasha . . . Sep 1997
Edwards, Mr Gareth M BA . . . *§Mar 1985
Elliott, Mr Adrian . . . Oct 1994
Farkas, Mr Alan C BA(Sussex) . . . Oct 1984
Farr, Miss Helen J LLB . . . *Nov 1993
Fell, Mr Jonathan M LLB . . . *Oct 1990
Fink, Mr Roger J MA(Oxon) . . . *§Oct 1983
Fischer, Mr Dale . . . May 1990
Flanagan, Mr Thomas D LLB(Hons)(Lond) . . . *Dec 1979
Fleetwood, Ms Bridget R . . . Nov 1996
Ford, Mr Richard . . . Nov 1999
Francis, Mr Barry H LLB(Bris) . . . *§Apr 1977
French, Mr Jonathan A . . . *Oct 1986
Fryer, Mr Laurence D . . . *Oct 1981
Garvie, Mr Carl P MA(Cantab) . . . *Oct 1986
Gill, Mr Howard . . . Nov 1998
Goodwyn, Mr Edward . . . *Nov 1994
Gray, Mr Seamus . . . Oct 1997
Griffith, Mr Matthew . . . *Jan 1996
Hambury, Mr Jason . . . *Apr 1991
Hann, Mr Martyn C LLB . . . *Nov 1992
Harman, Mr Martin J . . . *Nov 1972
Harris, Mr Jon LLB(Bris) . . . *Apr 1993
Hart, Mr Jonathan . . . *Sep 1992
Hawthorn, Ms Patricia . . . Dec 1985
Heaton, Mr Matthew . . . Sep 1998
Hew, Kian Heong . . . Dec 1994
Heyes, Ms Fiona J LLB(Sheff) . . . *Oct 1987
Hibbert, Mr Andrew J BA(Hons) . . . *Nov 1984
Howes, Mr Jonathan . . . *Nov 1995
Isaac, Mr David MA(Cantab) . . . *Oct 1985
Jacobs, Ms Lynette LLB(Hons)(B'ham); PhD(Law) . . . *Mar 1999
Johnson, Ms Liz . . . Sep 1998
Joyston-Bechal, Mr Simon . . . Sep 1993
Jucker, Miss Antoinette M BA; MA . . . Jul 1979
Kelly, Mr Christopher M LLB . . . Nov 1994
Khangura, Kultar LLB(Hons) . . . *Oct 1995
Kilvington, Ms Ann . . . *Jun 1991
Laing, Mr Ian . . . Sep 1993
Lancaster, Mr David Bernard . . . *Mar 1979
Lane, Mr Mark A . . . *Oct 1975
Laudy, Mr Richard B G . . . *Apr 1987
Leman, Mr Thomas R MA(Oxon) . . . *May 1996
Levy, Mr Stephen Peter LLB . . . Oct 1990
Lewington, Mr Andrew Darius . . . *Feb 1996
Lewis, Mr Dean . . . *Oct 1983
Lewis, Mr Wyn BA . . . *Apr 1987
McCallough, Mr Robert A . . . *Jun 1975
MacKenzie, Mr John . . . Oct 1992
McMillan, Mr Fraser . . . *Jan 1991
Masraf, Mr Andrew Mark BA(Hons) Sweet & Maxwell Law Prize . . . *Oct 1995
Mecrate-Butcher, Mr Robert J S LLB . . . *Nov 1994
Meeks, Mr Alastair S BA(Durham) . . . *Aug 1992
Membery, Mr Martin C LLB(Soton); LSF(Hons) . . . *Apr 1993
Moir, Mr Robert . . . Sep 1997
Monaghan, Mr J Iain . . . *Dec 1978
Morris, Mr Neal . . . *Oct 1992
Morrison, Mr Alasdair . . . Oct 1987
Moss, Mr Christopher John . . . Dec 1994
Mullarkey, Mr Michael Peter LLB . . . Feb 1994
Mullen, Mr Christopher P MA(Cantab) . . . *§Oct 1986
Mumford, Mr Simon LLB . . . *Nov 1994
Nash, Mr David . . . Jan 1979
Normington, Mr Andrew . . . Oct 1996
Nurse-Marsh, Ms Isabel Geraldine MA(Oxon) . . . *May 1991
O'Shea, Ms Judith LLB(Lond) . . . *Jul 1987
Oliver, Mr William H J MA(Cantab); LPC . . . *Apr 1997
Orviss, Ms Kate . . . Nov 1996
Paciorek, Mr Stefan LLB . . . *Sep 1992
Park, Mr Charles E BA(York) . . . *Nov 1989
Patmore, Ms Lisa . . . May 1997
Peter, Mr Wood . . . Jun 1985
Phillips, Mr Jeremy P LLB(B'ham) . . . *Oct 1984
Plunkett, Mr Simon . . . Sep 1995
Reardon, Mr Jonathan A MA(Cantab) . . . *§Apr 1984
Rice, Mr Paul . . . Oct 1996
Ridge, Ms Helen E LLB . . . Nov 1988
Riley, Mr Jonathan . . . Mar 1998
Roberts, Ms Alexis . . . Apr 1996
Roberts, Mr Geoffrey . . . Aug 1997
Roberts, Mr Martin C . . . *Apr 1979
Roe, Mr Mark R . . . *Mar 1981
Rowan, Mr Vincent B . . . *Feb 1989
Ryley, Mr Michael D MA(Oxon) . . . *Oct 1985
Salmon, Mr John . . . Oct 1993
Salway, Mr John . . . Mar 1997
Sawicki, Ms Sara . . . Oct 1996
Scholefield, Ms Stephen . . . Oct 1996
Seddon, Mr Clive C . . . *Sep 1987
Stevenson, Mr David . . . Oct 1988
Stroud, Mr Derek . . . Nov 1989
Thomas, Ms Sarah J LLB . . . *Jul 1997
Timmins, Ms Jacqui . . . Oct 1991
Taylor, Ms Clare . . . *Oct 1996
Trevethan, Mr John LLB(L'pool) . . . *Jun 1990
Tyerman, Mr John . . . Sep 1996
Tyler, Mr Geoffrey Richard . . . *Jan 1984
Valentine, Mr Kenneth . . . Jul 1994
Walker, Ms Kim . . . Jul 1983
Watney, Mr Adrian J . . . Jun 1968
Webster, Mr Martin MA(Cantab); ATII . . . *§Oct 1983
Whetham, Miss Anna C LLB . . . *Dec 1989
Whitaker, Ms Iona Ruth BA(Hons) . . . *Nov 1990
White, Mr Jamie BA . . . *Sep 1995
Whitton, Ms Anthea . . . Sep 1999
Williams, Mr Richard D . . . Nov 1986
Winton, Ms Anne-Marie . . . Dec 1997
Wood, Mr Peter . . . Feb 1997
Workman, Ms Catherine LLB(Dundee) . . . Oct 1994
Young, Ms Pamela . . . *Sep 1996

Con: Ellison, Mr Robin C . . . *Apr 1973

PIPER SMITH WATTON LLP ‡

29 Great Peter Street London SW1P 3LW
Tel: 020 7222 9900 *Fax:* 020 7222 9901
Dx: 148404 WESTMINSTER 5
E-mail: info@pswlaw.co.uk
List of partners: N J Battell, R M Berns, H E Bunker, D H Cornforth, I G Skuse, S M Solomons, M D Spash, R C Twyman
Work: B1 C1 C2 E F1 F2 J1 K1 K2 K3 K4 L M3 O R1 R2 S1 S2 T1 W Z(c,e,f,i,l,o)

Ptr: Battell, Ms Nancy J LLB . . . *Oct 1987
Berns, Mr Richard M . . . *Jul 1971
Bunker, Miss Helen E BA(Hons) . . . *Feb 1997
Cornforth, Ms Diana H . . . *Nov 1975
Skuse, Mr Ian G LLB . . . *Dec 1980
Solomons, Mr Stephen M LLB(Hons) . . . *Oct 1984
Spash, Mr Mark D LLB . . . *Feb 1986
Twyman, Mr Richard C LLB . . . *Oct 1986

Ast: Lloyd Jones, Mr John J HB . . . *Mar 1972
Sandhy, Miss Ruby LLM . . . Feb 2002

ALFRED PIROTTA ‡

95 New Wanstead Waltham Forest London E11 2SA
Tel: 020 8281 1771 *Fax:* 020 8926 3536
E-mail: a.pirotta@ntlworld.com
Languages: Italian, Maltese

PITMANS LLP

1 Crown Court 66 Cheapside London EC2V 6LR
Tel: 020 7634 4620 *Fax:* 020 7634 4621 *Dx:* 133108 CHEAPSIDE 2
Office: Reading (2 offices)
Work: G W Z(b,e,f,w)

Ptr: Summers, Mr Jeremy N LLB(Hons) . . . Oct 1993

PITMANS SK SPORT & ENTERTAINMENT LLP ‡

One Crown Court 66 Cheapside London EC2V 6LR
Tel: 020 7634 4620 *Fax:* 020 7634 4620 *Dx:* 133108 CHEAPSIDE 2
E-mail: jtang@pitmans.com

PITTALIS & CO ‡

Global House 303 Ballards Lane London N12 8NP
Tel: 020 8446 9555 *Fax:* 020 8446 9333 *Dx:* 57399 FINCHLEY
E-mail: info@pittalis.co.uk
List of partners: M R Pittalis, R R Pittalis
Languages: Greek
Work: B1 C1 E J1 L O Q S1 S2 W

Ptr: Pittalis, Mr Marios Robert BA(Hons); AKC . . . *§Dec 1988
Pittalis, Mr Roger Royiros BA(Hons) . . . *Nov 1991

Asoc: Shah, Ms Mita LLB . . . *Aug 1999

PLEXUS LAW (A TRADING NAME OF PARABIS LAW LLP)

32 Threadneedle Street London EC2R 8AY
Tel: 020 7763 6103 *Fax:* 020 7763 6115 *Dx:* 42606 CHEAPSIDE
Office: Colchester, Croydon, Evesham, Leeds, London EC3, Manchester (2 offices)

Ptr: Bushell, Mr Anthony BA(Hons) . . . Oct 2002
Gwilliam, Mr Michael James . . . Oct 1991

PLEXUS LAW (A TRADING NAME OF PARABIS LAW LLP)

Peninsular House 30-36 Monument Street London EC3R 8NB
Tel: 0844 245 4000 *Fax:* 0870 084 8300 *Dx:* 98944 CHEAPSIDE 2
Emergency telephone 0870 084 8200
Office: Colchester, Croydon, Evesham, Leeds, London EC2, Manchester (2 offices)
Work: A3 C1 E J2 N O P Q Z(j,q,r,u)
Fixed Fee Interview, Legal Aid undertaken and Member of Accident Line

Ptr: Beckwith, Mr Simon Matthew . . . Aug 1999
Birdi, Mr Kiran BA(Hons) . . . Jan 1995
Cobb, Mrs Concepta LLB(Hons); LPC . . . Mar 2004
Collins, Mr Justin Paul MA(Hons) . . . Mar 1996
Court, Mr Peter Geoffrey MA(Oxon) . . . *Nov 1983
Davies, Ms Sian M LLB . . . *Oct 1988
Fanning, Mr Mark LLB . . . Dec 1991
Gillespie, Ms Jacqueline Ann . . . *Nov 1988
Grimbaldstone, Ms Heather . . . *Oct 2002
Hanison, Mr Darren LLB . . . *Oct 1995
Kanwar, Mr Nish BA(Hons); MA; DipLaw . . . *Nov 1993
Maclachlan, Mr Luke Francis BA(Oxon) . . . Dec 1992
Morris, Mr Julian . . . Oct 2002
Mulligan, Ms Claire Michelle BA(Hons) . . . *Oct 1995
Newman, Mr Jeremy . . . *Nov 1991
Norrie, Ms Anna . . . *Mar 2000
Oldfield, Ms Kathryn LLB(Hons) . . . *Dec 1991
Oliver, Mr Timothy Gerald BA(Law); BA Surrey County Councillor . . . *Nov 1986
Phillips, Mr Steve BSc(Econ) . . . Jan 1988
Plant, Mr Nigel D LLB . . . Apr 1981
Ratcliff, Mr Mark Jonathan . . . Sep 1998
Roberts, Mr John Timothy LLB . . . *Jan 1987
Wicks, Gary . . . Nov 2008
Zimmerman, Felix . . . NSP

Asoc: Beazleigh, Mr Gary . . . Oct 2005
Blanchette, Ms Karen BA(Hons); CPE; LPC . . . May 2004
Bush, Mr Mark BA . . . May 1996
Colman, Mr Jeremiah M P LLB . . . *Oct 1983
Davies, Mr Richard T . . . *Apr 1997
Galliet, Ms Megan . . . *Nov 1995
Guest, Mr Richard . . . Aug 2004
Hockley, Ms Emma . . . Mar 2001
Howarth, Mr Jason . . . Aug 2005
Kochane, Mr Neil J . . . *Sep 2000
Luff, Ms Kirsty LLB(Hons) . . . *Nov 1995
Madichie, Miss Anna BA(Hons); LLB(Hons) . . . Sep 2004
Meltzer, Mr Daniel H . . . Sep 1989
Scott, Ms Karen J . . . *Jan 2000
Stokes, Mr George . . . Nov 1996
Turnbull, Mr Darren Peter LLM . . . *Jan 2005

Ast: Bell, Mr Alastair . . . Jan 2003
Desai, Ms Binita . . . Apr 2006
Fowle, Ruchi . . . Mar 2001
Ghai, Sunita . . . Apr 2004
Gray, Mr Robert Stewart BA; BProc . . . Dec 1995
Holbrook, Miss Janine . . . Apr 2006
Mikolajewski, Miss Susan J LLB . . . *§Oct 1988
Orengo, Mr Alain . . . *Jan 2003
Owen, Mr Anthony LLB . . . *Apr 1974
Sayers, Ms Deborah Louise LLB(Hons) . . . Jun 2006
Skinner, Ms Naomi . . . Mar 2007
Trundle, Mr Paul BSc(Hons) . . . *Nov 1996
Veiga, Ms Gloria . . . Sep 2005

Con: Squire, Mr Nicholas J BA . . . *Jun 1976

PLOWDEN-WARDLAW SOLICITORS ‡

149 Westwood Park London SE23 3QL
Tel: 020 7958 1676 *Fax:* 020 7958 1676

POLLECOFF SOLICITORS LTD ‡

41 Tabernacle Street London EC2A 4AA
Tel: 020 7608 2568 *Fax:* 020 7608 2751 *Dx:* 36649 FINSBURY
E-mail: reception@pollecofflaw.com
List of partners: P K Pollecoff
Work: C1 D1 D2 J1 K1 L N S1 W
Agency and Legal Aid Franchise

Ptr: Pollecoff, Mr Philip K BA . . . *Jul 1980

Ast: Archer, Ms Rachel Miranda . . . Dec 1992
Colby, Ms Sarah LLB . . . *Nov 1995
Kedge, Miss Natalie . . . Aug 1996
Kominsky, Ms Anne LLB . . . *Oct 1992
Subrero, Mr Ahmed . . . Jun 1996

LEE POMERANC ‡

33-35 Finchley Lane London NW4 1BX
Tel: 020 8201 6299 *Fax:* 020 8201 6296
E-mail: mail@leepomeranc.co.uk
List of partners: M S Lee, S Pomeranc
Work: B1 C1 E N O Q R1 R2 S1 S2 T1 W

Ptr: Lee, Mr Michael S LLB . . . *Oct 1983
Pomeranc, Mr Stephen LLB . . . *Feb 1984

POOLE & CO

6 Gray's Inn Square Gray's Inn London WC1R 5AX
Tel: 020 7269 9023 *Fax:* 020 7404 9731
Dx: 65 LONDON/CHANCERY LN
E-mail: enquiries@pooleandco.com
Office: Crewkerne, Ilminster

POPPLESTON ALLEN

88 Kingsway London WC2B 6AA
Tel: 020 7936 5869 *Fax:* 020 7681 6339
E-mail: mail@popall.co.uk
Office: Nottingham

PORTNER & JASKEL LLP ‡ (incorporating David Baker & Co)

63-65 Marylebone Lane London W1U 2RA
Tel: 020 7616 5300 *Fax:* 020 7258 8526 *Dx:* 9067 WEST END
E-mail: info@pjlaw.co.uk
List of partners: D A Baker, P J J Cairaschi, M R Griver, B Portner
Languages: French, Greek, Turkish
Work: B1 C1 C3 E I J1 K1 L N O P Q R1 R2 S1 S2 W Z(c,e,f,i,r)

Agency, Advocacy, Legal Aid undertaken and Member of Accident Line
Ptr: Cairaschi, Mr Paul Jean Joseph LLB(Hons) . . . . . . *Aug 1993
Mem: Baker, Mr David A BA; MA(Dublin) . . . . *Jan 1983
Griver, Mr Mitchell R LLB . . . . *Oct 1984
Portner, Mr Brian LLB. . . . . *Nov 1971
Ast: Broughton, Mr Daniel LLB(Hons) . . . . Apr 2006
Dev, Mrs Rita LLB(Hons) . . . . Sep 1994

PORTRAIT SOLICITORS ‡
(in association with SNR Denton)
1 Chancery Lane London WC2A 1LF
Tel: 020 7092 6990 *Fax:* 020 7430 1242
Dx: 69 LONDON/CHANCERY LN
Emergency telephone 020 7092 6990
E-mail: judith.portrait@portraitsolicitors.com
List of partners: D B Flynn, H E Johnston, J S Portrait
Work: S1 T2 W Z(d)
Ptr: Flynn, Mr Dominic B BA; LLM(Lond) . . . . *Oct 1983
Johnston, Miss Helen E LLB . . . . *Feb 1985
Portrait, Ms Judith S MA(Oxon) . . . . *Nov 1972
Ast: Burton, Ms Alison BA(Cantab); LSF . . . . *Nov 1994
Hovil, Miss Sarah E. . . . . *Dec 1989
Potts, Miss Christian . . . . Dec 2000

PORTWAY SOLICITORS ‡
335 Barking Road London E13 8EE
Tel: 020 7476 5500 *Fax:* 020 7476 5520
E-mail: info@portwaysolicitors.com

POSTLETHWAITE & CO ‡
11-15 Betterton Street Darden Studios Covent Garden London WC2H 9BP
Tel: 020 7470 8805

POTHECARY WITHAM WELD ‡
70 St George's Square Westminster London SW1V 3RD
Tel: 020 7821 8211 *Fax:* 020 7630 6484 *Dx:* 86164 VICTORIA 2
E-mail: info@pwwsolicitors.co.uk
List of partners: A M Beale, T H Cadman, P J M Hawthorne, P J O Herschan, A Hussain, G Kidd, T B Warren
Languages: French, German, Italian
Work: A3 C1 J1 K2 L Q S1 S2 T2 W X Z(d)
Agency and Advocacy undertaken
Ptr: Beale, Mrs Alexa M BA(Oxon). . . . . *Nov 1985
Cadman, Mr Thomas Harland BA . . . . Apr 2008
Hawthorne, Mr Peter J M KSG LLB(Lond). . . . . . *May 1974
Herschan, Mr Patrick J O . . . . *Jun 1980
Hussain, Mr Ajmal LLB(Hons)(English & European Law) . . . . Aug 2007
Kidd, Mr Gerald LLB . . . . *Nov 1991
Warren, Mr Timothy B LLB(Bris). . . . . *Nov 1974
Asoc: O'Connor, Mr John K BSc. . . . . *Sep 1993
Ast: Azhar, Mr Nadeem . . . . Apr 2011
Beringer, Ms Catherine Elizabeth Margaret BMus(Hons); BA(Cantab); LPC . . . . *Mar 2008
Byng Nelson, Mr Robert Arthur . . . . Oct 2007
Feeley, Mr Gerard. . . . . Oct 2009
Fuschillo, Miss Clara LLB(Hons). . . . . *Oct 2001
Gray, Ms Kim Lindsey BSc; PhD(Ecology); CPE. . . . Oct 1997
Hampton, Mr Adam Edward Hethelyi . . . . Sep 2006
Strauss, Mrs Maria . . . . Nov 2008

POWELL & CO ‡
77 Woolwich New Road Woolwich London SE18 6ED
Tel: 020 8854 9131 *Fax:* 020 8855 4174 *Dx:* 33318 WOOLWICH
E-mail: info@powell-solicitors.co.uk

POWELL FORSTER ‡
Eurolink Centre 49 Effra Road Brixton Lambeth London SW2 1BZ
Tel: 020 7737 8111 *Fax:* 020 7737 8222
E-mail: law@powellforster.co.uk
List of partners: D J Forster, T J Powell
Languages: French, German
Work: L N Q Z(q)
Emergency Action, Advocacy, Fixed Fee Interview, Legal Aid Franchise and Member of Accident Line
Ptr: Forster, Ms Deirdre J BA ♦ . . . . *Jun 1980
Powell, Mr Timothy J LLB ♦ Chairman of the Residential Property Tribunal Service (LVT) . . . . *Oct 1984

POWELL GILBERT LLP ‡
85 Fleet Street London EC4Y 1AE
Tel: 020 3040 8000 *Fax:* 020 3040 8001
Dx: 358 LONDON/CHANCERY LN
E-mail: zoe.butler@powellgilbert.com

POWELL SPENCER & PARTNERS ‡
290 Kilburn High Road London NW6 2DD
Tel: 020 7604 5600 *Fax:* 020 7328 1221 *Dx:* 123862 KILBURN 2
Emergency telephone 07659 118181
E-mail: gregpowell@psplaw.co.uk
List of partners: A J T Gillman, G D K Powell, M Tait, M E Yule
Languages: French, German, Hebrew, Portuguese, Spanish
Work: D1 G H K1 L N V Z(g,i,r)
Emergency Action, Agency, Advocacy, Fixed Fee Interview, Legal Aid undertaken, Legal Aid Franchise and Member of Accident Line
Ptr: Gillman, Mr Arthur J T LLB(Exon) . . . . *Apr 1981
Powell, Mr Gregory D K LLB; BSc(Lond) . . . . *Oct 1973
Tait, Mr Michael BA . . . . *Jan 1982
Yule, Mr Michael Edwards BA. . . . . *Dec 1991
Con: Jacobs, Mr Philip S LLB. . . . . *Jun 1974

POWELL SPENCER & PARTNERS ‡
8 Central Chambers The Broadway Ealing London W5 2NR
Tel: 020 8231 0956 *Fax:* 020 8556 1811 *Dx:* 5105 EALING
E-mail: martindavidson@psplaw.co.uk

PRAGASH & MCKENZIE ‡
894 Garrett Lane Wandsworth London SW17 0NB
Tel: 020 8682 2332

PREISKEL & CO LLP ‡
8-10 New Fetter Lane London EC4A 1RS
Tel: 020 7583 2120 *Fax:* 020 7583 2103
E-mail: info@preiskel.com
List of partners: D Preiskel, R Preiskel
Languages: French, German, Hebrew, Italian, Portuguese, Spanish
Work: C1 C2 C3 F2 I M1 U1 U2 Z(e,f,za)
Fixed Fee Interview undertaken
Ptr: Preiskel, Mr Daniel BA(Hons); MA(Hons) . . . . Sep 1991
Preiskel, Mr Ronnie BA(Hons); MA(Hons); MBA(Insead) . . . . Mar 1995
Asoc: Rainhartz, Mr Amit LLB; MSc . . . . Apr 2006
Saras, Mr Jose M. Oct 2005

PRESTON AND COMPANY ‡
7 Nottingham Street Marylebone London W1U 5EL
Tel: 020 7486 8666 *Fax:* 020 7486 9111
E-mail: law@prestonandcompany.com

MILES PRESTON & CO ‡
10 Bolt Court London EC4A 3DQ
Tel: 020 7583 0583 *Fax:* 020 7583 0128
E-mail: miles.preston@milespreston.co.uk
List of partners: R Freeman, A M Nice, A M Plum, C M C Preston, J M Stanczyk
Work: K1
Emergency Action and Agency undertaken
Ptr: Freeman, Miss Rachel MA . . . . Mar 2001
Nice, Miss Anna M LLB(Hons) . . . . *Nov 1994
Plum, Miss Andrea M LLB; LP. . . . . *Sep 1999
Preston, Mr C Miles C. . . . . *Jun 1974
Stanczyk, Miss Julia Maria LLB(Hons). . . . . *Oct 1984
Ast: Cox, Mrs Cynthia Pendias BA. . . . . Nov 2008

PRESTON-ROUSE & CO ‡
6 Gray's Inn Square Gray's Inn Camden London WC1R 5AX
Est: 1987
Tel: 020 7269 9020 *Fax:* 020 7404 9731
Dx: 65 LONDON/CHANCERY LN
E-mail: judith@preston-rouse.com
Languages: Russian, Spanish
Work: C1 E F1 O Q R2 S1 S2 U2 W X Z(b,e,q)

DAVID PRICE SOLICITORS & ADVOCATES ‡
21 Fleet Street London EC4Y 1AA
Tel: 020 7353 9999 *Fax:* 020 7353 9990
E-mail: enquiries@lawyers-media.com
List of partners: D J Price
Work: Z(k)
Agency and Advocacy undertaken
Ptr: Price, Mr David Jack ♦ . . . . *May 1990
Ast: Duodu, Korieh ♦. Jul 1999

PRICEWATERHOUSECOOPERS LEGAL LLP ‡
6 Hay's Lane London SE1 2HB
Tel: 020 7212 1616 *Fax:* 020 7212 1570
Dx: 138213 COVENT GARDEN 2
List of partners: A J Benham, S A Brookes, R A Carolina, R J Edmundson, D F Evans, A S Firth, L D Flavell, S J Walker, N P Willis
Work: C1 C2 C3 E I J1 L M1 O P R1 R2 S2 U1 Z(b,e,i,n,o)
Ptr: Benham, Ms Amanda J LLB(Lond); LLM(Cantab) . . . *Oct 1987
Brookes, Ms Shirley A LLB(Hons). . . . . *Jul 1989
Carolina, Mr Robert A BA; JD; LLM . . . . *May 1996
Edmundson, Mr Richard J LLB(B'ham) . . . . *Nov 1986
Evans, Darryl F BA . . . . Nov 1985
Firth, Mr A Simon BA(Cantab). . . . . Oct 1987
Flavell, Mr Leon D. . . . . Dec 1988
Walker, Mr Simon J LLB. . . . . *Nov 1989
Willis, Mr Nicholas P LLB; LLM . . . . *Nov 1987
Ast: Crocco, Mr Patrick BA; LLB . . . . Jul 1998

PRINCE EVANS ‡
Craven House 40-44 Uxbridge Road Ealing London W5 2BS
Tel: 020 8567 3477 *Fax:* 020 8840 7757 *Dx:* 5100 EALING
E-mail: info@prince-evans.co.uk
Web: www.prince-evans.co.uk
List of partners: A R Best, R J Jennings, T B Lemon, C B Neill, G Smith
Work: N Q Z(h)
Emergency Action, Agency, Advocacy, Fixed Fee Interview undertaken and Member of Accident Line
Ptr: Best, Mr Anthony R LLB(Hons) . . . . *Feb 1998
Jennings, Mr Robert J LLB . . . . *Feb 1987
Lemon, Mr Thomas B. . . . . *Jul 1969
Neill, Mr C Bryan LLB. . . . . *Jul 1979
Smith, Mr Gary . . . . May 2004
Ast: Allen, Elaine . . . . Nov 1992
Charalambous, Harris. . . . . Dec 2005
Collins, Kerry . . . . Sep 2009
Davies, Mr Ben . . . . Sep 2008
Erlam, Mrs Jane LLB . . . . *Nov 1992
Johnstone, Mrs Dorothy LLB . . . . *Nov 1989
O'Conner, Mr Chris . . . . Mar 2008
Pemberton, Alexy. . . . . Sep 2008
Porter-Gayle, Sharon . . . . Dec 1994
Ridgeon, Mrs Mary C LLB. . . . . *Oct 1983
Teall, Mr Jeremy BA. . . . . *§Oct 1988
Treszka, Miss Sophie LLB(Hons) . . . . Sep 1983
Turner, Rachel . . . . Dec 2007

The firm specialises in: Housing Association Law, Land Acquisition and Development, Building / Construction, Landlords / Tenant, Property and Commercial Litigation, Employment, Company Commercial, Conveyancing, Wills / Trusts, Family/ Matrimonial, Personal Injury and Catastrophic Injury. Agency Instructions accepted at short notice.

PRIOR LAW ‡
47 Canterbury Grove London SE27 0NX
Tel: 020 8761 2302 *Fax:* 020 8480 7690
E-mail: nicola.prior@priorlaw.co.uk

PRITCHARD ENGLEFIELD ‡
14 New Street London EC2M 4HE
Tel: 020 7972 9720 *Fax:* 020 7972 9722
Dx: 88 LONDON/CHANCERY LN
E-mail: po@pe-legal.com
List of partners: N Abeygunasekera, G Altmann, R S Ashby, B E Bletso, A M Colman, C W Dunston, D S Glass, J Greager, A H Harris, J B Havergal, M J W Joseph, D King-Farlow, D R Levene, S C McInnes, S Oehlert, N A Roche, F J Sieber, I J Silverblatt, M Stancliffe, S Steiner, D L Wright
Languages: French, German, Hebrew, Hindi, Russian, Spanish, Swedish
Work: B1 C1 C2 C3 D1 E F1 F2 I J1 K1 L M1 M2 N O P Q R1 R2 S1 S2 T1 T2 W X Z(b,c,d,e,f,h,i,j,k,l,o,p,q,r,t,w)
Agency, Legal Aid undertaken and Legal Aid Franchise
Ptr: Abeygunasekera, Ms Nelu . . . . *Jan 1993
Altmann, Ms Gitta LLB; LLM . . . . *Oct 1997
Ashby, Ms Rosalind S LLB(Bris). . . . . *Apr 1987
Bletso, Mr Bryan E LLB(Sheff) . . . . *Oct 1990
Colman, Mr Antony M BA; LLB Solicitor of the Supreme Court of NSW . . . . §Feb 1986
Dunston, Mr Colin W MA(Cantab). . . . . *§Oct 1982
Glass, Mr David S MA; LLB(Cantab) . . . . *Aug 1974
Greager, John. . . . . Jan 2002
Harris, Mr Anthony H LLB(Lond) . . . . *§Apr 1981
Havergal, Dr Jane B BA(Hons); PhD . . . . *§Oct 1987
Joseph, Ms Marian J W BA(Cantab). . . . . *Oct 1987
King-Farlow, Mr David MA(Oxon) . . . . §Jun 1970
Levene, Mr David R LLB(Lond) . . . . *§Apr 1969
McInnes, Mr Stuart C LLB(Hull) . . . . *§Sep 1981
Oehlert, Mr Sebastian. . . . . *Jan 1985
Roche, Mr Nicholas A MA(Cantab) . . . . Nov 1977
Sieber, Miss Frances J . . . . *Nov 1979
Silverblatt, Mr Ian J LLB(Hons) . . . . Oct 1988
Stancliffe, Mrs Melanie LLB . . . . Sep 1998
Steiner, Dr Sybille LLB; German Attorney at Law (Rechtsanwalt) . . . . Feb 1993
Wright, Ms Diana L MA(Oxon); CPE; LSF. . . . . . . *Apr 1989
Ast: Fabre, Miss Geraldine. . . . . Sep 1999
Lauzeral, Mrs Isabelle LLB; Maitrise en Droit . . . . . Sep 1999
Pedler, Ms Katherine S BSc. . . . . *Nov 1991
Schneider, Mr Thilo Heinrich LLB(Europe). . . . . . . Sep 2003
Con: Avery, Ms Belinda M LLB(Lond). . . . . *Mar 1988
Barley, Mr Michael Desmond Tennyson BA(Oxon). . . *Jun 1976

PROCOL & CANDOR SOLICITORS ‡
21 Horn Lane Ealing London W3 9NJ
Tel: 020 8993 4646 *Fax:* 020 8993 5656 *Dx:* 80268 ACTON
E-mail: info@procol.info
List of partners: N Kusturovic
Languages: Arabic, Cantonese, French, Gujarati, Hindi, Italian, Kiswahili, Mandarin, Russian, Serbo-Croat, Spanish, Urdu, Welsh
Work: B1 C1 E F1 G J1 K1 K4 L N O Q R1 S1 S2 T1 T2 U1 W Z(e,f,g,i,l,q,r)
Emergency Action, Agency, Advocacy and Fixed Fee Interview undertaken
Ptr: Kusturovic, Mr Nicholas LLB(Hons) . . . . Nov 2001
Asoc: McCarthy, Ms Judith H BA(Hons) . . . . Feb 2002
Rubie, Mr Michael A LLB(Hons). . . . . Jun 1972

PROCTOR MOORE SOLICITORS ‡
747 Green Lanes Winchmore Hill London N21 3SA
Tel: 020 8364 3111 *Fax:* 020 8364 3222
E-mail: xen@proctormoore.com

PROLEGAL LIMITED ‡
5th Floor 63 St Mary Axe London EC3A 8AA
Tel: 020 7743 6700 *Fax:* 020 7743 6794
E-mail: info@prolegal.co.uk

PROPERTY LEGAL SOLICITORS ‡
PO Box 47585 London N14 9AE
Tel: 020 8360 7259 *Fax:* 020 8364 3603
E-mail: info@propertylegalsolicitors.co.uk

PROSKAUER ROSE ‡
75 Davies Street London W1K 5HT
Tel: 020 7016 3600 *Fax:* 020 7016 3696

PROSPECT SOLICITORS ‡
Building 3 Chiswick Business Park 566 Chiswick High Road London W4 5YA
Tel: 020 8899 6063 *Fax:* 020 8899 6163 *Dx:* 3510 HOUNSLOW
List of partners: J Upil
Languages: Cantonese, Hindi, Punjabi, Tamil, Urdu
Work: E F1 K1 Q R1 S1 S2 Z(i,l)
Fixed Fee Interview undertaken
SPr: Upil, Mr Jeetendr BSc(Hons); PDIP Law. . . . . Aug 1998

PROTOPAPAS ‡
Queens House 180 Tottenham Court Road London W1T 7PD
Tel: 020 7636 2100 *Fax:* 020 7636 2101
Dx: 134203 LONDON/TOTTENHAM COURT ROAD 2
E-mail: enquiries@protopapas.co.uk
List of partners: E Joannou, S K Liveras, X S Protopapas, Z Protopapas
Languages: Greek
Work: A1 B1 B2 C1 C2 E F1 F2 G J1 K1 K3 L N O Q R1 R2 S1 S2 T1 T2 W Z(d,e,f,i,j,k,l,p,q,r)
Emergency Action and Advocacy undertaken
Ptr: Joannou, Miss Elena LLB(Hons) . . . . *May 2005
Protopapas, Mr Xenophon S BA. . . . . *May 1982
Protopapas, Mrs Zoe BA . . . . *Jun 1988
Liveras, Mr Savakis Kyriacou BSc(Hons) . . . . NSP
Ast: Pavlides, Miss Rena . . . . *Jun 2007

DONALD PUGH SOLICITOR ‡
169 Station Road London E4 6AG
Tel: 020 8524 6700

PUNATAR & CO SOLICITORS ‡
32 Junction Road London N19 5RE
Tel: 020 7272 3330 *Fax:* 020 7272 3331 *Dx:* 54758 ARCHWAY
E-mail: lawyers@punatar.biz
List of partners: P Anand, T Punatar, M Tmaira
Office: London E1
Ptr: Anand, Pritam. . . . . *Jan 1996
Punatar, Trushar ● . . . . *Jan 1995
Tmaira, Ms Mary ● . . . . *Jan 2002

PUNATAR & CO SOLICITORS
Suite 308 Frazer House 32-38 Leman Street London E1 8EW
Tel: 020 7173 6111 *Fax:* 020 7173 6115
E-mail: lawyers@punatar.biz
Office: London N19

FRANK PURDY ‡
Portman House 2 Portman Street Westminster London W1H 6DU
Tel: 020 7408 6190
List of partners: F Purdy
SPr: Purdy, Mr Frank. *Jul 1965

PUXON MURRAY LLP ‡
One Royal Exchange Avenue London EC3V 3LT
Tel: 020 7464 4390 *Fax:* 020 7464 4399
E-mail: admin@puxonmurrayllp.co.uk

JAMES PYKE & CO ‡
159 Herne Hill London SE24 9LR
Tel: 020 7733 0081 *Fax:* 020 7733 0085 *Dx:* 96303 HERNE HILL
E-mail: enquiries@jamespyke.com

PYSDENS SOLICITORS ‡
108 Fenchurch Street London EC3M 5JR
Tel: 020 7702 4442 *Fax:* 020 7702 1779
E-mail: info@pysdens.com

QUASTEL MIDGEN LLP ‡
74 Wimpole Street London W1G 9RR
Tel: 020 7908 2525 *Fax:* 020 7908 2626 *Dx:* 9021 WEST END
E-mail: reception@quastels.com
List of partners: A Blake, J P L Goldberg, J Greenberg, E Greenspan, J Gross, M S Haringman, J Mace, J Neilan, D A Quastel
Languages: French, Russian, Ukrainian
Work: A1 B1 B2 C1 C2 C3 D1 E F1 F2 G I J1 K1 K2 K3 L M2 N O P Q R1 R2 S1 S2 T1 T2 U2 V W Z(b,c,d,e,f,i,j,k,l,m,q,r,s,w)
Emergency Action, Agency, Advocacy and Fixed Fee Interview undertaken
Ptr: Blake, Ms Ann-Maree . . . *Jan 2003
Goldberg, Mr Jonathan P L . . . Jan 1982
Greenberg, Mr Jason . . . *Jan 2003
Greenspan, Mrs Eva . . . Oct 1997
Gross, Mr Jonathan LLM(Cantab) . . . *Dec 1989
Haringman, Mr Michael S LLB(Lond) . . . *Dec 1969
Mace, Ms Juliette . . . Nov 1995
Neilan, Mr Jonathan BA(Hons) . . . *Sep 2001
Quastel, Mr David Adam LLB . . . *Feb 1986
Ast: Booth, Ms Elizabeth . . . Jan 2004
Hay, Ms Anna . . . *Jan 2007
Minsky, Mrs Susan L LLB(Lond) . . . *Apr 1981
Ryatt, Mandeep . . . *Jan 2003
Williams, Miss Christine M BA . . . *Mar 1991

QUEE & MAYANJA SOLICITORS LTD ‡
60 Neasden Lane Neasden London NW10 2UW
Tel: 020 8438 4547 *Fax:* 020 8450 6619

QUERCUS LAW ‡
107-111 Fleet Street London EC4A 2AB
Tel: 020 7936 9816 *Fax:* 020 7936 9133
E-mail: robert_oakes@btinternet.com

QUINN EMANUEL URQUHART & SULLIVAN LLP ‡
16 Old Bailey London EC4M 7EG
Tel: 020 7653 2000 *Fax:* 020 7653 2100
E-mail: richardeast@quinnemanuel.com

QUINN MANTION ‡
Compass House 7 Clove Crescent East India Dock London E14 2BD
Tel: 020 7512 2600 *Fax:* 020 7512 2602 *Dx:* 42678 ISLE OF DOGS
E-mail: info@quinnmantion.co.uk
List of partners: M L Mantion, M H Quinn
Languages: Bengali, French
Work: B1 C1 D1 E F1 J1 K1 K3 L N O P Q R1 S1 W Z(d,h,k,l)
Agency and Fixed Fee Interview undertaken
Ptr: Mantion, Miss Monique Liliane LLB(Lond) . . . *Jun 1994
Quinn, Mr Martin Howard . . . *Dec 1989
Ast: Nkafu, Mr Asabgwiy J LLM; PGCE Councillor . . . Dec 2002

QUIST SOLICITORS ‡
12th Floor Broadgate Tower 20 Primrose Street London EC2A 2EW
Tel: 020 7596 2813
E-mail: mail@quistlaw.com
List of partners: A R Raja
Languages: Arabic, Urdu
Work: A3 C1 C2 E F1 F2 J1 L N O Q R2 S1 S2 Z(b,d,f,g,i,n)
Fixed Fee Interview undertaken
Ptr: Raja, Mr Akhtar Riaz LLB . . . *Oct 1991

RG LAW ‡
34 Brunswick Park Gardens London N11 1EJ
Tel: 020 8368 5155
E-mail: rg@rglaw.org.uk

RLS SOLICITORS ‡
4th Floor 388 Strand London WC2R 0LT
Tel: 020 7812 6607 *Fax:* 020 7836 4277
Dx: 138412 CHARING CROSS

RMPI SOLICITORS ‡
Moss House 15-16 Brooks Mews Mayfair London W1K 4DS
Tel: 020 7318 4444 *Fax:* 020 7318 4445 *Dx:* 44615 MAYFAIR
E-mail: lawyers@reidminty.co.uk
List of partners: Y Botiuk, W Christopher, M Fenn, K Grice, R Hart, N J Mills, C Minty, N Neocleous, M A Pulford, P J V Rake, A S Reid
Languages: Armenian, French, Greek, Russian, Spanish
Work: A1 A3 B1 C1 C2 C3 E F1 G J1 K1 L M1 M2 N O P Q R1 R2 S1 S2 T1 T2 U2 W Z(a,b,c,e,i,j,k,l,m,q,w)
Agency undertaken and Member of Accident Line
Ptr: Botiuk, Mr Yuri LLB; BA . . . Oct 2001
Fenn, Mr Michael BSc(Hons) . . . Oct 1997
Grice, Mr Kristian . . . Aug 2000
Hart, Mr Richard LLB . . . Oct 1996
Mills, Mr Nigel J MA(Cantab) . . . *§Dec 1977
Minty, Ms Christine LLB . . . Jan 1966
Neocleous, Neoclis BA; LLM . . . *Sep 1985
Pulford, Mr Michael Anthony BSocSc . . . Nov 1994
Rake, Mr Piers J V BA(Hons) . . . Jun 2005
Reid, Mr Andrew S LLB; ACIArb . . . *Mar 1979
Christopher, Mr William LLB(Hons) . . . Oct 1997
Asoc: Hessel, Mr Mark LLB . . . Jun 2000
Ast: Aslanian, Mr Ararat LLB . . . Sep 2005
Nawaz, Mr Faqir . . . Dec 2000
Knox, Ms Kelly . . . Jan 2003
Con: Sprawson, Mr Robert . . . Jan 1968

R O C K SOLICITORS ‡
151 Balham Hill London SW12 9DJ
Tel: 020 8673 5819 *Fax:* 020 8772 0040 *Dx:* 41604 BALHAM
E-mail: enquiries@rocksolicitors.com

R R & CO LONDON MARITIME & ENERGY SOLICITORS ‡
Gallery 4 The Lloyds Building 12 Leadenhall Street London EC3V 1LP
Tel: 020 7816 5496 *Fax:* 020 7816 5497
E-mail: law@rrco.co.uk

RVH SOLICITORS ‡
PO Box 57661 London NW7 0FW
Tel: 020 8371 6656 *Fax:* 020 8371 6656
E-mail: rharris@rvhsolicitors.com

RADCLIFFES LE BRASSEUR ‡
5 Great College Street Westminster London SW1P 3SJ
Tel: 020 7222 7040 *Fax:* 020 7222 6208
Dx: 113 LONDON/CHANCERY LN
E-mail: info@rlb-law.com
List of partners: R V Bassani, G M Benning, S W Blair, A P Brougham, P D R Brown, V Bryant, E S Caine, P Coats, S R Dinnick, C P Dixon, S R Everett, C A Farrer, P J Garland, R C G Gillott, A Green, W Hedley-Miller, S A G Janisch, S M Kernyckyj, A W Leslie, H Llewellyn-Morgan, A E Lynn, P J Maddock, D L Manghnani, K S Mayne, P D Merchant, T Newsome, J North, R V O'Donovan, A E Parsons, P J Peacock, C S Penfold, R P J Price, R Privett, N Rawson, N D A Rawson, R D Rowe, K M Shaw, R R H Shipway, R W Sumerling, M Thorniley-Walker, M J Thorniley-Walker, R R Vallings, S P Von Peltz, N G C West, C J E Williams, K Williams, S A Woodwark, G E Woolhouse
Office: Cardiff, Leeds
Languages: Afrikaans, French, German, Italian, Spanish
Work: A1 A3 B1 B2 C1 C2 C3 D1 D2 E F1 F2 I J1 J2 K1 K2 K3 L M1 M2 N O P Q R1 R2 S1 S2 T1 T2 U1 V W X Z(b,c,d,e,f,h,i,j,k,l,m,o,p,q,r,s,x)
Emergency Action, Agency and Advocacy undertaken
Ptr: Bassani, Mr Ricardo Vasco LLB . . . *Oct 1990
Blair, Mr Stephen W LLB . . . *Oct 1990
Brougham, Mr Antony P BA(Oxon) . . . *Nov 1976
Brown, Mr Peter D R LLB(Lond) Clerk to General Commissioner of Taxes . . . *Jul 1965
Bryant, Ms Virginia . . . Jul 1986
Caine, Ms Elizabeth Susan . . . *Nov 1994
Coats, Mr Peter . . . Apr 1994
Dinnick, Mr Simon R BA . . . *May 1978
Farrer, Mr Charles A MA(Cantab) . . . *Dec 1974
Garland, Mr Philip J LLB . . . *Nov 1972
Gillott, Mr Roland C G . . . *§Sep 1972
Green, Ms Anne . . . Sep 1997
Hedley-Miller, Mr William BA . . . Nov 1986
Janisch, Mr Stephen A G MA(Cantab) . . . *Nov 1972
Leslie, Mr Alexander W LLB(B'ham) . . . *Feb 1981
Llewellyn-Morgan, Mr Huw LLB . . . Mar 1980
Maddock, Mr Philip J BA(Cantab) . . . *Sep 1987
Manghnani, Mr Deepak L BA . . . *Nov 1982
Mayne, Miss Karen S LLB . . . *Oct 1984
Newsome, Mr Timothy BCom; LLB Commissioner Small Claims Court (South Africa) . . . *Sep 1991
North, Mr Jonathan LLB(B'ham) . . . *Mar 1971
O'Donovan, Mr Robert V MA(Cantab) . . . *Nov 1976
Parsons, Mr Andrew E LLB . . . *Oct 1987
Peacock, Mr Philip J LLM(Lond) . . . *Jun 1968
Penfold, Ms Caroline S . . . Nov 1988
Price, Mr Richard P J LLB(Nott'm) . . . *Mar 1972
Privett, Mr Richard LLB . . . *Nov 1995
Rawson, Mr Nicholas . . . Apr 1986
Rowe, Mr Robert D MA(Cantab); PhD . . . *Mar 1974
Shaw, Ms Katharine M BA . . . *Nov 1990
Shipway, Mr Ralph R H . . . *Oct 1973
Sumerling, Mr Robert W . . . *Jun 1969
Thorniley-Walker, Mr Michael . . . Jun 1972
Vallings, Mr Robert R . . . *Jan 1969
Von Peltz, Mr Stephen P . . . Jan 1966
West, Mr Nigel G C . . . *Sep 1989
Williams, Ms Kate . . . Jan 1985
Woolhouse, Mr Geoffrey E . . . *Jul 1979
Asoc: Bower, Ms Joanna . . . Nov 2000
Emberton, Miss Jane Liesel BA(Hons) . . . *Oct 1991
Hall, Mr Gordon Patrick BA; LLB(Cape Town); ACII . . . Mar 1996
Hill, Miss Kate . . . *Feb 1999
Lang, Ms Jane . . . Nov 1991
Parsons, Ms Lisa Anne BA . . . *Nov 1996
Pasquini, Mr Nello E Dr Jur . . . *Aug 1991
Patel, Miss Reena LLB; DipLP . . . *Aug 1996
Raja, Ms Sejal BA(Hons) . . . *Nov 1998
Screene, Ms Yvonne . . . Nov 1997
Thompson, Mr Paul . . . Oct 1999
Ast: Abrahamian, Ms Paula . . . Sep 2004
Baldwin, Mr Leighton BA(Hons) . . . *Mar 2001
Bancroft, Ms Suzannah . . . Sep 2003
Berner, Mr Tim . . . Jan 1986
Brophy, Ms Mary Louise LLB . . . Aug 1997
Bull, Linzi . . . Dec 2002
Chapman, Ms Clare . . . Sep 2000
Childs, Mr William . . . Oct 2003
Cooper, Nyree . . . Sep 2004
Crane, Miss Lara LLB . . . Oct 2002
Creamer, Mr Richard . . . Sep 2002
Dias, Miss Corrine LLB(Hons) . . . Sep 2000
Donald, Mr Oliver . . . Sep 2004
Fairley, Ms Victoria Jane . . . Sep 1999
Farahi, Mrs Shahnaz LLB(Hons) . . . Feb 1994
Flew, Mr Samuel Richard LLB(Hons) . . . Aug 1998
Frall, Ms Marianne . . . Oct 2001
Goodman, Mr Elliot Simon BA; DipLaw . . . Nov 2002
Johnstone, Miss Alexandra N . . . *Dec 1989
Keough, Mr Christopher . . . Feb 1986
Maciejewski, Ms Danuta Elizabeth LLB(Hons) . . . Oct 1985
Maginn, Mr Terence . . . *Jan 1991
Margetts, Ms Rachel . . . Sep 2003
Meacock, Ms Sarah Louise . . . Dec 1996
Nicholas, Miss Michaela . . . *Oct 1998
Oliver, Mrs Juliet . . . Sep 2000
Parfitt, Ms Emma Jane . . . Sep 1998
Patel, Mrs Leana LLB(Hons) . . . Sep 2003
Perry, Mr Hamish Balmanno Dyson LLB(Hons); LPC . . . Sep 2002
Ramsden, Miss Louise LLB . . . Sep 2001
Rivero, Ms Daryl LLB . . . Sep 2000
Rivett-Carnac, Ms Laura . . . Oct 2001
Sadler, Mr Ian Derrick . . . Jun 1996
Sangar, Sangita . . . May 2000
Scales, Mr Andrian . . . Feb 1998
Scott-Patel, Ms Kerry . . . Sep 2001
Sell-Peters, Ms Tracy . . . Mar 1996
Stevens, Ms Emma . . . May 2002
Thomas, Mrs Stephanie BA . . . Feb 1993
Thompson, Mr Paul Simon . . . Sep 1999
Tucker, Miss Anita Sabine BA(Hons); PGDipLaw; LPC . . . Sep 2002
Way, Mrs Judith A BSc Justice of the Peace . . . *May 1979
Wu, Mr Michael Lionel . . . *Nov 2000
Yates, Ms Clare . . . Aug 1997
Con: Bieber, Mr I Robert C Justice of the Peace . . . *§Jul 1965
Brown, Mr Peter . . . Jul 1965
Cash, Mr William N P MA(Oxon) . . . *Dec 1967
Elks, Mr Michael J MA(Cantab); FCIArb . . . *Apr 1974
Mellett, Mr Michael T . . . *§Jun 1972
Noel-Smith, Ms Kelly BA . . . Nov 1992
Simon, Lyddon . . . Dec 1963
Standen, Mr Trevor . . . Jan 1976

GILLIAN RADFORD & CO ‡
459 Harrow Road Westminster London W10 4RG
Tel: 020 8960 4366 *Fax:* 020 8969 7268 *Dx:* 46650 MAIDA HILL
E-mail: info@gillianradford.co.uk
List of partners: D W Best, G M Radford
Languages: Arabic, Bengali, Indonesian, Russian
Work: D1 D2 K1 K3 K4 L W
Emergency Action, Legal Aid undertaken and Legal Aid Franchise
Ptr: Best, Mr David W BA(Oxon) . . . *Jun 1978
Radford, Ms Gillian M LLB(Exon) . . . *Oct 1977
Asoc: Foley, Ms Martine R LLB . . . *Jun 1999
Ast: Ali, Ms Salina LLB . . . *Jun 2005
Jones, Mrs Caroline Elizabeth BA . . . *Oct 1998
McCormack, Ms Grainne BA . . . *Jan 2008
Ramtohul-Brindle, Ms Shanta LLB(Hons) . . . *Jul 2003

RAE & CO SOLICITORS ‡
2c Trinity Street Southwark London SE1 1DB
Tel: 020 7407 6256 *Fax:* 020 7404 6255
Dx: 144361 SOUTHWARK 4
E-mail: raecosolicitors@btconnect.com

RAE NEMAZEE LLP ‡
2 Baronsgate 33-35 Rothschilds Road Chiswick London W4 5HT
Tel: 020 8996 1722 *Fax:* 020 8400 6267 *Dx:* 80313 CHISWICK

RAFFLES HAIG SOLICITORS ‡
1 Sekforde Street Clerkenwell London EC1R 0BE
Tel: 020 7107 2343 *Fax:* 020 7107 2344
E-mail: info@raffles-haig.com

RAHMAN & CO ‡
33 West Green Road Tottenham London N15 5BY
Tel: 020 8809 4643 *Fax:* 020 8802 7203
Dx: 55601 SOUTH TOTTENHAM
List of partners: A Rahman
Languages: Bengali, Punjabi, Urdu
Work: D1 E G H K1 N Q S1 Z(i,l)
Emergency Action, Agency, Advocacy and Legal Aid undertaken
Ptr: Rahman, Mr Aman-Ur BA; LLB . . . *Jul 1980

RAJA & CO ‡
10 Upper Tooting Road Tooting Bec Wandsworth London SW17 7PG
Tel: 020 8772 4900 *Fax:* 020 8682 9425
Dx: 34006 TOOTING NORTH
Emergency telephone 07801 913749
E-mail: rajat@rajasolicitors.co.uk
List of partners: K Senthoorselvan, R Thavaraja
Work: C1 G J1 L Q S1 W Z(i)
Legal Aid undertaken and Legal Aid Franchise
Ptr: Senthoorselvan, Krishanthini . . . *Mar 2002
Thavaraja, Rajadurai LLB . . . *Jun 1986

RAJA & CO ‡
2a Robinson Road Colliers Wood London SW17 9DJ
Tel: 020 8543 4974
E-mail: info@raja-solicitors.co.uk

RANGA & CO ‡
112 High Road Willesden London NW10 2PN
Tel: 020 8451 4518 *Fax:* 020 8451 4610
E-mail: rangaandco@aol.com
List of partners: M N U P Jayatilaka, S I Peramunagama
Languages: Hindi, Sinhalese, Tamil
Work: E F1 G H K1 L M1 P S1 T1 Z(i,p)
Emergency Action, Agency, Advocacy, Fixed Fee Interview and Legal Aid undertaken
Ptr: Jayatilaka, Malwattege N U P . . . Jun 1985
Peramunagama, Miss Suranganie I . . . Sep 1982

RASIAH & CO ‡
180a Merton High Street South Wimbledon London SW19 1AY
Tel: 020 8543 4040 *Fax:* 020 8543 2400
Dx: 30044 WIMBLEDON SOUTH
Emergency telephone 020 8544 1250
List of partners: N Rasiah
Languages: Sinhalese, Tamil
Work: B1 E G J1 K1 L N Q S1 V W Z(i,l)
Legal Aid undertaken
SPr: Rasiah, Mr Nallathamby LLB(Hons) . . . *Oct 1990

RATIP SOLICITORS ‡
13 Belltrees Grove Streatham London SW16 2HZ
Tel: 020 8677 0625 *Fax:* 020 8677 0625
List of partners: A Ratip
Languages: Punjabi, Turkish, Urdu
Work: F1 G H J1 K1 Q S1 V Z(i)
Emergency Action, Fixed Fee Interview and Legal Aid undertaken
Ptr: Ratip, Mr Ahmet LLB(Hons) . . . *Jan 1992

RATNA & CO ‡
169a High Street North East Ham London E6 1JB
Tel: 020 8470 8818 *Fax:* 020 8475 0131 *Dx:* 4724 EAST HAM
E-mail: ratnaandco@hotmail.co.uk
List of partners: K Ratnapalan, M Ratnapalan
Languages: Bengali, Tamil, Urdu
Work: K1 Q S1 S2 Z(i,l)
Fixed Fee Interview, Legal Aid undertaken and Legal Aid Franchise
Ptr: Ratnapalan, Mrs Kulanayaki . . . Jan 1988
Ratnapalan, Mr Muthiah . . . Jan 1991

RAWAL & CO ‡
310 Ballards Lane London N12 0EY
Tel: 020 8445 0303 *Fax:* 020 8492 9385
Emergency telephone 07973 698745
List of partners: N Rawal
Languages: Gujarati
Work: B2 D1 F1 G H K1 K2 L Q V X Z(h,l)
Emergency Action, Agency, Advocacy, Legal Aid undertaken and Legal Aid Franchise
SPr: Rawal, Nikunj • . . . Sep 1991
Ast: Matini, Ardeshir • . . . Mar 1999

 See p2 for the Key to Work Categories & other symbols

RAWLINGS GILES ‡
The Lanterns Bridge Lane London SW11 3AD
Tel: 020 7223 2765 *Fax:* 020 7350 0156
List of partners: A P Giles
Languages: Spanish
Work: A3 C1 O
SPr: Giles, Mr Alan Patrick . . . Jan 2000

RAWLISON BUTLER LLP
2nd Floor Berkeley Square House Berkeley Square London W1J 6BD
Tel: 020 7887 4548 *Fax:* 020 7887 6001
E-mail: info@rawlisonbutler.com
Office: Crawley, Horsham

RAYMOND & CO ‡
Suite 1H Leroy House 436 Essex Road Islington London N1 3QP
Tel: 020 7359 0422 *Fax:* 020 7359 8342
E-mail: raymond.co@btclick.com
List of partners: S D Raymond
Work: B1 C1 E F1 J1 L Q S1 S2 T1 T2 W Z(e,l,m,q)
Fixed Fee Interview undertaken
SPr: Raymond, Mr Simon David LLB . . . *Dec 1988

FRANCIS READ ‡
19-20 Grosvenor Street London W1K 4QH
Tel: 020 7499 4055 *Fax:* 020 7499 5036
E-mail: francisread@grosvenorstreet.co.uk
List of partners: F N Read
Work: E S1 W
SPr: Read, Mr Francis N . . . *Jun 1968

M REALE SOLICITORS LTD ‡
117 Waterloo Road London SE1 8UL
Tel: 020 7921 0525 *Fax:* 020 7921 0573
E-mail: info@mreale.com

MICHAEL REASON & PARTNERS LLP ‡
Hamilton House 1 Temple Avenue London EC4Y 0HA
Tel: 020 7489 2048 *Fax:* 020 7353 5715
Emergency telephone 07973 317841
E-mail: michael@michael-reason.com
List of partners: M Reason
Work: C1 E M2 O Q S1 S2 T1 T2 W Z(e)
Emergency Action, Agency and Advocacy undertaken
Ptr: Reason, Mr Michael LLM(Lond); NZ Barrister . . . *Jun 1991

REBECCA EMMETT EMPLOYMENT LAW CONSULTANCY ‡
24 Greville Street London EC1N 8SS
Tel: 020 3008 4327
E-mail: becci@rebeccaemmettemploymentlaw.com

REBUCK LAW ‡
Summit House 12 Red Lion Square London WC1R 4QD
Tel: 020 7440 4744 *Fax:* 020 7440 7499
E-mail: info@rebucklaw.com

RECULVER SOLICITORS ‡
12-16 Clerkenwell Road London EC1M 5PQ
Tel: 020 7324 6271 *Fax:* 020 7477 2276
E-mail: jrc@reculversolicitors.co.uk

REDD ‡
29 Cloth Fair London EC1A 7JQ
Tel: 020 7776 4760 *Fax:* 020 7600 9868
List of partners: C J Maconald-Brown
Work: Z(e)
Ptr: Maconald-Brown, Mr Charters J. . . . *Oct 1974

REED SMITH LLP
(in association with Said Al-Shahry Law Office; Law Offices of Dr Najeeb Al-Nauimi; Advocacia Rodrigues)
Broadgate Tower 20 Primrose Street London EC2A 2RS
Tel: 020 3116 3000 *Fax:* 020 3116 3999 *Dx:* 1066 LONDON/CITY
E-mail: law@richardsbutler.com
Languages: Arabic, Cantonese, French, German, Greek, Italian, Japanese, Mandarin, Polish, Portuguese, Russian, Spanish
Work: A1 A3 B1 C1 C2 C3 D1 E F1 G I J1 L M1 M2 N P R1 R2 S1 S2 T1 T2 U1 Z(a,b,c,d,e,f,h,i,j,k,l,m,n,o,p,s)
Emergency Action, Agency undertaken and Member of Accident Line
Ptr: Alfandary, Mr Peter R BA; LLM(Lond) . . . *Mar 1979
Allford, Mr Philip Michael BA(Leeds) . . . *Dec 1993
Anderson, Mrs Mary Teresa LLB . . . *Oct 1984
Andrews, Mr Alexander T C MA(Oxon) . . . *Nov 1985
Archer, Mr Timothy J MA(Oxon) Alfred Syrett Prize . *§Jun 1969
Arghyrakis, Mr Epaminondas George . . . May 1994
Beale, Mr Giles W K LLB . . . Jun 1989
Beirne, Ms Nola M BComm(UCD) . . . *May 1991
Bhattacharyya, Gautam LLB(Hons); LLM . . . Oct 1993
Bird, Mr Andrew J BA . . . Dec 1990
Borrowdale, Mr Peter E M LLB(Manc) Industrial Law Prize . . . *Nov 1977
Boutcher, Mr David J BA . . . *Oct 1981
Brown, Mr Charles A BA; BCL(Oxon) . . . Feb 1983
Brown, Mr George LLB(Leics); MSc . . . *Oct 1983
Burton, Mr Alexander S LLB . . . Oct 1993
Campbell, Ms Margaret E BA(Oxon) . . . Aug 1981
Connoley, Mr Mark BA(Oxon) . . . Jun 1980
Davis, Mr Peter R . . . *Jun 1972
Douglas, Mr Mark James LLB . . . *Oct 1993
East, Lindsay T MA(Oxon) . . . §Jun 1973
Edwards, Mr A Duncan LLB(Natal); BA(Natal) . . . *Jan 1988
Edwards, Mr Stephen MA(Cantab) . . . Mar 1976
Elphicke, Mr Charles LLB . . . *Jan 1994
Emmott, Mr John F BA; LLB(Sydney) . . . *Oct 1985
Evagora, Kyriacos LLB . . . May 1994
Ewart, Mr Michael John MA . . . Oct 1991
Fagelson, Mr Ian B LLB(Soton); BCL(Oxon) . . . *Jun 1980
Fallon, Mr Paul F LLB(Hons) . . . *Oct 1985
Foster, Mr Timothy G MA(Cantab) . . . *Oct 1983
Galloway, Ms Diane BA(Cantab); LLM(Harv) . . . Nov 1986
Gunn, Mr Richard Malcolm . . . Sep 1996
Hargreaves, Mr Philip M LLB . . . *Oct 1977
Harris, Mr Graham D MA(Oxon) Charles Steele; New Inn Prizes . . . Oct 1981
Hartley, Mr Simon P LLB(Cantab) . . . May 1995
Harvey, Mr Richard H J P MA(Oxon) . . . §Jun 1980
Hewetson, Mr Charles M BA(Dunelm) . . . Nov 1989
Hibbert, Mr Thomas BA(Cantab) . . . Oct 1993
Hobson, Ms Jane . . . *Sep 1992
Holmes, Ms Katherine . . . Jun 1990
Holt, Ms Stella P LLB(Exon) . . . Jan 1984
Hull, Mr John A LLB . . . Nov 1989
Hunt, Mr Jonathan P . . . Feb 1977
Hunt, Mr Mark T F MA . . . Sep 1995
Jeffcott, Mr Robin Bryan LLB . . . Jul 1996
Jenkinson, Mr Andrew LLB . . . Oct 1993
Johnston, Mr Paul F LLB . . . *Dec 1982
Kirkpatrick, Mr Stephen BA(Cantab) . . . Nov 1989
McCarthy, Mr Michael P LLB(Hons) . . . *Oct 1989
Maxtone-Smith, Mr Michael J MA(Cantab) . . . Nov 1988
Mead, Mr Geoffrey H BA(Hons) . . . *Mar 1997
Miller, Mr Edward S MA(Oxon); LLM; Licence en Droit Europeen Oberlander Prize Member of the Law and Tax Committee . . . *Oct 1988
Montague-Jones, Mr Roy R BA(Cantab) . . . *Nov 1983
Morgan, Mr Adam R M MA(Cantab) . . . *Jun 1978
Nicoll, Mr Richard C LLB . . . *§Nov 1974
Nowinski, Mr Richard Stanley BA(Hons); LLM . . . Nov 1995
Paisley, Ms Belinda L LLB . . . *Nov 1986
Parker, Mr Roger J LLB(Lond) . . . *Oct 1984
Pearman, Mr Scott A LLB . . . Oct 1990
Philipps, Mr Richard P S MA(Cantab) . . . §Dec 1978
Pike, Mr Jonathan R LLB . . . *Oct 1983
Pope, Caron C LLB . . . *Sep 1990
Pullen, Mr David M BA(Oxon) . . . §Jun 1967
Radley, Mr Lawrence J LLB(Reading) . . . *Nov 1982
Rees, Mr Laurence G MA(Cantab) . . . Dec 1976
Reid, Mr Graham M BA(Law) . . . *Nov 1987
Rofe, Mr Douglas John LLB . . . *Nov 1993
Rymer, Mr Philip R BA(Warw) . . . Oct 1993
Sanford, Mr Frank R MA(Cantab) . . . Sep 1992
Shaw, Mr Nicholas LLB(Soton) . . . Apr 1992
Skrein, Mr S P Michael MA(Oxon); AM(S Calif) . . . *§Nov 1973
Smith, Mr Barry H LLB . . . §Oct 1974
Southorn, Mrs Elizabeth M MA(Oxon) . . . Jun 1974
Speed, Mr Nicholas P LLB(Warw) . . . *Apr 1981
Stewart, Mrs Fiona . . . *Sep 1996
Stewart, Mr Gordon BA(Dunelm) . . . *Mar 1978
Swinburn, Mr Richard G BA(Cantab) . . . Oct 1988
Taylor, Mr Andrew D MA(Oxon) . . . §Feb 1980
Taylor, Mr Phillip M BA(Oxon) . . . Nov 1993
Wallace, Mr Keith . . . *§Jun 1971
Warne, Mr David G . . . *§Jan 1972
Watts, Mr Timothy E LLB(Lond) . . . *Apr 1978
Weller, Mr Charles G LLB . . . Oct 1995
Williams, Ms Susannah L LLB(Soton) . . . Mar 1995
Woo, Mr Nicholas LLB(Hons) . . . *Apr 1996
Yorke, Mr Jonathan LLB . . . *Oct 1986
Asoc: Allen, Ms Sarah BA; LPC . . . *Sep 2001
Campbell, Ms Katherine A LLB . . . *Oct 1991
Carter, Ms Jane . . . Sep 2000
Chapman, Mr Oliver . . . *Sep 1999
Cummings, Mrs Diana A . . . *Jan 1994
Dennis, Ms Alison J LLB(Oxon) . . . Oct 1996
Elliot, Mr Nick BA(Hons) . . . *Mar 1993
Heath, Mrs Katherine . . . *Sep 2001
Jackson, Miss Amy Laura Gosset LLB(Euro); Dip(Hons) . . . *Oct 1999
Kelly, Mrs Theresa M M LLB . . . Dec 1989
Kitchener, Ms Joanna Margaret BA(Cantab); LPC . . . *Sep 2000
Morley, Mrs Christine . . . Sep 1998
Mulcahy, Ms Helen LLB . . . *Sep 1999
O'Brien, Miss Jennifer CPE; LPC . . . *Sep 1999
Purslow, Mr Neil BA(Oxon) . . . *Sep 1993
Rose, Ms Catherine . . . *Sep 2000
Sandlant, Mr Duncan LLB . . . *Aug 1997
Shaikh, Ms Shireen . . . *Oct 1995
Shine, Mr Richard LLB; LLM . . . *Jan 2000
Sturt, Mr Adam J LLB; LPC . . . *Jan 1998
Suleman, Sakil . . . *Sep 2000
Wilson, Mr James LLB(Hons) . . . *Oct 1998
Ast: Abesamis, Miss Maria N LLB(Hons) . . . *Sep 1998
Amador-Bedford, Miss Josie BA(Hons); DipLaw . . . Feb 2001
Austin, Mr Daniel T LLB . . . Jan 1999
Beale, Mr Patrick A E MB; BS; BSc . . . Sep 1998
Benham, Mr Adrian David BA(Oxon) . . . *Nov 1987
Bennett, Mr Simon Christopher LLB . . . Feb 1997
Berry, Ms Julia Mary LLB(Hons) . . . Aug 1996
Bezzant, Mr Charles D . . . *Aug 2000
Brown, Miss Sarah E BA(Hons) . . . *Jan 2000
Busato, Miss Carla Mary . . . Jan 2001
Cain, Mr Brian N LLB(Bris) . . . Jun 1986
Carter, Miss Emma Jane BA(Hons) . . . *Sep 1999
Chown, Miss Emma G . . . Oct 1992
Cottingham, Mr Robert MA . . . Sep 1989
Cullis, Ms Joanne BA; LLB . . . Aug 1997
Donnithorne, Mr Nicholas Crawford BA . . . Sep 1997
Dunn, Mr Malcolm R BA; CPE; LPC . . . Jan 1999
Freeman, Ms Lynne P S LLB(Hons) . . . *Oct 1988
Galloway, Mrs Fiona J MA(Hons); LLM . . . *Jan 2000
Gillard, Mr Neil D BA; LLB Welsh Office Constitutional Law Prize . . . *Feb 1998
Graham-Wilson, Miss Jocelyn BA(Jt Hons) . . . Sep 1999
Green, Mr Jonathan BA(Hons); LLB . . . Nov 1996
Hardy, Mr Jake LLB; LLM Sweet & Maxwell Law Prize 1996; Blackstone's Prize 1994; Sheffield Law Society Prize 1995 . . . Sep 2000
Hartley, Ms Sarah Julia Jane BA(Hons) . . . Feb 1997
Heaton, Mr Alexander J MA(Hons) . . . Jan 2000
Hogarty, Ms Karen LLB(Hons); LLM . . . Oct 1995
Howard, Mr William Anthony LLB(Hons) . . . *Sep 1997
Hudson, Ms Caroline Elizabeth LLB . . . Dec 1996
Jones, Ms Carolyn E LLB(Hons) . . . *Sep 1997
Kassi, Artemis BA(Cantab); LLM(Lond); MA . . . Mar 1998
Kerr, Indeg Laura Miles BA(Hons) . . . Mar 1996
Knowles, Sasha Deanne LLB . . . Sep 1997
Lau, Mei Lyn LLB . . . Mar 1998
Lenthall, Miss Emma L . . . *Jan 1999
McCarthy, Miss Jennifer E BA; CPE . . . *Sep 2000
Melvin, Mr Robert Bryan BA(Oxon) . . . Oct 1996
Morgan-Harris, Miss Lucy LLB(Hons); LPC . . . Mar 2001
Payiataki, Ms Vassiliki LLM . . . *Sep 2000
Pearson-Smith, Mr Anthony BA(Hons) . . . *Sep 1998
Perry, Ms Helen BA(Hons) . . . Oct 1995
Perry, Miss Helen L BA(Hons)(Law) . . . Jan 2001
Phillip, Mr Hywel Ap John BA(Hons); LLB(Hons) . . . Oct 1996
Quli, Mr David R LLB(Hons)(Reading); Grenoble(France) . . . *Sep 1996
Sando, Tue . . . Feb 2001
Sangha, Ms Kalvinder LLB . . . Sep 1997
Savage, Ms Suzanne Amanda BA(Hons); CPE; LPC . *Sep 1997
Steele, Mr Peter Mark . . . Aug 1996
Tinkler, Mr Kelly John BA; LLB . . . Jan 1996
Turner, Mr Julian Londsborough BA; MA(Cantab) . . . Apr 1997
Tyreman, Mr Martin J BA . . . *Sep 1999
Underhill, Ms Sally-Ann LLB . . . Mar 1991
Walkington, Mr Michael D BA(Cantab) . . . Oct 1994
Woodhouse, Miss Alice Emma MA(Cantab) . . . *Nov 1994
Wright, Mr Josef LLB . . . Sep 2000
Young, Mr Michael J G LLB . . . Aug 1998
Con: Beare, Mr Stuart N MA; LLB(Cantab) Hon Clerk to the Ward of Portsoken . . . *Jun 1964
Bowtle, Mr Graeme J MA(Oxon) . . . *§May 1966
Cranston, Mr Michael D . . . *May 1981
Edwards, Mr Hugh R LLB . . . *§Oct 1966
Sutton, Mr Paul W . . . Oct 1987

REES MYERS SOLICITORS ‡
16-18 Woodford Road London E7 0HA
Tel: 020 8534 4311 *Fax:* 020 8534 4360
E-mail: solicitors@reesmyers.co.uk

REGENCY SOLICITORS ‡
1st Floor 270 Kilburn High Road London NW6 2BY
Tel: 020 7625 5666 *Fax:* 020 7625 5330 *Dx:* 123856 KILBURN 2

REGENTS & CO SOLICITORS ‡
2nd Floor 1-3 Hildreth Street Balham London SW12 9RQ

REGNUM SOLICITORS ‡
44 Balls Pond Road London N1 4AP
Tel: 020 7923 3855 *Fax:* 020 7241 4272 *Dx:* 46808 DALSTON
E-mail: info@regnumsolicitors.com

REID SINCLAIR & CO ‡
12-16 Blenheim Grove London SE15 4QL
Tel: 020 7358 1110 *Fax:* 020 7358 1119

LAW OFFICES OF SUZANNE M REISMAN ‡
4-5 Park Place London SW1A 1LP
Tel: 020 7324 6244 / 7898 9338 *Fax:* 020 7898 9001
E-mail: suzanne@suzannereisman.com

RELIANCE LAW ‡
110 New Cavendish Street London W1W 6XR
Tel: 020 7436 8733 *Fax:* 020 7436 0570
E-mail: info@relilaw.co.uk

REMAR & CO ‡
319-321 Camberwell New Road London SE5 0TF
Tel: 020 7252 6722 *Fax:* 020 7277 1724
List of partners: K J Arden
Ptr: Arden, Ms Karina J . . . Mar 1989

JOACHIM G REMDE SOLICITORS ‡
53 Chandos Place London WC2N 4HS
Tel: 020 7812 6620

RENAISSANCE ‡
413 Hoe Street Walthamstow London E17 9AP
Tel: 020 8521 1100 *Fax:* 020 8521 1123 *Dx:* 52567 WANSTEAD
E-mail: enquiries@renaissancesolicitors.co.uk
Work: K3 S1 S2 Z(i)

REORIENT LEGAL ‡
148 Leadenhall Street London EC3V 4QT
Tel: 020 7645 8255 *Fax:* 020 7645 8213
E-mail: info@reorient.co.uk
List of partners: T Adams, A M Preston
Ptr: Adams, Mr Tim BSc; MSc(Hons) . . . *Oct 1989
Preston, Mrs Anila M LLB . . . *Aug 1989

REST HARROW & CO SOLICITORS ‡
238 Merton Road Wimbledon London SW19 1EQ
Tel: 020 8544 2752 *Fax:* 020 8544 2731
Dx: 300011 SOUTH WIMBLEDON
E-mail: solicitors@restharrow.com

REYNOLDS COLMAN BRADLEY LLP ‡
The London Underwriting Centre (LUC) 3 Minster Court Mincing Lane London EC3R 7DD
Tel: 020 7220 4700 *Fax:* 020 7220 4710 *Dx:* 506 LONDON/CITY
E-mail: steven.reynolds@rcbllp.com

REYNOLDS DAWSON ‡
34 John Adam Street Charing Cross London WC2N 6HW
Tel: 020 7839 2373 / 07659 130481 *Fax:* 020 7839 2344
Dx: 40040 COVENT GARDEN
Emergency telephone 0845 705 6767 (CODE 9571)
List of partners: E Fox, D Naaman, C D E Reynolds
Work: G H P
Emergency Action, Agency, Advocacy and Legal Aid undertaken
Ptr: Fox, Ms Elizabeth . . . Jan 1995
Naaman, Miss Dalia . . . Feb 2002
Reynolds, Mr Colin D E LLB . . . *Jun 1978

REYNOLDS MACDONALD ‡
2nd Floor Davina House 137-149 Goswell Road London EC1V 7ET
Tel: 020 7490 3336 *Fax:* 020 7490 3337

REYNOLDS PORTER CHAMBERLAIN LLP ‡
Tower Bridge House St Katharine's Way London E1W 1AA
Tel: 020 3060 6000 *Fax:* 020 3060 7000 *Dx:* 600 LONDON/CITY
E-mail: enquiries@rpc.co.uk
List of partners: A Anderson, T R B Anderson, A J Aylmer, J E Barnes, M E Bartlett, N D Bird, R R T Boswall, P J Boursnell, O Bray, T C Brown, T Bull, S Cornish, G P Coull, J M Davies, D Dennis-Browne, P Devine, P Dowsey, J Drew, G R Elliott, D J Flower, K Forsythe, R Gare, S O Goldring, S K P T Greenley, A N Hamer, D G Harman-Wilson, K Harris, E B A Hartley, D G Haywood, A G F Hobson, W R J Hogarth, D Hooper, J Howard, C Jaycock, M A R Kendall, S M Kilgour, M C W Lavers, E Mann, K A Mathieson, N A C McMahon, J Mee, E N Meerloo, C T Micklem, J P Miller, R P Moody, C Newsholme, R D Nobbs, C M Percy, K Y Pollock, S K Pritam, K Rees, G D Reese, C J Russell, E Smerdon, B Stimpson, C F E Suchett-Kaye, C H Thorpe, A M J Ulm, K L H Underhill, A C Usher, D K D Vander Cruyssen, F Walkinshaw, J P Watmough, S G White
Office: Bristol
Languages: Afrikaans, French, German, Gujarati, Italian, Japanese, Norwegian, Russian, Spanish, Swedish
Work: A1 A3 B1 C1 C2 C3 D1 D2 E F1 I J1 L M1 M2 N O P Q R1 R2 T1 T2 U1 U2 X Z(c,d,e,f,j,k,o,p,q,r)
Legal Aid undertaken
Ptr: Anderson, Ms Alexandra . . . Dec 2003
Anderson, Mr Timothy R B LLB(Soton) . . . Nov 1986

Aylmer, The Hon A Julian MA(Cantab) *Jun 1976
Bartlett, Ms Miriam E BA(Hons)(Oxon)(Jurisprudence) *Mar 1992
Bird, Mr Nicholas David Jan 2000
Boswall, Mr Rupert R T BA(Oxon) *Nov 1991
Boursnell, Mr Philip John LLB(Sheff) Jan 1978
Bray, Mr Oliver Apr 1995
Brown, Mr Timothy C BA(Newc) Dec 1979
Bull, Mr Tim LLB(B'ham); ACII Sep 1991
Cornish, Ms Sarah Feb 1982
Coull, Mr Gavin P BA(Oxon); DipLaw; PGCLP *Sep 1997
Davies, Mr Jonathan M MA(Oxon) *Oct 1986
Dennis-Browne, Mr Dominic Nov 1990
Devine, Mr Patrick Mar 1991
Dowsey, Mr Paul Sep 2002
Drew, Mr Jeremy Nov 1993
Elliott, Miss Geraldine R LLB(Bris) *Sep 1980
Flower, Ms Dorothy Jane LLB(Exon) Oct 1992
Forsythe, Mr Kevin Oct 1994
Gare, Mrs Rosemary MA(Cantab) *Apr 1980
Goldring, Mr Simon Oliver BA(Hons)(Econ) Nov 1995
Greenley, Mr Simon K P T Jan 1980
Hamer, Mr Alexander N LLB(Exon); ATII *Oct 1984
Harman-Wilson, Mr Duncan G Jun 1975
Harris, Ms Kathleen Dec 2000
Hartley, Ms Elizabeth B A LLB *Oct 1982
Haywood, Mr David G LLB(Manc) Harry Strouts Prize Apr 1971
Hobson, Mr Andrew G F MA(Cantab) *Dec 1982
Hogarth, Mr W Robert J BA(Oxon) *Apr 1978
Hooper, Mr David Dec 1978
Howard, Ms Jane Oct 1992
Jaycock, Mrs Clare BA(Warw) Samuel Herbert Easterbrook Prize; Daniel Rearden Prize; Travers Smith Scholarship *May 1980
Kendall, Mr Mark A R LLB(Hons)(Law) Sep 1997
Kilgour, Mr Simon M BA(Oxon) Dec 1990
Lavers, Mr Mark Christopher Wallis MA *Oct 1987
McMahon, Mr Nicholas A C LLB(Cardiff) *Nov 1989
Mann, Mr Edward BA(Nott'm) Mar 1996
Mathieson, Mr Keith A MA(Cantab) Nov 1983
Mee, Mr James Oct 1997
Meerloo, Mr Edward N *Nov 1973
Micklem, Mr C T *Apr 1974
Miller, Mr James Patrick *Sep 1997
Moody, Mr Richard P LLB; LLM Dec 1991
Newsholme, Mr Christopher LLB(B'ham) *Nov 1985
Nobbs, Mr Ronald D LLB Oct 1989
Percy, Miss Catherine M LLB(Lond) Nov 1983
Pollock, Ms Karen Y BA(Keele); LLM(Lond) *Apr 1983
Pritam, Mr Sanjay K BA; MA(East Anglia) Sep 1996
Rees, Ms Katherine BA(Hons)(Cantab) Oct 1994
Reese, Mr Gavin D LLB(Wales) Oct 1985
Russell, Mr Colin J Dec 1976
Smerdon, Mr Edward LLB(Hons)(Manc) Nov 1992
Stimpson, Mr Barry Oct 1987
Suchett-Kaye, Mr Charles F E BSc; LLB(Exon); LLM(Lond); AIIT Jan 1979
Thorpe, Ms Catherine H LLB(Leics) Apr 1991
Ulm, Mr Alexander M J BA(Reading) *Jul 1978
Underhill, Mr Kenneth Landers Hoffman LLB(Queensland); LLM(Lond); Adm Australia 1989 *Jun 1991
Usher, Mrs A Carolynn BA Dec 1975
Vander Cruyssen, Ms Dianne K D LLB Sep 1997
Walkinshaw, Ms Fiona Mar 1989
Watmough, Mr Jonathan Peter LLB(Hons) Oct 1993
White, Mr Stuart G MA(Oxon) *§Feb 1984
Asoc: Combe, Mr Simon J BA(Oxon) Apr 1989
Ast: Abu-Deeb, Maya Oct 2001
Adam, Mr Simon Sep 2001
Allsopp, Mr Iain Mark MA(Hons) Oct 1992
Armstrong, Ms Rebecca Oct 2001
Ashmore, Mr Richard Sep 2005
Atkinson, Mr Philip Hugh David BA *Oct 1990
Ballinger, Mr Michael R MA(Cantab) Nov 1996
Baxter, Mr Brendan Jul 1997
Beaumont, Ms Rachael Jessica BA(Hons) Nov 1992
Bell, Mr Alistair Sep 2005
Berkoff, Ms Jacqui Sep 2003
Beswetherick, Mr Mark Sep 2002
Blackburn, Miss Helen Jane LLB Sep 1998
Bowles, Mr Travis BA; LLB Mar 2005
Brewer, Miss Catherine M LLB; LPC *Sep 2000
Brown, Mr Jonathan Dec 2004
Browning, Ms Cass Sep 2005
Bruce, Mr John Feb 1999
Burge, Ms Amanda Apr 1996
Burns, Miss Lorraine D LLB(L'pool) Sep 1987
Burt, Chris Jun 1993
Burton, Mr Barnaby Sep 2002
Campbell, Mr Gordon Oct 2003
Campbell, Miss Tina A BA(Hons) *Sep 1997
Carlton, Ms Lisa Sep 2005
Carter, Miss Nicola J E Aug 1997
Chaplin, Ms Rachel Mar 1998
Chart, Mr Reynold P MA(Cantab) *Oct 1985
Chipperfield, Mr Marcus Oct 1997
Chmerling, Miss Geraldine A LLB(Lond) *§Apr 1986
Clayden, Mr Justin Sep 1997
Coffey, Ms Juliette Sep 2001
Conn, Ms Lise Sep 2004
Corcut, Ms Sarah Sep 2005
Cullis, Ms Gemma Sep 2000
Culy, Mr Adam D LLB(Hons) Apr 1998
Darrall, Mr Julian Sep 2004
Davies, Mr Guy Apr 1993
de Lisle, Ms Laura Sep 2005
Drake, Mr Jonathan Oct 1990
Dutta, Mamata Sep 2002
Edwards, Mr Gareth J Mar 1996
Elford, Ms Catherine Sep 2004
Flood, Mr Paul M MA Nov 1985
Fortune, Ms Kate Sep 2002
Fraser, Ms Gillian Sep 2005
Gittins, Mr John Alan BA(Cantab) Aug 1998
Godwin, Mr Nick Sep 2001
Goodrich, Mr Ross Jan 2000
Gordon, Mr Alex Mar 1998
Greenwood, Ms Lucy Dorothy Anne BSc(Hons); DipLaw *Oct 1995
Griffiths, Ms Isobel Sep 2000
Groves, Chris Sep 2003
Hahlo, Ms Fiona Sep 2000
Hall, Mr Tristan Sep 2003
Handy, Mr Oliver J MA Apr 1998
Haniff, Ms Selina Mar 1999
Hankin, Ms Faye Sep 2004
Haydon, Mrs Davina R LLB *§Nov 1990
Henthorn, Mr Simon Feb 2000
Hill, Chris Feb 2002
Hobsley, Mr James C BSc; CPE; LSF Nov 1996
Hodges, Mr Neal Sep 2003
Hodgins, Mr Peter Feb 2000
Hogue, Ms Pearl Sep 2004
Howarth, Ms Kirsty Sep 1996
Jackson, Miss Rebecca J BA; CPE; LPC Oct 1998
Jenkins, Mr Rory BA Sep 1997
Johnson, Mr Nicholas Feb 1990
Kelly, Mr Ian LLB May 1999
Kershaw, Ms Claire Aug 2002
Khamma, Simy Sep 2003
Knight, Mr Marcus Nov 1993
Koh, Mr Raymond Sep 2001
Laird, Mr Simon Sep 2005
Lee, Mr Robert William LLB Sep 2001
Lince, Mr Robin Nov 2003
Louden, Mr Ross Sep 2003
Love, Mr Simon LSF; LLB *Nov 1995
Lumb, Mr Philip S LLB Sep 2000
MacCartney, Ms Marie-Claire Dec 1997
MacDonnell, Mr Liam BA *Nov 1991
McKenzie, Mr Matt Feb 2002
McMorron, Ms Sonia Apr 2006
McNerlin, Mr Jason Apr 2002
Mandarino, Mr Frank Jan 2006
Manners-Wood, Mr James Peter BA(Hons) Apr 2002
Marsh, Ms Abigail Lucy Sep 2000
Marshall, Mr Richard William Paul BA(Hons); CPE; LSF Nov 1995
Montgomerie, Miss Fiona J LLB(Hons) *Oct 1992
Oldham, Mr Nicolas P S LLB(Hons) May 2000
Osborne, Mr Richard G LLB Jul 1973
Owen, Lindsay Nov 1997
Paisley, Ms Kathryn Mar 1998
Pennant, Ms Alison Sep 2004
Pester, Mr Nick Sep 2005
Peters, Ms Caroline LLB(Hons); MA *Sep 1996
Phillips, Ms Chloe Feb 1996
Phythian-Adams, Mr James Sep 2005
Pretorius, Rion Jul 2004
Rainger, Ms Erika Mar 2001
Raymond, Mr Charles Edward William BA Jan 1999
Read, Mr Christian Sep 2002
Sagoo, Mr Neil V Oct 1996
Saint, Mr Philip Jonathan BA(Hons) Oct 1996
Saville, Mr Daniel Jonathan LLB Sep 1998
Schopflin, Ms Julia Nov 2000
Serby, Mr Tom Dec 1995
Sharp, Mr Iain M BA Oct 1998
Skeggs, Ms Anne Sep 2002
Smith, Mr Alex Sep 2002
Sproston, Ms Lorna Mar 2003
Stockwell, Mr James Sep 2003
Stone, Mr Alan Sep 2001
Sutton, Mr Mark Sep 2000
Thomas, Ms Annabel Sep 2003
Thorne, Mr David A BA(Hons)(Politics) *Oct 1999
Trehy, Ms Wendy Sep 1999
Van Der Breggen, Corne Nov 2003
Walsh, Ms Cathy Nov 2003
Wheal, Ms Elizabeth Oct 1997
Wilkinson, Mr Roger J *Mar 1979
Wills, Miss Frances Sep 2001
Wilson, Mr Dean Oct 2002
Wolfarth, Mr Geoffrey Ernest BA(Cantab) *Jan 1983
Wyles, Mr Jonathan J A LLB(Lond) Bickerdike Allen Prize (Construction Law) *Oct 1987
Young, Miss Fiona S LLB(Hons) Nov 2000

RICE-JONES & SMITHS ‡
7 Ely Place Holborn London EC1N 6RY
Tel: 020 7831 2506 ***Fax:*** 020 7831 6465
Dx: 224 LONDON/CHANCERY LN
Emergency telephone 020 7242 6017
E-mail: law@londonrjs.com
List of partners: P K Burton, J S Petrou, J Quigley
Languages: French, Greek, Spanish
Work: B1 C1 C2 E F1 F2 J1 K1 K3 L M1 M2 N O P Q R1 R2 S1 S2 T1 T2 W X Z(b,d,e,j,k,l,p,q,r)
Agency, Fixed Fee Interview, Legal Aid undertaken and Member of Accident Line
Ptr: Burton, Mr Peter K LLB(Manc) *Mar 1979
Petrou, Mr John S BA(Hons) *Mar 1983
Quigley, Mr John LLB *Oct 1983

RICH & BAILY ‡
157 Tottenham Lane Crouch End Haringey London N8 9BT
Tel: 020 8340 2481 ***Fax:*** 020 8348 3272 ***Dx:*** 35950 CROUCH END
Work: K1 K3 L Q S1 W

RICHARDS KIBBE & ORBE ‡
7th Floor Broadgate West 9 Appold Street London EC2A 2AP
Tel: 020 7033 3150 ***Fax:*** 020 7033 3151

MARTIN B RICHARDS ‡
Burton House Burton Hole Lane Mill Hill London NW7 1AL
Tel: 020 8906 1841

RICHMOND & BARNES ‡
16 St Martin's-le-Grand London EC1A 4EN
Tel: 020 7195 2266
E-mail: info@richmondandbarnes.com

RIDER SUPPORT SERVICES ‡
2 Deodar Road London SW15 2NN
Tel: 020 8246 4900 ***Fax:*** 020 8246 4930
E-mail: rss@ridersupport.co.uk
Languages: Afrikaans, French, Polish, Portuguese, Spanish, Welsh
Work: N

RIDLEY & CO ‡
26 Wilfred Street Buckingham Gate Westminster London SW1E 6PL
Tel: 020 7828 7656 ***Fax:*** 020 7630 9256
E-mail: law@mwridley.co.uk
List of partners: M W Ridley
Work: C1 E L O Q S1 S2
SPr: Ridley, Mr Mark W *Mar 1976
Asoc: Burrow, Ms Jillian Ann Jan 1990

RIDOUTS ‡
15 Bentinck Mews London W1U 2AP
Tel: 020 7317 0340 ***Fax:*** 020 7935 8310

RIES SOLICITORS ‡
50 Essex Street London WC2R 3JF
Tel: 020 3397 0499 ***Fax:*** 0870 495 3541
Dx: 37952 LONDON/KINGSWAY
E-mail: er@familysolutions.eu

RILEY & CO ‡
1 Stradbroke Road London N5 2PZ
Tel: 07785 231190

RIPPON PATEL & FRENCH ‡
37 Harley Street Westminster London W1G 8QG
Tel: 020 7323 0404 ***Fax:*** 020 7580 2705
Dx: 42721 OXFORD CIRCUS NORTH
E-mail: rpfsols@aol.com
List of partners: A S Patel, D B Rippon
Languages: French
Work: B1 C1 D1 K1 L N O Q S1 T1 T2 W Z(e,i,l)
Emergency Action, Agency, Advocacy, Legal Aid undertaken and Legal Aid Franchise
Ptr: Patel, Ashok S LLB; MA *§May 1982

RISEAM SHARPLES ‡
2 Tower Street London WC2H 9NP
Tel: 020 7836 9555 ***Fax:*** 020 7836 9777
Dx: 140580 COVENT GARDEN 4
E-mail: cas@rs-law.co.uk
List of partners: C F Riseam, C A Sharples
Work: E R2 S1 S2
Ptr: Riseam, Mr Colin F *Dec 1977
Sharples, Mr Clive A LLB *May 1974

RIX & KAY SOLICITORS LLP
20a Berkeley Street Mayfair London W1J 8EF
Tel: 020 7871 1012
Office: Hove, Seaford, Sevenoaks, Uckfield

HELEN ROBBINS SOLICITORS ‡
Forest House 8 Gainsborough Road Waltham Forest London E11 1HT
Tel: 020 8558 0038 ***Fax:*** 020 8558 3186 ***Dx:*** 58217 LEYTONSTONE
E-mail: helenrobbinssols@aol.com
Work: D1 K1 L Q S1 V W Z(h)

ROBERTS MCCRACKEN ‡
69 Hanover Road Brent London NW10 3DL
Tel: 0870 420 5658 ***Fax:*** 0870 420 5659
List of partners: R Calzolari, M H McCracken
Languages: Italian
Work: B1 E F1 J1 K1 L N O Q S1 S2
Agency undertaken
Ptr: Calzolari, Mr Robert BA(Law) *Mar 1986
McCracken, Ms Melanie Hazel BSc(Hons) *Feb 1987

PAUL ROBERTS ‡
60-61 Mark Lane London EC3R 7ND
Tel: 020 7264 0500 ***Fax:*** 020 7264 0501

ROBINSON & CO ‡
5th Floor Diamond House 36-38 Hatton Gardens London EC1N 8EB
Tel: 020 7405 5180 ***Fax:*** 020 7405 5190 ***Dx:*** 53328 CLERKENWELL
E-mail: rmortlock@robinsonsonlegal.co.uk
List of partners: T R Mortlock
Languages: French, Italian
Work: A1 A2 B1 C1 D1 E J1 K1 O P Q S1 W Z(b)
Agency undertaken
Ptr: Mortlock, Mr Thomas Richard LLB(NZ) *§Oct 1975

MARK ROBINSON TRANSACTIONAL INTELLECTUAL PROPERTY SERVICES ‡
17 Bradley Gardens Ealing London W13 8HE
Tel: 07881 951308
E-mail: mark.robinson@mrtips.co.uk

MICHAEL ROBINSON ‡
6th Floor 5 Princes Gate London SW7 1QJ
Tel: 020 7584 5038 ***Fax:*** 020 7584 1404
E-mail: mail@robinsonlaw.co.uk
List of partners: M L B Robinson
Work: B1 C1 M2 O Q Z(j)
SPr: Robinson, Mr Michael Lyndon Beverley MA(Oxon) *Oct 1965

ROBINSON RAVANI & CO ‡
269a Green Street London E7 8LJ
Tel: 020 8548 9402 ***Fax:*** 020 8586 2137 ***Dx:*** 11735 UPTON PARK

VIVIENNE ROBINSON ‡
25 Lake House Road London E11 3QS
Tel: 020 8279 8899 ***Fax:*** 020 8928 1549
Emergency telephone 020 8279 8899
E-mail: v-r@vrobinson.co.uk
List of partners: V Robinson
Languages: French
Work: C3 M1 U1
SPr: Robinson, Ms Vivienne MA(Cantab); Licence en Droit Europeen; US Attorney *Oct 1987

ROCHE & CO ‡
The Gate House Clifford's Inn London EC4A 1BL
Tel: 020 7831 2209 ***Fax:*** 020 7430 1674
E-mail: office@rocheco.co.uk
List of partners: P M Roche
Work: B2
SPr: Roche, Mr Paul M ★ *Jun 1992

ROCHMAN LANDAU LLP ‡
Accurist House 44 Baker Street London W1U 7AL
Tel: 020 7544 2424 ***Fax:*** 020 7544 2400
Dx: 42700 OXFORD CIRCUS NORTH
E-mail: mail@rochmanlandau.co.uk
List of partners: T E Cullen, P Dolan, P E Dunbar, A Langleben, D R Liebeck, K Nakada, P M Negus-Fancey, A W Platman, J E G Toth, J P Wiese, V Williams
Languages: French, Italian, Japanese, Portuguese, Spanish
Work: B1 C1 C2 C3 E F1 I J1 K1 K2 L M1 M2 N O P Q R1 S1 S2 T1 T2 W Z(b,c,d,e,f,i,j,k,l,m,o,p,q,w)
Emergency Action, Agency and Advocacy undertaken

See p2 for the Key to Work Categories & other symbols

Ptr: Cullen, Miss Teresa E BA(Hons) . . . *Nov 1985
Dolan, Ms Philippa BA . . . *Dec 1981
Dunbar, Mr Paul Edward LLB(Hons). . . . Oct 1997
Langleben, Mr Alan LLB(Hons) . . . *Feb 1970
Liebeck, Mr David R BA; LLB(Cape Town). . . *Jul 1977
Nakada, Mr Koichiro . . . Oct 2006
Negus-Fancey, Mrs Patricia M LLB(Hons). . . *Dec 1968
Platman, Mr Anthony W. . . . *Jun 1975
Wiese, Mr Jonathan Paul BA(Hons). . . *Nov 1994
Williams, Mrs Vanessa BA(Hons)(Law) Director of the Woman of the Year Lunch . . . Jan 1994
Mem: Toth, Mr John Edward Gerald BA Notary Public . . . *Nov 1985
Ast: Holden, Miss Samara Jane Nicola LLB; MSc . . . Nov 2009
Con: Alter, Mr Stephen . . . *Dec 1975
Fernandes, Mr Arthur P LLB; MBA; MCIArb . . . *Apr 1999
Rechnic, Mr Grant L LLB(Hons). . . *Dec 1986
Rochman, Mr John H . . . *Apr 1968
Silver, Mr Derrick Martyn . . . §Jun 1970
Sparrow, Mr Andrew Peter LLB(Hons) National Lawyer Award 1999 . . . Jun 1989

ROCK SOLICITORS ‡
4-6 Westbury Avenue Turnpike Lane London N22 6BN
Tel: 020 8888 1555 *Fax:* 020 8888 2555
E-mail: law@rocksolicitors.co.uk

RODGERS & BURTON ‡
(incorporating Ashbys)
(in association with Saunders & Co)
15-17 Church Road Barnes London SW13 9HG
Tel: 020 8939 6300 *Fax:* 020 8939 6325 *Dx:* 59702 BARNES
E-mail: info@randb.law.co.uk
List of partners: D J Moore, D Sutherland
Languages: French, Spanish
Work: A3 B1 C1 C2 C3 E F1 F2 I J1 K1 K2 L N O Q S1 S2 T1 T2 W Z(b,c,h,j,l,q,r)
Agency, Advocacy and Legal Aid undertaken
Ptr: Moore, Mr David J BSc; FCIArb . . . *May 1979
Sutherland, D. . . . Jan 2000
Ast: Pattinson, Ms Anette H BA . . . Oct 1995
Tyndall, Miss Gillian BA(Law) . . . *Oct 1987
Woloshak, Mr Mark O O BA(Hons) . . . *Oct 1990
Con: Ashby, Mr David A . . . *Jun 1970
McCutcheon, Mrs Deborah J L LLB . . . Nov 1978

ROELENS SOLICITORS WIMBLEDON ‡
Highlands House 165 The Broadway Wimbledon London SW19 1NE
Tel: 020 8554 8002 *Fax:* 020 8554 8003
E-mail: info@roelens-wimbledon.co.uk

ROGERS & CO SOLICITORS ‡
2nd Floor 145-157 St John Street London EC1V 4PY
Tel: 020 7060 1189 *Fax:* 0845 474 1735
E-mail: london@rogerssolicitors.com

ROKEBY JOHNSON BAARS ‡
22 Gilbert Street London W1K 5HD
Tel: 020 7499 4990 *Fax:* 020 7491 2233 *Dx:* 9005 WEST END

ROLI SOLICITORS ‡
Flat 29 67 Lower Sloane Street Westminster London SW1W 8DD
Tel: 020 7224 9777 *Fax:* 020 7224 9090
Languages: Arabic, French, Greek

ROLLINGSONS ‡
Marlborough Court 14-18 Holborn London EC1N 2LE
Tel: 020 7611 4848 *Fax:* 020 7611 4849
Dx: 334 LONDON/CHANCERY LN
E-mail: law@rollingsons.co.uk
List of partners: I Khawaja, G Rollingson
Languages: Creole, Greek, Hebrew, Hindi, Punjabi, Urdu
Work: C1 C2 D1 E F1 J1 K1 K2 K3 N O Q S1 S2 W Z(j,p,q,r)
Emergency Action and Fixed Fee Interview undertaken
Ptr: Khawaja, Mr Imran . . . *Jan 1993
Rollingson, Mr Gregory LLB(Hons) . . . *Apr 1980
Ast: Balgobin, Aneil . . . Sep 2001
Critchley, Mr Paul . . . *Jul 2005
Eden, Miss Sharon . . . Mar 2005
Rahman, Miss Alma. . . . Feb 2007
Rideough, Mr Paul LLB(Hons). . . . *Oct 1995
Vincent, Ms Sarah LLB(Hons). . . . *Nov 1992

ROMAIN COLEMAN & CO ‡
Hoe Street Chambers 183-185 Hoe Street Walthamstow Waltham Forest London E17 3AP
Tel: 020 8520 3322 *Fax:* 020 8520 8837 *Dx:* 32010 WALTHAMSTOW
List of partners: C R Baldwin, A Cork, D A Dolties, S E Gulshan
Languages: French
Work: C1 E J1 L M1 N O Q R1 S1 S2 T1 W Z(c,e,h,j,l)
Agency, Advocacy, Legal Aid undertaken and Member of Accident Line
Ptr: Baldwin, Mr Christopher R BA. . . . *Mar 1980
Cork, Mr Andrew LLB(Lond). . . . *Jun 1975
Dolties, Mr David A LLB(Lond) . . . *Jun 1977
Gulshan, Ms Suzanne Elizabeth LLB(Hons). . . . Nov 1990
Ast: Timms, Mr Christopher P LLB. . . . Feb 1998
Westbrook, Mr Martin J BA(Oxon). . . . *Dec 1975

RONALD FLETCHER BAKER LLP ‡
326 Old Street London EC1V 9DR
Tel: 020 7613 1402 *Fax:* 020 7613 2711 *Dx:* 137773 FINSBURY 5
E-mail: info@rfblegal.co.uk
List of partners: J O'Callaghan, R B Rahim, J A Roberts
Office: London W1
Languages: Cantonese, French, Greek, Hakka, Hindi, Punjabi, Urdu
Work: A3 B1 B2 C1 C2 C3 D1 D2 E F1 F2 G H J1 K1 K2 K3 L M1 M2 N O P Q S1 S2 W Z(b,e,k,l)
Emergency Action, Agency, Advocacy, Legal Aid undertaken and Legal Aid Franchise
Ptr: O'Callaghan, Mr John LLB . . . *Feb 1983
Rahim, Miss Rakeebah Bibi LLB . . . *May 1993
Roberts, Mr Jonathan A MA(Oxon) . . . *Dec 1976
Ast: Hung, Miss Sarah LLB . . . May 2005

RONALD FLETCHER BAKER LLP
77a Baker Street London W1U 6RF
Tel: 020 7467 5757 *Fax:* 020 7613 2711
Dx: 42722 OXFORD CIRCUS NORTH
E-mail: info@rfblegal.co.uk
Office: London EC1

RONALDSONS ‡
55 Gower Street London WC1E 6HQ
Tel: 020 7580 6075 *Fax:* 020 7580 7429
Dx: 134201 TOTTENHAM COURT ROAD 2
E-mail: forum@ronaldsons.co.uk
List of partners: R C France-Hayhurst, N R Hayter, S F Ronaldson
Ptr: France-Hayhurst, Mr Roger C LLB . . . *May 1977
Hayter, Mr Neil R . . . Sep 1997
Ronaldson, Mr Stephen F MA. . . . *Oct 1981
Ast: Ellis, Miss Anne-Marie. . . . Mar 1993
Traynor, Mr Dominic. . . . Nov 2000

RONIK SOLICITORS ‡
1b Herbert Road London SE18 3TB
Tel: 020 8317 6778 *Fax:* 020 8855 8816 *Dx:* 33313 WOOLWICH
E-mail: info.ronik@btconnect.com

ROOKS RIDER ‡
Challoner House 19 Clerkenwell Close Clerkenwell London EC1R 0RR
Tel: 020 7689 7000 *Fax:* 020 7689 7001 *Dx:* 53324 CLERKENWELL
E-mail: lawyers@rooksrider.co.uk
List of partners: N Cheshire, C E C Cooke, L A Hemingway, R H N Jenkins, J L John, K J Methold, A D Shalet, C G Wright
Languages: French, German, Russian, Spanish
Work: C1 C2 D1 D2 E J1 K1 L O Q R1 R2 S1 S2 T1 T2 W Z(d,e,i,k,p,q)
Emergency Action undertaken
Ptr: Cheshire, Mr Nick LLM; BA(Hons). . . . Jan 1981
Cooke, Mr Christopher E C LLB; TEP. . . . *Jul 1969
Hemingway, Ms Lindsey Ann LLB; Dip d'Etudes Juridiques Francaises . . . *Oct 1991
Jenkins, Mr Richard H N BA. . . . *Oct 1983
John, Mr James Lloyd LLB . . . *Sep 1988
Methold, Mrs Karen Joan LLB; TEP. . . . *Oct 1988
Shalet, Mr Anthony D LLB. . . . *Oct 1985
Wright, Mr Christopher G LLB. . . . *Dec 1973
Asoc: Clark, Mrs Sarah BA(Hons) . . . Nov 1985
Nelson, Mr Gary BA(Hons) . . . Dec 1998
Pullinger, Ms Amanda Claire LLB; FCIArb. . . . Oct 1980
Riley, Mrs Lucy B LLB. . . . Sep 2000
Stewart, Ms Nicola BSc. . . . Sep 2001
Ast: Cash, Hannah BSc . . . *Jun 2005
Davis, Ms Gemma LLB . . . Oct 2006
Johnson, Charlotte BA(Hons); LPC . . . Sep 2003
Kearns, Lawrie . . . Sep 2005
Lee, Ms Victoria LLB . . . Sep 2008
Lyon, Ms Emma LLB(Hons). . . . Sep 2005
Rippon, Alice BA(Hons). . . . Sep 2010
Robbins, Ms Philippa LLB(Hons) . . . Oct 2007
Stephens, Mr Mathew BA(Hons); PGDipLaw . . . *Sep 2007
Con: Foinette, Miss E Clare LLB; AKC . . . *Jun 1968

RICHARD ROONEY & CO ‡
78a High Street Wimbledon Village Merton London SW19 5EG
Tel: 020 8947 8024 *Fax:* 020 8947 1887
Dx: 35063 WIMBLEDON VILLAGE
E-mail: richard@richardrooney.com
List of partners: R F Rooney
Languages: Gaelic
Work: B1 C1 E F1 G J1 K1 L M1 N O Q S1 S2 W Z(j,k,l)
Agency, Advocacy, Fixed Fee Interview and Legal Aid undertaken
Ptr: Rooney, Mr Richard F. . . . *Feb 1976
Asoc: Maclean, Ms Fiona . . . May 1986

ROOPER & WHATELY ‡
159 New Bond Street London W1S 2UD
Tel: 020 7399 0824 *Fax:* 020 7399 0050 *Dx:* 54277 PICCADILLY
E-mail: julian.whately@rooperwhately.co.uk

ROPEMAKERS SOLICITORS ‡
2b Holme Road East Ham London E6 1LY
Tel: 020 8586 8500 *Fax:* 020 8475 0488
E-mail: igor.ryabchuk@ropemakerslaw.com
List of partners: R Ali
SPr: Ali, Mr Rofik. . . . Oct 2005
Con: Ryabchuk, Mr Igor. . . . Dec 2007

ROPES & GRAY INTERNATIONAL LLP ‡
5 New Street Square London EC4A 3BF
Tel: 020 3122 1100 *Fax:* 020 3122 1101

ROSE SAMUEL ODELE & PARTNERS ‡
252 Kirkgate Sydenham London SE26 4NL
Tel: 020 8676 3449 *Fax:* 020 8676 3448

JOHN H ROSEN & CO ‡
Charlcote House 101 Crawford Street Westminster London W1H 1AN
Tel: 020 7262 2471 *Fax:* 020 7262 8733
List of partners: J H Rosen
Languages: French
Work: E G H S1 W
Advocacy and Legal Aid undertaken

R A ROSEN & CO ‡
Collette House 55 Piccadilly London W1J 0DX
Tel: 020 7629 6566 *Fax:* 020 7629 1950
E-mail: arnold@arnoldrosen.co.uk
List of partners: R A Rosen
SPr: Rosen, Mr Ronald Arnold LLB Paul Methven & Yardborough Anderson Scholar Inner Temple . . . *Dec 1981

ROSENBERG & CO ‡
673 Finchley Road Barnet London NW2 2JP
Tel: 020 7431 8832 *Fax:* 020 7431 6534
Dx: 33808 GOLDERS GREEN
E-mail: stuart@rosenberg-and-co.com
Work: S1 W

ROSENBLATT ‡
9-13 St Andrew Street London EC4A 3AF
Tel: 020 7955 0880 *Fax:* 020 7955 0888
Dx: 493 LONDON/CHANCERY LN
E-mail: info@rosenblatt-law.co.uk
List of partners: D P J Fairfield, T Ferns, A Field, N Foss-Pedersen, C J Hyer, A Kinsey, A London, J Lovitt, T MacLeod, W O'Neil, C Pulham, I I Rosenblatt, N Sampson
Languages: French, German, Italian
Work: B1 C1 C2 C3 E F1 F2 I J1 M1 M2 N O P Q R1 S1 T1 T2 U1 U2 W Z(c,e,f,j,k,l,q,s)
Legal Aid Franchise
Ptr: Fairfield, Mr David P J LLB(Lond); AKC . . . *Mar 1984
Ferns, Mr Tom LLB . . . Nov 1995
Field, Mr Anthony . . . *Sep 2001
Foss-Pedersen, Mr Nick. . . . Sep 2000
Hyer, Mr Clive J LLB . . . *Oct 1986
Kinsey, Mr Andrew . . . Dec 1992
London, Ms Andrea LLB . . . Oct 2002
Lovitt, Mr Jon LLB. . . . Nov 1990
MacLeod, Ms Tania LLB. . . . *Oct 1993
O'Neil, Mr Wayne . . . Mar 1999
Pulham, Mr Chris . . . Sep 2000
Rosenblatt, Mr Ian I LLB(Lond) . . . *Oct 1983
Sampson, Mr Neil. . . . *Feb 1983

ROSHANIAN PAYMAN INTERNATIONAL SOLICITORS ‡
Suite 3 55 Park Lane Mayfair London W1K 1NA
Tel: 020 7499 2712 *Fax:* 020 7629 1774

ROSLING KING ‡
10 Old Bailey London EC4M 7NG
Tel: 020 7353 2353 *Fax:* 020 7583 2035
Dx: 154 LONDON/CHANCERY LN
E-mail: info@roslingking.co.uk
List of partners: J D Beagley, S Geoghegan, A T H Hardman, P Lewis, O T Rafferty, G Squire, H M Thurkettle
Languages: French, Spanish
Work: A1 A3 B1 C1 C2 C3 E I J1 J2 L N O P Q R1 R2 S1 S2 T1 T2 W Z(b,c,e,j,n,o,q,s,w)
Agency and Advocacy undertaken
Ptr: Beagley, Mr John D BA . . . *Sep 1983
Geoghegan, Mr Simon LLB . . . *Sep 1994
Hardman, Mr Andrew T H LLB . . . *Oct 1986
Lewis, Mr Peter LLB . . . *Sep 1995
Rafferty, Mr Owen T MA. . . . *Dec 1976
Squire, Miss Georgina LLB . . . *Nov 1983
Thurkettle, Miss Helen Mary BA. . . . *Sep 1995
Ast: Bowers, Mr Craig MEng. . . . Oct 2002
Brown, Mrs Suzannah E LLB . . . *Jan 1998
Doerr, Ms Michelle Elizbeth LLB; BSc. . . . Mar 2003
Fleming, Miss Faye BA . . . Sep 2003
Hembling, Mr Barry J BA . . . *Sep 2000
Jenkins, Mr Rory BA . . . Sep 1997
Stafford, Mr Lee Paul BA . . . Oct 2002
Taylor, Miss Lisa LLB . . . Oct 2002
Williams, Mr Richard LLB(Hons). . . . Sep 2001
Wilson, Miss Noleen LLM; ALCM . . . Sep 2003

ROSS & CO ‡
1 New Square Lincoln's Inn London WC2A 3SA
Tel: 020 7831 1099 *Fax:* 020 7242 2460

ROSS & CRAIG ‡
12a Upper Berkeley Street Westminster London W1H 7PE
Tel: 020 7262 3077 *Fax:* 020 7724 6427 *Dx:* 44416 MARBLE ARCH
E-mail: reception@rosscraig.com
List of partners: H R G Barrett, I E Bloom, S A Gilbert, S E Katzenberg, J M Kosky, D I Leadercramer, K C Pearlman, A A Ring, E L Ross, S Ten Hove
Languages: French, German, Italian
Work: B1 C1 C2 D1 E F1 J1 K1 K2 L M1 N O P Q R1 R2 S1 S2 T1 W Z(d,e,f,k,p,r,w,z)
Ptr: Barrett, Mr Hugh R G BA . . . §Feb 1979
Bloom, Mr Ian E BA. . . . *Jul 1979
Gilbert, Mr Stephen Alfred LLB(Soton). . . . *Oct 1977
Katzenberg, Ms Simone Elaine . . . *Mar 1992
Kosky, Mr Joseph Michael BA(Hons) . . . Apr 1981
Leadercramer, Mr David I LLB. . . . Jun 1976
Pearlman, Mr Keith C BA . . . *Feb 1986
Ring, Mr Adrian Anthony . . . *Apr 2002
Ten Hove, Mr Stephen LLB(Lond). . . . *Nov 1990
Asoc: Miles, Mr John C O. . . . *Jun 1976
Payne, Mrs Jacqueline M BSc. . . . *Jun 1980
Ast: Bardsley, Mr Philip Gibson . . . Oct 1995
Butt, Mrs Farah . . . *Aug 2000
Coyne, Miss Niamh Bridget . . . *May 2002
McNab, Mrs Mei-Ling . . . Oct 2001

JOHN ROSS ‡
48-50 Corringham Road Golders Green London NW11 7BU
Tel: 020 8458 1924 *Fax:* 020 8201 8858
List of partners: J I B E Ross
Languages: French, German
Work: C1 M1 N P Z(b,c,e,j,k)
Ptr: Ross, Mr John I B E BA(Oxon) . . . *Sep 1969

MICHAEL ROSS & CO ‡
Suite 8497 16-18 Circus Road London NW8 6PG
Tel: 020 7286 0002 *Fax:* 020 7266 0541
E-mail: mrossco@aol.com
Work: E S1 S2 W

PHILIP ROSS & CO ‡
(in association with Cyrus Ross)
4 Chandos Street London W1A 3BQ
Tel: 020 7636 6969 *Fax:* 020 7785 9151 *Dx:* 9012 WEST END
E-mail: law@philipross.com
List of partners: D M Abrahams, A Ahmed, C J Atkinson, G C Constant, J Fisher, A D Fishman, L J Paltnoi, M Paramjorthy, A Pattihis, H Pattihis, G J Scott, I D Stone, D A Williams, C J Wilson
Office: Bushey
Languages: French, Greek
Work: B1 C1 D1 E F1 J1 K1 K3 L N O Q R1 R2 S1 S2 W Z(b,c,d,f,h,k,l,p,q,r)
Ptr: Abrahams, Mr Daniel Morris. . . . Sep 2003
Ahmed, Mr Asif . . . Sep 2007
Atkinson, Mr Christopher J LLB(Lond) Deputy District Judge (Surrey). . . . *Apr 1981
Constant, Mr George Christos LLB . . . Sep 2004
Fishman, Mr Andrew D . . . *Jul 1980
Paltnoi, Mrs Lucy Jayne BA(Hons) . . . Dec 2001
Paramjorthy, Mrs Mathura. . . . Nov 2003
Pattihis, Miss Alicia . . . May 2009
Pattihis, Mr Harry LLB. . . . *Oct 1980
Scott, Mr Gary James LLB . . . *Mar 2003
Stone, Mr Irving D. . . . *Feb 1964
Williams, Mr David Alun LLB(Hons) . . . Oct 2001
Wilson, Mrs Carolyn Jane LLB(Hons) . . . Dec 1995
Fisher, Jane FILEx . . . NSP
Ast: Buysman, Mrs Emma Louise . . . Sep 2008
Gould, Miss Charlotte . . . Sep 2008

Con: Mellon, Mrs Victoria LLB(Hons) . . . . *Jun 1996
Papadopulo, Mr Peter. . . . . Jan 2010

SAMUEL ROSS SOLICITORS ‡
253 Camberwell New Road London SE5 0TH
Tel: 020 7701 4664 *Fax:* 020 7701 4678
E-mail: solicitors@samuelross.com

S D ROSSER & CO ‡
25 High Road Willesden Green London NW10 2TE
Tel: 020 8451 3848 *Fax:* 020 8451 6585 *Dx:* 58153 WILLESDEN
E-mail: sdrosser@hotmail.com
List of partners: C A Asher, S D Rosser
Languages: French, Polish, Spanish
Work: C1 D1 E J1 K1 L N O Q R1 S1 S2 W Z(l)
Agency and Advocacy undertaken
Ptr: Asher, Mr Clive Alan LLB . . . . *Dec 1991
Rosser, Mr Simon D BA. . . . . *Aug 1978
Ast: Leff, Mr Joshua A R BA. . . . . May 1988

ROSSIDES CAINE ‡
22 Alderman's Hill Palmers Green London N13 4PN
Tel: 020 8882 9292 *Fax:* 020 8886 9341
Dx: 57871 PALMERS GREEN
List of partners: A Vittachi
Languages: Greek
Work: B1 C1 E F1 J1 J2 K1 L N O Q S1 W Z(l,q)
Agency and Advocacy undertaken
SPr: Vittachi, Adil LLB . . . . *Dec 1984

ROUSE LEGAL (FORMERLY WILLOUGHBY & PARTNERS) ‡
(in association with Rouse & Co International)
11th Floor Exchange Tower 1 Harbour Exchange Square London E14 9GE
Tel: 020 7536 4100 *Fax:* 020 7536 4200
E-mail: rouselegal@iprights.com
List of partners: S Adams, K Fong, E Hardcastle, J Newman, A Rajendra, R Ross-Macdonald, D Sternfeld
Languages: Cantonese, Farsi, French, German, Hungarian, Italian, Mandarin, Serbo-Croat, Urdu
Work: A3 F2 I U2 Z(e,f,z,za)
Ptr: Adams, Mr Stuart LLB(Hons) . . . . *Dec 1993
Fong, Ms Karen LLB(Hons) . . . . *Aug 1994
Hardcastle, Mr Edward . . . . Oct 1992
Newman, Mr Jeremy BA(Jt Hons) . . . . *Sep 1994
Rajendra, Mrs Arty LLB(Hons). . . . . *Dec 1997
Ross-Macdonald, Mr Rupert BA(Hons); MA(Cantab). . Jan 1994
Sternfeld, Ms Diana BSc . . . . *Jun 1980
Asoc: Baines, Miss Rebecca LLB(Hons); BCL(Oxon) . . . . Nov 2002
Lachmansingh, Miss Annie BSc(Hons) . . . . *Jan 2001
Con: Willoughby, Mr Anthony. . . . . *§Sep 1970

ROWEL GENN SOLICITORS ‡
33 Cavendish Square London W1G 0PW
Tel: 020 7182 4097
E-mail: mail@rowelgenn.com

JONATHAN ROWELL & CO ‡
Flat 15 Highcroft 170 Highgate Road London NW5 1EJ
Tel: 020 7482 2663

ROYCE & CO ‡
4 Stephendale Yard Stephendale Road London SW6 2LR
Tel: 020 7736 9103 *Fax:* 020 7751 0357
List of partners: A V Royce
Languages: French
Work: A1 C1 C2 E F1 G J1 N Q R1 S1 W Z(l,p)
Agency, Advocacy and Legal Aid undertaken
Ptr: Royce, Mrs Amanda V . . . . Jul 1981

ROYDS LLP ‡
65 Carter Lane London EC4V 5HF
Tel: 020 7583 2222 *Fax:* 020 7583 2034 *Dx:* 138762 CHEAPSIDE 2
E-mail: info@royds.com
List of partners: C Anderson, J M H Buckland, F R Davey, C Doran, C Hall, P W Hart, R J Lloyd-Davies, S McKirgan, J W R Millar Craig, J D North, G E D Ospedale, J N Rampton, C B Rodda, S B Welfare, S Wilkinson, G B Williams, R M Woodman
Office: Morden
Languages: Arabic, French, German, Spanish
Work: A1 B1 C1 C2 C3 D1 E F1 J1 K1 K3 L M1 M2 N O P Q R1 S1 S2 T1 T2 V W Z(b,c,d,e,f,i,k,l,o,p,q,r,w)
Emergency Action, Agency, Legal Aid undertaken and Member of Accident Line
Ptr: Anderson, Mr Claus. . . . . *Jan 2008
Doran, Ms Caroline . . . . *Sep 2000
Hall, Mr Chris. . . . . *Oct 1983
Hart, Mr Patrick William. . . . . Feb 1993
Lloyd-Davies, Mr Robert J. . . . . *§May 1973
McKirgan, Mr Simon BA(Hons)(York)(History) . . . . Mar 1999
Millar Craig, Mr James W R LLB(Lond) . . . . *§Apr 1977
North, Mr John D BA . . . . *Oct 1987
Ospedale, Miss Gemma E D . . . . Dec 2000
Rampton, Mr Julian N BA(Cantab) . . . . *§Sep 1989
Rodda, Mr Christopher B BA . . . . *Oct 1987
Welfare, Mr Stephen Barry . . . . *Nov 1993
Wilkinson, Mr Stewart LLM . . . . *§May 1981
Williams, Mr Gareth Brook . . . . *Oct 1983
Woodman, Mr Richard M LLB. . . . . *§Oct 1983
Asoc: Clark, Mr Relf MA(Oxon); MMus(Lond); MMus(Reading); FRCO; ARCM; LRAM. . . . . May 1982
Ast: Ayre, Miss Alison . . . . *Sep 2010
Boulter, Miss Emma. . . . . *Sep 2010
Bowman, Mr David Alexander BA(Hons); LLDip . . . . Feb 2009
Briggs, Mrs Lauren . . . . *Sep 2010
Dathi, Mr Samir LLB; LPC. . . . . Jun 2006
Hurst, Mrs Deanna BA(Law & Criminology); LPC Law Society Outstanding Performance on LPC. . . . . *Sep 2007
May, Ms Hannah Jane BA; PGDL; PSC . . . . Apr 2010
Murphie, Miss Helen . . . . Jun 2005
Nahar, Mr Bharat LLB(Hons) . . . . Mar 2004
Newbold, Mr Mark William LLB . . . . Nov 2009
Pestill, Mr Jack . . . . Sep 2010
Tangen, Mrs Lucy. . . . . Aug 2003
Wilks, Miss Alexandra. . . . . *Sep 2010
Con: Maberly, Mr Adam A BA(Cantab) . . . . *§Aug 1969
May, Mr Roger D B BA(Exon). . . . . *Nov 1988
Newcombe, Mr Tim. . . . . Jun 1998
Wright, Mr Christopher R . . . . *§Dec 1966

RUBICON LAW ‡
4th Floor 50 Essex Street London WC2R 3JF
Tel: 020 7438 2888 *Fax:* 020 7438 2889
E-mail: manfred.kuerten@rubiconlaw.co.uk

RUBINSTEIN PHILLIPS LLP ‡
19 Buckingham Street London WC2N 6EF
Tel: 020 7925 2244 *Fax:* 020 7925 2256

C J RUSSELL MA(CANTAB) ‡
105a Westbourne Grove London W2 4UW
Tel: 020 7243 2455 *Fax:* 020 7243 2455
E-mail: russellslaw@yahoo.co.uk

HOWARD RUSSELL & CO ‡
1a Devonshire Mews Chiswick London W4 2HA
Tel: 020 8747 0731

RUSSELL JONES & WALKER ‡
(in association with Edinburgh)
50-52 Chancery Lane London WC2A 1HL
Tel: 020 7657 1555 *Fax:* 020 7657 1557
Dx: 202 LONDON/CHANCERY LN
E-mail: enquiries@rjw.co.uk
List of partners: S J N Allen, B Brandon, M Buckeridge, J H Carlton, B J Clarke, J C Clarke-Williams, T Coolican, E J O Cooper, P A T Daniels, E E Dux, T A F Epps, R Fletcher, D F Franey, R Geraghty, E Hawksworth, N B Holroyd, C P Howard, M J Imperato, S G Ingram, A M Kerr, S S Kilka, N J Kinsella, P J Kitson, R C Langton, R Powell-Evans, J Seddon, G C Solly, J N Sturzaker, S L Webb, J M Webber, A F Whitehead, I D Wilson
Office: Birmingham, Bristol, Cardiff, Manchester, Newcastle upon Tyne, Sheffield, Wakefield
Languages: French, German, Italian
Work: B1 C1 C2 D1 E F1 G H I J1 K1 L N O S1 W Z(d,f,k,l,p,t)
Emergency Action, Fixed Fee Interview, Legal Aid undertaken, Legal Aid Franchise and Member of Accident Line
Ptr: Brandon, Mr Ben . . . . Aug 1996
Carlton, Mr James H LLB(Hons). . . . . *Sep 1991
Clarke, Mr Barry James BA; MSc(Econ) Wig & Pen Prize 1996; TF tout Prize 1991 . . . . *Nov 1996
Clarke-Williams, Mr Jeremy Charles LLB . . . . . . *Oct 1986
Cooper, Mr Edward J O LLB(Bris). . . . . *Feb 1984
Daniels, Mr Paul A T BA(Oxon) . . . . *Nov 1993
Dux, Miss Elizabeth Emma LLB(Hons) . . . . *Oct 1990
Epps, Mr Tom A F LLB . . . . *Sep 1995
Fletcher, Mr Rod . . . . Apr 1981
Geraghty, Mr Richard BA; LSF(Guildford) . . . . . . *Nov 1995
Hawksworth, Ms Emma. . . . . Oct 1997
Howard, Mr Clive P MA(Oxon) . . . . *Oct 1988
Ingram, Mr Scott G LLB. . . . . *Oct 1983
Kerr, Ms Alison Mary LLB . . . . *Nov 1989
Kilka, Ms Simone S LLB(Hons) . . . . *Apr 1995
Kitson, Mr Paul J LLB. . . . . *Sep 1987
Powell-Evans, Ms Ruth . . . . Dec 1995
Seddon, Ms Judith . . . . Nov 1997
Sturzaker, Mr John N BSc(Econ) . . . . *Oct 1991
Webb, Mrs Sarah L . . . . *May 1983
Webber, Mr John M. . . . . *Jan 1969
Whitehead, Mr A Fraser LLB . . . . *Jun 1975
Ast: Abbey, Mr Robert M BA(Keele) . . . . *§Jun 1974
Allanson, Ms Sara Victoria BA(Hons); LSFC. . . . . . *Sep 1996
Bradbury, Miss Juliette Jane LLB . . . . *Mar 1999
Buczynsky, Ms Helen BSc(Hons) . . . . *Dec 1995
Carlisle, Ms Julie C BA(Hons). . . . . *Sep 1991
Cuming, Ms Fiona. . . . . May 1999
Daniel, Mr Daniel. . . . . May 1999
Escritt, Ms Sarah . . . . Oct 1998
Hallam, Mr Tristan G LLB; LLM . . . . *Jan 1993
Halperin, Ms Claire . . . . Sep 1998
Hardwick, Ms Jayne BA(Hons); CPE; DipLP. . . . . . Nov 1999
Hooper, Ms Rosalind Elizabeth MA(Cantab). . . . . . *Jul 1991
Hopkinson, Ms Sarah . . . . Nov 1999
Jackson, Mr Christopher Howard BA Notary Public . . *Oct 1993
Keleman, Ms Rachel . . . . §Nov 1990
Kerridge, Ms Virginia A LLB. . . . . *Oct 1982
Klim, Mr Peter E LLB . . . . *Oct 1985
Le Petit, Ms Katharine. . . . . Sep 1998
McKensie, Mr Jason . . . . Sep 1999
Morris, Ms Julie E. . . . . Mar 1999
O'dwyer, Ms Lisa . . . . Oct 1993
Peacock, Miss Amanda Marie LLB(Hons) . . . . . . *Jan 1996
Rea, Miss Elizabeth LLB . . . . *Jul 1998
Riordan, Ms Maureen . . . . Apr 1999
Rocker, Mr Robert. . . . . Nov 1997
Russell, Mr David. . . . . Aug 1999
Ryan, Miss Theresa Mary BA(Hons). . . . . *Oct 1994
Storey, Ms Tracey. . . . . Oct 1994
Swan, Ms Katriona A LLB. . . . . *Oct 1991
Wolf, Miss Sarah . . . . Oct 1993
Young, Ms Jacqueline. . . . . Sep 1998

P RUSSELL & CO ‡
Suite 61 London House 271-273 King Street London W6 9LZ
Tel: 020 8233 2943 *Fax:* 020 8233 2944
E-mail: info@prcsolicitors.com
List of partners: P C Russell
Work: O Z(e,f,w)
SPr: Russell, Mr Paul C LLB . . . . *Oct 1984

TIM RUSSELL ‡
24 Upper Mall London W6 9TA
Tel: 020 8741 4403 *Fax:* 020 8741 4403
E-mail: tdrussell@btopenworld.com

RUSSELL WISE ‡
30-31 Shoreditch High Street London E1 6PG

RUSSELL WISE SOLICITORS ‡
67a High Road Wood Green London N22 6BH
Tel: 020 8889 8300 *Fax:* 020 8889 8222 *Dx:* 35664 WOOD GREEN
E-mail: info@russellwise.com

RUSSELL-COOKE LLP ‡
2 Putney Hill Putney London SW15 6AB
Tel: 020 8789 9111 *Fax:* 020 8780 1194 *Dx:* 59456 PUTNEY
Emergency telephone 020 8788 0005
E-mail: helpdesk@russell-cooke.co.uk
Web: www.russell-cooke.co.uk
List of partners: D Alderson, J Asher, A Bearman, D A Blythe, M Bosworth, P H Cadman, J Carroll, J Carwardine, O J Chapman, M M Cheves, S P Clarke, N H Coates, P M Dawson, A Dennis, H Edwards, D Fairclough, I R Ford, R M Frimston, J Gardner, J C Gould, P M Greatholder, J G R Hunter, A M Isaacson, F R Kaye, V L Kilby, J E Klauber, S Leonard, S Little, M J Maskey, J I McCallum, D Mears, D Murphy, T M Nichols, M Parkinson, L P Ranford, F B Read, A Regan, A Sakrouge, P Sidoli, J Sinclair Taylor, A Studd, H Swindall, C R Thornton, J M Thornton, S Towler, A H Walter, E Wanambwa
Office: Kingston upon Thames, London WC1
Languages: French, German, Spanish
Work: A1 A3 B1 B2 C1 C2 D1 D2 E F1 G H J1 K1 K3 K4 L N O Q R1 R2 S1 S2 T1 T2 V W Z(c,d,e,h,m,o,p,q,r,s,w)
Emergency Action, Advocacy, Legal Aid undertaken, Legal Aid Franchise and Member of Accident Line
Ptr: Alderson, Ms Dawn . . . . Oct 1985
Asher, Miss Jessica BSc; CPE; LPC . . . . *Nov 1996
Bearman, Mr Alex BA. . . . . *Sep 2000
Blythe, Ms Deborah A LLB . . . . *Mar 1984
Carwardine, Ms Jae ★ . . . . Sep 1996
Cheves, Mrs Mary Magdalen LLB(Hons) . . . . *Nov 1982
Clarke, Mr Stephen P BA; LLB . . . . *Apr 1974
Coates, Mr Nigel H MA(Cantab). . . . . *Apr 1981
Dennis, Ms Angela LLB . . . . Sep 1999
Edwards, Ms Helen . . . . Oct 2000
Fairclough, Mr Dominic BA(Hons). . . . . *Jul 1997
Frimston, Mr Richard M BSc; ARCS STEP Founders Award for Outstanding Achievement 2010 Notary Public. . . *Nov 1979
Gardner, Ms Janice BA . . . . *Nov 1993
Gould, Mr John C MA(Cantab) . . . . *Jun 1980
Isaacson, Mr Arnold Michael BA(Hons) . . . . *Aug 1990
Kaye, Mrs Francesca R BA(Oxon). . . . . *Mar 1991
Kilby, Ms Vickie L BA . . . . *Feb 1987
Klauber, Ms Jane E BA(Oxon). . . . . *May 1987
McCallum, Mr James I BA. . . . . *Dec 1987
Mears, Mr David LLB(Hons); MSc. . . . . *Jun 1988
Murphy, Mr Donall LLB . . . . *Nov 1997
Parkinson, Mr Michael . . . . Mar 2002
Ranford, Mr Lee Peter FILEx; LSF. . . . . *Dec 1992
Read, Ms Fiona B BA(Hons) Deputy District Judge; Mediator; Collaborative Family Lawyer. . . . . *Oct 1987
Regan, Ms Alison . . . . Mar 2002
Sakrouge, Mr Anthony BA; LLB . . . . *Jul 1993
Sidoli, Paolo . . . . Nov 1993
Sinclair Taylor, Mr James BA . . . . *Jul 1975
Studd, Mr Andrew BSc; DipLaw. . . . . Jun 1995
Swindall, Mr Howard . . . . Mar 1980
Thornton, Mr Jonathan M MA(Oxon) Notary Public . . §Oct 1988
Towler, Ms Sarah LLB. . . . . Dec 2004
Walter, Mrs Anne H BA . . . . *Jul 1976
Wanambwa, Mr Edward. . . . . Oct 2003
Ast: Bannister, Ms Katie . . . . Jan 2007
Beaumont, Ms Rachael . . . . Sep 2006
Bhargava, Miss Rita LLB . . . . *Sep 2000
Bird, Miss Jenny LLB . . . . Sep 2010
Blackman, Mr Luke . . . . Jan 2007
Cawthorpe, Miss Katie LLB; LPC . . . . Sep 2011
Chapman, Ms Jodi . . . . Jan 2006
Colledge, Mr Michael LLB. . . . . *Jan 2005
Cross, Miss Heather BA. . . . . Oct 2004
Dawes, Miss Elizabeth . . . . Oct 2005
Elsey, Elliot . . . . Sep 2009
Ewing, Mr Simon Alistair LLB; BA . . . . Sep 2010
Garrod, Mr Matthew. . . . . Dec 2005
Gate, Mr Peter . . . . Sep 2009
Griffiths, Mr Delme . . . . Sep 2005
Humphrey, Mrs Harriet Louise LLB; LPC . . . . Mar 2011
Hutchinson, Mr Matthew BA; PGDL; LPC . . . . Sep 2008
Ledsham, Mr Gareth . . . . Sep 2006
Minett, Ms Kate BA(Hons); LLB . . . . Oct 2010
Minty, Ms Hannah LLB . . . . Apr 2007
Nathan, Deborah . . . . Sep 2007
Nicholson, Mr Peter. . . . . Sep 2008
Norton, Miss Elizabeth . . . . Sep 2008
O'Byrne, Emma. Sep 2008
O'Connor, Ms Nicola LLB . . . . May 2000
O'Keeffe, Daniel. . . . . Feb 2008
O'Reilly, Mr Stephen BA. . . . . Sep 2004
Ouazzani, Ms Somaya Leonard Sainer Foundation Scholarship Undergraduate Teaching Fellow at UCL. . . . . . . Sep 2010
Palmer, Samantha . . . . Mar 2003
Pavlovic, Mr Andrew Nicholas LLB . . . . Sep 2010
Priddle, Ms Tamsin MA . . . . Sep 2003
Pritchard, Samantha . . . . Sep 2009
Ransford, Mrs Sukanya BSc . . . . Sep 1997
Raymond, Jenny . . . . Sep 2009
Rengger, Ms Jo LLB . . . . Sep 2002
Reynolds, Ms Angharad. . . . . Jan 2003
Roberts, Mrs Leigh . . . . Feb 2000
Slattery, Miss Kate BA . . . . Jan 2008
Smartt, Ms Fudia LLB. . . . . Dec 2006
Stewart, Mrs Rachel . . . . Jul 2002
Strong, Mrs Zoe Caroline Irene BA(Hons); CPE . . . *Sep 2002
Taylor, Mrs Sarah Elizabeth LLB; PGDip. . . . . Sep 2006
Totic, Ms Emilie . . . . Jan 2010
Walker, Miss Alexandra LLB. . . . . Sep 2010
Whalley, Ms Helen BA . . . . Mar 2005
Wilmot, Mr Guy BA . . . . Sep 2004
Wilton, Miss Lucy BA . . . . Sep 2007
Con: Lee, Mr Terry . . . . *Mar 1970

Other offices in London and Kingston upon Thames. Charity, Children & Family, Conveyancing, Criminal, Commercial Litigation, Commercial Property, Company Law, Employment, French, IP, PI & Clinical Negligence, Regulation & Sports, Trusts, Wills, Probate & Tax

RUSSELL-COOKE LLP
8 Bedford Row London WC1R 4BX
Tel: 020 7405 6566 *Fax:* 020 7831 2565
Dx: 112 LONDON/CHANCERY LN
E-mail: helpdesk@russell-cooke.co.uk
Office: Kingston upon Thames, London SW15
Work: A1 A3 C1 D1 D2 E F1 G H J1 K1 K3 K4 L N O Q R1 R2 S1 S2 T1 T2 V W Z(c,d,e,h,m,o,p,q,r,w)
Ptr: Bosworth, Mr Matthew . . . . Feb 2005
Cadman, Mr Peter H LLB ● . . . . *Apr 1976
Carroll, Mr James LLB(Hons) Chair of Family Law Committee; Mediator; Collaborative Lawyer . . . . *Oct 2001
Chapman, Mr Oliver John LLB . . . . *Dec 1999
Dawson, Mr Peter M LLB . . . . *Jun 1979
Greatholder, Mr Paul Michael BSocSc. . . . . *Nov 1995

See p2 for the Key to Work Categories & other symbols

Hunter, Mr Jason G R LLB . . . . *Apr 1992
Leonard, Mr Scott LLB . . . . *Sep 2000
Maskey, Mr Michael J LLB . . . . *Jun 1969
Thornton, Ms Camilla R LLB . . . . Oct 1991
Ast: Colegate, Mr Peter . . . . Sep 2004
Cracknell, Mr Edward . . . . Mar 2005
Danks, Mr James BA . . . . Jun 2007
Dineen, Mr Matthew LLB(Hons) . . . . *Sep 2010
Hamilton, Miss Kate . . . . Sep 2003
McDermott, Miss Juliet Emma BA(Hons); MA; GDL; LPC . . . . Sep 2010
Rock Perring, Mrs Marianne BSc . . . . *Oct 2001
Rudolph, Ms Amy . . . . Jan 2010
Small, Mr Stephen . . . . Sep 2009
Stockley, Mr David LLB; LLM; DipLP . . . . Jun 2007
Webster, Mr David LLB; LLM . . . . Sep 2003

Other offices in Putney and Kingston upon Thames. Charity, Children & Family, Conveyancing, Criminal, Commercial Litigation, Commercial Property, Company Law, Employment, French, IP, PI & Clinical Negligence, Regulation & Sports, Trusts, Wills, Probate & Tax

RUSSELLS ‡
Regency House 1-4 Warwick Street London W1R 6LJ
Tel: 020 7439 8692 *Fax:* 020 7494 3582 *Dx:* 37249 PICCADILLY 1
E-mail: media@russells.co.uk
List of partners: A J English, S M Esplen, C Gossage, B K Howard, G A Maude, C D Organ, J Reid, M E Sinnott, P W Smith, S M Tregear
Work: C1 C2 C3 E J1 K1 O Q S1 S2 W Z(e,f,k,w)
Ptr: English, Mr Anthony J . . . . Jul 1978
Esplen, Mr Simon M CPE; LPC . . . . Apr 1997
Gossage, Mr Christopher LLB . . . . Sep 2001
Howard, Mr Brian K LLB(Sheff) . . . . Apr 1979
Maude, Mr Gavin A . . . . Nov 1993
Organ, Mr Christopher D BA(Cantab) . . . . Oct 1982
Reid, Mr John BA(Hons) . . . . *Sep 1999
Sinnott, Mr Mark E . . . . Dec 1984
Smith, Mr Peter W LLB . . . . *Apr 1979
Tregear, Mr Steven M . . . . Nov 1986
Ast: Hall, Mr Michael BA(Hons) . . . . Sep 2002
McCarthy, Ms Natalie LLB . . . . Sep 2003
Con: Russell, Mr Anthony D . . . . Dec 1967
Wyllie, Mr Ewen James MA(Cantab) . . . . *Apr 1977

RUSSELLS ‡
119 Station Road Chingford London E4 6BN
Tel: 020 8529 5933 *Fax:* 020 8529 5504 *Dx:* 37854 CHINGFORD 2
E-mail: russsolicitors@btconnect.com
List of partners: J G Hughes
Work: C1 O S1 W
Ptr: Hughes, Mr John G LLB . . . . *Jun 1976

RUSTEM GUARDIAN SOLICITORS ‡
4th Floor 15 New Bridge Street Blackfriars London EC4V 6AU
Tel: 020 7936 8000 *Fax:* 020 7936 8001 *Dx:* 53303 CLERKENWELL
Emergency telephone 07921 728332
E-mail: t.rustem@rustemguardian.co.uk
List of partners: T D Rustem
Languages: Hebrew, Turkish
SPr: Rustem, Timur D LLB(Hons) . . . . Jul 1997

RYLATT CHUBB ‡
15 Old Bailey London EC4M 7EF
Tel: 020 3170 8978 *Fax:* 020 3170 8979
Dx: 152 LONDON/CHANCERY LN
E-mail: office@rylattchubb.com

RYMER MEDIA LAW ‡
50 Etheldene Avenue Muswell Hill London N10 3QH
Tel: 07767 887972
E-mail: phil@rymermedialaw.com

SB SOLICITORS ‡
228a Whitechapel Road London E1 1BJ
Tel: 020 7539 1900 *Fax:* 020 7539 1909
E-mail: contact@sb-solicitors.com

S C LAW ‡
145 Upland Road London SE22 0DF
Tel: 020 8693 0900 *Fax:* 020 8693 0900
E-mail: mail@sclaw.co.uk

SD SOLICITORS ‡
249-251 Mile End Road London E1 4BJ
Tel: 020 7702 7966 *Fax:* 020 7791 2848
Dx: 30071 TOWER HAMLETS
E-mail: info@sdsolicitors.com

SEB SOLICITORS ‡
328b Bethnal Green Road London E2 0AG
Tel: 020 7729 9042 *Fax:* 020 7729 8503
Dx: 40907 BETHNAL GREEN

SGH MARTINEAU LLP
One America Square Crosswall London EC3N 2SG
Tel: 020 7264 4444 *Fax:* 020 7264 4440 *Dx:* 700 LONDON/CITY
E-mail: lawyers@sghmartineau.com
Office: Birmingham
Languages: French, German, Italian, Spanish
Work: A3 B1 C1 C2 C3 E F1 I J1 L M1 O Q S2 U2 Z(c,e,j,q,s)
Fixed Fee Interview undertaken
Ptr: Bailey, Mr David Allen Jackson BSc . . . . Oct 1991
Grier, Mr Ian S LLM; FABRP . . . . *Jun 1972
Inguanta, Ms Carmela LLB(Hons) . . . . *Dec 1990
Judge, Mr Edward C J BA . . . . Oct 1987
Sejas, Mr Daniel LLB(Hons) . . . . *Sep 1996
Shipp, Ms Emma J LLB . . . . *Oct 1990
Sprecher, Mr David . . . . *Dec 1968
Asoc: Bates, Ms Cheryl Louise . . . . Jun 1997
Hughes, Mr Nicholas MA(Cantab) . . . . *Oct 1992

SJ BERWIN LLP ‡
(in association with InterLaw(Worldwide))
10 Queen Street Place London EC4R 1BE
Tel: 020 7111 2222 *Fax:* 020 7111 2000 *Dx:* 255 LONDON
E-mail: info@sjberwin.com
List of partners: C Abrams, D P Adams, P W Anderson, R S Bartlett, R D Black, J E Blake, M J Bowen, A D Brettell, R P Burrow, D A Calligan, R J Cohen, H Corben, D A Currie, S J Davis, R Day, D W Derbyshire, P J Diss, J S Djanogly, R G F Gallardo Garcia, E M Gibson-Bolton, J R Gold, M P Goldberg, M J Hainsworth, D T D Harrel, S E Holmes, T A Johnson, N M F Kerr, R J Klein, S D Kon, A Leitch, T B Little, H C Mervis, M Metliss, L N R Myers, G J Nicholson, H P O'Connor, E M H Page, D A Parkes, B J Pickup, J A Pittal, C Pollack, S Ricketts, D P Rose, D S Ryland, M Sanders, J R Schrire, A Shindler, R Slowe, J S Smith, T H C Taylor, P E Thomas, M A Trask, D Tunkel, N A Upton, J M Vivian, S P Willson, S R Witney, G S Woolf, P Yam
Languages: Afrikaans, Arabic, Armenian, Cantonese, Catalan, Czech, Dutch, French, German, Greek, Hebrew, Hindi, Italian, Japanese, Maltese, Polish, Portuguese, Romanian, Russian, Slovak, Spanish, Swedish, Turkish
Work: A3 B1 B2 C1 C2 C3 E F1 F2 J1 L M1 N O P Q R1 R2 S2 T1 T2 U1 U2 W Z(b,c,d,e,f,g,i,j,k,o,p,w,za)
Advocacy undertaken
Ptr: Abrams, Mr Charles BA(Cantab) College & University Prizes . . . . *Apr 1976
Adams, Mr Dominic P LLB Welfare Law Prize . . . . . *Oct 1987
Anderson, Mr Peter W MA(Cantab) . . . . *§Apr 1978
Bartlett, Rajendron S BC; BL . . . . *Sep 1991
Black, Mr Raymond D LLB . . . . *Apr 1976
Blake, Mr Jonathan E MA; LLB(Cantab); ATII . . . . *Feb 1975
Bowen, Mr Martin J BA . . . . *Dec 1983
Brettell, Mr Adrian D BA; BCL; ATII . . . . *Oct 1987
Burrow, Mr Robert P MA(Cantab) . . . . *Nov 1975
Calligan, Mr David Andrew . . . . *Dec 1992
Cohen, Mr Ralph J LLB(Soton) . . . . *Nov 1983
Corben, Miss Heather BA(Manc); ATII . . . . Oct 1987
Currie, Mrs Delphine A LLB . . . . *Nov 1990
Davis, Mr Steven J LLB . . . . *Nov 1989
Day, Mr Rob LLB(Lond) Prize for Best Paper on Commercial Law (KCL) . . . . *Nov 1995
Derbyshire, Dr David Wyn BSc(Hons); PhD . . . . . . Nov 1991
Diss, Mr Paul J BA(Cantab) . . . . Apr 1976
Djanogly, Mr Jonathan S BA . . . . *Nov 1990
Gallardo Garcia, Mr Ramon G F LLB; MA . . . . Sep 1988
Gibson-Bolton, Ms Elaine M LLB . . . . *Oct 1987
Gold, Mrs Josyane R LLB . . . . *Apr 1981
Goldberg, Mr Michael P LLB . . . . *Oct 1990
Hainsworth, Mr Mark John LLB(Hons) . . . . *Oct 1991
Harrel, Mr David T D LLB . . . . *Feb 1975
Holmes, Mr Simon E MA(Cantab); Licence Specialise en Droit Europeen(Brussels) . . . . *Oct 1983
Johnson, Mr Timothy A MA . . . . *Oct 1989
Kerr, Mrs Nicola M F BA . . . . *Nov 1988
Klein, Mr Robb James LLB(Hons) . . . . *Nov 1993
Kon, Mr Stephen D BA . . . . *Jan 1980
Leitch, Mr Alexander . . . . Nov 1991
Little, Ms Tamasin B LLM . . . . *May 1985
Mervis, Mr Hilton C LLB(Hons) . . . . Nov 1989
Metliss, Mr Michael BA; CPE . . . . *Mar 1984
Myers, Mr Lewis N R LLB(Hons) . . . . *Oct 1989
Nicholson, Mr Graham J LLB(Hons); MBA . . . . . . *Oct 1985
O'Connor, Ms Hilary P BA(Hons) . . . . Nov 1991
Page, Mr Edward M H LLB(Hons) . . . . *Oct 1989
Parkes, Mr David Anthony LLB(Hons) . . . . *Nov 1995
Pickup, Mr Bryan J BA; MA(Cantab) . . . . *Apr 1981
Pittal, Mr Jonathon Adam LLB(Hons); LSF(Hons) . . *Sep 1994
Pollack, Mr Craig BA; LLB; LLM . . . . *Nov 1995
Ricketts, Mr Simon LLB(Hons) . . . . *Jan 1991
Rose, Mr David P . . . . *Nov 1994
Ryland, Mr David S BA(Oxon) . . . . *Feb 1981
Sanders, Mr Mark . . . . *Sep 1992
Schrire, Mr Jeremy R BA; BA(Hons)(Cape Town); LLB(Lond) Maxwell Law Prize . . . . *Oct 1986
Shindler, Mr Andrew BA; LLM . . . . Oct 1989
Slowe, Mr Richard • . . . . *Jan 1970
Smith, Mr Jeffrey S BSc . . . . *Jun 1978
Taylor, Mr Timothy H C BA(Oxon) . . . . *Nov 1980
Thomas, Miss Patricia E MA(Oxon) . . . . *Dec 1974
Trask, Mr Michael A MA(Oxon) . . . . *Jun 1983
Tunkel, Mr Daniel BA(Cantab) . . . . *Oct 1987
Upton, Mr Neil Anthony LLB Sweet & Maxwell Law Prize . . . . *Nov 1991
Vivian, Mr Jonathan M MA; LLB(Cantab) . . . . Jun 1980
Willson, Mr Stephen P . . . . *Dec 1979
Witney, Mr Simon Richard BA(Oxon); MPhil; MBA . . *Apr 1994
Woolf, Mr Geoffrey S LLB . . . . Mar 1970
Yam, Mr Perry . . . . Sep 1994

SJ LAW ‡
157a High Street Walthamstow London E17 7BX
Tel: 020 8520 6600 *Fax:* 020 8509 1807 *Dx:* 32043 WALTHAMSTOW
E-mail: info@sj-law.co.uk
List of partners: R Johnson, V Saujani
Ptr: Johnson, Mr Robert . . . . Nov 1999
Saujani, Vijesh . . . . Aug 1998
Ast: Hussain, Sharaz . . . . Jan 2002

SJS SOLICITORS ‡
82 Balham High Road Wandsworth London SW12 9AG
Tel: 020 8675 4436 *Fax:* 020 8675 4920
Dx: 34002 TOOTING NORTH
E-mail: sjssolicitors@btconnect.com
Work: B2 G H J1 K1 K3 K4 Q W Z(i)
Emergency Action, Agency, Fixed Fee Interview, Legal Aid undertaken and Member of Accident Line

SLA SOLICITORS ‡
Suite 250 Camberwell Business Park 99-103 Lomond Grove London SE5 7HN
Tel: 020 7703 1070 *Fax:* 020 7708 4328
E-mail: slasolicitors@hotmail.co.uk

SMI GROUP LTD ‡
Great Guildford Business Square 30 Great Guildford Street London SE1 0HS
Tel: 020 7827 6725 *Fax:* 020 7827 6724
E-mail: cbixby@smi-online.co.uk

SMWLAW ‡
50 Broadway London SW1H 0RG
Tel: 020 7060 0766
E-mail: smw@smwlaw.co.uk

SNR DENTON ‡
(in association with Penton International)
One Fleet Place London EC4M 7WS
Tel: 020 7242 1212 *Fax:* 020 7246 7777
Dx: 242 LONDON/CHANCERY LN
List of partners: M B Andrews, R C Anthony, S J Ashworth, C Astruc, R E C Barham, N D Barnett, A J Barr-Smith, D Beggs, F Bi, C M Bingham, D Birchall, A M Bonsor, H M H Bowman, M J Boyle, R G Budge, P Bugingo, D Burge, N Chandler, H M Cleaveland, J L Cohen, A D Collins, J A Curtis, J A Dallas, P A Davies, L Davis, L De Silva, C J Denny, W E Doonan, J E Douglas, J E K Fairbairn, G N Fifield, R Finney, E Gates, V Glastonbury, P A Goodwin, N Grandage, N R Griffiths, M Hanslip-Ward, G D Harris, M J Harvey, I F Hodgson, P Holland, J Horridge, A L Jarvis, M N Jones, G R Kahn, M P Kitchen, R Kulasingam, R J W Macklin, E M Marlow, R McAlpine, P M McArdle, C M McGee Osborne, S C Mitchell, H P Morris, N E A Mott, G E H Paine, J L Pope, R M Pretorius, M R Ramphul, M Ratcliff, R A Rice, I M Roberts, J F Rosenheim, M Rutstein, C L Sallabank, G R Sandars, M A Smallwood, D M Spacie, S E Szlezinger, J Tatten, D B Tennant, E J Tout, R P Turner, N E Vickers, N L Webber, N B H West, C W C Wood, J N Worthy, G Wynne
Office: Milton Keynes
Languages: Arabic, Cantonese, Czech, Dutch, French, German, Hebrew, Italian, Japanese, Mandarin, Polish, Russian, Spanish, Thai
Work: A3 B1 B2 C1 C2 C3 E F1 I J1 M1 M2 M3 O P Q R1 R2 T1 T2 U1 U2 W X Z(a,b,c,d,e,f,g,h,i,j,k,l,n,o,q,u,w,z)
Agency undertaken
Ptr: Andrews, Mr Mark B BA(Oxon) . . . . *§Mar 1976
Anthony, Mrs Rachel C LLB . . . . *Oct 1986
Ashworth, Mr Stephen J BA . . . . *Feb 1989
Astruc, Ms Catherine . . . . Sep 1995
Barham, Mr Richard E C BA . . . . Sep 1989
Barnett, Mr Nigel D LLB . . . . Nov 1985
Barr-Smith, Mr Adrian J MA(Cantab) . . . . *Dec 1977
Beggs, Ms Danielle . . . . Aug 1998
Bi, Farmida . . . . Oct 2001
Bingham, Ms Catherine M BA(Oxon) . . . . Sep 1988
Birchall, Mr David BA(Cantab) . . . . *Jul 1993
Bonsor, Mr Anthony M LLB . . . . *Jul 1974
Boyle, Miss Marian J LLB(Wales) . . . . *Feb 1986
Budge, Mr Richard G LLB(Hull) . . . . Oct 1985
Bugingo, Mr Paul LLB(Hons) . . . . *Sep 1995
Burge, Mr Daniel . . . . Oct 1990
Chandler, Mr Nick LLB(Leeds) . . . . Mar 1989
Cleaveland, Ms Helen M BSc(Bris) . . . . Nov 1986
Cohen, Mr Jeremy L BA(Cantab) . . . . *Nov 1993
Collins, Mr Andrew D BA(Oxon) . . . . §Jan 1977
Curtis, Mr James A BA . . . . §May 1979
Dallas, Mr James A MA(Oxon) . . . . *Dec 1979
Davies, Ms Penelope A LLB(B'ham) . . . . Jun 1978
Davis, Ms Lorraine . . . . Nov 1993
De Silva, Ms Lucille . . . . Sep 1994
Doonan, Mr W Elmer . . . . Sep 1988
Douglas, Ms Jane E MA(Oxon) . . . . *Oct 1983
Fifield, Mr Guy N LLB . . . . *§Oct 1982
Finney, Mr Robert LLB . . . . Nov 1991
Gates, Ms Ellen . . . . Dec 1992
Glastonbury, Mrs Virginia MA . . . . *May 1982
Goodwin, Mr Philip A BA; LLB(Cape Town) . . . . . . Mar 1981
Grandage, Mr Nicholas . . . . Sep 1991
Griffiths, Mr Neil R MA(Oxon) . . . . *Nov 1986
Hanslip-Ward, Mr Matthew . . . . Sep 1992
Harris, Ms Gilla D MA(Edin) . . . . Mar 1980
Harvey, Mr Matthew J LLB . . . . *Oct 1988
Hodgson, Mr Ian F . . . . Sep 1979
Holland, Mr Paul LLB(Hons) . . . . *Sep 1990
Horridge, Ms Joanne . . . . Nov 1994
Jarvis, Mr Alan L LLB(Lond) . . . . *Dec 1976
Jones, Mr Matthew N LLB . . . . Nov 1989
Kahn, Mr Greg R BA . . . . Oct 1986
Kitchen, Mr Martin Paul . . . . Mar 1992
Kulasingam, Mr Raj . . . . *Dec 1995
McAlpine, Mr Rory ♦ . . . . Oct 1990
McArdle, Miss Pauline M LLB(Soton); Former Barrister Jan 1991
McGee Osborne, Mr Christopher M . . . . Apr 1983
Macklin, Mr Richard J W . . . . Dec 1988
Marlow, Mr Edwin M MA(Cantab) . . . . *Jun 1980
Mitchell, Mr Simon Charles MA(Cantab) . . . . *Nov 1988
Morris, Mr Howard P . . . . Apr 1991
Mott, Mr Nicholas E A BSc . . . . Nov 1984
Paine, Mr Graham E H LLB(Bris) . . . . *§Apr 1980
Pope, Mr Julian L BA . . . . *Dec 1977
Pretorius, Ms Rosali M BA; LLB(Wits); LLM(Lond) . . *Sep 1997
Ramphul, Ms Miranda R BA(Warw); LLB . . . . *Oct 1988
Ratcliff, Mr Michael BCL; MA(Oxon) . . . . Oct 1982
Rice, Mr Robert Anthony . . . . May 1982
Roberts, Mr Ian M MA(Cantab) . . . . *Oct 1985
Rosenheim, Mr John F LLB(Lond) . . . . *Jun 1969
Rutstein, Mr Michael BA(Cantab) Squire & College Scholarship; College Graeme Hall Prize . . . . *Oct 1989
Sallabank, Ms Charlotte L BSc; AKC; ATII . . . . . . *Sep 1985
Sandars, Mr George R LLB . . . . *§Nov 1978
Smallwood, Ms Madeleine A BA(Law) . . . . *Oct 1988
Spacie, Mr Dominic M BA(Cantab) . . . . *Sep 1990
Szlezinger, Mr Sam E MA(Cantab) . . . . *Nov 1989
Tatten, Mr Jonathan LLB(Exon) . . . . May 1976
Tennant, Mr David B MA(St Andrews); Dip ACC(Aberdeen) . . . . *Nov 1991
Tout, Miss Elizabeth J LLB . . . . *Nov 1983
Turner, Mr Robert P LLB . . . . Dec 1989
Vickers, Mr Neil E BA(Dunelm); LLM(Cantab) . . . . *Nov 1987
Webber, Mr Nigel L MA(Oxon) . . . . *Nov 1992
West, Ms Nichola B H LLB . . . . Oct 1985
Wood, Mr Charles W C MA . . . . Jun 1980
Worthy, Mr John N MA(Cantab) . . . . *Nov 1985
Wynne, Mr Geoffrey BA(Oxon) . . . . *Apr 1975
Ast: Cook, Mr Simon BA(Hons); MA; CPE; LPC . . . . . . Sep 1997

SSB SOLICITORS ‡
The Matrix Complex 91 Peterborough Road London SW6 3BU
Tel: 020 7348 7630 *Fax:* 020 7348 7631
E-mail: chris@ssb.co.uk
List of partners: P B Spraggon, S Stennett
Work: Z(e,f)
Ptr: Spraggon, Mr Paul B LLB . . . . Feb 1988
Stennett, Ms Sarah . . . . May 1992

ST ENTERTAINMENT LAW ‡
3 Glenhurst Avenue London NW5 1PT
Tel: 020 7504 5859 *Fax:* 020 7504 5860
E-mail: sarah@entlawint.com

SV LAW ‡
34 The Mall Ealing London W5 3TJ
Tel: 020 8567 8989
E-mail: office@sv-law.co.uk

SW19 LAWYERS ‡
Walnut Tree House 17A Church Road London SW19 5DQ
Tel: 020 8947 7997
E-mail: jennifer.ison@sw19lawyers.co.uk

SZ LAW LTD ‡
International House 1-6 Yarmouth Place London W1J 7BU
Tel: 020 3056 4761
E-mail: info@szlaw.co.uk

SABEERS SOLICITORS ‡
130a Uxbridge Road Shepherd's Bush London W12 8AA
Tel: 020 8740 7007 *Fax:* 020 8740 7006
Dx: 58701 SHEPHERDS BUSH
E-mail: info@sabeers.co.uk
Languages: Punjabi, Urdu

SABI & ASSOCIATES ‡
86 Brook Street London W1K 5AY
Tel: 020 7414 0069 *Fax:* 020 7339 9069

SACALOFFS SOLICITORS ‡
31 Southampton Row London WC1B 5HJ
Tel: 020 3178 6124 *Fax:* 020 3008 6011
E-mail: info@sacaloffs.co.uk

SACH SOLICITORS ‡
Albion Mills 18 East Tenter Street London E1 8DN
Tel: 020 7680 1133 *Fax:* 020 7680 1144
E-mail: mail@sach-solicitors.co.uk

SACKER & PARTNERS LLP ‡
20 Gresham Street London EC2V 7JE
Est: 1966
Tel: 020 7329 6699 *Fax:* 020 7248 0552 *Dx:* 42615 CHEAPSIDE
E-mail: enquiries@sackers.com
List of partners: H Baker, H Ball, J Berman, M Berry, A D Bradshaw, J E Brown, C Carey, C B Close, I Cormican, N J Couldrey, A J Cribbs, K H Dandy, K F Dickson, P J Docking, F M Franklin, M B Greenlees, E C Hayes, P R Murphy, P Phillips, I M Pittaway, D Saunders, J S D Seres, P E Sibbit, R P Simmons, S J Tier
Work: J1 O Z(o,q)
Emergency Action and Advocacy undertaken
Ptr: Baker, Ms Helen MA(Cantab); LPC(Notts). . . . . . *Mar 2001
Ball, Miss Helen BA(Jurisprudence) . . . . *Sep 1998
Berman, Mr Jonathan LLB(Cantab); MA. . . . . . . *Dec 1975
Berry, Ms Michaela LLB. . . . . *Dec 1991
Bradshaw, Mr Andrew D BA(Econ & Politics); PGDipLaw . . . . *Oct 1999
Brown, Miss Janet E LLB(Hons). . . . . *Sep 1997
Carey, Ms Claire LLB(Hons). . . . . *Nov 1993
Close, Mr Christopher B LLB(Lond); BA(York). . . . *Apr 1987
Cormican, Mr Ian LLB(Hons) . . . . *Sep 1999
Couldrey, Mr Nicholas J BA . . . . *Jan 1978
Cribbs, Ms Alison J MA(Cantab); APMI . . . . *Nov 1994
Dandy, Ms Katherine H BA(Law) . . . . *Nov 1984
Dickson, Ms Katharine Faith. . . . . *Mar 1996
Docking, Mr Peter J BA . . . . *Oct 1987
Franklin, Mrs Fiona M LLB . . . . *Dec 1984
Greenlees, Mr Mark B BA(Oxon) . . . . *Aug 1979
Hayes, Mr Edward C BA(Oxon) . . . . *Dec 1989
Murphy, Mr Peter Robert LLB . . . . *Jan 2003
Phillips, Mr Paul BA(Oxon) . . . . *Oct 1991
Pittaway, Mr Ian M LLB(Hull) . . . . *Apr 1980
Saunders, Mr David BA(Bris)(French & German) . . . *Jan 2001
Seres, Mr Jonathan S D MA(Oxon) . . . . *Jun 1971
Sibbit, Miss Pauline E LLB(Leeds). . . . . *Nov 1986
Simmons, Mr Robin Peter BA(Accounting & Law) . . *Sep 1999
Tier, Ms Sarah J LLB(Soton) . . . . *Nov 1986
Asoc: Daplyn, Ms Eleanor MA; PGDipLaw. . . . . *Sep 2003
Forrest, Mrs Emily LLB(Hons) . . . . *Sep 2001
Khan, Mr Arshad BA(Oxon)(Law) . . . . Sep 1999
Legg, Miss Caroline LLB(Hons) . . . . Sep 2003
Lynch, Miss Zoe LLB . . . . *Mar 1998
O'Brien, Mr Stuart LLB . . . . Sep 2003
Phillips, Miss Sarah LLB(Hons) . . . . *Jan 2001
Ast: Beechinor, Ms Georgina BA(French & Spanish) . . . *Sep 2001
Bingham, Mr James MA(Oxon); LPC(Sheffield) . . . . *Jan 2009
Brown, Miss Naomi LLB(Hons) . . . . *Jan 2006
Bruce, Miss Nicola BA; LPC; MA . . . . *Feb 2006
Bull, Miss Andrea . . . . *Jan 2004
Cayless, Mr Nigel BA(Hons)(Philosophy) . . . . . . *Jan 2006
D'Costa, Mr Ian LLB(International Studies) . . . . . *Feb 2006
Dunbar, Miss Lucy MA(Cantab) . . . . *Aug 2008
Ghelani, Mr Chirag LLB . . . . Feb 2009
Hames, Mr Michael LLB(Leeds). . . . . *Mar 2004
James, Mr David . . . . Mar 2004
Jones, Mrs Georgina LLB(Hons) . . . . Sep 2001
Lovett, Mr Ferdinand James Clark BA(Oxon) . . . . . Jan 2009
Maclennan, Mr Euan . . . . *Sep 2004
Sami, Mr Fuat BA(Modern History) . . . . Sep 2004
Stimson, Miss Sarah . . . . *Sep 2007
Swire, Miss Katharine. . . . . *Sep 2007

DAVID SACKER & CO ‡
Top Floor 32 Hollycroft Avenue Hampstead London NW3 7QL
Tel: 020 7433 1437 *Fax:* 020 7794 4608
List of partners: J E Sacker
Work: B1 E J1 O Q S1 T1 Z(w)
SPr: Sacker, Miss Jocelyn Emily BA; FILEx. . . . . *Jul 1986

SAGGARS SOLICITORS ‡
Law Suite 199 Uxbridge Road West Ealing Ealing London W13 9AA
Tel: 020 8579 5755 *Fax:* 020 8930 0013 *Dx:* 5128 EALING

SAHOTA SOLICITORS ‡
218 Strand London WC2R 1AT
Tel: 0845 630 2095 *Fax:* 020 7583 9521
Dx: 232 LONDON/CHANCERY LN
E-mail: sahota@libel-law.co.uk
List of partners: B S Sahota
Languages: Hindi, Punjabi
Work: Z(k)
Advocacy and Fixed Fee Interview undertaken
Ptr: Sahota, Mr Barjinder Singh BA ♦ . . . . *Jun 1990

SAL & CO ‡
191 Angel Place Fore Street London N18 2UD
Tel: 020 8807 5888 *Fax:* 020 8807 3888 *Dx:* 36212 EDMONTON
Emergency telephone 07957 459063
E-mail: ibrahim@salandco.co.uk
List of partners: D K Sal, I Sal
Languages: Turkish
Work: E L S2 Z(i,l)
Fixed Fee Interview undertaken
Ptr: Sal, Mrs Dilek K. . . . . *Apr 2003
Sal, Mr Ibrahim LLB. . . . . *Dec 1998
Ast: Sal, Mr Hasan BSc; CPE . . . . Nov 2007
Ucar, Miss Serpil LLB . . . . May 2005

SALANS ‡
Millennium Bridge House 2 Lambeth Hill London EC4V 4AJ
Tel: 020 7429 6000 *Fax:* 020 7429 6001
E-mail: london@salans.com
List of partners: R G Abrahams, J D Berger, M S Bronstein, J Bullen, H P Cohen, P S Cooke, M Davidovski, J A Elton, P M Enoch, S J Finch, A Giles, B Green, C S O Havers, P Howard, J McDonald, B I Mordsley, J Polin, P A Prowse, L T Rosenblatt, P Salmon, R I Starr, T J Stubbs, R L Thomas, M J Wilson
Office: Bromley
Languages: Arabic, Azeri, French, German, Hebrew, Italian, Kazakh, Polish, Russian, Spanish, Ukrainian
Work: A3 B1 C1 C2 C3 E F1 F2 J1 J2 L M1 M2 O Q R1 R2 S1 S2 T1 T2 U1 U2 W Z(b,c,e,f,i,l,n,o,p,q)
Agency undertaken
Ptr: Abrahams, Mr Roger G LLB. . . . . *Oct 1972
Berger, Mr Jonathan David BA(Hons) . . . . *Nov 1986
Bronstein, Mr Michael S MA(Cantab) . . . . *Oct 1983
Bullen, Ms Jane LLB . . . . Sep 1990
Cohen, Mr Howard Paul LLB(Hons). . . . . *Jun 1994
Cooke, Mr Peter S BSc . . . . *Jun 1974
Davidovski, Ms Mira. . . . . *Dec 1997
Elton, Mr Jeffrey A LLB(Leeds) . . . . *Oct 1975
Enoch, Mr Philip M MA(Oxon); ATII . . . . *Mar 1972
Finch, Mr Stephen J LLB . . . . *Apr 1975
Giles, Mr Adrian LLB . . . . *Dec 1991
Green, Mr Bryan BA; LLB. . . . . Jan 2001
Havers, Ms Caroline S O LLB(Leics) . . . . *Dec 1983
Howard, Ms Paula LLB(Hons). . . . . *Oct 1994
McDonald, Mr Joel BSc; JD. . . . . Jan 2001
Mordsley, Mr Barry I LLM; LLB(Lond) Chairman of the Industrial Tribunal (England and Wales). . . . . *Mar 1972
Polin, Mr Jonathan LLB(Hons). . . . . Sep 1987
Prowse, Mr Philip Anthony BA(Oxon) . . . . *Dec 1989
Rosenblatt, Mr Lionel T LLB(Lond) . . . . *Jun 1974
Salmon, Mr Paul . . . . Jan 2001
Starr, Mr Robert I . . . . *Jan 1998
Stubbs, Mr Timothy J . . . . *Dec 1997
Thomas, Mr Richard L MA(Cantab) . . . . *Apr 1981
Wilson, Mr Mark John BA(Hons) . . . . *Jun 1994
Asoc: Edgelow, Mr Jonathan LLB(Hons). . . . . Sep 2001
Jordan, Miss Sonia A M LLB(Hons) . . . . *Nov 1996
Kotani, Mr Nigel BSc . . . . *Oct 1995
Mac Lua, Ms Sinead LLB(Bucks) . . . . *Oct 1990
Mattison, Mr Richard LLB(Hons) . . . . Sep 1999
Mew, Mr David J . . . . *Nov 1973
Morrison, Mrs Penny LLB(Hons) . . . . Sep 2001
Nocton, Mr Nicholas . . . . Jan 2001
Palmer, Ms Sophie BA(Hons) . . . . Sep 2002
Spitz, Mr Graham BA(Hons). . . . . *Oct 1996
Steel, Ms Rachel LLB. . . . . May 1994
Thwaites, Mr Greg LLB(Hons). . . . . Mar 1999
Townley, Ms Abigail BA(Hons). . . . . Sep 2002
Valmond, Ms Claudette BA(Lond) . . . . *Jun 1987
Varley, Mr James FILEx . . . . Oct 1995
Volokhova, Ms Anna LLB(Hons). . . . . Sep 2001
Walker, Ms Ruth M BSc(Leeds) . . . . *Mar 1982
Ast: Collins, Mr Simon BA(Hons). . . . . *Jan 2000
Kakkad, Mr Smeetesh LLB(Hons). . . . . *Jun 1997
Con: McKnight, Mr Andrew BA; LLB(Sydney); LLM(Lond). *Dec 1983
Wollenberg, Mr Anthony. . . . . Jan 2001

SALINGER SOLICITORS & NOTARY PUBLIC ‡
15 Kensington High Street Kensington & Chelsea London W8 5NP
Tel: 020 7937 8524 *Fax:* 020 7937 4289
Dx: 47212 KENSINGTON HIGH STREET
E-mail: office@salingernotary.co.uk
List of partners: P K Salinger
Languages: Polish, Russian
Work: E J1 K4 L M2 S1 S2 W Z(i)
SPr: Salinger, Mr Pawel K LLB(Exon); LSF Notary Public. . *Jan 1990

SAM & CO ‡
79 Broad Lane London N15 4DW
Tel: 020 8808 0020 *Fax:* 020 8808 4673
E-mail: solicitors1@btconnect.com
List of partners: S V A R A Samarasinghe
Languages: Sinhalese
Work: B1 C1 D1 E F1 G H I J1 K1 L M1 N O Q S1 T1 T2 V W Z(g,i,k,l,m)
Emergency Action, Agency, Fixed Fee Interview and Legal Aid undertaken
SPr: Samarasinghe, Sam V A R A BSc. . . . . *May 1991

DAVID SAMPSON & CO ‡
67 Brim Hill London N2 0HA
Tel: 020 8458 0345 *Fax:* 020 8458 0121
List of partners: D C Sampson
Ptr: Sampson, Mr David C BA(Cantab) . . . . *Oct 1966

SAMUEL & CO ‡
169 Malden Road London NW5 4HT
Tel: 020 7267 4240 *Fax:* 020 7267 5113 *Dx:* 123983 BELSIZE PARK
E-mail: samuelsammo@aol.com

ALAN SAMUELS & CO ‡
315 Regents Park Road Finchley London N3 1DP
Tel: 0845 900 0116 *Fax:* 0845 900 0152 *Dx:* 57283 FINCHLEY 2
E-mail: alan@asamuels.co.uk
List of partners: A C Samuels
Work: C1 E R2 S1 S2
SPr: Samuels, Mr Alan Craig LLB(Hons) . . . . Oct 1994

SAMUELS & CO SOLICITORS ‡
Token House 11-12 Tokenhouse Yard London EC2R 7AS
Tel: 020 7073 2860 *Fax:* 0844 507 0990
E-mail: info@samuels-solicitors.net
List of partners: J Samuels
Office: Leeds

SANDHU & SHAH ‡
382 Katherine Road Forest Gate London E7 8NW
Tel: 020 8552 4100 *Fax:* 020 8552 4195 *Dx:* 117351 UPTON PARK
E-mail: sandhushah@aol.com
List of partners: P S Sandhu, S A Sheikh
Languages: Polish, Punjabi, Russian, Ukrainian
Work: E F1 K1 K3 L N O Q S1 S2 W
Advocacy and Fixed Fee Interview undertaken
Ptr: Sandhu, Mr Parmjit S LLB. . . . . *Nov 1987
Sheikh, Mr Sajid Ahmed BCom; LLB . . . . Jul 1994

SARACENS ‡
164 New Cavendish Street London W1W 6YT
Tel: 020 7631 0770 *Fax:* 020 7255 2464

SARACENS SOLICITORS LLP ‡
Regent House 24-25 Nutford Place London W1H 5YN
Tel: 020 7725 7115 *Fax:* 020 7725 7116
E-mail: info@saracenssolicitors.co.uk

SASTO & KLINGER ‡
Third Floor 201 Great Portland Street London W1W 5AB
Tel: 020 7631 4714 *Fax:* 020 7580 7316 *Dx:* 148183 EUSTON 10
List of partners: M K J Ball, A M Klinger, S G Sasto
Work: B1 C1 E F1 J1 L M1 O S1 T1 T2 W Z(b,c,e,f,i,l,w)
Ptr: Ball, Mr Matthew Keneric James BSc(Hons); CPE; LPC . . . . Nov 1999
Klinger, Mr Adrian M BSc(Lond). . . . . *Jul 1975
Sasto, Mr Stephen G BA . . . . *Apr 1981

S SATHA & CO ‡
376-378 High Street North Manor Park Newham London E12 6PH
Tel: 020 8471 9484 *Fax:* 020 8471 9485
Dx: 133012 UPTON PARK 2
Emergency telephone 07956 288671
E-mail: sssatha@aol.com
List of partners: P Pathmanathan, S Sathananthan
Languages: Gujarati, Hindi, Malay, Punjabi, Sinhalese, Tamil, Telugu, Urdu
Work: B1 B2 G H J1 K1 K3 L N Q S1 V W Z(h,i,l)
Emergency Action, Advocacy and Fixed Fee Interview undertaken
Ptr: Pathmanathan, Mr Poopala LLB. . . . . *Jul 2004
Sathananthan, Mr Selvanayagam . . . . *§Aug 1993

RAYMOND SAUL & CO ‡
32 Alie Street London E1 8DA
Tel: 020 7480 5840 *Fax:* 020 7480 7865
Dx: 110801 LONDON ALDGATE 2
E-mail: info@rslaw.co.uk
List of partners: R Saul
Work: B1 E K3 L Q S1 S2 W
Agency, Advocacy and Legal Aid undertaken
SPr: Saul, Mr Raymond . . . . *Dec 1974
Asoc: Green, Mr Andrew LLB(Hons); PGDipLaw. . . . . . Oct 2001
Reay, Mr Kevin LLB(Hons) . . . . Oct 1988

Particular areas of work include: Bankruptcy, Commercial Property, Divorce and Matrimonial, Housing, Landlord and Tenant, Litigation - General and Residential Conveyancing.

SAUNDERS BEARMAN LLP ‡
60 Wellbeck Street London W1G 9XB
Tel: 020 7224 2618 *Fax:* 020 7224 2652 *Dx:* 83311 WEST END 2
E-mail: cpbearman@sb-law.co.uk
List of partners: C P Bearman, P J Saunders
Work: C1 S1 S2
Mem: Bearman, Mr Clive P . . . . *May 1981
Saunders, Mr Philip J . . . . *Feb 1974
Asoc: Lewis, Miss Sarah Rhiannon . . . . *Jul 2000
Rosenthal, Mr Samuel . . . . Feb 2006

SAUNDERS LAW PARTNERSHIP LLP ‡
Essex Hall 1-6 Essex Street London WC2R 3HY
Est: 1974
Tel: 020 7632 4300 *Fax:* 020 7836 7975 *Dx:* 37995 KINGSWAY
Emergency telephone 020 7632 4300
E-mail: info@saunders.co.uk
List of partners: G H Bromelow, S N Gilchrist, J N Saunders, K Sturman, J Wright
Languages: German, Gujarati, Urdu
Work: B2 G H J1 K1 K3 N O Q S1 W Z(q)
Emergency Action, Advocacy, Legal Aid undertaken and Legal Aid Franchise
Ptr: Bromelow, Mr Gary Henry LLB(Hons) . . . . *Nov 1996
Gilchrist, Mr Stephen N . . . . *Nov 1974
Saunders, Mr James N LLB. . . . . *Aug 1972
Sturman, Miss Karen LLB. . . . . *Dec 2001
Wright, Judith. . . . . NSP
Ast: Almaz, Mr Noam LLB . . . . Jul 2004
Dogra, Mr Ravinder S BA(Hons) ★ . . . . Jun 1996
Forde, Mr Bellamy BSc . . . . May 2004
Haddow, Mr Callum LLB . . . . *Mar 2005
Jones, Ms Samantha LLB. . . . . Apr 2009
Legg, Mr Paul LLB . . . . Jan 2006
Newnham, Ms Ruth BA . . . . Jan 2003
Parker, Mr Alistair Dawood LLB . . . . *Aug 2004
Rose-Smith, Mr Brian M BA(Hons) . . . . *Dec 1975
Rothwell, Mr Graham LLB. . . . . Apr 2007
Sampson, Ms Hannah LLB . . . . Jan 2002
Williams, Ms Nia BSc . . . . May 2008

WGR SAUNDERS & SON ‡
13 Station Road London SE25 5AH
Tel: 020 8653 4482 *Fax:* 020 8771 4001
Dx: 37801 SOUTH NORWOOD

R A SAVAGE & CO
7 Gainsborough Gardens Hampstead London NW3 1BJ
Tel: 020 7431 7711 *Fax:* 01707 326961
Office: Welwyn Garden City

NORMAN SAVILLE & CO ‡
47 Muswell Hill Broadway London N10 3HA
Tel: 020 8883 9711 *Fax:* 020 8883 4554 *Dx:* 36016 MUSWELL HILL
E-mail: rosemarywakeley@normansaville.co.uk
List of partners: L R Abrey, C M Hall
Languages: Afrikaans
Work: E F1 J1 K1 K3 N O Q S1 S2 W Z(c,d,e,f,g,j,k,l,p,q)
Emergency Action, Agency, Fixed Fee Interview and Legal Aid undertaken
Ptr: Abrey, Miss Lana R LLB(Hons) . . . . *Feb 1998
Hall, Mr Christopher M LLB; LLM . . . . *Dec 1975
Ast: Mao, Mr Anthony LLB. . . . . *Apr 1999
Con: Andrewes, Mr Robert N. . . . . *Jul 1969
Saville, Mr Norman LLB(Lond) . . . . *Jun 1966

See p2 for the Key to Work Categories & other symbols

SAVIOURS SOLICITORS ‡
1a Barnard Close London SE18 6JQ
Tel: 020 8855 1855 *Fax:* 020 8854 5225

SAVJANI & CO ‡
138 High Street Harlesden London NW10 4SP
Tel: 020 8961 3352 *Fax:* 020 8961 3471
List of partners: S Savjani
Languages: Gujarati
Work: C1 E F1 L O Q S1 S2 W Z(e,i)
Ptr: Savjani, Suresh LLB(Lond) . . . . *Dec 1978

SAYER MOORE & CO ‡
190 Horn Lane Acton London W3 6PL
Tel: 020 8993 7571 *Fax:* 020 8993 7763 *Dx:* 99632 ACTON 2
E-mail: rs@sayermore.co.uk
List of partners: S Langford, R Sayer
Office: Harrow
Work: E J1 S1 S2 W Z(d)
Ptr: Sayer, Mr Robert BA . . . . *Jan 1979
Asoc: Daly, Miss Breege BCL . . . . Feb 1991

SCANLAN & CO ‡
8-12 New Bridge Street London EC4V 6AL
Tel: 020 7353 5215 *Fax:* 020 7353 5222
E-mail: mms@scanlansolicitors.com

SCHILLINGS ‡
41 Bedford Square London WC1B 3HX
Tel: 020 7034 9000 *Fax:* 020 7034 9200
Dx: 89265 SOHO SQUARE 1
Emergency telephone 07711 715345
E-mail: legal@schillings.co.uk
List of partners: R Atkins, R Christie-Miller, J R Kelly, K Schilling
Languages: French, German, Greek, Italian, Spanish
Work: C1 G I J1 K1 K2 O Q U2 Z(e,f,k,w)
Emergency Action undertaken
Ptr: Atkins, Ms Rachel MA(Cantab) . . . . *Nov 1994
Christie-Miller, Mr Rod . . . . Sep 1997
Kelly, Mr J Richard . . . . *Dec 1971
Schilling, Mr Keith MA(Eur Business Law) . . . . *Feb 1981

SCHNEIDER PAGE ‡
18 North Tenter Street Aldgate London E1 8DL
Tel: 020 7480 5477
E-mail: info@schneiderpage.com
List of partners: S F Page, E Schneider
Office: Guildford
Languages: French, German, Hungarian, Italian, Spanish
Work: C1 C2 C3 M1 M2 O Z(e,f)
Ptr: Page, Mr Simon Finlay BSc(Exon); BA(Exon) . . . . . *Oct 1988
Schneider, Mr Ernest BA . . . . *Apr 1986
Con: Campbell, Ms Glenda LLB(Edin) . . . . *Nov 1990

KAYE SCHOLER LLP ‡
5th Floor 120 Aldersgate Street London EC1A 4JQ
Tel: 020 7014 0550 *Fax:* 020 7014 0555

PETER SCHOLL & CO ‡
20-21 Jockeys Fields London WC1R 4BW
Tel: 020 7025 2292 *Fax:* 020 7025 2202
E-mail: jockeys@peterscholl.com
List of partners: P Scholl
Work: A1 E L R1 R2 S1 S2
Ptr: Scholl, Mr Peter BA . . . . *§Jan 1982

ROBERT SCHON TAX PLANNING ‡
West Hill House 6 Swains Lane Highgate London N6 6QS
Tel: 020 7267 5010 *Fax:* 020 7424 9965
E-mail: robertschon@aol.com

SCHUBERT MURPHY ‡
34 Compton Road London N21 3NX
Tel: 020 8360 2599 *Fax:* 020 8360 2711
List of partners: P A Murphy
Work: S1
Ptr: Murphy, Miss Pamela A MA(Cantab) . . . . *§Feb 1979

SCHULTE ROTH & ZABEL ‡
20 Savile Row London W1S 3PR
Tel: 020 7081 8000 *Fax:* 020 7081 8010

SCHULTZE & BRAUN LLP ‡
33 Throgmorton Street London EC2N 2BR
Tel: 020 7156 5029 *Fax:* 020 7156 5223

SCOTT-MONCRIEFF HARBOUR & SINCLAIR ‡
Office 5 19 Greenwood Place London NW5 1LB
Tel: 020 7485 5588 *Fax:* 020 7485 5577 *Dx:* 46465 KENTISH TOWN
List of partners: A G W Harbour, L A Scott-Moncrieff
Languages: Gujarati, Punjabi, Yiddish
Work: D1 J1 K1 N Z(g,i,m,p)
Legal Aid undertaken
Ptr: Harbour, Mr Anthony G W BA . . . . Dec 1980
Scott-Moncrieff, Ms Lucy A LLB; BA . . . . *Mar 1978

SCULLY & SOWERBUTTS SOLICITORS ‡
1st Floor Elscot House Arcadia Avenue London N3 2JU
Tel: 020 8346 2804 *Fax:* 020 8346 8160
E-mail: info@ssplaw.co.uk
List of partners: P Sowerbutts
Office: Brentford, Twickenham
Ptr: Sowerbutts, Mr Paul . . . . Feb 2003

SEARS TOOTH ‡
98 Park Lane London W1K 7TQ
Tel: 020 7499 5599 *Fax:* 020 7495 2970
List of partners: S E Apthorp, R C Tooth
Work: K1 K3
Ptr: Apthorp, Miss Susan Elizabeth BA(Hons)(Law) . . . . Aug 1994
Tooth, Mr Raymond C BA(Oxon) . . . . *§Dec 1966
Ast: Edwards, Miss Kelly Louise LLB; LPC . . . . Mar 2011
Specialise in Family (Divorce) Finance and Private Children cases. Matters of a complicated and international nature.

SEBASTIANS ‡
St Bartholomew House 92 Fleet Street London EC4Y 1PB
Tel: 020 7583 2105 *Fax:* 020 7353 1671
Dx: 259 LONDON/CHANCERY LN
E-mail: sebastians@seblaw.co.uk
List of partners: J A Charles, G J Murphy, S P T Robeson, A C P Sebastian, S Thomas
Languages: French, Italian
Work: A3 B1 B2 C1 C2 C3 D1 D2 E F1 G J1 K1 K3 K4 L M1 M2 N O P Q R1 S1 S2 T1 T2 W Z(b,c,d,e,f,g,h,i,k,l,o,p,q)
Emergency Action, Agency, Advocacy, Fixed Fee Interview undertaken and Member of Accident Line
Ptr: Charles, Mr Julian A MA(Cantab) . . . . *Dec 1978
Murphy, Mr Gerard J BA . . . . *§Oct 1981
Robeson, Mr Simon Paul Toby LLB(Hons) . . . . *Oct 1987
Sebastian, Mr Anthony C P . . . . *§Sep 1973
Thomas, Miss Samantha BA(Hons) . . . . *Sep 1997
Con: Gold, Mr John S MA(Oxon) . . . . *Dec 1963

SECRETAN TROYANOV ‡
9 Gray's Inn Square London WC1R 5JQ
Tel: 020 7404 1199 *Fax:* 020 7405 0240
E-mail: gva.mail@stswiss.com
List of partners: E Stormann
Languages: French, German
Work: A3 B1 C1 C2 J1 M2 T2 W Z(b)
SPr: Stormann, Ms Eva . . . . Jan 1997

ANTHONY SEDDON & CO ‡
4th Floor Eldon Chambers 30-32 Fleet Street London EC4Y 1AA
Tel: 020 7842 0800 *Fax:* 020 7100 9582
Dx: 498 LONDON/CHANCERY LN
E-mail: info@anthonyseddon.co.uk

SEDDONS ‡
5 Portman Square Westminster London W1H 6NT
Tel: 020 7725 8000 *Fax:* 020 7935 5049 *Dx:* 9061 WEST END
E-mail: postmaster@seddons.co.uk
List of partners: R A Austin, N El-Imad, L Golstein, G E Honey, K D Irvine, A J Jacobs, S P Jacobs, D Jeff, D I P Kent, J M Kosky, D C Marriott, D Maxwell, A Miller, T Naylor, C Robertson, S A G Ross, M Simons
Languages: Arabic, Cantonese, Czech, French, German, Gujarati, Hindi, Italian
Work: A3 B1 C1 C2 D1 E J1 K1 K3 L M2 N O Q R1 R2 S1 S2 W X Z(b,c,e,f,i,k,l,n,p,q,r,w)
Agency and Advocacy undertaken
Ptr: Austin, Mr Robin A . . . . Nov 1971
El-Imad, Mr Ned LLB . . . . Oct 2002
Golstein, Mr Leon BA(Hons) . . . . Jan 1988
Honey, Mr Graham E . . . . *Jun 1976
Irvine, Mr Kyle Douglas LLB(Hons) . . . . *Sep 2000
Jacobs, Mr Andrew J LLB(Leeds) . . . . *Dec 1983
Jacobs, Mr Simon P LLB(Middx) . . . . *Oct 1989
Jeff, Ms Deborah BA(Hons) . . . . Nov 1997
Kent, Mr David I P . . . . *Nov 1977
Kosky, Mr Joseph Michael BA(Hons) . . . . Apr 1981
Marriott, Mr David C BA(Oxon) . . . . *Jun 1972
Maxwell, Mr David MA; LLB; DipLP . . . . Mar 1997
Miller, Mr Adam LLB(Hons) . . . . Sep 1998
Naylor, Mrs Tessa LLB . . . . Sep 1982
Robertson, Mr Clive . . . . Nov 1979
Ross, Mr Simon A G . . . . *Dec 1983
Simons, Mr Marvin BSc . . . . *Nov 1982
Asoc: Canham, Miss Jane BA; CPE; LPC . . . . Sep 2004
Thomas, Ms Rebecca Jane LLB(Hons) . . . . *Oct 1994
Ast: Braham, Mr Paul Stewart BA(Hons) . . . . Oct 2002
Chan, Miss Jenny LLB(Hons)(Business Law); LPC . . . Apr 2004
Melville-Smith, Mr John David LLB(Hons) Simmons & Simmons Prize 1989 . . . . Sep 1996

SEDGWICK DETERT MORAN & ARNOLD ‡
Fitzwilliam House 10 St Mary Axe London EC3A 8BF
Tel: 020 7929 1829 *Fax:* 020 7929 1808
E-mail: abarker@sdmauk.co.uk
List of partners: M G Chudleigh
Languages: French, German, Spanish
Work: C1 M2 N O Q Z(e,f,j,k,q)
Ptr: Chudleigh, Mr Mark Guy . . . . *Mar 1994

ELIZABETH SEELEY ‡
17 Marlborough Road Ealing London W5 5NY
Tel: 020 8840 2788 *Fax:* 020 8840 2788
E-mail: elizabethseeley@hotmail.com
List of partners: E S Seeley
Work: J1 Z(p,za)
SPr: Seeley, Miss Elizabeth S LLB(Soton) . . . . *Apr 1980

A SEELHOFF SOLICITORS ‡
1 Lyric Square Hammersmith London W6 0NB
Tel: 020 3178 4337 *Fax:* 020 3008 6161
E-mail: adrian@seelhoff.com

SEGENS BLOUNT PETRE ‡
Glade House 52-54 Carter Lane Westminster London EC4V 5EF
Tel: 020 7332 2222 *Fax:* 020 7236 2112 *Dx:* 1030 LDE
E-mail: info@sbplaw.com
List of partners: N F Allan, B R Alleyne, M M Clark, J Golledge, D Isaacs, T G Milton, M K Segen
Languages: French, German
Work: B1 C1 E J1 K1 K3 L O Q R1 S1 S2 W Z(c,p,q)
Ptr: Allan, Mr Nicholas Faulds . . . . *Jan 1972
Alleyne, Brenda Royett . . . . Jan 2005
Clark, Mrs Michela Mary MA . . . . Jan 1999
Golledge, Ms Jane . . . . *Dec 1990
Isaacs, Mr David . . . . *Mar 1958
Milton, Mr Timothy Gareth . . . . Dec 1978
Segen, Mr Michael Keith BA . . . . *Mar 1985
Asoc: Pritchard, Mr David Vaughan . . . . Jan 2009
Con: Alfille, Mr Cyril Maurice . . . . Jul 1959
Knight, Ms Vivien Margaret Ann . . . . Mar 1996
Kramer, Mr Jonathan Michael LLB . . . . Mar 1961

MICHAEL SEIFERT ‡
Phipps House 50 Broadwick Street London W1V 1FF
Tel: 020 7734 3263

SELVA & CO ‡
203 Kilburn High Road Kilburn London NW6 7HU
Tel: 020 7328 3330 *Fax:* 020 7328 3339 *Dx:* 123867 KILBURN 2
E-mail: sl74@aol.com
List of partners: S Selvamuruganantham
Ptr: Selvamuruganantham, Selathamby LLB . . . . Feb 1987

SELVARAJAH & CO ‡
4 Honeypot Lane Kingsbury Barnet London NW9 9QD
Tel: 020 8204 7884 *Fax:* 020 8204 0104
E-mail: selvarajahandco@btconnect.com
List of partners: C Selvarajah
Languages: Gujarati, Hindi, Punjabi, Sinhalese, Tamil, Telugu, Urdu
Work: C1 E G H J1 K1 L M1 N P Q R2 S1 S2 V W Z(c,g,i)
Emergency Action, Advocacy and Legal Aid undertaken
SPr: Selvarajah, Mr Carupiah LLB; LLM(Lond) . . . . *Nov 1987

SELWYN & CO ‡
278 Langham Road Wood Green London N15 3NP
Tel: 020 8881 2272 *Fax:* 020 8889 5159
E-mail: mail@selwynandco.com
List of partners: M D Selwyn
Languages: French
Work: B1 C1 C2 E F1 F2 I J1 L M1 O P Q R1 R2 S1 S2 W Z(c,e,f,j,k,l,q,s)
Agency undertaken
Ptr: Selwyn, Mr Martin D . . . . *Dec 1980
Asoc: Selwyn, Mr Richard LLB . . . . Jan 2008

SEYMOURS ‡
75 Carter Lane London EC4V 5EP
Tel: 020 7236 4322 *Fax:* 020 7236 4353
Languages: French, Polish
Work: C1 C2 E O Q Z(e,j,q)

R A SHADBOLT ‡
Avery Court 29e Avery Row London W1K 4BA
Tel: 01737 844184
E-mail: shadbolts@btconnect.com

SHADDAI & COMPANY (SOLICITORS & ADVOCATES) LIMITED ‡
Basement Offices Gibson House 800 High Road London N17 0DH
Tel: 020 3417 6552 *Fax:* 020 3417 6553
E-mail: info@shaddaiandco.com

SYED SHAHEEN SOLICITORS ‡
88a Whitechapel High Street London E1 7QX
Tel: 020 7247 2470 *Fax:* 020 7247 0331
E-mail: info@syedshaheen.co.uk

SHAHID RAHMAN ‡
160 Mile End Road London E1 4JL
Tel: 020 7480 9090 *Fax:* 0560 312 4695

SHAHZADS SOLICITORS ‡
148 Plashet Road Upton Park London E13 0QS
Tel: 0845 466 2299 *Fax:* 020 8472 3018
E-mail: shahzads.solicit@btconnect.com

SHAHZADS SOLICITORS & ESTATE AGENTS ‡
271 Hoe Street London E17 9PT
Tel: 020 8503 7979 *Fax:* 020 8503 7050 *Dx:* 32025 WALTHAMSTOW
E-mail: shahzads.solicit@btconnect.com

SHAIDY & CO ‡
102 Queensway Westminster London W2 3RR
Tel: 020 7229 6703 *Fax:* 020 7229 2902
List of partners: A Shaidy
SPr: Shaidy, Asad LLB . . . . Aug 1994

SHANAZ & PARTNERS SOLICITORS ‡
38 Commercial Street Tower Hamlets London E1 6LT
Tel: 020 7375 2898 *Fax:* 020 7375 2894 *Dx:* 708 LONDON/CITY
E-mail: mail@spslaw.co.uk
List of partners: S Ahmed
Languages: Bengali
Work: C1 D1 E K1 K3 S1 S2 W
Ptr: Ahmed, Ms Shanaz . . . . Mar 1996

SHANTHI & CO ‡
206 Seven Sisters Road Finsbury Park London N4 3NX
Tel: 020 7561 9494

SHAPLAND & CO ‡
18 Camden High Street Camden London NW1 0JH
Tel: 020 7383 7030 *Fax:* 020 7383 7033
Emergency telephone 07693 321995
Work: B2 G H
Emergency Action, Agency, Advocacy and Legal Aid undertaken

SHARIFUL SOLICITORS ‡
25 Abbey Parade Merton High Street London SW19 1DS
Tel: 020 8542 4284 *Fax:* 020 8543 2464

SHARMA & CO SOLICITORS ‡
214a High Street North East Ham London E6 2JA
Tel: 020 8552 5022 *Fax:* 020 8552 5023
Emergency telephone 07983 329679
E-mail: info@sharmasolicitors.co.uk

L SHARMA & CO SOLICITORS ‡
21 Boundary Road Plaistow London E13 9PS
Tel: 020 8471 6676 *Fax:* 020 8548 0485
Office: Ilford

SHARMA SOLICITORS ‡
Hamilton House Mabledon Place London WC1H 9BB
Tel: 0845 430 0145 *Fax:* 0845 430 0146
E-mail: reception@sharmasolicitors.com

SHARPE PRITCHARD ‡
Elizabeth House Fulwood Place London WC1V 6HG
Tel: 020 7405 4600 *Fax:* 020 7242 2210
Dx: 353 LONDON/CHANCERY LN
E-mail: enquiries@sharpepritchard.co.uk
Languages: French, Italian, Welsh
Work: A3 B1 C1 D1 E J1 L M1 N O P Q R1 R2 S2 W X Z(c,d,e,g,h,j,k,s,u,za)

SHARPES ‡
4 The Avenue Highams Park London E4 9LD
Tel: 020 8527 2388
E-mail: danielle@sharpessolicitors.freeserve.co.uk
Work: C1 E J1 L N O Q S2 Z(p)

BARRY SHAW ‡
86 Crown Woods Way Eltham London SE9 2NN
Tel: 020 8850 7976 *Fax:* 020 8850 7421
E-mail: barry.shaw@dsl.pipex.com
Languages: German

SHAW GRAHAM KERSH ‡
35 Great Marlborough Street London W1F 7JF
Tel: 020 7734 9700 *Fax:* 020 7734 4340
Emergency telephone 07074 959594
E-mail: info@sgk-solicitors.co.uk
List of partners: P J Graham, P J Hill, D A Kersh, R D Shaw
Languages: French
Work: B2 G H P
Ptr: Graham, Mr Paul James BA(Hons) . . . . *Sep 1986
Hill, Mr Philip J . . . . Jun 1994
Kersh, Mr Daniel Anthony LLB(Hons) . . . . Nov 1987
Shaw, Mr Raymond David BA(Hons) . . . . *Oct 1996

SHAW LLOYD & CO ‡
3rd Floor Rooms 189-190 Temple Chambers London EC4Y 0DA
Tel: 020 7353 9936 *Fax:* 020 7353 9950
E-mail: shaw.lloyd@btconnect.com

SHEARMAN & STERLING LLP ‡
Broadgate West 9 Appold Street London EC2A 2AP
Tel: 020 7655 5000 *Fax:* 020 7655 5500
List of partners: C Atkins, C R Bright, N J R Buckworth, C Colbridge, J D S Coppin, I M Goalen, P D S King, C J Leeds, K Macritchie, M T McGowan, S D E Peppiatt, M J Raines, B W B Reynolds, N J Thompson, A J Ward
Work: A3 C1 C2 C3 J1 M1 M2 O T1 Z(b,e,n,o)
Ptr: Atkins, Mr Clifford BA; BCL(Oxon). . . . . *Apr 1980
Bright, Mr Christopher R LLB . . . . Sep 1985
Buckworth, Mr Nicholas J R LLB(Dundee) English Law Medal 1982 . . . . *Oct 1986
Colbridge, Mr Christopher. . . . . Oct 1992
Coppin, Mr Jonathan D S . . . . *Mar 1990
Goalen, Mr Iain M LLB . . . . Nov 1989
King, Mr Peter D S BA(Cantab) . . . . *Oct 1983
Leeds, Ms Caroline J LLB. . . . . *Oct 1988
McGowan, Mr Michael T BA; BCL(Oxon) . . . . Oct 1989
Macritchie, Mr Kenneth LLB; BD(Aberdeen); MA(Manc) Oct 1990
Peppiatt, Mr Stephen D E LLB . . . . May 1987
Raines, Marke J BA; LLB; LLM(Cantab). . . . . May 1990
Reynolds, Mr Barnabas William Bailie LLB; MA; LLM . *Oct 1993
Thompson, Mr Nigel J BA. . . . . Oct 1992
Ward, Mr Anthony J BA(Lond). . . . . Jan 1989
Con: Scoon, Mr Iain . . . . Dec 2000

SHEARMAN BOWEN & CO SOLICITORS ‡
3 Dyers Building Holborn London EC1N 2JT

SHEIKH & CO ‡
208 Seven Sisters Road Finsbury Park London N4 3NX
Tel: 020 7263 5588 *Fax:* 020 7263 5522
E-mail: sasheikh@u.genie.co.uk
Languages: Albanian, Greek, Hebrew, Hindi, Kiswahili, Punjabi, Russian, Somali, Turkish, Urdu
Work: D1 E G H K1 L O Q S1 V W Z(i)
Emergency Action, Agency, Advocacy, Fixed Fee Interview, Legal Aid undertaken and Legal Aid Franchise

SHEIKH & CO ‡
Lichfield House 2 Lichfield Grove Finchley London N3 2JP
Tel: 020 8343 0693 *Fax:* 020 8343 3330
Emergency telephone 07958 338345
Agency, Advocacy, Fixed Fee Interview and Legal Aid undertaken

SHEPHERD + WEDDERBURN LLP ‡
Condor House 10 St Paul's Churchyard London EC4M 8AL
Tel: 020 7429 4900 *Fax:* 020 7329 5939 *Dx:* 98945 CHEAPSIDE 2
E-mail: info@shepwedd.co.uk
List of partners: W Blake, A Bond, E Colville, G Harvey, S J Hubner, P Knowles, R Lyons, K McGrory, A Rollo, L Scott, S Turnbull, G Winter
Work: A3 C1 C2 C3 E J1 J2 M1 O P R1 R2 S2 T1 T2 U1 W X Z(b,c,e,n,o,p,q,v,w,za)
Ptr: Blake, Mr Walter . . . . Jan 1995
Bond, Mr Andrew . . . . May 1979
Colville, Mrs Elaine BA . . . . Jun 1978
Harvey, Mr Guy. . . . . May 1976
Knowles, Mr Philip . . . . Jan 1997
Lyons, Mr Robert . . . . Mar 1986
McGrory, Mr Kevin . . . . Jan 1983
Rollo, Mr Angus. . . . . Jan 1994
Scott, Mr Lynne . . . . Jan 1994
Turnbull, Mr Steven. . . . . Jun 1978
Winter, Mr Guy . . . . Jan 2001
Mem: Hubner, Mr Stephen J. . . . . Mar 1988
Asoc: Dunbar, Mr Matthew. . . . . Sep 1999
Graham, Miss Jane A. . . . . Oct 1987
Ast: Dunlop, Ms Kirsten BA(Hons) . . . . *Jul 2003
Logan, Katie . . . . Mar 2008
McLeod, Lauren. . . . . May 2008
Plewa, Mr Christopher. . . . . Apr 2009

Particular areas of work include: Arbitration, Mediation, Commercial and Company Law, Mergers and Acquisitions, Competition Law, Commercial Property.

M A SHEPHERD & CO ‡
11 Lyndhurst Gardens Finchley London N3 1TA
Tel: 020 8343 2346 *Fax:* 020 8371 0787
Emergency telephone 0778 948 3531
E-mail: michael.shepherd3@virgin.net
List of partners: M A Shepherd
Work: J1 Z(j,o)
Ptr: Shepherd, Mr Michael A BA; DPhil(Oxon) . . . . *Oct 1988

MARTIN SHEPHERD & CO
Croyland House 113 Hertford Road Edmonton London N9 7EE
Tel: 020 8373 8373 *Fax:* 020 8373 8383 *Dx:* 36250 EDMONTON 2
E-mail: edmonton@martinshepherd.co.uk
Office: Enfield
Work: B1 C1 E F1 G J1 K1 L M1 N P R1 S1 W
Emergency Action, Agency, Advocacy and Legal Aid undertaken

MARTIN SHEPHERD & CO ‡
753 High Road North Finchley London N12 8LG
Tel: 020 8446 4301 *Fax:* 020 8367 7472
E-mail: finchley1@martinshepherd.co.uk

SHERIDAN & STRETTON ‡
Riverside House 22a Bradmore Park Road London W6 0DT
Tel: 020 8748 7340 *Fax:* 020 8741 3367
Dx: 32751 HAMMERSMITH 2
List of partners: M S Sheridan, M C Stretton
Work: C1 D1 E J1 K1 L O Q S1 S2 W Z(l)
Ptr: Sheridan, Mr Michael S. . . . . *Nov 1967
Stretton, Mrs Margaret C LLB . . . . *Jul 1979

SHERIDANS ‡
6th Floor Whittington House Alfred Place London WC1E 7EA
Tel: 020 7079 0100 *Fax:* 020 7079 0200 *Dx:* 2110 EUSTON
E-mail: general@sheridans.co.uk
List of partners: Z Ali, K M Ashby, M Berardi, A Daniel, R D Gifford, H R Jones, N G Jones, C E Lewis, S G Luckman, R M Roberts, T J L Robinson, J S Soneji, S A Taylor, M H Thomas, C Walker, M P Wells
Languages: French, Gujarati, Italian, Urdu
Work: B1 C1 C2 C3 D1 E G I J1 K1 L M1 M2 O P Q R1 S1 S2 T1 T2 U2 W Z(b,c,e,f,g,i,k,o,p,w)
Agency and Legal Aid undertaken
Ptr: Ali, Miss Zareen BSc(Hons); LLB(Hons). . . . . . . *Sep 1998
Ashby, Mr Keith Michael LLB(Hons); LSF . . . . . . *Dec 1994
Berardi, Miss Marisa BA. . . . . *Oct 1997
Daniel, Mr Alan LLB. . . . . *Jan 1989
Gifford, Mr Richard D MA . . . . *May 1971
Jones, Mr Howard R LLB . . . . *Nov 1975
Jones, Mr Nigel Graham LLM . . . . *Oct 1992
Lewis, Miss Claire Elizabeth LLB . . . . *Sep 1996
Luckman, Mr Stephen G LLB . . . . *Nov 1990
Roberts, Mr Russell M LLB . . . . *Oct 1984
Robinson, Mr Timothy James Lucas LLB(Hons) . . . . *Oct 1996
Soneji, Jay S LLB. . . . . *Jan 1988
Taylor, Mr Stephen A LLB. . . . . *Nov 1986
Thomas, Mr Michael H BA(Econ) . . . . *Dec 1983
Walker, Miss Caroline LLB . . . . *Jul 2000
Wells, Mr Murray Paul LLB . . . . *Oct 1992
Asoc: Stafford, Mr Gregory E LLB . . . . *Jan 1969
Ast: Basheer, Mr Tahir LLB . . . . *Jan 2000
Bhatia, Miss Praveen . . . . *Sep 2003
Fox, Miss Charlotte Emma Francis . . . . *Sep 2000
Green, Miss Paula M E BA . . . . *Sep 1999
Griffiths, Miss Leigh. . . . . *Sep 2003
Kempner, Mr Stephen LLB . . . . *Oct 1999
Lomas, Miss Nina Kate . . . . *Jan 2001
Mainwaring, Mr Henry Jacobs LLB . . . . *Sep 2000
Con: Glasser, Mr Cyril CMG LLM. . . . . *Apr 1967

SHERRARDS
7 Swallow Place London W1B 2AG
Tel: 020 7478 9010 *Fax:* 020 7499 3846 *Dx:* 44620 MAYFAIR
E-mail: jlb@sherrards.com
Office: St Albans
Ptr: Staal, Miss Dawn Sheridan LLB. . . . . *Oct 1992
Staal, Mr Robin J BA(Leeds) . . . . *§Oct 1982

SHERRS ‡
Institute of Advanced Legal Studies 17 Russell Square London WC1B 5DR
Tel: 020 7862 5859
List of partners: A H Sherr
SPr: Sherr, Prof Avrom Hirsh LLB; PhD; Prof Law Professor of Legal Education, Institute of Advanced Legal Studies . . *Apr 1974

GORDON SHINE & CO ‡
63 Chamberlayne Road Kensal Rise London NW10 3NG
Tel: 020 8969 7033 *Fax:* 020 8968 4920 *Dx:* 53952 KENSAL RISE
E-mail: geffrey@geffreyshinelaw.co.uk
List of partners: J N Shine
Work: A1 B1 C1 C2 C3 D1 E F1 G H J1 K1 L M1 M2 N O P Q R1 S1 T1 T2 V W Z(i)
Emergency Action, Agency, Advocacy, Legal Aid undertaken, Legal Aid Franchise and Member of Accident Line
Ptr: Shine, Mr Jeffrey N LLB(Lond) . . . . *Apr 1975

SHOOK HARDY & BACON LLP ‡
25 Cannon Street London EC4M 5SE
Tel: 020 7332 4500 *Fax:* 020 7332 4600
E-mail: info.london@shb.com
List of partners: S J Castley, S L Croft
Languages: Dutch, French, Italian
Mem: Castley, Mr Simon J LLB(Lond) . . . . Apr 1987
Croft, Miss Sarah L LLB(Bris) . . . . *Dec 1988

SHOOSMITHS
25 Southampton Buildings London WC2A 1AL
Tel: 020 3178 7168 *Fax:* 020 3178 7241
E-mail: london@shoosmiths.co.uk
Office: Basingstoke, Birmingham, Fareham, Manchester, Milton Keynes, Northampton, Nottingham, Reading
Work: A3 B1 B2 C1 C2 C3 E F1 F2 I J1 J2 K4 L M1 N O Q R1 R2 S1 S2 T1 T2 U2 W X Z(b,c,e,f,h,i,j,k,l,m,n,o,p,q,r,s,t,u,y,za)

SHORES ANCHOR SOLICITORS ‡
41d Kilburn High Road London NW6 5SB
Tel: 020 7372 1966 *Fax:* 020 7372 1772 *Dx:* 37701 KILBURN
E-mail: office@shoresanchor.com

SHORTLANDS SOLICITORS ‡
7th Floor 3 Shortlands Hammersmith London W6 8DA
Tel: 020 8822 3330 *Fax:* 020 8822 3450
E-mail: info@shortlands.co.uk

SHRANKS ‡
Ruskin House 40/41 Museum Street London WC1A 1LT
Tel: 020 7831 6677 *Fax:* 020 7831 7627
Dx: 35741 BLOOMSBURY 1
E-mail: shranks@shranks.co.uk
List of partners: B J Milburn, J P Ticktum
Work: C1 E J1 L O Q R2 S1 S2 T1 W Z(c,e,k)
Ptr: Milburn, Mr Benjamin John . . . . May 2007
Ticktum, Mr Jeremy P LLB . . . . *Jan 1990

SHUPAK & CO SOLICITORS ‡
5th Floor West 14 Fenchurch Avenue London EC3M 5BS
Tel: 020 7236 4400 *Fax:* 020 7236 4446
E-mail: info@shupak.com

SIBLEY & CO ‡
415 Strand London WC2R 0NT
Tel: 020 7395 9790 *Fax:* 020 7379 3371
E-mail: email@sibleyco.net
Work: A3 C1 E J1 O R2 S2 Z(q)
Con: Laycock, Mr Anthony E MA(Cantab). . . . . *Dec 1967

SIDLEY AUSTIN BROWN & WOOD ‡
Woolgate Exchange 25 Basinghall Street London EC2V 5HA
Tel: 020 7360 3600 *Fax:* 020 7626 7937 *Dx:* 580 LONDON/CITY
E-mail: ukinfo@sidley.com
List of partners: A W H Bliss, N Brittain, D P Carslaw, J Casanova, P H M Corr, M Denning, M G J Duncan, J A Goodman, G G Harrower, R M Hughes, M Menhennet, S W Oliver, P S Pal, A K Parnell, R E Parsons, G A Penn, J Russell, A P Scott, S J Smith, E A Uwaifo, M Walsh, H J Waterman, J C Williams, J D Woodhall
Languages: Arabic, Bengali, Bulgarian, Chinese, French, German, Hindi, Italian, Malay, Norwegian, Punjabi, Russian, Spanish, Swedish
Work: C1 C2 E I R2 S2 T1 U2 Z(b,e)
Ptr: Bliss, Mr Andrew William Hugh MA . . . . *Nov 1992
Brittain, Mr Nicholas LSF; CPE; BSc(Hons) . . . . . *Sep 1992
Carslaw, Ms Debbie P LLB(Bris) Margaret Harrison Simpson Award. *Nov 1987
Casanova, Mr John JD Magna Cum Laude; AB . . . . Jan 2003
Corr, Mr Patrick H M LLB . . . . *Nov 1990
Denning, Mr Matthew BA . . . . Jan 1995
Duncan, Mr Matthew G J . . . . Jan 1990
Goodman, Mr Julian A BA. . . . . *Jan 1988
Harrower, Mr Graeme G BL. . . . . *Sep 1988
Hughes, Mr Richard M BA(Oxon) . . . . *Nov 1987
Menhennet, Mr Mark BA(Law). . . . . *Nov 1981
Oliver, Mr Struan W LLB(Hons) . . . . *Sep 1983
Pal, Mr Partha S . . . . Jan 2004
Parnell, Mr Andrew K BA . . . . *Dec 1979
Parsons, Mr Robin E LLB(Lond). . . . . *Jun 1973
Penn, Mr Graham A LLB . . . . *Feb 1989
Russell, Mr John LLB . . . . *Apr 1977
Scott, Mr Andrew P BA(Oxon) Wronker Prize 1976 . . *Oct 1979
Smith, Miss Sarah J LLB . . . . *Jan 1990
Uwaifo, Mrs Elizabeth Amede LLB(Lond); BCL(Oxon) Harmsworth Law Scholarship; Kenneth McKinnon Prize; Leonard Sainer Prize . . . . *Feb 1992
Walsh, Mr Mark BA(Mod); MLitt; BL. . . . . *Jul 1999
Waterman, Mr Howard J LLB(Soton) . . . . *May 1977
Williams, Ms Jenifer Caroline BA . . . . *Jan 1988
Woodhall, Mr John D LLB. . . . . *Jun 1980

DOUGLAS SILAS SOLICITORS ‡
239 Regents Park Road Finchley London N3 3LF
Tel: 0870 743 3377 *Fax:* 0870 743 3388 *Dx:* 57280 FINCHLEY 2

ADRIAN SILK SOLICITOR ‡
96 Shirland Road Maida Vale London W9 2EQ
Tel: 020 7266 5070 *Fax:* 020 7266 5070 *Dx:* 46259 LONDON
E-mail: info@adriansilksolicitor.co.uk

SILVER SHEMMINGS LLP ‡
18 Westminster Palace Gardens Artillery Row London SW1P 1RJ
Tel: 0845 345 1244 *Fax:* 0845 345 1039
E-mail: office@shemmingsllp.co.uk
List of partners: R J Shawyer, S A Shemmings, R Silver
Office: Cardiff, Epping
Work: A3 B1 C1 J1 J2 O P Q Z(c,q)
Ptr: Shawyer, Mr Robert John LLB(Hons); FRIOB; MCIArb May 2007
Shemmings, Mrs Sarah A. . . . . *May 1982
Silver, Mr Richard. . . . . Feb 2004

SILVERCOIN & CO ‡
52 Berkeley Square Mayfair London W1J 5BT
Tel: 020 7409 7474 *Fax:* 020 7629 5612 *Dx:* 82981 MAYFAIR
Emergency telephone 07770 315315
E-mail: lydia@silvercoinsolicitors.co.uk
Work: C1 E K4 O Q S1 S2 W Z(i)

SILVERMAN SHERLIKER LLP ‡
(incorporating Edward Kramer & Co; Freeman & Co)
7 Bath Place London EC2A 3DR
Tel: 020 7749 2700 *Fax:* 020 7739 4309 *Dx:* 137779 FINSBURY 5
E-mail: cjs@silvermansherliker.co.uk
List of partners: J C Abbott, M D Donoghue, R K Gordon, M E F Guida, J I Kreser, N C J Lakeland, D K T Lee, N J Moran, M O'Higgins, R H Pearlman, A C Powell, C J Sherliker, J T R Silverman
Languages: Arabic, Cantonese, Dutch, French, German, Italian, Japanese, Malay, Mandarin, Romanian, Spanish
Work: A3 B1 C1 C2 C3 E F1 F2 I J1 J2 K1 K2 K3 L M1 M2 N O P Q R1 R2 S1 S2 T1 U2 W Z(a,b,c,e,f,j,k,l,o,p,r,t,w,y,z,za)
Emergency Action, Agency and Advocacy undertaken
Ptr: Abbott, Mr John C LLB . . . . *Sep 1984
Donoghue, Mr Martin David LLB(Hons) . . . . *Oct 1990
Gordon, Mr Richard Keith LLB(Hons) . . . . *Nov 1980
Guida, Ms Maria Elena Francesca BA(Hons) . . . . . *Oct 1993
Kreser, Ms Jennifer Isabel JP LLB(Hons) . . . . Mar 1986
Lakeland, Mr Nicholas C J LLB(Lond); DipCOP . . . *Nov 1990
Lee, Mr Dennis Kwong Thye . . . . *Sep 2003
O'Higgins, Ms Maeve . . . . May 1978
Pearlman, Mr Richard H. . . . . *Jun 1968
Powell, Mr Adam Charles LLB(Hons) . . . . Sep 2001
Sherliker, Mr Christopher John MA(Cantab) . . . . . . *Apr 1980
Silverman, Mr Jonathan T R. . . . . *Aug 1977
Mem: Moran, Mr Nicholas James LLB(Hons) . . . . Sep 2002
Asoc: Kidd, Mr Andrew LLB(Hons). . . . . *Jul 2005
Robertson, Mr James Victor Alexander BA(Hons); LPC; PGDL . . . . *Sep 2005
Ast: Arestis, Mr Stefan LLB(Hons) . . . . *Sep 2008
Friend, Mrs Vanessa Olivia BA; MA; LLB . . . . *Aug 2009
Gurluk, Mr Ben LLB(Hons) . . . . Dec 2006
Mountford, Mrs Izabela Barbara BA; LLB University Award for Outstanding Achievements in Law. . . . . Sep 2010
Rodgers, Ms Fiona C . . . . Sep 2007
Russell, Ms Victoria J. . . . . Jun 2007
Con: Kramer, Mr Edward . . . . Oct 1954

See p2 for the Key to Work Categories & other symbols

SIMCOCKS
Central Court 25 Southampton Buildings London WC2A 1AL
Tel: 020 3043 4243 *Fax:* 020 3043 4247
E-mail: enquiries@simcocks.com

MICHAEL SIMKINS LLP ‡
Lynton House 7-12 Tavistock Square London WC1H 9LT
Tel: 020 7874 5600 *Fax:* 020 7874 5601
Dx: 7 LONDON/CHANCERY LN
E-mail: info@simkins.com
List of partners: N Bennett, J Bentley, D Campbell, C Fatemi, C Fehler, D T Franks, A Nelson, S O'Mahony, H Stacey, S Waddington
Languages: Farsi, French, German, Italian, Portuguese, Spanish
Work: B1 C1 C2 C3 D1 D2 E I J1 K1 K2 K3 L M1 N O Q R1 S1 S2 U1 U2 W Z(e,f,i,k,l,p,w,z)
Ptr: Bennett, Mr Nigel MA(Cantab) *May 1971
Bentley, Mr Julian BA(Exon) *Mar 1993
Campbell, Mr David LLB(Soton) *May 1970
Fatemi, Mr Cyrus LLB(Leeds) *Oct 1977
Fehler, Ms Catherine BA(Oxon) *Mar 1983
Franks, Mr David T *Dec 1973
Nelson, Mr Adrian LLB *Sep 1983
O'Mahony, Ms Susan BCL *§Jan 1991
Stacey, Mr Howard MA(Oxon) *Nov 1990
Waddington, Miss Sarah LLB(Hons) *Dec 1995
Asoc: Barry, Mr Stuart LLB *Oct 1999
Paul, Ms Patricia *May 2001
Ast: Twynam, Miss Leonora MA(Eng Lit); CPE; LLB Sep 2002
Con: Taylor, Mr Richard LLB(Bris) *Jun 1973

SIMMONS & SIMMONS ‡
Citypoint 1 Ropemarket Street London EC2Y 9SS
Tel: 020 7628 2020 *Fax:* 020 7628 2070
Dx: 12 LONDON/CHANCERY LN
List of partners: M A Alexander, R A Armitage, G G D Bacon, C Bankes, Q D F Bargate, T J W Barnard, S Beck, N J O Benwell, R B Binns, A F Bird, S Bowles, C M Braithwaite, J H Bresslaw, R Bryan, S Bryan, S Bulmer, A J Butler, I Cocking, F A Cohen, N S Cronkshaw, W I Cullen, M Curtis, J W Davies, M P Dawkins, W S Dawson, M A Dewar, D R Dickinson, R Dyton, S R Elvidge, S J Evans, P M Exley, M A Farquharson, N H Fisher, R C B Freeland, P J Freeman, C R S Fuller, C X Garnham, J M Gaymer, S J Gillings, W E M Godfrey, C P Goodall, P D Hale, I B Hammond, H M Hancock, M A Hewland, C L Hewson, J Houghton, N D Jones, G S Kamstra, A J Karter, J P Kelly, A N Kent, D R Le Maitre-George, C E Leaver, R W Leigh, P A Li, G G Littler, F M Loughrey, M Ma, C J Mayo, J Melrose, C T Millar, S Mok, S H Moller, K M Mooney, S R Morgan, J S Morton, K P Mylrea, H Newman, J E Newman, M Norris, D P Nunn, P T Nunn, P J Orange, A J W Orr, C J Passmore, R Perry, R C S Pollock, C M Potter, J R Qualtrough, J Reingold, W M Rodger, D Roylance, P Royou, D J Sandy, M Saywell, R L Schon, I Sideris, J Sirs, J D Sivyer, R E H Slater, M R Smith, C D Thompson, J E A Troup, P J H Vaughan, A K Walkling, J C Walter, S Walters, A Ward, S J Watson, J Weston, T R E Wheadon, C Whitehead, C Wilkinson, A N B Wingfield, K J Woffenden, H Wong, A J Woodgate, M J Wyman
Work: A3 B1 B2 C1 C2 C3 E F1 F2 I J1 J2 L M1 M2 M3 N O P Q R1 R2 S2 T1 T2 U1 W Z(a,b,c,d,e,f,g,h,i,j,n,o,p,q,w,y)
Ptr: Alexander, Mr Miles A LLB *Jan 1989
Armitage, Mr Richard A LLB Dec 1982
Bacon, Mr G Gavin D LLB Nov 1982
Bankes, Mr Charles Nov 1991
Bargate, Mr Quentin D F BA; MSc(Wales) *Dec 1981
Barnard, Mr Timothy J W MA(Cantab) *Dec 1978
Beck, Ms Susan BA Sep 1998
Benwell, Mr Nicholas J O LLB May 1991
Binns, Mr Richard B BSc; LLM(Lond) *Oct 1988
Bird, Mr Alistair F LLB Nov 1980
Bowles, Miss Sarah BA(Cantab) Sep 1989
Braithwaite, Mr Christoper M BA Oct 1984
Bresslaw, Mr James H BA Oct 1986
Bryan, Mr Robert BA(Law) *Nov 1981
Bryan, Mr Steven BA Oct 1988
Bulmer, Mr Sean BA Apr 1992
Butler, Mr Alan J BA(Oxon) *Apr 1972
Cocking, Mr Ian Mar 1991
Cohen, Mr Frederick A MA; LLB; Barrister Jun 1967
Cronkshaw, Mr Nicholas S MA; ATII Oct 1992
Cullen, Mr William I BA *Jun 1980
Curtis, Mr Mark Dec 1990
Davies, Mr John W MA *Apr 1980
Dawkins, Mr Mark P LLB *Feb 1985
Dawson, Mr William S BA(Cantab) Oct 1980
Dewar, Mr Mark A LLB Mar 1990
Dickinson, Mr David R Oct 1974
Dyton, Mr Richard LLB; AKC; MSc *Oct 1989
Elvidge, Mr Stephen R MA(Cantab) *Sep 1974
Evans, Mr Stuart J LLB(Leeds) Nov 1972
Exley, Mr Paul M LLB Oct 1987
Farquharson, Miss Melanie A BA Oct 1988
Fisher, Mr Nicholas H BA(Oxon) *Nov 1985
Freeland, Rowan C B BA(Oxon) *Oct 1982
Freeman, Mr Peter J MA(Cantab); Licence en Droit Europeen *Jun 1977
Fuller, Mr Charles R S LLB Oct 1991
Garnham, Miss Caroline X BSc *Oct 1981
Gaymer, Mrs Janet M MA(Oxon); LLM(Lond) *Oct 1973
Gillings, Miss Sarah J LLB Oct 1987
Godfrey, Mr W Edwin M MA(Cantab) *Jun 1971
Goodall, Mr Charles P MA(Cantab); LLM *Apr 1976
Hale, Mr Paul D BA(Oxon) Nov 1985
Hammond, Mr Ian B LLB Nov 1988
Hancock, Miss Helen M LLB Dec 1988
Hewland, Mr Mark A BA Dec 1991
Hewson, Miss Carol L LLB(Lond) *Apr 1980
Houghton, Mr John LLB; LLM(Lond) Dec 1988
Jones, Mr Nicholas D BA Jan 1986
Kamstra, Mr Gerald S BA; PhD *Oct 1986
Karter, Mr Alan J Nov 1979
Kelly, Mr Jonathan P BA Daton Studentship in Law Oct 1989
Kent, Mr Adrian N LLB *Nov 1985
Le Maitre-George, Mr Damon R LLB Oct 1990
Leaver, Mr Colin E MA(Oxon) Dec 1982
Leigh, Mr Robert W LLB *Jul 1981
Li, Mr Paul A BA Nov 1991
Littler, Mr George G *Jul 1978
Loughrey, Miss Fiona M LLB(Manc) *Oct 1985
Ma, Ms Monica BA(Oxon) Oct 1992
Mayo, Mr Charles J MA *Dec 1985
Melrose, Mr Jonathan BA(Oxon) Oct 1985
Millar, Mr Colin T Jan 1989
Mok, Mr Stephen Mar 1992
Moller, Mr Stephen Hans BA Oct 1992
Mooney, Mr Kevin M LLB *Dec 1971
Morgan, Mr Simon R LLB *Apr 1980
Morton, Mr Jeremy Spencer LLB Nov 1991
Mylrea, Ms Kathryn P LLB Mar 1992
Newman, Mrs Helen LLB; AKC Jun 1980
Newman, Miss Jane E LLB; BCL May 1987
Norris, Mr Mark BSc Sep 1991
Nunn, Mr David P Feb 1987
Nunn, Mr Philip T May 1974
Orange, Mr Philip J BA(Cantab) *May 1981
Orr, Mr Anthony J W MA(Oxon) *Jun 1975
Passmore, Mr Colin J LLB ♦ *Nov 1984
Perry, Mr Richard BA *Sep 1990
Pollock, The Hon Richard C S MA(Cantab) Feb 1976
Potter, Ms Clare M MA Jan 1986
Qualtrough, Mr John R BA *Dec 1978
Reingold, Ms Juliet LLB May 1992
Rodger, Mr William M LLB *Apr 1980
Roylance, Mr David BA Jul 1994
Royou, Mr Phillippe Nov 1990
Sandy, Mr David J BA(Oxon) *Apr 1981
Saywell, Mr Martin LLB(Hons) *Nov 1986
Schon, Mr Robert L LLB; LLM *Jul 1980
Sideris, Mr Ian LLM Nov 1990
Sirs, Mr John BA *Jul 1979
Sivyer, Mr Jeremy D LLB(Sheff) *Jun 1979
Slater, Mr Richard E H BSc(City); MA(Cantab) Jun 1977
Smith, Mr Martin R BA(Cantab); LLM(Penn) *Jun 1981
Thompson, Mr C David BA(Cantab) *Jun 1979
Troup, Mr J Edward A BA(Oxon); MSc; ATII Apr 1981
Vaughan, Mr Philip J H MA *Aug 1979
Walkling, Mr Anthony K LLB(Lond) Andrews Prize *Oct 1982
Walter, Mr Jeremy C MA(Cantab); LLB(Cantab) *Apr 1973
Walters, Mr Stephen LLB Nov 1988
Ward, Mr Andrew BSc *Apr 1994
Watson, Mr Simon J MA(Oxon) Oct 1983
Weston, Miss Joanne LLB May 1989
Wheadon, Mr Thomas R E LLB(Soton) Oct 1989
Whitehead, Miss Catherine LLB *Oct 1983
Wilkinson, Mr Christopher LLB(Lond) *Oct 1978
Wingfield, Mr Andrew N B *Dec 1985
Woffenden, Mr Kenneth J BA(Cantab) *Jun 1979
Wong, Huen Jun 1989
Woodgate, Mr Antony J BSc; LLB; LLM *Sep 1989
Wyman, Mr Michael J Mellersh Prize *Nov 1976
Asoc: Durell, Mr Geoffrey A A Nov 1973
Ast: Adler-Jensen, Ms Tine BA *Oct 1985
Atkinson, Mr Adam Mar 2000
Baird, Mr James Mar 2000
Barlow, Mr Christopher Mar 1999
Barnes, Mr Trevor W MA(Cantab) Judicial Assistant; Court of Appeal *Aug 1997
Barnett, Mr Gary D R LLB(Nott'm) Nov 1988
Bartlett, Mr Philip BA May 1994
Batteson, Miss Margarethe LLB(Reading) *Nov 1982
Baxter, Ms Jocelyn LLB Sep 1997
Beppu, Rika Oct 1994
Bird, Ms Pascale Mar 1994
Block, Ms Jennifer LLB Dec 1992
Booth, Mr George Alistair LLB Oct 1991
Brackenbury, Ms Anna LLB Nov 1994
Brandman, Mr Gregory Sep 1998
Brassil, Ms Leila BA Jan 1994
Brown, Mr Alexander BA Sep 1999
Browne, Mr Paul Nov 1994
Brydon, Mr Andrew Mar 2000
Buckingham, Ms Rosalind E LLB Dec 1991
Buczkiewicz, Ms Louise LLB Sep 1999
Bunce, Mr Richard J R BA Oct 1990
Campbell, Ms Catriona BA Sep 1999
Carson, Ms Jacqueline W LLB Oct 1993
Carter, Mrs Hilary Jane BA(Hons) *Nov 1994
Chin, Ms Joanna BA Oct 1999
Clark, Ms Karen Sep 1994
Clayton, Mr Richard BSc Dec 1995
Comben, Mr Andrew F *Apr 1973
Connell, Ms Michele Nov 1994
Cook, Mr William BA Oct 1994
Crawford, Mr Guy Mar 2000
Cristie, Ms Lisa BA Nov 1995
Cruickshank, Ms Karen *Dec 1997
Damia Diaz-Plaja, Mr Guillermo Jan 1999
Daniel, Mr Jason Sep 1998
Davis, Mr Nigel BA Sep 1999
De Lorenzo, Mr Alfredo Aug 1998
Dean, Mr Matthew Dec 1991
Debenham, Miss Katherine Anne Aug 1994
Dennison, Mr Giles LLB May 1996
Dent, Ms Jo L LLB *Nov 1992
Dent, Mr Nicholas Andrew Hazard BA Sep 1996
Dewson, Ms Fiona M BA *Nov 1994
Dodson, Mr Michael BA Oct 1996
Doring, Mr Marc BSc Mar 1997
Dreyfuss, Ms Nathalie Mar 1998
Driscoll, Mr Brian BSc Oct 1996
Eddy, Ms Bridget Jane BA *Oct 1982
Everitt, Mr Charlie BA Sep 1998
Fagge, Mr Nicholas BA Sep 1998
Fiaccavento, MS Silvia BA Sep 1997
Field, Mr Timothy LLB Dec 1993
FitzGerald, Mr James F BA Nov 1992
Fitzpatrick, Ms Deborah Dec 1987
Gagie, Mr Michael BA Sep 1997
Garrood, Mr Trevor A LLB *Oct 1983
Goodman, Mr Paul LLB Oct 1987
Hadden, Mr Morven M M LLB Mar 1996
Haines, Mr Lawrence J MA(Oxon) Apr 1977
Harris, Ms Caroline BA Nov 1995
Harvey-Hills, Mr Justin LLB Sep 1997
Hilditch, Mr Christopher Oct 1994
Hill, Mr Peter BA Oct 1990
Hillier, Mr Paul M LLB Nov 1989
Hirst, Mr Paul BA Sep 1998
Hope, Mr James BA Oct 1996
Howard, Mrs Jane E BA Oct 1992
Hunter-Yeats, Ms Caroline LLB Sep 1999
Iapichino, Mr Alex LLB Sep 1999
Inman, Mr Paul Maurice Nov 1995
James, Ms Michelle Dawn Jan 1994
Jellis, Ms Jane LLM Oct 1996
Kan, Mr Michael K Y BA Mar 1987
Kemp, Ms Nicola LLB Mar 1996
Lee, Ms Sharon LLB Mar 1998
Lewis, Ms Victoria BA Oct 1996
Lidstone, Mrs Amanda BA Sep 1997
Lueder, Ms Caroline LLB Oct 1993
Lukins, Mr Edward J *Nov 1992
Luxton, Ms Stephanie BA Mar 1998
McClung, Ms Andrea Mar 2000
Macfarlane, Mr Iain BA Sep 1999
Mardon, Mr Paul E *Nov 1998
Marsh, Ms Kitty Nov 1995
Mayer, Arian BSc Mar 1998
Miller, Ms Penny LLB Mar 1997
Nash, Mr Michael A BA Oct 1993
Neale, Ms Alison LLB Oct 1999
O'Keeffe, Mr Andrew P LLB Nov 1990
Oats, Ms Maria LLB Nov 1991
Pascoe, Miss Alison L LLB(Aberdeen) Nov 1991
Phillipson, Mr Paul BA Sep 1998
Polling, Mr Michael Laurence MA(Oxon) Nov 1993
Pope, Mr Tim BA Jan 1999
Rentoul, Ms Anna Mar 2000
Roberts, Ms Isabella BA Mar 1999
Roberts, Mr Jeremy LLB Sep 1998
Robinson, Mr Mark LLB Apr 1995
Roche, Ms Emily BA Sep 1999
Roskell, Mr Michael William LLB Nov 1988
Sainty, Ms Sophie Nov 1995
Sanderson, Ms Lisa-Jane BA Mar 1999
Saunders, Mr Mark David LLB *Dec 1996
Sharp, Mr Gideon Mar 1999
Shaw, Mrs Carol E LLB Dec 1988
Sheiham, Mr Mark BA Sep 1998
Shepherd, Mr Mark Dec 1996
Smith, Mr Adrian H BA Oct 1989
Symonds, Ms Helen Mar 2000
Taylor, Mr James Mar 2000
Taylor, Mr Ralph A *Feb 1970
Tudor-Price, Mr Simon T MA; LLM *Sep 1991
Turner, Mr Robert BA Oct 1993
Unger, Ms Harriet BA Mar 1997
Van Schoote, Ms Cecile LLB Mar 1999
Vassell, Mr Ricky LLB(Hons) *Oct 1994
Vertigen, Mr James LLB Mar 1998
Wadlow, Mr Christopher M MA(Cantab) Oct 1981
Wallis, Mr Richard MA Sep 1998
Watson, Ms Jennifer BA Oct 1995
Whittaker, Mr Steven J LLB *Oct 1992
Wiese, Mr Jonathan Paul BA(Hons) *Nov 1994
Wilkins, Mr Richard Nov 1996
Williams, Mr Rhys John Tudor BA(Cantab) Nov 1994
Wright, Mr Philip Jan 1999
Yates, Mr Simon R BA(Oxon) Nov 1992

SIMMONS GLEEK SOLICITORS ‡
1 Duchess Street London W1W 6AU
Tel: 020 7580 9090 *Fax:* 020 7580 9393
Dx: 53816 OXFORD CIRCUS NORTH
E-mail: simmonsgleek@aol.com
List of partners: G Gleek, J S Simmons
Languages: Gujarati, Hindi, Kachi, Kiswahili
Work: B1 C1 E F1 K4 L O R1 R2 S1 S2 T1 T2 W Z(c,f,k,m)
Emergency Action, Agency and Fixed Fee Interview undertaken
Ptr: Gleek, Mr Gerald *§Feb 1971
Simmons, Mr Jeffrey S LLB(Hons) *Jun 1981

PAUL L SIMON ‡
8 Durweston Street Westminster London W1H 1EW
Tel: 020 7486 0541 *Fax:* 020 7486 1267
E-mail: info@plsimon.co.uk

ROBIN SIMON LLP ‡
Minister House 42 Mincing Lane London EC3R 7AE
Tel: 0333 010 0000 *Fax:* 0333 010 0001 *Dx:* 130980 LONDON CITY
E-mail: info@robinsimonllp.com
List of partners: P Dally, N Innes, M Jenkyn-Jones, A L MacLeod
Office: Birmingham, Leeds, Manchester

ROSS SIMON & CO SOLICITORS ‡
Shakespeare Business Centre 245A Coldhabour Lane London SW9 8RR
Tel: 020 7738 7953 *Fax:* 020 7737 4467 *Dx:* 58786 BRIXTON
E-mail: legal@rosssimon.co.uk

SIMONS LEVINE & CO ‡
Hamdan House 760 High Road North Finchley Barnet London N12 9QH
Tel: 020 8446 4273 *Fax:* 020 8446 9234 *Dx:* 57353 FINCHLEY 1
E-mail: adriansim@aol.com
List of partners: A M Simons
Work: K1 K3 L N Q S1 S2 W
Fixed Fee Interview undertaken
SPr: Simons, Mr Adrian M LLB; BSc(Econ) *Jun 1981

SIMONS MUIRHEAD & BURTON ‡
8-9 Frith Street Soho London W1F 7AG
Tel: 020 7734 4499 *Fax:* 020 7734 3263
Dx: 144060 SOHO SQUARE 5
E-mail: mail@smab.co.uk
List of partners: A C Burton, L Charalambous, S Culshaw, N E Fleming, D A Fordham, S Goldberg, D N Kirk, R Mireskandari, S J Shotnes, M A Smith
Languages: Farsi, French, German, Italian, Spanish
Work: B1 B2 C1 C3 E F1 G J1 L M1 M2 N O P Q R1 S1 S2 W Z(d,e,f,g,h,i,k)
Emergency Action, Agency, Advocacy, Fixed Fee Interview, Legal Aid undertaken and Legal Aid Franchise
Ptr: Burton, Mr Anthony C ★ *Mar 1972
Charalambous, Mr Louis BA; MA *Oct 1987
Culshaw, Ms Sarah *Sep 1999
Fleming, Ms Nicola E *Nov 1992
Fordham, Mr Douglas Alan BA ★ *Jun 1989
Goldberg, Mr Simon MA *Dec 1989
Kirk, Mr David Neil MA(Oxon) ★ *May 1989
Mireskandari, Razi BA; MA ♦ *Nov 1986
Shotnes, Mr Stephen J MA; BA ♦ *Nov 1991
Smith, Mr Martin A LLB *Nov 1986
Ast: Wylie, Ms Sarah L BA(Hons) *Aug 1992

SIMONS RODKIN LITIGATION SOLICITORS ‡
Finchley House 707 High Road London N12 0BT
Tel: 020 8446 6223 *Fax:* 020 8446 7955 *Dx:* 57359 FINCHLEY
E-mail: enquiries@sr-law.co.uk
List of partners: S Aaron
Work: B1 C1 C2 D1 E F1 K1 K3 L N O P Q R1 S1 S2 W Z(b,c,g,j,q,r)

Agency, Advocacy and Fixed Fee Interview undertaken
SPr: Aaron, Mr Simon LLB(Hons) . . . . *Aug 1997

SIMPLEX LAW ‡
3 More London Riverside London SE1 2RE
Tel: 0844 736 5653 *Fax:* 020 3283 4001

SIMPLY LEGAL SOLICITORS ‡
Unit 2 819 Romford Road Manor Park London E12 6EA
Tel: 020 8514 7734
E-mail: vinod@sharmaandcosolicitors.co.uk
Languages: Hindi, Punjabi, Urdu
Work: B2 G H J1 K1 K3 L N Q V W Z(g,i,p)
Fixed Fee Interview and Legal Aid undertaken

SIMPSON MILLAR LLP
(incorporating Goslings)
Floor 2 33-41 Dallington Street London EC1V 0BB
Tel: 0844 858 3400 *Fax:* 0844 858 3499 *Dx:* 53329 CLERKENWELL
E-mail: info@simpsonmillar.co.uk
Office: Birmingham, Bristol, Cardiff, Gateshead, Leeds, London SW19, Manchester
Work: A1 A3 B1 C1 C2 D1 D2 E F1 J1 J2 K1 K2 K3 K4 M2 M3 N O P Q R1 R2 S1 S2 T1 T2 U2 V W X Z(b,c,d,e,h,j,m,o,p,q,r,t,za)
Agency, Legal Aid undertaken and Member of Accident Line
Mem: Davies, Miss A Louise LLB . . . . Oct 1992
Davies, Mr Howard R A F LLB . . . . *Oct 1991
Denham, Mr J Alistair C LLB . . . . *§Sep 1981
Fawden, Mr Adrian C LLB. . . . . *Jul 1990
Harpur, Ms Joanna Anne LLB. . . . . *Apr 1991
Latimer, Ms Jane V BA . . . . Nov 1992
Ross, Mr David MSc . . . . *Nov 1989
Wontner-Smith, Mr Anthony H Chairman of the Legal Aid Committee (South London) . . . . *§Jun 1978

SIMPSON MILLAR LLP
150 The Broadway Wimbledon London SW19 1RX
Tel: 0844 858 3800 *Fax:* 0844 858 3899
E-mail: info@simpsonmillar.co.uk
Office: Birmingham, Bristol, Cardiff, Gateshead, Leeds, London EC1, Manchester
Work: A1 A3 B1 C1 C2 D1 D2 E F1 F2 J1 J2 K1 K2 K3 K4 M2 M3 N O P Q R1 R2 S1 S2 T1 T2 U2 V W X Z(b,c,d,e,h,j,m,o,p,q,r,t,za)

SIMPSON THACHER & BARTLETT LLP ‡
Citypoint 1 Ropemaker Street London EC2Y 9HU
Tel: 020 7275 6500 *Fax:* 020 7275 6502

ALI SINCLAIR SOLUTIONS ‡
47-49 Plashet Grove Upton Park London E6 1AD
Tel: 020 8552 6001

SINCLAIRS ‡
20 Watford Way Hendon London NW4 3AD
Tel: 020 8202 8222 / 8202 2042 *Fax:* 020 8202 3501
Dx: 59300 HENDON
Emergency telephone 020 8202 2042
E-mail: info@sinclairssolicitors.co.uk
Languages: French
Work: B1 C1 C2 C3 D1 E F1 G H J1 K1 L N O P Q R1 S1 T1 T2 W Z(b,c,d,e,f,i,j,k,l,m,o,s)

G SINGH ‡
13 The Mall Ealing London W5 2PJ
Tel: 020 8567 2661 *Fax:* 020 8567 1175 *Dx:* 5112 EALING
E-mail: gsingh_solicitors@hotmail.com
List of partners: A Rajagopal, G Singh
Languages: Gujarati, Hindi, Kiswahili, Punjabi, Urdu
Work: D2 E K1 K3 N Q S2 Z(g,i)
Fixed Fee Interview undertaken
Ptr: Rajagopal, Achyuth . . . . May 2005
Singh, Mr Gurbachan . . . . *Mar 1976

SINGHANIA & CO LTD ‡
1 Queen Anne's Gate London SW1H 9BT
Tel: 020 7799 1688 *Fax:* 020 7799 1687
E-mail: vijay@singhaniauk.com
List of partners: T B T Purton
Work: C1 E K1 K3 O R2 S1 S2 U2 Z(l)
Dir: Purton, Mr Tony B T LLB(Hons); AKC. . . . . *Jun 1970

SKADDEN ARPS SLATE MEAGHER & FLOM (UK) LLP ‡
40 Bank Street Canary Wharf London E14 5DS
Tel: 020 7519 7000 *Fax:* 020 7519 7070
List of partners: J D A Adebiyi, J Anderson, H Baker, M Berkner, B Buck, L Corte, P Coulton, M L Darley, G DiBianco, R Ely, H Foulkes, M E Hatchard, J P L Healy, P Heneghan, D Kavanagh, A Knight, S Lascelles, B Macaulay, C Mallon, R Muglia, A G Murray-Jones, K Nairn, D Nordlinger, T S Sanders, S Simpson, D Tricot, P Trivedi, C Wells
Languages: French, German, Greek, Hindi, Italian, Russian, Spanish
Work: A3 B1 C1 C2 C3 M1 M2 O Q T1 U1 Z(b)
Ptr: Adebiyi, Mr John D A BA(Jurisprudence) . . . . Mar 1993
Anderson, Mr James . . . . Sep 1996
Baker, Mr Hunter . . . . Jan 1988
Berkner, Michal . . . . Jan 1997
Buck, Mr Bruce . . . . Jan 1970
Corte, Mr Lorenzo. . . . . Jan 1998
Coulton, Mr Peter. . . . . Jan 1997
Darley, Mr Mark L BA . . . . *Sep 1986
DiBianco, Mr Gary. . . . . Jan 1996
Ely, Mr Richard . . . . Jan 1988
Foulkes, Mr Hilary. . . . . Jan 1986
Hatchard, Mr Michael E LLB . . . . Oct 1980
Healy, Mr James P L BCL(NUI); LLM(Florence) . . . . . Apr 1992
Heneghan, Mr Patrick. . . . . Jan 2009
Kavanagh, Mr David . . . . Nov 1992
Knight, Mr Adrian BA(Cantab). . . . . *Apr 1984
Lascelles, Mr Shaun . . . . Sep 1995
Macaulay, Mr Bruce. . . . . Nov 1995
Mallon, Mr Christopher . . . . Oct 1987
Muglia, Mr Richard . . . . Jan 1982
Murray-Jones, Mr Allan G BEc; LLB. . . . . Feb 1981
Nairn, Karyl . . . . Nov 1991
Nordlinger, Mr Douglas . . . . Jan 2003
Sanders, Mr Timothy Simon LLB . . . . Mar 1984
Simpson, Mr Scott . . . . Jan 1982
Tricot, Mr Danny . . . . Jan 1998
Trivedi, Mr Pranav. . . . . Jan 1991
Wells, Mr Clive . . . . Nov 1991

SKANTHABALAN SOLICITORS ‡
1st Floor 150 The Grove Stratford London E15 1NS
Tel: 020 8555 2710 *Fax:* 020 8555 2712
E-mail: skanthabalan@btconnect.com
List of partners: I Skanthabalan
Languages: Portuguese, Tamil
Work: E L R1 R2 S1 S2 W
SPr: Skanthabalan, Mrs Ilamathi . . . . *Aug 1990

SLADE & FLETCHER SOLICITORS ‡
1st & 2nd Floor 348a Camberwell New Road London SE5 0RW
Tel: 020 7733 6506 *Fax:* 020 7733 2715

RICHARD SLADE & COMPANY ‡
9 Gray's Inn Square London WC1R 5JD
Tel: 020 7160 0900 *Fax:* 020 7806 8267
Dx: 141 LONDON/CHANCERY LN
E-mail: richard@richardslade.com

SLATER BRADLEY & CO ‡
198 Upper Richmond Road Putney Wandsworth London SW15 2SJ
Tel: 020 8788 1008 *Fax:* 020 8789 0214 *Dx:* 59455 PUTNEY
E-mail: lawyer@slaterbradley.co.uk
List of partners: J M Bradley, P T Hourmouzios, N P Singh, J A Slater
Work: D1 D2 E G H K1 K3 L O Q S1 W Z(c,l)
Emergency Action, Agency, Advocacy, Legal Aid undertaken and Legal Aid Franchise
Ptr: Bradley, Ms Jane M BA . . . . *Jun 1981
Hourmouzios, Mr Philip T BA(Lond) . . . . *Dec 1974
Singh, Ms Natasha Piyari LLB. . . . . *Feb 2003
Slater, Mr John A . . . . *Dec 1974

SLAUGHTER AND MAY ‡
One Bunhill Row London EC1Y 8YY
Tel: 020 7600 1200 *Fax:* 020 7090 5000 *Dx:* 11 LONDON/CITY

BARRY SLAVIN & CO ‡
Third Floor 28 Margaret Street London W1W 8RZ
Tel: 020 7612 9010 *Fax:* 020 7612 9019
E-mail: barry.slavin@thelchgroup.com
List of partners: B M Slavin
Ptr: Slavin, Mr Barry M LLB Justice of the Peace; General Commissioner. . . . . *Dec 1972

SLOAN & CO ‡
211 Piccadilly London W1J 9HF
Tel: 020 7917 2865 *Fax:* 020 7917 2866 *Dx:* 82997 MAYFAIR
E-mail: mail@sloan.uk.net
List of partners: C A Sloan
Work: S1 S2
Agency undertaken
SPr: Sloan, Ms Christobel A LLM; MSc(Lond) . . . . . . *Sep 1981

SLOTINE LEGAL ‡
36 Bloomfield Terrace London SW1W 8PQ
Tel: 020 8528 1049 *Fax:* 020 8528 1001
E-mail: info@slotinelegal.co.uk

HENRY SMEE & CO ‡
Chandos House 33 Chandos Avenue London N20 9ED
Tel: 020 8446 3131 *Fax:* 020 8445 3095
E-mail: admin@henrysmee.co.uk
List of partners: H Smee
Work: B1 C1 E J1 K1 L O Q S1 S2 W
SPr: Smee, Mr Henry BA; MA . . . . *Oct 1982

ASHLEY SMITH & CO ‡
4-6 Lee High Road Lewisham London SE13 5LQ
Tel: 020 8463 0099 *Fax:* 020 8463 9191 *Dx:* 200961 LEWISHAM 2
Emergency telephone 020 8463 0099
E-mail: ashley@ashleysmith.org.uk
List of partners: R A Bosworth, A J Smith
Work: B2 G H
Emergency Action, Agency, Advocacy, Fixed Fee Interview, Legal Aid undertaken and Legal Aid Franchise
Ptr: Bosworth, Miss Rosalynn A BA(Lond) ★. . . . . . . *Dec 1983
Smith, Ashley J ★. . . . . *Jul 1985
Ast: Prosser, Mr D Lyn ★ . . . . *Dec 1993

SMITH BRAITHWAITE ‡
23 Heddon Street London W1B 4BQ
Tel: 020 7437 4244 *Fax:* 020 7437 0642 *Dx:* 54251 PICCADILLY 1
E-mail: information@smithbraithwaite.com

F W SMITH, RICHES & CO ‡
18 Pall Mall London SW1Y 5LU
Tel: 020 7930 0833

SMITH-RAHMAN ASSOCIATES ‡
24 Hampden Court Muswell Hill London N10 2HN
Tel: 020 7566 8244
List of partners: J Smith
SPr: Smith, J. . . . . Feb 1986

SMITHFIELD PARTNERS LIMITED ‡
2nd Floor 107 Cannon Street London EC4N 5AF
Tel: 0845 539 1000 *Fax:* 0845 652 0775 *Dx:* 42627 CHEAPSIDE
E-mail: solicitors@smithfieldpartners.com

SMITHS LAW LLP ‡
17 Shorts Gardens Covent Garden London WC2H 9AT
Tel: 020 7395 8631 *Fax:* 020 7395 8633
E-mail: lewis@smiths-law.com

SMYTH BARKHAM ‡
2 Henrietta Street London WC2E 8PS
Tel: 020 7632 9550 *Fax:* 020 7632 9551
E-mail: info@smythbarkham.co.uk
List of partners: C J Barkham, H T J Bradshaw, P Edwards, J A Smyth
Work: T1 T2 W Z(d,f)
Ptr: Barkham, Miss Caroline J BSc . . . . *Nov 1988
Bradshaw, Mr Hugh T J BA(Oxon) . . . . *Oct 1989
Edwards, Mr Paul. . . . . Nov 1993
Smyth, Mrs Joyce A BA(Cantab) . . . . *Apr 1983

SNOW HILL LEGAL ‡
150 Aldersgate Street London EC1A 4AB
Tel: 020 7334 9191 *Fax:* 020 7248 3408
Dx: 15 LONDON/CHANCERY LN
E-mail: joanne.morgan@moorestephens.com

JERZY SOKOL SOLICITOR ‡
Suite 77 9 Holles Street London W1G 0BD
Tel: 020 8123 9513 *Fax:* 020 7900 2155
E-mail: jbsokol@yahoo.co.uk

SOLICITORS FIRST LLP ‡
192 Trinity Road Wandsworth London SW17 7HR
Tel: 0870 770 7016 *Fax:* 020 8767 2330 *Dx:* 41611 BALHAM
E-mail: enquiries@first.uk.net
List of partners: G A Wood
Office: London SW17
Languages: Portuguese, Spanish, Urdu
Work: C2 E L R2 S1 S2 W Z(l)
Mem: Wood, Mr Graeme Alfred LLB. . . . . *Nov 1981

SOLICITORS FIRST LLP
240 Balham High Road London SW17 7AW
Tel: 020 8673 0116 *Fax:* 020 8767 2330
E-mail: enquiries@first.uk.net
Office: London SW17

M J SOLOMON & PARTNERS ‡
3rd Floor Conveyancing Section 101 Commercial Road London E1 1RD
Tel: 020 7377 2778 *Fax:* 020 7377 1446

M J SOLOMON & PARTNERS ‡
12 Wordsworth Parade Green Lanes London N8 0SJ
Tel: 020 8888 4446 *Fax:* 020 8888 5698

SOLOMON SINCLAIR LAW FIRM ‡
8 Fontaine Court 45 High Street London N14 6LW
Tel: 020 8882 5091 *Fax:* 020 8886 6647
E-mail: mail@solomonsinclair.com

SOLOMON TAYLOR & SHAW ‡
(incorporating Marsh Regan)
3 Coach House Yard Hampstead High Street London NW3 1QD
Tel: 020 7431 1912 *Fax:* 020 7794 7485 *Dx:* 144580 HAMPSTEAD 2
E-mail: mail@solts.co.uk
List of partners: S Atkinson, A Bloom, J Harris, N J Mills, D T O'Brien, K L O'Brien, G M Phillips, B M H Shaw, M Summerfield, R C Taylor, M Vangeen
Work: A1 A3 B1 C1 C2 C3 E J1 L O P S1 W Z(b,h,i,k)
Emergency Action, Agency and Advocacy undertaken
Ptr: Atkinson, Mr Scott LLB(English & French Law) . . . *Sep 1996
Bloom, Ari. . . . . Sep 1998
Harris, Jeremy . . . . Sep 1998
Mills, Mr Nicholas J BA(Dunelm) . . . . *Mar 1979
O'Brien, Mr Declan T LLB. . . . . *Oct 1985
O'Brien, Mrs Karen L LLB(Hons) . . . . Oct 1995
Phillips, Mr Gary M . . . . *Nov 1984
Shaw, Mr Barry M H LLB . . . . *Apr 1980
Summerfield, Mr Mark LLB(Hons). . . . . *Mar 1992
Taylor, Mr Raymond C LLB . . . . *Apr 1979
Vangeen, Mrs Melissa. . . . . Sep 2001
Ast: Cataldo, Miss Natalie Sarah LLB; LPC . . . . May 2011
Cranton, Mr Matthew LLB(Hons) . . . . Jan 2009
Goldmeier, Mr Rupert LLB. . . . . Nov 2002
Nahon, Mr Colin LLB . . . . Jan 2000
Patel, Miss Rupa BA(Hons); CPE . . . . Jun 1999
Con: Segal, Mr David A BA(Hons)(Oxon). . . . . Dec 1968
Solomon, Sir Harry . . . . *May 1960

SOMERS & BLAKE ‡
49b Boston Road Hanwell London W7 3SH
Tel: 020 8567 7025 *Fax:* 020 8840 6917 *Dx:* 39506 HANWELL
List of partners: G A J Blake, W A Somers
Work: B1 E G H N O Q S1 W
Agency, Advocacy, Fixed Fee Interview, Legal Aid undertaken and Member of Accident Line
Ptr: Blake, Mr Gerald A J LLB(Hons) . . . . Jun 1992
Somers, Mr William A. . . . . Feb 1964

SONN MACMILLAN ‡
19 Widegate Street Tower Hamlets London E1 7HP
Tel: 020 7377 8889 *Fax:* 020 7377 8279 *Dx:* 857 LONDON/CITY
Emergency telephone 07659 591505
List of partners: E R C Macmillan, D J Sonn
Work: B2 G H
Agency, Advocacy and Legal Aid undertaken
Ptr: Macmillan, Mr Euan R C . . . . Oct 1987
Sonn, Mr David J LLB(Manc) . . . . Oct 1987

SOOKIAS & SOOKIAS ‡
15 Brooks Mews London W1K 4DS
Tel: 020 7465 8000 *Fax:* 020 7465 8001 *Dx:* 138875 MAYFAIR
Emergency telephone 020 7229 7219
E-mail: info@sookias.co.uk
List of partners: K A Jones, M E Mannell, M J Sookias, R J Sookias, D J Stringfellow
Languages: Armenian, Farsi
Work: B1 C1 E F1 I J1 K1 K3 L M1 M2 O P Q R1 S1 S2 T2 W Z(c,g,i)
Emergency Action, Agency and Advocacy undertaken
Ptr: Jones, Ms Karen Ann BA . . . . Jan 2003
Mannell, Mr Michael E BA. . . . . *Jul 1988
Sookias, Mr Michael J BSc . . . . *Nov 1978
Sookias, Mr Robert J . . . . *§Mar 1983
Stringfellow, Ms Deborah J LLB. . . . . *Nov 1989

MICHAEL SOUL & ASSOCIATES ‡
4 Lincoln's Inn Fields London WC2A 3AA
Tel: 020 7353 3358 *Fax:* 020 7240 0139
Dx: 199 LONDON/CHANCERY LN
E-mail: mailbox@spanishlawyers.eu.com
List of partners: M Soul
Languages: Spanish
Work: C1 C2 E K3 M1 M2 R2 S1 S2 T1 T2 W
Ptr: Soul, Mr Michael Member of the Madrid & Malaga Bars . . . . *Dec 1971

SOUND ADVICE LLP ‡
1-5 Exchange Court Maiden Lane Covent Garden London WC2R 0JU
Tel: 020 7420 4300
E-mail: legal-info@soundadvicellp.com

SOUTHAMPTON ROW SOLICITORS LIMITED ‡
31 Southampton Row London WC1B 5HJ
Tel: 020 3178 4463 *Fax:* 020 3008 6011

SOUTHBANK SOLICITORS ‡
213a Clapham Road London SW9 0QH

SOUTHBRIDGE SOLICITORS ‡
123 Westminster Bridge Road London SE1 7HR
Tel: 020 7928 5488 *Fax:* 020 7928 5480
E-mail: yeelim@btconnect.com

SOUTHCOMBE & HAYLEY ‡
5 Upper Wimpole Street Westminster London W1G 6HQ
Tel: 020 7935 6631 *Fax:* 020 7935 6315 *Dx:* 83303 WEST END 2
E-mail: post@5uws.com
List of partners: T Drew, C Hayley, D Stancliffe
Languages: French
Work: B1 C1 C2 C3 E J1 K3 L M1 M2 N O P Q S1 S2 W Z(c,e,f,k,l,m)
Emergency Action, Agency and Advocacy undertaken
Ptr: Drew, Mr Terence BA . . . . . Feb 1988
Hayley, Mr Clive BA . . . . . *Dec 1982
Stancliffe, Mr David . . . . . Jul 1999

SOUTHCOTE SCOTT ‡
83 Baker Street London W1U 6AG
Tel: 020 7034 7035 *Fax:* 020 7034 7200
Dx: 42712 OXFORD CIRCUS NORTH
E-mail: info@southcotescott.com
List of partners: A W J Scott, K D Southcote-Want
Work: B1 C1 E L N O Q S1 S2 W Z(c,l)
Agency and Fixed Fee Interview undertaken
Ptr: Scott, Mr Andrew William John BA(Hons) . . . . . *Aug 1994
Southcote-Want, Mr Kevin D BA(Hons) . . . . . *May 1994

SOUTHFIELDS SOLICITORS ‡
2nd Floor 81 Wandsworth High Street Wandsworth London SW18 4TU
Tel: 020 8877 3421 *Fax:* 020 8877 8931
Dx: 59053 WANDSWORTH NORTH

SOUTHGATE & CO ‡
631 Seven Sisters Road London N15 5LE
Tel: 020 8809 0010 *Fax:* 020 8809 5583
Dx: 55611 SOUTH TOTTENHAM
Languages: Greek
Work: A1 A3 B1 C1 C2 E F1 F2 J1 J2 K1 K2 K3 L N O Q R1 R2 S1 S2 W Z(c,d,e,h,j,k,l,p,q,s)
Agency and Fixed Fee Interview undertaken

SPARROW & TRIEU SOLICITORS ‡
76 Shaftesbury Avenue London W1V 7DG
Tel: 020 7287 6608 *Fax:* 020 7287 6389 *Dx:* 89255 SOHO SQUARE
E-mail: mail@sparrowandtrieu.plus.com
List of partners: D G Sparrow, M T Trieu
Languages: Cantonese, Mandarin
Work: K1 L N S1 S2 W Z(i,l)
Ptr: Sparrow, Mr David G MA(Oxon); Barrister . . . . . *Mar 1984
Trieu, Mrs M Therese . . . . . *Jan 1984
Ast: Giles, Ms Elizabeth Victoria LLB . . . . . *Sep 2002

THE SPECTER PARTNERSHIP
49 Britton Street London EC1M 5UL
Tel: 020 7251 9900 *Fax:* 020 7490 1275
Office: Birkenhead, Warrington

DR LINDA S SPEDDING ‡
36 Alder Lodge River Gardens Stevenage Road Fulham London SW6 6NP
Tel: 020 7610 2025 *Fax:* 020 7610 1213
E-mail: linda@spedding.org
List of partners: L S Spedding
Languages: French
Work: M1 M2 P W Z(d,z)
SPr: Spedding, Dr Linda Susan LLB(Hons); LLM; PhD Lord Alexander Maxwell Trust Scholarship . . . . . *Nov 1975

SpeechlyBircham

SPEECHLY BIRCHAM LLP ‡
6 New Street Square London EC4A 3LX
Tel: 020 7427 6400 *Fax:* 020 7427 6600
Dx: 54 LONDON/CHANCERY LN
E-mail: information@speechlys.com
Web: www.speechlys.com
List of partners: M Bailey, T Ball, E Bartlett, J Bayliss, W Begley, R Bell, M Bennett, T M C Bettany, B Bidder, R T J Bond, K S Bordell, A Broadberry, E Budd, C I Butler, S Carey, J Carp, J W Carter, A Carter-Silk, H Chohan, A J J Clarke, P Cogher, A M Collins, R Connell, M D Couve, J Crawford, S N Dobson, J Freeman, A Gill, C Gothard, W Granger, R Grove, D Gwillim, W Hancock, C M Harlowe, J C R Hudson, C R Hutton, J Innes, G Jackson, N Janmohamed, A J Julyan, P A Kay, R Kilgour, A King-Christopher, R C Kirby, G Kleiner, A M Kopitko, D Leedham, J Leggett, G S Ling, M R Lingens, R Linskell, H Luckhurst, M MacDougall, R Martin, L G Medlock, V Mercer, T J Moran, N Moreno, M J Musgrave, W Nash, M Newing, R J F Novak, C D Palmer, C Prior, C Putt, T A Raper, S Ridpath, D Rosenberg, J H Rosshandler, D A Salmon, D Scott, S Shah, T P Shaw, B Slack, M T Smith, J Souter, P Stockdale, D Sullivan, M Summers, N Tall, R Thomas, K L Troup, A G Walsh, D J M Ward, J W Whitehead, D Wills, J Wolstenholme, M Wright, A Zavos
Languages: French, German
Work: A1 A3 B1 B2 C1 C2 C3 E I J1 J2 K1 K2 K3 L N O P Q R1 R2 S1 S2 T1 T2 U1 U2 W Z(b,c,d,e,f,i,j,m,n,o,p,q,u,v,w,za)
Advocacy undertaken
Ptr: Bailey, Mr Mark BA . . . . . *Oct 1994
Ball, Mr Tim . . . . . *Nov 1993
Bartlett, Mrs Emma LLB . . . . . *Sep 1999
Bayliss, Mr Jonathan . . . . . *Apr 1988
Begley, Mr William . . . . . *Sep 1998
Bell, Mr Robert BA; LLM . . . . . *Jan 1990
Bennett, Ms Meriel . . . . . Sep 1998
Bettany, Mr Trevor M C LLB . . . . . *Oct 1987
Bidder, Mr Bill . . . . . *Mar 1979
Bond, Mr Robert Thomas James BA(Law); BSc Notary Public . . . . . *Jun 1979
Bordell, Mr Keith S LLB . . . . . Feb 1988
Broadberry, Alison . . . . . Mar 2008
Budd, Ms Elizabeth LLB(Bris) . . . . . *Nov 1991
Butler, Mr Christopher I . . . . . *Oct 1982
Carey, Mr Steven . . . . . Aug 1992
Carp, Juliet . . . . . Oct 1993
Carter, Mr James W LLB(Cantab) . . . . . *Sep 1990
Carter-Silk, Mr Alexander . . . . . Aug 1988
Chohan, Harbans . . . . . Aug 1981
Clarke, Mr Andrew James Joseph BA(Oxon) . . . . . Oct 1996
Cogher, Ms Penny LLB(Bham) . . . . . Oct 1991
Collins, Mr Andrew McKeown LLB(Hons) . . . . . *Jun 1991
Connell, Mr Rupert . . . . . May 1978
Couve, Mr Mervyn D LLM(Lond) . . . . . *§Apr 1978
Crawford, Mr Jonathan . . . . . Aug 1997
Dobson, Mr Stephen N MA(Oxon) . . . . . *Dec 1978
Freeman, Mr James MA(Oxon) . . . . . Jan 1999
Gill, Ms Anita . . . . . Feb 1988
Gothard, Mr Charles LLB(Hons) . . . . . *Nov 1997
Granger, Mr William BA Trustee of Property Trust . . . . . Nov 1992
Grove, Mr Robin LLB . . . . . Apr 1996
Gwillim, Mr David LLB ♦ . . . . . *Oct 1981
Hancock, Mr William LLB; BCL . . . . . *Oct 1987
Harlowe, Mr Christopher M . . . . . *Jan 1986
Hudson, Mr Jeremy C R MA(Cantab) . . . . . Dec 1977
Hutton, Mr Charles Robert BA(Durham)(Classics) . . . . . Sep 1998
Innes, Ms Jane . . . . . Jan 2005
Jackson, Miss Gaynor LLB . . . . . Dec 1989
Janmohamed, Mr Nick BA(Cantab) . . . . . *Oct 1985
Julyan, Mr Alan J BA . . . . . *§Jun 1974
Kay, Mr Paul A LLB . . . . . *Oct 1983
Kilgour, Mr Robert . . . . . Sep 1999
King-Christopher, Mr Ashley . . . . . Jan 2000
Kirby, Mr Richard C MA(Oxon) . . . . . *§Dec 1971
Kleiner, Mr Graeme . . . . . Sep 1999
Kopitko, Mr Ashley M BA . . . . . *Feb 1986
Leedham, Mr David LLB(Hons); LLM . . . . . Nov 1996
Leggett, Mr Jon LLB; LLM . . . . . Sep 1991
Ling, Mr Graham S LLB . . . . . *Oct 1988
Lingens, Mr Michael R MA(Oxon) . . . . . *Oct 1982
Linskell, Mr Richard . . . . . Nov 1984
Luckhurst, Helena . . . . . Sep 2000
MacDougall, Mr Malcolm . . . . . Mar 1997
Martin, Mr Richard LLB(Cantab) . . . . . Jan 1995
Medlock, Mr Lee G . . . . . Dec 1994
Mercer, Mr Vincent MSI . . . . . Nov 1978
Moran, Mr Thomas James MA(Oxon) . . . . . Apr 2000
Moreno, Ms Nathalie LLM(Harv) . . . . . *Mar 2006
Musgrave, Mr Mark J . . . . . *§Apr 1977
Nash, Mr William . . . . . Nov 1997
Newing, Mr Matthew LLB(Hons) . . . . . *Oct 1995
Novak, Mr Rhys J F . . . . . Sep 2000
Palmer, Mr Charles D . . . . . *Apr 1971
Prior, Ms Clare . . . . . Sep 1997
Putt, Mr Christopher . . . . . Oct 1984
Raper, Mr Timothy A BA . . . . . *Feb 1981
Ridpath, Mr Simon LLB(Hons) . . . . . Sep 2001
Rosenberg, Mr Daniel BA(Cantab) . . . . . Sep 1987
Rosshandler, Mr Jonathan H MA(Oxon) . . . . . *Jun 1977
Salmon, Mr Duncan A LLB . . . . . *Apr 1981
Scott, Mr Duncan . . . . . Sep 2002
Shah, Miss Sanjvee BSc(Econ); PDL; LPC . . . . . Jan 2001
Shaw, Mr Thomas P LLB . . . . . *Apr 1987
Slack, Mr Brendan . . . . . Sep 2001
Smith, Mr Mark T . . . . . *Oct 1989
Souter, Mr James . . . . . Oct 2001
Stockdale, Mr Peter . . . . . Dec 1974
Sullivan, Mr Daniel . . . . . May 1996
Summers, Mr Mark BSc; ARCS; CPE; LPC; TEP STEP President's Prize Excellence Award 2010 . . . . . Sep 2001
Tall, Mr Nicholas . . . . . Sep 1999
Thomas, Mr Robert LLB(Wales) . . . . . Jan 1981
Troup, Ms Kate L LLB(Birmingham) . . . . . Sep 2001
Walsh, Mr Andrew Geoffrey MA; LLB . . . . . *Jul 1979
Ward, Mr D John M LLB . . . . . *Jan 1983
Whitehead, Mr Jonathan Wright BA . . . . . Feb 1985
Wills, Mr David . . . . . May 1967
Wolstenholme, Ms Jane LLB; LSF . . . . . Feb 1991
Wright, Mr Martin . . . . . Nov 1981
Zavos, Ms Andrea LLB . . . . . *Nov 1993
Con: Guthrie, Mr Graeme . . . . . May 1974

SPENCE & HORNE ‡
343 Mare Street Hackney London E8 1HY
Tel: 020 8985 2277 *Fax:* 020 8985 1177 *Dx:* 35463 HACKNEY 1
E-mail: angelaspence@hotmail.com
List of partners: A A M Spence
Languages: Punjabi, Sinhalese, Urdu
Work: D1 E F1 J1 K1 K3 L M1 O Q S1 S2 V W Z(g,h,i)
Emergency Action, Agency, Advocacy, Fixed Fee Interview and Legal Aid undertaken
Ptr: Spence, Ms Angela A M BSc ♦ . . . . . *Oct 1987

SPENSER UNDERHILL NEWMARK LLP ‡
6 Gray's Inn Square Gray's Inn London WC1R 5AX
Tel: 020 7269 9026 *Fax:* 020 7242 3032
E-mail: dspenserunderhill@sunlaw.co.uk

J D SPICER & CO ‡
140 Kilburn High Road London NW6 4JD
Tel: 020 7625 5590 *Fax:* 020 7328 5330 *Dx:* 37714 KILBURN
Emergency telephone 07836 577556
List of partners: J A Armstrong, K Khushal, J D Spicer, P W Spicer, J Stanhope, U Zeb
Office: Birmingham, London EC4
Languages: Gujarati, Polish
Work: C1 D1 E F1 G H J1 K1 L N P R1 S1 T1 V W
Emergency Action, Agency, Advocacy, Legal Aid undertaken and Legal Aid Franchise
Ptr: Armstrong, Ms Julie Ann BSc(Hons); MSc . . . . . Sep 1988
Khushal, Kirit BA . . . . . Feb 1989
Spicer, Mr Jonathan D LLB(Lond) . . . . . *Oct 1973
Spicer, Mr Philip W LLB . . . . . *Oct 1980
Stanhope, Miss Julie LLB . . . . . *Jul 1982
Zeb, Mr Umar LLB . . . . . Jun 1997
Ast: Souper, Mr Richard J BMus . . . . . Jan 1993

J D SPICER & CO
Temple Bar House 23-28 Fleet Street London EC4Y 1AA
Tel: 020 7651 0850 *Fax:* 020 7842 0779 *Dx:* 297 CHANCERY LANE
Office: Birmingham, London NW6

SPIEGEL & UTRERA LTD ‡
11 Murray Street London NW1 9RE
Tel: 020 7284 3700 *Fax:* 020 7284 3533
E-mail: info@spiegelutrera.co.uk

SPIROPOULOS LAWAL SOLICITORS ‡
367 Brockley Road Brockley London SE4 2AG
Tel: 020 8469 0669 *Fax:* 020 8305 6659

SPRING LAW ‡
40 Craven Street London WC2N 5NG
Tel: 020 7930 4158 *Fax:* 020 7389 0565

SQUIRE SANDERS (UK) LLP
7 Devonshire Square London EC2M 4YH
Tel: 020 7655 1000 *Fax:* 020 7655 1001
Dx: 136546 BISHOPSGATE 2
Office: Birmingham, Leeds, Manchester
Languages: Cantonese, Dutch, French, German, Greek, Italian, Lithuanian, Malay, Portuguese, Punjabi, Russian, Serbo-Croat, Spanish, Turkish
Work: A2 A3 B1 B2 B3 C1 C2 C3 E F1 F2 I J1 J2 M1 M2 O P Q R1 R2 S2 T1 T2 U1 U2 Z(b,c,e,f,h,j,l,n,o,q,t,w,y,z)
Ptr: Abraham, Mr William . . . . . Jul 1999
Allen, Mr Nicholas P BA . . . . . Feb 1985
Brandt, Mr Keith M BA(Hons)(Warw) . . . . . *Feb 1985
Brigstocke, Mr Christopher Thomas LLB(Hons) . . . . . Mar 1985
Burns, Mr Richard LLB . . . . . Oct 1983
Carney, Mr Graeme Peter BA(Hons) . . . . . *Oct 1985
Cassidy, Mr Michael J BA(Cantab); MBA Master of the City of London Solicitors Company 2001-2 . . . . . Sep 1971
Colliver, Mr Douglas J LLB(Bris) . . . . . *Apr 1971
Cooke, Mr Richard LLB . . . . . *Sep 1991
Cooper, Mrs Jane MA(Dundee) . . . . . *§Dec 1980
Court, Ms Julia Alison . . . . . Jan 1991
Cowen, Mr Rupert C BA . . . . . *§Mar 1986
Danilunas, Ms Marija BSc; LLB; BCL(Oxon) . . . . . *§Dec 1989
Deacon, Mr John LLB; MSc; ACIArb . . . . . *Nov 1988
Dell, Mr Alex B LLB . . . . . *Oct 1995
Dillon, Mr Paul . . . . . Nov 1990
Donovan, Ms Colleen Mary BSc; LLB(Hons) . . . . . *Sep 1989
Doraisamy, Jayanthi . . . . . Sep 1992
Evans, Mr Mark . . . . . Oct 1985
Fisher, Ms Tracy . . . . . Nov 1993
Fox, Miss Francesca LLB(Hons) . . . . . *Dec 1992
Garford, Mr F Stephen . . . . . *§Nov 1966
Gilbey, Mr Bernhard David LLB; ATII . . . . . *Feb 1993
Gordon, Mr Simon M MA(Cantab) . . . . . *Oct 1983
Gravill, Mr Robert M Birmingham Law Society Bronze Medal . . . . . Oct 1988
Greenstreet, Mr Ian A BSc . . . . . Oct 1990
Handley, Mr Mark . . . . . Aug 1997
Harris, Ms Kathleen . . . . . Dec 2000
Harris, Mr Paul . . . . . Jan 1998
Higton, Mr Jonathan P BA . . . . . Apr 1994
Hodder, Mr Charles J R BSc . . . . . *Dec 1990
Hosie, Mr Jonathan P LLB; MSc . . . . . Oct 1984
Hubbard, Mr Christopher BA . . . . . *Jul 1995
Hunter, Ms Wendy . . . . . Oct 1995
Ingle, Mr Trevor F LLB(Hons) . . . . . *Apr 1991
Jones, Mr David M . . . . . *May 1976
Korman, Mr Andrew John BA(Hons)(Oxon) . . . . . *Nov 1995
Macaulay, Mrs Gwyneth A LLB(Belfast) . . . . . *Jul 1977
Marsh, Mr Jonathan . . . . . Oct 1993
Marshall, Mrs Jane M LLB(Hons) . . . . . *Apr 1978
Mason, Mr Nicolas P LLB . . . . . *Mar 1987
May, Miss Caroline E BA(Durham) . . . . . *Dec 1987
Middleton-Smith, Mr Charles C . . . . . *Jun 1978
Morshead, Mr Jonathan E LLB(B'ham) . . . . . Apr 1976
Noblet, Ms Caroline BA . . . . . Oct 1991
O'Neill, Mr Gerard J . . . . . Nov 1992
Oxnard, Mr Paul A LLB(Hons) . . . . . *Nov 1989
Powell, Mr Andrew M LLB(Wales) . . . . . *§Jun 1980
Price, Mr Simon L MA(Oxon) . . . . . *Nov 1984
Rees, Mr Philip R BA(Norwich) . . . . . *Oct 1986
Rohsler, Mr Carl A . . . . . *Dec 1995
Sale, Mr Simon A . . . . . Oct 1994
Savage, Mr David James . . . . . Apr 2001
Stephenson, Mr Justin BA(Hons) . . . . . Nov 1990
Stewart, Mr Gordon BA(Hons)(Law) . . . . . Jan 1978
Taylor, Mr Jonathan BA(Hons); LLM . . . . . *Jun 1997
Terry, Ms Caroline J . . . . . Jan 1993
Thomas, Mr Martin Keith LLB . . . . . *Oct 1988
Townley, Mr Stephen LLM Arbitrator for the Court of Arbitration for Sport . . . . . *Oct 1978
Visintin, Mr Andrew O LLB(Hons) . . . . . *Jan 1990
Watson, Mr Andrew J LLB . . . . . *Nov 1990
Weekes, Mr Robert J BSc . . . . . *Jan 1988
Wegenek, Mr Robert LLB . . . . . Sep 1991
Whincup, Mr David H BA(Oxon); MA . . . . . *Oct 1986
Williams, Mr Nicholas MA(Cantab) . . . . . *Sep 1984
Willison, Mr Christopher Alan BSc; LLB(Hons) . . . . . *Oct 1992
Winston, Mr Laurence M LLB . . . . . *Nov 1994
Ast: Aaron, Ms Rachel Elisabeth . . . . . May 1999
Abbate, Miss Francine Victoria MA(Hons) . . . . . *Oct 1995
Ajimal, Ms Omleen Kaur . . . . . Sep 2000
Anstey, Ms Nicola Gila LLB; BA . . . . . Sep 1997
Araf, Ms Fazya . . . . . Sep 1998
Atherton, Miss Sharon Lynne LLB(Hons)(Leics); LSF(Hons)(Chester) . . . . . *Dec 1994
Ball, Ms Caroline Louise . . . . . Sep 1999
Bew, Mr Jonathan . . . . . *Sep 1998
Bray, Mr Robert Paul . . . . . Sep 2000
Bryce, Mr James Kirk . . . . . Sep 2000
Burton, Mr Andrew James . . . . . Nov 1997
Burton, Mr Steven Paul LLB(Hons); LLM . . . . . Jul 1998
Butterworth, Ms Sasha . . . . . Oct 1997
Byrne, Ms Maria . . . . . Jan 2001
Cartwright, Mr Thomas James LLB(Hons) . . . . . *Sep 1996
Cessford, Ms Rebecca Kate . . . . . May 2001
Chan, Ms Evelyn Lillian Swee Lian . . . . . Apr 1999
Clark, Miss Victoria Judith BA; MA(Hons)(Oxon) . . . . . *Oct 1992
Coats, Mr Peter J MA(Cantab) . . . . . *Jun 1994
Cole, Mr Stephen LLB(Hons) . . . . . *Oct 1995
Corbett, Mr Iain LLB . . . . . *Feb 1990
Cornelius, Mr Jonathan . . . . . Sep 2000
Crichton-Stuart, Mr Charles . . . . . Apr 2000
Cripps, Ms Angela Claire . . . . . Mar 1998
Curran, Mr Richard James . . . . . Jul 1999
Dabydeen, Mr Robin . . . . . Sep 1996
Davidson, Mrs Samantha J LLB . . . . . Feb 1997
Davies, Mr Robert Leighton LLB . . . . . Nov 1995
Davies, Ms Susan J BA; LLB . . . . . Nov 1988
Davis, Mr Robert Emanuel . . . . . Sep 2000

Distin, Mr Giles Henry. . . . . Sep 1998
Dougherty, Ms Sarah Patricia . . . . Sep 2000
Duthie, Mr Maxwell Bryan MA(Cantab); LLM; DipLS. *Nov 1996
Fearn, Mr Bradley Frank . . . . May 2000
Foster, Mr Andrew Myles . . . . Sep 1998
Frost, Mr Charles Edward. . . . . Sep 1999
Gardiner, Ms Amy Elizabeth. . . . . Sep 2000
Gayner, Mr Nicholas Charles Davidson . . . . Sep 1998
Gibbons, Ms Linda Marie . . . . Feb 2000
Gildener, Mr Simon James . . . . Sep 1998
Gill, Ms Ravinder . . . . Oct 1999
Glew, Ms Deborah . . . . Apr 1999
Goodwin, Ms Anna Marie . . . . Sep 2000
Graham, Miss Katie LLB(Hons) . . . . Dec 1997
Hamilton, Mr John. . . . . *Apr 1978
Harvey, Ms Ruth M LLB. . . . . *Dec 1988
Haste, Miss Michelle BA; LLM. . . . . *Dec 1991
Haworth, Ms Lesley LLB . . . . *Nov 1995
Hazelton, Mr Gary A . . . . *Nov 1990
Hennigan, Mr James . . . . Sep 2000
Hesketh, Mr Joseph John Richard. . . . . Sep 1999
Hewens, Mr Timothy Mark Armstrong . . . . Sep 2000
Hughes, Mrs Amanda J LLB(Hons) . . . . *Sep 1988
Hughes, Mr Gareth LLB. . . . . May 1999
Hunter, Mr Simon . . . . May 2000
Ivey, Mr Nicholas John . . . . Nov 2000
Jackson, Ms Lindsey Anne . . . . Nov 1998
Kendrick, Mr Adam . . . . Jan 1998
Khan, Mr Aamir Ali BSc; CPE; LPC . . . . *Jul 1997
Kostelnyk, Miss Jane L BA(Bris). . . . . *Nov 1991
Kuhn, Ms Mandy Leigh . . . . Sep 2000
Lambert, Miss Wendy BSc(Hons) . . . . *Oct 1995
Lanaghan, Miss Karen BSc(Hons). . . . . *Nov 1993
Lewis, Mr Matthew Basil . . . . Nov 1997
Little, Mr John K LLB(Hons). . . . . *Mar 1990
Lloyd-Davies, Miss Helen C LLB(Hons) . . . . Aug 1997
Lucas, Ms Janette Helen . . . . Sep 1999
McCormick, Ms Nicola Jane. . . . . Nov 1997
Mace, Mr Andrew James . . . . Jul 1999
McKay, Mr Spencer James . . . . Nov 1997
Mallick, Miss Catherine Louise LLB . . . . Sep 1998
Marsh, Ms Abigail Lucy . . . . Sep 2000
Martin, Ms Annabel Polly . . . . Oct 1999
Mason, Ms Lisa Jane . . . . Sep 1998
Meer, Mr Nadim Mahomed . . . . Nov 1998
Miles, Mr Simon Justin LLM(Commercial Law); LLB(Hons) . . . . Oct 1995
Millar, Ms Lindsay BA(Oxon); LLM(Lond) . . . . *Oct 1988
Milner, Miss Marina J LLB(Warw) . . . . Nov 1992
Mitchell, Mr James BSc(Hons) . . . . Nov 1995
Moore, Mr Ian Clive. . . . . Jan 1999
Nateghi, Ms Misha . . . . Sep 1998
Nolan, Ms Fionnuala LLB(Hons). . . . . Sep 1997
Nunn, Miss Kathryn E LLB(Hons); LSF . . . . *Oct 1993
Panayiotou, Mr Mark I BA(Hons) . . . . Sep 2000
Peet, Mr Jonathan C BA . . . . Mar 1988
Perry, Ms Mandy . . . . Sep 2000
Powell, Mr Reuben David . . . . May 2000
Pugh, Miss Nerys S LLB . . . . *Sep 1997
Quigley, Ms Dearbhla Mary Eva. . . . . Sep 2000
Rajani-Shah, Mrs Anjli. . . . . Sep 1999
Rao, Miss Farzana LLB(Wales) . . . . *Oct 1991
Reece, Mr Oliver Peter Shekin BA . . . . *Oct 1996
Reed, Mr Antony James Thomas . . . . Oct 1993
Ries, Miss Emmanuelle. . . . . Apr 1996
Ritchie, Ms Malissa Samantha LLB . . . . *Aug 1996
Robinson, Mr Simon Michael LLM; LLB . . . . Oct 1998
Sampson, Mr Stephen John BA(Hons) Birmingham Law Society Book Prize 1997 . . . . Sep 1998
Savill, Ms Lorraine Rose . . . . Sep 2000
Scott-Russell, Miss Jennifer LLB(Hons); DipLP . . . . *Mar 1998
Searle, Ms Jo Anne. . . . . Sep 1999
Sergent, Mr Franck . . . . Feb 2001
Shackleton, Mr James F BA(Hons) . . . . Oct 1993
Sheridan, Mr Martin James . . . . Sep 2000
Sherlock, Ms Susan Patricia Kathleen. . . . . Sep 1999
Smith, Ms Catherine . . . . Sep 1997
Smith, Mr Mark James LLB . . . . Sep 1998
Sohal, Rajwant . . . . May 2001
Sparks, Mr Fraser Matthew . . . . Sep 2000
Spinks, Mr David Graeme. . . . . Oct 1998
Spooner, Mr Adrian BSc(Pharm); MRPharmS; MRPharmM . . . . §May 1998
Staveley, Mr Charles G S LLB(Hons) . . . . *Oct 1996
Theobald, Ms Tanya Louise. . . . . Sep 2000
Toft, Ms Kirsten . . . . May 1999
Towers, Ms Diane LLB . . . . Oct 1994
Vidal, Mr Robert. . . . . Sep 2000
Whalley, Mr Andrew Geoffrey . . . . Oct 1998
Whitehead, Mr Mark Andrew BA(Hons)(History); CPE; LSF . . . . Oct 1995
Whiteley, Ms Nicola LLB; LPC. . . . . *Oct 1997
Williams, Ms Cathryn E LLB. . . . . Nov 1992
Williams, Mr James Alistair Goronwy LLB; LLM . . . . Sep 2000
Wisbey, Mrs Juliette L BSc(Hons); CPE. . . . . *Aug 1996
Wise, Ms Lesley BA(Hons) . . . . *May 1998
Woolley, Mr Alistair . . . . Nov 1995
Wrightson, Mr Graham R BA(Hons). . . . . *Sep 1997
Con: Calow, Mr David F. . . . . *§Mar 1961
Simpson, Mr Peter F MA(Oxon). . . . . Apr 1973

LOUIS SSEKKONO SOLICITORS ‡
14-15 Craven Street London WC2N 5AD
Tel: 020 7839 1772 *Fax:* 020 7839 1773

TERENCE ST J MILLETT ‡
34 Sumner Place South Kensington London SW7 3NT
Tel: 020 7581 7500 *Fax:* 020 7581 7501
Dx: 35753 SOUTH KENSINGTON
E-mail: info@tstjm.com
List of partners: P R Riley, I P Sinclair, P R Skilbeck, D S Wilkinson
Work: E L S1
Ptr: Riley, Ms Pauline R LLB(Lond) . . . . *Apr 1981
Sinclair, Mr Ian P BA . . . . *Oct 1980
Skilbeck, Mr Paul R BA(Law) . . . . *Jul 1985
Wilkinson, Mr Derek S LLB(Newc). . . . . *Apr 1976
Ast: Hasler, Mr Philip B BA. . . . . *Nov 1990
Pufulete, Mrs Helena . . . . *Jan 2003
Con: Downing, Mr John William Wallace LLB(Hons). . . . *Apr 1979

ST LUCE & CO ‡
36a Peckham Rye London SE15 4JR
Tel: 020 7635 9131 *Fax:* 020 7639 7616 *Dx:* 152643 PECKHAM 3
List of partners: S St Luce
Work: D1 G H K1
Legal Aid undertaken and Legal Aid Franchise
SPr: St Luce, Ms Sandra LLB(Lond) . . . . *Nov 1983

STAFFORD YOUNG JONES ‡
The Old Rectory 29 Martin Lane London EC4R 0AU
Tel: 020 7623 9490 *Fax:* 020 7929 5704
Dx: 176 LONDON/CHANCERY LN
E-mail: stronga@s-yj.co.uk
List of partners: F T Backman, B S Christer, N A Fulton, M Gaston, A D Strong, K M Wallace, P E Yelland
Languages: French, Portuguese
Work: B1 C1 E J1 K1 K3 L N O Q S1 S2 T2 W Z(h)
Ptr: Backman, Mr Francis T LLB. . . . . *Dec 1975
Christer, Mr Bruce S LLB(St Andrews); MA(Keele). . *Jun 1972
Fulton, Mr Neil A . . . . *Dec 1975
Gaston, Mr Martin LLB(Newc). . . . . Jul 1975
Strong, Mr Andrew D MA(Cantab). . . . . Jul 1977
Wallace, Mrs Karen Mary LLB. . . . . Nov 1993
Yelland, Mrs Pamela E LLB . . . . Apr 1973
Ast: Butterworth, Miss Alyssia LLB(Hons) . . . . Aug 2007
Wenham, Mrs Helen BA. . . . . Nov 1988
Con: Gottler, Mr David J . . . . *Jan 1969
Hills, Mr Rodney J. . . . . Dec 1972
Steel, Mr Andrew H MA(Cantab) . . . . Jun 1968

STALA ERIMOS CHARALAMBOUS & CO ‡
10 Raith Avenue London N14 7DU
Tel: 020 8886 5970 *Fax:* 020 8886 1290
E-mail: stalacharalambous@btinternet.com

JAMES STALLARD & CO ‡
Central Court 25 Southampton Buildings London WC2A 1AL
Tel: 020 7430 1861 *Fax:* 020 7242 1185
E-mail: stallard@btinternet.com
List of partners: R J Stallard
Work: C1 C2 C3 E J1 O T1 T2 Z(b,e,f)
Ptr: Stallard, Mr Reginald J LLB Renoldson Memorial Prize . . . . *Nov 1970

STAPLETONS SOLICITORS ‡
263 Green Lanes Palmers Green London N13 4XE
Tel: 020 8886 6876 *Fax:* 020 8882 5019
Dx: 57850 PALMERS GREEN
E-mail: info@stapletonslaw.com
List of partners: J M Schamroth, G Stapleton
Languages: Turkish
Work: E J1 K1 L N O Q S1 S2 W
Agency and Fixed Fee Interview undertaken
Ptr: Schamroth, Mr Julian M BA . . . . *Nov 1982
Stapleton, Mr Greg BA(Hons) . . . . *Nov 1993

STARR & PARTNERS LLP ‡
21 Garlick Hill London EC4V 2AU
Tel: 020 7199 1450 *Fax:* 020 7248 1740
E-mail: info@starrlegal.com
List of partners: L Booth, I Burton, T Starr
Languages: German, Russian
Ptr: Booth, Ms Lisa . . . . Dec 1993
Burton, Mr Ian. . . . . Jan 1993
Starr, Mr Toby. . . . . Sep 1996

STATHAM GILL DAVIES ‡
54 Welbeck Street London W1G 9XS
Tel: 020 7317 3210 *Fax:* 020 7487 5925
Dx: 42724 OXFORD CIRCUS NORTH
E-mail: info@sgdlaw.com

STEEL & SHAMASH ‡
12 Baylis Road Waterloo Lambeth London SE1 7AA
Tel: 020 7803 3999 *Fax:* 020 7803 3900 *Dx:* 36503 LAMBETH
Emergency telephone 07973 489440
E-mail: solicitors@steelandshamash.co.uk
List of partners: R Bhasin, A Dowie, M A Harris, J G Kaufman, G D Shamash
Languages: French, Spanish
Work: D1 E G H J1 K1 L M1 N P S1 S2 V W Z(d,e,i,k,m,p)
Emergency Action, Agency, Advocacy, Fixed Fee Interview, Legal Aid undertaken and Legal Aid Franchise
Ptr: Bhasin, Rakesh. . . . . Dec 1996
Dowie, Mr Andrew BA(Hons); CPE . . . . *Dec 1998
Harris, Mrs Mary A . . . . *Jul 1991
Kaufman, Ms Janice G BA . . . . Apr 1980
Shamash, Mr Gerald D BSc(Surrey) Justice of the Peace Councillor of Borough of Barnet. . . . . *May 1976
Ast: O'Connell, Ms Anna. . . . . Oct 1997
Rattray, Ms Frances. . . . . Nov 2007
Con: Bowker, Ms Deborah Clare BA(Oxon). . . . . *Nov 1986

STEELES
53 New Broad Street London EC2M 1BB
Tel: 020 7421 1720 *Fax:* 020 7421 1749 *Dx:* 564 LONDON/CITY
E-mail: info@steeleslaw.co.uk
Office: Diss, Norwich
Work: A1 A3 B1 B2 C1 C2 C3 D1 E F1 G H I J1 J2 K1 K2 L M1 M2 N O Q R1 R2 S1 S2 T1 T2 V W Z(c,d,h,k,l,m,o,p,r,u)
Agency, Advocacy undertaken and Member of Accident Line
Ast: Thomas, Ms Jean Patricia. . . . . Jun 1999
Con: Edmonds, Miss Cheryl . . . . *Nov 1998

STEINFELD LAW LLP ‡
22 Manchester Square London W1U 3PT
Tel: 020 7725 1313 *Fax:* 020 7725 1314
E-mail: michael.steinfeld@steinfeldlaw.co.uk

STENNETT & STENNETT ‡
4 Winchmore Hill Road Southgate London N14 6PT
Tel: 020 8920 3190 *Fax:* 020 8882 6823 *Dx:* 34305 SOUTHGATE
E-mail: enquiries@stennett-stennett.co.uk
List of partners: E Beckford-Stennett, M Stennett
Work: D1 E G H K1 L N S1 V Z(h)
Emergency Action, Agency, Advocacy and Legal Aid undertaken
Ptr: Beckford-Stennett, Ms Elaine . . . . *Mar 1989
Stennett, Mr Michael BA . . . . *Feb 1985

STEPHEN & ASSOCIATES LIMITED ‡
11-12 Pall Mall London SW1Y 5LU
Tel: 020 7930 2500 *Fax:* 020 7930 0083
E-mail: tony@stephensandassociates.com

LAWRENCE STEPHENS ‡
4th Floor Morley House 26-30 Holborn Viaduct London EC1A 2AT
Tel: 020 7935 1211 *Fax:* 020 7935 1213
E-mail: sbernstein@lawstep.co.uk
List of partners: S Bernstein, A J Conway, D Eilon, L P Kelly, S Messias, G Palos, J L Rubenstein, D Schwarz
Languages: French, Greek, Hebrew
Work: B1 B2 C1 C2 C3 E F1 F2 G I J1 K3 L N O Q R2 S1 S2 U1 U2 W Z(c,e,f,i,k,l,p,q,za)
Legal Aid undertaken
Ptr: Bernstein, Mr Steven LLB. . . . . *Oct 1990
Conway, Mr Andrew Jonathan LLB(Hons) . . . . . . *Dec 1995
Eilon, Dr Daniel MA; PhD(Cantab). . . . . Sep 1992
Kelly, Mr Lawrence P LLB. . . . . *Oct 1990
Messias, Mr Stephen BSc. . . . . *Aug 1989
Palos, Mr Gregorios LLB(Hons) . . . . *Oct 1988
Rubenstein, Mr Jeffrey L LLB . . . . *Oct 1988
Schwarz, Mr Danny BA; PGDipLaw; PGDipLP. . . . . Jan 1997
Asoc: Constant, Mr George Christos LLB . . . . Sep 2004
Con: Kosky, Mr David MA(Oxon) . . . . *Jun 1973
Lindemann, Ms Jayne. . . . . Nov 1994
Park, Mr Andrew W D BA . . . . *Jun 1985
Seal, Mr David S BA(Manc). . . . . *Jan 1982
Wright, Ms Anne Elizabeth LLB; MSc Petit Law Prize *Feb 1983

STEPHENSON HARWOOD ‡
(in association with Colin Ng & Partners)
1 Finsbury Circus London EC2M 7SH
Tel: 020 7329 4422 *Fax:* 020 7329 7100
Dx: 64 LONDON/CHANCERY LN
E-mail: info@shlegal.com
List of partners: T Addis-Jones, J Atkinson, M R H Baily, R R Baker, A S Beadnall, A S Bercow, R H Blower, K L Bonavia, N V Bowen-Morris, C F N Brearley, M W S Brooks, G G Burns, G P Campbell, W L W Cawley, J M Clegg, P W U Corbett, J H Cottrell, R J Cowper, D M Cuckson, K J Dean, I Devereux, A C Dourish, K W Duncan, J Enstone, S C Fellows, P J M Fidler, E Field, S C P Fitzgerald, T D Flanagan, I M Fletcher, R A J Foord, J M Fordham, J E Forrester, M C Foster, S Gadhia, J S Gale, P S G Ghirardani, S Gibbons, N C Gibson, B J Glicksman, P D Gordon-Saker, M J Green, R Gwynne, R M J Haldane, M Haniff, D R L Harris, A N Hart, S E Heard, J Higham, M H Hoddinott, G H Hodgkinson, P N Howick, B S Jeeps, H W Jenney, M F Jennings, A H M Johnson, A Johnstone, I Kaiser, A J Keates, M B Kemp, S D Koehne, S Laud, G Le Fleming Shepherd, B Leach, R A Light, C J Mackenzie-Grieve, A S R Mair, S N Mannering, D E J McDonald, J Morgan, R J Newman, N Noble, C Perez, D N Phillips, J G Pike, N H Porter, Z Ramprakash, M S Reed, D Relf, S Roberts, J Robertson, S Robertson, F J Rodriguez Marin, M A Russell, W A Saunders, J A Scales, A Sidey, N R Simmonds, R J Slade, A H Stockwell, M D Stockwood, S H Sumpton, A L Sutch, S R Tatham, S J Wait, J G M Walsh, J P Ward, S White, A J J Woodcock, J S Woodward, I Young
Languages: Dutch, French, German, Hungarian, Italian, Mandarin, Norwegian, Romanian, Russian, Spanish, Vietnamese
Work: A1 A3 B1 C1 C2 C3 E L M1 O P R1 T1 Z(a,b,c,h,i,j,s)
Ptr: Addis-Jones, Mr Timothy LLB(Hons) . . . . Aug 1993
Atkinson, Joachim BA. . . . . *Mar 1988
Baily, Mr Mark R H MA(Oxon). . . . . *Jan 1966
Baker, Mr Rodney R BA; LLM(Cantab) . . . . *Oct 1988
Beadnall, Mr A Stuart LLB(Lond) . . . . *Oct 1984
Bercow, Mr Alan S BA . . . . *Oct 1983
Blower, Mr Robert H LLB; MA. . . . . *Dec 1991
Bonavia, Mr Kenneth L LLB(Lond). . . . . *Nov 1982
Bowen-Morris, Mr Nigel V. . . . . Nov 1988
Brearley, Ms Catherine F N LLB. . . . . May 1989
Brooks, Mr Michael W S LLB; FCIArb . . . . *Oct 1981
Burns, Mr Graham G BA(Dunelm). . . . . *Oct 1983
Campbell, Mr Gary P LLB; LLM . . . . Mar 1996
Cawley, Mr William L W LLB. . . . . *Feb 1988
Clegg, Ms Julie M. . . . . Nov 1994
Corbett, Mr P William U MA(Cantab) . . . . *Jun 1979
Cottrell, Ms Jenny H BA(Cantab) . . . . *Oct 1987
Cowper, Mr Roderick J MA(Cantab) TSB Articled Clerk Award . . . . *Sep 1984
Cuckson, Mr David M MA(Cantab) . . . . *Oct 1978
Dean, Mr Kevin J BA(Oxon). . . . . Apr 1979
Devereux, Mr Ian . . . . *Nov 1981
Dourish, Ms Arlene Carol LLB. . . . . *Jan 1991
Duncan, Mr Kenneth W MA(Cantab) . . . . *§Apr 1971
Enstone, Mr John BA(Hons); MA; LLB. . . . . *Jul 1988
Fellows, Miss Sian C LLB. . . . . *Oct 1985
Fidler, Mr Peter J M MA(Oxon) John Mackrell Prize; Daniel Reardon Prize; Cecil Karuth Prize. . . . . *Jun 1967
Field, Ms Elizabeth MA(Cantab). . . . . Apr 1989
Fitzgerald, Mr Sean Carmel Patrick BA(Hons)(Oxon) . May 1993
Flanagan, Mr Thomas D LLB(Hons)(Lond) . . . . . . *Dec 1979
Fletcher, Mr Ian M LLB; LTCL; LRAM; ARCO; WS Notary Public . . . . *Jul 1978
Foord, Mr Roland A J LLB(Lond) . . . . *May 1985
Fordham, Mr John M MA(Cantab). . . . . *Oct 1974
Forrester, Mr John E LLB . . . . Nov 1989
Foster, Mr M Charles MA(Cantab). . . . . Jun 1972
Gadhia, Mr Sunil LLB(Nott'm) . . . . *Sep 1990
Gale, Mr John S MA(Cantab) . . . . *Oct 1982
Ghirardani, Mr Paolo S G BA(Cardiff) . . . . Nov 1985
Gibbons, Mr Sean BA(Cantab) . . . . *Oct 1992
Gibson, Mr Neill C LLB(Hons). . . . . Jan 1990
Glicksman, Mr Bernard J MA(Cantab). . . . . *§Jun 1976
Gordon-Saker, Mr Paul D Licensed Insolvency Practitioner Notary Public . . . . *§Jun 1970
Green, Mr Martin Jon BA . . . . *Nov 1992
Gwynne, Mr Richard MA(Cantab) . . . . *Oct 1979
Haldane, Mr Robert M J. . . . . *§Jul 1986
Haniff, Mr Marcel MA(Oxon). . . . . *Apr 1984
Harris, Mr David Roland Law . . . . *Nov 1971
Hart, Mr Andrew N LLB . . . . *Apr 1987
Heard, Miss Sian E LLB. . . . . *Nov 1987
Higham, Mr John . . . . Jul 1999
Hoddinott, Mr Michael H LLB(Lond) . . . . *Sep 1970
Hodgkinson, Mr George H MA(Oxon) . . . . *§Jan 1970
Howick, Mr Paul N BA(Hull). . . . . May 1982
Jeeps, Mr Barry S BA(Oxon) . . . . *Nov 1982
Jenney, Mr Hugo W LLB(Hons) . . . . *Sep 1990
Jennings, Mr Michael F . . . . *§Mar 1969
Johnson, Mr Angus H M MA(Cantab) . . . . Nov 1989
Johnstone, Mr Andrew BA; LLB . . . . *Jun 1991
Kaiser, Mr Ingolf BA(Oxon) . . . . *Sep 1993

See p2 for the Key to Work Categories & other symbols

Keates, Mr Andrew J LLB . . . *Jun 1979
Kemp, Mr Malcolm B . . . *Apr 1980
Koehne, Mr Stephen D LLB(Bris) . . . *Jun 1971
Laud, Mr Stephen LLB(Hons)(Manc) . . . *May 1995
Le Fleming Shepherd, Mr Gavin MA(Cantab) . . . §Apr 1975
Leach, Mr Ben LLB . . . *§Oct 1971
Light, Mr Richard A MA(Cantab) . . . *Apr 1977
McDonald, Mr Duncan E J MA(Phil) . . . *Oct 1981
Mackenzie-Grieve, Mr Colin J MA(Cantab) . . . *Nov 1975
Mair, Mr Antony S R MA(Oxon) . . . *Aug 1976
Mannering, Mr Stuart N LLB . . . *Dec 1980
Morgan, Mr Jeff MA(Cantab) . . . Oct 1980
Newman, Mr Robert J MA . . . *Oct 1984
Noble, Mr Neil LLB(Leics) . . . *Oct 1989
Perez, Mr Carlos . . . Nov 1988
Phillips, Mr D Nicholas . . . *Nov 1977
Pike, Mr John G LLB(Lond) . . . *Dec 1978
Porter, Mr Nigel H LLB . . . Nov 1990
Ramprakash, Ms Zara BA(Hons); CPE; LSF . . . Nov 1992
Reed, Mr Mark S BA(Oxon) . . . *May 1981
Relf, Mr David LLB . . . Apr 1977
Roberts, Mr Stephen BA(Hons)(Bris); CPE; LSF(Hons)*Nov 1991
Robertson, Mr James . . . Nov 1992
Robertson, Struan . . . *Mar 1968
Rodriguez Marin, Mr Fernando Jose LLM(USA) . . . Sep 1988
Russell, Mr Mark A BA . . . *Oct 1983
Saunders, Mr William A LLB; Diplome de Droit Francais Oct 1994
Scales, Mr J Anthony BA(Oxon) . . . *Jan 1968
Sidey, Ms Alison LLB . . . Jun 1992
Simmonds, Mr Neil R LLB(Hons) . . . Dec 1990
Slade, Mr Robin J MA; LLM . . . *Sep 1974
Stockwell, Mr Anthony H BA(Cantab) Daniel Reardon Prize . . . *Apr 1974
Stockwood, Mr Michael D BA(Cantab) . . . *Oct 1981
Sumption, Mr Stephen Harry LLB(Lond) . . . *Nov 1992
Sutch, Mr Andrew L MA(Oxon) . . . *§Oct 1979
Tatham, Mr Simon Ralph LLB . . . *Oct 1980
Wait, Mr Steven J BA(Hons) . . . *Oct 1984
Walsh, Mr Jonathan G M . . . *Apr 1969
Ward, Mr Jonathon P BA . . . Aug 1992
White, Ms Sharon LLB . . . *Dec 1986
Woodcock, Mr Anthony J J LLB; LLM . . . *Dec 1989
Woodward, Ms Jen S LLB; MA . . . *Apr 1987
Young, Mr Iain LLB . . . Nov 1991
Ast: Abbott, Mr James Stuart Alexander BA(Hons) . . . *Apr 1996
Arscott, Mr Jeremy P . . . Dec 1993
Concagh, Mr Anthony N LLB . . . Dec 1992
Wilson, Mr Hugh A BA(Lond) . . . *§Apr 1975
Winterton, Mr Alexander D LLB(Hons); LLM . . . *Oct 1999
Wright, Mrs Caroline LLB . . . *Aug 1980
Con: Williams, Mr Harvey G . . . §Dec 1970
Wilson, Mr Michael J F T MA(Oxon) . . . *Dec 1961

STEPIEN LAKE ‡
57 Queen Anne Street London W1G 9JR
Tel: 020 7467 3030 *Fax:* 020 7467 3040 *Dx:* 44610 MAYFAIR
E-mail: enquiry@stepienlake.co.uk
List of partners: T M D Lake, K J Stepien, M W Thomas
Work: E R1 S1
Ptr: Lake, Mr Timothy Michael David LLB . . . Dec 1980
Stepien, Mr Kazimierz Jozef MA(Oxon) . . . *Apr 1975
Thomas, Mr Mark William BA . . . *Feb 1988

STEPTOE & JOHNSON ‡
99 Gresham Street London EC2V 7NG
Tel: 020 7367 8000 *Fax:* 020 7367 8001
Dx: 206 LONDON/CHANCERY LN
Emergency telephone 020 7367 8000
E-mail: london@steptoe.com
List of partners: A C Bloom, M Farmer, C Gibson, M Gordon-Russell, A Greaves, I C Macvay, R Nwakodo, B Patterson, F Rao, M D Shenk, M C Thompson, A M Wallace
Languages: Cantonese, French, Hebrew, Hokkien, Igbo, Malay, Mandarin, Norwegian, Russian, Spanish, Yoruba
Work: A3 B1 B2 C1 C2 C3 E F1 I J1 J2 L M1 M2 O P Q R1 R2 S1 S2 T1 U1 U2 Z(b,c,e,i,j,k,o,p,q,w)
Emergency Action, Agency and Advocacy undertaken
Ptr: Bloom, Mr Andrew C LLB(Hons); LPC . . . *Sep 1996
Farmer, Mr Matthew LLB(Bris) . . . *Apr 1996
Gibson, Mr Christopher JD; MPP; BA . . . Jul 2001
Gordon-Russell, Mr Martin BA(Nott'm) . . . *§Feb 1980
Greaves, Mr Adam LLB . . . Nov 1986
Macvay, Mr Iain Clouston LLM . . . *Aug 2001
Nwakodo, Mr Rex . . . Aug 1995
Patterson, Mr Brendan LLB(Cardiff) . . . *Jun 1981
Rao, Miss Farzana LLB(Wales) . . . *Oct 1991
Shenk, Mr Maury David . . . Dec 1992
Thompson, Mr Michael C LLB(Soton); LLM(LSE) . . . *Feb 1989
Wallace, Ms Alison M BA . . . *Apr 1977

ELLIOTT STERN SOLICITORS ‡
Imperial House 64 Willoughby Lane Tottenham London N17 0SP
Tel: 020 8801 0444 *Fax:* 020 8801 0555
E-mail: es@elliottsternsols.co.uk

VIVIEN STERN SOLICITOR ‡
30 Goldhurst Terrace Camden London NW6 3HU
Tel: 020 7328 5532 *Fax:* 020 7328 5532
E-mail: vivien.stern@gmail.com
List of partners: V C Stern
Work: S1 W
SPr: Stern, Miss Vivien C LLB(Hons) . . . *Oct 1982

STERNBERG REED
Suite 2 152-156 Kentish Town Road London NW1 9QB
Tel: 020 7485 5558 *Fax:* 020 7485 5556
E-mail: enquiries@sternberg-reed.co.uk
Office: Barking, Grays, Romford
Ptr: Carr, Mr Kenneth LLB(Lond) ★ . . . *Jun 1979
Taube, Mr Martin Q N BA . . . *Sep 1989
Ast: Brookes, Ms Karen Lindsey . . . *Dec 1998

G T STEWART SOLICITORS ‡
28 Grove Vale East Dulwich London SE22 8EF
Tel: 020 8299 6000 *Fax:* 020 8299 6009 *Dx:* 32160 EAST DULWICH
Emergency telephone 020 8299 6000
E-mail: info@gtstewart.co.uk
List of partners: G T Stewart
Languages: Cantonese
Work: B2 G H J2 K1 L Z(g,h)
Agency, Advocacy, Fixed Fee Interview, Legal Aid undertaken and Legal Aid Franchise
SPr: Stewart, Mr Gregory T LLB(Hons) ★ . . . *Apr 1993

Ast: Arnsby, Mr Mike . . . *Jun 1981
Boyle, Ms Julie Ann . . . Dec 2003
Cheema, Ms Harminder LLB . . . *Aug 1998
Fazal, Miss Shabana LLB; LLM . . . *Jul 2008
Foong, Mr James LLB . . . *Sep 2008
Krudy, Ms Melanie CPE; LPC ★ . . . *Jul 1998
Longley, Mr Sean LLB . . . *Oct 1997
McParland, Ms Dervla LLB . . . Jul 2009
Manek, Mr Ronnie LLB . . . *Nov 2004
Matheson, Miss Nadine LLB . . . *Apr 2006
Matthew, Mr Paul LLB . . . *Oct 2008
Roberts, Lynn . . . Apr 2007
Russell, Mr William LLB . . . *Aug 2008
Smith, Sophie . . . Aug 2004
Stephens, Ms Sara LLB . . . Mar 2009
Yau, Mr Ricky LLM; BA . . . *Oct 2001

STEWARTS LAW LLP ‡
5 New Street Square London EC4A 3BF
Tel: 020 7822 8000 *Fax:* 020 7822 8080
Dx: 369 LONDON/CHANCERY LN
E-mail: info@stewartslaw.com
List of partners: G Brahams, P D Brehony, J D Cahill, J C Chamberlayne, D J Chism, J M Colston, S H Dench, A Dinsmore, R Dransfield, C R Edwards, S G Foster, F C Gillett, K B Grealis, E Hatley, J S Healy-Pratt, D J Herman, R M Hogwood, A N Knowles, M L P Lyons, P A Paxton, F R Pinch, S D Preston, L Robinson, B T Rogers, C L Salmon, A W Shaw, J Sinclair, T A Spillane, F J Stewart, S F M Stewart, P Stringer, K G M Thomas, B H Townsend, D Turnbull, S N Upson, C H Zietman
Office: Leeds
Languages: Croatian, French, Italian, Russian, Spanish
Work: A3 B2 C3 J1 K1 K2 K3 M1 M2 M3 N O Q Z(b,j,p,q,r)
Legal Aid undertaken, Legal Aid Franchise and Member of Accident Line
Ptr: Brahams, Mr Gareth LLB(Hons) . . . *Nov 1995
Brehony, Mr Paul Dominic BA(Hons) . . . *Oct 1993
Cahill, Mr John D LLB; ACIArb . . . *Feb 1985
Chamberlayne, Mr Julian C LLB Treasurer of FOCIS . *Nov 1994
Chism, Ms Debbie J BA(Oxon) . . . *Oct 1993
Colston, Jane Margaret LLB . . . *Nov 1991
Dench, Mr Stuart Henry BA(Hons) . . . *Nov 1996
Dinsmore, Mr Andrew BA(Hons) . . . *Nov 1996
Dransfield, Mr Robert . . . *Apr 1999
Edwards, Mr Charles R BA(Hons); LLM; LPC . . . *Sep 1997
Foster, Mr Stephen George BA(Wales) . . . *Jan 1987
Gillett, Fiona Catherine . . . *Sep 2000
Grealis, Mr Kevin B LLB . . . *§Oct 1989
Hatley, Ms Emma MA(Hons) . . . *Oct 1996
Healy-Pratt, Mr James Simon BA(Hons); LLM; MRAeS *Apr 2006
Hogwood, Mr Richard Mark BA(Hons)(Geography); PGDL . . . *Oct 2001
Knowles, Mr Anthony N LLB(Hons) . . . *Oct 1979
Lyons, Mr Muiris Laurence Paul LLM Immediate Past President of Association of Personal Injury Lawyers (APIL) . *Oct 1991
Paxton, Mr Paul Anthony BSc(Hons) . . . *Oct 1997
Robinson, Mrs Lucy LLB . . . *Oct 2000
Rogers, Mr Benjamin Thomas LLB; LPC . . . *Aug 1999
Salmon, Miss Clare Louise LLB; LPC Alasdair Benzie Business Law Prize . . . *Sep 2002
Shaw, Mr Andrew W LLB . . . *Jun 1981
Spillane, Mr Timothy Alban . . . *Sep 2003
Stewart, Fiona Jane BEC; LLB(Hons) . . . *Aug 1996
Stewart, Miss Sarah Frances Marie LLB(Hons); LPC . *Aug 1997
Thomas, Mr Keith Gordon Milbourne MEng(Electronic Communications Systems) . . . *Mar 1996
Turnbull, Mr Daniel . . . *Apr 2008
Upson, Mr Sean Norman LLB(Hons) . . . *Nov 1995
Zietman, Mr Clive H LLB(Manc) Manchester University Industrial Law Prize 1982 . . . *Nov 1985
Asoc: Berry, Mrs Francesca BA(Bris)(Economic & Social History); PGDipLaw; LPC . . . *Dec 2006
Forster, Miss Inge Lucy BA(Hons)(Eng Lit & History of Art); PGDipLaw; LPC . . . *Sep 2007
Fosler, Mrs Nichola LLB(Hons) . . . *Sep 1996
Goodyer, Miss Megan Claire . . . *May 2005
Humphries, Mr Matthew Paul . . . *Oct 1998
Hutchinson, Miss Karen Laura LLB(Law & Business); LPC . . . *Sep 2007
Jones, Mrs Antonia BA; MA . . . *Aug 1998
Jones, Mr Marc . . . *Apr 1999
Loblowitz, Mr Daniel Siegmund Henry BA; PGDipLaw; PGDipLP . . . *Jan 2004
Longworth, Mr Sam BA(Hons) . . . *Aug 2003
Neenan, Mr Peter Kristian MSci(Theoretical Physics); GDL; LPC . . . *Aug 2009
Rigby, Mr Scott Charlton LLB(Hons) . . . *Nov 2003
Tardivat, Mr Charles-Henri BSEng; MS; JD Clerk for the NTSB Judges . . . *Jun 2009
Wiseman, Miss Anna Caroline LLB . . . *Sep 2002
Ast: Applegate, Mrs Carla LLB . . . *Oct 2009
Badrick, Miss Ruth LLB . . . Sep 2008
Bailes, Mrs Elaina Mary BA(Hons)(Oxon); GDL; LPC . *Mar 2010
Benzeval, Mr Andrew James LLB(Hons) . . . *Oct 2009
de Villiers, Mr Paul Simon BA; LLB . . . *Aug 2008
Erusalimsky, Mr Adam BSc(Hons); ARCS; MLitt; PGDipLaw . . . *Apr 2010
Fernandez Moreno, Ms Julia . . . *Apr 2006
Fielding, Amy Leanne BA(Hons)(Nursing) . . . *Jul 2007
French, Mr Alistair . . . *Sep 2005
Green, Mr Daniel BA(Law & Sociology); LPC . . . *Oct 2004
Heath, Miss Amy LLB(Hons) . . . *Nov 2006
Hogg, Miss Nicola Jane LLB . . . *Oct 2010
Incles, Mr Grant Christopher LLB(Hons) Secretary for North West London Headway Support Group . . . *Apr 2004
Jenkins, Ms Laura LLB . . . *Oct 2010
Johnson, Mr Hugh Michael LLB . . . *Sep 2005
Kinch, Mrs Carly LLB . . . *May 2009
Krishnan, Miss Anjali LLB; LPC . . . *Sep 2005
Mackay, Mrs Emma Perdita BA(Hons)(French); GDL; LPC . . . *Dec 2008
Mawi, Ms Gaggandeep Kaur LLB . . . *Nov 2007
Oliver, Victoria Jean LLB . . . *Dec 2006
Receveur, Miss Kerie Yvonne Mary . . . *Apr 2001
Redgrave, Mr Peregrine Carlyle LLB(Hons) . . . *Feb 1998
Rickenberg, Miss Catherine Jane BA(Hons)(History); CPE ♦ . . . *Sep 2007
Smith, Mrs Kara BSc(Applied Sciences)(Criminology) . *Mar 2008
Sullivan, Miss Lauren LLB . . . *Sep 2010
Turnbull, Mr Craig Stephen LLB Sir Samuel Evans Prize (2003); Calcott Pryce Awards for Company Law, Commercial Law, Intellectual Property Law . . . *Sep 2006
Ward, Mrs Lucy Nicola MA(Hons)(Hist); GDL; LPC . . *Feb 2009

STIBBE ‡
Exchange House 12 Primrose Street London EC2A 2ST
Tel: 020 7466 6300 *Fax:* 020 7466 6311
E-mail: info@stibbe.co.uk

STILEMANS ‡
(incorporating Saville & Mannooch)
(in association with Meade & Co)
45 Chase Side Southgate London N14 5BP
Tel: 020 8882 1047 *Fax:* 020 8882 8623 *Dx:* 34300 SOUTHGATE
List of partners: G J Jones, A Pallikarou
Work: C1 E K4 L S1 S2 W
Ptr: Jones, Mr Geoffrey J . . . *§Jan 1969
Pallikarou, Miss Androulla BA . . . *§Jul 1983

FRANK STIMPSON & SON ‡
179 Stanstead Road London SE23 1HR
Tel: 020 8699 7644 *Fax:* 020 8291 4695
List of partners: K J Fender
Work: E S1 S2 W
Ptr: Fender, Mr Keith J . . . *Jun 1972

STITT & CO ‡
11 Gough Square London EC4A 3DE
Tel: 020 7832 0840 *Fax:* 020 7832 0841
Dx: 1052 LONDON/CHANCERY LN
E-mail: info@stitt.co.uk
List of partners: P H Crawford, I Fitzherbert, A B Jeffrey, D C Rogers, N J Winter
Languages: French, German
Work: C1 D1 E J1 K1 L N O Q R1 R2 S1 S2 T2 W X Z(d,h,k,p,r,w)
Emergency Action, Agency and Advocacy undertaken
Ptr: Crawford, Mr Peter Hamilton BA . . . *Jan 1978
Fitzherbert, Mr Ivan . . . *Feb 1986
Jeffrey, Mr Andrew Buchanan LLB(Hons) . . . *May 1993
Rogers, Mrs Denise Claudia LLB(Hons) . . . *Sep 1991
Winter, Mr Neil Jonathan . . . *Jan 1997
Ast: Fisher, Miss Sally Elizabeth BA . . . *Oct 1986
Philippou, Miss Alexia BA . . . Apr 2001

STOCKINGER ‡
Albert Buildings 49 Queen Victoria Street London EC4N 4SA
Tel: 020 7833 0448 *Fax:* 020 7833 0448
E-mail: stockinger@statutelaw.net
Work: B1 B2 C1 C2 C3 E I K1 M1 M2 M3 M4 O P R1 U2 Z(a,b,c,e,n,o,u)

STOCKLER BRUNTON ‡
(in association with Member Of International Law Firms (ILF))
2-3 Cursitor Street London EC4A 1NE
Tel: 020 7404 6661 *Fax:* 020 7404 6717
Dx: 445 LONDON/CHANCERY LN
E-mail: office@stockbrun.com
List of partners: J S Brenan, G H S Brunton, W T Stockler
Languages: French, German
Work: A3 B1 C1 E L M2 N Q R1 R2 S1 S2 T1 T2 Z(a,b,j,k,q)
Emergency Action, Agency and Advocacy undertaken
Ptr: Brenan, Mr James S LLB ♦ . . . *Oct 1983
Brunton, Mr Geoffrey H S BA ♦ . . . *Oct 1980
Stockler, Mr William T BA(Oxon) ♦ . . . *Jul 1969
Con: Holding-Parsons, Mr Beresford G C BA(Cantab) . . *§Jul 1981

STOKOE PARTNERSHIP ‡
646-648 High Road Leytonstone Waltham Forest London E11 3AA
Est: 1994
Tel: 020 8558 8884 *Fax:* 020 8539 9007 *Dx:* 58205 LEYTONSTONE
Emergency telephone 020 8558 8884
E-mail: enquiries@stokoepartnership.com
List of partners: J Babar, M Theodoulou, H Tsiattalou
Office: London WC2, Manchester
Languages: Greek, Italian
Work: B2 G H Z(g)
Emergency Action, Fixed Fee Interview, Legal Aid undertaken and Legal Aid Franchise
Ptr: Babar, Mr Jawad LLB(Hons) . . . *Mar 2000
Theodoulou, Miss Maria ★ . . . *Aug 1998
Tsiattalou, Haralambos ★ . . . *Sep 1994
Ast: Charalambous, Mr Constandino BA(Hons) . . . *May 2004
Jackson, Mr Stuart C BA(Hons)(Law) . . . *Dec 1987
Okebu, Mr Paul . . . Jun 2004
Parviez, Ms Shazia LLB(Hons) . . . Mar 2004
Pringle, Mr Keith H BA(Hons) . . . *Mar 2003

STOKOE PARTNERSHIP
Central Court 25 Southampton Buildings London WC2A 1AL
Tel: 020 3427 5710 *Fax:* 020 3427 5711
Dx: 167 LONDON/CHANCERY LN
E-mail: enquiries@stokoepartnership.com
Office: London E11, Manchester

STONE JOSEPH SOLICITORS ‡
Beta House 10 Ifield Road London SW10 9AA
Tel: 020 7854 9098 *Fax:* 020 7854 9375
E-mail: law@stonejoseph.com

STONE KING LLP
16 St John's Lane London EC1M 4BS
Tel: 020 7796 1007 *Fax:* 020 7796 1017
Office: Bath, Cambridge
Work: W X Z(d)
Ptr: Phillips, Mrs Ann . . . *Apr 1977

STONEHAGE LAW LIMITED ‡
56 Conduit Street London W1S 2YZ
Tel: 020 7087 0000 *Fax:* 020 7087 0001
E-mail: info@stonehage.com

STONES ‡
131 Baker Street London W1U 6SE
Tel: 020 7935 4848
E-mail: info@stonessolicitors.co.uk
Work: C1
Con: Evans, Mr Glenn Colin LLB(Hons) . . . *Jun 1982
Hass, Mr Frederick LLB . . . *§Mar 1956
Timms, Mr Howard LLB(Hons) . . . Mar 1998

STORK & COLES ‡
40 Great James Street London WC1N 3HB
Tel: 020 7404 6021 *Fax:* 020 7831 6115
E-mail: storkcoles@btconnect.com
List of partners: B G S Coles, P D Stork
Work: B1 C1 C2 C3 E J1 O Q R2 S1 S2 Z(c,d,e,q)
Agency undertaken
Ptr: Coles, Mr Bruce G S BSc(Bris) . . . . *Jun 1972
Stork, Mr Peter D . . . . *§Jan 1972

A M STRACHAN & CO ‡
67 Falkirk Street Hackney London N1 6SD
Tel: 020 7729 0003 *Fax:* 020 7739 8416
Emergency telephone 07770 416425
E-mail: office@amstrachan.co.uk
List of partners: A M Strachan
Work: G H L N Q Z(l)
Emergency Action, Legal Aid undertaken and Legal Aid Franchise
SPr: Strachan, Mr Alisdair McGregor LLB(Lond) . . . . . *Dec 1973

STRAFFORD LAW LIMITED ‡
Georgian House 63 Coleman Street London EC2R 5BB
Tel: 020 7628 7975 *Fax:* 020 7756 9939
E-mail: info@straffordlaw.co.uk

STRAIN KEVILLE ‡
34 Newman Street Westminster London W1T 1PZ
Tel: 020 7323 5000 *Fax:* 020 7636 0111
E-mail: andrewstrain@strainkeville.co.uk
List of partners: A J Strain
Work: C1 E J1 K1 L S1 S2 W
SPr: Strain, Mr Andrew John . . . . *Sep 1974

STRAND SOLICITORS ‡
3rd Floor 218 Strand London WC2R 1AT
Tel: 020 3393 3009 *Fax:* 020 7583 9521
Dx: 232 LONDON/CHANCERY LN
E-mail: info@strandsolicitors.co.uk
Office: London W4

STRAND SOLICITORS
Building 3 Chiswick Park 566 Chiswick High Road London W4 5YA
Tel: 020 3393 3009 *Fax:* 020 8899 6001
E-mail: info@strandsolicitors.co.uk
Office: London WC2

STRASONS ‡
260 Mitcham Lane Streatham London SW16 6NU
Tel: 020 8677 7534 *Fax:* 020 8677 0679
E-mail: strasons@gmail.com
List of partners: M R Casoojee
Ptr: Casoojee, Mr Mohamed Raffick LLB . . . . *Dec 1987

STRATEM LAW ‡
44 Paxton Road London W4 2QX
Tel: 07816 440692
E-mail: info@stratemlaw.com

STREATHERS CLAPHAM LLP
53 Clapham High Street Clapham London SW4 7TH
Tel: 020 7622 7257 *Fax:* 020 7627 5223
E-mail: ssmith@streathers.co.uk
Office: London N6, London W1

STREATHERS HIGHGATE LLP
Tuscan Studios 14 Muswell Hill Road Highgate London N6 5UG
Tel: 020 3074 1900 *Fax:* 020 3074 1904
E-mail: ssmith@streathers.co.uk
Office: London SW4, London W1

STREATHERS SOLICITORS LLP ‡
(in association with Walters)
128 Wigmore Street London W1U 3SA
Tel: 020 7034 4200 *Fax:* 020 7034 4301 *Dx:* 9050 WEST END
E-mail: mail@streathers.co.uk
List of partners: D P Landi, J T Lankshear, M R Lindley, Z M Reynolds, M C Silverman, B G Streather, N J Taffs
Office: London N6, London SW4
Languages: French, German
Work: A1 B1 C1 C2 C3 D1 E F1 J1 K1 L M1 M2 N O P Q R1 R2 S1 S2 T1 T2 V W Z(a,b,c,d,e,f,h,i,j,k,l,m,n,o,s,t,w)
Agency and Legal Aid undertaken
Ptr: Landi, Mr Damian P LLB . . . . *Sep 1989
Lankshear, Mr James Terence LLB . . . . *Sep 1993
Lindley, Mr Michael Robert LLB(Hons). . . . . *Nov 1994
Reynolds, Mr Zach M LLB. . . . . Oct 1998
Silverman, Mr Milton C LLB. . . . . *Oct 1980
Streather, Mr Bruce Godfrey MA(Oxon) . . . . *§Nov 1971
Taffs, Mr Nicholas J LLB . . . . *Feb 1988
Asoc: Low-Chew-Tung, Mr Christian LLB(Hons) . . . . . . *Mar 2001
Ast: Clibbon, Mr James Anthony BA(Hons); DipLaw . . . *Sep 1997
Danaher, Mr James LLB . . . . *May 2003
Martin, Ms Elizabeth BA; PGDip. . . . . *Feb 2007
Stone, Mr Nicholas Charles BA(Hons). . . . . Sep 2004
Van Der Meer, Mr Anthony William MA; BA(Hons); MABM; LLDip . . . . *Oct 2003
Con: Walters, Mrs Lorna N . . . . *Oct 1961

JOHN STREET SOLICITORS ‡
Ground Floor Haines House 21 John Street London WC1N 2BP
Tel: 020 7623 8822 *Fax:* 020 7623 8833 *Dx:* 37901 KINGS CROSS
E-mail: info@johnstreetsolicitors.com
List of partners: R R Mariaddan
Languages: Bengali, Cantonese, Hindi, Japanese, Korean, Mandarin, Tagalog, Tamil, Urdu
Work: C1 D1 E F2 J1 J2 K1 K3 L O Q R1 S1 S2 W X Z(f,q,y)
Emergency Action, Fixed Fee Interview and Legal Aid undertaken
Ptr: Mariaddan, Mr Raj Rajan . . . . Nov 1995

STRINGER SMITH & LEVETT ‡
239a Finchley Road London NW3 6JB
Tel: 020 7435 0436 *Fax:* 020 7431 3331
Dx: 38854 SWISS COTTAGE
List of partners: P W Levett, J H Smith
Work: E J1 K1 L N Q S1 W
Legal Aid undertaken and Member of Accident Line
Ptr: Levett, Mr Paul W. . . . . *Dec 1977

STRINGFELLOW & CO ‡
41 North End Road West Kensington London W14 8SZ
Tel: 020 7371 4040 *Fax:* 020 7371 3744
Dx: 42161 WEST KENSINGTON
E-mail: admin@stringfellowsolicitors.co.uk

STRUBE & CO ‡
15a Sydenham Road London SE26 5EX
Tel: 020 8659 3020 *Fax:* 020 8659 5020
E-mail: sales@strube.co.uk
List of partners: P J Strube
Languages: German
Work: E S1 W
Fixed Fee Interview undertaken
SPr: Strube, Mr Paul John LLB(Soton) . . . . *Nov 1984

STUNT PALMER & ROBINSON ‡
Equity House 450 Hackney Road London E2 6QL
Tel: 020 7739 6927 *Fax:* 020 7729 0716
List of partners: S E Marley
Work: E F1 K1 K2 L O Q S1 S2 V W
Agency, Advocacy and Legal Aid undertaken
Ptr: Marley, Mr Stuart E . . . . *Jan 1980
Ast: Hendry, Miss Margaret C BA . . . . Jan 1980

WILLIAM STURGES & CO ‡
Burwood House 14-16 Caxton Street Westminster London SW1H 0QY
Tel: 020 7873 1000 *Fax:* 020 7873 1010 *Dx:* 2315 VICTORIA
E-mail: law@williamsturges.co.uk
List of partners: S L M Breakwell, S M Collins, R J Dugdale, R M Edwards, M M Franks, N M Garland, I Gavin-Brown, J P Gray, J Hannon, F Hill, A Howe, M H Lawson, A M Levinson, G A L Meyrick, D J Morris, N D Phillips, J M Picken, R B C Prescott, R C W Rench, A H Todd, A K Tuthill, T A Walshe
Languages: French
Work: A1 A3 B1 C1 D1 D2 E F1 I J1 K1 K3 L N O Q R1 S1 S2 T2 W Z(b,d,l,m,n,q,r)
Emergency Action, Agency and Legal Aid Franchise
Ptr: Breakwell, Miss Sophie Louise Moy LLB . . . . Sep 2004
Collins, Ms Susan Mary LLB . . . . Feb 2001
Dugdale, Mr Richard J LLB(Hons)(L'pool) . . . . *Nov 1982
Edwards, Miss Ruth M LLB(Lond). . . . . *Jul 1978
Franks, Mr Michael Morris LLB Law Society Council Member . . . . *Mar 1978
Garland, Mr Neil Michael LLB(Hons) . . . . *Nov 2001
Gavin-Brown, Mr Ian . . . . *Apr 1966
Gray, Mr John Paul . . . . *§Jul 1967
Hannon, Mr James . . . . Oct 2002
Hill, Ms Fiona LLB(Hons) . . . . *Nov 1992
Howe, Mr Alan LLB(Hons). . . . . *Jul 1981
Lawson, Mr Michael Howard . . . . *Jan 1966
Levinson, Mr Alan Maurice . . . . *§Dec 1967
Meyrick, Mr Grant Anthony Lawford. . . . . *Jan 1966
Morris, Mr David J BSc(Lond). . . . . Jan 1969
Phillips, Mr Nicholas D BA(Hons) . . . . *Oct 1979
Picken, Mr Jonathon Michael LLB(Hons) . . . . Dec 1992
Prescott, Mr Robert B C Assistant Deputy Coroner . *§Nov 1967
Rench, Mr Richard C W. . . . . *Jul 1978
Todd, Mr Andrew H LLB(Lond) Deputy District Judge; Principal Registry of the Family Division . . . . *Apr 1976
Tuthill, Mr Anthony K MA(Cantab). . . . . *Apr 1973
Walshe, Mr Thomas Alan BA(Hons); LLM . . . . Jan 1986
Ast: Carlisle, Miss Jessica Anne BA(UCL) . . . . Apr 2007
Kilner, Mrs Mary Josephine LLB(Hons) . . . . *Jun 1976
Long, Miss Jessica Candlish BSc(Hons). . . . . Mar 2005
Mitchell-Innes, Mr Charles Duncan MTheol . . . . Jan 2003
Newton, Miss Christine . . . . Sep 1996
Smith, Miss Joanne Cecilia LLB. . . . . *Jan 1992

STURTIVANT & CO ‡
18 Bentinck Street London W1U 2JA
Tel: 020 7486 9524 *Fax:* 020 7224 3164
E-mail: visis@sturtivant.co.uk

SULLIVAN & CROMWELL ‡
1 New Fetter Lane London EC4A 1AN
Tel: 020 7959 8900 *Fax:* 020 7959 8950

SULLIVAN CONSULTING ‡
29a Lakeside Road London W14 0DX
Tel: 020 7603 1893 *Fax:* 020 7603 1893
E-mail: jes@sullutioms.demon.co.uk

SUMMERS ‡
22 Wellbeck Street London W1G 8EF
Tel: 020 7224 2024 *Fax:* 020 7224 2028 *Dx:* 82961 MAYFAIR
E-mail: jms@summerssolicitors.co.uk
Work: C1 E J1 O Q R2 S1 S2 Z(i,q)

SUMMIT LAW LLP ‡
1 Bentinck Street London W1U 2ED
Tel: 020 7467 3980 *Fax:* 020 7467 3990
Dx: 42706 OXFORD CIRCUS NORTH
E-mail: info@summitlawllp.co.uk

SUNRISE SOLICITORS LIMITED ‡
206 Merton High Street South Wimbledon London SW19 1AX
Tel: 020 8543 0999 *Fax:* 020 8543 0900
E-mail: info@sunrisesolicitors.co.uk

SURIYA & CO ‡
277 Whitechapel Road Tower Hamlets London E1 1BY
Tel: 020 7247 0444

SURIYA & CO ‡
1081 Garratt Lane London SW17 0LN
Tel: 020 8682 1131 *Fax:* 020 8682 3104
E-mail: zasslaw@hotmail.com

SUTOVIC & HARTIGAN ‡
271 High Street Acton London W3 9BT
Tel: 020 8993 5544 *Fax:* 020 8993 2555
E-mail: jstojs6483@aol.com
List of partners: J S Savic, S Sutovic
Languages: French, Polish, Serbo-Croat
Work: Z(g,i)
Ptr: Savic, Ms J Stojsavljevic . . . . *Mar 2000
Sutovic, Snezana . . . . *May 1994
Ast: Bobb, Mr Terence. . . . . *Sep 2008
Kennedy, Ms Nicola. . . . . *Sep 2006
Nettleship, Mr Paul . . . . *May 2004

SUTTON-MATTOCKS & CO LLP ‡
1 Rocks Lane Barnes London SW13 0DE
Tel: 020 8876 8811 *Fax:* 020 8878 4425 *Dx:* 59701 BARNES
Emergency telephone 07774 259528
E-mail: enquiries@suttonmattocks.co.uk
List of partners: M P F Flexman, C M Mitchell, A J Sutton-Mattocks, G Tyndall, J P J Walsh
Office: London W4
Work: C1 E L S1 S2 T1 W Z(q)
Fixed Fee Interview undertaken
Ptr: Flexman, Mr Matthew Paul Franz LLB(Hons) . . . . *Nov 1994
Sutton-Mattocks, Miss Alison Jane BA . . . . *Jun 1977
Tyndall, Miss Gillian BA(Law) . . . . *Oct 1987
Walsh, Mr Jonathan Patrick James LLB . . . . *Jun 1988
Con: Cheshire, Mr Timothy . . . . *Jan 1974
Goddard, Mrs Susan Elizabeth BA(Dunelm). . . . . . Apr 1981

SUTTON-MATTOCKS & CO LLP
152 Chiswick High Road London W4 1PT
Tel: 020 8994 7344 *Fax:* 020 8995 6409 *Dx:* 80302 CHISWICK
E-mail: enquiries@suttonmattocks.co.uk
Office: London SW13
Work: S1 S2 W
Ptr: Mitchell, Mrs Catherine M BA . . . . *Jun 1979
Asoc: Bloom, Miss Naomi Sara BA; GDL . . . . *Jan 2009
Young, Mr Edward . . . . Nov 2004
Ast: Dean, Mr John Laurence Francis . . . . Oct 1997
Miller, Mrs Elizabeth Alison . . . . Jan 1970

SUTTONS ‡
15 Thayer Street London W1U 3JX
Tel: 020 7935 5279 *Fax:* 020 7486 4426
E-mail: sd.sutton@btinternet.com
List of partners: S D Sutton
Work: A3 E J1 M2 O Q S2 W Z(f,k,q,w)
Agency undertaken
SPr: Sutton, Mr Stephen D BA; LLM(Cantab). . . . . . . *Nov 1988
Ast: Nugent, Ms Grace LLB(Hons) . . . . *May 2011
Con: Grace, Ms Caroline . . . . *Nov 1979
Harris, Mr Brian B. . . . . *Jul 1971
Salter, Mr Howard Anthony BA . . . . *Oct 1968

SVEDBERG LAW ‡
125 Sloane Street London SW1X 9AU
Tel: 020 7368 7000 *Fax:* 020 7351 6896 *Dx:* 35104 CHELSEA
E-mail: mail@svedberglaw.com
List of partners: Y Khan, A V Svedberg
Languages: Punjabi, Urdu
Work: C1 E F1 J1 L P S1 S2 W Z(b,e)
Ptr: Khan, Miss Yasmin LLM. . . . . *Oct 2004
Svedberg, Mrs Annabelle V LLB. . . . . *Jun 1975

SVETLOVA LLP ‡
11-12 St James Square London SW1Y 4LB
Tel: 020 7117 6444
E-mail: contact@svetlovallp.com

SWABEY & CO ‡
410 Riverbank House 1 Putney Bridge Approach London SW6 3JD
Tel: 020 7731 7777 *Fax:* 020 7731 7770
E-mail: swabey.co@btconnect.com
Languages: Polish
Work: E F1 L O Q S1 S2

SWAIN & CO ‡
Deptford Reach Speedwell Street London SE8 4AT
Tel: 0800 021 3272 / 020 8692 9100 *Fax:* 020 8692 9102
Dx: 56711 DEPTFORD
E-mail: mail@swainandco.com

SWAN TURTON ‡
68a Neal Street London WC2H 9PA
Tel: 020 7520 9555 *Fax:* 020 7520 9556
E-mail: info@swanturton.com

SWEETMAN BURKE & SINKER ‡
158-160 Broadway West Ealing Ealing London W13 0TL
Tel: 020 8840 2572 *Fax:* 020 8567 8379 *Dx:* 5155 EALING
Emergency telephone 020 8840 2572
E-mail: info@sbs-law.co.uk
List of partners: J P Koffman, G Lizra, S Sinker, P D Sweetman
Languages: French, Punjabi, Urdu
Work: B2 D1 G H K1 K3 L N O Q S1 S2 W
Emergency Action, Agency, Legal Aid undertaken and Legal Aid Franchise
Ptr: Koffman, Mr Jonathan Paul BA(Hons)(Humanities) . . *Nov 1997
Lizra, Ms Gillie LLB(Hons). . . . . *Jul 1990
Sinker, Ms Sara-Jane BA . . . . *Oct 1982
Sweetman, Mr Peter D BA Karuth & Norden Prize. . *Jan 1987
Ast: Brar, Mr Tajinder Singh LLB(Hons) . . . . Sep 2004
Patel, Miss Amisha BA(Hons). . . . . *Apr 2006

SWINNERTON MOORE SOLICITORS ‡
3rd Floor Cannongate House 62-64 Cannon Street London EC4N 6AE
Tel: 020 7236 7111 *Fax:* 020 7236 1222
E-mail: info@swinmoore.com
List of partners: A L Moore, A R Swinnerton
Languages: Farsi, French, Greek, Spanish, Turkish
Work: C1 E L O Q R2 S1 S2 Z(a,j)
Agency and Advocacy undertaken
Ptr: Moore, Mr Arthur Lewis BSc(Econ) . . . . *Jun 1976
Swinnerton, Mr Anthony R BSc . . . . *Mar 1973
Ast: Christou, Mr Christopher . . . . *Apr 1998
Theophani, Fano . . . . *Nov 2001
Con: Poynter, Mr Adam Christopher . . . . *Dec 1970

See p2 for the Key to Work Categories & other symbols

SYKES ANDERSON LLP ‡
9 Devonshire Square London EC2M 4YF
Tel: 020 3178 3770 *Fax:* 020 3178 3771 *Dx:* 729 LONDON/CITY
E-mail: solicitors@sykesanderson.com
List of partners: D Anderson, A Massenhove, C Smith, C J Sykes, D Weinstock
Languages: French, Spanish
Work: C1 C2 E J1 O Q R1 R2 S1 S2 T1 T2 W Z(i,p)
Emergency Action, Agency and Advocacy undertaken
Ptr: Anderson, Mr David MA; (South African Attorney) . . . *Oct 1985
Massenhove, Mr Alan LLB . . . Oct 1994
Sykes, Mr Christopher John BA . . . *Jan 1984
Weinstock, Ms Diane . . . *Nov 2004
Smith, Mrs Catherine . . . NSP
Ast: Gallop Mildon, Ms Nicole LLB(English & French); Maitrise en Droit . . . Apr 2010
Perry, Mr Graeme LLB(Law with French Law) . . . Sep 2009

SYLVESTER AMIEL LEWIN & HORNE LLP ‡
Pearl Assurance House 319 Ballards Lane London N12 8LY
Tel: 020 8446 4000 *Fax:* 020 8492 0123 *Dx:* 57384 FINCHLEY 1
E-mail: lawyers@sylvam.co.uk
List of partners: J H Horne, B C Lewin
Work: B1 C1 E F1 L O Q S1 S2 W Z(e,k)
Emergency Action and Agency undertaken
Ptr: Horne, Mr Jonathan Howard LLB . . . *Apr 1980
Lewin, Mr Bruce Colin . . . *Jun 1967

P B SYLVESTER & CO ‡
73 Mitcham Lane Wandsworth London SW16 6LY
Tel: 020 8769 6767 *Fax:* 020 8696 9901
E-mail: team@paulsylvester.com
List of partners: P B Sylvester
Work: B1 C1 D1 E F1 J1 K1 K3 L O Q R1 R2 S1 S2 T1 T2 W Z(c,k)
Ptr: Sylvester, Mr Paul Bernard . . . *May 1985

SYNERGY EMPLOYMENT LAW SOLICITORS ‡
The Podium Gainsborough Studios 1 Poole Street London N1 5EB
Tel: 020 7851 4411 *Fax:* 020 7033 4443
E-mail: info@synergyemploymentlaw.com

SYSTECH SOLICITORS ‡
Chapter House 18-20 Crucifix Lane London SE1 3JW
Tel: 020 7234 3520 *Fax:* 020 7234 3521
Office: Leeds, Liverpool, Manchester

TKD SOLICITORS ‡
124 Glenthorne Road Hammersmith & Fulham London W6 0LP
Tel: 020 8741 8050 *Fax:* 020 8741 8090
E-mail: mail@tkdsolicitors.com
Languages: Arabic, Bengali, Hebrew, Krio
Work: A3 C1 E J1 K1 K3 L M4 Q R1 S1 S2 W Z(i,l)
Emergency Action, Advocacy and Fixed Fee Interview undertaken

TLT SOLICITORS
20 Gresham Street London EC2V 7JE
Tel: 020 3465 4000 *Fax:* 020 3465 4001
Dx: 431 LONDON/CHANCERY LN
E-mail: generalenquiries@tltsolicitors.com
Office: Bristol
Ptr: Brewster, Mr Michael J . . . *Jun 1977
Burton, Mr Anthony J W . . . Dec 1974
Dickinson, Mr John W . . . *Mar 1975
Fincham, Ms Nicola A LLB(Bris) . . . *Apr 1983
Gordon, Mr Neil G BA . . . *Nov 1990
Harries, Mr Andre C D BA; LLB . . . *Apr 1972
Lafont De Sentenac, Mr Jerome . . . Jan 1994
Meakin, Mr Neil R LLB . . . *May 1986
Murray, Mr Andrew R BA . . . *Oct 1980
Newport, Mrs Annette M LLB . . . *Sep 1990
Reynolds, Mr Timothy J D LLB . . . Jun 1971
Taylorson, Mr Ian M BA . . . Feb 1976
Thomas, Mr Jeremy J . . . *Jul 1972
Willson, Mr Nigel S LLB(Lond) . . . Jun 1977
Wilson, Mr Richard T H MA(Oxon) . . . *Jun 1973
Ast: Blackett, Ms Leila BA . . . Jun 1999
Dhooper, Piara LLB . . . Oct 1998
Haydon, Ms Susan J BA(Hons) . . . Feb 1983
Con: De Mello Kamath, Mr A Roy P . . . Jul 1973

TMP SOLICITORS LLP ‡
29th Floor 1 Canada Square Canary Wharf London E14 5DY
Tel: 020 7712 1732 *Fax:* 020 7712 1522
E-mail: mail@tmpsol.com

TPP LAW LIMITED ‡
53 Great Suffolk Street London SE1 0DB
Tel: 020 7620 0888 *Fax:* 020 7620 0778
E-mail: info@tpplaw.co.uk

TTS SOLICITORS ‡
13c Hoe Street London E17 4SD
Tel: 020 8521 4686 *Fax:* 020 8521 9919 *Dx:* 32034 WALTHAMSTOW

TV EDWARDS LLP ‡
Park House 29 Mile End Road Tower Hamlets London E1 4TP
Tel: 020 7790 7000 *Fax:* 020 3357 9587
Dx: 300700 TOWER HAMLETS
Emergency telephone 020 8367 1758
E-mail: enquiries@tvedwards.com
List of partners: M J Ashford, J Beck, C Blacklaws, F A Couchman, M Davis, A T A Edwards, J D Emmerson, S Fitzgerald, J Lake, A Leivesley, F J Nichol, J Nichol, J Overton, F Rahman-Cook, J A Starling, C S Taylor, A Wright
Office: Cambridge, London E1 (2 offices), London E15, London EC4, London N15, London SE8, London SW11
Work: B2 D1 G H K1 K2 L N O V Z(l,m,p,q)
Emergency Action, Agency, Advocacy, Fixed Fee Interview, Legal Aid undertaken, Legal Aid Franchise and Member of Accident Line
Ptr: Ashford, Mr Mark James ★ . . . *Aug 1993
Beck, Ms Jenny . . . Sep 1994
Emmerson, Mr John David BA(Hons) . . . Jun 1984
Fitzgerald, Ms Susan BA . . . Jul 1990
Lake, Mr Jamie MA ★ . . . *Dec 1995
Leivesley, Miss Alison LLB(Hons) . . . *Jun 1997
Nichol, Mr Fredrick James LLB ★ . . . *Oct 1984
Taylor, Ms Carolyn S LLB(Leeds) . . . *Nov 1983
Ast: Adams, Miss Maria LLB . . . *Jun 2006
Green, Ms Lorraine LLB(Hons) . . . Nov 1995
Hack, Miss Alia LLB; LPC . . . Sep 2006
Snow, Ms Susan LLB; LLM . . . *Oct 1995
Trundle, Ms Jemma . . . Jun 2007

TV EDWARDS LLP
Temple Chambers 3-7 Temple Avenue London EC4Y 0HP
Tel: 020 7790 7000 *Fax:* 020 3357 9587
Dx: 219 LONDON/CHANCERY LN
E-mail: enquiries@tvedwards.com
Office: Cambridge, London E1 (3 offices), London E15, London N15, London SE8, London SW11

TV EDWARDS LLP
190-196 Deptford High Street London SE8 3PR
Tel: 020 7790 7000 *Fax:* 020 3357 9587 *Dx:* 56706 DEPTFORD
E-mail: enquiries@tvedwards.com
Office: Cambridge, London E1 (3 offices), London E15, London EC4, London N15, London SW11
Work: D1 D2 K1 K2 K3
Emergency Action, Agency, Advocacy, Fixed Fee Interview, Legal Aid undertaken and Legal Aid Franchise
Ptr: Blacklaws, Ms Christina BA . . . Jan 1991
Davis, Maud . . . Jan 1992
Ast: Horne, Ms Marie Luise Lena BSc . . . Mar 2006
Johnson, Ms Melita BA(Hons) . . . Oct 2003
Rowe, Ms Aisling BA ★ . . . *Jan 2007
Weston, Ms Monica Athensia . . . Jan 2009
Con: Biggs, Ms Nancy N LLB; MA . . . *Dec 1985
Casterton, Miss Dawn Suzanne LLB . . . Nov 1992
Harbour, Mr Anthony G W BA . . . Dec 1980
Kavanagh, Ms Sheila . . . Jan 1989
Mackinder, Ms Penny . . . Jun 1976
Prince, Mrs Beth F BA . . . May 1981
Shaw, Ms Helen . . . Mar 1983
Singer, Ms Corrine . . . Nov 1974
Tish, Ms Roberta . . . Jul 1971
Vassie, Ms Heather BA . . . Jul 1975
Webber, Anne . . . Feb 2001

TV EDWARDS LLP
33 Mile End Road Tower Hamlets London E1 4TP
Tel: 020 7790 7000 *Fax:* 020 3357 9587
Dx: 300700 TOWER HAMLETS
Emergency telephone 020 8367 1758
E-mail: enquiries@tvedwards.com
Office: Cambridge, London E1 (2 offices), London E15, London EC4, London N15, London SE8, London SW11

TV EDWARDS LLP
27a Mile End Road Tower Hamlets London E1 4TP
Tel: 020 7790 7000 *Fax:* 020 3357 9587
Dx: 300700 TOWER HAMLETS
Emergency telephone 0870 350 1758
E-mail: enquiries@tvedwards.com
Office: Cambridge, London E1 (2 offices), London E15, London EC4, London N15, London SE8, London SW11
Work: B2 D1 D2 G H J1 K1 L N V Z(l,m,q)
Emergency Action, Agency, Advocacy, Legal Aid undertaken, Legal Aid Franchise and Member of Accident Line
Ptr: Couchman, Mr Felix Alexander . . . *Nov 1993
Edwards, Mr Anthony T A LLB . . . *§May 1974
Overton, Mr Julian . . . Jun 2001
Rahman-Cook, Farhana . . . Nov 2002
Starling, Ms Jacqueline Anne . . . Nov 1995
Asoc: Stanners, Mr Ben . . . *Nov 1994
Ast: Kolapo, Ms Michele Corrine BA(Hons) . . . Nov 1997
Leslie, Ms Julie . . . Mar 2002
Longe, Mr Daniel Iyiola LLB . . . *Jul 2006
Motegherie, Meezabin . . . Sep 2003
Nisbet, Ms Leigh . . . Sep 2004
Warden, Miss Elizabeth Lilian LLB . . . *Jul 2004

TV EDWARDS LLP
Emma House 214 High Road London N15 4NP
Tel: 020 7790 7000 *Fax:* 020 3357 9587
Dx: 55605 SOUTH TOTTENHAM
E-mail: enquiries@tvedwards.com
Office: Cambridge, London E1 (3 offices), London E15, London EC4, London SE8, London SW11
Ptr: Nichol, Mr James . . . Oct 1984
Wright, Ms Adrienne CPE; LPC . . . Nov 2000
Ast: Doherty, Mr Niall Francis BA(Hons); PGDipLaw; BVC . *Aug 2007
Ezzat, Mr Karim Mostafa Ali . . . Oct 2004
Leighton, Mr Rossie MA(Eng Lit); PGDipLaw; LPC . . *Jan 2007

TV EDWARDS LLP
The Advice Arcade 107-109 The Grove London E15 1HP
Tel: 020 3141 1000 *Fax:* 020 3357 9587
E-mail: enquiries@tvedwards.com
Office: Cambridge, London E1 (3 offices), London EC4, London N15, London SE8, London SW11

TV EDWARDS LLP
261 Lavender Hill London SW11 1JD
Tel: 020 7790 7000 *Fax:* 020 3357 9587
Dx: 58556 CLAPHAM JUNCTION
E-mail: enquiries@tvedwards.com
Office: Cambridge, London E1 (3 offices), London E15, London EC4, London N15, London SE8

TWM SOLICITORS LLP
7 & 9 Queens Road Wimbledon London SW19 8NG
Tel: 020 8946 6454 *Fax:* 020 8947 7134
Dx: 300100 WIMBLEDON CENTRAL
E-mail: wimbledon.reception@twmsolicitors.com
Office: Cranleigh, Epsom, Guildford, Leatherhead, Reigate
Languages: French
Work: B1 C1 C2 C3 D1 E F1 J1 K1 K2 L N P Q R1 S1 S2 T1 T2 W Z(m)
Emergency Action and Advocacy undertaken
Ptr: Barry, Miss Eileen BA . . . *§Jan 1984
Cornes, Ms Sarah E BA . . . *Feb 1989
Lambert, Mr Peter B . . . *Nov 1980
Potter, Mr Jonathan Colin . . . *Dec 1996
Ast: Russell, Miss Louise . . . Aug 2003
Vassallo, Miss Jovita Maria LLM . . . *Dec 1998

TW SOLICITORS ‡
Clan McDonald House 47 Bramhope Lane London SE7 7FH
Tel: 020 8293 8933
E-mail: info@twsolicitors.co.uk

DAVID TAGG & CO ‡
119 Harwood Road London SW6 4QL
Tel: 020 7736 0999 *Fax:* 020 7736 0207
Dx: 83816 FULHAM BROADWAY
E-mail: enquiries@davidtagg.co.uk
List of partners: F E Price, D L Tagg
Office: London SW6
Languages: French
Work: D1 E F1 J1 K1 L O Q S1 S2 W Z(q)
Emergency Action, Agency, Advocacy, Fixed Fee Interview, Legal Aid undertaken and Legal Aid Franchise
Ptr: Price, Mr Francis E BA(Hons)(Law) . . . *Mar 1986
Tagg, Mr David Leonard LLB(Hons)(Lond) . . . *Oct 1994
Asoc: Osbourne, Miss Ann Leilah Patricia . . . *Jan 2006
Ast: Bahia, Miss Suki LLB . . . Aug 2011

DAVID TAGG & CO
57b New Kings Road London SW6 4SE
Tel: 020 7610 6676 *Fax:* 020 7610 6461
Dx: 83816 FULHAM BROADWAY
E-mail: enquiries@davidtagg.co.uk
Office: London SW6
Work: S1 S2

M TAHER & CO SOLICITORS ‡
Suite 811 Lloyds Building One Lime Street London EC3M 7DQ
Tel: 020 7929 7600

TAJ SOLICITORS ‡
247 East India Dock Road London E14 0EG
Tel: 020 7537 3002 *Fax:* 020 7537 3006
E-mail: info@tajsolicitors.com

TANBURGHS ‡
185 Uxbridge Road London W12 9RA
Tel: 020 8749 8902 *Fax:* 020 8749 9699
List of partners: W Tan
Languages: Cantonese, Chinese, Malay, Urdu
Work: C1 D1 E G H J1 K1 L O Q S2 Z(e,g,i)
Emergency Action, Legal Aid undertaken and Legal Aid Franchise
Ptr: Tan, Mr Wah-Piow MA(Oxon) ● . . . *Apr 1996

TANBURGHS O'BRIEN LAHAISE ‡
(in association with Tanburghs)
108 Kilburn High Road Kilburn Camden London NW6 4HY
Tel: 020 7372 6614 *Fax:* 020 7625 0264 *Dx:* 37715 KILBURN
List of partners: P K Cheng, A P Lahaise, W Tan
Languages: Cantonese, Chinese, Malay
Work: B2 E G H J1 K1 L N O Q S1 S2 W Z(i)
Emergency Action, Agency, Advocacy, Fixed Fee Interview, Legal Aid undertaken and Legal Aid Franchise
Ptr: Cheng, Mr Peter Kwock-Kwan LLB; LLM . . . *Sep 2000
Lahaise, Mr Anthony Philip . . . *Jan 1974
Tan, Mr Wah-Piow MA(Oxon) ● . . . *Apr 1996
Ast: Ng, Mrs How Ming LLB; MCSP . . . *Nov 2002
Con: Quincey, Mr Allan H LLB(Nott'm) . . . *Jun 1970

TANDA MIGLIORINI & ASSOCIATES LLP ‡
31 Southampton Row Holborn London WC1B 5HJ
Tel: 020 3170 7687
E-mail: anne.gadd@tmalegal.com

T R TANER & CO ‡
36 Willoughby Road Haringey London N8 0JG
Tel: 020 8348 1267 *Fax:* 020 8348 4417
E-mail: solicitors@trtaner.co.uk
List of partners: A Riza, T R Taner
Languages: Turkish
Work: E G H J1 K1 L S1 W Z(i)
Ptr: Riza, Miss Ayten BA . . . *Feb 1988
Taner, Teoman Rauf . . . *Dec 1972

DAVID TANG & CO ‡
Suite 8 Nassau House 122 Shaftesbury Avenue London W1D 5ER
Tel: 020 7439 4675 *Fax:* 020 7494 3187 *Dx:* 44737 SOHO SQUARE
Emergency telephone 07831 527768 / 07956 439555
E-mail: david@davidtang.co.uk
List of partners: D Tang
Languages: Chinese
Work: K1 M3 Q S1 S2 W Z(i)
Emergency Action undertaken
SPr: Tang, Mr David LLB . . . *Sep 1989

BRIAN H TAUB & CO ‡
57 High Point North Hill London N6 4AZ
Tel: 020 8340 4471
List of partners: B H Taub
Ptr: Taub, Mr Brian H LLB . . . *Oct 1957

TAVISTOCK LAW LIMITED ‡
Painters Hall Chambers 8 Little Trinity Lane London EC4V 2AN
Tel: 0845 260 6034 *Fax:* 0845 260 6035
List of partners: N Akhtar, R S Takhar
Languages: Punjabi, Urdu
Work: C1 C2 E F1 I J1 R2 S1 S2 U1 U2 Z(b,e,i)
Dir: Akhtar, Mr Nadeem LLB(Hons) . . . Mar 1999
Takhar, Mr Rabinder Singh MA(Oxon) . . . Oct 1990

ALAN TAYLOR & CO ‡
Mynott House 14 Bowling Green Lane London EC1R 0BD
Tel: 020 7251 3222 *Fax:* 020 7251 6222
E-mail: info@alantaylorandco.com
List of partners: J E Burke, D J Moloney, A R M Taylor
Languages: French, Russian, Spanish
Work: B1 E J1 K3 N O Q S1 S2 W Z(b,i,p,q)
Emergency Action, Agency, Advocacy, Fixed Fee Interview undertaken and Member of Accident Line
Ptr: Burke, Ms Jacqueline Ellen LLB . . . *Mar 1994
Moloney, Mr Diarmuid J BA . . . *Feb 1983
Taylor, Mr Alan R M LLB(NZ) . . . *Nov 1976

TAYLOR BRIDGE LLP ‡
1 The Colour House 7 Bell Yard Mews 159 Bermondsey Street London SE1 3UW
Tel: 020 7407 2463 *Fax:* 020 7378 1967
E-mail: admin@taylorbridge.com

TAYLOR HAMPTON SOLICITORS LLP ‡
3rd Floor London Chambers 218 Strand London WC2R 1AT
Tel: 020 7427 5970 *Fax:* 020 7353 1238
Dx: 232 LONDON/CHANCERY LN
E-mail: enquiries@thlaw.co.uk

MARK TAYLOR & CO ‡
310 Harbour Yard Chelsea Harbour London SW10 0XD
Tel: 020 7349 7373 *Fax:* 020 7349 7374
E-mail: mark@marktaylor.co.uk
List of partners: R M Taylor
Work: C1 C2 E J1 O Q R2 S1 S2 Z(w)
Ptr: Taylor, Mr Richard Mark LLB(Lond) . . . . *Nov 1984

TAYLOR WESSING ‡
5 New Street Square London EC4A 3TW
Tel: 020 7300 7000 *Fax:* 020 7300 7100
Dx: 41 LONDON/CHANCERY LN
E-mail: london@taylorwessing.com
List of partners: N K D Andrews, A S L Askwith, A M Baker, K Beattie, C J C Bell, D Bell, M Bennett, C F Bourgeois, A Breward, N A Briant, P S Burke, N C Burkill, M Buzzoni, A C Campbell, L Cobb, D J Coffey, S C Cohen, E Colville, S C C Dayes, M L G Dillon, R J Dukes, T G Eyles, C M Ferguson, J M Ferguson, D M Findlay, D Fitzpatrick, M W Fletcher, B Fortin-Lees, M W Frawley, H E Garthwaite, E U Gaunt, R M Gayford, A S Goldthorp, M A F Goodwin, T Graham, A S Granger, D V Greig, R B Grosse, P Harrison, J J Haydn-Williams, A D Hine, M T Hodgson, G A Jackson, P A Jackson, P B Kempe, D N Kent, P Lawrence, J S Linneker, C C Lloyd, S W Lovell, M B Mackay, P R Manser, A C Marks, R D Marsh, J M Marshall, R W McDonald, J McKee, E P O Mercer, P E Mitchell, G C W Morgan, G Moss, M E Newey, T J R Oldridge, R J C D Pertwee, R G Pike, R C Price, J W D Rawkins, M S H Ring, D Rosenberg, D Ross, K Sandford, C L Saunders, R D Sharma, P R Shaw, P W C Shepherd, J Sleightholme, M D Stanford-Tuck, T Stocks, D J Tarpey, S Walker, S Westell, N G White, J D Whitfield, J G G Williams, P Willis, M A S Winter
Office: Cambridge
Languages: Arabic, Assamese, Cantonese, Farsi, French, Gaelic, German, Greek, Gujarati, Hebrew, Italian, Mandarin, Portuguese, Russian, Spanish
Work: A1 A3 B1 B2 C1 C2 C3 D1 E F1 F2 I J1 J2 K1 L M1 M2 N O P Q R1 R2 S1 T1 T2 U1 W Z(a,b,c,d,e,f,g,h,i,j,k,l,m,n,o,q,s,w,y,z)
Emergency Action and Agency undertaken
Ptr: Andrews, Ms Nichola K D LLB(Nott'm) . . . . *Feb 1989
Askwith, Miss Alison S L BSc . . . . *Nov 1986
Baker, Mr A Martin BSc . . . . *Dec 1975
Beattie, Ms Kerry-Jane LLB . . . . *Dec 1991
Bell, Mr Christopher J C BTech . . . . *Dec 1975
Bell, Mr Douglas . . . . *Jan 1991
Bennett, Mr Mark LLM(Bris) . . . . *§Nov 1984
Bourgeois, Mr Christopher F FCIArb . . . . *Jan 1975
Breward, Mr Alastair BA; SAB Diploma(NSW Australia) Mar 1992
Briant, Mr Nicholas A LLB . . . . *Apr 1977
Burke, Mr Paul S . . . . Nov 1994
Burkill, Mr Nicholas C BA . . . . Jan 1987
Buzzoni, Mr Mark LLB(Bris); ATII . . . . *Apr 1980
Campbell, Ms Audrey C LLB . . . . *Sep 1984
Cobb, Mr Laurence LLB(Hons); ACIArb . . . . . . *Nov 1986
Coffey, Mr D Joseph . . . . Jan 1968
Cohen, Mr Simon C BSc . . . . *Apr 1990
Colville, Mrs Elaine BA . . . . Jun 1978
Dayes, Mr Simon C C LLB . . . . *Oct 1987
Dillon, Mr Martin L G BA . . . . *§Jul 1967
Dukes, Mr Rodney J BSc . . . . *Nov 1985
Eyles, Mr Timothy G LLB . . . . *Jul 1981
Ferguson, Miss Clare M BSc . . . . *Dec 1976
Ferguson, Mr James M BA . . . . *Feb 1983
Findlay, Mr David Mair LLB(Hons) Struben Prize . . *Jun 1995
Fitzpatrick, Mr Dominic BA(Hons) . . . . *Nov 1992
Fletcher, Mr Mark W MA(Cantab) . . . . *Mar 1969
Fortin-Lees, Bibi LLB . . . . *Nov 1993
Frawley, Mr Michael W LLM . . . . *Jun 1990
Garthwaite, Ms Helen E LLB(Hons); MSc; ACIArb . . *Nov 1990
Gaunt, Dr Elisabeth U Dr Jur(Vienna) . . . . Nov 1983
Gayford, Mr Robert M LLB . . . . *Dec 1974
Goldthorp, Ms Alison S BA(Cantab) . . . . *Sep 1990
Goodwin, Mr Martin A F BSc . . . . *Jul 1975
Graham, Mr Toby LLB(Hons) . . . . *Feb 1992
Granger, Mr Andrew S MA(Cantab) . . . . *Nov 1985
Greig, Mr David V BBS . . . . *Jul 1979
Grosse, Mr Richard B MA(Cantab) . . . . *Jun 1977
Harrison, Mr Paul BA(Oxon) . . . . *Oct 1981
Haydn-Williams, Mr Jonathan J MA . . . . *Jun 1983
Hine, Mr Andrew D LLB(Bris) . . . . *§Dec 1989
Hodgson, Mr Mark T BA(Cantab) . . . . *Nov 1992
Jackson, Mr Gordon A LLB . . . . *Apr 1978
Jackson, Mr Peter A BA . . . . *Oct 1987
Kempe, Mr Peter B MA . . . . *Oct 1986
Kent, Mr David N BA . . . . *§Mar 1977
Lawrence, Mr Paul LLB . . . . Nov 1994
Linneker, Mr John S BA; DipLP . . . . *Dec 1986
Lloyd, Mr Charles C BA . . . . *Oct 1983
Lovell, Mr Simon W LLB . . . . *Oct 1989
McDonald, Mr Roger W MA(Cantab) . . . . *Nov 1989
Mackay, Mr Marcus B MA Broderip & Easterbrook Prize . . . . *Jan 1983
McKee, Miss Jane LLB . . . . *Aug 1980
Manser, Mr Paul R BA(Warw) . . . . *Jun 1977
Marks, Mr Adam C LLB . . . . *Oct 1985
Marsh, Mr Richard D BA . . . . *§Dec 1975
Marshall, Mr James M BSc(Bris) ♦ . . . . *Apr 1990
Mercer, Mr Edward Peter Opgard MA(Cantab) . . . . Dec 1980
Mitchell, Mr Paul E LLB . . . . *Apr 1976
Morgan, Mr Glyn C W LLB . . . . *Oct 1988
Moss, Mr Gary LLB(Leics) Mackrell Prize . . . . . *Jun 1977
Newey, Mr Martin E LLB . . . . *Dec 1976
Oldridge, Mr Timothy J R LLB(Lond) . . . . *Nov 1988
Pertwee, Mr Richard J C D BA . . . . *Apr 1980
Pike, Mr Richard Gordon LLB . . . . Oct 1987
Price, Mr Richard C LLB . . . . *Nov 1970
Rawkins, Mr Jason William David BA . . . . *Nov 1992
Ring, Mr Malcolm S H TD . . . . *§Jun 1969
Rosenberg, Mr Daniel BA(Cantab) . . . . Sep 1987
Ross, Mr Dominic . . . . Mar 1992
Sandford, Kiran LLB(Lond) . . . . *Mar 1984
Saunders, Ms Carolyn L MA(Hons)(Cantab) . . . . . *Nov 1987
Sharma, Raman D LLB . . . . *Jan 1985
Shaw, Mr Peter R BA(Hons) . . . . *Jul 1980
Shepherd, Mr Peter W C BA . . . . *Apr 1980
Sleightholme, Mr James MA(Cantab) . . . . May 1981
Stanford-Tuck, Mr Michael D LLB . . . . *Jun 1972
Stocks, Mr Timothy BA; LLB . . . . *§Oct 1983
Tarpey, Mr Declan J MA . . . . *Oct 1985
Walker, Mr Simon MA(Cantab) . . . . *Jun 1981
Westell, Ms Sherree LLB(Bris) . . . . *Oct 1992
White, Mr Neil G . . . . *§May 1975
Whitfield, Mr John D LLB . . . . *Jul 1981
Williams, Mr John G G . . . . *§Dec 1966
Willis, Mr Peter . . . . *Oct 1991
Winter, Mr Martin A S BA(Oxon) . . . . *§Dec 1978
Asoc: Austin, Mr Mark D LLB . . . . Oct 1984
Bailey, Mr Richard Leslie BA(Hons) . . . . Sep 1998
Ball, Mr Jonathan Frank BSc . . . . Sep 1999
Bates, Mr Malcolm Robert . . . . Dec 1995
Beer, Mr Philip . . . . *Sep 1998
Benson, Mr Christopher J BA . . . . *Oct 1990
Blazey, Miss Joanna R LLB . . . . *Sep 1997
Bradbury, Miss Sarah J . . . . *Oct 1996
Buxton, Mr Edward BSc . . . . *Dec 1994
Callaghan, Mr Paul A LLB . . . . Mar 1997
Campbell, Mr Stuart G LLB(Hons) . . . . *Nov 1995
Carl, Mr Thomas BA . . . . Sep 1999
Chandler, Miss Clare Elizabeth LLB . . . . *Oct 1993
Clark, Mr Patrick LLB . . . . Sep 1996
Clifton, Mr Richard William BA(Oxon) . . . . . . *Nov 1995
Cline, Ms Helen BA . . . . *Nov 1993
Collins, Ms Deborah A . . . . Sep 2000
Cumberpatch, Mr Matthew LLB(Hons) . . . . *Nov 1993
Currie, Ms Anne Patricia MA . . . . Apr 1995
Davies, Ms Ellen . . . . *Sep 1998
Day, Mr Alistair LLB . . . . Sep 2000
De Ferrars, Mr David Kilmaine Percy LLB(Hons) . . . *Oct 1995
Druiff, Ms Naomi Deborah Jessel LLB . . . . May 1978
Dunlop, Miss Teressa M BA(Hons) . . . . *Nov 1990
Evans, Mr Alan . . . . *Oct 1997
Exton, Mrs Anne Elizabeth LLB(Leics) . . . . *Nov 1993
Ferns, Mr Tom LLB . . . . Nov 1995
Finlayson, Ms Laura . . . . *Sep 1998
Fox-Murphy, Ms Kathleen . . . . Sep 1999
Gilmartin, Ms Clare . . . . Sep 1999
Glynn, Miss Sasha . . . . Sep 1999
Goodwin, Ms Lisa BA . . . . *Nov 1994
Grey, Miss Deborah Jane Kincaid BA . . . . *Nov 1995
Hall, Mr Jonathan M BSc . . . . *Sep 1996
Harvey, Ms Jane BA . . . . *Sep 1996
Hawkes, Miss Sophie LLB . . . . *Nov 1993
Hawks, Mr James LLB . . . . Sep 1999
Hazell, Mr Nicholas . . . . *Sep 1998
Hills, Ms Nina . . . . *Sep 1998
Holland, Mrs Nancy L BA . . . . *Oct 1986
Howard, Ms Caroline LLB . . . . Nov 1992
Howard, Mr Daniel . . . . *Mar 1999
Hubber, Mr Keith Michael BA(Hons) . . . . Nov 1994
Humphrey, Ms Elizabeth . . . . *Sep 1998
Jeffries, Ms Melissa BSc . . . . Sep 1999
Khan, Farah Arjmand BA . . . . Sep 1999
Kotzur, Mr Wolfgang LLB . . . . Sep 1999
Lehrer, Ms Suzanne . . . . Oct 1999
Liu, Ms Mun-Ling BA(Hons) . . . . Sep 1999
Livingstone, Ms Laura BA(Hons) . . . . *Nov 1994
Lordon, Mrs Anna Justine BA . . . . *Dec 1995
McGrath, Ms Catherine A BA(Hons) . . . . *Sep 1998
McKeown, Ms Keren . . . . *Jun 1998
May, Ms Charlotte LLB . . . . Oct 1997
Miller, Mr Christopher . . . . *Sep 1998
Moser, Mr Nick Simon BA(Oxon) . . . . *Nov 1995
Muxlow, Ms Fiona T MA(Cantab) . . . . Oct 1996
Noor, Marjan BSc . . . . *Sep 1996
Paradise, Mr Peter . . . . Apr 2000
Pavin, Mr Daniel MA(Cantab) . . . . *Oct 1997
Pease, Mr Ian P B BA(Hons) . . . . *Apr 1989
Perry, Miss Janet LLB . . . . *Sep 1996
Redmayne, Mr Jonathan H BA . . . . *Nov 1987
Rodrigues, Ms Michelle . . . . *Sep 1998
Schnider, Ms Jayne LLB . . . . *Sep 1996
Scott, Mr John . . . . *Sep 1998
Scutt, Ms Lindsey . . . . Mar 1997
Seager, Mr Andrew MA(Oxon) . . . . *Dec 1980
Shanmuganathan, Niranjan BA . . . . *Nov 1995
Smith, Mr Neil Martin LLB(Leics) . . . . Dec 1995
Smyth, Mr Neil . . . . *Sep 1998
Statham, Ms Alison LLB . . . . Mar 1997
Stevens, Mr Andrew G B BA; LLM . . . . *Nov 1995
Stoate, Mr Nigel Martin BEng . . . . *Nov 1997
Tarbutt, Ms Kathryn LLB . . . . Oct 1999
Thompson, Mr Robert Patrick Werner LLB(Hons) . . *Nov 1995
Thornham, Mr Christopher John BSc . . . . *Feb 1996
Tocher, Ms Justine . . . . *Sep 1997
Trenton, Mr Anthony MA ♦ . . . . *Mar 1997
Turkson, Ms Naa Akuyea . . . . Sep 1999
Turley, Mr Christopher James LLB; DipLP . . . . . *Oct 1996
Varuna Sanjaya, Samaratunga BSc . . . . Sep 1999
Wain, Mr Tim BA(Hons) . . . . Oct 1995
Watson, Mr Jonathan . . . . *Sep 1996
Westoby, Ms Rachel . . . . *Sep 1998
Wilcox, Miss Emma . . . . Apr 1999
Ast: Ashplant, Ms Elaine LLB; Maitrise en Droit . . . *Apr 1989
Brampton, Mr Paul . . . . Sep 1996
Branston, Ms Naomi . . . . Sep 1999
Brice, Mr Oliver C R . . . . Sep 2000
Cheng, Ms Juniper C L . . . . Sep 2000
Dahia, Miss Harender K LLB(Hons) . . . . Nov 1999
Deasy, Mr Patrick LLB(Bris) . . . . Oct 1994

TEACHER STERN LLP ‡
37-41 Bedford Row London WC1R 4JH
Tel: 020 7242 3191 *Fax:* 020 7197 8010
Dx: 177 LONDON/CHANCERY LN
E-mail: contact@teacherstern.com
List of partners: P J Adam, O Azzuri, C Benjamin, P A Berry, J A Davies, D Fenton, C A Glass, A L Green, D G Irwin, C V Maddows, J M McVeigh, S J Miles, M Nathan, P N J Otvos, D C S Phillips, J I Rabinowicz, R J Raphael, C Richman, D Salisbury, E J Shakespeare, G J Shear
Languages: Cantonese, Czech, French, German, Hebrew, Hindi, Italian, Mandarin, Punjabi, Russian, Spanish
Work: B1 C1 C2 C3 E F1 I J1 L M1 M2 N O P Q R1 R2 S1 S2 T1 T2 U1 U2 W X Z(b,c,e,f,k,l,n,p,q,r,w)
Emergency Action, Agency and Advocacy undertaken
Mem: Adam, Mr Paul J LLB(Hons) . . . . *Nov 1990
Azzuri, Mr Oliver BSc; LLM . . . . *Oct 1999
Benjamin, Ms Charlotte BA . . . . *Feb 1995
Berry, Mr Philip A LLB . . . . *Oct 1980
Davies, Mr Joby Alexander BA(Hons) . . . . *Oct 1997
Fenton, Mr David BA(Hons) . . . . *Oct 1991
Glass, Mr Colin Aidan BA(Hons) Office of the Public Guardian . . . . *Feb 1990
Green, Miss Alison Louise BA(Hons) . . . . *Sep 1996
Irwin, Mr David Gavin LLB(Hons) . . . . *Nov 1992
McVeigh, Mr James Michael MA(Hons) . . . . . . *Oct 2001
Maddows, Ms Clair Vee . . . . *Nov 1996
Miles, Mr Simon Justin LLM(Commercial Law); LLB(Hons) . . . . Oct 1995
Nathan, Ms Martine BA(Hons)(Cantab) . . . . . . *Oct 1996
Otvos, Mr Philip Nicholas John BA(Hons) . . . . . Sep 1997
Phillips, Mr David Colin Simon LLB(Hons) . . . . . *Oct 1993
Rabinowicz, Mr Jacob I LLB(Hons) . . . . *May 1977
Raphael, Mr Russell J BA . . . . *Oct 1986
Richman, Mr Colin BA(Oxon) . . . . Nov 1982
Salisbury, Mr David LLB(Hons) . . . . *May 1992
Shakespeare, Ms Emma Joanne . . . . *Oct 2000
Shear, Mr Graham J LLB . . . . *Feb 1989
Ast: Armsden, Ms Chantal Marie LLM . . . . *Oct 2006
Birdi, Mr Balraj Singh . . . . *Apr 2004
Bushaway, Ms Laura Louise LLB(Hons) . . . . . . *Oct 2004
Castro, Mr George BA(Hons) . . . . *Apr 2005
Dunlavy, Mr Allan MA . . . . *Oct 2005
Grover, Mr Navinder Singh LLB; Leg Dip . . . . . *Dec 1999
Hodges, Ms Victoria BA(Hons) . . . . *Oct 2007
Hussain, Ms Nazia LLB . . . . *Feb 2006
Janney, Ms Jane BA(Hons) . . . . *Nov 1985
Larner, Ms Joanne Rachel LLB(Hons) . . . . *Oct 2007
Newsham, Miss Sophie Jayne LLB(Hons) . . . . . . *Nov 2000
Rock, Mrs Alexia Jane LLM . . . . *Oct 1999
Stark, Mrs Sharon BA . . . . *Dec 1998
Taylor, Mr Edward Jack BA(Hons) . . . . Oct 2005
Teacher, Mr Aron LLB . . . . *Apr 2008
Whitfield, Miss Kelly LLB . . . . *Oct 2003
Con: Cantor, Mr Jonathan Marshall . . . . *Apr 1980
Stern, Mr Stuart S W BA; LLB . . . . *Jul 1965
Teacher, Mr David S LLB . . . . *Jul 1966

TECHNOLOGY LAW ALLIANCE ‡
53 Chandos Place Covent Garden London WC2N 4HS
Tel: 0845 351 9090
E-mail: info@tlawa.co.uk
Office: Birmingham

J TEHRANI SOLICITORS ‡
7th Floor St Georges House 15 Hanover Square London W1S 1HS
Tel: 020 7409 7878 *Fax:* 020 7409 1615
E-mail: jamitehrani@gmail.com

G J TEMPLEMAN SOLICITORS ‡
49 Boston Road Hanwell Ealing London W7 3SH
Tel: 020 8566 1200 *Fax:* 020 8566 1505 *Dx:* 39505 HANWELL
E-mail: info@gjtempleman.co.uk
List of partners: R Nahar
Languages: Hindi, Punjabi
Work: S1 S2 W Z(i,l)
SPr: Nahar, Rajan LLB(Hons) . . . . Aug 1999

TENNENTS ‡
14 Devonshire Place London W1G 6HX
Tel: 020 7935 0640 *Fax:* 020 7224 6256
E-mail: tennentslaw@btinternet.com

FLORENCE TERRY SOLICITOR & MEDIATOR ‡
218-221 Strand London WC2R 1AT
Tel: 020 7936 4664 *Fax:* 020 7583 5151
E-mail: fjt@florenceterry.com
Work: K1 K2

KAYE TESLER & CO INC MICHAEL D KAYE & CO ‡ (incorporating Michael D Kaye & Co)
Equity House 86 West Green Road London N15 5PD
Tel: 020 8809 6756 *Fax:* 020 8802 0660
Dx: 55600 SOUTH TOTTENHAM
E-mail: kt@uklaw.net
List of partners: M D Kaye
Work: G J1 K1 L N P R1 S1 T1 W Z(c,i,k,l,o)
Fixed Fee Interview and Legal Aid undertaken
Ptr: Kaye, Mr Michael David Sydney Spanger Prize 1970 *Dec 1971

TETLOW POWELL ‡
13 Blyths Wharf Narrow Street Lime House London E14 8BF

GERALD V TEW ‡
17 Crestway London SW15 5BX
Tel: 020 8788 1628 *Fax:* 020 8789 5002
List of partners: G V Tew
Languages: French, German, Hindi
Work: C1 E J1 Z(b,d,e)

JOSEPH THALIYAN SOLICITORS ‡
212a High Street North East Ham London E6 2JA
Tel: 020 8586 2222
E-mail: info@jtsolicitors.co.uk

THAMES CHAMBERS SOLICITORS ‡
2nd Floor 303 Whitechapel London E1 1BY
Tel: 020 7375 1500 *Fax:* 020 7375 1511
E-mail: info@tcsolicitor.com

THEA LIMITED ‡
3rd Floor 218 Strand London WC2R 1AT
Tel: 020 7277 8649 *Fax:* 020 7583 9521
Dx: 232 LONDON/CHANCERY LN
E-mail: peter@thea.ltd.uk

THEVA & CO ‡
90 High Street Colliers Wood London SW19 2BT
Tel: 020 8542 6667 *Fax:* 020 8542 6691
E-mail: info@theva.co.uk
List of partners: S V Thevarajah
Languages: Tamil
Work: B1 E G H J1 K1 L Q S1 W Z(i,l)
Legal Aid undertaken
Ptr: Thevarajah, Mrs Shirani V LLB . . . . *Jun 1981

See p2 for the Key to Work Categories & other symbols

THIRUS ‡
114 Runnymede Merton Abbey London SW19 2PH
Tel: 020 8542 3358 *Fax:* 020 8542 3358
List of partners: M Thiruketheeswaran
Languages: Sinhalese, Tamil
Work: L S1 S2
SPr: Thiruketheeswaran, Mrs Malathy . . . . *Oct 1990

THOMAS ANDREW & DAODU SOLICITORS ‡
42 Homer Street Westminster London W1H 4NN
Tel: 020 7224 9522 *Fax:* 020 7723 9238
Emergency telephone 020 7724 9584
E-mail: tadhs@dircon.co.uk
List of partners: A Daodu
Languages: French, Punjabi
Work: C1 D1 E H J1 K1 L N O Q S1 V Z(a,c,i)
Emergency Action, Agency and Legal Aid undertaken
Ptr: Daodu, Mr Adekunle LLB(Hons); LLM(Hons)(Cantab) Lizette Bentwich Prize . . . . *Oct 1994
Ast: Ahmed, Mr Naushad BA . . . . *Aug 1994
Uppal, Ms Sona LLB(Hons) . . . . Nov 1998

THOMAS CAPITAL PROPERTY LAWYERS
1-7 Harley Street London W1G 9QD
Tel: 020 7101 0300
E-mail: info@thomaslegalgroup.com
Office: Gloucester (2 offices)

DAVID THOMAS SOLICITORS ‡
3rd Floor 136 George Street London W1H 5LD
Tel: 020 7724 8605

H E THOMAS & CO ‡
(incorporating Lomas Jones & Co)
16 Beresford Square Greenwich London SE18 6AY
Tel: 020 8854 3036 *Fax:* 020 8854 3985 *Dx:* 33306 WOOLWICH
List of partners: J D Sharp
Work: B1 C1 D1 D2 E F1 G H J1 K1 L N O Q S1 W Z(c,k)
Emergency Action, Agency, Advocacy, Legal Aid undertaken and Legal Aid Franchise
Ptr: Sharp, Mr Jeffrey D . . . . *Feb 1985

THOMPSON & CO ‡
48a Tooting High Street Wandsworth London SW17 0RG
Tel: 020 8767 5005 *Fax:* 020 8672 0360
List of partners: A A Khan, J Thompson
Languages: Finnish, French, German, Italian, Punjabi, Swedish, Urdu
Work: E F1 G H J1 K1 L Q R1 S1 S2 Z(g,i,u)
Legal Aid undertaken
Ptr: Khan, Anas Ahmad MA(Law); LLB . . . . *Oct 1999
Thompson, Mr John. . . . . *Jan 1982

THOMPSON & LILLEY ‡
Media House 4 Stratford Place London W1C 1AT
Tel: 020 7499 3633 *Fax:* 020 7499 4248 *Dx:* 82989 MAYFAIR
E-mail: info@thompsonlilley.co.uk

GUY THOMPSON & CO ‡
4-14 Tabernacle Street London EC2A 4LU
Tel: 020 7074 0110

GUY THOMPSON & CO ‡
25 Poplar Walk London SE24 0BX
Tel: 020 7274 6874
E-mail: guy.thompson@guyt.co.uk

THOMPSONS (FORMERLY ROBIN/BRIAN THOMPSON & PARTNERS) ‡
(in association with Thompsons(Scotland); The Thompsons Partnership; Thompsons McClure(Belfast))
Congress House Great Russell Street London WC1B 3LW
Tel: 020 7290 0000 *Fax:* 020 7637 0000 *Dx:* 35722 BLOOMSBURY
E-mail: info@thompsons-law.co.uk
List of partners: J H Allan, S P Allen, P Andrews, M Antoniw, R Arthur, P Ballard, M J Berry, P Carson, L Carter, S Cavalier, D Christie, J A Connolly, S W Cottingham, J Dadd, N W Dandridge, A D Davies, C E Davies, A Denham, S P Dewsbury, D P J Feenan, F Foy, J Gledhill, S J Goodman, S J Harris, A F Herbert, N R Johnson, S Jones, T P R Jones, P N E King, A C Lawton, T P Loughrey, K McIntyre Ross, K M Mitchell, P A Mulhern, J M Mullen, J H Nickson, M O'Connor, F M O'Gorman, G Owen, K Patten, K Pattern, R Pringle, B M Prudham, G D Roberts, K Roberts, K M Ross, R N A Sarfas, N Saunders, G D Shears, M Singh, P A Smith, T Sterling, J M Stevens, M Stokes, D I Stothard, C J Strogen, D A Thompson, M J S Tollitt, R L Toms, D P Towler, I F Walker, T Weetch, J Wood, R A Wood, R D Woolley
Office: Belfast, Birmingham, Bristol, Cardiff, Chelmsford, Dagenham, Derby, Harrow, Leeds, Liverpool, London SW19, Manchester, Middlesbrough, Newcastle upon Tyne, Nottingham, Plymouth, Sheffield, South Shields, Southampton, Stoke-on-Trent, Swansea, Wolverhampton
Work: G J1 J2 M1 N Q V Z(g,o,p,q,u)
Agency, Legal Aid undertaken and Member of Accident Line
Ptr: Sarfas, Ms Rachel N A BA(Hons); LSF . . . . *Nov 1993
Stevens, Ms Joanna M LLB(Manc) . . . . *Nov 1991
Walker, Mr Ivan F MA; LLB; Attorney New York Bar . . *Oct 1984
Asoc: Godwin, Mr Nicholas James BA(Hons) . . . . Sep 2001
Harris, Mr David. . . . . Sep 1997
Ast: Bains, Miss Jagdip LLB(Hons); LSF. . . . . *Apr 1997
Bennett, Mr Nigel Andrew LLB(Hons); LLM . . . . . . Apr 1998
Hutson, Mr Andrew LLB. . . . . *Mar 1996
McBride, Mr Benedict Eugene LLB . . . . *Aug 1996
Mellor, Ms Clare LLB(Hons). . . . . Dec 1996
Patel, Rakesh LLB . . . . *Sep 1992
Phillips, Ms Victoria Mary LLB. . . . . *Sep 1996
Rollason, Miss Leonie BA(Hons); DipLS. . . . . *Jun 1999
Rooney, Ms Ann E LLB . . . . *Sep 1996
Scarth, Ms Debbie BSc; LSF . . . . Aug 1994
Tobin, Ms Brenda M BA(Civil Law) . . . . Jan 1998

THOMPSONS (FORMERLY ROBIN/BRIAN THOMPSON & PARTNERS)
22-24 Worple Road Wimbledon London SW19 4DD
Tel: 020 8947 4163 *Fax:* 020 8947 4163
Office: Belfast, Birmingham, Bristol, Cardiff, Chelmsford, Dagenham, Derby, Harrow, Leeds, Liverpool, London WC1, Manchester, Middlesbrough, Newcastle upon Tyne, Nottingham, Plymouth, Sheffield, South Shields, Southampton, Stoke-on-Trent, Swansea, Wolverhampton
Work: E J1 N S1 W
Fixed Fee Interview, Legal Aid undertaken and Member of Accident Line
Ptr: Carson, Mr Peter . . . . *Nov 1985
Carter, Mr Louis. . . . . Dec 1987
Dadd, Mr Jan LLB(Hons); Former Barrister . . . . . . *Jul 1992
Davies, Mr Andrew D . . . . Jul 1991
Johnson, Mr Neil R . . . . Mar 1990
Mullen, Mr John M . . . . *Apr 1988
O'Connor, Ms Mary . . . . Mar 1989
Pringle, Mr Ronald . . . . *Oct 1979
Roberts, Mr Keith . . . . *Oct 1984
Singh, Mr Martin . . . . *Oct 1987
Sterling, Mr Trevor . . . . Dec 1993
Stokes, Mr Michael . . . . Jul 1992
Weetch, Ms Tracey . . . . Jun 1993
Ast: Burns, Ms Susan . . . . *Nov 1985
De Souza, Ms Maya . . . . Jul 1995
Evans, Mr Paul Justin BA . . . . Nov 1995
Foley, Mr John P . . . . Aug 1996
Francois, Ms Lesley N S . . . . *Dec 1987
Gage, Ms Samantha . . . . Nov 1994
McNicholas, Mr Brendan . . . . *Nov 1991
Young, Mr Edmund LLB. . . . . *Jun 1991

PETER THOMSON ‡
203 Coldharbour Lane Loughborough Junction Lambeth London SW9 8RZ
Tel: 020 7733 6196 *Fax:* 020 7738 6928 *Dx:* 96304 HERNE HILL
Emergency telephone 01580 892802
E-mail: p.thomson@live.co.uk
List of partners: P D Thomson
Work: E G J1 K1 K3 L Q S1 S2 W Z(i)
Agency, Advocacy and Fixed Fee Interview undertaken
SPr: Thomson, Mr Peter D BA . . . . *May 1979

THOREE & CO SOLICITORS ‡
1st Floor 409-411 Brixton Road London SW9 7DG
Tel: 020 7924 9668 *Fax:* 020 7737 7756
E-mail: enquiry@thoreesolicitors.co.uk

THORNTON & CO ‡
1 Goldhawk Road Shepherd's Bush Hammersmith & Fulham London W12 8QQ
Tel: 020 8743 3000 *Fax:* 020 8749 3149
Dx: 58710 SHEPHERDS BUSH
E-mail: tc.thorn@lineone.net
List of partners: T S Cowan
Languages: French, German
Work: E R1 S1 S2 W
SPr: Cowan, Mr Trevor S LLB(Lond) . . . . *May 1978
Con: Ostrin, Mr Anthony ★. . . . . *Nov 1998
Rule, Ms Eloisa Joan . . . . *Jan 1968

THREE CLEAR SOLUTIONS LIMITED ‡
Unit A07 Atlas Business Centre Staples Corner London NW2 7HJ
Tel: 020 8438 0624 *Fax:* 020 8438 0657
E-mail: info@threeclearsolutions.com

THRINGS LLP ‡
Kinnaird House 1 Pall Mall East London SW1Y 5AU
Tel: 020 7766 5600 *Fax:* 020 7766 5675 *Dx:* 140554 PICCADILLY 5
E-mail: solicitors@thrings.com
Office: Bath, Bristol, Swindon
Languages: French
Work: A1 A2 A3 B1 C1 C2 D1 E F1 F2 J1 K1 K2 K3 M2 N O Q R1 R2 S1 S2 T1 T2 U2 W Z(d,e,k,m,n,o,p,q)

THURLOE & LYNDHURST LLP ‡
25 Southampton Buildings London WC2A 1AL
Tel: 0333 123 2255 *Fax:* 0333 123 2256
Dx: 157 LONDON/CHANCERY LN
E-mail: info@thurloelaw.com
List of partners: S A Kingsley, S R Stock
Office: London SW7
Work: C1 E O R1 R2 S1 S2 Z(f)
Ptr: Kingsley, Mr Stephen Alexander MA(Cantab) . . . . . *Jun 1978
Stock, Mr Stuart Roy LLB . . . . Jan 1999

THURLOE & LYNDHURST LLP
5 Thurloe Street London SW7 2SS
Office: London WC2

TIBB & CO ‡
569 Kingsbury Road Kingsbury Barnet London NW9 9EL
Tel: 020 8905 0486 *Fax:* 020 8204 7675 *Dx:* 99351 KINGSBURY 2
E-mail: tibbco@btinternet.com
List of partners: R D Tibb
Work: E L S1 W
Ptr: Tibb, Mrs Raksha D BA. . . . . *Mar 1985

SEAN C TICKELL ‡
62 Avenue Road London N6 5DR
Tel: 020 8341 1000 *Fax:* 020 8340 5051
E-mail: luba.tickell@btconnect.com
List of partners: S C Tickell
Work: C1 C2 C3 E J1 O Q S1 W
Ptr: Tickell, Mr Sean C BSc . . . . *Oct 1980

KAREN TICKNER ‡
PO Box 57766 London NW11 1GB
Tel: 07900 698899
E-mail: karen@karentickner.com

JOSEPH TILY SOLICITORS ‡
First Floor Unit 2 218 Kingsland Road London E2 8DB
Tel: 020 7101 0232

TIME SOLICITORS ‡
714 High Road Leytonstone London E11 3AJ
Tel: 020 8558 4455 *Fax:* 020 8558 4459
E-mail: info@timesolicitors.co.uk

ROBERTA TISH SOLICITORS ‡
Tempo House 15 Falcon Road Battersea Wandsworth London SW11 2PJ
Tel: 020 7223 6966 *Fax:* 020 7350 2220
List of partners: R S Tish
Languages: French
Work: K1 K2
SPr: Tish, Ms Roberta S . . . . *Jul 1971

ANDREW TOBIAS & CO ‡
53 Paddington Street London W1U 4HT
Tel: 020 7935 8399 *Fax:* 020 7935 8599 *Dx:* 41707 MARYLEBONE 2
E-mail: law@andrewtobias.co.uk

L ANNE TODD SOLICITOR ‡
31 Park Crescent London N3 2NL
Tel: 020 8343 1088

TOSSWILL & CO ‡
260 Brixton Hill Lambeth London SW2 1HP
Tel: 020 8674 9494 *Fax:* 020 8671 8987
Emergency telephone 020 8674 9494
E-mail: hearsay@criminallaw.co.uk
List of partners: T M S Tosswill
Work: G H
Emergency Action, Advocacy, Legal Aid undertaken and Legal Aid Franchise
Ptr: Tosswill, Timothy M S LLB; LLM. . . . . *Nov 1976
Asoc: Bretherick, Mr P R John LLB . . . . *Apr 1975
Hamill, Mr Peter Bennett BA ★ . . . . *Aug 1999
Con: Hall, Miss Jennifer M LLB ★. . . . . *May 1978

TOVELL & CO ‡
55 Dukes Avenue London W4 2AG

TOWERBRIDGE TAX PRACTICE ‡
142 Temple Chambers 3-7 Temple Avenue London EC4Y 0DA
Tel: 020 7407 9899 *Fax:* 020 7936 3723
E-mail: info@towerbridgetax.com

TOWERHOUSE CONSULTING LLP ‡
10 Fitzroy Square London W1T 5HP
Tel: 0870 800 5300 *Fax:* 020 7874 1883
E-mail: office@towerhouseconsulting.com

MATTHEW TRACKMAN & CO ‡
58 Acacia Road London NW8 6AG
Tel: 020 7355 4441 *Fax:* 020 7355 4442
Dx: 83412 ST JOHNS WOOD

TRADING TERMS LIMITED ‡
5 Melrose Avenue London SW19 8BU
Tel: 020 8946 2355
E-mail: info@tradingterms.co.uk

TRAVERS SMITH LLP ‡
10 Snow Hill London EC1A 2AL
Tel: 020 7295 3000 *Fax:* 020 7295 3500
Dx: 1111079 CHANCERY LANE
E-mail: travers.smith@traverssmith.com
List of partners: M J Ayre, M R Bardell, O W A Barnes, A J Barrow, R J Barry, J L Bass, R W Baty, K S Bordell, R C Brown, S Buckingham, C J Carroll, M Chamberlain, P Cheveley, H Croke, P J Dolman, A F Douglas, P M Esam, M N R Evans, R Fell, A J Foster, A J Gillen, A Gregson, C G Hale, D M Henderson, R M B Holmes, D Innes, A J Judge, S K Kay, S C Keall, A A King, J Leslie, T M Lewis, A J W Lilley, P Lyons, S McNab, M A Moore, V L Nicholl, S J Paget-Brown, D M Patient, T E Purton, D R Reavill, E C H Reed, J S Richards, A J Roberts, K A Russ, S A Rutman, P A Sanderson, N Seay, I K Shawyer, R N E Skelton, S Skinner, R R Spedding, P A C Stannard, P J A Stear, R A Stocks, R J Stratton, J Styles, S R Summerfield, J Tuckley, M Varia, J M Walsh, N F Watson, A Wilson, S R Yates
Languages: French, German, Italian, Spanish, Swedish
Work: A3 B1 B2 C1 C2 C3 E F1 F2 I J1 J2 K1 L M1 M2 N O P Q R1 R2 S1 S2 T1 T2 U1 U2 W Z(b,c,d,e,j,k,o,q,w)
Ptr: Ayre, Mr Matthew John BA(Hons). . . . . *Mar 2000
Bardell, Mr Michael R LLB. . . . . *Dec 1985
Barnes, Mr Oliver W A BA(Cantab) . . . . *Jun 1976
Barrow, Mr Andrew J LLB . . . . *Nov 1978
Barry, Mr Robert J LLB(Lond) . . . . *Nov 1995
Bass, Mr Julian L LLB. . . . . *Jun 1981
Baty, Mr Richard William BA(Oxon) . . . . *Sep 1998
Bordell, Mr Keith S LLB . . . . Feb 1988
Brown, Mr Richard Christopher LLB. . . . . *Sep 1998
Buckingham, Mr Simon LLB(L'pool) . . . . *Jul 1979
Carroll, Mr Christopher J BSc . . . . *Apr 1980
Chamberlain, Miss Margaret BA(Oxon) Chairman of the BVCA Regulatory Committee . . . . *Nov 1985
Cheveley, Mr Philip . . . . Oct 1997
Croke, Mrs Helen BA; CPE; LPC . . . . *Mar 2001
Dolman, Mr Paul James LLB . . . . *Sep 1998
Douglas, Mr Alasdair F LLB(Edin); LLM(Lond). . . . *Dec 1981
Esam, Mr Peter M BA; MA(Cantab); MSc(Lond). . . . *Dec 1994
Evans, Mr Mark N R BA(Oxon) . . . . *May 1992
Fell, Mr Rob. . . . . Mar 1998
Foster, Mr Anthony JOhn . . . . *Sep 2000
Gillen, Mr Andrew Joseph LLB . . . . *Apr 1996
Gregson, Mr Andrew BSc; PhD(B'ham) . . . . *Dec 1994
Hale, Mr Christopher George MA; LLM(Cantab). . . . *Apr 1981
Henderson, Miss Dorothy M BA(Cantab) . . . . *Oct 1985
Holmes, Mr Robin M B MA(Cantab). . . . . *Mar 1978
Innes, Mr David BA(Hons). . . . . *Dec 1989
Judge, Mr Anthony J BA(Oxon) . . . . *Nov 1990
Kay, Mr Samuel Kilbourne MA(Oxon) . . . . *Mar 2000
Keall, Ms Sian C BA(Oxon) . . . . *Oct 1996
King, Mr Andrew A MA(Cantab) Law Scholarship (Cambridge University) . . . . *Jun 1989
Leslie, Mr Jonathan MA(Oxon) . . . . *Jan 1978
Lewis, Mr Timothy Mark MA(Cantab) . . . . Nov 1998
Lilley, Mr Andrew J W LLB . . . . *Nov 1987
Lyons, Mr Paul BSc(Hons); DipLaw; Barrister . . . . . *Nov 1997
McNab, Mr Steven . . . . Sep 1997
Moore, Mrs Margaret A BA(Dunelm) City of London Solicitors Co Prize; John Marshall & Harry Strouts Prizes; Sheffield Prize Secretary for City of London Law Society and Commercial Law Sub-Committee . . . . *Aug 1984
Nicholl, Mrs Victoria L LLB . . . . *Oct 1987
Paget-Brown, Mr Stephen J MA(Cantab) . . . . *Apr 1984
Patient, Mr David M BA(Dunelm) . . . . *Nov 1992
Purton, Mr Thomas Edward LLB(Hons) . . . . *Nov 1990
Reavill, Mr Daniel Richard LLB(Hons); PGDip IP. . . . Oct 1999
Reed, Mr Edmund C H BA(Cantab) . . . . *Sep 1996
Richards, Mr James S MA(Oxon) . . . . *Feb 1984
Roberts, Mr Andrew J BA(Oxon)(Jurisprudence). . . . Nov 1988
Russ, Ms Kathleen A BA(Oxon). . . . . *Jan 1994
Rutman, Mr Simon Andrew BA . . . . *Nov 1992
Sanderson, Mr Philip A BA . . . . *Nov 1993
Seay, Mr Nigel . . . . Feb 2002
Shawyer, Mr Ian K BA. . . . . *Sep 1998
Skelton, Mr Richard N E MA . . . . *May 1993

Skinner, Mr Stuart BA *Oct 2000
Spedding, Mr Richard Rolland MA(Oxon) *Apr 1996
Stannard, Mr Paul A C MA(Cantab); APMI *Nov 1982
Stear, Mr Philip J A MA(Oxon) *Nov 1997
Stocks, Mr Robert Aaron MA(Cantab) *Mar 2000
Stratton, Mr Richard J MA; LLB(Cantab); ATII *Dec 1983
Styles, Mr James *Sep 1997
Summerfield, Mr Spencer R MA(Cantab) *Nov 1989
Tuckley, Ms Jane *Oct 1988
Varia, Mahesh LLB(Hons) *May 1999
Walsh, Mr Jeremy M LLB(Manc) *Nov 1985
Watson, Mr Neal F LLB *Nov 1993
Wilson, Mr Alistair BA(Oxon) *Apr 1983
Yates, Mr Simon R BA(Oxon) Nov 1992

TRAYMANS ‡
(incorporating Rose & Birn)
Newington House 189 Stoke Newington High Street Stoke Newington Hackney London N16 0LH
Tel: 020 7249 9980 *Fax:* 020 7923 0082
Dx: 58053 STOKE NEWINGTON 1
Emergency telephone 01860 590949
E-mail: info@traymans.co.uk
List of partners: B J Mathiason, T J Mutti, C P Trayman
Work: C1 D1 E F1 G H J1 K1 L N Q S1 T1 V W
Emergency Action, Agency, Advocacy, Legal Aid undertaken and Legal Aid Franchise
Ptr: Mathiason, Mr Barry John LLB(Lond) *Nov 1972
Mutti, Mr Timothy John LLB *May 1990
Trayman, Mr Charles P LLB(Lond) *May 1977

TREASURY SOLICITORS ‡
3rd Floor Attorney Generals Office 20 Victoria Street London SW1H 0NF

ALISON TRENT & CO ‡
149 Fleet Street London EC4A 3DL
Tel: 020 7583 3350 *Fax:* 020 7353 6618
E-mail: alison@alisontrent.co.uk
List of partners: A C Trent
Work: B1 C1 E F1 I J1 L N O Q R1 S1 S2 Z(b,c,d,f,h,j,k,l,p,q,r)
Legal Aid undertaken and Legal Aid Franchise
Ptr: Trent, Ms Alison C LLB *Oct 1984

TRINITY INTERNATIONAL LLP ‡
Hillgate House 26 Old Bailey London EC4M 7HQ
Tel: 020 7653 9700 *Fax:* 020 7900 3945

TRINITY SOLICITORS ‡
61a West Ham Lane London E15 4PH
Tel: 020 8555 3030 *Fax:* 020 8555 3032
Dx: 5428 STRATFORD (LONDON)
E-mail: law@trinitysolicitors.com
Office: Chelmsford

TRINITY SOLICITORS LLP ‡
Winchester House 259-269 Old Marylebone Road London NW1 5RA
Tel: 020 7428 0880
Emergency telephone 0903 434 444
Languages: Arabic, French, Kurdish, Russian
Work: A3 B1 C1 E G J1 K1 K2 L N O R2 S1 S2 V W X Z(c,d,e,f,i,j,n,p,q)
Legal Aid undertaken

TROTT & GENTRY ‡
Tagwright House 35-41 Westland Place London N1 7LP
Tel: 020 3119 3150 *Fax:* 020 3119 3151 *Dx:* 146642 ISLINGTON 4
E-mail: lawyer@trottgentry.co.uk
List of partners: D Bueno de Mesquita, S Landau, D Rosenberg, S Saffer
Work: B1 C1 D1 E G H J1 K1 L M1 N O P Q S1 W Z(i,l)
Emergency Action, Agency, Advocacy, Fixed Fee Interview and Legal Aid undertaken
Ptr: Bueno de Mesquita, Mr David *Oct 1981
Landau, Mr Stephen LLB *Dec 1974
Rosenberg, Mr David *Jun 1962
Saffer, Mr Stanley Jun 1975
Ast: Gadhia, Mrs Hina *Sep 1996
Sood, Ms Varsha LLB(Lond) *Jun 1986

TROUTMAN SANDERS LLP ‡
6th Floor Hasilwood House Bishopsgate London EC2N 4AW
Tel: 020 7038 6650 *Fax:* 020 7038 6651
List of partners: S Barrett-Williams, R Bata, J Varholy
Work: C1 M2
Ptr: Barrett-Williams, Ms Sally Jun 2006
Bata, Mr Robert Jun 1999
Varholy, Mr John Mar 2002

TROWERS & HAMLINS ‡
(in association with Ann Tan & Associates Singapore)
Sceptre Court 40 Tower Hill London EC3N 3DX
Tel: 020 7423 8000 *Fax:* 020 7423 8001 *Dx:* 774 LONDON/CITY
E-mail: enquiries@trowers.com
List of partners: H J Acton, J Acton, J P N Adlington, L F Aglionby, R Alder, M R Amison, S Angle, M J Atwell, S Bailey, J Bibbings, D Biggerstaff, A Bode, A F Bode, E G Burrows, S J Canham, A J Carter, N Cohen, L D Coopersmith, A W G Creed, I M K Davis, S Davis, M Donnellan, I G Doolittle, N Downes, N C Edmondes, C T Faller, N Gibson, S M Gooden, I D Graham, J M Gubbins, J Harbridge, R D Hart, A S Hashemi, P J Hawkins, S E Hayes, M Higginson, R Hildebrand, S Hinton, J P Hunt, M Iley, J Jarvis, T Jenkins, J Joiner, A Jones, P Keuls, P H Keuls, R T King, L Levy, J W Linwood, A J Lyne, P McDermott, J H A McHugo, D L Moorhouse, C J Morrish, D Mosey, C T Munday, A Mutawi, D A O'Neil, M Pattinson, P D Peters, R A Picken, A D Poole, S A Price, C Proudley, A Rae, H Randall, E H Rose, T Secker, D Semmens, R E J Thomas, G Turner, G F Turner, A B Vickery, P C Ward, N W White, J Winrow, J A Winrow, A J Yates
Office: Exeter, Manchester
Languages: Arabic, Cantonese, French, German, Mandarin, Russian, Spanish
Work: A1 A3 B1 B2 C1 C2 C3 D1 E I J1 J2 K1 K2 L M1 M2 N O P Q R1 R2 S1 S2 T1 T2 W X Z(b,c,d,e,f,h,i,j,k,l,m,n,o,p,q,r,u)
Ptr: Acton, Mr Joseph Nov 1991
Adlington, Mr Jonathan P N *§Jan 1974
Aglionby, Mrs Lynn Felicity MA *Nov 1989
Alder, Mr Richie LLB *Nov 1984
Amison, Mr Martin R *Oct 1983
Angle, Mr Sean Nov 1990
Atwell, Mr Michael James *Nov 1992
Bailey, Ms Sara BA *Nov 1992
Bibbings, Ms Jennifer Nov 1989
Biggerstaff, Mr David *Nov 1983
Bode, Mr Adrian Apr 1978
Burrows, Miss Emma G LLB *Jan 1991
Canham, Ms Stephanie J LLB Oct 1988
Carter, Mr Adrian J *Oct 1989
Cohen, Mr Neil LLB *Sep 1983
Coopersmith, Ms Linda D LLB(Exon) *Oct 1979
Creed, Mr Adrian W G May 1992
Davis, Mr Ian Martin Kittredge BA; MA(Cantab) *Oct 1993
Davis, Ms Susannah Jan 1991
Donnellan, Mr Michael *Oct 1996
Doolittle, Mr Ian G MA; DPhil(Oxon) Jan 1987
Downes, Neale Oct 1992
Edmondes, Mr Nicholas C *Mar 1987
Faller, Ms Carolyn T LLB(Exon) *Nov 1984
Gibson, Mr Neil Jan 1990
Gooden, Mrs Sarah M BA(Oxon) *Nov 1986
Graham, Mr Ian D *Nov 1986
Gubbins, Mrs Jennifer M *Sep 1982
Harbridge, Mr James Sep 1995
Hart, Ms Rosemary D *Oct 1978
Hashemi, Amir S *Oct 1987
Hawkins, Mr P James Dec 1989
Hayes, Ms Sarah Elizabeth MA(Cantab) *Dec 1988
Higginson, Mr Michael Oct 1983
Hildebrand, Mr Richard Nov 1992
Hinton, Ms Sara Mar 1992
Hunt, Mr Jeremy P BA Nov 1998
Iley, Mr Malcolm Jan 1975
Jarvis, Mr Jonathan Oct 1998
Jenkins, Mr Tim May 1996
Joiner, Mr Jeremy Dec 1980
Jones, Mr Adrian Sep 1997
Keuls, Mr Peter Jun 1977
King, Mr Roger T *Jun 1977
Levy, Mr Leroy Oct 1994
Linwood, Mr John W *Dec 1980
Lyne, Miss Angela J LLB *Oct 1987
McDermott, Mr Paul Dec 1994
McHugo, Mr John H A *Apr 1982
Moorhouse, Mr Donald L *Apr 1976
Morrish, Mr Charles John BA *Oct 1987
Mosey, Mr David *Feb 1980
Munday, Mr Christopher T MA(Cantab) *Oct 1989
Mutawi, Mr Abdullah Sep 1996
O'Neil, Mr Dominic A *Oct 1988
Pattinson, Mr Michael *Nov 1993
Peters, Mr Philip D LLB Oct 1987
Picken, Mr Ralph A *§May 1980
Poole, Mr Anthony D LLB(Hons) Oct 1984
Price, Mrs Shona A LLB(Wales) Oct 1982
Proudley, Mr Christopher LLB *Nov 1986
Rae, Mr Andrew Oct 2001
Randall, Ms Helen Mar 1992
Rose, Mr Edward H BA(Hons); CPE; LPC *Oct 1997
Secker, Miss Tonia *Nov 1993
Semmens, Mr David Dec 1979
Thomas, Mr Rhys E J LLB(Hons)(Soton) Mar 1996
Turner, Mr Graham Apr 1971
Vickery, Mr Andrew B BA(Oxon) *Oct 1984
Ward, Mr Peter C *May 1982
White, Mr Nicholas W *Feb 1983
Winrow, Ms Janet Oct 1982
Yates, Mr Anthony J LLB *Jul 1991
Ast: Armitage, Ms Clare Sep 2004
Armstrong, Mr Simon Oct 2002
Barnard, Mr Andrew Oct 2000
Bartolozzi, Ms Sara Oct 1993
Barwick, Ms Claire Sep 1997
Bawtree, Ms Juliet Nov 1999
Beiley, Mr Robert Oct 2000
Bethell-Jones, Ms Jessica Oct 2003
Bird, Ms Judith Dec 1993
Brazil, Ms Justine Mar 2000
Brodrick, Mr Robert Sep 1998
Bruce, Ms Eileen Jan 1999
Bryan, Mr Simon Sep 2001
Bryan, Ms Yvette Sep 2004
Campbell, Mr Rory Nov 1996
Carmody, Ms Sara Sep 2004
Childs, Ms Natasha Mar 2000
Copeland, Ms Emma Sep 2001
Cox, Mr Matthew Sep 2001
Dalton, Ms Jane Apr 2005
Djurisic, Jasna Sep 1996
Dobinson, Mr Ian Oct 2001
Dorling, Mr Scott Mar 1994
Eldred, Ms Jennifer Sep 1999
Evans, Mr Daniel Sep 2001
Evans, Ms Susan Mar 1993
Fane, Ms Emma Jul 2004
Ficht, Bayard May 1998
Ford, Mr Jeremy Jun 1999
Frith, Ms Michelle Sep 2000
Gardner, Mr Peter Oct 1999
Garnett, Mr Joshua May 1998
Gibson, Ms Rebecca Sep 2001
Gill, Amardeep Sep 2003
Green, Mr Nicholas Oct 2002
Hall, Ms Samantha Sep 2001
Hardman, Ms Suzanne Oct 2001
Harrisingh, Mr Nick Oct 2002
Hayward, Ms Caroline Dec 1993
Holden, Mr David Oct 2003
Holling, Kyle Nov 2003
Hooke, Mr Daniel Oct 1998
Horne, Mr Rob Feb 2001
Howard, Mr Brian Oct 2002
Howard, Mr Christopher Oct 2003
Hudson, Ms Emma Oct 2003
Hunt, Ms Catherine May 1979
Innes, Ms Catherine Sep 1997
James, Ms Lucy Oct 1999
Jefferies, Mr Bill Oct 2003
Johnson, Mr James Oct 1997
Jonker, Mr Jan-Willem Aug 2002
Kalp, Mr Anthony Nov 1987
Khan, Shazia Mar 2005
Kirby, Ms Kate Apr 2004
Lambert, Mr Benjamin Aug 1999
Lilleyman, Ms Karen Oct 2002
Lowe, Mr Jeremy Nov 1981
Mcmullan, Ms Sarah-Jane Sep 2004
Mao, Ms Yvonne Dec 1990
Maqbool, Assad Sep 2003
Mohammed, Mr Abdul Haq Oct 2000
Morgan, Mr Digby Oct 2003
Nash, Mr Adam Sep 2005
Nazhat, Jubeenh Mar 2000
Newns, Mrs Rebecca LLB(Hons); ATT; ATII Apr 2000
Nugent, Ms Caroline Nov 1994
Ooi, Ms Yang-May Oct 1988
Parsons, Mr Peter Oct 1993
Paul, Mr Christopher Oct 2000
Paul, Ms Sarah Oct 2003
Pedder, Mr Christopher Sep 2002
Perry, Mr Paul Jan 2002
Pierson, Mr Adam Sep 2004
Price, Ms Beth Nov 1989
Record, Ms Michelle Nov 1995
Rees, Ms Rebecca Oct 2003
Rhodes, Ms Clare Oct 1999
Riddle, Mr Anthony Oct 1999
Roper, Ms Naomi Sep 2003
Russell, Mr Huw Sep 2005
Sarker, Ms Emilie Sep 2004
Saunders, Mrs Katharine S A BA(Hons); CPE; LPC *Oct 1999
Scott, Ms Anna Oct 2001
Shaw, Ms Amy Oct 2002
Shaw, Ms Rowena Oct 2002
Smith, Mr Steven Oct 1998
Sneddon, Mr Andrew Jun 1996
Sweeting, Ms Julien Sep 1999
Tandon, Ms Tania Sep 2000
Target, Mr Laurence Nov 1991
Taylor, Ms Jessica Apr 1995
Thomas, Mr Rhys Sep 1994
Towers, Mrs Victoria Elizabeth LLB *Oct 2003
Townsend, Ms Tracey Jan 1995
Walsh, Ms Julianne Oct 1998
Warren-Dickens, Mr Christopher Oct 2002
Webster, Ms Sharron Oct 2002
Welchew, Mr Timothy Sep 2005
Wigley, Mr Thomas Sep 2004
Williams, Ms Andrea Oct 2003
Williams, Mr Nathan Mar 2002
Wilson, Mr Charles Sep 1999
Wiseman, Mr Andrew D LLB(Hons); FRSA *Feb 1989

TRUSTEE SOLUTIONS LIMITED ‡
Citypoint One Ropemaker Street London EC2Y 9AH
Tel: 020 7667 0216
E-mail: susan.andrews@trusteesolutions.co.uk

JAMES TSANG & CO ‡
1st Floor 45 Gerrard Street London W1D 5QQ
Tel: 020 7287 0451 *Fax:* 020 7287 9850 *Dx:* 44732 SOHO SQUARE
E-mail: info@jamestsang.com
List of partners: G S Y Tsang, J P M Tsang
Languages: Cantonese, Mandarin
Work: B1 C1 D1 E F1 G H J1 K1 L M1 M2 O Q S1 W Z(i,j,l)
Emergency Action, Agency, Advocacy, Legal Aid undertaken and Member of Accident Line
Ptr: Tsang, Ms Grace So Yu Aug 1996
Tsang, Mr James Pak Ming LLB; MA *Oct 1987

SUE TUCK & CO ‡
Suite 291 56 Gloucester Road Kensington & Chelsea London SW7 4UB
Tel: 020 7385 7733 *Fax:* 020 7385 7733
E-mail: sue@tuck-solicitor.freeserve.co.uk
List of partners: S R Tuck
Languages: French
Work: J1 J2 N O Q Z(b,c,j,l,p,q,r)
Emergency Action, Agency, Advocacy and Fixed Fee Interview undertaken
SPr: Tuck, Ms Susan R LLB(Exon) *Apr 1980

TUCKER TURNER KINGSLEY WOOD & CO ‡
(incorporating Turner Turner & Co; Kingsley Wood & Co; Clarke & Co)
18 Bedford Row London WC1R 4EQ
Tel: 020 7242 3303 *Fax:* 020 7831 1732
Dx: 220 LONDON/CHANCERY LN
E-mail: legal@ttkw.co.uk
List of partners: P A Davis, C D Jones, S R M Joyce, G A E Melville, D P H Pearce
Office: London WC1
Work: A1 B1 C1 C2 C3 D1 E G H J1 K1 L M1 M2 N O P Q R1 S1 T1 T2 W Z(b,c,d,e,f,i,j,k,l,o,t)
Agency undertaken
Ptr: Davis, Mr Paul A LLB(Wales) *May 1980
Jones, Mr Christopher D §Jan 1970
Joyce, Mr Stephen R M *Jul 1970
Melville, Mr George A E Clerk to Ward of Portsoken *§Jun 1970
Pearce, Mr David P H LLB(Lond) *Jun 1971
Ast: Banfield, Mr Simon J LLB *Oct 1988
Johal, Ms Rukhi K LLB *Jul 1993
Jordan, Mr Peter G M *Mar 1990
Con: Bryant, Mr John A BSc *May 1985

TUCKER TURNER KINGSLEY WOOD & CO
28 Great James Street London WC1N 2ES
Tel: 020 7242 3303 *Fax:* 020 7831 1732
Dx: 220 LONDON/CHANCERY LN
E-mail: legal@ttkw.co.uk
Office: London WC1

TUCKERS
18 Camberwell Church Street London SE5 8QU
Tel: 020 7703 2324 *Fax:* 0845 330 7268
Dx: 35303 CAMBERWELL GREEN
E-mail: london@tuckerssolicitors.com
Office: Birmingham, London W1, Manchester
Ast: Brown, Mr Timothy Raymond LLB(Hons) *Jan 1987

TUCKERS
39 Warren Street London W1T 6AF
Tel: 020 7388 8333 *Fax:* 020 7388 7333
Dx: 123596 REGENTS PARK 3
Emergency telephone 020 7706 1764
Office: Birmingham, London SE5, Manchester
Languages: French, German, Italian, Spanish
Work: D1 G H Z(i)

See p2 for the Key to Work Categories & other symbols

TULLOCH & CO ‡
4 Hill Street London W1J 5NE
Tel: 020 7318 1180 *Fax:* 020 7318 1150

TURNBULL RUTHERFORD SOLICITORS ‡
165 The Broadway Wimbledon London SW19 1NE
Tel: 020 8545 6600 *Fax:* 020 8545 6633
E-mail: info@turnbullrutherford.com

TURNER & CO SOLICITORS ‡
Suite 434 162-168 Regent Street London W1B 5TE
Tel: 020 7038 3701 *Fax:* 0845 287 3630
E-mail: dtplus@dircon.co.uk

A L TURNER & CO ‡
5 Goodwin Avenue London NW7 3RJ
Tel: 020 8906 8084

TYRER ROXBURGH & CO ‡
Unit C405 The Chocolate Factory Clarendon Road Haringey London N22 6XJ
Tel: 020 8889 3319 *Fax:* 020 8881 6089 *Dx:* 34704 WOOD GREEN 2
Emergency telephone 020 8889 3319
E-mail: lawmakers@tyrerroxburgh.co.uk
List of partners: L A Rand, L Sterlini, M J Wolfenden, J Wyman
Languages: Italian
Work: D1 D2 K1 K3 L Q S1 S2 V W Z(g)
Emergency Action, Agency, Legal Aid undertaken and Legal Aid Franchise
Ptr: Rand, Ms Linda A BA(Oxon) Deputy District Judge . *May 1986
Sterlini, Mr Luigi LLB . *Oct 1983
Wolfenden, Mr Martin J BA . *Sep 1990
Wyman, Ms Jessica BA(Sussex) . *Nov 1992

UK IMMIGRATION & PROPERTY SOLICITORS LTD ‡
17 Redan House 23 Redan Place London W2 4SA
Tel: 0845 463 1561 *Fax:* 020 7504 8082
E-mail: info@work-permitsuk.com

ULLAH LAW ASSOCIATES ‡
220 Church Road Willesden London NW10 9NP
Tel: 020 8830 4800 *Fax:* 020 8459 6261 *Dx:* 57656 HARLESDEN
E-mail: info@ulasolicitors.com

J G UNDERWOOD ‡
73 Pimlico Road London SW1W 8NE
Tel: 020 7730 4019 *Fax:* 020 7730 1477
E-mail: john@underwoodlegal.freeserve.co.uk
Work: C1 E S1 S2 W Z(g,x)

UNDERWOOD SOLICITORS LLP ‡
40 Welbeck Street Westminster London W1G 8LN
Tel: 020 7526 6000 *Fax:* 020 7526 6001 *Dx:* 9074 WEST END
E-mail: enquiries@underwoodco.com
List of partners: P K Hughes, N S Jandu, J McLean, P A Redfern, L Reid, J M Roche, N Sabharwal, M Smith
Languages: French, Spanish
Work: A1 B1 C1 C2 C3 E F1 J1 K1 L N O Q R2 S1 S2 T1 T2 W Z(b,d,e,f,i,j,k,l,p,q)
Agency undertaken
Ptr: Hughes, Mr Peter K LLB(Bris). *Apr 1979
Jandu, Mr Navtej Singh BA(Hons)(Law) *Dec 1981
McLean, Mr James MA(Oxon). *Sep 2000
Redfern, Mr Paul A . *Dec 1988
Reid, Ms Louise LLB . *Sep 1993
Roche, Mr Justin M BA . *Oct 1980
Sabharwal, Mr Neil . Oct 2000
Smith, Mr Mark LLB. Aug 1997
Ast: Ganley, Miss Simone Jill LLB . *Jun 2006
Hickling, Mrs Jeanine . Sep 2000
McDonnell, Mr Michael James. Jul 2006
Riding, Mr Jonathan Harry. *Aug 1997
Twomey, Mr Paul . Dec 1993
Wyatt, Mr David. Dec 2004
Zakir, Mrs Rashida LLB(Hons). Sep 1998
Con: Dawson, Mr Bernard W LLB(Auckland) *Apr 1979
Guest, Miss Hilary A E LLB(Lond). *May 1965

UNIVERSA LAW LTD ‡
5th Floor Suite 1/2 New Premier House London WC1B 5AL

UNIVERSAL SOLICITORS ‡
3rd Floor 94a Whitechapel High Street London E1 7RA
Tel: 020 7377 5511 *Fax:* 020 7377 8811

UNSWORTH ROSE ‡
19 Princess Road Regents Park Camden London NW1 8JR
Tel: 020 7483 4411 *Fax:* 020 7586 9388 *Dx:* 96852 PRIMROSE HILL
List of partners: I Aziz, P M Unsworth
Languages: French, German
Work: A1 C1 E L R1 S1 S2 W
Ptr: Aziz, Mr Ibrahim LLB . Mar 2005
Unsworth, Mr P Mark LLB. *Apr 1981

URIA & MENENDEZ ‡
5th Floor 100 Cannon Street London EC4N 6EU
Tel: 020 7645 0280 *Fax:* 020 7600 1718

VLS SOLICITORS ‡
Gibson House 800 High Road Tottenham London N17 0DH
Tel: 020 8808 7999 *Fax:* 020 8808 1999
E-mail: info@vlssolicitors.com

VMS SOLICITORS LLP ‡
Rooms 194-195 Temple Chambers 3-7 Temple Avenue London EC4Y 0DB
Tel: 020 7936 1999 *Fax:* 020 7936 3385
E-mail: info@vms-legal.com

JAY VADHER & CO ‡
Victoria House 185 Romford Road Stratford London E15 4JF
Tel: 020 8519 3000 *Fax:* 020 8519 3300 *Dx:* 52106 FOREST GATE
E-mail: j.vadher@jayvadher.co.uk
List of partners: B N D Vadher, R B Vadher
Languages: Gujarati, Hindi, Kiswahili, Punjabi
Work: C1 E K3 O Q S1 W
Legal Aid Franchise
Ptr: Vadher, Mr Babulal Nanji Damji . *May 1983
Vadher, Mr Rajay B BA(Hons)(Soc Sci) *Sep 1998

VAHIB & CO ‡
435 Green Lane London N4 2HE
Tel: 020 8348 0055 *Fax:* 020 8348 6655 *Dx:* 57754 HARRINGAY

VALENS SOLICITORS ‡
25 Floral Street London WC2E 9DS
Tel: 020 7745 7320 *Fax:* 020 7745 7321
E-mail: contact@valenssolicitors.co.uk

VAN DOORNE ‡
1st Floor 55 King William Street London EC4R 9AD
Tel: 020 7648 0400 *Fax:* 020 7283 5001

VAN EATON SOLICITORS ‡
71 Leigham Court Road Streatham Hill London SW16 2NJ
Tel: 020 8769 6739 *Fax:* 020 8769 6391

VAN STRATEN SOLICITORS ‡
RB Building Portobello Dock 557 Harrow Road London W10 4RH
Tel: 020 8588 9660 *Fax:* 020 8969 7285
E-mail: sinead@vanstraten.co.uk

VANCE HARRIS
3 Malvern House Meridian Gate 199 Marsh Wall London E14 9YT
Tel: 020 7538 5232 *Fax:* 020 7538 1859 *Dx:* 42666 ISLE OF DOGS
E-mail: london@vanceharris.co.uk
Office: Crowborough
Work: C1 C2 E K1 L R2 S1 S2 T2 W Z(c)
Ptr: Macdonald, Mr Keith M . *Nov 1978
Ast: Cheah, Miss Elizabeth . *May 1990

VANGUARDS LLP ‡
304 High Street North London E12 6SA
Tel: 020 8586 2426 *Fax:* 020 8586 2436 *Dx:* 4711 EAST HAM
E-mail: vanguardsllp@gmail.com

JAY VARA & CO ‡
27 Granville Gardens Norbury London SW16 3LN
Tel: 020 8679 1292

VARDAG SOLICITORS LTD ‡
Bell House 8 Bell Yard London WC2A 2JR
Tel: 020 7404 9290 *Fax:* 020 7404 8995
E-mail: contact@vardags.com

VASUKI SOLICITORS ‡
10 Shakespeare Crescent Manor Park London E12 6LN
Tel: 020 8470 6655 *Fax:* 020 8470 2877
E-mail: vasukisolicitors@hotmail.co.uk

VEALE WASBROUGH VIZARDS
Barnards Inn 86 Fetter Lane London EC4A 1AD
Tel: 020 7405 1234 *Fax:* 020 7405 4171
Dx: 6 LONDON/CHANCERY LN
E-mail: ajames@vwv.co.uk
Office: Bristol
Languages: French, German, Greek, Italian, Punjabi, Russian
Work: A1 A3 B1 C1 C2 C3 D2 E F1 I J1 K3 K4 L N O P Q R1 R2 S1 S2 T1 T2 W X Z(b,c,d,e,i,j,k,l,m,n,o,p,w)
Emergency Action, Agency, Advocacy, Fixed Fee Interview and Legal Aid undertaken
Ptr: Barber, Mr Richard T BSc. *Jun 1973
Barradale, Mr Christopher R J D Freeman of the City of London . *§Jun 1968
Blain, Mr Jeremy J LLB . *Jun 1976
Burden, Mr John J H . *§Dec 1968
Cuxson, Mrs Judith M. *Oct 1984
Green, Mrs Christine Mary BA. *Sep 1994
Hamilton, Mr Andrew James Roderick BA(Hons) . Dec 1980
Millson, Mr Anthony Edward LLB . *§Apr 1976
Mitchell, Mrs Sandra Ann FILEx Freeman of the City of London . *Jun 1997
Oddy, Mr Jonathan LLB. Apr 1998
Perry, Mr Ronald E LLB. *Mar 1970
Phelps, Tina . May 1993
Smith, Mr Nevil Irwin LLB(Hons). *May 1982
Soden-Bird, Mr Charles BA(Hons). *Jan 1998
Wilkins, Mrs Emma Louise LLB(Hons). *Sep 1996
Asoc: Burnige, Ms Martha. Jan 2005
Durham, Mr Jonathan Geoffrey LLB(Hons) Sep 2003
Eldridge-Hinmers, Mrs Tracey BA. Apr 1990
Ast: Giddy, Mr Nick LLB . Sep 2008
Godfrey, Mr Colin Robert LLB. *Sep 2009
Hall, Mr Alexander John. Sep 2007

VED & CO ‡
79a High Road Willesden London NW10 2SU
Tel: 020 8459 8686 *Fax:* 020 8459 1497
List of partners: V Ved
Languages: Gujarati
Work: D1 E F1 G H J1 L P S1 Z(i,l,p)
Emergency Action, Agency and Legal Aid undertaken
Ptr: Ved, Vijaykumar. *Mar 1981

VENNER SHIPLEY & CO ‡
20 Little Britain London EC1A 7DH
Tel: 020 7600 4212 *Fax:* 020 7600 4188

VENTERS SOLICITORS ‡
1-6 Camberwell Green Camberwell London SE5 7AD
Tel: 020 7277 0110 *Fax:* 020 7277 0132
Dx: 35310 CAMBERWELL GREEN
E-mail: info@venters.co.uk
List of partners: M Chapman, A Hinds, J M Venters
Office: Reigate
Work: B2 D1 D2 G H K1 K2 K3
Emergency Action, Agency, Advocacy, Fixed Fee Interview, Legal Aid undertaken and Legal Aid Franchise
Ptr: Hinds, Ms Annette LLB(Hons). *Dec 1998
Venters, Ms June Marion • Recorder . *Jan 1984
Chapman, Mr Micheal. NSP
Asoc: Nix, Miss Julie BA(Hons) . *Feb 2002
Ast: Cephas, Mrs Camella LLB(Hons) . *Mar 2011
Dawkins, Miss Andrea Loren LLB(Hons); LLM(Hons) . *Sep 1998
Nanovski, Ms Ana BA(Hons) . *May 2009

VICKERS & CO ‡
(in association with Leslie Oliver & Co)
183 Uxbridge Road West Ealing Ealing London W13 9AA
Tel: 020 8579 2559 / 8840 3999 *Fax:* 020 8567 6965
Dx: 5104 EALING
Emergency telephone 07831 271389
E-mail: reception@vickers-solicitors.co.uk
List of partners: A S Atchison, D Barnes, R S Drepaul, M Guyer, S J Ingall
Languages: French, Gujarati, Italian, Punjabi, Urdu
Work: B2 C1 D1 F1 G H K1 K2 K3 K4 L N Q S1 S2 T1 T2 V W
Emergency Action, Agency, Advocacy, Fixed Fee Interview and Legal Aid undertaken
Ptr: Atchison, Mr Alexander S LLB. *Dec 1974
Barnes, Mr David LLB. *Jul 1978
Drepaul, Mr Robert S BSc(Hons) . *Mar 1995
Guyer, Mr Maurice LLB ♦ . *§Oct 1984
Ingall, Mr Stephen J LLB(Warw). *§Jun 1980
Asoc: Chana, Miss Satbinder LLB . *Sep 1998
Ast: Chauhan, Miss Lina LLB . *Dec 1999
Kaur, Ms Manjit . *Sep 2007
McCorry, Mr David John BSc(Geography). *Dec 1999
McGrath, Mr Vincent Hugh LLB . *Feb 1990
Mitchell, Ms Laverne . Dec 2005
O'Sullivan, Mr Trevor Peter BA(Hons). *Aug 2003
Shergill, Ms Michelle . Jan 2009
Con: Enock, Mr John Richard. *Oct 1982
Friday, Ms Maxine LLB . *Dec 1988
Oliver, Mr Leslie M LLB ♦ . *Jun 1970
St Clair Evans, Ms Julie. *Jan 1995
Vickers, Mrs Lisa E LLB(Lond) . *Jan 1951

VICTOR LISSACK ROSCOE & COLEMAN ‡
70 Marylebone Lane London W1U 2PQ
Tel: 020 7487 2505 *Fax:* 020 7487 5005 *Dx:* 9020 WEST END
Emergency telephone 020 7487 2505
E-mail: law@victorlissack.co.uk
List of partners: R J Almond, M V Coleman, R M Dimmock, R S Dogra, R S Roscoe
Work: B2 E G H S1 S2 W Z(i,l,m)
Emergency Action, Agency, Advocacy, Legal Aid undertaken and Legal Aid Franchise
Ptr: Almond, Mr Richard J BA . *§Oct 1984
Coleman, Mrs Margot V LLB ★ Deputy District Judge *May 1978
Dimmock, Miss Rosalind M BA(Manc). *Jun 1986
Dogra, Mr Ravinder S BA(Hons) ★ . Jun 1996
Roscoe, Mr Robert S ★ Deputy District Judge. *§Nov 1976
Ast: Binns, Mr John David LLB; MPhil . Oct 2000

VICTORY AT LAW SOLICITORS ‡
74a Woolwich Road Greenwich London SE10 0JU
Tel: 020 8853 8335 *Fax:* 020 8853 8338
E-mail: solicitor@victoryatlaw.com

VICTORY SOLICITORS ‡
136 Streatham High Road London SW16 1BW
Tel: 020 8769 6838 *Fax:* 020 8769 3269
E-mail: admin@victorysolicitors.com

BENJAMIN VINCENT SOLICITORS ‡
49 High Street Wanstead London E11 2AA
Tel: 020 8532 2266

VINCENT FRENCH & BROWNE ‡
Rugby Chambers 2 Rugby Street London WC1N 3QU
Tel: 020 7831 4994 *Fax:* 020 7831 4054 *Dx:* 37993 KINGSWAY
Emergency telephone 020 8748 0991
E-mail: info@vfb.co.uk
List of partners: V M C S Browne, V M N Browne, J L McKenzie, G R Mehrji
Work: A2 A3 B1 B2 C1 C2 C3 D1 D2 E F1 F2 G I J1 J2 K1 K2 K3 L M1 M2 N O P Q R1 R2 S1 S2 T1 T2 U1 U2 V W Z(a,b,c,d,e,f,g,h,i,j,k,l,o,p,q,r,w,za)
Emergency Action, Agency, Advocacy, Fixed Fee Interview, Legal Aid undertaken and Member of Accident Line
Ptr: Browne, Valentine M C S LLB. *Sep 1976
Browne, Mr Vincent M N LLB(Hons). *May 1980
McKenzie, Mr John Laurence LLB(Auckland); Admitted Feb 1971(NZ) . *Dec 1979
Mehrji, Ms Gillian R BA . *Apr 1987

VINSON & ELKINS LLP ‡
33rd Floor CityPoint One Ropemaker Street London EC2Y 9UE
Tel: 020 7065 6000 *Fax:* 020 7065 6001
E-mail: amsimang@velaw.com

VIRGO SOLICITORS ‡
Imperial House 64 Willoughby Lane Tottenham London N17 0SP
Tel: 020 8885 3999 *Fax:* 020 8885 4114 *Dx:* 36211 EDMONTON
E-mail: virgosolicitors@btconnect.com

VIRTUAL LAWYERS LIMITED ‡
Hyde Park House 5 Manfred Road London SW15 2RS
Tel: 0330 100 0320
E-mail: info@virtuallaw.eu

JOAN VIS SOLICITORS ‡
Grove Business Centre Unit w58 London N17 9TA
Tel: 020 8808 8969

VIZARDS LIVESEY CAMERON WALKER ‡
Warwick House 64-65 Cowcross Street London EC1M 6EG
Tel: 020 7490 5861 *Fax:* 020 7253 9872
Dx: 138786 CLERKENWELL
E-mail: info@vlcw.com

DAVID VLAHOS SOLICITORS ‡
64 Knightsbridge London SW1X 7JF
Tel: 020 7590 3175 *Fax:* 020 7590 9601
E-mail: david@davidvlahos.co.uk

VOLKS HEDLEYS ‡
26 Old Brompton Road South Kensington Kensington & Chelsea London SW7 3DL
Tel: 020 7584 6733 *Fax:* 020 7584 9577
Dx: 35762 SOUTH KENSINGTON
E-mail: volkshedleys@btconnect.com
List of partners: C L Horsnell, K M Rimmer
Languages: French, German, Portuguese
Agency undertaken
Ptr: Horsnell, Mr Christopher L BA. *Apr 1988

Rimmer, Mr Keith M BA . . . . *Apr 1985
Con: Henshall, Mr David G LLB(Soton) . . . . *Nov 1983

WGS SOLICITORS ‡
133 Praed Street Westminster London W2 1RN
Tel: 020 7723 1656 *Fax:* 020 7724 6936 *Dx:* 38754 PADDINGTON
E-mail: sandrat@wgs.co.uk
List of partners: C M Farmer, J R M Gerber, C Law, D J Levy, M E A O'Hara, J Shapiro, S B Wegg-Prosser
Languages: French, Hebrew, Spanish
Work: C1 E F1 J1 K1 L M1 O P Q R2 S1 T1 T2 W Z(f,i,l)
Ptr: Farmer, Mr Christopher M LLB(Lond) . . . . *§Jan 1967
Gerber, Mr Jonathan R M LLB . . . . Sep 1991
Law, Mr Charles . . . . Jun 1980
Levy, Mrs Deborah Jane LLB(Hons) . . . . Aug 1983
O'Hara, Miss Moira Elizabeth Ann LLB . . . . Aug 1987
Shapiro, Mr Jerome LLB . . . . *Jun 1995
Wegg-Prosser, Mr Stephen B BA . . . . *§Nov 1971
Asoc: Farmer, Miss Charlotte BSc . . . . Sep 1998
Con: Glasner, Mr Danny S M LLB . . . . *Nov 1977

WSM SOLICITORS LLP ‡
Woodcock House Gibbard Mews 37-38 High Street London SW19 5BY
Tel: 020 8879 4300 *Fax:* 020 8946 8073
Dx: 35053 WIMBLEDON VILLAGE
E-mail: tim.sweetland@wsmsolicitors.com

WT LAW LLP ‡
3rd Floor 46 Aldgate High Street London EC3N 1AL
Tel: 020 7680 8620 *Fax:* 020 7709 0101 *Dx:* 514 LONDON/CITY
E-mail: info@wtlawllp.com

WTS LEGAL ‡
Flat 4 11 Parsifal Road London NW6 1UG
Tel: 020 7435 4588
E-mail: rachel@wtsassociates.co.uk

WADESONS SOLICITORS ‡
Riverbank House 1 Putney Bridge Approach London SW6 3JD
Tel: 020 7384 3333 *Fax:* 020 7371 9949
E-mail: law@wadesons.fsnet.co.uk
List of partners: R T Wadeson
Work: C1 E J1 N Q W Z(p)
Agency undertaken
SPr: Wadeson, Mr Roy T BA . . . . *Feb 1987
Con: Thakker, Mrs Daksha LLB(Hons); LLM(Hons)(Lond) . *Sep 1993

WAGNER & CO ‡
25 Church Crescent London N20 0JR
Tel: 020 8361 5588 *Fax:* 020 8368 4871
E-mail: mark@wagnerandco.com

WAINWRIGHT & CUMMINS ‡
413a Brixton Road Lambeth London SW9 7DG
Tel: 020 7737 9330 *Fax:* 020 7737 9331 *Dx:* 58753 BRIXTON
Emergency telephone 020 7737 9330
E-mail: solicitors@wainwrightcummins.co.uk
List of partners: J V Cummins, A J Wainwright
Office: London SW2
Languages: Arabic, Polish, Spanish, Swedish
Work: B2 D1 G H K1 L N Z(l)
Emergency Action, Agency, Advocacy, Legal Aid undertaken and Member of Accident Line
Ptr: Cummins, Mr Jonathan V BA . . . . *Mar 1981
Wainwright, Mr Andrew J BA . . . . *Mar 1981
Asoc: Antolin, Ms Sonia LLB(Hons); DipLaw . . . . Jun 2000
Cummins, Mrs Jane MA . . . . Feb 1998
Fitzgerald, Mr David . . . . Jan 2003
Kurtha, Mrs Sunila BSc; MPhil . . . . *May 1999
Ast: Amadi, Mr Emmanuel BA; LLB . . . . Mar 1998

WAINWRIGHT & CUMMINS
30a Acre Lane Lambeth London SW2 5SG
Tel: 020 7326 7460 *Fax:* 020 7733 0463 *Dx:* 58753 BRIXTON
E-mail: jonathan.cummins@wainwrightcummins.co.uk
Office: London SW9
Languages: Fanti, Ga, Twi
Work: B2 D1 D2 E G H K1 K3 L S1 S2 W Z(g,l)
Agency and Legal Aid undertaken
Asoc: Djan-Krofa, Mrs Maame Adjoa LLB . . . . Mar 2006
Con: Atkinson, Mr Edward Charles LLB . . . . Jan 1980
Burton, Mr Peter Harman ★ . . . . Jun 1970
Wynter, Mr Alphonso MA . . . . Sep 1984

WALDEGRAVES ‡
Ealing House 33 Hanger Lane London W5 3HJ
Tel: 020 8166 0881 *Fax:* 020 8150 7852

WALKER & CO SOLICITORS ‡
210 Borough High Street London SE1 1JX
Tel: 020 7939 7757 *Fax:* 020 3006 8936
E-mail: commodities@walkerandco.org

WALKER SMITH WAY
Shakespeare House 168 Lavender Hill London SW11 5TG
Tel: 0844 346 3100 *Fax:* 0844 346 3200
E-mail: enquiries@walkersmithway.com
Office: Ashton-under-Lyne, Birmingham, Chester, Liverpool, Wrexham

WALKER TOMASZEWSKI SOLICITORS ‡
79 Gloucester Avenue Primrose Hill Camden London NW1 8LB
Tel: 020 7722 7740 *Fax:* 020 7722 7057 *Dx:* 96855 PRIMROSE HILL
List of partners: A Tomaszewski, C R Walker
Languages: Polish
Work: B1 C1 C2 C3 E F1 I J1 L O Q R1 S1 W Z(c,e,f,l)
Agency undertaken
Ptr: Tomaszewski, Mr Andrew LLB . . . . Nov 1988
Walker, Mr Charles R LLB(L'pool) . . . . *Dec 1987

WALKERS ‡
6 Gracechurch Street London EC3V 0AT
Tel: 020 7220 4999 *Fax:* 020 7220 4998
E-mail: info@walkerseurope.com

WALTONS & MORSE LLP ‡
77 Gracechurch Street London EC3V 0DL
Est: 1848
Tel: 020 7623 4255 *Fax:* 020 7626 4153 *Dx:* 1065 LONDON/CITY
E-mail: waltons@wamlaw.co.uk
Web: www.waltonsandmorse.com
List of partners: C Chatfield, C Dunn, M A Lloyd, D A Perry, A Purssell
Languages: French, Japanese, Spanish
Work: A3 M2 O Q Z(a,j)
Ptr: Chatfield, Mr Christopher LLM; DipLP; LLB . . . . . *Sep 1997
Dunn, Mr Christopher . . . . *Oct 1991
Lloyd, Mr Mark Andrew LLB . . . . *Nov 1994
Perry, Mr David A LLB . . . . *§Dec 1973
Purssell, Mr Andrew LLB(Manc) . . . . *Apr 1994
Ast: Biltoo, Mr Michael Alexander LLB; LLM . . . . Jul 1983
Burton, Miss Shaan . . . . Sep 2009
Charles-Jones, Mr Peter LLB . . . . *May 2009
Clark, Mr David BSc(Econ)(Hons); CPE; LSF . . . . . Nov 1995
Cook, Miss Paula Denise LLB(Hons) . . . . Mar 2008
Cordonnier, Ms Sophie LLB; LLM; Maitrise de Droit Prive; Master en Droit Maritime . . . . Oct 2009
Kaijo, Ms Naoko LLB; LLM . . . . Oct 2007
McCulloch, Ms Emily LLB(Hons); LLM(Wales) . . . . . Sep 2006
Manthorpe, Ms Joanna . . . . *Jan 2003
Pratts, Mr Christopher . . . . *Oct 2003

Categories of work: Shipping and Transportation, Insurance and Reinsurance.

WARAN & CO ‡
5a Clapham Common Southside London SW4 7AA
Tel: 020 7498 3328 *Fax:* 020 7498 2305
Dx: 53254 CLAPHAM COMMON
E-mail: mail@waran.co.uk
List of partners: A Vigneswaran
Languages: Hindi, Sinhalese, Tamil, Urdu
Work: B1 C1 D1 E G J1 K1 L S1 V W Z(i)
Emergency Action, Fixed Fee Interview and Legal Aid undertaken
Ptr: Vigneswaran, Arunthathy . . . . *Sep 1983

WARD BENGER ‡
8 Warwick Court Gray's Inn London WC1R 5DJ
Tel: 020 7242 2900 *Fax:* 020 7242 2500
E-mail: ward.benger@virgin.net
List of partners: D J Benger
Ptr: Benger, Mr David J LLB . . . . *Oct 1988

WARD BOLTON ‡
38 Wigmore Street London W1U 2RU
Tel: 020 7060 1285 *Fax:* 020 7060 1288
E-mail: arfan.shaikh@wardbolton.com

WARNER ASSOCIATES ‡
85-86 Bayham Street London NW1 0AG
Tel: 020 7788 4111 *Fax:* 020 7788 4222 *Dx:* 57054 CAMDEN TOWN
E-mail: law@warnerassociates.org.uk

WATERFIELDS SOLICITORS ‡
445 Roman Road London E3 5LX
Tel: 020 8981 4460 *Fax:* 020 8981 1223
E-mail: gs@waterfieldssolicitors.co.uk

THE WATERFRONT PARTNERSHIP SOLICITORS ‡
The Leathermarket Lafone House Leathermarket Street London SE1 3ER
Tel: 020 7234 0200 *Fax:* 020 7234 0600
E-mail: info@waterfrontpartnership.com

WATERMANS ‡
Spencer House 2 Spencer Avenue Palmers Green London N13 4TR
Tel: 020 8888 2820 *Fax:* 020 8881 3001 *Dx:* 56951 BOWES PARK
List of partners: C Christodoulou
Languages: French, Hebrew
Work: B1 C1 G J1 K1 L M1 P S1 W Z(c,i,p)
Emergency Action and Legal Aid undertaken
Ptr: Christodoulou, Mr Christopher . . . . Dec 1976

WATERSON HICKS ‡
65 Fenchurch Street London EC3M 4BE
Tel: 020 7929 6060 *Fax:* 020 7929 3748
E-mail: law@watersonhicks.com
List of partners: J W Hicks
Languages: Catalan, French, Spanish
Work: A3 C1 M1 M2 O P Q Z(a,j)
Ptr: Hicks, Mr John W BA(Dunelm) . . . . *Dec 1986

WATMORES ‡
Chancery House 53-64 Chancery Lane London WC2A 1RP
Tel: 020 7430 1512 *Fax:* 020 7405 7382
Dx: 246 LONDON/CHANCERY LN
E-mail: enquiries@watmores.co.uk
List of partners: G N Alhadeff, J P T Curran, J P Grunewald, S C Johnson, R K Mullins, P J Parker, D Weir
Work: A3 J2 M2 N Q Z(c,j,q)
Ptr: Alhadeff, Mr Guy N BA . . . . *Jan 1989
Curran, Mr Jerome P T MA(Oxon) . . . . Nov 1978
Grunewald, Mr Jonathan P MA(Oxon) . . . . *May 1981
Johnson, Mr Simon C LLB(Hons) . . . . *Nov 1998
Mullins, Mr Ronald K MA . . . . *Jan 1986
Parker, Mr Philip John LLB . . . . *Nov 1994
Weir, Mr David MA . . . . *Mar 1995
Con: Mullins, Dawn . . . . Oct 1988

WATSON BURTON LLP
Floor 29 30 St Mary Axe London EC3A 8BF
Tel: 0845 901 2100 *Fax:* 0845 901 2030 *Dx:* 124408 LONDON/CITY
E-mail: enquiries@watsonburton.com
Office: Leeds, Newcastle upon Tyne
Work: A3 B1 B2 C1 C2 C3 E F1 F2 I J1 J2 L M1 M2 O P Q R1 R2 S1 S2 T1 T2 U1 U2 W X Z(b,c,d,f,h,j,n,o,p,q,u,w,za)
Ptr: Jones, Mr David . . . . May 1976
Dir: O'Donovon, Mr Robert . . . . Nov 1976
Asoc: Yates, Mr Gareth . . . . Oct 2001

WATSON FARLEY & WILLIAMS ‡
15 Appold Street London EC2A 2HB
Tel: 020 7814 8000 *Fax:* 020 7814 8141 *Dx:* 530 LONDON/CITY
E-mail: londoninfo@wfw.com
List of partners: A Baird, M E Buchan, C T Buss, J C C Comyn, F Dunne, P J Flint, M Greville, R S Henderson, A Hutcheon, D E Kavanagh, S J Kavanagh, J P Kellett, M A Kenny, M J L'Estrange, M J Lawson, M M Llewellyn, C C Lowe, J Mellmann, A J W Muriel, D N Osborne, R L Parry, C A L Preston, S A Rigg, A Rooth, C S C Smallwood, M L Vernell, C M H Walford, D J Warder, J D Wardle, M A Watson, J A D Watters, A H Wettern
Languages: Cantonese, Dutch, French, German, Greek, Hebrew, Italian, Norwegian, Punjabi, Russian, Spanish, Swedish
Work: A1 B1 C1 C2 C3 E I J1 L M1 M2 N O Q R1 S1 T1 T2 Z(a,b,e,i,j,o)
Emergency Action undertaken
Ptr: Baird, Mr Andrew . . . . Nov 1989
Buchan, Ms M Elizabeth BA(Cantab) . . . . Dec 1988
Buss, Mr Charles Tilden BA . . . . Jan 1993
Comyn, Mr John C C . . . . *Mar 1980
Dunne, Mr Frank . . . . Apr 1980
Flint, Mr Peter Jeremy BA(Oxon) . . . . Jan 1984
Greville, Mr Michael . . . . Jul 1990
Henderson, Mr Richard S LLB(Hons) . . . . Apr 1989
Hutcheon, Mr Andrew . . . . Oct 1992
Kavanagh, Mr David E BA . . . . Oct 1991
Kavanagh, Mr Simon J BA(Hons) . . . . Nov 1987
Kellett, Mr Jonathan P BA(Kent) . . . . *Feb 1980
Kenny, Mr Michael A BA(Oxon); MA . . . . Oct 1978
L'Estrange, Mr Michael J LLB; ATII . . . . Oct 1990
Lawson, Mr Mark J LLB . . . . *Oct 1984
Llewellyn, Mrs Maria M LLB . . . . Oct 1981
Lowe, Mr Christopher C . . . . Nov 1987
Mellmann, Ms Jan . . . . Nov 1989
Muriel, Mr Andrew J W LLB . . . . *Feb 1988
Osborne, Mr David N MA(Cantab) . . . . Apr 1981
Parry, Mr Robin L LLB . . . . *Jan 1987
Preston, Mr Christopher A L FTII . . . . *Jul 1975
Rigg, Ms Shirley A LLB(Newc) . . . . *Sep 1988
Rooth, Mr Anthony BA(Cantab) . . . . Apr 1975
Smallwood, Mr Charles St C MA(Oxon) . . . . Sep 1979
Vernell, Mr Michael L BA(Oxon) . . . . Jun 1975
Walford, Mr Charles M H MA(Cantab) . . . . *Apr 1980
Warder, Mr David J BA(Cantab) . . . . *Jul 1976
Wardle, Mr J Douglas MA(Oxon) . . . . *Nov 1986
Watson, Mr Martin A BA(Cantab) . . . . *Jun 1971
Watters, Mr James A D BA . . . . Oct 1972
Wettern, Mr Andrew H BA(Cantab) . . . . *Mar 1981
Ast: Budd, Mr Neil G LLB . . . . Nov 1988
Carstairs, Mr Philip . . . . Sep 1997
Cooper, Ms Lorna BA; MA(Cantab); DipLaw; DipLP . . Sep 1996
Dibble, Mr Richard D . . . . Oct 1991
Dolder, Mr Adam D MA; LLM . . . . Sep 1995
Glen, Miss Pauline H MA Swansea Law Society Prize . Sep 1996
Harris, Ms Angharad . . . . Sep 1993
Herard, Ms Florence . . . . Aug 1994
Howard, Miss Christina LLB . . . . *Oct 1997
Laurent, Ms Rachel A LLB . . . . *May 1993
Legezynska, Marzena . . . . Nov 1991
Lescure, Alison BA(Hons); CPE; LPC . . . . Oct 1997
Lokholm, Ms Ellen Sofie BSc . . . . Nov 1995
Margrett, Ms Susan R . . . . Mar 1994
O'Donnell, Mr Michael D . . . . Feb 1988
Paleokrassas, Mr George . . . . Sep 1994
Parrinder, Miss Anna . . . . Sep 1996
Penn, Mr James F W . . . . Jun 1981
Steel, Ms Frances LLB . . . . Nov 1991
Taylor, Ms Claire Louise LLB(Hons) . . . . *Oct 1995
Vervitsioti, Ms Katerina . . . . Feb 1997
Vig, Miss Rippan J K LLB(Hons); DipLP . . . . Oct 1996
Weston, Mr Rubin BA(Oxon) . . . . Sep 1995
Con: Berg, Mr Alan G J BA(Oxon) . . . . *§Jul 1974
Farley, Mr Alastair H MA(Cantab) . . . . *Jun 1971

WATSON MARSHAL ‡
(incorporating Watson Sons & Room; Marshal & Co)
4 Castle Row Horticultural Place Chiswick London W4 4JQ
Tel: 020 8987 0100 *Fax:* 020 8987 8600 *Dx:* 80312 CHISWICK
E-mail: watsonmarshal@btinternet.com
List of partners: S L Davies
Work: E K4 L S1 S2 W
Ptr: Davies, Ms Susan Louise BA(Hons); ACII Notary Public . . . . *Jan 1990
Ast: Stenning, Mrs Jane Louise . . . . *Sep 1988

WATTS & LEEDING ‡
4 Novar Road London SE9 2DN
Tel: 020 8850 6366 *Fax:* 020 8294 1099
List of partners: J V Leeding, M S Newton
Work: F1 J1 K1 L S1 S2 W
Fixed Fee Interview undertaken
Ptr: Leeding, Mr John V BA . . . . *Jan 1968
Newton, Mr Michael S BA . . . . *Jan 1982
Ast: Stewart, Miss Emma Joy LLB(Hons); DipLP . . . . . *Nov 1998

WEAVER ROSE SOLICITORS ‡
39 The Mall Ealing London W5 3TP
Tel: 020 8579 6060 *Fax:* 020 8579 3030

D J WEBB & CO ‡
24 Alie Street London E1 8DE
Tel: 020 7480 5999 *Fax:* 020 7488 2030
E-mail: djwebb@webbimmigration.com
List of partners: D J Webb
Languages: Bengali, Hindi
Work: Z(i)
Legal Aid Franchise
Ptr: Webb, Mr David J LLB(B'ham) . . . . *Aug 1992

WEBSTER DIXON LLP ‡
Fourth Floor Thavies House 3-4 Holborn Circus London EC1N 2HA
Tel: 020 7353 8300 *Fax:* 020 7353 8400
Dx: 55 LONDON/CHANCERY LN
E-mail: info@websterdixon.com
List of partners: D Dixon, M Webster
Work: B1 C1 C2 E F1 J1 L N O Q S2 U1 Z(d,e,f,h,k,l)
Agency and Legal Aid undertaken
Ptr: Dixon, Miss Dawn LLB . . . . *Oct 1990
Webster, Mr Michael LLB(Hons) . . . . *Nov 1989
Ast: Kidd, Mr Daniel LLB(Hons) . . . . *Aug 2003

See p2 for the Key to Work Categories & other symbols

WEDLAKE BELL LLP ‡
52 Bedford Row London WC1R 4LR
Tel: 020 7395 3000 *Fax:* 020 7395 3100
Dx: 166 LONDON/CHANCERY LN
E-mail: legal@wedlakebell.com
List of partners: M Arnold, J W Bellhouse, T Bird, A Cook, J P Cornthwaite, R Dabydeen, P J Day, R A Dolman, D M Earl, J R Fluker, S Freeman, M Gardner, A Gould, A P H Heath-Saunders, R J Hewitt, C A Hicks, R L V Isham, D E Israel, A L Joyce, K Lalli, E A K Loveday, R Mahal, P Matthews, E C Metcalf, J R Muncey, H S Platt, S Reeves, M Ridsdale, C A L Weber, J Wolstenholme
Languages: Dutch, French, German, Italian, Punjabi, Russian, Spanish, Swedish, Welsh
Work: A3 B1 C1 C2 C3 E F1 F2 I J1 L M1 O P Q R1 R2 S1 S2 T1 T2 U1 U2 W Z(b,c,d,e,f,j,k,n,o,p,w,y,z)
Emergency Action and Fixed Fee Interview undertaken
Ptr: Arnold, Mr Martin LLB(Hons) . . . . *Dec 1989
Bellhouse, Mr Joseph W BA(Hons); MSc Hudson Prize Best Dissertation 1996 . . . . *Nov 1985
Bird, Mr Tim. Oct 1996
Cook, Ms Anna BA(Leeds) . . . . Sep 1997
Cornthwaite, Mr Jonathan P MA(Cantab) . . . . . . *Sep 1979
Dabydeen, Mr Robin BA(Hons); LLM . . . . Nov 1996
Day, Mr Peter J LLB. . . . . *Oct 1991
Dolman, Mr Robert A MA(Oxon). . . . . *Jul 1971
Earl, Mr David M LLB . . . . *Nov 1986
Fluker, Mr John R BSc . . . . *Feb 1982
Freeman, Mr Simon. . . . . Nov 1995
Gardner, Mr Michael BA(Hons) . . . . Nov 1995
Gould, Ms Alice. . . . . Dec 1991
Heath-Saunders, Mr Adrian P H LLB Sweet & Maxwell Law Prize; Winston Churchill Memorial Prize. . . . . *Apr 1989
Hewitt, Mr Richard J LLM(Lond). . . . . §Mar 1976
Hicks, Mr Charles A MA(Cantab) . . . . *§Jan 1971
Isham, Mr Richard L V LLB . . . . *Nov 1986
Israel, Mr David E BA(Hons) . . . . *Oct 1993
Joyce, Mr Andrew L MA(Cantab) . . . . *§Oct 1978
Lalli, Ms Kim LLB . . . . Apr 1989
Loveday, Ms Emma A K LLB . . . . *Dec 1987
Mahal, Mr Ravinder. . . . . Oct 1994
Matthews, Mr Philip LLB(Hull). . . . . *Jun 1978
Metcalf, Miss Eleanor C LLB . . . . *May 1992
Muncey, Mr John R LLB. . . . . *Oct 1983
Platt, Miss Hilary S BA; MA . . . . *Sep 1992
Reeves, Ms Suzanne LLB(Exon) . . . . *Apr 1979
Ridsdale, Mr Michael . . . . Sep 2001
Weber, Mr Clive A L LLB(Bris). . . . . *Oct 1976
Wolstenholme, Mrs Jane . . . . Nov 1991
Ast: Allfree, Mr Thomas James BSc(Hons); DipLaw . . . . Oct 1999
Copeland, Miss Fay LLB Law Society Annual Prize for Outstanding Performance (LPC) 1999; Nigel Asquith Prize 1999 . . . . Oct 2001
Dickson, Miss Aisha LLB . . . . Sep 1998
Elliott, Miss Sarah BSc(Hons). . . . . Sep 2002
Lewis-Vivas, Mr Justin LLB . . . . Sep 1998
McCourt, Miss Grainne S LLB; LSF . . . . Mar 1994
Con: Beattie, Miss Jennifer J B. . . . . *§Jun 1972
Carr, Mr David J H LLB . . . . Apr 1981
Cowlishaw, Mr John P LLB . . . . *Dec 1975
Eyre, Ms Jennet. . . . . Oct 1978
Weatherill, Mr Barry N A MA(Cantab) . . . . *§Apr 1966

WEIGHTMANS LLP
2nd Floor 6 New Street Square New Fetter Lane London EC4A 3BF
Tel: 020 7822 1900 *Fax:* 020 7822 1901
Dx: 310 LONDON/CHANCERY LN
Office: Birmingham, Dartford, Knutsford, Leicester, Liverpool, Manchester (2 offices)
Mem: Bannister, Mr Alan LLB(Lond). . . . . *Jun 1975
Henry, Mr Thomas M LLB. . . . . *Oct 1982
Loveday, Mr Simon C BA . . . . *May 1983
Williams, Mr Brian. . . . . *§Jan 1965

WEIL GOTSHAL & MANGES ‡
110 Fetter Lane London EC4A 1AY
Tel: 020 7903 1000 *Fax:* 020 7903 0990 *Dx:* 124402 LONDON/CITY
E-mail: weil.london@weil.com
Work: A3 B1 C1 C2 C3 E O T1 U1 Z(b)

AUSTIN WEINBERG ‡
24a Church Lane London N2 8DT
Tel: 020 8815 0720 *Fax:* 020 8815 0503 *Dx:* 52063 EAST FINCHLEY
E-mail: austin@austinweinberg.co.uk
List of partners: A V Weinberg
Work: E S1 S2
SPr: Weinberg, Mr Austin V LLB . . . . *Apr 1972

PAUL WEISS ‡
Alder Castle 10 Noble Street London EC2V 7JU
Tel: 020 7367 1600 *Fax:* 020 7367 1600

WELBECK ANIN SOLICITORS ‡
92 Coldharbour Lane London SE5 9PU
Tel: 020 7733 3838 *Fax:* 020 7738 3939
Dx: 35306 CAMBERWELL GREEN
E-mail: welbeckanin92@btconnect.com

WELBECK LAW LLP ‡
1 Bentinck Street London W1U 2ED
Tel: 020 7467 3999 *Fax:* 020 7467 3990
Dx: 42706 OXFORD CIRCUS NORTH
E-mail: info@welbecklawllp.co.uk

MICHAEL WELCH & CO ‡
Ruskin House 40-41 Museum Street London WC1A 1LT
Tel: 020 7831 4668 *Fax:* 020 7831 4476
E-mail: michael@michaelwelch.co.uk
Languages: French
Work: B1 C1 C2 O Z(q)

WELLERS LAW GROUP LLP
7-8 Grays Inn Square London WC1R 5JQ
Tel: 020 7242 7265 *Fax:* 020 7405 1719
Dx: 36 LONDON/CHANCERY LN
E-mail: cm@wellerslawgroup.com
Office: Bromley
Work: A1 B1 C1 C2 C3 E F1 J1 K1 K2 K3 L N O Q R2 S1 S2 T1 W Z(c,d,e,f,i,j,k,l,m,o,p,q,r)
Ptr: Mallet, Mr Robert G MA(Dundee) . . . . *Apr 1978
Martin, Mr Paul J . . . . *§Nov 1978
Scott, Mr Stephen D BA(Dunelm) . . . . *§Jun 1978
Summers, Mr Anthony J MA(Oxon) . . . . *§Nov 1978
Topping, Mr Giles Q LLB . . . . *Nov 1977
Ast: Cooke, Mr Andrew LLB . . . . *Sep 2008
Georgiou, Mr George Stavros BA; LLB . . . . Nov 2005
Con: Cooke, Mr Jonathan C . . . . Nov 1970

WEST LONDON LAW SOLICITORS ‡
Boundary House Boston Road Ealing London W7 2QE
Tel: 020 8434 3508 *Fax:* 020 8434 3740

WESTMANS LAW ‡
6 Kings Parade Okehampton Road Kensal Rise London NW10 3ED
Tel: 020 8912 2470 *Fax:* 020 8181 7074 *Dx:* 53950 KENSAL RISE
E-mail: office@westmanslaw.co.uk

WHALE ROCK LEGAL LIMITED ‡
4th Floor 15 Basinghall Street London EC2V 5BR
Tel: 020 7726 5080 *Fax:* 020 7726 5099
E-mail: nigel.kushner@whalerocklegal.com

WHARTON & WHARTON ‡
614 Linen Hall 162-168 Regent Street Westminster London W1B 5TG
Tel: 020 7038 3577 *Fax:* 020 7038 3502 *Dx:* 140540 PICCADILLY 5
E-mail: cwharton@whartonlaw.com
List of partners: K C Wharton
Work: C1 C2 Z(o)
Ptr: Wharton, Mr Kurt Christian MA(Oxon). . . . . *Nov 1988

WHATLEY & CO ‡
10b Colin Parade Sheaveshill Avenue Colindale Barnet London NW9 6SG
Tel: 020 8205 1411 / 8205 8931 *Fax:* 020 8200 5636
E-mail: s.lee@whatleyandco.co.uk
List of partners: S M Lee
Work: E S1
SPr: Lee, Mr Stephen M . . . . *Feb 1974

J B WHEATLEY & CO ‡
190-196 Deptford High Street London SE8 3PR
Tel: 020 8479 8000 *Fax:* 020 8691 2835 *Dx:* 56700 DEPTFORD
Emergency telephone 020 8479 8030
E-mail: enquiry@jbwheatley.co.uk
List of partners: C Blacklaws, L S Kaiser, R G Scotter, P D Southern, K Spence
Work: D1 G H K1 K2 L N Q S1 S2 W Z(l,m)
Emergency Action, Agency, Advocacy, Legal Aid undertaken, Legal Aid Franchise and Member of Accident Line
Ptr: Blacklaws, Ms Christina BA . . . . Jan 1991
Kaiser, Ms Louise Sophie LLB. . . . . *Feb 1996
Scotter, Mr Richard G LLB . . . . *Mar 1984
Southern, Mr Paul D BA. . . . . *Apr 1979
Spence, Miss Kerry LLB. . . . . *Oct 1992
Ast: Grace, Mr Richard H . . . . Jun 1981
Kaiser, Miss Stephanie Catherine LLB. . . . . *Nov 1999
Lalli, Ms Amanjit Kaur. . . . . .Jul 2000

WHELAN WORNER LIMITED ‡
48 Charles Street London W1J 5EN
Tel: 020 7409 1872
E-mail: patrick.whelan@whelanworner.com

WHIMSTERS SOLICITORS ‡
72 Foyle Road Blackheath London SE3 7RH
Tel: 020 8269 2444 *Fax:* 020 8269 0101 *Dx:* 50918 BLACKHEATH
List of partners: P W Whimster
Fixed Fee Interview undertaken
Ptr: Whimster, Mr Peter William LLB(Hons) . . . . *§Jan 1990

WHITE & CASE LLP ‡
5 Old Broad Street London EC2N 1DW
Tel: 020 7532 1000 *Fax:* 020 7532 1001
List of partners: R J Bamforth, J M H Bellhouse, M R Cole
Ptr: Bamforth, Mr Richard J LLB(Lond) . . . . *Sep 1990
Bellhouse, Mr John M H BA(Cantab) . . . . *§Jun 1972
Cole, Ms Margaret R MA(Cantab). . . . . Oct 1985
Asoc: Baker, Mr David Gordon LLB(Dundee) . . . . Oct 1995
Worrall, Mr John N LLB(Warw) . . . . Nov 1991
Ast: Bissett, Mr Mark. . . . . Sep 1997
Con: Brett, Mr Hugh M D MA(Oxon) . . . . *Nov 1967

WHITE & CO ‡
190 Clarence Gate Gardens Glentworth Street London NW1 6AD
Tel: 020 7258 0206 *Fax:* 020 7258 1096 *Dx:* 41720 MARYLEBONE 2
E-mail: info@whiteandcosolicitors.com
List of partners: G H White, T D White
Office: Gloucester
Work: E L Q S1 S2 W
Ptr: White, Mrs Gillian H BA. . . . . Dec 1988
White, Mr Timothy D . . . . *Jun 1981

WHITECROSS SOLICITORS ‡
150 Whitecross Street Islington London EC1Y 8JL
Tel: 020 7251 5533 *Fax:* 020 7251 5566
Dx: 33858 FINSBURY SQUARE
E-mail: enquiries@whitecrosslawyers.com
List of partners: F Bishi, O Oluwole
Work: J1 Q S1 S2 W Z(i)
Ptr: Bishi, Mr Folarin LLB . . . . *Jan 1999
Oluwole, Mr Olurotimi LLB . . . . *Jun 2004

WHITEFIELDS SOLICITORS ‡
Bank House 618 Lea Bridge Road Leyton London E10 6AP
Tel: 020 3208 0980 *Fax:* 020 8558 7912 *Dx:* 32027 WALTHAMSTOW
E-mail: info@whitefieldslaw.co.uk

WHITEHORSE SOLICITORS ‡
Suite 217 Island Business Centre 18-36 Wellington Street London SE18 6PF
Tel: 020 8317 1293 *Fax:* 020 8465 7747 *Dx:* 33321 WOOLWICH
E-mail: info@whitehorsesolicitors.com

CAROLINE WHITELEY ‡
9 The Postern Barbican London EC2Y 8BJ
Tel: 020 7638 4219 *Fax:* 020 7588 4321
E-mail: clw@cwhiteley.co.uk

WHITELOCK & STORR ‡
4 Bloomsbury Square London WC1A 2RL
Tel: 020 7405 3913 *Fax:* 020 7404 4131 *Dx:* 35739 BLOOMSBURY
Emergency telephone 07766 407408
E-mail: info@whitelockandstorr.com
List of partners: H W Cox, D V Leccacorvi
Languages: French, Hebrew, Italian, Turkish, Yiddish
Work: B2 G H
Emergency Action, Agency, Advocacy, Fixed Fee Interview, Legal Aid undertaken and Legal Aid Franchise
Ptr: Cox, Mr Hugh William BSc . . . . *Sep 2005
Leccacorvi, Mr Dante Vincenzo LLB ★ . . . . *Feb 1992
Ast: Kerslake, Miss Sarrah Jayne LLB ● . . . . *Jan 2007
Kumrai, Ms Anita . . . . *Oct 1999
Stringer, Ms Rose LLB; MA ★. . . . . *Oct 2006

WHITSTONS ‡
87 Vanbrugh Park Blackheath London SE3 7AL
Tel: 020 8853 5226 *Fax:* 020 8853 5226
List of partners: M G Whitston
Agency and Advocacy undertaken
Ptr: Whitston, Mr Martin G LLB(Wales) . . . . *Jan 1982

WHITTINGDALES ‡
(in association with Studio Legale Di Stefano; Rome)
Chancery House 53-64 Chancery Lane London WC2A 1QU
Tel: 020 7831 5591 *Fax:* 020 7430 0448
Dx: 111 LONDON/CHANCERY LN
E-mail: mrw@whittingdales.com
List of partners: M R Whittingdale
Work: C1 C2 E F1 J1 L N O P Q R1 S1 S2 W Z(d,e,f,j,k,m,q,r)
Agency and Advocacy undertaken
Ptr: Whittingdale, Mr Michael Robin . . . . *Feb 1972

WIGGIN LLP
10th Floor Met Building 22 Percy Street London W1T 2BU
Tel: 020 7612 9612 *Fax:* 01242 224223 *Dx:* 37201 PICCADILLY
E-mail: law@wiggin.co.uk
Office: Cheltenham

WIGGIN OSBORNE FULLERLOVE
52 Jermyn Street London SW1Y 6LX
Tel: 020 7290 2456 *Fax:* 020 7290 2444 *Dx:* 37206 PICCADILLY 1
Office: Cheltenham
Languages: French, German
Work: C1 C2 K1 M2 T1 T2 W Z(d,f,j,o)
Ptr: Cain, Mr Matthew BA(Hons). . . . . *Sep 1995
Fullerlove, Mr Michael R LLB; BCL . . . . *Oct 1974
Green, Mr Stephen M C BA(Hons); CTA. . . . . . . *Sep 1999
Hunston, Mr Paul LLB. . . . . Jan 1985
Marlow, Mr C Roderick J MA; LLB(Cantab) . . . . . *Jan 1977
Osborne, Mr Timothy W LLB . . . . *Apr 1976
Payne, Mr Mark H D MA(Oxon). . . . . *Oct 1987
Ast: Cook, Mr Chris LLB(Hons); PGDip . . . . *Oct 2004
Shayle, Mr Matthew. . . . . Oct 2007

DOUGLAS WIGNALL & CO ‡
44 Essex Street Strand London WC2R 3JF
Tel: 020 7583 1362 *Fax:* 020 3318 0879
Dx: 48 LONDON/CHANCERY LN
E-mail: dw@douglaswignall.com
List of partners: D J Wignall
Work: C1 E L S1
Ptr: Wignall, Mr Douglas J LLB . . . . *Mar 1974

WIKBORG REIN ‡
Cheapside House 138 Cheapside London EC2V 6HS
Tel: 020 7367 0300 *Fax:* 020 7367 0301

WILKINS BEAUMONT SUCKLING ‡
150 Minories London EC3N 1LS
Tel: 020 7264 2226

WILKINSONS ‡
53 Blake Hall Blake Hall Road Wanstead London E11 2QW
Tel: 020 8532 9270 *Fax:* 020 8989 1974
E-mail: adrian@wilkinsons-solicitors.org
List of partners: S Mir, A J Wilkinson
Languages: Punjabi, Urdu
Work: E S1 S2
Ptr: Mir, Ms Sabah LLB . . . . .Jul 2003
Wilkinson, Mr Adrian J LLB . . . . *Sep 1972

A WILLIAMS & CO ‡
International House 1-6 Yarmouth Place Mayfair London W1J 7BU
Tel: 020 3287 3519 / 3516 *Fax:* 020 7900 2529

WILLIAMS GORMAN LLP ‡
76 Hewitt Road Haringey London N8 9SB
List of partners: T de Villiers, A Gorman, K Hale, T Williams
Work: A1 A2 A3 B1 B2 B3 C1 C2 C3 D1 D2 E F1 F2 G H I J1 J2 K1 K2 K3 K4 L M1 M2 M3 M4 N O P Q R1 R2 S1 S2 T1 T2 U1 U2 V W X Z(a,b,c,d,e,f,g,h,i,j,k,l,m,n,o,p,q,r,s,t,u,w,x,y,z,za)
Ptr: de Villiers, Mr Tarquin . . . . Feb 1982
Gorman, Mr Alexander . . . . Aug 1975
Hale, Ms Karen. . . . . Nov 1985
Williams, Mr Theo. . . . . Aug 1972
Ast: Allison, Mr John. . . . . Mar 1983

MARTIN J WILLIAMS & CO ‡
15 Northfields Prospect Northfields Wandsworth London SW18 1PE
Tel: 020 8875 9833 *Fax:* 020 8875 9834
List of partners: M J Williams
Work: A3 C1 E K1 L M2 O Q R2 S1 W Z(c)
SPr: Williams, Mr Martin J LLB. . . . . *Oct 1988

WILLIAMS POWELL ‡
Staple Court 11 Staple Inn Buildings London WC1V 7QH
Tel: 020 7242 7005 *Fax:* 020 7242 7115
E-mail: mail@williamspowell.com

RICHARD WILLIAMS ‡
First Floor (Left) 36B Notting Hill Gate London W11 3HX
Tel: 020 7221 1188
List of partners: G R Williams
Work: A1 T1
SPr: Williams, Mr George R . . . . *May 1972

JOHN WILLIAMSON SOLICITOR ‡
55 Carminia Road Tooting Bec Wandsworth London SW17 8AJ
Tel: 020 8673 7508 *Fax:* 020 8673 9376
List of partners: J R Williamson
Work: C1 E L S1 S2 W
SPr: Williamson, Mr John R . . . . *Nov 1983

WILLKIE FARR & GALLAGHER LLP ‡
1 Angel Court London EC2R 7HJ
Tel: 020 7696 5454 *Fax:* 020 7696 5455

GEORGE WILLS SOLICITORS ‡
213 Clapham Road London SW9 0QH
Tel: 020 7095 9001 *Fax:* 020 7095 9002

WILMERHALE ‡
Alder Castle 10 Noble Street London EC2V 7QJ
Tel: 020 7645 2400 *Fax:* 020 7645 2424
List of partners: G Born, S P Finizio, M Holter, W J Miles, J C Pillman, J A Trenor
Office: London W1, Oxford
Work: A3 C1 C2 C3 J1 M2 M3 O T1 U1 U2 Z(e,o,za)
Ptr: Born, Mr Gary. . . . . Jan 1981
Finizio, Mr Steven P. . . . . Jan 1993
Holter, Mr Michael. . . . . Mar 1998
Miles, Ms Wendy Jane . . . . Feb 2000
Pillman, Mr Joseph C MA(Cantab) . . . . *§Dec 1977
Trenor, Mr John A. . . . . Jan 1995
Ast: Barras, Mrs Tessa Wendy BA(Cantab) . . . . *Sep 1991

WILMERHALE
49 Park Lane London W1K 1PS
Tel: 020 7872 1000 *Fax:* 020 7839 3537
E-mail: mark.keppler@wilmerhale.com
Office: London EC2, Oxford

WILSON & CO ‡
697 High Road Tottenham London N17 8AD
Tel: 020 8808 7535 *Fax:* 020 8880 3393 *Dx:* 52200 TOTTENHAM 2
Emergency telephone 020 8808 7535
E-mail: info@wilsons-solicitors.org.co.uk
List of partners: M K P Davies, D Hanley, M G Hanley, C Jackson, A Soyer, A Tootell, A Vasisht, K G Vincent
Languages: French, Somali, Spanish, Turkish
Work: B2 D1 D2 G H K1 Z(i)
Emergency Action, Agency, Advocacy, Legal Aid undertaken and Legal Aid Franchise
Ptr: Davies, Mr Matthew K P BA(Hons) . . . . Nov 1992
Hanley, Mr Damian BA . . . . *Feb 1998
Hanley, Mr Michael G BA(Cantab). . . . . *Nov 1985
Jackson, Ms Caroline . . . . Jun 1996
Soyer, Ms Aysen LLB. . . . . *Aug 1996
Tootell, Miss Anne-Marie LLB; EUR. . . . . *Jun 1991
Vasisht, Ms Anita BSc. . . . . May 1997
Vincent, Kenroy G BA. . . . . Oct 1990
Ast: Beckett, Miss Patricia Louise LLB. . . . . Jan 2002
Blakely, Mr Russell MA . . . . *Dec 1999
Britton, Mr Alexander John . . . . Feb 2002
Elliot, Mr James BA. . . . . *Mar 2001
Gonzalez, Ms Ana BA. . . . . Jul 2003
Jamil, Mr Shakeel LLB ★ . . . . Jul 2002
Lonnen, Ms Jacinta LLM . . . . Oct 1998
Paramesuaran, Mr Muhuntan BA . . . . Jul 2003
Piccos, Miss Deborah Joanne LLB . . . . *Dec 2001
Pugh, Mr Simon BSc . . . . Apr 2003

ASHLEY WILSON ‡
(incorporating Mackworth Rowland)
57 Buckingham Gate St James's Park London SW1E 6AJ
Tel: 020 7802 4802 *Fax:* 020 7802 4803 *Dx:* 99971 VICTORIA
E-mail: mail@ashleywilson.co.uk
List of partners: T Wilson
Languages: French, Italian
Work: A1 C1 C3 E J1 L R1 S1 S2 T2 W Z(d,e,f,h)
Ptr: Wilson, Mr Tony. . . . . Jan 1984
Ast: Woodroffe, Mr Jonathan F. . . . . Oct 1996
Con: Rowland, Mrs Sheila . . . . *Jul 1976

WILSON BARCA LLP ‡
13-14 Dean Street London W1D 3RS
Tel: 020 7272 2072 *Fax:* 020 7439 4122 *Dx:* 44710 SOHO SQUARE
Emergency telephone 07768 907567
E-mail: soho@wilsonbarca.com
List of partners: R G Barca, D F Wilson
Office: London N19
Languages: French, Italian, Mandarin
Work: A3 B1 C1 C2 C3 D1 E F1 F2 G I J1 K1 L M1 M2 N Q R1 S1 S2 T2 V W Z(e,f,g,i,k,l,p,q,r,z)
Emergency Action, Agency, Advocacy, Legal Aid undertaken and Member of Accident Line
Ptr: Barca, Mr Richard G BA; LLB. . . . . *Jul 1986
Wilson, Mr David F . . . . Dec 1975
Ast: Hakim, Mr Mohammad Ahmed LLB(Hons); DipLP. . *Nov 1997
Con: Lo, Mr Eric Y M LLB; Dip Intellectual Property. . . . *Dec 1990

WILSON BARCA LLP
(incorporating Frasers)
8 Archway Close Archway Road London N19 3TD
Tel: 020 7272 2072 *Fax:* 020 7263 3008 *Dx:* 54751 ARCHWAY
Emergency telephone 07768 907567
E-mail: archway@wilsonbarca.com
Office: London W1
Languages: French, Russian
Work: C1 E F1 J1 K1 L N O Q R1 S1 W
Agency, Advocacy, Legal Aid undertaken and Member of Accident Line
Con: Fraser, Mr Alexander Ian BA(Lond) . . . . *May 1982
Lo, Mr Eric Y M LLB; Dip Intellectual Property. . . . *Dec 1990

WILSON FINLAY ‡
40 Madrid Road Barnes London SW13 9PG

P E WILSON & CO ‡
106 Norwood High Street London SE27 9NH
Tel: 020 8761 3555 *Fax:* 020 8761 1555
Dx: 34151 NORWOOD NORTH
E-mail: phillw1@tiscali.co.uk

WILSONS SOLICITORS LLP
4 Lincoln's Inn Fields London WC2A 3AA
Tel: 020 7998 0420 *Fax:* 020 7242 7661
E-mail: enquiries@wilsonslaw.com
Office: Salisbury

WIMBLEDON SOLICITORS ‡
191 Merton Road London SW19 1EE
Tel: 020 8543 3302 *Fax:* 020 8543 3303
Dx: 30000 WIMBLEDON SOUTH
E-mail: mail@wimbledonsolicitors.net
Office: London SW17

WIMBLEDON SOLICITORS
271 Balham High Road Tooting Bec London SW17 7BD
Tel: 020 8767 0800 *Fax:* 020 8767 0850
E-mail: mail@wimbledonsolicitors.net
Office: London SW19

WINCKWORTH SHERWOOD LLP ‡
(incorporating Sherwood & Co)
Minerva House 5 Montague Close London SE1 9BB
Tel: 020 7593 5000 *Fax:* 020 7593 5099
Dx: 156810 LONDON BRIDGE 6
E-mail: info@wslaw.co.uk
List of partners: R Barnes, R P Botkai, O Carew-Jones, D R F Fitton, A M H Gorlov, B J Hood, P M C F Irving, R H A MacDougald, P C E Morris, A J Murray, R S Rai, V J H Rees, C M Vine, H S Wiggs
Office: London SW1, Oxford
Languages: French, German, Hindi, Italian, Punjabi, Spanish
Work: A1 A3 C1 C2 C3 D1 D2 E I J1 J2 K1 K2 L M1 M2 N O P Q R1 R2 S1 S2 T1 T2 W X Z(b,c,d,e,g,h,l,p,q,r,u,w,x)
Emergency Action, Agency, Advocacy undertaken and Member of Accident Line
Ptr: Barnes, Ms Ruth . . . . Feb 1987
Botkai, Mr Robert P LLB . . . . *Oct 1989
Carew-Jones, Mr Owen. . . . . *Sep 1994
Fitton, Mr Duncan R F BA(Oxon) . . . . *Nov 1986
Gorlov, Mrs Alison M H . . . . *§Dec 1975
Hood, Mr Brian J LLM(Canterbury, NZ) Ecclesiastical Notary of Chelmsford Diocesan Registrar & Bishops Legal Secretary . . . . *Apr 1976
Irving, Mr Paul M C F MA(Oxon); DPhil . . . . *Jan 1991
MacDougald, Mr R Hugh A LLB(Exon) . . . . *Dec 1979
Morris, Mr Paul C E BA(Wales) . . . . *Jul 1978
Murray, Mr Andrew J BA(Manc) . . . . Sep 1987
Rai, Mr Ranjeev Singh LLB(Hons). . . . . *Aug 1995
Rees, Mr V John H LLB(Soton); MA(Oxon); MPhil(Leeds) Joint Registrar Diocese of Oxford. . . . . *Jun 1975
Vine, Mr Christopher M . . . . *Jun 1974
Wiggs, Mr H Stephen BA(Wales) . . . . *§Dec 1976
Ast: Clark, Ms Anna . . . . Feb 1998
Collinge, Ms Julie LLB. . . . . *Oct 1986
Crossley, Ms Karen A MA(Oxon) . . . . *Sep 1988
Enfield, Miss Christine C M . . . . Jul 1979
Eveleigh, Mr Robert J. . . . . Dec 1994
Hall, Ms Cordelia . . . . Sep 1999
Harrison, Mr Robert C LLB(B'ham) . . . . *Sep 1984
Manfield, Mrs Penelope J LLB(Lond) . . . . *Nov 1973
Paul-Roberts, Ms Barbara Ellen FILEx . . . . *Nov 1994
Walsh, Ms Mary Bernadette LLB; LSF. . . . . *Oct 1996
Yates, Mr Roger M LLB . . . . *Oct 1986
Con: Grosse, Miss Lorna M LLB(Lond) . . . . *Jun 1980

WINGATE WONG SOLICITORS ‡
Third Floor 228 Edgware Road London W2 1DW
Tel: 020 7723 1228 *Fax:* 020 7723 3288
E-mail: info@wingatewongsolicitor.co.uk

WINSTON & STRAWN LLP ‡
Citypoint 1 Ropemaker Street London EC2Y 9HU
Tel: 020 7011 8700 *Fax:* 020 7011 8800

PAUL WINTER & CO ‡
Fleet House 6-12 New Bridge Street London EC4V 6AL
Tel: 020 7936 2433
E-mail: paulwinter@paulwinterandco.com

WINTER SCOTT ‡
St Olave's House Ironmonger Lane London EC2V 8EY
Tel: 020 7367 8989 *Fax:* 020 7726 2371
Emergency telephone 020 7367 8989
E-mail: enquiry@winterscott.co.uk
Work: A3 M2 O Z(a,j)

WISEMAN LEE LLP ‡
2 High Street South East Ham Newham London E6 6EU
Tel: 020 8215 1000 *Fax:* 020 8215 1100 *Dx:* 4705 EAST HAM
E-mail: info@wiseman.co.uk
List of partners: J E Aldred, R Ameen, B J Browne, M Dennis, J P Diamond, D H Inkpin, P M J Kaufman, D L Ormonde, K Phillips, J A Smith, S C Watmore, A R Wershof, D L Wershof, P A Wershof
Office: London E11, London E17
Languages: Bengali, French, German, Hindi
Work: A3 B1 B2 C1 D1 D2 E F1 F2 G H J1 J2 K1 K2 K3 L N O Q R1 R2 S1 S2 T1 T2 W X Z(j,l,m,q,r)
Emergency Action, Agency, Advocacy, Fixed Fee Interview, Legal Aid undertaken, Legal Aid Franchise and Member of Accident Line
Ptr: Aldred, Ms Julie E LLB; LLM . . . . *Nov 1986
Phillips, Miss Karen . . . . Oct 2003
Mem: Diamond, Mr Jonathan P . . . . Oct 1986
Kaufman, Mr Paul M J BA; LLB. . . . . Mar 1983
Wershof, Mr Adam R LLB. . . . . *Mar 1988
Wershof, Mr Paul A. . . . . *Jul 1975

WISEMAN LEE LLP
229 Hoe Street Walthamstow Waltham Forest London E17 9PP
Tel: 020 8215 1000 *Fax:* 020 8215 1150
Dx: 32008 WALTHAMSTOW
E-mail: info@wiseman.co.uk
Office: London E11, London E6
Languages: Gujarati, Hindi, Punjabi
Work: A3 B1 B2 C1 C2 C3 D1 D2 E F1 F2 G H J1 J2 K1 K2 K3 L N O Q R1 R2 S1 S2 T2 W X Z(l,m,q,r)
Emergency Action, Agency, Advocacy, Fixed Fee Interview, Legal Aid undertaken, Legal Aid Franchise and Member of Accident Line
Ptr: Dennis, Ms Maria BA . . . . Jun 1994
Mem: Smith, Mr Jeremy A BA . . . . *Nov 1987
Ast: Judt, Miss Emma LLB(Hons) . . . . Jan 2000

WISEMAN LEE LLP
9-13 Cambridge Park Wanstead Redbridge London E11 2PU
Tel: 020 8215 1000 *Fax:* 020 8215 1170 *Dx:* 52553 WANSTEAD
E-mail: info@wiseman.co.uk
Office: London E17, London E6
Languages: Bengali, German
Work: C1 E J1 K1 L N O R1 S1 S2 W
Emergency Action and Advocacy undertaken
Ptr: Ameen, Mr Ruhul . . . . May 1999
Browne, Ms Beverley J BA . . . . *Mar 1980
Ormonde, Miss Devorah Leya. . . . . Jul 2007
Watmore, Mr Stephen C MA(Oxon) . . . . Oct 1984
Mem: Inkpin, Mr Derek H . . . . *Dec 1973
Wershof, Mr David L LLB . . . . *Jul 1976
Ast: Fernandez, Ms Christabel Angelica Rose . . . . . . Aug 2004
Ormonde, Mrs Frances E LLB. . . . . *Apr 1973
Rose, Ms Debra Simone . . . . *Oct 2008
Con: Williams, Mr Geoffrey I BA . . . . *Jun 1979

WITHERS & ROGERS ‡
Goldings House 2 Hays Lane London SE1 2HW
Tel: 020 7663 3500 *Fax:* 020 7663 3550
Office: Birmingham

WITHERS LLP ‡
16 Old Bailey London EC4M 7EG
Tel: 020 7597 6000 *Fax:* 020 7597 6543
Dx: 160 LONDON/CHANCERY LN
E-mail: enquiries.uk@withersworldwide.com
List of partners: R Abbate, J Abrey, J Arnold, P Brecknell, C Coffin, S Cooke, J Copson, C D Cutbill, C D'Ambrosio, D I Dannreuther, J Dearle, M Dearle, H Devlin, G Doran, P Durrance, P A H Elliott, A J Ford, D Goodman, M Gouriet, M Hallam, M J P Harper, A Indaimo, J Ingham, A H Lane, I A Marsh, J d A Maycock, P Milner, M Mitchell, S Morgan, R Moruzzi, A Paines, D Parker, R Paul, C A Pearson, C Pike, J Riches, M Robertson, V Rylatt, S K Satchell, M Schindler, J Scott, H Stuart, T Taylor, N C Terras, A Thompson, J Wheeler, P Williams, P Wood
Languages: French, German, Italian, Spanish
Work: A1 B1 C1 C2 C3 D1 E F1 I J1 K1 L M1 M2 N O P Q R1 S1 S2 T1 T2 W Z(b,c,d,e,f,g,i,j,k,l,m,o,p,q)
Emergency Action undertaken
Ptr: Abbate, Mr Riccardo BSc(Hons)(Econ) . . . . *Nov 1995
Abrey, Ms Julia MA(Oxon). . . . . *Oct 1987
Arnold, Mr Jeremy MA(Oxon). . . . . *Nov 1985
Brecknell, Mr Paul BA(Hons) . . . . *Nov 1990
Coffin, Mr Christopher BA(Oxon). . . . . *Nov 1980
Cooke, Mr Stephen Sidney Herbert Clay Prize. . . . *§Jul 1971
Copson, Mr James BA . . . . *Jan 1992
Cutbill, Mr Clive D LLB(Lond) . . . . *§Oct 1985
D'Ambrosio, Ms Claudia BA(Oxon) . . . . *Oct 1986
Dannreuther, Mr David I BA(Hons)(Oxon) . . . . . . *Dec 1978
Dearle, Ms Jane LLB . . . . *Oct 1992
Dearle, Mr Marcus LLB(Hons). . . . . *Jan 1990
Devlin, Mr Hugh MA; LLB; DipLP . . . . *Feb 1995
Doran, Ms Gill LLB(Hons). . . . . Jan 1974
Durrance, Mr Philip MA(Hons)(Oxon) . . . . *§Jun 1965
Elliott, Ms Penelope Ann Hylton MA(Cantab) . . . . *Nov 1985
Ford, Mr Andrew John LLB(Hons). . . . . *Dec 1994
Goodman, Ms Dawn . . . . *§Aug 1980
Gouriet, Mr Michael MA(Hons) . . . . *Nov 1995
Hallam, Mr Murray MA(Oxon) Notary Public. . . . . *§Jun 1973
Harper, Mr Mark J P BA(Hons) . . . . Jan 1988
Indaimo, Mr Anthony BJuris; LLB . . . . *Nov 1990
Ingham, Ms Judith MA(Hons)(Oxon). . . . . *Nov 1983
Lane, Mr Andrew Herbert MA . . . . Dec 1993
Marsh, Mr Ian A ATII . . . . *Dec 1978
Maycock, Mr John d'Auvergne MA; LLM. . . . . *§Jan 1970
Milner, Ms Patricia BSc(Hons). . . . . *Nov 1991
Mitchell, Mr Michael MA(Oxon); MA(Cantab) . . . . . *Jul 1976
Morgan, Ms Samantha LLB . . . . *Sep 1992
Moruzzi, Mr Roberto BSc(Econ). . . . . *Jul 1990
Paines, Ms Alison MA(Cantab) . . . . *Apr 1981
Parker, Ms Diana MA; MPhil(Cantab) . . . . *Oct 1983
Paul, Mr Robin MA(Oxon). . . . . *§Dec 1977
Pearson, Ms Craigie Anne LLB . . . . Feb 2001
Pike, Mr Charles MA(Cantab) . . . . *Nov 1980
Riches, Mr John LLB . . . . *Oct 1985
Robertson, Ms Margaret MA(Hons)(Oxon)(Jurisprudence) . . . . *Nov 1986
Rylatt, Ms Virginia BA(Oxon) . . . . *Oct 1980
Satchell, Mrs Susan K BA. . . . . *Oct 1986
Schindler, Ms Meriel BA(Hons) . . . . *Sep 1991
Scott, Mr Jeremy MA(Oxon). . . . . *Jun 1979
Stuart, Mr Henry LLB . . . . *Oct 1984
Taylor, Mr Timothy MA(Oxon) . . . . *Oct 1985
Terras, Mr Nicholas Charles. . . . . Sep 2002
Thompson, Mr Anthony MA; LLB(Cantab). . . . . . . *§Apr 1968
Wheeler, Mr Jonathan BA(Hons) . . . . *Nov 1994
Williams, Ms Penelope LLB . . . . Oct 1990
Wood, Mr Peter BA(Hons). . . . . Apr 1988
Ast: Baldwin, Ms Camilla MA(Cantab) . . . . *Dec 1992
Baldwin, Mr David. . . . . *§Jun 1972
Banfeild, Ms Claire BA(Hons) . . . . *Sep 1998
Bannon, Ms Lucy F BA(Oxon). . . . . *Jan 1999
Bonny, Mr Peter Ian. . . . . *Sep 1997
Brienza-Wooldridge, Ms Antonietta LLB(Hons) . . . . *Apr 1993
Burge, Ms Harriet LLB . . . . *Oct 1996
Burt, Mr Jonathan Edward. . . . . *Oct 1996

See p2 for the Key to Work Categories & other symbols

Carey, Ms Veronica J BA(Hons); CPE; LSF . . . . . . *Nov 1995
Charvet, Mr Charles BA. . . . . *May 1994
Clarke, Ms Dora L S LLB(Hons). . . . . *Nov 1985
Fox, Ms Suzanne J LLB(Hons) . . . . Sep 1999
Gibson, Miss J Lucy BA(Hons) . . . . *Sep 1997
Graves, Ms Katie A L LLB. . . . . *Nov 1991
Hamlin, Mr Patrick R P MA(Oxon). . . . . Jun 1978
Hatley, Ms Emma MA(Hons) . . . . *Oct 1996
Hender, Ms Laura MA. . . . . Sep 1999
Hewitt, Mr Anthony P BA(Hons); LPC . . . . *Sep 1997
Hill, Ms Catherine BA(Hons). . . . . *Oct 1996
Hirst, Ms Nicole LLB . . . . *Nov 1990
Hurst, Mr Guy Nicholas MRICS . . . . *Sep 1997
Hutchinson, Miss Vicki L LLB . . . . *Dec 1985
Ibbitson, Mr Mark E BA(Hons). . . . . *Mar 1999
Ignatius, Ms Nadia BCom . . . . *Jul 1993
Isaac, Mr Daniel Peter BA(Hons)(Oxon). . . . . . . *Mar 1995
Jenkins, Ms Caitlin MA(Cantab) . . . . *Nov 1994
King, Mr Christopher LLB(Hons). . . . . *Apr 1990
Kleiner, Mr Graeme . . . . Sep 1999
Lipson, Mr Julian D MA(Oxon) . . . . *Mar 1996
McGrath, Mr Paul G BA(Hons)(Oxon)(Jurisprudence) . *Sep 1997
Markovitz, Ms Justine BA(Hons); CPE; LSF. . . . . . *Apr 1996
Miller, Ms Ann LLB(Hons) . . . . *Sep 1997
Moss, Ms Caroline H BA(Hons) . . . . *Nov 1985
Page, Miss Katherine BSc(Hons) . . . . *May 1989
Parker, Mr Damon J MA(Hons); DipLaw. . . . . *Sep 1997
Penfold, Ms Lyn BCS; CPE; LPC . . . . Sep 1998
Priestley, Mr Christopher S S LLB(Hons) Notary Public*Aug 1998
Richards, Ms Katherine BA(Hons)(Oxon) . . . . *Sep 1997
Sanderson, Ms Emma S LLB . . . . *Sep 1997
Simpson, Mr Ben BA . . . . *Jan 1996
Spedding, Ms Jane BA(Hons)(Jurisprudence) . . . . *May 1995
Stone, Mr Edward R M LLB. . . . . *Oct 1986
Trustram Eve, Ms Moire C BA(Hons) . . . . *Oct 1996
Wakeham, Mr Jeremy LLB(Hons) . . . . Sep 1999
Wells, Ms Natalie Jane LLB(Hons) . . . . *Oct 1995
Whiley, Mrs Alexandra Mary BSc(Hons). . . . . . . *May 1996
Con: Doughty, Mr Charles BA(Oxon) . . . . *§Oct 1961
Duffield, Mr Peter MA(Oxon) . . . . *Nov 1961
Matthews, Mr Paul B J LLB; BCL; LLD; Barrister Mackaskie Award; Mould Scholarship Deputy Coroner . . . *May 1987

WIXTED & CO LTD ‡
57 Putney Bridge Road London SW18 1NP

MATTHEW WOKENSON ‡
660 Old Kent Road London SE15 1JF

WOLFE MCCLANCY & CO ‡
2 Cromwell Place London SW7 2JE
Tel: 020 7581 8033 *Fax:* 020 7591 0053
Dx: 35764 SOUTH KENSINGTON
E-mail: rod@ashleywilson.co.uk

WOLFE MYERS & CO ‡
53 Goodge Street London W1P 1FB
Tel: 020 7580 7426
Emergency telephone 020 8202 8546
List of partners: A J Myers, W Myers
Office: London NW4
Work: C1 E F1 J1 L N P S1 W Z(i,l)
Agency and Legal Aid undertaken
Ptr: Myers, Mr Anthony J . . . . *Dec 1979

WOLFE MYERS & CO
5 Denehurst Gardens London NW4 3QS
Tel: 020 8202 8546
Office: London W1
Work: C1 E F1 J1 L M1 P S1 W Z(i,l)
Agency and Legal Aid undertaken
Ptr: Myers, Mr Anthony J . . . . *Dec 1979

LESLIE WOLFSON & CO ‡
39 Hill Street London W1J 5LZ

ELIZABETH WONG & COMPANY ‡
Cameo House 11 Bear Street London WC2H 7AS
Tel: 020 7766 5228 *Fax:* 020 7766 5229
Emergency telephone 07802 888996
E-mail: elizabeth@elizabethwong.com
List of partners: E S Y Wong
Languages: Cantonese, French, Mandarin
Work: C1 E K1 L Q S1 S2 W Z(i,l)
Fixed Fee Interview undertaken
SPr: Wong, Ms Elizabeth Shui Yin BSocSc(Hons) . . . . *Nov 1989

NADINE WONG & CO ‡
45 Queensway London W2 4QJ
Est: 1994
Tel: 020 7243 8888 *Fax:* 020 7221 8802 *Dx:* 35815 QUEENSWAY
E-mail: info@nadinewongsolicitors.co.uk
List of partners: N S P Wong
Languages: Cantonese, Chinese, Malay, Mandarin, Spanish
Work: C1 E K1 K3 Q S1 S2 W Z(g,i)
Legal Aid Franchise
SPr: Wong, Ms Nadine Siu Ping LLB; LLM . . . . *Aug 1991

WONTNER & SONS ‡
226 The Strand London WC2R 1BA
Tel: 020 7936 2414 *Fax:* 020 7936 3330
Emergency telephone 07759 698877
List of partners: A G I Wontner
Emergency Action, Agency, Advocacy, Fixed Fee Interview and Legal Aid undertaken
Ptr: Wontner, Mr Arthur G I MA(Oxon). . . . . Nov 1968

JOHN G WOOD ‡
4th Floor Suite 3 1 Duchess Street London W1W 6AN
Tel: 020 7580 2277 *Fax:* 020 7631 3751
E-mail: johngwood@btinternet.com
List of partners: J G Wood
Work: C1 E M2 S1
Ptr: Wood, Mr John Geoffrey . . . . *Nov 1970

JOHN G K WOOD ‡
9 Golden Square Westminster London W1F 9HZ
Tel: 020 7439 1122 *Fax:* 020 7439 0234
E-mail: john.wood@gspg.co.uk
List of partners: J G K Wood
Work: L S1
SPr: Wood, Mr John G K MA(Oxon); LLB(Lond) . . . . . . *Mar 1962

WOODFORDS SOLICITORS LLP ‡
Bishops Park House 25-29 Fulham High Street London SW6 3JH
Tel: 020 7731 0750 *Fax:* 020 7736 2896 *Dx:* 59472 PUTNEY
E-mail: post@woodfords.co.uk
Work: B1 C1 D1 E F1 J1 K1 K3 K4 L N O Q R1 S1 S2 T1 T2 V W Z(c,d,j,l,w)
Fixed Fee Interview undertaken and Member of Accident Line

WOODGRANGE SOLICITORS ‡
46 Woodgrange Road London E7 0QH
Tel: 020 8534 2400 *Fax:* 020 8534 3600 *Dx:* 52107 FOREST GATE
E-mail: info@woodgrangesolicitors.com

WOODROFFES ‡
(incorporating Clement Daniels & Co)
7 Beeston Place Westminster London SW1W 0JJ
Est: 1877
Tel: 020 7730 0001 *Fax:* 020 7730 7900 *Dx:* 99923 VICTORIA
E-mail: mail@woodroffes.co.uk
List of partners: R Brown, P Gordon-Smith
Languages: French, German, Polish, Spanish
Work: A3 B1 B2 C1 E J1 K1 K3 L M4 O P Q R2 S1 S2 W X Z(b,c,d,e,g,h,k,l,q)
Fixed Fee Interview and Legal Aid undertaken
Ptr: Brown, Mr Roger LLB(Lancs) . . . . *Dec 1992
Gordon-Smith, Mr Philip LLB(B'ham) . . . . *Feb 1992
Asoc: Oliver-Bellasis, Mr John. . . . . Feb 2005
Ast: Beeson, Miss Clarissa MA(Soton). . . . . Nov 2006
Hillman, Mr Benjamin Daniel BVC; LLB; BA . . . . . . Jan 2005
Wheatcroft, Mr Richard F J BA(Oxon). . . . . *Jan 1977
Con: Kahn, Mrs Aina LLB. . . . . *Apr 1991

WOOLF SIMMONDS ‡
1 Great Cumberland Place Westminster London W1H 7AL
Tel: 020 7262 1266 *Fax:* 020 7723 7159 *Dx:* 44422 MARBLE ARCH
E-mail: email@woolfsimmonds.co.uk
List of partners: D Sichel, W F C Simmonds, N P Woolf
Languages: French
Work: B1 C1 C2 C3 E J1 K1 L N Q S1 S2 T1 T2 W Z(e,f,h,i,k,l)
Emergency Action, Agency and Advocacy undertaken
Ptr: Sichel, Mr David . . . . Jan 1985
Simmonds, Mr William F C . . . . *Jun 1976
Woolf, Mr Nicholas P LLB. . . . . *Apr 1979
Asoc: Fleming, Mr David K . . . . *Jan 1976
Sharp, Miss Sarah F BA . . . . *Nov 1986

WRAGGE & CO LLP
3 Waterhouse Square 142 Holborn London EC1N 2SW
Tel: 0870 903 1000 *Fax:* 0870 904 1099 *Dx:* 155790 BLOOMSBURY
E-mail: mail@wragge.com
Office: Birmingham
Work: C1 C3 E I J1 M1 N O Q S1 W Z(e,j)
Member of Accident Line
Ptr: Benson, Mr Christopher de G . . . . *Jun 1974
Cooke, Mr Adam N BSc(Dunelm); FRGS . . . . *May 1986
Gibbins, Mr David J S MA(Cantab) . . . . *Jan 1984
Marsh, Mr David J . . . . *Nov 1978
Ast: Daisley, Miss Julia D LLB . . . . *Oct 1988
Evans, Mr Huw Nigel LLB. . . . . *Nov 1992

WRIGHT & CO ‡
26 Ives Street London SW3 2ND
Tel: 020 7584 7557 *Fax:* 020 7584 4391
Dx: 38162 KNIGHTSBRIDGE
E-mail: info@wrightlaw.co.uk
List of partners: J C Wright
Work: C1 E G L N Q S1 W Z(c,e,w)
Ptr: Wright, Mr John C BA(Legal Studies) . . . . *Apr 1981

WRIGHT SON & PEPPER LLP ‡
9 Gray's Inn Square Camden London WC1R 5JF
Est: 1850
Tel: 020 7242 5473 *Fax:* 020 7831 7454
Dx: 35 LONDON/CHANCERY LN
E-mail: wsp@wsap.co.uk
Web: www.wsap.co.uk
List of partners: G H Adam, S M Alais, E Degirmen, M G Tulloch, S Wade
Languages: French, German, Turkish
Work: A3 B1 C1 C2 C3 E J1 K1 L M1 N O P Q R1 S1 S2 T1 T2 W Z(c,e,f,o,q)
Advocacy undertaken
Mem: Adam, Mr Gordon H BA. . . . . Jun 1989
Alais, Mr Steven M . . . . *Nov 1973
Degirmen, Esat LLB. . . . . Jun 1998
Tulloch, Mr Michael Guthrie LLB(Bris). . . . . Apr 1970
Wade, Mr Stephen . . . . *May 1996
Ast: Budibent, Ms Sarah M LLB; MA. . . . . *Jul 1981
Con: Wright, Mr Nicholas J. . . . . *Aug 1970

WRIGHTWAY SOLICITORS ‡
1st & 2nd Floor 83 Lewisham High Street London SE13 5JX
Tel: 020 8297 0044 *Fax:* 020 8297 0060
E-mail: contact@wrightwaysolicitors.com

ALEXANDRA WYATT DIVORCE AND FAMILY LAW SOLICITOR ‡
First Floor 218 Strand London WC2R 1AP
Tel: 020 7936 4446 *Fax:* 020 7583 5151
Dx: 252 LONDON/CHANCERY LN
E-mail: aw@alexandrawyatt.co.uk

WYCOMBE HURD & CO ‡
(in association with Commercial Lawyers Group)
13 Craven Street London WC2N 5PB
Tel: 020 7925 0313
E-mail: taxlaw@wycombehurd.co.uk
List of partners: M P W Hurd
Languages: French
Work: C1 T1 T2
SPr: Hurd, Mr Michael Patrick Wycombe BA(Law) . . . . *Nov 1981

MICHAEL WYDRA & CO ‡
Broughton House 6-8 Sackville Street Westminster London W1S 3DG
Tel: 020 7437 3640 *Fax:* 020 7287 9035
E-mail: michael@michaelwydralaw.com
List of partners: M N Wydra
Work: A1 B1 B2 C1 C2 C3 E I J1 K4 L N O Q R2 S1 S2 T1 T2 W Z(b,c,j,q,z)
SPr: Wydra, Mr Michael N LLB. . . . . *Apr 1972

DAVID WYLD & CO ‡
Fleet House 8-12 New Bridge Street London EC4V 6AL
Tel: 020 7583 7920 *Fax:* 020 7583 7921
E-mail: info@davidwyld.co.uk

YVA SOLICITORS ‡
811 High Road North Finchley London N12 8JT
Tel: 020 8445 9898 *Fax:* 020 8445 9199 *Dx:* 152740 FINCHLEY 3
E-mail: cy@yvasolicitors.com
List of partners: S Achillea, C Elias, L Lambrou, C A Pickwick, M C Votsis, C Yiannakas
Ptr: Achillea, Mr Stavros LLB(Hons) . . . . *Aug 1994
Elias, Mr Christopher LLB. . . . . Oct 1982
Lambrou, Lambros MA . . . . Oct 2000
Pickwick, Mr Christopher A LLB(Hons) . . . . Oct 1997
Votsis, Mr Michael Christos LLB. . . . . *Mar 1975
Yiannakas, Mr Christopher LLB . . . . *Oct 1987
Asoc: Christou, Miss Stella LLB; LLM . . . . Apr 2005
Procopi, Miss Sophia Natalia LLB(Hons) . . . . Aug 2003
Tsoukkas, Mr John LLB(Hons) . . . . Sep 2005
Con: Procopi, Mr Peter LLB. . . . . *Apr 1981
Yiannakas, Mr Apostolos M . . . . *§Jun 1970

YANAKAS VOTSIS ACHILLEA ‡
YVA House 811 High Road North Finchley London N12 8JP

P H YEUNG ‡
3 Rupert Court London W1D 6DX
Tel: 020 7287 1882 *Fax:* 020 7287 8815
E-mail: phyeung@phyeung.co.uk
List of partners: P H Yeung
Languages: Cantonese
Work: B2 E G H O
SPr: Yeung, Ping Hang. . . . . *Jan 1994

P C D YORK & CO ‡
97-99 King Street Hammersmith London W6 9JG
Tel: 020 8741 4512 *Fax:* 020 8741 2898
E-mail: info@yorklaw.co.uk
List of partners: P C D York
Languages: Afrikaans, Cantonese, Dutch, Igbo, Pari, Punjabi, Urdu
Work: B2 C1 D1 E F1 G H J1 K1 K2 L M1 M3 N Q S1 S2 T1 V W Z(m)
Emergency Action, Agency, Advocacy, Fixed Fee Interview and Legal Aid undertaken
SPr: York, Mr Phillip Charles David LLB(Hons) . . . . Jul 1979

D YOUNG & CO
120 Holborn London EC1N 2DY
Tel: 020 7269 8550 *Fax:* 020 7269 8555
E-mail: mail@dyoung.co.uk
Office: Southampton
Work: Z(e)

JULIAN YOUNG & CO ‡
118 Seymour Place Marylebone London W1H 1NP
Tel: 020 7724 8414 *Fax:* 020 7258 0466 *Dx:* 82951 MAYFAIR
Emergency telephone 07956 502069 / 07931 504601
E-mail: enquiries@jylaw.co.uk
List of partners: J R Ramjeet, J C O Weinberg, J D Young
Languages: Arabic, French, German, Italian, Serbo-Croat, Turkish
Work: B2 G H
Emergency Action, Agency, Advocacy, Fixed Fee Interview, Legal Aid undertaken and Legal Aid Franchise
Ptr: Ramjeet, Ms Judy Rajkumarie LLB(Hons) ★. . . . . . *Jul 1994
Weinberg, Mr Julian C O BA(Hons) ★. . . . . Oct 1985
Young, Mr Julian David LLB(Lond); MBA; MCIM ★ . . *May 1977
Ast: Pope, Mr Colin Alan LLB(Hons) . . . . *Jan 2004
Rehnema, Ms Shabnam LLB(Hons). . . . . *Dec 1993
Remi, Mrs Lynn LLB(Hons) . . . . *May 2004
Con: Burrows, Mrs Dawn Denise BA(Hons). . . . . *Jan 2002
Powell, Mr Dean BSc(Hons) ●. . . . . Jan 1999

SARAH YOUREN PLANNING SOLICITORS LIMITED ‡
Unit 11 Bridge Wharf 156 Caledonian Road London N1 9UU
Tel: 0845 481 8136 *Fax:* 020 7147 1374
E-mail: enquiries@sarahyouren.com

ZAHRA & CO ‡
50C Micro Business Park 46-50 Greatorex Street London E1 5NP
Tel: 020 7375 1231 *Fax:* 020 7377 9296

ZAIWALLA & CO ‡
Chancery House 53-64 Chancery Lane London WC2A 7QS
Est: 1982
Tel: 020 7312 1000 *Fax:* 020 7404 9473
E-mail: s.zaiwalla@zaiwalla.co.uk
List of partners: P R Gaddam, S R Zaiwalla
Languages: German, Gujarati, Hindi, Telugu
Work: C1 F1 M2 O T1 T2 Z(a)
Ptr: Gaddam, Ms Pavani Reddy . . . . May 2005
Zaiwalla, Mr Sarosh R BCom; LLB ICA . . . . *Jul 1978

A E P ZALESKI ‡
179-181 Replingham Road Southfields London SW18 5LY
Tel: 020 8875 1791 *Fax:* 020 8875 1794
E-mail: aep.zaleski@btconnect.com
List of partners: A E P Zaleski
Languages: Polish
Work: S1 W
SPr: Zaleski, Mr Andrew E P MA(Lond) . . . . *Jan 1983

ZAMAN SOLICITORS ‡
166A Commercial Road London E1 2JY
Tel: 020 7702 7555 *Fax:* 020 7702 7666
E-mail: zamansolicitors@btconnect.com

ZELIN & ZELIN ‡
5a Cuthbert Street London W2 1XT
Tel: 020 7262 1405 *Fax:* 020 7724 6587 *Dx:* 38752 PADDINGTON
E-mail: admin@zelin.co.uk
Office: London W1
Languages: Cantonese, Mandarin
Work: B1 C1 D1 E F1 G H J1 K1 L N O Q S1 S2 V W Z(i,l)

ZELIN & ZELIN
First Floor Office 82-84 Shaftesbury Avenue London W1D 6NG
Tel: 020 7287 1777 *Fax:* 020 7287 3020
Office: London W2
Languages: Cantonese, Mandarin
Work: E K1 L Q S2 V Z(i)

ZHONGLUN W&D LLP ‡
123 Cannon Street London EC4N 5AX
Tel: 020 7623 8889 *Fax:* 020 7623 9288 *Dx:* 98930 CHEAPSIDE 2
E-mail: hxue@zlwd.com

ZIADIES ‡
516 Brixton Road London SW9 8EN
Tel: 020 7737 0934 *Fax:* 020 7274 9493 *Dx:* 58752 BRIXTON
List of partners: D Abeyewardene, E M MacGregor
Languages: Amharic, Ga, Ganda, Sinhalese, Tigrinya, Twi
Work: D1 E K1 K3 K4 L N Q S1 V W Z(i)
Emergency Action, Advocacy, Fixed Fee Interview and Legal Aid undertaken
Ptr: Abeyewardene, Mrs Dakshini . . . . *Apr 1985
MacGregor, Mrs Esteddar Mariam MA. . . . . *Jul 1991
Ast: Addae-Anderson, Mrs Beatrice MA(Dev Studs); BA(Law/CC); BL(Prof Law) . . . . *Dec 2006
Adekanmi, Mrs Abiola LLB . . . . *May 1994
Arawwawala, Ms Shiroma Rukmal BSc(Hons); CPE; LPC . . . . Mar 2001
Edwards, John . . . . Jun 1974
Fouad, Manal . . . . Apr 2007
Gameethige, Tishani . . . . Oct 2007
Turner, Mr Nicholas Guy. . . . . *Jul 1987

ZIMMERS ‡
32 Corringham Road London NW11 7BU
Tel: 0870 770 0171 *Fax:* 0870 770 0172
List of partners: G H Zimmer
Languages: German
Work: A3 F1 M1 M2 N Z(f)
Emergency Action, Agency, Advocacy and Fixed Fee Interview undertaken
SPr: Zimmer, Mr Gunter H . . . . Apr 1992

ZIMMERS ‡
5 Water Lane London NW1 8NZ
Tel: 020 7284 6970 *Fax:* 020 7284 6980
E-mail: info@zimmerslaw.com

ZORRO LAW ‡
1379 High Road Whetstone London N20 9LP
Tel: 0845 000 0219 *Fax:* 020 8626 4563

ZURIEL SOLICITORS ‡
289 Kennington Lane London SE11 5QY
Tel: 020 7582 5543 *Fax:* 020 7820 6642 *Dx:* 37051 KENNINGTON
E-mail: info@zurielsolicitors.co.uk

See p2 for the Key to Work Categories & other symbols

LONDON FIRMS BY POSTAL DISTRICT

E1

AK Solicitors . . . p3
Adams Solicitors . . . p4
Akin Gump Strauss Hauer & Feld. . . . p4
Alexander JLO . . . p5
Allen & Overy LLP . . . p5
Arbis LLP. . . . p7
Armstrong Law LLP. . . . p7
Athuraliyage Solicitors . . . p8
A Bajwa & Co . . . p9
Barker Austin. . . . p9
Bentleys Stokes & Lowless . . . p12
Blick & Co . . . p14
Capital Solicitors LLP. . . . p18
Cavell Solicitors LLP . . . p19
Chowdhury & Co . . . p20
Citygate Solicitors . . . p20
Cleveland Solicitors . . . p20
J Cooper . . . p22
R T Coopers Solicitors . . . p22
Copper Stone Solicitors . . . p22
Corbin & Hassan . . . p22
Cormact Cawley & Co . . . p22
Dare Emmanuel Solicitors . . . p25
Diamond Solicitors Limited . . . p27
Dorman Joseph Wachtel . . . p27
Elder Rahimi Limited . . . p29
Ellum LLP . . . p29
Edward Fail Bradshaw & Waterson . . . p30
The Family Law Practice . . . p30
Angela Gaff . . . p34
Garcha & Co . . . p35
Gawor & Co . . . p35
Guise Solicitors . . . p37
HSR Solicitors . . . p37
Hafezis Solicitors. . . . p37
Hextalls Limited . . . p41
Ince & Co Services Ltd . . . p44
The International Property Law Centre LLP . p45
Jackson Parton. . . . p45
Kalam Solicitors . . . p47
Kuddus Solicitors. . . . p50
LB & Co Solicitors . . . p50
Lake Jackson . . . p51
Lincoln's Chambers Solicitors. . . . p54
Lovatt & Co . . . p55
McCormacks . . . p56
Malik & Michael . . . p58
Thomas Mansfield LLP . . . p58
Mays Brown . . . p60
Miles & Partners . . . p60
Monk & Turner Solicitors LLP. . . . p61
Paul Hastings Janofsky & Walker LLP . . . p66
David Phillips & Partners . . . p67
Punatar & Co Solicitors. . . . p69
Reynolds Porter Chamberlain LLP . . . p71
Russell Wise . . . p74
SB Solicitors . . . p75
SD Solicitors . . . p75
Sach Solicitors . . . p76
RAYMOND SAUL & CO . . . p76
Schneider Page . . . p77
Syed Shaheen Solicitors . . . p77
Shahid Rahman . . . p77
Shanaz & Partners Solicitors . . . p77
M J Solomon & Partners . . . p80
Sonn Macmillan . . . p80
Suriya & Co . . . p84
TV Edwards LLP. . . . p85
Thames Chambers Solicitors . . . p86
Universal Solicitors . . . p89
D J Webb & Co . . . p90
Zahra & Co. . . . p93
Zaman Solicitors . . . p93

E2

Alexander Johnson . . . p5
Hafiz & Haque Solicitors . . . p37
Ignatiou-Fakhouri & Co Solicitors . . . p44
Malcolm & Co Solicitors . . . p58
Miramar Legal . . . p61
Obaseki Solicitors. . . . p64
SEB Solicitors . . . p75
Stunt Palmer & Robinson . . . p84
Joseph Tily Solicitors . . . p87

E3

Holden Haie . . . p42
McMillen Hamilton McCarthy . . . p57
Waterfields Solicitors . . . p90

E4

Achillea & Co. . . . p3
Alexander JLO . . . p5
Barnes & Partners . . . p10
Coldham Shield & Mace . . . p21
Corford International LLP . . . p22
M R Solicitors. . . . p55
Donald Pugh Solicitor. . . . p69
Russells . . . p75
Sharpes . . . p77

E5

Graham Bash & Co. . . . p11
Debridge Solicitors . . . p26
Hutchins & Co . . . p44
Moss & Co . . . p62
Owens Stevens Solicitors. . . . p65

E6

AKP Solicitors Ltd . . . p3
Aravindans . . . p7
Bala & Co . . . p9
Norman H Barnett & Co. . . . p11
J Bon Solicitors. . . . p14
Edell Jones & Lessers . . . p28
Edwards Duthie. . . . p29
J H Hart & Co. . . . p39
Jacobs Solicitors . . . p46
Losanaa & Co Solicitors . . . p55
Loxford Solicitors . . . p55
Marziano Khatry Mak Solicitors . . . p59
Ratna & Co. . . . p70
Ropemakers Solicitors . . . p73
Sharma & Co Solicitors . . . p77
Ali Sinclair Solutions . . . p80
Joseph Thaliyan Solicitors . . . p86
Wiseman Lee LLP . . . p92

E7

AQSA Law Chambers . . . p3
Arora Solicitors . . . p7
Balinda & Co . . . p9
Bluestone & Co. . . . p14
Denning Solicitors . . . p26
Fadiga & Co Solicitors . . . p30
Howell & Co . . . p43
MKM Solicitors . . . p55
Mangala & Kalum Solicitors . . . p58
Markand & Co . . . p58
Martin-Simms Solicitors. . . . p59
Munro Solicitors . . . p62
Nandy & Co . . . p63
Nasim & Co Solicitors. . . . p63
Perera & Co . . . p67
Rees Myers Solicitors. . . . p71
Robinson Ravani & Co . . . p72
Sandhu & Shah. . . . p76
Woodgrange Solicitors . . . p93

E8

Absolute Law Ltd . . . p3
BWF Solicitors . . . p9
Barnet Solicitors. . . . p10
S A Carr & Co. . . . p18
Caulker & Ozkutan . . . p19
Dowse & Co . . . p27
Emerly Halil And Brown Solicitors . . . p29
Erica Peat & Diable . . . p29
Franks Solicitors . . . p34
Harrison Morgan . . . p39
KC Law Chambers Solicitors . . . p47
Stuart Karatas Solicitors. . . . p48
Kuddus Solicitors (UK) Ltd . . . p50
Duncan Lewis & Co . . . p53
Lucas Law Limited . . . p55
MartynsRose Solicitors . . . p59
Nathaniel & Co . . . p63
Spence & Horne . . . p81

E9

Cherith Solicitors LLP . . . p19
P M Mitchell. . . . p61

E10

FLK Solicitors . . . p30
Haq Hamilton Hughes . . . p38
Kalra & Co . . . p48
London Law Firm . . . p55
Whitefields Solicitors . . . p91

E11

CFB Partnership . . . p17
C K Solicitors . . . p17
Christofi Wells & Co. . . . p20
Church Lane Solicitors Limited . . . p20
Gants Hill Solicitors . . . p35
Gough & Co Solicitors. . . . p36
Charles Gregory Associates. . . . p37
David Harrisons Solicitors . . . p39
Julius & Co Solicitors . . . p47
Kennards Wells . . . p48
MacLeish Littlestone Cowan. . . . p57
Murdochs . . . p62
Partners & Co. . . . p66
Alfred Pirotta . . . p68
Helen Robbins Solicitors . . . p72
Vivienne Robinson . . . p72
Stokoe Partnership . . . p83
Time Solicitors . . . p87
Benjamin Vincent Solicitors . . . p89
Wilkinsons . . . p91
Wiseman Lee LLP. . . . p92

E12

Abiloye & Co . . . p3
Chipatiso & Co Solicitors . . . p20
Haslaw & Co LLP . . . p39
Ideal Solicitors . . . p44
D H K Jacobs & Co . . . p45
Jeya & Co. . . . p46
Joy & Co . . . p47
Khan & Partners . . . p49
Law & Lawyers . . . p51
J S Lazar . . . p52
Patricks Solicitors . . . p66
S Satha & Co . . . p76
Simply Legal Solicitors . . . p80
Vanguards LLP . . . p89
Vasuki Solicitors. . . . p89

E13

M H Banharally & Co . . . p9
Dhillon & Co. . . . p27
Edwards Duthie . . . p29
GMG . . . p34
Lincolns Solicitors . . . p54
Portway Solicitors . . . p69
Shahzads Solicitors . . . p77
L Sharma & Co Solicitors . . . p77

E14

E J C Album. . . . p4
Alexander JLO. . . . p5
Allen & Overy LLP. . . . p6
Bibi Gadwah Solicitors. . . . p12
Bond Solicitors . . . p14
CLS Services . . . p17
Clifford Chance . . . p20
Crisp & Co Solicitors. . . . p23
Dalton Barrett Solicitors . . . p25
Dockland Solicitors LLP . . . p27
Doyle Clayton Solicitors Limited . . . p27
Feltons . . . p31
Hugh James. . . . p43
Kaslers Solicitors LLP . . . p48
LL Law LLP . . . p51
Lane Graham Solicitors . . . p51
Dale Langley & Co. . . . p51
Lehman Brothers . . . p52
Miller Evans & Co . . . p60
C M Murray . . . p62
Quinn Mantion. . . . p70
Rouse Legal (Formerly Willoughby & Partners) . . . p74
Skadden Arps Slate Meagher & Flom (UK) LLP . . . p80
TMP Solicitors LLP . . . p85
Taj Solicitors. . . . p85
Tetlow Powell . . . p86
Vance Harris. . . . p89

E15

Bearing Sachs Solicitors LLP. . . . p11
BlackWhite Solicitors . . . p13
Bowling & Co . . . p15
Corper Solicitors. . . . p22
Daybells LLP . . . p26
Irvine Thanvi Natas . . . p45
JDS Solicitors . . . p45
Paul John . . . p46
Charles Kirit & Co . . . p50
McCormacks . . . p56
Marshall & Mason Solicitors . . . p59
Pillai & Jones . . . p67
Skanthabalan Solicitors . . . p80
TV Edwards LLP. . . . p85
Trinity Solicitors . . . p88
Jay Vadher & Co . . . p89

E16

ATE Solicitors . . . p3
Hereward & Foster. . . . p41
G M Hewett Solicitor. . . . p41

E17

Arona Sarwar LLP. . . . p7
Bentleys. . . . p12
Cartwright Cunningham Haselgrove & Co . . p19
Cornerstones . . . p22
Uma Duraisingam . . . p28
Fellowes Solicitors. . . . p31
Foresters Solicitors . . . p33
Gilbert Turner Coomber . . . p35
Henscott Solicitors. . . . p40
McLarty & Co . . . p57

Manogaran & Co p58
Mirza & Co p61
Nat Jen Soyege Solicitors p63
Onyems & Partners p65
Renaissance p71
Romain Coleman & Co p73
SJ LAW p75
Shahzads Solicitors & Estate Agents p77
TTS Solicitors p85
Wiseman Lee LLP p92

E18

Chase Solicitors p19
Denton Solicitors p27
Hudson Mcconaghugh Solicitors p43
Huggins & Lewis Foskett p43
Gary Jacobs & Co p45
Andrew Keen & Co p48
Laderman & Co p51

EC1

Abrahams Dresden p3
Addleshaw Goddard p4
Akin & Law LLP p4
S Ali & Company Solicitors p5
William Bache Solicitors Limited p9
Balsara & Co p9
J E Baring & Co p9
Arthur Barnes & Co p10
Janie Batchford Solicitors p11
Belmont & Lowe p11
Best & Soames Limited p12
Bevan Kidwell p12
Blackwell Sanders Peper Martin LLP p13
Blake Lapthorn p13
Brett Wilson LLP p15
Burton Woolf & Turk p16
CMS Cameron McKenna LLP p17
Caliskan Carter Solicitors p17
Campbell Chambers p18
Cannings Connolly p18
Capital Law LLP p18
Carter Lemon Camerons p18
Chan Neill Solicitors p19
Clegg Manuel p20
Crawford Solicitors p23
Crowther Solicitors p23
DKLM Solicitors p24
Ralph Davis p26
Deighton Guedalla p26
Divorce Solicitors Online p27
Duane Morris p28
England Palmer p29
J E Evans-Jackson & Co p30
Stephen Fidler & Co p31
Foyen & Co p33
Francis Wilks & Jones LLP p34
Fried Frank Harris Shriver & Jacobson LLP p34
GSC Solicitors p34
Kay Georgiou p35
Giambrone Law p35
Goodman Ray p36
Greenhouse Stirton & Co p37
Greenwood & Co p37
Harper & Odell p39
Harris da Silva p39
Harris Hagan p39
Hogan Lovells International LLP p42
Housing & Property Law Partnership p43
HOWARD STONE p43
Nick Howe Solicitors p43
Hoxtons Solicitors p43
Innstep (Nominees) Limited p45
Irvine & Partners p45
Mariel Irvine p45
Irwin Mitchell LLP p45
Israel Strange & Conlon p45
Jens Hills Solicitors LLP p46
C J Jones Solicitors p46
Josiah Lake Gardiner LLP p47
KLS Law p47
Kingsley Napley p50
Leslie Kovacs p50
Law Partners Solicitors Ltd p51
Lawford Davies Denoon p51
LEIGH DAY & CO p52
Loch Associates p55
Lorrells LLP p55
McCormacks p56
Magwells p57
Mathys & Squire p59
W H Matthews & Co p59
Mellersh & Co p60
Millbank Solicitors p60
Miller Rosenfalck p61
Henry Milner & Co p61
Morton Fraser LLP p62
Joseph Mynah & Co Solicitors p62
Olisakwe Vincent Onuegbu p64
PCB Litigation LLP p65
Parlett Kent p66
Pini Franco LLP p67
Raffles Haig Solicitors p70
Rebecca Emmett Employment Law Consultancy p71
Reculver Solicitors p71
Redd p71
Reynolds Macdonald p71
Rice-Jones & Smiths p72
Richmond & Barnes p72
Robinson & Co p72
Rogers & Co Solicitors p73
Rollingsons p73
Ronald Fletcher Baker LLP p73
Rooks Rider p73
Kaye Scholer LLP p77
Shearman Bowen & Co Solicitors p78
Simpson Millar LLP p80
Slaughter and May p80
Snow Hill Legal p80
The Specter Partnership p81
Lawrence Stephens p82
Stone King LLP p83
Alan Taylor & Co p85
Travers Smith LLP p87
Venner Shipley & Co p89
Vizards Livesey Cameron Walker p89
Webster Dixon LLP p90
Whitecross Solicitors p91
Wragge & Co LLP p93
D Young & Co p93

EC2

A City Law Firm LLP p3
Arion Law p7
Arnold & Porter LLP p7
Ashurst LLP p7
Baker Botts LLP p9
Banks Kelly p9
Bargate Murray p9
Berrymans Lace Mawer p12
Bingham McCutchen (London) LLP p12
Blavo & Co Solicitors p14
Broadgate Legal p16
Cahill Gordon & Reindel p17
Cains Advocates Limited p17
Calyon p18
Carey Olsen p18
Bryan Cave p19
Cavendish Law p19
City Law Financial LLP p20
Cleary Gottlieb Steen & Hamilton p20
John Collis Solicitors p22
Conyers Dill & Pearman p22
Cravath Swaine & Moore LLP p23
Stella Currie p24
Curtis Mallet-Prevost Colt & Mosle LLP p24
DLA Piper UK LLP p24
Davies & Davies Associates Limited p26
Debevoise & Plimpton p26
Claudio Del Giudice p26
Laura Devine Solicitors p27
Devonshires p27
Dewey Ballantine p27
Dickson Minto WS p27
Dorsey & Whitney p27
Doyle Clayton Solicitors Limited p27
Druces LLP p27
Edwards Angell Palmer & Dodge p28
Employment Solicitors London Limited p29
Evergreen Solicitors p30
Eversheds LLP p30
Fenchurch Law LLP p31
Figueiredo & Bowman p32
Fishers p32
P A Fleury p33
Forbes Hall LLP p33
Fox Williams p33
Fujioka Company Limited p34
GQ Employment Law p34
Gianni Origoni & Partners p35
Gide Loyrette Nouel LLP p35
Gill Jennings & Every p35
Glade Law Limited p35
Goodman Ray p36
Grier Olubi Solicitors p37
Harvey Camford LLP p39
Edward Hayes LLP p39
Heather Thomas Consulting p40
Herbert Reeves & Co p40
Herbert Smith LLP p40
Hextalls p41
Houthoff Burma p43
Jacobsens p46
Jo & Co Solicitors p46
KD Law Limited p47
KattenMuchinRosenmanCornish LLP p48
Keelys LLP p48
Kemp Little LLP p48
King & Spalding International LLP p49
Kromann Reumert p50
Latham & Watkins LLP p51
Lattey & Dawe p51
Legal Hobbit p52
Levi Solicitors LLP p53
Link2Law p54
Linklaters LLP p54
Logos UK Limited p55
Mhlaw p55
MMS Law p55
McDermott Will & Emery UK LLP p56
McFaddens LLP p56
Maclay Murray & Spens LLP p57
Maisto E Associati p57
Mallesons Stephen Jaques p58
Maples Teesdale LLP p58
Maurice Turnor Gardner LLP p59
Mayer Brown International LLP p59
Milbank Tweed Hadley & McCloy p60
Minter Ellison p61
Mintz Levin Cohn Ferris Glovsky & Popeo LLP p61
Mark Morris Solicitors p62
Morrison & Foerster (UK) LLP p62
Morton Pugh Welch p62
Nautadutilh p63
Ogier p64
Orrick Herrington & Sutcliffe LLP p65
Osborne Clarke p65
Parker & Co p65
Partners Employment Lawyers p66
Richard Pearlman LLP p66
Pembrokes Solicitors p66
Penningtons p66
Phoros Trustees (UK) Limited p67
Pillsbury Winthrop Shaw Pittman LLP p67
Pindoria Solicitors p67
Pinsent Masons LLP p67
Pitmans LLP p68
Pitmans SK Sport & Entertainment LLP p68
Plexus Law (A Trading Name of Parabis Law LLP) p68
Pollecoff Solicitors Ltd p68
Pritchard Englefield p69
Quist Solicitors p70
Reed Smith LLP p71
Richards Kibbe & Orbe p72
Sacker & Partners LLP p76
Samuels & Co Solicitors p76
Schultze & Braun LLP p77
Shearman & Sterling LLP p78
Sidley Austin Brown & Wood p78
Silverman Sherliker LLP p78
Simmons & Simmons p79
Simpson Thacher & Bartlett LLP p80
Squire Sanders (UK) LLP p81
Steeles p82
Stephenson Harwood p82
Steptoe & Johnson p83
Stibbe p83
Strafford Law Limited p84
Sykes Anderson LLP p85
TLT Solicitors p85
Guy Thompson & Co p87
Troutman Sanders LLP p88
Trustee Solutions Limited p88
Vinson & Elkins LLP p89
Watson Farley & Williams p90
Paul Weiss p91
Whale Rock Legal Limited p91
White & Case LLP p91
Caroline Whiteley p91
Wikborg Rein p91
Willkie Farr & Gallagher LLP p92
WilmerHale p92
Winston & Strawn LLP p92
Winter Scott p92

EC3

ALMT Legal p3
Amy & Co p6
Appleby p7
Azam & Co Solicitors p9
Bains Cohen LLP p9
Barlow Lyde & Gilbert LLP p10
Bivonas Limited Solicitors p13
Blake-Turner & Co p14
Bond Pearce LLP p14
Brookes & Co p16
Browne Jacobson LLP p16
CMS Cameron McKenna LLP p17
Cameron Deacon LLP p18
Carter Perry Bailey LLP p18
Cayton & Co p19
Chauncy & Co p19
Churchward & Co p20
City Net Law p20
Clausen Miller LLP p20
Clyde & Co LLP p21
Thomas Cooper p22
Cost Advocates Limited p23
Cozen O'Connor LLP p23
DAC Beachcroft p24
Davies Battersby Ltd p26
Davis & Co p26
Dewey & LeBoeuf p27
Duval Vassiliades Solicitors p28
Elborne Mitchell LLP p29
Edward Fail Bradshaw & Waterson p30
Field & Co p31
Field Fisher Waterhouse LLP p31
Fishburns p32
Fox Hartley p33
Fox p33
Furley Page LLP p34
Gates and Partners p35
Gowlings (UK) LLP p36
Greenberg Traurig Maher LLP p37
Greenwoods p37
Hill Dickinson LLP p41
Holman Fenwick Willan p42
Holme Roberts & Owen p42
Horn & Co p43
Housemans p43
Hunton & Williams p44
Independent Pension Trustee Limited p45
Kennedys p49
Kirkland & Ellis International LLP p50
Jon Lang p51
Dale Langley & Co p51
Lax & Co LLP p52
Leelanes Solicitors LLP p52
Legitimus Solicitors p52
Lord Bissell & Brook p55
B J Macfarlane & Co p56
Laurence Marron Solicitors p59
Matheson Ormsby Prentice p59
Mayer Brown International LLP p60
Mills & Reeve p61
Morgans Solicitors p62
NCTM LLP p62
Ogilvy Renault p64
Plexus Law (A Trading Name of Parabis Law LLP) p68
ProLegal Limited p69
Puxon Murray LLP p69
Pysdens Solicitors p70
R R & Co London Maritime & Energy Solicitors p70
Reorient Legal p71
Reynolds Colman Bradley LLP p71
Paul Roberts p72
SGH Martineau LLP p75
Sedgwick Detert Moran & Arnold p77
Shupak & Co Solicitors p78
Robin Simon LLP p79
M Taher & Co Solicitors p85
Trowers & Hamlins p88
WT Law LLP p90
Walkers p90
WALTONS & MORSE LLP p90
Waterson Hicks p90
Watson Burton LLP p90
Wilkins Beaumont Suckling p91

EC4

Abbiss Cadres LLP p3
Alexander Solicitors p5
S C Andrew LLP p6
Jonathan Angell & Co p6
Archon Solicitors p7
E G Arghyrakis & Co p7
Ashby Cohen Solicitors Limited p7
Alan Ashley & Co p7
Baker & McKenzie p9
Barclay Taylor p9
Bark & Co p9
Bates Wells & Braithwaite London LLP p11
Berwin Leighton Paisner LLP p12
Bevan Brittan LLP p12
Beynons Nicholls p12
Bird & Bird LLP p13
Blackfords LLP p13
Blake Cassels & Graydon LLP p13
Bonelli Erede Pappalardo LLP p14
Bower Cotton Khaitan p15
Bracewell & Giuliani LLP p15
Bristows p15
Bullivant & Partners p16
Burt Staples & Maner LLP p16
Byrne & Partners p16
Callistes p17
Campbell Commercial Law p18
Carrington & Associates p18
George Carter p18
Carter Moore Solicitors p18
CARTER-RUCK p18
Chadbourne & Parke p19
Chadwyck-Healey & Co p19
James Chan & Co p19
The Chancery Partnership Solicitors p19
Charles Russell LLP p19
Chua's Solicitors p20
Claremont Richards p20
Clarke Willmott p20
Claude Hornby & Cox p20
Cooke Young & Keidan LLP p22
David Cooper & Co p22
Cornelian Lawyers And Mediators p22
Creed Lane Law Group p23
Crossmans MTA p23
Crowell & Moring p23
Curtis Turner & Drukker Ltd p24
DAC Beachcroft p24
DMH Stallard LLP p25
DWF p25
Dale-Stevens LLP p25
De Brauw Blackstones Westbroek p26
Dechert p26
Dewar Hogan p27
Dickinson Dees p27
Eastwoods Solicitors p28
Thomas Eggar LLP p29
Egorov Puginsky Afanasiev & Partners LLP p29
Faegre & Benson LLP p30
Ferguson Solicitors p31
Fisher Scoggins Waters LLP p32
P A Fleury & Co p33
Franks & Co p34
Freshfields Bruckhaus Deringer LLP p34
Frisby & Co p34
Froriep Renggli p34
Fulbright & Jaworski LLP p34
GH Cornish LLP p34
Gateley LLP p35
Gibson Dunn & Crutcher LLP p35
Gillhams Solicitors LLP p35
Gomez Acebo & Pombo p36
Goodman Derrick LLP p36
H2O Law LLP p37
Harney Westwood & Riegels p39
Harrisons Solicitors p39

N1

N2

N3

N4

N5

N6

N7

N8

N9

N10

N11

N12

N13

N14

N15

N16

N17

N18

N19

N20

N21

N22

NW1

NW2

NW3

NW4

NW5

NW6

NW7

NW8

NW9

NW10

NW11

SE1

SE2

SE3

SE4

SE5

SE6

SE7

SE8

SE9

SE10

SE11

SE12

SE13

SE14

SE15

SE16

SE17

SE18

SE19

SE20

SE21

SE22

SE23

SE24

SE25

SE26

SE27

SE28

SW1

SW2

SW3

SW4

SW5

SW6

SW7

SW8

Akodu & Co Solicitors . . . p4
Ana Kanellos Furlong Solicitor . . . p6
Clapham & Co . . . p20
Dickinson Solicitors Limited. . . . p27

SW9

Afrifa & Partners . . . p4
Chancery CS Solicitors . . . p19
Children & Families Law Firm. . . . p20
Gani & Co . . . p35
Hornby & Levy . . . p43
John & Co . . . p46
Nag & Co Solicitors. . . . p63
John Neville & Co . . . p63
M Olubi Solicitors. . . . p64
Ross Simon & Co Solicitors . . . p79
Southbank Solicitors . . . p81
Peter Thomson. . . . p87
Thoree & Co Solicitors . . . p87
Wainwright & Cummins. . . . p90
George Wills Solicitors . . . p92
Ziadies . . . p94

SW10

John T P Mcguirk . . . p57
Oakleys Solicitors . . . p64
Stone Joseph Solicitors. . . . p83
Mark Taylor & Co. . . . p86

SW11

Baxter Brown McArthur. . . . p11
Cummings . . . p24
DG Law . . . p24
EBR Attridge LLP. . . . p28
Farrell Martin Nee . . . p30
Gibson Young . . . p35
Hanne & Co . . . p38
William Heath & Co. . . . p40
Hodders . . . p41
Leon Kaye Solicitors . . . p48
Michael Gerard Mcfall . . . p60
Rawlings Giles . . . p71
TV Edwards LLP. . . . p85
Roberta Tish Solicitors . . . p87
Walker Smith Way . . . p90

SW12

A-Z Law Solicitors . . . p3
Balham Law Partnership . . . p9
Ines De Vecchi . . . p26
P G Solicitors . . . p65
Parfitt Law . . . p65
R O C K Solicitors . . . p70
Regents & Co Solicitors . . . p71
SJS Solicitors . . . p75

SW13

Antell & Co. . . . p6
R J Frost & Co . . . p34
Rodgers & Burton . . . p73
Sutton-Mattocks & Co LLP . . . p84
Wilson Finlay. . . . p92

SW14

Abbott Cresswell LLP. . . . p3
Absolutely Legal . . . p3
Kervin Barnes Limited . . . p10
A S Croxson . . . p23
Michael Oppler & Co . . . p65

SW15

Ahmads Solicitors . . . p4
R Felstead Solicitors . . . p31
Kensington Solicitors . . . p49
Lawrence Law . . . p52
Clive Lovatt Solicitor . . . p55
Mapletoft & Co . . . p58
Murray Hay Solicitors. . . . p62
Rider Support Services. . . . p72
RUSSELL-COOKE LLP . . . p74
Slater Bradley & Co . . . p80
Gerald V Tew. . . . p86
Virtual Lawyers Limited. . . . p89

SW16

Alaga & Co. . . . p4
Alan Ambridge Solicitor. . . . p6
ANTHONY GOLD . . . p6
Cowles. . . . p23
Dexter Henry & Co . . . p27
Goodwin & Co . . . p36
Henry Hughes & Hughes . . . p40
A L Hughes & Co. . . . p43
Azam Khan & Co Solicitors . . . p49
Kris Sen Solicitors . . . p50
Mccauley-Slowe Solicitors . . . p56
Ratip Solicitors . . . p70
Strasons . . . p84
P B Sylvester & Co . . . p85
Van Eaton Solicitors . . . p89
Jay Vara & Co . . . p89
Victory Solicitors . . . p89

SW17

Alen-Buckley & Co . . . p4
C M Atif & Co. . . . p8
Benn Cameron Solicitors . . . p12
Broadway Solicitors . . . p16
CAS Law Limited . . . p17
Collis & Co . . . p22
Fadiga & Co Solicitors . . . p30
Fernando & Co . . . p31
Kenwright & Lynch . . . p49
Lee Associates . . . p52
Duncan Lewis & Co. . . . p53
Mahesen & Co . . . p57
Makka Solicitors Ltd . . . p58
Dean Manson Solicitors. . . . p58
Peter J Miller . . . p60
Mr Laws Solicitors . . . p62
Pragash & McKenzie . . . p69
Raja & Co . . . p70
Solicitors First LLP . . . p80
Suriya & Co. . . . p84
Thompson & Co . . . p87
John Williamson Solicitor . . . p92
Wimbledon Solicitors . . . p92

SW18

Amer Sargent & Co. . . . p6
Begum & Co . . . p11
Birds Solicitors . . . p13
BULCRAIGS . . . p16
Irving Caplin & Co . . . p18
Flack & Co . . . p32
Jenkins Law . . . p46
Southfields Solicitors . . . p81
Martin J Williams & Co . . . p92
Wixted & Co Ltd . . . p93
A E P Zaleski. . . . p93

SW19

Armstrongs . . . p7
Ashworths Solicitors . . . p8
Bazeer & Co . . . p11
Black Stone Solicitors. . . . p13
Brocklesby & Co . . . p16
Broadbridge Grimes & Solicitors . . . p16
Broome Palmer Solicitors . . . p16
Burnley-Jones Bate & Co . . . p16
Cahill De Fonseka Solicitors . . . p17
Capsticks Solicitors LLP. . . . p18
Courtyard Solicitors LLP . . . p23
D E T Child. . . . p24
Davies Morgante Law Limited. . . . p26
Dowse Baxter. . . . p27
Eagles Solicitors . . . p28
J Howard Fry Solicitor. . . . p34
Gregsons. . . . p37
Hart Brown Solicitors . . . p39
Johnson Crilly Solicitors LLP . . . p46
Kanaga Solicitors . . . p48
Kingstons Solicitors. . . . p50
Kirby & Co . . . p50
Lexis Law Solicitors. . . . p54
McGlennons . . . p56
Austin McKee. . . . p57
Jeremy Marozzi. . . . p58
Morrisons Solicitors LLP . . . p62
Nathan & Co . . . p63
Ormerods. . . . p65
Paton Walsh Laundy . . . p66
Peace Farnell Limited. . . . p66
Peacock & Co . . . p66
Phoenix Law Partnership . . . p67
Rasiah & Co . . . p70
Rest Harrow & Co Solicitors . . . p71
Roelens Solicitors Wimbledon. . . . p73
Richard Rooney & Co. . . . p73
SW19 Lawyers . . . p76
Shariful Solicitors . . . p77
Simpson Millar LLP. . . . p80
Sunrise Solicitors Limited . . . p84
TWM Solicitors LLP. . . . p85
Theva & Co. . . . p86
Thirus . . . p87
Thompsons (formerly Robin/Brian Thompson & Partners) . . . p87
Trading Terms Limited . . . p87
Turnbull Rutherford Solicitors . . . p89
WSM Solicitors LLP. . . . p90
Wimbledon Solicitors . . . p92

SW20

C L Clemo & Co. . . . p20
Howell-Jones LLP. . . . p43
Leslieowen . . . p53
Michael & Company. . . . p60

W1

APD Solicitors. . . . p3
Ablett & Stebbing . . . p3
D Abraham & Co . . . p3
Mark Adams LLB . . . p4
Adams Solicitors . . . p4
Advisa Solicitors . . . p4
Aequitas Law LLP. . . . p4
Alexander Lawyers LLP . . . p5
Alexander Marks LLP . . . p5
Alexiou Fisher Philipps . . . p5
R W Anderson & Co. . . . p6
Angel & Co . . . p6
Ankamah Gunn Ltd . . . p6
Arc Property Solicitors LLP . . . p7
Arnold Fooks Chadwick LLP. . . . p7
Ashby Cohen Solicitors Ltd . . . p7
Ashfords LLP . . . p7
Aslan Charles Kousetta LLP. . . . p8
Atlee Chung & Company . . . p8
Awtani Immigration Solicitors . . . p9
Farooq Bajwa & Co . . . p9
Barker Gillette. . . . p9
Beauchamps . . . p11
David W Beech . . . p11
Benson Mazure LLP. . . . p12
Berkeley Law Limted . . . p12
Bignalls . . . p12
Birchley Titmus Commercial Solicitors . . . p13
Blandfords . . . p14
Blokh Solicitors . . . p14
Boodle Hatfield . . . p14
Bowen Muscatt . . . p14
Mark Brady Law LLP . . . p15
Robert Brand & Co . . . p15
Henri Brandman & Co. . . . p15
Brecher . . . p15
Breedy Handerson LLP . . . p15
M M E Brenninkmeyer. . . . p15
Bridgehouse Partners LLP. . . . p15
Brook Martin & Co . . . p16
Brooke North LLP . . . p16
Philip Brown & Co. . . . p16
Brown Rudnick Berlack Israels LLP . . . p16
CJ Associates. . . . p17
CVS Solicitors. . . . p17
Callaghan & Co . . . p17
Callistes. . . . p17
Camerons Solicitors LLP . . . p18
Carritt & Co LLP. . . . p18
Carters . . . p19
Cartwright Adams Solicitors Limited . . . p19
Cavendish Law . . . p19
Guy Clapham & Co . . . p20
Clifford Harris & Co . . . p21
Garth Coates Solicitors . . . p21
Coffey Graham LLP . . . p21
Cole Associates. . . . p21
Collins Benson Goldhill LLP . . . p21
C E P Colombotti . . . p22
Conybeare Solicitors . . . p22
Cramer Pelmont. . . . p23
Crawford Solicitors . . . p23
Cromwells Law Limited . . . p23
Cruickshanks Solicitors . . . p23
Curry Popeck . . . p24
DWFM Beckman . . . p25
Gordon Dadds . . . p25
Dalton Holmes Gray. . . . p25
Davenport Lyons . . . p25
Aubrey David . . . p25
DAVID CONWAY & CO. . . . p26
Davidson Morris Solicitors. . . . p26
Leigh Davis . . . p26
De Cruz Solicitors. . . . p26
Devassey Legal. . . . p27
Dias Solicitors. . . . p27
Charles Douglas Solicitors. . . . p27
Driving Defences LLP . . . p27
Musa Dudhia & Co . . . p28
E&A Law . . . p28
Ebury House Solicitors . . . p28
Egmont Solicitors & Notary Public . . . p29
Evans Dodd LLP . . . p30
Evans London Solicitors. . . . p30
Evans Wallace Solicitors . . . p30
Fasken Martineau LLP. . . . p31
Filatov Goldberg Musatov LLP. . . . p32
Finers Stephens Innocent LLP. . . . p32
Fishman & Co Solicitors. . . . p32
J P Fletcher & Co . . . p33
Forbes Anderson Free . . . p33
Forsters LLP . . . p33
Forsyth Simpson . . . p33
Fortune Law. . . . p33
Frank & Co . . . p34
Freedmans Law. . . . p34
Freeman Box . . . p34
Freemans Solicitors . . . p34
Fuglers . . . p34
Gallant Macmillan LLP. . . . p34
Gherson & Co. . . . p35
Gilchrist Solicitors . . . p35
Glinert Davis. . . . p36
Glovers Solicitors LLP . . . p36
Mel Goldberg Law . . . p36
Richard S Goldstein . . . p36
Goodge Law. . . . p36
David Goodman & Co . . . p36
Gordon & Co . . . p36
Grace & Co . . . p36
Paul Gromett & Co . . . p37
HCLS LLP. . . . p37
Haldanes . . . p37
Halebury Ventures Limited. . . . p38
HAMLINS LLP . . . p38
Hammond Bale . . . p38
Hansel Henson LLP . . . p38
Harbottle & Lewis LLP . . . p38
Harris & Co . . . p39
Brian Harris & Co . . . p39
D Harris & Co International . . . p39
Hartwig Notary Chambers . . . p39
C H Hausmann & Co . . . p39
Hilmi + Partners LLP. . . . p41
Hogan Lisle . . . p42
Howard & Company . . . p43
Hudson Brown. . . . p43
Hughes Willson Solicitors . . . p43
Hyam Lehrer. . . . p44
Hyde Law . . . p44
JPS Law Solicitors. . . . p45
Jacksons Solicitors . . . p45
Jacobs Allen Hammond . . . p45
Charles James & Co. . . . p46
Jaswal Johnston Boyle . . . p46
Anthony Jayes LLP . . . p46
Jeffrey Green Russell . . . p46
Jiva Solicitors . . . p46
Joelson Wilson LLP . . . p46
Josiah-Lake Solicitors . . . p47
Kalber Struckley & Co . . . p47
Howard Kennedy LLP . . . p48
Khatry Solicitors . . . p49
Kingfields Solicitors . . . p49
Klein Solicitors. . . . p50
Klimt & Co. . . . p50
Kyriakides & Braier . . . p50
LK Baltica Solicitors . . . p51
LSG Solicitors . . . p51
LT Law . . . p51
Law Firm Ltd . . . p51
Lecote Solicitors. . . . p52
Lee & Kan. . . . p52
Lee & Thompson . . . p52
Christine Lee & Co (Solicitors) Ltd . . . p52
P S Levy & Co. . . . p53
Lewis Green & Co Solicitors . . . p53
Lexica Law . . . p54
Lightfoot O'Brien Westcott . . . p54
C S Lima & Co . . . p54
Link2Law . . . p54
Lithman & Co . . . p55
Littons. . . . p55
Loughran & Co International Lawyers . . . p55
Trevor Lyttleton MBE . . . p55
M Law. . . . p55
MTC Law Limited . . . p56
David McCarthy . . . p56
McEwen Parkinson . . . p56
McLee & Co Solicitors . . . p57
Magrath LLP. . . . p57
Manuel Martin & Associates . . . p58
Stella Maris Solicitors LLP . . . p58
Marrache & Co . . . p58
Marshall Hatchick . . . p59
Martine Alan. . . . p59
Matini Montecristo . . . p59
Maurice Nadeem & Atif . . . p59
Mayfair Solicitors . . . p60
S Merali Solicitor Advocate . . . p60
Michael Conn Goldsobel. . . . p60
Micheal Seifert. . . . p60
Michelmores LLP . . . p60
Moghadassi & Associates . . . p61
Morgan & Morgan . . . p61
Moss Beachley Mullem & Coleman . . . p62
Murray Armstrong Solicitors . . . p62
Muscatt Walker Hayim. . . . p62
Nellen . . . p63
New Media Law LLP. . . . p63
Newmans . . . p63
Nicholas & Co. . . . p63
Noorani Law. . . . p63
Notable Services LLP . . . p64
Oracle Solicitors. . . . p65
Ortolan Legal Limited . . . p65
PAIL Solicitors. . . . p65
PCB Lawyers LLP. . . . p65
Patton Moreno & Asvat . . . p66
Pearson Lowe. . . . p66
David Phillips & Partners . . . p67
Portner & Jaskel LLP . . . p68
Preston And Company. . . . p69
Proskauer Rose . . . p69
Protopapas . . . p69
Frank Purdy . . . p69
Quastel Midgen LLP. . . . p70
RMPI Solicitors . . . p70
Rawlison Butler LLP. . . . p71
Francis Read . . . p71
Reliance Law . . . p71
Ridouts . . . p72
Rippon Patel & French. . . . p72
Rix & Kay Solicitors LLP. . . . p72
Rochman Landau LLP. . . . p72

Rokeby Johnson Baars p73
Ronald Fletcher Baker LLP p73
Rooper & Whately p73
John H Rosen & Co p73
R A Rosen & Co p73
Roshanian Payman International Solicitors p73
Ross & Craig p73
Philip Ross & Co p73
Rowel Genn Solicitors p74
Russells p75
SZ Law Ltd p76
Sabi & Associates p76
Saracens Solicitors LLP p76
Saracens p76
Sasto & Klinger p76
Saunders Bearman LLP p76
Schulte Roth & Zabel p77
SEARS TOOTH p77
Seddons p77
Michael Seifert p77
R A Shadbolt p77
Shaw Graham Kersh p78
Sherrards p78
Silvercoin & Co p78
Simmons Gleek Solicitors p79
Paul L Simon p79
Simons Muirhead & Burton p79
Barry Slavin & Co p80
Sloan & Co p80
Smith Braithwaite p80
Jerzy Sokol Solicitor p80
Sookias & Sookias p80
Southcombe & Hayley p81
Southcote Scott p81
Sparrow & Trieu Solicitors p81
Statham Gill Davies p82
Steinfeld Law LLP p82
Stepien Lake p83
Stonehage Law Limited p83
Stones p83
Strain Keville p84
Streathers Solicitors LLP p84
Sturtivant & Co p84
Summers p84
Summit Law LLP p84
Suttons p84
David Tang & Co p85
J Tehrani Solicitors p86
Tennents p86
Thomas Andrew & Daodu Solicitors p87
Thomas Capital Property Lawyers p87
David Thomas Solicitors p87
Thompson & Lilley p87
Andrew Tobias & Co p87
Towerhouse Consulting LLP p87
James Tsang & Co p88
Tuckers p88
Tulloch & Co p89
Turner & Co Solicitors p89
Underwood Solicitors LLP p89
Victor Lissack Roscoe & Coleman p89
Ward Bolton p90
Welbeck Law LLP p91
Wharton & Wharton p91
Whelan Worner Limited p91
Wiggin LLP p91
A Williams & Co p91
WilmerHale p92
Wilson Barca LLP p92
Wolfe Myers & Co p93
Leslie Wolfson & Co p93
John G K Wood p93
John G Wood p93
Woolf Simmonds p93
Michael Wydra & Co p93
P H Yeung p93
Julian Young & Co p93
Zelin & Zelin p94

W2

AMZ Law p3
Austin Law Solicitors LLP p8
Ernest Bird & Sons p13
Bokhari & Co p14
Laurence Brown Solicitor p16
John B Calver & Co p17
Colvin & Partners p22
Fulcrum Law LLP p34
William Heath & Co p40
Herefords Solicitors Limited p41
Adonis Kyriakides & Co p50
MA Law (Solicitors) LLP p55
Mcevedys p56
Mills & Co p61
Morgan Reed Solicitors p61
Paul Gubbay Solicitors p66
C J Russell MA(Cantab) p74
Shaidy & Co p77
UK Immigration & Property Solicitors Ltd p89
WGS Solicitors p90
Wingate Wong Solicitors p92
Nadine Wong & Co p93
Zelin & Zelin p94

W3

A Kay Pietron & Paluch p3
George Anthony Andrews Solicitors p6
Arora Lodhi Heath p7
Aston Clark p8
W A G Davidson & Co p26
Fairchild Greig p30
Gramdan Solicitors p36
Robert Layton & Co p52
Lock & Marlborough p55
Minogue & Co p61
Procol & Candor Solicitors p69
Sayer Moore & Co p77
Sutovic & Hartigan p84

W4

AR Legal Solicitors p3
Albion Gee & Co p4
Austins Solicitors p8
Mark Beattie p11
J Patrick F Bradley p15
T H R Crawley p23
Cresswell & Co p23
Freedmans p34
C From & Co p34
M C Grumbridge p37
Haynes & Co p39
Kathryn Hickmott p41
Huntley Legal p44
M C Kirton & Co p50
Lancasters p51
Leonard Lowy p55
Geraldine McAleese & Co p56
J P Mitchell p61
Owen White & Catlin p65
Prospect Solicitors p69
Rae Nemazee LLP p70
Howard Russell & Co p74
Strand Solicitors p84
Stratem Law p84
Sutton-Mattocks & Co LLP p84
Tovell & Co p87
Watson Marshal p90

W5

Arden Solicitors (Immigration Specialist) p7
Ash Norton Solicitors p7
Bishop Lloyd & Jackson p13
Bluetts Solicitors p14
A S Croxson Solicitors p23
ELC Solicitors p28
Elliots Bond & Banbury p29
Elthorn Solicitors p29
Fearnley & Co p31
Gore Legal p36
Paul Harden & Co p39
Howe & Co p43
J R Jones p47
L G Laurella p51
Lewis Sidhu Solicitors p53
Montague Lambert & Co p61
Ned Nwoko p63
Powell Spencer & Partners p69
PRINCE EVANS p69
SV Law p75
Elizabeth Seeley p77
G Singh p80
Waldegraves p90
Weaver Rose Solicitors p90

W6

Charles Annon & Co p6
Attiyah Lone p8
Barnett Alexander Conway Ingram LLP p10
Dent Abrams Solicitors p27
Farrell Matthews & Weir p31
HRO Grant Dawe LLP p37
Harris Temperley p39
Hayes Law LLP p39
Hubbard Pegman & Witney p43
LKNY Law p51
Lansbury Worthington p51
Ledgisters p52
Mcallister Olivarius p56
Macs Law p57
Myers Fletcher & Gordon p62
Owen White & Catlin p65
Pierre Thomas & Partners p67
Francis Piesse p67
P Russell & Co p74
Tim Russell p74
A Seelhoff Solicitors p77
Sheridan & Stretton p78
Shortlands Solicitors p78
TKD Solicitors p85
P C D York & Co p93

W7

DH Law Solicitors LLP p24
Hanwell Chambers p38
Khattak Solicitors p49
Somers & Blake p80
G J Templeman Solicitors p86
West London Law Solicitors p91

W8

Aaronson & Co p3
Bromptons p16
Cobham Solicitors p21
Davidson Merali & Co p26
E G Law p28
ALAN EDWARDS & CO p28
Hamilton & Co Advokatbyra p38
Dorothy A Hurrell p44
Lita Gale p54
John May Law p59
Salinger Solicitors & Notary Public p76

W9

Camilla Baldwin p18
Michael Demidecki p26
Ronald Fletcher & Co p33
Johnson & Co p46
Knights p50
Lawrence & Co p52
Northrop McNaughtan Deller p64
Adrian Silk Solicitor p78

W10

Campbell-Taylor Solicitors p18
Peter Kandler & Co p48
Li & Co Solicitor p54
Gillian Radford & Co p70
Van Straten Solicitors p89

W11

Abbott Law LLP p3
Fiona Campbell p18
Peter Dovey and Co p27
Oliver Fisher p32
David Fishwick p32
Alida Guest p37
John Ireland & Co p45
JVA Law p45
Nicholas Morris p62
Richard Williams p92

W12

Duncan Lewis & Co p53
Sabeers Solicitors p76
Tanburghs p85
Thornton & Co p87

W13

Anthony Holden Crofts & Co p6
James E Barnes p10
Bartram & Co p11
Caladashins p17
Debidins p26
E D C Lord & Co p55
McPhersons p57
Mark Robinson Transactional Intellectual Property Services p72
Saggars Solicitors p76
Sweetman Burke & Sinker p84
Vickers & Co p89

W14

Peter Badham & Co p9
Gardiners Solicitors p35
E Michael Garston p35
Kensington Law Chambers p49
LLC Law p51
Guy Littler p55
Mark & Co p58
Stringfellow & Co p84
Sullivan Consulting p84

WC1

Abbot Beresford p3
BPE Solicitors LLP p9
Barretts p11
Batchelors Solicitors p11
Bindmans LLP p12
BISHOP & SEWELL LLP p13
Blavo & Co Solicitors p14
P R M Bond & Co p14
Bracher Rawlins LLP p15
Brion & Co p15
Brookman p16
Brooks & Co p16
Burtonwoods p16
Butcher Burns LLP p16
CB Legal p17
Central Law Practice p19
Clore & Co p21
Cobbetts LLP p21
Collyer Bristow LLP p22
Cooper Whiteman p22
Couchmans LLP p23
Coward and Sahdev Solicitors p23
Creighton & Partners p23
Cumberland Ellis Peirs p23
DL Legal LLP p25
Davis & Co (Solicitors) Limited p26
Dawson Cornwell p26
Daysparkes p26
Hector Diaz & Co p27
David Doble p27
David Du Pre & Co p28
EBR Attridge LLP p28
Equal Justice Ltd p29
Farani Taylor p30
Farringdons p31
Fernando Scornik Gerstein Solicitors p31
Fragomen LLP p33
Fridays Property Lawyers p34
Gannons Limited p35
Goldkorn Mathias Gentle Page LLP p36
Gordons p36
Greenwoods p37
GREGORY ROWCLIFFE MILNERS p37
Gulay Mehmet p37
Gulbenkian Andonian Solicitors p37
Hamilton Downing Quinn p38
Harpers p39
Haseltine Lake & Co p39
Hudson & Co p43
Hugh Cartwright & Amin p43
Ingram Winter Green p45
James Ware Baxter Schoenfeld LLP p46
Jirehouse Capital p46
Johns & Saggar p46
W T Jones p47
J A Kemp & Co p48
Kensington Solicitors p49
Key2Law LLP p49
Christian Khan Solicitors p49
Imran Khan & Partners p49
The Khan Partnership LLP p49
Khindria & Co p49
Kiers & Co p49
Lawson-Cruttenden & Co p52
Levenes Employment p53
Lockharts Solicitors p55
Lovell Son & Pitfield p55
Lyndales Solicitors p55
MacDonald Chapman p56
McKenzie Brackman p57
Maitland p58
Malletts Solicitors p58
Marriott Harrison p59
Mastrovito & Associates p59
Maxwell Alves Solicitors p59
Maxwell Alves p59
May May & Merrimans p59
Mishcon de Reya p61
Monro Fisher Wasbrough LLP p61
Warren Murton p62
NUT SOLICITORS p62
Nabarro LLP p63
Nahlis Christou p63
O'Callaghan & Co p64
Oberman Law p64
Olswang LLP p64
Oury Clark p65
Pascalides & Co p66
Pattinson & Brewer p66
Poole & Co p68
Preston-Rouse & Co p69
Rebuck Law p71
Ronaldsons p73
RUSSELL-COOKE LLP p74
Sacaloffs Solicitors p76
Schillings p77
Peter Scholl & Co p77
Secretan Troyanov p77
Sharma Solicitors p77
Sharpe Pritchard p77
Sheridans p78
Sherrs p78
Shranks p78
Michael Simkins LLP p79
Richard Slade & Company p80
Southampton Row Solicitors Limited p81
Spenser Underhill Newmark LLP p81
Stork & Coles p84
John Street Solicitors p84
Tanda Migliorini & Associates LLP p85
Teacher Stern LLP p86
Thompsons (formerly Robin/Brian Thompson & Partners) p87
Tucker Turner Kingsley Wood & Co p88
Universa Law Ltd p89
Vincent French & Browne p89
Ward Benger p90
Wedlake Bell LLP p91
Michael Welch & Co p91
Wellers Law Group LLP p91
Whitelock & Storr p91
Williams Powell p92
WRIGHT SON & PEPPER LLP p93

WC2

Addie & Co p4
Aitchison & Co p4
Alberto Perez Cedillo Spanish Lawyers And Solicitors p4
Alexen Avocats p5
Ambrose Appelbe p6

LONDON PUBLIC AUTHORITIES, COMMERCIAL ORGANISATIONS etc. – A-Z

3I PLC
16 Palace Street London SW1E 5JD
Tel: 020 7928 3131 ***Dx:*** 710030 BIRMINGHAM ***Fax:*** 020 7928 0058
E-mail: andrew.wallace@3i.com
Sol: Bradbury, Mr Paul Alan BA Senior Counsel . . . . . . Jan 1974
Brierley, Mr Anthony William Wallace BA(Hons)(Law) Company Secretary . . . . *Jan 1990
Decesare, Mr John LLB(Hons) Senior Counsel . . . *Nov 1992
Leavesley, Ms Sara J LLB(Hons) Sweet & Maxwell Law Prize Senior Counsel . . . . *Nov 1992
Murphy, Mr Jonathan Charles MA Deputy Company Secretary . . . . Sep 1986
Portman, Mrs Nicola LLB(Hons) Associate Counsel . . Sep 1999
Richardson, Mr Alastair Philip BA Senior Counsel . . . Sep 1995
Roberson, Mrs Linda LLB(Hons)(with French Law) Senior Counsel . . . . Apr 1994
Stoner, Mr Jim LLB Senior Counsel . . . . Mar 2005
Wallace, Mr Andrew LLB(Hons) Senior Counsel . . . *Nov 1995

ABN AMRO BANK NV
250 Bishopsgate London EC2M 4AA
Tel: 020 7628 7766 ***Fax:*** 020 7588 2975
Sol: Holden, Ms Kathryn A Solicitor . . . . Mar 1992
Scott, Mr Douglas A BA(Sheff) Solicitor . . . . *Dec 1973
Tennekoon, Ravi LLB; BCL(Oxon) . . . . *Jun 1993

ABN AMRO MANAGEMENT SERVICES
250 Bishopsgate London EC2M 4AA
Tel: 020 7601 0101 ***Fax:*** 020 7678 7130
Sol: Short, Ms Helen Solicitor . . . . Oct 1992

ABN AMRO UK SERVICES LTD
Legal & Compliance Department 250 Bishopsgate London EC2M 4AA
Tel: 020 7392 3500 ***Fax:*** 020 7392 3050
Sol: Viskovich, Mr Denis G Solicitor . . . . Aug 1997

AMEC GROUP LTD
76-78 Old Street London EC1V 9RU
Tel: 020 7089 7350 ***Fax:*** 020 7089 7351
E-mail: john.fenwick@amec.com
Sol: Fenwick, Mr John C BA Manager . . . . Dec 1974

AJILON GROUP LTD
5 Hammersmith Grove London W6 0QQ
Tel: 020 8600 6875
Sol: Rowlands, Mr Ian Richard BSc(Hons)(Econ) Group Legal Director . . . . Nov 1986

AKZO NOBEL LTD
26th Floor Portland House London SW1E 5BG
Tel: 020 7009 5000 ***Fax:*** 020 7009 5001
Sol: Martin, Ms Julia C LLB Solicitor . . . . *Sep 1997
Miller, Mr Russell H Group Legal Adviser . . . . . . *Jan 1969
Privett, Miss Philada J BA(Hons) Solicitor . . . . . . *Sep 2000
Shannon, Ms Julie A M Solicitor . . . . *Dec 1986

AMERICAN EXPRESS BANK LTD
Sussex House Civic Way London RH15 9AW
Tel: 020 7824 6000
Sol: Behan, Miss Lorraine BA; LLB Manager Legal Affairs . Jul 2004

ANDROS MARITIME LTD
Commonwealth House 1-19 New Oxford Street London WC1A 1NU
Tel: 020 7831 4388
Sol: Andreas, Mr Christos BA(Dunelm) Solicitor . . . . . . Nov 1991

ANGEL TRAINS LTD
Portland House Bressenden Place London SW1E 5BH
Tel: 020 7592 0500 ***Fax:*** 020 7592 0520
Sol: Althen, Mr Rolf Rechtsanwalt Senior Legal Advisor . . Feb 1994
Duderstadt, Miss Iliana Legal Advisor . . . . Mar 1999
Foley, Ms Emer MA Legal Advisor . . . . Jan 1997
Ginn, Ms Adeline Marie LLB; LLM Legal Adviser . . . Aug 1998
Oddy, Ms Louise Margaret LLB(Lond) Legal Director *May 1982
Tudor-Price, Mr Simon T MA; LLM Solicitor . . . . . . *Sep 1991
Webb, Mr Ben Lockerbie LLB(Hons) Legal Advisor . . Apr 2007

ANSBACHER & CO LTD
Two London Bridge London SE1 9RA
Tel: 020 7089 4700 ***Fax:*** 020 7089 4895
Sol: Gibbon, Mr Richard Solicitor . . . . *Dec 1989

AON LTD
8 Devonshire Square London EC2M 4PL
Tel: 020 7623 5500 ***Fax:*** 020 7972 9862
Sol: Caird, Mrs Josie LLB; LPC Senior Legal Adviser . . . *Oct 1997
Flowers, Ms Emily LLB Senior Legal Advisor . . . . . *Oct 1995
Head, Miss Nicola A LLB(Sheff); LLM(Soton) Senior Legal Adviser . . . . *Dec 1992
Rose, Ms Nicole LLB(Hons); PGDip Solicitor . . . . . *Jan 2000
Sayer, Mr Craig LLB Senior Legal Adviser . . . . . . *Jun 1998

ARCADIA GROUP LTD
Colegrave House 70 Berners Street London W1T 3NL
Tel: 020 7636 8040 ***Fax:*** 020 7927 7651
Sol: Crossland, Mrs Julie LLB Legal Adviser . . . . *May 1997
Goldman, Mr Adam A LLB(Exon) Head of Legal . . . *Nov 1990
Jackman, Mr Ian P LLB(Bris) Company Secretary . . . *Jan 1971

ASSOCIATION OF BRITISH TRAVEL AGENTS LTD
68-71 Newman Street London W1T 3AH
Tel: 020 7637 2444 ***Fax:*** 020 7631 4623
E-mail: sbunce@abta.co.uk
Sol: Bunce, Mr Simon BA Head of Legal Services . . . . . Jan 1992

ASSOCIATION OF TEACHERS AND LECTURERS
7 Northumberland Street London WC2N 5RD
Tel: 020 7930 6441 ***Fax:*** 020 7782 0070
Sol: Adeogun, Ms Kehinde Olamide LLB Solicitor . . . . . Jan 1991
Liburd, Ms Sharon G FILEx Solicitor . . . . May 1992
Lott, Mr Philip D MA(Oxon) Solicitor . . . . *Dec 1977
Pilkington, Mr Martin S BA Solicitor . . . . *Jun 1988
Towers, Mrs Mary LLB(Euro) Solicitor . . . . Sep 2001

ASSOCIATION OF TRAIN OPERATING COMPANIES
40 Bernard Street London WC1N 1BY
Tel: 020 7841 8000 ***Fax:*** 020 7841 8264
Sol: Francis, Mr Richard J LLB(Lond) Legal Counsel . . . *Dec 1977
Yelland, Mr Christopher J LLB(Lond); AKC Solicitor . *Jun 1973

ASTRAZENECA PLC
15 Stanhope Gate London W1Y 6LN
Tel: 020 7304 5000 ***Fax:*** 020 7304 5196
Sol: Grady, Mr Shaun F LLB Asistant General Solicitor . . *Oct 1985
Kemp, Mr Adrian C N LLB(Law & Politics) . . . . . . *Nov 1991
Musker, Mr Graeme H R LLB Secretary & Solicitor . *Jun 1976

AUSTRALIA AND NEW ZEALAND BANKING GROUP LTD
40 Bank Street Canary Wharf London E14 5EJ
Tel: 020 3229 2121 ***Fax:*** 020 3229 2378
Sol: Arthur, Mr Robin Llewellyn MA Senior Lawyer . . . . *Sep 1993
Campbell, Mr Gareth William BA Head of Legal, UK/Europe . . . . *Jun 1978
Tait, Ms Penelope Jessie Radcliffe LLB; BA Senior Lawyer . . . . *Apr 1993

AVIVA PLC
St Helens 1 Undershaft London EC3P 3DQ
Tel: 020 7283 7500 / 01603 687905 ***Fax:*** 01603 680660
Sol: Alcorn, Ms Helen M LLB Solicitor . . . . Oct 1999
Barber, Ms Georgina Ann Solicitor . . . . Sep 2002
Barlow, Mr George R Solicitor . . . . *Oct 1995
Brown, Mrs Jessica LLB; LSF Solicitor . . . . *Nov 1995
Calderbank, Ms Jane BA Solicitor . . . . *Oct 1987
Clark, Ms Lyndsey K Solicitor . . . . Sep 1999
Clarke, Mrs Joanna LLB(B'ham) Solicitor . . . . . . *Jun 1978
Clayden, Mr Dominic J BA(English) Solicitor . . . . . *Feb 1994
Colley, Ms Tania Solicitor . . . . Dec 2004
Commons, Ms April Marie Solicitor . . . . Nov 1993
Cooke, Mr James David LLB(Hons) Solicitor . . . . . Jan 2003
Cox, Mr Jonathan M LLB(Hons) Solicitor . . . . Jul 1977
Dixey, Miss Gabrielle Suzanne LLB; PGDip Solicitor . *Sep 1993
Donegan, Ms Louise BA(Hons); CPE Solicitor . . . . . *Sep 1997
Dyer, Mrs Lydia R M Solicitor . . . . Jun 2002
Eastham, Ms Jocelyn J LLB Solicitor . . . . *§Mar 1985
Eaton, Mr Angus G BSc(Hons) Solicitor . . . . *Oct 1995
Eleanor, Mr Nicholas J R TD BA(Hons) Solicitor . . . *§Jul 1984
Fish, Mr David R L BA Solicitor . . . . *§Dec 1978
Gammer, Ms Fay C BA; M Inst TMA Solicitor . . . . . *Oct 1981
Gidney, Mr Stephen J LLB; LLM Solicitor . . . . . . *Oct 1991
Gill, Ms Gillian Solicitor . . . . Apr 2005
Grand, Mr Howard Solicitor . . . . Sep 2000
Gray, Mr Alistair David Solicitor . . . . Sep 2000
Greaves, Mr Paul Nicholas FILEx; LPC Solicitor . . . . *Aug 1998
Hardy, Mrs Valerie Patricia Solicitor . . . . *Sep 2002
Harmer, Mr Alwin R J LLB Solicitor . . . . *May 1989
Harris, Ms Donna C LLB Solicitor . . . . *Oct 1983
Hartford, Mr Robert R Solicitor . . . . Sep 2005
Henderson, Mr James Gordon BA Solicitor . . . . . . Sep 2002
Holkham, Miss Anna M BA(Nott'm) Solicitor . . . . . . *Mar 1984
Howlett, Mr Paul L Solicitor . . . . *§Apr 1981
Jackson, Ms Alison L LLB Solicitor . . . . Oct 1984
Jackson-Nichols, Ms Amanda LLB; LLM Solicitor . . . Oct 1991
Janday, Ms Sonia Solicitor . . . . Sep 2004
Jones, Mr Edward G BA; MBA Group Legal Services Director . . . . *Jun 1977
Kay, Mr Andrew L T BA(Hons) Solicitor . . . . Sep 2003
Lawson, Mr Christopher J Solicitor . . . . Jun 1997
Leslie, Miss Siobhan B Comm; MSc; FCIArb Solicitor *Nov 1980
Lingwood, Mr William E LLB Solicitor . . . . *Nov 1988
McAnlis, Mrs Rosie LLB Solicitor . . . . Jan 2000
McWilliam, Mr Stuart A LLB(Hons) Solicitor . . . . . *Nov 1997
Madaan, Mr Ashish Solicitor . . . . Sep 2001
Mann, Mr Stephen A J Solicitor . . . . *Nov 2000
Marshall, Ms Clair Louise Solicitor . . . . Dec 1991
Maskell, Ms Anne C LLB Solicitor . . . . Jun 1975
Matthews, Mr Andrew N LLB Solicitor . . . . *Feb 1982
Milnthorpe, Mr Gavin Solicitor . . . . Sep 2006
Morgan, Mr Simon LLB(Law & French Law) Solicitor . Sep 1993
Orr, Ms Suzanne L Solicitor . . . . Dec 1999
Page, Miss Fiona J BA Solicitor . . . . *§Oct 1982
Ranson, Ms Susan J Solicitor . . . . Sep 2004
Robson, Miss Catherine L BA(Dunelm) Solicitor . . . *Feb 1985
Rodriguez-Moreno, German Solicitor . . . . Nov 1995
Rogers, Ms Alexandra N J Solicitors . . . . Nov 2005
Roy, Mr Stephen Russell BA Solicitor . . . . *Sep 1994
Santos, Ms Elizabeth M Solicitors . . . . Jan 1999
Scorah, Mr Ian A Solicitor . . . . *Sep 1997
Sorrell, Ms Michelle Aviva BA(Lond) Solicitor . . . . Nov 1990
Spicker, Mr Richard H BA Solicitor . . . . *Dec 1980
Street, Miss Louise Marie BA Solicitor . . . . Sep 2006
Stubbs, Mr Nicholas Guy LLB(Hons) Solicitor . . . . . *Sep 1999
Swallow, Mr Mark S J LLB(B'ham) Solicitor . . . . . . *Oct 1989
Sweet-Escott, Mrs Ellen R Solicitor . . . . Sep 1999
Thompson, Mrs Stephanie Joanne Solicitor . . . . . *Sep 2002
Tootell, Ms Emma L BA Solicitor . . . . Apr 1999
Tullo, Mr Russell K LLB(Hons) Solicitor . . . . Oct 1998
Turner, Mr Timothy Robert BA(Hons); MA Solicitor . *Nov 1993
Vickers, Mr Timothy R LLB Solicitor . . . . *Nov 1993
Ware, Mrs Alexandra M BA(Law) Solicitor . . . . . . *§Jun 1977
Wild, Miss Katrina BA(Hons)(Philosophy); CPE; LPC Solicitor . . . . Aug 2002
Will, Mr Dominic P J Solicitor . . . . Sep 2000
Willis, Mr Kevin Richard BA(Hons) Solicitor . . . . . *Sep 1997
Wilman, Ms Jennifer Jane BSc Solicitor . . . . *Sep 1987
Woodhouse, Ms Andrea L Solicitor . . . . *Oct 1997
Woodrow, Mr Richard David Solicitor . . . . *Sep 2002
Woollett, Mrs Jane Emily BA(Cantab)(Law) Solicitor . *Sep 2000
Woollett, Mr Martyn Charles LLB Solicitor . . . . . . Sep 2000

AXA UK PLC
5 Old Broad Street London E22N 1AD
Tel: 020 7920 5900 ***Fax:*** 020 7920 5224
Sol: Adam, Mrs Alison Alethia BA(Hons) Legal Adviser . . . Mar 2001
Ashby, Mr Tobin LLB Legal Adviser . . . . Sep 1999
Burnett, Mr Robert Patrick Anthony BA(Hons) Legal Adviser . . . . Oct 1994
Coupland, Ms Emily LLB General Counsel - Life . . . . May 1992
Davis, Mr Edward H C LLB Group General Counsel . . Dec 1990
Faulkner, Mr Warwick LLB Legal Adviser . . . . Feb 1993
Gardner, Mr Mark Andrew BA Senior Legal Adviser . . Nov 1994
James, Mrs Natalie LLB(Hons) Legal Adviser . . . . . Nov 1997
Johnstone, Mr Ian Stuart Shaw BA; CPE Legal AdviserSep 1999
Kalideen, Ms Shereen Roxane BA(Hons); DipLaw; MA(Cantab); CPE Legal Adviser . . . . Oct 1996
Noke, Miss Cathryn LLB Legal Adviser . . . . Oct 2001
Patel, Mr Samir LLB Legal Adviser . . . . *Mar 2001
Paulson, Mr Graham BA(Jt Hons) Senior Legal AdviserSep 1994
Simcox, Ms Joanne Louise LLB(Hons) Legal Adviser . Sep 1998
Surridge, Mr Robert LLB; MA; AC Senior Legal Adviser . . . . *May 1993
Weston, Mrs Joanne LLB(Hons) Senior Legal Advisor . Dec 1995
Whitehead, Miss Julie BA(Hons); PGDipLPC Legal Adviser . . . . Jan 2003

B A A PLC
Heathrow Point West 234 Bath Road London UB3 5AP
Tel: 0870 000 0123 ***Fax:*** 020 8745 4290
Sol: Biber, Mr Eddie Solicitor . . . . *Dec 1990
English, Mrs Elvira LLB(Hons); BCom Legal Counsel . Jan 1991
Herga, Mr Robert D LLB(Dundee); MSc; FCIArb Head of Legal Services . . . . *Oct 1983
Hutchings, Mrs Joanne MA Lawyer . . . . Jan 1998
Pickard, Miss Sarah V BSc Solicitor . . . . *Nov 1993
Welfare, Miss Carol LLB Solicitor . . . . Jun 2004
Woodhouse, Mrs Susan Jane LLB Solicitor . . . . . . *Sep 1992

BBA AVIATION PLC
7th Floor 20 Balderton Street London W1K 6TL
Tel: 020 7514 3999 ***Fax:*** 020 7629 4391
Sol: Lees, Miss Petra Corporate Counsel . . . . *Mar 2001
Shaw, Mrs Sarah M F Group Secretary . . . . *Oct 1982
Simm, Mr Iain D C LLB General Counsel . . . . *Nov 1991

BBC
BBC Litigation Department 201 Wood Lane London W12 7TS
Tel: 020 8752 5734 ***Fax:*** 020 8752 5080
Sol: Bradley, Mrs Shelley I BA Solicitor, Programme Legal Advice . . . . *Oct 1974
Cresswell, Mr James Solicitor, Property Legal . . . . Apr 2001
Del Medico, Mr Glenn G Head of Programme Legal Advice . . . . Jun 1966
Hall, Mrs Vanessa Senior Adviser, Commercial Policy & Fair Trading . . . . *Aug 1985
Law, Mr Roger M Solicitor, Programme Legal Advice . Dec 1976
Lewis, Mr Jaron Mark BA(Hons) Solicitor, Litigation & Brand Enforcement . . . . *Oct 1996
Nazareth, Ms Valerie C LLB Solicitor, Programme Legal Advice . . . . *Nov 1987
O'Hanlon, Mr Stephen P MA(Cantab) Head of Legal Affairs, Rights & Business Affairs . . . . *Apr 1977
Tippetts, Miss Rebecca M LLB Head of Property Legal*Nov 1985
Youngson, Ms Janet G BA Senior Solicitor, Litigation and Brand Enforcement . . . . *Dec 1981

BP OIL INTERNATIONAL LTD
International Headquarters 1 St James's Square London SW1Y 4PD
Tel: 020 7496 4000 *Fax:* 020 7496 4630
Sol: Kneen, Ms Julianne M LLB Solicitor . . . . Apr 1990

BP PLC
International Headquarters 1 St James's Square London SW1Y 4PD
Tel: 020 7496 4000 *Fax:* 020 7496 4242
E-mail: bevanb@bp.com
Sol: Bevan, Mr Peter B Pugh LLB(Hons) Group General Counsel and Executive Vice President . . . . *Dec 1969

BRB (RESIDUARY) LTD
Whittles House 14 Pentonville Road London N1 9HF
Tel: 020 7904 5087 *Dx:* 400658 ISLINGTON *Fax:* 020 7904 5092
Sol: Sinclair, Mr Paul O LLB(Nott'm) Litigation Solicitor. . *Nov 1976
Whiting, Mrs Gillian M LLB(Nott'm) Head of Property Legal Services . . . . *Jun 1975

BTG INTERNATIONAL LTD
5 Fleet Place Limeburner Lane London EC4M 7RD
Tel: 020 7575 0000 *Fax:* 020 7575 0010
E-mail: info@btgplc.com
Sol: Davison, Mr Richard BCL Principal Solicitor . . . . . *Dec 1975
Mussenden, Dr Paul J BA; PhD Lawyer . . . . *Oct 1996
Sekhri, Mrs Anita LLB(Jt Hons)(Law & Japanese) Solicitor . . . . Apr 1999
Simpson, Mr Edward C F BA(Oxon) Legal Adviser . . Oct 1991

BAE SYSTEMS PLC
Stirling Square 6 Carlton Gardens London SW1Y 5AD
Tel: 01252 373232 *Fax:* 01252 383094
Sol: Bambridge, Ms Clare J LLB Senior Counsel. . . . . . *Oct 1990
Gallagher, Mr Andrew J Associate General Counsel. *Sep 1987
Gelsthorpe, Mr Edward Head of Labour Law . . . . . *Oct 1991
Kent, Mr George Chief Counsel, BVT Surface Fleets *Sep 1993
Musgrave, Mr Colin J Head of Mergers & Acquisitions *Dec 1974
Serfozo, Mr Mark J LLB(Hons) Chief Counsel, Compliance & Regulation . . . . *Oct 1990
Wiltshire, Mr Roger Campbell BA Chief Counsel, UK-ROW . . . . Apr 1994
Wood, Mr S Christopher LLB(Lond) Head of Property Law . . . . *Jun 1981

BALFOUR BEATTY PLC
130 Wilton Road London SW1V 1LQ
Tel: 020 7216 6800 *Fax:* 020 7216 6940
E-mail: info@balfourbeatty.com
Sol: McCormack, Mr Francis D F T BA(L'pool) Head of Legal Services . . . . *Apr 1983
Pearson, Mr Christopher R O'N LLB(Bris) Company Secretary . . . . *Apr 1972

BANK OF CYPRUS UK
Legal Department 87 Chase Side Southgate London N14 5BU
Tel: 020 8267 7331 *Dx:* 34309 SOUTHGATE *Fax:* 020 8447 8066
Sol: Byrne, Mr Stephen George BA(Hons) Head of Legal & Compliance. . . . . Jul 1994

BANK OF SCOTLAND LEGAL OPERATIONS
155 Bishopsgate London EC2M 3YB
Tel: 0870 600 5000 *Fax:* 01422 334453
Sol: Fisher, Mr Brian W BA Head of Legal Operations . . . Aug 1981
Griffiths, Mr Nick B Comm; LLB Solicitor. . . . . . . Apr 1994
Thomas, Mrs Valerie A BA Solicitor . . . . *Oct 1990

THE BANK OF TOKYO MITSUBISHI UFJ LTD
Finsbury Circus House 12-15 Finsbury Circus London EC2M 7BT
Tel: 020 7330 5000 *Fax:* 020 7330 5555
E-mail: mark_riley@ufjbank.co.jp
Sol: Riley, Mr Mark H C BA(Econ) Legal Adviser. . . . . *Dec 1979
Vashisht, Ms Arti BA(Hons); DipLaw Legal Advisor . . Oct 2002

BANQUE NATIONALE DE PARIS LONDON BRANCH
8-13 King William Street London EC4P 4HS
Tel: 020 7895 7293 *Fax:* 020 7929 0310
Sol: Toubkin, Mr Michael D Legal Adviser . . . . *Jul 1969

BARCLAYS BANK PLC
54 Lombard Street London EC3P 3AH
Tel: 020 7699 5000 *Fax:* 01452 638319
E-mail: legal.communications@barclays.co.uk
Sol: Harding, Mr Mark Dominic MA(Law & Modern Languages) Group General Counsel. . . . . *Jan 1982
Ogden, Mr Jeremy J LLB Deputy Group General Counsel . . . . *Jan 1983

BARING ASSET MANAGEMENT LTD
155 Bishopsgate London EC2M 3XY
Tel: 020 7628 6000 *Fax:* 020 7638 7928
Sol: Brace, Mr James J BA(Oxon) Solicitor. . . . . *Oct 1995

BEAR STEARNS
1 Canada Square London E14 5AD
Tel: 020 7516 6000 *Fax:* 020 7516 6621
Sol: McGowan, Mr William LLB; DipLP Solicitor . . . . . . Sep 1991

BEN SHERMAN GROUP LIMITED
2 Eyre Street Hill Clerkenwell London EC1R 5ET
Tel: 020 7812 5300 *Fax:* 020 7812 5301
E-mail: allan.reid@bensherman.co.uk
Sol: Reid, Mr Allan Christopher LLB(Hons); DipLP Legal Director . . . . Jun 2006

BLACK ROCK
33 King William Street London EC4R 9AS
Tel: 020 7743 3000 *Fax:* 020 7743 1064
Sol: Clark, Mr Fletcher LLB(Business Law); LLM(Corporate & Commercial Law) Vice President . . . . Oct 1992
Floyd, Mrs Angela Mary BSc(Hons)(Business); CPE; New York Bar Vice President . . . . Mar 1994
Hall, Mr Nicholas C D MA(Cantab) General Counsel. *Mar 1978
Howard, Mr Stuart LLM Director. . . . . Mar 1992
Lewis, Mr Austen J E BA(Hons) Vice President . . . . Oct 2000
Nielson, Mr Guy Anthony Dickon BA(Hons)(German) Director & Senior Counsel . . . . Dec 1995
Ivinson, Ms Jane LLB; BCL; IMC Maxwell Law Prize 1984 Director. . . . . Nov 1992
Shah, Ms Palvi LLB First Vice President. . . . . *Oct 1987
Stratford, Mr James T LLB(Bris) First Vice President . Dec 1986
Valentine, Mrs Amy Vicotria CPE; LPC(French & Spanish) Assistant Vice President . . . . Sep 2001

BRENT MAGISTRATES COURT
Church End 448 High Road London NW10 2DZ
Tel: 020 8451 7111 *Dx:* 110850 WILLESDEN 2 *Fax:* 020 8451 2040
Sol: Levene, Miss Karen Denise LLB; Dip Mag Law Assistant Deputy Justices Clerk. . . . . *Dec 1993
Morgan, Ms Julie BA Legal Advisor . . . . *Oct 1988
Stephenson, Miss Tabitha Chloe LLB Assistant Deputy Justices Clerk . . . . *Apr 1992

BRITISH AMERICAN TOBACCO
Globe House 4 Temple Place London WC2R 2PG
Tel: 020 7845 1000 *Fax:* 020 7845 2783
Sol: Aung, Toe Su Solicitor. . . . . Jun 1996
Biss, Mr Mark S LLB Assistant Solicitor . . . . *Oct 1988
Briginshaw, J Solicitor. . . . . Oct 1992
Burford, Ms Elise Solicitor. . . . . Jan 2000
Casey, Mr Robert J Solicitor. . . . . Aug 1997
Cleverly, Mr Simon P C BA Solicitor. . . . . *Oct 1988
Cooper, Mr Gareth A LLB(Bris) Solicitor. . . . . *Oct 1992
Davison, Mr Peter C Solicitor . . . . Jan 1991
Dunaway, Miss Helen E LLB; LLM Solicitor . . . . . . *Oct 1984
Entwistle, Ms Lisa Solicitor . . . . *Mar 1996
Flanagan, Miss Kay Helen LLB Assistant Solicitor. . . *Oct 1990
Gilbey, Mr Martyn C LLB; FCIArb Solicitor. . . . . . . *Jun 1977
Godby, Mr Peter C MA(Cantab) Solicitor. . . . . *Sep 1978
Jenner, Ms Eileen BA; MSc Solicitor. . . . . *Mar 1986
Massey, Mr Paul J LLB Solicitor. . . . . *Oct 1971
O'Callaghan, Miss Elizabeth LLB Solicitor. . . . . . . *Dec 1988
Page, Ms Sonia K Solicitor . . . . Sep 1998
Porter, Mr Alan F LLB Solicitor . . . . Nov 1989
Roper, Mr Simon C W Solicitor . . . . *Nov 1981
Scourfield, Mr Philip T BA(Hons) Solicitor . . . . *Apr 1980
Snook, Ms Nicola Solicitor. . . . . *Oct 1990
Williams, Mr David R Solicitor. . . . . Nov 1994
Williams, Mr Richard Solicitor . . . . Oct 1995

THE BRITISH COUNCIL
10 Spring Gardens London SW1A 2BN
Tel: 020 7389 4385 *Fax:* 020 7389 6347
Sol: Robinson, Ms Deborah Jane LLB; MSc Legal Adviser . Apr 1990

BRITISH MEDICAL ASSOCIATION
BMA House Tavistock Square London WC1H 9JP
Tel: 020 7387 4499 *Fax:* 020 7383 6454
Sol: Allman, Ms Victoria A LLM Assistant Solicitor . . . . . Mar 1984
Dowsett, Mr Roger H Solicitor. . . . . *Jan 1970
Hadley, Ms Anne L LLB(Hons) Assistant Solicitor . . . Apr 2000
Whitehouse, Ms Elizabeth F C BSc Assistant Solicitor. Nov 1975
Wilkinson, Ms Louise Assistant Solicitor. . . . . Jun 1990

BRITISH OLYMPIC ASSOCIATION
1 Wandsworth Plain London SW18 1EH
Tel: 020 8871 2677 *Fax:* 020 8871 9104
E-mail: firstname.surname@boa.org.uk
Sol: Friend, Miss Sara J LLB(Hons) Director of Legal Services . . . . Apr 1997

BRITISH STANDARDS INSTITUTION
389 Chiswick High Road Chiswick London W4 4AL
Tel: 020 8996 7010 *Fax:* 020 8996 7356
E-mail: info@bsi.org.uk
Sol: Gould, Mrs Virginia BA(Law); LLB Solicitor . . . . . . Jan 2002
Thomas, Mr Antony L J MA(Oxon) Solicitor . . . . . . *Sep 1972
Williams, Mr Stanley Killa MA(Oxon) Herbert Ruse Prize Director of Legal Affairs . . . . *Mar 1969

BRITISH TELECOMMUNICATIONS PLC
PPC5A BT Centre 81 Newgate Street London EC1A 7AJ
Tel: 020 7356 6181 *Fax:* 01332 577374
E-mail: suzanne.ridley@bt.com
Sol: Bayley, Mr Paul Commercial Lawyer. . . . . *Nov 1993
Beedham, Mr Geoffrey LLB VP of UK Business Management . . . . *Oct 1978
Bracewell, Mr Amanda Jane Commercial Lawyer . . . *Nov 1993
Bruce-Watt, Mrs Linda LLB Corporate Lawyer. . . . *Sep 1996
Clegg, Mr Graham D LLB Chief Counsel . . . . *Dec 1979
Collymore, Ms Samantha Jane Solicitor. . . . . *Aug 2005
Corry, Mr Shaun N LLB Solicitor-Practice Leader . . . Jul 1980
Davy, Mr Clive G LLB(Bris) Chief Counsel of BT Global Services . . . . *Dec 1979
Dawkins, Ms Tracey-Leonie Solicitor . . . . *Dec 2002
De Ridder, Mr Kimon Celicourt Macris Senior Legal Counsel . . . . *Mar 2000
Elworthy, Mr Martin N LLB(L'pool) Commercial Lawyer *Apr 1975
Fellows, Mr Mark Solicitor. . . . . *Sep 2004
Fisher, Mr Jeffery W LLB(Lond) Head of Corporate Law . . . . *Jun 1975
Fletcher, Mrs Anne L MA Group General Counsel . . *Nov 1983
Gabrielli, Ms Isabelle MA(French) Lawyer . . . . Oct 1982
Gallagher, Mrs Jennifer Susan Chief Counsel Commercial Policy . . . . *Dec 1995
Gleeson, Ms Niamh Christina Senior Competition Lawyer . . . . *Sep 2000
Gohil, Ms Kajal Solicitor. . . . . *Sep 2004
Grace, Ms Eva Maria Lawyer . . . . *Oct 1992
Gray, Miss Elizabeth A C BA; CPE Solicitor. . . . . . *Sep 1996
Gribble, Mr David Walter Head of Network Operations Legal Team . . . . *Oct 2000
Hadden, Mr Jason Mark Solicitor . . . . *Jun 1997
Harding, Ms Hilary Head of Advocacy Team. . . . . . *Oct 1993
Haynes, Mrs Vivienne A LLB(Lond) General Counsel of Group Operations . . . . *Oct 1982
Helliwell, Mrs Elaine Solicitor . . . . *Oct 1997
Hewett, Mr David C Head of Carrier Contract Operations . . . . *Nov 1979
Hill, Mrs Jane Frances Commercial Legal Team Leader . . . . *Jan 1983
Hobbs, Mr Neil Spencer Commercial Lawyer . . . . . *Nov 2001
Kenny, Miss Ann Caroline Head of Public Liability . . . *Oct 1994
Kirstein, Ms Claire Fiona Senior Solicitor . . . . *Sep 1998
Laurenson, Ms Katherine Mcrere Ruth Commercial Lawyer . . . . *Mar 2004
Lynch, Ms Agnes Christina Lawyer . . . . *Sep 1999
May, Ms Joanna Louise Employment Lawyer . . . . . *Sep 2000
Moore, Miss Christine E LLB Head of Employment Law . . . . *Apr 1988
Murray, Mr Stuart Charles Network Operations Lawyer *Oct 2004
Orchard, Mr Rupert H MA(Cantab) Chief Counsel of Transactions . . . . *Mar 1984
Paine, Miss Lois G BA Corporate Lawyer . . . . *Nov 1984
Parker, Mr Andrew J LLB General Counsel of BT Retail . . . . *Oct 1984
Paterson, Mr Nigel MA(Hons) Senior Deal Leader and Counsel of Major Deals and Projects. . . . . *May 1995
Plantard, Ms Celine LLM Legal Counsel in Transactions . . . . Mar 1995
Ritchie, Mr George D LLB(Wales) Head of Competition and Regulatory Law . . . . *Nov 1985
Rowson, Mr Gavin Peter LLB(Hons) Solicitor . . . . *Sep 1997
Saunders, Ms Julie Amanda Solicitor . . . . *Jul 1996
Shaw, Mr Timothy J B MA(Oxon) Chief Counsel of Commercial Law. . . . . *Mar 1986
Shawley, Mr David M Solicitor Information Manager . *Dec 1988
Silke, Mr Terry J Commercial Lawyer . . . . *Oct 1977
Skyers, Ms Sandra E LLB Employment and Business Development . . . . *Apr 1990
Smith, Mr Anthony C MA(Oxon) BT Group Legal Regulatory Counsel. . . . . *Jul 1973
Townsend, Ms Lisa Yvette Commercial Lawyer . . . *Aug 1993
Vareis-Tharmaraj, Mrs Deepa Senior Commercial Lawyer . . . . *Jul 2004
Vaughan, Mr Andrew T W General Manager of Business Integrity and Assurance. . . . . *May 1980
Wardle, Miss Justine Jill Solicitor . . . . *Oct 1999
Williams, Mr Alan Head of Broadband Legal Team. . . *Jun 1996

THE BUILDING SOCIETIES ASSOCIATION
3 Savile Row London W1X 1AF
Tel: 020 7437 0655 *Dx:* 81550 SAVILE ROW *Fax:* 020 7734 6416
E-mail: chris.lawrenson@bsa.org.uk
Sol: Lawrenson, Mr Christopher D LLB(Hons) Head of Legal Services . . . . *Apr 1980

BUNZL PLC
Legal Department 45 Seymour Street London W1H 7JT
Tel: 020 7725 5000 *Fax:* 020 7725 5001
Sol: Hussey, Mr Paul Nicholas LLB General Counsel & Company Secretary . . . . *Oct 1983
Vance, Mr Matthew C L BA(Law with French); LLB Legal Adviser . . . . *Sep 1999

BUPA
BUPA House 15-19 Bloomsbury Way London WC1A 2BA
Tel: 020 7656 2305 *Fax:* 020 7656 2725
Sol: Baxendale, Miss Amanda Louise LLB(Hons); PGDip; MA; ACII Legal Adviser. . . . . *May 1999
Booth, Ms Rachel Louise . . . . Jan 1997
Cooper, Mr Damian Peter LLB Legal Adviser . . . . *Sep 2002
Davidson, Miss Serena Louise BSc; DipLaw Legal Manager, Solicitor. . . . . Jan 2000
Fell, Mrs Esther LLB(Hons) Legal Adviser. . . . . . . *Apr 2002
Flemington, Mr Hugh Meyrick BA(Oxon) Solicitor . . . Jul 1971
Flinton, Mr Matthew J BA(Cantab); MA Head of Legal. Jan 1992
Goldie, Miss Helena Elspeth DipLP Commendation Diploma in Legal Practise Legal Adviser . . . . Sep 1997
Hewitt, Mr John A Legal Manager, Property . . . . . *Apr 2000
Horevey, Mr Richard Astin BA(Hons) Head of Legal - Employment . . . . Jan 1998
Newton, Mr Paul R BA Group Legal Director, Solicitor. *Apr 1987
Pemberton, Ms Ailsa J BSc; CPE; LPC . . . . Dec 1999
Randall, Ms Deborah LLB(Hons) Senior Legal Advisor. Mar 1997
Stephen, Mr Neill Alexander Legal Adviser . . . . . . Mar 2002
Sturman, Mrs Elizabeth G BA(Hons) Group Legal Manager . . . . Sep 2002

CLS HOLDINGS PLC
26th Floor Portland House Bressenden Place London SE1E 5BG
Tel: 020 7582 7766 *Fax:* 020 7828 5508
Sol: Wickham, Mr Gary Stephen Solicitor . . . . *Dec 1995

CABLE & WIRELESS
26 Red Lion Square London WC1R 4HQ
Tel: 020 7315 4000 *Fax:* 020 7315 5093
Sol: Slight, Miss Christine E BSc(Lond); FC1S. . . . . . *Dec 1978

CADBURY SCHWEPPES PLC
25 Berkeley Square London W1J 6HB
Tel: 020 7409 1313 *Fax:* 020 7830 5200
Sol: Blanks, Ms Hester BA(Dunelm) Company Secretary. . *Apr 1977
Budd, Ms Gillian S BA(Cantab); LLM Legal Director. *Nov 1988
Llewellyn, Mrs Geraldine Hilary MA(Oxon) Group Senior Legal Counsel. . . . . *Jun 2000

CAMBERWELL GREEN MAGISTRATES COURT
15 D'Eynsford Road London SE5 7UP
Tel: 0845 601 3600 *Dx:* 35305 CAMBERWELL GREEN
Fax: 020 7805 9896
Sol: Mullins, Miss Thirza Jane BA(Hons) Bench Legal Manager . . . . Sep 1997

CAMBRIDGE HOUSE LEGAL CENTRE
Cambridge House 137 Camberwell Road London SE5 0HF
Tel: 020 7703 3051 / 7701 9499 *Fax:* 020 7277 0401
Sol: Ansah-Twum, Miss Wonta Nana Asuaa LLB; LLM Solicitor . . . . Jul 2003
Pritchard, Ms Kerry Lynne LLB(Hons) Senior Solicitor . Oct 1991

CAMDEN COMMUNITY LAW CENTRE
2 Prince of Wales Road London NW5 3LQ
Tel: 020 7284 6510 *Fax:* 020 7267 6218
E-mail: admin@cck.org.uk
Sol: Day, Miss Samantha BA(Eng); CPE; LPC . . . . Sep 2002
Russell, Mr Alan Solicitor . . . . Jan 1992

CAMDEN TRIBUNAL UNIT
2 Grafton Yard London NW5 2ND
Tel: 020 7267 2424 *Fax:* 020 7485 5495
Sol: Bouda, Miss Iva LLB Unit Solicitor. . . . . *Jun 1992

CANARY WHARF GROUP PLC
1 Canada Square London E14 5AB
Tel: 020 7418 2367 *Fax:* 020 7418 2195
Sol: Ashley-Brown, Mr Michael A Group Legal Counsel . . *Jan 1973

CANCER RESEARCH UK
61 Lincoln's Inn Fields London WC2A 3PX
Tel: 020 7242 0200 *Fax:* 020 7061 8381
E-mail: legal@cancer.org.uk
Sol: Deerness, Ms Yvette Senior Legal Adviser . . . . . . *Mar 2002
Ferrara, Ms Shantha LLB Legal Advisor. . . . . *Jan 2001
Joannou, Ellaris Senior Legal Adviser . . . . Dec 1991
Prosser, Mrs Rhian E LLB Legal Adviser . . . . *Sep 2001
Richardson, Miss Penelope MA Legal Advisor. . . . . *Nov 2001
Scott, Ms Diane E LLB Director of Legal. . . . . *Nov 1989
Shropshire, Miss April LLB; MBA . . . . *Oct 1985

CELADOR PRODUCTIONS LTD
39 Long Acre London WC2E 9LG
Tel: 020 7240 8101 *Fax:* 020 7845 6977
Sol: Quinn, Miss Angela M LLB Solicitor *Dec 1984
Robb-John, Mr Anthony LLB(B'ham) Solicitor *Nov 1988

CENTRAL LONDON COMMUNITY LAW CENTRE
19 Whitcomb Street London WC2H 7HA
Tel: 020 7839 2998
Sol: Lewis, Ms Tamara LLB Solicitor Sep 1982

CHANNEL FOUR TELEVISION
124 Horseferry Road London SW1P 2TX
Tel: 020 7396 4444 *Fax:* 020 7306 8367
Sol: Tomalin, Ms Janet A LLB(Sheff) Head of Legal & Compliance Oct 1986

LEONARD CHESHIRE DISABILITY
30 Millbank London SW1P 4QD
Tel: 020 7802 8200 *Fax:* 020 7802 8250
Sol: Silver, Mr Ashley Stephen BA(Hons)(Oxon) Head of Legal/Company Secretary Former Barrister *Apr 1991

CHEVRON TEXACO
1 West Circus Canary Wharf London E14 4HA
Tel: 020 7719 3000 *Fax:* 020 7719 5124
Sol: Rixon, Mr Peter Director & Regional General Counsel *Jun 1970

CHLORIDE GROUP PLC
23 Lower Belgrave Street London SW1W 0N
Tel: 020 7881 1440 *Fax:* 020 7730 5085
Sol: Williams, Ms Susan LLB Group Legal Adviser *Jun 1979

CHRISTIES INTERNATIONAL PLC
8 King Street London SW1Y 6QT
Tel: 020 7839 9060 *Fax:* 020 7839 1611
Sol: Hall, Mrs Johanna May BA Group Legal Adviser Dec 1988
Wilson, Mr Martin LLB General Counsel Europe Jun 1992

CHUBB INSURANCE COMPANY OF EUROPE S.A.
106 Fenchurch Street London EC3M 5NB
Tel: 020 7956 5000 *Fax:* 020 7956 5901
Sol: Munro, Ranald Torquil Ian CPE; BA(Hons) General Counsel, Company Secretary & Head of External Affairs Jun 1986
Van Til Leedham, Mrs Sophie J D European Counsel May 1996

CHURCHILL INSURANCE GROUP
Crocon House 145 City Road London EC1V 1LP
Tel: 020 7656 6838 *Dx:* 136229 FINSBURY 4 *Fax:* 020 7656 6842
Sol: Hussain, Miss Zahreen H BA(Hons)(History & Politics) Senior Solicitor *Dec 1984
Winnard, Miss Linda LLB Solicitor *Apr 1981

CITIBANK NATIONAL ASSOCIATION
Citigroup Centre 25-33 Canada Square London E14 5LB
Tel: 020 7500 5000
Sol: Gaulter, Mr Andrew Martin MA(Cantab) Co Secretary *Apr 1976

CIVIL AVIATION AUTHORITY
CAA House 45-59 Kingsway London WC2B 6TE
Tel: 020 7453 6162 *Fax:* 020 7453 6163
Sol: Allan, Mr Robin J Solicitor *Oct 1982
Baker, Mr Stephen D MA(Cantab) Assistant Legal Adviser *Mar 1988
Britton, Mr Rupert J MA(Oxon); FRAeS Secretary and Legal Adviser *Jan 1971
Brooks, Mrs Imogen MA(Oxon) Solicitor *Sep 1997
Caldera, Ms Dilsha LLB(Hons); LLM Solicitor *Mar 2002
Lim, Miss Serena LLB(Exeter); LLM Solicitor *Mar 2003

CLERICAL MEDICAL INVESTMENT GROUP
33 Old Broad Street London EC2N 1HZ
Tel: 020 7321 1425 *Fax:* 020 7321 1425
Sol: Davies, Mrs Rebecca LLB Commercial Solicitor *Jan 1995
Giles, Miss Katherine BA(Hons); CPE; LPC Solicitor *Oct 1999
Harvey, Mr Richard LLB Senior Commercial Property Solicitor *Oct 1989
Myers, Mr Julian BA Commercial Solicitor Mar 1997
Paton, Miss Victoria Jane BA(Hons) Commercial Solicitor *Oct 1998
Veale, Mr Peter J LLB Solicitor & Company Secretary *Jun 1980

THE COLLEGE OF LAW
14 Store Street Bloomsbury London WC1E 7DE
Tel: 0800 289997
Sol: Ahmad, Mr Faheem Lecturer Jan 2002
Ajai-Ajagbe, Ms Elizabeth LLB Lecturer *Nov 1988
Arden, Ms Elizabeth Lecturer Jan 1992
Baker, Ms Juliette Senior Lecturer Jan 1995
Barham, Mr Clive R LLB Tutor *Mar 1988
Barker, Ms Rachel Lecturer Jan 2001
Beamish, Mr Simon Charles MA(Cantab) Lecturer *Nov 1994
Bilas, Mr Walter LLB(Lond) Senior Lecturer Apr 1985
Bingham, Ms Jo Lecturer Oct 1999
Bishop, Mr Clive W LLB Senior Lecturer Sep 1984
Brill, Mr Stephen James BSc Senior Lecturer *Aug 1998
Browne, Mr Kevin C LLB Associate Professor Oct 1987
Burke, Mr Barry W L Principal Lecturer Sep 1987
Calleja, Ms Marie Senior Lecturer Dec 1992
Capron, Mr David Senior Lecturer Jan 1987
Catlow, Mrs Margaret J BA Senior Lecturer *Jul 1979
Cortis, Ms Vanessa Senior Lecturer *Oct 1995
Daly, Mr George Senior Lecturer Jan 1995
De-Friend, Mr Richard Director Jan 1991
De-Maine, Ms Sarah Senior Lecturer Jan 1998
Delbourgo, Ms Angela Senior Lecturer Jan 1980
Desforges, Miss Amanda B LLB(L'pool) Deputy Director Vocational *Nov 1984
Duffield, Ms Nancy Senior Lecturer Sep 1987
Embley, Ms Judith Lecturer Jan 1980
Foxton, Ms Rachel Senior Lecturer Jan 1997
Gee, Miss Elizabeth Anne BA Senior Lecturer *Nov 1993
Goodchild, Mr Peter John Cahn BA(Oxon); CPE; LPE Senior Lecturer *Oct 1997
Grant, Ms Theresa Senior Lecturer Nov 1990
Gray, Mr Anthony Senior Lecturer Jul 1993
Hawes, Ms Rachel Associate Professor Jan 1979
Hawkins, Mr Peter Principal Lecturer Jan 1969
Hawkins, Mr Timothy Senior Lecturer Jan 1986
Hayhurst, Ms Penelope S BA(Hons) Lecturer Sep 1999
Hill, Miss Coral E BA Senior Lecturer Oct 1986
Hill, Mr Daniel BA(Hons)(Cantab); MA(Cantab) Lecturer *May 1996
Jackson, Ms Morette Senior Lecturer Jan 1992
Kempton, Ms Jacqueline BA Lecturer *Oct 1987
King, Ms Lesley Lecturer Jan 1976
Kirkness, Ms Lucy Senior Lecturer Jan 1984
Laski, Mr Alex Senior Lecturer Jan 1996
Lewis, Ms Jane E BA Senior Lecturer *Oct 1985
McEwen, Ms Janet Claire Senior Lecturer *Sep 1996
Malone, Ms Jacqui Senior Lecturer Jan 1997
Martinez, Miss Aurora LLB(Hons) Lecturer Oct 1995
Matthews, Ms Margaret Lecturer Jan 1996
Mavrikakis, Mr Alexis Associate Professor Jan 1995
Mawer, Ms Louise Lecturer Sep 1997
Noakes, Ms Hazel Lecturer Oct 1984
Norris, Mr Martin Senior Lecturer Jan 1992
Palman, Ms Jessica Senior Lecturer Jan 1995
Porter, Mr Robin A LLB(Leeds) Senior Lecturer *§Jul 1971
Pothecary, Ms Judith M BA(Hons) Lecturer *Feb 1997
Price, Mr Frederick H C MA(Edin); MCC Senior Lecturer *Nov 1991
Price, Ms Gail Senior Lecturer Jan 1981
Raval, Ms Devika Senior Lecturer Dec 1994
Rawcliffe, Miss Lisa C LLB(Leics) Lecturer *Nov 1991
Richards, Mr Gareth BA Senior Lecturer Nov 1994
Robathan, Mr Errol Senior Lecturer Jan 1996
Roberts, Mr Stuart Senior Lecturer Jan 2000
Rote, Mrs Sybilla LLB Senior Lecturer Jun 1988
Sabine, Ms Christa BA Lecturer *Oct 1993
Sang, Ms Susan Lecturer Jan 1998
Scott, Ms Karen LLB; LLM Senior Lecturer Oct 1996
Sharpley, Ms Deborah Ann CPE; LPC; BA/LLB Lecturer/Consultant Solicitor Mar 2001
Shortland, Ms Debbie Deputy Director Academic Oct 1987
Tayleur, Mr Trevor N L BA(Oxon); BCL Senior Lecturer *Oct 1982
Vandervlies, Ms Jane Senior Lecturer Jan 1979
Vickery, Miss Valerie Patricia LLB Lecturer Sep 1996
Wadsworth-Jones, Mrs Carol BA(Keele) Deputy Director Academic *Apr 1979
Wallis, Ms Debra Lecturer Oct 1993
Whitwam, Ms Jennifer Lecturer Jan 1999
Wise, Ms Julia Lecturer *Nov 1982

COMMERCIAL UNION PLC
PO BOX 420 St Helen's 1 Undershaft London EC3P 3DQ
Tel: 020 7283 7500 *Fax:* 020 7662 7295
Sol: Dixey, Miss Gabrielle Suzanne LLB; PGDip Corporate Lawyer *Sep 1993
Martin, Mr John D Legal Adviser *May 1983
Miles, Mr Thomas George MBA; LLB; ACIS Legal Adviser *Jul 1983
Shaine, Mr Neil R Solicitor *Jun 1970
Shepherd, Mr Christopher T MA(Oxon) Solicitor *Nov 1987
Tullo, Mr Russell K LLB(Hons) Solicitor Oct 1998

COMMISSION FOR LOCAL ADMINISTRATION IN ENGLAND
Millbank Tower Millbank London SW1P 4QP
Tel: 020 7217 4620 *Dx:* 2376 VICTORIA 1 *Fax:* 020 7217 4211
E-mail: london@lgo.org.uk
Sol: MacMahon, Mr Peter J MA; LLB Deputy Ombudsman *Dec 1969

CONOCOPHILLIPS (UK) LTD
Portman House 2 Portman Street London W1H 6DU
Tel: 020 7408 6000 *Fax:* 020 7408 6466
Sol: Anderson, Ms Fiona Jane LLB(Edin); DipLP Legal Adviser *Mar 1991
Dunne, Ms Michelle Ann LLB Senior Legal Advisor Jan 1986
Gorham, Ms Ruth Maretta BA(Hons) Senior Legal Adviser *Jan 1993
Price, Ms Elaine Marie LLB(Hons) Senior Counsel *May 1997
Walker, Mr Nigel F C MA(Cantab) Managing Counsel Africa *Sep 1978

CONSUMERS' ASSOCIATION
2 Marylebone Road London NW1 4DF
Tel: 020 7770 7000 *Fax:* 020 7770 7600
E-mail: name@which.co.uk
Sol: Farrington, Mr David Head of In-House Legal Oct 1977
Farrington, Mr David J BA(Oxon) Head of Legal *Oct 1977
Richards, Ms Sarah Katherine Frean BSc(UCT) *Oct 1977

COOKSON GROUP PLC
165 Fleet Street London EC4A 2AE
Tel: 020 7822 0000 *Fax:* 020 7822 0100
Sol: O'Hara, Mr Simon Andrew LLB(Hons) Head of Legal *Dec 1992

COPYRIGHT PROMOTIONS LICENSING GROUP LTD
3 Shortlands London W6 8PP
Tel: 020 8563 6400 *Fax:* 020 8563 6465
E-mail: amirviss@cplg.com
Sol: Mirviss, Ms Adrienne Scott BA; JD Head of Legal Affairs *Aug 1997

CORUS GROUP LIMITED
30 Millbank London SW1P 4WY
Tel: 020 7717 4523 *Fax:* 020 7717 4642
E-mail: helen.matheson@corusgroup.com
Sol: Bonville-Ginn, Miss Monique LLM(Hons); LLB(Wales); PGDip EC Law Corporate Lawyer *Oct 1989
Brown-Hovelt, Ms Luscinia BA; PGDL; LPC Corporate Lawyer *Aug 2004
Matheson, Ms Helen Lochhead LLB(Hons); LLM; DipLP Group Legal & Compliance Director Notary Public *Aug 1996
Mayers, Miss Debbie BA(Oxon); LPC Corporate Lawyer *Sep 1997
Page, Mr Alastair MA(Cantab) Corporate Lawyer *Mar 2001

COUNTRY LAND AND BUSINESS ASSOCIATION LTD
16 Belgrave Square London SW1X 8PQ
Tel: 020 7235 0511 *Fax:* 020 7235 4696
Sol: Flanagan, Mrs Harriet Ann LLB Legal Adviser Sep 1995
Price, Mr Christopher BA(Hons) Chief Legal Adviser May 1994
Sinclair, Mrs Laura Cicely BA(Hons) Senior Legal Adviser Jan 1998
Tetlow, Mr John Roger BA Legal Adviser Nov 1985

COUTTS & CO
440 Strand London WC2R 0QS
Tel: 020 7753 1403 *Fax:* 020 7753 1082
E-mail: william.enderby@coutts.com
Sol: Amer, Mr Simon Nicholas MA Solicitor Jan 1986
Enderby, Mr William Kenneth BA Head of Legal May 1977
Francis, Miss Elizabeth Sarah BSc; PGDL; LPC Solicitor Mar 2004
Mcleod, Mrs Merrilie Ann BA(Hons)(Law) Solicitor Oct 1987
Marken, Mr Gareth Peter Anthony MA(Oxon)(Classics); BVC; CPE Solicitor Oct 2004
Parsons, Mr Tim H LLB Solicitor Jan 1984
Trott, Mrs Helen Clare LLB(Hons); DipLP Lawyer Oct 1996

CRAWFORD-THG LTD
Trinity Court 42 Trinity Square London EC3N 4TH
Tel: 020 7265 0611
Sol: Kearney, Miss Suzanne Kathleen LLB Solicitor *Oct 1992

CREDIT SUISSE PRIVATE BANKING
5 Cabot Square London E14 4QR
Tel: 020 7888 8888
Sol: Ratcliffe, Mr Adrian Charles BA(Hons); DipLaw Senior Lawyer Sep 1997

CRESTON PLC
30 City Road London EC1Y 1BQ
Tel: 020 7448 8950 *Fax:* 020 7638 9426
Sol: Churchill-Coleman, Mrs Wendy Jane LLB Solicitor *May 1984

THE CROWN ESTATE OFFICE
16 Carlton House New Burlington Place London W15 2HX
Tel: 020 7851 5168 *Fax:* 020 7851 5125
E-mail: vivienneking@thecrownestate.co.uk
Sol: Harris, Mr David K N MA(Oxon) Deputy Head of Legal *§Jun 1973
King, Mrs Vivienne I BSocSc(Keele) Head of Legal *Mar 1988
Pinner, Mr David R LLB(Lond) Solicitor *Jan 1976

DAWNAY DAY INTERNATIONAL LIMITED
17 Grosvenor Gardens London SW1W 0BD
Tel: 020 7861 0989 *Fax:* 020 7828 1992
E-mail: simon.killick@dawnayday.com
Sol: Killick, Mr Simon LLB Group Legal Counsel Jan 1985

HOWARD DE WALDEN ESTATES LTD
23 Queen Anne Street London W1G 9DL
Tel: 020 7580 3163 *Fax:* 020 7255 1643
Sol: Willett, Mr Michael A BA In-house Solicitor Jun 1996
Wyatt, Ms Dawn Head of Legal Services *Mar 1981

DECCA MUSIC GROUP LTD
347-353 Chiswick High Road London W4 4HS
Tel: 020 8742 5420 *Fax:* 020 8742 5416
Sol: Robb, Miss Sophia Mary MA(Cantab) Director, Legal & Business Affairs *Sep 1996

DEGUSSA UK SERVICES LTD
Tego House Chippenham Drive Kingston London MK10 0AF
Tel: 0845 128 9575 *Fax:* 0845 128 9579
Sol: Lipman, Mr Jonathan LLB(Hons); DipLP Senior Counsel & Company Secretary *Nov 1997

DEPARTMENT FOR BUSINESS, ENTERPRISE AND REGULATORY REFORM
1 Victoria Street London SW1H 0ET
Tel: 020 7215 0105
Sol: Antill, Ms Justine Sep 1992
Arora, Nisha Nov 1993
Baker, Mr Richard G BA(Oxon); MS(Stanford) *Jun 1969
Bell, Ms Alissa Oct 1998
Bennett, Ms Virginia Nov 1993
Bovey, Mr Philip H Oct 1974
Bradley, Miss Alison J LLB(Lond) *Feb 1983
Briggs, Mr Daren Oct 1995
Broad, Mr Keith M Oct 1974
Bucknill, Mr Mark R Aug 1980
Busk, Mr Christopher E BA(Law); Licence en Droit Nov 1988
Carter, Ms Susan Apr 1992
Chase, Ms Bridget Jun 1970
Choudhury, Perween Sep 1996
Conlon, Miss Maureen BA(Law) *Apr 1980
Cromarty, Miss Isabel M BA(Oxon) Wig & Pen *Nov 1990
Deru, Ms Kemi Jan 2000
Dowling, Mr Carl Jan 1998
Ellis, Ms Rebecca Jan 1992
Ennals, Mr Alastair M LLB *Jul 1972
Fausset, Mr Anthony R LLB Dec 1980
Forbes, Mrs Megan Jan 1993
Fox, Ms Cynthia V LLB *Jul 1975
Hanrahan, Ms Jane Mar 1995
Hardaker, Ms Wendy Sep 1997
Harris, Mr John B Mar 1991
Hodgson, Ms Jane Sep 1993
Huey, Mr Peter Douglas BA(Hons); LLM Nov 1995
Hyett, Mr Stephen Apr 1973
Jenkins, Mr Daniel Jan 1994
Kissane, Mrs Claire Dec 1991
Ladha, Navroza Oct 1996
Leslie, Ms Caroline F LLB *Apr 1978
Lewis, Ms Nicola Nov 1994
McMillan, Mrs Alison Jun 1974
Markbreiter, Mr Charles Peter BA(Bris) Oct 1986
Maskell, Mr James S BA Oct 1990
Mercer, Mrs Carole Mar 1990
Milligan, Mr Scott G Jan 1975
Morgan, Mr Richard G LLB *Nov 1990
Morley, Miss Claire L BA(Lond) Oct 1988
Mutum, Ms Angela J Oct 1990
Nelson, Mr Robin Jan 1983
Nissen, Mr David E J Jul 1969
Race, Mrs Eve M BA(Oxon) *Dec 1977
Raikes, Mr David Charles Dec 1975
Rhone, Ms Shirley Jan 1996
Roberts, Mr John Oct 1971
Rogers, Ms Helen LLB(Nott'm) Mar 1993
Smith, Ms Susan Oct 1986
Smyth, Mr Ivan Jan 1997
Stanley, Mr John M Dec 1967
Susman, Mr Anthony M Apr 1975
Talbot, Mr Michael B J Jan 1989
Tarleton, Ms Sophie R BA(Oxon) Nov 1995
Thompson, Mr Peter Oct 1998
Tooke, Mr Mark Jan 1998
Venables, Ms Lisa LLB; M Jur Oct 1994
Watson, Mr Richard Oct 1992
Whittaker, Mr Ian Jan 1994
Woodbridge, Miss Vivien C Apr 1975
Woods, Mr Alan J Apr 1980

DIAGEO PLC
8 Henrietta Place London W1G 0NB
Tel: 020 7927 5300 *Fax:* 020 7927 4600

Sol: Chalmers, Ms Sabine LLB Solicitor *Oct 1989
Donovan, Mr Andrew D LLB Legal Counsel School Governor *Nov 1990
Downey, Ms Geraldine M P Legal Counsel Oct 1985
Fisher, Miss Sarah L LLB In-house Legal Adviser *Oct 1989
Harlock, Mr David F LLB Solicitor *Oct 1985
Moffat, Mrs Felicity Ann MA(Cantab)(Law) Solicitor *Mar 1991
Watts, Ms Margot L BA Legal Counsel Dec 1986

DIAMANTIS LEMOS LTD
6/8 Luke Street London EC2A 4EE
Tel: 020 7613 1234 ***Fax:*** 020 7613 0510
Sol: Lemos, Ms Maritsa BPA; JD(NY); QLTT In-house Solicitor Aug 1996

DOUGHTY HANSON & CO MANAGERS LTD
Times Place 45 Pall Mall London SW1Y 5JG
Tel: 020 7663 9300
Sol: Bradford, Miss Mary-Clare LLB Solicitor *Nov 1984

DURRINGTON CORPORATION LTD
4 Grosvenor Place London SW1X 7HJ
Tel: 020 7235 6146 ***Fax:*** 020 7235 3081
E-mail: jocelinharris@durrington.com
Sol: Harris, Ms Jocelin M St J MA Director *Jun 1970

EDF ENERGY PLC
40 Grosvenor Place Victoria London SW1X 7EN
Tel: 020 7242 9050 ***Dx:*** 152180 KNIGHTSBRIDGE 2
Fax: 020 7752 2223
Sol: Anstice, Ms Rachel Nov 2000
Baker, Mr Christopher J *Jan 1982
Bennett, Ms Clare LLB; LLM Aug 1991
Higson, Mr Robert I Company Solicitor *Jan 1983
Moreton, Mr Toby S LLB *Jun 1990
Richards, Mr Mark BA; LLM Commercial Solicitor Jan 1997

EEF
Broadway House Tothill Street London SW1H 9NQ
Tel: 020 7222 7777 ***Fax:*** 020 7222 2782
Sol: Atherton, Miss Lucy Mary BA Senior Legal Adviser *May 1995
Hagestadt, Ms Charlotte Lucy BSc Legal Adviser *Jan 1995
Hogarth, Ms Judith F BA; MA Legal Adviser *Sep 1996
Nicholls, Miss Vanessa Elizabeth BA Legal Adviser *Apr 2001
Taylor, Miss Gemma BA(Law); LLM Legal Adviser Jan 1997

EMI MUSIC PUBLISHING LTD
27 Wrights Lane London W8 5SW
Tel: 020 3059 3059 ***Fax:*** 020 3059 2059
Sol: Bebawi, Mr Antony LLB(Euro) Director of Legal and Business Affairs *Sep 1997
Golding, Mr Simon Joel Joseph BSc(Hons) Business Affairs Manager *Nov 1995
Mileson, Mr Christopher LLB(Lond) Consultant *Jun 1981
Smith, Mrs Joanne Sian LLB Business Affairs Lawyer Sep 1998

EMI RECORDS LTD
27 Wrights Lane London W8 5SW
Tel: 020 7795 7000
Sol: Radice, Mr James H BSc(Bris); CPE *May 1989

THE ECONOMIST NEWSPAPER LTD
25 St James's Street London SW1A 1HG
Tel: 020 7830 7000 ***Fax:*** 020 7930 3092
E-mail: email@economist.com
Sol: Grut, Mr Oscar BA(Hons); LSF Group General Counsel & Company Secretary *Jun 1995

ENFIELD MAGISTRATES COURT
The Court House Lordship Lane Tottenham London N17 6RT
Tel: 020 8808 5411 ***Dx:*** 134490 TOTTENHAM 3 ***Fax:*** 020 8885 4343

Sol: Carroll, Mr Stephen BA(Hons)(Law) Maxwell Law Prize Deputy Clerk to the Justices *Oct 1980
Carter, Mr Martin P BA(Hons) Senior Legal Adviser *Jan 1988
Decardi-Nelson, Mr Reggie BA(Hons) *Oct 2005
Ivill, Mrs Froso CPE; LPC Legal Adviser Mar 2005
Liddell, Mrs Clare Margaret LLB(Hons); Dip Magisterial Law Legal Adviser Nov 2000
Pipkin, Mrs Julie A Principal Court Clerk *Dec 1989
Roberts, Mrs Amanda LLB Legal Team Manager *Dec 2002

ENGLISH HERITAGE
1 Waterhouse Square 138-148 Holborn London EC1N 2ST
Tel: 020 7973 3360 ***Fax:*** 020 7973 3001
Sol: Bradbeer, Ms Charlotte Legal Advisor Nov 2004
Burgess, Miss Jane Elizabeth LLB Legal Adviser *Oct 1990
Fisher, Mrs Joanne Kelly Dip; F Inst L Ex Legal Advisor *Nov 1999
Hewitson, Mr Nigel BA(Hons); LARTPI Legal Director (Member of the planning panel) *Dec 1988
Myska, Miss Helena BA(Hons) Legal Adviser Apr 1989
Pemberton, Mrs Ceri W LLM Legal Adviser *Jan 1981

ENODIS PLC
Washington House 40-41 Conduit Street London W1S 2YQ
Tel: 020 7304 6000
Sol: Hooper, Mr David Ross Company Secretary *Dec 1971

EUROPE ARAB BANK PLC
13-15 Moorgate London EC2R 6AD
Tel: 020 7315 8500 ***Fax:*** 020 7315 8743
Sol: Bicheno, Miss Janet Heather LLB Legal Adviser *Jan 1988

FAMILY RIGHTS GROUP
The Print House 18 Ashwin Street London E8 3DL
Tel: 020 7923 2628 ***Fax:*** 020 7923 2683
Sol: Ryan, Ms Mary T BA Maurice Norden Prize Solicitor *Jan 1981

FINANCIAL SERVICES AUTHORITY
25 The North Colonnade Canary Wharf London E14 5HS
Tel: 020 7066 1000
Sol: Alterman, Ms Lucy LLB Solicitor Nov 1992
Bannister, Ms Yvette BA(Oxon) Solicitor Dec 1991
Bedi, Ms Anila LLB(Hons) Solicitor Oct 1995
Brady, Mr Richard Solicitor Oct 1990
Brown, Ms Judith E LLB Solicitor Oct 1992
Callum, Mr Alasdair J BA(Cantab) Solicitor Oct 1987
Chambers, Ms Therese BA Solicitor Nov 1991
Choyce, Mr D Gregory BA(Oxon) Chief Counsel Banking & General May 1983
Cooper, Mr Philip V J BSc(Hons); CPE Solicitor Nov 1992
Cross, Miss Pamela Dorothy BA Solicitor Nov 1995
Dockrell, Mr Hayes Rodney LLB Legal Adviser Apr 1991
Everett, Mr Richard J C BSc(Hons) Solicitor Oct 1990
Fernandes, Ms Anna Enforcement Officer Nov 1994
Heffner, Mr Richard Manager PIA Litigation & Appeals Aug 1996
Jefferies, Miss A Elizabeth BA(Hons); CPE; LPC Solicitor Oct 1996
Johnson, Mrs Andrea J LLB(Hons) *Oct 1989
London, Mr James F J LLB(Hull) Solicitor Nov 1989
Marsh, Mr Roger LLB(Lond) Manager PIA Litigation & Appeals Jun 1976
Marshall, Miss Helen A BA(Hull) Solicitor Oct 1987
Marshall, Ms Helen J BA(Hons) Solicitor Nov 1987
Mason, Mr Dominic E LLB(Hons) Manager IMRO Firms Oct 1992
Mason, Mr Ian James MA(Cantab) Senior Enforcement Counsel Dec 1991
Minghella, Ms Loretta C MA(Cantab) Head of Department *Sep 1987
Parish, Mrs Nicola LLB(Hons) Solicitor Nov 1993
Phelan, Mr Jonathan J LLB Solicitor Oct 1994
Purves, Mr Robert BA; LLC; BCom(Hons) Legal Adviser May 1994
Reed, Mr Gareth David LLB(Wales); TEP Legal Adviser Nov 1983
Sears, Mr Guy R W MA(Cantab) *Dec 1987
Sinclair, Ms Christina M R LLB(Hons); ANU; LLM Solicitor Mar 1994
Stein, Tal LLB(Cardiff); LPC Solicitor Oct 1997
Stimson, Mr Giles BA; MCIArb; CEDR Solicitor Dec 1972
Symington, Mr James MA(Hons); CPE Law Solicitor Jul 1999
Thomas, Mr Jeffrey M LLB Head of Authorisation Enquiries *Jun 1971
Thompson, Ms Stella Jane LLB; LSF Solicitor Dec 1992
Threipland, Mr Mark Patrick Murray BSc John Mackrell Solicitor Dec 1992
Tomes, Mr Richard Associate Civil Litigation Mar 1997
Whittaker, Mr Andrew M MA(Oxon) Deputy General Counsel *Apr 1980
Wylde, Mr John R A LLB(Lond) Manager Insurance & Friendly Societies Jul 1979

FIRST DISCOUNT LTD
Morrell House 98 Curtain Road London EC2A 3AA
Tel: 020 7739 5992 ***Fax:*** 020 7739 3930
Sol: Castle, Mr Alan L LLB(Hons) Company Solicitor *Jul 1960

FIRST TITLE INSURANCE PLC
76 Shoe Lane London EC4A 3JB
Tel: 020 7832 3100 ***Fax:*** 020 7832 3101
Sol: Borders, Mr Ian J Solicitor & Underwriter *Nov 1998
Nakarja, Harsit LLB(Hons) Solicitor & Underwriter *Aug 2001
Oldcorn, Mr Phillip J LLB(Hons) CEO *Nov 1992
Smith, Mrs Kelly LLB Solicitor & Underwriter *May 2001
Swallow, Mr Mark Solicitor & Underwriter *Sep 1999

FRAMLINGTON GROUP LTD
155 Bishopsgate London EC2M 3XJ
Tel: 020 7374 4100 ***Fax:*** 020 7330 6406
Sol: Tubbs, Miss Josephine Vanessa LLB(Bris) Head of Legal *Nov 1992

FRESHWATER GROUP OF COMPANIES (LEGAL DEPT)
Freshwater House 158-162 Shaftesbury Avenue London WC2H 8HR
Tel: 020 7836 1555 ***Dx:*** 51650 COVENT GARDEN
Fax: 020 7240 9770
Sol: Hedden, Mr Robert LLB; AKC Cliffords Inn Prizeman 1972 Group Solicitor *Mar 1972

FULLER SMITH & TURNER PLC
Griffin Brewery Chiswick London W4 2QB
Tel: 020 8996 2000 ***Fax:*** 020 7995 0230
Sol: Turner, Mr Timothy J M Director *Jun 1977

FUTURE FILM FINANCING LTD
76 Dean Street London W1D 3SQ
Tel: 020 7009 6600 ***Fax:*** 020 7009 6602
Sol: Blackman, Ms Julia BSc Head of Tax & Legal Services *Nov 1995
Margolis, Mr Stephen H LLB Solicitor *May 1974

GARTMORE INVESTMENT MANAGEMENT PLC
8 Fenchurch Place London EC3M 4PB
Tel: 020 7782 2000 ***Fax:*** 020 7782 2075
Sol: Bandesha, Miss Sandeep LLB Lawyer Sep 1998
Buys, Mr Bernardus LLB; BLC Solicitor Apr 2001
Jemmett, Ms Elizabeth MA; BA(Oxon)(Law) Lawyer Sep 1997
Kenderdine-Davies, Mr Mark Dixon Garth LLB; MBA Lawyer *Jul 1989
McGuire, Ms Fiona Lee BEc; LLB In-House Solicitor Apr 2005
Martin, Mr Simon B BA(Cantab) Solicitor *Nov 1993
Thomas, Miss Rachel Hannah LLB; Dip Law & French; LPC Lawyer Jan 2000

GIRLS' DAY SCHOOL TRUST
100 Rochester Row London SW1P 1JP
Tel: 020 7393 6666 ***Fax:*** 020 7393 6789
Sol: Arnold, Mrs Samantha LLB Assistant Legal Adviser Mar 2001
Hoare, Ms Caroline Lucy BA(Hons) Legal Director *Oct 1995
Jones, Miss Helen Elizabeth BA; LPC Assistant Legal Adviser *Sep 2002

GLOBAL AEROSPACE UNDERWRITING MANAGERS LTD
Fitzwilliam House 10 St Mary Axe London EC3A 8EQ
Tel: 020 7369 2244 ***Fax:*** 020 7369 2840
Sol: Walsh, Mr Stephen Group General Counsel *Nov 1998
Wilkinson, Mr Robert J BA(Hons) *Apr 1983
Williamson, Miss Ashleigh MA *Jan 2000

GLOBECAST NORTHERN EUROPE LTD
ITN Building 200 Grays Inn Road London WC1X 8XZ
Tel: 020 7430 4400 ***Fax:*** 020 7430 4321
Sol: Butler, Ms Rachelle MA Head of Legal Affairs Oct 1996
Nasir, Miss Neelam LLB Assistant Solicitor *Sep 1999

M GOLD & CO (METALS) LTD
Enterprise Works Trego Road London E9 5HJ
Tel: 020 8986 6314 ***Fax:*** 020 8986 1860
Sol: Gold, Mr Lawrence M BA(Econ) Managing Director Nov 1972

GOVERNMENT LEGAL SERVICE
11th Floor Lower Castle Street Castle Mead London BS1 3AG
Tel: 0845 300 0793
Sol: Adams, Mr Gary Arthur Reginald LLB Apr 1979
Hathaway, Mr Stuart BA(Oxon) May 1981

GRAND METROPOLITAN PLC (LEGAL DEPT)
8 Henrietta Place London W1M 9AG
Tel: 020 7321 6000 ***Fax:*** 020 7321 6001
Sol: Myddelton, Mr Roger H MA; LLB(Cantab) Legal Director & Company Secretary *Dec 1966

GREENWICH COMMUNITY LAW CENTRE
187 Trafalgar Road London SE10 9EQ
Tel: 020 8305 3350 ***Fax:*** 020 8858 5253
E-mail: laws@greenwich187.fsnet.co.uk
Sol: Wickramasingha, Ms Thalatha MA Supervising Solicitor *Nov 1986

LONDON BOROUGH OF GREENWICH LEGAL SERVICES
5th Floor Riverside House Woolwich High Street London SE18 6DN
Tel: 020 8921 5123 ***Dx:*** 400851 WOOLWICH 5 ***Fax:*** 020 8921 5556
Sol: Akbar, Miss Gulnaz LLB(Hons) Solicitor Nov 2000
Amaso, Ms Nimi LLB; BL(Nigeria); MA Jan 1996
Crabbe, Ms Sarah LLB(Hons) Social Services Lawyer Apr 1999
Grewal, Ms Sukhpal Kaur PFI Solicitor Nov 1996
Jenkins, Ms Catherine N MA(Cantab) Social Services Lawyer Nov 1984
Joseph, Mr Howard LLB(Hons)(Lond) Solicitor *Nov 1972
Mole, Mr Anthony G LLB; PGDipLaw(NZ) Principal Solicitor *Sep 1986
Natzler, Ms Caroline A MA(Edin) Senior Lawyer *Jan 1980
Onourah, Ms Azuka LLB; LLM Principal Lawyer Dec 1990
Power, Mr Russell T LLB Head of Legal Services *Oct 1973
Reid, Mrs Debbie G N Lawyer *Sep 1996
Reid, Ms Kim LLB Senior Lawyer *May 1983
Strunk, Mrs Ania A Principal Lawyer *Jul 1972
Travis, Ms Kim V A BA Social Services Lawyer *Oct 1990
Vautier, Mrs Helen LLB(Hons) Principal Solicitor Oct 1991
Watson, Ms Katharine MA(Oxon) Principal Lawyer *Apr 1982
White, Mrs Susan Ann Lawyer *Nov 1994

GUARDIAN ROYAL EXCHANGE PLC
1 Old Gate London EC3N 1RE
Tel: 020 7283 7101 ***Fax:*** 020 7621 2598
Sol: Clayton, Mr John R W MA(Cantab) Secretary *Oct 1976
Hastings, Mr Jarrod BA(Hons) Solicitor *Nov 1994

H M REVENUE & CUSTOMS
Somerset House Strand London WC2R 1LB
Sol: Collins, Mrs Deborah BA(Jurisprudence) Director Legal Sep 1987
Collins Rice, Ms Rowena BA(Oxon) Director Legal (Tax Law) HMRC Sep 1995
Ghelani, Sandeep BA(Hons) Nov 1997
Hogg, Mr David A CB Acting General Counsel & Solicitor MMRC *Nov 1969
Ridout, Mr Arnold James Solicitor Sep 1979

HAMMERSMITH & FULHAM COMMUNITY LAW CENTRE
142-144 King Street Hammersmith London W6 0QU
Tel: 020 8741 4021 ***Dx:*** 32760 HAMMERSMITH 2
Fax: 020 8741 1450
Sol: Gooderson, Ms Pauline F Solicitor *Nov 1984
Taylor, Ms Carol E Solicitor Feb 1985

HANSON PLC
1 Grosvenor Place London SW1X 7JH
Tel: 020 7245 1245 ***Fax:*** 020 7245 9939
E-mail: graham.dransfield@hanson.biz
Sol: Dransfield, Mr Graham BA(Oxon) Legal Director *Apr 1976
Laurie, Mr Elliot John MA(Cantab) Solicitor *Nov 1996

LONDON BOROUGH OF HARINGEY
Legal Services Alexandra House 10 Station Road London N22 4TR
Tel: 020 8489 0000 ***Dx:*** 35651 WOOD GREEN 1
Fax: 020 8489 3835 / 5984
Sol: Cunliffe-Jones, Mr Philip J MA Planning & Re-generating Lawyer Jul 1972
Eaton, Ms Chloe BA(Hons); LLB; DipLP Principal Lawyer, Social Services, LB of Haringey Jan 1999
Fiore, Miss Davina Jo-Anne LLB Head of Legal Services Governor City of Westminster College *Nov 1988
Ginsburg, Ms Elaine A BA(Hons) Principal Solicitor School Governor *Jun 1979
Lottari, Ms Maria LLB(Hons) Senior Legal Assistant *Mar 1981
Marshall, Mrs Emma Siobhan BA(Hons)(Dunelm) Lawyer Apr 1999
Maru, Mrs Anixa LLB Senior Legal Assistant *Jan 1996
Matthews, Mr Khumo Sego BA(Hons) Housing Lawyer Dec 2000
Meehan, Mr Kieron Patrick Anthony BA(Hons); MPhil Senior Lawyer *Jan 1999
Mitchison, Mr Terence Anthony MA(Oxon) Senior Lawyer *Dec 1981
Nunes de Souza, Miss Haydee LLB(Hons) Lawyer *Feb 1997
O'Connor, Ms Margaret BA(Hons); MA Lawyer *May 2000
Owa, Mrs Olayinka BA(Hons); LLM; DipLG Principal Lawyer *Nov 1993
Rogers, Miss Nicola Cerisa LLB(Hons); PGDip Senior Lawyer *Feb 2004
Salim, Ms Fateha LLB Senior Solicitor *May 2000
Steward, Mr Leslie Charles BSc; Cert Ed; CPE Senior Lawyer *Apr 1992
Voznick, Ms Michele BSc Lawyer *Nov 1997

HARINGEY MAGISTRATES LEGAL ADVISERS OFFICE
The Court House Bishops Road off Archway Road Highgate London N6 4HS
Tel: 0845 601 3600 ***Dx:*** 123550 HIGHGATE 3 ***Fax:*** 020 8273 3838
E-mail: firstname.secondname@hmcourts-service.gsi.gov.uk
Sol: Gartshore, Mr Derrick Hender LLB(Hons) Legal Adviser *Jun 1995
Harris, Miss Emma Hazell M BA(Hons) Legal Adviser May 1997
Hazelton, Mr Matthew LLB(Hons) Legal Adviser Jul 1997
Hughes, Mr Trevor William Legal Adviser Nov 2002
May, Mr Peter E Team Leader *Mar 1990

HENDERSON GLOBAL INVESTORS
4 Broadgate London EC2M 2DA
Tel: 020 7818 1818 ***Fax:*** 020 7818 4639
Sol: Irvine, Ms Jacqui Manager Legal Apr 2000
Keswick, Ms Lindsay Manager Legal Nov 1991
Kumar, Benita Divisional Director Mar 1995
O'Brien, Mr Steven J LLB Executive Legal Counsel *Apr 1980

HESS LTD
Level 9 The Adelphi Building 1-11 John Adam Street London WC2N 6AG
Tel: 020 7331 3000 ***Fax:*** 020 7331 3004

See p2 for the Key to Work Categories & other symbols

Sol: Boret, Mrs Samantha J Solicitor- Assistant General Counsel . . . . . . Nov 1989
Hampstead, Ms Rachel Alice MA; DipLaw Solicitor- Assistant General Counsel . . . . . . Sep 1994
Harwood, Mr Roger Morris LLB(Hons) Associate General Counsel. . . . . . May 2006
Phillips, Mrs Rebecca Legal Counsel . . . . . . Jan 2005

IBM UNITED KINGDOM LTD
Southbank 76 Upper Ground London SE1 9PZ
Tel: 020 7202 3000 **Fax:** 020 7202 5935
Sol: Campbell, Mr Duncan MA; LLM General Counsel . . *Feb 1992
Dixon, Mr Jason LLB; LLM Senior Attorney . . . . . . Apr 2004
Doyle, Ms Alison Mary Catherine LLB; DEUG Solicitor *Nov 1991
Dunger, Mrs Fiona E LLB . . . . . . *Oct 1987
Gallagher, Mr Steven Paul MA Senior Attorney . . . . Oct 1994
Green, Mr Kevin MBA; LLB; BA Senior Attorney. . . . Jan 2001
McClung, Mr Gilbert Edwin BA(Hons)(Cantab); MA(Hons)(Cantab) . . . . . . Jun 1991
Mason, Mr Alexander George BA Solicitor. . . . . . May 1991
Michelson, Ms Louisa J LLB; BA Senior Attorney . . . . Aug 1992
Power, Mr Nicholas Damien LLB; BSc Staff Attorney . . Jan 2003
Sullivan, Mrs Alison LLB Senior Attorney . . . . . . Jan 1989
Witt, Mr David Walter MA(Cantab) Senior Counsel . . *Jan 1969

ICC UNITED KINGDOM
30 Chepstow Road London W2 5BE
Tel: 020 7792 8579 **Fax:** 020 7229 8639
Sol: Merrett, Mr John R Arbitration Consultant Advocate of the Supreme Court of Brunei . . . . . . *Dec 1970

IFPI SECRETARIAT
10 Piccadilly London W1J 0DD
Tel: 020 7878 7900 **Fax:** 020 7878 7950
E-mail: info@ifpi.org
Sol: Pearcy, Mr Trevor R BA(Bris) Director, Finance & Administration . . . . . . *Oct 1976
Taylor, Mr Geoffrey BA(Sussex) Solicitor . . . . . . Nov 1995

IBSTOCK GROUP LTD
Russet Farm Redlands Lane London TN32 5NG
Tel: 01580 883850 **Fax:** 01580 880845
E-mail: stephenhardy@ibstock.co.uk
Sol: Hardy, Mr Stephen Philip MBE; MA; LSDE Company Secretary . . . . . . *May 1974

IMMIGRATION APPELLATE AUTHORITY
Taylor House 88 Rosebury Avenue London EC1R 4QU
Tel: 020 7353 8060 **Fax:** 020 8542 9066
Sol: Mannion, Mrs Rosy N LLB; LLM Solicitor Member SSAT; Part time Chairman Immigration Appeals Tribunal; Deputy Chairman of CSAT . . . . . . *§May 1984

INSINGER DE BEAUFORT (INSINGER ENGLISH TRUST)
44 Worship Street London EC2A 2JT
Tel: 020 7608 0888 **Fax:** 020 7608 2648
Sol: Addison, Mr Gerald P L Director. . . . . . *Dec 1966

INTERNATIONAL MANAGEMENT GROUP
Pier House Strand on the Green Chiswick London W4 3NN
Tel: 020 8233 5000 **Fax:** 020 8233 5301
Sol: Clark, Mr Brian S LLB Solicitor . . . . . . *Nov 1961

INTERVAL INTERNATIONAL LTD
Coombe Hill House Beverley Way London SW20 0AR
Tel: 020 8336 9300 **Fax:** 020 8336 9399
Sol: Echenagusia, Mr Jose Miguel Vice President Legal Services EMEA. . . . . . *Aug 1998

INVESCO
30 Finsbury Square London EC2A 1AG
Tel: 020 7065 3057 **Fax:** 020 7012 0696
E-mail: michelle_moran@ldn.invesco.com
Sol: Harte, Ms Ada Lawyer. . . . . . *Feb 2004
Labuschagne, Mr Willem Solicitor. . . . . . Dec 1995
Moran, Ms Michelle J M LLB Head of Legal for UK & Ireland . . . . . . *Mar 2000
Treacy, Ms Joanna BCom; LLB Barrister & Solicitor . . Jan 1994

INVESTEC BANK (UK) LTD
2 Gresham Street London EC2V 7QP
Tel: 020 7597 4000 **Fax:** 020 7597 4491
E-mail: lauren.ekon@investec.co.uk
Sol: Ekon, Mrs Lauren Kim BA; LLB Group Solicitor . . . *Aug 1998

JP MORGAN CHASE BANK
125 London Wall London EC2Y 5AJ
Tel: 020 7777 2000 **Fax:** 020 7777 3141
Sol: Feeney, Ms Joanne MA(Hons)(Modern History); CPE Assistant Vice President, Legal Department. . . . . . Dec 1994
Halim, Miss Tanjiha L BA Vice President. . . . . . *Nov 1987
Rose, Mr Philip R BA Vice President & Assistant General Counsel. . . . . . *Oct 1985

JOHN LEWIS PLC
Corporate Offices Partnership House Carlisle Place London SW1P 1BX
Tel: 020 7828 1000 **Fax:** 020 7592 6566
Sol: Hauff, Reynold L Solicitor . . . . . . *Jul 1975
Hoyle, Miss Amy LLB; LPC Commercial Corporate Solicitor . . . . . . Sep 2006
Rice, Mr Peter Hugh BA(Hons) Solicitor. . . . . . *Oct 1981
Shann, Miss Amy BSc; DipLaw; LPC Assistant Property Manager . . . . . . Sep 2006
Stride, Mr Andrew William LLB(Hons); Law; ACIS Deputy Company Secreatry. . . . . . *Oct 1991
Walton, Mr Guy DipLaw Property Lawyer . . . . . . May 1998
Willmott, Miss Sasha Jane BA(Hons) Personnel Lawyer . . . . . . Sep 2006
Wright, Mr Stephen James BA Principal Lawyer (Planning) . . . . . . Sep 2003

JOHNSON MATTHEY PLC
40-42 Hatton Garden London EC1N 8EE
Tel: 020 7269 8400 **Fax:** 020 7269 8433
Sol: Farrant, Mr Simon LLB Company Secretary & Senior Legal Adviser. . . . . . *Aug 1990
Moore, Miss Elizabeth Ingrid BA Assistant Legal Advisor . . . . . . Mar 1999

JOINT COUNCIL FOR THE WELFARE OF IMMIGRANTS
115 Old Street London EC1V 9JR
Tel: 020 7251 8708
Sol: Ahmed, Miss Sameena LLM Solicitor . . . . . . *Jun 2000
Beoku-Betts, Mr Derek Samuel Edward LLB; LLM Casework Director. . . . . . *Mar 1996
Lewis, Ms Kathryn Emma MEng Solicitor . . . . . . *Mar 2003
Pasha, Tauhid LLB(Hons) Legal, Policy and Information Director . . . . . . *Nov 1993

JOHN LAING
Allington House 150 Victoria Street London SW1E 5LB
Tel: 020 7901 3200 **Fax:** 020 7901 3520
Sol: Dennett-Thorpe, Ms Louisa BSc; CPE; LPC Legal Adviser . . . . . . Jan 2001
Dillon, Mr Matthew James LLB(Hons) . . . . . . Jan 1997
Poxelaris, Miss Maria LLB(Hons); LPC Solicitor . . . Sep 2000
Shell, Mr Peter LLB General Counsel . . . . . . Dec 1976

LAMBERT FENCHURCH LTD
Friary Court Crutched Friars London EC3N 2NP
Tel: 020 7560 3000 **Fax:** 020 7560 3231
Sol: Merttens, Mr Robin W MA(Cantab) Solicitor. . . . . *Mar 1985

LAND REGISTRY
Lincoln's Inn Fields London WC2A 3PH
Tel: 020 7917 8888 **Dx:** 1098 LONDON/CHANCERY LN
Fax: 020 7955 0110
Sol: Donaldson, Mr Jeremy R BA Land Registrar. . . . . *Oct 1985
Timothy, Mr Joseph V LLB Director of Legal Services . *Apr 1976
Twambley, Mr Francis BA Land Registrar . . . . . . Apr 1980
Westcott Rudd, Mr Michael MA(Cantab) Head of Corporate Legal Services . . . . . . *Sep 1984

LAZARD & CO LTD
50 Stratton Street London W1J 8LL
Tel: 020 7187 2000 **Fax:** 020 7072 6411
Sol: Nightingale, Ms Judith C MA(Oxon) Director & General Counsel . . . . . . *Jul 1993
Watson, Mr Dicken LLB(Hons) Head of Regulatory . . Jan 1998

LEGAL AND PROFESSIONAL CLAIMS LTD
24 Martin Lane London EC4R 0DR
Tel: 020 7621 3900 **Dx:** 46601 BARBICAN **Fax:** 020 7621 3949
E-mail: stephen.sullivan@lpclaims.com
Sol: Chaudhri, Miss Tehmina BA Solicitor . . . . . . *Jan 1980
Collins, Mr Kenneth Peter BA Solicitor. . . . . . *Oct 1986
Mustafa, Miss Susan C BA(Law) Solicitor . . . . . . *Jun 1983
Sullivan, Mr Stephen J LLB(Exon) Head of Legal & Compliance . . . . . . *Jul 1978
Tonner, Mr Craig James LLB; BComm. . . . . . Jan 2004

LONDON BOROUGH OF LEWISHAM
Town Hall Catford London SE6 4RU
Tel: 020 8695 6000 **Dx:** 139500 LEWISHAM 4 **Fax:** 020 8314 3145
E-mail: tony.galead@lewisham.gov.uk
Sol: Glass, Ms Helen BA(Lond) Principal Lawyer. . . . . Dec 1979
Keating, Mr Graham John Lyde BA Senior Solicitor . . *Oct 1995
Nicholson, Ms Kathleen M BSc Head of Law . . . . . Aug 1979
Nunney, Ms Georgina G BA Principal Lawyer . . . . . Jan 1987
Walls, Mr Damian Lawyer. . . . . . Jul 1990

SOCIETY OF LLOYD'S
One Lime Street London EC3M 7HA
Tel: 020 7327 1000 **Fax:** 020 7626 2389
Sol: Brady, Mr Paul James BA Solicitor . . . . . . Nov 2004
Coldbeck, Mrs Susan Elizabeth BA(Hons)(Law) Solicitor . . . . . . Sep 1999
Davies, Mr David Gwynn LLB Solicitor. . . . . . Jan 2005
Demery, Mr Nicholas Paul BA Solicitor . . . . . . Jan 1980
Gill, Miss Jennifer Louise LLB; BSc Solicitor. . . . . . Jan 2005
Hardy, Mr Simon James LLB; ACII Solicitor . . . . . Oct 2002
Hoffman, Ms Jofie Charlotte BA(Hons); LLB Solicitor . Jan 1995
Kennedy, Ms Diane Yvonne Louis BA Solicitor. . . . Apr 2005
McGovern, Mr Sean Gerard Director and General Counsel . . . . . . Oct 1994
Mackenzie, Ms Susan Jane BA(Bris) Team Manager *Nov 1991
Martin, Mr Paul Anthony Solicitor . . . . . . Jun 1993
Schaefer, Mrs Susanne Marguerite BA(Hons) Solicitor. Jan 1996
Schrader, Mrs Claire BA(Law) Solicitor . . . . . . Sep 1998
Spires, Mr Peter David LLB Head of Advisory . . . . . Jan 1995
Twemlow, Mr Christopher McGowan LLB(Hons) Solicitor . . . . . . Sep 2003
Wight, Ms Julianne BA; DipEd Solicitor . . . . . . Jan 1983

LLOYDS TSB GROUP PLC
10 Gresham Street London EC2V 7HN
Tel: 020 7158 2729 **Fax:** 020 7158 3233
Sol: Baker, Mr Richard John LPC Associate Director, Structured Transactions Group. . . . . . Oct 2001
Ball, Miss Alexandra BA(Jurisprudence) Associate Director, Products & Markets Legal. . . . . . *Jan 2000
Harrison, Mr Robert William Mark BA Associate Director, Products & Markets Legal. . . . . . Apr 2002
Isaacs, Mr Robin A BA(Hons) Director, Structured Transactions Group. . . . . . *§Dec 1980

LOCAL GOVERNMENT ASSOCIATION
Local Government House Smith Square London SW1P 3HZ
Tel: 020 7664 3000 **Dx:** 119450 CLERKENWELL 3
Fax: 020 7664 3030
E-mail: info@lga.gov.uk
Sol: Rees, Mr John BA(Lond) Director (Central Services) . *Jan 1979

LOGICA PLC
Stephenson House 75 Hampstead Road London NW1 2PL
Tel: 020 7637 9111 **Fax:** 020 7446 1937
Sol: Walker, Mr David C LLB(Bris) Legal Adviser. . . . . *Jan 1979
Wilkin, Mr Robert Paul LLB(Lond) Legal Adviser. . . *Mar 1993

CITY OF LONDON CORPORATION
Guildhall London EC2P 2EJ
Tel: 020 7606 3030 **Dx:** 121783 GUILDHALL **Fax:** 020 7332 1992
Sol: Bennetts, Mr Alan LLB Chief Legal Assistant . . . . *Oct 1983
Best, Mrs Ronica Lorna LLB Solicitor - Senior Legal Assistant . . . . . . *Aug 1999
Chadha, Mr Paul A BSc Principal Legal Assistant . . *Apr 1988
Chopra, Ms Rashmi LLB(Hons) Head of Employment Team . . . . . . Feb 2003
Clift, Mr John Solicitor. . . . . . *Dec 1984
Colvin, Mr Andrew J Solicitor . . . . . . *May 1975
Groves, Mr Alan B LLB(Hons) Principal Property Lawyer . . . . . . Feb 1980
Hickson, Mr C Paul MA(Cantab) Chief Legal Assistant *Oct 1983
Jeffrey, Mr George D R BA(Law) Chief Legal Assistant *Oct 1980
Mirabelli, Mr Philip William BA; LLM Solicitor . . . . *Aug 1995
Rahman, Miss Rummana LLB(Hons) Solicitor. . . . . *Dec 1992
Rhodes, Mr Tim LLB(Hons)(KCL) Principal Property Lawyer . . . . . . *Mar 1985
Wells, Ms Vicki L D LLB Senior Legal Assistant . . . . *Jan 1989

LONDON FIRE & EMERGENCY PLANNING AUTHORITY
Legal Branch 169 Union Street London SE1 0LL
Tel: 020 8555 1200 **Fax:** 020 7587 4697
Sol: Armstrong, Mrs Linda LLB Solicitor . . . . . . *Sep 1996
Boomla, Mrs Valerie Anne LLB; MSc Society of Construction Law Prize Solicitor . . . . . . *Jan 1985
Clarke, Ms Caroline J BA(Hons) Solicitor . . . . . . *Oct 1989
D'Aloise, Ms Diana Julia BA; LLB; MBA; DipLG Solicitor . . . . . . *Aug 1993
Dempsey, Ms Joanna Elizabeth LLB(Hons)(English & German Law); DipLP Solicitor . . . . . . *Dec 1999
Laurence, Miss Fiona Mary Caroline LLB; DipLG Solicitor . . . . . . *Oct 1987
McKenna, Ms Yvonne Solicitor . . . . . . *Nov 1995
Rolfe, Mrs Michele Susan BA; LLB Solicitor. . . . . . *Jul 2003
Vexter, Ms Dara A LLB(Exon) Solicitor. . . . . . *Mar 1987

THE LONDON LAW AGENCY LTD
69 Southampton Row London WC1B 4ET
Tel: 020 7353 9471 **Dx:** 1053 LONDON/CHANCERY LN
Fax: 0870 432 0663
E-mail: info@londonlaw.co.uk
Sol: Cowdry, Mr John Jeremy Arthur Director Solicitor . . *Nov 1966

CITY OF LONDON MAGISTRATES COURT
1 Queen Victoria Street London EC4N 4XY
Tel: 020 7332 1830 **Dx:** 98943 CHEAPSIDE 2 **Fax:** 020 7332 1493
Sol: Fowler, Ms Helen P Senior Court Clerk . . . . . . Oct 1996
Griffith, Mrs Jocelyn M LLB(Hons) Principal Solicitor. . *Oct 1996
Kelleher, Mrs Kathrin M Court Clerk. . . . . . May 1982
Knight, Ms Charlotte LLB(Hons) Court Clerk. . . . . *Apr 1993
Matthews, Mr Richard Legal Adviser. . . . . . *Mar 1994

LONDON STOCK EXCHANGE LTD
Legal Department The Tower Old Broad Street London EC2N 1HP
Tel: 020 7797 1000 **Fax:** 020 7334 8921 / 8908
Sol: Barrington, Ms Lorna Solicitor. . . . . . Dec 1995
Condron, Ms Lisa M LLB Solicitor & Company Secretary . . . . . . Nov 1992
Courtenay, Mr William Solicitor . . . . . . Sep 1998
Croxford, Mrs Jennifer MA(Cantab) Solicitor. . . . . Mar 1996
George, Miss Natasha M J Solicitor . . . . . . *Sep 1992
Hinton, Mr Paul BA(Hons). . . . . . *Sep 2001
Johnson, Ms Catherine Anne MA(Cantab) Solicitor and Head of Legal Department. . . . . . Sep 1993
Marcus, Mr Daniel Solicitor . . . . . . Sep 1998

LONDON UNDERGROUND LTD
55 Broadway London SW1H 0BD
Tel: 020 7918 3126 **Dx:** 148901 TOTTENHAM COURT ROAD 3
Fax: 020 7918 4563
Sol: Atkins, Ms Sarah A BA; MA Head of Legal Services. . Feb 1983
Avon, Mrs Michelle Stella Mary BA(Jt Hons) Property & Rail Interface Manager. . . . . . Jan 1991
Congdon, Mr Adrian Solicitor . . . . . . Jan 1990
Gent, Ms Susan LLB(Hons) Disputes Risk & Regulatory Holt Manager . . . . . . Nov 1990
Graham, Mr Sean LLB(Hons) Commercial Dispute Management Solicitor. . . . . . *Oct 1991
Holt, Ms Michelle LLB PPP Contract Support Manager-London Underground . . . . . . Apr 2004
Mee, Mrs Jane A LLB(Hons) PFI & Project Manager. *Nov 1992
Morris, Mr George Jonathan LLB(Hons) Solicitor . . . Jul 1992
Nijjar, Ms Baljinder BA Solicitor . . . . . . Feb 1998

MGN LTD
One Canada Square Canary Wharf London E14 5AP
Tel: 020 7293 3934 **Fax:** 020 7293 3613
Sol: Partington, Mr Marcus Solicitor . . . . . . Oct 1989

M M & K LTD
1 Bengal Court Birchin Lane London EC3V 9DD
Tel: 020 7283 7200 **Fax:** 020 7283 4119
E-mail: info@mm-k.com
Sol: Chhatrisha, Miss Rajshree LLB; LSF Solicitor Law Society Council Member. . . . . . Apr 1994

MCDONALDS RESTAURANTS LTD
11-59 High Road East Finchley London N2 8AW
Tel: 0870 241 3300 **Dx:** 52051 EAST FINCHLEY
Sol: Hilton-Johnson, Mr Julian C BA(Hons) VP of Corporate Affairs & General Counsel . . . . . . Mar 1992
Upton, Mr John LLB(Hons) Legal Counsel. . . . . . Sep 1999

MARATHON OIL UK LTD
Capital House 25 Chapel Street London NW1 5DQ
Tel: 020 7298 2500 **Fax:** 020 7298 2502
Sol: Collison, Mr Simon Brian BA Solicitor . . . . . . *Nov 1996
Wilson, Ms Louise Mary Solicitor . . . . . . Dec 1991

MARKS & SPENCER PLC
Waterside House 35 North Wharf Road London W2 1NW
Tel: 020 7935 4422 **Fax:** 020 8718 7721
Sol: Bhaloo, Mrs Shital LLB(Hons). . . . . . *Feb 1999
Blakey, Miss Fiona LLB . . . . . . Oct 2002
Haynes, Mr Steven LLB. . . . . . Jan 2004
Howell, Mrs Patricia LLB Solicitor . . . . . . *Nov 1996
Hullah, Mrs Hannah Kate Vinson BSc Solicitor. . . . *Nov 2001
Ivens, Mr Robert John LLB Head of Legal Department *Oct 1983
Lock, Mrs Carolyn Michelle LLB. . . . . . *Apr 2000
MacRae, Miss Heather LLB(Hons) Solicitor . . . . . *Oct 1993
Miller, Ms Diane BA(Hons) Solicitor . . . . . . *Sep 1999
Oakley, Mr Graham John LLB Company Secretary & Group Legal Adviser. . . . . . *Apr 1982
Roberts, Mr Anthony John Solicitor . . . . . . *Jan 1983
Rogers, Mrs Sarah Frances CPA; LPC Solicitor . . . Mar 1997
Wain-Heapy, Ms Sara BA(Hons) . . . . . . Sep 2003

MARSH & MCLENNAN COMPANIES, INC
Sackville House 143-149 Fenchurch Street London EC3M 6BN
Tel: 020 7357 1000 *Fax:* 020 7357 3410
Sol: Flahive, Mr Jeremiah BA(Hons) Litigation Counsel . . . Oct 1992
Hemmin, Ms Susan LLB Corporate Counsel. . . . . . *Jun 1994
Luxmoore Styles, Mr Roger P L LLB European Corporate Counsel. . . . . *Mar 1988
McHugh, Miss Rosaleen BA(Hons)(Oxon) Litigation Counsel . . . . . Nov 1989
Pullan, Ms Michele M BA(Hons) MMC Chief Litigation Counsel UK & Europe . . . . . *Dec 1985
Siva, Mr Anand BA Litigation Counsel. . . . . *Sep 1998
Wright, Mr Jonathan P M LLM; LLB Litigation Counsel. Nov 1988

MARTELLO PROFESSIONAL RISKS LIMITED
Caveat House 14 Lovat Lane London EC3R 8DZ
Tel: 020 7337 7500 *Dx:* 582 LONDON/CHANCERY LN
Fax: 020 7337 7533
E-mail: mail@martelloprl.co.uk
Sol: Barnes, Mr Philip M BSc(Bris); LLB(Lond); MSc; MICE; FCIArb Solicitor. . . . . *Oct 1989
Boyd, Mr Stuart BSc(Hons) Solicitor. . . . . Sep 2003
Carter, Mr Gregory LLB(Hons) Solicitor . . . . . Sep 2004
Dingemans, Ms Ann LLB(Hons) Solicitor . . . . . *Jan 1999
Hindle, Ms Katherine BA(Hons) Solicitor. . . . . Jun 2006
Leathley, Mr John FCII Practice Manager . . . . . *Dec 1991
Luff, Ms Kirsty LLB(Hons) Solicitor . . . . . *Nov 1995
Lyon, Mr Andrew LLB(Hons) Solicitor . . . . . *Mar 1993
MacKintosh, Ms Alison BA(Lond) Solicitor. . . . . Sep 1988
MacSweeney, Mr Nigel BA(Hons) Solicitor. . . . . *Nov 2002
Owen, Mr Anthony LLB Solicitor. . . . . *Apr 1974
Parker, Ms Ruth LLB Solicitor . . . . . Mar 2006
Swift, Ms Claire BA(Law); MA Solicitor . . . . . *Nov 1995
Trundle, Mr Paul BSc(Hons) Solicitor . . . . . *Nov 1996
Twaites, Mr Stephen BA(Hons)(Manc) Solicitor . . . *Feb 1988
Walsh, Ms Elaine BA(Hons); MA Head of Claims Department . . . . . *Nov 1994
Wood, Mr Michael BCom; LLB(Hons); ACII Chief Executive & Claims Director . . . . . *Dec 1990

METROPOLITAN POLICE DIRECTORATE OF LEGAL SERVICES
First Floor Victoria Block New Scotland Yard London SW1H 0BG
Tel: 020 7230 7210 *Fax:* 020 7230 7209
Sol: Barnes, Mr Richard A BA(Hons) Lawyer. . . . . *Apr 1997
Bergin, Mr John Christopher BSc(Hons) Lawyer. . . *Jun 1994
Bird, Ms Samantha R A BA(Hons); LLB Senior Lawyer *Apr 1997
Boahen, Ms Cynara A LLB(Hons) Lawyer. . . . . *Sep 1995
Brannigan, Mr William Niall LLB(Hons) Senior Lawyer *Dec 1994
Burrows, Ms Sandra D M BA(Dunelm) Town Clerk's Educational Trust Prize 1979 Assistant Director . . . . . *Jun 1979
Castiglione, Ms Sabrina LLB(Hons) Senior Lawyer . *Sep 1997
Catcheside, Ms Susan Elizabeth Courtenay BA(Hons) Senior Lawyer . . . . . *Oct 1995
Cunningham, Ms Andrea BA; CPE; LSF Senior Lawyer . . . . . *Sep 1992
Davis, Mr Mark Francis BA(Hons) Lawyer. . . . . *Feb 1993
Emery, Mr David BA(Oxon) Senior Lawyer . . . . . *Mar 2002
Fairbrother, Mr Andrew J LLB(Hons) Senior Lawyer. *Nov 1997
Gale, Miss Susan B BA Geoffrey Howard Watson; Robert Innes Prizes Lawyer. . . . . *Jul 1975
Gluck, Mr Laurence M LLB Senior Lawyer. . . . . *Nov 1978
Harraway, Mrs Emma L LLB(Hons) Lawyer . . . . . *Oct 1998
Heron, Miss Sarah LLB(Hons) Lawyer. . . . . *Nov 1990
Hyams, Miss Laura D LLB(Lond) Senior Lawyer. . . *§Apr 1980
Jones, Ms Melanie LLB(Hons) Senior Lawyer . . . . *Mar 1996
Leonard, Ms Jennifer M BSc(Hons) Senior Lawyer . *Nov 1990
Loose, Mr Peter D BA Lawyer. . . . . *Oct 1984
McCahon, Mr David BA Senior Lawyer . . . . . *Apr 1994
Morgan, Mr Guy LLB Assistant Director . . . . . *Oct 1983
Morley, Mrs Veronica T BA(Hons) Senior Lawyer . . *Aug 1991
Morris, Mrs Jacqueline R BA(Hons); MA(Hons) Lawyer . . . . . *Nov 1987
Neville, Ms Colette O H LLB(Hons) Senior Lawyer. . *Dec 1983
O'Dwyer, Ms Jennifer Mary LLB(Hons) Lawyer . . . *Mar 1998
Pierce, Mr Nicholas BA(Keele) Senior Lawyer. . . . *Dec 1981
Rai, Mr Gurpreet BA(Hons) Lawyer . . . . . *Oct 1988
Royan, Ms Sara M BA(Hons) Senior Lawyer . . . . *Nov 1995
Saleh, Miss Nuzhat F LLB Assistant Director . . . . *May 1987
Skipper, Mr Richard J LLB Senior Lawyer. . . . . *Jan 1986
Solomons, Mr Edward Brian BA Director . . . . . *Apr 1979
Spanton, Mr Mark A LLB(Hons) Senior Lawyer . . . *Oct 1993
Tuffuor, Miss Tracey Asantewaa LLB(Hons) Lawyer. *Mar 2004
Wright, Mr Julian BA Lawyer . . . . . *Nov 2005

THOMAS MILLER & CO
International House 26 Creechurch Lane London EC3A 5BA
Tel: 020 7283 4646 *Dx:* 621 LONDON/CITY *Fax:* 020 7283 5614
Sol: Holford, Mr Mark D LLB Director of Corporate Development . . . . . *Apr 1975

MILLS & ALLEN LTD
Summit House 27 Sale Place London W2 1YR
Tel: 020 7298 8000 *Fax:* 020 8326 7738
Sol: Sankar, Mrs Parvathi LLB(Hons) Solicitor & Company Secretary . . . . . Nov 1991

MITSUBISHI SECURITIES INTERNATIONAL PLC
Legal Department 6 Broadgate London EC2M 2AA
Tel: 020 7577 2804 *Fax:* 020 7577 2872
Sol: Alvernhe, Mr Pierre MBA Associate Director. . . . . Jan 1993
Davidson, Miss Georgina Senior Manager. . . . . *Jan 1997
House, Mr Richard M LLB Head of Legal Department *Mar 1990
Manku, Ms Jaz Manager . . . . . *Jan 2002

MONTPELLIER GROUP PLC
39 Cornhill London EC3V 3NU
Tel: 020 7522 3200 *Fax:* 020 7522 3213
E-mail: recept@yjlovell.mhs.compuserve.com
Sol: Price, Mr Alan M A Company Secratary & Solicitor Justice of the Peace. . . . . *Jul 1970

MORE GROUP PLC
33 Golden Square London W1R 3PA
Tel: 020 7287 6100 *Fax:* 020 7287 9160
E-mail: giles.wynne.thomas@moregroup.com
Sol: Wynne Thomas, Mr Giles LLB(Hons) Solicitor. . . . *Mar 1992

J MURPHY & SONS LTD
Hiview House Highgate Road London NW5 1TN
Tel: 020 7267 4366 *Fax:* 020 7482 3107
E-mail: jpmurphy@murphygroup.co.uk
Sol: Murphy, Mr John Patrick Solicitor . . . . . *Nov 1991

NATIONAL AIR TRAFFIC SERVICES LTD
5th Floor South Brettenham House Lancaster Place London WC2E 7EN
Tel: 01489 616001 *Fax:* 01489 615219
Sol: Gregory, Ms Katherine M Legal Adviser . . . . . Mar 1992

NATIONAL ASSOCIATION OF LOCAL COUNCILS
109 Great Russell Street London WC1B 3LD
Tel: 020 7637 1865 *Fax:* 020 7436 7451
Sol: Birtwistle, Miss Katharine LLB(Hons) Solicitor . . . . Aug 2004
Tharmarajah, Ms Meera LLB(Hons) Head of Legal Services . . . . . *Nov 1998

NATIONAL AUSTRALIA BANK
88 Wood Street London EC2V 7QQ
Tel: 020 7710 2100
E-mail: michael.webber@ev.nabgroup.com
Sol: Webber, Mr Michael F Head of Legal Services . . . . Aug 1981

NATIONAL INSTITUTIONS OF THE CHURCH OF ENGLAND, LEGAL OFFICE
Church House Great Smith Street London SW1P 3AZ
Tel: 020 7898 1000 *Dx:* 148403 WESTMINSTER 5
Fax: 020 7898 1718
E-mail: legal@c-of-e.org.uk
Sol: Crow, Mr Timothy LLB(Hons) Deputy Official Solicitor to the Church Commissioners . . . . . *Jun 1980
Egar, Rev Judith A BA; MA(Oxon) Solicitor . . . . . *Oct 1983
Hammond, Sir Anthony H KCB MA; LLD(Hons) Standing Counsel to General Synod . . . . . *Aug 1965
Owens, Mr Terence P LLB(Hons)(Exon) Solicitor . . *Jun 1975
Slack, Mr Stephen MA Chief Legal Adviser . . . . . *Apr 1979
Smith, Mr Stewart Alan BA(Hons)(Law) . . . . . *Sep 1988
Webster, Mr Derek M Solicitor. . . . . *Apr 1978
York, Mr Stephen MA Solicitor. . . . . *Sep 1997

NATIONAL UNION OF STUDENTS
Nelson Mandela House 461 Holloway Road London N7 6LJ
Tel: 020 7272 8900 *Fax:* 020 7263 5713
Sol: Mawle, Mr Michael C J Union Solicitor. . . . . *Dec 1967

NETWORK RAIL
40 Melton Street London NW1 2EE
Tel: 020 7557 8000 *Dx:* 133075 EUSTON 3 *Fax:* 020 7557 9000
Sol: Andrew, Ms Catherine Mary LLB Legal Adviser . . . . Sep 2000
Camp, Mrs Jennifer Clarissa BA(Hons)(Law); MA Legal Adviser . . . . . Sep 2001
Davey, Mr Stephen Robert LLB(Hons) Solicitor . . . . Sep 2003
Gribben, Miss Karen Anne . . . . . *Jan 1996
Jackson, Ms Elizabeth Adrienne Legal Adviser . . . *Sep 1978
James, Mr Andrew Lee LLM Legal Adviser . . . . . Feb 1992
Jobling, Ms Natalie H LLB(Hons) Head of Legal Services - Commercial. . . . . *Nov 1987
Kayne, Mr Daniel LLB; LPC Solicitor/Legal Adviser . . Oct 2001
Kelly, Mr Stuart Malcolm BEng Legal Adviser . . . . Feb 1999
Morton, Mrs Judith LLB(Hons); DIPLP; NP First Class Merit Certificate (Comparative Law) Legal Adviser. . . Mar 1999
Parkinson, Mrs Alison LLB Head of Legal Services - Property . . . . . *Jul 1978
Smith, Mr Richard L LLB(Leeds) BB&O Law Society Prize for Litigation Head Of Legal Services - Litigation . . . *Oct 1988
Woodward, Ms Genevieve Anne LLB Legal Adviser . . *Apr 2000

THE NEWSPAPER SOCIETY
St Andrews House 18-20 St Andrews Street London EC4A 3AY
Tel: 020 7632 7400 *Fax:* 020 7632 7401
E-mail: ns@newspapersoc.org.uk
Sol: Courtney, Ms Catherine M BA(Hons); DipLaw Political, Editorial & Regulatory Affairs Dept. . . . . *Oct 1986
Dennehy, Ms Susan LLB Legal Advisor . . . . . *Sep 2001
Newell, Mr David R LLB(B'ham); MPhil(Soton) Director*Mar 1978
Oake, Ms Susan L Legal Adviser . . . . . *Nov 1991

NORTH KENSINGTON LAW CENTRE
74 Golbourne Road North Kensington London W10 5PS
Tel: 020 8969 7473 *Dx:* 46655 MAIDA HILL *Fax:* 020 8968 0934
Sol: Burton, Ms Marie Patricia LLB Assistant Solicitor . . . Feb 1994
Lee, Ms Virginia LLB; BA Solicitor. . . . . *May 1992
Lewis, Ms Ursula Ann BA Solicitor. . . . . *Dec 1985
Nash, Ms Juliette MA(Cantab) Assistant Solicitor . . . Oct 1995
Sephton, Ms Claire Solicitor. . . . . Jan 1991
Tyrrell, Ms Helen M BA(Hons) Assistant Solicitor . . *Oct 1983

OFCOM
Ofcom Contact Centre Riverside House 2a Southwark Bridge Road London SE1 9HA
Tel: 020 7981 3040 *Fax:* 0845 456 3333
Sol: Morgan, Ms Gwen MA(Hons) Legal and Licensing Officer . . . . . *Sep 1999
Salomon, Ms Eve C BSc Director of Legal Services . *§Oct 1985

OFFICIAL SOLICITOR AND PUBLIC TRUSTEE
81 Chancery Lane London WC2A 1DD
Tel: 020 7911 7127 *Dx:* 0012 LONDON/CHANCERY LN
Fax: 020 7911 7105
E-mail: enquiries@offsol.gsi.gov.uk
Sol: Clift, Ms Helen Mary BA(Hons) Solicitor . . . . . *Oct 1994
Hart, Mr Simon BA(Hons); MA Solicitor . . . . . *Sep 1997
Ilett, Ms Janet E LLB Solicitor . . . . . *Oct 1985
Ingham, Mr John BA Solicitor . . . . . *Dec 1978
Lock, Mr Keith John BA(Oxon) Solicitor . . . . . *May 1981
McKendry, Ms Susan BA Solicitor. . . . . *Feb 1994
McQuire, Miss Jennifer A LLB(Hons) Solicitor . . . *Nov 1995
Maughan, Mrs May BA Solicitor. . . . . *Jun 1980
Miller, Mr David Michael Ashley BA Solicitor. . . . *Sep 1995
Pearson, Miss Sheila BA; LLB Solicitor . . . . . Jul 1991
Sandars, Mrs Rosemary E LLB Solicitor. . . . . Jun 1978
Sanders, Ms Catherine Solicitor. . . . . *Nov 1985
Solomons, Mr Edward B Deputy Official Solicitor & Public Trustee . . . . . *Apr 1979
Taylor, Mrs Beverley J Solicitor . . . . . May 1982

P&O LEGAL DEPT
16 Palace Street London SW1E 5JQ
Tel: 020 7930 4343
Sol: Gradon, Mr R Michael MA(Cantab) Solicitor. . . . . *Oct 1983

PADDINGTON LAW CENTRE
439 Harrow Road London W10 4RE
Tel: 020 8960 3155 *Dx:* 46657 MAIDA HILL *Fax:* 020 8968 0417
E-mail: paddingtonlaw@dial.pipex.com
Sol: McNicholas, Ms Anne Adviser / Solicitor. . . . . Jul 2001
Michie, Ms Caroline BA Solicitor. . . . . Dec 1989

PALMER CAPITAL PARTNERS
Floor 6 Time & Life Building 1 Bruton Street London W1J 6TL
Tel: 020 7409 5500 *Fax:* 020 7409 5501
E-mail: property@palmercapital.co.uk
Sol: Digby-Bell, Mr Christopher Harvey Chief Executive and General Counsel. . . . . *Dec 1972
Zanellato, Miss Nichola Lawyer . . . . . *Dec 2005

PARIBAS LTD
10 Harewood Avenue Marylebone London NW1 6AA
Tel: 020 7595 2000 *Fax:* 020 7595 2555
Sol: Sowerbutts, Mr Kevin J LLB Head of Internal Finance & Legal Department. . . . . *Dec 1983

PEGASI MANAGEMENT COMPANY LTD
207 Sloane Street London SW1X 9QX
Tel: 020 7245 4500 *Fax:* 020 7235 5468
Sol: Lofthouse, Miss Julia Anne BA(Hons) Solicitor. . . . *Jan 1986

PENSIONS OMBUDSMAN
The Office of the Pensions Ombudman 11 Belgrave Road London SW1V 1RB
Tel: 020 7834 9144 *Fax:* 020 7821 0065
E-mail: enquiries@pensions-ombudman.org.uk
Sol: Laverick, Mr David LLB(Hons)(Lond) Bedfordshire Law Society Prize 1970 Pensions Ombudsman President; Adjudication Panel for England. . . . . Nov 1971

PENTLAND GROUP PLC
Pentland Centre Lakeside Squires Lane Finchley London N3 2QL
Tel: 020 8346 2600 *Fax:* 020 8343 4876
Sol: McLaren, Mr John S LLB Corporate Counsel . . . . Dec 1988

PERFORMING RIGHT SOCIETY LTD
Copyright House 29-33 Berners Street London W1P 4AA
Tel: 020 7580 5544 *Fax:* 020 7306 4650
Sol: Fishman, Miss Karen E LLB Solicitor . . . . . *Nov 1991
Lowe, Miss Frances M MA Solicitor . . . . . Oct 1990
Molesworth, Mr Robert S H MA(Oxon) . . . . . *§Jun 1963

PLUMSTEAD COMMUNITY LAW CENTRE
105 Plumstead High Street London SE18 1SB
Tel: 020 8855 9817 *Fax:* 020 8316 7903
Sol: Bisson, Mr Nicholas James LLB(Hons) . . . . . Nov 1977

POLYGRAM FILM OPERATIONS
Oxford House 76 Oxford Street London W1N 0HQ
Tel: 020 7307 1300 *Fax:* 020 7307 7639
Sol: Darbyshire, Miss Alex CPE; LSF; BA Senior Adviser, Legal & Business Affairs Director EU Lawyers' Society. . *Nov 1994

POLYGRAM INTERNATIONAL LTD
8 St James Square London SW1Y 4JU
Tel: 020 7747 4000 *Fax:* 020 7499 2596
Sol: Constant, Mr Richard M MA(Cantab) General Counsel Nov 1978

PORT OF LONDON AUTHORITY
London River House Royal Pier Road London DA12 2BG
Tel: 01474 562396 *Fax:* 01474 562398
E-mail: sally.mashiter@pola.co.uk
Sol: Mashiter, Miss Sally D C LLB Legal Adviser. . . . . *Nov 1979

PRESCRIPTION MEDICINES CODE OF PRACTICE AUTHORITY
12 Whitehall London SW1A 2DY
Tel: 020 7930 9677 *Fax:* 020 7930 4554
E-mail: info@pmcpa.org.uk
Sol: Logan, Ms Etta LLB Secretary to the ANCPA . . . . *Oct 1992

PRICEWATERHOUSECOOPERS LLP
Plumtree Court London EC4A 4HT
Tel: 020 7583 5000 *Fax:* 020 7822 4652
Sol: Humphries, Mrs Caroline BA Solicitor . . . . . *Nov 1989

PRISONERS' ADVICE SERVICE
PO Box 46199 London EC1M 4XA
Tel: 020 7253 3323
E-mail: admin@prisoneradvice.demon.co.uk
Sol: Collins, Ms Nancy Senior Solicitor. . . . . Sep 2000
Dean, Miss Victoria BA Solicitor. . . . . Sep 1998

PRUDENTIAL PLC
Group Legal Services Laurence Pountney Hill London EC4R 0HH
Tel: 020 7220 7588 *Dx:* 138761 CHEAPSIDE 2 *Fax:* 020 7548 3886
Sol: Bish, Mr Thomas Gregory LLB; LLM Legal Adviser . *May 1973
Bothamley, Mr Ian Antony LLB Legal Adviser . . . . *May 2003
Drew, Ms Anita BA(Hons)(Oxon) Senior Legal Adviser *Nov 1995
Green, Mr David G LLB(Lond) Senior Legal Adviser. . *Oct 1982
Griffith, Miss Shan Mary LLB Senior Legal Adviser . . *Apr 1978
Higgins, Mr David C BA Senior Legal Adviser . . . . *Jul 1981
Maynard, Mr Peter Martin MA(Cantab) Director, Group Legal Services . . . . . *Apr 1977
Wilson, Mr Malcolm George William MA(Oxon) Legal Adviser . . . . . *Feb 1982

PUBLIC AND COMMERCIAL SERVICES UNION
160 Falcon Road London SW11 2LN
Tel: 020 7924 2727 *Fax:* 020 7924 1847
Sol: Wiles, Mrs Emma K LLB(Hons) Director of Legal Services . . . . . *Dec 1990

THE REALLY USEFUL GROUP LTD
22 Tower Street London WC2H 9NS
Tel: 020 7240 0880 *Fax:* 020 7240 1204
E-mail: hullj@reallyuseful.co.uk
Sol: Hull, Mr Jonathan Philip Charles BA(Dunelm) Group Legal Director. . . . . *Nov 1988

REED EXECUTIVE PLC
Academy Court 94 Chancery Lane London WC2A 1DT
Tel: 020 7421 1640 *Fax:* 020 7421 1641
Sol: Abernethy, Mr Andrew James Solicitor. . . . . Dec 2007
Edmunds, Ms Joan LLB Group Legal Adviser . . . . *Nov 1975
Grimsdale, Miss Sally L Group Property Solicitor . . *Sep 1981
Hanson, Miss Elizabeth Josephine LLB Solicitor. . . . Mar 2005
Saayman, Mr Kobus BComm; LLB Solicitor . . . . . Jul 2003
Yuen, Siu F LLB(Hons) Assistant Group Solicitor . . . Oct 1996

RENTOKIL INITIAL PLC
Portland House Bressenden Place London SW1E 5BH
Tel: 020 7592 2700 *Fax:* 020 7592 2800
Sol: Brown, Mr Gareth T LLB(Manc) UK Company Secretary . . . . . *Jan 1983
Ward-Jones, Mr Robert TD LLB(Bris) Group Secretary *Jun 1971

See p2 for the Key to Work Categories & other symbols

REUTERS GROUP PLC
The Reuters Building South Colonnade Canary Wharf London E14 5EP
Tel: 020 7250 1122 *Fax:* 020 7542 5896
Sol: Fitt, Ms Catherine BA(Hons)(History); CPE; LSF Principal Legal Counsel. . . . *Mar 1997
Forbes, Miss Sonya LLB; BA Senior Legal Counsel . . Sep 1999
Martin, Miss Rosemary E S BA; MBA General Counsel & Company Secretary. . . . *Oct 1985
Murphy, Mrs Joanna L LLB(Hons) Principal Legal Counsel . . . *Oct 1998
Reisenthel, Miss Annick L E LLB(Lond); Maitrise De Droit Francais et Anglais Principal Legal Counsel. . . . Oct 1989
Rowsell, Ms Catherine Anne LLB; BA; Attorney of High Court Of South Africa. Senior Legal Counsel . . . May 2001
Whitehead, Ms Kirsty BA Principal Legal Counsel . . . Nov 1994

RIO TINTO PLC
2 Eastbourne Terrace London W2 6LG
Tel: 020 7781 2000 *Fax:* 020 7781 1800
E-mail: charles.lawton@riotinto.com
Sol: Ferguson, Miss Audrey J LLB; BA Solicitor . . . *Jun 1994
Lane, Mr Timothy Andrew LLB; BSc(Australia); LLM(UK) Legal Counsel. . . . May 2000
Lawton, Mr Charles H H Legal Adviser & Head of Legal Department . . . *Nov 1970
Lumley-Smith, Mr Adrian LLB Solicitor. . . . *Sep 1987
Rumsby, Mrs Sarah Louise BA(Law) Solicitor . . . Feb 1999
Walker, Mrs Sandra MA(Cantab) Solicitor . . . *Oct 1976

THE ROYAL BANK OF SCOTLAND
Waterhouse Square 138-142 Holborn London EC1N 2TH
Tel: 020 7427 8000
Sol: Jones, Mr Peter A P Solicitor . . . Mar 1968

THE ROYAL BOROUGH OF KENSINGTON & CHELSEA
Room 235/1 Town Hall Hornton Street London W8 7NX
Tel: 020 7361 2741 *Dx:* 84015 KENSINGTON HIGH STREET 2
Fax: 020 7361 3488
E-mail: margaret.mckeogh@rbkc.gov.uk
Sol: Allsup, Miss Claire Caroline BA(Hons); LPC Solicitor . Jul 1999
Biginton, Mr William Gary Solicitor. . . . *Feb 2001
Bradley, Mr Warren Spencer BA(Hons) Senior Solicitor Jul 1999
Edila, Ms Gifty LLB; LLM Director of Law and Administration . . . *Apr 1998
Grant, Ms Janet Senior Solicitor. . . . *May 1992
Jaskowiak, Mr Andre M Solicitor. . . . *Dec 1990
Le Masurier, Mrs Lindsey Catherine LLB Solicitor . . *Mar 2000
Lehane, Miss Anne B LLB Solicitor . . . *Aug 1988
Mariani, Mr Steven Gerard BA Solicitor . . . *Apr 1994
Parbat, Mr Vijay BA; LLM Assistant Solicitor. . . . May 2004
Parker, Ms Leverne S LLB Chief Solicitor . . . *Apr 1990
Ryan, Mr Bartholemew BA Principal Solicitor . . . *May 1994
Salisbury, Miss Hazel LLB(Hons) Solicitor. . . . *Aug 1999
Titcombe, Miss Heidi S C LLB(Hons) Solicitor. . . . *Jun 1989
Vachino, Ms Cynthia LLB; LPC Solicitor. . . . Aug 1996
Walker, Mr David K B MA(Cantab) Principal Solicitor *May 1981

ROYAL COLLEGE OF NURSING
20 Cavendish Square London W1G 0RN
Tel: 020 7409 3333 *Dx:* 53800 OXFORD CIRCUS NORTH
Fax: 020 7647 3404
Sol: Bernhard, Mr Richard C LLB Director of Legal Services . . . *Jan 1980
Blundy, Mr Patrick H Solicitor . . . *Nov 1983
Caulfield, Ms Helen M A LLB; MA Solicitor . . . *Nov 1986
Richmond, Mr Howard R BA(Dunelm) Deputy Director Legal Services . . . *Dec 1978
Shiels, Mrs Mary C BA Solicitor. . . . *Feb 1984

ROYAL MAIL GROUP
100 Victoria Embankment London EC4V 0HQ
Tel: 020 7250 2468
Sol: Andrews, Miss Katherine M J LLB Senior Solicitor. . *Nov 1988
Berridge, Miss Victoria E L LLB Solicitor. . . . *May 1979
Branson, Mr Caspar R MA(Hons) Senior Lawyer . . . *Sep 1995
Canton, Mr Philip M BSc Senior Lawyer. . . . *Dec 1995
Cheetham, Mr John L R Senior Legal Adviser. . . . *Dec 1977
Churchard, Mrs Catherine H LLB Solicitor. . . . Jun 1976
Haldane, Ms Liesl K BA; LLB; QLTT Senior Lawyer . . Jan 1999
Lyng, Miss Toni Solicitor. . . . *Jun 1991
McFarlane, Miss Juliet A LLM(Lond); DipLaw Solicitor. *Apr 1987
Madron, Ms Jessica M L BA(Oxon) Solicitor. . . . *Oct 1985
Martin, Miss Debra Jane LLB(Hons) Senior Lawyer . *Sep 1996
Mirwitch, Mr Joseph S LLM Solicitor. . . . *§Nov 1972
Poole, Mr David BA(Hons) Lawyer . . . Nov 1998
Sherrott, Mrs Susan N BA(Cantab) Solicitor. . . . *Jul 1983
Singh, Jarnail BSc Senior Lawyer. . . . Dec 1992
Talbot, Miss Mandy LLM; BSc(Bris)(Econ) Solicitor . *Nov 1987
Wilson, Mr Robert G BA Solicitor . . . Oct 1980
Winship, Mrs Joanne C BSc(Hons) Senior Lawyer. . *Nov 1996
Wyles, Mrs Brigid M LLB Senior Lawyer. . . . *May 1993

JAMES RUBINSTEIN & CO
149 Cholmley Gardens Mill Lane London NW6 1AB
Tel: 020 7431 5500 *Fax:* 020 7431 5600
E-mail: jr@jamesrubinstein.co.uk
Sol: Rubinstein, Mr James Richard LLB . . . *Oct 1988

J SAINSBURY PLC
33 Holborn London EC1N 2HT
Tel: 020 7695 6000 *Fax:* 020 7695 7610
Sol: Robertson, Mr George BSc; LLB Senior Legal Officer *Mar 1985

THE SALVATION ARMY
International Headquarters 101 Queen Victoria Street London EC4P 4EP
Tel: 020 7236 5222 *Fax:* 020 7236 6272
Sol: Smith, Capt Peter J M Legal & Parliamentary Secretary to the Salvation Army . . . *Jul 1970

SANPAOLO IMI SPA
6th Floor Warwick Court Paternoster Square London EC4M 7LZ
Tel: 020 7214 8000 *Fax:* 020 7236 2698
Sol: Boyd, Mr Nigel LLB; BA Legal Advisor. . . . Jan 1999
Davis, Mr Jeremy Elliott BSc(Banking & Int'l Finance); LLM Head of Legal, Area Europe. . . . *Sep 1997
Innes, Mr Hamish John Mackenzie LLB; MA(Cantab) Legal Advisor Coolum Surft Lifesaving Bronze Medallion Jul 1998

THE SCOUT ASSOCIATION
Gilwell Park Chingford London E4 7QW
Tel: 020 8433 7178 *Fax:* 020 8433 7184
E-mail: trust.corporation@scout.org.uk
Sol: Hinton, Mr David L LLB(Hons); DipLP Head of Legal Services . . . *Jul 1998

SEA CONTAINERS SERVICES LTD
Sea Containers House 20 Upper Ground Blackfriars London SE1 9PF
Tel: 020 7805 5202 *Fax:* 020 7805 5912
Sol: Huck, Ms Janet M BA Manager Legal Services . . . *Nov 1985

SEMA GROUP UK LTD
4 Triton Square London NW1 3HG
Tel: 020 7830 4213 *Fax:* 020 7830 4206
E-mail: andrew.vos@sema.co.uk
Sol: Corder, Mrs Rachel Anne Solicitor. . . . Mar 1994
Thomas, Mr Mark R Solicitor . . . *§Nov 1991
Wilson, Mr David Ian LLB(B'ham) . . . *Oct 1990

SERIOUS FRAUD OFFICE
Elm House 10-16 Elm Street London WC1X 0BJ
Tel: 020 7239 7272 *Dx:* 135896 LONDON GRAY'S INN ROAD
Fax: 020 7837 1689
E-mail: public.enquiries@sfo.gsi.gov.uk
Sol: Adjepong, Mr Kwadjo LLB(Hons) Solicitor. . . . Apr 1998
Donnabella, Miss Rosemary LLB Solicitor. . . . Jul 1999
More, Mr Graham R MA(Hons) Assistant Director, SFO Oct 1984
Shaw, Ms Claire LLB(Hons); LSF Case Controller. . . Nov 1991
Wilson, Mr Anthony R MA(Oxon)(Jurisprudence) Lawyer . . . Oct 1981

SHELL INTERNATIONAL LTD
Shell Centre York Road London SE1 7NA
Tel: 020 7934 1234 *Dx:* 473 LONDON/CHANCERY LN
Fax: 020 7934 3023
E-mail: l.dalsgaard@shell.com
Sol: Anatogu, Mrs Helen Chineze LLB; BL; LLM Legal Counsel . . . Aug 2004
Ashworth, Mr Michael J LLB(Hons) Senior Legal Counsel . . . *Jun 1987
Bambridge, Mr Martin Edward LLB Associate General Counsel . . . *Jan 1988
Banks, Roscoe S BA; LLB Senior Legal Counsel . . . *Jul 2000
Batey, Miss Janet LLB(Manc) Senior Legal Counsel. *Dec 1989
Berkovitz, Ms Justine Legal Counsel . . . Dec 1994
Blum, Ms Barbara F M Legal Counsel. . . . *Sep 1992
Busby, Mrs Julia Ann LLB(Exon); LSF Legal Counsel . *Oct 1985
Buxton, Mr Edward BSc(Hons) Legal Counsel. . . . Dec 1994
Cameron, Mr Jacob Thomas BA(Oxon) Legal Counsel*Sep 2002
Campailla, Mr Nicholas T LLB Senior Legal Counsel . *Apr 1988
Cardozo, Mr Hugh David MA Legal Counsel. . . . Mar 1993
Cheong, Mr Kah Wai LLB(Hons); LLM(Cantab) Legal Counsel . . . *Jul 1999
Crawford, Miss Ruth A MA Training & Know How Counsel . . . *Nov 1987
Crompton, Miss Joanne H LLB Senior Legal Counsel . Nov 1987
Dawson, Mrs Kim LLB Managing Counsel. . . . *Oct 1993
Dewey, Mr Adrian C MA(Cantab); MBA; DIC Legal Counsel . . . *Oct 1986
Eneberi, Mr Jeffrey BSc(Hons); DipLaw Solicitor / IP Counsel . . . Mar 1999
English, Mr Charles Warwick Foster Senior Legal Counsel . . . *Feb 1974
Evans, Ms Georgina LLB; Solicitor; Registered Trade Attorney Head of Trade Marks . . . Jan 1992
Goodall, Miss Sian LLB(Hons)(Euro) Senior Legal Counsel . . . *Feb 2000
Grayson, Mr Bob BA Senior In-House Counsel . . . Jun 1989
Green, Mr Michael J LLB Senior Legal Counsel. . . *Dec 1975
Griffin, Mr James BA(Exeter)(Arabic & Islamic Studies) Legal Counsel. . . . Nov 1995
Griffiths, Mr Matthew D BSc Legal Counsel . . . *Sep 1993
Hawkins, Mrs Karin J LLB(Bris) Senior Legal Counsel *Dec 1986
Henderson, Mr Robert Joseph LLB; LLM UK Head of Legal . . . Sep 1992
Heslop, Ms Karen BA(Hons)(Bris) Legal Counsel . . . Sep 1999
Kachikwu, Mirian LLB; BL; PhD Legal Counsel . . . *Jan 2000
Kennedy Harper, Mr Tristram John LLM; MBA Senior Legal Counsel. . . . Sep 1995
Lamb, Miss Susan BSc; MSc Group Records Manager . . . *Nov 1992
Lancaster, Ms Nicola Joy BA(Hons)(Cantab) Senior Legal Counsel. . . . Jan 1997
Lane, Mrs Nicola BSc; CPE Legal Counsel . . . *Nov 2002
Lawlor, Mr Christopher Senior Legal Counsel . . . *Oct 1996
Loughlin, Miss Helen BA(Hons); LLM Legal Counsel . Nov 2002
Lowe, Ms Brigid BA; DipLaw Managing Counsel, Supply & Distribution . . . Feb 1994
McCree, Ms Cheryl BA(Hons) Senior Legal Counsel, IP Nov 1993
Morony, Mr Matthew L BA(Dunelm) Legal Counsel . . Oct 1992
Murphy, Mr David F MA(Cantab) Legal Counsel. . . *Dec 1979
Osborne, Mr Andrew Legal Counsel. . . . Oct 1990
Palmer, Miss Victoria LLB; LSF Legal Counsel . . . Sep 1992
Parsons, Mr Michael Rupert BA(Hons) Associate Counsel . . . Jan 1990
Pocock, Miss Emma Victoria LLB Legal Counsel . . . Sep 2004
Reader, Ms Clare LLB(Sheff); LSF Legal Counsel. . . *Apr 1992
Riley, Mrs T Anne LLB(Hons) Meredith Ray & Littler; RWSTEAD (Junior & Senior Scholarship); R G Lawson Prize for Conflicts of Law & English Panel System Associate General Counsel Antitrust . . . *Oct 1985
Rouse, Mr Philip Dobson MA(Oxon) Senior Legal Advisor . . . Sep 1980
Ruddock, Mr Keith A BA(Cantab) General Counsel Exploration and Production . . . *Nov 1986
Shannon, Ms Moira E MA(Cantab)(Law) Senior Legal Counsel . . . *Jan 1987
Skinner, Mr Paul Andrew LLB; PGDip Legal Counsel, IP . . . *Mar 2006
Smith, Mr Michael William BA Legal Counsel . . . *Oct 1982
Sparrow, Mr Andrew James MA(Oxon) Legal Counsel. *Oct 1992
Symes, Mr Benedick MA(Cantab) Senior Legal Counsel IP . . . Sep 1996
Tanner, Mr Paul Martyn Roger MA(Oxon) Senior Legal Counsel . . . Sep 1998
Taylor, Mr Howard C LLB Associate Legal Counsel . . *Jun 1977
Taylor, Miss Joanne BA Legal Counsel . . . *Sep 1992
Tugal, Dr Bulent BSc(Hons); PhD Legal Counsel . . . May 2003
Uglow, Ms Susannah BA(Hons) Legal Manager, Shell E & P Ireland . . . *Dec 1991
Ward, Ms Alexandra BA Legal Counsel . . . *Sep 1995
Ware, Mr Timothy G LLB Legal Counsel. . . . *Apr 1973
Wiseman, Mr Richard M General Counsel M& A and Project Finance. . . . *Dec 1974

SHELTER LEGAL SERVICES
88 Old Street London EC1V 9HU
Tel: 020 7505 2000 *Fax:* 020 7505 2168
Sol: Antoniades, Mr Nikos LLB Solicitor . . . May 1994
Gallagher, Mr John D MA Senior Solicitor . . . *May 1976
Joshi, Ms Uma BA(Hons) Solicitor. . . . May 1999
Morshead, Ms Sally P A BA Senior Solicitor. . . . *Nov 1993
Parkinson, Mr Nigel BA(Hons) Solicitor . . . Jan 1994
Parmar, Ms Rita LLB . . . Apr 2000
Parry, Mr Michael Adam BA(Hons); CPE; LSF Solicitor Nov 1992
Sephton, Ms Claire . . . Jan 1991
Storer, Ms Carol Anne BA(Dunelm) Solicitor. . . . *Oct 1983

SOCIETE GENERALE ASSET MANAGEMENT
9th Floor Exchange House Primrose Street London EC2A 2EF
Tel: 020 7090 2500
Sol: Guest, Mr Robert Austin BA(Oxon) Director of Legal & Compliance. . . . *Sep 1986
Redston, Mrs Sheila L LLB(Lond); ACIS Legal & Compliance Officer . . . *Nov 1985

SOLICITORS DISCIPLINARY TRIBUNAL
3rd Floor Gate House 1 Farrington Street London EC4M 7NS
Tel: 020 7329 4808 *Dx:* 395 LONDON/CHANCERY LN
Fax: 020 7329 4833
E-mail: enquiries@solicitorsolt.com
Sol: Elson, Mrs Susan Caroline SDT Traffic & Parking Adjudicator; Immigration Adjudicator. . . . *§Dec 1970

SONY MUSIC ENTERTAINMENT (UK) LTD
Bedford House 69-79 Fulham High Street London SW6 3JW
Tel: 020 7384 7500
Sol: Sternberg, Mr Jonathan BA(Kent) Director Legal Affairs . . . *Apr 1979

SOUTH WESTERN MAGISTRATES COURT
176a Lavender Hill London SW11 1JU
Tel: 020 7805 1447 *Dx:* 58559 CLAPHAM JUNCTION
Fax: 020 7805 1448
Sol: Smith, Miss Susan Clare Dip ML Legal Adviser . . . *Jan 2002

LONDON BOROUGH OF SOUTHWARK
PO Box 64529 London SE1P 5LX
Tel: 020 7525 5000
Sol: Blackburn, Mr Gavin Allen BScEcon(Hons) . . . Jul 2004
Boateng, Amma. . . . Jan 1996
Bradbury, Nicola . . . Jan 2001
Campbell, Miss Margaret E LLB(Hons) Legal Officer Social Services . . . *Nov 1992
Dodson, Margaret. . . . Sep 1998
Easty, Ms Gillian M LLB Legal Officer Social Services *Mar 1984
Emore, Mrs Kate . . . Jul 2000
Fashola, Ms Nikki Legal Officer Employment Law . . . Mar 1997
Gbadamosi, Gafar. . . . Nov 2005
Gooch, Ms Deborah A LLB Solicitor. . . . Sep 1989
Grimshaw, Cathryn . . . Oct 1995
Hilson, Caroline. . . . Jul 2000
Hughes-Young, Carol . . . Sep 2004
Jeffery, Ms Gillian. . . . Nov 1997
Kar, Ms Chitra BSc(Hons)(Lond); LSF Principal Legal Officer Conveyancing. . . . *Feb 1988
McKoy, Rachel . . . Aug 2005
Micklewright, Ms Mary E Legal Officer. . . . Nov 1994
Morley, Justin. . . . Mar 2008
Mouton, Nicole . . . Jul 2006
Murray, Claudette. . . . Nov 2005
Oduyoye, Janet. . . . Apr 2003
Phillips, Mr D Gareth LLB(Soton) . . . *Apr 1982
Power, Miss Sarah C Legal Officer Social Services . *Dec 1985
Qureshi, Nazia . . . Sep 1999
Rechtman, Felix. . . . Oct 2001
Rose, Ms Maureen Legal Officer, General Litigation . Dec 1997
Stevens, Nagla . . . Jan 2005
Wright, Ms Melanie . . . Sep 2003

SPRINGFIELD ADVICE & LAW CENTRE
Admissions Block Springfield Uni Hospital 61 Glenburnie Road London SW17 7DJ
Tel: 020 8767 6884 *Fax:* 020 8767 6996
Sol: Baldwin, Miss Deborah Solicitor. . . . *Jul 1996
Roberts, Mr Jonathan David MA; BSc(Econ) Supervising Solicitor Appeals Service Tribunal Manager . . . *Jan 1999
Syed, Mrs Naaz Solicitor . . . *Jan 2000

STANDARD CHARTERED BANK
1 Aldermanbury Square London EC2V 7SB
Tel: 020 7457 7500 *Fax:* 020 7280 7112
Sol: Bacon, Mr Dominic C LLB Solicitor Member of C& I Group . . . *Oct 1989
Brimacombe, Mr David J MA Solicitor. . . . *May 1985

SUMITOMO MITSUI BANKING CORPORATION EUROPE LIMITED
99 Queen Victoria Street London EC4V 4EH
Tel: 020 7786 1000 / 1017 *Fax:* 020 7236 0049
Sol: Edwards, Mr Sean W LLB Legal Counsel Europe . . *Nov 1988
Martyn, Mr C Philip LLB General Counsel - Europe . *§Mar 1972
Pattman, Mr Nicholas Edward John MA Legal Counsel Europe . . . *Mar 2003

SVENSKA HANDELSBANKEN AB (PUBL) LONDON
Trinity Tower 9 Thomas More Street London E1W 1GE
Tel: 020 7578 8115 *Fax:* 020 7578 8442
Sol: Hankey, Mr Martin MA(Cantab) Legal & Compliance. . *Oct 1968

SWISS RE LIFE & HEALTH LTD
30 St Mary Axe London EC3A 8EP
Tel: 020 7933 3000 *Fax:* 020 7933 5000
E-mail: maryobrien@swissre.com
Sol: Buttle, Mr Richard A LLB(Hons) Legal Services Manager . . . *Nov 1973
O'Brien, Miss Mary F BA Solicitor. . . . *May 1980

TATE & LYLE PLC
Sugar Quay Lower Thames Street London EC3R 6DQ
Tel: 020 7626 6525
Sol: Corrigan, Miss Alyson Jane LLB; LSF Solicitor . . . *Nov 1990
Gibber, Mr Robert A BA General Counsel . . . Dec 1988
Wright, Mr Andrew J MSc; LLB Commercial Lawyer. . *Jun 1975

TAYLOR NELSON SOFRES PLC
AGB House Westgate London W5 1UA
Tel: 020 8967 4348 *Fax:* 020 8967 4058
E-mail: john.stobart@tnsofres.com

Sol: Bateson, Mr David J LLB Solicitor. . . . . *Sep 1989
Wright, Mr Paul Simon Kent BA; MA(Oxon) Solicitor. *Sep 1984

TELEGRAPH MEDIA GROUP
111 Buckingham Palace Road London SW1W 0DT
Tel: 020 7931 3131
Sol: Braybrook, Ms Julia M BA(Cantab) Solicitor . . . . . . *Jun 1974
Lindsay, Mr Richard BA(Hons) Group Legal Director. . *Jan 1996
Playford, Mrs Sharon LLB Assistant Solicitor . . . . . *Jan 2001

TELENT PLC
New Century Park PO Box 53 London CV3 1HJ
Tel: 024 7656 2000 *Fax:* 024 7656 7000
Sol: McGeever, Miss Claire BA(Hons); CPE; LPC Senior Contract & Legal Manager . . . . *§Oct 1999

TIMES NEWSPAPERS LTD
1 Pennington Street London E1 9XN
Tel: 020 7782 5858 *Fax:* 020 7782 5860
Sol: Brett, Mr Alastair J MA(Oxon) Solicitor. . . . . *Oct 1975

TOTTENHAM HOTSPUR PLC
748 High Road London N17 0AP
Tel: 020 8365 5023 *Fax:* 020 8365 5022
Sol: Ireland, Mr John LLB Solicitor. . . . . *Sep 1982

TREASURY SOLICITORS DEPARTMENT
7th Floor One Kemble Street London WC2B 4TS
Tel: 020 7210 3000 *Dx:* 123242 KINGSWAY *Fax:* 020 7210 3004
Sol: Aries, Mr John Dudley SCS . . . . Jan 1970
Ash, Mr Nicholas SCS . . . . Sep 1986
Ashford, Mr Christopher R LLB Solicitor (Grade 6). . *Oct 1982
Babar, Mrs Diana Solicitor (SCS) . . . . *Jul 1995
Barlow, Ms Kathryn Elizabeth Grade 6 Lawyer. . . . *Oct 1989
Barry, Ms Roisin Solicitor (Grade 6) . . . . *Oct 1991
Bennett, Mr Peter J LLB(Lond) Solicitor (SCS) . . . . *Oct 1984
Beresford, Mr Nicholas Grade 7 Lawyer. . . . . Sep 1999
Bowman, Ms Caroline Harriet Grade 6 Lawyer. . . . . Apr 1994
Brown, Miss Charlotte Grade 7 Lawyer . . . . Sep 1994
Brummell, Mr David Director (SCS) . . . . Sep 1973
Brunsdon, Mr Paul A LLB(Leeds) Solicitor (Grade 6) . *Jun 1971
Brzezina, Miss Siobhan J Solicitor (Grade 7) . . . . . *Oct 1987
Chapman, Mr Adam P Solicitor (SCS). . . . . *Nov 1987
Charan, Ms Paramjit Kaur BA Grade 7 Lawyer . . . *Nov 1993
Chubb, Ms Alison BA Solicitor (Grade 6) . . . . *Sep 1988
Clarke, Mr Francis D W Solicitor (SCS) . . . . Dec 1974
Cochrane, Ms Susan Solicitor (SCS) . . . . Jun 1978
Collett, Mrs Vivienne Solicitor (SCS). . . . . Jun 1976
Collins, Mr John Edwin Solicitor (SCS) . . . . Dec 1965
Coopman, Mr Peter David Lawyer. . . . . Dec 1969
Corrigan, Mrs Anne Vanessa Grade 7 Lawyer. . . . . Apr 1997
Cribb, Mrs Jacqueline Grade 7 Lawyer . . . . May 2000
Crowe, Ms Alison Jane Ramsey Grade 6 Lawyer . . . Nov 1987
Cull, Mr Peter G MA(Cantab) Solicitor (Grade 6). . . *Apr 1981
Dann, Ms Linda M BA(Cardiff) Solicitor (Grade 6) . . . *Oct 1985
Das, Ms Shanta Lawyer (Casual) . . . . *Jul 2000
Davies, Miss Carol J LLB Solicitor (Grade 6) . . . . . Dec 1980
Denton, Mr Zane William LPC Grade 7 Lawyer . . . . Sep 1999
Devitt, Mr Stephen John Grade 6 Lawyer . . . . Oct 1989
Evans, Mr John Trevor Solicitor (Grade 6). . . . . . . Nov 1994
Fitzgerald, Mr Michael E LLB(Lond) Solicitor (Grade 6) *Apr 1974
Gajjar, Neera Solicitor (Grade 6) . . . . Nov 1989
Garner, Mrs Michelle A LLB Solicitor (Grade 6) . . . . *Nov 1985
Garner-Patel, Miss Amanda M S LLB Solicitor (Grade 6) . . . . *Jan 1994
Gbejuade, Miss Hilda Oluremi Omolara LPC Grade 7 Lawyer . . . . Oct 1998
Geist-Divver, Ms Carola Grade 6 Lawyer . . . . . . *Dec 1992
Giles, Mr Hugh Peter SCS . . . . Sep 1991
Gleed, Mr David Solicitor (Grade 6) . . . . Jul 1975
Grant, Mr Charles Edward Legal Officer. . . . . Sep 1997
Griffiths, Mrs Nicola LLB Solicitor (Grade 7). . . . . . *Oct 1992
Halnan, Ms Penelope Ann BA; Dip(Local Govt Law & Practice) Grade 6 Lawyer. . . . . *Oct 1993
Harker, Mr Simon T Solicitor (SCS) . . . . Apr 1981
Heilpern, Mrs Anya E BA(Oxon) Solicitor (Grade 6) . *Feb 1986
Henderson, Miss Phinella F LLB; Cert Air & Space Law; Dip ECLaw SCS . . . . Oct 1982
Herberg, Mr Lucan G Grade 6 Lawyer. . . . . *Nov 1994
Hiles, Miss Sharon Grade 7 Lawyer. . . . . Sep 2000
Hill, Ms Jane Elisabeth Solicitor (Grade 6). . . . . . . Dec 1994
Holloway, Mr Nicholas Charles LLB(B'ham) Grade 7 Lawyer . . . . Sep 1988
Howard, Mr Stuart David Grade 6 Lawyer . . . . Oct 1994
Jarret, Ms Amanda Gwyneth Solicitor (Grade 6). . . . Dec 1994
John, Ms Helen Solicitor. . . . . Dec 1992
Johnstone, Mr Andrew R Solicitor (Grade 7). . . . . . Oct 1986
Jones, Mrs Joanne Solicitor (Grade 6). . . . . Sep 1995
Jones, Miss Victoria Ann Grade 7 Lawyer . . . . Sep 1995
Kaye, Mrs Victoria Claire Grade 7 Lawyer. . . . . . . Dec 1996
Kennedy, Miss Catherine M Solicitor (Grade 6) . . . . Oct 1987
Kennedy, Mr William Campbell Grade 6 Lawyer. . . . Sep 1994
Lane, Miss Emma C P Solicitor (Grade 6). . . . . Jun 1991
Latham, Mr Edward D A Solicitor (Grade 7) . . . . . . Sep 1997
Law, Miss Samantha LPC Grade 7 Lawyer . . . . . . *Aug 1997
Lawton, Mr Anthony D Solicitor (SCS). . . . . Feb 1969
Letwin, Ms Isabel G Solicitor (Director) (SCS) . . . . . Apr 1981
Lightman, Ms Susan R I LLB Solicitor (Grade 6). . . *Dec 1985
Loosley, Mr Peter R Grade 7 Lawyer . . . . *Nov 1991
McDonald, Mr Adrian C Solicitor (Grade 6) . . . . . . Oct 1991
McKay, Mr Barrie J Solicitor (SCS) . . . . *Sep 1985
McNally, Ms Margaret Solicitor (Grade 6) . . . . Dec 1986
Magrill, Mrs Rachel V Solicitor (Grade 6) . . . . Dec 1990
Marcus, Ms Katheryn Solicitor (Grade 7) . . . . Apr 1997
Martin, Mr Sean E BA(Oxon) Solicitor (Grade 6). . . . Nov 1990
Messer, Mr Peter R Solicitor (SCS) . . . . *Sep 1973
Miller, Mrs Caroline Solicitor (Grade 6) . . . . Feb 1985
Miller, Mr Robert Solicitor (Grade 6). . . . . Nov 1985
Morris, Mr Jonathan Solicitor (Grade 6) . . . . Jul 1992
Nicoll, Miss Lindsey Solicitor (SCS). . . . . Mar 1993
North, Ms Sarah M BA(Hons); CPE Solicitor (Grade 6) Sep 1994
O'Reilly, Mr John K Grade 6 Lawyer. . . . . *Jan 1982
Padwell, Miss Martine Solicitor (Grade 6) . . . . Mar 1993
Phillips, Mr Roland J Solicitor (SCS). . . . . Jun 1974
Quick, Miss Rachel Grade 6 Lawyer. . . . . Sep 1994
Ramnarine, Ms Jody A Solicitor (Grade 6). . . . . . . Oct 1991
Rawlings, Ms Deborah S BA(Cantab) Solicitor (Grade 6) . . . . Mar 1990
Ridout, Mr Arnold James SCS. . . . . Sep 1979
Robinson, Maise E Solicitor (Grade 6). . . . . Mar 1990
Ross, Mrs Grainne Solicitor (Grade 7). . . . . Sep 1992
Sandal, Mr Alan J Solicitor . . . . Nov 1970
Sims, Mr David Grade 7 Lawyer. . . . . *Apr 1981
Smith, Mrs Leslie K Solicitor (Grade 6) . . . . Oct 1997
Steele, Ms Sandra P LLB(Lond) Grade 7 Lawyer . . *Nov 1986
Sylvester, Miss Clare A BA Solicitor (Grade 6). . . . . Oct 1987
Thomas, Mr Michael Christopher Pryce Director (SCS) *Jun 1976
Truran, Mr Martin G Solicitor (Grade 6) . . . . Dec 1987
Turek, Mr Andrew T Solicitor (Grade 6) . . . . Oct 1977
Tuttle, Mr Graham J Solicitor (Grade 6) . . . . *Dec 1984
Walker, Mr David Christopher Grade 7 Lawyer. . . . . Jul 1999
Walkingshaw, Miss Fiona Margaret Anne Grade 7 Lawyer . . . . May 1996
Wallwork, Mrs Josephine Grade 7 Lawyer. . . . . . . Oct 1998
Whitehurst, Mr Peter F O SCS . . . . Dec 1972
Williams, Mr Peter David Grade 7 Lawyer. . . . . . . Oct 1994
Winton, Mr George Edward LPC Grade 7 Lawyer . . . Apr 1999
Wones, Miss Eleri C MA(Oxon) Solicitor (Grade 6) . . *Oct 1985
Wood, Mr Thomas W Solicitor (Grade 7) . . . . Jun 1994
Youdell, Mr John C BA Solicitor (Grade 6). . . . . . *Dec 1978

TRINITY MIRROR PLC
One Canada Square Canary Wharf London E14 5AP
Tel: 020 7293 3934 *Fax:* 020 7293 3613
Sol: Partington, Mr Marcus Solicitor . . . . *Oct 1989
Welsh, Ms Rachel Mary BA(Hons) Solicitor . . . . . . Dec 1996

UNILEVER PLC
Unilever House PO Box 68 Blackfriars London EC4P 4BQ
Tel: 020 7822 5252 *Fax:* 020 7822 5464
Sol: Dougal-Biggs, Miss Tonia LLB Solicitor . . . . *Nov 1993
Franklin, Ms Susan Ann LLB Solicitor . . . . Apr 1977
Hazell, Mr Richard C LLB Solicitor. . . . . *Nov 1992
Hinton, Miss Isobel BA(Cantab) Solicitor. . . . . . . Oct 1990
Kidley, Miss Rachel A BSc Solicitor . . . . *May 1991
Lagler, Mr Mark Solicitor. . . . . *Nov 1995
Leek, Mr Robert David LLB(Manc) Solicitor . . . . . . Oct 1990
Peat, Mr Andrew G M LLB Solicitor . . . . *Oct 1965
Williams, Mr Stephen G LLB General Counsel & Joint Secretary . . . . *Apr 1972

UNISON
Membership Legal Services 1 Mabledon Place London WC1H 9AJ
Tel: 020 7388 2366 *Fax:* 020 7387 1464
Sol: McKenna, Ms Bronwyn Mary LLB(B'ham) Director of Legal Services . . . . *Oct 1990

UNIVERSAL MUSIC
364-366 Kensington High Street London W14 8NS
Tel: 020 8910 5000
Sol: Antonini, Miss Lisa BA(Hons); CPE; LPC Business Affairs Manager . . . . Feb 1998
Damani, Mr Shamus Badru BA Business Affairs Manager . . . . *Oct 2003
Joy, Mr Matthew R BA Group Commercial Counsel . *Sep 1990
Kernick, Mr Paul Andrew LLB Business Affairs Director Jan 1992
Lindsay, Mr Simon Patrick BA(Hons) Business Affairs Executive . . . . Nov 2005

UNIVERSAL PICTURES INTERNATIONAL LTD
Prospect House 80-110 New Oxford Street London WC1A 1HB
Tel: 020 7079 6000 *Fax:* 020 7079 6500
E-mail: andrew.hall@nbcuni.com
Sol: Damon, Mr James . . . . Sep 2002
Hall, Mr Andrew N LLB(Hons); LSF SVP; Head of Legal & Business Affairs. . . . . Oct 1989
Laithwaite, Mrs Melanie. . . . . Oct 1998
Szyszko, Mr Peter Gregory Legal Adviser (Anti-Piracy) Sep 2000
Throssell, Mrs Joanna. . . . . Oct 2003
Walker, Miss Jacqueline. . . . . Sep 2001
Waterfield, Mr Philip Legal Adviser . . . . Sep 2002

UNIVERSITY AND COLLEGE UNION SOLICITORS OFFICE
Carlow Street London NW1 7LH
Tel: 020 7756 2500 *Fax:* 020 7756 2501
E-mail: solicitors@ucu.org.uk
Sol: Scott, Mr Michael K LLB(Wales) Solicitor . . . . . . *Feb 1981

VISA EUROPE
PO Box 39662 London W2 6WH
Tel: 020 7937 8111 *Fax:* 020 7937 0877
Sol: Harper, Mrs Sarah Elizabeth LLB; LPC; PGDipLaw Legal Advisor . . . . *Aug 2000
Fewkes, Mrs Christele Stephanie LLB; LLM; LPC Legal Advisor . . . . *Jan 1998
Hartnett, Mrs Annabel L BA(Hons) Vice President; Senior Legal Advisor . . . . Feb 1998
Pothos, Miss Mary BA; LLB; GCLP Legal Counsel . . Apr 2004
Stokes, Mr Hugh Richard BA; MPhil Senior Vice President . . . . *Nov 1993

W H SMITH PLC
180 Wardour Street London W1F 8FY
Tel: 020 7851 8809 *Fax:* 020 7851 8841
Sol: Havenhand, Miss Diana C MA(Oxon) Group Legal Manager . . . . *Nov 1994
Havenhand, Mr John B MA Group Legal Manager. . . Jan 1984
Houghton, Mr Ian BSc Director of Legal Services & Company Secretary . . . . *Oct 1992

WALTHAM FOREST MAGISTRATES' COURT
The Court House 1 Farnham Avenue Walthamstow London E17 4NX
Tel: 0845 601 3600 *Dx:* 124542 WALTHAM FOREST
Fax: 020 8527 9063
Sol: Cozens, Mr Peter F . . . . *Dec 1980

WANDSWORTH & MERTON LAW CENTRE LTD
101a Tooting High Street London SW17 0SU
Tel: 020 8767 2777 *Dx:* 58853 TOOTING SOUTH
Fax: 020 8767 2711
Sol: Jackson, Ms Amber C S Employment Solicitor. . . . . Jan 1993
Karavas, Ms Kathleen Solicitor . . . . Mar 1993
Macauley, Ms Bridget BA(Hons); CPE; LPC Solicitor . May 1998
Muriel-Sanchez, Mrs Maria Teresa MSc Solicitor . . . Jan 2000
O'Connor, Ms Gabrielle Juliet LLB Housing Solicitor. . Mar 1992
Tugbobo, Mrs Roseanne LLB; BL Solicitor Immigration Department. . . . . Jan 2001

LONDON BOROUGH OF WANDSWORTH
Administration Department The Town Hall Wandsworth High Street London SW18 2PU
Tel: 020 8871 6000 *Dx:* 59054 WANDSWORTH NORTH
Fax: 020 8871 7506
E-mail: legal@wandsworth.gov.uk
Sol: Beaumont, Mr Guy LLB Senior Assistant Solicitor . . . Aug 2004
Cooper, Mr Mark Joseph LLB(Hons); DipLP Assistant Solicitor . . . . Jan 2005
Hayward, Mr David S DMA Principal Solicitor (Social Services) . . . . *May 1981
Maimaris, Mr S Ray P Solr(Conveyancing Manager). . Jun 1973
Matharu, Miss Balbir BSc(Hons) Assistant Solicitor . . Aug 1999
Munnery, Mr Richard W Principal Solicitor (Property) . . Jul 1975
Novell, Mrs Sally A LLB(Bris) Assistant Borough Solicitor (Litigation) . . . . *Jun 1980
Pauw, Mr Kenneth Michael BA(Hons) Solicitor. . . . *Feb 1995
Phelps, Miss Lisa Rebecca Lesley BA(Hons) Assistant Solicitor . . . . *Dec 1997
Plank, Ms Courtney M BA Senior Solicitor (Social Services) . . . . *Feb 1987
Walker, Mr Martin B A BA; MSc; MBA Borough Solicitor . . . . *Mar 1979
White, Mr Clifford P LLB(Lond) Deputy Borough Solicitor . . . . *Apr 1988

MARY WARD LEGAL CENTRE
26-27 Boswell Street London WC1N 3JZ
Tel: 020 7831 7079 *Dx:* 35700 BLOOMSBURY *Fax:* 020 7831 5431
Sol: Burns, Ms Alison . . . . *Feb 1987
Dalton, Mr Christopher BA Solicitor . . . . Oct 1979
Newth, Ms Isabel S Solicitor. . . . . Dec 1981
Pearce, Ms Sarah H BA(Hons); LLM Solicitor . . . . . Oct 1990
Roots, Mr Michael BA Solicitor . . . . Jan 1994
Wiggins, Mr John David Langdon BA Solicitor. . . . . Nov 1990

WARNER BROS
Warner House 98 Theobalds Road London WC1X 8WB
Tel: 020 7984 5000 *Fax:* 020 7984 5001
Sol: Senat, Mr Rick LLB(Lond) Head of Business Affairs . . *Jan 1982

THE WATER COMPANIES ASSOCIATION
1 Queen Anne's Gate London SW1H 9BT
Tel: 020 7222 0644 *Fax:* 020 7222 3366
Sol: Swallow, Mr Michael A LLB(Lond) Director & Secretary *Jul 1969

WEST OF ENGLAND INSURANCE SERVICES (LUXEMBOURG)
Tower Bridge Court 224 Tower Bridge Road London SE1 2UP
Tel: 020 7716 6000 *Fax:* 020 7716 6100
Sol: South, Mr Christopher G BA(Law) Solicitor . . . . . . Apr 1981

WESTMINSTER CITY COUNCIL
City Hall 64 Victoria Street London SW1E 6QP
Tel: 020 7641 6000 *Dx:* 2310 VICTORIA *Fax:* 020 7641 3325
Sol: Bhela, Mrs Harjinder Kaur LLB(Hons) Solicitor. . . . . Feb 1993
Burden, Miss Linda D LLB Principal Solicitor. . . . . *Nov 1982
Castledine, Ms Christine BA(Hons)(Wales); DipLib(Lond) Senior Licensing Solicitor. . . . . *Nov 1993
Cutts, Ms Helen V LLB Principal Solicitor . . . . . . *Jun 1979
Davies, Ms Rhian BA(Econ). . . . . *Sep 1992
Gopeesingh, Ms Gitanjali LLB; PGDip Solicitor . . . . Jan 2003
Greenwood, Miss Helen Diana BA(Hons); LLM Solicitor . . . . *Dec 1992
Lambie, Ms Monique LLB Solicitor. . . . . Oct 2001
Large, Mr Peter G LLB(Hons) Deputy Director of Legal Services . . . . *Oct 1980
Nixon, Mr Peter J M MA(Cantab) Principal Solicitor . . *Apr 1979
Panto, Mr Barry N BA(Hons); Dip(Local Govt Law) Senior Assistant Solicitor; Advocate . . . . *Nov 1985
Sutton, Ms Noreen H BA Assistant Solicitor . . . . . *Dec 1989
Thain, Ms Karen A BA Senior Assistant Solicitor. . . *Feb 1988
Wilson, Mr Colin T LLB; MCMA Director of Legal and Administrative Services . . . . *Oct 1982

CITY OF WESTMINSTER MAGISTRATES' COURT
70 Horseferry Road London SW1P 2AX
Tel: 020 7805 1008 *Dx:* 120551 VICTORIA 6 *Fax:* 020 7805 1193
Sol: Bryer, Mr Jeffrey S LLB(Lond). . . . . *Jan 1984

WHITBREAD PLC
Houghton Hall Business Park London LU5 5XE
Tel: 01582 424200 *Fax:* 01582 889416
Sol: Barratt, Mr Simon C BA(Oxon) Company Secretary . . *Oct 1985
Fairhurst, Mr Russell W LLB(Sheff) Sheffield Law Senior Prize Group Legal Adviser . . . . *Oct 1988
Msimang, Ms Tanya L MA Solicitor . . . . Sep 1996

WILLS GROUP LTD
Ten Trinity Square London EC3P 3AX
Tel: 020 7488 8111 *Fax:* 020 7481 7183
E-mail: goodingeo@willis.com
Sol: Andrea, Mr Philip LLB Senior Counsel. . . . . *Nov 1992
Bolton-Jones, Mrs Marie Anastasia LLB Solicitor . . *Aug 2002
Butterfield, Mr Geoffrey BA(Hons) Corporate Counsel. Sep 1996
Goodinge, Mr Oliver Hew Wallinger LLB(Soton) General Counsel UK. . . . . *Nov 1984
O'Rourke, Miss Kirsten LLB(Hons) Solicitor . . . . . *Jan 2003
Oakley, Ms Berenise Anne BA; LLB; DipEd University Medal Solicitor. . . . . *Feb 2003
Pead, Mr Nick BA(Hons) Solicitor . . . . Sep 2001
Stenson, Miss Fiona Patricia LLB(Hons) Solicitor . . *Sep 2000
Thomson-Hall, Miss Pamela LLB(Hons) Deputy General Counsel, UK . . . . *Nov 1993
Walters, Ms Shirley LLB(Hons) Solicitor. . . . . . . *May 1996
Williamson, Mr Michael David Solicitor. . . . . Nov 2001
Young, Ms Jane K LLB Solicitor. . . . . *Oct 1993

WIMBLEDON MAGISTRATES COURT
The Law Courts Alexandra Road Wimbledon London SW19 7JP
Tel: 020 8946 8622 *Dx:* 116610 WIMBLEDON 4
Fax: 020 8946 7030
Sol: Packer, Mr Eric LLB Clerk to the Justice. . . . . . . *Jan 1980

WIMPEY HOMES HOLDINGS LTD
3 Shortlands London W6 8EZ
Tel: 020 8846 3107 *Fax:* 020 8846 3105
Sol: Bernard, Mr Peter D Legal Director . . . . *Dec 1979
Creed, Miss Bronwyn LLB(Hons); ACIS Solicitor. . . *Aug 1991

 See p2 for the Key to Work Categories & other symbols

SECTION 2

SOLICITORS

ENGLAND & WALES

CONTENTS

Work Categories for Solicitors Firms

A1 Agricultural Law, Holdings & Property
A2 Animals, Farming, Forestry
A3 Arbitration & Mediation
B1 Bankruptcy
B2 Fraud
B3 Accounting Standards
C1 Commercial & Company Law
C2 Mergers & Acquisitions
C3 Competition Law
D1 Child Care & Wardship
D2 Adoption
E Commercial Property
F1 Consumer Law – Agreements, Credit, Licensing, Sale of Goods
F2 Consumer Protection – Advertising, Trade Descriptions, Trading Standards, Product Liability
G Crime – General
H Crime – Juvenile
I Computer Law
J1 Employment Law
J2 Health & Safety at Work
K1 Family Law
K2 Family Mediation
K3 Divorce & Matrimonial
K4 Elderly
L Housing, Landlord & Tenant
M1 European Community Law
M2 International Law
M3 Air Law
M4 Islamic Law
N Litigation, Accidents, Injury, Criminal Injury Compensation, Personal Injury
O Litigation, Commercial
P Environmental Liability
Q Litigation, General
R1 Planning, Compulsory Purchase, Lands Tribunal
R2 Property – Finance, Development
S1 Residential Conveyancing
S2 Commercial Conveyancing
T1 Taxation – Business
T2 Taxation – Personal
U1 Communications & Telecommunications
U2 Internet & e-commerce
V Welfare Benefits
W Wills, Trusts & Probate
X Education Law
Za Admiralty
Zb Banking Law
Zc Building Law, Building Contracts
Zd Charity Law
Ze Copyright, Patents, Trade Marks & Intellectual Property
Zf Entertainment, Artists & Performers
Zg Human Rights & Civil Liberties
Zh Housing Association Law
Zi Immigration & Nationality
Zj Insurance Law
Zk Libel, Slander & Defamation
Zl Liquor, Betting & Gaming Licensing
Zm Mental Health
Zn Mines, Minerals, Oil & Gas
Zo Pensions, Investments & Financial Services
Zp Race & Sex Descrimination
Zq Professional Negligence
Zr Clinical Negligence
Zs Rating Law
Zt Road Haulage Licensing
Zu Local Government
Zv Regulated by the FSA for Investment Business
Zw Sports Law
Zx Ecclesiastical Law
Zy Food & Drugs
Zz Printing & Publishing
Zza Data Protection

Key to symbols

Asoc = Associate
Ast = Assistant
Con = Consultant
Dir = Director
Dx = Document Exchange
E-mail = Electronic mail box
Est = Year Established
Fax = Facsimile number
Mem = Member
NSP = Non Solicitor Partner
Ptr = Partner
Sol = Solicitor
SPr = Sole Practitioner
Tel = Telephone number
Higher Rights of Audience – ♦ = Civil
Higher Rights of Audience – ★ = Criminal
Higher Rights of Audience – • = All
† = Member of Notaries Society
* = Law Society member
‡ = Principal office
§ = Solicitors Benevolent Association

COUNTRY FIRMS, ENGLAND & WALES – BY TOWN

2

ABERAERON, Ceredigion

EVANS & DAVIES ‡
1 Cadwgan Place Aberaeron Ceredigion SA46 0BU
Tel: 01545 570335 ***Fax:*** 01545 571145 ***Dx:*** 92403 ABERAERON
E-mail: nigel@evansanddavies.co.uk
List of partners: N R Davies
Languages: Welsh
Work: A1 B1 C1 E F1 J1 K1 L N Q S1 W Z(l,w)
Ptr: Davies, Mr Nigel R LLB . . . . Nov 1982
Con: Evans, Mr John LLB . . . . Mar 1963

GWYNNE HUGHES ‡
(incorporating Mark R Rishko)
Council Chambers 26 Alban Square Aberaeron Ceredigion SA46 0AL
Tel: 01545 570861 ***Fax:*** 01545 571121 ***Dx:*** 92400 ABERAERON
Emergency telephone 01545 570427 / 570418
E-mail: gwynnehughes@ukgateway.net
List of partners: J D Gwynne-Hughes, J D Gwynne-Hughes
Office: New Quay
Languages: Norwegian, Welsh
Work: A1 C1 E F1 J1 K1 K3 K4 L N O Q R1 R2 S1 S2 T1 T2 W Z(l,q)
Emergency Action, Agency, Advocacy, Fixed Fee Interview, Legal Aid undertaken and Legal Aid Franchise
Ptr: Gwynne-Hughes, Mr John Denys . . . . *Jan 1969
Gwynne-Hughes, Mr John David LLB(Lond); LLM(Wales) . . . . *Oct 1996
Con: Rishko, Mrs Mary R BA . . . . Dec 1972

ABERDARE, Rhondda Cynon Taff

THE GWYN GEORGE PARTNERSHIP ‡
The Beehive 11a Victoria Square Aberdare Rhondda Cynon Taff CF44 7LA
Tel: 01685 874629 / 871133 ***Fax:*** 01685 871541
Dx: 53853 ABERDARE
Emergency telephone 01685 874629
E-mail: mail@ggplaw.co.uk
List of partners: G J George, S Green, B Harvey, G M Insley, W N Thomas
Office: Blackwood, Merthyr Tydfil (2 offices), Ystradgynlais
Work: B1 B2 D1 D2 F1 G H K1 K2 K3 L N Q S1 V W Z(l,q)
Emergency Action, Agency, Advocacy, Fixed Fee Interview, Legal Aid undertaken, Legal Aid Franchise and Member of Accident Line
Ptr: George, Gwynfryn J LLB(Wales) . . . . *§Jul 1979
Green, Mrs Sara LLB . . . . *Jul 1994
Harvey, Ms Bridgitte LLB . . . . *Nov 1983
Insley, Mr Grahame M LLB . . . . *Oct 1987
Thomas, Mr W Neale LLB Deputy District Judge (Crime) . . . . *§Oct 1983
Con: Evans, Mr John A BEd . . . . *Nov 1979

HUGHES JENKINS SOLICITORS ‡
27a High Street Aberdare Rhondda Cynon Taff CF44 7AA
Tel: 01685 886611 ***Fax:*** 01685 882881 ***Dx:*** 53854 ABERDARE

GRAEME JOHN SOLICITORS ‡
(in association with Berwyn Davies & A F Brooks)
1 Victoria Square Aberdare Rhondda Cynon Taff CF44 7AL
Tel: 01685 878563 ***Fax:*** 01685 872573 ***Dx:*** 53859 ABERDARE
E-mail: info@graemejohn.co.uk
List of partners: A F Brooks, G F Carter, M R Henderson, J Thomas
Office: Aberdare (2 offices), Tonypandy, Ystradgynlais
Work: D1 D2 J1 J2 K1 N Q S1 S2 V W Z(l,q,r)
Agency, Legal Aid undertaken and Legal Aid Franchise
Con: Davies, Mr Alun B ♦. . . . . *§Dec 1973

GRAEME JOHN SOLICITORS
(in association with Berwyn Davies & A F Brooks)
Ceffyl Gwyn Chambers 3 Victoria Square Aberdare Rhondda Cynon Taff CF44 7LA
Tel: 01685 872491 ***Fax:*** 01685 872573 ***Dx:*** 53850 ABERDARE
Emergency telephone 07885 451035
E-mail: info@graemejohn.co.uk
Office: Aberdare (2 offices), Tonypandy, Ystradgynlais
Languages: Welsh
Work: C1 D1 D2 E F1 J1 J2 K1 L N O Q R1 S1 S2 V W Z(c,g,l,q,r,w)
Emergency Action, Agency, Advocacy, Fixed Fee Interview, Legal Aid undertaken and Legal Aid Franchise
Ptr: Carter, Mr Gerald F LLB. . . . . *Jun 1980
Thomas, Mr Jeffrey LLB ● H M Deputy Coroner of the Glamorgan Valleys . . . . *Jun 1979

GRAEME JOHN SOLICITORS
(in association with Berwyn Davies & A F Brooks)
1-3 Victoria Square Aberdare Rhondda Cynon Taff CF44 7LA
Tel: 01685 873565 ***Fax:*** 01685 881227 ***Dx:*** 53859 ABERDARE
Emergency telephone 01443 472738
E-mail: info@graemejohn.co.uk
Office: Aberdare (2 offices), Tonypandy, Ystradgynlais
Languages: Welsh
Work: A1 B1 C1 D1 E F1 G H J1 K1 L N R1 S1 S2 T1 W
Emergency Action, Agency, Advocacy, Fixed Fee Interview and Legal Aid undertaken
Ptr: Brooks, Mr Alwyn F. . . . . *Dec 1976

MARCHANT HARRIES & CO ‡
Bute Chambers 17-19 Cardiff Street Aberdare Rhondda Cynon Taff CF44 7DP
Tel: 01685 885500 ***Fax:*** 01685 885500 ***Dx:*** 53851 ABERDARE
Emergency telephone 07836 315738
E-mail: admin@marchantharries.co.uk
List of partners: J S Bird, S D S Bird, K Butler, J S Morris, P M Williams
Office: Aberdare, Mountain Ash
Languages: French, Italian, Welsh
Work: D1 D2 F1 G H J1 K1 K2 N O Q R1 S1 S2 W Z(m,q,r)
Emergency Action, Agency, Advocacy, Fixed Fee Interview, Legal Aid undertaken, Legal Aid Franchise and Member of Accident Line
Ptr: Bird, Mr Jeremy S LLB ★ . . . . *Oct 1986
Bird, Mr Simon D S LLB(Wales) ● . . . . *Aug 1989
Butler, Mr Keith LLB(Wales). . . . . *Mar 1980
Morris, Miss Judith S LLB. . . . . *Nov 1986
Williams, Mr Peter M . . . . *Jun 1979
Con: Howells, Mr Colin LLB. . . . . *Jul 1967

MARCHANT HARRIES & CO
77 High Street Hirwaun Aberdare Rhondda Cynon Taff CF44 9SW
Tel: 01685 813655 ***Fax:*** 01685 813515
E-mail: admin@marchantharries.co.uk
Office: Aberdare, Mountain Ash
Work: A1 B1 C1 D1 F1 G H J1 K1 L M1 N P S1 W
Emergency Action, Agency, Fixed Fee Interview and Legal Aid undertaken
Ptr: Morris, Miss Judith S LLB. . . . . *Nov 1986

ROMANO FERRARI STROUD ‡
7 National Court Cardiff Street Aberdare Rhondda Cynon Taff CF44 7DG
Tel: 01685 883143 ***Fax:*** 01685 883144 ***Dx:*** 53858 ABERDARE
E-mail: enquiries@romanoferrariandco.com

ABERGAVENNY, Monmouthshire

R GEORGE DAVIES & CO ‡
5 Neville Street Abergavenny Monmouthshire NP7 5AA
Tel: 01873 852535 ***Fax:*** 01873 857580 ***Dx:*** 43754 ABERGAVENNY
Emergency telephone 01873 831236
E-mail: hmedlicott@rgeorgedavies.co.uk
List of partners: R A C Davies, H G Medlicott
Languages: Welsh
Work: A1 B2 C1 D1 D2 E F1 G H J1 J2 K1 K3 L N O Q S1 S2 W X Z(l,q)
Emergency Action, Agency, Advocacy, Legal Aid undertaken and Legal Aid Franchise
Ptr: Davies, Mr Robert A C LLB . . . . *Jul 1976
Medlicott, Mr Huw G BA. . . . . *§Apr 1981
Ast: Fraser, Mr David J LLB . . . . *Nov 1988
Medlicott, Mrs Katherine A LLB . . . . *§Sep 1982

KEITH EVANS & COMPANY
Tiverton Chambers Lion Street Abergavenny Monmouthshire NP7 5PN
Tel: 01873 852239 ***Fax:*** 01873 856846 ***Dx:*** 43750 ABERGAVENNY
E-mail: office@keith-evans.co.uk
Office: Cwmbran, Newport
Languages: French, Welsh
Work: A1 B1 D1 E F1 G J1 K1 L N O Q R1 S1 T2 W Z(l)

FONSECA & PARTNERS ‡
St Marys Chambers Monk Street Abergavenny Monmouthshire NP7 5ND
Tel: 01873 857114 ***Fax:*** 01873 855873 ***Dx:*** 43753 ABERGAVENNY
List of partners: S M Baldwin, R G F Lovell
Work: D1 E K1 L S1 S2 W
Emergency Action, Agency, Advocacy, Fixed Fee Interview and Legal Aid undertaken
Ptr: Baldwin, Ms Stella M . . . . *Mar 1989
Lovell, Mr Richard G F . . . . *§May 1977

GABB & CO ‡
32 Monk Street Abergavenny Monmouthshire NP7 5NW
Tel: 01873 852432 ***Fax:*** 01873 857589 ***Dx:*** 43752 ABERGAVENNY
E-mail: abergavenny@gabb.co.uk
List of partners: A H B Candler, A M Davies, D H C Lloyd, S R W Meredith, D J Vaughan, S K V Williams
Office: Crickhowell
Work: A1 C1 C2 C3 D1 E F1 G H J1 K1 L M1 M2 N P R1 S1 S2 T1 T2 W
Emergency Action, Agency, Advocacy, Fixed Fee Interview, Legal Aid undertaken and Member of Accident Line
Ptr: Candler, Mr Anthony H B BA . . . . *§Jan 1972
Davies, Mr A Myles LLB. . . . . *Jan 1979
Lloyd, Mr David H C BA. . . . . *§Jun 1977
Meredith, Mr Stephen R W BA(Oxon) . . . . *§Oct 1992
Vaughan, Mr David J MA(Cantab). . . . . *May 1967
Williams, Miss Sophie K V LLB(Hons); LPC . . . . . . Sep 1997
Con: Stock, Mr Michael J. . . . . *§Oct 1957

GARTSIDES
Rother House 11 Nevill Street Abergavenny Monmouthshire NP7 5AA
Tel: 01873 857555 ***Fax:*** 01873 858947 ***Dx:*** 43751 ABERGAVENNY
E-mail: gglencross@gartsides.com
Office: Ebbw Vale, Newport
Work: D1 D2 E G H K1 K2 K3 L N O Q S1 S2 V W
Agency, Advocacy, Fixed Fee Interview, Legal Aid undertaken and Member of Accident Line
Ptr: Davies, Mr Christopher L LLB. . . . . *Jun 1973
Williams, Mrs Suzanne Mary . . . . Jun 1994
Ast: Jones, Mrs Leanne LLB. . . . . Sep 1998

MORGANS ‡
Central Chambers Lion Street Abergavenny Monmouthshire NP7 5PE
Tel: 01873 859993 ***Fax:*** 01873 853492 ***Dx:*** 43761 ABERGAVENNY
List of partners: S K Langton, A W Morgan
Languages: Spanish
Work: A1 C1 E J1 L N O Q R1 S1 S2 W
Agency, Advocacy, Fixed Fee Interview and Legal Aid undertaken
Ptr: Langton, Mrs Sarah Kate BA . . . . *Jan 1992
Morgan, Mrs Alison W BA. . . . . *Feb 1991

ROWLANDS & CO ‡
Harrington House 6 Pen Y Pond Abergavenny Monmouthshire NP7 5UD
Tel: 01873 850983 ***Fax:*** 01873 852032

ABERGELE, Conwy

GAMLINS ‡
Within Santander 5-7 Market Street Abergele Conwy LL22 7AG
Tel: 01745 357333 ***Fax:*** 01745 822993
E-mail: gamlins@gamlins.co.uk

HOWELL JONES & CO
57 Market Street Abergele Conwy LL22 7AF
Tel: 01745 826282 / 825845 ***Fax:*** 01745 827038
Dx: 14052 ABERGELE
E-mail: enquiries.abergele@howelljoneslaw.co.uk
Office: Llanrwst
Languages: Welsh
Work: A1 A2 C1 C2 D2 E F1 G H J1 K1 K3 K4 L N O P Q R1 R2 S1 S2 T1 T2 V W Z(c,d,l,q)
Emergency Action, Agency, Advocacy, Fixed Fee Interview, Legal Aid undertaken, Legal Aid Franchise and Member of Accident Line
Ptr: Davies, Mr Hywel LLB(Wales). . . . . *Oct 1984
Hughes, Mr David W P LLB(Wales) . . . . *Apr 1981
Hughes Parry, Ms Nia BA(Hons) . . . . *Oct 1984
McAlinden, Mr Paul LLB(Hons) . . . . *Nov 1994
Roberts, Mrs Nia W LLB(Wales). . . . . *Feb 1987
Asoc: Galloway, Mrs Carol Gail LLB(Hons) . . . . *Apr 2001
Jones, Mrs Eleri FILEx; TEP. . . . . *Oct 2005
Morris, Miss Rhonwen BA(Hons) . . . . *Sep 2003
Con: Evans, Mrs Janet P LLB . . . . *Jun 1975

GLYN OWEN & CO
Unit 2 51-53 Market Street Abergele Conwy LL22 7AF
Tel: 01745 833411 ***Fax:*** 01745 824337
Office: Colwyn Bay

ABERTILLERY, Blaenau Gwent

GRANVILLE-WEST CHIVERS & MORGAN
49 Church Street Abertillery Blaenau Gwent NP13 1DB
Tel: 01495 217070 ***Fax:*** 01495 215605 ***Dx:*** 92151 ABERTILLERY
E-mail: abertillery@granville-west.co.uk
Office: Blackwood, Caldicot, Newport, Pontypool, Risca
Work: D1 F1 G H J1 K1 N O P Q R1 S1 V W Z(k,l)
Emergency Action, Agency, Advocacy, Fixed Fee Interview and Legal Aid undertaken
Ptr: Cox-Healey, Mr John P . . . . *Dec 1984

LEWIS & LINES ‡
Commercial Chambers High Street Abertillery Blaenau Gwent NP13 1YB
Tel: 01495 212286 ***Fax:*** 01495 320443 ***Dx:*** 92150 ABERTILLERY
List of partners: J Lewis, K L Lines, T Wilkes
Work: A1 A3 B1 B2 C1 D1 D2 E F1 G H J1 J2 K1 K3 K4 L N O P Q R1 S1 S2 T1 T2 V W Z(c,j,l,m,q,w)
Emergency Action, Agency, Advocacy, Fixed Fee Interview, Legal Aid undertaken and Legal Aid Franchise
Ptr: Lewis, Ms Jill LLB(Hons) ♦ . . . . *Oct 1987
Lines, Mr Kevan L LLB(Hons) ● . . . . *Jan 1988
Wilkes, Miss Tracy BSc(Econ) ●. . . . . Aug 2002

ABERYSTWYTH, Ceredigion

ALISON LEGAL PRACTICE ‡
PO Box 235 Aberystwyth Ceredigion SY23 9AP
Tel: 01970 610908 *Fax:* 01970 623426
E-mail: enquiries@alisonslegal.co.uk

ALUN THOMAS & JOHN ‡
Crynfryn 17 Eastgate Aberystwyth Ceredigion SY23 2AR
Tel: 01970 615900 *Fax:* 01970 611941 *Dx:* 92105 ABERYSTWYTH
E-mail: rsj@atj.co.uk
List of partners: R S John, A P Thomas
Languages: Welsh
Work: A1 B1 C1 D1 E F1 J1 K1 L N O Q R1 S1 S2 V W Z(c,l,t)
Emergency Action, Agency, Advocacy and Legal Aid undertaken
Ptr: John, Mr Richard S LLB(Soton) . . . . *Jun 1985
Thomas, Mr Alun P LLB(Wales) Deputy District Judge*§Jun 1971

BRUNTON & CO ‡
(incorporating D Emrys Williams & Co)
6 Upper Portland Street Aberystwyth Ceredigion SY23 2DU
Tel: 01970 612567 / 617931 *Fax:* 01970 615572
List of partners: P L Brunton, E M Davies
Office: Machynlleth
Languages: Welsh
Work: A1 B1 B2 C1 D1 E G J1 K1 L N Q R1 S1 S2 T2 W Z(c,l,t)
Emergency Action, Agency, Advocacy and Fixed Fee Interview undertaken
Ptr: Brunton, Mr Peter L Coroner . . . . *Jul 1975

DAVID JAMES & COMPANY ‡
PO Box 61 15 Eastgate Aberystwyth Ceredigion SY23 2AR
Tel: 01970 615789 *Fax:* 01970 625081 *Dx:* 92101 ABERYSTWYTH
E-mail: enq@djd15.fsnet.co.uk
List of partners: D W James, K A Mathias
Languages: Welsh
Work: G H K1 N S1 S2 W Z(l)
Emergency Action, Advocacy, Fixed Fee Interview, Legal Aid undertaken and Legal Aid Franchise
Ptr: James, Mr David W LLB(Wales). . . . . Jun 1972
Mathias, Miss Kathryn Alison . . . . Oct 1996

GODWINS
31 Portland Street Aberystwyth Ceredigion SY23 4WF
Tel: 01970 624244 *Fax:* 01970 617711 *Dx:* 92113 ABERYSTWYTH
E-mail: smj@godwinssolicitors.co.uk
Office: Llandovery, Llandrindod Wells
Languages: Welsh
Work: A1 B1 C1 D1 E F1 G H I J1 K1 L N O Q R1 S1 V W Z(b,c,l,q,r)
Emergency Action, Agency, Advocacy, Fixed Fee Interview, Legal Aid undertaken and Legal Aid Franchise
Ptr: Margrave-Jones, Mr Simon R. . . . . *Jul 1991

HUMPHREY ROBERTS & BOTT ‡
1 Alfred Place Aberystwyth Ceredigion SY23 2BS
Tel: 01970 617618 *Fax:* 01970 636645 *Dx:* 92104 ABERYSTWYTH
E-mail: action@hrbsolicitors.com
List of partners: W H Hughes, R M Thomas
Languages: Welsh
Work: A1 E G K1 L P S1 S2 T2 W Z(m)
Agency and Fixed Fee Interview undertaken
Ptr: Hughes, Wyn H LLB . . . . *May 1980
Thomas, Mrs Rachel M LLB. . . . . *Nov 1982

MORRIS & BATES ‡
(incorporating W A Bowen & Griffiths; Roberts & Evans)
PO Box 1 Ffordd Alexandra Road Aberystwyth Ceredigion SY23 1PT
Tel: 01970 625566 *Fax:* 01970 625611 *Dx:* 92100 ABERYSTWYTH
E-mail: law@morrisbates.co.uk
List of partners: A P Bates, J H Bates, A M Jones, D R H Jones, N C Jones-Steele, R J Morris, W G Morris
Office: Knighton, Llandrindod Wells
Languages: Welsh
Work: A1 B1 C1 C2 D1 D2 E F1 F2 G H J1 K1 L N O P Q R1 R2 S1 S2 T1 T2 V W X Z(b,c,d,f,g,j,k,l,m,o,p,q,r,s)
Emergency Action, Agency, Advocacy, Legal Aid undertaken and Legal Aid Franchise
Ptr: Bates, Mr Anthony P LLB(Wales) Former President of the Aberystwyth Law Society . . . . *Apr 1974
Bates, Mr Jonathan Huw . . . . *Jul 2005
Jones, Miss Annwen M LLB. . . . . *Dec 1992
Jones, Mr David R Hinton LLB(Wales); BA(Wales) . . *Oct 1988
Jones-Steele, Ms Nia Catherine. . . . . Sep 2008
Morris, Mr Richard John LLB(Nott'm) Deputy Under Sheriff of Ceredigion . . . . *Oct 1995
Morris, Mr W Gareth LLB(Wales) Under Sheriff of Ceredigion; Clerk to Tax Commissioners Notary Public . . . *Sep 1970

POWELL DAVIES SOLICITORS ‡
Market Chambers 27 Eastgate Street Aberystwyth Ceredigion SY23 2AR
Tel: 01970 636599 *Fax:* 01970 630033
Dx: 92106 ABERYSTWYTH 1
E-mail: mail@powelldavies.co.uk
List of partners: J O Powell
Languages: Welsh
Work: A1 B1 C1 D1 E F1 G H J1 K1 L M1 N P R1 S1 T1 W Z(d,l,o)
Emergency Action, Agency, Advocacy, Fixed Fee Interview, Legal Aid undertaken and Member of Accident Line
Ptr: Powell, Mr Jonathan O LLB . . . . *Feb 1988
Con: Powell, Mr Stanley W BA(Hons). . . . . Oct 1959

MAIR WILLIAMS SOLICITORS ‡
Parc Merlin Glan Yr Afon Aberystwyth Ceredigion SY23 3FF
Tel: 01970 615529 *Fax:* 01970 626372 *Dx:* 92116 ABERYSTWYTH
E-mail: enquiries@mairwilliams.com

ABINGDON, Oxfordshire

BROOKSTREET DES ROCHES LLP ‡
25 Milton Park Abingdon Oxfordshire OX14 4SH
Tel: 01235 836600 *Fax:* 01235 836700 *Dx:* 144160 ABINGDON 4
Work: A1 B1 C1 C2 E J1 L N O P Q S1 S2 Z(c,d,f,l,n)

CATER LEYDON MILLARD LIMITED ‡
68 Milton Park Milton Abingdon Oxfordshire OX14 4RP
Tel: 01235 821115 *Fax:* 01235 833112
E-mail: info@caterleydonmillard.co.uk
Work: J1

CHALLENOR & SON ‡
Stratton House 50 Bath Street Abingdon Oxfordshire OX14 3LA
Tel: 01235 520013 *Fax:* 01235 534311 *Dx:* 35856 ABINGDON
List of partners: D S Gordon, S C Pegram, T J Pegram
Work: A1 C1 E J1 K1 L M1 N R1 S1 S2 W
Fixed Fee Interview undertaken
Ptr: Gordon, Mr David S MA(Oxon) . . . . *Dec 1973
Pegram, Mr Stephen C . . . . *Dec 1977
Pegram, Mr Trevor J MA(Oxon). . . . . *Jun 1970

EMPLOYMENT LAW PLUS ‡
Stepstone House Old Moor Abingdon Oxfordshire OX14 4ED
Tel: 01235 861919

FRANKLINS ‡
Walton House 15 Ock Street Abingdon Oxfordshire OX14 5AN
Tel: 01235 553222 *Fax:* 01235 523823 *Dx:* 35855 ABINGDON
E-mail: info@franklins-solicitors.co.uk
List of partners: J F Cunliffe, H C Foreman, J D Kent
Languages: Italian
Work: C1 E K1 R1 S1 S2 T1 T2 W
Legal Aid Franchise
Ptr: Cunliffe, Mr John F MA(Oxon). . . . . *Nov 1972
Foreman, Mrs Helen C MA . . . . *Feb 1988
Kent, Mrs Julia D LLB. . . . . *Apr 1979
Ast: Bruce, Mrs Sarah E BA . . . . *Sep 1982
Elliot, Mr Roger B LLB Deputy District Judge of the Family Division. . . . . *Apr 1973
Firth, Mrs Amanda Lee LLB(Hons) . . . . *Oct 1988
Goodman, Mrs Aislinn Ruth LLB(Hons) . . . . *Aug 2003
Con: Shaw, Mr Nigel P S BA(Exon) Notary Public. . . . . *§Oct 1975

MACNAB CLARKE ‡
14 Lombard Street Abingdon Oxfordshire OX14 5BJ
Tel: 01235 555700 *Fax:* 01235 555459
E-mail: pam@macnabclarke.com

SLADE LEGAL ‡
The Greenhouse Stratton Way Abingdon Oxfordshire OX14 3QP
Tel: 01235 521920 *Fax:* 01235 527116 *Dx:* 35851 ABINGDON
E-mail: enquiries@slade-legal.co.uk
List of partners: E Ferguson, L Groom, D M Hodson, J Hodson, G A McTier, M H Rickard, D H Slade, S H Smith
Office: Didcot, Wallingford
Work: C1 D1 E F1 F2 G H J1 K1 K2 L N P Q S1 S2 W Z(i,l)
Emergency Action, Agency, Advocacy, Fixed Fee Interview, Legal Aid undertaken and Member of Accident Line
Ptr: Groom, Ms Lisa-Marie BA. . . . . *Nov 1999
Hodson, Mr David M . . . . *Jul 1969
Hodson, Mr Jeremy LLB . . . . *Apr 1993
McTier, Mrs Geraldine A LLB . . . . *Apr 1977
Rickard, Mr Marcus Hugh LLB(Hons) . . . . *Jan 2000
Ast: Macpherson, Ms Emma Louise LLB(Hons); LPC . . . Jan 2002

WITHY KING SOLICITORS
33 West St Helen Street Abingdon Oxfordshire OX14 5DY
Tel: 01235 555345 *Fax:* 01235 553489 *Dx:* 35862 ABINGDON
E-mail: enquiries@withyking.co.uk
Office: Bath (2 offices), Marlborough, Oxford, Swindon, Thame, Trowbridge
Languages: French
Work: A1 B1 C1 C2 C3 D1 E F1 G H J1 K1 L M1 M2 N O P Q R1 S1 T1 T2 V W Z(c,d,e,h,i,o)

ACCRINGTON, Lancashire

ACKLAM BOND NOOR ‡
Equity Chambers 10-12 St James Street Accrington Lancashire BB5 1LY
Tel: 01254 872272 *Fax:* 01254 233370 *Dx:* 23766 ACCRINGTON
E-mail: david@acklambond.co.uk
List of partners: D I Acklam, D Bond, W I Noor
Office: Blackburn, Dewsbury
Languages: Gujarati, Punjabi, Urdu
Work: B1 C1 C2 C3 D1 E F1 G H J1 K1 L N O Q R1 S1 S2 V W Z(i,l,r)
Emergency Action, Agency, Advocacy and Fixed Fee Interview undertaken
Ptr: Acklam, Mr David Ian BA . . . . *Jan 1980
Bond, Mrs Denise BA . . . . *Oct 1986
Noor, Waqar Ilyas LLB . . . . *Oct 1999

ALTON & CO SOLICITORS ‡
112 Abbey Street Accrington Lancashire BB5 1EE
Tel: 01254 385104 *Dx:* 23759 ACCRINGTON

BARLOW ROWLAND ‡
18-24 St James Street Accrington Lancashire BB5 1NY
Tel: 01254 300400 *Fax:* 01254 300401 *Dx:* 23751 ACCRINGTON
List of partners: T H Codling, T J Gabbutt, C Hooper, K Smith
Work: A1 B1 C1 C2 C3 E F1 J1 K4 L N O P Q R1 R2 S1 S2 T1 T2 W Z(b,c,d,g,h,j,k,l,m,n,o,p,q,s)
Agency and Advocacy undertaken
Ptr: Codling, Mr Thomas Henry . . . . *Dec 1959
Gabbutt, Mr Timothy J LLB . . . . *Nov 1983
Hooper, Mrs Catherine LLB(Sheff). . . . . *Dec 1976
Smith, Mr Kenneth LLB(Manc) . . . . *Apr 1971

FARLEYS SOLICITORS LLP
(incorporating Simpson Ashworth Slinger)
12-18 Willow Street Accrington Lancashire BB5 1LP
Tel: 01254 367853 *Fax:* 01254 235468 *Dx:* 23753 ACCRINGTON
Emergency telephone 01254 52552
E-mail: info@farleys.com
Office: Blackburn (3 offices), Burnley, Manchester
Languages: Punjabi, Urdu
Work: A1 A3 B1 C1 C2 D1 D2 E F1 G H J1 K1 K2 L M1 N O P Q R1 S1 S2 T1 V W Z(d,i,j,k,l,m,p,q,r)
Emergency Action, Agency, Fixed Fee Interview and Legal Aid undertaken
Ptr: Horne, Mr Bernard LLB(Hons). . . . . *Oct 1988
McNeill, Mr Stephen Patrick LLB(Hons) . . . . *Mar 1981
Ast: Chorkley, Ms Sara-Jane LLB(Hons) . . . . *May 1998
Foster, Miss Suzanne Clare LLB(Hons) . . . . *Jun 2001
Goodier, Miss Jane Emma . . . . *Sep 2006
Saddiq, Mrs Zahra LLB(Hons). . . . . *Sep 2004

ANTHONY FOLEY ‡
9-13 Dutton Street Accrington Lancashire BB5 1JR
Tel: 01254 391223 *Fax:* 01254 394311 *Dx:* 23757 ACCRINGTON
E-mail: info@anthonyfoley.co.uk
List of partners: A Foley
Languages: Punjabi, Urdu
Work: E L N S1 W Z(i)
SPr: Foley, Mr Anthony BA(Law) . . . . *Mar 1979

FORBES
(incorporating Sandeman Johnson Steele & Son)
13-15 Cannon Street Accrington Lancashire BB5 1NJ
Tel: 01254 872111 *Fax:* 01254 399795 *Dx:* 23755 ACCRINGTON
Emergency telephone 01254 872888
E-mail: graeme.parkinson@forbessolicitors.co.uk
Office: Accrington, Blackburn (3 offices), Chorley, Leeds, Manchester, Preston
Work: A1 B1 C1 D1 E F1 F2 G H J1 K1 L M1 N O P Q R1 R2 S1 S2 V W Z(i,j,k,l,m,o,p,q,r)
Emergency Action, Agency, Fixed Fee Interview, Legal Aid Franchise and Member of Accident Line

FORBES
Gothic House St James Street Accrington Lancashire BB5 1LY
Tel: 01254 872111 *Fax:* 01254 770535 *Dx:* 23755 ACCRINGTON
E-mail: petev.dugdale@forbessolicitors.co.uk
Office: Accrington, Blackburn (3 offices), Chorley, Leeds, Manchester, Preston
Work: N S1 S2
Ptr: Dugdale, Mr Peter A LLB . . . . *Jun 1980
Forbes, Mr David I . . . . *§Dec 1968
Parkinson, Mr Graeme T . . . . *Dec 1979
Asoc: Bennett, Mr John Watson . . . . *Aug 1992
Ast: Cannings, Mrs Yvonne BA; LPC. . . . . *Sep 1996
Linford, Mrs Sara BA . . . . *Jul 1996

HPA SOLICITORS ‡
123 Blackburn Road Accrington Lancashire BB5 0AA
Tel: 01254 238310 *Fax:* 01254 236285
E-mail: info@hpasolicitors.com

HAWORTH & NUTTALL
17 Cannon Street Accrington Lancashire BB5 1NW
Tel: 01254 236221 *Fax:* 01254 871209 *Dx:* 23752 ACCRINGTON
Emergency telephone 01254 667117
E-mail: david.mccraith@hn-a.co.uk
Office: Blackburn, Great Harwood
Work: A1 B1 C1 C2 D1 D2 E F1 J1 K1 K3 K4 L N Q R1 R2 S1 S2 V W X Z(i,j,l,m,p)
Emergency Action, Agency, Advocacy, Fixed Fee Interview, Legal Aid undertaken, Legal Aid Franchise and Member of Accident Line
Ptr: Heyes, Mr Martin John LLB . . . . *Oct 1983
McCraith, Mr David A LLB. . . . . *§May 1980
Asoc: Magell, Miss Tanya LLB(Hons) . . . . Sep 1992

ROEBUCKS
7 Cannon Street Accrington Lancashire BB5 1NJ
Tel: 01254 306560 *Fax:* 01254 306561
Office: Blackburn (2 offices)

ROSTHORNS SOLICITORS ‡
8 Peel Street Accrington Lancashire BB5 1EA
Tel: 01254 398213 *Fax:* 01254 871183 *Dx:* 23761 ACCRINGTON

RUST & CO ‡
48 Blackburn Road Accrington Lancashire BB5 1LE
Tel: 01254 390015 *Fax:* 01254 386670 *Dx:* 23763 ACCRINGTON
List of partners: C M Rust
SPr: Rust, Mr C Michael BA(Oxon). . . . . *Apr 1980

SIGMA SOLICITORS ‡
95 Union Road Oswaldtwistle Accrington Lancashire BB5 3DD
Tel: 01254 391222 *Fax:* 01254 391220
E-mail: info@sigmasolicitors.com

ADDLESTONE, Surrey

MACKRELL TURNER GARRETT
(in association with Mackrell International)
315 Woodham Lane New Haw Addlestone Surrey KT15 3PA
Tel: 01932 342181 *Fax:* 01932 336489 *Dx:* 118700 NEW HAW
Office: London WC2, Woking (2 offices)
Work: B1 C1 C2 C3 E F1 J1 K1 L M1 M2 N O P Q R1 S1 T1 T2 W Z(e,i,k,l,t)
Agency, Fixed Fee Interview and Legal Aid undertaken
Ptr: Adkin, Mr Michael G LLB . . . . *Jan 1978
Saviker, Ms Marion Y . . . . *Nov 1983
Ast: Score, Mrs Pauline LLB(Hons) . . . . *Jul 1978

OWEN WHITE & CATLIN
151 Station Road Addlestone Surrey KT15 2AT
Tel: 01932 845020 *Fax:* 01932 844614
E-mail: addlestone@owenwhitecatlin.co.uk
Office: Ashford, Feltham, Hounslow, London W4, London W6, Shepperton

AINSDALE, Merseyside

CHESTNUTTS ‡
660 Liverpool Road Ainsdale Merseyside PR8 3LT
Tel: 01704 572221 *Fax:* 01704 572224 *Dx:* 18305 AINSDALE
E-mail: liz@chestnutts.co.uk
List of partners: E M D Chestnutt, S Lapsley
Languages: French, Spanish
Work: C1 E F1 J1 K1 K3 K4 L N O Q S1 S2 W
Agency, Legal Aid Franchise and Member of Accident Line
Ptr: Chestnutt, Mrs Elizabeth M D LLB. . . . . *Jun 1975
Lapsley, Miss Sarah LSF; LLB . . . . *Nov 1991
Ast: Rostamlou, Miss Sarah Natalie BA . . . . *Jan 2008

COCKSHOTT PECK LEWIS
20 Station Road Ainsdale Merseyside PR8 3HS
Tel: 01704 574144 *Fax:* 01704 578250 *Dx:* 18303 AINSDALE
E-mail: ajgc@cockshotts.co.uk
Office: Southport (2 offices)
Work: A1 E F1 K1 K4 L N Q S1 S2 W Z(c,l)
Emergency Action, Agency, Advocacy, Fixed Fee Interview undertaken and Member of Accident Line
Ptr: Cottrell, Mr Arthur John Geoffrey LLB . . . . *§Jun 1975
Asoc: Lawrence, Mrs Fleur V LLB . . . . *Oct 1999

See p112 for the Key to Work Categories & other symbols

HODGE HALSALL
2 Liverpool Avenue Ainsdale Merseyside PR8 3LX
Tel: 01704 577171 *Fax:* 01704 576517
Office: Southport
Ptr: Hatton, Mr Gordon LLB . . . . *Nov 1971

ALCESTER, Warwickshire

HCB SOLICITORS
35 High Street Alcester Warwickshire B49 5AF
Tel: 01789 765522
Office: Lichfield, Redditch, Solihull, Stratford-upon-Avon, Walsall

ALDEBURGH, Suffolk

H T ARGENT & SON
159 High Street Aldeburgh Suffolk IP15 5AN
Tel: 01728 452133
Office: Saxmundham
Work: A1 E L S1 S2 T1 T2 W
Ptr: Clarke, Mr Alan Gerald . . . . *§Dec 1963
Ast: Mackinnon, Mrs Linda LLB . . . . *Apr 1974

FAIRWEATHER STEPHENSON & CO
16 Wentworth Road Aldeburgh Suffolk IP15 5BB
Tel: 01728 454595 *Fax:* 01728 454577 *Dx:* 99777 ALDEBURGH
E-mail: info@fairweatherstephenson.co.uk
Office: Leiston

KEANE & CO ‡
37 High Street Aldeburgh Suffolk IP15 5AU
Tel: 01728 453595 *Fax:* 01728 452787 *Dx:* 99775 ALDEBURGH
E-mail: mail@keanelegal.co.uk
List of partners: R S Keane
Languages: Spanish
Work: A1 C1 E G H J1 K1 L R1 R2 S1 S2 T1 T2 W Z(d,h,l,q)
Ptr: Keane, Mr Richard S . . . . *Dec 1970
Ast: Browning, Miss Elizabeth A . . . . *Jul 1989

DALE PARKINSON & CO ‡
(incorporating Wrinch & Fisher)
8 North Warren Aldeburgh Suffolk IP15 5QF
Tel: 01728 453338
List of partners: M R Price
SPr: Price, Miss Marian R LLB(Lond). . . . . Dec 1967

ALDERLEY EDGE, Cheshire

CHAFES
32 London Road Alderley Edge Cheshire SK9 7DZ
Tel: 01625 585404 *Fax:* 01625 586016 *Dx:* 15422 ALDERLEY EDGE
E-mail: mail@chafes.co.uk
Office: New Mills, Stockport, Wilmslow

CLIFFORDS ‡
25 Windermere Drive Alderley Edge Cheshire SK9 7UP
Tel: 01625 582257

KNIGHTS SOLICITORS LLP
28a London Road Alderley Edge Cheshire SK9 7DZ
Tel: 01625 586686 *Fax:* 01782 717821
E-mail: mail@knightsllp.co.uk
Office: Cheltenham, Newcastle under Lyme
Work: A1 A2 A3 B1 C1 C2 C3 D1 E F1 F2 I J1 J2 K1 K3 K4 L M1 M2 N O P Q R1 R2 S1 S2 T1 T2 U1 U2 V W X Z(b,c,d,e,f,g,k,l,m,n,o,p,q,r,s,t,w)
Emergency Action, Advocacy, Fixed Fee Interview undertaken and Member of Accident Line

ALDERSHOT, Hampshire

MICHAEL BAKERS SOLICITORS LIMITED
Beaumont House Auchinleck Way PO Box 259 Aldershot Hampshire GU11 1WT
Tel: 01252 744600 *Fax:* 01252 346830 *Dx:* 153582 ALDERSHOT 6
Office: Farnborough, Redhill

DRAPER & CO SOLICITORS ‡
(in association with Draper & Co)
Law House 2a Wellington Street Aldershot Hampshire GU11 1DZ
Tel: 01252 318151 *Fax:* 01252 341575 *Dx:* 50104 ALDERSHOT
E-mail: wm.draper@virgin.net
List of partners: J P M Draper
Work: E F1 K1 L Q S1 S2 W Z(m)
Fixed Fee Interview undertaken
Ptr: Draper, Mr Jonathan P M . . . . *Jan 1982

FOSTER WELLS ‡
126 Victoria Road Aldershot Hampshire GU11 1JX
Tel: 01252 343567 *Fax:* 01252 330366 *Dx:* 50100 ALDERSHOT
E-mail: enquiries@fosterwells.co.uk

FRAME SMITH & CO ‡
1a Station Approach Ash Vale Aldershot Hampshire GU12 5LP
Tel: 01252 330330 *Fax:* 01252 331221
E-mail: info@framesmithsoicitors.co.uk

C M GREEN & CO ‡
Newlends Brackendene Aldershot Hampshire GU12 6BN
Tel: 01252 326501 *Fax:* 01252 312212
List of partners: C M Green
SPr: Green, Ms Carole M . . . . Dec 1991

HILL & CO ‡
Imperial House 2 Grosvenor Road Aldershot Hampshire GU11 1DP
Tel: 01252 319441 *Fax:* 01252 336403
E-mail: hillandco@btconnect.com
List of partners: J P Hill
Work: C1 G H K1 L M1 N P R1 S1
Agency, Advocacy, Fixed Fee Interview and Legal Aid undertaken
Ptr: Hill, Mr John P BSc . . . . *Oct 1973

LEVALES SOLICITORS LLP ‡
Barfield House Grove Road Ash Vale Aldershot Hampshire GU12 5BD
Tel: 01252 334915 *Dx:* 99277 ASH VALE
E-mail: info@levales.com

PINTO POTTS LLP ‡
304 High Street Aldershot Hampshire GU12 4LT
Tel: 0800 316 4434 *Fax:* 01252 361201 *Dx:* 142380 ALDERSHOT 3
E-mail: david.pinto@pintopotts.co.uk
List of partners: D F Pinto
Office: Fleet
Work: B1 G H J1 K1 M1 N P S1 W
Emergency Action, Agency, Advocacy and Legal Aid undertaken
Ptr: Pinto, Mr David F LLB. . . . . *Sep 1980

TANNER & TAYLOR LLP ‡
Stratfield Place 149 Victoria Road Aldershot Hampshire GU11 1JS
Tel: 01252 316565 *Fax:* 01252 310792 *Dx:* 50113 ALDERSHOT
E-mail: aldershot@tanner-taylor.co.uk
List of partners: C J Barker, I C Hogg, N Mehta, J A O'Dowd-Booth
Office: Ascot, Farnborough, Farnham
Work: B1 C1 C2 C3 D1 E F1 G H J1 K1 L M1 M2 N O P Q R1 S1 T1 T2 W Z(c,e,i,j,k,l)
Emergency Action, Agency, Advocacy, Fixed Fee Interview, Legal Aid undertaken, Legal Aid Franchise and Member of Accident Line
Ptr: Hogg, Mrs Isabel C BA(Law) . . . . *Oct 1984

TAYLOR STREET SOLICITORS LLP ‡
378-380 Vale Road Ash Vale Aldershot Hampshire GU12 5NJ
Tel: 01252 400999 *Fax:* 01252 400998 *Dx:* 99283 ASH VALE
Emergency telephone 07625 578100
E-mail: lawyers@taylor-street.co.uk
Work: B2 G H V
Agency, Advocacy, Fixed Fee Interview, Legal Aid undertaken and Legal Aid Franchise

WHEELERS ‡
Vale House 30 Wharf Road Ash Vale Aldershot Hampshire GU12 5AR
Tel: 01252 316316 *Fax:* 01252 328312 *Dx:* 99275 ASH VALE
Emergency telephone 01252 725690
E-mail: info@wheelerslaw.co.uk
List of partners: P A Keogh, M H McCrum, S M Reyersbach
Languages: French, German
Work: A1 B1 C1 C2 C3 D1 D2 E F1 F2 J1 J2 K1 K2 L M3 N O Q R1 R2 S1 S2 T1 T2 W Z(c,d,e,k,l,m,p,q,r)
Emergency Action, Agency, Advocacy and Fixed Fee Interview undertaken
Ptr: Keogh, Mr Paul A BA . . . . *§Oct 1987
McCrum, Mr Melvin Hugh LLB . . . . *§Oct 1992
Reyersbach, Mrs Susan M BA(French) . . . . *§Dec 1982
Ast: Armstrong, Mr Richard . . . . Oct 1994
Campbell-Clause, Mrs Sally BA(Hons) . . . . *Dec 1997
Gray, Mrs Jane Kathleen FILEx . . . . Jan 2006
Hamblet, Ms Simona . . . . Sep 2001
Stones, Mr Gary. . . . . Feb 2004
Workman, Mr Adam Terence . . . . *May 1992

ALFORD, Lincolnshire

TINN CRIDDLE & CO ‡
(in association with Brough Hall & Co(Skegness))
6 High Street Alford Lincolnshire LN13 9DX
Tel: 01507 462882 *Fax:* 01507 462706 *Dx:* 29741 ALFORD
E-mail: alford@tinncriddle.co.uk
List of partners: G Allen, P R Brough, C J Hall, J Hynes
Office: Spilsby, Sutton-on-Sea
Work: A1 E J1 K1 L Q S1 T1 T2 W
Fixed Fee Interview undertaken
Ptr: Allen, Mr Geoffrey. . . . . *Jan 1989
Brough, Mr Peter R LLB. . . . . *Jan 1980
Hall, Mrs Clare Joanne LLB(Hons) . . . . *Apr 1998
Hynes, Mr John BA(Hons). . . . . *Jul 2001
Ast: Briggs, Mrs Ann BSc(Hons)(Econ) . . . . *§Aug 1993
Brooks, Mrs Pamela Joan Leeds LLB(Leeds) . . . . . *Jan 1977
Giles, Mr Simon. . . . . *Jul 2009
Con: Criddle, Mr Peter M MA(Oxon) . . . . *Dec 1967
Forman, Mr John W S LLB(Lond) . . . . *Mar 1963

WILKIN CHAPMAN GRANGE SOLICITORS
(incorporating Walkers Owen Craig)
15 South Market Place Alford Lincolnshire LN13 9AE
Tel: 01507 466767 *Fax:* 01507 466263 *Dx:* 29742 ALFORD
E-mail: alfd@grangewintringham.com
Office: Beverley, Grimsby (3 offices), Horncastle, Lincoln, Louth, Mablethorpe, Market Rasen, Sutton-on-Sea
Work: A1 K1 N Q S1 S2 W
Ptr: Houltby, Mr Rupert M BSc. . . . . *§Nov 1984
Con: Quantrell, Mr Richard BA . . . . *§Dec 1978

ALFRETON, Derbyshire

BROADBENTS ‡
16 King Street Alfreton Derbyshire DE55 7AG
Tel: 01773 832511 *Fax:* 01773 520408 *Dx:* 16901 ALFRETON
Emergency telephone 01773 832511 (24HR)
List of partners: P James, J Last, Q Robbins
Office: Chesterfield, Derby, Heanor, Mansfield, Sutton-in-Ashfield
Work: A1 B1 C1 D1 E F1 G H J1 K1 L M1 N P R1 S1 T1 V W Z(c,d,e,j,k,l,p)
Emergency Action, Agency, Advocacy, Legal Aid undertaken and Member of Accident Line
Ast: Kay, Mrs Felicity S A BA(Law). . . . . Nov 1986
McMahon, Miss Olive BA; LLB . . . . *Mar 1991
Rusbridge, Mr Peter D BSc(Hons). . . . . *Oct 1990

CLEAVER THOMPSON LTD ‡
5-7 King Street Alfreton Derbyshire DE55 7AE
Tel: 01773 832193 *Fax:* 01773 835197 *Dx:* 16903 ALFRETON
E-mail: enquiries@cleaverthompson.co.uk
List of partners: A Botham, S J Shaw, A J Turner
Office: Clay Cross
Work: B1 C1 D1 D2 E F1 J1 K1 K2 K3 K4 L N O Q S1 S2 V W Z(l,m,q,r)
Emergency Action, Agency, Advocacy, Fixed Fee Interview, Legal Aid undertaken, Legal Aid Franchise and Member of Accident Line
Dir: Botham, Mr Andrew LLB(Euro) . . . . *Nov 1999
Shaw, Mr Stuart John LLB(Hons) . . . . *Nov 1995
Turner, Ms Angela Jean BA(Law) . . . . *Mar 1984
Con: Thompson, Mr J Barrie LLB. . . . . *Dec 1970

HARDY MILES TITTERTON
Hailsham House 15 Market Street South Normanton Alfreton Derbyshire DE55 2AB
Tel: 01773 580280 *Fax:* 01773 580005
E-mail: enquiry@hmtlegal.com
Office: Duffield, Ripley
Work: C1 E F1 G J1 L N Q S1 S2 T1 T2 W
Agency, Advocacy and Fixed Fee Interview undertaken

QUALITY SOLICITORS CHAPMAN & CHUBB ‡
Shane House 157 Nottingham Road Alfreton Derbyshire DE55 4JH
Tel: 01773 540480 *Fax:* 01773 540466
E-mail: chapsol@qualitysolicitors.com
List of partners: A B Chapman
Office: Alfreton
Work: C1 E F1 J1 K1 K2 K3 K4 N O Q S1 S2 W Z(d,q)
Emergency Action, Agency, Advocacy, Fixed Fee Interview and Legal Aid undertaken
SPr: Chapman, Ms Aileen Barbara BA(Legal Studies) . . . *Nov 1986
Ast: Moore, Ms Fiona Ann BA(Hons). . . . . *Jan 1999
Polley, Mrs Rachel Daphene LLB(Hons); LPC. . . . . Aug 1999

QUALITY SOLICITORS CHAPMAN & CHUBB
5 High Street Alfreton Derbyshire DE55 7DR
Tel: 01773 540480 *Fax:* 01773 833316
E-mail: chapsol@qualitysolicitors.com
Office: Alfreton
Work: C1 E F1 K1 K2 K3 K4 N O Q S1 S2 W Z(d,q)
Emergency Action, Agency, Advocacy, Fixed Fee Interview and Legal Aid undertaken

RICKARDS & CLEAVER ‡
17 Church Street Alfreton Derbyshire DE55 7AJ
Tel: 01773 832204 *Fax:* 01773 520655 *Dx:* 16904 ALFRETON
Emergency telephone 01773 831518
List of partners: M D Cairns, J P Durcan
Work: A1 D1 E F1 G H J1 J2 K1 L N O Q R1 R2 S1 S2 T1 T2 V W Z(d,l,m,q,r)
Emergency Action, Agency, Advocacy, Fixed Fee Interview, Legal Aid undertaken, Legal Aid Franchise and Member of Accident Line
Ptr: Cairns, Mr Mark D BA. . . . . *Feb 1984
Durcan, Mr James P LLB(Nott'm) . . . . *§Apr 1976

ALMONDSBURY, South Gloucestershire

ABBEY LAW ‡
25 The Courtyard Woodlands Bradley Stoke Almondsbury South Gloucestershire BS32 4NH
Tel: 01454 202102 *Fax:* 01454 202832
Dx: 124893 ALMONDSBURY 3
Emergency telephone 0117 973 4778
E-mail: priority@abbeylawsolicitors.com
List of partners: D J D Brown
Work: E S1 W
SPr: Brown, Mr David J D LLB(Exon). . . . . *Jul 1979

DAVIES & PARTNERS
135 Aztec West Almondsbury South Gloucestershire BS32 4UB
Tel: 01454 619619 *Fax:* 01454 619696 *Dx:* 35007 ALMONDSBURY
Office: Birmingham, Gloucester
Languages: French
Work: A1 A3 B1 B2 B3 C1 C2 C3 D1 E F1 F2 J1 J2 K1 K2 L N O P Q R1 R2 S1 S2 T1 T2 V W X Z(b,c,d,e,f,h,j,k,l,o,p,q,r,w)
Agency, Fixed Fee Interview, Legal Aid undertaken, Legal Aid Franchise and Member of Accident Line
Ptr: Brennan, Mr Thomas P MA(Cantab) Benefactors Law Scholar 1974; Harmsworth Exhibitioner 1972 . . . . Mar 1991
Gibbs, Mr Roger K LLB . . . . *Nov 1975
James, Mr Mark R LLB(Hons). . . . . *§Sep 1983
Kilgour, Mr Ewan M LLB(Soton). . . . . Nov 1992
Lockhart, Mr Ewan T LLB . . . . *Jul 1989
McColgan, Mr Stephen Edward LLB(Bris) . . . . *Oct 1986
Tay-Lodge, Mr Gregor Stuart LLB; Dip PI . . . . . . *Dec 1989
Ast: Austin, Mrs Louise Victoria LLB . . . . *Sep 2004
Eames, Mrs Diana M LLB(Hons) . . . . *Mar 2001
Gorman, Ms Fiona . . . . *Nov 1997
Jackson, Mrs Sarah Jane LLB. . . . . *Aug 1998
Marriott, Miss Anita J LLB(Hons) . . . . Feb 2000
Stilwell, Ms Elizabeth Mary LLB; TEP . . . . *Nov 2001
Whittock, Mrs Sarah Louise LLB(Hons) . . . . *Sep 2004
Williams, Miss Suzanne Emma LLB(Hons) . . . . . . *Jun 1998

ALNWICK, Northumberland

ADAM DOUGLAS & SON ‡
Market Place Alnwick Northumberland NE66 1HP
Tel: 01665 602363 *Fax:* 01665 510079 *Dx:* 67800 ALNWICK
E-mail: nl@adamdouglas.co.uk
List of partners: H Almond, H J A Hughes, N Luke, J M Smith
Office: Amble, Berwick-upon-Tweed
Work: A1 D1 E F1 F2 J1 K1 K3 K4 L S1 S2 W Z(l)
Legal Aid Franchise
Ptr: Hughes, Mr Hugo James A LLB(Hons) . . . . *Mar 2002
Luke, Mr Norman LLB Clerk to the Tax Commissioners . . . . *§Nov 1982
Smith, Mrs Judith M LLB . . . . *Apr 1980
Asoc: Leech, Miss Sarah LLB . . . . *Jul 2007

HARDINGTON HOGG SOLICITORS ‡
43 Bondgate Without Alnwick Northumberland NE66 1PR
Tel: 01665 605566 *Fax:* 01665 605677 *Dx:* 67801 ALNWICK
Office: Morpeth

TWYFORDS PROPERTY LAW FIRM ‡
Dunstan House Dunstan Alnwick Northumberland NE66 3SY
Tel: 01665 576040 *Fax:* 01665 576335
E-mail: law@twyfords.co.uk
Work: E K4 S1 S2 W

WARCUP SKENE ‡
Lloyds Bank Chambers 24 Bondgate Within Alnwick Northumberland NE66 1TD
Tel: 01665 606100 *Fax:* 01665 606200 *Dx:* 67810 ALNWICK
E-mail: info@warcupskene.co.uk

ALRESFORD, Hampshire

TIMOTHY J GIBSONS ‡
Laurel House Station Approach Alresford Hampshire SO24 9JH
Tel: 01962 736926 *Fax:* 01962 735226
E-mail: mail@gibsonssolicitors.co.uk

JEANETTE SILBURN ‡
2 Dene Cottages Ropley Alresford Hampshire SO24 0BJ
Tel: 01962 773777 *Fax:* 01962 773622
List of partners: J M Silburn
Work: S1 W
Ptr: Silburn, Mrs Jeanette Marianne BA . . . . *Mar 1986

ALREWAS, Staffordshire

PETER ROBERTS SOLICITOR ‡
Mill End House 18 Mill End Lane Alrewas Staffordshire DE13 7BX
Tel: 01283 790045 *Fax:* 01283 790960
E-mail: robertsrpn@hotmail.com
List of partners: R P N Roberts
Languages: French
Work: A1 C1 E F1 L R1 R2 S1 S2 T2 W Z(c,d)
Agency undertaken
SPr: Roberts, Mr Robert P N BA(Hons); MA . . . . *§Feb 1969

ALSAGER, Cheshire

POOLE ALCOCK
2a Lawton Road Alsager Cheshire ST7 2BJ
Tel: 01270 876550 *Fax:* 01270 872683 *Dx:* 23301 ALSAGER
E-mail: alsager@poolealcock.co.uk
Office: Chester, Congleton, Crewe (2 offices), Nantwich, Northwich, Sandbach, Warrington
Work: A1 B1 D1 E F1 G J1 K1 L N Q R1 S1 T1 T2 W Z(c)
Emergency Action, Agency, Advocacy, Fixed Fee Interview, Legal Aid undertaken and Member of Accident Line
Ptr: Goodwin, Mr Geoffrey I LLB. . . . . *Apr 1976

WOOLLISCROFTS
44 Crewe Road Alsager Cheshire ST7 2ET
Tel: 01270 875915 *Fax:* 01270 883672 *Dx:* 23303 ALSAGER
Office: Hanley, Newcastle under Lyme, Stoke-on-Trent
Work: A1 B1 C1 C2 C3 D1 E F1 G H J1 K1 L N O Q R1 S1 T1 T2 V W
Emergency Action, Fixed Fee Interview and Legal Aid undertaken
Ptr: Lymer, Mr Philip J LLB(Hons) . . . . *§Nov 1970

ALTON, Hampshire

ROBERT A BOOKER ‡
76 Victoria Road Alton Hampshire GU34 2DE
Tel: 01420 83570 *Fax:* 01420 83570
E-mail: bbooker@btinternet.com

BOOKERS & BOLTON ‡
Eastbrook House 6 High Street Alton Hampshire GU34 1BT
Tel: 01420 82881 / 88903 *Fax:* 01420 89880 *Dx:* 46904 ALTON
E-mail: enquiries@bookersandbolton.co.uk
List of partners: P E Carey, G P Cristofoli, E J Whale
Languages: French
Work: A1 C1 C2 E J1 K1 L N O Q S2 W
Ptr: Carey, Mrs Philippa E LLB; BL(Rhod) . . . . *§Jan 1983
Cristofoli, Mr Gideon P BA(Hons) . . . . *Nov 1993
Whale, Mrs Emma Jane BSc(Hons)(French & Law) . *May 1997
Asoc: Spiers, Mrs Doreen . . . . *Sep 1978
Tan, Mrs Tsyrina LLB(Hons). . . . . *Nov 1992

BRADLY TRIMMER ‡
Bradly Trimmer House 63 High Street Alton Hampshire GU34 1AF
Tel: 01420 88024 *Fax:* 01420 89890 *Dx:* 46907 ALTON
E-mail: info@bradlytrimmer.co.uk
List of partners: S Pandya, J W Richardson, D A Stanbrough
Work: E S1 S2 W
Ptr: Pandya, Mrs Sumita LLB(Hons). . . . . *Sep 1997
Richardson, Mr John Wilberforce LLB(B'ham). . . . *Dec 1980
Stanbrough, Mr David Allan. . . . . *Feb 1970

CAREY LAW ‡
2 Wisteria Mews London Road Holybourne Alton Hampshire GU34 9SB
List of partners: L Charles, D Gorman
Work: A1 A2 A3 B1 B2 B3 C1 C2 C3 D1 D2 E F1 F2 G H I J1 J2 K1 K2 K3 K4 L M1 M2 M3 M4 N O P Q R1 R2 S1 S2 T1 T2 U1 U2 V W X Z(a,b,c,d,e,f,g,h,i,j,k,l,m,n,o,p,q,r,s,t,u,w,x,y,z,za)
Ptr: Charles, Ms Louisa . . . . Aug 1991
Gorman, Mr Dave. Sep 1998
Ast: Joyce, Mrs Olive . . . . Jul 2007

DOWNIE & GADBAN ‡
Rockbourne House 100 High Street Alton Hampshire GU34 1ER
Tel: 01420 82879 *Fax:* 01420 87572 *Dx:* 46902 ALTON
E-mail: post@downiegadban.co.uk
List of partners: S H A Acworth, R W Pigula
Work: B1 C1 E F1 J1 J2 K1 L N O P Q R1 R2 S1 W Z(c,m,r)
Emergency Action, Advocacy, Fixed Fee Interview undertaken and Member of Accident Line
Ptr: Acworth, Mr Simon Hugh Arden Notary Public. . . . *Sep 1971
Pigula, Mr Richard W LLB(Lond) . . . . *Jul 1980
Ast: De Giovanni, Mr Julian Robert . . . . *Nov 2001
Con: Orsborn, Mr Jeremy G . . . . *Jun 1970
Particular areas of work include: Commercial and Company Law, Family, Employment, Commercial Property, Probate, Wills, Residential Property.

ENERGY TRANSACT LLP ‡
Farringdon Hurst Gosport Road Lower Farringdon Alton Hampshire GU34 3DE
Tel: 020 7096 0116 *Fax:* 020 7993 8887

KEEPING & CO ‡
49 High Street Alton Hampshire GU34 1AW
Tel: 01420 85221 *Fax:* 01420 87090 *Dx:* 46900 ALTON
List of partners: H J Keeping, I A Turk
Work: A1 B1 C1 D1 F1 G H J1 K1 L M1 P S1 T1 W Z(l,m)
Agency, Advocacy, Fixed Fee Interview and Legal Aid undertaken
Ptr: Keeping, Ms Hilary J . . . . Jul 1973
Turk, Mr Ivor A . . . . *§Feb 1955

PAINSMITH ‡
1 Mansfield Business Park Station Approach Lymington Bottom Road Alton Hampshire GU34 5PZ
Tel: 01420 565310 *Fax:* 01420 562782 *Dx:* 400953 ALTON 2
E-mail: info@painsmith.co.uk

ALTRINCHAM, Greater Manchester

AEGIS LEGAL ‡
The Annexe 26 Church Street Altrincham Greater Manchester WA14 4DW
Tel: 0161 927 3800 *Fax:* 0161 927 3801
E-mail: info@aegislegal.co.uk

STEPHEN BLACK SOLICITORS ‡
2nd Floor Station House Stamford New Road Altrincham Greater Manchester WA14 1EP
Tel: 0161 924 2230 *Fax:* 0161 924 2231
E-mail: stephen@sbsolicitors.co.uk

CHARLES BUCKLEY ‡
91 Stamford Road Bowden Altrincham Greater Manchester WA14 2JJ
Tel: 0161 928 2439 *Fax:* 0161 929 4047

CRS SOLICITORS LIMITED ‡
15 Planetree Road Hale Altrincham Greater Manchester WA15 9JN
Tel: 0161 980 8500 *Fax:* 0161 980 2800
E-mail: info@crssolicitors.co.uk

COHEN FILIPPINI ‡
10 Greenwood Street Altrincham Greater Manchester WA14 1RZ
Tel: 0161 929 9993 *Fax:* 0161 929 8933 *Dx:* 29112 ALTRINCHAM 1
E-mail: emma@cohenfilippini.co.uk
List of partners: S E Cohen, E Filippini
Languages: French
Work: C1 E K1 L N Q S1 W
Agency, Advocacy, Fixed Fee Interview and Legal Aid undertaken
Ptr: Cohen, Mr Simon E LLB . . . . Jun 1977
Filippini, Miss Emma LLB . . . . *Jun 1997
Con: Cohen, Mr Alain E C . . . . Jul 1973

COLLIER LITTLER ‡
411-413 Stockport Road Timperley Altrincham Greater Manchester WA15 7XR
Tel: 0161 980 6046 *Fax:* 0161 904 9854
E-mail: collierlittler1@hotmail.co.uk
List of partners: J Fairbrother, D E Hallam
Work: B1 C1 D1 E F1 G H J1 K1 L N R1 S1 T2 W Z(c,l)
Emergency Action, Agency, Advocacy and Legal Aid undertaken
Ptr: Fairbrother, Mr James LLB . . . . Dec 1971
Hallam, Mr David E LLB. . . . . *Jun 1968

COOPER FORD ‡
Suite 69-70 Atlantic Business Centre Atlantic Street Altrincham Greater Manchester WA14 5NQ
Tel: 0161 929 2414 *Fax:* 0161 928 1117
E-mail: richard.cooper@cooperfordlaw.co.uk

PHILIP COWEN ‡
Downs Court Business Centre 29 The Downs Altrincham Greater Manchester WA14 2QD
Tel: 0161 928 1720 *Fax:* 0161 386 8627
E-mail: pgc@philipcowen.co.uk

DOBSONS SOLICITORS ‡
17 The Downs Altrincham Greater Manchester WA14 2QD
Tel: 01694 17775 *Fax:* 01692 95602
E-mail: enquiries@dobsonssolicitors.co.uk

DUNNE GRAY ‡
Albert Buildings 3 Scott Drive Altrincham Greater Manchester WA15 8AB
Tel: 0161 928 8877 *Fax:* 0161 928 7667 *Dx:* 29119 ALTRINCHAM
E-mail: law@dg-sols.com
Work: N

FLETCHER & CO SOLICITORS
213 Ashley Road Hale Altrincham Greater Manchester WA15 9TB
Tel: 0161 926 8026 *Fax:* 0161 929 4952 *Dx:* 22972 KNUTSFORD
E-mail: johnfletcher@fsolicitor.co.uk
Office: Knutsford

N J GOODMAN & CO ‡
5 Market Street Altrincham Greater Manchester WA14 1QE
Tel: 0161 928 0990 *Fax:* 0161 941 6254
E-mail: nick.goodman@njgoodman.co.uk

HAWORTH HOLT BELL LIMITED ‡
Grosvenor House 45 The Downs Altrincham Greater Manchester WA14 2QG
Tel: 0161 928 7136 *Fax:* 0161 941 7040 *Dx:* 22054 HALE
E-mail: postroom@hhbsolicitors.co.uk
List of partners: R J Bell, R C Haworth, T J Simister
Languages: French
Work: B1 C1 C2 C3 E F1 J1 K1 K3 L N O Q S1 S2 W Z(e,q)
Dir: Bell, Mr Richard J. . . . . *§Mar 1968
Haworth, Mr Robert Chester. . . . . *§Jun 1968
Simister, Ms Tanya Joanne . . . . *Mar 1996
Asoc: Evans, Mrs Rachel Louise LLB(Hons); LPC . . . . . . Jul 2003
Hodkinson, Mrs Collette Patricia BSc(Physics); PGDL; LPC; TEP. . . . . *Jan 2009
Jones, Miss Lindsay Sorcha. . . . . Jan 2005
Marsden, Mr Andrew LLB(Hons) . . . . *Dec 1990

DAVID J HIGGINSON ‡
8 Woodhead Drive Hale Altrincham Greater Manchester WA15 9LG
Tel: 0161 980 3321 *Fax:* 0161 980 3321
Work: W

HILL & CO ‡
4-8 Market Street Altrincham Greater Manchester WA14 1QD
Tel: 0161 928 3201 *Fax:* 0161 926 9363 *Dx:* 29106 ALTRINCHAM 2
E-mail: client.services@hillandcompany.co.uk
Work: C1 D1 D2 E F1 G H J1 K1 L N O Q R1 S1 T2 V Z(d,l,m)
Emergency Action, Agency, Advocacy, Fixed Fee Interview, Legal Aid undertaken and Member of Accident Line

HILLS SOLICITORS LIMITED
19-21 Kingsway Altrincham Greater Manchester WA14 1PN
Tel: 0161 928 0961 *Fax:* 0161 941 6916 *Dx:* 19857 ALTRINCHAM
E-mail: jn@hills-solicitors.co.uk
Office: Bolton
Work: B1 D1 D2 E F1 K1 L N O Q S1 W
Emergency Action, Agency, Advocacy, Fixed Fee Interview, Legal Aid undertaken, Legal Aid Franchise and Member of Accident Line
Dir: Nattrass, Mr John A. . . . . Apr 1981

JEFFERIES LLP ‡
Ashley House Ashley Road Altrincham Greater Manchester WA14 2DW
Tel: 0800 342 3191 *Fax:* 0161 908 5122 *Dx:* 19855 ALTRINCHAM
E-mail: info@jefferies-solicitors.com
List of partners: M I Jefferies, M Ramsden
Work: N Z(r)
Agency undertaken
Ptr: Jefferies, Mr Michael Ian . . . . Nov 1988
Ramsden, Mrs Monina . . . . Oct 1994
Ast: Elkin, Mrs Nadine Louise Anne LLB(Hons) . . . . . . Feb 2001
Ferguson, Miss Kathryn LLB . . . . Jul 2004
McClarry, Miss Christine Louise LLB . . . . *Sep 2004
Nathanson, Miss Marcella FILEx . . . . Oct 2007
Sutton, Mrs Susannah J BA(Hons)(Accounting & Law) Jul 1999

KEOGHS AND NICHOLLS, LINDSELL & HARRIS ‡
25 Market Street Altrincham Greater Manchester WA14 1QT
Tel: 0161 928 9321 *Fax:* 0161 928 8334 *Dx:* 29107 ALTRINCHAM 2
E-mail: admin@keoghssolicitors.co.uk
List of partners: J S Gorner, J H Jones, L M Knight, L M Pinto, Z E Raynes, M H Sandler, M Yasser
Office: Stockport
Work: A3 D1 D2 K1 K3 K4 L N Q S1 W Z(g,q,r)
Advocacy, Legal Aid undertaken and Legal Aid Franchise
Ptr: Gorner, Mr John S LLB . . . . *Jun 1984
Raynes, Mrs Zoe E . . . . Mar 2004
Sandler, Mr Michael H. . . . . *Sep 1979
Asoc: Dent, Mrs Helen. . . . . Oct 1996
O'Hare, Mrs Emma Christine . . . . May 2009
Stacey, Ms Louise S . . . . Apr 2008
Tattum, Ms Wendii . . . . Sep 2005
Ast: England, Miss Elizabeth Kate . . . . Jun 2008
Lloyd, Mrs Nicola A . . . . Mar 2006

KING & CO ‡
Station House Stamford New Road Altrincham Greater Manchester WA14 1EP
Tel: 0161 924 2274 *Fax:* 0161 924 2275
E-mail: enquiries@kinglaw.co.uk

LAND LAW LLP ‡
10-14 Market Street Altrincham Greater Manchester WA14 1QB
Tel: 0161 928 8383 *Fax:* 0161 928 8484 *Dx:* 29918 ALTRINCHAM 2
E-mail: awhyte@land-law.co.uk
List of partners: A Chapman, H Davidson, P M Grundy, A Lawrence, A A F Whyte
Work: A1 A3 B1 C1 C2 E L O P R1 R2 S2 Z(c,d,q)
Ptr: Chapman, Mr Andrew MA. . . . . Jan 1996
Davidson, Miss Helen LLB(Hons) . . . . Jan 1996
Grundy, Mr Paul M LLB(Hons) . . . . *Oct 1989
Lawrence, Mrs Andrea BA(Law & Sociology) . . . . *Nov 1986
Whyte, Mr Angus A F MA(Cantab); LLB. . . . . . . *May 1989
Ast: Clark, Ms Ruth . . . . Sep 2005
Dingle, Ms Jenny LLB. . . . . Mar 2007
Heritage, Miss Gwyneth LLB(Hons) . . . . Oct 1985
Howarth, Ms Rosamond Irene BA. . . . . Dec 1993
Morris, Mrs Jennifer Frances MA(Cantab). . . . . . Sep 2005
Stone, Mr Andrew Simon Gordon LLB. . . . . Sep 2005

LAVIN COPITCH
5 Lloyd Square Altrincham Greater Manchester WA14 2RL
Tel: 0161 941 6462 *Fax:* 0161 941 6467
E-mail: enquiries@accidentlaw.ltd.uk
Office: Manchester
Work: J2 N
Fixed Fee Interview undertaken
Ptr: Lavin, Mr Thomas BA(Hons) . . . . *Feb 1985

WILLIAM H LILL & CO ‡
16 Old Market Place Altrincham Greater Manchester WA14 4DD
Tel: 0161 928 8111 *Fax:* 0161 926 9410 *Dx:* 29102 ALTRINCHAM 2
E-mail: enquiries@whlill.co.uk
List of partners: G Cooper, M R Jackson, O Jackson
Office: Lymm
Work: B1 D1 E J1 K1 N O S1 S2 V W
Emergency Action, Agency, Advocacy and Fixed Fee Interview undertaken
Ptr: Cooper, Mrs Gail LLB(Hons) . . . . *May 2003
Jackson, Mr Michael Rothwell BSc(Mech Eng) . . . *§Jun 1966
Jackson, Mr Oliver BA; LPC. . . . . *Sep 1996
Ast: Toft, Ms Beverly Jane LLB . . . . *Dec 1987

MCBRIDE & CO SOLICITORS ‡
36-40 Railway Street Altrincham Greater Manchester WA14 2RD
Tel: 0161 929 0229 *Fax:* 0161 929 1982
E-mail: jmcbride@mcbridesolicitors.co.uk

MALCOLM MCGUINNESS ‡
19b The Downs Altrincham Greater Manchester WA14 2QD
Tel: 0161 928 7134 *Fax:* 0161 929 7731
Emergency telephone 0161 928 7134
List of partners: D L Campbell
Work: G H
Agency, Advocacy and Legal Aid undertaken
SPr: Campbell, Mr David Lawrence LLB(Hons). . . . . . *Dec 1992
Ast: Good, Mrs Rachael Ann. . . . . *Dec 1998

MCHALE & CO ‡
19-21 High Street Altrincham Greater Manchester WA14 1QP
Tel: 0161 928 3848 *Fax:* 0161 928 3228 *Dx:* 29101 ALTRINCHAM 2
E-mail: mch@mchaleandco.co.uk

 See p112 for the Key to Work Categories & other symbols

MAURA MCKIBBIN: COLLABORATIVE SOLICITOR ‡
5 Market Street Altrincham Greater Manchester WA14 1QE
Tel: 0161 928 5974
E-mail: info@mauramckibbin.com

MADDOCKS CLARKE ‡
Fairbank House 27 Ashley Road Altrincham Greater Manchester WA14 2DP
Tel: 0844 805 5170 *Fax:* 0161 929 8446 *Dx:* 29115 ALTRINCHAM 1
E-mail: maddoc@globalnet.co.uk
List of partners: V L Norman, B J Whitworth, N J Whitworth
Work: C1 D1 E F1 G J1 K1 L M1 N P R1 S1 S2 W Z(e,l,m,q,r,w)
Emergency Action, Agency, Advocacy, Fixed Fee Interview, Legal Aid undertaken and Member of Accident Line
Ptr: Norman, Mrs Vivienne L BA. . . . . *Nov 1982
Whitworth, Mr Brian J. . . . . Jan 1967
Whitworth, Mr Nicholas James LLB . . . . *Oct 1995
Con: Brooks, Mr David G. . . . . May 1967

MASON & CO ‡
Charmax House 14 Old Market Place Altrincham Greater Manchester WA14 4DF
Tel: 0161 941 5757 *Fax:* 0161 941 5005
E-mail: info@masonandco-solicitors.co.uk

MOTORINGLAWYERS.COM ‡
Fairbank House 27 Ashley Road Altrincham Greater Manchester WA14 2DP
Tel: 0161 233 0900 *Fax:* 0161 233 0442
Emergency telephone 0161 233 0900
E-mail: contact@motoringlawyers.com
List of partners: M Lodge, M Sylvester
Ptr: Lodge, Mr Mike . . . . . Dec 1987
Sylvester, Mio. . . . . Jul 2004

MYERS LISTER PRICE ‡
7 Market Street Altrincham Greater Manchester WA14 1QE
Tel: 0161 926 9969 *Fax:* 0161 926 1500 *Dx:* 29911 ALTRINCHAM 2
E-mail: info@mlpsolicitors.co.uk
List of partners: J A Lee, M H Lister, G M Price
Work: C1 D1 D2 E F1 J1 K1 K2 L N O Q R1 S1 S2 W X Z(p,q,r)
Emergency Action, Agency, Advocacy, Fixed Fee Interview, Legal Aid undertaken, Legal Aid Franchise and Member of Accident Line
Ptr: Lee, Mr Jeremy A LLB; LLM. . . . . *Nov 1988
Lister, Mr Michael H LLB . . . . *Oct 1983
Price, Miss Gillian M LLB . . . . *Dec 1983
Asoc: Goss, Ms Joan BA(Hons) . . . . *Nov 1995
Ast: Whitehead, Mr Simon . . . . *Sep 1999
Con: Myers, Mr Ronald H LLB . . . . Dec 1963

NEIL MYERSON LLP ‡
The Cottages Regent Road Altrincham Greater Manchester WA14 1RX
Tel: 0161 941 4000 *Fax:* 0161 941 4411 *Dx:* 19865 ALTRINCHAM
E-mail: lawyers@neilmyerson.co.uk
List of partners: J M Evans, M A Latif, R M Lloyd, A Maher, N E Myerson, C E Newton, T E Norman
Office: Altrincham
Languages: French, Punjabi, Urdu
Work: A1 A3 B1 C1 C2 C3 E F1 F2 I J1 M4 O Q R1 R2 S1 S2 T1 T2 U1 U2 W Z(b,d,e,f,k,l,q,za)
Ptr: Evans, Mrs Joanne Marie BA(Cantab). . . . . Jun 1996
Latif, Mr Mohammed A LLB(Hons) . . . . Sep 1999
Lloyd, Mr Richard Michael LLB(Hons) . . . . *Sep 1996
Maher, Mr Adam LLB; LPC . . . . Sep 2003
Myerson, Mr Neil E LLB. . . . . *Jun 1973
Newton, Mr Carl Edward LLB . . . . *Nov 1995
Norman, Mr Timothy Edward BA . . . . *Jan 1983
Ast: Chandler, Mr James. . . . . Sep 2011
Evans, Laura . . . . Dec 2009
Gilbert, Miss Charlotte Rachel LLB . . . . Sep 2008
Henderson, Joanne LLB(Hons)(Leeds); LSF. . . . . Nov 1994
Kenny, Mr Philip. . . . . Sep 2007
Morris, Mr John LLB . . . . *Jan 2005
Murray, Miss Carla LLB(Hons). . . . . Sep 2006
Perritt, Mrs Joanne Grace BA. . . . . Sep 2003
Porter, Mr Christopher LLB(Hons); LPC . . . . Sep 2003
Sanig, Mrs Morag D LLB . . . . *Dec 1987
Taylor, Mrs Virginia L LLB; LLM(B'ham) . . . . *May 1978
Wellicome, Miss Sarah Louise LLB . . . . Sep 2007
Williams, Ms Sarah Ann LLB(Hons) . . . . Sep 2004

NEIL MYERSON LLP
Esmond House New Street Altrincham Greater Manchester WA14 2QS
Tel: 0161 941 4000 *Fax:* 0161 941 4411
E-mail: lawyers@neilmyerson.co.uk
Office: Altrincham

NICHOLLS HENSTOCK & STEVENSON ‡
Mayfield Chambers 228a Stockport Road Timperley Altrincham Greater Manchester WA15 7UN
Tel: 0161 980 6099 *Fax:* 0161 980 7728
E-mail: sandra.fox@nhssolicitors.co.uk
List of partners: J H Moss, G P Nicholls, S D Stevenson, W S Usden
Work: B1 C1 E F1 K1 N O Q S1 S2 W Z(j)
Agency and Legal Aid Franchise
Ptr: Moss, Mr John Humphrey Notary Public. . . . . §Apr 1964
Nicholls, Mr George Patrick LLB ♦. . . . . *Nov 1984
Stevenson, Mrs Sheryl Dawn LLB(Hons) . . . . Jan 2000
Usden, Mr Warren Stuart LLB. . . . . Mar 1988
Asoc: Davies, Mr Carl A BSc ♦ . . . . *Mar 1993
Hensley, Mr David Anthony LLB. . . . . Feb 1992

NICHOLLS LOCKE ‡
367a Stockport Road Timperley Altrincham Greater Manchester WA15 7UR
Tel: 0161 904 9595 *Fax:* 0161 903 9105 *Dx:* 26359 TIMPERLEY
E-mail: enquiry@nichollslocke.co.uk

PAGE & CO ‡
52 Leigh Road Hale Altrincham Greater Manchester WA15 9BD
Tel: 07977 023944
E-mail: andrew.page@pageand.co.uk

PANNONE LLP
Ollerbarrow House 209-211 Ashley Road Hale Altrincham Greater Manchester WA15 9SQ
Tel: 0161 926 1960 *Fax:* 0161 926 1970
E-mail: law@pannone.co.uk
Office: Manchester

MARGARET PATTERSON ‡
Grafton House 17 Grafton Street Altrincham Greater Manchester WA14 1DU
Tel: 0161 941 4862 *Fax:* 0161 926 8554
E-mail: mrgrtpatt@aol.com
List of partners: M P Patterson
Work: K1 S1 W
Ptr: Patterson, Mrs Margaret P LLB . . . . *Apr 1977

PRICE & SLATER ‡
20 Market Street Altrincham Greater Manchester WA14 4PF
Tel: 0161 615 5554
E-mail: info@priceandslater.co.uk

J M SHAOUL ‡
20 Haslemere Avenue Altrincham Greater Manchester WA15 0AU
Tel: 0161 819 1133 *Fax:* 0161 819 1144
List of partners: J M Shaoul
Ptr: Shaoul, Mr Joseph M LLB; FCIArb . . . . *Oct 1964

SHEAN SOLICITORS LTD ‡
Ravenstone House 1 The Paddock South Road Altrincham Greater Manchester WA14 3HT
Tel: 07711 130677 / 0161 929 1922
E-mail: richard@sheansolicitors.com

STOWE FAMILY LAW LLP ‡
The Camellia Building 38 Oxford Road Altrincham Greater Manchester WA14 2EB
Tel: 0161 926 1410 *Fax:* 0161 929 1538 *Dx:* 22051 HALE
E-mail: chiefexecutive@stowefamilylaw.co.uk

ULTIMATE LAW LIMITED ‡
18 The Downs Altrincham Greater Manchester WA14 2PU
Tel: 0161 710 2030 *Fax:* 0871 971 2119
E-mail: info@ultimatelawltd.com

VECTOR ‡
28-32 Greenwood Street Altrincham Greater Manchester WA14 1RZ
Tel: 0161 929 3579 *Fax:* 0161 941 6053

AMBLE, Northumberland

ADAM DOUGLAS & SON
73 Queen Street Amble Northumberland NE65 0DA
Tel: 01665 710744 *Fax:* 01665 713089
Office: Alnwick, Berwick-upon-Tweed
Work: E K4 L S1 S2 W Z(l)

KEITH S THOMPSON SOLICITOR ‡
20 Bridge Street Amble Northumberland NE65 0DR
Tel: 01665 713723 *Fax:* 01665 713674
List of partners: K S Thompson
Work: E F1 G H J1 K1 N S1 V W Z(i,m,p)
Emergency Action, Agency, Advocacy, Fixed Fee Interview and Legal Aid undertaken
SPr: Thompson, Mr Keith S . . . . Jun 1977

AMBLESIDE, Cumbria

DAVENPORT & SCOTT ‡
14 Church Street Ambleside Cumbria LA22 0BT
Tel: 01539 431919 *Fax:* 01539 434693
E-mail: info@davenport-scott.co.uk
List of partners: N C Davenport
Work: L S1 S2 W Z(l)
Fixed Fee Interview undertaken
SPr: Davenport, Mr Nicholas Charles. . . . . May 1993

AMERSHAM, Buckinghamshire

BLASER MILLS
119 High Street Old Amersham Amersham Buckinghamshire HP7 0EA
Tel: 01494 728021
Office: Aylesbury, Chesham, Harrow, High Wycombe, Rickmansworth, Staines

BROWNS
51 Woodside Road Amersham Buckinghamshire HP6 6AA
Tel: 01494 723535 *Fax:* 01494 432167
Office: Aylesbury, Beaconsfield, Bourne End, High Wycombe (3 offices), Maidenhead, Marlow, Princes Risborough, Thame

COFFERS ‡
Unit 1 Stateside House Corrinium Estate Amersham Buckinghamshire HP6 6YJ
Tel: 01494 727323 *Fax:* 01494 729696
List of partners: J Coffer
Work: G H
Advocacy undertaken
Ptr: Coffer, Mrs Joy LLB. . . . . *Jun 1979

COYLE WHITE DEVINE ‡
Boughton Business Park Bell Lane Amersham Buckinghamshire HP6 6GL
Tel: 0845 094 5945 *Fax:* 0845 094 5995 *Dx:* 50705 AMERSHAM
Office: London WC2

DAVIS & CO ‡
Flint Barn Court Church Street Amersham Buckinghamshire HP7 0DB
Tel: 01494 787587 *Fax:* 01494 787588

FULTON ROBERTSON ‡
Equity House 57 Hill Avenue Amersham Buckinghamshire HP6 5BX
Tel: 01494 722326 *Fax:* 01494 722325 *Dx:* 400002 AMERSHAM 3
E-mail: info@frlaw.co.uk
List of partners: C J Dolton
Work: F1 J1 K1 K3 K4 L N O Q S1 W Z(q,r)
Ptr: Dolton, Mr Christopher J LLB . . . . *Oct 1984

JEREMY GIBBS & CO ‡
36 Sycamore Road Amersham Buckinghamshire HP6 5DR
Tel: 01494 724671 *Fax:* 01494 434420 *Dx:* 50703 AMERSHAM
List of partners: M J C Gibbs
Work: E L S1 W
Ptr: Gibbs, Mr M Jeremy C MA(Oxon). . . . . *Jun 1974
Asoc: Pluss, Mr Harold LLB . . . . Dec 1980
Ast: Infante, Mr David A BA . . . . *Jun 1978

C Z GOODWIN ‡
17 Elm Close Amersham Buckinghamshire HP6 5DD
Tel: 01494 724446 *Fax:* 01494 431144
List of partners: C Z Goodwin
Work: S1 W
Agency undertaken
Ptr: Goodwin, Mrs Caroline Z BMus . . . . *Apr 1985

LENNONS
22 Hill Avenue Amersham Buckinghamshire HP6 5BW
Tel: 01494 433177 *Fax:* 01494 431411 *Dx:* 50716 AMERSHAM 1
E-mail: enq@lennonsltd.co.uk
Office: Chesham
Work: S1 W
Ptr: Russell, Mrs Jennifer Frances LLB(Hons) . . . . *Mar 1990

ALAN LOWE & CO ‡
Eaton Mews Badminton Court Church Street Amersham Buckinghamshire HP7 0DD
Tel: 01494 787598 *Fax:* 01494 723305
E-mail: info@alan-lowe.com

LAURENCE SINGER SOLICITOR ‡
33a Hill Avenue Amersham Buckinghamshire HP6 5BX
Tel: 01494 431400 *Fax:* 01494 431245 *Dx:* 400003 AMERSHAM 3
E-mail: admin@laurencesingersolicitor.co.uk
List of partners: L M Singer
Work: D1 K1 K2 K3
Emergency Action, Agency, Fixed Fee Interview, Legal Aid undertaken and Legal Aid Franchise
Ptr: Singer, Mr Laurence M . . . . *Mar 1970

AMESBURY, Wiltshire

BONALLACK & BISHOP
Queensberry House Salisbury Street Amesbury Wiltshire SP4 7AW
Tel: 01980 622992 *Fax:* 01980 624685 *Dx:* 46150 AMESBURY
E-mail: amesbury@bishopslaw.com
Office: Andover, Salisbury, Verwood
Work: A1 A3 B1 B2 C1 C2 C3 D1 D2 E F1 F2 G H I J1 J2 K1 K2 K3 K4 L N O P Q R1 S1 S2 T1 T2 U2 V W Z(c,e,h,k,l,m,p,q,r,s,z)
Emergency Action, Agency, Advocacy, Fixed Fee Interview and Legal Aid undertaken
Asoc: Martin, Mr Nicholas J TEP Clerk to Commissioner of Taxes . . . . *Jun 1971

TYLER LAW ‡
Minton House London Road Amesbury Wiltshire SP4 7RT
Tel: 0870 403 0200 *Fax:* 0870 403 0500
E-mail: info@tyler-law.co.uk

AMLWCH, Anglesey

T R EVANS HUGHES & CO
Rhianfa Mona Street Amlwch Anglesey LL68 9AN
Tel: 01407 830400 *Fax:* 01407 830400
Office: Holyhead
Languages: Welsh
Work: A1 C1 D1 E F1 G H J1 K1 L N Q R1 S1 V W Z(l,s,t)
Emergency Action, Agency, Advocacy, Fixed Fee Interview and Legal Aid undertaken
Ptr: Hughes, Mr John R C LLB . . . . *Apr 1983
Williams, Mr William R LLB . . . . *§Aug 1973

PARRY DAVIES CLWYD-JONES & LLOYD
15 Salem Street Amlwch Anglesey LL68 9BP
Tel: 01407 831777 / 830665 *Fax:* 01407 831573
Office: Benllech, Caernarfon, Llangefni, Pwllheli
Languages: Welsh
Work: A1 B1 C1 D1 E F1 G H J1 K1 P R1 S1 T1 W Z(l,m)
Emergency Action, Agency, Advocacy and Legal Aid undertaken
Con: Egan, Mr Peter LLB. . . . . *Feb 1984

AMMANFORD, Carmarthenshire

PHILIP AVERY & CO
12a High Street Ammanford Carmarthenshire SA18 2LY
Tel: 01269 596655 *Fax:* 01269 596018 *Dx:* 40329 LLANELLI
E-mail: enquiries@philipaverysolicitors.co.uk
Office: Llanelli

CCW LAW SOLICITORS LIMITED ‡
The Old Surgery 5 Church Street Llandybie Ammanford Carmarthenshire SA18 3HZ
Tel: 01269 851905 *Fax:* 01269 851907
E-mail: enquiries@ccwlawsolicitors.co.uk

DAVID L R DAVIES & CO ‡
Trevor Villa Lloyd Street Ammanford Carmarthenshire SA18 3BY
Tel: 01269 593463 / 592119 *Fax:* 01269 591691
Dx: 53752 AMMANFORD
List of partners: S H R Davies
Languages: Welsh
Work: A1 B1 C1 E F1 K1 K3 K4 L N O Q S1 S2 T1 T2 W Z(c,n)
Agency and Fixed Fee Interview undertaken
SPr: Davies, Mr Stephen H R LLB . . . . *Oct 1993
Con: Davies, Mr David L R BA . . . . *Jun 1962

GARY JONES SOLICITORS ‡
42 College Street Ammanford Carmarthenshire SA18 3AF
Tel: 01269 597978
E-mail: reception1@garyjonessolicitors.co.uk

LLYS CENNEN SOLICITORS ‡
52 College Street Ammanford Carmarthenshire SA18 3AG
Tel: 01269 592658 / 592790 *Fax:* 01269 596133
Dx: 53754 AMMANFORD
E-mail: law@llyscennen.co.uk
List of partners: J H Tracy Phillips, K A Tracy Phillips
Languages: Welsh
Work: A1 B2 C1 D1 D2 E F1 F2 G H J1 K1 L N P R1 S1 T1 V W X Z(l)

Emergency Action, Agency, Advocacy, Fixed Fee Interview, Legal Aid undertaken, Legal Aid Franchise and Member of Accident Line
Ptr: Tracy Phillips, Mr John H MA(Cantab) Clerk to the General Commissioners of Income Tax . . . . *Jan 1965
Tracy Phillips, Ms Katrin Annelise LLB. . . . . Apr 1994

SALTER REES & KELLY
31 Quay Street Ammanford Carmarthenshire SA18 3BS
Tel: 01269 592023 *Fax:* 01269 597848
E-mail: pak9@salterkelly.co.uk
Office: Swansea

STEADMAN JONES & BELL ‡
12 College Street Ammanford Carmarthenshire SA18 3AF
Tel: 01269 592306 *Fax:* 01269 596127
E-mail: enq@steadmanjones.com
List of partners: S E Bell, S P Morris
Languages: Welsh
Work: A1 B1 E K1 L N P Q R1 S1 S2 W Z(c,j,l,n,t)
Advocacy and Fixed Fee Interview undertaken
Ptr: Bell, Mr S Elfan LLB(Wales). . . . . *Jul 1984
Morris, Mr Simon P LLB. . . . . *Dec 1989

AMPTHILL, Bedfordshire

MILLGATE WOODBRIDGE ‡
11 Jacques Lane Clophill Ampthill Bedfordshire MK45 4BS
Tel: 01525 864820 *Fax:* 0845 528 0595
E-mail: heather.millgate@millgatewoodbridge.com

SHARMAN LAW
(incorporating Sharman and Trethewy)
88 Dunstable Street Ampthill Bedfordshire MK45 2JR
Tel: 01525 750750 *Fax:* 01525 402392 *Dx:* 36900 AMPTHILL
E-mail: mail@sharmanlaw.co.uk
Office: Bedford
Work: C1 D1 D2 E J1 K1 K2 R1 S1 S2 V W Z(h)
Emergency Action, Agency, Advocacy, Fixed Fee Interview, Legal Aid undertaken, Legal Aid Franchise, S.I.G and Member of Accident Line
Ptr: Northey, Mr Anthony W MA; LLM(Cantab); MBA Notary Public . . . . *§Apr 1972
Ast: Kendrick, Mrs Lesley A LLB(Lond) . . . . *§Nov 1972
Marchant, Ms Esther R BA . . . . Jun 1985

WILLIAMS & CO ‡
3 Woburn Street Ampthill Bedfordshire MK45 2HS
Tel: 01525 405566 *Fax:* 01525 406203 *Dx:* 36902 AMPTHILL
E-mail: reception@wilcolaw.com
List of partners: D A Barton, J C Priest
Work: A1 C1 E F1 R1 R2 S1 S2 Z(b,c)
Ptr: Barton, Mr David A . . . . *Dec 1975
Priest, Mr John C . . . . Nov 1970

ANDOVER, Hampshire

BARKER SON & ISHERWOOD LLP ‡
32 High Street Andover Hampshire SP10 1NT
Tel: 01264 353411 *Fax:* 01264 356549 *Dx:* 90303 ANDOVER
E-mail: info@bsandi.co.uk
List of partners: J E F Butcher, R C F Gregory, C R Holland
Office: Andover, Overton, Whitchurch
Work: A1 B1 C1 C2 C3 D1 E F1 J1 J2 K1 K3 K4 L N O P Q R1 R2 S1 S2 T1 T2 V W Z(b,c,d,e,h,j,l,m,n,o,q,s,t)
Legal Aid Franchise
Ptr: Butcher, Mr John E F BA . . . . *Jun 1978
Gregory, Mr Richard C F BA(Law). . . . . *Nov 1982
Holland, Mr Clive R . . . . *§Dec 1978
Ast: Hutt, Mrs Helen Lisa . . . . Nov 2001
Con: Barlow, Mr John T BA(Law) . . . . *Jun 1975
Machin, Miss Sandra LLB. . . . . *Nov 1984

BARKER SON & ISHERWOOD LLP
7 Tidworth Road Ludgershall Andover Hampshire SP11 9QD
Tel: 01264 791156 *Fax:* 01264 791209 *Dx:* 90303 ANDOVER
E-mail: info@bsandi.co.uk
Office: Andover, Overton, Whitchurch
Work: A1 B1 C1 E F1 J1 J2 K1 K3 K4 L N O Q R1 R2 S1 S2 T1 T2 W Z(j,r)
Member of Accident Line
Ptr: Holland, Mr Clive R . . . . *§Dec 1978

BONALLACK & BISHOP
3 Eastgate House East Street Andover Hampshire SP10 1EP
Tel: 01264 364433 *Fax:* 01264 356713 *Dx:* 90302 ANDOVER
Emergency telephone 01264 364433
E-mail: andover@bishopslaw.com
Office: Amesbury, Salisbury, Verwood
Work: A1 B1 B2 C1 C2 C3 D1 D2 E F1 F2 G H I J1 J2 K1 K3 K4 L N O Q R1 R2 S1 S2 T1 T2 U2 W Z(c,e,h,l,p,q,r,z)
Emergency Action, Agency, Advocacy, Fixed Fee Interview and Legal Aid Franchise

BULL & CO ‡
41b London Street Andover Hampshire SP10 2NU
Tel: 01264 352495 *Fax:* 01264 350399 *Dx:* 90316 ANDOVER
List of partners: N C Bull
Work: A1 E S1 S2 W
SPr: Bull, Mr Nigel Cecil MA(Cantab). . . . . Oct 1979

JAMES DALY LEGAL CONSULTANCY ‡
Suite 543 Andover House George Yard Andover Hampshire SP10 1PB
Tel: 07870 592467 / 0870 420 5451 *Fax:* 0870 420 5452

HAMPSHIRE LAW ‡
48 Lynx House Basepoint Business Park Caxton Close Andover Hampshire SP10 3FG
Tel: 01264 326344 *Fax:* 01264 326345
E-mail: enquiries@hampshire-law.co.uk

KERRY HILTON WILSON SOLICITOR ‡
The Law Barn Middle Wyke Andover Hampshire SP11 6AL
Tel: 01264 738788

PARKER BULLEN
8 Newbury Street Andover Hampshire SP10 1DW
Tel: 01264 400500 *Fax:* 01264 355957 *Dx:* 90304 ANDOVER
Office: Salisbury
Languages: French
Work: A1 C1 C2 D1 E J1 K1 K3 K4 R1 R2 S1 S2 T2 W Z(d,e,m)
Agency and Advocacy undertaken
Ptr: Bevan-Thomas, Mr Giles LLB(Exon) . . . . *Jun 1990
Deverill, Mrs Isabel . . . . *Nov 1993
Asoc: Gwinn, Mr Christopher Hastings Stephen L . . . . . *Sep 1997
Wilders-Pratt, Miss Emma LLB(Hons). . . . . *Dec 2003
Ast: Radigois, Miss Claire Georgette Cecily LLB . . . . . *Sep 2008
Con: Hiscocks, Mr Robin Henry Stallibrass Clerk to Commissioner of Taxes. . . . . *§Mar 1975

PARKES BROWNE ‡
24-32 London Street Andover Hampshire SP10 2PE
Tel: 01264 333336 *Fax:* 01264 333320 *Dx:* 90301 ANDOVER
E-mail: admin@parkesbrowne.co.uk
List of partners: D J Browne, M E Duckworth, R E Parkes
Languages: French
Work: A1 E F1 J1 K1 L N O Q S1 W Z(j,l)
Advocacy undertaken
Ptr: Browne, Mr David J. . . . . *Nov 1981
Duckworth, Mrs Michelle Elizabeth LLB(Hons). . . . *Sep 2000
Parkes, Mr Richard E . . . . *Dec 1972

RANSON HOUGHTON ‡
1-5 Bridge Street Andover Hampshire SP10 1BE
Tel: 01264 351533 *Fax:* 01264 332294 *Dx:* 90305 ANDOVER
Emergency telephone 01264 351388
E-mail: rh@rhsolicitors.co.uk
List of partners: N M Barry-Walsh, H F Houghton
Office: Basingstoke, Salisbury
Work: A1 B1 D1 E F1 I J1 K1 K3 L N P R1 S1 S2 V W
Emergency Action, Agency, Advocacy, Legal Aid undertaken and Member of Accident Line
Ptr: Barry-Walsh, Mr Niall Michael BA . . . . *§Nov 1974
Asoc: Buttle, Lucy. Nov 2008
Ast: Board, Mrs Natalie J BA. . . . . *Oct 1993
Con: Russell-Smith, Mr Michael R . . . . *§Dec 1969

SEARS & CO ‡
(incorporating Sears & Mant)
Wessex Chambers West Wing South Street Andover Hampshire SP10 2BN
Tel: 01264 336951 *Fax:* 01264 369121 *Dx:* 90314 ANDOVER
E-mail: sears.co@tiscali.co.uk

TALBOT WALKER LLP ‡
16 Bridge Street Andover Hampshire SP10 1BJ
Tel: 01264 363354 *Fax:* 01264 721718 *Dx:* 90300 ANDOVER
E-mail: info@talbotwalker.co.uk
List of partners: S Adlem, D M Walker, J L Walker, S T Q Walker
Office: Basingstoke
Languages: Italian
Work: A1 B1 B2 C1 C2 E F1 F2 G H I J1 K4 L M1 N O P Q R1 S1 S2 T2 W Z(c,l,q,r,t,y)
Emergency Action, Agency, Advocacy, Legal Aid undertaken and Legal Aid Franchise
Mem: Adlem, Miss Sonia LLB(Hons). . . . . *Oct 1996
Walker, Mr David M LLB Notary Public . . . . §Apr 1969
Walker, Mrs Janet Lesley LLB. . . . . *Jan 1987
Walker, Mr Simon Timothy Quentin LLB Notary Public. Nov 1985
Asoc: Torah, Ms Alison Ann LLB. . . . . Jun 2002
Ast: Lawrence, Miss Samantha Jane. . . . . Jan 2008

APPLEBY, Cumbria

GAYNHAM KING & MELLOR
29 Boroughgate Appleby Cumbria CA16 6XG
Tel: 01768 351422 *Fax:* 01768 352722
E-mail: info@gkmsolicitors.co.uk
Office: Penrith
Work: D1 D2 K1 K3 S1 S2 W Z(l)
Emergency Action, Agency, Advocacy, Fixed Fee Interview and Legal Aid undertaken
Ptr: Graham, Mr Mark PGDipLaw; LPC . . . . Dec 2004
Lowther, Mr Kevin A BA(Hons) . . . . *Aug 1986
Metcalfe, Miss Kathryn Sarah BA(Hons). . . . . . . *Nov 1998
Ast: Mitchell, Mr Clive David LLB. . . . . Oct 1985
Con: King, Mrs Julia BSc(Lond). . . . . *Apr 1979

HEELIS SOLICITORS ‡
7 Boroughgate Appleby Cumbria CA16 6XF
Tel: 01768 351591 *Fax:* 01768 352057
Emergency telephone 01768 351985
E-mail: bobearnshaw@heelis.co.uk
List of partners: C E Birtles, W R Earnshaw
Work: A1 B1 C1 D1 E F1 G H J1 K1 L N O P Q R1 S1 T1 T2 V W Z(c,d,h,k,l,p,s,t)
Emergency Action, Agency, Advocacy, Fixed Fee Interview, Legal Aid undertaken and Member of Accident Line
Ptr: Birtles, Miss Charlotte Esther BA(Hons) . . . . *Nov 2003
Earnshaw, Mr Walter Robert . . . . *Mar 1968

ARUNDEL, West Sussex

GREEN WRIGHT CHALTON ANNIS
1 Tarrant Street Arundel West Sussex BN18 9AZ
Tel: 01903 881122 *Fax:* 01903 881120 *Dx:* 86903 ARUNDEL
E-mail: arundel@gwca.co.uk
Office: Lancing, Rustington, Steyning, Worthing (2 offices)
Work: A1 C1 C2 E F1 J1 K1 L N O Q R1 R2 S1 S2 T1 T2 W Z(b,c,d,l,o,q)
Ptr: Rogers, Mr Jonathon . . . . *Sep 2002
Ast: Clark, Mr Gavin LLB(Hons) . . . . *Nov 2004
Hoare, Ms Katie. . . . . Nov 2001

HOLMES DEAN & CO ‡
21 High Street Arundel West Sussex BN18 9BX
Tel: 01903 884949 *Fax:* 01903 883003
Emergency telephone 01903 884949
Languages: French
Work: A1 C1 E F1 J1 K1 L N O P Q R1 S1 T1 W
Agency, Advocacy, Fixed Fee Interview, Legal Aid undertaken and Member of Accident Line

KENNY SOLICITORS ‡
11 The Causeway Arundel West Sussex BN18 9JJ
Tel: 01903 331021
E-mail: susanne@kennysolicitors.co.uk

ASCOT, Windsor & Maidenhead

BENJAMIN H DORMAN ‡
Northwood House Sunning Avenue Ascot Windsor & Maidenhead SL5 9PW
Tel: 01344 622276 *Fax:* 01344 622191

K LAW SOLICITORS ‡
The Old Court House London Road Ascot Windsor & Maidenhead SL5 7EN
Tel: 01344 620344 *Fax:* 01344 297344
E-mail: info@klaw.biz

NOMOS LEGAL SERVICES LIMITED ‡
Rushpoint 2 The Avenue Ascot Windsor & Maidenhead SL5 7LY
Tel: 07894 253120
E-mail: enquiries@nomoslegal.com

SCHRODER REID SOLICITORS ‡
The Old Court House London Road Ascot Windsor & Maidenhead SL5 7FJ.
Tel: 0845 643 6413 / 01344 295309 *Fax:* 0845 643 6483
E-mail: info@schroder-reid.com

TANNER & TAYLOR LLP
61 Chobham Road Sunningdale Ascot Windsor & Maidenhead SL5 0DT
Tel: 01344 876633 *Fax:* 01344 873406
E-mail: mw@margowatson.co.uk
Office: Aldershot, Farnborough, Farnham

ASHBOURNE, Derbyshire

FLINT BISHOP SOLICITORS
St John's House 54 St John Street Ashbourne Derbyshire DE6 1GH
Tel: 01335 342208 *Fax:* 01335 342010 *Dx:* 26834 ASHBOURNE
Emergency telephone 01335 25496
E-mail: info@flintbishop.co.uk
Office: Derby, Nottingham
Work: A1 C1 D1 E F1 G J1 K1 L M1 M2 N O P Q R1 S1 T1 T2 V W Z(d,l,m,o)
Emergency Action, Agency, Advocacy, Fixed Fee Interview, Legal Aid undertaken and Member of Accident Line
Ptr: Crowther, Mr Adrian C LLB(Manc). . . . . *Jan 1979
Weaver, Miss P Anne BA(Hons). . . . . *May 1981

ASHBY-DE-LA-ZOUCH, Leicestershire

CRANE & WALTON
30 South Street Ashby-de-la-Zouch Leicestershire LE65 1BT
Tel: 01530 414111 *Fax:* 01530 417022
Dx: 22653 ASHBY-DE-LA-ZOUCH
Office: Coalville, Leicester
Emergency Action, Agency, Advocacy, Fixed Fee Interview and Legal Aid undertaken
Ptr: Arnold, Mr Richard G LLB. . . . . *§Apr 1973
Crane, Mr John M. . . . . *§Jun 1980
Scott-Jones, Mr Martyn G LLB . . . . Jan 1983

FISHERS ‡
4-8 Kilwardby Street Ashby-de-la-Zouch Leicestershire LE65 2FU
Tel: 01530 412167 *Fax:* 01530 416146
Dx: 22651 ASHBY-DE-LA-ZOUCH
E-mail: fishers@fisherslaw.co.uk
List of partners: J A Gillions, M C A Killin, S W R Musson, A Robinson, L Taylor
Office: Swadlincote
Languages: French
Work: A1 A2 B1 C1 C2 D1 D2 E J1 K1 K3 K4 L O P Q R1 R2 S1 S2 T1 T2 W Z(c,d,e,l,m,n,o,p,q,s)
Fixed Fee Interview undertaken
Dir: Gillions, Mr John A MA(Oxon). . . . . *§Nov 1982
Killin, Mr M Charles A MA(Cantab) . . . . *§Apr 1978
Musson, Mr Simon W R. . . . . *§Nov 1969
Robinson, Mr Andrew BA(Jt Hons); LPC . . . . Apr 1997
Taylor, Mrs Louise LLB(Hons). . . . . *§Sep 2000
Ast: Crowson, Miss Helen BA(Hons). . . . . Apr 2009
Dobson, Miss Natasha . . . . Sep 2010
Con: Neiland, Mr T Gerard . . . . *Jul 1964
Paine, Mr Arthur John. . . . . *§Sep 1996

ANDREW M FORD ‡
(incorporating G W Hammond & Co)
York House Smisby Road Ashby-de-la-Zouch Leicestershire LE65 2UG
Tel: 01530 561734 *Fax:* 01530 561777 *Dx:* 23657 COALVILLE
E-mail: info@andrewford.co.uk

JOHN F HARRISON ‡
First Floor 52 Market Street Ashby-de-la-Zouch Leicestershire LE65 1AN
Tel: 01530 563655 *Fax:* 01530 563703
Emergency telephone 07836 516821
E-mail: jfhsolicitors@hotmail.com
List of partners: J F Harrison
Work: Z(m)
Emergency Action, Agency, Advocacy, Fixed Fee Interview, Legal Aid undertaken and Legal Aid Franchise
SPr: Harrison, Mr John F LLB ♦ . . . . *Nov 1971

NBM EASON
(in association with Nigel Broadhead Maynard; N B M Charles Whiting; N B M Dale)
Castle House South Street Ashby-de-la-Zouch Leicestershire LE65 1BQ
Tel: 01530 560545 *Fax:* 01530 563204
E-mail: paul.eason@nbmlaw.co.uk
Office: Cambridge, Chelmsford
Work: S1 S2 W
Ptr: Eason, Mr N Paul BA(Dunelm) . . . . *Oct 1981

SCUTT BEAUMONT SOLICITORS LTD
1st Floor 58 Market Street Ashby-de-la-Zouch Leicestershire LE65 1AN
Tel: 01530 563999 *Fax:* 01530 563555 *Dx:* 17016 LEICESTER 2
E-mail: info@sbs-solicitors.co.uk
Office: Corby, Leicester

 See p112 for the Key to Work Categories & other symbols

TIMMS ‡
80 Market Street Ashby-de-la-Zouch Leicestershire LE65 1AP
Tel: 01530 564498 *Fax:* 01530 588089
Dx: 22669 ASHBY-DE-LA-ZOUCH
E-mail: legal@timms-law.com

ASHFORD, Kent

BETTS & CO SOLICITORS LTD ‡
9 North Street Ashford Kent TN24 8LF
Tel: 01304 213172 *Fax:* 01304 215196 *Dx:* 30204 ASHFORD (KENT)
Emergency telephone 01304 213172
E-mail: info@bettssol.co.uk
List of partners: K Betts, J G Smith
Languages: French
Work: B2 G H
Emergency Action, Agency, Advocacy, Fixed Fee Interview, Legal Aid undertaken and Legal Aid Franchise
Ptr: Betts, Mr Keith . . . . *Sep 2000
Smith, Mr James G BA(Kent) . . . . *§Jul 1973

THE COMPENSATION CLINIC ‡
211a Bank Street Ashford Kent TN23 1DG
Tel: 01233 645678 *Fax:* 01233 650910 *Dx:* 30229 ASHFORD
E-mail: dburrows@thecompensationclinic.co.uk

RONA DOYLE & CO ‡
Wynsham House Wye Road Boughton Aluph Ashford Kent TN25 4EP
Tel: 01233 812244 *Fax:* 01233 811881

GIRLINGS
Stourside Place 35 Station Road Ashford Kent TN23 1PP
Tel: 01233 664711 *Fax:* 01233 664722
Dx: 151141 ASHFORD (KENT) 7
E-mail: enquiries@girlings.com
Office: Ashford, Canterbury, Herne Bay, Margate
Work: A1 A3 B1 C1 C2 E F1 F2 J1 L M1 O Q R1 R2 S2 Z(b,c,d,e,q,t)
Ptr: Burke, Mr Jeremy Christopher David . . . . *Oct 1988
McBride, Mr Anthony G MA; BPhil(Oxon) . . . . . . *§Dec 1976
Mallinson, Mr David J LLB. . . . . *Nov 1986
Page, Mr Christopher J BSc. . . . . *Nov 1979
Sherlock, Mr Daniel . . . . Feb 2001
Turner, Mr Richard J BA. . . . . *Sep 1984
Vincent, Mr Carl Alan . . . . *Oct 1995
Watson, Mr Andrew D. . . . . *§May 1986
Ast: Sharp, Lindsay . . . . Sep 2007

GIRLINGS
Bank House 2a Bank Street Ashford Kent TN23 1BX
Tel: 01233 647377 *Fax:* 01233 647363 *Dx:* 30232 ASHFORD (KENT)
E-mail: enquiries@girlings.com
Office: Ashford, Canterbury, Herne Bay, Margate
Work: K1 K2 K3 S1 W
Legal Aid undertaken
Ptr: Boucher, Mr Paul James . . . . *Nov 1985
Cook, Ms Alison Julia . . . . *May 2000
Staines, Mrs Roberta Julie LLB . . . . *Apr 1976
Ast: Unwin, Miss Patricia Catherine BA . . . . *Oct 1984

GOLDSPRING JONES SOLICITORS LIMITED ‡
4th Floor Suite 3 International House Ashford Kent TN23 1HU
Tel: 01843 227631 *Fax:* 01843 298567 *Dx:* 200202 CLIFTONVILLE

GURNEY HARDEN SOLICITORS LIMITED ‡
108 High Street Ashford Kent TN24 8SD
Tel: 01233 624488 *Fax:* 01233 624483
Emergency telephone 078 9495 8858
E-mail: ghenquiries@btconnect.com

HALLETT & CO ‡
11 Bank Street Ashford Kent TN23 1DA
Tel: 01233 625711 *Fax:* 01233 643841 *Dx:* 30202 ASHFORD (KENT)
E-mail: info@hallettandco.co.uk
List of partners: M Dewey, R J Diplock, A Doinik, D G Fifield, L Finlayson, J D Hudson, C A McDonald, R H Rix, M D Stevens, D Thorneycroft
Office: Ashford, New Romney
Languages: French
Work: A1 B1 C1 C2 C3 D1 D2 E F1 G H J1 K1 L N O P Q R1 S1 S2 T1 T2 V W X Z(b,c,d,e,f,h,i,j,k,l,m,p,s,t)
Emergency Action, Agency and Advocacy undertaken
Ptr: Dewey, Mr Mark LLB . . . . *Nov 1985
Diplock, Miss Ruth Janet LLB(Hons) . . . . *Oct 2003
Doinik, Mr Andrew. . . . . Sep 2006
Fifield, Mr David Graham . . . . *Dec 1990
Finlayson, Ms Louise MA(Hons); MA . . . . *Sep 1996
Hudson, Mr Jonathan Douglas . . . . *Nov 1995
McDonald, Mr Charles A BSc . . . . *§Oct 1978
Rix, Mr Richard H BSc(Lond) . . . . *Jan 1979
Stevens, Mr Martin David BSc. . . . . *§May 1996
Thorneycroft, Mr Darren. . . . . Sep 2006
Ast: Agnihotri, Ms Rakhi . . . . Sep 2005
Post, Ms Michelle Jacqueline LLB. . . . . *Jul 2000
Con: Lowings, Mr John S MA(Oxon) . . . . *§Dec 1968

HALLETT & CO
Monument Way Orbital Park Ashford Kent TN24 0HB
Tel: 01233 504700 *Fax:* 01233 503940
E-mail: info@hallettandco.co.uk
Office: Ashford, New Romney

HASKELL & CO SOLICITORS ‡
Claridge House 5 Elwick Road Ashford Kent TN23 1PD
Tel: 01233 664020 *Fax:* 01233 664144

HOLDEN & CO
3a Bank Street Ashford Kent TN23 1BX
Tel: 01233 663000 *Fax:* 01233 663009
Dx: 30212 ASHFORD (KENT) 1
E-mail: law@holdenandco.co.uk
Office: Hastings, Maidstone

KAIM TODNER LTD
46 High Street Ashford Kent TN24 8TE
Tel: 01233 662002 *Fax:* 01233 662003 *Dx:* 30210 ASHFORD (KENT)
Emergency telephone 020 7353 6660
E-mail: solicitors@kaimtodner.com
Office: London EC4, London N1, London SE17
Work: B2 G H
Agency undertaken
Dir: Quinn, Mr Robert Daniel . . . . Dec 2004
Ast: Ashley, Mr Richard . . . . May 1997

KINGSFORDS ‡
2 Elwick Road Ashford Kent TN23 1PD
Tel: 01233 624545 *Fax:* 01233 610011 *Dx:* 30205 ASHFORD (KENT)
E-mail: crp@kingsfords.net
List of partners: J D P Edmonds, A J Glover, J Granger, A D Green, K A Harper, M B McNeil
Office: Ashford
Languages: French, Mandarin
Work: A1 B1 C1 C2 C3 D1 D2 E F1 J1 K1 L M1 M2 N O P Q R1 S1 S2 T1 T2 V W Z(c,d,e,f,l)
Emergency Action, Agency, Advocacy, Fixed Fee Interview, Legal Aid undertaken and Member of Accident Line
Ptr: Glover, Miss Amanda J BSc. . . . . *Apr 1981
Green, Mr Alan David LLB . . . . *Oct 1986
McNeil, Miss Marian B . . . . *Dec 1980
Con: Hayward, Mr Colin James. . . . . *§Jan 1979

KINGSFORDS
5-7 Bank Street Ashford Kent TN23 1BZ
Tel: 01233 665544 *Fax:* 01233 645836 *Dx:* 30205 ASHFORD (KENT)
E-mail: crp@kingsfords.net
Office: Ashford
Languages: French, Mandarin
Work: A1 B1 C1 C2 C3 D1 D2 E F1 G H J1 K1 L M1 M2 N O P Q R1 S1 T1 T2 V W Z(c,d,e,f,l)
Agency, Advocacy, Legal Aid undertaken, Legal Aid Franchise and Member of Accident Line
Ptr: Edmonds, Mr Jean-Daniel D P BA. . . . . *Jun 1973
Granger, Mrs Julie LLB . . . . *Nov 1995
Harper, Mr Kevin Adrian. . . . . *Nov 1997
Ast: Fuller, Mr Graham Dean TEP . . . . *Sep 2005

LEADER VAN BOSCH SOLICITORS ‡
10 Bank Street Ashford Kent TN23 1BX
Tel: 01233 622321 *Fax:* 01233 622335
E-mail: anthonie@leadervanboschsolicitors.co.uk

MARTIN TOLHURST PARTNERSHIP LLP
Exchange House Monument House Orbital Park Ashford Kent TN24 0BH
Tel: 01233 505555 *Fax:* 01233 505556
E-mail: mtpa@martintolhurst.co.uk
Office: Gravesend, Longfield
Work: S1
Ptr: Carter, Mr Richard J BA. . . . . *Dec 1991
Newell, Mr Kevin F . . . . *Dec 1990

MOON & CO ‡
Applewood House The Hill Charing Ashford Kent TN27 0LU
Tel: 01233 714055
E-mail: kevin@moon-and-co.co.uk
List of partners: K G Moon, K B F Moon
Work: J1 W
Ptr: Moon, Mr Kevin Gordon BA. . . . . *Mar 1988

NET EMPLOYMENT SOLICITORS ‡
PO Box 216 Charing Ashford Kent TN27 0WX
Tel: 020 8906 6804 *Fax:* 01233 800009
E-mail: enquiries@net-solicitors.co.uk
List of partners: B Fakoya
Languages: Edo, Spanish, Turkish, Yoruba
Work: J1 Q W Z(i,p)
Fixed Fee Interview undertaken
Ptr: Fakoya, Ms Bola . . . . Apr 1994

ORCHID LAW ‡
Suite 1 Thorne Business Park Forge Hill Ashford Kent TN26 3AF
Tel: 01233 822250 *Fax:* 0560 344 6212
E-mail: michellepost@orchidlaw.co.uk

REEVES & CO SOLICITORS LIMITED ‡
27 High Street Ashford Kent TN24 8TF
Tel: 01233 665054 *Fax:* 0560 313 8186
E-mail: solicitors@reevesandcosolicitors.co.uk

T K SIMMONS ‡
Tulip Tree House The Lees Challock Ashford Kent TN25 4DE
Tel: 01233 740664 *Fax:* 01233 740248
Emergency telephone 01233 740664
E-mail: timmo51@aol.com
Languages: French, German
Work: C1 C2 F1 J1 Z(j)

JOHN SWALES ‡
Woodreeve Oast Capel Road Ruckinge Ashford Kent TN26 2EJ
Tel: 01233 732590 *Fax:* 01233 732718
Work: D1 D2 K1
Agency, Advocacy and Legal Aid undertaken
Ast: Gleeson, Miss Patricia LLB(Hons). . . . . Jan 1991

ASHFORD, Middlesex

OWEN WHITE & CATLIN
74 Church Road Spelthorne Ashford Middlesex TW15 2TP
Tel: 01784 254188 *Fax:* 01784 257057
Dx: 38701 ASHFORD (MIDDLESEX)
E-mail: ashford@owenwhitecatlin.co.uk
Office: Addlestone, Feltham, Hounslow, London W4, London W6, Shepperton
Languages: German, Spanish
Work: B1 C1 D1 E G H J1 K1 L N O P Q R1 S1 T1 W Z(l,p)

SHARPE & CO
(incorporating T J P O'Donnell & Co)
2 Station Approach Ashford Middlesex TW15 2QP
Tel: 01784 247376 *Fax:* 01784 244245
Dx: 38700 ASHFORD (MIDDLESEX)
E-mail: sharpe@sharpeashford.co.uk
Office: Harrow
Ptr: O'Donnell, Mr Timothy James Patrick . . . . *Jul 1977
Ast: Asghar, Mr Jehangir. . . . . Jul 2000

ASHINGTON, Northumberland

2

ADAMS HETHERINGTON
(incorporating Yarwood Gray & Co)
15 Laburnam Terrace Ashington Northumberland NE63 0XX
Tel: 01670 850520 *Fax:* 01670 522492 *Dx:* 62405 ASHINGTON
Office: Cramlington
Work: B1 C1 D1 E F1 G H J1 K1 L M1 N P Q R1 S1 T1 V W Z(k,l,p)
Emergency Action, Agency, Advocacy, Fixed Fee Interview, Legal Aid undertaken and Member of Accident Line
Ptr: Hetherington, Mr Anthony N LLB(Hons) . . . . *§Nov 1985

BROWELL SMITH & CO
Ellington House 23 Lintonville Terrace Ashington Northumberland NE63 9UN
Tel: 0871 474 3030 *Fax:* 0845 302 4755
E-mail: advice@browells.co.uk
Office: Cramlington, Newcastle upon Tyne (3 offices), Stockton-on-Tees, Stoke-on-Trent, Sunderland

CUTHBERTSONS
6a Laburnum Terrace Ashington Northumberland NE63 0XX
Tel: 01670 813524 *Fax:* 01670 810802 *Dx:* 62404 ASHINGTON
E-mail: enquiries@cutherbertsonsashington.com
Office: Blyth
Work: S1 W
Ptr: Armstrong, Mr Eric Coroner for North Tyneside and South Northumberland. . . . . *Jul 1969

LAWSON & THOMPSON ‡
(incorporating Craigs)
Post Office Chambers Station Road Ashington Northumberland NE63 8RL
Tel: 01670 813588 *Fax:* 01670 818722 *Dx:* 62407 ASHINGTON
Office: Bedlington, Blyth
Work: C1 D1 F1 G H K1 L S1 W

PETER MILLICAN & CO ‡
Northumbria Centre for Enterprise Lintonville Enterprise Park Ashington Northumberland NE63 9JZ
Tel: 01670 528450 *Fax:* 01670 528460
E-mail: peter@petermillicansolicitors.co.uk

ASHTEAD, Surrey

A J LUTLEY ‡
Springfield Rookery Hill Ashtead Park Ashtead Surrey KT21 1HY
Tel: 01372 279066 *Fax:* 0870 132 3728
E-mail: alutley@elawuk.com
List of partners: A J Lutley
Work: C1 E F1 I J1 L Z(d)
SPr: Lutley, Mr Andrew John MA(Cantab) . . . . *Oct 1976

SCOTT SON & CHITTY ‡
50 The Street Ashtead Surrey KT21 1AZ
Tel: 01372 276211 *Fax:* 01372 272608
List of partners: P J Martin
Work: E G H L Q S1 S2 W Z(y)
Agency, Advocacy, Fixed Fee Interview and Legal Aid undertaken
SPr: Martin, Mr Patrick J BA(Dunelm) . . . . *Sep 1980

ASHTON-IN-MAKERFIELD, Greater Manchester

HOUGHTON PIGOT & CO
1b Bryn Street Ashton-in-Makerfield Greater Manchester WN4 9AX
Tel: 01942 270757 *Fax:* 01942 721579
Dx: 18705 ASHTON-IN-MAKERFIELD
E-mail: enquiries@houghtonpigot.co.uk
Office: Wigan
Languages: French, Spanish
Work: A1 B1 C1 C2 C3 E F1 G H J1 K1 L M1 M2 N P R1 S1 T1 T2 V W Z(e,k,m)
Emergency Action, Agency, Advocacy, Fixed Fee Interview undertaken and Member of Accident Line
Ptr: Houghton, Miss Susan Elizabeth LLB Notary Public . . *Jan 1994
Lawlor, Mrs Frances M BA . . . . *Oct 1983
Randall, Mr Mark J LLB(UWIST) . . . . *Oct 1986

MILLS & CO ‡
1st Floor 60-62 Gerard Street Ashton-in-Makerfield Greater Manchester WN4 9AF
Tel: 01942 719655 *Fax:* 01942 727048
Emergency telephone 01942 719655
E-mail: mills_co@btconnect.com
List of partners: P A Mills
Work: E S1 S2 W
SPr: Mills, Mr Peter Alan LLB(Lond) . . . . *Apr 1978

GARTH RIGBY & CO ‡
23 Wigan Road Ashton-in-Makerfield Greater Manchester WN4 9AR
Tel: 01942 717378 *Fax:* 01942 271137
Dx: 18701 ASHTON-IN-MAKERFIELD
List of partners: N J Crompton
Languages: French
Work: D1 E F1 G H J1 K1 L N O P Q S1 V W Z(k,l,p,q)
Emergency Action, Advocacy, Fixed Fee Interview, Legal Aid undertaken and Legal Aid Franchise
Ptr: Crompton, Mrs Natalie Jane LLB(Hons) . . . . *Sep 1999
Con: Rigby, Mr Garth L LLB . . . . *Jun 1971

ASHTON-UNDER-LYNE, Greater Manchester

BEEVERS SOLICITORS ‡
15 Booth Street Ashton-under-Lyne Greater Manchester OL6 7LD
Tel: 0161 339 9697 *Fax:* 0161 343 1718
Dx: 25615 ASHTON-UNDER-LYNE
Emergency telephone 0161 339 9697
E-mail: enquiries@beevers-solicitors.co.uk
List of partners: L A Burke, J K Davis, B Ellis-Dokubo, K Lawson
Languages: Punjabi, Urdu
Work: D1 E G H J1 K1 L N O Q R1 S1 S2 W Z(i)
Emergency Action, Agency, Advocacy, Legal Aid undertaken and Legal Aid Franchise

Ptr: Burke, Ms Lorraine Ann BSc . . . . *Jun 1996
Davis, Mr John Keith LLB(Manc) . . . . *Jun 1981
Ellis-Dokubo, Boma LLB(Hons) . . . . *Feb 1993
Lawson, Mr Karibo . . . . *Jan 2001

BROMLEYS SOLICITORS LLP ‡
50 Wellington Road Ashton-under-Lyne Greater Manchester OL6 6XL
Tel: 0161 330 6821 *Fax:* 0161 343 1719
Dx: 25616 ASHTON-UNDER-LYNE
Emergency telephone 07785 531221
E-mail: bromleys@bromleys.co.uk
List of partners: N J Clough, M J Hirst, J M Longworth, K A G Platts, P S Westwell
Office: Manchester
Languages: French
Work: A3 B1 C1 C2 D1 D2 E F1 J1 J2 K1 K2 K3 K4 L N O Q R1 R2 S1 S2 T2 W Z(k,l,p,q)
Agency, Advocacy, Fixed Fee Interview, Legal Aid undertaken and Legal Aid Franchise
Ptr: Clough, Mr Nicholas Jonathan LLB(Hons); Dip PI . . *Nov 1991
Hirst, Mr Mark Jeremy LLB(Hons) . . . . *Nov 1989
Longworth, Mr John Myles . . . . *Jul 1975
Platts, Mr Keith A G LLB . . . . *Apr 1976
Westwell, Mr Paul Steven . . . . *Sep 2009
Asoc: Davies, Jennifer Lyn ♦ . . . . *Sep 1996
Ast: Bell, Miss Olivia Ann LLB . . . . *Jun 2003
Gwenlan, Mr Stephen B BA . . . . *Dec 1976
Mehta, Mr Krishan K LLB . . . . *Dec 1992
Oakes, Miss Natalie . . . . *Aug 2008

CLINCH SOLICITORS ‡
37 The Arcades Warrington Street Ashton-under-Lyne Greater Manchester OL6 7JD
Tel: 0161 441 0390 *Fax:* 0161 441 0391
E-mail: help@clinchsolicitors.co.uk

DWYERS ‡
176 Stamford Street Ashton-under-Lyne Greater Manchester OL6 7LR
Tel: 0161 308 3928 *Fax:* 0161 343 2410
Dx: 25607 ASHTON-UNDER-LYNE
E-mail: solicitors@dwyers.net
List of partners: M H P Allweis, A Reed
Work: B1 C1 C2 C3 D1 E F1 G H J1 K1 L N O P Q R1 S1 T1 T2 V W X Z(b,c,d,e,f,h,i,j,k,l,m,n,o,p,s,t)
Emergency Action, Agency, Advocacy, Fixed Fee Interview, Legal Aid undertaken and Member of Accident Line
Ptr: Allweis, Mr Micheal H P BA . . . . *Jul 1991
Reed, Ms Amanda LLB(Hons) . . . . Jul 2002

PLUCK ANDREW & CO
(incorporating Hibbert Pownall & Newton)
127 Old Street Ashton-under-Lyne Greater Manchester OL6 7SA
Tel: 0161 330 2875 *Fax:* 0161 343 2584
Dx: 25617 ASHTON-UNDER-LYNE
Emergency telephone 0161 368 6311
E-mail: reception@pluckandrew.com
Office: Hyde
Work: B2 D1 D2 E G H K1 K2 L N O Q R1 S1 T1 T2 V W Z(h,i,k,l,m,o,y)
Emergency Action, Agency, Fixed Fee Interview, Legal Aid undertaken, Legal Aid Franchise and Member of Accident Line
Ast: Fitzpatrick, Miss Angela M LLB(Nott'm) . . . . *Jun 1974

QUALITYSOLICITORS GRUBER GARRATT
61-63 Old Street Ashton-under-Lyne Greater Manchester OL6 6BD
Tel: 0161 344 2244 *Fax:* 0161 308 5139
Dx: 25612 ASHTON-UNDER-LYNE
Emergency telephone 07971 163241
E-mail: info@qsgrubergarratt.co.uk
Office: Oldham, Radcliffe, Stalybridge, Worsley
Languages: Gujarati
Work: B1 B2 C1 C2 D1 E F2 G H K1 K3 L N O P Q R1 R2 S1 S2 V W Z(i,j,k,l,m,p,q,r)
Emergency Action, Agency, Advocacy, Fixed Fee Interview, Legal Aid undertaken, Legal Aid Franchise and Member of Accident Line
Ptr: Gruber, Mr Howard P LLB . . . . *Mar 1982

ROGERSON GALVIN ‡
159 Stamford Street Ashton-under-Lyne Greater Manchester OL6 6XW
Tel: 0161 344 2027 / 335 9005 *Fax:* 0161 343 2996
List of partners: J S Galvin, A Proudfoot, I C Ridgway, C M Rogerson
Languages: French
Work: A1 B1 C1 C2 D1 E F1 G H K1 K3 L M1 M2 N O P Q R1 S1 S2 T1 T2 W Z(i)
Emergency Action, Agency, Advocacy, Fixed Fee Interview and Legal Aid undertaken
Ptr: Galvin, Mr John S LLB . . . . *Aug 1977
Proudfoot, Mr Alan . . . . *Oct 1981
Ridgway, Mr Ian C LLB . . . . *Nov 1989
Rogerson, Ms Catherine M . . . . *Jan 1980
Asoc: Miller, Ms Carole Joan LLB . . . . *Apr 2002
Ast: Heylin, Mrs Alison . . . . *Feb 1988

SMITH & TETLEY ‡
23-25 Booth Street Ashton-under-Lyne Greater Manchester OL6 7LF
Tel: 0161 330 2865 *Fax:* 0161 343 3285
Dx: 25610 ASHTON-UNDER-LYNE
E-mail: smithandtetley@hotmail.com
List of partners: A J Parker, M J Tetley
Work: B1 C1 C3 D1 E F1 K1 N O Q R1 S1 V W Z(l)
Emergency Action, Advocacy, Fixed Fee Interview, Legal Aid undertaken and Member of Accident Line
Ptr: Parker, Ashley J LLB . . . . *§Oct 1981
Tetley, Mr Mark J LLB(Manc) . . . . *§Dec 1973

HAROLD STOCK & CO ‡
55-57 Stamford Street Mossley Ashton-under-Lyne Greater Manchester OL5 0LN
Tel: 01457 835597 / 835034 *Fax:* 01457 837410
Dx: 25618 ASHTON-UNDER-LYNE
Emergency telephone 01457 870445
E-mail: mlr@haroldstock.com
List of partners: A Doggett, K A Kenyon, D McGuinness, A M Murray, J A O'Donnell, M L Ryan, A P Stock
Office: Ashton-under-Lyne, Failsworth
Languages: French, Hebrew
Work: B1 C1 C2 D1 E J1 K1 K3 K4 N O Q R1 R2 S1 S2 T1 T2 W Z(l,q)
Emergency Action, Agency, Advocacy and Fixed Fee Interview undertaken
Ptr: Doggett, Miss Angela LLB . . . . Jan 2004
Kenyon, Miss Karen Anne LLB(Hons) . . . . *Jan 1991
Murray, Mr Andrew Martin LLB . . . . *Jan 1986
O'Donnell, Mr James A LLB(Hons) . . . . Apr 2005
Ryan, Mr Mark Leslie LLB . . . . *§Oct 1993
Stock, Mr Alan Paul MA; LLB(Cantab) . . . . *Sep 1978
Con: Himelfield, Mr Andrew Kingston LLB(Hons) . . . . . . Jul 1977
Ranken, Mr Nigel BA(Econ) . . . . *Jun 1995

HAROLD STOCK & CO
2a Argyle Street Mossley Ashton-under-Lyne Greater Manchester OL5 0HF
Tel: 01457 838136 *Fax:* 01457 838740
Dx: 25618 ASHTON-UNDER-LYNE
E-mail: info@haroldstock.com
Office: Ashton-under-Lyne, Failsworth
Work: B1 C1 C2 D1 E J1 K1 K3 K4 N O Q R1 R2 S1 S2 T1 T2 W Z(l,q)
Emergency Action, Agency, Advocacy, Fixed Fee Interview undertaken and Member of Accident Line
Asoc: Wood, Miss Rebecca Jane LLB . . . . *Jan 2007

HAROLD STOCK & CO ‡
1 Anthony Street Mossley Ashton-under-Lyne Greater Manchester OL5 0HU
Tel: 01457 836152 *Fax:* 01457 835180

TRAFFICLAWYERS4U LIMITED ‡
60-66 Wellington Road Ashton-under-Lyne Greater Manchester OL6 6DE
Tel: 0800 032 5930
E-mail: info@trafficlawyer4u.com

WALKER SMITH WAY
8 Warrington Street Ashton-under-Lyne Greater Manchester OL6 6XP
Tel: 0844 346 3100 *Fax:* 0844 346 3200
Dx: 25613 ASHTON-UNDER-LYNE
E-mail: enquiries@walkersmithway.com
Office: Birmingham, Chester, Liverpool, London SW11, Wrexham
Work: J1 N Z(p,r)
Fixed Fee Interview, Legal Aid undertaken and Member of Accident Line
Ast: Hughes, Mr Paul Robert . . . . Jul 2002

RUPERT WOOD & SON ‡
60-66 Wellington Road Ashton-under-Lyne Greater Manchester OL6 6DE
Tel: 0161 330 9121 *Fax:* 0161 343 1342
Dx: 25611 ASHTON-UNDER-LYNE
Emergency telephone 0161 303 9121
E-mail: law@rupertwood.co.uk
List of partners: D Lennie, M J Wood
Languages: French, Spanish
Work: D1 E K1 K3 K4 N S2 W Z(m,q,r)
Emergency Action, Agency, Advocacy, Fixed Fee Interview, Legal Aid undertaken, Legal Aid Franchise and Member of Accident Line
Ptr: Lennie, Mr David LLB . . . . *Oct 1978
Wood, Mr Michael J LLB . . . . *Dec 1974
Asoc: Haworth, Mr David LLB(Hons) . . . . Nov 1993
Ast: Beilby, Miss Helen M LLB ♦ . . . . *Nov 1992

YATES ARDERN ‡
131-133 Old Street Ashton-under-Lyne Greater Manchester OL6 7SA
Tel: 0161 330 3332 *Fax:* 0161 339 4150
Emergency telephone 0161 330 3332
E-mail: enquiries@yatesardern.co.uk
List of partners: J T Chapman, W P Dowdall, M W Harper
Office: Oldham
Work: B2 G H
Agency, Advocacy and Legal Aid undertaken
Ptr: Chapman, Mr J Timothy BA . . . . *Mar 1987
Dowdall, Mr William P BA . . . . *Jan 1985
Harper, Mr Mark William LLB(Hons) . . . . *Feb 1996
Ast: Martin, Miss Victoria . . . . *Jul 2001
Wilding, Miss Elizabeth A LLB . . . . *Jan 1979

ATHERSTONE, Warwickshire

GARNER CANNING
133 Long Street Atherstone Warwickshire CV9 1AD
Tel: 01827 713543 *Fax:* 01827 717638 *Dx:* 23952 ATHERSTONE
E-mail: enquiries@garnercanning.co.uk
Office: Birmingham, Sutton Coldfield, Tamworth
Work: A1 C1 C2 D1 D2 E J1 K1 K2 K3 K4 Q R1 R2 S1 S2 T1 T2 W Z(d,l)
Fixed Fee Interview and Legal Aid undertaken
Ptr: Lewis, Mr David J LLB; TEP . . . . *§Dec 1975
Rymell, Ms Emma . . . . Dec 1998
Dir: Taylor, Ms Rachel Margaret . . . . Jan 2004

ATHERTON, Greater Manchester

DOOTSONS LLP
6 Eckersley Precinct Alma Street Atherton Greater Manchester M46 0DR
Tel: 01942 882172
E-mail: lawyers@dootsons.co.uk
Office: Culcheth, Leigh

MALCOLM PEET & CO
63 Market Street Atherton Greater Manchester M46 0DA
Tel: 01942 876115 *Fax:* 01942 894173 *Dx:* 700874 ATHERTON
E-mail: mpeet@hotmail.co.uk
Office: Wigan
Work: E F1 G H J1 K1 L M1 N P S1
Emergency Action, Advocacy, Fixed Fee Interview and Legal Aid undertaken
Ptr: Rudd, Mr Stephen J . . . . Apr 1978

RUSSELL & RUSSELL
43 Market Street Atherton Greater Manchester M46 0GQ
Tel: 01942 884469 *Fax:* 01942 875895 *Dx:* 700873 ATHERTON
Emergency telephone 0800 731 7555
E-mail: infoatherton@russellrussell.co.uk
Office: Bolton (4 offices), Bury, Middleton
Work: D1 D2 K1 K3 N W
Emergency Action, Agency, Advocacy, Fixed Fee Interview, Legal Aid undertaken and Member of Accident Line
Ptr: Seddon, Mr Neil BA . . . . Mar 1984
Ast: Taylor, Ms Christina LLB . . . . Feb 2002
Whitelegge, Miss Sarah BA(Hons) . . . . Apr 2010

ATTLEBOROUGH, Norfolk

NICHOLAS DAYKIN SOLICITORS ‡
Connaught Lodge 10 Connaught Road Attleborough Norfolk NR17 2BN
Tel: 01953 453774 *Fax:* 01953 454099 *Dx:* 44003 ATTLEBOROUGH
E-mail: info@nicholasdaykin.co.uk
Work: A1 C1 D1 E F1 K1 K3 K4 R1 R2 S1 S2 W Z(d,l)

GREENLAND HOUCHEN POMEROY
The Pines Connaught Road Attleborough Norfolk NR17 2BP
Tel: 01953 453143 *Fax:* 01953 453970 *Dx:* 44000 ATTLEBOROUGH
E-mail: mail@ghlaw.co.uk
Office: Long Stratton, Norwich, Watton, Wymondham
Work: A1 B1 C1 D1 E F1 J1 K1 K2 K3 K4 L N Q R1 S1 S2 T1 V W Z(h,q)
Agency, Advocacy, Fixed Fee Interview and Legal Aid undertaken
Ptr: Wright, Mr Colin D LLB Clerk to East Harling Internal Drainage Board . . . . *§Apr 1978
Ast: Bunn, Mrs Carolyn BSc . . . . *Mar 2008
Harris, Mrs Sally A BA . . . . *Sep 1988
Con: Plumbly, Mr Robert C S Clerk to Attleborough Tax Commissioner . . . . *§Nov 1973

Particular areas of work include: Agricultural Law, Holdings and Property, Bankruptcy, Commercial and Company Law, Child Care and Wardship, Commercial Property and Matrimonial.

MORONEYS ‡
1 Exchange Street Attleborough Norfolk NR17 2AB
Tel: 01953 455806 *Dx:* 44001 ATTLEBOROUGH
Emergency telephone 01603 810484
E-mail: moroneyssolicitors@aol.com
List of partners: L A J Moroney
Office: Wymondham
Work: A1 C1 D1 F1 K1 P Q S1 W
Emergency Action, Agency, Advocacy, Fixed Fee Interview undertaken and Member of Accident Line
Ptr: Moroney, Mr Lawrence A J . . . . *§Jan 1971

AXMINSTER, Devon

BEVISS & BECKINGSALE ‡
Law Chambers Silver Street Axminster Devon EX13 5AH
Tel: 01297 630700 *Fax:* 01297 630701 *Dx:* 43300 AXMINSTER
E-mail: enquiries@bevissandbeckingsale.co.uk
List of partners: M A R Carlisle, N J Cole, Z Gaitskell, M E Ollier
Office: Chard, Honiton, Seaton
Work: A1 A2 A3 C1 D1 E F1 K1 L N O P Q R1 S1 S2 T1 T2 V W Z(l,o)
Emergency Action, Advocacy and Fixed Fee Interview undertaken
Ptr: Carlisle, Mr Mark Anthony Robert LLB . . . . *Mar 1991
Cole, Mr Nigel J LLB . . . . *§Apr 1973
Ast: Boyer, Ms Victoria LLB . . . . Jan 2006
Knight, Mrs Julia Elizabeth LLB . . . . Sep 2005

MILFORD & DORMOR ‡
Silver Street Axminster Devon EX13 5AJ
Tel: 01297 32206 / 32207 *Fax:* 01297 35239 *Dx:* 43302 AXMINSTER
Emergency telephone 01297 33618
E-mail: axminster@milfordanddormor.co.uk
List of partners: W C Bennett, C E Burdett, D T Fazio
Office: Chard, Ilminster, Seaton
Work: A1 D1 E F1 G H J1 K1 L N Q S1 T2 W Z(m)
Emergency Action, Agency, Advocacy, Fixed Fee Interview, Legal Aid undertaken and Member of Accident Line
Ast: Deekes, Mr David M . . . . *Jul 1978

SCOTT ROWE ‡
Chard Street Axminster Devon EX13 5DS
Tel: 01297 32345 *Fax:* 01297 35229
E-mail: enquiries@scottrowe.co.uk

AYLESBURY, Buckinghamshire

BESHOFFS SOLICITORS ‡
22 Holly Court Tring Road Wendover Aylesbury Buckinghamshire HP22 6PE
Tel: 01296 621180 *Fax:* 01296 624928
E-mail: jim@beshoffslaw.com

BLASER MILLS
1 Cambridge Street Aylesbury Buckinghamshire HP20 1RP
Tel: 01296 434416 *Fax:* 01296 436615 *Dx:* 4125 AYLESBURY
Office: Amersham, Chesham, Harrow, High Wycombe, Rickmansworth, Staines
Work: D1 G H K1 K3
Emergency Action, Agency, Legal Aid undertaken and Legal Aid Franchise
Ptr: Rogers, Mr Darren James BA(Hons) . . . . Mar 1999
Asoc: Abbott, Mr Mark LLB ★ . . . . *Jan 2003
Pitcher, Mrs Diane . . . . *Jun 1980
Ast: Berry, Mr John Roger Phipps LLB . . . . Oct 1987
Jarvis, Mr Neil Renny BSc . . . . Feb 1987

G BOYLE ‡
113 Weston Road Aston Clinton Aylesbury Buckinghamshire HP22 5EP
Tel: 01296 630090 *Fax:* 01296 630090

BROWNS
12 Temple Square Aylesbury Buckinghamshire HP20 2QL
Tel: 01296 338633 *Fax:* 01296 338655 *Dx:* 4160 AYLESBURY
E-mail: aylesbury@brownssolicitors.co.uk
Office: Amersham, Beaconsfield, Bourne End, High Wycombe (3 offices), Maidenhead, Marlow, Princes Risborough, Thame

BUCKS SOLICITORS ‡
Cherat House 32 Havelock Street Aylesbury Buckinghamshire HP20 2NX
Tel: 01296 331600

CROWN AND MEHRIA SOLICITORS ‡
18 Carrington Road Aylesbury Buckinghamshire HP21 8JD
Tel: 01296 392403 *Fax:* 01296 392403
E-mail: mail@crownmehria.com

See p112 for the Key to Work Categories & other symbols

STUART FANTHAM ‡
14a High Street Wendover Aylesbury Buckinghamshire HP22 6EA
Tel: 01296 620300 *Fax:* 01296 620600
E-mail: legal@stuartfantham.co.uk
List of partners: S A Fantham
Office: Milton Keynes
Work: E L S1 W Z(h,q)
SPr: Fantham, Mr Stuart A LLB . . . . *Oct 1988

G C GARLICK ‡
9 Mill Court Quainton Road Waddesdon Aylesbury Buckinghamshire HP18 0LP
Tel: 01296 651481 *Fax:* 01296 651481
Emergency telephone 01296 651481
List of partners: G C Garlick
Work: E S1 W

HORWOOD & JAMES LLP ‡
7 Temple Square Aylesbury Buckinghamshire HP20 2QB
Tel: 01296 487361 *Fax:* 01296 427155 *Dx:* 4102 AYLESBURY
E-mail: enquiries@horwoodjames.co.uk
List of partners: K M Pratt, A K M Thorpe, J M Warbey
Work: A1 B1 C1 C2 C3 D1 E F1 G J1 K1 L N O P Q R1 R2 S1 T1 T2 V W Z(c,d,j,k,l,p,t)
Emergency Action, Agency, Advocacy, Fixed Fee Interview, Legal Aid Franchise and Member of Accident Line
Ptr: Pratt, Miss Kristine M BSc. . . . . *§Dec 1974
Thorpe, Miss Alison K M BA(Hons) . . . . *Nov 1987
Warbey, Mr Jonathan Mark LLB. . . . . *§Nov 1990
Ast: Leach, Mrs Kathryn J BA . . . . *Jun 1988
Reddington, Mr John LLB(Hons) . . . . Oct 2008
Swift, Miss Jill C LLB . . . . *§Oct 1990
Con: Freeman, Mr Neil LLB. . . . . *§Jul 1975
Maison, Mrs Geraldine E C . . . . *§Nov 1973

HOUSEMAN SOLICITORS ‡
Unit 10 Wingbury Courtyard Business VI Aylesbury Buckinghamshire HP22 4LW
Tel: 01296 682791 *Fax:* 01926 682151
Dx: 90802 LEIGHTON BUZZARD
E-mail: gib@housemans.co.uk

THE HOWARD PARTNERSHIP LIMITED
The Open House Edgcott Road Doddershall Aylesbury Buckinghamshire HP22 4DE
Tel: 01296 770372 *Fax:* 0800 093 4212
E-mail: richard.howard@richardhoward.co.uk
Office: London WC2
Languages: French
Work: A3 C1 C2 I J1 K1 K2 O T1 Z(e,f,k,w)
Ptr: Howard, Ms Helen P LLB(Hons). . . . . *May 1983
Howard, Mr Richard V LLB(Hons). . . . . *§Jun 1981

KIDD RAPINET
Western House 14 Rickfords Hill Aylesbury Buckinghamshire HP20 2RX
Tel: 0845 017 9616 *Fax:* 01296 432303 *Dx:* 4107 AYLESBURY
E-mail: rbenz@kiddrapinet.co.uk
Office: Farnham, High Wycombe, London WC2, Maidenhead, Reading, Slough
Work: A1 B1 C1 C2 C3 D1 E F1 G H I J1 K1 L M1 M2 N O P Q R1 R2 S1 T1 T2 V W X Z(b,c,e,j,l,m,s)
Emergency Action, Agency, Advocacy, Fixed Fee Interview, Legal Aid undertaken, Legal Aid Franchise and Member of Accident Line
Ptr: Benz, Mr Richard L . . . . *§Nov 1970
McMahon, Edel . . . . *Aug 2005
O'Shea, Mr John F LLB . . . . *Mar 1978
White, Mr Jeff. *Oct 1994
Ast: Chubb, Miss Samantha Ruth BSc(Hons) . . . . *Nov 2003

LEGAL TEAM LIMITED ‡
1st Floor Barclays House Gatehouse Way Aylesbury Buckinghamshire HP19 8DB
Tel: 01296 336077 *Fax:* 01296 336088
E-mail: doc@legalteam.org.uk

PAUL LUCAS & CO ‡
12 Temple Street Aylesbury Buckinghamshire HP20 2RQ
Tel: 01296 484022 *Fax:* 01296 392189 *Dx:* 4120 AYLESBURY
E-mail: paullucas@paul-lucas.co.uk
List of partners: P E Lucas
Work: C1 C2 C3 K1 K3 K4 R2 S1 W Z(l)
Ptr: Lucas, Mr Paul Edward . . . . *Nov 1980

M & D LAW LLP ‡
14 Prebendal Court Oxford Road Aylesbury Buckinghamshire HP19 8EY
Tel: 01296 436703 *Fax:* 01296 437101 *Dx:* 4111 AYLESBURY
E-mail: mhalton@mndlaw.co.uk

K M MARDELL & CO ‡
3rd Floor Kingfisher Exchange Kingfisher House Aylesbury Buckinghamshire HP21 7AY
Tel: 01296 468575 *Fax:* 01296 468562

PARROTT & COALES LLP ‡
14 Bourbon Street Aylesbury Buckinghamshire HP20 2RS
Tel: 01296 318500 *Fax:* 01296 318531 *Dx:* 4100 AYLESBURY
E-mail: law@parrottandcoalesllp.co.uk
List of partners: J R Couzens, S C S Ellis, R T Friedlander, J Leggett, S Plumridge, C A Suttill
Work: A1 B1 C1 C2 D1 D2 E J1 K1 K3 L N O Q R1 S1 S2 T1 T2 W Z(c,d,l)
Agency, Advocacy, Fixed Fee Interview, Legal Aid undertaken and Legal Aid Franchise
Ptr: Couzens, Mr James R BA. . . . . *§Nov 1985
Ellis, Mr Shaun C S LLB . . . . *§Mar 1986
Friedlander, Mr R Timothy MA(Oxon) . . . . *§Oct 1979
Leggett, Mr John Clerk to Commissioner of Taxes; Under Sheriff of the County of Buckingham . . . . *§Jul 1967
Plumridge, Miss Sarah BA(Hons)(Lond). . . . . . . *Dec 1995
Suttill, Miss Clare A LLB(Hons); LLM . . . . *Nov 1998
Asoc: Montlake, Mr Stuart LLB; FCIArb . . . . *Dec 1962
Sauvain, Mr Richard Philip . . . . Oct 1993
Wanstall, Mr Iain Robertson BA(Hons); MA . . . . . . Sep 1996
Ast: Page, Miss Hazel LLB(Hons) . . . . Jan 2002
Wong, Miss Tina Yit Mee BA(Hons) . . . . Jan 1997

PICKUP & SCOTT ‡
6 Bourbon Street Aylesbury Buckinghamshire HP20 2RR
Tel: 01296 397794 *Fax:* 01296 397033 *Dx:* 4116 AYLESBURY
E-mail: reception@pickupandscott.co.uk
List of partners: D R Pickup, K P Scott
Languages: Bengali, Tagalog, Urdu
Work: G H L N S1 W Z(i,l,m)
Emergency Action, Advocacy and Legal Aid undertaken
Ptr: Pickup, Mr David R BA . . . . *Oct 1983
Scott, Mr Kevin P BA . . . . *Nov 1982
Ast: Johal-Basi, Harleena . . . . Jun 2005

WILKINS ‡
Lincoln House 6 Church Street Aylesbury Buckinghamshire HP20 2QS
Tel: 01296 424681 *Fax:* 01296 426213 *Dx:* 4104 AYLESBURY
Emergency telephone 01296 424681
E-mail: mail@wilkinssolicitors.co.uk
List of partners: S A Hemmings, M G L Pryer, R T Smith
Languages: French, German
Work: D1 E F1 J1 K1 K3 K4 L N O Q S1 T2 W Z(q)
Emergency Action, Agency, Advocacy, Fixed Fee Interview, Legal Aid undertaken and Member of Accident Line
Mem: Hemmings, Miss Sarah Anne BA . . . . *Sep 1997
Pryer, Mr Mark G L BA . . . . *Dec 1980
Smith, Mr Robert Thornton BA . . . . *Oct 1987
Ast: Munraknah, Miss Sheena Devi LLB(Hons). . . . . . . Jan 2009
Perkins, Mrs Elizabeth Sally Ann BA(Hons)(Business Law) . . . . Jun 1980
Sansom, Mrs Lorna LLB(Hons); MA. . . . . Sep 2010
Con: Ward, Mrs Rosanne J LLB . . . . *Apr 1972

WILSON & BIRD ‡
Ideal House Exchange Street Aylesbury Buckinghamshire HP20 1QY
Tel: 01296 436766 *Fax:* 01296 393103 *Dx:* 4114 AYLESBURY
Emergency telephone 01296 425770
E-mail: legal@wilsonandbird.co.uk
List of partners: P L Bird
Languages: French, German, Italian
Work: B2 C1 D1 E F1 F2 G H J2 K1 K3 K4 L N O Q R2 S1 S2 T2 W
Emergency Action, Agency, Advocacy, Fixed Fee Interview, Legal Aid undertaken and Legal Aid Franchise
Ptr: Bird, Mr Paul L BA(Law). . . . . *Sep 1981
Ast: Bamford, Mrs Rosie BA; LLB(Hons). . . . . Sep 2011
Lewis, Miss Alison BA(Hons) . . . . *Apr 2005

AYLSHAM, Norfolk

HANSELLS
1 Norwich Road Aylsham Norfolk NR11 6BN
Tel: 01263 734313 *Fax:* 01263 734781 *Dx:* 31050 AYLSHAM
Office: Cromer, North Walsham, Norwich (2 offices), Sheringham
Languages: French
Work: A1 B1 C1 D1 D2 E F1 J1 J2 K1 K2 L M3 N O P Q R1 R2 S1 S2 T1 T2 V W Z(c,d,e,k,l,o,p,q,r)
Agency, Advocacy, Fixed Fee Interview and Legal Aid undertaken
Ptr: Lansdell, Mr Hugh Peter LLB . . . . *§Jul 1975

HOOD VORES & ALLWOOD
3 Burgh Road Aylsham Norfolk NR11 6AH
Tel: 01263 732123 *Fax:* 01263 734099 *Dx:* 31053 AYLSHAM
E-mail: admin@hoodvoreslow.co.uk
Office: Dereham
Work: A1 F1 J1 K1 K3 K4 L N Q S1 S2 T2 V W Z(c,d,l,q)
Fixed Fee Interview undertaken
Ptr: Whigham, Mr Jeremy Francis TEP . . . . *§Jun 1972
Con: Brown, Mr Cedric Maynard LLB . . . . *Dec 1967

BACUP, Lancashire

C C SMALE SOLICITORS ‡
Lane Ends House Lane Ends Road Bacup Lancashire OL13 9RG
Tel: 01706 873737 *Fax:* 01706 873737

WOODCOCKS
3 Irwell Terrace Bacup Lancashire OL13 9AN
Tel: 01706 874487 *Fax:* 01706 878343 *Dx:* 26251 RAWTENSTALL
E-mail: info@woodcocks.co.uk
Office: Bury, Haslingden, Ramsbottom, Rawtenstall
Work: A1 B1 C1 C2 D1 D2 E G H J1 K1 K3 L N O P Q R1 R2 S1 S2 T1 T2 W Z(e,l,o,q)

BAILDON, West Yorkshire

KINSEY & CO SOLICITORS ‡
First Floor Oakminster House Northgate Baildon West Yorkshire BD17 6LR
Tel: 01274 589900 *Fax:* 01274 548100
E-mail: enquiries@kinseysolicitors.co.uk
List of partners: J M Kinsey
Work: K1 K3
Agency and Fixed Fee Interview undertaken
SPr: Kinsey, Miss Juliette M LLB(Hons) . . . . Jan 1999

LAST CAWTHRA FEATHER LLP (incorporating Stuart Carter & Co)
29 Westgate Baildon West Yorkshire BD17 5EH
Tel: 01274 583106 *Fax:* 01274 596881 *Dx:* 20917 SHIPLEY
Office: Bradford, Ilkley, Leeds, Shipley
Work: D1 D2 G H J1 K1 K2 L N S1 V W X Z(i,l,m)
Agency, Advocacy, Legal Aid undertaken and Legal Aid Franchise
Ptr: Smith, Mr John R S MA(Cantab) . . . . *Jun 1973

BAKEWELL, Derbyshire

COCKERTONS ‡
Bridge Street Bakewell Derbyshire DE45 1DS
Tel: 01629 812613 *Fax:* 01629 814781 *Dx:* 27533 BAKEWELL
E-mail: enquiries@cockertonslegal.com
List of partners: M R Cockerton, J E Haigh, R N Kay, S Porter, E M Wallis
Work: A1 C1 E F1 J1 K4 L O Q R1 S1 S2 T2 W Z(d,l,n)
Ptr: Cockerton, Mr Michael R BSc(Eng) Steward of the Barmote Courts . . . . *§Jun 1974
Haigh, Mrs Juanita Erica LLB . . . . *Sep 1980
Kay, Mr Richard Norman BA . . . . *Oct 1986
Porter, Ms Suzanne LLB . . . . *Nov 2002
Wallis, Mrs Elizabeth Mary LLB(Hons). . . . . *Aug 2000
Ast: Rogers, Mr Jonathan Paul LLB . . . . *Jan 2010

FRANKLIN & CO ‡
Town Hall Chambers Anchor Square Bakewell Derbyshire DE45 1DR
Tel: 01629 814461 *Fax:* 01629 812858 *Dx:* 27532 BAKEWELL
E-mail: p.bramall@franklin-solicitors.co.uk
List of partners: P E Bramall
Work: A1 E K1 L N O Q R1 S1 S2 T2 W Z(d)
Ptr: Bramall, Mr Philip E BA(Oxon) . . . . *Oct 1994
Ast: Short, Mr Jonathan F LLB. . . . . *Oct 1989

BALA, Gwynedd

THOMAS ANDREWS & PARTNERS
Fronfair High Street Bala Gwynedd LL23 7AD
Tel: 01678 520893 *Fax:* 01678 521243
Office: Wrexham
Languages: Welsh
Work: E F1 G K1 L M1 P S1 W
Emergency Action, Agency, Advocacy, Fixed Fee Interview and Legal Aid undertaken
Ptr: Thomas, Mr Robert J M LLB . . . . Jun 1976

HYWEL DAVIES & CO ‡
74 High Street Bala Gwynedd LL23 7BH
Tel: 01678 520307 *Fax:* 01678 520131
Emergency telephone 01678 520089
E-mail: mail@hyweldavies-solicitors.co.uk
List of partners: H L L Davies
Languages: Welsh
Work: A1 B1 C1 D1 E F1 G H J1 K1 L M1 N P Q R1 S1 T1 T2 V W Z(d,l,m)
Emergency Action, Agency, Advocacy, Fixed Fee Interview, Legal Aid undertaken and Legal Aid Franchise
Ptr: Davies, Mr Hywel L L LLB(Wales) Notary Public. . . *§Oct 1975

GUTHRIE JONES & JONES ‡
5 Stryd Y Plase Bala Gwynedd LL23 7SW
Tel: 01678 520428 *Fax:* 01678 521863
Emergency telephone 01678 540351
E-mail: bala@guthriejj.co.uk
List of partners: D Edwards, O Roberts, N R Thirsk
Office: Denbigh, Dolgellau
Languages: Welsh
Work: A1 A2 C1 D1 E F1 G H J1 K1 L M1 M2 N O P Q R1 R2 S1 S2 V W X Z(c,g,l,r,u)
Emergency Action, Agency, Advocacy and Fixed Fee Interview undertaken
Ptr: Edwards, Mr Dylan BA; LLB. . . . . *Oct 1993
Roberts, Mr Osian LLB . . . . *Jul 2003
Thirsk, Mrs Nansi Roberts LLB . . . . *Feb 1985
Ast: Bright, Mr Andre LLB . . . . *Jan 2008

BALDOCK, Hertfordshire

MELANIE BEST EMPLOYMENT LAWYER ‡
Regus House 1010 Cambourne Business Park Cambourne Baldock Hertfordshire SG7 5RR
Tel: 01223 597832 *Fax:* 01233 598001
E-mail: mlb@melaniebest.co.uk

BRIGNALLS BALDERSTON WARREN
11 Whitehorse Street Baldock Hertfordshire SG7 6PZ
Tel: 01462 490100 *Fax:* 01462 490050 *Dx:* 45002 BALDOCK
E-mail: enquiries@bbwlaw.biz
Office: Biggleswade, Knebworth, Letchworth, Stevenage
Work: E L S1 S2 T2 W
Ptr: Laing, Mr Andrew J H LLB . . . . *§Jul 1977
Nickels, Mr Anthony J. . . . . *Nov 1973

FOREMANS LLP ‡
Yorke Chambers 15 Royston Road Baldock Hertfordshire SG7 6NW
Tel: 01462 499077

OLDHAMS SOLICITORS & ADVOCATES ‡
1 High Street Baldock Hertfordshire SG7 6AZ
Tel: 01462 895444 *Fax:* 01462 892476 *Dx:* 45003 BALDOCK
Emergency telephone 07773 002783
E-mail: admin@oldhams.net
List of partners: J C Hennessey, R Singh
Languages: French, Punjabi, Shona
Work: D1 G H J1 K1 K2 K3 N O Q V Z(g,i,l,q)
Emergency Action, Agency, Advocacy, Fixed Fee Interview, Legal Aid undertaken and Legal Aid Franchise
Ptr: Hennessey, Mr James C . . . . *Oct 1997
Singh, Rabinderjit BA Part time Chairman of Social Security Appeals. . . . . *Feb 1991
Ast: Kingham, Mrs Kate . . . . *Sep 2010
Martin, Mrs Samantha. . . . . *Aug 2007
Phillips, Mrs Sylvia BA(Law). . . . . *Aug 2002
Shah, Mrs Tina LLB(Hons) . . . . *Sep 2010
Con: Broe, Mr Clive Immigration Judge; Recorder. . . . . . *Jun 1980
Oldham, Mr Martin D BA; MA ★ Recorder; Deputy Coroner . . . . *§Jun 1976

SIMKINS ‡
Manor House 21 High Street Baldock Hertfordshire SG7 6BD
Tel: 01462 892221 *Fax:* 01462 892175 *Dx:* 45000 BALDOCK
E-mail: simkins@btconnect.com
List of partners: T A G Simkins
Work: C1 C2 E J1 S1 S2 W
SPr: Simkins, Mr Timothy Arthur George . . . . *Jul 1979

BAMFORD, Derbyshire

J P SCHOLES ‡
Lane End The Hollow Hope Valley Bamford Derbyshire S33 0DU
Tel: 01433 651625 *Fax:* 01433 651625
Emergency telephone 01433 651625
E-mail: himself@jpscholes.co.uk
Languages: Dutch, French, German
Work: C1 C3 F1 F2 M1 Z(y)

BAMPTON, Oxfordshire

J M HARRISON ‡
Clanfield House Market Square Bampton Oxfordshire OX18 2JJ
Tel: 01993 852222 *Fax:* 01993 852553
E-mail: info@j-mharrison.co.uk
List of partners: J C Harrison
Work: G L S1 W Z(l)
Agency, Advocacy and Fixed Fee Interview undertaken
SPr: Harrison, Mrs Jane-Marie C. . . . . *Dec 1980

BANBURY, Oxfordshire

APLIN STOCKTON FAIRFAX ‡
36 West Bar Street Banbury Oxfordshire OX16 9RU
Tel: 01295 251234 *Fax:* 01295 270948 *Dx:* 24203 BANBURY
E-mail: reception@aplins.co.uk
List of partners: R J Henshaw, A Scott Andrews, P J Waters, N J Yeadon
Work: A1 C1 E F1 J1 K1 K3 K4 L O Q R1 S1 S2 T2 W Z(d)
Agency and Advocacy undertaken
Ptr: Henshaw, Mr Robert John LLB Notary Public . . . . . *Jun 1998
Scott Andrews, Mr Anthony LLB Notary Public . . . . *Jun 1974
Waters, Mr Philip James . . . . *Sep 1996
Yeadon, Mr Nigel J LLB(Lond). . . . . *May 1975
Ast: Dowler, Mrs Mary . . . . Apr 1998
Pugh, Mr Nicholas LLB . . . . *Oct 2000

BOWER & BAILEY
39 South Bar Banbury Oxfordshire OX16 9AE
Tel: 01295 265566 *Fax:* 01295 270536 *Dx:* 24214 BANBURY
E-mail: banbury@bowerandbailey.co.uk
Office: Oxford, Swindon, Witney
Languages: Arabic, French
Work: B1 C1 C2 E F1 F2 I J1 K1 K3 K4 L N O Q S1 S2 U2 W Z(b,e,l,q,r,za)
Emergency Action, Advocacy, Fixed Fee Interview undertaken and Member of Accident Line
Ptr: Brookes, Mr Robert P LLB(Hons) . . . . *Oct 2000
Cooksey, Mr Philip David BA; LSF. . . . . *Nov 1993
Jackson, Mr Robert Michael LLB(Hons) . . . . *§Aug 2000
Norman, Miss Susan Ann LLB Birmingham Law Society Gold Medal. *Dec 1979
Porter, Mr Stephen J BA(Law). . . . . *Jun 1979
Ast: Leach, Mr Jeremy Matthew Stuart LLB . . . . Jan 2005
Vanheems, Miss Josephine Gwendoline D'Arcy BA(Hons)(Durham); GDC; LPC . . . . Sep 2010

BRETHERTONS LLP
Strathmore House Waterperry Court Middleton Road Banbury Oxfordshire OX16 4QD
Tel: 01295 270999 *Fax:* 01295 257575 *Dx:* 151640 BANBURY 4
E-mail: enquiries@brethertons.co.uk
Office: Rugby (3 offices)
Languages: French, Hindi, Punjabi
Work: A1 B1 C1 C2 C3 D1 D2 E F1 I J1 J2 K1 K2 K3 L M1 M2 N O Q R1 S1 S2 U1 U2 V W Z(c,d,e,m,o,p,q,r,y,za)
Emergency Action, Agency, Advocacy and Fixed Fee Interview undertaken
Ptr: Auld, Mr Brian C LLB; Dip Eur Law . . . . *Oct 1983
Craddock, Mr Simon Geoffrey LLB . . . . *Nov 1990
Dawson, Mr Richard Goeffrey LLB(Hons) . . . . *Nov 1972
Dibben, Mr Michael Paul BA(Law). . . . . *Dec 1982
Jardine, Mr Shaun Michael LLB. . . . . *Nov 1986
Ast: Bible, Mr Edward LLB. . . . . Nov 1994
Fleming, Mrs Jean Helen LLB. . . . . Mar 1979
Payne, Ms Monica L LLB(Hons). . . . . *Sep 1982
Wales, Mrs Sophie Emma. . . . . Sep 2008

CARR & CO ‡
(in association with Leport & Co)
9 Broughton Road Banbury Oxfordshire OX16 9QB
Tel: 01295 275168 / 261744 *Fax:* 01295 257870
Dx: 24250 BANBURY
E-mail: richard@rpcarr.co.uk
List of partners: R P Carr
Work: A1 C1 E F1 L R1 S1 W Z(c)
Ptr: Carr, Mr Richard P . . . . *Oct 1976

DAVIES & DAVIES ASSOCIATES LIMITED
PO Box 597 Banbury Oxfordshire OX16 6DN
Tel: 0800 840 4025 *Fax:* 0800 840 4026
E-mail: enquiries@daviesanddavies.net
Office: London EC2

HANCOCKS ‡
The Old Vicarage 24 Horsefair Banbury Oxfordshire OX16 0YA
Tel: 01295 253211 *Fax:* 01295 273069 *Dx:* 24201 BANBURY
E-mail: partners@hancocks-legal.co.uk
List of partners: P M Barlow, W N Wainman
Work: D1 E F1 J1 J2 K1 N O Q R1 S1 S2 T2 W Z(l,q,r)
Emergency Action, Agency, Advocacy, Fixed Fee Interview, Legal Aid undertaken and Legal Aid Franchise
Ptr: Barlow, Mr P Michael LLB. . . . . *§Jan 1970
Wainman, Mr W Neil BA . . . . *Jun 1974
Asoc: Davies, Mrs Deborah Jane LLB . . . . *Jan 1996
Peppard, Mrs Toni Patricia LLB . . . . Oct 1998

HERBERT & CHOLMELEY ‡
17 West Bar Banbury Oxfordshire OX16 9SA
Tel: 01295 263556 *Fax:* 01295 272206 *Dx:* 24211 BANBURY
E-mail: law@hcholmeley.demon.co.uk
List of partners: C M Fairfax-Cholmeley
Work: K4 S1 W
SPr: Fairfax-Cholmeley, Mr C Martin MA(Cantab). . . . . *Jan 1969

INSPIRE LAW ‡
Mercia House 51 The Green Banbury Oxfordshire OX16 9AB
Tel: 01295 298211 *Fax:* 01295 298212
E-mail: malcolm@inspirelaw.co.uk
List of partners: M W Tuvey
Dir: Tuvey, Mr Malcolm W BA . . . . *Oct 1990

IVERSON STANLEY HOLMES COMMERCIAL SOLICITORS ‡
Unit 4 Sugarswell Business Park Shenington Banbury Oxfordshire OX15 6HW
Tel: 01295 688923

JOHNSON & GAUNT ‡
(incorporating Whitehorns & Haines)
47 North Bar Banbury Oxfordshire OX16 0TJ
Tel: 01295 256271 / 271200 *Fax:* 01295 266451
Dx: 24208 BANBURY
Emergency telephone 01869 338463
E-mail: mail@johnsongaunt.co.uk
List of partners: C O Edwards, T C Elkins, T M Lewis, R J B Marsden, J R Rose
Languages: French
Work: A1 B1 B2 C1 C2 C3 D1 D2 E F1 G H J1 K1 L M1 M2 N O P Q R1 S1 S2 T1 T2 V W Z(c,d,e,f,g,i,j,k,l,m,n,p,q,t,w)
Emergency Action, Agency, Advocacy, Fixed Fee Interview, Legal Aid undertaken, Legal Aid Franchise and Member of Accident Line
Ptr: Edwards, Mr Christopher O MA(Cantab) . . . . *Apr 1981
Elkins, Mr Timothy C LLB . . . . *Nov 1983
Lewis, Mr Timothy M LLB . . . . *Dec 1981
Marsden, Mr Rodney J B . . . . *§Jun 1968
Rose, Mr J Roger. . . . . *§Jun 1968
Ast: Cullington, Mr Roy Ellis . . . . *Dec 1966
Reeve, Ms Sarah BA(Hons). . . . . *Jul 1990
Rogers, Ms Nicola BA(Hons) . . . . *Oct 1995

LEPORT & CO ‡
Lincoln Chambers 11 Market Place Banbury Oxfordshire OX16 5UA
Tel: 01295 257328 / 268181 *Fax:* 01295 759898
Dx: 24207 BANBURY
E-mail: reception@leportandco.co.uk
List of partners: J S Leport, S Singh
Work: A1 B1 C1 D2 E F1 G H J1 K1 K3 K4 L N O Q S1 S2 V W Z(k,l,q)
Emergency Action, Agency, Advocacy, Fixed Fee Interview and Legal Aid undertaken
Ptr: Leport, Mr John S. . . . . *Jul 1979
Singh, Satyanam BA . . . . *May 1986
Ast: McKeown, Miss Shelly LLB(Hons). . . . . Nov 2004
Randall, Mr Barry N LLB Commissioner for Oaths. . *Dec 1963

SPRATT ENDICOTT ‡
52-54 The Green Banbury Oxfordshire OX16 9AB
Tel: 01295 204000 *Fax:* 01295 204010 *Dx:* 24204 BANBURY 1
E-mail: enquiries@se-law.co.uk
List of partners: G C Bryant, E Dimelor, D Endicott, D H N Inch, H G R Patel, C A Shaw, J E Spratt, G C Stephenson, A A Woods
Office: Banbury (2 offices)
Languages: French, German, Greek, Gujarati, Hindi, Italian, Portuguese, Punjabi, Spanish, Urdu
Work: A1 B1 C1 C2 C3 D2 E F1 I J1 K1 L O Q R1 S1 S2 T2 W X Z(b,c,d,e,p,s)
Emergency Action, Agency, Advocacy and Fixed Fee Interview undertaken
Ptr: Bryant, Mr Geoffrey C MA(Oxon) . . . . *May 1974
Dimelor, Miss Estelle . . . . *Sep 1993
Endicott, Mr David . . . . *§Oct 1981
Inch, Mr David Hugh Northcote . . . . *§Sep 1983
Patel, Hitendra G R LLB. . . . . *§Mar 1988
Shaw, Ms Carol A LLB . . . . *§Jun 1986
Spratt, Mr John E BA(Oxon). . . . . *§Jun 1972
Stephenson, Mr Guy C BA(Hons) . . . . *Oct 1998
Woods, Mr Andrew A BA . . . . *§Jan 1988
Asoc: Belcher, Mr Neil George Martin LLB(Hons) . . . . . *Aug 1999
Gibbs, Mrs Caroline Elizabeth BA(Hons) . . . . . . *§Oct 1987
Gordon, Mrs Lucy MA(Cantab) . . . . *Oct 1992
Green, Ms Paula Melanie BA(Law & Philosophy) . . *Sep 1999
Thomas, Mr Lewis Llewellyn LLB(Hons). . . . . . . *Jan 1984
Ast: Macartney, Mr Michael Charles LLB(Hons) . . . . . *Jan 1982
Muir, Ms Nicola Caroline BA; PGDipLaw. . . . . . . *Mar 2008
Mulcare, Mr Patrick Anthony MA(Cantab) . . . . . . *Mar 2008
O'Riordan, Miss Catherine L MA . . . . *Sep 1999
Price, Mrs Philomena LLB. . . . . *Sep 2002
Roberts, Mr Graham Lionel Peter BA . . . . Sep 1996
Stacey, Miss Emily Jayne LLB(Hons) . . . . *Jul 1999
Turrington, Ms Fleur BA. . . . . *Sep 2005
Con: Bettison, Mr Oliver Joseph Samuel BA(Hons) . . . . . *Apr 1976

SPRATT ENDICOTT
County Chambers 11 Horse Fair Banbury Oxfordshire OX16 0AH
Tel: 01295 204000 *Fax:* 01295 204010
E-mail: enquiries@se-law.co.uk
Office: Banbury (2 offices)

SPRATT ENDICOTT
Gilmarde House 47 South Bar Street Banbury Oxfordshire OX16 9AB
Tel: 01295 204000 *Fax:* 01295 204010 *Dx:* 24204 BANBURY
E-mail: enquiries@se-law.co.uk
Office: Banbury (2 offices)

J P WATERHOUSE & CO ‡
2 Horse Fair Banbury Oxfordshire OX16 0AA
Tel: 01295 267555
List of partners: A P Ramsey, J P Waterhouse
Work: F1 G H J1 K1 L M1 S1 V
Agency, Advocacy, Fixed Fee Interview and Legal Aid undertaken
Ptr: Ramsey, Mr Alan P BA(Lond) . . . . *Jan 1979
Waterhouse, Mr Jonathan P LLB(B'ham) . . . . Apr 1975

WISE GEARY ‡
The Courtyard Chapel Lane Bodicote Banbury Oxfordshire OX15 4DB
Tel: 01295 278500 *Fax:* 01295 278585 *Dx:* 24245 BANBURY
E-mail: office@wise-geary.co.uk
List of partners: R D Geary, R E Pearcy, S J S Wise
Languages: German
Work: B1 C1 C2 C3 E F1 I J1 K3 L M2 O Q R2 S1 S2 T1 T2 U1 U2 W Z(b,c,e,l,q)
Agency, Advocacy and Fixed Fee Interview undertaken
Ptr: Geary, Mr Robert D LLB. . . . . *Nov 1988
Pearcy, Miss Rebecca Elizabeth LLB . . . . *Dec 2000
Wise, Mr Simon J S MA(Oxon) . . . . *Oct 1985
Asoc: Guess, Mrs Angela C LLB(Hons) . . . . Sep 1998
Saunders, Mr Desmond Wallace . . . . Mar 2005
Werth, Mr Paul Stephen LLB . . . . *Oct 1984
Ast: Batten, Ms Harriet . . . . *Jul 2006
Millan, Ms Anna BA(Hons); CPE; LPC. . . . . *Sep 2000
Con: Franklin, Mr Ronald P LLB(Bris). . . . . *Mar 1970

BANGOR, Gwynedd

CHRISTOPHER BATE ‡
Bryn-y-mor Holyhead Road Bangor Gwynedd LL57 2HG
Tel: 01248 372395

JULIE BURTON ‡
62 Sgwar Kyffin Bangor Gwynedd LL57 1LA
Tel: 01248 364750 *Fax:* 01248 360235
E-mail: post@julieburtonlaw.co.uk
Languages: French, Welsh
Work: X Z(m)
Legal Aid undertaken and Legal Aid Franchise

MARTIN BUSST & CO ‡
8 Penrhos Drive Bangor Gwynedd LL57 2AZ
Tel: 01248 355564 *Fax:* 01248 360379
E-mail: martinbusst@o2.co.uk

CARTER VINCENT JONES DAVIS ‡
The Port House Port Penrhyn Bangor Gwynedd LL57 4HN
Tel: 01248 362551 *Fax:* 01248 353358 *Dx:* 23176 BANGOR 2
List of partners: M H R Davis, J E Jones, R A Jones
Languages: Welsh
Work: A1 B1 C1 D1 E F1 G H J1 K1 L M1 N P R1 S1 T1 V W Z(i,k,l,m,p)
Emergency Action, Agency, Advocacy, Fixed Fee Interview and Legal Aid undertaken
Ptr: Davis, Mr M Hugh R BA. . . . . *Dec 1976
Jones, Mr John E . . . . Mar 1957
Jones, Mr R Alwyn LLB . . . . Jun 1980

ELWYN JONES & CO ‡
123 High Street Bangor Gwynedd LL57 1NT
Tel: 01248 370224 *Fax:* 01248 352313 *Dx:* 18721 BANGOR 1
E-mail: elwyn-jones@btconnect.com
List of partners: S Dowding, H Elwyn Jones, A W Jones
Languages: Welsh
Work: A1 B1 D1 D2 E F1 G H J1 K1 K2 L N O P Q R1 S1 S2 V W Z(l,m)
Emergency Action, Agency, Advocacy, Legal Aid undertaken and Legal Aid Franchise
Ptr: Dowding, Miss Sally LLB(Manc) Deputy High and County Court District Judge . . . . *Jan 1979
Elwyn Jones, Mr Huw MA(Oxon) Deputy Lord Lieutenant . . . . *Jul 1969
Jones, Mr Aled W LLB(Wales) Deputy District Judge (Criminal) . . . . *Mar 1980
Asoc: Davies, Mr Peter C LLB(Wales) . . . . *Jan 1995
Gwyn, Mrs Lowri Angharad LLB(Wales) . . . . *Jan 1991

GAMLINS
3 Chestnut Court Bangor Gwynedd LL57 4FH
Tel: 01248 672414 *Fax:* 01248 672419 *Dx:* 21624 MENAI BRIDGE
E-mail: bangor@gamlins.com
Office: Colwyn Bay (2 offices), Conwy, Holywell, Llandudno, Rhyl
Languages: Welsh
Work: C1 E J1 L O Q R2 S2 W

PRITCHARD & CO ‡
104 High Street Bangor Gwynedd LL57 1NS
Tel: 01248 370017 *Fax:* 01248 351267
Emergency telephone 07768 373021
E-mail: brian-pritchard@btconnect.com
List of partners: B J Pritchard
Languages: French, German, Welsh
Work: D1 F1 G H J1 K1 L N S1 W Z(l,m)
Emergency Action, Agency, Advocacy and Fixed Fee Interview undertaken
SPr: Pritchard, Mr Brian John BSc(Lond). . . . . *§Jun 1974

TUDUR OWEN ROBERTS GLYNNE & CO
Victoria Court High Street Bangor Gwynedd LL57 3AN
Tel: 01248 600171 *Fax:* 01248 602333
E-mail: ed.jonesson@virgin.net
Office: Bangor, Blaenau Ffestiniog, Caernarfon, Holyhead, Menai Bridge
Languages: Welsh
Work: A1 C1 E J1 L S1 T1 T2 W
Ptr: Ellis, Mr Aled L LLB(Wales). . . . . *Feb 1970

TUDUR OWEN ROBERTS GLYNNE & CO
157 High Street Bangor Gwynedd LL57 1NU
Tel: 01248 362315 / 355826 *Fax:* 01248 353489
Dx: 18722 BANGOR 1
Emergency telephone 01248 354908
E-mail: torglawbangor@lineone.net
Office: Bangor, Blaenau Ffestiniog, Caernarfon, Holyhead, Menai Bridge
Languages: Welsh
Work: D1 G H K1 K3 S1 W
Emergency Action, Agency, Advocacy, Fixed Fee Interview, Legal Aid undertaken and Legal Aid Franchise
Ptr: Davies, Mr Gwyn E BA(Wales) . . . . *Sep 1985
Con: Lloyd, Mr Iwan ap Gruffydd . . . . *Jul 1974

BANSTEAD, Surrey

CUFF AND GOUGH LLP ‡
Lamborn Place 26 High Street Banstead Surrey SM7 2LJ
Tel: 01737 851827 *Fax:* 01737 353274
E-mail: info@cuffandgough.com

MONTLAKE & CO ‡
Burghside Brighton Road Banstead Surrey SM7 1BB
Tel: 01737 352211 *Fax:* 01737 370072 *Dx:* 37750 BANSTEAD
E-mail: enquiries@montlake-solicitors.co.uk
List of partners: S M Grant, L A Pond
Work: A1 C1 E L R1 S1 T1 T2 W Z(l)
Ptr: Grant, Mrs Susan M BA(Lond) . . . . *May 1980
Pond, Mrs Lesley A LLB. . . . . *Nov 1986

QUALITY SOLICITORS COPLEY CLARK
Pathtrace House 91/93 High Street Banstead Surrey SM7 2NL
Tel: 01737 362131 *Fax:* 01737 363101 *Dx:* 56401 SUTTON 1
E-mail: info@copleyclark.co.uk
Office: Sutton
Languages: French
Work: B1 C1 C2 C3 D1 E F1 J1 K1 L N O Q R1 S1 S2 T1 T2 V W Z(c,l,p,q)
Emergency Action, Agency, Advocacy, Fixed Fee Interview undertaken and Member of Accident Line
Ptr: Brigham, Mr Robert A LLB . . . . *§Dec 1978
Hughes, Mr Neil A LLB . . . . *§Apr 1981
Lawrence, Mr Malcolm J LLB(B'ham) . . . . *§Oct 1980

See p112 for the Key to Work Categories & other symbols

SINNERTONS ‡
175 High Street Banstead Surrey SM7 2NT
Tel: 01737 212000 *Fax:* 01737 212001
E-mail: law@sinnertons.co.uk
List of partners: G J Sinnerton
Languages: French, Spanish
Work: A1 J1 L R1 R2 S1 S2 W Z(l)
Fixed Fee Interview undertaken
SPr: Sinnerton, Mr Geoffrey J . . . . *Nov 1978

STANLEY SMITH HILL & CO
141a High Street Banstead Surrey SM7 2NS
Tel: 01737 358001 *Fax:* 01737 373318 *Dx:* 37752 BANSTEAD
E-mail: banstead@stanleysmithhill.co.uk
Office: Carshalton
Work: K1 K3 S1 W
Fixed Fee Interview undertaken
Ptr: Mahoney, Mr David J LLB(Exon) . . . . *Nov 1981

BARGOED, Caerphilly

EMPORIUM SOLICITORS ‡
1st Floor Emporium Buildings Bargoed Caerphilly CF81 8QY
Tel: 01443 878800 *Fax:* 01443 832074

GOUGH DAVIES ‡
1 Hanbury Square Bargoed Caerphilly CF81 8QQ
Tel: 01443 839393 *Fax:* 01443 839366 *Dx:* 55503 BARGOED
List of partners: E M Davies, B Gough
Ptr: Davies, Mrs Elizabeth M LLB . . . . *Mar 1973
Gough, Mr Barrie LLB. . . . . *Jul 1991

MICHAEL LEIGHTON JONES ‡
(incorporating Leighton G Jones & Co)
53 Hanbury Road Rhymney Valley Bargoed Caerphilly CF81 8XD
Tel: 01443 830228 *Fax:* 01443 836154 *Dx:* 55502 BARGOED
E-mail: info@michaelleightonjones.com
List of partners: A E Andrewartha, M L Jones
Languages: French
Work: A1 B1 C1 D1 D2 E F1 F2 J1 K1 K3 K4 L N O P Q R1 R2 S1 S2 T1 V W Z(c,h,k,l,n)
Emergency Action, Agency, Advocacy, Fixed Fee Interview and Legal Aid undertaken
Ptr: Andrewartha, Miss Anita E LLB . . . . *Nov 1987
Jones, Mr Michael L LLB(Wales) . . . . *Feb 1985

BARKING, Essex

ASHBURNS SOLICITORS ‡
Trocoll House Wakering Road Barking Essex IG11 8PD
Tel: 020 8591 5297 *Fax:* 020 8594 4356
E-mail: info@ashburnssolicitors.co.uk

BAINS COHEN LLP ‡
61a East Street Barking Essex IG11 8EJ
Tel: 020 8252 7373 *Fax:* 020 8252 7793 *Dx:* 8510 BARKING
Emergency telephone 020 8252 7373
E-mail: info@bainscohen.com
Office: London EC3, London N3, London N8
Languages: Hebrew, Hindi, Punjabi, Urdu
Work: E G H J1 K1 K3 O Q S1 S2 W Z(i)
Legal Aid Franchise

CHRISTCHURCH SOLICITORS ‡
Suite No 113-114 Wigham House Wakering Road Barking Essex IG11 8QN
Tel: 020 8591 5934 *Fax:* 020 8591 5935

COTISENS SOLICITORS ‡
3a Station Parade Barking Essex IG11 8ED
Tel: 020 8594 8683

CRIMSON PHOENIX SOLICITORS ‡
Suite 410a Trocoll House Wakering Road Barking Essex IG11 8PD
Tel: 020 8591 6500 *Fax:* 020 8591 6533

DANIEL & PARTNERS ‡
8 Monteagle Court Wakering Road Barking Essex IG11 8PL

GILEAD BALMS ‡
Suite 307 Trocoll House Barking Essex IG11 8PD
Tel: 020 8594 4788

GRACE-SPRINGS SOLICITORS ‡
72 Longbridge Road Barking Essex IG11 8SF
Tel: 020 8591 5290 *Fax:* 020 8594 8448
E-mail: help@gspsolicitors.co.uk

HARGREAVES ‡
44 Longbridge Road Barking Essex IG11 8RT
Tel: 020 8594 2473 *Fax:* 020 8594 4640
Work: B1 C1 C2 C3 D1 E F1 J1 K1 L M1 M2 N O Q R1 S1 V W Z(c,l)
Emergency Action, Agency, Advocacy and Legal Aid undertaken

H S KANG & CO ‡
13a Station Parade Barking Essex IG11 8ED
Tel: 020 8594 5465 *Fax:* 020 8594 5475 *Dx:* 8520 BARKING
E-mail: hskangco@hotmail.com
List of partners: J Bhatoa, H S Kang
Office: Southall
Work: D1 J1 K1 K3 L N S1 V W X Z(g,i,j,q)
Ptr: Bhatoa, Jasbinder. . . . . Aug 1999
Kang, Harjit Singh BSc . . . . *May 1993

MACLEISH LITTLESTONE COWAN
23 Longbridge Road Barking Essex IG11 8TN
Tel: 020 8514 3000 *Fax:* 020 8507 1191 *Dx:* 8504 BARKING
Office: Ilford, London E11, Sawbridgeworth
Languages: French
Work: E K1 L R1 S1 W
Emergency Action, Agency, Advocacy, Fixed Fee Interview, Legal Aid undertaken and Member of Accident Line
Ptr: Littlestone, Mr Robert P LLB(Lond) . . . . *May 1974
Ast: Sattar, Miss Fatema. . . . . Jul 2009

OKAFOR & CO SOLICITORS ‡
214 Trocoll House Wakering Road Barking Essex IG11 8PD
Tel: 020 8594 7266

SAMUEL & CO SOLICITORS ‡
58b Ripple Road Barking Essex IG11 7PG
Tel: 020 8594 5000 *Fax:* 020 8594 0200 *Dx:* 8500 BARKING

SANTERS SOLICITORS ‡
44-44a Longbridge Road Barking Essex IG11 8RT
Tel: 020 8594 7542 *Fax:* 020 8594 5079 *Dx:* 8506 BARKING
E-mail: legal@santers.net
List of partners: M H Santer
Languages: French, Italian
Work: B1 C1 E F1 G H J1 K1 L M1 N P R1 S1 W Z(a,b,c,d,e,f,h,i,j,k,l,p,t)
Emergency Action, Agency, Advocacy, Fixed Fee Interview, Legal Aid undertaken and Member of Accident Line
Ptr: Santer, Mr Martyn H ACIArb • President of West Essex Law Society 97-98; Chairman of Barking Havering Health Authority Disciplinary Panel . . . . *Jan 1982

SHARPFIELDS & CO ‡
4th Floor Suite 413 Trocoll House Barking Essex IG11 8PD
Tel: 020 8594 0010 *Fax:* 020 8594 0015

STERNBERG REED ‡
Focal House 12-18 Station Parade Barking Essex IG11 8DN
Tel: 020 8591 3366 *Fax:* 020 8594 4606 *Dx:* 8501 BARKING
Emergency telephone 01708 766155
E-mail: enquiries@sternberg-reed.co.uk
List of partners: J Abraham, F L Anderson, E M Bendall, K Carr, H A Cohen, A T Crossley, M S Gill, A P Harrison, N Jeffs, S Kokkinos, A Nunn, R Sharma, B St Prix, G J Sternberg, M Q N Taube, C J Taylor, D B B Thomas
Office: Grays, London NW1, Romford
Languages: Hindi, Punjabi
Work: B2 C1 D1 D2 F1 G H J1 K1 K3 L N O Q S1 S2 W X Z(l,r)
Emergency Action, Agency, Advocacy, Fixed Fee Interview, Legal Aid undertaken and Member of Accident Line
Ptr: Abraham, Mr Julian BA . . . . Feb 1989
Anderson, Ms Frances Louise LLB(Hons) ★. . . . . *Nov 1994
Bendall, Miss Elizabeth Marjorie MA. . . . . *Jul 1977
Cohen, Mr Howard A LLB. . . . . *Sep 1991
Crossley, Mr Andrew T LLB . . . . *Aug 1987
Gill, Mr Mohinder S . . . . *Dec 1981
Harrison, Mr Andrew Paul. . . . . Dec 1992
Jeffs, Mr Neil . . . . Nov 2003
Kokkinos, Ms Soulla . . . . Sep 1998
Nunn, Ms Angela . . . . Nov 1993
Sharma, Mr Rajendra LLB. . . . . *Jun 1986
St Prix, Ms Brenda ★ . . . . *Sep 1996
Sternberg, Mr Geoffrey J LLB . . . . *Aug 1972
Taylor, Mr Christopher J BA ★. . . . . *Dec 1985
Thomas, Mr David Benedict Bryn MA(Cantab) ★ . . . *Feb 1993
Asoc: Davis, Ms Arlegh . . . . Jan 2002
Kaur, Ms Desho. . . . . Nov 2004
Kresner, Ms Yvette ★ . . . . Sep 1999
Lawrence, Mr Neil. Feb 2002
Shaw, Mr Gerard ★. . . . . May 2001
Ast: Barbone, Mr David M BA ★. . . . . *Sep 1982
Brookes, Ms Karen . . . . Jan 2008
Charles-Ward, Mrs Johanne Tamika LLB . . . . May 2002
Dobson, Mr Damien. . . . . Jan 2008
Gamble, Ms Jeneane . . . . Jan 2009
Hall, Mr Martin . . . . Jul 2009
Jackson, Mr Daniel . . . . Aug 2009
Knowles, Mr Jonathan. . . . . Dec 1995
Lyndsey, Ms Nicolette. . . . . Dec 2006
McCluskey, Ms Jayne Louise . . . . Jul 1998
McGrath, Mrs Zoe. Jan 2010
Poole, Mr Andrew. Jan 2009
Sparkes, Mr Stephen . . . . Mar 2009
Stockley, Ms Anne Elizabeth BA(Hons) . . . . Mar 2004
Thrower, Miss Jessica. . . . . Jan 2007
White, Miss Natalie . . . . Jan 2007
Wiseman, Mr Anthony. . . . . Nov 1990
Con: Kelly, Mrs Colette H • . . . . *Dec 1986
Kelly, Mr Philip L ★ . . . . Jan 1980
Reed, Mr Gordon M LLB . . . . *Apr 1977

SWABY CLARKE & NORRIS ‡
Wigham House 16-24 Wakering Road Barking Essex IG11 8QN
Tel: 020 8507 1882 *Fax:* 020 8507 1891 *Dx:* 8507 BARKING
List of partners: N G Swaby
Languages: French, German
Work: S1 S2 W Z(d)
SPr: Swaby, Mr Nigel G LLB(Wales) . . . . *Sep 1983

WATES SOLICITORS ‡
Fortis House 160 London Road Barking Essex IG11 8BB
Tel: 020 8214 1010 *Fax:* 020 8214 1012
E-mail: wathala@watessolicitors.co.uk

WILSONS SOLICITORS ‡
Suite 205-206 Trocoll House Wakering Road Barking Essex IG11 8PD
Tel: 020 8185 6005 / 07985 207267 *Fax:* 020 8185 6004
E-mail: wilson@wsolicitors.co.uk

BARMOUTH, Gwynedd

BREESE-GWYNDAF
Glanaig High Street Barmouth Gwynedd LL42 1DW
Tel: 01341 280317 *Fax:* 01341 281306
E-mail: office@breesegwyndaf.f2s.com
Office: Harlech, Porthmadog

BARNARD CASTLE, Co Durham

DARLING & STEPHENSONS
24 Horsemarket Barnard Castle Co Durham DL12 8LZ
Tel: 01325 489000 *Fax:* 01833 690149
E-mail: barnardcastle@darlingstephensons.co.uk
Office: Darlington
Work: A1 C1 E F1 J1 K1 L N Q R2 S1 S2 T1 T2 W Z(c,d,l,q)
Agency and Fixed Fee Interview undertaken
Ptr: Stephenson, Mr Ian W LLB . . . . *§Jun 1980

MEIKLES
(incorporating Meikle Skene & Co; Hardesty Elleanor; Dawson Arnott & Pickering)
38 Horsemarket Barnard Castle Co Durham DL12 8NA
Tel: 01833 690505 *Fax:* 01833 690392
Dx: 61660 BARNARD CASTLE
E-mail: vicky.johnson@meikles-solicitors.co.uk
Office: Bishop Auckland, Ferryhill, Spennymoor, Stockton-on-Tees
Work: A1 C1 D1 D2 E F1 G H J1 K1 K3 K4 L N O Q S1 S2 V W Z(i,l,m)
Emergency Action, Agency, Advocacy, Fixed Fee Interview, Legal Aid undertaken and Legal Aid Franchise
Ptr: Haigh, Mrs Claire LLB(Hons) . . . . *Jun 2001
Johnson, Mrs Catherine Victoria LLB(Hons)(Dunelm) Northumbrian Water Property Solutions Award; Best LPC Conveyancing Student (Northumbria University) 2004 . . . . *Sep 2006
Roberts, Mr John LLB(Newc) . . . . *Jun 1975

TBI SOLICITORS
8 Newgate Barnard Castle Co Durham DL12 8NG
Tel: 01833 638326 *Fax:* 0845 302 2992
Dx: 61664 BARNARD CASTLE
E-mail: info@tbilaw.co.uk
Office: Billingham, Hartlepool, Stockton-on-Tees
Work: A1 B1 C1 D1 E F1 G H J1 K1 L M1 N P R1 S1 S2 T1 V W Z(a,b,c,d,e,f,g,h,i,j,k,l,m,n,o,p,s,t)
Emergency Action, Agency, Advocacy, Fixed Fee Interview and Legal Aid undertaken
Ptr: Dexter, Miss Helen Clare LLB. . . . . *Oct 1995
White, Mr Michael J. . . . . *§Jul 1973
Ast: Shaw, Ms Bridget BA . . . . *Sep 1994

BARNET, Hertfordshire

AMV LAW ‡
Finchley House 17 Station Road New Barnet Barnet Hertfordshire EN5 1HW
Tel: 020 8245 0039
E-mail: info@amvlaw.com

ALEXANDROU & CO ‡
Francis House 2 Park Road Barnet Hertfordshire EN5 5RN
Tel: 020 8447 1503 *Fax:* 020 8449 2830 *Dx:* 8602 BARNET
List of partners: A E Alexandrou, B Kazimierska
Languages: Greek
Work: B1 C1 D1 E F1 G H J1 K1 L N O Q R1 S1 W Z(i,l)
Emergency Action and Advocacy undertaken
Ptr: Alexandrou, Mr Andreas E BA(Hons) . . . . *Mar 1989
Kazimierska, Ms Barbara LLB(Hons)(Lond) . . . . . *May 1997

MICHAEL ANVONER & CO ‡
Constable House 5 Bulwer Road Barnet Hertfordshire EN5 5JD
Tel: 020 8449 0003 *Fax:* 020 8449 0006
E-mail: law@anvoner.co.uk
List of partners: M S Anvoner
Work: K4 W
SPr: Anvoner, Mr Michael Steven. . . . . *Jun 1985

BARNET FAMILY LAW ‡
Highstone House 165 High Street Barnet Hertfordshire EN5 5SU
Tel: 020 8440 2229 *Fax:* 020 8440 5520 *Dx:* 8611 BARNET
Emergency telephone 07837 968793
E-mail: info@barnetfamilylaw.co.uk

BILBEISI SOLICITORS ‡
Groupama House 17 Station Road Barnet Hertfordshire EN5 1NW
Tel: 020 8275 3355 *Fax:* 020 8275 3350
E-mail: abilbeisi@onetel.com

BOTTRILLS SOLICITORS ‡
169 High Street Barnet Hertfordshire EN5 5SU
Tel: 020 8440 8188 / 8441 1125 *Fax:* 020 8441 2759
Dx: 130030 BARNET 3
E-mail: info@bottrills.com
List of partners: J N Harling, N Thompson
Work: E S1 S2 W
Ptr: Harling, Miss Julia N BA(Hons) . . . . *Nov 1991
Thompson, Miss Nicola BSc(Hons) . . . . *Jul 1999

BOYES SUTTON & PERRY ‡
(incorporating Milnes & Milnes)
20 Wood Street Barnet Hertfordshire EN5 4BJ
Tel: 020 8449 9155 *Fax:* 020 8441 3584 *Dx:* 8605 BARNET
E-mail: solicitors@boyessuttonperry.co.uk
List of partners: C J Davies, M Foley, K McMeel, M A Timmis
Work: C1 E F1 J1 K1 K3 L N O Q S1 S2 T2 W
Ptr: Davies, Mr Christopher J . . . . *§Jun 1977
Foley, Mrs Marion BA; CPE; LPC . . . . *Jan 1997
McMeel, Mr Kevin LLB(Lond) . . . . *Nov 1975
Timmis, Mr Matthew A BSc . . . . *Oct 1997
Asoc: Dookhun, Mr Mamode Yousouf Ali LLB; LPC . . . . . Feb 2005
Ast: Thompson, Ms Frances Helen BA(Hons) . . . . Jan 1999

BRAIKENRIDGE & EDWARDS ‡
30 Church Hill Road Barnet Hertfordshire EN4 8TB
Tel: 020 8449 1171 / 8441 7862 *Fax:* 020 8441 7572
List of partners: C M Thomas
Languages: French, Spanish
Work: C1 G M1 N P S1 W
Emergency Action, Legal Aid undertaken and Member of Accident Line
SPr: Thomas, Mr Christopher Mark LLB(Nott'm) . . . . . . *Sep 1981

DERRICK BRIDGES & CO ‡
12 Wood Street Barnet Hertfordshire EN5 4BQ
Tel: 020 8449 7326 *Fax:* 020 8449 8286 *Dx:* 8606 BARNET
E-mail: solicitors@derrickbridges.co.uk
List of partners: S A Fuller, N J Osborn, S T Sloan, S D Ward, R L Weldhen
Work: D2 G J1 K1 L N Q R1 S1 W
Emergency Action, Advocacy and Legal Aid undertaken
Ptr: Fuller, Miss Sharon A LLB(Hons) . . . . *Dec 1995
Osborn, Mr Nicholas J LLB . . . . *§Oct 1984
Sloan, Mr Stephen T LLB . . . . *Jun 1978
Ward, Mr Stephen Douglas BA(Hons). . . . . *Apr 1997
Weldhen, Mr Roger L Notary Public. . . . . *Feb 1975
Asoc: Solomon, Mrs Victoria. . . . . Nov 1997

PETER BROWN & CO SOLICITORS LLP ‡
1st Floor Corner House 19 Station Road Barnet Hertfordshire EN5 1QJ
Tel: 020 8447 3277 *Fax:* 020 8447 3282 *Dx:* 47706 NEW BARNET
E-mail: info@peterbrown-solicitors.com
List of partners: P I Brown, J A L Dresner, S I Hamilton, R L Streat
Work: C1 E J1 L O Q R2 S1 S2 T1 W Z(b,l)
Ptr: Brown, Mr Peter I BA . . . *Apr 1987
Dresner, Mr John Alexander Leo BA(Hons) . . . *Aug 2001
Hamilton, Miss Sandra Imogene LLB . . . *Jul 1992
Mem: Streat, Mr Richard L MA(Cantab) . . . *Nov 1984
Asoc: Magnus, Mr Alan David LLB. . . . Sep 2003
Con: Farmer, Miss Ann BA Solicitor of the Supreme Court . *Jan 1982
Robinson, Mr Robert . . . May 1987

COLEMANS - CTTS
16 Cockfosters Parade Cockfosters Barnet Hertfordshire EN4 0BX
Tel: 020 8441 1213 *Fax:* 020 8441 7548 *Dx:* 49953 COCKFOSTERS
E-mail: enquiries@colemans-ctts.co.uk
Office: Kingston upon Thames, Manchester
Languages: French, Italian, Portuguese, Spanish
Work: B1 C1 C2 C3 D1 E J1 K1 L M1 N O P Q S1 W Z(b,c,d,e,f,k,m)
Member of Accident Line
Asoc: Purday, Ms Dorothy Ann . . . Jan 2002

E A LAW ‡
Knight House 29-30 East Barnet Road Barnet Hertfordshire EN4 8RN
Tel: 020 8805 5307 *Fax:* 020 8805 5308
E-mail: info@ealaw-solicitors.co.uk

FSU LAW LIMITED ‡
4 Plantagenet Road Barnet Hertfordshire EN5 5JQ
Tel: 0700 397 3240
E-mail: ifergusson@mac.com

HADLEY LAW ASSOCIATES LLP ‡
56 East View Barnet Hertfordshire EN5 5TN
Tel: 020 8441 1856 *Fax:* 020 8440 2077 *Dx:* 8603 BARNET

HOWARD SCHNEIDER SPIRO STEELE ‡
Constable House 5 Bulwer Road Barnet Hertfordshire EN5 5JD
Tel: 020 8216 2020 *Fax:* 020 8216 2022 *Dx:* 47716 NEW BARNET
E-mail: solicitor@conveyancing.co.uk
List of partners: J Finegold
Work: E L S1 S2
SPr: Finegold, Mr Jeffrey BA(Hons) . . . *May 1981
Con: Moscisker, Mr Arnold D LLB(Lond) . . . *Jun 1977

MHHP LAW LLP ‡
7b High Street Barnet Hertfordshire EN5 5UE
Tel: 020 8275 5556 *Fax:* 020 8275 5552 *Dx:* 130033 BARNET 3
E-mail: info@mhhplaw.com

MACRORY WARD ‡
27 Station Road Barnet Hertfordshire EN5 1PW
Tel: 020 8440 3258 *Fax:* 020 8440 5436
E-mail: mw@macroryward.co.uk
List of partners: W J G Macrory, M M J Ward
Work: B1 C1 E K1 L R2 S1 S2 T2 W Z(l)
Ptr: Macrory, Mr William J G BSc(Econ); MSc Deputy District Judge . . . Jun 1978
Ward, Miss Martina M J LLB(Manc) . . . Apr 1984

STEVEN DEAN MAGAC & CO ‡
159 High Street Barnet Hertfordshire EN5 5SU
Tel: 020 8441 3399 *Fax:* 020 8441 3134 *Dx:* 8604 BARNET
E-mail: info@magac.co.uk
List of partners: J H Payne, M A H Robinson, J P Tarbox
Work: K3 Q S1 S2 W
Ptr: Payne, Mr John H. . . . *§Jan 1976
Robinson, Mr Michael A H. . . . *§Jan 1972
Tarbox, Mr Jeremy P . . . *§Jan 1976

MALE & WAGLAND
69 High Street Barnet Hertfordshire EN5 5UR
Tel: 020 8449 9669 *Fax:* 020 8440 8703 *Dx:* 8600 BARNET
E-mail: barnet@mwlaw.co.uk
Office: Potters Bar
Languages: French
Work: A1 B1 C1 D1 E F1 G H J1 K1 L M1 N P R1 S1 T1 V W Z(c,h,k,l)
Emergency Action, Agency and Advocacy undertaken

C M MILLER SOLICITORS ‡
25 Evelyn Road Cockfosters Barnet Hertfordshire EN4 9JT
Tel: 020 8449 6151 *Fax:* 020 8440 0252
E-mail: c.martinmiller@ntlworld.com
List of partners: C M Miller
Work: C1 E L S1 S2
SPr: Miller, Mr Charles Martin . . . *Nov 1976

P W MOODY ‡
25 Station Road New Barnet Barnet Hertfordshire EN5 1PH
Tel: 020 8440 1443 *Fax:* 020 8440 5802 *Dx:* 49957 COCKFOSTERS
List of partners: P W Moody
Languages: French, Spanish
Work: K1 L N Q S1 W Z(l)
Ptr: Moody, Mr Peter William BA; LLM. . . . *Nov 1963

PARKES WILSHIRE JOHNSON ‡
1 Cockfosters Parade Cockfosters Barnet Hertfordshire EN4 0BX
Tel: 020 8441 1556 *Fax:* 020 8449 5774 *Dx:* 49951 COCKFOSTERS
E-mail: law@pwj-solicitors.co.uk
List of partners: J A Bleetman, J M G Crisp, C M B Johnson, R Thorp
Office: Barnet
Languages: French, Italian
Work: B1 C1 C2 C3 D1 E F1 G J1 K1 L M1 N O Q R1 S1 S2 T1 T2 W Z(c,d,e,k,l,m,p,q,w)
Emergency Action, Agency, Advocacy, Fixed Fee Interview, Legal Aid undertaken and Member of Accident Line
Ptr: Bleetman, Mrs Judith Ann LLB(Hons) . . . *Oct 1992
Crisp, Mr Jeremy Michael Gascoyne . . . Jan 1972
Johnson, Mr Christopher M B . . . *Oct 1967
Thorp, Mr Rory LLB(Hons) . . . *Aug 2000

PARKES WILSHIRE JOHNSON
Highstone House 165 High Street Barnet Hertfordshire EN5 5SU
Tel: 020 8364 9955 *Fax:* 020 8364 9959 *Dx:* 130034 BARNET 3
E-mail: law@pwj-solicitors.co.uk
Office: Barnet
Work: C1 C2 E F1 F2 J1 K1 L N O Q R1 S1 S2 T2 W
Ast: Thorp, Mr Rory LLB(Hons) . . . *Aug 2000
Yates, Mr Andrew Mark BA; LLB . . . *Feb 2000

RB PARTNERSHIP SOLICITORS ‡
7b High Street Barnet Hertfordshire EN5 5UE
Tel: 020 8275 3877 *Fax:* 020 8275 3878

FREDERICK RINE SOLICITORS ‡
Hadley House 17 Park Road Barnet Hertfordshire EN5 5RY
Tel: 020 8440 9833 *Fax:* 020 8440 7825
E-mail: info@frederickrinesolicitors.com

JONATHAN S ROSE ‡
1 Corner House 19 Station Road Barnet Hertfordshire EN5 1QJ
Tel: 020 8447 4870 *Fax:* 020 8440 8466 *Dx:* 47705 NEW BARNET
E-mail: jonathan@jonathansrose.com
List of partners: J S Rose
Languages: French
Work: C1 E J1 L S1 W
SPr: Rose, Mr Jonathan Simon LLB(Hons). . . . *Oct 1984
Ast: Man, Mr Daniel . . . Nov 2008

CHARLES ROSS SOLICITORS ‡
18 Station Parade Cockfosters Road Barnet Hertfordshire EN4 0DW
Tel: 020 8216 2300
E-mail: enquiries@charlesross.co.uk
List of partners: G C Patros, T Petrou
Languages: Greek, Italian
Work: E J1 K1 K3 L O Q R2 S1 S2 W
Ptr: Patros, Mr George C BSc(Hons); PGDip; LLB(Hons); LLM; MCIArb Estates Gazette Prize 1992. . . . Oct 1996
Petrou, Thymios . . . Mar 1979
Ast: Vassou, Mr Vassos Michael LLB(Hons) . . . Nov 2005

LAWRENCE STERNBERG & CO ‡
5 Bulwer Road Barnet Hertfordshire EN5 5JD
Tel: 020 8440 5550

WARING & CO ‡
6th Floor Kingmaker House Station Road Barnet Hertfordshire EN5 1NZ
Tel: 0870 444 2782 *Fax:* 020 8447 4650 *Dx:* 47709 NEW BARNET
E-mail: mail@waring.co.uk
List of partners: C J Weir, D R Winston
Office: Bolton
Work: L N S1 Z(w)
Member of Accident Line
Ptr: Weir, Mr Christopher John LLB . . . Nov 1998
Winston, Mr David Richard LLB(Hons) . . . Oct 1994

BARNOLDSWICK, Lancashire

STEELE & SON
Station Chambers 16 Fernlea Avenue Barnoldswick Lancashire BB18 5DP
Tel: 01282 813385 *Fax:* 01282 813443 *Dx:* 18551 BARNOLDSWICK
E-mail: info@steeleforlaw.com
Office: Clitheroe
Work: A1 C1 D1 E F1 G H J1 K1 L N R1 S1 S2 T1 V W
Emergency Action, Agency, Advocacy, Fixed Fee Interview, Legal Aid undertaken and Legal Aid Franchise
Ptr: Nadkarni, Mr Suresh LLB . . . *Jul 2005
Ast: Hindmarsh, Mrs Katie Victoria Louise LLB. . . . *Oct 2009
Sweeney, Mrs Helen LLB . . . *Apr 1974

STERRATT & CO ‡
10 Church Street Barnoldswick Lancashire BB18 5UT
Tel: 01282 813731 *Fax:* 01282 816978 *Dx:* 18552 BARNOLDSWICK
E-mail: barnoldswick@sterratt.co.uk
List of partners: J D W Sims, M C Sterratt
Office: Skipton
Work: J1 K1 K3 K4 L S1 S2 W
Ptr: Sims, Mr Jeremy D W LLB(Lond) . . . *Sep 1980

WALKER FOSTER
Craven House Newtown Barnoldswick Lancashire BB18 5UQ
Est: 1919
Tel: 01282 812340 *Fax:* 01282 812331 *Dx:* 18553 BARNOLDSWICK
E-mail: info@walkerfoster.com
Office: Ilkley, Silsden, Skipton
Work: A1 B1 C1 C2 C3 D1 E F1 G H J1 K1 L M1 M2 N P S1 W Z(l)
Agency, Advocacy, Fixed Fee Interview, Legal Aid undertaken and Member of Accident Line
Ptr: Walker, Mr Peter C . . . *§Jul 1979

BARNSLEY, South Yorkshire

ATTEYS
25/31 Regent Street Barnsley South Yorkshire S70 2HJ
Tel: 01226 212345 *Fax:* 01226 215275 *Dx:* 12254 BARNSLEY
Office: Doncaster, Retford, Sheffield, Wath-upon-Dearne
Work: A1 B1 C1 D1 E F1 G H J1 K1 L N O Q R1 S1 V W Z(c,l,n)
Emergency Action, Agency, Advocacy, Fixed Fee Interview, Legal Aid undertaken, Legal Aid Franchise and Member of Accident Line
Ptr: Gordon, Mr David C LLB . . . *Mar 1987
Jennings, Miss Rosalind M LLB. . . . Mar 1985
Knight, Mrs Gillian A BA. . . . *Nov 1982
Methley, Mr Alan . . . *Aug 1974
Ast: Argyle, Miss Victoria Louise LLB(Hons) . . . *Oct 1997
Beevers, Mr Paul LLB; MCIArb . . . *Jan 1980
Maylard, Mrs Victoria Jayne LLB(Hons) . . . *Oct 1995

BURY & WALKERS LLP ‡
Britannic House Regent Street Barnsley South Yorkshire S70 2EQ
Tel: 01226 733533 *Fax:* 01226 207610 / 283611
Dx: 12251 BARNSLEY
E-mail: barnsley@burywalkers.com
List of partners: M P Burke, J R Clark, A H Crothers, A L Duffin, D R Grimes, R O Jones, S G Nuttall, T J Quy, J Walden, M J M Walker
Office: Leeds, Wombwell
Languages: French
Work: A1 B1 C1 C2 C3 D1 E F1 G H I J1 K1 L M1 M2 N O P Q R1 S1 T1 T2 V W X Z(b,c,d,e,f,g,h,i,j,k,l,m,n,o,p,s,t,w,x)
Emergency Action, Agency, Advocacy, Fixed Fee Interview, Legal Aid undertaken and Legal Aid Franchise
Ptr: Clark, Mr John R LLB(Leeds) . . . *May 1971
Crothers, Mr Andrew H LLB(B'ham). . . . *§Jul 1977
Duffin, Mr Alan L MA(Oxon). . . . *Jun 1973
Grimes, Mr David R MA(Oxon) . . . *§Dec 1977
Quy, Mr Terry J LLB(Exon) . . . *Dec 1974
Walker, Mr Michael J M MA(Cantab) . . . *Oct 1963
Ast: Amiss, Ms Julie-Marie LLB; LLM . . . *Mar 2000
Barber, Miss Lisa BA(Hons)(Law) . . . Jan 1998
Britton, Miss Barbara LLB(Hons) . . . Nov 1997
Crothers, Mrs Christine LLB. . . . *Aug 1990
Fletcher, Ms Amanda . . . Sep 2008
Grimes, Mrs June Jacqueline MA . . . *Nov 1993
Jones, Ms Rebecca. . . . Oct 2003
Shorrock, Mrs Jayne Helen LLB(Hons); LPC; PSC . . Mar 2008
Other offices in Leeds, Wombwell. Holders of Legal Aid contract in family law.

ELMHIRST PARKER LLP ‡
17-19 Regent Street Barnsley South Yorkshire S70 2HP
Tel: 01226 282238 *Fax:* 01226 244153 *Dx:* 12260 BARNSLEY
E-mail: barnsley@elmhirstparker.com
List of partners: J P Bouvet, J C Cox, K Haggerty, B Legg, M P Legg, S L Maxton, S L Rounding
Office: Leeds, Selby (2 offices)
Work: A1 C1 E J1 K1 K3 L N Q S1 S2 T1 T2 W Z(d,l,r)
Agency and Fixed Fee Interview undertaken
Ptr: Legg, Mr Barry . . . NSP
Ast: Alton, Mr Clive Stephen. . . . *Feb 1988
Con: Crutch, Mr Alan LLB(Sheff) Clerk to Commissioner of Taxes . . . *Apr 1979

FRITCHLEY GOLDSMITH ‡
7 Eastgate Barnsley South Yorkshire S70 2EP
Tel: 01226 215600 *Fax:* 01226 215601
Work: B2 G H Z(l)
Emergency Action, Agency, Advocacy, Fixed Fee Interview, Legal Aid undertaken and Legal Aid Franchise
Con: Greaves, Mr Alan E LLB(Hons); LLM . . . Apr 1995
Orsborn, Mr Brian BA(Hons) . . . *Dec 1986

G V HALE & CO ‡
9a Shambles Street Barnsley South Yorkshire S70 2SQ
Tel: 01226 785100 *Fax:* 01226 785100
Work: G H
Emergency Action, Agency, Advocacy and Legal Aid undertaken

HESELTINE BRAY & WELSH ‡
29 Church Street Barnsley South Yorkshire S70 2AL
Tel: 01226 210777 *Fax:* 01226 210007 *Dx:* 12256 BARNSLEY
E-mail: info@hbw-law.co.uk
List of partners: E J H Bray, A J Heseltine, D I Sutcliffe, A J Welsh
Work: A1 B1 D1 E F1 G H J1 K1 L N Q S1 V W Z(l,m,t)
Emergency Action, Agency, Advocacy, Fixed Fee Interview, Legal Aid undertaken and Legal Aid Franchise
Ptr: Bray, Mr Eric J H . . . Aug 1982
Heseltine, Mr Alistair J LLB(Leeds) . . . *Jul 1984
Sutcliffe, Mr D Iain BSc(Lond). . . . *Jul 1979
Welsh, Ms Alison J LLB. . . . *Dec 1990

HOWARD & CO ‡
(incorporating Briscoe Burgess)
Harewood House 2-4 Victoria Road Barnsley South Yorkshire S70 2BB
Tel: 01226 215215 *Fax:* 01226 284592 *Dx:* 12252 BARNSLEY
Emergency telephone 0114 234 7398 / 01226 241284
E-mail: law@howardandco.co.uk
List of partners: P M Burgess, M P Homer, P G Howard, P G Stables, H Wheelhouse
Office: Barnsley
Work: G H K1 S1 W
Emergency Action, Agency, Advocacy, Legal Aid undertaken and Legal Aid Franchise
Ptr: Burgess, Mrs Penny M BA . . . *Nov 1987
Homer, Mr Michael P LLB. . . . *Apr 1978
Howard, Mr Peter G LLB . . . *§Apr 1973
Stables, Mr Philip Glynn. . . . *Aug 1997
Wheelhouse, Ms Heather LLB. . . . *May 1996
Ast: Kennedy, Mr Augustine . . . *Jan 1986

HOWARD & CO
(incorporating Briscoe Burgess)
5-7 Regent Street Barnsley South Yorkshire S70 2EG
Tel: 01226 211888 *Fax:* 01226 211999 *Dx:* 12252 BARNSLEY 1
Office: Barnsley
Work: D1 K1 N Q S1 W
Agency, Fixed Fee Interview and Legal Aid undertaken
Ast: Greaves, Mr Paul Nicholas . . . *Aug 1998
Reece, Mr Jonathan M LLB . . . *Jan 1984

PHILIP & ROBERT HOWARD
181 Pontefract Road Cudworth Barnsley South Yorkshire S72 8AE
Tel: 01226 780840 *Fax:* 01226 780841 *Dx:* 717550 BARNSLEY 6
Emergency telephone 01484 684390
Office: Castleford
Work: A1 B1 C1 D1 D2 E F1 G H J1 K1 L M1 N P Q R1 S1 T1 V W
Emergency Action, Agency, Advocacy and Legal Aid undertaken
Ptr: Howard, Mr Philip BA(Wales) . . . *§Jun 1974

HOWELLS LLP
The Core County Way Barnsley South Yorkshire S70 2JW
Tel: 01226 805190 *Fax:* 01226 320146 *Dx:* 12261 BARNSLEY
E-mail: enquiries@howellsllp.com
Office: Rotherham, Sheffield
Ast: Danaher, Mr William John ★. . . . Oct 1982
Walker, Ms Sarah Louise LLB(Hons) . . . *Aug 1997

MKB SOLICITORS LLP ‡
1-11 Huddersfield Road Barnsley South Yorkshire S70 2LP
Tel: 01226 210000 *Fax:* 01226 211110 *Dx:* 12258 BARNSLEY
E-mail: info@mkbsolicitors.co.uk
List of partners: L Baker, G F Beaumont, G Casey, S Dawson, A Glover, K Gray, P R Higgins, C Newsam, D R Wilson, C Worton, D A Wright
Work: A1 B1 C1 C2 C3 D1 E F1 G H J1 K1 L N O Q R1 S1 W
Emergency Action, Agency, Advocacy, Fixed Fee Interview, Legal Aid undertaken and Member of Accident Line
Ptr: Baker, Miss Lynn BA . . . *May 1988
Beaumont, Mr Guy F BA . . . *Oct 1991
Casey, Mr Gerard. . . . Nov 1997
Dawson, Mr Steven. . . . Sep 2001
Glover, Mr Alan. . . . *Dec 1990
Gray, Mrs Karen LLB(Hons). . . . *Sep 1998
Higgins, Mr Peter R LLB . . . *Dec 1976
Newsam, Mr Christopher LLB. . . . *May 1990
Wilson, D R. . . . Oct 1991
Worton, Cassie . . . Nov 2005

See p112 for the Key to Work Categories & other symbols

Wright, Mr David A . . . *May 1977
Ast: Coles, Mrs Angela . . . Oct 1992
Wilcock, Carol . . . Nov 1978
Con: Dearden, Mr John LLB . . . *Apr 1975

MALTAS & CO ‡
Unit 2 Barnsley Business & Innovation Centre Snydale Road Barnsley South Yorkshire S72 8RP
Tel: 01226 781596 *Fax:* 01226 781596
E-mail: maltasandco@hotmail.co.uk
List of partners: E Maltas
SPr: Maltas, Ms Elizabeth . . . Jan 1996

MASON PALMER ‡
7 Station Road Royston Barnsley South Yorkshire S71 4EW
Tel: 01226 709100 *Fax:* 01226 709100
List of partners: P J Mason, H Palmer
Work: D1 D2 E F1 G J1 K1 K2 L N O S1 S2 V W Z(l)
Emergency Action, Agency, Advocacy, Fixed Fee Interview and Legal Aid undertaken
Ptr: Mason, Mr Peter J LLB(Hons) . . . *Mar 1988
Palmer, Mrs Helen LLB(Hons) . . . *Aug 1995

MILNERS SOLICITORS
18 Blacker Road Barnsley South Yorkshire S75 6BW
Tel: 01226 391173 *Fax:* 01226 384620 *Dx:* 12042 LEEDS
E-mail: office@milnerslaw.com
Office: Leeds, Pontefract, Wakefield

NEWMAN & BOND ‡
35 Church Street Barnsley South Yorkshire S70 2AP
Est: 1796
Tel: 01226 213434 *Fax:* 01226 213435 *Dx:* 12259 BARNSLEY 1
E-mail: enquiries@newmanandbond.co.uk
List of partners: J Leece, J Leece, J A Munden
Work: A1 B1 C1 D1 E F1 J1 K1 K3 L N O Q S1 S2 W Z(q)
Emergency Action, Agency, Advocacy, Legal Aid undertaken and Legal Aid Franchise
Ptr: Leece, Mr Jack LLB(Sheff) . . . *Jun 1979
Leece, Mrs Jill LLB(Sheff) . . . *Apr 1979
Munden, Ms Jane Anne LLB . . . Nov 1994
Asoc: Nicholson, Miss Zoe Olivia LLB . . . Sep 2005
Wright, Mr St John P BA Notary Public . . . *Jan 2001
Ast: Fegan, Mrs Julie Victoria LLB(Hons) . . . Jul 2009

PEACE REVITT ‡
6-8 Barnsley Road Wombwell Barnsley South Yorkshire S73 8DD
Tel: 01226 341111 / 210077 *Fax:* 01226 210081
Emergency telephone 07699 740810
E-mail: law@peacerevitt.co.uk
List of partners: C M R Peace, A J Revitt
Office: Rotherham
Languages: Hindi, Punjabi, Urdu
Work: D1 E F1 G H J1 K1 K3 L N Q S1 S2 V W Z(l,q)
Emergency Action, Agency, Advocacy, Fixed Fee Interview, Legal Aid undertaken and Legal Aid Franchise
Ptr: Peace, Mr Christopher M R LLB(Lond) . . . *Jul 1980
Revitt, Mr Andrew J LLB . . . *Jan 1990

PENNINE LAW ‡
Riversdale 34 Market Street Hoyland Barnsley South Yorkshire S74 9QR
Tel: 01226 369600 *Fax:* 01226 369609
E-mail: mail@penninelaw.co.uk
List of partners: W H M Hoyland, I E Lofthouse
Office: Sheffield

RALEYS ‡
Regent House 11 Regent Street Barnsley South Yorkshire S70 2EG
Tel: 01226 211111 *Fax:* 01226 211112 *Dx:* 25210 BARNSLEY 2
E-mail: maxine.scott@raleys.co.uk
List of partners: D P Barber, D I Firth, C Gill, J W E Gladman, J Markham, K A Richards
Work: D1 D2 J1 J2 K1 K2 K3 N S1 W Z(q,r)
Legal Aid undertaken and Legal Aid Franchise
Ptr: Barber, Mr David P LLB . . . *Oct 1989
Firth, Mr D Ian LLB(L'pool) . . . *Apr 1973
Gill, Ms Carol BA(Hons) . . . Oct 1998
Gladman, Mr James W E LLB(Sheff) . . . *Nov 1987
Markham, Mr Jonathan MA . . . Nov 1996
Richards, Miss Katherine A LLB . . . Oct 1992

RIAZ KHAN & CO ‡
Richmore House 7 Princess Street Barnsley South Yorkshire S70 1PR
Tel: 01226 283006 *Fax:* 01226 285015

DAVID B RICHARDS ‡
9 Kensington Road Barnsley South Yorkshire S75 2TX
Tel: 01266 281929 *Fax:* 01266 281929
Work: G H Z(m)
Emergency Action, Agency, Advocacy and Legal Aid undertaken

SHEPHERDS SOLICITORS ‡
Kendray Business Centre Thornton Road Kendray Barnsley South Yorkshire S70 3NA
Tel: 0800 073 2221

L A STEEL ‡
Oxford Villa 123 Dodworth Road Barnsley South Yorkshire S70 6HL
Tel: 01226 770909 *Fax:* 01226 770655
E-mail: mail@lasteelsolicitors.com
List of partners: L A Steel
Work: F1 F2 J1 J2 N O Q R1 Z(p,q,r,w)
Agency and Advocacy undertaken
Ptr: Steel, Mr Lancelot A BEd . . . *Oct 1991
Ast: Clarke, Mr Robert L BA(Hons) . . . *Mar 2002

G M WILSON
4 Great Cliffe Court Great Cliffe Road Dodworth Barnsley South Yorkshire S75 3SP
Tel: 01226 794140 *Fax:* 0870 051 3518 *Dx:* 742600 BARNSLEY
E-mail: davidbrooke@gmwilson.co.uk
Office: Wakefield

BARNSTAPLE, Devon

BREWER HARDING & ROWE ‡
1 The Square Barnstaple Devon EX32 8LW
Tel: 01271 342271 *Fax:* 01271 377685 *Dx:* 34957 BARNSTAPLE
E-mail: lawyers@bhrlaw.co.uk
List of partners: R K Ball, T M Barnes, I D R Budge, S E Carter, M J Chittock, G S Cloke, A R Dart, S J A Dove, N J Emo, N H Treasaden, G J Triggs, J K Walker, K B Wigley, A T H Woo
Office: Barnstaple, Bideford, Braunton, Exeter, Ilfracombe
Languages: French, Spanish
Work: A1 A3 B1 C1 C2 C3 D1 E F1 G H J1 K1 K2 K3 L N O P Q R1 S1 S2 T1 T2 V W Z(c,d,h,k,l,m,r,t)
Emergency Action, Agency, Advocacy, Fixed Fee Interview, Legal Aid undertaken and Legal Aid Franchise
Ptr: Ball, Mr Roderick K LLB . . . *§Jan 1980
Barnes, Mr Toby Martin LLB(Hons) . . . *§Sep 1996
Budge, Mr Ian D R LLB . . . *Dec 1977
Cloke, Mr Gregory Staurt LLB . . . Sep 1996
Dart, Mr Anthony R BA . . . *§Jan 1984
Dove, Mr Stephen J A BA . . . *§Feb 1983
Triggs, Mr Geoffrey John LLB(Exon) . . . *§Oct 1978
Wigley, Mr Kevin B . . . *Nov 1980
Asoc: Brown, Mrs Lydia Charlotte LLB . . . *Nov 1994
Cheves, Mr Roger Bruce FRGS . . . *Jul 1982
Millen, Ms Victoria J BCom(Hons) . . . *Mar 1998
Welham, Mr Richard J LLB . . . *Jul 1978
Wendon, Mr Andrew BA(Hons) . . . *Sep 1998
Ast: Aston, Ms Julie Ann . . . *§Nov 2001
Barbeary, Mr Stephen G BA(Econ) . . . *Aug 1988
Congdon, Mr Richard J L BA(Hons) . . . *Jun 1979
Jenkins, Mrs Alex LLB . . . Aug 2004
Little, Miss Carol LLB . . . *Jul 2006
Symons, Mr John R LLB(Hons) . . . *Oct 1970

BREWER HARDING & ROWE
Bridge Buildings Barnstaple Devon EX32 8LW
Tel: 01271 342271 *Fax:* 01271 378664 *Dx:* 34957 BARNSTAPLE
E-mail: lawyers@bhrlaw.co.uk
Office: Barnstaple, Bideford, Braunton, Exeter, Ilfracombe

CHANTER FERGUSON
Bridge Chambers Barnstaple Devon EX31 1HF
Tel: 01271 342268 *Fax:* 01271 373813 *Dx:* 34961 BARNSTAPLE
Office: Bideford
Work: A1 B1 C1 C2 C3 D1 E F1 G H J1 K1 L N O P Q R1 S1 T1 T2 V W X Z(a,c,d,e,h,k,l,m,o,s)
Emergency Action, Agency, Advocacy, Fixed Fee Interview, Legal Aid undertaken, Legal Aid Franchise and Member of Accident Line
Ptr: Clark, Mr Maurice Notary Public . . . *§Jan 1982
Laugharne, Mr Andrew Charles BA . . . *Apr 1975
Mole, Mr Peter R LLB Clerk to General Commissioners of Inland Revenue . . . *§Mar 1974
Con: Ferguson, Mr Jeremy J Notary Public . . . *§Nov 1958

TONY DART SOLICITORS & ADVOCATE ‡
102 Boutport Street Barnstaple Devon EX31 1SY
Tel: 01271 341742 *Fax:* 01271 378459
E-mail: tony@tonydart.co.uk

M J ELSDON
4 Eastacombe Rise Heanton Barnstaple Devon EX31 4DG
Tel: 01271 817661 *Fax:* 01271 817662
Emergency telephone 01271 817661
E-mail: info@elsdons-solicitors.co.uk
Office: North Walsham
Languages: Italian, Maltese
Work: A1 B1 C1 C2 C3 D1 D2 E F1 J1 K1 K3 K4 L M1 M2 N O P Q R1 S1 S2 T1 T2 W Z(f,g,q,r)
Emergency Action, Agency and Advocacy undertaken

JAYNE MCKENZIE SMITH ‡
95 High Street Barnstaple Devon EX31 1HR
Tel: 01271 329020

MICHAEL OERTON ‡
22 Boutport Street Barnstaple Devon EX31 1RP
Tel: 01271 378686
List of partners: M T Oerton
Work: B1 D1 E G H K1 L N O Q S1 T1 T2 V W Z(q)
Emergency Action, Agency, Advocacy, Legal Aid undertaken and Legal Aid Franchise
Ptr: Oerton, Mr Michael T Notary Public . . . Jan 1967
Ast: Nock, Mr Timothy G BA . . . *Nov 1990

SAMUELS SOLICITORS ‡
18 Alexandra Road Barnstaple Devon EX32 8BA
Tel: 01271 343457 *Fax:* 01271 322187 *Dx:* 34953 BARNSTAPLE
Emergency telephone 01271 858374
E-mail: mail@samuels-solicitors.co.uk
List of partners: J Cluley, J M Samuel
Work: A3 B1 B2 C1 C2 D1 D2 E F1 F2 I J1 J2 K1 L M1 N O P Q R1 R2 S1 S2 T1 T2 W X Z(b,c,e,i,j,k,o,q,r)
Emergency Action, Agency, Advocacy, Fixed Fee Interview, Legal Aid undertaken, Legal Aid Franchise and Member of Accident Line
Ptr: Cluley, Mrs Julia . . . Oct 2002
Samuel, Ms Jan M BA(Hons) . . . *§Dec 1980

SCHOFIELDS SOLICITORS ‡
Montana Kentisbury Barnstaple Devon EX31 4NU
Tel: 01271 882790 *Fax:* 01271 889421

SLEE BLACKWELL ‡
(incorporating Montague Arthur & Partners)
10 Cross Street Barnstaple Devon EX31 1BA
Tel: 01271 372128 *Fax:* 01271 344885 *Dx:* 34952 BARNSTAPLE
E-mail: info@sleeblackwell.co.uk
List of partners: N J Arthur, A J Burke, L A Dawkins, C H Jones, C J E Jones, P Jordan, J A G Pearn
Office: Bideford, Braunton, Exeter, South Molton
Languages: French, Spanish
Work: A1 B1 C1 C2 C3 D1 D2 E F1 G H J1 K1 L M1 M2 N O P Q R1 R2 S1 T1 T2 V W Z(b,c,d,e,l,q,r)
Emergency Action, Agency, Advocacy, Fixed Fee Interview, Legal Aid undertaken, Legal Aid Franchise and Member of Accident Line
Ptr: Arthur, Mr Nicholas J . . . *§Mar 1984
Burke, Mr Andrew John BA . . . *Oct 1992
Dawkins, Mr Lee A BA . . . *Nov 1990
Jones, Mr Christopher J E LLB . . . *§Nov 1980
Jordan, Mr Paul LLB Sweet & Maxwell Law Prize; Leicester Law Society Prize . . . *Oct 1988
Ast: Cole, Mr Julian Henry LLB(Hons) . . . *Dec 1994
Sinclair, Ms Toni LLB(Hons) . . . *Nov 1991
Con: Whiteley, Mr David L . . . *§Nov 1982

SMITHS SOLICITORS ‡
102 Boutport Street Barnstaple Devon EX31 1SY
Tel: 01271 314888 *Fax:* 01271 378459
E-mail: lo@smiths-solicitors.co.uk

TOLLER BEATTIE LLP ‡
Devonshire House Riverside Road Pottington Business Park Barnstaple Devon EX31 1QN
Tel: 01271 341000 *Fax:* 01271 344445 *Dx:* 34954 BARNSTAPLE
E-mail: solicitors@tollerbeattie.co.uk
List of partners: D Baker, R H Beattie, J Dunkley, R W Gross, M D Kingman, G M Lindqvist-Jones, M S Roome
Languages: Danish
Work: A1 B1 C1 C2 C3 D1 D2 E F1 G H I J1 K1 K3 K4 L M1 M2 N O P Q R1 S1 S2 T1 T2 U2 V W Z(c,d,e,g,k,l,m,q,t,za)
Emergency Action, Agency, Advocacy, Fixed Fee Interview, Legal Aid undertaken and Member of Accident Line
Ptr: Baker, Ms Deborah LLB(Wales) . . . *§Oct 1985
Beattie, Mr Robert H . . . *§Jul 1969
Dunkley, Mr Jon LLB(Hons) . . . Aug 2006
Gross, Mr Robert William BA; DipLG . . . *Mar 1980
Kingman, Mr Michael Donald BA(Law); DipPIL . . . *Jul 1981
Lindqvist-Jones, Mrs Gillian Margaret LLB . . . *Oct 1980
Roome, Mr Mark Simon LLB; PGDip Professional Legal Skills Duke of Edinburgh Scholarship . . . Jan 2006
Ast: Dorey, Miss Stacimarie . . . Sep 2010
Hook, Mr Timothy S H LLB(Exon) . . . *§Jul 1977
Jenkins, Mrs Alexandra LLB . . . Aug 2004
Tollett, Mr Paul . . . Dec 1985
Con: Gordon-Lee, Mr Alan J LLB; MBIM . . . *Jun 1974

BARROW-IN-FURNESS, Cumbria

BROWN BARRON ‡
65 Duke Street Barrow-in-Furness Cumbria LA14 1RW
Tel: 01229 828814 *Fax:* 01229 812202
Dx: 63901 BARROW-IN-FURNESS
Emergency telephone 01229 585012
E-mail: enquiries@brown-barron.co.uk
List of partners: C A Barron, P S O'Donnell
Work: D1 D2 F1 J1 J2 K1 K3 L N O P Q S1 S2 W Z(l,q)
Emergency Action, Agency, Advocacy, Fixed Fee Interview and Legal Aid Franchise
Ptr: Barron, Mr Christopher A LLB(Newc) . . . *Nov 1980
O'Donnell, Mr Paul Simon LLB . . . *Aug 2000
Asoc: Hughes, Miss Georgina Kathryn BA . . . Mar 2006
Sharp, Mr Philip Alan LLB(Leics) Deputy Coroner . . . *Jun 1977

CLARKSON HIRST
105 Duke Street Barrow-in-Furness Cumbria LA14 1RH
Tel: 01229 820600
Office: Kendal, Lancaster

DENBY & CO ‡
(incorporating Hampson & Scott; Jobling & Knape)
119 Duke Street Barrow-in-Furness Cumbria LA14 1XE
Tel: 01229 822366 *Fax:* 01229 870109
Dx: 63904 BARROW-IN-FURNESS
Emergency telephone 01229 822807
E-mail: info@denbyco.co.uk
List of partners: J H Denby, R M Denby, A Gallagher, A Gallagher, M Sadler, J P Scott
Office: Ulverston
Work: D1 D2 E F1 G H J1 K1 K2 K3 K4 L N O P Q R1 S1 S2 T2 W Z(c,d,j,k,l,r)
Emergency Action, Agency, Advocacy, Fixed Fee Interview, Legal Aid undertaken, Legal Aid Franchise and Member of Accident Line
Ptr: Denby, Mr Richard Mark LLB(Hons) . . . *Dec 1993
Gallagher, Mr Andrew LLB(Hons) . . . *May 2000
Scott, Mr John Philip LLB(Hons) . . . *Dec 1993
Asoc: Hollins Gibson, Mr Andrew James BA(Hons) . . . *Jan 1977
Ast: Findlay, Miss Elanor Anne LLB . . . *Dec 2003

FORRESTERS ‡
117 Duke Street Barrow-in-Furness Cumbria LA14 1XA
Tel: 01229 820297 *Fax:* 01229 870017
Dx: 63906 BARROW-IN-FURNESS
E-mail: mail@forresterssolicitors.co.uk
List of partners: A S H Adams, J L Fish, M Graham
Work: A1 A2 B1 B2 C1 D1 D2 E G H K1 N Q S1 S2 T1 T2 W Z(c,d,l,q)
Emergency Action, Agency, Advocacy, Fixed Fee Interview, Legal Aid undertaken and Legal Aid Franchise
Dir: Adams, Mr Angus S H LLB(L'pool) . . . *Jun 1976
Fish, Mr Jeremy L BA(Oxon) . . . *Jan 1985
Graham, Mr Michael LLB ★ . . . *Aug 1990
Asoc: Lister, Mr Harry D MA(Cantab) . . . *Jan 1980
Ast: Templeton, Miss Karen Dawn LLB ★ . . . *Oct 1993
Thompson, Miss Nicola Clare LLB . . . *Mar 2008

LIVINGSTONS
Buccleuch House 75-77 Buccleuch Street Barrow-in-Furness Cumbria LA14 1QQ
Tel: 01229 828300 *Fax:* 01229 824796
E-mail: enquiries@livingstons.co.uk
Office: Dalton-in-Furness, Ulverston
Languages: French, German
Work: C1 E F1 J1 K1 K3 K4 N Q S1 T2 W Z(l)
Emergency Action, Agency, Advocacy, Fixed Fee Interview and Legal Aid undertaken
Dir: Hollis, Mr Simon J LLB(Hons) . . . *Oct 1990

POOLE TOWNSEND ‡
69-75 Duke Street Barrow-in-Furness Cumbria LA14 1RP
Tel: 01229 811811 *Fax:* 01229 824705
Dx: 63900 BARROW-IN-FURNESS
Emergency telephone 0800 389 2939
E-mail: mbeecham@pooletownsend.co.uk
List of partners: L Bayles, J C Copeland, M J Oates, S Pyne, T B Roberts, P J Yates
Office: Dalton-in-Furness, Grange-over-Sands, Kendal, Ulverston
Work: A1 B1 C1 C2 C3 D1 E F1 G H J1 K1 L M1 M2 N O P Q R1 S1 S2 T1 T2 V W X Z(c,i,k,l,o,r)
Emergency Action, Agency, Advocacy, Legal Aid undertaken, Legal Aid Franchise and Member of Accident Line
Ptr: Bayles, Lindsey . . . *Dec 1992
Copeland, Mrs Joanne C . . . *Nov 1993
Oates, Mr Martin J LLB . . . *Nov 1992
Pyne, Mrs Susan BSc(Hons); LPC . . . *Nov 1998
Roberts, Trystan Bleddyn LLB . . . *Nov 1995
Yates, Mr Peter J LLB . . . *§Jul 1975
Asoc: Redmond, Ms Mary Elizabeth Stennett BA(Hons) . . . *Jul 1981
Ast: Beecham, Mr Matthew . . . Nov 2005
Tunn, Miss Jane . . . Feb 2007
Con: Davies, Mr Michael . . . Jul 1967

BARROW-UPON-HUMBER, North Lincolnshire

SHK SOLICITORS ‡
Wood Lea Westoby Lane Barrow-upon-Humber North Lincolnshire DN19 7DJ
Tel: 01469 531388 / 07793 204890 *Fax:* 01469 531388
E-mail: shk@shksolicitprs.co.uk

BARRY, Vale of Glamorgan

CLODES SOLICITORS ‡
21 Thompson Street Barry Vale of Glamorgan CF63 4JL
Tel: 01446 720777
List of partners: M C J Clode
Office: Cardiff

CRANES ‡
(in association with Francis & Buck; Cardiff)
8 Broad Street Barry Vale of Glamorgan CF62 7AA
Tel: 01446 720444 *Fax:* 01446 738555
E-mail: cranes.sols@btconnect.com
List of partners: N J Crane, T J Crane
Work: E L R1 S1 T1 T2 W Z(c,h,j)
Ptr: Crane, Mr Nicholas J BA(Law) . . . . *Jul 1983
Crane, Mr Timothy J LLB . . . . *Oct 1980

FORTE LAW ‡
The Cottage Penmark Barry Vale of Glamorgan CF62 3BP
Tel: 01446 713599
E-mail: law@fortelaw.co.uk

GRIFFITHS INGS LTD ‡
70 High Street Barry Vale of Glamorgan CF62 7DW
Tel: 01446 725180 *Fax:* 01446 725181 *Dx:* 38573 BARRY
E-mail: info@griffithsings.com
Office: Cardiff

J A HUGHES ‡
Centenary House King Square Barry Vale of Glamorgan CF62 8HB
Tel: 01446 411000 *Fax:* 01446 411010 *Dx:* 38550 BARRY
Emergency telephone 07831 509272
E-mail: jahughes@qualitysolicitors.com
List of partners: J L Davies, T M Ellis, T G Hackett, S E Horwood, A D Kennedy
Office: Cardiff, Penarth
Languages: French, Welsh
Work: A1 B1 D1 D2 E G H J1 K1 N Q R1 S1 Z(d,e,f,g,j,k,p,r)
Emergency Action, Agency, Advocacy, Fixed Fee Interview, Legal Aid undertaken, Legal Aid Franchise and Member of Accident Line
Ptr: Ellis, Mrs Tracy Margaret LLB . . . . *Oct 1995
Hackett, Mr Timothy G LLB(Exon) ♦ . . . . *Nov 1989
Ast: Kelland, Mr Neil LLB . . . . Oct 1983
Landcastle, Miss Clarissa LLB . . . . *Sep 2006
McPherson, Mr Gavin LLB . . . . Nov 2006
Williams, Mrs Gayle LLB . . . . *Feb 2002

JEFF LLOYD ‡
87a Holton Road Barry Vale of Glamorgan CF63 4HG
Tel: 01446 741919 *Fax:* 01446 744635 *Dx:* 38552 BARRY
E-mail: enquiries@jefflloydsolicitor.co.uk
List of partners: J H Lloyd
SPr: Lloyd, Mr Jeffrey H LLB(Lond) . . . . *Jul 1975

COLIN JONES ‡
17 Thompson Street Barry Vale of Glamorgan CF63 4JL
Tel: 01446 420043 *Fax:* 01446 420045

PASSMORE LEWIS & JACOBS ‡
21 Tynewydd Road Barry Vale of Glamorgan CF62 8HB
Tel: 01446 721000 *Fax:* 01446 746949 *Dx:* 38557 BARRY
E-mail: mail@passmores.com
List of partners: J H Gifford, T G Hughes, C E Roblin, N Willetts
Work: C1 D1 E F1 G H J1 K1 L M1 P R1 S1 V W X Z(m)
Emergency Action, Agency, Advocacy, Fixed Fee Interview and Legal Aid undertaken
Ptr: Gifford, Mr Jonathan H LLB(Wales) . . . . *Dec 1976
Hughes, Mr Trefor Glyn LLB(Lond) . . . . *§Jul 1976
Roblin, Catherine E LLB . . . . *§Nov 1984
Willetts, Mr Neil LLB(Wales) . . . . *§May 1978
Con: Thomas, Mr Geoffrey F LLB(Wales) . . . . *Oct 1959

ANTHONY PUGH ‡
The Old Rectory Flemingston Barry Vale of Glamorgan CF62 4QJ
Tel: 01446 751493 *Fax:* 01446 750961
E-mail: anthonypugh@btopenworld.com
List of partners: A I Pugh
Work: K4 T2 W Z(d)
SPr: Pugh, Mr Anthony Ivor BA(Oxon) Deputy District Chairman of the Tribunal Service; General Commissioner of Income Tax . . . . *Aug 1968

ROBERTSONS
2-4 Buttrills Road Barry Vale of Glamorgan CF62 8EF
Tel: 01446 745660 *Fax:* 01446 744124 *Dx:* 38556 BARRY
E-mail: law@robsols.co.uk
Office: Cardiff (2 offices)
Work: B1 C1 D1 E F1 G H J1 K1 L M1 N P R1 S1 W Z(k,l,p)
Emergency Action, Agency, Advocacy, Legal Aid undertaken, Legal Aid Franchise and Member of Accident Line
Ptr: Hart, Miss Clare F LLB(Wales) . . . . *Jul 1979
Humphreys, Mr Andrew M LLB . . . . *Mar 1988

URRUTIA & CO ‡
PO Box 166 Barry Vale of Glamorgan CF62 7EN
Tel: 0800 013 2315 *Fax:* 01446 401414 *Dx:* 38567 BARRY
E-mail: new.enquiry@famile-law.co.uk

VALE SOLICITORS ‡
144 Holton Road Barry Vale of Glamorgan CF63 4UA
Tel: 01446 733191 *Fax:* 01446 749038 *Dx:* 38554 BARRY
Emergency telephone 029 2070 8207
E-mail: mail@valesolicitors.com
Office: Llantwit Major
Work: D1 F1 G H J1 K1 L M1 P S1 W
Emergency Action, Agency, Advocacy, Fixed Fee Interview, Legal Aid undertaken and Member of Accident Line

BARTON-UPON-HUMBER, North Lincolnshire

BARTON SOLICITORS ‡
Falkland Way Barton-upon-Humber North Lincolnshire DN18 5RL
Tel: 01652 618376

DE VITA NORRIS SOLICITORS ‡
26 High Street Barton-upon-Humber North Lincolnshire DN18 5PD
Tel: 01652 661960

KEITH READY & CO ‡
Market Place Barton-upon-Humber North Lincolnshire DN18 5DD
Tel: 01652 632215 *Fax:* 01652 660036
Dx: 29601 BARTON-UPON-HUMBER
E-mail: keith@ready.co.uk
List of partners: H K Ready
Work: B1 D1 E F1 J1 K1 K3 K4 L N Q S1 S2 T2 V W Z(c,k,m)
Agency and Fixed Fee Interview undertaken
Ptr: Ready, Mr H Keith BA(Oxon) . . . . *§Jan 1965
Asoc: Lyons, Mr Stephen Keith BA(Hons) . . . . *Jan 1990

S W SOLICITOR LTD ‡
2 Hassel View Barton-upon-Humber North Lincolnshire DN18 5QY
Tel: 01652 639051 / 07811 102086
E-mail: stuartward@swsolicitor.co.uk

BASILDON, Essex

BROWN & CO ‡
6 Capricorn Centre Cranes Farm Road Basildon Essex SS14 3JJ
Tel: 01268 243610 *Fax:* 01268 243611 *Dx:* 139485 BASILDON 9
Work: S1 S2

DORLING COTTRELL
1st Floor Suite Phoenix House Basildon Essex SS14 3EZ
Tel: 01268 796000
Office: Benfleet

JERMAN SIMPSON PEARSON & SAMUELS
Southgate House 88 Town Square Basildon Essex SS14 1BN
Tel: 01268 820111 *Fax:* 01268 820363 *Dx:* 53042 BASILDON
Emergency telephone 07717 713631
Office: Southend-on-Sea
Ptr: Jerman, Mr Mark C LLB(Hons) . . . . Sep 1987
Pearson, Mr Mark BA(Law) . . . . Nov 1983
Ast: Clift, Mr Ian . . . . Nov 2001
Fell, Paula . . . . Apr 2005
Morlham, Christina . . . . Jun 2005
Murrison, Mr Richard . . . . Jul 2006

ANTHONY KING & CO ‡
(in association with Anthony King LLB; Notary Public)
Southgate House Town Square Basildon Essex SS14 1BN
Tel: 01268 240400 *Fax:* 01268 240424 *Dx:* 53018 BASILDON
Emergency telephone 07766 918344
E-mail: jcowdrey@anthonyking.co.uk
List of partners: J E Cowdrey, A B King, M P Savage
Work: D1 D2 E F2 G H J1 J2 K1 K3 L N O Q S1 S2 V W Z(h,q)
Emergency Action, Agency, Advocacy, Fixed Fee Interview, Legal Aid undertaken and Legal Aid Franchise
Ptr: Cowdrey, Mrs Jane Elizabeth LLB . . . . *Nov 1992
King, Mr Anthony B LLB Notary Public . . . . *Apr 1977
Savage, Mr Mark Peter LLB ★ . . . . *Feb 1996
Ast: Bland, Mrs Kerry LLB . . . . *Feb 2010
Collins, Mr Seth LLB . . . . *Dec 2008
Cronin, Miss Erin LLB . . . . *Sep 2009
Dowie, Miss Sarah BA(Hons) . . . . *Aug 2008
McLoughin, Miss Joanne LLB . . . . *Feb 2010
Snow, Miss Yvonne LLB . . . . *Feb 2008
Thorne, Miss Claire LLB; BVC . . . . *Jun 2008

MWP SOLICITORS ‡
Freedom House East Square Basildon Essex SS14 1HS
Tel: 01268 527131 *Fax:* 01268 530089 *Dx:* 53000 BASILDON
E-mail: info@mwpsolicitors.co.uk
List of partners: L M Callaghan, L S Maudsley
Work: D1 E F1 J1 K1 K3 L N Q S1 W
Emergency Action, Agency, Advocacy, Fixed Fee Interview, Legal Aid undertaken, Legal Aid Franchise and Member of Accident Line
Ptr: Callaghan, Ms Lorraine May BA . . . . *Dec 1992
Maudsley, Mr Lawrence Stewart BA . . . . *Jul 1977

MCCORMACKS
74-76 Town Square Basildon Essex SS14 1DT
Tel: 01268 525999 *Fax:* 01268 525250
Emergency telephone 020 7791 2000
E-mail: messages@mccormacks.co.uk
Office: London E1, London E15, London EC1
Languages: British Sign Language, Spanish
Work: B2 G H
Emergency Action, Agency, Advocacy, Fixed Fee Interview and Legal Aid undertaken
Ptr: Cuthbert, Mr Leslie LLM ★ Part time Road Charge User Adjudicator . . . . *Jul 1996

MARTIN NOSSEL & CO ‡
10-12 Southernhay Basildon Essex SS14 1EL
Tel: 01268 289555 *Fax:* 01268 534661 *Dx:* 53005 BASILDON
Emergency telephone 01268 534644
E-mail: mnossel@aol.com
List of partners: M I Nossel
Work: B1 E F1 G J1 K1 L M1 M2 N P R1 S1 T1 T2 V X
Emergency Action, Agency, Fixed Fee Interview, Legal Aid undertaken and Legal Aid Franchise
Ptr: Nossel, Mr Martin I BA; LLM . . . . *Feb 1984
Asoc: Nossel, Miss Emma-Faye LLB(Hons) . . . . Sep 2010

PALMERS ‡
19 Town Square Basildon Essex SS14 1BD
Tel: 01268 240000 *Fax:* 01268 240001 *Dx:* 53002 BASILDON
E-mail: enquiries@palmerslaw.co.uk
List of partners: E Chong, C A Jacobs, L J McClellan, C J R Mowat, J R L Sirrell, A P Skinner, T C Steele, C W Tant
Office: Grays, South Woodham Ferrers
Languages: Cantonese
Work: A1 A3 B1 B2 B3 C1 C2 C3 D1 D2 E F1 F2 G H I J1 J2 K1 K2 K3 K4 L M1 O P Q R1 R2 S1 S2 T1 T2 U2 V W X Z(c,d,e,g,i,k,l,p,q,t,z)
Emergency Action, Agency, Advocacy, Fixed Fee Interview, Legal Aid undertaken and Legal Aid Franchise
Ptr: Jacobs, Miss Carey Anne LLB; LPC . . . . *Oct 1997
McClellan, Mr Lee John LLB . . . . *Sep 1998
Mowat, Mr Christopher J R LLB(Lond) . . . . *Dec 1973
Sirrell, Mr Jeremy R L BA(Hons) . . . . *May 1989
Tant, Mr Clive W BSc . . . . *Nov 1980
Asoc: Smith, Miss Joanne BA(Hons)(Law & Psychosocial Studies) . . . . Sep 2003
Ast: Barnes, Mr Karl George LLB . . . . Sep 1999
Derrick, Mrs Aldene Davina Ruth . . . . Oct 2003
Dixon, Mr Simon Charles LLB . . . . Oct 2009
Francis, Mrs Deborah LLB(Hons) . . . . Jan 2005
Goss, Ms Jacqueline Ann LLB . . . . *Jan 1999
Jago, Mrs Helen Alison . . . . Sep 2005
Poli, Mr Matthew Bruno . . . . Oct 2006
Smy, Miss Donna LLB(Hons); LPC . . . . Sep 2008
Verdi, Mrs Surjit . . . . Oct 2004

BASINGSTOKE, Hampshire

NICHOLAS BATES ‡
56 Southern Road Basingstoke Hampshire RG21 3EA
Tel: 01256 331278 *Dx:* 3015 BASINGSTOKE
Emergency telephone 07721 671765
E-mail: nbates@btconnect.com
List of partners: N J Bates
Languages: French, Spanish
Work: G H
Emergency Action, Agency, Advocacy, Fixed Fee Interview, Legal Aid undertaken and Legal Aid Franchise
SPr: Bates, Mr Nicholas John BA . . . . Dec 1976
Con: Coupland, Mr Cedric M . . . . *§Dec 1980

ANDREW BRADLEY ‡
Goldings London Road Basingstoke Hampshire RG21 4AN
Tel: 01256 478119 *Fax:* 01256 814292

BRAIN CHASE COLES ‡
Haymarket House 20-24 Wote Street Basingstoke Hampshire RG21 7NL
Tel: 01256 354481 *Fax:* 01256 841432 *Dx:* 3005 BASINGSTOKE
E-mail: enquiries@brainchasecoles.co.uk
List of partners: J M Coles, K A Martin, N G Massey-Chase, M S Stevenson
Work: D1 D2 E K1 K2 K3 L Q R1 S1 S2 V W Z(h,q)
Emergency Action, Agency, Advocacy, Fixed Fee Interview, Legal Aid undertaken and Legal Aid Franchise
Ptr: Coles, Mr Jonathan M LLB(Wales) Notary Public . . . *Oct 1983
Martin, Mrs Katharine Anne LLB ♦ . . . . *Jun 1999
Massey-Chase, Mr Nicholas G LLB(Bris) . . . . *Apr 1975
Stevenson, Mrs Margaret S LLB(Nott'm) . . . . *Nov 1985
Ast: Ford, Miss Elizabeth LLB; PGDL . . . . *Sep 2010
Harvey, Miss Sarah LLB . . . . Sep 2009
Palmer, Miss Sarah Elizabeth LLB; TEP STEP Excellence Award 2007 . . . . *Apr 2007
Parkes, Mrs Sheila C LLB(Aberdeen) . . . . *Jan 1986

IAN BURLINGHAM SOLICITOR ‡
4 Winton Square Basingstoke Hampshire RG21 8EN
List of partners: I W Burlingham
SPr: Burlingham, Mr Ian W LLB . . . . *May 1967

ADRIAN CHARD & CO ‡
1 Richmond Road Basingstoke Hampshire RG21 5NX
Tel: 01256 363944 *Fax:* 01256 356132 *Dx:* 3023 BASINGSTOKE
E-mail: admin@bedsonandchard.demon.co.uk
List of partners: A Chard
Work: C1 E N O Q S1
Agency, Advocacy and Legal Aid undertaken
SPr: Chard, Mr Adrian LLB . . . . *May 1983

THE CHILD LAW PARTNERSHIP
10 Sarum Hill Basingstoke Hampshire RG21 8SR
Tel: 01256 630080 *Fax:* 01256 543791 *Dx:* 3013 BASINGSTOKE
E-mail: infi@childlawpartnership.co.uk
Office: Guildford

COOMBER RICH ‡
Yard House May Place Basingstoke Hampshire RG21 7NX
Tel: 01256 812202 *Fax:* 01256 346349 *Dx:* 3020 BASINGSTOKE

ELIN & ASSOCIATES ‡
1a Queens Parade Basingstoke Hampshire RG21 7DA
Tel: 01256 358864 *Fax:* 01256 358290
E-mail: elinsolicitors@googlemail.com
List of partners: T Elin
Languages: Polish
Work: G H J1 J2 L S1 V W Z(l)
Agency, Fixed Fee Interview, Legal Aid undertaken and Legal Aid Franchise
SPr: Elin, Miss Teresa ★ . . . . Oct 1994

HENLEYS ‡
60 Southern Road Basingstoke Hampshire RG21 3EA
Tel: 01256 840084 *Fax:* 01256 844368 *Dx:* 3021 BASINGSTOKE
E-mail: jonathan.henley@henleyssolicitors.co.uk
List of partners: J A Henley
Work: E S1 W
Ptr: Henley, Mr Jonathan A BA . . . . *Jul 1981

LAMB BROOKS LLP ‡
Victoria House 39 Winchester Street Basingstoke Hampshire RG21 7EQ
Tel: 01256 844888 *Fax:* 01256 330933 *Dx:* 3000 BASINGSTOKE
E-mail: enquiries@lambbrooks.com
List of partners: D T Argent, S Aston, N M Bourne, A C Brooks, A Davies, R G Finlayson, M Izquierdo, A M Lowe, T Rogers, W J Sadler
Languages: French
Work: A1 B1 B2 C1 C2 C3 D1 D2 E F1 F2 J1 K1 K3 K4 L M1 M2 N O P Q R2 S1 S2 T1 T2 U1 U2 W Z(c,e,l,p,q,za)
Emergency Action, Agency, Advocacy, Fixed Fee Interview undertaken and Member of Accident Line
Ptr: Argent, Mr David T BSc . . . . *Jan 2000
Aston, Mrs Sheena . . . . *Dec 2000
Bourne, Mr Nigel M BA . . . . *§Dec 1979
Brooks, Mr Alexander C LLB . . . . *Nov 1990
Davies, Ms Ann LLB(Wales) H M Deputy Coroner of North East Hampshire . . . . *§Nov 1982
Finlayson, Mr Robert G BA . . . . *§May 1981

See p112 for the Key to Work Categories & other symbols

Izquierdo, Mr Mark LLB(Hons). . . . . *Sep 1997
Lowe, Mr Andrew M. . . . . *§Aug 1991
Rogers, Mrs Trudy-Jane LLB . . . . . *Aug 2001
Sadler, Mr Warren James BA(Hons). . . . . *Nov 1992
Asoc: Jaj, Balvinder . . . . . *Mar 2004
Johnson, Mrs Kirstie Jane LLB(Hons) . . . . . *Sep 2002
Latcham, Miss Julie Anne. . . . . *May 2001
Soccard, Mrs Joanne LLB. . . . . *Dec 2001
Whiteaker, Mrs Viviene Chai BA(Hons); LPC . . . . . *Apr 2000
Ast: Arran, Mrs Hannah May LLB . . . . . *Sep 2006
Barron, Ms Amy Claire LLB(Hons). . . . . Nov 2010
Christian, Miss Laura Bryony LLB(Hons) . . . . . *Sep 2009
Denza, Mr Paul LLB(Hons) . . . . . May 2004
Ervin, Miss Louise Kathleen. . . . . *Sep 2007
Squires, Miss Sue. . . . . *Mar 2007
Wilkins, Miss Susan Dessislava LLB . . . . . *May 2008
Con: Gaze, Miss Jennifer A LLB(Exon); TEP . . . . . *§Jul 1972
Innes-Ker, Mr Robert Notary Public . . . . . Nov 1970
Rossiter, Mr Thomas William . . . . . Dec 1979

LAWYER IN A HARD HAT LIMITED ‡
2 Kestrel Court Vyne Road Sherborne St John Basingstoke Hampshire RG24 9HJ
Tel: 01256 889840 *Fax:* 01256 889839
E-mail: graeme@lawyerinahardhat.com

JOE MCDERMOTT SOLICITORS ‡
29 Kendal Gardens Basingstoke Hampshire RG22 5HD
Tel: 07720 723072

MORGAN & CO ‡
6a London Street Basingstoke Hampshire RG21 7NU
Tel: 01256 329888 *Fax:* 01256 329888
List of partners: R J R Morgan
Work: J1 K1 L S1 S2 W
Emergency Action, Agency, Fixed Fee Interview and Legal Aid undertaken
SPr: Morgan, Mr Richard John Ruck . . . . . *Jul 1971

NEALE TURK
74 Bounty Road Basingstoke Hampshire RG21 3BZ
Tel: 01256 473013 *Fax:* 01256 811647 *Dx:* 3044 BASINGSTOKE
E-mail: j.foxley@nealeturk.com
Office: Fleet
Work: A1 C1 C2 E L R1 S1 S2 W Z(l)
Ptr: Ratcliffe, Mr John F LLB. . . . . Apr 1973
Wheeler, Mr Jonathan Charles LLB . . . . . Feb 1997

PENNINGTONS
Da Vinci House Basing View Basingstoke Hampshire RG21 4EQ
Tel: 01256 407100 *Fax:* 01256 479425
Dx: 148600 BASINGSTOKE 21
E-mail: info@penningtons.co.uk
Office: Godalming, London EC2
Languages: French, Italian, Spanish
Work: A1 B1 C1 D1 E F1 G H I J1 K1 L M1 N O P Q R1 S1 T1 W Z(c,d,e,k,l)
Emergency Action, Agency, Advocacy undertaken and Member of Accident Line
Ptr: Appelboam-Meadows, Mrs Alison Margaret BA(Hons). *Oct 1993
Bickford, Mr David LLB(Hons). . . . . Nov 1991
Bosi, Mr Gianfranco LLB(Hons) . . . . . *Oct 1985
Brooks, Mr Charles M Member of SEG, IBA, UAI . . *§Nov 1980
Burton, Julie MA(Oxon) . . . . . May 1981
Cardew, Sarah BA(Hons) . . . . . Sep 2000
Cash, Mr Michael LLB(Hons) . . . . . *Nov 1993
Davies, Mr Tim LLB(Hons) . . . . . Apr 1987
Palmer, Mr Timothy Michael BA(Hons) . . . . . *Nov 1995
Storey, Mrs Linda Anne LLB(Hons) . . . . . *Nov 1990
Underwood, Mr Richard L MA(Cantab) . . . . . *Apr 1973
Vengadesan, Joanne LLB(Hons) . . . . . Apr 2001
Asoc: Dixon, Mr Graham . . . . . Oct 2002
Geoghegan, Mr Conor LLB . . . . . Aug 1994
Hodgson, Sian . . . . . Sep 1997
Johnson, Alison. . . . . Sep 2001
Pooley, Mr Mark J LLB . . . . . *Jan 1987
Searle, Charlotte . . . . . Oct 2005
Spencer, Ms Justine. . . . . *Oct 1999
Wright, Mr Tim . . . . . Jun 1979
Ast: Aldous, Rachel . . . . . Sep 2010
Bevan, Ms Elise. . . . . Sep 2007
Gibson, Sarah. . . . . Sep 2007
Lee, Sarah . . . . . Dec 2010
Lindsay, Laura . . . . . Sep 2010
Ross, Georgina . . . . . Sep 1999
Stevenson, Charlotte . . . . . Sep 2007
Wonnacott, Camilla . . . . . Apr 1992
Woodhouse, Gemma . . . . . Sep 2007
Con: Rouse, Mr Jonathan M LLB(Hons) . . . . . *Jul 1974

PHILLIPS SOLICITORS ‡
Town Gate 38 London Street Basingstoke Hampshire RG21 7NY
Tel: 01256 460830 *Fax:* 01256 364333 / 854638
Dx: 123073 BASINGSTOKE 10
E-mail: legal@phillips-law.co.uk
List of partners: G Brown, J A Corrigan, H P K Gardener, S V Glyn-Owen, Z Naylor, J R Pender, A G Preshaw
Languages: Afrikaans, French, German, Portuguese, Spanish
Work: A3 C1 E J1 K1 K2 K4 O Q S1 W Z(l)
Agency and Advocacy undertaken
Dir: Brown, Ms Gillian LLB(Hons) ♦ . . . . . *Jun 1996
Corrigan, Mrs Judith Ann LLB; PGDipLaw. . . . . *Sep 2003
Gardener, Mr Howard Paul Keith BSc; FMA Mediator ♦ Deputy District Judge . . . . . *§Oct 1982
Glyn-Owen, Mrs Sheila V BA(Hons) ♦. . . . . *Mar 1991
Naylor, Miss Zoe LLB ♦ . . . . . *Oct 1995
Pender, Mr Jonathan Richard LLB(Hons) ♦ . . . . . *Apr 1983
Preshaw, Mr Alexander Grenville LLB ♦ . . . . . *§Jul 1979
Ast: Eachus, Ms Hayley Kristina LLB(Hons) . . . . . *Sep 2005
Parker, Mr Robert James LLB. . . . . *Sep 2007
Rayner, Ms Kelly-Jean . . . . . Apr 2006
Real, Miss Sarah . . . . . *Aug 2004
Roberts, Mrs Melanie BSc(Geography); PGDipLaw . . *Aug 2007

QUALITY SOLICITORS CLARKE & SON ‡
Manor House 8 Winchester Road Basingstoke Hampshire RG21 8UG
Tel: 01256 320555 *Fax:* 01256 843150 *Dx:* 3004 BASINGSTOKE
E-mail: mail@clarkeandson.co.uk
List of partners: P L Cowdery, I G F Kershaw, S Lakhani, C V Marchant-White, B Sankhla, P B Turner, N Wharry
Languages: French
Work: B1 C1 C2 C3 D1 D2 E F1 F2 J1 J2 K1 K2 K3 K4 L N O P Q R1 R2 S1 S2 T2 W Z(c,d,e,h,j,l,p,q,s)
Agency, Advocacy, Fixed Fee Interview undertaken and Member of Accident Line
Ptr: Cowdery, Mr Paul L BA . . . . . *Oct 1989
Kershaw, Mr Ian Graham Frederick LLB. . . . . *Apr 1972
Lakhani, Mr Sandeep LLB(Hons) . . . . . Dec 1988
Marchant-White, Mr Charles V. . . . . *May 1981
Sankhla, Bhupendra LLB . . . . . *Apr 1990
Turner, Mr Peter B RD LLB(Bris) . . . . . *Dec 1970
Wharry, Mrs Nia. . . . . *Jan 1998
Asoc: Hill, Mr John Robin Bertram. . . . . Jun 1973
Ast: Bowey, Miss Debbie Marie LLB; LPC . . . . . *Sep 2010
Hunt, Mr Thomas Edward LLB(Hons) . . . . . *Sep 2009
Lockley, Mr Christopher John . . . . . *Feb 1974
Muncer, Ms Amy Jane LLB; LPC . . . . . *Dec 2006
Redhead, Miss Claire . . . . . *Apr 2011
Con: Nichols, Mr Stephen Mark Deputy District Judge . . §Dec 1985

RANSON HOUGHTON
Eastlands 2 London Road Basingstoke Hampshire RG21 4AW
Tel: 01256 816759 *Fax:* 01256 816764
Office: Andover, Salisbury
Work: C1 E K1 K3 K4 S1 S2 V W Z(l)
Agency, Advocacy and Legal Aid undertaken

SHOOSMITHS
Quantum House Basing View Basingstoke Hampshire RG21 4EX
Tel: 0370 086 6200 / 01256 696200 *Fax:* 0370 086 6201
Dx: 159070 BASINGSTOKE 26
E-mail: basingstoke@shoosmiths.co.uk
Office: Birmingham, Fareham, London WC2, Manchester, Milton Keynes, Northampton, Nottingham, Reading
Work: A3 B1 B2 C1 C2 C3 E F1 F2 I J1 J2 K4 L M1 N O Q R1 R2 S1 S2 T1 T2 U2 W X Z(b,c,e,f,h,i,j,k,l,m,n,o,p,q,r,s,t,u,y,za)
Emergency Action, Agency, Advocacy, Fixed Fee Interview, Legal Aid undertaken and Member of Accident Line
Ptr: Ahmed, Ms Zarina . . . . . §Feb 1993
Donoghue, Miss Rosemary BA(Hons). . . . . *§Mar 1990

TALBOT WALKER LLP
60 New Road Basingstoke Hampshire RG21 7PW
Tel: 01256 332404 *Fax:* 01256 462645 *Dx:* 3003 BASINGSTOKE
E-mail: info@talbotwalker.co.uk
Office: Andover
Work: G H
Emergency Action, Agency, Advocacy, Legal Aid undertaken and Legal Aid Franchise
Ast: Stott, Mr Edward GDL. . . . . Nov 2008

MAX THUM ‡
Pond House Weston Road Upton Grey Basingstoke Hampshire RG25 2RH
Tel: 01256 862161 *Fax:* 01256 862621
E-mail: maxthum@btinternet.com
List of partners: M J A Thum
Languages: French
Work: A3

WALLIS PRANCE ‡
8 Cross Street Basingstoke Hampshire RG21 7DH
Tel: 01256 464311 *Fax:* 01256 842230
List of partners: P A Davies, T J Harris
Work: C1 E S1 S2 W
Ptr: Davies, Mr Philip A LLB. . . . . Jun 1980
Harris, Miss Tracey Jane BA . . . . . Mar 1992

WILLS CHANDLER ‡
76 Bounty Road Basingstoke Hampshire RG21 3BZ
Tel: 01256 322911 *Fax:* 01256 327811 *Dx:* 3007 BASINGSTOKE
E-mail: legal@wills-chandler.co.uk
List of partners: A Dodson, R Innes-Ker, M Le Fort
Work: C1 E F1 J1 K1 K3 O Q S1 S2 W Z(p)
Emergency Action, Agency, Advocacy and Fixed Fee Interview undertaken
Ptr: Dodson, Mr Anthony . . . . . *Sep 1999
Innes-Ker, Mr Robert Notary Public . . . . . Nov 1970
Le Fort, Mr Michael BSc(Hons) . . . . . *Aug 2003
Ast: Berk, Mr Andrew . . . . . Jan 2002

BATH, Bath & North East Somerset

ALAN TURNER & CO ‡
21 Gay Street Bath Bath & North East Somerset BA1 2PD
Tel: 01225 336260 *Fax:* 01225 421422 *Dx:* 8032 BATH
E-mail: info@alanturner.com
Web: www.alanturner.com
List of partners: L A Turner
Languages: German
Work: A1 C1 E K4 L S1 S2 T2 W Z(c)
SPr: Turner, Mr Lionel Alan. . . . . *Jun 1975

ALDERWICKS SOLICITORS LIMITED ‡
The Tramshed Beehive Yard Walcot Street Bath Bath & North East Somerset BA1 5BB
Tel: 01225 731400 *Fax:* 01225 731301
E-mail: info@alderwicks.com

ANGELL & CO ‡
5 Pierrepont Street Bath Bath & North East Somerset BA1 1LB
Tel: 01225 484244 *Fax:* 01225 461055
Emergency telephone 01225 484244
List of partners: S J Angell
Work: D1 D2 K1 K3
Emergency Action, Agency, Advocacy, Legal Aid undertaken and Legal Aid Franchise
Ptr: Angell, Miss Sarah Jane LLB; BEd . . . . . *Mar 1983

BLB SOLICITORS
1 Edgar Buildings George Street Bath Bath & North East Somerset BA1 2DU
Tel: 01225 462871 *Fax:* 01225 445060 *Dx:* 8011 BATH
Emergency telephone 01225 769787
E-mail: solicitors@bath.blandb.co.uk
Office: Bradford-on-Avon, Swindon, Trowbridge
Work: A1 B1 C1 C2 D1 E F1 G H J1 K1 L N O P Q R1 S1 T1 V W Z(l,m,t)
Emergency Action, Agency, Advocacy, Fixed Fee Interview, Legal Aid undertaken, Legal Aid Franchise and Member of Accident Line
Ptr: Bishop, Mr Terence A. . . . . *§Feb 1962
Morison, Mr David R . . . . . *Jul 1979
Asoc: Lowes, Mr Richard Edward LLB. . . . . *Oct 1993
Ast: Eaton, Miss Tracey . . . . . Sep 2001

BATH LAW
(incorporating Simcox Associates)
14 New Bond Street Bath Bath & North East Somerset BA1 1BE
Tel: 01225 401200 *Fax:* 01225 446913
Emergency telephone 01225 465833
E-mail: info@bathlaw.com
Office: Beaconsfield, Burnham, Rickmansworth, Windsor
Work: C1 E G H J1 K1 K2 K3 N O Q S1 W
Emergency Action, Agency, Advocacy and Fixed Fee Interview undertaken

BURNINGHAM & BROWN ‡
20 Queen Square Bath Bath & North East Somerset BA1 2HB
Tel: 01225 320090 *Fax:* 01225 447646 *Dx:* 8008 BATH
E-mail: law@burningham-and-brown.co.uk
List of partners: D J Gay, S Loveless, B Perry, E S K Vidnes
Work: E K1 L R2 S1 S2 W
Fixed Fee Interview undertaken
Ptr: Gay, Mr David J. . . . . *Dec 1977
Loveless, Sarah. . . . . Mar 2005
Perry, Mr Brendan. . . . . *Jun 1970
Vidnes, Mr Edward Sefton Knut . . . . . Sep 2005

COASTER LEGAL ‡
PO Box 3792 Bath Bath & North East Somerset BA1 3WY
Tel: 01225 421543

ROSAMUND COPPEN & COMPANY ‡
(incorporating Dale Johnston & Co)
6 Hayes Place Bear Flat Bath Bath & North East Somerset BA2 4QW
Tel: 0330 440 1802 *Fax:* 0844 443 2622
List of partners: R Coppen, J A Hammond, N K Turner
Work: E L R2 S1 S2 W
Ptr: Coppen, Mrs Rosamund . . . . . *Dec 1979
Hammond, Miss Julia A LLB . . . . . *Apr 1981
Turner, Mr Nicholas K BA . . . . . *Jun 1980

CRALLANS ‡
2 Wood Street Queen Square Bath Bath & North East Somerset BA1 2JQ
Tel: 01225 326417 *Dx:* 8028 BATH
E-mail: reception@crallans.co.uk

FREEMANS SOLICITORS ‡
4-5 Bridge Street Bath Bath & North East Somerset BA2 4AS
Tel: 01225 330733 *Fax:* 01225 333380
E-mail: shaun@freemans-solicitors.co.uk
List of partners: S R T Freeman
SPr: Freeman, Mr Shaun R T BA(Law). . . . . Sep 1987

JULIET HARDICK SOLICITORS ‡
7 Pierrepont Street Bath Bath & North East Somerset BA1 1LB
Tel: 01225 311177 *Fax:* 01225 481555
List of partners: S K Froster, J B Hardick, K F Syme
Work: E J1 L S1 W
Ptr: Froster, Mr Syme Keith . . . . . Jan 1994
Hardick, Miss Juliet Brenda BA . . . . . *Nov 1990
Syme, Mr Keith Fraser . . . . . Jan 1994

GEOFFREY HUETING & CO ‡
16 Forester Lane Bath Bath & North East Somerset BA2 6QX
Tel: 01225 465828 *Fax:* 01225 470200
E-mail: law@huetingsolicitors.co.uk
List of partners: G P Hueting
Work: C1 E L S1 S2 W
SPr: Hueting, Mr Geoffrey Paul BA. . . . . *Dec 1988

HUTCHESON FORREST ‡
(in association with Hutcheson Partnership)
1 Milsom Street Bath Bath & North East Somerset BA1 1DA
Tel: 01225 312311 *Fax:* 01225 462616
E-mail: simon@hutchsolicitors.com
List of partners: S A Hutcheson, B O'Donnell
Work: B1 C1 C2 E F1 G H J1 N O P Q R1 S1 T1 T2 W Z(c,e,f,h,j,l)
Emergency Action, Advocacy, Fixed Fee Interview and Legal Aid undertaken
Ptr: Hutcheson, Mr Simon A LLB(Hons) . . . . . *Nov 1989
O'Donnell, Mr Brendan . . . . . Jan 2002

LEECH & CO
Queen Square House Queen Square Place Charlotte Street Bath Bath & North East Somerset BA1 2LL
Tel: 01225 354673
E-mail: contact@leech.co.uk
Office: Manchester

G B LEWIS ‡
Monkspool House Wolverton Bath Bath & North East Somerset BA3 6QT
Tel: 01373 831004

ANDREW MAYNARD & CO ‡
4 Forefield Terrace Bath Bath & North East Somerset BA2 4PD
Tel: 01225 461146 *Fax:* 01225 469964
List of partners: A T Maynard
Work: C1 J1 Z(p)
Emergency Action, Agency, Advocacy and Fixed Fee Interview undertaken
Ptr: Maynard, Mr Andrew Thornton BA . . . . . Dec 1974

MOGERS ‡
24 Queen Square Bath Bath & North East Somerset BA1 2HY
Tel: 01225 750000 *Fax:* 01225 445208 *Dx:* 8003 BATH
E-mail: info@mogers.co.uk
List of partners: M A Blowers, D W M Campbell, F G Collins, S O'Sullivan, R Silcock, S Treharne, S J Veysey
Languages: French, Spanish
Work: A1 B1 C1 C2 C3 D1 E F1 J1 J2 K1 K3 K4 L N O P Q R1 R2 S1 S2 T1 T2 U2 V W Z(b,c,d,e,g,k,l,o,p,q,r)
Emergency Action, Agency, Advocacy, Fixed Fee Interview and Legal Aid Franchise
Ptr: Blowers, Mr Michael A BA(Law). . . . . *Mar 1984
Campbell, Mr Derwent W M. . . . . *§Jan 1982
Collins, Mr Frank G LLB. . . . . *Oct 1986
O'Sullivan, Ms Samantha . . . . . Oct 1988
Silcock, Rebecca . . . . . Jan 1996
Treharne, Mr Steven LLB(Hons). . . . . *Oct 1995
Veysey, Mr Simon J. . . . . *§Mar 1973
Asoc: Banks, Miss Nicola . . . . . Oct 1987

Davies, Mr Ian . . . . Nov 1999
Denny, Mr Neil . . . . Apr 1998
Drew, Ms Natalie . . . . Sep 2004
Gofton, Mr Tim . . . . Sep 2001
Ast: England, Ms Maeve. . . . . Sep 2007
Fairclough, Ms Emma. . . . . Feb 2008
Treble, Ms Alison . . . . Nov 2008

MOTORING LAW DEFENCE
2-4 Henry Street Bath Bath & North East Somerset BA1 1JT
Tel: 0808 178 3288 *Fax:* 01225 400667
E-mail: advice@motoringlawdefence.com
Office: Bath (2 offices)

MOWBRAY CITY ADVOCATES
2-4 Henry Street Bath Bath & North East Somerset BA1 1JT
Tel: 01225 400666 *Fax:* 01225 400667 *Dx:* 8023 BATH
E-mail: info@mowbraycityadvocates.co.uk
Office: Bath (2 offices)
Ast: Holden-White, Mr David LLB . . . . *Jan 1974

MOWBRAY WOODWARDS SOLICITORS ‡
3 Queen Square Bath Bath & North East Somerset BA1 2HG
Tel: 01225 485700 *Fax:* 01225 445064 *Dx:* 8023 BATH
Emergency telephone 07778 893836
E-mail: info@mowbraywoodwards.co.uk
List of partners: M Graham, M Moss, A R Phillips, T A Smith, L A F Watson, D L Whitworth
Office: Bath (2 offices)
Languages: French
Work: A1 B1 C1 C2 C3 D1 D2 E F1 F2 G H I J1 K1 K2 K3 K4 L N O Q R1 R2 S1 S2 T1 T2 V W X Z(d,f,k,l,m,r,w)
Emergency Action, Agency, Advocacy, Fixed Fee Interview, Legal Aid undertaken, Legal Aid Franchise and Member of Accident Line
Ptr: Graham, Mr Matthew . . . . Sep 2002
Moss, Mrs Meg LLB(Hons) . . . . *Sep 1992
Phillips, Mr Anthony Robin BA ★ . . . . *§Oct 1988
Smith, Ms Tracey A LLB(Hons) . . . . Oct 1989
Watson, Mr Luke Anthony F. . . . . *Dec 1999
Whitworth, Mr David Lloyd . . . . Nov 1994
Asoc: Greene, Mr John . . . . *§Jun 1976
Ast: Carrick, Mrs Sheila L LLB(Exon) School Governor. . *Oct 1987
Davies, Mrs Joanne. . . . . Apr 2006
Halling-Brown, Ms Rachael Jennifer. . . . . Jun 2004
Hambly, Mrs Jennifer LLB(Hons)(Law) . . . . Nov 2003
Hatvany, Mr Philip B BA. . . . . Nov 1995
Heard, Mrs Harriet L F LLB . . . . *Sep 2000
Martin, Mr Matthew Edward. . . . . Feb 2004
Wood, Ms Victoria. . . . . Nov 2005
Con: Northover, Mr Geoffrey J BA(Hons) . . . . *§Jul 1971

RENNEY & CO SOLICITORS ‡
Regency House 2 Wood Street Queen Square Bath Bath & North East Somerset BA1 2JQ
Tel: 01225 326435
E-mail: info@renneyandco.com

WILL ROLT SOLICITORS ‡
18 Charles Street Bath Bath & North East Somerset BA1 1HX
Tel: 01225 426390 *Fax:* 0870 762 5707 *Dx:* 8020 BATH
E-mail: info@willrolt.co.uk
Work: B1 L V Z(h)
Legal Aid Franchise

SHARP FAMILY LAW ‡
3 Miles's Buildings George Street Bath Bath & North East Somerset BA1 2QS
Tel: 01225 448955
E-mail: richard@sharpfamilylaw.com
Office: Bristol

STONE KING LLP ‡
13 Queen Square Bath Bath & North East Somerset BA1 2HJ
Tel: 01225 337599 *Fax:* 01225 335437 *Dx:* 8001 BATH
Emergency telephone 01225 324444
E-mail: admin@stoneking.co.uk
List of partners: A Acton, D G Ainslie, A J Allen, J G Brownrigg, J R Burchfield, R A S Butler, S R Greenwood, C E J Hayward, S M Howarth, R J W Inman, A M H King, L S Lever, R Meakin, A J Mortimer, H D Pearce, A Phillips, S H Ravenscroft, N S J Watson, P M Woodhouse
Office: Cambridge, London EC1
Work: A1 B1 C1 C2 D1 E F1 G H J1 K1 K2 K3 K4 L N O P Q R1 S1 S2 T1 T2 V W X Z(c,d,e,g,h,i,k,l,m,p,q,x,za)
Emergency Action, Agency, Advocacy, Fixed Fee Interview, Legal Aid undertaken, Legal Aid Franchise and Member of Accident Line
Ptr: Acton, Mr Anthony MA(Oxon) . . . . *§Mar 1972
Ainslie, Mr David Galbraith MA(Cantab); TEP . . . . *Jul 1973
Allen, Mrs Alison Jane BSc(Hons); CPE; LSF . . . . *Oct 1993
Brownrigg, Mr John G. . . . . *§Apr 1977
Burchfield, Mr Jonathan R MA(Cantab); ATII . . . . *Dec 1978
Butler, Mr Roy Alexander Sidney MA(Oxon); MBA. . . Jan 1977
Greenwood, Mr Steven R LLB. . . . . *Mar 1991
Hayward, Mr Charles E J BA(Bris) . . . . *Sep 1980
Howarth, Mrs Stephanie Margaret MA. . . . . *Sep 1998
Inman, Mr Roger John Wallace MA(Cantab) Harnsworth Award Middle Temple . . . . *Sep 1996
King, Mr A Michael H . . . . *§Mar 1974
Lever, Mrs Lynden S BSc . . . . *§Dec 1983
Meakin, Mr Robert LLB; LLM . . . . *Apr 1998
Mortimer, Mr Andrew John BA . . . . *Apr 1988
Pearce, Mr Hugh David BSc(Hons)(Dunelm) . . . . . *Sep 1991
Ravenscroft, Mr Stephen H MA; LLM(Cantab). . . . . *Jan 1997
Watson, Mr Nicholas Simon Joss BA . . . . *Dec 1982
Woodhouse, Mr Peter Mark LLB . . . . *Mar 1995
Asoc: Banks, Mr Andrew BA(Hons) . . . . *Oct 1996
Brotherton, Mr Michael G BA(Hons). . . . . *Jun 2000
Fell, Ms Caroline . . . . Jan 2002
Sanderson, Mrs Catherine LLB . . . . Oct 1986
Sutton, Mr Paul BA(Wales) . . . . Oct 1992
Turpin, Mr Kenneth Arthur LLB . . . . Jul 1992
Whittaker, Miss Alexandra Rebecca MA(Cantab); CPE; LPC . . . . *Nov 2003
Ast: Berry, Ms Lydia . . . . Jan 2007
Boyle, Ms Jean . . . . Jan 2006
Braithwaite, Mr Matthew Richard LLB . . . . Jul 2005
Burkey, Ms Lorraine. . . . . Jan 2007
Curtis, Miss Rachel Emma LLB(Hons); PGDipLaw Tutors' Prize for Outstanding Performance (UWE) 2002. . . . . Oct 2003
Eels, Miss Rebecca L LLB; PGDip; LPC. . . . . *Feb 1998
Haley, Ms Emma . . . . Jan 2002
Hayward, Mrs Julie Victoria LLB. . . . . Jan 1979
Hosking, Miss Deanna Janet Carol LLB(Reading) . . *Aug 1990
Layzell, Mrs Kathryn . . . . Jan 2003
Leviss, Miss Caroline Ruth LLB . . . . Nov 2001
Mills, Miss Alexandra LLB; LPC; BA(Law & French) . . Jun 2005
Rogers, Ms Kerry . . . . Jan 2007
Simpson, Mr Fraser. . . . . Jan 2007
Strathdee, Mrs Celia A P LLB(Bris) . . . . *Oct 1979
Walker, Mr Simon Thomas LLB . . . . *Sep 2004
White, Ms Sarah . . . . Jan 2007
Wilkinson, Ms Tamsin. . . . . Jan 2008
Wood, Ms Alice . . . . Jan 2004
Con: Gold, Mr Richard A MA; LLB . . . . *Dec 1968

TECHNOLOGY COMMERCIAL AND OUTSOURCING LAW LIMITED ‡
7 Homefield Timsbury Bath Bath & North East Somerset BA2 0LU
Tel: 07545 642724
E-mail: will.hull@tcosolicitors.com

THRINGS LLP
Midland Bridge Bath Bath & North East Somerset BA1 2HQ
Tel: 01225 340000 *Fax:* 01225 319735 *Dx:* 8002 BATH
Emergency telephone 0117 986 2739 / 01225 311383
E-mail: solicitors@thrings.com
Office: Bristol, London SW1, Swindon
Languages: French, German, Italian
Work: A1 A2 A3 B1 C1 C2 C3 D1 D2 E F1 F2 G J1 J2 K1 K2 L M1 M2 N O P Q R1 R2 S1 S2 T1 T2 U1 U2 V W X Z(b,c,d,e,f,h,i,j,k,l,m,n,o,p,q,t,w,x,z)

PETER F TOMLINSON & CO ‡
7a Northumberland Buildings Queen Square Bath Bath & North East Somerset BA1 2JB
Tel: 01225 484232 *Fax:* 01225 463952
E-mail: peter.tomlinson@peter-tomlinson.co.uk
List of partners: P F Tomlinson
Work: C1 C2 E J1 M1 S1 S2 W
Ptr: Tomlinson, Mr Peter F LLB . . . . *Jun 1970

SIMON WEST ‡
8 St Marys Buildings Bath Bath & North East Somerset BA2 3AT
Tel: 01225 482001 *Fax:* 0870 705 3077
Emergency telephone 07734 758959
E-mail: simon@westsolicitors.co.uk
Languages: French, Spanish
Work: G N Q Z(q)

WITHY KING SOLICITORS ‡
5-6 Northumberland Buildings Queen Square Bath Bath & North East Somerset BA1 2JE
Tel: 01225 425731 *Fax:* 01225 315562 *Dx:* 8014 BATH 1
E-mail: enquiries@withyking.co.uk
Office: Abingdon, Bath, Marlborough, Oxford, Swindon, Thame, Trowbridge
Languages: Cantonese, French, German, Italian
Work: A1 A3 B1 C1 C2 D1 D2 E F1 F2 G H I J1 J2 K1 K2 K3 L M1 N O P Q R1 R2 S1 S2 T1 T2 U2 V W Z(c,d,e,f,g,h,i,j,k,l,m,p,q,r,w,za)

WITHY KING SOLICITORS
James Street West Green Park Bath Bath & North East Somerset BA1 2BT
Tel: 01225 425731 *Fax:* 01225 352916 *Dx:* 8014 BATH
E-mail: enquiries@withyking.co.uk
Office: Abingdon, Bath, Marlborough, Oxford, Swindon, Thame, Trowbridge
Languages: Cantonese, French, German, Italian
Work: A1 A3 B1 C1 C2 D1 D2 E F1 F2 G H I J1 J2 K1 K2 K3 L N O Q R1 R2 S1 S2 T1 T2 U2 V W Z(c,d,e,f,g,h,i,j,k,l,m,p,q,r,w,za)

BATLEY, West Yorkshire

BASER & CO ‡
Office No4 Coach House Al-Hikmah Centre Batley West Yorkshire WF17 7AA
Tel: 01924 452950 *Fax:* 01924 455979
Emergency telephone 07949 854415
E-mail: baser@btinternet.com
Languages: Afrikaans, Gujarati, Urdu
Work: B1 F1 F2 J1 K1 K3 L M2 M4 N O Q W Z(b,i,k,l,p,w)
Agency and Fixed Fee Interview undertaken

BREARLEYS SOLICITORS ‡
1 Brunswick Street Batley West Yorkshire WF17 5DT
Tel: 01924 473065 *Fax:* 01924 443669 *Dx:* 700167 BATLEY
Emergency telephone 07836 778693 / 07831 155621
E-mail: nickbattye@brearleyssolicitors.com
List of partners: M Barber, N J Battye, E Clough
Office: Birstall, Cleckheaton
Work: A1 B1 C1 D1 E F1 G H J1 K1 L M1 N P R1 S1 T1 V W
Emergency Action, Agency, Advocacy, Fixed Fee Interview, Legal Aid undertaken, Legal Aid Franchise and Member of Accident Line
Ptr: Barber, Mr Michael BA(Lond) ♦ . . . . *Nov 1978
Battye, Mr Nicholas John LLB(Hons) ♦ . . . . *May 1995
Clough, Miss Emma LLB(Hons) ♦. . . . . *Oct 1995
Ast: Hood, Mrs Angela Mary BA(Hons). . . . . Aug 2001

HELEN DAVIES SOLICITORS ‡
Blakeridge Mill Mayman Lane Batley West Yorkshire WF17 7TB
Tel: 07855 965381 *Fax:* 01924 441528
E-mail: hdavies@branchwater-developments.com

HELLEWELL PASLEY & BREWER ‡
2 Nelson Street Birstall Batley West Yorkshire WF17 9EP
Tel: 01924 472596 *Fax:* 01924 470165 *Dx:* 700905 BIRSTALL
Emergency telephone 07771 863473
E-mail: lwall@hpandb.co.uk
List of partners: L Gaddes, L J Wall, R M Whitaker, R N Wiggans
Office: Dewsbury
Work: D1 D2 E J1 K1 K2 L N O Q S1 S2 T2 W Z(i)
Emergency Action, Agency, Advocacy, Fixed Fee Interview, Legal Aid undertaken, Legal Aid Franchise and Member of Accident Line
Ptr: Wall, Mrs Lesley Joan LLB(Hons). . . . . *Aug 1997
Wiggans, Mr R Nigel . . . . *Oct 1987
Ast: Gaddes, Ms Alison . . . . *Jan 2004
Con: Bottomley, Mr William J LLB. . . . . *Jan 1966

ANDREW HILL ‡
16 Branch Road Batley West Yorkshire WF17 5RY
Tel: 01924 423353 *Fax:* 01924 423393
Work: S1 W

BATTLE, East Sussex

EMIN READ SOLICITORS ‡
Beckett House Mitre Way Station Approach Battle East Sussex TN33 0BQ
Tel: 01424 775967 *Fax:* 01424 777241 *Dx:* 42106 BATTLE
E-mail: enquiries@eminread.co.uk

HERINGTONS ‡
1 Upper Lake Battle East Sussex TN33 0AN
Tel: 01424 772401 *Fax:* 01424 774550 *Dx:* 42101 BATTLE
List of partners: N C Brunt, R A Fisher, D Harding, S L Kinsey, D Longhurst, G E Longmire, R Parkes, T P Roberts, I M A Stewart, N J Thonger, J L B Thorpe
Office: Eastbourne, Hastings, Rye
Work: A1 E L S1 V W Z(d,l,m)
Emergency Action, Agency, Advocacy undertaken and Member of Accident Line
Ptr: Roberts, Mr Timothy P LLB(Bris) . . . . *§May 1977
Thonger, Mr Nigel J. . . . . *§Apr 1977
Ast: Campbell, Miss Sarah Holly LLB(Hons) . . . . *Jan 2009
Chivers, Mrs Angela M . . . . *Jan 1979

HOUSING LAW SERVICES ‡
HLS House Watchoke Business Centre Battle East Sussex TN33 0GB
Tel: 01424 774738

WYKEHAM HURFORD SHEPPARD & SON LLP ‡
6 High Street Battle East Sussex TN33 0AE
Tel: 01424 775088 *Fax:* 01424 775717
E-mail: battle@whss.co.uk
List of partners: S Buller, D J Lloyd, J L A B Wykeham-Hurford
Office: Chislehurst, Tenterden
Languages: French
Work: J1 L N Q R1 S1 T1 T2 V W Z(b,c,d,l,m,s)
Emergency Action, Agency, Advocacy, Legal Aid undertaken and Member of Accident Line
Ptr: Lloyd, Mr David J LLB. . . . . Jan 2008
Wykeham-Hurford, The Hon John Louis Andre Besme . . . . *§Dec 1975
Dir: Buller, Sally . . . . Oct 2008
Con: Brackett, Mr W Barry . . . . *§Jul 1959

BAWTRY, South Yorkshire

JONES & CO
48 High Street Bawtry South Yorkshire DN10 6JB
Tel: 01302 710555 *Fax:* 01302 711742 *Dx:* 701290 BAWTRY
E-mail: info@jonessolicitors.co.uk
Office: Retford
Languages: French, German
Work: A1 B1 C1 E F1 K1 L M1 S1 S2 T1 W Z(d,l,m)
Ptr: Hadfield, Mr Anthony . . . . *Jul 1980
Jenkins, Ms Rhona Kirsty LLB(Hons) . . . . *Aug 1993
Sharpe, Mr Matthew. . . . . Dec 1998

BEACONSFIELD, Buckinghamshire

BAILY GIBSON ‡
5 Station Parade Beaconsfield Buckinghamshire HP9 2PG
Tel: 01494 672661 *Fax:* 01494 678493 *Dx:* 34500 BEACONSFIELD
E-mail: beaconsfield@bailygibson.co.uk
List of partners: L P Owen, L G Owen, J N Young
Office: High Wycombe
Languages: Spanish
Work: A1 B1 C1 C2 C3 D1 E F1 G H J1 K1 L M1 M2 N O P Q R1 S1 T1 T2 V W Z(l)
Emergency Action, Agency, Advocacy, Legal Aid undertaken, Legal Aid Franchise and Member of Accident Line
Ptr: Owen, Mrs Lynne Geraldine LLB(Lond) . . . . *Apr 1977
Ast: Diez, Mrs Susana Veronica . . . . *Jun 2001
James, Ms Kathy . . . . *Nov 2000
John, Mrs Joanne. . . . . *Nov 2005
Lambert, Mr Martin Derek. . . . . *Dec 1991

BRITTONS
3a Station Parade Beaconsfield Buckinghamshire HP9 2PB
Tel: 01494 730722 *Fax:* 01494 730795 *Dx:* 34503 BEACONSFIELD
E-mail: lex@brittonsol.co.uk
Office: Bourne End
Languages: German, Italian, Portuguese
Work: C1 E S1 S2 W
Con: O'Hagan, Mr Anthony Richard BA(Hons) . . . . Jan 1999

MICHAEL BROUGH AND COHEN ‡
Burkes Court Burkes Road Beaconsfield Buckinghamshire HP9 1NZ
Tel: 01494 680420 *Fax:* 01494 680770 *Dx:* 34517 BEACONSFIELD
E-mail: beaconsfield@mbc-law.co.uk
List of partners: M J A Brough
Work: A1 B1 C1 D1 D2 E F1 J1 K1 K2 K3 L Q S1 S2 T2 W Z(d,e,h,l,m,x)
Agency and Fixed Fee Interview undertaken
SPr: Brough, Mr Michael James Arman BA. . . . . *Dec 1988
Con: Jackson, Mr Stephen LLB. . . . . Jan 1983

BROWNS
Eden House Reynolds Road Beaconsfield Buckinghamshire HP9 2FL
Tel: 01494 677771 / 677021 *Fax:* 01494 677023
Dx: 34519 BEACONSFIELD
E-mail: wills@brownssolicitors.co.uk
Office: Amersham, Aylesbury, Bourne End, High Wycombe (3 offices), Maidenhead, Marlow, Princes Risborough, Thame
Work: C1 E S1 S2 W
Fixed Fee Interview undertaken
Ast: Boynton, Mrs Marie B L LLB(Warw) . . . . *Apr 1986
Con: Stoll, Ms Suzanne J LLB(Hons) . . . . *Feb 1982

CHEBSEY & CO ‡
51 London End Beaconsfield Buckinghamshire HP9 2HW
Tel: 01494 670440 *Fax:* 01494 670276
Dx: 34504 BEACONSFIELD 1
Emergency telephone 07899 953415
E-mail: beaconsfield@chebsey.com
List of partners: K Chebsey, M C Fox, D M P Wachtel
Office: Bath, Burnham, Rickmansworth, Windsor
Languages: Punjabi, Spanish

See p112 for the Key to Work Categories & other symbols

Work: B2 C1 E G H J1 K1 K2 K3 M1 N O Q S1 S2 W Z(k,l,p,q)
Agency, Advocacy, Fixed Fee Interview and Legal Aid undertaken
SPr: Chebsey, Mr Keith . . . . Jan 1985
Ast: Crown, Mr Thomas Henry Robert LLB. . . . . *Sep 2007
Knott, Ms Johanna Louise BA. . . . . Mar 2001
Poole, Ms Laura . . . . Feb 2008
Thomas, Mr Jeffrey M LLB . . . . *Jun 1987
Woodend, Ms Helen . . . . Jan 2008
Con: Wade, Mr Brian Alan LLB(Bris) . . . . Feb 1966

DALE-LACE & CO ‡
2 Gregories Road Beaconsfield Buckinghamshire HP9 1HQ
Tel: 01494 675269 *Fax:* 01494 671081
Emergency telephone 01494 675269
E-mail: cdl@dale-lace.com
List of partners: C Dale-Lace
Work: S1 S2 W
SPr: Dale-Lace, Mrs Christine BA(Hons)(Law) . . . . . . *Jun 1976

J F DAWSON ‡
34 Tilsworth Road Beaconsfield Buckinghamshire HP9 1TP
Tel: 01494 670566 *Fax:* 01494 670566
E-mail: jonathan.dawson@virgin.net
List of partners: J F Dawson
Work: C1 J1 J2 L Z(d)
SPr: Dawson, Mr Jonathan Frank MA; LLB(Lond) . . . . . *Jun 1978

THE EMPLOYMENT LAW CONSULTANCY ‡
33 Hogback Wood Road Beaconsfield Buckinghamshire HP9 1JT
Tel: 01494 673123 *Fax:* 01494 673123
E-mail: sanjiv@emp-law.com

HINE SOLICITORS ‡
51 Amersham Road Beaconsfield Buckinghamshire HP9 2HB
Tel: 01494 685588 *Fax:* 01494 685584 *Dx:* 34508 BEACONSFIELD
List of partners: A J Glover, A Hine
Office: Bracknell, Cheltenham, Gerrards Cross, Oxford, Princes Risborough, Swindon, Yiewsley

HUTCHINSON ‡
43 Burgess Wood Road South Beaconsfield Buckinghamshire HP9 1EL
Tel: 01494 680775 *Fax:* 01494 677870
E-mail: geoff@hutchlaw.co.uk

HILARY JOHNSTON ‡
7 Manor Farm Way Seer Green Beaconsfield Buckinghamshire HP9 2YD
Tel: 01494 678230 *Fax:* 01494 677450
E-mail: hiljohns@aol.com
List of partners: H Johnston
Work: E S1 S2 W Z(m)
Ptr: Johnston, Mrs Hilary LLB(B'ham) . . . . *Dec 1979

LAWRENCE HAMBLIN ‡
8 Burkes Court Burkes Road Beaconsfield Buckinghamshire HP9 1NZ
Tel: 01494 683610 *Fax:* 01494 683615 *Dx:* 34511 BEACONSFIELD
E-mail: beaconsfield@lawrencehamblin.com

NICHOLAS LOWE ‡
1 Wooster Road Beaconsfield Buckinghamshire HP9 1SR
Tel: 01494 680480 *Fax:* 01494 680580

MCDONALD COHEN ‡
30 Highlands Road Seer Green Beaconsfield Buckinghamshire HP9 2XN
Tel: 01494 677421 *Fax:* 01494 681083 *Dx:* 34505 BEACONSFIELD
E-mail: anncohen@mcdonaldcohen.co.uk

BEAMINSTER, Dorset

KITSON & TROTMAN ‡
The Champions Hogshill Street Beaminster Dorset DT8 3AN
Tel: 01308 862313 *Fax:* 01308 862033
E-mail: kandt@legalchampions.freeserve.co.uk
List of partners: M J Conroy, R J King, T Scammell
Office: Bridport, Lyme Regis
Work: A1 A2 B1 C1 D1 E F1 G H J1 K1 L M1 N O P Q R1 R2 S1 S2 T1 T2 V W Z(d,e,h,k,l,p,q,r)
Emergency Action, Agency, Advocacy and Fixed Fee Interview undertaken
Ptr: Conroy, Mr Michael J Clerk to Commissioner of Taxes.*Dec 1972
Scammell, Miss Tracy. . . . . *Dec 1992

BEARWOOD, West Midlands

HEARNE & CO ‡
120-121 Poplar Road Bearwood West Midlands B66 4AP
Tel: 0121 420 3636 *Fax:* 0121 420 4572 *Dx:* 724220 SMETHWICK 3
E-mail: rjh@hearneandco.co.uk
List of partners: G J Hearne, R J Hearne, M R Thomas
Languages: French
Emergency Action, Agency, Advocacy, Fixed Fee Interview, Legal Aid undertaken and Member of Accident Line
Ptr: Hearne, Mr Roger J. . . . . *Nov 1971
Thomas, Mr Martin R BA(Hons). . . . . *May 1981
Ast: Jones, Mr Stuart R BA . . . . *Feb 1990

PATWA SOLICITORS ‡
25 Abbey Road Bearwood West Midlands B67 5RA
Tel: 0121 429 8666 *Fax:* 0121 420 8668
E-mail: info@patwasolicitors.co.uk
List of partners: F F Patwa
Languages: Gujarati, Punjabi, Urdu
Work: E K1 O Q R1 S1 S2 Z(d,g,l,u)
Fixed Fee Interview undertaken
Ptr: Patwa, Ms Fatemabai F LLB ♦ . . . . *Feb 1988

BEAUMARIS, Anglesey

R GORDON ROBERTS LAURIE & CO
(in association with R Gordon Roberts Laurie)
Regent Chambers 17 Church Street Beaumaris Anglesey LL58 8AB
Tel: 01248 810210 / 810532 *Fax:* 01248 811544
E-mail: beaumaris@rgrl.co.uk
Office: Llangefni
Languages: Welsh
Work: A1 B1 C1 D1 E F1 G H J1 K1 L M1 N P R1 S1 T1 W Z(a,c,e,h,j,k,l,o,p,s)
Emergency Action, Agency, Advocacy, Fixed Fee Interview and Legal Aid undertaken

BEBINGTON, Merseyside

HILLYER MCKEOWN LLP
2 Church Road Bebington Merseyside CH63 7PH
Tel: 0151 645 4255 *Fax:* 0151 644 1905 *Dx:* 18282 BEBINGTON
E-mail: bebington@law.uk.com
Office: Chester, Wrexham
Work: C1 C2 D1 E J1 K1 N O S1 S2 W Z(o,w)
Agency, Advocacy, Fixed Fee Interview, Legal Aid undertaken and Legal Aid Franchise
Ptr: McKeown, Mr Philip Henry LLB . . . . *Apr 1976
Ast: Clayton, Mr R Martin BA . . . . *Nov 1973
Entwistle, Mr Richard Ronald . . . . Oct 2007
Goldthorp, Mrs Janet Irene . . . . May 1979
Mitchell, Ms Joanne. . . . . Apr 2007
Con: Wise, Mr Peter Robinson LLB(Bris) . . . . *Jun 1974

BECCLES, Suffolk

CHAMBERLINS
3 Ballygate Beccles Suffolk NR34 9NB
Tel: 01502 713131 *Fax:* 01502 718040 *Dx:* 51456 BECCLES
E-mail: stephen@chamberlins.demon.co.uk
Office: Caister-on-Sea, Great Yarmouth (2 offices), Lowestoft
Work: A1 B1 C1 C2 C3 D1 E F1 J1 K1 L N P Q R1 S1 T1 T2 V W Z(b,c,d,h,k,l,m,s)

MEARS HOBBS & DURRANT
11 Ballygate Beccles Suffolk NR34 9NA
Tel: 01502 715818 *Fax:* 01502 717030 *Dx:* 51451 BECCLES
Office: Great Yarmouth, Lowestoft
Work: A1 C1 E F1 G H J1 K1 L N Q S1 W
Agency, Advocacy, Legal Aid undertaken and Member of Accident Line
Ptr: Swanbury, Mr John B LLB(Leeds). . . . . *Nov 1971

NORTON PESKETT
Exchange Square Beccles Suffolk NR34 9HP
Tel: 01502 718700 *Fax:* 01502 718709 *Dx:* 51450 BECCLES
E-mail: enquiries@nortonpeskett.co.uk
Office: Great Yarmouth, Halesworth, Lowestoft
Work: A1 C1 D1 E G H J1 K1 L N Q R1 S1 T2 W Z(d,l,m)
Agency, Advocacy, Fixed Fee Interview, Legal Aid undertaken and Legal Aid Franchise

SPRAKE & KINGSLEY
32 Blyburgate Beccles Suffolk NR34 9TB
Tel: 01502 713214 *Fax:* 01502 717428 *Dx:* 51452 BECCLES
E-mail: info@spakekingsley.co.uk
Office: Bungay
Work: A1 B1 C1 C2 C3 D1 E F1 G H J1 J2 K1 K3 K4 L N O Q R1 R2 S1 S2 T1 T2 V W Z(c,d,h,j,k,l,m,p,t)
Emergency Action, Agency, Advocacy undertaken and Member of Accident Line
Asoc: Hay, Mr John William Stephens BA(Hons). . . . . . . *Apr 2002
Con: Wells, Mr J Chris . . . . *Nov 1979

BECKENHAM, Kent

EDWARDS VAZIRANEY ‡
Provident House 6-20 Burrell Row Beckenham Kent BR3 1AT
Tel: 020 8249 6536 *Fax:* 020 8249 6537
Emergency telephone 020 8249 6536

HOLLS SOLICITORS ‡
183a High Street Beckenham Kent BR3 1AH
Tel: 020 8658 9767 *Fax:* 020 8650 7637
E-mail: lawyer@hollssolicitor.co.uk
List of partners: A Hollist, M Stewart
Languages: French
Work: K1 K3 L Q S1 S2 W X Z(i)
Fixed Fee Interview undertaken
Ptr: Hollist, Mr Abraham. . . . . Aug 2003
Stewart, Mr Martin . . . . Aug 2008

JBS SOLICITORS ‡
Junction House 4-6 Southend Road Beckenham Kent BR3 1SD
Tel: 0845 643 5050 *Fax:* 0845 643 5100
E-mail: info@jbslaw.co.uk

JONES NICKOLDS ‡
Angels House 5 Albemarle Road Beckenham Kent BR3 5HZ
Tel: 020 3405 2300 *Fax:* 020 3006 8804 *Dx:* 40608 BECKENHAM
E-mail: contact@jonesnickolds.co.uk

LESLEY LEPORATI ‡
160 Croydon Road Beckenham Kent BR3 4DE
Tel: 020 8639 3515 *Fax:* 020 8663 6723
E-mail: lesley.leporati@fabermaunsell.com
Work: P
Fixed Fee Interview undertaken

CLIFFORD MILLER ‡
Burnhill Business Centre 50 Burnhill Road Beckenham Kent BR3 3LA
Tel: 020 8663 0044 *Fax:* 020 8663 0011
E-mail: generalmail@cliffordmiller.com
List of partners: C G Miller
Work: C3 I Z(e,f)
SPr: Miller, Mr Clifford George BSc; ARCS; Dip IPL ♦ . . . *Mar 1984

ONE SOURCE FULL SERVICES ‡
5 Pembroke Court 41 Wickham Road Beckenham Kent BR3 6NA
Tel: 020 8432 4077
E-mail: info@onesourcepk.co.uk

PRITCHARD JOYCE & HINDS ‡
Kelsey House 77 High Street Beckenham Kent BR3 1AN
Tel: 020 8658 3922 *Fax:* 020 8658 8694 *Dx:* 40601 BECKENHAM
E-mail: postmaster@pj-h.co.uk
List of partners: K Blakesley, K M Davey, S A Hartwell, S M Hinds, H M Newman, A Ransley
Languages: Cantonese, French, German, Portuguese, Spanish
Work: A3 B1 C1 C2 D1 D2 E F1 J1 K1 K3 L N O Q R2 S1 S2 W Z(c,e,l,q)
Fixed Fee Interview undertaken
Ptr: Blakesley, Miss Karen BA(Hons) . . . . *Dec 1998
Davey, Miss Kim Michelle LLB. . . . . *§Sep 2003
Hartwell, Mrs Sally A BA(Wales). . . . . *§Jan 1983
Hinds, Mr Stewart M . . . . *§Dec 1980
Newman, Miss Helen M. . . . . *§Oct 1984
Ransley, Mr Andrew LLB . . . . *§Oct 1991
Ast: Biggs, Ms Natasha . . . . *Mar 2008
Gardiner, Mrs Sarah . . . . *Aug 1996
Johnston, Mrs Sarah . . . . *Sep 2009
Long, Ms Janet Frances. . . . . *Dec 1987
Mestre, Miss Paula LLB(Hons) . . . . *Oct 2000
Nobbs, Mr Christopher . . . . *Feb 2007
Salvidge, Miss Zoe . . . . *Mar 2010
Warren, Miss Helen Maria LLB(Law with German Law) *Jun 2001
Con: Joyce, Mr John Q. . . . . *§Dec 1975
Potts, Mrs Michelle . . . . *§Jan 1995

RAW & CO ‡
54 Manor Way Beckenham Kent BR3 3LJ
Tel: 020 8658 2965 *Fax:* 020 8658 0491 *Dx:* 40607 BECKENHAM
E-mail: neil@rawandco.co.uk

STOFFEL & CO ‡
48 High Street Beckenham Kent BR3 1AY
Tel: 020 8650 8157 *Fax:* 020 8658 3447 *Dx:* 40600 BECKENHAM
E-mail: stoffelandco1@tiscali.co.uk
List of partners: K J Bradford, G C Mann
Work: D1 K1 K3 L S1 S2 T2 W
Fixed Fee Interview undertaken
Ptr: Bradford, Miss Katherine J LLB . . . . *Aug 1978
Mann, Mr Gerard C LLB. . . . . *Jun 1972

TJM LAW ‡
247 High Street Beckenham Kent BR3 1AB
Tel: 020 8662 6090 *Fax:* 020 8711 5435 *Dx:* 40602 BECKENHAM
E-mail: info@tjmlaw.co.uk

THACKRAY WILLIAMS
225-235 High Street Beckenham Kent BR3 1BN
Tel: 020 8663 0503 *Fax:* 020 8658 2691
Office: Bromley, West Wickham
Work: C1 C2 D1 E F1 J1 K1 L N O P Q R1 S1 T1 V W Z(c)
Emergency Action, Fixed Fee Interview, Legal Aid undertaken and Member of Accident Line
Ptr: Raby, Mr Andrew S LLB; ACIArb . . . . *Oct 1990
Thackray, Mr Simon T E BA. . . . . *Apr 1981
Ast: Antoniou, Mr Paul. . . . . Oct 1998

TINKLIN SPRINGALL
(incorporating Attenboroughs; Kingsbury & Turner)
9-11 Rectory Road Beckenham Kent BR3 1JB
Tel: 020 8402 7222 *Fax:* 020 8402 8222 *Dx:* 40603 BECKENHAM
E-mail: mail@tinklinspringall.co.uk
Office: Bromley
Languages: Spanish
Work: A1 B1 C1 C2 C3 E F1 J1 K1 K4 L N Q R1 S1 T2 W
Agency undertaken
Ptr: Arnott, Mr David G LLB(Wales) . . . . *Oct 1988
Danger, Ms Gillian S LLB . . . . *Oct 1984
Springall, Mr Ian C LLB . . . . Oct 1982

BEDALE, North Yorkshire

ECCLES HEDDON
5 South End Bedale North Yorkshire DL8 2BJ
Tel: 01677 422422 *Fax:* 01677 424992 *Dx:* 65090 BEDALE
Office: Ripon, Thirsk
Work: A1 C1 D1 E G H J1 K1 L S1 T2 W Z(c,d)
Agency and Fixed Fee Interview undertaken

BEDFORD, Bedfordshire

ADAMS MOORE FAMILY LAW
62-64 Braham Road Bedford Bedfordshire MK40 2QG
Tel: 01234 330900
Office: Bletchley, Corby, Daventry, Luton, Milton Keynes, Northampton

BARBER-LOMAX ‡
The Old Surgery 22a High Street Harrold Bedford Bedfordshire MK43 7DQ
Tel: 01234 721108 *Fax:* 01234 721201
List of partners: P A Barber-Lomax
Ptr: Barber-Lomax, Mr Peter Anthony LLB. . . . . *Oct 1982

BEDFORD FAMILY LAW ‡
19 Grove Place Bedford Bedfordshire MK40 3JJ
Tel: 01234 363211 *Fax:* 01234 364012

C C BELL & SON ‡
(incorporating H G Langley & Co; Porter Jessop & Son)
48-50 Harpur Street Bedford Bedfordshire MK40 2QT
Tel: 01234 363251 *Fax:* 01234 345276 *Dx:* 5608 BEDFORD
E-mail: law@ccbell.co.uk
List of partners: L J Rose, R E Stubbings
Work: A1 C1 C2 C3 D1 E F1 G H J1 K1 L M1 M2 N P R1 S1 T1 T2 V W Z(b,c,d,k,l)
Agency, Advocacy and Legal Aid undertaken
Ptr: Rose, Mr L John OBE; DL . . . . *§Nov 1962
Stubbings, Mr Robin E BA . . . . *Dec 1975
Asoc: Martin-Moran, Mrs Patricia LLB . . . . *Jan 1974

CIAMPA SOLICITORS ‡
26 St Mary's Street Bedford Bedfordshire MK42 0AS
Tel: 01234 341525 *Fax:* 01234 341427
E-mail: enquiries@ciampasolicitors.co.uk
Languages: Italian, Polish
Work: E N S1 S2 W Z(r)
Fixed Fee Interview undertaken

COWLEY DI GIORGIO & CO ‡
63 Harpur Street Bedford Bedfordshire MK40 2SR
Tel: 01234 218171 *Fax:* 01234 327632 *Dx:* 5658 BEDFORD
E-mail: reception@cowleydigiorgio.co.uk
List of partners: S Cowley, P A Roberts
Languages: Italian

Work: B1 C1 E F1 J1 K1 K3 K4 L N Q S1 T1 V W Z(l)
Agency, Advocacy and Fixed Fee Interview undertaken
Ptr: Cowley, Mr Stephen BA. . . . . . *Jun 1976
Roberts, Mr Paul Anthony LLB(Hons) . . . . . *Nov 2003
Ast: Sacco, Miss Giuseppina LLB . . . . . *Sep 2005

DAVIDSON SMITH & CO ‡
Oxford Cottage 13 Grove Place Bedford Bedfordshire MK40 3JJ
Tel: 01234 351971 *Fax:* 01234 351828 *Dx:* 716009 BEDFORD 5
Emergency telephone 07973 919720
E-mail: d-smithandco@btconnect.com
List of partners: M A Davidson-Smith
Work: D1 K1 V
Emergency Action, Agency, Fixed Fee Interview, Legal Aid undertaken and Legal Aid Franchise
Ptr: Davidson-Smith, Mrs Michelle A BA. . . . . . *Nov 1988

DUCHENNES ‡
61-63 St Peters Street Bedford Bedfordshire MK40 2PR
Tel: 01234 356678 *Fax:* 01234 343282
E-mail: josephine@duchennes.com
List of partners: J M Duchenne
Work: B1 F1 K1 K3 L O Q
Agency, Advocacy and Fixed Fee Interview undertaken
SPr: Duchenne, Mrs Josephine May LLB(Hons)(Bucks) . *Nov 1988

EMMOTT SNELL & CO ‡
Leveson Cottage 32 Grove Place Bedford Bedfordshire MK40 3JJ
Tel: 01234 360140 *Fax:* 01234 357866 *Dx:* 716015 BEDFORD 5
E-mail: enquiries@emmottsnell.co.uk

FIRST DEFENCE ‡
30-32 Bromham Road Bedford Bedfordshire MK40 2QD
Tel: 01234 263263
Office: Northampton, Wellingborough

FULLERS FAMILY LAW PRACTICE LLP ‡
57-59 St Peters Street Bedford Bedfordshire MK40 2PR
Tel: 01234 343134 *Fax:* 01234 355567 *Dx:* 716013 BEDFORD 5
E-mail: enquiries@fullersfamilylaw.com
List of partners: J L Armstrong, M D Fuller
Work: D1 K1
Fixed Fee Interview, Legal Aid undertaken and Legal Aid Franchise
Ptr: Armstrong, Miss Judith Lorraine LPC . . . . . Nov 1996
Fuller, Mr Martin David . . . . . Nov 1996
Ast: Cooper, Mr David Colin LLB(Leeds). . . . . Jul 1978
Cox, Mr Joseph Gerald . . . . . May 1983
Rawlins, Miss Dreana Ursula LLB(Hons) . . . . . Apr 2004
Rees, Mr Nick. . . . . Apr 2009

HARVEY INGRAM BORNEOS
Dixon House 77-97 Harpur Street Bedford Bedfordshire MK40 2SY
Tel: 01234 353221 *Fax:* 01234 217955 *Dx:* 5607 BEDFORD
E-mail: mail@borneos.co.uk
Office: Birmingham, Leicester, Milton Keynes, Newport Pagnell
Languages: French, German, Italian, Polish, Spanish
Work: A1 B1 C1 C2 C3 D1 E F1 F2 G H I J1 J2 K1 K2 L M1 M2 N O P Q R1 S1 S2 W Z(c,d,e,h,k,l,m,p,q,t,w)
Emergency Action, Agency, Advocacy, Fixed Fee Interview, Legal Aid undertaken, Legal Aid Franchise and Member of Accident Line
Mem: Barker, Mr Derek L LLB. . . . . Oct 1988
Borneo, Mr Kenneth A . . . . . *§Apr 1968
Foley, Mr Vincent J LLB. . . . . *§Oct 1991
Harris, Mr Andrew J B. . . . . *Jul 1971
Holmes, Mr Stephen W LLB. . . . . *§Apr 1980
Humphrey, Mr Graham H LLB. . . . . §Nov 1973
Johnstone, Mr Hugh E MA(Cantab) . . . . . *§Jan 1970
Mills, Mr Dominic M LLB . . . . . Nov 1982
Phelan, Miss Samantha. . . . . Aug 1995
Thompson, Mr Mark BA. . . . . *Jan 1991
Ast: Church, Ms Susan J LLB . . . . . *Nov 1987

LAWTONS SOLICITORS LIMITED ‡
Mayfair House, Lurke Street, Bedford Bedfordshire MK40 3HZ
Tel: 01234 356235 *Fax:* 01234 218809 *Dx:* 716608 BEDFORD 5
E-mail: enquiries@lawtonslaw.co.uk

LOWE & CO ‡
9 Deacon Mews Marston Moretaine Bedford Bedfordshire MK43 0AQ
Tel: 01234 764731
E-mail: info@loweandco.co.uk
List of partners: S Lowe
SPr: Lowe, Mrs Susan LLB(Hons) . . . . . Jul 1998

PALMERS ‡
PO Box 455 Hasset Chambers Hassett Street Bedford Bedfordshire MK40 1WG
Tel: 01234 211161 *Fax:* 01234 211389 *Dx:* 5611 BEDFORD
E-mail: admin@palmers.co.uk
List of partners: H F J Fowler, J Palmer, R M Palmer, S Palmer
Work: A1 C1 E L R1 R2 S1 S2 T1 T2 W
Ptr: Fowler, Mr Harry Frederick Joseph LLB . . . . . *Jun 1984
Palmer, Ms Jill . . . . . *§May 1984
Palmer, Mr Roy M. . . . . *§Nov 1956
Palmer, Ms Sara . . . . . *§Oct 1995

PARK WOODFINE HEALD MELLOWS LLP ‡
1 Lurke Street Bedford Bedfordshire MK40 3TN
Tel: 01234 400000 *Fax:* 01234 401111 *Dx:* 716007 BEDFORD 5
E-mail: admin@pwhmllp.com
List of partners: S Burridge, G R Dannan, R C Levene, I G Pears, V Pope, J Thelwall, C Trundley, S Williamson, M Wills
Office: Northampton, Rushden
Languages: French, German, Italian, Punjabi, Spanish
Work: A1 A3 B1 C1 C2 C3 D1 E F1 J1 J2 K1 K2 K3 K4 L M1 M2 N O P Q R1 S1 T1 T2 V W Z(c,d,e,l,m,o,q,r)
Emergency Action, Agency, Advocacy, Fixed Fee Interview, Legal Aid undertaken, Legal Aid Franchise and Member of Accident Line
Ptr: Burridge, Mr Stephen BA(Hons). . . . . Jul 1984
Dannan, Mr Garry R LLB . . . . . Dec 1974
Levene, Rae C LLB. . . . . Jun 1980
Pears, Mr Ian Geoffrey LLB(Hons) . . . . . *§Jan 1986
Pope, Miss Vanessa BA; LLB . . . . . Oct 2000
Thelwall, Mr John BA(Hons)(Law). . . . . Apr 1975
Trundley, Miss Claire LLB. . . . . *Oct 1993
Williamson, Mr Steven . . . . . Jun 1977
Wills, Mr Michael LLB. . . . . Jun 1980
Ast: Hardy, Mr Michael BA. . . . . Jan 1982
Lawrence, Ms Melanie LLB . . . . . Dec 2006
Rampal, Ms Melany BA(Hons) . . . . . Aug 2006
Rana, Mr Asad LLB(Hons) . . . . . Aug 2005

PITMAN & CO ‡
PO Box 406 Bedford Bedfordshire MK44 3YZ
Tel: 01234 831333 *Fax:* 01234 831334

PREMIER SOLICITORS ‡
Mayfair House 11 Lurke Street Bedford Bedfordshire MK40 3HZ
Tel: 01234 358080 *Fax:* 01234 348112 *Dx:* 716006 BEDFORD 5
E-mail: info@premiersolicitors.co.uk
List of partners: D Dass, S Kambli, B Khetia, H Singh
Languages: Hindi, Italian, Punjabi, Urdu
Work: A1 B1 B3 C1 C2 D2 E J1 K1 K3 L N O Q S1 S2 T1 T2 W Z(e,i,o,p,r)
Agency and Fixed Fee Interview undertaken
Ptr: Kambli, Mr Sunil LLB; MBA; ACA; ACIS; FPC; CTA Notary Public. . . . . Jan 2004
Mem: Dass, Dinesh . . . . . Oct 2006
Khetia, Bhupendrakumar . . . . . May 1999
Singh, Hernak. . . . . Jan 2002

REHMANS SOLICITORS LTD ‡
71 Gwyn Street Bedford Bedfordshire MK40 1HH
Tel: 01234 350244 *Fax:* 01234 350246 *Dx:* 5602 BEDFORD
E-mail: info@rehmans.co.uk

SHARMAN LAW ‡
(incorporating Sharman and Trethewy)
1 Harpur Street Bedford Bedfordshire MK40 1PF
Tel: 01234 303030 *Fax:* 01234 409040 *Dx:* 5604 BEDFORD
E-mail: mail@sharmanlaw.co.uk
List of partners: P J Elliott, J G Moore, A W Northey
Office: Ampthill
Languages: French, German, Italian, Spanish
Work: D1 D2 E F1 G H J1 K1 K2 L N Q S1 S2 V W Z(d,l,m)
Emergency Action, Agency, Advocacy, Fixed Fee Interview, Legal Aid undertaken, Legal Aid Franchise, S.I.G and Member of Accident Line
Ptr: Elliott, Mr Philip J BA(Hons). . . . . Nov 1996
Moore, Mr John Graham LLB(Lond). . . . . *Jan 1970
Ast: Chandler, Mrs Susan Elizabeth BSocSc(Law) . . . . . *Oct 1989
Con: Codrington, Mr Ian C MA(Cantab) Notary Public. . . . *Oct 1962

TRINITY LEGAL SOLICITORS ‡
80 Neville Crescent Bromham Bedford Bedfordshire MK43 8JQ
Tel: 01234 826890 *Fax:* 01234 826659
E-mail: trinitylegal@btconnect.com

WOODFINES LLP ‡
Exchange Building 16 St Cuthberts Street Bedford Bedfordshire MK40 3JG
Tel: 01234 270600 *Fax:* 01234 210128 *Dx:* 5619 BEDFORD
E-mail: mail@woodfines.co.uk
List of partners: N J Ashton, A G H Buckley, A J Butler, M D Cox, D Davies, J Egan, A N Frost, N J Gibbs, S Goulding, B A Hall, C C Hallsworth, K Jones, J P Leadbeater, I D MacAskill, P J Mount, S Oliver, N P Quinn, A Salter, J D Webster, C Wingfield
Office: Bletchley, Cambridge, Milton Keynes, Sandy
Languages: French, German, Italian, Spanish
Work: A1 A3 B1 B2 C1 C2 C3 D1 D2 E F1 F2 G H I J1 J2 K1 K2 L M1 M2 N O P Q R1 R2 S1 S2 T2 U1 U2 V W Z(c,d,e,f,g,h,i,j,k,l,m,o,p,q,r,w,z)
Emergency Action, Agency, Advocacy, Legal Aid undertaken, Legal Aid Franchise and Member of Accident Line
Ptr: Ashton, Mr Nigel John BA(Dunelm) . . . . . *Dec 1986
Cox, Mr Michael D LLB . . . . . *Nov 1978
Goulding, Miss Sylvia LLB(Hons) . . . . . *Oct 1983
Jones, Mr Keith. . . . . *Jul 1979
Leadbeater, Mr John P LLB . . . . . *Nov 1992
Oliver, Mr Stephen MA . . . . . *Jul 1993
Mem: MacAskill, Mr Iain Donald . . . . . Apr 1989
Webster, Mr John David. . . . . *Oct 1980
Wingfield, Mr Christopher LLB(Exon) . . . . . *Oct 1975
Asoc: Byard, Miss Lorraine LLB; PGDip . . . . . *Mar 2003
Colling, Mr Robert John. . . . . *Jun 1973
Findlay, Mrs Valerie A. . . . . *Nov 1979
Ast: Eyre, Ms Lisa Danielle . . . . . Sep 2007
Findlay, Miss Marie LLB. . . . . Sep 2005
Marsh, Mr James John . . . . . *Sep 2008

YOUNG & CO ‡
65 Harpur Street Bedford Bedfordshire MK40 2SR
Tel: 01234 346411 / 344211 *Dx:* 5646 BEDFORD
List of partners: N J Crocker, C S Young
Work: E L S1 S2 W
Ptr: Crocker, Mr Nicholas John . . . . . *Jan 1979
Young, Mr Charles S . . . . . *Mar 1963
Ast: Young, Mrs Patricia LLB(Hons) . . . . . *Sep 1998

BEDLINGTON, Northumberland

DAVID AULD & CO
100-102 Front Street East Bedlington Northumberland NE22 5AE
Tel: 01670 826870 *Fax:* 01670 530237 *Dx:* 62701 BEDLINGTON
Emergency telephone 01670 512552
E-mail: tracey.connolly@david-auld.co.uk
Office: Morpeth
Work: D1 G K1
Emergency Action, Agency, Advocacy, Fixed Fee Interview and Legal Aid undertaken
Ptr: Auld, Mr M David E LLB. . . . . *Jun 1975
Lamond, Miss Michelle LLB . . . . . *Mar 1998
Con: Auld, Mrs Valerie Lynn BA(Hons) . . . . . *Dec 1981
Burrell, Miss Carole A LLB; MA Medical Law - Watson Burton Prize . . . . . *Jul 1997

LAWSON & THOMPSON
(incorporating Craigs)
108 Front Street East Bedlington Northumberland NE22 5AE
Tel: 01670 530700 *Fax:* 01670 531164 *Dx:* 62704 BEDLINGTON
E-mail: tim.barker@lawsonandthompson.co.uk
Office: Ashington, Blyth
Work: D1 G H J1 K1 L N Q S1 V W Z(l,q)

WHOLLEY GOODINGS LLP
1 Vulcan Place Bedlington Northumberland NE22 5DN
Tel: 01670 824080 *Fax:* 01670 824009 *Dx:* 62702 BEDLINGTON
E-mail: symmone@wholleygoodings.co.uk
Office: Morpeth
Work: C1 D1 D2 E F1 G H J1 K1 K2 K3 K4 L N Q S1 S2 W
Emergency Action, Agency, Advocacy, Fixed Fee Interview, Legal Aid undertaken and Member of Accident Line
Ptr: Goodings, Mr Richard Guy BA ♦ President of Newcastle Law Society (2006-07). . . . . Feb 1983
Wholley, Mr Richard D LLB . . . . . *Apr 1980
Con: Tocher, Mr David Richard LLB. . . . . *Jul 1969

BEDWORTH, Warwickshire

JOHN MOHAMED & CO ‡
Elliott House Rye Piece Ringway Bedworth Warwickshire CV12 8JH
Tel: 024 7649 1964 *Fax:* 024 7664 3007 *Dx:* 21656 BEDWORTH
Emergency telephone 07836 332989
List of partners: J Mohamed, P Rowlands
Work: B1 C1 D1 E F1 G H J1 L M1 N P S1 W Z(l)
Emergency Action, Agency, Advocacy and Legal Aid undertaken
Ptr: Mohamed, Mr John BA . . . . . *Nov 1981
Rowlands, Mr Philip. . . . . *Sep 1987
Ast: Gear-Evans, Mrs Joy LLB. . . . . *Mar 1990

PAYNES ‡
(incorporating W James Harris & Co; R G Frisby & Small; J F Tansley; Payne Skillington)
Marshall House 44 King Street Bedworth Warwickshire CV12 8JA
Tel: 024 7631 9820 *Fax:* 024 7664 3286 *Dx:* 21660 BEDWORTH
Emergency telephone 024 7667 9671
E-mail: martin.williams@paynes-solicitors.co.uk
List of partners: J Hickey, M R Williams
Work: B1 C1 D1 E G H J1 K1 L N Q S1 V W Z(k,l,m)
Emergency Action, Agency, Advocacy, Fixed Fee Interview and Legal Aid undertaken
Ptr: Hickey, Mr John BA. . . . . *Nov 1987
Williams, Mr Martin Royston LLB Canon of Coventry Cathedral . . . . . *Jun 2003

TUSTAIN JONES & CO
9 Bulkington Road Bedworth Warwickshire CV12 9DG
Tel: 024 7664 3222 *Fax:* 024 7664 3070 *Dx:* 21659 BEDWORTH
Office: Nuneaton
Agency, Legal Aid undertaken and Legal Aid Franchise
Ptr: Stanford, Miss Annamaria. . . . . *Jul 1997
Tustain, Mr Peter . . . . . *Jan 1990
Ast: Soar, Mrs Joanne LLB; BA . . . . . Feb 2005

BEESTON, Nottinghamshire

EDWARDS CLEGG ‡
10 Cross Street Beeston Nottinghamshire NG9 2NX
Tel: 0115 922 4537 *Fax:* 0115 922 4227 *Dx:* 11655 BEESTON
List of partners: J W Edwards
Work: C1 E R1 R2 S1 S2 W
Ptr: Edwards, Mr Jeffrey W BA . . . . . *Dec 1976
Ast: Edwards, Miss Philippa Claire. . . . . Sep 2005

ELLIS-FERMOR & NEGUS
2 Devonshire Avenue Beeston Nottinghamshire NG9 1BS
Tel: 0115 922 1591 *Fax:* 0115 925 9341 *Dx:* 11652 BEESTON
E-mail: beeston@ellis-fermor.co.uk
Office: Belper, Long Eaton, Ripley
Work: A1 B1 C1 C2 C3 D1 E F1 G H J1 K1 K2 L N O P Q R1 S1 S2 T1 T2 V W Z(d,e,j,k,l,m)
Emergency Action, Agency, Advocacy, Legal Aid undertaken and Legal Aid Franchise
Ptr: Hale, Mr Simon Peter LLB. . . . . *Dec 1990
Slack, Mrs Sarah J LLB . . . . . *Oct 1985
Ast: Bourne, Mr Benjamin . . . . . Sep 2009
Jordan, Mrs Sarah LLB . . . . . *Jan 2004
Con: Wells, Mr David R. . . . . Jun 1975

MACLAREN WARNER
40a High Road Beeston Nottinghamshire NG9 2JP
Tel: 0115 943 6696 *Fax:* 0115 943 6606 *Dx:* 711900 BEESTON
Office: Eastwood, Ilkeston, Stapleford
Ptr: Warner, Mr Stephen J BA(Law) . . . . . *Aug 1981

MURRAY BRAY ‡
50 Wollaton Road Beeston Nottinghamshire NG9 2NR
Tel: 0115 925 6300 *Fax:* 0115 925 7300
E-mail: info@murraybray.co.uk

ROTHERA DOWSON
Regent Chambers 103-105 High Road Beeston Nottinghamshire NG9 2JT
Tel: 0115 916 5200 *Fax:* 0115 916 5222 *Dx:* 11651 BEESTON
E-mail: enquiries@rotheradowson.co.uk
Office: Nottingham (3 offices), West Bridgford
Languages: French, German, Italian, Japanese, Punjabi, Urdu
Work: A1 A3 B1 C1 C2 C3 D1 D2 E I J1 J2 K1 K2 K3 K4 L M1 N O P Q R1 S1 S2 T1 T2 U2 W X Z(c,d,e,j,k,o,p,q,s,t,x)
Emergency Action, Agency, Advocacy, Fixed Fee Interview and Legal Aid undertaken
Ptr: Brydon, Mr David G LLB . . . . . *May 1972
Cobb, Mr Paul Anthony LLB(Hons) . . . . . *Feb 1992
Asoc: Tyas, Ms Ruth LLB(Hons). . . . . *Sep 2004

BELPER, Derbyshire

BRUCE ANTHONY SOLICITORS ‡
Hamilton House 4 Bullbridge Hill Ambergate Belper Derbyshire DE56 2EW
Tel: 01773 857999 *Fax:* 01773 857999 *Dx:* 16882 RIPLEY
E-mail: bruce.anthony@dsl.pipex.com
List of partners: B P Anthony
SPr: Anthony, Mr Bruce P BA . . . . . *Dec 1989

BRIGGS SAYER & CO ‡
46 Bridge Street Belper Derbyshire DE56 1AX
Tel: 01773 825246 *Fax:* 01773 821194 *Dx:* 15303 BELPER
List of partners: T E Briggs, H Y Brown, M B Sayer
Office: Ripley
Work: G H J1 K1 L N Q S1 S2 W
Emergency Action, Agency, Advocacy and Legal Aid undertaken
Ptr: Briggs, Mr Thomas E LLB(Sheff) . . . . . *Nov 1967
Brown, Miss Helen Yvonne . . . . . Sep 2004
Sayer, Mr Michael B LLB(Sheff). . . . . *Jul 1980
Asoc: Lamb, Mrs Sally Ann LLB(Hons) . . . . . Nov 1996

See p112 for the Key to Work Categories & other symbols

NIGEL DAVIS SOLICITORS ‡
The Sheepfold Carr Hall Farm Turnditch Belper Derbyshire DE56 2LW
Tel: 01335 372889 *Fax:* 01335 372891 *Dx:* 742820 BELPER
E-mail: nigeldavis@agriculturalsolicitors.co.uk
List of partners: N R Davis, M Elias, O Wilson
Languages: French, German, Greek, Italian, Lithuanian, Polish, Russian, Spanish
Work: A1 A2 A3 P R1 S1 U1 W
Agency and Advocacy undertaken
Ptr: Davis, Mr Nigel R MA(Cantab) . . . . *Jun 1975
Elias, Mr Matthew LLB(Hons) . . . . *Jul 2004
Wilson, Mr Oliver LLB(Hons) . . . . *Jul 2002
Asoc: Bastin, Miss Jane BA(Hons)(Dunelm) . . . . *Apr 1981
Osuch-Goodhead, Mrs Wanda Maria MA . . . . Oct 1994
Con: Corbett, Miss Helen Louise LLB. . . . . Dec 1993

ELLIS-FERMOR & NEGUS
7 Bridge Street Belper Derbyshire DE56 1AY
Tel: 01773 821665 *Fax:* 01773 826634
E-mail: belper@ellis-fermor.co.uk
Office: Beeston, Long Eaton, Ripley
Ptr: Whiteley, Mr Richard Ben LLB(Hons) . . . . Feb 2004

PYMS ‡
The Triangle 131 Bridge Street Belper Derbyshire DE56 1BJ
Tel: 01773 822307 *Fax:* 01773 826518 *Dx:* 15301 BELPER
Emergency telephone 01773 833977
E-mail: ronday@pyms-solicitors.co.uk
List of partners: R J H Day, A Goadby
Work: A1 C1 C2 D1 E K1 K2 K3 K4 L R1 R2 S1 S2 V W Z(c)
Agency and Fixed Fee Interview undertaken
Ptr: Day, Mr Ronald John Hugh . . . . *Jul 1979
Goadby, Mr Alan . . . . *Jan 1986

SHACKLOCKS
25 Chapel Street Belper Derbyshire DE56 1AR
Tel: 01773 822333 *Fax:* 01773 821551 *Dx:* 13504 BELPER
E-mail: enquiries@shacklocks.co.uk
Office: Derby, Mansfield, Ripley
Work: A1 C1 C2 C3 E F1 J1 K1 L N Q R1 S1 T1 T2 W Z(c,d,e,k,l,t)
Agency, Advocacy and Fixed Fee Interview undertaken
Ptr: Parr, Mrs Clare BA(Hons). . . . . *Jun 1975
Taylor, Mr Michael Ian. . . . . *Mar 1973
Asoc: Stubbins, Mr Benjamin Francis LLB . . . . Sep 2003
Vickers, Ms Clare Helene LLB. . . . . Oct 1993
Ast: Elliot, Mr Nick James . . . . May 2008

BENFLEET, Essex

ANP SOLICITORS ‡
290 Kiln Road Benfleet Essex SS7 1QT
Tel: 01702 556688 *Fax:* 01268 772633
Dx: 39601 HADLEIGH ESSEX
E-mail: info@anpsolicitors.com
Languages: Hindi, Punjabi, Urdu

BARNES COLEMAN & CO ‡
(incorporating Barnes Knowles & Taylor Heard & Coleman)
30 Rectory Road Hadleigh Benfleet Essex SS7 2ND
Tel: 01702 558211 *Fax:* 01702 551404
Dx: 39606 HADLEIGH ESSEX
E-mail: barnescolemanco@btconnect.com
List of partners: C W Knowles
Work: A1 B1 C1 D1 E F1 G H J1 K1 L N O Q S1 V W
Agency and Advocacy undertaken
Ptr: Knowles, Mr Charles W BA . . . . *Dec 1981

DORLING COTTRELL ‡
81a High Road Benfleet Essex SS7 5LE
Tel: 01268 795530
Office: Basildon

ANDREW HURRELL SOLICITORS ‡
Central Chambers 227 London Road Hadleigh Benfleet Essex SS7 2RE
Tel: 01702 558286 *Fax:* 01702 551235
Dx: 39617 HADLEIGH ESSEX
E-mail: alanlast@andrewhurrell.com
List of partners: A P Hurrell
Office: Thorpe Bay
Languages: French
Work: C1 E F1 J1 L S1 T1 T2 W Z(l)
Fixed Fee Interview undertaken
SPr: Hurrell, Mr Andrew P LLB(Lond); TEP Life Governor of Imperial Cancer Research Fund Notary Public . . . . *§Apr 1981

R E KNODT SOLICITOR ‡
7 Melcombe Road Benfleet Essex SS7 5NB
Tel: 01268 566465
E-mail: richardk.legal@virgin.net

LIDDELL AND COMPANY
206 High Road Benfleet Essex SS7 5LD
Tel: 01268 565769 *Fax:* 01268 566118
E-mail: jab@liddell-solicitors.co.uk
Office: Billericay, Romford
Work: K1 K2 K3 S1 S2 W
Fixed Fee Interview undertaken
Ast: Lodeto, Mrs Jane . . . . Sep 2003
Lyon, Mr Mark . . . . Nov 1989

NAIRNSEY FISHER & LEWIS ‡
105 London Road Benfleet Essex SS7 5TG
Tel: 01268 566655 *Fax:* 01268 565059 *Dx:* 48950 BENFLEET
E-mail: bm@n-f-l.co.uk
List of partners: R J Lord, B Morgan
Ptr: Lord, Mr Roderick James . . . . Jan 1988
Morgan, Ms Brenda. . . . . Jan 1988

TAYLOR HALDANE BARLEX LLP
204 High Road Benfleet Essex SS7 5LD
Tel: 01702 339168 *Fax:* 0845 658 7990 *Dx:* 2805 SOUTHEND
E-mail: mail@thblegal.com
Office: Braintree, Chelmsford, Ipswich, Southend-on-Sea

BENLLECH, Anglesey

PARRY DAVIES CLWYD-JONES & LLOYD
Trem-y-don Benllech Anglesey LL74 8TF
Tel: 01248 852782 *Fax:* 01248 852782
Office: Amlwch, Caernarfon, Llangefni, Pwllheli

BENTHAM, North Yorkshire

DEREK M JORDAN
Station Road Bentham North Yorkshire LA2 7LH
Tel: 01524 261254 *Fax:* 01524 263461
Office: Settle
Work: A1 G K1 M1 P S1 T1 W
SPr: Jordan, Mr Derek M. . . . . *Jun 1974

BERKHAMSTED, Hertfordshire

AUSTINS PENNY & THORNE
175 High Street Berkhamsted Hertfordshire HP4 3AP
Tel: 01442 872141 *Fax:* 01442 862222 *Dx:* 80851 BERKHAMSTED
E-mail: berkhamsted@austinslaw.com
Office: Luton
Work: C1 D1 E F1 J1 K1 L N O Q S1 S2 V W
Agency, Advocacy, Legal Aid undertaken and Member of Accident Line
Mem: Farrow, Mrs Lee-Ann BA; LLB. . . . . *Jul 1999
Frostick, Mr Nigel G LLB . . . . *§Apr 1976
Ast: Gibbs, Mrs Janine Tanya BA(Hons). . . . . Jul 1993
Houghton, Mr James Matthew BA(Hons) . . . . *Dec 2006

A F BARKER & CO ‡
40 Lower Kings Road Berkhamsted Hertfordshire HP4 2AA
Tel: 01442 863336 *Fax:* 01442 865825 *Dx:* 80867 BERKHAMSTED
List of partners: M Casotti
Ptr: Casotti, Mr Marco LLB . . . . Feb 1989

CAMERON SOLICITORS ‡
264b High Street Berkhamsted Hertfordshire HP4 1AQ
Tel: 01442 870303 *Fax:* 01442 871355

HARROWELL & ATKINS ‡
Boxwell House 275 High Street Berkhamsted Hertfordshire HP4 1BW
Tel: 01442 865671 *Fax:* 01442 865992 *Dx:* 80852 BERKHAMSTED
E-mail: legal@harrowell-atkins.co.uk
List of partners: M D Atkins, M I Avern, J R Comerford
Work: A1 B1 D1 E F1 G H J1 K1 L M1 N P R1 S1 T1 W Z(l)
Emergency Action, Agency, Advocacy, Fixed Fee Interview, Legal Aid undertaken and Member of Accident Line
Ptr: Atkins, Mr Michael Dennis LLB . . . . *Oct 1995
Avern, Mr Michael I BA . . . . *Oct 1983
Ast: Dowen, Mrs Helen BA(Hons) . . . . *Apr 1993

SUMNER & TABOR ‡
Lockhart House 295-299 High Street Berkhamsted Hertfordshire HP4 1AJ
Tel: 01442 862797 / 872311 *Fax:* 01442 872643
Dx: 80850 BERKHAMSTED
E-mail: sols@sumtab.co.uk
List of partners: K E Ainsworth, G C E Sumner, G M Tabor
Work: B1 C1 D1 E J1 K1 L N O Q R1 S1 S2 V W Z(c,q)
Emergency Action, Agency, Advocacy, Fixed Fee Interview, Legal Aid undertaken and Legal Aid Franchise
Ptr: Ainsworth, Mrs Kathryn E . . . . *Sep 1995
Sumner, Mr Geoffrey C E MA(Oxon) . . . . Jan 1969
Tabor, Mrs Gillian M LLB(Hons). . . . . *Nov 1981

PAUL S WILLIAMSON ‡
16 Priory Gardens Berkhamsted Hertfordshire HP4 2DS
Tel: 01442 862475 *Fax:* 01442 862475
E-mail: paul.williamson@lineone.net
List of partners: P S Williamson
Languages: French, Spanish
Work: C1 E F1 J1 K4 M1 M2 S1 S2 W
SPr: Williamson, Mr Paul Soulsby LLB(Hons) Notary Public *Dec 1990

BERWICK-UPON-TWEED, Northumberland

ADAM DOUGLAS & SON
49-51 Bridge Street Berwick-upon-Tweed Northumberland TD15 1ES
Tel: 01289 306479 *Fax:* 01289 330246
Dx: 67792 BERWICK-UPON-TWEED
E-mail: hja@adamdouglas.co.uk
Office: Alnwick, Amble
Work: D1 E F1 F2 J1 K1 K3 K4 L S1 S2 W Z(l)
Emergency Action, Agency, Advocacy, Fixed Fee Interview and Legal Aid Franchise
Ptr: Almond, Ms Hilary BA(Dunelm) . . . . *Sep 1989
Hughes, Mr Hugo James A LLB(Hons) . . . . *Mar 2002
Asoc: Twyford, Mr Richard BA. . . . . *Aug 2008

SANDERSON MCCREATH & EDNEY ‡
4 Quay Walls Berwick-upon-Tweed Northumberland TD15 1HD
Tel: 01289 306724 *Fax:* 01289 330323
Dx: 67790 BERWICK-UPON-TWEED
List of partners: G L Hill, S G Jones
Work: A1 B1 C1 D2 E J1 K1 L N O Q S1 T1 W Z(d,l,q)
Emergency Action, Agency and Advocacy undertaken
Ptr: Hill, Mrs Gaynor Louise Clerk to Commissioner of Taxes . . . . *May 2002
Jones, Mr Stuart Gavin BA(Law) . . . . *Apr 1987
Ast: Palin, Mr Samuel John LLB(Hons). . . . . Jan 2008

T C SMITH ‡
9 Church Street Berwick-upon-Tweed Northumberland TD15 1EF
Tel: 01289 307409 *Fax:* 01289 307515
Dx: 67793 BERWICK-UPON-TWEED
E-mail: mtb@tcsmith.co.uk
List of partners: M T Butson, J A Marshall, S J Stockdale
Work: A2 D1 D2 E F1 G H J1 K1 L M1 M2 N O P Q R1 S1 S2 T1 T2 V W Z(c,d,l,n,p,q)
Emergency Action, Agency, Advocacy, Legal Aid undertaken and Legal Aid Franchise
Ptr: Butson, Mr Mark T BA(Kent) Under Sheriff of Berwick-upon-Tweed . . . . *Mar 1985
Marshall, Mr John A. . . . . *Oct 1975
Stockdale, Miss Sara J BA Dickinson Dees Law Prize 1993 . . . . *Sep 1996

TAIT FARRIER GRAHAM
8 Sandgate Berwick-upon-Tweed Northumberland TD15 1EP
Tel: 01289 309851 *Fax:* 01289 309851
E-mail: info@gatesheadsolicitors.co.uk
Office: Gateshead, Newcastle upon Tyne

BEVERLEY, East Riding of Yorkshire

DAVIS DAVIDSON ‡
Tower House 65 North Bar Within Beverley East Riding of Yorkshire HU17 8AZ
Tel: 01482 881278 *Fax:* 01482 881395
Emergency telephone 01964 542496
E-mail: law@davisdavidson.demon.co.uk
List of partners: S B Davidson, W M Davis
Work: A1 B1 C1 D1 E G H J1 K1 L N O P Q S1 W Z(f)
Emergency Action, Agency and Advocacy undertaken
Ptr: Davidson, Mr Steven B BA . . . . *Oct 1985
Davis, Mr W Michael LLB(Wales) . . . . *Jan 1978

LOCKINGS
Highgate House 19 Wednesday Market Beverley East Riding of Yorkshire HU17 0DG
Tel: 01482 300500 *Fax:* 01482 300501 *Dx:* 28304 BEVERLEY
E-mail: mbrown@lockings.co.uk
Office: Hull (2 offices)
Work: C1 E L S1 S2 W
Ast: Breckon, Mr Malcolm . . . . Apr 1974

SANDERSONS
Morton House Morton Lane Beverley East Riding of Yorkshire HU17 9DD
Tel: 01482 324662 *Fax:* 01482 860118 *Dx:* 28301 BEVERLEY
Emergency telephone 01482 324662
E-mail: enquiries@sandersonssolicitors.co.uk
Office: Hull
Work: A1 B2 C1 D1 E F1 J1 K1 K2 K3 L N O Q R1 R2 S1 S2 T1 T2 V W Z(h,j,l,w)
Emergency Action, Agency, Advocacy, Legal Aid undertaken and Member of Accident Line

WARD SCOTT LLP
Appleton House 3a Wednesday Market Beverley East Riding of Yorkshire HU17 0DG
Tel: 01482 887667 *Fax:* 01482 888234
E-mail: info@wardscottllp.co.uk
Office: Hull
Work: C1 E K1 K3 K4 N O S1 S2 W

WILKIN CHAPMAN LLP
The Hall Lairgate Beverley East Riding of Yorkshire HU17 8HL
Tel: 01482 398398 *Fax:* 01482 870913 *Dx:* 28302 BEVERLEY
E-mail: it@wilkinchapman.co.uk
Office: Alford, Grimsby (3 offices), Horncastle, Lincoln, Louth, Mablethorpe, Market Rasen, Sutton-on-Sea
Work: A1 A3 C1 C2 D1 E F1 J1 K1 K2 K3 L N O Q R1 S1 S2 T1 T2 W Z(l,r)
Emergency Action, Agency, Advocacy, Fixed Fee Interview, Legal Aid undertaken and Member of Accident Line
Ptr: Adams, Mr Michael Stephenson LLB(Lond) . . . . *Jun 1973
Carlton, Mr James M BA . . . . *Oct 1985
Justice, Mr Martyn Robert LLB . . . . Dec 1982
Patrick, Mr Neil Bonthron . . . . *Jul 1975
Asoc: Archer, Mrs Lesley Adele LLB Oxley & Coward Prize in Taxation Law. . . . . *May 1994
Booth, Mr Timothy Richard LLB . . . . *Mar 1979
Moggridge, Mrs Virginia BA(Hons). . . . . *Sep 2001
Schofield, Mr John . . . . *Nov 2003
Ast: Butterfint, Ms Lucy . . . . Sep 2009
Huntingdon, Ms Emma . . . . Jun 2000

BEWDLEY, Worcestershire

DAVID A ASHWORTH ‡
The Hay Loft Hextons Farm Barns Arley Bewdley Worcestershire DY12 1SW
Tel: 01299 861056 *Fax:* 01299 861056
E-mail: davidashworth279@btinternet.com
List of partners: D A Ashworth
Work: A1 C1 E L S1 W
Ptr: Ashworth, Mr David Alan . . . . *Mar 1969

C&S SOLICITORS
PO Box 4896 Bewdley Worcestershire DY12 1YU
Tel: 01562 752199 *Fax:* 01562 747935
E-mail: newclaim@cs-solicitors.com
Office: Kidderminster

MARION EVANS ‡
67 High Street Bewdley Worcestershire DY12 2DJ
Tel: 01299 402741 *Fax:* 01299 401800 *Dx:* 29901 BEWDLEY
E-mail: info@marion-evans-solicitors.co.uk
List of partners: M Evans
SPr: Evans, Mrs Marion LLB(Lond). . . . . *Jul 1976

NICHOLAS SUTTON SOLICITORS ‡
Sydney Place 7 Kidderminster Road Bewdley Worcestershire DY12 1AQ
Tel: 01299 405626 *Fax:* 01299 405626 *Dx:* 29904 BEWDLEY
E-mail: nicksutton1@mac.com

THREE COUNTIES LAW ‡
Unit 4 70 Load Street Bewdley Worcestershire DY12 2AW
Tel: 07789 436481 *Fax:* 01562 510496

BEXHILL, East Sussex

DONALDSON DUNSTALL ‡
48 Parkhurst Road Bexhill East Sussex TN40 1DE
Tel: 01424 216329 *Fax:* 01424 730131 *Dx:* 8102 BEXHILL-ON-SEA
E-mail: info@donaldsondunstall.com
List of partners: P N Donaldson, C T P Dunstall, K Tynan

Work: B1 C1 E J1 K1 K3 K4 L N O Q R1 S1 S2 W Z(c,j,l,q)
Agency and Advocacy undertaken
Ptr: Donaldson, Mr Patrick Neville BA . . . . *Jun 1979
Dunstall, Mr Colin T P. . . . . *Sep 1994
Tynan, Miss Katherine LLB(Hons). . . . . *Sep 1995

FYNMORES ‡
10-12 Parkhurst Road Bexhill East Sussex TN40 1DF
Tel: 01424 732333 *Fax:* 01424 739832 *Dx:* 8100 BEXHILL-ON-SEA
E-mail: amilbox@fynmoreslaw.com
List of partners: J A Ball, M E Woolliams
Work: A1 B1 C1 D1 D2 E F1 J1 K1 K2 P R1 S1 S2 T1 W Z(m)
Emergency Action, Advocacy, Fixed Fee Interview, Legal Aid undertaken and Legal Aid Franchise
Ptr: Ball, Mr John A CBE LLB(Lond). . . . . *§May 1966
Woolliams, Mr Mervyn E . . . . *§Jan 1970
Ast: Ormrod, Mr David MA(Oxon) . . . . *§Apr 1971
Con: Foster, Mr Michael J . . . . *§Jun 1980

GRANARY CHAMBERS ‡
148 Ninfield Road Bexhill East Sussex TN39 5BD
Tel: 01424 733008 *Fax:* 01424 734988
Dx: 91555 BEXHILL (LITTLE COMMON)
E-mail: clerks@granarychambers.com
Work: A3 G H N Z(e)

GABY HARDWICKE ‡
2 Eversley Road Bexhill East Sussex TN40 1EY
Tel: 01424 730945 *Fax:* 01424 730043 *Dx:* 8105 BEXHILL
E-mail: info@gabyhardwicke.co.uk
List of partners: C J Bean, M R Bugden, A S Caulfield, D E Getty, J P Midgley, B C Sagar, P W Taylor, M V Walker, M E Williams, D G Young
Office: Bexhill, Eastbourne, Hastings
Languages: French
Work: B1 C1 C2 C3 D1 E J1 K1 K2 L N O Q R1 R2 S1 S2 T1 T2 V W Z(c,d,o,r,z)
Advocacy, Fixed Fee Interview, Legal Aid undertaken, Legal Aid Franchise and Member of Accident Line
Ptr: Bugden, Mr Michael R ACIB . . . . *§Dec 1974
Midgley, Mr Jonathan P LLB(Hons) . . . . *Feb 1993
Taylor, Mr Peter W . . . . *Dec 1972

GABY HARDWICKE
56 Cooden Sea Road Little Common Bexhill East Sussex TN39 4SL
Tel: 01424 842206 *Fax:* 01424 848060
E-mail: info@gabyhardwicke.co.uk
Office: Bexhill, Eastbourne, Hastings
Work: B1 C1 C2 C3 D1 E J1 K1 K2 L N O Q R1 R2 S1 S2 T1 T2 V W Z(c,d,o,r,z)

MENNEER SHUTTLEWORTH ‡
(incorporating Willett & Phillips; Michael Maurice Slot)
21 Eversley Road Bexhill East Sussex TN40 1HA
Tel: 01424 730630 *Fax:* 01424 730313 *Dx:* 8101 BEXHILL-ON-SEA
Emergency telephone 07968 208146
E-mail: legalbex@shuttleworth.co.uk
List of partners: D J Collins, J E S Crone, R J F Harrison, R Howlett, A G Reid, A C Shuttleworth, A J Wilson
Office: St Leonards-on-Sea
Languages: French
Work: A1 B1 C1 D1 D2 E F1 F2 G H J1 J2 K1 L M1 N O P Q R1 R2 S1 S2 T1 T2 W X Z(c,d,g,i,k,l,m,o,q,r)
Emergency Action, Advocacy, Fixed Fee Interview, Legal Aid Franchise and Member of Accident Line
Ptr: Crone, Mr John E S. . . . . *§Jul 1973
Shuttleworth, Mr Anthony C. . . . . *Jul 1973

YOUNG COLES & LANGDON
13 Eversley Road Bexhill East Sussex TN40 1JE
Tel: 01424 210013 *Fax:* 01424 218728 *Dx:* 8106 BEXHILL-ON-SEA
E-mail: rclane@btconnect.com
Office: Hastings
Work: B1 C1 E F1 L N Q S1 T1 W Z(b,e,m)
Agency and Fixed Fee Interview undertaken
Ptr: Lane, Mr Richard Carlisle BA . . . . *May 1982

BEXLEY, Kent

GRAHAM DAWSON & CO ‡
80d Bexley High Street Bexley Kent DA5 1LE
Tel: 01322 558811 *Fax:* 01322 558816 *Dx:* 90501 BEXLEY
E-mail: tdr@grahamdawsonandco.co.uk
List of partners: G J Dawson, T D Rees
Work: E N O S1 S2 T1 W
Fixed Fee Interview undertaken
Ptr: Dawson, Mr Graham J . . . . *§Dec 1973
Rees, Mr Timothy David BA(Hons) . . . . *Apr 1990

BEXLEYHEATH, Kent

ALETTA SHAW SOLICITORS ‡
130-132 Broadway Bexleyheath Kent DA6 6DP
Tel: 020 8301 4884 Fax: 020 8301 3477
Dx: 151363 BEXLEYHEATH 6
E-mail: enquiries@alettashaw.co.uk
List of partners: P Aletta, R F Andrews, H Scanlon
Work: D1 D2 G J1 K1 K3 L N Q S1 V W
Emergency Action, Agency, Advocacy, Fixed Fee Interview, Legal Aid undertaken and Legal Aid Franchise
Ptr: Aletta, Ms Patricia. . . . . Jun 1999
Andrews, Mr Richard Frederick BA(Hons). . . . . . . Mar 2003
Scanlon, Ms Hazel . . . . Jan 2001

APEX LAW LLP ‡
20 Winchester Road Bexleyheath Kent DA7 4TX
Tel: 020 8306 1455 *Fax:* 020 8306 3851
E-mail: mark@apexlaw.co.uk
Office: Bexleyheath

APEX LAW LLP
1 Thirlmere Road Bexleyheath Kent DA7 6PU
Tel: 01322 333201 *Fax:* 01322 338177
E-mail: maggie@apexlaw.co.uk
Office: Bexleyheath

BAYNARDS ‡
308b Broadway Bexleyheath Kent DA6 8AA
Tel: 020 8304 5113 *Fax:* 020 8301 4818 *Dx:* 31814 BEXLEYHEATH
E-mail: baynards.sols@btconnect.com
List of partners: V A Baynard
Work: C1 S1 W
Member of Accident Line
Ptr: Baynard, Mrs Veronica A LLB. . . . . *Jun 1982

T G BAYNES ‡
Broadway House 208 Broadway Bexleyheath Kent DA6 7BG
Tel: 020 8301 7777 *Fax:* 020 8301 7701
Dx: 151360 BEXLEYHEATH 6
E-mail: info@tgbaynes.com
List of partners: S J Burton, M A Clark, M J Dewar, K R Gough, R Higgins, K A Ioannou, E J Lee, A J Leiper, E Lewis, S C Potts, S Power, A J Robertson, D A Rose, N Sarwar, K K Shokar, R R Thomas, J T Wigginton
Office: Dartford, Orpington
Work: B1 C1 D1 D2 E F1 J1 J2 K1 K2 K3 K4 L N O Q R1 R2 S1 S2 T1 T2 V W Z(c,l,p,q,r)
Emergency Action, Agency, Advocacy, Fixed Fee Interview, Legal Aid undertaken, Legal Aid Franchise and Member of Accident Line
Ptr: Clark, Mr Michael A LLB . . . . *Jul 1978
Lee, Miss Emma Jane LLB(Hons). . . . . *Jul 2006
Lewis, Mr Edward. . . . . *Aug 1998
Potts, Mr Simon C BA. . . . . *§Feb 1983
Robertson, Mr Andrew J LLB . . . . *§Feb 1985
Rose, Mrs Donna Alison . . . . *Aug 1984
Sarwar, Mr Nadeem BSc; DipLaw. . . . . *Mar 2000
Shokar, Mrs Kulvinder Kaur BA; LPC;. . . . . *Jun 2003
Thomas, Mr Richard R LLB . . . . *Aug 1978
Dir: Gough, Mr Keith Robert. . . . . *Jul 1977
Asoc: Rogers, Mr Stephen. . . . . Nov 2003

CHANCELLORS LEA BREWER ‡
246 Broadway Bexleyheath Kent DA6 8BB
Tel: 020 8303 0077 *Fax:* 020 8304 4023 *Dx:* 31800 BEXLEYHEATH
E-mail: enquiries@chancellors.com
List of partners: R G Douglas, A K Kemsley, M R Lea, A O Wiles
Languages: British Sign Language, French
Work: A2 C1 D1 D2 E F1 G J1 K1 K3 K4 L N O Q R1 S1 S2 T1 T2 W Z(c,k,l,r)
Agency, Advocacy and Fixed Fee Interview undertaken
Ptr: Douglas, Mr Robin Gordon LLB . . . . *Oct 1979
Kemsley, Miss Alison K BA(Hons). . . . . *Nov 1990
Lea, Mr Martin R . . . . *§Dec 1972
Wiles, Mr Andrew O. . . . . *Jun 1977
Ast: Clarke, Miss Tara LLB(Hons) . . . . *Nov 2002

HOWARTH SCOTT ‡
The Old Vicarage 174a Broadway Bexleyheath Kent DA6 7EE
Tel: 020 8303 4658 *Fax:* 020 8303 3882
List of partners: S Howarth, J M H Scott
Languages: French, German
Work: D1 E J1 K1 L N S1 W
Emergency Action, Advocacy, Fixed Fee Interview and Legal Aid undertaken
Ptr: Howarth, Ms Sue BA . . . . *Apr 1981
Ast: Hall, Ms Alison LLB . . . . Feb 1994
Howarth, Ms Jane LLB . . . . Jan 1993
Stewart, Ms Sharon E BA. . . . . *Oct 1987

MCMILLAN WILLIAMS SOLICITORS ‡
4-5 Market Place Bexleyheath Kent DA6 7DU
Tel: 020 8303 0168 *Fax:* 020 8303 9125
Dx: 130386 BEXLEYHEATH 4
E-mail: enquiries@mcmillan-williams.co.uk
List of partners: C S Landes
Work: B2 D1 D2 E G H K1 K2 K3 S1 S2 W
Emergency Action, Agency, Advocacy, Fixed Fee Interview, Legal Aid undertaken and Legal Aid Franchise
Ptr: Landes, Mrs Caroline Suzanne LLB(Hons) Chairman of the Bexley Community Legal Services Partnership . *Sep 1988
Con: Earle-Hutton, Mrs Georgina C C BSc(Psych) . . . . . *Apr 1996

T N NUNNS ‡
15 Hawthorn Road Bexleyheath Kent DA6 7AF
Tel: 020 8304 2538
E-mail: timothy.nunns@btinternet.com

STUART HURRION & GREEN ‡
33 Crook Log Bexleyheath Kent DA6 8EB
Tel: 020 8298 1595 *Fax:* 020 8301 6336 *Dx:* 31802 BEXLEYHEATH
E-mail: shg@stuarthurriongreen.co.uk
List of partners: J A Belsham, M J Shirley
Work: E K4 R2 S1 S2 W
Ptr: Belsham, Ms Jane Anne LLB(Hons). . . . . *Nov 1982
Shirley, Mr Martin J LLB(Lond) . . . . *Nov 1982
Ast: Oborne, Mrs Sheila . . . . Jun 2001

THOMAS BOYD WHYTE ‡
302 Broadway Bexleyheath Kent DA6 8AB
Tel: 020 8303 7755 *Fax:* 020 8304 4284 *Dx:* 31804 BEXLEYHEATH
E-mail: enquiry@tbw.uk.com
List of partners: G T Luckhurst, B G Wilkey
Languages: French, German
Work: A1 B1 C1 D1 E F1 G H I J1 K1 L M1 N O P Q R1 S1 T1 V W Z(c,d,i,l,m,t)
Agency, Advocacy, Fixed Fee Interview, Legal Aid undertaken, Legal Aid Franchise and Member of Accident Line
Ptr: Luckhurst, Mr Gordon T BSc . . . . *§Jul 1981
Wilkey, Mr Bruce G LLB. . . . . *Oct 1987
Ast: Sokhal, Jatinder BSc(Econ Law & Politics) . . . . . *Sep 1996
Con: Dunton, Ms Margaret V . . . . *Nov 1966

BICESTER, Oxfordshire

ALFRED TRUMAN ‡
The Old Court House 5 Sheep Street Bicester Oxfordshire OX26 6JB
Tel: 01869 252761 *Fax:* 01869 246619 *Dx:* 40150 BICESTER
E-mail: alfred@trumans.co.uk
List of partners: D O Coxall, J H D Meakin, S S Pangu
Office: Buckingham
Languages: French, German, Malay
Work: A1 B1 C1 C2 D1 E F1 J1 K1 N O Q R1 S1 S2 T1 T2 W Z(c,i,k,l,p,q)
Ptr: Coxall, Mr David Oxford. . . . . *Dec 1968
Meakin, Mr John H D LLB. . . . . *May 1980
Pangu, Shamsher Singh LLB . . . . Feb 2001
Ast: Girton, Mrs Helen R LLB(Lond) . . . . *Dec 1977
Con: Corner, Mr Rodney Hunter Gordon LLB(Hons) Coroner for Milton Keynes Notary Public . . . . *§Jul 1965

BRIDGEHOUSE PARTNERS ‡
2 Market Square Bicester Oxfordshire OX26 6AA
Tel: 01869 243457 *Fax:* 01869 242323
List of partners: M C B Cox, J N Rowles-Davies
Work: A1 B1 C1 D1 E F1 G H J1 K1 L N O P Q R1 S1 T1 V W Z(c,l,p)
Emergency Action, Agency, Advocacy, Fixed Fee Interview and Legal Aid undertaken
Ptr: Cox, Mr Matthew Charles Benjamin BA(Hons). . . . . Jan 2004
Rowles-Davies, Mr John N BA(Hons) . . . . *§Nov 1994

CANTELLI & CO ‡
60 North Street Bicester Oxfordshire OX26 6NF
Tel: 01869 324899 *Fax:* 01869 325775 *Dx:* 40156 BICESTER
List of partners: R Cantelli
Languages: Spanish
Work: E F1 J1 K1 N Q S1
Fixed Fee Interview and Legal Aid undertaken
SPr: Cantelli, Mr Roderick . . . . *Jul 1989

HMG LAW LLP
32 Crown Walk Bicester Oxfordshire OX26 6HY
Tel: 01869 252244 *Fax:* 01869 247362 *Dx:* 40153 BICESTER
Emergency telephone 01869 245671
E-mail: info@hmg-law.co.uk
Office: Oxford
Languages: French, German
Work: A1 B1 C1 C2 E F1 J1 K1 K3 K4 L O Q R1 S1 S2 T1 T2 W Z(b,k,l,q)
Agency and Advocacy undertaken
Ptr: Baker, Mr Gary Stephen LLB . . . . *Nov 1984
Jackson, Mr Stevyn A LLB(Hons) . . . . *Oct 1991
Ast: Jessop, Ms Catherine Elizabeth BA . . . . *Oct 1995

NEASHAM LLOYD ‡
68 Sheep Street Bicester Oxfordshire OX26 6JW
Tel: 01869 252161 *Fax:* 01869 241775 *Dx:* 40158 BICESTER
E-mail: sneasham@neashamlloyd.co.uk
List of partners: S C Clark, S M Neasham
Work: D1 E F1 K1 K2 L S1 V W
Legal Aid Franchise
Ptr: Clark, Miss Sally C . . . . *Nov 1993
Neasham, Mr Steven M. . . . . *May 1982
Asoc: Howson, Mrs Abigail . . . . Sep 2005

BIDDULPH, Staffordshire

CHARLTONS SOLICITORS ‡
Saracen House 84 High Street Biddulph Staffordshire ST8 6AS
Tel: 01782 522111 *Fax:* 01782 522710
List of partners: G P Quinn
Work: A1 A2 A3 B1 C1 D1 D2 E F1 F2 G J1 J2 K1 K2 L O Q R1 R2 S1 S2 V W X Z(c,g,h,m,p,q,r,t)
Emergency Action, Agency, Advocacy, Fixed Fee Interview, Legal Aid undertaken, Legal Aid Franchise and Member of Accident Line
Ptr: Quinn, Mr Gerard P LLB(Hons) . . . . *§Jul 1964
Ast: Hambleton, Mr Michael S BA . . . . *Nov 1985
Peake, Mrs Linda BA(Law) . . . . *Dec 1987

BIDEFORD, Devon

BAZELEY BARNES & BAZELEY ‡
24 Bridgeland Street Bideford Devon EX39 2QB
Tel: 01237 473122 *Fax:* 01237 421531 *Dx:* 53608 BIDEFORD
E-mail: mail@bazeleys.co.uk
List of partners: A B Charles, J A Goodge, P R Sims
Work: A1 D1 G H J1 L N Q S1 W Z(d)
Agency and Advocacy undertaken
Ptr: Charles, Mr Andrew B LLB . . . . *Dec 1982
Goodge, Mr Jonathan Allenby LLB(Warw). . . . . . . *Jun 1979
Sims, Mr Peter Ralph LLB(Leics) . . . . *§Feb 1972
Ast: Bakehouse, Miss Debbie Ann LLB(Hons) . . . . . . *Jul 2004
Con: Rowe, Mr David George BA(Hons) . . . . *May 1967

BREWER HARDING & ROWE
29 Bridgeland Street Bideford Devon EX39 2PT
Tel: 01237 472666 *Fax:* 01237 470000 *Dx:* 53600 BIDEFORD
E-mail: lawyers@bhrlaw.co.uk
Office: Barnstaple (2 offices), Braunton, Exeter, Ilfracombe
Languages: Spanish
Work: A1 B1 C1 D1 E F1 K1 K3 L O P Q R1 S1 S2 V Z(b,c,d,h,j,k,l,m,o,q)
Emergency Action, Agency, Advocacy, Legal Aid undertaken and Legal Aid Franchise
Ptr: Chittock, Mr Michael J. . . . . *Feb 1982
Emo, Ms Nicola J LLB(Hons) . . . . *Oct 1995
Woo, Mr Andrew Teck Han LLB(Hons) Sweet & Maxwell Law Prize 1992 . . . . *Dec 1995

CHANTER FERGUSON ‡
17 The Quay Bideford Devon EX39 2EN
Tel: 01237 478751 *Fax:* 01237 470893 *Dx:* 53604 BIDEFORD
List of partners: M Clark, A C Laugharne, P R Mole
Office: Barnstaple
Work: A1 B1 C1 C2 C3 D1 E F1 G H J1 K1 L N O P Q R1 S1 T1 T2 V W X Z(a,c,d,e,h,k,l,m,o,s)
Emergency Action, Agency, Advocacy, Fixed Fee Interview, Legal Aid undertaken, Legal Aid Franchise and Member of Accident Line
Ptr: Clark, Mr Maurice Notary Public. . . . . *§Jan 1982
Laugharne, Mr Andrew Charles BA . . . . *Apr 1975
Mole, Mr Peter R LLB Clerk to General Commissioners of Inland Revenue . . . . *§Mar 1974
Con: Ferguson, Mr Jeremy J Notary Public . . . . *§Nov 1958

OPENSHAWS ‡
Tower House 26 The Strand Bideford Devon EX39 2ND
Tel: 01237 478900 *Fax:* 01237 470400
E-mail: oss@openshaws.com
List of partners: N H F Openshaw
Languages: French
Work: C1 C2 C3 M2 Z(b,e)
SPr: Openshaw, Mr Nicholas Henry Folliott LLB(Hons) . . . Nov 1985

See p112 for the Key to Work Categories & other symbols

PETER PETER & WRIGHT
Grenville House The Quay Bideford Devon EX39 2EZ
Tel: 01237 472233 *Fax:* 01237 471128 *Dx:* 53603 BIDEFORD
E-mail: mail@ppwbid.co.uk
Office: Bude, Holsworthy, Okehampton
Work: A1 C1 D1 D2 E F1 J1 K1 K2 K3 K4 L N O P Q R1 R2 S1 S2 T2 V W Z(d,l,o,p)
Ptr: Buckland, Ms Philippa J MSc . . . . . *§Apr 1993
Smale, Mr Clive E S TEP . . . . . *§Feb 1983
Ast: Brookes, Ms Suzanne J. . . . . . *Oct 1996
Mansell, Mrs Wendy LLB . . . . . *Nov 1987
Sims, Miss Zoe Claire LLB . . . . . *Jul 2007
Slade, Mrs Anne Rose LLB; TEP . . . . . *Jan 2006
Con: McNeill, Mr Allister Chairman of the Welfare Benefits Tribunal Notary Public . . . . . *§Aug 1971
Rowson, Mr Brian D MA(Cantab) . . . . . *§Apr 1970

DAVID ROWE & CO ‡
Bridge Chambers Lower Bridge Street Bideford Devon EX39 2BU
Tel: 01237 425525

SELDON WARD & NUTTALL ‡
18 The Quay Bideford Devon EX39 2HF
Tel: 01237 479121 *Fax:* 01237 471902 *Dx:* 53602 BIDEFORD
E-mail: solicitors@seldons.co.uk

SLEE BLACKWELL
12 Mill Street Bideford Devon EX39 2JT
Tel: 01237 425225 *Fax:* 01237 425985 *Dx:* 53614 BIDEFORD
Office: Barnstaple, Braunton, Exeter, South Molton
Work: C1 D1 E F1 G H J1 J2 K1 K2 L N O Q R1 S1 S2 V W X Z(p,q,r)
Emergency Action, Agency, Advocacy, Fixed Fee Interview, Legal Aid undertaken, Legal Aid Franchise and Member of Accident Line

BIDFORD-ON-AVON, Warwickshire

HALL REYNOLDS ‡
18 High Street Bidford-on-Avon Warwickshire B50 4BU
Tel: 01789 772955 *Fax:* 01789 490126
E-mail: email@hallreynolds.co.uk
List of partners: D C Hall, D F Ratcliffe
Languages: French
Work: B1 C1 C2 E F1 J1 K1 L N O Q S1 S2 W Z(b,c,l)
Agency, Advocacy, Legal Aid undertaken and Member of Accident Line
Ptr: Hall, Mr David C LLB(Lond) . . . . . Dec 1973
Ratcliffe, Mr David F BA(Cantab) . . . . . *Oct 1986

BIGGIN HILL, Kent

ROGER DEAN & CO ‡
134a Main Road Biggin Hill Kent TN16 3BA
Tel: 01959 542872 *Fax:* 01959 576065
E-mail: rogerdeanco@btconnect.com
List of partners: B N Sarney
Work: C1 E F1 J1 L P S1 S2 W
Ptr: Sarney, Mr Brian Nigel LLB(L'pool) . . . . . *Dec 1977

PETER ZELNIK & CO ‡
184 Main Road Biggin Hill Kent TN16 3BB
Tel: 01959 570730 *Fax:* 01959 570740
Emergency telephone 01892 523708
E-mail: admin@peterzelnikandco.co.uk
List of partners: P R Zelnik
Work: C1 D1 E F1 K1 K3 K4 L O Q S1 S2 W
Emergency Action, Agency, Advocacy and Fixed Fee Interview undertaken
Ptr: Zelnik, Dr Peter Robert BSc; MSc; PhD . . . . . *Oct 1984

BIGGLESWADE, Bedfordshire

BRIGNALLS BALDERSTON WARREN
2 London Road Biggleswade Bedfordshire SG18 8EP
Tel: 01767 313813 *Fax:* 01767 316978 *Dx:* 37153 BIGGLESWADE
E-mail: enquiries@bbwlaw.biz
Office: Baldock, Knebworth, Letchworth, Stevenage
Work: E J1 K1 L S1 S2 W
Fixed Fee Interview and Legal Aid undertaken
Ptr: Brain, Mr Terence P. . . . . . *Oct 1982
Whiddett, Mr Daniel S J LLB(Hons) Notary Public . . . Mar 2001
Ast: Willoughby, Mr Robert. . . . . . *Jan 2008

MOTLEY & HOPE ‡
The Manor House 11 Shortmead Street Biggleswade Bedfordshire SG18 0AT
Tel: 01767 600600 *Fax:* 01767 317939 *Dx:* 37151 BIGGLESWADE
E-mail: mail@motleyandhope.co.uk
List of partners: H C Hope, P J Motley
Work: D1 E J1 K1 K2 S1 W
Emergency Action, Agency, Advocacy, Fixed Fee Interview, Legal Aid undertaken and Legal Aid Franchise
Ptr: Hope, Mrs Helen C BSc. . . . . . *Nov 1986
Motley, Mr Paul J BA . . . . . *Aug 1977
Ast: Francis, Mr Robin LLB(Hons) . . . . . *Dec 1998
Frith, Mr Stephen LLB(Reading). . . . . . *Sep 1982

WOODWARDS ‡
3 High Street Biggleswade Bedfordshire SG18 0JE
Tel: 01767 601111 *Fax:* 01767 600010 *Dx:* 37161 BIGGLESWADE
Emergency telephone 01767 315611
E-mail: law@woodwards-solicitors.fsnet.co.uk
List of partners: N Woodward
Work: E S1 S2
SPr: Woodward, Mr Nigel BA(Law). . . . . . Sep 1985

BILLERICAY, Essex

ASPLEY LAW LIMITED ‡
203 Church Street Billericay Essex CM11 2TP
Tel: 07939 039850 *Fax:* 0844 357 2152
E-mail: omardin@aspleylaw.com

MICHAEL CULLEN & PARTNERS ‡ (incorporating Harvey Collins & Cullen)
102 High Street Billericay Essex CM12 9BY
Tel: 01277 623132 *Fax:* 01277 630098 *Dx:* 32200 BILLERICAY
E-mail: michaelcullen@michaelcullen.com
List of partners: A H Brown, S W Wallis
Work: A1 B1 C1 C2 D1 D2 E F1 F2 J1 J2 K1 K3 K4 L M1 N O P Q R1 R2 S1 S2 T1 V W Z(c,l)
Emergency Action, Agency, Advocacy, Fixed Fee Interview, Legal Aid undertaken, Legal Aid Franchise and Member of Accident Line
Ptr: Brown, Mr Andrew H MA(Cantab). . . . . . *Oct 1983
Wallis, Mr Stephen W. . . . . . *Dec 1979
Asoc: Booroff, Mr Kevin LLB. . . . . . *Apr 1994
Ast: Rudd, Mrs Diane E MA(Cantab). . . . . . *Oct 1985

E EDWARDS SON & NOICE ‡
Three Horseshoes House 139 High Street Billericay Essex CM12 9AF
Tel: 01277 658551 *Fax:* 01277 630024 *Dx:* 32206 BILLERICAY
E-mail: law@eesan.plus.com
List of partners: T Maylin, J D Orchard
Languages: Hindi, Punjabi
Work: C1 D1 E F1 J1 K1 K3 L N P Q R1 S1 S2 T2 V W Z(h,i,j,l,p,q,s)
Agency, Advocacy, Fixed Fee Interview, Legal Aid undertaken and Member of Accident Line
Ptr: Maylin, Mr Terry. . . . . . Oct 2000
Orchard, Miss Jane D LLB . . . . . *Jun 1980
Ast: Bhatta, Mr Balraj Singh BA(Hons). . . . . . *Jun 1993
Wells, Ms Kathleen Ellen LLB(Hons) . . . . . *Apr 2000
Con: Squire, Mr Aidan Ward LLB . . . . . *Oct 1974

DEBORAH GIBBINS & CO ‡
Suite 2c Union House 117 High Street Billericay Essex CM12 9AH
Tel: 01268 270866 *Fax:* 01268 271014
E-mail: sue@deborahgibbins.co.uk
List of partners: D K Gibbins
Work: D1 K1 K3
Emergency Action, Fixed Fee Interview and Legal Aid undertaken
SPr: Gibbins, Ms Deborah K BA . . . . . *May 1985

ROGER GREEN & CO ‡
100 High Street Billericay Essex CM12 9BY
Tel: 01277 659441 *Fax:* 01277 630596 *Dx:* 32203 BILLERICAY
E-mail: law@rogergreenco.co.uk

LIDDELL AND COMPANY
Church House 46 High Street Billericay Essex CM12 9BS
Tel: 01277 636426 *Fax:* 01277 659462
E-mail: mail@liddell-solicitors.co.uk
Office: Benfleet, Romford
Work: J1
Fixed Fee Interview undertaken
Ptr: Elgar, Dr Jane. . . . . . Mar 2005

MARKS MILLER & CO ‡
92b High Street Billericay Essex CM12 9BT
Tel: 01277 633991 *Fax:* 01277 657245 *Dx:* 32201 BILLERICAY
E-mail: kcmiller@marksmiller.co.uk
List of partners: L B Marks, K C Miller
Work: B1 C1 E K1 L N O Q S1 S2 W Z(c,d)
Ptr: Miller, Mr Keith C . . . . . *Nov 1978
Con: Rose, Mr Adrian M C . . . . . *Dec 1973

GEOFFREY SEARLE PLANNING SOLICITORS ‡
1 King George's Court High Street Billericay Essex CM12 9BY
Tel: 01277 633014 *Fax:* 01277 623585
Emergency telephone 01277 633014
E-mail: gjs@geoffreysearle.com
List of partners: D C H Evans, G J Searle
Work: R1 Z(u)
Ptr: Evans, Mr David Charles Heron MA(Hons)(Edin); DipLaw . . . . . Jun 2006
Searle, Mr Geoffrey John TD; FRSA . . . . . *§Dec 1968

BILLINGHAM, Stockton-on-Tees

COCHRANES LAW FIRM LIMITED ‡
67 Queensway Billingham Stockton-on-Tees TS23 2LU
Tel: 01642 366800 *Fax:* 01642 366809 *Dx:* 63160 BILLINGHAM
List of partners: J K Cochrane
Work: D1 K1 K3 S1 S2 W
Ptr: Cochrane, Mr James K . . . . . *Nov 1994

DAVIDSON LARGE LLP
Wellington House Wynyard Business Park Wynyard Billingham Stockton-on-Tees TS22 5TB
Tel: 01740 665050 *Fax:* 01740 665050
E-mail: info@davidsonlarge.com
Office: Harrogate

EASON LAW ‡
Haverton House Haverton Hill Industrial Estate Billingham Stockton-on-Tees TS23 1PZ
Tel: 01642 371371

TBI SOLICITORS
12 Evolution Wynyard Park Wynyard Billingham Stockton-on-Tees TS22 5TB
Tel: 01740 646000 *Fax:* 0845 302 2993 *Dx:* 742760 BILLINGHAM 3
E-mail: info@tbilaw.co.uk
Office: Barnard Castle, Hartlepool, Stockton-on-Tees

BILLINGSHURST, West Sussex

ANDERSON LONGMORE & HIGHAM
68 High Street Billingshurst West Sussex RH14 9QR
Tel: 01403 782710 *Fax:* 01403 784989
E-mail: billi@alhlaw.co.uk
Office: Chichester, Petworth, Storrington
Work: A1 B1 C1 C2 D1 D2 E F1 J1 K1 K2 K3 K4 L N O Q R1 R2 S1 S2 T2 V W Z(c,d,h,o,p)
Ast: Lee, Mr Julian Mark LLB . . . . . *Mar 2002

FRANCES J SILVERMAN ‡
PO Box 64 Billingshurst West Sussex RH14 9YD
Tel: 01403 783696 *Fax:* 01403 786669
E-mail: j3fjs@aol.com
List of partners: F J Silverman
Work: E J1 L S1 S2 Z(p,q)
SPr: Silverman, Mrs Frances J LLM Part time Employment Judge; Part time Chairman of Leasehold Valuation Tribunal . . . . . *Mar 1973

2

BILSTON, West Midlands

REES PAGE (incorporating Darbey Scott Rees; Pages & Skidmore Hares & Co)
17 Wellington Road Bilston West Midlands WV14 6AD
Tel: 01902 577776 *Fax:* 01902 577769 *Dx:* 23551 BILSTON
E-mail: info@reespage.co.uk
Office: Wolverhampton
Languages: French
Work: A1 B1 C1 C2 D1 D2 E F1 I J1 K1 K3 L N O Q R1 S1 S2 T1 T2 U2 W Z(c,d,h,j,l,q)
Emergency Action, Agency, Advocacy, Fixed Fee Interview, Legal Aid undertaken, Legal Aid Franchise and Member of Accident Line
Ptr: Dougall, Miss Perveen BA(Law). . . . . . *§Oct 1999
Horsley, Mr Peter C. . . . . . *§Apr 1975
Hughes, Mr Simon D LLB. . . . . . *§Apr 1991

RILEY HAYES & CO
36 Church Street Bilston West Midlands WV14 0AH
Tel: 01902 353300 *Fax:* 01902 353344
Office: Wolverhampton
Ptr: Misra, Mr Shiva Vinay LLB(Hons) . . . . . *Nov 1997
Ast: Mondair, Narjit . . . . . Oct 2003

ROSE LAW ‡
3 The Orchard Bilston West Midlands WV14 0EA
Tel: 01902 495049 *Fax:* 01902 491714
E-mail: rosy@rose-lawsolicitors.co.uk

SALHAN & COMPANY
Swank Bank House 27-29 Lichfield Street Bilston West Midlands WV10 0AQ
Tel: 01902 407207
Office: Birmingham

BINGHAM, Nottinghamshire

FRASER BROWN
19 Union Street Bingham Nottinghamshire NG13 8AD
Tel: 01949 830812 *Fax:* 01949 837631 *Dx:* 13879 BINGHAM
E-mail: bingham@fraserbrown.com
Office: Nottingham (2 offices)
Work: A1 E J1 K1 K3 S1 S2 W
Legal Aid undertaken
Ast: Buckley, Mrs Joanne Louise LLB(Hons) . . . . . Jan 2003
Fernandes, Socorina A LLB. . . . . . *Oct 1993
Small, Miss Emma Jane LLB(Hons). . . . . . *Jul 2007
Wollacott, Mr Richard Bernard LLB . . . . . *Apr 2001
Con: Suthers, Mr Martin William OBE; DL MA(Cantab) . . . *Jul 1965

HAWLEY & RODGERS
1 Fisher Lane Bingham Nottinghamshire NG13 8BQ
Tel: 01949 836879
E-mail: bingham@hawleyandrodgers.com
Office: Loughborough, Nottingham

LOVEJOY SOLICITORS LIMITED ‡
Suite 6 Church House East Street Bingham Nottinghamshire NG13 8DS
Tel: 01949 876105

HENRY THOMPSON & SONS
Old Court House Bingham Nottinghamshire NG13 8AL
Tel: 01949 836800
Office: Grantham

BINGLEY, West Yorkshire

CASEYS SOLICITORS ‡
2 Park Road Bingley West Yorkshire BD16 4JA
Tel: 01274 560105 *Fax:* 01274 568221 *Dx:* 21101 BINGLEY 2
E-mail: info@caseys.org.uk

CASEYS SOLICITORS ‡
8 Russell Court Wool Gate Cottingley Business Park Bingley West Yorkshire BD16 1PE
Tel: 01274 510656 *Fax:* 01274 560139 *Dx:* 21101 BINGLEY 2
E-mail: enquiries@caseys-solicitors.co.uk

CHIVERS SOLICITORS ‡
2 Wellington Street Bingley West Yorkshire BD16 2NB
Tel: 01274 561666 *Fax:* 01274 561555
E-mail: criminaldefence@chiverssolicitors.co.uk
Office: Durham

EMPLOYMENT LAW SOLICITORS DIRECT ‡
The Ramada Hotel Board Room Bradford Road Bingley West Yorkshire BD16 1TU
Tel: 01274 786056 *Fax:* 01274 786066
E-mail: info@elsdirect.org.uk

PACE LEGAL SERVICES LIMITED ‡
2 School Street Cottingley Bingley West Yorkshire BD16 1QB
Tel: 01274 566886
E-mail: legalpace@gmail.com

WEATHERHEAD & BUTCHER ‡
120 Main Street Bingley West Yorkshire BD16 2JJ
Tel: 01274 562322 *Fax:* 01274 551558 *Dx:* 21104 BINGLEY 2
E-mail: info@wandb.uk.com
List of partners: J Daykin
Work: E S1 W
SPr: Daykin, Mr John LLB(Hull) . . . . . *Sep 1975

WORGER HOWCROFT ‡
Skipton Chambers Chapel Lane Bingley West Yorkshire BD16 2NG
Tel: 01274 511246 *Fax:* 01274 511258 *Dx:* 21105 BINGLEY 2
E-mail: andrew@worgerhowcroft.co.uk
List of partners: A D Worger
Work: B1 C1 D1 F1 F2 J1 K1 K3 K4 L N O Q S1 S2 V W Z(i,q)

Emergency Action, Agency, Advocacy, Fixed Fee Interview, Legal Aid undertaken and Member of Accident Line
Ptr: Worger, Mr Andrew D . . . . *Nov 1993

BIRCHINGTON, Kent

BOYS & MAUGHAN
83 Station Road Birchington Kent CT7 9RB
Tel: 01843 842356 *Fax:* 01843 847811 *Dx:* 31101 BIRCHINGTON
E-mail: birchington@boysandmaughan.co.uk
Office: Broadstairs, Margate, Ramsgate
Work: K4 R2 S1 S2 T2 W
Ptr: Cox, Mr Allen G BA(Dunelm) . . . . *Jul 1975

MARSDEN DUNCAN
38 Station Road Birchington Kent CT7 9DQ
Tel: 01843 295743 / 841161 *Dx:* 31102 BIRCHINGTON
E-mail: duncanandco@kent-computers.com
Office: Cliftonville, Ramsgate
Work: E L S1 S2 W
Fixed Fee Interview undertaken
Ptr: Duncan, Mr Ian S . . . . *Jul 1980

BIRKENHEAD, Merseyside

174 LAW ‡
68 Whetstone Lane Birkenhead Merseyside CH41 2TF
Tel: 0151 647 7372 *Fax:* 0151 666 1399 *Dx:* 24254 BIRKENHEAD 2
E-mail: info@174law.co.uk
List of partners: K Bibby, M E Cottrill, D Hayhurst, R M Kendall, H L Pittard
Work: C1 D1 E K1 K2 K3 L N S1 S2 W Z(c,h)
Emergency Action, Agency, Advocacy, Fixed Fee Interview, Legal Aid undertaken, Legal Aid Franchise and Member of Accident Line
Ptr: Bibby, Mrs Kathryn BA(Law). . . . . *Oct 1985
Cottrill, Mr Mark E LLB . . . . *Sep 1989
Hayhurst, Mr David LLB. . . . . *Jun 1980
Kendall, Mr Robin M LLB . . . . *Apr 1981
Pittard, Ms Helen L LLB. . . . . *May 1995

A HALSALL & CO ‡
(incorporating Thompson Rigby & White)
(in association with J P Almond & Co)
17 Brandon Street Birkenhead Merseyside CH41 5BD
Tel: 0151 647 6323 *Fax:* 0151 647 9818 *Dx:* 17853 BIRKENHEAD 1
E-mail: info@halsalls.co.uk
List of partners: A J Almond, J D Conlon, R W Davies, A M Fountain
Office: Wirral (3 offices)
Work: C1 D1 E F1 J1 K1 K2 K3 L P Q R1 S1 S2 T1 V W Z(c,d,h,j,l,o)
Agency, Advocacy and Fixed Fee Interview undertaken
Ptr: Almond, Mr Andrew J LLB(L'pool). . . . . *§May 1967
Conlon, Mr John D LLB(B'ham) . . . . *Dec 1977
Fountain, Mr Alexander M LLB(Hons) . . . . *Oct 1995
Con: Johnson, Mr Christopher R . . . . *Jul 1971

Other offices in Greasby, Hoylake, Thingwall. We specialise in the following areas of work: Wills, Trusts and Probate, Housing Association Law, Liquor, Betting and Gaming Licensing. Agency Commissions gladly undertaken.

ANDERSON & CO SOLICITORS ‡
6 Mortimer Street Birkenhead Merseyside CH41 5EU
Tel: 0151 647 1500 *Fax:* 0151 647 1900

BDH SOLICITORS ‡
26 Hamilton Square Birkenhead Merseyside CH41 6AY
Tel: 0151 666 0300 *Fax:* 0151 647 8911 *Dx:* 17890 BIRKENHEAD

BALLAM ‡
58 Hamilton Square Birkenhead Merseyside CH41 5AT
Tel: 0151 647 8977 *Fax:* 0151 666 2161 *Dx:* 17885 BIRKENHEAD
Emergency telephone 07714 203130
List of partners: J A Ballam
Work: G H J1 Z(m)
Emergency Action, Agency, Advocacy and Legal Aid undertaken
Ptr: Ballam, Mr John A ★ . . . . *Jul 1978

BRUNSWICKS LLP ‡
Suite 3 56 Hamilton Square Birkenhead Merseyside CH41 5AS
Tel: 0870 766 8400 *Fax:* 0871 288 4089
Emergency telephone 07855 855588
E-mail: info@brunswick.com
List of partners: A W Dawson, K M Lewin
Languages: French, German, Russian
Work: A3 E J1 J2 O R1 S2 Z(a,c,e,g,m,p,q,u,y,za)
Agency undertaken
Ptr: Lewin, Mr Keith Malcolm LLB; FILEx . . . . *Oct 1986
Mem: Dawson, Mr Andrew William LLB . . . . Nov 1988
Con: Smith, Mr Leonard Christopher LLB Deputy District Judge . . . . Oct 1978

CAMPS SOLICITORS ‡
1 Europa House Conway Street Birkenhead Merseyside CH41 4FT
Tel: 0151 201 8080 *Fax:* 0151 201 8090
Dx: 714295 BIRKENHEAD 8
Emergency telephone 0800 092 9200
E-mail: frontoffice@camplaw.co.uk
List of partners: C D Billing, J Humphreys, S A Saul, L Southern
Languages: French, Polish, Welsh
Work: C3 E N
Agency, Advocacy and Fixed Fee Interview undertaken
Ptr: Billing, Mr Colin David BA. . . . . *Nov 1986
Humphreys, Miss Johanne LLB(Hons). . . . . *Sep 1996
Saul, Miss Stephanie Alison LLB(Hons) . . . . Sep 2000
Southern, Mrs Lynne LLB(Hons) . . . . *Jul 1998

CARPENTERS ‡
Leonard House Scotts Quays Birkenhead Merseyside CH41 1FB
Tel: 0870 780 1870 *Fax:* 0870 780 2820 *Dx:* 17879 BIRKENHEAD 1
E-mail: info@carpenters-law.co.uk
List of partners: J D Carpenter, J H Mead, D Scully, I Smith
Work: C1 C2 E J1 N O Q R2 S1 S2 W Z(c,d,e,k,l,p,w)
Fixed Fee Interview undertaken
Ptr: Carpenter, Mr John D. . . . . *§May 1975
Mead, Mr John H . . . . Jul 2000
Scully, Ms Donna . . . . Nov 1995
Smith, Mr Ian BA . . . . *May 1998

CARPENTERS ‡
Priory House Monks Ferry Birkenhead Merseyside CH41 5LH
Tel: 0844 249 0844 *Fax:* 0844 249 3939 *Dx:* 17879 BIRKENHEAD 1
E-mail: enquiries@carpenters-law.co.uk

DAVIDSON FLYNN DUKE SOLICITORS ‡
The Antiques Triangle 128 Chester Street Birkenhead Merseyside CH41 5DL
Tel: 0151 513 3333 *Fax:* 0151 513 3334
E-mail: paul.davison@dfd-solicitors.co.uk

FANSHAW PORTER & HAZLEHURST ‡
11-12 Hamilton Square Birkenhead Merseyside CH41 6AX
Tel: 0151 647 4051 *Fax:* 0151 666 1632 *Dx:* 17869 BIRKENHEAD
List of partners: D Garrett, K Harley, C Murphy
Ptr: Garrett, Mr David . . . . Jul 1978
Harley, Mrs Kate LLB . . . . Oct 1982
Murphy, Mr Christopher . . . . Sep 1980
Asoc: Bellringer, Sara . . . . Nov 2001
Ast: Evans, Rachel . . . . Feb 2006
Slight, Mr Andrew. . . . . Apr 2009
Williams, Mr Christopher . . . . May 2005

FORSTER DEAN LTD
27 Milton Pavement Grange Precinct Birkenhead Merseyside CH41 2YA
Tel: 0151 203 1281 *Fax:* 0151 203 1282
E-mail: enquiries@forsterdean.co.uk
Office: Bootle, Chorley, Crewe, Eccles, Ellesmere Port, Huyton, Leigh, Liverpool (5 offices), Oldham, Preston, Rochdale, Runcorn, St Helens, Stockport, Warrington, Widnes (2 offices), Wigan

H J WALKER SIBIA ‡
59 Hamilton Square Birkenhead Merseyside CH41 5AT
Tel: 0151 649 0950 *Fax:* 0151 649 0950
E-mail: law@hjws.com

HAWORTH & GALLAGHER ‡
(incorporating Swancott Morgan Hannaford & Taggart)
39 Hamilton Square Birkenhead Merseyside CH41 5BP
Tel: 0151 647 8624 *Fax:* 0151 647 3722 *Dx:* 17859 BIRKENHEAD
List of partners: J J Gallagher, C M Kehoe, A J Nelson
Office: Wallasey
Work: B1 C1 D1 E F1 G H J1 K1 L M1 N P R1 S1 T1 V W Z(b,f,i,k,l,p)
Emergency Action, Agency, Advocacy, Fixed Fee Interview and Legal Aid undertaken
Ptr: Nelson, Mr Anthony J. . . . . Jun 1984
Ast: Neal, Mr Quentin Mark BA(Wales). . . . . *Nov 1990

HIGGINS & CO ‡
10-12 Whetstone Lane Charing Cross Birkenhead Merseyside CH41 2QR
Tel: 0151 653 5222 *Fax:* 0151 653 8711 *Dx:* 24256 BIRKENHEAD 2
E-mail: jackey@injurysolicitor.com
List of partners: P J Higgins
Work: L N W
Agency and Legal Aid undertaken
SPr: Higgins, Mr Paul J BA(Law) . . . . *May 1981
Ast: Crowder, Ms Jane A LLB(Hons). . . . . Oct 1991
Fear, Mrs Joanna M LLB . . . . Jul 1985
Wareing, Mr Ian David LLB . . . . *Jul 1994

BARRY K HOLLAND ‡
47 Hamilton Square Birkenhead Merseyside CH41 5BD
Tel: 0151 666 2181 *Fax:* 0151 647 1025
E-mail: barry@barryholland.com
Work: F2 Z(l)
Advocacy undertaken

INTEGRUM LAW ‡
72 Argyle Street Birkenhead Merseyside CH41 6AF
Tel: 0151 649 1626 *Fax:* 0151 649 1620
E-mail: mail@integrulamlaw.co.uk

MARK JONES & PARTNERS
28 Hamilton Square Birkenhead Merseyside CH41 6AZ
Tel: 0151 647 9594 *Fax:* 0151 647 1661 *Dx:* 17889 BIRKENHEAD
E-mail: justice@mjpsolicitors.co.uk
Office: Liverpool
Ptr: Freckleton, Mr Philip John ● . . . . *Feb 1996
Gunn, Mr Neil Fraser LLB(Hons) . . . . *Dec 1998

NORMAN JONES - PERSONAL INJURY SPECIALISTS ‡
27 Hamilton Square Birkenhead Merseyside CH41 6AZ
Tel: 0151 647 7001 *Fax:* 0151 647 7004 *Dx:* 17874 BIRKENHEAD 1
E-mail: accounts@normanjones.co.uk

THE KEITH JONES PARTNERSHIP ‡
First Floor 17-21 Price Street Birkenhead Merseyside CH41 6JN
Tel: 0151 650 6830 *Fax:* 0151 666 2276 *Dx:* 17861 BIRKENHEAD 1
E-mail: info@kjplaw.co.uk

KIRWANS ‡
363 Woodchurch Road Prenton Birkenhead Merseyside CH42 8PE
Tel: 0151 608 9078 *Fax:* 0151 609 0030 *Dx:* 15505 PRENTON
Emergency telephone 07770 864037
E-mail: info@kirwanssolicitors.co.uk
List of partners: R J Dawson, P J Ford, S K Gibson, P F Hunt, D S Kirwan, S J Murray, M Sandys, J J F Tuson
Office: Liverpool, Moreton
Work: A1 B1 B2 C1 D1 E F1 F2 G H I J1 K1 K3 K4 L N O Q R1 R2 S1 S2 V W Z(e,k,l,p,q)
Emergency Action, Agency, Advocacy, Fixed Fee Interview, Legal Aid undertaken, Legal Aid Franchise and Member of Accident Line
Ptr: Dawson, Mr Richard Jasper. . . . . *Jan 1975
Ford, Mr Paul Josiah FILEx ★. . . . . *Oct 1996
Hunt, Mr Paul Forrester MA(Oxon) . . . . *Oct 1981
Asoc: Simmons, Mr Simon Andrew LLB(Hons). . . . . *Mar 2004
Stear, Mr Daniel Edward BA(Hons) . . . . *Sep 2004
Wood, Mr Paul J LLB(Hons) ★ . . . . *Oct 2000
Ast: Colvin, Mrs Victoria Sarah. . . . . *Aug 2007
Currie, Mrs Claire. . . . . *Aug 2008
Ellis, Miss Anna Louise . . . . *Sep 2006
Howard, Mr Neil Gareth BA(Hons). . . . . *Jul 2009
Reynolds, Mr Matthew John BA(Hons) ★ . . . . . . *Feb 2005
Sedgwick, Mr Nigel P LLB. . . . . *Jul 1979

LEES SOLICITORS LLP ‡
44-45 Hamilton Square Birkenhead Merseyside CH41 5AR
Tel: 0151 647 9381 *Fax:* 0151 649 0100 *Dx:* 17856 BIRKENHEAD 1
E-mail: info@lees.co.uk
List of partners: M W Broughton, M J Duckworth, T B Fisher, L S Flor, V Howley, J R Hurlbut, F Kemp, E Kinch, J Kingston-Davies, I F MacGregor, J A MacGregor, J P Morshead, M J Read, E W Roberts, D T Tweedie
Office: Heswall, West Kirby
Languages: French, Welsh
Work: B1 C1 C2 D1 E F1 J1 K1 K2 K3 K4 L N O Q R1 R2 S1 S2 T1 T2 U2 W Z(c,d,l,m,q,r)
Agency, Fixed Fee Interview, Legal Aid undertaken, Legal Aid Franchise and Member of Accident Line
Ptr: Duckworth, Mr Mark J BA(Hons) . . . . *Nov 1982
Flor, Mr Lancelyn S LLB(Hons) Muir Matthews Prize Awarded by Liverpool Law Society. . . . . *Sep 1999
Howley, Ms Veronica LLB . . . . *Apr 2001
Hurlbut, Julia R . . . . Nov 2008
Kemp, Miss Fiona MA(Cantab) Rebecca Flowers Scholarship 1996 . . . . Sep 2001
Kinch, Eleni. Sep 2001
MacGregor, Mr Ian F . . . . *Nov 1984
MacGregor, Ms Jane Alison. . . . . *Nov 1991
Morshead, Mr John P. . . . . Aug 1996
Roberts, Elen W LLB(Hons). . . . . *Nov 1998
Tweedie, Mr David T LLB . . . . *Dec 1975
Kingston-Davies, Ms Joanna . . . . NSP
Ast: Bloor, Mr Jon . . . . Sep 2001
Coventry, Ms Tania Victoria BSc. . . . . Sep 2006
Fisher, Mr Craig Alan . . . . Mar 2006
Hood, Mr Martin. . . . . Sep 2008
Lee, Mrs Joanne . . . . Aug 2009
Lewis, Mr Stephen John. . . . . Mar 2008
Lodh, Miss Roneeta. . . . . Dec 2009
McNally, Miss Joanne LLB . . . . Mar 2005
Oakes, Ms Catherine Anne LLB(Law & American Studies) . . . . Sep 2006
Passley, Mrs Katherine . . . . Feb 2009

CHERYL LEWIS & CO ‡
Chancery House 1-3 Westbourne Road Birkenhead Merseyside CH41 4FN
Tel: 0151 652 1451 *Fax:* 0151 653 9766 *Dx:* 24252 BIRKENHEAD 1
E-mail: mkg@cheryllewis.co.uk
List of partners: H A Davies, M K Green
Languages: French
Work: B1 C1 D1 E F1 G H J1 K1 L M1 N P R1 S1 T1 V W Z(c,d,e,h,i,j,k,l,m,o,p,s)
Emergency Action, Agency, Advocacy, Fixed Fee Interview, Legal Aid undertaken and Legal Aid Franchise
Ptr: Davies, Mrs Heather A LLB . . . . *Nov 1990
Green, Mr Martyn K BA . . . . *Nov 1986

MCDONAGH SOLICITORS ‡
The Old Post Office 30 Hamilton Street Birkenhead Merseyside CH41 5AD
Tel: 0151 650 2150 *Fax:* 0151 647 9205 *Dx:* 17855 BIRKENHEAD
E-mail: info@mcdonaghsolicitors.co.uk
List of partners: B McDonagh
Dir: McDonagh, Barbara. . . . . Mar 2000

MORECROFTS SOLICITORS LLP
30 Hamilton Square Birkenhead Merseyside CH41 6AZ
Tel: 0151 666 2210 *Fax:* 0151 666 2537 *Dx:* 17868 BIRKENHEAD
E-mail: mail@morecroft.co.uk
Office: Crosby, Liverpool (2 offices)
Work: C1 D1 E G H K1 L N Q S1 S2 Z(h,t)
Agency, Fixed Fee Interview and Legal Aid undertaken
Ptr: Davidson, Ms Stephanie Phyllis LLB . . . . *Nov 1995
Asoc: Perrigo, Mr Andrew James Francis LLB . . . . *Oct 1993
Ast: Lally, Ms Heather . . . . Dec 2005
White, Mr Darren LLB. . . . . *Feb 2009

NADIM ASSOCIATES SOLICITORS LIMITED ‡
4 Park Road North Birkenhead Merseyside CH41 4EZ
Tel: 0151 651 2040 *Fax:* 0151 652 3988
E-mail: info@solicitorslaw.com
Office: Liverpool

PERCY HUGHES & ROBERTS ‡
19 Hamilton Square Birkenhead Merseyside CH41 6AY
Est: 1919
Tel: 0151 666 9090 *Fax:* 0151 666 1080 *Dx:* 17862 BIRKENHEAD 1
E-mail: law@phrsols.co.uk
List of partners: A J Beech, M H Bland, G Edwards, J A Smith
Languages: Danish, French
Work: B2 D1 D2 E F1 J1 K1 K3 L N O Q S1 S2 W Z(j,p,q)
Agency, Advocacy, Fixed Fee Interview, Legal Aid undertaken and Legal Aid Franchise
Ptr: Beech, Mrs Alison J LLB . . . . *Oct 1989
Bland, Mr Mark H LLB. . . . . *May 1977
Edwards, Mr Gareth LLB(Hons). . . . . *Oct 1998
Smith, Miss Jacqueline A LLB. . . . . *§Oct 1981
Ast: Dejon-Stewart, Miss Emily. . . . . *Feb 2010
Evans, Miss Victoria LLB . . . . *Dec 2005
Hassall, Mr John Arthur LLB(Hons). . . . . Oct 1982
Knowles, Mrs Lindsey Margaret PGDipLaw; BSc . . *Dec 2007
Parkins, Mr Antony Simon LLB . . . . Dec 2009
Randall, Ms Wendy BA(Hons)(Law). . . . . *Sep 1988
Tibbett, Mrs Ruth Helen LLB(Hons) . . . . *Oct 1989
Townley, Miss Helen LLB(Hons). . . . . *Sep 2002

D P ROBERTS HUGHES & DENYE ‡
1 Hamilton Square Birkenhead Merseyside CH41 6AU
Tel: 0151 647 6000 *Fax:* 0151 647 9000 *Dx:* 17858 BIRKENHEAD
E-mail: info@dprobertshd.co.uk
List of partners: J A Ballam, M F H Brown, S M Delaney, A J Denye, F Moan
Office: Ellesmere Port
Work: A1 B1 C1 D1 E F1 G H J1 K1 K2 L M1 N O Q R1 S1 S2 V W Z(d,g,h,l,m,o,r)
Emergency Action, Agency, Advocacy, Legal Aid undertaken, Legal Aid Franchise and Member of Accident Line
Ptr: Ballam, Mr John A ★ . . . . *Jul 1978
Delaney, Miss Susan Mary LLB(Hons). . . . . *Dec 1990
Denye, Mr Anthony J LLB. . . . . *May 1967
Ast: Millington, Mr Ian David LLB. . . . . *Oct 1997
Wynne, Ms Vicki Lorraine . . . . *Nov 1997

ROBERTS MOORE NICHOLAS JONES ‡
63 Hamilton Square Birkenhead Merseyside CH41 5JF
Tel: 0151 647 0000 *Fax:* 0151 647 0002
Dx: 730420 BIRKENHEAD 14
Emergency telephone 0845 606 6800
E-mail: partners@rmnj.co.uk

 See p112 for the Key to Work Categories & other symbols

List of partners: G Brooks, J Creswick, H Gordon, R A London-Smith, L Millen, R W Nicholas, G F Pachter, D W Pontin, J D Robinson, J A Weate
Work: D1 G H K1 K2 K3 N S1 S2 W Z(m)
Emergency Action, Agency, Advocacy, Fixed Fee Interview, Legal Aid undertaken, Legal Aid Franchise and Member of Accident Line
Ptr: Brooks, Mr Gareth LLB . . . *Mar 2004
Creswick, Mrs Jacqueline MA . . . *Nov 1982
Gordon, Miss Helen LLB . . . *Aug 1998
London-Smith, Mr Raymond A LLB . . . *Mar 1984
Millen, Mrs Lianne BA(Hons) . . . *Aug 1999
Nicholas, Mr Richard W LLB(Lond) . . . *Dec 1979
Pachter, Mr Gerald Frederick BA . . . *Feb 1986
Pontin, Mr David W LLB. . . . *Jul 1979
Robinson, Mr John David LLB(Hons) . . . *Aug 1997
Weate, Mr John A DML(Hons) . . . *Mar 1985
Asoc: Fearon, Ms Sinead Elizabeth . . . *Nov 2003
Ast: Gallagher, Mr Thomas . . . *Dec 2008
Hinder, Ms Teresa Louise . . . *Sep 2000
Ormond, Ms Emma . . . *Jul 2008
Rogan, Mrs Moya LLB . . . *Oct 2006
Con: Hazlehurst, Mr Alan D LLB(L'pool). . . . *Dec 1977

J M SKINNER & CO ‡
2 Mortimer Street Birkenhead Merseyside CH41 5EU
Tel: 0151 666 1122 *Fax:* 0151 666 1134 *Dx:* 17854 BIRKENHEAD
E-mail: law@jmskinner.co.uk
List of partners: K Anderson
Languages: French
Work: E F1 J1 K1 L N O Q S1 S2 W Z(c)
Emergency Action, Agency, Fixed Fee Interview undertaken and Member of Accident Line
Ptr: Anderson, Miss Kirsty LLB(Hons) . . . Oct 1999

THE SPECTER PARTNERSHIP ‡
Ground Floor Rosebrae Court Woodside Ferry Approach Birkenhead Merseyside CH41 6DU
Tel: 0151 647 3000 *Fax:* 0151 647 7913 *Dx:* 24273 BIRKENHEAD 4
List of partners: J M Canter, K L Specter, G W Williams
Office: London EC1, Warrington
Work: C1 D1 E G H J1 K1 N O Q S1
Agency, Fixed Fee Interview, Legal Aid undertaken and Member of Accident Line
Ptr: Canter, Mr Jan Michael BA(Hons). . . . *Oct 1992
Specter, Mr Kenneth L BA(Hons) . . . *May 1981
Williams, Mr Gareth W . . . Jan 1981
Ast: Carter, Mr Robert J BA(Hons). . . . *Jan 1997
O'Neill, Mr Nicholas Jon LLB(Hons) . . . *Jul 1999
Sant, Miss Emma Victoria LLB . . . *Aug 1997

R A WILKINSON & CO ‡
5 Mortimer Street Hamilton Square Birkenhead Merseyside CH41 5EU
Tel: 0151 647 6259 *Fax:* 0151 647 2190 *Dx:* 17875 BIRKENHEAD
List of partners: R A Wilkinson
Work: B1 C1 C2 C3 E F1 G J1 K1 L N O Q S1 W
Emergency Action, Agency, Advocacy and Fixed Fee Interview undertaken
Ptr: Wilkinson, Mr Richard Andrew BA. . . . *Nov 1974

GARETH WILLIAMS SOLICITORS ‡
238-240 Conway Street Birkenhead Merseyside CH41 4AQ
Tel: 0845 490 0700

BIRMINGHAM, West Midlands

3 SPIRES SOLICITORS LIMITED ‡
Aston House 3 Aston Road North Aston Birmingham West Midlands B6 4DS
Tel: 0121 333 1296 *Fax:* 0121 333 5006
E-mail: richard.carroll@3spiressolicitors.co.uk

AKZ SOLICITORS ‡
712 Alum Rock Road Saltley Birmingham West Midlands B8 3PP
Tel: 0121 326 0500 *Fax:* 0121 326 9944

APC SOLICITORS ‡
30 Elmfield Crescent Birmingham West Midlands B13 9TN
Tel: 0121 242 3000

ARC SOLICITORS ‡
274a Ladypool Road Sparkbrook Birmingham West Midlands B12 8JU
Tel: 0121 449 1188 *Fax:* 0121 449 7289 *Dx:* 13031 BIRMINGHAM
E-mail: enquiries@arc-solicitors.co.uk

ADAMS & CO ‡
170a Soho Road Handsworth Birmingham West Midlands B21 9LP
Tel: 0121 523 3491 *Fax:* 0121 554 9917
E-mail: adams_co@btconnect.com
List of partners: W W Adams
Work: B1 C1 D1 E F1 G H J1 K1 L M1 N P R1 S1 T1 V W Z(a,b,c,d,e,f,g,h,i,j,k,l,m,n,o,p,s,t)
Agency, Advocacy, Fixed Fee Interview and Legal Aid undertaken
Ptr: Adams, Mr William W BA . . . *Jan 1976

ADDISON AARON (BIRMINGHAM) LIMITED ‡
65 Church Street Birmingham West Midlands B3 2DP
Tel: 0121 262 3773 *Fax:* 0121 262 3701
E-mail: info@addisonaaron.com

AHMAD & WILLIAMS SOLICITORS ‡
The Rock 201-203 Alum Rock Road Birmingham West Midlands B8 1EU
Tel: 0121 328 4282 *Fax:* 0121 328 4441
E-mail: info@ahmandwilliams.co.uk
Office: Birmingham

AHMAD & WILLIAMS SOLICITORS
69 Cape Hill Birmingham West Midlands B66 4SG
Tel: 0121 558 6881 *Fax:* 0121 558 6882
E-mail: info@ahmadwillams.co.uk
Office: Birmingham

AHMED SOLICITORS ‡
111 Villa Road Handsworth Birmingham West Midlands B19 1NH
Tel: 0121 507 1030 *Fax:* 0121 507 0200
Emergency telephone 07977 532536
List of partners: A Ahmed
Languages: Bengali, Hindi, Mirpuri, Pahari, Punjabi, Urdu
Work: G H
Agency and Advocacy undertaken
SPr: Ahmed, Astakhar LLB(Hons) . . . Dec 1996

ALEXANDRIAN SOLUTIONS LLP ‡
Unit 4200 Waterside Centre Solihull Parkway Birmingham West Midlands B37 7YN
Tel: 0121 663 0024

AMAN SOLICITORS ADVOCATES LTD
37 Alum Rock Road Saltley Birmingham West Midlands B8 1LR
Tel: 0121 328 4455 *Fax:* 0121 328 5544
E-mail: info@amansolicitors.co.uk
Office: Wembley

ANDERSON REEVES SOLICITORS ‡
5a New Street Erdington Birmingham West Midlands B23 6SD
Tel: 0800 014 1529 *Fax:* 0121 382 7548
E-mail: info@andersonreeves.com

MAURICE ANDREWS ‡
Alfred Andrews House 180/182 Soho Hill Hakley Birmingham West Midlands B19 1AG
Tel: 0121 554 4900 *Fax:* 0121 554 7282 *Dx:* 24961 HANDSWORTH
E-mail: maurice.andrews@btconnect.com
Work: D1 D2 G H K1 N Q S1 S2 V W Z(i)
Agency, Fixed Fee Interview and Legal Aid undertaken

ARK SOLICITORS ‡
411 Stratford Road Spark Hill Birmingham West Midlands B11 4JZ
Tel: 0121 753 7130

ASPEN COURT SOLICITORS LIMITED ‡
48 The Qube 12 Scotland Street Birmingham West Midlands B1 2EJ
Tel: 0845 094 4912 *Fax:* 0845 094 4913
E-mail: info@aspencourtsolicitors.com
Languages: Urdu
Work: J1 S1 Z(i)

ASTON CARTER SOLICITORS ‡
1464 Pershore Road 50 Salisbury Road Stirchley Birmingham West Midlands B30 2NT
Tel: 0121 684 3009 *Fax:* 0121 684 3004
Emergency telephone 07957 166410
E-mail: info@astoncartersolicitors.com
Office: Hounslow

ATKINSON SPENCE ‡
107 Soho Hill Birmingham West Midlands B19 1AY
Tel: 0121 507 9930

AVERTA EMPLOYMENT LAWYERS ‡
Vienna House Starley Way Birmingham International Park Birmingham West Midlands B37 7GN
Tel: 0870 421 1952 *Fax:* 0121 782 8159
E-mail: enquiries@averta.com

AVERY KNIGHTS SOLICITORS LTD ‡
130 Bradford Street Bradford Court Business Centre Birmingham West Midlands B12 0NS
Tel: 0845 458 6291 *Fax:* 0845 458 6292
Dx: 711804 BIRMINGHAM 28

AZIZ SOLICITORS LIMITED ‡
KMS House Kings Chambers 201 Streetly Road Birmingham West Midlands B23 7AJ
Tel: 0121 683 6938 *Fax:* 0121 661 6116
E-mail: ar@azizsolicitors.com

BA SOLICITORS ‡
436 Stratford Road Sparkhill Birmingham West Midlands B11 4AD
Tel: 0121 773 4200 *Fax:* 0121 777 7744
Languages: Hindi, Punjabi, Urdu
Work: B1 C1 E K1 O Q S1 S2 W Z(b,i)

BK SOLICITORS ‡
Crown House 28 George Street Birmingham West Midlands B12 9RG
Tel: 0121 440 1881 *Fax:* 0121 440 1991 *Dx:* 10790 MOSELEY
E-mail: info@bksolicitors.com
List of partners: S Khalil
Languages: Bengali, Mirpuri, Punjabi, Urdu
Work: E N O Q S1 S2 W Z(q)
Agency, Advocacy, Fixed Fee Interview undertaken and Member of Accident Line
Ptr: Khalil, Mr Siraj LLB . . . Nov 1999

BMG SOLICITORS ‡
3 Birmingham Road Birmingham West Midlands B43 6NW
Tel: 0121 358 8855 *Fax:* 0121 358 8866

BMV SOLICITORS ‡
3rd Floor Ruskin Chambers 191 Corporation Street Birmingham West Midlands B4 6RP
Tel: 0121 248 1980

BAILEY WRIGHT & CO ‡
Branston Court Branston Street Birmingham West Midlands B18 6BA
Tel: 0845 475 1996 *Fax:* 0121 523 5295
E-mail: solicitors@baileywright.com
List of partners: K A Bailey
Work: D1 J1 N X Z(p)
Emergency Action, Agency, Advocacy, Fixed Fee Interview, Legal Aid undertaken and Legal Aid Franchise
SPr: Bailey, Miss Karen Andrady LLB(Hons) Birmingham Law Society Sole Practitioner of the Year 2002. . . . *Feb 1988

BAKE & CO SOLICITORS ‡
52 Blucher Street Birmingham West Midlands B1 1QU
Tel: 0121 616 5025 *Fax:* 0121 616 5026
E-mail: info@bakesolicitors.co.uk

BASSI SOLICITORS ‡
220 Soho Road Handsworth Birmingham West Midlands B21 9LR
Tel: 0121 554 0868

DOREEN NEALE BASTABLE SOLICITOR ‡
2 Swanshurst Lane Moseley Birmingham West Midlands B13 0AJ
Tel: 0121 744 3611 *Fax:* 0121 744 3611
List of partners: D N Bastable
Work: E S1 S2 W
SPr: Bastable, Miss Doreen Neale . . . *Jul 1970

BENUSSI & CO ‡
7th Floor Newater House 11 Newhall Street Birmingham West Midlands B3 3NY
Tel: 0121 248 4001 *Fax:* 0121 248 3990 *Dx:* 13042 BIRMINGHAM 1
E-mail: birmingham@benussilaw.co.uk
List of partners: H J Arnold, D P Benussi, N Hobden
Work: K1 K2 K3 M2
Agency undertaken
Ptr: Arnold, Mrs Helen Jane BSc . . . *Oct 1984
Benussi, Mrs Diane P LLB(Hons) Former President of the Law Society Birmingham. . . . *Jul 1982
Hobden, Mr Neil BA(Hons)(Law) . . . *Nov 1984
Asoc: Sarabia, Mrs Mary S LLB . . . *Dec 1997
Ast: Burrows, Ms Georgina Jane BA(Hons) . . . *Feb 1991
Leach, Miss Susanne Janice BA(Hons) Law Society Best Student 2002/03; FBC Business Law & Practice 2002/03; Birmingham Law Society Criminal Law Prize 2001/02 . . . *Nov 2005
McKenna, Miss Denisa MA(Oxon). . . . *Sep 1998

BERRYMANS LACE MAWER
63 Temple Row Birmingham West Midlands B2 5LS
Tel: 0121 643 8777 *Fax:* 0121 643 4909 *Dx:* 13077 BIRMINGHAM 1
E-mail: info@blm-law.com
Office: Bristol, Cardiff, Leeds, Liverpool, London EC2, Manchester, Southampton, Stockton-on-Tees
Work: A3 G J2 N O Q Z(h,j,q,r)

BEVAN BRITTAN LLP
Interchange Place Edmund Street Birmingham West Midlands B3 2TA
Tel: 0870 194 1000 *Fax:* 0870 194 7800
Dx: 707927 BIRMINGHAM 65
E-mail: info@bevanbrittan.com
Office: Bristol, London EC4
Work: A3 C1 E J1 N Z(m,r)
Ptr: Cartwright, Ms Sarah L . . . Sep 1998
Dagnell, Mr Adrian . . . Oct 1991
Hodgetts, Mr Tim M. . . . Sep 1999
Hughes, Mr Stephen D BA . . . *§Jun 1987
Kendall, Mr Adam J. . . . Mar 1998
McCormack, Ms Colette. . . . *Sep 1998
Print, Ms Melanie . . . Mar 1987
Rinta-Suksi, Ms Penny . . . Oct 1995
Woffenden, Ms Sara Jane LLB(Hons) Part time Chairman Employment Tribunal (England & Wales) . . . Oct 1985

BEYNON & CO ‡
259 Alcester Road South Birmingham West Midlands B14 6DT
Tel: 0121 444 0099 *Fax:* 0121 444 3001
Emergency telephone 07976 258205
E-mail: gbeynonsolicitors@hotmail.com
Work: B2 G H

BICKLEY WHEATLEY & CO ‡
50 High Street Erdington Birmingham West Midlands B23 6RH
Tel: 0121 377 6266 *Fax:* 0121 377 7324 *Dx:* 21213 ERDINGTON
E-mail: bickwheatley@btconnect.com
List of partners: M L Darby, K Jarvis
Work: E K1 K3 N Q S1 W
Fixed Fee Interview, Legal Aid undertaken and Legal Aid Franchise
Ptr: Darby, Mrs Maisie L LLB Birmingham Law Society Bronze Medal . . . *Apr 1977
Jarvis, Ms Katherine BA. . . . Apr 2005

BLACKHAMS SOLICITORS ‡
Lancaster House 67 Newhall Street Birmingham West Midlands B3 1NR
Tel: 0121 233 6900 *Fax:* 0121 233 9880 *Dx:* 13072 BIRMINGHAM 1
E-mail: mpriestley@blackhams.com
List of partners: T P Cuthbertson, M G M Stocks
Work: C1 C2 E L S1 S2 T2 W Z(d,m)
Ptr: Cuthbertson, Mr Timothy P LLB. . . . *§Apr 1977
Stocks, Mr Michael Geoffrey Marland LLB Notary Public . . . *Apr 1977
Asoc: Smart, Mr Peter J LLB . . . *Dec 1987
Woodward, Mr Martin Paul LLB . . . *Jun 1970

BLAIR ALLISON & CO ‡
Fountain Court Steelhouse Lane Birmingham West Midlands B4 6DR
Tel: 0121 233 2904 *Fax:* 0121 236 8913 *Dx:* 23534 BIRMINGHAM 3
E-mail: marimeisel@blairallison.co.uk
List of partners: G Bird, J A Green, S M Meisel
Work: D1 K1 K2 L S1 W
Agency, Advocacy and Legal Aid undertaken
Ptr: Bird, Mr Grant LLB . . . *Oct 1993
Green, Mrs Judith A BA. . . . *Nov 1987
Meisel, Mrs Sian M LLB. . . . *Oct 1976
Ast: Hall, Mr Andrew LLB . . . *Sep 1994
Moat, Ms Harriet BA . . . *Oct 1992
Price, Ms Catherine BA . . . *Oct 1993

BLAKEMORES ‡
40 Great Charles Street Birmingham West Midlands B3 2AT
Tel: 0121 234 7200 *Fax:* 0121 234 7299 *Dx:* 13038 BIRMINGHAM
E-mail: birmingham@blakemores.co.uk
Office: Leamington Spa
Languages: French, German, Russian, Spanish
Work: K1 K3 S1

BOLLIN LEGAL ASSOCIATES LTD ‡
St Georges Court 1 Albion Street Birmingham West Midlands B1 3AH
Tel: 0121 200 8400 *Fax:* 0121 212 2759 *Dx:* 14039 BIRMINGHAM
E-mail: info@bollinlegal.com

BOURNE JAFFA ‡
5 Heathfield Road Kings Heath Birmingham West Midlands B14 7BT
Tel: 0121 443 3486 / 444 8440 *Fax:* 0121 693 3486
E-mail: kingsheath@bournejaffer.co.uk
List of partners: D M Morgan, B D Wild
Work: K1 L S1 W
Ptr: Morgan, Mrs Dianne Margaret LLB(Hons). . . . *Feb 1977
Wild, Mr Barrie D LLB(Leeds) . . . *Apr 1977

BOURNE JAFFA & CO ‡
72 The Green Kings Norton Birmingham West Midlands B38 8RU
Tel: 0121 451 3338 *Fax:* 0121 451 3455 *Dx:* 20302 COTTERIDGE
Emergency telephone 0121 459 3075
E-mail: litigation@bournejaffa.co.uk
Languages: French, Spanish
Work: C1 F1 G H J1 K1 L M1 N O Q S1 W

BOURNE JAFFA & CO ‡
1 Redditch Road Kings Norton Birmingham West Midlands B38 8RN
Tel: 0121 451 1661 *Fax:* 0121 433 3547
E-mail: conveyancing@bournejaffa.co.uk

BRASIERS LAW ‡
1 Victoria Square Birmingham West Midlands B1 1BD
Tel: 0845 130 8455

BREAKWELLS ‡
Aspect Court 4 Temple Row Birmingham West Midlands B2 5HG
Tel: 0121 222 2606 *Fax:* 0121 222 2607 *Dx:* 23524 BIRMINGHAM 3
List of partners: A M Breakwell
SPr: Breakwell, Mr Andrew Martin LLB(Hons) . . . . . . *Feb 1985

BREVITTS ‡
5 Oak Tree Lane Selly Oak Birmingham West Midlands B29 6JE
Tel: 0121 472 4131 *Fax:* 0121 471 3655
E-mail: jane@brevittsolicitors.co.uk
List of partners: J A Sutton
Work: K4 S1 W
Legal Aid Franchise
SPr: Sutton, Ms Jane Allison . . . . *Oct 1999

BRIDGEHOUSE PARTNERS LLP
Suite 2F St Georges Court 1 Albion Street Birmingham West Midlands B1 3AH
Tel: 0121 233 0919 *Fax:* 0121 233 2716
Office: London W1

BRIDGEHOUSE PARTNERS LLP ‡
Lancaster House 67 Newhall Street Birmingham West Midlands B3 1NQ
Tel: 0121 314 0000 *Fax:* 0121 314 0020
E-mail: sm@bridgehouselaw.com

BRINDLEY TWIST TAFFT & JAMES
1 Fountain Court Steel House Lane Birmingham West Midlands B4 6DR
Tel: 0121 214 8989 *Fax:* 0121 233 9559
Dx: 16074 BIRMINGHAM FOUNTAIN COURT
Office: Coventry
Ptr: Qasim, Mr Mohammed . . . . Sep 1991
Ast: Brogan, Miss Caroline Ann . . . . Jul 2006

BRITANNIA LAW PRACTICE ‡
353b Birchfield Road Perry Barr Birmingham West Midlands B20 3BJ
Tel: 0121 356 3030 *Fax:* 0121 345 0800
Emergency telephone 075 3400 5005
E-mail: info@britannialawpractice.com

BROOKS SULEMAN SOLICITORS LLP ‡
282 Slade Road Birmingham West Midlands B23 7LX
Tel: 0121 384 5768 *Fax:* 0121 384 3286
E-mail: bssllp@aol.com

BROOMHALL & CO ‡
Cheltenham House 14 Temple Street Birmingham West Midlands B2 5BG
Tel: 0121 633 4868 *Fax:* 0121 643 4927
Emergency telephone 0121 308 7362
E-mail: office@broomhallandco.co.uk
List of partners: J Broomhall, S A Broomhall
Work: C1 J1 K1 S1 W
Agency undertaken
Ptr: Broomhall, Ms Jeanine LLB . . . . *Dec 1991
Broomhall, Mr Stephen A BA(Law); ACIArb . . . . . . Jan 1980

HENRY BROWNE SOLICITORS ‡
Elite House 95 Stockfield Road Birmingham West Midlands B27 6AT
Tel: 0121 765 3332 *Fax:* 0121 765 3332
Dx: 19809 ACOCKS GREEN
E-mail: advice@henry-browne.co.uk
List of partners: A Henry
Ptr: Henry, Ms Angela LLB(Hons) . . . . Nov 1997

BROWNE JACOBSON LLP
Victoria House Victoria Square Birmingham West Midlands B2 4BU
Tel: 0121 237 3900 *Fax:* 0121 236 1291
Office: London EC3, Nottingham
Mem: Amphlett, Mr Mark Leslie . . . . Dec 1989

BULLER JEFFRIES ‡
36 Bennetts Hill Birmingham West Midlands B2 5SN
Tel: 0121 212 2620 *Fax:* 0121 212 2210 *Dx:* 13051 BIRMINGHAM 1
E-mail: info@bullerjeffries.com
List of partners: D P Adamson, C Bourne, D J Brosnan, C A Coates, R F Coates, R J Davis, R J Edwards, G J Lewis, R H Seagrove, C S Vernon, J R L Williams
Office: Coventry
Languages: French, German
Work: A1 B1 C1 E F1 F2 J1 J2 K4 L N O Q R1 S1 S2 T1 T2 V W Z(c,h,j,q)
Fixed Fee Interview undertaken
Ptr: Adamson, Mr Derek P LLB . . . . *Mar 1981
Bourne, Miss Collette . . . . *Jul 1993
Brosnan, Mrs Denise Jane PGDipLaw; FILEx . . . . . Jan 2005
Coates, Miss Caroline Amanda LLB. . . . . *Nov 1994
Coates, Mr Roger F LLB . . . . *Dec 1961
Davis, Mr Richard J BSc(Bris). . . . . *Feb 1986
Edwards, Mr Robert J LLB . . . . *Oct 1987
Lewis, Mr Geoffrey J LLB . . . . *§Apr 1973
Seagrove, Mr Richard H BA(Oxon) . . . . *Oct 1992
Vernon, Mr Clive Steven . . . . *Jan 1982
Williams, Mr John Roger Lloyd LLB . . . . *§Apr 1980
Asoc: Banks, Mrs Hannah LLB(Hons) Birmingham Law Society (2nd Prize). . . . . *May 2002
Tinkler, Mrs Helen BA(Hons) . . . . *Oct 1990
Ast: Powell, Mr Albert Edward BA; LLB; FCII; LLM; ACIArb*May 1996
Con: Dace, Mr Nigel H LLB(Hons) . . . . *§Jun 1973

DAVID BUNN & CO ‡
886 Bristol Road South Northfield Birmingham West Midlands B31 2NS
Tel: 0121 476 8481 *Fax:* 0121 411 1840 *Dx:* 26782 NORTHFIELD
E-mail: davidbunn.stirch@btconnect.com
List of partners: D T Bunn, J L S Bunn, G Lloyd
Office: Birmingham (2 offices)
Work: S1 S2 W
Ptr: Bunn, Mr David Thomas LLB . . . . *Dec 1977
Bunn, Mr James L S . . . . *Sep 2001
Lloyd, Mrs Gemma LLB(Hons) . . . . *Aug 2005
Ast: Bunn, Mr Andrew David Thomas . . . . Mar 2011

DAVID BUNN & CO
35 High Street Kingsheath Birmingham West Midlands B14 7BH
Tel: 0121 441 3322 *Fax:* 0121 443 3873
Office: Birmingham (2 offices)
Work: S1 S2 W
Ptr: Bunn, Mr David Thomas LLB . . . . *Dec 1977
Bunn, Mr James L S . . . . *Sep 2001
Ast: Bunn, Mr Andrew David Thomas . . . . Mar 2011
Lloyd, Mrs Gemma LLB(Hons) . . . . *Aug 2005

DAVID BUNN & CO
1468 Pershore Road Stirchley Birmingham West Midlands B30 2NT
Tel: 0121 459 9714 *Fax:* 0121 458 2682
Office: Birmingham (2 offices)

CAROLE BURGHER ‡
28 Bloomfield Road Birmingham West Midlands B13 9BY
Tel: 0121 449 2002

SIMON BURN SOLICITORS ‡
43 Temple Row Birmingham West Midlands B2 5LS
Tel: 0121 371 0301 *Fax:* 0121 371 0302
E-mail: enquiries@simonburn.com

BUTLER HALL & CO ‡
214 Hagley Road Edgbaston Birmingham West Midlands B16 9PH
Tel: 0121 456 3171 *Fax:* 0121 456 4813 *Dx:* 23059 EDGBASTON 1
E-mail: penny@butlerhall.co.uk
List of partners: I R Butler, P J R Hall
Languages: French, German
Work: C1 C2 E L S1 S2 W
Ptr: Butler, Mr Ian R LLB . . . . *Mar 1980
Hall, Mrs Penelope Jane Rosemary LLB . . . . . . *§Dec 1974

CALTHORPE SOLICITORS ‡
6 Vicarage Road Edgbaston Birmingham West Midlands B15 3ES
Tel: 0121 452 4955 *Fax:* 0121 452 4956 *Dx:* 23073 EDGBASTON
E-mail: info@calthorpesolicitors.com

LISA CAMPBELL SOLICITOR ‡
44 Third Avenue Selly Park Birmingham West Midlands B29 7EX
Tel: 07779 099870

CAMPBELL SOLICITORS ‡
6th Floor Waterloo House Waterloo Street Birmingham West Midlands B2 5TB
Tel: 0121 270 6343 *Fax:* 0121 472 2819
E-mail: info@campbell-solicitors.com

CANTY & CO ‡
6th Floor King Edward House New Street Birmingham West Midlands B2 4QJ
Tel: 0121 688 5000 *Fax:* 0121 688 5010 *Dx:* 13046 BIRMINGHAM
E-mail: enquiries@cantys.co.uk
List of partners: C R Canty, C L Law
Work: C1 C2 E K3 N O Q R1 R2 S1 S2 W Z(l)
Agency and Advocacy undertaken
Ptr: Canty, Ms Catherine Ruth LLB . . . . *Mar 1992
Law, Mr Christopher Leslie BA . . . . *Nov 1985

CAPE HILL SOLICITORS ‡
54 Waterloo Road Cape Hill Birmingham West Midlands B66 4JN
Tel: 0121 532 3018

CAPSTICKS SOLICITORS LLP
35 Newhall Street Birmingham West Midlands B3 3PU
Tel: 0121 230 1500 *Fax:* 0121 230 1515 *Dx:* 13003 BIRMINGHAM
E-mail: info@capstick.co.uk
Office: London SW19

CARLTONS SOLICITORS ‡
503 Coventry Road Small Heath Birmingham West Midlands B10 0LL
Tel: 0121 766 7447

BARBARA CARTER ‡
117 Vicarage Road Kings Heath Birmingham West Midlands B14 7QG
Tel: 0121 441 3238 *Fax:* 0121 441 2191
Emergency telephone 0121 441 3238
E-mail: childlaw@bcarter.entadsl.com
List of partners: B L Carter
Languages: German
Work: D1 D2
Emergency Action, Agency, Advocacy, Legal Aid undertaken and Legal Aid Franchise
SPr: Carter, Ms Barbara Linda BA(Hons) Recorder. . . . . *Jan 1983

CARTWRIGHT KING
Floor 14 McLaren Building 46 The Priory Queensway Birmingham West Midlands B4 7LR
Tel: 0121 270 1988 *Fax:* 0121 237 6100 *Dx:* 23514 BIRMINGHAM 3
Emergency telephone 080 8178 7119
E-mail: admin@cartwrightking.co.uk
Office: Derby, Gateshead, Leicester, Nottingham, Sheffield

CARVERS (PART OF THE WILKES PARTNERSHIP LLP)
10 Coleshill Road Hodge Hill Birmingham West Midlands B36 8AA
Tel: 0121 784 8484 *Fax:* 0121 783 4935
E-mail: enquiries@carverslaw.co.uk
Office: Birmingham
Work: D1 K1 S1 S2
Ptr: Keene, Mr Aaron Bardell LLB . . . . *Oct 1989
Vogel, Ms Susan Marie BA . . . . May 1982
Asoc: Gilkes, Mr Richard . . . . *Mar 1970
Ast: Chawdary, Mrs Shakti. . . . . Sep 2001
Whittall, Ms Stephanie . . . . Sep 2010
Con: Edmunds, Mr Keith BA(Law) . . . . *Dec 1977

CARVILL & JOHNSON LLP ‡
735 Bristol Road South Northfield Birmingham West Midlands B31 2NG
Tel: 0121 476 9000 *Fax:* 0121 478 2519 *Dx:* 26781 NORTHFIELD
E-mail: post@carvill-johnson.co.uk
List of partners: P A Carvill, R G Johnson, D J Sheldon
Work: B1 C1 D1 E F1 J1 K1 N O Q S1 S2 W Z(c)
Agency, Legal Aid undertaken and Legal Aid Franchise
Ptr: Carvill, Mr Peter A LLB . . . . *Oct 1987
Johnson, Mr Richard G LLB. . . . . *§May 1980
Sheldon, Mr David John. . . . . Oct 1990
Asoc: Fulford, Mrs Susan Kathleen LLB . . . . Oct 1995

CHALLINORS
Edmund House 12-22 Newhall Street Birmingham West Midlands B3 3EF
Tel: 0121 212 9393 *Fax:* 0121 212 3422
Dx: 707295 BIRMINGHAM 65
E-mail: info@challinors.co.uk
Office: Halesowen, Nottingham, West Bromwich, Wolverhampton
Work: D1 E F1 G H J1 K1 K2 L N O Q S1 V W Z(c,i,l,m,q,r)
Emergency Action, Agency, Fixed Fee Interview, Legal Aid undertaken, Legal Aid Franchise and Member of Accident Line
Ptr: Bannister, Mr Richard LLB . . . . *Oct 1990
Corser, Mr R David R Notary Public. . . . . *Jan 1970
Debney, Ms Fiona LLB(Hons) . . . . Oct 1994
Follis, Mr Michael I LLB . . . . *Apr 1985
Houston, Ms Angela Mary. . . . . Feb 1992
Howe, Ms Elisabeth BA(Law) . . . . *Nov 1986
Kang, Baldev S BA(Law) . . . . *Oct 1987
Kerrigan, Mr Joseph M D LLB. . . . . *Nov 1985
Lewis, Miss Nicola . . . . *Oct 1994
McHugh, Mr Peter J. . . . . *Oct 1990
O'Sullivan, Ms Fiona M LLB. . . . . *Dec 1986
Sellar, Mr Nigel P LLB Part time Chairman of Social Security Appeals. . . . . *Oct 1983
Walker, Mr Jonathan P LLB . . . . *Feb 1992
Asoc: Naylor, Mr Gavin LLB(Hons). . . . . Apr 1997
Skinner, Mr Robert . . . . *Jan 1993
Tubb, Mr Nicholas D C LLB(Hons) . . . . *Feb 1988
Ast: Carneiro, Mr Alan V. . . . . *Mar 1994
Corser, Ms Sarah M BA. . . . . Sep 2000
Derrett-Smith, Miss Tania . . . . *Sep 1999
Hammersley, Miss Fiona Sara LLB(Law & German) . *Mar 2001
Underwood, Ms Nicola . . . . *Sep 1995

CHANCELLOR SOLICITORS ‡
276 Moseley Road Birmingham West Midlands B12 0BS
Tel: 0121 446 4408 *Fax:* 0121 440 5622
E-mail: chancellorsolicitors@yahoo.co.uk

CHARLES & CO ‡
16-17 Caroline Street Birmingham West Midlands B3 1TR
Tel: 0121 236 1985 *Fax:* 0121 236 4652 *Dx:* 13012 BIRMINGHAM

CLAIM TIME LIMITED ‡
1206 Stratford Road Hall Green Birmingham West Midlands B28 8HN
Tel: 0845 051 8080

CLARKE WILLMOTT ‡
138 Edmund Street Birmingham West Midlands B3 2ES
Tel: 0845 209 1000 / 0117 305 6000 *Fax:* 0845 209 2001
Dx: 722320 BIRMINGHAM 75
E-mail: info@clarkewillmott.com
List of partners: M Anderson, M Askew, N B Baker, M J M Barker, A J Beedham, D Birchall, A M Breakwell, L Brown, P Chapman, C Charlton, M Clarke, S Clarke, L E Edwards, N Engert, R Evans, A C Fairweather, M C Farren, N D Francombe, K E Gardner, J Grigg, R Gupta, P Hall, N L Ham, K A Harvey, T Hayden, D W S Hayes, T W L Hyde, S C Ingram, K Jones, W Juckes, K Kennedy, P R Knight, S L Latham, N Lindsay, P H Livingstone, R O Lloyd Jones, G W Lovett, B Martin, G McIntyre, R Mohindra, R Morfee, J W Morton, M P Mundy, P Nellist, S Norcross Webb, J C Oakland, M K Parrott, H A J Pestell, M A Pettingell, C Piggott, B Pike, A Powles, C A Rankin, T Read, S Rosser, T Russ, J E Russell, N J Seager, R Seaton, S Slough, R J Smeath, O Smedley, E J Smithers, J L Stephens, C Taylor, S S W Thair, S Thomas, S Thorne, T Walker, T Watkins, A West, W Whiteley, V H Wilkes, M Wilson, J M Wiltshire, P H Winterborne, L Young
Office: Bristol, London EC4, Manchester, Southampton, Taunton
Languages: French
Work: A1 A2 A3 B1 C1 C2 C3 E F1 I J1 J2 K1 K3 L M2 N O P Q R1 R2 S1 S2 T1 T2 U2 W X Z(b,c,d,e,g,h,j,k,l,o,p,q,r,t,u,w,za)
Emergency Action, Agency, Advocacy, Fixed Fee Interview and Legal Aid undertaken
Ptr: Anderson, Ms Mary . . . . Oct 1984
Beedham, Mr Andrew John LLB; MBA . . . . *Oct 1983
Birchall, Mr David LLB(Hons) . . . . Oct 1995
Breakwell, Mr Andrew Martin LLB(Hons) . . . . . . *Feb 1985
Hayes, Mr David W S LSF. . . . . *Nov 1974
Knight, Mr Paul R BA . . . . *Oct 1988
Morton, Mr Jonathan W LLB . . . . *§Oct 1982
Piggott, Mr Christopher BSc(Hons)(Econ) . . . . . . Oct 1995
Powles, Mr Anthony LLB . . . . *Dec 1972
Read, Mr Thomas LLB(Hons); MA. . . . . Sep 1999
Wilkes, Ms Victoria Helen LLB . . . . Jan 1991

COBBETTS LLP
One Colmore Square Birmingham West Midlands B4 6AJ
Tel: 0845 404 2404 *Fax:* 0845 404 2434
Dx: 716703 BIRMINGHAM 43
E-mail: enquiries@cobbetts.com
Office: Leeds, London WC1, Manchester
Work: A1 B1 C1 C2 C3 E F1 I J1 K1 L M1 M2 N O P Q R1 R2 S1 S2 T1 T2 V W X Z(b,c,d,e,h,i,j,k,l,o,s,x)

COLEY & TILLEY ‡
(incorporating Piddock Wood & Co)
Neville House 14 Waterloo Street Birmingham West Midlands B2 5UF
Tel: 0121 643 5531 *Fax:* 0121 643 5711 *Dx:* 13065 BIRMINGHAM
Emergency telephone 0121 445 3833
E-mail: tc@coleyandtilley.co.uk
List of partners: G N Griffiths, J Leo, A C Piddock, B G Poultney, A Wilde, G I Wood
Work: A1 B1 C1 C2 C3 D1 E F1 I J1 K1 K3 K4 L M1 N O Q R1 S1 T1 T2 W Z(d,e,h,j,l)
Emergency Action, Agency, Advocacy, Fixed Fee Interview, Legal Aid undertaken, Legal Aid Franchise and Member of Accident Line
Ptr: Griffiths, Mr Grahame N LLB . . . . *§Jul 1978
Leo, Mr James LLB(Hons) . . . . *Nov 2000
Piddock, Mr Andrew C . . . . *Nov 1976
Poultney, Mr Bryan G LLB. . . . . *Oct 1988
Wilde, Ms Annmarie LLB . . . . *Oct 1993
Wood, Mr Geoffrey I LLB(Leeds) . . . . *Apr 1975
Asoc: Barclay, Ms Jane V LLB. . . . . *Sep 1987
Piercy, Mr Neil MA . . . . *Apr 1979
Thomas, Miss Rebecca Jane BA(Hons). . . . . Aug 2000
Ast: Dawson, Mrs Katy Louise LLB(Hons) . . . . Mar 2006
Hathaway, Miss Sally-Ann LLB . . . . Mar 2000
Lloyd-Smith, Mr Christopher BA(Jt Hons); LLM . . . Sep 2004
O'Neil, Mr Stephen LLB. . . . . Jul 1999
Pain, Miss Caroline LLB(Hons) . . . . Oct 2005
Ruddocks, Mrs Jo LLB(Hons) . . . . Sep 2005
Agency Commissions undertaken. Within short walking distance of all courts.

See p112 for the Key to Work Categories & other symbols

2

ANTHONY COLLINS SOLICITORS LLP ‡
134 Edmund Street Birmingham West Midlands B3 2ES
Tel: 0121 200 3242 *Fax:* 0121 212 7442 *Dx:* 13055 BIRMINGHAM 1
Emergency telephone 07626 951241
E-mail: info@anthonycollins.com
List of partners: A S J Bean, S D Belling, N A Carter, M Cook, J D Cox, S J Dalling, R Grinbergs, P A Hall, H E J Harrison, S M Hogan, P F Hubbard, A J Lancaster, A A Millross, S Ramshaw, R H Thompson, H J Tucker, J H Wearing, E J Wyatt
Work: A1 A3 B1 C1 C2 C3 D1 D2 E F1 I J1 J2 K1 K2 K3 L N O P Q R1 R2 S1 S2 T1 T2 U2 W X Z(c,d,e,h,l,m,q,r,u,x)
Emergency Action, Agency, Advocacy, Fixed Fee Interview, Legal Aid undertaken, Legal Aid Franchise and Member of Accident Line
Ptr: Bean, Mr Alan S J BA(Oxon); MA(Lond). . . . . *Dec 1977
Belling, Mr Stephen David LLB . . . . *Nov 1992
Carter, Mr Nicholas A BA(Hons); MA . . . . *Oct 1983
Cook, Mr Mark LLB(Lond). . . . . *Nov 1989
Cox, Mr Jonathan D. . . . . *Jan 1991
Dalling, Mr Stephen J LLB(Hons) . . . . *Oct 1987
Grinbergs, Miss Ruth LLB. . . . . *Sep 1979
Hall, Mr P Anthony BA . . . . *Nov 1986
Harrison, Mrs Hilary E J LLB(Hons) . . . . *§Oct 1985
Hogan, Mr Simon M BA. . . . . *Dec 1983
Hubbard, Mr Peter Fortescue LLB. . . . . Sep 1996
Lancaster, Mr Andrew J BA(Law) . . . . *Oct 1985
Millross, Mr Andrew A LLB; DipLG Birmingham Law Society Joint Gold Medal Winner . . . . *Oct 1987
Ramshaw, Mr Simon LLB(Hons) . . . . *Apr 1981
Thompson, Miss Romaine H MA(Cantab) . . . . *Oct 1988
Tucker, Mrs Helen Joy LLB Director of the Birmingham Bond Scheme. *Oct 1994
Wearing, Mr John H LLB . . . . *Oct 1987
Wyatt, Ms Elizabeth J BA(Hons). . . . . *Oct 1991
Asoc: Alcock, Mr David LLB(B'ham) . . . . *§Oct 1982
Basra, Miss Baljit K LLB(Hons); LPC Dip . . . . . . *Apr 1997
Batta, Mr Rankeshwar LLB(Hons); LSF . . . . *Oct 1995
Bevan, Mrs Julie Varnom LLB ILEX Prize . . . . . . *Mar 1994
Elphinston, Mr Alexander BA(Dunelm); TEP. . . . . . *§Oct 1980
Foster, Natasha BA(Hons) . . . . *Sep 2001
Gregson, Mr Matthew LLB . . . . *Sep 2001
Huntbach, Ms Sarah . . . . *Oct 1994
Lee-Mills, Mrs Joanna LLB(Hons) . . . . *Nov 2001
Margetson, Mrs Elizabeth Ann LLB(Hons). . . . . . . Sep 2003
Measures, Mrs Charlotte LLB(Hons). . . . . Nov 1997
More, Mr Richard MA . . . . *Nov 1991
Parker, Mr Colin. . . . . Oct 1987
Shone, Miss Jennifer A LLB(B'ham). . . . . *§Oct 1986
Thomas, Mr Heath LLB(Hons). . . . . *Jun 1996
Turner, Mrs Edwina E H LLB . . . . *Sep 1990
Vercoe, Miss Suzanne C LLB(Hons). . . . . Sep 1996
Walton, Mrs Deborah Ruth LLB . . . . *Jul 1997
Webb, Mrs Sarah LLB; DIPIP . . . . Sep 1991
Woodman, Mr Paul Richard BA Cozens Hardy Moot Prize . . . . *Nov 1992
Wort, Mr Matthew. . . . . Jan 2002
Ast: Bhangal, Rajinder BSc(Psychology & Education) . . . May 1998
Biddle, Miss Faye BA; LPC . . . . Mar 2009
Bisla, Mrs Sukhdip . . . . Sep 2005
Blackwell, Ms Kirsty FILEx . . . . *Dec 2001
Brooks, Mr Richard . . . . May 2005
Brown, Mrs Inez May LLB. . . . . *Sep 2002
Burgher, Ms CarolE BA; CPE Evershed Law Prize for Best Student Deputy District Judge (Civil) . . . . Nov 1991
Campsall, Ms Esther . . . . Sep 2005
Dabek, Miss Anna LLB; LPC . . . . Sep 2009
Duke, Miss Emma LLB(Hons); LPC . . . . Sep 2007
Freeth, Mr Richard LLB(Hons)(Law). . . . . Nov 1999
Green, Mrs Sheree BA Broderip & Easterbrook Prize 1991 . . . . Nov 1993
Hall, Mr David Iain John BA; MA . . . . *Aug 2001
Hallott, Mr Robert. . . . . Sep 1999
Hamir, Mr Osman LLB; LLM Best Obligatory Essay; Best Administrative & Constitutional Law Student. . . . Feb 2002
Holmes, Miss Donna LLB(Hons). . . . . Sep 2007
Jardine, Miss Victoria Louise LLB(Hons). . . . . . . *May 2000
Jones, Ms Julia LLB. . . . . Mar 2005
Knight, Mrs Michelle. . . . . Aug 2006
Lee, Mr Simon BA(Law & French); LPC. . . . . Sep 2004
Macheng, Monica. . . . . Feb 2002
Millward, Mr Adam BSc; PGDipLaw; LPC . . . . Mar 2008
Monk, Mrs Gayle MA(English Literature) . . . . Mar 2008
Monk, Mr James . . . . Sep 2007
Mullen, Mr Douglas James LLB(Hons). . . . . *Sep 2000
Patrice, Miss Sarah Louise LLB . . . . Dec 2003
Ramon, Miss Maria Elena LLB; LPC; PSC. . . . . . . *Mar 2004
Riley, Miss Emma LLB; LPC. . . . . Oct 2007
Robinson, Mrs Julie CPE; ILEX . . . . Feb 2006
Room, Miss Alison BA; GDL; LPC Equity & Trusts Prize from BLS. . . . . Mar 2009
Smith, Ms Jenny . . . . Oct 1984
Tamber, Mr Jas LLB(Hons) . . . . Jul 2005
Tomlinson, Ms Sarah LLB. . . . . Sep 2004
Zaki, Miss Nevine BA(Hons)(Ancient History) . . . . . May 2006
Con: Baldwin, Mr Peter N LLB . . . . *§Jul 1978
Dauncey, Mr Robert O . . . . *Apr 1969
Lloyd, Mr Jonathan S MA(Oxon) . . . . Apr 1976
Reading, Mr Paul . . . . Apr 1976
Walsh, Mr John MA(Oxon) . . . . *Dec 1976

GEORGE MITCHELL COLMAN & CO ‡
Colman House 6-10 South Street Harborne Birmingham West Midlands B17 0DB
Tel: 0121 427 7700 *Fax:* 0121 428 4688
List of partners: S H Colman, S R Colman
Work: E S1 W
Ptr: Colman, Mr Sidney H . . . . *Jun 1947
Colman, Ms Susan R LLB. . . . . *Sep 1979

COMMERCIAL & LEGAL GROUP (CLG) ‡
First Floor Offices 135 Alum Rock Road Birmingham West Midlands B8 1NH
Tel: 0121 326 6611

THE COMMUNITY LAW PARTNERSHIP ‡
4th Floor Ruskin Chambers 191 Corporation Street Birmingham West Midlands B4 6RP
Tel: 0121 685 8595 *Fax:* 0121 236 5121 *Dx:* 23525 BIRMINGHAM 3
E-mail: office@communitylawpartnership.co.uk
Languages: French, Italian, Romanian
Work: L V

THE CONNEXION PARTNERSHIP
63 Temple Row Birmingham West Midlands B2 5LS
Tel: 0121 633 6606 *Fax:* 0121 633 6617 *Dx:* 13077 BIRMINGHAM 1
E-mail: infobirmingham@cxp-law.com
Office: Manchester

K J CONROY SOLICITORS ‡
George Street Chambers 36-37 George Street Birmingham West Midlands B3 1QA
Tel: 0121 212 1575

CONSILIUM LEGAL ‡
121 Livery Street Birmingham West Midlands B3 1RS
Tel: 0845 241 5656 *Fax:* 0845 241 5658
Dx: 16077 BIRMINGHAM FOUNTAIN COURT
E-mail: contactus@consiliumlegal.com

COUSINS BUSINESS LAW ‡
Swan House PO Box 11543 Birmingham West Midlands B13 0ZL
Tel: 0121 778 3212 *Fax:* 0121 275 6155
E-mail: gary.cousins@business-lawfirm.co.uk

COX COOPER LIMITED ‡
Cambrai Court 1235 Stratford Road Hall Green Birmingham West Midlands B28 9AA
Tel: 0121 777 0015 *Fax:* 0121 325 5400 *Dx:* 714525 HALL GREEN 2
E-mail: law@coxcooper.co.uk
List of partners: D M Cooper, A B S Cox
Work: C1 C2 E I J1 O Q U2 Z(e,p)
Fixed Fee Interview undertaken
Dir: Cooper, Mr David Michael BA(Oxon) . . . . *Feb 1987
Cox, Mr Andrew B S LLB . . . . *Nov 1991
Ast: Stanley, Miss Denise LLB; PGDip . . . . *Apr 2006

CRAFFREY & COMPANY ‡
(incorporating Khattak-Pasha & Co Ltd)
57 Yardley Road Acocks Green Birmingham West Midlands B27 6LL
Tel: 0121 326 6977 / 706 7907 *Fax:* 0121 327 3084
Dx: 19808 ACOCKS GREEN
E-mail: law@caffreysolicitors.com

KENNETH CURTIS & CO ‡
88 Aldridge Road Perry Barr Birmingham West Midlands B42 2TP
Tel: 0121 356 1161 *Fax:* 0121 356 2973 *Dx:* 21502 PERRY BARR
Office: Redditch
Work: C1 C2 C3 D1 E G H J1 K1 L N P R1 S1 S2 V Z(h,i,l)

D & A SOLICITORS ‡
118a Soho Road Birmingham West Midlands B21 9DP
Tel: 0121 523 3601 / 0845 803 5961 *Fax:* 0121 523 0101

DAC BEACHCROFT
Nine Brindleyplace Oozells Square Birmingham West Midlands B1 2HE
Tel: 0121 698 5200 *Fax:* 0121 698 5290 *Dx:* 13057 BIRMINGHAM
Office: Bristol, Leeds, London EC3 (3 offices), London EC4 (2 offices), Manchester (2 offices), Newcastle upon Tyne, Newport, Winchester
Languages: French, German, Italian
Work: A3 B1 B2 C1 C3 E F1 F2 I J1 J2 L M1 N O P Q R1 R2 S2 T1 T2 U1 U2 W X Z(c,d,e,h,j,l,n,o,p,q,r,s,u,w,y,z)
Agency undertaken
Ptr: Archer, Ms Kate. . . . . Feb 1998
Cannon, Mr Martin J LLB; ACIArb. . . . . *Oct 1989
Carolan, Ms Lorraine M LLB. . . . . *Oct 1990
Leighton, Mr Paul . . . . Feb 2001
May, Miss Sara E LLB. . . . . Oct 1988
Murray, Mr Paul C LLB(Bris). . . . . *§Feb 1980
Ralston, Mr James Bruce LLB(Manc) . . . . *Dec 1983
Richards, Mr Rhod . . . . Nov 1996
Roach, Mr W D Andrew. . . . . Dec 1978

DBS LAW LTD ‡
Three Broadway Broad Street Birmingham West Midlands B15 1BQ
Tel: 0844 277 0800 *Fax:* 0844 277 0801 *Dx:* 70267 EDGBASTON 2
E-mail: info@dbslaw.co.uk

DLA PIPER UK LLP
Victoria Square House Victoria Square Birmingham West Midlands B2 4DL
Tel: 0870 011 1111 *Fax:* 0121 262 5794 *Dx:* 13022 BIRMINGHAM
Emergency telephone 0870 011 1111
E-mail: chris.rawstron@dlapiper.com
Office: Leeds, Liverpool, London EC2, Manchester, Sheffield
Languages: French, German, Spanish
Work: A1 B1 C1 C2 C3 D1 E F1 F2 G J1 J2 L M1 M2 N O P R1 S1 T1 W X Z(a,b,c,d,e,f,h,i,j,k,l,n,o,p,q,u)
Emergency Action, Agency undertaken and Member of Accident Line
Ptr: Arrand, Mr Charles W BA(Nott'm). . . . . Nov 1994
Bamford, Mr Nick . . . . Feb 1996
Beardmore, Mr Mark . . . . Sep 1996
Bointon, Ms Rosemary A BA(Oxon). . . . . Oct 1986
Bottley, Mr Stephen. . . . . Nov 1996
Bowker, Mr Neil David LLB(Hons). . . . . *Oct 1992
Bradley, Mr Graeme LLB(England)(Hong Kong) . . . . Dec 1985
Burgess, Mr Mark L LLB . . . . *Nov 1993
Campion, Mr John LLB(Lond) . . . . *Mar 1990
Collier, Mr Roger G BA . . . . *Oct 1988
Cook, Mr Charles . . . . Oct 1995
Davie, Mr Francis P LLB . . . . *Apr 1989
Dolphin, Mr Huw LLB(Manc); LSF. . . . . *Nov 1991
Glover, Mr David LLB . . . . *Oct 1987
Haywood, Mr Noel . . . . Sep 1996
Herring, Mr Andrew . . . . Oct 1995
Hirst, Mr Matthew V LLB . . . . *Nov 1991
Iliff, Mr Nicholas Patrick BA; DipLaw. . . . . *Jun 1995
Jacobs, Mr Alan S LLB(Sheff). . . . . *Jun 1981
Jeffreys, Mr John . . . . Sep 1998
Jew, Mr Nicholas LLB. . . . . *Apr 1995
Jones, Mr Alex BA(Oxon); MA. . . . . *Nov 1991
Jones, Mr Simon Huw BSc(Econ). . . . . *Nov 1989
Lavery, Mr James C LLB . . . . Sep 1990
McMorrow, Miss Marie Frances LLB(Sheff) . . . . . . *Oct 1989
Macpherson, Ms Karen . . . . Nov 1990
Miles, Ms Helen. . . . . Nov 1994
Mooney, Mr Eamon Fergal LLB(Hons). . . . . Oct 1993
Morris, Mr Greg. . . . . Aug 2003
Norris, Mr Robert John MEng Childs Prize. . . . . . *Oct 1995
Orme, Mr Russell P. . . . . *Feb 1989
Randle, Mr Anthony R LLB . . . . *Nov 1987
Rawstron, Mr Christopher D LLB(Hons) . . . . *Oct 1986
Seiger, Mr Radd BA. . . . . Nov 1992
Sullivan, Mr John C P BA(Oxon) . . . . *Oct 1980
Taylor, Mr Peter. . . . . Aug 1985
Thompson, Mr Peter K LLB; ACIArb Chairman of the Industrial Tribunals . . . . Nov 1970
Tozer, Mr Roy. . . . . Nov 1990
Wallace, Ms Sandra. . . . . Oct 1994
Woolcock, Mr Brian LLB(Hons) . . . . *Oct 1982

THE D M PARTNERSHIP ‡
Fifth Floor Ruskin Chambers 191 Corporation Street Birmingham West Midlands B4 6RP
Tel: 0121 200 0930 *Fax:* 0121 200 0931
E-mail: dm.partnership@btconnect.com

DASS SOLICITORS ‡
The Old Doctors Surgery 50 Newhall Street Birmingham West Midlands B3 3RJ
Tel: 0121 248 4000 *Fax:* 0121 248 4020 *Dx:* 13006 BIRMINGHAM 1
E-mail: law@dass-solicitors.com
List of partners: A Dass, D C Jotangia
Office: London SW1
Work: A3 B1 B2 C1 C2 E G H J1 K1 K3 M2 N O P Q R2 S1 S2 T1 T2 U2 Z(e,j,o,q,r)
Emergency Action and Advocacy undertaken
Ptr: Dass, Mr Alias LLB; LSF . . . . *May 1991
Jotangia, Dipak C LLB(Hons) . . . . *Dec 1990
Asoc: Holland, Mr Robert LLB . . . . *Mar 1996
Lowry-Mullins, Mr Kevin LLB(Hons) ★. . . . . *Oct 1999
Ast: Bhakta, Miss Nila BA(Hons). . . . . Dec 2007
Braich, Mr Aniel LLB . . . . *Jun 2009
Campbell, Ms Harriet Anna BA(Hons). . . . . Jan 2004
Colabawalla, Mr Roy LLB(Hons). . . . . *Apr 2011
Jones, Mr Mark Andrew LLB(Hons)(Law & French) . . *Sep 2005
Kaur, Miss Gurminder BA(Hons)(Law & International Studies); MA; LPC . . . . Aug 2011
Kausar, Miss Razwana LLB; PGDip LPC . . . . *Feb 2010
Redfern, Miss Gemma LLB; PGDip . . . . Nov 2008
Ubhi, Miss Navjit BA(Hons); PGDipLP. . . . . *Jan 2008
Walton, Mr Christopher Mark MA . . . . *Dec 1988
Con: Daly, Mr Steve . . . . *Jan 1974
Jaffa, Mr Richard H LLB. . . . . *Jul 1967

DASSAUR SOLICITORS ‡
700 Stratford Road Sparkhill Birmingham West Midlands B11 4AT
Tel: 0121 702 2758 *Fax:* 0121 777 7277
E-mail: kulraj@dassaursolicitors.com

DAVIES & PARTNERS
Latham House 33-34 Paradise Street Birmingham West Midlands B1 2BJ
Tel: 0121 616 4450 *Fax:* 0121 643 3928
Dx: 715358 BIRMINGHAM 78
Office: Almondsbury, Gloucester
Work: E J1 N O P Q R1 R2 S1 S2 Z(r)
Agency, Legal Aid undertaken, Legal Aid Franchise and Member of Accident Line
Ptr: Edwards, Ms Tracy D LLB(Hons) . . . . *Jul 1996
Stokes, Mr David C LLB(Hons) . . . . *Nov 1994
Ast: Bowen, Ms Rachel LLB(Hons). . . . . *Sep 1994
Katsionis, Mrs Pamela . . . . *Mar 2005
Singh, Mr Jaspal LLB(Hons). . . . . *Sep 2001
Watkins, Ms Helen LLB(Hons) ♦. . . . . Sep 2000

NEIL DAVIES & PARTNERS LLP ‡
Calcameron House 36b Water Street Birmingham West Midlands B3 1HP
Tel: 0121 200 7040 *Fax:* 0121 200 7041 *Dx:* 13037 BIRMINGHAM
E-mail: law@ndandp.co.uk

DAVISONS ‡
Ground Floor Sycamore House 54 Calthorpe Road Birmingham West Midlands B15 1TH
Tel: 0121 685 1234 *Fax:* 0121 685 1274 *Dx:* 702678 EDGBASTON 2
E-mail: lawyers@edg.davisons-solicitors.co.uk
List of partners: G A Davison, S Ingram, U Sadiq
Office: Birmingham (2 offices), Sutton Coldfield
Work: D1 F1 G H J1 K1 Q S1 W
Fixed Fee Interview, Legal Aid undertaken and Member of Accident Line
Ptr: Davison, Mr Gary A LLB . . . . *Oct 1983
Ingram, Mrs Samantha . . . . Oct 2006
Ast: Jones, Mr Nigel. . . . . Nov 1975
Parys, Rebecca. . . . . Oct 2007
Wilkes, Mr Darryl . . . . May 2006

DAVISONS
63-65 Beckbury Road Weoley Castle Birmingham West Midlands B29 5HS
Tel: 0121 685 1248 *Fax:* 0121 685 1254
Dx: 700983 WEOLEY CASTLE
E-mail: lawyers@weo.davisons-solicitors.co.uk
Office: Birmingham (2 offices), Sutton Coldfield
Work: C1 C2 C3 D1 F1 G H J1 K1 M1 M2 N P R1 S1 W
Emergency Action, Agency, Advocacy, Fixed Fee Interview and Legal Aid undertaken
Ptr: Sadiq, Mr Umran LLB(Hons) . . . . Sep 1998
Ast: Cadbury, Mrs Julie A BA . . . . *Mar 1983

DAVISONS
1841 Pershore Road Cotteridge Birmingham West Midlands B30 3DJ
Tel: 0121 685 1255 *Fax:* 0121 685 1264 *Dx:* 20301 COTTERIDGE
E-mail: lawyers@cot.davisons-solicitors.co.uk
Office: Birmingham (2 offices), Sutton Coldfield
Work: C1 C2 C3 D1 E F1 G H K1 L M1 M2 N P R1 S1 W
Emergency Action, Advocacy, Fixed Fee Interview and Legal Aid undertaken
Ast: Bailey-Bradshaw, Mrs Roxene Elesia LLB. . . . . . . Sep 2004
Con: Dixon, Mr John Christopher . . . . Jun 1972

DIVORCE & FAMILY LAW PRACTICE ‡
14 St Paul's Square Birmingham West Midlands B3 1RB
Tel: 0121 200 0890 *Fax:* 0121 233 9623
E-mail: jp@dflp.co.uk
List of partners: B J Morris, J C Price
Languages: French
Work: K1 K3
Emergency Action, Agency and Advocacy undertaken
Ptr: Morris, Miss Beverley Joy. . . . . Nov 1998
Price, Miss Joan C LLB(Hons) Deputy District Judge . . Jul 1977
Ast: Middleton, Mrs Vivienne LLB(Hons) Most Outstanding Student in Academic Year 2004/5 at UCE Birmingham . . . . *Apr 2006

SARAH DWIGHT SOLICITOR ‡
1340 Stratford Road Hall Green Birmingham West Midlands B28 9EH
Est: 2000
Tel: 0121 702 2100 *Fax:* 0121 702 2656 *Dx:* 714520 HALL GREEN 2
E-mail: info@sarahdwight.com
List of partners: S E Dwight

Work: S1 W
SPr: Dwight, Miss Sarah E LLB(Hons) . . . . Oct 1990

EATON RYAN & TAYLOR ‡
Lombard House 145 Great Charles Street Birmingham West Midlands B3 3LP
Tel: 0121 236 1999 *Fax:* 0121 236 1991 *Dx:* 13007 BIRMINGHAM 1
E-mail: info@ert-law.co.uk
List of partners: A Connock, S J Corner, N D Eaton, K F Ryan, M A Taylor, S E Whitehall
Work: A3 B1 B2 C1 F1 F2 I J1 J2 L N O P Q R1 S2 U1 U2 Z(b,c,e,j,k,p,q,r)
Emergency Action, Agency, Advocacy, Fixed Fee Interview, Legal Aid undertaken and Member of Accident Line
Ptr: Connock, Mr Andrew LLB(Hons) . . . . *Jan 2000
Corner, Mr Scott James LLB(Hons) . . . . *Nov 1994
Eaton, Mr Neil D LLB(Hons). . . . . *Oct 1989
Ryan, Mr Kieran Francis BA(Hons) . . . . *Mar 1988
Taylor, Mr Mark A. . . . . *Dec 1989
Whitehall, Mr Sean Eric LLB(Hons); LSF . . . . *Oct 1994
Asoc: Evans, Ms Emma Claire FILEx . . . . Jan 2005
Jack, Mrs Jill BSc. . . . . *Jul 2001
Ast: Bharya, Mrs Rajwinder FILEx; LPC Bradin & Trubshaw Partnership . . . . Nov 2005
Hanson, Miss Zoe LLB . . . . Aug 2006
Rawlings-Smith, Miss Kim Paulette LLB; LPC . . . . . Mar 2010

EDDOWES PERRY ADAMS ROBERTS & CO ‡
24 High Street Erdington Birmingham West Midlands B23 6RR
Tel: 0121 373 7395 *Fax:* 0121 377 8794 *Dx:* 21209 ERDINGTON
E-mail: info@epar.co.uk
List of partners: P E Stevens
Work: C1 E R2 S1 S2 W
Ptr: Stevens, Mr Paul E LLB. . . . . *Dec 1976

ELLIOTT & CO ‡
83 Newhall Street Birmingham West Midlands B3 1LP
Tel: 0121 236 9690 *Fax:* 0121 236 6697
E-mail: info@elliottco.co.uk

ELSE SOLICITORS LLP
39 Ludgate Hill Birmingham West Midlands B3 1EH
Tel: 0121 212 6560 *Dx:* 13019 BIRMINGHAM
E-mail: info@elsecommercialsolicitors.co.uk
Office: Burton-on-Trent

ENGLAND KERR HANDS & CO ‡
146 High Street Harborne Birmingham West Midlands B17 9NN
Tel: 0121 427 9898 *Fax:* 0121 427 9092 *Dx:* 19768 HARBORNE
E-mail: charlotte@englandkerr.co.uk
List of partners: A R England-Kerr, V Treloar
Work: C1 C2 C3 E F1 L M1 M2 N P S1
Agency and Legal Aid undertaken
Ptr: England-Kerr, Mr Andrew R BSc(Hons) . . . . *Jan 1985
Treloar, Ms Vicki . . . . Nov 2001

ENGLAND STICKLAND & NEALE ‡
Bank Chambers Six Ways Erdington Birmingham West Midlands B24 8AA
Tel: 0121 377 7773 *Fax:* 0121 377 6621 *Dx:* 21223 ERDINGTON
E-mail: info@esnsolicitors.com
List of partners: L D Neale, A K Stickland, J Sumner
Work: B1 B2 C1 D1 E F1 G H J1 K1 K3 L M1 N P R1 S1 S2 T1 V W Z(q)
Fixed Fee Interview and Legal Aid undertaken
Ptr: Neale, Mr Laurence D LLB . . . . *§Mar 1981
Stickland, Mr Adrian K LLB . . . . Dec 1974
Sumner, Mr John BA . . . . *Oct 1993

EQUITY SOLICITORS ‡
92 Grove Lane Handsworth Birmingham West Midlands B21 9HA
Tel: 0121 554 7470 *Fax:* 0121 554 7670 *Dx:* 24963 HANDSWORTH
Emergency telephone 07889 172848
E-mail: admin@equitysolicitors.com
List of partners: S Bhardwaj, M Tofayel-Sattar, M Zafir
Languages: Bengali, French, German, Hindi, Mirpuri, Punjabi, Urdu
Work: E J1 K3 L N Q S1 S2 W Z(i,l,q,r)
Agency and Fixed Fee Interview undertaken
Ptr: Bhardwaj, Ms Sunita . . . . Nov 2001
Tofayel-Sattar, Mr Mohammed . . . . Dec 1999
Zafir, Mr Mohammed . . . . Feb 2003

EVANS DERRY RENNIE & CO ‡
(in association with Wallace Robinson & Morgan)
46 Chelmsley Circle Chelmsley Wood Birmingham West Midlands B37 5UH
Tel: 0121 770 1721 *Fax:* 0121 770 8513
Dx: 23255 CASTLE BROMWICH
E-mail: info@evansderry.com
List of partners: J S Derry, M Evans
Office: Warwick
Work: B1 C1 D1 F1 G H I J1 K1 L M1 P S1 V W
Emergency Action, Agency, Advocacy, Fixed Fee Interview and Legal Aid undertaken
Ptr: Derry, Mr John S LLB . . . . *Oct 1984
Evans, Mr Mark BA . . . . *Aug 1984

EVERSHEDS LLP
115 Colmore Row Birmingham West Midlands B3 3AL
Tel: 0845 497 9797 *Fax:* 0845 497 1900 *Dx:* 13004 BIRMINGHAM 1
Office: Cambridge, Cardiff, Ipswich, Leeds, London EC2, Manchester, Newcastle upon Tyne, Nottingham
Work: A1 B1 C1 C2 C3 E F1 G J1 K1 L M1 M2 N P R1 S1 T1 T2 W Z(b,c,e,g,j,k,l,m,o,p,s)

EXLEX SOLICITORS ‡
The Woodlands 52 Grosvenor Road Birmingham West Midlands B20 3NH
Tel: 0121 331 4155

EYRE & CO ‡
866 Washwood Heath Road Ward End Birmingham West Midlands B8 2NG
Tel: 0121 784 4722 *Fax:* 0121 789 7065 *Dx:* 27432 HODGE HILL
E-mail: a.rimmington@eyrelaw.co.uk
List of partners: R J Guy, A R Rimmington
Work: E K4 S1 S2 W
Ptr: Guy, Mr Roger J . . . . *Jun 1969
Rimmington, Mr Andrew R BA. . . . . *Mar 1983

FABER & CO ‡
Ground Floor Coleridge Chambers 177 Coronation Street Birmingham West Midlands B4 6RG
Tel: 0121 236 5751 *Fax:* 0121 233 1990 *Dx:* 13048 BIRMINGHAM 1
Emergency telephone 07551 080800
E-mail: info@faberandco.co.uk
List of partners: A S Johal, A Mistry, H S Suthi
Work: D1 E G H K1 K2 K3 L Q R1 S1 S2 W
Emergency Action, Agency, Advocacy and Legal Aid undertaken
Ptr: Johal, Amritpal Singh LLB. . . . . Oct 1999
Mistry, Mr Ashok LLB . . . . Oct 1999
Suthi, Mr Hocknam Singh . . . . *Mar 2001
Ast: Harrison, Mr Mark N BA. . . . . *Dec 1981
Con: Faber, Mr Malcolm S D MA(Oxon). . . . . *Apr 1966
Faber, Mr Roger M . . . . *Dec 1975

FAWCETT & PATTNI
85-89 Colmore Row Birmingham West Midlands B3 2BB
Tel: 0121 200 1013 *Fax:* 0121 448 0706
E-mail: clients@fp-law.com
Office: Walsall

THE FIRM SOLICITORS LLP ‡
Suite 133 Gazette Building 168 Corporation Street Birmingham West Midlands B4 6TF
Tel: 0121 709 6506 *Fax:* 0121 236 1474 *Dx:* 23520 BIRMINGHAM 3
E-mail: info@thefamilyfirm.co.uk
Office: Redditch, Solihull

BRENDAN FLEMING ‡
165 Newhall Street St Pauls Square Birmingham West Midlands B3 1SW
Tel: 0121 683 5000 *Fax:* 0121 200 2176
Work: D1 G H K1 S1
Emergency Action, Agency, Advocacy, Fixed Fee Interview, Legal Aid undertaken, Legal Aid Franchise and Member of Accident Line
Ast: Maxim, Ms Rebecca . . . . Mar 1993

FORSTER & WHEELER ‡
817 Hagley Road West Quinton Birmingham West Midlands B32 1AD
Tel: 0121 421 4888 *Fax:* 0121 422 0888 *Dx:* 14515 HALESOWEN
E-mail: kate@forsterwheeler.co.uk
List of partners: C L Forster
Work: S1 S2 W
SPr: Forster, Ms Christine L . . . . Jul 1976

FREETH CARTWRIGHT LLP
3rd Floor 75 Colmore Row Birmingham West Midlands B3 2AP
Tel: 0845 634 2575 *Fax:* 0845 634 2576 *Dx:* 13024 BIRMINGHAM 1
E-mail: postmaster@freethcartwright.co.uk
Office: Derby, Leicester, Manchester, Nottingham
Ptr: Clifford, Mr Lee . . . . Nov 1998
Joyce, Mr Raymond Ernest BSc; MSc; LLB; ACIArb. . *Apr 1992
Mackintosh, Ms Mary Barbara BSc(Hons); CPE; LPC . Oct 1999
Osborn, Mr Richard . . . . Sep 1997
Walker, Ms Julie . . . . Jan 1998
Williamson, Mr Darren . . . . Sep 1998

GQS LIMITED ‡
288 Baldwins Lane Birmingham West Midlands B28 0XB
Tel: 0121 733 7070

GANDERTON SOLICITORS ‡
Barlett House 1075 Warwick Road Acocks Green Birmingham West Midlands B27 6QT
Tel: 0121 708 1944 *Fax:* 0121 708 1948
E-mail: leigh@gandertonsolicitors.co.uk

GARNER CANNING
301-303 Chester Road Castle Bromwich Birmingham West Midlands B36 0JG
Tel: 0121 749 5577 *Fax:* 0121 749 2765
Dx: 23251 CASTLE BROMWICH
E-mail: enquiries@garnercanning.co.uk
Office: Atherstone, Sutton Coldfield, Tamworth
Work: A1 C1 C2 D1 D2 E J1 K1 K2 K3 K4 L O Q R1 R2 S1 S2 T1 T2 W Z(d,l)
Agency, Fixed Fee Interview, Legal Aid undertaken and Legal Aid Franchise
Ptr: Canning, Mr Martin Paul LLB(Newc). . . . . *Jul 1975
Ast: Keene, Ms Joanna Sally. . . . . Nov 1996

GATELEY LLP ‡
One Eleven Edmund Street Birmingham West Midlands B3 2HJ
Tel: 0121 234 0000 *Fax:* 0121 234 0001 *Dx:* 13303 BIRMINGHAM 1
E-mail: info@gateleyuk.com
List of partners: J E Allen, P J Alton, R Armstrong, C A Betts, N W Brown, P Cliff, R M F Coles, P G Davies, A M Evans, V L Garrad, S N Gill, S Goodrham, J Gopsill, N J Handel, A C Hardingham, E J Hassall, P A Hayward, J Hobbs, J R G John, T A K Knight, T A Ledger, D I L Lloyd Jones, A D MacMillan, A J Madden, A J Matthews, B G McGeever, A D Messent, C L Mitchell, A J Moore, C L Nuttall, M A Park, R J Pettifor, C Reed, S Richards, P M A Rose, M J Rutherford, P Scott, R Sherwin, K A Silvester, J M Tomasin, N M Walser, M J Ward, S M Wilson
Office: Leicester, London EC4, Manchester, Nottingham
Languages: French, German, Italian, Punjabi
Work: A3 B1 C1 C2 C3 D1 E F1 F2 I J1 J2 L M1 M2 N O P Q R1 R2 S1 S2 T1 T2 U2 W Z(b,c,d,e,f,h,l,o,p,q,t)
Emergency Action, Agency, Advocacy, Fixed Fee Interview, Legal Aid undertaken and Member of Accident Line
Ptr: Alton, Mr Philip J LLB. . . . . *Oct 1983
Armstrong, Miss Ruth BA(Hons). . . . . *Oct 1992
Betts, Mrs Carol A . . . . Dec 1989
Cliff, Mr Paul LLB(Hons) . . . . *Oct 1988
Davies, Mr Peter G LLB. . . . . *Aug 1982
Evans, Mr Andrew Mark LLB(Hons)(Wales) . . . . . . *Oct 1993
Garrad, Ms Victoria L LLB(Hons) . . . . *Oct 1998
Gill, Mr Simon Nicholas BSc(Econ); MBS . . . . *Sep 1997
Goodrham, Mr Stephen LLB(Hons) . . . . *Mar 1993
Gopsill, Mr James. . . . . Jan 1997
Handel, Mr Neil J LLB. . . . . *Nov 1983
Hayward, Mr Paul A BA. . . . . *Oct 1984
John, Mr James Richard Gareth LLB(Hons). . . . . . . *Apr 1990
Ledger, Mr Timothy Adrian BA. . . . . *Feb 1983
Lloyd Jones, Mr David I L BA(Hons); FCIArb . . . . *§Dec 1979
McGeever, Mr Brendan G LLB . . . . *May 1983
MacMillan, Mr Andrew Duncan LLB(Hons). . . . . . . *May 1993
Madden, Mr Andrew J LLB; LSF Birmingham Law Society Book Prize . . . . *Sep 1987
Nuttall, Mr Callum Laing BA(Hons)(Oxon) . . . . . . *Oct 1994
Park, Mr Michael A LLB. . . . . Jun 1980
Pettifor, Mr Richard James LLB . . . . *Oct 1993
Reed, Mr Christopher MA . . . . Sep 1999
Scott, Mrs Pamela LLB . . . . Dec 1995
Sherwin, Ms Rebecca. . . . . Jan 1997
Silvester, Ms Katherine Ann BA; MA. . . . . *Sep 1993
Ward, Mr Michael James LLB(B'ham) Former President of the Birmingham Law Society . . . . *Oct 1984
Wilson, Mr Steven Mark BA(Econ) . . . . Mar 1991
Asoc: Davies, Mr A Iain LLB. . . . . *Mar 1987
Davies, Miss Michelle Rose BA . . . . *Sep 2002
Emms, Miss Fiona E BA(Law). . . . . Oct 1986
Hacking, Mrs Kathryn LLB. . . . . *Sep 2003
Halton, Mrs Jane M LLB. . . . . *Nov 1983
Haworth, Mr Mark C LLB; MCIPD . . . . Oct 1993
Huttley, Mrs Elaine . . . . Sep 2005
Jahreiss, Mr Martin MA(Oxon). . . . . *Sep 2001
Khan, Mr Mushtaq BSc(Hons); DMS; PGDipLaw . . . Apr 2000
Levesley, Mrs Karen Lesley BA(Hons). . . . . *Sep 2001
Mabe, Mr Adrian N LLB(Wales); ATII; TEP. . . . . . *Aug 1979
O'Byrne, Mr Rory LLB(Hons) . . . . Apr 1998
Wright, Ms Amber. . . . . Sep 2004
Ast: Griffiths, Ms Amy . . . . Sep 2005
Thomas, Mr Rebecca . . . . Mar 2006

GLAISYERS ‡
(incorporating Adie Evans & Warner; Reece Davis Wood Wild & Co)
(in association with Glaisyers in Manchester & Tamworth)
10 Rowchester Court Printing House Street Birmingham West Midlands B4 6DZ
Tel: 0121 233 2971 *Fax:* 0121 236 1534 *Dx:* 24933 BIRMINGHAM 4
Emergency telephone 0121 236 1885
E-mail: advice@glaisyers.co.uk
List of partners: S B Cole, N P Davis, D I Dollery, S Dunigan, K D C Good, J G Loveday, J A Powell, C P Royle, D P Simon, E M M Smith, H A Smith
Work: B1 B2 D1 E F1 G H J1 J2 K1 K2 L N Q R2 S1 S2 V W Z(g,h,i,k,l,m,p,q,r,t)
Emergency Action, Agency, Advocacy, Fixed Fee Interview, Legal Aid undertaken, Legal Aid Franchise and Member of Accident Line
Ptr: Cole, Mr Stephen B LLB(Nott'm) . . . . *Jul 1971
Davis, Mr Neil P LLB . . . . *Sep 1988
Dollery, Mr David I LLB . . . . *Jan 1975
Dunigan, Mr Stewart BA. . . . . *Jul 1979
Good, Mr Kevin D C LLB(Hons). . . . . Dec 1985
Loveday, Mr John G LLB(B'ham) . . . . *Oct 1983
Powell, Miss Julia A LLB . . . . *Oct 1991
Royle, Mr Charles P LLB(Sheff). . . . . *§Jun 1971
Simon, Mr David P LLB(Soton); MA(Brunel). . . . . . *Feb 1986
Smith, Mr Ewen M M . . . . *Sep 1996
Smith, Ms H Antonia BA . . . . *Oct 1984
Asoc: Burns, Miss Claire Elizabeth LLB . . . . *Nov 1993
Ast: Masih, Mr Steven LLB(Hons) . . . . *Jun 1998
Mian, Miss Najma LLB(Hons) . . . . *Mar 1993
Taylor, Mr Philip Mark LLB(Hons) . . . . Nov 1991
Con: Windmill, Mr John A LLB . . . . *Jun 1961

GORRARA HADEN SOLICITORS ‡
Quadrant Court 50 Calthorpe Road Birmingham West Midlands B15 1TH
Tel: 0121 452 8787

GOSHEN SOLICITORS ‡
14 Hylton Street Birmingham West Midlands B18 6HN
Tel: 0121 686 3170 *Fax:* 0121 241 7578
E-mail: info@goshensolicitors.co.uk
List of partners: O Obayelu
Ptr: Obayelu, Oluwakemi . . . . Jan 2007

GRAMDAN SOLICITORS ‡
1a Coleshill Road Hodge Hill Birmingham West Midlands B36 8DT
Tel: 0121 786 1196 *Fax:* 0121 785 2170 *Dx:* 27441 HODGE HILL
E-mail: info@gramdansolicitors.co.uk

GROVE TOMPKINS BOSWORTH ‡
54 Newhall Street Birmingham West Midlands B3 3QG
Tel: 0121 236 9341 / 236 8091 *Fax:* 0121 236 5169
Dx: 13040 BIRMINGHAM 1
Emergency telephone 07885 485283
E-mail: law@gtb-solicitors.com
List of partners: J A Cornwell, J R Devlin, D H Dudley, M W Ingamells, J Ingram
Work: A1 B1 C1 D1 E F1 G H J1 K1 K3 K4 L N O Q R1 S1 S2 T1 W Z(k)
Emergency Action, Agency, Advocacy, Fixed Fee Interview and Legal Aid undertaken
Ptr: Cornwell, Mr John A LLB(Newc). . . . . *§Apr 1971
Devlin, Mr James R BSc . . . . *Jan 1984
Dudley, Mr Dennis H . . . . *§Feb 1974
Ingamells, Mr Michael W BA(Law). . . . . *Apr 1981
Ingram, Mr James LLB . . . . *§Feb 1993

HK LAWYERS LIMITED ‡
6 Soho Road Birmingham West Midlands B21 9BH
Tel: 0121 515 0006 *Fax:* 0121 515 0008
E-mail: info@hklawyers.co.uk

HMA LAW SOLICITORS ‡
5 Tenby Street Birmingham West Midlands B1 3EL
Tel: 0121 200 1400 *Fax:* 0121 200 1480
E-mail: mafzal@hma-law.co.uk

HS SOLICITORS LIMITED ‡
828 Bristol Road South Birmingham West Midlands B31 2NS
Tel: 0121 477 3377 *Fax:* 0121 477 3355

HADGKISS HUGHES & BEALE ‡
83 Alcester Road Moseley Birmingham West Midlands B13 8EB
Tel: 0121 449 5050 *Fax:* 0121 442 4074 *Dx:* 10788 MOSELEY
Emergency telephone 07710 367398
E-mail: enquiries@hhb-law.co.uk
List of partners: P D Barnett, R G Brindley, C V Cattell, M J Eyre, E P Faithfull, A J Jones, A J Jones, G M Keir, M A Luscombe, J T Norton, G F Peters, S Sharif, A R Warner
Office: Birmingham (2 offices)
Work: C1 D1 E F1 G H J1 K1 K2 L N O Q R1 S1 S2 T2 V W Z(h,i,l,m,r)
Emergency Action, Agency, Advocacy, Legal Aid undertaken and Legal Aid Franchise
Ptr: Barnett, Mr Peter D. . . . . *Jan 1971
Brindley, Mr Roderick G LLB(Lond) . . . . *§Mar 1973
Cattell, Mr Colin V BA. . . . . Feb 1982
Faithfull, Mr Edward Philip. . . . . *§Feb 1966
Jones, Mr Anthony J LLB(L'pool) . . . . *Nov 1973

See p112 for the Key to Work Categories & other symbols

Jones, Mr Adrian J . . . . *Jun 1999
Keir, Mr Gordon M LLB . . . . Oct 1985
Norton, Mr James Timothy LLB(Hons). . . . . Nov 1992
Peters, Mr Gordon F LLB . . . . *Jun 1990
Warner, A R. . . . . *Jun 1971
Asoc: O'Connor, Ms Diane E A LLB . . . . *Jul 1973
Ast: Barnett, Mrs Hilary LLB . . . . *May 1972
Con: Mallatratt, Mr Roger S BSc . . . . *Oct 1981

HADGKISS HUGHES & BEALE
(incorporating Laurence Taylor & Co)
1041 Stratford Road Hall Green Birmingham West Midlands B28 8AS
Tel: 0121 778 2161 *Fax:* 0121 778 3290 *Dx:* 18656 HALL GREEN
E-mail: enquiries@hhb-law.co.uk
Office: Birmingham (2 offices)
Work: C1 J1 L O R2 S1 S2 W
Fixed Fee Interview undertaken
Ptr: Eyre, Mr Michael J MA(Oxon). . . . . *Oct 1984
Luscombe, Mr Martin A . . . . *Nov 1997

HADGKISS HUGHES & BEALE
47 Yardley Road Acocks Green Birmingham West Midlands B27 6HQ
Tel: 0121 707 8484 *Fax:* 0121 706 6309
Dx: 19802 ACOCKS GREEN
E-mail: enquiries@hhb-law.co.uk
Office: Birmingham (2 offices)
Languages: German, Gujarati, Hindi, Kiswahili, Russian, Urdu
Work: C1 D1 E F1 G H K1 K3 K4 L N O Q R1 S1 S2 V W Z(l,q)
Emergency Action, Agency, Advocacy, Legal Aid undertaken and Legal Aid Franchise
Ptr: Cattell, Mr Colin V BA. . . . . Feb 1982
Norton, Mr James Timothy LLB(Hons). . . . . Nov 1992
Sharif, Mr Sohale BA . . . . *Nov 2000
Asoc: O'Connor, Ms Diane E A LLB . . . . *Jul 1973
Con: Faithfull, Mr Edward Philip. . . . . *§Feb 1966

HAMSTEAD LAW PRACTICE ‡
5 Railway Terrace Old Walsall Road Birmingham West Midlands B42 1NR
Tel: 0121 357 6500 *Fax:* 0121 357 7670
E-mail: info@hamsteadlaw.com

HAMSTEAD LAW PRACTICE ‡
1 Vicarage Road Kings Heath Birmingham West Midlands B14 7QA
Tel: 0121 357 6500
012 1357 6500 *Fax:* 0121 357 7670
E-mail: info@hamsteadlaw.com

LEE HANDY & CO ‡
247 High Street Erdington Birmingham West Midlands B23 6SS
Tel: 0121 377 6773

HANIF SOLICITORS ‡
393 Coventry Road Small Heath Birmingham West Midlands B10 0SP
Tel: 0121 771 3399 *Fax:* 0121 771 3366
E-mail: enquiry@hanifsolicitors.co.uk

HARBANS SINGH ‡
(in association with Singh Tutt & Co Solicitors'(Wolverhampton))
Piara Ryat House 372 Soho Road Handsworth Birmingham West Midlands B21 9QL
Tel: 0121 551 4496 *Fax:* 0121 523 2271 *Dx:* 24957 HANDSWORTH
Emergency telephone 07831 355544 / 01922 625520
E-mail: hs@harbans-singh.co.uk
List of partners: J N Kakad, H Singh
Office: Oldbury
Languages: Farsi, French, Gujarati, Hindi, Pashto, Punjabi, Russian, Urdu
Work: B2 D1 D2 G H J1 K1 L R1 R2 S1 S2 T1 T2 U1 V W Z(d,g,i,l,p)
Emergency Action, Agency, Advocacy, Fixed Fee Interview, Legal Aid undertaken and Legal Aid Franchise
Ptr: Kakad, Jayantilal N . . . . *Jan 1989
Singh, Harbans LLB(Lond); MBIM Advocate(India); MCIArb Notary Public . . . . *May 1981

HARVEY INGRAM LLP
8th Floor Edmund House 12-22 Newhall Street Birmingham West Midlands B3 3EW
Tel: 0121 214 1200 *Fax:* 0121 214 1299
Office: Bedford, Leicester, Milton Keynes, Newport Pagnell

HARVEY SON & FILBY
3rd Floor Victoria Square House 81 New Street Birmingham West Midlands B2 4BA
Tel: 0121 632 6092 *Fax:* 0121 633 3107 *Dx:* 13016 BIRMINGHAM
Office: Ipswich, London WC2
Ptr: Kong, Mr Stephen LLB; LLM . . . . Jan 2006

HASAN SOLICITORS ‡
(incorporating Harry Jagdev & Co)
Falcon House 643 Stratford Road Spark Hill Birmingham West Midlands B11 4DY
Tel: 0121 778 4003 *Fax:* 0121 778 6221 *Dx:* 18665 HALL GREEN
Emergency telephone 07768 587057
Languages: Punjabi, Turkish, Urdu
Work: G H Z(i)
Emergency Action, Agency, Advocacy, Fixed Fee Interview and Legal Aid undertaken
Ast: Abdi, Mr Mahmood Saeed BA(Hons) . . . . Aug 2003
Deepak, Mrs Punam LLB(Hons). . . . . Mar 2005
Con: Jagdev, Mr Harjit Singh LLB(Hons) . . . . *Apr 1986

PHILLIP M HAYCOCK ‡
89 The Parade Birmingham West Midlands B37 6BB
Tel: 0121 788 1234 *Fax:* 0121 788 1330
Emergency telephone 07626 904141
Work: D1 D2 G H K1 W
Emergency Action, Agency, Advocacy, Fixed Fee Interview, Legal Aid undertaken and Legal Aid Franchise

HEARTLANDS SOLICITORS ‡
18 Alum Rock Road Birmingham West Midlands B8 1JB
Tel: 0121 327 0255 *Fax:* 0121 535 7070 *Dx:* 715911 PHOENIX PARK
E-mail: info@heartsol.com
Languages: Hindi, Mirpuri, Punjabi, Urdu
Work: E F1 K1 K3 L M4 S1 S2 Z(g,i)
Agency and Fixed Fee Interview undertaken

HEAVEN & COMPANY ‡
Charter House 297 Alcester Road South Birmingham West Midlands B14 6DT
Tel: 0121 444 0456 *Fax:* 0121 444 0456
E-mail: heavenandco@btinternet.com

HERITAGE SOLICITORS ‡
206 Rookery Road Handsworth Birmingham West Midlands B21 9PY
Tel: 07791 805116 *Fax:* 0121 554 8527
E-mail: seida@heritagesolicitors.com

HIMAYAH SOLICITORS ‡
291a Birchfield Road Perry Barr Birmingham West Midlands B20 3DD
Tel: 0121 356 5007 *Fax:* 0121 356 6007
E-mail: info@aasolicitors.co.uk
List of partners: K Ahmed
Languages: Hindi, Punjabi, Urdu
Work: L Q S1 S2 Z(i)
Ptr: Ahmed, Mr Khurshid . . . . Oct 2000
Ast: Ali, Murtaza BA(Hons) . . . . May 2001
Yakoob, Mr Asead LLB(Hons). . . . . Aug 2008

STUART HODGE CORPORATE LAWYERS ‡
3 Temple Row West Birmingham West Midlands B2 5NY
Tel: 0121 214 2490 *Fax:* 0121 214 2491

THOMAS HORTON LLP ‡
61 Hewell Road Barnt Green Birmingham West Midlands B45 8NL
Tel: 0121 445 7373
E-mail: receptionlg@thomashorton.co.uk

HOWELL & CO ‡
1341 Stratford Road Hall Green Birmingham West Midlands B28 9HW
Tel: 0121 778 5031 *Fax:* 0121 777 3967 *Dx:* 714513 HALL GREEN 2
E-mail: mail@howell-solicitors.co.uk
List of partners: P A Burden, B M Jobling, C J Leek
Work: B1 B2 C1 C3 D1 E F1 F2 G H K1 K3 L N O Q S1 S2 T1 T2 W
Emergency Action, Agency, Advocacy, Legal Aid undertaken and Legal Aid Franchise
Ptr: Burden, Mr Peter A BA(Hons)(Law) ★. . . . . *Oct 1988
Jobling, Mr Bruce M ●. . . . . *Nov 1972
Leek, Mr Christopher J ● . . . . Jul 1997
Con: Golden, Mr David Michael. . . . . *Dec 1986

HUJAN & CO SOLICITORS ‡
24a Showell Green Lane Birmingham West Midlands B11 4JP
Tel: 0121 766 7345

HUSSAIN SOLICITORS LIMITED ‡
481 Coventry Road Small Heath Birmingham West Midlands B10 0JS
Tel: 0121 766 7474

IEI SOLICITORS
Bank House 6 Hockley Hill Birmingham West Midlands B18 5AA
Tel: 0121 554 6445 *Fax:* 0121 270 4210
E-mail: contact@ieisolicitors.co.uk
Office: Edgware, Norwich

I WILL SOLICITORS LTD ‡
201 Streetly Road Erdington Birmingham West Midlands B23 7AJ
Tel: 0121 683 6940
Languages: Urdu
Work: C1 M4 W

IRWIN MITCHELL LLP
Imperial House 31 Temple Street Birmingham West Midlands B2 5DB
Tel: 0870 150 0100 *Fax:* 0121 643 6021 *Dx:* 13030 BIRMINGHAM
Office: Bristol, Leeds, London EC1, Manchester, Newcastle upon Tyne, Sheffield
Work: A1 A3 C1 C2 C3 D1 E J1 K1 L M1 M2 N O P Q R1 R2 T1 T2 W X Z(c,d,e,g,h,j,k,l,m,o,p,q,r,t,w)
Emergency Action, Agency, Advocacy, Fixed Fee Interview, Legal Aid undertaken and Member of Accident Line
Ptr: Billings, Mr David M. . . . . *May 1969
Cunningham, Mr Kevin Gerald BA. . . . . *Aug 1979
Fernandes, Miss Alison R LLB(Hons) . . . . *Apr 1997
Flathers, Mr John M LLB(Leeds) . . . . *Nov 1987
Follis, Mr Richard T LLB Deputy Vice President of the Birmingham Law Society . . . . *Dec 1981
Harris, Mr Paul Thomas BA(Hons)(Law) Chairman of R3 (Midlands) . . . . *Oct 1987
Henderson, Mr Stuart A LLB . . . . *Mar 1992
Jordan, Miss Lisa C LLB(Hons) . . . . *Oct 1993
Kirkpatrick, Mr Alasdair Robert Moore LLB R W Stead Memorial Scholarship 1982. . . . . *Oct 1986
Mewies, Miss Sally A LLB(Hons) . . . . *Oct 1988
Napier, Mr T Michael LLB. . . . . *Mar 1970
Peacock, Mr Jonathan LLB(Hons); LLM . . . . *Apr 1993
Simpson, Mr Wrightson LLB. . . . . *May 1980
Walters, Mr Gary Richard ACII . . . . *Dec 1990
Whiting, Mr John R LLB. . . . . *May 1991
Wylde, Mr Andrew LLB . . . . *Nov 1991
Ast: Allen, Ms Katherine L LLB(Hons) . . . . *Sep 1996
Banks, Mr Philip J. . . . . *Aug 1997
Burke, Ms Rachel Victoria LLB(Hons) . . . . *Sep 1994
Burns, Miss Sara . . . . *Sep 1996
Chhoker, Sukhdev. . . . . *Jan 1999
Coates, Miss Alida . . . . *May 1996
Cox, Miss Amanda Jane LLB(Hons). . . . . *Dec 1995
Currie, Mr Matthew James LLB(Hons). . . . . *Nov 1995
Dean, Mr Howard Michael LLB(Hons). . . . . *Jan 1994
Dowling, Mr Fergal Nicholas LLB(Hons). . . . . *Nov 1994
Edwards, Mr Philip Derek LLB(Hons) Wolverhampton Law Society's Centenary Prize 1992 Chairman of Headway Kidderminster. . . . . *Sep 1994
Hamilton, Ms Sandra . . . . *Oct 1997
Harris-James, Mr Kevin M LLB . . . . *Feb 1993
Jermine, Ms Rachel Elizabeth. . . . . *Sep 1997
Johal, Mr Resham S LLB(Hons). . . . . *Sep 1999
Ladva, Mrs Kavita LLB(Hons) . . . . *Dec 1995
Muscroft, Ms Julie BA(Dunelm) . . . . *Aug 1987
Nicol, Ms Tricia C . . . . *Sep 1999
Pickup, Miss Hilary . . . . *Sep 1999
Pinch, Mr Frank Roger . . . . *Oct 1993
Singh, Mr Devinder LLB(Hons) . . . . *Mar 1992
Skehan, Miss Louise . . . . *Oct 1998
Spurling, Mr Marc LLB . . . . *Oct 1998
Stockdale, Miss Sarah LLB; DipLaw. . . . . *Oct 1999
Taylor, Ms Annabel Lucy LLB(Hons); LPC. . . . . . . *Oct 1998
Taylor, Ms Irene SRN; DipNur; LLB(Hons). . . . . . . *Nov 1999
Thiara, Mrs Charanjit LLB(Hons) . . . . *Oct 1993
Wann, Ms Tessa Joanne Rose LLB(Hons). . . . . . . *Oct 1998
White, Dr John C . . . . *Sep 1999

ASHLEY JAMES SOLICITORS ‡
1301 Stratford Road Hall Green Birmingham West Midlands B28 9HH
Tel: 0845 643 1234 *Fax:* 0121 702 1410

JANSONS SOLICITORS ‡
348 Stratford Road Sparkhill Birmingham West Midlands B11 4AA
Tel: 0121 773 4142 *Fax:* 0121 773 4145
E-mail: enquiries@jansonsolicitors.com

THE JOHN HUGHES LAW PRACTICE ‡
Cheltenham House 14-16 Temple Street Birmingham West Midlands B2 5BG
Tel: 0845 130 2855 *Fax:* 0845 130 5299 *Dx:* 13008 BIRMINGHAM
E-mail: jrhughes@jhlp.co.uk

JONAS ROY BLOOM ‡
The Citadel 190 Corporation Street Birmingham West Midlands B4 6QD
Tel: 0121 212 4111 *Fax:* 0121 212 1770 *Dx:* 23540 BIRMINGHAM 3
Emergency telephone 0121 212 4111
E-mail: info@jrblegal.co.uk
List of partners: S G Bloom, F J Bloomer, P B Cox, B Henry, S M Jonas, N G Roy, J P Smitheman
Languages: German
Work: B2 G H N O Q Z(g,j,r)
Emergency Action, Agency, Advocacy and Legal Aid undertaken
Ptr: Bloom, Mr Stephen George BA . . . . *Jul 1981
Bloomer, Mr Fergal Joseph LLB(Hons) . . . . Feb 1988
Cox, Mr Patrick B BCL ★ . . . . *Mar 1990
Henry, Mr Ben . . . . Oct 2008
Jonas, Mr Steven Michael LLB(Manc) ★ Former President of Birmingham Law Society . . . . *§Apr 1981
Roy, Mr Nicholas G LLB ★ Notary Public . . . . *Oct 1969
Smitheman, Mr John P BA(Hons). . . . . *May 1980
Ast: Adams, Ms Natasha Louisa LLB . . . . Nov 2004
Jacob, Mr Michael H LLB . . . . *May 1975

DAVID WARREN JONES ‡
Sycamore House 23a Sycamore Road Bourneville Birmingham West Midlands B30 2AA
Tel: 0121 414 1949 *Fax:* 0121 471 3181 *Dx:* 20307 COTTERIDGE
E-mail: davidwarrenjones@btconnect.com

GORDON JONES & CO ‡
37/139 New Road Rubery Birmingham West Midlands B45 9JR
Tel: 0121 453 8151 *Fax:* 0121 453 9825 *Dx:* 20553 RUBERY
E-mail: gjones@gordonjonessolicitors.co.uk
List of partners: G Jones, D Watkins
Work: A1 C1 E F1 J1 J2 K1 K3 K4 L N O Q S1 S2 T2 W Z(d,g)
Emergency Action, Agency, Advocacy and Fixed Fee Interview undertaken
Ptr: Watkins, Mrs Denise . . . . *Feb 2005
Asoc: Akehurst, Mr Michael J LLB. . . . . *Dec 1977

J R JONES ‡
614-616 Stratford Road Birmingham West Midlands B11 4AP
Tel: 0121 777 7864

JOYCE LEGAL ‡
Suite 3a St Georges Court Birmingham West Midlands B1 3AH
Tel: 0121 262 1800

JUSMOUNT & CO ‡
7c Highgate Business Centre Ladypool Road Sparkbrook Birmingham West Midlands B12 8LD
Tel: 0121 773 8911 *Fax:* 0121 773 8911
E-mail: s.saini@jusmountsolicitors.com

KANGS SOLICITORS ‡
Tudor House 2a Wake Green Road Moseley Birmingham West Midlands B13 9EZ
Tel: 0121 449 9888 *Fax:* 0121 449 8849 *Dx:* 10787 MOSELEY
E-mail: enquiries@kangssolicitors.co.uk
List of partners: H S Kang
Office: Birmingham, London EC4, Manchester
Languages: Punjabi
Work: B2 G H S1
Agency, Advocacy and Legal Aid undertaken
Ptr: Kang, Hamraj Singh BA(Econ) . . . . *Oct 1996
Asoc: Veale, Mr John . . . . Sep 2003

KANGS SOLICITORS
854 Washwood Heath Road Ward End Birmingham West Midlands B8 2NL
Tel: 0121 784 3015 *Fax:* 0121 784 3182
E-mail: enquiries@kangssolicitors.co.uk
Office: Birmingham, London EC4, Manchester

KATARIA SOLICITORS ‡
338a Soho Road Handsworth Birmingham West Midlands B21 9QL
Tel: 0121 554 5404

KAULDHAR & CO ‡
1 Old Walsall Road Great Barr Birmingham West Midlands B42 1NN
Tel: 0121 358 6868

KENNEDYS
35 Newhall Street Birmingham West Midlands B3 3PU
Tel: 0121 214 8000 *Fax:* 0121 214 8001 *Dx:* 13043 BIRMINGHAM
Office: Belfast, Cambridge, Chelmsford, London EC3, Maidstone, Manchester, Sheffield, Taunton

A ZEB KHAN SOLICITORS ‡
19 Washwood Heath Road Washwood Heath Birmingham West Midlands B8 1SH
Tel: 0121 327 5999

T A KHOO SOLICITORS ‡
8th Floor Suite A Albany House Birmingham West Midlands B5 4BD
Tel: 0121 666 7088 / 0560 156 7863 *Fax:* 0121 666 6880
Dx: 71180 BIRMINGHAM 28
E-mail: enquiries@takhoosolicitors.co.uk

KILROYS ‡
Park Business Centre Wood Lane Erdington Birmingham West Midlands B24 9QR
Tel: 0121 270 1002 *Fax:* 0870 199 1459
E-mail: chris@kilroys.co.uk
List of partners: C T Kilroy
Work: C1 E F1 J1 N O Q S1 S2 Z(k,l)
Emergency Action, Agency and Advocacy undertaken
SPr: Kilroy, Mr Christopher T LLB(Hons); LLM . . . . *Jun 1976

KINGSWOOD LEGAL LIMITED ‡
1st Floor 385 Coventry Road Small Heath Birmingham West Midlands B10 0SW
Tel: 0121 772 7779 *Fax:* 0121 772 4886
E-mail: info@kingswoodsolicitors.com

LATHAR SOLICITORS ‡
41 Anstruther Road Edgbaston Birmingham West Midlands B15 3NW
Tel: 0121 454 2625

LAW CONNECT ‡
Chambers 221 27 Colmore Row Birmingham West Midlands B3 2EW
Tel: 0845 833 6690 *Fax:* 0845 833 6691

THE LAW PRACTICE (UK) LIMITED ‡
Combrai Court 1231 Staratford Road Hall Green Birmingham West Midlands B28 9AA
Tel: 0121 778 2371 *Fax:* 0121 778 5685 *Dx:* 18651 HALL GREEN
E-mail: ga@lawpracticeukltd.com

LAWRENCE-REYNOLDS SOLICITORS ‡
213 Station Road Stechford Birmingham West Midlands B33 8BB
Tel: 0121 784 5321 / 07983 377712 *Fax:* 0121 785 0688
E-mail: admin@lawrence-reynolds.com

CHRISTINE LEE & CO (SOLICITORS) LTD ‡
Cathay Building 86 Holloway Head Birmingham West Midlands B1 1NB
Tel: 0121 666 6228 *Fax:* 0121 666 6993
Dx: 720294 BIRMINGHAM 47
List of partners: D T W Ho, C C K Lee, M F Wilkes
Office: London W1
Languages: Cantonese, Chinese, Malay, Mandarin
Ptr: Ho, Mr David Tat Wai . . . . Nov 2003
Lee, Ms Christine C K LLB . . . . Feb 2002
Wilkes, Mr Martin F LLB. . . . . May 1977
Asoc: Ho, Mrs Jennifer BA(Hons) . . . . Oct 1994
Nall, Mrs Sandeep Kaur. . . . . Jun 2005

LEGAL SWAN SOLICITORS ‡
First Floor 168 Hampstead Road Handsworth Birmingham West Midlands B20 2QR
Tel: 0121 551 7866 *Fax:* 0121 551 7866
E-mail: info@legalswan.com

LEVENES SOLICITORS
The McLaren Building 35 Dale End Birmingham West Midlands B4 7LN
Tel: 0121 212 0000 *Fax:* 0121 233 1878 *Dx:* 23502 BIRMINGHAM 3
E-mail: enquiries@levenes.co.uk
Office: London N22
Languages: Punjabi
Work: D1 D2 G H K1 N V Z(q)
Emergency Action, Agency, Advocacy, Fixed Fee Interview, Legal Aid undertaken, Legal Aid Franchise and Member of Accident Line
Asoc: Taylor, Miss Joanne Marie LLB(Hons). . . . . *Jan 1998
Ast: Beasley, Mr Timothy John LLB(Hons); LPC . . . . . . *Oct 1992
Brown, Mr Stephen BA(Hons); LLDip . . . . *Aug 1997
Evans, Ms Ruth L. Jan 2000
Martyr, Mr Colin Richard BA; LLB Governor of Worthington School . . . . *Sep 1994
O'Hora, Ms Jasminka . . . . Apr 1999
Parapagga, Miss Balbir K LLB(Hons) . . . . *Aug 1998
Price, Miss Catherine M. . . . . *Jul 1995
Sivia, Miss Rosie P . . . . *Oct 1995

LEWIS ONIONS SOLICITORS ‡
Allium House 36 Water Street Birmingham West Midlands B3 1HP
Tel: 0121 200 7240 *Fax:* 0121 236 1492

LIA SOLICITORS ‡
6 Poplar Road Kings Heath Birmingham West Midlands B14 7AD
Tel: 0121 444 0020 *Fax:* 0121 444 0021

LIN & CO SOLICITORS ‡
1st Floor 80-82 Lower Essex Street Birmingham West Midlands B5 6SN
Tel: 0121 244 2300 *Fax:* 0121 244 2200
Dx: 711807 BIRMINGHAM 28
E-mail: linsolicitors@aol.com
List of partners: C K L Lin
Office: Sutton Coldfield
Languages: Cantonese, Mandarin
Work: E K1 K3 S1 S2 W Z(i)
SPr: Lin, Miss Callie K L LLB. . . . . *Dec 1992
Ast: Wong, Mr Kee Hiung Eric LLB; BEng . . . . *Apr 2011
Other offices in Birmingham. We conduct business in Cantonese, Mandarin. We specialise in the following areas of work Family Law, Commercial Conveyancing, Immigration and Nationality, Residential Conveyancing, Divorce, Wills.

LINCOLN-LEWIS & CO ‡
48 Frederick Road Edgbaston Birmingham West Midlands B15 1HN
Tel: 0121 454 7011 *Fax:* 0121 454 7070 *Dx:* 712632 EDGBASTON 1
Emergency telephone 01527 893246
List of partners: J D Lincoln-Lewis
Work: A1 C1 C2 C3 E F1 G H J1 K1 L M1 M2 N P S1 T1 T2 W Z(c,i,j,l)
Emergency Action, Agency, Advocacy, Fixed Fee Interview undertaken and Member of Accident Line
SPr: Lincoln-Lewis, Mr Jeremy D. . . . . *Oct 1962

LOVSEY MARSH ‡
Pitman Building 161 Corporation Street Birmingham West Midlands B4 6PH
Tel: 0121 212 0255 *Fax:* 0121 212 0266 *Dx:* 23506 BIRMINGHAM 3
E-mail: info@lovseymarsh.co.uk
List of partners: A McKie
Languages: Mirpuri, Punjabi, Urdu
Work: D1 K1 S1
Emergency Action, Agency, Advocacy and Legal Aid undertaken
Ptr: McKie, Miss Annette LLB Chairman of the DSA Board of Appeal . . . . *Dec 1980

LOYNTON & CO ‡
Suite 13 Thimblemill Lane Nechells Birmingham West Midlands B7 5HS
Tel: 0121 327 0118 / 327 0652 *Fax:* 0121 327 1167
List of partners: J Loynton
Languages: Bahasa, Cantonese, Thai
Work: C1 E K1 L S1 W
Agency, Fixed Fee Interview and Legal Aid undertaken
Ptr: Loynton, Ms Jenny LLB . . . . *Oct 1988

M&N SOLICITORS ‡
307a Birchfield Road Birmingham West Midlands B20 3BX
Tel: 0121 356 1999

MCCORMACKS ‡
Ruskin Chambers 191 Corporation Street Birmingham West Midlands B4 6RP
Tel: 0121 200 2777 *Fax:* 0121 236 1740
E-mail: mail@mccormacks.biz
List of partners: J P McCormack
Work: B2 G H N
SPr: McCormack, Mr John P ★. . . . . Dec 1979

ROBERTA MCDONALD ‡
12 Wake Green Road Moseley Birmingham West Midlands B13 9EZ
Tel: 0121 449 6821 *Fax:* 0121 449 5160
E-mail: rmdsolicitor@aol.com
List of partners: R A McDonald
Work: D1 D2
Agency, Advocacy, Legal Aid undertaken and Legal Aid Franchise
SPr: McDonald, Ms Roberta A LLB(Bris) . . . . *Dec 1973

MCFADDENS LLP
Vancouver House 111 Hagley Road Birmingham West Midlands B16 8LB
Tel: 0121 452 5040 *Fax:* 0121 452 5041 *Dx:* 23052 EDGBASTON
E-mail: reception@mcfaddenslaw.co.uk
Office: London EC2

MCGRATH & CO ‡
2nd Floor Gazette Buildings 168 Corporation Street Birmingham West Midlands B4 6TF
Tel: 0121 643 4121 *Fax:* 0121 236 7965 *Dx:* 13010 BIRMINGHAM 1
E-mail: info@mcgrath.co.uk
List of partners: S Kumar, G J McGrath, E F M Robinson, A Verma
Office: Birmingham (2 offices)
Work: G H L
Legal Aid undertaken
Ptr: McGrath, Mr Graham J MA(Oxon). . . . . *Oct 1976
Robinson, Mr Errol F M BA . . . . Jun 1988
Asoc: Ellis, Ms Georgina . . . . Jun 2008
Ast: Clarke, Mr Alan . . . . Oct 2004
Kelly, Ms Rosemary. . . . . Mar 2006

MCGRATH IMMIGRATION SOLICITORS PARTNERSHIP
2nd Floor Gazette Buildings 168 Corporation Street Birmingham West Midlands B4 6TF
Tel: 0121 643 4124 *Fax:* 0121 236 7965
Office: Birmingham (2 offices)
Work: Z(i)
Ptr: Kumar, Satish LLB(Hons); LLM . . . . Dec 1998
McGrath, Mr Graham J MA(Oxon). . . . . *Oct 1976
Robinson, Mr Errol F M BA . . . . Jun 1988

MCGRATH LITIGATION PARTNERSHIP
2nd Floor Gazette Buildings 168 Corporation Street Birmingham West Midlands B4 6TF
Tel: 0121 643 4828 *Fax:* 0121 236 7965 *Dx:* 13010 BIRMINGHAM 1
Emergency telephone 0870 238 5411
E-mail: info@mcgrath.co.uk
Office: Birmingham (2 offices)
Work: L N Q
Emergency Action, Agency, Advocacy, Fixed Fee Interview, Legal Aid undertaken and Member of Accident Line
Ptr: McGrath, Mr Graham J MA(Oxon). . . . . *Oct 1976
Robinson, Mr Errol F M BA . . . . Jun 1988
Verma, Ajay LLB(Hons) . . . . Sep 1994
Asoc: Chumber, Mr Haripal Lal LLB(Hons). . . . . Sep 2004

MACKAY & CO ‡
95 Summerfield Crescent Edgbaston Birmingham West Midlands B16 0EN
Tel: 0121 454 1814 *Fax:* 0121 242 3524
E-mail: law@robertmackay.biz
List of partners: R I Mackay
SPr: Mackay, Mr Robert I ★ . . . . *Dec 1972

MAIDMENTS
5 Rowchester Court Whittall Street Birmingham West Midlands B4 6DH
Tel: 0870 403 4000 *Fax:* 0845 017 6633
Emergency telephone 0121 200 2221
E-mail: contact@maidments.co.uk
Office: Bolton, Sale, Salford
Ptr: Manu, Mr Mahan . . . . Nov 2000

MANDLA BHOMRA & CO ‡
19 Soho Road Handsworth Birmingham West Midlands B21 9SN
Tel: 0121 523 3384 *Fax:* 0121 554 9089 *Dx:* 24956 HANDSWORTH
Emergency telephone 0121 525 6418 / 440 0783
List of partners: S S Bhomra, S S Mandla
Languages: Hindi, Punjabi, Urdu
Work: D1 E G H K1 M1 P S1 Z(i)
Emergency Action, Agency, Advocacy, Fixed Fee Interview and Legal Aid undertaken
Ptr: Bhomra, Sukhdev S LLB . . . . Aug 1985
Mandla, Sewa S . . . . *Dec 1976

THOMAS MANSFIELD LLP
Aspect Court 4 Temple Row Birmingham West Midlands B2 5HG
Tel: 0845 601 7756 *Fax:* 0121 222 4437
E-mail: info@thomasmansfield.com
Office: Croydon, London E1, Manchester

MANTILLA AND STONERWOOD SOLICITORS ‡
Unit 116 The Albert Wing The Argent Centre Birmingham West Midlands B1 3HS
Tel: 0121 236 7959 *Fax:* 0121 233 3771
Dx: 71208 BIRMINGHAM 29
E-mail: enquiries@mantillaandstonerwood.co.uk

MARGETTS & RITCHIE ‡
Coleridge Chambers 177 Corporation Street Birmingham West Midlands B4 6RL
Tel: 0121 236 5517 *Fax:* 0121 236 5520
List of partners: D Hetherington, G R Ritchie, J E Ritchie
Work: E F1 F2 J2 S1 S2 W Z(y)
Ptr: Hetherington, Mr David BA . . . . *Jun 1978
Ritchie, Mr Graham R. . . . . *§Dec 1973
Ritchie, Mr Jonathan Edward BA . . . . *Nov 1995

MARKS & CLERK
Alpha Tower Suffolk Street Queensway Birmingham West Midlands B1 1TT
Tel: 0121 643 5881 *Fax:* 0121 606 4766
Office: Cheltenham, Leeds, Leicester, Liverpool, London WC2, Manchester, Oxford

MAYFLOWER SOLICITORS ‡
Floor 2 3 Brindley Place Birmingham West Midlands B1 2JB
Tel: 0845 233 0003
E-mail: enquiries@mayflowersolicitors.com

MERCY MESSENGER ‡
Ash House Pinewood Court Coleshill Road Birmingham West Midlands B37 7HW
Tel: 0121 770 1221 *Fax:* 0121 770 7110
E-mail: family@mercymessenger.co.uk
List of partners: D F Messenger, M Messenger
Office: Daventry
Work: C1 D1 K1 K2 K3
Ptr: Messenger, Mr David Frank LLB(Lond) . . . . *§Jan 1966
Messenger, Ms Mercy. . . . . *Dec 1966
Asoc: Ganderton, Mrs Victoria Anne LLB . . . . *Sep 2005
Long, Miss Lucy BA. . . . . Sep 2005

MIAN & CO ‡
3rd Floor Suite 1 190 Corporation Street Birmingham West Midlands B4 6QD
Tel: 0121 684 8000 *Fax:* 0121 684 8001 *Dx:* 23505 BIRMINGHAM 3
Emergency telephone 07659 109742
E-mail: mians@btinternet.com
List of partners: A Mian, T S Mian
Languages: Hindi, Mirpuri, Punjabi, Urdu
Work: G H
Emergency Action, Agency, Advocacy, Fixed Fee Interview, Legal Aid undertaken and Legal Aid Franchise
Ptr: Mian, Ajmal LLB . . . . *Jun 1980
Mian, Tanweer S . . . . *Jan 1984
Ast: Duran, Mr Safdar Nawab Khan LLB(Hons) . . . . . . Jan 2004
Khan, Mr Mahmood LLB(Hons) . . . . *Nov 2001
Zahoor, Mr Aftab LLB(Hons). . . . . *Aug 2008

MILES-PIERCE SOLICITORS ‡
Cornwall Buildings 45-51 Newhall Street Birmingham West Midlands B3 3QR
Tel: 0800 987 5305 *Fax:* 0121 222 4177
E-mail: info@miles-pierce.com
List of partners: J P W Fallows, P H Fallows, H Hodgkinson
Languages: French
Work: B1 C1 D1 E F1 G H K1 L N O P Q S1 W Z(i)
Emergency Action, Agency, Advocacy, Fixed Fee Interview, Legal Aid undertaken and Member of Accident Line
Ptr: Fallows, Mr Julian Peter William LLB . . . . *Nov 1995
Fallows, Mr Peter H TD . . . . *Dec 1966
Hodgkinson, Mr Harry LLB . . . . Jun 1964

MILLS & REEVE
78-84 Colmore Row Birmingham West Midlands B3 2AB
Tel: 0121 454 4000 *Fax:* 0121 200 3028
Dx: 707290 BIRMINGHAM 65
E-mail: guy.hodgson@mills-reeve.com
Office: Cambridge, Leeds, London EC3, Manchester, Norwich
Work: C1 E J1 J2 N O Q R1 S1 S2 W Z(c,d,h,m,o,q,r,u)
Ptr: Cassidy, Mr Thomas M LLB(Lond) . . . . *Aug 1978
Hawker, Ms Fiona LLB . . . . *Mar 1994
Hinchley, Mr Guy R LLB. . . . . *Mar 1985
Hundle, Jogvinder. . . . . Dec 1991
Knowles, Mr Stuart P BA(Oxon)(Law) . . . . *Nov 1986
Turner, Mr Angus LLB. . . . . *Nov 1995
Waddington, Ms Sheila K I BA . . . . Mar 1989
Asoc: Brewer, Mr Martin BA; CPE . . . . Nov 1991
Ast: Brathwaite, Mrs Dawn Allison LLB; LLM. . . . . May 1991
Bull, Mr Christian Graham LLB; MA . . . . *Sep 2002
Burnett, Mr Martin MA(Oxon) . . . . *Dec 1981
Dhillon-Sidhu, Mrs Baljit Kaur . . . . *Feb 2000
Duce, Mr Kevin . . . . Oct 2000
Frankland, Mr Neil J LLB(Hons). . . . . *Oct 1997
Gooding, Mr David Jonathon Charles BA(Hons); DipLL; DipLP . . . . Sep 2002
Haines, Miss Jacqueline Marie LLB . . . . Nov 1992
Hall, Mr Wesley MSc(Econ) . . . . *Jun 1995
Herlihy, Mrs Jayne Elizabeth LLB; RGN . . . . Sep 2001
Horner, Miss Katy LLB(Hons) . . . . *Sep 2001
Jacks, Mr Howard LLB(Wales) . . . . *§Aug 1975
Jones, Mr Alban P LLB(Manc) Stephen Heelis Prize; George Hadfield & John Peacock Prizes. . . . . *Apr 1977
Macharaga, Mr Dennis Tungamirai LLB(Hons)(B'ham) Committee Member of the Northern Counties Housing Association Ltd . . . . *Oct 1987
Smith, Ms Wendy BA; LLB . . . . *Nov 2000
Wylly, Miss Johann Lee BA . . . . Sep 2001

B H MOHAMMED ‡
302 Stratford Road Birmingham West Midlands B11 1AA
Tel: 0121 772 4464 *Fax:* 0121 773 3846 *Dx:* 707271 SPARKHILL
Emergency telephone 0121 772 4464
E-mail: info@bh-mohammed.com
Languages: Bengali, Gujarati, Kiswahili, Mirpuri, Punjabi, Urdu
Work: B2 G H
Agency, Advocacy, Legal Aid undertaken and Legal Aid Franchise

JOHN MORGAN SOLICITORS ‡
The Citadel 190 Corporation Street Birmingham West Midlands B4 6TU
Tel: 0121 233 1852 *Fax:* 0121 236 2521 *Dx:* 23535 BIRMINGHAM 3
Emergency telephone 07659 104283
E-mail: enquiries@johnmorgansolicitors.co.uk
List of partners: J K Morgan
Languages: Punjabi
Work: G H
Emergency Action, Agency, Advocacy, Fixed Fee Interview and Legal Aid undertaken
Ptr: Morgan, Mr John K . . . . *§Jan 1964

MUSHTAQ & CO ‡
14-16 Bristol Street Birmingham West Midlands B5 7AA
Tel: 0121 622 1786 *Fax:* 0121 622 2786
Emergency telephone 0121 622 1786
List of partners: R S Mushtaq
Languages: Punjabi, Urdu
Work: D1 F1 G H J1 K1 L Q S1 W Z(i)
Emergency Action, Agency, Advocacy, Legal Aid undertaken and Member of Accident Line
SPr: Mushtaq, Miss Rifat S BA. . . . . *Feb 1988

See p112 for the Key to Work Categories & other symbols

NEW HAMPTON LAW ‡
63 Great Hampton Street Birmingham West Midlands B18 6EL
Tel: 0121 551 9777 *Fax:* 0121 523 9444
Dx: 712535 BIRMINGHAM 30
E-mail: legal@newhamptonlaw.com

NEWTON LAW PRACTICE ‡
30a Newton Road Great Barr Birmingham West Midlands B43 6BW
Tel: 0121 357 0100 *Fax:* 0121 357 0123
E-mail: mail@newtonlawpractice.co.uk

NICHOLAS & CO ‡
75a High Street Kings Heath Birmingham West Midlands B14 7BH
Tel: 0121 444 3822 *Fax:* 0121 444 6815
E-mail: info@nicholas-solicitors.co.uk

NICHOLLS & CO LIMITED ‡
Lonsdale House 52 Blucher Street Birmingham West Midlands B1 1QU
Tel: 0845 194 9570 *Fax:* 0845 194 9571
E-mail: enquiries@nichollsco.co.uk

O'MAHONEY & COMPANY ‡
653 Kingstanding Road The Circle Kingstanding Birmingham West Midlands B44 9RH
Tel: 0121 355 5571 *Fax:* 0121 355 8409
E-mail: joan@omahoney.uk.com

OSBORNE & CO ‡
168 Corporation Street Birmingham West Midlands B4 6TF
Tel: 0121 200 1074 *Fax:* 0121 212 3289 *Dx:* 22532 BIRMINGHAM 3
E-mail: enquiries@osbornesolicitors.co.uk

PARKER GREGO CULLEN & BALL ‡
101 Bath Street Birmingham West Midlands B4 6HG
Tel: 0121 200 3031 *Fax:* 0121 200 3029
List of partners: E S Ball, G K Cullen, R M Hill, J M Lewis
Work: G H S1
Agency, Advocacy, Legal Aid undertaken and Legal Aid Franchise
Ptr: Ball, Mr Edward Stevie . . . . Jan 2001
Hill, Mr Roger M. . . . . *Jan 1969
Cullen, Mr Gerard Kevin. . . . . .NSP
Lewis, Mr Joseph Morgan. . . . . .NSP

JAMES PEARCE & CO ‡
606 Bromford Lane Ward End Birmingham West Midlands B8 2DP
Tel: 0121 784 1886 *Fax:* 0121 783 6466 *Dx:* 27435 HODGE HILL
E-mail: ejfp@jamespearce.co.uk
List of partners: J James, E J F Pearce
Office: Birmingham (2 offices), Sutton Coldfield
Work: C1 C2 C3 D1 E F1 J1 K1 L M1 M2 N O P Q R1 S1 T1 T2 V W Z(c,i,l)
Agency, Advocacy, Fixed Fee Interview, Legal Aid undertaken, Legal Aid Franchise and Member of Accident Line
Ptr: James, Mr John BA(Hons); CPE . . . . *Jul 1997
Pearce, Mr Edward James Frederick LLB(Hons) . . . *Jan 1995
Ast: Johnson, Mrs Judy Juliet . . . . *Oct 1999
Jones, Mr Stuart BA(Hons) . . . . *Feb 1990

JAMES PEARCE & CO
9 York Road Erdington Birmingham West Midlands B23 6TE
Tel: 0121 382 6622 *Fax:* 0121 350 5855 *Dx:* 21201 ERDINGTON
Office: Birmingham (2 offices), Sutton Coldfield

JAMES PEARCE & CO
James Pearce House 379 Queslett Road Great Barr Birmingham West Midlands B43 7HH
Tel: 0121 360 1300 *Fax:* 0121 360 3800 *Dx:* 728744 GREAT BARR
Office: Birmingham (2 offices), Sutton Coldfield
Ptr: Pearce, Mr Edward James Frederick LLB(Hons) . . . *Jan 1995

PEARSON ROWE ‡
(incorporating Springthorpe Holcroft & Bishop)
55 St Pauls Square Birmingham West Midlands B3 1QS
Tel: 0121 236 7388 *Fax:* 0121 237 4307 *Dx:* 13021 BIRMINGHAM
E-mail: info@pearson-rowe.co.uk
List of partners: M Deeley, B J Flint, A Patel
Work: A1 B1 C1 D1 E J1 J2 K1 K2 K3 L N O Q S1 S2 W Z(c,h,q,w)
Agency, Advocacy, Fixed Fee Interview undertaken and Member of Accident Line
Ptr: Deeley, Mr Michael LLB(Wales) . . . . *May 1974
Flint, Mr Brian J. . . . . *May 1979
Patel, Mr Alpesh LLB(Hons). . . . . *Apr 2004
Asoc: Faulkner, Miss Jodi BSc(Hons); PGDipLaw . . . . . . *Sep 2003
Rouine, Mr Augustine Patrick LLB(Hons) Deputy District Judge . . . . *Nov 1991
Ast: Elliott, Mr Michael. . . . . Jan 1973
McDowall, Mr James I MA(Cantab) . . . . *Jul 1973

DAVID PETT & CO ‡
Colmore Plaza Executive 20 Colmore Circus Birmingham West Midlands B4 6AT
Tel: 0845 223 8822
E-mail: enquiries@pettfranklin.com

DAVID PHILLIPS & PARTNERS
120 Cornwall Buildings 45 Newhall Street Birmingham West Midlands B3 3QR
Tel: 0844 842 5525 *Fax:* 0121 222 4164 *Dx:* 13017 BIRMINGHAM
E-mail: info@dpp-law.com
Office: Bootle (2 offices), Chadwell Heath, Leicester, Liverpool, London E1, London SE18, London W1, Manchester, Nelson, Wealdstone

PINSENT MASONS LLP
3 Colmore Circus Birmingham West Midlands B4 6BH
Est: 2004
Tel: 0121 200 1050 *Fax:* 0121 626 1040
Dx: 703167 BIRMINGHAM 12
E-mail: enquiries@pinsentmasons.com
Office: Bristol, Leeds, London EC2, Manchester
Languages: Arabic, Cantonese, French, German, Greek, Hindi, Italian, Mandarin, Punjabi, Spanish
Work: A3 B1 C1 C2 C3 E F1 F2 I J1 J2 L M1 N O P R1 R2 T1 T2 U1 U2 W X Z(b,c,d,e,f,h,j,k,l,n,o,p,q,s,u,w,y,z,za)
Emergency Action, Agency and Advocacy undertaken
Ptr: Aisbett, Mr Alan LLB . . . . *Jan 1983
Bange, Mr Vijay K LLB(Hons) . . . . *Jan 1994
Bond, Ms Alison J BA(Cantab) . . . . *Nov 1988
Brown, Mr Stephen V BA(Cantab). . . . . *Oct 1982
Coley, Mr Jonathan David LLB . . . . *Sep 1994
Crow, Ms Linda J LLB(Hons) Chairman of the Quoted Companies Alliance Legal Committee. . . . . . . *Sep 1989
Dye, Miss Jayne Barbara BA . . . . *Nov 1995
Ellis, Ms Joanne BSc . . . . *Sep 1995
Fitton, Mr Christopher Anthony LLB . . . . *Aug 1995
Fortnam, Mr Jonathan R LLB(L'pool) . . . . *Oct 1990
Gill, Mr Joseph LLB; LLM . . . . *Nov 1994
Gronow, Mr Simon D V MA(Cantab). . . . . *Oct 1986
Harkin, Mr Paul M LLB(Hons). . . . . *May 1991
Hart, Ms Nicola J BA . . . . *Oct 1988
Hartshorn, Mr Richard Andrew BA(Hons)(Keele) . . . *Nov 1994
Hornigold, Mr Andrew S LLB(Nott'm) . . . . Oct 1991
Hyde, Mr Ian R BA(Oxon). . . . . *Oct 1990
Johnson, Mr Thomas BA(Hons)(Cantab) . . . . *Nov 1996
Jones, Mrs Linda J BA(Nott'm) . . . . *Nov 1994
Jones, Mr Neil F LLB(Hons) Chairman of the Joint Contracts Tribunal Drafting Sub-Committee . . . . *Mar 1974
Kent, Mr Paul LLB(Hons) . . . . *Oct 1990
Laight, Mr Simon B BA(Hons)(Lond). . . . . *Dec 1992
Lawson-King, Ms Joanna LLB(Lond) . . . . *Oct 1982
Lougher, Mr Guy BA(Hons)(York) . . . . *Dec 1989
Lowson, Mr Gregory J BA(L'pool) . . . . *Nov 1984
Miles, Mr Stephen J LLB . . . . Oct 1991
Morgan, Miss Elizabeth Rachel BA . . . . *Nov 1994
Norman, Mr Ashley James BA . . . . *Oct 1990
Parisi, Mrs Lisa LLB. . . . . *Nov 1992
Paton, Mr Andrew J LLB(Exon) . . . . *§Jul 1981
Pett, Mr David J MA(Oxon) . . . . *§Nov 1980
Philpot, Mr David J LLB(Bris) . . . . Dec 1987
Pigden, Mr Simon J LLB(Hons) . . . . *Oct 1988
Rees, Ms Kathryn J LLB(Exon) . . . . *Apr 1988
Richards, Mr Jim H MA(Hons)(Cantab) . . . . *Aug 1987
Robins, Miss Catherine A LLB(Bris). . . . . *Nov 1989
Ryan, Mr David P BA(Oxon); MBA . . . . *Nov 1985
Shelley, Mr Daniel William BA. . . . . *Jun 1985
Stephens, Mr Hugo Offley Prideaux LLB(Hons) . . . . *Oct 1989
Tonks, Mr Julian M J MA(Oxon). . . . . *Oct 1982
Twist, Mr G Patrick A BA(Keele). . . . . *Aug 1981
Warrington, Mr Giles LLB(Bris); LLM(Cantab) . . . . . *May 1996
Wood, Mr Alan K LLB. . . . . *Sep 1992
Wyn Davies, Mrs Cerys LLB(Exon) . . . . *Oct 1985
Yates, Mr Andrew P MA(Cantab) Karuth & Nordon Prizes . . . . *Nov 1988
Con: Denley, Mr Peter LLB . . . . Dec 1977
White, Mr Martin J MA(Cantab) . . . . *§Jun 1979

PRICE MISTRY ‡
3rd Floor Gazette Buildings 168 Corporation Street Birmingham West Midlands B4 6TF
Tel: 0121 200 1577 *Fax:* 0121 212 2035 *Dx:* 23511 BIRMINGHAM 3
E-mail: info@pricemistry.co.uk
List of partners: D Mistry
Ptr: Mistry, Miss Dipika LLB(Hons). . . . . Jun 1996

PRIOR CUMBERLIDGE & PUGH WITH JEFFERY PARR & CO ‡
1618-1620 Coventry Road Yardley Birmingham West Midlands B26 1AL
Tel: 0121 707 9211 *Fax:* 0121 765 4079
Dx: 701172 SWAN YARDLEY
E-mail: pcp@cumberlidge.co.uk
List of partners: P J Cumberlidge, P J Cumberlidge
Work: C1 E F1 J1 K1 L O Q S1 S2 W
Agency undertaken
Ptr: Cumberlidge, Mrs Pamela J LLB(Lond) . . . . *Jan 1970
Cumberlidge, Mr Paul J LLB(B'ham). . . . . *Dec 1966

PUBLIC INTEREST LAWYERS ‡
Eight Hylton Street Jewellery Quarter Birmingham West Midlands B18 6HN
Tel: 0121 515 5069 *Fax:* 0121 515 5129
E-mail: info@publicinterestlawyers.co.uk
List of partners: P J Shiner
Dir: Shiner, Mr Philip J LLB; LLM . . . . Nov 1981
Ast: Carey, Mr Daniel . . . . Sep 2003
Duffy, Mr Jim . . . . Jan 2005
Gregory, Ms Tessa . . . . May 2008
Jacobs, Mr Sam. . . . . Jan 2006
Webber, Mr Leigh. . . . . Jan 2010

PUBLIC LAW SOLICITORS ‡
8th Floor Albany House Hurst Street Birmingham West Midlands B5 4BD
Tel: 0121 256 0326 *Fax:* 0121 622 1426
Dx: 711803 BIRMINGHAM 28
E-mail: info@publiclawsolicitors.co.uk

Community Legal Service

Criminal Defence Service

PURCELL PARKER ‡
204-206 Corporation Street Birmingham West Midlands B4 6QB
Tel: 0121 236 9781 *Fax:* 0121 236 8243 *Dx:* 23508 BIRMINGHAM 3
Emergency telephone 0121 236 9781
E-mail: info@purcellparker.co.uk
List of partners: T P Davis, B P L Galletti, K D Good, A P Newport, R Parker, D C Purcell, M T Purcell, D P Rees, S M Stephens
Languages: German
Work: G H L S1 V W
Emergency Action, Agency, Advocacy, Fixed Fee Interview, Legal Aid undertaken, Legal Aid Franchise and Member of Accident Line
Ptr: Davis, Mr Tiernan Patrick . . . . Nov 1991
Galletti, Mr Benedict Piers Lutyens LLB . . . . *Sep 1999
Good, Mr Kevin Dermot. . . . . Feb 1992
Newport, Mr Alan Patrick . . . . Aug 1996
Parker, Mr Ronald LLB . . . . *§Jun 1975
Purcell, Mrs Deborah Claire. . . . . *Feb 1978
Purcell, Mr Michael T LLB(B'ham). . . . . *§May 1975
Rees, Mr David Peter. . . . . Jan 1992
Stephens, Mr Spencer Michael BA(Hons) ★. . . . . . . *Oct 1993
Ast: Daniels, Miss Sadie May LLB . . . . Aug 2008

Date established: 1979. Office hours: 0900 to 1700. Languages spoken: German. Agency Commissions willingly undertaken. Crime: General, Motoring or Juvenile. Legal aid. Property: Landlords, Tenants. Residential conveyancing. Wills, Trusts and Probates. A large legal aid crime practice.

RT LAW ‡
66 Northfield Road Kings Norton Birmingham West Midlands B30 1JH
Tel: 0121 459 1414 *Fax:* 0121 459 0090 *Dx:* 20314 COTTERIDGE

RAGHIB AHSAN SOLICITORS ‡
66 Hinstock Road Handsworth Birmingham West Midlands B20 2EU
Tel: 0121 551 1846 / 07941 284617 *Fax:* 0121 551 1846
E-mail: ra@raghibahsansolicitors.com

RAJPUT SOLICITORS ‡
41 Formans Road Sparkhill Birmingham West Midlands B11 3AA
Tel: 0121 777 0300 *Fax:* 0121 777 2570
Emergency telephone 07951 882637
E-mail: rajputsolicitors@btinternet.com
List of partners: A T Rajput
Languages: Hindi, Pashto, Punjabi, Urdu
Work: K3 M4 S1 S2 W Z(i)
SPr: Rajput, Mr Arshad Tanveer BSc; LLB . . . . Jan 2004

RASHID & CO SOLICITORS ‡
401 Witton Road Witton Birmingham West Midlands B6 6SP
Tel: 0121 356 0078 *Fax:* 0121 356 0079
E-mail: info@rashidandco.com
Ast: Asghar, Mr Kamran . . . . Oct 2010

RAVIAN SOLICITORS ‡
15 Alum Rock Road Birmingham West Midlands B8 1LL
Tel: 0121 322 4922 *Fax:* 0121 322 4923

REDFERN & CO ‡
Whitehall Chambers 23 Colmore Row Birmingham West Midlands B3 2BP
Tel: 0121 236 1801 *Fax:* 0121 236 9906 *Dx:* 13027 BIRMINGHAM 1
E-mail: l.jacobs@btconnect.com
List of partners: L L Jacobs
Work: C1 E K3 S1 S2 W
Fixed Fee Interview undertaken
SPr: Jacobs, Mr Leonard L LLB(Lond) . . . . *§Jun 1974

REID & CO SOLICITORS ‡
52 Frederick Road Edgbaston Birmingham West Midlands B15 1HN
Tel: 0121 450 4240 *Fax:* 0121 450 4250 *Dx:* 23055 EDGBASTON

REILLY & CO SOLICITORS ‡
(incorporating Williams Freeman & Lloyd)
Bank Chambers 1490 Stratford Road Hall Green Birmingham West Midlands B28 9EU
Tel: 0121 744 4090 *Fax:* 0871 384 1019 *Dx:* 20655 SHIRLEY
Ast: Latty, Miss Anne-Marie LLB . . . . *Nov 1993
Con: Christopher, Mr George . . . . *Jun 1983

RENATA & CO ‡
172 School Road Hall Green Birmingham West Midlands B28 8PA
Tel: 0121 777 7333 *Fax:* 0121 777 5050
E-mail: info@renatasolicitors.com
List of partners: R R E Baszynska-Kamrowska
Languages: Polish, Russian
Work: J1 J2 K1 N Q S1 W Z(f,q,r,w)
Emergency Action, Advocacy and Fixed Fee Interview undertaken
SPr: Baszynska-Kamrowska, Ms Renata Regina Elzbieta BA . . . . *Sep 1992
Asoc: Kamrowski, Mr Jerzy Leopold LLB . . . . *Feb 2003

RES IPSA SOLICITORS ‡
Neville House 14 Waterloo Street Birmingham West Midlands B2 5TX
Tel: 0121 643 0044 *Fax:* 0121 643 9200 *Dx:* 13074 BIRMINGHAM 1
E-mail: info@res-ipsa-solicitors.co.uk

REWARD LITIGATION LTD ‡
65 Church Street Birmingham West Midlands B3 2DP
Tel: 0845 366 9336 *Fax:* 0845 900 0550
E-mail: info@rewardlitigation.co.uk

ROGOLS SOLICITORS ‡
Branston Court Branston Street Birmingham West Midlands B18 6BA
Tel: 0121 329 2087 *Fax:* 0121 336 1871
E-mail: info@rogols.co.uk

ROSKELL DAVIES & CO ‡
661-665 Kingstanding Road Kingstanding Birmingham West Midlands B44 9RH
Tel: 0121 354 1515 / 355 1011 *Fax:* 0121 355 8906
E-mail: ianroskell@btconnect.com
List of partners: K A Davies, I Roskell
Work: E L N O Q S1 S2 W
Agency and Advocacy undertaken
Ptr: Davies, Mr Keith A LLB . . . . Oct 1979
Roskell, Mr Ian . . . . Oct 1978

RUBRIC LOIS KING & CO ‡
32-34 New Road Rubery Birmingham West Midlands B45 9HU
Tel: 0121 453 5133 / 453 3301 *Fax:* 0121 453 8299
Dx: 20552 RUBERY

RUDGE & CO ‡
Mansell House 200 Newhall Street Birmingham West Midlands B3 1SH
Tel: 0121 200 1775 *Fax:* 0121 200 1776
List of partners: A M Rudge
Languages: French
Work: B1 C1 C2 E F2 J1 N O P Q R1 S1 S2
Agency undertaken
Ptr: Rudge, Mr Alan M LLB . . . . *§Oct 1972

RUSSELL JONES & WALKER
11th Floor The McLaren Building 35 Dale End Birmingham West Midlands B4 7LN
Tel: 0121 233 8300 *Fax:* 0121 233 8303 *Dx:* 13028 BIRMINGHAM 1
E-mail: enquiries@rjw.co.uk
Office: Bristol, Cardiff, London WC2, Manchester, Newcastle upon Tyne, Sheffield, Wakefield
Work: G H J1 N Z(p,r)
Emergency Action, Agency, Legal Aid undertaken, Legal Aid Franchise and Member of Accident Line
Ptr: Langton, Mr Richard Crispian BA . . . . *Mar 1984
Ast: Griffiths, Ms Carol. . . . . Aug 1998
Wilson, Mr Adam Charles BA(Hons). . . . . *Sep 1991

RUTHERFORDS
264a-266 Chester Road Castle Bromwich Birmingham West Midlands B36 0LB
Tel: 0121 749 4488 *Fax:* 0121 749 4823
Dx: 23253 CASTLE BROMWICH
Office: Tamworth (2 offices)
Work: C1 D1 E F1 G H J1 K1 L M1 N P Q R1 S1 S2 T2 V W Z(e,h,i,k,r)

SGH MARTINEAU LLP ‡
No1 Colmore Square Birmingham West Midlands B4 6AA
Tel: 0870 763 2000 *Fax:* 0870 763 2001
Dx: 721090 BIRMINGHAM 43
E-mail: lawyers@sghmartineau.com
List of partners: A C Adams, D F Allison, D A J Bailey, I P Baker, W T Barker, Q H Butler, J E Byford, H B Carslake, S A E Coghlan, M J V Craik, H Driscoll, K M Dudley, M J Edwards, D Faulkner, I S Grier, C Inguanta, S Jamdar, E C J Judge, H Leeson, P Mountain, C S J Read, H A Readett, J C Rice, D Sejas, E J Shipp, D Sprecher, J E Spreckley, A J Stilton, A R Whitehead, R Wrigley
Office: London EC3
Languages: French, German
Work: A1 A3 B1 C1 C2 C3 D1 E F1 F2 G I J1 J2 K1 L M1 M2 N O P Q R1 R2 S1 S2 T1 T2 U1 U2 W X Z(b,c,d,e,f,g,h,j,k,l,m,n,o,p,q,r,s,u,w,x,y,z)
Emergency Action, Agency and Advocacy undertaken
Ptr: Adams, Mr Andrew C BA . . . *Oct 1989
Allison, Mr David F MA(Oxon) . . . *§Jun 1978
Baker, Mr Ian P BA(Oxon) . . . *§Oct 1983
Barker, Mr William T BSc(Keele) . . . *Oct 1986
Butler, Mr Quentin H BA(Oxon) . . . *Oct 1982
Byford, Ms Jane E . . . *Nov 1994
Carslake, Mr Hugh B BA; LLB(Dublin) Notary Public . *§Jun 1973
Coghlan, Mr Simon A E BA(Dunelm) . . . *Oct 1984
Craik, Mr Michael James Victor LLB(Hons); MSc . . *§Nov 1991
Driscoll, Mrs Helen LLB . . . *§Oct 1993
Dudley, Mr Keith M . . . *§Jan 1980
Edwards, Mr Martin J LLB(B'ham) . . . Nov 1988
Faulkner, Mr David . . . Nov 1996
Jamdar, Ms Smita . . . Sep 1996
Leeson, Ms Heather LLB(Hons) . . . *Jun 1981
Mountain, Mr Paul MA(Oxon) . . . *Sep 1989
Read, Mr Clive St John BA(Hons) . . . *Nov 1992
Readett, Ms Helen A BA(Hons) . . . *Sep 1982
Rice, Mr John C LLB . . . *Oct 1989
Spreckley, Mr James E LLB(Hons) . . . Oct 1992
Stilton, Mr Andrew J MA(Cantab) . . . *§Oct 1981
Whitehead, Mr Andrew R LLB . . . *Oct 1988
Wrigley, Mr Richard LLB . . . *Oct 1989
Asoc: Forbes, Ms Joanna J . . . *Nov 1995
Gunning, Miss Carol M LLB . . . *Nov 1989
Lane, Mr Stephen A BA(Hons)(Oxon) . . . *Nov 1994
McGiveron, Mr Adam T BSc(Hons) . . . *Nov 1998
Ast: Amlani, Mr Bhavesh . . . Mar 2001
O'Brien, Miss Michelle . . . Sep 2001
Patel, Miss Kavita . . . Sep 2001
Swanton, Ms Geraldine BA(Hons); MA(Hons) . . . Sep 1999
Thornber, Mr Ben . . . Sep 1999
Tudor, Ms Naomi LLB(Hons) . . . Sep 1999

SAFAAZ SOLICITORS ‡
38 Showell Green Lane Sparkhill Birmingham West Midlands B11 4JP
Tel: 0121 772 7428
E-mail: info@safaaz.com

SAFFRON SOLICITORS ‡
2nd Floor 3 Brindley Place Birmingham West Midlands B1 2JB
Tel: 0121 698 8558 *Fax:* 0121 698 8600
E-mail: info@saffronsolicitors.co.uk

SAINTS SOLICITORS ‡
45 Villa Road Birmingham West Midlands B19 1BH
Tel: 0121 523 7865 *Fax:* 0121 523 7856
E-mail: info@saintssolicitors.com

SALHAN & COMPANY ‡
1st Floor Murdoch Chambers 153a Corporation Street Birmingham West Midlands B4 6PH
Tel: 0121 605 6000 *Fax:* 0121 605 6001 *Dx:* 23532 BIRMINGHAM
Emergency telephone 0121 605 6000
E-mail: enquiries@salhan.co.uk
List of partners: T Salhan
Office: Bilston
Languages: Punjabi, Urdu
Work: G H
Emergency Action, Advocacy, Fixed Fee Interview and Legal Aid undertaken
Ptr: Salhan, Tarsem LLB . . . *Aug 1989

SEHDEVA LAW ‡
PineCroft 73 Monument Lane Lickey Birmingham West Midlands B45 9QJ
Tel: 0121 343 1316 *Fax:* 0121 453 8611
E-mail: vsehdeva@btinternet.com

SEHGAL & CO ‡
1 Nexus House 456 Stratford Road Sparkhill Birmingham West Midlands B11 4AE
Tel: 0121 772 2226 *Fax:* 0121 772 2011 *Dx:* 707263 SPARKHILL
Emergency telephone 07970 794173
List of partners: T S Ali, M S Sehgal
Languages: Punjabi, Urdu
Work: C1 F1 G H J1 L N O Q S1 V W Z(e,i,j)
Emergency Action, Fixed Fee Interview and Legal Aid undertaken
Ptr: Ali, Mr Tareq Saleem LLB(Hons) . . . *Jun 1993
Sehgal, Mr Mandyp Singh LLB(Hons) . . . *Dec 1995

SHAKESPEARES ‡
(incorporating Needham & James LLP)
Somerset House Temple Street Birmingham West Midlands B2 5DJ
Tel: 0121 237 3000 *Fax:* 0121 237 3011
Dx: 702312 BIRMINGHAM 10
E-mail: info@shakespeares.co.uk
List of partners: R C Adey, F M Allen, H Andrews, S R Archer, M J Beesley, C P Billyeald, R A Bolton, R Brackenbury, N J Briggs, R N Cox, G P Davie, S Dempsey, N A Drayson, A P Dudley, M B English, S P N Gilmour, A F Hannington, R S W Harcourt, A Hartshorn, V C Harvey, M J Hibbs, H J Holden, P A Huggins, J B Hughes, D Irwin, D A F James, J C D James, J P Jarvis, S N Jones, C A Laird, T O Lawrence, J L Lewis, J Mason, C Mifflin, A Millband, B A Money, K R Nagle, J M Park, J D Pears, J Pope, S J G Robb, C R Selby, V Simpson, S J Skiba, P M Snodgrass, K H Spedding, M J Sutton, L Teague, C A Walker, S Warburton, K R Webb, R J Wellington, P Whelan, C Williams, G E Wright
Office: Leicester, Moreton-in-Marsh, Nottingham, Shipston-on-Stour, Stratford-upon-Avon
Languages: French, German, Spanish
Work: B2 C1 C2 E I J1 K1 K2 K3 N O Q R2 S1 S2 U2 W Z(e,j,k,q,za)
Emergency Action, Agency, Advocacy, Fixed Fee Interview, Legal Aid undertaken and Member of Accident Line
Ptr: Adey, Mr Robert C LLB(Hons) . . . *Jan 1986
Beesley, Mr Mark J LLB . . . *Oct 1988
Bolton, Mr Richard A LLB(Bris) . . . *Apr 1978
Briggs, Mr Nicholas James LLB(Hons); Dip IP . . . *Nov 1991
Davie, Mr Gary P LLB(Hons) . . . *Nov 1992
Dempsey, Mr Sean . . . Jan 1981
English, Mr Mark B LLB; PGDip . . . *Oct 1985
Gilmour, Mr Simon P N LLB(Hons); LSF . . . *Nov 1994
Hannington, Mr Anthony F LLB . . . Oct 1993
Hartshorn, Mr Andrew . . . Nov 1994
Hibbs, Mr Michael J LLB Commissioner for the General Income Tax; Chairman of Central Region of the County Court Users Association . . . *§Oct 1983
Holden, Mrs H Julia LLB Deputy District Judge . . . *Jan 1985
Hughes, Mr John B LLB . . . *Jun 1974
Irwin, Ms Debbie . . . Jan 1994
Jones, Mr Stephen N LLB . . . *Dec 1979
Laird, Mrs Clare A BA(Hons) . . . Sep 1989
Lawrence, Mr Timothy O LLB(Hons) . . . *Nov 1989
Mason, Mr Justin . . . Jan 2001
Money, Mrs Beverley Ann DMS Shakespeare Prize for Commercial Law 1998 . . . *Oct 1998
Nagle, Mr Kevin R LLB . . . *§Oct 1984
Park, Mrs Julie Mary LLB . . . Sep 2000
Simpson, Ms Victoria . . . Jan 1994
Spedding, Mr Keith Hamilton LLB(Hons) . . . *Nov 1995
Sutton, Mr Matthew Jeremy MA(Oxon) . . . *Nov 1989
Teague, Mrs Lorraine BA(Hons); CPE; LSF . . . §Jan 1991
Warburton, Mr Steven LLB . . . *Dec 1995
Whelan, Ms Paula . . . Sep 1999
Williams, Mr Chris . . . Jan 1970
Con: James, Mr Keith R . . . *§Feb 1954

SHOOSMITHS
7th Floor 125 Colmore Row Birmingham West Midlands B3 3SH
Tel: 0370 086 4000 / 0121 335 4440 *Fax:* 0370 086 4001
Dx: 701863 BIRMINGHAM 6
E-mail: birmingham@shoosmiths.co.uk
Office: Basingstoke, Fareham, London WC2, Manchester, Milton Keynes, Northampton, Nottingham, Reading
Work: A3 B1 B2 C1 C2 C3 E F1 F2 I J1 J2 K4 L M1 N O Q R1 R2 S1 S2 T1 T2 U2 W X Z(b,c,e,f,h,i,j,k,l,m,n,o,p,q,r,s,t,u,y,za)
Ptr: Bishop, Mr Alex . . . Sep 1997
Boss, Mr Simon A LLB . . . *Oct 1988
Clegg, Mr Darren BA(Hons) . . . *§Sep 1997
Davis, Ms Joanne . . . Oct 2003
Dewes, Mr Chris . . . Jan 1995
Farooq, Mr Vaqas . . . Sep 2001
Follis, Mr Richard T LLB Deputy Vice President of the Birmingham Law Society . . . *Dec 1981
Gilbey, Mr Iain . . . *§Oct 1994
Heath, Mr Philip James LLB(Hons); MA; Former Barrister . . . *Jan 2000
Jackson, Mr David . . . Sep 2000
Jackson, Mr Jason . . . Jan 1996
Keates, Mr James Laurence LLB . . . *Nov 1996
Kordan, Mr Joel N BSc(LSE)(Econ) . . . *Jan 1990
McGuirk, Ms Rebecca . . . Mar 1999
Martin, Mr Oliver B BA(Hons) . . . Nov 1996
Mason, Mr Andrew LLB . . . Oct 1993
Peet, Mr Alastair . . . Sep 1999
Perry, Mr Geoffrey John Cochrane . . . Oct 1991
Sawbridge, Ms Rebecca . . . Sep 1999
Wilson, Ms Helen . . . Sep 1999

SIDHU & CO ‡
PO Box 12286 Birmingham West Midlands B16 6AB
Tel: 07831 293903 *Fax:* 0870 137 6739
Emergency telephone 07831 293903
List of partners: G S Sidhu
Languages: Hindi, Punjabi
Work: C1 E F1 L R1 S1 S2 W Z(j,l)
Emergency Action, Agency, Advocacy, Fixed Fee Interview and Legal Aid undertaken
Ptr: Sidhu, Gurmail S BA . . . *Dec 1982

ROBIN SIMON LLP
37a Waterloo Street Birmingham West Midlands B2 5TJ
Tel: 0333 010 0000 *Fax:* 0333 010 0005 *Dx:* 13070 BIRMINGHAM
E-mail: info@robinsimonllp.com
Office: Leeds, London EC3, Manchester

SIMPSON MILLAR LLP
47 Summer Lane Birmingham West Midlands B19 3TH
Tel: 0844 858 3500 *Fax:* 0844 858 3599
E-mail: info@simpsonmillar.co.uk
Office: Bristol, Cardiff, Gateshead, Leeds, London EC1, London SW19, Manchester
Work: C1 C2 D1 E F1 F2 J1 J2 K1 K2 K3 K4 M2 N O P Q R1 R2 S1 S2 T1 T2 U2 V W X Z(c,d,e,h,j,m,o,p,q,r,t,za)

SINCLAIRS ‡
173 Waterloo Road (off Coventry Road) Yardley Birmingham West Midlands B25 8LH
Tel: 0121 708 2144 *Fax:* 0121 708 0436
Dx: 701178 YARDLEY SWAN CENTRE
E-mail: m.mccormack@sinclairslaw.co.uk

ROBIN SINGH & CO SOLICITORS ‡
285 A Soho Road Birmingham West Midlands B21 9SA
Tel: 0121 515 1500

SPENCER SHAW ‡
2nd Floor 3 Brindley Place Birmingham West Midlands B1 2JB
Tel: 0121 698 8507 *Fax:* 0121 698 8600
E-mail: enquiries@spencershaw.co.uk

J D SPICER & CO
1st Floor Suite 109 Cornwall Buildings Birmingham West Midlands B3 3QR
Tel: 0121 222 4213 *Fax:* 0121 222 4219
Office: London EC4, London NW6

SQUIRE SANDERS (UK) LLP
(incorporating Stones Porter)
(in association with Buchanan Ingersoll(USA))
Rutland House 148 Edmund Street Birmingham West Midlands B3 2JR
Tel: 0121 222 3000 *Fax:* 0121 222 3001
Dx: 708610 BIRMINGHAM 17
Office: Leeds, London EC2, Manchester
Languages: French, German, Hebrew, Polish, Spanish
Work: A1 A2 A3 B1 B2 B3 C1 C2 C3 D1 E F1 F2 G I J1 J2 K1 L M1 M2 N O P Q R1 R2 S2 T1 T2 U1 U2 Z(b,c,d,e,f,h,i,j,k,l,m,n,o,p,q,w,y,z)
Emergency Action, Agency, Advocacy undertaken and Member of Accident Line
Ptr: Allen, Mrs Amanda J P LLB(B'ham) . . . *Oct 1986
Barker, Mr Francois LLB(Hons) . . . Sep 1997
Beswick, Mr David J LLB . . . *Oct 1987
Brown, Mr Jeffrey LLB; FCIArb; ACII . . . *Apr 1981
Egan, Mrs Caroline H MA(Oxon) . . . Oct 1982
Forrest, Mr John S . . . Oct 1989
Green, Mr Nicholas John BA(Hons) . . . *Sep 1991
Hull, Mr David J LLB(Sheff) . . . *Oct 1986
Jones, Mr Robert E LLB . . . *Oct 1991
Moorcroft, Mr Paul John . . . Sep 1993
Moore, Mr Jonathan Felix BSc(Hons) . . . *Jan 1992
O'Meara, Mrs Anne M LLB Chairman of the City of Birmingham Symphony Orchestra Development Trust . . . *May 1980
Perraton, Ms Stephanie L LLB . . . Oct 1990
Robertson, Ms Audrey M LLB . . . Oct 1990
Singh, Mr Devinder LLB(Hons) . . . *Mar 1992
Trainer, Mr Michael Reinhard LLB; DipLP Notary Public Aug 1994
Asoc: Jones, Mrs Heather L M LLB(B'ham) . . . Dec 1973
Joseph, Mr Paul Wolfe MA(Cantab) . . . Oct 1992
Sambrook, Ms Madeline LLB . . . Sep 1990
Shepherd, Ms Pamela LLB . . . *Oct 1992
Sutherland, Miss Monique Diane LLB . . . *Oct 1990
Sutton, Mr Philip LLB . . . Sep 1993
Walker, Mr Martin LLB; Dip Planning & Env Law . . . Nov 1984
Ast: Allen, Thornton . . . Jul 1997
Clifford, Mr Michael J BA . . . *Nov 1991
Dunnage, Ms Philippa Jane . . . Sep 2000
Essery, Ms Helen Joanne LLB . . . Oct 1996
French, Mr Daniel LLB(Hons) . . . *Sep 1999
Giles, Mr Matthew John LLB(Hons) . . . Sep 1998
Ishak, Mrs Julia Marie LLB; LPC . . . *Oct 1996
James, Mrs Fiona Catherine . . . Sep 2000
James, Mr Stuart . . . Sep 2000
Kalsi, Mr Harmesh Kaur . . . Apr 1999
King, Mrs Emma . . . Sep 1994
Leech, Mr Jonathan R A BA(Hons) . . . *Feb 1998
MacDonald, Mr Iain Charles Sinclair . . . Oct 1998
Maughan, Mrs Dympna BA(Hons) . . . *Sep 1990
Rankin, Ms Georgina Ann . . . Sep 2000
Shardlow, Mrs Janice B LLB . . . *Oct 1983
Sohi, Mr Jasvir Singh . . . Oct 2000
Stirling, Mrs Jane Elizabeth . . . Sep 1994
Thompson, Mrs Claire Louise LLB(Hons) . . . Mar 1998
Ward, Ms Denise Sharon . . . Dec 2000
Williams, Ms Melanie Z LLB . . . *Sep 1998
Con: James, Mr John A LLB(Bris) . . . *§Dec 1969

STEEL & CLUNIS ‡
30 Grove Lane Handsworth Birmingham West Midlands B21 9EP
Tel: 0121 523 9191 *Fax:* 0121 554 5641 *Dx:* 24953 HANDSWORTH
E-mail: info@steel-clunis.co.uk
Ast: Andrews, Phyton F H G . . . Apr 1986

STERLING SOLICITORS ‡
664 Coventry Road Small Heath Birmingham West Midlands B10 0UU
Tel: 0121 772 0777 *Fax:* 0121 772 1005
E-mail: law@sterlingsolicitors.co.uk
List of partners: D Pazir, S Perveen
Languages: Bengali, Hindi, Lithuanian, Mirpuri, Punjabi, Russian, Urdu
Work: E K1 K3 L N O Q S2 W
Ptr: Pazir, Dil . . . Sep 2003
Perveen, Saida . . . Mar 2001

SULTAN LLOYD ‡
514a Coventry Road Small Heath Birmingham West Midlands B10 0UN
Tel: 0121 248 2850 *Fax:* 0121 248 2851

SYDNEY MITCHELL ‡
Apsley House 35 Waterloo Street Birmingham West Midlands B2 5TJ
Tel: 0121 698 2200 / 0808 166 8827 *Fax:* 0121 200 1513 / 214 2131
Dx: 13054 BIRMINGHAM 1
E-mail: enquiries@sydneymitchell.co.uk
List of partners: F Ismail, T Lewis, K Moores, D Singh
Office: Birmingham, Solihull
Languages: Punjabi
Work: A1 B1 C1 C2 C3 D1 E F1 F2 J1 K1 M1 P R1 S1 S2 T2 V W Z(c,p,q)
Emergency Action, Agency, Advocacy, Fixed Fee Interview and Legal Aid undertaken
Ptr: Ismail, Miss Fahmida LLB Sweet & Maxwell Law Prize Notary Public . . . *Oct 1988
Lewis, Mr Tony LLB . . . *Dec 1972
Singh, Divinder BA . . . *Apr 1986
Ast: Simpson, Mr Jonathon M LLB(Hons) . . . *Aug 1996
Vinti, Mr Mauro BSc . . . *Aug 2001

SYDNEY MITCHELL
Shakespeare Buildings 2233 Coventry Road Sheldon Birmingham West Midlands B26 3NL
Tel: 0121 722 2969 / 0808 166 5638 *Fax:* 0121 722 3127
Dx: 21801 SHELDON
E-mail: enquiries@sydneymitchell.co.uk
Office: Birmingham, Solihull
Work: A1 B1 C1 C2 C3 D1 E F1 F2 J1 K1 M1 N O P Q R1 R2 S1 S2 T2 V W Z(c,l,p,q)
Emergency Action, Agency, Advocacy, Fixed Fee Interview, Legal Aid undertaken and Member of Accident Line
Ptr: Moores, Ms Karen LLB . . . *May 1993

SYEDS SOLICITORS ‡
86A Bristol Street Birmingham West Midlands B5 7AH
Tel: 0121 622 5800 *Fax:* 0121 440 7829
E-mail: info@syedssolicitors.com
Office: Manchester

TRP SOLICITORS ‡
6 Lee Bank Business Centre 55 Holloway Head Birmingham West Midlands B1 1HP
Tel: 0121 616 4700 *Fax:* 0121 643 0700
Dx: 720292 BIRMINGHAM 47
E-mail: pas@trpsolicitors.co.uk

TALLAR LLP ‡
44 Kingscote Road Edgbaston Birmingham West Midlands B15 3JY
Tel: 0845 555 1501
E-mail: enquiries@tallar.com

 See p112 for the Key to Work Categories & other symbols

TECHNOLOGY LAW ALLIANCE
2nd Floor Baskerville House Centenary Square Birmingham West Midlands B1 2ND
Tel: 0845 351 9090
E-mail: info@tlawa.co.uk
Office: London WC2

THOMAS & CO ‡
Springfield House 56 Springfield Road Kings Heath Birmingham West Midlands B14 7DY
Tel: 0121 444 0030 *Fax:* 0121 444 2112 *Dx:* 10794 MOSELEY
E-mail: info@thomas-law.co.uk
List of partners: A Thomas, S R Thomas
Work: K1 K3 K4 L N Q S1 S2 W
Agency undertaken
Ptr: Thomas, Mr Anthony Henry Malcolm Hubbard Scholarship Deputy District Judge . . . . *Feb 1969
Thomas, Mrs Sheila Rachel . . . . *Dec 1985

THOMPSONS (FORMERLY ROBIN/BRIAN THOMPSON & PARTNERS)
The McLaren Building 45 The Priory Queensway Birmingham West Midlands B4 7LF
Tel: 0121 262 1200 *Fax:* 0121 236 6715 *Dx:* 24915 BIRMINGHAM 4
Office: Belfast, Bristol, Cardiff, Chelmsford, Dagenham, Derby, Harrow, Leeds, Liverpool, London SW19, London WC1, Manchester, Middlesbrough, Newcastle upon Tyne, Nottingham, Plymouth, Sheffield, South Shields, Southampton, Stoke-on-Trent, Swansea, Wolverhampton
Work: J1 N Z(p)
Legal Aid undertaken and Member of Accident Line
Ptr: Carter, Mr Louis. . . . . Dec 1987
Dewsbury, Mr Simon Philip BA . . . . *Dec 1987
Feenan, Mr David P J. . . . . *Nov 1987
Loughrey, Mr Terence Patrick FILEx. . . . . *Oct 1998
Pringle, Mr Ronald . . . . *Oct 1979
Ast: Bailey, Mr Craig P D LLB . . . . *Aug 2000
Carter, Mr Aidan J BSc . . . . Jan 1999
Chester, Ms Celena Dawn LLB . . . . *Sep 1996
Fahy, Miss Alison Kathleen LLB(Hons) . . . . *Oct 1989
Fitzwalter, Mr Stephen Anthony . . . . *Oct 1993
Gardner, Mr James S LLM; LLB. . . . . *Jan 1987
Henderson Nee Grantham, Mrs Claire Felicity LLB(Hons) . . . . *Nov 1995
Hepplestone, Miss Victoria L K LLB . . . . Jul 1999
Juss, Warinder S LLB. . . . . *May 1993
Kelly, Mr Mark A R LLB(Hons). . . . . Dec 2000
Parkhouse, Mr John R O LLB(Hons) . . . . *Oct 1990
Ruff, Mr Marc Antony . . . . Nov 1998
Storer, Mrs Julie Ann LLB(Hons) . . . . *May 1997
Voss, Ms Marion Emily Olga LLB . . . . *Mar 1994
Webb, Miss Joanne LLB(Hons); LPC . . . . *Apr 1999

TIBBITS FISHER ‡
Barclays Bank Chambers 5 Westley Road Acocks Green Birmingham West Midlands B27 7UQ
Tel: 0121 707 3900 *Fax:* 0121 764 4281
Dx: 131815 ACOCKS GREEN 3
E-mail: info@tibbitfishersolicitors.co.uk
List of partners: A Tibbits
Work: K1 L S1 S2 W
Legal Aid undertaken and Legal Aid Franchise
Ptr: Tibbits, Mr Anthony . . . . *Jul 1977
Asoc: Hindmarsh, Mr Simon John LLB(Hons) . . . . *Jul 1991

TOUSSAINTS ‡
1st Floor 150 Soho Road Birmingham West Midlands B21 9LN
Tel: 0121 523 5050 *Fax:* 0121 523 3200
Dx: 24968 HANDSWORTH 1
Emergency telephone 07971 217575
E-mail: toussaints@lawyersonline.co.uk
List of partners: M M Toussaint
Work: B2 G H J1 K1 N O Q S1 S2 W Z(q)
Agency, Advocacy and Fixed Fee Interview undertaken
Ptr: Toussaint, Miss Mary M BA(Hons) •. . . . . *§Dec 1989

TOWNSHENDS LLP
Cornwall House 31 Lionel Street Birmingham West Midlands B3 1AP
Tel: 0121 214 1540 *Fax:* 0121 214 1549
Dx: 712087 BIRMINGHAM 29
Office: Coleshill, Coventry

TRINITY LAW PARTNERSHIP ‡
Blackthorn House 1-2 Mary Ann Street St Pauls Square Birmingham West Midlands B3 1RL
Tel: 0121 212 3141 *Fax:* 0121 212 3161

CAROL A TRIPLETT SOLICITOR ‡
307 Quelled Road Great Barr Birmingham West Midlands B43 7HB
Tel: 0121 682 8247 *Fax:* 0121 360 7364
E-mail: legalhr@blueyonder.co.uk

TUCKERS
210 Corporation Street Birmingham West Midlands B4 6QB
Tel: 0121 236 4324 *Fax:* 0121 236 4364 *Dx:* 23519 BIRMINGHAM 3
Emergency telephone 0121 449 1525
Office: London SE5, London W1, Manchester
Work: G H

TYNDALLWOODS ‡
12th Floor The McLaren Building 46 The Priory Queensway Birmingham West Midlands B4 7LR
Tel: 0121 624 1111 *Fax:* 0121 624 8401
Dx: 16073 BIRMINGHAM FOUNTAIN COURT
Emergency telephone 01467 888855
List of partners: K M Dyer, J A Dyke, S J Foster, N Garcia, S R Jones, M Kaur-Heer, E A Mitchell, M H Phillips
Office: Birmingham
Languages: Bengali, French, Punjabi, Spanish, Urdu
Work: B1 B2 D1 F1 G H J1 K1 L N O Q R1 X Z(g,h,i,l,m,p,q,u,y)
Emergency Action, Agency, Advocacy, Fixed Fee Interview, Legal Aid undertaken and Legal Aid Franchise
Ptr: Dyer, Mr K Michael MA(Oxon). . . . . *Nov 1976
Dyke, Mrs Judy Ann LLB Birmingham Law Society Pro Bono Award 2003. Jan 1982
Foster, Mr Simon J LLB. . . . . Oct 1985
Garcia, Ms Natalia . . . . Sep 1996
Jones, Miss Sally R LLB . . . . *Nov 1984
Kaur-Heer, Miss Manjit LLB(Hons) . . . . *May 1990
Mitchell, Exdol A BA . . . . *Oct 1981
Phillips, Mr Mark H BA . . . . *May 1981
Ast: Ebanks, Miss Janet Yvonne LLB . . . . Mar 1992
Jabeen, Miss Ferhut LLB . . . . Oct 2004
Latif, Ms Aisha . . . . Feb 2003
Nicholas, Mr Simon . . . . *Sep 2000
O'Gorman, Mr Thomas BA . . . . Jul 2001
Schneeberger, Mr Christoph. . . . . Feb 2005
Winarskie, Mr Lorick MA . . . . *Nov 1996

TYNDALLWOODS
29 Woodbourne Road Edgbaston Birmingham West Midlands B17 8BY
Tel: 0121 693 2222 *Fax:* 0121 693 0844
E-mail: mdyer@tyndallwoods.co.uk
Office: Birmingham
Languages: Bengali, French, Punjabi, Spanish, Urdu
Work: E R1 S1 S2 T2 W Z(d)
Emergency Action, Agency, Advocacy and Legal Aid undertaken
Ptr: Dyke, Mrs Judy Ann LLB Birmingham Law Society Pro Bono Award 2003. Jan 1982

UK MIGRATION LAWYERS LTD ‡
Centre Court 1301 Stratford Road Hall Green Birmingham West Midlands B28 9HH
Tel: 0121 702 1407 *Fax:* 0121 702 1494
E-mail: info@ukmigrationlawyers.co.uk

VESEYS SOLICITORS ‡
95 Spencer Street Birmingham West Midlands B18 6DA
Tel: 0121 523 1123 *Fax:* 0121 554 8153
Emergency telephone 0121 449 6351
Work: G H V W
Emergency Action, Agency, Advocacy, Fixed Fee Interview and Legal Aid undertaken
Con: Gold, Mr Ian H . . . . *Jul 1971

VICTOR HENRY ‡
13a St Paul's Square Birmingham West Midlands B3 1RB
Tel: 0121 236 3473 / 232 4666 *Fax:* 0121 212 3363
E-mail: info@victor-henry.co.uk

WK SOLICITORS ‡
First Floor 514 Moseley Road Birmingham West Midlands B12 9AH
Tel: 0121 440 7664 / 07841 290176 *Fax:* 0121 440 7686
E-mail: info@wksolicitors.co.uk

WALKER SMITH WAY
5th Floor 1 Victoria Square Birmingham West Midlands B1 1BD
Tel: 0844 346 3100 *Fax:* 0844 346 3200
E-mail: enquiries@walkersmithway.com
Office: Ashton-under-Lyne, Chester, Liverpool, London SW11, Wrexham

WARWICK SOLICITORS ‡
1168 Stratford Road Hall Green Birmingham West Midlands B28 8AF
Tel: 0121 778 1188 / 07956 822250 *Fax:* 0121 778 2277
Dx: 18664 HALL GREEN
E-mail: info@warwicksolicitors.com

WATERS & CO ‡
81 High Street Coleshill Birmingham West Midlands B46 3AG
Tel: 01675 463855 *Fax:* 01675 467496 *Dx:* 15052 COLESHILL
E-mail: office@waterssolicitors.co.uk
List of partners: T C Waters, V L B Waters
Work: A1 B1 C1 C2 E F1 J1 K1 L N O P Q S1 W
Ptr: Waters, Ms Teresa C LLB. . . . . Jun 1993
Waters, Mr Victor L B . . . . Mar 1959

GAIL WATKINS & CO ‡
1 Bull Street Harborne Birmingham West Midlands B17 0HH
Tel: 0121 427 9583 *Fax:* 0121 427 9583
E-mail: gail@gailwatkins.wanadoo.co.uk
List of partners: G Watkins
Languages: French, German
Work: C1 E S1 S2 Z(i)
SPr: Watkins, Ms Gail . . . . Jun 1977

WEIGHTMANS LLP
1st Floor St Philips Point 47 Cannon Street Birmingham West Midlands B2 5EF
Tel: 0121 632 6100 *Fax:* 0121 632 5410 *Dx:* 13035 BIRMINGHAM 1
Office: Dartford, Knutsford, Leicester, Liverpool, London EC4, Manchester (2 offices)
Mem: Lang, Mr Tim T MBA; BSc; LSF; CPE. . . . . Jan 1994
Yeaman, Mr Anthony G . . . . Feb 1988
Asoc: Charlton, Mr Simon R BA(Hons). . . . . *Mar 1993

WILDINGS ‡
864 Washwood Heath Road Ward End Birmingham West Midlands B8 2NG
Tel: 0121 786 2555 *Fax:* 0121 789 6360 *Dx:* 27433 HODGE HILL
List of partners: P D Wilding
Languages: French, Punjabi, Spanish
Work: D1 E F1 G H K1 L M1 N P S1
Emergency Action, Agency, Fixed Fee Interview, Legal Aid undertaken and Member of Accident Line
Ptr: Wilding, Mr Patrick D LLB. . . . . *Dec 1975

THE WILKES PARTNERSHIP LLP ‡
41 Church Street Birmingham West Midlands B3 2RT
Tel: 0121 233 4333 *Fax:* 0121 233 4546 *Dx:* 13047 BIRMINGHAM
E-mail: law@wilkes.co.uk
List of partners: M Abrol, D W Cleary, J Cooper, C J Csukas, A Garland, K Hackett, A Hasnip, S Hopkins, A B Keene, G T O'Hara, J Parkin, S Thomas, S M Vogel, N R Wood
Office: Birmingham
Languages: French, German, Italian
Work: A3 B1 B2 C1 C2 C3 D1 E F1 F2 I J1 J2 K1 K2 K3 L M1 M2 N O P Q R1 R2 S1 S2 T1 T2 U1 U2 V W Z(b,c,d,e,f,h,j,k,l,m,o,p,q,r,s)
Emergency Action, Agency, Advocacy, Fixed Fee Interview, Legal Aid undertaken, Legal Aid Franchise and Member of Accident Line
Ptr: Abrol, Mr Mark LLB . . . . *Oct 1993
Cleary, Mr David W LLB. . . . . *Nov 1986
Cooper, Mr John LLB(Hons). . . . . *Dec 1991
Csukas, Mr Carl J BA(Oxon) . . . . *Sep 1998
Garland, Mr Andrew. . . . . Nov 1993
Hackett, Ms Kathryn LLB(Hons). . . . . *Nov 1994
Hasnip, Mr Andrew . . . . *Nov 1996
Hopkins, Mr Stephen LLB . . . . Oct 1996
Keene, Mr Aaron Bardell LLB . . . . *Oct 1989
O'Hara, Mr Gareth T LLB . . . . *Oct 1990
Parkin, Mr Jeremy. . . . . *Jul 2000
Thomas, Mr Simon LLB. . . . . *Sep 2000
Wood, Mr Nigel R LLB . . . . *§Oct 1983
Asoc: Allen, Miss Jennifer LLB. . . . . *Sep 2006
Stowell, Ms Victoria . . . . Sep 2004
Ast: Adcock, Mr Hedley LLB . . . . Sep 2007
Beddows, Miss Jessica LLB. . . . . May 2009
Cooper, Ms Claire LLB(Hons) . . . . *Sep 2003
Hadley, Mr James LLB . . . . Jun 2010
Hennity, Mr Paul M LLB(Hons) . . . . Apr 2000
Huskisson, Mr Jon LLB(Hons). . . . . Sep 2008
Hutchison, Ms Emma LLB(Hons) . . . . Mar 2007
Joslyn, Miss Samantha BA(Hons)(Cantab) . . . . . . Sep 2009
Parr, Mr Matthew LLB. . . . . Sep 2010
Raybould, Mr Peter LLB(Hons) . . . . Sep 2008
Schuck, Mr Adrian LLB . . . . Aug 2008
Terrar, Mr Mark LLB(Hons) . . . . Sep 2009
Con: Blick, Mr Marcus . . . . *May 1982
Coplestone-Crow, Mr Timothy LLB(Hons) . . . . Nov 1995
Drury, Mr David Martin . . . . *§Jan 1966
Stevenson, Mr David LLB(Hons) . . . . Oct 1987

WILLIAMSON & SODEN
Windsor House 100 Windsor Street South Birmingham West Midlands B7 4HZ
Tel: 0121 333 4848 *Fax:* 0121 333 3737
Emergency telephone 0121 778 5000 (24HR)
Office: Solihull
Work: G H K1
Emergency Action, Agency, Advocacy, Legal Aid undertaken, Legal Aid Franchise and Member of Accident Line
Ptr: Bryce, Mr James A ★. . . . . *Mar 1983

J M WILSON SOLICITORS ‡
299-301 Birchfield Road Perry Barr Birmingham West Midlands B20 3BY
Tel: 0121 356 4556 *Fax:* 0121 356 4633
Emergency telephone 07711 709342
List of partners: S Sharma, J M Wilson
Languages: Bengali, Hindi, Mirpuri, Punjabi, Urdu
Work: G H K3 S1 V W X Z(g,i)
Emergency Action, Agency, Advocacy, Fixed Fee Interview, Legal Aid undertaken and Legal Aid Franchise
Ptr: Sharma, Mr Sanjeev LLB . . . . *Mar 2004
Wilson, Mr James M BA; MPhil . . . . *Nov 1985

WINCHESTERS SOLICITORS LIMITED ‡
40a High Street Erdington Birmingham West Midlands B23 6RH
Tel: 0800 634 4679 *Fax:* 0121 382 7287
E-mail: sarah.gordan@winchestersolicitors.co.uk

WITHERS & ROGERS
75 Colmore Row Birmingham West Midlands B3 2AP
Tel: 0121 245 3900 *Fax:* 0121 245 3930
Office: London SE1

MICHAEL G WOOLDRIDGE ‡
21 Shirley Road Acocks Green Birmingham West Midlands B27 7XU
Tel: 0121 706 2259 *Fax:* 0121 706 9512
Emergency telephone 0121 706 2259
List of partners: M G Wooldridge
Languages: Czech, French
Work: F1 G H K1 P S1 W Z(w)
Emergency Action, Agency, Advocacy, Fixed Fee Interview, Legal Aid undertaken and Legal Aid Franchise
Ptr: Wooldridge, Mr Michael G LLB . . . . *May 1975

WORNHAM & CO SOLICITORS ‡
Ground Floor 52 Albion Street Jewellery Quarter Birmingham West Midlands B1 3EA
Tel: 0121 236 7999 *Fax:* 0121 236 5999
E-mail: trevor@wornham.co.uk

WRAGGE & CO LLP ‡
55 Colmore Row Birmingham West Midlands B3 2AS
Tel: 0121 233 1000 *Fax:* 0121 214 1099 *Dx:* 13036 BIRMINGHAM 1
Office: London EC1
Languages: Cantonese, French, German, Italian, Mandarin, Polish, Russian, Spanish, Welsh
Work: A1 B1 C1 C2 C3 E F1 I J1 L M1 M2 N O P Q R1 S1 T1 T2 W X Z(b,c,d,e,f,i,j,k,l,n,o,s,t)

YOUNG & LEE ‡
No6 The Wharf Bridge Street Birmingham West Midlands B1 2JS
Tel: 0121 633 3233 *Fax:* 0121 632 5292 *Dx:* 701255 EDGBASTON 4
Emergency telephone 07956 581059
E-mail: timlee@younglee.co.uk
List of partners: K Barritt, B K Khatkar, P R Kimberley, T R Lee, J S Lloyd, S Price, I R Young
Languages: Bengali, Gujarati, Hindi, Punjabi, Urdu
Work: A1 C1 C2 D1 D2 E I J1 J2 K1 L N O Q R2 S1 S2 U2 W Z(c,d,e,f,p,q,w)
Emergency Action, Agency, Advocacy and Legal Aid Franchise
Ptr: Barritt, Mr Keith . . . . *§Dec 1958
Khatkar, Miss Baldish Kaur BA(Hons); LPE; LPC . . . *Jan 1998
Kimberley, Mr Paul R Notary Public . . . . *Jun 1981
Lee, Mr Timothy R MA(Cantab) . . . . *§Apr 1975
Lloyd, Mr Jonathan S MA(Oxon) . . . . Apr 1976
Price, Mr Stuart LLB(Hons) . . . . Nov 1995
Young, Mr Ian R LLB(B'ham) . . . . *§Dec 1975
Asoc: Jenkins, Mr Gareth LLB(Hons) . . . . *§Jan 1989
Whittle, Mr Andrew C BA . . . . *Sep 1991
Ast: Akram, Ms Salvia LLB(Hons) . . . . *Apr 2000

ZAK SOLICITORS ‡
20 College Road Handsworth Wood Birmingham West Midlands B20 2HX
Tel: 0121 554 8244 *Fax:* 0121 551 8800

BIRSTALL, Leicestershire

PETER ASTILL & CO ‡
7 Hannah Parade Stonehill Avenue Birstall Leicestershire LE4 4JE
Tel: 0116 221 4885 *Fax:* 0116 294 7589
E-mail: cpa@peterastill.co.uk
List of partners: C P Astill
SPr: Astill, Mr C Peter . . . . Mar 1982

JACKSON & CO
9 Sibson Road Birstall Leicestershire LE4 4DZ
Tel: 0116 267 6263
Office: Lutterworth
Work: S1 W
Ptr: Payne, Mr Michael John LLB . . . . *Mar 1987

W A TYLER & CO ‡
93 Sibson Road Birstall Leicestershire LE4 4NB
Tel: 0116 267 6900 *Fax:* 0116 267 9911
Work: E S1 W

BIRSTALL, West Yorkshire

BREARLEYS SOLICITORS
Lloyds Bank Chambers 10 Market Place Birstall West Yorkshire WF17 9EL
Tel: 01924 443900 *Fax:* 01924 444868 *Dx:* 700906 BIRSTALL
Emergency telephone 07836 778693
E-mail: nickbattye@brearleyssolicitors.com
Office: Batley, Cleckheaton
Work: C1 D1 E F1 K1 K3 K4 L N O Q R2 S1 S2 W Z(q,r)
Emergency Action, Agency, Advocacy, Fixed Fee Interview, Legal Aid undertaken, Legal Aid Franchise and Member of Accident Line

BIRTLEY, Tyne & Wear

JOHN BAYLES & CO ‡
26 Durham Road Birtley Tyne & Wear DH3 2QG
Tel: 0191 410 2142 *Fax:* 0191 410 7892
Emergency telephone 0191 386 3939
E-mail: jbayles@netcomuk.co.uk
List of partners: J F Bayles
Office: Durham
Work: B1 D1 E F1 K1 L S1 W
Fixed Fee Interview, Legal Aid Franchise and Member of Accident Line
Ptr: Bayles, Mr John F. . . . . *§Jan 1982

BISHOP AUCKLAND, Co Durham

C W BOOTH & CO ‡
PO Box 122 5 Cockton Hill Road Bishop Auckland Co Durham DL14 6EN
Tel: 01388 606660 *Fax:* 01388 604898
Emergency telephone 01388 661958
List of partners: C W Booth, L P D Brison, R G Willoughby
Office: Peterlee
Work: D1 G H K1 L N S1 W Z(l)
Emergency Action, Agency, Advocacy, Fixed Fee Interview, Legal Aid undertaken and Legal Aid Franchise
Ptr: Booth, Mr Clive W LLB . . . . *Aug 1976
Brison, Mr Liam Paul Dalton BA. . . . . *Aug 1996
Willoughby, Mr Robert Graham LLB. . . . . *Oct 1992

HEWITTS ‡
(incorporating Wager Turner)
207 Newgate Street Bishop Auckland Co Durham DL14 7EL
Tel: 01388 604691 *Fax:* 01388 607899
Dx: 60153 BISHOP AUCKLAND
E-mail: enquiries@hewitts.co.uk
List of partners: G F Burnett, B Davidson, J Drew, C J L Fountain, A D Green, M Hole, G Hunsley, R Kershaw, A G Nattrass, L E M Saunders-Jerrom, J A Turner, A Tweddle
Office: Crook, Darlington, Newton Aycliffe, Stockton-on-Tees
Work: A1 A2 A3 B1 B2 C1 C2 D1 D2 E F1 G H J1 K1 L M1 N O P Q R1 S1 S2 U2 V W X Z(c,d,e,f,g,h,i,j,k,l,m,n,o,p,q,s,t)
Emergency Action, Agency, Advocacy, Fixed Fee Interview, Legal Aid undertaken and Legal Aid Franchise
Ptr: Davidson, Ms Brenda BA Deputy Coroner. . . . . . . Mar 1989
Drew, Mrs Janet BA(Hons) . . . . *Jul 1997
Kershaw, Mr Roy . . . . *Jun 1974
Nattrass, Mr Alistair G LLB(Hons). . . . . *Sep 1993
Turner, Mr John A LLB . . . . *Jan 1980
Ast: Hargreaves, Mr Paul LLB . . . . *Oct 1988
Richardson, Mrs Claire LLB(Hons) . . . . Nov 2007
Walker, Mrs Debra Ann BEd. . . . . Mar 2004
Winship-Lee, Mrs Melanie LPC . . . . *Oct 2005
Con: Cunningham, Mr David B Part time DSS Tribunal Chairman . . . . *Jun 1975
Pattison, Mr David C . . . . *§Mar 1961
Penna, Mr Colin E LLB H M Coroner . . . . *§Mar 1962

ANTHONY HOOD FAMILY LAW SOLICITOR ‡
The Old Chapel 36 Westerton Bishop Auckland Co Durham DL14 8AH
Tel: 01388 609886
E-mail: mail@anthonyhood.co.uk

BERNARD JAMES ‡
10a Newgate Street Wear Valley Bishop Auckland Co Durham DL14 7EG
Tel: 01388 458868 *Fax:* 01388 458853
Dx: 60168 BISHOP AUCKLAND 1
List of partners: B James
Work: E F1 J1 K1 K3 L N O Q S1 S2 W Z(l)
Advocacy and Fixed Fee Interview undertaken
SPr: James, Mr Bernard BA(Law) . . . . *Oct 1981

MEIKLES
(incorporating Meikle Skene & Co; Dawson Arnott & Pickering)
23 Victoria Avenue Bishop Auckland Co Durham DL14 7NE
Tel: 01388 451122 *Fax:* 01388 661442
Dx: 60166 BISHOP AUCKLAND
Emergency telephone 01740 656324
Office: Barnard Castle, Ferryhill, Spennymoor, Stockton-on-Tees
Languages: French
Work: D1 D2 F1 F2 G H J1 J2 K1 L N O Q S1 S2 V W Z(l,q)
Emergency Action, Agency, Advocacy, Fixed Fee Interview, Legal Aid undertaken, Legal Aid Franchise and Member of Accident Line
Ptr: Clinton, Mr Andrew James . . . . *Aug 1996
Simpson, Mrs Lynne LLB(Hons). . . . . *Jul 1999
Ast: Passfield, Miss Zoe ★. . . . . Mar 1999

SMITH RODDAM ‡
56 North Bondgate Bishop Auckland Co Durham DL14 7PG
Tel: 01388 603073 *Fax:* 01388 450483
Dx: 60150 BISHOP AUCKLAND
List of partners: D L Harris, G Johnson, N Thompson
Office: Crook, Shildon
Work: A1 C1 C2 C3 D1 E F1 G H J1 K1 L N O Q R1 S1 V W Z(l)
Emergency Action, Agency, Advocacy, Fixed Fee Interview, Legal Aid undertaken, Legal Aid Franchise and Member of Accident Line
Ptr: Johnson, Mr Gerald BA(Law) . . . . *§Apr 1981
Thompson, Mr Neil . . . . *Nov 1997
Asoc: Bayles, Mrs Jill Diane LLB(Hons); LSF . . . . *Feb 1996
Ast: Monckton-Milnes, Miss Hilary LLB. . . . . *§Apr 1978
Con: Fairclough, Mr A Neville Notary Public. . . . . *§May 1967

ANTHONY WALTERS & CO ‡
Barrington Chambers 23a Victoria Avenue Bishop Auckland Co Durham DL14 7JH
Tel: 01388 662222 *Fax:* 01388 450603
Dx: 60157 BISHOP AUCKLAND
E-mail: aw@anthonywalters.co.uk
List of partners: A Walters
Work: B1 C1 E K1 K3 K4 L O Q R1 S2 W Z(b)
Agency undertaken
Ptr: Walters, Mr Anthony. . . . . *Oct 1979
Con: Chisem, Mr George Malcolm . . . . Jun 1973
Hood, Mr Anthony BA. . . . . *Oct 1990

BISHOP'S STORTFORD, Hertfordshire

BREEZE & WYLES SOLICITORS LLP
11 Ducketts Wharf South Street Bishop's Stortford Hertfordshire CM23 3AR
Tel: 01279 715333 *Fax:* 01279 715344
Dx: 146160 BISHOP'S STORTFORD 2
Office: Cheshunt, Enfield, Hertford
Work: E K1 K3 S1 S2 W Z(e,h)
Fixed Fee Interview and Legal Aid Franchise
Dir: Fraser, Mr Murray. . . . . Sep 1992
Gupta, Mrs Malina . . . . Sep 2002
O'Brien, Mr Brendan . . . . Feb 1998
Toulson, Mr Adrian . . . . Nov 1996
Ast: Brink, Jolanda. May 2009

EARTHRIGHTS SOLICITORS ‡
The Stansted Centre Parsonage Road Bishop's Stortford Hertfordshire CM22 6PU
Tel: 01279 874172
E-mail: jd1@earthrights.org.uk

LOCKYERS ‡
43 Church Manor Bishop's Stortford Hertfordshire CM23 5AF
Tel: 01279 505970
E-mail: lockyers@hotmail.co.uk

Lexcel

NOCKOLDS ‡
6 Market Square Bishop's Stortford Hertfordshire CM23 3UZ
Tel: 01279 755777 *Fax:* 01279 755149
Dx: 50400 BISHOP'S STORTFORD
E-mail: post@nockolds.co.uk
Web: www.nockolds.co.uk
List of partners: N J Belcher, J N Brunton, L Cowley, P E Dodd, D M Hayward, J S Jones, P J King, M S Stark, M J Talbot, A J Watts
Languages: Croatian, French, Italian, Portuguese, Spanish
Work: A1 B1 C1 C2 C3 D1 D2 E F1 F2 H J1 K1 K2 K3 K4 L M2 N O P Q R1 R2 S1 S2 T2 W X Z(c,d,e,g,h,j,k,l,m,p,q,r,t,u,w,y)
Emergency Action, Advocacy and Fixed Fee Interview undertaken
Ptr: Belcher, Mr Nicholas J Notary Public . . . . *§Dec 1973
Brunton, Mr James N. . . . . *Oct 2003
Cowley, Ms Lynn BA(Hons) . . . . *Dec 1988
Dodd, Mr Peter E BSc(Hons) . . . . *Mar 1996
Hayward, Mr Darren M BA(Hons) . . . . *Sep 1997
Jones, Miss Jennie Samantha LLB . . . . *Sep 2001
King, Mr Peter J BA(Law). . . . . *Apr 1990
Stark, Mr Michael S LLB . . . . *§Jul 1974
Talbot, Mr Michael J LLB . . . . *§Oct 1982
Watts, Miss Amanda J LLB(Hons). . . . . *Oct 2003
Ast: Corti, Ms Terri LLB(Hons) . . . . *Oct 1988
Cozens, Miss Francesca Marie BA(Hons)(Law & Sociology) . . . . *Mar 2007
Duffy, Miss Erin Charlotte LLB. . . . . Apr 2010
Hanes, Ms Carolyn BMus(Hons); MMus; LLB . . . . *Feb 2005
Hare, Mrs Alison Sarah LLB; LPC. . . . . Jan 2007
Menhinick, Mr Stevie . . . . *Oct 2007
Miles, Ms Sarah LLB . . . . Jul 2004
Moody, Mr Ivan Karl. . . . . Feb 1998
Moseley, Ms Bev LLB(Hons); LPC; BSc(Hons); PGCE Sep 2010
Peyman, Miss Maria-Christina LLB . . . . Apr 2004
Smith, Mr Gary . . . . *Jun 2009
Valero, Mr Alfonso PGDipLaw. . . . . Sep 2009
Wand, Miss Janette Susan BSc; PGDipLaw; LPC. . . *Apr 2007
Winter, Mr Daniel LLB(Hons) . . . . Sep 2004
Zilic-Munic, Mrs Bilyana PGDipLaw; LPC . . . . Sep 2003
Con: Wadham-Smith, Mr Clive Julian LLB . . . . Apr 1978

THE PLANNING LAW PRACTICE ‡
20 Oaklands Park Bishop's Stortford Hertfordshire CM23 2BY
Tel: 01279 652505 *Fax:* 01279 757618

REYNOLDS JOHNS PARTNERSHIP ‡
(incorporating WM GEE & Sons; Winter Johns & Co)
Apex House 18 Hockerill Street Bishop's Stortford Hertfordshire CM23 2DW
Tel: 01279 508626 *Fax:* 01279 503834
Dx: 50436 BISHOP'S STORTFORD
E-mail: law@reynoldsjohns.co.uk
List of partners: J P Clarke, N R Johns
Languages: Punjabi
Work: A1 B1 D1 E F1 J1 K1 K3 L N O Q R1 S1 S2 T1 T2 W Z(c,h,l,q)
Emergency Action, Agency, Advocacy and Fixed Fee Interview undertaken
Ptr: Clarke, Mrs Janet P LLB . . . . *Mar 1986
Johns, Mr Nicholas R . . . . *Nov 1981
Ast: Dhillon, Miss Jasdeep Kaur LLB. . . . . Mar 2005

CHRISTOPHER J L RYAN ‡
Maggots End Farm Maggots End Bishop's Stortford Hertfordshire CM23 1BJ
Tel: 01279 815970

ANTHONY STOCKTON
13 Ducketts Wharf South Street Bishop's Stortford Hertfordshire CM23 3AR
Tel: 01279 464530 *Fax:* 01279 464538

STANLEY TEE ‡
6 High Street Bishop's Stortford Hertfordshire CM23 2LU
Tel: 01279 755200 *Fax:* 01279 758400
Dx: 50404 BISHOP'S STORTFORD
E-mail: law@teeslaw.co.uk
List of partners: S N Becker, G P R Bramley, P R Bricknell, J R Donovan, R A Elms, S R Hynard, C M Izzard, D N Jacobs, M J Kirby, C A Metcalf, P F Osborne, P J Penney, D I Redfern, J M Sandford, P C Sellars, J R Tee, A S Wright
Office: Braintree, Great Dunmow, Saffron Walden
Languages: French, German, Welsh
Work: A1 B1 C1 C2 D1 D2 E F1 F2 G H J1 J2 K1 K3 L N O P Q R1 R2 S1 S2 T2 V W Z(c,d,h,j,l,p,q,r,s)
Emergency Action, Agency, Advocacy, Fixed Fee Interview, Legal Aid undertaken, Legal Aid Franchise and Member of Accident Line
Ptr: Becker, Mr Simon N BA(L'pool) . . . . *Oct 1986
Bramley, Govan P R LLB(Sheff). . . . . *Oct 1986
Donovan, Mr John R LLB(B'ham) . . . . *Jun 1974
Elms, Mr Robert A BA. . . . . *§Dec 1978
Izzard, Mrs Catherine M LLB(Sheff) . . . . *Oct 1989
Jacobs, Mr David N LLB . . . . *May 1981
Kirby, Mr Michael J BA(Kent) . . . . *Apr 1975
Metcalf, Mrs Caroline A LLB(East Anglia) . . . . . . *Oct 1987
Redfern, Mr David I LLB(Leics) . . . . *Apr 1981
Sandford, Mr Jonathan M LLB(Exon) . . . . *Oct 1994
Sellars, Mr Peter C LLB(Sheff) . . . . *Jul 1978
Tee, Mr J Richard MA(Cantab) . . . . *Apr 1978
Wright, Mr Allan S LLB(Soton) . . . . *Apr 1981
Asoc: Aitken, Mr Steven John LLB. . . . . *Aug 1996
Blunderfield, Mr Andrew. . . . . *Dec 1991
Dowson, Mr James H LLB(Hons) . . . . *Nov 1994
Mowat, Miss Catherine Elizabeth LLB . . . . Sep 2000
Overy, Miss Sarah J FILEx . . . . *Sep 1996
Robinson, Mr Ian Justin LLB . . . . *Sep 1998
Ast: Bell, Mr Graham John BSc(Econ) . . . . *Sep 2001
Cane, Mr Aaron John LLB(Hons) . . . . Mar 2005
Davies, Miss Tracy Anne . . . . *Sep 2000
Duffin, Miss Judith Elizabeth LLB(Hons). . . . . . . *Sep 2004
Glaister, Miss Letitia Pamela Campbell LLB . . . . . *Sep 2003
Henry, Mr Michael LLB . . . . Sep 2002
Hollis, Mr Robert J G LLB. . . . . *Oct 2001
Morris, Mr Oliver James BA. . . . . *Aug 2001
Myska, Ms Helena MA(Oxon) . . . . *Apr 1989
Powell, Miss Sally Jane BA . . . . Sep 2004
Purslow, Miss Abbie Louise BA . . . . Sep 2003
Seeley, Mr Nicholas R. . . . . *Dec 1979
Whitaker, Mr Robert Joseph LLM . . . . *Sep 2002

TRUST SOLICITORS LIMITED ‡
41 Dane Park Bishop's Stortford Hertfordshire CM23 2PR
Tel: 01279 655232
E-mail: info@trustsolicitorsltd.co.uk

WHISKERS
The Folly 18 Hadham Road Bishop's Stortford Hertfordshire CM23 2QR
Tel: 01279 501550 *Fax:* 01279 503004
Dx: 50403 BISHOP'S STORTFORD
E-mail: enquiries@whiskers.co.uk
Office: Epping, Harlow, Woodford

WRAY & CO ‡
34 Ellenborough Close Bishop's Stortford Hertfordshire CM23 4PB
Tel: 01279 505964

BISHOP'S WALTHAM, Hampshire

CHAMBERLAINS ‡
Red Lion Street Bishop's Waltham Hampshire SO32 1ST
Tel: 01489 896141 *Fax:* 01489 896020
E-mail: chamberlains@redlionstreet.freeserve.co.uk
List of partners: C Chamberlain, H E Mundy
Languages: French
Work: A1 C1 C3 E J1 L R1 R2 S1 S2 T1 T2 W
Ptr: Chamberlain, Mr Colin . . . . *Jun 1976
Mundy, Mr Henry E . . . . *Nov 1981
Asoc: Chamberlain, Miss Hannah Beth LLB . . . . Feb 2010

DRIVER BELCHER SOLICITORS ‡
The Square Bishop's Waltham Hampshire SO32 1GJ
Tel: 01489 892101 / 892102 *Fax:* 01489 895019
E-mail: pdbelcher@driverbelcher.co.uk
List of partners: P D Belcher, P D Belcher
Office: Southampton
Work: C1 D1 D2 E K1 K2 N O Q S1 S2 W Z(q,r)
Emergency Action, Agency, Advocacy, Fixed Fee Interview, Legal Aid undertaken and Legal Aid Franchise
Ptr: Belcher, Mrs Patricia Dawn . . . . Dec 1991

BISHOPS CASTLE, Shropshire

EMRYS JONES & CO
28 High Street Bishops Castle Shropshire SY9 5BQ
Tel: 01588 638793
E-mail: info@emrysjones.co.uk
Office: Welshpool
Work: A1 B1 C1 D1 E F1 G H J1 K1 K3 L N O P Q R1 S1 S2 T1 W Z(c,j,k,l,q,s,t)
Emergency Action and Advocacy undertaken

See p112 for the Key to Work Categories & other symbols

MEDLICOTT SNOWS ‡
The Old Picture House High Street Bishops Castle Shropshire SY9 5BQ
Tel: 01588 638425 *Fax:* 01588 638895
E-mail: solicitors@medlicottsnows.co.uk
List of partners: C Denham, P J Medlicott, R Wayne
Office: Knighton
Work: A1 C1 D1 E K1 K3 K4 L Q S1 S2 W
Emergency Action, Agency, Fixed Fee Interview, Legal Aid undertaken and Legal Aid Franchise
Ptr: Denham, Ms Caroline . . . . . *§Oct 1992
Medlicott, Mr Peter James . . . . . *§Jul 1968
Wayne, Mr Robin . . . . . *Aug 1970

BLABY, Leicestershire

JOSIAH HINCKS
33 Leicester Road Blaby Leicestershire LE8 4GR
Tel: 0116 264 3430 *Fax:* 0116 278 7269
E-mail: info@josiahhincks.co.uk
Office: Coalville, Leicester
Work: A2 A3 B1 C1 C2 D1 D2 E F1 J1 K1 K2 L N O P Q S1 S2 W Z(c,d,e,i,l,o,q,r)
Agency, Advocacy and Legal Aid undertaken
Ast: Chauhan, Mrs Zabin LLB(Hons) . . . . . Jan 2007

RICH & CARR FREER BOUSKELL
7 Lutterworth Road Blaby Leicestershire LE8 4DW
Tel: 0116 242 6039 *Fax:* 0116 277 6014 *Dx:* 29802 BLABY
E-mail: enquiries@richandcarr.co.uk
Office: Leicester, Lutterworth, Oadby, Syston
Work: C1 E K1 L N Q S1 S2 T1 W
Emergency Action and Advocacy undertaken
Ptr: Barr, Mr Edward John BA; MA; LSF . . . . . Nov 1997

BLACKBURN

AA LAW (LANCASHIRE) LTD ‡
7 Lord Street West Blackburn BB2 1LA
Tel: 0845 644 0786 *Fax:* 0845 644 0601
E-mail: aa_lawsolicitors@yahoo.co.uk

ACKLAM BOND NOOR
2 Strawberry Bank Blackburn BB2 6AA
Tel: 01254 56068 *Fax:* 01254 677415 *Dx:* 17980 BLACKBURN
E-mail: david@acklambond.co.uk
Office: Accrington, Dewsbury
Work: B1 C1 C2 E J1 K1 L N O R1 R2 S1 S2 W Z(i,l,r)
Emergency Action, Agency, Advocacy, Fixed Fee Interview and Legal Aid undertaken
Ptr: Acklam, Mr David Ian BA . . . . . *Jan 1980

BLAKEWATER SOLICITORS LTD ‡
3 Richmond Terrace Blackburn BB1 7AT
Tel: 01254 261515 *Fax:* 01254 261527 *Dx:* 15260 BLACKBURN 2
E-mail: info@blakewatersolicitors.com

CURTIS LAW SOLICITORS ‡
26 Limbrick Blackburn BB1 8AA
Tel: 01254 297130 *Fax:* 01254 297131 *Dx:* 15253 BLACKBURN 2
E-mail: info@curtislaw.co.uk

FARLEYS SOLICITORS LLP ‡
22-27 Richmond Terrace Blackburn BB1 7AF
Tel: 01254 367855 *Fax:* 01254 583526 *Dx:* 13604 BLACKBURN 3
Emergency telephone 01254 525552
E-mail: info@farleys.com
List of partners: J D Bridge, A Church-Taylor, M G Corrigan, P Corrigan, D Draper, B Horne, D King, I A Liddle, A Love, S P McNeill, N Molyneux, B T K O'Connor, C J Porter, P R Schofield, J Taylor, P J Taylor
Office: Accrington, Blackburn (2 offices), Burnley, Manchester
Languages: Gujarati, Hindi, Punjabi, Urdu
Work: A1 B1 B2 C1 C2 D1 E F1 G H J1 K1 K3 L M1 N O P Q R1 S1 S2 T1 V W Z(f,g,l)
Emergency Action, Agency and Advocacy undertaken
Ptr: Corrigan, Mr Michael G LLB. . . . . *Jun 1979
Draper, Mr Desmond BA; MA . . . . . *Aug 1994
Schofield, Mr Paul R LLB ★ . . . . . *Jun 1980
Taylor, Mr Philip J LLB(Huddersfield) . . . . . *Feb 1988
Asoc: Hibbert, Ms Bridgette . . . . . *Aug 2001
Preston, Mr Kevin F ★ . . . . . *Jun 1992
Ast: Gray, Miss Alison L LLB. . . . . *Dec 1995
Hall, Miss Sian LLB(Hons) . . . . . *Sep 2001
Shaw, Miss Annette LLB(Hons) ★ . . . . . *Mar 2006
Suleman, Mr Nadir LLB(Hons) . . . . . *Dec 2010
Walmsley, Mrs Laura Jane LLB(Hons) . . . . . *Sep 2008

FARLEYS SOLICITORS LLP
Unit C1 Hurstwood Court Duttons Way Blackburn BB1 2QR
Tel: 01254 367856 *Fax:* 01254 229830 *Dx:* 13604 BLACKBURN 3
E-mail: info@farleys.com
Office: Accrington, Blackburn (2 offices), Burnley, Manchester
Work: A1 B1 C1 D1 E F1 G H J1 K1 L M1 N O P Q R1 S1 T1 V W
Emergency Action, Agency, Advocacy, Fixed Fee Interview, Legal Aid undertaken, Legal Aid Franchise and Member of Accident Line
Ptr: King, Mrs Deborah . . . . . *Aug 2009
Liddle, Mr Ian Albert . . . . . *Apr 1997
O'Connor, Mr B T Kieran LLB(Hons) . . . . . *Jul 1986
Porter, Mr Christopher John LLB . . . . . *Apr 1981
Ast: Draper, Mr Daniel . . . . . *Aug 2007
Greenwood, Mr Stephen . . . . . *Aug 2008
Hindle, Rebecca . . . . . Jul 2009
Jenner, Rachael . . . . . *Sep 2009
Mitchell, Ms Victoria LLB(Hons) . . . . . *Oct 2006
Walsh, Mr Alex . . . . . *Aug 2006

FARLEYS SOLICITORS LLP
1-2 Richmond Terrace Blackburn BB1 7AT
Tel: 01254 367854 *Fax:* 01254 693941 *Dx:* 13604 BLACKBURN 3
E-mail: info@farleys.com
Office: Accrington, Blackburn (2 offices), Burnley, Manchester
Ptr: Church-Taylor, Mr Andrew LLB(Wales) . . . . . *Feb 1982
Love, Miss Antonia . . . . . *Sep 1998
Taylor, Mr Jonathan . . . . . Jun 1999
Asoc: Bunyan, Mr Barry Robert LLB Judge Coventry Prize . *Dec 1991
Rebello, Mr Anthony Francis Alan BA(Hons)(Law) Judge Coventry Prize 1983 . . . . . *Dec 1985
Ast: Drew, Mrs Angharad LLB(Hons) . . . . . *Sep 2010
Hall, Miss Sian LLB(Hons) . . . . . *Sep 2001
Hill, Miss Pauline Sally LLB(Hons) . . . . . *Jul 2003
Livesey, Mrs Toni LLB(Hons) . . . . . *Oct 2009
Pickup, Mr Damien Simon LLB(Hons) . . . . . *Aug 2009
Rossi, Mrs Angela Jane LLB(Hons) . . . . . *Aug 2008
Taylor, Mrs Marsaya Victoria LLB(Hons) ● . . . . . *Mar 2006
Whittingham, Miss Ruth Margaret LLB(Hons); LPG; DipLaw . . . . . *Oct 2001

FARNSWORTH MORGAN BAKHAT ‡
41a Richmond Terrace Blackburn BB1 7AW
Tel: 01254 274700

FORBES ‡
(incorporating Marsden & Marsden)
Rutherford House 4 Wellington Street (St Johns) Blackburn BB1 8DD
Tel: 01254 54374 *Fax:* 01254 52347 *Dx:* 17952 BLACKBURN 1
Emergency telephone 01254 265809
E-mail: andrea.stamp@forbessolicitors.co.uk
List of partners: D H Baker, J C Barker, M J Blacklidge, R M Bower, M G Crabtree, S J Dawson, P A Dugdale, G P Earnshaw, A M Ellis, D I Forbes, P D A Geldard, T J Hollingsworth, W J H Hood, S G Isherwood, D J King, G T Parkinson, P A Scholes, S T Shorthouse, P B Turner
Office: Accrington (2 offices), Blackburn (2 offices), Chorley, Leeds, Manchester, Preston
Work: A1 B1 C1 C2 C3 D1 E F1 G H J1 K1 L M1 N P R1 S1 T1 T2 V W Z(a,b,d,e,f,g,h,i,j,k,l,m,n,o,s,t)
Emergency Action, Agency, Advocacy, Fixed Fee Interview, Legal Aid undertaken, Legal Aid Franchise and Member of Accident Line
Ptr: Barker, Mr John C LLB . . . . . *§Jun 1975
Bower, Mr Robin M LLB. . . . . *Oct 1991
Hollingsworth, Mr Timothy J BA; LSF . . . . . *Mar 1990
Scholes, Mr Peter A. . . . . *§Feb 1964
Ast: Jones, Mr Rayner LLB . . . . . *Jun 1991
Milnes, Mr Daniel R LLB(Hons) Sweet & Maxwell Law Prize (Durham University) 1995. . . . . Sep 1998
Ormand, Mr Jonathan R LLB(Hons). . . . . Oct 1998
Patel, Mr Siraj Ahmed LLB . . . . . *Oct 1994
Smith, Mr Michael E BA(Law) . . . . . *Oct 1981
Smith, Mr Nigel J LLB. . . . . *Oct 1981
Spensley, Mrs Michelle LLB. . . . . *Feb 1993
Con: Haddow, Mr John C MA. . . . . *Jun 1970

FORBES
Marsden House 28 Wellington Street (St John's) Blackburn BB1 8DA
Tel: 01254 662831 *Fax:* 01254 681104 *Dx:* 17969 BLACKBURN 1
Emergency telephone 01254 265809
E-mail: martin.crabtree@forbessolicitors.co.uk
Office: Accrington (2 offices), Blackburn (2 offices), Chorley, Leeds, Manchester, Preston
Work: A1 B1 C1 C2 C3 D1 E F1 G H J1 K1 L N O P Q R1 S1 T1 T2 V W Z(b,c,e,f,h,i,j,k,l,m,o,s,t)
Emergency Action, Agency, Advocacy, Fixed Fee Interview, Legal Aid undertaken and Member of Accident Line
Ptr: Crabtree, Mr Martin G MA(Cantab) . . . . . *§May 1980
Ellis, Mr Andrew M BSc. . . . . *Sep 1990
Geldard, Mr Paul D A LLB. . . . . *Feb 1988
Ast: Bower, Mr Alistair. . . . . Mar 1998
Hardy, Miss Siobhan LLB . . . . . *Oct 1990
Howard, Mr Ian Paul Richard LLB. . . . . Oct 1990
Mychalkiw, Miss Anna MA. . . . . *Oct 1993
Myles, Mr John J LLB(L'pool) . . . . . Jul 1986
Pickford, Mr David LLB . . . . . *Mar 1993
Yates, Mr David Roland LLB(Hons); LSF . . . . . *Oct 1995

FORBES
73 Northgate Blackburn BB2 1AA
Tel: 01254 580000 *Fax:* 01254 682392 *Dx:* 17970 BLACKBURN 1
Emergency telephone 01254 265809
E-mail: mike.bracklidge@forbessolicitors.co.uk
Office: Accrington (2 offices), Blackburn (2 offices), Chorley, Leeds, Manchester, Preston
Work: G H J1 K1 V Z(h)
Emergency Action, Agency, Advocacy, Fixed Fee Interview, Legal Aid undertaken, Legal Aid Franchise and Member of Accident Line
Ptr: Blacklidge, Mr Michael J LLB(Leeds) . . . . . *May 1981
King, Mr Daniel J BA Judge Coventry Prize . . . . . *Jun 1986
Ast: Ditta, Mr Basharat Ali LLB(Hons) . . . . . May 1997
Shebon, Mrs Helen . . . . . *May 1997
Tempest, Mrs Shirley BA(Hons); LSF . . . . . *Oct 1991

GARRICKS SOLICITORS ‡
8 Cunningham Court Blackburn BB1 2QX
Tel: 01254 268790 *Fax:* 01254 696881
E-mail: info@garrickslaw.co.uk

HPA SOLICITORS ‡
Cambridge House 84-86 Randal Street Blackburn BB1 7LG
Tel: 01254 274786 *Fax:* 01254 427101
E-mail: info@hpasolicitors.com

HARDMAN WOOD ‡
(incorporating Arkwright Cooper)
11 Wellington Street St Johns Blackburn BB1 8BZ
Tel: 01254 295540 *Fax:* 01254 295541 *Dx:* 17959 BLACKBURN 1
E-mail: ed@hardman-wood.co.uk
List of partners: M J Hardman, A Wood
Work: C1 C2 D1 D2 E F1 K1 K2 K3 K4 L R1 S1 S2 T1 T2 V W
Emergency Action, Agency, Advocacy, Fixed Fee Interview, Legal Aid undertaken and Legal Aid Franchise
Ptr: Hardman, Mr Michael John . . . . . *§Nov 1973
Wood, Mr Anthony LLB . . . . . *§Jul 1980
Ast: Parr, Mrs Ellie. . . . . Nov 2010

HAWORTH & NUTTALL ‡
1a Strawberry Bank Preston New Road Blackburn BB2 6AS
Tel: 01254 272640 *Fax:* 01254 272641 *Dx:* 17954 BLACKBURN 1
E-mail: admin@hn-commercial.co.uk
List of partners: P D Barnes, I C Brunt, C R J Bury, M J Heyes, G H Ireland, D A McCraith, N Phelps, J J Riley
Office: Accrington, Great Harwood
Work: A1 B1 C1 C2 C3 D1 D2 E F1 J1 K1 K3 K4 L N O Q R1 R2 S1 S2 W Z(i,m,q)
Agency, Advocacy, Fixed Fee Interview, Legal Aid undertaken and Legal Aid Franchise
Ptr: Brunt, Mr Ian C BSc. . . . . *Oct 1992
Bury, Mr Charles R J LLB . . . . . *§Apr 1981
Heyes, Mr Martin John LLB . . . . . *Oct 1983
Ireland, Mr Graham H LLB . . . . . *§Feb 1998
Phelps, Mrs Nicola LLB(Leics). . . . . *Nov 1988
Riley, Mr John J LLB Judge Coventry Prize . . . . . *Jun 1978
Ast: Akhtar, Miss Shahin LLB(Hons)(Business Law) . . *Jun 2003
Barnes, Mr Peter D LLB(Hons) . . . . . *Jul 1976
Mann, Mr Daviv LLB; BA . . . . . Aug 2010
Slattery, Mr Michael B. . . . . *Jun 1973
Con: Leigh, Mr John RD RD; LLB. . . . . *§Jun 1969

NIGEL HOLDEN & CO
Richmond House 15 Richmond Terrace Blackburn BB1 7BQ
Tel: 01254 682424 *Fax:* 01254 682400
E-mail: nigel@nigelholden.co.uk
Office: Burnley, Nelson
Languages: Italian
Work: A1 C1 E F1 J1 N O Q R1 S1 T2 W Z(c)
Agency, Advocacy undertaken and Member of Accident Line
Ptr: Holden, Mr Arthur Nigel LLB(Hons)(Lond); MBA Notary Public . . . . . Mar 1972

JOSEPHS SOLICITORS LLP ‡
Lister House 6 St Andrews Street Blackburn BB1 8AE
Tel: 01254 677099

KG SOLICITORS LIMITED ‡
Lex House Capricorn House Blakewater Road Blackburn BB1 5QR
Tel: 01245 685695

LISA MARIE MCNULTY ‡
756 Whalley New Road Blackburn BB1 9BA
Tel: 01254 248209

NP LAWYERS ‡
7 St Andrews Street Blackburn BB1 8AE
Tel: 01254 671100 *Fax:* 01254 671103

NAPTHENS LLP
Greenbank Court Challenge Way Greenbank Business Park Blackburn BB1 5QB
Tel: 01254 667733 *Fax:* 01254 681166 *Dx:* 17964 BLACKBURN 1
E-mail: blackburn@napthens.co.uk
Office: Blackpool, Chorley, Preston
Languages: Japanese
Work: A1 B1 C1 C2 C3 D1 E F1 J1 K1 L N O Q R2 S1 S2 V W Z(f,l,q,r)
Emergency Action, Agency, Advocacy, Fixed Fee Interview undertaken and Member of Accident Line
Ptr: Clare, Mr Andrew David BA(Hons) . . . . . *Oct 1998
Eatough, Mr John A LLB(Manc). . . . . *Jun 1971
Hill, Mr David LLB(Hons) . . . . . Oct 1995
Windle, Mr J Martin B BA . . . . . *Oct 1981
Ast: Bromiley, Victoria . . . . . Jul 2005
Clithero, Mr Richard John LLB . . . . . Feb 2007
Ireland, Mr Malcolm. . . . . Jul 2008
Patefield, Mr Simon Mark LLB. . . . . Sep 1988

ROGER PICKLES & CO ‡
15 Richmond Terrace Blackburn BB1 7BQ
Tel: 01254 51000 *Fax:* 01254 59999 *Dx:* 17978 BLACKBURN
Work: D1 F1 G H J1 K1 K2 L N Q S1 V W Z(h,i,k,m,q,r)
Emergency Action, Agency, Advocacy and Legal Aid undertaken

QUALITYSOLICITORS C TURNER ‡
Oakfield House 93 Preston New Road Blackburn BB2 6AY
Tel: 01254 688400 *Fax:* 01254 688426
E-mail: law@turnerlaw.co.uk
List of partners: P Garner, R M Prew, N M B Turner
Languages: French
Work: B2 D1 E F1 G H J1 K1 K3 N O Q S1 S2 W Z(i,j,k,l,r,t)
Emergency Action, Agency, Advocacy, Legal Aid undertaken, Legal Aid Franchise and Member of Accident Line
Ptr: Garner, Mr Paul. . . . . *§Jun 1990
Prew, Mr Richard M LLB . . . . . *Sep 1990
Turner, Mr Nicholas M B MA(Oxon) . . . . . *§Dec 1979
Asoc: Bellis, Mr Paul LLB(Hons). . . . . Oct 1983
Procter, Mr Ian Mark LLB(Hons). . . . . *Nov 2002
Wrennall, Mrs Barbara Susan LLB(Hons) . . . . . Oct 1991
Ast: Chapman, Miss Suzanne . . . . . Apr 2009
Chowdhary, Waseem . . . . . Aug 2008
Suleman, Mr Sarfraz . . . . . Oct 2006

ROEBUCKS ‡
(incorporating Singletons & Rushton Ibbotson)
7 & 12 Richmond Terrace Blackburn BB1 7BG
Tel: 01254 274000 *Fax:* 01254 274002 *Dx:* 15254 BLACKBURN 2
Emergency telephone 07903 559919
E-mail: info@roebuckslaw.co.uk
List of partners: D P Grindrod, R W E Hall, T A Hoyle, R M Phoenix, G R Tootle, J E Watson
Office: Accrington, Blackburn
Languages: French, Gujarati, Kiswahili, Punjabi, Urdu
Work: A1 A2 B1 B2 D1 D2 E G H J1 K1 K4 L N O P Q R1 S1 S2 W X Z(c,d,e,j,l,m,q,w,x)
Emergency Action, Agency, Advocacy, Fixed Fee Interview, Legal Aid undertaken, Legal Aid Franchise and Member of Accident Line
Ptr: Grindrod, Mr David P LLB. . . . . *§Jul 1978
Hall, Mr Robert William Edwin LLB(Hons) Deputy Diocesan Registrar Notary Public . . . . . *§Oct 1982
Hoyle, Mr Thomas A LLB(Soton) Diocesan Registrar; Chapter Clerk to Blackburn Cathedral; Chairman of MHRT; President of the Notaries Society of England and Wales Notary Public . . . . . *§Jun 1976
Phoenix, Mr Robin Michael LLB(Hons) . . . . . *§Aug 1998
Tootle, Mr Graeme R BA . . . . . *§Mar 1984
Watson, Mrs Julia E LLB Deputy District Judge (Civil) *§Apr 1976
Asoc: Ashcroft, Miss Louise Catherine Elizabeth LLB . . . *Sep 2001
De-Mel, Miss Victoria Louise LLB(Hons). . . . . *Jul 2001
Hussain, Mr Imran LLB . . . . . *Jan 2005
Morrissey, Miss Emma Louise LLB(Hons) . . . . . *Feb 1993
Nolan, Miss Alison LLB(Hons). . . . . Oct 1990
Robson, Miss Sarah LLB . . . . . *Nov 2005
Wadsworth, Miss Vicky . . . . . *Sep 2004
Ast: Neville, Miss Louise Megan LLB. . . . . Jul 2008
Wade, Miss Karen Louise LLB(Hons) . . . . . Aug 2007
Con: Hamlin, Mrs Kate LLB(Leeds) . . . . . *§Nov 1977
King, Mr Peter John BA(Hons)(Law). . . . . §Jan 1982

ROEBUCKS
Diocesan Offices Cathedral Close Blackburn BB1 5AA
Tel: 01254 503070 *Fax:* 01254 699963
E-mail: registry@blackburnce.u-net.com
Office: Accrington, Blackburn
Work: Z(x)

Ptr: Hall, Mr Robert William Edwin LLB(Hons) Deputy Diocesan Registrar Notary Public . . . . *§Oct 1982
Hoyle, Mr Thomas A LLB(Soton) Diocesan Registrar; Chapter Clerk to Blackburn Cathedral; Chairman of MHRT; President of the Notaries Society of England and Wales Notary Public . . . . *§Jun 1976

SILK SOLICITORS ‡
59 James Street Blackburn BB1 6BE
Tel: 01254 266616 *Fax:* 01254 266615
E-mail: info@silksolicitors.co.uk
List of partners: H Pickles, K Teasdale
Ptr: Pickles, Helen. . . . . Feb 1997
Teasdale, Kay. . . . . Mar 1997

THE SOLOMON PARTNERSHIP SOLICITORS LLP ‡
20 Strawberry Bank Blackburn BB2 6AA
Tel: 01254 667358 *Fax:* 01254 699137 *Dx:* 17983 BLACKBURN
E-mail: info@thesolomonpartnership.com
Office: Manchester

JOHN SWINDELL AND CO SOLICITORS ‡
St John's House 22 Wellington Street (St Johns) Blackburn BB1 8AF
Tel: 01254 52400 *Fax:* 01254 52332 *Dx:* 17967 BLACKBURN 1
List of partners: J Swindell
Languages: Arabic, Gujarati, Urdu
Ptr: Swindell, Mr John. . . . . Feb 1994

TAYLORS ‡
Rawlings House Exchange Street Blackburn BB1 7JN
Tel: 0844 800 0263 *Fax:* 0844 800 0264
E-mail: contact@taylors.co.uk
List of partners: D Bailey, C D Bowers, A R Catterall, E Hurn, A J Livesey, O J McCann, M S Niven, C G Scott
Office: Manchester
Languages: French, German, Spanish
Work: B1 C1 C2 C3 E I J1 J2 L M1 M2 O P Q R1 R2 S2 U2 Z(b,c,e,o,q)
Ptr: Bailey, Mr David LLB(Hons) . . . . *Sep 2002
Hurn, Mrs Elaine LLB(B'ham) . . . . *§Apr 1980
McCann, Mr Oliver John BA(Hons) . . . . *Sep 2000
Scott, Mr Christopher Granville BA(Brunel College) . *Jan 1981
Asoc: Barnes, Mrs Claire Louise LLB; LLM(QMW). . . . . *Oct 1996
Challender, Mr Barry James LLB(Hons). . . . . . . *Jun 1976
Ast: Black, Mrs Elizabeth Patricia MA(Hons) . . . . . . *Sep 2002

A D VARLEY & CO ‡
26 Wellington Street (St Johns) Blackburn BB1 8AF
Tel: 01254 582777 *Fax:* 01254 582888 *Dx:* 17960 BLACKBURN
E-mail: mail@advarleyandco.co.uk
Office: Preston
Work: E N S1 W

VERITAS SOLICITORS LLP ‡
Blackburn Enterprise Centre Furthergate Blackburn BB1 3HQ
Tel: 01254 504999 *Fax:* 01254 504998
E-mail: info@veritassolicitors.co.uk

WALKER PRESTONS ‡
Suite 6 Blackburn Enterprise Park Furthergate Blackburn BB1 3HQ
Tel: 01254 772265 *Fax:* 01254 505088 *Dx:* 15252 BLACKBURN 2
E-mail: info@wpsolicitors.co.uk

THE WATSON RAMSBOTTOM PARTNERSHIP ‡
25-29 Victoria Street Blackburn BB1 6DN
Tel: 01254 672222 *Fax:* 01254 681723 *Dx:* 15251 BLACKBURN 2
E-mail: info@watsonramsbottom.com
List of partners: C N Bolton, E I Foolat, R Horman, P W Lamster, J Swanney, P D Thompson, P West
Office: Darwen, Great Harwood
Languages: French, Gujarati, Urdu
Work: A1 A2 A3 B1 B2 C1 C2 C3 D1 D2 E F1 F2 G H I J1 J2 K1 K3 K4 L M1 M2 N O P Q R1 R2 S1 S2 T1 T2 V W X Z(c,e,f,g,h,i,j,k,l,m,n,p,q,s,t,u,y,za)
Emergency Action, Agency, Advocacy, Fixed Fee Interview, Legal Aid undertaken, Legal Aid Franchise and Member of Accident Line
Ptr: Bolton, Mr Christopher Neil LLB(Hons) • . . . . . . Oct 2000
Foolat, Mr Ebrahim Ismail LLB . . . . *Mar 1992
Horman, Ms Rachel. . . . . *Feb 1998
Lamster, Mr Peter W LLB(Lond). . . . . *Nov 1971
Swanney, Mr John LLB(Sheff). . . . . *Apr 1981
Thompson, Mr Phillip David BA(Hons). . . . . Dec 1980
West, Mr Peter . . . . *Sep 1973
Asoc: Brown, Mr Ian LLB . . . . Dec 1978
Farry, Miss Geraldine LLB(Hons) . . . . Nov 1990
Ast: Hallmark, Ms Ann-Kathryn . . . . *Oct 1997
Holland, Ms Claire M LLB(Hons) . . . . Oct 1993
Hussain, Mr Ibrar LLB(Hons) . . . . Sep 2004
Pollitt, Miss Stephanie Justine BA; PGCE . . . . Jul 1998
Shaw, Miss Valerie Anne LLB(Hons)(Law with French)*Nov 1992
Unnisa, Mrs Fahrat LLB(Hons) . . . . *Sep 2000
Watson, Mrs Lisa LLB(Hons) . . . . Oct 2005
Whittaker, Mrs Michelle Ann LLB(Hons). . . . . Sep 2005
Con: Dewhurst, Mr John Turner •. . . . . Dec 1968

IAN WHALLEY ‡
1 Billinge Side Blackburn BB2 6QA
Tel: 01254 676472 / 07896 241032 *Fax:* 01254 676472
E-mail: ian@iwhalley.com

BLACKPOOL

ASCROFT WHITESIDE ‡
303 Whitegate Drive Blackpool FY3 9JS
Tel: 01253 766866 *Fax:* 01253 766826 *Dx:* 19366 BLACKPOOL 2
E-mail: mail@ascroftwhiteside.co.uk
List of partners: F Reid, L D Samuels
Work: A1 A3 C1 E F1 F2 J1 J2 K1 K3 K4 L N O Q S1 S2 T2 W Z(j,l,p,q)
Emergency Action, Agency, Advocacy and Fixed Fee Interview undertaken
Dir: Reid, Mrs Fiona FILEx . . . . *Sep 2005
Samuels, Mr Lester David. . . . . *Nov 1970
Ast: Booth, Mr Graeme Timothy LLB. . . . . *Sep 2007
Con: Richmond, Mr Robert Frederick . . . . *Mar 1957

ATKINSON CAVE & STUART ‡
45 Springfield Road Blackpool FY1 1PZ
Tel: 01253 293151 *Fax:* 01253 752289 *Dx:* 714351 BLACKPOOL 5
E-mail: lscott@acslawyers.co.uk
List of partners: P J S Cave, G Stuart
Work: A1 B1 B2 C1 D1 D2 E F1 G H J1 K1 L N O Q R1 S1 S2 V W Z(c,h,l,p,q,r)
Emergency Action, Agency, Advocacy, Legal Aid undertaken and Legal Aid Franchise
Ptr: Cave, Mr Peter J S LLB(Hons) . . . . *Apr 1973
Stuart, Mr Graham LLB(Hons). . . . . *Dec 1980
Ast: Quirke, Mrs Gillian LLB(Hons). . . . . Dec 1999
Splaine, Miss Leisa Marie LLB(Manc) . . . . *Dec 1994

BANKS CARRINGTON & CO ‡
12 Edward Street Blackpool FY1 1BA
Tel: 01253 622269 / 315223 *Fax:* 01253 315222
Dx: 17023 BLACKPOOL 1
E-mail: alan@bankscarrington.co.uk
List of partners: A M Carrington
Work: A1 S1 S2 W Z(l)
SPr: Carrington, Mr Alan M LLB(Hons) . . . . *Jun 1973

SARAH BARCLAY & CO ‡
8a Darwin Court Hawking Place Blackpool FY2 0JN
Tel: 01253 356051 *Fax:* 01253 356052
E-mail: sarah@sarahbarclay.co.uk
List of partners: S J Barclay
Work: Z(r)
Legal Aid undertaken
SPr: Barclay, Ms Sarah Jane LLB . . . . *Feb 1996

BARKER BOOTH & EASTWOOD ‡
346 Lytham Road Blackpool FY4 1DW
Tel: 01253 362500 *Fax:* 01253 341032
Dx: 27651 BLACKPOOL SOUTH
E-mail: info@barker-booth.co.uk
List of partners: T Fielding, S P Foy, K Gorman, D R Lowe, C A Morley
Work: B1 C1 D1 F1 J1 K1 K2 K3 L N O Q S1 S2 W Z(q)
Emergency Action, Agency, Advocacy, Fixed Fee Interview, Legal Aid undertaken, Legal Aid Franchise and Member of Accident Line
Ptr: Fielding, Mr Timothy LLB . . . . Oct 1991
Foy, Mr Shaun P . . . . *May 1984
Gorman, Mr Kevin LLB . . . . *Jul 1980
Lowe, Mr Darren Roy . . . . *Sep 1993
Morley, Ms Catherine A LLB. . . . . *May 1996
Ast: Morgan, Mrs Claire . . . . *Apr 2002

BARRETT NELLIGAN SOLICITORS
263 Church Street Blackpool FY1 3PB
Tel: 01253 292848 *Fax:* 01253 292860
Office: Fleetwood

BERRYS SOLICITORS ‡
247 Church Street Blackpool FY1 3PE
Tel: 01253 620022 *Fax:* 01253 297117
Emergency telephone 01253 620022
E-mail: berrys.mail@btconnect.com
List of partners: C J Berry
Languages: Filipino, Spanish
Work: J1 K4 N O Q S2 W
Agency undertaken
SPr: Berry, Mr Christopher J BA(Hons). . . . . *Apr 1982

BLACKHURST BUDD LLP ‡
22 Edward Street Blackpool FY1 1BA
Tel: 01253 629300 *Fax:* 01253 293519 *Dx:* 17026 BLACKPOOL 1
Emergency telephone 07770 304844
E-mail: info@blackhurstbudd.co.uk
Office: Blackpool (2 offices)
Work: A1 B1 C1 D1 E F1 G H J1 K1 K2 L N O Q S1 S2 T1 T2 V W Z(c,d,e,l,o,r,s)

BLACKHURST BUDD LLP
32 Edward Street Blackpool FY1 1BH
Tel: 01253 629300
E-mail: info@blackhurstbudd.co.uk
Office: Blackpool (2 offices)

BLACKHURST BUDD LLP
283 Church Street Blackpool FY1 3PG
Tel: 01253 629300
E-mail: info@blackhurstbudd.co.uk
Office: Blackpool (2 offices)

BRADSHAWS HAMER PARK & HAWORTH
285 Church Street Blackpool FY1 3PF
Tel: 01253 621531 *Fax:* 01253 752924 *Dx:* 714601 BLACKPOOL 6
Office: Lytham
Work: A1 B1 C1 E K1 L R2 S1 T1 T2 W Z(m)
Ptr: Shillito, Mr Christopher S LLB. . . . . *Sep 1976
Ast: Taylor, Miss Emma BA(Hons) . . . . *Nov 2007

BUTCHER MCPHEE SOLICITORS ‡
Briercliffe Barn Staining Old Road Staining Blackpool FY3 0BG
Tel: 01253 892888 *Fax:* 01253 886876
E-mail: info@butchermcphee.co.uk

COBAINS ‡
201-203 Church Street Blackpool FY1 3PA
Tel: 01253 290092 *Fax:* 01253 290459 *Dx:* 17069 BLACKPOOL 1
Emergency telephone 07860 808633 / 01253 394754
E-mail: gordon.haley@cobains.co.uk
List of partners: A E Cobain, L E Cobain
Languages: French
Work: B2 C1 C2 E F1 G H J1 K1 K2 K3 L N O Q S1 S2 W
Emergency Action, Agency, Advocacy, Legal Aid undertaken, Legal Aid Franchise and Member of Accident Line
Ptr: Cobain, Mr Allan E . . . . *Feb 1973
Cobain, Mrs Lynda E . . . . *Jun 1979
Ast: Duffy, Mr Stephen LLB(Hons) . . . . *May 1991
Lockwood, Ms Martha. . . . . Jul 2002

COLEBOURNES SOLICITORS AND ADVOCATES ‡
77 Adelaide Street Blackpool FY1 4LP
Tel: 01253 293195 *Fax:* 01253 751979 *Dx:* 17041 BLACKPOOL 1
Emergency telephone 07770 443466
List of partners: T Colebourne
Work: D1 E G H K1 K3 L N S1 S2 V W Z(l)
Agency, Advocacy, Legal Aid undertaken and Legal Aid Franchise
Ptr: Colebourne, Mr Trevor ★ . . . . *Dec 1977

COOPER NIMMO ‡
237 Church Street Blackpool FY1 3PB
Tel: 01253 626793 *Fax:* 01253 295567 *Dx:* 19364 BLACKPOOL 2
E-mail: enquiries@coopernimmo.co.uk
List of partners: J Nimmo, D A Wylie
Work: D1 D2 E K1 K3 K4 L S1 S2 W
Emergency Action, Advocacy, Fixed Fee Interview, Legal Aid undertaken and Legal Aid Franchise
Ptr: Nimmo, Mr John BSc . . . . *Feb 1985
Wylie, Ms Deborah Ann BA(Hons). . . . . *Jul 1997
Con: Cooper, Mrs Lindsey C LLB . . . . *Jul 1978

W H DARBYSHIRE & SON ‡
252 Lytham Road Blackpool FY1 6EX
Tel: 01253 346646 *Fax:* 01253 406069
Dx: 27653 BLACKPOOL SOUTH
Emergency telephone 01253 346646
E-mail: mail@whdarbyshire.co.uk
List of partners: D S Banting, R W Darbyshire, J W B McLaren, L S Williams
Office: Lytham
Work: B1 D1 D2 E F1 G H K1 K3 K4 L N O Q S1 S2 T1 T2 W Z(l)
Emergency Action, Agency, Advocacy, Fixed Fee Interview, Legal Aid undertaken and Legal Aid Franchise
Ptr: Banting, Mrs Denise Sandra LLB(Hons). . . . . . . *May 1998
Darbyshire, Mr Rowland W Part time Chairman of TAS . . . . *§Oct 1965
McLaren, Mr John W B LLB. . . . . *Oct 1986
Williams, Miss Lynn Suzanne LLB. . . . . *Aug 1994
Ast: Kipling, Mrs Janet M BA(Dunelm)(Law) . . . . *Aug 1979
Laszlo, Mr Martin George BA(Oxon). . . . . *Aug 2000

DICKINSONS ‡
24 Park Road St Annes-on-Sea Blackpool FY8 1PA
Tel: 01253 781010 *Fax:* 01253 780735 *Dx:* 716860 ST ANNES 2
E-mail: webenquiry@dickinsonssolicitors.co.uk
List of partners: N J Dickinson
Office: Blackpool
Work: A1 B1 C1 D1 D2 E F1 K1 L N O Q R1 S1 S2 T1 T2 W Z(c,h,j,l,p,r)
Agency, Fixed Fee Interview undertaken and Member of Accident Line
SPr: Dickinson, Mr Neville J . . . . *Jul 1975

DICKINSONS
5 Bath Street Lytham Blackpool FY8 5ES
Tel: 01253 795577 *Fax:* 01253 736665 *Dx:* 28441 LYTHAM
E-mail: stuart.harrison@dickinsonsolicitors.co.uk
Office: Blackpool

EASTHAMS SOLICITORS LIMITED ‡
Continental House 292-302 Church Street Blackpool FY1 3QA
Tel: 0800 032 1432 *Fax:* 0844 855 4405 *Dx:* 714600 BLACKPOOL 6
E-mail: info@easthams.co.uk
List of partners: J Bower, D Hepplestall
Languages: Polish
Work: C1 E L N O Q S1 S2 W
Dir: Bower, Mr John BA(Hons). . . . . Jul 1987
Hepplestall, Ms Debra. . . . . Sep 1997
Ast: Turner, Mr Gregory . . . . Jan 2007

ASHLEY FISHER & CO ‡
18 Edward Street Blackpool FY1 1BA
Tel: 01253 751585 *Fax:* 01253 751686
Emergency telephone 07885 708907
List of partners: A Fisher
Work: D1 F1 G H K1 L N Q S1 W
Emergency Action, Agency, Advocacy, Fixed Fee Interview and Legal Aid undertaken
SPr: Fisher, Mr Ashley LLB. . . . . *Jun 1980

INGHAMS ‡
(incorporating Irving Harris & Co)
4-8 Leopold Grove Blackpool FY1 4JR
Tel: 01253 626642 *Fax:* 01253 295590 *Dx:* 17043 BLACKPOOL 1
List of partners: C B Beckett, M P Beckett, B R Burrow, G G Cocker, A T W Hale, P J Isaacs, P M Jensen, J P Muir, R J H Statham, J I Yates
Office: Blackpool, Fleetwood, Knott-End-on-Sea, Poulton-le-Fylde, Thornton Cleveleys
Work: B1 D1 D2 E F1 G H J1 K1 L N Q R1 S1 V W Z(l,q)
Emergency Action, Agency, Advocacy, Fixed Fee Interview and Legal Aid undertaken
Ptr: Beckett, Mrs Marianne Petrina BA(Law). . . . . Jan 1999
Burrow, Mr Bradley R LLB. . . . . Oct 1990
Cocker, Mr Geoffrey G LLB; BA. . . . . *Apr 1975
Jensen, Mr Peter Michael BA(Law) . . . . Jan 1990
Yates, Mr John Ian LLB; LLM . . . . *Dec 1970
Ast: Buckley, Mrs Karen LLB Legal Practice Course Annual Prize 1999 . . . . Apr 2002
Con: Thompson, Mr Patrick. . . . . Jan 1974

INGHAMS
(incorporating Irving Harris & Co; Dorothy Heatons)
37 Red Bank Road Bispham Blackpool FY2 9HX
Tel: 01253 353308 *Fax:* 01253 356380
Office: Blackpool, Fleetwood, Knott-End-on-Sea, Poulton-le-Fylde, Thornton Cleveleys
Work: E L Q S1 W Z(l)
Ptr: Statham, Mr Richard J H BA(Law). . . . . *Apr 1981

LAYTON-LAW.COM ‡
3 Westcliffe Drive Layton Square Blackpool FY3 7BJ
Tel: 01253 399311 *Fax:* 01253 395445
E-mail: david-owen@lawyer.com
List of partners: D Owen
Work: K1 K3 S1 S2 W
Fixed Fee Interview undertaken
SPr: Owen, Mr David LLB(Manc). . . . . *Jun 1987

NAPTHENS LLP
Libra House Cropper Close Whitehills Business Park Blackpool FY4 5PU
Tel: 01253 622305 *Fax:* 01253 295591 *Dx:* 714350 BLACKPOOL 5
E-mail: blackpool@napthens.co.uk
Office: Blackburn, Chorley, Preston
Work: C1 D1 D2 E J1 K1 K3 K4 L N O Q S1 S2 W Z(c,l)
Emergency Action, Agency, Advocacy, Fixed Fee Interview, Legal Aid undertaken and Legal Aid Franchise
Ptr: Gledhill, Mr Simon J LLB . . . . *Oct 1981
Long, Mr Martin T LLB . . . . *Apr 1981
Lucking, Mrs Helen LLB. . . . . *Oct 1993
Ast: Bulmer, Leona . . . . Nov 1998
Kernot, Ms Helen Marie LLB(Hons) . . . . Aug 2007

 See p112 for the Key to Work Categories & other symbols

Mackinnon, Ms Jennifer LLB . . . . *Oct 2000
Richards, Mr Robert Francis LLB(Hons). . . . . *Apr 2004

NORTH SOLICITORS ‡
The Enterprise Centre 291-305 Lytham Road Blackpool FY4 1EW
Tel: 01253 200300 *Fax:* 01253 405706
E-mail: jonnajp@northsolicitors.co.uk

POND MARSH ‡
249 & 253 Church Street Blackpool FY1 3PB
Tel: 01253 620466 *Fax:* 01253 752675 *Dx:* 19361 BLACKPOOL
E-mail: hughpond@pondmarsh.fsnet.co.uk
List of partners: H S Marsh, H C Pond
Work: D1 D2 F1 G H J1 K1 N S1 W
Emergency Action, Agency, Advocacy, Legal Aid undertaken, Legal Aid Franchise and Member of Accident Line
Ptr: Marsh, Mr Howard S LLB(Hons). . . . . *Sep 1980
Pond, Mr Hugh C . . . . *Dec 1970

ROLAND ROBINSONS & FENTONS LLP ‡
85-89 Adelaide Street Blackpool FY1 4LX
Tel: 01253 621432 *Fax:* 01253 751161 *Dx:* 17039 BLACKPOOL 1
E-mail: csmc@rrfsolicitors.com
List of partners: M Batty, R J Castle, R Evans, C S Marquis Carr, D P Newell
Office: Lytham
Languages: French, German
Work: B1 C1 D1 E F1 G H J1 K1 K3 L N O P Q R1 S1 T1 T2 V W Z(c,d,j,k,l,q,r)
Emergency Action, Agency, Advocacy, Legal Aid undertaken and Member of Accident Line
Ptr: Castle, Mr Robert J LLB. . . . . *Oct 1989
Evans, Mr Robert BA(Hons). . . . . *Sep 1998
Marquis Carr, Mr Clive S BA(Hons) . . . . *Oct 1985
Newell, Mr Daniel P LLB(Lond) . . . . *Mar 1981
Ast: Jackson, Miss Clare A BA(Hons) . . . . Sep 2003
Manning, Mr Peter Read LLB . . . . *Jan 1980
Schofield, Mrs Emma FILEx. . . . . Sep 2007
Swindlehurst, Ms Fay LLB. . . . . Aug 2001
Con: Slater, Mr Anthony R . . . . Jul 1968

SHAW DAVENPORT & WARDLE ‡
17 King Street Blackpool FY1 3EJ
Tel: 01253 622281 *Fax:* 01253 752578 *Dx:* 17037 BLACKPOOL
Emergency telephone 01253 886181
E-mail: enquiries@shawdw.co.uk
List of partners: P D Atkin
Work: A1 B1 C1 C2 C3 D1 E F1 G H J1 K1 L M1 M2 N P R1 S1 T1 T2 W Z(c,d,l,m)
Emergency Action, Agency, Advocacy, Fixed Fee Interview, Legal Aid undertaken and Member of Accident Line
SPr: Atkin, Mr Paul Douglas LLB . . . . *Jul 1976

SNIPELAW ‡
Thompson Road Whitehill Business Park Blackpool FY4 5PN
Tel: 01253 844444 *Fax:* 01253 844488
E-mail: mail@iansnipe.com
List of partners: I M Snipe
Work: B1 E G J1 K1 M1 N P S1 W
Emergency Action, Agency, Advocacy and Legal Aid undertaken
Ptr: Snipe, Mr Ian M LLB(Hull). . . . . *§Nov 1973

WARINGS SOLICITORS ‡
Cedar Chambers Cedar Square Blackpool FY1 1BP
Tel: 01253 293106 *Fax:* 01253 623193 *Dx:* 17032 BLACKPOOL 1
E-mail: info@warings.org.uk
List of partners: K J Looby, G G F McAnulty
Languages: Greek
Work: B1 C1 D1 E G H K1 L N Q S1 S2 V W Z(l)
Emergency Action, Agency, Advocacy, Fixed Fee Interview, Legal Aid undertaken and Member of Accident Line
Ptr: Looby, Mr Kevin J BA . . . . *Apr 1980
McAnulty, Mr Gary G F LLB. . . . . *Mar 1996
Asoc: Stewart, Mrs Jennifer Margaret . . . . Oct 1997
Ast: Wilkinson, Mr Paul Jonathan LLB . . . . Nov 1998
Con: Waring, Mr Christopher J MA(Cantab). . . . . *Dec 1963

WHITWORTH & GREEN ‡
277 Church Street Blackpool FY1 3PB
Tel: 01253 772912 *Fax:* 01253 294582
Emergency telephone 01391 772912
List of partners: H A Green
Work: D1 F1 G H J1 K1 L M1 P S1 V W
Emergency Action, Agency, Advocacy, Fixed Fee Interview, Legal Aid undertaken and Member of Accident Line
Ptr: Green, Mr Howard A LLB . . . . *Dec 1982

WYLIE KAY ‡
6 Queen Street Blackpool FY1 1PE
Tel: 01253 296297 *Fax:* 01253 751345 *Dx:* 714352 BLACKPOOL 5
List of partners: M J Farrow
Work: A1 C1 E F1 J1 K1 K3 L N O Q R1 S1 S2 T1 T2 W Z(b,c)
Emergency Action, Agency, Advocacy and Fixed Fee Interview undertaken
SPr: Farrow, Mr Michael John BA . . . . *Jul 1979
Con: Apfel, Mr Brian LLB(Hons)(QUB) . . . . *Jun 1978

BLACKWOOD, Caerphilly

FAHM & CO ‡
81 Apollo Way Blackwood Caerphilly NP12 1WB
Tel: 01495 224973 *Fax:* 01495 222902
List of partners: S T Fahm
Work: B1 F1 J1 K1 L M2 N Q R1 V Z(c,h,i,m,p,u)
Advocacy, Fixed Fee Interview and Legal Aid undertaken
SPr: Fahm, Mr Sikiru Tungi MBE LLM(LSE); FCIS; FRSA; FREcons ● . . . . *Jan 1994

GRANVILLE-WEST CHIVERS & MORGAN (incorporating G Edward Williams & Son)
PO Box 1 182 High Street Blackwood Caerphilly NP12 1YB
Tel: 01495 223161 *Fax:* 01495 229827 *Dx:* 55453 BLACKWOOD
E-mail: blackwood@granville-west.co.uk
Office: Abertillery, Caldicot, Newport, Pontypool, Risca
Work: N S1 W
Fixed Fee Interview undertaken
Ptr: Erasmus, Mr John D LLB . . . . *Nov 1984

THE GWYN GEORGE PARTNERSHIP
114a High Street Blackwood Caerphilly NP12 1YL
Tel: 01495 222214 *Fax:* 01495 228469 *Dx:* 55458 BLACKWOOD 1
E-mail: mail@ggplaw.co.uk
Office: Aberdare, Merthyr Tydfil (2 offices), Ystradgynlais

PATCHELL DAVIES (TRADING NAME OF PD LAW LTD) ‡
183 High Street Blackwood Caerphilly NP12 1ZF
Tel: 01495 227128 *Fax:* 01495 222425 *Dx:* 55452 BLACKWOOD
Emergency telephone 029 2025 0194
E-mail: law@patchelldavies.co.uk
List of partners: G L S Davies, S J Morris, H Patchell, L Williams
Languages: French, Welsh
Work: A1 B1 C1 C2 C3 D1 E F1 G H J1 K1 L N O P Q R1 S1 T1 T2 V W Z(c,d,e,f,j,k,l,p,t)
Emergency Action, Agency, Advocacy, Fixed Fee Interview, Legal Aid undertaken, Legal Aid Franchise and Member of Accident Line
Ptr: Davies, Mr Graeme L S BSc(Econ) . . . . *Dec 1982
Morris, Mr Stephen J LLB(Wales) . . . . *Apr 1981
Patchell, Mr Howard LLB(Wales) . . . . *Dec 1976
Williams, Llyr LLB. . . . . *Oct 1991
Ast: Davies Williams, Miss Charlene Elizabeth LLB(Hons) . Sep 2004
Hall, Mr Jonathan. . . . . Jul 2003
Morris, Mrs Helen. . . . . *Oct 1988
Con: Patchell, Mrs Elinor M LLB . . . . *Dec 1976

TREVOR GRIFFITHS & HUMPHRIES ‡
The Square High Street Blackwood Caerphilly NP12 1ZD
Tel: 01495 225236 *Fax:* 01495 223225 *Dx:* 554451 BLACKWOOD
List of partners: M C U Davies, D W H Ellis, M S Humphries
Ptr: Davies, Mr Mark C U LLB. . . . . *Dec 1975
Ellis, Mr David W H LLB. . . . . *Jan 1970
Humphries, Miss Marcia S LLB . . . . *Jan 1979
Ast: Rogers, Mrs Glynis L LLB. . . . . *Oct 1983

BLAENAU FFESTINIOG, Gwynedd

ALWENA JONES & JONES ‡
9 High Street Blaenau Ffestiniog Gwynedd LL41 3DB
Tel: 01766 831882 *Fax:* 01766 831920
E-mail: awjones@btconnect.com
List of partners: A W Jones
Office: Tywyn
Languages: Welsh
Work: A1 C1 K1 L N S1 S2 W
Agency and Advocacy undertaken
SPr: Jones, Miss Alwena W LLB(L'pool) . . . . *§Mar 1990
Ast: Pearce, Ms Susan BA(Hons) . . . . Oct 2006

TUDUR OWEN ROBERTS GLYNNE & CO
40 High Street Blaenau Ffestiniog Gwynedd LL41 3AL
Tel: 01766 830206 *Fax:* 01766 830142
Office: Bangor (2 offices), Caernarfon, Holyhead, Menai Bridge
Languages: Welsh
Work: A1 B2 C1 D1 D2 E G H J1 J2 K1 K3 K4 L N Q R1 R2 S1 S2 T2 W X Z(l)
Agency, Advocacy, Legal Aid undertaken and Legal Aid Franchise
Ptr: Roberts, Mr Hywel G LLB. . . . . *Mar 1987
Williams, Mr Richard Owen LLB. . . . . *Jan 1989
Con: Ellis, Mr Aled L LLB(Wales) . . . . *Feb 1970

BLANDFORD FORUM, Dorset

BLANCHARDS BAILEY LLP ‡ (incorporating John Foster-Pegg)
Bunbury House Stour Park Blandford Forum Dorset DT11 9LQ
Tel: 01258 459361 *Fax:* 01258 483610
Dx: 90102 BLANDFORD FORUM
E-mail: bunbury@blanchardsbailey.co.uk
List of partners: M A J Bellman, J F Dodge, I L Holden, A D Horne, M D P Lewis
Office: Dorchester, Shaftesbury, Stalbridge
Work: A1 C1 C2 D1 E F1 F2 J1 K1 K2 K3 K4 L N O Q R1 S1 S2 T1 T2 V W X Z(d,k)
Agency, Advocacy, Fixed Fee Interview, Legal Aid undertaken and Legal Aid Franchise
Ptr: Bellman, Mr Mark A J LLB(Sheff) . . . . *May 1977
Dodge, Mr Jerome Francis LLB; TEP . . . . *Sep 2001
Holden, Ms Isobel Lisa . . . . *Jan 1989
Horne, Mr Alan D LLB. . . . . *Apr 1981
Lewis, Merlin D P BA . . . . *Apr 1988
Asoc: Jackson, Mrs Joanna . . . . Apr 2006
Jennings, Mr Christopher G BSocSc . . . . *Oct 1985
Ast: Gale, Genette. . . . . *Oct 2007
Martin, Mrs Laura. . . . . Oct 2008
Con: Johnston, Mr Michael C Coroner . . . . *§Jan 1970
Lang, Mr David M MA(Oxon) . . . . *Dec 1966

LOWE LEGAL SERVICES ‡
Cherokee Blandford Hill Blandford Forum Dorset DT11 0AA
Tel: 01258 881142 *Fax:* 01258 881142
E-mail: paul@lowelegal.co.uk
List of partners: P B Lowe
Work: C1 E F1 F2 L S1 S2 W
Ptr: Lowe, Mr Paul Bryan BA . . . . *Jan 1984

SHOARNS SOLICITORS CHRISTOPHER SHEEHAN LLB ‡
Talmine 2 St Marys Close Winterborne Blandford Forum Dorset DT11 0DJ
Tel: 01258 880214 *Fax:* 0870 762 7978
E-mail: cs@solicitor1.com
List of partners: C Sheehan
Work: A1 C1 E I L R2 S1 S2 W Z(c)
Ptr: Sheehan, Mr Christopher LLB. . . . . *Jun 1975

TRAILL & CO INCORPORATING BRENNAND & WILSON ‡
Greyhound House Market Place Blandford Forum Dorset DT11 7EB
Tel: 01258 452555 *Fax:* 01258 459384 *Dx:* 90101 BLANDFORD
E-mail: admin@traill.biz

GRENVILLE J WALKER ‡
45 East Street Blandford Forum Dorset DT11 7DX
Tel: 01258 459911 *Fax:* 01258 459996
E-mail: office@grenvillejwalker.co.uk
List of partners: G J Walker
Office: Bournemouth, Portland, Weymouth
Work: A1 D1 F1 G H J1 K1 L N Q R1 S1 T1 T2 V W Z(l)
Emergency Action, Agency, Advocacy, Fixed Fee Interview, Legal Aid undertaken and Legal Aid Franchise
Ptr: Walker, Mr Grenville James HND . . . . *§Jan 1986
Ast: Hazelton, Mr William ● . . . . *Jan 2001
Manley Topp, Mrs Helen D BA(Hons) . . . . *§Aug 1997

H D WALLACE-JONES ‡
Abbotts Court Winterborne Kingston Blandford Forum Dorset DT11 9BH
Tel: 01929 471236
List of partners: H D Wallace-Jones
Work: S1 W

JANE V WILKINSON ‡
Wrekin House Ibberton Blandford Forum Dorset DT11 0EN
Tel: 01258 817719 *Fax:* 01258 817719
List of partners: J V Wilkinson
Work: A1 A2 C1 E F1 F2 K4 L O Q S1 S2 T2 W
Agency and Fixed Fee Interview undertaken
SPr: Wilkinson, Ms Jane V. . . . . *Oct 1982

BLAYDON-ON-TYNE, Tyne & Wear

BAKER GRAY & CO ‡
30 The Garth Winlaton Blaydon-on-Tyne Tyne & Wear NE21 6DD
Tel: 0191 414 4869 *Fax:* 0191 414 8672
Emergency telephone 01860 526308
List of partners: A C Baker, C J P Gray
Office: Newcastle upon Tyne
Work: D1 G H K1 K3 L Q S1 S W
Emergency Action, Agency, Advocacy, Fixed Fee Interview, Legal Aid undertaken and Member of Accident Line
Ptr: Baker, Mr A Christopher LLB . . . . *Jan 1976

WAUGH MOODY & MULCAHY
Charteris Chambers 5 Upper Precinct Wesley Court Blaydon-on-Tyne Tyne & Wear NE21 5BT
Tel: 0191 414 2967 *Fax:* 0191 414 2286
Office: Newcastle upon Tyne
Work: A1 B1 C1 D1 E F1 G H J1 K1 L N O P Q R1 S1 T1 V W Z(c,f,k,l)
Emergency Action, Agency, Advocacy, Fixed Fee Interview and Legal Aid undertaken
Ptr: Moody, Miss J Carole LLB(Leeds). . . . . *Dec 1974

BLETCHLEY, Milton Keynes

ADAMS MOORE FAMILY LAW
192 Queensway Bletchley Milton Keynes MK2 2ST
Tel: 01908 640150
Office: Bedford, Corby, Daventry, Luton, Milton Keynes, Northampton

BRIDGEMAN KETTLE ‡
257 Queensway Bletchley Milton Keynes MK2 2EH
Tel: 01908 376321 *Fax:* 01908 643771
E-mail: info@bridgemankettle.com
List of partners: S T Kettle, L J Wakeman
Work: E J1 K1 K3 Q S1 S2 W
Fixed Fee Interview undertaken
Ptr: Kettle, Mr Shaun Thomas LLB . . . . *Feb 1988
Wakeman, Mrs Lynda Jane LLB. . . . . *Jun 1980

WOODFINES LLP
123-131 Queensway Bletchley Milton Keynes MK2 2DH
Tel: 01908 366333 *Fax:* 01908 644096 *Dx:* 100012 BLETCHLEY
E-mail: mail@woodfines.co.uk
Office: Bedford, Cambridge, Milton Keynes, Sandy
Languages: French
Work: A1 A3 B1 C1 C2 C3 D1 E F1 F2 J1 K1 K2 K4 L M1 M2 N O P Q R1 S1 S2 T1 T2 V W Z(c,d,e,i,j,k,l,m,n,o,p,x)
Emergency Action, Agency, Advocacy, Fixed Fee Interview, Legal Aid undertaken, Legal Aid Franchise and Member of Accident Line
Mem: Buckley, Mr Andrew Giles Holcroft . . . . *Sep 2000
Quinn, Mr Niall Peter ★ . . . . Jun 1974
Asoc: Birchall, Mr Christopher Antony . . . . *Apr 1981
Ast: Hayward, Mr Michael John . . . . *Sep 2008

BLYTH, Northumberland

ALDERSON DODDS ‡ (incorporating Sidney Son & Alderson; John R Parsons & Son)
4-8 Stanley Street Blyth Northumberland NE24 2BU
Tel: 01670 352293 *Fax:* 01670 354166 *Dx:* 62604 BLYTH
Emergency telephone 07659 818999 (QUOTE NO 15177)
E-mail: aldersondodds@aldersondodds.co.uk
List of partners: P W Dunn, S Johnson, T J Murray, G Shannon
Work: B1 C1 D1 D2 E F1 G H J1 K1 K3 L N O Q S1 S2 T2 V W Z(c,e,k,l,m,o,q,r)
Emergency Action, Agency, Advocacy, Fixed Fee Interview, Legal Aid undertaken, Legal Aid Franchise and Member of Accident Line
Ptr: Dunn, Mr Paul W LLB. . . . . *Nov 1986
Johnson, Mrs Susan BA. . . . . *Jul 1981
Murray, Mrs Tracey Jane BA(Hons) . . . . *Feb 1997
Shannon, Mr Graham LLB . . . . *Mar 1991
Asoc: Monkhouse, Mr John BA . . . . *May 1981
Ast: Bell, Ms Gail LLB(Hons). . . . . Jan 2006
Cowens, Miss Rebecca LLB. . . . . Apr 2011
Hall, Miss Penelope Mary . . . . *Mar 2009
Organ, Miss Helen Denyse LLB . . . . *Feb 2001
Rodgers, Mrs Judith Anne LLB . . . . *Nov 1980

CARR & CO ‡
22-24 Stanley Street Blyth Northumberland NE24 2BZ
Tel: 01670 351251 *Fax:* 01670 369405 *Dx:* 62608 BLYTH
Emergency telephone 01670 351251
E-mail: blyth@carrandcosolicitors.com
List of partners: G Iceton, S G Smith, V Wormald
Office: Gosforth, Morpeth
Languages: Turkish
Work: B1 D1 D2 E F1 J1 K1 K2 K4 L N Q S1 W
Emergency Action, Agency, Advocacy, Fixed Fee Interview and Legal Aid Franchise
Ptr: Smith, Mrs Sharon Grace LLB(Hons) . . . . *Nov 1989

Wormald, Miss Valerie LLB(Hons). . . . . *Jun 1981
Con: Easdon, Mr Alistair G . . . . *§Jan 1979

CUTHBERTSONS ‡
(incorporating Lynn & Rutherford & J W Cuthbertson & Co)
3 Stanley Street Blyth Northumberland NE24 2BS
Tel: 01670 352121 *Fax:* 01670 355951 *Dx:* 62601 BLYTH
E-mail: cuthbertsons.blyth@tiscali.co.uk
List of partners: E Armstrong, T L Carroll
Office: Ashington
Work: A1 B1 C1 D1 E F1 G H J1 K1 K2 K3 L N O P Q R1 S1 S2 T1 V W Z(l)
Emergency Action, Agency, Advocacy, Fixed Fee Interview undertaken and Member of Accident Line
Ptr: Carroll, Mr Trevor L BA(Hons)(Soc Sci) . . . . *Nov 1984

GOODYEAR & CO ‡
16a Regent Street Blyth Northumberland NE24 1PY
Tel: 01670 362379 *Fax:* 01670 351867
Work: D1 F1 G J1 K1 N Q S1 V W
Emergency Action, Agency, Advocacy, Fixed Fee Interview and Legal Aid undertaken

HEDLEY SOLICITORS ‡
3 Simpson Street Blyth Northumberland NE24 1AX
Tel: 01670 361055 *Fax:* 01670 551120 *Dx:* 62607 BLYTH
E-mail: nigelhedley@btinternet.com

LAWSON & THOMPSON
(incorporating Monkhouse)
5 Stanley Street Blyth Northumberland NE24 2BS
Tel: 01670 361959 *Fax:* 01670 351803 *Dx:* 62602 BLYTH
Emergency telephone 01661 871924
Office: Ashington, Bedlington
Work: C1 D1 F1 G H K1 L M1 P S1

WHITEHEAD & LOW ‡
Offshore House Euroseas Centre Blyth Northumberland NE24 1LZ
Tel: 01670 541531 *Fax:* 01670 541532 *Dx:* 62603 BLYTH
Emergency telephone 07881 783466
E-mail: john@whiteheadandlow.com
List of partners: J Whitehead
Languages: Chinese, Malay, Mandarin, Spanish
Work: B3 C1 E G S1 S2 W Z(i)
Ptr: Whitehead, Mr John. Mar 2001

YARWOOD & STUBLEY ‡
15 Stanley Street Blyth Valley Blyth Northumberland NE24 2BT
Tel: 01670 361211 *Fax:* 01670 360064 *Dx:* 62600 BLYTH
E-mail: secretaries@yarwoodstubley.co.uk
List of partners: R G Bird, A Brown, S W Gibson
Work: B2 D1 E F1 F2 G H J1 J2 K1 K2 L N Q R1 S1 S2 V W Z(l,w,y)
Agency, Advocacy, Legal Aid undertaken and Legal Aid Franchise
Ptr: Bird, Mr Richard Geoffrey LLB . . . . *Jul 1979
Brown, Mr Alan BA . . . . *Sep 1979
Gibson, Mr Stephen W LLB. . . . . *Feb 1980
Ast: Patterson, Mr Kyle BA . . . . Nov 2001

BODMIN, Cornwall

AP BASSETT SOLICITORS
Bryn Love Lane Bodmin Cornwall PL31 2BL
Tel: 01208 871485 *Fax:* 01208 873534
E-mail: allsorts@apbassettsolicitors.co.uk
Office: Lostwithiel

C NICHOLLS ‡
71 Fore Street Bodmin Cornwall PL31 2JB
Tel: 01208 76969 *Fax:* 01208 73796 *Dx:* 81851 BODMIN
Emergency telephone 07778 496058
E-mail: cnicholls@cnicholls.co.uk
Web: www.cnicholls.co.uk
List of partners: C Nicholls
Languages: French
Work: A3 D1 F1 G H J1 K1 K2 K3 N O Q S1 S2 W Z(c,q)
Emergency Action, Agency, Advocacy, Fixed Fee Interview, Legal Aid undertaken and Legal Aid Franchise
SPr: Nicholls, Mr Christopher MA(Cantab) ★ . . . . *Mar 1975
Ast: Argles, Mr Richard Varnier . . . . *Nov 1974
Farrell, Mr Antony LLB(Hons) . . . . *Jun 2000
Hazleton, Mr William LLB(Hons). . . . . *Jan 1978
Mitchell, Mr Christopher Alec CPE; PGDipLaw. . . . . *Jan 2006
Parsons, Mr Stephen J LLB(Lond). . . . . *Apr 1975

Franchised in crime and Family. Duty solicitors Agency Commissions undertaken in all local courts and police stations.

G & I CHISHOLM ‡
Bree Shute Court Bell Lane Bodmin Cornwall PL31 2JE
Tel: 01208 74242 *Fax:* 01208 72245 *Dx:* 81850 BODMIN
Emergency telephone 01208 72809
List of partners: G J Ingram, T J Symons
Work: A1 B1 C1 D1 E F1 G H J1 K1 L N O P R1 S1 S2 T1 V W Z(c,h,j,l,m,p,r,t)
Agency, Advocacy, Fixed Fee Interview and Legal Aid undertaken
Ptr: Ingram, Mr Gareth John. . . . . *Dec 1994
Symons, Mr Trevor J . . . . *Dec 1982
Con: Chisholm, Mr Ian LLB. . . . . *May 1972
Lander, Mr Alan J. . . . . *Jul 1972

MURRAYS ‡
8 Turf Street Bodmin Cornwall PL31 2DH
Tel: 01208 72863 *Fax:* 01208 78601 *Dx:* 81853 BODMIN
E-mail: jm@murraylegal.co.uk
List of partners: N R Gibbins, A J Lobb, J R Murray
Work: D1 D2 K1 Z(m)
Emergency Action, Agency, Advocacy, Legal Aid undertaken and Legal Aid Franchise
Ptr: Gibbins, Mr Nicholas Roger. . . . . *May 1999
Lobb, Mr Andrew John LLB(Hons). . . . . *§Oct 1991
Murray, Mr John Rupert. . . . . *Oct 1977

SPROULL SOLICITORS LLP
42 Fore Street Bodmin Cornwall PL31 2HW
Tel: 01208 72328 *Fax:* 01208 77881 *Dx:* 81854 BODMIN
E-mail: bodmin@sproulllp.co.uk
Office: Camelford, Port Isaac
Work: A1 B1 C1 E F1 K1 K3 K4 L N O Q R2 S1 S2 W Z(j,q,r)
Agency, Advocacy and Fixed Fee Interview undertaken
Mem: Hutchison, Mr David Stuart LLB. . . . . *Oct 1997
Sproull, Mr Daniel M LLB . . . . *Nov 1991
Ast: Pounder, Mr Jonathan BA(Hons) . . . . *Jul 1996

BOGNOR REGIS, West Sussex

CHAMBERLAIN MARTIN SOLICITORS ‡
42 Sudley Road Bognor Regis West Sussex PO21 1ES
Tel: 01243 825211 *Fax:* 01243 860682 *Dx:* 31203 BOGNOR REGIS
E-mail: robert.dunn@chamberlainmartin.com
List of partners: P M Bodkin, K Campbell, G R F Dunn, C E Vassall
Office: Littlehampton
Work: A1 B1 C1 C2 D1 E F1 J1 K1 L O Q R1 S1 S2 T1 T2 V W Z(c,l,o,q)
Emergency Action, Agency, Advocacy, Legal Aid undertaken and Legal Aid Franchise
Ptr: Bodkin, Mr Paul Martin BA(Hons) . . . . *Jun 1979
Campbell, Mr Keith . . . . *Dec 1976
Dunn, Mr G Robert F . . . . *Dec 1972
Vassall, Miss Charlotte Elena . . . . *Nov 2002
Ast: Grace, Miss Pauline Donna . . . . *Dec 1991
Rutherford, Miss Susan . . . . *Oct 2001
Con: Crockford, Mrs Susan A BA. . . . . *Dec 1983

GEORGE IDE LLP
Belmont Lodge Belmont Street Bognor Regis West Sussex PO21 1LE
Tel: 01243 829231 *Fax:* 01243 825553 *Dx:* 31204 BOGNOR REGIS
E-mail: maildesk@bognor.georgeide.co.uk
Office: Chichester (3 offices)
Work: A1 A3 B1 C1 C2 C3 D1 D2 E F1 G H J1 J2 K1 K2 L M1 N O P Q R1 R2 S1 S2 T1 T2 V W Z(c,g,h,j,k,l,m,o,p,q,r,s,t)
Emergency Action, Agency, Advocacy, Fixed Fee Interview, Legal Aid undertaken, Legal Aid Franchise and Member of Accident Line

EDWARD HAYES LLP
236 Chichester Road Bognor Regis West Sussex PO21 5BA
Tel: 01243 822655 *Fax:* 01243 827647 *Dx:* 30307 CHICHESTER
E-mail: info@edwardhayes.co.uk
Office: Chichester (2 offices), Havant, Littlehampton, London EC2, London EC4, Worthing
Work: E L S1 S2 W
Legal Aid Franchise
Ptr: Waite, Mr Douglas H . . . . *Jun 1972
Ast: Horlock, Mr Philip . . . . *Nov 1996
Sampson, Mr Stephen LLB(Hons). . . . . Jul 2008

THE OWEN-KENNY PARTNERSHIP
69 London Road Bognor Regis West Sussex PO21 1DE
Tel: 01243 864865 *Fax:* 01243 820455
Office: Chichester (2 offices)
Ptr: Hall, Mr Michael R . . . . Dec 1975

RITA SEN SOLICITORS ‡
4 Nyetimber Lane Rose Green Bognor Regis West Sussex PO21 3HG
Tel: 01243 263658 *Fax:* 01243 262370 *Dx:* 31202 BOGNOR REGIS
E-mail: rs@ritasen.co.uk
List of partners: H Gagan, R Sen
Office: Bognor Regis
Ptr: Sen, Miss Rita LLB(Hons). . . . . Oct 1984
Ast: Osmend, Elizabeth . . . . Nov 1994

RITA SEN SOLICITORS
33 Rose Green Road Rose Green Bognor Regis West Sussex PO21 3EU
Tel: 01243 263658 *Dx:* 31202 BOGNOR REGIS
E-mail: hg@ritasen.co.uk
Office: Bognor Regis
Ptr: Gagan, Helen. . . . . Nov 1997

HELEN AND IAN SAUL SOLICITORS ‡
6 Priory Close Bognor Regis West Sussex PO21 4HH
Tel: 01243 268996 / 07929 132111 *Fax:* 01243 268996
E-mail: hi@lawtoyourdoor.co.uk

NIGEL SEED SOLICITOR ‡
1 Middleton Court 57 Elmer Road Middleton-on-Sea Bognor Regis West Sussex PO22 6EH
Tel: 01243 855195 *Fax:* 01243 855878
E-mail: nigel.seed@btconnect.com

WANNOP FOX STAFFURTH & BRAY
York Road Chambers York Road Bognor Regis West Sussex PO21 1LT
Tel: 01243 864001 *Fax:* 01243 860708 *Dx:* 31212 BOGNOR REGIS
Emergency telephone 07730 577711
E-mail: bognor@wfsblaw.com
Office: Chichester, Havant, Littlehampton, Worthing (3 offices)
Work: A1 A3 B1 B2 C1 C2 C3 D1 D2 E F1 F2 G H J1 J2 K1 K2 K3 K4 L M1 M2 N O P Q R1 R2 S1 S2 T1 T2 V W X Z(b,c,d,e,f,h,i,j,k,l,m,o,p,q,r,s,t)
Emergency Action, Agency, Advocacy, Fixed Fee Interview, Legal Aid undertaken, Legal Aid Franchise and Member of Accident Line
Ptr: Baker, Miss Sarah Elizabeth Notary Public . . . . . *§Jan 2003
Green, Mr Paul Anthony. . . . . *§Sep 2006
Mason, Miss Joanne Margaret LLB(Hons) ★ . . . . *§Oct 2001
Poupart, Mr Nicholas K Notary Public . . . . *§Dec 1977
Ast: Andrews, Mrs Joanne. . . . . *Jul 2008
Careless-Shore, Mrs Sophie . . . . *Oct 2007

WINTLE & CO ‡
72 Aldwick Road Bognor Regis West Sussex PO21 2PE
Tel: 01243 863021 *Fax:* 01243 862431 *Dx:* 31201 BOGNOR REGIS
Emergency telephone 01243 603658
List of partners: N Pestelle, N R Seed, S L Smith, T G Stanton
Office: Bognor Regis, Selsey
Languages: French
Work: E F1 J1 K1 L N Q S1 T2 W Z(l)
Emergency Action, Agency, Advocacy, Legal Aid undertaken and Member of Accident Line
Ptr: Pestelle, Mr Nigel BA . . . . *Sep 1982
Stanton, Mr Terence G Deputy District Judge . . . . *§Jun 1966

WINTLE & CO
57 Elmer Road 3-5 Middleton Court Middleton-on-Sea Bognor Regis West Sussex PO22 6EH
Tel: 01243 586611 *Fax:* 01243 584402 *Dx:* 31201 BOGNOR REGIS
Office: Bognor Regis, Selsey
Work: E L S1 T2 W
Ptr: Seed, Mr Nigel R LLB(Leeds). . . . . *§Dec 1972
Smith, Mrs Stella L LLB. . . . . *Jan 1981

BOLTON, Greater Manchester

AGH SOLICITORS ‡
126 St George's Road Bolton Greater Manchester BL1 2BZ
Tel: 01204 364433 *Fax:* 01204 364488
Emergency telephone 07867 695495 / 01204 364433
E-mail: a.hussain@aghsolicitors.co.uk
List of partners: I Ahmed, D J Gradwell, A Hussain
Languages: Pahari, Punjabi, Urdu
Work: G J2 K1 K3 N Q S1 S2 Z(g,i)
Emergency Action, Agency, Advocacy, Fixed Fee Interview undertaken and Member of Accident Line
Ptr: Ahmed, Ms Ishtiaq LLB(Hons); Barrister. . . . . . . *Sep 2000
Gradwell, Mr Derek J LLB(Hons); LLM . . . . *Jan 1999
Hussain, Mr Ajmal LLB(Hons). . . . . Mar 2000

AI LAW LIMITED ‡
66 Chorley Street Bolton Greater Manchester BL1 4AL
Tel: 01204 454344 *Fax:* 01204 454342
E-mail: mail@ailawltd.com

ADAMSONS LAW ‡
122 St Georges Road Bolton Greater Manchester BL1 2BZ
Tel: 0808 129 3786 / 01204 362835 *Fax:* 01204 531940
E-mail: enquiries@adamsonslaw.co.uk

ALLANSONS LLP ‡
25 Chorley Old Road Bolton Greater Manchester BL1 3AD
Tel: 0161 220 8484 *Fax:* 01204 389398 *Dx:* 24123 BOLTON
Emergency telephone 07774 713333
E-mail: advice@allansons.com
List of partners: R B Allanson, M Patel
Office: Manchester
Languages: Gujarati, Urdu
Legal Aid Franchise
Ptr: Allanson, Mr Roger B LLB ●. . . . . Feb 1986
Patel, Mr Mohammed ● . . . . *Jul 2003

AMM SOLICITORS LTD (FAITH KING SOLICITORS) ‡
Estate House 4 Myrtle Street Bolton Greater Manchester BL1 3AH
Tel: 01204 369123 *Fax:* 01204 370297 *Dx:* 724045 BOLTON
E-mail: info@faithking.co.uk

ASONS SOLICITORS LIMITED ‡
32-36 Chorley New Road Bolton Greater Manchester BL1 4AP
Tel: 01204 520720 *Fax:* 0844 873 3670
E-mail: ia@asons.co.uk

ASPINALL & CO ‡
15 Wood Street Bolton Greater Manchester BL1 1EB
Tel: 01204 388200 *Fax:* 01204 394626
E-mail: aspinallco@aol.com
List of partners: J Meredith, T L Valenzuela
Work: C1 D1 E J1 K1 K3 K4 L N O Q S1 S2 T1 T2 W
Emergency Action, Agency, Advocacy, Legal Aid undertaken and Legal Aid Franchise
Ptr: Meredith, Mr John LLB . . . . Apr 1977
Valenzuela, Miss Tanya Louise LLB(Hons) . . . . . . Oct 1999

BARKERS ‡
29 Chorley New Road Bolton Greater Manchester BL1 4QR
Tel: 01204 370011 *Fax:* 01204 373111
Emergency telephone 07803 174070
E-mail: info@barkers-solicitors.co.uk
List of partners: J S Barker, M J Newton
Work: D1 K1 W
Emergency Action, Agency, Advocacy, Fixed Fee Interview, Legal Aid undertaken and Legal Aid Franchise
Ptr: Barker, Mr Jeremy Simon BA . . . . *Oct 1980
Newton, Mrs Michelle Jane LLB; PGDip. . . . . *May 2000

BOLTONS SOLICITORS ‡
99 Market Street Farnworth Bolton Greater Manchester BL4 7NS
Tel: 01204 704090

BUTTERWORTHS ‡
Mansell House Aspinal Close Horwich Bolton Greater Manchester BL6 6QQ
Tel: 01204 678334
E-mail: info@butterworths.co.uk

CMG LAW ‡
94 Chorley New Road Bolton Greater Manchester BL1 4DH
Tel: 01204 467400
E-mail: info@cmglaw.co.uk

CARRS SOLICITORS LIMITED ‡
1-3 The Courtyard Calvin Street Bolton Greater Manchester BL1 8PB
Tel: 01204 496898
E-mail: johncarr@carrsolicitors.co.uk

CORPORATEBLUE ‡
55 Chorley New Road Bolton Greater Manchester BL1 4QR
Tel: 01204 399966

CUMMING HODGKINSON DICKINSON ‡
(incorporating Gordon Cumming & Son; James Hodgkinson & Dickinson)
Taylor House 20-22 Silverwell Street Bolton Greater Manchester BL1 1PU
Tel: 01204 523108 / 528396 *Fax:* 01204 365481 *Dx:* 24128 BOLTON
E-mail: chd.sol@virgin.net
List of partners: R G Cumming, J R Gillies
Work: A1 B1 E F1 K1 L N O Q R1 S1 S2 W Z(l)
Emergency Action, Agency, Advocacy, Fixed Fee Interview, Legal Aid undertaken and Legal Aid Franchise
Ptr: Cumming, Mr Robert G LLB. . . . . *Jul 1979
Gillies, Mr J Roger BA. . . . . *Apr 1976

CYRIL MORRIS ARKWRIGHT ‡
Churchgate House 30 Churchgate Bolton Greater Manchester BL1 1HS
Tel: 01204 535261 *Fax:* 01204 363354 *Dx:* 24109 BOLTON
E-mail: info@cma-law.co.uk
List of partners: J M Barlow, J E Hutton, D P Millar
Work: A1 B1 C1 C2 C3 D1 D2 E F1 G H J1 K1 K2 K3 K4 L N O P Q R1 S1 S2 T1 T2 W Z(b,c,d,e,f,h,j,k,l,o,q,s,t)
Emergency Action, Agency, Advocacy, Fixed Fee Interview, Legal Aid undertaken and Legal Aid Franchise
Ptr: Barlow, Ms Joanne Marie LLB. . . . . *Nov 1994
Hutton, Ms Joanne Elizabeth LLB . . . . *Nov 1994
Millar, Mr Darin Patrick LLB . . . . *Oct 1994

 See p112 for the Key to Work Categories & other symbols

Asoc: Arkwright, Mr Tim Joseph Christian BEng(Hons). . . . *Nov 2004
Everett, Mrs Naomi Joy LLB. . . . . *Jun 2002
Gracie, Miss Mary P LLB . . . . *Dec 1978
Jackson, Ms Rhona Margaret LLB(Hons) . . . . *Oct 1995
Morton, Miss Kimberley LLB(Hons) ★ . . . . *Mar 2000
Ast: Arkwright, Mrs Lindsay Louise LLB . . . . *Jun 2005
Barton, Mr Stuart BA(Hons). . . . . Jan 2005
Dance, Ms Michelle LLB(Hons) . . . . *Dec 2006
Con: Arkwright, Mr David P Notary Public. . . . . Nov 1968
O'Brien, Mr Philip Anthony LLB(Hons). . . . . *Sep 1971
Tonge, Mr Paul G LLB(Hull) ★. . . . . *Jun 1975

JOE EGAN SOLICITORS ‡
13 Mawdsley Street Bolton Greater Manchester BL1 1JZ
Tel: 01204 386214 *Fax:* 01204 380900
Emergency telephone 01204 848874
List of partners: J B Egan
Office: Bolton
Languages: French, German, Gujarati, Spanish, Urdu
Work: G H K1 L M1 S1 V
Emergency Action, Agency, Advocacy, Fixed Fee Interview, Legal Aid undertaken and Member of Accident Line
Ptr: Egan, Mr Joseph B BA ★ . . . . Nov 1982

JOE EGAN SOLICITORS
18 Wood Street Bolton Greater Manchester BL1 1DY
Tel: 01204 368060 *Fax:* 01204 364030
Emergency telephone 01204 368060
Office: Bolton
Languages: French, German, Spanish
Work: D1 F1 G H K1 L M1 P S1 V W
Emergency Action, Agency, Advocacy, Fixed Fee Interview and Legal Aid undertaken
Ptr: Egan, Mr Joseph B BA ★ . . . . Nov 1982

J ESNER & CO ‡
Lloyds Bank Chambers Howell Croft North Bolton Greater Manchester BL1 1QY
Tel: 01204 522562 *Fax:* 01204 532699 *Dx:* 24111 BOLTON
List of partners: P A O'Brien
Work: E K1 K3 S1 S2 W Z(i)
Ptr: O'Brien, Mr Philip A LLB . . . . Sep 1971

FIELDINGS PORTER ‡
Silverwell House 32 Silverwell Street Bolton Greater Manchester BL1 1PT
Tel: 01204 540900 *Fax:* 01204 362129 *Dx:* 24144 BOLTON
Emergency telephone 01204 540900
E-mail: info@fieldingsporter.co.uk
List of partners: J N Birch, J C Birtwell, S A Duncan, H Dunn, A C Gibbons, K Gregory, A J McLoughlin, C S Morris, E Nally, J E A Webster, F C Young
Office: Westhoughton
Languages: French
Work: A1 B1 B2 C1 C2 C3 D1 D2 E F1 G H J1 J2 K1 K3 K4 L M1 N O P Q R1 S1 S2 T1 T2 U1 U2 W Z(c,d,e,g,h,l,m,o,p,q,r)
Emergency Action, Agency, Advocacy, Fixed Fee Interview, Legal Aid undertaken, Legal Aid Franchise and Member of Accident Line
Ptr: Birch, Mr John N MA; LLM(Cantab) . . . . *Dec 1988
Birtwell, Mr John C LLB . . . . *Apr 1979
Duncan, Mr Stuart A BA(Law). . . . . *Oct 1985
Dunn, Mrs Hilary LLB Deputy District Judge. . . . . . *Nov 1972
Gibbons, Mrs Andrea C LLB . . . . *Sep 1993
Gregory, Miss Kathryn BA. . . . . *Oct 1990
McLoughlin, Mr Andrew J MA(Cantab) ● . . . . *§Nov 1983
Morris, Mr Craig S LLB . . . . *Sep 1993
Nally, Mr Edward LLB President of the Law Society . *§Mar 1980
Webster, Mr John Edward Ashcroft LLB; LLM . . . . . *Sep 1996
Young, Mr Fraser C LLB . . . . *Oct 1989
Con: Porter, Mr David S LLB Clerk to Commissioner of Taxes . . . . *Oct 1966

FORD LEGAL SOLICITORS ‡
Suite F5 The I-Zone Bolton Greater Manchester BL3 5AB
Tel: 01204 374825

FORD LEGAL SOLICITORS ‡
114 St Helens Road Bolton Greater Manchester BL3 3PJ
Tel: 01204 656393 *Fax:* 01204 855322
E-mail: markpford@fordlegal.co.uk

GARSTANGS ‡
Bradshawgate Chambers 57-61 Bradshawgate Bolton Greater Manchester BL1 1DU
Tel: 01204 531118 *Fax:* 01204 392582
E-mail: info@garstangs.co.uk
List of partners: R B Cornthwaite, M E Garstang, A J H Harris, R Ingram
Office: London WC2
Languages: Greek, Italian
Work: A1 B1 C1 C2 C3 D1 E F1 G H J1 K1 L M1 M2 N O P Q R1 S1 T1 T2 V W Z(c,e,h,i,k,l,m,o,s,t)
Emergency Action, Agency, Advocacy, Fixed Fee Interview, Legal Aid undertaken and Member of Accident Line
Ptr: Garstang, Mr Michael Edward BA . . . . Jul 1978

GRAHAM CLAYTON SOLICITORS
25 Chorley New Road Bolton Greater Manchester BL1 4QR
Tel: 01204 521434
Office: Cardiff

ADAM F GREENHALGH & CO ‡
Mawdsley Chambers 20 Mawdsley Street Bolton Greater Manchester BL1 1LE
Tel: 0845 074 3491 *Fax:* 01204 364611 *Dx:* 24148 BOLTON 1
E-mail: info@afglaw.co.uk
Languages: Gujarati, Urdu
Work: A1 C1 C2 C3 D1 E F1 G H J1 K1 L M1 N O P Q R1 S1 S2 V W Z(c,d,k,l,m,p,q,r)

HR SOLICITORS ‡
27 Mawdsley Street Bolton Greater Manchester BL1 1LN
Tel: 01204 402000

HSK SOLICITORS
72 St George's Road Bolton Greater Manchester BL1 2DD
Tel: 01204 526465 *Fax:* 01204 386493 *Dx:* 24136 BOLTON
E-mail: hsk_sols@hotmail.com
Office: Manchester
Languages: Gujarati, Hindi, Punjabi, Urdu
Work: B2 E F1 L N O S1 S2 W Z(i,j,q)
Emergency Action, Agency, Advocacy, Fixed Fee Interview and Legal Aid undertaken
Ptr: Ali, Mr Asghar LLB(Hons) . . . . *Jan 2002
Hussain, Mr Ansar LLB(Hons). . . . . *Nov 1983
Singh, Mr Gurpralad Landa LLB(Hons) . . . . *May 1981

HILLS SOLICITORS LIMITED ‡
(incorporating Victor Rose & Co)
New Mansion House 63-65 Chorley New Road Bolton Greater Manchester BL1 4QR
Tel: 01204 388300 *Fax:* 01204 362500 *Dx:* 24141 BOLTON
List of partners: M Fletcher, J A Nattrass
Office: Altrincham
Work: B1 C1 D1 D2 E J1 K1 K2 L N R1 R2 S1 S2 V W Z(c,i,k,l,r)
Agency, Advocacy, Fixed Fee Interview, Legal Aid undertaken and Member of Accident Line
Dir: Fletcher, Mr Mark . . . . *Apr 1981
Ast: Chakrabarti, Mrs Sanchita LLB(Hons) . . . . *Nov 1988

W ELAINE HOLLAND ‡
Ashberry House 41 New Hall Lane Heaton Bolton Greater Manchester BL1 5LW
Tel: 01204 849253 *Fax:* 01204 849253

KBL SOLICITORS ‡
28 Mawdsley Street Bolton Greater Manchester BL1 1LF
Tel: 01204 527777 *Fax:* 01204 388940 *Dx:* 24135 BOLTON 1
E-mail: enquiries@kbl.co.uk
List of partners: M Beaumont, J Hassells, D W Johnson, N W Lewis, D S Roberts, J R Shorrock, M E Slater, P M J Stephenson, C A Taylor
Languages: German
Work: B1 C1 C2 E F1 J1 K1 K3 K4 L N O P Q R1 R2 S1 S2 T1 T2 W Z(c,d,e,l,o,w)
Emergency Action, Advocacy and Fixed Fee Interview undertaken
Ptr: Beaumont, Mr Michael BA(Law). . . . . *Nov 1973
Hassells, Mr John LLB . . . . *Oct 2002
Johnson, Mr David W LLB. . . . . *Oct 1982
Lewis, Mr Nicholas W LLB . . . . *May 1974
Roberts, Ms Debbie S LLB . . . . *Oct 1986
Shorrock, Mr Jonathan Robert LLB(Hons). . . . . . . *Nov 1985
Slater, Mr Michael Edward BA(Hons); LLM . . . . . . *Feb 1995
Stephenson, Mr Philip M J BA(Oxon) . . . . *Dec 1992
Taylor, Mr Christopher A LLB . . . . *Sep 1991
Asoc: Bell, Mr Stephen LLB(Hons); LLM. . . . . *Jun 1999
Hartley, Miss Susan LLB . . . . *May 1986
Marsh, Mrs Helen LLB(Hons) . . . . *Oct 2002
Ast: Dawson, Mrs Claire LLB . . . . *May 2005
Hart, Miss Christine Lorraine LLB(Hons). . . . . *Sep 2008
Hatton, Mr Paul Lee LLB . . . . *Apr 2005
McArdle, Mr Stephen Joseph BA(Hons) . . . . *Sep 2007
Traynor, Mrs Anneka BA(Hons); GDL; LPC . . . . . . *Oct 2006
Withnell, Miss Charlotte LLB; LPC. . . . . *Sep 2007

KAPADIA SOLICITORS ‡
312 Derby Street Bolton Greater Manchester BL3 6LF
Tel: 01204 655614 *Fax:* 01204 653322
E-mail: info@kapadiasolicitors.co.uk

KEOGHS LLP ‡
2 The Parklands Bolton Greater Manchester BL6 4SE
Tel: 01204 677000 *Fax:* 01204 677111
Dx: 723540 BOLTON (LOSTOCK)
E-mail: info@keoghs.co.uk
List of partners: D Banks, J Batchelor, P J Bibby, A Butt, K Cartmell, R D Clarke, J Dexter, S Drinkwater, A J Graham, R S Gray, J Heath, J Lowe, M McAleer, S N McLoughlin, M Mooney, C Pearson, M Pope, C Quinn, A J Robins, M H Rogers, A C Scholar, N D Southern, I R Tenquist, D R Tonge, D R Tyson, A R Underwood, D M Walton, D Ward, S Weeks, M A Whalley, J W Whittle, J W Whittle, G Williams, D M Wynn, K Young
Office: Coventry
Languages: French
Work: B2 C1 C2 E J1 L N O Q R2 S1 S2 U2 W Z(e,j,p,q,w)
Advocacy undertaken
Ptr: Banks, Ms Deborah LLB . . . . *Nov 1995
Batchelor, Mr Jon LLB. . . . . *Nov 1993
Bibby, Mr Peter James LLB . . . . *Oct 1992
Butt, Mr Asim LLB; LLM. . . . . *Nov 1992
Cartmell, Mr Keith LLB(Hons) . . . . Sep 1982
Clarke, Mr R Donald LLB . . . . *Feb 1988
Graham, Mr Alistair J LLB. . . . . *Oct 1993
Gray, Mr Robert S LLB . . . . *Oct 1991
Heath, Mr James LLB. . . . . *Jun 1997
Lowe, Mr Jonathan LLB. . . . . *Nov 1995
McAleer, Mr Martin LLB. . . . . Apr 1994
McLoughlin, Mrs S Nicola LLB . . . . *Oct 1986
Pearson, Ms Claire LLB. . . . . *Dec 1994
Pope, Mr Michael LLB. . . . . *Sep 1994
Robins, Mr Alan J LLB(Bris). . . . . *Jun 1973
Rogers, Mr Matthew H LLB . . . . *Oct 1993
Scholar, Mr Andrew C LLB . . . . *Dec 1987
Tenquist, Mr Iain R LLB. . . . . *Feb 1984
Tonge, Mr David Robert LLB . . . . *Nov 1992
Tyson, Mr David R LLB . . . . *Apr 1977
Underwood, Mr Andrew R LLB . . . . *Feb 1987
Walton, Mr David M LLB . . . . *May 1989
Ward, Mr Damian LLB. . . . . *Oct 1996
Whalley, Mr Mark A LLB. . . . . *Jan 1989
Whittle, Mr John W LLB. . . . . *Oct 1976
Williams, Mr Gareth LLB . . . . *Aug 1991
Wynn, Mr David Mark LLB(Hons) ● . . . . *May 1994
Young, Mr Ken LLB . . . . Sep 1998
Mem: Dexter, Mr Julian . . . . Sep 2000
Drinkwater, Miss Suzanne LLB(Hons) . . . . *§Oct 1993
Mooney, Melanie . . . . May 2000
Quinn, Claire . . . . Dec 1994
Southern, Mr Neil David LLB(Hons) . . . . *Nov 2000
Weeks, Sharon . . . . Dec 1994
Asoc: Birkbeck, Ms Rachel BA(Hons)(Cantab). . . . . *Sep 1996
Davies, Mr Robert LLB . . . . *Apr 1995
Dickinson, Rose. Mar 2004
Fitzpatrick, Mr Gary BSc(Hons) . . . . *Feb 1999
Hardman, Ms Tracy BA(Hons). . . . . Oct 1996
Hargan, Katherine. . . . . Aug 2002
Harris, Elizabeth . . . . Sep 2004
Hassan, Mr Paul LLB . . . . *Mar 1999
Hewitt, Mrs Jo LLB . . . . *Mar 1999
Howarth, Mr Tom LLB(Hons) . . . . *Sep 2000
Lewarne, Ruth . . . . Mar 2004
Lynch, Ms Paula LLB . . . . *Feb 1995
Montford, Mrs Kathryn LLB . . . . *Oct 1997
Moore, Ms Pamela LLB. . . . . *Sep 1998
Nuttall, Ms Amanda BA(Hons). . . . . *Aug 1998
Scholefield, Mrs Kate MA . . . . *Oct 1996
Shrimpton, Mrs Lis . . . . Oct 1996
Ast: Bagri, Mr Mandip Singh LLB(Hons) . . . . *Jun 1998
Baker, Mr Timothy. . . . . Mar 1991
Batchelor, Ms Caroline LLB(Hons). . . . . *Sep 1998
Carr, Miss Alison LPC. . . . . Dec 1998
Clayton, Mrs Clare . . . . Jan 2002
Davies, Ms Elaine BEd . . . . Jan 2001
Galloway, Miss Lisa BA(Hons). . . . . *Sep 1998
Garlick, Miss Sandra LLB . . . . *Sep 2000
Herricks, Mr Andrew LLB(Hons)(English & European Law) . . . . *Oct 1999
Higgins, Miss Michelle LLB(Hons). . . . . *Oct 1995
Holdsworth, Miss Fiona LLB. . . . . *May 2002
Ingram, Mr Timothy Alwyne LLB(Hons) . . . . *Aug 1995
Kirton, Mr Lee BA(Hons) . . . . *Aug 2001
Knapman, Joanna. . . . . Sep 2005
Lancaster, Miss Joanne. . . . . Sep 2000
Langridge, Ms Karen BA(Hons) . . . . Aug 2001
McIntosh, Miss Nicola BA(Hons); LSF. . . . . *Oct 1995
Morris, Mr James Dominic BA(Hons) . . . . *Nov 1998
Pathak, Miss Munju Bala LLB(Hons); LSF. . . . . . . *Mar 1997
Peters, Mr Andrew BSc . . . . *Sep 1999
Sharma, Mrs Neena. . . . . May 2002
Short, Mr Martin J BA(Hons) . . . . *Oct 1998
Tyson, Ms Lisa Jayne. . . . . *Sep 1991
Vary, Ms Tejal LLB(Hons) . . . . *Apr 2001
Walker, Miss Lucy. . . . . Jan 1999
Walkinshaw, Mr David LLB . . . . *Mar 2000
Webster, Ms Helen BA(Hons). . . . . Jul 1999

LANSDALE & HOLDSWORTH ‡
1 The Studios 316 Chorley Old Road Bolton Greater Manchester BL1 4JU
Tel: 01204 491111 *Fax:* 01204 792134
E-mail: law@lansdale.uk.com
List of partners: M Bartalotta, L D Shimmin
Languages: French, Italian
Work: N S1 W
Agency and Advocacy undertaken
Ptr: Bartalotta, Mr Marco LLB(Hons). . . . . Oct 1999
Shimmin, Mr Leslie Douglas LLB . . . . Nov 1993

LATIMER LEE LLP
854 Bury Road Bolton Greater Manchester BL2 6NY
Tel: 0161 798 9000 *Fax:* 0161 773 6578
E-mail: info@latimerlee.com
Office: Bury, Heywood, Prestwich

MJC SOLICITORS ‡
68 Kilworth Drive Lostock Bolton Greater Manchester BL6 4RL
Tel: 01204 491915 *Fax:* 01204 492772
E-mail: mike@mjcsolicitors.co.uk

MRH SOLICITORS ‡
Atria House Spa Road Bolton Greater Manchester BL1 4AG
Tel: 01204 535333 *Fax:* 01204 535444 *Dx:* 24129 BOLTON
E-mail: mail@mrhsolicitors.co.uk
List of partners: M Patel, A Qamruddin
Dir: Patel, Mohammed. . . . . May 2004
Qamruddin, Ahmed . . . . Feb 2000
Ast: Jamali, Femida . . . . Apr 2008

MAIDMENTS
5 Great Moor Street Bolton Greater Manchester BL1 1NZ
Tel: 0870 403 4000 *Fax:* 0845 017 6633
Emergency telephone 0870 403 4000
E-mail: contact@maidments.co.uk
Office: Birmingham, Sale, Salford
Work: B2 D1 G H J1 K1 K3
Ptr: Potter, Miss Jane LLB(Hons) . . . . *Sep 1996

MEADE LAW SOLICITORS ‡
Ground Floor Kennedy House 91 Manchester Road Bolton Greater Manchester BL2 1ET
Tel: 01204 365398 *Fax:* 01204 362404
E-mail: info@meadelaw.co.uk

PATERSONS SOLICITORS ‡
Glenfield House 1 Longsight Bolton Greater Manchester BL2 3HS
Tel: 01204 308889 *Fax:* 01204 309997
E-mail: enquiry@patersonssolicitors.com
List of partners: K Hall-Paterson, W Hall-Paterson
Ptr: Hall-Paterson, Kay . . . . Oct 1988
Hall-Paterson, Mr Wayne . . . . Dec 1999

PRESTIGE LAW SOLICITORS LLP ‡
First Floor 97-99 Derby Street Bolton Greater Manchester BL3 6HH
Tel: 01204 385555 *Fax:* 01204 388551
E-mail: info@prestigelaw.co.uk

COLIN RAYNER & CO ‡
(incorporating Balshaws)
546 Blackburn Road Astley Bridge Bolton Greater Manchester BL1 8NW
Tel: 01204 591145 *Fax:* 01204 305877
E-mail: colin@colinraynersolicitors.com
List of partners: H M Hodgson, C Rayner
Languages: Gujarati, Urdu
Work: A1 B1 C1 C2 C3 D1 D2 E F1 I J1 K1 L M1 M2 N O P Q R1 S1 T1 T2 V W Z(a,b,c,d,e,f,g,h,i,j,k,l,m,n,o,p,s,t)
Emergency Action, Agency, Advocacy, Fixed Fee Interview, Legal Aid undertaken, Legal Aid Franchise and Member of Accident Line
Ptr: Hodgson, Mrs Heather M LLB(Hons) . . . . *Nov 1992
Rayner, Mr Colin . . . . *Dec 1975
Asoc: Bau, Mrs Shema LLB(Hons). . . . . Jun 2001
Boardman, Mr Paul A LLB(Hons) . . . . *Feb 1988
Taylor, Mrs Elizabeth BA(Hons) . . . . *Nov 2003

RUSSELL & RUSSELL ‡
Churchill House Wood Street Bolton Greater Manchester BL1 1EE
Tel: 01204 399299 *Fax:* 01204 389223 *Dx:* 24146 BOLTON 1
Emergency telephone 01204 847999
E-mail: info@russellrussell.co.uk
List of partners: J Bromley, A L Connor, A J Costello, S G Crompton, Z A Harryman, S A Ibrahim, T P Leather, V Pearl, J A Penman, N S Ross, N Seddon, J D Smethurst, A D Whittaker
Office: Atherton, Bolton (3 offices), Bury, Middleton
Work: C1 D1 D2 E G H K1 K3 K4 N R1 S1 S2 W Z(l)
Emergency Action, Agency, Advocacy, Fixed Fee Interview, Legal Aid undertaken, Legal Aid Franchise and Member of Accident Line
Ptr: Bromley, Miss Judith BA . . . . *Feb 1988
Connor, Mrs Amanda L BA . . . . *Nov 1992
Costello, Mr Andrew James LLB(Hons) . . . . *Nov 2001

Crompton, Mr Stephen G LLB(B'ham). . . . . *Sep 1980
Harryman, Miss Zoe Amanda BSc(Hons) . . . . . . *Feb 2002
Leather, Mr Thomas P LLB . . . . *Oct 1986
Ross, Mr Nicholas S LLB . . . . *Mar 1986
Whittaker, Mr Adam David BSc(Hons); CPE. . . . . . Mar 2000
Ast: Duckworth, Mr Quentin James LLB . . . . Sep 2004
Field, Miss Rebecca LLB(Hons). . . . . Jan 2010
Flanagan, Mrs Jean LLB(Hons) . . . . Sep 2002
Hughes, Mrs Jill Alicia BSc(Hons). . . . . Jul 2005
McKail, Mr Thomas Oliver LLB(Hons) . . . . Apr 2008
Marsh, Miss Victoria Jayne BA(Hons) . . . . May 2009
Price, Ms Amy Victoria LLB . . . . Apr 2007
Towey, Mr James Raymond LLB(Hons) . . . . Feb 2007
Walsh, Miss Rachael Clare LLB(Hons) . . . . Sep 2005

RUSSELL & RUSSELL
21 Lee Lane Horwich Bolton Greater Manchester BL6 7BP
Tel: 01204 699432 *Fax:* 01204 668011 *Dx:* 19773 HORWICH
Emergency telephone 01204 847999
E-mail: infohorwich@russellrussell.co.uk
Office: Atherton, Bolton (3 offices), Bury, Middleton
Work: D1 K1 K3 S1 W
Emergency Action, Agency, Advocacy, Fixed Fee Interview, Legal Aid undertaken and Legal Aid Franchise

RUSSELL & RUSSELL
86 Market Street Farnworth Bolton Greater Manchester BL4 7NY
Tel: 01204 707926 *Fax:* 01204 861306 *Dx:* 24146 BOLTON
Emergency telephone 01204 847999
E-mail: infofarnworth@russellrussell.co.uk
Office: Atherton, Bolton (3 offices), Bury, Middleton
Work: D1 D2 K1 K3 S1 W
Emergency Action, Agency, Advocacy, Fixed Fee Interview and Legal Aid undertaken
Ast: Rance, Miss Louise BA . . . . Oct 2009
Sale, Mrs Rebecca Susannah LLB(Hons) . . . . Jun 2008
Wood, Ms Emma Jane LLB . . . . Feb 2006

RUSSELL & RUSSELL
Larkhill House 160 St George's Road Bolton Greater Manchester BL1 2PJ
Tel: 01204 375700 *Fax:* 01204 399923 *Dx:* 24146 BOLTON 1
Emergency telephone 0800 731 7555
E-mail: infolarkhill@russellrussell.co.uk
Office: Atherton, Bolton (3 offices), Bury, Middleton
Work: J1 N
Emergency Action, Agency, Advocacy, Fixed Fee Interview undertaken and Member of Accident Line
Ptr: Smethurst, Mr Julian Derrick BA. . . . . *Nov 1985
Ast: Ali, Mrs Saira LLB(Hons) . . . . Aug 2005
Grayson, Mrs Karen LLB(Hons). . . . . *Jul 2002
Pilkington, Miss Rebecca Louise LLB . . . . Apr 2010

SERIOUS LAW LLP - THE SERIOUS LAW PRACTICE ‡
Sherrington House 66 Chorley Street Bolton Greater Manchester BL1 4AL
Tel: 0800 616 681 *Fax:* 01204 362988
List of partners: M E Dixon, M Heap, B Priestley, J H Sherrington, T B Walters
Ptr: Dixon, Mr Matthew E . . . . *Oct 1996
Sherrington, Mr John H LLB(Hons) . . . . *Aug 1985
Walters, Mr Timothy B. . . . . *Oct 1995
Mem: Heap, Matthew . . . . Nov 2006
Priestley, Ben. . . . . Aug 2003
Ast: Syddall, Jonathan. . . . . Nov 2006

DEREK SMITH & CO ‡
76 Bradshawgate Bolton Greater Manchester BL1 1QW
Tel: 01204 389089 *Fax:* 01204 523115
E-mail: dereksmith4@btconnect.com
List of partners: C Smith, J D Smith
Office: Bury
Work: A1 E K1 K4 L N S1 S2 W
Fixed Fee Interview and Legal Aid undertaken
Ptr: Smith, Miss Caroline LLB; LSF . . . . *Jul 1994
Smith, Mr Joseph Derek. . . . . Jan 1968

STEPHENSONS SOLICITORS LLP
13 Silverwell Street Bolton Greater Manchester BL1 1PP
Tel: 01942 777777 *Fax:* 01204 389814 *Dx:* 24137 BOLTON
E-mail: enquiries@stephensons.co.uk
Office: Bolton, Leigh (2 offices), Manchester, St Helens, Wigan (2 offices)

STEPHENSONS SOLICITORS LLP
Sefton House Northgate Close Bolton Greater Manchester BL6 6PQ
Tel: 01942 777777
E-mail: enquiries@stephensons.co.uk
Office: Bolton, Leigh (2 offices), Manchester, St Helens, Wigan (2 offices)

WARING & CO
Caroline House Bradshawgate Bolton Greater Manchester BL2 1BJ
Tel: 01204 550160 *Fax:* 01204 550161 *Dx:* 24139 BOLTON
Office: Barnet
Work: N

THE WELLS LAW PARTNERSHIP ‡
58 Market Street Little Lever Bolton Greater Manchester BL3 1HN
Tel: 01204 709959 *Fax:* 01204 862918
E-mail: enquiries@wellslaw.co.uk
List of partners: D W Wells, J E Wells
Work: D1 D2 E S1 S2 W
Agency, Advocacy and Legal Aid undertaken
Ptr: Wells, Mr David W LLB(Lond). . . . . *Apr 1975
Wells, Mrs Jean E LLB(Lond) . . . . *May 1975

WINDER TAYLOR FALLOWS ‡
76 Bradshawgate Bolton Greater Manchester BL1 1QW
Tel: 01204 389908 / 522888 *Fax:* 01204 364570
E-mail: office@windertaylor.co.uk
List of partners: E J Titley, H C R Worthington
Office: Bolton (2 offices)
Work: A1 B1 C1 C2 C3 D1 E F1 G H J1 K1 L M1 M2 N O P Q R1 S1 T1 T2 V W Z(b,c,e,f,h,i,j,k,l,m)
Emergency Action, Agency, Advocacy, Fixed Fee Interview, Legal Aid undertaken and Member of Accident Line
Ptr: Titley, Mr Edward J LLB(Exon) . . . . *Jul 1969
Worthington, Mrs Heather C R . . . . *Apr 1977

WINDER TAYLOR FALLOWS
(incorporating J A A Taylor & Taylor)
139 Church Street Horwich Bolton Greater Manchester BL6 7BR
Tel: 01204 697467 *Fax:* 01204 669133 *Dx:* 19771 HORWICH
E-mail: office@windertaylor.co.uk
Office: Bolton (2 offices)
Work: C1 D1 E J1 K1 K2 K3 K4 L M1 P R1 S1 S2 T1 V W Z(c,e,j,l,m,t)
Agency, Advocacy, Fixed Fee Interview, Legal Aid undertaken and Member of Accident Line
Asoc: Seddon, Mr Andrew LLB . . . . *Apr 1981

WINDER TAYLOR FALLOWS
568 Chorley Old Road Bolton Greater Manchester BL1 6AB
Tel: 01204 498970 *Fax:* 01204 498979
E-mail: office@windertaylor.co.uk
Office: Bolton (2 offices)
Work: C1 C2 E J1 K4 R2 S1 S2 W
Asoc: Butler, Mr Adam Patrick LLB . . . . *Dec 1990

BOOTLE, Merseyside

FORSTER DEAN LTD
256 Stanley Road Bootle Merseyside L20 3ER
Tel: 0151 933 0062 *Fax:* 0151 922 2542
E-mail: enquiries@forsterdean.co.uk
Office: Birkenhead, Chorley, Crewe, Eccles, Ellesmere Port, Huyton, Leigh, Liverpool (5 offices), Oldham, Preston, Rochdale, Runcorn, St Helens, Stockport, Warrington, Widnes (2 offices), Wigan

JAMES MURRAY SOLICITORS ‡
41 Merton Road Bootle Merseyside L20 7AP
Tel: 0151 933 3333 *Fax:* 0151 933 3343 *Dx:* 18807 BOOTLE 1
Emergency telephone 0151 933 3333
E-mail: info@jamesmurray.law.co.uk
Office: Liverpool
Work: B2 D1 G H K1 L N Q

OPTIMUM LAW SOLICITORS ‡
Suite F04 The Bridgewater Complex Canal Street Bootle Merseyside L20 8AH
Tel: 0845 649 8101 *Fax:* 0808 280 0590
E-mail: mark.barter@optimumlaw.co.uk

DAVID PHILLIPS & PARTNERS ‡
202 Stanley Road Bootle Merseyside L20 3EP
Tel: 0151 922 5525 *Fax:* 0151 922 8298 *Dx:* 18806 BOOTLE
Emergency telephone 0151 922 5525
E-mail: info@dpp-law.com
List of partners: D R Dennis, S A Ewing, A J Murphy, S A Nolan, J D Norman, D H Phillips
Office: Birmingham, Bootle, Chadwell Heath, Leicester, Liverpool, London E1, London SE18, London W1, Manchester, Nelson, Wealdstone
Work: D1 E F1 G H J1 K1 L N Q S1 S2 V W Z(c,f,h,l)
Emergency Action, Agency, Advocacy, Fixed Fee Interview and Legal Aid undertaken
Ptr: Dennis, Mr Daniel Richard BA. . . . . *Mar 1998
Ewing, Mr Scott Alexander LLB . . . . Apr 1994
Murphy, Mr Anthony James BA . . . . *Oct 1993
Nolan, Mr Stuart A BA ★ . . . . *Feb 1988
Norman, Mr J David LLB . . . . *Jul 1984
Phillips, Mr David H LLB . . . . *Nov 1966
Ast: Fraser, Miss Louise Mary Yvonne LLB. . . . . Oct 1984

DAVID PHILLIPS & PARTNERS
268 Stanley Road Bootle Merseyside L20 3ER
Tel: 0151 933 5525 *Fax:* 0151 922 3425 *Dx:* 18806 BOOTLE
E-mail: info@dpp.law.com
Office: Birmingham, Bootle, Chadwell Heath, Leicester, Liverpool, London E1, London SE18, London W1, Manchester, Nelson, Wealdstone

SILVERSMITHS ‡
264 Stanley Road Bootle Merseyside L20 3ER
Tel: 0151 922 6066 *Fax:* 0151 922 2900 *Dx:* 18810 BOOTLE
Emergency telephone 0151 727 2141
List of partners: F P Dillon, J M Jones
Languages: French, Welsh
Work: G H
Agency, Advocacy, Legal Aid undertaken and Legal Aid Franchise
Ptr: Dillon, Mr Francis Patrick LLB(Hons) . . . . Sep 1993
Jones, Mr John Morris LLB . . . . Apr 1977

BORDON, Hampshire

GELLHORNS ‡
12 Chalet Hill Bordon Hampshire GU35 0TQ
Tel: 01420 205032 *Fax:* 01420 478252 *Dx:* 36150 BORDON
E-mail: jane.murphy@gellhorns.co.uk
List of partners: T S Rose
Work: B1 D1 E F1 J1 K1 L N O Q S1 S2 W Z(c,l)
Emergency Action, Agency, Advocacy, Fixed Fee Interview undertaken and Member of Accident Line
SPr: Rose, Mr Timothy Simon BA(Law). . . . . *Mar 1981

METCALFE HARVEYS ‡
22 Chalet Hill Bordon Hampshire GU35 0TQ
Tel: 01420 479962 *Fax:* 01420 487528 *Dx:* 155420 BORDON 2
E-mail: law@harveys-solicitors.co.uk

BOREHAMWOOD, Hertfordshire

THE DENTAL LAW PARTNERSHIP SOLICITORS ‡
6 Theobald Court Theobald Street Borehamwood Hertfordshire WD6 4RN
Tel: 020 8387 1587 *Fax:* 020 8387 1582
E-mail: info@dentallaw.co.uk

ELIAS & CO ‡
The Kinnetic Business Centre Theobald Street Borehamwood Hertfordshire WD6 4PJ
Tel: 020 8387 1333 *Fax:* 020 8346 9938
Dx: 45615 BOREHAMWOOD
E-mail: law@elias.myzen.co.uk

B K ELLIS & CO ‡
8a Shenley Road Borehamwood Hertfordshire WD6 1DL
Tel: 020 8386 8686 *Fax:* 020 8386 6168
Dx: 45620 BOREHAMWOOD
List of partners: N D Simmons
Languages: Hindi, Punjabi, Urdu
Work: C1 E J1 S1 S2 W Z(i)
Fixed Fee Interview undertaken
Ptr: Simmons, Mr Neale David BA. . . . . *Feb 1988
Con: Ellis, Mr Brian Kaye LLB(Lond) . . . . *Dec 1962

FS CONVEYANCING ‡
The Kinetic Centre Theobald Street Borehamwood Hertfordshire WD6 4PJ
Tel: 020 8387 4143

FISHER LAW ‡
Suite 38 Kinetic House The Kinetic Centre Borehamwood Hertfordshire WD6 4PJ
Tel: 020 8387 4057
E-mail: jonfisher16@hotmail.com

FREEDMAN SHARMAN & CO ‡
Kenwood House 77a Shenley Road Borehamwood Hertfordshire WD6 1AG
Tel: 020 8953 9111 *Fax:* 020 8953 7478
Dx: 45603 BOREHAMWOOD
List of partners: S D Barnett, S J F Dewis, D Freedman, J Sharman, A M Witkover
Work: C1 D1 E F1 G H J1 K1 L M1 N P R1 S1 T1 V W
Emergency Action, Agency, Advocacy, Fixed Fee Interview and Legal Aid undertaken
Ptr: Barnett, Mrs Sylvia D . . . . *Feb 1984
Dewis, Miss Samantha J F BA . . . . Oct 1985
Freedman, Mr David . . . . May 1974
Sharman, Mr Julian LLB. . . . . *Apr 1977
Witkover, Mr Adam Marc LLB(Hons) . . . . *Nov 1992

HERBERTLEWIS SOLICITORS ‡
Devonshire House Manor Way Borehamwood Hertfordshire WD6 1QQ
Tel: 020 8731 4560 *Fax:* 020 8731 4557
E-mail: mail@herbertlewissolicitors.com

KSRI SOLICITORS ‡
4 Imperial place Maxwell Road Borehamwood Hertfordshire WD6 1JN
Tel: 020 8357 6871 / 8213 3073 *Fax:* 020 8906 1313
E-mail: sri@srilegalservices.com

MARTIN SMITH & CO ‡
Majestic House 18 Shenley Road Borehamwood Hertfordshire WD6 1DL
Tel: 020 8953 0636 *Fax:* 020 8207 4835
Dx: 45608 BOREHAMWOOD
E-mail: martin.smith@martinsmith.biz
List of partners: S C Rehder, C A P Reimann
Languages: French
Work: C1 C2 E F1 J1 K1 K2 K3 K4 L N O Q S1 S2 W Z(c,j,k,l,q,r)
Emergency Action, Agency and Advocacy undertaken
Ptr: Rehder, Mr Stephen C . . . . *Oct 1974
Reimann, Mrs Carol Anne Prince LLB. . . . . *Nov 1983
Asoc: Peters, Mr Andrew LLB . . . . Dec 1987

BOROUGH GREEN, Kent

D FISHER & CO ‡
40 High Street Borough Green Kent TN15 8BJ
Tel: 01732 884299 *Fax:* 01732 885802
List of partners: D J W Fisher
Work: C1 E L S1 S2 W
SPr: Fisher, Mr Dennis Joseph William . . . . *§Jun 1970

BOROUGHBRIDGE, North Yorkshire

FITZGERALD-HARTS ‡
Claro Chambers Horsefair Boroughbridge North Yorkshire YO51 9LD
Tel: 01423 322312 *Fax:* 01423 324480
Dx: 61430 BOROUGHBRIDGE
E-mail: info@fitz-law.co.uk
List of partners: R W Rusby, A L Ware
Work: A1 A2 B1 C1 D1 E F1 J1 K1 L N O Q R1 S1 S2 T1 T2 W Z(c,d,l)
Advocacy and Fixed Fee Interview undertaken
Ptr: Rusby, Mr Richard William BA. . . . . *Dec 1976
Ware, Mr Alan Leslie . . . . *Sep 1988
Ast: Humphries, Mrs Louise Adele LLB . . . . Mar 2007
Moss, Mrs Marguerite Irma . . . . Dec 1986
Con: Fitzgerald-Hart, Mr Mark Edward Notary Public . . . . *Jul 1976
Stout, Mr Lionel Alty. . . . . Dec 1970

HETHERTONS LLP
St James Square Boroughbridge North Yorkshire YO51 9AR
Tel: 01423 322940 *Fax:* 01423 323437
Dx: 61433 BOROUGHBRIDGE
E-mail: law@hethertons.co.uk
Office: York
Work: A1 B1 C1 D1 E F1 J1 J2 K1 K3 L N O Q S1 S2 T1 T2 W Z(c,k,l,q)
Agency, Advocacy and Fixed Fee Interview undertaken
Ptr: Hallam, Mr David C LLB. . . . . *§Feb 1990

TAYLORS SOLICITORS ‡
18 St James Square Boroughbridge North Yorkshire YO51 9AR
Tel: 01423 325566 *Fax:* 01423 325545
Dx: 61436 BOROUGHBRIDGE

BOSCASTLE, Cornwall

CHRISTOPHER KEY & CO ‡
Trebiffen Farm Minster Boscastle Cornwall PL35 0BW
Tel: 01840 250200 *Fax:* 01840 250900
Emergency telephone 01840 250638
E-mail: admin@chriskey.plus.com
List of partners: C A Key
Work: A1 A2 J1 J2 L N O P S1 T2 W X Z(c,f,k,q)

See p112 for the Key to Work Categories & other symbols

Fixed Fee Interview undertaken and Member of Accident Line
SPr: Key, Mr Christopher A LLB . . . . *Apr 1980

BOSCOMBE, Bournemouth

QUALITYSOLICITORS D'ANGIBAU ‡
2 Sea Road Boscombe Bournemouth BH5 1DA
Tel: 01202 393506 *Fax:* 01202 394231 *Dx:* 46858 BOSCOMBE
E-mail: dangibau@qualitysolicitors.com
List of partners: R G S Fielding, T J Glover, J J K Harvey, F E McArthur, R J Turner
Office: Poole (2 offices)
Work: C1 D1 E F1 G H J1 K1 K3 K4 L N O Q S1 T2 V W Z(p)
Emergency Action, Agency, Advocacy, Fixed Fee Interview, Legal Aid undertaken, Legal Aid Franchise and Member of Accident Line
Ptr: Glover, Mr Timothy John LLB . . . . *Nov 1992
Harvey, Mr Jonathan J K . . . . *§Jul 1978
Asoc: Hill, Mr Kevin Richard ★. . . . . *Aug 2005
Johnson, Mr Peter LLB ● . . . . *§Dec 1970
Williams, Miss Katie LLB; LPC . . . . *Oct 2002

BOSTON, Lincolnshire

BAMBRIDGES SOLICITORS LIMITED ‡
27 Wide Bargate Boston Lincolnshire PE21 6SW
Tel: 01205 310510 *Fax:* 01205 310008 *Dx:* 26801 BOSTON
E-mail: advice@bambridges.com
List of partners: D C Bambridge, S L Spencer
Work: A1 B1 C1 D1 E F1 G H J1 J2 K1 L N O P Q R1 S1 T1 T2 W Z(c,d,e,j,l,o,q,r,t,y)
Agency and Advocacy undertaken
Ptr: Spencer, Sarah Louise . . . . Aug 2009
Dir: Bambridge, Mr Dennis C . . . . *§Dec 1975

CHATTERTONS SOLICITORS ‡
28 Wide Bargate Boston Lincolnshire PE21 6RT
Tel: 01205 351114 *Fax:* 01205 356018 *Dx:* 26803 BOSTON
E-mail: boston@chattertons.com
List of partners: R E Alcock, S Attfield, V L Barnard, R J Blezard, K L Bunting, P J Burns, R E Clark, E F Conway, P A B Cordingley, S C Cox, P L Cropley, C E Cunnington, C Dobbs, B M Ellis, R Freeman, J Harrison, E M Hopkins, J Johns, R A Knipe, P F Lawson, R R Ludlow, D L Miller, C F Mockford, E A A Nicholson, D S Rogerson, T D Salt, J L Speed, E S Thornton, D M Wellman
Office: Boston, Grantham, Horncastle, Lincoln, Newark, Sleaford, Spalding, Stamford
Languages: French
Work: A1 B1 C1 C2 E F1 J1 L M1 M2 P R1 S1 T1 T2 V W X Z(d,e,j,k,l,o)
Emergency Action, Agency, Advocacy, Fixed Fee Interview, Legal Aid undertaken, Legal Aid Franchise and Member of Accident Line
Ptr: Bunting, Mrs Katherine L MA(Oxon); APMI . . . . . *Nov 1988
Cropley, Mr Peter L . . . . *Feb 1970
Nicholson, Mrs Elizabeth A A LLB; Cert Ed; TEP . . . *Dec 1978
Ast: Marshall, Mrs Nicola LLB(Hons)(Business Law) . . . . Sep 2002
Con: Cammack, Mr Frank MA(Cantab) . . . . *Aug 1969

CHATTERTONS SOLICITORS
4 South Square Boston Lincolnshire PE21 6HX
Tel: 01205 310025 *Fax:* 01205 310027 *Dx:* 26822 BOSTON
E-mail: boston@chattertons.com
Office: Boston, Grantham, Horncastle, Lincoln, Newark, Sleaford, Spalding, Stamford
Work: A1 C1 C2 C3 D1 E F1 F2 G H J1 K1 L M1 M2 N O P Q R1 S1 T1 T2 V Z(j,k,l,q)
Emergency Action, Agency, Advocacy, Fixed Fee Interview, Legal Aid undertaken, Legal Aid Franchise and Member of Accident Line
Ptr: Conway, Mr Edward F LLB . . . . *May 1991
Lawson, Mr Peter F BA Herbert Ruse Prize . . . . . . *Apr 1980

CRIMINAL DEFENCE ASSOCIATES ‡
3 Trinity Street Boston Lincolnshire PE21 8RJ
Tel: 01205 364777 *Fax:* 01205 364778
E-mail: criminaldefenceassociates@gmail.com

MORLEY BROWN & CO ‡
(incorporating Rice Waite Marris; Laurence Brown & Co)
2 Main Ridge West Boston Lincolnshire PE21 6QH
Tel: 01205 364986 *Fax:* 01205 310824 *Dx:* 26807 BOSTON
E-mail: enquiries@morleybrown.co.uk
List of partners: L J Brown, P D Howden, C R Morley
Work: A1 A3 B1 C1 C2 C3 D2 E F1 J1 J2 K1 K3 K4 L N O P Q R1 S1 S2 T1 T2 V W Z(c,l,q)
Emergency Action, Agency, Advocacy, Fixed Fee Interview, Legal Aid undertaken, Legal Aid Franchise and Member of Accident Line
Ptr: Brown, Mr Laurence J. . . . . *§Feb 1983
Howden, Mr Paul D TEP; FILEx. . . . . *May 1986
Morley, Mr Charles Richard BA(Dunelm) . . . . . . *§Jan 1981

S R OUTRAM & CO ‡
66 Robin Hood's Walk Boston Lincolnshire PE21 9ES
Tel: 01205 365342
List of partners: S R Outram
Work: F1 G H J1 K1 L N Q R1 S1 T2 W
Member of Accident Line
SPr: Outram, Mr Stephen R FILEx; LLB(Hons)(Lond). . . . *Jan 1983

THE RINGROSE LAW GROUP - PAUL COOPER ‡
(incorporating Frost Gunning & Co; Grocock & Staniland; Adie Pickwell)
Endeavour House Gilbert Drive Boston Lincolnshire PE21 7TR
Tel: 01205 311511 *Fax:* 01205 310410 *Dx:* 26805 BOSTON
E-mail: paul.cooper@ringroselaw.co.uk
List of partners: J Atkinson, A J Clark, P S Cooper, P Hanby, R J Harwood, D W Hitchcock, S Khanna, J A P Knight, C E Pickwell, M O Roberts, G W Stenson, D G Thornley
Office: Grantham, Lincoln (2 offices), Newark, Sleaford, Spalding
Languages: French, German, Hindi, Punjabi
Work: A1 A3 B1 C1 C2 C3 D1 D2 E F1 F2 G H J1 J2 K1 K2 L M1 M2 N O P Q R1 S1 S2 T1 T2 W X Z(e,i,l,m,p,q,r)
Emergency Action, Agency, Advocacy, Fixed Fee Interview, Legal Aid undertaken, Legal Aid Franchise and Member of Accident Line
Ptr: Atkinson, Miss Julie LLB(Hons) . . . . *Sep 1995
Cooper, Mr Paul S BA Clerk to Commissioners of Taxes; H M Deputy Coroner. . . . . *Jun 1984
Roberts, Mr Martin O LLB(Leeds) . . . . *Oct 1987

SILLS & BETTERIDGE LLP
5 Main Ridge West Boston Lincolnshire PE21 6QL
Tel: 01205 364615 *Fax:* 01205 354340 *Dx:* 26804 BOSTON
E-mail: info@sillslegal.co.uk
Web: www.sillslegal.co.uk
Office: Coningsby, Gainsborough, Lincoln, Skegness, Sleaford, Spalding, Spilsby
Work: A1 A2 B1 B2 C1 C2 C3 D1 D2 E F1 F2 G H I J1 J2 K1 K2 K3 K4 L M1 N O P Q R1 R2 S1 S2 T1 T2 U2 V W X Z(b,c,d,e,g,h,i,k,l,m,o,p,q,r,s,t,u,v,w,za)
Emergency Action, Agency, Advocacy, Fixed Fee Interview, Legal Aid undertaken, Legal Aid Franchise and Member of Accident Line
Ptr: Brickles, Mr Beris BA(Law) . . . . *Jun 1994
Clarke, Mrs Yvonne . . . . Dec 1975
Tinn, Mr Richard . . . . Aug 1973
Asoc: Conduit, Mr James . . . . Aug 2008
Ast: Curtis, Miss Jennifer. . . . . Sep 2010
Goldsborough, Mr Andrew. . . . . Jun 2006
Waxman, Sacha . . . . *Jan 2009

BOTLEY, Oxfordshire

PATRICIA BHUTTA & RUTH CARO LLP
67 Eynsham Road Botley Oxfordshire OX2 9BU
Tel: 01865 863128 *Fax:* 01865 865052
Office: Cheltenham
Ptr: Bhutta, Mrs Patricia F M BA. . . . . *Mar 1980

BOURNE, Lincolnshire

ANDREWS STANTON & RINGROSE ‡
11 North Street Bourne Lincolnshire PE10 9AF
Tel: 01778 422626 *Fax:* 01778 421829 *Dx:* 27084 BOURNE
List of partners: J C Forster
Work: A1 B1 C1 D1 E F1 G H J1 K1 L M1 N P R1 S1 T1 V W Z(c,d,e,l,m,n,t)
Emergency Action, Agency, Advocacy, Fixed Fee Interview, Legal Aid undertaken and Member of Accident Line
Ptr: Forster, Mr Jonathan C BA; LLB. . . . . *§Jun 1958

DOUBLE & MEGSON
4 West Street Bourne Lincolnshire PE10 9NE
Tel: 01778 423376 *Fax:* 01778 421737 *Dx:* 27081 BOURNE
E-mail: jmegson@doubleandmegson.co.uk
Office: Market Deeping
Work: A1 B1 C1 D1 D2 E F1 F2 G H J1 K1 L N O P Q R1 S1 S2 T1 V W Z(c,i,l,q,r)
Emergency Action and Agency undertaken
Ptr: Megson, Mr John . . . . *Feb 1969
Wood, Mr Richard Robert . . . . *Dec 1990

DUNCAN A PICKERING ‡
4 Southfields Bourne Lincolnshire PE10 9TZ
Tel: 01778 421757 *Fax:* 01778 421565

BOURNE END, Buckinghamshire

DAVID L BAIN ‡
43 Goddington Road Bourne End Buckinghamshire SL8 5TU
Tel: 07974 257555 *Fax:* 01628 521179

BRITTONS ‡
28 The Parade Bourne End Buckinghamshire SL8 5SY
Tel: 01628 533350 *Fax:* 01628 533119
E-mail: lex@brittonsol.co.uk
Office: Beaconsfield
Work: C1 E S1 S2 W

BROWNS
14 The Parade Bourne End Buckinghamshire SL8 5SY
Tel: 01628 531800 *Fax:* 01628 531808
E-mail: bourneend@brownssolicitors.co.uk
Office: Amersham, Aylesbury, Beaconsfield, High Wycombe (3 offices), Maidenhead, Marlow, Princes Risborough, Thame
Work: S1 S2
Fixed Fee Interview undertaken

J D SOUTHWORTH ‡
Samarra House Hawks Hill Bourne End Buckinghamshire SL8 5JQ
Tel: 01628 522407 *Fax:* 01628 531341
E-mail: j.southworth@samara.demon.co.uk

BOURNEMOUTH

AFL SOLICITORS ‡
99 Harewood Avenue Bournemouth BH7 6NW
Tel: 01202 729999 *Fax:* 01202 729988
E-mail: yd@aflsolicitors.co.uk
List of partners: Y Dossabhoy
SPr: Dossabhoy, Miss Yasmin LLB . . . . *Nov 1995

ALDRIDGE BROWNLEE SOLICITORS LLP ‡
Kingsway House 13 Christchurch Road Lansdowne Bournemouth BH1 3JY
Tel: 01202 294411 *Fax:* 01202 295944 *Dx:* 7641 BOURNEMOUTH
E-mail: enquiries@aldridge-brownlee.co.uk
List of partners: L C E Barton, A M Cook, J A Giles, P A Griffin, R A Hall, P G Kirk, A P Lilley, A N Pitt
Office: Bournemouth (2 offices), Christchurch
Work: A3 B1 D1 E F1 G H J1 K1 K2 K3 K4 L N O Q R1 S1 S2 W Z(a,c,l,o,q)
Emergency Action, Agency, Advocacy, Fixed Fee Interview, Legal Aid undertaken, Legal Aid Franchise and Member of Accident Line
Ptr: Barton, Mrs Lynne C E LLB(Soton) . . . . *§Nov 1982
Cook, Ms Augustine M LLB . . . . *§Apr 1984
Kirk, Mr Peter G BSc; LLB . . . . *Apr 1992
Pitt, Mr Andrew N MA(Oxon) . . . . *§Jan 1979
Ast: Allen, Mr Brendan. . . . . Sep 2002
Jinks, Miss Nicola S C LLB(Hons). . . . . *Jun 1991
Proctor, Mr Mark Bernard LLB. . . . . Sep 2003

ALDRIDGE BROWNLEE SOLICITORS LLP
912 Wimborne Road Moordown Bournemouth BH9 2DJ
Tel: 01202 527008 *Fax:* 01202 532848 *Dx:* 7641 BOURNEMOUTH
E-mail: enquiries@aldridge-brownlee.co.uk
Office: Bournemouth (2 offices), Christchurch
Work: T1 T2 W
Fixed Fee Interview, Legal Aid undertaken and Member of Accident Line
Ptr: Giles, Mr John A BA . . . . *§Oct 1982
Hall, Mr Richard A LLB(Lond). . . . . *§Apr 1979
Ast: Dixon, Mrs Sarah . . . . Sep 2005
Newbold, Mr Michael John LLB; DipLP . . . . *Oct 2000

ALDRIDGE BROWNLEE SOLICITORS LLP
89 Wimborne Road Winton Bournemouth BH3 7AW
Tel: 01202 526343 *Fax:* 01202 530875 *Dx:* 7641 BOURNEMOUTH
E-mail: enquiries@aldridge-brownlee.co.uk
Office: Bournemouth (2 offices), Christchurch
Work: L S1
Ptr: Griffin, Mr Paul A BA . . . . *§Dec 1983
Ast: Adams, Miss Stephanie Louise LLB. . . . . *Mar 2011
Alahakoon, Mr Julian LLB. . . . . *Jul 2007

ANDREWS MCQUEEN ‡
Lorne Park House 1 Lorne Park Road Bournemouth BH1 1JJ
Tel: 01202 290628 *Fax:* 01202 551188 *Dx:* 7601 BOURNEMOUTH
List of partners: V V A Cowlard, K J O'Neill
Work: D1 G H N S1 W
Emergency Action, Agency, Advocacy, Fixed Fee Interview, Legal Aid undertaken and Legal Aid Franchise
Ptr: Cowlard, Miss Vanessa V A BA(Law) . . . . *§Dec 1986
O'Neill, Mr Keith J BA ★. . . . . *§Oct 1982
Ast: Codling, Mrs Lesley-Anne BA(Hons) . . . . *Apr 1988
Harris, Miss Julie-Ann. . . . . *§Sep 2003

BAEHRS ‡
Abchurch Chambers 24 St Peter's Road Bournemouth BH1 2LN
Tel: 01202 292075 *Fax:* 01202 295454
E-mail: litigation@baehrs.co.uk
List of partners: E R Baehr
Work: J1 K1 N O Q Z(k,q)
Emergency Action, Agency and Advocacy undertaken
SPr: Baehr, Mr Eric Robert. . . . . *Nov 1972

BAXTER & CO ‡
1 Stirling Road Bournemouth BH3 7JG
Tel: 01202 530249 *Fax:* 01202 534578
Emergency telephone 01202 530249 (24HR)
List of partners: C Baxter
Work: B1 C1 C3 E F1 J1 K1 L N O Q S1
Emergency Action, Agency, Advocacy, Fixed Fee Interview, Legal Aid undertaken and Member of Accident Line
SPr: Baxter, Mr Clifford LLM; MA. . . . . *Nov 1983

CHESTER & CO ‡
22 Argyll Road Bournemouth BH5 1ED
Tel: 01202 395395 *Fax:* 01202 395395
E-mail: john.jrchester@virgin.net
List of partners: J R Chester
Work: S1
SPr: Chester, Mr John Richard MA(Oxon); MBA(Columbia). *§Jul 1980

COLES MILLER SOLICITORS LLP
260-266 Charminster Road Bournemouth BH8 9RS
Tel: 01202 511512 *Fax:* 01202 530957
Dx: 122753 BOURNEMOUTH 10
E-mail: office@coles-miller.co.uk
Office: Bournemouth, Broadstone, Poole
Work: B1 C1 D1 E F1 J1 J2 K1 L N O Q R1 R2 S1 S2 T1 T2 V W Z(c,l,m,q,r)
Emergency Action, Agency, Advocacy, Fixed Fee Interview, Legal Aid undertaken, Legal Aid Franchise and Member of Accident Line
Ptr: Whittle, Mr Christopher David BA(Hons); PGDipLP . . *Feb 2001
Asoc: Hall, Mrs Tanya Jane LLB(Hons) . . . . *Sep 1993

COLES MILLER SOLICITORS LLP
4 Durley Chine Road Bournemouth BH2 5QT
Tel: 01202 293226 *Fax:* 01202 294963 *Dx:* 89308 WESTBOURNE
E-mail: office@coles-miller.co.uk
Office: Bournemouth, Broadstone, Poole
Work: C1 E J1 K1 K3 K4 L N O Q S1 T2 W Z(d,h,l,m)
Ptr: Howard, Mr Andrew BA . . . . *§Dec 1978
Knight, Miss Fiona O LLB(Hons) . . . . *Sep 1989
Steele-Williams, Mr Simon T LLB(Hons). . . . . . . *Oct 1991
Asoc: Barnett, Mr Jason LLB(Law & Business); PGDipLP . . *Apr 2004
Ast: Edwards, Miss Kathryn BA . . . . *Sep 2004
Oran, Miss Heidi LLB . . . . *Apr 2004
Smith, Mr Matthew Anthony. . . . . Jul 2008

DRUITTS ‡
Borough Chambers Fir Vale Road Bournemouth BH1 2JE
Tel: 01202 551863 *Fax:* 01202 294036 *Dx:* 7640 BOURNEMOUTH
E-mail: enquiries@druitts.co.uk
List of partners: C G Clifford, K Donalson
Work: D1 J1 K1 K3 K4 N Q S1 S2 W
Emergency Action, Agency, Advocacy and Fixed Fee Interview undertaken
Ptr: Clifford, Mr Christopher G BSc(Hons) . . . . *Aug 2000
Donalson, Miss Kay BA. . . . . *Apr 1990
Ast: Gates, Miss Stephanie Michele LLB; TEP . . . . . . *Feb 2006
Lloyds, Mrs Margaret Alison LLB . . . . *Jul 1979
Moore, Miss Samantha Jane Katherine BSSc(Hons); PGDipLaw; MA(Law) . . . . *Jan 2003
Partington, Miss Julie Audrey BA(Hons). . . . . *Apr 2007

DUTTON GREGORY
Kingsland House 21 Hinton Road Bournemouth BH1 2DE
Tel: 01202 315005 *Fax:* 01202 315004 *Dx:* 7635 BOURNEMOUTH
E-mail: contact@duttongregory.co.uk
Office: Southampton, Winchester

SIMON ELLIOTT SOLICITOR ‡
The Law Chambers 15a Westbourne Arcade Poole Road Bournemouth BH4 9AY
Tel: 01202 767200 *Fax:* 01202 760980
E-mail: simon.elliott@thelawchambers.co.uk

ELLIS JONES ‡
Sandbourne House 302 Charminster Road Bournemouth BH8 9RU
Tel: 01202 525333 *Fax:* 01202 535935
Dx: 122752 BOURNEMOUTH 10
E-mail: email@ellisjones.co.uk
List of partners: D E Leask, S McNally, P A Naser, N R Smith, N J Taylor, C Wells
Office: Poole, Ringwood, Swanage
Work: C1 C2 E J1 K1 K2 K3 L N O Q S1 S2 T2 W Z(i,l,q,r)

Agency, Advocacy, Fixed Fee Interview, Legal Aid Franchise and Member of Accident Line
Ptr: Leask, Miss Deborah E LLB(Hons) . . . . *Jan 1990
McNally, Mr Sean BSc(Brunel) ♦ . . . . *Mar 1991
Smith, Mr Nigel R LLB ♦ . . . . *Nov 1988
Taylor, Mr Nigel J BA . . . . *§Oct 1979
Wells, Mr Craig . . . . Sep 1996
Asoc: Arthur, Mr Nigel Lachlan BSc(Econ) ♦ . . . . *§Aug 1980
Clake, Mr Matthew . . . . Sep 2002
Dendle, Ms Sarah . . . . Jul 2002
McWilliam, Mr David LLB ♦ . . . . *Nov 1997
Stevens, Ms Donna ♦ . . . . *Nov 1999
Walford, Lesley . . . . Sep 2006
Williams, Mr David Geoffrey . . . . *Dec 1988
Ast: Hopcroft, Ms Sarah . . . . Oct 2006
Con: Crawford, Mr John W . . . . Oct 1970

FRENCH LAW MATTERS ‡
First Floor Suite 1 Richmond House Bournemouth BH2 6EZ
Tel: 01202 355480 *Fax:* 01202 355479
E-mail: lauren@frenchlawmatters.co.uk

GALES ‡
512 Wimborne Road Winton Bournemouth BH9 2ET
Tel: 01202 512227 / 512446 *Fax:* 01202 533072 *Dx:* 7700 WINTON
E-mail: mail@gales-solicitors.co.uk
List of partners: M J Moore, R H Williams
Work: D1 E F1 J1 K1 K3 L N Q S1 S2 W
Emergency Action, Agency, Advocacy and Fixed Fee Interview undertaken
Ptr: Moore, Mr Matthew John BA(Hons); BVC . . . . . . *§Apr 2002
Williams, Mr Richard H LLB . . . . *§Oct 1974
Ast: England, Mrs Sarah Louise LLB(Hons); LLM; PGDip . Apr 2008
Farrow, Mr Peter K BA . . . . *§May 1986

GENESIS LEGAL SERVICES LIMITED ‡
Beacon House 15a Christchurch Road Bournemouth BH1 3LB
Tel: 01202 552255

GRID LAW LIMITED ‡
Melbury House 1-3 Oxford Road Bournemouth BH8 8ES
Tel: 01202 961342

HAROLD G WALKER ‡
21 Oxford Road Bournemouth BH8 8ET
Tel: 01202 203200 *Fax:* 01202 294118 *Dx:* 7609 BOURNEMOUTH 1
E-mail: solicitors@hgwalker.co.uk
List of partners: J B Collins, A S Fairley, M R Hudson, N A Lowe, S J Nethercott, H Storry Deans
Office: Broadstone, Christchurch, Verwood, Wimborne
Work: A3 B1 C1 D1 D2 E J1 K1 K3 K4 L N O Q S1 S2 T2 W Z(j,k,l,q)
Emergency Action, Agency, Advocacy and Fixed Fee Interview undertaken
Ptr: Collins, Mr John B LLB(Lond) Deputy District Judge . *Jun 1975
Fairley, Mr Alan S LLB(L'pool) . . . . *May 1976
Hudson, Mr Martyn R . . . . *§May 1979
Lowe, Mrs Nicola Anne LLB(Hons) . . . . *Jan 2003
Nethercott, Mr Simon J . . . . *§Jun 1980
Storry Deans, Mr Hugh BA(Hons) . . . . *Oct 1981
Ast: Collins, Mrs Sheila Mary LLB(Lond) . . . . *May 1976
Cottrell, Mrs Erica Jane LLB . . . . Dec 1993
Findlay, Chantal . . . . *Oct 2007
Knight, Mr Matthew Simon BA; MA Law Society LPC Prize 2004 . . . . *Sep 2006
Woodcock, Mrs Dee BA(Hons)(Classical Studies) . . . Dec 2001
Con: Phillips, Mr David Andrew MA(Cantab) . . . . *Jan 1990

HORSEY LIGHTLY FYNN ‡
3 Poole Road Bournemouth BH2 5QJ
Tel: 01202 551991 *Fax:* 01202 295403 *Dx:* 7608 BOURNEMOUTH
E-mail: snightingale@hlf-law.co.uk
List of partners: P J Day, L C Fynn, J Godfrey-Payne, A John, S C Nightingale
Languages: French, German, Spanish
Work: A1 A3 B1 C1 D1 D2 E F1 F2 G J1 J2 K1 K2 K3 K4 L O P Q R1 R2 S1 S2 T2 U2 W Z(c,d,l,q,s,t,u,w,y)
Emergency Action, Agency, Advocacy and Fixed Fee Interview undertaken
Ptr: Day, Mr Philip J BA(Cantab) . . . . *Jan 1982
Fynn, Mr Lionel C . . . . *§Jun 1963
Godfrey-Payne, Mr Jon BSc(Hons); DipLaw; DipHSW; DMS Fellow Royal Institute of Public Health . . . . . *Jun 2006
John, Mr Anthony Certificate of Merit (Sorbonne Paris) *Jul 1973
Nightingale, Mr Simon C LLB Notary Public . . . . . *§Dec 1975
Asoc: Llewellyn, Mr Richard Guy Seys . . . . *Dec 1976
Ast: Lee, Miss Jessica Evelyn LLB(Business Law); PGDL *Sep 2010
Preece, Mr Mark Robert LLB(Hons); LLM(Hons) . . . *Oct 2008
Con: Graham, Mrs Sandra D BA(Law) . . . . *Dec 1984

HUMPHRIES KIRK
1 Southbourne Grove Bournemouth BH6 3RD
Tel: 01202 421111 *Fax:* 01202 417146 *Dx:* 50550 SOUTHBOURNE
Emergency telephone 01202 437155
E-mail: bournemouth@hklaw.eu
Office: Dorchester, Poole (2 offices), Swanage, Wareham
Languages: French, German, Italian, Spanish
Work: D1 E K1 K3 K4 L S1 S2 T2 V W Z(o)
Advocacy, Fixed Fee Interview, Legal Aid undertaken and Legal Aid Franchise
Ptr: Cross, Mr Simon David BSc(Hons) . . . . *Sep 2006
Levene, Ms Kay E BA . . . . *Dec 1983
Asoc: Anderson, Mr David M . . . . *Dec 1976
Ast: Hammersley, Mr James Joseph . . . . Oct 2008

HURLEYS ‡
1107 Christchurch Road Bournemouth BH7 6BQ
Tel: 01202 436100 *Fax:* 01202 417180 *Dx:* 50560 SOUTHBOURNE
E-mail: law@davidhurley.co.uk
List of partners: D Hurley
Work: D1 G H K1 V W
Emergency Action, Agency, Advocacy, Fixed Fee Interview and Legal Aid undertaken
SPr: Hurley, Mr David . . . . Nov 1981
Ast: Price, Mark . . . . Jan 1983
Stansfield-Glass, Melanie . . . . Jan 1995

INSLEY & PARTNERS ‡
Tremont House 225 Charminster Road Bournemouth BH8 9QL
Tel: 01202 510167 *Fax:* 01202 530529
List of partners: R M Aitkenhead, D R Aldersey, P G Bennett
Office: Ferndown
Work: B1 C1 C2 E J1 L O P R1 S1 T1 T2 W Z(b,c,l)
Ptr: Aldersey, Mr David Richard BA(Oxon) . . . . *§Jul 1975
Bennett, Mr Paul G LLB(Bris) . . . . *§Apr 1975

THE ISAACS PRACTICE ‡
15 Lansdowne Road Bournemouth BH1 1RZ
Tel: 01202 299999 *Fax:* 01202 555803
E-mail: johncarmichael@tiplaw.co.uk
List of partners: J Carmichael
Languages: French, German, Spanish
Work: B2 J1 K1 K3 N O Q Z(q,r)
Emergency Action, Agency, Advocacy and Fixed Fee Interview undertaken
SPr: Carmichael, Mr John . . . . Jun 1980

THE JONATHAN MORRISSEY PRACTICE ‡
Harris House 264-266 Old Christchurch Road Bournemouth BH1 1PF
Tel: 01202 310999 *Fax:* 01202 311994 *Dx:* 7644 BOURNEMOUTH
Emergency telephone 07802 351020
E-mail: jm@jmlaw.co.uk
List of partners: J Morrissey
Languages: French, Spanish
Work: G H
Emergency Action, Agency, Advocacy, Fixed Fee Interview, Legal Aid undertaken and Legal Aid Franchise
SPr: Morrissey, Mr Jonathan LLB H M Deputy Coroner of Bournemouth, Poole & Eastern Dorset . . . . . *Mar 1986

KALE & CO ‡
49 Ophir Road Bournemouth BH8 8LT
Tel: 01202 552375
List of partners: D M Kale
Work: S1 W Z(l)
Agency undertaken
Ptr: Kale, Mr David M LLB(L'pool); TEP . . . . *Nov 1982

KITELEYS SOLICITORS LIMITED ‡
7 St Stephens Court 15-17 St Stephens Road Bournemouth BH2 6LA
Tel: 01202 299992 *Fax:* 01202 297329
Dx: 156940 BOURNEMOUTH 3
E-mail: office@kiteleys.co.uk
List of partners: S Isaacs, M Kiteley
Office: Southampton
Work: F1 F2 J1 K1 N Q W Z(r)
Fixed Fee Interview undertaken
Ptr: Isaacs, Sarah . . . . Jan 1997
Kiteley, Mr Mark BA; LLB(Hons) . . . . *Oct 1997

LACEYS ‡
5 Poole Road Bournemouth BH2 5QL
Tel: 01202 557256 *Fax:* 01202 551925 *Dx:* 7605 BOURNEMOUTH
E-mail: 5pr@laceyssolicitors.co.uk
Office: Bournemouth, Poole
Languages: French, German
Work: A1 A3 C1 C2 D1 E I J1 K1 K2 K3 L N O Q R2 S1 S2 T2 U2 W Z(c,d,l,q,r)

LACEYS
9 Poole Road Bournemouth BH2 5QR
Tel: 01202 755980 *Fax:* 01202 755994 *Dx:* 7605 BOURNEMOUTH
E-mail: 5pr@laceyssolicitors.co.uk
Office: Bournemouth, Poole

LESTER ALDRIDGE LLP ‡
Russell House Oxford Road Bournemouth BH8 8EX
Tel: 01202 786161 *Fax:* 01202 786110 *Dx:* 7623 BOURNEMOUTH 1
E-mail: online.enquiry@la-law.com
List of partners: J M Allin, D J Ashplant, A J Corke, S E Cowan, M Coward, R H Deehan, S E Evans, R M Fairbairn, C T Flood, T G Ford, R A H Galloway, M P C Giddins, B E Glazier, P A Grose, D M Herbert, J P Howe, J L Kelly, J C Kings, R L Lapworth, O B McKinney, E A O'Keeffe, D L Parkhouse, J E H Porter, W J Rickard, R A Robertson, K L Savage, B H Skelding, S M Southgate, S N Stone, G D Thomas, K E Thompson, R D Woolley
Office: Bournemouth, London WC2, Southampton
Languages: Afrikaans, French, German, Spanish
Work: A1 B1 C1 C2 C3 D1 E F1 G H I J1 K1 L M1 M2 N O P R1 S1 T1 T2 W V X Z(b,c,d,e,h,i,k,l,m,o,s,t,w)
Emergency Action, Agency, Advocacy, Legal Aid undertaken and Member of Accident Line
Ptr: Allin, Mr Jeremy M . . . . *§Dec 1975
Ashplant, Mr David J MA(Cantab) . . . . *§Oct 1983
Corke, Mr Andrew J LLB(Bris) . . . . *Apr 1980
Cowan, Ms Susan E LLB . . . . *§Oct 1983
Coward, Mr Martin . . . . *§Nov 1983
Evans, Mrs Susan Elizabeth LLB . . . . *§Jul 1987
Giddins, Mr Michael P C LLB . . . . *Oct 1983
Glazier, Mr Barry E MA(Oxon) Notary Public . . . . *§Jun 1966
Grose, Mr Peter A MA(Oxon) . . . . *§Dec 1978
Howe, Mr Jonathan P BA Notary Public . . . . *§Nov 1972
Kelly, Mr Jonathan Lloyd MA(Cantab) . . . . Nov 1994
Lapworth, Ms Rachel L . . . . *Dec 1991
McKinney, Miss Oonagh B BA . . . . *May 1988
Parkhouse, Mr David L MA(Oxon) . . . . *§Jul 1974
Porter, Ms Jane E H BA(Hons) . . . . *Nov 1986
Robertson, Mr Robert A . . . . *Sep 1972
Savage, Mrs Karen Lea . . . . *Nov 1997
Southgate, Mr Stuart M LLB . . . . *Mar 1963
Thomas, Mr Geoffrey D LLB . . . . *§Apr 1979
Thompson, Mrs Karen E LLB . . . . *Oct 1987
Woolley, Mr Roger D LLB . . . . *§Feb 1983
Ast: Brodie, Mr Timothy J . . . . *Feb 1999
Esterhuizen, Mr Grant Andrew . . . . *Jul 2000
Hermer, Mrs Jenny L LLB . . . . *Jun 1994
Lucas, Mrs Ruth Deborah LLB . . . . *Nov 1989
Mason, Ms Paula Marie LLB . . . . Sep 2000
Millichap, Miss Suzanne Louise . . . . *May 2000
Trotter, Miss Clare Elizabeth BA; DipLS . . . . May 1995
Con: Boardman, Mr Peter R MA; LLB Notary Public . . . . *Apr 1975

LESTER ALDRIDGE LLP
Fast Track House 6 Enterprise Way Aviation Park West Bournemouth BH23 6EW
Tel: 01202 597700 *Fax:* 01202 597840
E-mail: online.enquiry@la-law.com
Office: Bournemouth, London WC2, Southampton

MJP LAW ‡
1613 Wimborne Road Kinson Bournemouth BH11 9AP
Tel: 01202 582582 *Fax:* 01202 576262 *Dx:* 44852 KINSON
E-mail: mp@mjplaw.co.uk
List of partners: P R Avis
Languages: French, Spanish
Work: E K1 L N Q S1 S2 V W
Advocacy undertaken
SPr: Avis, Mr Peter R BA(Hons) Deputy District Judge Notary Public . . . . *§Jun 1981

THE MENTAL HEALTH PRACTICE ‡
15 Wellington Road PO Box 5137 Bournemouth BH5 2WG
Tel: 01202 269023 / 07961 053639 *Fax:* 01202 247100
E-mail: tmhpractice@ntlworld.com

PRESTON REDMAN ‡
Hinton House Hinton Road Bournemouth BH1 2EN
Tel: 01202 292424 *Fax:* 01202 552758 *Dx:* 7611 BOURNEMOUTH
E-mail: office@prestonredman.co.uk
List of partners: J C Bridger, J J Buchanan, R J Clough, A C Falck, T E Flower, D J Francis, M Hensleigh, R M Kefford, H S McKeown, D J E Neville-Jones, P T B Smith
Languages: French
Work: A1 A2 B1 C1 C2 C3 D1 E F1 G H J1 K1 K2 K3 K4 L M1 N O P Q R1 S1 S2 T1 T2 V W Z(a,b,c,d,e,f,g,h,j,k,l,q,x)
Emergency Action, Agency, Advocacy, Fixed Fee Interview, Legal Aid undertaken, Legal Aid Franchise and Member of Accident Line
Ptr: Bridger, Mr John C BA(Law) . . . . *Mar 1985
Buchanan, Mr John J . . . . *§Jan 1976
Clough, Mr Richard J LLB(Lond) . . . . *May 1972
Falck, Mr Adrian Clive LLB . . . . *Jul 2004
Flower, Mr Timothy Edward . . . . *Jul 2007
Francis, Mr Daniel James LLB . . . . *Nov 1992
Hensleigh, Mr Mark BA(Law) . . . . *Oct 1988
Kefford, Mrs Rebecca Marie LLB . . . . Jan 2004
McKeown, Mr Henry S LLB(Lond) . . . . *Nov 1971
Neville-Jones, Mr Douglas J E Notary Public . . . . *Feb 1975
Smith, Mr Paul Thomas Boulton . . . . *Aug 1986
Asoc: Bar, Mr Justyn W BSc . . . . *Oct 1990
Ast: Ackroyd, Mrs Anne M . . . . *Dec 1977
Bryant, Mrs Janine LLB . . . . *Sep 2009
Clough, Mr Jeremy Edward . . . . *Oct 2009

RAWLINS DAVY PLC ‡
Rowland House Hinton Road Bournemouth BH1 2EG
Tel: 01202 558844 *Fax:* 01202 557175 *Dx:* 7629 BOURNEMOUTH
E-mail: enquiries@rawlinsdavy.com
List of partners: O M Baker, M E Davies, E J Kennar, N J White
Work: B1 C1 C2 E F1 F2 J1 J2 L M3 N O P Q R1 R2 S1 S2 T1 T2 W Z(c,d,e,f,k,l,o,p,q,u)
Advocacy and Fixed Fee Interview undertaken
Dir: Baker, Mr Owen M LLB; LPC; PSC . . . . *Nov 1999
Davies, Mr Martin E LLB . . . . *Nov 1987
Kennar, Mr Eliezer John FILEx . . . . Dec 1983
White, Mr Neil John BSc . . . . Sep 1966
Ast: Cavanagh, Miss Gemma . . . . Mar 2009
Duggal, Miss Shami . . . . Apr 2004
Norman, Mr Peter J LLB . . . . Jun 1976
Smith, Miss Julie Patricia . . . . Jan 1985
Con: Bodley, Mr Kevin F LLB(Hons); LLM; MSc Notary Public . . . . Mar 1979

RENSHAW DERRICK & CO ‡
1 Poole Road Bournemouth BH2 5QQ
Tel: 01202 552777 *Fax:* 01202 552989 *Dx:* 7642 BOURNEMOUTH
E-mail: mail@renshawderrick.co.uk

RICHARDS & MORGAN LLP ‡
67 Southbourne Grove Bournemouth BH6 3RN
Tel: 01202 424234 *Fax:* 01202 428884 *Dx:* 50552 SOUTHBOURNE
E-mail: mail@richards-morgan.co.uk
List of partners: J S Salway, A G Turle
Languages: French
Work: C1 E F1 J1 K1 K3 L S1 W Z(l)
Agency and Advocacy undertaken
Ptr: Salway, Mr James S BA . . . . *§Dec 1979
Turle, Mr Alan G . . . . *§Jul 1977

RICHARD SEDGLEY & CO ‡
228-230 Old Christchurch Road Bournemouth BH1 1PE
Tel: 01202 556222 *Fax:* 01202 555311 *Dx:* 7672 BOURNEMOUTH
E-mail: office@rsedgley.co.uk
List of partners: R N Sedgley
Work: B1 C1 C2 E F1 F2 J1 K1 K2 L M2 N O Q R1 R2 S1 S2 T2 W Z(d,f,k,l,q)
Fixed Fee Interview undertaken
Ptr: Sedgley, Mr Richard N . . . . *May 1978
Asoc: Annen, Mr Michael J . . . . *§Dec 1976
Wood, Mrs Sarah Naomi LLB . . . . *Oct 1993

SOLOMONS SOLICITORS ‡
(incorporating Billins & Co)
8 Seamoor Road Westbourne Bournemouth BH4 9AN
Tel: 01202 802807
Con: Billins, Mr Edward George . . . . *Feb 1972

STEELE RAYMOND ‡
Richmond Point 43 Richmond Hill Bournemouth BH2 6LR
Tel: 01202 294566 *Fax:* 01202 552285 *Dx:* 7643 BOURNEMOUTH
E-mail: timstone@steeleraymond.co.uk
List of partners: J I Andrews, R Bajaj, P R Causton, J Daniels, J L L Fenn, P D Longland, S F Middleton, S B Outten, P C A Rolph, D R Steele, L J Watkin
Work: A1 A2 A3 B1 C1 C2 C3 D1 E F1 F2 I J1 J2 K1 L M1 M2 M3 N O P Q R1 R2 S1 S2 T1 T2 U1 U2 W X Z(a,b,c,d,e,f,h,i,j,k,l,o,p,q,s,t,w)
Emergency Action, Agency, Advocacy, Legal Aid undertaken, Legal Aid Franchise and Member of Accident Line
Ptr: Andrews, Mr John I LLB(Manc) . . . . *§Apr 1980
Bajaj, Mr Robert LLB . . . . *§Oct 1991
Causton, Mr Paul R BA; ATII; TEP . . . . *§Nov 1974
Daniels, Mr John LLB(B'ham) . . . . §Jan 1979
Fenn, Mr Julian L L BA; LLM(Lond) . . . . *§Apr 1975
Longland, Mr Paul D LLB; BCL Clements Inn Prize; Daniel Reardon Prize . . . . *§Jun 1981
Middleton, Mrs Susan F BSc . . . . *§Nov 1981
Outten, Mr Simon B BA . . . . *§Apr 1977
Rolph, Mr Peter C A LLB . . . . *§Dec 1981
Steele, Mr David R LLB(Manc) . . . . *§Aug 1973
Watkin, Lindsey J LLB(Hons) Degree Prize 1982 Committee Member of the Chamber of Trade . . . . *§Oct 1984
Asoc: Hawker, Miss Amala J LLB(Hons); PGDipLP . . . . . *§Sep 1998
Mills, Mr Nigel BA(Hons)(Philosophy) . . . . Mar 1983
Stone, Mr Timothy P C LLB(Hons) . . . . §Apr 2000
Ast: Errihoui, Miss Fadwa Houyam LLB; LPC . . . . *§Mar 2005
Gilmour, Mrs Elizabeth . . . . Sep 1999
Hardman, Mr Craig Venmore LLB . . . . *§Apr 2003
James, Miss Deepa BSc(Hons) . . . . *§Sep 2002

 See p112 for the Key to Work Categories & other symbols

Knowles, Mr Richard M BSc; LLB(RSA); QLTT . . . *§Mar 2000
Con: Arnold, Mr Alan J BSc(Econ); MCIPS . . . . *§Jun 1977
Raymond, Mr John R . . . . *§Apr 1970

TURNERS SOLICITORS LLP ‡
1 Poole Road Bournemouth BH2 5QQ
Tel: 01202 291291 *Fax:* 01202 553606 *Dx:* 7637 BOURNEMOUTH
E-mail: info@turners-solicitors.co.uk
List of partners: D M Blackmore, S C Hobby, S C H Immins, E B B Monds, M J Shutler, R S Tombs, S R White, K R Whitlock
Work: A1 A3 B1 C1 C2 C3 D1 E F1 J1 K1 K2 K3 L M1 M2 N O P Q R1 S1 S2 T1 T2 V W Z(b,c,d,h,j,k,l,o,q,r,s)
Agency and Advocacy undertaken
Ptr: Blackmore, Mr David Michael LLB. . . . . *Jul 2000
Hobby, Mrs Susan Claire . . . . *Sep 1996
Immins, Mr Simon Charles Heighton BA(Hons) . . . . *Oct 1992
Monds, Mr Edward Brooks Beatty . . . . *§Dec 1975
Shutler, Mr Michael J BA . . . . *§Mar 1983
Tombs, Mr Richard S LLB(Hons) . . . . Nov 1989
White, Mr Stephen R LLB. . . . . Nov 1971
Whitlock, Mr Kevin R Deputy District Judge . . . . . . *Nov 1981
Asoc: Houston, Ms Kerry LLB . . . . Sep 2004
Ast: Nanavita, Miss Bina LLB(Hons) . . . . *Mar 2010
Pringle, Miss Jamilah LLB(Hons) . . . . *Nov 2007

SCOTT WALBY LLP ‡
10 Poole Hill Bournemouth BH2 5PS
Tel: 01202 311112 *Fax:* 01202 311114 *Dx:* 7618 BOURNEMOUTH
E-mail: info@scott-walby.com

GRENVILLE J WALKER
46 Poole Road Westbourne Bournemouth BH4 9DZ
Tel: 01202 752594 *Fax:* 01202 751376 *Dx:* 89305 WESTBOURNE
E-mail: office@grenvillejwalker.org.uk
Office: Blandford Forum, Portland, Weymouth

SEAN WATERS ‡
The Law Chambers 15a Westbourne Arcade Poole Road Bournemouth BH4 9AY
Tel: 01202 767200 *Fax:* 01202 760980

ROBERT WRYNNE SOLICITORS ‡
138-140 Tuckton Road Tuckton Bournemouth BH6 3JX
Tel: 01202 422622 *Fax:* 01202 422499
E-mail: enquiries@robertwrynne.co.uk

BOURTON-ON-THE-WATER, Gloucestershire

I R GANNICOTT ‡
Vine House High Street Bourton-on-the-Water Gloucestershire GL54 2AN
Tel: 01451 820265 *Fax:* 01451 822359
Dx: 11432 BOURTON-ON-THE-WATER
E-mail: gannicott@btconnect.com
List of partners: I R Gannicott
Languages: German
Work: A1 B1 C1 E L R1 S1 W
Ptr: Gannicott, Mr Ian R LLB(Leeds). . . . . *Feb 1966

KENDALL & DAVIES ‡
Station Road Bourton-on-the-Water Gloucestershire GL54 2AA
Tel: 01451 820277 *Fax:* 01451 822157
Dx: 11431 BOURTON-ON-THE-WATER
E-mail: bourton@kendallanddavies.co.uk
List of partners: H G Davies, R L Davies, R G Draper
Office: Burford, Moreton-in-Marsh, Stow-on-the-Wold
Languages: French
Work: A1 C1 C2 D1 E F1 J1 K1 K3 L N O Q R1 S1 S2 T2 W Z(c,h,l,q)
Dir: Davies, Mr Richard L BA . . . . *§Mar 1985

BOVEY TRACEY, Devon

WBW SOLICITORS
Union Square Bovey Tracey Devon TQ13 9AE
Tel: 01626 833263 *Fax:* 01626 835260
E-mail: lawyer@wbw.co.uk
Office: Exeter, Newton Abbot, Torquay
Languages: French
Work: A1 B1 B2 C1 C2 C3 D1 D2 E F1 G H J1 K1 K2 L M1 M2 N O P Q R1 S1 T2 V W X Z(m,r)
Emergency Action, Agency, Advocacy, Fixed Fee Interview, Legal Aid undertaken, Legal Aid Franchise and Member of Accident Line
Ast: Brown, Mr Adrian T . . . . *§Dec 1973

BRACKLEY, Northamptonshire

BCC SOLICITORS ‡
(in association with Bowerman & Partners)
16 Market Place Brackley Northamptonshire NN13 7BG
Tel: 01280 702238 *Fax:* 01280 705154 *Dx:* 16981 BRACKLEY
E-mail: crawley@barnescampling.co.uk
Office: Witney
Work: D1 K1 W

BAILEYS ‡
Tudor House 4a Banbury Road Brackley Northamptonshire NN13 6AU
Tel: 01280 701166 *Fax:* 01280 701177 *Dx:* 16990 BRACKLEY
E-mail: baileyslegal@yahoo.co.uk
List of partners: Y S Bailey, A M Bravo
Languages: Malay, Mandarin, Punjabi
Work: E J1 K1 N O Q S2
Ptr: Bailey, Mrs Yew See BA; LLB . . . . *Sep 1989
Bravo, Ms Angela Maria. . . . . *Feb 1997

CL MANAGEMENT SOLUTIONS LIMITED ‡
The Manor Hinton-in-the-Hedges Brackley Northamptonshire NN13 5NE
Tel: 01280 702605 *Fax:* 01280 706813

GILROY STEEL ‡
16 Market Place Brackley Northamptonshire NN13 7BG
Tel: 01280 709426 *Fax:* 01280 705154 *Dx:* 16981 BRACKLEY
Office: Buckingham, Northampton

RICHARD HORTH ‡
9 Market Place Brackley Northamptonshire NN13 7AB
Tel: 01280 703773 *Fax:* 07092 130586 *Dx:* 16982 BRACKLEY
E-mail: contactus@richardhorth.co.uk
List of partners: R A Horth
Languages: French
Work: D1 G H J1 K1 M1 P S1 W
Emergency Action, Agency and Advocacy undertaken
SPr: Horth, Mr Richard A LLB(Hull). . . . . *Oct 1975

BRACKNELL, Bracknell Forest

ASCOT LAWYERS ‡
Summit House London Road Bracknell Bracknell Forest RG12 2XH
Tel: 01344 783890

BAS SOLICITORS ‡
Gingers Court 36a High Street Bracknell Bracknell Forest RG12 1HE
Tel: 01344 862111 *Fax:* 01344 860157 *Dx:* 33603 BRACKNELL
E-mail: legal@bas-solicitors.co.uk
List of partners: P J Grindrod, S A Speed
Work: C1 C2 D1 D2 E F1 K1 L O Q R2 S1 S2 W Z(c)
Agency and Advocacy undertaken
Ptr: Grindrod, Mr Paul J LLB(Lond) . . . . *Nov 1973
Speed, Mr Simon Anthony BSc(Hons); MSc. . . . . . *Jun 1996

FAIRBROTHER & DARLOW ‡
13 Millbanke Court Millbanke Way Bracknell Bracknell Forest RG12 1RP
Tel: 01344 420808 *Fax:* 01344 421818 *Dx:* 33634 BRACKNELL
E-mail: info@fairbrotherdarlow.co.uk
List of partners: D P Darlow, J D Fairbrother
Work: D1 G H J1 K1 L N Q S1 V W
Emergency Action, Agency, Advocacy, Fixed Fee Interview, Legal Aid undertaken and Legal Aid Franchise
Ptr: Darlow, Mr Douglas P LLB . . . . *Oct 1989
Fairbrother, Mrs Jaki D BA . . . . *Oct 1987
Ast: Lewis, Miss Rebecca BSc(Hons) . . . . *Oct 2001

HINE SOLICITORS
Abbey House Grenville Place Bracknell Bracknell Forest RG12 1BP
Tel: 01344 667300
Office: Beaconsfield, Cheltenham, Gerrards Cross, Oxford, Princes Risborough, Swindon, Yiewsley

KITE GRIFFIN ‡
Brooke House High Street Bracknell Bracknell Forest RG12 1LL
Tel: 01344 425637 *Fax:* 01344 423536 *Dx:* 33604 BRACKNELL
Emergency telephone 0118 981 6265
E-mail: info@kitegriffin.co.uk
List of partners: C D P Kite
Work: B1 C1 C2 C3 D1 E F1 G I J1 K1 L N O Q R1 S1 S2 T1 T2 W Z(c,e,f,i,k,l,p,r,t,w)
Agency, Advocacy and Fixed Fee Interview undertaken
SPr: Kite, Mr Christopher Douglas Paul. . . . . *§Nov 1968

SHOURIEFEARS ‡
5 Newell Hall Warfield Street Bracknell Bracknell Forest RG42 6AQ
Tel: 01344 302136 *Fax:* 0870 861 1386
E-mail: info@shouriefears.com

WILSON & BERRY ‡
Coppid Hall Warfield Road Bracknell Bracknell Forest RG42 2LR
Tel: 01344 420555 *Fax:* 01344 860486 *Dx:* 33602 BRACKNELL
E-mail: enq@wilsonberry.co.uk
List of partners: A N Hone, R N Pringle, M I Weeks, S I Wilkes
Work: C1 E G H K1 L R1 S1 T1 T2 W
Agency, Advocacy, Legal Aid undertaken and Legal Aid Franchise
Ptr: Hone, Mr Alan N LLB ♦ . . . . Apr 1985
Pringle, Mr Robert N BA(Hons) ♦ . . . . May 1981
Weeks, Mr Michael I BA ★ . . . . Jun 1978
Wilkes, Mr Stuart Ian LLB ♦. . . . . Jan 1991

BRADFORD, West Yorkshire

AARONS ‡
16a Killinghall Road Bradford West Yorkshire BD3 8DS
Tel: 01274 668722

ALI & CO SOLICITOR
22 Easby Road Bradford West Yorkshire BD7 1QX
Tel: 01274 391197 *Fax:* 01274 735425
E-mail: aliandco@btconnect.com
Office: Huddersfield
Ptr: Hussain, Khalid . . . . Jan 2000
Ast: Ali, Marnat . . . . Apr 2006
Ali, Shahzad . . . . Oct 2009

ALLERTON KAYE ‡
7 Southbrook Terrace Bradford West Yorkshire BD7 1AB
Tel: 01274 370066

ALLERTON KAYE ‡
Callmate House 1 Wilton Street Bradford West Yorkshire BD5 0AX
Tel: 01274 379840 *Fax:* 01274 379841
E-mail: info@allertonkaye.com

ALTAF SOLICITORS ‡
227 Manningham Lane Bradford West Yorkshire BD8 7HH
Tel: 01274 400405 *Fax:* 01274 400342
E-mail: info@altafsolicitors.co.uk

APPLEBYS ‡
44 Sunbridge Road Bradford West Yorkshire BD1 2AB
Tel: 01274 728838 *Fax:* 01274 738849 *Dx:* 11738 BRADFORD
Emergency telephone 07973 418474
E-mail: enquiries@applebys-law.co.uk
List of partners: M A Ullah
Languages: Hindi, Punjabi, Urdu
Ptr: Ullah, Mr M Amin LLB. . . . . *Sep 1990

JAVID ARSHAD & CO ‡
Marlborough House 1 Marlborough Road Bradford West Yorkshire BD8 7LD
Tel: 01274 493153

AURANGZEB KHAN SOLICITORS ‡
39 Duckworth Lane Bradford West Yorkshire BD9 5ET
Tel: 01274 548549 *Fax:* 01274 549533
List of partners: A Khan
Languages: Bengali, Gujarati, Pashto, Urdu
SPr: Khan, Aurangzeb BSc(Hons) . . . . Nov 1993

AXIOM SOLICITORS ‡
Bradford Chamber Business Park New Lane Bradford West Yorkshire BD4 8BX
Tel: 01274 664471 *Fax:* 01274 664492
E-mail: info@axiomsolicitors.co.uk

ALASTAIR BATEMAN & CO ‡
46 Westgate Bradford West Yorkshire BD1 2QR
Tel: 01274 739973 *Fax:* 01274 745504
List of partners: A N Bateman
Work: G H Z(m)
Legal Aid Franchise
SPr: Bateman, Mr Alastair N LLB. . . . . *Oct 1986
Ast: Dhesi, Kamaldeep Singh . . . . Sep 1997

BERWICKS ‡
74a Duckworth Lane Bradford West Yorkshire BD9 5EZ
Tel: 01274 498784 *Fax:* 01274 507031
E-mail: qadier@berwickssolicitors.com

BLAKELEY SOLICITORS ‡
2 Sowden Grange Thornton Bradford West Yorkshire BD13 3TH
Tel: 01274 831141 *Fax:* 01274 831140
E-mail: sblakeley@btinternet.com

BROWNS SOLICITORS LIMITED ‡
Auburn House 8 Upper Piccadilly Bradford West Yorkshire BD1 3NU
Tel: 01274 778000 *Fax:* 01274 778001
E-mail: info@brownssolicitors.com

CARTER FOX SOLICITORS ‡
Bradford Chamber Business Park New Lane Bradford West Yorkshire BD4 8BX
Tel: 01274 665775 *Fax:* 01274 664775 *Dx:* 712513 BRADFORD 10
E-mail: info@carterfox.co.uk

CERTUS SOLICITORS ‡
33 Manor Row Bradford West Yorkshire BD1 4PS
Tel: 01274 722199 *Fax:* 01274 722741
E-mail: naheem.anwar@certuslegal.co.uk

CHAMBERS SOLICITORS ‡
37 Grattan Road Bradford West Yorkshire BD1 2LU
Tel: 01274 301450

CHAUDHURY SOLICITORS ‡
17 Salem Street Bradford West Yorkshire BD1 4QH
Tel: 01274 732999

CHIVERS WALSH SMITH AND IRVINE & CO ‡
(incorporating Stuart Carter & Co)
Refuge Buildings 9-11 Sunbridge Road Bradford West Yorkshire BD1 2AZ
Tel: 01274 740077 *Fax:* 01274 740442
Emergency telephone 07970 678666
E-mail: solicitors@cwsi.co.uk
List of partners: A J Chaplin, J R S Smith, P J Welch
Languages: French, Punjabi, Spanish, Urdu
Work: D1 D2 E F1 G H J1 K1 L N O Q R1 S1 V W X Z(i,m)
Emergency Action, Agency, Advocacy, Fixed Fee Interview, Legal Aid undertaken and Legal Aid Franchise
Ptr: Chaplin, Mr Anthony J LLB . . . . *Oct 1983
Smith, Mr John R S MA(Cantab) . . . . *Jun 1973
Welch, Mr P James LLB(Leeds). . . . . Oct 1985

BARRY CLARK SOLICITOR ‡
10 Mornington Vale Bradford West Yorkshire BD8 7HB
Tel: 01274 544844

JOHN B CORDINGLEY & CO ‡
14 Hallfield Road Bradford West Yorkshire BD1 3RQ
Tel: 01274 736646 *Fax:* 01274 723471
List of partners: J B Cordingley, I T Howe
Languages: German
Work: B1 E G H N S1 W Z(l)
Agency, Advocacy and Legal Aid undertaken
Ptr: Cordingley, Mr John B. . . . . *Jun 1968
Howe, Mr Ian Thornton LLB. . . . . *Nov 1963

CORNWELLS ‡
59 Towngate Wyke Bradford West Yorkshire BD12 9JD
Tel: 01274 675631 *Fax:* 01274 600258 *Dx:* 13931 WYKE
List of partners: S G Hardcastle
Office: Featherstone
Work: D1 E K1 L Q R1 S1 S2 W Z(c)
Ptr: Hardcastle, Mr Stanley G LLB(Lond) . . . . *Dec 1979
Ast: Murphy, Mrs Melissa LLB(Hons). . . . . *Jan 2001

SHAZAD H DAD SOLICITORS ‡
6 Eldon Place off Manningham Lane Bradford West Yorkshire BD1 3TH
Tel: 01274 731000 *Fax:* 01274 731010
E-mail: shazadhdad@hotmail.co.uk
List of partners: S Dad
SPr: Dad, Shazad . . . . Jan 2002

DOWNEY & CO ‡
1 Prospect House Sandbeds Queensbury Bradford West Yorkshire BD13 1AD
Tel: 01274 883515 *Fax:* 01274 814125 *Dx:* 742870 BRADFORD
E-mail: mariem@downeyandco.co.uk
Work: S1 S2 W

DRYDENS ‡
Shire House 2 Humboldt Street Bradford West Yorkshire BD1 5HQ
Tel: 01274 378000 *Fax:* 01274 378199 *Dx:* 11768 BRADFORD
E-mail: enquiries@drydenslaw.com
Work: F1 Q Z(q)

EATONS ‡
The Old Library 34 Darley Street Bradford West Yorkshire BD1 3LH
Tel: 0845 660 0660 *Fax:* 01274 305056 *Dx:* 11710 BRADFORD
E-mail: enquiries@eatons-solicitors.co.uk
List of partners: J G I Brown, P A Brunskill, F M Callow, C J Parker
Office: Leeds, Otley
Work: D1 E F1 G H J1 K1 L N O Q S1 V W Z(m)
Emergency Action, Agency, Advocacy, Fixed Fee Interview, Legal Aid undertaken, Legal Aid Franchise and Member of Accident Line

Ptr: Brown, Mr John Graeme Irvine LLB . . . . *Nov 1982
Brunskill, Mr Paul A BSc(Psych). . . . . *Jan 1984
Callow, Ms Fiona M BA(Hons). . . . . *Oct 1988
Parker, Mr Charles J LLB . . . . *Jul 1969
Ast: Nadel, Ms Gina . . . . *Jan 1980
Singleton, Mrs Maureen LLB(Hons) . . . . *Oct 1988
Steele, Miss Amanda E BA . . . . *Sep 1993

C K EDRUPT ‡
Water Lane Bradford West Yorkshire BD1 2JL
Tel: 01274 731111

STEVEN J EMMOTT ‡
Shipton Chambers 16-18 North Parade Bradford West Yorkshire BD1 3HT
Tel: 01274 309791 *Fax:* 01274 394838
Work: S1

GOOD & CO SOLICITORS LLP ‡
234 Manningham Lane Bradford West Yorkshire BD8 7BZ
Tel: 0845 388 8901 *Fax:* 0845 388 8902
E-mail: ingo@good-solicitors.com

GORDONS LLP ‡
Forward House 8 Duke Street Bradford West Yorkshire BD1 3QX
Tel: 01274 202202 *Fax:* 01274 202100 *Dx:* 11716 BRADFORD
E-mail: mail@gordonsllp.com
Office: Leeds
Work: B1 C1 C2 C3 D1 E F1 J1 K1 L M1 M2 N P R1 S1 V W Z(c,f,i,k,l,t)

HANSARDS SOLICITORS ‡
13 Duckworth Lane Bradford West Yorkshire BD9 5ER
Tel: 01274 403797 *Fax:* 01274 403798

HAYRE & CO ‡
Kenburgh House 28a Manor Row Bradford West Yorkshire BD1 4QU
Tel: 01274 744405 *Fax:* 01274 744406
List of partners: C Dixon, B Hayre
Work: C1 E I J1 N O Q S1 S2 U2 Z(e,i,k,za)
Ptr: Dixon, Mr Colin . . . . Apr 1993
Hayre, Mr Baljinder LLB. . . . . Feb 2002

ISMAIL & GHANI ‡
8-9 Southbrook Terrace Bradford West Yorkshire BD7 1AB
Tel: 01274 737546 *Fax:* 01274 720721
List of partners: M Ghani, B Ismail
Languages: Gujarati, Hindi, Hindko, Punjabi, Urdu
Work: B1 C1 C2 C3 D1 E F1 G H J1 K1 L M1 M2 N P R1 S1 W Z(i)
Emergency Action, Agency, Advocacy, Fixed Fee Interview, Legal Aid undertaken and Member of Accident Line
Ptr: Ghani, Mushtaq BA(Law) . . . . *Sep 1982
Ismail, Mr Bashir . . . . *Dec 1981

JOSEPH & CO SOLICITORS ‡
7 Southfield Lane Bradford West Yorkshire BD5 9HU
Tel: 01274 526940 *Fax:* 01274 526949
E-mail: info@josephandcosolicitors.co.uk

KBS SOLICITORS ‡
29a Tyrrel Street Bradford West Yorkshire BD1 1RU
Tel: 01274 725655

KABIR AHMED & CO SOLICITORS ‡
88 Lumb Lane Bradford West Yorkshire BD8 7QZ
Tel: 01274 739939 *Fax:* 01274 739949
E-mail: info@kabirahmedsolicitors.co.uk

KHAN SOLICITORS ‡
24 Sunbridge Road Bradford West Yorkshire BD1 2AA
Tel: 01274 301999 *Fax:* 01274 301997 *Dx:* 11788 BRADFORD 8
Emergency telephone 07976 958826
E-mail: khansolicitors@virgin.net.co.uk
List of partners: M S Khan
Languages: Gujarati, Hindi, Punjabi, Urdu
Work: B2 D1 E G H J1 K1 K2 L N Q S1 V W Z(h,k,l,p)
Emergency Action, Agency, Advocacy, Legal Aid undertaken and Member of Accident Line
Ptr: Khan, Mr Mohammed Sarwar LLB(Hons) . . . . . . *Jan 1996

LPS SOLICITORS LIMITED ‡
119 Little Horton Lane Bradford West Yorkshire BD5 0HT
Tel: 01274 392007

LAST CAWTHRA FEATHER LLP ‡
Airedale House 128 Sunbridge Road Bradford West Yorkshire BD1 2AT
Tel: 01274 848800 *Fax:* 01274 390644 *Dx:* 11723 BRADFORD
E-mail: enquiries@lcf.co.uk
List of partners: C Abraham, D P Anderson, A P Burkinshaw, S E Clark, E D Henry, A Lee, A T McDonald, S D Mordey, N Shaw, J R S Smith, S R B Stell, I M Underwood, J H Wright
Office: Baildon, Ilkley, Leeds, Shipley
Languages: French, Italian, Spanish
Work: C1 D1 E F1 J1 K1 L N O Q R1 R2 S1 S2 U2 V W Z(c,q)
Emergency Action, Agency, Advocacy, Fixed Fee Interview, Legal Aid undertaken and Legal Aid Franchise
Ptr: Anderson, Mr D Paul LLB . . . . *Feb 1985
Burkinshaw, Mr A Paul . . . . Mar 1965
Clark, Mrs Susan E LLB; ATII . . . . *Nov 1988
Henry, Ms Elizabeth D BA(Lond) . . . . Nov 1983
Stell, Mr Simon Richard Bradley LLB; MICM; MBA . . *Jun 1981
Underwood, Mr Ian M ♦ Deputy District Judge. . . . *§Nov 1978
Asoc: Morris, Mr Paul BA . . . . *§Dec 1977
Westcott, Mr Paul BA . . . . Nov 1991
Ast: Adams, Miss Zoe . . . . Oct 2006
Beaumont, Miss Rebecca. . . . . Jan 2007
Casey, Ms Ann-Marie . . . . Mar 2008
Christian, Mrs Ann LLB . . . . *Sep 2001
Hudson, Miss Harriet . . . . Mar 2008
Long, Ms Rachel . . . . Sep 2005
Montgomery, Ms Ragan Elizabeth. . . . . Jan 2001
Con: Verity, Mr Stuart A MA(Oxon) . . . . *Apr 1973

LEGAL MOVE ‡
PO Box 41 Well Street Bradford West Yorkshire BD1 5NU
Tel: 0870 600 4818 *Fax:* 01274 764710

LEVI SOLICITORS LLP
2nd Floor Arndale House Charles Street Bradford West Yorkshire BD1 1EH
Tel: 01274 709709 *Fax:* 01274 079711 *Dx:* 11774 BRADFORD
E-mail: info@levisolicitors.co.uk
Office: Leeds
Work: S1

LUMB & MACGILL ‡
Leeds House 4 James Street Bradford West Yorkshire BD1 3PZ
Tel: 01274 730666 *Fax:* 01274 723453 *Dx:* 11714 BRADFORD
Emergency telephone 01274 514109
E-mail: post@lumbandmacgill.fsnet.co.uk
List of partners: P G Ainge, P D Mawhinney, P D Milner
Languages: Punjabi, Urdu
Work: G H K1
Agency and Legal Aid undertaken
Ptr: Ainge, Mr Phillip G LLB ★. . . . . *Jun 1981
Mawhinney, Miss Paula D LLB(Manc) R G Lawson Prize . . . . *Oct 1985
Milner, Mr Paul D LLB(Hull) ★. . . . . *Jul 1980

MCMANUS SEDDON ‡
Lloyds Bank Chambers 43-45 Hustlergate Bradford West Yorkshire BD1 1PH
Tel: 01274 741841 *Fax:* 01274 394653 *Dx:* 11786 BRADFORD
Emergency telephone 07770 761291
E-mail: enquiries@mcmanusseddon.co.uk
List of partners: N J Leadbeater, C A McManus, R F Seddon
Languages: French, Pashto, Punjabi, Urdu
Work: B2 D1 D2 F1 G H K1 K3 K4 L N O Q S1 W Z(g,q)
Emergency Action, Agency, Advocacy, Fixed Fee Interview, Legal Aid undertaken and Legal Aid Franchise
Ptr: Leadbeater, Mr Nicholas J LLB . . . . *Sep 1993
McManus, Mrs Colette A BA . . . . *Jan 1993
Seddon, Mr Roger F LLB . . . . *Oct 1980
Asoc: Gullett, Mr Andrew James BA. . . . . *Dec 2001
Saliheen, Miss Shazia LLB . . . . *Aug 2005
Steele, Miss Amanda E BA . . . . *Sep 1993

MAKIN DIXON SOLICITORS ‡
Second Floor The Wool Exchange 10 Hustlergate Bradford West Yorkshire BD1 1RE
Tel: 01274 747747 *Fax:* 01274 747277 *Dx:* 11736 BRADFORD
E-mail: enquiries@makindixon.co.uk
List of partners: I Dixon, C Makin
Office: Halifax, Harrogate, Keighley, Skipton, Todmorden

MALIK SOLICITORS ‡
Royal Chambers 2 Upper Piccadilly Bradford West Yorkshire BD1 3PQ
Tel: 01274 727773 *Fax:* 01274 744088
E-mail: info@maliksolicitors.com

MEGSONS LLP
4th Floor Arndale House Charles Street Bradford West Yorkshire BD1 1EJ
Tel: 01274 738444 *Fax:* 01274 738404 *Dx:* 712514 BRADFORD 10
Office: Oldham
Work: F1 J1 O Q Z(c,q)
Agency and Legal Aid undertaken
Ptr: Hannam, Mr Ian Paul LLB. . . . . *Jun 1984

MILLAN SOLICITORS ‡
1368 Leeds Road Bradford West Yorkshire BD3 8ND
Tel: 01274 660111 *Fax:* 01274 660222 *Dx:* 721743 BRADFORD 19
E-mail: enquiries@millansolicitors.co.uk
List of partners: G Millan
Languages: Hindi, Punjabi, Urdu
Work: N O Q Z(i,q,r)
Agency, Advocacy, Fixed Fee Interview undertaken and Member of Accident Line
Ptr: Millan, Mrs Goldie LLB; LLM(Cantab) Sweet & Maxwell Law Prize . . . . *Nov 1995

MIR & CO SOLICITORS ‡
846 Manchester Road Bradford West Yorkshire BD5 8DJ
Tel: 0845 652 0720 *Fax:* 01274 725842
E-mail: info@mirsolicitors.co.uk

MORRISH SOLICITORS LLP
Landmark House 3 Broadway Bradford West Yorkshire BD1 1JD
Tel: 01274 745328 *Fax:* 01274 742758
E-mail: info@morrishsolicitors.com
Office: Leeds, Pudsey, Yeadon

MURRAYS SOLICITORS ‡
10 Piece Hall Yard Bradford West Yorkshire BD1 1PJ
Tel: 01274 304448 *Fax:* 01274 739036
List of partners: P Murray
SPr: Murray, Ms Philippa LLB . . . . Sep 1988
Ast: Bowden, Sarah . . . . Mar 2010

NEEDHAMS ‡
34 Peckover Street Little Germany Bradford West Yorkshire BD1 5BD
Tel: 01274 371088
E-mail: info@needhamssolicitors.co.uk
List of partners: P C Needham, K Wadsworth
Office: Bridport
Languages: French, Punjabi, Spanish, Urdu
Work: A1 B2 N R2
Emergency Action, Agency, Advocacy, Fixed Fee Interview, Legal Aid undertaken and Member of Accident Line
SPr: Needham, Mr Philip Charles BA. . . . . *Feb 1992
Ptr: Wadsworth, Ms Kate . . . . Nov 2009

NUR & CO SOLICITORS ‡
836 Leeds Road Bradford West Yorkshire BD3 9TX
Tel: 01274 656465 *Fax:* 0560 311 9532
E-mail: info@nursolicitors.com

OPTIMA LEGAL SERVICES LTD ‡
Arndale House Charles Street Bradford West Yorkshire BD1 1UN
Tel: 0871 880 8080 *Fax:* 01274 513708
E-mail: info@optimalegal.co.uk
Office: Newcastle upon Tyne

PATEL & BHATOA ‡
National House 951 Leeds Road Bradford West Yorkshire BD3 8JB
Tel: 01274 669023 *Fax:* 01274 656151 *Dx:* 721740 BRADFORD 19
E-mail: mail@pb-law.co.uk
List of partners: A Bhatoa, J S Bhatoa
Languages: Gujarati, Hindi, Punjabi, Urdu
Work: B1 C1 C2 C3 D1 E F1 J1 K1 L M1 M2 N O P Q R1 S1 T1 T2 V W Z(d,h,i,l,m)
Emergency Action, Agency, Advocacy, Fixed Fee Interview, Legal Aid undertaken and Member of Accident Line
Ptr: Bhatoa, Avtar . . . . Jan 1994
Bhatoa, Jagtar S LLB(Manc) . . . . *§Sep 1979

MUSA A PATEL & CO
56-58 Manningham Lane Bradford West Yorkshire BD1 3EB
Tel: 01274 747777 *Fax:* 01274 737575
Emergency telephone 07966 213165
E-mail: info@musapatels.co.uk
Office: Dewsbury
Languages: Gujarati, Punjabi, Urdu
Work: D1 G H K1 S1 S2 Z(i)
Agency, Advocacy, Legal Aid undertaken and Legal Aid Franchise

NICK PETERKEN SOLICITOR ‡
1 Ivegate Bradford West Yorkshire BD1 1SQ
Tel: 01274 733322 *Fax:* 01274 733377
E-mail: nick@npsolicitors.co.uk

PETHERBRIDGE BASSRA SOLICITORS ‡
Vintry House 18-24 Piccadilly Bradford West Yorkshire BD1 3LS
Tel: 01274 724114 *Fax:* 01274 724161 *Dx:* 11706 BRADFORD
Emergency telephone 01422 201222 / 01274 480902
E-mail: mail@petherbridgebassra.co.uk
List of partners: T P Hussain, L H Julian, A Petherbridge, R Singh, P J R Sweeney
Languages: Punjabi, Urdu
Work: G H
Emergency Action, Agency, Advocacy, Fixed Fee Interview, Legal Aid undertaken and Legal Aid Franchise
Ptr: Hussain, Mr Tariq P LLB(Hons) ● . . . . *Apr 1997
Julian, Miss Lisa H LLB(Hons) ●. . . . . *Sep 1996
Petherbridge, Mr Alan LLB(Hons) ● . . . . *Apr 1981
Singh, Rachim BA(Law) ★. . . . . *§Oct 1987
Sweeney, Mr Philip J R BA(Law) . . . . Dec 1980
Ast: Hutton, Ms Anne-Marie LLB(Hons) ● . . . . Jan 2006
Kelly, Mr John C R LLB . . . . *Jun 1975

PLATINUM PARTNERSHIP SOLICITORS ‡
Platinum House 3 Eldon Place Bradford West Yorkshire BD1 3AZ
Tel: 0845 490 5000 *Fax:* 0870 445 0505
E-mail: admin@ppsolicitors.com
List of partners: N Karim
Ptr: Karim, Miss Nasreen LLB(Hons) . . . . *Nov 2000

PROLEGIS SOLICITORS LLP ‡
First Floor 1-3 Kings Gate Bradford Business Park Bradford West Yorkshire BD1 4SJ
Tel: 07967 109388 / 01274 718690 *Fax:* 01274 724613
Dx: 11702 BRADFORD
E-mail: admin@prolegissolicitors.co.uk

QAYOUM & CO SOLICITORS ‡
26 Durley Avenue Bradford West Yorkshire BD9 5LG
Tel: 01274 225098
E-mail: enquiries@qayoumandcosolicitors.co.uk

RJ SOLICITORS ‡
105 Heaton Road Bradford West Yorkshire BD9 4RZ
Tel: 01274 900563 *Fax:* 01274 494157
E-mail: rjsolicitors@btconnect.com

READ DUNN CONNELL ‡
Manor Row Chambers 35-37 Manor Row Bradford West Yorkshire BD1 4PS
Tel: 01274 723858 *Fax:* 01274 728493 *Dx:* 712515 BRADFORD
E-mail: info@readdunnconnell.co.uk
List of partners: R E Anderson, J C Fitzpatrick, S D Littlewood, M R Millin, R Saroop
Office: Ilkley
Languages: Hindi, Punjabi, Urdu
Work: B1 C1 E F1 J1 K1 K3 K4 L N O Q S1 S2 T2 W Z(c,l,p,q,r)
Emergency Action, Agency, Advocacy, Fixed Fee Interview, Legal Aid undertaken, Legal Aid Franchise and Member of Accident Line
Ptr: Anderson, Mr Robert E BA . . . . *§Jun 1984
Fitzpatrick, Miss Judith C LLB(Hull) . . . . *Jun 1980
Littlewood, Miss Sarah Davina LLB(Hons). . . . . . . *Jul 2005
Millin, Ms Mary Rose BA; MBA . . . . Apr 1985
Saroop, Mr Ram LLB . . . . *Feb 1992
Ast: Mayne, Mr David . . . . Sep 2007
Con: Fox, Miss Belinda J LLB(Lond) . . . . *Oct 1986
Thomas, Mr James E K BA. . . . . *Dec 1979
Ward, Mr Nigel Henry . . . . *Jan 1965

REISS SOLICITORS ‡
102-104 Lumb Lane Bradford West Yorkshire BD8 7RS
Tel: 01274 395858 *Fax:* 01274 395878

RIAZ SOLICITORS ‡
955-959 Leeds Road Bradford West Yorkshire BD3 8JB
Tel: 01274 662154 *Fax:* 01274 664374
E-mail: mriazsolicitor@hotmail.co.uk

RUNHAMS ‡
89-93 Manningham Lane Bradford West Yorkshire BD1 3BN
Tel: 01274 532233 *Fax:* 01274 534399 *Dx:* 1126 BRADFORD
E-mail: info@runhams.com
List of partners: J D Dowling, C D Rhodes, E Wegorzewski
Languages: Polish
Work: B1 C1 C2 C3 E F1 J1 L N O Q R1 S1 S2 W Z(c,e,f,k,l,o,q)
Emergency Action, Agency and Fixed Fee Interview undertaken
Ptr: Dowling, Mr John David LLB . . . . *May 1989
Rhodes, Mr Christopher David LLB . . . . *Oct 2003
Wegorzewski, Mr Edward LLB. . . . . *Dec 1980
Asoc: Rasool, Nighat Kanser BA(Hons)(Law & Accountancy) *Apr 2006
Ast: Capaldi, Mr Joseph LLB. . . . . Mar 1978
Con: Kirkbride, Mr Bryan MA; LLB(Cantab) . . . . *Apr 1973
Runham, Mr John Stuart LLB . . . . *Jul 1972

SCHOFIELD SWEENEY ‡
Church Bank House Church Bank Bradford West Yorkshire BD1 4DY
Tel: 01274 306000 *Fax:* 01274 306111 *Dx:* 11755 BRADFORD
E-mail: law@schoeys.com
List of partners: H C Atkinson, D C Birkinshaw, P A N Knight, M R Millin, P R S Petchey, C E Schofield, J M Staton, M N Sweeney
Office: Leeds
Work: A1 B1 C1 C2 C3 E I J1 J2 M1 O Q R1 R2 S1 S2 T1 T2 Z(b,c,d,e,j,l,q,t)
Agency undertaken
Ptr: Atkinson, Mrs Hilary C LLB . . . . *§Apr 1978
Birkinshaw, Mr Darren C LLB . . . . *Oct 1990
Knight, Mr P A Nicholas LLB . . . . *§Jun 1970
Millin, Ms Mary Rose BA; MBA . . . . Apr 1985

See p112 for the Key to Work Categories & other symbols

Petchey, Mr P R Simon BSocSc. . . . . *Apr 1987
Schofield, Mr Christopher E MA(Cantab) . . . . *Feb 1988
Staton, Mr James M LLB Treasurer of Local Law Society . . . . *Nov 1982
Sweeney, Mr Martin N LLB . . . . *Oct 1986
Asoc: Cowan-Clark, Mrs Julie Patricia BA(Hons). . . . . . . *Oct 1996
Ast: Mathams, Ms Rosemary Helen . . . . Apr 2002
Umer, Mr Tariq Leslie LLB; BA(Hons) . . . . §Oct 2002

SHEIRS SOLICITORS ‡
64 Duckworth Lane Bradford West Yorkshire BD9 5HA
Tel: 01274 499922 *Fax:* 01274 499921
E-mail: sheir786@hotmail.co.uk

SHIRE SOLICITORS ‡
7 Eldon Place Bradford West Yorkshire BD1 3AZ
Tel: 01274 727373 *Fax:* 01274 724700
E-mail: info@shiresolicitors.co.uk

SIGMA LAW SOLICITORS ‡
Sigma House 15 Salem Street Manor Row Bradford West Yorkshire BD1 4QH
Tel: 01274 391100 / 0844 879 3447 *Fax:* 01274 390201
Dx: 11724 BRADFORD
E-mail: info@sigmalawyers.co.uk

SIMPSON DUXBURY ‡
(in association with Farrar Stead & Haley; Herbert Duxbury Son & Co; Rooley Temple Milnes)
2 Tyrrel Street Bradford West Yorkshire BD1 1RJ
Tel: 01274 734166 *Fax:* 01274 390182 *Dx:* 11709 BRADFORD
E-mail: lawyers@simpsonduxbury.co.uk
List of partners: H A Cox, J R Mason, P E Taber
Languages: Punjabi, Urdu
Work: C1 D1 E F1 G H J1 K1 K3 L N Q S1 S2 V W Z(i,l)
Emergency Action, Agency, Advocacy, Fixed Fee Interview, Legal Aid undertaken and Legal Aid Franchise
Ptr: Cox, Mr Howard A BSc(Wales)(Econ) . . . . *Jun 1979
Mason, Mr Jonathan R LLB . . . . *Mar 1987
Taber, Mr Philip E BA . . . . *Jun 1981
Ast: Tordoff, Mr Fraser BA . . . . *Sep 1993

SOLICITORS DIRECT ‡
109-113 Carlisle Road Bradford West Yorkshire BD8 8BY
Tel: 01274 776000 *Fax:* 01274 779000
E-mail: enquiries@solicitorsdirect.biz
List of partners: S A Khan, S Majid
Languages: Punjabi, Urdu
Work: C1 E N Q S1 S2 W Z(i)
Ptr: Khan, Shadab Ahmed. . . . . *Nov 1997
Majid, Mr Shakeel. . . . . Feb 2004

STACHIW BASHIR GREEN ‡
The Old Bank Building 499 Great Horton Road Great Horton Bradford West Yorkshire BD7 4EG
Tel: 01274 404010 *Fax:* 01274 404012
E-mail: info@sbglaw.co.uk
List of partners: R A Bashir, A C Green, J N Stachiw
Office: Bradford
Languages: French, Gujarati, Italian, Polish, Punjabi, Ukrainian, Urdu
Work: B1 C1 D1 E J1 K1 L N O Q S2 V W Z(c,e,k,p,q)
Emergency Action, Agency, Advocacy, Fixed Fee Interview, Legal Aid Franchise and Member of Accident Line
Ptr: Bashir, Mr Riaz Arif LLB(Hons); LSF Calcott Pryce Dissertation Prize . . . . Nov 1995
Stachiw, Mr Jaroslaw Nestor BA(Hons)(Law) . . . . . *Dec 1993

STACHIW BASHIR GREEN
656 Great Horton Road Bradford West Yorkshire BD7 4AA
Tel: 01274 404010 *Fax:* 01274 404012
Emergency telephone 07793 494253
E-mail: info@sbglaw.co.uk
Office: Bradford
Languages: Punjabi, Ukrainian, Urdu
Work: B1 C1 E F1 F2 J1 K1 L N O Q Z(c,e,h,k,p,q)
Emergency Action, Agency, Advocacy, Fixed Fee Interview and Legal Aid undertaken
Ptr: Green, Mr Adrian Charles LLB(Hons) President of Bradford Law Society . . . . Nov 1991

SWITALSKI'S
(incorporating Bridge & Co)
2a Darley Street Bradford West Yorkshire BD1 3HH
Tel: 01274 720314 *Fax:* 01274 721206 *Dx:* 11790 BRADFORD
Office: Dewsbury, Halifax, Huddersfield, Leeds, Wakefield
Languages: Urdu
Work: D1 G H J1 K1 K2 L Z(i,m,r)
Emergency Action, Agency and Legal Aid undertaken
Ptr: Bridger, Mr Alan S BSc ★ . . . . *Jun 1982

TARKEL SOLICITORS ‡
32 Horton Grange Road Bradford West Yorkshire BD7 3AQ
Tel: 01274 918481 / 0800 988 4471 *Fax:* 01274 577944
E-mail: info@tarkelsolicitors.co.uk

UMBRELLA LEGAL SOLICITORS ‡
722a Manchester Road Bradford West Yorkshire BD5 7QS
Tel: 01274 737001 *Fax:* 01274 737002

VIDESS LTD ‡
633 Halifax Ltd Liversedge Bradford West Yorkshire WF15 8HG
Tel: 01274 851577
E-mail: bmillet@videss.co.uk

WHITAKER FIRTH ‡
1 Manor Row Bradford West Yorkshire BD1 4PB
Tel: 01274 381900 *Fax:* 01274 392848 *Dx:* 11739 BRADFORD
E-mail: reception@whitakerfirth.co.uk
Work: A1 C1 C2 C3 D1 E F1 J1 K1 K3 K4 L N O Q R1 R2 S1 S2 T2 W Z(c,d,h)

WILLISCROFT & CO ‡
Pickwick Works 17 Peckover Street Bradford West Yorkshire BD1 5BD
Tel: 01274 305380 *Fax:* 01274 720715 *Dx:* 11769 BRADFORD
E-mail: williscroft@williscroft.co.uk
List of partners: S M Adams, L Cohen, L A Johnson, J Kelly
Languages: Punjabi, Urdu
Work: D1 D2 K1 K3 L V X
Emergency Action, Agency, Advocacy, Fixed Fee Interview, Legal Aid undertaken and Legal Aid Franchise
Ptr: Adams, Mrs Stephanie Mary . . . . *Sep 1998
Cohen, Ms Lucy LLB(Hons) . . . . *Oct 1998
Johnson, Ms Lindsey A LLB. . . . . *Oct 1987
Kelly, Ms June BA; QSW; CPE . . . . *Sep 1994
Asoc: Altman, Mr Adrian Jon LLB . . . . Feb 2005
Callow, Ms Fiona M BA(Hons). . . . . *Oct 1988
Davison, Mrs Ruth LLB . . . . *Sep 2003
Jennings, Miss Sarah Jane LLB(Hons) . . . . *Sep 2007
Majid, Miss Asia. . . . . Apr 2009
Smalley, Miss Emma LLB Law Society Award for LPC 2004 . . . . *Oct 2007

WILSONS
2-4 Fair Road Wibsey Bradford West Yorkshire BD6 1QN
Tel: 01274 693600 *Fax:* 01274 678874
Office: Bradford, Horsforth, Leeds, Pudsey
Asoc: Liburd, Miss Keira LLB . . . . *May 2006

WILSONS
21 The Green Idle Bradford West Yorkshire BD10 9PT
Tel: 01274 616400 *Fax:* 01274 612646
Office: Bradford, Horsforth, Leeds, Pudsey

S A YOUNIS SOLICITORS ‡
267 Legrams Lane Bradford West Yorkshire BD7 2HH
Tel: 01274 579900

BRADFORD-ON-AVON, Wiltshire

BLB SOLICITORS
3 Church Street Bradford-on-Avon Wiltshire BA15 1LR
Tel: 01225 866541 *Fax:* 01225 867780
Dx: 82650 BRADFORD-ON-AVON
Emergency telephone 01221 469787
E-mail: solicitors@bradford.blandb.co.uk
Office: Bath, Swindon, Trowbridge
Work: A1 B1 D1 E F1 G H J1 K1 L M1 N P R1 S1 T1 V W
Emergency Action, Agency, Advocacy, Fixed Fee Interview and Legal Aid undertaken
Ptr: Bagnall, Mr Guy LLB . . . . §Apr 1970

MCCLOY LEGAL ‡
4 The Shambles Bradford-on-Avon Wiltshire BA15 1JS
Tel: 01225 866563 *Fax:* 01225 867789
Dx: 82652 BRADFORD-ON-AVON
E-mail: law@mccloy.co.uk
List of partners: G R McCloy, P J McCloy
Languages: French
Work: A2 B1 C1 C2 C3 E F1 F2 J1 K1 L M2 N O Q R2 S1 S2 W Z(d,e,f,k,l,q,r,w,z)
Emergency Action, Agency, Advocacy and Legal Aid undertaken
Ptr: McCloy, Mr Graham R . . . . *May 1996
McCloy, Mr Patrick J . . . . *Jan 1978
Con: McCloy, Mrs Judith Melissa . . . . *Dec 1977
McCloy, Mr Matthew C . . . . *Feb 1974

BRAINTREE, Essex

BOYD CARTER ‡
Twyford House 6a Rayne Road Braintree Essex CM7 2QH
Tel: 01376 555000 *Fax:* 01376 359207 *Dx:* 56202 BRAINTREE
E-mail: bc@boydcarter.co.uk

CUNNINGTONS ‡
Great Square Braintree Essex CM7 1UD
Tel: 01376 326868 *Fax:* 01376 550003 *Dx:* 133225 BRAINTREE 3
E-mail: quotes@cunningtons.co.uk
List of partners: J P Bradshaw, N S Brothers, C Dias, D N Drake, A P Fenton, A J P Hutton, S E Kew, J S O'Brien, F S Parsons, N J Price, K Sharman, J R Simpkin, A Toulson, J C Withams
Office: Braintree, Croydon, Ilford, Solihull, Wickford
Work: E K1 L Q S1 S2 W
Ptr: Drake, Mr David Nigel LLB(Hons) . . . . *Jun 1979
Fenton, Mr A Paul BA(Hons) . . . . *Nov 1985
Kew, Mr Stephen E BA(Hons). . . . . *Apr 1981
O'Brien, Ms Jeanette Sylvia. . . . . *Dec 1985
Price, Ms Natasha J BSc(Hons). . . . . *Jan 1998
Sharman, Ms Katrina LLB. . . . . Dec 2003
Toulson, Mr Adrian LLB(Hons). . . . . *Nov 2006
Withams, Mrs Johanna Carole BA(Hons) . . . . *Jan 1987
Asoc: Perks, Ms Susan LLB(Hons) . . . . *Jun 2006
Ast: Eka, Ms Nnennaya LLB(Hons). . . . . *Dec 2001
Gemmell, Mr James BA(Hons) . . . . *Apr 2006

CUNNINGTONS
2 Tofts Walk Braintree Essex CM7 1JU
Tel: 01376 326868 *Fax:* 01376 550003 *Dx:* 133225 BRAINTREE 3
E-mail: info@cunningtons.co.uk
Office: Braintree, Croydon, Ilford, Solihull, Wickford

GT LAW SOLICITORS ‡
1 Park Farm Industries Witham Road Black Notley Braintree Essex CM77 8JX
Tel: 01245 360148
E-mail: enquiries@gtlaw.co.uk

HOLMES & HILLS LLP ‡
Dale Chambers Bocking End Braintree Essex CM7 9AJ
Tel: 01376 320456 *Fax:* 01376 342156 *Dx:* 56200 BRAINTREE 1
E-mail: legaladvice@holmes-hills.co.uk
List of partners: J E Brady, M B Cornell, H M Harris, R N Harris, S C Hopkins, C Livingston, R E Mason, E G Popham, J H Simpson, D W G Whipps, M J Wright
Office: Halstead
Work: A1 B1 C1 C2 C3 D1 E F1 J1 K1 K3 K4 L N O P Q R1 S1 S2 T2 V W Z(c,h,r,u)
Advocacy and Fixed Fee Interview undertaken
Ptr: Brady, Mr Jason Elliott LLB . . . . *§Sep 2001
Cornell, Mr Mark Brian LLB . . . . *§Sep 1994
Harris, Mrs Helen Margaret LLB; FILEx . . . . *§Mar 1990
Hopkins, Mr Steven Charles. . . . . *Oct 2004
Livingston, Mr Christopher LLB . . . . *§Sep 1998
Mason, Mrs Rebecca Elizabeth LLB. . . . . *§Sep 2005
Whipps, Mr David W G LLB. . . . . *§Oct 1978
Wright, Mr Michael J . . . . *§Jun 1970
Ast: Ashworth, Mr Robert David . . . . Jul 2007
Goldstone, Mrs Hayley Elizabeth . . . . Oct 2005
Kent, Mr Nicholas Peter. . . . . *Nov 1997
Khan, Mrs Ansa LLB . . . . *§Jun 2007
Lilliott, Mrs Joanna Kathryn BA(Hons)(Law); DipLG . . *Nov 1986
Sturman, Mr Daniel Christopher LLB . . . . *Oct 2005
Con: Simpson, Mr Colin O LLB(Lond) Chief Assessor to the Law Society Personal Injury Panel . . . . *§Jan 1975

KEW LAW LLP ‡
Old Manor House Little Square Braintree Essex CM7 1UT
Tel: 01376 550073 *Fax:* 01376 331215
E-mail: info@kewlaw.co.uk

LEVY & CO SOLICITORS LLP
Skyline 120 470 Avenue West Great Notley Braintree Essex CM77 7AA
Tel: 01376 511819 *Fax:* 01376 511781 *Dx:* 33403 WITHAM
E-mail: mail@levysolicitors.co.uk
Office: Witham

MOON BEEVER SOLICITORS ‡
260 Avenue West Skyline 120 Great Notley Braintree Essex CM77 7AA
Tel: 0844 736 9775 *Fax:* 01376 348542 / 345628
E-mail: info@moonbeever.com

SHERWINS LIMITED ‡
Sherwins House 3-4 Freeport Office Village Century Drive Braintree Essex CM77 8YG
Tel: 0845 890 9210 *Fax:* 0845 890 9201 *Dx:* 133230 BRAINTREE 3
E-mail: enquiries@sherwins.net

SMITH LAW PARTNERSHIP ‡
Gordon House 22 Rayne Road Braintree Essex CM7 2QW
Tel: 01376 321311 *Fax:* 01376 559239 *Dx:* 56205 BRAINTREE
E-mail: lawyers@slpsolicitors.co.uk
List of partners: S Carlile, R W R Smith
Work: A1 C1 E F1 J1 K1 K3 K4 L N O P Q S1 S2 T1 V W Z(c,d,n)
Emergency Action, Fixed Fee Interview undertaken and Member of Accident Line
Ptr: Carlile, Miss Susan . . . . *Nov 1989
Smith, Mr Robert W R MA(Cantab); MBA . . . . . . *§Apr 1974
Ast: Colgan, Ms Lara MBA ● . . . . *Sep 2004
Fireson, Ms Michelle . . . . *Oct 2007
Head, Ms Caroline ● . . . . *May 2004
Lewis, Ms Penny . . . . *Feb 1982

STEED & STEED LLP
76-82 & 86 Coggeshall Road Braintree Essex CM7 9BY
Tel: 01376 552828 *Fax:* 01376 550014 *Dx:* 56204 BRAINTREE
E-mail: info@steedandsteed.co.uk
Office: Sudbury
Work: D1 E G H K1 K2 K3 K4 L S1 V W
Legal Aid undertaken and Legal Aid Franchise
Ptr: Jarlett, Mr Stephen R LLB(Hons) . . . . *May 1981
Peachey, Mr Ash LLB(Hons) . . . . *Dec 1997
Ast: Andrews, Mr Andrew . . . . *Dec 2006
Connell, Mr Richard. . . . . *Jan 1997
King, Miss Sarah Elizabeth . . . . Jan 2010

TAYLOR HALDANE BARLEX LLP
First Floor Unit 10 Freeport Office Village Braintree Essex CM77 8YG
Tel: 0845 293 7688 *Fax:* 0845 293 7686 *Dx:* 133228 BRAINTREE 3
E-mail: mail@thblegal.com
Office: Benfleet, Chelmsford, Ipswich, Southend-on-Sea

ROLAND TAYLOR & CO ‡
74a High Street Braintree Essex CM7 1JP
Tel: 01376 330099 *Fax:* 01376 551164 *Dx:* 133232 BRAINTREE 3
E-mail: roland.d.taylor@btinternet.com
List of partners: R D Taylor
Languages: Polish, Spanish
Work: B1 G J1 K1 L N O Q S1 S2 Z(c,k,q)
Agency undertaken
SPr: Taylor, Mr Roland D LLB . . . . *Oct 1983

STANLEY TEE
Star House 38 Rayne Road Braintree Essex CM7 2QP
Tel: 01376 552277 *Fax:* 01376 551919 *Dx:* 56203 BRAINTREE
E-mail: law@stanleytee.co.uk
Office: Bishop's Stortford, Great Dunmow, Saffron Walden
Work: D1 K1 S1 W
Emergency Action, Agency, Advocacy, Fixed Fee Interview, Legal Aid undertaken and Legal Aid Franchise
Ast: Briggs, Mrs Andrea . . . . *Nov 1998
Ward, Miss Sally BA(Hons) . . . . *Oct 1994

BRAMHALL, Greater Manchester

BRAMHALL SOLICITORS ‡
Errwood House 212 Moss Lane Bramhall Greater Manchester SK7 1BD
Tel: 0161 439 9777 *Fax:* 0161 439 1793
E-mail: info@bramhallsolicitors.co.uk
Languages: Spanish
Work: E F1 G K1 N O Q S1 S2 W Z(q)

BUTCHER & BARLOW LLP
205 Moss Lane Bramhall Greater Manchester SK7 1BA
Tel: 0161 439 8228 *Fax:* 0161 439 9001 *Dx:* 25102 BRAMHALL
E-mail: enquiries@butcher-barlow.co.uk
Office: Bury (2 offices), Frodsham, Leigh, Northwich, Prestwich, Runcorn (2 offices), Sandbach, Tyldesley
Work: C2 D2 F1 F2 J1 K1 K2 K3 K4 N O Q S1 S2 W Z(k,l,q,r)
Agency and Fixed Fee Interview undertaken
Ptr: Kelly, Mr Justin Sean LLB Notary Public. . . . . . . *Sep 2001
Morris, Mr Robert G LLB . . . . *Oct 1984
Thompson, Mr Philip John BA(Hons) . . . . Nov 1984

CHAPMANS SOLICITORS ‡
23 Linney Road Bramhall Greater Manchester SK7 3JW
Tel: 0161 440 7702 *Fax:* 0161 440 7730

SAS DANIELS LLP
4 The Square Woodford Road Bramhall Greater Manchester SK7 1JJ
Tel: 0161 475 7680 *Fax:* 0161 475 7681
Emergency telephone 0161 475 7680
E-mail: help@sasdaniels.co.uk
Office: Chester, Congleton, Macclesfield, Stockport
Work: A1 B1 C1 C2 E F1 F2 J1 K1 L N O Q R1 S1 S2 W Z(l,q)
Emergency Action and Fixed Fee Interview undertaken
Ptr: Sinclair, Ms Sandra LLB(Hons) . . . . *Oct 1985
Con: Pattison, Mr Stuart Raymond . . . . *Jul 1969
Smith, Mrs Diana Warmington LLB . . . . *Apr 1978

2

NICOLA J TIERNAN SOLICITORS ‡
Sovereign House Bramhall Centre Bramhall Greater Manchester SK7 1AW
Tel: 0161 439 5286 *Fax:* 0161 439 7277
E-mail: office@nicolajtiernansolicitor.co.uk
List of partners: N Tiernan
Dir: Tiernan, Nicola . . . . Oct 1992

BRAMPTON, Cumbria

CARTMELL SHEPHERD
Gill Place Brampton Cumbria CA8 1SQ
Tel: 01697 72378 *Fax:* 01697 741023
E-mail: brampton@cartmells.co.uk
Office: Carlisle (2 offices), Haltwhistle, Penrith
Languages: French
Work: A1 B1 C1 E F1 J1 J2 K1 K2 K3 K4 L O Q S1 T1 W Z(d,f,h,k,q,r)
Emergency Action and Fixed Fee Interview undertaken
Ptr: Holland, Mrs Hilary Prudence BA . . . . *Sep 1997
Asoc: Crouch, Mrs Elizabeth LLB . . . . Sep 2003
Ast: Stephenson, Miss Rachael Mary . . . . Jan 2009

ALAN NIEKIRK SOLICITOR ‡
West Field Gelt Road Brampton Cumbria CA8 1QH
Tel: 01697 72833 *Fax:* 01697 72833
E-mail: alanniekirk@hotmail.com
List of partners: A F Niekirk
Work: T2 W Z(d)

BRANDON, Suffolk

RUDLINGS & WAKELAM
73 High Street Brandon Suffolk IP27 0AY
Tel: 01842 810300 *Fax:* 01842 810193 *Dx:* 33900 BRANDON
E-mail: jeremy.brooks@rudlings-wakelam.co.uk
Office: Bury St Edmunds, Long Melford, Thetford
Languages: French, German
Work: A1 D1 E F1 G J1 K1 N S1 V W Z(c,l)

BRAUNTON, Devon

BREWER HARDING & ROWE
2 Caen Shopping Centre Braunton Devon EX33 1EE
Tel: 01271 812033 *Fax:* 01271 815393
E-mail: lawyers@bhrlaw.co.uk
Office: Barnstaple (2 offices), Bideford, Exeter, Ilfracombe
Work: S1 S2
Ptr: Triggs, Mr Geoffrey John LLB(Exon) . . . . *§Oct 1978

ROBERT CAMPBELL & COMPANY ‡
Greenhills Winsham Braunton Devon EX33 2LX
Tel: 0870 241 2139 *Fax:* 0870 240 1136
E-mail: rob@carelaw.co.uk

SLEE BLACKWELL
6 South Street Braunton Devon EX33 2AA
Tel: 01271 812019 *Fax:* 01271 814204 *Dx:* 50451 BRAUNTON
Office: Barnstaple, Bideford, Exeter, South Molton
Work: S1 W
Ptr: Arthur, Mr Nicholas J . . . . *§Mar 1984
Burke, Mr Andrew John BA . . . . *Oct 1992
Dawkins, Mr Lee A BA . . . . *Nov 1990
Jones, Mr Christopher H LLB . . . . *Apr 1981
Jordan, Mr Paul LLB Sweet & Maxwell Law Prize; Leicester Law Society Prize . . . . *Oct 1988
Pearn, Mr John A G LLB(Wales) . . . . *§Nov 1974

TAYLORS SOLICITORS ‡
(incorporating Furse Sanders & Taylor, Braunton)
Sterling Court 4 The Square Braunton Devon EX33 2JD
Tel: 01271 812811 *Fax:* 01271 812818 *Dx:* 50456 BRAUNTON
Emergency telephone 01271 812811
E-mail: info@taylors-law.co.uk
List of partners: P W Taylor
Office: Ilfracombe
Languages: French
Work: A1 C1 E K4 L N O Q S1 S2 T1 T2 W Z(d,l,q)
Fixed Fee Interview undertaken
SPr: Taylor, Mr Philip Ward LLB(Exon) . . . . *§Dec 1976
Ast: Schofield, Mr Gregory Paul LLB. . . . . *Nov 1996

BRECON, Powys

CHARLES CROOKES WITH GEORGE TUDOR & DE WINTON
8a High Street Brecon Powys LD3 7AL
Tel: 01874 625151 *Fax:* 01874 622359 *Dx:* 200352 BRECON
E-mail: adavies@ccj-law.co.uk
Office: Cardiff
Work: A1 B1 C1 C2 E J1 K3 L N O Q S1 S2 T1 T2 W X Z(d,q,r,x)
Fixed Fee Interview undertaken
SPr: Davenport, Mr Timothy John Parry LLB(Lond) Registrar of the Diocese of Swansea & Brecon . . . . *Jun 1976

HORNSBY DE GRAY SOLICITORS LLP ‡
Parc View Hay Road Talgarth Brecon Powys LD3 0AL
Tel: 07791 747091
Office: Twickenham

JEFFREYS & POWELL ‡
4 Lion Street Brecon Powys LD3 7AU
Tel: 01874 622106 *Fax:* 01874 623702 *Dx:* 200350 BRECON
List of partners: B J Beck, W G T Griffiths, S C Morris
Office: Builth Wells
Languages: Welsh
Work: A1 B1 C1 D1 E F1 J1 K1 L P Q R1 S1 S2 T1 T2 W Z(c,d,h,l,m)
Agency and Advocacy undertaken
Ptr: Beck, Mr Barry John MA; BCL(Oxon) . . . . *§May 1977
Griffiths, Mr W Griffin T LLB(Wales). . . . . *§Apr 1965
Morris, Mrs Sian C LLB(Wales) . . . . *§Jun 1981
Ast: Anderson, Mr James Francis Rieu LLB(Hons)(Law) . . *Oct 2004
Deveney, Ms Joanne Elizabeth LLB(Hons)(Lond) . . . Aug 1996
Martin, Ms Gilian Alexandra BA. . . . . *Sep 2004

KEPPE ROFER ‡
11 Ship Street Brecon Powys LD3 9AB
Tel: 01874 624627 *Fax:* 01874 611495 *Dx:* 200351 BRECON
E-mail: enquiries@kepperofer.co.uk
List of partners: G G Lewis, G Martin, G Rofer
Languages: German, Welsh
Work: A1 B1 B2 D1 D2 E F1 F2 G H J1 K1 K2 L M1 M2 N O Q S1 S2 V W Z(l,m,p,q,r)
Emergency Action, Agency, Advocacy, Fixed Fee Interview, Legal Aid undertaken, Legal Aid Franchise and Member of Accident Line
Ptr: Lewis, Mr Gareth Glyn LLB(Hons). . . . . Dec 2003
Martin, Ms Gill . . . . Sep 2004
Rofer, Mr Gavin LLB . . . . *Nov 1992

RICHARDS THOMAS SOLICITORS ‡
2 The Struet Brecon Powys LD3 7LH
Tel: 01874 623371 *Fax:* 01874 622261
E-mail: info@richardsthomas.co.uk

THE WOODLAND DAVIES PARTNERSHIP LLP
4 Bulwark Brecon Powys LD3 7LB
Tel: 01874 624422 *Fax:* 01874 611303 *Dx:* 200354 BRECON
Office: Hay-on-Wye, Hereford, Kington, Talgarth

BRENTFORD, Middlesex

ANTHONY HOLDEN CROFTS & CO ‡
Dock House 79 High Street Brentford Middlesex TW8 8AE
Tel: 020 8568 7768 *Fax:* 020 8569 8657 *Dx:* 90358 BRENTFORD
E-mail: info@ahcrofts.co.uk
List of partners: M Cosstick, S I Williams
Office: London W13
Work: C1 E S1 S2 W
Ptr: Cosstick, Mr Mark LLB . . . . *Oct 1981
Williams, Mr Stephen I LLB . . . . *Feb 1984

DOUGLASS SIMON ‡
60 High Street Brentford Middlesex TW8 0AH
Tel: 020 8560 3888 *Fax:* 020 8569 7888 *Dx:* 90362 BRENTFORD
E-mail: info@douglass-simon.com
List of partners: L S Cabatbat
Office: London SW5
Languages: Hindi, Punjabi, Tagalog, Urdu
Work: D1 J1 K1 K3 L Q W Z(i)
Emergency Action, Agency, Advocacy, Fixed Fee Interview and Legal Aid undertaken
Ptr: Cabatbat, Ms Lira Simon LLB(Hons) . . . . Feb 1992
Ast: Khan, Mr Haroon LLB(Hons) . . . . Mar 2008
Reel, Ms Tish LLB(Hons) . . . . Sep 2005

FARRAH AND CO SOLICITORS ‡
PO Box 572 Brentford Middlesex TW8 1AF
Tel: 020 8582 5762 *Fax:* 020 8582 5762
E-mail: info@farrahandcosolicitors.co.uk

SAMUEL L LARYE & CO ‡
4 Country Parade High Street Brentford Middlesex TW8 8EP
Tel: 020 8568 7022 *Fax:* 020 8568 0065
Emergency telephone 07850 769678
E-mail: samuel.larye@aol.com
List of partners: S L Larye
Work: G H
Agency, Advocacy, Fixed Fee Interview, Legal Aid undertaken and Legal Aid Franchise
SPr: Larye, Mr Samuel Lartey BA(Hons)(Law) . . . . . . *Jan 1991

LLOYD BRENNAND ‡
202 High Street Brentford Middlesex TW8 8AH
Tel: 020 8569 9020 *Fax:* 020 8569 9511 *Dx:* 90352 BRENTFORD
Emergency telephone 07836 220900
E-mail: jbrennand@lloydbrennand.co.uk
List of partners: S Arora, J L Brennand, G R Lloyd, A Rai
Work: E G H J1 K1 S1 W Z(l)
Emergency Action, Agency, Advocacy, Legal Aid undertaken and Member of Accident Line
Ptr: Arora, Saneh LLB; LLM. . . . . *Feb 1990
Brennand, Ms Joanna L BA(Law). . . . . *Oct 1983
Lloyd, Mr Glyn R . . . . *Nov 1983
Rai, Ms Alexandra . . . . Nov 1998

SCULLY & SOWERBUTTS
99 Ealing Road Brentford Middlesex TW8 0LQ
Tel: 020 8758 9333 *Fax:* 020 8569 9628
E-mail: info@ssplaw.co.uk
Office: London N3, Twickenham

SONI & KAUR ‡
80 High Street Brentford Middlesex TW8 8AE
Tel: 020 8568 6464 *Fax:* 020 8568 3232 *Dx:* 90360 BRENTFORD
Emergency telephone 07976 353949

WARSI SOLICITORS ‡
2nd Floor 1000 Great West Road Brentford Middlesex TW8 9HH
Tel: 020 8261 4637 / 4639 *Fax:* 020 8261 4638
E-mail: warsisolicitors09@hotmail.com

BRENTWOOD, Essex

BARNES GILLETT ‡
25 Shenfield Road Brentwood Essex CM15 8AG
Tel: 01277 226491 *Fax:* 01277 260339
List of partners: J D Gillett
Work: A1 B1 C1 C2 C3 E L S1 S2 T1 T2 W
Ptr: Gillett, Mr James D BSc. . . . . *Jul 1971

BLACKLOCKS ‡
Jubilee House 3 The Drive Brentwood Essex CM13 3FR
Tel: 01277 725057

CHRISTINE EASTER SOLICITORS ‡
Pixies Halt Hook End Road Brentwood Essex CM15 0NR
Tel: 01277 821506 *Fax:* 0845 527 6250 *Dx:* 5006 BRENTWOOD
E-mail: office@christineeastersolicitors.co.uk

CLAIRE FLOOD SOLICITORS ‡
18 Edwards Way Hutton Brentwood Essex CM13 1BT
Tel: 01277 202869
E-mail: claire@claireflood18.plus.com

GB LAW ‡
Second Floor 190 Hutton Road Shenfield Brentwood Essex CM15 8NR
Tel: 0800 321 3328 *Fax:* 01277 231177
E-mail: info@gblawyers.co.uk

S B GOODMAN ‡
The Red House 8 Red Road Brentwood Essex CM14 5JE
Tel: 01277 262703 *Fax:* 01277 230304
E-mail: claremont99@gmail.com

ALEXANDER HAIGH & CO ‡
10 Queens Road Brentwood Essex CM14 4HE
Tel: 01277 216320 *Fax:* 01277 200910
Emergency telephone 07734 267287
E-mail: markhaigh10@hotmail.com
List of partners: M A Haigh
Work: G H K1 K3
Emergency Action, Agency, Advocacy, Fixed Fee Interview and Legal Aid undertaken
SPr: Haigh, Mr Mark Alexander. . . . . *Dec 1990

LANDONS ‡
(incorporating Crust Lane & Davidson)
Landon House 9 Shenfield Road Brentwood Essex CM15 8AH
Tel: 01277 210021 *Fax:* 01277 262801 *Dx:* 5002 BRENTWOOD 1
E-mail: enquiries@landons.co.uk
List of partners: G P Green, M K Seaman
Work: B1 C1 D1 E F1 J1 K1 L N O Q S1 S2 T2 W Z(d)
Emergency Action, Fixed Fee Interview, Legal Aid undertaken and Legal Aid Franchise
Ptr: Green, Mr Geoffrey P Clerk to Commissioner of Taxes*§Jul 1961
Seaman, Ms Miranda K BSc(Econ) . . . . *Nov 1992
Ast: Smith, Mr Patrick R LLB(Hons) . . . . Dec 1975

PINNEY TALFOURD LLP
39-41 High Street Brentwood Essex CM14 4RH
Tel: 01277 268700 *Fax:* 01277 268701 *Dx:* 5003 BRENTWOOD
Office: Hornchurch, Upminster
Mem: Cockram, Mr Philip Thomas LLB(Hons) . . . . *Jun 1996
Asoc: Edwards, Mr Matthew John . . . . Sep 2004
Loadman, Miss Catherine Mary Elizabeth LLB(Hons) . Nov 1998
Loveys, Ellen Louise . . . . Sep 2004

PRESTONS & KERLYS ‡
Security House Chambers 1 Shenfield Road Brentwood Essex CM15 8AL
Tel: 01277 211755 *Fax:* 01277 261154 *Dx:* 5004 BRENTWOOD
Work: D1 E F1 G H J1 K1 L N P Q R1 S1 T1 T2 V W Z(i,l,m,s)
Agency, Advocacy, Fixed Fee Interview, Legal Aid undertaken and Member of Accident Line
Ast: Abedin, Miss Syeda S BA(Hons)(Law). . . . . Dec 1989

PURE LAW LLP ‡
Lutea House (Commercial First Building) Warley Hill Business Park The Drive Great Warle Brentwood Essex CM13 3BE
Tel: 01277 897300 *Fax:* 01277 897301 *Dx:* 148522 BRENTWOOD 7
E-mail: enquiries@purelawllp.co.uk

RAINER HUGHES ‡
Oak House 46 Crossways Shenfield Brentwood Essex CM15 8QY
Tel: 01227 226644 *Fax:* 01227 224228 *Dx:* 32910 SHENFIELD
E-mail: info@rainerhughes.com
List of partners: A Johal, S S Panesar
Office: Brentwood
Work: B1 B2 E G H K1 K3 N O Q S1 S2 W Z(b)
Ptr: Johal, Mr Amritpal LLB . . . . Apr 2007
Panesar, Mr Sanjay S LLB(Hons). . . . . Sep 2002
Ast: Punpher, Miss Anita LLB(Hons) . . . . *Mar 2011

RAINER HUGHES
186 Hutton Road Shenfield Brentwood Essex CM15 8NR
Tel: 01277 226644 *Fax:* 01277 224228 *Dx:* 32910 SHENFIELD
E-mail: brian.hughes@rainerhughes.com
Office: Brentwood
Work: C1 E J1 K3 K4 R2 S1 S2 T1 T2 W
Con: Hughes, Mr Brian R J O MBE MA; MCIArb Council of Law Society . . . . *§Jan 1965

REEVES FISHER & SAMS ‡
47 Crown Street Brentwood Essex CM14 4BD
Tel: 01277 202500 *Dx:* 50121 BRENTWOOD
E-mail: rfslc@aol.com

SANDERS WITHERSPOON LLP ‡
Knight Court 51 Crown Street Brentwood Essex CM14 4BE
Tel: 01277 221010 *Fax:* 01277 219125 *Dx:* 5000 BRENTWOOD
Emergency telephone 07769 853580
E-mail: info@sanderswitherspoon.co.uk
List of partners: P C Witherspoon
Office: Brentwood
Work: A1 B1 B2 C1 C2 C3 D1 E F1 G H J1 K1 L M1 N O P Q R1 S1 V W Z(k)
Emergency Action, Agency, Advocacy, Fixed Fee Interview, Legal Aid undertaken, Legal Aid Franchise and Member of Accident Line
Ptr: Witherspoon, Mr Philip C LLB(Lond). . . . . *Jul 1979

SANDERS WITHERSPOON LLP
21 Hutton Road Shenfield Brentwood Essex CM15 8JU
Tel: 01277 221010 *Fax:* 01277 219125 *Dx:* 5000 BRENTWOOD
E-mail: info@sanderswitherspoon.co.uk
Office: Brentwood

SCANNELLS HUNT ‡
Parker House 104 Hutton Road Shenfield Brentwood Essex CM15 8NB
Tel: 01277 223242 *Fax:* 01277 261921 *Dx:* 32903 SHENFIELD
E-mail: contact@scannells.com
List of partners: E B A Cousins
Work: E J1 K1 K3 L N Q S1 S2 W Z(x)
SPr: Cousins, Miss Elizabeth Bessie Anne . . . . Jan 1995

WORTLEY BYERS ‡
Cathedral Place Brentwood Essex CM14 4ES
Tel: 01277 268368 *Fax:* 01277 268369 *Dx:* 96155 BRENTWOOD 2
E-mail: info@wortleybyers.co.uk
List of partners: A F Barrett, S P Chandler, D A Chapman, A Elliss, L Folley, R W Hawkings, A M Lightowler, B R Spencer, J Winfield
Languages: French, German
Work: A1 B1 C1 C2 C3 D1 E F1 J1 K1 K3 L M1 N O P Q R1 R2 S1 S2 T1 T2 W Z(c,d,h,l,n,o,s)
Emergency Action, Agency, Advocacy and Fixed Fee Interview undertaken

See p112 for the Key to Work Categories & other symbols

Ptr: Barrett, Mr Albert F LLB. . . . . *Oct 1974
Chandler, Mr Stephen P. . . . . *Dec 1975
Chapman, David A BA(Hons) . . . . *Jun 1978
Elliss, Miss Anne . . . . *Oct 1998
Folley, Mrs Lucy BA. . . . . *Nov 1994
Hawkings, Mr R Warren BA(Law) . . . . *Jul 1979
Lightowler, Mr A Michael LLB Notary Public . . . . . . *Apr 1977
Spencer, Mr Brian R MA(Cantab) . . . . *Oct 1984
Winfield, Mrs Jane LLB . . . . *Sep 1990
Ast: Cane, Mr Aaron LLB(Hons)(Essex) . . . . *Mar 2005
Chong, Ms Poh-Shan LLB. . . . . *Aug 1998
Dowman, Mrs Susan . . . . Oct 2001
Everett, Mr Christopher William . . . . Sep 2007
Hawley, Mr Nathan . . . . *Sep 2000
Massenhove, Mr Alan LLB . . . . Oct 1994
Spearman, Mr Andrew Frederick . . . . Sep 2006
Traill, Mr Nicholas D BA(Oxon) . . . . *Apr 1977

BRIDGEND

ANDREWS SOLICITORS ‡
11 Market Street Bridgend CF31 1LL
Tel: 0870 112 7330 *Fax:* 0870 112 7331
E-mail: enquiries@andrewssolicitors.com

ANTHONY & JARVIE ‡
6 Court Road Bridgend CF31 1BW
Tel: 01656 652737 *Fax:* 01656 657532 *Dx:* 38000 BRIDGEND
E-mail: law@anthonyandjarvie.co.uk
List of partners: G C Kemp, K A Kemp, M R Sherlock
Languages: French
Work: A1 A2 B1 C1 C2 D1 D2 E F1 F2 J1 J2 K1 L M1 M2 N O P Q R1 R2 S1 S2 W Z(b,c,d,f,g,i,j,k,l,p,q,r,u,w)
Agency, Advocacy, Fixed Fee Interview, Legal Aid undertaken and Member of Accident Line
Ptr: Kemp, Mr Gordon Christopher BSc(Econ). . . . . . . *Jul 1977
Kemp, Mrs Katherine A BSc(Econ) . . . . *Feb 1983
Sherlock, Mrs Marice R LLB Deputy District Judge . . *Oct 1983
Asoc: Morrish, Mr David Christopher. . . . . *Feb 1974
Con: Brace, Mr Marcus David LLB . . . . May 1996
Davies, Mr Reginald Gwyn LLB; MBA. . . . . *Dec 1977
Jarvie, Mr T Hunter LLB. . . . . *§Jun 1968

GORDON A BATTRICK & CO ‡
10 Court Road Bridgend CF31 1BN
Tel: 01656 768111 *Fax:* 01656 664140 *Dx:* 38020 BRIDGEND
E-mail: gbattrick@3net.co.uk
List of partners: G A Battrick
Work: A1 B1 C1 D1 E F1 J1 K1 L M1 N P R1 S1 W
Emergency Action, Agency, Advocacy undertaken and Member of Accident Line
Ptr: Battrick, Mr Gordon A BA . . . . *§Jan 1985

BERRY SMITH LLP
Brackla House Brackla Street Bridgend CF31 1BZ
Tel: 01656 645525 *Fax:* 01656 645174 *Dx:* 38004 BRIDGEND
E-mail: bridgend@berrysmith.com
Office: Bristol, Cardiff, London WC2
Languages: French, German, Welsh
Work: B1 C1 C2 C3 D1 E J1 K1 L M1 M2 N O P Q R1 S1 V W Z(e)
Legal Aid undertaken
Ptr: McColgan, Mrs Catherine E LLB . . . . *Feb 1986
Ast: Atherton, Mrs Marina LLB(Hons) . . . . *Oct 1993

DP LAW LTD T/A DAVID PROSSER & CO ‡
Bryn Ogwy 3 Court Road Bridgend CF31 1BL
Tel: 01656 645921 *Fax:* 01656 768008 *Dx:* 38003 BRIDGEND
E-mail: enquiries@davidprosser.co.uk
List of partners: D P Prosser, B A Sweeney, S D Thomas
Languages: Welsh
Work: D1 D2 J1 K1 N O Q S1 S2 W
Emergency Action, Agency, Advocacy, Fixed Fee Interview, Legal Aid undertaken, Legal Aid Franchise and Member of Accident Line
Dir: Prosser, Mr David P LLB(Wales) ♦ . . . . *§Jul 1979
Sweeney, Mr Brendan A LLB . . . . *Jan 1990
Thomas, Mr Simon D LLB. . . . . *Mar 1984
Ast: Radford, Ms Stevey-Leigh LLB . . . . Jun 2009
Williams, Ms Sarah Louise LLB . . . . Jan 2008
Con: Hillier, Mrs Rachel Louise BA . . . . *Oct 1999

DAVID & SNAPE ‡
Wyndham House Wyndham Street Bridgend CF31 1EP
Tel: 01656 661115 *Fax:* 01656 663138 *Dx:* 38001 BRIDGEND
Emergency telephone 01656 785004
E-mail: iain.llewellyn@davidandsnape.com
List of partners: J G Chubb, J R O David, I P Llewellyn, E A Thompson
Office: Porthcawl
Languages: Welsh
Work: A1 B1 C1 C2 D1 D2 E F1 G H J1 K1 L N O Q R1 S1 S2 V W Z(r)
Emergency Action, Agency, Advocacy, Legal Aid undertaken and Legal Aid Franchise
Ptr: David, Mr Jonathan R O. . . . . *§Jun 1974
Llewellyn, Mr Iain P LLB; MA . . . . *§Sep 1980
Thompson, Ms Elizabeth A LLB(Exon) . . . . *§Jun 1980
Ast: McGarrigle, Ms Sonia LLB(Hons) . . . . *Jul 1996

RUTH DAVIES LLB SOLICITOR ‡
Ty Newydd Maes-y-Deri Close Pencoed Bridgend CF35 6YY
Tel: 01656 860644 *Fax:* 01656 860644
E-mail: ruthdavieskemp@uku.co.uk

R L EDWARDS & PARTNERS ‡
(incorporating Brinley Richards & Partners; Williams Simons & Thomas)
4 Derwen Road Bridgend CF31 1LH
Tel: 01656 656861 *Fax:* 01656 668190
Emergency telephone 01656 653582
E-mail: bridgend.office@rledwards-partners.co.uk
Office: Maesteg, Porthcawl, Treorchy
Work: A1 B1 B2 C1 C2 D1 E F1 G H J1 K1 L M1 N O P Q R1 S1 T1 T2 V W X Z(c,d,e,h,i,j,k,l,m,n,o,t,w)
Emergency Action, Agency, Advocacy, Legal Aid undertaken, Legal Aid Franchise and Member of Accident Line
Ast: Rand, Miss Madeline . . . . Mar 1999
Thomas, Ms Hayley A LLB . . . . Aug 1995

GASKELL & WALKER ‡
12 Park Street Bridgend CF31 4AX
Tel: 01656 653122 *Fax:* 01656 767097 *Dx:* 38006 BRIDGEND
Emergency telephone 01656 657560
List of partners: J M Butler, G R Davies, J A Taylor
Office: Cowbridge
Work: C1 D1 G H K1 N Q S1 S2 V W Z(l)
Emergency Action, Agency, Advocacy, Fixed Fee Interview and Legal Aid undertaken
Ptr: Butler, Mr James M . . . . *Jun 1985
Davies, Mr Gwyn R LLB(Wales). . . . . *Dec 1980

DAVID W HARRIS & CO
13 Penybont Road Pencoed Bridgend CF35 5PY
Tel: 01656 862424 *Fax:* 01656 864735
Emergency telephone 01639 895697
Office: Pontypridd, Talbot Green

BARRIE Y JONES & CO
10 Court Road Bridgend CF31 1BN
Tel: 01656 657929 *Fax:* 01656 648055 *Dx:* 38027 BRIDGEND
Office: Llantwit Major
Work: C1 C2 C3 D1 E F1 G H J1 K1 L N O Q S1 T1 T2 W Z(l)
Emergency Action, Agency, Advocacy, Fixed Fee Interview, Legal Aid undertaken and Member of Accident Line
Ptr: Jones, Mr Barrie Y BSc(Econ). . . . . *Aug 1979

KTP SOLICITORS ‡
Ty Atebion Bocam Park Bridgend CF35 5LJ
Tel: 01656 869002 *Fax:* 01656 869003 *Dx:* 38022 BRIDGEND
E-mail: bridgend@ktpsolicitors.net
List of partners: R G Hammerton, P J Hinton, J Kitchen
Office: Bridgend, Pontypridd, Porth
Ptr: Hammerton, Mr Robert G LLB. . . . . *Oct 1982

KTP SOLICITORS
(incorporating Jongmans)
2-4 Nolton Street Bridgend CF31 1DU
Tel: 01656 655755 *Fax:* 01656 641789 *Dx:* 38022 BRIDGEND
E-mail: bridgend.noltonstreet@ktpsolicitors.net
Office: Bridgend, Pontypridd, Porth
Languages: French
Work: B1 D1 F1 G H K1 L M1 M2 O Q S1 V W Z(l,m)
Emergency Action, Agency, Advocacy, Fixed Fee Interview, Legal Aid undertaken and Member of Accident Line

MELANIE LAZARUS & CO ‡
38-40 Nolton Street Bridgend CF313BN
Est:
Tel: 01656 750888 *Fax:* 01656 750889 *Dx:* 38011 BRIDGEND
E-mail: melanielazarus@melanielazarusandcosolicitors.com

RTL SOLICITORS
Elm Court Cowbridge Road Bridgend CF31 3SR
Tel: 01656 665850 *Fax:* 01656 665851 *Dx:* 146940 BRIDGEND
E-mail: contact@rtl-law.co.uk
Office: Cardiff
Work: E S1 S2 W
Ptr: Lewis, Mr Matthew BA(Hons) . . . . Jun 1996
Rosser, Mr Alun LLB . . . . Jul 1980
Thomas, Mr Paul F LLB. . . . . Jan 1987

DAVID SEDGWICK SOLICITORS ‡
1st Floor 20 Dunraven Place Bridgend CF31 1EF
Tel: 01656 767766 *Fax:* 01656 767888
E-mail: d-sedgwick@btconnect.com

PHILIP THOMAS & CO SOLICITORS ‡
20a Queen Street Bridgend CF31 1HX
Tel: 01656 658123 *Fax:* 01656 658127
E-mail: p.thomas-co@btconnect.com

SIAN THOMAS & DAUGHTER SOLICITORS ‡
8 Court Road Bridgend CF31 1BN
Tel: 01656 645439 *Fax:* 01656 661455
E-mail: law@solicitors.co.uk
List of partners: C L Morgan, S Thomas
Languages: Welsh
Work: S1 S2 W
Ptr: Morgan, Ms Catrin Lisa . . . . Jan 2004
Thomas, Mrs Sian LLB . . . . *Jul 1978

TURNER SOLICITORS ‡
Great Barn Wallas Farm Ewenny Bridgend CF35 5AE
Tel: 01656 768500
E-mail: emma.turner@educationlawspecialists.co.uk

WHITTINGHAMS ‡
Alexandra House 5-7 Court Road Bridgend CF31 1BE
Tel: 01656 653485 *Fax:* 01656 656647 *Dx:* 38007 BRIDGEND
Emergency telephone 01656 650532
E-mail: bridgend@whittinghams.co.uk
List of partners: M Greenway, A C Harries, H L Jones
Office: Porthcawl
Languages: Welsh
Work: A1 B1 C1 D1 E F1 G J1 K1 L M1 N O P Q R1 S1 T1 V W Z(l,t)
Emergency Action, Agency, Advocacy, Fixed Fee Interview undertaken and Member of Accident Line
Ptr: Harries, Miss Andrea C LLB(Wales). . . . . *§Mar 1979
Jones, Mr Howard L LLB(Aberystwyth) . . . . *§Oct 1984

BRIDGNORTH, Shropshire

ANDREWSLAW SOLICITOR ‡
Stargate Business Centre Faraday Drive Bridgnorth Shropshire WV15 5BA
Tel: 01746 769700 *Fax:* 01746 769690
E-mail: christine@andrewslaw.co.uk

FBC MANBY BOWDLER LLP
1 St Leonard's Close Bridgnorth Shropshire WV16 4EL
Tel: 01746 761436 *Fax:* 01746 766764 *Dx:* 23202 BRIDGNORTH
E-mail: info@fbcmb.co.uk
Office: Shrewsbury, Telford, Willenhall, Wolverhampton
Languages: French, German
Work: A1 A2 D1 D2 E K1 L O Q R1 S1 S2 T2 W Z(c,d,x)
Ptr: Burn, Mrs Julie LLB. . . . . *§Apr 1981
Corfield, Mr Steven G LLB(Wales). . . . . *§Jul 1981
Cowell, Mr Philip Henry LLB. . . . . §Mar 1991
Kynnersley, Mr John . . . . *Jan 1974
Asoc: Price, Mr Peter C LLB. . . . . *§Jun 1975
Ast: Godwin, Mr Douglas HND(Agriculture); Dip Advanced Farm & Estate Management; PGDipLaw. . . . . *Oct 2002

ALISTAIR MITCHELL ‡
PO Box 3956 49 Chambers Bridgnorth Shropshire WV16 4NA
Tel: 01746 761545 *Fax:* 01746 767968 *Dx:* 23205 BRIDGNORTH
Emergency telephone 07939 529492
E-mail: 49chambers@googlemail.com
Work: D1 G H J1 K1 K3 N Z(g,i,p)
Agency, Advocacy and Legal Aid undertaken

MORTIMERS ‡
65 Whitburn Street Bridgnorth Shropshire WV16 4QP
Tel: 01746 761000 *Fax:* 01746 766765 *Dx:* 23217 BRIDGNORTH
E-mail: law@mortimers-solicitors.co.uk
List of partners: K L Brake, C J Waters, D Williams
Office: Hereford, Ludlow
Work: A1 B1 C1 D1 D2 E F1 F2 J1 K1 N Q S1 S2 W Z(m,q)
Emergency Action, Agency, Advocacy, Fixed Fee Interview, Legal Aid undertaken and Legal Aid Franchise
Ptr: Waters, Mr Christopher J . . . . Sep 1993
Williams, Mrs Deborah . . . . *Nov 1993

A R NUNN ‡
Regency House 7 West Castle Street Bridgnorth Shropshire WV16 4AB
Tel: 01746 768400 *Fax:* 01746 768448
E-mail: arnunn@fsmail.net
List of partners: A R Nunn
Work: A1 E L S1 S2 W
SPr: Nunn, Mr Alan Robert. . . . . *Jul 1980

PITT & COOKSEY ‡
82a High Street Bridgnorth Shropshire WV16 4DU
Tel: 01746 763101 / 763642 *Fax:* 01746 766032
Dx: 23203 BRIDGNORTH
List of partners: S P Whiston
Work: E L S1 S2 W
Ptr: Whiston, Mr Stephen Philip LLB. . . . . *Dec 1976

STREET & COMPANY SOLICITORS ‡
9 Firtrees Bridgnorth Shropshire WV155EA
Est:
Tel: 0845 544 0499 *Fax:* 0845 544 0599
E-mail: info@streetsolicitors.co.uk

THOMAS & CO ‡
51b High Street Bridgnorth Shropshire WV16 4DX
Tel: 01746 762929 *Fax:* 01746 762969 *Dx:* 719830 BRIDGNORTH

UNDERHILL LANGLEY & WRIGHT
St Leonards House 9 St Leonards Close Bridgnorth Shropshire WV16 4EJ
Tel: 01746 764171 *Fax:* 01746 766837 *Dx:* 23206 BRIDGNORTH
Office: Wolverhampton (2 offices)
Work: A1 C1 E J1 K4 S1 S2 W
Ptr: Smillie, Mr Angus C LLB Deputy Assistant Coroner for Wolverhampton. . . . . *Oct 1980

WILLIAMS & CO ‡
(incorporating R J R Haslewood & Co)
29 East Castle Street Bridgnorth Shropshire WV16 4AN
Tel: 01746 762157 / 765603 *Fax:* 01746 768496
Dx: 23220 BRIDGNORTH
E-mail: info@williams-law.co.uk
List of partners: B J Jones, D E Williams
Work: A1 E L S1 S2 T2 W
Fixed Fee Interview undertaken
Ptr: Jones, Mrs Beverley Jane LLB(Hons) . . . . *Sep 1999
Williams, Mr David E BSc(Hons) . . . . *May 1996

WOOLLEY & CO ‡
1 St Marys Street Bridgnorth Shropshire WV16 4DW
Tel: 01746 765311 *Fax:* 01746 767473 *Dx:* 23201 BRIDGNORTH

BRIDGWATER, Somerset

ALLETSONS LTD ‡
8 Castle Street Bridgwater Somerset TA6 3DB
Tel: 01278 456621 *Fax:* 01278 452494 *Dx:* 80610 BRIDGWATER
Emergency telephone 01278 456621
E-mail: info@alletsons.co.uk
List of partners: B Davies, C F Hayllar, S A Richards Bond
Languages: Bosnian, Croatian, French, German, Russian, Serbian
Work: D1 D2 E G H K1 K2 K3 K4 L Q S1 W
Emergency Action, Agency, Advocacy, Legal Aid undertaken and Legal Aid Franchise
Ptr: Davies, Mr Benjamin LLB . . . . *Jul 2004
Hayllar, Mr Crispin Francis BA. . . . . *Jun 1977
Richards Bond, Mr Stephen A. . . . . *Feb 1983
Ast: Arif, Mr Anjam. *Jan 2007
McClelland, Ms Lisa Kirsty . . . . *Mar 2010

AMICUS SOLICITORS AND ADVOCATES ‡
Sedgemoor Auction Centre Market Way North Petherton Bridgwater Somerset TA6 6DF
Tel: 01278 664060 *Fax:* 0844 209 8525
E-mail: info@amicuslaw.co.uk

ASH CLIFFORD ‡
14 Northgate Bridgwater Somerset TA6 3EU
Tel: 01278 451327 *Fax:* 01278 429750 *Dx:* 80601 BRIDGWATER
Emergency telephone 07699 748242
E-mail: mail@ashclifford.co.uk
List of partners: C M Bearman, I R Parker, N J Yeo
Work: A1 B1 B2 C1 D1 E F1 G H J1 J2 K1 K3 N P R1 S1 S2 V W Z(c,l,t)
Emergency Action, Agency, Advocacy, Fixed Fee Interview and Legal Aid undertaken
Ptr: Bearman, Mrs Caroline M BA(Law) . . . . *Oct 1987
Parker, Mr Ian Robert LLB(Exon) . . . . *Oct 1984
Yeo, Mr Nigel J BA . . . . *Nov 1982
Ast: Dodden, Miss Laura LLB . . . . *Sep 2010

BARRINGTON SCHOLFIELD ‡
(incorporating Barrington & Sons; Scholfield Roberts & Hill; Hugh Barran)
11-12 King Square Bridgwater Somerset TA6 3AH
Tel: 01278 422858 / 422873 *Fax:* 01278 453437
Dx: 80600 BRIDGWATER

E-mail: gpresley@barrington-scholfield.com
List of partners: C B Barrington, M C Broker
Work: A1 E L S1 S2 T2 W Z(h)
Ptr: Barrington, Mr Christopher B MA(Cantab) Notary Public . . . *Jan 1971
Broker, Mr Martin C BA . . . *Apr 1983

DUNN SIMPSON & CO ‡
21 King Square Bridgwater Somerset TA6 3DJ
Tel: 01278 424272 *Fax:* 01278 444187 *Dx:* 80606 BRIDGWATER
List of partners: A J Dunn, N C Simpson
Work: A1 B1 C1 D1 E F1 J1 K1 L N O Q S1 S2 V W Z(l)
Emergency Action, Agency, Advocacy and Fixed Fee Interview undertaken
Ptr: Dunn, Mr Anthony John LLB . . . *Dec 1972
Simpson, Mr Nicholas C LLB(Lond) Deputy District Judge . . . *Dec 1972

PARDOES ‡
West Quay House Northgate Bridgwater Somerset TA6 3EU
Tel: 01278 457891 *Fax:* 01278 429249 *Dx:* 80602 BRIDGWATER
E-mail: pardoes@pardoes.co.uk
List of partners: G A Adams, N J Dell, R C Fitzgerald, J L Goodman, K J Hughes, M D Hughes, D M Isaac, A F Kelly, K E Middle, K O'Brien, G H H Persson, J Rich, C J Spencer
Office: Taunton, Yeovil
Languages: Dutch, French, German
Work: A1 B1 C1 C2 C3 D1 E F1 G H J1 K1 L M1 M2 N O P Q R1 S1 T1 T2 V W X Z(c,d,e,f,j,k,l,o,p,t)
Emergency Action, Agency, Advocacy, Fixed Fee Interview, Legal Aid undertaken and Member of Accident Line
Ptr: Adams, Mr Guy A LLB(Exon) . . . *Oct 1989
Dell, Mr Nicholas John BA(Hons); LLM . . . *May 1990
Goodman, Mr Justin Luke LLB(Hons) . . . *May 1994
Hughes, Mr Kieran John BA; MA; PGDip; LP . . . Sep 2000
Isaac, Mr Daniel Matthew BA(Hons) . . . *Mar 2004
Kelly, Mr Andrew Francis LLB(Hons) . . . Aug 1997
Persson, Mr George Harold Hilding BA(Hons) . . . *Sep 2004
Spencer, Mr Christopher J . . . May 1976
Asoc: Light, Mr Paul C . . . Sep 1997
Palmer, Miss Rebecca Louise LLB(Hons) . . . Sep 2009
Starkey, Mr David Michael LLB(Hons) . . . Dec 2002
Ast: Counsell, Mrs Samantha LLB . . . *Oct 2005
Khodabocus, Mr Sheih Imran BSc; PGDipLaw . . . Sep 2008
Knowles, Miss Emily Blanche LLB(Hons) . . . Jul 2009
Mann, Imogen . . . Jan 2007
Needs, Mr Gareth LLB(Hons) . . . Oct 2003
Con: Eskell, Mr Guy P LLB(B'ham) . . . *Jun 1978

BRIDLINGTON, East Riding of Yorkshire

BROOKE WILLIAMS
1st Floor Natwest Chambers 14-16 Manor Street Bridlington East Riding of Yorkshire YO15 2SA
Tel: 01262 409409 *Fax:* 01262 602332
E-mail: brid@brookewilliams.co.uk
Office: Hull, Leeds, York

HOULTON CARR ‡
PO Box 185 Bridlington East Riding of Yorkshire YO15 9AG
Tel: 01262 677979
E-mail: enquiries@legalboffins.co.uk
List of partners: P Houlton Jones, T Schram
Work: C1 E F1 K1 S1 S2 W Z(l)
Agency and Advocacy undertaken
Ptr: Houlton Jones, Mr Peter . . . Jun 1995
Schram, Ms Theresa . . . Sep 1988

LANCASTERS ‡
11 Quay Road Bridlington East Riding of Yorkshire YO15 2AB
Tel: 01262 602401 *Fax:* 01262 400243 *Dx:* 61901 BRIDLINGTON
E-mail: lancasters_solic@hotmail.com
List of partners: V A L Lancaster
Work: A1 A2 B1 B2 C1 D1 D2 E F1 F2 G H I J1 J2 K1 K2 L N O P Q R1 R2 S1 S2 V W X Z(c,f,g,h,i,k,l,o,p,q,r,s,u,x,y)
Emergency Action, Agency, Advocacy, Fixed Fee Interview, Legal Aid undertaken, Legal Aid Franchise and Member of Accident Line
Ptr: Lancaster, Ms Victoria A L LLB . . . *Jan 1979
Ast: Sowerby, Mr Terence LLB(Dunelm) . . . §Jun 1968

MURRAY HILLS SOLICITORS ‡
10 King Street Bridlington East Riding of Yorkshire YO15 2DE
Tel: 01262 672249 *Fax:* 01262 604011 *Dx:* 61902 BRIDLINGTON
E-mail: info@murrayhillssolicitors.co.uk

PINKNEY GRUNWELLS LAWYERS LLP
8 Quay Road Bridlington East Riding of Yorkshire YO15 2AP
Tel: 01262 673445 *Fax:* 01262 672379 *Dx:* 61905 BRIDLINGTON
E-mail: solicitors@pinkneygrunwells.co.uk
Office: Filey, Scarborough, Whitby
Work: A1 D1 D2 E F1 J1 K1 L N Q S1 S2 T2 V W Z(d,l,m,o)
Agency, Advocacy, Legal Aid undertaken, Legal Aid Franchise and Member of Accident Line
Mem: Dean, Mr Roger Edward LLB . . . *Apr 1977
Harvey, Mrs Alison Jane MA . . . *Feb 1984
Jackson, Ms Helen Elizabeth LLB . . . *May 2005

STUART SMITH & BURNETT ‡
(incorporating Peter Wise & Co)
16 Wellington Road Bridlington East Riding of Yorkshire YO15 2BG
Tel: 01262 678128 *Fax:* 01262 400012 *Dx:* 61900 BRIDLINGTON
E-mail: solicitors@stuartsmithburnett.co.uk
List of partners: R E Bancroft, M J Bowen, D J Burnett, M E Burnett
Work: C1 D1 D2 E F1 J1 K1 K3 K4 L O Q S1 S2 T2 V W
Emergency Action, Advocacy, Fixed Fee Interview, Legal Aid undertaken and Legal Aid Franchise
Ptr: Bancroft, Mr Richard Ernest LLB . . . *May 1980
Bowen, Mr Michael J LLB . . . *Jul 1980
Burnett, Mr David J FIMgt . . . *Nov 1977
Burnett, Mrs Madeline E BA(Lond) . . . *May 1977
Con: Robson, Mr Frederick A LLB(Hull) . . . *Dec 1971

BRIDPORT, Dorset

AUSTEN WHETHAM & GUEST ‡
21 South Street Bridport Dorset DT6 3NR
Tel: 01308 422236 *Fax:* 01308 427772 *Dx:* 43202 BRIDPORT
Emergency telephone 01308 422236
E-mail: tc@awg-law.co.uk
List of partners: P J Alexander, S D Bowley, E A West
Work: A1 B1 C1 D1 E J1 K1 K3 L N O Q R1 S1 S2 T1 T2 W Z(l)
Advocacy undertaken
Ptr: Alexander, Mr Peter James LLB . . . *§Jan 1970
Bowley, Mr Scott D . . . *Jan 1999
West, Mrs Elizabeth Anne BSc(Econ) . . . *Jul 1981

ESSENTIAL EMPLOYMENT LAW SERVICES LIMITED ‡
Unit 27a Dreadnought Trading Estate Bridport Dorset DT6 5BU
Tel: 01308 459459

KITSON & TROTMAN
9 Chancery Lane Bridport Dorset DT6 3PX
Tel: 01308 427436 *Fax:* 01308 420335 *Dx:* 43217 BRIDPORT
E-mail: bridport@kitsonandtrotman.co.uk
Office: Beaminster, Lyme Regis
Work: A1 A2 B1 C1 D1 E F1 G H J1 K1 L M1 N O P Q R2 S1 S2 T1 T2 V W Z(c,d,h,k,l,p,q,r)
Emergency Action, Agency, Advocacy, Fixed Fee Interview undertaken and Member of Accident Line
Ptr: King, Mr Richard J BA(Hons) . . . *Nov 1983

MAX OWEN SOLICITORS ‡
PO Box 6923 Uploaders Bridport Dorset DT6 4PR
Tel: 01308 485680 *Fax:* 01308 485071
E-mail: maxowenlaw@aol.com

MILNE & LYALL ‡
Oxford House 33 West Street Bridport Dorset DT6 3QW
Tel: 01308 422362 *Fax:* 01308 427592 *Dx:* 43201 BRIDPORT
List of partners: D M Lester, C J G White
Work: A1 A2 B1 B2 C1 C2 D1 D2 E F1 F2 G H I J1 J2 K1 K3 L N O Q R1 R2 S1 S2 T1 T2 V W X Z(c,e,g,k,l,m,o,p,q,s,y)
Emergency Action, Agency, Advocacy, Fixed Fee Interview, Legal Aid undertaken and Legal Aid Franchise
Ptr: Lester, Mr David Marcus LLB . . . *Oct 1985
White, Mr Christopher J G . . . *§Oct 1970

NANTES ‡
36 East Street Bridport Dorset DT6 3LH
Tel: 01308 422313 *Fax:* 01308 456989 *Dx:* 43200 BRIDPORT
List of partners: D J Corp, G M Fribbance, M A Harvey, D M Holman, J S Smith
Office: Dorchester, Weymouth
Dir: Corp, Mr David J LLB(Lond) . . . Dec 1977
Fribbance, Ms Gillian M . . . *Nov 1994
Harvey, Mr Michael A BSc(Nott'm) . . . Sep 1980
Smith, Mr John Samuel . . . *Sep 1982
Ast: Harmer, Mrs Carolyn LLB . . . Mar 1999
Con: Lobb, Mr Andrew Notary Public . . . Jul 1967

NEEDHAMS
37 St Andrews Road Bridport Dorset DT6 3BJ
Tel: 01308 440034
E-mail: info@needhamssolicitors.co.uk
Office: Bradford

JOHN SOWERBY LIMITED ‡
12 South Street Bridport Dorset DT6 3NQ
Tel: 01308 424090

BRIERLEY HILL, West Midlands

BARRY GREEN ‡
28a High Street Quarrybank Brierley Hill West Midlands DY5 2JW
Tel: 01384 566332 *Fax:* 01384 566349

HIGGS & SONS ‡
3 Waterfront Business Park Brierley Hill West Midlands DY5 1LX
Tel: 0845 111 5050 *Fax:* 01384 342000 *Dx:* 22751 BRIERLEY HILL
E-mail: law@higgsandsons.co.uk
List of partners: R J P Austin, P Barnsley, D P Beard, P J Coleman, D S Ellis, D J Everall, G M Faber, P G Gosling, S Gupta, E Hickman, J M Higgs, P Hunt, S C Jackson, T M L Jones, C A Junor, R E Leek, J Lowe, P J Martin, P Martin-Summers, D J V Morgan, N Moxon, L J Obrey, C L Pottinger, J B Rostron, S Shepherd, I D Shovlin, N R Stockall, N A Taylor, J P Tonks
Office: Kingswinford
Languages: French
Work: A1 B1 C2 C3 E F1 F2 I J1 L M1 O P R1 S1 S2 T1 T2 V W X Z(c,d,e,k,l,m,o,p,q)
Emergency Action, Agency, Advocacy, Fixed Fee Interview, Legal Aid undertaken and Member of Accident Line
Ptr: Austin, Mr R Jonathan P BA(Bris) . . . *Nov 1981
Barnsley, Mr Philip LLB(Hons) . . . *Sep 1999
Beard, Mr Damian Paul LLB(Hons) . . . Apr 2001
Coleman, Mr Peter J LLB(Hons) . . . *Oct 1991
Ellis, Mr David S BA(Hons) . . . *Oct 1985
Everall, Miss Donna J LLB(Hons) . . . *Dec 1993
Faber, Mr Gavin Mark LLDip; BA(Hons) . . . *Sep 1999
Gosling, Mr Peter G LLB(Hons) . . . *Nov 1992
Gupta, Mr Susheel BA(Hons) . . . *Mar 2001
Hickman, Ms Elizabeth LLB(Hons) . . . *Sep 1996
Hunt, Mr Paul LLB(Hons) Maxwell Law Prize; Birmingham Law Society Gold Medal . . . *Nov 1990
Jackson, Mr Steven Charles LLB(Lond) . . . *§Oct 1977
Jones, Mr Timothy M L LLB(Hons); LLM . . . *§Oct 1989
Junor, Ms Catherine Anne BA(Hons) . . . *Nov 1995
Leek, Mr Robert E BA; LLM . . . *§Oct 1980
Lowe, Miss Julia LLB(Hons) Secretary for Network Midlands . . . *Nov 1993
Martin, Mr Philip J LLB(Lond) . . . *§Jun 1973
Morgan, Mr David J V LLB(Hons); PGDip Ed Law . . . *§Apr 1977
Moxon, Mr Nicholas LLB(Hons) . . . *Oct 1995
Obrey, Mrs Lucy Jayne . . . Sep 2000
Pottinger, Mrs Claire Louise . . . Sep 1999
Rostron, Mr John B BA(Business Law) . . . *§Apr 1976
Shepherd, Mrs Samantha . . . Sep 1999
Shovlin, Mr Ian D BA(Hons) . . . *Jul 1981
Stockall, Mr Neil R LLB(Hons) . . . *Nov 1995
Taylor, Mr Nicholas A LLB(Hons); DLP . . . *Sep 1999
Tonks, Mr John P LLB . . . *§Oct 1969
Asoc: Abbi, Sunil LLB; LPC; PSC . . . *Nov 1999
Burnell, Miss Claire Victoria LLB(Hons) . . . *Jul 2001
Cottam, Miss Debra . . . *Sep 1998
Kehel, Gurvinder Singh LLB . . . *Sep 1994
Kettle, Mr Geoffrey Ian Marshall . . . Apr 2002
Langford, Miss Clare Victoria LLB(Hons) . . . *Sep 2003
Legg, Miss Kate BA(Hons); LLDip . . . *Sep 2003
Newton, Ms Kate . . . Sep 2002
Parsons, Mr Mark D BA(Hons)(Dunelm) . . . *Sep 1997
Scriven, Mrs Beverley LLB(Hons) . . . *Oct 1993
Shaw, Mr Andrew John LLB(Hons) David Baxter Prize for Commercial Law 2002 . . . Aug 2003
Walker, Ms Joanne . . . Sep 2003
Ast: Cartwright, Miss Claire L BA(Hons); DipLaw . . . *Sep 1999
Probert, Miss Kate Elizabeth LLB(Hons) . . . *Sep 2002
Con: Cheadle, Mr Kenneth . . . *§Jul 1966
Higgs, Mr David H . . . *§Jun 1963
Nock, Mr Malcolm LLB(Lond) . . . *§Apr 1970

STEPHENSONS ‡
57-59 High Street Brierley Hill West Midlands DY5 3ED
Tel: 01384 79731 *Fax:* 01384 265825 *Dx:* 22753 BRIERLEY HILL
E-mail: info@stephensonsthelawyer.co.uk
List of partners: R H G Farrow, T Tomlinson
Office: Wombourne
Work: B1 C1 D1 E K1 K4 L N O Q S1 W
Agency and Advocacy undertaken
Ptr: Farrow, Mr Robert H G . . . *§Aug 1968
Tomlinson, Ms Tracey LLB . . . *Oct 1990
Ast: Hudson, Ms Julie . . . Sep 2006
Con: Hammersley, Mr Roger R LLB . . . *§Dec 1967

WALDRONS ‡
Wychbury Court Two Woods Lane Brierley Hill West Midlands DY5 1TA
Tel: 01384 811811 *Fax:* 01384 811822
Dx: 701422 BRIERLEY HILL 4
E-mail: lawyers@waldrons.co.uk
List of partners: T J Andrews, A M Dawson, J Ellis, S W Green, S G Hanns, L S Harrison, T A Pratt, J M Roberts, P W Waldron, S J Waterfield, N H Whitehouse, A Witt
Office: Dudley, Kingswinford, Tipton, Walsall, Worcester
Languages: French, German
Work: B1 C1 C2 D1 E F1 G H J1 K1 K2 L M1 N O P Q R1 S1 S2 T1 V W Z(d,e,k,l,m,p,r)
Emergency Action, Agency, Advocacy, Legal Aid undertaken, Legal Aid Franchise and Member of Accident Line
Ptr: Ellis, Mrs Joanne LLB(Hons) . . . Oct 1991
Green, Mr Stephen William LLB(Hons) . . . *Oct 1992
Pratt, Miss Trudy Angela LLB(Hons) . . . *Oct 1995
Roberts, Mr John M LLB . . . Oct 1984
Waldron, Mr Peter W LLB . . . *Dec 1973
Waterfield, Ms Suzanne Jane LLB; DipLP . . . Sep 1996
Witt, Mr Adrian LLB . . . Oct 1995
Ast: Battelley, Mr Christian BA . . . Sep 2001
Edwards, Mr David E LLB . . . Aug 2001
Gennard, Ms Natalie FILEx . . . Apr 1999
Jalota, Ms Kiran LLB(Hons) . . . Nov 1992
Pathan, Miss Sabhia LLB ★ . . . *Jul 2000

BRIGG, North Lincolnshire

HETTS JOHNSON WHITING ‡
11 Bigby Street Brigg North Lincolnshire DN20 8EP
Tel: 01652 655101 *Fax:* 01652 650351
E-mail: jaef@hjw.demon.co.uk
List of partners: J A E Ford, M Johnson, J Pountney
Languages: French, German
Work: A1 B1 D1 E F1 G H J1 K1 L N P Q R1 S2 T2 V W Z(b,c,d,h,l)
Agency, Fixed Fee Interview and Legal Aid undertaken
Ptr: Ford, Miss J Annabel E LLB Charles Herbert Reed Prize 1982 . . . *Sep 1985
Johnson, Mr Michael LLB(Leics) Leicester Law Society Prize 1970 . . . *Jun 1975
Pountney, Mr Jonathan BA . . . *Jan 1980

MASON BAGGOTT & GARTON
(incorporating Sowter & Gibson)
25 Bigby Street Brigg North Lincolnshire DN20 8ED
Tel: 01652 654111 *Fax:* 01652 658188 *Dx:* 24352 BRIGG
E-mail: brigg@lawlincs.co.uk
Office: Epworth, Scunthorpe
Work: A1 B1 C1 C2 C3 D1 D2 E F1 J1 K1 L M1 M2 N P Q R1 S1 S2 T1 T2 V W Z(l,t)
Emergency Action, Agency, Advocacy, Fixed Fee Interview, Legal Aid undertaken, Legal Aid Franchise and Member of Accident Line
Ptr: Mason, Mr Richard J S LLB(Hons) . . . Jul 1998

SCIOLTI & CO ‡
PO Box 88 Brigg North Lincolnshire DN20 8WT
Tel: 01652 655845 *Fax:* 01652 651122
E-mail: help@askgiles.info

BRIGHOUSE, West Yorkshire

ARMITAGE SYKES LLP
71 Bradford Road Brighouse West Yorkshire HD6 1RR
Tel: 01484 714431 *Fax:* 01484 400712 *Dx:* 25351 BRIGHOUSE
E-mail: info@armitagesykes.co.uk
Office: Huddersfield (2 offices)
Work: A1 B1 C1 C2 C3 D1 D2 E F1 F2 J1 J2 K1 K3 K4 L M1 N O P Q R1 S1 S2 T1 T2 W Z(b,c,d,e,h,k,l,p,q)
Emergency Action, Agency, Advocacy, Fixed Fee Interview and Legal Aid undertaken
Ptr: Brewer, Mr Philip MA(Oxon) . . . *§Apr 1980
Lewis, Mr Vivian J LLB . . . *Mar 1984
Asoc: Walker, Miss Ruth BSc(Hons) . . . *Aug 1998
Ast: Fish, Mrs Emily BA(Hons) . . . *Sep 2008

BEARDERS
3-5 King Street Brighouse West Yorkshire HD6 1NX
Tel: 01484 710571 *Fax:* 01484 400561
E-mail: r@c.com
Office: Halifax
Work: K1 S1 T2 W
Ptr: Cross, Mrs Yasmin MA . . . *Jul 1996
Smithies, Mr Richard David LLB(Hull) . . . May 1973

BREARLEYS ‡
The RoundHouse 12 King Street Brighouse West Yorkshire HD6 1NX
Tel: 01484 714400 *Fax:* 01484 716115 *Dx:* 25364 BRIGHOUSE
E-mail: nickbattye@brearleyssolicitors.com

See p112 for the Key to Work Categories & other symbols

BRIGHTLINGSEA, Essex

JOHN FOWLERS LLP SOLICITORS
12 Victoria Place Brightlingsea Essex CO7 0BX
Tel: 01206 302694 ***Fax:*** 01206 302961
Emergency telephone 01206 769342
E-mail: info@johnfowlers.co.uk
Office: Colchester
Work: D1 E G H K1 K2 L M1 M2 N O P Q S1 S2 W Z(c,l,m)
Emergency Action, Agency, Advocacy, Fixed Fee Interview, Legal Aid undertaken and Member of Accident Line
Ptr: Kennedy, Mr Kim N R BA . . . . *§May 1981
Root, Mr Derek L BA(Law) . . . . *Dec 1978
Ast: Brennan, Mrs Marisa Dawn LLB. . . . . *Apr 2005
Robinson, Mrs Marjorie Elaine LLB . . . . *Oct 1993
Con: Coomber, Miss Sharon A BA(Hons) . . . . *Mar 1986
Howell, Mr David LLB; Dip IntLaw Advocacy Prize Grays Inn 1979 . . . . Apr 1996

BRIGHTON, Brighton & Hove

ACT LEGAL ‡
Stanford House 9 South Road Brighton Brighton & Hove BN1 6SB
Tel: 01273 565656 ***Fax:*** 01273 540455
E-mail: mail@actlegal.co.uk
List of partners: D Sherwood, A C Thompson
Work: K4 S1 T2 W
Ptr: Sherwood, Mr David . . . . *Apr 1974
Thompson, Mr Alan C MA(Oxon) . . . . *Aug 1973

ARLINGTON SOLICITORS ‡
145 Islingword Road Brighton Brighton & Hove BN2 9SH
Tel: 01273 696962 ***Fax:*** 01273 682705
Emergency telephone 07734 350340
E-mail: info@arlingtonslaw.co.uk
Work: C1 D1 D2 J1 K3 N O Q Z(i)
Emergency Action, Agency and Fixed Fee Interview undertaken

BE LEGAL ‡
The Sussex Innovation Centre Science Park Square Falmer Brighton Brighton & Hove BN1 9SB
Tel: 01273 704525 ***Fax:*** 0870 421 4756
E-mail: info@be-legal.com

BWS ‡
PO Box 81 Brighton Brighton & Hove BN51 9AF
Tel: 0700 067 9000

BEELEY & CO SOLICITORS
25 Ship Street Brighton Brighton & Hove BN1 1AD
Tel: 01273 748464 ***Fax:*** 01273 774449 ***Dx:*** 2715 BRIGHTON 1
E-mail: paul.christmas@beeleyandco.co.uk
Office: Cheadle

BILMES LLP
95 Ditchling Road Brighton Brighton & Hove BN1 4ST
Tel: 01273 380202 ***Fax:*** 01273 380206
Dx: 30253 BRIGHTON PRESTON ROAD
E-mail: law@bilmesllp.com
Office: London WC2

BISHOP & LIGHT ‡ (incorporating Hunters)
171 Edward Street Brighton Brighton & Hove BN2 0JB
Tel: 01273 626288 ***Fax:*** 01273 676717 ***Dx:*** 2741 BRIGHTON
E-mail: law@bishopandlight.co.uk
Work: G H V
Agency, Fixed Fee Interview, Legal Aid undertaken and Legal Aid Franchise
Asoc: Hunter, Mr John LLB . . . . Jan 2003
Con: Hunter, Mr James MA; LLB . . . . *Sep 1994

BOSLEY & CO ‡
5 Marlborough Place Brighton Brighton & Hove BN1 1UB
Tel: 01273 608181 ***Fax:*** 01273 690237 ***Dx:*** 36665 BRIGHTON 2
E-mail: msh@bosley.co.uk
List of partners: S Amin, M S Hastilow, G McCullagh
Work: B1 C1 D1 D2 E G H J1 K1 K3 L M1 N P Q S1 S2 V W Z(l)
Emergency Action, Agency, Advocacy and Legal Aid undertaken
Ptr: Amin, Mr Shahjehan LLB . . . . *Aug 1995
Hastilow, Mr Michael S . . . . *Nov 1970
McCullagh, Mr Gerard LLB . . . . *Mar 1981
Ast: Whittaker, Miss Lianna Kate LLB(Hons) . . . . Feb 2011

DAVID BUCK & CO ‡
32 Foundry Street Brighton Brighton & Hove BN1 4AT
Tel: 01273 621745 ***Fax:*** 01273 623330 ***Dx:*** 36658 BRIGHTON 2
Emergency telephone 01893 261543
E-mail: davidbucksols@aol.com
List of partners: D H Buck, J McWilliam
Work: G H I J1 K1 Q Z(p)
Emergency Action, Agency, Advocacy and Legal Aid undertaken
Ptr: Buck, Mr David H BA(Durham) . . . . *Apr 1987
McWilliam, Ms Joanna . . . . *Jul 1995

BURCHELL WILLIAMS LIMITED ‡
William Street Offices Brighton Brighton & Hove BN2 0BG
Tel: 01273 606555 ***Fax:*** 01273 693999 ***Dx:*** 2707 BRIGHTON
Emergency telephone 07659 160747
E-mail: solicitors@burchellwilliams.co.uk
List of partners: N P Burchell, M A Williams
Work: G H
Agency, Legal Aid undertaken and Legal Aid Franchise
Ptr: Burchell, Mr Neil P LLB . . . . *Apr 1986
Williams, Mr Martyn Adrian LLB ★. . . . . *Aug 1995
Asoc: Frank, Mr Richard BA(Hons) . . . . *Oct 1996
Con: McPherson, Mr James Victor LLB ★. . . . . *Jul 1975

BURT BRILL & CARDENS ‡
30 Old Steyne Brighton Brighton & Hove BN1 1FL
Tel: 01273 604123 ***Fax:*** 01273 570837 ***Dx:*** 2709 BRIGHTON 1
E-mail: help@bbc-law.co.uk
List of partners: D J Edwards, A Rustemeyer, P Slot, K G Smyth
Languages: Afrikaans, French, Spanish
Work: A1 A3 B1 C1 E I J1 K1 K2 K3 K4 L N O Q R1 S1 S2 T2 W Z(d,l,q)
Agency, Advocacy and Fixed Fee Interview undertaken
Ptr: Edwards, Mr David J . . . . *§Oct 1982
Rustemeyer, Mr Alistair LLB. . . . . Nov 1994
Slot, Mr Paul PGDipLaw. . . . . *Oct 2002
Smyth, Mr Kevin G . . . . *Jul 1973
Ast: Clark, Mrs Joanna Lucy BA; PGDL; LPC . . . . Sep 2001
Davies, Miss Samantha LLB . . . . *Apr 2010
Hughes, Miss Jodi Karan BA(Law with Business) . . . *Sep 2011
Ryle, Miss Wendy LLB . . . . *Jun 1980
Wake, Miss Vanessa LLB . . . . Jun 2008
Warren, Mrs Sophie. . . . . Jun 2009

HENRY CANE & SON ‡
9 Marlborough Place Brighton Brighton & Hove BN1 1UB
Tel: 01273 604091 ***Fax:*** 01273 670497 ***Dx:*** 2726 BRIGHTON 1
E-mail: oliver@hcane.co.uk
List of partners: O W H Tuckley
Work: E S1 S2 W
Ptr: Tuckley, Mr Oliver William Home LLB . . . . *Sep 1979

CLAREMONT CRAWT ‡
4 Queen Square Brighton Brighton & Hove BN1 3FD
Tel: 01273 727906 ***Fax:*** 01273 206217
Work: E L S1 W

MARTIN CRAY & CO ‡
177 Edward Street Brighton Brighton & Hove BN2 0JB
Tel: 01273 673226 ***Fax:*** 01273 621715 ***Dx:*** 2725 BRIGHTON 1
Emergency telephone 01273 673226
E-mail: info@martincray.co.uk
List of partners: M W Cray, M F Mitten
Work: B2 E G H J1 K1 L N O Q S1 S2 W Z(c,q)
Emergency Action, Agency, Advocacy, Fixed Fee Interview, Legal Aid Franchise and Member of Accident Line
Ptr: Cray, Mr Martin W BA ♦. . . . . *Jun 1981
Mitten, Mr Martin F . . . . *Nov 1982
Asoc: Brown, Mrs Barbara. . . . . May 2005

DMH STALLARD LLP ‡ (in association with Law Europe EEIG)
98 Queens Road Brighton Brighton & Hove BN1 3YB
Tel: 01273 329833 ***Fax:*** 01273 747500 ***Dx:*** 2703 BRIGHTON 1
E-mail: enquiries@dmhstallard.com
Office: Crawley, London EC4
Languages: Dutch, French, German, Italian, Spanish
Work: A1 A3 B1 B2 C1 C2 C3 D1 D2 E F1 F2 G H I J1 K1 K3 K4 L M1 N O P Q R1 R2 S1 S2 T1 T2 U2 V W X Z(b,c,d,e,f,g,h,k,l,m,o,p,q,r,s,t,u,w,x,z,za)

DAKERS ‡
11 Queens Place Brighton Brighton & Hove BN1 4JY
Tel: 01273 571685 ***Fax:*** 01273 676323 ***Dx:*** 2759 BRIGHTON
Emergency telephone 01273 571685
E-mail: info@dslaw.co.uk
List of partners: T J Dakers
Languages: French
Work: B1 C1 C2 C3 D1 E F1 G H J1 K1 L N O P Q R1 S1 V W Z(c,d,i,l,m)
Emergency Action, Agency, Advocacy, Fixed Fee Interview undertaken and Member of Accident Line
Ptr: Dakers, Mr Timothy J LLB(B'ham). . . . . *Feb 1977

DEAN WILSON LAING ‡
96 Church Street Brighton Brighton & Hove BN1 1UJ
Tel: 01273 327241 ***Fax:*** 01273 770913 ***Dx:*** 2706 BRIGHTON 1
E-mail: thelawyers@dwl.uk.com
List of partners: D H Barling, S A Cox, J B Hunt, G V James, N J P Perkins, P M Scampton, C L Whiteman, I K R Wilson
Languages: French
Work: A1 A3 B1 C1 C2 C3 D1 E F1 F2 J1 J2 K1 K2 K3 K4 L N O P Q R1 R2 S1 S2 T1 T2 V W Z(a,c,d,g,h,i,k,l,o,p,q,r,w)
Agency, Advocacy undertaken and Member of Accident Line
Ptr: Barling, Mr David H . . . . *Sep 1972
Cox, Mrs Siobhan Anne. . . . . *Sep 2003
Hunt, Mr Julian B BA(Hons). . . . . *Aug 1998
James, Mrs Georgina V. . . . . *May 1978
Perkins, Mr Nicholas J P LLB . . . . *Sep 1982
Scampton, Mr P Michael BA . . . . *Dec 1976
Whiteman, Miss Claire Lisa LLB(Hons) . . . . *Sep 1996
Wilson, Mr Ian K R ● . . . . *Jan 1969
Ast: Dickinson, Ms Samantha . . . . *Dec 2001
Miles, Ms Rebecca . . . . Jul 2005
Roberts, Mrs Seema BA; LLM. . . . . *Nov 1997

JULIAN DOBSON SOLICITORS ‡
1 Frederick Terrace Frederick Place Brighton Brighton & Hove BN1 1AX
Tel: 01273 766355 ***Fax:*** 01273 766350
E-mail: info@juliandobson.com
Languages: French
Work: B1

FITZHUGH GATES ‡ (incorporating Ernest Cragg & Son)
3 Pavilion Parade Brighton Brighton & Hove BN2 1RY
Tel: 01273 686811 ***Fax:*** 01273 676837 ***Dx:*** 2727 BRIGHTON 1
E-mail: mail@fitzhugh.co.uk
List of partners: L F Ditchburn, A D Druce, A G Foot, P M Hill, H P Hunt, R A V Watson
Office: Shoreham-by-Sea
Languages: Spanish
Work: B1 C1 D1 E F1 J1 K1 L M1 N O P Q R1 R2 S1 T1 V W Z(b,c,d,e,h,j,k,l,m,o,p,q,r,s,t)
Emergency Action, Agency, Advocacy, Legal Aid undertaken, Legal Aid Franchise and Member of Accident Line
Ptr: Ditchburn, Miss Lucy F LLB. . . . . *Nov 1989
Druce, Mr Anthony D MA(Oxon). . . . . *Mar 1970
Foot, Mr Anthony Graeme MA(Cantab) . . . . *Jun 1972
Watson, Mr Robert A V LLB. . . . . Jun 1976
Ast: Lawton, Ms Nicole LLB(Hons). . . . . Oct 1996
MacFarlane, Miss Moira Patricia LLB(Hons). . . . . . *Nov 1993

GILLIES SOLICITORS LLP ‡
21-23 Middle Street Brighton Brighton & Hove BN1 1AL
Tel: 01273 206050 ***Fax:*** 01273 202737 ***Dx:*** 2730 BRIGHTON
E-mail: ed@gilliesllp.com

GLEDHILL SOLICITORS ‡
1a Powis Square Brighton Brighton & Hove BN1 3HH
Tel: 01273 719083 ***Fax:*** 01273 719084

GRIFFITH SMITH FARRINGTON WEBB ‡
47 Old Steyne Brighton Brighton & Hove BN1 1NW
Tel: 01273 324041 ***Fax:*** 01273 384000 ***Dx:*** 2701 BRIGHTON 1
E-mail: brighton@griffithsmith.co.uk
Office: Hassocks, Henfield
Languages: French, German
Work: A1 B1 C1 C2 D1 E F1 J1 K1 K3 K4 L N O Q S1 S2 V W Z(d,q,r,u)

HARNEY & WELLS ‡
30 Grand Parade Brighton Brighton & Hove BN2 9QA
Tel: 01273 684666 ***Fax:*** 01273 279974 ***Dx:*** 2714 BRIGHTON 1
List of partners: C A Harney
Work: D1 K1 K3
Emergency Action, Agency, Fixed Fee Interview and Legal Aid undertaken
SPr: Harney, Mrs Carol Ann LLB(Hons) . . . . *Oct 1984

HARRINGTONS ‡
83 Ditchling Road Brighton Brighton & Hove BN1 4SD
Tel: 01273 606069
Emergency telephone 07773 315822
E-mail: joseph@harringtons-solicitors.co.uk
List of partners: J Harrington
Work: R2 Z(q)
Advocacy and Fixed Fee Interview undertaken
Dir: Harrington, Mr Joseph. . . . . Aug 1990

HARRIS PALEY SCHONE LTD ‡
9 St Georges Place Brighton Brighton & Hove BN1 4GB
Tel: 01273 600009 ***Fax:*** 01273 600008
Emergency telephone 07061 006009
E-mail: law@hps-law.co.uk
Work: G H
Fixed Fee Interview undertaken

EDWARD HARTE LLP ‡
6 Pavilion Parade Brighton Brighton & Hove BN2 1RA
Tel: 01273 662750 ***Fax:*** 01273 662755 ***Dx:*** 36651 BRIGHTON 2
List of partners: B Donnan, A C Edgar, E M Taylor, C T Wibley
Work: B1 C2 D1 E F1 G J1 J2 K1 K2 L N O Q R2 S1 S2 V W Z(c,d,h,l,q)
Emergency Action, Agency, Advocacy, Fixed Fee Interview, Legal Aid undertaken and Legal Aid Franchise
Ptr: Donnan, Mr Brian LLB . . . . *Jan 1992
Taylor, Mrs Elizabeth M LLB(Manc) . . . . *Jun 1977
Wibley, Mr Colin T LLB(Soton) . . . . *Jul 1978
Edgar, Amanda Christina . . . . NSP
Asoc: Ansell, Miss Susan Lilian . . . . *Jul 1973
Callaghan, Mr Thomas Edward LLB. . . . . Jun 2006
Nagra, Ms Manjinder Kaur BSc . . . . *Jul 2001
Taylor, Miss Samantha BA . . . . *May 2008

HEALYS LLP
8 & 9 Old Steine Brighton Brighton & Hove BN1 1EJ
Tel: 01273 685888 ***Fax:*** 01273 685454 ***Dx:*** 2702 BRIGHTON 1
Emergency telephone 01273 685888
Office: London EC4
Languages: French, German, Greek, Spanish
Work: B1 C1 C2 C3 D1 E F1 G H J1 K1 K2 K3 L M1 M2 N O P Q R1 S1 S2 T1 T2 W Z(c,e,i,j,k,l,q,r)
Emergency Action, Agency, Advocacy undertaken and Member of Accident Line
Ptr: Austen-Jones, Mr Jonathan Douglas LLB(Hons). . . *Nov 1995
Healy, Mr John Andrew . . . . *Feb 1975
Skinner, Mr Dino E BA(Econ); LLM . . . . *Sep 1984
Taylor, Mr Nicholas Jamison LLB . . . . *Oct 1993
Asoc: Badain, Miss Melanie Robina LLB(Business Law); LPC . . . . *Aug 2006
Taylor, Miss Catherine Victoria . . . . Feb 1996
Ast: Ahmad, Miss Nazish LLB . . . . *Aug 2008
Catuara, Miss Daniela LLB; LPC . . . . Apr 2009
Con: Bolton, Mr Jeremy P. . . . . *Jul 1978
Mercer, Ms Margaret A W. . . . . *Mar 1958
Stockman, Mr David Howard . . . . *Jul 1973

HENNINGS SOLICITORS ‡
138 Old London Road Brighton Brighton & Hove BN1 8YA
Tel: 01273 505800

HOWLETT CLARKE CROWTHER WOOD ‡
8-9 Ship Street Brighton Brighton & Hove BN1 1AZ
Tel: 01273 327272 / 326341 ***Fax:*** 01273 328857
Dx: 36656 BRIGHTON 2
E-mail: brighton@lawhcc.co.uk
List of partners: R J G Dyson, C J Edmonds, W J T Fenton, W Robertson, S A Rowe, P R Schaverien, D J Shockley, B I Yates
Office: Hove
Languages: French
Work: A1 B1 C1 C2 C3 D1 E F1 G H K1 L N O R1 S1 T1 T2 W Z(c,j,k,l,o,t)
Emergency Action, Agency, Advocacy, Fixed Fee Interview, Legal Aid undertaken, Legal Aid Franchise and Member of Accident Line
Ptr: Dyson, Mr Richard J G . . . . *Jan 1970
Fenton, Mr William J T BA; FCIArb . . . . *Jun 1979
Rowe, Mr Simon A . . . . *Mar 1984
Schaverien, Mr Philip Richard BA(Law) . . . . *Nov 1982
Shockley, Mr David J . . . . *Jul 1965
Yates, Mr Bernard I LLB. . . . . *Jan 1970
Con: Brewins, Mr John D LLB(Nott'm) . . . . *Apr 1974

IRVING & CO
11 Marlborough Place Brighton Brighton & Hove BN1 1UB
Tel: 01273 665460 ***Fax:*** 01273 665461
Office: London NW1

JAMES & CO ‡
Premier House 11 Marlborough Place Brighton Brighton & Hove BN1 1UB
Tel: 01273 665470
List of partners: S J Fanning, P J Ward
Work: E J1 L O Q S2
Emergency Action, Agency and Fixed Fee Interview undertaken
Ptr: Fanning, Mr Stephen James BA(Hons) . . . . *Jun 1993
Ward, Paul J . . . . Jan 1995

JOHNSON MCCABE ‡
19 Queens Road Brighton Brighton & Hove BN1 3XA
Tel: 01273 822500 ***Fax:*** 01273 204743 ***Dx:*** 36683 BRIGHTON 2
E-mail: info@johnsonmccabe.co.uk
List of partners: B J Noonan
Work: E S1 W
Ptr: Noonan, Mr Brendan J . . . . *Jul 1979

JUST EMPLOYMENT
The Brighton Forum 95 Ditchling Road Brighton Brighton & Hove BN1 4ST
Tel: 01483 303636 ***Fax:*** 01483 459850

E-mail: info@justemployment.com
Office: Guildford, Reading

KELLYS ‡
9 St Georges Place Brighton Brighton & Hove BN1 4GB
Tel: 01273 674898 *Fax:* 01273 684008
E-mail: admin@kellys-solicitors.co.uk

SYLVIA KING ‡
Brighton Business Centre 95 Ditchling Road Brighton Brighton & Hove BN1 4ST
Tel: 01273 573837 *Fax:* 01273 689021
E-mail: sylviaking117@hotmail.com

MCMILLAN WILLIAMS SOLICITORS ‡
11 Prince's Street Brighton Brighton & Hove BN2 1RD
Tel: 01273 254004 *Fax:* 01273 621617 *Dx:* 2733 BRIGHTON
E-mail: brighton@mwsolicitors.co.uk

DEAN MARSH & CO ‡
73a Middle Street Brighton Brighton & Hove BN1 1AL
Tel: 01273 823770

MARTIN SEARLE ‡
9 Marlborough Place Brighton Brighton & Hove BN1 1UB
Tel: 01273 609911 *Fax:* 01273 609944
E-mail: info@ms-solicitors.co.uk
List of partners: F Martin
Office: Croydon
Dir: Martin, Miss Fiona BA(Hons); LSF . . . . Mar 1996

JOHN MATTHEWS SOLICITOR ‡
20 Inwood Crescent Brighton Brighton & Hove BN1 5AQ
Tel: 01273 928714 *Fax:* 01273 542589
E-mail: jmemploymentlaw@aol.com

GERARD MAYE LEGAL LIMITED ‡
4 Dorset Street Brighton Brighton & Hove BN2 1WA
Tel: 01273 560444 *Fax:* 01273 560445 *Dx:* 36662 BRIGHTON 2
Emergency telephone 07855 471893
E-mail: enquiries@gerardmaye.co.uk
List of partners: G S Maye
Office: Brighton, Littlehampton
SPr: Maye, Mr Gerard S LLB. . . . . Nov 1991

GERARD MAYE LEGAL LIMITED
36 Roberston Road Preston Park Brighton Brighton & Hove BN1 5NL
Tel: 01273 560426 *Dx:* 36662 BRIGHTON 2
Emergency telephone 01875 610178
E-mail: enquiries@gerardmaye.co.uk
Office: Brighton, Littlehampton

MAYO WYNNE BAXTER LLP ‡
Century House 15-19 Dyke Road Brighton Brighton & Hove BN1 3FE
Tel: 01273 775533 *Fax:* 01273 207744 *Dx:* 141292 BRIGHTON 5
E-mail: brighton@mayowynnebaxter.co.uk
List of partners: S M Bird, P R K Bristow, J R M Clarke, I R Coombs, M M Cooperman, C Coopey, E Coxall, B H Davis, C F Dodds, M S D Frankel, M E Gillingham, D G S Gordon, T Griffiths, P A Hall, A J Hooper, R Johnston, C S Le May, J R Lingwood, M Minter, K D Minto, D Orgill, J Porter, C J Randall, G S Stone, C G Strutt, R P Thompson, P R Ticehurst, L M Webster
Office: East Grinstead, Eastbourne, Lewes, Seaford
Work: A1 B1 C1 C2 C3 D1 E F1 J1 K1 L M1 M2 N P R1 S1 T1 T2 V W Z(c,d,e,h,l)
Emergency Action, Agency, Advocacy, Fixed Fee Interview, Legal Aid undertaken, Legal Aid Franchise and Member of Accident Line
Ptr: Bristow, Mr Peter R K LLB . . . . *Jun 1979
Cooperman, Mr Martyn M. . . . . *Jun 1981
Coopey, Mr Christopher. . . . . *Aug 1997
Frankel, Mr Michael S D LLB . . . . *§Nov 1970
Gillingham, Mr Mark E . . . . *Dec 1966
Gordon, Mr David George Strachan. . . . . *Oct 1994
Hooper, Mr Arthur J LLB ♦ Deputy District Judge . . . *Jun 1962
Lingwood, Mr John R BA . . . . *§Oct 1982
Minter, Ms Melanie LLB. . . . . Nov 1990
Orgill, Mr Dean LLB. . . . . Nov 1987
Webster, Lesley M LLB(Lond) Part time Chairman of CSAT . . . . *§Jul 1976
Ast: Brown, Mr Richard Auger LLB(Hons) . . . . *Nov 1997
Gage, Mrs Katherine Elizabeth BA(Hons) . . . . . . *Dec 1989
Holmes, Miss Victoria J. . . . . Feb 2001
Manton, Mrs Laura Michelle LLB; TEP. . . . . *Aug 1998
May, Mr Geoffrey Robert BSc(Hons) . . . . Sep 1996
Sheriff, Ms Memuna. . . . . Apr 2002
Tarrant, Ms Lucy BA . . . . Aug 1999
Con: Hall, Mr Stephen J • Recorder. . . . . *May 1971
Mercer, Mr Robin . . . . *§May 1974

JAMES MEAD ‡
61 Hanover Terrace Brighton Brighton & Hove BN2 9SP
Tel: 01273 677420

MULBERRY'S EMPLOYMENT LAW SOLICITORS
95 Ditchling Road Brighton Brighton & Hove BN1 4ST
Tel: 01273 573850 *Fax:* 01273 573851
E-mail: info@mulberryssolicitors.com
Office: London SW1

MULROONEY CRAGHILL LIMITED ‡
Basement 44 Grand Parade Brighton Brighton & Hove BN2 9QA
Tel: 01273 692020 *Fax:* 01273 684827 *Dx:* 2720 BRIGHTON
E-mail: law@mulrooneycraghill.com

OSLER DONEGAN TAYLOR ‡
Pavilion View 19 New Road Brighton Brighton & Hove BN1 1UF
Tel: 01273 710712 *Fax:* 01273 710713 *Dx:* 36663 BRIGHTON 2
E-mail: jdonegan@odt.uk.com
List of partners: J P Donegan, H R Osler, R J N Taylor
Office: Hassocks
Languages: French
Work: B1 E F1 J1 L N O Q S1 V W Z(h,i,p,q,r)
Emergency Action, Agency, Advocacy and Fixed Fee Interview undertaken
Ptr: Donegan, Mr Jeremy Patrick BSc . . . . *Nov 1991
Osler, Mr Harvey R LLB . . . . *Oct 1990
Taylor, Mr Rupert J N BA(Hons). . . . . *Sep 1996

M S PAGE ‡
3 The Rise Portslade Brighton Brighton & Hove BN41 2PY

RAILTON ‡
Premier House 11 Marlborough Place Brighton Brighton & Hove BN1 1UB
Tel: 01273 738285 *Fax:* 01273 665482

SAGELAW ‡
PO Box 228 24 Burrow Street Brighton Brighton & Hove BN1 3SZ
Tel: 01273 387246

SEYMOURS + SOLICITORS ‡
12 Queens Place Brighton Brighton & Hove BN1 4JY
Tel: 01273 628808 *Fax:* 01273 628174
Emergency telephone 07788 555262
E-mail: info@seymoursolicitors.co.uk
List of partners: A B Seymour
Office: Horsham
Ptr: Seymour, Mr Anthony B LLB; LLM . . . . Jun 1979

SHERWOOD SOLICITORS ‡
The Little Globe 153 Edward Street Brighton Brighton & Hove BN2 0JG
Tel: 01273 608221 *Fax:* 01273 670456 *Dx:* 94306 BRIGHTON 1
E-mail: mail@sherwood-solicitors.co.uk
List of partners: D Sherwood
Languages: French, German
Work: E S1 W
Ptr: Sherwood, Mr David LLB(Lond) . . . . *Mar 1973

SPEARPOINT FRANKS SOLICITORS LTD ‡
Suites 3 & 5 39-42 East Street Brighton Brighton & Hove BN1 1HL
Tel: 01273 748749 *Fax:* 01273 774189 *Dx:* 2737 BRIGHTON
E-mail: law@sfsolicitors.co.uk

SUSSEX LAW SOLICITORS ‡
45 Ladies Mile Road Brighton Brighton & Hove BN1 8TA
Tel: 01273 561312 *Fax:* 01273 563525

TENNANT & KNIGHT ‡
10 Prince Albert Street Brighton Brighton & Hove BN1 1HE
Tel: 01273 202050 *Fax:* 01273 206604 *Dx:* 36695 BRIGHTON 2
E-mail: solicitors@tennantknight.co.uk
List of partners: S M Knight, G M Tennant, C Youdan
Work: D1 K1 S1 W
Emergency Action, Legal Aid undertaken and Legal Aid Franchise
Ptr: Knight, Ms Susan M BA. . . . . *Feb 1988
Tennant, Mrs Gillian Mary. . . . . *Dec 1971
Youdan, Miss Charlotte BA(Hons); CPE; LPC . . . . . Jul 2006
Ast: Lynch, Mrs Jennifer BA(Hons). . . . . Sep 2006

THOMPSON ALLEN LLP ‡
(incorporating Peter J Wright)
6 Malborough Place Brighton Brighton & Hove BN1 1UB
Tel: 01273 608003 *Fax:* 01273 608004 *Dx:* 2754 BRIGHTON
E-mail: info@thompsonallen.co.uk
List of partners: M Allen, J L Thompson
Work: A1 A2 C1 E K4 L O Q S1 S2 W Z(c,d)
Ptr: Allen, Mr Mark LLB(Law with French) . . . . *May 1992
Thompson, Mr Justin Lee LLB. . . . . *Nov 2003
Asoc: Abbott, Miss Suzanne MA. . . . . *Oct 1994
Con: Foot, Mr Anthony Graeme MA(Cantab) . . . . *Jun 1972
Thompson, Mr Alan C MA(Oxon) . . . . *Aug 1973

RICHARD THORN & CO ‡
6 Marlborough Place Brighton Brighton & Hove BN1 1UB
Tel: 01273 625600 *Fax:* 01273 625650 *Dx:* 36661 BRIGHTON 2
E-mail: enquiries@richardthorn.net
List of partners: R L H Thorn
Languages: French
Work: G H K1 N O Q Z(q)
Agency, Advocacy, Legal Aid undertaken and Legal Aid Franchise
SPr: Thorn, Mr Richard L H . . . . *Jul 1980
Ast: Sells, Ms Cara LLB . . . . *Oct 2002

RONNIE TREMLETT & CO ‡
69 Grand Parade Brighton Brighton & Hove BN2 9TS
Tel: 01273 696132 *Fax:* 01273 696767 *Dx:* 2728 BRIGHTON
Emergency telephone 07626 800033
E-mail: office@tremletts.com
List of partners: R C Tremlett
Work: G H
Emergency Action, Agency, Advocacy, Legal Aid undertaken and Legal Aid Franchise
Ptr: Tremlett, Mr Ronnie C BA ★. . . . . May 1982

WALKERS SOLICITORS ‡
143e Ditchling Road Brighton Brighton & Hove BN1 6JA
Tel: 01273 564939 *Fax:* 01274 564840
E-mail: rw@walkersbrighton.com
Office: Brighton
Languages: German
Work: E J1 Q S1 W

WALKERS SOLICITORS
88 High Street Rottingdean Brighton Brighton & Hove BN2 7HF
Tel: 01273 309193 *Fax:* 01273 308430
E-mail: rw@walkersbrighton.com
Office: Brighton
Languages: German
Work: E J1 Q S1 W

WOOLLEY BEVIS DIPLOCK ‡
Lanes End House 15 Prince Albert Street Brighton Brighton & Hove BN1 1HY
Tel: 01273 323231 *Fax:* 01273 820350 *Dx:* 36652 BRIGHTON 2
List of partners: S P Alldis, F Amin, A G Darby, D J E Diplock, R H Edmondson, B L Ellis
Office: Hove
Agency, Advocacy, Legal Aid undertaken and Legal Aid Franchise
Ptr: Alldis, Mr Simon Paul . . . . *Feb 1973
Amin, Miss Farida BSc . . . . Mar 1997
Edmondson, Mr Richard H LLB . . . . *Jun 1970
Ast: Bruce, Romany M LLB . . . . *Jul 1985
Con: Bidwell, Mr Christopher John Stanley MA . . . . . . *§Apr 1968

BRISTOL

AMD SOLICITORS ‡
100 Henleaze Road Bristol BS9 4JZ
Tel: 0117 962 1460 *Fax:* 0117 962 1961
Dx: 33364 WESTBURY-ON-TRYM
E-mail: info@amdsolicitors.com
List of partners: M K Davies, P J Golding, R T Harris, A N Moore
Office: Bristol (3 offices)
Work: D1 E J1 K1 L O Q S1 S2 W X Z(d,m,t)
Agency and Legal Aid undertaken
Ptr: Davies, Mrs Marian K . . . . *Jul 1980
Moore, Mr Anthony N BA . . . . *Jun 1979
Ast: Brown, Mr Christopher G BSc. . . . . *May 1979
Demetriou, Ms Rebecca. . . . . Nov 2007
Dukes, Mrs Alison E LLB . . . . *§Nov 1986
Horowitz, Miss Claire LLB(Hons) . . . . Feb 2008
Hughes, Ms Katie. . . . . Mar 2008
Jack, Mr Andrew LLB(Hons). . . . . Aug 2009
McCall, Mr Grant LLB. . . . . Apr 2008
McIlveen, Ms Hilary BA(Hons). . . . . *Jun 1988
Muir, Miss Emma LLB. . . . . Apr 2009
Thistlethwaite, Miss Anne L LLB(Hons) . . . . *Oct 1984
Wilkinson, Miss Laura A LLB . . . . *Nov 1989

AMD SOLICITORS
15 The Mall Bristol BS8 4DS
Tel: 0117 974 4100 *Fax:* 0117 974 4106
E-mail: info@amdsolicitors.com
Office: Bristol (3 offices)
Ptr: Harris, Mr Richard T LLB . . . . *Dec 1965

AMD SOLICITORS
2 Station Road Shirehampton Bristol BS11 9TT
Tel: 0117 923 5562 *Fax:* 0117 982 2887
Dx: 33364 WESTBURY-ON-TRYM
E-mail: info@amdsolicitors.com
Office: Bristol (3 offices)
Work: D1 E F1 J1 K1 L N Q S1 S2 W X Z(d,m)
Emergency Action, Agency, Advocacy, Legal Aid undertaken and Legal Aid Franchise
Ast: Brown, Mr Christopher G BSc. . . . . *May 1979

AMD SOLICITORS
77, 79 & 81 Alma Road Clifton Bristol BS8 2DP
Tel: 0117 973 8205 *Fax:* 0117 923 7456 *Dx:* 130681 CLIFTON 4
E-mail: info@amdsolicitors.com
Office: Bristol (3 offices)
Work: A1 B1 C1 C2 D1 E F1 J1 K1 L M1 N O P Q S1 T1 T2 W Z(b,c,d,e,f,k,l)
Agency undertaken
Ptr: Golding, Mr Peter J LLB. . . . . *Oct 1988

ADAMS BURROWS ‡
34 Broad Street Staple Hill Bristol BS16 5NS
Tel: 0117 970 2246 *Fax:* 0117 970 2216 *Dx:* 31855 STAPLE HILL
E-mail: timadams@adamsburrows.co.uk
List of partners: T D S Adams
Languages: French
Work: D1 E G H K1 N P S1 Z(l,m)
Emergency Action, Agency, Advocacy, Fixed Fee Interview and Legal Aid undertaken
SPr: Adams, Mr Timothy D S LLB(Lond) . . . . *Dec 1980
Con: Crabbe, Mr Paul V LLB . . . . *Jan 1972

ALISTAIRS ‡
30 Mount Hill Hanham Bristol BS15 8QX
Tel: 0117 961 3952

ALLEN HOOLE SOLICITORS ‡
5 Portland Square Bristol BS2 8RR
Tel: 0117 942 0901 *Fax:* 0117 942 3180 *Dx:* 122083 BRISTOL 2
E-mail: lawyers@allenhoole.co.uk
List of partners: T D Allen, N Gordelier, D Heys, G Nelson, G X Percival, S A M Stevens
Office: Cheltenham
Work: C1 D1 E F1 G H J1 K1 L N Q R1 S1 T1 V W Z(c,i,l,m)
Emergency Action, Agency, Advocacy, Fixed Fee Interview, Legal Aid undertaken and Legal Aid Franchise
Ptr: Allen, Mr Terence D BA(Lond). . . . . *Jun 1979
Gordelier, Miss Nicola LLB(Hons); LPC Leonard Sainer Trust Award. . . . . *Dec 1999
Heys, Mrs Dianne LLB ★ . . . . *Oct 1990
Nelson, Mr Giles LLB(Hons). . . . . *Oct 1986
Percival, Mr Guy X LLB(Hons) . . . . *Sep 1991
Stevens, Ms Sheron Alfonsus Maria LLB ★ . . . . . . *Mar 1979

MARK ANDREWS & CO ‡
54 Ridingley Lawrence Weston Bristol BS11 0QD
Tel: 0117 983 8880 *Fax:* 0117 983 8882
List of partners: M Andrews
Ptr: Andrews, Mr Mark LLB . . . . *Oct 1990

ASHFORDS LLP
Tower Wharf Cheese Lane Bristol BS2 0JJ
Tel: 0117 321 8000 *Fax:* 0117 321 8001 *Dx:* 151760 BRISTOL 30
E-mail: info@ashfords.co.uk
Office: Exeter, London W1, Plymouth, Taunton, Tiverton
Work: C1 E J1 S2 U2 Z(za)
Ptr: Baines, Mr Andrew William BSc(Hons) . . . . Sep 1996
Betteridge, Mr Andrew Collins LLB(Hons) . . . . Sep 2000
Clarke, Ms Joanna Clare LLB . . . . Sep 1998
Livingston, Mr Eric . . . . Sep 1998
Mackay, Mr Garry LLB(Hons) . . . . Sep 1998
Pomeroy, Mr David Anthony William. . . . . Nov 1995
Smith, Mr Andrew BA; LLB . . . . Sep 2000

BARCAN WOODWARD ‡
31 North Street Bedminster Bristol BS3 1EN
Tel: 0117 963 5237 *Fax:* 0117 966 8582
Dx: 98975 BEDMINSTER (BRISTOL)
E-mail: info@bedmin.barcanwoodward.co.uk
List of partners: R A Barcan, G A Dobie, R E Harries, R O Howell, C M Miller, J H Scott, M Van Vessem, M E Voisin, G Woodward
Office: Bristol (2 offices)
Languages: Dutch, French
Work: D1 K1 K2 S1 W
Emergency Action, Agency, Advocacy, Fixed Fee Interview, Legal Aid undertaken and Legal Aid Franchise
Ptr: Dobie, Mr Gordon A LLB(L'pool). . . . . *§Jan 1984
Miller, Mr Christopher M BSc(Bris). . . . . *Aug 2006
Ast: Wathan, Miss Natalie LLB. . . . . Oct 2001

See p112 for the Key to Work Categories & other symbols

BARCAN WOODWARD
374 Gloucester Road Horfield Bristol BS7 8TP
Tel: 0117 923 2141 *Fax:* 0117 942 2287 *Dx:* 51804 HORFIELD
E-mail: info@bedmin.barcanwoodward.co.uk
Office: Bristol (2 offices)
Languages: French
Work: D1 E K1 K2 N S1 W Z(r)
Emergency Action, Agency, Advocacy, Fixed Fee Interview, Legal Aid undertaken and Legal Aid Franchise
Ptr: Howell, Mr Richard O BSc Deputy District Judge . . . *Mar 1985
Scott, Mrs Julie Helen LLB . . . Oct 1991
Woodward, Mr Giles LLB . . . Apr 1978
Ast: Joseph, Ms Kim LLB . . . *Oct 1987

BARCAN WOODWARD
6 King Street Bristol BS1 4EQ
Tel: 0117 925 8080 *Fax:* 0117 925 8081 *Dx:* 7854 BRISTOL
E-mail: info@qsquare.barcanwoodward.co.uk
Office: Bristol (2 offices)
Languages: Dutch, French
Work: D1 K1 K2 K3 N S1 W Z(r)
Emergency Action, Agency, Advocacy, Legal Aid undertaken and Legal Aid Franchise
Ptr: Barcan, Mr Richard A LLB(L'pool) . . . *Jan 1979
Harries, Mr Richard Essex . . . Nov 1999
Van Vessem, Ms Marina BSc(Hons) . . . Oct 1990
Voisin, Mrs Maria Eileen BSc(Hons) Assistant Deputy Coroner . . . *Nov 1991
Ast: Buckridge, Ms Myfanwy BA . . . *Oct 1988
Prowle, Miss Amie Louise LLB . . . Mar 2004

BARRY & BLOTT ‡
53 Westbury Hill Bristol BS9 3AD
Tel: 0117 962 9161 / 962 9171 *Fax:* 0117 962 8063
Dx: 33351 WESTBURY-ON-TRYM
E-mail: enquiries@barryandblott.com

BARTONS
22 Orchard Street Bristol BS1 5EH
Tel: 0117 925 6000 *Fax:* 0117 925 6001 *Dx:* 7881 BRISTOL
E-mail: bristol@bartons.co.uk
Office: Kingsbridge, Plymouth, Salcombe, Totnes
Languages: Punjabi, Urdu
Work: C1 C2 E R2 S1 S2 Z(l)
Ptr: Albery, Mr Philip J. . . . *Oct 1977

BATCHELOR SHARP ‡
Unit 3 Badminton Court Bristol BS37 5HZ
Tel: 01454 319100 *Fax:* 01454 313605 *Dx:* 47255 YATE
E-mail: mail@batchelorsharp.co.uk
List of partners: K Batchelor
Office: Kingswood, Knowle
Work: E L S1 W
Ptr: Batchelor, Mr Keith . . . *Dec 1977

BATTRICK CLARK SOLICITORS LTD ‡
151 Whiteladies Road Clifton Bristol BS8 2RA
Tel: 0117 973 1391 *Fax:* 0117 973 5782
Dx: 99892 BRISTOL REDLAND
E-mail: info@battrickclark.co.uk

BEALE AND COMPANY SOLICITORS LLP
Venturers House King Street Bristol BS1 4PB
Tel: 0117 915 4021 *Fax:* 0117 915 4340 *Dx:* 7809 BRISTOL
E-mail: reception@beale-law.com
Office: London WC2

BERRY SMITH LLP
1 Friary Temple Quay Bristol BS1 6EA
Tel: 0845 602 5846 *Fax:* 0117 344 5001
E-mail: bristol@berrysmith.com
Office: Bridgend, Cardiff, London WC2

BERRYMANS LACE MAWER
Broad Quay House Prince Street Bristol BS1 4DJ
Tel: 0117 975 8649 *Fax:* 0117 905 8810 *Dx:* 7807 BRISTOL
E-mail: info@blm-law.com
Office: Birmingham, Cardiff, Leeds, Liverpool, London EC2, Manchester, Southampton, Stockton-on-Tees

BEVAN BRITTAN LLP ‡
Kings Orchard 1 Queen Street Bristol BS2 0HQ
Tel: 0870 194 1000 *Fax:* 0870 194 7800 *Dx:* 7828 BRISTOL 1
E-mail: info@bevanbrittan.com
List of partners: G G Atkins, A J Buckingham, M J B Calverley, I Caplan, M Carroll, S L Cartwright, J T Chapman, J D Clarke, H Coetzee, K Cooksley, A Dagnell, A L Duthie, J L Easterbrook, T Ellis, B Evans, T M Fogarty, N A Grant, T R E Heywood, T M Hodgetts, J P Hoskins, M D Howe, S D Hughes, D J Hunter, D A Hutton, C Jarman, P Keith-Lucas, A J Kendall, J K Kirkbride, S Lamont, S A Lindsay, J C Lloyd, C McCormack, C A J Metherell, I G Miller, P H C Moody, S R Moore, K A M Mortimer, S J Mumford, D J Owens, M Print, C W N Proddow, S J Renouf, P Rinta-Suksi, J N Sinclair, S P Smith, M C Strathdee, P S Taverner, C M Taylor, A C Tobin, M S J Trinder, C A R Wade, D J Weir, S Westell, S J M Whitfield, D G Widdowson, S J Woffenden, A M T Woodward, A Young
Office: Birmingham, London EC4
Languages: French, German, Italian, Spanish
Work: A3 B1 B2 C1 C2 C3 E F2 I J1 J2 L M1 N O P Q R1 R2 S2 X Z(b,c,e,h,j,l,m,q,r,u)
Emergency Action, Agency and Advocacy undertaken
Ptr: Buckingham, Miss Alison Jane BA . . . *§Oct 1993
Calverley, Mr Mark Joseph Balmforth BA(Hons) . . . *Sep 1991
Carroll, Mr Martin LLB. . . . Sep 1997
Clarke, Mr John D BA. . . . *§Oct 1977
Ellis, Mr Tom . . . *§Dec 1991
Evans, Ms Bethan LLB . . . Oct 1993
Heywood, Mr Timothy R E BA; ACIArb . . . *Oct 1987
Hoskins, Mr Julian Peter BA(Hons) . . . *§May 1998
Howe, Mr Martin D LLB . . . *Oct 1983
Hunter, Mr David John BA(Hons)(Oxon). . . . *§Apr 1994
Hutton, Mr David A LLB(Hons) . . . *§Nov 1992
Jarman, Mr Christopher BA(History). . . . *§Nov 1987
Keith-Lucas, Mr Peter. . . . Jun 1976
Kirkbride, Mr J Kane . . . *§Oct 1990
Lamont, Ms Sarah-Jane MA(Hons)(Cantab); LSF . . . *Nov 1992
Lindsay, Mr Simon Alexander . . . *§Oct 1994
Lloyd, Ms Joanna Clare LLB; Barrister. . . . *§Apr 1997
Metherell, Mr Charles A J LLB(Hons) . . . *Nov 1985
Moore, Mr Simon Robert . . . Oct 1996
Mortimer, Mr Kenneth Adrian McKay . . . *§Dec 1975
Mumford, Ms Sarah J. . . . Nov 1981
Owens, Mr David J BA(Oxon) Innes & Howard Watson Prize . . . *§Dec 1984
Renouf, Ms Sharon Jayne LLB . . . *Nov 1994
Smith, Miss Susan Penelope LLB. . . . *§Nov 1991
Strathdee, Mr Michael Courtland LLB(Bris) . . . *§Jun 1979
Taverner, Mr Paul Stephen LLB(Hons). . . . *Dec 1991
Taylor, Ms Caroline Maria BA(Econ); DMS. . . . *§Jul 1989
Wade, Mr Christopher A R LLB(Hons); PGDip Env Law . . . *§Nov 1993
Weir, Mr Duncan J BA(Hons)(History) . . . *Sep 1993
Whitfield, Mr Stuart J M LLB(Hons) . . . *§Oct 1990
Woodward, Mr A M Tim. . . . Mar 1996
Young, Mr Anthony . . . Sep 1999

BEVANS ‡
Grove House Grove Road Bristol BS6 6UL
Tel: 0117 923 7249 *Fax:* 0117 923 7253
Dx: 99880 BRISTOL REDLAND
E-mail: info@bevans.co.uk
List of partners: A H Bevan, G R Hollebon
Office: London WC2
Languages: French, German, Italian
Work: A3 C1 E J1 O Q S1 S2 Z(e,p,q)
Emergency Action, Agency, Fixed Fee Interview and Legal Aid undertaken
Dir: Bevan, Mr Alexander Henry MA(Oxon) . . . *Nov 1977
Hollebon, Mr Guy Robin LLB CCH Business Law LPC Prize 1999 . . . *Sep 2001
Ast: Bromfield, Ms Lucinda . . . *Oct 2007
Broughton, Ms Harriet Katherine . . . *Sep 2008
Mason, Mr Neil . . . *Sep 2000
Millward Jones, Mr Robert. . . . Oct 1985
Power, Mr William MA(Cantab) Director of the North Somerset Housing; Governor of City of Bath College . . . *Mar 1980
Simpson, Mishka . . . *Sep 2006

BOBBETTS MACKAN ‡
17 Berkeley Square Clifton Bristol BS8 1HB
Tel: 0117 929 9001 *Fax:* 0117 922 5697
Dx: 122815 BRISTOL GREAT GEORGE STREET
Emergency telephone 0117 929 8987
E-mail: info@bobbetts.com
List of partners: S Marsh, A C Miles, S A Mitchell, G Tippett, K J Wood
Languages: French, German
Work: B2 D1 D2 E F1 G H J1 J2 K1 K3 K4 N O Q S1 S2 W Z(d,g,l,p,q,r,y)
Emergency Action, Agency, Advocacy, Fixed Fee Interview, Legal Aid undertaken, Legal Aid Franchise and Member of Accident Line
Ptr: Marsh, Mrs Sara . . . *§Jun 1991
Miles, Mr Anthony C ★ . . . *§Jun 1972
Mitchell, Miss Sally A LLB(Leics) . . . *§Jul 1977
Tippett, Mr Giles ★ . . . *§Sep 1999
Wood, Mr Kevin J BA(York) . . . *§Apr 1979
Asoc: George, Mr Stephen ★ . . . *§Apr 2003
Hullis, Mrs Catherine Marianna BSc; LPC . . . *Sep 2004
Tagg, Mr Christopher . . . *§Sep 1996
Ast: Cummins, Ms Donna . . . *Jan 2006
Hanson, Mrs Bessie. . . . Dec 2008
Pearce, Mrs Rebecca Kathryn. . . . *May 2005
Pitman, Mrs Sarah Anne . . . Oct 2004
Con: Williams, Mr Peter Leslie LLB(Lond). . . . *§Apr 1974

BOND PEARCE LLP
3 Temple Quay Temple Back East Bristol BS1 6DZ
Tel: 0845 415 0000 *Fax:* 0845 415 6900
Dx: 200561 BRISTOL TEMPLE MEADS
E-mail: info@bondpearce.com
Office: London EC3, Plymouth, Southampton
Ptr: Davies, Mr Timothy L LLB(Lond) . . . §Jun 1978
Dunn, Mr Ian H BA(York) . . . *§Oct 1981
Evans, Ms Nerys H . . . Apr 1997
Guyatt, Mr Richard D . . . Oct 1996
Hewes, Mr Simon P LLB(Warw). . . . *§Oct 1987
Houghton, Mr John E R MA(Oxon) . . . *Jun 1973
Hughes, Mr Simon J L BA. . . . *Sep 1998
Jones, Mr Gareth . . . Jul 1980
Kinsey, Mr C Julian M LLB(Sheff) . . . *Oct 1984
Lister, Mr Stephen M LLB . . . *Apr 1991
Mallender, Mr James D R LLB(Hons) . . . Oct 1998
Martyn, Mr Ian A BA . . . *Nov 1989
Maxwell, Ms Anna. . . . Sep 2001
O'Kane, Miss Fiona Therese BA . . . *May 1989
Oldroyd, Mr Gary . . . *Sep 1997
Parry, Mr Emrys J BSc(Lond)(Econ); FIMgt . . . *§Jan 1974
Peacey, Mr Nathan J . . . Sep 1997
Peacock, Mr Ian D LLB(Manc) . . . *§Nov 1984
Rees, Mr James . . . Oct 1991
Robson, Mr Charles R . . . Dec 1989
Rumley, Ms Joanne. . . . Sep 1998
Stockley, Mr Paul J LLB. . . . *Sep 1993
Stone, Mr Paul A BA(Hons) . . . *Sep 1998
Tettmar, Mr Victor S D LLB(Manc). . . . *§Dec 1985
Theyer, Mr Nigel A MA(Cantab) . . . *§Oct 1977
Wetherall, Mr Patrick LLB . . . *Aug 1997
Woodward, Mr Tony LLB . . . *Apr 1978

SABINA BOWLER-REED ‡
PO Box 2930 Bristol BS8 9FY
Tel: 01275 373111 *Fax:* 01275 373666 *Dx:* 130680 CLIFTON 4
E-mail: office@bowler-reed.co.uk
List of partners: S Bowler-Reed
Work: D1 D2 K1
Emergency Action, Agency, Advocacy, Fixed Fee Interview, Legal Aid undertaken and Legal Aid Franchise
Ptr: Bowler-Reed, Ms Sabina BA(Bris). . . . *Oct 1977

BRADFORD & CO
28 Cannon Street Bedminster Bristol BS3 1BN
Tel: 0117 963 5261 *Fax:* 0117 966 9778 *Dx:* 48202 NAILSEA
Emergency telephone 0117 963 5261
E-mail: bradford@bradfordlaw.freeserve.co.uk
Office: Nailsea
Languages: French, German, Italian
Work: D1 E G H K1 L N Q S1 S2 W Z(i,l)
Agency and Advocacy undertaken
Ast: Miller, Mrs Isobel BA; LLB. . . . *Apr 1988
Con: Bradford, Mr Paul A. . . . *Nov 1976

BRAIN SINNOTT & CO
713-715 Fishponds Road Fishponds Bristol BS16 3UH
Tel: 0117 965 1030 *Fax:* 0117 965 1031 *Dx:* 30764 FISHPONDS
E-mail: fishponds@brainsinnott.co.uk
Office: Kingswood
Emergency Action, Agency, Advocacy, Fixed Fee Interview, Legal Aid undertaken and Legal Aid Franchise
Ast: Carrick, Mr Brian J LLB(Nott'm) . . . Jun 1978
Sherahilo, Mr John I. . . . Jan 1985

BRICE & CO ‡
145 Whiteladies Road Clifton Bristol BS8 2QB
Tel: 0117 973 7484 *Fax:* 0117 923 7867
Dx: 99881 BRISTOL REDLAND
E-mail: briceandco@btinternet.co.uk
Work: A1 C1 E F1 K1 M1 N Q S1 S2 W Z(l)
Agency, Fixed Fee Interview, Legal Aid undertaken and Member of Accident Line
Ast: Maxwell, Mr Andrew D LLB . . . *Sep 1980

PETER BROWNE ‡
The Law Shop 48 Gloucester Road Bishopston Bristol BS7 8BH
Tel: 0117 944 1966 *Fax:* 0117 924 8688
E-mail: peter@pb-solicitors.co.uk
List of partners: P W F Browne, M R White
Languages: French, German, Spanish
Work: J1 K1 K3 L Q S1 S2 W Z(d)
SPr: Browne, Mr Peter W F MBE BA(Cantab) . . . *Jul 1967
Ptr: White, Mr Marc Robert LLB(Jt Hons)(Law & French) Notary Public. . . . *Dec 1998

BURGES SALMON ‡
One Glass Wharf Bristol BS2 0ZX
Tel: 0117 939 2000 *Fax:* 0117 902 4400 *Dx:* 7829 BRISTOL
E-mail: email@burges-salmon.com
List of partners: R A Barr, R J Bedford, C E Bewley, P A Browne, L E Claydon, P C Davey, A A Dunlop, J B Dunn, D E Evans, M J Evans, C Fletcher-Wood, S E M Forbes, D G Gidney, C M J Godfrey, P S N Haggett, C M Hallam, M R Harling, T M Illston, C M Jackson, R J Leeming, A Llewelyn Evans, D J Marsh, C A McFarlane, S J McNulty, A W M Mitchell, P H A Morris, A C Morrison, W J W Neville, N M Olley, R S Owen, M A Paterson, N F M Popplewell, P C Robinson, I K Salter, H J Scott-Lawler, C S T Seaton, R A B Spink, P R Williams, C J C Wyld
Languages: French, German, Italian, Spanish, Turkish
Work: A1 A2 A3 B1 B2 C1 C2 C3 D1 D2 E F1 F2 I J1 J2 K1 K2 L M1 M2 M3 N O P Q R1 R2 S1 S2 T1 T2 U1 U2 W X Z(b,c,d,e,f,g,h,i,j,k,l,m,n,o,p,q,s,t,u,w,y,z)
Emergency Action, Agency, Advocacy, Fixed Fee Interview, Legal Aid undertaken and Legal Aid Franchise
Ptr: Barr, Mr R Alan LLB Sweet & Maxwell Law Prize; Calcott Memorial Essay Prizes . . . *Sep 1982
Bedford, Mr Richard J LLB . . . *Oct 1986
Bewley, Mrs Colette E BSc . . . *Oct 1990
Browne, Mr Paul A LLB . . . *Apr 1992
Claydon, Miss Laura E LLB . . . *Oct 1988
Davey, Mr Philip C LLB . . . *Oct 1991
Dunlop, Mr Andrew A . . . Jun 1991
Dunn, Mr John B . . . *Dec 1977
Evans, Mrs Della E BA; LLM(Bris) Maxwell Law Prize 1980 . . . *Nov 1991
Evans, Mr Michael J LLB(Bris) . . . *Oct 1992
Fletcher-Wood, Mr Clive OBE BA . . . *Nov 1994
Forbes, Miss Sandra E M LLB. . . . *Nov 1989
Gidney, Mr David G BA(Oxon) . . . Dec 1977
Godfrey, Mr Christopher M J MA(Oxon) . . . *Oct 1986
Haggett, Mr Paul S N BA(Cantab). . . . *Oct 1985
Hallam, Miss Catherine M BA(Oxon) . . . Nov 1984
Harling, Mr Marcus R LLB. . . . *Oct 1985
Illston, Mr Timothy M BA . . . *Feb 1986
Jackson, Mr Christopher M MA(Cantab). . . . *Oct 1990
Leeming, Mr Richard J BA . . . Dec 1993
Llewelyn Evans, Mr Adrian BA(Dunelm); FCIArb . . . *Apr 1979
McFarlane, Ms Carol Ann LLB; DipLP. . . . *Aug 1995
McNulty, Mr Stephen J MA(Oxon); PhD . . . *Apr 1981
Marsh, Mr David J MA(Oxon) . . . *§Sep 1968
Mitchell, Mr A W Martin MA(Oxon) . . . *Aug 1976
Morris, Mr Peter H A BA; CPE . . . Nov 1982
Morrison, Mr Alastair Charles MA(Cantab). . . . *Mar 1987
Neville, Mr William J W ● . . . *Dec 1987
Olley, Mr Nicholas M MA(Oxon). . . . Oct 1987
Owen, Mr Richard S BA(Hons) . . . Mar 1996
Paterson, Mr Mark A . . . May 1994
Popplewell, Mr Nigel F M MA(Cantab); ATII; TEP . . . *Oct 1989
Robinson, Mr Patrick C LLB Legal Associate of the Royal Town Planning Institute . . . *Feb 1989
Salter, Mr Ian K LLB. . . . *Oct 1992
Scott-Lawler, Miss Helen J BA . . . Nov 1995
Seaton, Mr Christopher S T BSc . . . *Oct 1993
Spink, Mr Richard A B MA; LLM Harris Scholar . . . Dec 1991
Williams, Mr Peter R BA; ACIArb; BIAC. . . . *Oct 1982
Wyld, Mr Charles J C MA(Oxon) . . . *Dec 1982
Asoc: Barnett, Mr John Edward MA(Oxon). . . . Jan 1997
Benson, Mr Jeremy C LLB; LPC. . . . *Sep 1996
Bridgwater, Mrs Jane M LLB . . . *Mar 1989
Briggs, Mr Justin H C BSc(Econ) . . . *Dec 1995
Bull, Mr Roger BA(Hons); LPC . . . Jan 1997
Bulman, Mrs Deborah Helen BSc(Hons). . . . *Nov 1995
Clark, Mr Richard J R BA(Hons)(Dunelm) . . . Nov 1995
Handler, Ms Jenny A LLB Longman Prize for Planning & Environmental Law . . . Oct 1996
Hewitt, Mr Thomas R M BSc; MRICS . . . Sep 1997
Horrocks, Mrs Nicola J LLB Maxwell Law Prize; Richard Linzey Memorial Prize (Land Law); Lyons Davidson Prize *Oct 1989
Tanner, Mrs Alyson F R LLB. . . . Sep 1997
Warren, Mr Andrew N H. . . . Sep 1994
Weston, Mr W Rupert J BA(Hons). . . . Sep 1997
Whale, Miss Alyson LLB; DipLP. . . . Oct 1999
Whitehall, Mr Ian Richard BSc(Hons) . . . *Nov 1995
Ast: Aldridge, Mrs Carol Anne LLB(Leics) . . . Oct 1987
Higgins, Mrs Rose-Anna M BA(Oxon). . . . *Oct 1989

BURKE & CO
1 Baileys Court Webbs Wood Road Bradley Stoke Bristol BS32 8EJ
Tel: 0117 931 4499 *Fax:* 0117 979 8889
Dx: 124895 ALMONDSBURY 3
E-mail: info@burkeandco.co.uk
Office: Bristol
Work: E S1 W
SPr: Burke, Mr Peter F LLB . . . *Oct 1982

MARTIN BYNE ‡
182 Whiteladies Road Clifton Bristol BS8 2XU
Tel: 0117 973 1019 *Fax:* 0117 973 8258
E-mail: byne2001@yahoo.com
List of partners: M H Byne
Work: L T1 T2

Agency and Advocacy undertaken
Ptr: Byne, Mr Martin Howard . . . . *Jun 1972

CMS CAMERON MCKENNA LLP
Merchants House North Wapping Road Bristol BS1 4RW
Tel: 0117 930 0200 *Fax:* 0117 934 9300 *Dx:* 78116 BRISTOL
E-mail: info@cmck.com
Office: London EC1, London EC3
Work: B1 C1 C2 E O Z(b,j)
Ptr: Agar, Mr Nicholas S D LLB(Lond) . . . . *May 1979
Badham, Ms Sally. . . . . Sep 1993
Billington, Mr Guy MA(Cantab) . . . . *§Apr 1971
Hegarty, Mr Simon C LLB . . . . *Jun 1981
Wallace, Ms Louise H LLB(Lond) . . . . Nov 1990
Ast: Woodfield, Mr Philip John . . . . *Sep 1996

CW LAW SOLICITORS LIMITED ‡
North Quay Temple Back Bristol BS1 6FL
Tel: 0845 604 7298 *Fax:* 0117 934 9111 *Dx:* 141844 BRISTOL 19

ELIZABETH CAPLE ‡
77 Howard Road Westbury Park Bristol BS6 7UX
Tel: 0117 907 5699

ALISON CASTREY LIMITED ‡
PO Box 267 Bristol BS9 4XJ
Tel: 0117 962 2356
List of partners: A J E Castrey
SPr: Castrey, Ms Alison Jane Elizabeth MA(Hons)(Oxon). . Nov 1991

H N E CHESTERFIELD ‡
11 Old Sneed Road Stoke Bishop Bristol BS9 1ES
Tel: 0117 968 8148 *Fax:* 0117 968 8148
E-mail: nchesterfield@blueyonder.co.uk
List of partners: H N E Chesterfield
Work: J1 Z(p)
SPr: Chesterfield, Mr Hugh N E LLB . . . . *Apr 1981

CLARKE WILLMOTT
1 Georges Square Bath Street Bristol BS1 6BA
Tel: 0845 209 1000 / 0117 305 6000 *Fax:* 0845 209 2002
Dx: 78247 BRISTOL
E-mail: info@clarkewillmott.com
Office: Birmingham, London EC4, Manchester, Southampton, Taunton
Work: A1 A2 A3 B1 C1 C2 C3 E F1 F2 I J1 J2 K1 K3 L M2 N O P Q R1 R2 S1 S2 T1 T2 U2 W X Z(b,c,d,e,h,j,k,l,o,p,q,r,t,u,w,za)
Advocacy, Fixed Fee Interview, Legal Aid undertaken, Legal Aid Franchise and Member of Accident Line
Ptr: Askew, Mr Martin . . . . *Oct 1992
Baker, Mr Neil Bristol BSc. . . . . *Dec 1994
Brown, Mrs Louise LLB . . . . *Oct 1995
Chapman, Mr Paul MA(Cantab) . . . . *Dec 1995
Charlton, Mr Christopher BA(Hons)(Law) . . . . . *Feb 1995
Clarke, Mr Michael LLB(Exon). . . . . *§Mar 1973
Clarke, Mr Stephen BA(Hons)(Manc) . . . . *Nov 1995
Edwards, Miss Lorraine E LLB(Hons) . . . . *Nov 1987
Engert, Mr Nicholas LLB(Soton). . . . . *§Jul 1973
Gardner, Mrs Kate E LLB . . . . *Dec 1992
Gupta, Mr Robin LLB . . . . Oct 2000
Hall, Ms Priscilla . . . . *Oct 1989
Ham, Mr Neil L LLB(Bris) . . . . *Oct 1987
Harvey, Mr Kit Alexander LLB(Hons) . . . . *Sep 1996
Jones, Mr Kevin LLB(Cardiff) . . . . *Mar 1990
Juckes, Mr William . . . . *Oct 1982
Latham, Ms Sharon Louise LLB. . . . . *Dec 1994
Lindsay, Mr Nigel . . . . *May 1967
Livingstone, Mr Peter H LLB . . . . *Oct 1988
Lovett, Mr Gregory W LLB . . . . *§Oct 1984
McIntyre, Mr Graham BA(Hons); LPC. . . . . Sep 1997
Martin, Bonnie . . . . *Nov 1985
Morfee, Mr Robert LLB(Hons). . . . . *§Dec 1971
Oakland, Mrs Jane C LLB(B'ham). . . . . *§Jun 1979
Parrott, Mr Michael K LLB(Leics) . . . . *§Apr 1979
Pestell, Mr Hugh A J BA . . . . *Nov 1991
Pettingell, Mr Martin A BA. . . . . *Oct 1983
Pike, Ms Beverley LLB(Leics) . . . . *Nov 1982
Rankin, Ms Claire Alison BA . . . . *May 1993
Rosser, Mr Stephen BA . . . . *Oct 1984
Seager, Ms Nicola Jane. . . . . *Nov 1991
Seaton, Mr Roger MA(Oxon) . . . . *Apr 1981
Slough, Mr Steven . . . . *§May 1983
Smedley, Mr Oliver . . . . Nov 1999
Smithers, Miss Elizabeth Janet MA; TEP . . . . . . *Aug 1992
Taylor, Mr Christopher LLB(Lond) . . . . *Nov 1988
Thomas, Mr Simon . . . . Sep 1997
Watkins, Mr Trevor LLB(Hons) . . . . *Nov 1991
Whiteley, Mr William. . . . . Nov 1987
Winterborne, Mr Philip Howard BA(Hons); DipLP . . . Feb 1999

ROY COLES & CO ‡
11 Berkley Square Cliffton Bristol BS8 1HG
Tel: 0117 925 6257 *Dx:* 37004 CLIFTON
E-mail: info@roycoles.com

COOKE PAINTER LIMITED ‡
26 & 32 Gilda Parade Wells Road Whitchurch Bristol BS14 9HY
Tel: 01275 835569 *Fax:* 01275 540050
E-mail: whitchurch@cps-sols.co.uk
List of partners: C L O'Malley, S G Porter, A M Stone
Office: Bristol (3 offices), Knowle
Work: B1 K1 K3 L S1 S2
Agency undertaken
Ptr: O'Malley, Ms Claire Louise . . . . *Nov 1990
Ast: Fraser, Ms Jean. . . . . *May 2001

COOKE PAINTER LIMITED
40 Sandy Park Road Brislington Bristol BS4 3PF
Tel: 0117 971 4074 *Fax:* 0117 907 0054 *Dx:* 51051 BRISLINGTON
E-mail: brislington@cps-sols.co.uk
Office: Bristol (3 offices), Knowle
Work: E S1 S2 W
Ptr: Stone, Mr Andrew M LLB . . . . *Nov 1982

COOKE PAINTER LIMITED (incorporating Shepstones)
PO Box 1193 Backwell Bristol BS48 9AD
Tel: 01275 400037 *Fax:* 01275 463786
E-mail: backwell@cps-sols.co.uk
Office: Bristol (3 offices), Knowle
Work: E S1 S2 W
Fixed Fee Interview undertaken
Ptr: Stone, Mr Andrew M LLB . . . . *Nov 1982
Ast: Tolson, Mr Richard Martin LLB . . . . Oct 1979

COOKE PAINTER LIMITED
12 West Town Lane Brislington Bristol BS4 5BN
Tel: 0117 971 6765 *Fax:* 0117 971 9913
E-mail: westtownlane@cps-sols.co.uk
Office: Bristol (3 offices), Knowle

CORFIELD SOLICITORS ‡
2 The Avenue Sneyd Park Bristol BS9 1PA
Tel: 0117 968 8890 *Fax:* 0117 968 8891
E-mail: info@corfieldsolicitors.com

DAC BEACHCROFT
Portwall Place Portwall Lane Bristol BS99 7UD
Tel: 0117 918 2000 *Fax:* 0117 918 2100 *Dx:* 7846 BRISTOL 1
Office: Birmingham, Leeds, London EC3 (3 offices), London EC4 (2 offices), Manchester (2 offices), Newcastle upon Tyne, Newport, Winchester
Languages: French, German, Italian, Kiswahili, Norwegian, Russian, Spanish, Swedish
Work: A3 B1 B2 B3 C1 C2 C3 E F1 F2 I J1 J2 L M1 N O P Q R1 S2 T1 T2 U1 U2 W X Z(c,d,e,h,j,l,n,o,p,r,s,u,w,y,z)
Emergency Action, Agency, Advocacy undertaken and Member of Accident Line
Ptr: Austwick, Mr Malcolm P LLB . . . . *Oct 1983
Bothamley, Mr H L Michael BA(Dunelm). . . . . . . *§Apr 1982
Brothwood, Mr Graham Charles LLB . . . . *Feb 1988
Butcher, Mr Nathan James BSc(Hons); CPE; LSF. . *Nov 1994
Campbell, Mr John Marcus LLB. . . . . Oct 1990
Cherry, Mr Anthony John LLB. . . . . *May 1979
Corrigan, Mr Thomas G LLB(Manc) . . . . Oct 1985
Esam, Mr David R BA Clements Inn Prize. . . . . . *§Dec 1977
Faulkner, Mrs Helen Louise BA . . . . *Nov 1992
Hindle, Mr Giles M . . . . *Nov 1996
Knapman, Mr Nicholas . . . . Nov 1995
Lock, Mr Alex. . . . . Aug 2002
Metcalfe, Mr Stephen J BA(Oxon). . . . . Oct 1983
Montgomery, Mr Nigel BA(Cantab) . . . . *Oct 1985
Morris, Mr James S BA; CPE; LSF . . . . *Jul 1991
Ormond, Ms Jocelyn L BA(Oxon) . . . . *Oct 1997
Parke, Mr Paul F BSc; DipLaw . . . . Jun 1990
Pollitt, Mr David E BA(Bris) . . . . Dec 1993
Pratt, Mr Alan J LLB. . . . . Nov 2000
Preddy, Mr Daniel Seth . . . . Sep 1999
Roberts-Jenkins, Ms Rachel. . . . . Sep 1996
Roff, Ms Sally LLB . . . . Sep 1991
Roper, Mr Jeremy J LLB . . . . *Apr 1979
Simpson, Miss Helen . . . . *Nov 1997
Slingo, Ms Corinne . . . . Sep 1996
Staines, Ms Helen C LLB . . . . *Oct 1983
Stokes, Mr Andrew M LLB . . . . *Nov 1986
Taylor, Mr Giles . . . . Oct 1996
Thompson, Miss Susan J BA(Law); MCL . . . . *§Jul 1985
Thomson, Mr Marcus S BA . . . . *Nov 1990
Thornycroft, Mr Ben LLB . . . . *Nov 1994
Williams, Mr John B A LLB(Bris). . . . . Aug 1993
Yuill, Mrs Sally E BA . . . . *Oct 1988

DAVIS WOOD ‡
884 Fishponds Road Fishponds Bristol BS16 3XB
Tel: 0117 965 3504 *Fax:* 0117 958 3382 *Dx:* 30751 FISHPONDS
E-mail: admin@daviswood.co.uk
List of partners: J A Davis, S H Pressdee, P C Wood
Work: A1 B1 C1 C2 C3 D1 E F1 J1 K1 L N O P R1 S1 T1 T2 V W Z(j)
Emergency Action, Agency, Advocacy, Fixed Fee Interview, Legal Aid undertaken and Member of Accident Line
Ptr: Davis, Mr James A LLB. . . . . *Apr 1976
Pressdee, Mr Simon H LLB . . . . *Nov 1987
Wood, Mr Peter C LLB . . . . *Feb 1984
Asoc: Hitchings, Mr Michael LLB. . . . . *Apr 1995
Ast: Bale, Mrs Shirley A . . . . *Dec 1989
Benefield, Ms Rachel M BA(Hons) . . . . *Dec 1996

MAUREEN DE PIETRO ‡
3 Cavendish Road Henleaze Bristol BS9 4DZ
Tel: 0117 962 8772 *Fax:* 0117 940 9082

DEVEREUX & CO ‡
52 High Street Westbury-on-Trym Bristol BS9 3DZ
Tel: 0117 959 3344 *Fax:* 0117 959 3355
Dx: 33354 WESTBURY-ON-TRYM
List of partners: R J Devereux
Office: Bristol
Work: C1 D1 E K1 L S1 W
Agency undertaken
Ptr: Devereux, Mr Richard John MA(Oxon) . . . . *§Dec 1980
Ast: McCallum, Ms Elizabeth. . . . . *Jul 2005

DEVEREUX & CO
28 High Street Shirehampton Bristol BS11 0DL
Tel: 0117 938 0222 *Fax:* 0117 938 0244
Dx: 33354 WESTBURY-ON-TRYM
Office: Bristol
Work: K1 S1 S2 W
Legal Aid Franchise
SPr: Devereux, Mr Richard John MA(Oxon) . . . . *§Dec 1980
Ast: Gittoes-Davis, Miss Alexandra Mansell BA; LLB. . . *Sep 2002

AMANDA DOYLE LAW SERVICES ‡
12 Knole Park Almondsbury Bristol BS32 4BS
Tel: 07973 201327
E-mail: amanda@doylelaw.co.uk

ELITE SOLICITORS LIMITED ‡
217-219 Stapleton Road Easton Bristol BS5 0PD
Tel: 0117 952 5777

MARTIN EVANS SOLICITOR ‡
36 Laurie Crescent Bristol BS9 4TA
Tel: 0117 975 4460 *Fax:* 0117 914 1804
Emergency telephone 07971 045977
E-mail: martinevans@bristol936.freeserve.co.uk
Work: E R1 S2 Z(u)

FARRELLS SOLICITORS ‡
16 Portland Square Bristol BS2 8SJ
Tel: 0117 944 4664 *Fax:* 0117 944 4665
E-mail: info@farrells.co.uk
List of partners: S E Armitage, N D Farrell, C L O'Malley
Work: A3 B1 B2 C1 C2 E F1 I J1 K1 L N O Q S1 S2 W Z(c,e,q,r)
Emergency Action, Agency, Advocacy undertaken and Member of Accident Line
Ptr: Armitage, Mrs Sally E BSc . . . . *Oct 1991
Farrell, Mr Nigel D LLB; FCIArb . . . . *Oct 1981
O'Malley, Ms Claire L LLB(Hons) . . . . *Nov 1990

FEENY & CO ‡
177 Whiteladies Road Clifton Bristol BS8 2RY
Tel: 0117 923 9477 *Fax:* 0117 973 7189
Dx: 99875 BRISTOL REDLAND
List of partners: H D Feeny
Work: E S1 W
SPr: Feeny, Mr Hugh Denis BA. . . . . *Jun 1981

FLEET SOLICITORS LLP ‡
1 Friary Temple Quay Bristol BS1 6EA
Tel: 0845 603 3273 *Fax:* 0845 603 3274
E-mail: mail@fleetlaw.co.uk
Office: Cheltenham
Work: O Q Z(c,e,j,q)

FOSTER & PARTNERS ‡
International House Bank Road Kingswood Bristol BS15 8LX
Tel: 0117 961 5300 *Fax:* 0117 961 2981 *Dx:* 43352 KINGSWOOD
E-mail: kingswood@fostersbristol.co.uk
List of partners: V P Foster, A J T King, G W Moss, J Pratley
Office: Bristol
Languages: French
Work: D1 K1 K3 N S1 W Z(j)
Emergency Action, Agency, Advocacy, Fixed Fee Interview, Legal Aid undertaken, Legal Aid Franchise and Member of Accident Line
Ptr: King, Mr Andrew J T MA(Oxon) Deputy District Judge *Aug 1986
Moss, Mr Gregory William LLB . . . . *Feb 1987
Ast: Harris, Miss Helen LLB . . . . *Sep 2001

FOSTER & PARTNERS
1st Floor Office Suite 48 Corn Street Bristol BS1 1HQ
Tel: 0117 922 0229 *Fax:* 0117 929 8621 *Dx:* 7867 BRISTOL 1
E-mail: bristol@fostersbristol.co.uk
Office: Bristol
Languages: French, Greek
Work: D1 D2 K1 K3 N S1 V W X
Emergency Action, Agency, Advocacy, Fixed Fee Interview, Legal Aid undertaken, Legal Aid Franchise and Member of Accident Line
Ptr: Foster, Mr V Paul ♦ . . . . *§Dec 1979
Pratley, Mr John BA. . . . . *Feb 1992
Ast: Chrisfield, Ms Carol . . . . *Sep 1997
Sproull, Ms Zoe LLB . . . . *Nov 1999
Stambouleiu, Mr Hector Nicholas LLB. . . . . *Apr 1991

FOX HARTLEY ‡
St Lawrence House Broad Street Bristol BS1 2HF
Tel: 0117 917 7210 *Fax:* 0117 917 7211
Office: London EC3

FUSSELL WRIGHT ‡
59 Queen Charlotte Street Bristol BS1 4HL
Tel: 0117 927 9117 *Fax:* 0117 921 4177 *Dx:* 7858 BRISTOL
E-mail: admin@fussellwright.co.uk
Web: www.fussellwrightsolicitors.co.uk
List of partners: M R D Buck, M C Dickman
Office: Bristol
Work: C1 E L R1 S1 W
Advocacy and Fixed Fee Interview undertaken
Ptr: Dickman, Mr Michael C . . . . *§May 1987

Particular areas of work include: Bankruptcy, Commercial and Company Law, Commercial Property, Agreements, Credit, Sale.

FUSSELL WRIGHT
105 Sandy Park Road Brislington Bristol BS4 3PG
Tel: 0117 971 3535 *Fax:* 0117 972 3611 *Dx:* 51050 BRISLINGTON 2
E-mail: admin@fussellwright.co.uk
Web: www.fussellwrightsolicitors.co.uk
Office: Bristol
Work: E S1 S2 W
Ptr: Buck, Mr Malcolm Richard David LLB(Hons) . . . . . Oct 1988

Fussell Wright is a professional law firm, based in Bristol, specialising in conveyancing, wills & probate. Est over 100 years.

DAVID GIST SOLICITORS ‡
21-23 Clare Street Bristol BS1 1TZ
Tel: 0117 927 9111 *Fax:* 0117 927 9101 *Dx:* 7880 BRISTOL
E-mail: info@davidgist.co.uk
List of partners: D Gist, A G Grady, P D Honess, S Nichols
Work: J1 N O Q Z(c,j,r,w)
Agency, Advocacy, Fixed Fee Interview, Legal Aid undertaken, Legal Aid Franchise and Member of Accident Line
Ptr: Gist, Mr David Deputy District Judge . . . . *§Jan 1969
Grady, Mr Antony G LLB . . . . *Oct 1990
Honess, Mr Paul D LLB. . . . . *§Oct 1986
Nichols, Ms Sarah LLB . . . . *Nov 1990
Asoc: Mayne, Ms Helen E LLB . . . . *Nov 1996
Ast: Chisnall, Mr Justin S C LLB. . . . . *Apr 1998
Edmonds, Mr Crispin William Irvine BA(Hons); CPE; LSF . . . . *Sep 1996
Gist, Mr Stuart BA . . . . *Nov 1996
Griffith, Mrs Nia LLB . . . . *Oct 1995
Kinneon, Mr Samuel LLB . . . . *Jul 1991

GLYNNS SOLICITORS ‡
Burnts House Chelwood Bristol BS39 4NL
Tel: 01761 490883 *Fax:* 01761 490873
E-mail: info@glynns.co.uk
List of partners: J A Glynn
Languages: French
Work: C1 F1 F2 J2 N O P Q Z(q,r)
SPr: Glynn, Miss Julie A BA(Law) . . . . *Mar 1980
Ast: Bird, Mr Christopher P LLB . . . . *Aug 1991
Gomersall, Mr John Stuart BA(Hons)(English). . . . *Nov 1998

GREENWOODS
One Redcliff Street Bristol BS1 6NP
Tel: 0117 910 0200 *Fax:* 0117 910 0201
E-mail: contact@greenwoods-solicitors.com
Office: Fareham, London EC3, London WC1, Manchester, Milton Keynes
Ptr: Guy, Mr Michael LLB . . . . May 1976

GREGG LATCHAMS LLP ‡
7 Queen Square Bristol BS1 4JE
Tel: 0117 906 9400 *Fax:* 0117 906 9401 *Dx:* 7845 BRISTOL
E-mail: enquiries@gregglatchams.com

See p112 for the Key to Work Categories & other symbols

List of partners: W J Dalby, V A Daniell, R A Gore, A D M Gregg, P B Hardman, R J Hill, B L Hunt, D Langley, K B McEwan, M J Rapps
Languages: French
Work: A1 A3 B1 B2 C1 D1 D2 E F1 F2 G H J1 J2 K1 K2 L N O P Q R1 R2 S1 S2 W X Z(b,c,d,e,f,h,i,j,k,l,m,o,q,r,t,w,y)
Emergency Action, Agency, Advocacy and Fixed Fee Interview undertaken
SPr: Langley, Mr David MA(Oxon) . . . . . *Apr 1981
Ptr: Dalby, Mr William J LLB(Lond) . . . . . *Oct 1977
Daniell, Mrs Victoria A BA(General Arts). . . . . *May 1979
Gore, Mr Richard A LPC; PSC; BA(Jt Hons). . . . . *Oct 1996
Gregg, Mr Andrew D McC Notary Public. . . . . *§Dec 1970
Hardman, Mr Paul Barnsley . . . . . *Jan 1988
Hill, Mr Richard J LLB(Hons) . . . . . *Mar 1985
Hunt, Mrs Barbara L LLB . . . . . *§Apr 1974
McEwan, Mr Kenneth B BA(Hons). . . . . *Nov 1985
Rapps, Mr Michael J MA(Oxon); TEP . . . . . *Apr 1976
Asoc: Atkinson, Sarah. . . . . Mar 2006
Gupwell, Mr Michael John PGDipLaw; PGDipLP; PGDipNP Notary Public . . . . . Jun 2007
Hopkins, Mrs Clare Louise LLB . . . . . *Nov 1995
James, Mr Michael H LLB(Bris) . . . . . *Dec 1980
Langley, Mr David MA(Oxon) . . . . . *Apr 1981
McColl, Mr Iain . . . . . *Mar 2004
Orme, Ms Sally . . . . . *May 1979
Wareham, Mr Andrew John LLB. . . . . *Sep 2002
Ast: Brown, Mr Philip LLB(Hons); PGDip; DipLG Distinction - DipLG - Awarded by the Law Society . . . . . Jun 2008
Fairbairn, Mrs Maxine BA(Hons) . . . . . *Jun 1975
Foote, Mr Colin Jefferson BA(Hons); LLB(Law & Italian)Feb 2006
Frost, Miss Polly Hayllar LLB; LPC . . . . . Oct 2010
James, Miss Emma-Rose LLB; LPC. . . . . Oct 2010
Pitt, Mr Edward . . . . . Sep 2009
Con: Quinn, Mr Patrick J . . . . . *Nov 1970

HARNETT & CO ‡
729a Fishponds Road Fishponds Bristol BS16 3UW
Tel: 0117 965 5366 *Fax:* 0117 958 3891 *Dx:* 30752 FISHPONDS
E-mail: kharnett@harnettandco.co.uk
List of partners: K M Harnett
Work: C1 E K4 S1 S2 T1 T2 V W
SPr: Harnett, Miss Kathleen Mary BSc(Econ). . . . . *Oct 1986

HENRIQUES GRIFFITHS ‡
18 & 20 Portland Square Bristol BS2 8SJ
Tel: 0117 909 4000 *Fax:* 0117 942 0017 *Dx:* 122076 BRISTOL 11
E-mail: info@henriquesgriffiths.com
List of partners: M R W Griffiths, S M Halligan, P R Hogan, T P J Salvidge, A J Whiles, U A Woodburn
Office: Bristol (2 offices), Winterbourne
Languages: British Sign Language, French, German, Greek, Italian, Portuguese, Russian, Spanish
Work: B1 C1 D1 E F1 J1 K1 K2 L M1 N O P Q S1 S2 V W Z(c,d,e,f,i,j,k,l,m)
Emergency Action, Agency, Advocacy, Fixed Fee Interview, Legal Aid undertaken, Legal Aid Franchise and Member of Accident Line
Ptr: Griffiths, Mr Mark R W LLB . . . . . *Jun 1977
Halligan, Mrs Susan Margaret LLB . . . . . *Feb 1997
Hogan, Mr Phillip R LLB(Soton); LLM(Bris) . . . . . *May 1981
Salvidge, Mrs Tina Patricia Joy . . . . . *May 1990
Whiles, Ms Alison Jane LLB. . . . . *Dec 1993
Woodburn, Mr U Antony Deputy District Judge; Assistant Deputy H M Coroner . . . . . *Nov 1981
Asoc: Killough, Miss Leana Jane . . . . . Sep 2002
Marshall, Mr Richard Stephen John LLB(Hons) ♦ . . . . . *Apr 1994
Turpin, Mr Kenneth Arthur LLB . . . . . Jul 1992
White, Mrs Rosalind Kay . . . . . Sep 2001
Ast: Goda, Mrs Jennifer Mary . . . . . Mar 2005
Head, Miss Rebecca Joanne . . . . . Jan 2004
Con: Pitt, Mr A Bryan FCMI. . . . . *Dec 1973

HENRIQUES GRIFFITHS
5 Rodney Place Clifton Bristol BS8 4HY
Tel: 0117 973 2950 *Fax:* 0117 946 7461 *Dx:* 130671 CLIFTON 4
E-mail: info@henriquesgriffiths.com
Office: Bristol (2 offices), Winterbourne
Work: C1 E S1 W

HENRIQUES GRIFFITHS
(in association with Dolmans Windows)
770a Fishponds Road Fishponds Bristol BS16 3UA
Tel: 0117 965 9444 *Fax:* 0117 958 3690 *Dx:* 30750 FISHPONDS
E-mail: info@henriquesgriffiths.com
Office: Bristol (2 offices), Winterbourne
Work: S1 W
Con: Windows, Mr Anthony R MA(Cantab) . . . . . Jun 1969

DAVID HODES & CO ‡
Broad Quay House Broad Quay Bristol BS1 4DJ
Tel: 0117 905 8705 *Fax:* 0117 905 8805 *Dx:* 7804 BRISTOL
E-mail: info@davidhodes.co.uk

ALAN HODGE SOLICITORS ‡
Wellspring House 4 Castle Street Bristol BS35 1HB
Tel: 01454 888098 *Fax:* 01454 888101 *Dx:* 48354 THORNBURY
E-mail: info@alanhodge.co.uk
List of partners: A J H Hodges
SPr: Hodges, Mr Alan J H . . . . . *§Jul 1971

JOHN HODGE SOLICITORS
Venturers House Kings Street Bristol BS1 4PB
Tel: 0117 929 2281 *Dx:* 8403 WESTON-SUPER-MARE
E-mail: mailbox@johnhodge.co.uk
Office: Clevedon, Wedmore, Weston-super-Mare (2 offices), Yatton
Work: A1 C1 D1 D2 E J1 J2 K1 K2 K3 K4 N O Q R2 S1 S2 W Z(q,r)
Fixed Fee Interview undertaken

HOOLE & CO ‡
65 Gloucester Road Patchway Bristol BS34 5JH
Tel: 0117 969 1436 *Fax:* 0117 923 6311 *Dx:* 35019 ALMONDSBURY
Emergency telephone 0117 969 1436
E-mail: william.nicks@hooleandco.co.uk
List of partners: D N Miller, W A Nicks
Office: Bristol
Work: B2 C1 D1 E J1 J2 K1 L N P Q S1 S2 V W Z(i)
Emergency Action, Agency, Advocacy, Fixed Fee Interview and Legal Aid undertaken
Ptr: Miller, Mr David N LLB(Lond) ★. . . . . *May 1988
Nicks, Mr William Anthony LLB Part time Chairman of SSAT . . . . . *Jul 1965
Ast: Avery, Mr Mark D BA ♦ . . . . . *Aug 1989
Green, Ms Helen C BA . . . . . *Mar 1979

HOOLE & CO
St Pauls Chambers 2 Brighton Street St Pauls Bristol BS2 8XA
Tel: 0117 942 8871 *Fax:* 0117 924 4859
Office: Bristol
Work: K1 Z(i)
Legal Aid Franchise
Ptr: Miller, Mr David N LLB(Lond) ★ . . . . . *May 1988
Ast: Gage, Mr Richard LLB(Hons) . . . . . *Sep 2003
Singh, Mr Robby . . . . . Nov 2000

ROBERT HOWE ‡
46 Grange Road Saltford Bristol BS31 3AG
Tel: 01225 873480 *Fax:* 01225 874042
E-mail: roberthowe@saltford56.freeserve.co.uk

HUGHES ENTERPRISE LAW PRACTICE ‡
Tyrm Lodge 1 Henbury Road Bristol BS9 3HQ
Tel: 0117 959 6424 *Fax:* 0117 959 6425
E-mail: info@enterpriselaw.co.uk
List of partners: A D Hughes
Work: A3 C1 I J1 O U2 Z(e,q)
SPr: Hughes, Mr Anthony D MA(Oxon). . . . . *§Apr 1981

HUMPHREYS & CO ‡
14 King Street Bristol BS1 4EF
Tel: 0117 929 2662 *Fax:* 0117 929 2722 *Dx:* 78239 BRISTOL
E-mail: lawyers@humphreys.co.uk
List of partners: S M Burbidge, R A Humphreys, P L G Montgomery, P L B Siddons
Languages: French, German, Spanish
Work: A1 A3 B1 C1 C2 C3 E F1 F2 I J1 J2 L M1 M2 N O P Q R1 R2 S1 S2 U1 U2 W Z(c,d,e,f,g,i,j,k,l,p,q,r,w,z,za)
Emergency Action, Agency, Advocacy, Fixed Fee Interview and Legal Aid undertaken
Ptr: Burbidge, Mr Stephen Mark LLB(Soton). . . . . *Oct 1992
Humphreys, Mr Robert A BA(Oxon); MA(Oxon) . . . . *Jun 1981
Montgomery, Mr Peter L G BA(Bris). . . . . *Nov 1981
Siddons, Mr Philip Ll B LLB; BA(Bris); LLB(Wales) . . *Nov 1983
Asoc: Annand, Prof Ruth Elaine LLB(Hons)(Dunelm) . . . . *Jun 1974
Lipman, Mr Peter Anand BSc(Warw) . . . . . *Oct 1992
Morris, Mr David Phillip LLB(Cardiff). . . . . *Apr 1979
Ast: Holly, Mr Neil Allan BA(Law & Sociology)(Warw); LPC(UWE) . . . . . Apr 2010
Hotson, Ms Leanne LLB(Law & Psychology)(Swansea); LPC(swansea) . . . . . Apr 2011
Kumar, Ms Nisha LPC; BA(Oxon) . . . . . Jan 2009
Morse, Mr Tristan Matthew LLB . . . . . Jan 2009

IRWIN MITCHELL LLP
One Castlepark Tower Hill Bristol BS2 0JA
Tel: 0870 150 0100 *Fax:* 0845 609 9920
Office: Birmingham, Leeds, London EC1, Manchester, Newcastle upon Tyne, Sheffield

KELCEY & HALL ‡
Fosters Chambers 17 Small Street Bristol BS1 1DE
Tel: 0117 927 9604 *Fax:* 0117 925 0609 *Dx:* 78206 BRISTOL
Emergency telephone 07659 104004
E-mail: enquiry@kelceyandhall.co.uk
List of partners: N J Clough, G Hall, I C P Kelcey
Languages: Spanish
Work: B2 D1 D2 G H I J1 J2 K1 N S1 W Z(c,i,j,r)
Emergency Action, Agency, Advocacy, Fixed Fee Interview, Legal Aid undertaken, Legal Aid Franchise and Member of Accident Line
Ptr: Clough, Mr Nicholas John ★. . . . . *Jul 1975
Hall, Miss Gillian BA . . . . . *Oct 1982
Kelcey, Mr Ian C P . . . . . *§May 1980
Asoc: Adams, Mrs Susan MA(Cantab). . . . . *Dec 1978
Chamberlain, Miss Nicola BA(Hons). . . . . Sep 1999
Ast: Arthur, Mr Nicholas J . . . . . *Oct 1996
Thornton, Miss Amanda Jane BA . . . . . *Aug 1999

RODNEY KING & PARTNERS ‡
All Saints House 6 All Saints Lane Bristol BS1 1JH
Tel: 0117 926 5201 *Fax:* 0117 927 6526 *Dx:* 78137 BRISTOL
Emergency telephone 0117 929 3377 (CRIMINAL DEFENCE)
E-mail: enquiries@rodneyking.co.uk
List of partners: R E King, D J Stone
Work: D1 G H K1 K3 S1 W
Emergency Action, Agency, Advocacy, Legal Aid undertaken and Legal Aid Franchise
Ptr: King, Mr Rodney E MBA . . . . . *Mar 1972
Stone, Miss Deborah J LLB. . . . . *Oct 1985
Ast: Brooker, Mr Neil Christopher BA(Hons); DipLaw. . . . *Aug 2004
Petters, Mr Leigh David BA(Hons)(Bris)(German); CPE(UWE) . . . . . *Jan 2006
Powles, Mr Thomas James Joseph LLB. . . . . *Nov 2003

KIRBY SHEPPARD
(incorporating Kirby Fixsen & Godwin; Watson Sinnott)
49/50 Queen Square Bristol BS1 4LW
Tel: 0845 840 0045 *Dx:* 7855 BRISTOL
E-mail: info@kirbysheppard.co.uk
Office: Kingswood, Thornbury
Languages: French, German
Work: A1 B1 C1 C2 C3 D1 D2 E F1 J1 K1 K4 L M1 M2 N O P Q S1 T1 T2 W Z(c,j,k,l,m,p)
Emergency Action, Agency, Advocacy, Fixed Fee Interview, Legal Aid undertaken and Member of Accident Line
Ptr: Bell, Mr James LLB . . . . . *Feb 2005
Curwen, Mr David B BA; MA . . . . . *Oct 1978
Gridley, Mr James R BSc ♦ . . . . . *Jun 1980
Pennelegion, Ms Hanni LLB(Hons)(Law & French) ♦ . Feb 1999
Willcocks, Mr Andrew G LLB(Hons); LSF ♦ . . . . . *Jan 1994
Ast: Firth, Ms Amanda J BA . . . . . *May 1979
Francis, Ms Sara S V BA(Lond) ♦. . . . . *Jul 1978
Moger, Miss Charmaine LLB; DipLP. . . . . Oct 2010
Shepherd, Miss Carrie Denise LLB(Jt Hons)(Law & Psychology) . . . . . Aug 2006
Williams, Miss Samantha Mary LLB . . . . . Aug 2008

LAW EXPRESS ‡
10 The Sanctuary Macrae Road Ham Green Bristol BS20 0DD
Tel: 01275 378700 *Fax:* 0870 043 4283

LEUNG & CO ‡
111 Victoria Street Bristol BS1 6AX
Tel: 0117 920 9230 *Fax:* 0117 920 9239
Emergency telephone 07092 227788
E-mail: info@leung-solicitors.co.uk
List of partners: W H A Leung
Languages: Cantonese, Mandarin
Work: B1 C1 E F1 J1 K1 L M1 Q S1 S2 V W Z(c,d,e,i,l,p,y)
Emergency Action, Agency and Fixed Fee Interview undertaken
SPr: Leung, Ms Wing Hing Amelia BSocSc(Hons); LLM ♦ Notary Public. . . . . *§Mar 1992

LINDLEYS ‡
(incorporating Lindleys; David Johnstone Co; Stevens & Co)
11 Great George Street Bristol BS1 5RR
Tel: 0117 926 2408 *Fax:* 0117 922 5866
Dx: 122802 BRISTOL GREAT GEORGE STREET
E-mail: administrators@lindleyjohnstone.com
List of partners: D W Hendey
Office: Clevedon
Work: B1 C1 D1 E F1 J1 K1 L N O P R1 S1 S2 W Z(c,e,f,l,q)
Agency, Advocacy and Legal Aid undertaken
Ptr: Hendey, Mr David W LLB . . . . . *Apr 1976

GORDON LOWE & CO ‡
132 Station Road Yate Bristol BS37 4PQ
Tel: 01454 326833 *Fax:* 01454 326843 *Dx:* 47256 YATE
E-mail: info@gordonlowe.co.uk
List of partners: G F A Lowe, G Plessier
Work: D1 D2 K1 K3 N Q
Legal Aid undertaken
Ptr: Lowe, Mr Gordon F A BA; Cert Ed . . . . . *Apr 1971
Plessier, Mr Guy BA(Hons) . . . . . Nov 1999

LYONS DAVIDSON ‡
Victoria House 51 Victoria Street Bristol BS1 6AD
Tel: 0117 904 6000 *Fax:* 0117 904 6006 *Dx:* 7834 BRISTOL
E-mail: info@lyondavidson.co.uk
List of partners: R J Acock, S Alexander, M R Bastow, G J A Brand, Z Browne, R T Charles, J Darlington, I Davies, J Gore, A Hewitt, A J Hibbard, J P Hicks, T Jones, J Kelbie, M Lennaghan, K P Morgan, J W Myatt, T B Naylor, C Parsons, P Revell, B V Rowe, J E Scowen, R J Squire, T A Still, S Upton, R Voke, M Walsh
Office: Cardiff, Leeds, New Malden, Plymouth, Solihull
Work: C1 C2 D1 E J1 J2 K1 K2 K3 N O P Q S1 S2 W Z(j,o,p,q,r,y)
Advocacy, Fixed Fee Interview and Legal Aid undertaken
Ptr: Acock, Mr Roger J LLB . . . . . *§Oct 1980
Alexander, Mrs Susan BA. . . . . *Apr 1996
Bastow, Mr Martin R LLB . . . . . *Oct 1988
Brand, Mr Graham J A LLB . . . . . *§Dec 1982
Browne, Mr Zak. . . . . Oct 1992
Charles, Mr Richard Tudor BA . . . . . Oct 1992
Darlington, Jo. . . . . Sep 1993
Gore, Mr John . . . . . Sep 1992
Hewitt, Mr Alex . . . . . Jun 1991
Hibbard, Miss Amanda J LLB . . . . . *Nov 1989
Hicks, Mr John P BA . . . . . *Oct 1981
Jones, Mr Trevor . . . . . Oct 1994
Lennaghan, Ms Michelle . . . . . Sep 1998
Morgan, Mr Kevin Paul LLB. . . . . *Sep 1996
Myatt, Mr James W LLB(Wales). . . . . Mar 1983
Naylor, Mr Thomas Barry LLB. . . . . *May 1995
Parsons, Ms Carol . . . . . Dec 1999
Revell, Mr Peter. . . . . Sep 1996
Rowe, Mr Bernard V BA. . . . . *§Nov 1976
Scowen, Miss Jennifer E LLB . . . . . *Aug 1987
Squire, Mr Richard J LLB . . . . . *Apr 1980
Still, Mr Trevor A MA(Cantab) . . . . . *Oct 1987
Upton, Ms Susan . . . . . Aug 1996
Voke, Mr Richard . . . . . Mar 2002
Ast: Partridge, Mr Nigel LLB . . . . . *Sep 1990
Richardson, Mr James I LLB . . . . . *Sep 1990
Sage, Ms Jill E . . . . . Oct 1992
Savill, Mr Mark BA(Cantab) . . . . . *Feb 1992

LYONS ROUNSFELL
95 Regent Street Kingswood Bristol BS15 8LJ
Tel: 0117 967 5252 *Fax:* 0117 935 2122 *Dx:* 43355 KINGSWOOD
E-mail: enquiries@lyonsrounsfell.co.uk
Office: Westbury-on-Trym
Work: A1 B1 C1 C2 C3 D1 E F1 G H I J1 K1 L M1 M2 N P Q R1 S1 T1 T2 V W Z(c,e,h,k,l)
Emergency Action, Agency, Advocacy, Fixed Fee Interview, Legal Aid undertaken and Member of Accident Line
Ptr: Lyons, Miss Clancy A LLB. . . . . *Nov 1981

GARY MCFARLANE ‡
Rivermead Lower Conham Vale Bristol BS15 3AU
Tel: 0117 941 4844

MAGNA LAW ‡
The Coach House Magna House Battle Lane Bristol BS40 8PX
Tel: 01275 332000 *Fax:* 0870 487 7511
E-mail: enquiries@magnalaw.co.uk

MEADE-KING ‡
11-12 Queen Square Bristol BS1 4NT
Tel: 0117 926 4121 *Fax:* 0117 929 7578 *Dx:* 7812 BRISTOL
E-mail: gen@meadeking.co.uk
List of partners: C A Ainley, R J Boulding, P J Burbidge, A J Chivers, J N G Hawkins, N W Hughes, E A Langford, K W Mahoney
Work: A3 B1 C1 C2 E J1 J2 K4 L O P Q R2 S1 S2 T1 T2 W Z(c,d,e,l,q)
Agency, Advocacy and Fixed Fee Interview undertaken
Ptr: Ainley, Miss Catherine A LLB . . . . . *Oct 1991
Boulding, Mr Richard J LLB; TEP . . . . . *§Jun 1980
Burbidge, Mr Philip John ACIArb; LLB(Soton) . . . . *Apr 1995
Chivers, Mr Adam J MA(Oxon); FCIArb; MPNLA . . . *Dec 1978
Hawkins, Mr James N G LLB . . . . . *Oct 1985
Hughes, Miss Nicola Wynne BA. . . . . *Sep 2001
Langford, Mr Edward A LLB. . . . . *Dec 1992
Mahoney, Mr Keith W BSc; FABRP . . . . . *Apr 1996
Asoc: East, Mr Simon Robert LLB(Hons); PGDipLP . . . . . *Oct 1998
McCartney, Miss Mary LLB; LLM; TEP. . . . . *Oct 1980
Ast: Dymock, Mr Adam Rhys LLB . . . . . *Jan 2009
Francetti, Mr David Andrew BA(Hons); LLM. . . . . *Jun 2007
Hardingham, Ms Sheila Mary LLB. . . . . *Apr 1976
Hartigan, Miss Lauren Alexandra LLB . . . . . *Sep 2010
Hesbrook, Miss Clare Stephanie LLB; LPC . . . . . *Oct 2009
Molter, Miss Anna LLB(Hons) . . . . . *Aug 2002

MENZIES LAW ‡
St Brandon's House 29 Great George Street Bristol BS1 5QT
Tel: 0845 113 0150 *Fax:* 0871 989 6159
E-mail: enquiries@menzieslaw.co.uk

MERRETT & CO ‡
Hazel Farm Upper Littleton Winford Bristol BS40 8HG
Tel: 01275 331228 *Fax:* 01275 331248
E-mail: info@merrettandco.com

2

List of partners: T Merrett
Work: E P R1 Z(u)
SPr: Merrett, Ms Tracey LLB(Hons) . . . . Oct 1985

METCALFES ‡
46-48 Queen Square Bristol BS1 4LY
Tel: 0117 929 0451 *Fax:* 0117 929 9551 *Dx:* 7835 BRISTOL
Emergency telephone 0117 971 4050
E-mail: info@metcalfes.co.uk
List of partners: D Boniface, S J Duddell, J Y Ellery, H E Falconer, A J B Forster, R D Forster, A M Heath, L K McCluskey, A Rigby, J B Smart, A J Stone
Languages: French
Work: A1 A3 B1 C1 C2 C3 D1 E F1 I J1 J2 K1 K2 K3 K4 L M1 M2 N O P Q R1 R2 S1 S2 T1 T2 U1 U2 W Z(b,c,d,e,f,j,l,m,p,q,r)
Emergency Action, Agency, Advocacy, Legal Aid undertaken, Legal Aid Franchise and Member of Accident Line
Ptr: Boniface, Mr David LLB(Bris) . . . . *Dec 1980
Duddell, Mr Stephen J LLB(Hons). . . . . *Jun 1981
Ellery, Ms Judith Y LLB . . . . *Nov 1987
Falconer, Ms Helen E LLB. . . . . *Jun 1993
Forster, Mr Anthony J B BA(Law) . . . . *Mar 1984
Forster, Mrs Rhona D BA(Hons). . . . . *Mar 1984
Heath, Mr Anthony M BA . . . . *Dec 1979
McCluskey, Ms L Kay LLB Legal Secretary of the Bristol Medico-Legal Society; Chairwoman of Bristol NBPA. . . . *Oct 1982
Rigby, Miss Angelina BSc(Econ) . . . . *Sep 1993
Smart, Miss Julia B LLB Chairman of the Bristol Collaborative Family Lawyers Pod; Committee Member of Bristol Resolution . . . . *Sep 1979
Stone, Mr Adrian Jeremy LLB . . . . *Nov 1986
Asoc: Bliss, Miss Natasha Kirsten LLB(Hons)(with French Law) . . . . *Jan 2005
Burgess, Ms Martino Lois . . . . *Jan 2001
Evans, Mrs Caroline Helen Samantha LLB(Hons) . . *May 2002
Ast: Bateman, Miss Heidi Caroline . . . . *Dec 2006
Baynton, Mr David Andrew LLB(Hons) . . . . *Jan 2010
Block, Miss Claire Victoria. . . . . Nov 2008
Duggan, Mr Paul Anthony MSc . . . . *Feb 2007
Con: Bragg, Mr James R LLB(Bris) . . . . *Jul 1969

MONTAGUE HARRIS ‡
Hartley House 35 High Street Bristol BS37 6BA
Tel: 01454 322722 / 313362 *Fax:* 01454 273009
E-mail: montag@globalnet.co.uk
List of partners: N L Nagle
Work: A1 B1 C1 D1 E F1 J1 L R1 S1 S2 T1 V W Z(l,p)
Agency undertaken
SPr: Nagle, Mrs Nancy L. . . . . *§May 1982

MORGAN COLE
3rd Floor South Plaza Marlborough Street Bristol BS1 3NX
Tel: 0117 916 7220 *Fax:* 0117 924 9192 *Dx:* 7865 BRISTOL
E-mail: info@morgan-cole.com
Office: Cardiff, Oxford, Reading (2 offices), Swansea
Ptr: Bradley, Miss Deborah A BA(L'pool). . . . . *Oct 1987
Morgan, Ms Zoe L BA; PGDipLaw. . . . . *Sep 1997
Ottley, Mr Richard J BA(Kent) . . . . *Sep 1990
Poole, Mr Ian T PGDipLaw . . . . *Mar 1998
Asoc: Anderson, Mr Philip Thursfield LLB(Hons). . . . . . *Oct 1982
Brock, Miss Sally A . . . . *Nov 2003
Jones, Mrs Tessa F L. . . . . *Aug 1998
Weldon, Mrs Claire Rachel LLB . . . . Sep 2002
Ast: Drew, Miss Naomi J M LLB(Hons). . . . . *Sep 1998
Morgan, Mr Jonathan Alexander LLB(Hons). . . . . . *Apr 1990
Snook, Miss Holly. . . . . Nov 2006
Swanton, Miss Laura Elizabeth LLB. . . . . *Sep 1997
Twort, Miss Georgina E. . . . . *Jul 2002

JOHN A NEIL ‡
1 Friary Temple Quay Bristol BS1 6EA
Tel: 0117 344 5003 *Fax:* 0117 344 5220
E-mail: post@johnaneil.co.uk
List of partners: J A Neil
Ptr: Neil, Mr John A . . . . *Oct 1980

NICOLE LITTLE ‡
35 Burghley Road St Andrews Bristol BS6 5BL
Tel: 07909 966231
E-mail: nicole.a.little@googlemail.com

NILE ARNALL SOLICITORS ‡
11 Cotham Road South Kingsdown Bristol BS6 5TZ
Tel: 0117 909 8898 *Fax:* 0117 909 6347
List of partners: G Arnall, R P Morgan-Jones, R J Nile
Work: G H Z(i)
Agency, Advocacy, Fixed Fee Interview and Legal Aid undertaken
Ptr: Arnall, Mr Graham LLB(Bris) . . . . Nov 1994
Morgan-Jones, Mr Robert Paul LLB(Hons) . . . . . . *Oct 1992
Nile, Mr Richard J LLB(B'ham) . . . . Nov 1972

OCEAN PROPERTY LAWYER ‡
199 Gloucester Road Bristol BS7 8BG
Tel: 0117 916 6600 *Fax:* 0117 916 6609 *Dx:* 51805 HORFIELD
E-mail: j.aldons@ocean-propertylawyers.co.uk

OSBORNE CLARKE ‡
2 Temple Back East Temple Quay Bristol BS1 6EG
Tel: 0117 917 3000 *Fax:* 0117 917 3005 *Dx:* 7818 BRISTOL
E-mail: enquiries@osborneclarke.com
List of partners: O Al-Nuaimi, K L A Almond, J Barker, M G Bell, M Bennett, R Berg, T D Birt, A J A Bott, R Bowyer, A Boyle, A L Braithwaite, R J Bretton, J Brooks, S Brown, S C Bulman, P V Clough, D Cubitt, D Darnton, R N F Drewett, C D Dyer, S Fielder, A J Finnegan, W Fongenie, R C C Gait, P A Gardner, S Groom, J S J Hemming, S P Jebb, A R John, N Johnson, C F Kearney, P J Killen, D J Kingdon, G Leyshon, A M Lifely, A Livingstone, J A Lougher, M C L Macpherson, P Matthews, H C C Minto, P G S Moss, J H Moule, J J Mullock, C L Robinson, L Roma, B Rutherford, A J Saul, T A Savvides, S J Speirs, P Staunton, N R G Strahl, F Sweeting, S C Wilson, M R A Womersley, M Woodward, D Wright
Office: London EC2, Reading
Languages: Danish, Dutch, French, German, Italian, Spanish
Work: A1 B1 C1 C2 C3 E F1 I J1 L M1 M2 N O P Q R1 S1 T1 T2 W X
Emergency Action, Agency and Advocacy undertaken
Ptr: Al-Nuaimi, Mr Omar. . . . . Sep 1997
Bell, Mr Michael Guest BSc(Lond). . . . . *Apr 1993
Bennett, Mr Matthew MA(Cantab). . . . . *Nov 1994
Boyle, Miss Anne-Marie LLM; BA(Hons)(Law) . . . . *Sep 1997
Braithwaite, Mr Andrew L LLB. . . . . *Feb 1985
Bretton, Mr Richard J LLB(Bris) . . . . *§Apr 1978
Brooks, Mr Jonathan . . . . Jan 1993
Brown, Mrs Sandra LLB(Bris) . . . . *Oct 1986
Bulman, Mr Sean Christopher LLB . . . . *Oct 1993
Clough, Mr Peter V . . . . Nov 1989
Darnton, Dolf . . . . Apr 1994
Drewett, Mr Robert N F MA(Oxon) . . . . *Mar 1987
Hemming, Mr Julian St John MA(Cantab); LLM . . . . *Oct 1989
John, Mr Alan R BA(Oxon) . . . . Oct 1984
Killen, Mr Paul J. Jan 2000
Livingstone, Mr Alisdair . . . . Oct 1995
Matthews, Mr Paul . . . . Oct 1993
Moss, Mr Philip G S. . . . . *Oct 1983
Moule, Ms Jocelyn Handley BSc; FIMLS . . . . . . *Dec 1992
Mullock, Mr James Justin . . . . Sep 1996
Robinson, Ms Clare L LLB . . . . Nov 1987
Speirs, Mr Simon J MA(Cantab). . . . . *Nov 1982
Sweeting, Ms Fiona. . . . . Jan 1995
Womersley, Mr Mark Richard Arthur MA(Cantab) . . *§Nov 1992
Woodward, Mr Mark LLB(Soton) . . . . Apr 1999
Wright, Mr Daniel . . . . Sep 2002
Asoc: Boobier, Mr Nigel J LLB. . . . . *Oct 1994
Briggs, Ms Leona Jane . . . . Oct 1992
Clarkson Webb, Mr D William . . . . *Jul 1992
Clayton, Mr Andrew BA(Hons). . . . . *Apr 1994
Higgs, Mr David Geoffrey . . . . Dec 1994
Jordan, Hallam A MA(Oxon). . . . . Oct 1987
Luker, Mr Charles C MA(Oxon) . . . . *§Dec 1976
McPherson, Mr Hugh A BA . . . . *Oct 1980
Morgan, Mrs Maureen J LLB . . . . Apr 1976
Murphy, Ms Breige LLB . . . . *Dec 1991
Nankervis, Ms Marianne V LLB . . . . *Nov 1987
O'Haire, Mr Michael J. . . . . Dec 1980
Rogers, Miss Jane M LLB. . . . . *Jun 1979
Tithecott, Mrs Andrea LLB. . . . . *Oct 1992
Ast: Arnold, Mr Simon LLB(Hons) . . . . Nov 1998
Barker, Mr John. Nov 1992
Bridges, Mr Kevin D. . . . . Sep 1997
Burch, Ms Lara F M. . . . . Mar 1996
Chivers, Mr Phillip M . . . . Nov 1996
Cook, Mr Patrick D MA . . . . *Sep 1981
Dawe-Lane, Mr Patrick J LLB . . . . Jun 1994
Ferris, Mr David J. . . . . Sep 1997
Fitzsimons, Ms Linda . . . . Oct 1993
Groom, Mr Stephen W BA(Oxon) . . . . *§Apr 1975
Heyes, Ms Jennifer C . . . . Sep 1997
Jones, Mr Hugh. Nov 1989
Lewis, Mr Matthew . . . . Mar 1999
Mant, Mr Julian D. . . . . Dec 1996
Milkins, Mr Jason R. . . . . Sep 1997
Om, Miss Erika E H LLB(Hons) . . . . *Dec 1990
Peden, Mr Douglas . . . . Sep 1996
Perrin, Leslie C BA Secretary for Bristol Old Vic. . . . *Nov 1985
Roxburgh, Mr Bruce O . . . . *Dec 1986
Shute, Mrs Colleen . . . . *Feb 1986
Sian, Herdeep. . . . . Mar 1998
Squire, Mr Grant LLB(Hons). . . . . Oct 1997
Walker, Ms Lucy. Oct 1998
Watts, Mr Clive R. . . . . *Dec 1977
Welchman, Ms Cecilia E . . . . Sep 1997
Wilkinson, Mr Ian R. . . . . Sep 1997

PALMER RAY ‡
64-68 Stokes Croft Bristol BS1 3QU
Tel: 0117 944 4678 *Fax:* 0117 944 4789

PARKHOUSE & CO ‡
106 Henleaze Road Henleaze Bristol BS9 4JZ
Tel: 0117 962 9978 *Fax:* 0117 962 8535
E-mail: david.parkhouse@parkhousesolicitors.co.uk
List of partners: P F Burke, D L Parkhouse
Office: Bristol
Work: C1 D1 E F1 J1 K1 L N O Q R1 S1 T1 T2 V W Z(c,j,l)
Agency, Advocacy, Fixed Fee Interview undertaken and Member of Accident Line
Ptr: Burke, Mr Peter F LLB . . . . *Oct 1982
Parkhouse, Mr David L BA . . . . *Oct 1980

PATTINSON & BREWER
Transport House Victoria Street Bristol BS1 6AY
Est: 1891
Tel: 0117 917 1100 *Fax:* 0117 917 1101
Dx: 200554 BRISTOL TEMPLE MEADS
E-mail: bristol-enquiries@pattinsonbrewer.co.uk
Office: London WC1, York
Work: N Q Z(q)
Member of Accident Line
Ptr: Lightwood, Mr Gary. . . . . *Nov 1986

PETER BURROWS & CO ‡
194 North Street Southville Bristol BS3 1JF
Tel: 0117 963 6366 *Fax:* 0117 963 6366
E-mail: info@peterburrowssolicitors.co.uk

PIERCE GLYNN
Executive Centre Bristol Centre Gate Colston Avenue Bristol BS1 4TR
Tel: 0117 317 8133 *Fax:* 020 7407 0444
E-mail: mail@pierceglynn.co.uk
Office: London SE1

PINSENT MASONS LLP
33-35 Queen Square Bristol BS1 4LU
Est: 2004
Tel: 0117 924 5678 *Fax:* 0117 924 6699 *Dx:* 78154 BRISTOL
E-mail: enquiries@pinsentmasons.com
Office: Birmingham, Leeds, London EC2, Manchester
Languages: French, German
Work: A3 E J2 N O P R1 R2 S1 S2 Z(c,u)
Emergency Action, Agency and Advocacy undertaken
Ptr: Collingwood, Mr Mark A. . . . . *Oct 1980
Davies, Mr Lawrence M. . . . . *Oct 1984
Foley, Mr Richard E. . . . . May 1988
Harris, Mr Adam P. . . . . May 1981
Vickers, Miss Cathryn J BSc(Econ) . . . . *§Nov 1989

PRICE & CO SOLICITORS ‡
16 Hotwell Road Bristol BS8 4UD
Tel: 0117 949 4144 *Fax:* 0117 949 4148
E-mail: priceandco@tiscali.co.uk

QUALITY SOLICITORS BURROUGHS DAY ‡
14 Charlotte Street Bristol BS1 5PT
Tel: 0117 929 0333 *Fax:* 0117 929 0335 *Dx:* 7825 BRISTOL 1
E-mail: contact@qsbd4law.com
List of partners: J C Baden-Daintree, J H C Balchin, J Beasley, H B Craig, F M Dawrant, C W I Edmonds, M Huang, A F McPherson, A Minihane, H E Phillips, A Putin, M J Ryan
Office: Portishead
Languages: Cantonese, French, German, Greek, Italian
Work: A1 A3 B1 C1 C2 C3 D1 D2 E F1 F2 I J1 J2 K1 K3 K4 L M1 M2 N O Q R1 R2 S1 S2 T1 T2 V W Z(c,d,e,h,j,k,l,o,p,q,r,s)
Emergency Action, Agency, Advocacy, Fixed Fee Interview, Legal Aid Franchise and Member of Accident Line
Ptr: Baden-Daintree, Mr John Christopher LLB. . . . . . *Nov 1989
Balchin, Mr John Hugh Charles LLB. . . . . *Oct 1991
Beasley, Ms Julia BA; PGDip; LPC Civil Justice Council Essay Competition - 1st Prize 2002 . . . . *Nov 2002
Craig, Mrs Helena Begum LLB(Hons) . . . . *Feb 1996
Dawrant, Ms Fiona Mary BSc(Hons). . . . . *Sep 1996
Edmonds, Mr Crispin William Irvine BA(Hons); CPE; LSF . . . . *Sep 1996
Huang, Ms Mei-Ling BA; JD. . . . . Jan 2004
McPherson, Miss Anne F BA(Hons)(Lancs) . . . . . *§Dec 1975
Minihane, Miss Anne LLB Panel Receiver for Court of Protection . . . . *Sep 1989
Phillips, Miss Hazel E LLB. . . . . *Sep 2000
Putin, Mr Andrew LLB(Lond) . . . . *§Dec 1978
Ryan, Mr Martin John LLB. . . . . *Feb 1981
Asoc: Andrews, Ms Jennifer. . . . . Nov 2001
Donohue, Mr Brendan Kevin BA(Hons) . . . . *Mar 2003
Pratt, Miss Fiona Jane BA. . . . . *Mar 2002
Woodham, Mr Leigh Spencer LLB. . . . . *Aug 1999
Ast: Fox, Miss Helga M LLB(Hons). . . . . *Mar 2004
Hamilton, Mrs Sophie Anita LLB; PGDipLP . . . . . *Mar 2002
Jones, Julia. . . . . Oct 2002
Lamont, Ms Alison . . . . Sep 2009
Lucas, Ms Susanna. . . . . Sep 2007
Neagle, Ms Samantha. . . . . Mar 2008
Nottidge, Mr James E. . . . . *Oct 1995
Pinchin, Ms Claire. . . . . Jan 2005
Thomas, Ms Rhiannon . . . . Sep 2008
Walters, Miss Bonita BA(Oxon) . . . . *Sep 1999
Zikking, Ms Katy LLB . . . . Oct 2000

QUAY LEGAL ‡
1 Friary Temple Quay Bristol BS1 6EA
Tel: 0117 344 5108 *Fax:* 0117 344 5001
E-mail: query@quaylegal.co.uk

REYNOLDS PORTER CHAMBERLAIN LLP
Temple Circus Temple Way Bristol BS1 6LW
Tel: 020 3060 6000 *Fax:* 020 3060 7000 *Dx:* 7842 BRISTOL
E-mail: enquiries@rpc.co.uk
Office: London E1
Ptr: Barnes, Mr Jeremy E BA(Hons). . . . . *§Oct 1989

RICHARD NELSON BUSINESS DEFENCE SOLICITORS
Centre Gate Colston Avenue Bristol BS1 4TR
Tel: 0117 942 5678 *Fax:* 0115 986 2626
E-mail: defencebristol@richardnelsonllp.co.uk
Office: Cardiff, Manchester, Nottingham, Solihull

RIGG & CO ‡
Box No 1492 23 Russell Grove Bristol BS6 7UD
Tel: 0117 377 7473
E-mail: riggandco@blueyonder.co.uk

ROXBURGH MILKINS ‡
Merchants House North Wapping Road Bristol BS1 4RW
Tel: 0845 241 9500 *Fax:* 0845 241 9496
E-mail: info@roxburghmilkins.com

RUSSELL JONES & WALKER
Broad Key House Prince Street Bristol BS1 4DJ
Tel: 0117 374 2222 *Fax:* 0117 374 2233 *Dx:* 7840 BRISTOL 1
E-mail: enquiries@rjw.co.uk
Office: Birmingham, Cardiff, London WC2, Manchester, Newcastle upon Tyne, Sheffield, Wakefield
Work: G H J1 N Z(p,r)
Emergency Action, Advocacy, Fixed Fee Interview, Legal Aid undertaken, Legal Aid Franchise and Member of Accident Line
Ptr: Buckeridge, Ms Myfanwy BA(Hons) . . . . *Oct 1988
Solly, Ms Gillian C LLB . . . . *Apr 1981
Wilson, Mr Ian David LLB(Hons) . . . . *Nov 1983
Ast: Godson, Mr Alan . . . . Nov 1995
Grady, Ms Helen . . . . Jun 1996
Rumley, Mr Paul . . . . Feb 1987
Trump, Mr Stephen F LLB; LLM. . . . . *Jul 1995
Turnbull, Miss A Kathryn LLB . . . . *Nov 1991

SH FAMILY LAW ‡
51 High Street Hanham Bristol BS15 3DQ
Tel: 0117 960 1437 *Fax:* 0117 960 2208
E-mail: enquiries@shfamilylaw.co.uk

SANSBURY DOUGLAS ‡
6 Unity Street Bristol BS1 5HH
Tel: 0117 926 5341 *Fax:* 0117 922 5621 *Dx:* 7821 BRISTOL
Emergency telephone 07659 105457
E-mail: dcampbell@sansburydouglas.co.uk
List of partners: D A Campbell, G M Crowther, D J Fanson, P Richardson, C J L Roberts, T J Rose
Office: Bristol, Knowle
Languages: French
Work: C1 G H N O Q W
Emergency Action, Agency, Advocacy, Fixed Fee Interview and Legal Aid undertaken
Ptr: Campbell, Mr David A LLB Chief Assessor for the Criminal Litigation Accreditation Scheme. . . . . *Nov 1985
Crowther, Mr Garry Michael CPE; LPC . . . . *Feb 1996
Richardson, Mr Peter . . . . *Nov 1997
Roberts, Mr C John L. . . . . *Feb 1972

SANSBURY DOUGLAS
116 Grosvenor Road St Pauls Bristol BS2 8YA
Tel: 0117 955 2663 *Fax:* 0117 954 0527
Emergency telephone 07659 105457
E-mail: dfanson@sansburydouglas.co.uk
Office: Bristol, Knowle
Work: G H
Emergency Action, Agency, Advocacy, Legal Aid undertaken and Legal Aid Franchise
Ptr: Fanson, Mr David J BA(Law) . . . . *Mar 1985
Rose, Mr Timothy J LLB(Bris). . . . . *Nov 1982
Ast: Chamberlin, Ms Jane . . . . *Jun 1997
Cormack, Mrs Rose. . . . . Mar 2008
Ibe, Mrs Gaynor. Sep 2005

van Wely, Ms Anna M LLB . . . . *Feb 1979
Con: Hodgen, Mr Hamish R BA. . . . . *§Jan 1984

SCRASE EMPLOYMENT SOLICITORS ‡
The Coach House 52a Egerton Road Bristol BS7 8HL
Tel: 0117 985 1026 *Fax:* 0117 985 0063
E-mail: info@scraselaw.com

SHARP FAMILY LAW
Venturers House King Street Bristol BS1 4PB
Tel: 01225 448955
E-mail: richard@sharpfamilylaw.com
Office: Bath

SHARPLES & CO ‡
62 Gloucester Road Bishopston Bristol BS7 8BH
Tel: 0117 942 8214 *Fax:* 0117 942 0498
E-mail: enquiries@sharples-solicitors.com
List of partners: R D Vooght
Work: E K4 S1 S2 W Z(x)
Ptr: Vooght, Mr Richard Denis. . . . . *§Aug 1971
Ast: Speake, Mrs Claire L LLB(Hons); LSF. . . . . *Oct 1988
Con: Sharples, Mr Stephen M . . . . *§Jul 1968

SIMPSON MILLAR LLP
20 Church Road Lawrence Hill Bristol BS5 9JA
Tel: 0844 858 3600 *Fax:* 0844 858 3699
E-mail: info@simpsonmillar.co.uk
Office: Birmingham, Cardiff, Gateshead, Leeds, London EC1, London SW19, Manchester
Work: A1 A3 B1 C1 C2 D1 D2 E F1 F2 J1 J2 K1 K2 K3 K4 M2 M3 N O P Q R1 R2 S1 S2 T1 T2 U2 V W X Z(b,c,d,e,h,j,m,o,p,q,r,t,za)

SIMS COOK & TEAGUE
3 All Saints Court Bristol BS1 1JN
Tel: 0117 927 2141 *Fax:* 0117 925 2826 *Dx:* 7837 BRISTOL
E-mail: info@simscookteague.com
Office: Thornbury
Work: A1 B1 C1 D1 E F1 G H J1 K1 L M1 N P R1 S1 T1 V W Z(c,l)
Emergency Action, Agency, Advocacy, Fixed Fee Interview and Legal Aid undertaken
Ptr: Teague, Mr Gavin Richard LLB(Hull) . . . . *Jun 1971
Ast: Allingham, Mr Edmund F LLB. . . . . *Jun 1975

BS SINGH & CO ‡
182 Stapleton Road Easton Bristol BS5 0NZ
Tel: 0117 935 4500
E-mail: info@bssinghsolicitors.co.uk

SOUTH WEST LAW LIMITED ‡
1 Hide Market West Street St Phillips Bristol BS2 0BH
Tel: 0117 314 6400 *Fax:* 0117 314 6419
E-mail: enquiries@southwestlaw.org.uk

STANDISH ASSOCIATES ‡
198 Cheltenham Road Bristol BS6 5QZ
Tel: 0117 924 9204 *Fax:* 0117 924 9205
E-mail: alexhs@standish-associates.com

STEER AND CO ‡
St Brandons House 29 Great George Street Bristol BS1 5QT
Tel: 0117 230 9700
E-mail: enquiries@steerandco.com

STEPHEN GISBY & CO ‡
Park House 10 Park Street Bristol BS1 5HX
Tel: 0117 915 4562 *Fax:* 0117 907 4701 *Dx:* 7810 BRISTOL
E-mail: stephen@stephengisby.co.uk

PAUL STEVENS & CO ‡
48 Gloucester Road Bishopston Bristol BS7 8BH
Tel: 0117 942 9308 *Fax:* 0117 924 8688
Emergency telephone 07659 130140
List of partners: P B M Stevens
Work: G H S1
Agency, Advocacy and Legal Aid undertaken
SPr: Stevens, Mr Paul B M LLB . . . . Feb 1983
Ast: Comer, Mr Matthew. . . . . Mar 2003

STIRLING & CO ‡
8 Gloucester Road North Filton Bristol BS7 0SF
Tel: 0117 931 4435 *Fax:* 0117 931 4220
E-mail: enquiries@stirlingandco.com
List of partners: D A J D Stirling, M E Stirling
Work: F1 J1 K1 K2 N Q S1 S2 V W
Emergency Action, Agency, Fixed Fee Interview, Legal Aid undertaken and Member of Accident Line
Ptr: Stirling, Mr David A J D BA(Oxon). . . . . *Jul 1977
Stirling, Ms Maura E LLB(Hons). . . . . *Oct 1978

TLT SOLICITORS ‡
One Redcliff Street Bristol BS1 6TP
Tel: 0117 917 7777 *Fax:* 0117 917 7778 *Dx:* 7815 BRISTOL
E-mail: generalenquiries@tltsolicitors.com
List of partners: D I Bird, R H G Bourns, M J Brewster, J E Brown, A J W Burton, T J Claridge, R D Clothier, E S E Cooke, J W Dickinson, K R Evans, N A Fincham, R A Flowerdew, A D Glynn, N G Gordon, C P Goulden, K Gwyther, A C D Harries, A Hawes, J C Hoey, W J Hull, J Lafont De Sentenac, N A Little, J Lucas, P N S May, S McBride, N R Meakin, N A Moss, S J Mumford, A R Murray, A M Newport, D P L Pester, N D M Pritchard, T E Pyper, P M Rees, T J D Reynolds, G Shaw, R M Staunton, I M Taylorson, J J Thomas, A D Troup, J C J Waddell, R G L Waller, A D Weeks, W J Williams, N S Willson, R T H Wilson, D W Woodward
Office: London EC2
Work: A3 B1 C1 C2 C3 D1 E F1 I J1 K1 K2 L M1 M2 O P Q R1 R2 S1 S2 T1 T2 U2 W Z(b,c,d,e,h,j,k,l,o,p,q,z)
Emergency Action, Agency, Advocacy, Fixed Fee Interview, Legal Aid undertaken, Legal Aid Franchise and S.I.G
Ptr: Bird, Mr David Iain BSocSc; FCII . . . . *Oct 1994
Bourns, Mr Robert H G LLB Secretary for Bristol Law Society . . . . *Dec 1980
Brown, Ms Judith E BA; LLM . . . . *Oct 1987
Claridge, Mr Tobias J BSc(Hons) . . . . Dec 1992
Clothier, Mr Roger D LLB . . . . *Mar 1986
Cooke, Mr Edward S E LLB(Hons) Chairman of the Faculty of Building Great Western Branch . . . . *Jul 1979
Evans, Ms Katherine R BA(Hons); LLB; MRTPI . . . . Sep 1997
Flowerdew, Mr Richard A LLB(Soton); FCIArb ♦. . . . Apr 1972
Glynn, Mr Andrew D LLB . . . . *Oct 1985
Goulden, Mr Christopher P BA(Hons); CPE . . . . . . *Oct 1982
Gwyther, Ms Kerry LLB(B'ham) . . . . *Oct 1983
Hawes, Ms Alison. . . . . *Sep 1994
Hoey, Mr Jonathan Christopher LLB. . . . . *Sep 1992
Hull, Mr William John LLB Sanderson Wells Speech Prize . . . . *Sep 1995
Little, Mrs Nicole A . . . . Jan 1988
Lucas, Miss Julia LLB(Hons); LLM . . . . *Mar 1994
McBride, Mr Stuart LLB . . . . *Oct 1995
May, Mr Philip N S BA(Oxon) . . . . *Oct 1986
Moss, Mr Nicholas A BA; MSPI . . . . *Jun 1982
Mumford, Miss Sarah J LLB; ACIArb . . . . *Nov 1981
Pester, Mr David P L BA(Hons) . . . . *Oct 1989
Pritchard, Mr Nicholas D M . . . . *§Mar 1970
Pyper, Mr Timothy E MA . . . . *§Jun 1970
Rees, Mr Patrick M BA(Hons). . . . . *Oct 1981
Shaw, Mr Graham MA; PGCE. . . . . *Oct 1994
Staunton, Mr Robin M LLB . . . . *Apr 1984
Troup, Mr Andrew D LLB(Bris) . . . . *Dec 1972
Waddell, Mr Jeremy C J BA(Oxon); LLM(Lond) . . . *§Mar 1962
Waller, Mr Richard G L BA(Hons) . . . . *Oct 1983
Weeks, Mrs Alana D BA; MEd . . . . *Oct 1989
Williams, Mr William J BSc(Eng) . . . . Feb 1966
Woodward, Mr David W LLB(Bris). . . . . *Apr 1975
Ast: Brazier, Mr James S BA; MPhil . . . . *Sep 1996
Clifford, Ms Alison C BA. . . . . *Mar 1988
Denny, Mr Neil Richard BA(Hons); CPE; LPC . . . . . *Apr 1998
Mulvaney, Ms Jennifer M BA; LLM . . . . Nov 1990

ROBERT TARREN SOLICITORS ‡
12 St Edwards Road Bristol BS8 4TS
Tel: 0845 121 4716 *Fax:* 0871 594 4202
E-mail: rt@roberttarren.co.uk

TEMPLE BRIGHT LLP ‡
St Brandon's House 29 Great George Street Bristol BS1 5QT
Tel: 0117 920 0056 *Fax:* 0117 920 0057
E-mail: enquiries@templebright.com

THOMPSONS (FORMERLY ROBIN/BRIAN THOMPSON & PARTNERS)
18 Lawford Street Bristol BS2 0DZ
Tel: 0117 304 2400 *Fax:* 0117 941 1460 *Dx:* 78123 BRISTOL
Office: Belfast, Birmingham, Cardiff, Chelmsford, Dagenham, Derby, Harrow, Leeds, Liverpool, London SW19, London WC1, Manchester, Middlesbrough, Newcastle upon Tyne, Nottingham, Plymouth, Sheffield, South Shields, Southampton, Stoke-on-Trent, Swansea, Wolverhampton
Languages: Welsh
Work: G J1 N Z(r)
Agency, Legal Aid undertaken, Legal Aid Franchise and Member of Accident Line
Ptr: Arthur, Mr Richard BA; LSF . . . . *Sep 1990
Ast: Grayson, Mr Richard Keith LLB . . . . *Oct 1993
Gregor, Ms Lisa. . . . . *Nov 1998
MacGregor, Miss Eileen S BA. . . . . *Nov 1988
Waite, Mrs Sara Christina LLB(Cardiff) . . . . *Jun 1994
Williams, Ms Helen Sarah. . . . . *Sep 1996

THRINGS LLP
(in association with Libralex; Gesica)
The Paragon Counterslip Bristol BS1 6BX
Tel: 0117 930 9500 *Fax:* 0117 929 3369 *Dx:* 7895 BRISTOL
E-mail: solicitors@ttuk.com
Office: Bath, London SW1, Swindon
Work: A3 B1 C1 C2 C3 E F1 F2 I J1 J2 L M1 M2 N O P Q R1 R2 S1 S2 T1 T2 U1 W X Z(a,b,c,d,e,f,i,j,k,l,n,o,p,q,t,y,z)

ADAM TUCKER & CO ‡
3 Druetts Close Bristol BS10 5BE
Tel: 020 7193 6341 *Fax:* 020 7193 6341
E-mail: adam@adamtuckerlegal.com

VEALE WASBROUGH VIZARDS ‡
Orchard Court Orchard Lane Bristol BS1 5WS
Tel: 0117 925 2020 *Fax:* 0117 925 2025 *Dx:* 7831 BRISTOL
E-mail: ajames@vwv.co.uk
List of partners: W S Baker, R T Barber, C R J D Barradale, D Bellew, J J Blain, J J H Burden, T Cave, R Collier, J M Cuxson, J Davies, J Deakin, K Deakin, D Emanuel, C M Green, N Guest, A J R Hamilton, S Heald, S Linnitt, D Locke, J Markland, S McGuigan, A E Millson, S A Mitchell, S Nokes, B Northover, J Oddy, R E Perry, T Phelps, G Philpott, J Prosser, N Puddicombe, M Rose, P Sampson, N I Smith, N Smith, T Smithers, C Soden-Bird, J Webster, E L Wilkins, B Willis, D Worthington
Office: London EC4
Languages: Afrikaans, Dutch, French, German, Hindi, Italian, Polish, Spanish
Work: A1 A3 B1 B2 C1 C2 C3 D1 E F1 F2 I J1 J2 K1 K2 L M1 M2 N O P Q R1 R2 S1 S2 T1 T2 U2 W X Z(b,c,d,e,f,g,h,j,k,l,m,n,o,p,q,r,s,u,w,z)
Emergency Action, Agency, Advocacy, Fixed Fee Interview, Legal Aid undertaken, Legal Aid Franchise and Member of Accident Line
Ptr: Baker, Mr W Simon BA(Cantab); LLB . . . . *§Jun 1971
Bellew, Mr Derek BA(Oxon). . . . . *§Jul 1967
Cave, Miss Tabitha BSc(Hons) . . . . Sep 1996
Collier, Mr Robert LLB. . . . . *Sep 2000
Davies, Miss Julie LLB(Hons) . . . . *Oct 1995
Deakin, Mr John LLB . . . . *Oct 1999
Deakin, Mr Karl LLB(Hons) . . . . *Sep 2002
Emanuel, Mr David BA(Oxon). . . . . *Oct 1992
Guest, Mr Nathan BA . . . . *Sep 2000
Heald, Mr Simon BA(Hons) . . . . *Oct 1989
Linnitt, Mr Simon LLB(Hons) . . . . *Sep 1997
Locke, Mr Doug LLB(Hons); PGDip IPL . . . . *Apr 1999
McGuigan, Mr Steven. . . . . Sep 2003
Markland, Ms Janice LLB(Hons). . . . . *Oct 1990
Nokes, Mrs Susan MA(Oxon) . . . . *Apr 1980
Northover, Mr Barnaby BA(Econ) . . . . *Mar 2002
Philpott, Mr Gary MA(Cantab); ACIArb; AIIT. . . . . . *Sep 1985
Prosser, Mr Jason LLB(Hons) . . . . *Sep 1998
Puddicombe, Mr Nigel LLB(Soton). . . . . *Apr 1979
Rose, Ms Michelle BSc . . . . *Dec 1995
Sampson, Mr Paul BSc . . . . *Jan 1992
Smith, Mr Nicholas LLB . . . . *Oct 1985
Smithers, Mr Timothy LLB. . . . . *Oct 1982
Webster, Mr John LLB . . . . *Oct 1985
Willis, Mr Benjamin LLB(Hons) . . . . *Nov 1991
Worthington, Mr David LLB . . . . *Dec 1975
Asoc: Bendall, Ms Michelle BA . . . . *May 1994
Bevan, Mr Simon LLB; LLM. . . . . *Sep 1999
Bird, Mr David John. . . . . Sep 2003
Campbell, Mrs Joanne ILEX; FILEx . . . . *Oct 2002
Cook, Ms Allison LLB . . . . *Mar 2000
Early, Mr Oliver LLB(Hons) . . . . *Nov 1993
Larter, Mrs Felicity LLB(Hons). . . . . Sep 2002
Lawrence, Miss Fiona LLB . . . . *Sep 2000
Pool, Mr Oliver . . . . Sep 2004
Robertson, Mrs Helen LLB . . . . *Oct 1983
Stott, Mrs Rachel BA(Hons). . . . . *Dec 1992
Ast: Anniss, Ms Caitlin BSc; MSc . . . . *Mar 2001
Booz, Jessica. . . . . Sep 2009
Brewin, Mr Christopher . . . . Aug 2007
Burnell, Emma-Jane . . . . Sep 2006
Evans, Naomi. . . . . Apr 2009
Finch, Kate . . . . Nov 2004
Foot, Mr Tristan. Sep 2003
Ford, Annette . . . . Sep 2008
Forrest, Cara . . . . Sep 2004
Osman, Claire. . . . . Sep 2005
Pemberton, Mr Neill. . . . . Mar 2008
Rushton, Miss Sally BA(Hons)(Law & History). . . . . *Nov 1988
Tate, Mary. . . . . Apr 2006
Williams, Paula . . . . Mar 2008
Con: King, Mr Stuart LLB(Lond). . . . . *Oct 1984
Rathbone, Mr Jonathan BA(Hons). . . . . *Sep 2001

WARDS SOLICITORS ‡
52 Broad Street Bristol BS1 2EP
Tel: 0117 929 2811 *Fax:* 0117 929 0686 *Dx:* 7824 BRISTOL
E-mail: info@wards.uk.com
List of partners: J N Brentnall, M J Keegan, M McCabe, N J Murray, R E E Parkman, G Peacock, D J Sheridan, P J Simon, A R Underhill, C J Westlake, L J Wilson
Office: Bristol, Clevedon, Nailsea, Portishead, Staple Hill, Weston-super-Mare (3 offices), Yate
Languages: French, German
Work: A1 B1 C1 C2 C3 D1 E F1 G J1 K1 L N O P Q R1 S1 T1 T2 V W X Z(b,c,d,h,j,l,n,t)
Emergency Action, Fixed Fee Interview, Legal Aid undertaken, Legal Aid Franchise and Member of Accident Line
Ptr: Brentnall, Mr John N LLB President of Weston-Super-Mare RFU . . . . *Apr 1973
Keegan, Mr Martin J LLB . . . . Oct 1975
Murray, Mr Nigel J LLB(Lond) . . . . *Oct 1975
Sheridan, Mr David J BA(Dunelm) Honorary Solicitor to North Somerset CAB . . . . *May 1980
Underhill, Ms Alison R LLB . . . . *Oct 1989
Ast: Gough, Mrs Jane H McN CPE; BA(Hons) . . . . *Sep 1992
Williamson, Dr Ian Brian BA; MA; PhD . . . . *Oct 1995

WARDS SOLICITORS
6-7 Fountain Court New Leaze Woodlands Lane Bristol BS32 4LA
Tel: 01454 204880 *Fax:* 01454 201391
Dx: 35005 ALMONDSBURY (AZTEC WEST)
E-mail: info@wards.uk.com
Office: Bristol, Clevedon, Nailsea, Portishead, Staple Hill, Weston-super-Mare (3 offices), Yate
Work: C1 C2 D1 D2 E J1 K1 K2 N Q S1 S2 W
Fixed Fee Interview, Legal Aid undertaken and Legal Aid Franchise
Ptr: Wilson, Mrs Linda J LLB . . . . *Nov 1985

WATKINS SOLICITORS ‡
192 North Street Bedminster Bristol BS3 1JF
Tel: 0117 939 0350 *Fax:* 0117 939 0351
Dx: 98981 BEDMINSTER (BRISTOL)
E-mail: info@watkinssolicitors.co.uk

ANDREW WEBB ‡
Windsor House Greville Road Bristol BS3 1LL
Tel: 0117 953 8408 *Fax:* 0117 953 1059
Emergency telephone 0117 953 1059
List of partners: A Webb
Work: G H Z(m)
Agency and Advocacy undertaken
SPr: Webb, Mr Andrew BA(Hons) . . . . *Feb 1982

JOHN WHITCROFT ‡
59 Queen Charlotte Street Bristol BS1 4HL
Tel: 0117 922 7740 *Fax:* 0117 925 0202
E-mail: johnwhitcroft@onetel.com
Work: N

WILMOT THOMPSON ‡
73 Park Street Bristol BS1 5PG
Tel: 0117 927 6583 *Fax:* 0117 929 0673
Dx: 122810 BRISTOL GREAT GEORGE STREET
List of partners: C A Moon, J Radford
Work: E S1 W
Ptr: Moon, Miss Christine Anne LLB. . . . . *Dec 1986
Radford, Mr John LLB. . . . . *Jun 1976

WITHERS & ROGERS
1 Redcliff Street Bristol BS1 6NP
Tel: 0117 925 3030 *Fax:* 0117 925 3530

KEVIN WITHEY SOLICITOR ‡
Hillcrest Homefield Road Saltford Bristol BS31 3EG
Tel: 01225 874569
E-mail: k.withey@hotmail.co.uk

DANIEL WOODMAN AND CO LTD ‡
Ground Floor 286 Coronation Road Southville Bristol BS3 1RT
Tel: 0117 902 8003 *Fax:* 0117 902 8004
Dx: 98986 BEDMINSTER (BRISTOL)
E-mail: dwoodman@danielwoodman.co.uk

AIDAN WOODS & CO ‡
238 Stapleton Road Eastville Bristol BS5 0NT
Tel: 0117 952 2006 *Fax:* 0117 935 4115
Emergency telephone 0117 952 2006
E-mail: enquiries@aidanwoods.co.uk
List of partners: A S C d F Woods
Languages: French
Work: B2 G H Z(m)
Emergency Action, Agency, Advocacy, Legal Aid undertaken and Legal Aid Franchise
SPr: Woods, Mr Aidan St Clair de F LLB ★. . . . . Jun 1980
Asoc: Clarke, Ms Debbie BA(Hons) ★. . . . . Jun 1980
Ast: Rollason, Ms Patricia R LLB ★ . . . . Jan 1984
Rowland, Mr Robyn P J BA(Hons). . . . . *Jul 2005

BRIXHAM, Devon

EASTLEYS
3 New Road Brixham Devon TQ5 8LZ
Tel: 01803 853266 *Fax:* 01803 856302 *Dx:* 58900 BRIXHAM
E-mail: brixham@eastleys.co.uk
Office: Paignton, Totnes
Languages: French
Work: A1 B1 C1 C2 D1 D2 E F1 G J1 K1 K2 L N O Q R1 R2 S1 S2 T2 W Z(c,l,m,o,p,r)
Emergency Action, Agency, Advocacy, Fixed Fee Interview, Legal Aid undertaken, Legal Aid Franchise and Member of Accident Line
Ptr: Hopkins, Mr John BA; FPC . . . . *§Jun 1979
Ast: Nicholson, Miss Luisa LLB . . . . *May 2003

K E CONVEYANCING ‡
3/5 New Road Brixham Devon TQ5 8LZ
Tel: 01803 882024 *Fax:* 01803 852441 *Dx:* 58906 BRIXHAM
E-mail: brixham@eastleys.co.uk

PROWSE THOMAS ‡
(incorporating Robertson Owen & Son; Parsons & Outfin)
3 Bolton Street Brixham Devon TQ5 9DA
Tel: 01803 882210 *Fax:* 01803 882713 *Dx:* 58901 BRIXHAM
E-mail: brixlaw@cs.com
List of partners: A B Prowse, D L Thomas
Work: A1 B1 C1 C2 C3 D1 E F1 G H J1 K1 L N P R1 S1 T1 T2 V W Z(d,l)
Emergency Action, Agency, Advocacy, Fixed Fee Interview, Legal Aid undertaken and Member of Accident Line
Ptr: Prowse, Mr Anthony B . . . . *Jun 1971
Thomas, Mr David L . . . . Jan 1979

ROGER RICHARDS
10a Bolton Street Brixham Devon TQ5 9DE
Tel: 01803 854123 *Fax:* 01803 856700
E-mail: enquiries@rogerrichards.co.uk
Office: Paignton

BROADSTAIRS, Kent

BARNES MARSLAND
103 High Street Broadstairs Kent CT10 1JS
Tel: 01843 861595 *Fax:* 01843 862250 *Dx:* 32452 BROADSTAIRS
E-mail: enquiries@barnesmarsland.co.uk
Office: Margate
Languages: French
Work: K4 L S1 T2 W Z(o,v)
Ptr: Mackenzie, Mrs Jane . . . . Apr 2008
Miles, Ms Jacqueline . . . . *Jul 1988
Con: Brohier, Mr Malcolm R . . . . *Nov 1981

BOYS & MAUGHAN
99 High Street Broadstairs Kent CT10 1NQ
Tel: 01843 868861 *Fax:* 01843 860556 *Dx:* 32457 BROADSTAIRS
E-mail: broadstairs@boysandmaughan.co.uk
Office: Birchington, Margate, Ramsgate
Work: S1 S2 W
Emergency Action, Agency, Advocacy, Fixed Fee Interview, Legal Aid undertaken, Legal Aid Franchise and Member of Accident Line
Ptr: Michael, Mr Antonios . . . . *Jul 1998

FOSTERS LAW LIMITED
64 High Street Broadstairs Kent CT10 1JT
Tel: 01843 340200 *Fax:* 01843 340202
Office: Herne Bay

HARDMAN & WATSON ‡
5 Lloyd Road Broadstairs Kent CT10 1HX
Tel: 01843 863479 *Fax:* 01843 603303 *Dx:* 32450 BROADSTAIRS
List of partners: R M Cobb, J J Dillon, I F Goldup
Languages: French
Work: K1 K3 S1 S2 W
Legal Aid undertaken
Ptr: Cobb, Miss Rebecca M LLB H M Coroner. . . . . . §Dec 1972
Dillon, Mr James Jerome LLB H M Assistant Deputy Coroner . . . . *Nov 1999
Goldup, Mr Ian F LLB(Nott'm) H M Deputy Coroner . *May 1978

MACKENZIE DILLON ‡
The Old Police Station 60 Gladstone Road Broadstairs Kent CT10 2TA
Tel: 01843 604222 *Fax:* 01843 600855

ROBINSON ALLFREE
142 High Street Broadstairs Kent CT10 1JD
Tel: 01843 865261 *Fax:* 01843 601526 *Dx:* 32453 BROADSTAIRS
E-mail: broadstairs@robinson-allfree.co.uk
Office: Cliftonville, Ramsgate
Languages: French, German
Work: A1 C1 C2 E F1 J1 K1 L N O Q R1 S1 T1 T2 V W Z(j)
Emergency Action, Agency, Advocacy, Fixed Fee Interview, Legal Aid undertaken, Legal Aid Franchise and Member of Accident Line

BROADSTONE, Poole

COLES MILLER SOLICITORS LLP
Arrowsmith Court 10 Station Approach Broadstone Poole BH18 8AX
Tel: 01202 694891 *Fax:* 01202 694920 *Dx:* 34552 BROADSTONE
E-mail: office@coles-miller.co.uk
Office: Bournemouth (2 offices), Poole
Work: D1 K1 S1 W
Emergency Action, Agency, Advocacy, Fixed Fee Interview, Legal Aid undertaken, Legal Aid Franchise and Member of Accident Line
Ptr: Hamilton-Cole, Ms Emma LLB(Hons)(Soton) . . . . *Sep 1996
Kerley, Ms Ruth Helen . . . . Sep 2002

DICKINSON MANSER
221 The Broadway Broadstone Poole BH18 8DN
Tel: 01202 692308 / 694490 *Fax:* 01202 601353
Dx: 34551 BROADSTONE
Office: Poole
Work: C1 E F1 G J1 L R1 S1 W Z(l,m)
Agency and Fixed Fee Interview undertaken
Ptr: Yeoman, Mr Gareth E. . . . . *Apr 1985

HAROLD G WALKER
196a-200a The Broadway Broadstone Poole BH18 8DR
Tel: 01202 692448 / 695361 *Fax:* 01202 601847
Dx: 34556 BROADSTONE
Office: Bournemouth, Christchurch, Verwood, Wimborne
Work: K1 S1 W

LAWRENSON SOLICITORS ‡
6 Gladelands Close Broadstone Poole BH18 9JX
Tel: 01202 657058
E-mail: leslawrenson@btinternet.com
Languages: French

BROADWAY, Worcestershire

BAILEY & TOFIELD ‡
Broadway Chambers 7 Keil Close High Street Broadway Worcestershire WR12 7DP
Tel: 01386 854851 *Fax:* 01386 858864 *Dx:* 742680 BROADWAY
E-mail: enquiries@baileyandtofield.co.uk

ANTONY A HOLMES ‡
The Old British School Room 47b High Street Broadway Worcestershire WR12 7DP
Tel: 01386 858107 *Fax:* 01386 859454
List of partners: A A L Holmes
Work: L S1 S2 W
SPr: Holmes, Mr Antony A L . . . . *Sep 1980

BROCKENHURST, Hampshire

ROSS CARTER ‡
Fairhaven Rhinefield Road Brockenhurst Hampshire SO42 7SQ
Tel: 01590 624422 *Fax:* 01590 624433
E-mail: lawyers@rosscarter.co.uk
List of partners: S K R Carter
Work: E K4 S1 T2 W
Fixed Fee Interview undertaken
SPr: Carter, Miss Susan Kathryn Ross . . . . Jan 1984

BRETT JOHNSON ‡
Hill Top House Beaulieu Brockenhurst Hampshire SO42 7YG
Tel: 01590 612731 *Fax:* 01590 612743
Emergency telephone 07836 247896
E-mail: bretros@aol.com
List of partners: R D B Johnson
Languages: French, Italian
Work: C1 F1 J1 K1 L N R1 S1 T1 W Z(a,c,i,j,l)
Emergency Action, Advocacy undertaken and Member of Accident Line
Ptr: Johnson, Mr R D Brett . . . . *§Nov 1970

LAYZELL SOLICITORS LIMITED ‡
82 Brockley Road Brockenhurst Hampshire SO42 7RA
Tel: 01590 623770

MARTINS
(in association with Pye-Smiths)
3 Courtyard Mews Brookley Road Brockenhurst Hampshire SO42 7RB
Tel: 01590 623252 *Fax:* 01590 623786
E-mail: sue.martin@martinsolicitors.co.uk
Languages: French, Spanish
Agency, Advocacy and Fixed Fee Interview undertaken
SPr: Martin, Mrs Susan R LLB . . . . *Dec 1978

BROMBOROUGH, Merseyside

WIRRAL FAMILY LAW & MEDIATION ‡
15-19 Allport Lane Bromborough Merseyside CH62 7HH
Tel: 0151 343 3150 *Fax:* 0151 482 8638
E-mail: graham.roberts@wslms.co.uk

BROMLEY, Kent

APPLETON MASSEY ‡
Wells House 15-17 Elmfield Road Bromley Kent BR1 1LT
Tel: 0845 812 1002 *Fax:* 0845 812 1003 *Dx:* 121105 BROMLEY
E-mail: info@appletonmassey.co.uk

ARNHEIM & CO ‡
7 Denbridge Road Bromley Kent BR1 2AG
Tel: 020 8295 4818

ASCOT & CHASE ‡
16a London Road Bromley Kent BR1 3QR
Tel: 020 8313 9009 *Dx:* 5710 BROMLEY
Office: Bromley

ASCOT & CHASE
26 Station Approach Hayes Bromley Kent BR2 7EH
Tel: 020 8462 3344 *Fax:* 020 8462 5000 *Dx:* 5710 BROMLEY
E-mail: info@ascotchase.co.uk
Office: Bromley

BATCHELORS SOLICITORS ‡
Charles House 35 Widmore Road Bromley Kent BR1 1RW
Tel: 020 8768 7000 *Fax:* 020 8768 7045 *Dx:* 117614 BROMLEY 7
E-mail: batchelors@batchelors.co.uk
Web: www.batchelors.co.uk
List of partners: A E J Harmer, S Hickey, M A Martil, M Miles, D J Skinner, N P S Stotesbury, M Walkington, A M Whichcord, S D Wilbourn, T C Wilson
Office: London WC1
Languages: French
Work: A1 A3 C1 C2 E J1 K1 K3 K4 L O Q R1 R2 S1 S2 T1 T2 W Z(c,h,m,p,q)
Agency and Fixed Fee Interview undertaken
Ptr: Harmer, Mr Andrew E J Deputy District Judge. . . . *Nov 1991
Hickey, Ms Sarah . . . . *Feb 2003
Martil, Mrs Mary A LLB(Hons). . . . . *Oct 1989
Miles, Mr Matthew. . . . . *May 2005
Skinner, Mr Daniel J BSc(Hons). . . . . *Oct 1993
Stotesbury, Mr Nicholas P S. . . . . *May 1979
Walkington, Mr Mark . . . . *Nov 1993
Whichcord, Mr Adrian Michael LLB(Hons) . . . . . . *Mar 2004
Wilbourn, Mr Steven D BA(Hull). . . . . *Dec 1980
Wilson, Mr Thaine Cornel LLB(Hons) . . . . *Sep 2002
Asoc: Bell, Miss Sharon Leanne LLB(Hons) . . . . *Mar 2006
McKnight, Mr Nick LLB(Law with French Law). . . . *Sep 2004
Rattray, Ms Claire. . . . . *Sep 1999
Ryait, Mrs Gavinder LLB(Hons) . . . . *Jan 2003
Ast: Agrawal, Akanshi . . . . *Mar 2008
Bodley, Mrs Alexandra Esme LLB(Hons) . . . . . . *Jan 2005
Churchill, Ms Amy Elizabeth FILEx; LPC . . . . . . *Aug 2011
Herbert, Miss Simone Rhiannon BA(Hons)(History) . *Mar 2008
White, Mr Edward LLB . . . . *Sep 2003

A J BOND & CO ‡
Universal House 1 Walters Yard High Street Bromley Kent BR1 1QA
Tel: 020 8464 2229 *Fax:* 020 8466 6009 *Dx:* 117606 BROMLEY 7
List of partners: A J Bond, N M Bond
Work: B1 C1 D1 E J1 K1 K3 L O Q S1 W Z(p)
Emergency Action, Agency, Fixed Fee Interview, Legal Aid undertaken and Legal Aid Franchise
Ptr: Bond, Mr Anthony J. . . . . *May 1971
Bond, Mr Nicholas M . . . . Jan 1987

BROWNS SOLICITORS ‡
51 Tweedy Road Bromley Kent BR1 3NH
Tel: 020 7831 8111

DAVIES & CO ‡
Cambridge Chambers 200-202 High Street Bromley Kent BR1 1PW
Tel: 020 8460 6668 *Fax:* 020 8460 1249 *Dx:* 117616 BROMLEY
List of partners: D J Davies
Work: D1 D2 K1
Legal Aid undertaken and Legal Aid Franchise
SPr: Davies, Mr David John LLB; BA; MCIArb . . . . . . *§Apr 1969

EDWARDS DAVIES SOLICITORS ‡
Leonard House 5-7 Newman Road Bromley Kent BR1 1RJ
Tel: 020 8437 0900 *Fax:* 020 8437 0901 *Dx:* 5706 BROMLEY
E-mail: enquiries@edwardsdavies.com

FALCON LEGAL ‡
41 Hayesford Park Drive Bromley Kent BR2 9DA
Tel: 020 8290 6787 *Fax:* 020 8290 1033
E-mail: info@falconlegal.co.uk

FORTRESS LAW ‡
38 Beckenham Lane Shortlands Bromley Kent BR2 0DQ
Tel: 020 8466 8998 *Fax:* 020 8466 0180 *Dx:* 121102 BROMLEY 9
E-mail: info@fortresslaw.co.uk

FRAZER BRADSHAW ‡
248 High Street Bromley Kent BR1 2RL
Tel: 020 8466 5588
E-mail: office@fblaw.co.uk

HARDY MCBRIDE & CO ‡
Shaftesbury House 20 Tylney Roads Bromley Kent BR1 2RL
Tel: 020 8460 1999 *Fax:* 020 8460 1977
Emergency telephone 07774 265943
E-mail: hardymcbricleco@btconnect.com
List of partners: K R T Hardy-McBride
Work: G H
Emergency Action, Agency, Advocacy and Legal Aid undertaken
Ptr: Hardy-McBride, Mr Kimball Robert Thomas LLB. . . *Mar 1995
Ast: Jones, Mr Mark LLB. . . . . Apr 2000

HERMELING ‡
27 Birch Row Bromley Kent BR2 8BX
Tel: 020 8295 1573 *Fax:* 0560 004 0401
E-mail: contact@hermeling.co.uk

MARIA JONES ‡
41 Rochester Avenue Bromley Kent BR1 3DN
Tel: 020 8290 5103 *Fax:* 020 8289 5060
E-mail: mariajones@ukgateway.net

JUDGE & PRIESTLEY ‡
Justin House 6 West Street Bromley Kent BR1 1JN
Tel: 020 8290 0333 *Fax:* 020 8464 3332 *Dx:* 117600 BROMLEY 7
E-mail: info@judge-priestley.co.uk
List of partners: K Barrowman, A L Clarke, M Henwood, A Nurse, M D Oakley, T Shaah, R A N Stanger, P Stevens, S Taylor
Languages: Afrikaans, British Sign Language, Cantonese, French, Hindi, Punjabi, Spanish, Urdu
Work: A1 A3 B1 C1 C2 C3 E F1 J1 K1 K2 K3 L N O Q R1 R2 S1 S2 T1 W Z(b,c,e,h,i,j,k,l,p,q,r,u,y)
Emergency Action, Agency, Advocacy, Fixed Fee Interview, Legal Aid Franchise and Member of Accident Line
Ptr: Barrowman, Ms Kay. . . . . Jan 1994
Clarke, Mr Anthony L . . . . *Jan 1970
Henwood, Ms Madelaine . . . . Nov 1999
Nurse, Anne . . . . Jan 1975
Oakley, Mr Mark D LLB . . . . *Oct 1989
Shaah, Miss Thowheetha LLB(Hons) . . . . *Jul 1991
Stanger, Mr Ralph A N . . . . *§Dec 1972
Stevens, Mr Paul . . . . Jan 1993
Taylor, Mr Steven BA . . . . *Oct 1987
Asoc: Constantine, Marie . . . . Jan 2002
Cuffe, Mr Neil. . . . . Sep 2005
Dhooper, Suki. . . . . Jan 1993
Ast: Addai, Ms Rachel. . . . . Jan 2006
Chan, Tina . . . . Sep 2002
Davies, Ms Linda . . . . Feb 1988
Parsons, Mr Marcus. . . . . Jan 2005
Rudd, Lucy . . . . Jan 2007
Singh, Nitika . . . . Jun 2007

VIRGINIA JURAS & CO ‡
13 Kinnaird Avenue Bromley Kent BR1 4HG
Tel: 020 8402 9403 *Fax:* 020 8290 0285
Emergency telephone 07703 219140
E-mail: vaj@ntlworld.com
List of partners: V A Juras
Languages: Lithuanian
Work: S1 T2 W Z(i)
Fixed Fee Interview undertaken
SPr: Juras, Ms Virginia A LLB . . . . *May 1981

MARSONS SOLICITORS LLP ‡
4 Newman Road Bromley Kent BR1 1RJ
Tel: 020 8313 1300 *Fax:* 020 8466 7920 *Dx:* 119599 BROMLEY 8
E-mail: bromley@marsons.co.uk
List of partners: S Adabadze, G Bush, S T Day, E M King, J M White

See p112 for the Key to Work Categories & other symbols

Work: C1 E J1 L N O Q S2 Z(c,h,q)
Agency undertaken and Member of Accident Line
Ptr: Adabadze, Mr Steven. . . . . *Apr 2004
Bush, Mr Gregory LLB; BComm. . . . . *Aug 1999
Day, Miss Sara T LLB. . . . . *Oct 1991
King, Miss Elizabeth M LLB(Hons) . . . . *Oct 1986
White, Miss Jennifer Mary LLB(Hons) . . . . *Dec 1991

DANIEL MILLER ‡
16 Hildenlea Place Bromley Kent BR2 0YH
Tel: 020 8460 3247
E-mail: dmillersolicitor@aol.com

RUDD JEPSON ‡
131-133 Southlands Road Bromley Kent BR2 9QT
Tel: 020 8313 0555 *Fax:* 020 8466 3444
E-mail: enquiries@ruddjepson.co.uk
List of partners: D A Brindle, A Jepson, J M Rudd
Work: E R1 S1 S2 W Z(l)
Ptr: Brindle, Miss Debra Ann LLB . . . . *Jan 1998
Jepson, Mr Anthony LLB . . . . *Apr 1976
Rudd, Mr John Michael LLB(Newc) Commissioner of Taxes . . . . *Oct 1971

R SAIFUDDIN ‡
62 Widmore Road Bromley Kent BR1 3BD
Tel: 020 8466 1266
E-mail: r_saifuddin@hotmail.co.uk
List of partners: R Saifuddin
Ptr: Saifuddin, Mrs Rubina BA(Law) . . . . *Feb 1986

SALANS
7th Floor 26 Elmfield Road Bromley Kent BR1 1WA
Tel: 020 8460 2237 *Fax:* 020 8466 9374 *Dx:* 94704 BROMLEY 3
E-mail: bromley@salans.com
Office: London EC4

MICHAEL TAYLOR & ASSOCIATES ‡
1 Elmfield Park Bromley Kent BR1 1LU
Tel: 020 8437 0707 *Fax:* 020 8437 0701 *Dx:* 149510 BROMLEY 8
E-mail: info@mtasolicitors.com
List of partners: M Taylor
Office: Manchester, Urmston
Work: A3 J1 L N Q S2 W Z(j,q,r)
Agency undertaken and Member of Accident Line
Ptr: Taylor, Mr Michael BA. . . . . May 1983

THACKRAY WILLIAMS ‡
Kings House 32-40 Widmore Road Bromley Kent BR1 1RY
Tel: 020 8290 0440 *Fax:* 020 8464 5282 *Dx:* 119600 BROMLEY 8
List of partners: K R Gauntlett, D A Hacker, A J Porter, A S Raby, M E Ridley, S T E Thackray, P M Thomas, A Wood
Office: Beckenham, West Wickham
Languages: German, Norwegian, Spanish
Work: B1 C1 E J1 K1 L M1 N O P Q R1 S1 T1 W Z(b,c,d,e,h,j,l,m,o)
Emergency Action, Agency, Advocacy, Legal Aid undertaken, Legal Aid Franchise and Member of Accident Line
Ptr: Gauntlett, Mr Kevin Rees LLB(Hons) . . . . *Jan 1989
Hacker, Mr David A . . . . Oct 1983
Porter, Mr Alan J LLB . . . . *§Mar 1983
Ridley, Mr Mark Ellis LLB . . . . Oct 1992
Wood, Miss Amanda . . . . Oct 1985
Ast: MacLeod, Ms Jane . . . . Sep 1996

TINKLIN SPRINGALL ‡
(incorporating Lamb & Furness)
Devonshire House Elmfield Road Bromley Kent BR1 1TF
Tel: 020 8402 6222 *Fax:* 020 8402 9222 *Dx:* 121101 BROMLEY
E-mail: mail@tinklinspringall.co.uk
List of partners: D G Arnott, G S Danger, I C Springall, R F Tinklin
Office: Beckenham
Work: E J1 K1 K3 N O Q S1 S2 W
Agency undertaken
Ptr: Tinklin, Mr Roger F LLB. . . . . *Jan 1972
Con: Lamb, Mr Peter L . . . . *§Dec 1976

WELLERS LAW GROUP LLP ‡
Tenison House 45 Tweedy Road Bromley Kent BR1 3NF
Est: 1881
Tel: 020 8464 4242 *Fax:* 020 8464 6033 *Dx:* 5713 BROMLEY
E-mail: enquiries@wellerslawgroup.com
List of partners: R G Mallet, P J Martin, S D Scott, A J Summers, G Q Topping
Office: London WC1
Work: B1 C1 C2 D1 D2 E F1 F2 J1 K1 L N O Q R1 R2 S1 S2 T2 W Z(c,d,e,h,o,p,q)
Agency, Advocacy and Legal Aid Franchise
Ptr: Martin, Mr Paul J . . . . *§Nov 1978
Scott, Mr Stephen D BA(Dunelm) . . . . *§Jun 1978
Summers, Mr Anthony J MA(Oxon) . . . . *§Nov 1978
Ast: Baird, Mr James BA. . . . . Jan 1993
Bastian-Carter, Mrs Nimalee BSc; CPE; LPC . . . . . Oct 2003
Hine, Mrs Lesley Denise TEP . . . . Dec 1993
McParland, Miss Claire LPC. . . . . *Sep 2006
Majiyagbe, Ms Juliana Jokotola LLB(Hons) . . . . . . *Jan 2004
Rumjahn, Miss Yasmin BA(Hons); PGDipLaw . . . . . Jan 1999
Toal, Miss Lorraine Clare LLB(Hons) . . . . *Nov 2004
Whitfield, Miss Jane Deborah BA; PGDip . . . . . . *§Nov 2000
Con: Charman, Ms Linda A LLB(Lond) . . . . May 1989
Gore, Mr Anthony John BA Deputy District Judge . . . §Jul 1977

WESTFIELD SOLICITORS ‡
South Tower 26 Elmfield Road Bromley Kent BR1 1WA
Tel: 020 8228 1260 *Fax:* 020 8228 1263 *Dx:* 121100 BROMLEY 9
E-mail: info@westfieldsolicitors.com

BROMSGROVE, Worcestershire

HOLLIES SOLICITORS AND ADVOCATES LIMITED ‡
60 Birmingham Road Bromsgrove Worcestershire B61 0DD
Tel: 01527 831800
Office: Stourbridge

THOMAS HORTON LLP ‡
Strand House 70 The Strand Bromsgrove Worcestershire B61 8DQ
Tel: 01527 871641 *Fax:* 01527 836762 *Dx:* 17271 BROMSGROVE 1
Emergency telephone 01527 77889
E-mail: tmh@thomashorton.co.uk
List of partners: P P Biddle, J H Fisher, T M Horton, R A Hull, F M R Lawson-Hughes, G W Morgan, J A Sommerville
Work: A1 D1 D2 E G H J1 K1 L N Q S1 S2 W Z(l)
Emergency Action, Agency, Advocacy, Fixed Fee Interview, Legal Aid undertaken and Legal Aid Franchise
Ptr: Biddle, Mr Paul P LLB. . . . . *Dec 1978
Fisher, Mr John Hamilton LLB(Hons) . . . . *Jan 1993
Horton, Mr T Matthew BA . . . . Dec 1974
Hull, Mr Richard A LLB . . . . *Oct 1999
Lawson-Hughes, Mrs Fiona M R LLB . . . . *Nov 1991
Morgan, Mr Graham W LLB(B'ham). . . . . *§Nov 1973
Sommerville, Mr James A MA. . . . . *Dec 1978
Ast: Elvins, Ms Kirsty Gail LLB. . . . . Mar 2007
Oliver, Miss Katie BA(Hons)(Law) . . . . Apr 2008

MFG SOLICITORS
(incorporating Fisher Holyoake)
1 High Street Bromsgrove Worcestershire B61 8AJ
Tel: 01527 831691 *Fax:* 01527 831531
Dx: 715776 BROMSGROVE 2
Emergency telephone 01527 31201
E-mail: bromsgrove@mfgsolicitors.com
Office: Halesowen, Kidderminster, Oswestry, Telford, Worcester
Work: A1 B1 C1 C2 C3 D1 E F1 G H J1 K1 L M1 M2 N P R1 S1 T1 T2 V
Emergency Action, Agency, Legal Aid undertaken, Legal Aid Franchise and Member of Accident Line
Ptr: Bishop, Mr Simon J LLM . . . . *Oct 1974
Bovey, Mr Christopher J LLB . . . . *Jan 1981
Cooke, Mr Simon M LLB . . . . *Oct 1988
Noble, Mr Michael H W LLB(Hons) . . . . *§Oct 1964
Trenchard, Ms Grace S LLB. . . . . *Nov 1987
Ast: Aston, Ms Isabel LLB(Hons). . . . . *Sep 2002
Colley, Miss Anna Sian . . . . Sep 2002
Hackett, Miss Marisa Caroline. . . . . Sep 2000
Con: Morgan, Mr Terence. . . . . *§Jul 1961

MARTYN AMEY & CO ‡
7 Kidderminster Road Kidderminster Bromsgrove Worcestershire B61 7JJ
Tel: 01527 576060 *Fax:* 01527 579708
E-mail: mail@martynamey.co.uk

PATTMANS ‡
18 St John Street Bromsgrove Worcestershire B61 8QY
Tel: 01527 872947 *Fax:* 01527 558804
E-mail: enquiries@pattmans.co.uk
List of partners: J M Morley, R J Murray-Peters
Ptr: Morley, Mrs Jane M LLB . . . . Nov 1986
Murray-Peters, Mr Richard James. . . . . *Jan 1970

SCOTTS HOLT & SELLARS ‡
Steps House 10 St John Street Bromsgrove Worcestershire B61 8QY
Tel: 01527 872711 *Fax:* 01527 836075
Dx: 715778 BROMSGROVE 2
E-mail: info@shs-solicitors.co.uk
List of partners: A J Borley, A J Morris, P J Samuels
Work: E F1 J1 K1 K3 L N Q S1 S2 W
Agency, Advocacy and Fixed Fee Interview undertaken
Ptr: Borley, Mr Andrew J BA. . . . . *May 1989
Morris, Mr Alan J BA . . . . *Mar 1977
Samuels, Mr Peter John LLB(B'ham) . . . . *Oct 1980
Asoc: Morley, Mrs Jane M LLB . . . . Nov 1986
Nazir, Miss Nesheela BA(Hons)(Law with English). . . *Jul 2001
Side, Ms Tracey LLB(Hons). . . . . *Aug 2004
Con: Gorman, Mr Martin M . . . . *Nov 1962

BROMYARD, Worcestershire

BEAUMONTS
38 High Street Bromyard Worcestershire HR7 4AY
Tel: 01885 488442 *Fax:* 01885 488533 *Dx:* 17201 HEREFORD
E-mail: jstephenson@beaumonts-solicitors.co.uk
Office: Hereford

BROSELEY, Shropshire

A BUNNING SOLICITOR ‡
Floyer Hall Floyer Lane Benthall Broseley Shropshire TF12 5RW
Tel: 01952 883688 *Fax:* 01952 883688
E-mail: annabunning@aol.com

BROUGH, East Riding of Yorkshire

ST STEPHENS CONSULTANCY SERVICES LIMITED ‡
2 Main Road Newport Brough East Riding of Yorkshire HU15 2PP
Tel: 01430 441383 *Fax:* 01430 449873
E-mail: taylornewport@aol.com

YORKSHIRE LAW SOLICITORS ‡
21 Westgate North Cave Brough East Riding of Yorkshire HU15 2NG
Tel: 01430 422422 *Fax:* 01430 424678
E-mail: walter@sweeney.lawlite.net
Languages: French
Work: S1 W

BROUGHTON-IN-FURNESS, Cumbria

THOMAS BUTLER & SON ‡
Syke House Church Street Broughton-in-Furness Cumbria LA20 6ER
Tel: 01229 716336 *Fax:* 01229 716652
List of partners: W J Ilett
Office: Millom
Languages: French
Work: A1 C1 E F1 K4 L R1 S1 S2 T2 W Z(l)
SPr: Ilett, Mr William John LLB. . . . . *Oct 1974
Ast: Tattersall, Mr J Philip . . . . *Sep 1971

BROWNHILLS, West Midlands

CMHT SOLICITORS
82 High Street Brownhills West Midlands WS8 6EW
Tel: 01543 372347 *Fax:* 01543 373769
Emergency telephone 01922 646425
E-mail: cox.mcqueen.@nbol.co.uk
Office: Walsall (2 offices)
Work: D1 G H K1 L S1 V W Z(m)
Emergency Action, Agency, Advocacy, Legal Aid undertaken and Member of Accident Line
Ptr: Bellshaw, Mr Philip A LLB. . . . . *Oct 1987
Ast: Froggatt, Miss Sarah LLB. . . . . Oct 2007
McFarlane, Miss Kirstine Fiona LLB(Hons); DipLP. . . Sep 2000

BROXBOURNE, Hertfordshire

MADDERSONS ‡
97 High Road Broxbourne Hertfordshire EN10 7BN
Tel: 01992 444421 *Fax:* 01992 443111 *Dx:* 44550 BROXBOURNE
E-mail: info@maddersons.co.uk
List of partners: M Madderson
Work: D1 E F1 J1 K1 K3 K4 L N O Q S1 S2 W Z(q)
Fixed Fee Interview undertaken
Ptr: Madderson, Ms Maxine . . . . *Sep 2002

BRYNMAWR, Blaenau Gwent

BEHR & CO ‡
Hollymount Market Square Brynmawr Blaenau Gwent NP23 4AJ
Tel: 01495 310581 *Fax:* 01495 312060 *Dx:* 84801 BRYNMAWR
E-mail: andrew@behr.co.uk
List of partners: S A L B Behr, A L Campbell
Languages: Welsh
Work: B1 D1 D2 F1 J1 K1 K3 K4 L N Q S1 S2 V W Z(q)
Emergency Action, Agency, Advocacy, Fixed Fee Interview, Legal Aid undertaken and Legal Aid Franchise
Ptr: Behr, Mrs Sonia Amelia Le Breton BSc; LLB . . . . . *Jun 1992
Campbell, Mr Andrew L MA; DipLaw; DipLP. . . . . . *Nov 1997
Ast: Hall, Mr Jason Stewart LLB(Hons); Diploma Bar Vocational Studies; QLTT. . . . . *May 2006
Huish, Miss Gill LLB. . . . . *Feb 2009
Wilsher, Miss Carly Anne LLB. . . . . *Mar 2005

BUCKHURST HILL, Essex

CARTER DEVILE
82 Queen's Road Buckhurst Hill Essex IG9 5BS
Tel: 020 8506 0636 *Fax:* 020 8506 0736
Dx: 40451 BUCKHURST HILL
Office: Ilford

DIAMONDS ‡
Lincoln House 184 Queens Road Buckhurst Hill Essex IG9 5BD
Tel: 020 8559 0778 *Fax:* 020 8559 0728
Dx: 40456 BUCKHURST HILL
Emergency telephone 020 8559 0778
E-mail: enquiries@diamondssolicitors.com
List of partners: L R Diamond
Work: B1 C1 E F1 J1 K1 L N O Q S1 W Z(c,k)
Agency and Advocacy undertaken
Ptr: Diamond, Ms Lesley R . . . . *Oct 1987
Ast: Culverhouse, Mr Graham John LLB . . . . *Sep 1997
Power, Ms Joanne Elizabeth LLB(Hons). . . . . *Sep 2002

ROGERS & CO ‡
8 Princes Way Buckhurst Hill Essex IG9 5DU
Tel: 020 8498 9910 *Fax:* 020 8281 1984
E-mail: ellis.mizrahi@ntlworld.com
List of partners: E R Mizrahi
SPr: Mizrahi, Mr Ellis R. . . . . *Mar 1983

BUCKINGHAM, Buckinghamshire

ALFRED TRUMAN
First Floor Old Brewery House Castle Street Buckingham Buckinghamshire MK18 1BS
Tel: 01280 822217 *Fax:* 01280 813269 *Dx:* 39958 BUCKINGHAM
E-mail: rodney.corner@trumans.co.uk
Office: Bicester
Work: A1 B1 C1 C2 C3 E F1 G H J1 K1 L N P Q R1 S1 T1 T2 W Z(b,c,d,i,j,l,o,s)
Emergency Action, Agency, Advocacy and Fixed Fee Interview undertaken
Con: Corner, Mr Rodney Hunter Gordon LLB(Hons) Coroner for Milton Keynes Notary Public . . . . *§Jul 1965

CHANDLER RAY ‡
22 West Street Buckingham Buckinghamshire MK18 1HG
Tel: 01280 814040 *Fax:* 01280 817207 *Dx:* 39950 BUCKINGHAM
E-mail: reception@chandlerray.co.uk
List of partners: C H M Chandler, V T H Guse, D C Wigg
Office: Buckingham, Winslow
Work: A1 A2 B1 C1 C2 D1 E F1 J1 K1 K3 K4 L N O Q R1 R2 S1 S2 T2 V W Z(q)
Emergency Action, Agency and Fixed Fee Interview undertaken
Ptr: Chandler, Mr Christopher Henry Morgan. . . . . *Mar 1972
Wigg, Mr David C BL . . . . *Jun 1978
Ast: Davis, Mrs Diana S BA(Dunelm) . . . . *Oct 1984
Haskew, Mr Jack BA; JD . . . . Jan 2006
Odedra, Miss Nita LLB(Hons). . . . . Jun 2006

CHANDLER RAY
Unit 7 Home Ground Buckingham Industrial Park Buckingham Buckinghamshire MK18 1UH
Tel: 01280 821572 / 825555 *Fax:* 01280 815729
Dx: 39950 BUCKINGHAM
Office: Buckingham, Winslow

GILROY STEEL
2nd Floor 1a West Street Buckingham Buckinghamshire MK18 1HL
Tel: 01280 815538 *Fax:* 01280 705154 *Dx:* 39954 BUCKINGHAM
Office: Brackley, Northampton

LORIMERS ‡
25-26 West Street Buckingham Buckinghamshire MK18 1HF
Est: 1785
Tel: 01280 812132 / 813405 *Fax:* 01280 814214
E-mail: bmingham@lorimers.org.uk
List of partners: B P Mingham
Work: A1 D1 E F1 J1 K1 L Q S1 W
Ptr: Mingham, Mr Brian P . . . . *Jul 1973

MCGREGOR WILSHIRE LIMITED ‡
Old Priory Farm Bletchley Road Thornborough Buckingham Buckinghamshire MK18 2DZ
Tel: 01280 815301 *Fax:* 01280 821740
E-mail: stephen.wilshire@mcgw.co.uk

BUCKLEY, Flintshire

E A HARRIS & CO LTD
The Cross Buckley Flintshire CH7 2JL
Tel: 01244 541505 *Fax:* 01244 545599 *Dx:* 26502 BUCKLEY
E-mail: solicitors@eaharris.com
Office: Shotton
Work: D1 E F2 J1 J2 K1 K3 L N O Q S1 S2 W
Legal Aid undertaken and Legal Aid Franchise
Dir: Connah, Mr Gary BSc(Hons)(Econ) . . . . *§Oct 1988
Jones, Mr Keith A LLB(Lond) . . . . *§Sep 1972

P LLOYD JONES & CO
Belgrave Chambers 25a Brunswick Road Buckley Flintshire CH7 2ED
Tel: 01244 547119 / 547110 *Fax:* 01244 546570
Dx: 26503 BUCKLEY
Office: Mold
Work: E G H K1 L M1 P R1 S1 T1 V W
Emergency Action, Agency, Advocacy, Fixed Fee Interview and Legal Aid undertaken
Ptr: Jesse, Mr Christopher LLB . . . . *Oct 1980

MACASKILL'S ‡
19a Brunswick Road Buckley Flintshire CH7 2ED
Tel: 01244 544477 *Fax:* 01244 548604 *Dx:* 26501 BUCKLEY
Emergency telephone 01244 818437
E-mail: macaskills@macaskillssolicitors.co.uk
List of partners: J M Macaskill
Work: D1 G H J1 K1 M1 P S1 W Z(l)
Emergency Action, Agency, Advocacy, Fixed Fee Interview, Legal Aid undertaken and Member of Accident Line
Con: Marner, Mr John M LLB . . . . *May 1967

BUDE, Cornwall

BUSBYS SOLICITORS ‡
The Strand Bude Cornwall EX23 8TJ
Tel: 01288 359000 *Fax:* 01288 356000 *Dx:* 118529 BUDE
E-mail: lawyer@busbyslaw.co.uk
List of partners: J Busby
Work: A1 A3 B1 C1 D1 D2 E F1 F2 J1 J2 K1 K3 K4 L N O Q R1 R2 S1 S2 V W Z(c,d,h,k,p,q,r)
Emergency Action, Agency, Advocacy and Legal Aid undertaken
SPr: Busby, Mr John BA(Dunelm) . . . . *§Dec 1980
Ast: Helman, Mr David S Notary Public . . . . *Jan 1974

PAUL FINN SOLICITORS ‡
The Strand Bude Cornwall EX23 8SY
Tel: 01288 356256 *Fax:* 01288 354900 *Dx:* 118531 BUDE
E-mail: finnp@finnlaw.co.uk
List of partners: P H Finn
Languages: French
Work: A1 A3 B1 C1 D1 E F1 J1 K1 L N O P Q R1 S1 S2 T1 T2 V W Z(c,d,h,j,k,l,m,p,q,r,s)
Emergency Action, Agency, Advocacy, Fixed Fee Interview, Legal Aid undertaken, Legal Aid Franchise and Member of Accident Line
Ptr: Finn, Mr Paul H MCIArb; FCMI . . . . *§Jul 1973
Ast: Dart, Mr Philip R BA(Law) . . . . *Nov 1980

PETER PETER & WRIGHT
1 Queen Street Bude Cornwall EX23 8AZ
Tel: 01288 352101 *Fax:* 01288 355860 *Dx:* 118527 BUDE
E-mail: mail@peterslaw.co.uk
Office: Bideford, Holsworthy, Okehampton
Work: A1 A2 C1 C2 D1 D2 E F1 J1 K1 K2 K4 L N O Q R2 S1 S2 T2 W Z(c,d,l,p,q)
Ptr: Bennett, Mr Adrian . . . . *§Sep 1971
Rowland, Mr Toby James MA(Cantab) . . . . *§Feb 1994
Ast: Pritchard, Ms Lucy LLB . . . . *Dec 2002
Weeks, Miss Rebecca LLB . . . . Sep 2011

BUDLEIGH SALTERTON, Devon

CORFIELD SOLICITORS ‡
9 The Green Otterton Budleigh Salterton Devon EX9 7HQ
Tel: 01395 567102 *Fax:* 01395 567102
E-mail: info@corfieldsolicitors.com

EVERYS
Council Chambers Station Road Budleigh Salterton Devon EX9 6RL
Tel: 01395 442223 *Fax:* 01395 446374
Dx: 122841 BUDLEIGH SALTERTON
E-mail: law@everys.co.uk
Office: Exeter, Exmouth, Honiton (2 offices), Ottery St Mary, Seaton, Sidmouth, Taunton
Work: A1 B1 C1 C2 C3 D1 E F1 G H J1 K1 L N O P Q R1 S1 T1 T2 W X Z(a,c,d,e,i,l,p)
Emergency Action, Agency, Advocacy, Fixed Fee Interview, Legal Aid undertaken, Legal Aid Franchise and Member of Accident Line
Asoc: Izzett, Mrs Sarah Louise Jane. . . . . *§May 1980
Ast: Beamer, Mrs Barbara Jean . . . . *§May 1997
Woodford, Mrs Helen Kate . . . . *§Sep 2005

SYMES ROBINSON & LEE
51 High Street Budleigh Salterton Devon EX9 6LG
Tel: 01395 445581 *Fax:* 01395 446248
Dx: 122840 BUDLEIGH SALTERTON
E-mail: mail@srl-solicitors.co.uk
Office: Crediton, Exeter
Work: D1 E F1 J1 K1 K3 K4 L N P Q R1 S1 S2 T1 T2 V W Z(l,o,q,r)
Agency undertaken
Ptr: Langrishe, Mr Patrick du P LLB . . . . *Dec 1980
Middlemost, Mr Donald James Peel BL(Hons); LLB . *Nov 2001
Ast: Govier, Mr Stephen C G. . . . . *§Nov 1976

BUILTH WELLS, Powys

JEFFREYS & POWELL
46 High Street Builth Wells Powys LD2 3AB
Tel: 01982 553224 *Fax:* 01874 623702 *Dx:* 200350 BRECON
Office: Brecon
Work: A1 K1 L Q S1 T1 T2 W
Agency and Advocacy undertaken
Ptr: Griffiths, Mr W Griffin T LLB(Wales) . . . . *§Apr 1965

SYDNEY G THOMAS & CO ‡
West End House West Street Builth Wells Powys LD2 3AH
Tel: 01982 553289 *Fax:* 01982 553590
List of partners: A R I Vanhees
Work: A1 E K1 L S1 T1 T2 W Z(l)
Ptr: Vanhees, Mr Alfons R I LLB(Wales) . . . . *Jul 1974
Ast: Stephens, Mr David H. . . . . Jan 1970

H VAUGHAN VAUGHAN & CO ‡
(incorporating Marsden & Co)
Manchester House 50 High Street Builth Wells Powys LD2 3AD
Tel: 01982 552331 / 553571 *Fax:* 01982 552860
Dx: 100653 BUILTH WELLS
E-mail: david@hvaughan.co.uk
List of partners: D T Lloyd
Office: Rhayader
Languages: French, German
Work: A1 A2 D2 E K1 K3 L Q R1 R2 S1 S2 T1 T2 W
Advocacy undertaken
SPr: Lloyd, Mr David Thomas . . . . *§Apr 1975
Con: Dunn, Conal M . . . . *Nov 1984

BUNGAY, Suffolk

ALLENS ‡
2 St Marys Street Bungay Suffolk NR35 1AX
Tel: 01986 893928 *Fax:* 01986 875775
E-mail: allens@tetnet.co.uk
List of partners: R C B Allen
Office: Halesworth
Work: D1 F1 G H J1 K1 L M1 P S1 W Z(l)
Emergency Action, Agency, Fixed Fee Interview, Legal Aid undertaken and Member of Accident Line
Ptr: Allen, Mr Roger C B. . . . . *Oct 1977

CADGE & GILBERT ‡
8 Earsham Street Bungay Suffolk NR35 1AG
Tel: 01986 893134 *Fax:* 01986 893600 *Dx:* 83700 BUNGAY
E-mail: cadgegilbert@btinternet.com
List of partners: B Ferguson, M J Simpson
Office: Loddon
Languages: French, Spanish
Work: A1 B1 C1 D1 E F1 G H J1 K1 L M1 N O P Q R1 S1 T1 V W Z(c,f,i,l,m,o,t)
Emergency Action, Agency, Advocacy, Fixed Fee Interview and Legal Aid undertaken
Ptr: Simpson, Mr Malcolm J BA . . . . *Feb 1983

FOSTERS
(incorporating Russell Steward)
3 Trinity Street Bungay Suffolk NR35 1EQ
Tel: 01986 895251 *Fax:* 01986 895671 *Dx:* 83701 BUNGAY
E-mail: enquiries@fosters.co.uk
Office: Lowestoft, Norwich, Wymondham
Work: A1 B1 B2 C1 C2 C3 D1 D2 E F1 G H J1 K1 K2 L M1 M2 N O P Q R1 S1 S2 T1 T2 V W Z(b,c,i,l,m,p,q,r)
Emergency Action, Agency, Advocacy, Fixed Fee Interview, Legal Aid undertaken, Legal Aid Franchise and Member of Accident Line
Ptr: Saul, Mr Andrew P LLB(Lond). . . . . *§Dec 1980

SPRAKE & KINGSLEY ‡
16 Broad Street Bungay Suffolk NR35 1EN
Tel: 01986 892721 *Fax:* 01986 893380 *Dx:* 83704 BUNGAY
E-mail: info@sprakekingsley.co.uk
List of partners: F J Davy, N P Kingsley, K J Phillips, D J Sprake
Office: Beccles
Work: A1 A2 B1 C1 C2 C3 D1 E F1 G H J1 K1 K2 K3 K4 L N O Q R1 R2 S1 S2 T1 T2 V W Z(c,d,h,j,k,l,m,p,t)
Emergency Action and Agency undertaken
Ptr: Davy, Miss Frances J . . . . *Feb 2003
Kingsley, Mr Nicolas P. . . . . *Oct 1980
Phillips, Miss Karen J LLB. . . . . *Oct 1990
Sprake, Mr David J . . . . *May 1981

BUNTINGFORD, Hertfordshire

C J HILL SOLICITOR ‡
Friars Grange Offley Green Rushden Buntingford Hertfordshire SG9 0TF
Tel: 07973 781670
E-mail: chill.office@virgin.net
Work: G H
Advocacy undertaken

D M KREMPEL ‡
Traf House Roe Green Sandon Buntingford Hertfordshire SG9 0QE
Tel: 01763 288569 *Fax:* 01763 288570
E-mail: sjk@dmkrempel.co.uk
List of partners: D M Krempel, S J Krempel
Work: C1 E S1 S2 W
Ptr: Krempel, Mrs Deborah Mary BA. . . . . *Jan 1983
Krempel, Mr Steven James BA . . . . *May 1981

BURES, Suffolk

BRICE & CO ‡
The Old Vicarage Church Square Bures Suffolk CO8 5AA
Tel: 01787 227199 *Fax:* 01787 227140
Dx: 99881 BRISTOL REDLAND
Emergency telephone 01787 227199
E-mail: briceandco@hotmail.com
List of partners: J Brice
Languages: French
Work: G H
Emergency Action, Agency, Advocacy, Legal Aid undertaken and Legal Aid Franchise
SPr: Brice, Mrs Julie LLB(B'ham). . . . . *Oct 1980

BURFORD, Oxfordshire

KENDALL & DAVIES
7 Sheep Street Burford Oxfordshire OX18 4LS
Tel: 01993 822025 *Fax:* 01993 823634 *Dx:* 709254 BURFORD
E-mail: burford@kendallanddavies.co.uk
Office: Bourton-on-the-Water, Moreton-in-Marsh, Stow-on-the-Wold
Work: A1 E L S1 S2 W
Dir: Davies, Mr Huw G . . . . *§Mar 1979
Ast: Bird, Mr Roger BA . . . . *Jan 2003
Vienot, Miss Juliette Ann LLB(Hons). . . . . *Nov 1992

BURGESS HILL, West Sussex

ACUMEN BUSINESS LAW
50 Victoria Road Victoria Business Park Burgess Hill West Sussex RH15 9LH
Tel: 01444 810070 *Fax:* 0871 714 2698
Office: Hove

BENNETT OAKLEY & PARTNERS ‡
13 Mill Road Burgess Hill West Sussex RH15 8DN
Tel: 01444 235232 *Fax:* 01444 236327 *Dx:* 300400 BURGESS HILL
E-mail: lawyers@bennettoakley.co.uk
List of partners: J T Fisher, A J Oakley
Work: A1 B1 C1 E J1 K1 L N O Q S1 W Z(d)
Ptr: Fisher, Mr James T BA(Legal Studies) . . . . *Mar 1980
Oakley, Mr Alan J MA(Oxon) Notary Public . . . . . *Jun 1972
Ast: Pullen, Miss Kate Helen Louise BA . . . . Dec 1991

SDK LAW ‡
23 The Forum 277 London Road Burgess Hill West Sussex RH15 9QU
Tel: 01444 240393 *Fax:* 01444 220475
E-mail: steven@sdk-law.co.uk

STEVENS SON & POPE ‡
Jubilee House 56-58 Church Walk Burgess Hill West Sussex RH15 9AN
Tel: 01444 246377 *Fax:* 01444 870919 *Dx:* 300402 BURGESS HILL
E-mail: info@ssandp.com
List of partners: Y Cordwell, R J B Jackson
Work: D1 E F1 J1 K1 K2 K3 L N Q R1 S1 S2 T2 V W Z(l)
Emergency Action, Agency, Legal Aid undertaken and Legal Aid Franchise
Ptr: Cordwell, Ms Yvonne LLB(Hons) . . . . *Sep 1993
Jackson, Mr Roger J B LLB. . . . . *Nov 1972

WHETHAM & GREEN ‡
54 Crescent Road Burgess Hill West Sussex RH15 8EQ
Tel: 01444 233403 *Fax:* 01444 870248 *Dx:* 300403 BURGESS HILL
List of partners: J A Green
Work: B1 E F1 P R1 S1 W Z(i,l)
Emergency Action, Agency, Fixed Fee Interview and Legal Aid undertaken
Ptr: Green, Mr John A. . . . . *Jul 1971

BURLEY-IN-WHARFEDALE, West Yorkshire

CHRIS DENTON ‡
Crossfell Station Road Burley-in-Wharfedale West Yorkshire LS29 7NT
Tel: 01943 607828
List of partners: C M Denton
Agency, Advocacy, Fixed Fee Interview and Legal Aid undertaken
SPr: Denton, Mr Christopher M LLB . . . . *Jan 1970

BURNHAM, Buckinghamshire

BROWNS ‡
98 High Street Burnham Buckinghamshire SL1 7JT
Tel: 01628 660440 *Fax:* 01628 660450

CHEBSEY & CO
10-12a High Street Burnham Buckinghamshire SL1 7JH
Tel: 01628 660077 *Fax:* 01628 660041 *Dx:* 38214 BURNHAM
Emergency telephone 07899 953415
E-mail: burnham@chebsey.com
Office: Bath, Beaconsfield, Rickmansworth, Windsor
Languages: Hindi, Punjabi, Urdu
Work: B2 G H K1 K2 K3 M1 N O Q W Z(k,l,p,q)
Agency, Advocacy and Legal Aid undertaken
Ast: Bains, Mrs Manjit . . . . Apr 1999
Cole, Nicky . . . . *Jan 1991
Dunne, Miss Caroline Anne LLB. . . . . *Oct 1992
Tanner, Mr Malcolm John BSocSc. . . . . *§Nov 1972
Tufail, Mrs Safeena LLB. . . . . Apr 2005
Con: Francis, Mr John George . . . . Dec 1971
Sommer, Mrs Josephine Margaret. . . . . *Feb 1980

KILPATRICK & CO ‡
The Priory Stomp Road Burnham Buckinghamshire SL1 7LS
Tel: 07834 258605 *Fax:* 01628 662555
List of partners: R M Kilpatrick
Work: C1 C2 E J1 K1 N O Q S1 Z(c,f,j,k)
Agency and Advocacy undertaken
Ptr: Kilpatrick, Mr Robert M BA . . . . *Mar 1983

See p112 for the Key to Work Categories & other symbols

BURNHAM-ON-CROUCH, Essex

HARVEY ESCOTT & CO ‡
36 High Street Burnham-on-Crouch Essex CM0 8AA
Tel: 01621 784838 / 784839 *Fax:* 01621 782210
E-mail: info@harvey-escott.co.uk
List of partners: H J Escott
Languages: French, German, Spanish
Work: D1 E F1 J1 K1 K3 K4 L O Q S1 W
Emergency Action and Fixed Fee Interview undertaken
SPr: Escott, Mrs Hilary J LLB. . . . . . *Oct 1990
Ast: Smith, Mr Patrick R LLB(Hons) . . . . . . Dec 1975

BURNHAM-ON-SEA, Somerset

ALLETSONS ‡
31 College Street Burnham-on-Sea Somerset TA8 1AS
Tel: 01278 780151 *Fax:* 01278 781004
Dx: 47552 BURNHAM-ON-SEA
E-mail: info@alletsons.com
List of partners: M I Merryweather, D H Williams, R H Williams
Work: A1 C1 C2 E F1 J1 K1 L N O Q R1 S1 T1 T2 V W Z(e,l,q)
Agency and Advocacy undertaken
Ptr: Merryweather, Milford I LLB . . . . . . *Nov 1984
Williams, Mr David H LLB. . . . . . *§Oct 1971
Williams, Mr Richard Haydn LLB . . . . . . *Mar 2000
Ast: Palmer, Mr John S A LLB . . . . . . *§Jul 1979
Con: Watkis, Mr J Brian H LLB . . . . . . *§Nov 1962

BARRINGTON & SONS ‡
60 High Street Burnham-on-Sea Somerset TA8 1AG
Tel: 01278 782371 *Fax:* 01278 792781
Dx: 47550 BURNHAM-ON-SEA
Emergency telephone 07702 631663
E-mail: admin@barrington-sons.co.uk
List of partners: P C F Caley, N Redding
Work: A1 B1 C1 E F1 K1 K3 L O Q S1 S2 W Z(l)
Emergency Action and Advocacy undertaken
Ptr: Caley, Miss Patricia Corran Frances LLB . . . . . . *Oct 1982
Redding, Mr Nicholas LLB. . . . . . *Oct 1984

GOULD & SWAYNE
64 High Street Burnham-on-Sea Somerset TA8 1PE
Tel: 01278 783272 *Fax:* 01278 781040
Dx: 47553 BURNHAM-ON-SEA
E-mail: c.haskins@gouldandswayne.co.uk
Office: Glastonbury, Street, Wells
Work: A1 B1 C1 E F1 J1 K1 K4 L O Q S1 S2 T1 T2 W Z(d,l,m)
Dir: Culshaw, Mr Charles J BA(Law). . . . . . *§Nov 1984

HOLLEY & STEER ‡
1 Berrow Road Burnham-on-Sea Somerset TA8 2ET
Tel: 01278 788991 *Fax:* 01278 792159
Dx: 47551 BURNHAM-ON-SEA
Emergency telephone 01278 781490
List of partners: A J F Holley, B M J Steer
Languages: French
Work: A1 D1 G H K1 M1 P S1 T1 W
Emergency Action, Agency, Advocacy, Legal Aid undertaken and Member of Accident Line
Ptr: Steer, Mr Brendan M J LLB(Lond). . . . . . *Jan 1982

HENRY NEVILL & CO ‡
Post Office Chambers Victoria Street Burnham-on-Sea Somerset TA8 1AL
Tel: 01278 793936 *Fax:* 01278 793787
Emergency telephone 01278 788103
E-mail: info@henrynevill..co.uk
List of partners: P H Nevill
Work: E L S1 S2 W
SPr: Nevill, Mr Philip Henry. . . . . . *Jun 1982

JOHN SHIRLEY & CO ‡
24 College Street Burnham-on-Sea Somerset TA8 1AT
Tel: 01278 780202 *Fax:* 01278 792612
Dx: 47555 BURNHAM-ON-SEA
List of partners: J M Booth, W J Shirley
Ptr: Booth, Mrs Jean M LLB. . . . . . *§Oct 1984
Shirley, Mr W John LLB(L'pool) . . . . . . *Dec 1978

BURNLEY, Lancashire

APPLEYARD LEES
10 Hargreaves Street Burnley Lancashire BB11 1ED
Tel: 01282 412506
E-mail: burnley@appleyardlees.com
Office: Chester, Halifax, Harrogate, Huddersfield, Leeds, Liverpool, Manchester, Preston, Sheffield, Stockton-on-Tees, York

BALDWIN WYATT SOLICITORS ‡
Proctors Chambers 24 Hammerton Street Burnley Lancashire BB11 1NA
Tel: 01282 429999 *Fax:* 01282 448866 *Dx:* 23880 BURNLEY
E-mail: team@bwlawyers.co.uk
List of partners: R Baldwin, C Wyatt
Work: E J1 K4 L N Q S1 S2 W
Agency undertaken
Ptr: Baldwin, Mr Roger . . . . . . *Oct 1978
Wyatt, Mr Christopher LLB(Sheff) . . . . . . *Oct 1982
Asoc: Kay, Mr John Michael LLB(Hons) . . . . . . *Dec 1977

CLIFFORD SMITH & BUCHANAN ‡
(incorporating Lambert & Parker)
36 Manchester Road Burnley Lancashire BB11 1HJ
Tel: 01282 452611 *Fax:* 01282 454832 *Dx:* 23852 BURNLEY
E-mail: burnley@cs-b.co.uk
List of partners: I A Buchanan, A Riley
Office: Colne, Nelson
Work: K3 S1 W
Emergency Action, Agency, Advocacy, Fixed Fee Interview undertaken and Member of Accident Line
Ptr: Riley, Mr Alan BA(Hons)(Law). . . . . . *§Dec 1976

DONALD RACE & NEWTON
5-7 Hargreaves Street Burnley Lancashire BB11 1EN
Tel: 01282 433241 *Fax:* 01282 831720 *Dx:* 23859 BURNLEY
Office: Burnley, Colne

FARLEYS SOLICITORS LLP
Prudential Buildings Manchester Road Burnley Lancashire BB11 1HJ
Tel: 01282 798664 *Fax:* 01282 718009 *Dx:* 23862 BURNLEY
Emergency telephone 01254 52552
E-mail: info@farleys.com
Office: Accrington, Blackburn (3 offices), Manchester
Work: A3 B2 C1 D1 E F1 F2 G H J1 K1 K2 L N P Q S1 T1 T2 V W X Z(i,j,l,m,p,q,r,w)
Emergency Action, Agency, Advocacy, Fixed Fee Interview, Legal Aid undertaken, Legal Aid Franchise and Member of Accident Line
Ptr: Corrigan, Mr Paul. . . . . . *Jul 1997
Molyneux, Mr Nicholas . . . . . . Jan 2001
Ast: Chorkley, Ms Sara-Jane LLB(Hons) . . . . . . *May 1998
Crompton, Ms Tracy. . . . . . Sep 2007
Frankland, Mrs Karen J LLB. . . . . . *Oct 1990
Lyle, Miss Sara Louise LLB(Hons). . . . . . *Sep 2004
Con: Kearsley, Miss Joanne LLB(Hons). . . . . . *Feb 1999

GEORGE H GUYER ‡
18 Carleton Avenue Simonstone Burnley Lancashire BB12 7JA
Tel: 01282 773438
List of partners: G H Guyer
Legal Aid undertaken
Ptr: Guyer, Mr George H . . . . . . *Aug 1970

HOLT & LONGWORTH ‡
4 Bull Street Burnley Lancashire BB11 1DW
Tel: 01282 414740 *Fax:* 01282 458666
E-mail: burnley@holtandlongworth.co.uk

JGT ‡
8 Elizabeth Street Burnley Lancashire BB11 2BQ
Tel: 01282 426722 *Fax:* 01282 458543 *Dx:* 23871 BURNLEY
Emergency telephone 01282 844272 / 0200 22498
List of partners: J R S Greenwood, A N Holden, G S Tindall
Office: Blackburn, Nelson
Languages: French, German
Work: A1 B1 C1 D1 E F1 G H J1 K1 L M1 N P R1 S1 T1 V W Z(c,d,e,k,l,m,s)
Emergency Action, Agency, Advocacy, Fixed Fee Interview and Legal Aid undertaken
Ptr: Greenwood, Mr John R S . . . . . . *Dec 1988
Holden, Mr Arthur Nigel LLB(Hons)(Lond); MBA Notary Public . . . . . . Mar 1972
Tindall, Mr Graeme S LLB. . . . . . *Oct 1990

LAWSON TAYLOR LLP ‡
Dylan Harvey Business Centre Liverpool Road Burnley Lancashire BB12 6HH
Tel: 01282 477588 *Fax:* 01282 477589
E-mail: info@lawson-taylor.co.uk

A B MARSH SOLICITORS ‡
121 Colne Road Burnley Lancashire BB10 1LN
Tel: 0800 169 4849
E-mail: info@abmsolicitors.co.uk

MAYSONS SOLICITORS LLP ‡
27-29 Manchester Road Burnley Lancashire BB11 1HG
Tel: 01282 416069 *Fax:* 01282 436924

NGA ‡
33a-43 Parker Lane Burnley Lancashire BB11 2BU
Tel: 01282 457295 *Fax:* 01282 458396
E-mail: enquiries@ngasolicitors.co.uk
List of partners: A J Allen, S Brown, N J Campbell, T Grice, G F Ireland
Office: Burnley, Colne
Work: E G H K1 L N S1 W
Emergency Action, Agency, Advocacy, Fixed Fee Interview and Legal Aid undertaken
Ptr: Allen, Mr Anthony J. . . . . . Sep 1998
Grice, Mr Trevor LLB . . . . . . *Aug 1986
Ireland, Mr Geoffrey F LLB . . . . . . Jul 1979

NGA
85 Hammerton Street Burnley Lancashire BB11 1LE
Tel: 01282 450144 *Fax:* 01282 455033 *Dx:* 18202 COLNE
E-mail: enquiries@ngasolicitors.co.uk
Office: Burnley, Colne

POLLARD BOWER SOLICITORS ‡
8-10 Hargreaves Street Burnley Lancashire BB11 1ED
Tel: 01282 457624 *Fax:* 01282 412574 *Dx:* 23854 BURNLEY
E-mail: info@pollardbower.co.uk
List of partners: C J Baldwin, D J Harris
Work: B1 C1 C2 D1 E F1 F2 J1 K1 L N P Q R1 S1 S2 W
Emergency Action, Agency, Advocacy, Fixed Fee Interview, Legal Aid undertaken, Legal Aid Franchise and Member of Accident Line
Ptr: Baldwin, Mr Craig J BA(Law) ♦ . . . . . . *Oct 1984
Harris, Mr Darran J FILEx ♦. . . . . . *Sep 1998
Asoc: Hindsley, Mrs Joanne Karen. . . . . . Apr 2004
Mitchell, Miss Louise BA(Hons); LLB(Hons) . . . . . . *Apr 2010

DONALD RACE & NEWTON ‡
4 Nicholas Street Burnley Lancashire BB11 2EU
Tel: 01282 433241 *Fax:* 01282 831720 *Dx:* 23859 BURNLEY
Emergency telephone 07990 585494
E-mail: indo@drnlaw.co.uk
List of partners: S M Anderson, S J Newton, A Norris, P J Reynolds
Office: Burnley, Colne
Work: A1 B1 C1 C2 C3 D1 E F1 G H J1 K1 L M1 M2 N O P Q R1 S1 T1 T2 V W
Emergency Action, Agency, Advocacy, Fixed Fee Interview, Legal Aid undertaken, Legal Aid Franchise and Member of Accident Line
Ptr: Anderson, Mr Stephen Martin LLB. . . . . . Aug 2000
Newton, Mr Simon J Clerk to Commissioner of Taxes *§Dec 1970
Norris, Mr Adrian LLB Leicester Law Society Prize . . *Oct 1991
Ast: Austin, Ms Sarah J BBA; PGDipLaw; AMSI . . . . . . *Sep 1996
Con: Hartley, Mr John A LLB . . . . . . *§Jun 1966

SFN SOLICITORS ‡
3-5 Red Lion Street Burnley Lancashire BB11 2AE
Tel: 01282 421284 *Fax:* 01282 412299 *Dx:* 23856 BURNLEY
E-mail: info@sfn.co.uk
List of partners: K Bridge, G J S Lonsdale, J C McNabb, T Stansfield
Work: A1 A2 A3 B1 C1 C2 D1 D2 E F1 G H J1 K1 K2 K3 K4 L M4 N O P Q R1 R2 S1 S2 T1 V W Z(c,d,e,f,g,h,i,j,k,l,m,p,q,r,s,w)
Emergency Action, Agency, Advocacy, Fixed Fee Interview and Legal Aid undertaken
Ptr: Bridge, Mrs Kimberley. . . . . . *Oct 1996
Lonsdale, Mr George James Stanley LLB . . . . . . Nov 1990
McNabb, Mr John Charles LLB(Hons) Panel Receiver for Court of Protection . . . . . . *§May 1981
Stansfield, Mrs Tracy . . . . . . Sep 1994
Ast: Aksa, Miss Yousaf Naureen LLB(Hons) . . . . . . Aug 2001
Charnley, Mrs Rachel Claire LLB(Hons) . . . . . . Jul 2000
Dearing, Mr Nicholas LLB(Hons) . . . . . . *Sep 1998
Evans, Mrs Catherine Elisabeth LLB(Hons) . . . . . . Sep 1998
Khan, Miss Sajada LLB(Hons). . . . . . Jan 2005
Law-Riding, Miss Anita Marie LLB(Hons) . . . . . . May 2000
Con: Dearing, Mr Basil LLB(Hons) . . . . . . *Oct 1967
Dearing, Mr Ian B LLB(Leeds) Notary Public. . . . . . *Apr 1971

ERIC H SMITH ‡
22 Manchester Road Burnley Lancashire BB11 1HH
Tel: 01282 432141 *Fax:* 01282 423329 *Dx:* 23851 BURNLEY
E-mail: info@erichsmith.co.uk
List of partners: S M Smith
Work: E F1 R1 S1 S2 W
Agency and Fixed Fee Interview undertaken
SPr: Smith, Mr Stuart M . . . . . . *§Jan 1980

SMITH SUTCLIFFE ‡
50 Manchester Road Burnley Lancashire BB11 1HJ
Tel: 01282 426251 *Fax:* 01282 420766 *Dx:* 23855 BURNLEY
E-mail: burnley@smithsutcliffe.com
List of partners: S Dakers, D Fort, P G Halstead, D Hendleman, P Wilkinson
Office: Padiham
Work: A1 C1 C2 D1 D2 E F1 J1 K1 L N O P Q R1 R2 S1 S2 T2 V W X Z(d,i,m,q)
Emergency Action, Agency, Advocacy, Fixed Fee Interview, Legal Aid undertaken and Legal Aid Franchise
Ptr: Dakers, Mr Simon. . . . . . Apr 1998
Fort, Mr Derek LLB; AKC . . . . . . *§Jul 1980
Halstead, Mr Paul G BTech . . . . . . *§Mar 1986
Hendleman, Mr Darren BA . . . . . . *Aug 1997
Wilkinson, Mr Peter. . . . . . *Dec 1977

SMITHJONES SOLICITORS LTD ‡
King Edward House 9 Finsley Gate Burnley Lancashire BB11 2FS
Tel: 01282 855400 *Fax:* 01282 855401 *Dx:* 742730 BURNLEY 10
E-mail: info@sjlaw.co.uk
List of partners: C Bibby, A J Graham, P A G Jones, P J Smith, D C Woodhead
Office: Kenilworth
Work: N Q Z(q)
Emergency Action, Fixed Fee Interview undertaken and Member of Accident Line
Ptr: Bibby, Mr Craig LLB. . . . . . Jan 2005
Graham, Mr Alexander J LLB(Manc) . . . . . . *Apr 1977
Jones, Mr Peter Anthony Glyn BSc . . . . . . *Oct 1984
Smith, Mr Paul J LLB . . . . . . *Jun 1984
Woodhead, Mr Dermot C LLB. . . . . . *Oct 1985
Con: Willoughby, Mr Robin LLB. . . . . . *§Mar 1969

SOUTHERNS ‡
Mackenzie House 66-68 Bank Parade Burnley Lancashire BB11 1UB
Tel: 01282 422711 *Fax:* 01282 470320 *Dx:* 23860 BURNLEY
Emergency telephone 01282 422711
E-mail: bankparade@southernslaw.info
List of partners: S A Bentley, A M Buchanan, N Cronin, J S Hunter, K Morgan, G Rodwell, J H Rusius, R G Taylor, M H Williams
Office: Burnley, Colne, Nelson
Work: B1 C1 C2 C3 D1 E F1 J1 K1 L N O Q R1 S1 T1 T2 V W Z(d,l,m,o)
Emergency Action, Agency, Advocacy, Fixed Fee Interview, Legal Aid undertaken, Legal Aid Franchise and Member of Accident Line
Ptr: Bentley, Miss Sarah A LLB . . . . . . Oct 1986
Buchanan, Mr Andrew M LLB(L'pool) . . . . . . *§Mar 1979
Cronin, Mr Neil LLB. . . . . . *Oct 1998
Hunter, Mr James S. . . . . . *Apr 1974
Ast: Anwar, Mr Shazad LLB . . . . . . *§Sep 2002
Barton, Mr David Richard . . . . . . Sep 2003
Pollard, Mr Jonathan Mark LLB . . . . . . *§Aug 2001
Taylor, Mr Gary Alan LLB(Hons). . . . . . *§Oct 1995

SOUTHERNS
6a Hargreaves Street Burnley Lancashire BB11 1ES
Tel: 01282 438446 *Fax:* 01282 446525 *Dx:* 23860 BURNLEY
E-mail: hargreavesstreet@southernslaw.info
Office: Burnley, Colne, Nelson
Work: G H J1 K1 L N Q V
Emergency Action, Agency, Advocacy, Fixed Fee Interview, Legal Aid undertaken, Legal Aid Franchise and Member of Accident Line
Ptr: Taylor, Mr Richard G BA ★ H M Coroner . . . . . . *§Nov 1980
Williams, Mr Mark H LLB . . . . . . *§Dec 1986

WADDINGTON & SON ‡
28 Manchester Road Burnley Lancashire BB11 1HH
Tel: 01282 426666 *Fax:* 01282 427974 *Dx:* 23858 BURNLEY
Emergency telephone 07976 236958 / 07976 236962
E-mail: enquiries@waddingtonandson.co.uk
List of partners: D J Baldwin, D J Bradshaw, P J Turner
Office: Padiham
Work: B1 C1 D1 D2 E F1 G H J1 K1 L M1 N O Q R1 S1 S2 V W Z(i,l,q,r)
Emergency Action, Agency, Advocacy, Fixed Fee Interview, Legal Aid undertaken and Legal Aid Franchise
Ptr: Baldwin, Mr Duncan John BA . . . . . . *Oct 1987
Bradshaw, Mr Dylan John LLB . . . . . . *Sep 1990
Turner, Mr Philip J LLB(Leics). . . . . . *Apr 1980
Asoc: Marshall, Mrs Kathrine Elaine LLB. . . . . . *Sep 2005
Warner, Mr Colin LLB . . . . . . Apr 1998
Ast: Fell, Miss Cathryn Helen BSc; CPE; LPC . . . . . . Jun 2005

WALKERS
43 Parker Lane Burnley Lancashire BB11 2BU
Tel: 01282 411138 *Fax:* 01282 414671
Office: Rossendale
Work: G H
Agency and Legal Aid undertaken

WARD LEGAL LTD ‡
Simonstone Business Park Blackburn Road Simonstone Burnley Lancashire BB12 7NQ
Tel: 01282 775788 *Fax:* 01282 771186
E-mail: david.ward@wardlegal.co.uk

BURNTWOOD, Staffordshire

HELEN M MULLINS ‡
3 Linchfield Road Burntwood Staffordshire WS2 0HQ
Tel: 01543 674295 *Fax:* 01543 674953
Work: K1 S1 S2 W

ROSEBLADE & CO ‡
9 Cannock Road Chase Terrace Burntwood Staffordshire WS7 1JS
Tel: 01543 898591 *Fax:* 01543 671040
List of partners: E Roseblade
Work: B1 C1 E F1 G H J1 K1 K3 L N O Q R1 S1 S2 V W Z(h,k,l,q)
Emergency Action, Agency and Advocacy undertaken
Ptr: Roseblade, Mr Edwin . . . . *§Jul 1980

BURTON-IN-KENDAL, Cumbria

NIGEL DAVIS SOLICITORS ‡
The Stable Yard Dalton Hall Burton-in-Kendal Cumbria LA6 1NJ
Tel: 01524 784260 *Fax:* 01524 784261
E-mail: enquiries@agriculturalsolicitors.co.uk

BURTON-ON-TRENT, Staffordshire

ABBEY LAW SOLICITORS ‡
Abbey House 127 Horninglow Street Burton-on-Trent Staffordshire DE14 1PJ
Tel: 01283 539718 *Fax:* 01283 539717
E-mail: enquiries@abbeylawsolicitors.co.uk
List of partners: S Dean
Ptr: Dean, Mr Simon. *Oct 1994

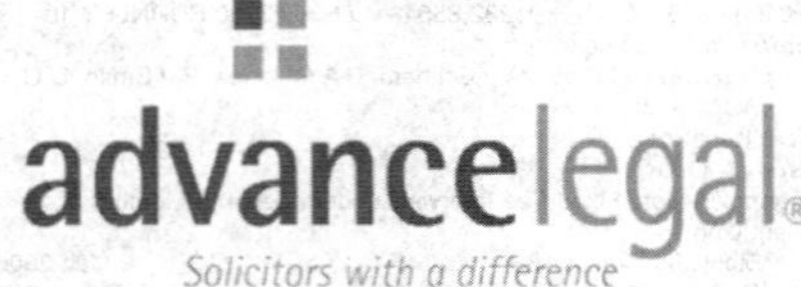

ADVANCE LEGAL ‡
Suites 3-9 Imex Business Park Shobnall Road Burton-on-Trent Staffordshire DE14 2AZ
Tel: 01283 544492 *Fax:* 01283 545584
E-mail: help@advancelegal.co.uk
Web: www.advancelegal.co.uk
List of partners: M D J House, S A Kehoe
Work: C1 J1 J2 N O Q S1 W Z(g,p,r)
Agency undertaken
Ptr: House, Mr Mark David John LLB(Hons) . . . . Dec 2004
Kehoe, Mr Sean A BSocSc; Also qualified as an attorney in California . . . . *Nov 1989
Ast: Barker, Mrs Dianne LLB(Hons) . . . . Oct 1991

We are happy to undertake all categories of Agency work in the High Court/County Court. Please contact us at the above address.

ASTLE PATERSON LTD ‡
181 Horninglow Street Burton-on-Trent Staffordshire DE14 1NJ
Tel: 01283 531366 *Fax:* 01283 510996
Dx: 715426 BURTON-ON-TRENT 6
E-mail: enquiries@astlepaterson.co.uk
List of partners: E M Astle, J C Paterson, J C Trubshaw, P G Walters, N E Wilson
Work: B1 C1 C2 D1 E J1 K1 K2 K3 L N O Q R1 R2 S1 S2 T1 T2 W Z(c,l)
Emergency Action and Agency undertaken
Mem: Walters, Mr Paul Godfrey . . . . *Jan 1971
Dir: Astle, Mr E Martin Notary Public. . . . . *Jun 1963
Paterson, Miss Jean C LLB Notary Public . . . . *Jun 1981
Trubshaw, Mr John Cyril BA. . . . . *Apr 1980
Wilson, Mrs Naomi Estelle LLB . . . . *Sep 2000
Ast: Hume, Miss Fiona L MA(Hons) . . . . *Jun 1986
O'Shea, Mr Liam Timothy Joseph LLB. . . . . *Sep 2007

BE LEGAL ‡
Parkway House 2nd Avenue Burton-on-Trent Staffordshire DE14 2WF
Tel: 01283 517717

ELSE SOLICITORS LLP ‡
First Avenue Centrum 100 Burton-on-Trent Staffordshire DE14 2WE
Tel: 01283 526200
Office: Birmingham

HELEN MASON & CO SOLICITORS ‡
17 Rangemore Hall Mews Rangemore Burton-on-Trent Staffordshire DE13 9RE
Tel: 01629 815175

OMW SOLICITORS ‡
Worthington House 146 High Street Burton-on-Trent Staffordshire DE14 1JE
Tel: 01283 563401 / 530333 *Fax:* 01283 547314
Dx: 10701 BURTON-ON-TRENT
Emergency telephone 01283 561078 / 566077
E-mail: info@omwsolicitors.co.uk
List of partners: P M Levy, R P Mills, S D Woodall
Languages: Urdu
Work: A1 B1 D1 E F1 G H J1 K1 L N O Q R1 S1 T1 V W Z(d,h)
Emergency Action, Agency, Advocacy, Fixed Fee Interview and Legal Aid undertaken
Ptr: Levy, Mr Peter M LLB. . . . . *Jul 1969
Mills, Mr Raymond P LLB . . . . *Jul 1968
Woodall, Mrs Susan D BA(Hons) . . . . *Dec 1979
Asoc: Ball, Mrs Christine V BA(Hons) . . . . *Apr 1977
Khunkhuna, Mrs Dee BA(Hons). . . . . *Feb 1999

SAMBLE BURTON & WORTH ‡
(in association with Irvings)
Abbey Arcade Market Place Burton-on-Trent Staffordshire DE14 1HQ
Tel: 01283 565731 *Fax:* 01283 510569
Dx: 10702 BURTON-ON-TRENT
List of partners: L G Conner, A R Picken
Office: Derby
Languages: French
Work: A1 C1 E G J1 K1 R1 S1 T1 W Z(m)
Agency, Advocacy, Fixed Fee Interview, Legal Aid undertaken and Member of Accident Line
Ptr: Conner, Mr Lionel G LLB . . . . *Mar 1974

R W SKINNER & SON ‡
12 Market Place Burton-on-Trent Staffordshire DE14 1HA
Tel: 01283 561694 *Fax:* 01283 548346
Dx: 10710 BURTON-ON-TRENT
E-mail: johns@rwskinnerandson.co.uk
List of partners: J W D Skinner, R C V Skinner
Work: A1 B1 B2 C1 D1 E F1 G H J1 K1 K3 K4 L M1 N P Q R1 S1 S2 V W Z(c,i,k,l,m)
Emergency Action, Agency, Advocacy, Fixed Fee Interview, Legal Aid undertaken and Legal Aid Franchise
Ptr: Skinner, Mr John William Douglas LLB . . . . *Jan 1994
Skinner, Mr Robin C V. . . . . *Nov 1958

THE SMITH PARTNERSHIP
158 High Street Burton-on-Trent Staffordshire DE14 1JE
Tel: 01283 536471 *Fax:* 01283 510987
Dx: 10708 BURTON-ON-TRENT
E-mail: burton@smithpartnership.co.uk
Office: Burton-on-Trent, Derby, Leicester (2 offices), Stoke-on-Trent, Swadlincote
Work: D1 F1 G H J1 K1 L M1 M2 P S1 V Z(i,l,m)
Emergency Action, Agency, Advocacy, Fixed Fee Interview, Legal Aid undertaken, Legal Aid Franchise and Member of Accident Line
Ptr: O'Driscoll, Mr Neil BSc . . . . Mar 1992
Ast: Green, Mr Nicholas S LLB. . . . . Oct 1982
Shaw, Mr Stuart John LLB(Hons) . . . . *Nov 1995

THE SMITH PARTNERSHIP
45 High Street Burton-on-Trent Staffordshire DE14 1JP
Tel: 01283 548282 *Fax:* 01283 511365
Dx: 10705 BURTON-ON-TRENT
E-mail: drewrys@drewrys45.com
Office: Burton-on-Trent, Derby, Leicester (2 offices), Stoke-on-Trent, Swadlincote
Work: A1 C1 C2 D1 E F1 J1 K1 K2 K3 K4 L Q S1 S2 T2 V W Z(m)
Emergency Action, Agency, Advocacy, Fixed Fee Interview and Legal Aid undertaken
Ptr: Phillips, Mr Andrew M LLB . . . . *May 1974
Smith, Mr Anthony D LLB . . . . *Mar 1979

FRANK E L SPEARS ‡
245 Waterloo Street Burton-on-Trent Staffordshire DE14 2NJ
Tel: 01283 511474

TALBOT & CO ‡
148 High Street Burton-on-Trent Staffordshire DE14 1JY
Tel: 01283 564716 *Fax:* 01283 510861
Dx: 10717 BURTON-ON-TRENT
E-mail: tombramall@talbotco.co.uk
List of partners: T J Bramall
Work: A1 C1 C2 E F1 J1 K1 K2 L N O Q R1 S1 S2 T1 T2 W Z(d,h,l,o,q,r)
Emergency Action, Agency, Advocacy, Fixed Fee Interview, Legal Aid Franchise and Member of Accident Line
Ptr: Bramall, Mr Thomas J LLB ♦ . . . . *Nov 1991
Asoc: Bramall, Mr Anthony LLB ♦ . . . . *§Dec 1968
Ast: Milburn, Mr Robert J ♦ . . . . *§Jan 1970
O'Connor, Mr Stephen LLB(Hons). . . . . *Sep 1999

TIMMS
7-8 Lichfield Street Burton-on-Trent Staffordshire DE14 3RE
Tel: 01283 561531 / 544417 *Fax:* 01283 511332
Dx: 10706 BURTON-ON-TRENT 1
E-mail: legal@timmslaw.co.uk
Office: Derby, Swadlincote
Work: A1 C1 C2 D1 E F1 G H J1 K1 L N Q R1 S1 V W Z(c,l,m,r,t)
Agency, Advocacy, Fixed Fee Interview, Legal Aid undertaken, Legal Aid Franchise and Member of Accident Line

JOHN WALLER & CO ‡
128 New Street Burton-on-Trent Staffordshire DE14 3QW
Tel: 01283 505950

MOIRA L WALLER ‡
The Hollies High Street Hanbury Burton-on-Trent Staffordshire DE13 8TF
Tel: 01283 821365
Emergency telephone 01283 821365
Work: G H P
Agency and Advocacy undertaken

BURY, Greater Manchester

ABT LAW LLP ‡
3rd Floor 1 The Rock Bury Greater Manchester BL9 0JP
Tel: 0161 764 6476 *Fax:* 0161 764 9320 *Dx:* 20524 BURY
E-mail: info@abtlaw.co.uk

AST HAMPSONS (INCORPORATING WARHURST AND CO) ‡
23 Knowsley Street Bury Greater Manchester BL9 0ST
Tel: 0161 764 3317 *Fax:* 0161 763 1978 *Dx:* 20504 BURY 1
E-mail: info@warhurst.co.uk
List of partners: R J K Hudson
Work: C1 E J1 K1 R1 S1 S2 W
Ptr: Hudson, Mr Robert J K . . . . *§Jul 1982
Con: Holden, Mr David C. . . . . *§Jan 1965

JEAN BIRTWELL SOLICITOR ‡
39 Longsight Road Ramsbottom Bury Greater Manchester BL0 9SL
Tel: 01204 866533

BUTCHER & BARLOW LLP ‡
2-6 Bank Street Bury Greater Manchester BL9 0DL
Tel: 0161 764 4062 *Fax:* 0161 797 2912 *Dx:* 20506 BURY 1
E-mail: enquiries@butcher-barlow.co.uk
List of partners: J A Aldersley, R J Ashton, C J M Barlow, E M Byrom, R Cryan, A S Gleave, A R Higham, S D Holland, C Hopkins, J R Hyatt, J S Kelly, R G Morris, A S Norman, S D Pinnington, A G Sandland, J M Shelmerdine, R Taylor, P J Thompson, L Walker, J G Whitaker
Office: Bramhall, Bury, Frodsham, Leigh, Northwich, Prestwich, Runcorn (2 offices), Sandbach, Tyldesley
Languages: German
Work: A1 B1 C1 C2 C3 D1 D2 E F1 J1 K1 K3 K4 L M1 M2 N O P Q R1 R2 S1 S2 T1 T2 V W X Z(c,d,e,j,l,m,o,p,q,r,t)
Emergency Action, Agency, Advocacy, Fixed Fee Interview, Legal Aid undertaken, Legal Aid Franchise and Member of Accident Line
Ptr: Byrom, Mr Edward Martin LLB(Hons) . . . . *§May 1971
Higham, Mr Anthony Richard BA(Hons)(Econ) Notary Public . . . . *Mar 1997
Ast: Hodgson, Mr James LLB . . . . *Sep 2008

BUTCHER & BARLOW LLP
18 Silver Street Bury Greater Manchester BL9 0ER
Tel: 0161 764 5141 *Fax:* 0161 762 9505 *Dx:* 20506 BURY
Emergency telephone 07831 808950
E-mail: enquiries@butcher-barlow.co.uk
Office: Bramhall, Bury, Frodsham, Leigh, Northwich, Prestwich, Runcorn (2 offices), Sandbach, Tyldesley
Work: C1 C2 D1 E F1 G H J1 K1 L N P R1 S1 S2 W Z(c,i,q,r)
Emergency Action, Agency, Advocacy, Legal Aid undertaken, Legal Aid Franchise and Member of Accident Line
Ptr: Holland, Mr Stephen David LLB(Hons) . . . . Mar 1984
Pinnington, Mr Stephen David LLB . . . . *Jan 1993
Ast: Smith, Mrs Abigail Catherine . . . . Dec 1999

CLOUGH & WILLIS ‡
(incorporating Clayton Castle & Monks)
2 Manchester Road Bury Greater Manchester BL9 0DT
Tel: 0161 764 5266 *Fax:* 0161 797 6157 *Dx:* 20508 BURY 1
E-mail: info@clough-willis.co.uk
List of partners: P H Breedon, F A Gaskell, T J Gray, C J Macwilliam, L R Marston, L Stratton-Webb, S Talukdar, E M Whittaker
Work: A1 B1 C1 C2 D1 D2 E F1 J1 J2 K1 K2 L N O Q R1 R2 S1 S2 T1 W Z(c,l,q,r,s,w)
Emergency Action, Agency, Advocacy, Fixed Fee Interview, Legal Aid undertaken, Legal Aid Franchise and Member of Accident Line
Ptr: Breedon, Mr Paul H LLB . . . . *§Jun 1976
Gaskell, Ms Fiona A LLB . . . . *§Oct 1987
Gray, Mr Timothy Jonathan LLB. . . . . *§Nov 1993
Macwilliam, Mr Christopher J LLB. . . . . *§Sep 1983
Marston, Mr Lee Raymond LLB(Hons); LSF. . . . . *§May 1997
Stratton-Webb, Mrs Lorraine . . . . *§Oct 2002
Talukdar, Miss Shefali LLB(Hull). . . . . *§Oct 1988
Whittaker, Mrs Eileen Marie. . . . . *§Feb 1998
Asoc: Azam, Mr Shahid M M LLB . . . . *§Mar 2002
Oliviero, Miss Dominique LLB; LPC . . . . Sep 2010
Webster, Miss Helen Fiona LLB. . . . . Feb 2006

CROMPTON HALLIWELL ‡
4-6 St Marys Place Bury Greater Manchester BL9 0EA
Tel: 0161 797 9222 *Fax:* 0161 762 9635
List of partners: C Brogan, B Clayton, J Grant, D E Hantom
Work: C1 D1 E F1 G H J1 K1 L M1 N O P Q R1 S1 V W Z(k,l)
Emergency Action, Agency, Advocacy, Fixed Fee Interview, Legal Aid undertaken and Member of Accident Line
Ptr: Brogan, Mr Christopher LLB. . . . . *§Apr 1980
Clayton, Mr Bernard BA(Hons)(Law) . . . . Dec 1975
Grant, Miss Joanne BA(Hons)(Politics); CPE; LPC . . Sep 1997
Hantom, Mr Donald E LLB . . . . *§Dec 1972
Ast: Daly, Mr James Barry BA(Hons). . . . . Dec 2001

DRIVING DEFENCES LLP ‡
Warth Park Radcliffe Road Bury Greater Manchester BL9 9TB
Tel: 0844 335 0767
E-mail: info@drivingdefences.com

EXCEL LEGAL ‡
27 Knowsley Street Bury Greater Manchester BL9 0ST
Tel: 0161 764 1035 *Fax:* 0161 761 5417 *Dx:* 20705 BURY
E-mail: enquiries@excellegal.co.uk

JOSEPH FOXLER & CO ‡
22 The Rock Bury Greater Manchester BL9 0NT
Tel: 0161 797 4126 *Fax:* 0161 272 0204
List of partners: J H Foxler
Work: D1 G H K1 N S1 V W
Emergency Action, Agency, Advocacy, Fixed Fee Interview, Legal Aid undertaken, Legal Aid Franchise and Member of Accident Line
Ptr: Foxler, Mr Joseph H LLB . . . . *Mar 1974

GHW SOLICITORS ‡
Glengarry 397 Holcombe Road Bury Greater Manchester BL8 4HF
Tel: 01204 882373
E-mail: gareth.williams@ghwsolicitors.co.uk

GLP SOLICITORS
Maple House Haymarket Street Bury Greater Manchester BL9 0AR
Tel: 0161 764 1818 *Fax:* 0161 761 1555 *Dx:* 20539 BURY
E-mail: bury@glplaw.com
Office: Manchester (4 offices), Middleton, Prestwich
Work: C1 F1 J1 N Q R2 W Z(p,q)
Agency, Legal Aid Franchise and Member of Accident Line
Ptr: Leigh, Mr Graham S BA. . . . . *Dec 1981
Ast: Davies, Mr Richard Neil BA(Hons); DipLaw . . . . . . Oct 2005

GEORGE HAWORTH CHAPPELL & WHITWORTH ‡
13-15 Square Street Ramsbottom Bury Greater Manchester BL0 9BL
Tel: 01706 824811 *Fax:* 01706 821928
List of partners: J C J Cavill, E J Whitworth
Work: F1 G H J1 K1 L N S1 T2 W
Emergency Action, Agency, Advocacy and Fixed Fee Interview undertaken
Ptr: Cavill, Mr John Charles J BA . . . . *§Jan 1985

HUGHES WALKER ‡
82 Bolton Street Bury Greater Manchester BL2 0LL
Tel: 0870 744 5952 *Fax:* 0845 108 5381

AUBREY ISAACSON SOLICITORS
60 Sunny Bank Road Sunny Bank Bury Greater Manchester BL9 8HJ
Tel: 0161 959 5050 *Fax:* 0161 959 5051
E-mail: jeffrey@aubreyisaacson.co.uk
Office: Prestwich (2 offices), Whitefield
Work: G J1 J2 K1 N Q S1 S2 W Z(q,r)
Member of Accident Line

See p112 for the Key to Work Categories & other symbols

LATIMER LEE LLP
Sankey Street Bury Greater Manchester BL9 0JE
Tel: 0871 128 9000 *Fax:* 0871 288 9010
E-mail: info@latimerlee.com
Office: Bolton, Heywood, Prestwich

NESBIT LAW GROUP LLP ‡
Warth Business Centre Warth Road Bury Greater Manchester BL9 9NB
Tel: 0161 763 0050 *Fax:* 0161 763 0066 *Dx:* 20533 BURY
E-mail: mail@nesbitlawgroup.co.uk
Office: Leeds, Liverpool, Wembley

QUARTERS SOLICITORS ‡
33 Bolton Street Ramsbottom Bury Greater Manchester BL0 9HU
Tel: 01706 829553 *Fax:* 0870 762 1062
E-mail: enquiries@quartersonline.co.uk

RECOVERY ASSIST LLP ‡
41-43 Walmersley Road Bury Greater Manchester BL9 5AE
Tel: 0161 762 4949 *Fax:* 0161 762 3480
E-mail: info@recoveryassist.co.uk

RUSSELL & RUSSELL
Belgrave Terrace 10 Manchester Road Bury Greater Manchester BL9 0EB
Tel: 0161 762 2888 *Fax:* 0161 762 2889 *Dx:* 20510 BURY 1
Emergency telephone 01204 847999
E-mail: infobury@russellrussell.co.uk
Office: Atherton, Bolton (4 offices), Middleton
Work: D1 D2 K1 K3 N S1 W
Emergency Action, Agency, Advocacy, Fixed Fee Interview, Legal Aid undertaken, Legal Aid Franchise and Member of Accident Line
Ptr: Ibrahim, Mr Saleem Abdullah BA(Hons) . . . . Sep 2004
Pearl, Mr Vincent BA . . . . *Sep 1990
Ast: Entwistle, Ms Teresa Helen LLB(Hons) . . . . Apr 2004
Morris, Miss Nichola Louise LLB(Hons) . . . . Sep 2010
Moss, Miss Michelle LLB . . . . Oct 2008
Whitehead, Ms Samantha BA(Hons) . . . . *§Jun 2001

SALT VEEDER ‡
10 Union Street Bury Greater Manchester BL9 0NY
Tel: 0161 797 5650 *Fax:* 0161 797 5619
Emergency telephone 0161 792 3149
E-mail: claire.jackson@saltveeder.com
Work: B1 C1 D1 E K1 L N O Q S1 S2 W

DEREK SMITH & CO
138 Bolton Road West Ramsbottom Bury Greater Manchester BL0 9PD
Tel: 01706 829750 *Fax:* 01706 823859
Emergency telephone 01204 887423
E-mail: csmith2@tiscali.co.uk
Office: Bolton
Work: A1 B1 E K1 K2 L N O P Q R1 S1 S2 W
Emergency Action, Agency, Advocacy, Fixed Fee Interview and Legal Aid undertaken
Ptr: Smith, Mr Joseph Derek . . . . Jan 1968

SOVEREIGN SOLICITORS ‡
35 Knowsley Street Bury Greater Manchester BL9 0ST
Tel: 0161 280 0582 *Fax:* 0161 280 0583
E-mail: info@hsovereignpartnership.co.uk

TAYLOR VAUGHAN SOLICITORS ‡
44-48 Bolton Street Bury Greater Manchester BL9 6RA
Tel: 0161 763 1066 *Fax:* 0161 763 1501
E-mail: info@taylorvaughan.co.uk

WOODCOCKS
12 & 14 Manchester Road Bury Greater Manchester BL9 0DX
Tel: 0161 761 4611 *Fax:* 0161 797 1238 *Dx:* 20501 BURY
E-mail: info@woodcocks.co.uk
Office: Bacup, Haslingden, Ramsbottom, Rawtenstall
Work: A1 B1 C1 C2 C3 D1 D2 E G H J1 K1 K3 L N O Q S1 S2 T1 T2 W Z(c,d,e,l,o,q)

BURY ST EDMUNDS, Suffolk

ABLE BISHOP LTD ‡
1st Floor Sampson House The Street Bury St Edmunds Suffolk IP30 9QN
Est: 2002
Tel: 01359 245141 *Fax:* 01359 245085
Emergency telephone 01359 242941
E-mail: info@ablebishop.biz
Languages: German, Spanish
Work: G H J1 L P Q R1 S1 X Z(c,h,n,p,t)

ASHTON KCJ
81 Guildhall Street Bury St Edmunds Suffolk IP33 1PZ
Tel: 01284 762331 *Fax:* 01284 764214
Dx: 57200 BURY ST EDMUNDS
E-mail: enquiries.bury@ashtonkcj.co.uk
Office: Bury St Edmunds, Cambridge, Felixstowe, Ipswich, Norwich (2 offices), Thetford
Languages: French, German, Swedish
Work: A1 A2 A3 B1 C1 C2 C3 D1 D2 E F1 G H J1 J2 K1 K2 L M1 M2 N O P Q R1 R2 S1 S2 T1 T2 V W X Z(b,c,d,e,f,g,h,i,j,k,l,m,n,o,p,q,s,t)
Emergency Action, Advocacy, Fixed Fee Interview, Legal Aid undertaken, Legal Aid Franchise and Member of Accident Line
Ptr: Adam, Mr Robert C BA(Hons) . . . . *§Nov 1995
Barnes, Mr David J LLB(Lond) . . . . *§Sep 1972
Brown, Mr Alan M LLB . . . . *§Oct 1987
Long, Mr Jonathan L E LLB . . . . *§Oct 1984
Merriam, Mr Mark R BA . . . . *§Jan 1982
Roe, Mr Andrew J BA(Cantab) . . . . *§Dec 1979
Winterbone, Mr Ian M LLB(Hons) . . . . *Dec 1976
Ast: Beaton, Mr Mark J LLB(Hons) . . . . *§Nov 1993
Budge, Miss Alison G MA(Oxon) . . . . *§Nov 1986
Griffiths, Mr James Paul BA(Hons)(History); DipLaw . . Sep 2000
Kumari, Miss Nisha LLB(Hons); LPC; PSC . . . . . *May 2000
Stephenson, Miss Polly BA . . . . Sep 2002
Wangermann, Mr Michael A LLB(Law & German) . . *Sep 1998

ASHTON KCJ
Beacon House Kempson Way Suffolk Business Park Bury St Edmunds Suffolk IP32 7AR
Tel: 01284 761233 *Fax:* 01284 702225
Dx: 130760 BURY ST EDMUNDS 4
Emergency telephone 01842 752409
E-mail: enquiries.bury@ashtonkcj.co.uk
Office: Bury St Edmunds, Cambridge, Felixstowe, Ipswich, Norwich (2 offices), Thetford
Languages: French, German, Swedish
Work: A1 A2 A3 B1 C1 C2 C3 D1 D2 E F1 F2 I J1 J2 K1 K2 K3 L M1 M2 N O P Q R1 R2 S1 S2 T1 T2 U2 V W X Z(c,d,e,g,h,j,k,l,m,n,o,p,q,r,u,z)
Emergency Action, Agency, Advocacy, Fixed Fee Interview, Legal Aid undertaken, Legal Aid Franchise and Member of Accident Line

ATKINS THOMSON
Low Green Barn Nowton Bury St Edmunds Suffolk IP29 5ND
Tel: 01284 767766 *Fax:* 01284 767800
Dx: 57212 BURY ST EDMUNDS
E-mail: suffolklaw@atkinsthomson.com

D R BAKER SOLICITOR ‡
13 Vision Centre 5 Eastern Way Bury St Edmunds Suffolk IP32 7AB
Tel: 01284 764600

BURNETT BARKER ‡
3 Hatter Street Bury St Edmunds Suffolk IP33 1LZ
Tel: 01284 701131 *Fax:* 01284 760310
Dx: 57204 BURY ST EDMUNDS
E-mail: law@burnettbarker.co.uk
List of partners: D J Barker, R N R Burnett, D B Gallagher
Languages: French, Spanish
Work: B1 B2 C1 D1 E F1 F2 G H J1 J2 K1 K3 K4 L N O Q S1 S2 T1 T2 V W Z(d,e,g,i,k,l,p,q)
Emergency Action, Agency, Advocacy, Fixed Fee Interview, Legal Aid undertaken, Legal Aid Franchise and Member of Accident Line
Ptr: Barker, Mr David J LLB . . . . *§Jan 1980
Burnett, Mr Robin N R . . . . *§Jun 1970
Gallagher, Mr Declan B LLB . . . . *Mar 1994
Ast: Furlong, Ms Claire Alexandra . . . . *Jun 2003
Matthews, Miss Joanne LLB(Hons) . . . . *Jul 1994
Mortlock, Miss Miranda . . . . *Oct 2004
Sadek, Miss Rania LLB . . . . *Dec 2009

CHARLES FRASER & CO ‡
(in association with Irena Spence & Co (Cambridge))
Johnson's building Northgate Street Bury St Edmunds Suffolk IP33 1HY
Tel: 01284 750111 *Fax:* 01284 750888
Dx: 130762 BURY ST EDMUNDS 4
E-mail: charles@charlesfraser.co.uk
List of partners: C A K Fraser, I J Spence
Languages: Polish
Work: E L P S1 S2 W Z(d,l)
Fixed Fee Interview undertaken
Ptr: Fraser, Mr Charles A K . . . . *Jul 1983
Spence, Mrs Irena Josefa LLB(Leics) . . . . *Oct 1984

GEORGE & CO ‡
Orchard Vale Borley Green Woolpit Bury St Edmunds Suffolk IP30 9RW
Tel: 01449 737582 *Fax:* 01449 737254
E-mail: law@georgeandco.co.uk
List of partners: N P George
Work: C1 E J1 S1 S2 U2 W Z(c,e)
SPr: George, Mr Nigel P . . . . *May 1984

GREENE & GREENE ‡
80 Guildhall Street Bury St Edmunds Suffolk IP33 1QB
Tel: 01284 762211 *Fax:* 01284 717499
Dx: 57205 BURY ST EDMUNDS
E-mail: mail@greene-greene.com
List of partners: I S Alston, M D Batt, M Batty, K S E Chandler, N J Grigg, M R Kay, F C Paskell, S Poole, S Ratcliffe, C J Thomson, N R Walmsley, H M Wingfield
Work: A1 B1 C1 C2 C3 D1 E F1 J1 K1 K2 K3 L M1 M2 N O P Q R1 S1 T1 T2 W Z(c,d,e,h,i,j,k,l,m,p,q,t)
Emergency Action, Agency and Advocacy undertaken
Ptr: Alston, Mrs Isabella S MA(Oxon) . . . . *§Sep 1983
Batt, Mr Michael D Notary Public . . . . *§Jun 1973
Batty, Mr Michael LLB . . . . *§Oct 1990
Chandler, Miss Katharine Sarah Elizabeth BA(Hons) *§Apr 1983
Grigg, Mr Neil John LLB . . . . *§Jan 1998
Kay, Mr Martin R LLB Vice President of Suffolk & North Essex Law Society . . . . *§Apr 1973
Paskell, Mr Fraser Charles BA(Business Law) . . . . *§Nov 1983
Poole, Miss Selene LLB . . . . *Sep 2004
Ratcliffe, Mr Simon . . . . *§Apr 2004
Thomson, Mr Christopher J LLB Charles Hebert Smith Memorial Prize 1985 . . . . *§Oct 1988
Walmsley, Mr Neil R LLB . . . . *§Nov 1991
Wingfield, Mrs Helen Margaret LLB . . . . *May 1975
Ast: Barrell, Mr Mark Gavin Anderson LLB(Hons) . . . . *Oct 1994
Butler, Mr Alun John BA(Hons) . . . . *Nov 1989
Kinnison, Mr Andrew Keith LLB(Hons) . . . . *May 1993
McWilliam, Mr Stuart A LLB(Hons) . . . . *Nov 1997
Mathers, Mr Jonathan David BA(Hons) . . . . *Oct 1996
Melia, Mrs Nadezhda Alexandra BA(Hons) . . . . . . *Sep 2003
Mortenson, Mrs Anna Lindsay Stoodley LLB(Hons) . . *Sep 2006
Taylor, Mr Christopher Arthur LLB . . . . *Nov 1995

GROSS & CO ‡
83-84 Guildhall Street Bury St Edmunds Suffolk IP33 1LN
Tel: 01284 763333 *Fax:* 01284 762207
Dx: 57203 BURY ST EDMUNDS
E-mail: mp@gross.co.uk
List of partners: N R Amor, J Cobbold, G De'Ath, E A Hodder, G D Kirk, S Sidhu
Languages: French, Spanish
Work: A1 C1 C2 E I J1 J2 K1 K2 K3 K4 L M1 P R1 S1 S2 U1 U2 W Z(d,e,i,p)
Emergency Action and Agency undertaken
Ptr: Amor, Dr Nicholas Richard MA(Oxon); PhD . . . . . . *Oct 1983
Cobbold, Mr Jonathan BA(Keele) . . . . *Sep 1989
De'Ath, Mr Gary LLB(Hons) Honorary Consul Cote d'Ivoire . . . . *Dec 1976
Hodder, Miss Elizabeth A LLB(Hons) . . . . *Oct 1984
Kirk, Mr Graeme Donald BA(Hons) Clerk to General Commissioners for Tax . . . . *Apr 1981
Sidhu, Mr Sohan LLB(Hons) . . . . *Nov 1998
Ast: McDonald, Mrs Julie MA(Cantab) . . . . *Jan 2008

MPH SOLICITORS
Unit 3 The Wheelwrights Shop Lower Green Bury St Edmunds Suffolk IP28 6NL
Tel: 01284 811870 *Fax:* 01284 811893 *Dx:* 50506 NEWMARKET
E-mail: postbox@mphsolicitors.co.uk
Office: Manchester
Work: N
Dir: Harrington, Mr Simon Paul James LLB(Hons) Law Society Prize for Outstanding Performance on LPC 2003 . . . . May 2004

MCCARTHY STEWART & BOOTY SOLICITORS ‡
Suffolk House Angel Hill Bury St Edmunds Suffolk IP33 1UZ
Tel: 01284 748927 *Fax:* 01284 753929
Dx: 57244 BURY ST EDMUNDS
E-mail: enquiries@mccarthyandbooty.co.uk
List of partners: P Booty, K McCarthy, D M C Stewart
Office: Stowmarket
Ptr: Booty, Mr Paul . . . . Jan 1999
McCarthy, Mr Kevin LLB . . . . Jun 1981

MADLEY HUGHES & CO SOLICITORS ‡
White Horse Cottage Newmarket Road Risby Bury St Edmunds Suffolk IP28 6RD
Tel: 01284 810612
E-mail: annmadley@btinternet.com

PARTRIDGE & WILSON ‡
88 Guildhall Street Bury St Edmunds Suffolk IP33 1PT
Tel: 01284 762281 *Fax:* 01284 761214
Dx: 57201 BURY ST EDMUNDS
E-mail: bse@partridgeandwilson.co.uk
List of partners: M C Dawson, P F Herriott, S H Williams
Work: A1 B1 C1 C2 S3 D1 E F1 G H J1 K1 L M1 N O P Q R1 R2 S1 S2 T1 T2 V W Z(c,d,e,h,j,k,l,m,n,o,q,t)
Emergency Action, Agency, Advocacy, Fixed Fee Interview, Legal Aid undertaken and Legal Aid Franchise
Ptr: Dawson, Mrs Mary Clare LLB . . . . *Sep 1994
Herriott, Mr Peter Francis LLB; TEP . . . . *Jun 1981
Williams, Mrs Sonja H BA(Law) . . . . *Jan 1986

RISBYGATE SOLICITORS ‡
101 Risbygate Street Bury St Edmunds Suffolk IP33 3AA
Tel: 01284 756822 *Fax:* 01284 756823
Dx: 57208 BURY ST EDMUNDS
Work: K4 S1 T2 W

RUDLINGS & WAKELAM
14 Woolhall Street Bury St Edmunds Suffolk IP33 1LA
Tel: 01284 755771 *Fax:* 01284 762436
Dx: 57202 BURY ST EDMUNDS
E-mail: info@rudlings-wakelam.co.uk
Office: Brandon, Long Melford, Thetford
Languages: French
Work: A1 A3 C1 D1 D2 E F1 G H J1 J2 K1 K2 L N O P Q R1 S1 S2 T2 V W Z(d,e,f,i,l,m,p,q,r)

SEN LEGAL LIMITED ‡
9 Looms Lane Bury St Edmunds Suffolk IP33 1HE
Tel: 01284 723952 *Fax:* 01284 702008
E-mail: manager@senlegal.co.uk

MARK THOMPSON SOLICITOR ‡
16 Euston Close Bury St Edmunds Suffolk IP33 3PY
Tel: 01842 766353
E-mail: m_thompson_03@yahoo.co.uk

WANHAM LONGHURST & CO ‡
Old Pastures Tuffields Road Whepstead Bury St Edmunds Suffolk IP29 4TN
Tel: 01284 735808 *Fax:* 01284 735684
E-mail: wanhamlonghurst@btinternet.com
List of partners: A W Longhurst
Work: A1 C1 E L S1 S2 W
Fixed Fee Interview undertaken
Ptr: Longhurst, Mr Anthony Wanham LLB . . . . *§Dec 1971

WHATLEY LANE
30 St Andrews Lodge Bury St Edmunds Suffolk IP33 1SZ
Tel: 01284 330251 *Dx:* 130766 BURY ST EDMUNDS 4
E-mail: reception@whatleylane.co.uk
Office: Newmarket

WILLETT & CO ‡
(incorporating L Lewis Palmer & Co; Whiteheads)
18 Angel Hill Bury St Edmunds Suffolk IP33 1XQ
Tel: 01284 701323 *Fax:* 01284 750548
Dx: 57207 BURY ST EDMUNDS
Emergency telephone 01394 460473
E-mail: law@willettsolicitors.com
List of partners: G Gregory, D G R Shipman, C N Willett
Languages: French
Work: A1 B1 C1 C2 C3 D1 E F1 G H I J1 K1 L M1 M2 N O P Q R1 S1 T1 T2 V W Z(b,c,d,f,j,k,l,n,o,s)
Emergency Action, Agency, Advocacy, Fixed Fee Interview, Legal Aid undertaken and Legal Aid Franchise
Ptr: Gregory, Mr Graham . . . . Jan 1993
Shipman, Mr David G R . . . . *Nov 1971
Willett, Mr Clive N . . . . *Feb 1966
Asoc: Griffiths, Mrs Hilary Rosalind BA . . . . Nov 1971

BUSHEY, Hertfordshire

ANAMI LAW IINCORPORATING KIRKWOODS ‡
51 High Road Bushey Heath Bushey Hertfordshire WD23 1EE
Tel: 020 8950 1155 *Fax:* 020 8950 0207
E-mail: info@anami-law.eu
List of partners: M A Scott
Work: E L S1 S2 W
Ptr: Scott, Mr Michael A LLB(Bris) . . . . *Mar 1973

BSG SOLICITORS LLP
Prestige House 16 Melbourne Road Bushey Hertfordshire WD23 3LN
Tel: 020 8955 7690 *Fax:* 020 8950 8707 *Dx:* 42553 BUSHEY
Office: London N3

JULIAN BLOOM & CO ‡
151 Sparrows Herne Bushey Hertfordshire WD23 1AQ
Tel: 020 8950 3001 *Fax:* 020 8950 3015 *Dx:* 42566 BUSHEY
E-mail: mail@jbloom.co.uk
List of partners: J D Bloom, A W Morris
Work: C1 C2 E J1 S1 S2 W
Ptr: Bloom, Mr Julian David LLB(Hons)(B'ham) . . . . . *Oct 1973
Morris, Mr Alan W LLB(Lond) . . . . *Jun 1972

FOREMAN & CO ‡
83 High Street Bushey Hertfordshire WD23 1BL
Tel: 07956 513563
E-mail: andrew@lawsol.co.uk

J S LANE & CO ‡
(in association with Russell Hobson & Co)
High Street Bushey Hertfordshire WD23 3HE
Tel: 020 8950 1782 *Fax:* 020 8950 9398 *Dx:* 42554 BUSHEY
E-mail: info@jslane.co.uk
List of partners: J S Lane
Work: B1 C1 D1 E J1 K1 L N O Q R1 S1 W Z(m,q)
Fixed Fee Interview, Legal Aid undertaken and Member of Accident Line
SPr: Lane, Mr Jonathan S . . . . *Nov 1972

MOERAN OUGHTRED & CO ‡
Suite 2 Ivy House 35 High Street Bushey Hertfordshire WD23 1BD
Tel: 020 8421 7175 *Fax:* 020 8421 7156 *Dx:* 42560 BUSHEY
E-mail: general@molaw.co.uk

PHILIP ROSS & CO
Grosvenor House 25-27 School Lane Bushey Hertfordshire WD23 1SS
Tel: 020 8090 9191 *Fax:* 020 3326 5528
E-mail: remortgage@philipross.co.uk
Office: London W1
Work: L S1
Ptr: Paramjorthy, Mrs Mathura. . . . . Nov 2003

D R SHERIDAN & CO ‡
(in association with Sheridan & Co)
106 High Street Bushey Hertfordshire WD23 3DE
Tel: 020 8950 6768 *Fax:* 020 8950 7005 *Dx:* 42555 BUSHEY
E-mail: drs@sheridan.org.uk
List of partners: D R Sheridan
Work: B1 C1 D1 E F1 J1 K1 N O S1 S2 W Z(r)
Emergency Action, Agency, Advocacy, Fixed Fee Interview undertaken and Member of Accident Line
Ptr: Sheridan, Mr Dennis R LLB. . . . . *Jul 1977

GRAHAM WHITE & CO ‡
94 High Street Bushey Hertfordshire WD23 3HD
Tel: 020 8950 5304 *Fax:* 020 8950 0250 *Dx:* 42550 BUSHEY
E-mail: law@grahamwhite.co.uk
List of partners: C Gray
Work: B2 C1 D1 E F1 F2 G H J1 J2 K1 K2 K3 K4 L N O Q S1 S2 W Z(p,q)
Advocacy, Fixed Fee Interview undertaken and Member of Accident Line
Ptr: Gray, Mr Charles . . . . May 1981
Ast: Fairless, Mrs Susan LLB(Hons); BSc(Hons). . . . . . Oct 2005

BUXTON, Derbyshire

BROOKE-TAYLORS ‡
4 The Quadrant Buxton Derbyshire SK17 6AW
Tel: 01298 22741 *Fax:* 01298 77065 *Dx:* 26732 BUXTON
E-mail: post@brooke-taylors.co.uk
List of partners: C L S Broadhurst, L S Crowe, T J Oaks, R A Wood
Languages: French
Work: A1 C1 C2 D1 E F1 G H J1 K1 K3 K4 L N O P Q R1 S1 S2 T1 T2 V W Z(c,f,h,i,k,l,m,n,s,t)
Emergency Action, Agency, Advocacy, Fixed Fee Interview, Legal Aid undertaken and Legal Aid Franchise
Ptr: Broadhurst, Miss Clare Louise Saxon . . . . *Sep 2001
Crowe, Mrs Lindsay S BA. . . . . *Mar 1987
Oaks, Mr Timothy J BA . . . . *Mar 1982
Wood, Ms Rosemary A BA . . . . *Mar 1984
Ast: Bunting, Mrs Diane J BA(Hons) . . . . *Sep 1989
Jones, Mr Philip LLB . . . . *Nov 1989
Ward, Miss Katharine Jane MA(Law); LPC; MA(Hons)(French & German) . . . . Jan 2008

BUNTING & RILEY ‡
37 Spring Gardens Buxton Derbyshire SK17 6BJ
Tel: 01298 767495 *Fax:* 01298 78883
E-mail: buntingandriley@btconnect.com
Work: G H
Agency, Fixed Fee Interview and Legal Aid undertaken

COOPER SONS HARTLEY & WILLIAMS ‡
9 Terrace Road Buxton Derbyshire SK17 6DU
Tel: 01298 77511 *Fax:* 01298 72138 *Dx:* 26736 BUXTON
E-mail: post@cshw.co.uk
List of partners: H S Carter, A J Cullimore, L H Middleton, N S Sharpe, S R Shuff
Office: Chapel-en-le-Frith
Languages: French, German
Work: B1 C1 D1 J1 K1 K3 K4 L N O Q S1 S2 T2 W
Emergency Action, Advocacy, Fixed Fee Interview and Legal Aid undertaken
Ptr: Carter, Mr Howard Stephen LLB(Manc) . . . . *Apr 1978
Cullimore, Mr Andrew J LLB(Manc) . . . . *Mar 1977
Sharpe, Mr Nicholas S LLB(Manc) . . . . *Nov 1989
Asoc: Beckett, Mrs Alison Jayne MA(Cantab) . . . . *Oct 1988
Rolf-McGregor, Mr Edgar LLB(Hons)(Manc). . . . . . *§Oct 1986
Woodhead, Miss Dawn A LLB. . . . . *Apr 1987
Ast: Hall, Miss Debra LLB(Hons). . . . . *Feb 1998
Proven, Ms Katie Judith LLB(Hons) . . . . Oct 2006

PRICKETTS
12 Hardwick Street Buxton Derbyshire SK17 6BN
Tel: 01298 22874 *Fax:* 01298 24408 *Dx:* 26734 BUXTON
E-mail: martin.wragg@pricketts.co.uk
Office: Stockport
Work: A1 B1 C1 C2 C3 D1 E F1 J1 J2 K1 K3 K4 L N O P Q R1 R2 S1 S2 W Z(c,d,e,j,k,l,q,r)
Advocacy undertaken
Ptr: Ince, Mrs Elizabeth Anne . . . . *Sep 2005
Shackleton, Mr Alan BA(Hons) ♦ . . . . *Oct 1988
Wragg, Mr B Martin LLB. . . . . *Jun 1976

CAERNARFON, Gwynedd

BENNETT SMITH PARTNERSHIP ‡
Garth Bach Nant Y Garth Y Felinheli Caernarfon Gwynedd LL56 4QF
Tel: 01248 679000

DAVIES & CO SOLICITORS CYFREITHWYR ‡
36 Y Maes Caernarfon Gwynedd LL55 2NN
Tel: 01286 675715 / 07754 715113
E-mail: info@daviesandcosolicitors.com

ELLIS DAVIES & CO ‡
27 Bangor Street Caernarfon Gwynedd LL55 1AT
Tel: 01286 672437 *Fax:* 01286 672288 *Dx:* 23222 CAERNARFON
E-mail: post@ellisdavies.co.uk
List of partners: D Ellis-Davies, R W Jones
Languages: Welsh
Work: A1 E G H L N R1 R2 S1 S2 T1 T2 V W Z(d,l,t)
Agency, Advocacy, Legal Aid undertaken and Legal Aid Franchise
Ptr: Ellis-Davies, Mr Dewi LLB. . . . . *Dec 1997
Jones, Mr Richard Wyn BSc(Wales)(Econ) . . . . . *§Dec 1980
Con: Ellis-Davies, Mr Richard H LLB(L'pool) . . . . *§Jun 1968

GARETH GRIFFITH & COMPANY ‡
6 Pepper Lane Caernarfon Gwynedd LL55 1RG
Tel: 01286 676869 *Fax:* 01286 677705
E-mail: ggco@btconnect.com
Languages: Welsh
Work: S1 S2 V W Z(l)
Emergency Action, Agency, Advocacy, Legal Aid undertaken and Legal Aid Franchise

PARRY DAVIES CLWYD-JONES & LLOYD
2a Bridge Street Caernarfon Gwynedd LL55 1AB
Tel: 01286 673381 *Fax:* 01286 674476 *Dx:* 23232 CAERNARFON
Office: Amlwch, Benllech, Llangefni, Pwllheli
Languages: Welsh
Work: A1 A2 A3 B1 B2 C1 D1 D2 E F2 G H J1 K1 K2 L M1 N P Q R1 R2 S1 S2 W Z(q)
Agency and Legal Aid undertaken
Ptr: Davies, Ms Lena Rees ♦ . . . . Dec 1993

PRITCHARD JONES EVANS LANE ‡
37 Castle Square Caernarfon Gwynedd LL55 2NN
Tel: 01286 673387 *Fax:* 01286 675217 *Dx:* 23224 CAERNARFON 1
List of partners: W T Jones, M E Jones-Evans, T Om, J D Pritchard-Jones
Languages: Welsh
Work: A1 C1 C2 D1 E F1 G H J1 K1 L N O Q R1 S1 S2 T1 T2 W Z(h,l,s)
Agency, Advocacy, Fixed Fee Interview undertaken and Member of Accident Line
Ptr: Jones, Mr Wyn Trefor LLB(Wales). . . . . *Oct 1991
Jones-Evans, Merfyn E LLB(Wales). . . . . *Oct 1985
Om, Mr Tony . . . . *Oct 1982
Pritchard-Jones, Mr J Dewi LLB(Wales) H M Coroner *Nov 1970

EMYR THOMAS & SON ‡
4 Castle Street Caernarfon Gwynedd LL55 1SE
Tel: 01286 672307 / 672308 *Fax:* 01286 678244
Dx: 23225 CAERNARFON
E-mail: office@emyrthomas.fsnet.co.uk
List of partners: O G Jones
Languages: Welsh
Work: A1 C1 K1 L N S1 T1 W
Agency, Advocacy and Fixed Fee Interview undertaken
Ptr: Jones, Mr Owen Gerallt LLB . . . . *Jun 1978
Ast: Jones, Ms Gail LLB(Hons) TA Levi Prize 1986; Llewelfryn Davies Prize 1987; Mevrig Williams Prize 1988; Calcott Law Prize 1988 . . . . *Nov 1991

TUDUR OWEN ROBERTS GLYNNE & CO ‡
Lloyds Bank Chambers Eastgate Street Caernarfon Gwynedd LL55 1AG
Tel: 01286 672207 / 672851 *Fax:* 01286 677574
Dx: 23223 CAERNARFON
List of partners: G E Davies, A L Ellis, J T Owen, H G Roberts, R O Williams
Office: Bangor (2 offices), Blaenau Ffestiniog, Holyhead, Menai Bridge
Languages: Welsh
Work: B2 D1 F1 G H J1 K1 K3 L N O Q R1 S1 S2 V W Z(l)
Emergency Action, Agency, Advocacy, Fixed Fee Interview, Legal Aid undertaken, Legal Aid Franchise and Member of Accident Line
Ptr: Davies, Mr Gwyn E BA(Wales) . . . . *Sep 1985
Owen, Mr John T LLB. . . . . *Oct 1984
Roberts, Mr Hywel G LLB. . . . . *Mar 1987
Ast: Huws, Mr Sion Wyn. . . . . *Sep 2000
Jones, Mrs Frances P LLB . . . . *Jun 1980
Tudur, Meleri LLB. . . . . *Oct 1983
Williams, Mr Richard LLB . . . . *Nov 1989
Con: Lloyd, Mr Iwan ap Gruffydd . . . . *Jul 1974

CAERPHILLY

CASWELL JONES ‡
Portcullis House 18 Cardiff Road Caerphilly CF83 1JN
Tel: 029 2086 4888 *Fax:* 029 2086 3912 *Dx:* 43858 CAERPHILLY
E-mail: enquiries@caswelljones.com
Office: Ystrad Mynach
Work: C1 D1 D2 E F1 J1 K1 K2 K3 L R1 S1 S2 V W

COSTLEY & PARTNERS SOLICITORS ‡
Clive Chambers 2 Clive Street Caerphilly CF83 1GE
Tel: 029 2086 4666 / 2088 5705 *Fax:* 029 2086 5188
Dx: 43863 CAERPHILLY

CHARLES CROOKES & JONES ‡
(incorporating Murray Evans Clinch & Co)
The Bluebell Market Street Caerphilly CF83 1NX
Tel: 029 2086 0628 *Fax:* 029 2088 6201 *Dx:* 43861 CAERPHILLY
Emergency telephone 029 2086 0628
List of partners: M J Downey, R W Evans, E A Jones, G Lucas
Languages: Welsh
Work: A1 B1 C1 C3 D1 D2 E F1 G H J1 K1 K3 K4 L M1 M2 N O P Q R1 S1 S2 V W Z(c,l)
Emergency Action, Agency, Advocacy, Fixed Fee Interview, Legal Aid undertaken, Legal Aid Franchise and Member of Accident Line
Ptr: Downey, Mr Michael J LLB . . . . *May 1989
Evans, Mr Ralph W LLB(Wales); LLM(Cantab) . . . . *Jan 1979
Jones, Mr E Aidan LLB(Wales) . . . . *Dec 1974
Lucas, Mr Graham LLB . . . . *May 1993
Ast: O'Brien, Mrs Sharon E LLB(Hons). . . . . *Oct 1992
Con: Charles, Mr David W T BA(Oxon). . . . . *§Jan 1964

DAVIES SULLY WILKINS ‡
3 Station Terrace Caerphilly CF83 1HD
Tel: 029 2088 7828 *Fax:* 029 2086 4575 *Dx:* 43853 CAERPHILLY
Emergency telephone 029 2062 5724
E-mail: admin@daviessullywilkins.co.uk
List of partners: G Davies, M A Wilkins
Languages: French
Work: B1 C1 C2 D1 D2 E F1 F2 J1 J2 K1 L N O P Q S1 S2 V W X Z(l,q)
Emergency Action, Agency, Advocacy, Fixed Fee Interview, Legal Aid undertaken, Legal Aid Franchise and Member of Accident Line
Ptr: Davies, Mrs Gaynor LLB(Hons) . . . . *Apr 1990
Wilkins, Mr Michael A . . . . *Jul 1969
Ast: Kelland, Mr Neil LLB . . . . Oct 1983
Thomas, Mrs Tanya H. . . . . *Aug 2002
Thorne, Ms Lorraine LLB(Hons). . . . . *Jul 2005

EVANS & GREAVES ‡
5 Piccadilly Square Caerphilly CF83 1PB
Tel: 029 2086 6001 *Fax:* 029 2086 3182 *Dx:* 43860 CAERPHILLY
Emergency telephone 07970 866001
E-mail: admin@evansandgreaves.co.uk
List of partners: G R Evans, C S Greaves
Work: D1 D2 E G H K1 K2 M1 P S1 Z(l)
Emergency Action, Agency, Advocacy, Fixed Fee Interview, Legal Aid undertaken and Legal Aid Franchise
Ptr: Evans, Mr Geoffrey R. . . . . *Sep 1981
Greaves, Mr Christopher Stephen LLB(Wales). . . . . Dec 1987
Ast: Evans, Ms Leanne E . . . . Jun 1997

EVANS QUARTERMAINE SOLICITORS ‡
67 High Street Rhymney Caerphilly NP22 5LP
Tel: 01685 840404
E-mail: mail@evansquartermaine.co.uk

LINDSAY FORD SOLICITORS LTD ‡
93 Cardiff Road Caerphilly CF83 1WS
Tel: 029 2088 2441 *Fax:* 029 2085 1386 *Dx:* 43851 CAERPHILLY
E-mail: info@lindsay-ford.co.uk
List of partners: R L Ford
Work: C1 C2 D1 E K1 S1 S2 W Z(c)
Emergency Action, Agency, Advocacy, Fixed Fee Interview, Legal Aid undertaken and Legal Aid Franchise
Ptr: Ford, R Lindsay LLB . . . . *Mar 1971

HOWELLS
72-74 Cardiff Road Caerphilly CF83 1JQ
Tel: 029 2086 7111 *Fax:* 029 2086 6346 *Dx:* 43854 CAERPHILLY
E-mail: info@howellslegal.com
Office: Cardiff, Newport, Swansea, Talbot Green
Work: C2 D1 E J1 K1 K3 L N Q S1 S2 W
Agency, Fixed Fee Interview and Legal Aid undertaken
Ptr: Hunt, Mrs Angela Jayne LLB . . . . *Jul 1980
Ast: Selfridge, Ms Emma Kathryn LLB . . . . Jul 2002

LEWIS WHITTLE ‡
34 White Street Caerphilly CF83 1HB
Tel: 029 2088 1378 *Fax:* 029 2088 1894 *Dx:* 43868 CAERPHILLY
Emergency telephone 01443 403447
List of partners: P G Lewis
Work: G H J1 V
Emergency Action, Agency, Advocacy, Fixed Fee Interview and Legal Aid undertaken
Ptr: Lewis, Mr Paul G BSc. . . . . Feb 1993

CAISTER-ON-SEA, Norfolk

CHAMBERLINS
5 High Street Caister-on-Sea Norfolk NR30 5EL
Tel: 01493 720019 *Fax:* 01493 722328
E-mail: jbt@chamberlins.demon.co.uk
Office: Beccles, Great Yarmouth (2 offices), Lowestoft
Work: K1 S1 S2 W Z(l)

CAISTOR, Lincolnshire

BATES & MOUNTAIN
6 Market Place Caistor Lincolnshire LN7 6TL
Tel: 01472 851224 *Fax:* 01472 852615
E-mail: andrew.dollery@batesandmountain.com
Office: Grimsby
Work: S1 S2 W
Legal Aid undertaken
Ptr: Dollery, Mr Andrew James BA Clerk to Caistor Grammar School . . . . *Mar 1985

CALDICOT, Monmouthshire

GRANVILLE-WEST
12a Newport Road Caldicot Monmouthshire NP26 4BQ
Tel: 01291 423999 *Fax:* 01291 424957 *Dx:* 86957 CALDICOT
E-mail: caldicot@granville-west.co.uk
Office: Abertillery, Blackwood, Newport, Pontypool, Risca
Languages: Welsh
Work: C1 D1 E F1 J1 K1 L N O P Q R1 S1 S2 W Z(m,p,q)
Emergency Action, Agency, Fixed Fee Interview and Legal Aid undertaken
Ast: Telang, Mr Justin Mohit LLB(Hons) . . . . *Oct 1995

NUTTER & RICHARDS SOLICITORS ‡
89 Treetops Portskewett Caldicot Monmouthshire NP26 5RT
Tel: 01291 420361 *Fax:* 01291 431458
E-mail: nutrich@sols2.fsnet.co.uk
Work: D1 D2 K1 K3 Q S1 S2 W
Agency and Advocacy undertaken

PROPERTS
The Square Magor Caldicot Monmouthshire NP26 3EP
Tel: 01633 882282 *Fax:* 01633 889099
E-mail: contact@properts.co.uk
Office: Chepstow
Ptr: Propert, Mr John P MA(Oxon) Notary Public. . . . . *§Jun 1967
Propert, Mrs Jane Elizabeth LLB(Hons) . . . . *§Aug 2006

TWOMLOWS ‡
Griffyn Chambers 20 Newport Road Caldicot Monmouthshire NP26 4BQ
Tel: 01291 422753 *Fax:* 01291 430471 *Dx:* 86950 CALDICOT
Emergency telephone 01291 422753
E-mail: j.painter@twomlows.com
List of partners: C M Prigg, A J Twomlow, M A Twomlow

 See p112 for the Key to Work Categories & other symbols

Office: Chepstow, Monmouth
Work: C1 F1 G H J1 K1 L M1 P S1 V W
Emergency Action, Agency, Advocacy, Fixed Fee Interview and Legal Aid undertaken
Ptr: Prigg, Mr Christopher M LLB . . . . Oct 1985
Twomlow, Mr Andrew J BA . . . . *May 1981
Twomlow, Mrs Molly A LLB . . . . *Mar 1980
Ast: Campbell, Mr James Mervyn John LLB(Hons). . . . . *Sep 1998

CALLINGTON, Cornwall

BLIGHT BROAD & SKINNARD ‡
George Place Callington Cornwall PL17 7JH
Tel: 01579 382213 *Fax:* 01579 383878
Emergency telephone 01579 351094
E-mail: info@blightsolicitors.co.uk
List of partners: N P W Skinnard
Languages: French
Work: A1 C1 E F1 G J1 K1 K2 K3 K4 L N Q R1 S1 S2 W Z(c,l,m,n,t)
Emergency Action, Agency, Advocacy and Fixed Fee Interview undertaken
Ptr: Skinnard, Mr Nicholas P W MA(Oxon). . . . . *Sep 1983
Ast: Anderson, Ms Gillian Clare BA(Hons) Notary Public . . *Dec 1999
Smith, Mrs Laura Janice LLB . . . . *Oct 1994

R HANCOCK & SON ‡
9 Fore Street Callington Cornwall PL17 7AA
Tel: 01579 383101 *Fax:* 01579 384254
E-mail: office@hancock.ssnet.co.uk
List of partners: V M Carne
Work: A1 L S1 W
Emergency Action, Agency, Advocacy, Fixed Fee Interview and Legal Aid undertaken
Ptr: Carne, Ms Vivian M LLB . . . . *§Dec 1971

CALNE, Wiltshire

AWDRY BAILEY & DOUGLAS
Westhill House 4 Market Hill Calne Wiltshire SN11 0BU
Tel: 01249 815110 *Fax:* 01249 817467 *Dx:* 44803 CALNE
E-mail: abd@awdrys.co.uk
Office: Devizes, Marlborough, Wootton Bassett
Languages: French, German
Work: A1 B1 C1 C2 D1 E F1 J1 J2 K1 K3 L N O P Q R1 S1 S2 T1 T2 W Z(c,d,h,j,k,l,o,q,r)
Emergency Action, Agency, Advocacy, Fixed Fee Interview, Legal Aid undertaken, Legal Aid Franchise and Member of Accident Line
Ptr: Awdry, Mr G Antony. . . . . *§Dec 1978
Douglas, Mr Andrew J BA(Law) . . . . *§Oct 1983
Everett, Mr Alistair Munro . . . . *§Nov 1992
Robinson, Mr Nicholas LLB(Hons). . . . . *Nov 2000
Shah, Mr Peter Vipin LLB . . . . *Dec 1992
Ast: Matthieson, Mrs Samantha Isabell LLB(Hons). . . . . *Apr 2000

BEVIRS
Market Hill House 3 Market Hill Calne Wiltshire SN11 0EG
Tel: 01249 814536 *Fax:* 01249 816761 *Dx:* 44802 CALNE 1
E-mail: bevirs@bevirs.co.uk
Office: Swindon, Wootton Bassett
Work: A1 D1 D2 E F1 J1 K1 K3 K4 L N O Q S1 T1 T2 W Z(d,q)
Emergency Action, Agency, Advocacy and Legal Aid undertaken
Ptr: Sewell, Mr Nicholas John LLB(Hons) . . . . *Oct 1990
Spearey, Mr Edward A . . . . *§Mar 1976
Asoc: Smith, Mr Ian Graham BA(Hons) . . . . *Jun 1980
Ast: Hambleton, Mrs Julie Irene Christine BA(Law). . . . *Feb 1984
Willott, Ms Emma Jane LLB(Hons) . . . . Sep 1999

GOUGHS ‡
The Strand Calne Wiltshire SN11 0JU
Tel: 01249 812086 *Fax:* 01249 816378 *Dx:* 44800 CALNE
E-mail: info@goughs.co.uk
List of partners: K Basnett, P J Boyce, S L Cave, N J R Davis, K G Dobson, M Drew, S W C Howard, M C Lang, D Moir, J Pridmore, J M Shipton, P G Vingoe, I M Young
Office: Chippenham, Corsham, Devizes, Melksham, Trowbridge
Languages: Afrikaans, Portuguese
Work: A1 A3 B1 C1 C2 C3 D1 D2 E F1 J1 J2 K1 K2 K3 K4 L N O P Q R1 R2 S1 S2 W Z(d,h,q,r)
Emergency Action, Agency and Advocacy undertaken
Ptr: Basnett, Mr Kevin LLB . . . . *Nov 1983
Cave, Mr Stephen L Gloucester & Wiltshire Law Society Prize . . . . *Apr 1976
Asoc: Figueiredo, Miss Isabel Maria Lopes Notary Public . . Feb 2006
Ast: Corp, Mrs Gabrielle Alice BA(Law) . . . . Feb 2009

JAC LAW ‡
26 Spirthill Calne Wiltshire SN11 9HP
Tel: 01249 760717 *Fax:* 01249 760750
E-mail: info@jaclaw.co.uk

CAMBERLEY, Surrey

BROOKS & PARTNERS ‡
Lyons House 2 Station Road Frimley Camberley Surrey GU16 7JA
Tel: 01276 681217 *Fax:* 01276 691290 *Dx:* 46953 FRIMLEY
E-mail: law@brooks-partners.co.uk
List of partners: M T Brooks, S P Groves
Work: B1 C1 C2 D1 D2 E J1 K1 K3 K4 L N O Q R1 R2 S1 S2 W Z(c,m)
Emergency Action, Agency, Advocacy and Fixed Fee Interview undertaken
Ptr: Brooks, Mr Michael T . . . . *§Jan 1980
Groves, Mr Simon Paul . . . . *Dec 1977
Ast: Prance, Ms Deborah Susan LLB(Hons) . . . . *Apr 1984
Stack, Miss Carrie. . . . . *Jan 2009

CAMPBELL COURTNEY & COONEY ‡
(in association with The Bileghan Law Office(Famagusta))
Maybury House Frimley High Street Frimley Camberley Surrey GU16 7HJ
Tel: 01276 25100 *Fax:* 01276 691276 *Dx:* 46950 FRIMLEY
E-mail: chris@ccc-law.co.uk
List of partners: C M Cooney
Languages: French
Work: B1 C1 C2 D1 E G J1 J2 K1 L N S1 W Z(q,r)
Emergency Action, Agency, Advocacy, Fixed Fee Interview, Legal Aid undertaken, Legal Aid Franchise and Member of Accident Line
Ptr: Cooney, Mr Christopher Martin LLB(Hons). . . . . . *Nov 1985
Ast: Radia, Mr Rajan LLB(Hons) . . . . *Nov 1995

CONSTANTINE & SUMMERS ‡
143b Frimley Road Camberley Surrey GU15 2PS
Tel: 01276 23211 *Fax:* 01276 25327 *Dx:* 32735 CAMBERLEY
E-mail: info@constantineandsummers.co.uk
List of partners: G V Constantine, J E Summers
Work: D1 K1 L S1
Emergency Action, Agency, Fixed Fee Interview, Legal Aid undertaken and Legal Aid Franchise
Ptr: Constantine, Miss Griselda V LLB(Lond) . . . . *Mar 1975
Summers, Ms Julie Elizabeth BSc. . . . . *Nov 1995

FOSTER HARRINGTON ‡
52 Park Street Camberley Surrey GU15 3PT
Tel: 01276 692233 *Fax:* 01276 692244
E-mail: info@fosterharr.freeserve.co.uk
List of partners: E Bradshaw, A N Cox, T R Foster
Work: C1 E J1 K1 L N O Q S1 S2 W
Ptr: Bradshaw, Mrs Elaine. . . . . *Dec 1993
Cox, Mr Andrew N LLB . . . . *Oct 1984
Foster, Mr Timothy R LLB. . . . . *Jun 1980

HARRISON LI SOLICITORS LLP ‡
2 Stanhope Gate Stanhope Road Camberley Surrey GU15 3DW
Tel: 01276 27700 *Fax:* 01276 27799 *Dx:* 32706 CAMBERLEY
E-mail: info@harrisonli.co.uk
List of partners: D L Harrison, T K M Li
Languages: Cantonese
Work: E L R1 R2 S1 S2 W
Mem: Harrison, Mr David Lionel . . . . *Dec 1974
Li, Mr Tom Kwing Ming . . . . Jan 2005

R J HAWKSLEY & CO ‡
32-36 Bladen Court Bell Lane Blackwater Camberley Surrey GU17 0NW
Tel: 01252 890400 *Fax:* 01252 890306 *Dx:* 93458 YATELEY
Emergency telephone 07736 356991
E-mail: reception@rjhawksley.co.uk
List of partners: R J Hawksley
Work: B1 C1 D1 F1 G H J1 K1 N O Q R1 S1 S2 W Z(l)
Emergency Action, Agency, Advocacy and Fixed Fee Interview undertaken
SPr: Hawksley, Mrs Rebecca J LLB(Hons) . . . . Sep 1997

HEALD NICKINSON ‡
Lansdowne House Knoll Road Camberley Surrey GU15 3SY
Tel: 01276 680000 *Fax:* 01276 680068 *Dx:* 32701 CAMBERLEY
E-mail: info@healdnickinson.co.uk
List of partners: D M Flynn, A M Illingworth, A N Struve, G Thomas, M J Wright
Languages: French, German, Greek
Work: B1 C1 C2 D1 E F1 J1 K1 K2 K3 K4 L N O Q R1 R2 S1 S2 T2 V W Z(c,g,h,i,k,l,m,p,q,r)
Fixed Fee Interview, Legal Aid undertaken and Legal Aid Franchise
Ptr: Flynn, Mr Dermot M LLB(Hons) . . . . *Oct 1992
Illingworth, Mrs Anna Mary BA(Hons) . . . . *Jul 1998
Struve, Mr Anthony N BA . . . . *Oct 1979
Thomas, Mrs Gendy BA. . . . . *Mar 1983
Wright, Mr Michael John . . . . *Jan 1976
Asoc: Jay, Miss Sarah LLB . . . . *Oct 1987
Lillywhite, Ms Patricia . . . . *Sep 1996
Moon, Ms Sarah LLB(Hons). . . . . *Jan 2004
Ast: Prentice, Miss Zara Michelle LLB(Hons). . . . . *Jan 1994
Struve, Mr Matthew Edward BA(Hons); LLB(Hons) . . *Jul 2009
Con: Daniels, Mr Michael J . . . . *Dec 1979

HERRINGTON & CARMICHAEL LLP ‡
Waters Edge Riverside Way Watchmoor Park Camberley Surrey GU15 3YL
Tel: 01276 686222 *Fax:* 01276 28041 *Dx:* 32700 CAMBERLEY
E-mail: info@herrington-carmichael.com
List of partners: A D Annette, Y Brar, M S Buckeldee, J W Eatwell, T J Hardesty, A D B Holden, J A Job, D G Keighley, A R S C Tahourdin, F J Tierney
Office: Wokingham
Languages: French, German
Work: A1 B1 C1 C2 C3 D1 E F1 G H I J1 K1 L M2 N O P Q R1 S1 T1 T2 V W Z(c,e,f,j,k,l,t)
Emergency Action, Agency, Advocacy, Fixed Fee Interview, Legal Aid undertaken and Legal Aid Franchise
Ptr: Annette, Mr Andrew Douglas . . . . Sep 1999
Buckeldee, Mr Martin S LLB(Hons) . . . . *Feb 1981
Hardesty, Mr Timothy John BA(Hons) . . . . Sep 2001
Job, Mr J Adrian LLB(Leeds) . . . . *Jun 1969
Keighley, Mr David G . . . . *§Jan 1982
Tahourdin, Mr Anthony R St C BA(Hons)(Law); TEP. . *Mar 1979
Tierney, Ms Frances J BA(Law) . . . . *Oct 1985
Ast: Batchelor, Miss Elizabeth . . . . Jan 2006
Boulter, Ms Andrea . . . . Dec 1990
Hothersall, Mr Nicholas BA; PG Dip EC Competition Law . . . . Aug 1998
House, Miss Rachael . . . . Aug 2005
McSorley, Miss Claire Louise LLB(Hons) . . . . Feb 2005
Con: Stanbury, Mr Christopher C . . . . Oct 1965
Sutton, Mr Kenneth David BA . . . . *Dec 1975

LEE & COMPANY ‡
2 Princess Way Camberley Surrey GU15 3SP
Tel: 01276 20911 *Fax:* 01276 22145 *Dx:* 32716 CAMBERLEY
Emergency telephone 01252 879218
E-mail: jbl@leeandcompany.co.uk
List of partners: J B Lee, M A Lee
Work: B1 C1 D1 E F1 F2 J1 J2 K1 K3 L N O Q R1 S1 S2 V W Z(l,q,r)
Emergency Action, Agency, Advocacy, Fixed Fee Interview, Legal Aid undertaken and Legal Aid Franchise
Ptr: Lee, Mr Jeffrey B . . . . *Nov 1978
Lee, Ms Maureen A . . . . *Dec 1979
Ast: Lee, Miss Jennifer LLB(Hons) . . . . *Nov 2010

MELIA & MUMFORD ‡
11-13 Sturt Road Frimley Green Camberley Surrey GU16 6HT
Tel: 01252 836554 *Fax:* 01252 837893
List of partners: P J Melia
Work: D1 E F1 G H J1 K1 N S1 W
Agency, Advocacy, Fixed Fee Interview and Legal Aid undertaken
Ptr: Melia, Mr Paul J. . . . . Dec 1978

MORRISONS SOLICITORS LLP
90 Park Street Camberley Surrey GU15 3NY
Tel: 01276 686005 *Fax:* 01276 605949 *Dx:* 32711 CAMBERLEY
E-mail: info@morrlaw.com
Web: www.morrlaw.com
Office: London SW19, Redhill, Woking
Languages: Spanish
Work: A1 C1 D1 E F1 J1 K1 K3 K4 L N Q S1 S2 W Z(d,m)
Emergency Action and Fixed Fee Interview undertaken
Ptr: Fowles, Mr Andrew R LLB. . . . . *Mar 1976
Humphreys, Mr D Gareth LLB; MA . . . . *Apr 1980
Asoc: Lovering, Mr Thomas Allan LLB(Hons) . . . . *Jan 1999
Con: Close, Mr Peter M W . . . . *§Jan 1969
We conduct business in Spanish. We specialise in the following areas of work Family Law, Residential Conveyancing, Wills, Trusts and Probate.

MARIA D MULROE SOLICITOR ‡
Lake View House 34 Minehurst Road Mytchett Camberley Surrey GU16 6JP
Tel: 01252 521556 *Fax:* 01252 521556

NEALE TURK ROCHFORT
12 Kings Ride Camberley Surrey GU15 4JG
Tel: 01276 20551 *Fax:* 01276 66877
E-mail: info@nealeturkrochfort.co.uk
Office: Farnborough
Work: A1 E J1 K1 K3 K4 L Q R1 S1 S2 W Z(l)
Advocacy and Fixed Fee Interview undertaken
Ptr: Gallagher, Mr Stephen David . . . . *Sep 1975
Rochfort, Miss Eila De Burgh . . . . *§Dec 1971
Ast: Reynolds, Mr David Mark MA(Hons)(Oxon) . . . . . . *Jul 1989

PARK LAW ‡
Quatro House Lyon Way Camberley Surrey GU15 1AL
Tel: 01276 804788 *Fax:* 01276 691640
E-mail: info@parklaw.co.uk
List of partners: I G Park
Ptr: Park, Mr Ian G BA; LLB; FCIArb. . . . . *Oct 1978

WEBB & CO PROPERTY SOLICITORS ‡
Cedar House Cedar Lane Camberley Surrey GU16 7HZ
Tel: 01276 26994

CAMBORNE, Cornwall

RONALD BUTLER ‡
South Drive Tehidy Camborne Cornwall TR14 0EZ
Tel: 01209 716620 *Fax:* 01209 610860

DB LAW ‡
(incorporating Trott & Battell; Daniell & Thomas; Vivian Thomas & Jervis)
13 Chapel Street Camborne Cornwall TR14 8EJ
Tel: 01209 712428 *Fax:* 01209 612137 *Dx:* 82759 CAMBORNE
List of partners: C C Baker, J P Battell, G D Calderwood, J Mepham, E Moore, A J Smith, J Thomas, J M Timmis, S C West
Office: Falmouth, Penzance, St Ives
Languages: French, German
Work: A1 C1 C3 D1 E F1 G H J1 K1 K2 K3 K4 L N P Q R1 S1 S2 V W Z(c,j,l)
Emergency Action, Agency, Advocacy, Fixed Fee Interview, Legal Aid undertaken and Legal Aid Franchise
Ptr: Baker, Mr Christopher C MA . . . . *Jul 1999
Battell, Mr Jonathan P LLB(Manc). . . . . *§Jul 1967
Mepham, Mrs Janet LLB . . . . May 1981
Smith, Mr Alister J BA. . . . . *Apr 1980
Timmis, Mr John M LLB(Hons) . . . . Apr 1986
West, Mr Stephen C LLB(Wales) . . . . Mar 1975
Asoc: Hulley, Mr Charles Maxwell LLB(Hons) . . . . Sep 2004
Ast: Kehler, Mr Hans Dieter BJuris; LLB; MA. . . . . Apr 2002
Con: Jacoby, Mr James D . . . . *§Dec 1975

HOWELL HYLTON ‡
(incorporating Peter Hylton & Co)
24 Cross Street Camborne Cornwall TR14 8EX
Tel: 01209 613014 *Fax:* 01209 613035 *Dx:* 82758 CAMBORNE
E-mail: howellhylton.cam@btconnect.com
List of partners: R K Eccleston, F N Howell, P R Hylton
Work: D1 G H K1 N S1 W Z(l)
Emergency Action, Agency, Advocacy and Legal Aid undertaken
Ptr: Eccleston, Mr Robert Keith . . . . Jan 1998
Howell, Mr Frederick N LLB • . . . . Jul 1993
Hylton, Mr Peter R LLB(York, Ontario). . . . . *§Feb 1967

NALDERS QUALITY SOLICITORS
6 Chapel Street Camborne Cornwall TR14 8EG
Tel: 01209 714278 *Fax:* 01209 710437 *Dx:* 82754 CAMBORNE
E-mail: post@nalders.co.uk
Office: Falmouth, Helston, Newquay, Penzance, St Austell, Truro (2 offices)
Work: D1 E F1 J1 K1 L M1 N O P Q R1 S1 S2 W

ALISTER PILLING ‡
45 Cross Street Camborne Cornwall TR14 8ET
Tel: 01209 613800 *Fax:* 01209 613777 *Dx:* 82763 CAMBORNE
Emergency telephone 01209 613800
E-mail: alister.pilling@btinternet.com
List of partners: A G D W Pilling
Work: D1 D2 E F1 F2 G H J1 K1 L N Q S1 S2 W Z(l,m)
Emergency Action, Agency, Advocacy, Fixed Fee Interview and Legal Aid undertaken
SPr: Pilling, Mr Alister Grenville De Winton LLB(Hons)(Warw) . . . . *Oct 1988

WALLER & HART ‡
Hazelberry 29 Basset Road Camborne Cornwall TR14 8SH
Tel: 01209 714064 / 719871 *Fax:* 01209 710069
E-mail: solicitors@wallerandhart.co.uk
List of partners: P C Hart, S K Morris
Languages: French
Work: A1 A2 B1 C1 C2 C3 E F1 J1 K1 K4 L N O P Q R1 R2 S1 S2 T1 T2 W Z(c,d,e,i,k,l,m,n,q,t)
Emergency Action, Fixed Fee Interview undertaken and Member of Accident Line
Ptr: Hart, Mr Peter Clive LLB . . . . *Jun 1976
Morris, Mrs Stephanie Kelly LLB . . . . *Oct 2007

WALTERS & BARBARY ‡
Basset Chambers 18 Basset Road Camborne Cornwall TR14 8SG
Tel: 01209 712454 *Fax:* 01209 710074 *Dx:* 82750 CAMBORNE
E-mail: reception@waltersbarbary.co.uk

List of partners: A P K Blair, A R Butterfield, R F Cope, S P Rutherford, R J Wiles
Work: A1 B1 C1 C2 C3 D1 E F1 G H J1 K1 L N R1 S1 T1 T2 V W Z(l)
Emergency Action, Agency, Advocacy, Fixed Fee Interview, Legal Aid undertaken, Legal Aid Franchise and Member of Accident Line
Ptr: Blair, Mr Alexander Peter Kevin PGDipLaw . . . . . *Sep 1999
Butterfield, Mr Alan R LLB. . . . . *§Nov 1971
Cope, Mr Robert F . . . . §Dec 1973
Rutherford, Mr Stephen P LLB . . . . *§May 1977
Wiles, Miss Rachel Jane LLB . . . . *Oct 1992

CAMBRIDGE, Cambridgeshire

AMEER MEREDITH ‡
35 Hills Road Cambridge Cambridgeshire CB2 1NT
Tel: 01223 577077 *Fax:* 01223 577066 *Dx:* 5855 CAMBRIDGE
E-mail: partners@ameermeredith.com
List of partners: Y S Ameer
Work: N Z(q,r)
Agency, Advocacy, Fixed Fee Interview undertaken and Member of Accident Line
SPr: Ameer, Miss Yasmin S BSc(Hons); LSF. . . . . . . *Mar 1984
Ast: Ciaffey, Mr Ciaran. . . . . Oct 2009

ASHTON KCJ
Chequers House 77-81 Newmarket Road Cambridge Cambridgeshire CB5 8EU
Tel: 01223 363111 *Fax:* 01223 323370 *Dx:* 122893 CAMBRIDGE 4
E-mail: enquiries.cambridge@ashtonkcj.co.uk
Office: Bury St Edmunds (2 offices), Felixstowe, Ipswich, Norwich (2 offices), Thetford
Languages: French, German, Swedish
Work: A1 A2 A3 B1 C1 C2 C3 D1 D2 E F1 F2 I J1 J2 K1 K2 K3 L M1 M2 N O P Q R1 R2 S1 S2 T1 T2 U2 V W X Z(c,d,e,g,h,j,k,l,m,n,o,p,q,r,u,z)
Emergency Action, Agency, Advocacy, Fixed Fee Interview, Legal Aid undertaken, Legal Aid Franchise and Member of Accident Line

MICHAEL BARHAM & CO ‡
168 Mill Road Cambridge Cambridgeshire CB1 3LP
Tel: 01223 415797 *Fax:* 01223 415793
E-mail: info@michaelbarham.co.uk

BARR ELLISON LLP ‡
39 Parkside Cambridge Cambridgeshire CB1 1PN
Tel: 01223 417200 *Fax:* 01223 417201 *Dx:* 5806 CAMBRIDGE
E-mail: law@barrellison.co.uk
List of partners: A C Barr, R K Curry, M Denmead, F T Durrant, S H A Hefferon, M M Tucker
Office: Cambridge
Languages: French, Italian, Serbo-Croat
Work: A1 B1 C1 C2 C3 D1 E F1 J1 K1 K3 K4 L M1 M2 N O P Q R1 S1 S2 T1 T2 W Z(c,e,l,o,q,r)
Agency, Advocacy and Fixed Fee Interview undertaken
Ptr: Barr, Mrs Alison Claire LLB(Lond). . . . . *Apr 1974
Curry, Mr Robert K . . . . Oct 1996
Denmead, Mr Michael BSc . . . . Sep 2004
Durrant, Mr Francis T MA . . . . *Nov 1986
Tucker, Miss Marion M LLB(Leics). . . . . *Apr 1981
Ast: Greensitt, Mrs Judith Diane LLB. . . . . *Apr 1974
Henderson, Ms Beverley LLB . . . . *Oct 1985
Mallott, Miss Charlotte . . . . *Apr 2009
Payne, Miss Sarah . . . . *Dec 1995
Saggers, Mrs Helen. . . . . *Jun 1991

BARR ELLISON LLP
The Concourse Addenbrookes Hospital Hills Road Cambridge Cambridgeshire CB2 2QQ
Tel: 01223 411315 *Fax:* 01223 411279 *Dx:* 5806 CAMBRIDGE
E-mail: law@barrellison.co.uk
Office: Cambridge
Work: A1 B1 C1 C2 C3 D1 E F1 G H J1 K1 L M1 M2 N O P Q R1 S1 T1 T2 W Z(c,i,l)
Emergency Action, Agency, Advocacy, Fixed Fee Interview, Legal Aid undertaken, Legal Aid Franchise and Member of Accident Line
Ptr: Hefferon, Mrs Sarah H A MA . . . . *Oct 1985

BIRKETTS LLP
Daedalus House Station Road Cambridge Cambridgeshire CB1 2RE
Tel: 01223 326600 *Fax:* 01223 326629 *Dx:* 131969 CAMBRIDGE 6
E-mail: mail@birketts.co.uk
Office: Chelmsford, Ipswich, Norwich

ANDREW BRYCE & CO ‡
Unit 23 Cambridge Science Park Cambridge Cambridgeshire CB4 0GN
Tel: 01223 437011 *Fax:* 01223 437012
E-mail: bryce@ehslaw.co.uk
List of partners: A J Bryce
Work: J2 P Z(n)
SPr: Bryce, Mr Andrew John LLB(Newc) . . . . *Jun 1971

RICHARD BUXTON ‡
19b Victoria Street Cambridge Cambridgeshire CB1 1JP
Tel: 01223 328933 *Fax:* 01223 301308
E-mail: law@richardbuxton.co.uk
List of partners: R M Buxton, S Ring, P A Stookes
Work: M1 M2 O P Q R1 Z(a,g,n)
Emergency Action, Agency, Advocacy and Legal Aid undertaken
Ptr: Buxton, Mr Richard Moberly BA(Cantab); MA(Cantab); MES(Yale) . . . . *Oct 1978
Ring, Ms Susan BA. . . . . *Nov 1991
Stookes, Mr Paul A LLB(Hons); MSc; MIEMA; CENV ♦Mar 1998
Asoc: Copithorne, Ms Adrienne BA; MA . . . . Mar 2010
Kelton, Mr Andrew BA(Cantab); MA. . . . . Aug 2007

JOHN BYRNE & CO ‡
Sheraton House Castle Park Cambridge Cambridgeshire CB3 0AX
Tel: 01223 370063 *Fax:* 01223 307277
E-mail: jb@johnbyrne.co.uk
Work: A3 J1 K1 O Q Z(e,f)

CB4LAW ‡
10 Milton Road Cambridge Cambridgeshire CB4 1JY
Tel: 01223 316666 *Fax:* 01223 323262 *Dx:* 5824 CAMBRIDGE 1
Emergency telephone 01223 300625
E-mail: info@cb4law.com
List of partners: S Matthews
Work: D1 E K1 K2 S2 V
Emergency Action, Agency, Advocacy, Fixed Fee Interview, Legal Aid undertaken and Legal Aid Franchise
SPr: Matthews, Mr Simon LLB(Lond). . . . . *Dec 1976
Ast: Casey, Mrs Helen MA. . . . . *Oct 1993
Davies, Mrs Elizabeth MA Clabon Prize; Geoffrey Howard Watson Prize; Robert Innes Prize . . . . *Nov 1979
Con: Cunnah, Mr Robin J. . . . . *Oct 1985

CAMBRIDGE FAMILY LAW PRACTICE LLP ‡ (incorporating Marchant Daisley)
20 Cambridge Place Cambridge Cambridgeshire CB2 1NS
Tel: 01223 443333 *Fax:* 01223 443330 *Dx:* 132993 CAMBRIDGE 7
E-mail: info@cflp.co.uk

CHARLES RUSSELL LLP
Clarendon House Clarendon Road Cambridge Cambridgeshire CB2 8FH
Tel: 01223 465465 *Fax:* 01223 465400 *Dx:* 131971 CAMBRIDGE 6
E-mail: enquiries@charlesrussell.co.uk
Office: Cheltenham, Guildford, London EC4, Oxford

ALEXANDER CRAIG SOLICITORS ‡
1st Floor 98a Mill Road Cambridge Cambridgeshire CB1 2BD
Tel: 01223 348910

CREED LANE LAW GROUP ‡
12 Tredgold Lane Napier Street Cambridge Cambridgeshire CB1 1HN
Tel: 01223 327771 *Fax:* 01223 327780
E-mail: creed.lane@virgin.net

CROSSMANS MTA ‡
Wellington House East Road Cambridge Cambridgeshire CB1 1BH
Tel: 01223 451442 *Fax:* 01223 451107
E-mail: rachel.dunne@crossmansmta.com
List of partners: L J G Browne, R A Dunne, C V Nunes
Office: London EC4, Manchester
Languages: French, Spanish
Work: B1 C1 C2 C3 D1 E F1 F2 J1 K1 K2 K3 K4 L N O Q R2 S1 S2 T2 U2 V W Z(c,d,f,g,l,p,q,y)
Emergency Action, Agency, Advocacy, Fixed Fee Interview and Legal Aid Franchise
Ptr: Browne, Mr Louis J G BA(Lond). . . . . *§Jun 1979
Dunne, Mrs Rachel Ann BA . . . . *Dec 1995
Nunes, Mrs Claire Virginia LLB . . . . *Jun 1981
Ast: Simons, Ms Sara Ann FILEx . . . . Sep 2004

DAVIES SOLICITORS ‡
30 Woollards Lane Great Shelford Cambridge Cambridgeshire CB22 5LZ
Tel: 01223 842211 *Fax:* 01223 842323
E-mail: law@daviessolicitors.co.uk
Office: Cambridge

DAVIES SOLICITORS
Richmond House 16-20 Regent Street Cambridge Cambridgeshire CB21 1DB
Tel: 01223 696444
Office: Cambridge

DIXON PHILLIPS LTD ‡
22 Hills Road Cambridge Cambridgeshire CB2 1JP
Tel: 01223 352007
E-mail: info@dixon-phillips.co.uk

EPITOME LAW ‡
St Johns Innovation Centre Cowley Road Cambridge Cambridgeshire CB4 0WS
Tel: 01223 303162
E-mail: info@epitomelaw.co.uk

EVERSHEDS LLP
Kett House Station Road Cambridge Cambridgeshire CB1 2JY
Tel: 0845 497 9797 *Fax:* 0845 497 3777 *Dx:* 5807 CAMBRIDGE
Office: Birmingham, Cardiff, Ipswich, Leeds, London EC2, Manchester, Newcastle upon Tyne, Nottingham
Languages: French
Work: A1 B1 C1 C2 C3 E F1 H J1 K1 N O P Q R1 S1 T1 T2 W X Z(e,j,l,m)

FOWLER DE PLEDGE ‡
Unit 14 Frenchs Mill Frenchs Road Cambridge Cambridgeshire CB4 2NP
Tel: 01223 311291 *Fax:* 01223 300107
E-mail: enquiries@fdp.co.uk
List of partners: P D de Pledge, A R Fowler
Languages: German
Work: B1 C1 C2 E J1 J2 L N O Q Z(c,e,q,r)
Agency undertaken and Member of Accident Line
Ptr: de Pledge, Mr Paul D . . . . *Oct 1980
Fowler, Mr Andrew R BA Deputy District Judge . . . *Nov 1986
Con: Brewer, Mr Andrew Paul LLB(Warw) Part time Chairman of the Appeals Service Tribunals. . . . . *Jun 1980

FURSDON KNAPPER
18 Orchard Way Great Cambourne Cambridge Cambridgeshire CB23 5BN
Tel: 020 8123 3872 *Fax:* 01954 710089
Office: Plymouth

GEOFF TAYLOR SOLICITOR ‡
12 High Street Coton Cambridge Cambridgeshire CB3 7PL
Tel: 01954 211761 *Fax:* 01954 211761
E-mail: geoff@geofftaylor.co.uk

PETER GIDDENS & CO ‡
266 High Street Cottenham Cambridge Cambridgeshire CB24 8RZ
Tel: 01954 250089 *Fax:* 01954 252026
E-mail: peter.giddens@btconnect.com
List of partners: P J Giddens
Work: E S1 W
Fixed Fee Interview undertaken
SPr: Giddens, Mr Peter John. . . . . *Jun 1981

GINN & CO ‡
Sidney House Sussex Street Cambridge Cambridgeshire CB1 1PE
Tel: 01223 358275 *Fax:* 01223 324271 *Dx:* 131968 CAMBRIDGE 6
E-mail: ginn.co@virgin.net
List of partners: M Barham, J P Copper, J H Jones
Work: A1 C1 D1 E F1 J1 K1 K3 L N O Q R1 S1 S2 T1 W Z(c,d,l,p)
Emergency Action, Agency, Fixed Fee Interview, Legal Aid undertaken and Legal Aid Franchise
Ptr: Barham, Mrs Madeline BA . . . . *Jul 1975
Copper, Mr Jonathan P . . . . *Apr 1999
Jones, Mrs Jill H . . . . *Mar 1989
Ast: Grove, Ms Nichola . . . . *Jan 1998
Hastings, Mrs Joanne C LLB . . . . *Dec 1991
Howard, Ms Fay A BA . . . . *Apr 1991

COLINA GREENWAY ‡
Wellington House East Road Cambridge Cambridgeshire CB1 1BH
Tel: 01223 451072 *Fax:* 01223 451134
E-mail: info@colinagreenway.com

ANDREW GROVE & CO ‡
11 Norfolk Street Cambridge Cambridgeshire CB1 2LD
Tel: 01223 367133 *Fax:* 01233 323817
E-mail: andrewgroveandco@virgin.net
List of partners: A W Grove
Languages: Spanish
Work: D1 H J1 K1 L N Q S1 W Z(c,i,p)
Emergency Action, Agency and Advocacy undertaken
SPr: Grove, Mr Andrew W LLB(Melbourne); Dip Soc Stud(Melbourne) . . . . *Dec 1979

HAYS & COMPANY SOLICITORS ‡
St John's Innovation Centre Cowley Road Cambridge Cambridgeshire CB4 0WS
Tel: 0800 011 6489 *Fax:* 01223 421558
E-mail: admin@tehays.com

HEWITSONS ‡
Shakespeare House 42 Newmarket Road Cambridge Cambridgeshire CB5 8EP
Tel: 01223 461155 *Fax:* 01223 316511 *Dx:* 133155 CAMBRIDGE 8
E-mail: mail@hewitsons.com
List of partners: N Ackermann, T F Bacon, C L Bangor-Jones, I G Barnett, S G Biggin, D G Bradley, A K Brett, D W Browne, C E V Colacicchi, P J Cooch, E A Davies, S J De Loynes, J T Dix, M G Elmslie, P W Ewart, K P W Fletcher, P R D Gutteridge, N Hall, N T Harpham, C R B Hewitson, D E Hollest, D A Hopkins, S M Hughes, R G Ingram, C D Jones, E J Jones, J Lawrence, M E Legg, L Leone, R McLellan, T S Middleton, Y M Morgan, S Portman, T J Richards, D R Sabberton, P R Saffron, G B Sampson, N T Sayer, D J Sharples, J Shephard, J C Simpson, P J A Taylor, W G H Thatcher, H W Thomas, J A White, D Wilkinson, J Williams, D M Williamson
Office: Milton Keynes, Northampton, Saffron Walden
Languages: French, German, Italian, Spanish
Work: A1 A3 B1 B2 C1 C2 C3 D1 E F1 G H I J1 K1 L M1 M2 N O P Q R1 R2 S1 S2 T1 T2 U1 U2 W Z(b,c,d,e,f,h,i,j,k,l,m,n,o,p,q,r,s,u,y)
Agency, Advocacy, Fixed Fee Interview, Legal Aid undertaken and Legal Aid Franchise
Ptr: Ackermann, Niel BA; LLB . . . . *Jul 1981
Bacon, Mr Timothy F BA(Dunelm). . . . . *Nov 1991
Biggin, Mr Simon G LLB. . . . . *Mar 1983
Bradley, Mr David G MA(Cantab) . . . . *Apr 1972
Brett, Mr Alan K LLM(Cantab); LLM(B'ham); Dip Int Law(Cantab) . . . . *§Nov 1972
Davies, Ms Elizabeth Anne LLB. . . . . *Sep 1996
Dix, Mr John T BA; LLB. . . . . *Aug 1991
Elmslie, Mr Mark G LLB; LLM . . . . Nov 1988
Ewart, Mr Peter W MA(Cantab) . . . . *May 1974
Gutteridge, Mr Peter R D . . . . *§May 1967
Harpham, Mr Neil T BA(Hons). . . . . *Oct 1994
Hewitson, Mr Charles R B LLB . . . . *Nov 1977
Jones, Mr Colin David BA(Hons) . . . . *Dec 1993
Jones, Mrs Elizabeth J . . . . *Nov 1975
Lawrence, Mr James LLB . . . . Dec 1987
Leone, Ms Luisa . . . . Oct 1990
McLellan, Mr Robert LLB . . . . Sep 1991
Morgan, Mrs Yvette Morgan LLB . . . . *Aug 1994
Portman, Mr Simon . . . . Sep 1996
Richards, Mr Timothy J LLB. . . . . *Sep 1985
Sabberton, Mr David R MA(Cantab). . . . . *§Dec 1968
Saffron, Mr Philip R MA(Cantab) . . . . *Apr 1980
Sampson, Mr Graeme B LLB . . . . *Nov 1982
Sayer, Mr Nicholas T LLB; LLM; FSALS. . . . . Oct 1987
Sharples, Mrs Deborah Jane LLB . . . . *Nov 1990
Simpson, Mr James Christopher BSc . . . . *Sep 1996
Thatcher, Mr William G H . . . . *Nov 1990
Thomas, Mr Huw W LLB(Leics) . . . . *Oct 1984
Wilkinson, Mrs Denise BA. . . . . *Oct 1984
Williams, Mr Jason LLB(Hons) . . . . *Oct 1987
Williamson, Mrs Dee M LLB. . . . . *Nov 1992
Ast: Aldred, Mrs Hilary MA(Cantab) . . . . Oct 1998
Backhaus, Mrs Jacqueline A BSc(Hons). . . . . *Sep 1999
Bearpark, Miss Lisa E LLB . . . . Nov 1993
Chalk, Mr William Alexander Matthew LLB . . . . . . *Jul 1999
Church, Miss Katherine M BA . . . . *Oct 1989
Cumberbatch, Mr Christopher LLB . . . . *Oct 2002
Curtis, Mr Daniel J LLB(Hons); TEP. . . . . *Oct 1997
Dennett, Mrs Karen L . . . . Oct 2000
Drayton, Miss Helen Mary LLB(Hons) . . . . *Sep 2001
Fields, Mr Andrew LLB(Hons). . . . . *Sep 1999
Gannon, Miss Christine Ann BA(Jt Hons) CPE Prize For EC Law 1997/98. . . . . *Sep 2001
Gearing, Mr Mark Christopher LLB(Hons); Dip French Legal Studies . . . . *Sep 2000
Greenbank, Mrs Susan MA(Cantab). . . . . Jul 1990
Hall, Ms Sarah Elizabeth MA(Cantab); CPE; LPD . . *Sep 1998
Heath, Mr Paul BA . . . . Sep 2001
Li-Yan-Hui, Mr Daniel . . . . Apr 2002
McElhone, Mr Stephen J LLB(Hons). . . . . *Sep 1998
McGowan, Mr Michael . . . . Jan 1997
Makin, Mr Colin . . . . *Aug 1999
Morris, Dr Ruth BSc; MB . . . . Sep 2002
Parekh, Hemal LLB(Hons) . . . . *Apr 2001
Scally, Dr David MSc; PhD CPE Prize. . . . . Sep 1999
Simms, Miss Justine BA(Hons) . . . . Aug 2002
Swinburn, Ms Elizabeth Jane BA; MA(Oxon) . . . . . *Sep 2000
Tweddle, Miss Victoria . . . . *Dec 2000
Wild, Mr Paul Spencer BA(Hons); DipLaw; LPC . . . *Sep 2001

HIGHFIELDS LAW PRACTICE ‡
74 Highfields Road Highfields Caldecote Cambridge Cambridgeshire CB23 7NX
Tel: 01954 210363 *Fax:* 01954 211305
List of partners: J H Tarrant
Work: C1 E J1 K1 Q S1 S2 W
Ptr: Tarrant, Mr John H . . . . *Dec 1970

KENNEDYS
2nd Floor Terrington House 13-15 Hills Road Cambridge Cambridgeshire CB2 1NL
Tel: 01223 533060 *Fax:* 01223 533076 *Dx:* 5827 CAMBRIDGE

Office: Belfast, Birmingham, Chelmsford, London EC3, Maidstone, Manchester, Sheffield, Taunton
Work: Q Z(j,q,r)
Ptr: Barlow, Mr Philip BMedSci; MB; SHB; MA. . . . . . . .Jul 1997
Lapraik, Mr John D LLB. . . . . *Oct 1983
Ast: Baker, Alexandra . . . . Sep 2006
Duncan, Ms Margaret BA . . . . *Oct 1992
Mead, Amanda . . . . Sep 2006
Topham, Ms Lin. . . . . Sep 1988

KING & CO ‡
St Andrew's House 59 St Andrew's Street Cambridge Cambridgeshire CB2 3DD
Tel: 01223 365432 / 566038 *Fax:* 01223 464241
Dx: 5829 CAMBRIDGE
E-mail: kingco@btconnect.com
List of partners: R S Covell, R A Freeman, P Gittins, A P Huskinson
Office: Cambridge
Work: A1 B1 C1 C2 C3 E F1 J1 L M1 M2 P R1 S1 T1 T2 V W Z(c,d,l,m,o)
Agency and Fixed Fee Interview undertaken
Ptr: Freeman, Mr Ralph A LLB(Lond) . . . . *May 1971
Gittins, Mr Paul LLB Notary Public . . . . *Nov 1991
Huskinson, Mr A Paul LLB Notary Public . . . . *Mar 1984
Con: Hindmarsh, Mr J David MA; LLM; LMRTPI Notary Public . . . . *Oct 1960

KING & CO
238 High Street Cottenham Cambridge Cambridgeshire CB24 8RZ
Tel: 01954 251818 *Fax:* 01954 251672 *Dx:* 5829 CAMBRIDGE
E-mail: king238@tiscali.co.uk
Office: Cambridge
Work: A1 E L S1 S2 W
Fixed Fee Interview undertaken
Ptr: Covell, Mr Roger S . . . . *Dec 1981
Ast: Cumberland, Mrs Stephanie Jane LLB(Hons) . . . . . *Oct 1983

LAWSOLVE LLP ‡
Granthams House 19 Babraham Road Cambridge Cambridgeshire CB2 2RB
Tel: 01223 412333

MONICA LENTIN & CO ‡
69a Maids Causeway Cambridge Cambridgeshire CB5 8DE
Tel: 01223 314452 *Fax:* 01223 460385
List of partners: M R Lentin
Languages: French, German, Hebrew
Work: G H
Advocacy, Fixed Fee Interview and Legal Aid undertaken
SPr: Lentin, Mrs Monica Ruth BA(Hons) . . . . Jun 1982

MARKS & CLERK SOLICITORS LLP ‡
62-68 Hills Road Cambridge Cambridgeshire CB2 1LA
Tel: 01223 345539
E-mail: solicitors@marks-clerk.com

MASSUCCO BUTTRESS ‡
162 Tenison Road Cambridge Cambridgeshire CB1 2DP
Tel: 01223 463183 *Fax:* 01223 463180
E-mail: mail@massuccobuttress.co.uk
List of partners: A D Buttress, M X Massucco
Languages: French, Italian
Work: S1
Ptr: Buttress, Mrs Amanda D BA(Hons) . . . . Sep 1999
Massucco, Mr Mark Xavier MA . . . . .Jul 1987

JAN MENTHA SOLICITORS ‡
24 Cheney Way Cambridge Cambridgeshire CB4 1UD
Tel: 01223 502090 *Fax:* 01223 579369
E-mail: jan@mentha.com

LINDSAY MESSENGER SOLICITORS ‡
46 St Johns Street Duxford Cambridge Cambridgeshire CB2 4RA
Tel: 01223 508860 *Fax:* 01223 508860

MILLER SANDS ‡
Regent House 133 Station Road Impington Cambridge Cambridgeshire CB24 9NP
Tel: 01223 202345 *Fax:* 01223 202333 *Dx:* 5816 CAMBRIDGE
E-mail: info@millersands.com
List of partners: W S Cowell, J D Landy
Languages: Afrikaans, Dutch, French, German, Italian, Spanish
Work: A1 B1 C1 D1 D2 E F1 J2 K1 K2 K3 K4 L N O Q R1 R2 S1 S2 T1 T2 V W Z(c,d,k,l,m,q)
Emergency Action, Agency, Advocacy and Fixed Fee Interview undertaken
Ptr: Cowell, Mr William Scott . . . . *Jun 1994
Landy, Mr Julian David BA(Sheff) . . . . *Dec 1978
Ast: Barkas, Ms Katharine . . . . *Jan 2009
Bradberry, Ms Louisa BA(Hons). . . . . *Jul 2005
Con: Hawthorn, Mr George Ryan LLB; BA . . . . Jun 1977

MILLS & REEVE ‡
Francis House 112 Hills Road Cambridge Cambridgeshire CB2 1PH
Tel: 01223 364422 *Fax:* 01223 355848 *Dx:* 122891 CAMBRIDGE 4
List of partners: M Aizlewood, T K E Allsop, M R Arrowsmith-Brown, G Attle, M J Aubrey, R J Bamber, J R Barclay, W D W Barr, G S Barrett, D M J Brock, N H Brown, E J Callaghan, T M Cassidy, S R Christy, C M Clarke, D A Cowper, C A de Ferrars Green, P J Driscoll, J M G Falkner, B J Firth, N J Fischl, P W Furnivall, F Hawker, J W F Herring, R J Higgs, G R Hinchley, G J Hodgson, J Hundle, J M Hunter, R D Hutton, S Jack, R M Jeffries, S King, S P Knowles, B Marshall, I J Mayers, G G Menzies, D Mills, I J S Napper, D M Ogilvy, T Pickthorn, R J C Pickup, R H Plascow, A D Poore, E Powell, A K Ray, J J P Ripman, H Robinson, T Ryan, C J H Scott, G P L Scoular, N Stone, G Thomas, C J Townsend, A Turner, S K I Waddington, J G Wheatley, A Wood
Office: Birmingham, Leeds, London EC3, Manchester, Norwich
Work: A1 A2 A3 B1 C1 C2 C3 D1 E F1 F2 I J1 J2 K1 K2 L M1 N O P Q R1 R2 S1 S2 T1 T2 U1 V W X Z(b,c,d,e,f,g,h,j,l,m,n,o,p,q,r,t,u,x,y,z)
Emergency Action, Agency, Advocacy, Fixed Fee Interview, Legal Aid undertaken and Legal Aid Franchise
Ptr: Allsop, Mr Timothy Keith Edward . . . . *Oct 1994
Attle, Mr Gary BA . . . . *Oct 1992
Aubrey, Mr Michael J BSc. . . . . *Nov 1991
Bamber, Mr Roger J MA(Cantab) . . . . *Oct 1981
Barr, Mr William D W LLB. . . . . §Apr 1973
Brock, Mr David M J LLB(Lond). . . . . *§Jun 1980
Brown, Miss Nicola H LLB. . . . . *Nov 1987
Callaghan, Mr Edward J LLB . . . . *Jun 1974
Christy, Mr Stephen R LLB . . . . *Apr 1974
Clarke, Mrs Claire Margaret MA(Oxon) . . . . *Mar 1993
Cowper, Mr D Anthony . . . . *§May 1973
de Ferrars Green, Ms Christine A BA(Hons)(York). . . *Nov 1989
Firth, Mrs Beverley J LLB . . . . *Jun 1981
Marshall, Mr Brian BA; MPhil . . . . *Jan 1984
Menzies, Mr Graeme G BA . . . . *§Jul 1980
Mills, Mr David BSc(Hons) . . . . *Nov 1995
Napper, Miss Isabel J S BA(Law); LLM . . . . *Nov 1984
Ogilvy, Mr Duncan M . . . . *§Nov 1976
Pickthorn, Mr Thomas BA; CPE; LSF . . . . *Nov 1994
Pickup, Raith J C BA(Oxon). . . . . *Nov 1987
Plascow, Mr Ronald H LLB . . . . *Jun 1981
Poore, Mr Alasdair D MA(Cantab); CPA; RTMA Harmsworth Exhibitioner Council Member of the Chartered Institute of Patent Agents. . . . . *Dec 1989
Powell, Mr Edward BA(Hons); DPhil. . . . . *Nov 1993
Ray, Mr Andrew Keith LLB(Hons) . . . . *Feb 1989
Robinson, Mr Herbert . . . . *§Jul 1969
Thomas, Dr Gillian DPhil; CPE . . . . Oct 1996
Townsend, Mr Christopher John MA(Cantab) . . . . *§Jan 1991
Wheatley, Mr Jamieson G. . . . . Feb 1987
Wood, Mr Andrew MA(Cantab) . . . . *Jan 1995
Asoc: Bearcroft, Mrs Sandra Mary BA . . . . *Nov 1988
Finlayson-Brown, Mr Nicholas M BA(Hons); CPE . . . Sep 1993
Peel, Miss Jane E BA(Law) . . . . *Nov 1989
Prandy, Ms Helen. . . . . Nov 1992
Roy, Miss Judy BA; MA . . . . Sep 1994
Thornton-Swan, Ms Carol A LLB . . . . *§Nov 1986
Turner, Ms Helen LLB. . . . . *Oct 1992
Ast: Adamson, Ms Anne L E MA(Cantab) . . . . Sep 2002
Anthony, Miss Barbara Susan LLB(Hons) . . . . Sep 2002
Atwal, Miss Harpreet Kaur LLB; LPC . . . . *Sep 2002
Baggaley, Miss Joanna LLB(Hons) . . . . *Sep 1998
Bartlett, Ms Lisa. . . . . Nov 1999
Baseley, Miss Rachel Louise MA(Oxon); CPE; LPC . . Sep 2002
Betts, Mr Giles LLB . . . . *Oct 1999
Bolton, Ms Helen Margaret LLB . . . . Mar 1997
Burr, Miss Sarah Elke LLB . . . . *Sep 2002
Calder, Mr Kevin E . . . . Oct 1999
Carrier, Mr Andrew . . . . Sep 2000
Corner, Mr Hamish Richard LLB. . . . . Sep 2001
Craig, Mr Stuart C BA(Hons) . . . . Nov 1996
Davenport, Miss Julia N S LLB(Law with German) Tolley Publishing Prize - Best Performance in Constitutional & Administrative Law . . . . Aug 2002
Davies, Ms Alison Jane BSc . . . . *Oct 1980
Elvin, Mrs Laura Catherine BA(Hons); CPE; LPC . . . *Nov 1996
Evans, Ms Annabelle BSc; CPE; LPC. . . . . *Apr 2000
Falvey, Miss Sarah Louise LLB(Hons); PGDip. . . . . *Sep 1999
Farrand, Mr Daniel J BSc(Hons). . . . . *Feb 1999
Fox, Mrs Catherine BA; MA; LLM(Cantab). . . . . . . Oct 1997
Garrett, Miss Alison M LLB . . . . *Dec 1988
Goodger, Mr Martyn. . . . . Jan 1999
Harris, Mrs Samantha Caroline BA(Hons)(Law with Geography) . . . . Sep 2001
Holdaway, Mrs Laura LLB. . . . . .Jul 1998
Horrocks, Miss Claire L LLB; DipLP. . . . . *Sep 1998
Johnston, Mr Edward Conor LLB . . . . May 2001
Jones, Mrs Amanda MA; BA(Hons); CPE; LPC . . . . . Oct 1997
Kwan, Miss Kathleen BSc; LLB . . . . Feb 2002
Lapraik, Ms Nichola E P LLB . . . . *Oct 1983
Lass, Ms Rosemary BA; MA(Cantab) . . . . *Jul 1994
Lim, Ms Zickie . . . . Oct 2000
Maggio, Mr Vincenzo . . . . Sep 2002
Mobed, Ms Julie BA(Hons); CPE; LPC . . . . Oct 1997
Noble, Mr Richard Thomas Joseph BSc(Hons) . . . . *Oct 1995
Patel, Hinal LLB(Hons); LPC . . . . Sep 2001
Patten, Mr Dwight BA; CPE; LPC . . . . Nov 2001
Pemble, Mr Stuart CPE; LPC Former Judicial Assistant to the Court of Appeal. . . . . *Oct 1997
Renfree, Mr Robert Peter LLB(Hons) . . . . *Sep 1997
Seed, Mrs Sarah . . . . Apr 1997
Spencer, Mr Jonathan A LLB; LPC . . . . Sep 2001
Stead, Mr David LLB . . . . Sep 2001
Thorne, Mrs Claire Louise LLB(Hons) . . . . Sep 1997
Turner, Mr Ben Eliot BA(Hons) . . . . Sep 2001
Wakeman, Mr Michael David LLB . . . . Sep 2001
Walton, Ms Vanessa LLB(Hons). . . . . Sep 1999
Weston, Miss Kimbra S BA; MA(Oxon) . . . . *Nov 1989
Whatley, Mr Michael LLB(Hons). . . . . Sep 1997
Wicks, Mrs Charlotte E MA Law Society Prize for Good Work on the LPC 1999. . . . . Sep 2001
Con: Archibald, Ms Bridget E H BA. . . . . *Nov 1983

NBM MASSUCCO SHELBOURNE
Lincoln House The Paddocks 347 Cherry Hinton Road Cambridge Cambridgeshire CB1 8DH
Tel: 01223 211992 *Fax:* 01223 242831
Office: Ashby-de-la-Zouch, Chelmsford
Work: B1 C1 C2 C3 D1 E F1 J1 K1 L N O Q S1 W Z(l)
Emergency Action, Agency, Advocacy, Fixed Fee Interview, Legal Aid undertaken, Legal Aid Franchise and Member of Accident Line
Ptr: Broadhead, Mr Robert W N LLB. . . . . *§Jun 1970
Ast: May, Mrs Joanne Claire LLB . . . . *Sep 1994

O'MALLEY SOLICITORS ‡
84 Rampton Road Willingham Cambridge Cambridgeshire CB24 5JQ
Tel: 01954 202075
E-mail: omalleysolicitors@googlemail.com

JANE OAKES ‡
Collaborative Chambers Compass House Chivers Way Cambridge Cambridgeshire CB24 9AD
Tel: 01223 253733
E-mail: enquiries@collaborativechambers.co.uk

OSLERS SOLICITORS ‡
48 Mill Road Cambridge Cambridgeshire CB1 2AS
Tel: 01223 352558 *Fax:* 01223 365369
E-mail: cambs@oslers.co.uk
List of partners: M Cleaver, C R Lockwood, J S Yardy
Office: Stowmarket
Ptr: Cleaver, Miss Mary LLB(Hons) . . . . *Sep 1996

PELLYS SOLICITORS ‡
Second Floor Suite 4 Ravenscroft House Cambridge Cambridgeshire CB2 1AB
Tel: 01223 654220 *Dx:* 131975 CAMBRIDGE 6
E-mail: office@pellys.co.uk

PETERSFIELDS LLP ‡
Wellington House East Road Cambridge Cambridgeshire CB1 1BH
Tel: 01223 451010 *Fax:* 01223 451126
E-mail: enquiries@petersfields.com

REDDIE & GROSE ‡
5 Shaftsbury Road Cambridge Cambridgeshire CB2 8BW
Tel: 01223 360350 *Fax:* 01223 360280

SARFO SOLICITORS ‡
99 Victoria Road Cambridge Cambridgeshire CB4 3BS
Tel: 01223 305551 *Fax:* 01223 305554 *Dx:* 5836 CAMBRIDGE
Emergency telephone 07859 895679
E-mail: contact@sarfosolicitors.co.uk
List of partners: E Sarfo-Akrade
SPr: Sarfo-Akrade, Elfreda . . . . Apr 1995
Ast: Candy, Ms Veronica A BA; MA(Cantab) . . . . *Oct 1998

SHELBOURNES SOLICITORS ‡
1 Munro House Trafalgar Way Bar Hill Cambridge Cambridgeshire CB23 8SQ
Tel: 01954 208064 *Fax:* 0870 350 1664
E-mail: mshelbourne@shelbournes.com

SHELLEY & CO ‡
46 Eden Street Cambridge Cambridgeshire CB1 1EL
Tel: 01223 359441 *Fax:* 01223 355099 *Dx:* 5826 CAMBRIDGE
Emergency telephone 01223 359441
E-mail: enquiries@shelleyandco.co.uk
List of partners: M F J Benn, J T Dignan, C L Metcalfe, M F Shelley
Work: B2 G H
Emergency Action, Agency, Advocacy, Fixed Fee Interview, Legal Aid undertaken and Legal Aid Franchise
Ptr: Benn, Ms Melanie F Jane MA(Hons)(Anthropology) ★. *Oct 1993
Dignan, Mr James T BA(Hons)(Law) . . . . *Aug 1981
Metcalfe, Miss Christina Louise MA(Oxon); LLB(Hons) *Oct 1996
Shelley, Mr Mark Frank BA(Hons) ★. . . . . *Mar 1988
Asoc: Bradd, Miss Catherine BA. . . . . *Nov 1999
Con: Milsom, Mr Robert Charles MA(Cantab). . . . . *Jan 1980

SILVER FITZGERALD ‡
15-17 Castle Street Cambridge Cambridgeshire CB3 0AH
Tel: 01223 562001 *Fax:* 01223 518310 *Dx:* 88009 CAMBRIDGE 1
E-mail: enquiries@silverfitzgerald.co.uk
List of partners: K L Anker, R Silver
Languages: French
Work: D1 D2 F1 J1 K1 K3 L N Q V
Emergency Action, Agency, Advocacy, Fixed Fee Interview, Legal Aid undertaken and Legal Aid Franchise
Ptr: Anker, Mrs Karen L MA(Cantab). . . . . *Dec 1991
Silver, Mr Raphael BA(Dunelm) . . . . *Oct 1984
Ast: Macduff, Mr Douglas . . . . *Jan 2005
Sherwin, Desley. *Jan 1992

DAVID W SKINNER SOLICITOR ‡
30 Lambs Lane Cottenham Cambridge Cambridgeshire CB4 8TA
Tel: 01954 201075

SMART LAW SOLICITORS LLP
Wellington House East Road Cambridge Cambridgeshire CB1 1BH
Tel: 01223 451057 *Fax:* 0870 446 0904
E-mail: contact@smartlawfirm.co.uk
Office: Ely

SMITH MAY SOLICITORS ‡
14 Barnwell House Barnwell Business Park Barnwell Drive Cambridge Cambridgeshire CB5 8UU
Tel: 01223 415372 *Fax:* 01223 415370
E-mail: sarah.smith@smslaw.co.uk

SOMERTON & FLETCHER ‡
The Trapezium 186a Victoria Road Cambridge Cambridgeshire CB4 3LG
Tel: 01223 566596 *Fax:* 01223 566598
E-mail: pcfletcher.sandf@btclick.com
List of partners: P C Fletcher, J M Somerton
Languages: Farsi
Work: E F1 L Q S1 S2 W
Ptr: Fletcher, Mr Peter C MA(Cantab) Notary Public . . . . *Dec 1987
Somerton, Mr J Major BA . . . . *Mar 1980
Con: Christie, Mrs Anne BA. . . . . *Oct 2003

IRENA SPENCE ‡
68-70 Castle Street Cambridge Cambridgeshire CB3 0AJ
Tel: 01223 713300 *Fax:* 01223 509237 *Dx:* 88019 CAMBRIDGE 1
E-mail: mail@irenaspence.co.uk
List of partners: C A K Fraser, N R Houlder, I J Spence, T S Spilsbury
Office: Cambridge
Languages: Polish
Work: B1 D1 D2 E F2 J1 K1 L N O Q S1 S2 V W Z(q,t)
Agency, Fixed Fee Interview and Legal Aid undertaken
Ptr: Fraser, Mr Charles A K . . . . *Jul 1983
Houlder, Mr Nicholas R LLB. . . . . Nov 1972
Spence, Mrs Irena Josefa LLB(Leics) . . . . *Oct 1984
Spilsbury, Miss Tracy S BA(Hons). . . . . *Oct 1988

IRENA SPENCE
(incorporating Verity Hickford & Co)
5 Green End Comberton Cambridge Cambridgeshire CB23 7DY
Tel: 01223 713300 *Fax:* 01223 263718 *Dx:* 88019 CAMBRIDGE 1
E-mail: mail@irenaspence.co.uk
Office: Cambridge
Work: S1 W
Con: Hickford, Ms Verity A . . . . *§Oct 1961

STANLEY TEE LLP ‡
Devonshire House 89 Regent Street Cambridge Cambridgeshire CB2 1AW
Tel: 01223 311141 *Fax:* 01223 460749 *Dx:* 5811 CAMBRIDGE
E-mail: law@teeslaw.co.uk
List of partners: R Conn, J Lees, A C Lorimer, P D Taylor
Work: C1 E K1 N O Q S1 S2 T2 W Z(r)
Advocacy, Fixed Fee Interview, Legal Aid undertaken and Legal Aid Franchise
Ptr: Conn, Miss Rachel . . . . Apr 1981
Lees, Mr John BA(Dunelm) . . . . *Apr 1977
Lorimer, Mr Alastair C MA(Cantab) . . . . *§Jun 1971
Taylor, Mr Paul D BA . . . . *Jun 1993
Ast: Copeland, Mr Adam Aaron Peter BA(Hons)(English Lit); CPE; LPC. . . . . Feb 1998
Toovey, Mr Nicholas Charles MA(Cantab) . . . . Apr 1976
Walker, Mrs Jennifer . . . . Sep 2007

STONE KING LLP
Wellington House East Road Cambridge Cambridgeshire CB1 1BH
Tel: 01223 451070 *Fax:* 01223 451100
Office: Bath, London EC1
Work: X Z(d)

TV EDWARDS LLP
The Advice Hub Cambridge 66 Devonshire Road Cambridge Cambridgeshire CB1 2BL
Tel: 020 7790 7000 *Fax:* 020 3357 9587
E-mail: enquiries@tvedwards.com
Office: London E1 (3 offices), London E15, London EC4, London N15, London SE8, London SW11

TAYLOR VINTERS ‡
Merlin Place Milton Road Cambridge Cambridgeshire CB4 0DP
Tel: 01223 423444 *Fax:* 01223 423486 *Dx:* 724560 CAMBRIDGE 12
E-mail: info@taylorvinters.com
List of partners: J A Allen, S W Beach, C A Berry, A J Butler, N D Campbell, G W A Chadwick, C D A Falvey, J A Fox, Q R Golder, M J Henson, A P Horwood-Smart, A M Lyne, J V Packer, E F V Perrott, O C P Pryke, J R Short, P Tapner, E D Turner, J M Warren, J A Wells
Languages: French, German
Work: A1 A3 B1 C1 C2 C3 D1 D2 E F1 F2 G I J1 J2 K1 K2 L M1 M2 N O P Q R1 R2 S1 S2 T1 T2 U1 U2 W X Z(c,d,e,g,h,i,k,l,n,o,p,q,r,t,u,y)
Agency, Advocacy, Fixed Fee Interview, Legal Aid undertaken, Legal Aid Franchise and Member of Accident Line
Ptr: Allen, Mr James Alexander BA(Hons); LLM . . . . . *Nov 1993
Beach, Mr Steven W BA(Oxon) . . . . . Nov 1985
Berry, Mrs Christine A MA. . . . . *Mar 1992
Butler, Mr Alun John BA(Hons) . . . . . *Nov 1989
Campbell, Mr Neill D . . . . . *§Mar 1975
Chadwick, Mr Gerard W A MA; LLM(Cantab) . . . . *§Aug 1971
Falvey, Mr Christopher D A MA(Cantab); Licence en Droit Europeen(Brussels). . . . . *Oct 1988
Fox, Miss Jocelyn A LLB . . . . . Oct 1985
Golder, Mr Quentin Robert LLB; LLM . . . . . Mar 1999
Henson, Ms Michaela Jane MA(Cantab). . . . . *Aug 1995
Horwood-Smart, Mr Adrian P . . . . . *Nov 1977
Lyne, Mrs Amanda M MA; LLB(Cantab) . . . . . *Jan 1982
Packer, Mr James Vernon BSc; CPE; LPC . . . . . *Oct 1996
Perrott, Mr Edward F V MA(Cantab). . . . . *Nov 1976
Pryke, Mr Oliver Charles Patrick BA(Hons) . . . . . *Sep 1996
Short, Mr John R LLB(Sheff) . . . . . *§Apr 1974
Tapner, Mr Paul. . . . . *Jan 1988
Turner, Mr Edmund David BSc . . . . . Dec 1995
Warren, Mrs Jennifer M BA Governor of Anglia Polytechnic University. . . . . *Dec 1981
Wells, Miss Jacqueline A LLB. . . . . *Nov 1991
Asoc: Beric, Miss Angela LLB(Hons); LLM. . . . . Jul 1998
Flynn, Miss Rachel E BA(Hons). . . . . *Sep 1994
Hall, Mr Tim LLB; LLM . . . . . Oct 1993
James, Mr Roger Benjamin BSc(Hons) . . . . . Aug 1996
Lee, Ms Alison Helen LLB. . . . . Oct 1996
Maguire, Mr Nigel LLB . . . . . Sep 1999
Melville-Ross, Mr Rupert W BA(French). . . . . *Sep 1998
Rainford, Dr David . . . . . Oct 1987
Stabler, Mrs Sara Louise LLB(Hons). . . . . Oct 1995
Ast: Ambrose, Miss Katherine . . . . . Sep 1999
Deyong, Miss Elizabeth M BA(Oxon) . . . . . *Oct 1984
Gaffney, Mr Richard D. . . . . Sep 2000
Martin, Mrs Clare Ann LLB; BIURIS. . . . . Aug 1998
Moran, Miss Victoria Louise LLB . . . . . Sep 2002
Wheeler, Mr Guy A . . . . . Sep 1999

TAYLOR WESSING
24 Hills Road Cambridge Cambridgeshire CB2 1JP
Tel: 01223 446400 *Fax:* 01223 446401 *Dx:* 88010 CAMBRIDGE
Office: London EC4

THOMSON WEBB & CORFIELD ‡
16 Union Road Cambridge Cambridgeshire CB2 1HE
Tel: 01223 578070 *Fax:* 01223 578050 *Dx:* 5840 CAMBRIDGE
E-mail: enquiries@twclaw.co.uk
List of partners: N V Barnes, A Blackman, P A Carr, N E Corfield, S A Hollis, S Kainth, D Parker, P R Speer, T J Thomson
Office: Cambridge (2 offices)
Work: B2 C1 C2 D1 D2 E F1 F2 G H J1 K1 L N O Q R2 S1 S2 W Z(i,j)
Agency and Fixed Fee Interview undertaken
Ptr: Carr, Miss Philippa A MA(Hons). . . . . *Nov 1998
Corfield, Mr Nicholas E . . . . . *Jun 1976
Hollis, Mr Steven Alexander LLB(Hons) . . . . . *Oct 1995
Parker, Mr David . . . . . Jun 2003
Speer, Mr Philip R BA(Cantab) . . . . . Apr 1976
Thomson, Mr Timothy J LLB . . . . . *Apr 1981
Ast: Burns, Ms Claire . . . . . Nov 2007
Other Offices in Cambridge and Histon. Holders of LA Franchise for Crime and Family.

THOMSON WEBB & CORFIELD
94 Regent Street Cambridge Cambridgeshire CB2 1DP
Tel: 01223 578068 *Fax:* 01223 477639 *Dx:* 5840 CAMBRIDGE
E-mail: enquiries@twclaw.co.uk
Office: Cambridge (2 offices)
Work: B1 C1 C2 D1 D2 E G H J1 K1 K3 L N O Q S1 S2 W Z(e,i,l,m)
Agency and Fixed Fee Interview undertaken
Ptr: Barnes, Mr Nicholas Vincent LLB(Hons). . . . . *Dec 1997
Blackman, Miss Alison LLB . . . . . Oct 1995
Kainth, Mr Sandeep. . . . . *Nov 1995
Ast: Woodruff, Mrs Sheila J LLB . . . . . *Jul 1976

THOMSON WEBB & CORFIELD
22 High Street Histon Cambridge Cambridgeshire CB4 9JD
Tel: 01223 518317 *Fax:* 01223 500075 *Dx:* 5840 CAMBRIDGE
E-mail: enquiries@twclaw.co.uk
Office: Cambridge (2 offices)
Work: S1 W
Ptr: Parker, Mr David . . . . . Jun 2003
Ast: Watson, Mr Gary LLB(Hons) . . . . . Dec 1991

WALKER WALLIS SOLICITORS ‡
Trinity House Cambridge Business Park Cowley Road Cambridge Cambridgeshire CB4 0WZ
Tel: 01223 393805 *Fax:* 01223 393501
E-mail: info@walkerwallis.com

ANNE WEBBER & CO ‡
Castle Business Park Sheraton House Cambridge Cambridgeshire CB3 0AX
Tel: 01223 370073 *Fax:* 01233 323233
E-mail: annewebbersolicitors@ntlworld.com

WOODFINES LLP
Ground Floor Lockton House Clarendon Road Cambridge Cambridgeshire CB2 8FH
Tel: 01223 411421 *Fax:* 01223 413710 *Dx:* 5869 CAMBRIDGE
E-mail: mail@woodfines.co.uk
Office: Bedford, Bletchley, Milton Keynes, Sandy
Work: A1 A3 B1 C1 C2 C3 D1 E F1 F2 J1 K1 K2 K4 L M1 M2 N O P Q R1 S1 S2 T1 T2 V W Z(c,d,e,i,j,k,l,m,n,o,p,x)
Emergency Action, Agency, Advocacy, Fixed Fee Interview, Legal Aid undertaken, Legal Aid Franchise and Member of Accident Line
Mem: Butler, Mr Alun John BA(Hons) . . . . . *Nov 1989
Davies, Mrs Denise . . . . . Nov 1984

CAMELFORD, Cornwall

SPROULL SOLICITORS LLP ‡
8 Fore Street Camelford Cornwall PL32 9PG
Tel: 01840 212315 *Fax:* 01840 212792
E-mail: camelford@sproullllp.co.uk
List of partners: D S Hutchison, D M Sproull, D Sproull
Office: Bodmin, Port Isaac
Work: A1 B1 C1 E K1 K3 K4 L N O Q R2 S1 S2 W Z(q)
Agency, Advocacy and Fixed Fee Interview undertaken
Mem: Sproull, Dugald LLB. . . . . *Jun 1966

CANNOCK, Staffordshire

ANSONS LLP
Commerce House Ridings Park Eastern Way Cannock Staffordshire WS11 2FJ
Tel: 01543 466660 *Fax:* 01543 571682
E-mail: info@ansonsllp.com
Office: Lichfield
Work: A1 A3 C1 E J1 K1 K2 K3 L N O P Q R1 S1 S2 W Z(c,d)
Fixed Fee Interview undertaken

NIGEL W BEAMAN ‡
98 High Green Cannock Staffordshire WS11 1BE
Tel: 01543 574474 *Fax:* 01543 500010
E-mail: nwb@nigelwbeaman.co.uk
List of partners: N W Beaman
Work: J1 K1 K3 O Q Z(c,p,q)
Emergency Action and Advocacy undertaken
SPr: Beaman, Mr Nigel W LLB ♦ M C Hugall Memorial Prize . . . . . *Dec 1988

BURRELL JENKINS ‡
17 Wolverhampton Road Cannock Staffordshire WS11 1AP
Tel: 01543 505040 *Fax:* 01543 579724 *Dx:* 16093 CANNOCK
Emergency telephone 01543 578371
List of partners: P S G Jenkins, I S Thind
Work: C1 D1 E F1 G H J1 K1 L N S1 V W Z(h,k,l,o,p)
Emergency Action, Agency, Advocacy, Fixed Fee Interview, Legal Aid undertaken and Legal Aid Franchise
Ptr: Jenkins, Mr Paul S G LLB(Lond) . . . . . *§Jul 1977
Thind, Inderjit S LLB . . . . . *Mar 1985
Ast: Emery, Miss Janet D BA(Law). . . . . *Nov 1983
Osgerby, Mrs Hazel F BSocSc . . . . . *Oct 1985

CHRIS CLARK (incorporating S B Sheldon)
98 High Green Cannock Staffordshire WS11 1BE
Tel: 01543 573004 *Fax:* 01543 573006
Emergency telephone 07802 364741
E-mail: sbsheldon@gmail.com
Office: Stafford
Work: G H S1 S2 W
Emergency Action, Agency, Advocacy, Fixed Fee Interview, Legal Aid undertaken and Legal Aid Franchise
Con: Sheldon, Mr Stephen B LLB(Manc) . . . . . *Apr 1976

DUNHAM GUEST & LYONS ‡
29 Wolverhampton Road Cannock Staffordshire WS11 1AP
Tel: 01543 462121 *Fax:* 01543 466414 *Dx:* 16091 CANNOCK
E-mail: enquiries@dglyons.co.uk
List of partners: A J Binns, D A James
Work: A1 B1 C1 D1 E F1 K1 K3 L O P Q R1 S1 S2 T2 W Z(c,e,k,m,q)
Emergency Action, Agency and Advocacy undertaken
Ptr: Binns, Mr Allan J LLB. . . . . *Mar 2000
James, Mr David Anthony FILEx . . . . . *May 1989

FRISBY SOLICITORS LIMITED ‡
Suite 1 Pendragon House Cannock Staffordshire WS11 7FJ

GARDNER ILIFF & DOWDING ‡
14 Wolverhampton Road Cannock Staffordshire WS11 1AN
Tel: 01543 466941 *Fax:* 01543 462316 *Dx:* 16090 CANNOCK
E-mail: gardners@gidsolicitors.com
List of partners: N A Dowding, R K Sherriff
Work: A1 E K1 N R1 S1 S2 W Z(l)
Emergency Action, Advocacy, Fixed Fee Interview undertaken and Member of Accident Line
Ptr: Dowding, Mr Nicholas Ashley LLB(Hons) . . . . . *§Oct 1987
Sherriff, Mr R Kevin. . . . . *§Feb 1983
Asoc: Hartshorne, Ms Joanne Louise LLB(Hons). . . . . *Oct 2002

R GOVIER SOLICITORS ‡
25-27 Wolverhampton Road Cannock Staffordshire WS11 1AP
Tel: 01543 469919 *Fax:* 01543 469919 *Dx:* 16100 CANNOCK
E-mail: rgoviersolicitor@btconnect.com

IMPERIUM LAW LLP ‡
Suite 5 Bermar House Rumer Hill Business Estate Cannock Staffordshire WS11 0ET
Tel: 01543 437203 *Fax:* 01543 437204

JEWELS SOLICITORS
91 High Green Cannock Staffordshire WS11 1BH
Tel: 01543 577505 *Fax:* 01543 578083
E-mail: ccooper@jewelssolicitors.co.uk
Office: Stafford

W R JOYCE SOLICITORS LLP ‡
5 Lysander Way Cannock Staffordshire WS11 9SB
List of partners: S Daniels, R Joyce
Work: A1 A2 A3 B1 B2 B3 C1 C2 C3 D1 D2 E F1 F2 G H I J1 J2 K1 K2 K3 K4 L M1 M2 M3 M4 N O P Q R1 R2 S1 S2 T1 T2 U1 U2 V W X Z(a,b,c,d,e,f,g,h,i,j,k,l,m,n,o,p,q,r,s,t,u,w,x,y,z,za)
Ptr: Daniels, Ms Simone. . . . . Apr 1982
Joyce, Mr Ronald. . . . . Nov 1968
Ast: Skate, Mr Arthur. . . . . May 1984

CANTERBURY, Kent

BEADLE PITT & GOTTSCHALK ‡
1 St Margaret's Street Canterbury Kent CT1 2TT
Tel: 01227 464481 *Fax:* 01227 762311 *Dx:* 5305 CANTERBURY
E-mail: enquiries@bpgsolicitors.co.uk
List of partners: P N Gottschalk, R A Pitt
Languages: German
Work: C1 E J1 K1 N Q S1 W
Agency and Advocacy undertaken
Ptr: Gottschalk, Mr Peter N . . . . . *Jul 1979
Pitt, Mr Richard A LLB(Soton). . . . . *§Jun 1972

BOND JOSEPH ‡
65 Burgate Canterbury Kent CT1 2HJ
Tel: 01227 453545 *Fax:* 01227 453888 *Dx:* 5327 CANTERBURY 1
Emergency telephone 01227 450779
List of partners: I R Bond, G Joseph
Work: D1 G H K1 K2 Z(m)
Emergency Action, Agency, Advocacy, Legal Aid undertaken and Legal Aid Franchise
Ptr: Bond, Mr Ian R BA . . . . . Mar 1986
Joseph, Ms Gillian LLB . . . . . Apr 1986

BULL & BULL ‡
98 Thomas Way Lakesview International Business Park Canterbury Kent CT3 4NH
Tel: 01227 714860 *Fax:* 01227 713477
E-mail: canterbury@bull-and-bull.co.uk
List of partners: G Baldock, K J Brazier
Office: Faversham, Herne Bay
Languages: French
Work: A1 E L S1 T2 W Z(i,l)
Ptr: Brazier, Mr Kenneth J. . . . . *Jun 1985

EMPLOYMENT RELATIONS ‡
Yewgate Barn Old Road Elham Canterbury Kent CT4 6UH
Tel: 01303 840001 *Fax:* 01303 840097
E-mail: info@employment-relations.co.uk

FAIRWEATHER & CO SOLICITORS ‡
16 Station Road West Canterbury Kent CT2 8AN
Tel: 01227 784337 *Fax:* 01227 471649
Dx: 49052 CANTERBURY WEST
E-mail: info@fairweather-solicitors.co.uk
List of partners: N Fairweather, D Tamplin
Work: D1 D2 J1 K1 K2 K3 N Z(g,m,r)
Legal Aid undertaken
Ptr: Fairweather, Mr Nick . . . . . Dec 1991
Tamplin, Mr Darren . . . . . Jun 2004

FOSTERS LAW LIMITED ‡
75 St Dunstan's Street Canterbury Kent CT2 8BN

FURLEY PAGE LLP ‡
39 St Margarets Street Canterbury Kent CT1 2TX
Tel: 01227 763939 *Fax:* 01227 762829 *Dx:* 5301 CANTERBURY
E-mail: info@furleypage.co.uk
List of partners: P F Addis, U H B Alexander, H M S Barrett, A J Gough, T D O Hall, P W Hawkes, J N Jones, J P W Licence, M C J C Longmore, A S Masters, M McDonagh, B N B Mowll, J A Muir-Little, R G O'Connor, J R Pigott, N Ryan, C B Wacher, G E Wallace, S E A Wolfe, R Wright
Office: Chatham, London EC3, Whitstable
Languages: French, German
Work: A1 A3 B1 C1 C2 C3 D1 E F1 J1 K1 L M1 M2 N O P Q R1 R2 S1 S2 T1 T2 U1 U2 V W X Z(c,d,e,i,j,k,l,n,o,p,q,s,t)
Advocacy, Fixed Fee Interview undertaken and Member of Accident Line
Ptr: Alexander, Utrick H B MBE; DL. . . . . *§Jul 1939
Barrett, Mr Harvey M S BA . . . . . *§Oct 1979
Gough, Mr Andrew J LLB(Manc) . . . . . *§Jul 1980
Hall, Mr T David O BA . . . . . *§Oct 1981
Hawkes, Mr Peter W LLB . . . . . *§Jul 1981
Jones, Mr J Nigel MA(Cantab) . . . . . *§Nov 1970
Licence, Mr Jeremy Paul William . . . . . Oct 1998
Longmore, Mr Michael C J C . . . . . *§Apr 1983
Masters, Mr Andrew Steven BA(Hons) . . . . . *§Oct 1995
Mowll, Mr Benjamin Nicholas Bullen LLB . . . . . *Feb 1993
Muir-Little, Mr James A . . . . . *Oct 1993
O'Connor, Mr Rory G LLB(Bris) . . . . . Apr 1988
Pigott, Mr James R LLB. . . . . *§Oct 1988
Ryan, Mr Neille LLB. . . . . *§Nov 1990
Wacher, C B . . . . . *§Oct 1984
Wallace, Mrs Gillian E. . . . . *§Dec 1966
Wolfe, Mr Simon E A MA(Cantab). . . . . *Jun 1981
Wright, Mr Russell LLB(Hons). . . . . *§Dec 1974

GARDNER CROFT LLP ‡
2 Castle Street Canterbury Kent CT1 2QH
Tel: 01227 813400 *Fax:* 01227 451018 *Dx:* 5302 CANTERBURY
E-mail: enquiries@gardnercroft.co.uk
List of partners: H D H G Barton, D S Bennett, P C Le Fleming, E J Sutton, T L Townsend
Languages: Afrikaans, German
Work: A1 B1 C1 C2 D1 D2 E F1 J1 K1 K3 K4 L N O Q R1 S1 S2 T1 T2 V W Z(c,d,h,j,k,l,p,q,s,t)
Emergency Action, Agency, Advocacy and Fixed Fee Interview undertaken
Mem: Barton, Mr Hugo David Harvey Garbutt BSc(Hons); MA(Law); PGDipLP European Law Students Association Scholarship . . . . . *Sep 1996
Bennett, Mr Daniel Simon BA(Hons). . . . . *Oct 2002
Le Fleming, Peer C BA . . . . . *Apr 1977
Sutton, Mrs Eileen Jane LLB(Hons) . . . . . *Nov 2002
Townsend, Mr Timothy L LLB . . . . . *Oct 1984
Ast: Lockyer, Miss Hannah Julia . . . . . *Sep 2002
Pinder, Mr Ian LLB(Hons) . . . . . *Oct 2003
Riordan Nicholas, Mr David BA(Hons); PGDL . . . . . *Oct 2006
Russell, Mrs Georgette Ann PGDipLaw . . . . . *May 2009
Con: Vine, Mr Roger S BA; LLB . . . . . *Jul 1978

See p112 for the Key to Work Categories & other symbols

GIRLINGS ‡
16 Rose Lane Canterbury Kent CT1 2UR
Tel: 01227 768374 *Fax:* 01227 450498 *Dx:* 5303 CANTERBURY
E-mail: enquiries@girlings.com
List of partners: P J Boucher, R J R K Browne, J C D Burke, I N Burrow, A J Cook, S F Finnis, G R Harvey, D J Mallinson, A G McBride, C Neeve, C J Page, S E Record, L Rushton, D Sherlock, R J Staines, C L Trim, R J Turner, C Vernon, C A Vincent, A D Watson
Office: Ashford (2 offices), Herne Bay, Margate
Languages: French, German, Spanish
Work: C1 D1 D2 E G H K1 K2 K3 K4 N R2 S1 T1 T2 V W Z(l,o,q,v)
Advocacy, Legal Aid undertaken, Legal Aid Franchise and Member of Accident Line
Ptr: Finnis, Ms Sarah Frances LLB(Hons) . . . . *Sep 1998
Harvey, Mr Gareth R . . . . *§Jul 1979
Rushton, Ms Lesley. . . . . *Nov 1992
Vernon, Mr Christopher . . . . Oct 1991
Con: Elton, Mr Francis P-W. . . . . *§Nov 1970
Keel, Mr Andrew BA Herbert Ruse Prize; Clabon Prize *Oct 1982
Morgan, Mr Peter B MA(Oxon) . . . . *§May 1967

GIRLINGS PERSONAL INJURY CLAIMS LIMITED ‡
16 Rose Lane Canterbury Kent CT1 2UR
Tel: 01227 768374 *Fax:* 01227 450498
List of partners: J P A Pidduck
Work: N Z(r)
Dir: Pidduck, Mr Jonathan Peter Anthony . . . . *May 1996
Ast: Milne, Mrs Clare Rebecca. . . . . Sep 1997

ANDREW M JOHNSON ‡
Canterbury Innovation Centre University Road Canterbury Kent CT2 7FG
Tel: 01227 811713 / 811714 *Fax:* 01227 811715
E-mail: a.johnson@spanish-law.net

THE LAW PRACTICE ‡
Hunstead House Chartham Canterbury Kent CT4 7PE
Tel: 01227 733595 *Fax:* 01227 733596
E-mail: lawyers@tlpsolicitors.co.uk
Languages: Finnish
Work: C1 E F1 F2 L O Q S1 S2

LETTS & CO ‡
Bartletts Tyler Hill Road Blean Canterbury Kent CT2 9HT
Tel: 01227 471555 *Fax:* 01227 471556
E-mail: lettsco@btconnect.com
List of partners: J R Letts
SPr: Letts, Mr John R . . . . *§Jan 1975

LEXICA LAW
31 Watling Street Canterbury Kent CT1 2UD
Tel: 01227 764141 *Fax:* 01227 781614 *Dx:* 5346 CANTERBURY
E-mail: enquiries@hsalaw.co.uk
Office: London W1
Languages: French
Work: A3 C1 C2 E F1 J1 L O Q R1 S1 S2 T1 Z(h,k,q)
Emergency Action, Agency and Advocacy undertaken
Ptr: Calliste, Ms Gillian . . . . *Dec 1986
Gurr, Mr Simon . . . . *Oct 1987
Hutchings, Mr Nicholas A BA . . . . *Mar 1987
Sharratt, Mr Jonathan J BA(Law) . . . . *Mar 1985

MORRIS SOUTHERLAND ‡
South Oast The Street Canterbury Kent CT4 5BZ
Tel: 01227 830462 *Fax:* 01227 830414
E-mail: celia.morris@dial.pipex.com

WAITT & CO SOLICITORS ‡
Court Chambers 9/10 Broad Street Canterbury Kent CT1 2LW
Tel: 01227 470600 *Fax:* 01227 764393 *Dx:* 5321 CANTERBURY
E-mail: info@waittlaw.com
List of partners: K L Waitt
Office: Folkestone
Work: G H
Emergency Action, Agency, Advocacy, Legal Aid undertaken and Legal Aid Franchise
Ptr: Waitt, Ms Kerry L BSc. . . . . Nov 1983

CANVEY ISLAND, Essex

BEECROFT MAXWELL ‡
Lakeside House 9 Knightswick Road Canvey Island Essex SS8 9PA
Tel: 01268 511999 *Fax:* 01268 510827 *Dx:* 55000 CANVEY ISLAND
Emergency telephone 01702 582589
List of partners: D R Capp, J M Mason, J Penman
Work: D1 E F1 J1 K1 K3 K4 L N O Q S1 S2 W X Z(l,p)
Emergency Action, Agency, Advocacy, Fixed Fee Interview and Legal Aid undertaken
Ptr: Capp, Mr David Ronald . . . . *May 1985
Mason, Mrs Judith M LLB(Hons) . . . . *Dec 1976
Penman, Ms Janis LLB . . . . *Jun 2002

HOOK & PARTNERS ‡
92-98 High Street Canvey Island Essex SS8 7SU
Tel: 01268 692255 *Fax:* 01268 510075 *Dx:* 55002 CANVEY ISLAND
E-mail: info@hookandpartners.com
List of partners: D J Hook, D R Hook
Languages: French, German
Work: C1 C2 D1 E I J1 K1 K3 L N O Q S1 S2 T1 T2 W Z(l,q)
Emergency Action, Agency, Advocacy and Fixed Fee Interview undertaken
Ptr: Hook, Mr David J . . . . *§Dec 1973
Hook, Mr David Russel LLB(Hons) . . . . *Nov 2009
Ast: Brazier, Miss Lorna LLB(Hons) . . . . *Sep 2009

TYLER LAW ‡
91 Furtherwick Road Canvey Island Essex SS8 7AY
Tel: 01268 630850 *Fax:* 01268 699543 *Dx:* 55003 CANVEY ISLAND
E-mail: info@tyler-law.co.uk

CARDIFF

AMA LAW ‡
Argyle Chambers 2 St Martins Row Albany Road Cardiff CF24 3RP
Tel: 029 2048 1313 *Fax:* 029 2048 1366

GLEN ABRAHAM & CO ‡
76 Crwys Road Cathays Cardiff CF24 4NT
Tel: 029 2037 7226 *Fax:* 029 2037 7095
E-mail: post@glen-abraham.co.uk

ACKLAND & CO ‡
68 Llandaff Road Canton Cardiff CF11 9NL
Tel: 029 2064 1461 *Fax:* 029 2022 6667 *Dx:* 95410 CANTON
E-mail: info@acklandslegal.co.uk
List of partners: S R Ackland
SPr: Ackland, Mr Simon Robert . . . . May 1992

ALBANY SOLICITORS ‡
168 Richmond Road Cardiff CF24 3BX
Tel: 029 2047 2728 *Fax:* 029 2049 5096
E-mail: info@albanysolicitors.co.uk

ANTHONY JEREMY & MAY ‡
Hill Court Cefn Coed Road Cardiff CF23 6AQ
Tel: 029 2034 0313 *Fax:* 029 2076 4716
Ast: Jeremy, Mr Anthony W . . . . Oct 1963

BJ LAW SOLICITORS LIMITED ‡
1 Neptune Court Vanguard Way Ocean Park Cardiff CF24 5PJ
Tel: 029 2046 1006 *Fax:* 029 2047 1180
E-mail: solutions@bjlsolicitors.com

BECKERLEY HALL SOLICITORS ‡
38 Heol St Denys Lisvane Cardiff CF14 0RU
Tel: 029 2075 5777 *Fax:* 029 2068 9516

BEECH JONES DE LLOYD ‡
72 Merthyr Road Whitchurch Cardiff CF14 1DJ
Tel: 029 2062 3247 *Fax:* 029 2061 6054
E-mail: solutions@beechjones.com
Office: Liverpool

BENSON WATKINS & CO LIMITED ‡
18 Churchill Way Cardiff CF10 2DY
Tel: 029 2038 2486 *Fax:* 029 2038 3856 *Dx:* 50761 CARDIFF 2
Work: C1 E S1 S2 W
Con: John, Mr Nicholas H H . . . . *Apr 1970

BERRY SMITH LLP ‡
Haywood House Dumfries Place Cardiff CF10 3GA
Tel: 029 2034 5511 *Fax:* 029 2034 5945 *Dx:* 33097 CARDIFF 1
E-mail: cardiff@berrysmith.com
List of partners: C M Beames, R J Berry, R A Bound, I Doull, N Greenaway, D C Jones, C E McColgan, N Parker, M L Pursall
Office: Bridgend, Bristol, London WC2
Languages: Arabic, French, German, Hindi, Punjabi, Urdu, Welsh
Work: C1 C2 E J1 O S1 W
Ptr: Beames, Mr Christopher M LLB. . . . . Oct 1985
Berry, Mr Roger J MA(Cantab) . . . . *Dec 1978
Bound, Mr R Andrew LLB . . . . Nov 1989
Doull, Mr Iwan BSc(Hons); CPE; LPC. . . . . *Oct 1997
Greenaway, Mr Nigel LLB . . . . Sep 1999
Jones, Mr David C LLB . . . . *Apr 1992
Parker, Mr Nicholas LLB . . . . *Mar 1992
Pursall, Mr Martin L LLB(Hons) . . . . *Oct 1987
Ast: Akram, Mr Sheraz LLB . . . . *Sep 2006
Askins, Mrs Karen. . . . . *Sep 2005
Atkins, Miss Talia . . . . Jan 2003
Attwood, Miss Beth LLB. . . . . Oct 2008
Bartlett, Mrs Katrina. . . . . Sep 1999
Bashir, Miss Sally LLB . . . . *Sep 2006
Benjamin, Mr Deian LLB(Hons) . . . . *Jul 2008
Borrington, Miss Emma Louise LLB . . . . *Sep 2004
Care, Mr Simon. . . . . Jan 2007
Clewett, Miss Sarah. . . . . Jan 2004
Coughlan, Mr Christopher LLB(Hons); LLM . . . . . . Sep 2010
Emery, Miss Jane LLB . . . . Nov 2007
Evans, Miss Selena LLB(Hons) . . . . Sep 2010
Grech, Mr Fabio LLB . . . . Sep 2003
Lewis, Mrs Elizabeth Claire LLB. . . . . Aug 2009
Norton, Miss Jean LLB . . . . Sep 2010
Pinder, Mrs Jennifer LLB . . . . Mar 2010
Prendergast, Ms Alice E LLB . . . . *Oct 1992
Rickaby, Miss Alexandra LLB . . . . Jan 2011
Senior, Mr Robert LLB . . . . *Sep 1999
Shamo, Miss Helen Rhiannon LLB . . . . Jul 2005
Sutton, Mr Matthew LLB. . . . . Sep 2008
Westerman, Miss Erica . . . . *Jan 2005

BERRYMANS LACE MAWER
23 Neptune Court Vanguard Way Cardiff CF24 5PJ
Tel: 029 2044 7667 *Fax:* 029 2048 9041 *Dx:* 33066 CARDIFF
E-mail: info@blm-law.com
Office: Birmingham, Bristol, Leeds, Liverpool, London EC2, Manchester, Southampton, Stockton-on-Tees

BEVERLEY DAVIES GUTHRIE ‡
Brunswick House 43 Brunswick Street Canton Cardiff CF5 1LJ
Tel: 029 2037 3582 *Fax:* 029 2064 1460

BISHOP MCBRIDE OLDEN ‡
60-62 James Street Cardiff Bay Cardiff CF10 5EZ
Tel: 029 2049 0111 *Fax:* 029 2049 4904 *Dx:* 200756 CARDIFF BAY
E-mail: bishop_co@freenet.co.uk
List of partners: M Bishop, T McBride, M Olden
Work: G H
Legal Aid Franchise
Ptr: Bishop, Ms Marilyn ★. . . . . Jan 1990
McBride, Ms Trudy LLB ★. . . . . *Jul 1979
Olden, Mr Martin . . . . Jul 1979

BLACKFORDS LLP
One Caspian Point Cardiff Bay Cardiff CF10 4DQ
Tel: 029 2044 4070 *Fax:* 029 2044 4071
Dx: 744691 CARDIFF BAY 3
Emergency telephone 07876 081080
E-mail: cardiff@blackfords.com
Office: Croydon, London EC4, Woking

BOWDEN JONES SOLICITORS ‡
19 Newport Road Cardiff CF24 0AA
Tel: 029 2048 4550 *Fax:* 029 2048 4101 *Dx:* 33074 CARDIFF
E-mail: enquiries@bowdenjones.co.uk

R M BRETT & CO ‡
First Floor 39 Charles Street Cardiff CF10 2GB
Tel: 029 2023 0440 *Fax:* 029 2023 0442
E-mail: rmbrettco@btconnect.com
List of partners: R M Brett
Work: A1 C1 E L S1 T1 T2 W
Fixed Fee Interview undertaken
Ptr: Brett, Mr Roy Maitland LLB . . . . *Jul 1974
Ast: Brett, Mrs Claudine Ann LLB . . . . *Dec 1973

2

DAVID BRINNING ‡
Temple Chambers 32 Park Place Cardiff CF10 3BA
Tel: 029 2039 7364 *Fax:* 029 2023 8423 *Dx:* 50769 CARDIFF 2
E-mail: dbrinning@temple-chambers.co.uk
Work: B2 D1 G H K1 K3 N Q Z(i)
Legal Aid undertaken

BRODIE SMITH & MAHONEY ‡
78 Whitchurch Road Cardiff CF14 3LX
Tel: 029 2022 1848 / 2022 7680 *Fax:* 029 2022 0518
Dx: 50757 CARDIFF 2
E-mail: mahoney@clara.net
List of partners: A C Mahoney, P D Mahoney
Languages: Italian
Work: A1 B1 C1 E S1 W
Ptr: Mahoney, Ms Anna C . . . . *Jan 1971
Mahoney, Mr Paul D . . . . *Jun 1969

CAPITAL LAW LLP ‡
Capital Building Tyndall Street Cardiff CF10 4AZ
Tel: 0333 240 0489 *Fax:* 0333 240 0487 *Dx:* 33013 CARDIFF
E-mail: info@capitallaw.co.uk
Office: London EC1

CHETNA & CO SOLICITORS ‡
150a City Road Cardiff CF24 3DR
Tel: 029 2049 4322 *Fax:* 029 2045 2552
E-mail: enquiries@chetnasolicitors.co.uk

CHURCHGATE LEGAL LLP ‡
9 Kings Road Cardiff CF11 9BZ
Tel: 0800 533 5795 *Fax:* 029 2066 0158 *Dx:* 141860 CARDIFF 28
E-mail: enquiries@churchgatelegal.co.uk

CITY LAW SOLICITORS ‡
12a Albany Road Cardiff CF24 3RP
Tel: 029 2045 5797 *Fax:* 029 2045 5898
E-mail: info@citylawsolicitors.uk.com

CLARKE & HARTLAND SOLICITORS ‡
48 The Parade Roath Cardiff CF24 3AB
Tel: 029 2048 3181 *Fax:* 029 2049 8377
Emergency telephone 07971 016070
E-mail: enq@clarkeandhartland.co.uk
List of partners: S Clarke, S A Enever, T J Hartland, D W Pinnell
Office: Penarth
Work: C1 C3 D1 E G H K1 L P S1 V W Z(l)
Emergency Action, Agency, Advocacy, Fixed Fee Interview, Legal Aid undertaken and Legal Aid Franchise
Ptr: Clarke, Mr Stephen BA(Law) ★ . . . . *Dec 1980
Enever, Mrs Sally A. . . . . *Feb 1981
Hartland, Mr Timothy J LLB ★. . . . . *Oct 1986
Pinnell, Mr David William LLB(Hons) ★ . . . . *Oct 1995
Ast: Masterman, Mrs Lisa LLB(Nott'm). . . . . *§Mar 1981

CLARKSLEGAL LLP
2 Caspian Point Caspian Way Cardiff Bay Cardiff CF10 4DQ
Tel: 029 2055 7500 *Fax:* 029 2055 7501
Office: London WC2, Reading, Swansea
Work: C1 E J1 P Z(c,d,p,u)
Ptr: Downes, Mr Dafydd Gwn LLB(Hons); PGDipLP . . . . *Sep 1999
Asoc: Huffer, Mr Nicholas D BA(Hons). . . . . *Nov 1995
Ast: Flett, Ms Alison . . . . *Oct 2007
Hall, Ms Victoria. . . . . *Jun 2006
Holtham, Miss Rhiannon Victoria LLB . . . . *Jun 2004
Lendrum, Mrs Caroline Lucy BA(Law). . . . . Sep 2003

CLEMENTS AND CO ‡
75 Caeglas Road Rumney Cardiff CF3 3JX
Tel: 029 2036 1771 *Fax:* 07092 844045
E-mail: mail@clementsandco.org.uk
List of partners: M Clements
Work: B1 C1 E F1 F2 J1 K1 K3 L N O Q S1 S2 W Z(l,q,t)
Agency undertaken
SPr: Clements, Mr Michael LLB(Hons) . . . . Oct 2000

CLODES SOLICITORS
15a Station Road Llanishen Cardiff CF14 5LS
Tel: 029 2076 5050 / 01446 720777 *Fax:* 029 2074 7193
Emergency telephone 07850 511793 (24HR)
E-mail: clodev@clodes-solicitors.com
Office: Barry
Work: D1 D2 G H J1 K1 K3 K4 N Q S1 W Z(l,m)
Emergency Action, Agency, Advocacy, Fixed Fee Interview and Legal Aid undertaken
Ptr: Clode, Mr Michael Charles John BA. . . . . *Nov 1987
Ast: Clode, Mr Damian LLB . . . . Apr 2008
Clode, Miss Victoria Emma LLB. . . . . Feb 2008

COMMERCIAL LEGAL SOLUTIONS ‡
Llwyn y Brain Mawr Creigiau Cardiff CF15 9SG
Tel: 029 2089 2211 *Fax:* 029 2092 0335

CONFREYS ‡
56 Mackintosh Place Roath Cardiff CF24 4RQ
Tel: 029 2045 8080 *Fax:* 029 2045 2199
Emergency telephone 029 2045 8080
List of partners: D E Blackhurst, N P Confrey
Work: Z(m)
Emergency Action and Legal Aid undertaken
Ptr: Blackhurst, Ms Debra E. . . . . Aug 1998
Confrey, Mr Neil Patrick LLB Part time Chairman of Special Education Needs Tribunal. . . . . *Nov 1985

CORDNER LEWIS ‡
25/26 Neptune Court Vanguard Way Cardiff CF24 5PJ
Tel: 029 2047 5640 *Fax:* 029 2047 5641 *Dx:* 33076 CARDIFF 1
E-mail: info@cordnerlewis.co.uk
Work: N

COUNTRYWIDE PROPERTY LAWYERS
8th Floor Brunel House Fitzalan Road Cardiff CF24 0ZZ
Tel: 029 2044 2100
Office: Manchester

CHARLES CROOKES LIMITED ‡
51 The Parade Cardiff CF24 3AB
Tel: 029 2049 1271 *Fax:* 029 2047 1211 *Dx:* 33025 CARDIFF
E-mail: postmaster@ccj-law.co.uk
List of partners: J J M Arter, R F Crookes, T J P Davenport, T R Howorth
Office: Brecon
Languages: Cantonese, French, Hakka, Mandarin, Spanish, Welsh
Work: A1 B1 B2 B3 C1 C2 C3 E F1 I J1 L M1 M2 N O P Q R1 R2 S1 T1 T2 W Z(c,e,f,j,k,l,q,w,y)
Emergency Action, Agency, Advocacy, Fixed Fee Interview and Legal Aid undertaken
Ptr: Arter, Mr Jonathan J M LLB . . . . *§Dec 1975
Crookes, Mr Robert Frank BSc(Econ) Notary Public . *§Jul 1969
Howorth, Mr Tim Robert LLB . . . . *Nov 1993
Ast: Lado, Mr Ricky BA(Hons); PGDipLaw; LPC Notary Public . . . . *Oct 2003
Con: Fisher, Mr Richard John Hindle MA(Oxon) . . . . Apr 1997

CROWLEY & CO ‡
Oxford House 10-16 Vere Street Roath Cardiff CF24 3DS
Tel: 029 2045 8895 *Fax:* 029 2045 8894
Emergency telephone 07974 919292
E-mail: admin@crowleysolicitors.co.uk
List of partners: J M Crowley
Languages: Afrikaans, Gujarati, Hindi, Urdu, Zulu
Work: B2 E G H J1 K1 S1 S2 V W Z(d,i,l)
Emergency Action, Agency, Advocacy, Fixed Fee Interview and Legal Aid undertaken
Ptr: Crowley, Mr Jonathan M BSc(Econ) . . . . *Dec 1985
Asoc: Aslam, Miss Fazila LLB . . . . Sep 2005
Bhamjee, Mr Mohamed Hanef OBE BSc . . . . *Jun 1996
Pearce, Miss Joanne BA(Hons) . . . . Jan 2004
Stuart, Mrs Anna Maria LLB(Hons) . . . . Sep 2002

DARWIN GRAY ‡
Helmont House Churchill Way Cardiff CF10 2HE
Tel: 029 2082 9100 *Fax:* 029 2082 9101 *Dx:* 33053 CARDIFF 1
E-mail: bdarwin@darwingray.com
List of partners: B S Darwin, D Gray, R Lewis, J R Smith
Office: Newport
Work: B1 C1 E F1 F2 J1 O Q R2 S2 U2 Z(b,c,e,f,j,l,p,q,w)
Ptr: Darwin, Miss Bethan S LLB(Lond) . . . . *Sep 1990
Gray, Mr Donald . . . . Oct 1985
Lewis, Mr Rhodri . . . . Jul 1997
Smith, Mr Jason Robert LLB(Hons) . . . . *Oct 1995

DAVIES & JONES SOLICITORS ‡
32 The Parade Roath Cardiff CF24 3AD
Tel: 029 2046 5296 *Fax:* 029 2048 2377
Emergency telephone 07970 969 357
List of partners: D C H Rees
Work: G H
Emergency Action, Agency, Advocacy, Legal Aid undertaken and Legal Aid Franchise
Ptr: Rees, Mr David C H LLB(Hons) . . . . *Apr 1994
Ast: Mitchard, Mr Edward BSc(Hons) . . . . *Sep 1999
Sharp, Mr Adam . . . . *Jul 2002

DAVIES PRICHARD & WEATHERILL ‡
6 St Andrews Crescent Cardiff CF10 3DD
Tel: 029 2037 7471 *Fax:* 029 2037 2066 *Dx:* 50770 CARDIFF 2
List of partners: G W Eveleigh, P J E Needham
Work: K1 N O Q R2 S1 S2 W
Agency, Advocacy and Fixed Fee Interview undertaken
Ptr: Eveleigh, Mr Graham William LLB(Wales) . . . . *Apr 1982
Needham, Mr Patrick John Easthope . . . . *Jan 1981

RHIDIAN DAVIES & CO SOLICITORS ‡
15 Waungron Road Cardiff CF5 2JJ
Tel: 029 2056 2913
E-mail: rhidiandavies@sky.com

DE MAID SOLICITORS & ADVOCATES ‡
2 Park Court Mews Park Place Cardiff CF10 3DQ
Tel: 029 2023 5575 *Fax:* 029 2022 2191
Emergency telephone 07785 795023
E-mail: info@demaidsolicitors.co.uk
List of partners: B K de Maid, M W de Maid
Work: B2 G H Z(g)
Emergency Action, Agency, Advocacy, Legal Aid undertaken and Legal Aid Franchise
Ptr: de Maid, Mr Bernard K ★ . . . . *Dec 1968
de Maid, Mr Mathew William LLB; BA(Hons)(Cantab) ★ . . . . *Mar 1997
Ast: Britton, Mr Vaughan . . . . Dec 1998

DEVONALDS
The Old Library East Road Tylorstown Cardiff CF43 3DA
Tel: 01443 755189 *Fax:* 01443 757738
E-mail: tylorstown@devonalds.co.uk
Office: Pontypridd (2 offices), Talbot Green, Tonypandy

DOLMANS ‡
One Kingsway Cardiff CF10 3DS
Tel: 029 2034 5531 *Fax:* 029 2039 8206 *Dx:* 122723 CARDIFF 12
E-mail: info@dolmans.co.uk
List of partners: P H E Bennett, P D Boobier, P P S Bradley, S M Evans, N L Gower, J Harris, A Henders-Green, C Hoskins, A P Oliver, M Standley, P E Veysey
Languages: Welsh
Work: C1 C2 E F1 F2 J1 J2 L M1 N O P Q R1 R2 S1 S2 T1 T2 V W X Z(b,c,d,e,f,h,j,k,o,p,q,u,w,x,za)
Emergency Action, Agency and Advocacy undertaken
Ptr: Bennett, Mr Peter H E LLB . . . . *§Mar 1995
Boobier, Mr Philip D LLB . . . . *§Oct 1984
Bradley, Mr Philip P S LLB . . . . *§Apr 1992
Evans, Mr Simon M BA . . . . *§Sep 1994
Gower, Mr Nicholas L BSc(Econ) . . . . *§Jul 1980
Harris, Mr Justin LLB . . . . *§Feb 1993
Henders-Green, Mrs Alison BA(History) . . . . *§Oct 1993
Hoskins, Mrs Clare BA . . . . *§Nov 1994
Oliver, Mr Adrian P LLB . . . . *Mar 1984
Standley, Mrs Melanie LLB . . . . *§Sep 1999
Veysey, Mr Paul Edward LLB Law Society Award for Outstanding Achievement on the LPC 2002 . . . . *Jul 2004
Asoc: Alexander, Miss Nicola E L BSc; CPE; LSF Grant Thornton - Top Commercial Law Student . . . . *Oct 1998
Blades, Mrs Judith LLB . . . . *Sep 2003
Cottle, Mrs Jennifer LLB; DipLaw Cardiff & District Law Society - Junior Lawyer of the Year 2011 . . . . *Oct 2007
Danter, Mr Thomas A BA; LLM . . . . *Dec 1993
David, Mr Ryan Ralph BSc . . . . *Nov 2004
Edwards, Mrs Nicola M LLB . . . . *Oct 1995
Evans, Mrs Amanda J LLB; LLM . . . . *Nov 1995
Mitchell, Mr Jamie LLB . . . . *Sep 2002
Thomas, Mrs Claire E LLB . . . . *Nov 1996
Ast: Davies, Miss Teleri Mair LLB . . . . *Sep 2005
Hind, Mrs Anna Michelle BA; PGDipLaw; LPC . . . . *Oct 2007
Parry, Mrs Anna E LLB . . . . *Oct 2003
Rees, Miss Rhian Clair LLB . . . . *Feb 2007
Tucker, Mr Paul J BA . . . . *Jul 1999
Watermeyer, Mrs Vikki LLB . . . . *Sep 2005

ELLISON & CO ‡
13 Kings Road Canton Cardiff CF11 9BZ
Tel: 029 2038 2508 *Fax:* 029 2066 6582
List of partners: A G Hughes
Work: E S1 W
Ptr: Hughes, Mr Adrian G . . . . *Jan 1982

ELY LAW PRACTICE ‡
Suite 20 65 Penarth Road Cardiff CF10 5DL
Tel: 029 2038 7738
E-mail: jones38@yahoo.co.uk

EMERITUS LEGAL ‡
St Michael's Room The Old Probate Registry 49 Cardiff Road Cardiff CF5 2DQ
Tel: 029 2056 7836 *Fax:* 029 2056 7836
E-mail: rhys@emerituslegal.co.uk

ERGO LAW LIMITED ‡
Falcon Drive Cardiff Bay Cardiff CF10 4RU
Tel: 0845 300 6441 *Fax:* 0845 300 6442
E-mail: enquiries@ergo-law.com

EVANS & CO ‡
29-31 City Road Cardiff CF24 3BJ
Tel: 029 2048 0054 *Fax:* 029 2046 2504
E-mail: evansandco@pintel.co.uk

EVANS AND JONES SOLICITORS LLP ‡
8b Station Road Radyr Cardiff CF15 8AA
Tel: 029 2002 0909 *Fax:* 029 2084 4543
E-mail: dalia.evans@evansandjones.co.uk

EVERSHEDS LLP
1 Callaghan Square Cardiff CF10 5BT
Tel: 0845 497 9797 *Fax:* 0845 498 7333
Office: Birmingham, Cambridge, Ipswich, Leeds, London EC2, Manchester, Newcastle upon Tyne, Nottingham

FIRST BEACON LEGAL SERVICES
6 Park Place Cardiff CF10 3RS
Tel: 029 2023 7777 *Fax:* 029 2038 1828
E-mail: law@robsols.co.uk
Office: Barry, Cardiff

FRANCIS & BUCK ‡
(in association with Cranes Solicitors)
Celtic House 20 Cathedral Road Cardiff CF11 9FB
Tel: 029 2034 4995 *Fax:* 029 2039 9646 *Dx:* 141870 CARDIFF 28
E-mail: enquiries@francisandbuck.co.uk
List of partners: K J Crane, N J Crane, T J Crane, C M Jenkins
Languages: Welsh
Work: L R1 S1 W Z(h)
Agency undertaken
Ptr: Crane, Mr Nicholas J BA(Law) . . . . *Jul 1983
Crane, Mr Timothy J LLB . . . . *Oct 1980
Jenkins, Miss Catrin Mary LLB . . . . *Dec 1983
Ast: Bowen, Mr Steven LLB(Hons) . . . . *Apr 1997

FREED & CO ‡
19 St Andrews Crescent Cardiff CF10 3DB
Tel: 029 2022 2685 *Fax:* 029 2039 6605 *Dx:* 50765 CARDIFF 2
E-mail: questions@freedandco.com

GELDARDS LLP ‡
Dumfries House Dumfries Place Cardiff CF10 3ZF
Tel: 029 2023 8239 *Fax:* 029 2023 7268 *Dx:* 33001 CARDIFF
E-mail: info@geldards.co.uk
List of partners: G C Banks, K Baranski, A T Borkowski, R L Brace, S E Bradley, E Burns, J Butler, M G Butler, G R Davies, S Davies, C E Dean, C L Delemore, P J Dickens, A Evans, E A Ganderton, E Gardner-Browne, K L Gates, W A Gill, J M Gordon, J C Griffiths, H M Hacking, C P Hackney, P M Hopkins, K Howell, R James, M Jeffs, S M Jenkins, D Jenkins Jones, B T Johnson, M W Jones, G R Latham, M Lindsey, D A Makin, D Martin, E P Meggitt, R Moore, A W Morris, E G Morris, P G Murphy, A J Norris, I Owen, A J K Pearson, T G Shock, N J Simone, A Slater, H Strickland, R Surma, D W Tilly, F Tschentscher, D A Watson, D H Williams, H R C Williams, I G Williams, S L Williams
Office: Derby, Nottingham
Languages: French, German, Welsh
Work: A1 A3 B1 C1 C2 C3 E F1 F2 I J1 L M1 M2 N O P Q R1 R2 S1 T1 T2 U1 W Z(b,c,d,e,h,k,r,u,y)
Emergency Action, Agency, Advocacy, Fixed Fee Interview, Legal Aid undertaken, Legal Aid Franchise and Member of Accident Line
Ptr: Baranski, Mr Karl LLB(Wales) . . . . *Dec 1982
Brace, Ms Rhian L LLB . . . . *§Nov 1992
Bradley, Ms Suzanne E LLB(B'ham) . . . . Apr 1988
Burns, Ms Emma . . . . Oct 1999
Davies, Mr Glynne Roland . . . . Jun 1978
Davies, Ms Sandra . . . . *Oct 1991
Delemore, Miss Ceri Lynn BA(Kent); Diplome en Droit Francais . . . . Oct 1986
Evans, Mr Andrew . . . . Sep 1993
Ganderton, Mrs Elizabeth A LLB Notary Public . . . . *Oct 1989
Gates, Miss Kathryn Louise BA(Hons)(Law) . . . . *Mar 1987
Gill, Mr William Anthony LLB(Wales) . . . . *§Jun 1976
Griffiths, Mr Jonathan C . . . . Nov 1991
Hopkins, Mr Paul Marcus BA(Oxon) . . . . Oct 1987
Howell, Ms Kim . . . . Nov 1993
James, Mr Rob . . . . Apr 1978
Jeffs, Mr Michael LLB . . . . *Mar 1983
Jenkins, Mr Stephen Martin . . . . Oct 1989
Jones, Mr Michael Wilson BA . . . . *Jun 1976
Latham, Mrs Gillian Ruth LLB(Bris) . . . . *Dec 1983
Lindsey, Mr Michael . . . . May 1987
Makin, Mrs Donna A LLB Manchester University Year Prize . . . . *Nov 1992
Meggitt, Mr Edward P . . . . Nov 1993
Moore, Mr Richard . . . . Dec 1998
Morris, Mr Andrew William LLB(Wales) . . . . Oct 1989
Morris, Ms Elin Gwenllian BA(Oxon)(Law) . . . . Oct 1990
Murphy, Mrs Penelope Gay LLB(Lond) . . . . *§Feb 1976
Norris, Mr Anthony J LLB . . . . *§Nov 1991
Owen, Mr Ioan . . . . Oct 1997
Pearson, Mr Allan Jeffery Keith LLB . . . . Oct 1987
Williams, Mr Huw Rhys Charles MA(Oxon) . . . . *Jun 1978
Williams, Ms Sian L LLB(Wales) . . . . *§Dec 1978

GLAMORGANLAW ‡
24 Park Place Cardiff CF10 3BA
Tel: 029 2022 5472 *Fax:* 029 2022 8462 *Dx:* 33019 CARDIFF
E-mail: info@glamlaw.co.uk
Office: Cowbridge, Pontypridd

GRAHAM CLAYTON SOLICITORS
122 Bute Street Cardiff CF10 5AE
Tel: 029 2049 1818 *Fax:* 029 2049 2491
E-mail: s.morgan@nut.org.uk
Office: Bolton

WILLIAM GRAHAM LAW LIMITED ‡
24 Neptune Court Ocean Way Cardiff CF24 5PJ
Tel: 029 2089 5100 *Fax:* 029 2048 9864 *Dx:* 200765 CARDIFF BAY

THE GRECH GOODEN PARTNERSHIP LLP ‡
Clifton House 8 Four Elms Road Roath Cardiff CF24 1LE
Tel: 029 2022 2255 *Fax:* 029 2045 0162
Dx: 122152 ROATH (CARDIFF)
Emergency telephone 07860 483378
List of partners: C Cormack, S Grech, D McSorley, J J D Wilkins
Office: Cardiff
Languages: Greek, Welsh
Work: G H
Emergency Action, Agency, Advocacy, Legal Aid undertaken and Legal Aid Franchise
Ptr: Cormack, Mr Christian LLB(Hons) . . . . Aug 1999
Grech, Spiro LLB ★ . . . . *Jul 1979
McSorley, Mr Declan LLB . . . . *Oct 1993
Wilkins, Mr Johnathan James Douglas BSc(Hons) . . *Aug 1999
Ast: Slough, Mr Philip Justin LLB(Hons); LLM . . . . Apr 2003

THE GRECH GOODEN PARTNERSHIP LLP
4 Ocean House Harrowby Street Cardiff Bay Cardiff CF10 5GA
Tel: 029 2045 0600 *Fax:* 029 2049 2593
Office: Cardiff

GRIFFITHS INGS LTD
9 Kings Road Canton Cardiff CF11 9BZ
Tel: 029 2034 0178 *Fax:* 01446 725181
E-mail: info@griffithsings.com
Office: Barry

SUSANNE M E HAMILTON & CO ‡
3 Willowford Cottages Gwaelod-y-Garth Cardiff CF4 8JI
Tel: 01443 842347

A G HEALE LTD ‡
51 Cardiff Road Llandaff Cardiff CF5 2DQ
Tel: 029 2056 2566 *Fax:* 029 2056 2393
E-mail: a@agheale.com
List of partners: A G Heale
Work: A3 C1 O
SPr: Heale, Mr Adrian G LLB; FCIArb . . . . *§Mar 1970

A G HEALE LTD ‡
7 Heol y Deri Rhiwbina Cardiff CF14 6HA
Tel: 029 2062 3121 / 07802 442624 *Fax:* 029 2062 3132
E-mail: a@agheale.com

HERMER & EVANS ‡
10 St Andrews Crescent Cardiff CF10 3DD
Tel: 029 2038 7766 / 2022 4009 *Fax:* 029 2038 7500
Dx: 50785 CARDIFF 2
Emergency telephone 029 2048 2054
List of partners: G W W Evans, S H Hermer
Languages: Welsh
Work: C1 E F1 G H J1 K1 L N Q S1 S2 V W Z(h,i)
Emergency Action, Agency, Advocacy, Fixed Fee Interview undertaken and Member of Accident Line
Ptr: Evans, Mr Gareth W W LLB(Wales) . . . . *Dec 1973
Hermer, Mr Stuart H BSc(Econ) . . . . *Jun 1971

HOPKINS LAW LLP ‡
26 Windsor Place Cardiff CF10 3BZ
Tel: 029 2039 5888 *Fax:* 029 2039 6888 *Dx:* 50753 CARDIFF 2
E-mail: enquiries@hopkinslawltd.com
List of partners: K A Mordey
Office: Cardiff, Cowbridge

HOPKINS LAW LLP
3 Ashtree Court Cardiff Gate Business Park Cardiff CF23 8RW
Tel: 029 2073 3000 *Fax:* 029 2073 3010 *Dx:* 11847 RUMNEY
E-mail: enquiries2@hopkinslawltd.com
Office: Cardiff, Cowbridge
Dir: Mordey, Mrs Kerry Anne LLB . . . . *Jun 1991

WENDY HOPKINS FAMILY LAW PRACTICE LLP ‡
13 Windsor Place Cardiff CF10 3BY
Tel: 029 2034 2233 *Fax:* 029 2034 3828 *Dx:* 33030 CARDIFF 1
E-mail: enquiries@wendyhopkins.co.uk
List of partners: M A Hamer, R Howells, T L Hughes, D James, S E Wyburn
Languages: Welsh
Work: D1 D2 K1 K2 K3 K4 W
Emergency Action, Agency, Advocacy, Legal Aid undertaken and Legal Aid Franchise
Ptr: Hamer, Miss Melanie A LLB . . . . *Nov 1989
Howells, Mrs Rhian LLB . . . . *Mar 1988
Hughes, Ms Thea Louise LLB . . . . *Sep 1992
James, Mr David LLB(Hons) . . . . *Nov 1991
Wyburn, Miss Sarah Elizabeth LLB . . . . Jul 2002
Ast: Baker, Miss Jane LLB . . . . *Oct 2007
Cooper, Miss Claire LLB . . . . *Sep 2008
Edwards, Miss Kate LLB . . . . *Apr 2006
Watts, Miss Lorraine LLB . . . . *Oct 2007
Williams, Miss Elizabeth Anne LLB . . . . *Oct 2007

HOWELLS ‡
Hallinans House 22 Newport Road Cardiff CF24 0TD
Tel: 029 2040 4020 *Fax:* 029 2047 0275 *Dx:* 33009 CARDIFF
E-mail: info@howellslegal.com

See p112 for the Key to Work Categories & other symbols

List of partners: T M Hobbs, P J Howell, A J Hunt, J V O'Connell, M G Phillips
Office: Caerphilly, Newport, Swansea, Talbot Green
Languages: French, Spanish
Work: C2 D1 E J1 K1 K3 L N Q S1 S2 W
Agency, Fixed Fee Interview, Legal Aid undertaken and Legal Aid Franchise
Ptr: Hobbs, Mr T Mark LLB . . . . . *Jun 1980
Howell, Mr Philip J . . . . . Dec 1979
O'Connell, Mr John V TEP. . . . . *§Jul 1977
Phillips, Mrs Margaret G LLB . . . . . *Mar 1981
Asoc: Davies, Mrs Rosalind Mary LLB(Hons) . . . . . Sep 2001

HUGH JAMES ‡
Hodge House 114-116 St Marys Street Cardiff CF10 1DY
Tel: 029 2022 4871 *Fax:* 029 2038 8222 *Dx:* 33000 CARDIFF 1
E-mail: cardiff@hughjames.com
List of partners: G W Adams, C D Asbrey, C T Breeze, J C Clement-Evans, A K Davies, P Dicken, M Evans, P Evans, A J Harding, M A Harvey, I Herbert, A Ivin, M G Jefferies, R J A Jenkins, A Jones, L Jones, M L N Jones, C E King, P Lewis, A J Love, W J C Lysaght, A J Manners, C Milford, G M Morgan, N C Morgan, H Noakes, D C W Preece, H M Price, D L Roberts, M Rosser, W P Salen, I A Scott, W D Snowdon, M Stephens, M Tossell, S C L Warren, S J Webber, L Wheeldon, M S Whittaker, G J Williams, N D Wilson, C E Wright
Office: London E14
Work: A1 A3 B1 B2 C1 C2 C3 D1 E F1 G H I J1 J2 K3 L M1 M2 N O P Q R1 R2 S1 S2 T1 T2 U1 V W X Z(b,c,d,e,f,h,i,j,k,l,m,n,o,p,q,r,u,x)
Emergency Action, Agency, Advocacy, Fixed Fee Interview, Legal Aid undertaken, Legal Aid Franchise and Member of Accident Line
Ptr: Adams, Mr Geoffrey W LLB . . . . . *§Jun 1975
Asbrey, Mr Colin D BSc(Econ) Deputy District Judge . *Jun 1977
Breeze, Ms Ceri T LLB . . . . . *Oct 1986
Clement-Evans, Mr J Cenric LLB(Wales) . . . . . *Dec 1986
Davies, Mr Andrew K LLB. . . . . *Oct 1988
Dicken, Mr Phillip . . . . . *Nov 1992
Evans, Mr Malcolm . . . . . *Jan 1992
Evans, Mr Peter BA. . . . . *Jan 1981
Harding, Mr Andrew J LLB Chairman of Headway Cardiff . . . . . *Oct 1984
Harvey, Mr Mark A LLB . . . . . *Dec 1990
Herbert, Mr Ian LLB. . . . . *Dec 1990
Ivin, Mrs Alison . . . . . Sep 1995
Jefferies, Mr Michael G LLB(Lond); ACIArb . . . . . *Apr 1972
Jenkins, Mr Russel J A LLB. . . . . *Jun 1969
Jones, Mr Alun LLB(Hons) . . . . . *Sep 1994
Jones, Leighton LLB . . . . . *Oct 1976
Jones, Mr Michael L N MA(Oxon); ACIArb ♦ Associated Law Societies of Wales Prize . . . . . *Jun 1966
King, Mrs Christine E BA . . . . . *Jun 1980
Lewis, Ms Pauline. . . . . *Mar 1996
Love, Miss Alison June LLB; AIPM; LSF. . . . . *Nov 1993
Lysaght, Mr William J C. . . . . *Jan 1981
Manners, Mr Andrew J LLB . . . . . *Oct 1990
Milford, Mr Christopher BSc. . . . . *Dec 1978
Morgan, Mr Gareth M MA. . . . . *Jun 1980
Morgan, Mr Neil C LLB . . . . . *Nov 1991
Noakes, Ms Helen . . . . . *Nov 1983
Preece, Ms D Ceri W LLB(Wales) President of Cardiff Chamber of Commerce . . . . . *Jul 1980
Price, Mr Hugh M. . . . . *§Dec 1975
Roberts, Mr David L MA; LLB(Cantab) . . . . . *§Oct 1974
Rosser, Mari LLB . . . . . *Feb 1992
Salen, Wiljo P LLB(Lond) . . . . . *Jun 1975
Scott, Mr Iain A. . . . . *Oct 1990
Snowdon, Mr William D LLB(Hons) Chairman of Investors in People . . . . . *Dec 1979
Stephens, Mr Malcolm . . . . . Dec 1977
Tossell, Mr Matthew LLB(Wales) . . . . . *Oct 1985
Warren, Ms Sian C L . . . . . *Oct 1988
Webber, Mr Stephen J LLB . . . . . Sep 1996
Wheeldon, Ms Lynn. . . . . *Sep 1994
Whittaker, Mairwen S LLB . . . . . *Oct 1987
Williams, Mr Gareth J LLB(Wales). . . . . *Jun 1976
Wilson, Mr Neil D. . . . . *Dec 1980
Wright, Mrs Cherry E LLB. . . . . *Jul 1969
Asoc: Davies, Ms Yvonne . . . . . *Oct 1987
Driscoll, Ms Victoria. . . . . Sep 1997
Hughes, Mared Wyn LLB . . . . . *Nov 1992
Morgan, Mr Robert L LLB . . . . . *Nov 1988
Morris, Miss Joanne LLB(Hons). . . . . *Oct 1997
Pulman, Mr Ralph LLB(Hons); LLM . . . . . Jan 1997
Wilde, Ms Catherine. . . . . *Oct 1993
Williams, Mr Rhys A LLB . . . . . *Jul 1980
Ast: Agius, Ms Ruth LLB(Hons) . . . . . Sep 2000
Barnes, Mr Phillip LLB(Hons) . . . . . Sep 2000
Choudhary, Chui . . . . . Feb 2000
Coates, Mr Christopher John . . . . . *Aug 1996
Ellis, Mr Simon LLB. . . . . Sep 2000
Evans, Ms Gwen LLB(Hons) . . . . . Sep 2001
Evans, Mr Gavin Sior Cadwaladr BA(Hons); CPE; LSF *Jan 1998
Harrison-Jones, Mrs Angela T LLB . . . . . *Sep 1992
Hazzard, Ms Lynsey. . . . . Mar 2002
Hill, Ms Melissa F LLB(Hons) . . . . . *Oct 1998
Hurn, Mr Peter LLB(Hons). . . . . Sep 2001
Lane, Mr Richard LLB. . . . . Sep 1999
Locke, Mr Richard LLB . . . . . Sep 1999
Rees, Mr Jonathan B LLB(Hons)(Exon); DipLP . . . *Sep 1998
Rees, Ms Rebecca . . . . . Sep 1999
Roberts, Ms Mair . . . . . Oct 2001
Rogers, Mr Paul BA. . . . . *Mar 1995
Scourfield, Miss Emma LLB. . . . . *Aug 1996
Shorney, Miss Kate LLB; LPC; PSC. . . . . *Sep 1999
Watkins, Miss Melanie C LLB; Dip. . . . . *Sep 1999
Williams, Ms Erica . . . . . Sep 2001
Wisdom, Mr Gareth LLB(Hons) . . . . . Nov 2000

J A HUGHES
89 Beulah Road Rhiwbina Cardiff CF14 6LW
Tel: 029 2061 9700 *Fax:* 029 2052 1275
Dx: 136741 LLANISHEN CARDIFF
E-mail: jahughes@qualitysolicitors.com
Office: Barry, Penarth
Work: D1 G J1 K1 K3 K4 N O Q S1 S2 W
Ptr: Horwood, Miss Sandra E LLB. . . . . *Nov 1987
Kennedy, Mr A Duncan BA . . . . . *Oct 1986
Ast: Lane, Ms Hayley Louise LLB . . . . . *Aug 2003

HUNT & MORGAN ‡
4 Park Court Mews Park Place Cardiff CF10 3DQ
Tel: 029 2034 1234 *Fax:* 029 2034 2350 *Dx:* 33031 CARDIFF 1
E-mail: office@hunt-morgan.co.uk
List of partners: M S Hunt, D C Morgan, M C Rostron
Languages: French
Work: B1 C1 E J1 O Z(b,l)
Emergency Action and Advocacy undertaken
Ptr: Hunt, Mr Matthew Sherborne LLB. . . . . *Jun 1979
Morgan, Mr Dennis Charles LLB . . . . . *Oct 1991
Rostron, Mr Mark Charles LLB(Hons) . . . . . *Sep 1992

HURLOW & PARTNERS ‡
176 Cowbridge Road East Canton Cardiff CF11 9NE
Tel: 029 2039 6087 *Fax:* 029 2023 8038 *Dx:* 95412 CANTON
E-mail: enquiries@hurlowandpartners.co.uk
List of partners: L Harper, C A Hurlow
Work: D1 G H K1
Emergency Action, Agency, Advocacy, Fixed Fee Interview, Legal Aid undertaken and Legal Aid Franchise
Ptr: Harper, Miss Lydia LLB(Hons) ★ . . . . . *Feb 1989
Hurlow, Ms Carole Ann LLB. . . . . *Nov 1982
Asoc: Kukielka, Ms Cindy Elizabeth Laura BA . . . . . *Oct 1994
Walker, Miss Vicky Marie LLB(Hons) . . . . . *Oct 1995
Ast: McDaid, Mr Mark LLB(Hons) . . . . . *Nov 2004

HUSBAND SAYE ‡
Cadogan House 273 Cowbridge Road East Canton Cardiff CF5 1JB
Tel: 029 2034 5217 *Fax:* 029 2037 4437 *Dx:* 95400 CANTON
E-mail: husbandsaye@btconnect.com
List of partners: D C Husband, N Saye
Work: E J1 K1 L N O P Q S1 S2 T1 T2 W
Ptr: Husband, Mr David C BA . . . . . *§Jan 1978
Saye, Mr Norman BA . . . . . *Dec 1977

HUTTON'S ‡
16 St Andrews Crescent Cardiff CF10 3DD
Tel: 029 2037 8621 *Fax:* 029 2038 8450 *Dx:* 33065 CARDIFF
Emergency telephone 029 2079 1646
E-mail: stuart.hutton@huttons-solicitors.co.uk
List of partners: S M C Hutton
Languages: French, Gujarati, Spanish
Work: B1 C1 C2 D1 E F1 G H J1 K1 K3 L N O Q S1 V W X Z(c,e,f,h,i,k,l,m,p,q,s,t)
Emergency Action, Agency, Advocacy, Fixed Fee Interview, Legal Aid undertaken and Legal Aid Franchise
Ptr: Hutton, Mr Stuart M C Chairman of SSAT. . . . . *§Jun 1975
Ast: Culverwell, Ms Alison M LLB . . . . . Sep 1989
Stowbridge, Ms Clare P BA . . . . . *Jan 1989

JMD LAW LIMITED ‡
26-28 James Street Cardiff Bay Cardiff CF10 5EX
Tel: 029 2045 6780 *Fax:* 029 2045 6781 *Dx:* 200754 CARDIFF BAY
Emergency telephone 07811 208211
E-mail: nigel.jones@jmdlaw.co.uk
List of partners: N Davis, N A Jones
Languages: Welsh
Work: B1 B2 C1 E F1 F2 J1 J2 K1 K2 K4 L N O Q R1 R2 S1 S2 W Z(c,f,g,j,k,p,q,r,t)
Emergency Action, Agency, Advocacy, Fixed Fee Interview and Legal Aid Franchise
Ptr: Davis, Mrs Nicola BA(Hons) ●. . . . . *Apr 1992
Jones, Mr Nigel Anthony BA(Hons) ● . . . . . *Nov 1986
Asoc: Howells, Mr Rhodri LLB(Hons) . . . . . *Jan 2007
Ast: Jones, Mr Adam Richards LLN(Hons). . . . . Oct 2001
O'Sullivan, Mr Nicholas LLB(Hons) . . . . . *Dec 2008

ANTHONY JACOBS & CO ‡
91 Albany Road Cardiff CF24 3LP
Tel: 029 2048 3509 *Fax:* 029 2046 5512
E-mail: anthonyjacobs@btconnect.com
List of partners: A M Jacobs
Work: E K1 L N O S1
Legal Aid undertaken
Ptr: Jacobs, Mr Anthony M LLB(Wales) . . . . . *Oct 1979

HEK JONES SOLICITORS ‡
Second Floor The Wharf Schooner Way Cardiff CF10 4EU
Tel: 029 2044 0070 *Fax:* 029 2045 5874 *Dx:* 200758 CARDIFF BAY
E-mail: ajones@hekjones.com

WYNNE D A JONES ‡
3 Ely Road Llandaff Cardiff CF5 2JE
Tel: 029 2056 9496 *Fax:* 029 2056 9496
E-mail: wynnedajones@hotmail.com
List of partners: W D A Jones
SPr: Jones, Mr Wynne D A. . . . . *§Jan 1966

JANET L JORDAN SOLICITORS ‡
Elliott Buildings 23 Cardiff Road Taffs Well Cardiff CF15 7RB
Tel: 029 2081 0439 *Fax:* 029 2081 1344

KINSEY-JONES SOLICITORS ‡
6 Raleigh Walk Brigantine Place Cardiff CF10 4LN
Tel: 0560 126 7303 *Fax:* 029 2047 3169
E-mail: mail@kinsey-jones-solicitors.co.uk

KRUZINS ‡
Harris House 92a Crwys Road Cathays Cardiff CF24 4NP
Tel: 029 2039 0101 *Fax:* 029 2072 6722
E-mail: kruzsols@aol.com
List of partners: S J Kruzins
Work: J1 K1 N O Q S1 S2 V W
Emergency Action, Agency, Advocacy, Fixed Fee Interview and Legal Aid undertaken
Ptr: Kruzins, Miss Sarita Josephine LLB(Hons) . . . . . *Feb 1990

LEO ABSE & COHEN ‡
40 Churchill Way Cardiff CF10 2SS
Tel: 029 2038 3252 / 2034 5421 *Fax:* 029 2034 5572
Dx: 33002 CARDIFF
E-mail: law@leoabse.co.uk
List of partners: Y E Agnew, M A J Jenkins, R J Norman, R G Williams
Office: Newport, Swansea
Languages: French, Italian, Welsh
Work: B1 C1 D1 D2 E F1 G H J1 K1 K2 K3 L N O Q R1 S1 T1 T2 V W Z(b,c,d,j,k,l,o)
Emergency Action, Agency, Advocacy, Legal Aid undertaken and Legal Aid Franchise
Ptr: Agnew, Ms Yvonne E LLB(Hons) . . . . . *Oct 1986
Jenkins, Mr Mike A J . . . . . Oct 1992
Norman, Mr Richard J LLB . . . . . *Nov 1987
Williams, Mr Robin G LLB. . . . . *Nov 1980
Asoc: Church, Mr Mark LLB . . . . . Sep 1993
Gwynne, Ms Anne LLB . . . . . Sep 1994

Owen, Mr Andrew John LLB(Hons) . . . . . *Jan 1988
White, Mr James D R LLB. . . . . *Mar 1991
Ast: Browne, Mr John Christian CPE. . . . . *Sep 1997
Davies, Mr Richard M LLB(Hons) . . . . . Aug 1996
Edwards, Miss Susan J BA; CPE; LPC . . . . . Jan 1999
Loxton, Mr Gareth Clive BA(Hons) . . . . . *Dec 1989
Morris, Ms Andrea . . . . . Nov 1994
O'Brien, Ms Janet Lorraine LLB. . . . . Jun 1996
Owen, Mr Nicholas S R L LLB. . . . . *Jul 1991
Rees, Mr Ian . . . . . Jan 1998
Rosser, Mr Jonathan P LLB; DipLP; LPC . . . . . Mar 1999
Saunders, Mr Edward J MA(Cantab) . . . . . Mar 1994

LLOYD & ROWE ‡
205 City Road Roath Cardiff CF24 3JD
Tel: 029 2045 8999 *Fax:* 029 2045 8999
Emergency telephone 07812 077251
List of partners: N L Lloyd, D R Rowe, A M Sampson
Work: E G H J1 K1 L N S1 V W
Emergency Action, Agency, Advocacy, Fixed Fee Interview, Legal Aid undertaken and Legal Aid Franchise
Ptr: Lloyd, Mr Nicholas L LLB . . . . . Jun 1993
Rowe, Ms Deborah R LLB. . . . . *Nov 1988
Sampson, Mr Aubrey Martin. . . . . May 1995

LOOSEMORES ‡
Alliance House 18-19 High Street Cardiff CF10 1PT
Tel: 029 2022 4433 *Fax:* 029 2080 3100 *Dx:* 33008 CARDIFF
E-mail: post@loosemores.co.uk
List of partners: P A Brindley, M J Culley, L A Jones, B R Melrose, K Thomas
Work: B1 C1 C2 C3 E F1 J1 L N O P Q R1 S1 S2 T1 T2 W Z(b,c,d,e,f,j,k,l,p,w)
Emergency Action, Agency, Advocacy and Fixed Fee Interview undertaken
Ptr: Brindley, Mr Peter Anthony BSc. . . . . *Oct 1995
Culley, Mr Michael J LLB . . . . . *Apr 1983
Jones, Miss Linda A LLB . . . . . *Mar 1980
Melrose, Mrs Bridget Ruth LLB . . . . . *Oct 1991
Thomas, Mr Karl LLB . . . . . *Apr 2001
Asoc: Pascoe, Mr Hugh R LLB . . . . . *Nov 1979
Ast: Edwards, Mr Christopher LLB. . . . . *Oct 1994
Fox, Mr Simon Gary LLB . . . . . *Mar 1997
Jones, Mr Paul Lloyd LLB. . . . . Sep 2003
Joseph, Mr Martin Howard LLB . . . . . *Jul 1975
Kaur, Mrs Lakhbir LLB; LLM. . . . . *May 2002
Khan, Mrs Leanne LLB . . . . . *Aug 2007

Our specialisations are: Commercial & Company Law, Accidents, Injury, Employment, Property, Probate, Wills, Tax planning and Trusts, Charities, Powers of Attorney, Intellectual Property Protection.

A G LUCAS & CO ‡
Malthouse Avenue Cardiff Gate Business Park Cardiff CF23 8RU
Tel: 029 2026 3628 *Fax:* 029 2026 3700
E-mail: aglucasco@aol.com

LYONS DAVIDSON
Greyfriars House Greyfriars Road Cardiff CF10 3AL
Tel: 029 2030 3710 *Fax:* 029 2030 3711
E-mail: info@lyondavidson.co.uk
Office: Bristol, Leeds, New Malden, Plymouth, Solihull
Ptr: Davies, Mr Ian . . . . . Aug 1999

M&A SOLICITORS LLP ‡
3 Assembly Square Britannia Quay Cardiff Bay Cardiff CF10 4PL
Tel: 029 2048 2288 *Fax:* 029 2049 5588 *Dx:* 200750 CARDIFF BAY
E-mail: info@manda.uk.com
List of partners: S Berry, E C Evans, J Geen, D A Rees, R L Sellek, B Thomas, A Whiteley, G R Wilson
Languages: Welsh
Work: C1 C2 E J1 R1 R2 S2 Z(c,e,s)
Ptr: Berry, Mr Stephen. . . . . Jan 1993
Evans, Mr Eric Christopher . . . . . Oct 1980
Geen, Mr Jonathan . . . . . Jan 1996
Rees, Ms Deryn Anne BA; MA; ACA . . . . . Sep 1996
Sellek, Ms Rachelle Louise LLB. . . . . Oct 1995
Thomas, Miss Betsan LLB . . . . . Oct 1996
Whiteley, Mr Alan . . . . . Jan 1987
Wilson, Mr Gareth Rosser LLB . . . . . Jan 2002

MLM CARTWRIGHT ‡
Pendragon House Fitzalan Court Newport Road Cardiff CF24 0BA
Tel: 029 2046 2562 *Fax:* 029 2049 1118 *Dx:* 33011 CARDIFF 1
E-mail: enquiries@mlmcartwright.com
List of partners: M J Baggott, J S Fernandez Lewis, D R King, C J Mayers, N L T Morgan, A C Pay, A Thomas, A Walters
Languages: French, Welsh
Work: A1 B1 C1 C2 E F1 I J1 J2 L N O Q R1 R2 S1 S2 U1 U2 W Z(c,e,f,l,m,p,q,r,t)
Agency and Advocacy undertaken
Ptr: Baggott, Mr Michael John LLB Notary Public . . . . . *Oct 1990
Fernandez Lewis, Mr Jonathan S LLB. . . . . *Oct 1984
King, Mr David Robert LLB(Hons). . . . . *Dec 1994
Mayers, Mr Christopher J LLB(Wales). . . . . *Oct 1983
Morgan, Mr Nigel L T LLB. . . . . *§Jan 1969
Pay, Mr Alex Charles LLM; BA; BSc. . . . . *Apr 1985
Thomas, Miss Andrea BSc(Econ); DipLP . . . . . *Jul 1996
Walters, Mr Aled LLB University of Wales Evan Morgan Scholarship. . . . . *Oct 1997
Asoc: Ackland, Mr Michael BA. . . . . *May 1995
Brown, Mrs Joanne Sian LLB . . . . . *Sep 1999
Childs, Mr Christopher Greenslade LLB(Hons)(Soton). Apr 1980
Morgan, Mr Daniel James Lindon . . . . . *Sep 2000
Phillips, Miss Elin Mai LLB . . . . . Oct 1997
Willis, Mr Robert BSc(Hons). . . . . Jan 1997
Ast: Bechares, Mr Stuart John LLB . . . . . *Oct 2006
Corrigan, Mr James Peter Edward LLB(Hons); LPC . *Sep 2006
McCarthy, Miss Rachael Louise LLB(Hons); LPC . . . *Jan 2009
Mahapatra, Mrs Daniela Emily Itala LLB. . . . . *Sep 2005
Sheppard, Mr David Alexander BA; LPC . . . . . Sep 2007
Thacker, Mr Peter LLB . . . . . *Sep 2005
Tinning, Mr Michael Thomas BA; LLDip . . . . . Aug 2003
Con: Parnell, Mrs Susan G T BA . . . . . *§Dec 1977

MCTAGGART SOLICITORS ‡
24 St Andrews Crescent Cardiff CF10 3DD
Tel: 029 2023 4090 *Fax:* 029 2039 8077 *Dx:* 50795 CARDIFF 2
E-mail: enquiries@mctlaw.co.uk

MALEKIN LAW ‡
11 Corporation Road Grangetown Cardiff CF11 7AN
Tel: 029 2023 1222 *Fax:* 029 2023 1406
List of partners: P S S A Malekin
Ptr: Malekin, Mr Paul S St A LLB(Wales) ★ . . . . Aug 1981

MALLIA & CO ‡
196 Cowbridge Road East Cardiff CF5 1GX
Tel: 029 2022 0044 *Fax:* 029 2023 8618
Dx: 95401 CANTON CARDIFF
Emergency telephone 029 2070 8207 / 2035 9770
E-mail: law@mallia.com
List of partners: P J Mallia
Languages: French, German
Work: A1 B1 B2 C1 D1 E F1 G H J1 K1 L M1 N P S1 W Z(i,l,m,t)
Emergency Action, Agency, Advocacy, Fixed Fee Interview, Legal Aid undertaken and Legal Aid Franchise
SPr: Mallia, Mr Peter Joseph. . . . . *§Jul 1971

MALLOY & BARRY ‡
194 Cowbridge Road East Canton Cardiff CF5 1GW
Tel: 029 2034 3434 *Fax:* 029 2034 1434 *Dx:* 95415 CANTON
Emergency telephone 07659 190347
E-mail: info@malloybarry.co.uk
List of partners: M T Barry, K P Malloy
Work: B2 C1 D1 E F1 G H J1 K1 K3 L N O Q R1 S1 S2 T2 V W Z(i,l,q,r,s,t,w)
Emergency Action, Agency, Advocacy, Fixed Fee Interview and Legal Aid undertaken
Ptr: Barry, Mr Michael T BSc(Econ) ♦ . . . . *Mar 1985
Malloy, Mr Kieron P LLB ★ . . . . *§Aug 1984

MANSFIELD FELLOWES SOLICITORS ‡
Regus House Falcon Drive Cardiff Bay Cardiff CF10 4RU
Tel: 029 2050 4101 *Fax:* 029 2050 4101
E-mail: contact@mansfieldfellowes.co.uk

MARTYN PROWEL ‡
Ground & 3rd Floor Hallinans House 22 Newport Road Cardiff CF24 0DB
Tel: 029 2047 0909 *Fax:* 029 2049 8566 *Dx:* 33037 CARDIFF
Emergency telephone 07836 297082
E-mail: enquiries@martynprowel.co.uk
Web: www.martynprowel.co.uk
List of partners: H Davies, J Lynch, G H Richards, C Rockey
Languages: French, Welsh
Work: A2 B2 C1 D1 D2 E F1 G H J1 K1 K3 N O P Q R1 S1 S2 W Z(l,p,q,r)
Emergency Action, Agency, Advocacy, Fixed Fee Interview, Legal Aid undertaken, Legal Aid Franchise and Member of Accident Line
Ptr: Davies, Mr Hywel BA(Hons). . . . . *May 1981
Lynch, Mr James LLB(Hons) . . . . *Nov 1995
Richards, Mr Geraint H LLB ★. . . . . *Mar 1984
Rockey, Ms Caron BA. . . . . *Dec 1992
Asoc: Stephens, Mr Grant James LLB; LPC . . . . *May 2007
West, Ms Catherine Victoria LLB . . . . Nov 2001
Ast: Goldsworthy, Miss Rebecca Jane LLB. . . . . *Nov 2004
Griffiths, Miss Janine FILEx . . . . *Jan 2007
Harris, Mr James Alexander LLB(Hons); DipLaw. . . . *Jul 2005
Lambert, Miss Krystle LLB; LPC. . . . . *Feb 2010
Rees, Mr Thomas LLB; DipLaw . . . . Apr 2011
Ritchie, Mrs Ceri LLB(Hons) Sweet & Maxwell. . . . *Oct 2004
Watkins, Mr Richard Aled LLB; DipLaw . . . . *Aug 2000
Con: Edwards, Mr Robert N LLB(Wales) . . . . *Mar 1975
Prowel, Mr William M LLB. . . . . *Dec 1971

Holders of LSC Contract for Crime, Family, Clinical Negligence. We conduct business in French & Welsh. We specialise in Fraud, Child Care, Commercial Property, Employment, Personal Injury.

MERRILS EDE SOLICITORS ‡
(incorporating T J Morgan & Co)
27 Park Place Cardiff CF10 3BA
Tel: 029 2037 1131 *Fax:* 029 2022 5540 *Dx:* 33032 CARDIFF
Emergency telephone 029 2070 4217 / 2022 5755
E-mail: central@merrilsede.co.uk
List of partners: H M James, A D Morris, J L Tillyard
Office: Penarth
Languages: French, German, Welsh
Work: A1 B1 C1 C2 C3 D1 E F1 G H J1 K1 L M1 M2 N P Q R1 S1 T1 T2 V W Z(c,f,h,i,j,k,l,m)
Emergency Action, Agency, Advocacy, Fixed Fee Interview, Legal Aid undertaken and Member of Accident Line
Ptr: Tillyard, Mrs Janet L LLB Part time Chairman of Social Section, Disability and Child Support Appeal Tribunals . *Dec 1979
Ast: James, Mr David LLB(Hons) . . . . *Nov 1991
Lawrie, Ms Annette . . . . Sep 1998
McCarthy, Mr Paul J LLB; MSc; MA. . . . . Oct 1984

DUNCAN MOGHAL
134 Woodville Road Cardiff CF24 4EE
Tel: 029 2064 4999 *Fax:* 029 2066 5620
E-mail: cardiff@duncanmoghal.com
Office: Newport

MOONEERAMS LIMITED ‡
36 Richmond Road Cardiff CF24 4AS
Tel: 029 2048 3615 *Fax:* 029 2045 4986
E-mail: alistair@mooneerams.com

MORGAN COLE ‡
Bradley Court Park Place Cardiff CF10 3DP
Tel: 029 2038 5385 *Fax:* 029 2038 5300 *Dx:* 33014 CARDIFF
E-mail: info@morgan-cole.com
Office: Bristol, Oxford, Reading (2 offices), Swansea
Languages: Bemba, French, German, Hebrew, Italian, Mandarin, Polish, Portuguese, Punjabi, Spanish, Welsh
Work: A1 B1 C1 C2 C3 D1 E F1 G H I J1 K1 L M1 M2 N O P Q R1 S1 T1 T2 V W Z(b,c,d,e,f,g,h,j,k,l,m,n,o,t)

MORGAN DENTON JONES LLP ‡
Ground Floor Park House Greyfriars Road Cardiff CF10 3AF
Tel: 029 2053 7740 *Fax:* 029 2053 7749 *Dx:* 33073 CARDIFF 1

JAMES MORGAN SOLICITORS ‡
Morgan Arcade Chambers 33 St Mary Street Cardiff CF10 1PH
Tel: 029 2038 2111 / 2022 1600 *Fax:* 029 2038 3510
Dx: 33024 CARDIFF 1
List of partners: T Evans, S Keller
Work: A1 C1 E F1 J1 L S1 S2 W Z(c,l,q)
Ptr: Evans, Mr Tudor . . . . Sep 1962
Keller, Mr Steven LLB(Leics) Clerk to Cornelly Community Council . . . . *Nov 1985
Ast: Penn, Miss Emma Mary Sarah BSc; CPE . . . . . . Mar 2002

MORGANS ‡
Elgin House 106-107 St Mary Street Cardiff CF10 1DX
Tel: 029 2072 9888 *Fax:* 029 2072 9898 *Dx:* 33040 CARDIFF
Emergency telephone 07831 568274
E-mail: info@morgans-sols.co.uk
List of partners: R A Morgan
Office: Cardiff, Milford Haven, Swansea
Languages: Welsh
Work: A3 B1 B2 C1 C2 D1 D2 E F1 F2 G H J1 J2 K1 K3 K4 L N O P Q R2 S1 S2 T1 T2 V W Z(h,j,k,m,p,q,y)
Emergency Action, Agency, Advocacy, Fixed Fee Interview, Legal Aid undertaken and Legal Aid Franchise
SPr: Morgan, Mr Roy A LLB ★ . . . . *§Oct 1981
Asoc: Walker, Miss Vicky Marie LLB(Hons) . . . . *Oct 1995
Ast: Almeida, Ms Catherine . . . . Jun 2009
Butler, Mrs Rhiannon LLB. . . . . Jan 2004
Davies, Mrs Rachel LLB. . . . . *Jul 1981
Goodall, Ms Carolyn Mary LLB(Hons) . . . . *Oct 1997
Grace, Miss Sarah Jane LLB ★ . . . . *Oct 1999
Harris, Mr James Alexander LLB(Hons); DipLaw. . . *Jul 2005
Howells, Mrs Lynda Joy LLB . . . . May 1996
Humphreys, Ms Rhiannon LLB . . . . *Dec 2003
Menard, Miss Hannah LLB . . . . Mar 2007
Mitchard, Mrs Nicola LLB . . . . *Aug 1997
Stocks, Mr Andrew PGDipLaw; BA(Hons). . . . . . Feb 2007
Stubbs, Miss Ele BSc(Hons) . . . . *Nov 2007

MORGANS
31 Wilson Road Ely Cardiff CF5 4LL
Tel: 029 2059 5155 *Fax:* 029 2059 1355 *Dx:* 33040 CARDIFF
Emergency telephone 029 2056 2054
E-mail: info@morgans-sols.co.uk
Office: Cardiff, Milford Haven, Swansea
Work: D1 F1 G H J1 K1 L N S1 V
Emergency Action, Agency, Advocacy, Fixed Fee Interview and Legal Aid undertaken

JOHN MORRIS SOLICITORS ‡
Kenneth Pollard House 5-19 Cowbridge Road East Cardiff CF11 9AB
Tel: 029 2066 7788 *Fax:* 029 2066 5798 *Dx:* 141879 CARDIFF 28
E-mail: john_morris_enqs@btconnect.com

D J MURPHY SOLICITORS ‡
19 St Andrews Crescent Cardiff CF10 3DB
Tel: 029 2022 1300 *Fax:* 029 2022 1341 *Dx:* 33067 CARDIFF 1
E-mail: djmurphy.co@virgin.net
Languages: French, German, Japanese, Welsh
Work: B1 C1 C3 E F1 F2 J1 L M1 M3 N O P Q R1 S1 S2 T1 T2 W Z(a,b,c,e,f,k,l,q,r)

NEWLAW SOLICITORS ‡
2nd Floor Ross House Scott Harbour Cardiff CF10 4PJ
Tel: 0870 756 6870 *Fax:* 0870 756 6871 *Dx:* 200759 CARDIFF BAY
E-mail: info@new-law.co.uk

NEWLAW SOLICITORS ‡
Helmont House Churchill Way Cardiff CF10 2HE
Tel: 0845 521 0945 *Fax:* 0845 521 0946 *Dx:* 200759 CARDIFF BAY
E-mail: info@new-law.co.uk

NICOL DENVIR & PURNELL ‡
798 Newport Road Rumney Cardiff CF3 4FH
Tel: 029 2079 6311 *Fax:* 029 2077 9261 *Dx:* 118475 RUMNEY
E-mail: paulinehutchings@ndplegal.com
List of partners: A M Denvir, A M Donnelly, G F D Nicol, J Purnell, J M Treharne
Work: D1 D2 K1 K2 K3 S1 V W
Emergency Action, Agency, Advocacy, Fixed Fee Interview, Legal Aid undertaken and Legal Aid Franchise
Ptr: Denvir, Miss Aine M LLB ♦ . . . . *§Mar 1985
Donnelly, Mr Anthony M LLB ♦ . . . . *Nov 1986
Nicol, Mr G Frazer D ♦ . . . . *Jun 1979
Purnell, Ms Joanna BA . . . . *Jan 1992
Treharne, Ms Joni May LLB. . . . . *Aug 1999
Asoc: Whiting, Miss Rhian LLB(Hons) . . . . Nov 1998
Ast: Dixon, Mr Luke Stephan LLB . . . . May 2009
Morgan, Miss Emma Louise BSc(Econ). . . . . . . Jun 1998
Tucker, Mr William Patrick. . . . . Sep 2010
Con: Morgan, Ms Myfanwy Elizabeth BA . . . . *Dec 1977

O'BRIEN LEWIS & JAMES
2 Heol-y-Deri Rhiweina Cardiff CF14 6HF
Tel: 029 2061 1471 *Fax:* 029 2052 2095
Office: Cardiff
Work: C1 D1 E F1 G H J1 K1 L N O Q S1 V W

OWEN & OSULLIVAN ‡
1 Caspian Point Pierhead Street Cardiff Bay Cardiff CF10 4DQ
Tel: 029 2044 4082

EMYR PIERCE & CO ‡
5a Heol-y-Deri Rhiwbina Cardiff CF14 6HA
Tel: 029 2061 6002 *Fax:* 029 2052 2772
Dx: 96180 WHITCHURCH (CARDIFF)
E-mail: law@emyrpierce.co.uk
List of partners: E Pierce
Languages: Welsh
Work: E L S1 S2 W
Ptr: Pierce, Mr Emyr. . . . . *Oct 1980

PRIME LAW ‡
Sophia House 28 Cathedral Road Cardiff CF11 9LJ
Tel: 0845 519 0266 *Fax:* 029 2066 3001
E-mail: nick.corney@primelaw.co.uk

PRINCIPLE LAW LIMITED ‡
122 Clifton Street Cardiff CF24 1LW
Tel: 029 2047 0800 *Fax:* 029 2079 6030
E-mail: admin@principlelaw.co.uk
Work: B1 C1 E J1 O Q Z(b,i,k,q)
Agency, Advocacy and Fixed Fee Interview undertaken

RG LEGAL SOLICITORS ‡
50 Cyncoed Road Cardiff CF23 5SH
Tel: 029 2049 0047 *Fax:* 029 2048 6037
E-mail: enquiries@rglegal.co.uk
List of partners: S J Kruzins, J K G Watkins
Work: F1 G H J1 K1 L N O Q S1 V W Z(l,p)
Agency, Advocacy and Fixed Fee Interview undertaken
Ptr: Kruzins, Miss Sarita Josephine LLB(Hons) . . . . . *Feb 1990
Watkins, Mr James Kenneth Giles BA. . . . . *Jul 1985

RTL SOLICITORS ‡
Waterloo House Fitzalan Court Fitzalan Road Cardiff CF24 0EL
Tel: 029 2023 4030 *Fax:* 029 2023 4031 *Dx:* 33060 CARDIFF
E-mail: info@rtllegal.co.uk
List of partners: M Lewis, A Rosser, P F Thomas
Office: Bridgend
Work: A1 C1 C2 E F1 F2 J1 J2 L R2 S1 S2 W Z(c,h,w)
Ptr: Lewis, Mr Matthew BA(Hons) . . . . Jun 1996
Rosser, Mr Alun LLB . . . . Jul 1980
Thomas, Mr Paul F LLB. . . . . Jan 1987

RADCLIFFES LE BRASSEUR
25 Park Place Cardiff CF10 3BA
Tel: 029 2034 3035 *Fax:* 029 2034 3045 *Dx:* 33063 CARDIFF 1
Office: Leeds, London SW1
Languages: French, Welsh
Work: J1 N Q Z(k,m,q,r)
Agency undertaken
Ptr: Llewellyn-Morgan, Mr Huw LLB . . . . Mar 1980
Ast: Lang, Miss Jane Louise LLB . . . . *Nov 1988

RAUSA MUMFORD ‡
(incorporating S J Cottrell)
35 Park Place Cardiff CF10 3RL
Tel: 029 2034 4341 *Fax:* 029 2023 1153
Emergency telephone 07860 363816
E-mail: mail@rausamumford.co.uk
List of partners: P A Beckerley, S A R Mumford, D M Olden, S Rausa, E D Thomas
Languages: French, Italian, Welsh
Work: B2 D1 E F1 G H J1 K1 L M1 N P Q R1 S1 V W Z(j,l,m,t)
Emergency Action, Agency, Advocacy, Fixed Fee Interview, Legal Aid undertaken, Legal Aid Franchise and Member of Accident Line
Ptr: Beckerley, Mr Peter A LLM; BA . . . . Oct 1989
Mumford, Mr Simon A R LLB; GIPM ★ . . . . *Dec 1981
Olden, Mr D Martyn BA . . . . *Jul 1979
Rausa, Mr Salvatore BSc(Econ). . . . . *Dec 1978
Thomas, Eirian D BSc(Econ) . . . . Mar 1990

ALUN REES SOLICITOR ‡
28 Cathedral Road Cardiff CF11 9LJ
Tel: 029 2056 3732 *Fax:* 029 2056 3117
E-mail: ar@arlaw.co.uk

REES WOOD TERRY ‡
9 St Andrews Crescent Cardiff CF10 3DG
Tel: 029 2040 8800 *Fax:* 029 2040 8808 *Dx:* 33028 CARDIFF
E-mail: info@reeswoodterry.co.uk
List of partners: A P M Hickey, M L Hood, D G Williams
Languages: Welsh
Work: A1 B1 C1 C2 C3 E F1 J1 K1 L N O P Q R1 S1 S2 T1 T2 W Z(d,f,g,i,l,q,r)
Emergency Action, Agency, Advocacy and Fixed Fee Interview undertaken
Ptr: Hickey, Ms Angela Pauline Mary LLB(Hons). . . . . *Oct 1984
Hood, Mr Martin L LLB . . . . *Apr 1975
Williams, Mr Dafydd Gareth LLB . . . . *Dec 2004
Ast: Morgans, Ms Clair LLB. . . . . *Oct 2009
Pitt, Mrs Frances Eirian LLB. . . . . *Jan 2009

RENDERS ‡
189 Whitchurch Road Cardiff CF14 3JR
Tel: 029 2054 4900 *Fax:* 029 2054 4909
Emergency telephone 07860 710680
E-mail: enquiries@renders-solicitors.co.uk
List of partners: J B D Render, D A Stephens
Work: G H N Q S1 W
Emergency Action, Agency, Advocacy, Fixed Fee Interview, Legal Aid undertaken and Legal Aid Franchise
Ptr: Render, Mr Justin B D. . . . . Jun 1995
Stephens, Mr David Anthony . . . . Mar 1997
Ast: Unsworth, Mr Ian T LLB. . . . . Apr 1987

RICHARD NELSON BUSINESS DEFENCE SOLICITORS
Castle Court 6 Cathedral Road Cardiff CF11 9LJ
Tel: 029 2064 7513 *Fax:* 029 2064 7514
E-mail: defencecardiff@richardnelsonllp.co.uk
Office: Bristol, Manchester, Nottingham, Solihull

RICHARDS THOMAS SOLICITORS ‡
14 The Strand Ferndale Cardiff CF43 4LY
Tel: 01443 757738 *Fax:* 01443 755581

ROBERTSONS ‡
6 Park Place Cardiff CF10 3RS
Tel: 029 2023 7777 *Fax:* 029 2038 1828 *Dx:* 33039 CARDIFF
E-mail: enquiries@robsols.co.uk
List of partners: L E L Hallinan, C F Hart, A M Humphreys, R A Lloyd, D F Paddison, A W Reynolds, I M Williams, M H Williams
Office: Barry, Cardiff
Languages: Welsh
Work: B1 B2 C1 C2 C3 D1 E F1 G H J1 K1 K2 L N O Q R1 S1 T1 T2 V W Z(b,c,d,e,h,i,k,l)
Emergency Action, Agency, Advocacy, Fixed Fee Interview, Legal Aid undertaken, Legal Aid Franchise and Member of Accident Line
Ptr: Hallinan, Mr Lincoln E L LLB . . . . Oct 1989
Lloyd, Mr R Alun LLB . . . . *Jul 1977
Paddison, Mr David F. . . . . Dec 1972
Reynolds, Mr Alun W LLM; LLB. . . . . *Nov 1980
Williams, Mr Ian M LLB . . . . *Oct 1985
Williams, Martell H LLB . . . . *Nov 1976

RUBIN LEWIS O'BRIEN
10 Crickhowell Road St Mellons Cardiff CF3 0EF
Tel: 029 2077 9988 *Fax:* 029 2079 7031 *Dx:* 95602 ST MELLONS
E-mail: reception@rlobcdf.co.uk
Office: Cwmbran
Languages: Welsh
Work: A1 B1 C1 C2 D1 E K1 L N O Q R1 S1 W Z(i,k,l)
Emergency Action, Advocacy, Fixed Fee Interview and Legal Aid undertaken
Ptr: Lee, Mr Richard A BA. . . . . *§Mar 1990
Asoc: Wood, Ms Amanda . . . . Feb 2005

RUSSELL JONES & WALKER
Landore Court 51 Charles Street Cardiff CF10 2GD
Tel: 029 2026 2800 *Fax:* 029 2026 2828 *Dx:* 99764 CARDIFF
E-mail: enquiries@rjw.co.uk

See p112 for the Key to Work Categories & other symbols

Office: Birmingham, Bristol, London WC2, Manchester, Newcastle upon Tyne, Sheffield, Wakefield
Languages: Welsh
Work: B2 E G J1 J2 N O Q X Z(g,k,p,q,r,w)
Emergency Action, Legal Aid undertaken, Legal Aid Franchise and Member of Accident Line
Ptr: Clarke, Mr Barry James BA; MSc(Econ) Wig & Pen Prize 1996; TF tout Prize 1991 . . . *Nov 1996
Coolican, Mr Timothy BA(Hons) . . . *Mar 1998
Imperato, Mr Michael J BA(Hons) . . . *Nov 1990
Ast: Bradbury, Miss Juliette Jane LLB . . . *Mar 1999
Collins, Mr Nicholas Giles LLB . . . *Oct 1995
Harfield, Miss Rachel Louise LLB . . . Sep 2000

SAVERY & PENNINGTON ‡
11 Moira Terrace Cardiff CF24 0EJ
Tel: 029 2045 7222 *Fax:* 029 2045 2211
E-mail: saverypennington@btconnect.com

SHANAHAN WORMALD DAVIS SOLICITORS & ADVOCATES ‡
The Ground Floor 19 Cathedral Road Cardiff CF11 9HA
Tel: 029 2019 0184 *Fax:* 029 2019 0183
E-mail: shanahans@ntlbusiness.com

SILVER SHEMMINGS LLP
Walters Buildings Clarence Road Cardiff CF10 5FA
Tel: 029 2047 4570 *Fax:* 029 2047 4575
E-mail: cardiff@shemmingsllp.co.uk
Office: Epping, London SW1
Work: A3 O Z(c)

THOMAS SIMON ‡
62 Newport Road Cardiff CF24 0DF
Tel: 029 2055 7200 *Fax:* 029 2055 7203 *Dx:* 33068 CARDIFF 1
List of partners: K J S Cooper, W J Graham, S H James, A D Lewis, H J O'Brien, P A O'Brien, P N Simon, R J Thomas
Office: Cardiff
Work: E F1 J1 K1 L N O Q S1 S2 V W
Ptr: Graham, Mr W John BA(Law) . . . *Jun 1984
James, Mr Simon H LLB Part time Chairman of the Social Security Appeals Tribunal . . . *Jul 1973
O'Brien, Mr Howard J LLB . . . *Jun 1972
O'Brien, Mr Philip A BSc(Econ) . . . *Mar 1977
Simon, P N . . . Dec 1991
Thomas, Mr Rupert J LLB(Wales) Member of the Management Committee United Welsh Housing Association . . . *Nov 1983
Asoc: Croucher, Mr Damian John LLB . . . Sep 2001
Hilton, Mrs Susan Jayne LLB . . . Sep 1993
James, Mrs Sarah Elizabeth FILEx . . . Dec 2004
Owen, Mr Nicholas S R L LLB . . . *Jul 1991
Simon, Mr Paul Nathan LLB . . . Dec 1999
Ast: Daniel, Mr David Nigel LLB(Hons) . . . Sep 1994
Hughes, Mr Niall Liam LLB; LLM . . . Jan 2001
Jones, Ms Nicola Andrea LLB . . . Sep 2002
Rea, Ms Elena LLB Trustee of Fairbridge Cymn (Charity) . . . Mar 1995
Smith, Miss Danielle LLB . . . Jan 2001
Con: Jenkins, Mr Edward K . . . Sep 1984

SIMPSON MILLAR LLP
273 Cowbridge Road East Cardiff CF5 1JB
Tel: 0844 858 3700 *Fax:* 0844 858 3799 *Dx:* 95404 CANTON
E-mail: info@simpsonmillar.co.uk
Office: Birmingham, Bristol, Gateshead, Leeds, London EC1, London SW19, Manchester
Work: A1 A3 B1 C1 C2 D1 D2 E F1 F2 J1 J2 K1 K2 K3 K4 M2 M3 N O P Q R1 R2 S1 S2 T1 T2 U2 V W X Z(b,c,d,e,h,j,m,o,p,q,r,t,za)

SINCLAIRS
234b Cowbridge Road Cardiff CF5 1GY
Tel: 029 2038 8398 *Fax:* 029 2039 4448 *Dx:* 95416 CANTON
E-mail: g.evans@sinclairslaw.co.uk
Office: Penarth

SPENCER SKUSE ‡
12 Park Grove Cardiff CF10 3BN
Tel: 029 2034 3993 *Fax:* 029 2022 2165 *Dx:* 33010 CARDIFF 1
E-mail: mail@spencerskuse.com
List of partners: G M Skuse, G M Spencer
Work: A1 B1 C1 C2 C3 E F1 J1 K1 L N O Q R1 S1 T1 T2 W Z(c,h,i,k,l,p)
Emergency Action, Agency, Advocacy, Fixed Fee Interview, Legal Aid undertaken and Legal Aid Franchise
Ptr: Skuse, Mr Graeme M LLB . . . *Nov 1996
Spencer, Miss Gillian M LLB . . . *Dec 1980
Ast: Potter, Mr John Michael LLB . . . *Apr 2003

SPICKETTS BATTRICK LAW PRACTICE
126 Clifton Street Roath Cardiff CF24 1LX
Tel: 029 2046 1480 *Fax:* 029 2048 7505
E-mail: enquiries@spickettsbattrick.co.uk
Office: Cardiff, Pontypridd
Work: B1 D1 D2 F1 J1 K1 K2 K3 N S1 S2 W
Emergency Action, Agency, Advocacy, Fixed Fee Interview, Legal Aid undertaken and Legal Aid Franchise
Ptr: Battrick, Mr Richard J LLB . . . *Nov 1984
Greenhough, Mr Ryan LLB . . . *Nov 1996
Ast: Alexander, Mr Stephen Andrew LLB(Hons) Vice Chair of Local Children's Contact Centre . . . Oct 1992
Davidson, Mr Gareth Lloyd LLB . . . *Oct 1992
Richetta, Mrs Aumeneh . . . Jul 2005
Wells, Mr Matthew David LLB; LPC . . . *Nov 2008

SPICKETTS BATTRICK LAW PRACTICE
56 Albany Road Roath Cardiff CF24 3RR
Tel: 029 2046 7150 *Fax:* 029 2048 7505
E-mail: enquiries@spickettsbattrick.co.uk
Office: Cardiff, Pontypridd
Work: D1 D2 K1 K2 K3

STEWARTS LEGAL ‡
1st Floor Oxford House 16 Vere Street Cardiff CF24 3BJ
Tel: 0845 621 6217
E-mail: darren@stewartslegal.com

TAJ SOLICITORS ‡
242 Cowbridge Road East Canton Cardiff CF5 1GY
Tel: 029 2023 5332 *Fax:* 029 2023 5859
E-mail: info@tajsolicitors.com

TEMPLE LAW SOLICITORS ‡
The Old Probate Registry 49 Cardiff Road Cardiff CF5 2DQ
Tel: 029 2083 8970 *Fax:* 029 2083 8974 *Dx:* 141875 CARDIFF 28
E-mail: enquiries@tlsolicitors.com
List of partners: R I Cassam
Ptr: Cassam, Mr Roland Ivor . . . Dec 1977

THOMPSONS (FORMERLY ROBIN/BRIAN THOMPSON & PARTNERS)
Agincourt House 14-18 Newport Road Cardiff CF24 0SW
Tel: 029 2044 5300 *Fax:* 029 2048 0028
Office: Belfast, Birmingham, Bristol, Chelmsford, Dagenham, Derby, Harrow, Leeds, Liverpool, London SW19, London WC1, Manchester, Middlesbrough, Newcastle upon Tyne, Nottingham, Plymouth, Sheffield, South Shields, Southampton, Stoke-on-Trent, Swansea, Wolverhampton
Languages: French, German, Welsh
Work: G J1 N Z(r)
Legal Aid undertaken, Legal Aid Franchise and Member of Accident Line
Asoc: Gasson, Mr William D LLB(Hons) . . . *Nov 1995
Ast: Jones, Miss Catherine Anne . . . Oct 1996
Jones, Mrs Michaela BA(Hons) . . . *Jul 1996
Parkes, Ms Karen Jayne LLB(Hons); LSF . . . *Sep 1994
Westlake, Ms Louise Anne BSc . . . Oct 1996

SIMON J VOLLANS & CO ‡
The Chancery Suite Chapel House 4 Meadow View Cardiff CF3 2TQ
Tel: 01633 680478 *Fax:* 01633 689007
E-mail: simon.vollans@virgin.net

GEOFFREY WILLIAMS & CHRISTOPHER GREEN ‡
The Mews 38 Cathedral Road Cardiff CF11 9LL
Tel: 029 2034 3377 *Fax:* 029 2034 3566 *Dx:* 141877 CARDIFF 28
E-mail: law@gwcg.globalnet.co.uk
List of partners: C Green, G Williams
Work: G J2 Z(q,t)
Advocacy undertaken
Ptr: Green, Mr Christopher LLB; BA ★ . . . *§Nov 1970
Williams, Mr Geoffrey BA(Law) ♦ . . . *Apr 1978

L G WILLIAMS & PRICHARD ‡
22 St Andrews Crescent Cardiff CF10 3DD
Tel: 029 2022 9716 *Fax:* 029 2037 7761 *Dx:* 50752 CARDIFF 2
E-mail: mail@cardiff-law.co.uk
List of partners: D M Evans, P C Evans, S Pengilley, M J Stephens
Languages: Welsh
Work: B1 C1 C2 E F1 J1 K1 K3 K4 L N O Q R1 S1 S2 W Z(c,r)
Advocacy and Fixed Fee Interview undertaken
Ptr: Evans, Mr David Michael LLB . . . Oct 1982
Evans, Mr Philip C LLB . . . *Oct 1976
Pengilley, Miss Sian LLB . . . *Sep 2001
Stephens, Mr Martin John BA . . . Jun 1993

YOUNGS ‡
52 Station Road Llanishen Cardiff CF14 5LU
Tel: 029 2076 3211 *Fax:* 029 2076 6123
Emergency telephone 07712 624907
E-mail: info@youngs-solicitors.co.uk
List of partners: J R Young
Work: B1 D2 E F1 F2 G H J1 K1 L N Q R1 S1 S2 V W Z(q,u,y)
Emergency Action, Agency, Advocacy, Fixed Fee Interview, Legal Aid undertaken and Legal Aid Franchise
SPr: Young, Mr John R LLB(Lond) . . . *Jan 1975

YUNGS SOLICITORS ‡
68 St Anthony Road Heath Cardiff CF14 4DJ
Tel: 029 20 62 8019 *Fax:* 029 2062 5632
E-mail: enquiries@yungs-solicitors.co.uk

CARDIGAN, Ceredigion

GEORGE DAVIES & EVANS LIMITED ‡
(incorporating W Evans George & Sons)
Castle Chambers Grosvenor Hill Cardigan Ceredigion SA43 1HX
Tel: 01239 612308 *Fax:* 01239 612869 *Dx:* 92653 CARDIGAN
E-mail: gdaviesevans@btconnect.com
List of partners: H Cole, D John, R E Jones, J B Nicholl
Office: Newcastle Emlyn
Languages: Welsh
Work: A1 D1 E K1 L Q S1 S2 W Z(c)
Emergency Action, Agency, Advocacy, Fixed Fee Interview and Legal Aid undertaken
Dir: John, Dawn . . . Jan 2006
Jones, Miss Rebecca Elizabeth LLB . . . *Sep 2002
Nicholl, Mr John B . . . *Jan 1969

MORGAN & RICHARDSON ‡
7 St Mary Street Cardigan Ceredigion SA43 1HB
Tel: 01239 612302 *Fax:* 01239 612533 *Dx:* 92650 CARDIGAN
List of partners: D R Harries, I R Harries, A M Reed
Languages: Welsh
Work: A1 C1 C2 C3 D1 E G H K1 L M1 M2 P S1 T1 T2 W
Agency, Advocacy, Fixed Fee Interview, Legal Aid undertaken and Member of Accident Line
Ptr: Harries, Mr Ian R LLB(Wales) . . . *Aug 1989
Reed, Mr Arwyn Morris . . . *Jun 2000
Ast: Rattenbury, Mr Michael Kenneth LLB . . . *Jun 2005
Con: Thomas, Mr Alan P LLB(Wales) . . . *May 1964

MOSELEY GEORGE ‡
Siambre Pendre 20 Pendre Aberteifi Cardigan Ceredigion SA43 1JT
Tel: 01239 623960 *Fax:* 01239 623969 *Dx:* 92657 CARDIGAN
Emergency telephone 07815 450863
List of partners: S A George, C G Moseley
Languages: French, Welsh
Work: A1 K1 K2 K3 K4 L S1 S2 W
Fixed Fee Interview and Legal Aid undertaken
Dir: George, Miss Sian Angharad LLB . . . *Nov 1992
Moseley, Ms Catrin G BA; MA(Wales) . . . *Feb 1990

TAYLOR LEWIS ‡
Bingham House Pendre Cardigan Ceredigion SA43 1JU
Tel: 01239 621999 *Fax:* 01239 621865
Emergency telephone 01239 613820
E-mail: enquiry@colin-tay-law.co.uk
List of partners: A V Lewis
Languages: French, Welsh
Work: A1 B1 C1 D1 E F1 F2 G H J1 K1 L N O Q R1 S1 S2 V W Z(c,i,l,p,q,r)
Emergency Action, Agency, Advocacy, Legal Aid undertaken, Legal Aid Franchise and Member of Accident Line
SPr: Lewis, Mr Alan V . . . *Dec 1996

WELCH & CO ‡
40 St Marys Street Cardigan Ceredigion SA43 1ET
Tel: 01239 614070 *Fax:* 01239 615222 *Dx:* 92654 CARDIGAN
Emergency telephone 01239 654573
E-mail: louisewelch@welchlaw.co.uk
List of partners: M L Welch, S A H Welch
Office: Cardigan
Languages: Welsh
Work: D1 D2 E G H K1 K3 L Q S1 V W Z(q)
Emergency Action, Agency, Advocacy, Fixed Fee Interview, Legal Aid undertaken and Legal Aid Franchise
Dir: Welch, Mrs Madeleine Louise LLB . . . *Mar 1979
Welch, Mr Stephen A H LLB . . . *Sep 1979
Ast: Dyer, Miss Carys LLB . . . Jun 2008
Hanson, Ms Katy Charlotte Emma . . . Oct 2003
Wigan, Mr Peter BA(Hons) . . . *Apr 1996

WELCH & CO
Dolwar Fach High Street Cilgerran Cardigan Ceredigion SA43 2SG
Office: Cardigan

W J WILLIAMS & DAVIES ‡
Glyncoed Chambers Priory Street Cardigan Ceredigion SA43 1BX
Tel: 01239 612262 *Fax:* 01239 615319 *Dx:* 92652 CARDIGAN
E-mail: enquiries@wmsdavies.co.uk
List of partners: C A Dyer, J S Dyer
Languages: Welsh
Emergency Action, Agency, Advocacy, Fixed Fee Interview and Legal Aid undertaken
Ptr: Dyer, Ms Christine A LLB . . . *May 1978
Dyer, Mr John S LLB . . . *Apr 1978
Con: Watts, Mr John M LLB . . . Oct 1957

CARLISLE, Cumbria

ATKINSON RITSON ‡
(incorporating Atkinson & North; Hetherington Ritson & Co; Saul & Lightfoot; J A Coupland & Co; K Messenger; Moore & Emery)
15 Fisher Street Carlisle Cumbria CA3 8RW
Tel: 01228 525221 *Fax:* 01228 515409 *Dx:* 63001 CARLISLE
E-mail: info@atkinson-ritson.com
List of partners: A L C Barnard, M C Emery, H J B Fitzgerald, K J Wheeler, P D Yardley
Office: Wigton
Work: A1 B1 C1 D1 E F1 G H J1 K1 L M1 N O P Q R1 S1 S2 V W Z(c,d,i,k,l,m,r,t)
Emergency Action, Agency, Advocacy, Fixed Fee Interview, Legal Aid undertaken, Legal Aid Franchise and Member of Accident Line
Ptr: Barnard, Mr Andrew Lindsay Curtis BA . . . Sep 1999
Emery, Mr Malcolm C . . . May 1982
Wheeler, Miss Kathryn J . . . *Nov 1990
Yardley, Mr Peter D LLB . . . *§Jan 1979
Con: Ward, Mr David BA(Oxon) . . . *§Feb 1962

BAINES WILSON LLP ‡
2 Merchants Drive Carlisle Cumbria CA3 0JW
Tel: 01228 552600 *Fax:* 01228 549560 *Dx:* 741450 CARLISLE 10
E-mail: law@baineswilson.co.uk
List of partners: A R Hill, J Holborn, S F Logue, J S R Wilson
Languages: French
Work: C1 C2 C3 E I J1 L O S2 U1 U2 Z(e,p)
Ptr: Hill, Mr Andrew Robert LLB . . . Jun 1994
Holborn, Ms Joanne LLB . . . May 1995
Logue, Mr Sean Francis LLB(Hons); MBA . . . *Mar 1990
Wilson, Mr John S R LLB(Hons) . . . *Nov 1988
Asoc: Harty, Mr Duncan Alexander LLB . . . Nov 2005
Ast: Hawley, Mr James Alexander LLB . . . Apr 2008
Scaife, Mr Thomas Jardine LLB . . . Jul 2011
Sewell, Mrs Elizabeth Clare LLB(Hons) . . . Jul 2001

BELL PARK KERRIDGE ‡
Clifford Court Cooper Way Parkhouse Carlisle Cumbria CA3 0JG
Tel: 01228 888999 *Fax:* 01228 888998 *Dx:* 63014 CARLISLE
E-mail: info@bpkcumbria.co.uk
List of partners: J Bell, D G Carter
Work: A1 E F1 J1 N O Q S1 S2 W Z(m,r)
Emergency Action, Agency, Advocacy, Fixed Fee Interview undertaken and Member of Accident Line
Ptr: Bell, Mr James LLB Deputy District Judge . . . *Feb 1985
Carter, Mr Duncan Gilchrist LLB(Hons) . . . *Aug 1996
Ast: Harrison, Mrs Claire LLB; LPC . . . Sep 2001
Con: Tattersall, Mr Stephen LLB . . . *Oct 1988

BENDLES ‡
22 Portland Square Carlisle Cumbria CA1 1PE
Tel: 01228 522215 *Fax:* 01228 515442 *Dx:* 63010 CARLISLE
Emergency telephone 01228 75302
E-mail: solicitors@bendles.org
List of partners: A C Bone, V M Clough, M J Johnson, D C Kendrew, A J Stevenson
Languages: French, German, Melanesian, Spanish
Work: A1 A2 A3 B1 C1 D1 D2 E F1 J1 K1 K2 L M1 N O P Q S1 V W Z(c,d,l)
Emergency Action, Agency, Advocacy, Fixed Fee Interview and Legal Aid undertaken
Ptr: Bone, Ms Alison C BSc . . . *Feb 1990
Clough, Ms Vivienne M . . . *Oct 1986
Johnson, Mr Michael John LLB(Hons); LLM . . . *Dec 1996
Kendrew, Mr David C LLB . . . *§Apr 1976
Stevenson, Mr Andrew J MA . . . *Jan 1990
Ast: Hanlon, Mr John Thompson LLB . . . Jan 2005
Rawsthorn, Mrs Frances Claire BA . . . Oct 1988
Con: Lewis, Ninian LLB . . . *Oct 1974

BURNETTS ‡
6 Victoria Place Carlisle Cumbria CA1 1ES
Tel: 01228 552222 *Fax:* 01228 522399 *Dx:* 63005 CARLISLE
E-mail: info@burnetts.co.uk
List of partners: J D Claxton, M E Cousins, A Curran, A J Fallows, N Gutteridge, P M Hall, J V Jagger, R M V Jones, A J Lake, T S Leach, C J G Marshall, R W Miller, J E Morris, S N Mortimer, J Noctor, W J Priddle, N Ruane, J D Stronach, K Z B Strycharczyk, V R Watson, M P M Wrightson
Office: Carlisle, Newcastle upon Tyne, Whitehaven
Languages: Danish, Dutch, French, German, Mandarin, Polish
Work: A1 B1 C1 C2 C3 D1 D2 E F1 G I J1 J2 K1 K3 K4 L M1 N O P Q R1 R2 S1 S2 T1 U2 V W X Z(b,c,d,e,h,i,j,k,l,m,n,o,p,q,r,s,t,u,za)
Emergency Action, Agency, Advocacy, Fixed Fee Interview, Legal Aid undertaken, Legal Aid Franchise and Member of Accident Line

Ptr: Ruane, Mrs Natalie BA(Hons)(German & French) . . *Sep 2001
Claxton, Mr J Douglas LLB(Lond) . . . . *§Oct 1974
Cousins, Mr Michael E MA(Oxon) . . . . *§Apr 1971
Curran, Mrs Angela LLB . . . . *Oct 1994
Fallows, Miss Amy Jasmine LLB(Hons) Cavendish Law Prize; Alasdair Benzie Business Law Prize . . . . . . *Nov 2001
Gutteridge, Mr Nicholas LLB(Hons)(Hull) . . . . . . *May 1991
Hall, Ms Patricia M MA(Oxon) . . . . *§Oct 1981
Jagger, Miss Janet Victoria BA(Law) Harold Wyatt Scholarship; Cooper Exhibition (Nottingham University) . . . . *Apr 1981
Jones, Mr Richard M V LLB . . . . Nov 1986
Lake, Mr Anthony J . . . . *Nov 1990
Leach, Mr Tom Simpson LLB(Lond) . . . . *§Jul 1978
Marshall, Mr Charles Jonathan Guy LLB . . . . *Dec 1986
Miller, Mr Richard William LLB(Hons)(Newc) . . . . . *Aug 2007
Morris, Mr John E LLB . . . . *Dec 1974
Mortimer, Mr Simon N BA(Law) . . . . *§Oct 1982
Noctor, Mr John MA(Cantab) . . . . *§Nov 1985
Priddle, Mr W John LLB(Newc) . . . . *§Jun 1974
Stronach, Mrs Joanne Denise LLB(Hons) . . . . Nov 1994
Strycharczyk, Kuba Z B BA(Dunelm) . . . . *Dec 1978
Watson, Mrs Victoria Roy LLB(Hons) . . . . *Sep 1997
Wrightson, Mr Martyn P M . . . . *§Nov 1981
Asoc: Chappell, Mrs Susan Marie LLB . . . . Jan 2004
Lyon, Mr Samuel John BA(Hons)(Newc)(Accounting & Law) . . . . *Sep 2006
Phillips, Miss Hazel LLB . . . . *Sep 2006
Redhead, Mrs Caroline Anne Bocking . . . . *Nov 1994
Ast: Barnes, Miss Diane Katherine LLB(Hons)(Durham) . *Sep 2009
Child, Miss Leigh Crawford LLB(Hons) . . . . Dec 2003
Dodds, Mrs Sarah Elizabeth LLB(Sheff) . . . . *Sep 2008
Hall, Ms Lynne Jane . . . . *Sep 2003
Hill, Miss Miranda Jane LLB . . . . Sep 2010
Johnston, Mr James LLB . . . . Jul 2010
Keenleyside, Mrs Patricia Ruth BA(Hons) . . . . . . *Nov 1990
Logan, Mrs Christina Hestbech LLB(Shef) . . . . Jan 2002
McMurchie, Mr Andrew LLB . . . . Oct 1994
Mather, Mr Robert BA . . . . Sep 2010
Spencer, Mrs Sian Louise Hellier MA . . . . Oct 2006
Con: Cornish, Mr Tony . . . . Nov 1986
McGill, Mr David John MA . . . . *Nov 1995
Southorn, Mr Andrew Timothy MA(Oxon) . . . . . . *Jun 1974

BURNETTS
Montgomery Way Rosehill Industrial Estate Carlisle Cumbria CA1 2TQ
Tel: 01228 552222 *Fax:* 01228 552299
E-mail: info@burnetts.co.uk
Office: Carlisle, Newcastle upon Tyne, Whitehaven
Languages: Cantonese, Dutch, French, German, Mandarin, Polish
Work: A1 J2 N Z(r)
Legal Aid undertaken
Ptr: Ruane, Mrs Natalie BA(Hons)(German & French) . . *Sep 2001
Claxton, Mr J Douglas LLB(Lond) . . . . *§Oct 1974
Cousins, Mr Michael E MA(Oxon) . . . . *§Apr 1971
Curran, Mrs Angela LLB . . . . *Oct 1994
Fallows, Miss Amy Jasmine LLB(Hons) Cavendish Law Prize; Alasdair Benzie Business Law Prize . . . . . . *Nov 2001
Gutteridge, Mr Nicholas LLB(Hons)(Hull) . . . . . . *May 1991
Hall, Ms Patricia M MA(Oxon) . . . . *§Oct 1981
Jagger, Miss Janet Victoria BA(Law) Harold Wyatt Scholarship; Cooper Exhibition (Nottingham University) . . . . *Apr 1981
Jones, Mr Richard M V LLB . . . . Nov 1986
Lake, Mr Anthony J . . . . *Nov 1990
Leach, Mr Tom Simpson LLB(Lond) . . . . *§Jul 1978
Miller, Mr Richard William LLB(Hons)(Newc) . . . . . *Aug 2007
Morris, Mr John E LLB . . . . *Dec 1974
Mortimer, Mr Simon N BA(Law) . . . . *§Oct 1982
Noctor, Mr John MA(Cantab) . . . . *§Nov 1985
Priddle, Mr W John LLB(Newc) . . . . *§Jun 1974
Stronach, Mrs Joanne Denise LLB(Hons) . . . . Nov 1994
Strycharczyk, Kuba Z B BA(Dunelm) . . . . *Dec 1978
Watson, Mrs Victoria Roy LLB(Hons) . . . . *Sep 1997
Wrightson, Mr Martyn P M . . . . *§Nov 1981
Asoc: Chappell, Mrs Susan Marie LLB . . . . Jan 2004
Lyon, Mr Samuel John BA(Hons)(Newc)(Accounting & Law) . . . . *Sep 2006
McMurchie, Mr Andrew LLB . . . . Oct 1994
Phillips, Miss Hazel LLB . . . . *Sep 2006
Redhead, Mrs Caroline Anne Bocking . . . . *Nov 1994
Ast: Dodds, Mrs Sarah Elizabeth LLB(Sheff) . . . . *Sep 2008
Hall, Ms Lynne Jane . . . . *Sep 2003
Hill, Miss Miranda Jane LLB . . . . Sep 2010
Keenleyside, Mrs Patricia Ruth BA(Hons) . . . . . . *Nov 1990
Williams, Miss Emma Marie LLB(Newc) . . . . *Oct 2008
Con: McGill, Mr David John MA . . . . *Nov 1995
Southorn, Mr Andrew Timothy MA(Oxon) . . . . . . *Jun 1974

BUTTERWORTHS ‡
24 Lowther Street Carlisle Cumbria CA3 8DA
Tel: 01228 593939 *Fax:* 01228 525465 *Dx:* 63017 CARLISLE
E-mail: info@butterworths-solicitors.co.uk
List of partners: A M Butterworth, A M Nelson
Office: Penrith
Work: C1 D1 E G H J1 K1 L N O P Q S1 V W Z(i,m,p)
Emergency Action, Agency, Advocacy, Fixed Fee Interview, Legal Aid undertaken, Legal Aid Franchise and Member of Accident Line
Ptr: Butterworth, Mr Anthony M LLB . . . . *§Jun 1987
Nelson, Mrs Angela Michelle LLB . . . . *Nov 1993
Ast: Chuku, Mr John Nathaniel LLB . . . . *Nov 1994
Parkinson, Ms Marian Elizabeth BSc(Hons); MA(Environmental Law) . . . . *Sep 1984

BUTTERWORTHS ‡
The Orchards Carleton Carlisle Cumbria CA1 3DZ
Tel: 01228 516400 *Fax:* 01228 516419
E-mail: info@butterworths-solicitors.co.uk

CARTMELL SHEPHERD ‡
Viaduct House Carlisle Cumbria CA3 8EZ
Tel: 01228 516666 *Fax:* 01228 401490 *Dx:* 63006 CARLISLE
E-mail: post@cartmells.co.uk
List of partners: D F Armstrong, J J Carroll, T H Cartmell, S E Duff, C Fish, D H Flynn, C M Hansford, H P Holland, J M H Jeeves, J M R Nelson, T V Sykes, J E Y Wright
Office: Brampton, Carlisle, Haltwhistle, Penrith
Work: A1 B1 C1 C2 C3 D1 E F1 J1 K1 L M1 M2 N P R1 S1 T1 T2 V W Z(b,c,d,e,f,h,i,j,k,l,m,n,o,s,t)
Emergency Action, Agency, Advocacy, Fixed Fee Interview, Legal Aid undertaken and Member of Accident Line
Ptr: Duff, Mrs Susan Elizabeth . . . . *Nov 1992
Fish, Mrs Carol LLB . . . . *May 1989
Flynn, Mrs Deborah Helen LLB(Hons) . . . . *Oct 1995
Jeeves, Mrs Joanna M H LLB . . . . *Oct 1985
Nelson, Mrs Julian M R MA; LLB . . . . *Aug 1989
Sykes, Mr Timothy V BA(Dunelm) . . . . *Apr 1979
Asoc: Johnson, Mrs Stephanie C . . . . *Sep 1999
Minihan, Miss Jayne C LLB . . . . Sep 2004
Stafford, Mr Peter J LLB . . . . *Sep 1997
Ast: Aspin, Mr Mark Gareth . . . . Jan 2010
Davies, Ms Ann Claire . . . . Oct 1985
Logan, Mrs Claire L LLB . . . . Sep 2007
Marrs, Mr Peter LLB . . . . Sep 2006

CARTMELL SHEPHERD
Montgomery Way Rosehill Carlisle Cumbria CA1 2RW
Tel: 01228 514077 *Fax:* 01228 514470 *Dx:* 63006 CARLISLE
E-mail: rosehill@cartmells.co.uk
Office: Brampton, Carlisle, Haltwhistle, Penrith
Work: A1 C1 C2 C3 E L T1 T2 W
Agency undertaken and Member of Accident Line
Ptr: Carroll, Mr Jonathan James LLB(Hons) . . . . *Sep 2001
Cartmell, Mr Timothy H BA(Cantab); ACII . . . . . . *§Mar 1972
Ast: McAlister, Mrs Samantha Claire . . . . Jan 2009
McKenzie, Miss Joanne . . . . Jan 2008
Pretswell-Walker, Mrs Katherine . . . . Sep 2008

GEOFFREY CLAPP ‡
Earl Street Chambers 11 Earl Street Carlisle Cumbria CA1 1DP
Tel: 01228 810228 *Fax:* 01228 810071 *Dx:* 63004 CARLISLE
List of partners: G N Clapp
SPr: Clapp, Mr Geoffrey N . . . . Jun 1964

K J COMMONS & CO
54 Warwick Road Carlisle Cumbria CA1 1DR
Tel: 01228 822666 *Fax:* 01228 822667 *Dx:* 63051 CARLISLE
E-mail: helen.mcneil@kjcommons.co.uk
Office: Whitehaven, Workington
Work: G K1 S1 Z(r)
Emergency Action, Agency, Advocacy, Fixed Fee Interview and Legal Aid undertaken
Ptr: Nickson, Mr Marcus P LLB . . . . *§Nov 1977

CRUTES
13 Castle Street Carlisle Cumbria CA3 8SY
Tel: 01228 525195 *Fax:* 01228 522620
E-mail: info@crutes.co.uk
Office: Newcastle upon Tyne, Stockton-on-Tees
Work: A1 A3 B1 C1 D1 E F1 G H J1 K1 K3 L M1 N O P Q S1 V W Z(h,k,l,q,r,u)
Emergency Action, Agency, Advocacy, Fixed Fee Interview, Legal Aid undertaken and Member of Accident Line
Ptr: O'Neil, Mr Shaun LLB . . . . *Jun 1995
Robson, Mr Michael Kenneth Deputy District Judge . *Feb 1985
Ast: Graham-Jones, Ms Judith Alison LLB(Hons) . . . . . Nov 1995

MALCOLM DODDS & CO ‡
18 Spinners Yard Fisher Street Carlisle Cumbria CA3 8RE
Tel: 01228 529444 *Dx:* 63044 CARLISLE
E-mail: mdodds@malcolmdodds.co.uk

SCOTT DUFF & CO
3 Devonshire Street Carlisle Cumbria CA3 8LG
Tel: 01228 531054 *Fax:* 01228 511497
E-mail: aduff@scottduff.co.uk
Office: Keswick, Penrith
Work: E F1 G H J1 K1 L N O R1 S1 S2 V W Z(c,l)
Emergency Action, Agency, Advocacy, Fixed Fee Interview, Legal Aid undertaken, Legal Aid Franchise and Member of Accident Line
Ptr: Connell, Mrs Suzanne Elizabeth LLB(Hons) . . . . . *Mar 2000
Wright, Miss Katharine Abigail LLB(Hons) . . . . . . *Sep 2001
Ast: Broad, Miss Cheryl Teresa . . . . Jul 2008
Sterling, Mr Matthew BSc . . . . Jun 2011

MICHAEL J FISHER & CO ‡
49 Spencer Street Carlisle Cumbria CA1 1BB
Tel: 01228 592686 *Fax:* 01228 592674
E-mail: info@mjfisher.co.uk

HOUGH HALTON & SOAL ‡
32 Abbey Street Carlisle Cumbria CA3 8RJ
Tel: 01228 524379 *Fax:* 01228 511249 *Dx:* 63012 CARLISLE
E-mail: enquiries@halton-soal.co.uk
List of partners: J Ditchburn, A J Kirkpatrick, J K Leiper
Work: F1 J1 J2 K1 L N Q R1 S1 S2 T2 W Z(q,r)
Agency, Advocacy, Fixed Fee Interview and Legal Aid undertaken
Ptr: Ditchburn, Mr Jonathan LLB(Hons) . . . . *Mar 1998
Kirkpatrick, Mr Andrew J LLB . . . . *§Dec 1988
Leiper, Mr John K BA . . . . *Jun 1977
Asoc: Elliot, Mr Ashley LLB(Hons) . . . . *Feb 2001
Grounds, Mr Alastair J LLB . . . . *Jun 1987
Oakley, Dr Catherine Ann BSc; PhD; PGDipLaw . . . . Sep 2005
Unwin, Mr Stephen John MBA . . . . *Sep 2000
Warwick, Miss Kim BA . . . . Jul 2004

JENNINGS LEGAL SERVICES ‡
Clifford House Clifford Court Cooper Way Carlisle Cumbria CA3 0JG
Tel: 0870 777 7100 *Fax:* 0870 777 7600 *Dx:* 7300300 CARLISLE 9
E-mail: info@jenningslegalservices.co.uk

ANITA LEAKER SOLICITOR ‡
49 Spencer Street Carlisle Cumbria CA1 1BB
Tel: 01228 521383 *Fax:* 01228 818169

MPG SOLICITORS ‡
32 The Enterprise Centre James Street Carlisle Cumbria CA2 5BB
Tel: 01228 625700 *Fax:* 01228 818169
E-mail: kgheard@aol.com

MARGARET PAYNE ‡
49 Spencer Street Carlisle Cumbria CA1 1BB
Tel: 01228 521383 *Fax:* 01228 818169
Emergency telephone 07710 050100
E-mail: info@margaretpayne.co.uk
List of partners: M P Payne
Work: B2 G H I J2 Z(m,t)
Emergency Action, Agency, Advocacy, Fixed Fee Interview, Legal Aid undertaken and Legal Aid Franchise
SPr: Payne, Mrs Margaret Patricia LLB(Nott'm) ★ Serjeants Inn Prize . . . . *Apr 1981

PETER WILLIAM PICKLES ‡
Harp Hill Armathwaite Carlisle Cumbria CA4 9PW
Tel: 01697 472223
List of partners: P W Pickles
Work: S1 W

ROYS ‡
PO Box 185 Carlisle Cumbria CA1 1GL
Tel: 01228 526385 *Fax:* 01228 537700
List of partners: I A Roy
Work: S1 W
SPr: Roy, Mr Iain A LLB . . . . *Dec 1977

J H SMITH ‡
Carlisle Criminal Law Chambers 49 Spencer Street Carlisle Cumbria CA1 1BB
Tel: 01228 521383 *Fax:* 01228 818169
Emergency telephone 07831 374958
List of partners: J H Smith
Work: G H
Emergency Action, Agency, Advocacy, Fixed Fee Interview and Legal Aid undertaken
SPr: Smith, Mr John Hartley BA(Hons) . . . . *§Feb 1981

WILLIAMS & AIREY ‡
24 Spencer Street Carlisle Cumbria CA11BG
Est:
Tel: 01228 829530 *Fax:* 01228 549666

WRAGG MARK-BELL SOLICITORS ‡
16-17 The Square Dalston Carlisle Cumbria CA5 7PY
Tel: 01228 711728 *Fax:* 01228 711330
Emergency telephone 01228 710184
E-mail: theoffice@wraggmarkbell.co.uk
List of partners: W D Mark-Bell, G L Wragg
Office: Carlisle
Languages: Arabic, Farsi, French
Work: A1 A2 B2 C1 C2 C3 D1 D2 E F1 F2 G H J1 J2 K1 K2 K3 K4 L N O P Q R1 S1 S2 W Z(b,c,d,e,h,i,l,t,u,y)
Agency, Advocacy, Fixed Fee Interview, Legal Aid undertaken and Legal Aid Franchise
Ptr: Mark-Bell, Mr William D MA(Oxon) ★ Part time Immigration Judge . . . . *Dec 1977
Dir: Wragg, Mrs Gaynor L BA(Oxon) Council Member of the Law Society . . . . *Dec 1988
Ast: Berry, Mrs Elizabeth MA(Hons)(Geography); CPE; LPCSep 2003
Kennon, Mr Nicholas Todhunter LLB . . . . Apr 1997
Lloyd-Osborne, Miss Susan Elizabeth BA(Hons); CPE; LPC . . . . Oct 1991

WRAGG MARK-BELL SOLICITORS
80 English Street Carlisle Cumbria CA3 8HP
Tel: 01228 510077 *Fax:* 01228 511188
E-mail: theoffice@wraggmarkbell.co.uk
Office: Carlisle

CARMARTHEN, Carmarthenshire

MARY EVANS & CO ‡
Waverley House 22 Lammas Street Carmarthen Carmarthenshire SA31 3AL
Tel: 01267 233881 *Fax:* 01267 232952 *Dx:* 51423 CARMARTHEN
E-mail: mail@maryevanssolicitors.com
List of partners: E M Evans, H C Morcom
Languages: Welsh
Work: C1 C2 C3 E F1 G H J1 K1 L N O S1 W
Emergency Action, Agency, Advocacy, Fixed Fee Interview, Legal Aid undertaken and Legal Aid Franchise
Ptr: Evans, Miss E Mary LLB . . . . *Oct 1982
Morcom, Mr Huw C LLB(Wales) . . . . *Jul 1989
Ast: Jones, Miss Sally Verona LLB . . . . *May 1999

JOHN FARR-DAVIES & CO ‡
3 Queen Street Carmarthen Carmarthenshire SA31 1JR
Tel: 01267 231818 *Fax:* 01267 236581
Emergency telephone 01267 233803
E-mail: alison@johnfarr-davies.fsbusiness.co.uk
List of partners: A K John
Languages: French, Welsh
Work: A1 A2 B1 C1 E F1 J1 S1 S2 T1 T2 U2 W Z(c,d,l,t,u)
SPr: John, Miss Alison K LLB(Wales) . . . . *Dec 1979
Asoc: Campbell, Ms Mair Anne LLB(Hons)(Wales) . . . . . *Jan 1982

HAINS & LEWIS LTD
32 Quay Street Carmarthen Carmarthenshire SA31 3JT
Tel: 0845 408 0125 *Fax:* 01834 861340
E-mail: law@hainsandlewis.co.uk
Office: Haverfordwest, Narberth

LEWIS LEWIS & COMPANY LTD
County Chambers 20 Blue Street Carmarthen Carmarthenshire SA31 3LE
Tel: 01267 231666 *Fax:* 01267 238334 *Dx:* 98375 ST CLEARS
Office: St Clears, Tenby
Work: A1 J1 K1 N Q S1 S2 W Z(l,q)
Agency undertaken

ANDREW MARKHAM & CO ‡
(incorporating Seventeen Bridge Street Solicitors & Gwilym Thomas Solicitor)
1 Queen Street Carmarthen Carmarthenshire SA31 1JR
Tel: 01267 221550 / 236199 *Fax:* 01267 229330
Dx: 51438 CARMARTHEN 1
Emergency telephone 07812 049296
E-mail: mail@andrewmarkham.co.uk
List of partners: A J Markham
Languages: French, Spanish
Work: D1 G H J1 K1 K3 L N Q S1 S2 W Z(m)
Emergency Action, Agency, Advocacy, Fixed Fee Interview, Legal Aid undertaken and Legal Aid Franchise
SPr: Markham, Mr Andrew Joel LLB . . . . *Jan 1999
Ast: Isaac, Miss Lynne Mary LLB(Hons)(Law & Italian); LPC Apr 2005
Jones, Mr Peter Rhys LLB(Wales) . . . . Nov 1975
Weeks, Miss Alison BA . . . . Apr 2004
Williams, Mrs Julia . . . . *Mar 1999
Con: Collen, Miss Jocelyne Sarah LLB . . . . *Nov 1994

PRITCHARD EDWARDS & CO ‡
Golden Grove House 10 Quay Street Carmarthen Carmarthenshire SA31 3JT
Tel: 01267 234022 *Fax:* 01267 231867 *Dx:* 51404 CARMARTHEN
List of partners: M K Edwards, E Pritchard
Languages: Welsh
Work: A1 B1 C1 C2 C3 D1 E F1 J1 K1 L N P Q R1 S1 T1 T2 W Z(l,m,t)
Emergency Action, Agency, Advocacy, Fixed Fee Interview, Legal Aid undertaken and Member of Accident Line

See p112 for the Key to Work Categories & other symbols

Ptr: Edwards, Ms Melanie K LLB . . . . *Apr 1985
Pritchard, Mr Eryl LLB. . . . . *§Jun 1978
Ast: Davies, Miss Hayley M LLB . . . . *May 2005

RED KITE LAW
St John Street Carmarthen Carmarthenshire SA34 0AN
Tel: 01994 240305
Office: Carmarthen, Haverfordwest, Milford Haven, Pembroke, Pembroke Dock, Tenby

RED KITE LAW
14-15 Spilman Street Carmarthen Carmarthenshire SA31 1SR
Tel: 01267 239000 *Fax:* 01267 238521
Emergency telephone 01207 239000
Office: Carmarthen, Haverfordwest, Milford Haven, Pembroke, Pembroke Dock, Tenby
Languages: Welsh
Work: A1 B1 C1 D1 E F1 F2 G H J1 K1 K3 K4 L N O Q R1 S1 S2 T2 W X Z(c,l,q,t)
Emergency Action, Agency, Advocacy, Fixed Fee Interview, Legal Aid undertaken, Legal Aid Franchise and Member of Accident Line
Ptr: Evans, Mr D Michael BSc. . . . . *Sep 1989
Griffiths, Mr John L LLB. . . . . *Dec 1975
Griffiths, Mr K Michael LLB(Lond) . . . . *Dec 1977
Lewis, Mr John R LLB. . . . . *Jun 1974
Williams, Mr David I BA. . . . . *Sep 1985
Ast: Bowen, Mr Mathew Isaac LLB. . . . . Sep 2003
Griffiths, Miss Catrin Mary LLB . . . . Nov 2002
Hopwood, Mr Richard Martin LLB(Wales) . . . . . . *§Oct 1981
Jones, Enfys W D LLB . . . . *Jan 1985
Owen, Mr Aled Rhys LLB . . . . Apr 1999
Powell, Miss Dymphna Maria BA . . . . Mar 2001
Voyle, Luned . . . . *Feb 1995
Con: Hughes, Mr John M. . . . . *Jul 1967

MICHAEL J REED LTD ‡
Trawsmawr Manor Farm Henfwlch Road Carmarthen Carmarthenshire SA33 6AE
Tel: 01267 281675 *Fax:* 01267 281693
E-mail: mike@mjreedsolicitors.co.uk
List of partners: M J Reed
Work: G H
Emergency Action, Advocacy, Legal Aid undertaken and Legal Aid Franchise
SPr: Reed, Mr Michael J LLB. . . . . Oct 1971

RUNNETT AND CO ‡
Walsall House Pentre Road St Clears Carmarthen Carmarthenshire SA33 4LR
Tel: 01994 438068 *Fax:* 01994 231126 *Dx:* 98379 ST CLEARS
E-mail: info@runnettlawyers.co.uk

STEEL & HITCHCOCK ‡
9 Quay Street Carmarthen Carmarthenshire SA31 3JT
Tel: 01267 236781 *Fax:* 01267 237771
List of partners: R T Hitchcock
Languages: Welsh
Agency, Advocacy, Fixed Fee Interview, Legal Aid undertaken and Member of Accident Line

TRANT & RICHARDS ‡
4 St Mary Street Carmarthen Carmarthenshire SA31 1TN
Tel: 01267 236426 *Fax:* 01267 223154
List of partners: R T Hitchcock
Work: S1 S2 T2 W Z(d)

UNGOED-THOMAS & KING LIMITED ‡
Gwynne House 6 Quay Street Carmarthen Carmarthenshire SA31 3JX
Tel: 01267 237441 *Fax:* 01267 238317 *Dx:* 51400 CARMARTHEN
E-mail: mail@utk.co.uk
List of partners: H A F Bruce, C A Kirby, R A J Lewis, A C Owen, T H Owen
Languages: Welsh
Work: A1 B1 C1 D1 E F1 J1 J2 K1 K2 L N O Q R1 S1 V W X Z(d,h,k,l,m,q,r)
Emergency Action, Agency, Advocacy and Fixed Fee Interview undertaken
Dir: Bruce, The Hon Henry Adam Francis MA(Oxon); TEP*§Nov 1988
Kirby, Mr Christian Alexander LLB. . . . . *Aug 1997
Lewis, Mr Roland A J LLB. . . . . *§Mar 1990
Owen, Mrs Ann Carys LLB(Wales); LLM(Cantab) . . . *Sep 1982
Owen, Mr Thomas Huw LLB(Wales). . . . . *§Jul 1980
Con: Jenkins, Mr Anthony LLB(Wales) . . . . *§Jul 1975

WALTERS & WILLIAMS ‡
31 Quay Street Carmarthen Carmarthenshire SA31 3JZ
Tel: 01267 236686 *Fax:* 01267 230678
List of partners: R J M Griffiths
Work: S1 S2 W
SPr: Griffiths, Mr Roger John Morris . . . . *§Jun 1977

CARNFORTH, Lancashire

ADVOCACY DIRECT ‡
198 Coastal Road Bolton Le Sands Carnforth Lancashire LA5 8JW
Tel: 01524 824606
E-mail: cgh@advocacydirect.co.uk

JENNIFER KNOWLES SOLICITORS ‡
1 Bowland View Clapham Old Road Ingleton Carnforth Lancashire LA6 3JN
Tel: 01524 241417 *Fax:* 01524 242395
E-mail: jk@jklaw.co.uk

RATCLIFFE & BIBBY ‡
3-7 New Street Carnforth Lancashire LA5 9BU
Tel: 01524 734884 *Fax:* 01524 736449 *Dx:* 63982 CARNFORTH
E-mail: carnforth@rblegal.co.uk
List of partners: N Anderton, V R Drinkall, I S Gardner
Office: Lancaster, Morecambe
Work: A1 B1 C1 C2 C3 D1 E F1 G H J1 K1 L N O P Q R1 S1 T1 T2 V W Z(d,j,k,l,m,s,t)
Emergency Action, Agency, Advocacy, Fixed Fee Interview, Legal Aid undertaken and Member of Accident Line

CARSHALTON, Surrey

PAUL R BARON ‡
34 Warnham Court Road Carshalton Surrey SM5 3LZ
Tel: 020 8401 2251 *Fax:* 020 8286 4694
Emergency telephone 07778 211791
E-mail: paulbaron99@hotmail.com
List of partners: P R Baron
Languages: French, Malay, Punjabi
Work: B2 G H
Agency and Advocacy undertaken
Ptr: Baron, Mr Paul R MA(Cantab). . . . . *§May 1967

MCMILLAN WILLIAMS
The Orangery The Square Carshalton Surrey SM5 3BN
Tel: 020 8432 2041 *Fax:* 020 8432 2042 *Dx:* 59958 WALLINGTON
Emergency telephone 020 8660 3383
E-mail: carshalton@mcmillan-williams.co.uk
Office: Coulsdon, Croydon, Mitcham, South Croydon, Thornton Heath, Wallington
Languages: French, German
Ptr: Jones-King, Mrs Nicola Jayne LLB(Hons) . . . . Jan 1993
Manning, Ms Nicola. . . . . *Jan 1981
Ast: Hall, David . . . . Oct 2003

PIRES LAW FIRM ‡
38 Newstead Walk Carshalton Surrey SM5 1AW
Tel: 020 8648 1671 *Fax:* 07985 339948
E-mail: kenneth@pireslawfirm.com

STANLEY SMITH HILL & CO ‡
(incorporating Warmingtons; W V Hill)
35 High Street Carshalton Surrey SM5 3BG
Tel: 020 8669 0044 *Fax:* 020 8669 8827 *Dx:* 59956 WALLINGTON
E-mail: carshalton@stanleysmithhill.co.uk
List of partners: D J Mahoney, G R Nunn
Office: Banstead
Work: C1 D1 E F1 J1 K1 K3 L N Q S1 S2 T2 W
Emergency Action, Agency, Fixed Fee Interview undertaken and Member of Accident Line
Ptr: Nunn, Mr Geoffrey R LLB(Warw) . . . . *Apr 1975
Ast: Gridley, Mrs Rosemary A LLB(Sheff) . . . . *Oct 1983

KEITH WALMSLEY ‡
61 Strawberry Lane Carshalton Surrey SM5 2NG
Tel: 020 8669 3643
List of partners: K Walmsley
Work: C1
SPr: Walmsley, Mr Keith LLB(Lond); FCIS . . . . *Jun 1979

CARTERTON, Oxfordshire

DUNNING ANDERSON ‡
5 The Clockhouse Carterton Oxfordshire OX18 3HN
Tel: 01993 840200 *Fax:* 01993 844855
E-mail: stephen@cartertonlaw.com
List of partners: S J Dunning
Work: C1 E J1 K1 N S1 S2 W Z(r)
SPr: Dunning, Mr Stephen J . . . . *Dec 1978

CASTLE CARY, Somerset

BARTLETT GOODING & WEELEN
(incorporating Robin Weelen & Co)
Old Bank House High Street Castle Cary Somerset BA7 7AW
Tel: 01963 350888 *Fax:* 01963 351107
Emergency telephone 01749 346354
E-mail: mail@bgwcastlecary.co.uk
Office: Cheddar, Glastonbury, Shepton Mallet
Work: A1 A2 B1 C3 E F1 G H J1 K1 L N P R1 S1 S2 W Z(c,l,q,t)
Emergency Action, Agency, Advocacy, Fixed Fee Interview, Legal Aid undertaken, Legal Aid Franchise and Member of Accident Line
Ptr: Bartlett, Mr Basil W . . . . *Apr 1967
Nash, Mrs Dervla LLB(Hons) . . . . *Sep 2002
Rae, Miss Elizabeth LLB(Hons) . . . . *Sep 2004
Reynolds, Mr Gareth LLB . . . . *Oct 1985
Weelen, Mr Robin A. . . . . *Jun 1973

CASTLEFORD, West Yorkshire

EMSLEYS
26 Bank Street Castleford West Yorkshire WF10 1JD
Tel: 01977 550115 *Fax:* 01977 514163 *Dx:* 700131 CASTLEFORD
E-mail: law@emsleys.co.uk
Office: Crossgates, Garforth, Leeds, Rothwell (2 offices)
Languages: French, German
Work: K1 K2 K3 S1 W
Emergency Action, Agency, Advocacy, Fixed Fee Interview, Legal Aid Franchise and Member of Accident Line
Asoc: Bellhouse, Mr Robert Mark LLB(Hons) . . . . *Oct 1990
Johnson, Mr Dean . . . . *Nov 1994

HARTLEY & WORSTENHOLME ‡
20 Bank Street Castleford West Yorkshire WF10 1JD
Tel: 01977 732222 *Fax:* 01977 603105 *Dx:* 700134 CASTLEFORD
E-mail: info@hartley-worstenholme.co.uk
List of partners: M M C Andrews, T F Day, D J Gaythorpe, V J Maude, D S McClure, J Sharp, C Wilton
Office: Pontefract
Work: C1 C2 D1 D2 E J1 K1 K2 K3 L N O Q R1 S1 S2 T1 T2 V W Z(l,p,q)
Emergency Action, Advocacy, Fixed Fee Interview, Legal Aid undertaken and Legal Aid Franchise
Ptr: Andrews, Mrs Margaret M C LLB; TEP . . . . *§May 1978
Day, Mr Tom F LLB(Hons). . . . . *Feb 1983
McClure, Mr Donald S LLB . . . . *Dec 1976
Maude, Miss Victoria Jane LLB . . . . Mar 2007
Ast: Cashman, Mr Oliver LLB . . . . Nov 2008
Markham, Miss Sarah J L BA(Hons). . . . . *Nov 1992
Smales, Mrs Anna Louise LLB(Hons) . . . . *Jul 2008

PHILIP & ROBERT HOWARD ‡
14 Wesley Street Castleford West Yorkshire WF10 1AE
Tel: 01977 551320 *Fax:* 01977 517166 *Dx:* 700133 CASTLEFORD
Emergency telephone 01977 617536
List of partners: P Howard, R Howard
Office: Barnsley
Work: B1 D1 F1 G H J1 K1 L N V
Ptr: Howard, Mr Robert BA(Keele). . . . . *Mar 1983

JORDANS
2 Wesley Street Castleford West Yorkshire WF10 1AE
Tel: 01977 518778 *Fax:* 01977 518085 *Dx:* 700141 CASTLEFORD
E-mail: enquiries@jordanssolicitors.co.uk
Office: Dewsbury, Wakefield
Work: A3 B1 C1 D1 D2 E F1 F2 G H J1 J2 K1 K2 K3 K4 L N O Q R1 R2 S1 S2 V W Z(c,h,l,p,q,s,t)
Emergency Action, Agency, Advocacy, Fixed Fee Interview, Legal Aid undertaken and Legal Aid Franchise
Ptr: Sands, Mrs Christine LSF; LLB(Hons). . . . . *Nov 1994
Ast: Dosanjh, Miss Amandeep LLB . . . . May 2005
Hubery, Miss Sarah Joanna May BA . . . . *Jan 2007
Worrall, Mr Edward LLB. . . . . *Oct 1994

LOFTHOUSE & CO ‡
16 Wesley Street Castleford West Yorkshire WF10 1AE
Tel: 01977 603347 *Fax:* 01977 603477 *Dx:* 700139 CASTLEFORD
E-mail: lofthouse@btconnect.com
List of partners: D Lofthouse
Ptr: Lofthouse, Mr Denis LLB . . . . *Dec 1988
Ast: Cooper, Mr Charles L BSc; MPhil . . . . *Nov 1991

MAURICE SMITHS ‡
Lexsmith Chambers Bradley Street Castleford West Yorkshire WF10 1HP
Tel: 01977 557171 *Fax:* 01977 517274 *Dx:* 700135 CASTLEFORD
Emergency telephone 07774 169274
E-mail: richardpinto@mauricesmiths.co.uk
List of partners: A Gale, R J Pinto, R J Warsop
Office: Pontefract
Work: A1 B2 D1 D2 E F1 G H J1 K1 L Q R1 S1 S2 V W Z(c,j,l,p,q,r)
Emergency Action, Agency, Advocacy, Fixed Fee Interview, Legal Aid undertaken and Legal Aid Franchise
Ptr: Gale, Mr Anthony LLB. . . . . *Feb 1990
Pinto, Mr Richard John BA(Law) . . . . *Jan 1979
Warsop, Mrs Rachel Jane. . . . . *Sep 1997

CATERHAM, Surrey

K J DESBOTTES & CO ‡
28 Westway Caterham Surrey CR3 5TP
Tel: 01883 343460 *Fax:* 01883 340901
E-mail: kjdesbottes@btconnect.com
List of partners: K J Desbottes
Work: K1
Fixed Fee Interview undertaken
SPr: Desbottes, Mrs Katherine J . . . . *Nov 1981

DOLLMAN & PRITCHARD ‡
8 The Square Caterham Surrey CR3 6XS
Tel: 01883 347823 *Fax:* 01883 340628 *Dx:* 36801 CATERHAM
E-mail: info@dollman.co.uk
List of partners: A S Allward, E Carter-Birch, G J Norman, J R A Ronald
Languages: French, Greek, Urdu
Work: D1 E F1 G H J1 K1 K3 L O Q S1 S2 W Z(d,h,l)
Emergency Action, Agency, Advocacy, Fixed Fee Interview, Legal Aid undertaken and Legal Aid Franchise
Ptr: Allward, Mr Alasdair S. . . . . *Jul 1977
Carter-Birch, Mrs Emily BA(Law) . . . . *§Jan 2001
Norman, Mr Graham John BA(Wales). . . . . *Mar 1995
Ronald, Mr John R A . . . . *Dec 1969
Asoc: Durnin, Mr Martin BA(Hons). . . . . §Aug 1996
Leather, Mr David. . . . . Jul 1971
Tsoukkas, Mr John LLB(Hons) . . . . Sep 2005
Yamin, Mansoor BA(Hons) . . . . §May 1996
Con: Elias, Mr Christopher LLB . . . . Oct 1982
Tomlin, Mr Robert L LLB(Wales). . . . . *§Mar 1972

M SELVI REDDY ‡
32 Tupwood Lane Caterham Surrey CR3 6DA
Tel: 01883 340578
List of partners: M Reddy
Work: S1
SPr: Reddy, Mrs Moganaselvi LLB(Hons)(Business Law); Former Barrister(1987) . . . . *Apr 1993

CATTERICK GARRISON, North Yorkshire

CLARK WILLIS
18 Richmond Road Catterick Garrison North Yorkshire DL9 3JA
Tel: 01748 830000 *Fax:* 01748 830850
E-mail: enquiries@clarkwillis.co.uk
Office: Darlington (2 offices)
Work: B2 D1 D2 E G H J1 K1 K3 K4 L N O Q S1 S2 W Z(m,q)
Emergency Action, Agency, Advocacy, Fixed Fee Interview, Legal Aid undertaken and Member of Accident Line
Asoc: Jones, Mr Alister Mark LLB(Hons). . . . . *Sep 2005

SCOTTS WRIGHT
22 Richmond Road Catterick Garrison North Yorkshire DL9 3JD
Tel: 01748 832431 *Fax:* 01748 836269 *Dx:* 31660 LEYBURN
E-mail: enquiries@scottswright.com
Office: Hawes, Leyburn
Languages: French, German
Work: A1 C1 D1 D2 E F1 G H J1 J2 K1 K3 K4 L N Q R1 S1 S2 V W Z(d,l,r)
Emergency Action, Agency, Advocacy, Fixed Fee Interview, Legal Aid undertaken and Legal Aid Franchise
Ptr: Scott, Mr Malcolm W MA(Cantab). . . . . *Jul 1969
Ast: Flynn, Miss Louise LLB . . . . Apr 2010
Harrison, Mr Christopher E LLB(Lond). . . . . *Jun 1971
Moore, Miss Kathryn Ann . . . . Sep 2009

CHADWELL HEATH, Essex

CHARLES DE ALWIS ‡
157 High Road Chadwell Heath Essex RM6 6NL
Tel: 020 8597 5717 *Fax:* 020 8597 7327
E-mail: charlesdealwis@btconnect.com
List of partners: C De Alwis

Languages: Gujarati, Hindi, Sinhalese, Urdu
Work: C1 C3 E F1 F2 J1 K1 L M1 O Q S1 S2 W Z(i,l)
Fixed Fee Interview and Legal Aid Franchise
Ptr: De Alwis, Mr Charles . . . . *Sep 1987
Ast: Gill, Miss Sarabjit . . . . Jul 2002
Muhammad, Mrs Jacqueline E A Y . . . . *Feb 2002

MULLIS & PEAKE
(incorporating A Martin & Co; Sanders Poulten & Co)
3 High Road Chadwell Heath Essex RM6 6QA
Tel: 020 8599 2417 *Fax:* 020 8599 6713
Dx: 90051 CHADWELL HEATH
Office: Romford
Work: S1
Emergency Action, Agency and Advocacy undertaken
Ptr: Shipton, Mr Michael M BA. . . . . Mar 1987
Asoc: Clark, Mr Roger Paul LLB. . . . . *Nov 1984
McAulay, Mrs Germain Elizabeth LLB(Hons). . . . . *Oct 1993

DAVID PHILLIPS & PARTNERS
150 High Road Chadwell Heath Essex RM6 6NT
Tel: 020 8597 5557 *Fax:* 020 8599 3435
Dx: 90057 CHADWELL HEATH
E-mail: info@dpp.law.com
Office: Birmingham, Bootle (2 offices), Leicester, Liverpool, London E1, London SE18, London W1, Manchester, Nelson, Wealdstone

CHAGFORD, Devon

MATTHEW BOYER SOLICITORS ‡
Appletree Barn Chagford Devon TQ13 8JQ
Tel: 01647 432222 *Fax:* 01647 432580

HELDER ROBERTS & CO
(in association with Mann Jenkins)
58-60 The Square Chagford Devon TQ13 8AE
Tel: 01647 433161 *Fax:* 01647 432058
Office: Moretonhampstead
Work: E R2 S1 S2 W
Ptr: Floyd-Walker, Mr David Arnold . . . . *Sep 1970

CHALFONT ST GILES, Buckinghamshire

BROWN & CO ‡
Lychgate Offices High Street Chalfont St Giles Buckinghamshire HP8 4QH
Tel: 01494 874175 *Fax:* 01494 874798
List of partners: R W Brown
Work: S1 W
Ptr: Brown, Mr Raymond W . . . . *§Jun 1970

CHALFONT ST PETER, Buckinghamshire

DAVIS-LAW ASSOCIATES ‡
Bishops House Market Place Chalfont St Peter Buckinghamshire SL9 9HE
Tel: 01753 888776 *Fax:* 01753 880407
Dx: 31957 CHALFONT ST PETER
Emergency telephone 01753 888776
List of partners: J Davis
Work: B2 C1 G Q S2
Advocacy and Fixed Fee Interview undertaken
Ptr: Davis, Mr John • . . . . Jul 1978
Con: Pearson, Mr Alan William LLB(Leeds). . . . . *§Jan 1976

KNIPE WOODHOUSE-SMITH ‡
145-147 High Street Chalfont St Peter Buckinghamshire SL9 9QL
Tel: 01753 887877 / 889149 *Fax:* 01753 885485
Dx: 31950 CHALFONT ST PETER
List of partners: P K T Chong, P Cooper, B P Knipe
Work: C1 D1 E F1 J1 K1 L N O Q R1 S1 V W Z(c)
Emergency Action, Agency, Advocacy, Fixed Fee Interview, Legal Aid undertaken and Member of Accident Line
Ptr: Chong, Mr Peter K T LLB . . . . *Dec 1988
Cooper, Mrs Petra LLB . . . . *Jun 1979
Knipe, Mr Brian P BSc . . . . *Feb 1988

CHANDLERS FORD, Hampshire

BLAKE LAPTHORN
New Kings Court Tollgate Chandlers Ford Hampshire SO53 3LG
Tel: 023 8090 8090 *Fax:* 023 8090 8092
Dx: 38538 SOUTHAMPTON 3
E-mail: info@bllaw.co.uk
Office: London EC1, Oxford, Portsmouth
Work: A1 A3 B1 C1 C2 C3 E F1 F2 J1 J2 L M1 N O P Q R1 R2 S1 S2 Z(b,c,d,e,f,g,k,r)
Emergency Action, Agency, Advocacy, Fixed Fee Interview, Legal Aid undertaken, Legal Aid Franchise and Member of Accident Line
Ptr: Agnew, Mr Donald LLB . . . . *§Apr 1976
Albuery, Mr Bradley LLB . . . . *Oct 1988
Bainbridge, Ms Jill LLB(Hons); LSF(Hons); Dip Adv Litigation . . . . *Oct 1994
Barber, Mr Peter W B MA(Oxon); BCL; Barrister Society of Construction Law Hudson Prize 1988 . . . . . *Nov 1983
Blake, Mr Carey S MA(Cantab) Notary Public . . . . *§Jun 1968
Brockman, Mr Christopher C LLB . . . . *Jul 1988
Brook, Mr Niall P BA . . . . *Jun 1981
Broom, Mr Philip D . . . . *Dec 1990
Burge, Mr Simon N LLB(Hons) Deputy Coroner for Central Hampshire . . . . *Oct 1985
Chant, Mrs Mary L LLB . . . . *§Oct 1986
Charter, Mr Mark . . . . Sep 1984
Craft, Mr Maxwell C MA(Cantab) Part time Employment Tribunal Chairman. . . . . *§Nov 1978
Crier, Mr Phillip B LLB. . . . . *Oct 1983
Dobson, Mr Julian A H . . . . *Nov 1988
Dolan, Mr Christopher P BA(Hons) . . . . *Dec 1985
Dryden, Mrs Susan J LLB; LLM . . . . *Oct 1985
Harlow, Mr Alan J. . . . . *Nov 1986
Higham, Mr David R G LLM. . . . . *§Sep 1979
Keitley, Mr Nicholas LLB . . . . *Oct 1985
Kennedy, Mr James I BA Under Sheriff of Hampshire *§Jan 1979
McClure, Ms Alison LLB. . . . . *Nov 1986
McClure, Mr Christopher Bonnar LLB(Hons). . . . . *Nov 1990
Marshland, Miss E M Clare BA(Lond) . . . . *§Jun 1982
Mitchell, Mr John MA(Cantab). . . . . *§Dec 1979
Morris, Miss Amanda Claire. . . . . *Sep 1994
Munro, Ms Lorna E LLB. . . . . *§Oct 1986
Murfitt, Mr Stephen E LLB; LLM Solicitor to the General Optical Council . . . . *§Dec 1974
Oliver, Mr David C . . . . *§Dec 1973
Palmer, Miss Sarah A. . . . . *Oct 1990
Peck, Mr Andrew D . . . . *§Jan 1972
Penfold, Mr Bob. . . . . Jan 1988
Portlock, Mr Richard A LLB(Wales) . . . . *Oct 1987
Rayner, Mr David MA(Cantab). . . . . Oct 1983
Riccio, Miss Maria C FILEx . . . . *Sep 1996
Shepherd, Mr P Mark LLB. . . . . *Mar 1987
Shimmin, Miss Kathryn J LLB. . . . . *Nov 1988
Short, Mr Grahame A MA(Cantab) H M Coroner of Mid Hants . . . . *Jun 1979
Sowton, Mr Oliver BSc(Hons) . . . . Sep 1998
Steel, Mr John R MA(Cantab); MA(De Montfort). . . *§Jun 1975
Sturgess, Mr Geoffrey H BA. . . . . *Jun 1980
Taunt, Mr Christopher J BA(Oxon). . . . . *Apr 1979
Thurston, Mr Martyn R LLB(Bris) . . . . *Jun 1971
Woodhouse, Ms Susan J . . . . *Sep 1992
Asoc: Harry, Mrs Jacquie . . . . *Jul 1996
Herklots, Radu W BA . . . . *Mar 1985
Ast: Alder, Mr Christopher B . . . . Sep 2000
Allnutt, Mr Christopher Anthony Robert LLB(Hons) . *Nov 1991
Archibald, Mr Stephen. . . . . Apr 1996
Aspinall, Mrs Patricia W LLB Notary Public . . . . . *Nov 1971
Brown, Miss Clare LLB . . . . Sep 2002
Browne, Ms Natasha Martha . . . . *Dec 2001
Chandler, Miss Victoria Anne LLB. . . . . Sep 2002
Christy, Mrs Ruth Victoria . . . . Sep 2001
Connor, Miss Claire Louise . . . . *Mar 2002
Cook, Mrs Frances M E LLB . . . . *Oct 1995
Cooper, Mr Anthony. . . . . *Sep 1997
Dannan, Miss Rachel Sarah LLB(Hons). . . . . Sep 2001
Drake, Mr Stephen P LLB(Hons) William Hutton Prize. *Jul 1997
Driver, Mr Timothy J BSc(Econ); DMA. . . . . *Jan 1981
Fairley, Mrs Victoria. . . . . Sep 1999
Foden, Mr Mark Roger LLB(Hons). . . . . Sep 2002
Fowler, Mrs Clare E LLB . . . . *Sep 1999
Harris-Deans, Mrs Marian LLB(Hons) . . . . *Sep 1998
Heywood, Mrs Elaine M MA(Hons) . . . . *Nov 1993
Hill, Mr Richard BA(Hons); CPE; LPC . . . . Sep 1998
Hillier, Miss Marianne Louise LLB . . . . Nov 1999
Hills, Miss Nicola E BA(Hons)(Law Accounting & Finance) . . . . *Oct 1993
Howard, Mrs Claire LLB; LLM. . . . . *Nov 1994
Howlett, Mr Ian . . . . *Nov 1984
Knight, Mrs Lynn Fraser Arnold LLB(Hons) . . . . . Nov 1996
Kovacs, Mr Gabor T LLB . . . . *Oct 1983
Lasenby, Ms Deborah Jane LLB Monitor Press Prize 1992 . . . . *Nov 1994
Lewis, Mr James BA(Hons); MA. . . . . *Sep 2002
Mackenzie, Mrs Jane Lindsey LLB . . . . *Sep 2002
Olley, Mr David Russell . . . . *Feb 2001
Paget, Mrs Catherine MA(Cantab) Member of the Property Litigation Association . . . . *Jun 1993
Patel, Ms Kirti LLB(Hons). . . . . *§Sep 1993
Pavitt, Mr Michael G J LLB(Hons). . . . . *Sep 1999
Porter, Mr Stephen Dennis . . . . *Jan 2001
Shallcross, Mr John S MA Hanson Prize For Contracts 1986 . . . . *Dec 1991
Simpson, Mr Robert. . . . . Sep 2003
Smedley, Mrs Lynda J BA(Hons) . . . . *Sep 1997
Somarakis, Mr Philip . . . . Oct 1990
Stewart, Mr Neil MSc . . . . Sep 1998
Sturdy, Mr Justin William MA(Cantab). . . . . *Nov 1993
Sullivan, Mrs Sara Louise LLB . . . . *Oct 1994
Thomas, Ms Hilary C BA . . . . *Jul 1995
Townsend, Mr Allen Notary Public. . . . . *Sep 1987
Wallsgrove, Mr Jon Stuart DML; LLB . . . . *Oct 1993
Wheadon, Mrs Sarah . . . . Oct 1993
Wilder, Ms Vanessa LLB(Hons) . . . . Jul 1997
Willetts, Ms Michelle Rachael L BA(Law) . . . . . . Sep 2002
Williams, Mrs Gillian M BSc(Hons); MCIEH; PGDip . . Jan 2001
Williams, Miss Sara Louise BA(Hons). . . . . Sep 2002
Winkworth, Miss Caroline LLB(Hons) . . . . *Sep 1996
Wright, Mr Stephen C LLB . . . . Apr 1975
Young, Ms Holly Tamsin Shelley LLB(Hons). . . . . Sep 2002
Con: Hewitt, Mr Richard Charles . . . . *Oct 1997
Prideaux, Mr Walter. . . . . Oct 1964

DEMPSTER BINNING LLP ‡
5 West Links Tollgate Chandlers Ford Hampshire SO53 3TG
Tel: 023 8062 1790 *Fax:* 023 8062 1799
Dx: 48115 CHANDLERS FORD 2
List of partners: S S Binning, P E A Dempster
Work: E R2 S2
Ptr: Binning, Sulinder S LLB. . . . . *§Jan 1987
Dempster, Mr Peter E A LLB . . . . *§Nov 1984
Ast: Searles, Ms Dawn LLB(Hons). . . . . *Oct 1992
Con: Tranah, Mrs Eleanor R LLB . . . . *Apr 1980

ERIC ROBINSON SOLICITORS
6-8 Brownhill Road Chandlers Ford Hampshire SO53 2EA
Tel: 023 8025 4676 *Fax:* 023 8025 1206
Dx: 45950 CHANDLERS FORD
Emergency telephone 0870 238 5687
E-mail: chandlersford@ericrobinson.co.uk
Office: Hythe, Southampton (4 offices)
Languages: French
Work: B1 C1 C2 C3 D1 E F1 G H J1 K1 L M1 M2 N O P Q S1 V W X Z(m)
Emergency Action, Agency, Advocacy, Fixed Fee Interview, Legal Aid undertaken, Legal Aid Franchise and Member of Accident Line
Ptr: Maxfield, Mrs Catherine E E LLB(Hons); BA(Hons) . *Sep 1994
Payne, Mr Graham P W LLB(Soton); TEP. . . . . . . *Apr 1974
Ast: McIntyre, Miss Emily Anne LLB . . . . Sep 2007
Storry, Mr David Austin Wynn BA . . . . Jan 1991

ML LAW LTD
146 Bournemouth Road Chandlers Ford Hampshire SO53 3AL
Tel: 023 8026 9570 *Fax:* 023 8025 4461
Dx: 48107 CHANDLERS FORD 2
E-mail: central@mllaw.co.uk
Office: Eastleigh

CHAPEL-EN-LE-FRITH, Derbyshire

COOPER SONS HARTLEY & WILLIAMS
25 Market Street Chapel-en-le-Frith Derbyshire SK23 0HS
Tel: 01298 812138 *Fax:* 01298 815097
E-mail: legal@cshw.co.uk
Office: Buxton
Languages: French, German
Work: A1 B1 C1 C2 C3 D1 E F1 J1 K1 K3 K4 L M2 N O P Q R1 R2 S1 S2 T1 T2 V W Z(b,c,d,e,h,i,j,k,l,m,n,o,q,r,s,t,w)
Emergency Action, Agency, Advocacy, Fixed Fee Interview, Legal Aid undertaken, Legal Aid Franchise and Member of Accident Line
Ptr: Middleton, Mrs Lesley Helen LLB; Grad IPD. . . . . *Sep 1996
Shuff, Mr Stephen R LLB . . . . Oct 1986
Ast: Bradd, Miss Victoria Louise LLB(Hons) . . . . *Jun 2011
Proven, Mrs Kate LLB(Hons) . . . . *Oct 2006
Con: Williams, Mr J Michael MBE MA(Oxon) . . . . *Jun 1967

CHARD, Somerset

BEVISS & BECKINGSALE
Law Chambers Holyrood Street Chard Somerset TA20 2AJ
Tel: 01460 269700 *Fax:* 01460 269701 *Dx:* 43701 CHARD
E-mail: enquiries@bevissandbeckingsale.co.uk
Office: Axminster, Honiton, Seaton
Work: A1 A2 C1 D1 E J1 K1 L N P Q R1 S1 S2 T1 T2 V W Z(c,l,o,r)
Emergency Action, Agency, Advocacy and Fixed Fee Interview undertaken
Ast: Griffiths, Mrs Frances BSc . . . . Sep 2001
Harley, Mrs Christine LLB . . . . Sep 2006
Micklethwait, Mr Michael St John BA(Hons) . . . . . . Sep 1998

MILFORD & DORMOR
45 Fore Street Chard Somerset TA20 1PT
Tel: 01460 65335 / 61000 *Fax:* 01460 65319
E-mail: chard@milfordanddormor.co.uk
Office: Axminster, Ilminster, Seaton
Work: E K1 N S1 W
Agency, Advocacy and Fixed Fee Interview undertaken
Ptr: Bennett, Mr William C. . . . . *§Jun 1980
Burdett, Mr Colin Edgar LLB . . . . *Jan 1979
Ast: Rex, Mr Nicholas Peter . . . . *§Dec 1969
Con: Blackmore, Mr Michael Rubert . . . . *Nov 1978

SCOTT ROWE
36a Fore Street Chard Somerset TA20 1PT
Tel: 01460 63336 *Fax:* 01460 63338
Office: Lyme Regis

CHARLBURY, Oxfordshire

HOPE & CO ‡
Farthing Hall Sprigs Holly Lane Chinnor Charlbury Oxfordshire OX39 4BY
Tel: 01494 483182

CHATHAM, Medway Towns

ALSTON ASHBY ‡
75 High Street Chatham Medway Towns ME4 4EE
Tel: 01634 845051 *Fax:* 01634 828540
E-mail: info@alstonashby.co.uk
List of partners: I G Alston, C J A Ashby
Office: Chatham
Work: C1 C2 E F1 J1 K1 L N O Q S1 W Z(c,l)
Agency, Advocacy, Fixed Fee Interview and Legal Aid undertaken
Ptr: Alston, Mr Ian G LLB . . . . *May 1976

ALSTON ASHBY
25 Military Road Chatham Medway Towns ME4 4JG
Tel: 01634 842017 *Fax:* 01634 811036
E-mail: alstonashby@tsuki.demon.co.uk
Office: Chatham
Work: C1 C2 E J1 L N O Q S1 S2 W Z(c,q,r)
Agency, Advocacy and Fixed Fee Interview undertaken
Ptr: Ashby, Mr Christopher J A LLB(Lond) . . . . *Jul 1975

RAYMOND BEER & CO ‡
16 Manor Road Chatham Medway Towns ME4 6AG
Tel: 01634 814911 *Fax:* 01634 826826 *Dx:* 6723 CHATHAM

BORG KNIGHT EMPLOYMENT SOLICITORS ‡
Innovation Centre Maidstone Road Kent Chatham Medway Towns ME5 9FD
Tel: 01634 757001 / 020 7099 8135 *Fax:* 01634 757663
E-mail: info@borgknight.com
Office: Rochester

DGB SOLICITORS ‡
The Captain's House Central Avenue Pembroke Chatham Medway Towns ME4 4UF
Tel: 01634 304000 *Fax:* 01634 304440
E-mail: enquiries@dgblaw.co.uk
List of partners: P P Fox, J E Gomme, C M Moore, I E Pentecost, M G Smith
Work: A1 A3 B1 C1 C2 D1 E J1 J2 K1 K2 K3 K4 L N O P Q R2 S1 S2 T1 T2 U2 W Z(c,e,h,k,l,p,q,r)
Emergency Action, Agency, Advocacy and Fixed Fee Interview undertaken
Ptr: Fox, Mr Paul Philip LLB(Hons); ACIB . . . . *Jun 1987
Gomme, Mr James Edward LLB(Hons) . . . . *Nov 2001
Moore, Mr Colin Marcus. . . . . *Nov 2001
Pentecost, Mr Ian Edward LLB(Lond) . . . . *Nov 1985
Smith, Mr Mark Geoffrey LLB(Hons). . . . . *Jan 2003
Ast: Gibbs, Miss Caroline . . . . *Jan 2006
Maggiulli, Mr Dario Massimo BA(Hons) . . . . Sep 2004
Mannooch, Mrs Sarah. . . . . *Feb 2006

EMERALD SOLICITORS ‡
17 New Road Avenue Chatham Medway Towns ME4 6BA
Tel: 01634 407500 *Fax:* 01634 407500
E-mail: info@emeraldsolicitors.co.uk

See p112 for the Key to Work Categories & other symbols

FURLEY PAGE LLP
Admiral's Offices Main Gate Road The Historic Dockyard Chatham Medway Towns ME4 4TZ
Tel: 01634 828277 *Fax:* 01634 830056 *Dx:* 131400 ROCHESTER 2
E-mail: info@furleypage.co.uk
Office: Canterbury, London EC3, Whitstable

HATTON LAW ‡
Suite 2 6-8 Chestnut Avenue Walderslade Chatham Medway Towns ME5 9A
Tel: 01634 686822 *Fax:* 01634 683238 *Dx:* 49902 WALDERSLADE
E-mail: lo@hattonlaw.co.uk

DEREK J HAYWARD & CO ‡
19 Railway Street Chatham Medway Towns ME4 4HU
Tel: 01634 815651 *Fax:* 01634 840068 *Dx:* 6714 CHATHAM
List of partners: D J Hayward
Work: G H
Ptr: Hayward, Mr Derek J LLB. . . . . *Dec 1976

KINGSLEY SMITH SOLICITORS LLP ‡
81 High Street Chatham Medway Towns ME4 4EE
Tel: 01634 811118 *Fax:* 01634 831046 *Dx:* 6718 CHATHAM 1
E-mail: mail@kslaw.co.uk
List of partners: M J Dugdale, E Kingsley-Smith, N M Kingsley-Smith
Work: A1 A2 B1 C1 C2 C3 D1 E F1 F2 J1 J2 K4 L M1 M2 N O P Q R1 R2 S1 S2 T1 T2 W Z(c,e,g,h,j,k,l,p,q,t,u,za)
Emergency Action, Advocacy and Fixed Fee Interview undertaken
Mem: Dugdale, Mr Mathew James. . . . . *Sep 2001
Kingsley-Smith, Ms Elizabeth BA(Dunelm). . . . . . *Oct 1988
Kingsley-Smith, Mr Nicholas M LLB . . . . *Feb 1989

JOHN MORLEY & CO
15-16 Walderslade Centre Walderslade Chatham Medway Towns ME5 9LR
Tel: 01634 668516 *Fax:* 01634 836921 *Dx:* 49907 WALDERSLADE
E-mail: walderslade@morlaw.com
Office: Rainham

ROBIN MURRAY & CO ‡
The Old Ragged School Kings Street (Off Rope Walk) Chatham Medway Towns ME4 4LY
Tel: 01634 832332 *Fax:* 01634 831331 *Dx:* 6744 CHATHAM
E-mail: chatham.enquiries@robinmurrayandco.com
List of partners: R J F Atkinson, A D Balneaves, R J Murray
Languages: French
Work: B2 G H
Agency, Advocacy, Legal Aid undertaken and Legal Aid Franchise
Ptr: Atkinson, Mr Richard J F BSc(Econ) ★ . . . . *Sep 1990
Balneaves, Mr Alan Douglas LLB . . . . *Aug 1996
Murray, Mr Robin James . . . . *Dec 1980
Ast: Farley, Mr Henry Richard BA(Hons). . . . . *Nov 1990
Norton, Mr John C . . . . *§Dec 1976
Rowberry, Miss Christina Charlotte LLB(Hons); PGDip *Sep 2000
Shrimpton, Mr Harold Edward. . . . . §Jun 1969
Slater, Ms Deborah Elaine BA(Hons) . . . . Oct 1982

MYBRIEF SOLICITORS ‡
The Joiners Shop Historic Dockyard Chatham Medway Towns ME4 4TZ
Tel: 01634 544544 *Fax:* 0845 544 0879
Emergency telephone 07835 975800
E-mail: reception@mybrief.com
List of partners: J J Betts
Work: B2 G H Q U2 W Z(e,g)
Emergency Action, Advocacy and Fixed Fee Interview undertaken
Ptr: Betts, Mr Jeremy James LLB(Hons). . . . . *Oct 1993

STEPHENS & SON LLP ‡
Rome House 39-41 Railway Street Chatham Medway Towns ME4 4RP
Tel: 01634 811444 *Fax:* 01634 831532 *Dx:* 6700 CHATHAM 1
E-mail: email@stephens-son.co.uk
List of partners: C M Brooks-Johnson, C V Fuchter, K J Gladwell, A Johnston, D A Nicholson, J A Shicluna
Work: A3 B1 C1 C2 D2 E F1 G J1 K1 K3 K4 L N O Q R1 S1 S2 W Z(d,l,q)
Emergency Action, Agency, Advocacy, Fixed Fee Interview undertaken and Member of Accident Line
Ptr: Brooks-Johnson, Mrs Caroline Mary LLB(Hons) . . . . *Nov 1994
Gladwell, Mr Kevin J . . . . *May 1989
Nicholson, Mrs Deborah A LLB(Hons). . . . . *Oct 1987
Shicluna, Miss Jacqueline Ann MA(Oxon). . . . . . *Nov 1988
Mem: Fuchter, Mr Charles Victor. . . . . Dec 1977
Johnston, Mr Alan. . . . . NSP
Asoc: Daniels, Mr Peter E . . . . *§Jan 1983
Con: Bailey, Mr Michael Robin . . . . *Jun 1981
Holder, Mr John K LLB(Hons) . . . . *§Jun 1975

T S LAW LIMITED ‡
5 Shirley Avenue Chatham Medway Towns ME5 9UP
Tel: 01634 311876 *Fax:* 01634 302261
E-mail: manjittesse@tslawchatham.co.uk

WINCH & WINCH ‡
(incorporating Arnold Tuff & Grimwade(Chatham))
5 New Road Avenue Chatham Medway Towns ME4 6AR
Est: 1894
Tel: 01634 830111 *Fax:* 01634 408891 *Dx:* 6707 CHATHAM
Emergency telephone 01634 830111
E-mail: solicitors@winch-winch.co.uk
Work: A1 B1 C1 C2 E F1 G J1 K1 K3 L N O Q R1 S1 S2 T1 T2 W Z(d,i,l,p,q)

CHATTERIS, Cambridgeshire

G CARTWRIGHT & CO ‡
9 Park Street Fenland Chatteris Cambridgeshire PE16 6AB
Tel: 01354 692607 *Fax:* 01354 693857 *Dx:* 56852 CHATTERIS
E-mail: info@gcartwright.co.uk
List of partners: G Cartwright
Languages: Dutch, French, Spanish
Work: A1 C1 C2 C3 D1 D2 E F1 J1 K1 L N Q R1 S1 T2 W Z(g)
Ptr: Cartwright, Mr Gordon LLB . . . . *Jul 1975
Asoc: Threlfall, Mrs Karen Jane LLB(Hons) . . . . *Feb 1993
Con: Vipas, Mr Kenneth Edward MA(Oxon). . . . . *Jan 1974

GRAHAM DACK & COMPANY (INC BATTERSBY JAMES) ‡
(incorporating Battersby James)
10 Park Street Chatteris Cambridgeshire PE16 6AE
Tel: 01354 695885 *Fax:* 01354 694275
E-mail: admin@grahamdack.com
List of partners: R F Battersby, G M C Dack
Office: March
Work: A1 C1 C2 C3 D1 E J1 K1 K3 L N O P Q S1 T1 T2 W Z(l)
Agency undertaken and Member of Accident Line
Ptr: Battersby, Mr Richard F. . . . . *§Jun 1979

CHEADLE, Greater Manchester

ABNEY GARSDEN MCDONALD ‡
37 Station Road Cheadle Greater Manchester SK8 5AF
Tel: 0161 482 8822 *Fax:* 0870 990 9350
Dx: 18605 CHEADLE HULME
E-mail: reception@abneys.co.uk
List of partners: P W A Garsden
Work: B1 C1 C2 C3 D1 E F1 G H J1 K1 L M1 M2 N P R1 S1 V W Z(c,j,l,m)
Emergency Action, Agency, Advocacy, Fixed Fee Interview, Legal Aid undertaken, Legal Aid Franchise and Member of Accident Line
Ptr: Garsden, Mr Peter W A BA . . . . *Apr 1981
Ast: Chandler, Mrs Caroline LLB. . . . . Apr 2001
Corcoran, Ms Deborah BSc; CPE; LSF . . . . Nov 1996
Curran, Mr Phillip LLB(Hons); DipLaw. . . . . Jan 1994
Durkin, Mr Paul P BA(Hons). . . . . Dec 1991
Follows, Ms Samantha Jayne BA(Hons). . . . . . . Aug 1996
Goss, Ms Joan BA(Hons) . . . . *Nov 1995
Thomas, Mr Hywel Gruffydd LLB(French & Law); Cert d'Etudes Juridiques (Nantes) . . . . Sep 1996

ASHFIELDS ‡
Strathblane House Ashfield Road Cheadle Greater Manchester SK8 1BB
Tel: 0161 495 2960 *Fax:* 0161 495 7116 *Dx:* 22352 CHEADLE
E-mail: mail@ashfields-solicitors.co.uk

BAILEYS ‡
37 Station Road Cheadle Hulme Cheadle Greater Manchester SK8 5AF
Tel: 0161 488 4688 *Fax:* 0844 824 3982
E-mail: info@baileyslegal.net

BEARDSELLS ‡
Vienna House Eden Place Cheadle Greater Manchester SK8 1AT
Tel: 0161 477 2288 *Fax:* 0161 474 7268 *Dx:* 22356 CHEADLE
E-mail: cathy@beardsel.u-net.com
List of partners: B S Azariah, P Christmas, S K Colquhoun, J D Halstead, H A Miles, W Y Suen, C J Worthy
Work: F1 G N O P Q Z(c,j,t)
Agency, Advocacy, Legal Aid undertaken and Member of Accident Line
Ptr: Azariah, Ms Breda S LLB(Hons)(with French) Horton Jones Memorial Prize . . . . *Oct 1991
Christmas, Mr Paul LLB. . . . . *Oct 1994
Colquhoun, Miss Sara Katharine LLB . . . . *Jun 1995
Halstead, Mr John Darrell BA(Hons); CPE. . . . . . *Jan 1994
Miles, Miss Harriet Anne LLB(Hons). . . . . *Nov 1994
Suen, Mrs Wai Yi LLB(Hons) . . . . *May 1989
Worthy, Mr Christopher J LLB . . . . *Jun 1972
Ast: Cray, Miss Joanne Lesley LLB(Hons) . . . . Sep 1996
Jones, Mrs Bernadette C LLB. . . . . *Nov 1990
Stone, Mr Richard H BA(Hons) . . . . *Dec 1996
Torkisz, Miss Julia LLB(Hons); LSF . . . . Apr 1997
Con: Hodson, Mr Philip MA(Oxon); FCIArb . . . . *Jun 1969

BEELEY & CO SOLICITORS ‡
Sovereign House Stockport Road Cheadle Greater Manchester SK8 2EA
Tel: 0800 195 2537 / 0161 492 5970 *Fax:* 0161 492 5980
Dx: 22353 CHEADLE
E-mail: nancy@beeleyandco.co.uk
Office: Brighton

BLUE SKY LAW ‡
5300 Lakeside Cheadle Royal Business Park Cheadle Greater Manchester SK8 3GP
Tel: 0161 246 6077 *Fax:* 0161 491 1927

CRANGLE EDWARDS
159 Councillor Lane Cheadle Greater Manchester SK8 2JE
Tel: 0161 428 2331 *Fax:* 0161 428 7436
E-mail: cheadlecrangleedwards@yahoo.co.uk
Office: Stretford
Work: D1 D2 K1 K2 N S1 W Z(l,q)
Agency, Advocacy, Legal Aid undertaken and Legal Aid Franchise
Ast: Malpas, Mrs Emma BA . . . . Jan 2005
Con: Crangle, Mr Gerald P LLB(Dunelm) . . . . Jul 1964

HL LAW ‡
301 Hollyhedge Road Gatley Cheadle Greater Manchester SK8 4HH
Tel: 0161 428 1000 *Fax:* 0161 428 7722 *Dx:* 700780 HEALD GREEN

JMS SOLICITORS ‡
Landmark House Station Road Cheadle Hulme Cheadle Greater Manchester SK8 7BS
Tel: 0161 486 3390 *Fax:* 0161 486 3391
E-mail: info@jms-solicitors.co.uk

LOWICK MCKAY ‡
44-46 Church Road Cheadle Greater Manchester SK8 4NQ
Tel: 0161 491 5588 *Fax:* 0161 491 5599
E-mail: reception@lowickmckay.com
List of partners: M W Lowick, B Mckay
Work: B1 D1 D2 E F1 J1 K1 L N O Q S1 V W Z(p)
Ptr: Lowick, Mr Michael W. . . . . *§Jul 1977
Mckay, Miss Bernadette. . . . . *Sep 1988

MARTINS
40 Foxland Road Gatley Cheadle Greater Manchester SK8 4QB
Tel: 0161 428 3102 *Fax:* 0161 428 3100
Office: Eccles

SAVILLES ‡
87a High Street Cheadle Greater Manchester SK8 1AA
Tel: 0161 491 8540
E-mail: info@savilles-solicitors.co.uk

E JOHN STIFF ‡
28 Daylesford Road Cheadle Greater Manchester SK8 1LF
Tel: 0161 491 0461
E-mail: john.stiff@e-mail.co.uk

ANDREW J TAYLOR ‡
Westend Chambers 10 Wilmslow Road Cheadle Greater Manchester SK8 1BT
Tel: 0161 428 1875 *Fax:* 0161 428 1876
E-mail: general@andrewjtaylor.co.uk
List of partners: D Lovett, A J Taylor
Work: A1 B1 C1 E F1 J1 L O P R1 S1 S2 T1 W Z(b,d,f,l,w,z)
Fixed Fee Interview undertaken
Ptr: Lovett, Mrs Doreen . . . . *Nov 2000
Taylor, Mr Andrew J LLB(Manc) . . . . *Feb 1982

CHEADLE, Staffordshire

A H BROOKS & CO
(incorporating H G Terry & Co)
73 High Street Cheadle Staffordshire ST10 1AN
Tel: 01538 754253 *Fax:* 01538 755698
E-mail: lawyers@ahbrooks.co.uk
Office: Leek
Work: A1 B1 C1 D1 D2 E F1 F2 J1 K1 K2 K3 K4 L N O Q S1 S2 W Z(c,e,l,m,q)
Emergency Action, Agency, Advocacy, Fixed Fee Interview undertaken and Member of Accident Line
Ptr: Williamson, Miss Greta LLB(Hons); LPC . . . . . . *§Dec 1996

DICKSONS SOLICITORS LTD
82-84 High Street Cheadle Staffordshire ST10 1AJ
Tel: 01782 262424
Office: Stoke-on-Trent (2 offices)

THE ERIC WHITEHEAD PARTNERSHIP ‡
St Giles Chambers 14 Chapel Street Cheadle Staffordshire ST10 1DY
Tel: 01538 755761 *Fax:* 01538 757361 *Dx:* 27981 CHEADLE
Emergency telephone 01538 702476
E-mail: mailbox@ericwhitehead.co.uk
List of partners: T Halliday, N J John, N John
Work: A1 B1 C1 D1 E F1 G H J1 K1 K2 K3 K4 L N P Q R1 S1 S2 T1 T2 V W Z(q,r)
Emergency Action, Agency, Advocacy, Fixed Fee Interview, Legal Aid undertaken, Legal Aid Franchise and Member of Accident Line
Ptr: Halliday, Mr Timothy BA. . . . . *§Oct 1985
John, Mr Nicolas . . . . *§Jun 1972
John, Mr Nicholas J BA(Hons) . . . . *Jun 1998

CHEADLE HULME, Greater Manchester

HILARY MCCAULEY SOLICITORS LIMITED ‡
37 Ramillies Avenue Cheadle Hulme Greater Manchester SK8 7AQ
Tel: 0161 485 6723 *Fax:* 0161 486 6548
E-mail: hilary@hilarymccauley.co.uk
List of partners: H A McCauley
Work: S1 W
Dir: McCauley, Ms Hilary A LLB . . . . *May 1977

MINAHAN HIRST & CO ‡
33 Station Road Cheadle Hulme Greater Manchester SK8 5AF
Tel: 0161 485 8131 *Fax:* 0161 485 3526
Dx: 18603 CHEADLE HULME
E-mail: solicitors@minahan-hirst.co.uk
List of partners: R L Hirst, M J J Minahan
Work: D1 E K1 N S1 W
Emergency Action, Agency, Advocacy and Fixed Fee Interview undertaken
Ptr: Hirst, Mr R Leslie LLB(Hons) . . . . *Jul 1980
Minahan, Mr Michael J J LLB(Hons). . . . . *Jun 1972
Ast: Buckley, Miss Christine L LLB(Hons) . . . . *Mar 1985
Holmes, Mrs Karen Elizabeth LLB. . . . . Jul 1998
Sullivan, Mrs Carolynn Susan Ann LLB . . . . Jul 1974

SIMPSONS SOLICITORS ‡
3rd Floor 36 Station Road Cheadle Hulme Greater Manchester SK8 2AJ
Tel: 0161 485 6030 *Fax:* 0161 485 6040
E-mail: law@simpsonssolicitors.co.uk

CHEAM, Surrey

ARORA BAILEY ‡
14-16 Ewell Road Cheam Surrey SM3 8BU
Tel: 020 8661 0000 *Fax:* 020 8661 0110 *Dx:* 200614 CHEAM
E-mail: enquiries@arorabailey.co.uk
List of partners: A Arora, D L Bailey
Languages: Hindi, Punjabi
Work: J1 K1 S1 S2 W
Fixed Fee Interview undertaken
Ptr: Arora, Ms Ashma . . . . *Jan 1998
Bailey, Ms Deborah L LLB. . . . . *Nov 1990

BELL & CO ‡
3 The Broadway Cheam Surrey SM3 8BQ
Tel: 020 8642 6099 *Fax:* 020 8643 0916 *Dx:* 200600 CHEAM
E-mail: info@bellsolicitors.com
List of partners: N J Brocklehurst, S H Liddington, J C Mill, D C Patel
Office: Cheam, Sutton
Work: E K1 K3 N Q S1 W Z(q)
Fixed Fee Interview undertaken
Ptr: Brocklehurst, Mr Neil James LLB(Hons). . . . . *Mar 1995
Liddington, Mr Stuart Henry. . . . . *Jun 1970
Con: Sherriff, Mr Angus W G . . . . *§Jan 1970
Williams, Mr John G. . . . . *§Nov 1970

BELL & CO
57 The Broadway Cheam Surrey SM3 8BL
Tel: 020 8642 6099
E-mail: info@bellsolicitors.com
Office: Cheam, Sutton

BRAND & CO ‡
Nonsuch House London Road North Cheam Cheam Surrey SM3 9AA
Tel: 020 8641 2771 *Fax:* 020 8644 2687
Dx: 200701 CHEAM NORTH
E-mail: dawnw@brandandco.com
List of partners: A H Brand, B J Hubert
Work: B1 C1 C2 C3 D1 D2 E F1 G H I J1 K1 K3 L O Q R1 S1 S2 T1 T2 W Z(c,e,g,h,j,k,l,m,o,q,s)

Emergency Action, Agency, Advocacy, Fixed Fee Interview, Legal Aid undertaken and Legal Aid Franchise
Ptr: Brand, Mr Alan H . . . . . *Mar 1962
Hubert, Mr Barry John LLB . . . . . *Aug 1992
Asoc: McNeill, Ms Clare . . . . . *Aug 2002
Ast: Boueh, Miss Emma . . . . . *Jan 2007
Wright, Miss Holly BA; LPC; PGDipLaw . . . . . *Dec 2004

HOWELL-JONES LLP
(incorporating Taylor Willcocks)
10 Upper Mulgrave Road Cheam Surrey SM2 7BA
Tel: 020 8642 8142 *Fax:* 020 8642 2863 *Dx:* 200601 CHEAM
E-mail: cheam@howell-jones.com
Office: Kingston upon Thames, Leatherhead, London SW20, London WC2, Walton-on-Thames
Languages: French
Work: B1 B2 C1 C2 C3 E F1 I J1 J2 L M1 M2 N O Q R1 R2 S1 S2 T1 T2 W Z(d,e,f,g,i,j,k,l,o,p,q,r,u,w,z)
Advocacy and Fixed Fee Interview undertaken
Ptr: Addison, Mrs Sarah Anne LLB . . . . . *Dec 1978
Thorpe, Mr Colin J . . . . . *Jun 1969
Trim, Mr Paul B H . . . . . *Dec 1973
Asoc: Courtney, Miss Mary C E I BA . . . . . *Oct 1986
Ast: Chowdhry, Mrs Laila . . . . . Apr 2004
Dalgetty, Ms Elizabeth . . . . . *Jun 1996
Jacobs, Mr Jonathan LLB . . . . . *Aug 2000

MCGLINCHEY & CO ‡
703a London Road Cheam Surrey SM3 9DL
Tel: 020 8330 7979 *Fax:* 020 8330 4910
Dx: 200705 CHEAM NORTH
E-mail: lawmcg@aol.com
List of partners: S L McGlinchey
Work: S1
Ptr: McGlinchey, Mrs S Lesley BA . . . . . *Mar 1982

CHEDDAR, Somerset

BARTLETT GOODING & WEELEN
Roley House Church Street Cheddar Somerset BS27 3RA
Tel: 01934 745400 *Fax:* 01934 744011 *Dx:* 130365 CHEDDAR
E-mail: gareth.bgw@btinternet.com
Office: Castle Cary, Glastonbury, Shepton Mallet

GREAVES BREWSTER LLP ‡
Indigo House Wedmore Road Cheddar Business Park Cheddar Somerset BS27 3EB
Tel: 01934 745880 *Fax:* 01934 745881
E-mail: info@greavesbrewster.co.uk

CHARLES HART SOLICITORS ‡
Glebe House Chamber Vicarage Lane Draycott Cheddar Somerset BS27 3SH
Tel: 01934 742315
E-mail: charles@charles-hart.co.uk
List of partners: D G Foster, C H Hart, M G Lloyd
Work: C1 E G H J1 K1 L N O Q S1 T1 W
Emergency Action, Agency, Fixed Fee Interview, Legal Aid undertaken and Legal Aid Franchise
Ptr: Foster, Mr David Geoffrey LLB(Hons) . . . . . Jun 1988
Hart, Mr Charles H LLB ★ . . . . . *Feb 1988
Lloyd, Mr Martin Grahame LLB . . . . . Oct 1987
Asoc: Williams, Mr Rhys Gildas . . . . . Nov 2003
Williams, Mr Richard . . . . . Aug 2001

TIM MARKS ‡
Pilgrims Cottage Lower North Street Cheddar Somerset BS27 3HH
Tel: 01934 744133 *Fax:* 020 7681 2012
E-mail: tjmlcv@tiscali.co.uk

CHELMSFORD, Essex

ALEXANDER LAWYERS LLP ‡
Bervale House 35-37 Moulsham Street Chelmsford Essex CM2 0HY
Tel: 01245 216050 *Fax:* 01245 216089
E-mail: info@alexanderlawyersllp.com
List of partners: M Alexander, R Puri
Office: London W1
Work: C1 E J1 O P Q S1 T1 T2 W Z(h,i)
Ptr: Alexander, Mr Michael . . . . . *§Nov 1973

ALLISON SOLICITORS ‡
Lyttleton House 64 Broomfield Road Chelmsford Essex CM1 1SW
Tel: 01245 218244 *Fax:* 01245 820204

ARCHERS SOLICITORS ‡
78 New London Road Chelmsford Essex CM2 0PD
Tel: 01245 216888 *Fax:* 01245 216880 *Dx:* 3313 CHELMSFORD
List of partners: M B Calvy
Work: J1 O Q
SPr: Calvy, Miss Maria Beverley LLM . . . . . Nov 1998

BACKHOUSE SOLICITORS ‡
Unit 56 The Waterhouse Business Centre 2 Cromar Way Chelmsford Essex CM1 2QE
Tel: 01245 216626 *Fax:* 01245 216627
E-mail: info@backhouse-solicitors.co.uk
List of partners: M Backhouse
Work: J1 Q
Fixed Fee Interview undertaken
Ptr: Backhouse, Minal . . . . . Jan 1997

THE BEAVIS PARTNERSHIP ‡
Rochester House 275 Baddow Road Chelmsford Essex CM2 7QA
Tel: 01245 264748 *Fax:* 01245 260338
E-mail: mail@beavis-law.co.uk
List of partners: R M Chinery, M J Cornberg, T J Wayman
Office: Witham
Work: B1 B2 C1 D1 E F1 J1 K1 K2 L N O P Q R1 R2 S1 S2 V W Z(l)
Emergency Action, Agency, Advocacy, Fixed Fee Interview and Legal Aid undertaken
Ptr: Chinery, Mr Richard M LLB(Hons) . . . . . *Jan 1981
Cornberg, Mr Martin J . . . . . *Dec 1979
Wayman, Mr Trevor J LLB . . . . . *Oct 1988
Ast: Dattani, Ms Suniti LLB(Hons) . . . . . *Jan 2004
Harrison, Miss Claire LLB . . . . . *Mar 1984

BIRKETT LONG LLP
One Legg Street Chelmsford Essex CM1 1JS
Tel: 01245 453800 *Fax:* 01245 453801 *Dx:* 3394 CHELMSFORD
E-mail: mail@birkettlong.co.uk
Office: Colchester
Work: A1 A2 A3 B1 C1 C2 C3 D1 D2 E F1 F2 I J1 J2 K1 K2 K3 K4 L M1 M2 N O P Q R1 R2 S1 S2 T1 T2 U1 U2 W X Z(c,d,e,f,g,h,i,j,k,l,m,n,o,p,q,r,s,t,u,z)
Agency, Advocacy, Legal Aid undertaken and Legal Aid Franchise
Ptr: Allen, Mr Peter C LLB Notary Public . . . . . *Sep 1993
Hopkins, Mr Martin LLB; DipLPC . . . . . *Jun 1998
Rayner, Mr David MA(Cantab) . . . . . Oct 1983
Read, Mrs Claire Louise Zita LLB; MA . . . . . *Aug 2000
Ridley, Miss Justina LLB(Hons) . . . . . *Jan 1992
Wisbey, Mr David J LLB(Nott'm) . . . . . *Apr 1986
Wolny, Mr Robert Martin LLB(Hons) . . . . . Jun 1975
Asoc: Brunning, Miss Emma Louise LLB(Hons) . . . . . *Oct 1997
Curtis, Mrs Andrea . . . . . Feb 2005
Edmondson, Miss Nadina BA . . . . . *Sep 1989
Radford, Ms Anya . . . . . Jan 2002
Ast: Bruce, Mrs Jenny LLB; LPC . . . . . Sep 2008
Collins, Miss Lisa Marie LLB . . . . . Sep 2010
Parmenter, Mr Benjamin Mark Grimmer . . . . . Sep 2010
Pritchard, Mr Julien M BSc(Hons) . . . . . *May 1999
Russo, Ms Maria Gerarda . . . . . Dec 1999
Thurlow, Mr Marc . . . . . Feb 2010
Waters, Ms Emma Joanne LLB . . . . . Sep 2006
Wiles, Ms Claire . . . . . Sep 2002
Con: Avila, Mr Stephen Carlos LLB; LLM . . . . . Sep 2002

BIRKETTS LLP (WOLLASTONS LLP)
Brierly Place New London Road Chelmsford Essex CM2 0AP
Tel: 01245 211211 *Fax:* 01245 354764 *Dx:* 89703 CHELMSFORD 2
Emergency telephone 07834 603939
E-mail: mail@birketts.co.uk
Office: Cambridge, Ipswich, Norwich
Languages: French, German, Italian
Work: A1 A3 B1 C1 C2 C3 D1 D2 E F1 F2 I J1 J2 K1 K3 L M1 M2 N O P Q R1 R2 S1 S2 T1 T2 U1 U2 W X Z(b,c,d,e,f,h,i,k,l,n,o,p,q,t,w,y,z,za)
Agency undertaken
Mem: Burnett, Mr Nicholas J BA(Leeds) . . . . . *Mar 1980
Kerr, Ms Grace Elizabeth . . . . . Jan 1995
Palmer, Mr Kevin J LLB(Hons) Part time Chairman of Employment Tribunals . . . . . *Oct 1984
Payne, Mr Richard James LLB(Hons) . . . . . *Apr 1991
Ruiz, Rafael J BA . . . . . Sep 1997
Thompson, Mr Nigel H BA(Law) . . . . . *Oct 1984
Wilson, Mrs Melanie T LLB . . . . . *Nov 1989
Wollaston, Mr Richard H . . . . . *May 1973
Asoc: Barlow, Mrs Clare Anne LLB . . . . . *Aug 1993
Hunt, Mr Daden Henry Edward . . . . . *Sep 2002
Jones, Mr Adam Mark BA(Hons)(Law with German) . . Mar 2003
Kudryl, Mr Adam Joseph LLB . . . . . Sep 2003
Weston, Mr Matthew R LLB(Exon) . . . . . *Sep 1996
Ast: Coombe, Mr Joshua . . . . . *Aug 1997
Con: Cook, Mr Nicholas D LLB Notary Public . . . . . *Nov 1982
Little, Mr A James LLB(Lond); DPA(Lond); Barrister . *Jun 1973
Wollaston, Mrs Catherine Frances BA . . . . . *May 1973

BRETTS SOLICITORS ‡
PO Box 7370 Chelmsford Essex CM3 8WF
Tel: 01245 401233 *Fax:* 01245 401233
List of partners: S C Brett
SPr: Brett, Ms Susan Clare BSc(Hons)(Sociology) . . . . . *Jun 1996

ROGER BROOKER & CO ‡
70-72 New London Road Chelmsford Essex CM2 0PE
Est: 1973
Tel: 01245 351924 *Fax:* 01245 492428 *Dx:* 3305 CHELMSFORD
E-mail: info@rogerbrooker.co.uk
Web: www.rogerbrooker.co.uk
List of partners: R L Brooker, C I Perrin
Work: C1 D1 E J1 K1 O Q R2 S1 S2 W
Emergency Action, Advocacy and Fixed Fee Interview undertaken
Ptr: Brooker, Mr Roger L LLB . . . . . *Jul 1973
Perrin, Mrs Charlotte Isabel LLB(Hons); AKC . . . . . *Oct 1991
Ast: Macfarlane, Mrs Vivenne LLB . . . . . Nov 1985

B A CHAPPELL & CO ‡
115 Longstomps Avenue Chelmsford Essex CM2 9BZ
Tel: 01245 251650 *Fax:* 01245 251570 *Dx:* 89701 CHELMSFORD
E-mail: chappellsol@btinternet.com
List of partners: B A Chappell
Work: D1 E K1 L N S1 W
Fixed Fee Interview undertaken
Ptr: Chappell, Ms Barbara A LLB(Leics) . . . . . Jun 1974

PETER J COCKLE ‡
6 Lyndhurst Drive Bicknacre Chelmsford Essex CM3 4XL
Tel: 01245 225534 / 020 7015 1850 *Fax:* 01245 227038
List of partners: P J Cockle
Work: S1 W
SPr: Cockle, Mr Peter J LLB . . . . . *§Oct 1981

COLEMANS ‡
(in association with Cunningtons)
141 New London Road Chelmsford Essex CM2 0QT
Tel: 01245 264494 *Fax:* 01245 494537 *Dx:* 89710 CHELMSFORD
Work: A3 D2 E F1 J1 K1 K2 S1 S2 W Z(l)
Emergency Action, Agency, Advocacy, Fixed Fee Interview, Legal Aid undertaken and Legal Aid Franchise
Ast: Farrow, Miss Jacqueline Elizabeth LLB(Hons); DipLP . *Apr 2000
Paynter, Miss Louise LLB(Hons) . . . . . *Nov 1999

SHIRLEY CROFT SOLICITORS ‡
Lawrence House The Street Chelmsford Essex CM3 2DN
Tel: 01245 380019 *Fax:* 01245 381147
E-mail: shirleycroft@btinternet.com
List of partners: S A Croft
SPr: Croft, Mrs Shirley Anne . . . . . Oct 1994

DUFFIELD STUNT ‡
71 Duke Street Chelmsford Essex CM1 1JU
Tel: 01245 262351 *Fax:* 01245 492821
E-mail: mail@duffieldstunt.co.uk
List of partners: S R Chesney, N F Welch
Languages: Cantonese, Hakka, Hokkien, Malay, Mandarin, Teochew
Work: A1 C1 E J1 K1 K3 K4 L S1 S2 T2 W Z(d,q)
Ptr: Chesney, Mr Stephen Richard LLB(Lond) . . . . . *§Nov 1975
Welch, Mr Nicholas F LLB(Lond) . . . . . *Oct 1980
Ast: Bennett-Helps, Mrs Ann BA . . . . . Aug 2004
Chew, Ms Linda G S LLM . . . . . Jul 2005

Nicholas, Miss Lucy Sophia LLB(Hons) . . . . . *Nov 1989
Con: Harpur, Mr G R Travers LLB(Lond) . . . . . *§Sep 1969
Tattersall, Mr Richard John MA; BA . . . . . Jan 1974

FISHER JONES GREENWOOD LLP
Steeple House Church Lane Chelmsford Essex CM1 1NH
Tel: 01245 890110 *Fax:* 01245 890111 *Dx:* 3303 CHELMSFORD
Emergency telephone 01245 222004
E-mail: chelmsford@fjg.co.uk
Office: Clacton-on-Sea, Colchester (2 offices)
Work: B1 C1 C2 C3 D1 E F1 F2 G H I J1 J2 K1 L M1 N O P Q R1 R2 S1 S2 U2 V W Z(c,e,g,h,j,k,l,p,q,r)
Emergency Action, Agency, Advocacy, Fixed Fee Interview, Legal Aid undertaken, Legal Aid Franchise and Member of Accident Line
Ptr: Jones, Mr Christopher Rodney Vaughan BA(Hons)(Business Law) . . . . . *§Oct 1979
Lawton, Mr David L D BA(Oxon) ★ . . . . . *§May 1967

GADSBY WICKS ‡
Priory Place New London Road Chelmsford Essex CM2 0PP
Tel: 01245 494929 *Fax:* 01245 495347 *Dx:* 89707 CHELMSFORD 2
E-mail: mail@gadsbywicks.co.uk
List of partners: T A Frankel, G M Gadsby, A Mendham, F Pollard, R R Wicks
Work: N Q Z(r)
Legal Aid undertaken and Legal Aid Franchise
Ptr: Frankel, Ms Tamar Aliza LLB(Hons) . . . . . *May 1994
Gadsby, Mrs Gillian M LLB . . . . . *Sep 1989
Mendham, Mr Alan LLB(Hons) . . . . . *Sep 2004
Pollard, Ms Frances RGN; BA(Hons); DipLaw . . . . *Nov 2000
Wicks, Mr Roger R . . . . . *§Nov 1971
Ast: Fitzpatrick, Mrs Penelope J LLB . . . . . *Aug 2000

GARRODS SOLICITORS ‡
82 Springfield Road Chelmsford Essex CM2 6JY
Tel: 01245 492494 *Fax:* 01245 493840 *Dx:* 3375 CHELMSFORD 1
E-mail: enquiries@garrodslaw.com
List of partners: A J Garrod
Work: B1 C1 C2 D1 D2 E F1 J1 K1 K2 K3 L N O Q S1 S2 V W Z(d,q,r)
Emergency Action, Agency, Fixed Fee Interview, Legal Aid undertaken and Member of Accident Line
Ptr: Garrod, Miss Anita Jane BA(Hons) . . . . . May 1985

GEPP & SONS ‡
58 New London Road Chelmsford Essex CM2 0PA
Tel: 01245 493939 *Fax:* 01245 493940 *Dx:* 3306 CHELMSFORD
Emergency telephone 01245 358894
E-mail: mail@gepp.co.uk
List of partners: N G M Ashford, R P J Brice, P Butterfield, D R Carter, A L Dean, J P Douglas-Hughes, P G Littlefield, J Moore, S P Payne, L S Stradling, E M Worthy, H M A Young
Office: Colchester
Languages: French
Work: A1 B1 C1 D1 E F1 G H J1 K1 N O Q R1 S1 T1 T2 V W Z(l)
Agency, Legal Aid undertaken, Legal Aid Franchise and Member of Accident Line
Ptr: Ashford, Mr Neil G M MA(Cantab) . . . . . *§Jun 1979
Brice, Mr Roger P J LLB(Wales) . . . . . *§Dec 1978
Butterfield, Mr Peter LLB . . . . . Sep 1997
Carter, Mr Daniel R . . . . . *Dec 1990
Dean, Miss Alexandra L LLB(Hons) . . . . . Aug 2000
Douglas-Hughes, Mr Jonathan P DL Under Sheriff; Clerk to the Commissioner of Taxes . . . . . *§Dec 1969
Littlefield, Mr Peter G . . . . . *Feb 1972
Moore, Ms Joanna LLB(Hons) . . . . . *Feb 1994
Payne, Mr Steven P BA(Law) . . . . . *Nov 1984
Stradling, Miss Louise S LLB . . . . . *Sep 2000
Worthy, Mr Edward Malcolm LLB(Hons) . . . . . Jan 1998
Young, Mrs Hannah Marie Antoinette BCL . . . . . Oct 1994
Asoc: Buttress, Ms Claire LLB . . . . . Oct 2003
Emerson, Mr Justin R LLB . . . . . Oct 1999
Ast: Abu Bakar, Mr Muhammad Shah LLM . . . . . *Aug 2006
Carver, Mrs Lincey Indira LLB . . . . . Oct 2008
Davenport, Mrs Emma LLB(Hons) . . . . . *Jan 2002
Insley, Mr Jonathan David . . . . . Dec 2007
Nair, Miss Natasha LLB(Hons) . . . . . May 2006
Plomp, Miss Hendrika LLB(Hons) . . . . . §Mar 2005
Pumfrey, Mrs Joanne LLB; LLM . . . . . Nov 2004

LEONARD GRAY ‡
(incorporating Raggett Tiffen & Harries)
72-74 Duke Street Chelmsford Essex CM1 1JY
Tel: 01245 504904 *Fax:* 01245 490728 *Dx:* 3309 CHELMSFORD 1
Emergency telephone 01245 504904
E-mail: legal@leonardgray.co.uk
List of partners: C R Burrell, J R T M Oakley, R M Randall, C A Smith
Languages: French
Work: A1 A3 B1 C1 C2 D1 E F1 G H J1 K1 K2 K3 L M1 N O P Q R1 S1 S2 V W
Emergency Action, Agency, Advocacy, Fixed Fee Interview, Legal Aid undertaken, Legal Aid Franchise and Member of Accident Line
Ptr: Burrell, Mr Clive R LLB . . . . . *Sep 1999
Oakley, Mr Justin R T M MA(Oxon) . . . . . *Dec 1979
Randall, Mr Richard M LLB . . . . . *Nov 1972
Smith, Colin A LLB . . . . . *Jan 1982
Ast: Appleby, Mr John P LLB . . . . . *Sep 2003
Orrell, Ms Sarah . . . . . Jan 2006

A S GREENSTREET SOLICITOR ‡
86 Mildmay Road Chelmsford Essex CM2 0EA
Tel: 01245 603505 *Fax:* 01245 601308
E-mail: andrew@asgreenstreet.com

HARVEY COPPING & HARRISON
(in association with Harvey Collins Tipman & Co)
6 Chandlers Way South Woodham Ferrers Chelmsford Essex CM3 5TB
Tel: 01245 322956 *Fax:* 01245 322401 *Dx:* 50802 WICKFORD (S)
E-mail: woodham@hchsolicitors.co.uk
Office: Wickford
Work: A1 B1 C1 C2 C3 D1 E F1 J1 K1 L M1 M2 N P R1 S1 T1 T2 W Z(c,i)
Emergency Action, Fixed Fee Interview, Legal Aid undertaken and Member of Accident Line
Ptr: Shepard, Mrs Susan Jane LLB(Hons) . . . . . *Nov 1993

KENNEDYS
Greenwood House 91/99 New London Road Chelmsford Essex CM2 0PP
Tel: 0845 838 4800 *Fax:* 0845 838 4801
Dx: 89702 CHELMSFORD 2
E-mail: mailbox@kennedys-law.com

 See p112 for the Key to Work Categories & other symbols

Office: Belfast, Birmingham, Cambridge, London EC3, Maidstone, Manchester, Sheffield, Taunton
Work: B1 M1 P S1 Z(j)
Ptr: Bowman, Mr Nicholas BA(Hons); DipLP. . . . . *Nov 1998
Brewer, Mr Charles W. . . . . *Jun 1965
Penrose-Stevens, Ms Joti A LLB . . . . *Dec 1985
Sutton, Ms Mary Josephine MBA . . . . Apr 1991
West, Mr Kieran L. . . . . *§Jul 1978
West, Mr Richard Paul LLB . . . . *Oct 1993
Yates, Mr John David . . . . *Dec 1987
Mem: Harris, Ms Jennifer Kay . . . . *Nov 1993
Ast: Caplan, Mr Andrew LLB(Hons) . . . . Jan 1997
Harris, Mr Richard M C BA . . . . *Mar 1985
Harrison, Mr Andrew Paul LLB(Hons) . . . . *Dec 1992
Marriott, Ms Anne BA . . . . Apr 1999
Mayes, Wendy . . . . Sep 2003
Middleton, Joy . . . . Sep 2005
O'Reilly, Ms Pauline LLB(Hons) . . . . Sep 1995
Ruston, Mr Ronald LLB . . . . *§Oct 1994
Smithers, Mrs Victoria LLB(Hons) . . . . Sep 2001
Stevenson, Ms Clare . . . . Nov 1998
Con: Rogers, Mr David . . . . Jul 1975

LLOYD GREEN SOLICITORS ‡
Kensal House 77 Springfield Road Chelmsford Essex CM2 6JG
Tel: 01245 294600 *Fax:* 01245 294666 *Dx:* 3359 CHELMSFORD 1
E-mail: mail@lloyd-green.co.uk
List of partners: N Chatters, J W Duncombe, L S Green
Work: F1 J1 J2 N Q Z(j,q)
Agency and Fixed Fee Interview undertaken
Ptr: Chatters, Mr Nicholas LLB(Hons) . . . . *Oct 1990
Duncombe, Mr John W LLB(Hons) . . . . *Jul 1997
Green, Mr Lloyd S BSocSc . . . . *Oct 1985

MORRIS & CO SOLICITORS ‡
123 New London Road Chelmsford Essex CM2 0QT
Tel: 01245 345999 *Fax:* 01245 345900 *Dx:* 89717 CHELMSFORD 2
E-mail: enquiries@morrisandcosolicitors.co.uk

NIGEL BROADHEAD MYNARD ‡
(in association with NBM Charles Whiting; NBM Dale; NBM Charles White; NBM Eason)
32 Rainsford Road Chelmsford Essex CM1 2QG
Tel: 01245 269909 *Fax:* 01245 261932
List of partners: R W N Broadhead, N P Eason
Office: Ashby-de-la-Zouch, Cambridge
Work: B1 C1 C2 E F1 F2 G J1 L N Q R1 R2 S1 S2 W
Emergency Action, Agency and Advocacy undertaken
Ptr: Broadhead, Mr Robert W N LLB. . . . . *§Jun 1970
Con: Mynard, Mr Stephen A . . . . *Oct 1986

PWP SOLICITORS ‡
Cloville Hall Ship Road West Hanningfield Chelmsford Essex CM2 9XA
Tel: 01277 841104 *Fax:* 01277 841616
E-mail: pwpsolicitors@aol.com

PETERS & CO
Faircross House 206 Springfield Road Chelmsford Essex CM2 6BN
Tel: 01279 453331
E-mail: info@peterslegal.co.uk
Office: Dunstable, Harlow

PRETTYS
Number One Legg Street Chelmsford Essex CM1 1JS
Tel: 01245 295295 *Fax:* 01245 295299 *Dx:* 3323 CHELMSFORD
E-mail: djohnson@prettys.co.uk
Office: Ipswich
Work: A3 B1 C1 C2 E F1 F2 I J1 J2 K1 K2 K3 K4 L M1 N O Q R1 R2 S1 S2 T2 U1 U2 W Z(a,b,c,d,e,h,j,k,l,o,p,q,r,t,w)
Emergency Action, Agency, Fixed Fee Interview undertaken and Member of Accident Line
Ptr: Chasmer, Mrs Michelle . . . . Sep 2000
McMutrie, Ms Fiona. . . . . Sep 2000
Sleight, Mr Tom. . . . . Sep 2000
Thompson, Dr Guy . . . . Sep 1999
White, Mr Matthew . . . . Dec 1995

QUALITYSOLICITORS HILL & ABBOTT ‡
Threadneedle House 9 & 10 Market Road Chelmsford Essex CM1 1XH
Tel: 01245 258892 *Fax:* 01245 490480 *Dx:* 3301 CHELMSFORD 1
E-mail: info@qshalaw.com
List of partners: R T Clarke, B M Crawford, J M Melvin, J M H Newson, R H Penn, A A J Royle
Languages: Hindi, Polish, Punjabi, Russian, Urdu
Work: B1 C1 C2 C3 D1 D2 E F1 J1 K1 K2 K3 K4 L M1 M2 N O P Q R1 S1 S2 T1 T2 V W X Z(b,c,d,e,g,h,j,k,l,m,o,p,q,r,w)
Emergency Action, Agency, Advocacy, Fixed Fee Interview, Legal Aid undertaken, Legal Aid Franchise and Member of Accident Line
Ptr: Clarke, Mr Ronald Terence LLB(Hons) . . . . *Feb 1997
Crawford, Mr Barry M LLB Social Security Appeals Tribunal Chairman . . . . *Oct 1973
Melvin, Mr J Michael BA. . . . . *Apr 1980
Newson, Mr Jeremy Michael Hugh LLB Sweet & Maxwell Law Prize . . . . *Nov 1993
Penn, Mr Richard Howard LLB(Hons) . . . . *Oct 1992
Royle, Mr Aidan Albert Julian BA(Law) . . . . *Mar 1985
Ast: Bishop, Ms Karen LLB . . . . *Nov 2003
Blythe, Mr Richard J BA. . . . . *Nov 1985
Huggins, Miss Kim Samantha BA(Hons). . . . . Mar 2011
Letts, Miss Katherine BA . . . . *Sep 2009
Stock, Mr Justin M A LLB . . . . *Nov 1989
Walls, Mr Stephen Mark LLB; LSF. . . . . *Jan 1992

ISABELLE E RASTALL ‡
Lancaster House 234 Springfield Road Chelmsford Essex CM2 6BP
Tel: 01245 349966 *Fax:* 01245 349970
List of partners: I E Rastall
Work: S1
Ptr: Rastall, Miss Isabelle E BA(Lond) . . . . *Oct 1981

AL RAYMENT ‡
50 Paddock Drive Chelmsford Essex CM1 6UX
Tel: 01245 466624

PETER RICHBELL & CO SOLICITORS ‡
Signal Chambers Railway Street Chelmsford Essex CM1 1QS
Tel: 01245 355300 *Fax:* 01245 355310 *Dx:* 121927 CHELMSFORD 6
List of partners: A J Mitty, P L Richbell
Work: N
Member of Accident Line
Ptr: Mitty, Mr Anthony J LLB. . . . . *Oct 1991
Richbell, Mr Peter Leonard LLB Maxwell Law Prize . *§Oct 1988

SILVERBECK RYMER ‡
County House County Square 100 New London Road Chelmsford Essex CM2 0RG
Tel: 0845 050 8001 *Fax:* 01245 291777 *Dx:* 139166 CHELMSFORD
E-mail: law@silverbeck-rymer.co.uk

STANTON-DUNNE & CO ‡
The Generals Main Road Boreham Chelmsford Essex CM3 3HJ
Tel: 01245 460303 *Fax:* 01245 460331
E-mail: enquiries@stanton-dunne.co.uk

TAYLOR HALDANE BARLEX LLP ‡
Copt House 73 Springfield Road Chelmsford Essex CM2 6JG
Tel: 0845 293 7688 *Fax:* 01245 455590
Dx: 160020 CHELMSFORD 19
Emergency telephone 07946 706444
E-mail: mail@thblegal.com
List of partners: P A Barlex, R D Haldane, S M Steggles, M Taylor
Office: Benfleet, Braintree, Ipswich, Southend-on-Sea
Work: G H
Advocacy and Legal Aid undertaken
Ptr: Barlex, Mr Peter Andrew LLB ★. . . . . *Dec 1994
Haldane, Mr Russell Duncan LLB . . . . *Dec 1999
Steggles, Ms Sarah Maria LLB; LLM . . . . *Sep 2001
Taylor, Mr Matthew LLB. . . . . *Jan 1994
Ast: Donegan, Mr Paul Gerard BA. . . . . *Oct 2005
Lindsey, Ms Alexandra Fiona Polly BA. . . . . *Oct 2004
Reader, Ms Louise Jacqueline LLB . . . . *Sep 2005

THOMPSONS (FORMERLY ROBIN/BRIAN THOMPSON & PARTNERS)
(in association with The Thompsons Partnership; Thompsons McClure(Belfast); Thompsons(Scotland))
2nd Floor Grosvenor House 53 New London Road Chelmsford Essex CM2 0ND
Tel: 01245 228800 *Fax:* 01245 352259 *Dx:* 3326 CHELMSFORD
Office: Belfast, Birmingham, Bristol, Cardiff, Dagenham, Derby, Harrow, Leeds, Liverpool, London SW19, London WC1, Manchester, Middlesbrough, Newcastle upon Tyne, Nottingham, Plymouth, Sheffield, South Shields, Southampton, Stoke-on-Trent, Swansea, Wolverhampton
Work: F1 G J1 N

TOLHURST FISHER LLP
Marlborough House Victoria Road South Chelmsford Essex CM1 1LN
Tel: 01245 495111 *Fax:* 01245 494771 *Dx:* 3314 CHELMSFORD
E-mail: info@tolhurstfisher.com
Office: Southend-on-Sea
Languages: French
Work: A1 B1 C1 C2 C3 E F1 J1 L M1 M2 N O R1 S1 T1 T2 W Z(b,c,d,e,n,o)
Agency undertaken
Ptr: Cuthbert, Ms Julie. . . . . Mar 1989
Provan, Mr Graeme. . . . . Nov 1997
Tolhurst, Mr Philip. . . . . May 1973
Ast: Holmes, Mr Oliver James . . . . Oct 1982

TRINITY SOLICITORS
Suite 125 Waterhouse Business Centre 2 Cromar Way Chelmsford Essex CM1 2QE
Tel: 0870 850 1153 *Fax:* 0870 850 5526
E-mail: law@trinitysolicitors.com
Office: London E15

CHARLES WHITING ‡
Moulsham Court 39 Moulsham Street Chelmsford Essex CM2 0HY
Tel: 01245 496911 *Fax:* 01245 496141
Dx: 139163 CHELMSFORD 11
E-mail: enquiries@cwhiting.co.uk
List of partners: C W Whiting
Work: B1 C1 E F1 K1 K3 L O Q R2 S1 S2 W Z(l,q)
Ptr: Whiting, Mr Charles William LLB . . . . *§Nov 1982

JANE WILLIAMS EMPLOYMENT LAW SOLICITORS ‡
34 Chichester Drive Chelmsford Essex CM1 7RY
Tel: 01245 251007 / 07740 409054 *Fax:* 0870 051 2106
E-mail: jane@janewilliamsemploymentlaw.co.uk

WILSON & CO ‡
Mayes Lane Mayesfield Danbury Chelmsford Essex CM3 4NJ
Tel: 01245 202602 *Fax:* 01245 226925
E-mail: juliawilson@wilsonandcolegal.com

WORTLEY REDMAYNE KERSHAW ‡
Stonebridge House Stonebridge Walk High Street Chelmsford Essex CM1 1EY
Tel: 01245 491122 *Fax:* 01245 281229 *Dx:* 3312 CHELMSFORD 1
List of partners: F M Ashworth, G R Atkinson, D B Perry, G R Yeldham
Work: A1 B1 C1 C2 C3 D1 E F1 G H J1 K1 K3 L M1 N O P Q R1 S1 S2 T1 T2 V W Z(c,e,k,l)
Emergency Action, Agency, Advocacy, Fixed Fee Interview, Legal Aid undertaken and Legal Aid Franchise
Ptr: Ashworth, Mrs Fiona M LLB. . . . . *Jul 1999
Atkinson, Mr Graeme Ross BA(Law) . . . . *Oct 1983
Perry, Mr David Brian . . . . *Jul 1995
Yeldham, Mr Grahame R BA . . . . *§Dec 1977
Asoc: Clifton-Thompson, Mrs Petra . . . . *Sep 1999
Coombe, Mr Joshua. . . . . *Aug 1997
Mcgann, Mrs Eleanor K. . . . . *Jun 1996
Ast: Ashworth, Mr Robert David . . . . Jul 2007
Curtis, Miss Tamasin Anne LLB . . . . May 2009
Fraser, Mr Donald Simon . . . . Dec 1993
Gillam, Miss Emma LLB. . . . . Jan 2008
Insley, Mr Jonathan David. . . . . Dec 2007
Johnston, Mr Ian Christopher LLB. . . . . Aug 2007
Lowe, Mr Kieran . . . . Aug 2007
Smith, Miss Lucinda. . . . . Aug 2005

CHELTENHAM, Gloucestershire

AT@LAW LLP ‡
4 Court Mews London Road Charlton Kings Cheltenham Gloucestershire GL52 6HS
Tel: 0800 019 5933 *Fax:* 0845 190 7124 *Dx:* 7410 CHELTENHAM
E-mail: enquiries@atlawsolicitors.co.uk

ROSS ALDRIDGE LLP ‡
5th Floor Eagle Tower Montpellier Drive Cheltenham Gloucestershire GL50 1TA
Tel: 01242 707400 *Fax:* 0870 161 1055 *Dx:* 7441 CHELTENHAM
Emergency telephone 01242 707400
E-mail: enquiries@ra-sol.com
List of partners: R P Aldridge, J M Depner, S Sriwardene
Work: N
Ptr: Aldridge, Mr Ross P MA(Cantab) . . . . *Jun 1974
Depner, Mr John M BA . . . . *Oct 1987
Sriwardene, Mr Siri . . . . NSP

2

ALLEN HOOLE SOLICITORS
31 St George's Road Cheltenham Gloucestershire GL50 3DU
Tel: 01242 522201 *Fax:* 01242 521651
E-mail: lawyers@allenhoole.co.uk
Office: Bristol

ASTBURY AND COMPANY ‡
Castle Chambers High Street Winchcombe Cheltenham Gloucestershire GL54 5LJ
Tel: 01242 604303 *Fax:* 01242 604409 *Dx:* 118775 WINCHCOMBE
E-mail: paul.astbury@astburyandco.co.uk

BPE HOMEMOVE LLP ‡
St James's House St James's Square Cheltenham Gloucestershire GL50 3PR
Tel: 01242 708800 *Fax:* 01242 708806
Dx: 141661 CHELTENHAM 11
E-mail: info@bpehomemove.co.uk
Work: S1
Fixed Fee Interview undertaken

BPE SOLICITORS LLP ‡
St James' House St James' Square Cheltenham Gloucestershire GL50 3PR
Tel: 01242 224433 *Fax:* 01242 574285 *Dx:* 141660 CHELTENHAM
E-mail: bpe@bpe.co.uk
List of partners: T Adamson, M A J Anton-Smith, R J H Bretherton, J E A Briano, N C Corner, W J R Evans, R D Handley, G R Hughes-Jones, H Lovatt, M R Ovington, J C Pyrke, P J Radford, A A D N Rudge, D Sherborne, A Shield, T Ward, J K Workman
Office: London WC1
Languages: French, German, Italian, Spanish, Welsh
Work: A3 B1 B2 C1 C2 E F1 F2 J1 J2 L N O Q R1 R2 S1 S2 T2 U2 W Z(c,e,h,l,p,q,za)
Emergency Action, Agency, Fixed Fee Interview undertaken and Member of Accident Line
Ptr: Adamson, Miss Theresa LLB(Lond) . . . . *Jun 1981
Anton-Smith, Mr Mark Alexander John . . . . *Oct 1989
Briano, Ms Julia E A LLB . . . . *Nov 1995
Corner, Miss Nicola C MA. . . . . *Sep 1981
Evans, Mrs Wendy J R . . . . Oct 1993
Handley, Mr Richard D MA(Cantab). . . . . *Apr 1979
Hughes-Jones, Mr Gavin R LLB. . . . . *Apr 1975
Lovatt, Mrs Helen . . . . Oct 1984
Ovington, Mr Mark R . . . . *Jun 1968
Pyrke, Mr Julian Charles BSc(Hons). . . . . *Nov 1994
Radford, Mr Philip J BA . . . . *§Mar 1985
Rudge, Mr Anthony A De N LLB(Hons)(Exon) . . . . . Oct 1988
Sherborne, Mr Darren BA(Hons); LLM(Hons) . . . . . Mar 2002
Shield, Miss Antonia . . . . Aug 1999
Ward, Mr Tim . . . . Sep 1997
Workman, Mr John Kerrison BA(Dunelm) . . . . *Nov 1984
Asoc: Garfield, Mr Iain LLB . . . . Sep 2002
Taylor, Mr Andrew BSc(Hons). . . . . Jun 2003
Ast: Lacey, Mrs Joanne . . . . Sep 2002

BAILEYS ‡
7 Royal Crescent Cheltenham Gloucestershire GL50 3DF
Tel: 01242 514477 *Fax:* 01242 226189 *Dx:* 7421 CHELTENHAM
List of partners: A D Chapman, C W Jenkins
Work: A1 C1 D1 E K1 L S1 S2 T2 V W Z(d)
Fixed Fee Interview undertaken
Ptr: Chapman, Mr Andrew D LLB . . . . *§Dec 1974
Jenkins, Mr Christopher William LLB . . . . *Jul 1973
Ast: Cahill, Ms Mary T P BA . . . . *Jun 1990
FitzGerald, Ms Georgina A BA(Hons) . . . . *Apr 1988
Hart, Mr Andrew Wallace FILEx . . . . *Jan 1993

BEVAN-EVANS & CAPEHORN SOLICITORS ‡
Loreburn House 7 Montpellier Terrace Cheltenham Gloucestershire GL50 1US
Tel: 01242 234564 *Fax:* 0870 051 5791 *Dx:* 37463 CHEPSTOW
E-mail: enquiries@beandc.co.uk

DAVID BILLINGHAM & PARTNERS ‡
2 Church Road Bishops Cleeve Cheltenham Gloucestershire GL52 8LR
Tel: 01242 676224 *Fax:* 01242 677131
Dx: 96553 BISHOPS CLEEVE
Emergency telephone 01242 675645
E-mail: dgb@billinghampartners.co.uk
List of partners: D G Billingham
Office: Tewkesbury
Work: A1 B2 C1 D1 D2 E F1 G H J1 K1 L P S1 S2 V W
Emergency Action, Agency, Advocacy, Fixed Fee Interview, Legal Aid undertaken and Member of Accident Line
Ptr: Billingham, Mr David G ACIArb H M Coroner of Gloucestershire Gloucester District; Chairman of Gloucestershire Independent Advocacy Project for Children in Need *Jul 1973
Ast: Harbinson, Mr Matthew BA(Hons). . . . . Feb 2005

BRAND MELLON LLP
10 Church Street Charlton Kings Cheltenham Gloucestershire GL53 8AR
Tel: 01242 227266 *Fax:* 01242 226735
Office: Gloucester
Work: A1 B1 C1 D1 E F1 G H J1 K1 L M1 N P R1 S1

SIMON BURN SOLICITORS ‡
Lower Ground Floor 123 Promenade Cheltenham Gloucestershire GL50 1NW
Tel: 01242 228444 *Fax:* 01242 516888 *Dx:* 7404 CHELTENHAM
Emergency telephone 07736 430270
E-mail: enquiries@simonburn.co.uk
List of partners: S Burn
Work: B1 C1 E J1 L M2 O Q S2 Z(b,e,k)
Emergency Action, Agency, Advocacy and Fixed Fee Interview undertaken
Ptr: Burn, Mr Simon LLB . . . . Aug 1998

CHARLES RUSSELL LLP
Compass House Lypiatt Road Cheltenham Gloucestershire GL50 2QJ
Tel: 01242 221122 *Fax:* 01242 584700 *Dx:* 7442 CHELTENHAM
E-mail: enquiries@charlesrussell.co.uk
Office: Cambridge, Guildford, London EC4, Oxford

Work: A1 B1 C1 C2 C3 E F1 I J1 L M1 M2 O P Q R1 R2 S1 S2 T1 T2 U1 W Z(b,c,d,e,f,h,j,k,o,s)
Agency undertaken and Member of Accident Line
Ptr: Adlard, Ms Helen E MA . . . *Nov 1993
Brothwood, Mr Ian J LLB(Nott'm) . . . *Nov 1988
Davis, Mr Martin M MA(Oxon) . . . *§Dec 1968
Gearon, Mr Patrick . . . *Nov 1994
Jordan, Mr Geoffrey W BA; LLB; LARTPI . . . *Oct 1975
Mayer, Mr Adrian George Alan . . . Mar 1998
Morton, Mr Nigel J BA . . . *Oct 1983
Norton, Mr Richard W F LLB . . . *Feb 1985
Page, Mr Christopher J MA(Oxon) . . . *§Nov 1985
Pallister, Mr Stephen BA; MA . . . *Sep 1989
Rundall, Mr Francis R S BA(Dunelm) . . . *Apr 1975
Russell, Mr Colin P BA(Oxon) . . . *§Jan 1970
Scandrett, Mr Peter D MA(Cantab) . . . *Oct 1977
Asoc: Turcan, Ms Sarah Jane . . . *Sep 1997
Ast: Jenkins, Mr Timothy Paul LLB Clyde & Co Common Law Prize . . . *Nov 1995

CLIFFORD HOLMES SOLICITORS ‡
37 St George's Square Cheltenham Gloucestershire GL50 3DU
Tel: 01242 529933 ***Fax:*** 01242 529955 ***Dx:*** 7426 CHELTENHAM
E-mail: rch@cliffordholmes.co.uk
Work: E R2 S2

COWLE SMART ‡
29 Leckhampton Road Cheltenham Gloucestershire GL53 0AZ
Tel: 01242 222744 / 570700 ***Fax:*** 01242 584518
Dx: 90850 CHELTENHAM 3
E-mail: vc@cowle-smart.co.uk
List of partners: V W Cowle
Work: A1 B1 C1 E F1 K1 L N O Q R2 S1 S2 W Z(c,e,l,r)
Agency undertaken
SPr: Cowle, Mr Vivian Wilson . . . *Jul 1973

CHRISTOPHER DAVIDSON SOLICITORS LLP ‡
2 & 3 Oriel Terrace Oriel Road Cheltenham Gloucestershire GL50 1XP
Tel: 01242 581481 ***Fax:*** 01242 221210 ***Dx:*** 7408 CHELTENHAM
E-mail: info@cdlaw.co.uk
List of partners: K A Ellis, D R Mason, A S Raistrick, J S Richardson
Work: A1 A3 B1 B2 C1 C2 C3 E F1 I J1 J2 K4 L M1 M2 N O P Q R1 S1 S2 U2 W X Z(b,c,d,e,f,j,k,l,o,q)
Emergency Action, Agency, Advocacy, Fixed Fee Interview undertaken and Member of Accident Line
Ptr: Ellis, Mr Keith A BA(Law) . . . *Nov 1989
Mason, Mr David R LLB . . . *Mar 1991
Raistrick, Mr Andrew S LLB . . . *Nov 1980
Richardson, Mr John Stuart MA(Oxon) . . . *Dec 1971

DAVIS GREGORY LTD ‡
25 Rodney Road Cheltenham Gloucestershire GL50 1HX
Tel: 01242 235202 ***Fax:*** 01242 224716 ***Dx:*** 7423 CHELTENHAM 1
E-mail: law@davisg.co.uk
List of partners: S P Greener, T C Howarth, L B Srodon
Work: A3 B1 C1 E J1 J2 K1 K2 K3 K4 N O Q R1 S1 S2 T2 W Z(o,q)
Member of Accident Line
Dir: Greener, Mr Simon P LLB . . . *Dec 1985
Howarth, Mr Timothy C LLB(Leics) Notary Public . . . *§Apr 1977
Srodon, Miss Laura B LLB(B'ham) J F Gregg Memorial Prize; Amphlett Prize Notary Public . . . *§Oct 1983
Ast: Banister, Mrs Hilary Jean LLB . . . Nov 1988
Newman, Miss Angela Claire LLB(Hons) . . . Sep 2001
Taylor, Ms Alison Jane LLB(Hons) . . . Oct 1995

FAMILY LAW CONSULTANTS ‡
7 Rodney Road Cheltenham Gloucestershire GL50 1HX
Tel: 01242 222201
E-mail: joanne.bennett@flcsolicitors.co.uk
List of partners: J M Bennett, S C Harris
Ptr: Bennett, Miss Joanne Marie LLB(Hons) . . . Sep 1999
Harris, Miss Samantha Carole LLB; LPC . . . *Oct 2003

FLEET SOLICITORS LLP
Visage House Lansdown Place Lane Cheltenham Gloucestershire GL50 2LB
Est: 2006
E-mail: mail@fleetlaw.co.uk
Office: Bristol
Work: O Z(j,q)

J H GABB & CO SOLICITORS ‡
9 Gainsborough House Battle Brook Drive Chipping Campden Cheltenham Gloucestershire GL55 6JX
Tel: 07970 011693 ***Fax:*** 01386 840483
E-mail: jamesgabb@btconnect.com

GILLANDERS ‡
1 North Place Cheltenham Gloucestershire GL50 4DW
Tel: 01242 583434 ***Fax:*** 01242 583435 ***Dx:*** 7452 CHELTENHAM 1
E-mail: dsg@gillanders-law.com
List of partners: D S Gillanders, M Lynham
Work: A1 B1 C1 E F1 J1 L N O Q S1 S2 W Z(k,l,q,r)
Emergency Action, Agency, Advocacy and Fixed Fee Interview undertaken
Ptr: Gillanders, Mr Donald S BA(TCD); LLB(Lond) . . . Nov 1985
Lynham, Mr Mark LLB(Hons) . . . Sep 1999

HARRISON CLARK LLP
(incorporating Jordans)
Kings House 127 Promenade Cheltenham Gloucestershire GL50 1NW
Tel: 01242 269198 ***Fax:*** 01242 584195 ***Dx:*** 7452 CHELTENHAM
E-mail: lawyers@harrison-clark.co.uk
Office: Hereford, Ross-on-Wye, Worcester (2 offices)
Work: A1 A2 A3 B1 C1 C2 C3 D1 D2 E F1 F2 I J1 J2 K1 K2 K3 K4 L M1 N O P Q R1 R2 S1 S2 T1 U2 V W X Z(b,c,d,e,h,j,l,m,o,p,q,r,s,u)
Emergency Action, Agency, Advocacy, Fixed Fee Interview, Legal Aid undertaken, Legal Aid Franchise and Member of Accident Line
Ptr: Bateman, Ms Andrea Louise LLB . . . Sep 2000
Bexfield, Ms Cindy April BA(Hons) . . . *Jan 1988
Brew, Mr Jonathan LLB . . . *§Oct 1980
Caldicott, Mr Andrew . . . *Feb 1994
Capper, Mr Robert Matthew LLB . . . *Sep 1997
Cave, Mr Michael A . . . Sep 1987
Green, Mr Richard BA . . . *Jan 1983
Irvine, Miss Caroline Jane BA(Hons) . . . *Oct 1990
James, Mr Andrew M BA(Oxon) . . . *Oct 1990
Jordan, Mrs Barbara Glenys BA(Hons)(Philosophy) . . . *Mar 1981
Morgan, Mr Richard Charles . . . *Mar 1984
Oliver, Miss Dawn E LLB(Hons) . . . *Oct 1992
Savage, Mr Peter . . . *Mar 1997
Spain, Mrs Brenda V BA . . . *Nov 1987
Thomas, Mr Rod . . . *Aug 1998
Thornton-Smith, Miss Charlotte Jane . . . *Oct 2003
Whitbread, Mr Jonathan R . . . *Sep 1999
Asoc: Baker, Ms Ruth . . . Jan 2007
Cambridge, Mr Daniel . . . *Jan 2004
Dhillon, Miss Arpinder LLB . . . *Oct 1999
Gilhooly, Miss Suzzane Jane . . . Oct 2005
Goodwin, Mr Michael BA . . . *Sep 1999
Hodgetts, Ms Joanne . . . *Jan 2006
Leask, Rebecca . . . *Oct 2007
Lowe, Ms Tracey . . . Jan 2006
Priest, Ms Emma . . . *Jan 2002
Scott, Ms Alison . . . *Jan 2001
Small, Miss Lucinda LLB . . . *Nov 1996
Smith, Mr Frank Richard LLB(Hons)(Law & Italian) . . . *Jan 2003
Thompson, Ms Claire . . . *Jan 1998
Tipple, Ms Lorna . . . *Jan 2004
Waddington, Mr Mathew Nicholas George . . . *Oct 2003
Ast: Berry, Constantine . . . *Jan 2006
Haq, Ms Suraiya . . . May 1994
Wathen, Ms Mary . . . Jul 2008

HINE SOLICITORS
149-151 Fairview Road Cheltenham Gloucestershire GL52 2EX
Tel: 01242 256686 ***Fax:*** 01242 261360
Office: Beaconsfield, Bracknell, Gerrards Cross, Oxford, Princes Risborough, Swindon, Yiewsley

HUGHES PADDISON ‡
10 Royal Crescent Cheltenham Gloucestershire GL50 3DA
Tel: 01242 574244 ***Fax:*** 01242 221631 ***Dx:*** 7453 CHELTENHAM
E-mail: info@hughes-paddison.co.uk
List of partners: J S Brothwood, J G Hughes, M S Paddison, G H Parry, D T Sterrett, R A Stewart, J M Witek
Languages: French, Italian
Work: B1 D1 E F1 J1 J2 K1 K2 K3 K4 L N O Q R1 S1 S2 T2 V W X Z(q)
Emergency Action, Agency, Advocacy and Fixed Fee Interview undertaken
Dir: Brothwood, Ms Jane S LLB . . . *Oct 1989
Hughes, Mrs Julie G LLB . . . *Sep 1982
Paddison, Mr Mark S . . . *May 1977
Parry, Mr Gareth Huw LLB . . . *Apr 1999
Sterrett, Mr David Thomas LLB(Lond) . . . *Feb 1990
Stewart, Miss Rachel Anne LLB . . . *Jun 1999
Witek, Mrs Jane Marie . . . *Sep 2001
Asoc: Allen, Miss Jennifer Laurel LLB . . . Apr 2008
Ast: Armstrong, Mr Douglas Charles BA; LLB . . . Apr 2010
Buswell, Miss Katie Hannah LLB(Hons) . . . Apr 2009
Gamblin, Mrs Catherine Gail LLB(with French) . . . Apr 2009
Con: Hughes, Mr John M BA(Law) . . . *Nov 1978

HUNTS ‡
6 Ormond Terrace Regent Street Cheltenham Gloucestershire GL50 1HR
Tel: 01242 525777 ***Fax:*** 01242 261728
E-mail: hunts@btinternet.com
List of partners: N P Hunt
Work: K4 T2 W
SPr: Hunt, Mr Nicholas P LLB(B'ham) . . . *Mar 1981

NICK HUTCHINSON & CO ‡
3 Rodney Road Cheltenham Gloucestershire GL50 1HX
Tel: 01242 261515 ***Fax:*** 01242 581937 ***Dx:*** 7405 CHELTENHAM
E-mail: mail@nickhutchinson.co.uk
List of partners: V L Hammond, N G Hutchinson
Languages: French
Work: A1 C1 E J1 K1 K3 L N Q S1 S2 W
Fixed Fee Interview undertaken
Ptr: Hammond, Mrs Vanessa Louise . . . *Mar 1995
Hutchinson, Mr Nicholas G BA(Lond) . . . *Mar 1981

KNIGHTS SOLICITORS LLP
Eagle Tower Montpellier Drive Cheltenham Gloucestershire GL50 1TA
Tel: 01242 524654 ***Fax:*** 01242 524590 ***Dx:*** 7443 CHELTENHAM
E-mail: mail@knightsllp.co.uk
Office: Alderley Edge, Newcastle under Lyme
Work: A1 A2 A3 B1 C1 C2 C3 D1 E F1 F2 I J1 J2 K1 K3 K4 L M1 M2 N O P Q R1 R2 S1 S2 T1 T2 U1 U2 V W X Z(b,c,d,e,f,g,k,l,m,n,o,p,q,r,s,t,w)
Emergency Action, Fixed Fee Interview undertaken and Member of Accident Line
Ptr: Anton-Smith, Mr Mark Alexander John . . . *Oct 1989
Coddington, Mr Russell Graham LLB . . . *§Sep 2001

LANE & CO ‡
Saint George's House 101 St George's Place Cheltenham Gloucestershire GL50 3QZ
Tel: 01242 524785 / 222421 ***Fax:*** 01242 222784
Dx: 7413 CHELTENHAM
List of partners: J D Hueston, S Rosbottom
Languages: French
Work: S1 S2 W
Ptr: Hueston, Mr James D LLB(Lond); TEP . . . *§Dec 1974
Rosbottom, Mr Stephen LLB . . . *§Apr 1981

LESTER MADDRELL ‡
PO Box 386 Cheltenham Gloucestershire GL51 3YW
Tel: 01242 222147 ***Fax:*** 01242 222147
List of partners: A L Maddrell
SPr: Maddrell, Mr Alan Lester Deputy Traffic Commissioner; Deputy Tribunal Judge . . . *Oct 1971

MCWALTER & CO ‡
8 Mill Parade Church Road Bishop Cleeve Cheltenham Gloucestershire GL52 8RL
Tel: 01242 676106 ***Fax:*** 01242 675805 ***Dx:*** 96552 BISHOP CLEEVE
List of partners: E McWalter
SPr: McWalter, Miss Elizabeth BA . . . Oct 1986

MAITLAND WALKER
19 Imperial Square Cheltenham Gloucestershire GL50 1QZ
Tel: 01242 285855 ***Fax:*** 01242 285856 ***Dx:*** 7445 CHELTENHAM
E-mail: cheltenham-office@maitlandwalker.com
Office: Minehead
Languages: Afrikaans, French
Work: C1 C3 J1 M1 N O Q Z(l,q)
Emergency Action, Agency, Advocacy and Fixed Fee Interview undertaken
Ptr: Croft, Mr Rupert . . . Oct 1992
Asoc: Rowe, Mr Nicholas Francis LLB . . . Sep 2002
Ast: Rowe, Mr Scott Michael BA; CPE . . . Sep 2004

MANLEY TURNBULL ‡
Turnbull House 1 Tally Ho Lane Guiting Power Cheltenham Gloucestershire GL54 5TY
Tel: 01451 851882 ***Fax:*** 01451 657777
E-mail: info@manleyturnbull.co.uk

MARKS & CLERK
27 Imperial Square Cheltenham Gloucestershire GL50 1RQ
Tel: 01242 524520 ***Fax:*** 01242 579383
Office: Birmingham, Leeds, Leicester, Liverpool, London WC2, Manchester, Oxford

MIDWINTERS ‡
(incorporating Gareth Gregory & Co)
1-3 Crescent Place Cheltenham Gloucestershire GL50 3PJ
Tel: 01242 514674 ***Fax:*** 01242 221968 ***Dx:*** 7411 CHELTENHAM
E-mail: enquiries@midwinters.co.uk
List of partners: A J Cassin, G N Gregory, H J O Harries
Work: C1 D1 E J1 J2 K1 K3 L N O Q S1 S2 T2 W Z(q)
Agency, Advocacy, Fixed Fee Interview, Legal Aid Franchise and Member of Accident Line
Ptr: Cassin, Mrs Alexis J BA(Law) Borough Councillor . . . *§Jun 1976
Gregory, Mr Gareth Nicholas BA . . . *§Sep 1985
Harries, Mr Hugh J O LLB . . . *§Aug 1985
Asoc: Iliffe, Mrs Kathryn M BA . . . *Mar 1985
Keddie, Mr John Richard BA . . . *Feb 1997
Leigh, Ms Jane C BA(Warw) . . . *Dec 1988
Petrie, Mrs Diana MA . . . *Nov 1979
Ryder, Mrs Catherine A BA(Bris) . . . *Oct 1986
Con: Lyall, Mr David B . . . *§Nov 1955

MORRIS ORMAN HEARLE ‡
Wynnstay House St James Square Cheltenham Gloucestershire GL50 3PU
Tel: 01242 257188 ***Fax:*** 01242 257199 ***Dx:*** 7481 CHELTENHAM
E-mail: claims@mohlaw.co.uk
List of partners: J R Barker, D J Hearle, M R Orman, N Scrivens, C Wright
Work: J1 N Z(j,q)
Agency undertaken and Member of Accident Line
Ptr: Barker, Mr John Roger BA; Barrister . . . Mar 1998
Hearle, Mr David J MA . . . Nov 1983
Orman, Mr Mark R BA(Law) . . . *Nov 1986
Scrivens, Nicola . . . Apr 2005
Wright, Mr Christopher LLB . . . Jun 1995

PATRICIA BHUTTA & RUTH CARO LLP ‡
Hope Cottage Chapel Street Stow On The Wold Cheltenham Gloucestershire GL54 1DA
Tel: 01451 832386
E-mail: ruth@bhuttacarolaw.co.uk
List of partners: P F M Bhutta
Office: Botley

PEARNE & CO ‡
Eagle Tower Montpellier Drive Cheltenham Gloucestershire GL50 1TA
Tel: 01242 530622 ***Fax:*** 0844 443 2662
E-mail: info@pearne.co.uk
List of partners: H Pearne, S Pearne
Languages: French
Work: C1 U2 Z(e,za)
Ptr: Pearne, Mrs Helen MA(Oxon) . . . Sep 1996
Pearne, Mr Stephen . . . Jul 1998

PINKERTON LEEKE & CO ‡
7-8 Ormond Terrace Regent Street Cheltenham Gloucestershire GL50 1HR
Tel: 01242 237477 ***Fax:*** 01242 224019 ***Dx:*** 7417 CHELTENHAM 1
Emergency telephone 0138 689 317
E-mail: heidi@pinkertonleeke.co.uk
List of partners: C E Gent, A P Leeke
Work: A1 B1 C1 D1 E F1 G H J1 K1 K3 K4 L M1 N O P Q R1 S1 S2 T1 V W Z(c,l)
Emergency Action, Agency, Advocacy and Fixed Fee Interview undertaken
Ptr: Gent, Mrs Catherine Elizabeth LLB(Hons) . . . *Sep 1999
Leeke, Mr Andrew Phillip LLB(Lond) . . . *Jun 1974
Ast: Aitken, Miss Heidi Louise LLB(Hons) . . . *Nov 2003
Hanks, Mrs Kathryn Joy BA(Hons) . . . *Sep 1996
Con: Dagley-Morris, Mr John Howard . . . *Jan 1964

RICKERBYS LLP ‡
Ellenborough House Wellington Street Cheltenham Gloucestershire GL50 1YD
Tel: 01242 224422 ***Fax:*** 01242 518428 ***Dx:*** 7415 CHELTENHAM 1
E-mail: info@rickerbys.com
Languages: French, German, Spanish
Work: A1 B1 C1 C2 C3 D1 E F1 I J1 K1 K2 K3 K4 L M1 M2 N O P Q R1 S1 S2 T1 T2 W X Z(b,c,d,e,f,h,i,l,o,p)

PHILIP SMART & ASSOCIATES ‡
213 London Road Charlton Kings Cheltenham Gloucestershire GL52 6HY
Tel: 01242 529333 ***Fax:*** 01242 527404
E-mail: philip-smart@btconnect.com

HELEN SMITH SOLICITOR ‡
160 Leckhampton Road Cheltenham Gloucestershire GL53 0DH
Tel: 07766 412615 ***Fax:*** 01242 514514
E-mail: hrsmith@talk21.com

STEVEN YOUNG & CO
19 St Georges Road Cheltenham Gloucestershire GL50 3DT
Est: 1999
Tel: 01242 257269 ***Fax:*** 01242 243897
Emergency telephone 01452 332882
E-mail: syc@stevenyoungsolicitors.co.uk
Office: Gloucester
Work: G H
Agency and Advocacy undertaken
Ptr: Malvern-White, Mrs Clare BA(Hons) . . . Nov 1996
Young, Mr Steven L LLB(Bris) . . . Mar 1984
Ast: Bond, Miss Gemma LLB; LPC . . . Sep 2010

TOWN & COUNTRY LAWYERS ‡
10 Imperial Square Cheltenham Gloucestershire GL50 1QB
Tel: 01242 587900 ***Fax:*** 01242 254796 ***Dx:*** 7475 CHELTENHAM
E-mail: property@tcountry.co.uk
List of partners: V H O'Neil, P M Wilson
Languages: French, Italian, Spanish
Work: E S1 S2

See p112 for the Key to Work Categories & other symbols

Ptr: O'Neil, Mr Vincent Howard LLB(Hons) School Governor . . . . . *Dec 1980
Wilson, Mr Paul Marcel . . . . . Apr 1981

WHITEMANS SOLICITORS ‡
1st Floor Regal House 61 Rodney Road Cheltenham Gloucestershire GL50 1HX
Tel: 01242 529514 *Fax:* 01242 263217 *Dx:* 7457 CHELTENHAM
E-mail: info@whitemans.com

WIGGIN LLP ‡
95 The Promenade Cheltenham Gloucestershire GL50 1WG
Tel: 01242 224114 *Fax:* 01242 224223
E-mail: law@wiggin.co.uk
List of partners: S J Baggs, M J Bullock, J M Chess, S Crawford, A M Jones, C M Kean, M Ketley, S R Lowde, C H Moore, A G C Ross, S St John James
Office: London W1
Languages: French, German
Work: A3 B1 C1 C2 C3 E F2 J1 J2 L M1 O Q R2 S1 S2 T1 T2 U1 W Z(e,f,i,j,k,m,q,w,z)
Ptr: Baggs, Mr Simon James BA(Hons) . . . . . *Sep 1994
Bullock, Mr Matthew J MA(Cantab) . . . . . *Oct 1985
Chess, Mr Jason M MA; MPhil(Oxon) . . . . . Aug 1995
Crawford, Mrs Sue Lillian Knowles Scholarship for Law; Child & Pilkington Prize for Family & Consumer Law . . . . Sep 1984
Jones, Mr Adrian M . . . . . *Oct 1998
Kean, Ms Caroline Mary MA(Cantab) . . . . . *Jan 1985
Ketley, Mr Miles BA(Hons) . . . . . *Jan 1995
Lowde, Mr Shaun R LLB; DIPIP . . . . . *Nov 1989
Moore, Mr Charles Henry LLB . . . . . *Feb 1988
St John James, Mr Sean . . . . . Oct 1990
Asoc: Sheppard, Mr Guy BA . . . . . *Sep 2000
Ast: De Silva, Ms D Amali LLB . . . . . Jan 1994
Doble, Mrs Anna Michelle BA(Hons) . . . . . *Sep 1998
Gorski, Mr Philip Edward MA(Oxon) . . . . . Sep 2002
Headicar, Mr Benedict Matthew BA . . . . . Sep 2004
Khurana, Miss Deepti LLB; DEJF; LPC . . . . . *Sep 2003
Otway, Ms Katherine Ann LLB; LLM . . . . . Sep 1995
Panesar, Mr Gurminder Singh LLB; MA . . . . . *Sep 2004
Parkes, Mr Neil Thomas LLB(Hons) . . . . . Mar 2001
Southgate, Ms Katie LLB . . . . . Sep 2001
Thomas, Mr Simon Michael BA(Hons); LLM . . . . . *Sep 2003

WIGGIN OSBORNE FULLERLOVE ‡
3rd Floor 95 The Promenade Cheltenham Gloucestershire GL50 1HH
Tel: 01242 710200 *Fax:* 01242 710201 *Dx:* 7430 CHELTENHAM
List of partners: M Cain, M R Fullerlove, S M C Green, P Hunston, C R J Marlow, T W Osborne, S Pallister, M H D Payne
Office: London SW1
Languages: French, German
Work: C1 C2 M2 T1 T2 W Z(d,f,j,o)
Ptr: Cain, Mr Matthew BA(Hons) . . . . . *Sep 1995
Fullerlove, Mr Michael R LLB; BCL . . . . . *Oct 1974
Green, Mr Stephen M C BA(Hons); CTA . . . . . *Sep 1999
Hunston, Mr Paul LLB . . . . . Jan 1985
Marlow, Mr C Roderick J MA; LLB(Cantab) . . . . . *Jan 1977
Osborne, Mr Timothy W LLB . . . . . *Apr 1976
Pallister, Mr Stephen BA; MA . . . . . *Sep 1989
Payne, Mr Mark H D MA(Oxon) . . . . . *Oct 1987
Ast: Cook, Mr Chris LLB(Hons); PGDip . . . . . *Oct 2004
Shayle, Mr Matthew . . . . . Oct 2007

WILLANS LLP ‡
28 Imperial Square Cheltenham Gloucestershire GL50 1RH
Tel: 01242 514000 *Fax:* 01242 519079 *Dx:* 7420 CHELTENHAM
E-mail: law@willans.co.uk
List of partners: P Allen, M D Austen, S Brazier, N P Cox, J M Gillman, P D Gordon, J A Grigg, L D Lucas, C Middleton, J A H Mills, W T Morse, B L Redmond, P H Symes-Thompson, S L Wynne
Work: A1 A3 B1 C1 C2 C3 D1 D2 E F1 I J1 K1 K2 K3 L M1 N O P Q R1 R2 S1 S2 U1 U2 W X Z(c,d,e,l,q)
Agency, Advocacy, Fixed Fee Interview undertaken and Member of Accident Line
Ptr: Allen, Mr Philip BA . . . . . May 1998
Austen, Ms Margaret D MA(Cantab) . . . . . *§Oct 1983
Brazier, Mr Simon LLB . . . . . *Sep 1999
Cox, Mr Nicholas P LLB(Leics) . . . . . *Mar 1983
Gillman, Mrs Jenifer May . . . . . Apr 1979
Gordon, Mr Paul Dean LLB . . . . . *Sep 1999
Grigg, Mr James Alexander LLB(Hons) . . . . . Oct 1998
Lucas, Mr Laurence D BA(Dunelm) . . . . . *§Nov 1985
Middleton, Mr Charles LLB . . . . . *Oct 1983
Mills, Mr Jonathan A H . . . . . *May 1981
Morse, Mr William T BA(Hons); LLDip . . . . . *Aug 1997
Redmond, Ms Bridget Louise LLB . . . . . Aug 1996
Symes-Thompson, Mr Paul H MA(Cantab) . . . . . *Oct 1985
Wynne, Ms Susan L LLB . . . . . *Dec 1995
Ast: Evans, Ms Alisha Catherine LLB . . . . . Apr 2010
Froude, Ms Katie Sarah BA . . . . . Oct 2010
Hodges, Mr Simon LLB . . . . . Sep 2003
Senkbeil, Ms Susan . . . . . Apr 2009

CHEPSTOW, Monmouthshire

BARNES RICHARDS RUTTER ‡
St Maur Beaufort Square Chepstow Monmouthshire NP16 5EP
Tel: 01291 628898 *Fax:* 01291 628979 *Dx:* 37455 CHEPSTOW
Emergency telephone 01291 625631
E-mail: postmaster@brrsol.co.uk
List of partners: S L Richards, P D S Rutter
Work: A1 B1 C1 E F1 J1 K1 L N O S1 S2 W
Fixed Fee Interview undertaken
Ptr: Richards, Mr Simon L . . . . . *Dec 1973
Rutter, Mr Paul D S BA(Dunelm) . . . . . *Jun 1976

MARIE DARK SOLICITORS ‡
Rose Cottage Chapel Lane Pwllmeyric Chepstow Monmouthshire NP16 6JU
Tel: 01291 621638 *Fax:* 01291 622102
E-mail: marie@mariedark.co.uk
List of partners: M R Dark
Work: E F1 F2 K1 K3 K4 L Q S1 S2 T2 W
Fixed Fee Interview undertaken
Ptr: Dark, Mrs Marie R LLB(Wales) . . . . . *§Mar 1978

EVANS & ELLIS ‡
Cas-Gwent Chambers Welsh Street Chepstow Monmouthshire NP16 5XG
Tel: 01291 622814 *Fax:* 01291 624735 *Dx:* 37453 CHEPSTOW
E-mail: evansandellis@btconnect.com
List of partners: S J Howells
Languages: Hindi, Punjabi
Work: A1 C1 E F1 J1 K1 K3 L N P R1 S1 T1 W Z(l)
Emergency Action, Agency, Advocacy and Fixed Fee Interview undertaken
Ptr: Howells, Mr Sydney John LLB . . . . . *Jun 1977
Ast: Nair, Mrs Pinky LLB . . . . . *Mar 2001

FRANCIS & CO ‡
17 Welsh Street Chepstow Monmouthshire NP16 5YH
Tel: 01291 622237 *Fax:* 01291 623880 *Dx:* 37450 CHEPSTOW
E-mail: jenniferl@francisandco.co.uk
List of partners: J M Burke, J Lewis
Work: A1 B1 C1 E F1 G J1 K1 L N P R1 S1 T1 W Z(c,d,e,l,o,s)
Emergency Action, Agency, Advocacy, Fixed Fee Interview, Legal Aid undertaken and Member of Accident Line
Ptr: Burke, Mrs Judith Mary LLB . . . . . *§Apr 1981
Lewis, Jennifer . . . . . May 1997

MARK HOARE ‡
Manor House Bank Street Chepstow Monmouthshire NP16 5EL
Tel: 01291 630356 *Fax:* 01291 630368
E-mail: chepstowlaw@aol.com
Languages: French, Spanish

PROPERTS ‡
Albion Chambers Albion Square Chepstow Monmouthshire NP16 5DA
Tel: 01291 627268 *Fax:* 01291 620030
E-mail: contact@properts.co.uk
List of partners: J E Propert, J P Propert
Office: Caldicot

MALCOLM REYNOLDS & ASSOCIATES ‡
11-11a Welsh Street Chepstow Monmouthshire NP16 5LN
Tel: 01291 628217 *Fax:* 01291 629386
E-mail: info@mcrandassociates.co.uk

SEVERN LAW SOLICITORS ‡
First Floor Unit 1a Beaufort Park Way Chepstow Monmouthshire NP16 5UH
Tel: 01291 630451 *Fax:* 01291 637329

TWOMLOWS
15-16 Upper Church Street Chepstow Monmouthshire NP16 5EX
Tel: 01291 623323 *Fax:* 01291 628131 *Dx:* 37456 CHEPSTOW
E-mail: sols@twomlows.com
Office: Caldicot, Monmouth

CHESHAM, Buckinghamshire

BLASER MILLS
Carlton House 33 Red Lion Street Chesham Buckinghamshire HP5 1DN
Tel: 01494 782291 *Fax:* 01494 773970 *Dx:* 50300 CHESHAM
Office: Amersham, Aylesbury, Harrow, High Wycombe, Rickmansworth, Staines
Work: E L R1 S1 T2 W Z(c)
Ptr: Palmer, Mr Adrian J . . . . . *Jul 1981
Asoc: Akram, Ms Nosheen . . . . . Sep 2008
Coleman, Miss Abigail BA(Hons) . . . . . Aug 2005
Hussain, Miss Shabina . . . . . Sep 2008
Morrisey, Ms Doreen S . . . . . *Dec 1985
Partington, Mr Ian K BA(Hons)(Law) . . . . . Feb 1988
Con: Aldridge, Mrs Janian Mary MA(Oxon) . . . . . *Apr 1980
Bazzard, Mr S Roy . . . . . *Jun 1975
Wetherell, Mr Ian S DMA . . . . . *Mar 1974

BRAMWELL BROWNE ODEDRA ‡
85 High Street Chesham Buckinghamshire HP5 1DE
Tel: 01494 782244 *Fax:* 01494 791581 *Dx:* 50307 CHESHAM
E-mail: admin@bbosolicitors.co.uk
List of partners: J E Bramwell, J R Browne, D Odedra
Languages: French, Gujarati
Work: D1 D2 E G H J1 K1 K3 L N P Q R1 S1 S2 V W Z(l)
Emergency Action, Agency, Advocacy, Fixed Fee Interview and Legal Aid undertaken
Ptr: Bramwell, Ms Jane E BA(Oxon) . . . . . *Dec 1978
Browne, Mr Jeremy Robert LLB; Dip Soc Admin . . . *Feb 1979
Odedra, Mr Dipak LLB(Hons) . . . . . *May 1999

BREAKTHROUGH FAMILY LAW SOLUTIONS ‡
22a High Street Chesham Buckinghamshire HP5 1EP
Tel: 01494 776696 *Fax:* 01494 774851 *Dx:* 50305 CHESHAM
E-mail: info@breakthroughfls.com

FRANCIS & HOW ‡
Botley House East Street Chesham Buckinghamshire HP5 1DQ
Tel: 01494 782541 *Fax:* 01494 791590
E-mail: andrew@francisandhow.com
List of partners: A P D Murray, A Murray
Work: E L S1 W
Agency, Advocacy undertaken and Member of Accident Line
Ptr: Murray, Mr Anthony ACIArb Clerk to General Commissioners for Spelthorne Division Notary Public . . . . Jan 1969
Murray, Mr Andrew Petrocokino Dalrymple LLB(Hons); ACIR . . . . . Sep 2000

IBB SOLICITORS
The Bury Church Street Chesham Buckinghamshire HP5 1JE
Est: 1994
Tel: 0845 638 1381 *Fax:* 0845 638 1391 *Dx:* 50302 CHESHAM
E-mail: enquiries@ibblaw.co.uk
Office: Uxbridge
Languages: French, German, Gujarati, Hindi, Italian, Punjabi
Work: K1 K2 K3 K4 S1 T2 W Z(o)
Emergency Action, Agency, Advocacy, Fixed Fee Interview, Legal Aid undertaken and Legal Aid Franchise
Ptr: Almond, Miss Jacqueline . . . . . *Apr 1992
Booth, Mr Steven . . . . . *Jun 1978
Galloway, Ms Jan . . . . . Sep 1991
Murray, Ms Gillian . . . . . *Apr 1978
Outram, Mrs Gillian . . . . . *Dec 1992
Silverman, Mr Martin Notary Public . . . . . *Sep 1983
Asoc: Mehta, Ms Shital . . . . . Aug 1998
Ast: Howard, Mr John Howard LLB . . . . . Aug 2005
Johnson, Miss Natalie . . . . . Sep 2003
Con: Outram, Mr Rex . . . . . *Aug 1979
Roberts, Mr Shon . . . . . *Dec 1986

JOHAL LAKER SOLICITORS ‡
5 Swan Close Chesham Buckinghamshire HP5 2LW
Tel: 01494 771743 *Fax:* 01494 771743

DAVINA KIRBY SOLICITOR ‡
Higher Blackwell Blackwell Hall Lane Chesham Buckinghamshire HP5 1TN
Tel: 01494 764646 *Fax:* 01494 764440
E-mail: djk@davina-kirby.demon.co.uk
Work: K1 K3

LENNONS ‡
Chess Chambers 2 Broadway Court Chesham Buckinghamshire HP5 1EG
Tel: 01494 773377 *Fax:* 01494 773100 *Dx:* 50309 CHESHAM
E-mail: enq@lennonsltd.co.uk
List of partners: A J Coyle, A J King, H Kmotrasova, J F Russell
Office: Amersham
Languages: Czech
Work: B1 C1 C2 D1 E F1 J1 K1 K3 L N O P Q R1 R2 S1 S2 T1 W Z(c,k,l,p,q,r,t)
Emergency Action, Agency and Advocacy undertaken
Dir: Coyle, Mr Andrew J LLB(Hons) . . . . . *Oct 1990
King, Mr Andrew J LLB(Hons) . . . . . Jul 2008
Kmotrasova, Hana BA . . . . . Mar 2008
Asoc: Craigs, Laura LLB(Hons) . . . . . Jul 2009

RACHAEL MATTHEWS SOLICITORS ‡
Fieldview Hawridge Chesham Buckinghamshire HP5 2UQ
Tel: 01494 758573 *Fax:* 01494 758202
E-mail: rachael@rmatthewssolicitor.co.uk

RICHARDSON SMITH & CO ‡
35 High Street Chesham Buckinghamshire HP5 1BW
Tel: 01494 772773 *Fax:* 01494 772112 *Dx:* 50303 CHESHAM
E-mail: angelaphelan@richardsonsmithsolicitors.co.uk
List of partners: A M Phelan, P R Smith
Work: D1 G H K1 L N Q W Z(l)
Emergency Action, Agency, Advocacy, Fixed Fee Interview, Legal Aid undertaken and Legal Aid Franchise
Ptr: Phelan, Miss Angela M FILEx . . . . . *Jan 2001
Smith, Mr Paul R LLB . . . . . *Nov 1972

CHESHUNT, Hertfordshire

AUSTIN RYDER & CO
Hope House 1 High Street Cheshunt Hertfordshire EN8 0BZ
Tel: 01992 624804 *Fax:* 01992 621016
E-mail: enquiries@austinryder.com
Web: www.austinryder.com
Office: London N9, London NW1
Work: C1 C2 E L N Q S1 W
Fixed Fee Interview and Legal Aid undertaken

BARNES & PARTNERS
103 Crossbrook Street Cheshunt Hertfordshire EN8 8LY
Tel: 01992 626366 *Fax:* 01992 623322
Dx: 80801 WALTHAM CROSS
E-mail: people@barnesandpartners.com
Office: Enfield, Harlow, London E4, London N15, London N16, London N18, London N8, Pinner, Ware
Work: D1 E G K1 L N Q S1 W
Legal Aid undertaken and Member of Accident Line

BREEZE & WYLES SOLICITORS LLP
Turners Hill Chambers 1 Albury Grove Road Cheshunt Hertfordshire EN8 8XR
Tel: 01992 642333 *Fax:* 01992 643355 *Dx:* 30154 CHESHUNT
Office: Bishop's Stortford, Enfield, Hertford
Work: E J1 K1 K3 L Q R1 S1 S2 W Z(h)
S.I.G
Asoc: Gautam, Henal . . . . . Jan 2004

BERNIE COMISKEY ‡
128 Turners Hill Cheshunt Hertfordshire EN8 9BN
Tel: 01992 632606 *Fax:* 01992 634040

CURWENS
College House College Road Cheshunt Hertfordshire EN8 9BL
Tel: 01992 631461 *Fax:* 01992 639332 *Dx:* 30150 CHESHUNT
E-mail: enquiries@curwens.co.uk
Office: Enfield, Hoddesdon, Waltham Abbey
Languages: Greek
Work: A1 E K3 L O Q R1 S1 W Z(d)

GISBY HARRISON ‡
Goffs Oak House Goffs Lane Cheshunt Hertfordshire EN7 5HG
Tel: 01707 878300 *Fax:* 01707 876185 *Dx:* 98302 CUFFLEY
E-mail: postroom@gisbyharrison.co.uk
List of partners: S Argyrou, M C Browne, D H Goldberg, M P Lane, D R Mitson, J G Nugent, N S Tatum, D J Ward
Work: A1 B1 C1 C2 E F1 J1 K1 L N O Q R1 R2 S1 S2 T2 W Z(c,e,h,j,l)
Member of Accident Line
Ptr: Argyrou, Miss Sarra LLB; LLM . . . . . *Nov 1998
Browne, Mr Martin C BA . . . . . *Apr 1980
Goldberg, Mr David Harvey BA(Hons) . . . . . *Dec 1993
Lane, Mr Michael P BA . . . . . Oct 1984
Mitson, Mr David R LLB . . . . . *Mar 1990
Nugent, Mr John G LLM . . . . . *§May 1986
Tatum, Mr Nigel S BA . . . . . *Oct 1980
Ward, Mr Duncan Jeremy LLB(Hons) . . . . . *Aug 1983
Asoc: Jackson, Mr Christopher Howard BA Notary Public . . *Oct 1993
Ast: Chambers, Mr Gary LLB . . . . . *Nov 1982

EDWARD OLIVER & CO ‡
38 Crossbrook Street Cheshunt Hertfordshire EN8 8JQ
Tel: 01992 633491 *Fax:* 01992 634004
Dx: 142400 WALTHAM CROSS 5
E-mail: kim@edwardoliver.co.uk
List of partners: D Aumayer, A Goldberg
Work: B2 C1 D1 D2 E G H J1 K1 K2 L N Q R2 S1 S2 W Z(c,l,q,r)
Emergency Action, Agency, Advocacy, Fixed Fee Interview, Legal Aid undertaken and Member of Accident Line
Ptr: Aumayer, Mr David BA . . . . . *Sep 1978
Goldberg, Mr Alan . . . . . Jan 1972

CHESTER, Cheshire

AARON & PARTNERS LLP SOLICITORS ‡
5-7 Grosvenor Court Foregate Street Chester Cheshire CH1 1HG
Tel: 01244 405555 *Fax:* 01244 405566 *Dx:* 19990 CHESTER
E-mail: enquiries@aaronandpartners.com
List of partners: R Barge, C Brook, S A Carter, K E Catherall, N Clarke, D A Cooney, T J P Culpin, J M Devoy, D S M Edwards, S E H Ellis, R D Forrester, C M Gray, D A Harries, T Jones, C Pointon, C Rowe, L A Saunders, S J Scott-Goldstone, H A Watson
Office: Manchester
Languages: French, German, Spanish, Welsh
Work: A1 A2 A3 B1 C1 C2 C3 E F1 F2 I J1 J2 K1 K3 L O P Q R1 R2 S1 S2 T1 T2 U1 U2 W Z(b,c,d,e,f,g,j,k,l,n,o,p,q,r,s,t,u,x)
Agency, Advocacy and Fixed Fee Interview undertaken
Ptr: Barge, Mr Richard LLB . . . . Sep 1996
Brook, Miss Claire LLB . . . . Sep 2004
Carter, Mr Simon A LLB; MCIArb . . . . *May 1976
Catherall, Ms Kate Elizabeth LLB; MA. . . . . *§Sep 1999
Clarke, Mr Nicholas BA Colleges Scholarship in Jurisprudence from Wadham College, Oxford 1996/97 & 1997/98*Sep 2001
Cooney, Mr David Anthony LLB(Hons) . . . . *Oct 2003
Culpin, Mr Timothy James Philip LLB . . . . *Sep 1994
Devoy, Mr John M LLB . . . . *Nov 1990
Edwards, Mr D Simon M LLB(Lond) Notary Public. . . *Oct 1983
Ellis, Mr Simon Edgar Hargreaves. . . . . *Oct 1997
Forrester, Mr Richard D LLB . . . . *Nov 1976
Gray, Mrs Clare Mary LLB(Hons) . . . . *Oct 2001
Harries, Mr David Andrew LLB(Hons) . . . . *Oct 1993
Jones, Mr Trefor MA(Cantab) . . . . *Jan 1980
Pointon, Mr Clive LLB Notary Public. . . . . *Nov 1994
Rowe, Mr Colin Notary Public . . . . *Feb 1978
Saunders, Ms Lorraine Anne BA(Hons); LLB(Hons) . *Dec 1998
Scott-Goldstone, Mr Stuart James MA(Cantab) . . . *Sep 1997
Watson, Mrs Helen Andrea . . . . *Sep 2002
Asoc: Chillery, Ms Janette Louise BA(Hons) . . . . Aug 2003
Corcoran, Miss Elizabeth LLB(Hons) . . . . Feb 2004
Hibbert, Mr Eliot BA. . . . . Jul 2006
Kerfoot, Mr Emyr Lloyd BSc(Hons)(Econ); MA. . . . *Mar 2004
Kerr, Mr Adam . . . . *May 2006
Kidd, Mrs Helen. . . . . *Sep 2004
Tarne, Mrs Joanna E LLB . . . . *Mar 2004
Woodward, Mr Raymond BA(Hons); PGCE . . . . . . Feb 1989
Ast: Ali, Miss Shabina . . . . *Mar 2006
Coombs, Mr Paul David LLB . . . . Apr 2009
Dunning, Mr Andrew . . . . Oct 2010
Furber, Miss Sarah Louise . . . . *Sep 2007
Hadzik, Miss Laura . . . . Oct 2009
Hilyer, Miss Jane . . . . Sep 2005
McCartney, Miss Catherine . . . . *Jun 2007
Murphy, Miss Anna . . . . Oct 2007
Parkes, Miss Naomi Elizabeth. . . . . *Jun 2007
Petricca-Riding, Mrs Claire . . . . Apr 2005
Pugh, Ms Elisabeth . . . . Sep 2004
Ridgway, Rowena. . . . . Mar 2009
Sillito, Miss Julie . . . . Sep 2008
Wiegand, Mrs Lois . . . . Sep 2004
Con: Aaron, Mr Julian MA(Oxon) . . . . *Nov 1966
Kinloch, Mr William A A I LLM; BA; DPA; LMRTPI; AIL*§Jul 1967
Moore, Mr Robin G Notary Public . . . . Oct 1961

ALLINGTON HUGHES
Newgate Walk The Precinct Chester Cheshire CH1 1JU
Tel: 01244 312166 *Fax:* 01244 348876 *Dx:* 19983 CHESTER
E-mail: enquiriesc@allingtonhughes.com
Office: Wrexham
Languages: French, German

ANGELS SOLICITORS ‡
17 Smithford Walk 19-24 Grange Mount Prenton Chester Cheshire L35 1SF
Tel: 0151 480 6636 *Fax:* 0151 480 6415
E-mail: info@angelssolicitors.co.uk

APPLEYARD LEES
34 Cuppin Street Chester Cheshire CH1 2BN
Tel: 01244 321124
E-mail: chester@appleyardlees.com
Office: Burnley, Halifax, Harrogate, Huddersfield, Leeds, Liverpool, Manchester, Preston, Sheffield, Stockton-on-Tees, York

BGR BLOOMER ‡
4 Telford Court Dunkirk Trading Estate Chester Cheshire CH1 6LT
Tel: 01244 852040 / 0800 180 4169 *Fax:* 01244 852041
E-mail: info@bgrb.co.uk

BALLANTYNE GRANT LLP ‡
6 Mollington Grange Parkgate Road Chester Cheshire CH1 6NP
Tel: 01244 394230 *Fax:* 01244 851908
E-mail: agrant@ballantynegrantllp.com
List of partners: A Grant, N Grant
Work: A3 B1 B2 F1 J1 L O Q Z(c,g,h,p,q)
Ptr: Grant, Mr Andrew. . . . . Sep 1993
Grant, Ms Nia. . . . . Oct 1995

E J BAMFORTH SOLICITORS ‡
9 Hunter Street Chester Cheshire CH1 2AQ
Tel: 01244 357209 *Fax:* 01244 357226
E-mail: martyn.tucker@ejbamforth.co.uk
List of partners: E J Bamforth
Languages: German
Work: G H L V Z(h,l)
Agency, Advocacy, Legal Aid undertaken and Legal Aid Franchise
Ptr: Bamforth, Mr Erwin J BA . . . . *Mar 1986

BARTLETTS SOLICITORS
1 Frodsham Street Frodsham Square Chester Cheshire CH1 3JS
Tel: 01244 313301 *Fax:* 01244 405398
E-mail: piclaims@bartlettslaw.co.uk
Office: Chester, Liverpool (3 offices)
Work: N Q
Ptr: Morris, Mr Trevor R BA(Hons). . . . . *Oct 1995
Ast: Austin-Lea, Mrs Elizabeth. . . . . Jan 1997
Birchwood, Mrs Grace S . . . . Jul 2000
Dodd, Mr Owain A . . . . Jun 2003
Kenealy, Miss Natalie . . . . Feb 2009

BARTLETTS SOLICITORS
16 Nicholas Street Chester Cheshire CH1 2NX
Tel: 01244 313301 *Fax:* 01244 319398 *Dx:* 19989 CHESTER
E-mail: advice@bartlettslaw.co.uk
Office: Chester, Liverpool (3 offices)
Languages: French, Italian
Work: A1 B1 C1 D1 E F1 G H J1 K1 L M1 N P R1 S1 T1 V W Z(c,i,j,l)
Fixed Fee Interview undertaken
Ptr: Bartlett, Mr Pierre N MA(Oxon) . . . . *Jul 1967
Latimer, Mr Eric J LLB. . . . . *Jul 1973

BIRCHALL BLACKBURN LLP
Regus House Herons Way Chester Business Park Chester Cheshire CH4 9QR
Tel: 0844 980 2430 *Fax:* 0161 236 0687
Office: Chorley, Formby, Leyland, Manchester, Morecambe, Preston (2 offices), Southport

BRAMHALLS ‡
10 Mollington Grange Parkgate Road Mollington Chester Cheshire CH1 6NP
Tel: 01244 888002 / 07843 472356 *Fax:* 01244 851759
E-mail: phil.bramhall@blegal.co.uk

CHAMBERS & CO ‡
Stable House Heath Lane Chester Cheshire CH3 5SX
Tel: 01244 403411 *Fax:* 01244 310588
E-mail: law@chambersandco.com

CULLIMORE DUTTON ‡
20 White Friars Chester Cheshire CH1 1XS
Tel: 01244 356789 *Fax:* 01244 312582 *Dx:* 19985 CHESTER
E-mail: info@cullimoredutton.co.uk
List of partners: J F C Arnold, G M Crump, N Cummings, H Davenport, C O Hyatt, C E Jones, R J S Lea, D G Mason, T M Parker, J L Rawcliffe, L A Stuart, U D M Williams, D Woodward
Languages: Welsh
Work: A1 A2 B1 C1 C2 C3 D1 E J1 K1 K2 K3 K4 L N O P Q R1 S1 S2 T1 T2 V W Z(d,l,m,n,o,q,v,x)
Agency, Advocacy and Fixed Fee Interview undertaken
Ptr: Arnold, Mr John F C BA. . . . . *§Oct 1984
Crump, Miss Gillian M LLB . . . . *§Jun 1980
Cummings, Mr Nicholas LLB . . . . *§Dec 1977
Davenport, Mrs Helen BA(Hons)(Law). . . . . *§Dec 1981
Hyatt, Mrs Catherine O BA . . . . *§Mar 1987
Jones, Mrs Caroline E BA. . . . . *§Mar 1987
Lea, Mr Rory John Spencer MA(Cantab) . . . . . . *§Nov 1975
Mason, Mr David G LLB. . . . . *§Jun 1975
Parker, Mr Timothy Mayor. . . . . *§Feb 1976
Rawcliffe, Mrs Jacqueline Lesley LLB(Hons). . . . . *Dec 1992
Stuart, Mrs Lesley A LLB . . . . *§Oct 1985
Williams, Miss Ursula Diana MacDonald LLB . . . . *§May 1977
Woodward, Mrs Denise . . . . *§Sep 1997
Asoc: Bebbington-Plant, Mrs Adele BA(Hons) . . . . *Sep 2007
Goddard, Mr James Christopher H LLB(Hons); LLM. . *Jul 2007
Haywood, Mr Melanie Jayne LLB . . . . *Jul 2002
Lunt, Mr James . . . . Aug 2008
McFall, Mrs Helen Joan LLB(Hons) Diocesan Registrar . . . . *Sep 1989
Ast: Wright, Ms Helen Catherine BA(Hons)(Oxon) . . . . . *Jul 2009
Con: McAllester, Mr Alan K MA(Oxon) . . . . *Jan 1968

LAW OFFICES OF PAUL D'AMBROGIO ‡
Crown Buildings 121a Saughall Road Chester Cheshire CH1 5ET
Tel: 0870 442 2654 *Fax:* 0870 442 2876
E-mail: paul@pda-law.co.uk
List of partners: P D'Ambrogio
Languages: Italian
Work: A1 J1 K4 N S1 W Z(r)
Emergency Action, Agency, Advocacy and Fixed Fee Interview undertaken
SPr: D'Ambrogio, Mr Paul LLB(Hons). . . . . Sep 1996

DTM LEGAL LLP ‡
Archway House Station Road Chester Cheshire CH1 3DR
Tel: 01244 354800 *Fax:* 01244 403485 *Dx:* 20004 CHESTER1
E-mail: newbusiness@dtmlegal.com

GUY DODD SOLICITORS ‡
Suite H2A Chester Enterprise Centre Hoole Bridge Chester Cheshire CH2 3NE
Tel: 01244 315577 *Fax:* 01244 344655
E-mail: guy@guydodd.co.uk

DRUMMONDS ‡
Windsor House Pepper Street Chester Cheshire CH1 1DF
Tel: 01244 408300 *Fax:* 01244 408310 *Dx:* 20028 CHESTER
E-mail: enquiries@drummonds-solicitors.co.uk
List of partners: E J Bellamy, K N Cartwright, N P M Tuson
Work: E F2 J1 J2 K1 K3 K4 N O Q R2 S1 S2 W Z(l,r)
Agency and Fixed Fee Interview undertaken
Ptr: Bellamy, Miss Elisabeth J BA(Oxon). . . . . *Oct 1987
Cartwright, Mr K Neill LLB(Manc) . . . . *Oct 1978
Tuson, Mr Nicholas Peter Maxwell LLB(Hons). . . . *Mar 1994
Ast: Dennis, Mr Timothy David BA . . . . *Jan 2006
John, Mr Owain Alun . . . . Sep 2008
Jolly, Miss Kathryn Elizabeth BA(Hons); CPE; LPE . *May 2000
Lloyd, Mr Gethin Russell BA(Hons); CPE; LPC . . . . Jan 2004
Magee, Mr Paul LLB(Hons) . . . . *Jul 1995
Skinner, Ms Elinor Anne LLB . . . . Oct 1993

DYNE SOLICITORS LIMITED ‡
The White House High Street Tattenhall Chester Cheshire CH3 9PX
Tel: 01829 773100 *Fax:* 01829 773109
E-mail: info@dynesolicitors.co.uk
List of partners: J B Dyne, C L Simmons
Languages: French, German, Italian
Work: A1 E J1 J2 P R1 R2 S2 Z(n,t)
Agency and Fixed Fee Interview undertaken
Ptr: Dyne, Mr John B LLB; MIQ; MINSTTA Honorary Member of the Heavy Transport Association . . . . *Oct 1987
Simmons, Ms Clare Louise MA(Cantab); FGS. . . . *Sep 1997
Con: Denton, Mr Lewis A LLB . . . . *Nov 1971

ELLIS & CO ‡
10 Castle Street Chester Cheshire CH1 2DS
Tel: 01244 319388 *Fax:* 01244 319333 *Dx:* 20007 CHESTER
E-mail: inbox@ellis-solicitors-chester.co.uk
List of partners: S R Cornes, J W Ellis
Work: E F1 J1 K1 K3 L S1 T1 W Z(l)
Fixed Fee Interview undertaken
Ptr: Cornes, Mrs Sarah R LLB. . . . . *Oct 1982
Ellis, Mr James W LLB . . . . *Jun 1980

FOREMANS LLP ‡
Claytons House Sandpiper Close Chester Business Park Chester Cheshire CH4 9QU
Tel: 01244 625500 *Fax:* 01244 625599
E-mail: admin@foremansllp.com

GKR LAW SOLICITORS ‡
Unit 83d Chester Enterprise Centre Poolebridge Chester Cheshire CH2 3NE
Tel: 0151 549 4120

JONATHAN GOODWIN SOLICITOR ADVOCATE ‡
Unit 17e Telford Court Dunkirklee Chester Cheshire CH1 6LT
Tel: 01244 853120 *Fax:* 01244 853125 *Dx:* 14905 LITTLE SUTTON
E-mail: jongoodwin@jglaw.co.uk

HEMSLEYS ‡
(incorporating Ronald Davies & Co)
Mason House 2 Mason Street Chester Cheshire CH1 4DR
Tel: 01244 382400 *Fax:* 01244 372335
Dx: 22159 CHESTER (NORTHGATE)
Emergency telephone 01244 382400
E-mail: hemsleys@btconnect.com
List of partners: M J Hemsley
Work: G H Q
Emergency Action, Agency, Advocacy and Legal Aid undertaken
Ptr: Hemsley, Mr Michael J . . . . *Jan 1970

HILL DICKINSON LLP
34 Cuppin Street Chester Cheshire CH1 2BN
Tel: 01244 896600 *Fax:* 01244 896601 *Dx:* 19991 CHESTER
E-mail: law@hilldickinson.com
Office: Liverpool, London EC3, Manchester, Sheffield
Languages: Cantonese, Danish, French, German, Italian, Latin, Norwegian, Portuguese, Spanish, Swedish, Welsh
Work: A1 A2 A3 B1 B2 B3 C1 C2 C3 D1 D2 E F1 F2 G H I J1 J2 K1 K2 L M1 M2 M3 N O P Q R1 R2 S1 S2 T1 T2 U1 U2 V W X Z(a,b,c,d,e,f,g,h,i,j,k,l,m,o,p,q,t,u,w,x,y,z)
Emergency Action, Agency, Advocacy, Fixed Fee Interview, Legal Aid undertaken, Legal Aid Franchise and Member of Accident Line
Ptr: Campbell, Mr Iain LLB(Hons) . . . . *Dec 1980
Gibson, Mr Andrew P LLB. . . . . *Oct 1989
Jones, Mr Robin W LLB. . . . . *§Nov 1970
Lewis-Ethelston, Mrs Christine A BA(Jt Hons). . . . *Oct 1980
McGarva, Mr Jack LLB(Hons). . . . . *Jan 1987
Milburn, Miss Paula M LLB . . . . Sep 1990
Parrington, Mr Simon H Deputy District Judge. . . . *Jan 1975
Wightman, Ms Sally LLB . . . . *Nov 1987
Williams, Mr Brent M BA . . . . *Oct 1987

HILLYER MCKEOWN LLP ‡
Murlain House Union Street Chester Cheshire CH1 1QP
Tel: 01244 318131 *Fax:* 01244 344749 *Dx:* 22153 CHESTER
E-mail: mail@law.uk.com
List of partners: S L Bayley, S J Harvey, V J Jones, L Kidd, D S McAllister, P H McKeown, J C Shelley, J M Watkinson, D M J Wright
Office: Bebington, Wrexham
Work: C1 C2 D1 E F1 J1 K1 L N O Q S1 S2 W Z(e,l,o,w)
Emergency Action, Agency, Advocacy, Fixed Fee Interview, Legal Aid undertaken, Legal Aid Franchise and Member of Accident Line
Ptr: Bayley, Miss Sarah Louise LLB . . . . *Dec 2003
Harvey, Mr Steven James. . . . . Sep 1996
Jones, Mrs Victoria Jane . . . . Nov 1994
Kidd, Mrs Lindsey. . . . . Oct 1999
McAllister, Mr Duncan Stuart . . . . Oct 1995
McKeown, Mr Philip Henry LLB . . . . *Apr 1976
Shelley, Mrs Joanne Catherine . . . . Oct 1996
Watkinson, Mrs Justine Michelle LLB . . . . Oct 1995
Wright, Mr David Michael John LLB . . . . Oct 1983
Asoc: Benskin, Mrs Lisa Jane . . . . Sep 2006
Jones, Ms Caroline . . . . Oct 2006
Marston, Mr Carl Brian . . . . Oct 2001
Stirrett, Mr Anton Dominic LLB . . . . Sep 2001
Ast: Corley, Miss Sara Lynne . . . . Mar 2008
Dooey, Miss Karla. . . . . Sep 2008
Evans, Miss Alison . . . . Nov 1997
Morris, Ms Katherine Anne . . . . Oct 2009
Pownall, Miss Amy Louisa. . . . . Sep 2009
Con: Korff, Mr Jonathan P D . . . . *Nov 1977
Wise, Mr Peter Robinson LLB. . . . . Jun 1974

JOLLIFFE & CO ‡
Exchange House White Friars Chester Cheshire CH1 1DP
Tel: 01244 310022 *Fax:* 01244 345628 *Dx:* 19997 CHESTER
E-mail: law@jolliffes.com
List of partners: P J Anderson, A J Bartley, H J Butler, J A Harris, A Newall
Work: A1 B1 C1 C2 C3 E F1 F2 J1 K1 K3 L N O Q R1 R2 S1 S2 T1 T2 U2 V W Z(c,d,l,q,r)
Agency undertaken
Ptr: Anderson, Mr Peter J LLB. . . . . *Apr 1975
Bartley, Mr Andrew James BSc(Hons) ♦. . . . . . . *Nov 2004
Butler, Mr Hugh J LLB(Hons) . . . . *Jan 1989
Harris, Mr James Alexander LLB . . . . *Sep 2003
Newall, Mr Alan LLB; Dip Wel Law . . . . *Oct 1978
Asoc: Drew, Mr Richard John Patrick . . . . *Nov 1993
Ast: Elford, Miss Clare Louise LLB(Hons) . . . . Aug 2009
Hughes, Miss Angela Carole BA(History) . . . . Sep 2009
Williams, Mr Simon John LLB . . . . Sep 2008
Young, Mr Robert LLB(Hons) . . . . Sep 2006

KELSALL & COMPANY ‡
Watergate House 85 Watergate Street Chester Cheshire CH1 2LF
Tel: 01244 320610 *Fax:* 01244 409563
E-mail: john.kelsall5@btopenworld.com

KNIGHT MCGOLDRICK SOLICITORS ‡
W19a Chester Enterprise Centre Hoole Bridge Chester Cheshire CH2 3NE
Tel: 01244 349710

LEGAL MANAGEMENT SOLUTIONS ‡
Park House Chantry Court Chester Cheshire CH1 4QN
Tel: 0871 871 0286 *Fax:* 0871 871 0287
E-mail: suzannejervis@integrity.co.uk

MACKENZIE JONES ‡
Concorde House 6 Canal Street Chester Cheshire CH1 4EJ
Tel: 01244 355523 *Fax:* 01244 344360
E-mail: mailroom@macjones.com

See p112 for the Key to Work Categories & other symbols

MATTHEWS LEWIS & CO ‡
Martins Bank Chambers 31 Hoole Road Hoole Chester Cheshire CH2 3NF
Tel: 01244 327750 *Fax:* 01244 342982
Dx: 21601 CHESTER (HOOLE)
Emergency telephone 01244 311633
E-mail: lawyers@matthewslewis.co.uk
List of partners: A S Holliday, S F Woodside
Work: F1 J1 K1 K3 L N Q S1 S2 W
Agency, Advocacy and Fixed Fee Interview undertaken
Ptr: Holliday, Mr Anthony Stanley MA(Oxon) Notary Public. Jan 1980
Woodside, Mr Stephen F LLB; PGDipLP. . . . . *Oct 1996

MERCURY LEGAL LLP ‡
Murlain House Union Street Chester Cheshire CH1 1QP
Tel: 0800 612 7703 *Fax:* 01244 344749 *Dx:* 22153 CHESTER
E-mail: info@mercurylegal.co.uk

MODUS LEGAL ‡
Modus House 104 Garden Lane Chester Cheshire CH1 4EY
Tel: 01244 372584 *Fax:* 01244 379451
E-mail: james.pressley@moduslegal.co.uk
List of partners: J Pressley
Work: C1 C2 C3 F1 F2 I J1 U2 Z(e,f,za)
Agency, Advocacy and Fixed Fee Interview undertaken
SPr: Pressley, Mr James LLB(Hons) . . . . *Dec 1998

OLIVER & CO ‡
Douglas House 117 Foregate Street Chester Cheshire CH1 1HE
Est: 1961
Tel: 01244 312306 *Fax:* 01244 350261 / 354666
Dx: 19977 CHESTER 1
Emergency telephone 07623 960292
E-mail: info@oliverandco.co.uk
Languages: Welsh
Work: B1 C1 D1 E F1 G J1 K1 N R1 S1 W Z(c,j,p,q)

PJ THORNILEY SOLICITORS ‡
4 Chantry Court Sovereign Way Chester Cheshire CH1 4QN
Tel: 01244 394225

POOLE ALCOCK
43 Whitefriars Chester Cheshire CH1 1NZ
Tel: 01244 408130 *Fax:* 01244 341854 *Dx:* 19987 CHESTER 1
E-mail: chester@poolealcock.co.uk
Office: Alsager, Congleton, Crewe (2 offices), Nantwich, Northwich, Sandbach, Warrington

ALAN ROBERTS & CO ‡
(in association with Offices in Perth Australia)
Unit H11A Chester Enterprise Centre Hoole Bridge Chester Cheshire CH2 3NE
Tel: 01244 562754 *Fax:* 01244 346653
Dx: 21610 CHESTER (HOOLE)
Emergency telephone 07885 274671
E-mail: arobertssolicitor@seeyouincourt.co.uk
List of partners: A Roberts
Work: A3 B1 J1 K1 K3 K4 L N O Q R1 V W Z(c,k,p,r)
Emergency Action, Agency, Advocacy, Fixed Fee Interview, Legal Aid undertaken and Member of Accident Line
SPr: Roberts, Mr Alan LLB(Hons); LLM. . . . . *May 1977
Con: Malpass, Mr Colin LLB(Hons) . . . . May 1971

THE ROLAND PARTNERSHIP ‡
St Marks House 52 St Marks Road Saltney Chester Cheshire CH4 8DQ
Tel: 01244 659404 *Fax:* 01244 659535 *Dx:* 179430 CHESTER 16
E-mail: enquiries@therolandpartnership.co.uk
List of partners: K G N Roland, T R Roland
Work: N Q S1 Z(r)
Legal Aid undertaken and Legal Aid Franchise
Ptr: Roland, Ms Kim G N LLB . . . . *Feb 1987
Roland, Mr Trevor Ross BA(Hons) . . . . *Sep 1996
Ast: Greenall, Mr John LLB(Hons) . . . . *Jan 2002
Jones, Miss Justine Alexandra LLB . . . . *Aug 2006
Tinsley, Miss Fiona Rachel LLB . . . . *Sep 2010
Con: Soutter, Mr Ian D LLB(Hons) . . . . *Apr 1987

RUSSELL & RUSSELL ‡
9 White Friars Chester Cheshire CH1 1NZ
Tel: 01244 405700 *Fax:* 01244 405750 *Dx:* 19974 CHESTER
E-mail: infochester@russellrussell.co.uk
List of partners: S W Alexander, J M Bagby, S J Coupe, S G Crompton, H K Jones, K M Woods
Work: D1 D2 G H K1 K3 W
Emergency Action, Agency, Advocacy, Fixed Fee Interview and Legal Aid undertaken
Ptr: Alexander, Ms Susan Whitehead LLB . . . . *Aug 1994
Bagby, Mr James Matthew LLB(Hons). . . . . Sep 2001
Coupe, Mr Stephen James BA . . . . Aug 2002
Crompton, Mr Stephen G LLB(B'ham). . . . . *Sep 1980
Jones, Mr Howard Kenneth LLB. . . . . *Nov 1992
Woods, Ms Karen M LLB . . . . *Jun 1991
Ast: Moghaddam, Miss Mina Khadij BSc(Hons) . . . . . . Nov 2009
Porter, Miss Claire Louise LLB(Hons) . . . . Jun 2008

SAS DANIELS LLP
35 White Friars Chester Cheshire CH1 1QF
Tel: 01244 305900 *Fax:* 01244 305901
E-mail: help@sasdaniels.co.uk
Office: Bramhall, Congleton, Macclesfield, Stockport

SM SOLICITORS ‡
Old Bank Buildings Foregate Street Chester Cheshire CH1 1JT
Tel: 01244 314722 *Fax:* 01244 314698 *Dx:* 19975 CHESTER
List of partners: S McKeown
Work: B1 C1 E J1 K4 N O Q S1 S2 W Z(e,l,q)
Ptr: McKeown, Mr Stephen BA . . . . *Oct 1992

SALAM & CO ‡
44 Brook Street Chester Cheshire CH1 3DZ.
Tel: 01244 344577 / 07738 719265 *Fax:* 01244 343755
E-mail: info@salamimmigration.co.uk

R T STEELE & SPENCER ‡
43 Hoole Road Chester Cheshire CH2 3NH
Tel: 01244 318016 / 314531 *Fax:* 01244 321813
Dx: 21602 CHESTER (HOOLE)
E-mail: all@steeleandspencer.co.uk
List of partners: R J Spencer
Work: E K1 K3 L N Q S1 S2 W
Fixed Fee Interview undertaken
SPr: Spencer, Mr Rodney John. . . . . *Dec 1975

STORRAR COWDRY ‡
25 White Friars Chester Cheshire CH1 1NZ
Tel: 01244 400567 *Fax:* 01244 403377 *Dx:* 19993 CHESTER
E-mail: reception@storrarcowdry.co.uk
List of partners: P Brindley-Slater, D M Cowdry, E E Richardson, D D Storrar, C J A Wright
Office: Chester
Work: A1 B1 C1 C2 E F1 J1 K1 K3 L N O P Q R1 S1 S2 T1 T2 W Z(b,q)
Emergency Action, Agency, Advocacy and Fixed Fee Interview undertaken
Ptr: Brindley-Slater, Mr Peter . . . . Apr 2004
Cowdry, Mr David M. . . . . *§Aug 1981
Richardson, Ms Elaine Elizabeth BA . . . . *Mar 1999
Storrar, Mrs Darlene D LLB . . . . *Oct 1982
Wright, Mr Craig John Andrew LLB(Hons). . . . . *Aug 2003
Ast: Devine, Mrs Jane Elizabeth BSc(Hons) . . . . Jan 2008
Lucas, Miss Karen Kristina BA . . . . Aug 2007
Woolley, Mrs Kelly Louise LLB(Hons) . . . . Jun 2009
Con: Davies, Mr Paul LLB . . . . *Oct 1990
Storrar, Mr Christopher J . . . . *§Jul 1977

STORRAR COWDRY
India House 21 Castle Street Chester Cheshire CH1 2DS
Tel: 01244 400567 *Fax:* 01244 403377 *Dx:* 19993 CHESTER
E-mail: reception@storrarcowdry.co.uk
Office: Chester
Work: A1 B1 C1 C2 E F1 J1 K1 K3 L N O P Q R1 S1 S2 T1 T2 W Z(b,q)
Agency and Fixed Fee Interview undertaken
Ast: Burnett, Mr John Joseph LLB(Hons). . . . . Nov 1997

WALKER SMITH WAY ‡
26 Nicholas Street Chester Cheshire CH1 2PQ
Tel: 0844 346 3100 *Fax:* 0844 346 3200 *Dx:* 19982 CHESTER 1
E-mail: enquiries@walkersmithway.com
List of partners: J Baines, A P Britlin, A R Bruce, J Clark, R Coppack, H E Davies, B M Dawson, M G Denholm, L Eccleston, M A Elliott, C Graham, H G Humphreys, M Keenan, I B Lewis, J M Lewis, J M Meakin, H M Nash, G M D Prestt, P A Randles, D C Rudd, J Sharples, R C T Thomas, N H Turnbull, R M Vasmer, J P Weaver, R J Williams, A Woods, R Wynn-Jones
Office: Ashton-under-Lyne, Birmingham, Liverpool, London SW11, Wrexham
Languages: French, Welsh
Work: A1 D1 E F1 G H J1 K1 K2 K3 K4 L N O P Q R1 R2 S1 S2 T2 W Z(c,k,n,p,q,r)
Emergency Action, Agency, Advocacy, Fixed Fee Interview, Legal Aid undertaken and Legal Aid Franchise
Ptr: Baines, Mrs Janet. . . . . *§Sep 1995
Britlin, Mr Anthony P LLB . . . . *§Aug 1991
Bruce, Mr Alexander Richard LLB . . . . *Sep 1999
Clark, Mr Jonathon LLB. . . . . *§Oct 1987
Coppack, Mrs Rhian LLB(Hons). . . . . *§Sep 1997
Davies, Mr Huw Ellis LLB(L'pool) . . . . *§May 1981
Dawson, Mr Brian Michael LLB(Manc). . . . . *§Feb 1980
Eccleston, Mrs Louise BA(Hons)(Dunelm). . . . . . *Oct 1993
Graham, Miss Clare LLB(Hons) . . . . *Sep 2000
Humphreys, Mr H Gareth LLB(Wales) . . . . *Sep 1990
Keenan, Mr Michael BA(Bris) . . . . *§Sep 1992
Meakin, Ms Jane M LLB. . . . . *Jun 1988
Nash, Mrs Helen Mair LLB; LP . . . . *Nov 1999
Prestt, Mr Gray M D LLB(Manc). . . . . *§May 1974
Randles, Miss Patricia A LLB . . . . *§Sep 1990
Thomas, Mr Richard Charles Thornton LLB . . . . . *Sep 1999
Weaver, Mr Jeremy P BA . . . . *Oct 1990
Williams, Mr Richard John. . . . . *Oct 1995
Woods, Mrs Angela BA(Dunelm) . . . . *§Oct 1986
Asoc: Saul, Mr Kevin LLB . . . . *Sep 2002
Ast: Brassington, Mrs Catherine Joan . . . . *Sep 2004
Collingwood, Mr Paul Richard. . . . . *Sep 2008
Davies, Miss Amanda Joy. . . . . *Sep 2002
Evans, Miss Ceri Angharad . . . . *Oct 2001
Holmes, Miss Frances Ann . . . . *Nov 2005
Humphreys, Mr Roland John Trevor. . . . . *Sep 2005
James, Mr Simon Christopher. . . . . *Sep 2008
Lunt, Mr Stephen David. . . . . *Sep 2002
Makinson, Mr Paul Jeffrey. . . . . Sep 2003
Neden, Miss Stephanie . . . . *Sep 2007
Price, Miss Rachel Elizabeth . . . . *Sep 2004
Smith, Mr Stewart Peter. . . . . *May 2005
Thomas, Mr Jason Maxwell LLB. . . . . *Apr 2002
Tippetts, Miss Katherine. . . . . *Sep 2003
Wise, Miss Deborah Jane. . . . . *Oct 2006

WOODS SOLICITORS ‡
19 White Friars Chester Cheshire CH1 1NZ
Tel: 01244 340560 *Fax:* 01244 314606
E-mail: info@woodslaw.co.uk
Work: N

CHESTER-LE-STREET, Co Durham

GORDON BROWN ASSOCIATES ‡
(incorporating Mason Brown Associates)
143 Front Street Chester-le-Street Co Durham DH3 3AU
Tel: 0191 388 1778 *Fax:* 0191 389 1476
Dx: 60251 CHESTER LE STREET
Office: Newcastle upon Tyne
Work: C1 D1 D2 E G H J1 J2 K1 L N O Q S1 S2 V W Z(c,l,o,p)

GILES HUNTER PARTNERSHIP ‡
Victoria House 4 High Chare Chester-le-Street Co Durham DH3 3PX
Tel: 0191 388 7041 *Fax:* 0191 388 3884
E-mail: info@ghplaw.co.uk

GRAHAM CLAYTON SOLICITORS ‡
Ouckland House High Chare Chester-le-Street Co Durham DH3 3PX
Tel: 0191 389 0999
Office: Doncaster, Ilford, Stafford

NIGEL J HUMES & CO ‡
Jubilee Cottages 3-5 High Chare Chester-le-Street Co Durham DH3 3PX
Tel: 0191 388 8737 *Fax:* 0191 389 0862
Dx: 60264 CHESTER-LE-STREET
Emergency telephone 0191 387 3177 / 388 2054
E-mail: nigel.humes@btconnect.com
List of partners: N J Humes
Work: S1 W
Legal Aid Franchise
Ptr: Humes, Mr Nigel John BA(York)(Econ) . . . . *Feb 1989

RICHMOND ANDERSON GOUDIE ‡
Flake Cottages Cone Terrace Chester-le-Street Co Durham DH3 3QH
Tel: 0191 388 7884 *Fax:* 0191 387 1576
Dx: 60253 CHESTER-LE-STREET
Emergency telephone 07659 131292
E-mail: jwa@richmondanderson.co.uk
List of partners: J W Anderson, J D Barker, D Bradley, J P Newton
Work: B1 C1 C2 D1 E G H J1 K1 N O Q S1 W Z(l,m)
Emergency Action, Agency, Advocacy, Fixed Fee Interview, Legal Aid undertaken, Legal Aid Franchise and Member of Accident Line
Ptr: Anderson, Mr John Wallace LLB . . . . *Oct 1969
Barker, Mr Jonathan D LLB . . . . *Oct 1993
Bradley, Mr David BA . . . . *Feb 1984
Newton, Mr James P LLB William Hutton Prize . . . *§Dec 1982
Ast: Hanson, Ms Suzanne LLB. . . . . *Jan 1995
Lauder, Ms Mary C K . . . . *Feb 1990

SWINBURNE & JACKSON LLP
Cestria House High Chare Chester-le-Street Co Durham DH3 3PY
Tel: 0191 388 7221 *Fax:* 0191 389 1475
Dx: 60250 CHESTER-LE-STREET
E-mail: chester-le-street@swinburnejackson.com
Office: Gateshead, Hexham, Ryton, Washington
Work: A1 B1 C1 D1 E F1 G H J1 K1 L N P Q R1 R2 S1 S2 V W Z(b,d,h,j,l,p,s,t)
Emergency Action, Agency, Advocacy, Fixed Fee Interview, Legal Aid undertaken and Legal Aid Franchise
Ast: Scales, Miss Susanne. . . . . Apr 2007

CHESTERFIELD, Derbyshire

ANDERSON PARTNERSHIP ‡
(incorporating John Cutts)
71 Saltergate Chesterfield Derbyshire S40 1JS
Tel: 01246 220737 *Fax:* 01246 221081 *Dx:* 12369 CHESTERFIELD
E-mail: enquiries@andersonslaw.co.uk
List of partners: J N Anderson, S Peach, L G Saunders
Work: C1 C2 C3 D1 E F1 J1 K1 K2 L N O Q R1 S1 S2 W Z(c,h,k,l,q,r)
Emergency Action, Agency, Advocacy, Fixed Fee Interview, Legal Aid undertaken, Legal Aid Franchise and Member of Accident Line
Ptr: Anderson, Mr James Nigel BA(Hons) Deputy Coroner. *Jan 1980
Peach, Miss Sarah BA(Hons) . . . . Nov 1995
Saunders, Mr Leslie G BA. . . . . *Nov 1980
Ast: Bradley, Mr Neil R. . . . . May 2004
Hannan, Miss Laura. . . . . *Jun 2007
Holland, Ms Nicola A . . . . May 2006
Robinson, Ms Nadine J . . . . Apr 2006

BRM SOLICITORS ‡
Gray Court 99 Saltergate Chesterfield Derbyshire S40 1LD
Tel: 01246 555111 *Fax:* 01246 554411 *Dx:* 12358 CHESTERFIELD
E-mail: post@brmlaw.co.uk
List of partners: P Berresford, P J McGowan, A J Sheehan, R A Shiers, J C Skelton, R S Thompson
Languages: French, German, Spanish
Work: B1 C1 C2 E F1 J1 L N O Q R2 S1 S2 T2 W Z(c,d,e,l,q,r)
Emergency Action, Agency, Advocacy, Fixed Fee Interview undertaken and Member of Accident Line
Ptr: Berresford, Mr Paul . . . . *Nov 1999
McGowan, Mr Peter J BA . . . . *Feb 1983
Sheehan, Mr Adrian James BA . . . . *Nov 1998
Shiers, Mr Rodney A Vice President North Derbyshire Chamber of Commerce Notary Public. . . . . *Feb 1976
Skelton, Mr Jason Craig. . . . . *Nov 2001
Thompson, Mr Russell S LLB(Hons). . . . . *Oct 1995
Asoc: Woodhead, Mr Robert BA. . . . . *Aug 1998
Ast: Hallam, Miss Amy Rebecca LLB; DipLaw . . . . Sep 2002
Swingewood, Miss Anna . . . . *Sep 2005
Con: Brown, Mr Neil A LLB . . . . *Oct 1991

BANNER JONES ‡
(in association with Netuschil-Breunig (Germany))
24 Glumangate Chesterfield Derbyshire S40 1UA
Tel: 01246 560560 *Fax:* 01246 220390 *Dx:* 12360 CHESTERFIELD 1
E-mail: info@bannerjones.co.uk
List of partners: R R Banner, H K Downing, W J Fletcher, S Gordon, A N Hay, J E Henshaw, T D Hughes, P W E Jones, R A Joy, C J Sellars, S P Wright
Office: Chesterfield (3 offices), Dronfield, Sheffield
Work: A1 B1 B2 C1 C2 D1 E F1 F2 G H J1 K1 K2 K3 L N O Q R1 S1 S2 W Z(c,e,o,p,q,r)
Emergency Action, Agency, Advocacy, Fixed Fee Interview, Legal Aid undertaken and Legal Aid Franchise
Ptr: Hay, Mr Andrew N BA. . . . . *Jan 1985
Henshaw, Mrs Jayne E LLB. . . . . *Mar 1988
Sellars, Mr Christopher Jason BA(Hons)(Dunelm) . . . *Oct 1994
Dir: Gordon, Mr Stephen LLB Notary Public . . . . *Oct 1987
Joy, Mr Richard A BA . . . . *Nov 1997

BANNER JONES
(in association with Netuschil-Breunig (Germany))
4 Cotton Street Bolsover Chesterfield Derbyshire S44 6HA
Tel: 01246 827516 *Fax:* 01246 562080
E-mail: info@bannerjones.co.uk
Office: Chesterfield (3 offices), Dronfield, Sheffield
Work: A1 B1 C1 C2 C3 D1 E F1 G H I J1 K1 K3 L N O Q R1 S1 V W Z(c,d,m)
Emergency Action, Agency, Advocacy, Fixed Fee Interview and Legal Aid undertaken

BANNER JONES
(in association with Netuschil-Breunig (Germany))
Marsden Chambers 2-4 Marsden Street Chesterfield Derbyshire S40 1JY
Tel: 01246 209773 *Fax:* 01246 231188 *Dx:* 12360 CHESTERFIELD
E-mail: info@bannerjones.co.uk
Office: Chesterfield (3 offices), Dronfield, Sheffield
Work: B1 C1 C2 D1 E F1 G H J1 K1 K2 K3 L N O Q S1 S2 V W
Emergency Action, Agency, Advocacy, Fixed Fee Interview and Legal Aid undertaken
Ptr: Banner, Mr Robert R LLB(Lond). . . . . *§Dec 1976
Downing, Miss Helena K BA(Dunelm). . . . . *§Oct 1984
Hughes, Mr Trevor D LLB. . . . . *§Jul 1978
Jones, Mr Peter W E BA . . . . *§Nov 1980
Wright, Mr Simon P LLB. . . . . *Oct 1989
Ast: Gunn, Ms Diane E BA. . . . . *Oct 1993

BANNER JONES
(in association with Netuschil-Breunig (Germany))
The Old Council Chamber 95 High Street Clay Cross Chesterfield Derbyshire S45 9DZ
Tel: 01246 861250 *Fax:* 01246 861232
E-mail: info@bannerjones.co.uk
Office: Chesterfield (3 offices), Dronfield, Sheffield
Languages: French
Work: A1 B1 C1 C2 C3 D1 D2 E F1 G H I J1 K1 K3 L N O Q R1 S1 S2 W Z(c,l)
Emergency Action, Agency, Advocacy, Fixed Fee Interview, Legal Aid undertaken and Legal Aid Franchise
Ptr: Fletcher, Mr William J LLB . . . . *Oct 1974

ROBERT L BASHFORTH & CO ‡
2-4 Corporation Street Chesterfield Derbyshire S41 7TP
Tel: 01246 200204 *Fax:* 01246 200207
List of partners: R L Bashforth
Work: G H
Agency undertaken
SPr: Bashforth, Mr Robert L LLB(Sheff) . . . . Jan 1984

BILTON HAMMOND LLP
51 Rutland Road Chesterfield Derbyshire S40 1ND
Tel: 01246 232418 *Fax:* 01246 210930 *Dx:* 12365 CHESTERFIELD
E-mail: julianhammond@biltonhammond.co.uk
Office: Mansfield
Work: E G H K1 K2 K3 L S1 S2 W
Emergency Action, Agency, Advocacy, Fixed Fee Interview, Legal Aid undertaken and Legal Aid Franchise
Con: Hammond, Mr Julian C LLB(Newc) . . . . *Jun 1973

BROADBENTS
Stephenson's Chambers 8a Stephenson Place Chesterfield Derbyshire S40 1XL
Tel: 01246 540955 *Fax:* 01246 224988 *Dx:* 720374 CHESTERFIELD
E-mail: broadbentmail@btconnect.com
Office: Alfreton, Derby, Heanor, Mansfield, Sutton-in-Ashfield

BROOKS SOLICITORS ‡
77 Saltergate Chesterfield Derbyshire S40 1JS
Tel: 01246 220552 *Fax:* 01246 220567
E-mail: info@brookssolicitors.co.uk
List of partners: P W G Brook
Ptr: Brook, Mr Paul W G LLB(Sheff). . . . . *Sep 1978

ELLIOT MATHER LLP ‡
The Courtyard 49 Low Pavement Chesterfield Derbyshire S40 1PB
Tel: 01246 231288 *Fax:* 01246 204081 *Dx:* 12362 CHESTERFIELD
E-mail: admin@elliotmather.co.uk
List of partners: R A Anderton, J S Barber, N L Delgado-Bush, R Froggatt, S A Gill, N Heppell, P A Hollyer, M E Honeyben, A T Johnston, S R J King, J L Page, A C Seel, J Skill, A Yates
Office: Chesterfield, Mansfield, Matlock
Work: A1 B1 C1 C2 C3 D1 E F1 G H J1 K1 L M1 M2 N P R1 S1 T1 T2 V W Z(b,c,d,e,h,i,j,k,l,m,n,o,p,s,t)
Emergency Action, Agency, Advocacy, Fixed Fee Interview, Legal Aid undertaken and Member of Accident Line
Mem: Barber, Mr Jonathan Simon LLB. . . . . *Oct 1992
Honeyben, Mrs Mary E BA . . . . *Oct 1991
Skill, Mrs Julie . . . . *Aug 2006
Asoc: Brint, Mr Steven Francis LLB(Hons). . . . . *Jul 2005
Wood, Mrs Libby Rebecca LLB(Hons). . . . . *May 2002
Ast: Beckworth, Mr Vincent Alan. . . . . Mar 2008
Brown, Ms Sarah Jane BA(Politics); CPE; LPC . . . . May 2000
Butcher, Miss Louise LLB(Hons) . . . . Jan 2005
Harvey, Mr Joseph LLB; PGDipLP; DipIT . . . . Sep 2007
Iredale, Miss Alicen Astrid BA; GDipLaw. . . . . . . Nov 2009

ELLIOT MATHER LLP
12 Soresby Street Chesterfield Derbyshire S40 1JN
Tel: 01246 231288 *Fax:* 01246 558598
E-mail: admin@elliotmather.co.uk
Office: Chesterfield, Mansfield, Matlock
Mem: Hollyer, Mr Paul A LLB(Leics); MIPD; ACIArb . . . . *Mar 1979
Seel, Mr Alastair Crawford BA; MA . . . . Mar 1999
Yates, Mr Andrew. . . . . Mar 2007
Asoc: Dawson, Miss Joanna Louise LLB(Hons) . . . . . . *Aug 2006
Dixon, Miss Amy Jayne BA(Hons); DipLaw . . . . . *Sep 2007
Yates, Mrs Kathryn LLB(Hons) . . . . *Sep 2002

GRAYSONS
100 Saltergate Chesterfield Derbyshire S40 1LG
Tel: 01246 229393 *Fax:* 01246 229494
E-mail: enquiries@graysons.co.uk
Office: Sheffield

THE JOHNSON PARTNERSHIP
2nd Floor No3 Burlington House 19 Burlington Street Chesterfield Derbyshire S40 1RX
Tel: 01246 520930 *Fax:* 01246 550526
Emergency telephone 01246 520930
E-mail: mail@thejohnsonpartnership.co.uk
Office: Derby, Mansfield, Nottingham
Work: B2 F2 G H J2
Emergency Action, Agency, Advocacy, Fixed Fee Interview and Legal Aid undertaken
Ast: Fowkes, Miss Katie LLB(Hons) . . . . *Mar 2011
Wilford, Mr John BA(Hons) . . . . *Oct 1984

JUST COSTS SOLICITORS
Dunston Innovation Centre Dunston Road Chesterfield Derbyshire S41 8NG
Tel: 01246 267961 *Fax:* 01246 267965 *Dx:* 743530 CHESTERFIELD
E-mail: info@justcosts.com
Office: Leeds, London WC2, Manchester (2 offices)

KIERANCLARKEGREEN ‡
36 Clarence Road Chesterfield Derbyshire S40 1XB
Tel: 01246 211006 *Fax:* 01246 209786 *Dx:* 12352 CHESTERFIELD
Emergency telephone 01246 211006
E-mail: enquiries@kieranclarke.co.uk
List of partners: S M Dewson, T Evans, J M Green, E Leek, L C Price, S R Smith, K P Tomlinson
Office: Chesterfield, Staveley
Work: A1 A3 B2 D1 D2 E F1 G H J1 K1 K2 K3 L N O Q S1 S2 T2 V W Z(c,j,l,m)
Emergency Action, Agency, Advocacy, Fixed Fee Interview, Legal Aid undertaken and Member of Accident Line
Ptr: Evans, Mr Timothy BA(Hons) . . . . *Dec 1979
Leek, Mrs Emma LLB. . . . . *Aug 2001
Price, Miss Lesley C . . . . *Dec 1984
Smith, Mrs Susan R LLB . . . . *Jul 1974
Tomlinson, Mr Kevin P BA. . . . . *Feb 1985
Asoc: Bosworth, Miss Julia E LLB(Hons). . . . . *Dec 2003
Haigh, Mr Gavin Malcolm LLB(Hons) . . . . *Oct 2002
Rogers, Miss Jessica LLB(Hons) . . . . *Apr 2007
Ast: Norman, Mrs Katrina . . . . *Sep 1997
Con: Kieran, Mr James A LLB(Hons); LSF . . . . *Jun 1975

KIERANCLARKEGREEN
88 Saltergate Chesterfield Derbyshire S40 1LG
Tel: 01246 230359 / 234937 *Fax:* 01246 554997
Dx: 12352 CHESTERFIELD
Office: Chesterfield, Staveley
Work: C1 C2 C3 E F1 J1 K1 L S1 T1 T2 W
Fixed Fee Interview and Legal Aid undertaken
Ptr: Green, Mr John M. . . . . Aug 1980

NFLA LTD
91a New Square Chesterfield Derbyshire S40 1AH
Tel: 01246 471900 *Fax:* 01246 471901
Emergency telephone 0115 945 4555
E-mail: mail@nflaw.co.uk
Office: Nottingham, Rotherham, Sheffield, Wellingborough
Work: D1 K1 K3
Dir: Gibbons, Mrs Julia . . . . Oct 2001
Ast: Foster, Ms Julie BSc . . . . *Apr 2006
Mullis, Mr Cary LLB(Hons) . . . . Feb 2010

PRINCE MCCULLOCH SOLICITORS ‡
3 Royal Court Basil Close Chesterfield Derbyshire S41 7SL
Tel: 0845 331 2723 *Fax:* 01426 221934
E-mail: info@princemcculloch.co.uk

IAN R SCUTT ‡
Chatsworth Lodge 110 Chatsworth Road Chesterfield Derbyshire S40 3BQ
Tel: 01246 203952
List of partners: I R Scutt

SHIPTON HALLEWELL & CO ‡
23 West Bars Chesterfield Derbyshire S40 1AB
Tel: 01246 232140 *Fax:* 01246 220582 *Dx:* 12353 CHESTERFIELD
E-mail: shipton-hallewell@legalisp.net
List of partners: D G Jones, S C Walker
Work: A1 D1 D2 E G H K1 K2 L S1 S2 W
Emergency Action, Agency, Advocacy, Fixed Fee Interview, Legal Aid undertaken and Legal Aid Franchise
Ptr: Jones, Mr David G LLB(B'ham) . . . . *Jan 1977
Walker, Mrs Susan C LLB. . . . . *Dec 1980

DEAN THOMAS & CO
31 Mill Street Clowne Chesterfield Derbyshire S43 4JN
Tel: 01246 810050 *Fax:* 01246 570578
E-mail: enquiries@deanthomas.co.uk
Office: Retford, Worksop
Work: C1 E F1 K1 N Q S1 W
Agency, Legal Aid undertaken and Member of Accident Line
Ptr: Dixon, Mr Steven LLB. . . . . *Nov 1983

WOODHEAD & HOOLE ‡
Britannia Buildings 2 The Shambles Chesterfield Derbyshire S40 1PX
Tel: 01246 233149 / 209001 *Fax:* 01246 200909
Dx: 12351 CHESTERFIELD
E-mail: bev@woodheadhall.co.uk
List of partners: R A C Woodhead
Languages: French
Work: C1 E F1 L N S1 W Z(c,e,l)
SPr: Woodhead, Mr Roger Anthony Clive. . . . . *§Jan 1969

YOUR LAWYERS LIMITED ‡
Prospect House Chesterfield Derbyshire S43 3QE
Tel: 0871 310 0144
E-mail: aman@yourlawyers.co.uk

CHICHESTER, West Sussex

ANDERSON LONGMORE & HIGHAM
38 Southgate Chichester West Sussex PO19 1DP
Tel: 01243 787899 *Fax:* 01243 839423 *Dx:* 30320 CHICHESTER
E-mail: chich@alhlaw.co.uk
Office: Billingshurst, Petworth, Storrington
Work: C1 D1 D2 E K1 K2 K3 L S1 S2 W
Ptr: Cooke, Mr Edward William Geoffrey BA(History); PG DipLaw . . . . *May 2000
Stisted, Mr William John BA(Religious Studies); DipLaw . . . . *Oct 2000

BROOKES & CO ‡
1st Floor Dominican House St John's Street Chichester West Sussex PO19 1TU
Tel: 01243 780333 *Fax:* 01243 773442
Emergency telephone 01243 783553
List of partners: T H Brookes, S Collett
Languages: Polish
Work: D1 G H
Emergency Action, Agency, Advocacy, Fixed Fee Interview, Legal Aid undertaken and Legal Aid Franchise
Ptr: Brookes, Mr Terence H BA ★. . . . . *Jul 1975
Collett, Mr Stephen . . . . Nov 1995
Asoc: Fisher, Mr James Roger LLB(Hons). . . . . Nov 1995
Ast: Ferguson, Mrs Julie Elizabeth LLB . . . . May 1998

CK SOLICITORS ‡
Clock House 128 High Street Chichester West Sussex PO20 0QE
Tel: 01243 603393 *Fax:* 01243 603394

CHARLES HILL HUBBARD ‡
27-28 Southgate Chichester West Sussex PO19 1ES
Tel: 01243 781000 *Fax:* 01243 779390 *Dx:* 30323 CHICHESTER
E-mail: info@charleshillhubbard.co.uk
List of partners: P A Bradley, G R Hitch, D G Ryan, C R A Spirit
Work: D1 E K1 K2 L Q S1 S2 T2 W
Emergency Action, Advocacy, Fixed Fee Interview, Legal Aid undertaken and Legal Aid Franchise
Ptr: Bradley, Mr Paul A BSc(Soton) . . . . *Apr 1981
Hitch, Mr Graham Roger TEP. . . . . *Jan 1969
Ryan, Mr Dominic G BA(Hons)(Law) . . . . *Apr 1987
Spirit, Mr Christopher R A BA(Hons)(Law). . . . . . *May 1988
Con: Hubbard, Mrs Sylvia D . . . . *Apr 1962

CHICHESTER FAMILY LAW PRACTICE ‡
Forum House Stirling Road Chichester West Sussex PO19 7DN
Tel: 01243 787335 *Fax:* 01243 788471 *Dx:* 30316 CHICHESTER
E-mail: info@chichesterflp.co.uk

THOMAS EGGAR LLP ‡
(in association with Avrio; Lexcel; The Bridge Group)
The Corn Exchange Baffins Lane Chichester West Sussex PO19 1GE
Tel: 01243 786111 *Fax:* 01243 775640 *Dx:* 30300 CHICHESTER
E-mail: chichester@thomaseggar.com
Office: Crawley, London EC4, Newbury, Southampton, Worthing
Languages: French, German, Greek, Italian, Polish, Portuguese, Punjabi, Russian, Spanish
Work: A1 A2 A3 B1 B2 C1 C2 C3 D1 D2 E F1 F2 J1 J2 K1 K2 K3 K4 L N O P Q R1 R2 S1 S2 T1 T2 U2 W X Z(b,c,d,e,g,h,m,o,p,q,r,s,t,w,x,y)

GEORGE IDE LLP
solicitors

Lexcel

GEORGE IDE LLP ‡
52 North Street Chichester West Sussex PO19 1NQ
Est: 1966
Tel: 01243 786668 *Fax:* 01243 831000 *Dx:* 30306 CHICHESTER
Emergency telephone 07850 644908
E-mail: julian.bobak@georgeide.co.uk
Web: www.georgeide.co.uk
List of partners: J Bobak, R W Enticott, P A Fretwell, A J Goff, P Lewis, I H Mellor, I P Oliver, F J S Poole, S J Ward, C J Watson, L U Watt
Office: Bognor Regis, Chichester (2 offices)
Languages: French
Work: A1 B1 C1 C2 C3 E F1 J1 J2 K1 M1 N O P Q R1 S1 S2 T1 T2 V W Z(l,m,o,p,r)
Emergency Action, Agency, Advocacy, Fixed Fee Interview, Legal Aid undertaken, Legal Aid Franchise and Member of Accident Line
Ptr: Enticott, Mr Robert W MA(Oxon) . . . . *Oct 1980
Mellor, Mr Ian Hague LLB(Hons); Cert PFS . . . . . *Mar 1992
Ward, Mr Stephen James LLB(Hons) . . . . *Feb 1988
Watt, Ms Louise U LLB . . . . *Nov 1986
Ast: Jhurry-Wright, Mrs Danielle Louise BSc; PGDip . . . *Nov 2005
Richards, Siobhan . . . . Nov 2009
Smith, Mr Nicholas Stuart BA(Hons); CPE; LPC. . . *Aug 2002

Established: 1966. Languages: French. Medical Negligence, Insolvency, Employment, Divorce, Mental Health, Family, Commercial and Domestic Conveyancing, Landlord and Tenant, Commercial, Wills and Probate, Town and County Planning and Financial Services.

GEORGE IDE LLP
Lion House 79 St Pancras Chichester West Sussex PO19 4NL
Tel: 01243 786668 *Fax:* 01243 831000
Office: Bognor Regis, Chichester (2 offices)
Ptr: Bobak, Mr Julian LLB . . . . *§Jul 1976
Fretwell, Mr Paul Anthony LLB . . . . *Oct 1990
Goff, Mr Anthony J . . . . *May 1980
Oliver, Mr Ian P. . . . . Oct 1986
Watson, Miss Claire J LLB . . . . *Nov 1989
Lewis, Mr Paul . . . . NSP
Ast: Jenkins, Miss Karen Suzanne LLB; BA . . . . *Nov 2009
Patel, Tejal . . . . *Oct 2008
Riches, Ms Sheila Margarey BA; MSc(Medical Ethics). *Oct 1994
Rogers, Mrs Rachel Charissa Rose LLB(Hons) . . . *Nov 2004

GEORGE IDE LLP
44 North Street Chichester West Sussex PO19 1NQ
E-mail: julian.bobak@georgeide.co.uk
Office: Bognor Regis, Chichester (2 offices)
Ptr: Poole, Mr Fraser J S BA . . . . *Oct 1984

GREENFIELDS ‡
22 East Street Chichester West Sussex PO19 1HS
Tel: 01243 773654 *Fax:* 01243 773689 *Dx:* 30317 CHICHESTER
Work: C1 E I J1 K1 K3 L O Q S1 S2 W Z(c,h,m,q)
Agency and Fixed Fee Interview undertaken

EDWARD HAYES LLP ‡
22 West Street Chichester West Sussex PO19 1HZ
Tel: 01243 781431 *Fax:* 01243 536651 *Dx:* 30307 CHICHESTER
Emergency telephone 0800 085 9684
E-mail: info@edwardhayes.co.uk
List of partners: G Ambridge, H J Fitzsimons, M S French, C C E Hayes, C I Long, M Monan, Y Patel, D H Waite
Office: Bognor Regis, Chichester, Havant, Littlehampton, London EC2, London EC4, Worthing
Work: B2 D1 D2 G H J1 K1 K2 K3 L M2 N Q S1 S2 W Z(l,q,r,w)
Emergency Action, Agency, Advocacy, Legal Aid undertaken and Legal Aid Franchise
Ptr: Fitzsimons, Miss Helen Jane PGDipLaw. . . . . . . *Nov 1996
Hayes, Mr Christopher Charles Edward LLB(Hons) ★ *Dec 1991
Monan, Miss Maria HB(Hons) ★. . . . . Mar 1995
Ast: Benfield, Mrs Eleanor . . . . Oct 2004
Halsey, Mr Jason ★ . . . . *Jan 1998

EDWARD HAYES LLP
14 Shore Road East Wittering Chichester West Sussex PO20 8DZ
Tel: 01243 672124 *Fax:* 01243 672818 *Dx:* 30307 CHICHESTER
Emergency telephone 0800 085 9684
E-mail: info@edwardhayes.co.uk
Office: Bognor Regis, Chichester, Havant, Littlehampton, London EC2, London EC4, Worthing
Work: A1 B1 B2 D1 E F1 G H J1 K1 K2 L N R1 S1 S2 W Z(w)

See p112 for the Key to Work Categories & other symbols

Emergency Action, Agency, Advocacy, Legal Aid undertaken and Legal Aid Franchise
Ast: Watson, Mr Graham J. . . . . *Nov 1982

PAUL HILLS & CO ‡
1 Kingfisher Parade East Wittering Chichester West Sussex PO20 8BJ
Tel: 01243 671782 *Fax:* 01243 671794
E-mail: paulhillssolicitors@eastwittering.freeserve.co.uk
List of partners: P Hills
Work: L R2 S2 W
SPr: Hills, Mr Paul . . . . Dec 1974
Ast: Miller, Ms Anna . . . . Jan 1990

JUMP & CO SOLICITORS ‡
11 North Pallant Chichester West Sussex PO19 1TQ
Tel: 01243 778508 *Fax:* 01243 778509 *Dx:* 30311 CHICHESTER
E-mail: info@jumpsolicitors.co.uk
List of partners: D W Jump
Work: E S1 S2 W
SPr: Jump, Mr David W . . . . *Jan 1981

KENNY SOLICITORS ‡
6 Whyke Lane Chichester West Sussex PO19 7UR
Tel: 01243 887880 *Fax:* 01243 887959
E-mail: victoria@kennysolicitors.co.uk

LAWBYWEB SOLICITORS ‡
99 Westgate Chichester West Sussex PO19 3HB
Tel: 01243 773072 *Fax:* 01243 780397
E-mail: steve@lawbyweb.co.uk

THE OWEN-KENNY PARTNERSHIP ‡
Old Market House Market Avenue Chichester West Sussex PO19 1JR
Tel: 01243 532777 *Fax:* 01243 539650 *Dx:* 135816 CHICHESTER 5
E-mail: victoria@oweken.co.uk
List of partners: E Allchurch, S Fildes, M R Hall, J E M Jones, S P Kenny, V Kenny, D R Small
Office: Bognor Regis, Chichester
Work: E F1 K1 K3 L Q S1 S2 W Z(l)
Agency, Advocacy and Legal Aid undertaken
Ptr: Allchurch, Ms Emily . . . . Sep 2004
Fildes, Ms Sara-Jayne . . . . Nov 2000
Hall, Mr Michael R . . . . Dec 1975
Jones, Mrs Julie E M BSc(Econ); TEP. . . . . *Dec 1978
Kenny, Mr Simon P . . . . *May 1981
Kenny, Mrs Victoria . . . . *Feb 1984
Small, Mr David Richard LLB . . . . *Nov 1994

THE OWEN-KENNY PARTNERSHIP
38 South Street Chichester West Sussex PO19 1EL
Tel: 01243 532790
Office: Bognor Regis, Chichester

PURE EMPLOYMENT LAW ‡
1 Little London Chichester West Sussex PO19 1PH
Tel: 01243 836840
E-mail: nicola.brown@pureemploymentlaw.co.uk

STONE MILWARD RAPERS ‡
50 Westgate Chichester West Sussex PO19 3HE
Tel: 01243 780211 *Fax:* 01243 782619 *Dx:* 30309 CHICHESTER
E-mail: rogerstone@smrsolicitors.co.uk
List of partners: S L Evans, M J W Field, M D Milward, A Sinclair, R J Stone, F H Winskell
Office: Chichester
Work: C1 E F1 J1 K1 L N S1 S2 T1 W Z(i,j,l,m)
Emergency Action, Agency, Advocacy, Fixed Fee Interview and Legal Aid undertaken
Ptr: Milward, Mr Martin D BA Assistant Deputy Coroner . . *Oct 1981
Sinclair, Mr Alastair . . . . *Nov 2000
Stone, Mr Roger J . . . . *Jul 1973
Winskell, Miss Fiona Home . . . . Aug 1972

STONE MILWARD RAPERS
87 High Street Selsey Chichester West Sussex PO20 0QL
Tel: 01243 602832 *Fax:* 01243 602644 *Dx:* 153584 SELSEY
E-mail: sevans@smrselsey.co.uk
Office: Chichester
Work: D1 E K1 K3 L R2 S1 S2 W
Ptr: Evans, Mrs Sarah Louise BSc(Hons) . . . . *Nov 2001
Field, Mr Matthew James William . . . . *Oct 2005

WANNOP FOX STAFFURTH & BRAY ‡
South Pallant House Chichester West Sussex PO19 1TH
Tel: 01243 778844 *Fax:* 01243 788349 *Dx:* 30305 CHICHESTER
Emergency telephone 01243 778844
E-mail: chichester@wfsblaw.com
List of partners: C Albon, S E Baker, J E M Brotherton, S Collett, J Dahill, C Fletcher, P A Green, J M Mason, G Morgan, C Osborne, N K Poupart, P J Seear
Office: Bognor Regis, Havant, Littlehampton, Worthing (3 offices)
Languages: French, German
Work: A1 B1 B2 C1 C2 C3 D1 E F1 G H I J1 K1 K2 L N O P Q R1 R2 S1 S2 T1 T2 U2 V W X Z(c,d,e,h,k,l,m,o,q)
Emergency Action, Advocacy, Legal Aid undertaken and Member of Accident Line
Ptr: Brotherton, Mr James E M LLB . . . . Nov 1991
Asoc: Kessler, Mr Mark ● . . . . *Aug 1999
Ast: Hayward, Miss Maria LLB(Hons) . . . . *Sep 1998

CHIPPENHAM, Wiltshire

FORRESTER & FORRESTER ‡
(incorporating Keary Stokes & White)
61 St Mary Street Chippenham Wiltshire SN15 3JH
Tel: 01249 444300 *Fax:* 01249 443223 *Dx:* 34202 CHIPPENHAM
E-mail: mail@forrester-forrester.com
List of partners: A J Gill, M J Paterson, J Watts
Office: Malmesbury
Work: A1 C1 C2 C3 D1 E F1 J1 K1 L O Q S1 S2 T1 T2 V W Z(d,h,l)
Emergency Action, Agency, Advocacy, Fixed Fee Interview, Legal Aid undertaken and Legal Aid Franchise
Ptr: Watts, Mr Jonathan. . . . . Dec 2001
Asoc: Coates, Mr Richard . . . . Nov 1993
King, Mrs Rachael . . . . Jun 1998
Ast: Morris, Mrs Anne G LLB . . . . Mar 1990

GOUGHS
Mill House 1 New Road Chippenham Wiltshire SN15 1EJ
Tel: 01249 444499 *Fax:* 01249 443116 *Dx:* 34200 CHIPPENHAM
E-mail: info@goughs.co.uk
Office: Calne, Corsham, Devizes, Melksham, Trowbridge
Work: A1 C1 C2 C3 D1 D2 E F1 F2 J1 K1 K2 K3 L N O P Q R1 R2 S1 S2 W Z(c,e,o,q,r,z)
Emergency Action, Agency and Advocacy undertaken
Ptr: Boyce, Mr Peter J LLB; LLM . . . . *Dec 1977
Dobson, Mr Kevin George. . . . . Dec 1991
Howard, Mr Stephen W C LLB . . . . *Jun 1974
Young, Mrs Ira Margaret BSc . . . . *Nov 1993
Asoc: Bowles, Mrs Hilary Margaret . . . . Apr 1998
Ast: Bennett, Mrs Rachel Hannah LLB. . . . . Jul 2004
Carr, Ms Hannah BSc; PGDip. . . . . Oct 2005
Heeley, Mrs Helen Elizabeth BA(Hons); GDL; LPC . . Sep 2010

RICHARD GRIFFITHS & CO
12b St Mary Street Chippenham Wiltshire SN15 3JJ
Tel: 01249 446300 *Fax:* 01249 446301
E-mail: info@richardgriffithsandco.com
Office: New Milton, Salisbury

H&G PROPERTIES ‡
190 London Road Chippenham Wiltshire SN15 3BE
Tel: 01249 656144 *Fax:* 01249 656144
E-mail: ian.hodges@btopenworld.com

J K HARMSHAW ‡
12 High Street Marshfield Chippenham Wiltshire SN14 8LP
Tel: 01225 891786

JEARY & LEWIS ‡
46 Market Place Chippenham Wiltshire SN15 3HU
Tel: 01249 444484 *Fax:* 01249 444434 *Dx:* 34211 CHIPPENHAM
E-mail: mparfitt@jeary-lewis.co.uk
List of partners: S Goldson, M A Jeary, A Moghal
Office: Swindon
Work: D1 G H K1 K3 K4 R1 S1 V W Z(i,k,l,t)
Emergency Action, Agency, Advocacy, Fixed Fee Interview, Legal Aid undertaken and Legal Aid Franchise
Ptr: Goldson, Mr Simon . . . . Jan 1995
Jeary, Mr Michael A. . . . . *Dec 1970
Moghal, Mr Asif. . . . . Jan 2006
Ast: Brereton, Ms Kim . . . . Jan 2009
Ervine, Miss Cindy LLB(Hons). . . . . *Oct 1995

MARK D OWEN SOLICITORS ‡
The Peninsula 2 Cheetham Hill Road Chippenham Wiltshire M4 4FB
Tel: 0161 827 8525 *Fax:* 0870 243 9843

RAYNERS ‡
(incorporating Wills Beesley)
57 Market Place Chippenham Wiltshire SN15 3HL
Tel: 01249 650394 *Fax:* 01249 444069
List of partners: S Goldson, C E Rayner, K E J Rayner
Languages: French
Work: E F1 J1 L N Q S1 W
Ptr: Goldson, Mr Simon LLB(Hons) . . . . *Nov 1994
Rayner, Mrs Carole Elizabeth LLB. . . . . Nov 2001
Rayner, Mr Keith E J . . . . *Jun 1978

SHEARER & CO SOLICITORS ‡
64a Market Place Chippenham Wiltshire SN15 3HG
Tel: 01249 657744 *Fax:* 01249 657774
E-mail: p.shearer@shearerandco.com

WYKEHAM & CO ‡
Trey House Lower Seagry Chippenham Wiltshire SN15 5EP
Tel: 01249 721010 *Fax:* 01249 720002
E-mail: nick@nwykeham.co.uk
List of partners: N P Wykeham
Work: E L R1 S1 T2 W
Fixed Fee Interview undertaken
SPr: Wykeham, Mr Nicholas P LLB(Newc) . . . . *May 1975

CHIPPING NORTON, Oxfordshire

BRADLEY SAUL SOLICITORS ‡
Market Chambers 2 Market Street Chipping Norton Oxfordshire OX7 5NQ
Tel: 01608 648020 *Fax:* 01608 641698
E-mail: office@bradleysaul.co.uk

DALE AND DALE ‡
3 Threshers Yard West Street Kingham Chipping Norton Oxfordshire OX7 6YF
Tel: 0845 603 1573 *Fax:* 0845 603 1574
E-mail: info@ddlaw.co.uk

DYAKOWSKI GAFFORD ‡
2 New Street Chipping Norton Oxfordshire OX7 5LJ
Tel: 01608 643051 *Fax:* 01608 641019
Dx: 16951 CHIPPING NORTON
E-mail: dyakowski.gafford@btinternet.com
List of partners: J A G Dyakowski, G Gafford
Work: A1 K1 L S1 W
Advocacy undertaken
Ptr: Dyakowski, Mr John A G LLB . . . . *Aug 1979
Gafford, Mr Geoffrey . . . . Dec 1979

WHITE & BLACK LEGAL LLP ‡
Chalford Park Oxford Road Old Chalford Chipping Norton Oxfordshire OX7 5QR
Tel: 0800 035 2656 *Fax:* 0845 201 3155
E-mail: enquiries@wablegal.com

DENIS WYNN & CO ‡
6a Market Place Chipping Norton Oxfordshire OX7 5NA
Tel: 01608 643036 *Fax:* 01608 641025
Dx: 16953 CHIPPING NORTON
E-mail: wynnlaw@tiscali.co.uk
List of partners: D C Wynn
Work: K1 L S1 S2 V W Z(l)
Agency, Advocacy and Fixed Fee Interview undertaken
Ptr: Wynn, Mr Denis C . . . . *§Dec 1975

CHIPPING ONGAR, Essex

NICOLA HARRIES SOLICITOR ‡
157 High Street Chipping Ongar Essex CM5 9JD
Tel: 01277 362332
List of partners: N Harries
SPr: Harries, Miss Nicola BA ♦. . . . . Dec 1979

SORRELLS SOLICITORS ‡
157 High Street Chipping Ongar Essex CM5 9JD
Tel: 01277 365532 *Fax:* 01277 365518 *Dx:* 47955 ONGAR
E-mail: info@sorrells.org.uk

TILBROOK'S ‡
Quires Green Willingale Chipping Ongar Essex CM5 0QP
Tel: 01277 896000 *Fax:* 01277 896050
List of partners: R C W Tilbrook
Work: B1 F1 J1 L N O Q Z(g,q)
Agency, Advocacy and Fixed Fee Interview undertaken
SPr: Tilbrook, Mr Robin C W BA . . . . *§Sep 1990

CHIPPING SODBURY, South Gloucestershire

BEAUFORT LAW ‡
Old Bank House 79 Broad Street Chipping Sodbury South Gloucestershire BS37 6AD
Tel: 01225 339329 *Fax:* 01454 316453
E-mail: gjames@beaufortlaw.co.uk

CLUTTON COX SOLICITORS ‡
Parliament House 4 High Street Chipping Sodbury South Gloucestershire BS37 6AH
Tel: 01454 312125 *Fax:* 01454 324682
E-mail: info@cluttoncox.co.uk
List of partners: S P J Hajek
Ptr: Hajek, Mr Stephen P J BA . . . . *Jan 1983

GRUNDY & CO ‡
The Bake House Chipping Campden Chipping Sodbury South Gloucestershire GL55 6HL
Tel: 01386 849290 *Fax:* 0870 731 9111
E-mail: juliet@conveywithcare.com

HORNBY BAKER JONES & WOOD
1st Floor Back Offices Brick House Chipping Sodbury South Gloucestershire BS37 6DA
Office: Newport

CHIRK, Wrexham

STEVENS LUCAS ‡
Spring House Holyhead Road Chirk Wrexham LL14 5NA
Tel: 01691 777949 *Fax:* 01691 777775 *Dx:* 712200 CHIRK
Emergency telephone 01978 861237
E-mail: chirk@stevenslucas.co.uk
List of partners: M S Davies, L Hill, E R Stevens, P J Stevens
Office: Oswestry
Work: A1 B1 C1 E G H J1 K1 K4 L N O Q R1 S1 S2 W X Z(d,l,q)
Fixed Fee Interview undertaken
Ptr: Stevens, Mrs Elizabeth Ruth LLB . . . . *Apr 1975
Stevens, Mr Patrick J LLB. . . . . *§Dec 1980
Con: Lucas, Mr Ian C MP; BA(Oxon) . . . . *Nov 1985

CHISLEHURST, Kent

SUSAN HEADS & COMPANY ‡
1a Bromley Lane Chislehurst Kent BR7 6LH
Tel: 020 8467 5544 *Fax:* 020 8467 7799
E-mail: susanheads@law-chislehurst.co.uk
List of partners: S E Heads
Work: O S1 S2
SPr: Heads, Mrs Susan Elsie. . . . . *Dec 1991

NIGEL OWEN & CO ‡
1a Bromley Lane Chislehurst Kent BR7 6LH
Tel: 020 8295 1989 *Fax:* 020 8295 1660
E-mail: nigelowen@law-chislehurst.co.uk
List of partners: N V Owen
Work: B1 O Q S1 S2 W
SPr: Owen, Mr Nigel Vaughan . . . . *Jun 1977

PRESTON MELLOR HARRISON ‡
30 High Street Chislehurst Kent BR7 5AS
Tel: 020 8468 7025 *Fax:* 020 8467 5388 *Dx:* 59500 CHISLEHURST
E-mail: jha@pmhsolicitors.com
List of partners: J Harrison, J P Meisner
Languages: French, German
Work: C1 E F1 J1 K1 K3 K4 Q R1 S1 W
Ptr: Harrison, Mr John. . . . . *Dec 1974
Meisner, Mrs Janet P BA(Dunelm). . . . . *§Jun 1981

WYKEHAM HURFORD SHEPPARD & SON LLP
Kingsley House 5 High Street Chislehurst Kent BR7 5AB
Tel: 020 8297 0393 / 8467 8307 *Fax:* 020 8467 4381
E-mail: chislehurst@whss.co.uk
Office: Battle, Tenterden
Languages: French
Work: C1 L S1 W
Dir: Buller, Sally. . . . . Oct 2008
Wykeham-Hurford, The Hon John Louis Andre Besme . . . . *§Dec 1975

CHOBHAM, Surrey

CAG SOLICITORS ‡
Arcadia 44 Chertsey Road Chobham Surrey GU24 8PJ
Tel: 01276 488082 *Fax:* 01276 488190
E-mail: info@caglaw.co.uk
List of partners: C A Gregorious
SPr: Gregorious, Mrs Carol Ann FILEx Parish Councillor . . Nov 2002

CHORLEY, Lancashire

D J AHERN SOLICITORS ‡
Limbrick House Long Lane Chorley Lancashire PR6 9EE
Tel: 01257 268944

MALCOLM G BEVERLEY SOLICITORS ‡
33a Cunliffe Street Chorley Lancashire PR7 2BA
Tel: 01257 231462 *Fax:* 0871 266 8090 *Dx:* 18408 CHORLEY
E-mail: enquiry@mgblaw.co.uk
Work: L N O Q S1 W

BIRCHALL BLACKBURN LLP
24 St Thomas's Road Chorley Lancashire PR7 1HY
Tel: 01257 279011 *Fax:* 01257 261890 *Dx:* 18406 CHORLEY
E-mail: info@birchallblackburn.co.uk
Office: Chester, Formby, Leyland, Manchester, Morecambe, Preston (2 offices), Southport
Languages: Chinese, Gujarati, Punjabi, Urdu
Work: A1 B1 D1 D2 E J1 K1 K2 K3 N O Q R2 S1 S2 W Z(b,g,l,m,q)
Legal Aid Franchise
Ptr: Harris, Mrs Christine J LLB Licensed Insolvency Practitioner . . . *Jun 1981
Taylor, Mr Andrew J BA(Hons); DipOSH. . . . *Mar 2000
Asoc: Green, Ms Anne Mary Moreau BA(Hons); MA. . . . Oct 1985
Thompson, Mrs Esther Mary BSc . . . *§Nov 1992
Ast: Evans, Mr Stephen Edward LLB(Hons) . . . Mar 2008
Limbachia, Miss Seijal LLB(Hons). . . . *May 2008

C&P SOLICITORS ‡
Vantage House Buckshaw Court Chorley Lancashire PR7 6TU
Tel: 0845 601 2101 *Fax:* 0845 601 2102
E-mail: info@cplaw.org
Work: N
Agency undertaken

STANLEY H CROSS & CO ‡
10 Ashfield Road Chorley Lancashire PR7 1LJ
Tel: 01257 272222 *Fax:* 01257 261967 *Dx:* 18415 CHORLEY 1
E-mail: chris.hall@shcandco.co.uk
List of partners: D M Edwards, C I J Hall
Work: D1 D2 F1 G H J1 K1 K3 L N Q S1 W Z(k,l)
Emergency Action, Agency, Advocacy, Fixed Fee Interview, Legal Aid undertaken and Legal Aid Franchise
Ptr: Edwards, Mr David M LLB. . . . *Feb 1989
Hall, Mr Christopher I J LLB(L'pool) . . . *Dec 1979
Ast: Elsden, Miss Charlotte Ruth LLB; PGDip . . . *Apr 2009
Kirkham, Miss Clare. . . . Jul 2010

ANTHONY J DEWHURST ‡
5 Brentwood Road Anderton Chorley Lancashire PR6 9PL
Tel: 01257 480715 *Fax:* 01257 480573
E-mail: tony@ajd1.demon.co.uk

FORBES
55 St Thomas's Road Chorley Lancashire PR7 1JE
Tel: 01257 260600 *Fax:* 01257 260602 *Dx:* 18425 CHORLEY
E-mail: info@forbessolicitors.co.uk
Office: Accrington (2 offices), Blackburn (3 offices), Leeds, Manchester, Preston
Work: D1 G H K1 K2 V
Agency, Advocacy, Legal Aid undertaken and Legal Aid Franchise
Ptr: Dawson, Mr Steven James LLB. . . . *Oct 1993

FORSTER DEAN LTD
13-17 Cleveland Street Chorley Lancashire PR7 1BH
Tel: 01257 262960 *Fax:* 01257 275168
E-mail: enquiries@forsterdean.co.uk
Office: Birkenhead, Bootle, Crewe, Eccles, Ellesmere Port, Huyton, Leigh, Liverpool (5 offices), Oldham, Preston, Rochdale, Runcorn, St Helens, Stockport, Warrington, Widnes (2 offices), Wigan
Languages: Punjabi, Urdu
Work: N S1
Ptr: Taylor, Mrs Rachel Jane LLB . . . *Oct 1995

GARLANDS SOLICITORS ‡
Margaret House Unit 2 Chorley Lancashire PR7 4HD
Tel: 01257 474477 *Fax:* 01257 474488

I S LAW ‡
Jubilee House 15 Queens Road Chorley Lancashire PR7 1JU
Tel: 01257 754854 *Fax:* 0870 288 7483
E-mail: info@is-law.co.uk

KEVILL KIRKHAM & GRAYSON ‡
High Street Chambers High Street Chorley Lancashire PR7 1DU
Tel: 01257 263676 / 269212 *Fax:* 01257 265670
Dx: 700930 CHORLEY 2
Emergency telephone 01257 269486
E-mail: kkgrayson@btconnect.com
List of partners: R Grayson, N H Saunt
Work: A1 E K1 L R1 S1 W Z(c)
Ptr: Grayson, Mr Richard LLB(Lond). . . . *Jan 1969
Saunt, Mr Neil H LLB; LLM . . . Oct 1979

KEVILLS ‡
(incorporating John B Kevill & Son; Kevill Brown & Co)
Astley House 5 Park Road Chorley Lancashire PR7 1QS
Tel: 01257 265711 *Fax:* 01257 266925 *Dx:* 18402 CHORLEY
E-mail: p.singleton@kevills.net
List of partners: V K Nicholson, S A Robinson, P A Singleton
Work: B1 C1 E F1 J1 K1 L N O Q S1 S2 V W Z(c,e,l)
Emergency Action, Agency, Advocacy, Fixed Fee Interview undertaken and Member of Accident Line
Ptr: Nicholson, Ms Vicky K LLB . . . *Aug 1996
Robinson, Mr Simon A LLB . . . *Sep 1991
Singleton, Mr Peter A. . . . *May 1974

MARSDEN RAWSTHORN LLP
(incorporating Marsdens Solicitors LLP & Rawsthorns)
43 St Thomas's Road Chorley Lancashire PR7 1JE
Tel: 01257 279511 *Fax:* 01257 271022 *Dx:* 18401 CHORLEY
E-mail: info@marsdenrawsthorn.com
Office: Preston
Languages: French
Work: A1 A3 B1 B2 C1 C2 D1 D2 E F1 F2 G H J1 J2 K1 K2 K3 K4 L N O Q R2 S1 S2 T1 T2 W X Z(c,d,l,m,p,q,r)
Emergency Action, Agency, Advocacy, Legal Aid undertaken and Legal Aid Franchise
Ptr: Jolly, Mr Philip G Tax Tribunal Member (First Tier- Non Legal) . . . *Jun 1971
Margey, Mr Paul . . . *Mar 1991
Ast: Moseley, Katherine . . . *Sep 2010
Pearson, Mrs Anna Louise LLB(Hons). . . . *Oct 1995
Stephenson, Mr Simon Paul LLB(Hons) . . . *Dec 2000
Con: Hardwick, Mr John F . . . *§Jun 1981
Jackson, Mr Paul H LLB. . . . *Mar 1985
Milner, Mr Peter LLB(Leeds); MA Tribunal Judge (Lower Tier) . . . *May 1981

Mr Jackson is a member of the Child Care Panel.

I ANTHONY D MARTIN ‡
Alderley House Andertons Mill Chorley Lancashire PR7 5PY
Tel: 01257 451383 *Fax:* 01257 450130
Emergency telephone 01257 451383
E-mail: iadmartin@aol.com
List of partners: I A D Martin
Work: C1 I M1 M2 U2
SPr: Martin, Mr I Anthony D MA; LLM(Cantab) Notary Public . . . *§May 1968

NAPTHENS LLP
10-12 St Thomas's Road Chorley Lancashire PR7 1HR
Tel: 0845 260 2111 *Fax:* 01257 260096 *Dx:* 18412 CHORLEY
E-mail: chorley@napthens.co.uk
Office: Blackburn, Blackpool, Preston
Ptr: Crompton, Mr John M LLB . . . *May 1987
Hawksworth, Mr William D LLB . . . *Jul 1977
Ast: Austin, Eve LLB. . . . *Apr 2005
James, Nichola . . . Dec 1999
Khan, Mr Zulfi LLB(Hons) . . . Aug 2003
Richmond, Pamela . . . Aug 2004

NICHOLSONS ‡
Ligan House 32 Town Road Croston Chorley Lancashire PR26 9RB
Tel: 01772 601700 *Fax:* 01772 601702
List of partners: A Nicholson
Work: E K1 N Q S1 W
Fixed Fee Interview undertaken
Ptr: Nicholson, Miss Amanda BA(Hons) . . . *Jan 1983

NORTH WEST EMPLOYMENT LAW ‡
311 Doncaster House Moorland Gate Chorley Lancashire PR6 9FE
Tel: 01257 231458 *Fax:* 01257 231581
E-mail: info@nwelaw.co.uk

O'RIORDAN & CO ‡
1-3 Queens Road Chorley Lancashire PR7 1JU
Tel: 01257 262837 *Fax:* 01257 261766 *Dx:* 18403 CHORLEY
List of partners: G T Hegarty, J M O'Riordan
Work: B1 D1 E G H J1 K1 L M1 P R1 S1 W
Agency, Advocacy, Fixed Fee Interview, Legal Aid undertaken and Legal Aid Franchise
Ptr: Hegarty, Ms Geraldine T. . . . *Apr 1990
O'Riordan, Mr James M. . . . *Jan 1969

QUINN & CO ‡
2 St Mary's Walk Chorley Lancashire PR7 2RT
Tel: 01257 241818 *Fax:* 01257 261758
E-mail: graham@quinnsolicitors.co.uk
List of partners: G A Quinn
Work: S1 W
Ptr: Quinn, Mr Graham A BA . . . *Dec 1981

LYNNE STEEN COMMERCIAL SOLICITOR ‡
Heskin Hall Wood Lane Heskin Chorley Lancashire PR7 5PA
Tel: 01257 452044 *Fax:* 01257 450690
List of partners: L C Steen
Work: B1 C1 C2 C3 E F1 I J1 M1 M2 O P Z(d,e,y)
Agency undertaken
SPr: Steen, Ms Lynne C LLB(Hons) . . . *Feb 1989

WHITEHEADS SOLICITORS LIMITED ‡
PO Box 125 Chorley Lancashire PR7 2GD
Tel: 01257 266008 *Fax:* 01257 249704 *Dx:* 700931 CHORLEY 2
E-mail: info@whiteheadsols.co.uk
List of partners: P Lloyd, P Whitehead
Work: J1 L Z(h)
Dir: Lloyd, Mr Paul . . . Jan 2002
Whitehead, Mr Peter . . . Jan 1975

C WILSON SOLICITORS ‡
The Carrington Centre The Green Eccleston Chorley Lancashire PR7 5UP
Tel: 01257 451333 *Fax:* 01257 451333
E-mail: enquiries@cwilsonsolicitors.co.uk

YATES BARNES ‡
20 St Thomas's Road Chorley Lancashire PR7 1HR
Tel: 01257 267014 *Fax:* 01257 269276 *Dx:* 18404 CHORLEY
E-mail: yates@yatesbarnes.com
List of partners: S M Barnes, A E Yates
Work: C1 E J1 L N O Q S1 S2 W
Ptr: Barnes, Ms Susan Mary. . . . *Jan 1984
Yates, Mr Allan E LLB. . . . Mar 1975

CHORLEYWOOD, Hertfordshire

TURBERVILLES
Witton House Lower Road Chorleywood Hertfordshire WD3 5LB
Tel: 01923 284112 / 285869 *Fax:* 01923 284909
Dx: 52303 CHORLEYWOOD
Emergency telephone 01923 785385
E-mail: chorleywood@turbervilles.co.uk
Office: Uxbridge (3 offices)
Languages: French, German
Work: C1 E F1 J1 K1 K3 K4 L Q S1 S2 W Z(c,j)
Fixed Fee Interview undertaken

CHRISTCHURCH, Dorset

ALDRIDGE BROWNLEE SOLICITORS LLP
277 Lymington Road Highcliffe Christchurch Dorset BH23 5EB
Tel: 01425 282150 *Fax:* 01425 282110 *Dx:* 45350 HIGHCLIFFE
E-mail: enquiries@aldridge-brownlee.co.uk
Office: Bournemouth (3 offices)
Work: E L S1 S2 T2 W Z(d)
Ptr: Lilley, Mr Andrew Paul. . . . *Sep 1996
Ast: Marshall, Mrs Sara L LLB . . . *§Apr 1978

THE CARERS'S LEGAL CENTRE ‡
109 Burley Road Bransgore Christchurch Dorset BH23 8AY
Tel: 07740 432159 / 01425 674844
E-mail: carerslegalcentre@googlemail.com

FRETTENS SOLICITORS ‡
The Saxon Centre 11 Bargates Christchurch Dorset BH23 1PZ
Tel: 01202 491777 *Fax:* 01202 471743 *Dx:* 51101 CHRISTCHURCH
Emergency telephone 01202 488998
E-mail: info@frettens.co.uk
List of partners: I Fretten, K Fretten, M I Fretten, O B McKinney, I Slinger, L Young
Office: New Milton
Languages: French
Work: A1 C1 C2 D1 D2 E F1 F2 J1 J2 K1 K2 K3 K4 L N O P Q R1 R2 S1 S2 T1 T2 U2 V W Z(c,h,i,j,k,l,m,o,p,q,r,s,t)
Emergency Action, Agency, Advocacy, Fixed Fee Interview, Legal Aid Franchise and Member of Accident Line
Ptr: Fretten, Mr Ian LLB(Lond). . . . *§Dec 1971
Fretten, Ms Kate . . . *Jul 2001
Fretten, Mr Matthew Ian BA(Hons) . . . *Sep 2000
McKinney, Miss Oonagh B BA. . . . *May 1988
Slinger, Miss Ianthe MA(Cantab) . . . *Nov 2001
Young, Mr Lee BA; CTA; TEP. . . . *Sep 1996
Asoc: Hayter, Ms Michelle. . . . *Mar 2002
Ast: Burton, Mr Paul. . . . *Mar 2007
Dominey, Ms Hannah . . . Jul 2006
Muncer, Ms Amy Jane LLB; LPC . . . *Dec 2006

HAROLD G WALKER
33a Bargates Christchurch Dorset BH23 1QD
Tel: 01202 482202 *Fax:* 01202 473151 *Dx:* 51117 CHRISTCHURCH
E-mail: christchurch@hgwalker.co.uk
Office: Bournemouth, Broadstone, Verwood, Wimborne
Work: K1 K3 S1 S2 W

MORRIS SCOTT & CO ‡
280 Lymington Road Highcliffe Christchurch Dorset BH23 5ET
Tel: 01425 278866 *Fax:* 01425 276656 *Dx:* 45351 HIGHCLIFFE
Emergency telephone 01202 706852
E-mail: postmaster@morrisscott.co.uk
List of partners: I V Richards, A L Rohr
Work: B1 D1 E G H J1 K1 K3 L N O Q S1 S2 W Z(k,l)
Emergency Action, Agency, Advocacy, Fixed Fee Interview, Legal Aid undertaken, Legal Aid Franchise and Member of Accident Line
Ptr: Richards, Mr Ian V BA ● . . . *Dec 1980
Rohr, Mrs Andrea L LLB(Leics) . . . *Oct 1985
Asoc: Longland, Mrs Caryl M LLB(Hons). . . . *Oct 1981
Osman, Ms Lynn LLB. . . . *May 2002

ROY SMITH & CO ‡
47 Bargates Christchurch Dorset BH23 1QD
Tel: 01202 473413 / 473414 *Fax:* 01202 481820
Dx: 51107 CHRISTCHURCH
E-mail: roysmithco@btinternet.com
List of partners: J P Smith, R A Smith
Languages: French
Work: E L S1 S2 W
Fixed Fee Interview undertaken
Ptr: Smith, Miss Julie Patricia . . . Jan 1985
Smith, Mr Roy A . . . *§Jul 1972

SPURLINGS SOLICITORS ‡
2a Church Street Christchurch Dorset BH23 1BW
Tel: 01202 473321 *Fax:* 01202 479178 *Dx:* 51102 CHRISTCHURCH
List of partners: J Spurling
Work: S1 S2 T2 W Z(d)
Ptr: Spurling, Mr John Notary Public. . . . *§Feb 1977

TRUMAN-MOORE
7a Oaktree Parade Bransgore Christchurch Dorset BH23 8AB
Tel: 01425 673994 *Fax:* 01425 674343
Dx: 130690 CHRISTCHURCH 2
Office: Verwood
Languages: French
Work: A1 B1 C1 E F1 J1 K1 L N O P Q S1 S2 T1 W Z(l)
Agency and Fixed Fee Interview undertaken
Ptr: Durant, Mr Peter J C LLB. . . . §Nov 1981

WB LEGAL LLP ‡
43 Bargates Christchurch Dorset BH23 1QD
Tel: 0870 402 0555
E-mail: enquiries@wb-legal.co.uk

WILLIAMS THOMPSON ‡
Avon House 4 Bridge Street Christchurch Dorset BH23 1DX
Tel: 01202 484242 *Fax:* 01202 481327 *Dx:* 51106 CHRISTCHURCH
E-mail: enquiries@williamsthompson.co.uk
List of partners: J A G Hoare, A Randall, P J Watson-Lee, N J Williamson
Work: D1 E K1 K3 K4 S1 W
Emergency Action, Agency, Advocacy, Fixed Fee Interview and FLA; STEP; APIL
Ptr: Hoare, Mr J Alastair G LLB . . . *Dec 1977
Randall, Mrs Anne-Marie . . . *Mar 1973
Watson-Lee, Mr Peter J BSc(Econ) . . . *Jun 1978
Williamson, Mr Nicholas John BA . . . *Nov 1997
Ast: Jubb, Ms Susan. . . . *Jan 2005
Moore, Miss Samantha Jane Katherine BSSc(Hons); PGDipLaw; MA(Law) . . . *Jan 2003
Partington, Miss Julie Audrey BA(Hons). . . . *Apr 2007
Con: Chedgy, Mrs Carole A LLB . . . *Nov 1984
Watson-Lee, Mrs Anne P. . . . *Jan 1983

CHURCH STRETTON, Shropshire

PCB SOLICITORS LLP
44 Sandford Avenue Church Stretton Shropshire SY6 6BH
Tel: 01694 723818 *Fax:* 01694 724511
E-mail: info@pcblaw.co.uk
Office: Knighton, Ludlow, Shrewsbury, Telford
Languages: French
Work: A1 C1 D2 E F1 G H J1 K1 N O Q S1 S2 W
Legal Aid undertaken
Ptr: Hughes, Ms Rachael Esther. . . . Jul 1996

PI+ SOLICITORS ‡
14 Ludlow Road Church Stretton Shropshire SY6 6AA
Tel: 01694 722134
E-mail: info@personalinjuryplus.co.uk

See p112 for the Key to Work Categories & other symbols

L V PRIESTLEY & SON ‡
10 High Street Church Stretton Shropshire SY6 6BU
Tel: 01694 722254
List of partners: V M Priestley
Languages: French, Spanish
Agency and Legal Aid undertaken
Ptr: Priestley, Mr Vincent M . . . . *Dec 1977

CHURCHDOWN, Gloucestershire

LANGLEY WELLINGTON
33a Morley Avenue Churchdown Gloucestershire GL3 2BL
Tel: 01452 856846 *Fax:* 01452 856846 *Dx:* 7525 GLOUCESTER 1
Office: Gloucester
Work: E L S1 S2 T2 W
Ptr: Thompson, Mr Alan R MA(Cantab) . . . . *Nov 1970

CINDERFORD, Gloucestershire

GWYN JAMES SOLICITORS
14 Commercial Street Cinderford Gloucestershire GL14 2RR
Tel: 01594 822277 *Fax:* 01594 826262 *Dx:* 92500 CINDERFORD
Emergency telephone 07811 359125
E-mail: cinderford@gwynjames.co.uk
Office: Coleford
Work: A1 C1 D1 D2 E F1 J1 K1 K3 L N Q S1 S2 T1 T2 W Z(l)
Emergency Action, Agency, Advocacy, Fixed Fee Interview, Legal Aid undertaken and Legal Aid Franchise
Ptr: Feltham, Mrs Deborah Frances BA(Hons). . . . . . *Oct 1995
Wilkey, Mr Jonathan P BA(Law). . . . . *Dec 1979

CIRENCESTER, Gloucestershire

ALAN CARR SOLICITORS ‡
Park Lodge Hatherop Cirencester Gloucestershire GL7 3NA
Tel: 01285 710358
E-mail: alancarr01@btconnect.com

DAVEY FRANKLIN JONES ‡
10-12 Dollar Street Cirencester Gloucestershire GL7 2AL
Tel: 01285 654875 *Fax:* 01285 650963 *Dx:* 39403 CIRENCESTER
E-mail: enquiries@dfjlaw.co.uk
List of partners: P M Davies, A H Fletcher, V S Hancock, J C Leyland
Office: Gloucester
Languages: French, German
Work: A1 B1 B2 C1 C2 C3 D1 D2 E F1 F2 J1 J2 K1 K3 K4 L M1 N O P Q S1 T2 W Z(d,e,k,l,p,r)
Emergency Action, Agency, Advocacy, Fixed Fee Interview undertaken and Member of Accident Line
Ptr: Hancock, Miss Valerie S BA. . . . . *Dec 1970
Ast: Atkins, Mrs Meryl C LLB(Hons) . . . . *Jun 1980
Brady, Mr Michael Paul . . . . *Jan 1979
Leivers, Ms Amy Louise. . . . . Sep 2003
Saunders, Miss Rachel Mary . . . . May 2004

ALISON FIELDEN & CO ‡
The Gatehouse Dollar Street Cirencester Gloucestershire GL7 2AN
Tel: 01285 653261 *Fax:* 01285 885372 *Dx:* 39418 CIRENCESTER
E-mail: alison@alisonfielden.co.uk
List of partners: A J Fielden
Languages: French, German, Russian
Work: E K1 K3 S1 S2 W
Emergency Action, Agency, Advocacy, Fixed Fee Interview and Legal Aid undertaken
Ptr: Fielden, Mrs Alison J MA(Oxon) Notary Public. . . . *§Dec 1979
Ast: Weavill, Ms Heather BA(Hons) . . . . Nov 1992

LODDERS SOLICITORS LLP
Lorraine House Market Place Cirencester Gloucestershire GL7 2NW
Tel: 01285 659535 *Fax:* 01285 652787 *Dx:* 39410 CIRENCESTER
E-mail: lawyers@lodders.co.uk
Office: Henley-in-Arden, Stratford-upon-Avon
Work: A1 C1 E S1 S2 T2 W
Ptr: Samworth, Miss Penelope Andrea LLB(with French). .*Nov 1989

MORGAN CLARKE SOLICITORS ‡
Cotswold Villas Dyer Street Cirencester Gloucestershire GL7 2PP
Tel: 01285 650066 *Fax:* 01285 642999
List of partners: D M Clarke, M Iqbal
Ptr: Clarke, Mr Dermot Martin BA(Hons); MSc(Econ); LSF. Mar 1995
Iqbal, Mazar. . . . . Sep 2005
Asoc: Coleman, Mr Christopher Francis LLB(Hons) . . . . . Sep 2005
Kingsbury, Wendy. Mar 2007

RESIDENTIAL PROPERTY LAWYERS LTD ‡
Unit 4 Sterling Corner Esland Place Cirencester Gloucestershire GL7 1YG
Tel: 01285 651515 *Fax:* 01285 656748
E-mail: info@residentialpropertylawyers.co.uk

SANDERS BRICKWOOD ‡
8 Park Street Cirencester Gloucestershire GL7 2BN
Tel: 01285 654601 *Fax:* 01285 650380 *Dx:* 39402 CIRENCESTER
E-mail: sandbrick@aol.com
List of partners: R L Brickwood, R H Sanders
Languages: French
Work: A1 C1 C2 C3 D1 E G H J1 K1 L M1 N P S1 S2 T1 T2 W Z(b,e,f,l)
Agency and Advocacy undertaken
Ptr: Brickwood, Mr Roger L LLB(Lond). . . . . *Nov 1975
Sanders, Mr Rupert H. . . . . *Jun 1972
Ast: McDonagh, Mrs Patricia BSc . . . . *Oct 1980

SEWELL MULLINGS LOGIE LLP ‡
7 Dollar Street Cirencester Gloucestershire GL7 2AS
Tel: 01285 650000 *Fax:* 01285 649898 *Dx:* 39400 CIRENCESTER

TANNERS ‡
Lancaster House Thomas Street Cirencester Gloucestershire GL7 2AX
Tel: 01285 659061 *Fax:* 01285 655603 *Dx:* 39409 CIRENCESTER
E-mail: law@tanners.co.uk
List of partners: C A Alexander, R A Isaac, P E Marrow, N S Tanner
Work: A1 A2 A3 C1 C2 E F2 J1 J2 L M1 N O Q R1 R2 S1 S2 U1 U2 W Z(c,d,e,k,q)
Ptr: Alexander, Mr Christopher A . . . . *Nov 1982
Isaac, Mr Richard A. . . . . *§Apr 1981
Marrow, Mr Peter Edward. . . . . *Oct 1993
Tanner, Mr Nicholas S. . . . . *§Jun 1978
Asoc: Craig, Mrs Geraldine LLB . . . . *Aug 2000
Hasler, Mrs Julia Katherine Louise . . . . *Jul 1998
Ast: Corris, Mrs Catherine LLB. . . . . *Oct 2000
Saunders, Mrs Harriet Mary Elizabeth LLB . . . . . . *Jan 1999
Taylor, Mr Jeremy . . . . *Sep 2006

WILMOT & CO SOLICITORS LLP ‡
38 Castle Street Cirencester Gloucestershire GL7 1QH
Tel: 01285 650551 *Fax:* 01285 654007 *Dx:* 39417 CIRENCESTER
E-mail: cirencester@wilmots.co.uk
List of partners: M L Gray, A M Grazebrook, M G Grenfell, S H Mumford, P L G Nicholas, C E Young
Work: A1 B1 C1 E J1 K1 K3 K4 L N O Q S1 S2 T2 W Z(d,e,q,r)
Ptr: Gray, Mr Michael L . . . . *§Jan 1995
Grazebrook, Mr Adrian M TD . . . . *§May 1966
Grenfell, Mr Michael G . . . . *§Nov 1976
Mumford, Mr Simon H BA(Exon) . . . . *§Oct 1981
Nicholas, Mr Philip L G LLB. . . . . *§Feb 1989
Young, Mrs Clare Elizabeth LLB. . . . . *§Sep 2000
Ast: Sharpe, Mr Phillip LLB; LPC. . . . . *May 2005

CLACTON-ON-SEA, Essex

BENNETTS LAW PRACTICE LTD ‡
10 & 12 Crusader Business Park Stephenson Road West Clacton-on-Sea Essex CO15 4TN
Tel: 01255 254400 *Fax:* 01255 254401
E-mail: nbennett@bennettsolicitors.co.uk
List of partners: N J H Bennett, J D E Shawe
Work: C1 D1 D2 E F1 F2 J1 J2 K1 K2 K3 L N O Q R1 R2 S1 S2 V W X Z(c,j,k,l,q)
Dir: Bennett, Mr Nicholas J H LLB. . . . . *Sep 1989
Shawe, Mr Jonathan Dudley Ellis . . . . *Jun 1981

ELLISONS
63-65 Station Road Clacton-on-Sea Essex CO15 1SD
Tel: 01255 421248 *Fax:* 01225 476485
Dx: 34650 CLACTON-ON-SEA
E-mail: enquiries@ellisonssolicitors.com
Office: Colchester, Frinton-on-Sea, Harwich
Work: J1 K1 K2 K3 K4 S1 W Z(p)
Agency and Fixed Fee Interview undertaken
Ptr: Connal, Mr Stuart A M . . . . *Dec 1980
Lansley, Mr Stephen C . . . . *§Mar 1984
Con: Baldwin, Mr Jeremy F BA(Bris) . . . . *Jul 1975

FISHER JONES GREENWOOD LLP
Essex House 98 Pier Avenue Clacton-on-Sea Essex CO15 1NJ
Tel: 01255 323103 *Dx:* 34658 CLACTON-ON-SEA
E-mail: clacton@fjg.co.uk
Office: Chelmsford, Colchester (2 offices)

ALISTAIR KEEBLE ‡
106 Kings Avenue Holland-on-Sea Clacton-on-Sea Essex CO15 5EP
Tel: 01255 818900 *Fax:* 01255 818909 *Dx:* 34672 CLACTON
Emergency telephone 01206 262032
E-mail: law@alistairkeeble.co.uk
List of partners: A C Keeble
Languages: French
Work: A1 C1 E F1 J1 L S1 S2 W X Z(l)
Fixed Fee Interview undertaken
SPr: Keeble, Mr Alistair C . . . . *May 1979
Ast: Benham, Mr John G. . . . . *Dec 1975

LINN & ASSOCIATES SOLICITORS ‡
100 Pier Avenue Clacton-on-Sea Essex CO15 1NJ
Tel: 01255 224660 *Fax:* 01255 470143
Dx: 34652 CLACTON-ON-SEA
E-mail: solicitors@linnandassociates.co.uk
Office: Gillingham, Harwich

NINA MORAN-WATSON ‡
The Lodge House Crow lane Tendring Clacton-on-Sea Essex CO16 9AP
Tel: 0845 241 5633 *Fax:* 0870 770 1623
E-mail: nina@nmoran-watson.co.uk
List of partners: N Moran-Watson
Work: C1
SPr: Moran-Watson, Ms Nina LLB . . . . *Oct 1988

PLEASS THOMSON & CO ‡
Rosemary Chambers 91 Rosemary Road West Clacton-on-Sea Essex CO15 1EP
Tel: 01255 221133 *Fax:* 01255 220055 *Dx:* 34654 CLACTON
Emergency telephone 01255 221010
E-mail: solicitors@pleassthomson.co.uk
List of partners: V Patten, J C Pleass
Office: Colchester
Languages: French, German
Work: C1 D1 D2 E F1 J1 K1 K3 K4 L M2 N O Q R1 R2 S1 S2 T2 W Z(l,p)
Emergency Action, Agency, Advocacy, Legal Aid undertaken, Legal Aid Franchise and Member of Accident Line
Ptr: Patten, Mrs Veronica LLB(Hons) ● . . . . *Feb 1996
Pleass, Miss Jane Christine BA(Hons)(Law) ● . . . . *§Mar 1986
Asoc: Goodfrey, Ms Andrea J LLB(Hons) . . . . *§Jun 1999

POWIS & CO ‡
57 Station Road Clacton-on-Sea Essex CO15 1RU
Tel: 01255 233400 *Fax:* 01255 420419 *Dx:* 34653 CLACTON
E-mail: mervynbaker@powis-law.co.uk
List of partners: M Baker, J J Roberts
Work: A1 B1 C1 D1 E F1 J1 K1 L N Q R1 S1 S2 T1 T2 V W Z(d,j,m,p)
Emergency Action, Agency, Advocacy, Fixed Fee Interview, Legal Aid undertaken and Legal Aid Franchise
Ptr: Baker, Mr Mervyn LLB . . . . *Sep 1976
Roberts, Mr Jonathan J LLB. . . . . *Jan 1991

THOMPSON SMITH & PUXON
39 Station Road Clacton-on-Sea Essex CO15 1RN
Tel: 01255 221919 *Fax:* 01255 220240 *Dx:* 34651 CLACTON
Emergency telephone 01255 475077
E-mail: info@tsplegal.com
Office: Colchester
Languages: French
Work: D1 D2 E K1 N O Q S1 S2 T2 V W Z(m,o,q)
Emergency Action, Agency, Advocacy, Legal Aid undertaken and Member of Accident Line
Ptr: Porter, Mr Richard S BA; MSc ★ . . . . *§Nov 1984
Ast: Barnes, Miss Fay Jessica LLB . . . . *Nov 2004
Welham, Mr Samuel Paul Christopher LLB . . . . . . Sep 2005
Con: Baldwin, Mr Robin Geoffrey. . . . . *§Nov 1975

CLAY CROSS, Derbyshire

CLEAVER THOMPSON LTD
6a Eyre Street Clay Cross Derbyshire S45 9NS
Tel: 01246 865048 *Fax:* 01246 860030
Office: Alfreton
Work: D1 D2 E F1 J1 K1 K3 N S1 S2 W Z(l,m)
Emergency Action, Agency, Advocacy, Fixed Fee Interview, Legal Aid undertaken and Member of Accident Line
Con: Ripley, Mr David LLB . . . . *Dec 1982

CLECKHEATON, West Yorkshire

BREARLEYS SOLICITORS
4, 6 & 6a Cheapside Cleckheaton West Yorkshire BD19 5AF
Tel: 01274 864002 *Fax:* 01274 864012 *Dx:* 25551 CLECKHEATON
E-mail: nickbattye@brearleyssolicitors.com
Office: Batley, Birstall

CADMANS LAW & PROPERTY ‡
Churchill House Northgate Cleckheaton West Yorkshire BD19 3HH
Tel: 01274 874231 *Fax:* 01274 866066 *Dx:* 25552 CLECKHEATON
E-mail: reception@cadmans-solicitors.com
List of partners: T R Conroy, E J McBennett, S Nazam, K Reid
Languages: Punjabi, Urdu
Work: D1 E F1 K1 L N O Q S1 S2 W Z(r)
Emergency Action, Agency, Advocacy, Fixed Fee Interview, Legal Aid undertaken, Legal Aid Franchise and Member of Accident Line
Ptr: Conroy, Mr Timothy R. . . . . *Aug 1971
McBennett, Mrs E Jane BA . . . . *Dec 1984
Nazam, Mr Sajad LLB. . . . . *Feb 2002
Reid, Mrs Kris. . . . . *Oct 1996
Ast: Nazia, Ms Safia. Mar 2006

INESONS ‡
Provincial House Albion Street Cleckheaton West Yorkshire BD19 3JG
Tel: 01274 872202 *Fax:* 01274 869652 *Dx:* 25554 CLECKHEATON
Emergency telephone 01274 877931
List of partners: P T Normandale, J M Potentier
Work: C1 D1 D2 E F1 G H J1 K1 L N O Q S1 S2 T1 T2 W Z(c,d,l)
Emergency Action, Agency, Advocacy, Fixed Fee Interview, Legal Aid undertaken and Legal Aid Franchise
Ptr: Normandale, Mr Paul T LLB. . . . . *Mar 1972
Potentier, Miss Joy M LLB(Manc) . . . . *Jun 1980
Ast: Hussain, Miss Sureya LLB(Hons) . . . . Jun 2001
Reid, Mrs Yvonne LLB(Hons) . . . . *Jul 2000
Whitehead, Miss Joanne Marie BA(Hons). . . . . . . *Apr 2007

ROTHERYS ‡
22 Albion Street Cleckheaton West Yorkshire BD19 3JD
Tel: 01274 876785 *Fax:* 01274 851230 *Dx:* 25553 CLECKHEATON
E-mail: malcolm@rotherys.com
List of partners: C Hewison
Work: A1 C1 D1 E F1 J1 K1 K2 L M1 N O P Q R2 S1 S2 W Z(l,r)
Agency, Advocacy, Fixed Fee Interview undertaken and Member of Accident Line
Ptr: Hewison, Mr Christopher . . . . Jul 1977

WILLIAMS & CO SOLICITORS LLP ‡
Brooke House 3-5 Dewsbury Road Cleckheaton West Yorkshire BD19 3RS
Tel: 01274 851608 *Fax:* 01274 852293
E-mail: peter@williamscleck.co.uk
List of partners: P J Williams
Work: C1 E J1 K4 S1 S2 W
SPr: Williams, Mr Peter Jeffrey LLB(Hons) . . . . *Jun 1970
Ast: Ahmed, Mrs Ambreen LLM . . . . *Dec 2003

CLEETHORPES, North East Lincolnshire

JOHN BARKERS
12 St Peters Avenue Cleethorpes North East Lincolnshire DN35 8HJ
Tel: 01472 695218 *Fax:* 01472 692344
E-mail: clt@jbarkers.co.uk
Office: Grimsby, Louth, Mablethorpe
Work: A1 B1 C1 C2 D1 D2 E F1 F2 G H J1 K1 K3 K4 L N O Q R1 S1 S2 T1 T2 V W Z(b,h,l)
Emergency Action, Agency, Advocacy, Fixed Fee Interview, Legal Aid undertaken, Legal Aid Franchise and Member of Accident Line
Asoc: Longbottom, Mr Jonathan Peter LLB . . . . *Mar 1993

R J SOLICITORS LTD ‡
64 St Peters Avenue Cleethorpes North East Lincolnshire DN35 8HP
Tel: 01472 699599 *Fax:* 01472 699599
E-mail: raj@rjsolicitors.com

CLEOBURY MORTIMER, Shropshire

MFG SOLICITORS ‡
High Street Cleobury Mortimer Shropshire DY14 8DG
Tel: 01299 270210
E-mail: cleoburymortimer@mfgsolicitors.com

CLEVEDON, North Somerset

J R BROWN & CO ‡
8 Station Road Clevedon North Somerset BS21 6NH
Tel: 01275 879292 *Fax:* 01275 870202 *Dx:* 30357 CLEVEDON
E-mail: gareth.richards@jrbrown.co.uk
List of partners: G Richards, S J Wilmot
Work: A1 C1 C2 E F1 J1 K1 L N O P Q R1 S1 T1 T2 V W Z(c)
Emergency Action, Agency, Advocacy, Fixed Fee Interview, Legal Aid undertaken and Member of Accident Line
Ptr: Richards, Mr Gareth LLB . . . . May 1979
Wilmot, Mr Stephen J BA . . . . *Jul 1979

GRIMSHAWS SOLICITORS LIMITED ‡
PO Box 145 Clevedon North Somerset BS21 7JQ
Tel: 01275 875216 *Fax:* 01275 875216
E-mail: info@grimshawssolicitors.co.uk

JOHN HODGE SOLICITORS
14 Kenn Road Clevedon North Somerset BS21 6EL
Tel: 01275 874213 *Fax:* 01275 340063 *Dx:* 30355 CLEVEDON
E-mail: mailbox@johnhodge.co.uk
Office: Bristol, Wedmore, Weston-super-Mare (2 offices), Yatton
Work: A1 B1 C1 D1 E J1 K1 K2 K3 K4 N O Q S1 S2 W Z(p,q,r)
Fixed Fee Interview undertaken
Ast: Cole, Mr Christopher J LLB(Hons) Harry Strutts Prize . Jun 1966

LINDLEYS
The Reading House 11 Alexandra Road Clevedon North Somerset BS21 7QH
Tel: 01275 877277 *Fax:* 01275 877477 *Dx:* 30360 CLEVEDON
E-mail: dhenjey@lindleys.net
Office: Bristol
Ptr: Hendey, Mr David W LLB . . . . *Apr 1976

WARDS SOLICITORS
1-3 Alexandra Road Clevedon North Somerset BS21 7QF
Tel: 01275 850470 *Fax:* 01275 343559 *Dx:* 30353 CLEVEDON
E-mail: info@wards.uk.com
Office: Bristol (2 offices), Nailsea, Portishead, Staple Hill, Weston-super-Mare (3 offices), Yate
Work: A1 C1 C2 E F1 J1 K1 L N O P Q R1 S1 S2 W Z(c,j,k,l,o,s)
Advocacy undertaken and Member of Accident Line
Con: Murray, Mr Robert R . . . . Jun 1979

CLEVELAND, Redcar & Cleveland

CYGNET FAMILY LAW ‡
Ground Floor Portland House West Dyke Road Cleveland Redcar & Cleveland TS10 1DH
Tel: 01642 777680 *Fax:* 01642 777688 *Dx:* 60022 REDCAR
E-mail: enquiries@cygnetfamilylaw.co.uk
Work: D1 D2 K1 K3 S1 W
Agency, Advocacy and Legal Aid undertaken

CLIFTON, Bristol

HANDS LAW ‡
Westpoint 78 Queens Road Clifton Bristol BS8 1QU
Tel: 0117 905 9262

CLIFTONVILLE, Kent

FST SOLICITORS LIMITED ‡
176 Northdown Road Cliftonville Kent CT9 2QN
Tel: 01843 234160 *Dx:* 200204 CLIFTONVILLE

NORMAN HUNTER ‡
Mainsale 168 Northdown Road Cliftonville Kent CT9 2QN
Tel: 07766 313613
Emergency telephone 07766 313613
List of partners: N Hunter
Work: G H
SPr: Hunter, Mr Norman . . . . Oct 1979

MARSDEN DUNCAN ‡
Westminster Bank Chambers 160 Northdown Road Cliftonville Kent CT9 2QN
Tel: 01843 295741 *Fax:* 01843 295742 *Dx:* 200203 CLIFTONVILLE
E-mail: info@marsdenduncan.co.uk
List of partners: I S Duncan, K G Marsden
Office: Birchington, Ramsgate
Languages: Dutch, French
Work: B1 D1 E F1 J1 K1 L N O Q R1 S1 S2 V W Z(l)
Agency, Advocacy, Fixed Fee Interview and Legal Aid undertaken
Ptr: Marsden, Mr Kim Gordon LLB. . . . . *Dec 1983

ROBINSON ALLFREE
253 Northdown Road Cliftonville Kent CT9 2PN
Tel: 01843 228635 *Fax:* 01843 224560 *Dx:* 200201 CLIFTONVILLE
E-mail: cliftonville@robinson-allfree.co.uk
Office: Broadstairs, Ramsgate
Work: C1 C2 C3 D1 E F1 G H J1 K1 L M1 M2 N P S1 W Z(i,p)
Emergency Action, Agency, Advocacy, Legal Aid undertaken and Member of Accident Line
Ptr: Longdon, Mr Michael R . . . . *Nov 1974
Worth, Miss Sandra LLM . . . . *Nov 1997
Con: Robinson, Mr James E . . . . *Dec 1963

CLITHEROE, Lancashire

ABBEY COURT SOLICITORS ‡
Unit 6 Abbey Works Clitheroe Lancashire BB7 9SP
Tel: 01254 824963

BACKHOUSE JONES LTD ‡
The Printworks Heys Road Clitheroe Lancashire BB7 9WD
Tel: 01254 828300 *Fax:* 01254 828301 *Dx:* 15166 CLITHEROE
E-mail: enquiries@backhouses.co.uk
List of partners: J A Backhouse, J N Backhouse, C A Branton, M J Cunningham, I K Jones, S C Meyerhoff, A Woolfall
Work: B1 C1 C2 E F1 F2 G I J1 J2 N O P Q R1 R2 S1 S2 T1 W X Z(b,e,j,k,t)
Emergency Action, Agency, Advocacy and Fixed Fee Interview undertaken
Dir: Backhouse, Mr James Anderson LLB(Hons). . . . . *Nov 1992
Backhouse, Mr Jonathon Norman LLB(Hons); DipLaw. *Jul 1999
Branton, Ms Christine Anne BA(Hons); LLB . . . . . *Oct 1991
Cunningham, Mr Michael John BA(Hons); MCIT. . . . *§Jul 1978
Jones, Mr Ian Kenneth LLB; Dip PI . . . . *Nov 1992
Meyerhoff, Mr Steven Carl . . . . *Oct 2005
Woolfall, Mr Andrew LLB . . . . *Oct 1993
Ast: Bell, Mrs Jennifer LLB(Hons) . . . . *Jul 2005
Bell, Mr Scott Thomas LLB . . . . *Sep 2010
Coe, Ms Natalie. . . . . Mar 2008
Davies, Mr Mark Nicholas LLB(Hons) . . . . *Sep 2006
Flynn, Mrs Lucy Elizabeth BA(Hons) . . . . *May 2007
Grindrod, Miss Claire BA(Hons). . . . . *Sep 2008
Hornsby, Ms Alexa LLB . . . . *Nov 1985
Jones, Mrs Ursula E BA. . . . . *Sep 1999
Lawton, Miss Michelle BA(Hons) . . . . *Aug 2009
Lomax, Mr James Richard BA(Hons) . . . . *Sep 2010
Newbury, Ms Wendy Louise LLB(Hons) . . . . *Oct 1991
Whitehead, Miss Frances BSc(Hons) . . . . *Jan 2009
Williams, Ms Josiane . . . . *Sep 2000
Con: Heaton, Mr John Graham LLB(Hons) . . . . *Jun 1981

CHENERY MAHER & CO ‡
21 Church Street Clitheroe Lancashire BB7 2DF
Tel: 01200 422264 *Fax:* 01200 428986
E-mail: mail@chenerymaher.co.uk
List of partners: I L A Chenery, C L Maher
Languages: Cantonese
Work: A1 D1 E K1 K2 K3 K4 L S1 S2 W
Agency and Advocacy undertaken
Ptr: Chenery, Mrs Irene L A LLB. . . . . *§Oct 1982
Maher, Mrs Carol L BA(Hons). . . . . *§Oct 1982
Asoc: Herd, Mrs Anthea Pui Sang LLB(Hons) . . . . Oct 2004

DRM CONVEYANCING ‡
18 Railway View Road Clitheroe Lancashire BB7 2HE
Tel: 01200 428102
E-mail: info@drmconveyancing.co.uk

FIELDEN LAW LLP ‡
Manor Buildings Moor Lane Wiswell Clitheroe Lancashire BB7 9DG
Tel: 01254 828410 *Fax:* 01254 823097
E-mail: enquiries@fieldenlaw.co.uk

HOULDSWORTHS ‡
The Old Coach House 2 Accrington Road Whalley Clitheroe Lancashire BB7 9DT
Tel: 01254 825757 *Fax:* 01254 825758 *Dx:* 15152 CLITHEROE
Emergency telephone 01200 426469
E-mail: law@houldsworths.co.uk
List of partners: J H Houldsworth
Office: Clitheroe
Work: A1 B1 C1 D1 E F1 G H J1 K1 L N O P Q R1 S1 S2 T1 T2 V W Z(l)
Emergency Action, Agency, Advocacy, Fixed Fee Interview, Legal Aid undertaken, Legal Aid Franchise and Member of Accident Line
Ptr: Houldsworth, Mr John H. . . . . *Nov 1973

HOULDSWORTHS
Pullman House 2-4 Duck Street Clitheroe Lancashire BB7 9SP
Tel: 01200 422152 *Fax:* 01200 428983 *Dx:* 15152 CLITHEROE
E-mail: law@houldsworths.co.uk
Office: Clitheroe

LORDS LEGAL SERVICES LIMITED ‡
Monks Lodge Sawley Clitheroe Lancashire BB7 4LE
Tel: 01200 440977

MICHAEL A LOVERIDGE ‡
40 Well Terrace Clitheroe Lancashire BB7 2AD
Tel: 01200 442600 *Fax:* 01200 442528
E-mail: michael@loveridgelaw.co.uk
List of partners: M A Loveridge
Work: E N O Q S1 W Z(j)
Emergency Action and Fixed Fee Interview undertaken
SPr: Loveridge, Mr Michael A LLB . . . . *Jun 1980

SFN SOLICITORS ‡
Stanley House Lowergate Clitheroe Lancashire BB7 1AD
Tel: 01200 426811 *Fax:* 01200 428223
E-mail: bdearing@sfn.co.uk

STEELE & SON ‡
Castlegate Clitheroe Lancashire BB7 1AZ
Tel: 01200 444321 *Fax:* 01200 425428 *Dx:* 15858 CLITHEROE
Emergency telephone 01254 822302
E-mail: steeleandson@aol.com
List of partners: K G Bagot, S J Barker, S Nadkarni, J M Taylor
Office: Barnoldswick
Languages: French
Work: A1 C1 E F1 G H J1 K1 K3 K4 L N O Q R1 S1 S2 W Z(c,d,l)
Emergency Action, Agency, Advocacy, Fixed Fee Interview, Legal Aid undertaken and Member of Accident Line
Ptr: Bagot, Mr Keith Gordon LLB . . . . *Oct 1982
Barker, Mr Stephen John BA(Law) . . . . *Jun 1980
Taylor, Mr John M. . . . . *Jul 1967

COALVILLE, Leicestershire

CRANE & WALTON ‡
21-25 London Road Coalville Leicestershire LE67 3JB
Tel: 01530 834466 *Fax:* 01530 810886 *Dx:* 23652 COALVILLE
E-mail: enquiries@craneandwalton.com
List of partners: R F Adkinson, R G Arnold, J M Crane, A Klimowicz, M J C Needham, M G Scott-Jones
Office: Ashby-de-la-Zouch, Leicester
Work: A1 B1 C1 D1 E F1 J1 K1 K3 L M1 N O P Q R1 R2 S1 S2 T1 T2 V W
Emergency Action, Agency, Advocacy, Fixed Fee Interview and Legal Aid undertaken
Ptr: Arnold, Mr Richard G LLB. . . . . *§Apr 1973
Needham, Mr Matthew J C LLB. . . . . May 1994

JOSIAH HINCKS
39-41 Belvoir Road Coalville Leicestershire LE67 3PD
Tel: 01530 835041 *Fax:* 01530 811778 *Dx:* 23654 COALVILLE
E-mail: info@josiahhincks.co.uk
Office: Blaby, Leicester
Work: A1 A2 A3 B1 C1 C2 D1 D2 E F1 J1 K1 K2 L N O P Q S1 S2 W Z(c,d,e,i,l,o,q,r)
Agency, Advocacy and Legal Aid undertaken

M&S SOLICITORS LIMITED ‡
20 Newton Road Heather Coalville Leicestershire LE67 2RD
Tel: 01530 266000 *Fax:* 01530 266020 *Dx:* 715546 SWEPSTONE
E-mail: info@mslaw.co.uk

MANDER CRUICKSHANK SOLICITORS LLP ‡
Berrisford Row 101-105 Belvoir Road Coalville Leicestershire LE67 3PH
Tel: 01530 510666 *Fax:* 01530 811543 *Dx:* 23651 COALVILLE
Emergency telephone 01530 814166
E-mail: enquiries@mandersol.co.uk
List of partners: J A G Abbott, W P Chadwick, K S Hicklin
Office: Hinckley
Work: B1 C1 D1 E F1 G H J1 K1 K2 K4 L N O Q S1 S2 V W Z(l)
Emergency Action, Agency, Advocacy, Fixed Fee Interview, Legal Aid undertaken, Legal Aid Franchise and Member of Accident Line
Mem: Abbott, Mr James A G LLB(Manc). . . . . *Apr 1979
Chadwick, Mr W Peter BA. . . . . *Jun 1980
Hicklin, Miss Kathryn Sarah LLB(Hons) . . . . *Jul 1999
Ast: Christison, Mrs Ann Katharine MA(Cantab) . . . . . . Oct 1995
Cole, Gemma. *Aug 2008
Dixon, Miss Kelly LLB. . . . . Mar 2009
Hubbard, Miss Deborah LLB(Hons) . . . . *May 1996
Tubb, Mr Paul Michael LLB(Hons). . . . . *Jan 2006
Con: Mander, Mr Charles Ewan. . . . . *Mar 1963

MOSS SOLICITORS LLP
Unit 11a Whitwick Business Centre Stenson Road Coalville Leicestershire LE67 4JP
Tel: 01530 815747
Office: Loughborough

COBHAM, Surrey

DAVID BELLCHAMBER & CO ‡
18 Lockhart Road Cobham Surrey KT11 2AX
Tel: 01932 702233 *Fax:* 01932 883277
E-mail: davidbellchamber@aol.com
List of partners: D C Bellchamber
Work: I J1 K1 K3 K4 Q S1 U2 W Z(za)
Ptr: Bellchamber, Mr David C LLB(Lond). . . . . Mar 1975

THE BERKELEY GROUP PLC ‡
Berkeley House 19 Portsmouth Road Cobham Surrey KT11 1JG
Tel: 01932 868555 *Fax:* 01932 865819

DAVID BOLTON & ASSOCIATES ‡
11 Harebell Hill Cobham Surrey KT11 2RS
Tel: 01932 868074 *Fax:* 01932 589783
E-mail: davbolton@msn.com

HART BROWN SOLICITORS
33 High Street Cobham Surrey KT11 3ES
Est: 1919
Tel: 0800 068 8177 *Fax:* 01932 866396 *Dx:* 46101 COBHAM
E-mail: lawyers@hartbrown.co.uk
Office: Cranleigh, Godalming, Guildford, London SW19, Woking
Work: A1 A3 B1 C1 C2 C3 D1 D2 E F1 I J1 K1 K2 K3 K4 L M1 M2 N O P Q R1 R2 S1 S2 T2 V W Z(b,c,d,e,i,k,l,m,o,p,q,r,s,t)
Emergency Action, Agency, Advocacy, Fixed Fee Interview, Legal Aid undertaken and Legal Aid Franchise
Ptr: Pearce, Mr Timothy J BA . . . . *May 1980
Asoc: Abbott, Mr Julian R LLB(Lond) . . . . *Apr 1978
Ast: Higgins, Miss Sonia BSc(Econ) . . . . *Sep 2005
Howe, Mr Peter David LLB . . . . *Nov 1991

LOWRIE & CO ‡
The Old Coaching Mews 7b High Street Cobham Surrey KT11 3DH
Tel: 01932 865818 *Fax:* 01932 867587
E-mail: lowrieco@btinternet.com
List of partners: J C Lowrie
Work: E L S1 S2 W
Ptr: Lowrie, Mrs Julia C BA . . . . *Apr 1983

MUNDAYS LLP ‡
Cedar House 78 Portsmouth Road Cobham Surrey KT11 1AN
Est: 1960
Tel: 01932 590500 *Fax:* 01932 590220 *Dx:* 156970 COBHAM
E-mail: enq@mundays.co.uk
List of partners: M A Andrew, N A Andrews, V E Barker, J D Bell, N J Broadhurst, G S Coy, M Dharamsi, S Duckworth, G Georgiou, V I J Gilmour, R A B Harris, K P Healy, D P Irving, F R McAllister, S H Morris, J P O'Flinn, I J Saffin, D B Squire, V A Toon, M S Unwin, D I Willis
Languages: French, German
Work: A3 B1 C1 C2 C3 D1 E F1 F2 I J1 K1 K2 K3 M3 O Q R2 S1 S2 T1 T2 U1 U2 W Z(b,c,e,k,l,p,w)
Ptr: Andrew, Mr Mark A JD . . . . Jul 2005
Andrews, Mr Neale Alan . . . . Oct 1988
Barker, Mr Victor E MA(Cantab). . . . . *Apr 1981
Bell, Mr John Denham . . . . *Feb 1988
Broadhurst, Mrs Nicola Jane LLB . . . . *Sep 1993
Coy, Mr Graham S MA(Cantab). . . . . *§Feb 1978
Dharamsi, Meboob TEP. . . . . *§Jan 1987
Duckworth, Miss Sarah . . . . *Sep 1996
Georgiou, Mr George BSc. . . . . *Oct 1996
Gilmour, Miss Veronica I J LLB(Hons) . . . . *Oct 1986
Harris, Mr Robert A B. . . . . *§Dec 1973
Healy, Mr Kevin Patrick LLB(Hons) . . . . §Jan 1994
Irving, Mr David P LLB(Hons) . . . . *§Mar 1984
McAllister, Ms Fiona R LLB(Hons). . . . . *§Nov 1985
Morris, Mr Stephen H LLB(Hons) . . . . *§Apr 1981
O'Flinn, Mr James Patrick LLB(Hons) . . . . *Nov 1995
Saffin, Mrs Ingrid J FILEx . . . . *§Apr 1997
Squire, Mr David B . . . . *Apr 1965
Toon, Ms Valerie A BA(Hons) . . . . *§Nov 1987
Unwin, Mr Miles S LLB(Hons) . . . . *§Oct 1980
Willis, Mr David Ian LLB(Hons) . . . . *Oct 1997
Ast: Green, Ms Miranda . . . . *Sep 1999
Jackson, Mr Oliver James Faux BA; LLDip . . . . . . Sep 2000
Jardine-Brown, Mr Magnus . . . . Oct 2005
Lawrence, Mr James Thomas LLB . . . . *Sep 2004
Lowery, Mr Paul BSc(Hons). . . . . Aug 2002
Martyn, Mr Nicholas. . . . . Feb 2007
Picknell, Mr James LLB . . . . Jan 2003
Regan, Mr David John LLB(Hons). . . . . *Apr 2006
Walton, Mr Philip BA . . . . *Sep 2000
Young, Mr Alexander LLB. . . . . *Sep 1997
Con: Morton, Mr J Andrew BA(Oxon) . . . . *§Jun 1966

SEIFERT & CO ‡
2 Fairmile Lane Cobham Surrey KT11 2DJ
Tel: 01932 866788 *Fax:* 01932 866883
E-mail: seifertandco@tiscali.co.uk
List of partners: L C Seifert
Languages: Hebrew
Ptr: Seifert, Lesley C . . . . *Jul 1979

See p112 for the Key to Work Categories & other symbols

COCKERMOUTH, Cumbria

BELL PARK KERRIDGE ‡
4 Main Street Cockermouth Cumbria CA13 9LQ
Tel: 01900 820800 *Fax:* 01900 826798 *Dx:* 62801 COCKERMOUTH
E-mail: lakeland@bpkcumbria.co.uk

BROCKBANK CURWEN CAIN & HALL
Norham House Main Street Cockermouth Cumbria CA13 9JS
Tel: 01900 827222 *Fax:* 01900 827755 *Dx:* 62807 COCKERMOUTH
E-mail: bt@brockbanks.co.uk
Office: Keswick, Maryport, Whitehaven, Workington
Work: C1 D1 D2 E F1 F2 J1 K1 K2 K3 L N O P Q R1 R2 S1 S2 V W Z(c,h,r)
Agency, Advocacy, Legal Aid undertaken and Member of Accident Line
Dir: Bevan, Ms Ceri J LLB. . . . . *§Oct 1987
Dunn, Mr John M W LLB(L'pool) Notary Public . . . *§Dec 1975
Greenwood, Mrs Lorraine BSc(Hons) . . . . *§Jan 1982
Con: Pratley, Mr S Graham MA; LLB Notary Public . . . . *§Dec 1976

JACQUELINE GOODLAD ‡
18 Mayo Street Cockermouth Cumbria CA13 0BY
Tel: 01900 825524 *Fax:* 01900 825524

MILBURNS ‡
3-5 Main Street Cockermouth Cumbria CA13 9LE
Tel: 01900 898010 *Fax:* 01900 829113 *Dx:* 62805 COCKERMOUTH
E-mail: cockermouth@milburns.org

WAUGH & MUSGRAVE ‡
1 Main Street Cockermouth Cumbria CA13 9LA
Tel: 01900 823127 *Fax:* 01900 827538 *Dx:* 62800 COCKERMOUTH
Emergency telephone 01900 823127
E-mail: enquiries@waughandmusgrave.co.uk
List of partners: G R Quigley
Languages: French, German
Work: A1 C1 C2 E F1 G J1 L R1 S1 W Z(d,l,t)
Agency and Advocacy undertaken
Ptr: Quigley, Mr Graham Robert LLB . . . . *Feb 1975
Ast: Scott, Mr Roger I LLB; MBA; ACIS . . . . *Jan 1980

CODSALL, Staffordshire

DBL TALBOTS LLP
2 Station Road Codsall Staffordshire WV8 1BX
Tel: 01902 843427 *Fax:* 01902 847424 *Dx:* 18037 CODSALL
E-mail: info@dbltalbots.co.uk
Office: Dudley (2 offices), Kidderminster, Stourbridge (2 offices), Wolverhampton
Work: C1 D1 D2 E F1 G H J1 K1 K3 K4 L N Q S1 S2 W
Emergency Action, Agency, Advocacy, Fixed Fee Interview and Legal Aid undertaken
Ptr: Jones, Ms Diane Elizabeth BA . . . . Jul 1994
Wetherall, Mr John BA . . . . *Dec 1975

COLCHESTER, Essex

ASHER PRIOR BATES ‡
(in association with Bates Travell and Bates HVH)
Blackburn House 32 Crouch Street Colchester Essex CO3 3HH
Tel: 01206 573089 *Fax:* 0870 054 3630 *Dx:* 3602 COLCHESTER
Emergency telephone 07770 305977
E-mail: buston@apblaw.co.uk
List of partners: R T D Buston
Work: A1 C1 C2 E L R1 R2 S1 S2 W Z(c,d,l)
SPr: Buston, Mr Roger T D TD LLB(Lond); FCMI; TEP Territorial Army Officer . . . . *Dec 1977

BIRKETT LONG LLP ‡
Essex House 42 Crouch Street Colchester Essex CO3 3HH
Tel: 01206 217300 *Fax:* 01206 572393 *Dx:* 3603 COLCHESTER
E-mail: mail@birkettlong.co.uk
List of partners: P C Allen, B R Ballard, J M Calnan, D J Cammack, T J Dickens, K W Goddard, P M Hoddell, M Hopkins, A W Livesley, S Loome, T Ogle, D Rayner, C L Z Read, J Ridley, K Songhurst, D J Wisbey, R M Wolny, D K Wybar
Office: Chelmsford
Work: A1 A2 A3 B1 C1 C2 C3 D1 D2 E F1 F2 I J1 J2 K1 K2 K3 K4 L M1 M2 N O P Q R1 R2 S1 S2 T1 T2 U1 U2 W X Z(c,d,e,f,g,h,i,j,k,l,m,o,p,q,r,t,u,z,za)
Emergency Action, Agency, Advocacy and Fixed Fee Interview undertaken
Ptr: Ballard, Mr Bruce Robert ATII; LSF Notary Public . . *Dec 1990
Calnan, Mrs Jane M LLM . . . . *Jan 1986
Cammack, Mr David James LLB(Hons) Notary Public . *Feb 1996
Dickens, Mrs Tracey Jane LLB(Hons); DipLP . . . . *Sep 1998
Goddard, Mr Kurt W LLB . . . . *Dec 1981
Hoddell, Mr Philip Michael BSc(Econ) . . . . *Oct 1989
Livesley, Mr Adrian W LLB . . . . *§Apr 1981
Loome, Mr Simon LLB(Hons)(Kingston) . . . . *Nov 1995
Ogle, Mr Timothy BSc; MA; ATT. . . . . *Oct 1996
Songhurst, Mr Keith LLB(Hons) . . . . *Sep 2001
Wybar, Mr David K MA . . . . *§Dec 1988
Asoc: Jones, Miss Elizabeth Mandy LLB; LSF ♦ . . . . *Oct 1992
Leate, Mrs Miranda Jane BA(Hons); MA. . . . *Sep 1995
Lloyd, Mr Reginald William LLM. . . . . Nov 2002
Loxley, Ms Melanie . . . . Sep 2002
Rosenthal, Mr Ronald H LLB . . . . *Mar 1980
Smallcombe, Ms Leonora Amanda Felicity LLB(Hons). *Nov 1998
Sullivan, Mr Kevin John LLB. . . . . Sep 1999
Yates, Miss Melaine LLB . . . . *Aug 2005
Ast: Brown, Miss Emily LLB(Hons); LPC . . . . Sep 2009
Bunting, Miss Laura Elizabeth. . . . . Sep 2010
Gibbs, Mr David. . . . . Sep 2005
Hogarth-Jones, Mr Bruce . . . . Dec 2004
Raynes, Ms Vicky. . . . . Sep 2007
Savage, Miss Annabelle BSc; CPE; LPC . . . . Sep 2008
Temperton, Mr David J . . . . *Jun 1986
Wrinch, Mr Mark Peter James PGDipLaw; LPC . . . . Oct 2008
Con: George, Mr Philip W MA(Cantab) . . . . *Apr 1975
Larkman, Mr Keith H TEP. . . . . *§Jul 1965

BRICE & CO ‡
3 Balkerne House Balkerne Passage Colchester Essex CO1 1PA
Tel: 01206 710168
E-mail: briceandco@hotmail.com

DENNIS BROWN SOLICITORS ‡
The Willows Westwood Hill Colchester Essex CO4 5BN
Tel: 01206 505060 *Fax:* 01206 505051
List of partners: D Brown
Work: G K1 L N O Q R1 Z(q)
Emergency Action, Agency, Advocacy, Legal Aid undertaken and Legal Aid Franchise
Ptr: Brown, Mr Dennis. . . . . *Jan 1998

SHARON COOMBER ‡
Holly Villa 15 Beverley Road Colchester Essex CO3 3NG
Tel: 01206 769342
Work: Z(m)
Emergency Action, Agency, Advocacy, Legal Aid undertaken and Legal Aid Franchise

CROWN LAW SOLICITORS ‡
12 Langham Barns Langham Lane Langham Colchester Essex CO4 5ZS
Tel: 01206 273499 *Fax:* 01206 272934
E-mail: info@crownlaw.co.uk

MARTIN ELLIOTT & CO ‡
Audley House Berechurch Hall Road Colchester Essex CO2 9NW
Tel: 01206 767112 *Fax:* 01206 769434
E-mail: info@martinelliott.com
List of partners: M G Elliott
Work: E S1 S2 W
SPr: Elliott, Mr Martin George LLB(Hons). . . . . *Aug 1982

ELLISONS ‡
Headgate Court Head Street Colchester Essex CO1 1NP
Tel: 01206 764477 *Fax:* 01206 764455 *Dx:* 3601 COLCHESTER
E-mail: enquiries@ellisonssolicitors.com
List of partners: L Bland, S J Clifford, N M Coates, S A M Connal, A C Holden, J P Hollington, R Jones, S C Lansley, K A List, T D Logan, G W Longhurst, A Miranda, L Pearce, C G Penfold, E Powell, P D Powell, J Scott, A R Tilsley, G Wallington, K R Wilsher
Office: Clacton-on-Sea, Frinton-on-Sea, Harwich
Work: A1 A2 A3 B1 C1 C2 C3 E F1 I J1 K2 K3 K4 L M1 N O Q R1 R2 S1 S2 T2 U2 W Z(c,d,f,h,j,l,p,q,t,u)
Emergency Action, Agency, Advocacy, Legal Aid undertaken and Legal Aid Franchise
Ptr: Bland, Miss Louise LLB . . . . *Sep 1999
Clifford, Mr Seamus J LLB(Law & Politics). . . . . Oct 1998
Coates, Mrs Nicola M LLB. . . . . *Apr 1991
Connal, Mr Stuart A M . . . . *Dec 1980
Hollington, Miss Jeanette P LLB; TEP. . . . . *May 1984
Lansley, Mr Stephen C . . . . *§Mar 1984
List, Mr Keith A LLB. . . . . *May 1977
Logan, Mr Timothy D BA(Hons) . . . . *Jun 1987
Longhurst, Mr Guy Wanham BSc . . . . *Sep 1997
Miranda, Mr Andrew LLB . . . . *Jan 1999
Penfold, Mr Charles G MA(Cantab) . . . . *§Jun 1976
Powell, Mr Edward LLB . . . . *Nov 1998
Powell, Mr Peter D . . . . *§Dec 1971
Scott, Mrs Jayne BA(Hons) . . . . *Oct 2000
Tilsley, Mr Andrew Robert LLB . . . . *Nov 1974
Wallington, Mr Graeme BA . . . . *Oct 1992
Wilsher, Mr Kevin R. . . . . *May 1979
Jones, Mr Robert . . . . NSP
Pearce, Mr Lee . . . . NSP
Asoc: Westbrook, Mrs Gina LLB(Hons) . . . . Jul 2004
Ast: Brice, Ms Harriet . . . . Sep 2010
Dawson, Mrs Lisa Jane LLB; LPC. . . . . Sep 2004
Forsyth, Mr Paul . . . . Jan 2009
Hunt, Mrs Kay LLB . . . . Nov 2002
McPhie, Mr Thomas LLB . . . . *Apr 1999
Roberts, Mr Philip. . . . . Sep 2006
Rogers, Ceri . . . . Sep 2007
Simpkins, Ms Natalie . . . . Sep 2010
Con: Baldwin, Mr Jeremy F BA(Bris) . . . . *Jul 1975
Beresford-Jones, Mr Nicholas Paul MA(Cantab). . . . *Jul 1991

FISHER JONES GREENWOOD LLP ‡
2nd Floor Norfolk House 23 Southway Colchester Essex CO2 7BA
Tel: 01206 578282 *Fax:* 01206 760282 *Dx:* 3600 COLCHESTER
E-mail: info@fjg.co.uk
List of partners: S L L Boyes, J H Burkett, A G Fisher, C J L Graves, N G Humphreys, C R V Jones, D E Jones, D L D Lawton, S J Osborn, P R Tawn, K L Taylor, C M Theeman, M R Welch, J M Wilson, C A M Yemm
Office: Chelmsford, Clacton-on-Sea, Colchester
Languages: French
Work: A1 A3 B1 C1 C2 D1 D2 E F1 F2 G H J1 J2 K1 K2 K3 L N O Q S1 S2 V W X Z(c,d,g,h,i,l,m,p,r)
Emergency Action, Agency, Advocacy, Fixed Fee Interview, Legal Aid undertaken, Legal Aid Franchise and Member of Accident Line
Ptr: Boyes, Miss Sonia L L LLB . . . . *Nov 1999
Burkett, Mr James Henry . . . . Sep 2002
Fisher, Mr Anthony G LLB. . . . . *Feb 1981
Graves, Mr Christopher John Lang MA(Cantab). . . . *Apr 1973
Humphreys, Mr Nigel Gordon LLB(Nott'm). . . . . *Dec 1979
Osborn, Mr Simon John. . . . . *Oct 1984
Tawn, Mr Paul Richard BA . . . . May 1989
Taylor, Mrs Kathryn L . . . . *Oct 1984
Theeman, Mr C Michael BA. . . . . *Aug 1988
Welch, Mr Matthew R LLB. . . . . *Aug 1981
Wilson, Ms Jane M LLB. . . . . *Feb 1987
Yemm, Mr Christopher Alan Michael BA(Nott'm). . . . *Jun 1976
Asoc: Graves, Ms Hannah Kelza BA(Hons) . . . . Jun 2006
Ast: Clark, Ms Alison. . . . . Apr 2005
Cooper, Ms Natasha . . . . Jan 2005
Craig, Mr Glenn. . . . . Apr 2005
Earnshaw, Ms Rachel Anne. . . . . Aug 2002
Frank, Ms Elizabeth LLB . . . . May 1993
Grimwade, Ms Susanne. . . . . Jul 2001
Hildrow, Mr Richard . . . . Aug 2005
Knappett, Ms Charlotte . . . . Feb 2005
Petersen, Mrs Ellen Lorraine Maria LLB(Hons) . . . . Sep 2001
Surgenor, Ms Simone LLB(Hons) . . . . Mar 2002

FISHER JONES GREENWOOD LLP
(in association with Legalex Cost Drafting)
Charter Court Newcomen Way Severalls Business Park Colchester Essex CO4 9YA
Tel: 01206 835300 *Fax:* 01206 835301 *Dx:* 3600 COLCHESTER
Emergency telephone 01206 578282
E-mail: info@fjg.co.uk
Office: Chelmsford, Clacton-on-Sea, Colchester
Languages: French
Work: A1 B1 C1 D1 E F1 G H J1 K1 L N O Q S1 W Z(g,h,l,m)
Emergency Action, Agency, Advocacy, Fixed Fee Interview, Legal Aid undertaken, Legal Aid Franchise and Member of Accident Line
Ptr: Jones, Mr David E LLB . . . . *Jul 1969

JOHN FOWLERS LLP SOLICITORS ‡
Town Hall Chambers St Runwald Street Colchester Essex CO1 1DS
Tel: 01206 576151 *Fax:* 01206 761916 *Dx:* 3605 COLCHESTER
Emergency telephone 01206 769342
E-mail: info@johnfowlers.co.uk
List of partners: C J Andrews, W E Cronshey, S Crosby, K N R Kennedy, K E Morovic, D L Root, N A Watts
Office: Brightlingsea
Work: B1 B2 C1 C2 C3 D1 E F1 G H J1 K1 K2 L M1 N O Q R1 S1 S2 V W Z(l,m,q)
Emergency Action, Agency, Advocacy, Fixed Fee Interview, Legal Aid undertaken, Legal Aid Franchise and Member of Accident Line
Ptr: Andrews, Mr Christopher James LLB; LLM . . . . *Jan 2008
Cronshey, Mrs Wendy Elizabeth LLB(Hons) Hill & Abbott Family Law Prize 2000 . . . . Aug 2007
Crosby, Mrs Sheila FILEx; LPC . . . . Dec 2007
Kennedy, Mr Kim N R BA . . . . *§May 1981
Morovic, Mrs Karen Elizabeth LLB. . . . . *Sep 2001
Root, Mr Derek L BA(Law) . . . . *Dec 1978
Watts, Mr Neil Andrew LLB . . . . NSP
Ast: Bradford, Mr Ian Clifford. . . . . *Dec 1988
Brennan, Mrs Marisa Dawn LLB. . . . . *Apr 2005
Chandraratna, Mrs S K Visaka LLB . . . . *Feb 2004
Dare, Ms Cheryl. . . . . *Oct 2010
O'Toole, Mr James LLB . . . . Jan 2006
Robinson, Mrs Marjorie Elaine LLB . . . . *Oct 1993
Welch, Mrs Louise Joanne LLB . . . . Nov 2009
Con: Coomber, Miss Sharon A BA(Hons). . . . . *Mar 1986

GEPP & SONS
56 North Hill Colchester Essex CO1 1PX
Tel: 01206 369889 *Fax:* 01206 369019 *Dx:* 3640 COLCHESTER
Emergency telephone 01245 358894
E-mail: mail@gepp.co.uk
Office: Chelmsford
Work: A1 B1 C1 D1 E F1 G H J1 K1 N O Q R1 S1 T1 T2 W Z(l)
Emergency Action, Advocacy and Legal Aid undertaken
Ptr: Ashford, Mr Neil G M MA(Cantab). . . . . *§Jun 1979
Brice, Mr Roger P J LLB(Wales). . . . . *§Dec 1978
Butterfield, Mr Peter LLB . . . . Sep 1997
Carter, Mr Daniel R . . . . *Dec 1990
Dean, Miss Alexandra L LLB(Hons) . . . . Aug 2000
Douglas-Hughes, Mr Jonathan P DL Under Sheriff; Clerk to the Commissioner of Taxes . . . . *§Dec 1969
Littlefield, Mr Peter G . . . . *Feb 1972
Moore, Ms Joanna LLB(Hons). . . . . *Feb 1994
Payne, Mr Steven P BA(Law) . . . . *Nov 1984
Stradling, Miss Louise S LLB . . . . *Sep 2000
Worthy, Mr Edward Malcolm LLB(Hons). . . . . Jan 1998
Young, Mrs Hannah Marie Antoinette BCL. . . . . Oct 1994
Asoc: Buttress, Ms Claire LLB . . . . Oct 2003
Emerson, Mr Justin R LLB . . . . Oct 1999
Ast: Abu Bakar, Mr Muhammad Shah LLM. . . . . *Aug 2006
Bradshaw, Miss Elizabeth Jane BA . . . . Aug 2005
Carver, Mrs Lincey Indira LLB. . . . . Oct 2008
Davenport, Mrs Emma LLB(Hons). . . . . *Jan 2002
Insley, Mr Jonathan David. . . . . Dec 2007
Nair, Miss Natasha LLB(Hons) . . . . May 2006
Plomp, Miss Hendrika LLB(Hons) . . . . §Mar 2005
Pumfrey, Mrs Joanne LLB; LLM. . . . . Nov 2004

GOODYBURRETT LLP ‡
St Martins House 63 West Stockwell Street Colchester Essex CO1 1HE
Tel: 01206 577676 *Fax:* 01206 548704 *Dx:* 3663 COLCHESTER
E-mail: law@goodyburrett.co.uk
List of partners: D J Brown, M G Hammett, D F Howe, B C Johnston
Work: A1 A3 B1 C1 C2 E F1 F2 G H J1 K1 K2 K3 K4 L N O Q R1 S1 S2 T1 W Z(d,i,n,p,q,r)
Emergency Action, Agency, Advocacy, Fixed Fee Interview and Legal Aid undertaken
Ptr: Brown, Mr David J LLB(Lond) . . . . *§Jun 1972
Hammett, Mr Myles G MA(Cantab) . . . . *§Jul 1979
Howe, Mr Donald F LLB(Hons) . . . . *Oct 2001
Johnston, Mr Bryan Campbell. . . . . *§Jun 1995
Asoc: Howe, Mr Donald F LLB(Hons) . . . . *Oct 2001
Money, Miss Sarah Jane LLB(Hons). . . . . *Nov 1999
Morgan, Miss Catherine Maria LLB(Hons). . . . . Sep 2004
Morley, Miss Anna Christine LLB . . . . Apr 2007
Sadler, Miss Lauren LLB(Hons) . . . . Oct 2001

H & S LEGAL ‡
Suite 208 The Business Centre Wellington House Colchester Essex CO3 3DA
Tel: 01206 500181 / 020 7096 9060 *Fax:* 01206 710200
E-mail: info@hs-legal.co.uk

DAVID MORGAN JONES ‡
49 North Hill Colchester Essex CO1 1PY
Tel: 01206 766749 *Fax:* 01206 765104 *Dx:* 3684 COLCHESTER
E-mail: david.m.jones@btconnect.com
List of partners: D M Jones
Work: C1 C2 E I N O Q S1 S2 W
Ptr: Jones, Mr David M . . . . *Oct 1968

KEW LAW LLP ‡
55 North Hill Colchester Essex CO1 1PX
Tel: 01206 564546 *Fax:* 01206 560793
E-mail: info@kewlaw.co.uk

MATHER & CO ‡
Hill House Grove Hill Langham Colchester Essex CO4 5PJ
Tel: 01206 322763 *Fax:* 01206 322895
E-mail: gillmather@aol.com
List of partners: G Mather
Work: E K1 L S1 S2 W
Ptr: Mather, Mrs Gillian . . . . *Jan 1979

OBW PERERA ‡
21-23 Head Street Colchester Essex CO1 1NH
Tel: 01206 541111 *Fax:* 01206 540660 *Dx:* 3614 COLCHESTER
Emergency telephone 07795 217638
E-mail: enquiries@obwperera.co.uk
List of partners: P Baker, L M Osborn, A Perera, C A Woodley
Dir: Baker, Mr Paul BA(Hons) . . . . Oct 1990
Osborn, Miss Lucy Margaret LLB(Hons). . . . . Sep 1996
Perera, Anna . . . . Jan 1981
Woodley, Miss Caroline A LLB . . . . *Sep 1997
Asoc: Swash, Mr Matthew LLB(Hons) . . . . *Feb 2004

PLEASS THOMSON & CO
1 Laysmith Avenue Brightlingsea Colchester Essex CO7 0JB
Tel: 01206 307454 *Fax:* 01206 308991
E-mail: solicitors@pleassthomson.co.uk
Office: Clacton-on-Sea

PLEXUS LAW (A TRADING NAME OF PARABIS LAW LLP)
886 The Crescent Colchester Business Park Colchester Essex CO4 9YQ
Tel: 0844 245 4950 *Dx:* 154140 COLCHESTER 17
Office: Croydon, Evesham, Leeds, London EC2, London EC3, Manchester (2 offices)
Ptr: Edwards, Mr Darshan J D LLB(Hons) . . . *Nov 1992
Francis, Mr Timothy Needham BA(Hons) . . . Oct 1994
Gaston, Mr Keith R LLB(Hons) . . . Nov 1988
Whybrew, Mr Richard BA(Hons); CPE; LSP . . . Oct 1993
Asoc: Tilling, Mr Simon . . . Jul 2001
Ast: Thomas, Ms Helen . . . Jan 2000

SPARLING BENHAM & BROUGH ‡
3 West Stockwell Street Colchester Essex CO1 1HQ
Tel: 01206 733733 *Fax:* 01206 564551 *Dx:* 3607 COLCHESTER
E-mail: sjm@sparlings.co.uk
List of partners: R O Bartholomew, M R Carr, P M Connolly, R J Ennals, J B Juby, L W F North, I G Richardson, L M Stansfield
Office: Frinton-on-Sea
Work: A1 C1 D1 D2 E F1 J1 K1 K2 K3 K4 L N O Q R1 S1 S2 T1 T2 W Z(c,d,h,j,l,q)
Emergency Action, Agency, Advocacy, Fixed Fee Interview, Legal Aid undertaken and Legal Aid Franchise
Ptr: Bartholomew, Mr Robert O . . . *§Dec 1977
Carr, Mr Martyn R LLB . . . *§Oct 1982
Connolly, Mr Paul M LLB . . . Oct 1988
Ennals, Mr Roger J LLB(Lond) . . . *§Nov 1972
North, Mr Lloyd W F LLB ♦ . . . *Oct 1989
Richardson, Mr Ian G LLB . . . *Sep 1994
Stansfield, Miss Linda M BA(Law) . . . *Apr 1980
Ast: Golding, Mrs Katherine A MA; BA . . . *Oct 1992
Gomm, Mr James Alexander BSc . . . *Jan 2004

THOMPSON SMITH & PUXON ‡
4 North Hill Colchester Essex CO1 1EB
Tel: 01206 574431 *Fax:* 01206 563174 *Dx:* 3617 COLCHESTER
E-mail: info@tsplegal.com
List of partners: M W H Cooksley, M A Fedeyko, R S Porter, M J S Price, S J Webb, J G Wilson, M G Wilson
Office: Clacton-on-Sea
Languages: French
Work: A1 B1 C1 C2 C3 D1 E F1 F2 J1 K1 K3 K4 M1 N O P Q R1 S1 S2 T1 T2 V W Z(b,c,d,k,l,q,r)
Emergency Action, Agency, Advocacy, Fixed Fee Interview, Legal Aid undertaken, Legal Aid Franchise and Member of Accident Line
Ptr: Cooksley, Mr Mark W H BA(Lond) Deputy District Judge; Council Member and Former President of the Suffolk & North Essex Law Society . . . *Jul 1979
Fedeyko, Ms Mary Anne LLB Dean Ivan Rand Award; Malcolm J McKinnon Award . . . *§Jan 1989
Price, Mr Marcus J S LLB(Nott'm) . . . *§Nov 1981
Webb, Mr Steven John LLB(Leeds) . . . *§Oct 1990
Wilson, Mr Julian G LLB(Cantab) . . . *§Dec 1981
Wilson, Mr M Graham BA(Dunelm) Deputy District Judge . . . *§Dec 1977
Ast: Cantor, Mrs Alison J BA(Hons) . . . Oct 1982
Davies, Ms Amanda C LLB . . . Nov 1993
Sheeran, Ms Clare Frances BA . . . *Sep 2001
Wicks, Miss Kathryn Margaret BA(Hons)(Combined Studies); LLM . . . Apr 2005
Con: Welham, Mr David S BA(Lond) . . . Dec 1977

WERENOWSKI SOLICITORS ‡
9 East Stockwell Street Colchester Essex CO1 1SS
Tel: 01206 367907 *Fax:* 01206 367911
E-mail: lsw@werenowski.com
List of partners: L S Werenowski
SPr: Werenowski, Mr Leszek S LLM . . . *Apr 1990

WILLIAMS SOLICITORS ‡
Burnt Oak Corner Oak Cottage Colchester Essex CO7 6TJ
Tel: 01206 584320 / 298877 *Fax:* 0560 0757 036
E-mail: williams@bizlegal.biz

COLEFORD, Gloucestershire

GWYN JAMES SOLICITORS ‡
11 High Street Coleford Gloucestershire GL16 8HE
Tel: 01594 833042 *Fax:* 01594 836104 *Dx:* 94103 COLEFORD
E-mail: coleford@gwynjames.co.uk
List of partners: D F Feltham, J P Wilkey
Office: Cinderford
Work: A1 D1 J1 K1 K3 K4 S1 S2 T2 W Z(k,l,m)
Agency, Fixed Fee Interview, Legal Aid undertaken and Member of Accident Line
Ptr: Feltham, Mrs Deborah Frances BA(Hons) . . . *Oct 1995

JAMES WARRY & CO ‡
4 High Street Coleford Gloucestershire GL16 8HF
Tel: 01594 833184 *Fax:* 01594 837353 *Dx:* 94100 COLEFORD
List of partners: J R Warry
Work: K3 S1 S2 W
Fixed Fee Interview undertaken
Ptr: Warry, Mr James R LLB . . . *§Jul 1979
Ast: Duberley, Miss Helen E LLB . . . *Nov 1991

COLESHILL, Warwickshire

TOWNSHENDS LLP ‡
Clinton House High Street Coleshill Warwickshire B46 3BP
Tel: 01675 467333 *Fax:* 01675 467373 *Dx:* 15051 COLESHILL
List of partners: N J Ireland, P D Townshend
Office: Birmingham, Coventry
Work: B1 B2 C1 C2 E G J1 K1 L N O Q R2 S1 S2 W Z(d,k,l,p,q)
Agency and Advocacy undertaken
Ptr: Ireland, Mr Neil John LLB(Hons) ● . . . *Oct 1994
Townshend, Mr Philip D LLB(Hons) . . . *Oct 1997
Con: Christensen, Mrs Carolyn F LLB(B'ham); TEP Notary Public . . . *Jul 1971

COLNE, Lancashire

CLIFFORD SMITH & BUCHANAN
1 Market Street Colne Lancashire BB8 0LJ
Tel: 01282 860606 *Fax:* 01282 860818
E-mail: rachel@cs-b.co.uk
Office: Burnley, Nelson
Work: S1 S2 W
Ptr: Buchanan, Mr Ian Alexander . . . *Jan 1968
Ast: Buchanan, Mr David Alexander BA; MA; GDL . . . Aug 2008

DONALD RACE & NEWTON (incorporating Bracewell & Dyson)
59 Albert Road Colne Lancashire BB8 0BX
Tel: 01282 864500 *Fax:* 01282 869579 *Dx:* 18203 COLNE
Emergency telephone 07788 555212
E-mail: info@drnlaw.co.uk
Office: Burnley (2 offices)
Work: A1 B1 D1 E F1 G H J1 K1 L N P Q R1 S1 V W Z(e,i)
Emergency Action, Agency, Advocacy, Fixed Fee Interview, Legal Aid undertaken, Legal Aid Franchise and Member of Accident Line
Ptr: Reynolds, Mr Peter J LLB Deputy District Judge . . . *Dec 1978
Ast: Barnes, Miss Louise LLB(Hons) . . . *Apr 2005
Barrowclough, Miss Jean . . . *Nov 1986

FARNWORTH SHAW ‡
65 Albert Road Colne Lancashire BB8 0BZ
Tel: 01282 865885 *Fax:* 01282 868677 *Dx:* 18207 COLNE
E-mail: enquiries@farnworthshaw.co.uk
List of partners: A W Berry, P Bolton, E Ennis, A J Payne
Office: Colne, Nelson
Work: A1 B1 C1 C2 D1 E F1 G H J1 K1 K3 K4 L N O P Q S1 S2 T1 T2 V W Z(c,i,k,l,q)
Agency and Advocacy undertaken
Ptr: Payne, Mr Andrew J BA(Oxon) . . . Oct 1988
Ast: Dakin, Miss Katharine . . . Jul 2005
Newberry, Miss Angela Claire . . . Apr 2003
Palmer, Lauren . . . Apr 2009

FARNWORTH SHAW
50 Albert Road Colne Lancashire BB8 0AW
Tel: 01282 864081 *Fax:* 01282 861339 *Dx:* 18204 COLNE
E-mail: enquiries@farnworthshaw.co.uk
Office: Colne, Nelson
Languages: French, Italian
Work: A1 B1 C1 C2 D1 E F1 G H J1 K1 K3 K4 L N O P Q S1 S2 T1 T2 V W Z(c,i,k,l,q)
Emergency Action, Agency, Advocacy, Fixed Fee Interview, Legal Aid undertaken, Legal Aid Franchise and Member of Accident Line
Ptr: Bolton, Mr Peter LLB . . . *May 1975

NGA
32 Albert Road Colne Lancashire BB8 0AL
Tel: 01282 862000 *Fax:* 01282 869884 *Dx:* 18202 COLNE
Emergency telephone 01282 450144
E-mail: enquiries@ngasolicitors.co.uk
Office: Burnley (2 offices)
Work: B1 D1 E G H J1 K1 L S1 V W Z(l)
Emergency Action, Agency, Advocacy, Fixed Fee Interview, Legal Aid undertaken and Member of Accident Line
Ptr: Brown, Mr Stephen . . . *Dec 1976
Campbell, Mr Neil John LLB . . . *Jan 1984

SOUTHERNS
73 Albert Road Colne Lancashire BB8 0BP
Tel: 01282 863113 *Fax:* 01282 857727 *Dx:* 18206 COLNE
E-mail: albertroad@southernslaw.info
Office: Burnley (2 offices), Nelson
Work: E G H K1 L S1 S2 W
Emergency Action, Agency, Advocacy, Fixed Fee Interview, Legal Aid undertaken, Legal Aid Franchise and Member of Accident Line
Ptr: Morgan, Miss Kirsten LLB . . . *Jul 1999
Ast: Jackson, Mr Steven A LLB . . . *§Sep 2000
Nightingale, Mr Duncan S LLB . . . *Jun 1991

STEELE & SON ‡
28 Albert Road Colne Lancashire BB8 0AB
Tel: 01282 868000 *Fax:* 01282 868314 *Dx:* 18201 COLNE
E-mail: info@steeleandson.com
List of partners: G M Smith
Languages: French
Work: A1 C1 D1 E F1 G H J1 K1 K3 L N P Q R1 S1 T1 V W Z(c,l)
Emergency Action, Agency, Advocacy, Fixed Fee Interview, Legal Aid undertaken, Legal Aid Franchise and Member of Accident Line
Ptr: Smith, Mr Glen M . . . *Sep 1982
Con: Campbell, Mr Neil John LLB . . . *Jan 1984

COLWYN BAY, Conwy

AMPHLETTS ‡
49 Conway Road Colwyn Bay Conwy LL29 7AN
Tel: 01492 532296 *Fax:* 01492 534505 *Dx:* 17905 COLWYN BAY
E-mail: administrator@amphlettslegal.co.uk
List of partners: G A Edmondson, C J Hind
Languages: Welsh
Work: B1 C1 D1 D2 E F1 J1 K1 K2 K3 K4 L N O Q S1 S2 W Z(h,q)
Emergency Action, Agency, Advocacy, Fixed Fee Interview, Legal Aid undertaken and Legal Aid Franchise
Ptr: Edmondson, Mr Gareth A LLB(Wales) . . . *Dec 1987
Hind, Mr Christopher J BA . . . *Dec 1979

BONE & PAYNE LLP
13 Wynnstay Road Colwyn Bay Conwy LL29 8NB
Tel: 01492 532385 *Fax:* 01492 539879 *Dx:* 17902 COLWYN BAY
E-mail: enquiries@boneandpayne-cb.co.uk
Office: Llandudno, Old Colwyn
Languages: Welsh
Work: A1 D1 E G H J1 K1 L N O Q S1 S2 W Z(l)
Agency, Advocacy, Fixed Fee Interview, Legal Aid undertaken and Member of Accident Line
Mem: Davies, Mr Gareth H LLB . . . *Nov 1984
Asoc: Corry, Miss Karen LLB(Hons) . . . Aug 1996
Sethi, Mr Sunil LLB . . . Sep 1986
Ast: Dutton, Ms Claire Elizabeth LLB . . . Dec 2004
Con: Marston, Mr John W LLB . . . *Dec 1976

GAMLINS (incorporating Gamlin Kelly & Beattie G D Armitage Bate & Co)
4 Wynnstay Road Colwyn Bay Conwy LL29 8NB
Tel: 01492 532275 *Fax:* 01492 533119 *Dx:* 17903 COLWYN BAY
E-mail: colwynbay@gamlins.com
Office: Bangor, Colwyn Bay, Conwy, Holywell, Llandudno, Rhyl
Work: D1 E G K1 L N P S1 W
Emergency Action, Agency, Advocacy, Fixed Fee Interview and Legal Aid undertaken
Ptr: Oliver, Mr Vernon LLB . . . *Feb 1992
Ast: Jones, Mr Owain D LLB . . . Mar 1991

GAMLINS
13 Everard Road Rhos on Sea Colwyn Bay Conwy LL28 4EU
Tel: 01492 547156 *Fax:* 01492 543266 *Dx:* 17903 COLWYN BAY
E-mail: rhosonsea@gamlins.com
Office: Bangor, Colwyn Bay, Conwy, Holywell, Llandudno, Rhyl

EDWARD HUGHES ‡
30 Wynnstay Road Colwyn Bay Conwy LL29 8NB
Tel: 01492 535640 *Fax:* 01492 531792

HUMPHRYS & CO (incorporating Dawsons)
65 Abegele Road Colwyn Bay Conwy LL29 7RU
Tel: 01492 532255 *Fax:* 01492 530107 *Dx:* 17913 COLWYN BAY
Office: Rhyl, Wrexham

OSBORNS ‡
19 Wynnstay Road Colwyn Bay Conwy LL29 8NB
Tel: 01492 532056 / 532820 *Fax:* 01492 530134
Dx: 17907 COLWYN BAY
E-mail: osbornslegal@btconnect.com
List of partners: M Eames-Hughes, D H Twine
Work: B2 C1 D1 E F1 F2 G H J1 J2 K1 L N P Q R1 S1 S2 T2 V W X Z(g,l,u,w,y)
Fixed Fee Interview undertaken
Ptr: Eames-Hughes, Maxen LLB . . . *Jul 1976
Twine, Mr D Howard LLB(L'pool) . . . *Nov 1971

GLYN OWEN & CO ‡
25 Princes Drive Colwyn Bay Conwy LL29 8HT
Tel: 01492 532649 *Fax:* 01492 533114 *Dx:* 17900 COLWYN BAY
E-mail: glynowen@btconnect.com
List of partners: M Evans, G Owen
Office: Abergele
Languages: Welsh
Work: A1 E F1 J1 K1 L M1 P S1 S2 V W Z(l)
Agency, Advocacy and Fixed Fee Interview undertaken
Ptr: Evans, Mrs Maureen . . . *Mar 1980
Owen, Mr Glyn . . . *§Jan 1962

CONGLETON, Cheshire

BIRCHALL RYAN SOLICITORS ‡
23-25 West Street Congleton Cheshire CW12 1JN
Tel: 01260 297070 *Fax:* 01260 297977
E-mail: reception@birchallryan.com
List of partners: A W Birchall
Office: Crewe
Ptr: Birchall, Mr Anthony W LLB(Hons) . . . *Jun 1981
Ast: Derbyshire, Mr Anthony LLB(Hons); DipLP . . . *Sep 1996

POOLE ALCOCK
7 Moody Street Congleton Cheshire CW12 4AN
Tel: 01260 275337 *Fax:* 01260 299157 *Dx:* 20285 CONGLETON
E-mail: congleton@poolealcock.co.uk
Office: Alsager, Chester, Crewe (2 offices), Nantwich, Northwich, Sandbach, Warrington
Work: A1 B1 C1 D1 E F1 G J1 K1 L M1 N P R1 S1 T1 V W
Emergency Action, Agency, Advocacy, Fixed Fee Interview and Legal Aid undertaken
Ptr: Boston, Mr Peter LLB . . . *Nov 1975

S J POWELL & CO ‡
Sunnyside Mill Highfield Road Congleton Cheshire CW12 3AQ
Tel: 01206 292592 *Fax:* 01260 292582
E-mail: simon@sjpowell.co.uk
List of partners: S J Powell
Work: E L N R2 S1 S2 W
SPr: Powell, Mr Simon J BA(Hons) . . . *Mar 1984

SAS DANIELS LLP
8-10 West Street Congleton Cheshire CW12 1JS
Tel: 01260 282300 *Fax:* 01260 274243
E-mail: help@sasdaniels.co.uk
Office: Bramhall, Chester, Macclesfield, Stockport
Work: A1 B1 C1 C2 C3 D1 E F1 J1 K1 K3 K4 L N P R1 S1 T1 T2 V W Z(b,c,e,k,l,m,o,p,s)
Emergency Action, Agency, Advocacy, Fixed Fee Interview, Legal Aid undertaken, Legal Aid Franchise and Member of Accident Line
Ptr: Ridings, Mr Martin David LLB ♦ . . . Mar 1998
Simpson, Mrs Rebecca LLB(Hons) ♦ . . . Sep 1997
Ast: Palmer, Miss Lindsey . . . Aug 2004
Con: Cope, Mr Robert I LLB(L'pool) ♦ . . . Mar 1972

WAINS
28 West Street Congleton Cheshire CW12 1JR
Tel: 01260 279414 *Fax:* 01260 299573 *Dx:* 20259 CONGLETON 1
E-mail: lb@wainssolicitors.co.uk
Office: Macclesfield
Work: A1 D1 E G H K1 K3 L Q S1 S2 W Z(l)
Agency, Advocacy, Fixed Fee Interview, Legal Aid undertaken and Legal Aid Franchise
Ptr: Gough, Mr Roger E N . . . *§Aug 1979

CONGRESBURY, North Somerset

LAURENCE HOLMES SOLICITORS ‡
The Elms Farm Brinsea Road Congresbury North Somerset BS49 5JL
Tel: 01934 838445 *Fax:* 01934 838166
E-mail: email@laurenceholmes.co.uk
List of partners: L Holmes
Work: K1 N W
SPr: Holmes, Mr Laurence . . . *Dec 1993

See p112 for the Key to Work Categories & other symbols

2

CONINGSBY, Lincolnshire

SILLS & BETTERIDGE LLP
45 Silver Street Coningsby Lincolnshire LN4 4SG
Tel: 01526 344444 *Fax:* 01526 345555
E-mail: info@sillslegal.co.uk
Web: www.sillslegal.co.uk
Office: Boston, Gainsborough, Lincoln, Skegness, Sleaford, Spalding, Spilsby
Work: A1 A2 B1 B2 C1 C2 C3 D1 D2 E F1 F2 G H I J1 J2 K1 K2 K3 K4 L N O P Q R1 R2 S1 S2 T1 T2 U2 V W Z(b,c,d,e,g,h,i,k,l,m,o,p,q,r,s,t,u,w,za)
Emergency Action, Agency, Advocacy, Fixed Fee Interview, Legal Aid undertaken, Legal Aid Franchise and Member of Accident Line
Ptr: Stapleton, Mr David P. . . . . *Aug 2000

CONNAH'S QUAY, Flintshire

CROSS SOLICITORS ‡
New Cross House 2 High Street Connah's Quay Flintshire CH5 4DA
Tel: 01244 822101 *Fax:* 01244 822104 *Dx:* 22781 CONNAHS QUAY
E-mail: bgc@cross-solicitors.co.uk
List of partners: B G Cross, S M Hollywood
Work: A1 B1 C1 C2 C3 D1 E F1 G H J1 K1 L M1 M2 N P R1 S1 T1 T2 V W
Agency, Advocacy, Fixed Fee Interview, Legal Aid undertaken and Legal Aid Franchise
Ptr: Cross, Mr Brian Garry LLB . . . . . *Jul 1976
Hollywood, Ms Susan Marie. . . . . Nov 2001

CONSETT, Co Durham

BENNETT RICHMOND
33 Front Street Consett Co Durham DH8 5AB
Tel: 01207 504141 *Fax:* 01207 580408 *Dx:* 61932 CONSETT
E-mail: info@bennett-richmond.co.uk
Office: Lanchester

CKM SOLICITORS
82 Medomsley Road Consett Co Durham DH8 5HS
Tel: 01207 509020 *Fax:* 01207 590595 *Dx:* 61937 CONSETT
E-mail: consett.office@ckm-solicitors.co.uk
Office: Durham

ROBERT GALLACHER SOLITICORS ‡
21 Hope Street Blackhill Consett Co Durham DH8 5TS
Tel: 01207 581143
Work: S1

GILES HUNTER PARTNERSHIP ‡
16 Victoria Road Consett Co Durham DH8 5BQ
Tel: 01207 590285 *Fax:* 01207 581647
E-mail: info@ghplaw.co.uk

MASKERY & CO ‡
63a Medomsley Road Consett Co Durham DH8 5HQ
Tel: 01207 588300 *Fax:* 01207 588301

ROW & SCOTT
4 Church Street Consett Co Durham DH8 5QA
Tel: 01207 591810 *Fax:* 01207 508642 *Dx:* 61942 CONSETT
Emergency telephone 01207 591810
E-mail: rowandscott@btconnect.com
Office: Morpeth, Newcastle upon Tyne
Emergency Action, Agency, Advocacy, Fixed Fee Interview, Legal Aid undertaken and Member of Accident Line
Ptr: Row, Mr Barry T BA. . . . . *Jul 1978
Scott, Mr J Richard . . . . . Dec 1978

SWINBURNE SNOWBALL & JACKSON ‡
2 Edith Street Consett Co Durham DH8 5DW
Tel: 01207 502532 *Fax:* 01207 503385 *Dx:* 61930 CONSETT
E-mail: info@ssj-solicitors.com
List of partners: J Cowie, V J Dobbie, J A Flynn
Work: A1 B1 C1 D1 E F1 G H J1 K1 K3 K4 L N O P Q R1 S1 S2 V W Z(h,k,l,p,q,u)
Emergency Action, Agency, Advocacy, Legal Aid undertaken and Legal Aid Franchise
Ptr: Cowie, Miss Joanne LLB(Hons) Notary Public. . . . . *Jul 1991
Dobbie, Ms Verity J LLB. . . . . *Jan 1985
Flynn, Mr John A LLB. . . . . *§Jun 1973
Ast: Flynn, Mrs Jennifer MBE; DL LLB Liverpool Law Society Prize . . . . . *Jul 1975

CONWY

BARRIGA MCDONALD SOLICITORS ‡
45 St George Crescent Wrexham Conwy LL13 8DB
Tel: 01978 358157 *Fax:* 01978 361827

ALLAN L BAYLISS ‡
Erw Ty Horeb Hope Mountain Conwy LL12 9HE
Tel: 01978 761595
E-mail: erwty@ukonline.co.uk

JOHN BELLIS & CO
Compton House Station Road Conwy LL33 0AL
Tel: 01248 680527 *Fax:* 01248 681443 *Dx:* 22417 PENMAENMAWR
Office: Penmaenmawr
Languages: French, German
Work: D1 D2 E F1 G H J1 K1 K2 K3 L N Q S1 S2 V W X Z(l)
Emergency Action, Agency, Advocacy, Fixed Fee Interview and Legal Aid undertaken

GAMLINS
(incorporating Porter & Co)
Bank Building Castle Street Conwy LL32 8AU
Tel: 01492 593201 *Fax:* 01492 593202 *Dx:* 24629 CONWY
E-mail: conwy@gamlins.co.uk
Office: Bangor, Colwyn Bay (2 offices), Holywell, Llandudno, Rhyl
Languages: Welsh
Work: A1 B1 C1 C2 C3 D1 E F1 G H J1 K1 L M1 M2 N P R1 S1 T1 T2 V W Z(i,k,l)
Emergency Action, Agency, Advocacy, Fixed Fee Interview, Legal Aid undertaken and Legal Aid Franchise
Ptr: Ranson, Mr Francis Newman Charles LLB Clerk to Commissioner of Taxes. . . . . *§Oct 1970
Salisbury, Mr Mark P LLB. . . . . *Oct 1981

J W HUGHES & CO ‡
Lancaster Square Conwy LL32 8AD
Tel: 01492 596596 *Fax:* 01492 592587 *Dx:* 24627 CONWY
E-mail: mailroom@jwhugheslaw.co.uk
List of partners: P B Kentish, J G Parry, N R J Passey, D C Roberts, A W Thomas, P J Watters
Office: Llandudno
Languages: French, Welsh
Work: A1 B1 B2 C1 D1 E F1 G H J1 K1 K2 K3 L N O Q R1 S1 S2 V W Z(c,d,k,m)
Emergency Action, Agency, Advocacy, Fixed Fee Interview, Legal Aid undertaken, Legal Aid Franchise and Member of Accident Line
Ptr: Parry, Mr John G BSc(Econ) . . . . . Dec 1987
Passey, Mr Nicholas R J BA. . . . . *Feb 1986
Roberts, Mr Donald C LLB(Wales). . . . . *§Jun 1976
Thomas, Mr Alun W LLB . . . . . *Jul 1980
Ast: Brown, Mr Peter BA(Hons) • . . . . . *Sep 1995
Sargent, Mr Simon . . . . . *Jun 1998

CORBRIDGE, Northumberland

SAVAGES ‡
(in association with Joyce & Co)
Robson House 4 Middle Street Corbridge Northumberland NE45 5AT
Tel: 01434 632505 *Fax:* 01434 633220 *Dx:* 69251 CORBRIDGE
E-mail: corbridge@savages-solicitors.co.uk
List of partners: E P Savage, R L Savage
Work: A1 B1 C1 C2 E F1 J1 L N O Q S1 W Z(c,e,j,k,l,m)
Emergency Action, Agency and Advocacy undertaken
Ptr: Savage, Mrs Eileen Patricia BA(Hons). . . . . *Nov 1980
Savage, Mr Richard Latham BA(Hons) . . . . . *Apr 1981
Ast: Crowder, Mr Peter. . . . . *Dec 1974

CORBY, Northamptonshire

ADAMS MOORE FAMILY LAW
34 Elizabeth Street Corby Northamptonshire NN17 1PN
Tel: 01536 201600
Office: Bedford, Bletchley, Daventry, Luton, Milton Keynes, Northampton

LAMB & HOLMES
Uppingham House Headway Business Park 5 Saxon Way West Corby Northamptonshire NN18 9EZ
Tel: 01536 745168 *Fax:* 01536 746603 *Dx:* 12902 CORBY
E-mail: law@lamb-holmes.co.uk
Office: Kettering
Work: A1 A3 B1 C1 D1 E F1 F2 I J1 J2 K1 K2 K3 L N O Q R1 R2 S1 S2 W Z(c,d,l,p,q,r,t)
Agency, Advocacy, Fixed Fee Interview, Legal Aid Franchise and Member of Accident Line
Ptr: Davies, Mr James N W BA . . . . . *Feb 1983
Ast: Routen, Mrs Julia C LLB . . . . . *Oct 1984
Staite, Miss Zoe LLB(Hons); BVC . . . . . Nov 2010

M D T LAW ‡
7 High Street Weldon Corby Northamptonshire NN17 3JJ
Tel: 01536 400038 *Fax:* 01536 400039
E-mail: mdtlaw@btconnect.com

R J OSBORNE & CO ‡
82 George Street Corby Northamptonshire NN17 1QE
Tel: 01536 204111 *Fax:* 01536 402115 *Dx:* 12903 CORBY
Emergency telephone 01536 266981
E-mail: mail@rjo-corby.co.uk
List of partners: V A Blow, B Bushell, A Gibson
Office: Northampton, Wellingborough
Work: G H
Emergency Action, Agency, Advocacy, Fixed Fee Interview and Legal Aid undertaken
Ptr: Blow, Miss Valerie A LLB . . . . . *Aug 1976
Bushell, Mr Brian BA . . . . . Mar 1981

SCUTT BEAUMONT SOLICITORS LTD
5 Manitoba Close Corby Northamptonshire NN18 9HX
Tel: 01536 744847 *Fax:* 0116 254 5511 *Dx:* 17016 LEICESTER 2
E-mail: info@sbs-solicitors.co.uk
Office: Ashby-de-la-Zouch, Leicester

SEATONS SOLICITORS ‡
1 Alexandra Road Corby Northamptonshire NN17 1PE
Tel: 01536 276300 *Fax:* 01536 276333 *Dx:* 12910 CORBY
E-mail: info@seatons.co.uk
List of partners: A P Chambers, P W Seaton
Office: Kettering (2 offices)
Work: E F1 G H J1 K1 L N Q S1 S2 W Z(r)
Agency, Advocacy, Fixed Fee Interview, Legal Aid undertaken and Member of Accident Line
Ptr: Chambers, Mr Adrian P LLB(Hons) . . . . . *§Dec 1988
Seaton, Mr Paul W BA(Hons) . . . . . *§Dec 1979
Ast: Chan, Miss Sarah M FILEx; PGDipLaw . . . . . *Nov 1998

TOLLERS LLP
2 Exchange Court Cottingham Road Corby Northamptonshire NN17 1TY
Tel: 01536 276727 *Fax:* 01536 276700 *Dx:* 12901 CORBY
E-mail: enquiries@tollers.co.uk
Office: Kettering, Milton Keynes, Northampton
Ast: Benson, Mr Tristan . . . . . Feb 2008

CORRINGHAM, Thurrock

PENMANS
83a St Johns Way Corringham Thurrock SS17 7LL
Tel: 01375 673968 *Fax:* 01375 361811
Dx: 34603 STANFORD-LE-HOPE
E-mail: l.carver@penmanslaw.co.uk
Office: Stanford-le-Hope
Work: C1 C2 E K1 L Q R1 S1 V W Z(l)
Agency and Legal Aid undertaken
Ptr: Buggle, Mr Gerard Joseph LLB(Hons). . . . . *Jun 1978

CORSHAM, Wiltshire

GOUGHS
23 Pickwick Road Corsham Wiltshire SN13 9BH
Tel: 01249 712193 *Fax:* 01249 716274 *Dx:* 47352 CORSHAM
E-mail: info@goughs.co.uk
Office: Calne, Chippenham, Devizes, Melksham, Trowbridge
Work: A1 C1 E K1 R1 S1 S2 W Z(c)
Fixed Fee Interview and Legal Aid Franchise
Ptr: Drew, Mr Matthew BA(Hons) . . . . . *Mar 1994
Lang, Mr Martin C BA; CMA. . . . . Oct 1980
Ast: Given, Mr Andrew. . . . . Sep 2007
Heley, Miss Beth Sarah LLB(Cardiff); LPC(UWE) . . . Sep 2009

COTTINGHAM, East Riding of Yorkshire

DANBY & CO ‡
5a High Street Cottingham East Riding of Yorkshire LE16 8XL
Tel: 01536 771110 *Fax:* 01536 771110

GWENDOLINE DRURY ‡
The Studio 14/16 George Street Cottingham East Riding of Yorkshire HU16 5PQ
Tel: 01482 840201 *Fax:* 01482 844647
List of partners: G Drury
Work: S1 S2 W
SPr: Drury, Mrs Gwendoline . . . . . *Jul 1979

HJD SOLICITORS ‡
14 King Street Cottingham East Riding of Yorkshire HU16 5QE
Tel: 01482 310870 *Fax:* 01482 214042

COULSDON, Surrey

COULSDON SOLICITORS (TREMONT MIDWEST SOLICITORS) ‡
160 Brighton Road Town Centre Coulsdon Surrey CR5 2NE
Tel: 020 8660 0810 *Fax:* 020 8660 8303
E-mail: info@tremontmidwestsolicitors.co.uk

DKLL SOLICITORS ‡
139 Brighton Road Coulsdon Surrey CR5 2NJ
Tel: 020 8668 0419

DORAN & CO ‡
45 Woodmansterne Road Coulsdon Surrey CR5 2DJ
Tel: 020 8660 6947
List of partners: V J Doran
Work: E S1 W
Ptr: Doran, Mr Vincent J BA(Law) . . . . . *Mar 1983

TERENCE FLYNN & CO ‡
26a Chipstead Valley Road Coulsdon Surrey CR5 2RA
Tel: 020 8660 8061 *Fax:* 020 8660 4393 *Dx:* 59854 COULSDON
E-mail: info@terenceflynn.co.uk
List of partners: T N Flynn
Work: C1 D1 E F1 G H J1 K1 L M1 P R1 S1 T1 W Z(k,p)
Fixed Fee Interview and Legal Aid undertaken
Ptr: Flynn, Mr Terence N LLB(Hons). . . . . *Dec 1981

D H GARLAND ‡
48 The Chase Coulsdon Surrey CR5 2EG
Tel: 020 8660 7049

LUDLOW LANE SOLICITORS ‡
46 Outwood Lane Chipstead Coulsdon Surrey CR5 3NB
Tel: 01737 550967 *Fax:* 01737 550967
E-mail: sara@ludlowlanesolicitors.com

MCMILLAN WILLIAMS ‡
35 Malcolm Road Coulsdon Surrey CR5 2DB
Tel: 020 8668 4131 *Fax:* 020 8660 4289 *Dx:* 59850 COULSDON
Emergency telephone 020 8660 3383
E-mail: coulsdon@mcmillan-williams.co.uk
List of partners: T N Channer, N J Jones-King, N Manning, D McKeown, J G S McMillan, H O Oghoetuoma, N S Perot, C J Smith, G P Stagg
Office: Carshalton, Croydon, Mitcham, South Croydon, Thornton Heath, Wallington
Work: K1 K3 S1
Agency, Fixed Fee Interview, Legal Aid undertaken and Legal Aid Franchise
Ptr: McMillan, Mr John G S BA . . . . . *Jul 1980
Stagg, Mr Geoffrey P LLB. . . . . Oct 1987
Asoc: Osborne, Mr Anton . . . . . Jun 2008
Ast: Christoforou, Ms Maria Angela LLB . . . . . *May 2003
Keeble, Mr Adam . . . . . Mar 2005
William, Mr Michael . . . . . Aug 2008

SARAH WOOTTON SOLICITORS ‡
36 Portnalls Road Coulsdon Surrey CR5 3DE
Tel: 01737 553812 *Fax:* 01737 536760
E-mail: sarahwootton@yahoo.co.uk

COVENTRY, West Midlands

ABBEY GATE LIMITED ‡
10 Holbrook Lane Coventry West Midlands CV6 4AB
Tel: 024 7666 1511 *Fax:* 024 7666 4893
E-mail: sakhan@abbeygatesolicitors.com

ALSTERS KELLEY
1 Manor Terrace Friars Road Coventry West Midlands CV1 2NU
Tel: 0844 561 0100 *Fax:* 0844 561 0199 *Dx:* 11211 COVENTRY
Emergency telephone 07626 313 233 / 07818 048 481
E-mail: enquiries@alsterskelley.com
Office: Leamington Spa, Nuneaton
Languages: French, German, Italian, Punjabi
Work: B1 B2 C1 C2 D1 D2 E G H J1 J2 K1 K2 K3 K4 L N O Q S1 S2 W Z(c,d,i,k,l,q,r)
Emergency Action, Agency, Advocacy, Fixed Fee Interview, Legal Aid undertaken, Legal Aid Franchise and Member of Accident Line
Ptr: Bannister, Mr Adrian C J BA. . . . . *Dec 1990
Harvey, Mrs Louise Caroline . . . . . *Nov 1994

Hunka, Mr Stefan John BA . . . . . *Dec 1978
Kemp, Mrs Erica Jane BA . . . . . Sep 2001
Mannion, Ms Teresa . . . . . *Jun 1998
Asoc: Gill, Mrs Sharanjit Vaur . . . . . Aug 1999
Hunt, Mrs Louise . . . . . Sep 1995
McSheen-Bailey, Mrs Cheryl Angela . . . . . Oct 1997
Ast: Elias, Ms Nancy . . . . . Oct 2007
Ghuman, Mrs Tanya . . . . . Apr 2006
Grewal, Ms Gurminder Honey . . . . . Oct 2006
Samuda, Miss Fiona BA(Hons)(Law) . . . . . *Jun 2003
Thapar, Miss Jaswinder LLB; MA; LLM . . . . . Oct 2006
Thiara, Jaz . . . . . *Jul 2001

ANGEL & CO ‡
117-119 New Union Street Coventry West Midlands CV1 2NY
Tel: 024 7625 2211 *Fax:* 024 7652 5339 *Dx:* 11236 COVENTRY 1
E-mail: susan.wharton@angelandco.net
List of partners: L J Duff, C J Holland, M J Taberner
Work: B1 C1 D1 E F1 J1 K1 K2 K3 K4 L N O Q S1 S2 W Z(p)
Emergency Action, Agency, Fixed Fee Interview, Legal Aid undertaken and Legal Aid Franchise
Ptr: Duff, Ms Lesley J LLB . . . . . *Dec 1990
Holland, Mr Christopher James LLB(Hons) . . . . . *Oct 2003
Taberner, Mr Michael J MA(Oxon); FCMI . . . . . *Apr 1974
Ast: Kesic, Mr Elvis LLB(Hons) . . . . . *Aug 2008
Rowland, Mr Mark David BA . . . . . *Jul 1990

BHB LAW LIMITED ‡
149-151 New Union Street Coventry West Midlands CV1 2NT
Tel: 024 7655 5191
E-mail: info@bhblaw.co.uk

BAND HATTON LLP ‡
1 Copthall House Station Square Coventry West Midlands CV1 2FY
Tel: 024 7663 2121 *Fax:* 024 7622 9038 *Dx:* 11207 COVENTRY 1
Emergency telephone 024 7663 2121
E-mail: law@bandhatton.co.uk
List of partners: P D Costigan, H R Jones, D M Mobbs, J J Wilby
Languages: French, German
Work: A1 B1 C1 C2 C3 D1 E F1 F2 J1 K1 L M1 N O P Q R1 R2 S1 S2 T1 T2 V W X Z(b,c,d,e,j,k,l,o,p,w)
Agency, Fixed Fee Interview, Legal Aid undertaken, Legal Aid Franchise and Member of Accident Line
Ptr: Costigan, Mr Philip D LLB(Bris) . . . . . *§Apr 1977
Jones, Mr Haydn R LLB(Newc) . . . . . *§Jul 1977
Mobbs, Mrs Dawn Marie . . . . . *Oct 1996
Wilby, Mr Jonathan James LLB . . . . . *May 1996
Ast: Bennell, Mrs Joyce E . . . . . *Nov 1978
Checketts, Ms Helen A BA . . . . . Aug 2001
Cross, Mrs Tracy Ann . . . . . *Oct 1997
French, Mr John LLB . . . . . Oct 2005
Morgan, Mr Richard LLB(Hons) . . . . . Jan 2005
Ridley, Mr Mark Ellis LLB . . . . . Oct 1992

BATE EDMONDS SNAPE ‡
Manor Court Manor House Drive Coventry West Midlands CV1 2EY
Tel: 024 7622 0707

BRINDLEY TWIST TAFFT & JAMES ‡
Lowick Gate Siskin Drive Coventry West Midlands CV3 4FJ
Tel: 024 7653 1532 *Fax:* 024 7630 1300 *Dx:* 11202 COVENTRY 1
E-mail: admin@bttj.com
List of partners: S R Grindlay, D R Hawley, C L James, M Qasim, J C Ruddick, J F Ward, S J Wright
Office: Birmingham
Languages: French
Work: B1 C1 C2 E F1 I J1 K1 K3 L N O P Q R1 S1 S2 V W Z(d,e,l,q,r)
Agency, Advocacy, Fixed Fee Interview, Legal Aid undertaken and Member of Accident Line
Ptr: Grindlay, Mr Simon R . . . . . *§Feb 1980
Hawley, Mr David Robin LLB(Lond) . . . . . *Feb 1983
James, Mr Colin L MA(Cantab) . . . . . *Jul 1973
Qasim, Mr Mohammed . . . . . Sep 1991
Ruddick, Mr John C LLB . . . . . *§Apr 1975
Ward, Mr John Francis . . . . . *Aug 2000
Wright, Ms Samantha Jane . . . . . *Nov 1990
Ast: Alcock, Mr Jason Martin . . . . . Jan 2008
Allen, Mr Stephen Joseph . . . . . Apr 2008
Bailes, Mr Alistair James Christopher . . . . . *Oct 2002
Bevan, Mrs Sarah Jane . . . . . Oct 1998
Cooper, Mr Mark Andrew . . . . . *May 2006
Giddings, Mr Ian Thomas . . . . . Feb 2003
Howell, Ms Samantha Jane . . . . . Aug 2001
Porter, Miss Lindsay . . . . . *Feb 1975

Other offices in Birmingham. We specialise in the following areas of work Commercial and Company Law, Commercial Property, Personal Taxation, Employment Law, Clinical Negligence, Personal Injury.

BULLER JEFFRIES
Bank House 23 Warwick Road Coventry West Midlands CV1 2EW
Tel: 024 7622 8734 *Fax:* 024 7663 2820 *Dx:* 12235 COVENTRY
E-mail: cov@bullerjeffries.co.uk
Office: Birmingham
Languages: French, German
Work: C1 E F1 F2 J2 K4 N O Q S1 S2 W Z(c,j,q)
Fixed Fee Interview undertaken and Member of Accident Line
Ptr: Coates, Miss Caroline Amanda LLB . . . . . *Nov 1994
Coates, Mr Roger F LLB . . . . . *Dec 1961

BUTTON LEGAL LLP ‡
25 Warwick Road Coventry West Midlands CV1 2EZ
Tel: 024 7652 5457 *Fax:* 024 7652 0240
E-mail: nick@button-law.co.uk
List of partners: L Barber, R N Button, N J Ireland
Work: A1 C1 E F1 K1 L S1 T2 V W Z(l)
Emergency Action, Agency, Advocacy, Fixed Fee Interview and Legal Aid undertaken
Ptr: Button, Mr Robert N . . . . . *Sep 1986
Mem: Barber, Ms Louise LLB(Hons); PGDipLP . . . . . *Dec 1995
Ireland, Mr Neil John LLB(Hons) ● . . . . . *Oct 1994

COLTMAN WARNER CRANSTON LLP ‡
3 The Innovation Village Cheetah Road Coventry West Midlands CV1 2TL
Tel: 024 7662 7262 *Fax:* 024 7022 7691 *Dx:* 74261 COVENTRY 26
E-mail: lcoltman@coltmanco.com
List of partners: L Coltman
Work: O Q
Mem: Coltman, Mr Larry . . . . . *Apr 1984

Asoc: Khan-Hussain, Alia LLB . . . . . *Jan 2000
Shaw, Ms Bettina LLB . . . . . *Jan 1984
Ast: Hailey, Miss Jennifer Ann . . . . . *Jan 1985

DE MARCO HUNTER ‡
Number Three Siskin Drive Middlemarch Business Park Baginton Coventry West Midlands CV3 4FJ
Tel: 024 7621 4440 *Fax:* 024 7699 8273
E-mail: enquiries@demarcohunter.com

DREW JONES SOLICITORS ‡
17 Queens Road Coventry West Midlands CV1 3EG
Tel: 024 7655 5511 *Fax:* 024 7655 5577
E-mail: law@drewjones.co.uk

FIELD OVERELL
8-10 Corporation Street Coventry West Midlands CV1 1GF
Tel: 024 7622 9582 *Fax:* 024 7622 5034 *Dx:* 11223 COVENTRY
E-mail: coventry@fieldoverell.com
Office: Leamington Spa
Work: D1 E F1 G H J1 K1 K3 L N O P Q S1 W Z(l)
Emergency Action, Agency, Advocacy, Fixed Fee Interview, Legal Aid undertaken and Member of Accident Line
Ptr: McCusker, Mr Andrew Patrick Michael LLB . . . . . *Sep 1992

GUILDHALL SOLICITORS ‡
242 Stoney Stanton Road Foleshill Coventry West Midlands CV1 4FP
Tel: 024 7622 5556 *Fax:* 024 7622 5557
E-mail: info@guildhallsolicitors.co.uk

HAMMON OAKLEY ‡
403 Walsgrave Road Coventry West Midlands CV2 4AH
Tel: 024 7644 8585 *Fax:* 024 7644 1611 *Dx:* 723720 COVENTRY 19
E-mail: enquiries@hammonoakleysolicitors.co.uk
List of partners: M A Hammon, J L Oakley
Languages: French
Work: A1 C1 D1 E F1 G H J1 K1 K3 L M1 N P R1 S1 T1 V W Z(c,i,j,k,l,m,t)
Emergency Action, Agency, Advocacy, Fixed Fee Interview and Legal Aid undertaken
Ptr: Hammon, Mr Michael A . . . . . *Jun 1964
Oakley, Mr John L LLB . . . . . *Jan 1970
Ast: Arab, Miss Sophia BA; LLM . . . . . *Oct 2007
Skudra, Andris D LLB . . . . . *§Jul 1979
Williams, Mr Nicholas J BA . . . . . Aug 2001
Con: King, Mr Peter G . . . . . *§Apr 1962

HEER MANAK ‡
434 Foleshill Road Coventry West Midlands CV6 5JX
Tel: 024 7666 4000 *Fax:* 024 7666 4904 *Dx:* 18869 COVENTRY 2
Emergency telephone 07956 143968
E-mail: solicitor@heermanak.co.uk
List of partners: B S Dahil, R Heer, K Manak
Office: Coventry
Languages: Hindi, Punjabi, Urdu
Work: B1 B2 C1 C2 D1 D2 E F1 F2 G H J1 K1 K2 L N O P R1 R2 S2 W Z(i,p)
Emergency Action, Agency, Advocacy, Fixed Fee Interview, Legal Aid undertaken and Legal Aid Franchise
Ptr: Dahil, Mr Balbir Singh LLB(Hons) . . . . . *Apr 1995
Heer, Mr Robin LLB(Hons) . . . . . *§Apr 1992
Manak, Kulwant LLB . . . . . *§Feb 1993

HEER MANAK
5 Queen Victoria Road Coventry West Midlands CV1 3JL
Tel: 024 7666 4000 *Fax:* 024 7666 4904
Office: Coventry

NOEL KELLY SOLICITOR ‡
192 Dulverton Avenue Coventry West Midlands CV5 8HB
Tel: 024 7671 5720 *Fax:* 024 7671 5720

KEOGHS LLP
Compton Court Harry Weston Road Binley Business Park Coventry West Midlands CV3 2SU
Tel: 024 7665 8200 *Fax:* 024 7665 8268 *Dx:* 721682 COVENTRY 15
E-mail: info@keoghs.co.uk
Office: Bolton
Work: A3 B2 N O Q Z(j,q)
Advocacy undertaken
Ptr: Whittle, Mr John W LLB . . . . . *Nov 1991
Asoc: Coleman, Mr Neil Leonard LLB(Hons) . . . . . *Oct 1993
Mabey, Mr Paul . . . . . Sep 1978
Shrimpton, Mrs Elisabeth Anne BA(Hons)(Law) . . . . . Oct 1996
Young, Mr Ken LLB . . . . . Sep 1998
Ast: Bagri, Mr Mandip Singh LLB(Hons) . . . . . *Jun 1998
Chapman, Mr James LLB . . . . . Oct 1993
Davies, Ms Elaine BEd . . . . . Jan 2001
Hill, Ms Sarah LLB(Hons) . . . . . *Aug 2000
Howarth, Mr Tom LLB(Hons) . . . . . *Sep 2000
Ingram, Mr Timothy Alwyne LLB(Hons) . . . . . *Aug 1995
Langridge, Ms Karen BA(Hons) . . . . . Aug 2001
Pathak, Miss Munju Bala LLB(Hons); LSF . . . . . *Mar 1997
Temperley, Mr Andrew LLB . . . . . *Sep 1999

KUNDERT & CO ‡
3 Copthall House Station Square Coventry West Midlands CV1 2FD
Tel: 024 7622 7741 *Fax:* 024 7625 1417 *Dx:* 11246 COVENTRY
E-mail: info@kundert.co.uk
List of partners: P T Hughes, C Jones, C J D Jones, P Shrimpton, S L Warwick, H J S Whitney
Office: Coventry
Work: C1 C2 D1 D2 E F1 F2 G H J1 K1 L N O Q S1 S2 V W Z(i,k,l,m,p)
Emergency Action, Agency, Advocacy, Fixed Fee Interview, Legal Aid undertaken and Member of Accident Line
Ptr: Hughes, Mr Paul Thomas LLB(Hons) . . . . . Sep 2001
Jones, Mr Christopher John David LLB(B'ham) ★ . . . . . *§Dec 1970
Shrimpton, Mr Peter LLB(B'ham) . . . . . *§Jun 1967
Whitney, Mr Henry J S LLB(Nott'm) . . . . . *May 1979
Ast: Rees, Mr David Vernon LLB(Hons) . . . . . *Oct 2004

KUNDERT & CO
14 Old Church Road Bell Green Coventry West Midlands CV6 7BY
Tel: 024 7668 4928 *Fax:* 024 7666 2031 *Dx:* 11246 CONVENTRY
Emergency telephone 024 7641 5713
E-mail: info@kundert.co.uk
Office: Coventry
Work: C1 C2 D1 D2 F1 F2 G H J1 K1 L M1 M2 N O P Q S1 S2 V W Z(i,k,l,m,p)
Emergency Action, Agency, Advocacy, Fixed Fee Interview, Legal Aid undertaken and Legal Aid Franchise

Ptr: Jones, Chris . . . . . Jun 1971
Warwick, Ms Sarah Louise LLB ♦ . . . . . *Dec 2000
Ast: Freeman, Ms Emma . . . . . Aug 2006
Morgan, Ms Catrin Anne LLB . . . . . Aug 2006

THE LAW PARTNERSHIP ‡
452 Foleshill Road Coventry West Midlands CV6 5LB
Tel: 024 7668 7211 *Fax:* 024 7668 2472

LAWYERS 4 IT ‡
12 Ransome Road Gun Hill Coventry West Midlands CV7 8GZ
Tel: 07747 806651 *Fax:* 020 7900 6420
E-mail: office@lawyers4it.com

LOUGHRIDGE BOWLER ‡
2 The Quadrant Coventry West Midlands CV1 2EL
Tel: 024 7663 1632 *Fax:* 024 7663 2828
E-mail: info@lb-law.co.uk
List of partners: J A Bowler, C A M Dobson, E J Loughridge
Languages: French, German
Work: K4 T2 V W
Ptr: Bowler, Miss Jill Alison BA . . . . . *Mar 1985
Dobson, Mrs Caroline A M BA(Hons) . . . . . *Dec 1987
Loughridge, Miss Eileen Jane . . . . . *§Apr 1981
Ast: Watts, Mrs Lorna May . . . . . *Sep 1997

MACNAMARA KING SOLICITORS
2 Meeting House Lane Balsall Common Coventry West Midlands CV7 7FX
Office: Warwick

MANDER HADLEY & CO ‡
(incorporating Browetts)
1 The Quadrant Coventry West Midlands CV1 2DW
Tel: 024 7663 1212 *Fax:* 024 7663 3131 *Dx:* 11204 COVENTRY 1
E-mail: enquiries@manderhadley.co.uk
List of partners: J C Hall, C A Jones, D C Mander, P I Mander, G M Matthews, M C McNally, R G Pascall, A W Sharp, A B Turner, D M Webb
Languages: French, German, Spanish
Work: A1 C1 D1 E F1 G H J1 K1 L N P Q S1 S2 T2 W Z(c,d,i,m)
Emergency Action, Agency, Advocacy, Fixed Fee Interview, Legal Aid undertaken, Legal Aid Franchise and Member of Accident Line
Ptr: Hall, Mr Jonathan C LLB . . . . . *Feb 1983
Jones, Mr Carl A . . . . . *Oct 1992
McNally, Mr Mark C LLB(Hons) ★ . . . . . *Oct 1992
Mander, Mr David C LLB(B'ham) J F Gregg Memorial Prize . . . . . *§Mar 1960
Mander, Mr Peter I . . . . . *Jan 1966
Matthews, Miss Gillian M LLB . . . . . *Jun 1976
Pascall, Mr Roger G LLM . . . . . *Apr 1980
Sharp, Mr Andrew W LLB(Bris) . . . . . *Jun 1979
Turner, Mrs Anne B . . . . . *Jun 1975
Webb, Mr David M LLB . . . . . *Dec 1982
Ast: Norgate, Ms Clare LLB . . . . . Oct 1991
Con: Foottit, Mr George T W MA(Cantab) . . . . . *Jun 1981

MAYA & CO SOLICITORS ‡
1 Holmsdale Road Foleshill Coventry West Midlands CV6 5BL
Tel: 024 7670 0417 *Fax:* 0560 341 7518
E-mail: info@mayaandcosolicitors.com

MILLERCHIP PEACHEY ‡
3 The Quadrant Coventry West Midlands CV1 2DY
Tel: 024 7624 3615 *Fax:* 024 7624 3615
E-mail: info@mpcrime.com
List of partners: S J Millerchip, R A Murray
Languages: French, Mirpuri, Punjabi, Urdu
Work: G H
Emergency Action, Advocacy, Legal Aid undertaken and Legal Aid Franchise
Ptr: Millerchip, Mr Stephen J BA(Law) . . . . . *Oct 1984
Murray, Mr Richard Andrew LLB(Hons) . . . . . *Jul 1996
Ast: Farooq, Mr Mohammed BA(Hons) . . . . . *Mar 2003

MURRAY BAYLISS ‡
1st Floor 4-6 Hay Lane Coventry West Midlands CV1 5RF
Tel: 024 7663 2950 *Fax:* 024 7652 0592 *Dx:* 18852 COVENTRY 2
E-mail: david.murray@murraybayliss.co.uk

NEWSOME VAUGHAN LLP ‡
Greyfriars House Greyfriars Lane Coventry West Midlands CV1 2GW
Tel: 024 7663 3433 *Fax:* 024 7625 6496
E-mail: pauls@n-v.co.uk
List of partners: C W Bates, L S Drew, R M B Griffiths, I S Grindal, P Saunders
Languages: French, Italian, Maltese, Spanish
Work: A1 B1 C1 C2 C3 E F1 G J1 K4 L M1 N O P Q R1 S1 S2 T1 T2 U2 W Z(c,d,e,h,j,l,o,p,q)
Agency, Advocacy, Legal Aid undertaken, Legal Aid Franchise and Member of Accident Line
Ptr: Bates, Mrs Caroline Wendy LLB President of Warwickshire Young Lawyers . . . . . *Apr 1997
Drew, Ms Louise Suzanne LLB Council Member of the Warwickshire Law Society . . . . . Oct 1995
Griffiths, Mr Rupert M B BA; MBA . . . . . *§Jun 1977
Grindal, Mr Ian Sinclair MA(Oxon) . . . . . *§Oct 1980
Saunders, Mr Paul LLB . . . . . *Aug 1989
Asoc: Essery, Ms Helen Joanne LLB . . . . . Oct 1996
James, Mr Howard Owen LLB . . . . . *Sep 1994
Judge, Mr John B LLB(Hons) . . . . . Feb 1988
Ogunshakin, Mr Ifeolu Olumide LLB(Hons) . . . . . *Dec 2002
Ast: Bisal, Mrs Satinder BA(Hons) . . . . . *Feb 2000
Grigg, Mrs Verity Louise LLB . . . . . Feb 2002
Heywood, Miss Lucie J . . . . . *May 2001

PAYNE SKILLINGTON ‡
Lex House 12 Manor Road Coventry West Midlands CV1 2LG
Tel: 024 7663 3044 *Fax:* 024 7652 5470 *Dx:* 11219 COVENTRY
E-mail: s.mcgrath@payneskillington.co.uk
List of partners: R J Brown, S A McGrath
Languages: Hindi, Punjabi
Work: A1 B1 C1 C2 E F1 G H J1 K1 L N O P Q R1 S1 S2 V W Z(c,h,i,j,k,l,s)
Agency and Advocacy undertaken
Ptr: Brown, Mr Robert James . . . . . *§Jul 1969
McGrath, Mr Simon Anthony . . . . . *§Jan 1979
Ast: Sachdev, Rajiv LLB(Hons) . . . . . *Sep 1988

PENMANS ‡
17a Queens Road Coventry West Midlands CV1 3DH
Tel: 024 7622 6575 *Fax:* 024 7625 6248 *Dx:* 706790 COVENTRY 9

See p112 for the Key to Work Categories & other symbols

List of partners: C J Aldridge, T C Chatham, R R G Griffiths, P I Holmes, P J Jones, J M Schmid, A C Sharpe, S R Sharpe, D F Tandy, E L Wyatt
Office: Kenilworth, Wellesbourne
Languages: French, German, Italian, Punjabi, Urdu
Work: A1 B1 C1 D1 E F1 G H J1 K1 L M1 N P R1 S1 T1 V W Z(i,l,m,p,t)
Emergency Action, Agency, Advocacy, Fixed Fee Interview, Legal Aid undertaken and Member of Accident Line
Ptr: Holmes, Ms Patricia I . . . . Feb 1986
Jones, Mr Philip J LLB(CNAA) . . . . *Dec 1990
Schmid, Miss Judith M BA(Hons) . . . . Oct 1985
Sharpe, Mr Andrew C. . . . . *Oct 1982
Sharpe, Mr Simon R BA. . . . . *Mar 1987
Tandy, Mr David F BA. . . . . *Jun 1980

RBM SOLICITORS ‡
4 Station Square Coventry West Midlands CV1 2GT
Tel: 024 7652 0999 *Fax:* 0845 302 8332
E-mail: info@rbmsolicitors.co.uk
List of partners: R Bvunzawabaya
SPr: Bvunzawabaya, Rumbiadzai . . . . Dec 2003

RICHARDSON & DAVIES ‡
3 Park Road Station Square Coventry West Midlands CV1 2LE
Tel: 024 7622 2001 *Fax:* 024 7622 6246 *Dx:* 11217 COVENTRY
List of partners: M E Barker-Davies, W R Evans
Work: B1 C1 C2 C3 D1 E F1 J1 K1 L M1 M2 N O P Q R1 S1 T1 T2 V W Z(d,l)
Agency, Advocacy and Fixed Fee Interview undertaken
Ptr: Barker-Davies, Mr Miles E. . . . . *§May 1977
Evans, Mr William R LLB(Lond) . . . . *§Apr 1978

ROTHERHAM & CO ‡
8-9 The Quadrant Coventry West Midlands CV1 2EG
Tel: 024 7622 7331 *Fax:* 024 7622 1293 *Dx:* 11212 COVENTRY
E-mail: info@rotherham-solicitors.co.uk
Work: C1 D1 E F1 G H J1 K1 L N O Q S1 S2 W X Z(d,h,l,q,r,x)

R H ROWLEY ‡
Braughing Mead Ryton Road Bubbenhall Coventry West Midlands CV8 3BH
Tel: 024 7630 1996 *Fax:* 024 7630 3252
E-mail: roy@rhrowley.co.uk
List of partners: R H Rowley
Work: E K1 L N O Q S1 S2 W
Agency and Advocacy undertaken
Ptr: Rowley, Mr Roy Hall LLB Deputy District Judge; NPAS Adjudicator . . . . *Aug 1969

SARGINSONS LAW LLP ‡
10 The Quadrant Coventry West Midlands CV1 2EL
Tel: 024 7655 3181 *Fax:* 024 7625 8573 *Dx:* 11200 COVENTRY
Emergency telephone 024 7622 1514
E-mail: info@sarginsons-solicitors.co.uk
List of partners: C Bailey, S J Booth, I D G Cox
Work: C1 E G H K1 K3 L N O Q S1 S2 W Z(l)
Agency, Advocacy, Legal Aid undertaken and Legal Aid Franchise
Ptr: Bailey, Mr Christopher. . . . . *Jul 1979
Booth, Mr Simon J LLB(Lond). . . . . *Dec 1974
Cox, Mr Ian D G BA. . . . . *Jul 1973
Ast: Paremain, Mr Richard Mare LLB . . . . *Oct 1990
Con: Sarginson, Mr David R . . . . *Oct 1958

SEYMOURS ‡
(incorporating Roland Hollick & Co)
Queens House Queens Road Coventry West Midlands CV1 3JN
Tel: 024 7655 3961 *Fax:* 024 7625 1634 *Dx:* 706792 COVENTRY 9
E-mail: law@seymours.co.uk
List of partners: A J Blay, R J Fardoe, A W Hardy
Work: A1 B1 C1 D1 E F1 J1 K1 K3 L N O Q R1 S1 S2 T1 W Z(e,h,o,s)
Emergency Action, Agency, Advocacy, Fixed Fee Interview and Legal Aid undertaken
Ptr: Blay, Mr Adrian J . . . . *Dec 1973
Fardoe, Mr Robert J LLB . . . . *§Apr 1975
Hardy, Mr Andrew W LLB(Soton) . . . . *Mar 1979
Ast: Colledge, Mr Duncan J . . . . *Feb 2008
Ferguson, Mr Mark Andrew . . . . *Sep 2005
Sangha, Tarsem . . . . *Feb 1999

CAROL SKETCHLEY SOLICITOR ‡
Asbury House 17 Asbury Road Balsall Common Coventry West Midlands CV7 7QN
Tel: 01676 530514 *Fax:* 01676 535526
E-mail: carolsketchley@employmentuk.com
List of partners: C A Sketchley
Work: J1 S1 W
Emergency Action, Agency, Advocacy and Fixed Fee Interview undertaken
Ptr: Sketchley, Mrs Carol A BA . . . . *Sep 1985

ROGER DAVID SMALLMAN ‡
28 Balsall Street Balsall Common Coventry West Midlands CV7 7PJ
Tel: 01676 535283 *Fax:* 01676 535283
Dx: 13705 BALSALL COMMON
E-mail: r.d.smallman@btinternet.com

SMITH & WELLS ‡
4-6 Hay Lane Coventry West Midlands CV1 5RF
Tel: 024 7655 3040 *Fax:* 024 7655 0150
E-mail: melonie_smith@btinternet.com

ANTHONY STOCKTON ‡
8 Shortfield Close Balsall Common Coventry West Midlands CV7 7UN
Tel: 01676 535790 *Fax:* 01676 535646
Dx: 13706 BALSALL COMMON
E-mail: enquiries@anthonystockton.co.uk
List of partners: K Satsavia, M A Stockton
Languages: Hindi, Punjabi
Work: S1 S2 W
Ptr: Satsavia, Mrs Kirandeep LLB . . . . *Jan 2000
Stockton, Mr Mark A BA(Hons) . . . . *Jan 1983
Asoc: Taylor, Ms Jayne Pamela . . . . Mar 1998
Ast: Dosanjh, Miss Parminder Kaur LLB(Hons). . . . . . *Dec 2003

TOWNSHENDS LLP
2 Brays Lane Coventry West Midlands CV2 4DZ
Tel: 024 7644 8606 *Fax:* 024 7645 8725 *Dx:* 700111 COVENTRY 4
E-mail: s.melling@townshends.co.uk
Office: Birmingham, Coleshill
Agency and Legal Aid undertaken
Ptr: Townshend, Mr Philip D LLB(Hons) . . . . *Oct 1997

VARLEY HIBBS LLP ‡
3 Coventry Innovation Villa Coventry University Technology Park Cheetah Road Coventry West Midlands CV1 2TL
Tel: 024 7663 1000 *Fax:* 024 7663 0808 *Dx:* 742360 COVENTRY 26
E-mail: info@varleyhibbs.com
List of partners: S P Byrne, S E Pearce, M V Thomas, J H Woodhouse
Languages: French, Hindi, Punjabi
Work: A1 A3 B1 C1 C2 C3 D1 D2 E F1 F2 I J1 K1 K2 K3 L M1 N O P Q R1 R2 S1 S2 T1 T2 U2 V W Z(b,c,d,e,f,h,j,k,l,o,p,q,r,t,za)
Emergency Action, Agency, Advocacy and Legal Aid undertaken
Mem: Byrne, Mr Sean P MA(Cantab) . . . . *Nov 1987
Pearce, Ms Susan E LLB ♦ . . . . *Dec 1980
Thomas, Mr Malcolm Vaughan LLB(Hons). . . . . . *§Feb 1994
Woodhouse, Ms Julia Helen LLB ♦ . . . . *Nov 1995
Ast: Maini, Miss Arti LLB(Hons) . . . . *Nov 1996
Sarbjit, Mrs Nahl BSc(Hons); MA . . . . *Sep 2006
Shield, Mr Matthew . . . . *Nov 2007
Zala, Mr Panjak LLB(Hons) . . . . *Sep 1993
Con: Coludrick, Mr Tim . . . . *Nov 1993
Sharp, Mrs Caroline E LLB ♦ . . . . *Jul 1979

WALLACE MCNALLY ‡
Suite 2 6 The Quadrant Coventry West Midlands CV1 2EL
Tel: 024 7622 0300 *Fax:* 024 7622 0301 *Dx:* 11205 COVENTRY
Emergency telephone 07818 048481
E-mail: emily@wallacemcnally.co.uk
List of partners: M Farooq, M C McNally, E N A Wallace
Work: G H
Ptr: Farooq, Mr Mohammad ★. . . . . *Sep 2003
McNally, Mr Mark C LLB(Hons) ★. . . . . *Oct 1992
Wallace, Ms Emily N A LLB; BA. . . . . *Oct 1990

WARD & RIDER LIMITED ‡
2 Manor Yard New Union Street Coventry West Midlands CV1 2PF
Tel: 024 7655 5400 *Fax:* 024 7622 4717 *Dx:* 11209 COVENTRY
E-mail: enquiry@wardrider.co.uk
List of partners: J C M Claridge, A C Pettersen
Languages: Hindi, Polish, Punjabi, Urdu
Work: J1 K1 K3 K4 N Q S1 W Z(j)
Emergency Action, Advocacy, Fixed Fee Interview undertaken and Member of Accident Line
Ptr: Claridge, Mr Jason C M LLB . . . . *Jan 1995
Pettersen, Mr Alistair Charles BA(Hons). . . . . . . *§Jun 1981
Ast: Beynon, Mrs Fiona Marion Ruth BA(Hons); MA . . . . *Oct 1995
Daniel, Mr Stuart John . . . . *Oct 2006
Hart, Mr Geoffrey Allan . . . . *Jan 1998
Kaur, Anita . . . . *Mar 2009
Khalil, Mrs Nasreen . . . . *Jul 2007
Kumari, Miss Anu . . . . *Mar 1999
Nagra, Mr Arvinder Singh LLB. . . . . *Oct 2008
O'Rourke, Ms Pauline L LLB . . . . *Nov 1991
Phillips, Mr Huw David LLB(Hons). . . . . *Nov 1986
Venables, Miss Sarah Jane LLB. . . . . *Jul 2008
Walker, Mr Giles S LLB(Hons). . . . . *Jul 1998
Williams, Miss Lucy Jayne LLB . . . . *Sep 2010

ELLEN YEE-MAN WINDSOR ‡
3 Birmingham Road Stoneleigh Coventry West Midlands CV8 3DD
Tel: 024 7641 4984 *Fax:* 024 7641 4984
List of partners: E Y M Windsor
Languages: Chinese, German, Spanish
Work: B1 B2 J1 K1 M2 N O Q Z(b,i,q)
Agency undertaken
SPr: Windsor, Mrs Ellen Y M LLB(Lond) . . . . *May 1988

COWBRIDGE, Vale of Glamorgan

CASTLE LAW ‡
Penllyn Castle Penllyn Cowbridge Vale of Glamorgan CF71 7RQ
Tel: 07772 368086
E-mail: enquiries@castlelawsols.co.uk

GASKELL & WALKER
89 Eastgate Cowbridge Vale of Glamorgan CF71 7AA
Tel: 01446 772212 *Fax:* 01446 773921 *Dx:* 50951 COWBRIDGE
E-mail: info@gaskellandwalker.com
Office: Bridgend
Agency, Advocacy, Fixed Fee Interview, Legal Aid undertaken and Member of Accident Line
Ptr: Taylor, Mr John A Associated Law Societies of Wales Prize 1973 . . . . *§Mar 1974

GLAMORGANLAW
The Business Centre Town Hall Square Cowbridge Vale of Glamorgan CF71 7EE
Tel: 01446 771742 *Fax:* 01446 771380
E-mail: richard@beechandco.com
Office: Cardiff, Pontypridd

HOPKINS LAW LLP
50-50a High Street Cowbridge Vale of Glamorgan CF71 7AH
Tel: 01446 774151 *Fax:* 01446 776894
E-mail: enquiries3@hopkinslawltd.com
Office: Cardiff (2 offices)

LARBY WILLIAMS WITH GWYN & GWYN ‡
The Pavilion 60 Eastgate Cowbridge Vale of Glamorgan CF71 7AB
Tel: 01446 775535 *Fax:* 01446 775156 *Dx:* 50954 COWBRIDGE
E-mail: cowbridge@larby-williams.co.uk
List of partners: P Haines, J A Holley, A G B Larby, F W Williams
Languages: Welsh
Work: A1 E K1 K3 K4 L R2 S1 S2 T2 W Z(c,l)
Agency and Advocacy undertaken
Ptr: Haines, Mrs Pamela BA(Hons); MA . . . . *Feb 1996
Holley, Mrs Judith Anne LLB . . . . *Oct 1977
Larby, Mr Adrian G B MA; LLB Tax Commissioner. . . *Jun 1970
Williams, Miss Frances Wynne BA . . . . *Jan 1976
Ast: Baker, Ms Susan Rosemary LLB . . . . Aug 1991
Carter, Mr Julian David Robert . . . . *Nov 1980
Lane, Ms Hayley Louise LLB . . . . *Aug 2003
Con: Hughes, Mrs Nest M LLB(Wales) . . . . *§Jul 1975
Williams, Mr Lawrence Hugh Wyndham BA; TEP . . *§Sep 1962

COWES, Isle of Wight

URSULA BAGNALL DIVORCE & FAMILY LAW SOLICITORS ‡
18 Medina Village Cowes Isle of Wight PO31 7HT
Tel: 01983 247221 *Fax:* 01983 247223
E-mail: ub@ursulabagnallsolicitor.co.uk
List of partners: U M W Bagnall
Languages: French, German, Spanish
Work: A2 D1 D2 F1 F2 K1 N O Q S1 S2 W Z(w)
Emergency Action, Agency, Advocacy, Legal Aid undertaken and Legal Aid Franchise
SPr: Bagnall, Mrs Ursula M W . . . . Aug 1992

WALTER GRAY & CO
Baring Chambers 13 Denmark Road Cowes Isle of Wight PO31 7SY
Tel: 01983 281188 / 296010 *Fax:* 01983 200719
Emergency telephone 01983 526625
E-mail: cowes@waltergray.co.uk
Office: Ryde
Work: E K4 S1 S2 W

CRADLEY HEATH, West Midlands

W M ATTWOOD & SON ‡
143-146 High Street Cradley Heath West Midlands B64 5HJ
Tel: 01384 566523 / 566128 *Fax:* 01384 634470
Dx: 20754 CRADLEY HEATH
List of partners: A W Attwood
Work: A1 E R1 S1 T1 T2 W
Fixed Fee Interview undertaken
Ptr: Attwood, Mr Arthur W. . . . . *Dec 1976

GEORGE GREEN LLP ‡
195 High Street Cradley Heath West Midlands B64 5HW
Tel: 01384 410410 *Fax:* 01384 634237 *Dx:* 20752 CRADLEY HEATH
List of partners: P R Bennett, R M Cliff, J R Coles, G Green, T M Lang, C Mort, K A Styles, N R Williams, S J Wyer
Languages: French, German, Gujarati, Hindi, Punjabi
Work: A3 B1 C1 C2 C3 D1 D2 E I J1 K1 K2 L O Q R2 S1 S2 T1 T2 U2 W Z(b,c,d,e,k,l,q)
Agency and Advocacy undertaken
Ptr: Styles, Mr Kevin A BA. . . . . *§Oct 1984
Mem: Bennett, Mr Paul R LLB(Dunelm) . . . . *Nov 1997
Cliff, Mr Richard M LLB(Bris) . . . . *Nov 1971
Coles, Mr James R LLB. . . . . *Sep 2003
Green, Mr Guy BA(Law & Philosophy). . . . . Nov 1985
Lang, Mr Timothy Mark LLB(Hons) . . . . *Oct 1991
Mort, Miss Ceri LLB. . . . . *Oct 1989
Williams, Mr Neil R LLB(Leics) . . . . *Oct 1989
Wyer, Mr Stephen John MA(Oxon) . . . . *Oct 1988
Asoc: Allen-Jones, Mr Christopher James . . . . *Oct 1996
Fitzsimmons, Miss Julia Margaret MA; CPE. . . . . . Oct 1996
Griffiths, Mr Simon LLB . . . . *Sep 2005
Martin, Miss Clare Rachel LLB(Hons) . . . . *Aug 2002
Meade, Mr Stephen John PGDipLaw; BVC . . . . . . *Oct 2006
Rabani, Mrs Nirmla LLB Highest National A Level Law Award . . . . Sep 2002
Round, Mr Philip James LLB Birmingham Law Society Bronze Medal 1999. *Sep 2000
Unarkat, Mrs Shilpa Roopen LLB . . . . *Oct 2002
Ast: Bains, Miss Kelly LLB(Hons) . . . . *Apr 2008
Beal, Ms Deborah Janet BA; GDC; LPC. . . . . *Sep 2008
Choudhary, Miss Aasha LLB . . . . *Sep 2009
Lewis, Miss Jane Mary LLB(Hons) . . . . *Dec 2006
Taylor, Miss Louise Rose LLB. . . . . Sep 2010

Other offices in Birmingham. We conduct business in French, German, Gujarati, Hindi, Punjabi. We specialise in the following areas of work Corporate and Commercial Law, Commercial Property, Litigation - Commercial, Employment.

CRAMLINGTON, Northumberland

ADAMS HETHERINGTON ‡
(incorporating Yarwood Gray & Co)
Suites 18 & 19 Dudley Court East East Square Cramlington Northumberland NE23 6QW
Tel: 01670 714622 / 714635 *Fax:* 01670 739169
Dx: 62304 CRAMLINGTON
E-mail: adamsh-cram@btconnect.com
List of partners: R D Adams, A N Hetherington
Office: Ashington
Work: B1 C1 D1 E F1 G H J1 K1 L N P Q R1 R2 S1 S2 T1 U1 V W Z(c,l,m)
Emergency Action, Agency, Advocacy, Fixed Fee Interview, Legal Aid undertaken and Member of Accident Line
Ptr: Adams, Mr Roderick D BA(Hons) . . . . *Mar 1973
Hetherington, Mr Anthony N LLB(Hons) . . . . *§Nov 1985

BROWELL SMITH & CO
Units 42-44 Apex Business Village Annitsford Cramlington Northumberland NE23 7BF
Tel: 0871 474 3030 *Fax:* 0845 302 4755
E-mail: advice@browells.co.uk
Office: Ashington, Newcastle upon Tyne (3 offices), Stockton-on-Tees, Stoke-on-Trent, Sunderland

ANDREW J FENNY & CO ‡
(incorporating Nat Punshon & Co)
3-4 Dudley Court East Square Cramlington Northumberland NE23 6QW
Tel: 01670 737393 *Fax:* 01670 730606 *Dx:* 62300 CRAMLINGTON
Emergency telephone 01670 737393
E-mail: info@andrewjfenny.co.uk
List of partners: A J Fenny
Work: A1 B1 C1 D1 E F1 G H J1 K1 L N R1 S1 T1 T2 V W Z(c,l)
Emergency Action, Agency, Advocacy, Fixed Fee Interview and Legal Aid undertaken
Ptr: Fenny, Mr Andrew J LLB . . . . *Apr 1974

JFS LAW LIMITED ‡
Durken Business Park Seghill Cramlington Northumberland NE23 7EB
Tel: 0191 237 1216 *Fax:* 0191 237 1216
E-mail: info@jfslaw.co.uk

CRANBROOK, Kent

LAWRENCE BROOKS ‡
Merriecroft The Common Sissinghurst Cranbrook Kent TN17 2AE
Tel: 01580 715175 *Fax:* 01580 715185
List of partners: L Brooks
Work: C1 C2 C3 E J1 R1
SPr: Brooks, Mr Lawrence . . . . *Feb 1971

BUSS MURTON LLP
31 High Street Cranbrook Kent TN17 3EE
Tel: 01580 712215 *Fax:* 01580 714496 *Dx:* 38950 CRANBROOK
E-mail: info@bussmurton.co.uk
Office: Dartford, Tunbridge Wells
Work: C2 E J1 K1 K2 L Q S1 S2 T1 T2 W Z(h)
Ptr: Browne, Mrs Corinne L LLB(Lond) . . . . *Oct 1979

CROOKESLAW SOLICITORS ‡
Suite 3 W & D Offices Conghurst Lane Cranbrook Kent TN18 5ED
Tel: 01580 754884 *Fax:* 01580 754884
E-mail: crookeslaw@aol.com
Work: A1 A2 A3 B1 B2 C1 C2 C3 E F1 F2 I J1 J2 K4 L M1 M2 M3 O P R1 R2 S1 S2 U1 W Z(b,c,d,e,f,g,j,k,n,o,p,q,r,w,y,za)

DAVID GILLIES SOLICITOR ‡
Rohan House 35 Joyce Close Cranbrook Kent TN17 3LZ
Tel: 01580 715523

GRIFFIN LAW ‡
Highgate Hawkhurst Cranbrook Kent TN18 4ER
Tel: 01580 236120 *Fax:* 01580 236121 *Dx:* 38954 CRANBROOK
E-mail: justice@griffinlaw.co.uk

WALKERS SOLICITORS ‡
Satins Hill Oast Spongs Lane Cranbrook Kent TN17 2AH
Tel: 01580 713649 *Fax:* 01580 713340
E-mail: ivanwalker@walkers-law.co.uk

CRANLEIGH, Surrey

FRANCIS & CO ‡
Mapledrakes Farm Ewhurst Cranleigh Surrey GU6 7QP
Tel: 01483 267222 *Fax:* 01483 272051
E-mail: julie-francis@bigwig.net
List of partners: J A Francis
Languages: German
Work: W
Ptr: Francis, Mrs Julie A BSc(Hons) . . . . *Oct 1990

HART BROWN SOLICITORS
2 Bank Buildings 147 High Street Cranleigh Surrey GU6 8BE
Est: 1919
Tel: 0800 068 8177 *Fax:* 01483 275302 *Dx:* 300501 CRANLEIGH
E-mail: lawyers@hartbrown.co.uk
Office: Cobham, Godalming, Guildford, London SW19, Woking
Work: A1 B1 C1 C2 C3 D1 D2 E F1 F2 G H I J1 J2 K1 K2 K3 K4 L M1 M2 N O P Q R1 R2 S1 S2 T1 T2 V W Z(b,c,d,e,i,j,k,l,m,o,p,q,r,z)
Emergency Action, Agency, Advocacy, Fixed Fee Interview, Legal Aid undertaken and Legal Aid Franchise
Ptr: Coulson, Miss Alyson Clare LLB(Hons) . . . . *Apr 1993
Spencer, Mr Stuart D LLB(Lond) . . . . *Apr 1975
Ast: Glenister, Mrs Josephine BA . . . . *May 1985
Taylor, Mr Luke . . . . *Jan 2000

LYNN MURRAY & CO ‡
The Old Bakery Collins Court 39 High Street Cranleigh Surrey GU6 8AS
Tel: 0844 815 0373 *Fax:* 0844 815 0738 *Dx:* 300510 CRANLEIGH
E-mail: lynn@lynnmurray.plus.com

TWM SOLICITORS LLP
Broadoak House Horsham Road Cranleigh Surrey GU6 8DJ
Tel: 01483 273515 *Fax:* 01483 278075 *Dx:* 300500 CRANLEIGH
E-mail: cranleigh.reception@twmsolicitors.com
Office: Epsom, Guildford, Leatherhead, London SW19, Reigate
Work: A1 E L R1 R2 S1 S2 T2 V W Z(l)
Asoc: Adams, Victoria . . . . Jan 2004

CRAVEN ARMS, Shropshire

DIXON LEWIS SOLICITORS
Unit 2 The Craven Centre Shrewsbury Road Craven Arms Shropshire SY7 9PY
Tel: 01588 672399
E-mail: j.taylor11@btconnect.com
Office: Wellington
Work: K3 N Q S1 W
Ptr: Taylor, Mr Jeremy BSc . . . . Nov 1991

CRAWLEY, West Sussex

ASB LAW ‡
Innovis House 108 High Street Crawley West Sussex RH10 1AS
Tel: 01293 603600 *Fax:* 01293 603666 *Dx:* 57100 CRAWLEY 1
Emergency telephone 01293 603603
E-mail: crawley@asb-law.com
List of partners: C D Armitage, M D Bailey, J E Barry, R W Bell, M E Brown, J W Catterick, J R B Cavell, A J Clinton, R Cowell, R M Curtis, M W Cutler, U M T Danagher, J Grant, I J Greenfield, R C Harris, J A Innes, C A King, F J Lacy Scott, A T J Nosek, A J Pawlik, J K Simmons, A C Taylor, S Thomas, R Thornley-Gibson, C Trelfer
Office: Maidstone
Languages: Afrikaans, Danish, Dutch, French, German, Hebrew, Italian, Polish, Spanish, Turkish
Work: A1 A2 A3 B1 C1 C2 C3 D1 E F1 I J1 K1 K2 L M1 M2 M3 N O P Q R1 S1 S2 T1 T2 W Z(c,e,g,i,l,r)
Emergency Action, Agency, Advocacy, Legal Aid undertaken, Legal Aid Franchise and Member of Accident Line
Ptr: Armitage, Mrs Caroline D MA(Cantab) Director of the Crawley Horsham NHS Trust 1992-1996. . . . . *Oct 1984
Bailey, Mr Michael David Borlase Prize; Harry Strouts Prize President of Sussex Law Society; Legal Aid Area Committee . . . . *§Jun 1965
Barry, Mr John E . . . . *Jan 1969
Bell, Mr Russell W LLB . . . . *§Jun 1975
Clinton, Mr Andrew J LLB(Hons) . . . . *Jan 1990
Grant, Mr Jonathan BA . . . . Oct 1989
Greenfield, Mr Ian J BA; TEP . . . . *Mar 1984
Innes, Mr John A . . . . *Dec 1976
Lacy Scott, Mr Francis J LLB . . . . *Nov 1981
Nosek, Miss Alina T J BA . . . . *Oct 1980
Pawlik, Mr Andrew J . . . . Nov 1978
Taylor, Mr Andrew C LLB . . . . *Oct 1983
Thornley-Gibson, Mrs Rebecca LLB(Hons); LSF. . . . *Oct 1992
Asoc: Cooper, Mr Derek C. . . . . *Dec 1974
Knorpel, Mr Andrew Mark David LLB . . . . *Sep 1997
Loufer, Ms Ashleigh. Sep 1996
Martell, Ms Jan LLB. Oct 1989
Shepherd, Ms Penina . . . . Jan 1999
Ast: Bond, Ms Katy BSc(Hons). . . . . Jul 2002
Gould, Mr Robert LLB(Hons) . . . . Jan 2001
Hussain, Ms Shaheena BA(Hons). . . . . Sep 1997
Huxtable, Mr James. Nov 1999
Kong, Miss Lai BEd(Hons) . . . . *§Nov 1997
Lake, Mrs Denise LLB(Hons); LPC . . . . Sep 1999
Longden, Mr Christopher LLB(European) . . . . *Nov 1997
Lord, Miss Karen . . . . *Oct 1998
Mead, Ms Helen BSc(Hons). . . . . Oct 2000
Philcox, Ms Caroline A BSc; BA. . . . . Aug 1998
Scully, Miss Eleanor LLB(Hons); LPC . . . . *May 1998
Wicks, Ms Catherine . . . . Sep 1998
Con: Hockings, Ms Dorothy LLB(Hons) . . . . Jan 2000

JAMES B BENNETT & CO ‡
Nightingale House 1-3 Brighton Road Crawley West Sussex RH10 6AE
Tel: 01293 544044 *Fax:* 01293 449579 *Dx:* 57103 CRAWLEY
E-mail: info@jbb-law.co.uk
List of partners: G S Bennett, K J Newell
Work: A1 C1 E J1 K1 L R1 S1 W Z(e,h)
Ptr: Bennett, Mr Graeme S Notary Public . . . . *Jun 1979
Newell, Mr Kevin J Mellersh Prize Notary Public. . . . Mar 1974
Ast: Klimaytys, Ms Michelle Laurel. . . . . Mar 2006

BOOTS STARKE GOACHER ‡
Buxton House 2 East Park Crawley West Sussex RH10 6AS
Tel: 01293 539789 *Fax:* 01293 539753 *Dx:* 57108 CRAWLEY 1
E-mail: bsglaw@btconnect.com

CLEMATIS LAW ‡
Nightingale House 1-3 Brighton Road Crawley West Sussex RH10 6AE
Tel: 01293 45 647 / 07595 469023 *Fax:* 01293 404216
Dx: 57111 CRAWLEY
E-mail: info@clematislaw.co.uk

DMH STALLARD LLP
(in association with Law Europe EEIG)
Gainsborough House Pegler Way Crawley West Sussex RH11 7FZ
Tel: 01293 605000 *Fax:* 01293 543760 *Dx:* 57102 CRAWLEY
E-mail: enquiries@dmhstallard.com
Office: Brighton, London EC4
Languages: Dutch, French, German, Italian, Spanish
Work: A1 A3 B1 B2 C1 C2 C3 D1 D2 E F1 F2 G H I J1 K1 K3 K4 L M1 N O P Q R1 R2 S1 S2 T1 T2 U2 V W X Z(b,c,d,e,f,g,h,k,l,m,o,p,q,r,s,t,u,w,x,z,za)

ADRIAN DAGGER ‡
St Andrews House 26 Brighton Road Crawley West Sussex RH10 6AA
Tel: 01293 403399 *Fax:* 01293 403390

THOMAS EGGAR LLP
(in association with Avrio; The Bridge Group; Lexcel)
Belmont House Station Way Crawley West Sussex RH10 1JA
Tel: 01293 742700 *Fax:* 01293 742999 *Dx:* 85715 CRAWLEY
E-mail: gatwick@thomaseggar.com
Office: Chichester, London EC4, Newbury, Southampton, Worthing
Work: A1 A2 A3 B1 B2 C1 C2 C3 D1 D2 E F1 F2 J1 J2 K1 K2 K3 L M2 M3 N O P Q R1 R2 S1 S2 T1 T2 U2 W X Z(b,c,d,e,g,m,o,p,q,r,s,t,w,x,y)

PETER GREENE & CO ‡
International Business Centre Spindle Way Crawley West Sussex RH10 1TG
Tel: 07546 231812 *Fax:* 01293 565504

HARRIS & CO ‡
6 Brighton Road Southgate Crawley West Sussex RH10 6AA
Tel: 01293 537551 *Fax:* 01293 561590 *Dx:* 57101 CRAWLEY
E-mail: info@harrissols.demon.co.uk
List of partners: K R Harris
Work: B1 C1 E J1 L N O P Q S1 S2 T1 T2 W Z(g,h,l,q)
Ptr: Harris, Mr Kenneth R LLB(Lond) . . . . *Jul 1979

C J HOUGH & CO LTD ‡
2 Oak Cottage County Oak Way Crawley West Sussex RH111 7ST
Tel: 01293 734592 / 734596 *Fax:* 020 7023 4927
E-mail: reception@cjhough.co.uk

JEREMY JONES ‡
Little Orchard Chapel Lane Crawley West Sussex RH10 3ET
Tel: 01342 713148 *Fax:* 01342 713148

LEWIS & DICK
18a Brighton Road Crawley West Sussex RH10 6AA
Tel: 01293 526031 *Fax:* 01293 562390 *Dx:* 57109 CRAWLEY
E-mail: crawley@lewis-dick.com
Office: Epsom
Work: C1 D1 E J1 K1 K2 L R2 S1 S2 V W Z(c,d,h)
Fixed Fee Interview undertaken
Ptr: Jones, Mr Owen P LLB . . . . *Jun 1976
Con: Bardell, Mr Eric E LLB(Hons) . . . . *Jun 1975

M23LAW SOLICITORS (HEDLEY-SAUNDERS & CO) ‡
Golf House Horsham Road Pease Pottage Crawley West Sussex RH11 9SG
Tel: 0844 264 0999 *Fax:* 020 3292 1586
Emergency telephone 07973 803727
E-mail: help@m23law.co.uk
List of partners: P F Hedley-Saunders
Languages: French
Work: G H Z(x)
Fixed Fee Interview and Legal Aid undertaken
SPr: Hedley-Saunders, Mr Paul F ★ . . . . Jul 1977
Ast: Wise, Mr Geoffrey. . . . . Aug 2006

ANTHONY MORRIS SOLICITORS ‡
8 Ifield Road Crawley West Sussex RH11 7YY
Tel: 01293 519619 *Fax:* 01293 541898
E-mail: info@anthonymorris.co.uk
List of partners: D Knight, A Morris
Ptr: Knight, Ms Debbie . . . . Jan 2000
Morris, Mr Anthony . . . . Jan 1977

PB LEGAL LIMITED ‡
174 Three Bridges Road Crawley West Sussex RH10 1LE
Tel: 01293 553000 *Fax:* 01293 553001
E-mail: info@pblegal.co.uk

RAWLISON BUTLER LLP ‡
Griffin House 135 High Street Crawley West Sussex RH10 1DQ
Tel: 01293 527744 *Fax:* 01293 520202 *Dx:* 120750 CRAWLEY 8
E-mail: info@rawlisonbutler.com
List of partners: D R Armstrong, N Benson, S J Evans, A Hyams-Parish, A J King, C A Lee, B Matthews, R Munroe, M N O'Shea, A Owen, N A Pentecost, S M Ryan, T D Sadka, C Strange, R M Worthing
Office: Horsham, London W1
Languages: French, German, Italian
Work: A1 A3 B1 B2 C1 C2 C3 E F1 F2 I J1 K1 K2 K3 L M1 M2 M3 N O P Q R1 R2 S1 S2 T1 T2 U1 U2 W X Z(b,c,d,e,i,j,k,l,p,q,w,za)
Emergency Action undertaken
Ptr: Ryan, Mr Sean M. . . . . *Nov 1981
Mem: Armstrong, Mr Digby R . . . . *May 1978
Benson, Mr Neil LLB(Hons)(B'ham) Chairman of the Property Association Training Committee. . . . . Nov 1995
Evans, Mr Stuart J BA(Law); LLM(Cantab) . . . . . *Nov 1987
Hyams-Parish, Mr Antony. . . . . Dec 2000
King, Mr Andrew J . . . . Oct 1993
Lee, Mr Clive A LLB. . . . . *Nov 1986
Munroe, Ms Rachael LLB(Hons). . . . . Sep 2004
O'Shea, Mr Mark Nigel LLB . . . . *Oct 1988
Owen, Miss Abigail BA(Hons)(Law & Criminology). . . *Oct 1998
Pentecost, Mr Nicholas A LLB(Hons) . . . . *Sep 1997
Sadka, Mr Timothy D . . . . *Feb 1987
Worthing, Mr Robert M BA(Hons) . . . . *Aug 1991
Asoc: Arneill, Mr James Iestyn LLB . . . . Sep 2002
Beames, Mr Martin Andrew LLB. . . . . *Oct 1991
Hoad, Mr Andrew M G LLB(Hons). . . . . *Sep 1996
Joll, Ms Vanessa . . . . Sep 2000
Leah, Mrs Elizabeth BA(Hons); LLDip . . . . *Nov 1998
Walsh, Mr William Thomas Alastair LLB. . . . . Oct 2001
Winter, Mr Nigel Carr LLB . . . . Nov 1994
Ast: Axe, Mr Michael Woodstock. . . . . *Apr 2004
Burke, Ms Lorraine Natalia LLB . . . . Sep 2009
Bylett, Miss Liane LLB(Surrey) . . . . Sep 2010
Carlin, Mrs Diane Wendy LLB. . . . . Nov 1995
Hawkins, Mr Andrew . . . . Feb 2005
Hulmes, Ms Kathryn LLB . . . . Aug 2006
Jethwa, Ms Reema LLB(Brunel). . . . . Jan 2010
Jones, Mr Peter. . . . . Nov 2007
McAlister, Mrs Katherine Ann LLB. . . . . Jan 2004
McCarthy, Ms Cassandra LLB(Sussex) . . . . Jul 2006
Miles, Mrs Kay BA(Hons)(Econ & Law) . . . . *Sep 1999
Noble, Mr Brian LLB(Coventry) . . . . Dec 2005
Sutton, Ms Beth. . . . . *Sep 2008
Wiles, Ms Amaris BA(Hons)(History) . . . . Sep 2010

RUSSELL & CO SOLICITORS AND ESTATE AGENTS ‡
12-13 Queens Square Crawley West Sussex RH10 1DY
Tel: 01293 561965 / 0845 300 2809 *Fax:* 01293 521301
Dx: 57110 CRAWLEY
E-mail: post@russell-co-legal.co.uk
List of partners: A Kinnersley, G Parker
Work: B2 I J1 K1 K3 M2 N O Q R2 S1 S2 T1 T2 W Z(j,q,r)
Emergency Action, Agency and Legal Aid Franchise
Ptr: Kinnersley, Mrs Alison. . . . . *Nov 1998
Parker, Mr Grant LLB; BSc . . . . Jan 2003

STEVENSDRAKE ‡
117-119 High Street Crawley West Sussex RH10 1DD
Est: 1782
Tel: 01293 596900 *Fax:* 01293 596968 *Dx:* 57104 CRAWLEY
Emergency telephone 01293 596900
E-mail: info@stevensdrake.com
List of partners: S L Grimshaw, S J Jago, J Lovatt, A Mitchell, M O'Halloran, M K Patel, I C D Paul, G P Penn, G J Pickering, I Price, M Randall
Languages: French, Gujarati
Work: A1 B1 C1 C2 C3 D1 D2 E F1 I J1 K1 K2 K3 L M1 M2 N O P Q R1 S1 S2 T1 T2 U2 V W X Z(b,c,d,e,f,m,q)
Emergency Action, Agency, Advocacy, Fixed Fee Interview, Legal Aid Franchise and Member of Accident Line
Ptr: Grimshaw, Mr Spencer L LLB(Hons) . . . . *§Nov 1987
Jago, Ms Susan Jennifer . . . . Jan 1996
Lovatt, Mr John FILEx. . . . . Oct 2002
Mitchell, Mr Alex . . . . Nov 1995
O'Halloran, Mr Mark. . . . . Jan 2002
Patel, Mr Minesh K LLB . . . . *§Dec 1989
Paul, Mr Ian Charles David BA(Hons). . . . . Jan 1998
Penn, Mr Graham P BA Notary Public. . . . . *Oct 1982
Pickering, Mr Gavin J LLB(NZ) . . . . *Sep 1991
Price, Mr Ian . . . . *Sep 1993
Randall, Mr Michael LLB(Hons) . . . . *Sep 1986
Asoc: Ladd, Miss Emma Clare LLB; PGDipLPC Notary Public Jul 2004
Richards, Ms Eleanor BA(Hons)(Politics & Intern. Relations) . . . . Oct 1993
Ast: Burraston, Mr Richard LLB(Hons). . . . . *Sep 2005
Grindley, Mr Matthew James LLB(Hons)(Law with French Law) . . . . Sep 2007
Jago, Miss Alexa Laura Kate LLB . . . . *Aug 2007
Youngs, Miss Rachel Katherine BSc; MSc; PGDipLaw; LPC . . . . Sep 2006

DAVID STREET & COMPANY ‡
Eagle House 19 Brighton Road Crawley West Sussex RH10 6AE
Tel: 01293 616191 *Fax:* 01293 616404 *Dx:* 57133 CRAWLEY 1
Emergency telephone 07711 105641
E-mail: info@streetlegal.co.uk
List of partners: D L Street
Work: C1 E G H I Q S1 S2 W Z(l,s,t)
Emergency Action, Agency, Advocacy and Legal Aid undertaken
Ptr: Street, Mr David Leonard MA(Cantab) ★ . . . . . . *§Mar 1982
Ast: Luttman, Mr Paul LLB ★. . . . . *Apr 1999

DL THOMAS SOLICITORS ‡
Herondale Herons Lea New Domewood Crawley West Sussex RH10 3HE
Tel: 01342 715215 / 07988 699140 *Fax:* 01342 715215
E-mail: dlt@dlthomas-legal.co.uk

See p112 for the Key to Work Categories & other symbols

VIKING LAW ‡
Worth Corner Business Centre Worth Corner Turners Hill Road Crawley West Sussex RH10 7SL
Tel: 01293 886807
E-mail: info@vikinglaw.co.uk

CREDITON, Devon

CHARLESWORTH NICHOLL & CO ‡
31 High Street Crediton Devon EX17 3AJ
Tel: 01363 774706 *Fax:* 01363 775604 *Dx:* 54200 CREDITON
E-mail: mail@charlesworthnicholl.co.uk
List of partners: M J Nation, C S Nicholl
Languages: French, German, Italian, Spanish
Work: A1 C1 D1 E J1 K1 K3 K4 L P Q R1 S1 S2 T1 T2 V W X Z(c,d)
Emergency Action, Agency, Advocacy, Fixed Fee Interview, Legal Aid undertaken and Legal Aid Franchise
Ptr: Nation, Mrs Mary J LLB . . . . *Apr 1979
Nicholl, Miss Christine Sylvia LLB(Wales) . . . . *§Oct 1982

FILOR EMPLOYMENT LAWYERS ‡
Thorn Park Spreyton Crediton Devon EX17 5AG
Tel: 01647 231475 / 07891 055856 *Fax:* 01647 231265

HOTCHKISS WARBURTON ‡
34 High Street Crediton Devon EX17 3JP
Tel: 01363 774752 *Fax:* 01363 777813 *Dx:* 54202 CREDITON
E-mail: enquiries@hotchkiss-warburton.co.uk
List of partners: G N Hotchkiss, P H Taylor
Work: A1 B1 C1 J1 L R1 R2 S1 S2 T1 W
Fixed Fee Interview undertaken
Ptr: Hotchkiss, Mr Gordon N LLB . . . . *Apr 1976
Taylor, Mr Paul H . . . . *Oct 1998
Ast: Rapley, Miss Lindsay LLB. . . . . *Jul 2005

SYMES ROBINSON & LEE ‡
Manor Office North Street Crediton Devon EX17 2BR
Tel: 01363 775566 *Fax:* 01363 772706 *Dx:* 54203 CREDITON
E-mail: mail@srl-solicitors.co.uk
List of partners: J D Brindley, P d P Langrishe, J C R B Lee, D J P Middlemost, C Trevelyan-Thomas
Office: Budleigh Salterton, Exeter
Languages: French, German
Work: A1 D1 E F1 J1 K1 K3 K4 L N O P Q R1 S1 S2 T2 W Z(k,o,r)
Advocacy undertaken
Ptr: Lee, Mr Jeremy C R B . . . . *§Oct 1978
Trevelyan-Thomas, Mrs Clare LLB(Hons) . . . . *Oct 1983
Ast: Arden, Mr Mark Richard LLB(Hons) . . . . *Jan 1984
Brookes, Miss Naomi BA(Hons); CPD; LPC . . . . *Nov 2010
Justice, Mr Martin BA(Hons). . . . . *Jan 2000

VEITCH PENNY
2 Market Street Crediton Devon EX17 2AL
Tel: 01363 772244 *Fax:* 01363 775874 *Dx:* 54201 CREDITON
Emergency telephone 01363 774771
E-mail: credlaw@veitchpenny.co.uk
Office: Exeter
Work: A1 E L R1 S1 S2 T2 W

SIMON YOUNG ‡
Hill View 1 Waresfoot Drive Crediton Devon EX17 2DG
Tel: 01363 774248 / 07815 291487
E-mail: simon@syoung.co.uk

CREWE, Cheshire

BENTLEY SOLICITORS ‡
No1 Imperial Chambers Prince Albert Street Crewe Cheshire CW1 2DJ
Tel: 01270 509800 *Fax:* 01270 509888
E-mail: info@bentleysolicitor.co.uk
List of partners: A D T Bentley
Work: N Z(q,r)
Ptr: Bentley, Mr Anthony D T BA. . . . . *Jan 1982
Asoc: Bate, Mr Richard BA; LPC . . . . Aug 1999
Cruise, Mrs Jan LLB(Hons) . . . . Aug 1995

BIRCHALL RYAN SOLICITORS
190 Nantwich Road Crewe Cheshire CW2 6BP
Tel: 01270 211115 *Fax:* 01270 580620
E-mail: reception@birchallryan.com
Office: Congleton

FISH AND FISH SOLICITORS ‡
21a Station Road Goostrey Crewe Cheshire CW4 8PJ
Tel: 0844 736 1887 *Fax:* 0844 736 1887
E-mail: info@fishandfish.co.uk

FORSTER DEAN LTD
213 Nantwich Road Crewe Cheshire CW2 6DA
Tel: 01270 254064 *Fax:* 01270 254065 *Dx:* 708521 CREWE 5
E-mail: enquiries@forsterdean.co.uk
Office: Birkenhead, Bootle, Chorley, Eccles, Ellesmere Port, Huyton, Leigh, Liverpool (5 offices), Oldham, Preston, Rochdale, Runcorn, St Helens, Stockport, Warrington, Widnes (2 offices), Wigan
Ptr: Hussain, Abid LLB(Hons) . . . . *Oct 1997

GREEN IMMIGRATION CONSULTANCY ‡
Mensa Meadowfields Buerton Crewe Cheshire CW3 0DF
Tel: 01270 811617 *Fax:* 01270 811617
E-mail: info@greenimmigration.co.uk

HALL SMITH WHITTINGHAM LLP
172-174 Nantwich Road Crewe Cheshire CW2 6BW
Tel: 01270 212000 *Fax:* 01270 259727 *Dx:* 708512 CREWE 5
E-mail: law@hswsolicitors.co.uk
Office: Nantwich
Work: A1 B1 C1 C2 D1 E F1 J1 K1 K2 K3 K4 L N O P Q R1 S1 S2 T1 T2 V W Z(j,l,m,o,p)
Emergency Action, Agency, Advocacy, Fixed Fee Interview, Legal Aid undertaken, Legal Aid Franchise and Member of Accident Line
Ptr: Dodd, Mr Christopher W. . . . . *Jun 1980
Masters, Mrs A Kay LLB • Deputy District Judge . . *Dec 1986
Morgan-Wynne, Mr Richard J LLB. . . . . . *Nov 1983
Percival, Mr John C LLB . . . . *Dec 1975
Wilson, Mrs S Jane LLB • Leeds University Torts Prize 1976 . . . . *Mar 1980
Ast: Coles, Mr Steven LLB(English & French Law) . . . . Nov 2004
Greatbanks, Miss Alison . . . . *Oct 2001
Hilton, Ms Claire . . . . *Apr 2011
Con: Fox, Mr Charles R LLB • Deputy District Judge; Assistant Recorder . . . . *§Apr 1974

HIBBERTS LLP
144 Nantwich Road Crewe Cheshire CW2 6BG
Tel: 01270 215117 *Fax:* 01270 500494 *Dx:* 708510 CREWE 5
E-mail: enquiries@hibberts.com
Office: Ellesmere, Nantwich, Tarporley, Whitchurch
Work: A1 B1 C1 C2 C3 D1 E F1 G H J1 K1 L M1 M2 O P Q R1 S1 T1 T2 V W Z(l,m,t)
Emergency Action, Agency, Advocacy, Fixed Fee Interview and Legal Aid undertaken
Ptr: Badman, Mr Roger LLB. . . . . *Jan 1983
Bailey, Mr Stewart Alexander LLB(Hons) . . . . *Dec 1993
Dimelow, Mr Anthony Stephen BA(Law). . . . . *Sep 1988
Flood, Mr Stuart Macdonald LLB . . . . . . *Dec 1980
Ast: Brooksbank, Miss Carolyn. . . . . Sep 2009
Burton, Ms Rachael. . . . . Jul 2008
Renaudon, Ms Camille . . . . Jun 2008

DAVID LAGO & CO SOLICITORS AND MEDIATORS ‡
Imperial Chambers Prince Albert Street Crewe Cheshire CW1 2DX
Tel: 01270 504850 *Fax:* 01270 504859
E-mail: solicitors@davidlago.co.uk

POOLE ALCOCK
Datum House Electra Way Crewe Cheshire CW1 6ZF
Tel: 01270 502880 *Fax:* 01270 502881 *Dx:* 743390 CREWE
E-mail: crewedatum@poolealcock.co.uk
Office: Alsager, Chester, Congleton, Crewe, Nantwich, Northwich, Sandbach, Warrington

POOLE ALCOCK
(incorporating Timperley & Co)
238-246 Edleston Road Crewe Cheshire CW2 7EH
Tel: 01270 256665 *Fax:* 01270 500482 *Dx:* 20154 CREWE
Emergency telephone 0800 389 7093
E-mail: crewe@poolealcock.co.uk
Office: Alsager, Chester, Congleton, Crewe, Nantwich, Northwich, Sandbach, Warrington
Languages: French, German
Work: A1 B1 C1 D1 E F1 G H J1 K1 L M1 N P R1 S1 T1 V W Z(a,b,c,d,e,f,g,h,j,k,p,s,t)
Emergency Action, Agency, Advocacy, Fixed Fee Interview, Legal Aid undertaken and Member of Accident Line
Ptr: Gaut, Mr David M LLB . . . . *Oct 1988
Rose, Mr Ian M. . . . . *Dec 1974

SPEAKMAN & CO ‡
(incorporating Garnett & Culey)
180 Nantwich Road Crewe Cheshire CW2 6BS
Tel: 01270 214237 *Fax:* 01270 255751
E-mail: law@speakman.co.uk
List of partners: D J Britton, L L Britton, E G Williams
Work: C1 E F1 J1 K1 L N Q S1 W
Emergency Action, Agency, Advocacy, Fixed Fee Interview undertaken and Member of Accident Line
Ptr: Britton, Mr David J LLB(Lond). . . . . . . *Jan 1979
Britton, Ms Laura Louise LLB . . . . Feb 2002
Williams, Mr E Gareth LLB(Lond) . . . . . . *Jun 1977
Ast: Carlisle, Ms Patricia E BA. . . . . *Sep 1988
Con: Meadows, Mr John R LLB(B'ham). . . . . . *§Mar 1968

TAYLOR LEGAL ‡
(incorporating Robert Bygott & Sons)
Old Bank Chambers 24a Market Street Crewe Cheshire CW1 2EL
Tel: 01270 500844 *Fax:* 01270 589806 *Dx:* 20175 CREWE
E-mail: info@taylorhollinshead.co.uk
Work: E J1 N Q R1 S1 S2 W Z(w)
Agency and Fixed Fee Interview undertaken

THORNEYCROFT SOLICITORS ‡
16A The Square London Road Holmes Chapel Crewe Cheshire CW4 7AB
Tel: 01477 536999 *Fax:* 01477 536991 *Dx:* 28102 HOLMES CHAPEL
E-mail: info@thorneycrofts.co.uk

LYNN THORNTON ‡
50 Crewe Road Shavington Crewe Cheshire CW2 5JB
Tel: 01270 567987 *Fax:* 01270 567987

TYRER LAW ‡
7 Westgate Park Hough Crewe Cheshire CW2 5GY
Tel: 01270 842424 *Fax:* 01270 842525

CREWKERNE, Somerset

FASTTRAC SOLICITORS ‡
The Old Warehouse Bincombe Lane Crewkerne Somerset TA18 7BH
Tel: 01460 279288 *Fax:* 0870 738 6254
E-mail: mailbox@fasttrac.co.uk

POOLE & CO ‡
17 Market Street Crewkerne Somerset TA18 7JU
Tel: 01460 279100 *Fax:* 01460 73988 *Dx:* 43401 CREWKERNE
E-mail: enquiries@pooleandco.com
List of partners: J D B Martin, P J L North
Office: Ilminster, London WC1
Work: A1 A2 A3 B1 C1 C2 C3 D1 D2 E F1 F2 J1 K2 L M1 M2 N O P Q R1 R2 S1 T1 T2 V X Z(a,b,c,d,e,f,h,j,k,l,m,o,p,q,r,s,t,u,w,x)
Emergency Action, Agency, Advocacy, Fixed Fee Interview, Legal Aid undertaken and Member of Accident Line
Ptr: Martin, Mr Justin D B . . . . *§Dec 1971
North, Mr Peter J L MA(Cantab). . . . . . . *§Jun 1974
Ast: De Mowbray, Ms Vanessa BA. . . . . . . *Nov 1994
Poole, Mr Adrian . . . . Sep 2001
Con: Collins, Mr Geoffrey S LLB . . . . *Jun 1970

THE STOKES PARTNERSHIP ‡
Kingfisher House Market Square Crewkerne Somerset TA18 7LH
Tel: 01460 279279 *Fax:* 01460 279289 *Dx:* 43400 CREWKERNE
E-mail: info@law-solutions.co.uk
List of partners: J L Butler, B Pang, D Stokes, J Stokes, M R Williamson
Languages: Chinese, French, Malay, Spanish
Ptr: Butler, Ms Joanne Louise LLB. . . . . . . *Nov 1992
Pang, Mr Brendan. . . . . Dec 1991
Stokes, Mr David . . . . Jul 1980
Stokes, Mr Jonathan LLB(Bris) . . . . Oct 1982
Williamson, Mr Michael R LLB; MICM. . . . . . Nov 1986
Ast: Austin, Ms Anna . . . . Sep 2004
Bollington, Mr David LLB(Aberdeen) Notary Public . . *Jun 1972
Lewis, Ms Katherine. . . . . Jul 1998
Newbery, Mrs Melinda Jane. . . . . Nov 1995
Warren, Mrs Sarah T LLB. . . . . *Nov 1991
Wright, Mr Robert Charles BA(Jurisprudence) . . . . *Nov 1992

WILLIAMSONS SOLICITORS ‡
2 Church Street Crewkerne Somerset TA18 7HR
Tel: 01460 200450 *Fax:* 01460 200456
E-mail: info@mrw-law.co.uk

CRICCIETH, Gwynedd

MICHAEL J PARRY ‡
Council Offices High Street Criccieth Gwynedd LL52 0BS
Tel: 01766 523114 *Fax:* 01766 522590
List of partners: M J Parry
Languages: Welsh
Work: K1 L S1 W
Ptr: Parry, Mr Michael J LLB. . . . . *Jun 1977

CRICKHOWELL, Powys

GABB & CO
Old Bank House Beaufort Street Crickhowell Powys NP8 1AD
Tel: 01873 810629 *Fax:* 01873 810485 *Dx:* 100751 CRICKHOWELL
Emergency telephone 01873 854923
E-mail: crickhowell@gabb.co.uk
Office: Abergavenny
Languages: Welsh
Work: A1 B1 C1 C2 C3 D1 E F1 G J1 K1 L M1 M2 N O P Q R1 S1 T1 T2 V W X Z(c,d,h,k,l,m)
Emergency Action, Agency, Advocacy, Fixed Fee Interview, Legal Aid undertaken, Legal Aid Franchise and Member of Accident Line
Con: Maddocks, Mr Glyn F MA. . . . . *Oct 1985

CROMER, Norfolk

HANSELLS
10 Church Street Cromer Norfolk NR27 9ER
Tel: 01263 512003 *Fax:* 01263 515022 *Dx:* 31002 CROMER
E-mail: cromerreception@hansells.co.uk
Office: Aylsham, North Walsham, Norwich (2 offices), Sheringham
Languages: French, German
Work: E L R1 S1 W
Emergency Action, Agency, Advocacy, Fixed Fee Interview, Legal Aid undertaken, Legal Aid Franchise and Member of Accident Line
Asoc: Care, Mr Jonathan P . . . . *May 1978

POPE & CO ‡
The Old Town Hall Prince of Wales Road Cromer Norfolk NR27 9HS
Tel: 01263 513355 *Fax:* 01263 514832 *Dx:* 31001 CROMER
E-mail: admin@popeandcocromer.co.uk
List of partners: G V Pope
Work: A3 B1 C1 C2 D1 E F1 J1 K1 K3 K4 L N O Q S1 S2 W Z(e,l)
Agency, Advocacy and Fixed Fee Interview undertaken
Ptr: Pope, Mr Gregory Victor LLB(Warw); FCIArb . . . . *§Apr 1975
Con: Crosbie, Miss Rachel Marie LLB . . . . . . Dec 2001

WORKING LAW SOLICITORS ‡
The Garden House Cromer Road Sidestrand Cromer Norfolk NR27 0LT
Tel: 01263 576607 *Fax:* 01263 579128
E-mail: sallydavenport@workinglawsolicitors.co.uk

CROOK, Co Durham

HEWITTS
(incorporating Booth & Dixon; Marquis Penna; J R Waite & Alsop; Wager Turner; Cohens)
Post Office House 1-2 Elliott Street Crook Co Durham DL15 8QH
Tel: 01388 762466 *Fax:* 01388 762914 *Dx:* 715826 CROOK 2
E-mail: enquiries@hewitts.co.uk
Office: Bishop Auckland, Darlington, Newton Aycliffe, Stockton-on-Tees
Work: A1 A2 A3 B1 B2 C1 C2 D1 D2 E F1 G H J1 J2 K1 K2 L M1 N O P Q R1 S1 S2 U2 V W X Z(c,d,e,f,g,h,i,j,k,l,m,n,o,p,q,s,t)
Emergency Action, Agency, Advocacy, Fixed Fee Interview, Legal Aid undertaken and Legal Aid Franchise
Ptr: Tweddle, Mr Andrew LLB Coroner. . . . . . . *§Feb 1981
Ast: Foster, Mrs Lorraine. . . . . Oct 2005
Terry, Mr Callum Robert BA(Hons) . . . . . . *Aug 2001

SMITH RODDAM
Corner Chambers Market Place Crook Co Durham DL15 8NE
Tel: 01388 762564 *Fax:* 01388 767120
Dx: 60150 BISHOP AUCKLAND
Office: Bishop Auckland, Shildon
Work: A1 C1 C2 C3 E G H K1 M1 M2 P S1 W Z(l)
Emergency Action, Agency, Advocacy, Fixed Fee Interview and Legal Aid undertaken
Ptr: Harris, Mr David L LLB(Hons). . . . . . . *Oct 1982
Ast: Whittle, Miss Donna Louise LLB(Hons) . . . . . Sep 2002

CROSBY, Merseyside

BLACK NORMAN ‡
67-71 Coronation Road Crosby Merseyside L23 5RE
Tel: 0151 931 2777 *Fax:* 0151 931 4950 *Dx:* 20403 CROSBY
Emergency telephone 0151 931 2777
E-mail: coralmadden@blacknorman.co.uk
List of partners: J J Clark, H S Norman
Work: B1 C1 C2 D1 E G J1 K1 L P Q R1 S1 S2 W Z(l)
Emergency Action, Agency, Advocacy, Fixed Fee Interview, Legal Aid undertaken and Legal Aid Franchise
Ptr: Clark, Ms Jennifer Jane. . . . . Sep 2001
Norman, Mr Howard S . . . . *Jun 1976
Ast: Howard, Mr David S LLB Notary Public . . . . *Jan 1969
Con: Black, Ms S Leslie . . . . *Nov 1941

MORECROFTS SOLICITORS LLP
2 Crown Buildings Liverpool Road Crosby Merseyside L23 5SR
Tel: 0151 924 9234 *Fax:* 0151 931 3165 *Dx:* 20410 CROSBY

E-mail: mail@morecroft.co.uk
Office: Birkenhead, Liverpool (2 offices)
Work: A1 A3 B1 C1 C2 C3 D1 D2 E F1 F2 G H J1 J2 K1 K2 K4 L M1 M2 N O P Q R1 R2 S1 S2 T1 T2 V W X Z(e,i,l,p,q,r)
Emergency Action, Agency, Advocacy, Fixed Fee Interview, Legal Aid undertaken, Legal Aid Franchise and Member of Accident Line
Ptr: Brennan, Miss Carole A LLB . . . . *Oct 1987
Rimmer, Miss Barbara M LLB . . . . *Apr 1978
Ast: Reynolds, Ms Patricia LLB . . . . *Dec 1981

CROSS HILLS, North Yorkshire

TURNERS ‡
41 Main Street Cross Hills North Yorkshire BD20 8TT
Tel: 01535 634149 *Fax:* 01535 636607 *Dx:* 702813 SILSDEN
E-mail: mail@turners.uk.net
List of partners: D T King
Work: A1 C1 D1 E F1 G H J1 K1 L M1 N P Q R1 S1 T2 W Z(d,g,k,l)
Emergency Action, Agency, Advocacy and Fixed Fee Interview undertaken
Ptr: King, Mr David Thomas LLB . . . . *Jun 1979
Asoc: Brockett, Mrs Ruth Elizabeth BSc(Hons) . . . . Oct 1992
Vallow, Mr Michael Philip BA . . . . May 1991

CROSSGATES, North Yorkshire

EMSLEYS
35 Austhorpe Road Crossgates North Yorkshire LS15 8BA
Tel: 0113 260 3115 *Fax:* 0113 260 6693 *Dx:* 13905 CROSSGATES
Emergency telephone 0113 273 7440
E-mail: law@emsleys.co.uk
Office: Castleford, Garforth, Leeds, Rothwell (2 offices)
Languages: French, German
Work: D1 J1 K1 K3 L P R1 S1 W Z(c,h,l,n,p,s)
Emergency Action, Agency, Advocacy, Fixed Fee Interview undertaken and Member of Accident Line
Ptr: Murray, Mr John N LLB . . . . *Dec 1989
Asoc: Abbott, Ms Tina Dawn LLB(Hons) . . . . *Dec 1992
Caines, Miss Juliana LLB(Hons) . . . . *Apr 2002
Higgins, Mr David MCIH . . . . Nov 2005

CROWBOROUGH, East Sussex

CHAPPELL PASCOE ‡
Croham House Croham Road Crowborough East Sussex TN6 2RW
Tel: 01892 664348 *Fax:* 01892 664984 *Dx:* 36854 CROWBOROUGH
Emergency telephone 01892 664348
E-mail: info@chappellpascoe.com
List of partners: C D Chappell, L O Pascoe
Work: D1 F1 J1 J2 K1 K3 L N O Q
Emergency Action, Agency, Advocacy, Fixed Fee Interview, Legal Aid undertaken and Legal Aid Franchise
Ptr: Chappell, Mr Crispin D MA . . . . *Oct 1992
Pascoe, Mr Lee O BA(Hons); DipLaw Talbot Criminal Prize 1992 . . . . *Aug 1995

DONALDSON WEST ‡
Croham House Croham Road Crowborough East Sussex TN6 2RL
Tel: 01892 662233 *Fax:* 01892 601010 *Dx:* 36852 CROWBOROUGH
E-mail: ped@dwlaw-online.com
Languages: French, German
Work: A1 B1 C1 C2 C3 D1 E F1 J1 K1 L M1 N O P Q R1 S1 T1 T2 V W Z(b,c,d,e,h,i,j,k,l,m,p,s,t)
Emergency Action, Agency, Advocacy undertaken and Member of Accident Line

FINCH LEGAL SOLICITORS ‡
4 Spring Gardens Park Lane Crowborough East Sussex TN6 2QN
Tel: 01892 610046 *Fax:* 01892 655292
E-mail: lf@finchlegal.co.uk

GLADSTONES ‡
2 The Broadway Crowborough East Sussex TN6 1DF
Tel: 01892 610260 *Fax:* 01892 610916
List of partners: E N Panton
Languages: French
Work: K1 S1 W
Ptr: Panton, Mr Eric N. . . . . *Jun 1962

LEIGH WHITE ‡
Park Grove Lye Green Crowborough East Sussex TN6 1UU
Tel: 01892 655808 *Fax:* 01892 655808
E-mail: info@leighwhite.co.uk

VANCE HARRIS ‡
1 Beacon Road Crowborough East Sussex TN6 1AF
Tel: 01892 653434 *Fax:* 01892 654760 *Dx:* 36850 CROWBOROUGH
E-mail: crowborough@vanceharris.co.uk
List of partners: V A Gerdes, K M Macdonald, S P S Vance
Office: London E14
Work: C1 C2 E K1 L R1 R2 S1 S2 T2 W Z(c)
Ptr: Gerdes, Mrs Valerie Ann . . . . *Jun 1970
Vance, Mr Simon P S . . . . *Nov 1967
Ast: Miller, Mrs Julie Ann. . . . . *Oct 1995

G A WAITE SOLICITOR ‡
PO Box 156 Crowborough East Sussex TN6 1RX
Tel: 01892 652800 *Fax:* 01892 610795
E-mail: info@waiteslegal.co.uk
List of partners: G A Waite
Work: C1 E R2 S1 S2 W Z(h)
Ptr: Waite, Mr Graham A . . . . *Jan 1980

TREVOR WEST PROPERTY LAWYER ‡
Glenholme Church Road Rotherfield Crowborough East Sussex TN6 3LG
Tel: 01892 853135 *Fax:* 01892 853870
E-mail: mail@rotherfieldlawyer.co.uk
List of partners: T J West
Ptr: West, Mr Trevor John. . . . . Nov 1962

CROWTHORNE, Bracknell Forest

DICKENS & CO ‡
Richmond House 281 High Street Crowthorne Bracknell Forest RG45 7AH
Tel: 01344 772901 / 776151
List of partners: K C Dickens, M T Dickens
Work: A1 B1 C1 D1 E F1 G H J1 K1 L M1 N O P Q R1 S1 T1 V W Z(c,j,m)
Emergency Action, Agency, Advocacy, Fixed Fee Interview and Legal Aid undertaken
Ptr: Dickens, Mr Kenneth Clive . . . . *Dec 1976
Dickens, Ms Marian T LLB . . . . *May 1976

ANTHONY IGBINIYESU ‡
18 Talavera Close Dukes Ride Crowthorne Bracknell Forest RG45 6DS
Tel: 01344 779579

ROWBERRYS ‡
Sherwood House 104 High Street Crowthorne Bracknell Forest RG45 7AX
Tel: 01344 775311 *Fax:* 01344 779353 *Dx:* 48600 CROWTHORNE
E-mail: info@rowberrys.co.uk
List of partners: N Bhatti, S G Halliday
Work: A1 C1 C2 D1 E J1 K1 K3 L N O Q R2 S1 S2 T2 W Z(c,j,q,r)
Ptr: Bhatti, Miss Nilu LLB . . . . Jul 1992
Halliday, Mr Stirling George LLB. . . . . *Dec 1987

ROSEMARY SMITH & CO ‡
Sydenham House Chambers 97 High Street Crowthorne Bracknell Forest RG45 7AD
Tel: 01344 777441 *Fax:* 01344 778873 *Dx:* 48601 CROWTHORNE
E-mail: law@rosemarysmithandco.com
List of partners: S Durairajah, H M Johnson
Work: C1 C2 E F1 J1 K1 K3 L N O Q S1 S2 T2 V W Z(m)
Emergency Action, Agency, Advocacy, Fixed Fee Interview, Legal Aid undertaken and Legal Aid Franchise
Ptr: Durairajah, Ms Shanthi LLB(Lond). . . . . Nov 1992
Johnson, Mrs Helen Marie LLB(Soton) . . . . Jun 1978

CROYDON, Surrey

APT SOLICITORS ‡
128 Sutherland Road Croydon Surrey CR0 3QJ
Tel: 020 8689 7292 *Fax:* 020 8684 4574
E-mail: admin@aptsolicitors.com

AISTON SOLICITORS ‡
43 Friends Road Croydon Surrey CR0 1ED
Tel: 020 8681 0123 *Fax:* 020 8688 1629
E-mail: enquiries@aistonsolicitors.co.uk
List of partners: N A Aiston
Languages: French, German
Work: B1 C1 C2 E F1 F2 J1 K1 K2 K3 L O Q R2 S1 S2 T1 T2 W Z(q)
Agency undertaken
Ptr: Aiston, Mr Neil A LLB . . . . *Jun 1979

ALFRED JAMES & CO ‡
406a Brighton Road South Croydon Surrey CR2 6AN
Est: 2000
Tel: 020 8681 4627 *Fax:* 020 8681 8281
Emergency telephone 07958 288920
E-mail: solicitors@alfred-james.com
List of partners: A Sijuwade
Languages: Yoruba
Work: G J1 K1 K3 L N O Q S1 S2 W Z(a,i,p,r)
Fixed Fee Interview undertaken
Ptr: Sijuwade, Mr Adedeji LLB(Hons) . . . . Jan 2006

ALLEN BARFIELDS ‡
Woolwich House 43 George Street Croydon Surrey CR9 1EY
Tel: 020 8680 2050 *Fax:* 020 8686 6948 *Dx:* 2632 CROYDON
E-mail: mail@allenbarfields.co.uk
List of partners: P N Colman, N Leonard, I H Miller, C E Thomas
Office: West Wickham
Work: C1 C2 E J1 K1 K3 K4 L N O Q R2 S1 S2 W Z(i,l,r)
Agency, Fixed Fee Interview undertaken and Member of Accident Line
Ptr: Leonard, Mr Nigel. . . . . May 1981
Thomas, Mr Christopher Edward . . . . Dec 1987
Con: Addington-Smith, Mr Nigel . . . . *Dec 1970
Copeland, Mr Roger A LLB . . . . *Oct 1970
Kirby, Mr Alan David . . . . *Jan 1971

AMOSU ROBINSHAW SOLICITORS ‡
Suite 25 Suffolk House George Street Croydon Surrey CR0 1PE
Tel: 020 8688 2573 *Fax:* 020 8760 9239 *Dx:* 2618 CROYDON
E-mail: dipali@amosurorobinshaw.co.uk

ANDERSONS ‡
Boswell Cottage 19 South End Croydon Surrey CR0 1BE
Tel: 020 8680 3131 *Fax:* 020 8688 7058
Dx: 38456 SOUTH CROYDON
E-mail: info@anderlaw.co.uk
List of partners: R A Ainsworth
Languages: French, German, Italian
Work: B1 C1 C2 E G I J1 K1 L M2 N O P Q R1 R2 S1 T1 T2 V W Z(c,h,i,j,o)
Emergency Action, Agency, Advocacy, Legal Aid undertaken and Member of Accident Line
Ptr: Ainsworth, Mr Robert A . . . . *Jan 1984
Ast: Christofi, Mr Christopher Ian LLB(Hons)(Wales) . . . *Nov 1994
Con: Anderson, Mr Christopher J . . . . *Dec 1967
Coe, Mr Peter H. . . . . *Jun 1975
Fletcher, Mr Digby Martin BA ♦ . . . . Dec 1974

ANDREWS & MONROE SOLICITORS ‡
41 Flagon Court 18 St Andrews Road Croydon Surrey CR0 1BU
Tel: 020 8686 5862 / 07521 844993 *Fax:* 0871 900 4422
E-mail: info@andrewsmonroe.co.uk

ATKINS HOPE SOLICITORS ‡
North End Chambers 74-78 North End Croydon Surrey CR9 1SD
Tel: 020 8680 5018 *Fax:* 020 8688 8347 *Dx:* 2629 CROYDON
Emergency telephone 020 8771 7789
E-mail: enquiries@atkinshope.co.uk
List of partners: J R Bull, C R Collier, C G Furness, N J P Thomas
Work: B2 D1 D2 F1 G H K1 N Q W Z(q,r)
Emergency Action, Agency, Advocacy, Fixed Fee Interview, Legal Aid undertaken, Legal Aid Franchise and Member of Accident Line
Ptr: Bull, Mr Jeremy R LLB . . . . Mar 1984
Collier, Ms Charlotte R LLB . . . . *Oct 1984
Furness, Mr Colin G BSc . . . . *Dec 1974
Thomas, Mr Nicholas J P LLB. . . . . *Sep 1980

AWAN SOLICITORS
Airport House Purley Way Croydon Surrey CR0 0XZ
Tel: 020 8781 1838
Emergency telephone 07949 660118
E-mail: info@awansolicitors.co.uk
Office: Kenley
Languages: French, Italian, Punjabi, Spanish, Urdu
Work: B1 G J1 K1 K3 L M4 N O Q S2 Z(i,p,q)
Emergency Action, Agency, Advocacy and Fixed Fee Interview undertaken
Ptr: Awan, Mr Mumtaz Ahmed Justice of the Peace . . . . Nov 1993

BADHAMS LAW (A TRADING NAME OF PARABIS LAW LLP) ‡
8 Bedford Park Croydon Surrey CR0 2AP
Tel: 0844 245 4000 *Fax:* 020 8688 3166 / 0844 245 4501
Dx: 144481 CROYDON 25
List of partners: E F Adams, L Allan, A J Baker, J A Bates, S M Beckwith, K Birdi, R Bramall, D R Burt, J D Burt, A Bushell, C Cobb, J P Collins, A Colombo, C L Cooper, S G Cornfield, H N E Cotes, P G Court, S M Davies, R J Dell, S N Dhillon, J L Dixon, M J Dyson, D J D Edwards, M Fanning, C M Foulkes, T N Francis, K R Gaston, J A Gillespie, C Gough, H Grimbaldstone, M J Gwilliam, D Hanison, M B Harrison, A S A Hills, P James, N Kanwar, S Killip, L F Maclachlan, A H McDougall, J E Messervy-Whiting, D R Metcalfe, J Morris, C M Mulligan, J Newman, A Norrie, K Oldfield, T G Oliver, J W J Parker, S Phillips, N D Plant, M J Ratcliff, A Rennie, J T Roberts, R M Salvini, L Shaw, T Short, M R Sivil, M Smith, A Steel, P D Taylor, J L B Tetley, C Wallace, L Watts, A R N White, P M Whitfield, R Whybrew, G Wicks, J A Wilkinson, N P R Yates, F Zimmerman
Office: Colchester, Evesham, Leeds, London EC2, London EC3, Manchester (2 offices)
Work: E J2 N O Q Z(j,u)
Ptr: Colombo, Mr Alexander. . . . . *Nov 1997
Dell, Mr Robert John LLB(Hons). . . . . *Jan 1999
Dhillon, Mrs Sharanjit N LLB . . . . *Sep 1997
Dyson, Mr Mark J. . . . . Nov 1992
Harrison, Mr Myles Brewster LLB . . . . Nov 1999
James, Mr Peter LLB(Hons). . . . . Jul 1994
Killip, Ms Samantha LLB . . . . Oct 1999
Taylor, Mr Paul D . . . . *Dec 1975
Wilkinson, Mrs Julia Annette LLB(Hons)(Law & French); SFE . . . . *Jun 1990
Asoc: Ison, Miss Rebecca Ann LLB(Hons). . . . . *Oct 2000
Thompson, Ms Antonia . . . . Aug 1997
Ast: Ginnaw, Ms Joanna. . . . . Sep 1996
Hogg, Ms Jennifer. . . . . Nov 2003
Kemp, Ms Allison . . . . Nov 2006

BARNES HARRILD & DYER ‡
76 London Road Croydon Surrey CR0 2TB
Tel: 020 8681 5128 *Fax:* 020 8686 9776 *Dx:* 2646 CROYDON
Emergency telephone 020 8686 0731
E-mail: bhdsolicitors@yahoo.co.uk
List of partners: B K Barnes, M D Dyer
Work: D1 G H J1 K1 Z(l,p)
Emergency Action, Agency, Advocacy, Fixed Fee Interview, Legal Aid undertaken and Legal Aid Franchise
Ptr: Barnes, Mr Barry K . . . . *Nov 1969
Dyer, Mr Michael D LLB. . . . . *Oct 1975

BECKETT SOLICITORS ‡
22 Outram Road Croydon Surrey CR0 6XE
Tel: 020 8405 0750
E-mail: nadia.beckett@beckett-solicitors.co.uk

BERKELEYS SOLICITORS ‡
3rd Floor Vistec House 185 London Road Croydon Surrey CR0 2RJ
Tel: 020 8760 5064 *Fax:* 020 8688 0119 *Dx:* 2611 CROYDON
E-mail: info@berkeleyssolicitors.com

BLACKFORDS LLP ‡
Hill House 1 Mint Walk Croydon Surrey CR0 1EA
Tel: 020 8686 6232 *Fax:* 020 8681 5078 *Dx:* 2617 CROYDON
Emergency telephone 07876 081080
E-mail: croydon@blackfords.com
List of partners: G R Bloxsome, T Francis, P M Troy
Office: Cardiff, London EC4, Woking
Work: B2 D1 E G H J1 K1 L N Q S1 W Z(c)
Emergency Action, Advocacy, Fixed Fee Interview, Legal Aid undertaken and Member of Accident Line
Ptr: Bloxsome, Mr Gary Roy. . . . . *Dec 1991
Troy, Ms Pauline M LLB ♦. . . . . *Aug 1989
Ast: Ball, Ms Lynn H LLB(L'pool) ♦. . . . . Jun 1979
Floyd, Mr Andrew V BA ★. . . . . Feb 1996
Payne, Miss Diana BA ★ . . . . *Nov 1990
Con: Barnes, Mr Francis J ♦ . . . . *Dec 1968
Thompson, Ms Elaine J LLB . . . . *Apr 1974

BRAIDWOOD LAW PRACTICE SOLICITORS ‡
19 Stafford Road Croydon Surrey CR0 4NG
Tel: 020 8726 7926 *Fax:* 020 8686 9186
E-mail: braidwoodlaw@ymail.com

COGENT LAW (incorporating Rymills)
Exchange Court 8 Bedford Park Croydon Surrey CR0 2AP
Tel: 0844 245 4452 *Fax:* 0870 832 5302 *Dx:* 144482 CROYDON 25
E-mail: info@cogentclaims.co.uk
Office: Leeds
Ptr: Addyman, Mr Nicholas James Springett. . . . . Nov 1992
Cure, Mr Jonathan Peter LLB . . . . *Nov 1990
O'Callaghan, Mr Mark P LLB . . . . Nov 1992
Rodgers, Mr Simon Patrick . . . . Nov 1997
Ast: Badcock, Miss Joanne Margaret LLB . . . . *Jul 1990
Fowle, Ruchi . . . . Mar 2001
Hussain, Ms Hena . . . . Jan 2003
Kusi-Appauh, Miss Adwoa BA(Hons) . . . . *Dec 1997
Lloyd, Mr Mark . . . . Jan 2001
Millar, Ms Suzanne . . . . Sep 2002
Tahsin, Mr Omar H . . . . Jul 2000

COOK & PARTNERS ‡
241 Lower Addiscombe Road Croydon Surrey CR0 6RD
Tel: 020 8655 4466 *Fax:* 020 8656 7755 *Dx:* 2656 CROYDON
List of partners: C J Cook, I J Douglas

See p112 for the Key to Work Categories & other symbols

Work: B1 C1 C2 C3 E F1 J1 K1 L N O P Q R2 S1 S2 W Z(d,h,l,q)
Emergency Action, Agency and Advocacy undertaken
Ptr: Cook, Mr Christopher James LLB(Hons). . . . . *Jul 1978
Douglas, Mr Ian James LLB ♦. . . . . *Feb 1991

CUNNINGTONS
Toronto House 49b South End Croydon Surrey CR0 1BF
Tel: 020 8688 8446 *Fax:* 020 8686 2147 *Dx:* 2612 CROYDON
E-mail: jason.bradshaw@cunningtons.co.uk
Office: Braintree (2 offices), Ilford, Solihull, Wickford
Work: E L S1 S2 W
Ptr: Bradshaw, Mr Jason Peter . . . . Mar 1999
Brothers, Mr Nicholas S LLB(Hons). . . . . *Nov 1992
Dias, Mr Christopher LLB(Hons). . . . . Oct 2001
Asoc: Crystal, Mr Celestino LLB(Hons) . . . . Aug 2003

DANIEL CURRY & CO ‡
46 High Street Croydon Surrey CR0 1YB
Tel: 020 8680 2188 *Fax:* 020 8688 8278 *Dx:* 84210 CROYDON 1
E-mail: curryddc@aol.com
List of partners: D D Curry
Languages: Hindi, Urdu
Work: B1 C1 D1 D2 E F1 F2 J1 K1 K3 K4 L N O P Q R2 S1 S2 W Z(c,d,j,l,p,q,r)
Emergency Action, Agency, Advocacy, Fixed Fee Interview, Legal Aid undertaken and Legal Aid Franchise
SPr: Curry, Mr Daniel D BA(Law). . . . . *Jun 1983
Ast: Andrews, Mr Paul I BA(Kent) . . . . Jun 1977
Gulliver, Mrs Sheila Ann LLB(Hons) . . . . *Nov 1982
Hussain, Mr Saleem LLB(Hons). . . . . *Aug 2002
McGilvray, Mrs Patrcia Jean LLB(Hons). . . . . Oct 1992
Saika, Mrs Hersha Shamjibhai Sherein . . . . *May 2007

DZIMITROWICZ YORK ‡
The White House 6 Laud Street Croydon Surrey CR0 1ST
Tel: 020 8667 0340 *Fax:* 020 8667 0690
List of partners: A P Dzimitrowicz, K M York
Work: B1 C1 E K1 L N Q S1 S2
Agency and Advocacy undertaken
Ptr: Dzimitrowicz, Mr Antony P LLB(Soton) . . . . *Dec 1981
York, Mrs Krystyna M . . . . *Dec 1991

EL MURPHY & CO ‡
Streeter Marshall 74 High Street Croydon Surrey CR9 2UU
Tel: 020 8680 2638 *Fax:* 020 8253 4870 *Dx:* 2623 CROYDON
E-mail: info@streetermarshall.com

G H LAW ‡
22 Barclay Road Croydon Surrey CR0 1JN
Tel: 020 8680 5095 *Fax:* 020 8760 9544
E-mail: ghowardco@aol.com

GOWENS LLP ‡
Davis House Robert Street Croydon Surrey CR0 1QQ
Tel: 020 8680 2200 *Fax:* 020 8688 1804 *Dx:* 2624 CROYDON
E-mail: info@gowens.co.uk

GRANTS SOLICITORS ‡
The Old Tithe Barn 520 Purley Way Croydon Surrey CR0 4RE
Tel: 020 8288 8899 *Fax:* 020 8781 1227 *Dx:* 151220 CROYDON 34
E-mail: email@grantssolicitors.com
Languages: French, Hindi
Work: D1 K1 K3 L S1 S2 V W Z(p)
Emergency Action, Advocacy, Fixed Fee Interview, Legal Aid undertaken and Legal Aid Franchise

GREATER LONDON SOLICITORS ‡
First Floor 343 London Road Croydon Surrey CR0 3PA
Tel: 020 8684 7044

HARTWIG NOTARY CHAMBERS ‡
4 Dingwall Road Croydon Surrey CR9 3RG
Tel: 020 8681 2893 *Fax:* 020 8681 8183
E-mail: hartwig@beeb.net
List of partners: H J Hartwig
Office: London SW1, London W1
Languages: French, German, Italian, Spanish
Work: A1 B1 C1 C2 C3 D1 E J1 K1 M1 M2 N P R1 S1 T1 T2 W Z(b,d,e,f,i)
Legal Aid undertaken and Member of Accident Line
Ast: Aspden, Miss Janet LLB(Lond) Notary Public . . . . *May 1980
Kuhn, Mr Manfred Philipp LLM Notary Public . . . . *Mar 1993

HEDLEYS SOLICITORS LLP
308 High Street Croydon Surrey CR0 1NG
Tel: 020 8667 0677 *Fax:* 020 8680 1710
Office: East Horsley, Leatherhead

HIACE SOLICITORS ‡
24 Barclay Road Croydon Surrey CR0 1JN
Tel: 020 8686 3777 *Fax:* 020 8686 3778 *Dx:* 2607 CROYDON
Emergency telephone 07904 091877
E-mail: admin@hiacesolicitors.com
List of partners: H Anyiam
Work: G H Z(g,i)
Agency, Legal Aid undertaken and Legal Aid Franchise
SPr: Anyiam, Mr Herbert . . . . Aug 1998

ICS SOLICITORS ‡
1st Floor Crown House 405 London Road Croydon Surrey CR0 3PE
Tel: 020 8664 4670
E-mail: icssolicitors@yahoo.co.uk

DAVID L JONES ‡
8 Barnfield Avenue Croydon Surrey CR0 8SE
Tel: 020 8656 1915

KKS SOLICITORS ‡
286 Mitcham Road Croydon Surrey CR0 3JN
Tel: 020 8239 8585 *Fax:* 020 8251 8351

LAM & MEERABUX SOLICITORS ‡
Cygnet House 12-14 Sydenham Road Croydon Surrey CR0 2EE
Tel: 020 8253 0099 *Fax:* 020 8688 4722 *Dx:* 2621 CROYDON
E-mail: info@lammeerabux.com

LEACH RAWLENCE & HART ‡
53 Chatsworth Road Croydon Surrey CR9 1LE
Tel: 020 8680 5850 *Fax:* 020 8681 3169 *Dx:* 97475 CROYDON 6
List of partners: J W E Leach, P R Tanner
Languages: French, German
Work: C1 E F1 J1 K3 L O Q S1 S2 T2 W
Ptr: Leach, Mr John W Edward . . . . *§Jun 1963
Tanner, Mr Peter R BA(Hons) . . . . *Jun 1981
Asoc: Webster, Mr John Scott LLB(Lond); TEP. . . . . *Jun 1981
Ast: Lowe, Miss Fiona Vanessa LLB . . . . *May 2008
Miah, Mr Koysor LLB . . . . *Jul 2010

ANTHONY LEONARD ASSOCIATES ‡
Airport House Purley Way Croydon Surrey CR0 0XZ
Tel: 020 8288 3548 *Fax:* 020 8288 3549
E-mail: info@anthonyleonard.co.uk
List of partners: A L Webb
Office: Croydon
SPr: Webb, Mr Anthony Leonard LLB . . . . *Oct 1990

ANTHONY LEONARD ASSOCIATES
242 Wickham Road Shirley Croydon Surrey CR0 8BJ
Tel: 020 8654 7757 *Fax:* 020 8654 4336
E-mail: info@anthonyleonard.co.uk
Office: Croydon

LIM & PARTNERS ‡
Unit 13 Wing Yip Centre 544 Purley Way Croydon Surrey CR0 4NZ
Tel: 020 8649 9988

ROGER LONG & CO ‡
PO Box 2939 Purley Croydon Surrey CR8 1WN
Tel: 020 8668 5071
Emergency telephone 07850 388688
E-mail: solicitors@rogerlong.co.uk
List of partners: R B Long
Work: D1 D2 G H K1 K3
Emergency Action, Agency, Advocacy, Fixed Fee Interview, Legal Aid undertaken and Legal Aid Franchise
SPr: Long, Mr Roger B BA; LLM(Lond). . . . . *Oct 1982
Ast: Hardy, Mr Robert Charles BSc . . . . *May 2002

MCMILLAN WILLIAMS
56-58 Central Parade New Addington Croydon Surrey CR0 0JD
Tel: 01689 848311 *Fax:* 01689 846946 *Dx:* 53360 WARLINGHAM
Emergency telephone 020 8660 3383
E-mail: newaddington@mcmillan-williams.co.uk
Office: Carshalton, Coulsdon, Mitcham, South Croydon, Thornton Heath, Wallington
Languages: Bengali, French, Hindi, Italian, Punjabi, Urdu
Work: A3 D1 G H L N O Q S1 Z(b,q,r)
Fixed Fee Interview and Legal Aid undertaken
Ptr: McKeown, Miss Denise LLB. . . . . *Nov 1995
Oghoetuoma, Mr Henry Oritsematosan . . . . *Aug 1996
Smith, Mr Colum Jeffrey LLB . . . . *Oct 1993
Ast: Choudhury, Hasina Khatun . . . . Sep 2006
Corbett, Ms Sarah. . . . . Oct 2008
Hurney, Ms Lauren . . . . Sep 2008
James, Mr Justin . . . . Jan 2006

THOMAS MANSFIELD LLP ‡
Ground Floor Unit 2 Christopher Wren Yard Croydon Surrey CR0 1QG
Tel: 0845 601 7756 *Fax:* 020 8681 8141
E-mail: info@thomasmansfield.com
Office: Birmingham, London E1, Manchester

MANSOURI & SON ‡
37a-37b High Street Croydon Surrey CR0 1QB
Tel: 020 8401 7352 *Fax:* 020 8401 7351
Emergency telephone 07966 259252
E-mail: info@solicitorsfirm.com
List of partners: C Mansouri
Languages: Arabic, Farsi
Work: B1 B2 C1 E F1 G H K1 K3 L M2 M4 N O Q S2 W Z(f,g,i,l,n)
Emergency Action, Agency, Fixed Fee Interview, Legal Aid undertaken and Legal Aid Franchise
SPr: Mansouri, Dr Cyrus LLB(Hons); LLM . . . . Sep 2000

MARTIN SEARLE
8 Bedford Park Croydon Surrey CR0 2AP
Tel: 020 8256 4490
E-mail: info@ms-solicitors.co.uk
Office: Brighton

NIKKI MODIE & CO ‡
Crown House 405 London Road Croydon Surrey CR0 3PE
Tel: 0870 700 0160 *Fax:* 07092 807422
Emergency telephone 0870 700 0160
E-mail: info@nikkimodie-solicitors.co.uk
Languages: Bengali, Punjabi, Urdu, Yoruba
Work: B2 D2 E F1 F2 I J1 J2 K1 K3 L M4 N O P Q R2 S1 S2 W X Z(c,d,e,f,i,j,k,q,r,w)
Agency, Advocacy, Fixed Fee Interview undertaken and Member of Accident Line

ORMERODS ‡
(incorporating Gray Marshall & Campbell; The Heap Partnership; Quirke & Wombwell & Coningsbys)
45 Friends Road Croydon Surrey CR0 1ED
Tel: 020 8686 5000 *Fax:* 020 8680 0972 *Dx:* 2619 CROYDON
E-mail: enquiries@ormerods.co.uk
List of partners: J A Borrow, P A Conrathe, S J H Cook, G D Jones, M Jones, P I King, S P McIlwaine, M R Walters, P M Woods
Office: London SW19, Reigate
Languages: French, Gujarati, Hindi
Work: B1 B2 C1 C2 D1 D2 E F1 H I J1 K1 K3 K4 L N O Q R1 R2 S1 W X Z(c,d,g,i,l,m,p,q)
Emergency Action, Agency, Advocacy, Fixed Fee Interview, Legal Aid undertaken and Member of Accident Line
Ptr: Borrow, Mrs Janet A LLB(Lond) . . . . *Oct 1982
Conrathe, Mr Paul Antony BA(Hons) . . . . *Oct 1995
Cook, Mr Simon J H BA. . . . . *Oct 1986
Jones, Mr Graham D BA(Oxon). . . . . *§Jul 1974
Jones, Mr Mark LLB(Hons) . . . . Sep 1996
King, Miss Patricia Irene BSc . . . . *Dec 1993
McIlwaine, Mr Simon P . . . . Apr 1986
Walters, Miss Maureen R LLB. . . . . *Oct 1991
Woods, Mr Peter M LLB. . . . . *Oct 1985
Ast: Bates, Mr Roger Philip . . . . Mar 2000
Bogan, Mr Howard . . . . Sep 1994
Bush, Mr Gregory LLB; BComm. . . . . *Aug 1999
Chapman, Ms Emma LLB. . . . . *Jul 1990
Eldridge-Hinmons, Mrs Tracey BA(Hons) . . . . Apr 1990
Goldstein, Mr David BA(Hons) ★ . . . . *Jul 2001
Ryan, Miss Mary . . . . Feb 2001
Tunbridge, Mrs Rosamond E . . . . *May 1978
Con: Marshall, Mr Stephen . . . . *Dec 1978
Patterson, Mr Philip H LLM; BA . . . . *Dec 1977

PERCY HOLT & NOWERS ‡
42 George Street Croydon Surrey CR9 1NE
Tel: 020 8688 3603 *Fax:* 020 8681 3830 *Dx:* 2613 CROYDON
List of partners: G A Nowers, D A Patterson
Work: E S1 T1 T2 W
Ptr: Nowers, Mr Graham A . . . . *Apr 1962
Patterson, Mr Derek A . . . . *Jan 1967

PRO-LEAGLE ‡
Acorn House 74-94 Cherry Orchard Road Croydon Surrey CR0 6BA
Tel: 020 8680 0088 *Fax:* 020 8680 1996

R&H LAW ‡
Southbridge House Southbridge Place Croydon Surrey CR0 4HA
Tel: 0800 046 1472 *Fax:* 020 8240 6636
List of partners: R Rocker
Ptr: Rocker, Mr Robert. . . . . Nov 1997

THOMAS SANCHEZ SOLICITORS ‡
32 Leslie Park Road Croydon Surrey CR0 6TN
Tel: 020 3372 5387 *Fax:* 020 3489 0874
E-mail: info@thomassanchez.co.uk

SIMMAN SOLICITORS ‡
107 Church Street Croydon Surrey CR0 1RN
Tel: 020 8686 1085 *Fax:* 020 8686 4385
E-mail: legal@simmansolicitors.org.uk
List of partners: N Bakshi
SPr: Bakshi, Navaljit . . . . Mar 1998

STATUS LEGAL ‡
86 South End Croydon Surrey CR0 1DQ
Tel: 020 8649 9204 *Fax:* 020 8688 4625

STREETER MARSHALL ‡
(incorporating E L Murphy & Co)
74 High Street Croydon Surrey CR9 2UU
Tel: 020 8680 2638 *Fax:* 020 8253 4870 *Dx:* 2623 CROYDON
E-mail: info@streetermarshall.co.uk
List of partners: P S Bowness, P J Cook, I S Dosanjh, T J Farrington, R T Fielding, G R Hopkins, D G Moore, J J Moore, T C Moore, A R Pickering, M B Smeed
Office: Purley, Warlingham
Work: B1 C1 C2 D1 E F1 J1 K1 L N O Q R1 S1 T1 T2 W X Z(b,c,d,e,j,k,l,o,q,t)
Emergency Action, Agency, Legal Aid undertaken and Legal Aid Franchise
Ptr: Dosanjh, Inderjit S LLB . . . . *Nov 1990
Farrington, Mr Timothy J BA(Hons)(Nott'm) . . . . . . *Nov 1999
Fielding, Mr Richard T LLB . . . . *May 1983
Moore, Mr David G . . . . *Dec 1975
Moore, Mr Jonathan J. . . . . *Dec 1975
Moore, Mr Timothy C . . . . *Oct 1972
Smeed, Mr Mark Bryan LLB(Leics) . . . . *Nov 1994
Asoc: Howes, Miss Charlotte Lucy. . . . . Mar 2006
Ast: Adams, Mr Darren . . . . Apr 2002
Boodt, Mr Pieter LLB . . . . May 2008
Gilbert, Miss Sophie. . . . . Dec 2006
Haxton, Sian . . . . *May 2004
Jenkins, Mr Matthew Roy LLB. . . . . Jan 2009
Mendes da Costa, Mr Tim. . . . . *Sep 2006
Con: Pearce, Mr Gregory E LLB . . . . *Dec 1978

SURREY SOLICITORS ‡
Charter House 29a London Road Croydon Surrey CR0 2RE
Tel: 020 8666 0330 *Fax:* 0870 211 5889
E-mail: surreysolicitors@blueyonder.co.uk

VICTOR CLIFFORD SOLICITORS ‡
Cambridge House 16-18 Wellesley Road Croydon Surrey CR0 2DD
Tel: 07947 446310 *Fax:* 020 8289 9993

ROBERT G WILLIAMS & CO SOLICITORS ‡
77a George Street Croydon Surrey CR0 1LD
Tel: 020 8681 3121 *Fax:* 020 8681 3242 *Dx:* 2681 CROYDON
Work: L N Q S1 W Z(c)

CUCKFIELD, West Sussex

GUEST & CO ‡
West Riddens Farm Anstye Cross Cuckfield West Sussex RH17 5AH
Tel: 01444 413731
List of partners: J A T Guest
Work: E L R1 S2 T1 W
Ptr: Guest, Mr John A T . . . . *Dec 1969

CULCHETH, Warrington

DOOTSONS LLP
23 Jackson Avenue Culcheth Warrington WA3 4EJ
Tel: 01925 765212 *Dx:* 13837 CULCHETH
E-mail: lawyers@dootsons.co.uk
Office: Atherton, Leigh
Work: A1 C1 D1 E J1 K1 L O Q R1 S1 T1 W Z(l)
Mem: Howells, Mr Ian LLB. . . . . *Jun 1976

CULLOMPTON, Devon

JAMES CALDERBANK ‡
Ashculme House Brownheath Heymock Cullompton Devon EX15 3SU
Tel: 01823 680697 *Fax:* 01823 681021
E-mail: james.calderbank@btopenworld.com
List of partners: J R Calderbank
Languages: French
Work: G H Z(m)
Emergency Action, Agency, Advocacy, Fixed Fee Interview, Legal Aid undertaken and Legal Aid Franchise
SPr: Calderbank, Mr James Richard MA(Cantab). . . . . . *Jun 1976

DUNN & BAKER
Chudleigh House 38 High Street Cullompton Devon EX15 1AE
Tel: 01884 33818 *Fax:* 01884 32356 *Dx:* 49600 CULLOMPTON
E-mail: mail@dunnandbaker.co.uk
Office: Exeter
Work: B1 C1 D1 E F1 G H J1 K1 L N O Q S1 V W Z(l,m,o)

Emergency Action and Legal Aid undertaken
Asoc: Newman, Mr Jonathan R . . . . *Jun 1978

MILFORD & DORMOR ‡
Halifax House Hemyock Devon Cullompton Devon EX15 3QW
Tel: 01823 680846
E-mail: chard@milfordanddormor.co.uk

CWMBRAN, Torfaen

BALDWIN TOWNSEND & CO ‡
(in association with Geoffrey Townsend & Co)
9 Victoria Street Cwmbran Torfaen NP44 3JS
Tel: 01633 866007 *Fax:* 01633 866097
List of partners: J Baldwin
Work: B1 E F1 G H J1 K1 L N O Q S1 V W Z(l)
Emergency Action, Agency, Advocacy, Fixed Fee Interview and Legal Aid undertaken
Ptr: Baldwin, Mr Julian BSc . . . . *Nov 1993

KEITH EVANS & COMPANY
2nd Floor Room 7 Cwmbran Torfaen NP44 1PB
Tel: 01633 860900 *Fax:* 01633 484095
E-mail: office@keith-evans.co.uk
Office: Abergavenny, Newport

L J LAW ‡
Churchill House The Manor Llantarnam Cwmbran Torfaen NP44 3AQ
Tel: 01633 626977 *Fax:* 01633 626977
E-mail: laurence@ljlaw.co.uk

NEWBOLD & CO ‡
12a Russell Street Cwmbran Torfaen NP44 1EA
Tel: 01633 874715 *Fax:* 01633 867414 *Dx:* 43659 CWMBRAN
E-mail: reception@newboldandco.co.uk
List of partners: G B Newbold, M Van De Weyer
Work: B1 D1 D2 E F1 F2 J1 K1 L N O Q R2 S1 S2 W
Emergency Action, Fixed Fee Interview and Legal Aid Franchise
Ptr: Newbold, Mrs Glynis Betty LLB(Hons). . . . . Dec 1991
Van De Weyer, Mrs Margaret LLB(Hons)(Lond) . . . . *Jun 1976

RUBIN LEWIS O'BRIEN ‡
Gwent House Gwent Square Cwmbran Torfaen NP44 1PL
Tel: 01633 867000 *Fax:* 01633 485612 / 626390
Dx: 43650 CWMBRAN
E-mail: reception1@rlob.co.uk
List of partners: C R Davies, C Davis, S R George, V C Henley, R A Lee, R W Lewis, J R O'Brien, A R Williams
Office: Cardiff
Languages: Flemish, Welsh
Work: A1 B1 B2 C1 C2 C3 D1 E F1 G H J1 K1 L M1 M2 N O P Q R1 S1 S2 T1 T2 V W Z(l,r,t)
Emergency Action, Agency, Advocacy, Fixed Fee Interview, Legal Aid undertaken and Legal Aid Franchise
Ptr: Davies, Mr Christopher R LLB(Lond) . . . . *Apr 1979
Davis, Miss Claire. . . . . Oct 1985
George, Mr Samuel Richard BA(Hons) . . . . Aug 1999
Henley, Ms Valerie C LLB . . . . *Nov 1988
Lewis, Mr Richard W . . . . *Jun 1980
O'Brien, Mr Jerome R LLB . . . . *§Apr 1977
Williams, Mr Alun R LLB . . . . *Oct 1984
Con: Rubin, Mr Jeremy M . . . . *§Nov 1965

KEITH SMART & CO ‡
6 New Street Pontnewydd Cwmbran Torfaen NP44 1EE
Tel: 01633 872031 *Fax:* 01633 838118 *Dx:* 43651 CWMBRAN
E-mail: keithsmartandco@btconnect.com
List of partners: K Smart
Work: A1 B1 C1 D1 E F1 G H J1 K1 L M1 N P R1 S1 T1 V W Z(e,f,i)
Emergency Action, Agency, Advocacy, Fixed Fee Interview, Legal Aid undertaken and Member of Accident Line
Ptr: Smart, Mr Keith LLB . . . . *Jul 1979

DAGENHAM, Essex

ISAAC AKANDE & CO SOLICITORS ‡
42 Lockwell Road Dagenham Essex RM10 7RE
Tel: 020 8593 2992 *Fax:* 020 8593 5177
E-mail: isaac.akande@btconnect.com

GILEAD BALMS SOLICITORS ‡
PO Box 891 Dagenham Essex RM9 9HF
Tel: 020 8595 2211 *Fax:* 020 8595 2235 *Dx:* 8529 BARKING
E-mail: solicitors@gileadbalmssolicitors.co.uk

LILLYWHITE WILLIAMS & CO ‡
Elliott House 1 Cinema Parade Green Lane Dagenham Essex RM8 1AA
Tel: 020 8593 7471 *Fax:* 020 8592 6558 *Dx:* 52002 DAGENHAM
E-mail: lillywhitewilliams@btconnect.com
List of partners: I J Lillywhite, A R Williams
Agency, Advocacy, Fixed Fee Interview and Legal Aid undertaken
Ptr: Lillywhite, Mr Ian J LLB . . . . Dec 1977
Williams, Mr Andrew R . . . . Nov 1976

MILNER ELLEDGE ‡
1a Station Parade Heathway Dagenham Essex RM9 5AW
Tel: 020 8984 0940 *Fax:* 020 8593 2235 *Dx:* 8508 BARKING
E-mail: admin@milnerelledge.co.uk
List of partners: K Elledge, S M Milner
Work: K1
Emergency Action, Legal Aid undertaken and Legal Aid Franchise
Ptr: Elledge, Ms Kim LLB(Hons). . . . . Nov 2002
Milner, Mr Simon M BA . . . . Feb 1988
Asoc: Dowling, Ms Jean BA(Hons)(Law). . . . . Oct 2002
Wigul, Mr Scott BA(Hons). . . . . Feb 1997

THOMPSONS (FORMERLY ROBIN/BRIAN THOMPSON & PARTNERS)
Transport House 50-52 New Road Dagenham Essex RM9 6YS
Tel: 020 8596 7700 *Fax:* 020 8595 6124 *Dx:* 52003 DAGENHAM
Office: Belfast, Birmingham, Bristol, Cardiff, Chelmsford, Derby, Harrow, Leeds, Liverpool, London SW19, London WC1, Manchester, Middlesbrough, Newcastle upon Tyne, Nottingham, Plymouth, Sheffield, South Shields, Southampton, Stoke-on-Trent, Swansea, Wolverhampton

WILKINS & CO ‡
34 Ellerton Gardens Dagenham Essex RM9 4HT
Ast: Wilkins, Mrs Lorraine . . . . Mar 1985

DALTON-IN-FURNESS, Cumbria

LIVINGSTONS
57-61 Market Street Dalton-in-Furness Cumbria LA15 8AW
Tel: 01229 462126 *Fax:* 01229 462083
E-mail: enquiries@livingstons.co.uk
Office: Barrow-in-Furness, Ulverston
Work: C1 D1 E F1 J1 K1 K3 K4 N O Q S1 T2 W Z(l)
Emergency Action, Agency, Advocacy, Fixed Fee Interview and Legal Aid undertaken
Dir: Dacre, Mrs Lisa J. . . . . *Aug 1998

POOLE TOWNSEND
66 Market Street Dalton-in-Furness Cumbria LA15 8AA
Tel: 01229 467565 *Fax:* 01229 467566
Office: Barrow-in-Furness, Grange-over-Sands, Kendal, Ulverston

DARLINGTON

BHP LAW
Westgate House Faverdale Darlington DL3 0PZ
Tel: 01325 466794 *Fax:* 01325 376509 *Dx:* 69285 DARLINGTON 6
E-mail: info@bhplaw.co.uk
Office: Durham, Halifax, Newcastle upon Tyne, Newton Aycliffe, North Shields, Stockton-on-Tees
Work: A3 B1 C1 C2 C3 D1 D2 E F1 F2 G H J1 J2 K1 K2 K3 K4 L N O Q R1 R2 S1 S2 T1 T2 U1 U2 W X Z(c,e,l,o,p,q,r,u,x,za)
Legal Aid undertaken
Ptr: Biglin, Miss Helen BSc(Hons) . . . . *Dec 1993
Blackett, Mr Peter Rodney Notary Public . . . . . . *§Jun 1970
Gaudern, Miss Emma. . . . . *Sep 1999
Hamer, Mr Terence Paul LPE; LPC . . . . *Jul 1987
Hunter, Mrs Sonia Joan LLB . . . . *Nov 1992
Pratt, Mrs Karen Stephanie IFA . . . . *Jan 1986
Asoc: Dick, Miss Zoe LLB . . . . Feb 2007
Wood, Mr Adam Notary Public . . . . Nov 2007
Ast: Copeland, Mr Gary James LLB . . . . Feb 1986

CLARK WILLIS ‡
105 Bondgate Darlington DL3 7LB
Tel: 01325 281111 *Fax:* 01325 289800 *Dx:* 60121 DARLINGTON
E-mail: p.furness@clarkwillis.co.uk
List of partners: C J Bunting, P J Duffy, P J Furness, J Willis
Office: Catterick Garrison, Darlington
Languages: French
Work: B2 D1 D2 G H J1 K1 K3 N Q V Z(q)
Emergency Action, Agency, Advocacy, Fixed Fee Interview, Legal Aid undertaken and Legal Aid Franchise
Ptr: Bunting, Mr Christopher John LLB(Hons) . . . . . . *Sep 1996
Duffy, Mr Philip John LLB(Hons). . . . . *Dec 1996
Furness, Mr Peter Jeremy LLB ★ . . . . *Jun 1989
Ast: Bloomfield, Miss Tanya Louise LLB(Hons). . . . . . *Dec 2008
Clish, Mr John Leslie LLB. . . . . *Aug 2008
Harley, Mr Jonathan LLB(Hons); PGDL(BVC) Justice of the Peace. . . . . *Feb 2010
Jandoo, Mr Amrit Singh . . . . *Feb 2010
Mahon, Miss Joanna LLB(Hons). . . . . *Sep 2009
Payne, Miss Rebecca Catherine LLB(Hons). . . . . . *Oct 2007

CLARK WILLIS
Enterprise House Valley Street Darlington DL1 1GY
Tel: 01325 281111 *Fax:* 01325 745299
E-mail: j.willis@clarkwillis.co.uk
Office: Catterick Garrison, Darlington
Work: L V W Z(m)
Fixed Fee Interview and Legal Aid undertaken
Ptr: Willis, Mr Jonathan LLB(Hons); PGDipLaw Mental Health Review Tribunal Judge; Deputy District Judge. . *Nov 1985
Asoc: Burrows, Mrs Victoria LLB(Hons); LLM . . . . *Jul 2004
Mafham-Jackson, Mrs Jane LLB . . . . *Sep 2004
Ast: Alexander, Mrs Susan BA. . . . . *Apr 1996
Bushby, Mrs Kelly LLB(Hons); LLM . . . . *Jul 2004
Hall, Miss Diane LLB . . . . *Feb 2011
Leighton, Miss Sarah LLB. . . . . *May 2009
McCabe, Miss Katherine Elizabeth LLB . . . . *May 2011
Moss, Miss Nicola LLB . . . . *Feb 2009
Sigsworth, Mr Matthew James BA(Hons) . . . . *Apr 2011

CLOSE THORNTON ‡
2 Duke Street Darlington DL3 7AB
Tel: 01325 466461 *Fax:* 01325 465121 *Dx:* 60107 DARLINGTON
E-mail: law@close-thornton.co.uk
List of partners: S K Burke, D Hogg, I Robson, C R Wiper, M A Woolfe
Work: A1 A2 A3 B1 C1 C2 C3 D1 D2 E F1 F2 J1 K1 K2 L N O P Q S1 S2 T1 T2 W Z(c,k,l,q,r)
Emergency Action, Agency, Advocacy, Fixed Fee Interview, Legal Aid undertaken, Legal Aid Franchise and Member of Accident Line
Ptr: Burke, Mr Shaun K LLB. . . . . *Nov 1989
Hogg, Mr David. . . . . *Sep 1996
Robson, Mr Iain MA(Hons)(History); CPE; LSF . . . . May 2000
Wiper, Mr Christopher R. . . . . *Jan 1983
Woolfe, Mr Malcolm Aaron LLB(Hons) Northumberland University Employment Law Prize 1999 . . . . Sep 2002
Asoc: Henderson, Miss Kelly Louise. . . . . Nov 2005

DARLING & STEPHENSONS ‡
53 Coniscliffe Road Darlington DL3 7EN
Tel: 01325 489000 *Fax:* 01325 466490
E-mail: darlington@darlingstephensons.co.uk
List of partners: I W Stephenson, P S G Stephenson
Office: Barnard Castle
Work: A1 C1 D1 D2 E F1 J1 K1 L N O P Q R1 R2 S1 S2 T1 T2 V W X Z(c,d,k,l,p,q,r)
Emergency Action, Agency and Fixed Fee Interview undertaken
Ptr: Stephenson, Mr Ian W LLB . . . . *§Jun 1980
Stephenson, Mr Philip St George . . . . *§Jun 1972
Asoc: Ellis, Mr Simon . . . . Jan 2000

DONNELLY MCARDLE ADAMSON
56 Duke Street Darlington DL3 7AN
Tel: 01325 482299 *Fax:* 01325 382918 *Dx:* 60125 DARLINGTON
E-mail: enquiries@mcardles.co.uk
Office: Hartlepool, Peterlee, Stockton-on-Tees, Sunderland (2 offices)
Work: D1 G H J1 K1 K3 L N O Q S1 W Z(k,q,r)
Advocacy, Fixed Fee Interview, Legal Aid undertaken and Member of Accident Line
Ptr: Cardwell, Mr Geoffrey H. . . . . *Jan 1986
Mathieson, Ms Julie Isobel . . . . Aug 1996
Mitchell, Mr Phillip G BA. . . . . Feb 1989
Phillips, Mr James. . . . . Sep 1980
Russell, Mr Andrew C. . . . . Nov 1993
Ast: Hawks, Mrs Sally . . . . Oct 1986
Killick, Mrs Karen . . . . Feb 1983
Con: McArdle, Mr John. . . . . Dec 1978

FREEMAN JOHNSON ‡
11 Victoria Road Darlington DL1 5SP
Tel: 01325 466221 *Fax:* 0845 389 3201 *Dx:* 60108 DARLINGTON
Emergency telephone 07711 661179
E-mail: darlington@freemanjohnson.co.uk
List of partners: C H Atterton, J K Campbell, M D Clarke, C A Middleton, D Smark, P F Town, G A Turnbull, D M Williams, H C Wrigley
Office: Durham, Northallerton, Spennymoor
Work: A1 B1 C1 C2 D1 D2 E F1 F2 G H J1 K1 L N O Q R1 R2 S1 S2 T2 V W Z(c,e,g,l,m,n,p,r)
Emergency Action, Agency, Advocacy, Fixed Fee Interview, Legal Aid undertaken and Member of Accident Line
Asoc: Thompson, Miss Anne Helen BA(Hons); CPE; PGDipLaw; LPC . . . . Mar 2004
Ast: Woodland, Mrs Janette LLB(Hons) . . . . *§Feb 1988

HEWITTS
(incorporating Booth & Dixon; Marquis Penna; J R Waite & Alsop; Cohens)
Provincial House 100-102 Bondgate Darlington DL3 7LB
Tel: 01325 468573 *Fax:* 01325 485631 *Dx:* 69289 DARLINGTON 6
E-mail: enquiries@hewitts.co.uk
Office: Bishop Auckland, Crook, Newton Aycliffe, Stockton-on-Tees
Work: A1 A2 A3 B1 B2 C1 C2 D1 D2 E F1 G H J1 J2 K1 K2 L M1 N O P Q R1 S1 S2 U2 V W X Z(c,d,e,f,g,h,i,j,k,l,m,n,o,p,q,s,t)
Emergency Action, Agency, Advocacy, Fixed Fee Interview, Legal Aid undertaken and Legal Aid Franchise
Ptr: Hunsley, Mr Graham LLB(Newc) . . . . *Nov 1971
Saunders-Jerrom, Mrs Laura Elizabeth Mary CPE; LPCJun 1998
Ast: Hare, Ms Jennifer M . . . . *Nov 1962
Snowdon, Ms Heather LLB; LPC Cavendish Prize for the best mark in a non-core subject 1997 . . . . Apr 2004
Spurr, Mr Alexander Irving BA(Hons) . . . . Sep 2005
Strike, Mrs Autumn Lenore LLB . . . . Dec 2002

HODGSONS & MORTIMER ‡
34 Duke Street Darlington DL3 7TZ
Tel: 01325 250111 / 355956 *Fax:* 01325 245475
Dx: 60122 DARLINGTON
E-mail: enquiries@hodgsons-mortimer.co.uk
List of partners: N J Hodgson, R A Hodgson
Office: Richmond
Work: A1 C1 D1 D2 E J1 J2 K1 L N O Q S1 S2 W Z(d,g,l,q)
Emergency Action, Agency and Legal Aid Franchise
Ptr: Hodgson, Mr Richard Anthony LLB . . . . Mar 1977
Asoc: Adeola, Mrs Oluwapelumi Amanda LLB; LLM . . . . . Oct 2009
Ast: Richardson, Mrs Miranda LLB. . . . . *Mar 1980
Con: Patterson, Mr Ernest Barry LLB(Lond). . . . . *Jul 1979

LATIMER HINKS ‡
5-8 Priestgate Darlington DL1 1NL
Tel: 01325 341500 *Fax:* 01325 381072 *Dx:* 69282 DARLINGTON 6
E-mail: lh@latimerhinks.co.uk
Web: www.latimerhinks.co.uk
List of partners: A E Elliott, W M Gardner, T J Haggie, N H Neilson, N J V Poole, P N Stevenson, A P Way
Languages: French, German, Russian, Spanish
Work: A1 A2 A3 B1 C1 C2 D1 D2 E F1 F2 I J1 K1 K2 K3 K4 L M1 O P Q R1 S1 S2 T1 T2 W Z(b,c,d,e,f,h,i,j,k,l,m,n,o,p,q,w)
Agency, Advocacy and Fixed Fee Interview undertaken
Ptr: Elliott, Mrs Anne E LLB . . . . *§Jun 1976
Gardner, Mr William Mark LLB . . . . *Sep 1988
Haggie, Mr Timothy J MA(Cantab) Notary Public . . *§Mar 1971
Neilson, Mrs Nicola Helen LLB; LLM . . . . Sep 2003
Poole, Mr Nicholas J V BA . . . . *Apr 1986
Stevenson, Mr P Neil LLB(Sheff) . . . . *§Apr 1980
Way, Mr Andrew Peter FILEx . . . . NSP
Ast: Armstrong, Mrs Elizabeth Fyfe BA(Jt Hons)(Dunelm); CPE; LPC; TEP. . . . . Sep 1998
Booth, Miss Helen Jane LLB(Hons); DPP . . . . Mar 2008
McLoughlin, Miss Kelly LLB . . . . Sep 2010
Moremon, Miss Victoria Anne LLB. . . . . Jul 2010
Perkins, Miss Gillian Emma BA(Hons)(Econ & Law); LPC . . . . *Jun 2008
Sweeney, Miss Nadine BA(Hons)(Philosophy & Politics); LLB . . . . Sep 2009
Walker, Miss Natalie BA. . . . . *Oct 2007
Williams, Mr Daniel Steven BA(Econ); CPE; LPC . . . Sep 2011

Agricultural Law, Commercial & Company, Wills Trusts & Tax Planning. Commercial & Residential Property, Renewable Energy.

THE LETTING GROUP
33 Bondgate Darlington DL3 7JJ
Tel: 01325 460330 *Fax:* 01325 460238
E-mail: info@lettinggroup.com
Office: South Shields

AUSTIN SANDERS LAW FIRM LIMITED ‡
Oakwood House Eastmount Road Darlington DL1 1LA
Tel: 01325 360360 *Fax:* 01325 360234 *Dx:* 69283 DARLINGTON 6
E-mail: pa@austinsanders.co.uk

WATSON WOODHOUSE
70 Victoria Road Darlington DL1 5JG
Tel: 01642 670634
Office: Middlesbrough, Stockton-on-Tees

K J WIPER ‡
PO Box 166 Darlington DL1 9EQ
Tel: 01325 242645 *Fax:* 01325 242644
E-mail: kjw@kjwiper.com

DARTFORD, Kent

ALL ABOUT RIGHTS LAW PRACTICE ‡
Suite G27 Crown House Dartford Kent DA1 1DZ
Tel: 01322 424570

See p112 for the Key to Work Categories & other symbols

APEX LAW LLP ‡
Instone House Instone Road Dartford Kent DA1 2AG
Tel: 01322 277732

T G BAYNES
(incorporating Chancellor & Ridley)
Baynes House 5 Market Street Dartford Kent DA1 1DB
Tel: 01322 295555 *Fax:* 01322 295501 *Dx:* 31905 DARTFORD
E-mail: info@tgbaynes.com
Office: Bexleyheath, Orpington
Work: C1 C2 D1 D2 E J1 K1 K3 K4 L R1 R2 S1 S2 W Z(c)
Emergency Action, Advocacy, Fixed Fee Interview, Legal Aid undertaken and Legal Aid Franchise
Ptr: Burton, Mr Stephen J LLB. . . . . *Dec 1989
Dewar, Mr Martin John LLB(Hons). . . . . *Sep 2002
Higgins, Mr Robbie . . . . . *Aug 2001
Ioannou, Ms Karen A . . . . . *Nov 1996
Leiper, Miss Andrea Jane. . . . . *Mar 2003
Ast: De Souza, Mrs Shabnim . . . . . *Nov 1993

BRADY EASTWOOD PIERCE & STEWART
4 Summerhill Road Dartford Kent DA1 2LP
Tel: 020 8692 8181 *Fax:* 020 8692 8585 *Dx:* 56703 DARTFORD
Office: London SE8

BUSS MURTON LLP
Crown House Home Gardens Dartford Kent DA1 1DZ
Tel: 01322 220235 *Fax:* 01322 293841 *Dx:* 142725 DARTFORD 7
Office: Cranbrook, Tunbridge Wells
Work: D1 E J1 K1 K3 K4 N Q S1 S2 W Z(l)
Agency, Fixed Fee Interview and Legal Aid undertaken

COOK TAYLOR WOODHOUSE
12 High Street Dartford Kent DA1 1BY
Tel: 01322 223223
E-mail: nwoodhouse@ctwsolicitors.co.uk
Office: London SE9

ESTATE AND CORPORATE SOLICITORS ‡
1a Spital Street Dartford Kent DA1 2DJ
Tel: 01322 292101 *Fax:* 0560 342 0614 *Dx:* 31902 DARTFORD
E-mail: info@eandcsolicitors.co.uk

HEWITT BURROUGH & CO ‡
82 High Street Dartford Kent DA1 1DE
Tel: 01322 273833 *Fax:* 01322 282420 *Dx:* 31900 DARTFORD
Emergency telephone 07693 391210
E-mail: hewittburrough@btconnect.com
List of partners: J H McGhie
Work: A1 D1 E F1 G H J1 K1 L N Q S1 V W
Emergency Action, Agency, Advocacy, Fixed Fee Interview and Legal Aid undertaken
Ptr: McGhie, Mr John H . . . . . *Aug 1978
Asoc: Golding, Mr Alan C . . . . . *Jun 1976

HITCHMAN & CO ‡
36 Crayford High Street Dartford Kent DA1 4HG
Tel: 01322 556648

CAROLINE MATHEWS SOLICITORS ‡
57 Perry Street Crayford Dartford Kent DA1 4RB
Tel: 01322 552275 *Fax:* 01322 552275

NEVES SCOTT ‡
Ground Floor Offices Instone House Instone Road Dartford Kent DA1 2AG
Tel: 01322 277732 *Fax:* 0870 052 0408
E-mail: markn@neves-scott.co.uk

HOWARD OUTRED & CO ‡
57 Hythe Street Dartford Kent DA1 1BG
Tel: 01322 224881 *Fax:* 01322 292719 *Dx:* 31903 DARTFORD
E-mail: howardoutred@btconnect.com
List of partners: R Mitchell
Work: E L S1 W Z(l)
Fixed Fee Interview undertaken
Ptr: Mitchell, Mr Roger BA. . . . . Jul 1975
Ast: Franklin, Mrs Donna J LLB(Wales) . . . . . *Oct 1986

ROSS GREEN & CROWE ‡
3 Bullace Lane Dartford Kent DA1 1BB
Tel: 01322 225353 *Fax:* 01322 224537
List of partners: S Crowe, I P Ross
Languages: French
Work: A1 C1 C2 C3 D1 E F1 G H J1 K1 L N O P Q R1 S1 T1 T2 W Z(l,m)
Emergency Action, Agency and Advocacy undertaken
Ptr: Crowe, Mr Stephen LLB. . . . . *Jun 1979
Ross, Mr Ian P . . . . . *§Jul 1973

SHARPE & PERL ‡
23 The Row New Ash Green Longfield Dartford Kent DA3 8JB
Tel: 01474 872576 / 873359 *Fax:* 01474 873350
Dx: 41952 NEW ASH GREEN
E-mail: sharpeandperl@breathe.com
List of partners: N Perl, J Williams
Languages: French
Work: B1 C1 C2 C3 E F1 G K1 L N S1 W Z(c,l)
Emergency Action, Agency and Advocacy undertaken
Ptr: Perl, Mr Nicholas LLB. . . . . *Jul 1976
Williams, Ms Jane LLB(Hons). . . . . *Nov 1995

THOMSON SNELL & PASSMORE
The Old Rectory St Mary's Road Greenhithe Dartford Kent DA9 9AS
Tel: 01322 623700 *Fax:* 01322 623701 *Dx:* 157310 DARTFORD 12
Office: Tunbridge Wells
Ptr: Aggarwal, Mr Kamal K LLB; LLM . . . . . *Oct 1992

WEIGHTMANS LLP
Riverbridge House Anchor Boulevard Crossways Business Park Dartford Kent DA2 6SL
Tel: 020 7822 1900 *Fax:* 020 7822 1901 *Dx:* 146000 DARTFORD 9
Office: Birmingham, Knutsford, Leicester, Liverpool, London EC4, Manchester (2 offices)
Languages: French
Work: C1 C2 C3 D2 E J1 J2 K1 K2 K3 L O Q R2 S1 S2 U1 U2 W Z(c,h,j,l,q,za)
Agency, Fixed Fee Interview undertaken and Member of Accident Line
Mem: Bannister, Mr Alan LLB(Lond). . . . . *Jun 1975
Brannigan, Ms Karyn . . . . . *Oct 1994
Brenlund, Miss Louise Rachel DipLaw; PGDip; FILEx . Nov 2005
Challis, Mr Thomas J LLB. . . . . *Nov 1984
Dudley, Mr Stephen William. . . . . *Nov 1995
East, Miss Fiona M BA(Law) . . . . . *Oct 1982
Johnson, Mr David LLB(Hons). . . . . Mar 2001
Kenyon, Mr Crispin S V. . . . . *§Dec 1980
Newman, Mr Mark R MA . . . . . Oct 1977
Shaer, Mr Jonathan. . . . . *Jun 1979
Spriggs, Ms Sally Elizabeth . . . . . Sep 1994
Dir: Williams, Mr Brian. . . . . *§Jan 1965

DARTMOUTH, Devon

DORADE LAW ‡
1 Broadstone House Dartmouth Devon TQ6 9NR
Tel: 01803 835187 *Fax:* 020 7900 6972
E-mail: jojo.szota@doradelaw.com

HANSELL DREW & CO ‡
49 Newcomen Road Dartmouth Devon TQ6 9BJ
Tel: 01803 834555 *Fax:* 01803 839019 *Dx:* 81353 DARTMOUTH
E-mail: admin@hanselldrew.com
List of partners: J R Hansell
Work: G H Z(l)
Agency, Advocacy, Fixed Fee Interview, Legal Aid undertaken and Legal Aid Franchise
SPr: Hansell, Mr John R LLB(Hons) . . . . . *Mar 1969
Ast: Drew, Mr Mark LLB . . . . . *Dec 1992

HANSELL WILKES & CO ‡
St Georges Chambers 14 Newcomen Road Dartmouth Devon TQ6 9BN
Tel: 01803 833993 *Fax:* 01803 833814 *Dx:* 81352 DARTMOUTH
E-mail: enquiries@hansellwilkes.co.uk
List of partners: R A Wilkes
Languages: French
Work: A1 C1 E F1 J1 K1 L O P Q R1 S1 S2 V W
Emergency Action, Legal Aid undertaken and Legal Aid Franchise
Ptr: Wilkes, Mr Richard Arnold BA(Law); TEP . . . . . *§Oct 1973
Ast: Malley, Mr Christopher Charles William Member of Chartered Institute of Arbitrators . . . . . *Nov 1973
Con: Carpanini, Mr Philip J LLB; LLM. . . . . *Dec 1980

WOLLEN MICHELMORE SOLICITORS
10 The Quay Dartmouth Devon TQ6 9PT
Tel: 01803 213251 *Fax:* 01803 835662
Office: Newton Abbot, Paignton, Torquay
Work: A1 A2 C1 C2 C3 D1 E F1 I J1 K1 L N O P Q R1 S1 T1 T2 V W Z(a,c,d,e,f,h,k,l,m)

DARWEN, Blackburn

DLC SOLICITORS LIMITED ‡
38 Railway Road Darwen Blackburn BB3 2RJ
Tel: 01254 761234 *Fax:* 01254 760929 *Dx:* 18009 DARWEN
Emergency telephone 01254 761234
E-mail: info@dlcsolicitors.co.uk
List of partners: S J Rees, R Stanley
Work: D1 G H J1 K1 L N S1 V W Z(g,h,i,l,m,t)
Emergency Action, Agency, Advocacy, Fixed Fee Interview, Legal Aid undertaken and Legal Aid Franchise
Ptr: Rees, Mr Stephen John BA . . . . . *Oct 1987
Stanley, Mr Russell LLB. . . . . *Sep 2000
Asoc: Siddique, Mr Fiaz . . . . . Jan 2009

LESLEY HALLIWELL SOLICITORS ‡
Bank Chambers Belgrave Square Darwen Blackburn BB3 1BU
Tel: 01254 773800 *Fax:* 01254 703903
E-mail: info@lhalliwellsolicitors.com

THE WATSON RAMSBOTTOM PARTNERSHIP
33-39 Railway Road Darwen Blackburn BB3 2RL
Tel: 01254 701111 *Fax:* 01254 873658 *Dx:* 18005 DARWEN
Emergency telephone 01254 701111
E-mail: info@watsonramsbottom.com
Office: Blackburn, Great Harwood
Work: B2 D1 E F1 G H J1 K1 L N O Q S1 S2 T1 T2 W
Emergency Action, Agency, Advocacy, Fixed Fee Interview, Legal Aid undertaken, Legal Aid Franchise and Member of Accident Line
Ptr: Lamster, Mr Peter W LLB(Lond). . . . . *Nov 1971
Thompson, Mr Phillip David BA(Hons). . . . . Dec 1980
Ast: Unnisa, Mrs Fahrat LLB(Hons) . . . . . *Sep 2000
Con: Dewhurst, Mr John Turner •. . . . . Dec 1968

DAVENTRY, Northamptonshire

ADAMS MOORE FAMILY LAW
Moot Hall Market Square Daventry Northamptonshire NN11 4BH
Tel: 01327 300771
Office: Bedford, Bletchley, Corby, Luton, Milton Keynes, Northampton

BRIGID TURNER & CO LTD ‡
Cherry Tree Barn Upper Boddington Daventry Northamptonshire NN11 6DH
Tel: 01327 263950 *Fax:* 01327 263996 *Dx:* 21955 DAVENTRY
E-mail: brigid@brigidturner.co.uk

HATTON ‡
1 Sheaf Street Daventry Northamptonshire NN11 4AA
Tel: 01327 301201 *Fax:* 01327 706226 *Dx:* 21954 DAVENTRY
E-mail: tracey@hattonsolicitors.co.uk
List of partners: J R Hatton
Work: A1 B1 B2 C1 C2 C3 E G K1 L M1 M2 N P R1 S1 S2 T1 T2 U2 W Z(j,m,q,r)
Emergency Action, Agency, Advocacy, Legal Aid undertaken and Member of Accident Line
Ptr: Hatton, Mr Jonathan R LLB . . . . . *May 1983

J C LAWRENCE & CO ‡
Woodhill House Stockwell Lane Hellidon Daventry Northamptonshire NN11 6LG
Tel: 07837 287747 *Fax:* 01327 260565
E-mail: jcl@jenniferlawrencesolicitoradvocate.co.uk

MERCY MESSENGER
45 Sheaf Street Daventry Northamptonshire NN11 4AA
Tel: 01327 301745 *Fax:* 01327 301748
E-mail: dfm@mercymessenger.co.uk
Office: Birmingham

PATEL & CO ‡
Lloyds Bank Chambers 18 High Street Daventry Northamptonshire NN11 4HT
Tel: 01327 311213 *Fax:* 01327 311210 *Dx:* 21953 DAVENTRY
E-mail: shashi@patelandco.co.uk
List of partners: S Patel
Languages: Greek, Gujarati, Hindi, Punjabi, Urdu
Work: A1 B1 C1 D1 E F1 F2 G H I J1 J2 K1 K3 K4 L N O P Q S1 T1 T2 V W Z(c,j,l,o,q,r)
Emergency Action, Agency, Advocacy, Fixed Fee Interview undertaken and Member of Accident Line
SPr: Patel, Mr Shashi LLB . . . . . *Apr 1991

ROLLASONS ‡
9 New Street Daventry Northamptonshire NN11 4BT
Tel: 01327 301771 *Fax:* 01327 301755 *Dx:* 21957 DAVENTRY
E-mail: admin@rollasons.com
List of partners: J H Caddoo, C C L Phelan, P J Rollason
Languages: French
Work: A1 B1 C1 C2 C3 E G J1 K1 L O Q R1 R2 S1 S2 T2 V W Z(b,h,k,l)
Agency, Advocacy and Fixed Fee Interview undertaken
Ptr: Caddoo, Mrs Joanne Helen FILEx. . . . . Jan 1997
Phelan, Mr Christopher Charles Lawrence BA Parish Clerk . . . . . *Nov 1983
Rollason, Mr Peter John BA. . . . . *§Dec 1983

TEMPLE & CO COMMERCIAL SOLICITORS ‡
Natwest Bank Chambers 46 High Street Daventry Northamptonshire NN11 4HU
Tel: 0845 241 4045 *Fax:* 0845 241 4046 *Dx:* 21958 DAVENTRY
E-mail: eft@templesols.com
List of partners: J Cato, E M F Temple
Languages: French, German
Work: A3 C1 C2 C3 E J1 M1 M2 O S2 Z(e)
Ptr: Cato, Mr John LLB . . . . . *Feb 1989
Temple, Mr Euan M F MA. . . . . *Dec 1970
Ast: Jones, Miss Katie. . . . . *Mar 2009

MICHAEL WHEELER ‡
The Old Post Office Whilton Daventry Northamptonshire NN11 2NN
Tel: 01327 844299 *Fax:* 01327 842483
E-mail: mwheeler@globalnet.co.uk

WOODCOCK & THOMPSON
Foundry House 53a High Street Daventry Northamptonshire NN11 4BQ
Tel: 01327 312121 *Fax:* 01327 314100 *Dx:* 21956 DAVENTRY
E-mail: rwoodward@wtsolicitors.co.uk
Office: Northampton

DEAL, Kent

EMMERSON BROWN & BROWN ‡
127 High Street Deal Kent CT14 6BD
Tel: 01304 362146 *Fax:* 01304 374468 *Dx:* 32253 DEAL
List of partners: J W Eyley, J M Hartridge, B P Hazelton, J A Turner, T W Wade
Office: Dover, Sandwich
Work: A1 B1 D1 E F1 J1 K1 K3 L Q R1 S1 S2 V W Z(c,l)
Agency, Advocacy and Fixed Fee Interview undertaken
Ptr: Eyley, Mr John W . . . . . *Jun 1976
Hazelton, Mr Barry P LLB. . . . . *May 1978

HARDMANS ‡
4-6 Park Street Deal Kent CT14 6AQ
Tel: 01304 373377 *Fax:* 01304 363895 *Dx:* 32251 DEAL
E-mail: info@hardmans-law.co.uk
List of partners: J P Daniell, C A Hobson, E A Plews
Work: A1 B1 C1 C2 C3 D1 E F1 G H I J1 K1 L M1 M2 N O P Q R1 S1 T1 T2 V W X Z(d,k,l,m,q)
Emergency Action, Agency, Advocacy, Fixed Fee Interview, Legal Aid undertaken and Legal Aid Franchise
Ptr: Daniell, Mr Jonathan P MA(Cantab). . . . . *May 1967
Hobson, Miss Catherine A LLB(Hons). . . . . *Aug 1998
Plews, Miss Eleanore A LLB(Hons) . . . . . *Nov 1996

PALMERS CRIMINAL DEFENCE SOLICITORS ‡
90 Mill Hill Deal Kent CT14 9JB
Tel: 01304 380572 *Fax:* 01304 373639 *Dx:* 32260 DEAL
Emergency telephone 01304 380572 / 07968 185524
E-mail: pcdsdeal@hotmail.co.uk
List of partners: R Marinaccio, S C Palmer
Languages: Italian
Work: G H K1
Emergency Action, Agency, Advocacy and Legal Aid undertaken
SPr: Marinaccio, Mr Rocco ★. . . . . *Dec 1996
Ptr: Palmer, Mrs Sandra C BA(Kent) • Mooting Shield. . . *Dec 1987
Ast: Leader, Miss Nicola Jane BA(Hons). . . . . Dec 2000

PAYNES SOLICITORS ‡
38 The Strand Walmer Deal Kent CT14 7DX
Tel: 01304 372441 *Fax:* 01304 372637
E-mail: info@paynes-solicitors.com
List of partners: D Payne
SPr: Payne, Donna. . . . . Oct 1995

C M ROBINSON ‡
47 Queen Street Deal Kent CT14 6EY
Tel: 01304 363236 *Fax:* 01304 362210
List of partners: C M Robinson
Work: A1 E S1 S2 W
Ptr: Robinson, Mr Christopher M. . . . . *Mar 1972

WILLIAMSON & BARNES ‡
12-14 Queen Street Deal Kent CT14 6EU
Tel: 01304 373154 *Fax:* 01304 368709 *Dx:* 32252 DEAL
E-mail: legal@williamson-barnes.co.uk
List of partners: N Bowles, J C Griffiths, M S R Griffiths
Work: A1 B1 D1 E F1 J1 K1 L N O Q R1 S1 S2 T1 T2 W Z(d,l,q)
Emergency Action, Agency, Advocacy, Fixed Fee Interview, Legal Aid undertaken and Legal Aid Franchise
Ptr: Bowles, Mr Nathan LLB. . . . . *Apr 2000
Griffiths, Mr Jonathan Charles LLB . . . . . *Oct 1995
Griffiths, Mr Michael S R . . . . . *Nov 1985
Con: James, Mr Keith LLB . . . . . *Apr 1970

WOLTON & CO ‡
PO Box 327 Deal Kent CT14 7FZ
Tel: 01304 389789 *Fax:* 01304 371122
List of partners: K M Wolton

Work: Z(m)
Agency, Advocacy and Legal Aid undertaken
SPr: Wolton, Ms Karen Mai BA(Hons) . . . . *Sep 1995
Ast: George, Ms Katherine LLB . . . . Apr 2004

DEESIDE, Flintshire

C&G SOLICITORS ‡
78 High Street Connah's Quay Deeside Flintshire CH5 4DD
Tel: 01244 821255 *Fax:* 0870 750 9595

HARVEYS ‡
26 Chester Road West Shotton Deeside Flintshire CH5 1BX
Tel: 01244 836667 *Fax:* 01244 810087 *Dx:* 24376 SHOTTON
Office: Flint

LAMPKIN & CO ‡
Aled House Lakeside Business Village St David's Park Deeside Flintshire CH5 3XA
Tel: 01244 525725 *Fax:* 01244 537116 *Dx:* 26567 MOLD
E-mail: mark@lampkinco.co.uk

DENBIGH, Denbighshire

J M LYNN DAVIES ‡
Perth y Rhos Ystrad Road Denbigh Denbighshire LL16 3HE
Tel: 01745 817564 *Fax:* 01745 813404
E-mail: jml@jmldavies.co.uk

GAMLINS ‡
Llys Aneurin 1 Crown Lane Denbigh Denbighshire LL16 3SY
Tel: 01745 812422 *Fax:* 01745 815028
E-mail: gamlins@gamlins.co.uk

GUTHRIE JONES & JONES
33 Vale Street Denbigh Denbighshire LL16 3AH
Tel: 01745 814817 *Fax:* 01745 798003
E-mail: dinbych@guthriejj.co.uk
Office: Bala, Dolgellau

SWAYNE JOHNSON SOLICITORS ‡
2 Hall Square Denbigh Denbighshire LL16 3PA
Tel: 01745 812835 *Fax:* 01745 814852 *Dx:* 23284 DENBIGH
E-mail: law@swaynejohnson.com
List of partners: R C Chamberlain, E T A Lloyd, J G Moriarty, S J Noton, D P Scott, M A H Taylor, M D Tree, C Vaughan, D R Williams
Office: Llandudno, Ruthin, St Asaph
Languages: Welsh
Work: A1 A2 C1 D1 D2 E F1 J1 K1 K4 L N O P Q S1 S2 T1 T2 V W Z(c,d,k,l,q,r,x)
Emergency Action, Agency, Advocacy, Legal Aid undertaken and Legal Aid Franchise
Dir: Chamberlain, Mr Richard C LLB(Lond) . . . . *Jun 1980
Lloyd, Mr Edward T A BA . . . . *Feb 1983
Moriarty, Mr Jonathon G LLB(Hons) . . . . *Nov 2000
Noton, Mrs Sarah J . . . . *Dec 1990
Scott, Mr David P LLB . . . . *Oct 1983
Tree, Mr Michael Dorian LLB(Hons) . . . . *Aug 1999
Vaughan, Caryl . . . . Jun 2009
Asoc: Lewis, Mrs Judith K BA(Lond) . . . . *Jun 1973
Con: Hooson, Mr David J LLB(Lond) Diocesan Registrar . *May 1967

DENHAM, Buckinghamshire

LEVMAN SOLICITORS ‡
12 Poplar Road Denham Buckinghamshire UB9 4AN
Tel: 0845 603 8362

DENTON, Greater Manchester

BOOTH INCE & KNOWLES (incorporating Sleigh & Son)
1 Market Street Denton Greater Manchester M34 2BN
Tel: 0161 336 7011 *Fax:* 0161 320 3667
Emergency telephone 0161 336 7011
E-mail: brian@bikdenton.com
Office: Droylsden (2 offices), Hyde
Work: K3 K4 L O Q S1 S2 W
Ptr: Musgrave, Mr Brian Peter Laubach . . . . *§Dec 1975
Shaw, Mr Gregory Gerald LLB . . . . *Dec 1991

JOHN M DEAN & CO ‡
PO Box 22 Denton Greater Manchester M34 3JG
Tel: 0161 337 9665 *Fax:* 0161 337 9560
E-mail: johnmdean@hotmail.co.uk
List of partners: J M Dean
Work: B1 B2 C1 E N S1 S2 W Z(r)
Fixed Fee Interview undertaken
SPr: Dean, Mr John Michael MA(Cantab) . . . . *Mar 1963

NORTON & CO ‡
99 Reddish Lane Denton Greater Manchester M34 2NF
Tel: 0161 223 5411
List of partners: H Abbott, C N Penson
Office: Hyde
Work: D1 E F1 K1 K3 K4 L N R1 S1 S2 W Z(c,j,l)
Agency and Fixed Fee Interview undertaken

SAINSBURYS ‡
26 & 28 Ashton Road Denton Greater Manchester M34 3EX
Tel: 0161 336 7027 *Fax:* 0161 336 0535
E-mail: admin@sainsburyssolicitors.co.uk
List of partners: M F Sainsbury
Work: C1 D1 D2 E F1 K1 L N O Q S1 S2 V W Z(d,e,h)
Emergency Action, Agency, Advocacy, Fixed Fee Interview and Legal Aid undertaken
Ptr: Sainsbury, Mr Michael F . . . . *Dec 1971

DERBY

ALEXANDER & CO ‡
56 Friar Gate Derby DE1 1DF
Tel: 01332 600005 *Fax:* 01332 600010 *Dx:* 11537 DERBY 1
E-mail: enquiries@aandco.co.uk
List of partners: D A L Alexander, K Blake, N F Smith
Office: Derby
Work: A1 B1 C1 C2 C3 D1 E F1 G H J1 K1 L M1 M2 N P R1 S1 T1 T2 V W Z(c,d,l)
Emergency Action, Agency, Advocacy and Fixed Fee Interview undertaken
Ptr: Alexander, Mr David A L LLB(Leeds) . . . . *Oct 1973
Blake, Ms Katie . . . . *Jul 2006
Smith, Mr Nigel F BA(Law) . . . . *Mar 1983

ALEXANDER & CO
2 Chapel Street Spondon Derby DE21 7JP
Tel: 01332 600011 *Fax:* 01332 600010 *Dx:* 11537 DERBY 1
E-mail: enquiries@aandco.co.uk
Office: Derby
Work: A1 B1 C1 C2 C3 D1 E F1 G H J1 K1 L M1 M2 N P S1 T1 T2 V W Z(c,d,l)
Emergency Action, Agency, Advocacy and Fixed Fee Interview undertaken
Ptr: Alexander, Mr David A L LLB(Leeds) . . . . *Oct 1973
Smith, Mr Nigel F BA(Law) . . . . *Mar 1983

ASHBY FAMILY LAW PRACTICE ‡
13 Cheapside Derby DE1 1BR
Tel: 01332 293293 *Fax:* 01332 298675 *Dx:* 11522 DERBY
E-mail: solicitors@aflp.co.uk
List of partners: D E Guthrie, N A Herbert
Work: D2 K1 K3 S1
Agency undertaken
Ptr: Guthrie, Mr David E BA; MA . . . . *Oct 1993
Herbert, Mr Nicholas A LLB(Hons) . . . . *Feb 1985

BAKEWELLS ‡
64 Friar Gate Derby DE1 1DJ
Tel: 01332 348791 *Fax:* 01332 739063 *Dx:* 11527 DERBY 1
E-mail: help@bakewells.co.uk
List of partners: M G Jinks, A R Murfin
Work: A1 B1 C1 C2 C3 D1 D2 E F1 F2 J1 J2 K1 L M1 M2 N O P Q R1 R2 S1 S2 T1 T2 V W X Z(c,e,k,l,o,p,r)
Emergency Action, Agency, Advocacy and Legal Aid Franchise
Ptr: Jinks, Mr Martin G LLB Notary Public . . . . *May 1979
Murfin, Mr Andrew R BA . . . . *Jul 1980
Asoc: Collins, Mr Victor J LLB . . . . Jul 1983

BEIGHTONS ‡
4 Victoria Street Derby DE1 1EQ
Tel: 01332 346430 *Fax:* 01332 298529
E-mail: jsb@beightons.com
List of partners: J S Beighton
Languages: French, German
Work: A1 B1 C1 E J1 L Q R1 S1 S2 W X Z(d,h,l)
Agency undertaken
Ptr: Beighton, Mr John Stuart LLB(Lond) . . . . *Oct 1974
Con: Dobson, Mr Richard A LLB(Leics) . . . . *Dec 1977
Passmore, Mr Alan M L BA(Oxon); BCL(Oxon) . . . . *Apr 1974

BEMROSE & LING ‡
Victoria Chambers 30 St Peter's Churchyard Derby DE1 1NR
Tel: 01332 347300 *Fax:* 01332 290329 *Dx:* 700318 DERBY 3
E-mail: admin@bemroseandling.com
List of partners: S M Busby, I S Donald, T A Dunleavy, M J Pattullo
Work: B1 C1 D1 D2 E K1 K2 L N O Q S1 S2 W Z(l)
Emergency Action, Agency, Advocacy, Fixed Fee Interview, Legal Aid undertaken, Legal Aid Franchise and Member of Accident Line
Ptr: Busby, Miss Sharon May LLB(Hons) . . . . *Mar 1999
Donald, Mr Iain S LLB . . . . *Jun 1976
Dunleavy, Miss Theresa Ann BA(Hons) . . . . Feb 1998
Pattullo, Mr Malcolm John BA(Law) . . . . *Dec 1981
Ast: Chipman, Ms Nelly LLB; LLM . . . . *Apr 2003
Duffin, Mr Robert Ian LLB(Hons) . . . . Oct 1994

BHATIA BEST
71-73 Osmaston Road Derby DE1 2JH
Tel: 01332 203000 *Fax:* 01332 203555 *Dx:* 700307 DERBY 3
E-mail: derby@bhatiabest.co.uk
Office: Mansfield, Nottingham

BRADLEY & JEFFERIES SOLICITORS LIMITED ‡
58 Friar Gate Derby DE1 1DF
Tel: 01332 221722 *Fax:* 01332 221727
E-mail: info@bradleyandjefferies.co.uk
List of partners: M C Bradley, A J Jefferies
Work: C1 E J1 O Q
Fixed Fee Interview undertaken
Dir: Bradley, Mr Matthew C . . . . *Nov 1990
Jefferies, Mrs Amanda Jane LLB . . . . Nov 1992
Ast: Linge, Kate . . . . Oct 2008
Neiland, Mr Matthew . . . . Oct 1996

BROADBENTS
1st Floor 25 Irongate Derby DE1 3GL
Tel: 01332 369090 *Fax:* 01332 371765
Office: Alfreton, Chesterfield, Heanor, Mansfield, Sutton-in-Ashfield

CJH SOLICITORS ‡
119 Osmaton Road Derby DE1 2GD
Tel: 01332 362509 *Fax:* 01332 362574
E-mail: admin@cjhsolicitors.co.uk

CARTWRIGHT KING
Majority House 51 Lodge Lane Derby DE1 3HB
Tel: 01332 346111 *Fax:* 0808 168 1500 *Dx:* 700895 DERBY 4
E-mail: admin@cartwrightking.co.uk
Office: Birmingham, Gateshead, Leicester, Nottingham, Sheffield
Ptr: Cash, Mr Andrew J LLB . . . . Nov 1979
Hollingsworth, Mr Wayne K BA . . . . *Jul 1981
Langton, Mr Robert John . . . . *Aug 2001
Lumb, Mr Timothy P LLB . . . . *Mar 1990
Waddingham, Mr Kevin LLB . . . . Oct 1986
Ast: Hodgson, Ms Emma . . . . Oct 1995
Holt, Ms Jacqueline LLB . . . . *Oct 2005
Hunter, Ms Nicola . . . . Feb 2001
Kaur, Kalminder . . . . *Jul 2000
Pallett, Miss Hannah Elizabeth . . . . *Oct 2008
Patterson, Ms Emily . . . . Jan 2010
Smith, Mr Martin . . . . Nov 1996
Stanbanks, Emma Jane . . . . *Apr 2002

MARK CROFT SOLICITOR ‡
PO Box 6595 Oakwood Derby DE21 2YQ
Tel: 01332 671133 *Fax:* 0870 420 5087
E-mail: info@mark-croft-solicitor.co.uk

DEDICATED ACCIDENT SOLICITORS ‡
The College Business Centre Uttoxeter New Road Derby DE22 3WZ
Tel: 01332 869286 *Fax:* 01332 869287
E-mail: enquiries@dedicatedaccidentsolicitors.co.uk
List of partners: J Das
Work: N Z(r)
SPr: Das, Mr John LLB(Hons) . . . . *May 1995
Asoc: Stokes, Mrs Alison R BA Sweet & Maxwell Law Prize (Durham Uni); Local Law Soc. . . . . Oct 1994

DERWENT LAW SOLICITORS ‡
5 Buxton Drive Little Eaton Derby DE21 5AN
Tel: 01332 416655 *Fax:* 01332 780718
E-mail: info@derwentlaw.co.uk

DORIANS ‡
Wyvern Chambers Wyvern Court Wyvern Business Court Derby DE21 6BF
Tel: 01332 680580 *Fax:* 01332 672300 *Dx:* 17505 DERBY 2
E-mail: enquiries@dorianssolicitors.co.uk
List of partners: F L Dorian, C J Hook
Work: G H N
Agency, Advocacy, Fixed Fee Interview, Legal Aid undertaken, Legal Aid Franchise and Member of Accident Line
Ptr: Dorian, Mr Fintan L . . . . *§Jul 1980
Hook, Mr Christopher J . . . . Feb 1984
Ast: Soodi, Mr Jas LLB . . . . *Nov 1995

EDDOWES WALDRON ‡ (incorporating G R Eddowes & Waldron; A J Cash & Sons)
12 St Peters Churchyard Derby DE1 1TZ
Tel: 01332 348484 *Fax:* 01332 291312 *Dx:* 17501 DERBY 2
Emergency telephone 07831 442334
E-mail: info@ewlaw.co.uk
List of partners: C M Gabb, C B Hackney, J R N Waldron, N Waldron
Languages: French, German
Work: A1 B1 C1 D1 E F1 G H I J1 K1 K2 K3 N O Q R1 S1 S2 T2 V W Z(e,l,m,p,q,r,t,x)
Emergency Action, Agency, Advocacy, Fixed Fee Interview, Legal Aid undertaken, Legal Aid Franchise and Member of Accident Line
Ptr: Gabb, Mr Christopher M BA . . . . *Oct 1986
Hackney, Ms Catherine B Notary Public . . . . *Oct 1994
Waldron, Mr John R N BSc(Eng) Frederick Drinkwater Prize . . . . *Oct 1976
Waldron, Mrs Nadine BA . . . . *Oct 1976
Ast: Hardy, Mr Wayne LLB . . . . *Feb 2005
Jamal, Deepa BA(Hons) . . . . *Jan 2005
Pattullo, Mr Malcolm John BA(Law) . . . . *Dec 1981
Stevens, Mr Simon LLB(Hons) . . . . Dec 2005

FLINT BISHOP SOLICITORS ‡
St Michaels Court St Michaels Lane Derby DE1 3HQ
Tel: 01332 340211 *Fax:* 01332 207601 *Dx:* 729320 DERBY 24
E-mail: info@flintbishop.co.uk
List of partners: Z I Bashir, I D Beardmore, A Cochrane, A C Crowther, H L Dixon, K J Dixon, Q Ghafoor, W Hooley, T H Jacobs, F A Lazenby, S G McCarthy, R Oren, C Pickup, A E Pilkington, B Sankey, B Simms, G Steele, S J R Taylor, R P Tice, M L Tyler, P A Weaver, G White
Office: Ashbourne, Nottingham
Languages: French, German, Spanish, Urdu
Work: A1 A3 B1 C1 C2 D1 E F1 J1 K1 K2 K3 L N O Q R1 R2 S1 S2 T1 T2 W Z(c,d,l,o,p,q,r)
Emergency Action, Agency, Legal Aid Franchise and Member of Accident Line
Ptr: Bashir, Zafar I LLB . . . . *Oct 1993
Beardmore, Mr Ian D LLB(Hons) . . . . *Oct 1987
Cochrane, Mr Andrew MA . . . . *Dec 1992
Crowther, Mr Adrian C LLB(Manc) . . . . *Jan 1979
Dixon, Mrs Heather L . . . . *Nov 1997
Dixon, Mr Kenneth J LLB . . . . *Nov 1988
Ghafoor, Qamer . . . . Jan 2002
Hooley, Ms Wendy . . . . Jan 2003
Lazenby, Ms Fiona A LLB(Hons) . . . . *Oct 1988
McCarthy, Mr Stephen G BA(Hons)(Law) . . . . *Nov 1982
Oren, Mr Ran LLB . . . . Sep 2002
Pickup, Ms Christine . . . . Jan 2002
Pilkington, Mr Andrew E . . . . *Nov 1997
Sankey, Mr Barry . . . . Jan 1983
Simms, Mrs Beverley . . . . Jan 2002
Steele, Mrs Grace . . . . *Nov 1988
Taylor, Mr Simon J R LLB(Hons) . . . . *Jul 1979
Tice, Mr Robert Peter LLB . . . . Oct 1998
Weaver, Miss P Anne BA(Hons) . . . . *May 1981

FREETH CARTWRIGHT LLP
2nd Floor West Point Cardinal Square Derby DE1 3QT
Tel: 01332 361000 *Fax:* 01332 546111 *Dx:* 729800 DERBY 25
E-mail: postmaster@freethcartwright.co.uk
Office: Birmingham, Leicester, Manchester, Nottingham
Ptr: Bird, Mr Michael S BA . . . . *Oct 1991
Copestake, Mr Michael G LLB . . . . *Apr 1976
Jefferies, Mr Jonathan D F LLB . . . . *Jul 1989
Macnab, Mr A Murray LLB . . . . *§Jun 1990
Taplin, Mr Michael John . . . . *§Dec 1991

GELDARDS LLP
Number One Pride Place Pride Park Derby DE24 8QR
Tel: 01332 331631 *Fax:* 01332 294295 *Dx:* 11509 DERBY 1
E-mail: info@geldards.co.uk
Office: Cardiff, Nottingham
Languages: Dutch, French, German, Italian
Work: A1 A3 B1 C1 C2 C3 D1 E F1 F2 I J1 L M1 N O P Q R1 R2 S1 T1 T2 U1 W Z(b,c,d,e,h,k,r,u,y)
Emergency Action, Agency, Advocacy, Legal Aid undertaken and Member of Accident Line
Ptr: Banks, Mr Graham C LLB . . . . *Oct 1993
Borkowski, Mr Andrew Thomas LLB(Nott'm) . . . . . . *Oct 1988
Butler, Mr Jonathan . . . . Jul 1999
Dean, Mr Colin E . . . . *Nov 1989
Hackney, Mr C Paul LLB(Lond) . . . . *Dec 1975
Martin, Mrs Debra LLB . . . . Dec 1991
Simone, Mr Nino John . . . . Dec 1991
Surma, Mr Roman LLB(Nott'm) . . . . *Oct 1987

See p112 for the Key to Work Categories & other symbols

Watson, Mr David A BA(Hons) . . . . *§Nov 1982
Williams, Mr David Henry BA . . . . *§Mar 1984

GLADSTONE SOLICITORS
13 Charnwood Street Derby DE1 2GT
Tel: 01332 203403 *Fax:* 01332 203686
Office: Newark, Nottingham (2 offices)

HANNELLS SOLICITORS DERBY ‡
55-57 High Street Chellaston Derby DE73 6TB
Tel: 01332 705505 *Fax:* 01332 691009
E-mail: info@hannells.co.uk

INSAAF SOLICITORS ‡
216 Normanton Road Derby DE23 6WB
Tel: 01332 595020 *Fax:* 01332 595021
E-mail: info@insaafsolicitors.co.uk

IRVINGS SOLICITORS
(in association with Samble Burton & Worth)
Iron Gate House 10 Iron Gate Derby DE1 3FJ
Tel: 01332 346036 *Fax:* 01332 297337 *Dx:* 11514 DERBY
E-mail: enquiries@irvsol.co.uk
Office: Burton-on-Trent
Work: D1 D2 E G H J1 K1 K3 K4 L Q S1 S2 W Z(g,m)
Agency, Advocacy, Fixed Fee Interview, Legal Aid undertaken and Legal Aid Franchise
Ptr: Picken, Ashley R BA; MBA . . . . *Dec 1976
Ast: Mowle, Mrs Lisa Fiona BSc(Hons). . . . . Nov 1994

THE JOHNSON PARTNERSHIP
(incorporating Sarah Margiotta)
10 Dovedale House 73 Wilson Street Derby DE1 1PL
Est: 2006
Tel: 01332 370473 *Fax:* 01332 370637
Emergency telephone 01332 370473
E-mail: mail@jpderby.co.uk
Web: www.thejohnsonpartnership.co.uk
Office: Chesterfield, Mansfield, Nottingham
Work: B2 G H
Emergency Action, Agency, Advocacy, Fixed Fee Interview, Legal Aid undertaken and Legal Aid Franchise
Ptr: Smith, Mr Timothy J BA(Law) . . . . *Feb 1987
Ast: Kalyan, Mr Pardeep LLB(Hons) . . . . *Jul 2008
Margiotta, Miss Sarah LLB ★ . . . . *Jul 1992
Simons, Ms Marcelle LLB(Hons) . . . . *Nov 1994

Criminal Litigation, In-House Counsel, Specialist Fraud Panel Members, Higher Rights Advocate, Prison Law Specialists, Youth Court Specialists, Taxi Licensing.

KASH TUTTER & CO ‡
34 Stenson Road Cavendish Derby DE23 1JB
Tel: 01332 272727 *Fax:* 01332 272722 *Dx:* 701533 DERBY 5
E-mail: kashtutter@kashtutter.co.uk

MATRIX SOLICITORS ‡
Normanton Business Centre 258 Normanton Road Derby DE23 6WD
Tel: 01332 363454 *Fax:* 01332 362338 *Dx:* 11565 DERBY 1

MOODY & WOOLLEY ‡
40 St Mary's Gate Derby DE1 3JZ
Tel: 01332 344221 *Fax:* 01332 295243 *Dx:* 11524 DERBY 1
E-mail: amp@moodyandwoolley.co.uk
List of partners: I D H Griffiths
Languages: Punjabi
Work: A1 B1 C1 C3 D1 E F1 G H J1 K1 L P R1 S1 T1 T2 V W Z(d,h,i,l,m,s)
Emergency Action, Agency, Advocacy and Legal Aid undertaken
Ptr: Griffiths, Mr Ian D H. . . . . *Oct 1989

NELSONS
Sterne House Lodge Lane Derby DE1 3WD
Tel: 01332 372372 *Fax:* 01332 345831 *Dx:* 700889 DERBY 4
Office: Leicester, Nottingham
Languages: French, German, Spanish
Work: A1 C1 D1 E F1 G H J1 K1 L N O Q R1 S1 T1 T2 W Z(c,k,l)
Agency, Advocacy, Fixed Fee Interview, Legal Aid undertaken and Member of Accident Line
Ptr: Cash, Mr Andrew J LLB. . . . . Nov 1979
Copestake, Mr Ian T LLB . . . . *§Jun 1978
Irish, Mr Stephen A LLB. . . . . *Dec 1973
Jefferies, Mrs Amanda Jane LLB . . . . Nov 1992
Taylor, Mrs Jocelyn E LLB(Cantab); BA(Law) . . . . . §Oct 1983
Asoc: Barlow, Mr Stuart A LLB(Lond) . . . . *Jun 1977
Ast: Eaton, Mr Andrew A BA(Hons) . . . . *Jun 1996
Greatbatch, Mr Paul. . . . . Apr 2000
Hawkins, Mrs Karin J LLB(Bris) . . . . *Dec 1986
Haysom, Mrs Elizabeth . . . . *Nov 1995
Margiotta, Miss Sarah LLB ★ . . . . *Jul 1992
O'Sullivan, Ms Karen A . . . . Oct 1998
Sore, Ms Justine . . . . Sep 2001
Con: Tornbohm, Mr P Noel LLB. . . . . *§Dec 1967

JOHN O'CONNOR SOLICITORS ‡
The Old Courthouse 18-20 St Peters Churchyard Derby DE1 1NN
Tel: 01332 345533 *Fax:* 01332 386446 *Dx:* 17511 DERBY 2
List of partners: N Akroyd, J B O'Connor
Office: Nottingham
Work: A1 C1 E F1 J1 K1 L Q R1 S1 W Z(c,l)
Fixed Fee Interview, Legal Aid undertaken and Member of Accident Line
Ptr: Akroyd, Mr Nigel . . . . *Jul 1964

OCL SOLICITORS LIMITED ‡
1280 London Road Alvaston Derby DE24 8QP
Tel: 01332 753572 *Fax:* 01332 757274
E-mail: oclsolicitors@aol.com

PINDERS ‡
10-11 St Mary's Gate Derby DE1 3JJ
Tel: 01332 364751 *Fax:* 01332 291451 *Dx:* 11516 DERBY
Emergency telephone 01850 358847
E-mail: solicitors@pinderslaw.co.uk
List of partners: S T Hoyle, I Robertson, W A Watson, J A Young
Work: A1 B1 C1 C2 D1 D2 E F1 G H J1 K1 K2 L N O P Q R1 S1 T1 T2 V W Z(c,j,k,l,m,q,r,s,t)
Emergency Action, Agency, Advocacy, Fixed Fee Interview, Legal Aid undertaken and Member of Accident Line
Ptr: Hoyle, Mr Stephen T BA(Law); LLB(Sussex) . . . . . *Nov 1986
Robertson, Mr Ian BA. . . . . *Oct 1982
Watson, Mr William A BA . . . . *Jan 1983
Young, Mr John A BA(Law) . . . . *Oct 1983
Ast: Wright, Mr Nicholas V LLB . . . . *Oct 1983

J H POWELL & CO ‡
Cathedral Chambers 2 Amen Alley Derby DE1 3GT
Tel: 01332 372211 *Fax:* 01332 290413 *Dx:* 11515 DERBY 1
E-mail: reception@jhpowell.co.uk
List of partners: P J Collinson, J M Fleming, J A Hill, G W P Potter, J M Thomson, D J Tomlinson
Work: A1 B1 C1 C2 C3 D1 E F1 I J1 K1 K3 K4 L N O P Q R1 R2 S1 S2 T1 T2 U2 W X Z(b,c,d,e,f,i,j,l,m,n,o,t,x,z)
Agency, Advocacy and Fixed Fee Interview undertaken
Ptr: Collinson, Mr Peter J MA(Cantab). . . . . *Mar 1975
Fleming, Mr John M. . . . . *Jul 1968
Hill, Mr Jonathan Andrew LLB(Hons) . . . . *Nov 1995
Potter, Mr Guy W P. . . . . *Jan 1982
Thomson, Mr J Michael . . . . *May 1975
Tomlinson, Mr David J LLB . . . . *Oct 1989

PROSPECT LAW ‡
The Old Gunroom Langley Priory Diseworth Derby DE74 2QQ
Tel: 01332 818785 *Fax:* 0330 809 0084
E-mail: info@prospectlaw.co.uk

ROBINSONS ‡
10-11 St James Court Derby DE1 1BT
Tel: 01332 291431 *Fax:* 01332 254185 *Dx:* 11544 DERBY 1
Emergency telephone 07889 609992
E-mail: info@robinsons-solicitors.co.uk
List of partners: F M K Apthorpe, N Barnes, B Holloway, C P Johnson, S F Marshall, S L Nash, C E Rosser, S J D Woolley
Office: Ilkeston
Languages: French
Work: A1 B1 C1 C2 C3 D1 E F1 J1 K1 K2 K3 L M1 M2 N O P Q R1 S1 T1 T2 V W Z(c,d,e,h,j,l,m,n,o)
Emergency Action, Agency, Advocacy, Legal Aid undertaken, Legal Aid Franchise and Member of Accident Line
Ptr: Apthorpe, Ms Fiona M K LLB . . . . Oct 1988
Barnes, Mr Neil . . . . *Dec 1977
Holloway, Mr Brian BA . . . . *Mar 1973
Johnson, Mr Charles P BA . . . . *May 1982
Marshall, Mr Stephen F LLB(Sheff) . . . . *Apr 1976
Nash, Mrs Sarah Louise LLB(Hons)(Law with French Law & Language) Mills E Reeve Land Law Prize . . . . . *Jan 2000
Rosser, Miss Charlotte Elizabeth MA(Cantab) . . . . . *Jun 2000
Woolley, Mr Stephen J D . . . . Dec 1974
Asoc: Pearce, Miss Heidi J LLB(Hons). . . . . *Nov 1998
Rose, Mr Adrian Graham LLB. . . . . *Nov 1995
Ast: Brookes, Miss Emma Jane LLB(Hons) . . . . Feb 2007
Hemming, Miss Charlotte Jayne LLB . . . . Oct 2008
Hopwood, Miss Eleanor BA(Law & Criminology). . . . *Jan 2010
Mills, Miss Rachel LLB . . . . *Dec 2001
Nayler, Miss Laura Faye LLB(Hons); LPC. . . . . Jun 2006
Saum, Mr Richard John BA(Hons); CPE; LPC. . . . . *Oct 2006
Sivanesan, Miss Kishanie LLB(Hons) . . . . Aug 2007
Yasmin, Mrs Musarrat LLB . . . . *Sep 2006

ROBOTHAM & CO ‡
(incorporating Whiston & Son; Randolph Eddowes & Co)
3 St Mary's Gate Derby DE1 3JE
Tel: 01332 346018 *Fax:* 01332 294368
E-mail: ncg@robotham-solicitors.co.uk
List of partners: N C Green, T C Robotham
Work: A1 E S1 S2 T2 W
Ptr: Green, Mr Nigel C. . . . . *Jun 1975
Robotham, Mr Timothy C Notary Public . . . . *§Jan 1969

RUDZKI AND JONES ‡
2a City Road Derby DE1 3RQ
Tel: 0845 519 2999 *Fax:* 01332 650555
E-mail: info@rudzkiandjones.co.uk

SAWARN & CO LTD SOLICITORS ‡
526 Arleston Lane Stenson Fields Derby DE24 3AG
Tel: 07984 431319 *Fax:* 01332 602912
E-mail: info@sawarn.com

SHACKLOCKS
110 Park Farm Drive Park Farm Centre Allestree Derby DE22 2QN
Tel: 01332 559281 *Fax:* 01332 553475
E-mail: enquiries@shacklocks.co.uk
Office: Belper, Mansfield, Ripley
Work: C1 J1 K1 K3 K4 L N O Q W
Ast: Birtwistle, Mr Guy. . . . . Jan 2001

SHEEHY-SMITH ‡
5 Raynesway Derby DE24 0DW
Tel: 01332 755409 *Fax:* 01332 755057 *Dx:* 742883 DERBY 28
E-mail: sheehysmith@tiscali.co.uk
List of partners: D J Sheehy-Smith
Work: K1 S1 S2 W
Fixed Fee Interview, Legal Aid undertaken and Legal Aid Franchise
SPr: Sheehy-Smith, Mr Derek J BA(Law). . . . . Apr 1983

THE SMITH PARTNERSHIP ‡
25 Wardwick Derby DE1 1HA
Tel: 01332 225300 *Fax:* 01332 225303
E-mail: info@smithpartnership.co.uk

THE SMITH PARTNERSHIP ‡
4th Floor Celtic House Heritage Gate Derby DE1 1LS
Tel: 01332 225225 *Fax:* 01332 225444 *Dx:* 11528 DERBY 1
E-mail: info@smithpartnership.co.uk
List of partners: M O Brealey, S V Chittenden, D E Clark, R Davies, G R B Dean, C Else, G Hart, S Mann, E A Mansfield, K T McGrath, A Neate, S C Newcombe, N O'Driscoll, A J Oldroyd, D R Oldroyd, A M Phillips, S D Richardson, S Rowley, A D Smith, P H Smith, J Wood
Office: Burton-on-Trent (2 offices), Leicester (2 offices), Stoke-on-Trent, Swadlincote
Work: B1 C1 C2 C3 D1 D2 E J1 K1 K2 L N O R1 S2 T1 T2 W X Z(b,c,e,j,m,o,r)
Emergency Action, Agency, Advocacy, Fixed Fee Interview, Legal Aid undertaken and Member of Accident Line
Ptr: Chittenden, Mr Stephen V LLB . . . . *Nov 1975
Clark, Mr David E BA(Law) . . . . *Feb 1989
Davies, Mr Russell LLB . . . . Nov 1993
Dean, Mr Graham R B . . . . *Apr 1969
Else, Mr Christopher LLB . . . . *Jun 1985
Mann, Mr Steven LLB. . . . . *Apr 1981
Oldroyd, Mr Andrew J LLB . . . . Jul 1990
Richardson, Mr Simon D BA . . . . *Jan 1982
Rowley, Mr Simon LLB . . . . *Dec 1983
Smith, Mr Peter H. . . . . *Feb 1979
Wood, Mr Jason BA. . . . . *Mar 1988
Asoc: Curran, Mr Kevin John LLB . . . . *Dec 1990
Johal, Muctar LLB(Hons) . . . . *Nov 1991
Jones, Miss Ruth Wynne LLB(Wales) . . . . *Oct 1992
Ast: Atwal, Baljinder . . . . Sep 1999
Dadswell, Mr Peter John LLB(Hons). . . . . *Oct 1992
Dunleavy, Miss Theresa Ann BA(Hons) . . . . Feb 1998
Gibbons, Mr John Richard. . . . . Aug 2001
Hinson, Mrs Azalina LLB . . . . *Nov 1997
Midgley, Ms Sally . . . . Sep 2001
Newsam, Mr Stuart BA; LLB . . . . *Sep 1993
Partridge, Mr Mark L J . . . . May 1998
Reeve, Mr Philip E LLB . . . . *Nov 1992
Wall, Ms Tracey. . . . . May 2001
Ward, Ms Alison Helen LLB(Hons) . . . . *Sep 1998
Wood, Ms Phillippa A . . . . Oct 1988

TLS ‡
11 Chester Court Alfreton Road Derby DE21 4AB
Tel: 01332 372182 *Fax:* 01332 372183
E-mail: celia.copestake@teleser.co.uk

THOMAS & EDGE ‡
32 Osmaston Road The Spot Derby DE1 2HS
Tel: 01332 346681 *Fax:* 01332 294084 *Dx:* 17502 DERBY 2
E-mail: mail@thomasandedge.co.uk
List of partners: R V Thomas
Work: E S1 S2 W
SPr: Thomas, Mr Roger V . . . . *Nov 1976

THOMPSONS (FORMERLY ROBIN/BRIAN THOMPSON & PARTNERS)
Peat House 5 Stuart Street Derby DE1 2EQ
Tel: 01332 224680 *Fax:* 01332 201872 *Dx:* 17504 DERBY 2
Office: Belfast, Birmingham, Bristol, Cardiff, Chelmsford, Dagenham, Harrow, Leeds, Liverpool, London SW19, London WC1, Manchester, Middlesbrough, Newcastle upon Tyne, Nottingham, Plymouth, Sheffield, South Shields, Southampton, Stoke-on-Trent, Swansea, Wolverhampton

TIMMS ‡
4 Babington Lane Derby DE1 1SU
Tel: 01332 364436 *Fax:* 01332 293510 *Dx:* 718110 DERBY 14
Emergency telephone 01462 151634
E-mail: legal@timmssol.co.uk
List of partners: J M Barnes, D Boot, J Hampton, N Hickman, F E C Moffat
Office: Burton-on-Trent, Swadlincote
Languages: Punjabi
Work: A1 B1 C1 D1 D2 E F1 G H J1 K1 L N O Q R1 S1 S2 V W Z(m)
Emergency Action, Agency, Advocacy, Fixed Fee Interview, Legal Aid undertaken, Legal Aid Franchise and Member of Accident Line
Ptr: Barnes, Miss Judith Marjorie LLB . . . . *Mar 1970
Boot, Mr David BA(Keele). . . . . *Oct 1976
Hampton, Mrs Jill BA . . . . *Sep 1993
Hickman, Miss Naomi LLB . . . . Nov 1993
Moffat, Miss Fiona Elizabeth Campbell BA(Hons) . . . Jan 1981

UNDERWOOD VINECOMBE LLP ‡
Telford House Outram's Wharf Little Eaton Derby DE21 5EL
Tel: 01332 836666 *Fax:* 01332 832486
Dx: 744780 DERBY (LITTLE EATON)
E-mail: enquiries@uvlegal.co.uk

DEREHAM, Norfolk

ROSEMARY DITCHMAN ‡
Ferndale House Rectory Road Wood Norton Dereham Norfolk NR20 5BA
Tel: 01362 683530 *Fax:* 01362 683530
List of partners: R Ditchman
Work: S1 S2 W Z(d)
SPr: Ditchman, Ms Rosemary BA(Hons) . . . . *Jul 1977

HOOD VORES & ALLWOOD ‡
The Priory Church Street Dereham Norfolk NR19 1DW
Tel: 01362 692424 *Fax:* 01362 698858 *Dx:* 45050 DEREHAM
E-mail: enquiries@hoodvoreslaw.co.uk
List of partners: D N Humberston, S E Kiddle-Morris, R P Margand, D A W Rose, J F Whigham
Office: Aylsham
Languages: French, Punjabi
Work: A1 B1 C1 C2 D1 D2 E F1 J1 K1 K3 K4 L N O Q R1 R2 S1 S2 T1 T2 V W Z(b,c,d,e,k,l,n,o,q,r)
Emergency Action, Agency, Advocacy, Legal Aid undertaken and Legal Aid Franchise
Ptr: Humberston, Mr Desmond Nigel LLB(Reading); TEP *§Sep 1987
Kiddle-Morris, Mrs Sally E BA School Governor . . *§Feb 1981
Margand, Mr Roger Patrick LLB(Hons) School Governor; Mentor for Princes Trust and the Eastern Association of Enterprise Agencies . . . . *§Sep 1996
Rose, Mr David A W LLB(Leics). . . . . *§Oct 1980
Whigham, Mr Jeremy Francis TEP . . . . *§Jun 1972
Asoc: Gosal, Mr Sarbjit Singh LLB. . . . . *Sep 2003
Con: Brown, Mr Cedric Maynard LLB . . . . *Dec 1967

W F SMITH LLP
Glencoe House 25 Market Place Dereham Norfolk NR19 2AX
Tel: 01362 852900 *Fax:* 01362 698404 *Dx:* 45052 DEREHAM
E-mail: rosie.molony@wfsmith.co.uk
Office: Swaffham, Watton
Work: B1 D1 E J1 K1 L N O Q S1 T1 V W Z(l,t)
Emergency Action, Advocacy, Fixed Fee Interview, Legal Aid undertaken and Legal Aid Franchise
Ptr: Stokes, Mr Arthur George H. . . . . *§Jan 1970
Upton, Mrs Jaqueline Anne . . . . *Nov 1998
Molony, Rosemarie . . . . .NSP

STEVENSONS SOLICITORS ‡
Gorgate Chambers Gorgate Drive Hoe Dereham Norfolk NR20 4HB
Tel: 01362 860300 *Fax:* 01362 860050 *Dx:* 45061 DEREHAM
E-mail: glenn@stevensonssolicitors.co.uk
List of partners: G N Stevenson
Work: A1 C1 E J1 K1 L N O P Q R1 S1 S2 W Z(l)
SPr: Stevenson, Mr Glenn Nigel LLB(Hons)(Manc) . . . . . *Mar 1983

DEVIZES, Wiltshire

AWDRY BAILEY & DOUGLAS ‡
33 St John's Street Devizes Wiltshire SN10 1BW
Tel: 01380 722311 *Fax:* 01380 721113 *Dx:* 42900 DEVIZES
E-mail: abd@awdrys.co.uk
List of partners: G A Awdry, A J Douglas, A M Everett, N Robinson, P V Shah
Office: Calne, Marlborough, Wootton Bassett
Languages: French, German
Work: A1 B1 C1 C2 D1 E F1 J1 K1 K3 L N O P Q R1 S1 S2 T1 T2 W Z(d,h,j,k,l,o,q,r)
Emergency Action, Agency, Advocacy, Fixed Fee Interview, Legal Aid undertaken, Legal Aid Franchise and Member of Accident Line
Ptr: Awdry, Mr G Antony. . . . . *§Dec 1978
Douglas, Mr Andrew J BA(Law) . . . . *§Oct 1983
Everett, Mr Alistair Munro . . . . *§Nov 1992
Shah, Mr Peter Vipin LLB . . . . *Dec 1992
Ast: Bressington, Mr Adrian N BA(Dunelm). . . . . . . *§Jun 1977
Chadwick, Mr Roger Eric BA(Hons) . . . . *Jan 2002
Fereday, Mrs Rachel Mary BSc . . . . *Apr 2005
Hughes, Miss Samantha Kate LLB(Hons) . . . . . . *Dec 1990

GOUGHS
Ramsbury House 30 Market Place Devizes Wiltshire SN10 1JG
Tel: 01380 726913 *Fax:* 01380 729107 *Dx:* 42904 DEVIZES
E-mail: info@goughs.co.uk
Office: Calne, Chippenham, Corsham, Melksham, Trowbridge
Languages: French
Work: A1 B1 C1 C2 C3 D1 D2 E F1 J1 J2 K1 K2 K3 K4 L N O P Q R1 R2 S1 S2 W X Z(c,d,e,h,l,m,za)
Emergency Action, Agency, Advocacy, Fixed Fee Interview and Legal Aid Franchise
Ptr: Davis, Dr Nicholas John Rutherford LLB; MBA; PhD. . *Apr 1972
Shipton, Mr Jonathan M LLB(Lond) . . . . *§Jan 1982
Ast: Broadbent, Gemma . . . . Sep 2008
Rubython, Emma . . . . Dec 2004

MORRIS GODDARD & WARD SOLICITORS ‡
28 St John Street Devizes Wiltshire SN10 1BN
Tel: 0845 680 2425
E-mail: info@mgwlaw.co.uk

WANSBROUGHS ‡
Northgate House Northgate Street Devizes Wiltshire SN10 1JX
Tel: 01380 733300 *Fax:* 01380 733600 *Dx:* 42901 DEVIZES
E-mail: mail@wansbroughs.com
List of partners: S J Beresford-Smith, C J B Bromfield, J M Bruton, A F Ciechan, S J Clifford, A Daymond, R J Hams, R A Jeffcoate, A M Jenkins, S McGregor-Johnson, A D Northall, N D Patterson, T J Prees, O G Price, A Wensley-Stock
Office: Melksham
Languages: French, Gujarati, Italian, Japanese
Work: A1 A2 A3 B1 C1 C2 C3 D1 D2 E F1 F2 G H J1 J2 K1 K2 K3 K4 L M1 N O P Q R1 R2 S1 S2 T1 T2 V W X Z(c,d,e,g,j,k,l,o,p,q,r,s,t,u)
Agency, Advocacy, Fixed Fee Interview, Legal Aid undertaken and Legal Aid Franchise
Ptr: Beresford-Smith, Mrs Sarah Jane LLB(Hons) . . . . *May 1995
Bromfield, Mr Christopher J B BA(Oxon) . . . . *Jun 1976
Bruton, Mr Jonathan Michael . . . . Oct 1999
Ciechan, Mr Alan Francis LLB(Nott'm). . . . . Apr 1981
Hams, Mr Robert J Cooks Law Prize . . . . *Dec 1978
Jeffcoate, Mr Richard A BSc . . . . Jan 1984
Jenkins, Mr Andrew M LLB . . . . Oct 1987
McGregor-Johnson, Mr Stuart LLB(Bris). . . . . . . *Apr 1976
Northall, Mr Adrian D LLB(Leeds) . . . . Mar 1986
Patterson, Mr Neil D MA . . . . Oct 1992
Prees, Mr Timothy J BSc(Econ) . . . . *Nov 1988
Price, Mr Oliver G BSc; PGDipLaw; LPC . . . . Jul 1996
Wensley-Stock, Mrs Anna LLB(Hons) . . . . *Sep 2002
Asoc: Bew, Mrs Kathryn A LLB(Hons) . . . . *Nov 1993
Davies, Mr Michael John LLB(Hons). . . . . Feb 2001
Hannaford, Mr Glyn Robert LLB; FILEx . . . . Jul 1998
Moor, Ms Jackie. . . . . Sep 1998
Rees, Mrs Lucy Jane . . . . Oct 1998
Watts, Mrs E Cynthia E LLB(Hons) . . . . *Oct 1992
Ast: Birch, Miss Rowena Ursula Isabel. . . . . Oct 2006
Clark, Mrs Mary C LLB . . . . Apr 1994
Conway, Miss Helen Mary Bridget BA . . . . Dec 1989
Dawson, Ms Kelly Louise . . . . Sep 2007
Fitzgeorge-Balfour, Ms Charlotte . . . . Mar 2008
Ladwa, Mr Rishi. . . . . Mar 2007
Lester, Mr James . . . . Sep 2008
Osman, Mr John Derek . . . . Sep 2003
Owen, Mrs Naomi LLB; LPC . . . . Sep 2002
Parker, Ms Helen Louise . . . . Mar 2008
Peterson, Rebecca . . . . Sep 2008
Vooght, Jennifer. . . . . Sep 2009
Con: Bousfield, Mr David S. . . . . *Jan 1966
Drury, Mr Richard J LLB(Bris) . . . . *Apr 1975

DEVONPORT, Devon

CROSSE WYATT & CO ‡
Old Bank House Fore Street Chulmleigh Devonport Devon EX18 7BR
Tel: 01769 580059

DEWSBURY, West Yorkshire

ACKLAM BOND NOOR
9 Leeds Road Dewsbury West Yorkshire WF12 7BB
Tel: 01924 465786
E-mail: jackie@acklambond.co.uk
Office: Accrington, Blackburn
Languages: Punjabi, Urdu

ASHMANS SOLICITORS ‡
First Floor 26 Market Place Dewsbury West Yorkshire WF12 7BB
Tel: 01924 501717 *Fax:* 01924 501407
E-mail: info@ashmanssolicitors.com

DISKEN & CO ‡
(incorporating J Bryan Smith & Co.)
20 Bond Street Dewsbury West Yorkshire WF13 1AT
Tel: 01924 464101 *Fax:* 01924 452880 *Dx:* 23355 DEWSBURY
List of partners: B T Disken, T Disken, K L Storey
Languages: French, Gujarati, Russian, Urdu
Work: B1 C1 E K1 K3 K4 L O Q R1 R2 S1 S2 W Z(i,l,q,w)
Ptr: Disken, Mr Bernard T MA . . . . *Oct 1993
Disken, Mr Thomas MA; LLM . . . . *§Nov 1958
Storey, Mrs Katharine Louise LLB. . . . . *Oct 1993
Ast: Collins, Mrs Sephora Maria BA . . . . *Nov 1998
McCullough, Mr Joseph David LLB . . . . *Feb 2008

MICHAEL GEORGE & COMPANY ‡
The Dewsbury Business & Media Centre 13 Wellington Road Dewsbury West Yorkshire WF13 1HF
Tel: 01924 488884 *Fax:* 01924 488843 *Dx:* 23370 DEWSBURY
Emergency telephone 07969620858
E-mail: em@mg-company.co.uk

HELLEWELL PASLEY & BREWER
66 Daisy Hill Dewsbury West Yorkshire WF13 1LS
Tel: 01924 455515 *Fax:* 01924 459861 *Dx:* 23361 DEWSBURY
E-mail: rwhitaker@hpandb.co.uk
Office: Batley
Work: A3 C1 C2 D1 D2 E F1 J1 J2 K1 K2 K3 L M4 N O Q R1 S1 S2 T1 T2 V W Z(c,i,l)
Emergency Action, Agency, Advocacy, Fixed Fee Interview, Legal Aid undertaken, Legal Aid Franchise and Member of Accident Line
Ptr: Gaddes, Mr Lee LLB(Hons) . . . . *§Sep 2004
Whitaker, Mr Richard M LLB Litigator at CPIL . . . . *Dec 1992
Ast: Cookson, Miss Sarah Louise LLB(Hons); PGDip. . . . Mar 2004
Vesely, Mrs Susan F LLB(Leeds) ♦ . . . . *Jun 1980
Con: Vesely, Mr Martin W. . . . . *§Dec 1975

IBA SOLICITORS ‡
13 Wellington Road Dewsbury West Yorkshire WF13 1HF
Tel: 01924 455000

JORDANS ‡
Neil Jordan House Wellington Road Dewsbury West Yorkshire WF13 1HL
Tel: 01924 457171 *Fax:* 01924 456131 *Dx:* 23357 DEWSBURY
E-mail: enquiries@jordanssolicitors.co.uk
List of partners: L Durham, D A Greenwood, P I Kirrane, S Lewis, S R Lindley, D J Mactaggart, S T Proctor, C Sands, S Shergill
Office: Castleford, Wakefield
Work: A3 B1 C1 D1 D2 E F1 F2 G H J1 J2 K1 K2 K3 K4 L M2 N O P Q R1 R2 S1 S2 V W Z(c,h,j,k,l,p,q,s,t)
Emergency Action, Agency, Advocacy, Fixed Fee Interview, Legal Aid undertaken and Legal Aid Franchise
Ptr: Durham, Ms Lynn LLB . . . . *Mar 1999
Greenwood, Mr David A LLB . . . . *Sep 1994
Kirrane, Mr Peter Ignatius BA(Hons); CPE. . . . . . *Jun 1995
Lindley, Mr Simon R BA. . . . . *Mar 1988
Ast: Asquith, Mrs Joy DML. . . . . *Jan 1989
Atkinson, Mrs Helen Margaret BA. . . . . *Mar 1984
Brocklebank, Ms Emma LLB . . . . Jun 2002
Chatterton, Mr Kieran LLB. . . . . Mar 2008
Hughes, Miss Helen Louise BA . . . . *Sep 2003
Mahil, Miss Sundeep LLB . . . . Nov 2009
Mercer, Miss Beverley Lauraine BSc . . . . *Oct 2001
Taylor-True, Mrs Catherine Anne LLB . . . . *Jun 2009

KINGSWELL WATTS ‡
Church Street Dewsbury West Yorkshire WF13 1JX
Tel: 01924 461236 *Fax:* 01924 453175 *Dx:* 23351 DEWSBURY
E-mail: enquiries@kingswellwatts.co.uk
List of partners: A Abubaker
Languages: Gujarati, Punjabi, Urdu
Work: C1 E L N S1 S2 W Z(c)
SPr: Abubaker, Mr Asif. . . . . *Nov 1994
Ast: Amin, Mrs Khuram LLB; LLM . . . . *Apr 2008

NADAT SOLICITORS ‡
2nd Floor Suite 4 Bond Street Dewsbury West Yorkshire WF13 1AG
Tel: 01924 505071

MUSA A PATEL & CO ‡
73 Bradford Road Dewsbury West Yorkshire WF13 2EG
Tel: 01924 437800 *Fax:* 01924 488810 *Dx:* 23371 DEWSBURY
Emergency telephone 07966 213165 / 07970 151056
E-mail: info@musapatels.co.uk
List of partners: Z Iqbal, M A Patel
Office: Bradford
Languages: Arabic, Gujarati, Hindi, Punjabi, Urdu
Work: D1 G H K1 K2 L S1 S2 W Z(i,p)
Emergency Action, Agency, Advocacy, Legal Aid undertaken and Legal Aid Franchise
Ptr: Iqbal, Zafar LLB(Hons) ♦ . . . . *Oct 1993
Patel, Mr Musa A LLB(Hons) ★ . . . . *Sep 1991

PRASAD SOLICITORS ‡
1st Floor 9 Wellington Road Dewsbury West Yorkshire WF13 1HF
Tel: 01924 464949 *Fax:* 01924 465100 *Dx:* 23369 DEWSBURY
E-mail: law@prasads.co.uk
List of partners: D Prasad
Ptr: Prasad, Mr Deepak LLB. . . . . *Oct 1989

QAMAR SOLICITORS ‡
9 Halifax Road Dewsbury West Yorkshire WF13 2JH
Tel: 01924 488199 *Fax:* 01924 488348 *Dx:* 23364 DEWSBURY
E-mail: qamar@qamar.co.uk

RKS SOLICITORS ‡
71 Daisy Hill Dewsbury West Yorkshire WF13 1LT
Tel: 01924 439106 *Fax:* 01924 439107
E-mail: info@rkssolicitors.com

RAMSDENS SOLICITORS
27 Union Street Dewsbury West Yorkshire WF13 1AY
Tel: 01924 455391 *Fax:* 01924 469299 *Dx:* 23360 DEWSBURY
E-mail: info@ramsdens.co.uk
Office: Elland, Halifax, Holmfirth, Huddersfield (3 offices), Mirfield
Languages: French, Punjabi, Urdu
Work: D1 E F1 G H J1 K1 L N O Q S1 V W

SWITALSKI'S
22 Bond Street Dewsbury West Yorkshire WF13 1AU
Tel: 01924 869940 *Fax:* 01924 869941 *Dx:* 23367 DEWSBURY
Office: Bradford, Halifax, Huddersfield, Leeds, Wakefield
Work: D1 G H J1 K1 K2 L Z(i,m,r)
Emergency Action, Agency and Legal Aid undertaken

DIDCOT, Oxfordshire

BARRETT & CO SOLICITORS LLP
7 The Business Centre Blewbury Didcot Oxfordshire OX11 9QA
Tel: 01235 851220 *Fax:* 01235 851445
E-mail: info@barrettandco.co.uk
Office: Reading
Work: A1 B1 C1 C2 C3 D1 E F1 F2 I J1 J2 K1 K2 K3 K4 L M1 O P Q R1 R2 S1 S2 W Z(c,e,p)
Advocacy and Fixed Fee Interview undertaken

CROSSLANDS EMPLOYMENT LAW PLUS ‡
Harwell Innovation Centre 173 Curie Avenue Didcot Oxfordshire OX11 0QG
Tel: 01235 838606
E-mail: beverley@crosslandsolicitors.com

DINNING CONSULTANCY ‡
62 Westwater Way Didcot Oxfordshire OX11 7TY
Tel: 07900 215065

HEDGES
The Glass Tower 6 Station Road Didcot Oxfordshire OX11 7LL
Tel: 01235 811888 *Fax:* 01235 816322 *Dx:* 40856 DIDCOT
E-mail: info@hedgeslaw.co.uk
Office: Wallingford
Work: A1 C1 D1 E K1 K2 K3 K4 L S1 S2 T1 T2 W
Fixed Fee Interview and Legal Aid Franchise
Ptr: Buxton, Mrs Mary Elizabeth LLB; BA(Hons) . . . . . Sep 1995
Ast: Nelson, Mrs Louise Elizabeth LLB. . . . . *Oct 1995

SLADE LEGAL
The Old Bank 137 The Broadway Didcot Oxfordshire OX11 8RQ
Tel: 01235 511211 *Fax:* 01235 815489 *Dx:* 40850 DIDCOT
E-mail: enquiries@slade-legal.co.uk
Office: Abingdon, Wallingford
Work: C1 D1 E F1 J1 K1 L N S1 W Z(l)
Fixed Fee Interview and Legal Aid Franchise
Ptr: Ferguson, Mr Eric. . . . . *Dec 1979
Hodson, Mr David M . . . . *Jul 1969

DINNINGTON, South Yorkshire

TIERNEY & CO ‡
The Old Dispensary Barleycroft Lane Dinnington South Yorkshire S25 2LE
Tel: 01909 550730 *Fax:* 01909 566537 *Dx:* 29786 DINNINGTON
Emergency telephone 07860 587133
E-mail: adpt@tierneyandco.co.uk
List of partners: A D P Tierney, G Tierney, S D G Tierney
Office: Rotherham
Languages: German
Work: E F1 G J1 J2 K1 K3 K4 L N O Q R1 S1 S2 V W Z(l,q,r,u)
Emergency Action, Agency, Advocacy and Fixed Fee Interview undertaken
Ptr: Tierney, Mr Adam Damian Peter LLB(Hons). . . . . *Dec 1995
Tierney, Mr George . . . . *Jan 1966
Tierney, Mr Simon D G ● . . . . Jan 1983
Ast: Inger, Mrs Janine April . . . . Aug 2009

DISLEY, Cheshire

CARTER & CARTER SOLICITORS ‡
14 Market Street Disley Cheshire SK12 2AA
Tel: 01663 761890
E-mail: chris@candcsolicitors.co.uk

WOOD'S SOLICITORS ‡
15 Buxton Old Road Disley Cheshire SK12 2BB
Tel: 01663 765511 *Fax:* 01663 765582
E-mail: postmaster@woodssolicitors.demon.co.uk
List of partners: R A Earland
Work: C1 E J1 K1 L O Q S1 S2 T2 W
Agency and Fixed Fee Interview undertaken
SPr: Earland, Mr Richard A LLB . . . . *Dec 1976

DISS, Norfolk

FRANCIS H CHENERY ‡
The Warehouse Norfolk House Courtyard St Nicholas Street Diss Norfolk IP22 4LB
Tel: 01379 644055 *Fax:* 01379 643911
Emergency telephone 01379 641725
E-mail: francis.chenery@btconnect.com
List of partners: F H Chenery
Work: A1 B1 C1 E F1 J1 K1 K3 L O Q S1 S2 W
Emergency Action, Agency, Advocacy and Fixed Fee Interview undertaken
SPr: Chenery, Mr Francis H . . . . *Sep 1980

COMERCRAWLEY ‡
Chancery House Victoria Road Diss Norfolk IP22 4HZ
Tel: 01379 644311 *Fax:* 01379 644299
E-mail: enquiries@comercrawley.co.uk
List of partners: I R Comer, E Crawley
Work: N
Member of Accident Line
Dir: Comer, Mr Ian R . . . . May 1981
Crawley, Miss Emma LLB(Hons); LSF. . . . . Oct 1992
Ast: Cole, Mrs Judith Ann LLB . . . . Nov 1997
Dougan, Ms Keely. . . . . Nov 2000
Flack, Mr Mark . . . . Nov 1992

JACKAMANS
Park House Mere Street Diss Norfolk IP22 4JY
Tel: 01379 643555 *Fax:* 01379 652221 *Dx:* 42500 DISS
Emergency telephone 01953 681362
E-mail: mail@jackamans.co.uk
Office: Felixstowe, Harleston, Ipswich
Languages: French, German
Work: A1 B1 C1 D1 E F1 G H K1 L N O Q R1 S1 T1 W Z(c,d,j,l,t)
Emergency Action, Agency, Advocacy, Fixed Fee Interview, Legal Aid undertaken and Member of Accident Line
Ptr: Laband, Mr James Lenford LLB . . . . *Oct 1984
Rowlands, Mr Mark Roymaur . . . . Dec 2006
Ast: Sharpe, Ms Anita BA . . . . Dec 1979

See p112 for the Key to Work Categories & other symbols

OVERBURYS & RAYMOND THOMPSON
2 Victoria Road Diss Norfolk IP22 4EY
Tel: 01379 641221 *Fax:* 01379 641227 *Dx:* 42521 DISS
E-mail: info@overburys.co.uk
Office: Norwich
Languages: French
Work: A1 A2 C1 C2 E F1 F2 J1 L R1 R2 S1 S2 T2 W Z(l)

STEELES
2 Mount Street Diss Norfolk IP22 4QE
Tel: 01379 652141 *Fax:* 01379 650150 *Dx:* 42507 DISS
E-mail: info@steeleslaw.co.uk
Office: London EC2, Norwich
Languages: French, German
Work: A1 A3 B1 B2 C1 C2 C3 D1 E F1 G H I J1 K1 K2 L M1 M2 N O Q R1 R2 S1 S2 T1 T2 V W Z(c,d,h,k,l,m,o,r,u)
Agency, Advocacy, S.I.G and Member of Accident Line
Ptr: Addinell, Mr Timothy J MA(Cantab); LLB(Hons) . . . *Mar 1986
Drake, Mr Stephen K . . . *Jan 1984
Grearson, Mr Neale LLB(Hons) . . . Oct 1986
Ast: Palmer, Mr Nicholas George LLB . . . Sep 2000

DOLGELLAU, Gwynedd

GUTHRIE JONES & JONES
Waterloo Chambers Dolgellau Gwynedd LL40 1AU
Tel: 01341 422604 *Fax:* 01341 422934
E-mail: dolgellau@guthriejj.co.uk
Office: Bala, Denbigh
Languages: Welsh
Work: A1 A2 G J1 K1 K3 K4 L N O Q R2 S1 S2 W X Z(l,m,t,u)
Agency, Advocacy and Fixed Fee Interview undertaken
Ptr: Roberts, Mr Osian LLB . . . *Jul 2003

J CHARLES HUGHES & CO ‡
Bridge End Dolgellau Gwynedd LL40 1AY
Tel: 01341 422464 *Fax:* 01341 423986 *Dx:* 711441 DOLGELLAU
E-mail: office@jcharleshughesandco.com
List of partners: G Evans
Office: Harlech
Languages: Welsh
Work: A1 B2 E G H K1 L N Q R1 S1 S2 T1 T2 W Z(d,l)
Emergency Action, Agency, Advocacy, Fixed Fee Interview, Legal Aid undertaken and Legal Aid Franchise
Ptr: Evans, Mr Gareth LLB(Wales). . . . *Dec 1975
Con: Wynne, Mr Thomas M LLB . . . *§Jan 1965

DONCASTER, South Yorkshire

MARK APPLEYARD LIMITED ‡
Consort House Waterdale Doncaster South Yorkshire DN1 3HR
Tel: 01302 640210 *Fax:* 0871 528 4191
E-mail: ma@malaw.co.uk

ATHERTON GODFREY ‡
8 Hall Gate Doncaster South Yorkshire DN1 3LU
Est: 1979
Tel: 01302 320621 *Fax:* 01302 340692 *Dx:* 12553 DONCASTER
E-mail: info@athertongodfrey.co.uk
List of partners: D J Bird, C H Godfrey, K Marriott, J McQuater, D Parker, J F Sutherland, S A Veysey
Languages: French
Work: B1 C1 D1 D2 E F1 F2 J1 K1 K2 K3 K4 L N O Q R1 S1 S2 V W Z(c,l,q,r)
Emergency Action, Agency, Advocacy, Fixed Fee Interview, Legal Aid undertaken, Legal Aid Franchise and Member of Accident Line
Ptr: Bird, Mr Donald John LLB. . . . *§Jun 1980
Godfrey, Mr Charles H LLB . . . *§Apr 1973
McQuater, Mr John LLM ♦ President of APIL 2009 . *§Nov 1983
Marriott, Ms Kay LLB . . . *Sep 1995
Parker, Ms Diane LLB. . . . *Nov 1991
Sutherland, Mr James F BA. . . . *Oct 1984
Veysey, Ms Stephanie Anne BA(Hons)(Classical Studies(Ancient History)) . . . *Dec 1995
Asoc: Baker, Miss Beverley LLB. . . . Nov 2008
Baker, Mrs Rachel Anne LLB(Hons). . . . Jun 2005
Beazley, Mrs Emma Louise BSc; MA; PGDip . . . *Jul 2002
Gallagher, Mr Sean Robert LLM. . . . *May 2005
Houghton, Miss Maria Ingrid. . . . *Jan 2007
King, Mrs Joanne . . . Sep 2001
Noble, Mr Christopher James Gerald LLB(Hons); PGDip Personal Injury Litigation . . . *Jun 1994
Ast: Buckle, Miss Katie Margaret LLB . . . Sep 2008
Cameron, Mrs Kate BA(Hons)(English); PGDipLaw; LPC . . . Oct 2009
Das, Miss Shantha BA(Hons) . . . *Jan 1999
Evans, Miss Keelie Jayne LLB(Hons) . . . *Mar 2009
Jennings, Miss Philipa BSc(Hons)(Psychology); GDL . Oct 2009
Lawrence, Miss Clare LLB . . . Oct 2007
Lawton, Miss Janine GDL; LPC . . . Sep 2010
Murgatroyd, Miss Caroline Deanna LLB. . . . Sep 2009
Naylor, Miss Sarah Louise. . . . *Oct 2007
Tansey, Ms Julie Ann LLB(Hons) Blackstone Prize 2001 . . . Sep 2007
Wood, Mr Nigel LLB(Hons) . . . *Sep 2010

ATTEYS ‡
82 Cleveland Street Doncaster South Yorkshire DN1 3DR
Tel: 01302 340400 *Fax:* 01302 323710 *Dx:* 12558 DONCASTER
List of partners: R C Allen, M E Browne, J W Buckley, R A Carlisle, C A Dudley, D C Gordon, R T Grove, R S F Haigh, A R Hattrell, C R P Hennis, R M Jennings, I M Jones, P N Jones, G A Knight, A Methley, M F Neeves, J E Oliver, G M Sampson, V A Sladdin, S P Taylor, J G W Wood
Office: Barnsley, Retford, Sheffield, Wath-upon-Dearne
Work: A1 B1 C1 C2 C3 D1 E F1 G H J1 K1 L N O P Q R1 S1 V W Z(c,e,h,l,m)
Emergency Action, Agency, Advocacy, Fixed Fee Interview, Legal Aid undertaken, Legal Aid Franchise and Member of Accident Line
Ptr: Allen, Mr Robert C BA(Law). . . . *Mar 1983
Carlisle, Mr Robert A . . . *May 1985
Dudley, Ms Cheryl A . . . *Oct 1986
Grove, Mr Roger T LLB. . . . *Jan 1988
Haigh, Mr Richard S F BA. . . . *Dec 1979
Hattrell, Mr Adrian R LLB . . . *Nov 1970
Hennis, Mr Cedric R P. . . . *Jun 1972
Jones, Mr Ian M. . . . *Jun 1970
Jones, Mr Philip Nigel LLB(Hons) . . . *Jan 1990
Oliver, Mrs Judith E LLB . . . *Oct 1983
Sampson, Mr G Michael LLB . . . *Jul 1974
Sladdin, Vicky A. . . . Oct 1990
Taylor, Mr Steve P. . . . May 1999
Wood, Mr John G W . . . *Oct 1986
Ast: Ward, Ms Victoria A. . . . *Oct 1992

BRUCE BOWLING & CO ‡
5 Thorne Road Doncaster South Yorkshire DN1 2HJ
Tel: 01302 320607 *Fax:* 01302 761639
E-mail: info@brucebowling.co.uk
List of partners: W B C Bowling
Office: Doncaster
Work: A1 L S1 S2 W
Ptr: Bowling, Mr William Bruce Clifford. . . . *Dec 1980

BRUCE BOWLING & CO
13 King Avenue Doncaster South Yorkshire DN11 0PG
Office: Doncaster

BRIDGE SANDERSON MUNRO ‡
55 Hallgate Doncaster South Yorkshire DN1 3PD
Tel: 01302 321621 *Fax:* 01302 340313 *Dx:* 12567 DONCASTER
E-mail: info@bsmlaw.co.uk
List of partners: N J Ball, P D Davies, B J Edwards, J L Goodwin
Office: Thorne, Wath-upon-Dearne
Work: A1 B1 C1 C2 C3 D1 E F1 J1 K1 L N O Q R1 S1 S2 T1 T2 V W Z(c,d,e,h,i,k,l,m,o,p,q,r,s)
Emergency Action, Agency, Advocacy, Fixed Fee Interview, Legal Aid undertaken, Legal Aid Franchise and Member of Accident Line
Ptr: Ball, Mr Nigel J LLB. . . . *Oct 1974
Davies, Mr Paul D LLB . . . *Dec 1976
Edwards, Mr Bevil John LLB . . . *Oct 1986
Goodwin, Mr Jonathan L LLB . . . *Nov 1992

PAUL BULLEN & CO ‡
5 Copley Road Doncaster South Yorkshire DN1 2PE
Tel: 01302 819000 *Fax:* 01302 812500 *Dx:* 28683 DONCASTER 2
E-mail: pbullen@paulbullen.co.uk
List of partners: P V Bullen, A B Rawlings
Work: C1 E K1 K3 K4 Q R2 S1 S2 W
Ptr: Bullen, Mr Paul Vincent BSc. . . . Jun 1977
Rawlings, Mr Anthony B LLB; LLM . . . *Oct 1991
Con: Wrigglesworth, Mr Peter Anthony . . . *Jul 1974

THE BYRNE PRACTICE ‡
10 South Parade Bawtry Doncaster South Yorkshire DN10 6JH
Tel: 01302 711211 *Fax:* 01302 711608
E-mail: admin@tbplaw.co.uk

CA LAW ‡
4 Nidd House Richmond Business Park Sidings Court Doncaster South Yorkshire DN4 5NL
Tel: 01302 347755 *Fax:* 01302 730777
E-mail: info@calaw.co.uk

COWLINGS
244 Great North Road Doncaster South Yorkshire DN6 7HN
Tel: 01302 723366 *Fax:* 01302 337888 *Dx:* 27703 MEXBOROUGH
Office: Mexborough

DAWSON & BURGESS WITH BELL DALLMAN & CO ‡
3 South Parade Hall Cross Hill Doncaster South Yorkshire DN1 2DZ
Tel: 01302 349463 *Fax:* 01302 329069 *Dx:* 28694 DONCASTER 2
Emergency telephone 01302 349463
E-mail: rmw@dawsonandburgess.co.uk
List of partners: T A Dallman, W Hezseltine, T Sanders, M J Toseland, R M Williams
Office: Doncaster (2 offices)
Languages: French, Italian
Work: A1 C1 C2 E F1 F2 J1 J2 K1 K3 K4 L N O Q R1 R2 S1 S2 T1 T2 V W X Z(c,d,e,n,q,r)
Emergency Action, Agency, Advocacy undertaken and Member of Accident Line
Ptr: Hezseltine, Mrs Wendy LLB. . . . *§Oct 1992
Sanders, Mr Timothy LLB . . . *§Dec 1977
Toseland, Mr Mark J BA(Law). . . . *§Dec 1984
Williams, Mr Roger Menai MA(Oxon) . . . *§Apr 1970

DAWSON & BURGESS WITH BELL DALLMAN & CO
87 High Street Bentley Doncaster South Yorkshire DN5 0AP
Office: Doncaster (2 offices)

DAWSON & BURGESS WITH BELL DALLMAN & CO
33 Church Street Armthorpe Doncaster South Yorkshire DN3 3AE
Tel: 01302 834744 *Fax:* 01302 834592 *Dx:* 708972 DONCASTER 10
E-mail: enquiries@belldallman.com
Office: Doncaster (2 offices)
Languages: French, Italian, Turkish
Work: A1 B1 C1 C2 C3 D1 D2 E F1 J1 K1 K2 K4 L M1 M2 N O P Q R1 S1 S2 T1 T2 V W Z(c,d,e,j,k,l,r,t)
Emergency Action, Agency, Advocacy, Fixed Fee Interview, Legal Aid undertaken, Legal Aid Franchise and Member of Accident Line
Ptr: Dallman, Mr Tony A LLB . . . *Dec 1977
Ast: Canli, Miss Gemma A D LLB . . . *Sep 2009

DICKINSON WOOD ‡
28 South Parade Doncaster South Yorkshire DN1 2DJ
Tel: 01302 329504 *Fax:* 01302 323636 *Dx:* 12572 DONCASTER
E-mail: lgb@dickinsonwood.co.uk
List of partners: M R Dickinson, K F Wood
Work: B1 C1 D1 D2 E K1 K2 L R1 S1 S2 W
Ptr: Dickinson, Mr Mark R LLB. . . . *Feb 1992
Wood, Ms Kay F LLB . . . *Nov 1986

C H DOWNTON ‡
Number One Railway Court Ten Pound Walk Doncaster South Yorkshire DN4 5FB
Tel: 01302 360060 *Fax:* 01302 360505
E-mail: mail@chdownton.com
List of partners: C H Downton
Work: C1 E S1 S2 W Z(c,n)
SPr: Downton, Mr Christopher H . . . *Mar 1977

FOREMAN & CO ‡
9 Ashdown Way Misterton Doncaster South Yorkshire DN10 4BP
Tel: 01427 891892 *Fax:* 01427 891354

MALCOLM C FOY & CO ‡
52 Hallgate Doncaster South Yorkshire DN1 3PB
Tel: 01302 340005 *Fax:* 01302 322283 *Dx:* 28698 DONCASTER 2
E-mail: info@malcolmcfoy.co.uk
List of partners: D J Carr, M C Foy, A Pashley
Office: Rotherham
Languages: French, German, Spanish
Work: B1 C1 C2 D1 D2 E F1 J1 J2 K1 K3 L N O Q R1 S1 S2 V W Z(i,l,m,p,q,r)
Emergency Action, Agency, Advocacy, Fixed Fee Interview, Legal Aid undertaken and Legal Aid Franchise
Ptr: Carr, Mr Daniel J ♦ . . . *Oct 1996
Foy, Mr Malcolm Clive LLB ♦ . . . *Mar 1969
Pashley, Mrs Andrea ♦ Notary Public . . . *Oct 2005
Ast: Clarke, Miss Lauren LLB(Hons) ♦ . . . *Aug 2006
Jenkins, Mr Hywel M BA ♦ . . . *Sep 1996
Johnson, Mr Robert Graham LLB ♦ . . . *Sep 2006
Kong, Ms Julie . . . Oct 2008
Roberts, Ms Victoria . . . Dec 2007
Turner, Mrs Alison Fiona LLB ♦ . . . *Jan 1993
White, Mrs Amanda LLB ♦ . . . *Oct 2007

FOYS SOLICITORS ‡
PO Box 111 Kingsgate House Kingsgate Doncaster South Yorkshire DN1 3DQ
Tel: 01302 327136 *Fax:* 01302 367656 *Dx:* 12563 DONCASTER
E-mail: info@foys.co.uk
List of partners: A J Chatterton, S J Derbyshire, P Evans, A Firth, K Green, D C Harris, G D A Kite, N J Misson, S J Paramore, D A Verity
Office: Rotherham, Sheffield (2 offices), Worksop
Languages: Punjabi
Work: A1 B1 B2 C1 C2 C3 D1 D2 E F1 F2 G H J1 J2 K1 L M1 M2 N O P Q R1 S1 S2 V W Z(b,c,e,g,h,j,l,m,p,q,r,t)
Emergency Action, Agency, Advocacy, Fixed Fee Interview and Legal Aid undertaken
Ptr: Chatterton, Mr Andrew J . . . *Dec 1981
Derbyshire, Ms Samantha J LLB . . . *Jan 1996
Green, Mr Keith. . . . *Dec 1991
Harris, Mr Dale C LLB ★ . . . *Oct 1993
Misson, Mr Nigel John LLB(Hons). . . . *Feb 1994
Paramore, Mr Stephen J LLB(Leics) ★ . . . *Apr 1972
Asoc: Walshe, Mr Nigel George MA(Oxon) . . . *Dec 1978
Ast: Baldwin, Ms Joanne Sarah Louise BA(Hons) . . . *Jul 2002
Gilberthorpe, Miss Helen Laura LLB. . . . *Feb 2006
Jones, Miss Kim Louise LLB . . . *Apr 2004

GRAHAM CLAYTON SOLICITORS
7-9 Chequer Road Doncaster South Yorkshire DN1 2AA
Tel: 01302 342448
Office: Chester-le-Street, Ilford, Stafford

GRAINGER APPLEYARD ‡
26-27 Hallgate Doncaster South Yorkshire DN1 3NL
Tel: 01302 327257 *Fax:* 01302 322470 *Dx:* 28685 DONCASTER 2
E-mail: info@graingerappleyard.co.uk
List of partners: C J Borrowdale, J P Grainger
Work: A1 B1 C1 D1 E G H J1 K1 L M1 O Q R1 S1 T1 T2 W Z(l,n,o,t)
Emergency Action, Agency, Advocacy, Fixed Fee Interview, Legal Aid undertaken and Legal Aid Franchise
Ptr: Borrowdale, Mr Christopher J LLB. . . . *Nov 1990
Grainger, Mr John P BA. . . . *§Feb 1982
Ast: Clark, Mrs Janice . . . *Jul 1982
Newall, Mr Jason . . . *Sep 2005

HLW KEEBLE HAWSON LLP
14 Prince's Street Doncaster South Yorkshire DN1 3NJ
Tel: 01302 366831 *Fax:* 01302 329718 *Dx:* 12562 DONCASTER
E-mail: info@hlwkeeblehawson.co.uk
Office: Leeds, Sheffield (2 offices)
Work: A1 B1 C1 C2 C3 D1 E F1 G H J1 K1 L N O P Q R1 S1 S2 T1 T2 V W Z(c,f,i,l,q,t)
Emergency Action, Agency, Advocacy, Fixed Fee Interview, Legal Aid undertaken, Legal Aid Franchise and Member of Accident Line
Ptr: Cunliffe, Mr David R Chairman of the Social Security & Disability Appeals Tribunal . . . *Dec 1968
Goel, Mr Paul Vinod MA(Oxon) . . . *Mar 1996
Hollinghurst, Mr Mark W BA(Cantab) . . . Dec 1991
Pennington, Mr Martin T. . . . *Feb 1974
Pennington, Mr Paul R . . . *Oct 1967
Ast: Lunn, Ms Tina. . . . Apr 2006
Con: Powell, Mr Keith Notary Public . . . *Dec 1973

HSR LAW (HAYES, SON & RICHMOND)
The Law Chambers 7-8 South Parade Doncaster South Yorkshire DN1 2ED
Tel: 01302 347800 *Fax:* 01302 363466 *Dx:* 711895 DONCASTER 2
Emergency telephone 07774 677465
E-mail: doncasterenquiries@hsrlaw.co.uk
Office: Epworth, Gainsborough
Languages: French, Punjabi, Urdu
Work: A1 A2 B2 C1 C2 D1 D2 E G H J1 K1 K2 K3 N O Q R2 S1 S2 V W Z(l,q)
Emergency Action, Agency, Advocacy, Fixed Fee Interview, Legal Aid undertaken and Legal Aid Franchise
Ptr: Allwood, Mr Richard J TD BA(Hons)(Soton); PGCE(Lond) . . . *Oct 1984
Best, Mr Andrew W LLB. . . . Sep 2001
Bradley, Mr John E MBIM Member of the Legal Aid Area Committee . . . Dec 1976
Braithwaite, Mr Fabian BA; JD . . . Nov 2004
Flinders, Mrs Tracy Jayne LLB; LSF Parish Councillor. *Oct 1995
Fullwood, Mr Richard Ellis. . . . *Jun 1980
Harris, Mr David Keith OBE; TD; DL LLB(Lond) . . . *Dec 1969
Kirkham, Ms Lucy Anne LLB . . . Oct 1997
Ast: Burnett, Mr Russell . . . Sep 2004
Coddington, Ms Catherine LLB . . . Apr 2008
Davies, Mr David P E LLB. . . . *Jul 1977
Hayles, Mr Nicholas P LLB ★ . . . *Dec 1977
Macdonald, Miss Kirstin-Anne LLB . . . Nov 2006
Russell, Mr Paul LLB . . . Nov 2007
Wood, Mr Mark LLB. . . . Jun 2005
Con: Vickers, Mr Peter G. . . . *§Jan 1970

G V HALE & CO ‡
70 Waterdale Doncaster South Yorkshire DN1 3BU
Tel: 01302 360606
E-mail: info@gvhale.co.uk

HALLIDAY REEVES
2nd Floor Kingsgate House Waterdale Doncaster South Yorkshire DN1 3JZ
Tel: 01302 560969 *Fax:* 01302 560663
Office: Gateshead

PAUL INMAN & CO ‡
3 Armthorpe Lane Doncaster South Yorkshire DN2 5LZ
Tel: 01302 349395 *Dx:* 28687 DONCASTER 2

E-mail: paulinmansols@btinternet.com
List of partners: P R Inman
Work: G H K1
Emergency Action, Agency, Advocacy, Fixed Fee Interview, Legal Aid undertaken and Legal Aid Franchise
SPr: Inman, Mr Paul Roger LLB . . . . *Jul 1976

ANDREW ISAACS ‡
7 Shaw Wood Business Park Shaw Wood Way Leger Way Doncaster South Yorkshire DN2 5TB
Tel: 01302 349480 *Fax:* 01302 368572
E-mail: agi@andrewisaacs.co.uk

GLYN JONES & CO ‡
15a Hall Gate Doncaster South Yorkshire DN1 3NA
Tel: 01302 340430 *Fax:* 01302 340437
E-mail: glynjones@glynjoneslaw.co.uk

KENYON SON & CRADDOCK ‡
(in association with Henshaw Pratt)
32 South Parade Thorne Doncaster South Yorkshire DN8 5DX
Tel: 01405 813108 *Fax:* 01405 740156 *Dx:* 13916 THORNE
E-mail: elizabethb@ksandc.co.uk
List of partners: P R Bainbridge, T J Bysouth
Office: Goole
Work: A1 C1 C2 C3 D1 E F1 G H J1 K1 L N O P Q R1 S1 S2 W X Z(c,d,j,l)
Emergency Action, Agency, Advocacy, Fixed Fee Interview, Legal Aid undertaken, Legal Aid Franchise and Member of Accident Line
Ptr: Bysouth, Mr Trevor J LLB . . . . *§Jun 1976
Asoc: Green, Mr Jonathan William Leonard LLB . . . . Nov 1988
Con: Pennington, Mr Peter R . . . . *§Dec 1960

KEYPOINT LAW LLP ‡
Quaypoint Lakeside Boulevard Doncaster South Yorkshire DN4 5PL
Tel: 01302 329655 *Fax:* 01302 732755
E-mail: enquiries@keypointlaw.co.uk
List of partners: E Beresford
Work: N Q W
Ptr: Beresford, Mrs Esta LLB . . . . Jun 2002
Asoc: Barnes, Mr Ian L O LLB(Hons) . . . . Dec 1974
Ast: Earley, Celia . . . . Nov 1985

NA COMMERCIAL ‡
1 Thorne Road Doncaster South Yorkshire DN1 2HJ
Tel: 01302 341300 *Fax:* 0845 299 2148
E-mail: contact@nacommercial.co.uk

NUMBER ONE LEGAL LTD ‡
23 Thorne Road Doncaster South Yorkshire DN1 2RP
Tel: 01302 760457 *Fax:* 01302 327050
Office: High Wycombe

QUALITYSOLICITORS JORDANS ‡
4 Priory Place Doncaster South Yorkshire DN1 1BP
Tel: 01302 365374 *Fax:* 01302 327521 *Dx:* 12555 DONCASTER 1
E-mail: info@jordansllp.com
List of partners: M Newby, R Sharp
Office: Sheffield
Languages: German
Work: A1 D1 E F1 G H K1 K3 K4 L N O Q S1 S2 T2 V W Z(d,l)
Emergency Action, Agency, Advocacy, Fixed Fee Interview and Legal Aid undertaken
Mem: Sharp, Mrs Rosemarie LLB . . . . *§Oct 1981
Ast: Crossling, Mr David . . . . *Nov 1983

SHAW & CO
6 Portland Place Doncaster South Yorkshire DN1 3DF
Tel: 0800 019 1248
E-mail: info@shawandco.com
Office: Newcastle upon Tyne, Telford

IAN SMITH & CO SOLICITORS ‡
3 Deans Close Misterton Doncaster South Yorkshire DN10 4BN
Tel: 01427 892884
E-mail: iandcsmith@hotmail.com

CHRIS STEVENSON ‡
Whitegates 103 Thorne Road Doncaster South Yorkshire DN2 5BE
Tel: 01302 341243 *Fax:* 01302 761969 *Dx:* 28693 DONCASTER 2
Emergency telephone 07623 807835
E-mail: chris.stevenson@chris-stevenson.co.uk
List of partners: C L Stevenson
Work: D1 E G H K1 S1 S2 W
Emergency Action, Agency, Advocacy, Fixed Fee Interview, Legal Aid undertaken and Legal Aid Franchise
SPr: Stevenson, Mr Christopher L LLB ★ . . . . *Jun 1975

TAYLOR BRACEWELL ‡
17-23 Thorne Road Doncaster South Yorkshire DN1 2RP
Tel: 01302 341414 *Fax:* 01302 340156 *Dx:* 28699 DONCASTER 2
E-mail: enquiries@taylorbracewell.co.uk
List of partners: S Beck, M A Beresford, R E Fullwood, J Gray, R M Parkinson, A A V Straw
Work: A1 B1 C1 D1 D2 E F1 G H J1 K1 K2 K3 L M1 N P Q R1 S1 S2 T1 V W Z(b,c,d,f,j,k,l,m,p,s)
Emergency Action, Agency, Advocacy, Fixed Fee Interview, Legal Aid undertaken, Legal Aid Franchise and Member of Accident Line
Ptr: Beck, Mrs Sharon . . . . Nov 1994
Beresford, Mr Mark A MA(Cantab) . . . . Dec 1986
Fullwood, Mr Richard Ellis . . . . *Jun 1980
Gray, Mr James BA(Hons) . . . . *Sep 1995
Parkinson, Mr Richard M LLB . . . . *Jan 1986
Straw, Mrs Alison Ann Victoria LLB(Hons) . . . . Oct 1991

WILLEM LOUW SOLICITOR-ADVOCATE ‡
2nd Floor Consort House Waterdale Doncaster South Yorkshire DN1 3HR
Tel: 01302 562590 *Fax:* 01302 562589
E-mail: willemlouw@wwmail.co.uk

DORCHESTER, Dorset

BPL SOLICITORS LTD ‡
Mey House Bridport Road Poundberry Dorchester Dorset DT1 3GY
Tel: 01305 214200 *Fax:* 01305 269945 *Dx:* 8707 DORCHESTER
E-mail: info@bplaw.co.uk
Office: Yeovil
Work: A1 C1 C2 E L O R1 R2 S1 S2 W Z(c,h,l)

BATTENS
Savernake House 42 High West Street Dorchester Dorset DT1 1UU
Tel: 01305 250560 *Fax:* 01305 260876 *Dx:* 8705 DORCHESTER
Emergency telephone 01305 251707
E-mail: webenquiry@battens.co.uk
Office: Sherborne, Weymouth, Yeovil
Work: A1 B1 C1 C2 C3 D1 E F1 G H J1 K1 L M1 M2 N O P Q R1 S1 T1 T2 V W Z(a,b,c,d,e,f,g,h,i,j,k,l,m,o,p,s)
Emergency Action, Agency, Advocacy, Legal Aid undertaken and Member of Accident Line
Ptr: Bell, Mr David Macmillan ACIArb Chairman of the Rent Assessment Committee; Deputy District Judge . *§Jun 1969
Blackmore, Mr Michael Rubert . . . . *Nov 1978
Con: Thomas, Mr Paul C . . . . *§Jul 1971

BLACKBURN & CO ‡
33 Trinity Street Dorchester Dorset DT1 1TT
Tel: 01305 858050 *Fax:* 01305 458191 *Dx:* 8718 DORCHESTER
E-mail: jafb@blackburnand.co.uk

BLANCHARDS BAILEY LLP
Stowey House Bridport Road Poundbury Dorchester Dorset DT1 3SB
Tel: 01305 251222 *Fax:* 01305 251095
E-mail: dorchester@blanchardsbailey.co.uk
Office: Blandford Forum, Shaftesbury, Stalbridge
Work: A1 C1 C2 D1 E F1 F2 J1 K1 K2 K3 K4 L N O Q R1 S1 S2 T1 T2 V W X Z(d,h,k)
Agency, Advocacy, Fixed Fee Interview, Legal Aid undertaken and Legal Aid Franchise
Ptr: Lewis, Merlin D P BA . . . . *Apr 1988
Asoc: Johns, Sheila BA(Hons) . . . . *Nov 1995
Ast: Martin, Mrs Laura . . . . Oct 2008
Con: Lang, Mrs Jean M BA(Wales) Part time Tribunal Judge; Deputy Lieutenant . . . . *Jun 1978

IAN F BRAZIER SOLICITORS ‡
2 Green Barton Swyre Dorchester Dorset DT2 9DN
Tel: 01308 898682

JAMES M R DEBENHAM ‡
East Farm House Affpuddle Dorchester Dorset DT2 7HH
Tel: 0845 230 0644 *Fax:* 0845 230 0622
Emergency telephone 0845 230 0644
E-mail: jmrd@jamesmrdebenham.f2s.com
List of partners: J M R Debenham
Work: C1 E L O P Q S1 S2 W Z(e,q)
Legal Aid undertaken
SPr: Debenham, Mr James Martin Robert . . . . *Jan 1980

GERALD DUKE SOLICITOR ‡
50 South Street Dorchester Dorset DT1 1DQ
Tel: 01305 340100 *Fax:* 01305 250913 *Dx:* 8717 DORCHESTER
E-mail: enquiries@geraldduke.com

HUMPHRIES KIRK
40 High West Street Dorchester Dorset DT1 1UR
Tel: 01305 251007 *Fax:* 01305 251045 *Dx:* 8703 DORCHESTER
Emergency telephone 01305 251145
E-mail: dorchester@hklaw.eu
Office: Bournemouth, Poole (2 offices), Swanage, Wareham
Languages: French, German, Italian, Spanish
Work: A1 A3 C1 C2 D1 E K1 K3 K4 L M2 O R1 R2 S1 S2 T2 W Z(o)
Agency, Advocacy, Fixed Fee Interview, Legal Aid undertaken and Legal Aid Franchise
Ptr: Carretta, Ms Caroline LLB . . . . *Oct 1987
Hedger, Mrs R Felicity BA(Wales) Part time Chairman of Social Security Appeals Tribunals; Ex President of Dorset Law Society; Director of DCCI . . . . *Oct 1969
Jones, Mrs Katharine BA . . . . *Oct 1990
Yarnold, Mr Howard W BA(Dunelm) . . . . *Oct 1982
Ast: Rowsell, Miss Louise . . . . Sep 2007

LAYZELL SOLICITORS LIMITED ‡
Burnside House 29 Queens Avenue Dorchester Dorset DT1 2EP
Tel: 01305 264657 *Fax:* 01305 261859
E-mail: steven.layzell@btconnect.com

MUSTOE SHORTER
41 High West Street Dorchester Dorset DT1 1UT
Tel: 01305 250900 *Fax:* 01305 250901 *Dx:* 8755 WEYMOUTH
Emergency telephone 07792 278513
E-mail: info@mustoeshorter.co.uk
Office: Weymouth
Languages: French, German
Work: D1 G H J1 K1 N Q S1 V W Z(k,l)

NANTES
Antelope Business Centre Antelope Walk Dorchester Dorset DT1 1BE
Tel: 01305 250100 *Fax:* 01305 250232 *Dx:* 8701 DORCHESTER
Office: Bridport, Weymouth
Dir: Holman, Mr David M LLB(Lond) . . . . *Dec 1979

PENGILLYS LLP
Challacombe House Beechwood Square Poundbury Dorchester Dorset DT1 3SS
Tel: 01305 768888 *Fax:* 01305 768777
E-mail: contact@pengillys.co.uk
Office: Weymouth
Work: A1 B1 C1 C2 C3 D1 E F1 J1 K1 K2 L N P Q R1 S1 T1 T2 V W Z(c,k,l,m,s)
Agency, Advocacy, Fixed Fee Interview and Legal Aid undertaken
Ptr: Edmonds, Mr Michael J LLB(Wales) . . . . *Jul 1981
Ast: Parsons, Ms Tracey LLB . . . . Nov 1989

PORTER DODSON
53 High West Street Dorchester Dorset DT1 1UX
Tel: 01305 262525 *Fax:* 01305 260733 *Dx:* 8700 DORCHESTER
E-mail: porterdodson@porterdodson.co.uk
Office: Sherborne, Taunton, Wellington, Yeovil
Languages: French
Work: A1 B1 C1 D1 E F1 J1 K1 K2 L N O Q R1 S1 S2 T1 T2 V W Z(c,m)

D H REYNOLDS ‡
Trinity Street 8 The Forum Centre Dorchester Dorset DT1 1TT
Tel: 01305 269740 *Fax:* 01305 257552

THORNE & CO SOLICITORS ‡
14 High West Street Dorchester Dorset DT1 1UW
Tel: 01305 251166 *Fax:* 01305 251140 *Dx:* 8706 DORCHESTER
E-mail: info@thorneandco.com
List of partners: L F Thorne
SPr: Thorne, Mr Lionel Frederick BA(Hons) . . . . *§Jan 1980

DORKING, Surrey

BEVAN BURROWS SOLICITORS ‡
Paper Mews Place 290/294 High Street Dorking Surrey RH4 1QT
Tel: 01306 876960 *Fax:* 01306 876961 *Dx:* 57301 DORKING
E-mail: enquiries@bevanburrows.co.uk

CORDELL & CO ‡
176-180 High Street Dorking Surrey RH4 1QR
Tel: 01306 743003 *Fax:* 01306 740539 *Dx:* 57304 DORKING
Emergency telephone 01306 743003
E-mail: cpcordell@msn.com
List of partners: C P Cordell
Work: N
Fixed Fee Interview, Legal Aid undertaken and Member of Accident Line
SPr: Cordell, Mr Christopher Paul LLB . . . . *Mar 1986

DAVID COWAN ‡
114 South Street Dorking Surrey RH4 2EW
Tel: 01306 886622 *Fax:* 01306 740183 *Dx:* 57312 DORKING
Emergency telephone 07718 871869 / 07885 752282
E-mail: enquiries@cowansdorking.co.uk
List of partners: D J Cowan
Work: D1 D2 E G H K1 K3 L S1 W Z(l,m)
Emergency Action, Agency, Advocacy, Fixed Fee Interview, Legal Aid undertaken and Legal Aid Franchise
Ptr: Cowan, Mr David John MA(Cantab) . . . . *§Apr 1972
Asoc: Longes, Mr Philip Charles . . . . *Nov 1971
MacLeod, Mrs Geraldine Annie . . . . *Jan 1984
Ast: Bevan, Miss Michelle Diane . . . . *Aug 2002
Masters, Miss Victoria Jane . . . . *Sep 2004
Con: Bradley, Mr Peter John BA(Soton)(Law) Clerk to Commissioner of Taxes . . . . *Jan 1966

DOWNS ‡
156 High Street Dorking Surrey RH4 1BQ
Tel: 01306 880110 *Fax:* 01306 502283 *Dx:* 57300 DORKING
Emergency telephone 01306 883699
E-mail: info@downslaw.co.uk
List of partners: A C Baldwin, A M Christmas, M S Debens, T J B Hughes, C I Millar, C C Shipley, S E Thomas
Languages: French, German, Spanish
Work: A1 B1 C1 C2 C3 D1 E F1 I J1 K1 L M1 M2 N O P Q R1 S1 S2 T1 T2 V W Z(c,d,h,j,k,l,m,n,p,s,t)
Emergency Action, Agency and Advocacy undertaken
Ptr: Baldwin, Miss Alison C LLB . . . . *Mar 1977
Christmas, Mr Andrew M . . . . *Mar 1980
Debens, Mr Michael S BA . . . . *§Apr 1981
Hughes, Mr Timothy J B BA . . . . Dec 1982
Millar, Mr Christopher I . . . . *§Nov 1987
Shipley, Mr Christopher C LLB; MBA . . . . *Oct 1982
Thomas, Miss Sarah E Clerk to Commissioner of Taxes Notary Public . . . . *§Nov 1976
Asoc: Bracher, Mr James H BA(Oxon)(Law) . . . . *Oct 1980
Kilgannon, Mr Matthew James LLB(Hons) . . . . *Oct 2000
Walton, Miss Caroline A BA . . . . *Nov 1987
Ast: Muston, Miss Elizabeth L BA . . . . *Nov 1984
Nixon, Mr Michael Paul LLB(Hons) . . . . *Oct 2003
Scott, Miss Kate Louise MSocSc . . . . *Feb 2003
Tilley, Mrs Stephanie L LLB(Hons) . . . . *Nov 1979
Warren, Ms Louise Catherine LLM . . . . *May 2000
Con: Martin, Ms Anne BA . . . . *Oct 1988

MEABY & CO TRADING AS HART SCALES & HODGES ‡
159 High Street Dorking Surrey RH4 1AD
Tel: 01306 884432 *Fax:* 01306 742370 *Dx:* 57302 DORKING
E-mail: info@hartscales.co.uk
List of partners: H E Gentry
Work: C1 C2 E K4 L R1 S1 T2 W Z(d,m)
Ptr: Gentry, Mr Hugh E LLB . . . . *§Jul 1973
Ast: Ward, Miss Tamsyn Louise LLB . . . . *Sep 2003

CAROLINE MILLER & CO ‡
Unit 4 Ockley Court Farm Yard Dorking Surrey RH5 5LS
Tel: 01306 627160

PWT ADVICE LIMITED ‡
Rill Cottage Vann Lake Road Ockley Dorking Surrey RH5 5NS
Tel: 0845 833 9025 *Fax:* 020 8715 0703
E-mail: info@pwtadvice.co.uk

DOVER, Kent

BKRW LIMITED
60 Castle Street Dover Kent CT16 1PJ
Tel: 01304 219282 *Fax:* 01304 219272
E-mail: info@bkrwsolicitors.co.uk
Office: Folkestone, Ramsgate

BRADLEYS ‡
15-21 Castle Street Dover Kent CT16 1PU
Tel: 01304 204080 *Fax:* 01304 215092 *Dx:* 6300 DOVER
List of partners: M A Potts, P R Wilkinson
Work: A1 B1 C1 D2 E F1 J1 L N O Q R1 S1 S2 T2 V W Z(c,l,q)
Agency and Fixed Fee Interview undertaken
Ptr: Potts, Miss Maureen Ann BA . . . . *§Nov 1985
Wilkinson, Mr Peter R LLB . . . . *§Jun 1980
Ast: Sherred, Mr Peter W BA(Kent) Deputy & Surrogate to the Judge Official & Commissary of the Confederation of the Cinque Ports . . . . *§Nov 1973
Sweeney, Miss Jayne LLB . . . . *Feb 2007

EMMERSON BROWN & BROWN
20 Castle Street Dover Kent CT16 1PW
Tel: 01304 211766 *Fax:* 01304 211466 *Dx:* 6308 DOVER
E-mail: christine.platt@ebandb.co.uk
Office: Deal, Sandwich
Work: A1 B1 C1 D1 D2 E F1 J1 K1 L N R1 S1 T1 V W Z(d,l,m,r)
Emergency Action, Agency, Advocacy and Legal Aid undertaken
Ptr: Hartridge, Mrs Jane M LLB(Leeds) . . . . *Dec 1976
Wade, Mr Trevor W LLB(Leics) . . . . *Apr 1977

See p112 for the Key to Work Categories & other symbols

FREDERIC HALL
77 Biggin Street Dover Kent CT16 1BB
Tel: 01304 202411 *Fax:* 01304 207111
E-mail: info@frederic-hall.co.uk
Office: Folkestone
Work: B1 C1 C2 D1 E F1 G H J1 K1 L N O Q S1 S2 V W Z(c,l,t)
Emergency Action, Agency, Advocacy, Legal Aid undertaken and Member of Accident Line
Ptr: Kirk, Mr Michael S . . . . . . *Jul 1967
Medlicott, Mr Richard C P MA(Cantab) . . . . . . *§Nov 1982
Saynor, Mr Jeremy P LLB. . . . . . *Oct 1988
Ast: Lodwick, Mr Malcolm J LLB(Manc) . . . . . . *Mar 1984

LAWSON TURNER & GILBERT
54 Castle Street Dover Kent CT16 1PJ
Tel: 01304 226338 *Fax:* 01304 226345
Office: London SE16
Work: S1 S2 Z(i)

MOWLL & MOWLL ‡
Trafalgar House Gordon Road Whitfield Dover Kent CT16 3PN
Tel: 01304 873344 *Fax:* 01304 873355 *Dx:* 6302 DOVER
E-mail: enquiries@mowll.co.uk
List of partners: J E Cousins, M W Diomede, R Hamilton, V A Scott
Work: C1 C2 D1 E F1 J1 K1 K3 K4 L M1 N O Q S1 S2 T1 V W Z(d,l,p,q,x)
Agency, Advocacy and Fixed Fee Interview undertaken
Ptr: Cousins, Mrs Janet E LLB Sweet & Maxwell Law Prize; Cavendish Prize . . . . . . *Jul 1999
Diomede, Mr Mark W LLB Clerk to Municipal Charities of Dover . . . . . . *Jun 1985
Hamilton, Mr Ross BA(Hons) . . . . . . *Nov 1986
Scott, Mrs Valerie A BA(Hons); TEP. . . . . . *Jan 1992
Ast: Mounsey, Miss Sara Caroline FILEx. . . . . . *Oct 1994
Con: Sturt, Mr Richard H B MA(Cantab) Registrar of the Diocese and Legal Secretary to the Bishop of Canterbury. . . *§Apr 1966

PIGOTTS ‡
10 Victoria Crescent High Street Dover Kent CT16 1DU
Tel: 01304 210614 / 212206 *Fax:* 01304 225212 *Dx:* 6317 DOVER
E-mail: stephen.cowell@pigotts.co.uk
List of partners: S R Cowell
Work: E J1 L O Q S1 W Z(d,l)
Agency and Advocacy undertaken
Ptr: Cowell, Mr Stephen Robert BSc. . . . . . *Oct 2000
Con: Wilkes, Mr Jeremy Douglas LLB(Lond); FCIArb; DipGen . . . . . . *§Mar 1977

SC LEGAL SERVICES LTD ‡
10 Victoria Crescent High Street Dover Kent CT16 1DU
Tel: 01304 210514

SINGLETON SAUNDERS FLOOD SOLICITORS ‡
45 Castle Street Dover Kent CT16 1PT
Tel: 01304 240080 *Fax:* 01304 240129 *Dx:* 6304 DOVER
E-mail: lawyers@ssf-law.co.uk
List of partners: I R Farthing, E F Flood, M M Islam, P J Singleton
Languages: Bengali
Work: B1 C1 C2 E F1 J1 K1 K3 K4 L N O Q S1 S2 W Z(e,i)
Fixed Fee Interview undertaken
Ptr: Farthing, Mr Ian R BA(Hons) . . . . . . *Jul 1978
Flood, Mrs Elizabeth Frances BA . . . . . . *Nov 1988
Islam, Mr Manzurul Micky. . . . . . *Nov 2007
Singleton, Mr Paul Joseph LLB(Hons). . . . . . *Dec 1998

STILWELL & HARBY ‡
110 Maison Dieu Road Dover Kent CT16 1RT
Tel: 01304 206850 *Fax:* 01304 206950 *Dx:* 6303 DOVER
E-mail: enquiries@stilwellandharby.co.uk
List of partners: J R Garner, P E Sayers
Languages: French
Work: A3 D1 D2 E K1 K3 L S1 S2 V W
Emergency Action, Agency, Advocacy, Legal Aid undertaken and Legal Aid Franchise
Ptr: Garner, Mr Jeremy R LLB. . . . . . *Sep 1977
Sayers, Ms Patricia E LLB . . . . . . *Jun 1988
Ast: Curtis, Miss Sarah Jane LLB(Hons) . . . . . . *Oct 1994
Muir, Ms Charis . . . . . . *Aug 1999

DOWNHAM MARKET, Norfolk

FRASER DAWBARNS
29 London Road Downham Market Norfolk PE38 9AS
Tel: 01366 383171 *Fax:* 01366 385034
Dx: 40950 DOWNHAM MARKET
E-mail: receptiondownham@fraserdawbarns.com
Office: King's Lynn, March, Wisbech
Work: A1 B1 B2 C1 C2 C3 D1 D2 E F1 G H J1 J2 K1 K2 L M1 N O P Q R1 S1 S2 T1 T2 V W Z(c,d,e,k,l,m,q,t)
Emergency Action, Agency, Advocacy, Legal Aid undertaken and Member of Accident Line
Ptr: Barratt, Mr Anthony J BA(Law) . . . . . . *May 1982
Charlton, Mr Alan H BA. . . . . . *Oct 1976
Grimes, Mr Iain R BA(Hons). . . . . . *Mar 2000
Ast: Woodley, Mrs Rebecca Jane . . . . . . Sep 1998

DRIFFIELD, East Riding of Yorkshire

BLAKESTONS ‡
50 Market Place Driffield East Riding of Yorkshire YO25 6AW
Tel: 01377 253476 *Fax:* 01377 240077 *Dx:* 61691 DRIFFIELD
E-mail: blakestons@marketplace.freeserve.co.uk
List of partners: N E Hutchings, V L Williamson
Languages: French, German
Work: A1 E J1 K1 K2 K3 K4 L N O Q S1 S2 W
Fixed Fee Interview, Legal Aid undertaken and Legal Aid Franchise
Ptr: Hutchings, Mr Nicholas E LLB. . . . . . *Aug 1992
Williamson, Mrs Vivienne L BA(Soton). . . . . . *§Nov 1976

N CUNLIFFE-LISTER ‡
3 Croome Road Sledmere Driffield East Riding of Yorkshire YO25 3XJ
Tel: 01377 236006 *Fax:* 01377 236560
Emergency telephone 01377 236006
E-mail: nclsewerby@hotmail.com
List of partners: N Cunliffe-Lister
Work: A1 G K1 L N P R1 R2 S1 S2 T2 W Z(h,l,s)
Emergency Action, Agency, Advocacy and Fixed Fee Interview undertaken
Ptr: Cunliffe-Lister, Earl of Swinton Nicholas BA(Oxon) Clerk to Sledmere and Croome Parish Council. . . . . . *Jan 1966

LUNDYS ‡
17 Exchange Street Driffield East Riding of Yorkshire YO25 6LA
Tel: 01377 252831 *Fax:* 01377 241317 *Dx:* 61693 DRIFFIELD
E-mail: david.lundy@btconnect.com
List of partners: D E Lundy
Work: A1 E L S1 T1 T2 W
SPr: Lundy, Mr David E LLB(Leeds) . . . . . . *Mar 1974

WILLIAMSONS
23 Exchange Street Driffield East Riding of Yorkshire YO25 6LF
Tel: 01377 252022 *Fax:* 01377 241018 *Dx:* 61690 DRIFFIELD
E-mail: bgc@williamsons-solicitors.co.uk
Office: Hull
Work: A1 D1 E G H K1 L N P Q R1 S1 S2 T1 T2 V W Z(l,r)

DROITWICH, Worcestershire

PARKINSON WRIGHT LLP
64 Friar Street Droitwich Worcestershire WR9 8EF
Tel: 01905 775533 *Fax:* 01905 794487 *Dx:* 19922 DROITWICH
E-mail: droitwich@parkinsonwright.co.uk
Office: Evesham, Worcester
Work: A1 B1 C1 D1 D2 E F1 J1 K1 L N O Q R1 R2 S1 S2 T2 V W Z(c,g,h,j,l,q)
Emergency Action, Agency, Advocacy, Fixed Fee Interview, Legal Aid undertaken, Legal Aid Franchise and Member of Accident Line
Ptr: Houghton, Mr David LLB(Lond) . . . . . . *§Dec 1977
Penn, Miss Susan LLB(Hons). . . . . . *Nov 1994

DRONFIELD, Derbyshire

BANNER JONES
(in association with Netuschil-Breunig (Germany))
1 Sheffield Road Dronfield Derbyshire S18 2DH
Tel: 01246 414438 *Fax:* 01246 414430
E-mail: info@bannerjones.co.uk
Office: Chesterfield (4 offices), Sheffield
Work: A1 B1 C1 C2 C3 D1 E F1 G H I J1 K1 K3 L N O Q R1 S1 S2 V W Z(c)
Emergency Action, Agency, Advocacy, Fixed Fee Interview, Legal Aid undertaken and Legal Aid Franchise

TAYLOR & EMMET LLP
57 Sheffield Road Dronfield Derbyshire S18 2GF
Tel: 0114 218 4000 *Fax:* 01246 416195 *Dx:* 10549 SHEFFIELD 1
E-mail: info@tayloremmet.co.uk
Office: Sheffield (2 offices)
Work: E S1 S2
Fixed Fee Interview and Legal Aid undertaken

DROYLSDEN, Greater Manchester

BERKELEY SOLICITORS ‡
100-102 Market Street Droylsden Greater Manchester M43 6DE
Est: 1996
Tel: 0161 371 0011 *Fax:* 0161 371 0022 *Dx:* 24755 DROYLSDEN
Emergency telephone 07000 269252
E-mail: post@claim.co.uk
List of partners: A R Berkeley
Work: B1 C1 C2 D1 D2 E F1 I J1 K1 L N O Q R1 S1 S2 T1 T2 V W Z(p,q,r)
Agency, Advocacy, Fixed Fee Interview, Legal Aid undertaken and Legal Aid Franchise
Ptr: Berkeley, Mr Adrian Robert LLB. . . . . . *Oct 1993

SLEIGH & SON
112-114 Market Street Droylsden Greater Manchester M43 7AA
Tel: 0161 370 2198 *Fax:* 0161 371 7309
E-mail: chris@sleighandson.com
Office: Denton, Droylsden, Hyde
Work: K4 L R1 S1 S2 T2 W Z(m)
Ptr: Sleigh, Mr Christopher T. . . . . . *Nov 1962

SLEIGH SON & BOOTH ‡
1 Ashton Road Droylsden Greater Manchester M43 7AB
Tel: 0161 370 9524 *Fax:* 0161 301 4849
List of partners: W Allen, J E Davies, B P L Musgrave, G G Shaw, C T Sleigh, S T Sleigh
Office: Denton, Droylsden, Hyde
Work: A1 E K4 L S1 S2 T2 W Z(m)
Ptr: Sleigh, Mr Christopher T. . . . . . *Nov 1962
Sleigh, Mr Simon Thomas LLB . . . . . . *Jan 1994
Ast: Sanderson, Miss Lauren Jane LLB . . . . . . *Jun 2007

DUDLEY, West Midlands

THE BANAHAN TENNANT PARTNERSHIP LIMITED ‡
Hawkins Hatton Buildings Unit 3 Castle Court Dudley West Midlands DY1 4RH
Tel: 01384 253288 *Fax:* 01384 456908 *Dx:* 12746 DUDLEY
E-mail: info@btplaw.co.uk

CLB LAWYERS (CASWELL LANE BOWATER SOLICITORS) ‡
CLB House 13-14 Stone Street Dudley West Midlands DY1 1NS
Tel: 01384 451731 *Fax:* 01384 242532 *Dx:* 12750 DUDLEY
E-mail: info@clblawyers.co.uk
Office: Dudley
Languages: Punjabi
Work: C1 E S1 S2 W Z(l)

CLB LAWYERS (CASWELL LANE BOWATER SOLICITORS)
3rd Floor Dudley House Stone Street Dudley West Midlands DY1 1NP
Tel: 01384 451731 *Fax:* 01384 242532
E-mail: info@clblawyers.co.uk
Office: Dudley

DBL TALBOTS LLP
195 Wolverhampton Street Dudley West Midlands DY1 1JW
Tel: 01384 459551 *Fax:* 01384 459945 *Dx:* 12748 DUDLEY
E-mail: info@talbotslaw.co.uk
Office: Codsall, Dudley, Kidderminster, Stourbridge (2 offices), Wolverhampton
Languages: French
Work: E S1 S2 W Z(h)
Mem: Wetherall, Mr John BA . . . . . . *Dec 1975

DBL TALBOTS LLP
Fountain Arcade Chambers Dudley West Midlands DY1 1PE
Tel: 01384 252471 *Fax:* 01384 239086 *Dx:* 741441 DUDLEY 7
Emergency telephone 01384 252471
E-mail: info@dbltalbots.co.uk
Office: Codsall, Dudley, Kidderminster, Stourbridge (2 offices), Wolverhampton
Work: B2 D1 D2 G H J1 K1 K3 K4 N O Q S1 S2 W Z(i,l,q)
Emergency Action, Agency, Advocacy, Fixed Fee Interview, Legal Aid undertaken and Legal Aid Franchise
Asoc: Graham, Mr John R B LLB . . . . . . *May 1981

DEAN & CO
Dudley Court 31 The Inhedge Dudley West Midlands DY1 1RR
Tel: 01384 352525 *Fax:* 01384 352526 *Dx:* 710679 STOURBRIDGE
E-mail: agd@deananco.com
Office: Stourbridge
Work: C1 E J1 K1 K3 K4 L R1 S1 S2 W Z(d)

HRS FAMILY LAW SOLICITORS ‡
204a Wolverhampton Street Dudley West Midlands DY1 1ED
Tel: 01384 458835 *Fax:* 01384 456473
E-mail: cir@hrsfamilylawsolicitors.co.uk

HAWKINS HATTON LLP ‡
3 Castle Court Castlegate Way Dudley West Midlands DY1 4RH
Tel: 01384 216840 *Fax:* 01384 216841 *Dx:* 12746 DUDLEY
E-mail: info@hawkinshatton.co.uk
List of partners: M J Banahan, S J A Garrett, C Rodrigues, M R Rogers, A Tennant
Languages: German
Work: A3 C1 C2 E J1 J2 L N O P Q R1 S1 S2 W Z(j,l,q,r,w)
Ptr: Banahan, Mr Michael J LLB(Hull) . . . . . . *Jun 1978
Garrett, Mr Stephen John Andrew. . . . . . *Nov 1973
Rodrigues, Mr Colin LLB . . . . . . Nov 1994
Rogers, Mr Michael Richard LLM . . . . . . Feb 1986
Tennant, Mr Anthony . . . . . . *Dec 1977
Asoc: Pugh, Mrs Sarah Elizabeth . . . . . . Nov 1991
Sandhu, Miss Harminder LLB Sweet & Maxwell Law Prize 1993 . . . . . . Feb 1997
Tarbuck, Miss Daniella BSocSc(Hons); PGCertL; PGDipLaw . . . . . . *Jun 2002

SILVESTERS SOLICITORS ‡
Ferndale House 3 Firs Street Dudley West Midlands DY2 7DN
Tel: 01384 240880 *Fax:* 01384 240880
E-mail: aws@silvesters.org.uk
Work: E J1 K4 L N S1 S2 U2 W Z(i)
Agency and Fixed Fee Interview undertaken

LOUIS SPRAGG & CO ‡
Holloway Chambers Priory Street Dudley West Midlands DY1 1EJ
Tel: 01384 211621 / 211622 *Fax:* 01384 241326
Dx: 741442 DUDLEY 7
Emergency telephone 07659 107224
E-mail: louisspragg@aol.com
List of partners: L S Spragg
Work: A1 B1 C1 C3 D1 E F1 G H J1 K1 L M1 P R1 S1 T1 T2 V W Z(c,d,e,k,l,m,p,s)
Emergency Action, Agency, Advocacy, Fixed Fee Interview, Legal Aid undertaken and Legal Aid Franchise
Ptr: Spragg, Mr Louis Stanley TD LLB. . . . . . Jan 1968
Ast: Burch, Mr Richard D LLB(Sheff). . . . . . *Jun 1975

M R TIMMS & CO LIMITED ‡
4 Louise Street Gornal Wood Dudley West Midlands DY3 2UB
Tel: 01384 458848 *Fax:* 01384 457088
E-mail: info@mrtimms.org
List of partners: M R Timms
Languages: French
Work: E L S1 S2 W
Ptr: Timms, Mr Michael R LLB. . . . . . *Jun 1969

TURNER BAYLEY THOMPSON WARMINGTON ‡
24 Wolverhampton Street Dudley West Midlands DY1 1DB
Tel: 01384 253331 / 253771 *Fax:* 01384 240663 *Dx:* 12742 DUDLEY
List of partners: J R Burton
Work: C1 E K1 L N Q S1 S2 T2 W
Agency undertaken
Ptr: Burton, Mr Jonathan Richard LLB(Manc) . . . . . . Jun 1969

WH LAW LLP ‡
Trafalgar House 47-49 King Street Dudley West Midlands DY2 8PS
Tel: 01384 216920 *Fax:* 01384 458131 *Dx:* 12741 DUDLEY
List of partners: S E Pugh, M R Rogers
Languages: French, German
Work: J1 J2 N P Z(r)
Ptr: Pugh, Mrs Sarah Elizabeth . . . . . . Nov 1991
Rogers, Mr Michael Richard LLM . . . . . . Feb 1986

WALDRONS
(in association with Waldrons at Brierley Hill; Mobberleys at Lye)
34 Dudley Court The Inhedge Dudley West Midlands DY1 1RR
Tel: 01384 811811 *Fax:* 01384 811844 *Dx:* 12760 DUDLEY
E-mail: lawyers@waldrons.co.uk
Office: Brierley Hill, Kingswinford, Tipton, Walsall, Worcester
Work: B1 C1 D1 E F1 G H J1 K1 L M1 N P R1 S1 T1 W Z(l)
Emergency Action, Agency, Advocacy, Fixed Fee Interview and Legal Aid undertaken
Ptr: Hanns, Mr Simon Gregory LLB ★. . . . . . *Oct 1990
Ast: Pathan, Miss Sabhia LLB ★. . . . . . *Jul 2000
Con: Hathway, Mr Peter E M ★. . . . . . *Dec 1972

WALTERS & CO ‡
58 Brook Street Woodsetton Dudley West Midlands DY3 1AG
Tel: 01902 661400 *Fax:* 01902 674337 *Dx:* 28902 SEDGLEY
E-mail: mail@waltersandco.co.uk

WILLIAM WRIGHT & SON ‡
Lutley House 13 St James's Road Dudley West Midlands DY1 1JF
Tel: 01384 255344 *Fax:* 01384 252024 *Dx:* 741440 DUDLEY 7

E-mail: enquiries@williamwrightandson.com
List of partners: J M Allely, C J French, S L Williets
Work: D1 D2 E K1 K3 K4 L S1 V W
Emergency Action, Agency, Advocacy, Legal Aid undertaken and Legal Aid Franchise
Ptr: Allely, Miss Julia Margaret LLB(Hons) . . . . *Nov 1992
French, Mrs Caroline J LLB . . . . *Oct 1987
Williets, Mr Stanley Leonard DML . . . . Feb 1990
Asoc: Bloxwich, Mrs Rachel LLB(Hons) . . . . Sep 2007
Brown, Mrs Melanie J LLB(Hons) . . . . *Oct 1990

DUFFIELD, Derbyshire

MAUREEN P GRENVILLE ‡
(in association with Timms)
98 Eaton Bank Duffield Derbyshire DE56 4BH
Tel: 01332 841789 *Fax:* 01332 842762
List of partners: M P Grenville
Work: D1 D2 K1 Z(m)
Emergency Action, Agency, Advocacy and Legal Aid undertaken
Ptr: Grenville, Mrs Maureen P MA(Cantab); LLM(Leics) Chairman of CSAT, DAT, SSAT and SENDIST . . . . *Jun 1977

HARDY MILES TITTERTON
Duffield Chambers 14 Town Street Duffield Derbyshire DE56 4EH
Tel: 01332 841115 *Fax:* 01773 841116 *Dx:* 171000 DUFFIELD
E-mail: ccroxall@hmtlegal.com
Office: Alfreton, Ripley
Ptr: Titterton, Mr Arthur . . . . Dec 1980
Con: Clarke, Mr John A. . . . . *Dec 1976
Hardy, Mr Ian David. . . . . Aug 1968

DULVERTON, Somerset

RISDON HOSEGOOD
Bank Chambers Dulverton Somerset TA22 9BU
Tel: 01398 322100 *Fax:* 01398 322110
E-mail: dulverton@risdonhosegood.com
Office: Minehead, Taunton, Williton, Wiveliscombe
Work: A1 D1 E F1 G H J1 K1 L N O Q R1 S1 V W Z(d)
Emergency Action, Agency, Advocacy, Fixed Fee Interview, Legal Aid undertaken and Member of Accident Line
Ptr: Sunderland, Mr James P . . . . *Dec 1974

DUNSTABLE, Bedfordshire

BYRON FEARN ‡
Scotson Chambers 80 High Street South Dunstable Bedfordshire LU6 3HD
Tel: 01582 605822 *Fax:* 01582 608629 *Dx:* 57002 DUNSTABLE
E-mail: byron.co@enablis.co.uk
List of partners: A W Fearn
Work: E J1 K1 L N S1 S2 W
Emergency Action, Agency, Advocacy and Fixed Fee Interview undertaken
Ptr: Fearn, Mr Arthur W LLB(Manc) . . . . *Dec 1963

FRANKLINS ‡
7 Albion Street Dunstable Bedfordshire LU6 1SA
Tel: 01582 699111 *Fax:* 01582 471141 *Dx:* 57009 DUNSTABLE
E-mail: bhartishah@franklinssolicitors.co.uk
List of partners: I Banks
Work: D1 D2 E K1 K3 S1 W
Emergency Action, Agency, Advocacy, Fixed Fee Interview and Legal Aid undertaken
Ptr: Banks, Mr Ian. . . . . *Mar 1987

KNOWLES BENNING
24 West Street Dunstable Bedfordshire LU6 1SN
Tel: 01582 667711 *Fax:* 01582 666893 *Dx:* 57010 DUNSTABLE
E-mail: info@knowlesbenning.com
Office: Luton, Shefford
Work: A1 B1 C1 C2 C3 D1 E F1 G H J1 K1 L M1 M2 N O P Q R1 S1 T1 T2 V W Z(b,c,d,e,j,k,l,m,o,p)
Emergency Action, Agency, Advocacy, Fixed Fee Interview undertaken and Member of Accident Line
Ast: Bentley, Mrs Cheryl BA . . . . Jan 2002

MORTON SOLICITORS ‡
75 West Street Dunstable Bedfordshire LU6 1ST
Tel: 01582 501240 *Fax:* 01582 501241 *Dx:* 57015 DUNSTABLE
E-mail: morton@morton-solicitors.com
List of partners: M Chater, D R Morton
Languages: French, German
Work: C1 E F1 J1 K1 L O S1 W Z(e,l)
Emergency Action, Agency, Advocacy and Fixed Fee Interview undertaken
Ptr: Chater, Mr Martin . . . . Jun 1986
Morton, Mr David Reginald LLB(Hons) Notary Public *Aug 1977

PETERS & CO
Unit 9a Tavistock Place Tavistock Street Dunstable Bedfordshire LU6 1NE
Tel: 01279 453331 *Fax:* 01279 453339
E-mail: info@peterslegal.co.uk
Office: Chelmsford, Harlow

SMITH BROWN & SPRAWSON ‡
46 High Street South Dunstable Bedfordshire LU6 3HE
Tel: 01582 601233 *Fax:* 01582 471416 *Dx:* 57008 DUNSTABLE
E-mail: dunstable@lawsbs.co.uk
List of partners: S J Brown, M Gentilella, A C Smith, S A Sprawson
Office: Luton

DURHAM, Co Durham

AMBROSE ‡
Rosslyn House The Avenue Durham Co Durham DH1 4DX
Tel: 0191 386 7260
E-mail: ambrose.sol@physics.org
List of partners: M A Heather
Ptr: Heather, Dr Michael A BSc(Dunelm); MSc; PhD; MIEE; MBCS; MInstP; CEng; FCIArb . . . . *Mar 1983

ANDREWS ANGEL SOLICITORS ‡
Second Floor 41-42 Saddler Street Durham Co Durham DH1 3NU
Tel: 0191 370 9890 *Fax:* 0191 374 1425 *Dx:* 60215 DURHAM

BHP LAW ‡
Kepier House Belmont Business Park Durham Co Durham DH1 1TW
Tel: 0191 384 0840 *Fax:* 0191 384 1523 *Dx:* 60209 DURHAM
E-mail: info@bhplaw.co.uk
List of partners: R Baker, H Biglin, D Birks, P R Blackett, J D J Burnett, G Crawford, J Dixon, E Gaudern, T P Hamer, A Hewitson, S J Hunter, M Leadbitter, D Lucas, M S Moffitt, A Noble, J A Pratt, K S Pratt, G Ritzema, S Robinson, P S Saxon, D J M Wilson, H Wood, J L Wood
Office: Darlington, Halifax, Newcastle upon Tyne, Newton Aycliffe, North Shields, Stockton-on-Tees
Work: A3 B1 C1 C2 C3 D1 D2 E F1 F2 G H J1 J2 K1 K2 K3 K4 L N O Q R1 R2 S1 S2 T1 T2 U1 U2 W X Z(c,e,o,p,q,r,u,w,x,za)
Legal Aid undertaken
Ptr: Burnett, Mr James Daniel Julius BA(Hons) . . . . . . *Oct 1993
Pratt, Mr John Anthony BA . . . . *Dec 1977
Wood, Mr John Lawrence . . . . *Jan 1983
Ast: Donnelly, Miss Fiona M BA(Law) . . . . *Apr 1980
Hodgson, Miss Claire LLB. . . . . Nov 1991
Wills, Mr Philip LLM. . . . . Mar 2010

JOHN BAYLES & CO
68 Saddler Street Durham Co Durham DH1 3NP
Tel: 0191 386 1161 *Fax:* 0191 410 7892
Emergency telephone 0191 386 3939
E-mail: jbayles@netcomuk.co.uk
Office: Birtley
Work: A1 B1 C1 D1 E F1 G H J1 K1 L M1 N P R1 S1 T1 V W
Emergency Action, Agency, Advocacy, Fixed Fee Interview, Legal Aid undertaken and Member of Accident Line
Ptr: Bayles, Mr John F. . . . . *§Jan 1982

CKM SOLICITORS ‡
14 Market Place Durham Co Durham DH1 3NE
Tel: 0191 384 9080 *Fax:* 0191 384 9144 *Dx:* 60207 DURHAM
E-mail: durham.office@ckm-solicitors.co.uk
List of partners: D Malone
Office: Consett
Dir: Malone, Mr David LLB . . . . Feb 1991
Ast: Musgrove, Mr Nicholas . . . . Oct 2003

CHIVERS SOLICITORS
Abbey Business Centre Abbey Road Pity Me Durham Co Durham DH1 5JZ
Tel: 0191 383 2222
E-mail: criminaldefence@chiverssolicitors.co.uk
Office: Bingley

COOPER STOTT ‡
Aykley Vale Chambers Durham Road Aykley Heads Durham Co Durham DH1 5NE
Tel: 0191 384 7210 *Fax:* 0191 384 4882 *Dx:* 60215 DURHAM
E-mail: paula.allam@cooper-stott.co.uk
List of partners: K Cooper, N C Cooper, A M Stott
Work: D1 F1 J1 K1 M1 P S1 W
Emergency Action, Agency, Advocacy, Fixed Fee Interview, Legal Aid undertaken and Member of Accident Line
Ptr: Cooper, Mrs Kathryn LLB William Hutton Memorial Prize . . . . Mar 1979
Cooper, Mr Nigel C LLB(Newc) . . . . *Mar 1979
Stott, Mrs Alison M BA . . . . *Nov 1981

FREEMAN JOHNSON
31 Old Elvet Durham Co Durham DH1 3JA
Tel: 0191 386 4843 / 386 9619 *Fax:* 0845 389 3203
Dx: 60210 DURHAM
Emergency telephone 01429 821809 / 0191 386 4596
E-mail: durham@freemanjohnson.co.uk
Office: Darlington, Northallerton, Spennymoor
Work: A1 B1 C1 D1 E F1 G H J1 K1 L M1 N P S1 T1 V W Z(l,m,n)
Emergency Action, Agency, Advocacy, Fixed Fee Interview, Legal Aid undertaken, Legal Aid Franchise and Member of Accident Line
Ptr: Atterton, Mr Clive H. . . . . *Dec 1972
Campbell, Mr J Kevin BA(Hons). . . . . *Apr 1984
Clarke, Mr Michael D LLB. . . . . Oct 1983
Middleton, Ms Carole Ann LLB . . . . Oct 1994
Smark, Mr David LLB(Nott'm) . . . . *Oct 1984
Town, Mr Peter Francis LLB. . . . . Jun 1978
Turnbull, Mr George A LLB Notary Public . . . . . . *Dec 1978
Williams, Mr Dorian Maurice BA(Hons)(Construction Engineering) . . . . Feb 1995
Wrigley, Mr Hugh Charles BA(Cantab). . . . . Dec 1975
Ast: Lannagan, Mrs Helen Anne . . . . *Mar 2005

GRIERSON SHAW & CO ‡
Lumsden House 19 Old Elvet Durham Co Durham DH1 3HL
Tel: 0191 386 2434 *Fax:* 0191 384 2084 *Dx:* 60202 DURHAM
List of partners: J S Grierson, J S Shaw
Work: D1 F1 G H J1 K1 L N P Q S1 W Z(k,l)
Emergency Action, Agency, Advocacy, Fixed Fee Interview and Legal Aid undertaken
Ptr: Grierson, Mr John S. . . . . *§Nov 1973
Shaw, Mr John S LLB. . . . . *Jan 1980
Ast: McManners, Mrs Margaret A LLB . . . . *Apr 1973

ILS SOLICITORS ‡
Whitfield House St John's Road Meadowfield Durham Co Durham DH7 8XL
Tel: 0191 378 2030
E-mail: stephen@ilssolicitors.co.uk
List of partners: S D Gowland
Work: F1 F2 J2 N O Q Z(r)
Agency, Advocacy, Fixed Fee Interview undertaken and Member of Accident Line
Ptr: Gowland, Mr Stephen David. . . . . Jan 2001

KEPIER LAW ‡
7 Ferens Park Durham Co Durham DH1 1NU
Tel: 0191 374 1402 *Fax:* 0191 374 1402
E-mail: kathryn-raine@kepierlaw.co.uk

SHEILA MOORE ‡
1 Almoners Barn Potters Bank Durham Co Durham DH1 3TZ
Tel: 0191 386 5621
List of partners: S Moore
Work: G
Advocacy undertaken
Ptr: Moore, Ms Sheila LLB. . . . . *Apr 1973

RILEY LANGDON ‡
1 St John's Road Meadowfield Durham Co Durham DH7 8ER
Tel: 0191 378 7620 *Fax:* 0191 378 7621
E-mail: mail@rileylangdon.co.uk
List of partners: Y Kemp, M Riley
Work: C1 E F1 J1 K1 L N O P Q S1 S2 W Z(l,q,x,y)
Agency, Advocacy, Fixed Fee Interview undertaken and Member of Accident Line
Ptr: Kemp, Mrs Yvonne . . . . Oct 2002
Riley, Ms Marie . . . . *Aug 1996
Ast: Rogers, Mr Owen Adrian BA . . . . *Jan 1988

SWINBURNE MADDISON ‡
Venture House Aykley Heads Business Park Durham Co Durham DH1 5TS
Tel: 0191 384 2441 / 384 7455 *Fax:* 0191 386 6141
Dx: 60206 DURHAM
E-mail: web@swinburnemaddison.co.uk
List of partners: A J Davison, R M Furness, S P Robson
Work: A1 B1 C1 C2 C3 D1 E F1 F2 G H J1 K1 K2 L O P Q R1 S1 S2 T1 T2 V W Z(b,c,d,f,h,i,j,k,l,n,o,s,t)
Emergency Action, Agency, Advocacy, Fixed Fee Interview, Legal Aid undertaken, Legal Aid Franchise and Member of Accident Line
Ptr: Davison, Mr Andrew J BA. . . . . *Nov 1981
Furness, Mr Robert M LLB . . . . *Dec 1975
Robson, Mr Samuel P LLB . . . . Jun 1976
Ast: Cooper, Miss Carolyn . . . . *Aug 2003
Devine, Mr Allan N LLB . . . . *Dec 1980
Moreland, Mr Jonathan Michael LLB . . . . *§Oct 1993

TMJ LEGAL SERVICES LLP
Gilesgate House 94 Gilesgate Durham Co Durham DH1 1JA
Tel: 0191 383 0111 *Fax:* 0191 370 9610
Emergency telephone 07793 201274
E-mail: legal@tmjlegal.co.uk
Office: Hartlepool, Peterlee, Wingate
Work: A1 B1 C1 C2 C3 D1 D2 E F1 J1 K1 K3 K4 L N O P S1 S2 W
Emergency Action, Agency, Advocacy, Fixed Fee Interview, Legal Aid undertaken and Member of Accident Line
Ast: Christie, Mrs Victoria Elizabeth LLB . . . . *Feb 2008

BARBARA THUBRON ‡
9 New Elvet Durham Co Durham DH1 3AQ
Tel: 0191 383 0600 *Fax:* 0191 383 0659
E-mail: barbara@barbarathubron.co.uk

WANSTALLS SOLICITORS ‡
Senate Suite Palatine House Belmont Business Park Durham Co Durham DH1 1TW
Tel: 0191 375 6676 / 375 6658 *Fax:* 0191 375 6651
E-mail: claim@wanstalls.co.uk

DURSLEY, Gloucestershire

GLRS PHOENIX LLP
Hollis House May Lane Dursley Gloucestershire GL11 4JW
Tel: 01453 547221 *Fax:* 01453 543961 *Dx:* 47152 DURSLEY
Office: Stonehouse, Stroud (2 offices)
Languages: French
Work: A1 B1 C1 C2 C3 D1 E F1 J1 K1 L M1 M2 N O P Q S1 T1 T2 V W Z(c,e,l)
Emergency Action, Agency, Advocacy, Legal Aid undertaken and Member of Accident Line
Ptr: Young, Mrs Lynda MA. . . . . *Nov 1982
Asoc: Playford, Ms Susan LLB(Hons); BA(Hons); CQSW . *Mar 1998

MARSHALL GLOVER LIMITED ‡
Suite 5 Harrison House Hawthorn Terrace Dursley Gloucestershire DH1 4EL
Tel: 0844 801 1422 / 07917 356064 *Fax:* 0191 519 7461
E-mail: enquiries@marshallglover.com

WINTERBOTHAM SMITH PENLEY LLP
26 Long Street Dursley Gloucestershire GL11 4JA
Tel: 01453 541940 *Fax:* 01453 548527 *Dx:* 47151 DURSLEY
E-mail: mail@wspsolicitors.com
Office: Nailsworth, Stroud
Languages: French, German
Work: E J1 K1 Q S1 S2 T2 W Z(d)
Emergency Action, Agency, Fixed Fee Interview, Legal Aid undertaken and Legal Aid Franchise
Ptr: Knight, Mr David G BA . . . . *Jun 1986
Penley, Mr John F OBE; TD Notary Public. . . . . . *§Jun 1973
Ast: Hosken, Mrs Samantha Jane BA . . . . Oct 2004
O'Donnell, Mr Kevin William LLB(Hons) . . . . Jan 1983
Smith, Miss Natalie Sarah BSc . . . . *Feb 2010

EARL SHILTON, Leicestershire

BLACK & CO ‡
14 Wood Street Earl Shilton Leicestershire LE9 7ND
Tel: 01455 844005 *Fax:* 01455 851434
Emergency telephone 07905 137335 / 07804 525469
List of partners: C E Black
Work: B2 G H
Emergency Action, Agency, Advocacy, Fixed Fee Interview and Legal Aid undertaken
SPr: Black, Mr Christopher E BA(Hons) . . . . *Oct 1984
Ast: Tubb, Mr Paul Michael LLB(Hons). . . . . *Jan 2006

THOMAS FLAVELL & SONS
4 Wood Street Earl Shilton Leicestershire LE9 7ND
Tel: 01455 842297 *Fax:* 01455 851108 *Dx:* 716424 HINCKLEY
E-mail: law@thosflavell.co.uk
Office: Hinckley, Market Bosworth
Work: E F1 K1 K3 S1 W
Ptr: Cowlard, Mr Michael John LLB . . . . *§Dec 1974

See p112 for the Key to Work Categories & other symbols

EASINGWOLD, North Yorkshire

G E EDMONDSON-JONES ‡
Richmond Garth Oulston Road Easingwold North Yorkshire YO6 3PR
Tel: 01347 821615
List of partners: G E Edmondson-Jones
Ptr: Edmondson-Jones, Mr Gerald E LLB; LMRTPI . . . *Nov 1954

HILEYS
The Market Place Easingwold North Yorkshire YO61 3AB
Tel: 01347 821234 *Fax:* 01347 823186
E-mail: sue@hileys.co.uk
Office: Thirsk
Work: A1 L S1 S2 W
Fixed Fee Interview undertaken
Ptr: Hannam, Mr Peter D LLB(Nott'm) . . . . *§Apr 1975

YORKLAW LTD (T/A BURN & COMPANY) (incorporating Coomer Harrow)
Rowntree House Market Place Easingwold North Yorkshire YO61 3AG
Tel: 01347 822188 *Fax:* 01347 823082
E-mail: enquiries@burn-company.co.uk
Office: York
Work: C1 C2 D1 E F1 J1 K1 K2 K3 K4 Q S1 S2 W
Dir: Burn, Mr Graeme N BA(Hons)(Law). . . . . §Sep 1982
Burn, Mr Steven M LLB; ACIArb. . . . . §Jul 1984
Knowles, Mr Stephen LLB(Hons) . . . . Jun 1993
Rutter, Ms Claire L LLB . . . . §Oct 1983

EAST GRINSTEAD, West Sussex

BURT BRILL & CARDENS ‡
The Center 201-203 London Road East Grinstead West Sussex RH19 1HA
Tel: 01342 306288 *Fax:* 01273 570837
E-mail: help@bbc-law.co.uk

HODKIN & CO ‡
42-44 Copthorne Road Felbridge East Grinstead West Sussex RH19 2NS
Tel: 01342 325765 *Fax:* 01342 325479
Dx: 300232 EAST GRINSTEAD
List of partners: P D Hodkin
Work: B1 C1 E F1 J1 K1 L N O Q S1 T1 T2 V W Z(d,e,i,j,k)
SPr: Hodkin, Mr Peter David LLB(Hons) ♦ . . . . *Oct 1989

IFOCUS ‡
72 Halsford Park Road East Grinstead West Sussex RH19 1PS
Tel: 020 7566 8244
E-mail: maureen.m.milne@btinternet.com
List of partners: M Milne
Ptr: Milne, Mrs M . . . . Feb 2004

ELAINE MCGLOIN ‡
Crown Lodge Cantelupe Road East Grinstead West Sussex RH19 3BJ
Tel: 01342 328000 *Fax:* 01342 322373
Dx: 300223 EAST GRINSTEAD
E-mail: elaine@elainemcgloin.com
List of partners: E McGloin
Work: F1 L R1 S1 S2 W
Ptr: McGloin, Mrs Elaine LLB . . . . *Apr 1978

MASON & BEER ‡ (in association with P R Vince & Co)
6 High Street East Grinstead West Sussex RH19 3AP
Tel: 01342 311255 *Fax:* 01342 315155
Dx: 300203 EAST GRINSTEAD
E-mail: masonandbeer@btinternet.com
List of partners: S J Carr, A N Osborn
Work: C1 D1 E G H K1 L N O Q S1 W
Emergency Action, Agency, Advocacy and Legal Aid undertaken
Ptr: Carr, Miss Sarah J BA(Hons) . . . . *Sep 1996
Osborn, Mr Antony N LLB(Nott'm). . . . . *Nov 1970

MAYO WYNNE BAXTER LLP
The Studio 43-45 Cantelupe Road East Grinstead West Sussex RH19 3BL
Tel: 01342 310600 *Fax:* 01342 410020
Dx: 300206 EAST GRINSTEAD
Office: Brighton, Eastbourne, Lewes, Seaford
Work: B1 E J1 K1 K3 L N Q S1 S2 W Z(c,l,r)
Emergency Action, Agency, Fixed Fee Interview, Legal Aid undertaken and Legal Aid Franchise
Ptr: Bird, Mr Stephen M . . . . *Sep 1968
Ticehurst, Mr Peter R BA . . . . *Jun 1967
Ast: Coppard, Mrs Paula L LLB(Hons) . . . . Nov 1997
Monaghan, Miss Marika Jane BA(Hons); CPE. . . . . *Oct 2001
Pike, Mr Daniel Richard BA(Hons)(Politics & English) . *Sep 2001
Wilmot, Mr Stephen John LLB. . . . . *Sep 1993

PEARLESS DE ROUGEMONT & CO ‡
8 Church Lane East Grinstead West Sussex RH19 3BA
Tel: 01342 323687 *Fax:* 01342 312503
Dx: 300200 EAST GRINSTEAD
E-mail: pearless1@btconnect.com
List of partners: G B Clarke, W M Ross
Languages: French
Work: C1 D1 E F1 G H J1 K1 L N O Q S1 T1 W Z(d,i)
Emergency Action, Agency, Advocacy, Fixed Fee Interview, Legal Aid undertaken and Member of Accident Line
Ptr: Clarke, Mr Geoffrey B LLB(Leeds) Notary Public . . *§Jan 1969
Ross, Mr William M BA; LLB(Cantab) . . . . *§Oct 1965
Ast: Bowman, Mrs Suzanne Jane LLB(Hons) . . . . *Oct 1988

ANN J TATE & CO ‡
1 Bulldogs Bank Top Road East Grinstead West Sussex RH19 4PH
Tel: 01342 811278

WAUGHS ‡
Clarendon House Judges Terrace East Grinstead West Sussex RH19 3AD
Tel: 01342 323545 *Fax:* 01342 325405
Dx: 300202 EAST GRINSTEAD
Emergency telephone 01342 313995
List of partners: A M Groat, R W Lumley, C L Moore
Work: A1 B1 C1 C2 C3 D1 E F1 G H J1 K1 L N O P Q R1 S1 T1 T2 W Z(c,d,l)
Emergency Action, Agency, Advocacy, Legal Aid undertaken and Member of Accident Line
Ptr: Groat, Mr Alexander M LLB . . . . *Apr 1981
Lumley, Mr Roger W . . . . *Feb 1963
Moore, Mr Christopher L LLB . . . . *Dec 1972
Ast: Lumley, Miss Clare C LLB. . . . . Aug 1997

EAST HORSLEY, Surrey

HEDLEYS SOLICITORS LLP ‡
6 Bishopsmead Parade East Horsley Surrey KT24 6SR
Tel: 01483 284567 *Fax:* 01483 284817 *Dx:* 141174 EAST HORSLEY
E-mail: reception@hedleys-solicitors.co.uk
List of partners: S E Christmas, C A R Hughes, R S Taylor
Office: Croydon, Leatherhead
Work: C1 E F1 J1 K1 K2 K3 K4 L O Q R1 S1 T1 T2 W Z(i,l,p)
Fixed Fee Interview undertaken
Ptr: Christmas, Mrs Sarah Elizabeth MSc . . . . May 2003
Hughes, Mr Christopher A R BA; TEP Notary Public. . *Dec 1979
Taylor, Mr Roger S Notary Public . . . . *§Jan 1970
Asoc: Hulatt, Mr Lewis LLB . . . . Nov 1988
Jackson, Kate. . . . . Sep 2006

EAST MOLESEY, Surrey

BOSWORTHS ‡ (incorporating Gurney Underwood & Co)
63 Bridge Road Hampton Court East Molesey Surrey KT8 9ER
Tel: 020 8941 3151 *Fax:* 020 8979 1115 *Dx:* 80051 EAST MOLESEY
E-mail: molesey@bosworths.co.uk
List of partners: P E J E Bosworth, J L Osborne, V W Tunney
Ptr: Bosworth, Mr Patrick E J E . . . . Feb 1969
Osborne, Mr James L. . . . . *Jun 1974
Tunney, Mr Vincent W LLB . . . . Dec 1974
Ast: Pickard, Mr Andrew David LLB; DipLP. . . . . Mar 2003

KENWRIGHT WALKER WYLLIE ‡ (incorporating Maynard James Rosen)
70 Walton Road East Molesey Surrey KT8 0DL
Tel: 020 8979 1131 *Fax:* 020 8941 0033 *Dx:* 80055 EAST MOLESEY
E-mail: solicitors@kww.co.uk
List of partners: D R Anstee, G C Coleman, R D Preece, S Sole, M J S Wyllie
Languages: Greek, Italian
Work: A1 B1 C1 C2 C3 D1 E F1 J1 K1 L M2 N O P Q R1 S1 S2 T1 T2 W Z(c,l,p)
Agency, Advocacy, Legal Aid undertaken, Legal Aid Franchise and Member of Accident Line
Ptr: Anstee, Mr David R LLB(Hons) . . . . *Feb 1990
Coleman, Mr Gary C BA . . . . *May 1981
Preece, Mr Robert D LLB . . . . *Jun 1976
Sole, Mr Salvatore . . . . *Nov 2003
Wyllie, Mr Martin J S . . . . *Jul 1978
Con: Walker, Mr Robert L LLB . . . . *Jun 1974

ROBERTSON RIVERS ‡
Mole Cottage 23 Creek Road Hampton Court East Molesey Surrey KT8 9BE
Tel: 020 8979 6077 *Fax:* 020 8224 6078 *Dx:* 80050 EAST MOLESEY
E-mail: david@robertsonrivers.co.uk
List of partners: P A Rivers, D B Robertson
Work: E J1 K1 K3 L S1 S2 W
Fixed Fee Interview undertaken
Ptr: Rivers, Mrs Pauline Anne Notary Public. . . . . . . *Oct 1983
Robertson, Mr David B Notary Public . . . . *Jul 1973
Ast: Robertson, Mr Ian Charles LLB(Hons). . . . . Aug 1977

EASTBOURNE, East Sussex

BARWELLS ‡
6 Hyde Gardens Eastbourne East Sussex BN21 4PN
Tel: 01323 411505 *Fax:* 01323 410288 *Dx:* 6918 EASTBOURNE
E-mail: advice@barwells.com
List of partners: S Ash, W J Elliott, D T J George, N C Jones, T J Morgan, A S Woods
Office: Newhaven, Peacehaven, Seaford
Work: A1 B1 C1 C2 C3 D1 E F1 J1 K1 K2 L N O Q S1 S2 T1 T2 V W Z(r)
Emergency Action, Agency, Advocacy, Fixed Fee Interview, Legal Aid undertaken, Legal Aid Franchise and Member of Accident Line
Ptr: George, Mr David T J ♦. . . . . *Jun 1978
Morgan, Mr Timothy J BA. . . . . *Feb 1980
Con: Harris, Mr David J LLB . . . . *Dec 1991
Hayler, Mrs Anne . . . . *Nov 1994

BISHOP & LIGHT ‡
2 Hyde Gardens Eastbourne East Sussex BN21 4PN
Tel: 01323 434822 *Fax:* 01323 646121 *Dx:* 6909 EASTBOURNE
E-mail: madeleine.priestley@bishopandlight.co.uk

CORNFIELD LAW ‡
Dial House 47 Cornfield Road Eastbourne East Sussex BN21 4QN
Tel: 01323 412512 *Fax:* 01323 411611 *Dx:* 6903 EASTBOURNE
List of partners: A E Board, R W Dicker, J J Q Howes
Languages: French, German
Work: C1 D1 E F1 G H J1 K1 L N O Q R1 S1 T1 T2 W Z(j,o)
Emergency Action, Agency, Advocacy, Fixed Fee Interview, Legal Aid undertaken, Legal Aid Franchise and Member of Accident Line
Ptr: Board, Mr Andrew E MA(Oxon) . . . . *§Nov 1973
Dicker, Mr Roderic W LLB(Lond) . . . . *Nov 1985
Howes, Mr Jeremy J Q LLB Notary Public. . . . . . . *Jun 1978
Ast: Hobden, Mrs Angela Victoria LLB(Hons). . . . . . . *Sep 2001

CRAMP & CO ‡
The White House 97 South Street Eastbourne East Sussex BN21 4LR
Tel: 01323 720581 *Fax:* 01323 721329 *Dx:* 6911 EASTBOURNE
Emergency telephone 01323 737640 / 01424 843754
List of partners: R E Bates, S M Cramp, T Stirmey
Work: C1 D1 D2 E F1 G H J1 K1 K3 K4 L N O Q S1 S2 V W Z(j)
Emergency Action, Agency, Advocacy, Fixed Fee Interview, Legal Aid undertaken and Legal Aid Franchise
Ptr: Bates, Mr Robin E LLB . . . . *§Dec 1980
Cramp, Mrs Sheila M LLB. . . . . *Nov 1979
Stirmey, Mr Tim. *Oct 1999
Ast: Clarke, Miss Sarah LLB(Hons) ★ . . . . *Mar 2006

DALTONS ‡
16 The Avenue Eastbourne East Sussex BN21 3YD
Tel: 01323 720040 *Fax:* 01323 724705
Emergency telephone 07932 461573
E-mail: admin@daltons-solicitors.co.uk
List of partners: S E Georgiou
Languages: Greek
Work: C1 C2 C3 D1 E F1 K1 K3 K4 L N O Q R1 S1 S2 W Z(c,i,l)
Emergency Action, Agency, Advocacy, Fixed Fee Interview and Legal Aid undertaken
SPr: Georgiou, Ms Sotira E. . . . . *Feb 1976

STUART GRACE ASSOCIATES ‡
25 Gildredge Road Eastbourne East Sussex BN21 4RU
Tel: 01323 433000 *Fax:* 01323 433009
E-mail: reception@stuartgraceassociates.co.uk

GABY HARDWICKE
33 The Avenue Eastbourne East Sussex BN21 3YD
Tel: 01323 435900 *Fax:* 01323 435921 *Dx:* 6916 EASTBOURNE
E-mail: info@gabyhardwicke.co.uk
Office: Bexhill (2 offices), Hastings
Work: B1 C1 C2 C3 D1 E J1 K1 K2 L N O Q R1 R2 S1 S2 T1 T2 V W Z(c,d,o,r,z)
Advocacy, Fixed Fee Interview, Legal Aid undertaken, Legal Aid Franchise and Member of Accident Line
Ptr: Bean, Mr Christopher James LLB . . . . *Oct 1994
Caulfield, Mr Antony S . . . . *Sep 1999
Getty, Mr David E LLB(Hons) . . . . *Nov 1988
Williams, Mr Mark Emlyn BA(Hons) . . . . *Sep 1998
Con: Crouch, Mrs Jeanette Ann Elaine TEP. . . . . *Oct 1987

HART READE ‡
104 South Street Eastbourne East Sussex BN21 4LW
Tel: 01323 727321 *Fax:* 01323 721097 *Dx:* 6904 EASTBOURNE
E-mail: info@hartreade.co.uk
List of partners: J W Benson, G Brown, N P A Dennis, A Funnell, H Maddison-White, J Penfold, A C Pluck, A Rannie, H D Smith
Office: Hailsham, Polegate
Work: C1 C2 D1 E F1 J1 K1 L N O Q S1 S2 T1 T2 W Z(l,p)
Ptr: Benson, Mr John Walter LLB . . . . *Sep 1994
Brown, Mr Guy . . . . *Dec 2008
Dennis, Mr Nicholas P A . . . . *May 1982
Funnell, Ms Alexandra . . . . *Oct 1999
Penfold, Mrs Jacqueline. . . . . *Dec 2000
Pluck, Mr Andrew C BA(Law) . . . . *Dec 1989
Rannie, Mr Andrew LLB(Hons) . . . . *Sep 2004
Smith, Miss Heather D LLB . . . . *Oct 1990
Ast: Ripley, Ms Tina . . . . *Jan 2009
Summers, Miss Zoe. . . . . *Jul 2009
Taylor, Mrs Neisha LLB(Hons). . . . . *Nov 2009
Con: Perry, Mr Roger C V D LLB . . . . *May 1975

HERINGTONS
39 Gildredge Road Eastbourne East Sussex BN21 4RY
Tel: 01323 411020 *Fax:* 01323 411040 *Dx:* 6908 EASTBOURNE
Emergency telephone 01323 833450
E-mail: istewart@heringtons.net
Office: Battle, Hastings, Rye
Work: A1 B1 B2 C1 C2 C3 D1 E F1 G H J1 K1 L M1 M2 N O P Q R1 S1 S2 T1 T2 V W Z(d,k,l,m,t)
Emergency Action, Agency, Advocacy, Fixed Fee Interview, Legal Aid undertaken, Legal Aid Franchise and Member of Accident Line
Ptr: Brunt, Mr Nigel C . . . . *Dec 1986
Kinsey, Ms Sally L . . . . *Jan 1999
Stewart, Mr Ian M A LLB(B'ham) . . . . *§Jun 1975
Thorpe, Mr John L B . . . . *Jun 1976

LAWSON LEWIS & CO ‡ (incorporating Nella & Co; Russell Gardner)
11 Hyde Gardens Eastbourne East Sussex BN21 4PP
Tel: 01323 720142 *Fax:* 01323 725349 *Dx:* 6902 EASTBOURNE
List of partners: N Ashford, J H Sogno, D Woodley
Office: Peacehaven
Languages: French, German
Work: B1 C1 C2 E F1 J1 K1 K2 K3 L N O Q R1 R2 S1 S2 T1 T2 V W Z(c,d,i,j,m,q)
Emergency Action, Agency, Advocacy, Legal Aid undertaken, Legal Aid Franchise and Member of Accident Line
Ptr: Ashford, Miss Nadine BA(Hons). . . . . *Nov 1999
Sogno, Mr Jeremy H BA . . . . *§Nov 1986
Woodley, Mr Daniel BSc; PGDip. . . . . Apr 2001
Asoc: Judge, Mr Steven BSc(Hons) . . . . *Sep 2007
MacDonald, Ms Barbara . . . . Feb 2005
Ast: Browne, Mrs Mary LLB . . . . *Oct 1987
Eleady-Cole, Mrs Rebecca BA; LLB(Hons) . . . . . . Oct 1995
Fitzgraham, Mrs Rosetta BSc; DipEd . . . . Dec 1997
Hamilton, Mr Robert MA(Hons)(St Andrews). . . . . . Jan 1982

MAYO WYNNE BAXTER LLP
20 Gildredge Road Eastbourne East Sussex BN21 4RP
Tel: 01323 730543 *Fax:* 01323 737214 *Dx:* 6900 EASTBOURNE
E-mail: eastbourne@mayowynnebaxter.co.uk
Office: Brighton, East Grinstead, Lewes, Seaford
Languages: French, Polish, Spanish
Work: A1 B1 C1 C2 D1 D2 E F1 F2 J1 K1 K2 K3 K4 L N O Q R1 S1 S2 T1 T2 U2 V W Z(b,c,d,e,f,h,i,j,l,m,o,p,q,r,u,z)
Emergency Action, Agency, Advocacy, Fixed Fee Interview, Legal Aid undertaken, Legal Aid Franchise and Member of Accident Line
Ptr: Coombs, Mr Ian R LLB(Bris) . . . . *Oct 1975
Coxall, Mr Edward . . . . Nov 1989
Davis, Mr Barry H LLB . . . . *Nov 1984
Griffiths, Mr Timothy LLB . . . . Nov 1990
Hall, Mrs Peggy Anne BA(Hons) . . . . *Mar 1994
Minto, Miss Kimberley D BA. . . . . *Nov 1985
Porter, Mr Jonathan. . . . . Oct 2002
Stone, Glendon S. *Dec 1980
Strutt, Mr Christopher G LLB . . . . *Oct 1984

MULLANEY & CO ‡
1 Gildredge Road Eastbourne East Sussex BN21 4RD
Tel: 01323 431292 *Fax:* 01323 412327 *Dx:* 6907 EASTBOURNE
E-mail: angela@mullaney-solicitors.co.uk
List of partners: E Mullaney, J F Mullaney
Work: D1 F1 G H J1 K1 L Q S1 S2 V W Z(l)
Emergency Action, Agency, Advocacy, Fixed Fee Interview and Legal Aid undertaken
Ptr: Mullaney, Elizabeth . . . . *May 2009
Mullaney, Mr John F LLB . . . . *Dec 1977

STEPHEN RIMMER LLP ‡
28-30 Hyde Gardens Eastbourne East Sussex BN21 4PX
Tel: 01323 644222 *Fax:* 01323 733034 *Dx:* 6906 EASTBOURNE
E-mail: enquiries@stephenrimmer.com
List of partners: A C Hobden, L M J Kerin, N A Manning, S Rimmer, J A Stebbing, J Waters
Languages: Spanish
Work: A3 B1 C1 C2 D1 D2 E F1 F2 G H J1 K1 K2 K3 L N O Q R1 R2 S1 S2 V W Z(c,h,i,k,l)
Emergency Action, Agency, Advocacy, Fixed Fee Interview, Legal Aid undertaken, Legal Aid Franchise and Member of Accident Line
Ptr: Hobden, Mr Alan Charles LLB. . . . . . *Sep 1991
Kerin, Miss Leta M J . . . . . *§Jul 1973
Manning, Mr Nicholas A MA(Cantab) . . . . . *Apr 1978
Rimmer, Mr Stephen . . . . . *§Dec 1975
Stebbing, Mr John A LLB . . . . . *Dec 1978
Waters, Mr Jonathan . . . . . *Jan 2006
Asoc: Martin, Francesca. . . . . . Dec 2007
Poulton, Mr Mark . . . . . Jul 2005
Richardson, Mr Joseph Francis . . . . . *Oct 2004
Shah, Mr Jay . . . . . May 2006
Stannard, Mr Anthony George. . . . . . *Jan 2003
Whelpton, Mr Andrew. . . . . . Feb 2008

GEOFFREY SPILLER SOLICITORS ‡
36a Saffrons Road Eastbourne East Sussex BN21 1DT
Tel: 01323 419566 *Fax:* 01323 419633
E-mail: gbhs@btinternet.com
List of partners: G Spiller
Work: S1 S2
Ptr: Spiller, Mr Geoffrey . . . . . Apr 1973

TERRY BALLARD AND CO ‡
Compass House 45 Gildredge Road Eastbourne East Sussex BN21 4RY
Tel: 01323 413413 *Fax:* 01323 413475
E-mail: terryballard@live.co.uk

RODNEY WARREN & CO ‡
Berkeley House 26 Gildredge Road Eastbourne East Sussex BN21 4RW
Tel: 01323 430430 *Fax:* 01323 412141 *Dx:* 6969 EASTBOURNE
Emergency telephone 07000 430430
E-mail: enquiries@rodneywarren.co.uk
List of partners: R S R Warren
Work: B1 B2 D1 D2 G H K1 N O Q Z(g,l)
Emergency Action, Agency, Advocacy, Fixed Fee Interview, Legal Aid undertaken and Member of Accident Line
Ptr: Warren, Mr Rodney S R LLB . . . . . *§Jul 1979
Asoc: Rivett, Mr Justin LLB . . . . . *Mar 1996

EASTCOTE, Middlesex

HOUGHTONS SOLICITORS LTD ‡
Audit House 260 Field End Road Eastcote Middlesex HA4 9LT
Tel: 020 8429 7451 *Fax:* 020 8429 7452 *Dx:* 35165 EASTCOTE
E-mail: hsl@hsllaw.co.uk
Work: B1 C1 C2 E J1 L O Q R1 R2 S1 S2 U2 W Z(b)
Fixed Fee Interview undertaken

MILLS CURRY ‡
90a Field End Road Eastcote Middlesex HA5 1RL
Tel: 020 8868 8841 *Fax:* 020 8869 9833
E-mail: davidmillscurry@aol.com
List of partners: D M Knox
Work: S1 T2 W
Ptr: Knox, Mr David Michael. . . . . . *Nov 1977
Con: Beake, Mr Howard Bedford LLB(Hons) . . . . . *§Jul 1977

R E REDRUP & COMPANY ‡
41 Field End Road Eastcote Middlesex HA5 2QQ
Tel: 020 8866 4097

THE SETHI PARTNERSHIP SOLICITORS ‡
The Barn House 38 Meadow Way Eastcote Middlesex HA4 8TB
Tel: 020 8866 6464 *Fax:* 020 8866 3232 *Dx:* 35159 EASTCOTE
E-mail: ritu@sethi.co.uk
List of partners: P Greenwood, S Rajdev, R Sethi
Languages: French, Gujarati, Hindi, Italian, Punjabi, Urdu
Work: A1 D1 E F1 G H J1 K1 L N O Q S1 S2 W Z(i,k,m,q,r)
Emergency Action, Agency, Advocacy, Fixed Fee Interview, Legal Aid undertaken and Legal Aid Franchise
Ptr: Greenwood, Mr Peter. . . . . . *Oct 1990
Rajdev, Shreeti . . . . . May 1991
Sethi, Mrs Ritu LLB(Hons) ★ . . . . . *Mar 1990
Con: Nandhra, Mr Dave LLB(hons) . . . . . May 1996

EASTLEIGH, Hampshire

BERNARD CHILL & AXTELL
103 Leigh Road Eastleigh Hampshire SO50 9ZQ
Tel: 023 8061 3197 *Fax:* 023 8061 2559 *Dx:* 34121 EASTLEIGH
E-mail: admin@bcasol.co.uk
Office: Southampton
Work: D1 E K1 S1 S2 V W
Emergency Action, Advocacy, Fixed Fee Interview, Legal Aid undertaken and Legal Aid Franchise
Ptr: Harvey, Mr Paul C BA. . . . . . *Dec 1980

GAMMON BELL & CO ‡
91 Leigh Road Eastleigh Hampshire SO50 9DQ
Tel: 023 8068 4900 *Fax:* 023 8061 2737 *Dx:* 34114 EASTLEIGH
List of partners: J C Bell, N J Gammon
Work: A1 A3 B1 C1 C2 C3 D1 E F1 G H J1 K1 K2 K3 L M1 M2 N O P Q R1 S1 S2 T1 T2 V W Z(l,m)
Emergency Action, Agency, Advocacy, Fixed Fee Interview, Legal Aid undertaken and Member of Accident Line
Ptr: Bell, Mrs Jayne C BA . . . . . *Apr 1981
Gammon, Mr Nicholas J BA. . . . . . *Nov 1981

GAMMON PIERCY & GAIGER ‡
77 Leigh Road Eastleigh Hampshire SO50 9DQ
Tel: 023 8065 8200 *Fax:* 023 8064 3474
E-mail: enquiries@gpglaw.co.uk
Office: Southampton

HAYES LAW LLP ‡
56 Leigh Road Eastleigh Hampshire SO50 9DT
Tel: 023 8061 2890 *Fax:* 023 8061 1529 *Dx:* 34104 EASTLEIGH
E-mail: info@hayeslaw.co.uk
Office: London W6

HEDLEY VISICK & CO ‡
109 Leigh Road Eastleigh Hampshire SO50 9DR
Tel: 023 8061 1133
List of partners: W A Visick
Work: B1 C1 E L R1 R2 S1 S2 T1 T2 W Z(l)
Fixed Fee Interview undertaken
SPr: Visick, Mr William A LLB(Nott'm) . . . . . *Dec 1978

JULIA HODGSON SOLICITORS ‡
297 High Street Eastleigh Hampshire SO50 5NB
Tel: 023 8065 1100

KNIGHT POLSON SOLICITORS ‡
2/4 Leigh Road Eastleigh Hampshire SO50 9FH
Tel: 023 8064 4822 *Fax:* 023 8064 3951
E-mail: enquiries@knightpolson.co.uk
List of partners: P Butler, F C Dunton, C J Knight
Office: Fareham, Winchester
Ptr: Butler, Mr Paul LLB . . . . . *Jun 1981
Dunton, Mrs Frances C LLB. . . . . . *Apr 1981
Knight, Mr Christopher J LLB . . . . . *Jun 1980
Asoc: Baverstock, Mrs Helen Frances LLB. . . . . . Jan 1973
Colley, Miss Alison LLB(Hons). . . . . . Jun 2006
Ast: Carreras, Mr Ralph Michael LLB(Hons) . . . . . Jun 1971
Hills, Mrs Sarah BSc(Hons); PGDipLaw. . . . . . *Sep 2001
Kaur, Ms Baljinder LLB(Hons). . . . . . May 2005
Mitchell, Ms Nicola LLB(Hons). . . . . . *Aug 2001
Con: Cledwyn, Mr David A . . . . . *Nov 1979
Martyn, Mr John King . . . . . *Jul 1964

ML LAW LTD ‡
463 Fair Oak Road Fair Oak Eastleigh Hampshire SO50 7AJ
Tel: 023 8060 0661 *Fax:* 023 8069 4166 *Dx:* 155180 EASTLEIGH 6
E-mail: central@mllaw.co.uk
List of partners: L F Jackson, M R Moore
Office: Chandlers Ford
Languages: French
Work: A1 B1 C1 C2 D1 E F1 J1 K1 L O Q R1 S1 S2 T2 W Z(l,q)
Dir: Jackson, Ms Lynn Fiona LLB . . . . . Oct 1990
Moore, Mr Michael R LLB. . . . . . *Jun 1980
Ast: Beg, Ms Farzana . . . . . Jun 2007
Kaur, Ms Baljinder LLB(Hons). . . . . . May 2005

RICHARD WEBSTER & CO ‡
30 Leigh Road Eastleigh Hampshire SO50 9DT
Tel: 023 8061 4583 *Fax:* 023 8061 1698 *Dx:* 34102 EASTLEIGH
E-mail: mail@rwco.co.uk
List of partners: R B Webster
Work: E R1 S1 W Z(d)
Ptr: Webster, Mr Richard B LLB . . . . . *Jun 1972

EASTWOOD, Nottinghamshire

ROBERT BARBER & SONS
7 Church Street Eastwood Nottinghamshire NG16 3BP
Tel: 01773 787878 *Fax:* 0115 878 9705 *Dx:* 19292 EASTWOOD
E-mail: reception@robertbarber.co.uk
Office: Hucknall, Nottingham
Work: A3 C1 E F1 J1 K1 K2 K3 L N O Q S1 S2 W Z(c,k,l)
Emergency Action undertaken

MACLAREN WARNER
45 Nottingham Road Eastwood Nottinghamshire NG16 3AN
Tel: 01773 713846 *Fax:* 01773 530903 *Dx:* 19293 EASTWOOD
Office: Beeston, Ilkeston, Stapleford

CHARLES NEWTON & CO ‡
5 Alexandra Street Eastwood Nottinghamshire NG16 3BD
Tel: 01773 535535 *Fax:* 01773 530844 *Dx:* 19291 EASTWOOD
E-mail: info@charlesnewton.co.uk
List of partners: B A Harasym, C C Newton, G R Newton, G M Williams
Office: Ilkeston
Work: C1 C2 C3 D1 E F1 G H J1 K1 L N P Q R1 S1 T1 T2 V W Z(c,h,j,k,l,m)
Emergency Action, Agency, Advocacy, Fixed Fee Interview undertaken and Member of Accident Line
Ptr: Harasym, Mrs Barbara Ann . . . . . *Aug 1996
Newton, Mr Charles C MBIM . . . . . *Dec 1986
Newton, Mr Gavin Richard BA(Hons); PGDipLaw; LLB Sep 2010
Williams, Mr Geraint Meredydd . . . . . Feb 1986

EBBW VALE, Blaenau Gwent

FONSECA & PARTNERS ‡
New County Buildings 59 Bethcar Street Ebbw Vale Blaenau Gwent NP23 6HW
Tel: 01495 303124 *Fax:* 01495 302676 *Dx:* 43950 EBBW VALE
E-mail: enquiries@fonsecalaw.co.uk
List of partners: J F A Fonseca, D T Johns, D R G Thickins
Work: A1 B1 C1 D1 E F1 G H J1 K1 L M1 N P R1 S1 T1 V W Z(c,m,n,t)
Emergency Action, Agency, Advocacy, Fixed Fee Interview and Legal Aid undertaken
Ptr: Fonseca, Mr Julian F A . . . . . *Dec 1977
Johns, Mr David T LLB . . . . . *Feb 1984
Thickins, Mr David R G LLB. . . . . . *Oct 1986
Ast: Bolton, Mrs Lucy V LLB. . . . . . *Nov 1999

GARTSIDES
Equity Chambers Market Street Ebbw Vale Blaenau Gwent NP23 6HP
Tel: 01495 302109 *Fax:* 01495 309234 *Dx:* 43951 EBBW VALE
Office: Abergavenny, Newport
Work: D1 D2 G H K1 K2 K3 V W

MACQUILLAN & CO ‡
13 Market Street Ebbw Vale Blaenau Gwent NP23 6HL
Tel: 01495 304382 *Fax:* 01495 309643
List of partners: J A V MacQuillan, J A J Williams
Office: Tredegar
Languages: French
Work: B1 D1 E F1 G H K1 L M1 N P R1 S1 W
Emergency Action, Agency, Advocacy, Fixed Fee Interview and Legal Aid undertaken
Ptr: MacQuillan, Ms Juliet A V LLB . . . . . May 1972
Williams, Mr Jonathon A J LLB . . . . . Apr 1982

RICHARDS & LEWIS ‡
19 Market Street Ebbw Vale Blaenau Gwent NP23 6HL
Tel: 01495 350018 *Fax:* 01495 301901 *Dx:* 43952 EBBW VALE
E-mail: neil@richardsandlewissolicitors.com
List of partners: D G Lewis, J N Mark, N A Richards
Work: C1 D1 E G H J1 K1 L N Q S1 V W Z(l,q)
Emergency Action, Agency, Advocacy, Legal Aid undertaken and Member of Accident Line
Ptr: Lewis, Mr David G LLB(Wales) Notary Public . . . . . *Oct 1987
Mark, Mr Jeffrey Neil DipLP(Cardiff). . . . . . *Oct 1997
Richards, Mr Neil A LLB Notary Public . . . . . *Nov 1983

ECCLES, Greater Manchester

BERRY & BERRY
124 Church Street Eccles Greater Manchester M30 0LS
Tel: 0161 789 7414 *Fax:* 0161 787 8224 *Dx:* 15856 ECCLES
E-mail: email.eccles@berryberry.co.uk
Office: Manchester (2 offices), Walkden
Emergency Action, Agency, Advocacy, Fixed Fee Interview, Legal Aid undertaken and Member of Accident Line
Ptr: Regan, Mr Patrick C LLB . . . . . Oct 1984
Ast: Draper, Ms Sarah L BA . . . . . *Oct 1994
Wearing, Mr Jonathan L M BA; LLB. . . . . . *Oct 1996

FORSTER DEAN LTD
22 Church Street Eccles Greater Manchester M30 0DF
Tel: 0161 707 4000 *Fax:* 0161 789 2070
E-mail: enquiries@forsterdean.co.uk
Office: Birkenhead, Bootle, Chorley, Crewe, Ellesmere Port, Huyton, Leigh, Liverpool (5 offices), Oldham, Preston, Rochdale, Runcorn, St Helens, Stockport, Warrington, Widnes (2 offices), Wigan

MARTINS ‡
9 Church Street Eccles Greater Manchester M30 0DF
Tel: 0161 707 3660 *Fax:* 0161 787 7047 *Dx:* 15865 ECCLES
E-mail: martinslawyers@btconnect.com
List of partners: G Neild, A J Wilson
Office: Cheadle
Work: C1 D1 E K1 N S1 S2 W
Emergency Action, Agency, Advocacy, Fixed Fee Interview, Legal Aid undertaken and Legal Aid Franchise
Ptr: Neild, Mr Graham BA . . . . . *Dec 1986
Wilson, Mr Anthony Jack LLB . . . . . Dec 1965
Ast: Newton, Ms Janet E. . . . . . *Sep 1989

METCALFE JOHNSTON MCCORMICK ‡
88-90 Church Street Eccles Cross Eccles Greater Manchester M30 0DA
Tel: 0161 789 3481 / 788 9021 *Fax:* 0161 787 7087
Dx: 15851 ECCLES
List of partners: I C Johnston, D Metcalfe
Work: B1 C1 D1 E F1 G H J1 K1 L M1 N P S1 S1 W Z(i,l)
Emergency Action, Agency, Advocacy, Fixed Fee Interview, Legal Aid undertaken, Legal Aid Franchise and Member of Accident Line
Ptr: Johnston, Mr Ian C LLB(Sheff) . . . . . Jul 1975
Metcalfe, Mr David John Peacock Prize; Rylands Brothers Scholarship . . . . . *Dec 1972

OGDEN LYLES & FOX ‡
32 Wellington Road Eccles Greater Manchester M30 0NP
Tel: 0161 789 2793 *Fax:* 0161 787 7642
Emergency telephone 07976 360256
E-mail: enquiries@olfsolicitors.co.uk
List of partners: H S M Landey, A D Partington
Office: Irlam
Work: B1 C1 D1 D2 E F1 G H J1 K1 L M1 N P R1 S1 T1 V W Z(l,m,q,r)
Emergency Action, Agency, Advocacy, Fixed Fee Interview, Legal Aid undertaken, Legal Aid Franchise and Member of Accident Line
Ptr: Landey, Mr Howard S M BA(Law) . . . . . *Jul 1980
Partington, Mr Albert D LLB(Reading) . . . . . *Mar 1984

ECKINGTON, Derbyshire

KAVANAGH & CO ‡
61 Market Street Eckington Derbyshire S21 5JG
Tel: 01246 432349 *Fax:* 01246 435876
Emergency telephone 07774 887733
E-mail: louise@jwkavanagh.f9.co.uk
List of partners: J W Kavanagh
Work: G H S1
Agency and Legal Aid undertaken
Ptr: Kavanagh, Mr John W LLB . . . . . *Sep 1983

EDENBRIDGE, Kent

F B JEVONS RILEY & POPE ‡
2c High Street Edenbridge Kent TN8 5AG
Tel: 01732 864411 *Fax:* 01732 866921 *Dx:* 52802 EDENBRIDGE
E-mail: admin@jrplaw.co.uk
List of partners: J C Rogers, W M Woodrow
Work: E S1 S2 W
Ptr: Rogers, Mr James C . . . . . *Nov 1974
Woodrow, Mr William M. . . . . . *Oct 1970
Ast: Weaver, Mrs Ruth Alison . . . . . *Oct 1988

HAMWAYS WALKER OWENS ‡
(incorporating Burbidge & Co; Wheeler John & Son)
Timbers Station Road Edenbridge Kent TN8 5NB
Tel: 01732 866666 *Fax:* 01732 866126 *Dx:* 52800 EDENBRIDGE
E-mail: christine.edwards@hwo-law.com
List of partners: M R Owens
Work: B1 C1 C2 D1 E F1 J1 K1 L N O Q S1 S2 V W Z(l)
Agency undertaken
SPr: Owens, Mr Martin R LLB . . . . . *Feb 1986

See p112 for the Key to Work Categories & other symbols

EDGWARE, Middlesex

AGAPE SOLICITORS ‡
1st Floor 130 Burnt Oak Broadway Edgware Middlesex HA8 0BB
Tel: 020 8952 9694 *Fax:* 020 8951 5565 *Dx:* 57166 EDGWARE
E-mail: info@agapesolicitors.com

AXIOM STONE ‡
DVS House 4 Spring Villa Road Edgware Middlesex HA8 7EB
Tel: 020 8951 6989 *Fax:* 020 8951 0999
E-mail: info@axiomstone.co.uk

COMPENSATION SOLICITORS ONLINE ‡
93 Whitchurch Gardens Edgware Middlesex HA8 6PG
Tel: 0845 345 7144 *Fax:* 020 8952 5010
E-mail: csolegal@aol.com

DARLINGTONS ‡
48 High Street Edgware Middlesex HA8 7EQ
Est: 1930
Tel: 020 8952 0033 / 8951 6666 *Fax:* 020 8951 6665
Dx: 57157 EDGWARE
E-mail: enquiries@darlingtons.com
List of partners: A Cenizo, D J Rosen, D Ross, D Serota, J R Swede
Languages: Gujarati, Spanish
Work: C1 C2 D1 E J1 K1 K3 L N O Q R2 S1 S2 W Z(l)
Ptr: Cenizo, Miss Alicia . . . . . . *Mar 2009
Rosen, Mr David Joseph LLB ♦ . . . . . . *Jan 1999
Ross, Dalia . . . . . . *Nov 2005
Serota, Ms Debbie . . . . . . *Sep 2006
Swede, Mr James Robert LLB. . . . . . *Oct 1995
Ast: Bhatiani, Miss Maya. . . . . . Sep 2011
Jones, Mr Ben . . . . . . *Jan 2008
Con: Shah, Rati . . . . . . Dec 1976
Slatner, Miss Nicole. . . . . . *Apr 1996
Swede, Mr David S . . . . . . *Nov 1970

DAVIDSON & CO ‡
Premier House 112 Station Road Edgware Middlesex HA8 7BJ
Tel: 020 8951 5656
List of partners: R Davidson
SPr: Davidson, Mr Robert BA(Law). . . . . . May 2000

FARMAR MILLER RABIN GORDON ‡
(incorporating Rubens Rabin & Co)
Elizabeth House 54-58 High Street Edgware Middlesex HA8 7EJ
Tel: 020 8381 3339 *Fax:* 020 8381 3336
List of partners: B C Gordon, P J Rabin
Languages: Hebrew
Work: C1 E F1 G H J1 K1 L S1 S2 W
Emergency Action, Agency and Fixed Fee Interview undertaken
Ptr: Gordon, Mr Brian C LLB. . . . . . *Dec 1979
Rabin, Mr Peter J . . . . . . *Jun 1976

FERNANDES VAZ ‡
109 High Street Edgware Middlesex HA8 7DB
Tel: 020 8381 3932 *Fax:* 020 8381 3935
E-mail: fernandesvaz@aol.com
Work: Z(i,m)
Fixed Fee Interview, Legal Aid undertaken and Legal Aid Franchise

GERSHON & GOLDSTEIN ‡
9th Floor Suite 9 Premier House Edgware Middlesex HA8 7BJ
Tel: 020 8952 5272 *Fax:* 020 8952 4359 *Dx:* 57152 EDGWARE
E-mail: k.goldstein@ggsolicitors.co.uk
List of partners: L Gershon, K C Goldstein
Languages: Hebrew
Work: Q S1 S2
Ptr: Gershon, Mr Louis . . . . . . *Dec 1977
Goldstein, Mr Keith C LLB(Lond) . . . . . . *Apr 1979

MAURICE HACKENBROCH & CO ‡
297 Hale Lane Edgware Middlesex HA8 7AX
Tel: 020 8958 4000 *Fax:* 020 8958 2300
E-mail: mhack@lineone.net
List of partners: M Hackenbroch
Languages: French
Work: E G K1 L O Q S1 W Z(i)
Emergency Action, Agency and Advocacy undertaken
SPr: Hackenbroch, Mr Maurice. . . . . . *Nov 1977

IEI SOLICITORS ‡
Suite 316-317 Premier House 112 Station Road Edgware Middlesex HA8 7BJ
Tel: 020 8952 7047 *Fax:* 020 8952 5541
E-mail: admin.london@ieisolicitors.co.uk
Office: Birmingham, Norwich

H LANDAU & CO ‡
202 Hale Lane Edgware Middlesex HA8 9RD
Tel: 020 8959 6991 *Fax:* 020 8959 7920 *Dx:* 57153 EDGWARE
List of partners: H Landau
Work: J1 N S1 W
Fixed Fee Interview undertaken
SPr: Landau, Mr Harvey LLB. . . . . . *Dec 1977

WAYNE LEIGHTON ‡
3rd Floor 54-58 High Street Edgware Middlesex HA8 7EJ
Tel: 020 8951 2988 *Fax:* 020 8951 2989 *Dx:* 57186 EDGWARE
E-mail: howard@wayneleighton.com
List of partners: D Cameron, R S Shah, H N Wayne
Languages: French, German, Gujarati, Kiswahili
Work: B2 C1 E J1 K1 K3 K4 N O Q R2 S1 S2 W Z(b,i,k)
Agency and Advocacy undertaken
Ptr: Shah, Mr Rahul Sobhag BA. . . . . . *Dec 1994
Wayne, Mr Howard N LLB. . . . . . *Apr 1976
Cameron, Dennis . . . . . . NSP
Con: Golstein, Mr Joseph LLB(Hons) . . . . . . *Dec 1976
Ziman, Mr Peter D LLB . . . . . . *§Jan 1969

LU OLIPHANT SOLICITORS ‡
Premier House 112-114 Station Road Edgware Middlesex HA8 7AQ
Tel: 020 8238 2822 *Fax:* 020 8238 2898 *Dx:* 57168 EDGWARE
List of partners: C W Lu, A D Oliphant
Languages: Cantonese, Mandarin
Work: Q S1 W
Agency and Advocacy undertaken
Ptr: Lu, Mr Chi Wai LLB. . . . . . *May 1992
Oliphant, Mr Allan D LLB(Hons). . . . . . *Nov 1992

MOERANS ‡
123 Station Road Edgware Middlesex HA8 7JR
Tel: 020 8952 0242 *Fax:* 020 8381 3511
E-mail: info@moerans.com
List of partners: J M Cookson, S J Shaffer
Office: Radlett
Work: C1 E K4 L M2 S1 S2 T2 W
Ptr: Cookson, Mr John M LLB(Lond). . . . . . *May 1973
Shaffer, Mr Simon J LLB(Hons) . . . . . . *Apr 2000
Ast: Marks, Mr Benjamin Alexander LLB(Hons) . . . . . . Jan 2007

MYLES REBACK & CO ‡
34 Hillcrest Avenue Edgware Middlesex HA8 8PA
Tel: 020 8958 8525 *Fax:* 07092 139317

RPN SOLICITORS ‡
166 Whitchurch Lane Edgware Middlesex HA8 6QL
Tel: 020 8621 4380 / 07870 567245 *Fax:* 020 8621 4380
E-mail: rubianoordin@googlemail.com

CHRIS RAJA ‡
3rd Floor 1 High Street Edgware Middlesex HA8 7TA
Tel: 020 8952 1990 *Fax:* 020 8952 9606
E-mail: chris@bmylawyer.co.uk
Languages: Burmese, French, Gujarati, Hindi, Sinhalese
Work: K1 S2 Z(i)

RICHARDS SOLICITORS ‡
5th Floor Premier House 112 Station Road Edgware Middlesex HA8 7BJ
Tel: 020 8731 5929 *Fax:* 020 8381 1759 *Dx:* 51364 MILL HILL
E-mail: post@richards-solicitors.co.uk
List of partners: A D Begbie, R L Buchalter
Ptr: Begbie, Mr Alisdair D . . . . . . *Oct 1988
Buchalter, Mr Richard Leon BA(Econ). . . . . . *May 1992

TENNAKOONS ‡
2nd Floor 11 The Quadrant Edgware Middlesex HA8 7LU
Tel: 020 8442 8484 *Fax:* 020 8442 8451
E-mail: tennakoons@btinternet.com
List of partners: M A Tennakoon
Work: F1 K1 L Q Z(i)
Emergency Action and Fixed Fee Interview undertaken
SPr: Tennakoon, Mudiyanselage A LLB. . . . . . Nov 1991

D B THAKERAR & CO ‡
35 Queensbury Station Parade Edgware Middlesex HA8 5NN
Tel: 020 8951 3113 *Fax:* 020 8951 4537
List of partners: D B Thakerar
Languages: Gujarati, Hindi
Work: B1 C1 C2 C3 E F1 G L N S1 W Z(b,c,d,f,i,l)
Emergency Action, Agency, Advocacy, Legal Aid undertaken and Member of Accident Line
Ptr: Thakerar, Deenesh B BA . . . . . . *Jun 1985

VERDANT SOLICITORS ‡
309 Hale Lane Edgware Middlesex HA8 7AX
Tel: 020 8905 3199 *Fax:* 020 8905 3389

WALLER POLLINS ‡
Premier House 112 Station Road Edgware Middlesex HA8 7BJ
Tel: 020 8238 5858 *Fax:* 020 8952 0295 *Dx:* 57164 EDGWARE
E-mail: info@wallerpollins.com
List of partners: J H Pollins, J Waller
Languages: Hebrew
Work: E L S1 S2 W Z(d)
Agency and Fixed Fee Interview undertaken
Ptr: Pollins, Mr Jeremy H LLB(Lond). . . . . . *Oct 1985
Waller, Mr Jeremy LLB(Lond) . . . . . . *Oct 1986
Con: Taylor, Mr Alan BA(Hons) . . . . . . *Jul 1974
Waller, Mr Gerald A LLM(Lond) Cecil Karuth Prize. . . *Oct 1957

J K WALMSLEY ‡
10 Grove Road Edgware Middlesex HA8 7NW
Tel: 020 8952 0211

WHITEHORNS ‡
Premier House 112 Station Road Edgware Middlesex HA8 7BJ
Tel: 020 8440 9900 *Fax:* 020 8440 3939
List of partners: K Whitehorn
SPr: Whitehorn, Mr Keith. . . . . . Nov 1983

WILLIAMS & CO ‡
12th Floor Premier House 112 Station Road Edgware Middlesex HA8 7BJ
Tel: 020 8952 8882 *Fax:* 020 8952 6668 *Dx:* 57167 EDGWARE
List of partners: L Williams
Languages: French, Hebrew, Italian
Emergency Action, Agency, Advocacy, Fixed Fee Interview and Legal Aid undertaken
Ptr: Williams, Miss Lesley . . . . . . *May 1988
Ast: Yeshua, Mrs Naomi. . . . . . *Aug 2003

EGHAM, Surrey

HORNE ENGALL & FREEMAN LLP ‡
47a High Street Egham Surrey TW20 9ES
Est: 1870
Tel: 01784 432292 *Fax:* 01784 433897 / 431964 *Dx:* 53100 EGHAM
E-mail: reception@hefllp.co.uk
List of partners: N D Jamison, S Webster
Office: Sunbury-on-Thames
Work: J1 K1 Q S1 W
Ptr: Jamison, Mr Nicholas Derrick Notary Public . . . . . . §Dec 1987
Webster, Miss Susan Notary Public . . . . . . Jan 1976
Ast: Phillips, Ms Amanda LLB(Hons). . . . . . Jan 2009
Particular areas of work include: Employment Law, Family Law, Litigation, Accidents, Injury, Residential Conveyancing, Wills, Trusts and Probate.

M J LEGAL ‡
Bank House 81 St Judes Road Egham Surrey TW20 0DF
Tel: 01784 433780

ELLAND, West Yorkshire

RAMSDENS SOLICITORS
94-96 Southgate Elland West Yorkshire HX5 0ET
Tel: 01422 372478 *Fax:* 01422 310032 *Dx:* 700954 ELLAND
E-mail: info@ramsdens.co.uk
Office: Dewsbury, Halifax, Holmfirth, Huddersfield (3 offices), Mirfield
Languages: French, German
Work: A1 B1 C1 D1 E F1 J1 K1 L N Q R1 S1 S2 W Z(c,l,m)
Agency undertaken
Ptr: Garsed, Mr David Fowler . . . . . . *May 1977
Ast: Blackburn, Mrs Julie Marie LLB(Hons). . . . . . May 2004

ELLESMERE, Shropshire

GOUGH-THOMAS & SCOTT ‡
8 Willow Street Ellesmere Shropshire SY12 0AQ
Tel: 01691 622413 *Fax:* 01691 623226
Dx: 701590 ELLESMERE (SALOP)
Emergency telephone 01691 655014
List of partners: C Kendall, M J Kendall, K D Law
Office: Oswestry
Work: A1 B1 C1 D1 E F1 G H J1 K1 L N O P Q R1 S1 T1 T2 V W Z(c,k,l,q)
Emergency Action, Agency, Advocacy, Fixed Fee Interview undertaken and Member of Accident Line
Ptr: Kendall, Mr Michael J BA . . . . . . Nov 1984
Law, Mr Kenneth D . . . . . . Oct 1997
Ast: Andrews, Miss Claire LLB; LPC . . . . . . Sep 2002

HIBBERT LUCAS BUTTER
2 Willow Street Ellesmere Shropshire SY12 0AG
Tel: 01691 622408 *Fax:* 01691 623115
Dx: 701594 ELLESMERE (SALOP)
E-mail: srs@hibberts.com
Office: Crewe, Nantwich, Tarporley, Whitchurch
Work: A1 L S1 W Z(l)
Ptr: Sorfleet, Mr Stephen R MA(Cantab). . . . . . *Jan 1977

ELLESMERE PORT, Cheshire

BDH SOLICITORS ‡
27-29 Whitby Road Ellesmere Port Cheshire CH65 8AA
Tel: 0151 355 7171 *Fax:* 0151 355 9168

BERKSON WALLACE SOLICITORS
82 Station Road Ellesmere Port Cheshire CH65 4DB
Tel: 0151 355 4412 *Fax:* 0151 355 0035
Dx: 15360 ELLESMERE PORT
E-mail: solicitors@berksonwallace.co.uk
Office: Wallasey
Work: C1 E F1 J1 J2 L N O Q R2 S1 S2 V W Z(c,e,q,r)
Emergency Action, Fixed Fee Interview, Legal Aid undertaken and Member of Accident Line
Ptr: Mather, Mr James Stuart . . . . . . Aug 2006
Morris, Mr Peter D F. . . . . . *Oct 1979
Ast: Tipping, Miss Sally BA(Hons) . . . . . . Jul 2003

BLAIN BOLAND & THOMAS LTD ‡
102 Whitby Road Ellesmere Port Cheshire CH65 0AB
Tel: 0151 355 2645 *Fax:* 0151 355 2829
Dx: 15354 ELLESMERE PORT
E-mail: michael.blain@blainboland.co.uk
List of partners: M J H Blain, B D Boland, N D W Thomas
Office: Willaston
Work: C1 E J1 K1 L S1 S2 T1 W Z(x)
Dir: Blain, Mr Michael John Heygarth LLB . . . . . . *Jul 1969
Boland, Mr Bernard David LLB . . . . . . *Jul 1974
Thomas, Mr Nicholas D W BA; LLM(Canon Law) . . *§Jan 1982

DEVINE & CO ‡
13 Chester Road Whitby Ellesmere Port Cheshire CH65 9BE
Tel: 0151 356 2009 *Fax:* 0151 356 2007
Dx: 15365 ELLESMERE PORT

ETTINGER & VICKERS ‡
396 Chester Road Little Sutton Ellesmere Port Cheshire CH66 3RB
Tel: 0151 339 1640 *Fax:* 0151 339 1666 *Dx:* 14906 LITTLE SUTTON
E-mail: info@ettingervickers.co.uk

FORSTER DEAN LTD
58 Whitby Road Ellesmere Port Cheshire CH65 8AE
Tel: 0151 356 7484 *Fax:* 0151 350 3489
E-mail: enquiries@forsterdean.co.uk
Office: Birkenhead, Bootle, Chorley, Crewe, Eccles, Huyton, Leigh, Liverpool (5 offices), Oldham, Preston, Rochdale, Runcorn, St Helens, Stockport, Warrington, Widnes (2 offices), Wigan

JACOBS SOLICITORS ‡
(incorporating De Cordova Alis & Filce)
76 Whitby Road Ellesmere Port Cheshire CH65 0AA
Tel: 0151 355 8481 *Fax:* 0151 357 1899
Dx: 15355 ELLESMERE PORT
E-mail: info@jacobslaw.co.uk
List of partners: S P Alis, R J D Boag, S C N Burton, S C Harrop
Office: Shotton
Work: B1 C1 D1 D2 E F1 G H J1 K1 L N Q S1 W Z(q)
Emergency Action, Agency, Advocacy and Legal Aid undertaken
Ptr: Boag, Mr Robin J D BA ★. . . . . . *Apr 1975
Burton, Miss Susan C N BA. . . . . . *Oct 1987
Harrop, Miss Susan C BA. . . . . . *Mar 1977
Ast: Axon, Mr Philip . . . . . . Mar 2010
Crawford, Miss Barbara Elizabeth LLB(Hons); LSF . . *Aug 1994
Ferns, Mr Stephen . . . . . . Nov 2004
McCrimmon, Mr Scott. . . . . . Jan 2011
Shell, Elaine . . . . . . Oct 2009

MALITS SOLICITORS ‡
72A Whitby Road Ellesmere Port Cheshire CH65 0AA
Tel: 07966 203386 / 0151 356 9046
E-mail: jm@malits.co.uk

D P ROBERTS HUGHES & DENYE
78-80 Whitby Road Ellesmere Port Cheshire CH65 0AA
Tel: 0151 355 6699 *Fax:* 0151 357 2023
Dx: 15353 ELLESMERE PORT
E-mail: info@dprobertshd.co.uk
Office: Birkenhead

Work: B1 C1 E F1 J1 L M1 N P R1 S1 T1 W Z(c,k,l)
Emergency Action, Agency, Advocacy, Fixed Fee Interview, Legal Aid Franchise and Member of Accident Line
Ptr: Brown, Mr Mark Frederick Howard LLB . . . . *Oct 1990
Moan, Mr Francis BA . . . . *Jun 1977

SAVAS & SAVAGE SOLICITORS LIMITED ‡
20 Stanney Lane Ellesmere Port Cheshire CH65 9AD
Tel: 0151 357 2375 ***Fax:*** 0151 356 8094
E-mail: cm@savasandsavage.co.uk

ELMSWELL, Suffolk

MICHAEL A JONES & CO ‡
Orchard House 2 Grange Meadows Elmswell Suffolk IP30 9DG
Tel: 01359 242941 ***Fax:*** 01359 241453
Emergency telephone 07850 888769 / 07889 288514
E-mail: majadvocate@btinternet.com
Languages: German, Spanish
Work: G H J1 L P Q R1 S1 X Z(c,h,l,n,p,t)

ELSTREE, Hertfordshire

ALPHA LEXIS LAW FIRM ‡
Boundary House 51 Barnet Lane Elstree Hertfordshire WD6 3JP
Tel: 0845 194 7340 / 01923 731150 ***Fax:*** 0845 194 7341
E-mail: mahesh.kakkar@alphalexislaw.co.uk

BRIGHTSTONE LAW LLP ‡
(incorporating E M Solomons)
Brightstone House 511 Centennial Park Centennial Avenue Elstree Hertfordshire WD6 3FG
Tel: 020 8731 3080 ***Fax:*** 020 8731 3081 ***Dx:*** 57165 EDGWARE
E-mail: info@brightstonelaw.co.uk
List of partners: J Newman, R M Sherrington, S B Simmons
Languages: French, German, Russian, Spanish
Work: B1 C1 E F1 J1 K1 K2 L M1 N P S1 S2 W Z(b,w)
Emergency Action, Legal Aid undertaken, Legal Aid Franchise and Member of Accident Line
Ptr: Newman, Mr Jonathan LLB . . . . *Oct 1986
Sherrington, Mr Richard M MA(Oxon) . . . . *Dec 1969
Simmons, Mr Stephen B . . . . *Nov 1980
Asoc: Glass, Mr Colin Aidan BA(Hons) Office of the Public Guardian . . . . *Feb 1990
Ast: Aman, Ms Satinder . . . . *Dec 2000
Levy, Mrs Deborah J LLB . . . . *Aug 1983

LANDAU & COHEN ‡
Medburn Lodge Butterfly Lane Elstree Hertfordshire WD6 3AD
Tel: 0845 331 2477 ***Fax:*** 020 8993 0621
Dx: 45612 BOREHAMWOOD
E-mail: enquiries@landaucohen.co.uk
List of partners: J M Turofsky
Languages: French, Gujarati, Spanish, Turkish
Work: C1 C2 C3 E F1 G H J1 K1 L M1 M2 N R1 S1 W Z(i,l,p)
Emergency Action, Agency, Advocacy and Legal Aid undertaken
Ptr: Turofsky, Mr Jeffrey M. . . . . Nov 1983

STEENE & CO ‡
1 Blattner Close Elstree Hertfordshire WD6 3PD
Tel: 020 8953 7707 ***Fax:*** 020 8207 6912
E-mail: dianne@steene.co.uk
List of partners: D K Steene
Work: W
SPr: Steene, Mrs Dianne K LLB . . . . *Nov 1985

ELY, Cambridgeshire

ARCHER & ARCHER ‡
Archer House Market Place Ely Cambridgeshire CB7 4QN
Tel: 01353 662203 ***Fax:*** 01353 667714 ***Dx:*** 41002 ELY
E-mail: info@archerandarcher.co.uk
List of partners: M J Judkins, R L Shaw, J T N Thorogood
Languages: Italian
Work: A1 C1 C2 C3 D1 D2 E F1 F2 G H J1 J2 K1 K2 K3 K4 L N O P Q R1 S1 S2 T1 T2 V W Z(c,d,h,j,k,l,p,q,r)
Emergency Action, Agency, Advocacy, Fixed Fee Interview, Legal Aid undertaken, Legal Aid Franchise and Member of Accident Line
Ptr: Judkins, Mr Michael J BA . . . . *§Dec 1979
Shaw, Miss Rachel Louise LLB(Hons). . . . . *Nov 1996
Thorogood, Mr John T N BA . . . . *§Oct 1982
Ast: Jahangir, Ms Sally Anne Nasim LLB(Hons) . . . . . . Feb 2006
Judkins, Mrs Barbara Janet BA . . . . *Oct 1980
Porter, Ms Zara Rian LLB . . . . *Sep 2008
Con: Bamford, Mr Richard MA(Cantab) Clerk to Commissioners of Taxes. . . . . Dec 1964

BENDALL ROBERTS ‡
53 Market Street Ely Cambridgeshire CB7 4LR
Tel: 01353 663581 ***Fax:*** 01353 667955 ***Dx:*** 41000 ELY
E-mail: j.roberts@bendallroberts.co.uk
List of partners: J H A Roberts
Work: S1 W
SPr: Roberts, Mr Jeremy H A . . . . *§Oct 1967
Ast: Meehan, Miss Amy Louise LLB . . . . Jan 2009
Roberts, Ms Briony Jane . . . . *§Sep 1998

HALL ENNION & YOUNG ‡
8 High Street Ely Cambridgeshire CB7 4JY
Tel: 01353 662918 ***Fax:*** 01353 662747 ***Dx:*** 41003 ELY
List of partners: J E Aspinall, K J Irons
Office: Ely
Work: A1 B1 E F1 G H J1 K1 L N O Q S1 V W Z(c,l)
Emergency Action, Agency, Fixed Fee Interview, Legal Aid undertaken, Legal Aid Franchise and Member of Accident Line
Ptr: Aspinall, Mr John E LLB. . . . . Apr 1979
Irons, Mr Karl Jason. . . . . Jul 2002

HALL ENNION & YOUNG
5 Main Street Littleport Ely Cambridgeshire CB6 1PH
Tel: 01353 860453 ***Fax:*** 01353 862811 ***Dx:*** 41003 ELY
Office: Ely
Work: S1 S2 W

LEE & TALLAMY SOLICITORS ‡
42 High Street Soham Ely Cambridgeshire CB7 5HE
Tel: 01353 722723 ***Fax:*** 01353 722860
E-mail: noel.lee@leeandtallamy-solicitors.co.uk

THOMAS MILNER & CO ‡
41a Station Road Littleport Ely Cambridgeshire CB6 1QF
Tel: 01353 860005 ***Fax:*** 01353 860005
List of partners: T Milner
Work: T2 W
SPr: Milner, Mr Thomas BA . . . . *Dec 1980

Community Legal Service

Lexcel

P B & W SOLICITORS LLP T/A POOLEY BENDALL & WATSON ‡
2 Three Cups Walk Forehill Ely Cambridgeshire CB7 4AN
Tel: 01353 666075 ***Fax:*** 01353 666162 ***Dx:*** 41022 ELY
E-mail: info@pbw.uk.com
Web: www.pbw.uk.com
List of partners: J J Lacey-Eresh, J M Pooley, J R Watson
Office: Ely
Work: A1 C1 D1 E K1 K2 K3 L S1 S2 V W
Fixed Fee Interview, Legal Aid undertaken and Legal Aid Franchise
Ptr: Lacey-Eresh, Mrs Jacqueline Jane LLB . . . . *§Mar 1987
Pooley, Miss Joanne M . . . . *§Feb 1987
Watson, Mrs Judith Rachael. . . . . *§Jun 1970
Ast: White, Mr Alvin Hilton LLB(Lond) . . . . *Jan 1983

Lexcel

P B & W SOLICITORS LLP T/A POOLEY BENDALL & WATSON
4b Church Street Isleham Ely Cambridgeshire CB7 5RX
Tel: 01638 780170 ***Fax:*** 01638 780190 ***Dx:*** 41022 ELY
E-mail: isleham@pbw.uk.com
Web: www.pbw.uk.com
Office: Ely
Work: A1 C2 K1 K2 K3 K4 S1 S2 W
Fixed Fee Interview and Legal Aid undertaken
Ast: White, Mr Alvin Hilton . . . . Jan 1983

SMART LAW SOLICITORS LLP ‡
1st Floor 42 High Street Soham Ely Cambridgeshire CB7 5HE
Tel: 01353 720903 ***Fax:*** 0870 446 0905
E-mail: nlee@smartlaw-solicitors.co.uk
Office: Cambridge

VIVIENNE ROBINSON ‡
The Hall Soham Ely Cambridgeshire CB7 5AA
Tel: 01353 722020
E-mail: vrobinson@vrobinson.co.uk

ALVIN H WHITE ‡
8 Main Street Prickwillow Ely Cambridgeshire CB7 4UN
Tel: 01353 688228
List of partners: A H White
Work: I K1 Q S1 W
Emergency Action, Agency and Fixed Fee Interview undertaken
SPr: White, Mr Alvin Hilton LLB(Lond) . . . . *Jan 1983

EMSWORTH, Hampshire

ADDISON LAW ‡
8 North Street Emsworth Hampshire PO10 7DD
Tel: 01243 372306 ***Fax:*** 01243 371021 ***Dx:*** 56100 EMSWORTH
E-mail: info@addisonlaw.co.uk

BELCHER FROST ‡
3 West Street Emsworth Hampshire PO10 7DX
Tel: 01243 377231 ***Fax:*** 01243 378114 ***Dx:*** 56101 EMSWORTH
E-mail: pennysmith@bfprobate.co.uk
List of partners: J A C Frost, P A Smith
Work: S1 S2 W
Ptr: Frost, Mr John Arthur Couch . . . . *May 1981
Smith, Mrs Penelope Ann BA . . . . *Dec 1980

MEDIATION NOW LTD
Bridge Cottage Aldsworth Westbourne Emsworth Hampshire PO10 8QR
Tel: 01243 377426 ***Fax:*** 01243 377426
E-mail: claire@mediation-now.co.uk
Office: Fareham, Petersfield (2 offices), Portsmouth

ENDERBY, Leicestershire

BRIDLE HATHAWAY ‡
Chancery House 16 Narborough Wood Business Park Enderby Leicestershire LE9 5XT
Tel: 0116 239 4014 ***Fax:*** 0116 238 8879

PREMIER PROPERTY LAWYERS LTD ‡
PO Box 7130 1 Francis Way Grove Park Enderby Leicestershire LE19 1SH
Tel: 0845 234 0217 ***Fax:*** 0116 289 0173 ***Dx:*** 724762 ENDERBY 2
E-mail: info@myhomemove.com
List of partners: P E Gegan
Work: S1
Ptr: Gegan, Mr Philip E . . . . *Jun 1973

ENFIELD, Middlesex

ADEL JIBS SOLICITORS ‡
517b Hertford Road Enfield Middlesex EN3 5UA
Tel: 020 3417 3859 ***Fax:*** 020 8804 0501
E-mail: info@adeljibssolicitors.co.uk

ANDERSON FIDLER ‡
Lincoln House 464 Lincoln Road Ponders End Enfield Middlesex EN3 4AH
Tel: 020 8804 6596 ***Fax:*** 020 8804 6528 ***Dx:*** 133182 ENFIELD 6
List of partners: S Razzaq
Languages: Bengali, French, Punjabi, Turkish, Urdu
Work: E F1 J1 K1 L O P Q R1 S1 S2 W Z(h)
Ptr: Razzaq, Mr Shaid. . . . . Aug 1999

BARKER GOOCH & SWAILES ‡
(incorporating H Raymond Welch)
1 Cecil Court London Road Enfield Middlesex EN2 6BU
Tel: 020 8366 3161 ***Fax:*** 020 8367 9927 ***Dx:*** 133176 ENFIELD 6
E-mail: bgssolicitors@btconnect.com
List of partners: I C M Fletcher, C F M Roer, M J Shreeves
Office: London N21
Work: D1 D2 E F1 G H J1 J2 K1 L N O P Q S1 S2 W Z(l,m,q,y)
Emergency Action, Agency, Advocacy, Fixed Fee Interview, Legal Aid undertaken and Member of Accident Line
Ptr: Fletcher, Mr Iain C M BA . . . . May 1982
Shreeves, Mr Martin J MA. . . . . Dec 1978

BARNES & PARTNERS
4 Little Park Gardens Enfield Middlesex EN2 6PQ
Tel: 020 8366 3333 ***Fax:*** 020 8367 7491 ***Dx:*** 90612 ENFIELD
E-mail: people@barnesandpartners.com
Office: Cheshunt, Harlow, London E4, London N15, London N16, London N18, London N8, Pinner, Ware
Work: B1 C1 C2 C3 D1 E F1 G H J1 K1 L M1 M2 N P R1 S1 T1 T2 V W

BLAVO & CO SOLICITORS
5 Chase Side Crescent Enfield Middlesex EN2 0JQ
Tel: 020 8363 8296
E-mail: enquiries@legalblavo.co.uk
Office: Guildford, London EC2, London N3, London WC1, St Albans, Uxbridge

BREEZE & WYLES SOLICITORS LLP
River House 90 Church Street Enfield Middlesex EN2 6AR
Tel: 020 8366 6411 ***Fax:*** 020 8367 7288 ***Dx:*** 90611 ENFIELD
Office: Bishop's Stortford, Cheshunt, Hertford
Work: C1 E J1 K1 K3 L Q R2 S1 S2 W
S.I.G
Dir: Appleton, Mr John M LLB. . . . . *Nov 1989
Thompson, Mr Roger John . . . . *Mar 1983

CHRISTOS WYBREW KENNETH SHAW & CO ‡
39a Church Street Enfield Middlesex EN2 6AJ
Tel: 020 8366 1345 / 8367 0840 ***Fax:*** 020 8363 3861
Dx: 90608 ENFIELD
E-mail: enquiries@christoswybrew.co.uk
List of partners: M L Cross, C Neocleous, P H Wybrew
Languages: Greek
Emergency Action, Agency, Advocacy and Legal Aid undertaken
Ptr: Cross, Miss Mandy L LLB. . . . . *Nov 1988
Neocleous, Mr Christos LLB. . . . . *Oct 1983
Wybrew, Mr Paul H LLB. . . . . *Jun 1980

CLEVERDONS ‡
7 Rendlesham Road Enfield Middlesex EN2 0TS
Tel: 020 8367 5375 ***Fax:*** 020 8373 1758 ***Dx:*** 90601 ENFIELD
E-mail: jccleverdon@mac.com
List of partners: J Cleverdon
Work: K1 S1 W
SPr: Cleverdon, Ms Jane-Claire LLB . . . . *Dec 1978

CURWENS ‡
(incorporating Trefor R James)
Crossfield House Gladbeck Way Enfield Middlesex EN2 7HT
Tel: 020 8363 4444 ***Fax:*** 020 8367 1301 ***Dx:*** 142501 ENFIELD 7
E-mail: enquiries@curwens.co.uk
Office: Cheshunt, Hoddesdon, Waltham Abbey
Work: A1 B1 C1 C2 C3 D1 D2 E F1 G H I J1 J2 K1 L M1 N O P Q R1 R2 S1 S2 V W X Z(b,e,i,j,k,l,m,p,q,r,w)

EMBERTONS ‡
(in association with Nagi & Co(Enfield); Dixon Emberton(London N16))
Estate House 151 Lancaster Road Enfield Middlesex EN2 0JN
Tel: 020 8364 4249 ***Fax:*** 020 8367 0532
List of partners: E M Emberton
Work: E L N Q S1 W
Agency, Fixed Fee Interview and Legal Aid undertaken
SPr: Emberton, Miss Elizabeth M TEP . . . . *Jun 1972

GRAHAM FEAR & CO ‡
Nicholas House River Front Enfield Middlesex EN1 3TF
Tel: 020 8363 3331 ***Fax:*** 020 8364 4405 ***Dx:*** 90602 ENFIELD
E-mail: info@grahamfear.co.uk
List of partners: G G Fear
Work: B1 C1 C2 E J1 K1 L N O Q S1 W Z(e,h)
Emergency Action and Agency undertaken
SPr: Fear, Mr Graham G . . . . Dec 1965

FOSTER & FOSTER ‡
8 Riverside Place Ladysmith Road Enfield Middlesex EN1 3AA
Tel: 0844 568 6877 ***Fax:*** 0844 568 6899 ***Dx:*** 133181 ENFIELD 6
E-mail: enquiries@foster-foster.co.uk

HAYAT & CO ‡
326 Lincoln Road Enfield Middlesex EN3 4AA
Tel: 020 8360 4485 ***Fax:*** 020 8360 4485
Emergency telephone 07909 510338
E-mail: info@hayatandco.com
List of partners: A Hayat
Languages: Dari, Farsi, French, Kurdish, Pashto, Polish, Russian, Spanish, Turkish, Urdu
Work: B1 C1 E F1 F2 G H J1 K1 K2 L N R2 S1 S2 V W Z(g,i,l,p)
Emergency Action, Agency, Fixed Fee Interview, Legal Aid undertaken and Legal Aid Franchise
Ptr: Hayat, Amar LLB(Hons). . . . . *Oct 1997

ISMAIL & CO ‡
288 Southbury Road Enfield Middlesex EN1 1TR
Tel: 020 8804 1065 ***Fax:*** 020 8804 1199 ***Dx:*** 133186 ENFIELD 6
E-mail: info@ismailco.co.uk
Languages: Turkish
Work: D1 F1 K2 Q Z(q,r)
Emergency Action, Agency, Advocacy, Fixed Fee Interview, Legal Aid undertaken and Member of Accident Line

See p112 for the Key to Work Categories & other symbols

JADE LAW SOLICITORS ‡
31 Church Street Enfield Middlesex EN2 6AJ
Tel: 020 8363 7000 *Fax:* 020 8363 1031
E-mail: jadelaw@btconnect.com

KARIS SPYRIS LLP ‡
Gor-Ray House 758 Great Cambridge Road Enfield Middlesex EN1 3PN
Tel: 020 8443 7000 *Fax:* 020 8443 7051
List of partners: N G Karis, T Spyris
Languages: Greek
Mem: Karis, Ntinos G . . . . Nov 1981
Spyris, Mr Terry LLB(Hons) . . . . *Apr 2003

LIZ SOLICITORS ‡
46a Church Street Enfield Middlesex EN2 6AZ
Tel: 020 8370 4980 *Fax:* 07796 064373 *Dx:* 90605 ENFIELD
E-mail: info@lizsolicitors.co.uk

MARSH & PARTNERS SOLICITORS ‡
177 Hoe Lane Enfield Middlesex EN1 4LW
Tel: 020 8805 1184 *Fax:* 020 8804 9428
E-mail: marshandpartners@hotmail.co.uk

OJN SOLICITORS ‡
7b London Road Enfield Middlesex EN2 6BN
Tel: 020 3232 2135 *Fax:* 020 8342 1648
E-mail: obi@ojnsolicitors.com

BERNARD PEARCE & CO ‡
626a Hertford Road Enfield Middlesex EN3 5TG
Tel: 020 8804 5271 *Fax:* 020 8804 0422
Dx: 133981 WALTHAM CROSS 3
E-mail: bernardpearce@btinternet.com
List of partners: M A M Pearce, D L White
Work: D1 D2 E J1 K1 N O Q S1 S2 W
Agency, Fixed Fee Interview, Legal Aid undertaken and Legal Aid Franchise
Ptr: Pearce, Mrs Margaret A M . . . . *Jan 1967
White, Mr David L LLB(Hons) . . . . *Nov 1991

A V RILLO & CO ‡
Gor-Ray House 758-760 Great Cambridge Road Enfield Middlesex EN1 3PN
Tel: 0800 093 7623

ADRIANNE ROY ‡
48 Lombard Avenue Enfield Middlesex EN3 5LN
Tel: 020 8292 9101 *Fax:* 020 8351 6054
List of partners: A Roy
Languages: Greek
Work: S1 W
SPr: Roy, Miss Adrianne LLB(Hons) . . . . *Feb 1990

SHEPHERD HARRIS & CO ‡
Nickel House 96 Silver Street Enfield Middlesex EN1 3EL
Tel: 020 8363 8341 *Fax:* 020 8367 7440 *Dx:* 144341 ENFIELD 8
Emergency telephone 07813 605612
E-mail: mail@shepherd-harris.co.uk
List of partners: I M Godfrey, D F Ritchie
Office: Waltham Cross
Languages: French, German, Italian, Punjabi, Urdu
Work: B2 C1 D1 D2 E F1 G H J1 K1 K3 L N O Q R2 S1 S2 T1 T2 V W X Z(i,l,p,q)
Emergency Action, Agency, Advocacy, Legal Aid undertaken, Legal Aid Franchise and Member of Accident Line
Ptr: Godfrey, Mr Ian M LLB ★ . . . . *Apr 1977
Ritchie, Mr Duncan F LLB. . . . . *Aug 1983
Ast: Costa, Mrs Georgia BA(Hons). . . . . *Feb 1997
Hetherington, Miss Georgina LLB . . . . *Apr 1985
Khaliq, Miss Tazeen LLB . . . . *Oct 1992
Mann, Mrs Harvinder LLB(Hons) . . . . Jan 2000
Ogilvie, Mr Hugh Marshall LLB(Hons) ★. . . . . *Nov 1995
Paddock, Miss Lynne Rachel BA(Hons)(Oxon) . . . . Sep 2009
Zimareva-Locke, Ms Natalia BSc; CPE; LPC . . . . *Mar 2005
Con: Burrowes, Mr David John Barrington LLB . . . . . . *Feb 1995

MARTIN SHEPHERD & CO ‡
29 Southbury Road Enfield Middlesex EN1 1YZ
Tel: 020 8367 3230 *Fax:* 020 8367 7472 *Dx:* 133179 ENFIELD 6
E-mail: reception@martinshepherd.co.uk
List of partners: M A Salida
Office: London N9
Work: B1 C1 C2 C3 D1 E F1 F2 J1 K1 K2 K3 L N O Q R2 S1 S2 W Z(c,l,q,r)
Emergency Action, Agency and Advocacy undertaken
Ptr: Salida, Mr Michael A LLB . . . . *Apr 1975

SINGLETONS AUSTIN RYDER ‡
2 Crossfield Chambers Gladbeck Way Enfield Middlesex EN2 7HT
Tel: 020 8363 0101 *Fax:* 020 8367 0387 *Dx:* 90604 ENFIELD
List of partners: A J Singleton, M J J Singleton
Office: Enfield
Work: B1 C1 C2 C3 D1 D2 E F1 G J1 K1 L M1 N O P Q R1 R2 S1 S2 T1 T2 W Z(b,c,d,j,l,p,q)
Legal Aid undertaken and Member of Accident Line
Ptr: Singleton, Miss Ann J. . . . . *Apr 1981
Singleton, Mr Michael J J . . . . *§May 1980
Asoc: Allen, Mrs Sara Elizabeth . . . . Oct 1998
Fox, Mr David Benjamin LLB . . . . *Sep 2004
Hatter, Mrs Pernilla Bettina . . . . *May 1998

SINGLETONS AUSTIN RYDER
18a Bush Hill Parade Village Road Enfield Middlesex EN1 2HB
Tel: 020 8364 0500 *Fax:* 020 8364 0602
Office: Enfield

SULLIVANS SOLICITORS LLP ‡
3 Cecil Court 49-55 London Road Enfield Middlesex EN2 6DE
Tel: 020 8363 3888 *Fax:* 020 8363 3999 *Dx:* 133184 ENFIELD 6
List of partners: G Sullivan
Mem: Sullivan, Mr Gerard . . . . Aug 1999

TRIUNE SOLICITORS ‡
15a Queensway Enfield Middlesex EN3 4SJ
Tel: 020 8804 5410 *Fax:* 020 8804 5483 *Dx:* 133175 ENFIELD 6
E-mail: triune-solicitor@btconnect.com

VANDERPUMP & SYKES ‡
(incorporating Billinghursts)
Lough Point 2 Gladbeck Way Enfield Middlesex EN2 7JA
Tel: 020 8367 3999 *Fax:* 020 8367 6252 *Dx:* 142500 ENFIELD 7
E-mail: vs@vanderpumps.co.uk
List of partners: M Heselton, S J Quy, K D Thompson
Work: C1 D2 E J1 K1 K2 K3 L N O Q R2 S1 S2 T1 T2 W Z(l)
Ptr: Heselton, Mr Mark MA(Hons) . . . . *Oct 1988
Quy, Mr Stephen J LLB(B'ham) . . . . *Jun 1976
Thompson, Mr Keith D LLB . . . . *Mar 1982
Ast: Barrett, Mr Andrew D . . . . *Dec 1999
Chapman, Miss Karen. . . . . Apr 2004
Howe, Miss Jennifer Anne BA(Hons); CPE . . . . . . Aug 2004
Porter, Mr James Edward BA(Hons); PGDipLaw. . . . Jan 2003
Stephens, Mr Richard Michael Morris BSc; LB. . . . *Nov 1992
Want, Mrs Maureen J BSc . . . . *Aug 1984

WELD & BEAVAN ‡
32 Little Park Gardens Enfield Middlesex EN2 6PF
Tel: 020 8363 1281 *Fax:* 020 8366 4085 *Dx:* 90643 ENFIELD 1
E-mail: info@weldbeavan.co.uk
List of partners: T C Constable
Work: K4 S1 S2 W
Ptr: Constable, Mr Timothy C MA(Cantab). . . . . *Jul 1964
Ast: Constable, Mrs Ailsa G . . . . *Aug 1970
Con: Fraser, Mr Alexander Ian BA(Hons) . . . . *Jun 1981

ANNE WHITEHORN ‡
44 Park Avenue Enfield Middlesex EN1 2HW
Tel: 020 8360 1882 *Fax:* 020 8351 3845
E-mail: anne.whitehorn@blueyonder.co.uk

EPPING, Essex

CHILDLAW ‡
134-136 High Street Epping Essex CM16 4AG
Tel: 01992 570300 *Fax:* 01992 570320 *Dx:* 40410 EPPING
E-mail: murph@childlaw.co.uk

FOSKETT MARR GADSBY & HEAD ‡
181 High Street Epping Essex CM16 4BQ
Tel: 01992 578642 *Fax:* 01992 572586 *Dx:* 40401 EPPING
E-mail: email@foskettmarr.co.uk
Office: Loughton
Work: A1 C1 C2 D1 D2 E F1 J1 K1 L N O Q R1 S1 S2 T1 T2 W Z(c,d,l,s)

KENNARDS WELLS
84a High Street Epping Essex CM16 4AE
Tel: 01992 570505 *Fax:* 01992 570515 *Dx:* 40405 EPPING
E-mail: sstubbings@kennardwells.co.uk
Office: London E11, Redbridge
Languages: French, Greek
Work: C1 D1 E J1 K1 R1 S1 S2 W Z(l)

PARTNERS EMPLOYMENT LAWYERS
261a High Street Epping Essex CM16 4BP
Tel: 0844 800 9239 *Fax:* 020 7681 1857
E-mail: hina@partnerslaw.co.uk
Office: London EC2

SILVER SHEMMINGS LLP
Purlieu House 11 Station Road Epping Essex CM16 4HA
Tel: 0845 345 1244 *Fax:* 0845 345 1039
E-mail: epping@shemmingsllp.co.uk
Office: Cardiff, London SW1
Work: A3 O Q Z(c)

WHISKERS
265 High Street Epping Essex CM16 4BS
Tel: 01992 561111 *Fax:* 01992 573502 *Dx:* 40400 EPPING
Emergency telephone 01279 434228 (CRIME) / 07968 734903
E-mail: enquiries@whiskers.co.uk
Office: Bishop's Stortford, Harlow, Woodford
Languages: French, German, Italian, Spanish
Work: A1 B1 C1 C2 C3 D1 E F1 G H J1 K1 K2 K3 K4 L M1 M2 N P R1 S1 T1 T2 V W Z(h,k,l,m,t)

EPSOM, Surrey

BWTLAW LLP ‡
6 South Street Epsom Surrey KT18 7PF
Tel: 01372 725655 *Fax:* 01372 721372 *Dx:* 30702 EPSOM
E-mail: contact@bwtlaw.co.uk
List of partners: S D Patel, D R Steed
Office: Sutton
Languages: French
Work: B1 C1 C2 C3 D1 E F1 J1 K1 L M1 M2 N P S1 W Z(c,f,k,l)
Emergency Action, Agency, Advocacy, Fixed Fee Interview, Legal Aid undertaken and Legal Aid Franchise
Ptr: Patel, Mr Shilpav D . . . . Mar 2001
Steed, Mr David R . . . . *Jan 1980
Asoc: Dalgetty, Ms Elizabeth. . . . . *Jun 1996
Con: Newman, Mrs Norma Mary LLB. . . . . *Jul 1977

LIONEL BLACKMAN ‡
Upper Chambers 7 Waterloo Road Epsom Surrey KT19 8AY
Tel: 01372 728941
Emergency telephone 01372 728941
List of partners: L F Blackman
Work: G H Z(g)
Emergency Action, Agency, Advocacy, Fixed Fee Interview and Legal Aid undertaken
SPr: Blackman, Mr Lionel F LLB(Leics) ●. . . . . Dec 1986
Ast: Haines, Mrs Suzy . . . . *Nov 1999
Jennings, Miss Billiejoe LLB(Hons) . . . . *Nov 1998

BOWLES & CO ‡
18 Church Street Epsom Surrey KT17 4QD
Tel: 01372 725241 *Fax:* 01372 724429 *Dx:* 30709 EPSOM
E-mail: law@bowlesco.co.uk
List of partners: A E Jones, S E Lambert, D J Read
Work: A1 C1 E J1 K1 L O Q R1 R2 S1 S2 T2 W Z(d)
Ptr: Jones, Mr Adrian Ewart BA; LLB . . . . Oct 1993
Lambert, Ms Sarah Elizabeth . . . . *Nov 1993
Read, Mr David J BA . . . . *Oct 1985

D E DAVIES & CO ‡
61a South Street Rosbury Lodge Epsom Surrey KT18 7PX
Tel: 020 8368 0048 *Fax:* 020 8368 0037
Languages: Welsh
Work: E L S1 W
Fixed Fee Interview undertaken

GUMERSALLS ‡
The White House 16 Waterloo Road Epsom Surrey KT19 8AZ
Tel: 01372 721122 *Fax:* 01372 741580 *Dx:* 30701 EPSOM
E-mail: solicitors@gumersalls.co.uk
Work: E K1 K3 L O Q S1 S2 T1 T2 W

HARBORD & CO ‡
The Pavilions Weston Road Epsom Surrey KT17 1JG
Tel: 01372 720077 *Fax:* 01372 740011 *Dx:* 30717 EPSOM
List of partners: R Harbord
SPr: Harbord, Mr Richard LLB(Hons). . . . . Jan 2002

BRETT HOLT SOLICITORS
21a Stoneleigh Broadway Stoneleigh Epsom Surrey KT17 2JA
Tel: 020 8393 0102 *Fax:* 020 8393 7001
Dx: 200800 WORCESTER PARK
E-mail: brettholt@qualitysolicitors.com
Office: Surbiton, Worcester Park

LANCASTERS ‡
4 Upper High Street Epsom Surrey KT17 4QJ
Tel: 01372 724931 *Fax:* 01372 728631 *Dx:* 30711 EPSOM
E-mail: info@lancasters-lawyers.com
List of partners: J L Wayt
Work: J1 L R2 S1 S2 W
SPr: Wayt, Mr John Lancaster MA; FIMgt; MCIArb; FNAEA; FInstD; FRSA; FILCA; FFA . . . . *Dec 1961

LEWIS & DICK ‡
443 Kingston Road Ewell Epsom Surrey KT19 0DG
Tel: 020 8393 0055 *Fax:* 020 8393 3317 *Dx:* 48303 EWELL
E-mail: ewell@lewis-dick.com
List of partners: O P Jones, J G Owens
Office: Crawley
Languages: French, Spanish
Work: C1 D1 E J1 K1 K2 L R2 S1 S2 T1 T2 V W Z(c,d,h,l)
Fixed Fee Interview undertaken
Ptr: Owens, Mr Jonathan Glyn LLB . . . . *Sep 2004
Ast: Kemp, Mrs Christine Judge Duveen Memorial Prize 2001 . . . . *Mar 2003

J A STEVENS & CO ‡
3a High Street Epsom Surrey KT19 8DA
Tel: 01372 745288 *Fax:* 01372 742667
List of partners: J A Stevens
Work: A1 C1 E L R1 S1 T1 W
Ptr: Stevens, Mr John A MA(Oxon) . . . . *Dec 1980
Con: Lewis, Mr Richard E. . . . . Jan 1975

TWM SOLICITORS LLP
123 High Street Epsom Surrey KT19 8AU
Tel: 01372 729555 *Fax:* 01372 742101 *Dx:* 30710 EPSOM
E-mail: epsom.reception@twmsolicitors.com
Office: Cranleigh, Guildford, Leatherhead, London SW19, Reigate
Work: A3 C1 C2 D1 E J1 K1 K2 L N O Q R2 S1 S2 T2 W Z(i,l,o,p,r)
Emergency Action, Agency, Advocacy undertaken and Member of Accident Line
Ptr: Adler, Miss Charlotte BA(Hons) . . . . *Sep 2000
Chignell, Mr James B . . . . *Dec 1970
Fowler, Mrs Anne Valerie LLB. . . . . *Oct 1984
Harding, Mr Nigel P LLB(Lond) Notary Public . . . . . *Jun 1980
Hast, Mrs Charmaine Kathleen BA; LLB Trustee of Surrey Family Mediation Society . . . . *Jan 1996
Levene, Mr Michael L . . . . *§May 1967
McAuley, Mr John David LLB . . . . *Sep 1996
Asoc: Miles, Fiona. . . . . Sep 2004
Ast: Caulcrick, Miss Folasade Monisola . . . . *Sep 2001
Setford, Mr Guy Michael David . . . . Nov 2001
Shelley, Mr Steve . . . . Mar 2001

EPWORTH, North Lincolnshire

HSR LAW (HAYES, SON & RICHMOND)
Staynor House Newborn Court 30 Chapel Street Epworth North Lincolnshire DN9 1HH
Tel: 01427 872206 *Fax:* 01427 872280 *Dx:* 18781 EPWORTH
Emergency telephone 01427 872876
E-mail: enquiries@taylorbracewell.co.uk
Office: Doncaster, Gainsborough
Work: A1 B1 E F1 J1 K1 L N P R1 S1 W Z(d,t)
Emergency Action, Agency, Advocacy, Fixed Fee Interview, Legal Aid undertaken and Member of Accident Line
Ptr: Fullwood, Mr Richard Ellis. . . . . *Jun 1980

MASON BAGGOTT & GARTON
1 Market Place Epworth North Lincolnshire DN9 1EU
Tel: 01427 872661 *Fax:* 01427 874257 *Dx:* 18782 EPWORTH
E-mail: epworth@lawlincs.co.uk
Office: Brigg, Scunthorpe
Work: A1 B1 C1 C2 C3 D1 E F1 G H J1 K1 L M1 M2 N O P Q R1 S1 T1 T2 V W Z(l,p,q,r)
Emergency Action, Agency, Advocacy, Fixed Fee Interview, Legal Aid undertaken and Legal Aid Franchise
Ptr: Garton, Mr Rex . . . . *Nov 1971

SYMES BAINS BROOMER
56 High Street Epworth North Lincolnshire DN9 1EP
Tel: 01427 872479 *Fax:* 01427 875547 *Dx:* 18784 EPWORTH
E-mail: info@sbblaw.com
Office: Goole, Grimsby, Howden, Scunthorpe
Legal Aid Franchise

ERITH, Kent

DORCAS FUNMI & CO ‡
12 Brook Street Erith Kent DA8 1JQ
Tel: 01322 335005 *Fax:* 01322 333505 *Dx:* 99677 ERITH

ESHER, Surrey

AW LAW ‡
North Lodge Esher Park Avenue Esher Surrey KT10 9NP
Tel: 01372 469100 *Fax:* 01372 462172
E-mail: andrewwills@aw-law.co.uk
List of partners: A N Wills
Work: C1 E J1 K1 O Q S1 S2 W Z(l)
Advocacy undertaken
Ptr: Wills, Mr Andrew Nicholas. . . . . *Sep 1980

ATKINS & CO ‡
Thames House 77a High Street Esher Surrey KT10 9QA
Tel: 01372 477188 *Fax:* 01372 473802 *Dx:* 36315 ESHER
E-mail: janine@atkinsandco.uk.com
List of partners: J A Atkins
Work: K1 K3 S1
Ptr: Atkins, Miss Janine A LLB. . . . . *Oct 1991

CREAGH BROWN & CO SOLICITORS ‡
65 Grove Way Esher Surrey KT10 8HQ
Tel: 020 8224 0610 *Fax:* 020 8873 8810 *Dx:* 36325 ESHER
E-mail: chris@creaghbrown.co.uk
Work: D1 K1 K3 K4 W
Agency undertaken

MICHAEL FRIEND ‡
Hunters Lodge Hillbrow Road Esher Surrey KT10 9UD
Tel: 01372 468098 *Fax:* 01372 468810
List of partners: M J Friend
Languages: French
Work: A3 C1 E G J1 J2 N O P Q R1 S1 S2 W Z(c,j,k,q,r,w)
Agency, Legal Aid undertaken and Member of Accident Line
SPr: Friend, Mr Michael John. . . . . *Nov 1967

GALLOWAY HUGHES SOLICITORS ‡
Warwick House 1 Claremont Lane Esher Surrey KT10 9DP
Tel: 01372 237070 / 020 8398 8188 *Fax:* 01372 237071
Dx: 36308 ESHER

HUNTER PEDDELL PROPERTY LAW ‡
Albany House Claremont Lane Esher Surrey KT10 9DA
Tel: 01372 477900 *Fax:* 01372 479829
E-mail: ihunter@hpplaw.co.uk

CAROLE MONTANO ‡
14 Brendon Close Esher Surrey KT10 9EH
Tel: 01372 465128

MORGAN RUSSELL LLP ‡
Hillbrow House Hillbrow Road Esher Surrey KT10 9NW
Tel: 01372 461411 *Fax:* 01372 461401
E-mail: advice@morganrussell.co.uk

PORTMANS SOLICITORS ‡
1 Meadway Esher Surrey KT10 9HG
Tel: 01372 464488 *Fax:* 01372 465317
E-mail: contact@portmans.org.uk
List of partners: M J Watson
Work: N
Ptr: Watson, Mr Michael John . . . . Jan 1978

TZANEV & CO LAWYERS ‡
49 Severn Drive Hinchley Wood Esher Surrey KT10 0AJ
Tel: 020 8224 2779 *Fax:* 020 8224 2779
E-mail: nik.tzanev@gmail.com

ETCHINGHAM, East Sussex

HENNAH & CO ‡
Holly Lodge High Street Etchingham East Sussex TN19 7SD
Tel: 01580 819171

EVESHAM, Worcestershire

ATTER MACKENZIE & CO ‡
Bridge Court 64 Bridge Street Evesham Worcestershire WR11 4RY
Tel: 01386 425300 *Fax:* 01386 765170 *Dx:* 16165 EVESHAM
E-mail: info@attermackenzie.co.uk
List of partners: R J Atter, J D Cooper, C M Hilton, A Hussain, P G Jackson
Languages: French, German
Work: A1 B1 C1 C2 C3 D1 D2 E F1 G H J1 J2 K1 K2 K3 L M1 M2 N O P Q R1 R2 S1 S2 T1 T2 V W Z(c,d,e,f,g,j,l,m,p,q,s,t)
Emergency Action, Agency, Advocacy, Fixed Fee Interview, Legal Aid undertaken and Legal Aid Franchise
Ptr: Atter, Mr Roger J BA(Hons) . . . . *Jun 1979
Cooper, Miss Julia D BA(Hons) . . . . *Sep 1998
Hilton, Mr Christopher M LLB . . . . *Mar 1993
Hussain, Mr Amer LLB . . . . *Sep 1999
Jackson, Mr Peter G BA . . . . *Dec 1980
Ast: Ham, Mr William Richard BA; GDL; LPC . . . . . . *Sep 2008
Jones, Mr Timothy S D LLB. . . . . *§Oct 1987

J R CHAMPKIN ‡
Little Moat House Abbots Salford Evesham Worcestershire WR11 8UT
Tel: 01386 871287 *Fax:* 01386 871885
Emergency telephone 07831 656500
E-mail: jamie@champkin.co.uk
List of partners: J R Champkin
Work: B1 C1 C2 E J1 O S2 Z(e,q,w)
Ptr: Champkin, Mr Jamie R LLB. . . . . *Jun 1981

COX & HODGETTS ‡
De Montfort House 115 High Street Evesham Worcestershire WR11 4HS
Tel: 01386 442513 *Fax:* 01386 765452 *Dx:* 16166 EVESHAM
List of partners: J M Brookes, C N T Campbell, I D Long, J A Pratt, P A Spencer
Work: A1 B1 C1 D2 E F1 J1 J2 K1 K3 K4 L N O Q R1 S1 S2 T2 U1 W Z(c,l,q,r)
Ptr: Brookes, Mr John M. . . . . *§Aug 1973
Campbell, Mr Colin Niall T BA. . . . . *§Oct 1985
Long, Mr Ian David . . . . *Dec 1999
Pratt, Mrs Julie A BSocSc. . . . . *Oct 1983
Spencer, Mr Paul Anthony. . . . . Oct 2006

THE INFORMATION LAW PRACTICE ‡
Mistletoe House Rous Lench Evesham Worcestershire WR11 4UW
Tel: 01386 793632 *Fax:* 01386 661111
E-mail: info@theinformationlawpractice.com

PARKINSON WRIGHT LLP
4 Abbey Lane Court Abbey Lane Evesham Worcestershire WR11 4BY
Tel: 01386 761176 *Fax:* 01386 765489 *Dx:* 700285 EVESHAM 2
E-mail: evesham@parkinsonwright.co.uk
Office: Droitwich, Worcester
Work: A1 C1 C2 D1 D2 E F1 G H J1 K1 K2 L N O Q S1 S2 V W Z(e,k,l,q)
Emergency Action, Agency, Advocacy, Fixed Fee Interview, Legal Aid undertaken and Legal Aid Franchise

PLEXUS LAW (A TRADING NAME OF PARABIS LAW LLP)
Vale Chambers 110-112 High Street Evesham Worcestershire WR11 4EJ
Tel: 01386 769160 *Fax:* 01386 769196 *Dx:* 16167 EVESHAM
Office: Colchester, Croydon, Leeds, London EC2, London EC3, Manchester (2 offices)
Work: J1 N
Agency undertaken
Ptr: Adams, Mrs Elmira Fiona BA; LLB; Advocate of the Supreme Court of South Africa . . . . Jul 2000
Bates, Miss Jennifer Anne BA(Hons)(Law & Management Scheme) Rich & Carr Solicitors Law Student of the Year Award 1998. . . . . *Sep 2001
Burt, Mr Damon R. . . . . *Oct 2000
Burt, Mr Jason Drew . . . . *Oct 1996
Bushell, Mr Anthony BA(Hons) . . . . Oct 2002
Cooper, Charlotte Louisa . . . . Sep 2003
Cornfield, Mr Stephen Graham BA(Hons); CPE; LPC . Sep 1997
Cotes, Mr Howard N E BA . . . . *Feb 1983
Messervy-Whiting, Mrs Julia E MA(Cantab) . . . . . *Nov 1989
Rennie, Mr Alan FILEx . . . . *Dec 1988
Sivil, Mr Michael R LLB . . . . *Jun 1977
Yates, Mr Nicholas P R BA . . . . *Dec 1979
Ast: Barnet, Mrs Nicola . . . . Apr 2008
Beesley, Miss Stephanie . . . . May 2010
Bennett, Mrs Holly Katriina . . . . Nov 2006
Brownsword, Mrs Fiona Jane . . . . Nov 1989
Conway, Mr Steven Philip . . . . Sep 2009
Coote, Ms Deborah Mary LLB. . . . . Sep 2000
De La Porte, Mr Paul . . . . Apr 2006
Deer, Ms Susan. . . . . Jul 2009
Delaney, Mr Robert . . . . Oct 2000
Desai, Ms Binita. . . . . Apr 2006
Fisher, Mrs Joanne LLB. . . . . Nov 1990
Godwin, Miss Marsha . . . . Dec 2003
Grant, Miss Deborah MacDonald MA(Hons); CPE. . . Aug 2004
Handley, Ms Sarah . . . . Mar 2010
Jones, Miss Nicola . . . . Mar 2010
Kikkine, Miss Natacha Anne. . . . . Sep 2005
Lewis, Mr Jonathan Philip . . . . Feb 1988
Mclachlan, Ms Joanna . . . . Oct 2003
Malone, Mrs Stephenie . . . . Sep 2005
Payton, Miss Rebecca LLM; LLB(Hons). . . . . Sep 2003
Povey, Mr Paul John LLB; FILEx . . . . May 2004
Sheret, Mrs Ruth . . . . Oct 1991
Simpson, Mr Alan. . . . . Jun 1980
Stokes, Mr Michael . . . . Jul 1992
Wagstaffe, Mrs Vicki . . . . Sep 2010
Walker, Ms Rebekah . . . . Sep 2008

SAUNDERS ROBERTS ‡
1 Crown Courtyard Evesham Worcestershire WR11 4RY
Tel: 01386 442558 *Fax:* 01386 49448 *Dx:* 700283 EVESHAM 2
List of partners: P R Boyd, J F Kirkham, P R Leach, J D Shipton, R S Wilson
Work: B1 C1 C2 C3 D1 E F1 J1 K1 L M1 N O P Q R1 S1 T1 T2 V W Z(c,d,i,t)
Agency and Advocacy undertaken
Ptr: Boyd, Mr Patrick Russell BCL; LLM . . . . Mar 2005
Kirkham, Mrs Julia Fay BSc. . . . . *Oct 1993
Leach, Mr Philip R LLB(L'pool) . . . . *Oct 1980
Shipton, Mr Jeremy D LLB(Manc) . . . . *Apr 1976
Wilson, Mr Robert Stephen . . . . *Dec 1972
Ast: Barklam, Mr John Robert Brighton BSc; DipLS; DipLP. Oct 1999

EWELL, Surrey

HAROLD BELL & CO ‡
Devon House 174 Kingston Road Ewell Surrey KT19 0SD
Tel: 020 8393 0231 *Fax:* 020 8393 0155
E-mail: info@haroldbell.co.uk
List of partners: M A Bell, T E Poolman
Work: A1 B1 C1 C2 C3 E F1 J1 K1 K2 K3 L M1 M2 N O Q R1 S1 T1 T2 W Z(c,j,l)
Legal Aid undertaken and Member of Accident Line
Ptr: Bell, Mr Malcolm A . . . . Dec 1978
Poolman, Miss Tracy E BA(Law) Notary Public . . . *Sep 1983
Ast: Haskew, Mr Derek C BA; JD . . . . Jan 2006

KEY2LAW LLP ‡
61 High Street Ewell Surrey KT17 1RX
Tel: 020 8393 0941 *Fax:* 020 8393 2281 *Dx:* 48304 EWELL
E-mail: info@key2law.co.uk
List of partners: G T C Musgrave
Office: London WC1
Languages: Swedish
Work: C1 D1 E G J1 K1 L N Q S1 W Z(o,w)
Emergency Action, Agency, Legal Aid undertaken and Member of Accident Line
Ptr: Musgrave, Mr Gavin T C MA(Cantab) . . . . *Apr 1981
Asoc: Davies, Mrs Delyth Eurios LLB(Hons)(Wales) . . . . *Jun 1979
Lewis, Miss Jacqueline A MA(Hons)(Cantab) . . . . *Nov 1985
Ast: Demelo, Mr Alwyn. . . . . Dec 1995
Gulliver, Mrs Sheila Ann LLB(Hons). . . . . *Nov 1982
Kay, Mrs Myra A . . . . *Jun 1969
Patel, Mr Viresh LLB . . . . *Feb 1995
Read, Ms Susan I K. . . . . Sep 1995
Con: Pond, Mrs Lesley A LLB. . . . . *Nov 1986

EXETER, Devon

ARMITAGE & CO ‡
Pearl Assurance House 236 High Street Exeter Devon EX4 3NE
Tel: 01392 251364 / 214786 *Fax:* 01392 413587
List of partners: S M Armitage
Languages: French
Work: A1 C1 E K1 L N O P R1 S1 W Z(l)
Agency, Advocacy undertaken and Member of Accident Line
SPr: Armitage, Mr Simon Michael LLB(Exon). . . . . . . *§Nov 1974

ASHFORDS LLP ‡
Ashford House Grenadier Road Exeter Devon EX1 3LH
Tel: 01392 337000 *Fax:* 01392 337001 *Dx:* 150000 EXETER 24
E-mail: info@ashfords.co.uk
List of partners: M A Alden, A W Baines, P L Barton, A J Bauer, D P S Beadel, A Bennett, A C Betteridge, J D Blackburn, J W Bosworth, C L Brewer, G J O Channer, J C Clarke, G A L Cruwys, I C Daniells, A J Dodd, R J Edwards, M Fox, P R Fox, S Gibbon, E Gibson, N Gosden, C J Gregson, J M Hadley-Piggin, C W Hattersley, T R Heal, D J S Heard, B C Hegarty, A S C Holyoak, S J Homer, R D Horsey, T Howells, M D Jury, A T Lee, R M Lewis, E Livingston, M M Lomas, S A Lomas, R J J Mac Neice, G Mackay, A MacMillan-Scott, M C Manning, A Mason, R K Murray, C B Pallot, J M Park, J E Pettit, D A W Pomeroy, A C Rothwell, S R Rous, A Smith, J S Smith, J S Squire, C B Steele, G C Trobridge, S J Walker, D P White, G T N Wilkinson, F C Wood, C B Wright
Office: Bristol, London W1, Plymouth, Taunton, Tiverton
Languages: French, German, Italian, Spanish, Swedish, Welsh
Work: A3 B1 C1 C2 E I J1 L N O P R1 R2 S1 T1 U2 W X Z(b,c,d,e,g,h,l,o,u,w)
Emergency Action, Agency, Advocacy, Fixed Fee Interview, Legal Aid undertaken, Legal Aid Franchise and Member of Accident Line
Ptr: Alden, Mr Michael Alistair BA(Nott'm) . . . . *Oct 1994
Bauer, Mr Angus James BSc(Hons); ATII; DipLP . . *Dec 1997
Bennett, Mr Alan LLB(Hons). . . . . Feb 2000
Blackburn, Mr J Darren LLB. . . . . *Dec 1991
Bosworth, Mr John William LLB . . . . Oct 1998
Brewer, Ms Clare Louise . . . . *Sep 1996
Daniells, Mr Ian C BA(Hons) . . . . Nov 1986
Gibbon, Miss Sian LLB . . . . *Oct 1990
Gibson, Ms Elizabeth . . . . Mar 2005
Gosden, Mr Nigel LLB. . . . . *Oct 1983
Hadley-Piggin, Mr Jonathan Mark . . . . Oct 1995
Heal, Mr Timothy Ralph BA(Hons). . . . . *Sep 1998
Hegarty, Mr Brian Charles BA(Hons) . . . . *Oct 1986
Holyoak, Mrs Annabel S C BA(Hons) . . . . *Oct 1987
Homer, Mr Stephen John LLB; FCIArb; FFB. . . . . . *Oct 1988
Horsey, Mr Robert Dirk LLB(Hons) . . . . *Nov 1992
Jury, Mr Mark David. . . . . Sep 2001
Lee, Mr Antony T MA(Cantab). . . . . *Nov 1990
Lomas, Mr Mark Mallyon BA(Hons) . . . . *Oct 1989
Mac Neice, Mr Rory John James LLB(Hons) . . . . . Nov 1998
MacMillan-Scott, Mr Andrew LLB(Hons). . . . . Jun 1992
Manning, Mr Mark Charles LLB(Hons). . . . . Sep 2001
Murray, Ms Ruth Kathryn LLB(Hons); LPC. . . . . . . Sep 2002
Pallot, Mr Charles Benedict . . . . May 1985
Park, Mrs Judith M BA(Hons) . . . . *May 1985
Pettit, Mr James Eaton Notary Public . . . . *Dec 1973
Rothwell, Mr Andrew C LLB; LSF Company Secretary for Advoc Limited . . . . *Apr 1980
Rous, Mr Simon Roderick MA(Cantab) . . . . *Jun 1976
Steele, Mr Carl Bryan LLB; LPC; Dip Sports Law; Dip IP Law & Practice. Sep 1997
Trobridge, Mr Geoffrey Charles . . . . Apr 1981
White, Mr Darren Paul LLB(Hons). . . . . Jul 2001
Wright, Mr Colin Bruce BA(Hons) . . . . Mar 1994
Asoc: Yendole, Mr Andrew. . . . . Sep 2000
Ast: Ferguson, Ms Victoria. . . . . Sep 2004
Hill, Ms Charlotte . . . . Sep 2005
Howson, Mr Andrew. . . . . Sep 2005

ATKINS LAW SOLICITORS ‡
The Red House St David's Hill Exeter Devon EX4 4BS
Tel: 01392 671657 *Fax:* 01392 671659
E-mail: enquiries@atkinslaw.co.uk
Work: G J1 Z(i)
Agency, Advocacy, Fixed Fee Interview, Legal Aid undertaken and Legal Aid Franchise
Asoc: Hockin, Mrs Judith Lavinia BSc(Hons). . . . . *Apr 2004
Huddleson, Mr Matthew James BA(Hons) . . . . . . *Oct 2002

JANET AUCKLAND SOLICITOR ‡
Queensgate House 48 Queen Street Exeter Devon EX4 3SR
Tel: 01392 210152 *Fax:* 0560 126 5922

BHR LAW
17a Gandy Street Exeter Devon EX4 3LS
Tel: 01392 496100 *Fax:* 01392 495900
E-mail: lawyers@bhrlaw.co.uk
Office: Barnstaple (2 offices), Bideford, Braunton, Ilfracombe
Ptr: Carter, Ms Susan Elizabeth BA . . . . Sep 2000
Walker, Mrs Jillian Kim MA(Oxon). . . . . May 1981

CBY SOLICITORS ‡
Paddock Cottage Exeter Devon EX5 2ES
Tel: 01404 822452
E-mail: bryan@cbysolicitors.com

CARTRIDGES ‡
144 Cowick Street St Thomas Exeter Devon EX4 1AS
Tel: 01392 256854 *Fax:* 01392 286790
Dx: 89850 EXETER ST THOMAS
E-mail: enquiries@cartridgeslaw.co.uk
List of partners: J G Cartridge, B M Garrood, A J C Griffin, F A Parffrey, P A Scott
Languages: French, Spanish
Work: A1 D1 D2 F1 F2 K1 L N O P Q S1 S2 V W Z(p,q)
Emergency Action, Agency, Advocacy, Fixed Fee Interview, Legal Aid undertaken and Legal Aid Franchise
Ptr: Cartridge, Mr John G LLB. . . . . *Apr 1970
Garrood, Ms Bridget Mary. . . . . *Sep 1997
Griffin, Mr Antony J C BA . . . . *Jul 1975
Parffrey, Mr Francis Anthony LLB . . . . *Jul 1978
Scott, Ms Penelope Anne . . . . *Sep 1995
Ast: Strange, Ms Julie BA(Hons); PhD; PGCE . . . . Sep 1997

CROSSE & CROSSE ‡
14 Southernhay West Exeter Devon EX1 1PL
Tel: 01392 258451 *Fax:* 01392 278938 *Dx:* 8313 EXETER
E-mail: mail@crosse.co.uk
List of partners: S A Bryant, W M Kemp, D M Merrick, T P Selley, R J Stevinson
Languages: French
Work: C1 D1 D2 E F1 J1 J2 K1 K3 K4 L N O Q S1 S2 T2 V W Z(j,l,m,p,q,r)
Emergency Action, Agency, Advocacy, Fixed Fee Interview, Legal Aid undertaken and Member of Accident Line
Ptr: Bryant, Miss Stacey Anne. . . . . *§Sep 1998
Kemp, Ms Wendy Merriel LLB(Hons) . . . . *§Sep 1998
Merrick, Mr David M BSc . . . . *§May 1981
Selley, Mr Timothy P LLB . . . . *§Oct 1984
Stevinson, Mr Richard J LLB(Bris). . . . . *§Oct 1989
Asoc: Adams, Mr Richard A LLB(Hons) . . . . *Feb 1989
Osborn, Miss Karen Jane BA(Hons). . . . . *Jan 1994
Ast: Brush, Mr Phillip Leslie LLB . . . . *Nov 1975

 See p112 for the Key to Work Categories & other symbols

Gregory, Mrs Nicola Jane LLM(Cantab) . . . *Oct 1991
Smith, Mrs Sabina May LLB. . . . *Jan 1996

DUNN & BAKER ‡
21-22 Southernhay East Exeter Devon EX1 1QQ
Tel: 01392 285000 *Fax:* 01392 285001 *Dx:* 8311 EXETER
E-mail: mail@dunnandbaker.co.uk
List of partners: E G Bowser, D E Cleverdon, J M Green, N Penwell, C E Salvatore, E Smith, A Wendon
Office: Cullompton
Work: A1 B1 B2 B3 C1 C2 C3 D1 E F1 G H I J1 K1 L M1 M2 N O P Q R1 S1 S2 T1 T2 V W X Z(c,d,e,i,j,k,l,m,o,p,q,r,s,y)
Emergency Action, Agency, Advocacy, Fixed Fee Interview, Legal Aid undertaken, Legal Aid Franchise and Member of Accident Line
Ptr: Bowser, Mr Edward G. . . . Dec 1977
Cleverdon, Mr Darren E BA(Hons) . . . *Aug 1998
Green, Ms Julia M BA. . . . Jun 1976
Penwell, Mr Nicholas TEP. . . . *Nov 2004
Salvatore, Mrs Caroline E LLB(Hons) . . . *Sep 1985
Smith, Miss Elga BA(Hons) . . . *May 2000
Wendon, Mr Andrew BA(Hons) . . . *Sep 1998
Con: Williams, Mr Roger Michael Linton MA(Oxon) Francis Bennion Prizeman Oxford . . . *Nov 1971
Woodhorse, Mr John Gordon Irvine LLB. . . . *Oct 1971

EVELING LEGAL & ADVISORY LTD ‡
Balliol House Southernhay Gardens Exeter Devon EX1 1NP
Tel: 01392 479002 *Fax:* 01392 474387 *Dx:* 8319 EXETER
E-mail: info@evelinglegal.co.uk

EVERYS
Hertford House Southernhay Gardens Exeter Devon EX1 1NP
Tel: 01392 477983 *Fax:* 01392 477984 *Dx:* 8314 EXETER
Emergency telephone 01404 822123
E-mail: law@everys.co.uk
Office: Budleigh Salterton, Exmouth, Honiton (2 offices), Ottery St Mary, Seaton, Sidmouth, Taunton
Work: A1 A2 B1 B2 C1 C2 C3 D1 D2 E F1 F2 G H J1 J2 K1 L M1 N O P Q R1 R2 S1 S2 T1 T2 V W X Z(c,d,e,h,i,k,l,m,n,o,p,q,r,s,t,u,w,x,y)
Emergency Action, Agency, Advocacy, Fixed Fee Interview and Legal Aid undertaken
Ptr: Cuthbert, Mr Charles K BA . . . *Oct 1984
Powell, Mrs Lesley Jane BA(Hons) . . . *§Nov 1997
Scott, Mr Robert A LLB . . . *§Oct 1991
Ast: Hodgson, Mrs Lynda May. . . . *§Sep 2003
Sandel, Miss Katy Ann LLB(Hons). . . . Sep 2005
Walker, Miss Lesley Margaret. . . . *§Jul 1996

FOLLETT STOCK LLP
Woodwater Park Pynes Hill Exeter Devon EX2 5WT
Tel: 01392 449370 *Fax:* 01392 449371
E-mail: enquiries@follettstock.co.uk
Office: Truro

FOOT ANSTEY
Senate Court Southernhay Gardens Exeter Devon EX1 1NT
Tel: 01392 411221 *Fax:* 01392 685220 *Dx:* 8308 EXETER
E-mail: contact@footanstey.com
Office: Plymouth, Taunton, Truro
Languages: French, Italian, Spanish, Thai
Work: A1 A3 B1 B2 C1 C2 C3 D1 D2 E F1 F2 G H I J1 J2 K1 K2 L M1 N O P Q R1 R2 S1 S2 T1 T2 U1 U2 V W X Z(a,b,c,d,e,f,g,h,j,k,l,n,o,p,q,s,t,u,w,y,z)
Emergency Action, Agency, Advocacy, Fixed Fee Interview, Legal Aid undertaken, Legal Aid Franchise and Member of Accident Line
Ptr: Bagwell, Mr Richard. . . . Sep 1998
Biggs, Mr Keith M BA. . . . *§Oct 1988
Coombs, Mr Richard G MA(Cantab) Harrison Exhibition . . . *§Jun 1979
Evans, Mr James LLB. . . . *Sep 1996
Gregory, Mr Simon H BA(Oxon). . . . *Apr 1981
Guard, Mr John P BA(Soton) . . . *§Apr 1982
Jaffa, Mr Anthony R BA(Oxon) Notary Public . . . *§Nov 1980
McNicol, Mr Angus M MA(Lond). . . . *§Jun 1981
Miller, Mr Adrian W M MA(Oxon) . . . *Jan 1975
Pinwell, Mr Gareth David . . . *Jan 1992
Priddis, Mrs Vanessa M L BA(Law) . . . *§Oct 1987
Probert, Mr Edmund A W MA(Cantab). . . . *§Jun 1978
Smith, Mrs Cathryn F LLB. . . . *§Oct 1986
Smith, Mrs Gillian LLB; LLM. . . . *§Jun 1980
Sykes, Mr Duncan LLB(Hons). . . . *Sep 1999
Thorne, Mr Christopher Gordon LLB. . . . *§Oct 1985
Turner, Mr David . . . Sep 2007
Whitehead, Mr Michael V BSc; ARCS; LLB . . . *§Oct 1990
Widley, Miss Louise. . . . Sep 1999
Asoc: Johnson, Mr Nicholas T BA . . . *Sep 1990
Ast: Cook, Mrs Rachel Elizabeth BSc(Econ); CPE; LPC Trustee of Womens Refuge . . . Sep 1997
Hall, Mr Jonathan James Foster LLB(Hons). . . . *Oct 1993
Harding, Mr Simon LLB(Hons). . . . *§Sep 1999
Hogarty, Mrs Bhavani R L BA(Hons). . . . *Nov 1991
Musannif, Mr Simon LLB . . . *Jan 1992
Naumann, Ms Marlene . . . Apr 1998
Parker, Miss Tracy J BA. . . . *Oct 1998
Sharp, Mrs Alexandra. . . . *Sep 1996
Con: Diver, Miss Isabel B MA(Cantab) . . . *§Jun 1972
Lawson, Mr Stephen A Deputy Bankruptcy Registrar . *Oct 1969
Willoughby, Mr Paul M . . . *§Jul 1973
Woodhouse, Mr John Gordon Imrie LLB(Exon) . . . *§Oct 1971

FORD SIMEY LLP ‡
The Senate Southernhay Gardens Exeter Devon EX1 1UG
Tel: 01392 274126 *Fax:* 01392 422098 *Dx:* 8316 EXETER
Emergency telephone 01392 275036
E-mail: info@fordsimey.co.uk
List of partners: S W Arnold, D P Boyle, T M Burford, P A Derbyshire, V A Donson, M Gaye, D S Harvey, A N R Hill, A J Holdich, M G Horwood, T Kelly, J R McIntosh, F G Medland, C A Mellanby, G H Palmer, M R P Redman, S J Sanger-Anderson, M Saxl, T C Underhill, A D Wheaton, D R Williams
Office: Exmouth, Honiton, Sidmouth
Work: A1 B1 C1 C2 D1 E F1 G H J1 K1 K2 L N O Q R1 S1 S2 T1 T2 W Z(c,h,j,k,l,o,q)
Agency, Advocacy, Fixed Fee Interview, Legal Aid undertaken and Legal Aid Franchise
Ptr: Arnold, Mr Stephen W BA ★ Deputy District Judge . *§Apr 1976
Burford, Miss Tina M BA(Hons)(Dunelm); TEP. . . . *§Jan 1992
Derbyshire, Mr Paul A LLB Deputy District Judge; Recorder . . . *§May 1973
Donson, Mr Victor A LLB . . . *§May 1969
Gaye, Mr Michael LLB(Leics) . . . *§May 1974
Harvey, Mr David S. . . . *Dec 1976
Kelly, Ms Tina. . . . Dec 1991
Mellanby, Ms Carolyn A LLB ★ Deputy District Judge (Crime) . . . *§Feb 1990
Palmer, Mr George H LLB. . . . *§Oct 1983
Redman, Mr Michael R P MA(Oxon) . . . *§Aug 1970
Sanger-Anderson, Mr Simon J . . . *Jan 1981
Saxl, Ms Miriam. . . . *§Dec 1992
Underhill, Mr Timothy C LLB(Lond) . . . *§Apr 1972
Williams, Mr David R LLB. . . . *§Jun 1981
Ast: Edwards, Mrs Frances May ACIArb. . . . *Sep 1995
Francis, Ms Vanessa LLB. . . . *Nov 1993
Henley, Miss Lucy E LLB(Hons). . . . *Apr 1980

GILBERT STEPHENS ‡
15-17 Southernhay East Exeter Devon EX1 1QE
Tel: 01392 424242 *Fax:* 01392 410925 *Dx:* 8338 EXETER
E-mail: law@gilbertstephens.co.uk
List of partners: T A J Bastyan, A J Bates, P D Dunn, B J Gawn, R A Heron, N I McKay, P J Symons, R S Walford
Office: Ottery St Mary, Sidmouth
Languages: French
Work: A1 B1 C1 C2 C3 D1 E F1 G H J1 K1 K2 L N O P Q R1 S1 S2 T1 T2 V W Z(b,c,d,i,j,l,m,o,t)
Emergency Action, Agency, Advocacy, Fixed Fee Interview, Legal Aid undertaken and Member of Accident Line
Ptr: Bastyan, Mr Terry A J. . . . *§Nov 1979
Bates, Mr Alastair J MA(Cantab) . . . *Mar 1984
Dunn, Mr Paul D BA(East Anglia) Sir George Fowler Prize . . . *§Jul 1978
Gawn, Miss Brenda Jane BA . . . *§Dec 1992
Heron, Mr R Alistair LLB(Reading) . . . *§Nov 1980
McKay, Mr Nigel I BSc(Hons) . . . *Mar 1998
Symons, Mr Philip John LLB(Hons) . . . *Sep 1988
Walford, Mr Richard Simon MA(Cantab). . . . *Dec 1989
Ast: Clegg, Miss Helen Susan BA . . . *§Dec 1994
Elphick, Miss Claire Amanda LLB . . . *Feb 2006
Govier, Miss Elizabeth Ann LLB; TEP . . . Oct 1989
McDonald, Miss Kim Marie LLB. . . . *Mar 2009
Warne, Ms Isabel . . . *Apr 2008
Con: Canning, Mrs Frances Grace LLB; Dip in Social Admin .Jul 1981
Willcox, Mr Timothy N V LLB(Bris). . . . *§Aug 1978

GRAHAM GOVER SOLICITOR ‡
10 Southernhay West Exeter Devon EX1 1JG
Tel: 01392 423090 *Fax:* 01392 423446
E-mail: graham@ggsol.co.uk
List of partners: G R Gover
Languages: Japanese
SPr: Gover, Mr Graham R LLB(Brunel). . . . *May 1983

HARTNELL CHANOT & PARTNERS FAMILY LAW SPECIALISTS ‡
Oriel House Southernhay Gardens Exeter Devon EX1 1NP
Tel: 01392 421777 *Fax:* 01392 421237 *Dx:* 8388 EXETER
E-mail: enquiries@hartnellchanot.co.uk
List of partners: J E Chanot, N A Hartnell, C Ryan, S J Sowden, C J Turner
Work: D1 D2 K1 K2 K3
Emergency Action, Agency, Advocacy, Legal Aid undertaken and Legal Aid Franchise
Ptr: Chanot, Mrs Jane E LLB . . . *§Sep 1992
Hartnell, Mr Norman A MA(Cantab) . . . *§Dec 1979
Ryan, Miss Caroline LLB(Hons). . . . *§Nov 1993
Sowden, Mr Stephen John . . . *Sep 1994
Turner, Mrs Carol Jayne LLB(Hons). . . . *Dec 1995
Asoc: Ellingham, Miss Susan LLB(Hons). . . . *Oct 1993
Reynolds, Mrs Claire Suzanne BA(Hons) . . . *Jan 2003

HINE & CO ‡
Haldon Brake High Ashton Exeter Devon EX6 7QY
Tel: 01392 832937 *Fax:* 01392 833797
E-mail: solicitors@hineco.co.uk

KITSONS LLP
The Forum Barnfield Road Exeter Devon EX1 1QR
Tel: 01392 455555 *Fax:* 01392 455961
E-mail: advice@kitsons-solicitors.co.uk
Office: Newton Abbot, Plymouth, Torquay
Work: A1 B1 C1 C2 C3 D1 D2 E F1 G H J1 K1 K2 K3 L M1 N O P Q R1 S1 S2 T1 T2 V W Z(b,c,d,e,f,g,h,i,j,k,l,m,o,r,s,t)
Emergency Action, Agency, Advocacy, Fixed Fee Interview, Legal Aid undertaken, Legal Aid Franchise and Member of Accident Line
Ptr: Davy, Mrs Emma LLB(Hons); LLM(Euro) Deputy District Judge . . . Sep 1998
Perkins, Mr Andrew S LLB . . . *Apr 1997
Smith, Mr Andrew. . . . Sep 1999
Asoc: Biddick, Lucie. . . . Sep 2004
Pope, Mr Nick. . . . Feb 2005
Scott-Tucker, Mr Matthew LLB(Hons) . . . *Sep 2005
Ast: Dunstone, Karen . . . Sep 2008
Sandel, Miss Katy Ann LLB(Hons). . . . Sep 2005
Con: Gaye, Mr Michael. . . . May 1975
O'Connor, Mr John Bernard LLB(Wales). . . . May 1979

MICHELMORES LLP ‡
Woodwater House Pynes Hill Exeter Devon EX2 5WR
Tel: 01392 688688 *Fax:* 01392 360563 *Dx:* 135608 EXETER 16
Emergency telephone 0800 072 4333
E-mail: enquiries@michelmores.com
List of partners: S Barnett, S J Billingham, C N Butcher, F Button, R Cobb, A J Cockayne, J M Damerell, M K Dickinson, N Duncan, C P Elias, M J Follett, J Gribble, R M Hedger, I D Holyoak, E Honey, R W Honey, D L Howe, P J Lowless, C Maunder, C McCormack, B J McGhie, W F Michelmore, A W M Miller, G Morgan, S A Morse, R Nicholson, R Noormohamed, G Offen, S Pickering, Z Porter, V Priddis, S Rice, T C Richards, J Riley, P J Sigler, G Smith, S M Thomas, A B Tobey, L N Vick, J Whitfield, P Wolfgang
Office: London W1, Sidmouth
Languages: French, Spanish
Work: A1 A2 A3 B1 B2 C1 C2 C3 D1 D2 E F1 F2 I J1 J2 K1 K2 K3 K4 L M1 N O P Q R1 R2 S1 S2 T1 T2 U1 U2 V W X Z(b,c,d,e,f,g,h,j,k,l,m,n,o,p,q,r,u,w,x,y,z,za)
Emergency Action, Agency, Advocacy, Fixed Fee Interview, Legal Aid undertaken, Legal Aid Franchise and Member of Accident Line
Ptr: Barnett, Mr Simon BA Under Sheriff of Devon. . . . *§Oct 1983
Billingham, Ms Samantha Jane LLB(Hons); LSF. . . . *Oct 1989
Butcher, Mr Christopher N LLB(Soton); TEP Notary Public . . . *Jun 1973
Button, Ms Fran LLB; MCs(Construction Law & Arbitration) . . . *Nov 1996
Cobb, Mr Richard MA(Cantab) . . . May 1994
Cockayne, Mr Anthony John . . . *Sep 2002
Damerell, Miss Joanna M BA . . . *Nov 1987
Dickinson, Mr Malcolm K MA(Cantab). . . . *§Mar 1980
Duncan, Mrs Nikki LLB . . . Oct 1979
Elias, Mr Christopher Paul. . . . *Nov 1977
Follett, Mr Martin J MA(Cantab) Diocesan Registrar for the Dioceses of Exeter and Truro . . . *Jun 1977
Hedger, Mr Richard Michael BA(Hons); LSF; FPC Trustee of Kennaway House . . . *Oct 1995
Holyoak, Mr Ian D. . . . *Oct 1988
Honey, Mrs Emma BSc(Hons). . . . *Nov 1996
Honey, Mr Richard William BA(Hons); CPE; LSF . . *Nov 1992
Howe, Mr David L BA . . . *§Oct 1986
Lowless, Mr Peter J LLB . . . *§Apr 1976
McCormack, Ms Carol OBE. . . . *Dec 1985
McGhie, Mrs Bernadette Julia BA . . . *Oct 1998
Michelmore, Mr William F LLB Chairman of STEP West of England Branch. . . . *§Oct 1984
Miller, Mr Adrian W M MA(Oxon) . . . *Jan 1975
Morgan, Mr Gareth . . . *Dec 1990
Morse, Mr Stephen A LLB(Lond) . . . *Nov 1985
Nicholson, Mr Rob BA(Hons) . . . Aug 1998
Noormohamed, Mr Rehman BEng(Hons); LLB(Hons) Dean of Law Faculty Commendation Award . . . *Sep 2001
Offen, Mr Gerald . . . *Oct 1989
Pickering, Mr Sacha LLB . . . *Sep 2000
Porter, Ms Zoe LLB(Hons). . . . *Sep 2001
Priddis, Miss Vanessa BA(Hons)(Law). . . . *Oct 1985
Rice, Ms Sally BA(Hons); LLB. . . . *§Mar 1999
Richards, Mr Timothy C LLB(Hons) . . . *Nov 1987
Riley, Mr Jonathan LLB . . . *Sep 1996
Sigler, Mr Peter J BA(Hons)(Oxon) . . . *Jun 1975
Smith, Mrs Gillian LLB; LLM. . . . *§Jun 1980
Thomas, Mr Simon M BA . . . *Apr 1990
Tobey, Mr Andrew B LLB . . . Dec 1983
Vick, Mr Laurence Nigel BA; ACII; CIP; LLB(Hons) . . *Apr 1981
Whitfield, Mr Joseph BA(Hons) . . . *Nov 1987
Wolfgang, Mr Philip LLB. . . . Sep 2001
Asoc: Baker, Mr James . . . *Sep 2005
Bonning, Mr Michael . . . *Sep 1999
Carver, Ms Annelie BA(Hons)(Law) . . . *Sep 2001
Close, Mr Christopher John LLB Deputy Coroner for West Somerset . . . *Sep 1978
Cook, Mrs Rachel Elizabeth BSc(Econ); CPE; LPC Trustee of Womens Refuge . . . Sep 1997
Davies, Mr Timothy John BA(Hons); PGDipLaw. . . . Sep 2001
Eagle, Ms Karen BA(Hons) . . . *Jun 2003
Howard, Mr Mark . . . Mar 2002
Phelps, Mr Jason LLB; LLM. . . . *Sep 1997
Probert, Mrs Johanna. . . . *Dec 1998
Ryley, Mr Philip BA(Hons). . . . *Apr 1987
Smallwood, Mrs Lucy Jane LLB. . . . *May 1994
Thompson, Mr David Ian . . . *Sep 2003
Ast: Ager, Mr David G BA(Hons). . . . *§Jun 1977
Archer, Miss Chrysten LLB(Hons); LPC . . . Sep 2008
Bond, Mr Ian BA; TEP. . . . Sep 2003
Brearley, Mr Thomas H MA; CPE; LPC . . . *May 2003
Brechin, Miss Katherine BA(Hons); PGDipLP . . . Sep 2011
Bryers, Ms Sally-Anne . . . *Dec 1997
Carey, Mrs Sophie Anne LLB . . . *Sep 2001
Carpenter, Mr Crispin William . . . *Jan 2001
Chisholm-Batten, Mrs Sara MA(History); PGDipLaw; LPC . . . *Sep 2006
Cooper, Mrs Danica BA; MA(Oxon); LPC . . . Sep 2005
Cross, Miss Alexandra LLB . . . *Sep 2010
Culver, Miss Lex LLB . . . *Nov 2010
Cunningham, Miss Naomi BA(Hons)(History) . . . *Oct 2005
Davies, Mrs Charlotte. . . . Sep 2008
Feather, Mr Andrew LLB . . . *Sep 2011
Finneran, Mr Kevin A P LLB(Hons) . . . *Apr 1989
Follett-Carman, Mrs Lynne LLB; CeMAP Best English Legal Systems Student; Land Law Prize; Best Dissertation; Best Law Graduate. . . . Sep 2011
Hadwick, Ms Lucie . . . *Apr 2008
Hall, Ms Polly LLB. . . . Sep 2007
Hargreaves, Ms Sarah LLB(Hons)(with French) Leicestershire Law Society Prize. . . . *Jan 2001
Heywood, Miss Anna LLB; BA(Hons)(English). . . . Sep 2010
Howard-Smith, Ms Chloe CPE; LPC. . . . *Oct 2006
Howels, Mr Benjamin Michael. . . . *Oct 2002
Jones, Ms Bethan BA(Hons); LLB; LPC . . . Sep 2011
Lane, Mr Nathaniel LLB; MBA; DipLP . . . *Sep 2003
Maunder, Clare BA . . . Oct 1995
Maxwell, Mrs Angela . . . *Sep 2003
Meadows, Miss Chloe LLB; LPC . . . Sep 2011
Merchant, Ms Catherine BA(Hons)(Jurisprudence); CPC . . . *Sep 2002
Mesley, Miss Lucy LLB . . . Sep 2009
Nicholls, Mr Max LLB(Law & French) . . . *Sep 2002
Parfitt, Mrs Sarah LLB. . . . *Sep 2008
Rogers, Ms Penny LLB . . . *Nov 1995
Rushton, Ms Denise. . . . *Nov 1987
Shearmur, Miss Rachael A MA(Cantab). . . . *Nov 1989
Stenner-Evans, Mr Tom LLB . . . *Jul 2009
Taylor, Mr Henry LLB(Hons). . . . *Sep 2008
Thompson, Miss Anna . . . *Sep 2006
Tilley, Mr Robin LLB(Hons) . . . *Mar 1978
Tilley, Miss Rachel . . . *Jun 2006
Torkar, Mr Tom LLB. . . . Sep 2005
Tribble, Ms Louise LLB . . . *Dec 2007
Walker, Mrs Julie C BA(Oxon). . . . *Apr 1981
Warren, Miss Rachel LLB . . . Sep 2009
Webber-Brown, Caroline LLB . . . *Sep 2009
Williams, Ms Anita LLB(Hons); LPC Town Councillor & Chairman of Planning & Highways Committee - Lyme Regis Town Council. . . . Sep 2005
Williams, Mr Alex. . . . *Sep 2006
Wilson, Mrs Emma . . . Sep 2007
Con: Langdon, Mr Michael Charles MA(Oxon) . . . *Oct 1981
Lawson, Mr Stephen A Deputy Bankruptcy Registrar . *Oct 1969

MILN MACLEOD SOLICITORS ‡
14 Cathedral Close Exeter Devon EX1 1EZ
Tel: 01392 686920 *Fax:* 01392 686921 *Dx:* 8350 EXETER
E-mail: advice@mmlaw.co.uk

STEPHEN MORGAN & CO ‡
Argyle House New Buildings Lane Gandy Street Exeter Devon EX4 3LS
Tel: 01392 215121 *Fax:* 01392 433115 *Dx:* 136194 EXETER 18
E-mail: enquiries@stephenmorgan.co.uk
List of partners: T W Chetwood, S J Morgan
Work: B1 C1 E F1 J1 K1 K3 L N O Q S1 S2 W Z(l)
Agency, Advocacy and Fixed Fee Interview undertaken
Ptr: Chetwood, Mr Terence W LLB(Lond) . . . *Dec 1977
Morgan, Mr Stephen John BA. . . . *Jun 1975

MOTOR INDUSTRY LEGAL SERVICES
Canonteign House Lower Ashton Exeter Devon EX6 7RH
Tel: 020 7244 6790 *Fax:* 020 7244 7139
E-mail: legal@mils.co.uk
Office: London SW5

NUNN RICKARD SOLICITORS ADVOCATES ‡
24 Southernhay East Exeter Devon EX1 1QN
Tel: 01392 200888 *Fax:* 01392 204426
E-mail: advocates@nunnrickard.co.uk

JONATHAN OGLEY & ASSOCIATES - SPANISH PROPERTY LAWYERS ‡
14 Juniper Close Exeter Devon EX4 9JT
Tel: 01392 462282 *Fax:* 01392 464739
E-mail: jon@ogleylaw.com
List of partners: J H Ogley
Languages: Spanish
Work: S1
SPr: Ogley, Mr Jonathan H FILEx . . . . . *§Dec 1985

OVER TAYLOR BIGGS ‡
4 Cranmere Court Lustleigh Close Matford Business Park Exeter Devon EX2 8PW
Tel: 01392 823811 *Fax:* 01392 823812 *Dx:* 300350 EXETER 5
E-mail: law@otb.uk.com
List of partners: R A Biggs, C J Over, D I Smith
Languages: French
Work: B1 C1 C2 C3 E F1 M1 M2 N O P Q R1 S1 Z(c,e,f,h,j,l,r,t)
Emergency Action, Advocacy, Fixed Fee Interview, Legal Aid undertaken, Legal Aid Franchise and Member of Accident Line
Ptr: Biggs, Mr Richard A MA(Cantab) . . . . . *Nov 1978
Over, Mr Christopher J LLB(B'ham) . . . . . *§Oct 1977
Smith, Mr David Ian LLB . . . . . *Jul 1979
Asoc: Belina, Miss Suzanne . . . . . May 1996
Ast: Atkinson, Mr Paul D. . . . . . *Oct 1993
Carr, Ms Patricia Lesley LLB . . . . . *May 1979

PARLETT KENT
11-15 Dix's Field Exeter Devon EX1 1QA
Tel: 01392 494455 *Fax:* 01392 491199 *Dx:* 8328 EXETER
Emergency telephone 01392 494455
E-mail: enquiries@exeter.parlettkent.co.uk
Office: London EC1
Languages: British Sign Language, German, Gujarati, Sinhalese
Work: N X Z(q,r)
Legal Aid undertaken, Legal Aid Franchise and Member of Accident Line
Ptr: Hurrell, Ms Claire LLB(Hons) . . . . . May 2009
Nathwani, Miss Jayshree LLB(Hons) . . . . . *Jan 1999
Robins, Mrs Katja LLB; LPC Best 1st Year Law Student 2000; Best 2nd Year Law Student 2001 . . . . . *Oct 2004
Young, Ms Magi BSocSc . . . . . *Jun 1987

J & S P POPE ‡
1st Floor 22 Cathedral Yard Exeter Devon EX1 1HB
Tel: 01392 274006 *Fax:* 01392 420065
Emergency telephone 01363 866261
E-mail: admin@jandsppope.co.uk
List of partners: S M Meads, R M Phillips
Work: B1 D1 F1 G H K1 L N S1 T2 V W Z(l)
Emergency Action, Agency, Advocacy, Fixed Fee Interview and Legal Aid undertaken
Ptr: Meads, Mrs Susan M MA(Oxon) . . . . . *§Jan 1987
Phillips, Mr Richard M LLB(Bris). . . . . . *Jul 1987

QUINN & CO ‡
The Vicarage Dunsford Exeter Devon EX6 7AA
Tel: 07951 450282 / 01392 248858 *Fax:* 01647 253314
E-mail: mail@quinnlaw.co.uk

RUNDLEWALKER ‡
Kings Wharf The Quay Exeter Devon EX2 4AN
Tel: 01392 209209 *Fax:* 01392 209208 *Dx:* 8379 EXETER 1
Emergency telephone 07843 388953
E-mail: solutions@rundlewalker.com
List of partners: N D Dudman, R E Shaw
Work: A1 A3 B1 B2 C1 C2 D1 D2 E F1 F2 G H J1 J2 K1 K2 L N O Q R2 S1 S2 V W Z(e,g,i,j,k,l,n,p,q,s)
Emergency Action, Agency, Fixed Fee Interview, Legal Aid undertaken, Legal Aid Franchise and Member of Accident Line
Dir: Dudman, Mr Nicholas D LLB(Exon) . . . . . *May 1985
Shaw, Mr Robert Edward BSc. . . . . . *Dec 1987
Asoc: Jury, Miss Susan Nicola LLB(Hons) . . . . . *Feb 1990
Ast: Dymond, Mr Nick LLB. . . . . . *Oct 2004
Wallace, Ms Helen BA(Hons) . . . . . Jan 1996

SLEE BLACKWELL
31 Queen Street Exeter Devon EX4 3SR
Tel: 01392 423000 *Fax:* 01392 494773 *Dx:* 136189 EXETER 18
E-mail: exeter@sleeblackwell.co.uk
Office: Barnstaple, Bideford, Braunton, South Molton
Work: D1 E F1 G H J1 J2 K1 L N O Q R1 R2 S1 S2 V W X Z(p,q)
Agency, Fixed Fee Interview, Legal Aid undertaken, Legal Aid Franchise and Member of Accident Line
Ast: Kelly, Mr Thomas Matthew BA(Hons) . . . . . *Nov 1995
Robson, Mrs Samantha BSc(Hons); DipLaw. . . . . *Aug 1997

SOLICITORS TITLE ‡
Portland House Longbrook Street Exeter Devon EX4 6AB
Tel: 01392 207900 *Fax:* 01392 496101 *Dx:* 134058 EXETER 15
E-mail: info@solicitorstitle.co.uk
Work: E L S1 S2 W Z(b,j)

STEPHENS & SCOWN ‡
Curzon House Southern Hay West Exeter Devon EX1 1RS
Tel: 01392 210700 *Fax:* 01392 274010 *Dx:* 8305 EXETER
E-mail: solicitors@stephens-scown.co.uk
List of partners: E A Allen, T R Atkins, R G Baker, A P Bassett, M J S Beadel, R M Camp, D Corsellis, G P E Curry, M J Evans, P D Gregory, C M Harper, J M Hoggett, R P Jones, J A Keliher, I D Lamond, M P Lowry, P G Marshall, S Mitchell, N R Moore, G I Murdoch, A H L Nicholls, M J Northcott, P A H Payne, P H Reed, M Richardson, M Smith, P G Snell, J P Stone, M Stubbs, M C Wald, A R H Welford, W Wilkins, A Williamson, K Wright
Office: St Austell, Truro
Languages: French, German, Spanish
Work: A1 A3 B1 C1 C2 C3 D1 D2 E F1 J1 J2 K1 L M1 M2 N O P Q R1 R2 S1 S2 T1 T2 V W X Z(b,c,d,e,h,i,j,k,l,m,n,q,s,t)
Agency, Advocacy, Legal Aid undertaken and Legal Aid Franchise
Ptr: Allen, Mrs Elizabeth A LLB Sir George Fowler Prize. . *Oct 1986
Baker, Mr Richard G BA. . . . . . *Nov 1992
Camp, Mr Robert M MA. . . . . . *Nov 1986
Corsellis, Mr David LLB . . . . . *Sep 1990
Curry, Mr Guy P E LLM . . . . . *Oct 1975
Gregory, Mr Phillip D LLB(Hons). . . . . . *Jan 1993
Harper, Mr Christopher M MA(Oxon) . . . . . *Apr 1977
Hoggett, Mr Jonathan M BA(Dunelm) . . . . . *Dec 1978
Keliher, Mr James A LLB . . . . . *Mar 1983
Moore, Mr Nigel R LLB ♦ Harmsworth Scholarship Middle Temple . . . . . *Dec 1989
Northcott, Mr Michael J . . . . . *Nov 1984
Payne, Mr Peter A H LLB . . . . . *Apr 1976
Richardson, Mr Mark LLB . . . . . *Nov 1992
Smith, Mr Mark LLB(Hons) . . . . . *Sep 1997
Wald, Mr Matthew C ●. . . . . . *Apr 1991
Wilkins, Mr William LLB . . . . . *Nov 1992
Williamson, Mr Alan LLB(Exon) . . . . . *Jun 1971
Asoc: Barton, Mr Andrew . . . . . *Oct 2003
Mogridge, Mr Philip BA(Hons). . . . . . *Apr 2000
Ast: Coleman, Ms Clare . . . . . *Oct 2004
Dymond, Mr Nick LLB. . . . . . *Oct 2004
Gawler, Mr Simon. . . . . . *Sep 2003
Green, Ms Catherine LLB. . . . . . *Jan 2005
Hamilton, Ms Kate LLB . . . . . *Oct 2002
Kale, Miss Elaine LLB. . . . . . *Nov 1995
Con: Clayden, Mr Martin J R . . . . . *Nov 1970

STONES SOLICITORS LLP ‡
Linacre House Southernhay Gardens Exeter Devon EX1 1UG
Tel: 01392 666777 *Fax:* 01392 666770 *Dx:* 8306 EXETER
Emergency telephone 07973 290895 (CRIME)
E-mail: mail@stones-solicitors.co.uk
List of partners: J D Browne, B K Courtenay-Stamp, J C Dobie, N J Dyer, T Falcao, H M Honeyball, D I Howell-Richardson, P Keeling, A Lugger, L Onyett, S Pucci, C Rundle, G Simm, H Winterbotham
Office: Okehampton
Languages: French, German
Work: A1 A3 B1 B2 C1 C2 D1 D2 E F1 J1 J2 K1 K2 K3 K4 L N O P Q R1 R2 S1 S2 T1 W X Z(d,h,j,l,p,q,s,t,w)
Emergency Action, Agency, Fixed Fee Interview, Legal Aid undertaken, Legal Aid Franchise and Member of Accident Line
Ptr: Browne, Mr James D BA(Hons) . . . . . Dec 1980
Courtenay-Stamp, Mrs Bronwen K LLB . . . . . Oct 1987
Dobie, Mr John C . . . . . Apr 1979
Dyer, Mr Nicholas J MA(Cantab) . . . . . Jul 1972
Falcao, Mr Terry. . . . . . Sep 2002
Honeyball, Mrs Helen M LLB(B'ham) . . . . . Jun 1986
Howell-Richardson, Mr David I BSc(Wales) . . . . . Apr 1978
Keeling, Mr Paul LLB . . . . . Nov 1982
Onyett, Ms Lynn . . . . . Jul 2001
Pucci, Miss Samantha BA(Hons) . . . . . Feb 2001
Rundle, Mr Christopher BA . . . . . Nov 1988
Simm, Mr Graham LLB(Hons). . . . . . *Oct 1988
Winterbotham, Mr Hugh. . . . . . Dec 1978
Asoc: Boden, Ms Louise. . . . . . *Jul 2002
Lovett, Mr Andrew. . . . . . Oct 2000
Reavey, Charlotte. . . . . . Oct 2003
Ast: Agnew, Claire. . . . . . Dec 2002
Cann, Mr Scott . . . . . Oct 2002
Cook, Mr Frank . . . . . Sep 2005
Cox, Rebecca. . . . . . Nov 1996
Govier, Claire BA . . . . . Aug 2001
Ruttledge, Mr James LLB(Law) . . . . . *§Jul 1987
Seymour, Nadine . . . . . Jan 2007

SYMES ROBINSON & LEE
16 Southernhay West Exeter Devon EX1 1PJ
Tel: 01392 270867 *Fax:* 01392 411286 *Dx:* 8340 EXETER
E-mail: mail@srl-solicitors.co.uk
Office: Budleigh Salterton, Crediton
Work: A1 D1 E F1 G H J1 K1 K3 K4 L N O P Q S1 S2 T2 W Z(c,o,q,r)
Emergency Action, Advocacy, Fixed Fee Interview and Legal Aid Franchise
Ptr: Brindley, Mr John D LLB . . . . . *§Mar 1976
Ast: Gray, Mrs Emma MA(Hons)(History of Art) . . . . . *Sep 2005
Green, Ms Emily LLB(Hons). . . . . . *Jan 2005
Marshall, Mr B Charles F MA(Hons). . . . . . *May 1979
Merrison, Miss Ida LLB . . . . . Mar 2005
Oliver, Mr Craig Conrad LLB; MBA . . . . . *Oct 1993
Perry, Mr Mark LLB . . . . . *Oct 2003
Underhill, Mr Timothy Cavill LLB(Lond) . . . . . *Apr 1972

PAUL TAYLOR SOLICITORS ‡
PO Box 451 Exeter Devon EX4 2WX
Tel: 0870 850 8045 / 07810 836696 *Fax:* 0870 850 8046
E-mail: paul@taylorsolicitors.co.uk

MARK THOMPSON LAW ‡
1 Emperor Way Exeter Business Park Exeter Devon EX1 3QS
Tel: 01392 314086 *Fax:* 01392 314001
E-mail: mark@markthompsonlaw.com

TOZERS ‡
Broadwalk House Southernhay West Exeter Devon EX1 1UA
Tel: 01392 207020 *Fax:* 01392 207018 *Dx:* 8322 EXETER
E-mail: p.edwards@tozers.co.uk
List of partners: A C W Beard, G G N Bond, M M Brotherton, F V Clarke, A J Dodd, T P Dyde, P W Edwards, B H Hayes, J W Headford, P D Kelly, A R G King, T Lambert, C A Mills, S J Sanger-Anderson, J E W Shrimpton, R C Thorneycroft, P A Towey, I S Walker, A Wood
Office: Newton Abbot, Plymouth, Teignmouth
Languages: French, Twi
Work: A1 A3 B1 C1 C2 C3 D1 D2 E F1 F2 J1 J2 K1 K2 L M1 N O P Q R1 R2 S1 S2 T1 T2 V W X Z(a,b,c,e,h,k,l,m,n,o,p,q,r,s)
Emergency Action, Agency, Advocacy, Fixed Fee Interview, Legal Aid undertaken, Legal Aid Franchise and Member of Accident Line
Ptr: Beard, Mr Anthony C W BA . . . . . *§Dec 1977
Bond, Mr Graham G N LLB . . . . . *§Jun 1971
Brotherton, Mr Michael M LLB. . . . . . *§Apr 1975
Clarke, Mr F Vernon MA(Oxon) . . . . . *§Nov 1986
Dyde, Mr Timothy P LLB(Hons) . . . . . *Nov 1995
Edwards, Mr Peter W BA(Dunelm) . . . . . *Jun 1978
Hayes, Mr Barry H LLB; LLM . . . . . *Oct 1984
Headford, Mrs Jill Wendy LLB. . . . . . *Nov 1990
Kelly, Mr Paul D BA(Dunelm) . . . . . *Jun 1992
Mills, Mr C Anthony LLB. . . . . . Apr 1977
Sanger-Anderson, Mr Simon J . . . . . *Jan 1981
Thorneycroft, Mr Richard C LLB. . . . . . *§May 1980
Walker, Mr Ian Stuart LLB. . . . . . *Sep 1992
Asoc: Arthur, Miss Endurance E BSc; CPE; LSF. . . . . *Apr 1995
Bramley, Mr Stuart William LLB(Hons). . . . . . *§Nov 1992
Dyde, Mrs Gillian Alexandra BA(Hons) . . . . . Nov 1995
Hemming, Miss Clair Anne LLB . . . . . Aug 2001
McLennan, Miss Kirsty LLB . . . . . May 1999
Ast: Apps, Miss Kirstie M LLB(Hons). . . . . . Sep 2004
Barkley, Mr Paul A M LLB(Hons)(Lond); MSc . . . . . *Oct 1986
Benyon-Tinker, Miss Emma L LLB(Hons); LPC . . . *Nov 2001
Cooper, Mr Peter LLB(Hons) . . . . . *Mar 2005
Jennings, Mr Stephen C. . . . . . Sep 2001
Kempson, Mr Dominic Michael Benignus . . . . . *Dec 1978
Powell, Miss Nicola BA(Hons)(Law & Criminology) . . Apr 2004

TRINITY ADVOCATES ‡
18a South Street Exeter Devon EX1 1DZ
Tel: 01392 927111 *Fax:* 01392 477783
E-mail: defence@trinityadvocates.co.uk

TROWERS & HAMLINS
The Senate Southernhay Gardens Exeter Devon EX1 1UG
Tel: 01392 217466 *Fax:* 01392 221047
E-mail: enquiries@trowers.com
Office: London EC3, Manchester
Work: B1 C1 E F1 J1 K1 L Q S1 T1 W Z(c,h)
Agency, Advocacy and Fixed Fee Interview undertaken
Ptr: Acton, Mr H Joseph. . . . . . *Nov 1991
Keuls, Mr Peter H. . . . . . *Jun 1977
Ast: Hewitt, Mrs Linda J BA . . . . . *Apr 1981

TRUELEGAL SOLICITORS ‡
76 Fore Street Topsham Exeter Devon EX3 0HQ
Tel: 01392 879414 *Fax:* 01392 879429
E-mail: advice@truelegal.co.uk
List of partners: M Truman
Work: C1 C2 E I J1 S2 U2 Z(c,e,za)
Fixed Fee Interview undertaken
Ptr: Truman, Mr Martin . . . . . Nov 1996

VEITCH PENNY ‡
1 Manor Court Dix's Field Exeter Devon EX1 1UP
Tel: 01392 278381 *Fax:* 01392 410247 *Dx:* 8309 EXETER 1
Emergency telephone 01392 412048
E-mail: law@veitchpenny.co.uk
Office: Crediton
Languages: French
Work: C1 C2 C3 E F1 F2 J1 J2 L N O P Q R1 R2 S1 S2 T1 T2 W X Z(c,d,e,g,j,l,p,q,u,w)

WBW SOLICITORS
County Chambers 75 Queen Street Exeter Devon EX4 3RX
Tel: 01392 202404 *Fax:* 01392 666555
E-mail: lawyer@wbw.co.uk
Office: Bovey Tracey, Newton Abbot, Torquay
Work: A1 A3 B1 B2 C1 C2 D1 D2 E F1 G H J1 K1 K2 L N O Q R1 S1 S2 T1 T2 V W Z(g,h,l,m,r)
Emergency Action, Agency, Advocacy, Fixed Fee Interview, Legal Aid undertaken, Legal Aid Franchise and Member of Accident Line
Ptr: Coram, Mr Robert S LLB . . . . . *§Apr 1973
Goddard, Mr Francis LLB . . . . . *Nov 1993
Martin, Mr Michael G LLB(Lond). . . . . . *§Oct 1976
Ogle, Miss Deborah Jane BA . . . . . *Oct 1989
White, Mr Martin BA(Hons) . . . . . *Oct 1993
Witheridge, Miss Sarah Mary LLB. . . . . . *Sep 1996
Ast: Dandy, Mr Robert Iain LLB(Hons) . . . . . *Mar 1993
Green, Miss Eleanor . . . . . May 2002
Hamblin, Mr James . . . . . Aug 2003
Hamzij, Miss Debbie . . . . . Sep 2003
Maxwell, Mrs Angela . . . . . *Sep 2003
Screech, Miss Jennifer BA(Hons) . . . . . *Jul 2001
Woodgates, Mrs Julia Ann . . . . . *Nov 1978
Con: Silverthorne, Miss Valerie Ann BA. . . . . . *§Jul 1973

EXMOUTH, Devon

EVERYS
Magnolia House Church Street Exmouth Devon EX8 1HQ
Tel: 01395 264384 *Fax:* 01395 267643 *Dx:* 48851 EXMOUTH
Emergency telephone 07900 151737
E-mail: law@everys.co.uk
Office: Budleigh Salterton, Exeter, Honiton (2 offices), Ottery St Mary, Seaton, Sidmouth, Taunton
Work: A1 A2 B1 B2 C1 C2 C3 D1 D2 E F1 F2 G H J1 J2 K1 L M1 N O P Q R1 R2 S1 S2 T1 T2 V W X Z(c,d,e,h,i,k,l,m,n,o,p,q,r,s,t,u,w,x,y)
Emergency Action, Agency, Advocacy, Fixed Fee Interview, Legal Aid undertaken and Legal Aid Franchise
Ptr: Cherryson, Miss Gay Maria BA(Hons)(Oxon) . . . . . *Oct 1995
Dixon, Mr Clive St J. . . . . . *§Dec 1969
Hawkins, Mr John T. . . . . . *§Dec 1970
Izzett, Mr Mark D N LLB. . . . . . *§Dec 1976
Pearson, Mr Andrew M LLB. . . . . . *§Jun 1972
Stradling, Miss Kimberley Joan LLB(Hons) . . . . . *§Dec 1992
Asoc: Durham Hall, Mrs Patricia Helene . . . . . *Mar 2001
Ast: Dixon, Mr Hugh B. . . . . . *§May 1978
Harding, Mr Simon LLB(Hons). . . . . . *§Sep 1999
Preston, Mr Mark . . . . . *§Nov 2004
Salway, Miss Gail Elizabeth . . . . . *Oct 1997
Con: Dawe, Mr Roger J. . . . . . *§Jan 1965

FORD SIMEY LLP
17 High Street Exmouth Devon EX8 1NR
Tel: 01395 272241 / 0800 169 3741 *Fax:* 01395 263112
Dx: 48853 EXMOUTH
Emergency telephone 01392 275036
E-mail: info@fordsimey.co.uk
Office: Exeter, Honiton, Sidmouth
Languages: French
Work: A1 C1 D1 D2 E F1 F2 G H J1 K1 L N O Q S1 S2 T2 V W Z(d,h,j,k,l,q,r)
Emergency Action, Agency, Advocacy, Fixed Fee Interview, Legal Aid undertaken, Legal Aid Franchise and Member of Accident Line
Ptr: Boyle, Mr David P LLB Archbold Exeter University. . *§Oct 1984
Hill, Ms Alison Nicolene R. . . . . . *§Nov 1993
McIntosh, Mr James Robert ★. . . . . . Dec 1990
Medland, Mr Felix G LLB . . . . . *Apr 1982
Ast: Holdich, Mrs Vivien Helen. . . . . . Jan 1980
Scott, Miss Lesley LLB . . . . . *Dec 1990
Wright, Miss Lucinda Jane . . . . . Oct 1999

F ARTHUR JONES & CO ‡
35 The Strand Exmouth Devon EX8 1AQ
Tel: 01395 265668 *Fax:* 01395 272318 *Dx:* 48862 EXMOUTH
E-mail: wade@ajoneslaw.co.uk
List of partners: A L Wade

See p112 for the Key to Work Categories & other symbols

Work: E S1 S2 W Z(l)
Ptr: Wade, Mr Anthony L . . . . *§Dec 1964

BARBARA MITCHELS SOLICITOR ‡
11 Oakleigh Road Exmouth Devon EX8 2LN
Tel: 0870 405 1957 *Fax:* 0870 405 1957
E-mail: barbara@mitchels.co.uk
Work: D1 K2 K4 W Z(m)
Agency and Advocacy undertaken

VINE ORCHARDS ‡
(incorporating Orchard & Co; Vine Edwards & Co)
Trinity Chambers 49 Rolle Street Exmouth Devon EX8 2RS
Tel: 01395 273035 / 264646 *Fax:* 01395 264650
Dx: 48852 EXMOUTH
Emergency telephone 01392 873084
E-mail: law@vineorchards.co.uk
List of partners: J A Orchard, R E Spencer, S A Stamm, A Williams
Work: A1 C1 D1 E F1 G H J1 K1 L N O Q R1 S1 T1 T2 V W Z(c,d,k,l,m)
Emergency Action, Agency, Advocacy, Fixed Fee Interview and Legal Aid undertaken
Ptr: Orchard, Mr John A Notary Public. . . . . *§Nov 1966
Spencer, Mr Roger E . . . . *Jul 1972
Stamm, Mrs Sigrid A LLB . . . . *Oct 1974
Williams, Mr Anthony LLB. . . . . *§Jan 1974

EYE, Suffolk

ANDERSONS ‡
9a Cross Street Eye Suffolk IP23 7AB
Tel: 01379 873510 *Fax:* 01379 873511 *Dx:* 425150 DISS

EYNSHAM, Oxfordshire

BEECHWOOD SOLICITORS ‡
1 Aelfric Court 2 Oxford Road Eynsham Oxfordshire OX29 4HG
Tel: 01865 883344 *Fax:* 01865 389585 *Dx:* 48406 EYNSHAM
E-mail: info@beechwoodsolicitors.com

FLANAGANS SOLICITORS ‡
2 Swinford Farm Eynsham Oxfordshire OX29 4BL
Tel: 01865 430040 *Fax:* 01865 430046 *Dx:* 48405 ENYSHAM
E-mail: info@flanaganssolicitors.com
Work: N
Emergency Action, Fixed Fee Interview undertaken and Member of Accident Line
Ast: Barnett, Mrs Amy LLB. . . . . Mar 2005

PELLMANS ‡
1 Abbey Street Eynsham Oxfordshire OX29 4TB
Tel: 01865 884400 *Fax:* 01865 884411 *Dx:* 48402 EYNSHAM
E-mail: mail@pellmans.co.uk
List of partners: G M Clark, A J G Pellman, I D Pellman, J Pellman
Languages: French, Spanish
Work: A1 A2 C1 E J1 K1 K3 K4 O Q S1 S2 T1 T2 W
Ptr: Clark, Mr Gavin McKinnon LLB . . . . *Dec 1998
Pellman, Mr Adrian John Gerald LLB(Lond) . . . . . *§Jun 1956
Pellman, Mr Ian Donald LLB(Hons)(Bucks) . . . . . *May 2011
Pellman, Ms Joanna LLB(Reading) . . . . *Nov 1997
Asoc: Burrows, Ms Rachel Jane MA(Oxon) . . . . *Sep 1986
Peto, Mrs Verity Robertson MA(Oxon). . . . . *Sep 1975

FAILSWORTH, Greater Manchester

APPLEBYS WILLS & PROBATE SOLICITORS ‡
318 Oldham Road Failsworth Greater Manchester M35 0EN
Tel: 0161 669 4365 / 07900 246677
E-mail: enquiries@applebysolicitors.co.uk

H L F BERRY & CO
(in association with M C Darlington)
758 Oldham Road Failsworth Greater Manchester M35 9XB
Tel: 0161 681 4005 *Fax:* 0161 681 4005
E-mail: info@hlfberrysolicitors.co.uk
Office: Manchester
Work: E F1 K1 N P S1 S2 W Z(l)
Emergency Action, Agency, Advocacy, Fixed Fee Interview undertaken and Member of Accident Line
Ptr: Citron, Mr Paul LLB . . . . *Nov 1982
Ast: Woodward, Ms Eleanor Margaret BA . . . . *Oct 2002
Con: Darlington, Mr Michael Clifford LLB Diocesan Registrar Notary Public. . . . . *Oct 1968
Park, Mr J Graham CBE LLB Parole Board Appraiser; Criminal Injuries Compensation Appeal Panel Member. . . *Jan 1968

FENTONS ‡
485 Oldham Road Failsworth Greater Manchester M35 9FS
Tel: 0161 682 7101 *Fax:* 0161 684 6500 *Dx:* 703120 FAILSWORTH
E-mail: enq@fentons.co.uk
List of partners: M D Evans, R E Gibson, M E Loftus, K J Maguire, M S Thomson, K Tonks
Office: Manchester
Languages: Chinese, Dutch, French, German, Spanish, Urdu
Work: J1 L N W
Emergency Action, Agency, Advocacy, Fixed Fee Interview, Legal Aid undertaken, Legal Aid Franchise and Member of Accident Line
Ptr: Evans, Mr Matthew David LLB . . . . Feb 1998
Gibson, Ms Rosemary Evelyn LLB; DipLP. . . . . . *Aug 1996
Loftus, Mr Martin Edward LLB; LSF . . . . *Dec 1995
Maguire, Mr Kieran J . . . . *Jan 1991
Thomson, Mr Mark S LLB. . . . . Jan 1990
Tonks, Mr Karl LLB(Hons). . . . . *Oct 1990
Ast: Bradley, Mr Damian P LLB . . . . Nov 1999
Cheetham, Ms Nicola Jayne. . . . . Mar 2003
Dobbs, Miss Angela June BA(Hons). . . . . Sep 2001
Hill, Miss Caroline LLB . . . . Jan 2000
Kavanagh, Miss Karen Patricia . . . . Dec 2001
Macdonald, Mr Alistair Innes . . . . Jan 2003
Roberts, Miss Phillipa Jane BA . . . . Jun 2001
Sparrow, Mr Matthew Timothy. . . . . Feb 2003
Taylor, Mr Andrew David BA(Hons) . . . . Sep 2001
Whitehouse, Miss Suzanne L LLB. . . . . Aug 2000

HEATH SONS & BROOME
461 Oldham Road Failsworth Greater Manchester M35 0AA
Tel: 0161 682 8535 *Fax:* 0161 682 6337 *Dx:* 703122 FAILSWORTH
Emergency telephone 0161 764 1403 / 682 0575
E-mail: hbroome@btclick.com
Office: Manchester
Work: D1 F1 G H K1 N S1 S2 W Z(i)
Emergency Action, Agency, Advocacy, Fixed Fee Interview, Legal Aid undertaken and Legal Aid Franchise
Ptr: Hayes, Mr Martin J LLB. . . . . *Oct 1974

HAROLD STOCK & CO
(incorporating Stock Beever & Stratton; Stratton & Co; Lees & Co)
56-58 Pole Lane Failsworth Greater Manchester M35 9PB
Tel: 0161 682 2400 *Fax:* 0161 688 5491
E-mail: dmc@haroldstock.com
Office: Ashton-under-Lyne (2 offices)
Work: B1 C1 C2 D1 D2 E J1 J2 K1 K3 K4 L N O Q R1 R2 S1 S2 T1 T2 W Z(c,e,i,l,p,q)
Emergency Action, Agency, Advocacy and Fixed Fee Interview undertaken
Ptr: McGuinness, Mr Darren. . . . . *Mar 1998

FAIRFORD, Gloucestershire

PETER J EWART & CO SOLICITORS ‡
East End House East End Fairford Gloucestershire GL7 4AP
Tel: 01285 713715 *Fax:* 01285 713505
E-mail: peter@ewart.uk.com

FAKENHAM, Norfolk

BUTCHER ANDREWS ‡
1 Old Post Office Street Fakenham Norfolk NR21 9BL
Tel: 01328 863131 *Fax:* 01328 864705 *Dx:* 31351 FAKENHAM
E-mail: webmaster@butcherandrews.co.uk
List of partners: A S Kirby, D C Linthwaite, C C Mordaunt, A Payne, A J M Taylor
Office: Holt
Languages: French
Work: A1 A2 B1 C1 C3 D1 E F1 J1 J2 K1 K3 K4 L M1 M2 N O P Q R1 S1 S2 T1 T2 V W Z(d,h,k,l,m,q,r,w)
Emergency Action, Agency, Advocacy, Fixed Fee Interview undertaken and Member of Accident Line
Ptr: Kirby, Mrs Anne Seymour LLB(Hons) . . . . *§May 1977
Linthwaite, Mr Darren C LLB . . . . *§Apr 1996
Mordaunt, Mr Christopher Charles BA. . . . . *Dec 2002
Payne, Adney MA(Cantab) . . . . *§Jul 1980
Taylor, Mr Andrew James McCowat BA; MA. . . . . . Nov 1994
Ast: Duff, Mrs Fiona Sara LLB . . . . *§Jul 2001
Hammond-Chambers-Borgnis, Mrs Jennifer Anne LLB *Sep 2002
Underwood, Mr Simon John LLB . . . . *Sep 2009
Con: Thomson, Miss Barbara. . . . . *Dec 1972

HAYES & STORR ‡
18-19 Market Place Fakenham Norfolk NR21 9BH
Tel: 01328 863231 *Fax:* 01328 855455 *Dx:* 31350 FAKENHAM
E-mail: law@hayes-storr.com
List of partners: C R H Abel, A H Craig, N Grearson, A Hallworth, F M Hewitt, R P Hewitt, I C MacBrayne, M L Marshall, J K Morgan, E M Ni Charthaig, J F T Pallister, C J Simpson, G J Simpson, M E Taylor
Office: Holt, King's Lynn, Sheringham, Wells-next-the-Sea
Work: A1 A3 B1 C1 C2 C3 D1 E F1 F2 I J1 J2 K1 K3 K4 L M1 M2 N O P Q R1 S1 S2 T1 T2 U2 V W Z(c,d,e,f,k,l,p,q,s,t,za)
Emergency Action, Agency, Advocacy, Fixed Fee Interview, Legal Aid undertaken and Legal Aid Franchise
Ptr: Grearson, Mr Neale LLB(Hons) . . . . Oct 1986
Hallworth, Mrs Anissa LLB . . . . Sep 2004
Hewitt, Mrs Fiona Macdonald MA(Cantab). . . . . . *Nov 1992
MacBrayne, Mr Iain Campbell LLB(Hull). . . . . . . *§May 1971
Simpson, Mr Christopher John LLB; TEP . . . . . . *§Dec 1972
Simpson, Mr Gordon James LLB . . . . Mar 1997
Ast: Findlay, Mr Alex LLB(Hons) . . . . Jul 1999
Game, Mr Mathew BA; LLB. . . . . Apr 2011
Smith, Margaret Anne BA . . . . Apr 1977

FALMOUTH, Cornwall

MALCOLM ASHTON ‡
8b North Parade Falmouth Cornwall TR11 2TD
Tel: 01326 313100 *Fax:* 01326 212773
E-mail: maa@maalaw.com
List of partners: M A Ashton
Work: E L S1 S2 W Z(d)
Agency and Fixed Fee Interview undertaken
SPr: Ashton, Mr Malcolm A MA(Cantab) . . . . *Dec 1975

BRAY & DILKS
71 Killigrew Street Falmouth Cornwall TR11 3PR
Tel: 01326 212021 *Fax:* 01326 212031 *Dx:* 81153 FALMOUTH
E-mail: office@braydilks.co.uk
Office: Truro
Work: A1 C1 D1 E F1 G H J1 K1 K3 L N O Q R1 S1 S2 W Z(l,m,q)
Agency, Advocacy and Fixed Fee Interview undertaken
Con: Dilks, Mrs Angela Mary LLB. . . . . Dec 1974

DB LAW
5 The Moor PO Box 23 Falmouth Cornwall TR11 3UF
Tel: 01326 211609 *Fax:* 01326 211609 *Dx:* 81151 FALMOUTH
Emergency telephone 07693 424607
Office: Camborne, Penzance, St Ives
Work: B1 C1 D1 D2 E F1 G H J1 K1 L N O Q S1 V W Z(a,c,l)
Emergency Action, Agency, Advocacy, Fixed Fee Interview, Legal Aid undertaken and Member of Accident Line

M J R GRIFFITHS ‡
Pennance Farmhouse Swanpool Falmouth Cornwall TR11 5BH
Tel: 07768 644006 / 01326 218711
E-mail: m@mjrgriffiths.co.uk

HINE DOWNING SOLICITORS ‡
8-14 Berkeley Vale Falmouth Cornwall TR11 3PA
Tel: 01326 316655 *Fax:* 01326 313448 *Dx:* 81150 FALMOUTH
E-mail: general@hinedowning.com
List of partners: A R Deacon, J W Lowry, E M J Richards, W R Richards, J C Rutherford, R B Stephens, P B Stonehouse, A K Upfold, M J Wilson
Work: A1 A3 C1 C2 D1 E F1 J1 K1 K2 K3 K4 L N Q S1 S2 T2 W Z(a,l)
Emergency Action, Agency, Fixed Fee Interview, Legal Aid undertaken and Legal Aid Franchise
Ptr: Deacon, Mr Anthony R LLB . . . . *Feb 1989
Lowry, Mr John W LLB . . . . *Feb 1990
Richards, Mr Edward Michael John LLB; Diploma in Notarial Practice; DASL Mediator Notary Public . . . . . . *Dec 1993
Richards, Mr William Raile LLB(Hons). . . . . *Jan 1999
Stephens, Mr Roger B LLB(Bris) . . . . *Apr 1979
Stonehouse, Mr Peter B LLB(Hons); LPC . . . . . . *Sep 1997
Upfold, Mrs Anne K. . . . . *Nov 1997
Wilson, Mr Michael John . . . . *Jun 1976
Mem: Rutherford, Mr John Campbell LLB(Hons). . . . . . *Dec 1994
Asoc: Standen, Mrs Diana. . . . . *Nov 1994
Con: Barrington, Mr Nicholas J F C. . . . . *Nov 1962
Dilks, Mr Brian M BSc. . . . . *Jun 1978
Peters, Mr David E MA(Oxon). . . . . *Jun 1977
Stonehouse, Mr David M . . . . *Nov 1962

NALDERS QUALITY SOLICITORS
49 Arwenack Street Falmouth Cornwall TR11 3LB
Tel: 01326 313441 *Fax:* 01326 315971 *Dx:* 81154 FALMOUTH
E-mail: post@nalders.co.uk
Office: Camborne, Helston, Newquay, Penzance, St Austell, Truro (2 offices)
Work: A1 B1 C1 C2 D1 D2 E F1 F2 J1 J2 K1 K2 L M1 N Q R1 S1 S2 T1 V W Z(c,g,h,i,k,o,s,u)

PRESTON GOLDBURN ‡
Pendennis Court Falmouth Business Park Bickland Water Road Falmouth Cornwall TR11 4SZ
Tel: 01326 318900 *Fax:* 01326 219375 / 311275
Dx: 81169 FALMOUTH
E-mail: legal@prestongoldburn.com
List of partners: T J Goldburn, H S Preston
Languages: French, Portuguese
Work: A1 C1 D1 E J1 K1 K2 K3 K4 L N O Q R1 S1 S2 W Z(l,q,r)
Emergency Action, Agency, Advocacy, Fixed Fee Interview, Legal Aid undertaken, Legal Aid Franchise and Member of Accident Line
Ptr: Goldburn, Mr Timothy J LLB(Soton). . . . . *Jun 1977
Preston, Mr Henry S BA(Law). . . . . *Jun 1977
Asoc: Edwards, Mr Jeremy Charles LLB(Hons) . . . . . . *Jul 1990
Ast: Grigg, Mrs Kelly Marie LLB . . . . *Aug 2010

FAREHAM, Hampshire

BRUTTON & CO ‡
West End House 288 West Street Fareham Hampshire PO16 0AJ
Tel: 01329 236171 *Fax:* 01329 289915 *Dx:* 40809 FAREHAM
E-mail: enquiries@brutton.co.uk
List of partners: B R Gulliver, A Robinson, D P Snatt, H A G Tyler
Languages: Dutch, Polish
Work: B1 C1 C2 D1 D2 E F1 F2 J1 J2 K1 K3 L N O Q R1 R2 S1 S2 T1 T2 V W X Z(a,c,d,g,h,j,k,o,p,q,x)
Agency, Advocacy, Fixed Fee Interview, Legal Aid undertaken and Legal Aid Franchise
Ptr: Gulliver, Mr Brian R LLB. . . . . *Dec 1979
Robinson, Mr Andrew . . . . *Nov 1983
Snatt, Mr Derek P LLB(Bris). . . . . *Apr 1974
Tyler, Miss Hilary A G LLB(Bris) Diocesan Registrar for the Diocese of Portsmouth . . . . *Jun 1978
Ast: Douglass, Mrs Anna Agnieszka LLB(Hons) Sweet & Maxwell Law Prize 2001 . . . . Jan 2005
Hill, Mrs Marianne BA(Hons) . . . . *Oct 1995

THE CHILDRENS LEGAL PRACTICE LTD ‡
Unit E4 Eefore House Fareham Heights Fareham Hampshire PO16 8XT
Tel: 01329 823322 *Fax:* 01329 822234
E-mail: info@childrenslegalpractice.com

CHURCHERS ‡
12 High Street Fareham Hampshire PO16 7BL
Tel: 01329 822333 *Fax:* 01329 822267 *Dx:* 40807 FAREHAM
E-mail: solicitors@churchers.co.uk
List of partners: M P W Bailey, A Bryan, W S Donnelly, N Eve, R C Foster, J D Guest, M Hazlewood, A C Joll, C P Mackey, B O'Hagan, R I Robinson, I A Sandilands
Office: Gosport, Lee-on-the-Solent, Portsmouth (2 offices), Ryde
Work: B1 C1 C2 C3 D1 E F1 G H J1 K1 K2 K3 L N O P Q S1 S2 V W Z(i,j,k,l)
Emergency Action, Agency, Advocacy, Fixed Fee Interview, Legal Aid undertaken, Legal Aid Franchise and Member of Accident Line
Ptr: Bailey, Mr Matthew P W LLB . . . . *Mar 1987
Eve, Mr Nick LLB . . . . Jan 1998
Foster, Mr Robert C LLB(Bris). . . . . *§Jul 1972
Guest, Mr John D. *Apr 1972
Hazlewood, Miss Mary BSc . . . . Oct 1984
Joll, Mrs Alison C LLB(Hons) . . . . *Nov 1991
Asoc: Pope, Miss Emma Rosemary LLB. . . . . *May 1999
Ast: Bennett, Mr Tim LLB . . . . Aug 2007
Matthews, Mr Christopher LLB . . . . Aug 2007

COFFIN MEW & CLOVER ‡
Fareham Point Wickham Road Fareham Hampshire PO16 7AU
Tel: 01329 825617 *Fax:* 01329 825619 *Dx:* 40831 FAREHAM
E-mail: fareham@coffinmew.co.uk
List of partners: J Bennett, J Bridges, A J Brockwell, D Cook, P Fellows, N M Gross, R D Hancock, J Hansford, G D Johns, P E Johnson, C R F Kenny, W A Meads, D M Neil, M E Padgett, W J R Pinniger, K J Steele, C M Upfield, R G Wassall, P J Yetman
Office: Gosport, Portsmouth, Southampton
Work: B1 C1 C2 C3 D1 D2 E F1 F2 G H J1 J2 K1 K2 L M1 M2 N O P Q R1 R2 S1 S2 T1 T2 V W X Z(c,d,h,i,j,k,l,o,p,q,r,s)
Agency, Advocacy, Fixed Fee Interview, Legal Aid undertaken, Legal Aid Franchise and Member of Accident Line
Ptr: Bennett, Miss Jennifer LLB(Lond) . . . . *§Apr 1979
Bridges, Mr Jonathan BA(Dunelm) . . . . *Mar 1979
Cook, Mr David BSc . . . . *Jul 1989
Fellows, Mr Peter MA(Hons)(Cantab) . . . . *Oct 1989
Hancock, Mr Roger D TD MA(Cantab) . . . . *§Apr 1978
Padgett, Mr Malcolm E MA(Oxon). . . . . *Jun 1977
Pinniger, Mr W James R LLB(Leeds) . . . . *Dec 1979
Steele, Mr Kevin J LLB . . . . *Feb 1989
Upfield, Mr Christopher M BA(Law) . . . . *§Apr 1984
Wassall, Mr Robert G LLB. . . . . *Jun 1981
Asoc: Bowler, Miss Susan Janet LLB(Hons) . . . . *Oct 1995
Busst, Ms Caroline Lisa. . . . . *Oct 1990

2

Ikin, Miss Hilary A BSc(Econ) . . . . *Oct 1983
Johnson, Ms Tracy J LLB(Hons) . . . . *Apr 1990
Klopenstein, Ms Tamara Lea BBA; JD; RN(Florida) . . Sep 1995
Murray, Miss Sarah BSc(Hons) . . . . Jun 1993
Ast: Deighton, Miss Sarah LLB . . . . *Mar 2000
Pickburn, Mrs Gillian L F BA(Hons) . . . . *Dec 1977
Webb, Mrs Karen Louise . . . . Oct 1997
Winter, Mrs Rhiannon Esher LLB(Hons) . . . . Sep 2000
Wong, Miss Oi-Yuyn . . . . Aug 2000
Con: Chapman, Mr Giles H L LLB(Lond) . . . . *Dec 1975

GB SOLICITORS LTD ‡
Eefore House Fareham Heights Fareham Hampshire PO16 8XT
Tel: 01329 282817 *Fax:* 01329 282818
E-mail: enquiries@gbsolicitors.co.uk
Work: S1 W

GLANVILLES ‡
(incorporating Buckell & Drew; Damant & Sons)
West Wing Cams Hall Camshill Fareham Hampshire PO16 8AB
Tel: 01329 282841 *Fax:* 01329 822052 *Dx:* 40819 FAREHAM
E-mail: fareham@glanvilles.co.uk
List of partners: P R Bateman, S Craven, G J R Lambie, P K Latham, S E Ledger, J G Melrose, C K Samuelson, C G Small
Office: Havant, Newport
Work: C1 D1 E G H K1 L M1 P R1 S1
Emergency Action, Agency, Advocacy, Fixed Fee Interview, Legal Aid undertaken and Member of Accident Line
Ptr: Craven, Ms Susan BA . . . . *Dec 1982
Latham, Mr Peter K LLB(Bris) . . . . *Mar 1970

GREENWOODS
3600 Parkway The Solent Centre Solent Business Park Fareham Hampshire PO15 7AN
Tel: 01489 882900 *Fax:* 01489 882959
E-mail: contact@greenwoods-solicitors.com
Office: Bristol, London EC3, London WC1, Manchester, Milton Keynes

HAYWARD BAKER ‡
18 High Street Fareham Hampshire PO16 7AF
Tel: 0800 107 7321 *Fax:* 0870 112 9646
E-mail: info@hayward-baker.com

KNIGHT POLSON
25 Barnes Wallis Road Segensworth East Fareham Hampshire PO15 5TT
Tel: 01329 339455
E-mail: enquiries@knightpolson.co.uk
Office: Eastleigh, Winchester

LAWCOMM SOLICITORS ‡
Unit 2 Victory Park Solent Way Fareham Hampshire PO15 7FN
Tel: 01489 864100 *Fax:* 01489 864101 *Dx:* 45251 PARK GATE
E-mail: advice@lawcomm.co.uk
List of partners: M Dhariwal
Work: B1 C1 E F1 J1 L N O P Q S1 W Z(l)
Emergency Action, Agency, Advocacy, Fixed Fee Interview and Legal Aid undertaken
Ptr: Dhariwal, Mr Mandeep . . . . Oct 1996
Con: Woolgar, Mr Neil D LLB(Hull) . . . . *May 1982

M V LLOYD ‡
164 West Street Fareham Hampshire PO16 0EJ
Tel: 023 9228 0944 *Fax:* 023 9228 4053
List of partners: M V Lloyd
Office: Portsmouth
Work: E L S1 S2 T2 W Z(l)
Agency undertaken
SPr: Lloyd, Mr Michael V TD MA(Cantab) Commissioner for Oaths . . . . *Oct 1955

ROBERT LOCKE ‡
4 St Christopher Avenue Fareham Hampshire PO16 7BY
Tel: 01329 822722 *Fax:* 01329 282766 *Dx:* 40823 FAREHAM
E-mail: info@robertlocke.co.uk
List of partners: R A Locke
Languages: French, Spanish
Work: F1 G Q S1 Z(t)
Agency, Advocacy and Fixed Fee Interview undertaken
SPr: Locke, Mr Robert A BA(Hons) . . . . *Jan 1985

MEDIATION NOW LTD
Cams Hall Cams Hill Fareham Hampshire PO16 8AB
Tel: 01329 232114
Office: Emsworth, Petersfield (2 offices), Portsmouth

MUGFORD & CO ‡
Abbey House Mill Lane Titchford Fareham Hampshire PO15 5RB
Tel: 01329 844555 *Fax:* 01329 849455
E-mail: richardmugford@mugford.co.uk
List of partners: R J Mugford
Work: C1 E F1 L O Q S1 S2 W Z(j)
Emergency Action, Agency and Advocacy undertaken
SPr: Mugford, Mr Richard James LLB(Hons) . . . . *Oct 1991

NOW LEGAL ‡
4 Brunel Way Segensworth Fareham Hampshire PO15 5TX
Tel: 0845 678 0150 *Fax:* 0845 678 0152 *Dx:* 45262 PARK GATE
E-mail: enquiries@now-legal.com

SHOOSMITHS
Russell House 1550 Parkway Solent Business Park Fareham Hampshire PO15 7AG
Tel: 0370 086 6800 / 01489 616800 *Fax:* 0370 086 6801
Dx: 124693 WHITELEY
E-mail: solent@shoosmiths.co.uk
Office: Basingstoke, Birmingham, London WC2, Manchester, Milton Keynes, Northampton, Nottingham, Reading
Languages: French, German
Work: A3 B1 B2 C1 C2 C3 E F1 F2 I J1 J2 K4 L M1 N O Q R1 R2 S1 S2 T1 T2 U2 W X Z(b,c,e,f,h,i,j,k,l,m,n,o,p,q,r,s,t,u,y,za)
Fixed Fee Interview, Legal Aid undertaken and Member of Accident Line
Ptr: Bennett, Mr Graham R LLB . . . . §Feb 1980
Derbyshire, Ms Helena . . . . Jan 1993
Dolan, Mr Christopher P BA(Hons) . . . . *Dec 1985
Hadley, Mr Jonathon . . . . Oct 1995
Hewson, Ms Kirsten . . . . Aug 1996
Jackson, Mr John D . . . . *Jun 1980
Knight, Ms Lynn . . . . Nov 1996
Knott, Mr Simon . . . . *§Jan 1991
Murphy, Mr Niall . . . . Feb 1990
Porter, Mr Stephen . . . . Jan 2001
Sfar-Gandoura, Ms Emna . . . . Oct 2001
Wright, Mr Sean . . . . Jan 1990

STARBUCK & MACK ‡
227 West Street Fareham Hampshire PO16 0HA
Tel: 01329 285341 *Fax:* 01329 822027
E-mail: mail@starbuckandmack.co.uk
List of partners: M T S C James, I S Mack
Languages: French
Work: C1 C2 E J1 K1 K3 K4 R1 R2 S1 S2 W Z(c,d)
Agency, Advocacy and Legal Aid Franchise
Ptr: James, Mr Matthew Timothy St Clair LLB(Exon) Charity Trustee; Church Leader . . . . *Nov 1993
Mack, Mr Iain S LLB(Soton) . . . . *Jan 1981

TANG BENTLEY & JACKSON ‡
151 West Street Fareham Hampshire PO16 0DZ
Tel: 01329 220401 *Fax:* 01329 828347 *Dx:* 40801 FAREHAM
List of partners: S F Bentley, E Jackson, T P Tang
Work: B2 G H
Emergency Action, Agency, Advocacy, Fixed Fee Interview and Legal Aid undertaken
Ptr: Bentley, Mr Stephen F BA(Hons) . . . . *Jun 1985
Jackson, Mr Edward LLB(Hons) . . . . *Apr 1981
Tang, Miss Theresa Poi-Ling LLB(Hons); DipLP . . . . *Jan 1998

VICTORY LEGAL COSTS SOLICITORS ‡
18 High Street Fareham Hampshire PO16 7AF
Tel: 0844 980 1690 *Dx:* 40802 FAREHAM
E-mail: keith.hayward@victorylegal.co.uk

WARNER GOODMAN LLP ‡
Portland Chambers 66 West Street Fareham Hampshire PO16 0JR
Tel: 01329 288121 *Fax:* 01329 822714 *Dx:* 40804 FAREHAM
E-mail: enquiries@warnergoodman.co.uk
List of partners: G S Barclay, C Battye, S E L Brooks, I Curtis, M Giles, S Grant, K B J Horn, S J Miles, A J Munden, D Y Oatham, H Robson, C Sheerin, D E Thompson, E Voller, W R R Ware, S J Whitemore, P J Winslade
Office: Portsmouth, Southampton
Work: A1 B1 C1 C2 D1 E F1 F2 G H J1 J2 K1 N O Q R1 R2 S1 S2 T2 W Z(a,c,j,l,m,o,p,q,r)
Emergency Action, Agency, Advocacy, Fixed Fee Interview, Legal Aid undertaken, Legal Aid Franchise and Member of Accident Line
Dir: Brooks, Ms Sarah Elizabeth Louise . . . . May 2002
Curtis, Mr Ian LLB(B'ham) . . . . *Apr 1977
Giles, Mr Martin . . . . Sep 2009
Ware, Mr William Reginald Richard . . . . Sep 1982
Asoc: Cox, Mrs Jane Louise . . . . Jul 2007
Hounsome, Miss Victoria Rhiannon . . . . Mar 2005
Johnstone, Miss Caroline Louise . . . . Nov 2005
Knight, Mrs Claire Louise . . . . Dec 2002
Sheppard, Miss Suzanne Marie . . . . Sep 2002
Ast: Jubb, Mrs Catherine Sian . . . . Jan 2001

FARINGDON, Oxfordshire

CROWDY & ROSE ‡
(in association with Pryce & Co)
2 Market Place Faringdon Oxfordshire SN7 7HW
Tel: 01367 240285 *Fax:* 01367 242138 *Dx:* 81000 FARINGDON
Emergency telephone 01793 765068
E-mail: info@crowdyandrose.co.uk
List of partners: S J Clarke, R C Noyce, P E T Widdrington
Office: Lechlade
Work: A1 C1 D1 E F1 G H J1 K1 L M1 P R1 S1 T1 V W Z(b,c,d,l,m)
Emergency Action, Agency, Advocacy, Fixed Fee Interview and Legal Aid undertaken
Ptr: Noyce, Mr Richard C LLB(Soton) . . . . *Oct 1977
Widdrington, Mr Peregrine E T . . . . *Jun 1970

DIANE JONES ‡
26 Cockswell Road Faringdon Oxfordshire SN7 7EZ
Tel: 01367 240624 *Fax:* 01367 243870

FARNBOROUGH, Hampshire

MICHAEL BAKER SOLICITORS LIMITED ‡
7 Queens Road Farnborough Hampshire GU14 6DJ
Tel: 01252 744600 *Fax:* 01252 744611
Dx: 146180 FARNBOROUGH 6
List of partners: M J Baker, J Oldfield
Office: Aldershot, Redhill
Work: N
Ptr: Baker, Mr Michael J LLB . . . . *Jan 1970
Oldfield, Mr Julian . . . . Jun 1999
Ast: Dryden, Ms Emma LLB . . . . Jan 2001

DAVIES BLUNDEN & EVANS ‡
43-45 Victoria Road Farnborough Hampshire GU14 7PD
Tel: 01252 541633 *Fax:* 01252 545015 *Dx:* 59553 FARNBOROUGH
E-mail: law@dbande.co.uk
List of partners: C N Jones, C J Rennison, D P Rowe
Office: Yateley
Work: D1 E G J1 K1 K3 L N Q R1 S1 S2 T2 V W Z(i,l,w)
Emergency Action, Agency, Advocacy, Fixed Fee Interview, Legal Aid undertaken and Legal Aid Franchise
Ptr: Jones, Mrs Chhui Nee LLB . . . . *Dec 1994
Rennison, Mr Christopher J BA . . . . *Mar 1983
Rowe, Mr Deglan P BA(Law) Notary Public . . . . . *§Jan 1985
Ast: Fickling, Mrs Renee Paula LLB . . . . *Aug 1997
Fisher, Mr Simon John LLB(Hons) . . . . *Nov 2007
Con: Evans, Mr Michael R MBE . . . . *§Dec 1957
Podger, Mr Christopher J . . . . *Jun 1984

FULCHERS OF FARNBOROUGH ‡
15 Cove Road Cove Farnborough Hampshire GU14 0EH
Tel: 01252 522475 *Fax:* 01252 522523 *Dx:* 59565 FARNBOROUGH
E-mail: litigation@fulchers-solicitors.co.uk
List of partners: J S Beards, K H R Izod
Work: B2 C1 E F1 G H J1 K1 K2 K3 K4 L N O P Q R1 R2 S1 S2 W Z(p,q)
Emergency Action, Agency, Advocacy, Fixed Fee Interview, Legal Aid undertaken and Legal Aid Franchise
Ptr: Beards, Mr Jonathan S LLB . . . . *Aug 1981
Izod, Mr Kevin H R ACIS ● . . . . *May 1982
Asoc: Packer, Ms Belinda LLB . . . . *Aug 2009
Ast: Jones, Ms Claire Louise LLB . . . . *Feb 2007

JAE MAHMOOD SOLICITOR ‡
9 Hatfield Gardens Farnborough Hampshire GU14 7ED
Tel: 01252 517459
E-mail: julie.mahmood@knightsbridge.resources.com

NEALE TURK ROCHFORT ‡
41 Victoria Road Farnborough Hampshire GU14 7PA
Tel: 01252 515155 *Fax:* 01252 376604
E-mail: info@nealeturkrochfort.co.uk
List of partners: S D Gallagher, E D B Rochfort
Office: Camberley
Work: J1 K1 K3 K4 Q S1 W
Ptr: Gallagher, Mr Stephen David . . . . *Sep 1975
Ast: Vinall-Morgan, Mrs Keren Angela Marie LLB(Hons) . *Dec 2002

PPG CRIMINAL LAW LTD ‡
Suite 2 Rushmoor Business Centre Kingsmead Farnborough Hampshire GU14 7SR
Tel: 01252 362626 *Fax:* 01252 362625 *Dx:* 59560 FARNBOROUGH
E-mail: trudi@ppg-solicitors.co.uk
Work: G H
Fixed Fee Interview and Legal Aid undertaken

TANNER & TAYLOR LLP
5th Floor Rushmoor Business Centre Kingsmead Farnborough Hampshire GU14 7SR
Tel: 01252 549555 *Fax:* 01252 544946 *Dx:* 59550 FARNBOROUGH
Emergency telephone 01256 862527
E-mail: farnborough@tanner-taylor.co.uk
Office: Aldershot, Ascot, Farnham
Work: C1 D1 D2 E F1 G H J1 K1 K2 L N S1 S2 V W Z(l,m,p)
Emergency Action, Agency, Advocacy, Fixed Fee Interview, Legal Aid undertaken, Legal Aid Franchise and Member of Accident Line
Ptr: Mehta, Ms Neeta LLB(Hons) . . . . *Apr 1993
O'Dowd-Booth, Mr John A . . . . *§Jun 1974
Ast: Atkins, Mrs Natasha Jane LLB . . . . *Sep 1999
Monk, Miss Heather J BA(Hons) . . . . *Mar 2000

WOODFORD STAUFFER ‡
Church Path House 63a Lynchford Road Farnborough Hampshire GU14 6EJ
Tel: 01252 375376 *Fax:* 01252 375399 *Dx:* 59563 FARNBOROUGH
E-mail: connorj@woodfordstauffer.co.uk
List of partners: D A Bowen, E Fairbairn, V S Stauffer
Work: C1 C2 C3 D1 E F1 J1 K1 K2 K3 L M1 N O P Q R1 S1 S2 W Z(c,l,m,q,r)
Emergency Action, Fixed Fee Interview and Legal Aid undertaken
Ptr: Bowen, Mr Darren Anthony LLB . . . . *Sep 1994
Stauffer, Miss Verity S MA(Oxon); Jurisprudence . . *May 1982
Fairbairn, Emma FILEx . . . . NSP

FARNHAM, Surrey

JACKIE ANDERSON ‡
1 Charlotte Close Heath End Farnham Surrey GU9 0LF
Tel: 01252 332132 / 07752 329079 *Fax:* 01252 332132
E-mail: jackie@jeasolicitors.co.uk

BARRINGTONS SOLICITORS ‡
6 St George's Yard Castle Street Farnham Surrey GU9 7LW
Tel: 01252 741751 *Fax:* 01252 734162
E-mail: deborah@barringtonlaw.co.uk
List of partners: D A Barrington, Y M Fuller
Work: C1 C2 E F1 F2 J1 S1 S2 W Z(e)
Ptr: Barrington, Ms Deborah Ann . . . . Jan 1988
Fuller, Mrs Yvonne M LLB . . . . *Jun 1978

BELLS SOLICITORS ‡
11 South Street Farnham Surrey GU9 7QX
Tel: 01252 733733 *Fax:* 01252 723718 *Dx:* 32801 FARNHAM
E-mail: mail@bells-solicitors.co.uk
List of partners: D F Burke, J S C Cave, F H Dutton
Languages: French
Work: B1 C2 D1 D2 E F1 J1 K1 K4 O Q S1 S2 T2 W Z(c,k,o,p,q)
Advocacy and Fixed Fee Interview undertaken
Ptr: Burke, Mr Dermot F LLB . . . . *§Oct 1989
Cave, Mr Jeremy S C LLB . . . . *§Oct 1982
Dutton, Ms Fiona Helen BA(Hons) . . . . *§Apr 1994
Ast: Connolly, Mr Liam GDL; BA(Hons); PGCE . . . . . . Feb 2009
Leighton, Mrs Georgina Elaine BA(Intl Business) . . . Sep 2010
Markall, Miss Karen Sara BSc(Hons); GDL . . . . . . Oct 2007
Pennington, Mr Edward Bartlett BA(Hons) . . . . . . §Jan 2004
Con: Rivers, Mr Tony LLB(Hons) . . . . Dec 1970

BURKILL GOVIER ‡
2 Maritime House The Hart Farnham Surrey GU9 7HW
Tel: 01252 717171 *Fax:* 01252 717188 *Dx:* 32804 FARNHAM
E-mail: enquiries@burkillgovier.com
List of partners: J J Burkill, M McCormack, J R Parker
Work: A1 A3 C1 C2 E J1 L M2 O P R1 R2 S1 S2 U2 Z(b,c,f,n,w)
Dir: Burkill, Mr Justin John LLB; ACIArb Andrews Prize . *Sep 1983
McCormack, Ms Maryanne LLB . . . . *Feb 1995
Parker, Mr James R LLB . . . . *Nov 1982

CALLAGHANS ‡
Firlex House 18 Firgrove Hill Farnham Surrey GU9 8LQ
Tel: 01252 723477 *Fax:* 01252 723488 *Dx:* 32803 FARNHAM
E-mail: bbutlersmith@callaghans.co.uk
List of partners: B C Butler-Smith, S C Izod, J K O'Callaghan, M P Wells
Languages: French, Greek, Turkish
Work: B1 D1 E J1 K1 K2 N O Q S1 S2 W Z(p)
Agency, Advocacy undertaken and Member of Accident Line
Ptr: Butler-Smith, Ms Belinda C BA(Dunelm) . . . . *Mar 1980
Izod, Mr Stephen C LLB(L'pool) . . . . *Oct 1978
O'Callaghan, Mr Jerome K LLB(B'ham) . . . . *Apr 1979
Wells, Mr Murray Paul LLB . . . . *Oct 1992
Asoc: Bradley, Mr Ian N BA . . . . *Dec 1987
Ast: Burford, Rebecca Anne . . . . Jul 2009
Dosani, Dipesh . . . . Jul 2009
Meadows, Miss Sonia Marie LLB . . . . *Sep 1999
Con: Henderson, Lynn . . . . Apr 1981
Ludick, Mrs Selena Veronica LLB(Hons) . . . . *Apr 1996

CLIFFORD COWLING & CO ‡
9-10 Upper Church Lane Farnham Surrey GU9 7PW
Tel: 01252 725726 *Fax:* 01252 737100 *Dx:* 32824 FARNHAM
E-mail: clifcow@btclick.com
List of partners: G D C Meyjes
Languages: French

See p112 for the Key to Work Categories & other symbols

Work: A1 C1 E F1 L P R1 S1 S2 T1
Ptr: Meyjes, Mr Gareth D C LLB Notary Public. . . . . . . *Jul 1973

DAWSON MASON & CARR
The Old Hop Kiln 1 Long Garden Walk Farnham Surrey GU9 7HX
Tel: 01252 725771 *Fax:* 01252 725774
Office: Guildford

ABIGAIL DAYKIN & CO ‡
94 Weydon Hill Road Farnham Surrey GU9 8NZ
Tel: 01252 719155 / 07774 259331 *Fax:* 0871 433 5832
Emergency telephone 07774 259331
E-mail: advice@abigaildaykin.co.uk
List of partners: A H Daykin
Work: J1 J2 Z(p)
Fixed Fee Interview undertaken
SPr: Daykin, Mrs Abigail Hall LLB(Hons) . . . . *Oct 1992

DRAPER & CO ‡
(in association with Wendy M Draper)
8 Borelli Yard Farnham Surrey GU9 7NU
Tel: 01252 727374 *Fax:* 01252 726165 *Dx:* 32809 FARNHAM
Emergency telephone 01420 475158
E-mail: vdg@totalise.co.uk
List of partners: J P M Draper, W M Draper
Work: A1 B1 D1 E F1 G H J1 K1 L N R1 S1 T1 T2 V W Z(c,k,l,p)
Emergency Action, Agency, Advocacy, Fixed Fee Interview and Legal Aid undertaken
Ptr: Draper, Mr Jonathan P M . . . . *Jan 1982
Draper, Ms Wendy M . . . . *Dec 1984
Ast: Mackie, Mrs Karen Frances BA(Hons). . . . . Oct 1987
Con: Draper, Leslie J BA . . . . *§Jun 1963

HADFIELDS BUTT & BOWYER ‡
104 West Street Farnham Surrey GU9 7ET
Tel: 01252 716101 *Fax:* 01252 733482 *Dx:* 32802 FARNHAM
E-mail: enquiries@hadfields.co.uk
List of partners: K G Duffy, M C Wise
Work: C1 E F1 J1 K1 K3 K4 L N O Q R1 S1 S2 T2 V W Z(d,h,l,m,q)
Emergency Action, Agency, Advocacy and Fixed Fee Interview undertaken
Ptr: Duffy, Mr Kevin Gerrard. . . . . *Dec 2008
Wise, Miss Mary Catherine LLB . . . . *§Mar 1995
Asoc: Clare, Miss Emma Louise LLB . . . . *§Sep 2004
Ast: Rothstein, Miss Emma Dorit LLB . . . . *Jul 2006
Con: Butt, Mr F Allan . . . . *§Dec 1963
MacAndrew, Mr Robert A MA(Cantab). . . . . *§Jul 1976
Valentine, Mr David S. . . . . *§Jan 1973

JLS SOLICITORS ‡
Mayfield Suite Alexandra House 1 Waverley Lane Farnham Surrey GU9 8BB
Tel: 01252 726741 *Fax:* 01252 728356
E-mail: info@jlssolicitors.co.uk
Work: K1 K2
Emergency Action, Agency and Fixed Fee Interview undertaken

JMA HR & LEGAL LTD ‡
2 Keep House 33 Castle Street Farnham Surrey GU9 7JB
Tel: 01252 821792
E-mail: enquiries@jma-hrlegal.co.uk

KIDD RAPINET
Sovereign House 17 South Street Farnham Surrey GU9 7QU
Tel: 0845 017 9609 *Fax:* 01252 737506 *Dx:* 32810 FARNHAM
E-mail: pwood@kiddrapinet.co.uk
Office: Aylesbury, High Wycombe, London WC2, Maidenhead, Reading, Slough
Work: A1 B1 C1 C2 C3 D1 E F1 I J1 K1 L R1 R2 S1 S2 T2 U2 W Z(d,e,f,m,o)
Ptr: Aylwin, Miss Joanne M BA(Hons) . . . . *Feb 1983
Meakins, Mrs Sandra LLB. . . . . *Oct 1983
Wood, Mr Peter Stewart LLB . . . . *Apr 1975
Ast: Panton, Mrs Rebecca Jayne BA(English/History); LLB.*Mar 2010

LEGAL SERVICES FOR BUSINESS ‡
Mill Cottage Mill Lane Crondall Farnham Surrey GU10 5RR
Tel: 01252 850853 *Fax:* 07789 773985
E-mail: lynda.lawson@legalservicesforbusiness.co.uk

KAREN MACKIE SOLICITOR ‡
9 Weydon Lane Farnham Surrey GU9 8QG
Tel: 01252 713013 *Fax:* 01252 715419
E-mail: karen@karenmackiesolicitor.co.uk

THE PURKISS PARTNERSHIP ‡
The Hayloft Badshot Farm Farnham Surrey GU9 9HR
Tel: 01252 344311 *Fax:* 01252 318536
Emergency telephone 079 7372 7420
E-mail: office@thepurkisspartnership.co.uk

SUGIYAMA & CO ‡
Meadow Lodge Lobs Wood Manor Farnham Surrey GU10 3RW
Tel: 01252 820500 *Fax:* 01252 820510
E-mail: enquiries@sugiyama.co.uk
List of partners: S H T Sugiyama
Languages: Japanese
Work: C1 F1 F2 J1 O Q Z(f,i)
SPr: Sugiyama, Saiichi H T. . . . . Oct 1990

TANNER & TAYLOR LLP
Ground Floor Suite B Gostrey House Farnham Surrey GU9 7PT
Tel: 01252 733770 *Fax:* 01252 730751 *Dx:* 32815 FARNHAM
E-mail: farnham@tanner-taylor.co.uk
Office: Aldershot, Ascot, Farnborough
Work: B2 C1 D1 E F1 G H J1 K1 K2 L M1 N O Q R2 S1 S2 T1 W
Emergency Action, Agency, Advocacy, Fixed Fee Interview, Legal Aid undertaken, Legal Aid Franchise and Member of Accident Line
Ptr: Barker, Mr Clive J. . . . . *May 1968

THORNE LEGAL CONSULTING ‡
18 Three Stiles Road Farnham Surrey GU9 7DE
Tel: 01252 708105
E-mail: enquiries@thornelegal.com

MALCOLM A H M WILLIAMSON ‡
Planning Environmental and Property Lawyers 7 Finns Business Park Mill Lane Farnham Surrey GU10 5RX
Tel: 0845 230 1022 *Fax:* 01252 851918
E-mail: lawyers@malcolmwilliamson.co.uk
List of partners: M A H M Williamson
Languages: French
Work: C1 C2 E J1 L M1 P R1 S1 S2 W Z(h,s)
SPr: Williamson, Mr Malcolm A H M FCMI . . . . *§Apr 1970

FAVERSHAM, Kent

BULL & BULL
4 Preston Street Faversham Kent ME13 8NS
Tel: 01795 534553 *Dx:* 32400 FAVERSHAM
E-mail: faversham@bullandbull.co.uk
Office: Canterbury, Herne Bay

DOMINIC GOWARD & CO ‡
4 Market Street Faversham Kent ME13 7AH
Tel: 01795 529025 *Fax:* 01795 535635
E-mail: dgoward@nildram.co.uk

MACKAY & CO ‡
6a East Street Faversham Kent ME13 8AD
Tel: 01795 536061 *Fax:* 01795 538813 *Dx:* 32401 FAVERSHAM
Work: C1 E N Q S1 S2 W Z(c,j,q)
Ast: Murr, Mr Richard C . . . . *Jun 1974

TASSELLS ‡
20 West Street Faversham Kent ME13 7JF
Tel: 01795 533337 *Fax:* 01795 530375 *Dx:* 32404 FAVERSHAM
E-mail: law@tassells-solicitors.co.uk
List of partners: M S Day, J B Mathews, A R Matthews
Languages: Italian, Russian, Spanish
Work: A1 B1 C1 C2 D1 E F1 F2 J1 J2 K1 K3 K4 L N O P Q R1 R2 S1 S2 T2 V W X Z(c,d,g,l,m,p,q,r,u)
Emergency Action, Agency, Advocacy and Fixed Fee Interview undertaken
Ptr: Day, Mr Michael S LLB(Bris) ♦ . . . . *§Jan 1970
Mathews, Mr James B BA ♦. . . . . *Apr 1987
Matthews, Mrs Ann Rachel MB; BS; BSc ♦ . . . . . . *Nov 1994
Ast: Anderson, Mrs Susan Lucy LLB(Hons) . . . . *Jul 2000
Wessels, Mr William Ian MA; PGCE. . . . . *Jul 2004

FEATHERSTONE, West Yorkshire

HEWISONS
24 Station Lane Featherstone West Yorkshire WF1 5BE
Office: Bradford

FELIXSTOWE, Suffolk

ASHTON KCJ
Anglia House 22-24 Hamilton Road Felixstowe Suffolk IP11 7AN
Tel: 01394 277188 *Fax:* 01394 670726 *Dx:* 31454 FELIXSTOWE
E-mail: enquiries.felixstowe@ashtonkcj.co.uk
Office: Bury St Edmunds (2 offices), Cambridge, Ipswich, Norwich (2 offices), Thetford
Languages: Dutch, French, German
Work: A1 A3 B1 B2 C1 C2 C3 D1 D2 E F1 F2 G H J1 J2 K1 K2 L M1 M2 N O P Q R1 S1 S2 T1 T2 U2 V W X Z(a,c,d,h,i,j,k,l,m,o,p,q,t)
Emergency Action, Advocacy, Fixed Fee Interview, Legal Aid undertaken, Legal Aid Franchise and Member of Accident Line
Ptr: Foyster, Mr Richard Michael LLB . . . . *Sep 1996

BLOCKS
97 Hamilton Road Felixstowe Suffolk IP11 7AH
Tel: 01394 283241 *Fax:* 01394 282428 *Dx:* 31451 FELIXSTOWE
E-mail: info@blockslegal.co.uk
Web: www.blockslegal.co.uk
Office: Ipswich
Work: A1 A2 A3 B1 C1 C2 C3 E F1 F2 I J1 K1 K3 K4 L O P Q R1 R2 S1 S2 T1 T2 W Z(c,d,e,h,k,l,p,q)
Agency and Fixed Fee Interview undertaken
Ptr: Boast, Mr Matthew David LLB. . . . . *§Oct 1995
Asoc: Weldon, Mrs Nicola Mary . . . . *Oct 2002

CREANS SOLICITORS ‡
105 Ranelagh Road Felixstowe Suffolk IP11 7HU
Tel: 01394 273481

DALE-STEVENS LLP
10 Victoria Street Felixstowe Suffolk IP11 7ER
Tel: 020 7929 2247
E-mail: law@dalestevens.com
Office: London EC4
SPr: Dale, Mr Michael LLB(Lond); MSc(Wales). . . . . . . *Sep 1981

FAIRWEATHER STEPHENSON & CO ‡
174-176 Hamilton Road Felixstowe Suffolk IP11 7DU
Tel: 01394 277941 *Fax:* 01394 670737 *Dx:* 31457 FELIXSTOWE
Emergency telephone 01394 284959
E-mail: enquiries@fairweatherstephenson.co.uk
List of partners: P D O Cooney, M F Stephenson
Work: D1 E F1 G H J1 K1 K2 L N Q S1 V W
Emergency Action, Agency, Advocacy, Fixed Fee Interview, Legal Aid undertaken and Member of Accident Line
Ptr: Cooney, Mr Patrick D O LLB . . . . *May 1991
Stephenson, Mr Michael F MA(Cantab) . . . . *Oct 1982
Ast: Broadhurst, Mr Stephen R BSc; MA; MPhil . . . . . . Dec 1992
Little, Mrs Elizabeth Mary LLB. . . . . *Oct 1999

JACKAMANS
167-171 Hamilton Road Felixstowe Suffolk IP11 7DR
Tel: 01394 279636 *Fax:* 01394 670179 *Dx:* 31452 FELIXSTOWE
Emergency telephone 01473 659908
E-mail: mail@jackamans.co.uk
Office: Diss, Harleston, Ipswich
Work: A1 B1 C1 C2 C3 D1 E F1 G H J1 K1 L M1 M2 N P S1 W Z(a,c,l,t)
Emergency Action, Agency, Advocacy, Fixed Fee Interview, Legal Aid undertaken, Legal Aid Franchise and Member of Accident Line
Ptr: Nainthy, Mr Priya Jerome LLB(Hons) . . . . Sep 1997
Owers, Mr Timothy . . . . *Dec 1991
Ast: Ribbands, Ms Maya BSc; PG DipLaw; DLCC . . . . . Jan 2004
Con: Berry, Mr Norman Boulton LLB . . . . *Jul 1976
Lockett, Miss Carol Joan LLB . . . . Nov 1982

MARGARY & MILLER ‡
5 Crescent Road Felixstowe Suffolk IP11 7BY
Tel: 01394 273333 *Fax:* 01394 670719 *Dx:* 31455 FELIXSTOWE
E-mail: info@margary-miller.co.uk
List of partners: D J Gaffney, S M J Leach
Office: Southwold, Woodbridge (2 offices)
Languages: French, German, Spanish
Work: A1 B1 C1 D1 E F1 J1 K1 K3 K4 L N O Q S1 S2 T1 T2 W Z(c,h,l,q,t)
Agency, Advocacy, Fixed Fee Interview undertaken and Member of Accident Line
Ptr: Leach, Mr Stephen M J Notary Public. . . . . *Jun 1973
Asoc: Cronin, Miss Rachel BA(Hons) . . . . *Sep 1994
Ast: McLauchlan, Mr Philip James LLB. . . . . Jun 2003

JOHN WESTON & CO ‡
10 Victoria Street Felixstowe Suffolk IP11 7ER
Tel: 01394 282527 *Fax:* 01394 276097
Emergency telephone 01473 659996
E-mail: info@johnweston.co.uk
List of partners: N J Weston
Languages: French, Italian
Work: C1 M1 M2 N O Q Z(a,j,t)
Emergency Action undertaken
SPr: Weston, Mr Nigel John BSc. . . . . Jul 1989

FELTHAM, Middlesex

MCCARTNEYS ‡
483b Staines Road Bedfont Feltham Middlesex TW14 8DH
Tel: 020 8751 6051 *Fax:* 020 8844 0301
List of partners: R W McCartney
Ptr: McCartney, Mr Roderick W . . . . Jul 1979

OWEN WHITE & CATLIN ‡
(incorporating Feldman Nicholls; Butler & Co)
Gavel House 90-92 High Street Feltham Middlesex TW13 4ES
Tel: 020 8890 2836 *Fax:* 020 8751 4581 *Dx:* 133826 FELTHAM 3
Emergency telephone 07860 806856
E-mail: feltham@owenwhitecatlin.co.uk
Office: Addlestone, Ashford, Hounslow, London W4, London W6, Shepperton
Languages: French, German, Spanish
Work: A1 A3 B1 B2 C1 C2 C3 D1 D2 E F1 F2 G H I J1 J2 K1 K2 K3 K4 L M1 M2 N O P Q R1 R2 S1 S2 T1 T2 V W Z(a,b,c,d,e,g,h,i,j,k,l,m,o,p,q,r,t,w,y)

FERNDOWN, Dorset

BLACKWELL-WEST ‡
The Annexe Moorlands Lodge 76 Moorlands Road Ferndown Dorset BH22 0JW
Tel: 01202 892300 *Fax:* 01202 855566
E-mail: info@blackwell-west.co.uk
List of partners: J D Blackwell-West
Work: N
SPr: Blackwell-West, Ms Julie Dorothy LLB(Hons) . . . . . Jul 1989
Asoc: Thomas, Mr Neil . . . . *Jan 1965

JAMES BOWIE CATON & CO ‡
499 Ringwood Road Ferndown Dorset BH22 9AG
Tel: 01202 875646 / 877225 *Fax:* 01202 861310
Dx: 45153 FERNDOWN
E-mail: mail@jbclaw.co.uk
List of partners: J D Bowie, P M H Caton
Work: A1 B1 C1 D1 E F1 G J1 K1 L M1 N O P Q R1 S1 T1 V W Z(a,b,c,d,e,f,j,k,l,m,n,o,p,s)
Emergency Action, Agency, Advocacy, Fixed Fee Interview, Legal Aid undertaken and Member of Accident Line
Ptr: Bowie, Mr James D . . . . *§Dec 1966
Caton, Mr Paul M H. . . . . *§Jun 1968

BUCHANAN & LLEWELLYN ‡
18 & 20 Victoria Road Ferndown Dorset BH22 9HZ
Tel: 01202 873355 *Fax:* 01202 870576 *Dx:* 45155 FERNDOWN
List of partners: A F Holmes, J R Rance
Office: Westbourne
Work: E F1 K1 K3 K4 N R2 S1 S2 T2 W Z(q)
Ptr: Rance, Mr John R. . . . . *Dec 1972

CHEAL ASSOCIATES LTD ‡
17 Henchard Close Ferndown Dorset BH22 8LH
Tel: 0845 508 9370 *Fax:* 0845 527 3416
E-mail: dani@employmentlegaladvice.co.uk

INSLEY & PARTNERS
66 Victoria Road Ferndown Dorset BH22 9JA
Tel: 01202 876117 *Fax:* 01202 895998 *Dx:* 45151 FERNDOWN
Office: Bournemouth
Work: B1 C1 C2 E F1 J1 K4 L O P Q R1 S1 S2 T2 W Z(b,c,d,l)
Ptr: Aitkenhead, Mr Robert M MA(Oxon); BCL. . . . . . . *§Apr 1981

LUFF BROOK CARTER SOLICITORS ‡
521 Ringwood Road Ferndown Dorset BH22 9AQ
Tel: 01202 871311 *Fax:* 01202 861286

FERRING, West Sussex

BENNETT GRIFFIN
Sea Lane Chambers 11 Sea Lane Ferring West Sussex BN12 5DR
Tel: 01903 229999 *Fax:* 01903 229174 *Dx:* 3703 WORTHING
Emergency telephone 01903 229949
E-mail: recw@bennett-griffin.co.uk
Office: Rustington, Worthing
Languages: French
Work: A1 A3 B1 C1 C2 C3 E F1 F2 J1 K4 L M1 M2 O P Q R1 S1 S2 T1 T2 V W Z(c,g,h,j,l,p,q)
Emergency Action, Agency, Advocacy, Fixed Fee Interview, Legal Aid undertaken, Legal Aid Franchise and Member of Accident Line
Ptr: Bennett, Mr Peter George MA(Hons); Dip Ed Member of Worthing Borough Council . . . . *Oct 1976
Fawcett, Mr Robert BA(Hons)(Politics) . . . . *Apr 2005
Smith, Mrs Elaine LLB . . . . *Feb 2001
Asoc: Clapham, Ms Tania Ann BA(Hons) . . . . *Nov 2002
Edwards, Mr Darren Richard LLB . . . . *Jan 2005
Hammond, Mrs Charlotte Elizabeth . . . . *Dec 2002
Ostrom, Jo . . . . *Oct 2007
Ast: Haffenden, Katie . . . . *Jul 2008
Con: Peterkin, Mr Ian Brock . . . . *Jul 1969

FERRYHILL, Co Durham

EVANS & CO
3 Durham Road Ferryhill Co Durham DL17 8LD
Tel: 01740 657444 *Fax:* 01740 655533
E-mail: ferryhill@evansco.co.uk
Office: Spennymoor
Work: D1 E F1 L S1 T1 T2 W Z(d,l,m)
Agency and Fixed Fee Interview undertaken
Ptr: Evans, Mr Robert G LLB; LLM; TEP. . . . . *Nov 1975

MEIKLES ‡
8 North Street Ferryhill Co Durham DL17 8HX
Tel: 01740 652811 *Fax:* 01740 655854 *Dx:* 60180 FERRYHILL
Emergency telephone 01740 656324
List of partners: A J Clinton, C E Coates, E Forrest, C Haigh, C V Johnson, L A Petterson, J Roberts, L Simpson, L M Steinberg
Office: Barnard Castle, Bishop Auckland, Spennymoor, Stockton-on-Tees
Work: A1 D1 D2 F1 G H J1 K1 L N Q S1 V W Z(l,m)
Emergency Action, Agency, Advocacy, Fixed Fee Interview, Legal Aid undertaken and Legal Aid Franchise
Ptr: Coates, Miss Claire Estelle LLB(Hons)(Law). . . . . *Sep 2000
Petterson, Mr Lawrence Albert LLB(Leeds) . . . . . . *Apr 1979

FETCHAM, Surrey

BROOKS & CO ‡
15 Cedar Drive Fetcham Surrey KT22 9ET
Tel: 01372 362042 *Fax:* 01372 363375
Office: London WC1
Work: O Q

QUALITYSOLICITORS PALMERS ‡
1 Hazel Parade Fetcham Surrey KT22 9PY
Tel: 01372 454791 *Fax:* 01372 451308
E-mail: palmers@qualitysolicitors.com
List of partners: L A Palmer, P J Palmer
Languages: German
Work: A3 B1 E F1 K1 K4 L Q S1 S2 V W Z(q)
Ptr: Palmer, Mrs Lesley Ann LLB(Soton) The Appeals Service Tribunal Judge (Part-time). . . . . *Mar 1983
Palmer, Mr Philip J LLB(Bris) OSS Local Conciliation Officer . . . . *Oct 1982
Con: Mahoney, Mrs Caroline BA(Hons); CPE; LSF . . . . . Sep 1991

FILEY, North Yorkshire

BIRDSALL & SNOWBALL
(incorporating Eagle-Clarke & Co; Moody Beanland & Co)
12 West Avenue Filey North Yorkshire YO14 9AA
Tel: 01723 515151 *Fax:* 01723 513321
E-mail: reception@birdsall-snowball.co.uk
Office: Scarborough
Work: A1 C1 E K1 K3 K4 L Q S1 T2 W
Agency and Fixed Fee Interview undertaken
Ptr: Cathcart, Mr Thomas C BA(Law) . . . . *Jun 1979
Ast: Nickson, Mrs Jane C LLB . . . . Apr 1981

PINKNEY GRUNWELLS LAWYERS LLP
25 Bridlington Street Hunmanby Filey North Yorkshire YO14 0JR
Tel: 01723 890634 *Fax:* 01723 890787
E-mail: solicitor@pinkneygrunwells.co.uk
Office: Bridlington, Scarborough, Whitby
Con: Summers, Mr Martin William . . . . *Nov 1971

THORPE & CO
10-12 Belle Vue Street Filey North Yorkshire YO14 9HY
Tel: 01723 515555 *Fax:* 01723 515550
Emergency telephone 01723 354077
E-mail: filey@thorpeandco.com
Office: Malton, Scarborough, Whitby
Languages: French, German
Work: A1 B1 C1 C2 C3 D1 D2 E F1 F2 G H J1 K1 K2 L M1 M2 N O P Q R1 S1 S2 T1 T2 V W Z(b,c,d,h,i,j,k,l,o,q,s,t)
Emergency Action, Agency, Advocacy, Fixed Fee Interview, Legal Aid undertaken, Legal Aid Franchise and Member of Accident Line
Ptr: Nickson, Mrs Jane C LLB . . . . Apr 1981
Shaw, Mr Nicholas J . . . . *§Jan 1984
Asoc: Scholey, Mr Peter David LLB(Hons). . . . . Jan 1991

FILTON, South Gloucestershire

BARNARD & CO
130 Gloucester Road North Filton South Gloucestershire BS12 7BQ
Tel: 0117 969 2773 *Fax:* 0117 923 6179
Work: E F1 G J1 K1 P S1 W Z(c)
Agency, Advocacy, Fixed Fee Interview and Legal Aid undertaken
Ast: Miller, Mr Neil Hugh BA . . . . *May 1982

FISHGUARD, Pembrokeshire

V J G JOHNS & SON ‡
Goodwick House Chambers 19 West Street Fishguard Pembrokeshire SA65 9AL
Tel: 01348 873671 *Fax:* 01348 874048 *Dx:* 98327 FISHGUARD
E-mail: enquiries@vjgjohns.co.uk
List of partners: A B C Davies, I L Phillips
Languages: Welsh
Work: A1 B1 C1 D1 D2 E F1 G H K1 L P Q R1 S1 S2 W Z(l,m)
Agency and Advocacy undertaken
Ptr: Davies, Mr Arwel B C LLB(Wales). . . . . *Mar 1984
Phillips, Mr Ifor L BA . . . . *Nov 1970
Ast: Potter, Mr Robin W D MA(Oxon) . . . . *Oct 1981

WALTER WILLIAMS ‡
(incorporating Alan Cook)
Sycamore Lodge Hamilton Street Fishguard Pembrokeshire SA65 9HL
Tel: 01348 873223 *Fax:* 01348 873699 *Dx:* 98325 FISHGUARD
E-mail: wwld@btconnect.com
List of partners: P W S Cross, P L Davies
Languages: Welsh
Work: A1 B1 C1 C2 C3 E G H J1 K1 Q R1 S1 W Z(c,f,l)
Emergency Action, Agency, Advocacy, Fixed Fee Interview and Legal Aid undertaken
Ptr: Cross, Mr Peter W S Notary Public . . . . *§Nov 1968
Davies, Mr Paul L LLB(Bris). . . . . *§Oct 1971

FLEET, Hampshire

BATES NVH
(in association with Bates & Partners)
67 Fleet Road Fleet Hampshire GU51 EPJ
Tel: 01252 629292 *Fax:* 01252 626592 *Dx:* 32602 FLEET
Emergency telephone 01252 625633
E-mail: fleet@batesnvh.co.uk
Office: Hook (3 offices), Leigh-on-Sea, London WC2
Languages: German
Work: A1 B1 C1 C2 C3 D1 E F1 G H J1 K1 L M1 M2 N O P Q R1 S1 T1 T2 V W Z(c,i,l,o)
Emergency Action, Agency, Advocacy, Fixed Fee Interview and Legal Aid undertaken
SPr: Hodgson, Mr Christopher A C. . . . . *§Jul 1979
Ptr: Wasem, Mr Roger E BA(Soton) . . . . *Dec 1977
Ast: Browett, Mrs Nicola LLB. . . . . Oct 1990
Con: Hooker, Mr Malcolm McD . . . . *Jan 1965

A J COLFER SOLICITORS ‡
121 Albert Street Fleet Hampshire GU51 3SR
Tel: 01252 623565

ROBERT COOK & CO SOLICITORS ‡
16 Reading Road South Fleet Hampshire GU52 7QL
Tel: 01252 812957 *Fax:* 01252 811667
E-mail: email@cookslaw.com
List of partners: R J Cook
Work: B1 C1 D1 D2 E F1 J1 K1 K2 K3 K4 L N O Q S1 S2 W Z(c,d,h,q)
Emergency Action, Agency, Advocacy and Fixed Fee Interview undertaken
SPr: Cook, Mr Robert J . . . . *Jul 1979

GRANTS SOLICITORS ‡
West Point House 32-34 Albert street Fleet Hampshire GU51 3RW
Tel: 01252 622288 *Fax:* 01252 622286
E-mail: ag@grantssolicitors.uk.net
List of partners: A Grant
Work: S1
SPr: Grant, Mrs Alice LLB . . . . Aug 1998

LEAN & CO ‡
12 Dinorben Avenue Fleet Hampshire GU52 7SG
Tel: 01252 816757
List of partners: S F Lean
Work: E O Q S1
SPr: Lean, Mr Stephen Frank LLB . . . . *Oct 1986

NEALE TURK ‡
Bridge House 27-31 Reading Road South Fleet Hampshire GU2 7QP
Tel: 01252 811070 *Fax:* 01252 811133 *Dx:* 32645 FLEET
E-mail: lwaller@nealeturk.com
List of partners: A D D Green, P D Lucas, J F Ratcliffe, J C Wheeler, J R C Wheeler
Office: Basingstoke
Work: A1 B1 B2 C1 C2 C3 D1 E F1 G H J1 K1 K3 L N O Q R1 S1 S2 T1 T2 W Z(c,k,l)
Agency, Advocacy and Fixed Fee Interview undertaken
Ptr: Green, Mr Andrew D D . . . . Jan 1991
Lucas, Mr Phillip D . . . . *May 1981
Ratcliffe, Mr John F LLB. . . . . Apr 1973
Wheeler, Mr Jonathan R Charles BA . . . . *Feb 1997
Asoc: Thorn, Mr Andrew E LLB . . . . *Jan 2003

PEYTO LAW ‡
Bryslan House Upper Street Fleet Hampshire GU51 3PE
Tel: 01252 617119 *Fax:* 01252 617029 *Dx:* 32605 FLEET
E-mail: info@peytolaw.com
List of partners: L Humphreys
SPr: Humphreys, Mrs Louise BA(Hons); PGDip; DipLG. . . Jan 2000

PINTO POTTS LLP
34 Reading Road South Fleet Hampshire GU52 7QL
Tel: 01252 361200 *Fax:* 01252 625649 *Dx:* 32623 FLEET
Office: Aldershot
Languages: French, German, Spanish
Work: B1 D1 E G H K1 M1 P S1 W Z(j,l,t)
Agency, Advocacy, Fixed Fee Interview, Legal Aid undertaken and Member of Accident Line

WILLS CHANDLER BEACH ‡
161 Fleet Road Fleet Hampshire GU51 3PD
Tel: 01252 613351 *Fax:* 01252 613353
Emergency telephone 01256 702650
E-mail: info@wcblaw.co.uk
List of partners: P M Beach
Office: Hook
Languages: French, German
Work: A1 B1 C1 C2 C3 D1 E F1 F2 G H J1 K1 K3 K4 L N O P Q R1 R2 S1 S2 T1 T2 W Z(b,c,d,g,h,j,k,l)
Emergency Action, Agency, Advocacy and Fixed Fee Interview undertaken
SPr: Beach, Mr Piers Matthew . . . . *Feb 1980

FLEETWOOD, Lancashire

ADDIES ‡
58-62 Adelaide Street Fleetwood Lancashire FY7 6EE
Tel: 01253 772128 *Fax:* 01253 771080 *Dx:* 18252 FLEETWOOD
E-mail: lawyers@addies.co.uk
List of partners: R T Jones, J Jorgenson
Work: C1 D1 E F1 J1 K1 K3 L N Q S1 S2 V W Z(l)
Emergency Action, Fixed Fee Interview and Legal Aid undertaken
Ptr: Jones, Mr Richard Timothy LLB. . . . . *Dec 1989
Jorgenson, Mr John LLB(Hons) . . . . *Aug 1997
Ast: McGinn, Miss Jennifer Louise. . . . . *Nov 2008

BARRETT NELLIGAN SOLICITORS ‡
(incorporating Steven G Pope)
Equity Chambers 50 Adelaide Street Fleetwood Lancashire FY7 6EE
Tel: 01253 771664 *Fax:* 01253 778530
Emergency telephone 07623 176818
List of partners: S C L Barrett, P M Nelligan
Office: Blackpool
Work: D1 E G H J1 K1 K2 L N Q S1 S2 V W Z(i,l,m)
Emergency Action, Agency, Advocacy and Legal Aid undertaken
Ptr: Barrett, Mr Simon C L. . . . . *Mar 1986
Nelligan, Mr Patrick Mark . . . . Oct 1995
Ast: Hillson, Mr Martin David. . . . . May 1991

BLACKBURN & CO ‡
13-15 Preston Street Fleetwood Lancashire FY7 6JD
Tel: 01253 872238 *Fax:* 01253 773576
List of partners: A G Godwin, D R Green, A M O'Brien
Office: Thornton Cleveleys
Work: C1 E G H K1 L N R1 S1 S2 T2 V W Z(c,l)
Agency, Advocacy, Fixed Fee Interview and Legal Aid undertaken
Ptr: Godwin, Mr Alan G LLB. . . . . *Dec 1975
O'Brien, Mr Anthony M BA . . . . *Dec 1981
Ast: Platt, Miss Sharon Ann LLB . . . . *Jan 1998

INGHAMS
32-38 North Albert Street Fleetwood Lancashire FY7 6AW
Tel: 01253 873481 *Fax:* 01253 772322 *Dx:* 18251 FLEETWOOD
Emergency telephone 01253 884610
Office: Blackpool (2 offices), Knott-End-on-Sea, Poulton-le-Fylde, Thornton Cleveleys
Work: D1 D2 E F1 G H J1 K1 L N Q R1 S1 S2 V W Z(h,l,q)
Emergency Action, Advocacy, Fixed Fee Interview, Legal Aid undertaken and Legal Aid Franchise
Ptr: Beckett, Mr Christopher Barry LLB(Hons) . . . . . . *Nov 1998
Isaacs, Mr Peter J. . . . . *Dec 1973
Muir, Mr John P BA(Dunelm) . . . . *Oct 1980
Ast: McCormick, Miss Helen BA(Hons). . . . . *Mar 2002
Weaver, Mr Andrew Paul . . . . *Jul 2001

PALMER HODGSON & HEYES
23-25 Poulton Street Fleetwood Lancashire FY7 6LP
Tel: 01253 778231 *Fax:* 01253 878996 *Dx:* 18256 FLEETWOOD
Office: Thornton Cleveleys
Work: B1 C1 D1 E F1 G H J1 K1 L M1 N P S1 T1 V W Z(l,m)
Emergency Action, Agency, Advocacy, Fixed Fee Interview, Legal Aid undertaken, Legal Aid Franchise and Member of Accident Line
Ptr: Heyes, Mr Gary BA . . . . *Nov 1988
Palmer, Mr Christopher J MA(St Andrews). . . . . . *Nov 1980

RENSHAW GILCHRIST & CO ‡
9 St Peters Place Fleetwood Lancashire FY7 6ED
Tel: 01253 873569 *Fax:* 01253 777205
List of partners: R M R Gilchrist
Ptr: Gilchrist, Mr Roderick M R . . . . *May 1962

ROWNTREE & BERRY ‡
33 North Albert Street Fleetwood Lancashire FY7 6AN
Tel: 01253 872581 *Fax:* 01253 777809 *Dx:* 18254 FLEETWOOD
Emergency telephone 01253 891346
E-mail: rowntreeandberry@btconnect.com
List of partners: R J D Berry, J Durning
Office: Poulton-le-Fylde
Emergency Action, Agency, Fixed Fee Interview and Legal Aid undertaken
Ptr: Berry, Mr Roger J D LLB . . . . Jul 1969
Durning, Mr John BA . . . . Feb 1983

VINCENTS SOLICITORS ‡
110 Lord Street Fleetwood Lancashire FY7 6LB
Tel: 01253 773377 *Fax:* 01253 770911 *Dx:* 18259 FLEETWOOD

FLINT, Flintshire

HARVEYS SOLICITORS
45 Church Street Flint Flintshire CH6 5AE
Tel: 01352 734003 *Fax:* 01352 734069
Office: Deeside
Ast: Larkin, Fiona . . . . Apr 2008

STEPHEN MULLARKEY SOLICITORS
54 Church Street Flint Flintshire CH6 5AE
Tel: 01352 733770 *Fax:* 01352 734085
Emergency telephone 01352 763727
E-mail: sm.solicitors@btconnect.com
Office: Holywell
Work: D1 G H K1 N Q S1 W
Emergency Action, Agency, Advocacy, Fixed Fee Interview, Legal Aid undertaken, Legal Aid Franchise and Member of Accident Line
SPr: Mullarkey, Mr Stephen BA(Nott'm). . . . . *Oct 1987

FLITWICK, Bedfordshire

REBECCA L FARET SOLICITORS ‡
Bridge House 3 Station Square Flitwick Bedfordshire MK45 1DP
Tel: 01525 712112 *Fax:* 01525 718136 *Dx:* 47000 FLITWICK
E-mail: p.derosaire@rlfaret.co.uk
List of partners: P Derosaire, R L Faret
Work: J1 K1 K3 L N S1 S2 W Z(l,r)
Agency, Advocacy and Fixed Fee Interview undertaken
Ptr: Derosaire, Mrs Penelope LLB . . . . *Aug 2005
Faret, Miss Rebecca L LLB . . . . *§Jul 1986

SYDNEY MITCHELL ‡
7 Station Square Flitwick Bedfordshire MK45 1DP
Tel: 01525 175520

FOLKESTONE, Kent

BKRW LIMITED ‡
5 Shellons Street Folkestone Kent CT20 1BW
Tel: 01303 255369 *Fax:* 01303 244575 *Dx:* 4902 FOLKESTONE
E-mail: info@bkrwsolicitors.co.uk
List of partners: H G B Roberts
Office: Dover, Ramsgate
Work: D1 E G H K1 L N O Q S1 W
Emergency Action, Agency, Advocacy, Legal Aid undertaken and Member of Accident Line
Ptr: Roberts, Mr Hugh G B . . . . *§Jul 1971

 See p112 for the Key to Work Categories & other symbols

BOWERS & JESSUP ‡
Westholme Chambers 134a Sandgate Road Folkestone Kent CT20 2BW
Tel: 01303 850678 *Fax:* 01303 220236 *Dx:* 4901 FOLKESTONE
List of partners: A J Bowers, L J Jessup
Work: K1 K3 Q S1 W Z(c)
Emergency Action, Agency and Fixed Fee Interview undertaken
Ptr: Bowers, Mr Adrian James BA(Hons) . . . . May 1998
Jessup, Ms Linda J . . . . May 1987

P H BROTHWELL ‡
16 Church Street Folkestone Kent CT20 1SE
Tel: 01303 253368 *Fax:* 01303 255758
List of partners: P H Brothwell
Work: S1 W
Ptr: Brothwell, Mr Peter Hobson . . . . *Oct 1974

ELDER RAHIMI LIMITED
Channel Business Centre Ingles Manor Castle Hill Avenue Folkestone Kent CT20 2RD
Tel: 07920 747475
E-mail: office@elderrahimi.co.uk
Office: London E1

FREDERIC HALL ‡
York House 32 Cheriton Gardens Folkestone Kent CT20 2UR
Tel: 01303 851185 *Fax:* 01303 850700 *Dx:* 4907 FOLKESTONE
E-mail: ash@frederic-hall.co.uk
List of partners: A S L Head, M Ivor-Jones, M S Kirk, R C P Medlicott, N G Price, J P Saynor
Office: Dover
Work: D1 E F1 G H J1 K1 K3 L N O Q S1 S2 V W Z(l,q)
Emergency Action, Agency, Advocacy, Legal Aid undertaken and Legal Aid Franchise
Ptr: Head, Ms Abigail S L LLB. . . . . *§Dec 1997
Ivor-Jones, Mr Michael BA . . . . *§Nov 1981
Medlicott, Mr Richard C P MA(Cantab) . . . . *§Nov 1982
Price, Mr Nicholas George LLB . . . . §Jan 1996

PARABIS LAW LLP ‡
The Saga Building Middelburg square Folkestone Kent CT20 1AZ
E-mail: info@parabis.co.uk

RIXONS SOLICITORS ‡
12 Cheriton Place Folkestone Kent CT20 2AZ
Tel: 01303 850090 *Fax:* 01303 850412 *Dx:* 4918 FOLKSTONE

ROOTES & ALLIOTT ‡
(incorporating T R S Miller)
27 Cheriton Gardens Folkestone Kent CT20 2AR
Tel: 01303 851100 *Fax:* 01303 851150 *Dx:* 4903 FOLKESTONE
E-mail: mail@rootes-alliott.co.uk
List of partners: A M Bevington, M N Duncombe, A P Isaacson, J K Morrison, S M J Watler, G Wynn Green
Office: Hythe
Languages: French, German
Work: A1 B1 C1 C2 C3 D1 D2 E F1 J1 K1 K3 K4 L M1 N O P Q R1 S1 S2 T1 T2 V W Z(c,d,h,j,k,l,m,p,s,t)
Emergency Action, Agency, Advocacy, Fixed Fee Interview, Legal Aid undertaken and Legal Aid Franchise
Ptr: Bevington, Mr Anthony M LLB. . . . . *§Nov 1970
Duncombe, Mr Martin Neil. . . . . *Oct 1981
Isaacson, Mr Anthony P Notary Public. . . . . *§Dec 1980
Morrison, Mr James K LLB . . . . *Nov 1984
Watler, Mrs Susan M J BA . . . . *§Oct 1979
Wynn Green, Mrs Gilian BA. . . . . *§Oct 1987
Ast: Barter, Mrs Sally Amanda BA(German & French); PGDL; LPC College of Law Guildford Family Law Prize . . . *Mar 2008
Garrard, Ms Sarah Lynette BA . . . . *§Oct 1995
Medlicott, Mrs Judith Margaret BA(Hons) . . . . . . Jan 1986
Toms-Wilson, Mrs Melanie Jane. . . . . *§Jul 2002

WAITT & CO SOLICITORS
Ingles Cottage Ingles Yard Jointon Road Folkestone Kent CT20 2RY
Tel: 01303 211999 *Fax:* 01303 250250 *Dx:* 5321 CANTERBURY
E-mail: info@waittlaw.com
Office: Canterbury

WORTHINGTONS ‡
28 Cheriton Gardens Folkestone Kent CT20 2AU
Tel: 01303 850206 *Fax:* 01303 246706 *Dx:* 4905 FOLKESTONE
Emergency telephone 01233 750170
E-mail: enquiries@weh.co.uk
List of partners: A H Butler, R C Jardella, B G Keating
Languages: French
Work: A3 B1 B2 C1 D1 D2 E F1 F2 G J1 K1 K2 L M1 N O Q R1 S1 S2 T1 T2 V W Z(e,h,i,l,m,p,q,r)
Emergency Action, Agency, Advocacy, Fixed Fee Interview, Legal Aid undertaken and Legal Aid Franchise
Ptr: Butler, Mr Andrew H BA. . . . . *§Nov 1981
Jardella, Mrs Rhona Campbell . . . . *Dec 1992
Keating, Mr Barry G BA(Law) . . . . *§Nov 1981
Ast: Coley, Mr Thomas Lionel . . . . *Sep 2000

FORDINGBRIDGE, Hampshire

DIXON & TEMPLETON ‡
(incorporating Truman-Moore (Ringwood))
43 High Street Fordingbridge Hampshire SP6 1AU
Tel: 01425 652194 *Fax:* 01425 657288 *Dx:* 46051 FORDINGBRIDGE
E-mail: law@dixon-templeton.com
List of partners: K French, W S Templeton, S J Wyatt
Office: Ringwood
Work: A1 A3 B1 C1 C2 C3 D1 D2 E F1 J1 K1 K2 K3 K4 L M1 M2 N O P Q R1 S1 S2 T1 T2 V W Z(c,d,h,l,m,o,q,r)
Emergency Action, Agency and Advocacy undertaken
Ptr: French, Mr Kevin LLB. . . . . *Mar 1986
Templeton, Mr William S . . . . *Oct 1969
Wyatt, Mr Stephen John LLB(Exon); TEP . . . . . . *Dec 1974
Ast: Prado, Mr Anthony Bernard LLB(Hons); LLM ● . . . . *Dec 1988

JACKSONS ‡
5 Provost Street Fordingbridge Hampshire SP6 1AZ
Tel: 01425 652110 *Fax:* 01425 654606 *Dx:* 46050 FORDINGBRIDGE
E-mail: info@fordingbridgesolicitors.co.uk
List of partners: D J Bowen-Ashwin, N J Donell, R G Eason
Languages: French
Work: A1 A2 C1 C2 E F1 J1 J2 K1 L N O P Q R1 R2 S1 S2 T1 T2 W Z(c,d,l,m,n,p,q)
Emergency Action, Agency and Advocacy undertaken
Ptr: Bowen-Ashwin, Mr David J BSc. . . . . *May 1981
Donell, Mr Nigel J. . . . . *§Nov 1978
Eason, Mr Robert G. . . . . Jun 1976

MEESONS
22 Salisbury Street Fordingbridge Hampshire SP6 1AF
Est: 1801
Tel: 01425 655251 *Fax:* 01425 656768 *Dx:* 46052 FORDINGBRIDGE
E-mail: fordingbridge@meesonssolicitors.co.uk
Office: Ringwood
Work: A1 B1 C1 D1 E F1 G H J1 K1 L M1 P S1 T1 V W Z(d,m)
Emergency Action, Agency, Advocacy, Fixed Fee Interview and Legal Aid undertaken
Ptr: Quain, Mrs Meriel. . . . . *Nov 1983

FOREST ROW, East Sussex

P R VINCE SOLICITORS ‡
Ashorne House Lewes Road Forest Row East Sussex RH18 5AB
Tel: 01342 822112 *Fax:* 01342 824964 *Dx:* 117777 FOREST ROW
E-mail: enquiries@vincelaw.com
List of partners: N C Tompkin, P R Vince
Languages: French
Work: A1 C1 C2 E J1 Q R2 S1 S2 T1 T2 W
Ptr: Tompkin, Mr Nicholas Charles LLB(Hons); LPC . . . . *Jan 2005
Vince, Mr Peter Richard. . . . . *Jan 1966

FORMBY, Merseyside

BIRCHALL BLACKBURN LLP
Ryeground House 6 Ryeground Lane Formby Merseyside L37 7EQ
Tel: 01704 832222 *Fax:* 01704 832111 *Dx:* 15409 FORMBY
Office: Chester, Chorley, Leyland, Manchester, Morecambe, Preston (2 offices), Southport

GABRIELS SOLICITORS ‡
38 Church Road Formby Merseyside L37 3NF
Tel: 01704 831554 *Fax:* 01704 831567
Languages: Italian
Work: B1 C1 E F1 F2 G H J1 K1 K2 K3 K4 L N O Q R1 S1 S2 W X Z(e,g,k,q)
Agency, Fixed Fee Interview and Legal Aid undertaken

MAXWELL HODGE SOLICITORS
(incorporating Goffey & Co)
Turret House 3 Chapel Lane Formby Merseyside L37 4DL
Tel: 01704 872156 *Fax:* 01704 831902 *Dx:* 15405 FORMBY
E-mail: info@maxweb.co.uk
Office: Heswall, Huyton, Kirkby, Liverpool (2 offices), Maghull, West Kirby
Work: A1 C1 E K4 L R1 R2 S1 S2 W
Ptr: Langfeld, Mr Allan L F LLB(Hons) . . . . *§Apr 1976
Williams, Mr Francis C . . . . *Dec 1974
Yates, Mr Michael John LLB(Hons) . . . . *Dec 1974

WHITFIELDS ‡
Marion House 23-25 Elbow Lane Formby Merseyside L37 4AB
Tel: 01704 878501 *Fax:* 01704 872145 *Dx:* 15403 FORMBY
Emergency telephone 01704 831592
E-mail: phil@whitfieldssolicitors.com
List of partners: T J McGraw, M L Osman, J R Pedley, J Smith, B Whitfield
Languages: French
Work: A1 B1 B2 C1 C2 D1 D2 E F1 G H J1 K1 K2 L M1 N O P Q R1 S1 S2 T1 T2 V W Z(a,b,c,d,e,f,g,h,i,j,k,l,m,n,p,q,r,s,t,y)
Emergency Action, Agency, Advocacy, Fixed Fee Interview, Legal Aid undertaken and Member of Accident Line
Ptr: McGraw, Mr Terry J LLB . . . . Apr 1981
Osman, Ms Margaret L LLB. . . . . Dec 1975
Pedley, Mr Jeffrey R LLB . . . . Nov 1980
Smith, Mr James LLB. . . . . Oct 1996
Whitfield, Mr Brian LLB . . . . *Dec 1973
Con: Bryan, Mr Joseph F. . . . . *Dec 1977
Parry, Mr James Neil Robertson. . . . . *Jul 1994

FRAMLINGHAM, Suffolk

CROSS RAM & CO
3 Church Street Framlingham Suffolk IP13 9BG
Tel: 01728 724111 *Fax:* 01728 724747 *Dx:* 123920 FRAMLINGHAM
E-mail: info@crossramfram.co.uk
Office: Halesworth
Work: A1 E L S1 W
Ptr: Parkes, Mrs Lorraine Daphne MA(Cantab) . . . . . . *Nov 1991

GURNEYS ‡
6 Riverside Framlingham Suffolk IP13 9AG
Tel: 01728 621372 *Fax:* 01728 723057
E-mail: mail@gurneys-solicitors.co.uk
List of partners: L F Gurney
Work: K1 K3 N W
Ptr: Gurney, Miss Lynne F LLB(Hons)(Leeds) . . . . *Oct 1985

FRESHWATER, Isle of Wight

ELDRIDGES
Avenue House Avenue Road Freshwater Isle of Wight PO40 9UZ
Tel: 01983 752492 *Fax:* 01983 754247
E-mail: info@eldridges.co.uk
Office: Newport, Ryde
Work: A1 C1 E F1 J1 K4 L P S1 S2 T2 W Z(d)
Ptr: Friend, Mrs Marian J BA(Hons)(Law) . . . . *§Jun 1977
Suggett, Mr John Anthony LLB(Lond) . . . . *§Apr 1972
Ast: Chave-Hill, Mrs Laura Louise . . . . *§Oct 2004

PHILLIPS ‡
Myrtle House High Street Freshwater Isle of Wight PO40 9JX
Tel: 01983 755050 *Fax:* 01983 759058

RJR SOLICITORS
Clayton House Queens Road Freshwater Isle of Wight PO40 9EN
Tel: 01983 752115 *Fax:* 01983 755494
Emergency telephone 01983 752115
E-mail: freshwater@rjr.co.uk
Office: Newport, Ryde
Languages: French, German
Work: A1 C1 E K4 R1 R2 S1 S2 W

2

FRIMLEY, Surrey

ROBERT SIMMONS LEGAL SERVICES LIMITED ‡
3 Wharf Road Frimley Surrey GU16 6LE
Tel: 01252 267980 *Fax:* 01252 835217
E-mail: david.simmons@robert-simmons.co.uk

VIHPS LEGAL ‡
7 Wyvern House 55-61 Frimley High Street Frimley Surrey GU16 7HJ
Tel: 0845 450 8445 *Fax:* 0845 280 1777
E-mail: paul@vihps.com

FRINTON-ON-SEA, Essex

ELLISONS
143 Connaught Avenue Frinton-on-Sea Essex CO13 9AB
Tel: 01255 851000 *Fax:* 01255 850041
E-mail: nicky.coates@ellisonssolicitors.com
Office: Clacton-on-Sea, Colchester, Harwich
Work: K1 K2 K3 K4 S1 W
Ptr: Coates, Mrs Nicola M LLB. . . . . *Apr 1991

SPARLING BENHAM & BROUGH
(incorporating Kenneth Elliott & Co)
62a Connaught Avenue Frinton-on-Sea Essex CO13 9QH
Tel: 01255 679222 *Fax:* 01255 679229
E-mail: sparlings.frinton@dial.pipex.com
Office: Colchester
Work: A1 C1 D1 E J1 K1 L N O Q R1 S1 S2 T1 T2 W Z(d)
Agency undertaken
Ptr: Juby, Mr Jonathan B . . . . *§Jul 1975

FRODSHAM, Cheshire

APP LAW ‡
3 Fingerpost Lane Frodsham Cheshire WA6 8LE
Tel: 01928 788537 *Fax:* 01928 787937

BUTCHER & BARLOW LLP
6 Church Street Frodsham Cheshire WA6 7EB
Tel: 01928 733871 *Fax:* 01928 739439 *Dx:* 15602 FRODSHAM
Emergency telephone 01928 733871 / 733546
Office: Bramhall, Bury (2 offices), Leigh, Northwich, Prestwich, Runcorn (2 offices), Sandbach, Tyldesley
Work: A1 B1 C1 C2 C3 D1 E F1 G H J1 K1 L N O R1 S1 T1 T2 V W
Agency, Advocacy, Fixed Fee Interview and Legal Aid undertaken
Ptr: Ashton, Mr Richard James LLB(Hons). . . . . Mar 1979
Taylor, Miss Rachael LLB(Hons). . . . . Apr 1996

FORSHAWS DAVIES RIDGWAY LLP
20 High Street Frodsham Cheshire WA6 7HE
Tel: 01928 739300 *Fax:* 01928 735190 *Dx:* 15603 FRODSHAM
E-mail: info@forshaws.co.uk
Office: Warrington (4 offices)
Work: A1 D1 F1 K1 K2 K3 N R1 S1 V W Z(q,r)
Emergency Action, Agency, Advocacy, Fixed Fee Interview, Legal Aid undertaken, Legal Aid Franchise and Member of Accident Line
Ptr: Hetherington, Miss Ruth Claire Part Time Assessor for the Law Society . . . . *Nov 1996
Lawson, Mr Stephen P LLB . . . . *Oct 1984
Asoc: Andrews, Ms Victoria . . . . Jan 2004

ROWLINSONS ‡
9 Church Street Frodsham Cheshire WA6 7DN
Tel: 01928 735333 *Fax:* 01928 735183 *Dx:* 15601 FRODSHAM
E-mail: info@rowlinsons.co.uk
List of partners: D E Eland, L B Rowlinson, D Stevenson
Work: A1 E J1 K1 K3 L R1 S1 S2 W Z(l,w)
Dir: Eland, Miss Donna Elizabeth LLB(Hons) STEP Diploma Outstanding Student of the Year. . . . . *Sep 2004
Rowlinson, Mrs Lynne Barbara LLB(Lond). . . . . . . *Sep 1979
Stevenson, Mr Denis FILEx . . . . *§Jan 1983
Ast: Frayne, Miss Carolyn LLB(Hons) . . . . *Oct 1995
Higgins, Ms Karen LLB(Hons). . . . . *Dec 2006
Parkinson, Mr Thomas James LLB(Hons) . . . . *Jan 2007
Con: Daly, Mr Michael BA(Hons)(Law) . . . . *Oct 1981

FROME, Somerset

AMES KENT ‡
Bridge House Bridge Street Frome Somerset BA11 1BD
Tel: 01373 462017 *Fax:* 01373 452196 *Dx:* 43800 FROME
E-mail: law@ames-kent.co.uk
List of partners: M M Rogers
Work: A1 B1 C1 E F1 J1 K3 L N O P Q R1 S1 S2 W Z(d,i,m)
Agency undertaken
Ptr: Rogers, Mr Michael M. . . . . *Sep 1975

BROWN & VAUTIER ‡
(incorporating Ritson & Vautier; Simon Brown)
Ken House Cork Street Frome Somerset BA11 1BL
Tel: 01373 465222 *Fax:* 01373 468816 *Dx:* 43805 FROME
E-mail: law@brownandvautier.com
List of partners: D D A Vautier
Work: A1 B1 C1 D1 D2 E F1 J1 K1 K4 L N O Q R1 S1 T1 V Z(f,g,l,q,r)
Emergency Action, Agency, Advocacy, Fixed Fee Interview, Legal Aid undertaken and Legal Aid Franchise
Ptr: Vautier, Mr David D A LLB(Lond) . . . . *Dec 1971
Ast: Vernalls, Ms Penelope BA(Hons) . . . . Oct 1999

DO I HAVE A CASE? (TOM STREET & CO) ‡
Maidsgrove Farm Standerwick Frome Somerset BA11 2PY
Tel: 0800 014 8727
E-mail: cgeorge@doihaveacase.co.uk

FDC LAW ‡
Argyll House Bath Street Frome Somerset BA11 1DP
Tel: 01373 465051 *Fax:* 01373 467414 *Dx:* 43801 FROME
E-mail: frome@fdc-law.co.uk
List of partners: D A Collins, S E Emery, D Gazzard, J Hollis, M L A Taylor, B J Whelan, J D Wood
Office: Frome, Keynsham, Radstock
Languages: French, German
Work: A1 B1 C1 C2 D1 E F1 G J1 J2 K1 K2 K3 K4 L N O Q R1 S1 S2 T1 T2 V W X Z(c,l)
Emergency Action, Agency, Advocacy and Fixed Fee Interview undertaken
Ptr: Gazzard, Mr David . . . . . *Dec 1993
Hollis, Mr James BA . . . . . *Jun 1980
Asoc: Roberts, Mrs Susan BA; MEd . . . . . Oct 1992

FDC LAW
22 Bath Street Frome Somerset BA11 1DL
Tel: 01373 463311 *Fax:* 01373 455780 *Dx:* 43801 FROME
E-mail: info@fdc-law.co.uk
Office: Frome, Keynsham, Radstock
Languages: French, German
Work: A1 A3 B1 C1 C2 C3 D1 D2 E F1 K1 K2 K3 L M1 M2 P R1 S1 S2 T1 T2 V Z(c,d,e,r)
Emergency Action, Agency, Advocacy, Fixed Fee Interview, Legal Aid undertaken and Legal Aid Franchise
Ptr: Emery, Ms Sandra E LLB . . . . . *Dec 1977
Asoc: Short, Mr Martin Geoffrey . . . . . *Jan 1985

GOTLEYS SOLICITORS ‡
2a Bath Street Frome Somerset BA11 1DL
Tel: 01373 454546 *Fax:* 01373 454030
E-mail: gotley@gotleys.co.uk

HARRIS & HARRIS
11 Stony Street Frome Somerset BA11 1BU
Tel: 01373 463366 *Fax:* 01373 468468 *Dx:* 43804 FROME
Emergency telephone 07967 197005
E-mail: reception@fromeharris-harris.co.uk
Office: Wells
Languages: French
Work: A1 A3 C1 C2 C3 D1 D2 E F1 F2 J1 J2 K1 K2 K3 K4 L N O Q R1 S1 S2 U2 W X Z(c,e,f,p,q)
Advocacy, Fixed Fee Interview and Legal Aid undertaken
Ptr: Clare, Mr John Edwin MA(Cantab) . . . . . *Apr 1976
Howlett, Mr Neil Michael MA(Cantab) . . . . . *Nov 1984
Macaulay, Mrs Alison Rosemary BA(Law) . . . . . *Jul 1980
Asoc: Clare, Mrs Jennifer M LLB . . . . . *Oct 1976

NEIL MCCORMICK ‡
1a Church Steps Frome Somerset BA11 1PL
Tel: 01373 455700 *Fax:* 01373 455015
List of partners: M N McCormick
Work: E L N O Q S1 S2 Z(q)
SPr: McCormick, Mr M Neil . . . . . *May 1978

TOWLER BROWN ‡
5 The Bridge Frome Somerset BA11 1AR
Tel: 01373 452955 *Fax:* 01373 452978 *Dx:* 43819 FROME
List of partners: S C Brown
Work: A1 E F1 S1 W Z(d)
Agency, Advocacy undertaken and Member of Accident Line
Ptr: Brown, Mr Simon Christopher BA(Hons) . . . . . *Feb 1983

KAREN WALLIS LAW LLP ‡
2 West End Frome Somerset BA11 3AD
Tel: 01373 473240 *Fax:* 01373 471530
E-mail: info@karenwallislaw.com

GAINSBOROUGH, Lincolnshire

BELL WRIGHT & CO ‡
7 Lord Street Gainsborough Lincolnshire DN21 2DF
Tel: 01427 611722 *Fax:* 01427 611173 *Dx:* 27204 GAINSBOROUGH
E-mail: bwd.gainsborough@ukonline.co.uk
List of partners: J Flowers, P D Wright
Languages: French
Work: A1 B1 C1 D1 E F1 G H J1 K1 K4 L N O P Q R1 S1 T1 V W Z(b,c,d,e,f,g,h,i,k,l,n,o,p,s,t)
Emergency Action, Agency, Advocacy, Fixed Fee Interview, Legal Aid undertaken and Member of Accident Line
Ptr: Flowers, Mr Jolyon BSc(Hons) . . . . . *§Oct 1989
Wright, Mr Peter D BA . . . . . *§Aug 1977

BURTON & DYSON ‡
22 Market Place Gainsborough Lincolnshire DN21 2BZ
Tel: 01427 610761 *Fax:* 01427 616866
E-mail: enquiries@burtondyson.com
List of partners: S R Hardy, P G Westcott, L J Whitelam
Languages: French, Italian, Spanish
Work: A1 C1 C2 D1 D2 E F2 J1 K1 K3 K4 L N O Q S1 S2 W Z(e,m)
Legal Aid undertaken, Legal Aid Franchise and Member of Accident Line
Ptr: Hardy, Mr Steven R LLB . . . . . *Oct 1990
Westcott, Mr Philip G BSc Notary Public . . . . . Nov 1974
Whitelam, Mrs Lisa Jane LLB(Hons) . . . . . Feb 2003
Ast: Carr, Sarah . . . . . Apr 2009
Dunphy, Mr David LLB . . . . . Oct 2004
Elwess, Mrs Alison Rachel BA; PGDipLaw; LPC . . . . . *Sep 2006
Foyster, Elizabeth . . . . . Feb 2002
Lockwood, Mrs Sharon LLB(Hons) . . . . . Sep 2003

CRADDOCK HODGSON & WILDIN ‡
47a Lord Street Gainsborough Lincolnshire DN21 2DD
Tel: 01427 615221 *Fax:* 01427 677079 *Dx:* 27208 GAINSBOROUGH
E-mail: davidhodgson@ch-w.co.uk

EDMUNDS & CO ‡
17 Morley Street Gainsborough Lincolnshire DN21 2NF
Tel: 01427 679817

HSR LAW (HAYES, SON & RICHMOND) ‡
Ship Court Silver Street Gainsborough Lincolnshire DN21 2DN
Tel: 01427 613831 *Fax:* 01427 611022 *Dx:* 27201 GAINSBOROUGH
Emergency telephone 07774 677465
E-mail: gainsboroughenquiries@hsrlaw.co.uk
List of partners: R J Allwood, A W Best, J E Bradley, F Braithwaite, T J Flinders, R E Fullwood, D K Harris, L A Kirkham
Office: Doncaster, Epworth
Languages: French, Punjabi, Urdu
Work: A1 A2 B1 B2 C1 C2 D1 D2 E F1 G H J1 J2 K1 K2 L N O P Q S1 S2 V W X Z(d,l,q)
Emergency Action, Agency, Advocacy, Fixed Fee Interview and Legal Aid undertaken
Ptr: Allwood, Mr Richard J TD BA(Hons)(Soton); PGCE(Lond) . . . . . *Oct 1984
Best, Mr Andrew W LLB . . . . . Sep 2001
Bradley, Mr John E MBIM Member of the Legal Aid Area Committee . . . . . Dec 1976
Braithwaite, Mr Fabian BA; JD . . . . . Nov 2004
Flinders, Mrs Tracy Jayne LLB; LSF Parish Councillor . *Oct 1995
Fullwood, Mr Richard Ellis . . . . . *Jun 1980
Harris, Mr David Keith OBE; TD; DL LLB(Lond) . . . . . *Dec 1969
Kirkham, Ms Lucy Anne LLB . . . . . Oct 1997
Ast: Burnett, Mr Russell . . . . . Sep 2004
Coddington, Ms Catherine LLB . . . . . Apr 2008
Davies, Mr David P E LLB . . . . . *Jul 1977
Hayles, Mr Nicholas P LLB ★ . . . . . *Dec 1977
Macdonald, Miss Kirstin-Anne LLB . . . . . Nov 2006
Russell, Mr Paul LLB . . . . . Nov 2007
Wood, Mr Mark LLB . . . . . Jun 2005
Con: Vickers, Mr Peter G . . . . . *§Jan 1970

ANDREW JAY & CO (PHILIP HANBY LIMITED) ‡
26 Lord Street Gainsborough Lincolnshire DN21 2DB
Tel: 01427 612412 *Fax:* 01427 810551 *Dx:* 27202 GAINSBOROUGH
Emergency telephone 01427 612412
E-mail: reception@andrewjay.co.uk
List of partners: A P Jay
Office: Lincoln
Languages: French
Work: D1 F1 G H J1 K1 L N Q R1 S1 V W X
Emergency Action, Agency, Advocacy, Fixed Fee Interview, Legal Aid undertaken, Legal Aid Franchise and Member of Accident Line
Ptr: Jay, Mr Andrew P LLB . . . . . *Jan 1980
Ast: Cunningham, Mr Anthony BA(Hons); CPE; LPC; PSC *Nov 1999
Forman, Mr Tim . . . . . *Apr 1999

SILLS & BETTERIDGE LLP
Unit 1C The Pattern Store Station Approach Gainsborough Lincolnshire DN21 2AU
Tel: 01427 616816 *Fax:* 01427 678817
E-mail: info@sillslegal.co.uk
Office: Boston, Coningsby, Lincoln, Skegness, Sleaford, Spalding, Spilsby
Work: G J1 N O Q S1 W Z(m)
Ptr: Capes, Mr Edward LLB(Hons); Licence en Droit . . . . Sep 2003
Hayes, Miss Maureen LLB(ELS) . . . . . *Sep 2003
Jaehrig, Mrs Shan FILEx; CPE . . . . . Jan 1994
Woods, Mr Anthony C LLB . . . . . Sep 1984

Particular areas of work include: Crime - General, Employment Law, Litigation, Accidents, Injury, Criminal Injury Com, Litigation - Commercial, Litigation - General.

TRENTSIDE LEGAL ‡
Catharine Place Chambers 10-14 Hickman Street Gainsborough Lincolnshire DN21 2DZ
Tel: 01427 616977 *Fax:* 01427 677188

GARFORTH, West Yorkshire

EMSLEYS
6 Main Street Garforth West Yorkshire LS25 1EZ
Tel: 0113 286 8746 *Fax:* 0113 286 2742 *Dx:* 29761 GARFORTH
E-mail: law@emsleys.co.uk
Office: Castleford, Crossgates, Leeds, Rothwell (2 offices)
Languages: French, German
Work: K1 K2 K3 S1 W Z(g)

ISON HARRISON
29 Main Street Garforth West Yorkshire LS25 1DS
Tel: 0113 286 1455 *Fax:* 0113 287 3014 *Dx:* 29766 GARFORTH
E-mail: garforth@isonharrison.co.uk
Office: Guiseley, Ilkley, Leeds (3 offices)
Work: E K1 K3 K4 N Q S1 S2 T2 W Z(q)
Emergency Action, Agency, Advocacy, Fixed Fee Interview, Legal Aid undertaken and Member of Accident Line
Ptr: Phillips, Mr Martyn J LLB . . . . . *Mar 1972
Ast: Beddoe, Mrs Beatrice Emma Clare LLB; LSF . . . . . *Sep 1994
Hynd, Ms Alison Clare LLB . . . . . *Dec 1980

GARSTANG, Lancashire

THURNHILLS
Cross House Market Place Garstang Lancashire PR3 1ZA
Tel: 01995 603142 *Fax:* 01995 600163
E-mail: adam.thurnhills@thurnhills.co.uk
Office: Preston
Languages: French
Work: A1 C1 D1 E F1 J1 K1 L N O Q R1 S1 W Z(c,j,k,l)
Emergency Action, Agency, Fixed Fee Interview, Legal Aid undertaken and Member of Accident Line
Ptr: Thurnhill, Mr Joseph A . . . . . *Feb 1975
Asoc: Thurnhill, Mr Marcus George . . . . . Dec 2001

TURNER PEARSON
Old Posthouse Market Place Garstang Lancashire PR3 1ZA
Tel: 01995 604536 *Fax:* 01995 605631 *Dx:* 17129 PRESTON 1
Emergency telephone 0800 132 383
E-mail: tracey@turnerslaw.co.uk
Office: Preston
Work: D1 E F1 J1 K1 K2 N Q S1 S2 W Z(l)

VINCENTS SOLICITORS ‡
Castle View Bridge Street Garstang Lancashire PR3 1YB
Tel: 01995 606442
Office: Poulton-le-Fylde
Work: C1 D1 E F1 J1 J2 K3 N O Q S1 S2 W Z(d,q)

GATESHEAD, Tyne & Wear

CARTWRIGHT KING
19 Kingsway House Kingsway Team Valley Gateshead Tyne & Wear NE11 0HW
Tel: 0191 487 6775 *Fax:* 0808 168 1500
Office: Birmingham, Derby, Leicester, Nottingham, Sheffield

JOHN DONKIN & CO ‡
Unit 9 Concept 2000 Sunderland Road Gateshead Tyne & Wear NE10 9LQ
Tel: 0191 495 2896 / 477 1781 *Fax:* 0191 495 9530
List of partners: J A Donkin, G Langlands
Office: Washington
Languages: French
Work: B2 C1 D1 D2 E F1 G H K1 L M1 N P Q S1 S2 T1 V W Z(g,l)
Emergency Action, Agency, Advocacy, Fixed Fee Interview, Legal Aid undertaken and Member of Accident Line
Ptr: Donkin, Mr John A . . . . . Jun 2004
Ast: Foley, Miss Jane . . . . . Aug 2001
Howd, Mrs Karen . . . . . *Jul 2001
McBride, Miss Caroline LLB . . . . . *Aug 1995
Wilkinson, Mr Andrew C . . . . . *Dec 1991

FOLEY HARRISON ‡
10 Regent Terrace Gateshead Tyne & Wear NE8 1LU
Tel: 0191 477 6333 *Fax:* 0191 477 1225
Emergency telephone 07831 463422
E-mail: mail@foley-harrison.co.uk
List of partners: M Foley, M Harrison
Work: D1 D2 G H K1 L N
Emergency Action, Agency, Advocacy, Fixed Fee Interview, Legal Aid undertaken and Legal Aid Franchise
Ptr: Foley, Mr Michael . . . . . Jan 1976
Harrison, Mr Mark . . . . . Jan 1985

GSE LEGALS ‡
The Lindum Chambers The Lindum Club Lindum Road Gateshead Tyne & Wear NE9 5AY
Tel: 0191 215 5008 / 07711 047335 *Fax:* 0191 490 1134
E-mail: info@gse-legals.co.uk

ALAN HALL ‡
15 Walker Terrace Gateshead Tyne & Wear NE8 1EB
Tel: 0191 477 7224 *Fax:* 0191 478 7892
List of partners: A Hall
Agency, Advocacy and Legal Aid undertaken
Ptr: Hall, Mr Alan . . . . . *Jul 1980

HALLIDAY REEVES ‡
8th Floor Chad House Tynegate Precinct Gateshead Tyne & Wear NE8 3HY
Tel: 0191 477 7728 *Fax:* 0191 477 9109
Emergency telephone 07623 523523
E-mail: enquiries@hallidayreeves.co.uk
List of partners: M D Halliday, M D Reeves
Office: Doncaster
Work: G H
Emergency Action, Agency, Advocacy, Fixed Fee Interview, Legal Aid undertaken and Legal Aid Franchise
Ptr: Halliday, Mr Martin D BA . . . . . *Dec 1979
Reeves, Mr Mark D LLB . . . . . *Feb 1989

HALLIDAY REEVES LAW FIRM ‡
PO Box 481 Gateshead Tyne & Wear NE8 9DW
Tel: 0191 477 7728 / 0844 811 2147 *Fax:* 0844 811 2148
E-mail: enquiries@hallidayreeves.com

HATHAWAYS ‡
(incorporating F S Lowe)
19 Regent Terrace Gateshead Tyne & Wear NE8 1LU
Tel: 0191 477 2288 *Fax:* 0191 490 0358 *Dx:* 60313 GATESHEAD
Emergency telephone 07889 007466
E-mail: jean@edwardhathaway.co.uk
List of partners: K F Graham, C J Kyle, C O Weidner
Office: Gateshead
Work: A1 B1 C1 D1 D2 E F1 G H J1 K1 L N O Q R1 S1 S2 T2 V W Z(g,i,k,l,m,q,r)
Emergency Action, Agency, Advocacy, Fixed Fee Interview, Legal Aid undertaken, Legal Aid Franchise and Member of Accident Line
Ptr: Graham, Mr Kevin F LLB . . . . . *Mar 1985
Kyle, Mr Christopher J LLB . . . . . *Oct 1990
Weidner, Mr Charles O LLB . . . . . *Dec 1979
Asoc: McManus, Mr Francis LLB . . . . . *May 1992

HATHAWAYS
572a-574a Durham Road Gateshead Tyne & Wear NE9 6HX
Tel: 0191 482 8700 *Fax:* 0191 482 6396 *Dx:* 60840 LOW FELL
Emergency telephone 07889 007466
E-mail: jean@edwardhathaway.co.uk
Office: Gateshead

HUTHARTS LAW FIRM ‡
Hillsyde House 17 Valley Gardens Low Fell Gateshead Tyne & Wear NE9 5EB
Tel: 0191 490 0031
E-mail: gillian@hutharts.com

IRIS LAW FIRM ‡
1st Floor Kent House Church Street Gateshead Tyne & Wear NE8 2AT
Tel: 0191 477 0055
E-mail: info@iris-law.co.uk

KD SOLICITORS ‡
88c High Street Felling Gateshead Tyne & Wear NE10 9LU
Tel: 0191 469 3322 *Fax:* 0191 469 3377
E-mail: legal.enquiries@kdsolicitors.co.uk
Work: C1 D1 E F1 J1 K1 K3 K4 L N O Q S1 S2 V W Z(e,k,l,m,p,u)
Agency, Advocacy, Fixed Fee Interview undertaken and Member of Accident Line

LAMBERT TAYLOR & GREGORY ‡
(incorporating Lambert & Lambert; Carr & Taylor; Lumsden Ramsey & Galbraith)
9 Walker Terrace Gateshead Tyne & Wear NE8 1EB
Tel: 0191 477 0616 *Fax:* 0191 490 0347 *Dx:* 60300 GATESHEAD
Emergency telephone 07733 018758
List of partners: T A W Gregory, A P Weldon
Work: A1 C1 D1 E G H J1 K1 L N O Q R1 R2 S1 S2 T1 T2 W Z(b,c,j,l,q)

See p112 for the Key to Work Categories & other symbols

Emergency Action, Agency, Advocacy, Fixed Fee Interview, Legal Aid undertaken and Legal Aid Franchise
Ptr: Gregory, Mr Timothy A W BA(Hons)(History) . . . . . *Aug 1991
Weldon, Mr Andrew Peter LLB . . . . *Apr 1994
Ast: Platt, Miss Margaret Mary BA; MA . . . . *Feb 1993

THOMAS MAGNAY & CO ‡
(incorporating Williamson & Jackson(Whickham))
13 Regent Terrace Gateshead Tyne & Wear NE8 1LU
Tel: 0191 477 3333 *Fax:* 0191 477 0978 *Dx:* 60305 GATESHEAD
List of partners: P S Bailey, P Magnay, W O'Grady, G G Smith
Office: Whickham
Work: A1 B1 C1 C2 C3 D1 E F1 J1 K1 K3 K4 L M1 M2 N P Q R1 S1 T1 T2 V W Z(c,d,f,i,j,k,l,m)
Emergency Action, Agency, Advocacy, Fixed Fee Interview, Legal Aid undertaken and Legal Aid Franchise
Ptr: Bailey, Miss Paula Sharon LLB(Hons) . . . . *Nov 1999
Magnay, Mr Peter DL . . . . *§Jun 1972
O'Grady, William . . . . Dec 1991
Smith, Mr Gregory Gordon . . . . Jul 2003
Con: Mitford, Mr David Coroner for the City of Newcastle-upon-Tyne . . . . Dec 1970

MULCAHY SMITH ‡
Regent House 21-23 Regent Terrace Gateshead Tyne & Wear NE8 1LU
Tel: 0191 490 1000 *Fax:* 0191 477 1996 *Dx:* 60302 GATESHEAD
E-mail: law@mulcahysmith.co.uk
List of partners: G Blackburn, P Hanratty, K L Henry
Work: A1 A3 B1 B2 C1 D1 D2 E F1 G H J1 K1 K2 K3 L N P Q R1 R2 S1 S2 T1 V W Z(h,l,m,o)
Emergency Action, Agency, Advocacy, Fixed Fee Interview, Legal Aid undertaken, Legal Aid Franchise and Member of Accident Line
Ptr: Blackburn, Mr Gerard BA . . . . *Feb 1983
Hanratty, Mr Paul BA . . . . *Feb 1990
Henry, Mrs Karen Lynne . . . . *Sep 1996
Ast: Martin, Ms Lisa Marie . . . . Oct 2010

SIMPSON MILLAR LLP
15a Walker Terrace Gateshead Tyne & Wear NE8 1EB
Tel: 0844 858 3000 *Fax:* 0844 858 3015
E-mail: info@simpsonmillar.co.uk
Office: Birmingham, Bristol, Cardiff, Leeds, London EC1, London SW19, Manchester

SWINBURNE & JACKSON LLP ‡
(incorporating Armstrong Rose & Appleby; J A Dixon & Son)
7 Walker Terrace Gateshead Tyne & Wear NE8 1DH
Tel: 0191 477 2531 / 477 3222 *Fax:* 0191 490 0371
Dx: 60303 GATESHEAD
Emergency telephone 07778 649842
E-mail: gateshead@swinburnejackson.com
List of partners: R Brennen, K M Pescott, J L Scott, C H S Swinburne
Office: Chester-le-Street, Hexham, Ryton, Washington
Work: B1 B2 C1 D1 D2 E F1 G H J1 J2 K1 K2 K4 L M1 M2 N O P Q R1 R2 S1 S2 V W Z(g,i,j,l,m,n,p,r)
Emergency Action, Agency, Advocacy, Fixed Fee Interview, Legal Aid undertaken, Legal Aid Franchise and Member of Accident Line
Ptr: Pescott, Miss Katrina Mary LLB(Hons) . . . . *Oct 1998
Swinburne, Mr Christian Hugh Stuart LLB(Hons)(Northumbria) . . . . *§Sep 1996
Asoc: Graham, Mr Richard LLB(Hons) . . . . Oct 2003
Ast: Blackburn, Mr Christopher . . . . *Dec 1978
Kerr, Miss Sarah Armstrong . . . . Mar 2004
Mackie, Mr David Andrew James . . . . Oct 2001
Sarwar, Mrs Naila . . . . Sep 2009
Simpson, Mrs Caroline Anne . . . . Mar 1991
Wood-Williams, Mr Michael Andrew . . . . Mar 2006
Con: Swinburne, Miss Lalage L LLB . . . . Mar 1956

TAIT FARRIER GRAHAM ‡
16 Regent Terrace Gateshead Tyne & Wear NE8 1LU
Tel: 0191 490 0108 *Fax:* 0191 490 1543 *Dx:* 60304 GATESHEAD
Emergency telephone 0191 285 1740
E-mail: info@gatesheadsolicitors.co.uk
List of partners: P J Farrier, T F Iceton, P Shepherd, R Tait
Office: Berwick-upon-Tweed, Newcastle upon Tyne
Work: B1 C1 D1 E F1 G H J1 K1 L M1 N P S1 V W Z(f,l,t)
Emergency Action, Agency, Advocacy, Fixed Fee Interview, Legal Aid undertaken, Legal Aid Franchise and Member of Accident Line
Ptr: Farrier, Mr Peter J LLB(Newc) . . . . Mar 1980
Iceton, Mr Thomas F BA . . . . *Feb 1983
Shepherd, Mr Philip BA . . . . Mar 1985
Tait, Mr Richard LLB(Leeds) . . . . Dec 1974

GERRARDS CROSS, Buckinghamshire

B P COLLINS LLP ‡
Collins House 32-38 Station Road Gerrards Cross Buckinghamshire SL9 8EL
Est: 1966
Tel: 01753 889995 *Fax:* 01753 889851
Dx: 40256 GERRARDS CROSS
Emergency telephone 01753 889995
E-mail: enquiries@bpcollins.co.uk
List of partners: S V Andrews, M J Brandis, J E Collis, J L Davis, S J Deans, D E Gill, N W Hallchurch, C D Hardy, M P Larcombe, D R Pritchard, D J Smellie, D R Stanning, J Townsend, C J Williams, A A Zachary
Languages: French, Greek
Work: A3 C1 C2 E I J1 K1 K2 K3 K4 L N O P Q R1 R2 S1 S2 T2 U2 W Z(d,e,k,m,o,p,q,w)
Ptr: Andrews, Miss Susan V LLB(Hons) . . . . *Jun 1980
Brandis, Mr Matthew Jason LLB . . . . *Sep 1997
Collis, Mrs Janet E . . . . *Nov 1981
Davis, Mrs Joanne L LLB . . . . *Oct 1991
Deans, Mr Simon John LLB . . . . *Nov 1997
Gill, Mrs Diane Elizabeth LLB . . . . *Oct 2003
Hallchurch, Mr Nicholas W LLB . . . . *Apr 1983
Hardy, Mr Christopher D MA(Oxon) . . . . *Dec 1980
Larcombe, Mr Michael P BA(Hons) . . . . *Nov 1993
Pritchard, Mr David R MA(Cantab) . . . . *Jul 1990
Smellie, Mr David John . . . . *Oct 1988
Stanning, Mr David R LLB(St Andrews) . . . . *Jan 1970
Townsend, Mr James BA(Hons) . . . . *Jun 2002
Williams, Mr Craig John LLB(Hons) . . . . *Oct 2003
Zachary, Mr Alexander A LLB . . . . *Sep 1999
Asoc: Baillie, Miss Emma Louise LLB(Hons) Blackstone Prize for Clinical Legal Education (2000) . . . . *Mar 2004
Baines, Mr Thomas Christopher BA; PGDL . . . . . . *Oct 2009
Caldecourt, Petrova . . . . *Aug 2007
Clark, Mr Robert James . . . . *Sep 2005
Congreves, Ms Julie Ann BSc(Hons) . . . . *Sep 2009
Davidoff, Mr Paul Daniel MA(Cantab); TEP STEP Student Excellence Award 2009 . . . . *Nov 2004
Deacon, Ms Sue . . . . *Mar 2004
Dunning, Mrs Shona Marie LLB(Hons) . . . . *Aug 2003
Fielder, Ms Kathryn LLB . . . . *Oct 1988
Galic, Miss Dara LLB . . . . *Oct 1990
Hipperson, Mrs Frances Elizabeth LLB(Hons) . . . . *May 2006
Holland, Ms Victoria Glenys LLB; DipLaw . . . . . . *Aug 1999
James, Ms Camilla . . . . *Oct 2007
Jones, Mr Alexander David LLB . . . . *Jan 2010
Jones, Mrs Harriet Elizabeth . . . . *Oct 2008
Kirk, Ms Elizabeth Joanna LLB(Law with Criminology) . *Aug 2010
McLoughlin, Mrs Sarah . . . . *Nov 1999
McSherry, Miss Laura Joyce LLB; LPC . . . . *Dec 2010
Moore, Mrs Christine Sara BSc . . . . *Nov 1990
Mowberry, Ms Maria BA(Hons) . . . . *Aug 2006
Nicolaou, Ms Nicola . . . . *Mar 2009
Pells, Ms Heather M LLB . . . . *Nov 1983
Price, Mrs Gillian Denise LLB(Hons) . . . . *Mar 2003
Rendell, Mrs Sara Alexandra BA(Hons) . . . . *Nov 1997
Smith, Miss Suzanne Natalie BA . . . . *Aug 2006
Con: Arundel, Mr Michael J . . . . *Feb 1972
Wilkinson, Mr P David MA(Oxon) Notary Public . . . . *Sep 1979

FAIRCHILD DOBBS ‡
(in association with Fairchild Greig(London W3))
Oak House 58-60 Oak End Way Gerrards Cross Buckinghamshire SL9 8BR
Tel: 01753 883127 *Fax:* 01753 886162
Dx: 40263 GERRARDS CROSS
E-mail: info@fairchilds.co.uk
List of partners: N C O Spoor, J J Worthington
Work: C1 E L R1 S1 S2 W Z(c,d)
Ptr: Spoor, Mr Nigel C O BA(Dunelm); TEP . . . . *§Dec 1976
Worthington, Mr Jonathan James BA; TEP . . . . . *§Dec 1974

HINE SOLICITORS
17 East Common Gerrards Cross Buckinghamshire SL9 7AG
Tel: 01753 482400 *Fax:* 01753 482401
Dx: 40265 GERRARDS CROSS
Emergency telephone 078 7065 8110
E-mail: mail@hineassociates.co.uk
Office: Beaconsfield, Bracknell, Cheltenham, Oxford, Princes Risborough, Swindon, Yiewsley
Work: D1 E G H K1 K3 L O Q S2 W Z(h)
Emergency Action, Agency, Advocacy, Fixed Fee Interview and Legal Aid undertaken
Ptr: Glover, Ms Alison Jane LLB ★ . . . . Sep 1999
Hine, Mr Anthony LLB ★ . . . . Feb 1998

MARCUS LEE & CO ‡
21 Station Road Gerrards Cross Buckinghamshire SL9 8ES
Tel: 01753 887991
E-mail: mary@marcuslee.co.uk

LISTEN (LAW) LIMITED ‡
71 Camp Road Gerrards Cross Buckinghamshire SL9 7PF
Tel: 01753 883531 *Fax:* 01753 883531

MOSS & CO SOLICITORS ‡
Suite 2 52 Packhorse Road Gerrards Cross Buckinghamshire SL9 8EF
Tel: 01753 895428 *Fax:* 01753 880346

SVS SOLICITORS ‡
60a Packhorse Road Gerrards Cross Buckinghamshire SL9 8EF
Tel: 01753 889123 *Fax:* 01753 889314
E-mail: mail@svssolicitors.com

SUKHY SANGHERA ‡
Fourways Oxford Road Gerrards Cross Buckinghamshire SL9 7DJ
Tel: 01753 885006
Emergency telephone 07718 911259

STUARTS
42 Packhorse Road Gerrards Cross Buckinghamshire SL9 8EB
Tel: 01753 892244 *Fax:* 01753 887906
E-mail: kareen.stuart@stuartslegal.co.uk
Office: Marlow, Sheerness, Sittingbourne
Work: D1 E J1 K1 K3 K4 L N O Q S1 S2 T1 T2 W Z(q)
Advocacy undertaken

WOODHOUSE DAUGHTREY SOLICITOR ‡
Kenway Cottage Ellis Avenue Gerrards Cross Buckinghamshire SL9 9UA
Tel: 01753 883309 *Fax:* 01753 899199
E-mail: advice@wd-law.demon.co.uk

GILLINGHAM, Dorset

DAVIS SIMMONDS DONAGHEY ‡
5 High Street Gillingham Dorset ME7 1BE
Tel: 01634 852700 *Fax:* 01634 850669 *Dx:* 6608 GILLINGHAM
Office: Herne Bay, Sittingbourne

DUGDALE SOLICITORS ‡
113 Watling Street Gillingham Dorset ME7 2YX
Tel: 01634 580606 *Fax:* 01634 789535 *Dx:* 6656 GILLINGHAM 2
E-mail: info@dugdalesolicitors.co.uk

FARNFIELD & NICHOLLS ‡
The Square Gillingham Dorset SP8 4AX
Tel: 01747 825432 *Fax:* 01747 822204
Dx: 100050 GILLINGHAM DORSET
E-mail: info@farnfields.com
List of partners: C Gundry, S A Jones, F Thomas
Office: Shaftesbury, Sturminster Newton, Warminster
Work: A1 B1 C1 C2 C3 D1 E F1 J1 K1 K2 L M1 M2 O P R1 R2 S1 T1 T2 V W Z(c,h)
Emergency Action, Agency and Advocacy undertaken
Ptr: Jones, Ms Sarah Ann LLB . . . . *May 1998
Thomas, Fiona . . . . Oct 2001
Asoc: Bovell, Mr John P A LLB . . . . Sep 1999
Ellis, Pauline . . . . Oct 2004
Howe, Mrs Nicola Jane BA(Hons) . . . . *Oct 1994

MACLACHLAN
Blackmore Vale House Newbury Gillingham Dorset SP8 4QJ
Tel: 01747 822103 *Fax:* 01747 821834
Dx: 100053 GILLINGHAM DORSET
E-mail: enquiries@maclachlansolicitors.co.uk
Office: Sherborne
Languages: French, German
Work: A1 A2 B1 C1 C2 D1 D2 E F1 F2 G J1 K1 K3 N O Q S1 S2 W Z(d,h,l,p)
Agency, Advocacy and Fixed Fee Interview undertaken

RUTTERS
Stone House High Street Gillingham Dorset SP8 4AN
Tel: 01747 822005 *Fax:* 01747 825191
E-mail: p.sutherland@ruttersla w.co.uk
Office: Shaftesbury
Work: A1 C1 D1 E F1 J1 K1 K3 K4 L M1 N O P Q R1 S1 S2 T1 T2 V W Z(l,m,q)
Emergency Action, Agency, Advocacy, Fixed Fee Interview undertaken and Member of Accident Line
Ptr: Rowntree, Mr Derek J LLB(Lond) . . . . *May 1979
Ast: Sutherland, Mr Phillip Wayne LLB . . . . *Mar 1989

GILLINGHAM, Medway Towns

BASSETS
Connaught Chambers 33-35 Balmoral Road Gillingham Medway Towns ME7 4QB
Tel: 01634 575464 *Fax:* 01634 576516 *Dx:* 6601 GILLINGHAM 1
E-mail: info.gill@bassetsolicitors.co.uk
Office: Rochester
Languages: French, German, Hindi, Punjabi, Urdu
Work: K1 L S1
Emergency Action, Agency, Advocacy, Fixed Fee Interview, Legal Aid undertaken and Member of Accident Line
Ptr: Ruse, Mr Paul N LLB(Hons) ★ . . . . *Oct 1993
Smith, Mr Martin Phillip Notary Public . . . . *Dec 1984
Sparks, Mr Paul Dominic James LLB(Hons) . . . . . *Dec 1993
Ast: Pang, Wing Yeung . . . . *Dec 1990
Stawell, Mr Kenneth F BA . . . . *§Feb 1981
Sulh, Mrs Sarbjit Kaur LLB . . . . *Aug 2000
Tadhunter, Miss Sandra Jane LLB(Hons) Notary Public *Nov 1998

BECKETT SOLICITORS ‡
27 High Street Rainham Gillingham Medway Towns ME8 7HX
Tel: 01634 263774 *Fax:* 01634 263775 *Dx:* 7227 RAINHAM
E-mail: nadia.beckett@beckett-solicitors.co.uk

EVANS & CO ‡
PO Box 293 Gillingham Medway Towns ME7 1WF
Tel: 020 7232 1325 *Fax:* 020 7231 8316
Emergency telephone 01322 69421
Work: D1 E F1 G K1 L M1 P S1 W Z(c,j,m)
Emergency Action, Agency, Advocacy, Fixed Fee Interview, Legal Aid undertaken and Member of Accident Line
Ast: Heaton, Mr Glenn LLB . . . . Dec 1988

HAWKRIDGE & CO ‡
39 Canterbury Street Gillingham Medway Towns ME7 5TR
Tel: 01634 854381 *Fax:* 01634 280200 *Dx:* 6602 GILLINGHAM 1
E-mail: enquiries@hawklaw.co.uk
List of partners: J H Hawkridge
Work: A1 C1 D1 E F1 J1 K1 L N O Q R1 S1 V W Z(c,l)
Fixed Fee Interview, Legal Aid undertaken and Member of Accident Line
Ptr: Hawkridge, Mr John H . . . . *§Dec 1970

KEEPERS LEGAL LLP ‡
Keepers House 34 High Street Gillingham Medway Towns ME7 1AQ
Tel: 0845 609 9069

LINN & ASSOCIATES SOLICITORS
175 Canterbury Street Gillingham Medway Towns ME7 5TU
Tel: 01634 577154 *Fax:* 01634 578120
Dx: 34652 CLACTON-ON-SEA
E-mail: solicitors@linnandassociates.co.uk
Office: Clacton-on-Sea, Harwich

PEARSONS ‡
29 Balmoral Road Gillingham Medway Towns ME7 4NX
Tel: 01634 280150 *Fax:* 01634 280520 *Dx:* 6600 GILLINGHAM
List of partners: A J Bailey
Work: G H K1 S1 S2
Emergency Action, Agency, Advocacy, Fixed Fee Interview, Legal Aid undertaken and Legal Aid Franchise
Ptr: Bailey, Mr Allen J . . . . Jun 1982

WHYTE & CO ‡
Albany House 85 Duncan Road Gillingham Medway Towns ME7 4JZ
Tel: 01634 852377 *Fax:* 01634 583388 *Dx:* 6604 GILLINGHAM 1
E-mail: info@whytesolicitors.co.uk
List of partners: R F Chowne, T M Hammond
Work: E K1 K3 Q S1 S2 W
Emergency Action and Fixed Fee Interview undertaken
Ptr: Chowne, Mr Richard F LLB; LLM . . . . *Mar 1973
Hammond, Mrs Tracey Margaret LLB . . . . *Nov 1994

GLASTONBURY, Somerset

BARTLETT GOODING & WEELEN
(incorporating Austin & Bath)
11 Chickwell Street Glastonbury Somerset BA6 8DL
Tel: 01458 832510 *Fax:* 01458 832202
E-mail: dervla@bgwglastonbury.co.uk
Office: Castle Cary, Cheddar, Shepton Mallet
Work: A1 B1 C2 E F1 G J1 J2 K1 K3 L N O Q S1 S2 V W Z(c,j,k,q)
Emergency Action, Agency, Advocacy, Fixed Fee Interview, Legal Aid undertaken, Legal Aid Franchise and Member of Accident Line
Ptr: Nash, Mrs Dervla LLB(Hons) . . . . *Sep 2002

GOULD & SWAYNE
31 High Street Glastonbury Somerset BA6 9HA
Tel: 01458 833700 *Fax:* 01458 834944 *Dx:* 45502 GLASTONBURY
E-mail: c.haskins@gouldandswayne.co.uk
Office: Burnham-on-Sea, Street, Wells
Languages: French
Work: A1 B1 C1 E F1 J1 K4 L O Q S1 S2 T1 T2 W Z(d,l,m)
Dir: Cann, Mr Julian G LLB(Hons) . . . . Aug 1992
Clark, Mr Stuart Trevelyan BA(Dunelm) . . . . *Dec 1980

DAVID MCCRUM LTD ‡
The Long House Lubborn Lane Baltonsborough Glastonbury Somerset BA6 8QP
Tel: 01458 851530 *Fax:* 0870 706 1157
E-mail: david@mccrum.uk.net

MILLER LYONS SOLICITORS ‡
48 High Street Glastonbury Somerset BA6 9DX
Tel: 01458 833660 *Fax:* 01458 834580
E-mail: info@desmondmiller.co.uk
List of partners: D P B Miller
Work: A1 K4 L S1 S2 W
SPr: Miller, Mr Desmond P B LLB(Leeds) Margaret Simpson Harrison Law Prize for Jurisprudence. . . . . *Apr 1974
Con: Ryan, Mr David Francis . . . . Aug 1966

RUPERT BEDFORD SOLICITOR ‡
Longacre Parbrook Glastonbury Somerset BA6 8PB
Tel: 01458 850120 *Fax:* 07860 472316
E-mail: rupert@rupertbedford.co.uk

GLOSSOP, Derbyshire

ABBOTTS SOLICITORS ‡
PO Box 112 Glossop Derbyshire SK13 6WL
Tel: 01457 858483 *Fax:* 01457 855501
E-mail: enquiries@abblaw.co.uk

ASPINALL WRIGHT ‡
Notary House 65 High Street West Glossop Derbyshire SK13 8AZ
Tel: 01457 854645 *Fax:* 01457 854640 *Dx:* 28486 GLOSSOP
E-mail: aw@awandco.co.uk
List of partners: P M Aspinall, P M Bunting, A M Wright
Languages: French
Work: B1 C1 C2 C3 D1 E F1 F2 J1 K1 K3 K4 L N O Q S1 S2 V W Z(l)
Emergency Action, Agency, Fixed Fee Interview, Legal Aid undertaken and Legal Aid Franchise
Ptr: Aspinall, Mr Peter M LLB . . . . *Jun 1971
Bunting, Mr Paul Michael . . . . *Nov 2008
Wright, Mr Anthony M LLB Notary Public . . . . *Apr 1976
Ast: Crawford, Miss Rebecca LLB . . . . *Sep 2008

BAKERS SOLICITORS ‡
89 High Street West Glossop Derbyshire SK13 8BB
Tel: 01457 859123 *Fax:* 01457 859093 *Dx:* 28487 GLOSSOP
E-mail: enquiries@bakers-solicitors.com

BARBER & CO ‡
1 Surrey Street Glossop Derbyshire SK13 7AH
Tel: 0845 803 0991 *Fax:* 0845 803 0992
E-mail: enquiries@barbersolicitors.co.uk
List of partners: R I Barber
Work: N
SPr: Barber, Mr R Ian LLB(Hons). . . . . *Oct 1986

HOWARD BERNSTEIN SOLICITORS ‡
6 Howard Street Glossop Derbyshire SK13 7DD
Tel: 01457 863999 *Fax:* 01457 805999
E-mail: enquiries@howardbernsteinsolicitors.co.uk

DAVIS BLANK FURNISS
10 Ellison Street Glossop Derbyshire SK13 8BZ
Tel: 01457 860606 *Fax:* 01457 869468 *Dx:* 28489 GLOSSOP
E-mail: glossop@dbf-law.co.uk
Office: Manchester
Work: A1 B1 C1 D1 E F1 G H J1 K1 L M1 N O P Q R1 S1 T1 V W Z(b,c,d,e,f,g,h,i,j,k,l,m,n,o,p,s,t)
Emergency Action, Advocacy, Fixed Fee Interview undertaken and Member of Accident Line
Ptr: Evans, Mr Keith Norman BA . . . . *§Jun 1975
Gee, Mr Martyn R LLB . . . . *§Jul 1981
Litherland, Mr Jonathan R C LLB . . . . *§Dec 1977
Wood, Mrs Susan LLB . . . . *Nov 1988
Asoc: Rose, Mrs Lorraine M. . . . . *Dec 1986
Smith, Miss Claire LLB(Hons) . . . . Sep 2001
Con: Taylor, Mr Anthony G LLB(Vict) . . . . *Oct 1961

PETER D GREENHALGH ‡
10 Edward Street Glossop Derbyshire SK13 7AF
Tel: 01457 861319 *Fax:* 01457 856069 *Dx:* 28488 GLOSSOP
E-mail: general@pdgs.co.uk
List of partners: P D Greenhalgh
Languages: French
Emergency Action, Agency, Advocacy, Fixed Fee Interview and Legal Aid undertaken
Ptr: Greenhalgh, Mr Peter D. . . . . *Jun 1977
Ast: Abbott, Mr Kenneth LLB. . . . . *Oct 1982

HT LEGAL LIMITED T/A HARRISON TOWNEND & ORMESHERS
Norfolk Chambers Norfolk Street Glossop Derbyshire SK13 7QU
Tel: 01457 868825 *Fax:* 01457 853695 *Dx:* 28493 GLOSSOP
E-mail: townend@easynet.co.uk
Office: Hyde
Work: A1 E F1 J1 K1 L N P R1 S1 W Z(c,e,i,l)
Emergency Action, Agency, Advocacy, Fixed Fee Interview and Legal Aid undertaken

HENRYS SOLICITORS LTD ‡
1D Market Street Glossop Derbyshire SK12 8AX
Tel: 01457 864143 *Fax:* 0161 474 7667
E-mail: reception@henrysolicitors.co.uk

YATES ARDERN ‡
12 Market Street Glossop Derbyshire SK13 8AR
Tel: 01457 857863
E-mail: enquiries@yatesardern.co.uk

GLOUCESTER, Gloucestershire

BRAND MELLON LLP ‡
Copner House 43 Southgate Street Gloucester Gloucestershire GL1 1TX
Tel: 01452 524088 *Fax:* 01452 307943 *Dx:* 7520 GLOUCESTER
E-mail: lawyers@brandmellon.co.uk
Office: Cheltenham
Work: B1 C1 C2 C3 D1 E F1 F2 G H J1 K1 L M1 M2 N P Q S1 V W Z(b,f,h,j,k,l,p,q,r)

COTSWOLD CONVEYANCING CENTRE ‡
60 Royal House Bruton Way Gloucester Gloucestershire GL1 1EP
Tel: 01452 545678 *Fax:* 01452 550529 *Dx:* 7511 GLOUCESTER
E-mail: ccc@langleywellington.co.uk
Work: S1 S2

DAVEY FRANKLIN JONES
Bearland House Longsmith Street Gloucester Gloucestershire GL1 2HJ
Tel: 01452 508800 *Fax:* 01452 508805
Dx: 133289 GLOUCESTER 11
Office: Cirencester
Work: A1 B1 C1 C2 C3 D1 D2 E F1 J1 K1 K3 K4 L N O P Q R1 S1 W Z(d,e,k,l,p,q,r)
Agency, Advocacy, Fixed Fee Interview undertaken and Member of Accident Line
Ptr: Davies, Mr Peter M LLB(Lond) . . . . *Jun 1979
Fletcher, Mr Adrian H BA . . . . *§Dec 1978
Leyland, Mrs Janice Celia. . . . . Sep 1999
Ast: Arora, Ms Anita . . . . Jun 1998
Dawson, Mrs Stephanie Margaret BA(Law); MA. . . . *Jan 1991

DAVIES & PARTNERS ‡
Rowan House Barnett Way Barnwood Gloucester Gloucestershire GL4 3RT
Tel: 01452 612345 *Fax:* 01452 611922
Dx: 149320 GLOUCESTER 18
List of partners: J P J Bourne, T P Brennan, A E Cooley, T D Edwards, S P Fletcher, R K Gibbs, S F Hart, M R James, E M Kilgour, E T Lockhart, P Loughlin, R M A Maisey, S E McColgan, R A Perry, S J Rowland, A G Smith, D C Stokes, G S Tay-Lodge, N G Tillott
Office: Almondsbury, Birmingham
Work: A1 A3 B1 B2 B3 C1 C2 C3 D1 E F1 J1 J2 K1 K3 L N O P Q R1 R2 S1 S2 T1 T2 W X Z(b,c,d,e,f,h,j,k,l,p,q,r)
Emergency Action, Agency, Fixed Fee Interview, Legal Aid undertaken and Member of Accident Line
Ptr: Bourne, Mr Julian P J MA(Oxon) . . . . *Jan 1982
Cooley, Mr Anthony E LLB . . . . *Oct 1986
Fletcher, Mr Stephen P MA(Cantab). . . . . *Nov 1983
Hart, Mr Simon F LLB(Hons) . . . . *Nov 1992
Loughlin, Miss Paula LLB; LLM . . . . *Apr 2000
Maisey, Mr Richard M A BA. . . . . *Apr 1979
Perry, Mr Raymond A LLB. . . . . *Dec 1987
Rowland, Mr Simon J LLB. . . . . *Dec 1978
Smith, Mr Adrian G LLB. . . . . *Feb 1983
Tillott, Mr Nigel G LLB. . . . . *Oct 1987
Ast: Davies, Miss Caroline M BSc(Hons). . . . . *Jul 1998
Edwards, Mrs Joy LLB . . . . Apr 2002
Lymer, Mrs Lorna Antoinette LLB ♦ . . . . *Oct 1993
Parker, Mr Timothy G BA(Lond). . . . . *May 1987
Playfair, Ms Julia L MA . . . . *Oct 1984
Smith, Mrs Geraldine A LLB. . . . . *Jun 1980

DEE & GRIFFIN ‡
Hucclecote Court 76 Hucclecote Road Gloucester Gloucestershire GL3 3RU
Tel: 01452 617288 *Fax:* 01452 610087
List of partners: A L Dee, K P Griffin
Office: Gloucester
Languages: French, German
Work: A1 E F1 K1 K3 L M1 N P R1 S1 V W
Emergency Action, Agency, Advocacy, Fixed Fee Interview undertaken and Member of Accident Line
Ptr: Dee, Mr Andrew L. . . . . *Jan 1983
Griffin, Mr Kieron P BA . . . . *§Mar 1983
Ast: Barnard, Mr Dean. . . . . Apr 2005

DEE & GRIFFIN
9a School Lane Quedgeley Gloucester Gloucestershire GR2 4PJ
Tel: 01452 724343 *Fax:* 01452 724843
Office: Gloucester

EQUILAW LTD ‡
Brunswick House Gloucester Business Park Gloucester Gloucestershire GL3 4AA
Tel: 01452 657999
E-mail: equityrelease@equilaw.uk.com

LEO GOATLEY & CO ‡
11 Denmark Road Gloucester Gloucestershire GL1 3HZ
Tel: 01452 548293

K W HUBBARD & CO ‡
3 Russell Street Gloucester Gloucestershire GL1 1NE
Tel: 01452 414406 *Fax:* 01452 506898 *Dx:* 7548 GLOUCESTER
List of partners: K W Hubbard
Work: K1 N Q S1 W
Ptr: Hubbard, Mr Keith W . . . . *Jul 1975

IACOPI PALMER SOLICITORS LLP ‡
Spinnaker House Spinnaker Road Gloucester Gloucestershire GL2 5FD
Tel: 01452 416452

LANGLEY WELLINGTON ‡
(incorporating C.H Fowler and Cook & Hickman)
Royal House 60 Bruton Way Gloucester Gloucestershire GL1 1EP
Tel: 01452 521286 *Fax:* 01452 307935 *Dx:* 7525 GLOUCESTER
E-mail: lawyers@langleywellington.co.uk
List of partners: M K Coughlan, P M Day, R J Love, H R Stephens, A R Thompson
Office: Churchdown
Work: A1 D1 D2 E J1 K1 K3 N Q R1 S1 S2 W X Z(l)
Emergency Action, Advocacy, Fixed Fee Interview, Legal Aid undertaken, Legal Aid Franchise and Member of Accident Line
Ptr: Coughlan, Mr Michael K LLB Deputy District Judge; Assistant Deputy Coroner. . . . . *Oct 1986
Day, Mr Philip M BSc(Econ). . . . . *Jun 1979
Love, Mr Robert Julian . . . . *Mar 1975
Stephens, Miss Helen R LLB(Hons)(Wales) Maxwell Law Prize Assistant Deputy Coroner. . . . . *§Nov 1988
Ast: Brennan, Miss Imelda Mary BSocSc . . . . *Nov 1990
Evans, Mr Matthew LLB. . . . . Jan 2007
Henderson, Mrs Lorna LLB(Hons); PGDip. . . . . . . Jul 2008
Keyte, Mrs Rosemary LLB . . . . *§Apr 1993
Manley, Miss Harriet Elizabeth BA(Sociology with Law); BA(Law); LPC. . . . . Sep 2007
Con: Fowler, Mr Christopher H . . . . *§Jun 1970

LUTTONS DUNFORD ‡
49 Brunswick Road Gloucester Gloucestershire GL1 1JS
Tel: 01452 529751 *Fax:* 01452 782388
E-mail: luttons55@aol.com
List of partners: S J Fisher, C A Lutton, D G Mouland
Work: A1 B1 C1 C2 D1 E F1 J1 K1 L N O Q R1 S1 S2 T1 W Z(j,q,r)
Agency, Fixed Fee Interview undertaken and Member of Accident Line
Ptr: Fisher, Mr Simon J LLB . . . . Mar 1984
Lutton, Mr Christopher A . . . . *Jun 1975
Mouland, Mr David Glenn BA . . . . *May 1996
Ast: Pearson, Mrs Dianne . . . . *Oct 1993

PETER M MCMURTRIE SOLICITOR AND NOTARY PUBLIC ‡
Walk Farm Moorend Road Gloucester Gloucestershire GL19 4NS
Tel: 01452 840373 *Fax:* 01452 840749

MADGE LLOYD & GIBSON ‡
34 Brunswick Road Gloucester Gloucestershire GL1 1JW
Tel: 01452 520224 *Fax:* 01452 306866 *Dx:* 7505 GLOUCESTER
E-mail: chris.peak@madgelloyd.com
List of partners: A K Bishop, R D P Jones, A J Langsford, C G Peak
Office: Gloucester, Newent
Work: A1 D1 D2 E K1 K3 K4 Q S1 S2 T1 T2 W Z(d,x)
Emergency Action, Agency, Advocacy, Fixed Fee Interview, Legal Aid undertaken and Legal Aid Franchise
Ptr: Bishop, Mr Andrew Keith LLB . . . . *§Apr 1978
Jones, Mr Robert D P. . . . . *Jan 1981
Peak, Mr Christopher G MA(Cantab) Diocesan Registrar . . . . *§Jun 1975

PITMAN BLACKSTOCK WHITE
Unit A Greyhound Gardens Longlevens Gloucester Gloucestershire GL2 0XH
Tel: 01452 381818 *Fax:* 01452 383636
E-mail: pbwlonglevens@tiscali.co.uk
Office: Lydney

ROWBIS SOLICITORS ‡
Morroway House Station Road Gloucester Gloucestershire GL1 1DW
Tel: 01452 301903 *Fax:* 01452 411115 *Dx:* 7500 GLOUCESTER
E-mail: enquiries@rowbis.co.uk
List of partners: T Ashford, J Crooknorth, M C Crooknorth, A A Holloway
Languages: French
Work: A1 A2 B1 B2 C1 D2 E F1 F2 G H J1 K1 L N O Q S1 S2 T1 T2 V W Z(d,l,q)
Emergency Action, Agency, Advocacy, Fixed Fee Interview, Legal Aid undertaken and Legal Aid Franchise
Ptr: Ashford, Mrs Tracey LLB . . . . *Nov 1996
Crooknorth, Jaron LLB . . . . *Mar 1999
Crooknorth, Mrs Michelle Clare LLB(Hons) . . . . . . *Oct 1995
Holloway, Mr Andrew A BA(Hons). . . . . *Jul 1981
Con: Leather, Mrs Penelope F BA(Hons) . . . . *Jan 1993

LINDA STAPLETON & CO
24 Clarence Street Gloucester Gloucestershire GL1 1DP
Tel: 01452 423870 *Fax:* 01452 301682 *Dx:* 7505 GLOUCESTER
E-mail: amandal@madgelloyd.com
Office: Gloucester, Newent
Work: A1 C1 D1 D2 E K1 K3 K4 L S1 S2 V W Z(d,x)
Emergency Action, Agency, Fixed Fee Interview, Legal Aid undertaken and Legal Aid Franchise
Ptr: Langsford, Ms Amanda J LLB(Hons) . . . . *Oct 2000
Ast: Cantwell, Miss Rachel LLB(Hons). . . . . *Apr 2008

STEVEN YOUNG & CO ‡
43 Park Road Gloucester Gloucestershire GL1 1LN
Est: 1999
Tel: 01452 332882 *Fax:* 01452 332883
Emergency telephone 01452 332882
E-mail: mail@stevenyoungsolicitors.co.uk
List of partners: C Malvern-White, S L Young
Office: Cheltenham
Work: G H
Agency and Advocacy undertaken
Ptr: Malvern-White, Mrs Clare BA(Hons). . . . . Nov 1996
Young, Mr Steven L LLB(Bris). . . . . Mar 1984
Ast: Ellis, Miss Lisa Jeanette LLB(Hons) . . . . Oct 2003
Griffiths, Mr Matthew Stephen LLB(Hons) . . . . . . Jan 2000
Jenkins, Mrs Sarah LLB; LPC . . . . Sep 2002

TAYNTONS LLP SOLICITORS ‡
8-12 Clarence Street Gloucester Gloucestershire GL1 1DZ
Tel: 01452 522047 *Fax:* 01452 424659 *Dx:* 7560 GLOUCESTER
E-mail: info@tayntons.co.uk
List of partners: A D Bird, J T G Cook, J Davies, S E Mitchem, A J Ollerenshaw, C M Price, J Thompson
Work: A1 C1 D1 E J1 K1 L N O Q S1 W Z(d,h,o,r)
Emergency Action, Agency, Advocacy, Fixed Fee Interview, Legal Aid undertaken and Legal Aid Franchise
Ptr: Bird, Mr Alan D LLB(Hull) . . . . *Apr 1976
Cook, Mr James Thomas Gregory. . . . . Dec 1974
Davies, Miss Jane LLB(Hons). . . . . Jun 1987
Mitchem, Miss Sarah E LLB. . . . . *Apr 1980
Ollerenshaw, Mr Andrew J LLB . . . . Dec 1992
Price, Mr Christopher Martin LLB . . . . Oct 2003
Thompson, Ms Joanne CPE; BA(York) . . . . Oct 1995
Asoc: Duthie, Miss Helen Frances LLB(Hons) . . . . Feb 2004
Hale, Mrs Katerina LLB(Hons). . . . . Oct 1993
Pettifer, Mr Ian LLB; MA; MCIPD . . . . Sep 1997
Ast: Fitzgerald, Miss Emma Louise LLB . . . . Apr 2010
Lacey, Miss Elizabeth Grace . . . . Oct 2007
Lewis, Mr Tristan Anthony BSc(Law); PGDipLaw . . . *Feb 2007
Weldrake, Miss Rachel LLB(Hons); LSF(Hons) . . . *Dec 1995

THOMAS CAPITAL PROPERTY LAWYERS ‡
Brunswick House Gloucester Business Park Gloucester Gloucestershire GL3 4AA
Tel: 01452 657950 *Fax:* 0871 471 7007 / 01452 657962
E-mail: info@thomaslegalgroup.com
Office: Gloucester, London W1

THOMAS CAPITAL PROPERTY LAWYERS
33a Morley Avenue Churchdown Gloucester Gloucestershire GL3 2BL.
Tel: 01452 857033 *Fax:* 0871 471 7007
E-mail: info@thomaslegalgroup.com
Office: Gloucester, London W1

TREASURES ‡
17 St Johns Lane Gloucester Gloucestershire GL1 2AZ
Tel: 01452 525351 *Fax:* 01452 506735 *Dx:* 7507 GLOUCESTER
Emergency telephone 01531 821549

See p112 for the Key to Work Categories & other symbols

E-mail: rec@treasures-solicitors.co.uk
List of partners: M D Hammond, C H Rivers, V Solomon
Languages: French
Work: A1 A3 B1 C1 C2 D1 D2 E F1 G H J1 K1 L N O Q R1 S1 S2 T1 V W Z(c,d,k,l,m,p,q,r,t)
Emergency Action, Agency, Advocacy, Fixed Fee Interview, Legal Aid undertaken, Legal Aid Franchise and Member of Accident Line
Ptr: Hammond, Mr Mark D. . . . *§Jun 1981
Rivers, Mr C Henry Notary Public . . . *§Jun 1970
Solomon, Mrs Victoria BA(Hons) . . . *§Apr 1992
Ast: Meredith, Ms Helen Elizabeth LLB. . . . Aug 2003
Scoffham, Mr Thomas William LLB(Hons) . . . Aug 2005

WALLIS SOLICITORS ‡
PO Box 3150 Gloucester Gloucestershire GL2 4HY
Tel: 01452 720827 *Fax:* 01452 720827
E-mail: graham@wallissolicitorslimited.co.uk

WHITE & CO
8 Canal Way Over Gloucester Gloucestershire GL2 8BY
Tel: 01452 413222 *Fax:* 01452 413222
Office: London NW1
Work: E Q S1 W Z(d)
Ptr: White, Mr Timothy D . . . *Jun 1981

WHITEMANS ‡
(incorporating James Blakeway & Pepper; Wells & Co (Cheltenham))
2nd Floor 65 London Road Gloucester Gloucestershire GL1 3HF
Tel: 01452 411601 *Fax:* 01452 300922 *Dx:* 7514 GLOUCESTER
Emergency telephone 01452 730297
E-mail: info@whitemans.com
List of partners: N B R Alexander, A W Ewart-James, A D M Wallace-Cook
Languages: French
Work: A1 B1 C1 C2 C3 D1 D2 E F1 J1 K1 L N P Q R1 S1 S2 T1 T2 V W Z(c,d,e,j,l,m,p,q,r,t)
Emergency Action, Agency, Advocacy, Fixed Fee Interview, Legal Aid Franchise and Member of Accident Line
Ptr: Alexander, Mr Nicholas B R BA Under Sheriff of City of Gloucester; High Court Enforcement Officer. . . *May 1980
Ewart-James, Mr Andrew W BA(Oxon); TEP Under Sheriff of Gloucestershire; High Court Enforcement Officer . *Feb 1977
Wallace-Cook, Mr Ashley D M MA(Oxon); LLB; DipLP. *Dec 2003
Asoc: Rai, Ms Rupinder BA(Hons). . . . *Oct 2001
Ast: McCarthy, Mr Julian Alexander BA(Law). . . . Aug 2005

GODALMING, Surrey

BAKER & CO ‡
Elm House Business Centre Shackleford Road Elstead Godalming Surrey GU8 6LB
Tel: 01428 687717 *Fax:* 01428 788469 *Dx:* 58363 GODALMING 2
E-mail: general@bakerlegal.co.uk

STAN BARING SOLICITOR ‡
Suite 3 21 Woodside Park Catteshall Lane Godalming Surrey GU7 1LG
Tel: 01483 860986 *Fax:* 01483 414006
E-mail: stan@stanbaring.com
List of partners: S Baring
Work: B1 C1 D1 E F1 G H J1 K1 L N O Q S1 W Z(e)
Agency, Advocacy and Fixed Fee Interview undertaken
Ptr: Baring, Mr Stan. . . . *Jan 1983

BARLOW ROBBINS LLP
Church House 30 Church Street Godalming Surrey GU7 1EP
Tel: 01483 417121 *Fax:* 01483 426836 *Dx:* 58351 GODALMING 2
E-mail: godalming@barlowrobbins.com
Office: Guildford (2 offices), Woking
Languages: French, German, Italian, Japanese, Polish, Spanish
Work: A1 A3 D1 D2 E K1 K2 K3 K4 L M2 Q S1 S2 T2 V W Z(d,k)
Emergency Action and Advocacy undertaken
Ptr: Ambrose, Mrs Sarah Anne BSc(Management Services); LPC . . . *Jul 1991
Goodridge, Mr Michael R LLB(Bris) . . . *§Apr 1970
Sanders, Mrs Belinda J MA(Oxon) . . . *Oct 1991
Asoc: Garcia-Deleito, Mr Anthony Samuel BSA(Hons)(German Law) . . . *Sep 2002
Habershon, Ms Helen. . . . *Sep 1999
Ast: Eyre, Miss Elizabeth LLB; TEP; ATT. . . . *§Oct 1989
Con: Barham, Ms Karen Lynne BA(Hons)(Law & Politics). *Dec 1988
Keer, Mrs Mary C LLB. . . . *Jul 1978
Purser, Mrs Candida Nicola Kirby Notary Public. . . . *Jan 1983

We specialise in the following areas of work Family Law, Divorce and Matrimonial, Residential Conveyancing, Probate, Wills & Trusts

BROCKINGTON CARROLL ‡
Elm House Shackleford Road Elstead Godalming Surrey GU8 6LB
Tel: 01252 703770 *Fax:* 01252 703787
E-mail: info@brockingtoncarroll.com
List of partners: S J Wade
Work: L S1 T2 W
SPr: Wade, Mr Simon J LLB . . . *Dec 1968

DOWNS ‡
The Tanners 75 Meadrow Godalming Surrey GU7 3HU
Tel: 01483 861848 *Fax:* 01483 861856 *Dx:* 58308 GODALMING 1
E-mail: info@downslaw.co.uk
List of partners: P J C Leach
Languages: French
Work: A1 B1 C1 E J1 L O P Q R1 R2 S1 W
Fixed Fee Interview undertaken
Ptr: Leach, Mr Paul J C . . . *Jan 1983
Ast: Everard, Ms Katherine LLB(Hons). . . . *Nov 1993

HART BROWN SOLICITORS
1 Lower South Street Godalming Surrey GU7 1BZ
Est: 1919
Tel: 0800 068 8177 *Fax:* 01483 887756 *Dx:* 58350 GODALMING 2
E-mail: lawyers@hartbrown.co.uk
Office: Cobham, Cranleigh, Guildford, London SW19, Woking
Languages: German
Work: A1 A3 B1 C1 C2 C3 D1 D2 E F1 F2 I J1 J2 K1 K2 K3 L M1 M2 N O P Q R1 R2 S1 S2 T2 V W Z(b,c,d,e,i,k,l,o,p,q,r,z)
Emergency Action, Agency, Advocacy, Fixed Fee Interview, Legal Aid undertaken and Legal Aid Franchise
Ptr: Parry-Jones, Mr Shaun D BA(Hons); PGDipLaw. . . *Nov 1997
Asoc: Sanders, Mrs Claire A LLB . . . *Nov 1989
Score, Mr Gary C A LLB(Hons) . . . *Jun 1977

Ast: Mills, Mrs Lorraine Ann LLB. . . . *Mar 2002
Wiggins, Miss Emily LLB . . . *Jan 2004

MARSHALLS ‡
102 High Street Godalming Surrey GU7 1DS
Tel: 01483 416101 *Fax:* 01483 427265 *Dx:* 58354 GODALMING 2
E-mail: reception@marshalls.uk.net
List of partners: S C Coate, B Kilburn, L G Rabinowitz
Office: Woking
Work: A1 C1 C2 D1 E F1 J1 K1 K3 L O Q R1 S1 S2 W Z(c,d,e,l)
Ptr: Coate, Ms Sara C LLB . . . *Oct 1982
Kilburn, Mr Barry LLB. . . . *Dec 1979
Rabinowitz, Mrs Lisa G MA(Oxon). . . . *Oct 1993
Ast: Dyke, Mr Nathan LLB. . . . *Mar 2008
Con: Duncan, Mrs Vivienne A M MA(Oxon); BCL. . . . *Sep 1981

PENNINGTONS
Highfield Brighton Road Godalming Surrey GU7 1NS
Tel: 01483 791800 *Fax:* 01483 424177 *Dx:* 58300 GODALMING 1
E-mail: info@penningtons.co.uk
Office: Basingstoke, London EC2
Languages: French, German
Work: A1 A2 B1 C1 C2 C3 D1 D2 E F1 G I J1 J2 K1 K2 L M1 M2 N O P Q R1 R2 S1 S2 T1 T2 U2 W Z(c,d,e,f,h,i,k,l,o,p,q,r,s,t,w,z)
Emergency Action, Agency, Advocacy, Legal Aid undertaken, Legal Aid Franchise and Member of Accident Line
Ptr: Bickerdike, Mr Simon LLB(Hons) . . . *Nov 1992
Cole, Mr Michael Giles LLB(Hons). . . . *Nov 1994
Cole, Mr Terence Arthur MA(Cantab) . . . *§Apr 1975
Dadswell, Miss Laura MA(Cantab). . . . *Sep 2000
Ewens, Mr John BA(Hons) . . . *Oct 1983
Kendall, Mr David. . . . Sep 2001
Law, Mr Stephen . . . Dec 1995
Lee, Mr Mark LLB(Hons) . . . Oct 2000
Luscombe, Miss Philippa F B LLB(Hons) . . . §Nov 1998
Rafter, Mr Timothy Simon BA(Hons). . . . *Oct 1985
Whitwell, Mr Anthony Reese BA(Hons) . . . *Mar 1983
Asoc: Barton, Ms Grainne LLB(Hons) . . . Oct 1989
Busby, Mr Mike . . . Sep 2005
Capper, Dr Brian S MA(Cantab); PhD . . . Oct 1996
Coley, Clare. . . . Sep 2000
Forde, Diana . . . Jan 1981
Hetherington, Ms Christine . . . Jan 1980
McCheyne, Emma . . . Sep 2002
Ward, Cecelia. . . . Sep 1997
Ast: Brassington, Liz. . . . Apr 2009
Cardy, Liz. . . . Sep 2007
Clayton, Mr Andrew. . . . Nov 2006
Garvey, Liz . . . Apr 2004
Gearey, Hannah. . . . Sep 2010
Hall, Rebecca. . . . Sep 2011
Harvey, Mr Graham BA(Politics); LPC; CDL. . . . Oct 2007
Hertzell, Anne. . . . Feb 1985
Holland, Victoria. . . . Nov 2003
John, Mr Steven . . . Apr 2006
Meers, Mrs Christine LLB . . . Aug 2002
Prothero, Lucie . . . Sep 2009
Stafford, Charlotte. . . . Dec 2010
Wood, Victoria . . . Sep 2007
Wylie, Mrs Joanna . . . Nov 2010
Con: Graham-Smith, Mr David Notary Public . . . Jan 1970
Mathe, Mr John BA(Bangor). . . . Dec 1973
Scarlett, Ms Sarah Elizabeth BA(Hons) . . . Nov 1993
Stedman, Mr David BA(Oxon). . . . Jan 1966

JOHN S WAYMAN ‡
125a High Street Godalming Surrey GU7 1AQ
Tel: 01483 429822

GOLDTHORPE, South Yorkshire

W BROOK & CO ‡
2a Doncaster Road Goldthorpe South Yorkshire S63 9HQ
Tel: 01709 898697 *Fax:* 01709 881156 *Dx:* 711253 GOLDTHORPE
Emergency telephone 01709 895696
E-mail: walterbrook@wbrooksolicitors.f9.co.uk
List of partners: J T Brook, W Brook
Work: F1 G H J1 K1 L M1 P S1 V W Z(c)
Emergency Action, Agency, Advocacy, Fixed Fee Interview and Legal Aid undertaken
Ptr: Brook, Mr Julian Taras LLB(Hons). . . . Oct 2002
Brook, Mr Walter BA(Business Law). . . . *Jul 1979

GOOLE, East Riding of Yorkshire

BAILEY & HAIGH
58 Pasture Road Goole East Riding of Yorkshire DN14 6HD
Tel: 01405 780200 *Fax:* 01405 708201 *Dx:* 28837 GOOLE
E-mail: baileys@solsl.fsn.co.uk
Office: Selby

HEPTONSTALLS LLP ‡
7-15 Gladstone Terrace Goole East Riding of Yorkshire DN14 5AH
Tel: 01405 765661 *Fax:* 01405 764201 *Dx:* 28831 GOOLE
E-mail: legal@heptonstalls.co.uk
List of partners: J Burman, C Cawood, A Hart, S S Hensman, S J Johnson, A S Pinchbeck, S Tilson, N J L Ward-Lowery
Office: Howden, Pontefract (2 offices), Scunthorpe
Languages: Bengali, French, Italian, Maltese, Punjabi, Urdu
Work: A1 B1 C1 C2 D1 E G H J1 K1 K2 K3 K4 L N O Q R1 R2 S1 S2 T1 T2 V W Z(b,c,d,h,j,l,n,o,p,q,r,s,t)
Emergency Action, Agency, Advocacy, Fixed Fee Interview, Legal Aid undertaken, Legal Aid Franchise and Member of Accident Line
Ptr: Burman, Mr John LLB(L'pool) . . . *May 1977
Johnson, Mrs Sarah Jane BA . . . *Oct 1991
Pinchbeck, Mr Arthur S LLB. . . . *Nov 1989
Asoc: Gill, Mr John C H . . . *§Jul 1980
Ast: Councell, Mrs Rebecca BA(Hons). . . . Nov 2001
Darwin, Mrs Samantha . . . Nov 1995
Garnett, Miss Hayley Elizabeth BA(Hons) . . . Jul 2002
Green, Miss Claire Antonia Rosemary BA; PGDipLaw. Sep 2005
Jones, Mrs Sandra LLB . . . Aug 2004
Lock, Mrs Julia BA(Hons); PGDipLaw . . . *Sep 2005
Maliakal, Mrs Elizabeth . . . Nov 1998
Platten, Mrs Victoria Maria LLB . . . Sep 1999
Russell, Ms Helen C LLB . . . *Jul 1999

KENYON SON & CRADDOCK
(in association with Henshaw pratt)
15 Paradise Place Goole East Riding of Yorkshire DN14 5DL
Tel: 01405 720850 *Fax:* 01405 720695 *Dx:* 28836 GOOLE
E-mail: emailinfo@ksandc.co.uk
Office: Doncaster
Work: A1 C1 C2 D1 D2 E F1 G H J1 K1 L N Q R1 S1 V W X Z(c,t)
Emergency Action, Agency, Advocacy, Fixed Fee Interview, Legal Aid undertaken, Legal Aid Franchise and Member of Accident Line
Ptr: Bainbridge, Mr Peter R PGDipLaw . . . *Dec 1989
Asoc: Webster, Mr Jonathan Michael . . . *Jan 1986

SYMES BAINS BROOMER
157 Boothferry Road Goole East Riding of Yorkshire DN14 6AL
Tel: 01405 763853 *Fax:* 01405 720246 *Dx:* 28832 GOOLE
E-mail: info@sbblaw.com
Office: Epworth, Grimsby, Howden, Scunthorpe
Work: A1 E K1 K3 S1 S2 T2 W
Agency and Legal Aid undertaken

GORING, Oxfordshire

RICHARD WILSON SOLICITORS LTD ‡
Cymbal House High Street Goring Oxfordshire RG8 9AU
Tel: 01491 879100 *Fax:* 01491 874187
Dx: 99175 GORING-ON-THAMES
E-mail: goring@richard-wilson.co.uk
List of partners: K A Charles, J B Howell-Pryce
Languages: French
Work: A1 E I J1 K1 L N Q S1 S2 T1 T2 U2 W Z(l)
Advocacy and Legal Aid Franchise
Ptr: Charles, Mrs Karen A LLB. . . . *§Feb 1990
Howell-Pryce, Mr John B TD Notary Public . . . *§May 1977
Con: Apley, Mr Richard B G MA(Cantab) . . . *Jan 1995

GORSEINON, Swansea

ROY KENNETH CHURCH ‡
Mill Buildings Parkmill Gorseinon Swansea SA3 2EH
Tel: 01792 371420 *Fax:* 01792 371584
List of partners: R K Church
Work: C1 C2 E R1 R2 S1
SPr: Church, Mr Roy Kenneth LLB. . . . *Apr 1981

T R HARRIS ARNOLD & CO ‡
25 Pontardulais Road Gorseinon Swansea SA4 4FE
Est: 1905
Tel: 01792 892166 / 891331 *Fax:* 01792 899489
Dx: 52450 GORSEINON
E-mail: nrp@harrisarnold.co.uk
List of partners: G J Davies, P Evans, I R Jones, N R Packer, P J Sims, A Williams
Languages: Welsh
Work: D1 D2 E F1 J1 K1 K2 L N Q S1 S2 T2 W Z(l,q)
Emergency Action, Agency, Advocacy, Fixed Fee Interview, Legal Aid undertaken, Legal Aid Franchise and Member of Accident Line
Ptr: Davies, Mr Geraint J LLB(Wales) . . . *Oct 1982
Evans, Mr Philip LLB(Leics). . . . *Nov 1986
Jones, Mr Ian Roderick BA(Wales) . . . *Nov 1994
Packer, Mr Nigel R LLB(Lond). . . . *Oct 1977
Sims, Mr P Jeremy LLB(Lond) . . . *§Jan 1983
Williams, Miss Andrea LLB; LLM . . . *Sep 2000

MARK SAUNDERS & CO ‡
4-14 Pontardulais Road Gorseinon Swansea SA4 4FE
Tel: 01792 892692 *Fax:* 01792 897431 *Dx:* 52457 GORSEINON
List of partners: M J Saunders
Work: D1 G H K1 N S1 W
Emergency Action, Agency, Advocacy, Fixed Fee Interview and Legal Aid undertaken
Ptr: Saunders, Mr Mark Julian LLB . . . *Feb 1988

GOSFORTH, Tyne & Wear

BIRCH & CO ‡
15 Lansdowne Terrace Gosforth Tyne & Wear NE3 1HN
Tel: 0191 284 5030 / 284 6040

CARR & CO
229 High Street Gosforth Tyne & Wear NE3 1HQ
Tel: 0191 284 0363 *Fax:* 0191 213 2757
Emergency telephone 0191 284 0363
E-mail: gosforth@carrandcosolicitors.com
Office: Blyth, Morpeth
Languages: Turkish
Work: B1 D1 D2 E F1 J1 K1 K2 K3 K4 L N Q S1 W
Emergency Action, Agency, Advocacy, Fixed Fee Interview, Legal Aid undertaken and Legal Aid Franchise
Ptr: Iceton, Miss Gemma LLB(Hons); LPC. . . . Nov 2006
Smith, Mrs Sharon Grace LLB(Hons) . . . *Nov 1989
Wormald, Miss Valerie LLB(Hons). . . . *Jun 1981

EMMERSON SOLICITORS
145 High Street Gosforth Tyne & Wear NE3 1HA
Tel: 0191 284 6989 *Fax:* 0191 285 1556
E-mail: amrobinson@emmersons-solicitors.co.uk
Office: Sunderland
Ptr: Robinson, Mr Arthur Michael LLB . . . *Oct 1992

CAROLINE GOORNEY SOLIICITOR ‡
1a Elmfield Road Gosforth Tyne & Wear NE3 4DD
Tel: 0191 285 9411 *Fax:* 0191 285 6677
E-mail: cgsolicitor@legaltx.com

MCKEAG & CO ‡
1-3 Lansdowne Terrace Gosforth Tyne & Wear NE3 1HN
Tel: 0191 213 1010 *Fax:* 0191 213 1704 *Dx:* 60353 GOSFORTH
Emergency telephone 07850 565543
List of partners: C T Cairns, D C McKeag, C E Moss, I S Ord, P Rafferty, P W Walton, A C Wilkinson
Work: A1 B1 C1 D1 E F1 G H J1 K1 L M1 N P R1 S1 T1 V W Z(e,f,i,j,k,l,p,t)
Emergency Action, Agency, Advocacy, Legal Aid undertaken and Member of Accident Line
Ptr: Cairns, Mr Conrad T MA(Edin); PhD; CPD . . . *Dec 1989
Moss, Mrs Carol E LLB. . . . Jul 1985
Ord, Mr Iain S LLB . . . Dec 1987

Rafferty, Mr Patrick BA . . . . Sep 1986
Walton, Mr Philip W LLB . . . . Dec 1988
Wilkinson, Mr Andrew C. . . . . *Dec 1991
Asoc: Cassidy, Mrs Amanda Irene LLB . . . . *Oct 1989
Jewitt, Ms Dorothy LLB . . . . Jun 1974
Ast: Laidlaw, Mr Keith J . . . . Jul 1992

GLYNIS M MACKIE ‡
29a Princes Road Gosforth Tyne & Wear NE3 5TT
Tel: 0191 236 5308 *Fax:* 0191 236 6920
E-mail: info@gmmlegal.co.uk
List of partners: G M Mackie
Work: E F1 L S1 W Z(d)
Fixed Fee Interview undertaken
SPr: Mackie, Mrs Glynis Margaret BA . . . . *Apr 1983
Ast: Birch, Miss Rosemary A LLB(Soton). . . . . *Oct 1988

LEONARD B G MUSCAT ‡
10 Lansdowne Terrace Gosforth Tyne & Wear NE3 1HN
Tel: 0191 285 8510 *Fax:* 0191 285 8510
Emergency telephone 0191 285 7698
List of partners: L B G Muscat
Languages: French, Hebrew
Work: B1 F1 K1 N R1 S1 T1 T2 W Z(c,j)
Emergency Action, Agency and Advocacy undertaken
SPr: Muscat, Mr Leonard Brian Geoffrey LLB(Dunelm) ♦ . . *Oct 1957

JOHN O'NEILL & CO ‡
(incorporating Stanton Croft)
1-2 Lansdowne Terrace East Gosforth Tyne & Wear NE3 1HL
Tel: 0191 246 4000 *Fax:* 0191 213 0134 *Dx:* 60351 GOSFORTH
E-mail: info@stantoncroft.co.uk
List of partners: D M Gold, R W S Hird, F A Jones, J M O'Neill
Languages: French
Work: A1 B1 C1 C2 D1 D2 E F1 J1 K1 K2 K3 K4 L N O P Q R1 S1 S2 T1 T2 W X Z(c,d,e,h,i,l,o,p,t)
Emergency Action, Agency, Advocacy, Fixed Fee Interview and Legal Aid Franchise
Ptr: Gold, Mr David Michael MA . . . . *Jan 1968
Hird, Mr Roger William Stanton BA(Cantab) . . . . . *Oct 1964
Jones, Mr Frederick Andrew LLB; STEP. . . . . *Jan 1971
O'Neill, Mr John Murdo BA(Law) . . . . *May 1981
Asoc: Burn, Mrs Alison BA(Hons) . . . . *Nov 1996
Charnock-Neal, Ms Gillian Margaret LLB Deputy District Judge . . . . *Oct 1986
Harbron, Ms Rebecca LLB(Hons) . . . . *Sep 2003
Con: Thom, Ms Anne LLB; TEP. . . . . *Dec 1960

CHRISTINE SANDERSON ‡
3 Rectory Drive Gosforth Tyne & Wear NE3 1XU
Tel: 0191 285 9633 *Fax:* 0191 285 9633
List of partners: C Sanderson
Work: S1
Agency undertaken
SPr: Sanderson, Miss Christine . . . . *Jul 1969

L L SWINBURNE ‡
(in association with Swinburne & Jackson)
6 Westfield Drive Gosforth Tyne & Wear NE3 4XT
Tel: 0191 285 7544 *Fax:* 0191 490 0371
Work: C1 D1 E F1 G H J1 K1 L M1 N P R1 S1 T1 W
Emergency Action, Agency, Advocacy, Fixed Fee Interview and Legal Aid undertaken
Con: Swinburne, Miss Lalage L LLB . . . . Mar 1956

GOSPORT, Hampshire

BISCOES
42 High Street Gosport Hampshire PO12 1DF
Tel: 023 9251 2030 *Fax:* 023 9251 2031 *Dx:* 136570 GOSPORT 2
E-mail: bcg@biscoes-law.co.uk
Office: Petersfield, Portchester, Portsmouth, Waterlooville, Wickham
Work: A2 A3 B1 D1 D2 E F1 I J1 J2 K1 K2 L N O Q S1 S2 V W X Z(b,c,d,f,j,k,l,q,r)
Emergency Action, Agency, Advocacy, Fixed Fee Interview, Legal Aid undertaken, Legal Aid Franchise and Member of Accident Line
Ptr: Hodge, Ms Jane . . . . *Apr 2006
Asoc: Chaffer, Miss Liza Rebecca LLB. . . . . *Nov 2008

BILL CHARLTON SOLICITORS ‡
53 Stoke Road Gosport Hampshire PO12 1LX
Tel: 023 9250 3366 *Dx:* 48168 GOSPORT

CHURCHERS
3 High Street Gosport Hampshire PO12 1BX
Tel: 023 9260 3400 *Fax:* 023 9251 1639 *Dx:* 136568 GOSPORT 2
Emergency telephone 023 9252 0204
E-mail: solicitors@churchers.co.uk
Office: Fareham, Lee-on-the-Solent, Portsmouth (2 offices), Ryde
Work: A1 B1 C1 D1 E F1 G H J1 K1 L M1 N P S1 T1 V W Z(b,e,k,l,m)
Emergency Action, Agency, Advocacy, Fixed Fee Interview, Legal Aid undertaken and Legal Aid Franchise
Ptr: Sandilands, Mr Ian A LLB(Lond). . . . . *Aug 1973

COFFIN MEW & CLOVER
60 Stoke Road Gosport Hampshire PO12 1PA
Tel: 023 9252 3111 *Fax:* 023 9251 0460 *Dx:* 48151 GOSPORT
E-mail: gosport@coffinmew.co.uk
Office: Fareham, Portsmouth, Southampton
Work: C2 L S1 T2 V W Z(o,s)
Emergency Action, Agency, Advocacy, Fixed Fee Interview, Legal Aid undertaken, Legal Aid Franchise and Member of Accident Line
Ptr: Kenny, Mr Courtney R F LLB . . . . *Jun 1975
Asoc: Baverstock, Mr David P . . . . *Apr 1969

DONNELLY & ELLIOTT LIMITED ‡
38 Stoke Road Gosport Hampshire PO12 1JG
Tel: 023 9250 5500 *Fax:* 023 9250 3980 *Dx:* 48150 GOSPORT
E-mail: enq@donnelly-elliott.co.uk
List of partners: J B C Donnelly, M Donnelly, R J Parrott, H Wilson
Work: C1 C2 D1 D2 E F1 J1 K1 K3 K4 L N O Q S1 S2 W Z(a,l,q)
Emergency Action, Fixed Fee Interview, Legal Aid undertaken and Legal Aid Franchise
Ptr: Donnelly, Mr John B C . . . . *May 1969
Donnelly, Mr Michael . . . . *Jun 1972
Parrott, Mr Richard J LLB(Hull) . . . . *Nov 1981
Wilson, Miss Helen LLB; BA(Hons); LawDip. . . . . . *Sep 1997
Ast: Cozeros, Mr David LLB(Hons). . . . . Jul 2001
Jenkins-Powell, Mrs Michelle Marie BA(Cantab). . . *Aug 2008
Mills, Mr Christopher John. . . . . *Mar 1995

KINGSWELL BERNEY ‡
2 Stoke Road Gosport Hampshire PO12 1JB
Tel: 023 9258 2211 *Fax:* 023 9251 0464 *Dx:* 48153 GOSPORT
Emergency telephone 023 9258 4137
E-mail: admin@kingswell-berney.co.uk
List of partners: V H Lowry, R A Money
Work: B1 D1 D2 E F1 F2 J1 J2 K1 L M1 N Q S1 S2 T1 T2 V W Z(m)
Emergency Action, Agency, Advocacy, Fixed Fee Interview, Legal Aid undertaken, Legal Aid Franchise and Member of Accident Line
Ptr: Lowry, Mr Victor H LLB; Dip EU Law & Practice . . . . *§Jul 1975
Money, Mr Robin A LLB. . . . . *§Jun 1980

KREMERS SOLICITORS LIMITED ‡
21 Solent Way Gosport Hampshire PO12 2NR
Tel: 0845 021 2222

GRANGE-OVER-SANDS, Cumbria

SHIRLEY M EVANS ‡
5 Lowther Gardens Grange-over-Sands Cumbria LA11 7EX
Tel: 01539 535208 *Fax:* 01539 534820
Dx: 63967 GRANGE-OVER-SANDS
E-mail: info@shirleymevans.co.uk
List of partners: S M Evans
Work: A1 B1 C1 C2 E F1 G H J1 L R1 R2 S1 S2 T1 T2 V W X Z(l,m)
Agency undertaken
SPr: Evans, Mrs Shirley M LLB. . . . . *Oct 1982

GEDYE & SONS (SOLICITORS) LTD ‡
Chancery House Kents Bank Road Grange-over-Sands Cumbria LA11 7HD
Tel: 01539 532313 *Fax:* 01539 532474
Dx: 63960 GRANGE-OVER-SANDS
E-mail: info@gedye.co.uk
List of partners: M E Jones, R A Roberts
Work: C1 E K4 L S1 S2 T1 T2 W Z(d,m)
Ptr: Jones, Mr Mark E BA . . . . *Feb 1988
Roberts, Mr Richard A BA. . . . . *Oct 1982
Ast: Bell, Miss Hannah Elizabeth LLB(Hons). . . . . Sep 2010
Craig, Mrs Geraldine LLB . . . . *Aug 2000
Lovell, Mrs Bridget Rachel LLB . . . . Oct 1990
Murphy, Miss Sarah Louise LLB(Hons) . . . . *Jun 2006

POOLE TOWNSEND
Main Street Grange-over-Sands Cumbria LA11 6AB
Tel: 01539 533316 *Fax:* 01539 534949
Emergency telephone 0800 389 2939
E-mail: mbeecham@pooletownsend.co.uk
Office: Barrow-in-Furness, Dalton-in-Furness, Kendal, Ulverston
Work: K4 S1 W
Asoc: Gregory, Mrs Fiona Susan LLB . . . . Jun 1995
Con: Davies, Mr Ieuan Michael LLB. . . . . *Jul 1967

GRANTHAM, Lincolnshire

BIRD & CO ‡
15 Castlegate Grantham Lincolnshire NG31 6SE
Tel: 01476 591711 *Fax:* 01476 593235 *Dx:* 27002 GRANTHAM
E-mail: enquiries@birdandco.co.uk
Web: www.birdandco.co.uk
List of partners: E Conron, C P Milligan, J L Overland
Office: Newark
Work: B1 C1 C2 C3 D1 E F1 G H J1 K1 L M1 M2 N P Q R1 S1 S2 W Z(c)
Emergency Action, Agency, Advocacy, Fixed Fee Interview, Legal Aid undertaken and Legal Aid Franchise
Ptr: Conron, Mrs Estelle LLB(Hons) . . . . *Nov 1995
Milligan, Mr Christopher Peter LLB ★ . . . . *Jul 1994
Overland, Mrs Jane Louise BA(Hons) . . . . *Apr 1999
Asoc: Arthur, Mr Robert LLB(Hons) . . . . Apr 1997
Macmillan, Mrs Katherine BA; DipLaw. . . . . Oct 2002
Macmillan, Mr Rory Duncan Hamilton BA . . . . . . *Mar 1991
Pye-Smith, Mr Christopher John BA(Hons) . . . . . . *Oct 1991
Rogerson, Mrs Mikaela . . . . *Jul 1996
Wild, Mr Stuart Patrick BSc(Hons). . . . . *Oct 1995
Ast: Christopher, Ms Caroline . . . . Sep 1997
Gallaher, Mrs Lydia Jane LLB(Hons) . . . . *Nov 2001
Tarlton-Weatherall, Ms Sally. . . . . Oct 2004
Con: Hardy, Mr Paul LLB(Hons) . . . . Nov 1998

CHATTERTONS SOLICITORS
30 Avenue Road Grantham Lincolnshire NG31 6TH
Tel: 01476 591550 *Fax:* 01476 591552 *Dx:* 27003 GRANTHAM
Emergency telephone 07860 721177
E-mail: grantham@chattertons.com
Office: Boston (2 offices), Horncastle, Lincoln, Newark, Sleaford, Spalding, Stamford
Work: A1 B1 C1 D1 E F1 J1 K1 L N O P Q R1 S1 S2 T1 T2 W Z(c,d,k,l,m,o,q)
Emergency Action, Agency, Advocacy, Fixed Fee Interview, Legal Aid undertaken, Legal Aid Franchise and Member of Accident Line
Ptr: Blezard, Mr Rodney John LLB(Hons) . . . . *Dec 1987
Clark, Mr Robert Eugar LLB(Hons) . . . . Apr 1979
Harrison, Ms Jayne . . . . Oct 2002
Johns, Miss Jacquelina LLB(Hons) . . . . Nov 2003
Ludlow, Mr Richard R . . . . *Nov 1997
Salt, Mr Timothy D BA(Law). . . . . *Oct 1983

FRASER WISE & CO ‡
28 Avenue Road Grantham Lincolnshire NG31 6TH
Tel: 01476 566646 / 561870 *Fax:* 01476 567617
Dx: 27006 GRANTHAM
List of partners: W L Fraser
Languages: French, Spanish
Work: C1 D1 E F1 G H J1 K1 S1 W
Emergency Action, Agency, Advocacy, Fixed Fee Interview and Legal Aid undertaken
SPr: Fraser, Mr William L BA. . . . . *Jul 1977
Ast: Fraser, Miss Gillian Mary LLB(Hons) . . . . Sep 1997

JMP SOLICITORS ‡
Newton Chambers Newton Business Park Isaac Newton Way Grantham Lincolnshire NG31 9RT
Tel: 01476 568100 *Fax:* 01476 566149 *Dx:* 713628 GRANTHAM
E-mail: enquiries@jmp-solicitors.com
List of partners: I Howard
Office: Warrington
Dir: Howard, Mr Ian . . . . Sep 2001

PERT & MALIM ‡
79 Westgate Grantham Lincolnshire NG31 6LD
Tel: 01476 561631 *Fax:* 01476 573274 *Dx:* 27012 GRANTHAM
Emergency telephone 01476 585352 / 585863
E-mail: perts@btinternet.com
List of partners: S J Pert
Work: A1 A2 B1 C1 D1 D2 E F1 G H I J1 J2 K1 L N O P R1 S1 S2 V W Z(c,e,g,i,k,l,o,q,r)
Emergency Action, Agency, Advocacy, Fixed Fee Interview undertaken and Member of Accident Line
Ptr: Pert, Mrs Sarah J LLB(Nott'm) . . . . *Oct 1983
Ast: Bagshaw, Mrs Sally Jane . . . . *Oct 1994

THE RINGROSE LAW GROUP - DAVID THORNLEY
(incorporating Nortons)
4 St Peter's Hill Grantham Lincolnshire NG31 6QD
Tel: 01476 590200 *Fax:* 01476 573822 *Dx:* 27001 GRANTHAM
E-mail: david.thornley@ringroselaw.co.uk
Office: Boston, Lincoln (2 offices), Newark, Sleaford, Spalding
Work: A1 B1 C1 D1 D2 E F1 G J1 J2 K1 K2 L N O Q S1 S2 T1 T2 V W Z(l,q)
Emergency Action, Agency, Advocacy, Fixed Fee Interview, Legal Aid undertaken, Legal Aid Franchise and Member of Accident Line
Ptr: Thornley, Mr David G LLB(Lond) . . . . *Jul 1977
Asoc: Armstrong, Ms Judith LLB(Hons) . . . . Sep 2005
Ast: Corringan, Mrs Sally Vanessa. . . . . *Oct 2002
Farmer, Mrs Nerina Lesley BA(Hons)(Dunelm)(Law). *Nov 1996
Green, Mrs Amanda J LLB . . . . Feb 1994
Jenkins, Mrs Jane LLB(Hons) . . . . *Apr 1991

HUGH STAUNTON ‡
Glebe House Main Street Gunby Grantham Lincolnshire NG33 5LF
Tel: 01476 861972 *Fax:* 0845 009 4435
E-mail: hugh@countylaw.co.uk
List of partners: H C T Staunton
Languages: French
Work: C1 W
Ptr: Staunton, Mr Hugh C T Henry Malcolm Hubbard Scholarship . . . . *Dec 1971

HENRY THOMPSON & SONS ‡
7 Elmer Street Grantham Lincolnshire NG31 6RE
Tel: 01476 563226 *Fax:* 01476 563893 *Dx:* 27005 GRANTHAM
E-mail: md.elliott@thompsols.com
List of partners: S L O Bukraba, M D Elliott
Office: Bingham
Work: C1 D1 E F1 K1 K3 L O Q S1 S1 T1 T2 W
Fixed Fee Interview undertaken
Ptr: Bukraba, Miss Susan L O BA . . . . *Apr 1983
Elliott, Mr Martin D LLB . . . . *Dec 1980
Ast: Alladin, Mrs Sameena Bashir BEd(Hons); MA . . . . . Jan 1998

GRASSINGTON, North Yorkshire

SPENCER DAVIES ‡
6 Station Road Grassington North Yorkshire BD23 5NQ
Tel: 01756 753015 *Fax:* 01756 753020
E-mail: amd@spencerdavies.co.uk
List of partners: A M Davies, J S Spencer
Languages: French, German
Work: A1 E G H K1 N P Q S1 S2 W Z(d,l,q,w,y)
Advocacy undertaken
Ptr: Davies, Mr Antony M LLB. . . . . *Sep 1984
Spencer, Mr John S MA(Cantab) . . . . *Jun 1974
Ast: Clare, Mrs Elaine R LLB Notary Public . . . . *Nov 1972

GRAVESEND, Kent

ROBIN F CLARK & CO ‡
198 Parrock Street Gravesend Kent DA12 1EW
Tel: 01474 334444 *Fax:* 01474 334362 *Dx:* 6812 GRAVESEND
E-mail: mail@robinfclark.co.uk
List of partners: R F Clark, S Gill
Languages: Punjabi
Work: B1 B2 C1 D1 D2 E F2 G H J1 K1 K3 K4 L N O P Q R1 S1 S2 W X Z(g,i,l,p,w)
Advocacy and Fixed Fee Interview undertaken
Ptr: Clark, Mr Robin F. . . . . *Jan 1968
Gill, Miss Sarabjit . . . . Jul 2002

FS LAW SOLICITORS & ADVOCATES ‡
27 Milton Road Gravesend Kent DA12 2RF
Tel: 01474 533338

M K GILL SOLICITORS ‡
63 Windmill Street Gravesend Kent DA12 1BJ
Tel: 01474 353399 *Fax:* 01474 354455
E-mail: info@mkgillsolicitors.co.uk

HATTEN WYATT ‡
18-21 Wrotham Road Gravesend Kent DA11 0PF
Tel: 01474 351199 *Fax:* 01474 334345 *Dx:* 6800 GRAVESEND
E-mail: advice@hatten-wyatt.com
List of partners: A L D Croud, K M Du Rocher, R L Giles, J S Gill, D J Jones, S Williams
Office: Gravesend
Languages: Gujarati, Hindi, Punjabi, Urdu
Work: B2 D1 D2 E F1 F2 G H J1 J2 K1 K2 K3 K4 L N O P Q S1 S2 W Z(d,g,i,k,l,m,p,q,r,v)
Emergency Action, Agency, Advocacy, Fixed Fee Interview, Legal Aid undertaken and Legal Aid Franchise
Ptr: Croud, Ms Avril Linda Denise BA(Exon) . . . . *Jun 1988
Du Rocher, Ms Karen M Notary Public . . . . *Oct 1988
Giles, Mr Richard Lionel. . . . . *Dec 1990
Gill, Mr Jasvinder Singh LLB(Hons); LLM Notary Public . . . . *Dec 1999
Jones, Mr Damien John LLB(Hons) . . . . *May 1999
Williams, Miss Sara LLB(Hons) . . . . *Aug 2001
Asoc: Ratchford, Ms Yvette Julia. . . . . *Sep 2006
Ast: Bhangra, Manprit . . . . *Jun 2009
Brooks, Gail Louise . . . . *May 2009
Lea, Mr David. . . . . *Sep 2010
Con: Brasington, Mr John. . . . . *Feb 1957
Girach, Farook Mahomed Husen Jusab . . . . *Jun 1981

See p112 for the Key to Work Categories & other symbols

HATTEN WYATT
51/54 Windmill Street Gravesend Kent DA12 1BD
Tel: 01474 351199 *Fax:* 01474 328315 *Dx:* 6800 GRAVESEND
E-mail: advice@hatten-wyatt.com
Office: Gravesend

MICHAEL JENKINS ‡
Mill Cottage Gravesend Kent DA12 3HA
Tel: 01474 822787 *Fax:* 01474 822520
Work: G H

ANDREW J KILBY ‡
36-37 The Hill Northfleet Gravesend Kent DA11 9EX
Tel: 01474 355758 *Fax:* 01474 350921
List of partners: A J Kilby
Work: A1 B1 C1 E K1 L S1 S2 W
Fixed Fee Interview and Legal Aid undertaken
Ptr: Kilby, Mr Andrew J . . . . *Jan 1970

KING PRIOR MACDONALD BRIDGE ‡
183 Parrock Street Gravesend Kent DA12 1EN
Tel: 01474 325678 *Fax:* 01474 569482
E-mail: reception@kingprior.co.uk
List of partners: R MacDonald Bridge, R D Prior
Office: Rochester
Languages: French
Work: E S1 W Z(l)
SPr: Prior, Mr Ronald D BA(Hons) . . . . *Jun 1980

PATRICK LAWRENCE ‡
5 Railway Place Gravesend Kent DA12 1AP
Tel: 01474 356441 *Fax:* 01474 333426 *Dx:* 6808 GRAVESEND
E-mail: pwl@patlaw.co.uk
List of partners: P W Lawrence
Languages: French, Punjabi, Urdu
Work: D1 E K1 K3 S1 S2 V W
Emergency Action, Agency, Advocacy, Fixed Fee Interview, Legal Aid undertaken and Legal Aid Franchise
SPr: Lawrence, Mr Patrick William . . . . *Oct 1980
Ast: Penaser, Talvinder Kaur BA(Hons) . . . . *Feb 2002

MARTIN TOLHURST PARTNERSHIP LLP ‡
7 Wrotham Road Gravesend Kent DA11 0PD
Tel: 01474 325531 *Fax:* 01474 560771 *Dx:* 6801 GRAVESEND
E-mail: mtpg@martintolhurst.co.uk
List of partners: J B C Carter, R J Carter, S F Franklin, J Hunt, K F Newell, P S Rothwell, B M Stewart, J Williams
Office: Ashford, Longfield
Work: B1 C1 E J1 K1 L N O Q S1 S2 W Z(l,q)
Emergency Action, Agency, Advocacy, Fixed Fee Interview undertaken and Member of Accident Line
Ptr: Carter, Mr James B C . . . . *Dec 1978
Franklin, Mr Simon F LLB. . . . . *Nov 1982
Hunt, Mr Julian LLB. . . . . *Aug 1999
Rothwell, Mr Philip S LLB(Lond) Notary Public. . . . . *Apr 1977
Ast: Denny, Mr Kevin John. . . . . Jan 1999
Dobson, Mr Giles Mackenzie BA(Hons) . . . . *Jan 2004
Fong, Miss Angela LLB . . . . *Dec 1999
Reid, Mr Hugh LLB . . . . *Apr 2006
Rothwell, Mr Paul Leonard LLB(Hons). . . . . Oct 2007

CHRIS MILESON ‡
Winnats Farm Wrangling Lane Gravesend Kent DA13 0XF
Tel: 01474 816517 *Fax:* 01474 813292
E-mail: chris@chrismileson.com
List of partners: C Mileson
Work: Z(f)
SPr: Mileson, Mr Christopher LLB(Lond) . . . . *Jun 1981

MIKE NORTHERN LEGAL ‡
7 Old Road West Gravesend Kent DA11 0LH
Tel: 01474 329961 *Fax:* 0870 706 1978
E-mail: mrln@mnlegal.co.uk

MARTIN SEWELL FAMILY LAW SOLICITOR & ADVOCATE ‡
8 Appleshaw Close Gravesend Kent DA11 7PB
Tel: 01474 323251 *Fax:* 01474 536752
E-mail: martinsewell@martinsewell.co.uk
List of partners: M D Sewell
Languages: French
Work: D1 D2 K1
Emergency Action, Agency, Advocacy, Fixed Fee Interview, Legal Aid undertaken and Legal Aid Franchise
SPr: Sewell, Mr Martin D LLB(Hons) . . . . *Jul 1975

SK NAGRA SOLICITORS ‡
33 Darnley Road Gravesend Kent DA11 0SD
Tel: 01474 333270 *Fax:* 01474 364714
E-mail: satbirnagra@yahoo.co.uk

STANTONS ‡
24 Wrotham Road Gravesend Kent DA11 0LX
Tel: 01474 579940 *Fax:* 01474 328230 *Dx:* 6831 GRAVESEND
E-mail: jan@stanlaw.co.uk
List of partners: J E Stanton
Work: D1 D2 K1 S1 W
Agency, Advocacy, Fixed Fee Interview and Legal Aid Franchise
Ptr: Stanton, Mrs Janet E BA . . . . *Dec 1977
Ast: Harris, Miss Emma Elizabeth LLB(Hons) . . . . Aug 2010
Palmer, Mrs Emma Rachel . . . . *Oct 1998

VYMAN SOLICITORS ‡
26 Harmer Street Gravesend Kent DA12 2AX
Tel: 01474 537270 *Fax:* 01474 537037 *Dx:* 6832 GRAVESEND
E-mail: admin@vyman.co.uk
List of partners: J P Berg, G S Mander, A Vyas
Office: Harrow, Maidstone
Languages: Gujarati, Punjabi
Ptr: Mander, Mr Gurnam Singh LLB(Hons). . . . . Oct 1996
Vyas, Mr Anup LLB(Hons). . . . . *Oct 1993
Ast: Hart, Ms Victoria LLB(Hons). . . . . Aug 1997

GRAYS, Thurrock

AKHIGBE & AKHIGBE SOLICITORS (A & A SOLICITORS) ‡
21a Orsett Road Grays Thurrock RM17 5DS
Tel: 01375 384386 *Fax:* 0560 343 9083 *Dx:* 54014 GRAYS
E-mail: info@akhigbe2solicitors.co.uk

ANGLO LAW SOLICITORS ‡
Excel Chambers 641a London Road Grays Thurrock RM20 3HD
Tel: 01708 862786
E-mail: rhussain@anglolaw.co.uk

ATTWOOD & CO ‡
20 London Road Grays Thurrock RM17 5XY
Tel: 01375 378122 / 378123 *Fax:* 01375 384111 *Dx:* 54006 GRAYS
E-mail: enquiry@attwoodandco.co.uk
List of partners: C Attwood, R D Bradbury, A Law
Work: B1 C1 C2 C3 D1 E F1 J1 J2 K1 K3 K4 L N O Q S1 S2 T1 T2 V W X Z(c,e,i,j,k,l,m,q,r,s)
Emergency Action, Agency, Advocacy, Legal Aid undertaken, Legal Aid Franchise and Member of Accident Line
Ptr: Attwood, Mr Clive General Commissioner of Taxes Deputy District Judge. . . . . *Jan 1968
Bradbury, Mr Richard D BA; MA. . . . . Jul 1981
Law, Mr Andrew LLB . . . . *Oct 1990
Ast: Kaur, Mrs Ranjit LLB(Hons) . . . . *Aug 2003

T A CAPRON & CO ‡
Milton House 68 Orsett Road Grays Thurrock RM17 5EJ
Tel: 01375 378331 *Fax:* 01375 390153 *Dx:* 54002 GRAYS
Emergency telephone 07974 355979
E-mail: tacapron@plus.com
List of partners: T J Taylor, C M H Ward
Work: A1 A3 B1 C1 C2 E F1 J1 K1 K3 L M1 N O P Q R1 R2 S1 S2 T1 W Z(a,b,c,d,e,f,g,h,i,j,k,l,m,n,p,s,t)
Emergency Action, Agency, Advocacy, Fixed Fee Interview and Legal Aid undertaken
Ptr: Taylor, Mr Terence J LLB . . . . *Apr 1975
Ward, Mr Christopher M H BA Notary Public. . . . . . *Jan 1965
Ast: Beasley, Mr Simon M . . . . *Jan 2009
Chesher, Mrs Arianne E. . . . . *Oct 2008

CUMMING & RILEY ‡
11a High Street Grays Thurrock RM17 6NB
Tel: 01375 383691 *Fax:* 01375 386708 *Dx:* 54005 GRAYS
Emergency telephone 07939 843435
E-mail: reception@cummingriley.com
List of partners: G A Cumming, J Michell
Languages: Spanish
Work: B1 C1 D1 E F1 G H J1 K1 L N R1 S1 T1 V W Z(l,t)
Emergency Action, Agency, Advocacy, Fixed Fee Interview and Legal Aid undertaken
Ptr: Cumming, Mr Gerald Anthony LLB(Soton). . . . . . . *Mar 1980
Michell, Mr John . . . . Jan 1979
Ast: Barham, Mrs Joanna Clare . . . . Oct 2001
Majid, Miss Tahmina Naz . . . . Nov 2004
Rogers, Ms Melanie Cristina LLB(Hons). . . . . *Sep 1997
St Clair-Haslam, Mr Stuart BSocSc; PGDipLaw; LLB . Feb 1998

FASHANU & CO ‡
6-18 High Street Grays Thurrock RM17 6LU
Tel: 01375 385588 *Fax:* 01375 386688

HATTENS SOLICITORS ‡
90 Orsett Road Grays Thurrock RM17 5ER
Tel: 01375 374851 / 373516 *Fax:* 01375 374332 *Dx:* 54000 GRAYS
E-mail: jtrull@hagsols.demon.co.uk
Work: A1 B1 C1 D1 E F1 G H J1 K1 L M1 N P R1 S1 T1 W Z(d,h,j,l,o)

PALMERS
Ascension Chambers Fleming Road Grays Thurrock RM16 6HH
Tel: 01375 484444 *Fax:* 01375 484448 *Dx:* 54016 GRAYS
E-mail: enquiries@palmerslaw.co.uk
Office: Basildon, South Woodham Ferrers
Languages: Cantonese
Work: C1 C2 D1 E F2 J1 K1 K2 K3 M1 O P Q R1 S1 S2 W Z(c,e)
Ptr: Chong, Enghet LLM(Lond) . . . . *Mar 1993
Skinner, Mr Andrew P. . . . . *Oct 1989
Ast: Kelly, Ms Hannah Lucy LLB(Hons) . . . . Sep 2004

PANESAR & CO ‡
3-5 Derby Road Grays Thurrock RM17 6QD
Tel: 01375 383283 *Fax:* 01375 383300
Emergency telephone 07939 965207
E-mail: enquiries@panesarandco.co.uk
Languages: Gujarati, Punjabi
Work: D1 G H K1 N Q
Ast: Patel, Ms Binta . . . . Jul 2004
Sparrow, Ms Hannah . . . . Jan 2002

MARGARET REYNOLDS SOLICITOR ‡
24 London Road Grays Thurrock RM17 5XY
Tel: 01375 390239 *Fax:* 01375 391808 *Dx:* 54009 GRAYS
E-mail: admin@mrpsolicitors.co.uk
List of partners: H Millane, M Reynolds
Work: E K1 K2 K3 K4 S1 S2 W
Fixed Fee Interview undertaken
Ptr: Millane, Ms Heather. . . . . Nov 1995
Reynolds, Mrs Margaret. . . . . *Dec 1979

STERNBERG REED
Upper Floors 6-8 High Street Grays Thurrock RM17 6LU
Tel: 01375 486500 *Fax:* 01708 486509 *Dx:* 54030 GRAYS
Emergency telephone 07626 917962
E-mail: enquiries@sternberg-reed.co.uk
Office: Barking, London NW1, Romford

TMB ASSOCIATES SOLICITORS ‡
34 Orsett Road Grays Thurrock RM17 5EB
Tel: 01375 378809

TAHMINA & CO ‡
8a London Road Grays Thurrock RM17 5XY
Tel: 01375 384200 *Fax:* 01375 378977

TAYLOR WOOD SOLICITORS ‡
71 Lancaster Road Chafford Hundred Grays Thurrock RM16 6EA
Tel: 01375 480053 / 01375 651543 *Fax:* 01375 480083
E-mail: info@taylorwoodsolicitors.com

GRAYSHOTT, Hampshire

BROWN-HOVELT VEALE NELSON ‡
Stewart House Crossways Road Grayshott Hampshire GU26 6HF
Tel: 01428 607433 *Fax:* 01428 607089 *Dx:* 52652 GRAYSHOTT
E-mail: bhvlawco@dsl.pipex.com
List of partners: R H Brown-Hovelt
Work: E K4 L S1 S2 W
Ptr: Brown-Hovelt, Mr Roger H LLB . . . . *Dec 1975

BURLEY & GEACH
International House Headley Road Grayshott Hampshire GU26 6NG
Tel: 01428 605355 *Fax:* 01428 604859 *Dx:* 52651 GRAYSHOTT
Emergency telephone 01428 656344
E-mail: grayshott@burley-geach.co.uk
Office: Haslemere, Liphook, Petersfield
Languages: French, German
Work: A1 B1 C1 C2 C3 D1 E F1 G H J1 K1 L M1 M2 N O P Q R1 S1 S2 T1 T2 V W Z(c,d,e,h,l,m,r)
Emergency Action, Agency, Advocacy, Fixed Fee Interview, Legal Aid undertaken, Legal Aid Franchise and Member of Accident Line
Ptr: Andrews, Mr Timothy J R LLB. . . . . *Oct 1977
Bather, Mr Stephen R LLB(Hull). . . . . *§Jun 1979
Baylis, Mr Richard J BA. . . . . *§Jul 1976
Jennings, Mr Howard M. . . . . *Jan 1983
Nellthorp, Mrs Alison E LLB(Exon) . . . . *Nov 1981
Spirit, Miss D Anna Jane BA . . . . *Dec 1985

LEWIS WHEELER SOLICITOR ‡
Whitebeam Cottage Church Lane Grayshott Hampshire GU26 6LY
Tel: 01483 600099 *Fax:* 01483 600099
E-mail: cw@lewiswheeler.co.uk

GREAT AYTON, North Yorkshire

KITCHING KNEALE & CO ‡
81 High Street Great Ayton North Yorkshire TS9 6NS
Tel: 01642 723713 *Fax:* 01642 725011
Languages: French, Kiswahili
Work: A1 C1 F1 J1 K1 L N O Q S1 W Z(k,l)
Agency, Advocacy, Legal Aid undertaken and Member of Accident Line
Asoc: Kitching, Mr Nigel H LLB Chairman of the Cleveland Social Security Appeal Tribunal . . . . *Jul 1969

GREAT BOOKHAM, Surrey

FORTESCUE GRAHAM & LLOYD
22a High Street Great Bookham Surrey KT23 4AG
Tel: 01372 456221 *Fax:* 01372 450155
Dx: 117527 GREAT BOOKHAM
E-mail: law@fortescuegl.co.uk
Office: Leatherhead
Work: C1 E K1 L S1 W
Fixed Fee Interview undertaken
Ptr: Lloyd, Mr Peter K LLB. . . . . *Jan 1969

WISMAYERS ‡
2 Butler House Guildford Road Great Bookham Surrey KT23 4HB
Tel: 01372 451114 *Fax:* 0870 762 5856
E-mail: clive.wismayer@virgin.net
List of partners: C R Wismayer
Languages: German
Work: B1 C1 E F1 J1 L M2 N O Q W Z(c)
Agency undertaken
Ptr: Wismayer, Mr Clive Richard BA(Leeds) . . . . *Nov 1981

GREAT DUNMOW, Essex

FOORT TAYLER ‡
75 High Street Great Dunmow Essex CM6 1AE
Tel: 01371 875200 *Fax:* 01371 875515 *Dx:* 89805 GREAT DUNMOW
Emergency telephone 01371 856632
E-mail: info@foort-tayler.co.uk
List of partners: S M Foort, S A Tayler
Work: E S1 W
Ptr: Foort, Miss Sheelagh M LLB(B'ham) . . . . *Nov 1979
Tayler, Ms Shelley Ann . . . . *Aug 1998

PDJ LAW ‡
Office 1 & 5 Rood End House 6 Stortford Road Great Dunmow Essex CM6 1DA
Tel: 01371 871600 *Fax:* 01371 871555
E-mail: paul.johnson@pdjlaw.co.uk

STANLEY TEE
42 High Street Great Dunmow Essex CM6 1AH
Tel: 01371 872166 *Fax:* 01371 875747 *Dx:* 89803 GREAT DUNMOW
E-mail: law@stanleytee.co.uk
Office: Bishop's Stortford, Braintree, Saffron Walden
Work: A1 C1 E F1 G J1 K1 L P S1 T1
Fixed Fee Interview and Legal Aid undertaken
Ptr: Osborne, Mr Paul F LLB . . . . Apr 1974

WADE & DAVIES ‡
28 High Street Great Dunmow Essex CM6 1AH
Tel: 01371 872816 *Fax:* 01371 872324 *Dx:* 89800 GREAT DUNMOW
E-mail: enquiries@wadeanddavies.co.uk
List of partners: M R Chapman
Work: A1 C1 E K1 M1 R1 S1 T1 W Z(d,m)
Emergency Action, Agency, Advocacy and Fixed Fee Interview undertaken
SPr: Chapman, Mr Michael R Clerk to Commissioner of Tax for West Essex, Stratford & Walthamstow Divisions Notary Public . . . . *§Jun 1972
Ast: Harper, Miss Lisa Marie LLB(Hons) . . . . Oct 2007

GREAT ECCLESTON, Lancashire

JOBLING & KNAPE
Town View West End Great Eccleston Lancashire PR3 0ZL
Tel: 01995 670083 *Fax:* 01995 671313
Office: Lancaster, Morecambe
Work: A1 B1 C1 D1 E F1 G H J1 K1 L M1 N P R1 S1 T1 V W Z(b,c,d,l,m)
Emergency Action, Agency, Advocacy, Fixed Fee Interview and Legal Aid undertaken
Ptr: Harrison, Mr David LLB(L'pool) . . . . *§May 1971

GREAT HARWOOD, Lancashire

HAWORTH & NUTTALL
Bancroft Chambers Town Hall Street Great Harwood Lancashire BB6 7HB
Tel: 01254 884253 *Fax:* 01254 883505
Office: Accrington, Blackburn
Work: A1 C1 D1 E F1 G H J1 K1 L M1 N P R1 S1 T1 W
Emergency Action, Agency, Advocacy, Fixed Fee Interview, Legal Aid undertaken and Member of Accident Line
Ptr: Barnes, Mr Peter D LLB(Hons) . . . . *Jul 1976
Ast: Slattery, Mr Michael B. . . . . *Jun 1973

THE WATSON RAMSBOTTOM PARTNERSHIP
18a-20 Queen Street Great Harwood Lancashire BB6 7QQ
Tel: 01254 884422 / 883020 *Fax:* 01254 877130
Dx: 15251 BLACKBURN 2
E-mail: info@watsonramsbottom.com
Office: Blackburn, Darwen
Languages: French
Work: A1 B1 C1 C2 C3 D1 E F1 J1 K1 L M1 M2 N P R1 S1 T1 T2 W Z(c,i,k,l)
Emergency Action, Agency, Advocacy, Fixed Fee Interview, Legal Aid undertaken and Legal Aid Franchise
Ptr: Swanney, Mr John LLB(Sheff). . . . . *Apr 1981

GREAT MISSENDEN, Buckinghamshire

D C KAYE & CO ‡
Old Bank Chambers 2 Wycombe Road Prestwood Great Missenden Buckinghamshire HP16 0PW
Tel: 01494 864650 / 862226 *Fax:* 01494 865406
Dx: 141430 PRESTWOOD
Emergency telephone 07970 166804
E-mail: office@dc-kaye.co.uk
List of partners: R I Cartmell, P Prikryl
Office: Wendover
Languages: Czech, German, Slovak
Work: A1 B1 B2 C1 D1 E F1 F2 G H J1 J2 K1 K3 K4 L M1 N O P Q R1 R2 S1 S2 V W Z(c,e,g,i,j,k,l,m,p,q,r,w,za)
Emergency Action, Agency and Fixed Fee Interview undertaken
Ptr: Cartmell, Mr Robert Ian BSc(Hons) . . . . *Dec 1996
Prikryl, Mr Paul LLB. . . . . *Jan 2002
Ast: Bagshaw, Mr Stuart BA . . . . Oct 2008
Waller, Miss Imogen BSc . . . . *Apr 2004
Con: Kaye, Mr Donald C MA(Econ). . . . . *Jun 1974

TIMOTHY KENCH & CO ‡
First Floor Suite 6 Chequers Parade Prestwood Great Missenden Buckinghamshire HP16 0PN
Tel: 01494 864153 *Fax:* 01494 864283 *Dx:* 141432 PRESTWOOD
E-mail: office@timothykench.com
List of partners: T R Kench
Languages: French
Work: F1 K1 N Q S1 W
Legal Aid undertaken and Member of Accident Line
Ptr: Kench, Mr Timothy R . . . . *Nov 1978

GREAT YARMOUTH, Norfolk

ARCHER & WILCOCK ‡
The Old Rectory Repps Road Clippesby Great Yarmouth Norfolk NR29 3BH
Tel: 01493 369700 *Fax:* 01493 369569

BREYDONS SOLICITORS ‡
64a North Quay Great Yarmouth Norfolk NR30 1JB
Tel: 01493 331057

CHAMBERLINS ‡
4-6 Crown Road Great Yarmouth Norfolk NR30 2JP
Tel: 01493 857621 *Fax:* 01493 330026
Dx: 41107 GREAT YARMOUTH
E-mail: pbw@chamberlins.demon.co.uk
Office: Beccles, Caister-on-Sea, Great Yarmouth, Lowestoft
Work: A1 B1 C1 C3 D1 E J1 K1 L N O P Q S1 S2 W Z(c,h,l,m)

CHAMBERLINS
9 Baker Street Gorleston Great Yarmouth Norfolk NR31 6QT
Tel: 01493 600113 *Fax:* 01493 443854
Dx: 41107 GREAT YARMOUTH
E-mail: adf@chamberlins.demon.co.uk
Office: Beccles, Caister-on-Sea, Great Yarmouth, Lowestoft
Work: A1 C1 D1 E F1 J1 K1 L N R1 S1 S2 V W Z(c,l)

COLE BENTLEY & CO ‡
21 Church Plain Great Yarmouth Norfolk NR30 1NE
Tel: 01493 330660 *Fax:* 01493 330747
Emergency telephone 07931 354666
E-mail: info@cole-bentley.fsnet.co.uk
Work: G H W
Legal Aid undertaken

GORDON DEAN SOLICITORS
19 Church Plain Great Yarmouth Norfolk NR30 1NE
Office: Norwich

ENGLAND & CO ‡
7-8 South Quay Great Yarmouth Norfolk NR30 2QN
Tel: 01493 844308 / 844309 *Fax:* 01493 330219
Dx: 41101 GREAT YARMOUTH
E-mail: pmason@englandandco.co.uk
List of partners: P R Mason
Office: Great Yarmouth (2 offices)
Work: A1 A3 B1 C1 C2 C3 D1 D2 E F1 F2 J1 J2 K1 K3 K4 L O Q R1 R2 S1 S2 W X Z(d,h,l,p,q)
Emergency Action, Agency, Advocacy, Fixed Fee Interview, Legal Aid undertaken and Legal Aid Franchise
SPr: Mason, Mr Peter Ralph LLB. . . . . *§Nov 1976
Asoc: Porter, Mr Christopher John LLB . . . . *Jul 1997
Smyth, Mr Christopher John BA(Hons) . . . . *Apr 1991
Ast: Anderson, Ms Lorna Ray LLB . . . . *Aug 1992
Hemmings, Ms Rebecca LLB . . . . *Jul 2008

ENGLAND & CO
137 Bells Road Gorleston Great Yarmouth Norfolk NR31 6AG
Tel: 01493 604990 *Fax:* 01493 655520 *Dx:* 41051 GORLESTON
E-mail: landerson@englandandco.co.uk
Office: Great Yarmouth (2 offices)
Work: A1 C1 C2 D1 D2 E F1 F2 J1 K1 K2 K3 K4 L O Q R1 S1 S2 T1 T2 W Z(d,h,l,p)
Emergency Action, Agency, Advocacy, Legal Aid undertaken and Legal Aid Franchise
Asoc: Porter, Mr Christopher John LLB . . . . *Jul 1997

ENGLAND & CO
Prospect House The Green Martham Great Yarmouth Norfolk NR29 4PA
Tel: 01493 740795 / 748174 *Fax:* 01493 740536
E-mail: csymth@englandandco.co.uk
Office: Great Yarmouth (2 offices)
Work: A1 B1 C1 C2 D1 D2 E F1 F2 J1 K1 K2 K3 K4 L O Q R1 S1 S2 T1 T2 W Z(d,h,l,p)
Emergency Action, Agency, Advocacy, Legal Aid undertaken and Legal Aid Franchise

HKB WILTSHIRES ‡
(incorporating Howard Killin & Bruce; Wiltshires)
16-17 South Quay Great Yarmouth Norfolk NR30 2RA
Tel: 01493 855676 *Fax:* 01493 843695
Dx: 41104 GREAT YARMOUTH
E-mail: info@hkbw.co.uk
List of partners: S J Brannigan, S L Harris, A J W Low, J Puxley, M J Tolladay, P I Tuttle, D G Young
Office: Lowestoft
Work: A1 C1 C2 D1 E J1 K3 P R1 S1 S2 T1 T2 W Z(l,m,n,o,t)
Emergency Action, Agency, Advocacy and Legal Aid undertaken
Ptr: Brannigan, Mrs Samantha Jane BA(Hons) Assistant Coroner . . . . *Jan 1998
Harris, Ms Sarah Louise LLB(Hons). . . . . Jul 2004
Low, Mr Alistair J W. . . . . *§Mar 1981
Puxley, Mr Jonathan . . . . Mar 1994
Tolladay, Mr Michael J LLB(Hons). . . . . *§Nov 1978
Young, Mr Derek Gunther Notary Public. . . . . . . *§Jul 1975
Con: Holroyd, Mr Nicholas J Deputy Coroner; Deputy District Judge . . . . *§May 1966
Wiltshire, Mr Hugh E C . . . . *Nov 1962

DAVID HOLMES & CO ‡
Humberside House 47 Englands Lane Gorleston Great Yarmouth Norfolk NR31 6BE
Tel: 01493 658291 *Fax:* 01493 658022
List of partners: D J Holmes
Work: K1 K3
Agency and Advocacy undertaken
SPr: Holmes, Mr David John BA(Law) . . . . *Dec 1979

LUCAS & WYLLYS ‡
11 Queen Street Great Yarmouth Norfolk NR30 2QW
Tel: 01493 855555 *Fax:* 01493 330055
Dx: 41100 GREAT YARMOUTH
E-mail: legal@lucasandwyllys.co.uk
List of partners: E C Benest, N P Craske, T J Parsons, N Riseborough, R R Swanston
Office: Great Yarmouth (2 offices), Lowestoft
Work: C1 D1 E F1 J1 K1 L N S1 S2 T1 T2 V W Z(j)
Emergency Action, Agency, Advocacy, Fixed Fee Interview, Legal Aid undertaken, Legal Aid Franchise and Member of Accident Line
Ptr: Benest, Miss Emma Charlotte LLB . . . . *Nov 1992
Craske, Mr Nigel Paul LLB . . . . *Oct 1986
Parsons, Mr Timothy James LLB(Hons). . . . . *Oct 1993
Riseborough, Ms Nicola. . . . . May 2004
Swanston, Mr Robert R LLB(L'pool) Notary Public. . *§Oct 1976
Asoc: Easter, Mrs Francesca . . . . Oct 2009
Gower, Ms Amy. Aug 2009
Pennington, Miss Kirsty Helen May LLB; PGDip. . . . *Oct 2007

LUCAS & WYLLYS
5 & 6 South Quay Great Yarmouth Norfolk NR30 2QJ
Tel: 01493 855555 *Fax:* 01493 330055
Dx: 41100 GREAT YARMOUTH
E-mail: admin@lucasandwyllys.co.uk
Office: Great Yarmouth (2 offices), Lowestoft

LUCAS & WYLLYS
61-62 Bells Road Gorleston Great Yarmouth Norfolk NR31 6AQ
Tel: 01493 663124 *Fax:* 01493 655488 *Dx:* 41052 GORLESTON
E-mail: gorleston@lucasandwyllys.co.uk
Office: Great Yarmouth (2 offices), Lowestoft
Work: A1 C1 D1 E K1 L M1 N P S1 V W
Emergency Action, Agency, Advocacy, Fixed Fee Interview, Legal Aid undertaken and Legal Aid Franchise

MEARS HOBBS & DURRANT
92 High Street Gorleston Great Yarmouth Norfolk NR31 6RH
Tel: 01493 665413 *Fax:* 01493 652836
Office: Beccles, Lowestoft
Work: A1 B1 C1 C2 C3 D1 E F1 G H J1 K1 L M1 N O P Q R1 S1 T1 T2 V W Z(a,b,c,d,e,f,g,h,i,j,k,l,m,n,o,p,s,t)
Emergency Action, Agency, Advocacy, Legal Aid undertaken and Member of Accident Line
Ptr: Mears, Mr Martin J P MA(Oxon); BCL. . . . . *Mar 1966

NORTON PESKETT
141 King Street Great Yarmouth Norfolk NR30 2PQ
Tel: 01493 849200 *Fax:* 01493 849201
Dx: 41125 GREAT YARMOUTH
E-mail: r-barley@nortonpeskett.co.uk
Office: Beccles, Halesworth, Lowestoft
Work: B1 D1 G H J1 K1 L N O Q R1 S1 Z(i,m)
Emergency Action, Agency, Advocacy, Fixed Fee Interview and Legal Aid undertaken
Ptr: Ambrose, Mr Anthony L. . . . . *§Jan 1968
Gibbons, Mr Julian R BSc. . . . . *Nov 1981
Stephenson, Mrs Alex. . . . . Aug 1998
Ast: Batch, Mr Kevin W . . . . *Dec 1989
Collins, Ms Claire A LLB . . . . *§Oct 1988
Hall, Ms Annette . . . . Nov 1997

NORTON PESKETT ‡
66a Bells Road Gorleston Great Yarmouth Norfolk NR31 6AF
Tel: 01493 652204 *Fax:* 01493 653462 *Dx:* 41050 GORLESTON

POLLOK WEBB & GALL ‡
(in association with Howard Pollok & Webb)
Fastolff House 29 Regent Street Great Yarmouth Norfolk NR30 1RR
Tel: 01493 853725 *Fax:* 01493 331108
E-mail: pollokwebbgall@aol.com
List of partners: G R Gall, C A Webb
Work: B1 C1 C2 D1 E F1 J1 K1 K3 L N O Q R1 S1 S2 V W Z(g,l,q)
Emergency Action, Agency and Advocacy undertaken
Ptr: Gall, Mr Graham R ♦ . . . . *§Jul 1977
Webb, Ms Carole A. . . . . *§Dec 1968

SHERIDAN BOWLES SOLICITORS ‡
1 Crown Road Great Yarmouth Norfolk NR30 2JN
Tel: 01493 859848 *Fax:* 01493 331017
Dx: 41123 GREAT YARMOUTH
E-mail: info@sheridanbowles.co.uk
List of partners: C R G Bowles
Work: G H Z(l)
Agency, Advocacy, Fixed Fee Interview, Legal Aid undertaken and Legal Aid Franchise
Ptr: Bowles, Mr Christopher R G LLB Notary Public . . . . *Jul 1977

PETER STEWARD & CO ‡
22 Church Plain Great Yarmouth Norfolk NR30 1NE
Tel: 01493 332277 *Fax:* 01493 332271
Emergency telephone 07768 823295 / 01508 550746
List of partners: P D Steward
Work: N
Emergency Action, Agency, Advocacy, Fixed Fee Interview and Legal Aid undertaken
SPr: Steward, Mr Peter Derek BSc(Hons)(Biochemistry) . . Aug 1992

GREENFORD, Middlesex

BERRI'S ‡
Research House Fraser Road Greenford Middlesex UB6 7AQ
Tel: 020 8537 3377

BIRD & LOVIBOND
44 The Broadway Greenford Middlesex UB6 9PT
Tel: 020 8578 6936 *Fax:* 020 8575 6170 *Dx:* 44500 GREENFORD
E-mail: greenford@bird-lovibond.co.uk
Office: Ruislip, Uxbridge
Work: C1 E J1 K1 K3 L N O Q S1 S2 W
Agency, Fixed Fee Interview undertaken and Member of Accident Line
Ptr: Matthews-Stroud, Mr Clinton W BA(Hons)(Law). . . . *Oct 1987

CONWAY & CO
299 Greenford Road Greenford Middlesex UB6 8RE
Tel: 020 8575 2191 *Fax:* 020 8575 7504 *Dx:* 80401 WEALDSTONE
Office: Harrow
Languages: Hebrew, Hindi, Urdu
Work: C1 D1 E F1 K1 K3 N S1 W

A DUA & CO ‡
146 Whitton Avenue East Greenford Middlesex UB6 0PY
Tel: 0845 430 4086 *Fax:* 0845 430 4087
E-mail: a.dua.co@gmail.com
List of partners: A Dua
Languages: Gujarati, Hindi, Punjabi, Urdu
Work: B1 D1 J1 K1 Q S1 Z(l)
Emergency Action, Agency and Advocacy undertaken
SPr: Dua, Mrs Ashoo LLB(Hons). . . . . Oct 1990

HS LAW SOLICITORS & NOTARIES ‡
Allied Sainif House 412 Greenford Road Greenford Middlesex UB6 9AH
Tel: 020 8578 5688

KEITH HALL JUVILER & CO ‡
420-422 Greenford Road Greenford Middlesex UB6 9AG
Tel: 020 8578 3133 / 8578 5373 *Fax:* 020 8575 8645
E-mail: plask@keithhalljuviler.co.uk
List of partners: P A Lask
Work: D1 E F1 G H J1 K1 L N O P Q S1 V W X Z(c,h,i,k,l,m,p)
Emergency Action, Agency, Advocacy, Fixed Fee Interview and Legal Aid undertaken
Ptr: Lask, Mr Paul Adam . . . . §Jul 1979
Ast: Andrews, Ms Cheryl C BA(Hons) . . . . *Dec 1987

SOHAL & CO ‡
412 Greenford Road Greenford Middlesex UB6 2AH
Tel: 020 8575 2424 *Fax:* 020 8575 1616 *Dx:* 44511 GREENFORD
E-mail: sohaljustice@hotmail.com
Languages: Gujarati, Hindi, Punjabi, Urdu
Work: A3 B1 B2 C1 D2 E F1 F2 G J1 K1 L N O Q S1 S2 W Z(b,i,k,l,r)
Advocacy undertaken

GRIMSBY, North East Lincolnshire

MARGARET ADAMS LAW ‡
1b Osborne Street Grimsby North East Lincolnshire DN31 1EY
Tel: 01472 358999 *Fax:* 01472 360450
E-mail: info@adamsscottlaw.co.uk
Office: Malton, Scarborough

JOHN BARKERS ‡
9-11 Old Market Place Grimsby North East Lincolnshire DN31 1JN
Tel: 01472 358686 *Fax:* 01472 240890 *Dx:* 13501 GRIMSBY 1
Emergency telephone 07710 511721
E-mail: hsf@jbarkers.co.uk
List of partners: H S Field, A D Havery, S R Makey, J L Needley, R Rushby, J C Stones
Office: Cleethorpes, Louth, Mablethorpe
Work: A1 B1 C1 C2 D1 D2 E F1 F2 G H J1 K1 K3 K4 L N O Q R1 S1 S2 T1 T2 V W Z(h,k,l,r)
Emergency Action, Agency, Advocacy, Fixed Fee Interview, Legal Aid undertaken, Legal Aid Franchise and Member of Accident Line
Ptr: Field, Mr Howard Stephen LLB(Warw). . . . . *Aug 1989
Havery, Mr Andrew David BA . . . . Dec 1996
Makey, Mr Stuart R . . . . *§Jan 1981
Rushby, Ms Ronda . . . . *Oct 2003
Stones, Mr Jonathan C LLB. . . . . *Mar 2003
Ast: Norman, Ms Jennifer Mary . . . . Feb 2005
Stockdale, Mr Christopher LLB(Hons) . . . . Apr 2007
Con: Cooke, Mr Malcolm Kenneth LLB(Hull) . . . . *§Sep 1969
Robinson, Mr Ian FILEx. . . . . Nov 1997

See p112 for the Key to Work Categories & other symbols

BATES & MOUNTAIN ‡
The Old Courthouse 42 Brighowgate Grimsby North East Lincolnshire DN32 0QW
Tel: 01472 357291 *Fax:* 01472 241118 *Dx:* 13512 GRIMSBY 1
E-mail: accounts@batesandmountain.com
List of partners: A J Dollery, G Ives, S Maguire, L A Studd, C B Wilson
Office: Caistor
Work: A1 B1 C1 C2 D1 D2 E F1 G H J1 K1 L N R1 S1 S2 T1 T2 V W Z(c,d,l,s)
Emergency Action, Agency, Advocacy, Legal Aid undertaken and Legal Aid Franchise
Ptr: Ives, Mr Graham LLB(Hons). . . . . *Apr 1973
Maguire, Mr Scott. . . . . *Apr 2006
Studd, Mr Lindsay A BA; PGCE. . . . . *Sep 1985
Wilson, Mr Christopher B Clerk to Commissioner of the Inland Revenue Notary Public . . . . *Nov 1975

BEETENSON & GIBBON ‡
Lauriston House Town Hall Square Grimsby North East Lincolnshire DN31 1JB
Tel: 01472 240251 *Fax:* 01472 241728 *Dx:* 13502 GRIMSBY 1
E-mail: jeanwilliams@bgsolicitors.com
List of partners: B R Barber, P Braithwaite, P R C Braithwaite, S A Carr, C R Ekberg, R L Gibbon, S Hall, M A Jackson, J W M King, J N Scammell, D R Smith, G Swann
Office: Louth
Work: A1 B1 C1 C2 C3 D1 E F1 G H J1 K1 L M1 M2 N O P R1 S1 S2 T1 T2 V W Z(b,c,d,e,f,h,i,j,k,l,m,o,p,q,s,t,w)
Emergency Action, Agency, Advocacy, Fixed Fee Interview, Legal Aid undertaken, Legal Aid Franchise and Member of Accident Line
Ptr: Barber, Mr Benjamin Robert BA(Hons) . . . . Feb 2003
Braithwaite, Mr Peter . . . . Jan 1977
Carr, Mrs Sharon Anne LLB. . . . . *Dec 1993
Ekberg, Mr Charles R BA . . . . *Mar 1980
Gibbon, Mr Richard L BA . . . . *§Oct 1984
Hall, Mrs Sandra . . . . *Oct 1997
Jackson, Mr Michael A . . . . *Mar 1980
King, Mr J William M LLB . . . . *Mar 1984
Smith, Mr David R BA(Law). . . . . *Apr 1979
Swann, Mr Gary BA(Oxon) . . . . *Oct 1990

BRIDGE MCFARLAND ‡
(incorporating Graville Chapman Geo; A White & Co; Hadden Owen & Son)
19 South St Mary's Gate Grimsby North East Lincolnshire DN31 1JE
Tel: 01472 311711 *Fax:* 01472 311500 *Dx:* 13507 GRIMSBY 1
Emergency telephone 01507 604940
E-mail: info@bmcf.co.uk
List of partners: P W Ashton, G H G Chapman, C J Cooper, D R Crombleholme, J C Doughty, R J Edwards, L Foston, D Harvey, D A Holmes, A J Horne, K M Hudson, K Hughes, S D Jones, S J Lambert, P R E McFarland, L S Moore, S T Oldridge, R J Parnell, J A Pennock, P M Purves, K A E Roebuck, J R Skelton, I C Sprakes, P J Taylor
Office: Grimsby (2 offices), Hull, Lincoln, Louth, Mablethorpe, Market Rasen, Skegness
Languages: Cantonese, French, Hokkien, Malayalam, Spanish
Work: A1 D1 E F1 G H J1 K1 L N O Q S1 S2 T1 T2 V W X Z(i,j,l,m,q,r)
Emergency Action, Agency, Advocacy, Fixed Fee Interview, Legal Aid undertaken and Legal Aid Franchise
Ptr: Chapman, Mr Gordon H G LLB . . . . *§Jun 1968
Cooper, Mr Christopher J LLB. . . . . *Oct 1986
Crombleholme, Mr Dale R. . . . . Oct 2001
Doughty, Mr Jonathan Charles BSc(Hons). . . . . . . *Sep 1997
Edwards, Mr Robert J LLB . . . . *§Dec 1977
Foston, Ms Leanne . . . . Aug 2001
Harvey, Mr Dave . . . . Nov 2001
Holmes, Mr David A. . . . . *§Jan 1967
Hudson, Ms Kathryn M . . . . Sep 2005
Hughes, Mr Kevin. . . . . Jun 1985
Lambert, Mr Stephen J BA . . . . *Apr 1981
Moore, Miss Lisa Samantha LLB . . . . *Aug 1996
Oldridge, Mr Stephen T . . . . Aug 2005
Parnell, Mr Richard John BA(Hons) . . . . Sep 1999
Pennock, Ms Jacqueline Ann LLB. . . . . *Mar 1993
Purves, Mr Patrick M Deputy Clerk to the Commissioner of Taxes. . . . . *Dec 1980
Roebuck, Mrs Kathryn A E LLB . . . . *Oct 1983
Skelton, Ms Jacqueline R LLB(Hons) . . . . Nov 1990
Sprakes, Mr Ian C BA. . . . . *Nov 1991
Taylor, Mr Patrick J . . . . *Oct 1996
Asoc: Harris, Mrs Bernadette A LLB(Hons) . . . . Oct 1983

BRIDGE MCFARLAND
21 Wellowgate Grimsby North East Lincolnshire DN32 0RA
Tel: 01472 311711 *Fax:* 01472 311500 *Dx:* 13507 GRIMSBY
E-mail: info@bmcf.co.uk
Office: Grimsby (2 offices), Hull, Lincoln, Louth, Mablethorpe, Market Rasen, Skegness

BRIDGE MCFARLAND
New Street Chambers New Street Grimsby North East Lincolnshire DN31 1HH
Tel: 01472 311711 *Fax:* 01472 311500 *Dx:* 13507 GRIMSBY
E-mail: info@bmcf.co.uk
Office: Grimsby (2 offices), Hull, Lincoln, Louth, Mablethorpe, Market Rasen, Skegness
Ptr: Ashton, Mr Philip W LLB(Lond) . . . . *Dec 1980
Jones, Mr Simon D LLB(Hons) . . . . *Nov 1997
Con: Ede, Mr Stephen A LLB(Nott'm). . . . . *§Jun 1975

ROY FOREMAN & CO ‡
Royal Oak Chambers 190 Victoria Street Grimsby North East Lincolnshire DN31 1NX
Tel: 01472 355262 *Fax:* 01472 356204
Emergency telephone 07575 949938
E-mail: office@rforeman.com
List of partners: M R Foreman
Languages: Bengali
Work: B2 G H
Emergency Action, Agency, Advocacy and Legal Aid undertaken
Ptr: Foreman, Mr Michael R LLB(Nott'm) . . . . *Jun 1971
Ast: Banerjee, Miss Anita . . . . *Apr 2009
Ellis, Mr Geoffrey David. . . . . Aug 2000
Sloane, Mr Nigel LLB . . . . Nov 1993

E C LIDSTER & CO ‡
Nelson Street Chambers 46 Nelson Street Grimsby North East Lincolnshire DN32 7SH
Tel: 01472 348417 *Fax:* 01472 251740 *Dx:* 13514 GRIMSBY
Emergency telephone 07768 598707
List of partners: N R Furman, E C Lidster
Work: G H V
Emergency Action, Agency, Advocacy, Fixed Fee Interview, Legal Aid undertaken and Legal Aid Franchise
Ptr: Furman, Mr Nicholas R LLB(Hons) . . . . *Oct 1989
Lidster, Mr Ernest C LLB(Hull) ★ . . . . *Oct 1976
Ast: Freeston, Mr Steven Thomas . . . . *Jan 2002
Hackfath, Mr Matthew Richard LLB . . . . *Jan 1998
Lee, Miss Vicky Anne . . . . *Sep 1999

PAUL RUDD ‡
Riverhead Chambers 9 New Street Grimsby North East Lincolnshire DN31 1HQ
Tel: 01472 350881 *Fax:* 01472 242234 *Dx:* 13521 GRIMSBY 1
Emergency telephone 01472 352879
E-mail: info@paulrudd.net
List of partners: T J Carson, P R F Rudd
Work: E N O Q S1 S2 W
Fixed Fee Interview undertaken and Member of Accident Line
Ptr: Carson, Mr Timothy Joseph LLB(Lond) . . . . *§Feb 1960
Rudd, Mr Paul R F BA(Humberside). . . . . *§Apr 1966
Ast: Johnson, Mr Stephen BA . . . . Feb 2009

PETER R SARGENT ‡
PO Box 393 Grimsby North East Lincolnshire DN37 9YZ
Tel: 01472 887670
Emergency telephone 01472 887670
E-mail: peter.r.sargent@talk21.com
List of partners: P R Sargent
Work: E L R1 R2 S1 S2 W
Agency and Fixed Fee Interview undertaken
Ptr: Sargent, Mr Peter Rodney FILEx . . . . *§Dec 1981

SYMES BAINS BROOMER
10 Abbey Walk Grimsby North East Lincolnshire DN31 1NB
Tel: 01472 360991 *Fax:* 01472 360993 *Dx:* 13506 GRIMSBY
E-mail: info@sbblaw.com
Office: Epworth, Goole, Howden, Scunthorpe
Work: A1 A3 B1 C1 C2 D1 E F1 F2 G H J1 K1 K2 L N O P Q R1 S1 S2 T1 T2 V W Z(l,q)

WILKIN CHAPMAN GOOLDEN
PO Box 16 New Oxford House Town Hall Square Grimsby North East Lincolnshire DN31 1EY
Tel: 0870 460 2586 *Fax:* 01472 360198
E-mail: jgoolden@wilkinchapman.co.uk
Office: Alford, Beverley, Grimsby (2 offices), Horncastle, Lincoln, Louth, Mablethorpe, Market Rasen, Sutton-on-Sea

WILKIN CHAPMAN GRANGE SOLICITORS
St Mary's Chambers West St Mary's Gate Grimsby North East Lincolnshire DN31 1LD
Tel: 01472 262626 *Fax:* 01472 359904 *Dx:* 13505 GRIMSBY 1
E-mail: gy@grangewintringham.com
Office: Alford, Beverley, Grimsby (2 offices), Horncastle, Lincoln, Louth, Mablethorpe, Market Rasen, Sutton-on-Sea
Work: A1 B1 C1 C2 C3 D1 E F1 F2 G J1 K1 K3 K4 L M1 M2 N O P Q R1 R2 S1 S2 T1 T2 V W X Z(c,e,l,o,q,t)
Emergency Action, Agency, Advocacy, Fixed Fee Interview and Legal Aid undertaken
Ptr: Houltby, Mr Richard W B LLB Notary Public. . . . . . *§Jul 1982
McKay, Mr Craig J BA(Law) Sweet & Maxwell Law Prize . . . . *Oct 1987
Plumtree, Mrs Sharon Elaine . . . . Oct 1991
Sheridan, Mr Paul R TD BA(Kent) Notary Public. . . *§Oct 1979
Ast: Davies, Ms Michelle. . . . . May 2002
Overton, Ms Emma Juliet LLB(Hons); LPC . . . . . . *Jul 2008
Con: Overton, Mr David V. . . . . *§Jun 1966

WILKIN CHAPMAN LLP ‡
1 Town Hall Street Grimsby North East Lincolnshire DN31 1HE
Tel: 01472 262626 *Fax:* 01472 340870 *Dx:* 13511 GRIMSBY 1
E-mail: elaister@wilkinchapman.co.uk
List of partners: M S Adams, F M Bennett, G T Blades, L M Boileau, R Brewin, D J Buckle, N M E Burn, T M Butcher, J M Carlton, M D Chilvers, P D Day, J Eatock, R J Eke, J T Goolden, C R Grocock, A D Holt, R W B Houltby, R M Houltby, L Howes, J Judge, M R Justice, P S Krick, J Lloyd, R A S MacMillan, C J McKay, G Morris, C E Parker, N B Patrick, J Peacock, S E Plumtree, M Robinson, J M Savage, S J Savage, I Sherburn, P R Sheridan, P R Tollerton, A D Wareing, N S Welch, J West
Office: Alford, Beverley, Grimsby (2 offices), Horncastle, Lincoln, Louth, Mablethorpe, Market Rasen, Sutton-on-Sea
Languages: French, German, Spanish
Work: A1 A3 B1 B2 C1 C2 C3 D1 D2 E F1 F2 G H J1 J2 K1 K2 K3 L N O P Q R1 R2 S1 S2 T1 T2 V W X Z(b,e,g,i,k,l,m,p,q,r,y)
Emergency Action, Agency, Advocacy, Fixed Fee Interview, Legal Aid undertaken, Legal Aid Franchise and Member of Accident Line
Ptr: Brewin, Ms Ruth BA(Dunelm) . . . . *Dec 1984
Buckle, Mr David J LLB(Bris) . . . . *Oct 1982
Chilvers, Mr Martyn D LLB(Hons) . . . . *May 1980
Eatock, Ms Jane LLB(Hons). . . . . *Mar 1991
Goolden, Mr Jonathan Thornes BA(Sheff)(Law) . . . . *Oct 1990
Grocock, Mr Christopher R . . . . *Nov 1997
Morris, Mr Graham LLB(Sheff) . . . . *Apr 1978
Peacock, Mr John. . . . . *§Dec 1981
Savage, Mrs Juliet Mary LLB(Exon). . . . . *§May 1977
Savage, Mr Stephen J . . . . *§Jan 1976
Sherburn, Mr Ian LLB(Hons) . . . . *May 1994
Tollerton, Mr Paul Robert MA(Oxon). . . . . Nov 2004
Wareing, Mr Andrew David LLB . . . . *Oct 1983
West, Mr Jonathan LLB . . . . *Sep 1998
Asoc: Blow, Miss Emma Lynsey LLB(Hons) . . . . Mar 2007
Gladding, Miss Katie Jacqueline LLB . . . . *Sep 2006
Ast: Atkin, Mr Edward . . . . Sep 2005
Burnett, Mr Andrew . . . . Nov 2000
Dix, Mr Matthew Thomas George LLB. . . . . *Sep 2004
Hornsby, Mrs Helen LLB . . . . *Oct 1998
Warwick, Ms Elizabeth . . . . Jul 2005

GUILDFORD, Surrey

AWB PARTNERSHIP LLP ‡
Braemar 3-5 Jenner Road Guildford Surrey GU1 3AQ
Tel: 01483 302345 *Fax:* 01483 301339 *Dx:* 146540 GUILDFORD 8
E-mail: info@awb.co.uk
List of partners: R J Batchelor, J R Compton, B E Dean, M Derrick, J Farr, R H Middlehurst, M Murtagh, C H Pfister, P D Servian
Work: C1 E F1 J1 K1 K3 L N O Q S1 S2 W
Ptr: Batchelor, Mr Roger J BA(Keele) . . . . *Apr 1978
Compton, Mr Jonathan Robert LLB; LLM . . . . *Jan 1999
Dean, Mr Bryan E LLB(Soton). . . . . *§Oct 1985
Derrick, Mr Michael BA(Hons). . . . . *Jun 2004
Farr, Ms Joanne BSc(Hons). . . . . *Jun 2001
Middlehurst, Mr Richard Hugh BA(Hons) . . . . *Feb 1988
Murtagh, Ms Maureen LLB . . . . *Nov 1989
Pfister, Mr Charles H Notary Public . . . . *Nov 1973
Servian, Mr Peter D BA Notary Public. . . . . *Apr 1976
Asoc: Brafield, Mr Mark MA(Oxon) Deputy District Judge . . *Dec 1989
Searle, Mrs Cathy MA(Oxon) . . . . *Oct 1989
Ast: Thompson, Mrs Gillian E BA(Hons) . . . . *Oct 1988
Con: Butler, Mr Richard Jesty Owen LLB(Edin); LLS . . . . *Jan 1978
Hemingway, Mr Richard William D'Oyly MA; TEP . . *§Jan 1970

BBL SOLICITORS LLP ‡
64a Chertsey Street Guildford Surrey GU1 4HL
Tel: 01483 838154 *Fax:* 01483 838156
E-mail: hema.lukha@blueberrylaw.com
Languages: Gujarati, Hindi
Work: K1 K3 N Q S1

BARLOW ROBBINS LLP ‡
The Oriel Sydenham Road Guildford Surrey GU1 3SR
Tel: 01483 562901 *Fax:* 01483 464260 *Dx:* 2407 GUILDFORD
E-mail: enquiries@barlowrobbins.com
List of partners: T C J Adams, S A Ambrose, H J Archibald, J E Ball, R Black, D G Foster, R J Glazebrook, H M Goatley, M R Goodridge, J A M Lada-Walicki, M R Lucas, D C H Ludlow, N P Phillips, G W Reid, B J Sanders, P J M Sisson, P Stephenson, A S Tishler, G Wilson
Office: Godalming, Guildford, Woking
Languages: French, German, Polish
Work: B1 B2 C1 C2 E J1 K1 K2 L N O Q R1 S2 W X Z(d,k,q,r,za)
Agency undertaken and Member of Accident Line
Ptr: Foster, Mr David G LLB. . . . . *Mar 1988
Glazebrook, Ms Rebecca Joanne . . . . *Sep 2000
Lada-Walicki, Ms Joanna A M LLB Member of the Executive Committee of British Polish Legal Association. . . *Nov 1986
Lucas, Mr Mark R BA(Hons) . . . . *Apr 1996
Phillips, Mr Nicholas Peter LLB(Hons); Dip IP Law & Practice . . . . *Oct 1995
Reid, Mr Gordon William LLB . . . . *Oct 1987
Sisson, Mr Peter J M LLB. . . . . *Feb 1983
Stephenson, Mr Philip. . . . . *Sep 1996
Tishler, Miss Andrea S . . . . *Nov 1998
Black, Mr Raymond . . . . .NSP
Asoc: Fulford, Mr Simon Richard Glynne BA. . . . . *Nov 1991
Green, Mrs Lisa. *Jan 1988
Parks, Mr Robert David. . . . . *Sep 2002
Ast: Fisher, Ms Catherine Rachel . . . . *Nov 1992
Green, Mr Paul . . . . *Jan 2008
Hunter, Ms Ena . . . . *Mar 2006
Kershaw, Miss Rebecca Louise . . . . *Mar 2010
Millard, Mrs Esther Jane . . . . *Oct 2001
Sellahewa, Miss Tanuja LLB. . . . . *May 2002
Steele, Mr Jonathan. . . . . *Sep 2008
Tudor, Ms Michelle . . . . *Oct 2007
Con: Harvie, Mrs Helen Laurette . . . . *Apr 2003
Other offices in Godalming, Guildford, Woking. We specialise in the following areas of work Commercial and Company Law, Commercial Property, Employment Law.

BARLOW ROBBINS LLP
55 Quarry Street Guildford Surrey GU1 3UE
Tel: 01483 543200 *Fax:* 01483 573325 *Dx:* 2407 GUILDFORD
E-mail: enquiries@barlowrobbins.com
Office: Godalming, Guildford, Woking
Languages: French, German
Work: D1 J2 K1 K2 K3 K4 L N Q R1 R2 S1 T1 T2 W Z(q,r)
Agency, Advocacy and Fixed Fee Interview undertaken
Ptr: Adams, Mr Timothy C J MA(Cantab) . . . . *§Mar 1985
Ball, Mrs Judith Elizabeth BA(Hons)(Law) Secretary for Surrey Resolution . . . . *Apr 1983
Goatley, Mrs Helen M BA(Hons). . . . . *Oct 1990
Asoc: Colman, Mrs Lynsey LLB . . . . *Sep 2005
Kemp, Ms Joanna Helen . . . . *Sep 2007
Potter, Miss Emma Jane LLB . . . . *Sep 1999
Ast: Davis, Mr Roger. . . . . *Sep 2008
Griffiths, Mrs Nicola. . . . . *Sep 2008
Hastie, Mrs Claire Louise . . . . *Jan 2007
Magnussen, Mrs Mariana . . . . *Jul 2003
Rees-Knowlden, Mrs Charlotte LLB(Hons). . . . . . *May 2003
Whitney, Mr Tim. Jan 2009
We specialise in the following areas of work: Family Law, Probate, Wills & Trusts, Residential Conveyancing. Agency Commissions gladly undertaken.

BLAVO & CO SOLICITORS
Crossweys House 28-30 High Street Guildford Surrey GU1 3HY
Tel: 01483 243456 *Fax:* 01483 243458
E-mail: enquiries@legalblavo.co.uk
Office: Enfield, London EC2, London N3, London WC1, St Albans, Uxbridge

BRUFFELL WILLIAMS SOLICITORS ‡
Castle House Castle Street Guildford Surrey GU1 3UW
Tel: 01483 511108 *Fax:* 01483 326500 *Dx:* 2438 GUILDFORD
E-mail: legal@bruffellwilliams.com

THE CASTLE PARTNERSHIP ‡
2 Wey Court Mary Road Guildford Surrey GU1 4QU
Tel: 01483 300905 *Fax:* 01483 409749
E-mail: enquiries@castlepartnership.co.uk
List of partners: D T Castle, J L Evans, I A Wilkinson
Office: Woking
Work: G H Z(l)
Ptr: Castle, Mr David T LLB ★. . . . . Oct 1984
Evans, Mr John L BA(Law) ★ . . . . Oct 1987
Wilkinson, Mr Ian Anthony LLB ★ . . . . Oct 1995

CHARLES RUSSELL LLP
Buryfields House Bury Fields Guildford Surrey GU2 4AZ
Tel: 01483 252525 *Fax:* 01483 252550 *Dx:* 2436 GUILDFORD
E-mail: enquiries@charlesrussell.co.uk
Office: Cambridge, Cheltenham, London EC4, Oxford
Work: A1 A3 B1 C1 C2 C3 D1 E F1 I J1 K1 K2 K3 L M1 M2 N O P Q R1 R2 S1 S2 T1 T2 U2 W Z(b,c,d,e,f,g,h,i,j,k,l,m,n,o,p,q,r,w)
Ptr: Critchley, Mr Paul A LLB(Lond) . . . . *Dec 1971
Drew, Ms Catherine Ann . . . . *Oct 1982
Elson, Mr Duncan W LLB . . . . *Nov 1985
Fordyce, Mr Rory P H. . . . . *Jan 1979

Jenkins, Mr Tim LLB(Hons) Clyde & Co Common Law Prize . . . . . *Sep 1995
Levaggi, Mr Peter D M BA(Hons) . . . . . *Nov 1991
Marriott, Mrs Suzanne Jane BA(Hons); AKC . . . . . *Nov 1996
Pidgeon, Mr Nicholas John . . . . . *Jun 1975
Pierce, Mr Roger T W LLB . . . . . *Apr 1979
Savage, Mr David BA(Hons)(Lond) Lady Templeman Scholarship 1994; Benefactors Scholarship 1992; Blackstone Major Entrance Exhibition 1992 . . . . . *Apr 2001
Sparks, Mr Geoff TD BA(Hons) . . . . . *Oct 1987
Stevens, Mrs Amanda BA(Hons); DipIHSM APIL Executive Committee Member . . . . . *Sep 1990
Tyson, Mrs Margaret A . . . . . *Oct 1980
Asoc: Duncan, Mr Matthew LLB(Hons); TEP . . . . . *Sep 1998
Haines, Mr David K LLB(Hons) . . . . . *Sep 1997
Hyne, Mr James LLB(Hons) . . . . . *Aug 1999
Wilsher, Ms Karen BA(Hons); LPC . . . . . Nov 1996
Ast: Ashford, Mrs Sally Louise BA(Hons)(Oxon) . . . . . *Oct 1992
Con: Marriott, Mr Jack . . . . . *§Jun 1975

CHEYNEY GOULDING ‡
Ward House 6 Ward Street Guildford Surrey GU1 4LH
Tel: 01483 567676 *Fax:* 01483 300538 *Dx:* 83174 GUILDFORD 2
Emergency telephone 01737 761970
E-mail: legal@cheyneygoulding.co.uk
List of partners: J Goulding, G R Young
Work: A1 C1 E J1 L N O P Q S1 W Z(c,d,l)
Ptr: Goulding, Mr Julian LLB . . . . . *Jun 1976
Young, Mr Graham R BA . . . . . *Nov 1985
Ast: Marshall, Mr Thomas Matthew . . . . . Nov 2006
Mullins, Miss Anna Louise BA(Hons) . . . . . Sep 2006
Williams, Mr Aled W . . . . . Jul 2002

THE CHILD LAW PARTNERSHIP ‡
2 Faraday Road Guildford Surrey GU1 1EA
Tel: 01483 543790 *Fax:* 01483 543791 *Dx:* 83182 GUILDFORD 2
E-mail: info@childlawpartnership.co.uk
List of partners: P Bennett, P Malthouse
Office: Basingstoke
Work: K1 K2 K3 X
Fixed Fee Interview undertaken
Ptr: Bennett, Mr Philip . . . . . *Apr 1979
Malthouse, Ms Peta . . . . . Dec 1992
Ast: Atkins, Mrs Natasha Jane LLB . . . . . *Sep 1999
Moors, Miss Karen E LLB(Hons) . . . . . Mar 1991
Whitby, Mrs Sarah Laurie BA(Oxon) Deputy Coroner for North East Hampshire . . . . . *Nov 1986

CLYDE & CO ‡
The merged firm of Barlow Lyde & Gilbert and Clyde & Co
1 Stoke Road Guildford Surrey GU1 4HW
Tel: 020 7876 5000 *Fax:* 020 7876 5120 *Dx:* 2406 GUILDFORD
E-mail: infoguildford@clydeco.com

COCKBURNS SOLICITORS ‡
Panorama 56 Guildown Road Guildford Surrey GU2 4EY
Tel: 01483 452848 *Fax:* 01483 452849
E-mail: gill@cockburns.co.uk

JONATHAN P COOPER ‡
Perren Buildings 19 Pewley Hill Guildford Surrey GU1 3SN
Tel: 07956 551898

HELEN E F CORBETT ‡
3 Grasmere Close Guildford Surrey GU1 2TG
Tel: 01483 450777 *Fax:* 01483 450580
Work: K3 S1 W
Fixed Fee Interview undertaken

ANTHONY F COX ‡
26 Manor Way Onslow Village Guildford Surrey GU2 7RP
Tel: 01483 562422 *Fax:* 01483 872396
E-mail: afc@fortnoms.com
List of partners: A F Cox
Work: E S1 S2 W
SPr: Cox, Mr Anthony Fortnom LLB(Hons) . . . . . *Sep 1979

CRACKNELLS ‡
14 Howard Gardens Guildford Surrey GU1 2NX
Tel: 01483 535558 *Fax:* 01483 535586
List of partners: R M Cracknell
Work: E R2 S1 S2 W
SPr: Cracknell, Mr Roger M BA . . . . . *Jun 1980

CRISP & CO SOLICITORS ‡
Turret House 77 Portsmouth Road Guildford Surrey GU2 4BS
Tel: 01483 570810 *Fax:* 01483 456516 *Dx:* 2402 GUILDFORD
E-mail: info@crispandco.com
List of partners: H C Crisp
Office: Kingston upon Thames, London E14
Work: D1 E K1 Z(e)
Emergency Action, Agency, Advocacy, Fixed Fee Interview, Legal Aid undertaken and Legal Aid Franchise
SPr: Crisp, Mr Henry Charles BA(Hons) . . . . . *Mar 1992

DR SOLICITORS ‡
Laneside Guildown Avenue Guildford Surrey GU2 4HB
Tel: 01483 511555 *Fax:* 0870 762 0245
E-mail: info@drsolicitors.com
List of partners: D Robertson
Languages: Danish, French, German, Norwegian, Swedish
Work: C1 E J1 R2 S2 Z(r)
Ptr: Robertson, Ms Daphne MA . . . . . *Oct 1993
Con: Denovan-Smith, Mr David John BA(Hons) . . . . . Mar 1991
Fisher, Mr Ian M LLB(L'pool) . . . . . Mar 1971

DAWSON MASON & CARR ‡
69 High Street Guildford Surrey GU1 3DY
Tel: 01483 576169 *Fax:* 01483 300026 *Dx:* 2422 GUILDFORD
E-mail: postroom@dawsoncarr.co.uk
List of partners: M J Carr, M C Dawson, A F Mason
Office: Farnham
Work: E S1 S2
Ptr: Carr, Mr Mark J LLB . . . . . *Jul 1976
Dawson, Mr Michael C . . . . . *Nov 1975
Mason, Mr Alan F LLB . . . . . *Apr 1977

DENHAMS ‡
Onslow House Onslow Road Guildford Surrey GU1 4HU
Tel: 01483 456450 *Fax:* 01483 456451
E-mail: enquiries@denlaw.co.uk
List of partners: S C Denham, J Lappage
Work: G H K1 Q S1 W
Emergency Action, Agency, Advocacy, Legal Aid undertaken and Legal Aid Franchise
Ptr: Denham, Mr Stephen C LLB(Hons) . . . . . *Feb 1990
Lappage, Miss Julia LLB(Hons) . . . . . *Nov 1991

THE DISPUTE RESOLUTION PRACTICE ‡
Brookview Queen Street Gomshall Guildford Surrey GU5 9LY
Tel: 01483 205325 *Fax:* 01483 205347
E-mail: britlawjb@btinternet.com
Languages: French
Work: A3 E F2 J1 O Q S1 S2 Z(a,q)

ENGLAND PALMER
Castle House Castle Street Guildford Surrey GU1 3UW
Tel: 01483 459161 *Fax:* 01483 300844 *Dx:* 141452 GUILDFORD 12
E-mail: guildford@englandpalmer.co.uk
Office: London EC1
Work: B1 C1 E F1 J1 K1 L N Q S1 S2 W Z(c,l,p,q,r)
Agency and Advocacy undertaken

FEARON & CO ‡
6 Faraday Road Guildford Surrey GU1 1EA
Tel: 01483 540840 *Fax:* 01483 540844 *Dx:* 2411 GUILDFORD
E-mail: enquiries@fearonlaw.com
List of partners: F L E Nash, A J Phillips
Languages: French
Work: A1 B1 C2 E F1 K1 K3 L N O Q R1 S1 S2 T1 W Z(d,e,l,n,r)
Agency, Fixed Fee Interview and Legal Aid Franchise
Ptr: Nash, Ms Francesca L E BA(Hons) . . . . . *Nov 1998
Phillips, Mr Alexander John . . . . . *Dec 1981
Ast: Williams, Mr Martin J BA . . . . . *May 1987

KIM FINNIS SOLICITOR ‡
59 Quarry Street Guildford Surrey GU1 3UA
Tel: 01483 539100 *Fax:* 01483 539110
E-mail: kimfinnis@stmaryschambers.org

FITCHETT & CO SOLICITORS ‡
3000 Cathedral Hill Guildford Surrey GU2 7YB
Tel: 01483 243587 *Fax:* 01483 243686
E-mail: leighfitchett@fitchettandco.co.uk

FRAME SMITH & CO ‡
The Studio Hitherbury House 97 Portsmouth Road Guildford Surrey GU2 4DL
Tel: 01483 599377

JULIA FRIMOND SOLICITORS ‡
Edgeborough House Upper Edgeborough Road Guildford Surrey GU1 2BJ
Tel: 01483 452224 *Fax:* 01483 452007 *Dx:* 2432 GUILDFORD 1
E-mail: lawyer@frimond.co.uk
List of partners: J M Frimond
Languages: French
Work: K1 K3 S1 W
Ptr: Frimond, Mrs Julia Mary LLB(Bris) Deputy District Judge . . . . . *Nov 1974
Ast: Greenhalgh, Mrs Stephanie LLB . . . . . Apr 2009
Con: Warner, Mrs Diana Patricia Weston BA(Hons)(Bris) . . Apr 1979

GCL SOLICITORS ‡
Connaught House Alexandra Terrace Guildford Surrey GU1 3DA
Tel: 01483 577091 *Fax:* 01483 579252 *Dx:* 141450 GUILDFORD 12
E-mail: partners@gcl-solicitors.co.uk
List of partners: C J Cooney, A R Inkin, R J Laugharne, P N Tustin
Work: E R2 S1 S2
Ptr: Cooney, Mr Christopher J LLB(NZ) . . . . . *Jul 1987
Inkin, Mr Anthony Roy Annual Prize for Outstanding Performance . . . . . *Oct 1996
Laugharne, Mr Richard J BA . . . . . *Jul 1980
Tustin, Mr Peter N BA(Hons) . . . . . *Dec 1986

GMH SOLICITORS ‡
31 Tangier Road Guildford Surrey GU1 2DF
Tel: 07545 571569
E-mail: gill@gmhsolicitors.com

GORDONS
Edgeborough House Upper Edgeborough Road Guildford Surrey GU1 2BJ
Tel: 01483 451900 *Fax:* 01483 451888 *Dx:* 2432 GUILDFORD 1
E-mail: guildford@gordonsols.co.uk
Office: London WC1
Work: E S1
Ptr: Austin, Mr John Stewart MA(Cantab) . . . . . *Apr 1980
Ferguson, Mr Hamish Dempster BA(Hons)(Law) . . *Nov 1985
Asoc: Clifford, Mrs Mary Penelope BA(Hons) . . . . . Oct 1996
Ast: Slade, Mr Michael John LLB . . . . . Jan 2003

HART BROWN SOLICITORS ‡
Resolution House Riverview Walnut Tree Close Guildford Surrey GU1 4UX
Est: 1919
Tel: 0800 068 8177 *Fax:* 01483 887759 *Dx:* 2403 GUILDFORD 1
E-mail: lawyers@hartbrown.co.uk
List of partners: P M Allamand, M S Bednarczyk, R A A Brown, B Brueggemann, R Campbell, A C Coulson, P J Grimwood, D S Knapp, N J Maud, S D Parry-Jones, T J Pearce, S D Spencer, P A Tobias
Office: Cobham, Cranleigh, Godalming, London SW19, Woking
Languages: German
Work: A1 A3 B1 C1 C2 C3 D1 D2 E F1 F2 I J1 J2 K1 K2 K3 L M1 M2 N O P Q R1 R2 S1 S2 T1 T2 V W Z(b,c,d,e,i,j,k,l,o,p,q,r,z)
Emergency Action, Agency, Advocacy, Fixed Fee Interview, Legal Aid undertaken and Legal Aid Franchise
Ptr: Allamand, Mr Paul M LLB . . . . . *Jun 1970
Bednarczyk, Mr Marek S BA . . . . . *Oct 1991
Brown, Mr Robert A A LLB . . . . . *Apr 1970
Brueggemann, Miss Bettina LLB . . . . . *May 1987
Campbell, Mr Roderick LLB . . . . . *Nov 1985
Grimwood, Mr Paul J LLB . . . . . *Oct 1987
Maud, Mr Nigel Jonathon BA; LLB . . . . . *Oct 2000
Tobias, Mr Paul A LLB . . . . . *May 1980
Ast: Dodd, Mrs Samantha LLB(Hons); LPC; Financial Planning Certificate . . . . . *Jan 1999
Gibbs, Mr Gerard LLB; BA(Hons) . . . . . *Jan 1996
Jones, Mr Owain LLB . . . . . *Jan 2006
Sacks, Ms Tara LLB; PGDipLP . . . . . *Jul 2004
Thurlow, Mr Christopher LLB . . . . . *Sep 2007
Watts, Mrs Celia BA(Hons)(English); DipLaw . . . . . *Oct 1997
Wickwar, Mr Peter F LLB(Lond); MBA(Cape Town) . . *Oct 1980

HAYMAN SOLICITORS ‡
5 Quarry Street Guildford Surrey GU1 3UP
Tel: 01483 600900 *Fax:* 01483 600902 *Dx:* 2440 GUILDFORD
List of partners: A Vadgama
SPr: Vadgama, Anjna . . . . . May 1999

V L HUMPHREYS & CO ‡
248-250 High Street Guildford Surrey GU1 3JG
Tel: 01483 574342 *Fax:* 01483 303470
List of partners: V L Humphreys
Work: A1 C1 E L S1
Agency undertaken
Ptr: Humphreys, V L . . . . . §Jun 1970

COLIN D JAMES
4 Station Road Shalford Guildford Surrey GU4 8HB
Tel: 01483 303456 *Fax:* 01483 575899 *Dx:* 52917 WEST BYFLEET
Office: West Byfleet
Work: S1
Ptr: James, Mr Colin D . . . . . Jan 1971

JUST EMPLOYMENT ‡
St Mary's Chambers 59 Quarry Street Guildford Surrey GU1 3UA
Tel: 01483 303636 *Fax:* 01483 459850 *Dx:* 2432 GUILDFORD 1
E-mail: info@justemployment.com
List of partners: F G Bignell
Office: Brighton, Reading
Work: C1 J1 J2 N T2 Z(p)
Advocacy and Fixed Fee Interview undertaken
Ptr: Bignell, Mr Francis G MA(Cantab) . . . . . *Dec 1977
Asoc: Henrion, Mr J Paul LLB . . . . . *Jun 1977
O'Connell, Ms Rachel Ann BA(Hons) . . . . . *Mar 1998
Ast: Haley, Mr James Alexander LLB . . . . . *Sep 2008
McDairmant, Ms Clare Marie LLB(Hons) . . . . . *Oct 2001

JUST IMMIGRATION SOLICITORS ‡
3000 Cathedral Hill Guildford Surrey GU2 7YB
Tel: 01483 243566 *Fax:* 01483 207806
E-mail: info@just-immigration.co.uk

KARSLAKES SOLICITORS LIMITED ‡
11-13 Frensham Suite 13-21 High Street Guildford Surrey GU1 3DG
Tel: 01483 454242 *Fax:* 01483 454243 *Dx:* 2417 GUILDFORD
E-mail: info@karslakes.com
List of partners: D N Cockle, D Yeates
Work: A3 B1 J1 K1 K3 O Q
Ptr: Yeates, Mr David . . . . . Jun 1985
Dir: Cockle, Mr Derek N LLB(Hons) . . . . . *Dec 1988

LAYTONS
(in association with Libralex; Gesica)
Tempus Court Onslow Street Guildford Surrey GU1 4SS
Tel: 01483 407000 *Fax:* 01483 407070 *Dx:* 2410 GUILDFORD
E-mail: guildford@laytons.com
Office: London EC4, Manchester
Work: B1 C1 C3 I J1 L Q R1 R2 S2 U2 Z(c,e)
Emergency Action, Agency and Advocacy undertaken
Ptr: Bannister, Mr Brian Nicholas MA(Cantab) . . . . . *Feb 1988
Bucknell, Mr Neil John MA(Cantab) . . . . . *Apr 1980
Chapman, Mr Simon J . . . . . Oct 1991
Cook, Mr Ian Anthony LLB(Wales) . . . . . *Apr 1980
Emmerson, Mr Simon James LLB . . . . . *Jul 1996
Knight, Mr David . . . . . Jan 1992
Lochner, Mr Pieter Ludolf BSc; LLB; Attorney & Patent Agent(S Africa) . . . . . *Nov 1980
Melville-Harris, Ms Zoe Kate LLB . . . . . *Sep 1992
Mendelsohn, Mr Geoffrey Ian LLB(Leeds) . . . . . *Oct 1987
Morley, Mr James . . . . . Jan 1978
Quibell, Mr John B LLB(Hons) . . . . . *Nov 1984
Sturge, Mr Colin A MA(Cantab) Director of Properties 2000 . . . . . *Dec 1982
Ast: Austin, Mr Derek Keith LLB(Hons) . . . . . *Aug 2000
De Bruin, Miss Karen BA; LLB . . . . . Jan 2000
De Giovanni, Mr Julian Robert . . . . . *Nov 2001
Hoare, Ms Geraldine Ann LLB(Hons); RGN . . . . . *Mar 2001
Hothersall, Mr Nicholas BA; PG Dip EC Competition Law . . . . . Aug 1998
Johnson, Mrs Kirstie Jane LLB(Hons) . . . . . *Sep 2002
McClenaghan, Mr David Thomas BA(Hons) . . . . . *Aug 1998
Martin, Mr James Richard LLB(Hons) . . . . . *Mar 1977
Millen, Ms Karen Kai-Ling BA(Hons) . . . . . *Jul 1998
Sellahewa, Miss Tanuja LLB . . . . . *May 2002

LOVETTS PLC ‡
Bramley House The Guildway Old Portsmouth Road Guildford Surrey GU3 1LR
Tel: 01483 457500 *Fax:* 01483 457700 *Dx:* 58306 GODALMING
E-mail: debt@lovetts.co.uk
List of partners: J E Liggins, G P McCulloch, C H Wilson
Work: O
Dir: Liggins, Mr Jonathan E . . . . . *Dec 1973
McCulloch, Mr G Paul . . . . . *Mar 1975
Wilson, Mr Charles H BA; FICM; MCIM . . . . . *Dec 1977

MWA SOLICITORS ‡
Ground Floor Chancery House Leas Road Guildford Surrey GU1 4QW
Tel: 01483 506100 *Fax:* 01483 505222
E-mail: info@mwalegal.com

MAJOR & CO ‡
(in association with Frederick Hass & Stone)
51 Quarry Street Guildford Surrey GU1 3UA
Tel: 01483 455771 *Fax:* 01483 455772 *Dx:* 83177 GUILDFORD 2
E-mail: reception@majorlaw.co.uk
List of partners: M A Brafield, D C Major
Work: C1 E K1 O Q S1 W
Ptr: Brafield, Mr Mark Allan MA(Oxon) . . . . . *Oct 1989
Major, Mr David Charles LLB . . . . . *Apr 1983

JENNIFER C MARGRAVE ‡
Courtyard Entrance (Down Road) Old Post Office 130 Epsom Road Guildford Surrey GU1 2PX
Tel: 01483 562722 *Fax:* 01483 829074
E-mail: jennifer@jennifermargrave.co.uk
List of partners: J C Margrave
Work: K4 T2 V W
SPr: Margrave, Mrs Jennifer C . . . . . *§May 1984
Ast: Lohn, Ms Keira . . . . . Dec 2007
Mason, Miss Joanne Christine LLB . . . . . *Sep 2003

See p112 for the Key to Work Categories & other symbols

MEABY & CO (TRADING AS SETFORDS)
14 Haydon Place Guildford Surrey GU1 4LL
Tel: 01483 408780 *Fax:* 01483 300487 *Dx:* 2401 GUILDFORD
E-mail: info@setfords.co.uk
Office: London SE5

RICHARD PIETROWSKI & CO ‡
4 The Mount Guildford Surrey GU2 4HN
Tel: 01483 505398 *Fax:* 01483 302494
E-mail: richard.pietrowskiandco@yahoo.co.uk
List of partners: R W J Pietrowski
Languages: Polish
Work: C1 E L Q S1
Fixed Fee Interview undertaken
Ptr: Pietrowski, Mr Richard W J BA . . . . Aug 1980

RHW SOLICITORS LLP ‡
Ranger House Walnut Tree Close Guildford Surrey GU1 4UL
Tel: 01483 302000 *Fax:* 01483 301242 *Dx:* 2445 GUILDFORD 1
E-mail: post@rhw.co.uk
List of partners: C Barnard, J H Britten, R P Brown, C M Pomfret, N E Richardson, B M Shacklady, C A Shacklady, M B Whiteman
Languages: French
Work: B1 C1 C2 C3 D1 E F1 I J1 K1 K3 L M1 M2 N O P Q R1 S1 T1 T2 W X Z(c,e,j,l,p)
Agency, Advocacy and Fixed Fee Interview undertaken
Ptr: Barnard, Mr Clive ACIB; TEP . . . . §Apr 1973
Britten, Mr John Howard . . . . Nov 1982
Brown, Mr Richard Powell LLB . . . . *Oct 1990
Pomfret, Mr Christopher M . . . . *Jan 1980
Richardson, Mr Nicholas Edward . . . . *May 1984
Shacklady, Mr Brian Murray MA(Cantab) . . . . *Jun 1977
Shacklady, Mrs Catherine Anne LLB . . . . *Oct 1984
Whiteman, Mr Martyn Bertram . . . . *Nov 1970
Asoc: Steer, Mr Martin LLB(Hons)(Business Law) . . . . . *Oct 1995
Ast: Clark, Mr Simon Andrew Lothian BSc(Hons). . . . . *Mar 2003
Cockburn, Miss Gillian Eleanor LLB; LLM(Tax); TEP. . *Jun 1979
Gillingham, Mr Giles Alfred BSc(Hons) . . . . *Mar 1981
Jago, Ms Samantha Catherine Jade. . . . . Apr 2005
Lyford, Mrs Elsie Mary. . . . . *Sep 2009
Sturge, Mrs Caroline Anne BA . . . . *Oct 1984

SCHNEIDER PAGE
12 Semaphore Road Guildford Surrey GU1 3PS
Tel: 01483 535997
E-mail: simon@schneiderpage.com
Office: London E1

STEVENS & BOLTON ‡
Wey House Farnham Road Guildford Surrey GU1 4YD
Tel: 01483 302264 *Fax:* 01483 302254 *Dx:* 2423 GUILDFORD 1
E-mail: mail@stevens-bolton.co.uk
List of partners: N Acomb, A T Alexander, R A Baxter, G A Brett, A C W Bussy, C F Davey, N J C Fieldhouse, M C Frisby, M S W Hunter, R W M King, P J Lambdin, M H Laver, H J Lupton, J B Mitchell, J V H Murray, J R Porteous, A R Quick, P R Snowden, K G Syson, J N Waine, B Whittaker
Languages: French, German
Work: A1 B1 C1 C2 C3 D1 E F1 I J1 K1 L M1 O P Q R1 S1 S2 T1 W Z(d,e,f,g,h,i,k,n,o,p,s)
Ptr: Acomb, Mr Nicholas LLB(B'ham) . . . . *Nov 1984
Alexander, Mr A Tudor LLB(Wales) . . . . *Jun 1977
Baxter, Mr Richard A LLB(Exon). . . . . *Nov 1986
Brett, Mr Garry A LLB(Hons) . . . . *Oct 1983
Bussy, Mr Andrew C W . . . . *§May 1977
Davey, Ms Catherine F BA(Exon) . . . . *Jan 1980
Fieldhouse, Mr Nicholas J C LLB(Bris) . . . . *Jul 1979
Frisby, Mr Michael C LLB(Hons). . . . . *Oct 1988
Hunter, Mr Michael S W. . . . . *§Jan 1972
King, Mr Richard W M BA(Hons) . . . . *Nov 1986
Lambdin, Mr Paul J LLB(Hons) . . . . *Oct 1982
Laver, Mr Michael H LLB(Lond) . . . . *§Apr 1981
Lupton, Mr Howard J LLB . . . . *Nov 1989
Mitchell, Mr James B BSc; ARCS; FSS; LLB(Lond) . . *Apr 1980
Murray, Mr John V H LLB(Lond). . . . . *May 1982
Porteous, Mr Jonathan R . . . . Sep 1992
Quick, Mr Andrew R LLB . . . . Nov 1990
Snowden, Mr Peter R. . . . . *§Apr 1978
Syson, Mr Keith Gordon LLB(Soton). . . . . *Dec 1991
Waine, Miss Janet N . . . . *§Aug 1978
Whittaker, Ms Beverley LLB. . . . . *Nov 1985
Asoc: Holmes-Siedle, Ms Rebbeca BA(Hons) . . . . Nov 1991
Lloyd, Mr Jeremy N LLB(Lond) . . . . *Jan 1989
Potter, Mr Keith W MA(Cantab) . . . . *Jan 1983
Ast: Bedford, Mr Joseph B P A LLB(Hons). . . . . Nov 1998
McLaughlan, Miss Claire . . . . *Oct 1998

TWM SOLICITORS LLP ‡
65 Woodbridge Road Guildford Surrey GU1 4RD
Tel: 01483 752700 *Fax:* 01483 752899 *Dx:* 2408 GUILDFORD 1
E-mail: info@twmsolicitors.com
List of partners: C Adler, E Barry, W Bosler, P M Bradley, J B Chignell, S Cloud, S E Cornes, A V Fowler, N P Harding, C K Hast, H G M D House, M C Jones, P B Lambert, M L Levene, G H P Maberly, J D McAuley, P R McCullough, A B P O'Loughlin, T Patel, D Patricio, G R Perkins, J C Potter, J W S Sandford-Pike, C C Sharpe, M A Stevenson, P D Stewart, A Storer, M C Truelove, K G A Walker
Office: Cranleigh, Epsom, Leatherhead, London SW19, Reigate
Work: A1 B1 C1 C2 C3 D1 E F1 J1 K1 L N O Q R1 S1 S2 T1 T2 W Z(c,d,e,h,k,l,p,q,x)
Agency, Advocacy, Fixed Fee Interview and Legal Aid undertaken
Ptr: House, Mr Howard G Mc D LLB. . . . . *§Jul 1978
O'Loughlin, Mr Adrian B P BSc Notary Public . . . . *§Jun 1977
Perkins, Mr Guy R LLB . . . . *Jan 1983
Sandford-Pike, Mr John W S . . . . *Nov 1981
Stewart, Mr Patrick D. . . . . *Feb 1984
Truelove, Mr Matthew C LLB(Lond) . . . . *Apr 1995
Walker, Ms Karin G A LLB . . . . *Feb 1988
Asoc: Fitzpatrick, Michelle. . . . . Jan 2004
Ast: Jenking, Mr Daniel John. . . . . *Sep 2002
Khanna, Sonali . . . . Jan 2008
Rabheru, Mrs Sonal LLB . . . . Feb 1999

WHELTONS ‡
162 High Street Guildford Surrey GU1 3HN
Tel: 01483 537633 *Fax:* 01483 576454 *Dx:* 2419 GUILDFORD 1
E-mail: solicitors@wheltons.com
List of partners: I L Child, C Fountain, J Watts
Work: D1 K1 K3 S1 W
Agency, Advocacy, Legal Aid undertaken and Legal Aid Franchise
Ptr: Child, Ms I Lynn LLB . . . . *Nov 1975
Fountain, Ms Claire . . . . *Nov 1999
Watts, Ms Julie . . . . *Jan 1994

WRIGHT & WRIGHT ‡
54 Chertsey Street Guildford Surrey GU1 4HD
Tel: 01483 531264 *Fax:* 01483 531448 *Dx:* 83153 GUILDFORD 2
E-mail: law@wrightandwright.com
List of partners: J S Sampson, A G M Wright, A M Wright
Work: C1 E F1 J1 O Q R1 S1 T2 W
Ptr: Sampson, Mr Julian Stracey LLB; TEP . . . . *Dec 1998
Wright, Mr Andrew Guy Malcolm BA . . . . *Oct 1976
Wright, Mrs Angela Mary BA . . . . *Apr 1976

GUISBOROUGH, Redcar & Cleveland

ASKEW BUNTING SOLICITORS LLP
Town Hall Guisborough Redcar & Cleveland TS14 6BH
Tel: 01287 635151 *Fax:* 01287 636627 *Dx:* 60002 GUISBOROUGH
E-mail: annette@askewbuntingllp.co.uk
Office: Middlesbrough
Work: A1 C1 D1 D2 E K1 L N Q R1 S1 W Z(l,m,r)
Emergency Action, Agency, Advocacy, Fixed Fee Interview, Legal Aid undertaken, Legal Aid Franchise and Member of Accident Line
Mem: Towler, Mr D William LLB . . . . *Dec 1974

ATHA BARTON & CO ‡
66 Westgate Guisborough Redcar & Cleveland TS14 6AY
Tel: 01287 633242 *Fax:* 01287 630522 *Dx:* 60003 GUISBOROUGH
Emergency telephone 07850 259907
E-mail: enquiries@athabarton.co.uk
List of partners: R S Barton, C L Gent
Office: Skelton-in-Cleveland
Work: D1 D2 E F1 F2 G H J1 K1 L N Q S1 S2 V W Z(r)
Emergency Action, Agency, Advocacy, Fixed Fee Interview and Legal Aid undertaken
Ptr: Barton, Mr Richard S LLB. . . . . *May 1988
Gent, Miss Clare L LLB . . . . *Nov 1997

IAN COWIE ‡
14 Chaloner Street Guisborough Redcar & Cleveland TS14 6QD
Tel: 01287 636401 *Fax:* 01287 632874
Emergency telephone 01947 895383
E-mail: ian@cowiesolicitors.co.uk
List of partners: I G Cowie
Work: F1 G H K1 L N S1 S2 V W
Emergency Action, Agency, Advocacy, Fixed Fee Interview, Legal Aid undertaken and Member of Accident Line
Ptr: Cowie, Mr Ian G. . . . . *Dec 1974

NEWBYS
Town Hall Market Place Guisborough Redcar & Cleveland TS14 6BQ
Tel: 01287 632208 / 632209 *Fax:* 01287 631855
Dx: 60001 GUISBOROUGH
Office: Middlesbrough, Stockton-on-Tees
Work: A1 B1 C1 C2 C3 D1 D2 E F1 G J1 K1 L N O Q S1 S2 T1 T2 W Z(p)
Emergency Action, Agency, Advocacy, Fixed Fee Interview, Legal Aid undertaken and Legal Aid Franchise
Ptr: Bosomworth, Mr Stephen J LLB. . . . . *Apr 1979
Ast: Hards, Mr Mark Lee LLB(Hons) . . . . *Nov 1994

KATHY WEBB & CO ‡
6-10 Church Street Guisborough Redcar & Cleveland TS14 6BS
Tel: 01287 633331 *Fax:* 01287 631133 *Dx:* 68740 GUISBOROUGH
E-mail: info@kathywebb.com
List of partners: C S Reed
Work: D1 D2 K1
Emergency Action, Agency, Legal Aid undertaken and Legal Aid Franchise
Ptr: Reed, Mr Carl Stephen LLB(Hons) . . . . *Jun 1994
Asoc: Fox, Ms Laura Jane Elizabeth LLB(Hons). . . . . . . *Sep 2004

GUISELEY, West Yorkshire

ISON HARRISON
65 Victoria Road Guiseley West Yorkshire LS20 8DQ
Tel: 01943 889080 *Fax:* 01943 262011 *Dx:* 29026 GUISELEY
E-mail: mail@isonharrison.co.uk
Office: Garforth, Ilkley, Leeds (3 offices)
Ast: Brook, Miss Elizabeth Anne. . . . . Oct 2009

HADLEIGH, Suffolk

GOTELEE
6 Church Street Hadleigh Suffolk IP7 5DU
Tel: 01473 822102 *Fax:* 01473 827832 *Dx:* 85050 BABERGH
E-mail: info-hadleigh@gotelee.co.uk
Office: Ipswich
Work: A1 C1 C3 D1 E F1 J1 K1 K4 L N O Q S1 S2 T2 W
Emergency Action, Agency, Advocacy, Fixed Fee Interview undertaken and Member of Accident Line

HAILSHAM, East Sussex

ELSBYS SOLICITORS ‡
7-9 Cortlandt George Street Hailsham East Sussex BN27 1AE
Tel: 01323 440030 / 0800 011 2797 *Fax:* 01323 449553
E-mail: ask@elsbylaw.co.uk

HART READE
Old Manor House Market Street Hailsham East Sussex BN27 2AE
Tel: 01323 841481 *Fax:* 01323 845687 *Dx:* 38304 HAILSHAM
E-mail: info@hartreade.co.uk
Office: Eastbourne, Polegate
Work: K1 K3 S1 T2 W
Ptr: Maddison-White, Mrs Helen LLB(Hons) . . . . *Aug 2002
Ast: Richards, Miss Carolyn LLB(Hons) . . . . *Nov 2005

LYCETT CONVEYANCING SOLICITORS ‡
PO Box 162 Hailsham East Sussex BN27 3FS
Tel: 01323 449552 *Fax:* 01323 449552
List of partners: J M Lycett
Work: S1 S2
SPr: Lycett, Miss Jennifer M LLB. . . . . *Oct 1984

HALE, Greater Manchester

BETESH PARTNERSHIP
3a Cecil Road Hale Greater Manchester WA15 9NY
Tel: 0161 926 1430 *Dx:* 14305 MANCHESTER 1
E-mail: enquiries@bpslaw.co.uk
Office: Manchester (2 offices)

DAVID S GANDY ‡
4 The Ridgeway Broad Lane Hale Greater Manchester WA15 0DD
Tel: 0161 980 2334 *Fax:* 0161 980 2334

PROPERTY LEGAL SOLICITORS ‡
2 Broomfield Lane Hale Greater Manchester WA15 9AG
Tel: 0161 941 7449 *Fax:* 0161 941 4078
E-mail: rthomas@proplegal.co.uk

HALESOWEN, West Midlands

CHALLINORS
Hyefield House 36 Hagley Road Halesowen West Midlands B63 4RH
Tel: 0121 550 0481 *Fax:* 0121 585 5124 *Dx:* 14507 HALESOWEN
Office: Birmingham, Nottingham, West Bromwich, Wolverhampton
Languages: French, German, Italian
Work: A1 B1 C1 D1 E F1 G H J1 K1 L M1 N P R1 S1 T1 W Z(e,l,p)
Emergency Action, Agency, Advocacy, Fixed Fee Interview, Legal Aid undertaken and Member of Accident Line
Ptr: Billingham, Mr Roger BA . . . . *May 1974
Chapple, Mr John L LLB . . . . *May 1977
Kelsall, Mr Steven T LLB . . . . *§Oct 1975
Price, Mr Richard E. . . . . *Dec 1981
White, Mr Philip J L. . . . . *Dec 1974

CUTLER BUTTERY SOLICITORS ‡
50 Summer Hill Halesowen West Midlands B63 3BU
Tel: 0121 550 0010 *Fax:* 0121 550 0040
E-mail: contact@cutlerbuttery.com

M J DARBY & CO ‡
107 Kent Road Halesowen West Midlands B62 8PB
Tel: 0121 421 7933 *Fax:* 0121 421 6397 *Dx:* 28652 QUINTON
E-mail: darbysolse@aol.com
List of partners: M J Darby
Work: A1 C1 E F1 G K1 L M1 P S1 W Z(j,n)
Legal Aid undertaken and Member of Accident Line
Ptr: Darby, Mr Michael J. . . . . *Oct 1977
Ast: Taft, Mr Colin M. . . . . *Jun 1977

FRASER-MACNAMARA LIMITED ‡
Helen House Great Cornbow Halesowen West Midlands B63 3AB
Tel: 0121 550 7308 *Fax:* 0121 550 3882 *Dx:* 14506 HALESOWEN
E-mail: frasermacnamara@btconnect.com

JACK KLAR SOLICITORS ‡
74 Long Lane Halesowen West Midlands B62 9DJ
Tel: 0121 561 5958

MFG SOLICITORS
5 Centre Court Vine Lane Halesowen West Midlands B63 3EB
Tel: 0121 550 0777 *Fax:* 0121 550 6888
E-mail: mail@mfgsolicitors.com
Office: Bromsgrove, Kidderminster, Oswestry, Telford, Worcester
Ptr: Neal, Mr Alan J MA(Oxon); ATII; TEP. . . . . *Jun 1976
Ast: Rosenbloom, Mrs Julia Louise. . . . . Sep 2002

N S PARRY SOLICITOR ‡
10 Ainsdale Gardens Halesowen West Midlands B63 1HW
Tel: 0121 550 0194

P M PETHERBRIDGE & CO ‡
60 Whitehall Road Halesowen West Midlands B63 3JS
Tel: 0121 550 0271 *Fax:* 0121 585 6823
Dx: 20757 CRADLEY HEATH
E-mail: pmp@pmpetherbridge.co.uk
Work: E L R2 S1 S2 W Z(g,i)

STABLES & CO ‡
70 High Street Halesowen West Midlands B63 3BA
Tel: 0121 585 3820 *Fax:* 0121 501 2211
E-mail: enquiries@stables-solicitors.co.uk
List of partners: J L Bird, N Jordan, N A Mills, D J Moore
Office: Kidderminster, Stourbridge
Work: C1 E F1 G H J1 K1 N O Q S1 S2 W Z(l)
Agency, Advocacy, Fixed Fee Interview and Legal Aid undertaken
Ptr: Bird, Ms Jessica Louise. . . . . Jan 2005
Mills, Mr Nicholas A. . . . . Jan 1996
Moore, Mr David J LLB . . . . *Nov 1985

KATHRYN WILLIETS SOLICITOR ‡
86 Blackberry Lane Halesowen West Midlands B63 4NY
Tel: 0121 501 2731 *Fax:* 0121 336 1818
E-mail: kathryn.williets@btinternet.com

HALESWORTH, Suffolk

ALLENS
55 Thoroughfare Halesworth Suffolk IP19 8AR
Tel: 01986 875246 *Fax:* 01986 893669
E-mail: allens@tetnet.co.uk
Office: Bungay
Work: D1 F1 G H J1 K1 M1 P S1 S2 W Z(l)
Emergency Action, Agency, Advocacy, Fixed Fee Interview and Legal Aid undertaken
Ptr: Allen, Mr Roger C B. . . . . *Oct 1977

CROSS RAM & CO ‡
18 The Thoroughfare Halesworth Suffolk IP19 8AJ
Tel: 01986 873636 *Fax:* 01986 872224 *Dx:* 51200 HALESWORTH
E-mail: info@crossram.co.uk
List of partners: J M Margarson, L D Parkes
Office: Framlingham
Work: A1 C1 C2 C3 E F1 J1 L P R1 S1 T1 T2 W Z(c,d,e,l,m,s)
Fixed Fee Interview undertaken

Ptr: Margarson, Mr Jonathan Marshall TEP . . . . *Oct 1968
Ast: Hewitt, Mr Daniel Jon LLB(Hons) . . . . *Sep 2000
Con: Jordan-Fisher, Ms Josephine M BA(Hons). . . . . . . Dec 1973

NORTON PESKETT
52 Thoroughfare Halesworth Suffolk IP19 8AR
Tel: 01986 872513 *Fax:* 01986 875484 *Dx:* 51202 HALESWORTH
E-mail: enquire@nortonpeskett.co.uk
Office: Beccles, Great Yarmouth, Lowestoft
Work: D1 D2 E G H J1 K1 K3 N Q S1 S2 W
Agency, Legal Aid undertaken and Legal Aid Franchise

HALIFAX, West Yorkshire

ADL SOLICITORS ‡
Kent House 16 Bull Close Lane Halifax West Yorkshire HX1 2EF
Tel: 01422 339994 *Fax:* 01422 383665 *Dx:* 16030 HALIFAX
E-mail: yasin.din@adl-solicitors.co.uk

ABRAHAMS SOLICITORS ‡
6 Water House Street Halifax West Yorkshire HX1 1UQ
Tel: 01422 381333 *Fax:* 01422 384747

APPLEYARD LEES
15 Clare Road Halifax West Yorkshire HX1 2HY
Tel: 01422 330110 *Fax:* 01422 330090
E-mail: ip@appleyardlees.com
Office: Burnley, Chester, Harrogate, Huddersfield, Leeds, Liverpool, Manchester, Preston, Sheffield, Stockton-on-Tees, York

BHP LAW
27 Harrison Road Halifax West Yorkshire HX1 2AT
Tel: 01422 250650 *Fax:* 01422 348792 *Dx:* 16020 HALIFAX
E-mail: info@bhplaw.co.uk
Office: Darlington, Durham, Newcastle upon Tyne, Newton Aycliffe, North Shields, Stockton-on-Tees
Work: A3 B1 C1 C2 C3 D1 D2 E F1 F2 G H J1 J2 K1 K2 K3 K4 L N O Q R1 R2 S1 S2 T1 T2 U1 U2 W X Z(c,e,o,p,q,r,u,w,x,za)
Legal Aid undertaken
Ptr: Dixon, Mr Jonathan . . . . Jun 1977
Leadbitter, Mrs Melanie LLB. . . . . Aug 2003
Noble, Mrs Ann . . . . Apr 1980

BAXENDALE VANZIE ‡
Prescott House 26 Prescott Street Halifax West Yorkshire HX1 2LG
E-mail: baxendalevanzie@hotmail.com

BEARDERS ‡
85 Northgate Halifax West Yorkshire HX1 1XF
Tel: 01422 365215 / 343427 *Fax:* 01422 348679 *Dx:* 16010 HALIFAX
E-mail: halifaxbearders@btopenworld.com
List of partners: Y Cross, R D Smithies
Office: Brighouse
Work: K1 K3 K4 S1 S2 W
Fixed Fee Interview undertaken
Ptr: Cross, Mrs Yasmin MA . . . . *Jul 1996
Ast: Edwards, Mrs Claire BSc(Hons). . . . . Jan 2011

BRIMBLE & CO ‡
16 Carlton Street Halifax West Yorkshire HX1 2AL
Tel: 01422 322121 *Fax:* 01422 322122 *Dx:* 720332 HALIFAX
List of partners: J Brimble
Ptr: Brimble, Mrs Julie BA . . . . *Nov 1991

CHADWICK LAWRENCE
23a Bull Close Lane Halifax West Yorkshire HX1 2EF
Tel: 01422 330601 *Fax:* 01422 321334 *Dx:* 16032 HALIFAX
E-mail: michaelb@chad-law.co.uk
Office: Huddersfield, Morley, Wakefield
Work: B1 C1 D1 D2 E F1 F2 G H J1 K1 K2 L M1 N O P Q R1 S1 T1 V W Z(e,k,l,p,q,r)

DIN SOLICITORS ‡
Janjua Chambers Black Swan Passage George Street Halifax West Yorkshire HX1 1HA
Tel: 01422 320485 *Fax:* 01422 322657
E-mail: info@dinsolicitors.co.uk

FINN GLEDHILL ‡
1-4 Harrison Road Halifax West Yorkshire HX1 2AG
Tel: 01422 330000 *Fax:* 01422 342604 *Dx:* 16022 HALIFAX
E-mail: enquiries@finngledhill.co.uk
List of partners: R M Gledhill, K S Green, D J L Lee, S J Mattock, M C Nowell, A J Palfreman, C Stevenson
Office: Hebden Bridge
Work: A1 B1 C1 C2 C3 D1 D2 E F1 F2 G H J1 K1 K3 L M1 M2 N O P Q R1 R2 S1 S2 T1 T2 V W X Z(b,c,d,g,i,j,k,l,m,o,p,q,s,t)
Emergency Action, Agency, Advocacy, Fixed Fee Interview, Legal Aid undertaken, Legal Aid Franchise and Member of Accident Line
Ptr: Gledhill, Mr R Marc LLB. . . . . *§Feb 1988
Green, Mr Kieron S . . . . *Dec 1979
Lee, Mr David J L. . . . . §Nov 1971
Mattock, Mr Stephen J LLB . . . . *Mar 1986
Nowell, Mr Malcolm C LLB . . . . Jul 1980
Palfreman, Miss Amanda J LLB. . . . . *§Oct 1991
Stevenson, Ms Carol LLB(Lond) . . . . *§Apr 1977
Ast: Jackson, Mrs Elaine LLB . . . . *Oct 1984

GOODWIN STEVENS SOLICITORS ‡
5 Carlton Street Halifax West Yorkshire HX1 2AL
Tel: 01422 300101

HADDOCK & COMPANY ‡
62 Gibbet Street Halifax West Yorkshire HX1 5BP
Tel: 01422 366010 *Fax:* 01422 322789 *Dx:* 16027 HALIFAX 1
E-mail: haddockandco@btconnect.com
List of partners: R W Campbell, C Haddock
Work: G N S1
Emergency Action, Agency, Advocacy, Legal Aid undertaken and Legal Aid Franchise
Ptr: Campbell, Mr Robert W LLB . . . . *Dec 1979
Haddock, Mr Christopher . . . . May 2000
Asoc: Flaga, Miss Michelle LLB(Hons). . . . . Jan 2006

HAIDER SOLICITORS ‡
9 Carlton Street Halifax West Yorkshire HX1 2AL
Tel: 01422 321632

MAKIN DIXON SOLICITORS
Clare Chambers 2 Clare Road Halifax West Yorkshire HX2 2HX
Tel: 01422 363184 *Fax:* 01422 381153 *Dx:* 16002 HALIFAX
E-mail: enquiries@makindixon.co.uk
Office: Bradford, Harrogate, Keighley, Skipton, Todmorden
Asoc: Jarockyj, Hannah . . . . Jan 2004

NEWELLS ‡
Unit D422 Dean Clough Mill Halifax West Yorkshire HX3 5AX
Tel: 01422 250250 *Fax:* 01274 603713

ON LEGAL ‡
16 Wade House Road Shelf Halifax West Yorkshire HX3 7PB
Tel: 01274 608353 *Fax:* 01274 608007
E-mail: mail@onlegal-solicitors.com
List of partners: I R Holdsworth
Languages: French
Work: C1 E K3 K4 O Q S1 S2 W Z(q)
Ptr: Holdsworth, Mr Ian R BA; LLM; PGDip Law Society Gazette Essay Prize 1995. . . . . *Dec 1982

PARABIS LAW LLP ‡
G1 G Mill Dean Clough Halifax West Yorkshire HX3 5AX
Tel: 0844 984 4900
E-mail: info@parabis.co.uk

PATTERSONS SOLICITORS ‡
31 Harrison Road Halifax West Yorkshire HX1 2AF
Tel: 01422 353555 *Fax:* 01422 353444
E-mail: pattersonssolicitors@googlemail.com

JOHN PICKERING & PARTNERS LLP ‡
20 Clare Road Halifax West Yorkshire HX1 2HX
Tel: 0808 144 0959 *Fax:* 01422 438500 *Dx:* 16023 HALIFAX
E-mail: pg@johnpickering.co.uk
List of partners: R Davies, N Fisher, P Glanville, C A Hepworth, K T Johnson
Office: Liverpool, Manchester
Languages: Punjabi, Urdu
Work: J1 N Z(p,r)
Legal Aid undertaken and Legal Aid Franchise
Ptr: Davies, Ms Ruth . . . . Apr 1996
Glanville, Mr Paul LLB . . . . Nov 1992
Hepworth, Ms Carol A. . . . . Dec 1977
Johnson, Mr Kevin Thomas Best Student Liverpool University 1998 . . . . Apr 1999
Asoc: Donovan, Mrs Rachel BSc . . . . *Jun 2003
Horton, Ms Claire MA(Cantab); CPE; LSF. . . . . . . *Mar 1990
Hussain, Mrs Fozia LLB(Hons) Best Student in Employment Law, Business Law & Practice 2002. . . . . Nov 2004
Ast: O'Hara, Mr Ryan . . . . *Nov 2007
Waterson, Miss Jo-Anne Elaine LLB Liverpool Law Society Prize 2005 . . . . Oct 2009
Wilson, Miss Helen . . . . Nov 2007

RAHMAN RAVELLI SOLICITORS ‡
Saracen House 10 Pellon Lane Halifax West Yorkshire HX1 5SP
Tel: 01422 346666 *Fax:* 01422 430526 *Dx:* 16001 HALIFAX 1

RAMSDENS SOLICITORS
(incorporating Jubb Longbothams; Rice-Jones)
6-8 Harrison Road Halifax West Yorkshire HX1 2AQ
Tel: 01422 330700 *Fax:* 01422 330184 *Dx:* 16018 HALIFAX
E-mail: info@ramsdens.co.uk
Office: Dewsbury, Elland, Holmfirth, Huddersfield (3 offices), Mirfield
Work: B1 C1 D1 E F1 J1 K1 K3 L N O Q S1 S2 T2 W Z(l,q)
Agency, Advocacy and Legal Aid undertaken
Ptr: Dolan, Mr Greg BA(Hons); CPE; LPC; PSC . . . . . *Sep 1996
Hepworth, Mr Mark Andrew . . . . *Oct 1985
Hofton, Mr David BA . . . . *Nov 1986
Asoc: Scott, Ms Anne Margaret LLB. . . . . *Jun 1996
Ast: Mullins, Miss Veronica Jane LLB . . . . *Sep 2004

BENJAMIN ROBERTS SOLICITORS ‡
4 Wards End Halifax West Yorkshire HX1 1BX
Tel: 01422 356633 *Fax:* 01422 383688
Emergency telephone 07809 472734
E-mail: help@benjaminrobertssolicitors.co.uk
List of partners: G Roberts
Work: N
Member of Accident Line
SPr: Roberts, Mr Graham . . . . Aug 1998

ANTHONY ROBERTSHAW SOLICITORS ‡
Lodge Lane End Lodge Lane Halifax West Yorkshire HX2 7TU
Tel: 01422 246002
E-mail: a.robertshaw@virgin.net

JOHN RYAN SOLICITOR ‡
1 Upper Lane Northowram Halifax West Yorkshire HX3 7DL
Tel: 01422 207684

SMITH SOLICITOR LLP ‡
18 Portland Place Halifax West Yorkshire HX1 2QN
Tel: 01422 383380 *Fax:* 01422 383370 *Dx:* 16016 HALIFAX
E-mail: reception@smithsolicitorsllp.co.uk
Work: E F1 G H K1 L N Q S1 W
Emergency Action, Advocacy, Fixed Fee Interview, Legal Aid undertaken, Legal Aid Franchise and Member of Accident Line

SWITALSKI'S
(incorporating Gaunts Solicitors)
Venture House Silver Street Halifax West Yorkshire HX1 1HS
Tel: 01422 284350 *Fax:* 01422 284351 *Dx:* 16014 HALIFAX
Office: Bradford, Dewsbury, Huddersfield, Leeds, Wakefield
Work: D1 G H J1 K1 K2 L Z(i,m,r)
Emergency Action, Agency and Legal Aid undertaken
Con: Rhodes, Mr Keith MA(Oxon); TEP. . . . . *Oct 1984

WILKINSON WOODWARD ‡
11 Fountain Street Halifax West Yorkshire HX1 1LU
Tel: 01422 339600 *Fax:* 01422 339601 *Dx:* 16004 HALIFAX
Emergency telephone 01850 745336
E-mail: law@wilkinsonwoodward.co.uk
List of partners: R A Brown, M S Cawthorn, A M Crabtree, L A Crabtree, J M H Dyson, P J Manock, C A Price, R M Scott
Office: Huddersfield
Languages: French
Work: A1 B1 C1 C2 C3 D1 D2 E F1 G H J1 K1 K2 K3 L M1 M2 N O P Q R1 R2 S1 T1 T2 V W Z(c,d,e,f,h,i,j,k,l,m,n,p,q,r,s)
Emergency Action, Agency, Advocacy, Fixed Fee Interview, Legal Aid undertaken, Legal Aid Franchise and Member of Accident Line
Ptr: Brown, Mr Richard A LLB . . . . *§Nov 1989
Cawthorn, Ms Maureen S LLB(Manc) Notary Public . *§Feb 1989
Crabtree, Mr Andrew M LLB; PGDip Planning & Environmental Law. *§Jan 1988
Crabtree, Mrs Lynn A BA(Keele) . . . . *§Jan 1989
Dyson, Mr Jonathan M H BA . . . . *Oct 1987
Manock, Ms Penelope J LLB . . . . *§Oct 1988
Price, Ms Caroline Anne . . . . *Apr 1994
Scott, Mr Robert M LLB(L'pool) . . . . *§Jul 1982
Ast: Booker, Ms Katie Louise LLB . . . . *Jul 2005
Jackson, Mr Henry Samuel LLB. . . . . *Sep 2009
Kurowski, Ms Laura. . . . . *Sep 2008
Meskimmon, Mrs Hayley Louise LLB . . . . *Apr 2010
Sands, Mrs Angeline Bridget BA . . . . *Sep 2010

HALSTEAD, Essex

HOLMES & HILLS LLP
Trinity Street Halstead Essex CO9 1JE
Tel: 01787 475312 *Fax:* 01787 473731 *Dx:* 41451 HALSTEAD
E-mail: legaladvice@holmes-hills.co.uk
Office: Braintree
Work: A1 B1 C1 C2 C3 D1 E F1 J1 J2 K1 K3 L O P Q S1 S2 T1 T2 W Z(c,d)
Fixed Fee Interview undertaken
Ptr: Harris, Mr Richard N LLB . . . . *§Nov 1982
Popham, Mr Edward Giles LLB(Hons). . . . . *§May 1969
Simpson, Ms Judith H LLB(Lond) . . . . *§Jul 1976

HALTWHISTLE, Northumberland

CARTMELL SHEPHERD
Main Street Haltwhistle Northumberland NE49 9AB
Tel: 01434 320362 *Fax:* 01434 320901
E-mail: haltwhistle@cartmells.co.uk
Office: Brampton, Carlisle (2 offices), Penrith
Languages: French
Work: A1 E F1 L S1 T1 W Z(d)
Fixed Fee Interview and Legal Aid undertaken
Ptr: Armstrong, Ms Diana F BA(Oxon). . . . . *Jan 1985
Asoc: Forrester, Mrs Catherin E MBE; CBE MA . . . . . . *Apr 1981

HAM, Surrey

DIXON WARD
Gate House 11 Upper Ham Road Ham Surrey TW10 5LE
Tel: 020 8546 0225 / 8549 2615 *Fax:* 020 8547 2038
Dx: 100251 RICHMOND 2
E-mail: ismith@dixon-ward.co.uk
Office: Richmond upon Thames
Work: E S1 S2 W
Con: Smith, Mr Ian J LLB. . . . . *Oct 1974

HAMPTON, Middlesex

ADAMS DELMAR ‡
56 Ashley Road Hampton Middlesex TW12 2HU
Tel: 020 8941 2097 *Fax:* 020 8979 4051 *Dx:* 115721 HAMPTON
E-mail: sols@adamsdelmar.co.uk
List of partners: J A D Adams
Work: E K1 S1 W
Ptr: Adams, Mr John A D BA(Warw). . . . . *Jun 1981
Ast: Marsh, Mr Simon F T BA(Kent) . . . . *Dec 1979
Nash, Ms Jacqueline A MA(Cantab). . . . . Oct 1987

COZENS MOXON & HARTS
35 Ashley Road Hampton Middlesex TW12 2JA
Tel: 020 8979 4333 *Fax:* 020 8979 1393 *Dx:* 115722 HAMPTON
E-mail: teddington@cmhlaw.co.uk
Office: Teddington
Work: A1 B1 C1 C2 C3 D1 E F1 G H J1 K1 L M1 M2 N P R1 S1 T1 T2 V W Z(d)
Agency, Fixed Fee Interview, Legal Aid undertaken and Member of Accident Line
Ptr: Farrer, Mr Robin E G . . . . *Jun 1977

JP MITCHELL ‡
Office 16 114 Tudor Road Hampton Middlesex TW12 2NF
Tel: 020 3151 2711 *Fax:* 020 8929 0087
E-mail: office@jpmitchell.co.uk

RICHARD KANANI & CO ‡
4 Cranmer Road Hampton Hill Hampton Middlesex TW12 1DW
Tel: 020 8941 8363 *Fax:* 020 8941 8853
E-mail: legal@richard-kanani.demon.co.uk
List of partners: R Kanani
Work: E L R1 S1 Z(l)
Ptr: Kanani, Mr Richard BA(Law) Maxwell Law Prize. . . . *Apr 1988

TRELFA & CO ‡
Milton House 28 Cranmer Road Hampton Hill Hampton Middlesex TW12 1DW
Tel: 020 8941 1249 *Fax:* 020 8979 6525
E-mail: jt@jilltrelfa.co.uk
List of partners: J M Trelfa
Work: K1
SPr: Trelfa, Miss Jill Marian LLB(Nott'm) . . . . *§Nov 1976

HANHAM, South Gloucestershire

MICHAEL KELLY & CO ‡
52 High Street Hanham South Gloucestershire BS15 3DR
Tel: 0117 967 6559 *Fax:* 0117 961 1366
List of partners: M J Kelly
Work: E J1 K1 K3 K4 L S1 S2 W
Agency and Advocacy undertaken
Ptr: Kelly, Mr Michael J . . . . Apr 1966

See p112 for the Key to Work Categories & other symbols

HANLEY, Stoke-on-Trent

BESWICKS
Alexander House Bethesda Street Hanley Stoke-on-Trent ST1 3DX
Tel: 01782 205000 *Fax:* 01782 404665 *Dx:* 20716 HANLEY
Emergency telephone 07788 426426
Office: Stoke-on-Trent
Languages: Dutch, French, German, Polish, Ruganda, Spanish, Urdu
Work: A1 A3 B1 B2 C1 C2 C3 D1 D2 E F1 F2 G H I J1 J2 K1 K2 K3 K4 L N O P Q R1 R2 S1 S2 T1 T2 V W Z(c,e,g,l,p,q,r,w,za)
Emergency Action, Agency, Advocacy, Fixed Fee Interview, Legal Aid undertaken and Legal Aid Franchise
Ptr: Bailey, Mr Tim. Jan 1981
Craig, Ms Fiona. Jan 1997
Heath, Mr Howard C LLB . . . . *§Dec 1973
Howland, Mr Peter J LLB(B'ham) . . . . *Oct 1979
McGuiness, Mrs Joanne LLB(Hons). . . . . *Feb 1992
Mellor, Mr Gary N LLB . . . . *Feb 1991
Stephenson, Mr Michael J LLB . . . . Jan 1979
Turnock, Mr Andrew. . . . . Jan 2002
Asoc: Bell, Mrs Nicola . . . . Jul 2004
Evans, Ms Kirsty . . . . Mar 2003
Welsh, Mr Robert . . . . Nov 2008
Yates, Mr Lee. Nov 2000
Ast: Matranga, Miss Natalie . . . . Mar 2009

BOWCOCK & PURSAILL
2 Ridge House Ridgehouse Drive Festival Park Hanley Stoke-on-Trent ST1 5SJ
Tel: 01782 200000 *Fax:* 01782 207018 *Dx:* 701708 HANLEY 2
E-mail: cw@bowcockpursaill.co.uk
Office: Leek
Work: A1 A2 B1 C1 C2 E F1 J1 K1 K2 K3 K4 L N O Q R1 R2 S1 S2 T1 T2 W Z(c,d,e,l,q)
Agency undertaken
Ast: Voce, Mrs Holly Kerr LLB . . . . *Sep 2009

CARNEY SOLICITORS LTD ‡
Gitana Street Hanley Stoke-on-Trent ST1 1DT
Tel: 01782 272999 *Fax:* 01782 202088 *Dx:* 20747 HANLEY
Emergency telephone 07970 495596
E-mail: michaelcarney@carneysolicitors.co.uk
List of partners: M A Carney
Office: Leek
Work: D2 E G H K1 K3 S2 W
Legal Aid undertaken
SPr: Carney, Mr Michael Alan CPE; LSF . . . . *Oct 1995

TINSDILLS ‡
Hays House 25 Albion Street Hanley Stoke-on-Trent ST1 1QF
Tel: 01782 262031 *Fax:* 01782 287571 *Dx:* 20710 HANLEY
E-mail: lawyers@tinsdills.co.uk
List of partners: K Boyle, A C Brian, A J Burrows, N Chadwick, A T Cogan, P J C Hamilton, P Hawksworth, P J Hawksworth, L V C Lovewell, K Moore, M Proud, M W Roberts, R Torr
Office: Leek, Newcastle under Lyme, Sandbach
Work: A1 A2 B1 B2 C1 C2 D1 D2 E F1 F2 J1 K1 K2 K3 K4 L N O P Q R1 R2 S1 S2 T1 V W Z(b,c,d,e,f,g,h,j,k,l,m,n,o,p,q,r,s,t)
Emergency Action, Agency, Advocacy, Fixed Fee Interview undertaken and Member of Accident Line
Ptr: Boyle, Kerry. . . . . Dec 2004
Brian, Mr Andrew C Notary Public. . . . . *§Nov 1989
Burrows, Mr Andrew J LLB(Hons) Polytechnic of Wales Merit Award 1989 (Law FT) . . . . *Oct 1992
Cogan, Mr A Timothy LLB. . . . . *Oct 1984
Hamilton, Mr Peter J C BA(Hons) . . . . *Jul 1997
Hawksworth, Mr Paul J . . . . *§Oct 1974
Lovewell, Mr Leonard V Christopher BA. . . . . . . *§Nov 1985
Moore, Mr Karl LLB. . . . . *§Dec 1986
Proud, Ms Marie . . . . May 2004
Roberts, Mr Martin W . . . . *§Mar 1988
Torr, Mrs Rebecca LLB(Hons). . . . . *Nov 1999
Asoc: Want, Mr James LLB(Hons). . . . . Sep 2002
Ast: Norman, Miss Emily LLB . . . . Sep 2006
Pickerin, Ms Sara Marie. . . . . Jul 2006
Con: Whitehouse, Mr Richard J LLB . . . . *§Apr 1977

WOOLLISCROFTS ‡
6-10 Broad Street Hanley Stoke-on-Trent ST1 4EU
Tel: 01782 204000 *Fax:* 01782 202413 *Dx:* 20708 HANLEY
E-mail: enquiries@woolliscrofts.co.uk
List of partners: R J G Basnett, W D Harrop, T W Jones, P A Lawton, P J Lymer, C M Mason
Office: Alsager, Newcastle under Lyme, Stoke-on-Trent
Work: A1 B1 C1 D1 D2 E F1 J1 K1 L N O P Q R1 S1 S2 T1 T2 W Z(c,i,k,r)
Emergency Action, Agency, Advocacy, Fixed Fee Interview undertaken and Member of Accident Line
Ptr: Basnett, Mr Raymond J G BA(Hons) . . . . Jun 1978
Jones, Mr Thomas W BA(Law) . . . . *Apr 1981
Lawton, Mr Phillip Andrew LLB(Lond) . . . . *Jun 1978
Mason, Mr Christopher M LLB(Wales). . . . . *Jun 1978
Asoc: Adams, Mr Edward J R BA(Hons). . . . . *Aug 1997
Barnett, Mr Andrew J . . . . *Nov 1996
Deavall, Mr Mark LLB(Hons) . . . . *Sep 2000
Jones, Miss Amanda LLB(Hons) . . . . Nov 1999
Ast: Johnson, Miss Victoria BA(Hons) . . . . May 2001

HAREFIELD, Middlesex

WORSDELL & VINTNER
12 High Street Harefield Middlesex UB9 6BU
Tel: 01895 824713 *Fax:* 01895 678270
Office: Ickenham
Work: A1 C1 E J1 L P R1 S1 T1 W
Ptr: Barrett, Mrs Alison C LLB. . . . . *Jun 1985
Crowther, Mr Neil BA . . . . *Dec 1978
Con: Vintner, Mr Barry S . . . . *Jun 1972

HARLECH, Gwynedd

BREESE-GWYNDAF
(incorporating Richard Williams)
Llys Y Graig Harlech Gwynedd LL46 2YE
Tel: 01766 780334 *Fax:* 01766 514227 *Dx:* 711470 PORTHMADOG
Emergency telephone 01286 830075
E-mail: breesegwyndaf@compuserve.com
Office: Barmouth, Porthmadog
Languages: Welsh
Work: A1 D1 D2 E F1 F2 G H J1 K1 L N O Q R1 S1 S2 V W Z(i,p,q,r)
Emergency Action, Agency, Advocacy, Fixed Fee Interview, Legal Aid undertaken and Legal Aid Franchise
Ptr: Williams, Mr John B LLB . . . . *Jun 1977

J CHARLES HUGHES & CO
Capel Dwr Harlech Gwynedd LL46 2YH
Tel: 01766 780818
Office: Dolgellau
Ptr: Evans, Mr Gareth LLB(Wales). . . . . *Dec 1975

HARLESTON, Norfolk

JACKAMANS
(incorporating Taylor & Co)
Ancient House The Thoroughfare Harleston Norfolk IP20 9AS
Tel: 01379 854455 *Fax:* 01379 854386 *Dx:* 92376 BUNGAY
E-mail: mail@jackamans.co.uk
Office: Diss, Felixstowe, Ipswich
Work: A1 C1 E J1 K1 K3 K4 L N Q S1 S2 W Z(c,q)
Agency, Fixed Fee Interview, Legal Aid undertaken and Legal Aid Franchise
Con: Taylor, Mr John Chillman LLB . . . . *§Mar 1984

HARLOW, Essex

ATTWATERS
Rothwell House West Square Harlow Essex CM20 1LQ
Tel: 01279 638888 *Fax:* 0845 508 5909 *Dx:* 40504 HARLOW
E-mail: enquiries@attwaters.co.uk
Office: Loughton
Work: A1 B1 B2 C1 C2 D1 D2 E F1 J1 K1 K3 K4 L N O Q R1 S1 S2 T1 T2 V W Z(c,l,q,r)
Emergency Action, Advocacy, Fixed Fee Interview, Legal Aid undertaken and Legal Aid Franchise
Ptr: Clarke, Mr Jonathan C LLB(Lond). . . . . §Sep 1975
Henchie, Mrs Manjot Kaur LLB(Hons). . . . . *Apr 1995
Kenny, Mrs Tracy Ann LLB(Hons). . . . . *Jul 1999
Kerry, Mr David G LLB; ACIB . . . . *Apr 1979
Mayhew, Miss Lesley-Ann LLB(Hons). . . . . Sep 2005
Parsons, Mrs Sheenagh Bernadette Joan LLB. . . . . *Mar 1991
Seibert, Ms Madeline LLB(Hons) . . . . *Jul 2000
Westbrook, Mrs Joanne Esther LLB(Hons) . . . . . . *Nov 1995
Westbrook, Mr Peter . . . . *Jan 1993
Ast: Carter, Mr Timothy James BA(Hons); PGDip; CPE; LPC; LLM . . . . May 2008
Heelis, Miss Rachel Camilla LLB . . . . Aug 2006
Wealleans, Miss Sarah Jane LLB(Hons)(UCL). . . . . *Mar 2010

BARNES & PARTNERS
5 West Square The High Harlow Essex CM20 1JJ
Tel: 01279 418601 *Fax:* 01279 450552 *Dx:* 40500 HARLOW
E-mail: people@barnesandpartners.com
Office: Cheshunt, Enfield, London E4, London N15, London N16, London N18, London N8, Pinner, Ware
Work: D1 E F1 K1 L N O Q S1 W

BUXTON RYAN & CO SOLICITORS ‡
7-10 Market House The High Harlow Essex CM20 1BL
Tel: 01279 420288 *Fax:* 01279 641336 *Dx:* 40516 HARLOW
Emergency telephone 01279 420288
E-mail: info@buxtonryan.co.uk
Work: G H
Agency and Legal Aid undertaken

HARRIS CUFFARO & NICHOLS ‡
Lion Court 8-10 Market Street Harlow Essex CM17 0AH
Tel: 01279 444456 *Fax:* 01279 439390 *Dx:* 95856 OLD HARLOW
E-mail: enquiry@hanlaw.co.uk
Languages: Bengali, Hindi, Italian, Portuguese, Urdu
Work: A1 E G H R1 S1 W Z(l)

LD LAW ‡
1 West Walk Harlow Essex CM20 1LR
Tel: 01279 441266 *Fax:* 01279 444440
E-mail: law@leedavies.co.uk
List of partners: M Casson, M J M Joseph, J Marie-France, M A Morgan, M E F Wales
Office: Norwich
Work: B1 D1 D2 E F1 J1 K1 L N O Q R1 S1 S2 W Z(c,k,l,m,p,q,t)
Emergency Action, Agency, Advocacy, Fixed Fee Interview, Legal Aid undertaken, Legal Aid Franchise and Member of Accident Line
Ptr: Marie-France, Mr Joseph . . . . Feb 1988
Morgan, Ms Michele Ashley BA(Hons)(Law). . . . . . *Jun 1995
Mem: Casson, Mr Michael MA(Cantab) . . . . *Jan 1978
Joseph, Ms Marie-France J M. . . . . Feb 1988
Morgan, Ms Michele Ashley BA(Hons)(Law). . . . . . *Jun 1995

M R LAW ‡
Harlow Enterprise Hub Kao Hockham Building Edinburgh Way Harlow Essex CM20 2NQ
Tel: 01279 430166 *Fax:* 01279 311480 *Dx:* 40503 HARLOW
E-mail: robertbarker@mrlaw.co.uk

PETERS & CO ‡
Level 9 Terminus House Terminus Street Harlow Essex CM20 1XA
Est: 2004
Tel: 01279 453331 *Fax:* 01279 453339 *Dx:* 40505 HARLOW
Emergency telephone 07979 353665
E-mail: info@peterslegal.co.uk
Office: Chelmsford, Dunstable
Languages: Shona
Work: J1 L S1 V W Z(i,m)

WHISKERS ‡
6 Mitre Buildings Kitson Way Harlow Essex CM20 1DR
Tel: 01279 439439 *Fax:* 01279 439100 *Dx:* 40502 HARLOW
Emergency telephone 01279 434338 (CRIME) / 0860 615170 (FAMILY)
E-mail: enquiries@whiskers.co.uk
Office: Bishop's Stortford, Epping, Woodford
Languages: French, German
Work: A1 B2 C1 C2 D1 E F1 G H J1 K1 K2 K3 K4 L N O P Q R1 S1 S2 T1 T2 V W Z(h,i,k,l,m,t,w)

WILSON DAVIES & CO ‡
Faircotes Station Road Harlow Essex CM17 0AP
Tel: 01279 426486 *Fax:* 01279 426255 *Dx:* 95850 OLD HARLOW
Emergency telephone 01279 734001
E-mail: info@wilsondavies.co.uk
List of partners: D Davies, G B Davies
Languages: Spanish
Work: C1 E L N P S1 W Z(i,l)
Ptr: Davies, Ms Denise . . . . Nov 1984

HAROLD WOOD, Essex

SANDERS & CO
2 Queen's Park Road Harold Wood Essex RM3 0HJ
Tel: 0844 353 3553
E-mail: enquiries@sanderssolicitors.co.uk
Office: Rainham
Work: E R2 S1 S2 W
Ptr: Gearing, Mr Daniel Leonard BA(Hons); Spanish Law Degree . . . . Sep 1999

HARPENDEN, Hertfordshire

PAUL BERG & TAYLOR ‡
Clayton House 7 Vaughan Road Harpenden Hertfordshire AL5 4EF
Tel: 01582 760161 *Fax:* 01582 461457 *Dx:* 80464 HARPENDEN
E-mail: harpenden@pbtlaw.com
List of partners: P R Berg, D J Taylor
Work: C1 E R1 S1 S2 T1 W
Fixed Fee Interview undertaken
Ptr: Berg, Mr Paul R BA. . . . . *Nov 1985
Taylor, Mr David J. . . . . *Oct 1984

MITCHELL SOLICITORS ‡
65 High Street Harpenden Hertfordshire AL5 2SW
Tel: 01582 414002 *Fax:* 01582 400166

NEVES SOLICITORS
(incorporating Wade & Jackson; Tuckey & Rylatt & McCaws; Rexwothy)
2 Sun Lane Harpenden Hertfordshire AL5 4ET
Tel: 01582 715234 *Fax:* 01582 768504 *Dx:* 80451 HARPENDEN
E-mail: info@neves-solicitors.co.uk
Office: Luton, Milton Keynes, Northampton
Languages: French
Work: A1 A3 C1 C2 D1 E F1 J1 K1 K2 K3 K4 L M4 O Q R1 R2 S1 S2 T1 T2 W Z(c,h,l,p)
Fixed Fee Interview undertaken
Ptr: Joseph, Mrs Jane LLB . . . . *Oct 1985
Simpson, Mr R Ian BA(Dunelm) Notary Public. . . . *§May 1977
Ast: Cowen, Mrs Mandy R BA(Lond). . . . . *Jun 1985
Halsey, Ms Fiona Ruth . . . . *Oct 1996

PERRINS SOLICITORS LLP ‡
10 Waterside Station Road Harpenden Hertfordshire AL5 4US
Tel: 01582 466140 *Fax:* 01582 766140 *Dx:* 152800 HARPENDEN 2
E-mail: mail@perrins-solicitors.co.uk
List of partners: C J D Bosher, A Miller, F Perrin
Work: E L R2 S1 S2 Z(h)
Ptr: Bosher, Mr Colin James Derek BSc . . . . Jun 1981
Miller, Mrs Amanda LLB. . . . . Oct 1988
Perrin, Mr Frederick LLB(Bris). . . . . *Feb 1972
Asoc: Pickersgill, Mr Nicholas Sebastian David BA(Hons) . . Oct 1993
Sharpe, Mr Richard Samuel CPE; LPC . . . . Sep 2003
Sheer, Miss Natalie . . . . May 2007
Con: Braun, Mr Simon LLB(Hons) ♦ . . . . Oct 1990
Byrne, Mrs Angela Ann LLB(Hons) . . . . Feb 1992

PHOTIADES
43 High Street Harpenden Hertfordshire AL5 2SF
Tel: 01582 766261 *Fax:* 01582 765018 *Dx:* 80460 HARPENDEN
Office: St Albans
Work: A3 E F1 J1 K1 K2 L N Q S1 S2 V W X Z(k)
Advocacy and Legal Aid undertaken
Ptr: Cox, Mr Jonathan M LLB(Hons). . . . . Jul 1977
Photiades, Mr John G P LLB(Lond) . . . . *Jul 1965

TAYLOR WALTON LLP
Station Approach Harpenden Hertfordshire AL5 4SP
Tel: 01582 765111 *Fax:* 01582 769089 *Dx:* 80450 HARPENDEN
E-mail: harpenden@taylorwalton.co.uk
Office: Luton, St Albans
Work: A1 B1 C1 D1 E F1 I J1 K1 L M1 N O P Q R1 S1 T1 U2 W X Z(b,c,d,e,f,h,j,k,l,m,o,p,s)
Ptr: Hartnett, Ms Aileen P M. . . . . *Jan 1980
Ast: Nixon, Ms Catherine S LLB(Nott'm) . . . . *Apr 1979

MARIA WATKINS (LEGAL SERVICE) LIMITED ‡
25 Greenway Harpenden Hertfordshire AL5 1NQ
Tel: 07702 817433

RICHARD A WOODMAN ‡
18 Wood End Road Harpenden Hertfordshire AL5 3ED
Tel: 01582 768222 *Fax:* 01582 624379
Emergency telephone 01582 768078
E-mail: richardwoodman@hotmail.com
List of partners: R A Woodman
Work: S1 W
SPr: Woodman, Mr Richard A . . . . *§Nov 1970

WRIGHT & CO ‡
9 Harding Parade Station Road Harpenden Hertfordshire AL5 4SW
Tel: 01582 767686 *Fax:* 01582 767979 *Dx:* 80457 HARPENDEN
Emergency telephone 07887 887275
E-mail: gpw@wrightand.co.uk
List of partners: G P Wright
Work: C1 E F1 J1 K1 L O P Q R1 S1 S2 W Z(f,n)
SPr: Wright, Mr Graham Peter LLB(Newc) . . . . *Oct 1986

HARROGATE, North Yorkshire

ANDERSONS SOLICITORS ‡
(incorporating P.J. Scott & Co)
Regent House 13-15 Albert Street Harrogate North Yorkshire HG1 1JX
Tel: 01423 527852 *Fax:* 01423 527677 *Dx:* 11979 HARROGATE
Emergency telephone 07802 306027
E-mail: anderson-sol@btconnect.com
List of partners: C L Farndon, P J Scott
Work: B2 D1 F1 G H K1 L N Q S1 S2 V W Z(l,m)

Emergency Action, Agency, Advocacy, Fixed Fee Interview, Legal Aid undertaken and Legal Aid Franchise
Ptr: Farndon, Mr Clive L LLB . . . . *Dec 1976
Scott, Mr Peter John . . . . *Dec 1963

APPLEYARD LEES
2 Northpark Road Harrogate North Yorkshire HG1 5PA
Tel: 01423 538448 *Fax:* 01423 538566
E-mail: harrogate@appleyardlees.com
Office: Burnley, Chester, Halifax, Huddersfield, Leeds, Liverpool, Manchester, Preston, Sheffield, Stockton-on-Tees, York

ARC PROPERTY SOLICITORS LLP ‡
The Studio Greengate Cardale Park Harrogate North Yorkshire HG3 1GY
Tel: 0800 612 9097 *Fax:* 0845 260 0777 *Dx:* 11953 HARROGATE
E-mail: info@arcpropertysolicitors.com
List of partners: R Ali, R Chan, W Mitchell
Office: London W1
Languages: Bengali, Hindi, Urdu
Work: A3 B1 E O Q S1 S2 W Z(q)
Ptr: Ali, Mr Rajob LLB . . . . Sep 2005
Chan, Mr Richard LLM . . . . Oct 1997
Mitchell, Mr William . . . . *Oct 1999

ASHWORTH LAW LLP ‡
7 Grove Park Court Harrogate North Yorkshire HG1 4DP
Tel: 01423 534500 *Fax:* 01423 522609

ATKINSON MCCALL ‡
18 Raglan Street Harrogate North Yorkshire HG1 1LF
Tel: 01423 501531 *Fax:* 01423 504935 *Dx:* 11951 HARROGATE
E-mail: law@atkinsonmccall.co.uk
List of partners: S N Berry, J G P Holroyd
Work: A1 B1 D1 E F1 G H J1 K1 L P Q R1 S1 S2 W Z(c,j,k,l,p,t)
Emergency Action, Agency, Advocacy, Fixed Fee Interview, Legal Aid undertaken and Legal Aid Franchise
Ptr: Berry, Mr Stuart N LLB(Sheff) . . . . *§Jun 1972
Holroyd, Mr Jeremy G P. . . . . *Dec 1971

BARBER TITLEYS ‡
6 North Park Road Harrogate North Yorkshire HG1 5PA
Tel: 01423 502211 *Fax:* 01423 503835 *Dx:* 11959 HARROGATE 1
E-mail: lawmail@barbertitleys.co.uk
List of partners: B T Axe, M J Blackham, R C Davies, J A Grimshaw, P M Henry, R M Jones, J M Long, R T D Mellors
Work: A1 A2 B1 C1 C2 D1 D2 E F1 J1 K1 K3 L N O P Q R1 R2 S1 S2 T2 W Z(c,d,l,m,q,r,u)
Agency undertaken
Ptr: Axe, Mr B Timothy MA(Oxon); DipLG . . . . *Dec 1984
Blackham, Mr Martin J BA. . . . . *§Nov 1974
Davies, Mr Richard C LLB. . . . . *Jan 1974
Grimshaw, Mr James A LLB. . . . . *Nov 1968
Henry, Mr Patrick M BCL . . . . *Nov 1971
Jones, Mr Ronald Mark BSocSc; TEP. . . . . *Oct 1989
Long, Mrs Judith M BA; TEP . . . . *Jul 1980
Mellors, Mr R Timothy D LLB; Dip PI . . . . *Mar 1987
Asoc: Henry, Mr Thomas St John BA . . . . May 2004
Holey, Mr Adrian Stuart BA(Hons); MSI(Dip); FSI . . *Mar 1997
Ast: Moore, Miss Sara LLB . . . . Sep 1999
Poole, Ms Susan Margaret LLB; MBA. . . . . Oct 1986

BECK SOLICITORS ‡
7 West Park Harrogate North Yorkshire HG1 1BL
Tel: 01423 528808

BERWINS SOLICITORS LIMITED ‡
2 North Park Road Harrogate North Yorkshire HG1 5PA
Tel: 01423 509000 *Fax:* 01423 503213 *Dx:* 25505 HARROGATE 2
E-mail: law@berwin.co.uk
List of partners: P D Berwin, S K Blake, J Jewers, C J Peace, R Robinson, S M Root, N Saunders, S Smith
Languages: French
Work: A1 B1 B2 C1 C2 D1 D2 E F1 F2 G I J1 K1 K2 K3 K4 L N O Q R2 S1 S2 U1 U2 W Z(e,l)
Emergency Action, Agency, Advocacy, Fixed Fee Interview and Legal Aid Franchise
Ptr: Root, Mr Stephen M BA(Law). . . . . *Dec 1985
Dir: Berwin, Mr Paul David BA; MA . . . . *Oct 1982
Blake, Mrs Susan K LLB . . . . *Nov 1990
Jewers, Mrs Julie . . . . Jul 2007
Peace, Ms Carolynn J MA; BA . . . . *Jul 1991
Robinson, Miss Rachel BSc(Hons) . . . . *Jan 1998
Saunders, Mrs Natalie MA . . . . Sep 2000
Smith, Sarah . . . . Sep 1996
Asoc: Barton, Miss Sophie LLB(Hons). . . . . *Jan 2001
Myerson, Ms Deborah S LLB . . . . *Oct 1993
Ast: Acton, Miss Caroline BA . . . . Apr 2009
Armer, Ms Claire . . . . Sep 2002
Farrell, Emma. Feb 2010
Harvey, Mr Robert. . . . . Oct 2009
Marland, Mr Gareth Andre. . . . . Jul 2007
Walsh, Marie LLB(Hons) . . . . Sep 2001
Con: Barrett, Mr John BSc . . . . *Jun 1975

BYWATERS TOPHAM PHILLIPS LLP ‡
17 Hornbeam Square South Hornbeam Business Park Harrogate North Yorkshire HG2 8NB
Tel: 01423 879556 *Fax:* 01423 874142 *Dx:* 11961 HARROGATE 1
E-mail: info@btp-law.co.uk
List of partners: S Arundel, B M Mawer, S G Petty, L E Tuck
Work: A1 E L S1 S2 T1 T2 W
Ptr: Mawer, Beverley Mary. . . . . NSP
Mem: Arundel, Miss Sara-Jane LLB . . . . *§Aug 2002
Petty, Mr Stephen G BA. . . . . *§Mar 1978
Tuck, Mrs Leslie Emilie . . . . *Apr 2005
Ast: Mills, Mrs Angela M LLB . . . . *§Jun 1977
Nelson, Miss Marie Notary Public . . . . *§Aug 1998

CAWTHRON KELBRICK LANE & CO ‡
14 Victoria Avenue Harrogate North Yorkshire HG1 1ED
Tel: 01423 561661 *Fax:* 01423 531025

DAVIDSON BROADBENT & CO ‡
5 Raglan Street Harrogate North Yorkshire HG1 1LE
Tel: 01423 561229 *Fax:* 01423 530984 *Dx:* 11980 HARROGATE
List of partners: M M Davidson, R K Ellis
Office: Leeds
Work: S1 S2 W
Ptr: Davidson, Mr Michael M LLB(Lond) . . . . *Jun 1977

DAVIDSON LARGE LLP ‡
Royal House 110 Station Parade Harrogate North Yorkshire HG1 1EP
Tel: 01423 727272 *Fax:* 01423 727200 *Dx:* 25520 HARROGATE
E-mail: info@davidsonlarge.com
List of partners: R M Davidson
Office: Billingham
Work: A1 A3 B1 B2 C1 C2 E F1 J1 J2 L N O P Q R1 R2 S1 S2 U1 U2 Z(b,e,k,l,q,r,s,w,z,za)
Agency, Advocacy and Fixed Fee Interview undertaken
Ptr: Davidson, Mr Russell M MA Harmsworth Exhibitioner . *Oct 1984
Ast: Fozard, Ms Rebekah MA(Hons)(Cantab) . . . . Sep 2003
Con: Bond, Ms Charlotte Lucy LLB(Hons)(Dunelm); LPC(LMU) Law Society Prize for Outstanding Performance in the LPC 2006 . . . . Sep 2008
Hill, Mr David MA(Hons)(Oxon) . . . . Jan 1978
Walton, Mr David James BA(Hons)(Leeds); CPE(York); LPC(York). . . . . Jul 1996

A M DAVIES ‡
Reynard Crag Reynard Crag Lane High Birstwith Harrogate North Yorkshire HG3 2JQ
Tel: 01423 772860 *Fax:* 01423 772862
E-mail: a.davies@amdavies.co.uk
List of partners: A M Davies
Work: A3 C1 K3 K4 L O Q Z(q)
Ptr: Davies, Mrs Angela Mary LLB. . . . . *Apr 1979

GRAHAME STOWE BATESON
Raglan Chambers 4 Raglan Street Harrogate North Yorkshire HG1 1LT
Tel: 01423 562121 *Fax:* 01423 505669 *Dx:* 11954 HARROGATE
Emergency telephone 07626 214264
E-mail: harrogate@gsbsolicitors.com
Office: Leeds (4 offices)
Work: A1 C1 D1 D2 E F1 J1 K1 L S1 S2 T2 W Z(c)
Emergency Action, Agency, Advocacy and Fixed Fee Interview undertaken
Ptr: Hurwood, Mr Michael Alan LLB; BA; CQSW. . . . . . *Oct 1993
Reed, Mr Richard Selby BA(Law) ★. . . . . *Feb 1985
Thompson, Mr Jonathan S . . . . *§Oct 1964
Ast: Astwood, Miss Meryn . . . . Jan 2003
Crowther, Mr Richard . . . . Jan 2006
Tinning, Mr Andrew Roberts. . . . . Apr 1998

HEMPSONS
The Exchange Station Parade Harrogate North Yorkshire HG1 1TS
Tel: 01423 522331 *Fax:* 01423 724047 *Dx:* 11965 HARROGATE 1
E-mail: enquiries@hempsons.co.uk
Office: London WC2, Manchester, Newcastle upon Tyne
Work: B1 C1 D1 E J1 J2 L N O P Q R1 R2 S2 Z(c,d,e,j,k,m,p,q,r)
Emergency Action, Agency and Advocacy undertaken
Ptr: D'Arcy, Miss Adrienne E LLB(Hons) William Hutton Prize . . . . *Nov 1984
Donaldson, Miss Paulene LLB; Dip PI. . . . . *Oct 1989
Evans, Mr Stephen P LLB. . . . . *Nov 1989
Hartrick, Mr Adam Keith LLB(Hons) . . . . *Oct 1996
Holroyd, Mrs M Louise LLB . . . . *Jan 1980
Hugh-Jones, Mr Charles LLB . . . . Sep 1999
Lazonby, Mr Ian A BVMS . . . . *Sep 1996
Lovel, Mr W John M LLB . . . . *Dec 1974
Parker, Mr Adrian Bruce BA(Dunelm) . . . . *§Dec 1994
Roberts, Mr David LLB . . . . *Oct 1996
Wilson, Mrs Kathleen J LLB. . . . . *Oct 1987
Ast: Burrows, Mr Craig LLB . . . . *Nov 1992
Figon, Mr Henry LLB; MBA . . . . *Jun 1973
Haigh, Mr John S. . . . . *Sep 1980
Hayre, Mr Baljinder LLB. . . . . Feb 2002
Holman, Mr Timothy R F MA(Cantab) . . . . *§Nov 1984
Liley, Miss Susan Jayne LLB . . . . Oct 1995
Lounds, Miss Joy BA(Hons); CPE; LPC. . . . . *Nov 1997
Pearson, Ms Heather J LLB. . . . . *Jan 1994

DOMINIC HIRST LLB ‡
PO Box 697 Harrogate North Yorkshire HG1 9LL
Tel: 01423 701527
E-mail: info@dhirstlaw.com

ANNE JARVIS & CO ‡
19 North Park Road Harrogate North Yorkshire HG1 5PD
Tel: 01423 858582 *Fax:* 01423 858583 *Dx:* 715729 HARROGATE
E-mail: lawyers@annejarvis.co.uk
List of partners: A E Jarvis
Work: D1 D2 K1 K3
Emergency Action, Agency, Advocacy and Fixed Fee Interview undertaken
SPr: Jarvis, Mrs Anne E LLB(Hons) . . . . *Apr 1981
Ast: Whelan, Mrs Francina LLB . . . . *Nov 1995

KIRBYS ‡
32 Victoria Avenue Harrogate North Yorkshire HG1 5PR
Tel: 01423 542000 *Fax:* 01423 542001 *Dx:* 11956 HARROGATE 1
E-mail: mail@kirbyssolicitors.co.uk
List of partners: R J Dooley, A Gray, M G Greenheld, M E Hutchinson, J M Robertshaw, K J Thompson
Work: A1 B1 C1 C2 D1 E F1 J1 K1 L N O P Q S1 T1 T2 W Z(b,c,d,e,k,l,o)
Emergency Action, Agency, Advocacy, Legal Aid undertaken and Member of Accident Line
Ptr: Dooley, Mr Roger J LLB. . . . . *§Jul 1987
Gray, Miss Alison LLB(Hons) . . . . Oct 1995
Greenheld, Miss M Georgina LLB(Exon). . . . . *Jun 1981
Hutchinson, Mr Mark E MA(Oxon). . . . . *Oct 1987
Robertshaw, Mr Jonathan Marcus LLB(Hons) . . . . *Sep 1993
Thompson, Miss Karen J MA; BA(Hons). . . . . Nov 1999
Ast: Balmforth, Mrs Elizabeth BA(Hons) . . . . Nov 1996
Bi, Shakeela . . . . Jan 2003
Chapman, Mr Ellis . . . . Jan 2002

JAMES LOVE & CO SOLICITORS LIMITED ‡
One Sceptre House Hornbeam Square North Harrogate North Yorkshire HG2 8PB
Tel: 0845 621 8000

MCCORMICKS ‡
Wharfedale House 37 East Parade Harrogate North Yorkshire HG1 5LQ
Tel: 01423 530630 *Fax:* 01423 530709 *Dx:* 11974 HARROGATE 1
Emergency telephone 07785 747567
E-mail: enquiries@mccormicks-solicitors.com
List of partners: N J Goodrum, P D G McCormick, G A Rogers
Languages: French, Spanish
Work: A1 A2 A3 B1 B2 C1 C2 C3 D1 D2 E F1 F2 G H I J1 J2 K1 K2 L M1 M2 M3 N O P Q R1 R2 S1 S2 T1 T2 U1 U2 W X Z(b,c,d,e,f,j,k,l,m,p,q,t,w,x,y,z)
Emergency Action, Agency, Advocacy, Fixed Fee Interview, Legal Aid undertaken, Legal Aid Franchise and Member of Accident Line
Ptr: Goodrum, Mr Neil J BA; FCI ●. . . . . *Oct 1981
McCormick, Mr Peter D G OBE LLB ★ . . . . *Dec 1976
Rogers, Mr Geoffrey A LLB . . . . *Oct 1985
Asoc: Anysz, Miss Lauren Katie MA(Hons)(Cantab) . . . . *Sep 2000
Arundel, Mr David John LLB. . . . . *Oct 1992
Baker, Mrs Philippa J LLB. . . . . *Nov 1991
Burns, Mr Mark Richard LLB . . . . *Sep 1990
Garfield, Mrs Rachael Francesca BA . . . . *Sep 2000
Greaves, Mr Paul Nicholas FILEx; LPC . . . . *Aug 1998
Hugill, Miss Lucie-Jane Pineau LLB . . . . *Jun 2002
Hutton, Mr C N Roger LLB; BA(Hons). . . . . *Dec 1991
Lawrence, Mr Clive Sydney MA(Cantab) . . . . *Nov 1993
Mackie, Mr John BA; MA(Oxon). . . . . Jan 2001
Marshall, Miss Sarah E BSc. . . . . *May 2000
Millmore, Mr Ryan Gregory LLB. . . . . *Sep 1999
Milner, Miss Joanne Elizabeth LLB . . . . *Sep 2002
Milner, Mr Steven James BA; MA . . . . *Sep 1999
Moran, Mr Richard John BA(Hons); LLB. . . . . *Aug 1996
Newman, Miss Victoria Alice BA(Hons) . . . . *Apr 2003
Proctor, Mr Stephen Thomas LLB. . . . . *Nov 1993
Rode, Mr Robert Charles LLB(Hons) ★ . . . . Oct 1994
Rogers, Mrs Sara BA(Hons)(Law). . . . . *Apr 1976
Sadler, Mrs Deborah Elizabeth LLB . . . . *Jul 2002
Spencer Robb, Mrs Rachel . . . . Nov 2002
Young, Mr Simon LLB. . . . . *Nov 1994
Ast: Harrison, Mrs Lynsey LLB(Hons) . . . . *Sep 2001

MAKIN DIXON SOLICITORS
Westminster House 23 Victoria Avenue Harrogate North Yorkshire HG1 5RD
Tel: 01423 500035 *Fax:* 01423 509172 *Dx:* 11973 HARROGATE
E-mail: enquiries@makindixon.co.uk
Office: Bradford, Halifax, Keighley, Skipton, Todmorden
Asoc: Boulongne, Isla . . . . Sep 2005

NICHOLLS & CO ‡
96 Station Parade Harrogate North Yorkshire HG1 1HQ
Tel: 01423 530103 *Fax:* 01423 525045 *Dx:* 11985 HARROGATE 1
E-mail: lucy@nichollssolicitors.co.uk
List of partners: G J M Nicholls
Work: E Q S1 W
Ptr: Nicholls, Mr Gavin J M . . . . Aug 1976

RODNEY W NOON & CO SOLICITORS ‡
Raglan House Raglan Street Harrogate North Yorkshire HG1 1LE
Tel: 01423 564555 *Fax:* 01423 564755

PEMBERTON REID ‡
Hammerain House Hookstone Avenue Harrogate North Yorkshire HG2 8ER
Tel: 01423 87308 *Fax:* 01423 873999
E-mail: katie.reid@pembertonreid.com

POWELL EDDISON FREEMAN & WILKS ‡
14 Albert Street Harrogate North Yorkshire HG1 1JW
Tel: 01423 564551 *Fax:* 01423 522775 *Dx:* 11958 HARROGATE
E-mail: info@powell-eddison.co.uk
List of partners: M B Plumbley, M P Slimming, T R Sutcliffe
Work: A1 A2 A3 B1 C1 C2 E F1 F2 J1 K1 K3 K4 L N O P Q R2 S1 S2 T1 T2 W X Z(c,d,l,p,q,r,u,y)
Emergency Action, Agency, Advocacy and Fixed Fee Interview undertaken
Ptr: Plumbley, Mr Michael B LLB. . . . . *Jun 1974
Slimming, Mr Michael P BA(Law) . . . . *Oct 1982
Sutcliffe, Mr Timothy Rufus . . . . *Dec 2004
Asoc: Beddow, Ms Helena MA; PhD. . . . . *Nov 1994

RAWORTHS LLP ‡
Eton House 89 Station Parade Harrogate North Yorkshire HG1 1HF
Tel: 01423 566666 *Fax:* 01423 504572 *Dx:* 11960 HARROGATE
List of partners: N T Adamson, C T Ardren, D Boylan, C J Butterworth, J M Dale, S K Hinds, J S Hutchinson, S Morris, J Mortimer, Z R Robinson, E M Sheldon, I Shuttleworth, J L Thirsk
Languages: Albanian, French, German, Italian, Spanish
Work: A1 A3 B1 C1 C2 C3 D1 D2 E F1 I J1 J2 K1 K2 K3 L O P Q R1 R2 S1 S2 T1 T2 U2 V W Z(b,c,d,e,j,k,l,m,p,q)
Emergency Action, Agency, Advocacy and Fixed Fee Interview undertaken
Ptr: Adamson, Mr Neil Thaines LLB . . . . *Aug 1972
Ardren, Mrs Carmelita Theresa LLB(Hons) . . . . . . *§Oct 1997
Boylan, Miss Deborah LLB . . . . *§May 2000
Butterworth, Mr Christopher J FCIArb; CEDR Accredited Mediator . . . . *§Jul 1971
Dale, Miss Janice M LLB . . . . *§Oct 1982
Hutchinson, Mr John Stephen LLB . . . . *Nov 1973
Morris, Mr Simon BA(Hons). . . . . *§Sep 1999
Mortimer, Mr Jonathan LLB(Hons). . . . . Oct 1993
Robinson, Mrs Zoe R LLB. . . . . *Nov 1985
Sheldon, Mr E Michael BA(Hons) . . . . *§Nov 1987
Shuttleworth, Mr Ian. . . . . *§Dec 1990
Thirsk, Mrs Joanna Louise BSc . . . . §Nov 1997
Hinds, Mrs Selena Kate FILEx . . . . NSP
Ast: Butt, Mrs Ruth BA(Hons)(History & Politics); GDL; LPC . . . . §Dec 2007
Coupe, Mrs Joanne LLB(Hons) . . . . *§Oct 1990
Gilroy-Thomas, Mrs Maureen BA; LLB; TEP. . . . . . . Jan 1992
Hill, Mr Matthew James LLB(Hons) . . . . *§Aug 2005
Lawson, Mr Andrew John LLB(Hons) . . . . Oct 1985
Mannakee, Mrs Madeline LLB(Hons) . . . . *§Nov 2006
Maybury, Miss Kate Elizabeth LLB(Hons) . . . . Mar 2005
Minors, Mrs Sarah Helen LLB(Hons) . . . . *§Nov 2003
Pennington, Miss Stephanie Jane LLB(Hons) . . . . . Nov 2006
Scanlan, Ms Fionula LLB(Hons). . . . . §Jul 2003
Togher, Mrs Sally Katharine LLB . . . . *§Sep 2000
Whitaker, Miss Elizabeth LLB . . . . §Oct 2001

RESOLUTE SOLICITORS ‡
Unit 4 Castle Hill Close Harrogate North Yorkshire HG2 9JH
Tel: 01423 526444 *Fax:* 01423 301081
E-mail: info@resolutelaw.co.uk

SPENCER EWIN MULVIHILL ‡
179 Kings Road Harrogate North Yorkshire HG1 5JQ
Tel: 01423 509826 *Fax:* 01423 531221 *Dx:* 11971 HARROGATE 1
E-mail: reception@semlaw.co.uk
List of partners: N J Ewin, S A Hoath, E R Mulvihill, S J Ramsbottom
Work: E S1 S2 W Z(l)
Ptr: Ewin, Mrs Nicola J LLB(Leeds) . . . . *Jun 1985
Hoath, Mr Sean Andrew LLB . . . . *Sep 1992
Mulvihill, Mr E Rory LLB(Manc) . . . . *Apr 1981
Ramsbottom, Mr Stephen J LLB(Lond) . . . . *May 1981

See p112 for the Key to Work Categories & other symbols

STOWE FAMILY LAW LLP ‡
Old Court House Raglan Street Harrogate North Yorkshire HG1 1LT
Tel: 01423 532600 *Fax:* 01423 532601
E-mail: chiefexecutive@stowefamilylaw.co.uk

TAYLOR FAWCETT ‡
7 Princes Square Harrogate North Yorkshire HG1 1ND
Tel: 01423 538111 *Fax:* 01423 536678 *Dx:* 720350 HARROGATE
E-mail: mail@taylorfawcett.co.uk
List of partners: J A Fawcett, S E Taylor
Work: D1 D2 K1 K3 K4 S1 W
Emergency Action, Agency, Advocacy, Fixed Fee Interview and Legal Aid undertaken
Ptr: Fawcett, Mrs Julie Ann . . . . Mar 1997
Taylor, Mrs Sarah E. . . . . Oct 1986
Ast: Rudland, Mrs Norma Jane LLB(Hons) Edward Bramley Prize 1973 . . . . *Nov 1979

HARROW, Middlesex

AB LAW ‡
PO Box 645 Harrow Middlesex HA2 2EN
Tel: 020 8426 5613 *Fax:* 020 8426 5613
E-mail: legal.info@ab-law.co.uk
List of partners: A R Bhagwandeen
Languages: Hindi
Work: C1 E J1 O Q
Agency and Fixed Fee Interview undertaken
SPr: Bhagwandeen, Ms Angena Ragini BA(Law); LLB(Hons) . . . . *Feb 1988

ALD LEGAL LIMITED ‡
2 Peterborough Road Harrow Middlesex HA1 2BQ
Tel: 020 8869 0422 *Fax:* 020 8869 0447 *Dx:* 4230 HARROW
E-mail: reception@ald-legal.co.uk

ALANROSS SOLICITORS ‡
41 Joel Street Harrow Middlesex HA6 1NZ
Tel: 01923 848200 *Fax:* 01923 845320 *Dx:* 35501 NORTHWOOD
E-mail: partners@alanross.co.uk
Languages: Gujarati, Hindi
Work: C1 E F1 J1 L O Q R1 S1 W Z(l)

ALEXANDER SOLICITORS ‡
166 Greenford Road Harrow Middlesex HA1 3QS
Tel: 020 8426 9060 *Fax:* 020 8426 9260 *Dx:* 43255 SUDBURY HILL
E-mail: legal@alexandersolicitors.co.uk

ALLIANCE SOLICITORS ‡
595 Kenton Road Harrow Middlesex HA3 9RT
Tel: 020 8206 3530 *Fax:* 020 8204 4972 *Dx:* 47516 KENTON
E-mail: pp@alliance-solicitors.com

ANDERSON ROSS SOLICITORS ‡
79 College Road Harrow Middlesex HA1 1BD
Tel: 020 3170 6030 *Fax:* 020 3170 6031 *Dx:* 4215 HARROW
Emergency telephone 020 3170 6030
E-mail: info@andersonrosssolicitors.com
Languages: Creole, Gujarati, Hindi, Punjabi, Urdu
Work: Z(i)

J ANDREWS ‡
83a Vaughan Road Harrow Middlesex HA1 4EF
Tel: 020 8422 9814

ANTARES LEGAL LLP ‡
Suite 557 State House 176 Station Road Harrow Middlesex HA1 2AE
Tel: 020 8621 5313
E-mail: contact@antareslegal.com

ASHBOURNES SOLICITORS ‡
Fifth Floor Suite C Queens House Harrow Middlesex HA1 1US
Tel: 020 8863 6966 *Fax:* 020 8863 6988

ASTON BROOKE SOLICITORS ‡
2 Gayton Road Harrow Middlesex HA1 2XU
Tel: 020 8901 7901 *Fax:* 020 8901 4115
E-mail: info@astonbrooke.co.uk

AUSTIN & BERNS SOLICITORS ‡
Talbot House 204-206 Imperial Drive Harrow Middlesex HA2 7HH
Tel: 020 8429 5937 *Fax:* 020 8429 5296
E-mail: austin.erhabor@hotmail.co.uk

BEEMANS SOLICITORS ‡
2 Gayton Road Harrow Middlesex HA1 2XU
Tel: 020 8901 7565

HAROLD BENJAMIN ‡
Hill House 67-71 Lowlands Road Harrow Middlesex HA1 3EQ
Tel: 020 8422 5678 *Fax:* 020 8864 0322 *Dx:* 4243 HARROW
E-mail: enquiries@haroldbenjamin.com
List of partners: C W A Batty, K R T Boddy, J Dorman, P Dutch, K C Flavell, R A Lane, D R Onnie, R Oshry, K S Paul, C J Snodin, M P Vincent
Work: C1 C2 E G J1 K1 K3 L N O P Q R1 R2 S1 S2 T1 W Z(c,e,f,l,q)
Legal Aid Franchise
Ptr: Batty, Mr Christopher W A LLB . . . . *Oct 1978
Boddy, Mr Keith R T LLB . . . . *Mar 1984
Dorman, Mr Jonathan LLB; LLM. . . . . *Nov 1983
Dutch, Mr Paul . . . . Jan 1987
Flavell, Mr Keith C BA Chairman of the Melton & Belvoir Duty Solicitor Committee . . . . *Jan 1983
Lane, Mr Roger A MA(Cantab) . . . . *Oct 1964
Onnie, Mr David R BSc(Econ); LLB(Hons). . . . . Dec 1996
Oshry, Mr Raymond BA. . . . . Oct 1985
Paul, Ms Kathrine S MA(Oxon) . . . . *Apr 1980
Snodin, Mr Christopher J . . . . Nov 1988
Vincent, Ms Marina P LLB. . . . . *Dec 1987
Con: Tomkins, Mr Gerald R A. . . . . *Jul 1962
Wilner, Miss Lindsay E BA . . . . *Jun 1977

BLASER MILLS
12 College Road Harrow Middlesex HA1 1JF
Tel: 020 8427 6262 *Fax:* 020 8427 0116 *Dx:* 4214 HARROW 1
Office: Amersham, Aylesbury, Chesham, High Wycombe, Rickmansworth, Staines
Work: D1 E K1 L N Q R1 S1 S2 Z(l)
Agency, Advocacy, Fixed Fee Interview, Legal Aid undertaken, Legal Aid Franchise and Member of Accident Line
Ptr: Herman, Miss Denise E LLB ♦ . . . . *Oct 1987
Kirk, Miss Alexandra . . . . *Sep 2005
Manek, Mrs Sangita LLB(Hons). . . . . Sep 1997
Tollinton, Mr Desmond A BA; BPhil . . . . *Oct 1984
Asoc: Jamal, Miss Tanya . . . . *Apr 2001
Nash, Miss Emma. Sep 2008
Con: Moore, Mr Laurence LLB . . . . *Mar 1970

BLATCHFORDS ‡
192 Northolt Road South Harrow Harrow Middlesex HA2 0EN
Tel: 020 8422 1181 *Fax:* 020 8864 7686
Dx: 37603 SOUTH HARROW
List of partners: A C Samuels
Agency undertaken and Member of Accident Line
Ptr: Samuels, Mr Alan Craig LLB(Hons) . . . . *Sep 1994
Con: Bogard, Mr Harvey P . . . . Oct 1959

BONNINGTONS SOLICITORS ‡
276 Preston Road Harrow Middlesex HA3 0QA
Tel: 020 8908 6363 *Fax:* 020 8908 6363
E-mail: info@bonningtonssolicitors.com

BROOKLYN SOLICITORS ‡
Miller House Rosslyn Crescent Harrow Middlesex HA1 2RZ
Tel: 020 8861 4004

BURROWS ‡
298-300 Preston Road Harrow Middlesex HA3 0QB
Tel: 020 8904 7725 / 8904 4150 *Fax:* 020 8908 3620
Dx: 97125 WEMBLEY PRESTON ROAD
List of partners: J M Bartlett, R M Heath-Brown
Work: E J1 K1 K2 K3 K4 L O Q S1 S2 W
Ptr: Bartlett, Miss Janice M BA(Hons) . . . . *Dec 1983
Heath-Brown, Mr Richard M LLB . . . . *Nov 1973
Particular areas of work include: Commercial Property, Employment Law, Family Law, Residential Conveyancing, Wills and Probate.

CS LAW ‡
KBC Harrow Exchange 2 Gayton Road Harrow Middlesex HA1 2XU
Tel: 020 8901 4089 *Fax:* 020 8901 4067

CAMERONS JONES ‡
200 Northolt Road South Harrow Harrow Middlesex HA2 0EN
Tel: 020 8423 6666 *Fax:* 020 8423 8617
Dx: 37611 SOUTH HARROW
Emergency telephone 020 8427 8000
E-mail: admin@cameronsjones.co.uk
List of partners: D R J Jones, I H Lloyd, G R Wheeler
Languages: Gujarati
Work: C1 E F1 J1 K1 L N O Q S1 S2 T1 W
Emergency Action, Advocacy, Fixed Fee Interview, Legal Aid undertaken and Legal Aid Franchise
Ptr: Jones, Mr Derek R J LLB . . . . *Jun 1974
Lloyd, Mr Ian H LLB; AKC. . . . . *Jun 1977
Wheeler, Mr Gordon R LLB . . . . *Nov 1976
Ast: Barot, Mrs Seema LLB . . . . Nov 2006
Brinicombe, Ms Hazel Jan LLB . . . . *Oct 1998
Caruthers-Little, Mr Peter G LLB(Bris). . . . . *Jun 1971

CAPLANS ‡
12 Peterborough Road Harrow Middlesex HA1 2Bq
Tel: 020 8864 0111 *Fax:* 020 8864 4514 *Dx:* 4201 HARROW 1
Emergency telephone 07956 639659
E-mail: natalie@caplans.net
List of partners: L Barker, R Caplan
Languages: French, German, Hungarian
Work: C1 C2 C3 D1 E F1 G H J1 K1 L N O Q S1 V W Z(e,f,l)
Emergency Action, Agency, Advocacy, Fixed Fee Interview, Legal Aid undertaken and Legal Aid Franchise
Ptr: Barker, Ms Linda . . . . Nov 1993
Caplan, Mr Richard LLB(B'ham). . . . . *Apr 1977
Con: Shelton, Mr Michael H MCIArb Deputy District Judge . *Jan 1976

ALEXANDER CHRISTIAN ‡
2 Imperial Drive Harrow Middlesex HA2 7LF
Tel: 020 8863 7800

CONWAY & CO ‡
109 High Street Wealdstone Harrow Middlesex HA3 5DL
Tel: 020 8863 0535 *Fax:* 020 8427 0349 *Dx:* 80401 WEALDSTONE
List of partners: A D Barnett, R Hermon, M Slater
Office: Greenford
Languages: Hebrew, Hindi, Urdu
Work: B1 C1 D1 E F1 K1 K3 N O P Q S1 S2 V W Z(i)
Legal Aid Franchise
Ptr: Barnett, Mr Alan David LLB . . . . *Dec 1976
Hermon, Mr Ronnie LLB(Hons) . . . . Dec 1997
Slater, Mrs Margaret BA. . . . . Sep 1998
Ast: Balakrishnan, Mrs Suvendrini . . . . Sep 1988
Con: Segall, Mr Edwin R LLB(Hons) . . . . Dec 1972

PATRICK J CUSACK & CO ‡
66 Station Road Harrow Middlesex HA1 2SQ
Tel: 020 8863 3414 *Fax:* 020 8424 0393 *Dx:* 30453 HARROW 3
E-mail: patrickjcusackco@btopenworld.com
List of partners: D Badiani, P J Cusack
Languages: French, German
Work: B1 C1 E G H J1 L N Q R1 S1 W Z(k,l,m,t)
Emergency Action, Agency, Advocacy, Legal Aid undertaken and Legal Aid Franchise
Ptr: Badiani, Mrs Dilpa LLB . . . . *Nov 2002
Cusack, Mr Patrick Joseph MA ● . . . . *Dec 1966
Con: Lynch, Mr William McTerence . . . . *Oct 1962

DECCAN PRIME SOLICITORS ‡
79 College Road Harrow Middlesex HA1 1BD
Tel: 020 3008 6769 *Fax:* 020 3008 6770
E-mail: mail@deccanprime.com

EVERATT'S ‡
6 Churchill Court 58 Station Road Harrow Middlesex HA2 7SA
Tel: 020 8424 0088 *Fax:* 020 8424 0454
E-mail: mail@everatts.co.uk
List of partners: S N Shah
Languages: Gujarati, Kiswahili
Work: B1 B2 C1 C2 E F1 F2 J1 K1 K3 L N O Q S1 S2 W Z(e,i,k,l,p,q,r,y)
Agency and Advocacy undertaken
Ptr: Shah, Shilan N LLB ♦. . . . . *Nov 1983
Ast: Bhatti, Ms Sangeet Kaur LLB(Hons). . . . . *Sep 2007
Shah, Mrs Binal LLB(Hons) . . . . *Apr 2010

P K P FRENCH ‡
Queens House Kymberly Road Harrow Middlesex HA1 1US
Tel: 020 8861 8832 *Fax:* 020 8861 8823 *Dx:* 4297 HARROW 4
Emergency telephone 07973 516535
E-mail: info@pkpfrench.com
List of partners: J Patel, P K Patel, P Patel
Languages: Gujarati, Hindi
Work: B1 C1 D1 E F1 G H J1 K1 N O Q S1 V W Z(e,i,l)
Emergency Action, Agency, Advocacy, Fixed Fee Interview and Legal Aid Franchise
Ptr: Patel, Jaushree LLB. . . . . Sep 2001
Patel, Priti LLB . . . . Dec 1991
Patel, Pankaj K LLB. . . . . *May 1986
Ast: Sanghavi, Ms Nita BA(Hons) . . . . Jul 2006

GANDHI & CO SOLICITORS ‡ (incorporating PGH Solicitors LLP)
181a Kenton Road Harrow Middlesex HA3 0EY
Tel: 020 8909 0800 *Fax:* 020 8909 0802
E-mail: paresh@pgasolicitors.co.uk

GATTAS DENFIELD SOLICITORS
207 Streatfield Road Harrow Middlesex HA3 9DA
Tel: 020 8204 9290 *Fax:* 020 8204 9292 *Dx:* 42802 KINGSBURY
Office: London NW9

GOODWINS FAMILY LAW SOLICITORS ‡
5 Warner House Harrovian Business Village Bessborough Road Harrow Middlesex HA1 3EX
Tel: 020 8423 3525 *Fax:* 020 8423 7383 *Dx:* 4235 HARROW 1
E-mail: nicholas.goodwin@goodwinsfamilylaw.co.uk
List of partners: R Barda, N J Goodwin
Work: K1
Emergency Action, Agency and Advocacy undertaken
Ptr: Barda, Mr Raymond. . . . . Jan 1987
Goodwin, Mr Nicholas J BA . . . . *Aug 1982

HANSON YOUNG AND CO LTD ‡
Temple House 221-225 Station Road Harrow Middlesex HA1 2TH
Tel: 020 8861 8374 *Fax:* 020 8861 8358
E-mail: info@hansonyoung.co.uk

HARROW LAW PRACTICE ‡
101 Kenton Road Harrow Middlesex HA3 0AN
Tel: 020 8909 0202 *Fax:* 020 8909 0203 *Dx:* 47520 KENTON
E-mail: enq@harrow-law.com
Work: A1 E L O Q R2 S1 S2 W Z(l)

A V HAWKINS & CO ‡
161a Greenford Road Harrow Middlesex HA1 3RA
Tel: 020 8422 2364 / 8422 2466 *Fax:* 020 8423 6454
Dx: 43251 SUDBURY HILL
List of partners: D B Parkhouse
Work: E L S1 W
SPr: Parkhouse, Mr David B LLB(Leeds) . . . . *Apr 1977

HESELTONS SOLICITORS ‡
62 Hesta Building 58-62 High Street Harrow Middlesex HA1 3LL
Tel: 020 8864 6171

T VINCENT HOWELLS & CO ‡
60 Station Road North Harrow Harrow Middlesex HA2 7SL
Tel: 020 8863 6655 *Fax:* 020 8427 9789
Dx: 83901 NORTH HARROW
List of partners: A D Ward
Work: C1 E F1 J1 L S1 W
Ptr: Ward, Mr Adrian D BA . . . . *Nov 1976

INAYAT SOLICITORS ‡
79 College Road Harrow Middlesex HA1 1BD
Tel: 020 3178 2450 *Fax:* 020 3178 4475
E-mail: info@inayatsolicitors.com

IRELAND ABRAHAMS ‡
23 High Street Harrow Middlesex HA1 3HT
Tel: 020 8864 5557 *Fax:* 020 8864 5558 *Dx:* 4203 HARROW 1

IRVINGS ‡
Scottish Provident House 76/80 College Road Harrow Middlesex HA1 1BQ
Tel: 020 8427 6600 *Fax:* 020 8427 4225 *Dx:* 4241 HARROW
E-mail: jayshree@irvings.co.uk
List of partners: J Radia, U M Radia
Languages: Gujarati, Hindi
Work: B1 C1 C2 E J1 K1 L M2 O Q R2 S1 S2 W Z(b,c,i,l,o)
Emergency Action, Agency and Advocacy undertaken
Ptr: Radia, Mrs Jayshree LLB . . . . *Dec 1989
Radia, Uday M LLB . . . . *Dec 1987

JOHAL & CO ‡
5-7 Northolt Road South Harrow Harrow Middlesex HA2 0HL
Tel: 020 8422 1221 *Dx:* 37600 SOUTH HARROW

JUMA LAW PRACTICE ‡
4th Floor Scottish Provident House 76-80 College Road Harrow Middlesex HA1 1BQ
Tel: 020 8861 1199 *Fax:* 020 8424 9625 *Dx:* 4205 HARROW
E-mail: jumalawpractice@btconnect.com
List of partners: H Juma
Languages: Gujarati
SPr: Juma, Mr Hussein BSc . . . . Jan 1983

KSL SOLICITORS ‡
702a Kenton Road Harrow Middlesex HA3 9QP
Tel: 020 8206 2666

J E KENNEDY & CO ‡
59-61 High Street Harrow-on-the-Hill Harrow Middlesex HA1 3HT
Tel: 020 8864 3056 *Fax:* 020 8864 4900
List of partners: J E Kennedy
Work: B1 E P Q S1 S2 W
Ptr: Kennedy, Mr Joseph E . . . . *Nov 1973

KINGS SOLICITORS ‡
KBC Harrow Exchange 2 Gayton Road Harrow Middlesex HA1 2XU
Tel: 020 8901 7585 *Fax:* 020 8338 3022

KINGSLEY KNIGHT ‡
PO Box 927 Harrow Middlesex HA3 3GX
Tel: 020 8931 3441 *Fax:* 020 8931 3441
E-mail: info@kingsleyknight.co.uk

L R P SOLICITORS ‡
17 Manor Way Harrow Middlesex HA2 6BZ
Tel: 020 8581 1292 *Fax:* 020 8904 7790
E-mail: info@lrpsolicitors.co.uk

THE LAW PARTNERSHIP ‡
The Poet's Corner 74-76 Station Road Harrow Middlesex HA1 2SQ
Tel: 020 8416 7004 *Fax:* 020 8416 7005 *Dx:* 30454 HARROW 3
List of partners: M R Patel, G Vagjiani
Languages: Gujarati, Urdu
Work: B1 C1 D1 D2 F1 J1 K1 L N O Q W Z(b,q)
Emergency Action and Legal Aid undertaken
Ptr: Patel, Mr Mineshkumar R LLB. . . . . Jan 1992
Vagjiani, Ms Gita LLB(Hons) . . . . . May 1998

DUNCAN LEWIS & CO
Spencer House 29 Grove Hill Road Harrow Middlesex HA1 3BN
Tel: 020 7923 4020 *Fax:* 020 7923 3320
E-mail: admin@duncanlewis.com
Office: London E8, London SE14, London SW17, London W12, Romford

LIGHTHOUSE SOLICITORS ‡
79 College Road Harrow Middlesex HA1 1BD
Tel: 020 3170 7588 / 3170 7589 *Fax:* 020 8181 6959
E-mail: fz@lhlegal.co.uk
List of partners: R Mirza, F Zuberi
Work: Z(i)
Ptr: Mirza, Mr Rizwan . . . . . Aug 1999
Zuberi, Mr Fawzi BA(Econ) . . . . . Dec 1996

JANE LILES SOLICITORS ‡
96 Dorchester Way Kenton Harrow Middlesex HA3 9RB
Tel: 020 8248 0301 *Fax:* 020 8204 6730
E-mail: jane@janelileslaw.com

LYNCH HALL & HORNBY ‡
(incorporating Swatton Hughes & Co; Bird & Kelly)
Hornby House 23 Peterborough Road Harrow Middlesex HA1 2BD
Tel: 020 8864 0722 *Fax:* 020 8423 4503 *Dx:* 4210 HARROW
E-mail: peter.lever@lynch-hall.co.uk
List of partners: J R Gough, R W J Hornby, S F Hornby, N T Kelly, F P Lever, H C Smith
Work: B1 C1 E F1 F2 H J1 K1 L M1 N O P Q R1 S1 S2 T1 W Z(e,j,k,l,q,r)
Emergency Action, Agency and Fixed Fee Interview undertaken
Ptr: Gough, Mr John R LLB . . . . . Jul 1971
Hornby, Mr Richard W J. . . . . May 1983
Hornby, Ms Suzi F. . . . . Nov 1991
Kelly, Mr Nigel T. . . . . Jul 1976
Lever, Mr F Peter . . . . . Oct 1962
Smith, Mr Howard C . . . . . Jan 1990

M A MAKINDE SOLICITOR ‡
101 Elgin Avenue Kenton Harrow Middlesex HA3 8QN
Tel: 020 8099 1780

MARKS AND MARKS SOLICITORS ‡
18 Peterborough Road Harrow Middlesex HA1 2BQ
Tel: 020 8426 8000

DOUGLAS MORGAN SOLICITORS ‡
25 Springfield Road Harrow Middlesex HA1 1QF
Tel: 020 8863 3655 *Fax:* 020 8863 3726

MORGANS SOLICITORS ‡
52 Sudbury Court Road Middlesex Harrow Middlesex HA1 3SH
Tel: 020 7912 9390 *Fax:* 020 8904 3069

NICHOLLS CHRISTIE & CROCKER
41 Station Road North Harrow Harrow Middlesex HA2 7SX
Tel: 020 8863 6366 *Fax:* 020 8863 4908
Dx: 83906 NORTH HARROW
Office: Uxbridge
Work: L S1 W
Asoc: Oakley, Mrs Rachel Margaret BA(Hons). . . . . *Oct 1991
Reid, Mr Richard Norman BA . . . . . *Dec 1978
Wood, Mrs Jennifer Mary LLB(Hons) . . . . . *Jan 1989
Con: Christie, Mr Michael John . . . . . *§Mar 1961

PATANI & CO ‡
1st Floor Pacific House 382 Kenton Road Harrow Middlesex HA3 8DP
Tel: 020 8909 0449 *Fax:* 020 8909 0469 *Dx:* 47505 KENTON
Languages: Gujarati

PATTERSON SEBASTIAN & CO ‡
79 College Road Harrow Middlesex HA1 1BD
Tel: 020 3178 5867 *Fax:* 020 3178 5868
E-mail: yvonne@pscosolicitors.co.uk

PHILLIPS & PHILLIPS ‡
220 Northolt Road South Harrow Harrow Middlesex HA2 8DS
Tel: 020 8422 4435 / 8422 8155 *Fax:* 020 8422 1414
Dx: 37606 SOUTH HARROW
List of partners: N Jobanputra, K Keeble, H J Ludlow
Work: C1 E K1 L S1 S2 T1 W
Ptr: Jobanputra, Nilesh BSc. . . . . Apr 1984
Keeble, Mrs Karin. . . . . *Jun 1996
Ludlow, Mr Howard J LLB(Lond) . . . . . *Apr 1976

RADIA & CO ‡
Rosslyn House 34 Railway Approach Harrow Middlesex HA3 5AA
Tel: 020 8424 2261 *Fax:* 020 8424 2095
List of partners: M Radia
Languages: Gujarati
Work: C1 E M1 P S1
Ptr: Radia, Mukesh BA . . . . . *May 1985

RAVI SOLICITORS ‡
457b Alexandra Avenue Rayners Lane Harrow Middlesex HA2 9RY
Tel: 020 8426 1178 *Fax:* 020 7429 3847 *Dx:* 48002 RAYNERS LANE
E-mail: info@ravisolicitors.co.uk

REDFERNS ‡
9 Churchill Court 58 Station Road North Harrow Harrow Middlesex HA2 7SA
Tel: 020 8424 7070 *Fax:* 020 8424 7050
List of partners: A W Randle, S Simmons, D A Tracey
Languages: French
Work: B1 C1 C2 D1 E F1 J1 K1 L M1 N O Q R1 S1 T1 T2 V W Z(c,h,i,j,l,o,p,q)
Emergency Action, Agency, Advocacy, Fixed Fee Interview, Legal Aid undertaken and Member of Accident Line
Ptr: Randle, Mr Antony W BA(Law) . . . . . *Oct 1980
Simmons, Mr Stephen . . . . . *Oct 1980
Tracey, Mr David A BA . . . . . *Oct 1980

C ROBERTS ‡
143 Eastcote Lane Harrow Middlesex HA2 8RW
Tel: 020 8864 9929 *Fax:* 020 8864 9946
Emergency telephone 07836 722905
Work: B2 E F1 F2 G H J1 K1 L M2 N O Q X Z(f,g,i,k,n,t)
Emergency Action undertaken

SC LAW ‡
36a Exeter Road Harrow Middlesex HA2 9PP
Tel: 020 8864 4913 *Fax:* 020 8864 4913

SAMY & CO ‡
29 High Street Wealdstone Harrow Middlesex HA3 5BY
Tel: 020 8861 2424 *Fax:* 020 8861 3939
E-mail: samy-co-solicitors@theseed.net
List of partners: P S Sivakumar
Work: B2 F1 G H J1 K1 L N Q V Z(h,i)
Emergency Action, Advocacy, Fixed Fee Interview, Legal Aid undertaken and Member of Accident Line
SPr: Sivakumar, Periathamby S ● . . . . . *Mar 1994

R R SANGHVI & CO ‡
(incorporating Sthalekar & Co)
Sherwood House 176 Northolt Road Harrow Middlesex HA2 0NP
Tel: 020 8515 0490 *Fax:* 020 8422 4268
Dx: 37604 SOUTH HARROW
E-mail: rohit@pchouse.net
List of partners: R R Sanghvi
Languages: Gujarati, Hindi
Work: C1 E G M1 N P S1 W Z(k)
SPr: Sanghvi, Rohit R LLB . . . . . *Oct 1983
Con: Sthalekar, Mr Rohit LLB(Hons) . . . . . *Nov 1989

J V SAUJANI & CO ‡
2nd Floor Suite 213 Signal House Harrow Middlesex HA1 2AQ
Tel: 020 8861 2606 *Fax:* 020 8863 4534
List of partners: J V Saujani
Languages: Gujarati, Hindi
Work: B1 C1 D1 E J1 K1 K3 K4 L N O Q S1 S2 W Z(b,c,i,l,q,r)
Legal Aid undertaken
SPr: Saujani, Mr Jayantilal Vallabhdas ♦ . . . . . *Nov 1983

SAYERS
242 High Road Harrow Weald Harrow Middlesex HA3 7BB
Tel: 020 8861 4191 *Fax:* 020 8427 3684 *Dx:* 80402 WEALDSTONE
Office: London W3
Work: E F1 G H K1 L N P S1 S2 W Z(l)
Emergency Action and Legal Aid undertaken
Ptr: Langford, Mr Simon LLB . . . . . *Jun 1979

INDRA SEBASTIAN SOLICITORS ‡
144 Station Road Harrow Middlesex HA1 2RH
Tel: 020 8427 3303 *Fax:* 020 8427 3313

SHAN & CO ‡
189 Northolt Road Harrow Middlesex HA2 0LY
Tel: 020 8864 7070 *Fax:* 020 8864 6070
Emergency telephone 07976 439141
List of partners: K Shanmugarajah
Work: F1 H K1 Q V Z(i)
Emergency Action, Fixed Fee Interview and Legal Aid undertaken
Ptr: Shanmugarajah, Mr Kanapathipillai LLB. . . . . *Apr 1991

SHARPE & CO ‡
Sherbourne House 23-25 Northolt Road Harrow Middlesex HA2 0LH
Tel: 020 8422 4555 *Fax:* 020 8426 8933
Dx: 37605 SOUTH HARROW
List of partners: I F Barry, T J P O'Donnell, G N Sharpe
Office: Ashford
Work: C1 E G H K1 L M1 N P
Agency, Advocacy and Legal Aid undertaken
Ptr: Barry, Mr Ivan F LLB(Hons) . . . . . *Nov 1996
Sharpe, G N BA. . . . . *Oct 1985

SHARPE & CO ‡
Brigade House Brigade Close Harrow Middlesex HA2 0LQ
Tel: 020 8423 7323 *Fax:* 020 8423 7616
Dx: 37605 SOUTH HARROW
E-mail: mail@sharpenadco.co.uk

SIDDIQUI & CO ‡
21-23 The Bridge Harrow Middlesex HA3 5AG
Tel: 020 8423 2400 *Fax:* 020 8427 7077
Emergency telephone 020 8863 5295
E-mail: crimelaw@btconnect.com
List of partners: A Burns, F Siddiqui
Languages: Hindi, Italian, Punjabi, Urdu
Work: G H
Emergency Action, Agency, Advocacy, Fixed Fee Interview, Legal Aid undertaken and Legal Aid Franchise
Ptr: Burns, Mrs Andrea BSc(Econ) . . . . . *Nov 1997
Siddiqui, Mrs Farida LLB(Hons) ★. . . . . *Dec 1996

ROGER SIMMONS & CO ‡
103 Kenton Lane Harrow Middlesex HA3 8UJ
Tel: 020 8909 9298 *Fax:* 020 8907 6297 *Dx:* 47515 KENTON
E-mail: rogerslaw@onetel.com

SIMO & CO ‡
91 Church Drive Harrow Middlesex HA2 7NR
Tel: 020 8866 6333

SOMA & CO SOLICITORS ‡
34 Eastcote Lane South Harrow Harrow Middlesex HA2 8DB
Est: 1998
Tel: 020 8423 0203 *Fax:* 020 8423 6465
E-mail: admin@somasolicitors.co.uk
List of partners: C Somasuntharam
Languages: Sinhalese, Tamil
Work: L S1 S2 W Z(i,l)
Agency and Fixed Fee Interview undertaken
SPr: Somasuntharam, Mrs Chandra . . . . . *Oct 1992

STENFIELD SOLICITORS ‡
88-90 High Street Harrow Middlesex HA1 3LP
Tel: 020 8422 2179
E-mail: mahesh@stenfield.com

P M SUCHAK & CO
Imperial Chambers 111 Park Lane Harrow Middlesex HA2 8NN
Tel: 020 8422 7707
Office: Leicester

TANN & TANN SOLICITORS
113b Kenton Road Harrow Middlesex HA3 0AN
Tel: 020 8909 3688 *Fax:* 020 8907 1323
Office: Wembley

TEMPLETONS SOLICITORS ‡
Temple House 221-225 Station Road Harrow Middlesex HA1 2TH
Tel: 020 8861 8310 *Fax:* 020 8732 2950
E-mail: enquire@templetonslaw.com

THAKKER & CO ‡
Second Floor 88-98 College Road Harrow Middlesex HA1 1BQ
Tel: 020 8424 0571 *Fax:* 020 8424 0572 *Dx:* 4248 HARROW 1
E-mail: info@thakkerandco.com
List of partners: V Archer, D Thakker
Languages: Gujarati
Work: D2 F1 K1 L S1 S2 W
Emergency Action, Fixed Fee Interview, Legal Aid undertaken and Legal Aid Franchise
Ptr: Archer, Ms Vivien LLB. . . . . *Oct 1977
Thakker, Mrs Damyanti BA . . . . . *Dec 1978

THAKRAR & CO ‡
1a Central Parade Station Road Harrow Middlesex HA1 2TW
Tel: 020 8427 3480 *Fax:* 020 8424 0573
E-mail: sundip@thakrarlaw.com

THOMPSONS (FORMERLY ROBIN/BRIAN THOMPSON & PARTNERS)
Grove House 55 Lowlands Road Harrow Middlesex HA1 3AP
Tel: 020 8872 8600 *Fax:* 020 8423 3104
Office: Belfast, Birmingham, Bristol, Cardiff, Chelmsford, Dagenham, Derby, Leeds, Liverpool, London SW19, London WC1, Manchester, Middlesbrough, Newcastle upon Tyne, Nottingham, Plymouth, Sheffield, South Shields, Southampton, Stoke-on-Trent, Swansea, Wolverhampton
Ast: Altman, Mr Philip R LLB(Lond) . . . . . *Jan 1957
Richards, Ms Sandra BA . . . . . *May 1999

VAN ARKADIE ‡
Pentax House South Hill Avenue Northolt Road Harrow Middlesex HA2 0DU
Tel: 020 8938 4687 *Fax:* 020 8938 4605
Dx: 37615 SOUTH HARROW
E-mail: info@van-arkadie.co.uk

VROOBEL KAYE ‡
8 Churchill Court 58 Station Road North Harrow Middlesex HA2 7SA
Tel: 020 8427 5006 *Fax:* 020 8427 6617
Dx: 83914 NORTH HARROW
List of partners: R D Vroobel
Ptr: Vroobel, Mr Russell D BA(Law) . . . . . *May 1984

VYMAN SOLICITORS
Vyman House 104 College Road Harrow Middlesex HA1 1BQ
Tel: 020 8427 9080 *Fax:* 020 8427 9050 *DS:* 4242 HARROW
E-mail: admin@vyman.co.uk
Office: Gravesend, Maidstone
Languages: Gujarati, Punjabi
Work: A3 B1 C1 C3 E F1 F2 J1 J2 L N O Q R2 S1 S2 W Z(b,e,i,k,q)
Fixed Fee Interview undertaken
Ptr: Berg, Mr Jeremy Paul LLB(Hons) . . . . . *Mar 1990
Mander, Mr Gurnam Singh LLB(Hons). . . . . Oct 1996
Vyas, Mr Anup LLB(Hons). . . . . *Oct 1993
Ast: Johal, Mrs Mandeep Kaur LLB(Hons) . . . . . *Nov 2005
Con: Pall, Mr Ashok Kumar LLB(Hons) . . . . . Jul 1991

W&J SOLICITORS ‡
York House 353a Station Road Harrow Middlesex HA1 1LN
Tel: 020 8863 8700 *Fax:* 020 8863 8609
E-mail: info@wandjsolicitors.co.uk

WALTER WILSON RICHMOND ‡
360b Station Road Harrow Middlesex HA1 2DE
Tel: 020 8427 8484 *Fax:* 020 8861 3362 *Dx:* 4209 HARROW 1
E-mail: wwr@walterwilson.co.uk
List of partners: V M Manek
Languages: French, Gujarati, Hindi, Punjabi, Urdu
Work: B1 C1 D1 E F1 G H J1 K1 L N O Q S1 S2 W Z(i,l)
Emergency Action, Agency, Advocacy, Fixed Fee Interview and Legal Aid undertaken
SPr: Manek, Vikram M . . . . . *Jul 1979

WHEELER GALVIN & WHEELER ‡
11 Village Way East Rayners Lane Harrow Middlesex HA2 7LX
Tel: 020 8868 7344 *Fax:* 020 8429 8591 *Dx:* 48003 RAYNERS LANE
E-mail: info@wgwsolicitors.co.uk

WHITE & CO ‡
58 Harrow View Harrow Middlesex HA1 1RQ
Tel: 020 8933 6192 *Fax:* 020 8863 9274 *Dx:* 30460 HARROW 3
E-mail: kevin@whiteandco.co.uk

HARTLEPOOL

R BELL & SON ‡
Durham House 32a Victoria Road Hartlepool TS26 8DD
Tel: 01429 273165 *Fax:* 01429 863461 *Dx:* 60657 HARTLEPOOL
E-mail: rbellandson@gmail.com
List of partners: D Brough, T Creed
Office: Peterlee
Work: A1 B1 C1 D1 D2 E K1 K3 K4 L N O Q S1 S2 W
Emergency Action, Agency, Advocacy, Legal Aid undertaken, Legal Aid Franchise and Member of Accident Line
Ptr: Brough, Mrs Diane . . . . . *Dec 1990

See p112 for the Key to Work Categories & other symbols

Creed, Mr Terence BA(Law); LLM. . . . . *Oct 1981
Ast: Waller, Ms Christine. . . . . *Oct 1998

DONNELLY MCARDLE ADAMSON
155 York Road Hartlepool TS26 9EQ
Tel: 01429 274732 *Fax:* 01429 260199 *Dx:* 60666 HARTLEPOOL
Office: Darlington, Peterlee, Stockton-on-Tees, Sunderland (2 offices)
Work: D1 F1 G H J1 K1 N W
Emergency Action, Agency, Advocacy, Fixed Fee Interview, Legal Aid undertaken, Legal Aid Franchise and Member of Accident Line
Ptr: Adamson, Mr Geoffrey ♦ . . . . *Jul 1987
Bennett, Mr Neil BA(Hons) ★ . . . . Aug 1997
Donnelly, Mr Charles W M LLB; HM Coroner ♦ . . . . May 1975
Mitchell, Mr Phillip G BA. . . . . Feb 1989
Morris, Mr Adrian CA LLB ★. . . . . Nov 1989
Relton, Mr John ★. . . . . Nov 1990
Ast: Duncan, Ms Victoria Louise . . . . Oct 1998
Gibson, Mrs Gillian M BA . . . . *Dec 1980
Taylor, Mr Jaxon . . . . Sep 2000
Ward, Caroline . . . . Sep 2006

MSP LEGAL SERVICES LLP ‡
Havelock House 24 Victoria Road Hartlepool TS26 8DD
Tel: 01429 232204 *Fax:* 01429 232236 *Dx:* 60656 HARTLEPOOL
E-mail: enquiries@msplegalservices.co.uk
List of partners: A L Jones, F J Smith, M Smith
Work: C1 E F1 F2 K4 N O Q S1 S2 T2 W Z(d,j,q)
Agency, Advocacy and Fixed Fee Interview undertaken
Ptr: Jones, Mr Andrew L. . . . . *Nov 2000
Smith, Ms Fiona Jane. . . . . *Nov 2000
Smith, Mr Malcolm MA(Oxon). . . . . *§Jun 1973
Asoc: Dixon, Mr Michael LLB . . . . *Jan 1995

TBI SOLICITORS ‡
York Chambers York Road Hartlepool TS26 9DP
Tel: 0800 052 6824 / 01429 264101 *Fax:* 0845 302 2990
Dx: 60650 HARTLEPOOL
Emergency telephone 01429 222772
E-mail: info@tbi.law.co.uk
List of partners: M L Brown, H C Dexter, M H Ellis, J R Ellwood, J B Hall, N A J Hall, S F Horsley, M A Levinson, V J S Moreton, R N Taylor, C J Tilly, J Walters, M J White, D L Whittle, T J Wilsdon, A C Winfield
Office: Barnard Castle, Billingham, Stockton-on-Tees
Work: A1 B1 C1 C2 D1 D2 E F1 G H J1 K1 K2 L M1 N O P Q R1 S1 S2 T2 V W Z(a,b,c,d,e,f,g,h,i,j,k,l,m,n,o,p,r,s,t)
Emergency Action, Agency, Advocacy, Fixed Fee Interview, Legal Aid undertaken, Legal Aid Franchise and Member of Accident Line
Ptr: Brown, Mr Martin Leigh LLB(Newc) William Hutton Prize . . . . *Mar 1978
Ellis, Mr Mark H LLB . . . . *Oct 1988
Ellwood, Mr John R LLB(Newc) . . . . *Nov 1980
Hall, Mr John B LLB. . . . . *§Apr 1976
Hall, Mr Nicholas Adam John . . . . Sep 1997
Horsley, Mr Steven Francis . . . . Sep 1996
Levinson, Mr Martin A LLB(L'pool). . . . . *Jun 1975
Moreton, Ms Victoria Jane Suzanne LLB(Hons) Deputy District Judge. . . . . *Oct 1995
Whittle, Ms Donna Louise. . . . . Oct 2002
Taylor, Mr Robert Neil. . . . . *Sep 1996
Tilly, Ms Carolyn J LLB . . . . *§May 1992
Walters, Mr John LLB. . . . . *Apr 1984
Winfield, Mr Anthony C BA(Newc). . . . . *§Jul 1977
Ast: Barber, Mrs Annalise . . . . Apr 2002
Garnett, Mrs Sara Rebecca . . . . Aug 2002
Howe, Ms Linsey Anne . . . . Nov 2000
Maloney, Ms Kirstey. . . . . Sep 1997

TMJ LEGAL SERVICES LLP ‡
Foster House 99 Raby Road Hartlepool TS24 8DT
Tel: 01429 235616 *Fax:* 01429 862859 *Dx:* 60665 HARTLEPOOL
E-mail: legal@tmjlegal.co.uk
List of partners: K L Claxton, K I Morgan, C J A Turner
Office: Durham, Peterlee, Wingate
Languages: Spanish
Work: C1 D1 D2 E F1 G J1 K1 K3 L N O S1 W
Emergency Action, Agency, Advocacy, Fixed Fee Interview, Legal Aid undertaken, Legal Aid Franchise and Member of Accident Line
Ptr: Claxton, Miss Kate L LLB . . . . *Sep 2005
Morgan, Mr Keith I LLB . . . . *Dec 1984
Turner, Miss Catherine J A BA . . . . *May 1978
Ast: Bell, Miss Lindsay LLB . . . . *Mar 2005
Dunkerley, Miss Clair LLB. . . . . *Nov 2003
Greggs, Mrs Amanda J LLB. . . . . *Nov 2001
Liddle, Mrs Helen BA . . . . *Nov 1994
Ryan, Mrs Lyn Marie LLB . . . . *Feb 1997
Stannard, Mr Christopher LLB. . . . . *Dec 2007

WILSON & CO SOLICITORS ‡
56 Avenue Road Hartlepool TS24 8AT
Tel: 01429 869523 *Fax:* 01429 868796

HARWICH, Essex

WILLIAM H BROWN ‡
276 High Street Dovercourt Harwich Essex CO12 3PD
Tel: 01255 503125

ELLISONS
London House 45 Kingsway Dovercourt Harwich Essex CO12 3JU
Tel: 01255 502428 *Fax:* 01255 504651
Dx: 49503 HARWICH (DOVERCOURT)
E-mail: alan.holden@ellisonssolicitors.com
Office: Clacton-on-Sea, Colchester, Frinton-on-Sea
Work: K1 K2 K3 K4 S1 W
Emergency Action, Agency, Advocacy, Fixed Fee Interview, Legal Aid undertaken, Legal Aid Franchise and Member of Accident Line
Ptr: Holden, Mr Alan C . . . . *Jul 1980

LINN & ASSOCIATES SOLICITORS
Haven House Albermarle Street Harwich Essex CO12 3HL
Tel: 01255 240880 *Fax:* 01255 240990
Dx: 34652 CLACTON-ON-SEA
E-mail: solicitors@linnandassociates.co.uk
Office: Clacton-on-Sea, Gillingham
Work: G H
Emergency Action, Agency, Advocacy, Legal Aid undertaken and Legal Aid Franchise

HASLEMERE, Surrey

BURLEY & GEACH
2 West Street Haslemere Surrey GU27 2AG
Tel: 01428 656011 *Fax:* 01428 656344 *Dx:* 58101 HASLEMERE
E-mail: haslemere@burley-geach.co.uk
Office: Grayshott, Liphook, Petersfield
Languages: French
Work: A1 B1 C1 C2 C3 D1 E F1 G H J1 K1 L M1 M2 N P R1 S1 T1 T2 V W Z(d,m)
Emergency Action, Advocacy, Fixed Fee Interview, Legal Aid undertaken, Legal Aid Franchise and Member of Accident Line
Ptr: Bather, Mr Stephen R LLB(Hull). . . . . *§Jun 1979
Ast: Brocklehurst, Mr David A LLB . . . . *Mar 1979
Chapman, Mrs O Alexandra M LLB(Hons)(Wales); LLB(Cantab) TA Levi Prize; Calcott Pryce Mooting Prize; Heather Meredith Parry Prize; Samuel Evans Prize . . . . *Oct 1981
Cook, Miss Sharon LLB. . . . . *Oct 1993

MARTIN COAKLEY ‡
72 High Street Haslemere Surrey GU27 2LA
Tel: 01428 648888 *Fax:* 01428 648899 *Dx:* 58116 HASLEMERE
E-mail: incoming@martincoakleysolicitors.co.uk
Work: B1 E J1 K4 L O Q S1 S2 W Z(l)

GARDNER THORPE
48 High Street Haslemere Surrey GU27 2LA
Tel: 01428 661151 *Fax:* 01428 645434 *Dx:* 58112 HASLEMERE
E-mail: gardnerthorpe@talk21.com
Office: Haslemere, Petworth
Languages: French
Work: E J1 K1 N O Q S1 S2 W Z(p)
Fixed Fee Interview undertaken
Ptr: Gardner, Mr Paul John FILEx; Dip Com Law(Wales). . *Dec 1992
Thorpe, Mr Steven John Howett BA(Hons) . . . . . . *Dec 1998

ANDREW M HIGGS & CO ‡
Oakwood Chase Lane Haslemere Surrey GU27 3AG
Tel: 07771 725541 *Fax:* 01428 644006

POTTER OWTRAM & PECK ‡
42 West Street Haslemere Surrey GU27 2AN
Tel: 01428 642321 *Fax:* 01428 653643
Dx: 58117 HASLEMERE (SURREY)
E-mail: potterop@haslemere.com
List of partners: S C Loveless, A H Ramsden, K E Shires
Work: A1 B1 C1 D1 E F1 G H J1 K1 L M1 N O P Q R1 S1 T1 V W X Z(b,c,d,e,f,g,h,i,j,k,l,m,n,o,p,s,t)
Emergency Action, Agency, Advocacy, Fixed Fee Interview and Legal Aid undertaken
Ptr: Loveless, Mr Simon Charles BA Notary Public. . . . . *Oct 1982
Ramsden, Mr Anthony H . . . . *§Nov 1977
Shires, Mrs Katherine E BSc . . . . *§Oct 1994
Ast: Hinchliffe, Ms Elizabeth . . . . Sep 2005

WILLIAMS WOOLLEY
48-50 High Street Haslemere Surrey GU27 2LA
Office: Haslemere, Petworth

R I YONGE SOLICITORS ‡
Pilgrims Marley Lane Haslemere Surrey GU27 3RF
Tel: 01428 644219 *Fax:* 01428 651258

HASLINGDEN, Lancashire

WOODCOCKS ‡
West View Princess Street Haslingden Lancashire BB4 6NW
Tel: 01706 213356 *Fax:* 01706 211494 *Dx:* 26252 RAWTENSTALL
E-mail: info@woodcocks.co.uk
Office: Bacup, Bury, Ramsbottom, Rawtenstall
Work: A1 B1 C1 C2 C3 D1 D2 E F1 J1 K1 K3 K4 L N O P Q R1 S1 S2 T1 T2 W Z(d,e,l,o,q)

HASSOCKS, West Sussex

LEONA DANIEL ‡
Laine Field Dumbrells Court Road Ditchling Hassocks West Sussex BN6 8GT
Tel: 01273 845024 *Fax:* 01273 846588
E-mail: suesouth@leonadaniel.co.uk
List of partners: L S Daniel
Work: D1
Legal Aid undertaken
SPr: Daniel, Mrs Leona S LLB(Hons). . . . . *Jun 1972

GRIFFITH SMITH FARRINGTON WEBB
32 Keymer Road Hassocks West Sussex BN6 8AL
Tel: 01273 843405 *Fax:* 01273 846422 *Dx:* 59650 HASSOCKS
E-mail: hassocks@griffthsmith.co.uk
Office: Brighton, Henfield
Languages: French
Work: A1 B1 C1 C2 D1 E F1 J1 K1 L N O Q S1 S2 T2 V W Z(d,q,r,u)

LINDSAY J KEITH SOLICITOR ‡
1 Bedlam Street Hurstpierpoint Hassocks West Sussex BN6 9EW
Tel: 01273 832444 *Fax:* 01273 832555
E-mail: law@keithsolicitors.co.uk

NICHOLAS HANCOCK SOLICITOR ‡
43 Chancellors Park Hassocks West Sussex BN6 8EY
Tel: 01273 841815

OSLER DONEGAN TAYLOR
133 High Street Hurstpierpoint Hassocks West Sussex BN6 9PU
Tel: 01273 831574 *Fax:* 01273 221584 *Dx:* 59654 HASSOCKS
Office: Brighton

HASTINGS, East Sussex

ABS SOLICITORS ‡
Administration Centre The Priory Meadow Centre Hastings East Sussex TN34 1PH
Tel: 0845 083 0003 *Fax:* 01424 448800 *Dx:* 7065 HASTINGS
Work: S1

BENSON & CO ‡
89 Queens Road Hastings East Sussex TN34 1RL
Tel: 01424 433601 *Fax:* 01424 433601
List of partners: A J Benson
Work: A1 E L Q S1 W
Agency and Legal Aid undertaken
Ptr: Benson, Mr Andrew J . . . . *Apr 1979

MICHAEL BLANDY SOLICITORS ‡
Elm Lodge 60 Old London Road Hastings East Sussex TN35 5LZ
Tel: 01424 712545 *Fax:* 01424 712545 *Dx:* 7003 HASTINGS
E-mail: michael@michaelblandy.co.uk

BUTTERS DAVID GREY & CO ‡
(incorporating Butters Olien; David Grey & Co)
25 Havelock Road Hastings East Sussex TN34 1BP
Tel: 01424 424949 / 715171 *Fax:* 01424 721535
Dx: 7045 HASTINGS
E-mail: reception@bdgconvey.co.uk
List of partners: J A W Butters, B P Collins, J D Grey
Work: B1 C1 D1 E F1 G H K1 L N R1 S1
Emergency Action, Agency, Advocacy, Fixed Fee Interview and Legal Aid undertaken
Ptr: Butters, Mr John A W LLB(Lond) . . . . Apr 1977
Collins, Mr Barry P LLB. . . . . *Apr 1991
Grey, Mr John D . . . . *May 1973

SAMANTHA DENHAM SOLICITORS ‡
10 Cambridge Road Hastings East Sussex TN34 1DJ
Tel: 01424 718822 / 719111 *Fax:* 01424 718833
Dx: 7062 HASTINGS
E-mail: sdenhamsolicitor@aol.com
List of partners: S M Denham
Languages: German
Work: S1 S2
SPr: Denham, Miss Samantha M BA(Hons) . . . . *Jul 1997

FUNNELL & PERRING ‡
192-193 Queens Road Hastings East Sussex TN34 1RG
Tel: 01424 426287 *Fax:* 01424 434372 *Dx:* 7023 HASTINGS
Emergency telephone 01424 426287
E-mail: law@funnellperring.co.uk
List of partners: J Eichler, G Lake, S J Long
Work: B1 D1 E G H J1 K1 K3 Q S1 S2 W Z(d)
Emergency Action, Agency, Advocacy, Fixed Fee Interview, Legal Aid undertaken and Legal Aid Franchise
Ptr: Eichler, Ms Jackie. . . . . Oct 2004
Lake, Mr Gary. Aug 2005
Long, Mr Stephen John LLB(Hons) . . . . *Feb 1991

GABY HARDWICKE
34 Wellington Square Hastings East Sussex TN34 1PN
Tel: 01424 438011 *Fax:* 01424 722409 *Dx:* 7028 HASTINGS
E-mail: info@gabyhardwicke.co.uk
Office: Bexhill (2 offices), Eastbourne
Languages: French
Work: B1 C1 C2 C3 D1 E J1 K1 K2 L N O Q R1 R2 S1 S2 T1 T2 V W Z(c,d,o,r,z)
Advocacy, Fixed Fee Interview, Legal Aid undertaken, Legal Aid Franchise and Member of Accident Line
Ptr: Sagar, Mr Bryan C . . . . *Dec 1980
Young, David G. Jan 2001
Con: Dennis, Mrs Sandra. . . . . *Nov 1996

HERINGTONS
Lacuna Place Havelock Road Hastings East Sussex TN34 1BG
Tel: 01424 434192 *Fax:* 01424 444824 *Dx:* 7006 HASTINGS
Emergency telephone 01424 812440
Office: Battle, Eastbourne, Rye
Work: D1 E J1 K1 L N S1 T2 W Z(m)
Emergency Action, Advocacy, Fixed Fee Interview, Legal Aid Franchise and Member of Accident Line
Ptr: Longhurst, Mrs Denise LLB(Soton) . . . . *Nov 1984
Longmire, Mr Geoffrey E LLB(Vict) . . . . *§Jul 1980
Parkes, Mr Russell BA ★ . . . . *Oct 1986

HOLDEN & CO ‡
Liberty Building The America Ground 32-33 Robertson Street Hastings East Sussex TN34 1HT
Tel: 01424 722422 *Fax:* 01424 720108 *Dx:* 7037 HASTINGS
E-mail: law@holdenandco.co.uk
List of partners: J Holden
Office: Ashford, Maidstone
Work: B1 C1 D1 E F1 G H J1 K1 K3 L M1 N P Q S1 S2 T1 T2 V W Z(g,h,l,p,q)
Emergency Action, Agency, Advocacy, Fixed Fee Interview, Legal Aid undertaken, Legal Aid Franchise and Member of Accident Line
Ptr: Holden, Jolyon ● . . . . *§Dec 1980
Ast: Deaves, Mr Graham L G . . . . *Jun 1975
Glendenning, Mr Mark LLB(Hons). . . . . *Dec 1984

MORGAN & LAMPLUGH ‡
12 Wellington Square Hastings East Sussex TN34 1PB
Tel: 01424 721821 *Fax:* 01424 722321 *Dx:* 7008 HASTINGS
Emergency telephone 01424 428738
List of partners: M J Gratton, G L Howard-Smith
Work: C3 D1 E F1 J1 K1 R1 S1 V W
Emergency Action, Agency, Advocacy, Fixed Fee Interview, Legal Aid undertaken and Legal Aid Franchise
Ptr: Gratton, Mr Michael J LLB . . . . *Apr 1980
Howard-Smith, Mr Gordon L LLB(B'ham) . . . . . . *May 1981
Asoc: Tyman, Miss Sarah L BA(Hons). . . . . *May 1997

JANET SINDEN & CO ‡
11 Wellington Square Hastings East Sussex TN34 1PB
Tel: 01424 425285 *Fax:* 01424 424794 *Dx:* 7039 HASTINGS
E-mail: info@janetsinden.co.uk
List of partners: J S Sinden
Work: F1 S1 S2 W
Ptr: Sinden, Mrs Janet S . . . . May 1973

PERCY WALKER & CO ‡
Robertson Chambers The Memorial Hastings East Sussex TN34 1JB
Tel: 01424 721234 *Fax:* 01424 721376 *Dx:* 7030 HASTINGS
List of partners: A G Earons, A S Francis
Work: E K4 L S1 S2 T2 W
Ptr: Earons, Mr Alan Graeme LLB. . . . . *Oct 1977
Francis, Mrs Aileen Stacey BSc(Hons) . . . . Jan 1994
Con: Deacon, Mr Andrew A R LLB . . . . *§Mar 1969

YOUNG COLES & LANGDON ‡
Langham House Albert Road Hastings East Sussex TN34 1QT
Tel: 01424 437878 *Fax:* 01424 444173 *Dx:* 7018 HASTINGS
E-mail: omnes@juvens.com
List of partners: R C Lane, C M F Langdon, D R Millgate
Office: Bexhill
Work: A1 C1 E K4 L M1 M2 R1 S1 S2 T1 T2 W Z(d,e,h,s,x)
Ptr: Langdon, Mr Christopher M F MA(Cantab) Notary Public . . . . *§Mar 1970
Millgate, Mr Derek R . . . . *§Nov 1981

HATCH END, Middlesex

MILLS CHODY LLP
388 Uxbridge Road Hatch End Middlesex HA5 4HP
Tel: 020 8428 2272 *Fax:* 020 8420 1351 *Dx:* 52157 HATCH END
E-mail: info@millschody.com
Office: Kenton
Languages: French, German
Work: B1 C1 D1 D2 E J1 K1 K2 N O Q R2 S1 S2 W Z(i,l,m,q,r)
Legal Aid Franchise
Ptr: Ford, Mr David J T LLB . . . . *§Nov 1988
Ast: Nyiri, Mr James Alexander LLB . . . . Jul 2006

HATFIELD, Hertfordshire

BTLAW SOLICITORS ‡
1 Waight Close Salisbury Village Hatfield Hertfordshire AL10 9GA
Tel: 01707 258154 *Fax:* 01707 258154
E-mail: mark.titmus1@btinternet.com

BAXTER WEBBE SOLICITORS ‡
43 Park Street Hatfield Hertfordshire AL9 5AB
Tel: 01707 259354

DW LAW ‡
Suite 2 Marquis House 68 Great North Road Hatfield Hertfordshire AL9 5ER
Tel: 01707 261177 *Fax:* 01707 265089 *Dx:* 100700 HATFIELD
E-mail: office@dwlaw.co.uk

FAHRI JACOB
53 Kentish Lane Brookmans Park Hatfield Hertfordshire AL9 6NG
Tel: 07908 144464
Office: London N8

KSP SOLICITORS ‡
Suite G 19-25 Salisbury Square Old Hatfield Hatfield Hertfordshire AL9 5BT
Tel: 01707 264277 *Fax:* 01707 260473
E-mail: kit@kspsolicitors.com
List of partners: K Pung
SPr: Pung, Kit . . . . Sep 2001

PINDERS SOLICITORS ‡
72 Walker Grove Hatfield Hertfordshire AL10 2AA
Tel: 01707 871514 *Fax:* 01707 329006

HATFIELD, South Yorkshire

A P TANSEY ‡
52 High Street Hatfield South Yorkshire DN7 6RY
Tel: 01302 843859 *Fax:* 01302 843859
List of partners: A P Tansey
Work: S1 S2 W
SPr: Tansey, Mr Arthur Philip MA(Oxon) . . . . *Jan 1980

HATHERSAGE, Derbyshire

ANGLO-SPANISH LAW ‡
6 Lower Burch Row Eyam Hope Valley Hathersage Derbyshire S32 5QF
Tel: 01433 631508 *Fax:* 01433 630329
E-mail: anglospanishlaw@legalisp.net
List of partners: E R Wagner
Languages: Spanish
Work: G M2 W
SPr: Wagner, Mr Edgar R LLB; LLM; LDO En Derecho Notary Public . . . . *Dec 1992

FAVELL SMITH & LAWSON
Suite 6 Brunel House Hathersage Business Park Hathersage Derbyshire S32 1DP
Tel: 01433 650718 *Fax:* 01433 651003
E-mail: legal@branch.favells.co.uk
Office: Sheffield
Work: A1 F1 K1 L S1 S2 W
Fixed Fee Interview and Legal Aid undertaken

JANE LITHERLAND SOLICITOR ‡
Heatherfield House Sheffield Road Hathersage Derbyshire S32 1DA
Tel: 01433 659990 *Fax:* 01433 659995
E-mail: jane@hathersagehall.fsnet.co.uk

RYLANDS LAW ‡
PO Box 4373 Hope Valley Hathersage Derbyshire S32 1WU
Tel: 01433 650878 *Fax:* 01433 650878
E-mail: info@rylandslaw.co.uk

HATTON, Derbyshire

QUENTIN SOLT LLP ‡
Turkey Farm House Beausale Lane Hatton Derbyshire CV35 7PE
Tel: 01926 808080
E-mail: quentin@qsolt.com

HAVANT, Hampshire

GLANVILLES
(incorporating Buckell & Drew; Damant & Sons)
Langstone Gate Solent Road Havant Hampshire PO9 1TR
Tel: 023 9249 2300 *Fax:* 023 9249 2361 *Dx:* 131355 HAVANT 2
E-mail: havant@glanvilles.co.uk
Office: Fareham, Newport
Languages: French
Work: A1 D1 E F1 H J1 K1 L N Q R1 S1 T1 T2 V W Z(l)
Emergency Action, Agency, Advocacy, Fixed Fee Interview, Legal Aid undertaken, Legal Aid Franchise and Member of Accident Line
Ptr: Melrose, Mr James Gordon BA; TEP . . . . *§Aug 1975
Small, Mr Charles G BA; TEP Notary Public. . . . *§Oct 1981
Asoc: Green, Mrs Sonia Marie LLB . . . . Sep 2001
Woodhouse, Miss Charlotte Ellen Sundby LLB(Hons) . *Oct 1990
Ast: Callaway, Miss Marie LLB. . . . . *May 2004
Reynolds, Mrs Elizabeth Celia LLB; TEP . . . . Nov 1998

EDWARD HAYES LLP
Suite 5 Langstone Gate Solent Road Havant Hampshire PO9 1TR
Tel: 023 9247 9872 *Fax:* 01243 536651 *Dx:* 30307 CHICHESTER
E-mail: info@edwardhayes.co.uk
Office: Bognor Regis, Chichester (2 offices), Littlehampton, London EC2, London EC4, Worthing
Work: B2 D1 D2 G H J1 K1 K2 K3 L M2 N Q S1 S2 W Z(i,l,q,w)
Emergency Action, Agency, Advocacy, Legal Aid undertaken and Legal Aid Franchise

HUGHES WAY ‡
10 South Street Havant Hampshire PO9 1DA
Tel: 023 9245 9020 *Fax:* 023 9249 8185
Work: C1 S1 T1 W

DAVID MCELDOWNEY ‡
42 Market Parade Havant Hampshire PO9 1QF
Tel: 023 9245 1007 *Fax:* 023 9249 2295

ROWE SPARKES PARTNERSHIP ‡
Unit 6 8 Park Road South Havant Hampshire PO9 1HB
Tel: 023 9248 6886 *Fax:* 023 9249 2921 *Dx:* 50009 HAVANT
Emergency telephone 0844 880 0969
E-mail: office@rowe-sparkes.co.uk
Office: Southampton, Southsea

SWAIN & CO
3-5 South Street Havant Hampshire PO9 1BU
Tel: 023 9248 3322 *Fax:* 023 9248 3366 *Dx:* 131359 HAVANT 2
E-mail: mail@swainandco.com
Office: Southampton
Work: D1 D2 G H J1 J2 K1 K2 K3 L N Q V X Z(h,m,q,r)
Emergency Action, Agency, Legal Aid undertaken, Legal Aid Franchise and Member of Accident Line
Ptr: Lee, Mrs Samantha A BSc(Hons) . . . . *Oct 1995
Swain, Mr Graeme Frederick LLB . . . . *Sep 1980
Asoc: Rayner, Miss Angela BA(Hons) . . . . *Sep 2000
Wright, Miss Victoria LLM . . . . *Dec 1996
Ast: Kainth, Mrs Jagjit LLB. . . . . Oct 2005
Moffatt, Miss Julia LLB(Hons) . . . . *Oct 1990
Stonehouse, Ms Rhiannon LLB(Hons). . . . . Dec 2006

VERISONA SOLICITORS
64 West Street Havant Hampshire PO9 1PA
Tel: 023 9249 2472 *Fax:* 023 9249 2472
Office: Portsmouth, Waterlooville

WANNOP FOX STAFFURTH & BRAY
First Floor Room 3 Block 201 Havant Hampshire PO7 1TR
Tel: 01243 778844 *Fax:* 01243 788349 *Dx:* 30305 CHICHESTER
E-mail: havant@wfsblaw.com
Office: Bognor Regis, Chichester, Littlehampton, Worthing (3 offices)

HAVERFORDWEST, Pembrokeshire

BISSMIRE FUDGE & CO ‡
19 Market Street Haverfordwest Pembrokeshire SA61 1NF
Tel: 01437 764723 *Fax:* 01437 760493
Dx: 98275 HAVERFORDWEST
E-mail: enquiries@bissmirefudge.co.uk
List of partners: M J Bissmire, I G Fudge, P J Radford, H G Scale
Office: Pembroke Dock
Work: A1 A2 A3 B1 C1 D1 E F1 G J1 K1 K2 K3 K4 L N O Q R1 S1 S2 W Z(c,l,n,q,r)
Agency and Advocacy undertaken
Ptr: Bissmire, Mr Michael J LLB(Lond). . . . . Jun 1971
Fudge, Mr Ian G LLB(Lond) . . . . *May 1979
Radford, Mr Peter J BA(Hons). . . . . *Nov 1983
Scale, Mr Howard G BA(Law) . . . . *Dec 1983

EATON-EVANS & MORRIS ‡
12 High Street Haverfordwest Pembrokeshire SA61 2DB
Tel: 01437 763383 *Fax:* 01437 766613
Dx: 98277 HAVERFORDWEST
E-mail: enquiries@eaton-evans.com
List of partners: S D Dyer, H L Hodges, M C E Raggett
Languages: Welsh
Work: A1 B1 B2 D1 D2 E F1 G H J1 K1 K3 K4 L N O Q R1 R2 S1 S2 V W Z(j,k,l,q)
Emergency Action, Agency, Advocacy, Fixed Fee Interview, Legal Aid undertaken and Legal Aid Franchise
Ptr: Dyer, Mr Sean D LLB(Hons). . . . . *Oct 1998
Hodges, Ms Helen Louise LLB . . . . *Nov 1993
Raggett, Mr Matthew C E BA . . . . *Mar 1984

HAINS & LEWIS LTD ‡
Penffynnon Hawthorn Rise Haverfordwest Pembrokeshire SA61 2BQ
Tel: 0845 408 0125 *Fax:* 01437 769434
Dx: 98283 HAVERFORDWEST
E-mail: law@hainsandlewis.co.uk
List of partners: V H Hains, S I Knox, R D P Lewis, C Taylor
Office: Carmarthen, Narberth
Work: A1 D1 E F1 G H I J1 K1 L N Q S1 S2 V W Z(d,l,o,p)
Emergency Action, Agency, Advocacy, Legal Aid undertaken and Legal Aid Franchise
Dir: Hains, Miss Victoria Helen BA. . . . . *Jul 1980
Knox, Miss Sharon I BSc . . . . May 1998
Lewis, Mr Richard Daniel Price LLB(Lond). . . . . *Jul 1980
Taylor, Mr Christopher. . . . . *Oct 2000

Ast: Brindley, Ms Joanne LLB; LPC . . . . *Nov 2007
Griffiths, Mrs Tracy . . . . *Dec 2003
Hughes, Miss Michelle Ann LLB. . . . . *Aug 2004
Smith, Mrs Karen LLB; LSF . . . . *Sep 1993
Con: Mumford, Mr Simon Anthony Rhys LLB; GIPM; AccMed Mental Health Act Commissioner 1989-1994 . . . . *Dec 1981

LAYTON & CO ‡
3 Picton Place Haverfordwest Pembrokeshire SA61 2LE
Tel: 01437 766671 *Fax:* 01437 769797
Dx: 98289 HAVERFORDWEST
Emergency telephone 07774 638231
E-mail: enquiries@laytonandco.co.uk
List of partners: J Brooks, J R R Webb
Work: B2 D1 F1 G H J1 K1 L N Q S1 S2 Z(r)
Emergency Action, Agency, Advocacy, Fixed Fee Interview, Legal Aid undertaken, Legal Aid Franchise and Member of Accident Line
Ptr: Brooks, Miss Jessica LPC. . . . . Jan 2003
Webb, Mr Jonathan Richard Rolfe BA(Hons) . . . . *Jan 2001
Asoc: Kelleher, Mr Michael J LLB . . . . *Oct 1982
Con: Layton, Mr J Mark LLB ★ . . . . *Dec 1987

T O L LLEWELLIN & CO ‡
Balfour Chambers Quay Street Haverfordwest Pembrokeshire SA61 1BG
Tel: 01437 767140 *Fax:* 01437 762206
E-mail: tollco@aol.com
List of partners: W O Llewellin
Work: A1 E K4 L R1 S1 T2 W Z(m)
SPr: Llewellin, Mr William O . . . . *Sep 1980

PRICE & SON ‡
33 Hill Lane Haverfordwest Pembrokeshire SA61 1PS
Tel: 01437 765331 *Fax:* 01437 768663
E-mail: mail@priceandson.co.uk
List of partners: S O Hill, W D Hill
Work: A1 B1 C3 D1 E J1 K1 L N O Q R1 S1 S2 T1 T2 W Z(c,d,l,q,t)
Emergency Action, Agency and Advocacy undertaken
Ptr: Hill, Mr Stephen O BCL(Oxon); LLB(Nott'm). . . . . *Oct 1981
Hill, Mr W David LLB(Nott'm) . . . . *Jun 1979

RED KITE LAW
Cleddau Chambers 18-20 Old Bridge Haverfordwest Pembrokeshire SA61 2ET
Tel: 01437 763332 *Fax:* 01437 760052
Dx: 136816 HAVERFORDWEST
Office: Carmarthen (2 offices), Milford Haven, Pembroke, Pembroke Dock, Tenby
Languages: French, Spanish, Welsh
Work: A1 B1 C1 D1 D2 E F1 F2 G H J1 K1 K3 K4 L N O Q S1 S2 T2 V W Z(c,d,l,m,t)
Emergency Action, Agency, Advocacy, Fixed Fee Interview, Legal Aid undertaken and Legal Aid Franchise
Ptr: Davies, Ms Rhian BA(Econ). . . . . *Sep 1992
Smith, Mr Luke BSc. . . . . Aug 1999
Ast: Brown, Mrs Christine . . . . *May 2000
Gunning, Mrs Elaine . . . . Jul 1999
Purbrick, Mrs Sarah Anne BSc(Hons)(Econ). . . . . Oct 2000
Con: Gates, Mr Rhett R BA. . . . . Oct 1993
Pagett, Ms Anne-Marie LLB. . . . . Dec 1986

STEVE THOMAS & CO ‡
Deerland Chambers Deerland Road Haverfordwest Pembrokeshire SA62 4NG
Tel: 01437 890500 *Fax:* 01437 890031
E-mail: jo@deerlandchambers.co.uk
List of partners: S Thomas
SPr: Thomas, Mr Stephen LLB. . . . . Oct 1991

RTP WILLIAMS LIMITED ‡
35 High Street Haverfordwest Pembrokeshire SA61 2BW
Tel: 01437 762321 *Fax:* 01437 763447
Emergency telephone 01646 621805
E-mail: reception@rtpsolicitors.co.uk
List of partners: M G Allingham
Work: A1 D1 D2 E K1 K2 K3 K4 L Q R1 S1 S2 W Z(l,q)
Emergency Action, Agency and Advocacy undertaken
SPr: Allingham, Mr Malcolm George BA . . . . *§Jul 1978
Ast: Curtlin, Mrs Helen J LLB . . . . *Jan 1977

HAVERHILL, Suffolk

ADAMS HARRISON
52a High Street Haverhill Suffolk CB9 8AR
Tel: 01440 705731 / 702485 *Fax:* 01440 706820
Dx: 80350 HAVERHILL
Emergency telephone 01440 704778
E-mail: enquiries@adams-harrison.co.uk
Office: Saffron Walden, Sawston
Work: A1 B1 C1 C2 D1 E F1 F2 G H J1 K1 L M2 N O P Q R1 S1 T1 T2 V W Z(l)
Emergency Action, Agency, Advocacy, Fixed Fee Interview, Legal Aid undertaken, Legal Aid Franchise and Member of Accident Line
Ptr: Cammiss, Mr Paul G LLB . . . . *§Mar 1973
Harrison, Mr Tom B LLB(Lond) . . . . *Dec 1977
Rees, Mr Rhodri E LLB(Wales) . . . . *Jul 1981

STEVENS ‡
25 High Street Haverhill Suffolk CB9 8AD
Tel: 01440 762511 *Fax:* 01440 703873 *Dx:* 80351 HAVERHILL
E-mail: info@stevens-law.co.uk
List of partners: A Caldwell
Office: Saffron Walden
Languages: French
Work: C1 D1 D2 E F1 G H J1 K1 K3 K4 L O Q R1 S1 S2 W Z(l,p)
Emergency Action, Agency, Advocacy, Fixed Fee Interview, Legal Aid undertaken and Legal Aid Franchise
Ast: Burden, Miss Rebecca LLB(Hons). . . . . *Apr 2003
Denham, Mrs Jennifer Mary LLB(Hons) . . . . *Sep 2002
Douch, Mrs Katherine E LLB(Hons) . . . . *Feb 1985
Halford, Miss Stephanie LLB(Hons) . . . . *Aug 2001
Jones, Miss Sarah Lesley LLB(Hons) . . . . *May 2009

NICHOLAS WRAY SOLICITOR ‡
PO Box 54 Haverhill Suffolk CB9 0BG
Tel: 01440 704467 *Fax:* 01440 704468
Emergency telephone 07885 560427
E-mail: nicholastwray@aol.com
List of partners: N Wray
Work: D2 G H J1 W X Z(l)

See p112 for the Key to Work Categories & other symbols

Emergency Action, Agency, Advocacy, Fixed Fee Interview, Legal Aid undertaken and Legal Aid Franchise
SPr: Wray, Mr Nicholas LLB . . . . *Jan 1991

HAWES, North Yorkshire

DAVID GALL LLB SOLICITOR ‡
Fulford House Town Foot Hawes North Yorkshire DL8 3NN
Tel: 01969 667171 *Fax:* 01969 667171
E-mail: david.gall@virgin.net
List of partners: D H Gall
Work: A1 L S1 W
SPr: Gall, Mr David Harry LLB . . . . *Nov 1970

RICHARD JOHNSON & PARTNERS ‡
Market Place Hawes North Yorkshire DL8 3QS
Tel: 01969 667000 *Fax:* 01969 667888
Emergency telephone 01969 663347
E-mail: johnson.hawes@dial.pipex.com
List of partners: E R D Johnson, M B McGarry, G C Mochrie
Office: Leyburn
Work: A1 A2 C1 E F1 G H J1 K1 K4 L N P R1 S1 S2 T1 T2 V W
Emergency Action, Agency, Advocacy, Fixed Fee Interview undertaken and Member of Accident Line
Ptr: Johnson, Mr E Richard D . . . . *§Jan 1970
McGarry, Mr Michael Bernard . . . . *§Dec 2004

SCOTTS WRIGHT
Market Place Hawes North Yorkshire DL8 3QX
Tel: 01969 667215 *Fax:* 01969 667222
E-mail: enquiries@scottswright.com
Office: Catterick Garrison, Leyburn

HAY-ON-WYE, Powys

GABBS LLP
1-2 Chancery Lane Hay-on-Wye Powys HR3 5DJ
Tel: 01497 820312 *Fax:* 01497 821174 *Dx:* 100850 HAY-ON-WYE
E-mail: hay@gabbs.biz
Office: Hereford, Leominster
Work: A1 C1 E F1 K1 L N S1 T1 W Z(d,l,m)
Agency, Fixed Fee Interview and Legal Aid undertaken
Ptr: Stenner-Evans, Mr John LLB(Bris) . . . . *Dec 1971

JANETTE HILL & CO SOLICITORS ‡
7 Market Street Hay-on-Wye Powys HR3 5AF
Tel: 01497 821000 *Fax:* 01497 821144 *Dx:* 100856 HAY-ON-WYE
E-mail: enquiries@janettehill.co.uk
List of partners: J L Hill
Dir: Hill, Miss Janette Linda MA; MPhil(Cantab)(Criminology) . . . . Oct 1996
Ast: Pallant, Miss Demelza Jane LLB(Hons) . . . . *Aug 2003

WILLIAMS BEALES & CO ‡
9 Broad Street Hay-on-Wye Powys HR3 5DB
Tel: 01497 820302 *Fax:* 01497 820462 *Dx:* 100853 HAY-ON-WYE
List of partners: M E Harris, T D d C Ryall
Work: A1 A2 B1 C1 D1 E F1 J1 K1 K2 K3 K4 L N O Q R1 S1 S2 W Z(c)
Ptr: Ryall, Ms Teresa Dorothy de Courcy BA. . . . . *Mar 1983
Harris, Michael Edward FILEx. . . . . .NSP
Ast: Tompkins, Mr John Leonard Paul LLB. . . . . Oct 1985

THE WOODLAND DAVIES PARTNERSHIP LLP ‡
Dol Y Coed 18 Castle Street Hay-on-Wye Powys HR3 5DF
Tel: 01497 820406 *Fax:* 01497 821269 *Dx:* 100852 HAY-ON-WYE
List of partners: E A Davies, P G Davies
Office: Brecon, Hereford, Kington, Talgarth
Work: A1 A2 D2 E K1 K2 K3 L N Q S1 S2 W Z(l)
Agency undertaken
Ptr: Davies, Miss E Ann . . . . *Nov 1979
Davies, Mr Peter G BSc(Econ) . . . . *Jan 1982
Asoc: Theobald, Miss Carolyn M LLB . . . . *Nov 1978

HAYES, Middlesex

ABM SOLICITORS ‡
61 Station Road Hayes Middlesex UB3 4BE
Tel: 020 8848 8600 *Fax:* 020 8848 8700

ABV SOLICITORS ‡
Kingshott Business Centre 23 Clayton Road Hayes Middlesex UB3 1AN
Tel: 0844 587 9996 *Fax:* 0844 587 9998 *Dx:* 44650 HAYES (MIDDX)
E-mail: admin@abvsolicitors.co.uk
Ast: Godhania, Hanisha . . . . May 2007

BANA VAID & ASSOCIATES
Bridgewater House 866-868 Uxbridge Road Hayes Middlesex UB4 0RR
Tel: 020 8813 6262 *Fax:* 020 8813 7710 *Dx:* 146921 HAYES 7
E-mail: rakhi@banavaid.com
Office: Uxbridge

BRADBERRYS ‡
452 Uxbridge Road Hayes Middlesex UB4 0SD
Tel: 020 8813 6962 *Fax:* 020 8813 5151
E-mail: enquiries@bradberrys.co.uk
Work: C1 E S1 S2 W Z(b)

CHEQUERS SOLICITORS LTD ‡
58 Coldharbour Lane Hayes Middlesex UB3 3ES
Tel: 020 8606 1000 *Fax:* 020 8606 1001 *Dx:* 44652 HAYES
E-mail: asha@chequers-solicitors.com
List of partners: A R Heer, Y H Teli
Languages: Gujarati, Hindi, Punjabi
Work: B1 C1 D1 E F1 J1 J2 K1 K3 L M4 N O Q S1 S2 W Z(i)
Agency, Fixed Fee Interview undertaken and Member of Accident Line
Ptr: Heer, Miss Asha Rani LLB(Hons) . . . . *Oct 1998
Teli, Mr Yogendra H LLB(Hons) . . . . *Feb 2001

DH LAW SOLICITORS LLP
Capital Place 120 Bath Road Heathrow Hayes Middlesex UB3 5AN
Tel: 020 8840 8008 *Fax:* 020 8567 4550
E-mail: heathrow@dhlaw.org.uk
Office: London SW1, London W7

DESOR & CO ‡
768 Uxbridge Road Hayes Middlesex UB4 0RU
Est: 1995
Tel: 020 8569 0708 *Fax:* 020 8561 6857
Dx: 44657 HAYES MIDDLESEX
E-mail: neeta@desorandco.co.uk
List of partners: K K Desor, N Desor
Languages: Gujarati, Hindi, Punjabi, Urdu
Work: B1 D1 D2 E F1 K1 K3 L N O Q S1 S2 W Z(c,l,q)
Emergency Action, Agency, Fixed Fee Interview, Legal Aid undertaken and Member of Accident Line
Ptr: Desor, Mr Kamal Kumar ♦. . . . . *Jan 1989
Desor, Mrs Neeta ♦ Former President of the Middlesex Law Society . . . . *Mar 1988
Ast: Webb, Mr Darrell LLB. . . . . *Sep 2005

EDEN SOLICITORS ‡
First Floor 368 Uxbridge Road Hayes Middlesex UB4 0SE
Tel: 020 8848 7999 *Fax:* 020 8848 8444
Work: K1 K3 L S1 S2 W Z(i)
Advocacy and Fixed Fee Interview undertaken

JS LAW ‡
KBC Hayes Exchange 23 Clayton Road Hayes Middlesex UB3 1AN
Tel: 020 8817 1004 *Fax:* 020 8817 1173
List of partners: S Charandeep, J Nerwan
Languages: Hindi, Punjabi, Urdu
Work: S1 S2 Z(i,l)
Ptr: Charandeep, Sehmi. . . . . Jun 1999
Nerwan, Jasbinder . . . . Sep 1998

LAWMEN SOLICITORS ‡
2nd Floor Suite B Bridge House Hayes Middlesex UB3 4BX
Tel: 020 8561 6090 *Fax:* 020 8813 5090
E-mail: info@lawmensolicitors.com

E D C LORD & CO ‡
Link House 1200 Uxbridge Road Hayes Middlesex UB4 8JD
Tel: 020 8848 9988 *Fax:* 020 8561 0101
Dx: 51750 HAYES MIDDLESEX 3
E-mail: mail@edclord.com
List of partners: G S Bloom, A Isitt, P J Pulsford, G Seers, P B Urwin, A R Wright
Office: London W13, Potters Bar
Work: E J1 L N O P Q S1 S2 W Z(l)
Agency undertaken and Member of Accident Line
Ptr: Bloom, Mr Grahame S . . . . *Dec 1981
Isitt, Mr Andrew. . . . . Dec 1990
Pulsford, Mr Patrick J LLB. . . . . *Jul 1975
Seers, Mr Graham . . . . Oct 1986
Urwin, Mr Paul B . . . . *§Jul 1980
Wright, Mr A Robert. . . . . .Jul 1985
Ast: Cowlin, Mr Jonathan R BA(Wales). . . . . *Jan 1980
Con: Parkhouse, Mr Norman W. . . . . Jan 1991

MTG SOLICITORS ‡
61 Coldharbour Lane Hayes Middlesex UB3 3EE
Tel: 020 8569 3131 *Fax:* 020 8569 3434
Office: Hayes

MTG SOLICITORS
2nd Floor Warley Chambers Warley Road Hayes Middlesex UB4 0PU
Tel: 020 8754 5577 *Fax:* 020 8561 2800 *Dx:* 44655 HAYES
E-mail: info@mtgsolicitors.com
Office: Hayes

RAIT & CO ‡
1 Willow Tree Lane Hayes Middlesex UB4 9BB
Tel: 020 8842 0101 *Fax:* 020 8842 0999
Dx: 44661 HAYES MIDDLESEX

TAYLOR PHILLIPS ‡
81 Coldharbour Lane Hayes Middlesex UB3 3EF
Tel: 020 8561 7367 *Fax:* 020 8561 7574
E-mail: taylorphillips@btconnect.com
List of partners: P Behal, A K Khullar
Languages: Gujarati, Hindi, Punjabi, Tamil, Telugu
Ptr: Behal, Parminder . . . . Nov 2005
Khullar, Ajay K . . . . Sep 1990

VS LAW SOLICITORS ‡
Union House 23 Clayton Road Hayes Middlesex UB3 1AN
Tel: 020 8817 1027 *Fax:* 020 8817 1200

VEJA & CO SOLICITORS ‡
593 Uxbridge Road Hayes Middlesex UB4 8HR
Tel: 020 8581 1502 *Fax:* 020 8581 1503
Dx: 51756 HAYES MIDDLESEX 3
Emergency telephone 07958 349747
E-mail: mail@vejaandco.com
List of partners: D J Marks, R Veja
Office: Leicester, Southall
Languages: Gujarati
Work: B2 G H
Agency, Advocacy, Legal Aid undertaken and Legal Aid Franchise
SPr: Veja, Rajshi LLB(Hons) ★. . . . . *§Dec 1988

VERMA & SHARMA LAW ASSOCIATES ‡
MWB Business Exchange 23 Clayton Road Hayes Middlesex UB3 1AN
Tel: 020 8817 1052

VIJAY & CO ‡
366B Uxbridge Road Hayes Middlesex UB4 0SE
Tel: 020 8573 5578 *Fax:* 020 8573 5578
E-mail: vijaytunga@aol.com

DESMOND WRIGHT & CO ‡
1094a Uxbridge Road Hayes Middlesex UB4 8QH
Tel: 020 8561 4888 *Fax:* 020 8569 1814
Dx: 51761 HAYES MIDDLESEX 3
Emergency telephone 020 8561 4888
Work: D1 G H
Agency, Advocacy and Legal Aid undertaken

HAYLE, Cornwall

CVC SOLICITORS
52 Fore Street Hayle Cornwall TR27 4DY
Tel: 01736 752246 *Fax:* 01736 756620
Dx: 151321 PENZANCE (HAYLE)
E-mail: enquirieshayle@cvc-solicitors.co.uk
Office: Penzance, St Ives
Languages: French
Work: A1 B1 C1 D1 E F1 J1 K1 M1 N P R1 S1 T1 V W Z(d,j,k,l,m,n,o,s)
Emergency Action, Agency, Fixed Fee Interview and Legal Aid undertaken
Dir: Jones, Mr Nicholas W S LLB . . . . Dec 1981

VINGOE LLOYD SOLICITORS (incorporating J R Lloyd & Co)
33 St John's Street Copper House Hayle Cornwall TR27 4LL
Tel: 01736 754075 *Fax:* 01736 756439
Dx: 151320 PENZANCE (HAYLE)
Emergency telephone 01736 752323
E-mail: info@vingoelloyd.co.uk
Office: Helston, St Ives
Work: A1 C1 D1 E K1 K3 L R1 S1 S2 T1 T2 W Z(c,d,l)
Fixed Fee Interview undertaken
Ptr: Lloyd, Mr John Richard LLB. . . . . *Dec 1973
Vingoe, Mr Anthony Gary . . . . *Sep 2001

HAYLING ISLAND, Hampshire

RAMSBOTTOM & CO SOLICITORS LIMITED ‡
5 Seagrove Avenue Hayling Island Hampshire PO11 9EU
Tel: 023 9246 5931 *Fax:* 023 9246 8349
Dx: 53154 HAYLING ISLAND
E-mail: dr@ramsbottom.co.uk
List of partners: D A Ramsbottom
Work: E I J1 L N O Q S1 S2 U2 W Z(l,q)
Agency and Fixed Fee Interview undertaken
Dir: Ramsbottom, Mr Donald Anthony BA(Hons); LLB . . *Dec 1988
Ast: Van Baskerville, Mr Glenroy Sinclair. . . . . Feb 1998

WILSON WAKEFIELD SOLICITORS ‡
63 Station Road West Town Hayling Island Hampshire PO11 0EB
Tel: 023 9246 4475 *Fax:* 023 9217 8583

HAYWARDS HEATH, West Sussex

SUSAN CLARK SOLICITOR ‡
3 Lucastes Mews Paddockhall Road Haywards Heath West Sussex RH16 1HE
Tel: 01444 454530 *Fax:* 01444 454580

COLEMANS ‡
Paddockhall Chambers Paddockhall Road Haywards Heath West Sussex RH16 1HF
Tel: 01444 459555 *Fax:* 01444 40306
Dx: 300301 HAYWARDS HEATH 1
E-mail: law@colemans-solicitors.com
List of partners: T C Cotterill, I A Morcowitz
Work: A1 B1 C1 C2 C3 D1 E F1 I J1 L M1 M2 N O P Q R1 S1 T1 T2 V W Z(c,d,e,j,k,l,m,p,t)
Emergency Action, Agency and Advocacy undertaken
Ptr: Cotterill, Mr Timothy C LLB . . . . *Nov 1988
Morcowitz, Mr Isaac Anthony BProc; TEP. . . . . . . *Dec 1986
Asoc: Taylor, Ms Fiona L LLB . . . . *§Nov 1988
Towns, Mr Robin P LLB(Lond); TEP Cecil Karuth Prize *Mar 1968
Ast: Abraham, Mr Bryan T. . . . . *Jan 1966
Bevis, Mr John H . . . . *Jan 1982
Con: Hancock, Mr Nicholas P MA(Oxon) . . . . *§Sep 1979
Stevenson, Mr Peter Robert BA(Soton) . . . . *§Jun 1968
Waistell, Mr Michael K LLB Notary Public . . . . . . *Jun 1971

B D H COOPER LTD ‡
Hamlyns Lewes Road Haywards Heath West Sussex RH17 7NG
Tel: 01444 831127 *Fax:* 01444 831182
List of partners: B D H Cooper
Ptr: Cooper, Mr Brian D H LLB . . . . *May 1974

FURNIVALS SOLICITORS ‡
2nd Floor 4 Heath Square Haywards Heath West Sussex RH16 1BL
Tel: 01444 473082 *Fax:* 01444 473472
Dx: 30060 HAYWARDS HEATH 2
E-mail: enquiries@furnivals.co.uk

STEPHEN GALLICO SOLICITORS ‡
Merlin House 6 Boltro Road Haywards Heath West Sussex RH16 1BB
Tel: 01444 411333 *Fax:* 01444 440604
Dx: 300311 HAYWARDS HEATH
List of partners: M E J Allen, S Gallico, F Taylor
Languages: French, German
Work: E J1 K4 S1 S2 T2 W
Ptr: Allen, Ms Melanie Elizabeth Jayne . . . . *Sep 1993
Gallico, Mr Stephen MA(Cantab) . . . . *Jun 1976
Taylor, Ms Fiona . . . . *Jan 1988
Asoc: McCarthy, Ms Katie . . . . *Jan 1990

HAMNETT OSBORNE TISSHAW ‡
3 Hazelgrove Road Haywards Heath West Sussex RH16 3PH
Tel: 01444 443030 *Fax:* 01444 443553
Dx: 155893 HAYWARDS HEATH 7
Emergency telephone 07767 058128
E-mail: info@hotsol.co.uk
List of partners: R Hayler, D Osborne, G D J Tisshaw
Languages: French, Italian, Punjabi, Urdu
Work: B2 D1 D2 G H K1 K3
Emergency Action, Agency, Advocacy, Fixed Fee Interview, Legal Aid undertaken and Legal Aid Franchise
Ptr: Hayler, Mr Rod LLB(Hons) ★ . . . . §Aug 2001
Osborne, Mr David BSc(Hons) ★ . . . . *§Dec 1996
Tisshaw, Miss Gilva D J BA(Hons) Assistant Deputy Coroner of the City of Brighton & Hove . . . . *§Sep 1989
Ast: Beighton, Mr Robert. . . . . *Jun 2001
Bullivant, Mr Andrew . . . . Jun 2005
L'Estrange, Mr Paul Nicholas BA(Hons) . . . . Jul 1992
Walker, Mrs Lisa V LLB(Hons). . . . . *Jan 1998

ALISTAIR HARPER & CO ‡
Broadway Chambers 19-31 The Broadway Haywards Heath West Sussex RH16 3AB
Tel: 01444 457890 *Fax:* 01444 451455
Dx: 300622 HAYWARDS HEATH 1 & 2
Emergency telephone 07623 971134
E-mail: enquiries@alistairharper.co.uk

List of partners: A Harper
Work: G H S1 V
Emergency Action, Agency, Advocacy, Fixed Fee Interview, Legal Aid undertaken and Legal Aid Franchise
SPr: Harper, Mr Alistair ★ . . . . *Nov 1981
Ast: Blunden, Mr Philip L BA(Hons) ★ . . . . *May 1998
Leete, Mr Tim ★. . . . . *Jul 1978
Rowland, Miss Sarah F LLB(Hons) . . . . Sep 1997

B G HINDLE ‡
Suite B The Priory Haywards Heath West Sussex RH16 3LB
Tel: 01444 443636

HOUSEMAN BENNER ‡
Commercial House 52 Perrymount Road Haywards Heath West Sussex RH16 3DT
Tel: 01444 414081 *Fax:* 01444 457384
Dx: 300600 HAYWARDS HEATH 2
E-mail: haywardsheath@houbenlaw.demon.co.uk
List of partners: P C Benner
Languages: French
Work: E K1 L R1 S1 S2 W
SPr: Benner, Mr Peter C MA(Cantab) Notary Public . . . *§Mar 1963

JACQUELINE LEE SOLICITOR ‡
6 Sunte Avenue Lindfield Haywards Heath West Sussex RH16 2AA
Tel: 01444 473372 *Fax:* 01444 473372
E-mail: jacqueline.lee@dsl.pipex.com

MILLER & CO SOLICITORS ‡
4th Floor Oakfield House 35 Perrymount Road Haywards Heath West Sussex RH16 3BW
Tel: 01444 443366 *Fax:* 01444 443369
E-mail: miller_sharkline@yahoo.co.uk

MULCARE JENKINS ‡
5a Muster Green Haywards Heath West Sussex RH16 4AP
Est: 1948
Tel: 01444 459954 *Fax:* 01444 413639
Dx: 300614 HAYWARDS HEATH
E-mail: info@mulcarejenkins.co.uk
List of partners: A G Blok
Work: E J1 K4 L R2 S1 S2 W
Fixed Fee Interview undertaken
SPr: Blok, Mr Alan Geoffrey . . . . *May 1981
Asoc: Rodemark, Mr Timothy James BA. . . . . *Oct 1981
Con: Miller, Mr David Patrick Henry. . . . . Jan 1970

ROHAN & CO ‡
Aviation House 1-7 Sussex Road Haywards Heath West Sussex RH16 4DZ
Tel: 01444 450901 *Fax:* 01444 440437
E-mail: partners@rohansolicitors.co.uk
List of partners: M T Cremin, R F Rohan
Work: B1 C1 E J1 J2 K1 K3 L N O Q S1 S2 U2 W Z(d,e,f,p)
Ptr: Cremin, Mr Martyn Timothy LLB. . . . . Jan 1982
Rohan, Mr Rupert F. . . . . Feb 1999
Asoc: Samuel, Mr Adrian Paul. . . . . Dec 1991

SHERRARDS ‡
Grosvenor Hall Bolnore Road Haywards Heath West Sussex RH16 4BX
Tel: 01444 473344 *Fax:* 01444 473249
E-mail: advice@harrysherrard.com
List of partners: H Sherrard
Office: West Drayton
Work: J1
SPr: Sherrard, Mr Harry LLB . . . . *Sep 1988

STARKE & CO FAMILY LAW ‡
LGM House Mill Green Road Commercial Square Haywards Heath West Sussex RH16 1XJ
Tel: 01444 416116 *Fax:* 01444 416414
Dx: 300302 HAYWARDS HEATH

WAUGH & CO ‡
(incorporating Waugh Brumell & Baron)
3 Heath Square Boltro Road Haywards Heath West Sussex RH16 1BD
Tel: 01444 451666 *Fax:* 01444 415401
Dx: 300300 HAYWARDS HEATH 1
E-mail: enquiries@waughandco.co.uk
List of partners: J S Cookson, A G McGowan
Languages: French
Work: A1 C1 E J1 K4 L R2 S1 S2 T1 T2 V W Z(d,h)
Fixed Fee Interview undertaken
Ptr: Cookson, Mr Jack S. . . . . *§Jun 1976
McGowan, Mr Anthony Gordon BSc. . . . . *Aug 2003
Ast: Cookson, Mr Christian Jack. . . . . Aug 2008

HEANOR, Derbyshire

BROADBENTS
14 High Street Heanor Derbyshire DE75 7EX
Tel: 01773 769891 *Fax:* 01773 530396 *Dx:* 19279 HEANOR
Emergency telephone 01773 769891
Office: Alfreton, Chesterfield, Derby, Mansfield, Sutton-in-Ashfield
Work: A1 B1 C1 C2 C3 D1 E F1 G H J1 K1 L M1 M2 N P R1 S1 T1 T2 V W Z(c,d,e,j,k,l,p)
Emergency Action, Agency, Advocacy, Legal Aid undertaken and Member of Accident Line
Ptr: James, Mr Paul LLB . . . . Oct 1985
Last, Mr John LLB . . . . *Dec 1976
Ast: Barrett, Mrs Hilary LLB . . . . Nov 1992

MILES & CASH ‡
2 Godfrey Street Heanor Derbyshire DE75 7GD
Tel: 01773 530000 *Fax:* 01773 530843
List of partners: N R Chappell, C Sedgwick
Office: Ripley
Ptr: Chappell, Mr Nigel R LLB(Newc) . . . . *Oct 1985
Sedgwick, Mr Christopher BA. . . . . *§Nov 1982

HEATHFIELD, East Sussex

H&R HUGHES SOLICITORS LLP ‡
27A High Street Heathfield East Sussex TN21 8JR
Tel: 01435 890101 *Fax:* 01435 864828
E-mail: info@hrhlaw.co.uk

HEBBURN, Tyne & Wear

TERENCE CARNEY ‡
35 Station Road Hebburn Tyne & Wear NE31 1LA
Tel: 0191 483 5422 / 483 8771 *Fax:* 0191 483 9761
Dx: 60832 HEBBURN
Emergency telephone 0191 388 5687
E-mail: enquiries@terence-carney.co.uk
List of partners: T Carney, T V Laffey
Office: South Shields
Work: D1 F1 G H J1 K1 K2 K3 K4 N P S1 S2 V W Z(l)
Emergency Action, Agency, Advocacy, Fixed Fee Interview, Legal Aid undertaken and Legal Aid Franchise
Ptr: Carney, Mr Terence. . . . . *Jun 1971
Laffey, Mr Thomas Victor LLB(Newc) . . . . . . *Jan 1985
Ast: Hargreaves, Mrs Carolyne LLB; MSc(Econ) . . . . . *Nov 2000
Owens, Mrs Ann LLB(Hons). . . . . Feb 1994

HEBDEN BRIDGE, West Yorkshire

DUFFY FOWLER GABBI SOLICITORS ‡
5-6 Wragley House Valley Road Hebden Bridge West Yorkshire HX7 7BZ
Tel: 01422 844110 *Fax:* 01422 845770

FINN GLEDHILL
29 West End Hebden Bridge West Yorkshire HX7 8UQ
Tel: 01422 842451 *Fax:* 01422 843114 *Dx:* 16022 HALIFAX
E-mail: enquiries@finngledhill.co.uk
Office: Halifax
Work: A1 B1 C1 C2 D1 D2 E F1 F2 G H J1 K1 K3 L N O Q R1 R2 S1 S2 T2 V W X Z(b,c,d,k,l,m,o,p)
Emergency Action, Agency, Advocacy, Fixed Fee Interview, Legal Aid undertaken and Member of Accident Line
Ptr: Gledhill, Mr R Marc LLB. . . . . *§Feb 1988
Green, Mr Kieron S . . . . *Dec 1979
Lee, Mr David J L. . . . . §Nov 1971
Mattock, Mr Stephen J LLB . . . . *Mar 1986
Nowell, Mr Malcolm C LLB . . . . Jul 1980
Palfreman, Miss Amanda J LLB. . . . . *§Oct 1991
Stevenson, Mrs Carol LLB(Lond) . . . . *§Apr 1977
Ast: Jackson, Mrs Elaine LLB . . . . *Oct 1984

MARY MAHON SOLICITORS ‡
8 Wragley House Valley Road Hebden Bridge West Yorkshire HX7 7BZ
Tel: 01422 844997 *Fax:* 01422 844797
Dx: 742982 HEBDEN BRIDGE
E-mail: enquiries@marymahonsolicitor.co.uk

HECKMONDWIKE, West Yorkshire

STANLEY HAYS ‡
2 Oldfield Lane Heckmondwike West Yorkshire WF16 0JQ
Tel: 01924 403809 *Fax:* 01924 406247 *Dx:* 25451 HECKMONDWIKE
Emergency telephone 07771 915398
E-mail: law@stanleyhays.co.uk
List of partners: R P H Dawson, C R Walker
Work: D1 G H K1 K3 K4 L S1 S2 W Z(v)
Emergency Action, Agency, Advocacy, Fixed Fee Interview, Legal Aid undertaken and Legal Aid Franchise
Ptr: Dawson, Mr Robert P H LLB(Leeds). . . . . *May 1985
Walker, Mr C Richard BA(Hons). . . . . *Jun 1981

REDFEARNS ‡
Midland Bank Chambers Market Place Heckmondwike West Yorkshire WF16 0HZ
Tel: 01924 403745 / 404601 *Fax:* 01924 404913
Dx: 25453 HECKMONDWIKE
E-mail: info@redfearns-solicitors.co.uk
List of partners: T F Joyce, M G Mangano
Work: D1 E F1 G H K1 L N O Q S1 S2 W
Emergency Action, Agency, Advocacy, Fixed Fee Interview, Legal Aid undertaken and Legal Aid Franchise
Ptr: Joyce, Mr Thomas F LLB(Hons). . . . . *Apr 1991
Mangano, Mr Mark George LLB(Hons) . . . . *Nov 1990
Ast: Pilkington, Mr James E LLB(Leeds). . . . . *Jun 1977
Con: Turton, Mr Stephen D W . . . . *Jan 1969

HEDNESFORD, Staffordshire

STOWE SIMON ‡
Post Office Chambers 92 Market Street Hednesford Staffordshire WS12 1AG
Tel: 01543 877131 *Fax:* 01543 423201
Emergency telephone 01543 877131
E-mail: mail@simonstowe.co.uk
List of partners: S Stowe
Work: E G J1 K1 L M1 P S1 T1 W Z(c,j,l)
Emergency Action, Agency, Advocacy, Fixed Fee Interview and Legal Aid undertaken
Ptr: Stowe, Mr Simon LLB. . . . . *Mar 1980

HELMSLEY, North Yorkshire

DEREK CROSSAN ‡
45 Bridge Street Helmsley North Yorkshire YO62 5DX
Tel: 01439 770070 *Fax:* 01439 770928
E-mail: derek@crosslex.com
List of partners: D J Crossan
Languages: French
Work: C1 C2 E F1 F2 J1 L O P R2 S1 S2 W Z(l,y)
SPr: Crossan, Mr Derek J LLB(Lond). . . . . *Dec 1968

NORTH YORKSHIRE LAW
4 Bondgate Helmsley North Yorkshire YO62 5BS
Tel: 01439 770207 *Fax:* 01439 771650 *Dx:* 63752 HELMSLEY
E-mail: info@northyorkshirelaw.com
Office: Scarborough, Whitby
Work: A1 A2 E K1 L N O P R1 S1 S2 T2 W Z(q)
Emergency Action, Agency, Advocacy and Fixed Fee Interview undertaken

HELSTON, Cornwall

BORLASE & COMPANY ‡
45 Coinagehall Street Helston Cornwall TR13 8EU
Tel: 01326 574988 *Fax:* 01326 573261 *Dx:* 81616 HELSTON
E-mail: hb@borlase-co.co.uk
List of partners: P C Fitzmaurice, J A Wilkin
Work: A1 A3 D1 D2 E J1 K1 K2 L N Q R2 S1 S2 W Z(l)
Ptr: Fitzmaurice, Mr Peter Charles. . . . . *Jan 1976
Wilkin, Mr John Andrew LLB . . . . *Oct 1994
Asoc: Cornish, Mrs Jessica BA(Hons) Cornwall Law Society Junior Lawyer 2011 . . . . Jan 2011
Micciche, Mr Angelo LLB(Hons). . . . . *Feb 1999
Ast: Mason, Mrs Eileen MA(Oxon). . . . . *Jan 1980
Con: Muirhead, Mr James David Charles LLB(Hons) . . . . *Jan 1989

DAVIES PARTNERSHIP ‡
43 Meneage Street Helston Cornwall TR13 8RB
Tel: 01326 573767 *Fax:* 01326 564756
E-mail: helston@thedaviespartnership.co.uk
List of partners: K Martin, R B D Palmer
Office: St Agnes
Languages: French
Work: A1 B1 C1 D1 E F1 K1 K3 L S1 S2 W
Ptr: Palmer, Mr Richard Bernard David . . . . *Dec 1969

NALDERS QUALITY SOLICITORS
32a Coinagehall Street Helston Cornwall TR13 8EQ
Tel: 01326 574001 *Fax:* 01326 564547 *Dx:* 81601 HELSTON
E-mail: post@nalders.co.uk
Office: Camborne, Falmouth, Newquay, Penzance, St Austell, Truro (2 offices)
Work: A1 B1 C1 D1 E F1 K1 L N O Q S1 S2 W
Agency, Legal Aid undertaken, Legal Aid Franchise and Member of Accident Line
Ptr: Reid, Mr Derek M. . . . . *Jul 1969

RANDLE THOMAS LLP ‡
2 Wendron Street Helston Cornwall TR13 8PP
Tel: 01326 572951 *Fax:* 01326 563122 *Dx:* 81606 HELSTON
E-mail: rt@randlethomas.co.uk
List of partners: G R J Adams, R J Stillwell
Work: A1 A2 D1 D2 E F1 K1 K3 K4 L Q S1 S2 T2 V W
Advocacy and Fixed Fee Interview undertaken
Mem: Adams, Mr Gregory R J LLB(Hons) . . . . *§Oct 1971
Stillwell, Mr Roger J. . . . . *§Apr 1976
Ast: Craner, Mrs Janet Helen BA. . . . . *§May 1981
Lock, Miss Zoe Kalandra LLB . . . . *Aug 2008

VINGOE LLOYD ‡
Great Office Cross Street Helston Cornwall TR13 8NF
Tel: 01326 555800 *Fax:* 01326 563828 *Dx:* 81602 HELSTON
E-mail: info@vingoelloyd.co.uk
List of partners: T P King, J R Lloyd, A G Vingoe
Office: Hayle, St Ives
Ptr: King, Mr Trevor P. . . . . *Dec 1974
Ast: Bartle, Kimberley . . . . *Sep 2007
Mandalia, Ms Mala . . . . Feb 1992
Watkins, Mr Paul LLB. . . . . Oct 2006

BRIAN WATTERS SOLICITORS ‡
53 Osborne Parc Helston Cornwall TR13 8TZ
Tel: 01326 565975 *Fax:* 01326 569493
E-mail: bws@brianwatters.co.uk

HEMEL HEMPSTEAD, Hertfordshire

BATEMANS ‡
58 High Street Bovingdon Hemel Hempstead Hertfordshire HP3 0HG
Tel: 01442 834344 *Fax:* 01442 832042
E-mail: law@batemans-solicitors.co.uk
List of partners: J F A Bateman, M C Skinner
Work: A1 B1 C1 C2 C3 E G J1 K1 L N O P Q R1 S1 W Z(c,e)
Agency and Fixed Fee Interview undertaken
Ptr: Bateman, Mr Joseph F A . . . . *Jul 1967
Skinner, Miss Mary Clare BA . . . . *Dec 1982

ANDREW CAMPBELL & CO ‡
Boston House 64-66 Queensway Hemel Hempstead Hertfordshire HP2 5HA
Tel: 01442 355215 *Fax:* 01442 355001

CARR HEPBURN SOLICITORS LTD ‡
60 Alexandra Road Hemel Hempstead Hertfordshire HP2 4AQ
Tel: 01442 241466 *Fax:* 01442 219008 / 259966
Dx: 8808 HEMEL HEMPSTEAD
E-mail: info@carrhepburn.co.uk
List of partners: P J Carr, J A Hepburn
Work: C1 C2 D1 D2 E K1 S1 S2 W
Emergency Action, Advocacy, Fixed Fee Interview, Legal Aid undertaken and Legal Aid Franchise
Ptr: Carr, Mr Philip Jonathan LLB . . . . *May 1974
Hepburn, Ms Jane A LLB . . . . *May 1979
Ast: Ramsey, Mrs Christine M LLB. . . . . *May 1981
Seath, Miss Rebecca BA(Hons); DipLaw . . . . . . *Nov 2008
Watson, Mrs Ursula LLB . . . . *Dec 2008

JOHN FULLER & PARTNERS LIMITED ‡
3 The Waterhouse Waterhouse Street Hemel Hempstead Hertfordshire HP1 1ES
Tel: 01422 233856 *Fax:* 01422 234744
E-mail: info@jfpcrime.com

KEER-KEER & CO ‡
39 Stephyns Chambers Bank Court Hemel Hempstead Hertfordshire HP1 1DA
Tel: 01442 216755 / 216756 *Fax:* 01442 214111
Dx: 8822 HEMEL HEMPSTEAD
E-mail: law@keer-keer.co.uk
List of partners: P W Keer-Keer
Work: B3 E J1 K1 N S1 W
Emergency Action, Agency, Advocacy, Fixed Fee Interview, Legal Aid undertaken and Member of Accident Line
Ptr: Keer-Keer, Mr Peter William LLB(Bris). . . . . . . *§Dec 1969
Ast: Tidbury, Miss Laura BA . . . . *Nov 1996
Turner, Mr Joseph Lionel BSc(Hons) . . . . *Oct 1993

See p112 for the Key to Work Categories & other symbols

LAW ABROAD ‡
79 Marlowes Hemel Hempstead Hertfordshire HP1 1LF
Tel: 0800 298 4298
E-mail: info@lawabroad.co.uk

PICKWORTHS ‡
55 Marlowes Hemel Hempstead Hertfordshire HP1 1LE
Tel: 01442 261731 *Fax:* 01442 230356
Emergency telephone 01442 261731
E-mail: info@pickworths.co.uk
List of partners: G Y Ferneyhough, I T Tottman, B S Walkinshaw
Work: A1 C1 C2 C3 D1 E F1 J1 J2 K1 K2 K3 L N O Q R1 S1 S2 W Z(h,p,q,r)
Emergency Action, Fixed Fee Interview undertaken and Member of Accident Line
Ptr: Ferneyhough, Mrs Glenda Y LLB . . . . *Apr 1980
Tottman, Mr Ian T LLB(Manc) . . . . *Nov 1977
Walkinshaw, Miss Belinda S BSc(Hons) . . . . *Oct 1989
Ast: Carroll, Mrs Linsey Clair LLB(Hons) . . . . *Jan 2006
Leadbeater, Miss Jane Elizabeth LLB . . . . *Jun 2004
Smith, Miss Kimberley Louise LLB(Hons) . . . . *Jun 2009
Yap, Miss June May Kim LLB . . . . *Sep 2008

PICTONS SOLICITORS LLP
1 The Waterhouse Waterhouse Street Hemel Hempstead Hertfordshire HP1 1ES
Tel: 01442 242441 *Fax:* 01442 248569
E-mail: info@pictons.co.uk
Office: Luton, Milton Keynes
Languages: Danish, Finnish, French, Gujarati, Hindi, Italian, Punjabi, Urdu
Work: B1 C1 C2 C3 D1 E F1 G H J1 K1 L N O Q R1 S1 S2 T1 T2 U2 V W Z(e,h,l,p,r,w)
Emergency Action, Agency, Advocacy, Fixed Fee Interview, Legal Aid undertaken, Legal Aid Franchise and Member of Accident Line
Ptr: Fuller, Mr Richard J . . . . *Jun 1971
King, Mr John R. . . . . *May 1975
Ast: Bugg, Miss Emma L LLB(Hons); DipLP . . . . *Nov 1996

RICHARDSONS SOLICITORS ‡
41 Marlowes Hemel Hempstead Hertfordshire HP1 1LD
Tel: 01442 500500 *Fax:* 01442 500583
Dx: 8807 HEMEL HEMPSTEAD
E-mail: info@richardsonslaw.co.uk

UK TRAFFIC LAW ‡
11-13 Alexandra Road Hemel Hempstead Hertfordshire HP2 5BS
Tel: 01442 209200 *Fax:* 01442 229399
E-mail: info@uktrafficlaw.co.uk

ANDREW WHELDON SOLICITORS ‡
11-13 Alexandra Road Hemel Hempstead Hertfordshire HP2 5BS
Tel: 01442 242999 *Fax:* 01442 284699
Dx: 8858 HEMEL HEMPSTEAD
E-mail: enquiry@wheldonlaw.co.uk

WITTS MOLONEY SOLICITORS ‡
3 Marlowes Court 67 Marlowes Hemel Hempstead Hertfordshire HP1 1LE
Tel: 0845 127 1333 *Fax:* 01442 214051
Dx: 8818 HEMEL HEMPSTEAD
E-mail: admin@wmsolicitors.com

HEMSWORTH, West Yorkshire

DAVID LEWIS & CO ‡
14a Cross Hills Hemsworth West Yorkshire WF9 4LK
Tel: 01977 614064 *Fax:* 01977 611113

HENFIELD, West Sussex

GRIFFITH SMITH FARRINGTON WEBB
Croft House High Street Henfield West Sussex BN5 9DJ
Tel: 01273 492045 *Fax:* 01273 493530
E-mail: henfield@griffithsmith.co.uk
Office: Brighton, Hassocks
Languages: French
Work: A1 B1 C1 C2 D1 E F1 J1 K1 L N O R1 S1 S2 V W Z(d,q,r,u)

HENGOED, Caerphilly

T S EDWARDS & SON
1 The Square Hengoed Caerphilly CF82 7DU
Tel: 01443 814161 *Fax:* 01443 812055 *Dx:* 132152 CAERPHILLY 3
E-mail: info@tsedwards.co.uk
Office: Newport
Emergency Action, Agency, Advocacy, Fixed Fee Interview, Legal Aid undertaken and Member of Accident Line
Ptr: Thomas, Mr Hugh L BA. . . . . Dec 1977

MICHAEL LEIGHTON JONES ‡
Suite 3 Tredomen Innovation Centre Tredomen Park Hengoed Caerphilly CF82 7FQ
Tel: 01443 816400 *Fax:* 01443 819551
E-mail: info@michaelleightonjones.com

LEGAL SERVICES FOR CHILDREN ‡
Tredomen Innovation and Technology Centre Tredomen Business Park Ystrad Mynach Hengoed Caerphilly CF82 7FN
Tel: 01443 866296 *Fax:* 01443 814045
E-mail: enquiries@lsforchildren.com

HENLEY-IN-ARDEN, Warwickshire

LODDERS SOLICITORS LLP
5-7 High Street Henley-in-Arden Warwickshire B95 5BW
Tel: 01564 792261 *Fax:* 01564 794821
Dx: 28131 HENLEY-IN-ARDEN
E-mail: lawyers@lodders.co.uk
Office: Cirencester, Stratford-upon-Avon
Work: K4 L S1 W
Ptr: Lapidge, Mr Stanley PhD(Princeton) Samuel Herbert Easterbrook Prize. . . . . *§Jul 1979

VALERIE PACK SOLICITOR ‡
White Gates Redditch Road Ullenhall Henley-in-Arden Warwickshire B95 5NY
Tel: 01564 792806 *Fax:* 01564 792806
E-mail: v.pack-whitegates@homecall.co.uk

THEO PRITCHETT ‡
Woodnorton Ullenhall Henley-in-Arden Warwickshire B95 5PW
Tel: 01564 742215 *Fax:* 01564 742215
Emergency telephone 07801 947620
List of partners: T Pritchett
Languages: French
Work: A1 D2 S1 S2 W
Advocacy undertaken

HENLEY-ON-THAMES, Oxfordshire

BLORES ‡
Delegate House 30A Hart Street Henley-on-Thames Oxfordshire RG9 2AL
Tel: 01491 579265 *Fax:* 01491 579358
E-mail: seb@blores.co.uk

COLLINS DRYLAND & THOROWGOOD LLP ‡
12 Hart Street Henley-on-Thames Oxfordshire RG9 2AU
Tel: 01491 572323 *Fax:* 01491 576766
Dx: 80504 HENLEY-ON-THAMES
List of partners: W Fursman, G D Tanner
Office: Tilehurst
Work: A1 B1 C1 C2 C3 E F1 J1 K1 L M1 M2 N O P Q R1 S1 W Z(c,e,l)
Agency and Advocacy undertaken
Ptr: Tanner, Mr Gordon D . . . . *Mar 1983
Asoc: Holmes, Mrs Wendy Elizabeth MA(Oxon) . . . . . . *§Jun 1976
McMath, Mr Luke W T BSc . . . . Sep 1997
Ast: Robson-Hemmings, Mr Gary Donald BSc(Hons); MRICS . . . . *Nov 2001

CONWAY & CO ‡
6 Grange Avenue Rotherfield Peppard Henley-on-Thames Oxfordshire RG9 5JP
Tel: 01491 411122 *Fax:* 01491 411122
Dx: 80513 HENLEY-ON-THAMES
E-mail: 003@conwayandco.co.uk
List of partners: L R R Conway, W McAllister
Office: Henley-on-Thames
Work: C1 C2 E J1 L O Q R1 S1 W Z(e,l)
Fixed Fee Interview and Legal Aid undertaken
Ptr: Conway, Mr Leslie R R BA . . . . *Dec 1986
McAllister, Mr William LLB. . . . . Dec 2000

CONWAY & CO
8 Reading Road Henley-on-Thames Oxfordshire RG9 1AG
Tel: 01491 411122 *Fax:* 01491 410680
Dx: 80513 HENLEY-ON-THAMES
E-mail: 001@conwayandco.co.uk
Office: Henley-on-Thames
Languages: Greek
Work: C1 C2 E J1 L O Q R1 S1 W Z(e,l)
Fixed Fee Interview and Legal Aid undertaken
Ast: Blanchard, Miss Catherine LLB(Hons). . . . . Nov 2002

COOPER SON & CALDECOTT ‡
2 West Street Henley-on-Thames Oxfordshire RG9 2DU
Tel: 01491 574203 *Fax:* 01491 410268
Dx: 80506 HENLEY-ON-THAMES
E-mail: legal@coopersolicitors.demon.co.uk
List of partners: S Bucknill, A T J Greenwood
Work: A1 B1 C1 C2 C3 D1 E F1 G H I J1 K1 L N O P Q R1 S1 S2 T2 W Z(c,d,e,l,q)
Emergency Action, Agency and Advocacy undertaken
Ptr: Bucknill, Mr Stephen BA . . . . *Sep 1991
Greenwood, Mr Andrew T J LLB(Bris). . . . . *§Jan 1979

THE HEAD PARTNERSHIP
64 Bell Street Henley-on-Thames Oxfordshire RG9 2BN
Tel: 01491 570900 *Fax:* 01491 636267
Dx: 80502 HENLEY-ON-THAMES
Office: Reading

KEALY FARMAR & CO ‡
73a Bell Street Henley-on-Thames Oxfordshire RG9 2BD
Tel: 01491 410393 *Fax:* 01491 410431
Dx: 80509 HENLEY-ON-THAMES
E-mail: rkealy@btconnect.com
List of partners: R N Farmar, R J C Kealy
Work: C1 C2 E J1 K1 L R2 S1 T1 T2 W
Ptr: Farmar, Mr Richard N BA . . . . *Dec 1979
Kealy, Mr Richard J C MA(Oxon) . . . . *Jul 1977

LAWRENCE HAMBLIN ‡
Concept House 9-11 Greys Road Henley-on-Thames Oxfordshire RG9 1SB
Tel: 01491 411884 *Fax:* 01491 411881
Dx: 80517 HENLEY-ON-THAMES
E-mail: henley@lawrencehamblin.com
List of partners: B S Bains, M L Hamblin, N Stanbrook
Office: Reading
Languages: Hindi, Punjabi, Urdu
Work: E N Q S1 S2 Z(r)
Advocacy, Fixed Fee Interview, Legal Aid undertaken and Legal Aid Franchise
Ptr: Bains, Mr Balkar S BSc(Hons) . . . . *Nov 1996
Hamblin, Mr Michael Lawrence LLB. . . . . *Jul 1991
Stanbrook, Mr Nigel. . . . . *Mar 1981
Ast: McQueen-Turner, Ms Alexa . . . . *Jun 2005

A C B HURST & CO ‡
54 New Street Henley-on-Thames Oxfordshire RG9 2BT
Tel: 01491 572699 *Fax:* 01491 577472
Dx: 80505 HENLEY-ON-THAMES
E-mail: info@acbhurst.go-plus.net
List of partners: A C B Hurst
Languages: French, Spanish
Work: E K1 L S1 W
Ptr: Hurst, Mr Andrew C B MA(Oxon) . . . . *§Jul 1965
Ast: Batty, Mrs Sally P BA . . . . *Jun 1970

DAVID ISAACS ‡
1 Berkshire Road Henley-on-Thames Oxfordshire RG9 1ND
Tel: 01491 577130 *Fax:* 01491 413873
E-mail: davidi@davislaw.fsnet.co.uk
List of partners: D L Isaacs
Office: Sutton
Work: C1 E I J1 M1 O S2 U1 U2 Z(e,f,w,z)
SPr: Isaacs, Mr David L MA(Oxon). . . . . *Jun 1981

2

JOHN MACKENZIE ‡
Rotherfield House 7 Fairmile Henley-on-Thames Oxfordshire RG9 2JR
Tel: 01491 411022

MERCERS ‡
50 New Street Henley-on-Thames Oxfordshire RG9 2BX
Tel: 01491 572138 *Fax:* 01491 572223
Dx: 80503 HENLEY-ON-THAMES
E-mail: mail@mercerslaw.co.uk
List of partners: M F Beadsworth, C S Bowler, M J Brunwin, A Carpenter, J E Sandars, P R K Stott, D J Weston
Office: Henley-on-Thames
Languages: French
Work: A1 B1 C1 C2 C3 D1 E F1 G H J1 K1 L M1 M2 N O P Q R1 S1 T1 T2 W Z(c,d,e,h,i,o)
Emergency Action, Agency, Advocacy, Legal Aid undertaken and Member of Accident Line
Ptr: Beadsworth, Mr Michael F BA(Law). . . . . *§Oct 1986
Bowler, Mr Christopher S LLB(Exon) . . . . *§Apr 1977
Brunwin, Mr Malcolm J . . . . *§Jul 1975
Carpenter, Miss Amanda LLB(Hons)(Leics) . . . . . *§Nov 1995
Sandars, Mr J Edward . . . . *§Jan 1970
Stott, Mr Paul R K LLB(Lond) . . . . *§Aug 1981
Weston, Mr David J. . . . . *§May 1967
Ast: Barker, Mr Guy William BA . . . . *Oct 1999
Bell, Mrs Carolyn A BA(Oxon). . . . . *Apr 1977
Hall, Mr Christopher David Kenneth BA; CPE; LPC . . *Sep 1998
Hopkins, Mr Peter A W BA . . . . *Sep 1997
Savin, Ms Zoe LLB(Hons). . . . . *Aug 2001
Con: Riley, Mr J Martin MA(Cantab) . . . . *§Mar 1963

MERCERS
50a Bell Street Henley-on-Thames Oxfordshire RG9 2BG
Tel: 01491 572138 *Fax:* 01491 579820
E-mail: mail@mercerslaw.co.uk
Office: Henley-on-Thames

MESSENGER & CO ‡
42b Bell Street Henley-on-Thames Oxfordshire RG9 2BG
Tel: 01491 576272 *Fax:* 01491 579972
Dx: 80501 HENLEY-ON-THAMES
E-mail: email@messengerandco.co.uk
List of partners: C A Messenger
Languages: French, Spanish
Work: A1 B1 C1 D1 E F1 K1 K3 L N O Q R1 R2 S1 S2 W
Ptr: Messenger, Mr Christopher A . . . . *Mar 1974
Ast: Streatfeild, Mrs Jane F BA . . . . *Feb 1977

K J SMITH SOLICITORS ‡
33-35 Station Road Henley-on-Thames Oxfordshire RG9 1AT
Tel: 01491 630000 *Fax:* 01491 636243
E-mail: info@kjsmith.co.uk

THORBURN & CO ‡
Belmont House 23 New Street Henley-on-Thames Oxfordshire RG9 2BP
Tel: 01491 577625 *Fax:* 01491 577694
E-mail: thorburnandco@aol.com
List of partners: J Muirhead
Languages: French, Italian
Work: B1 C1 E K1 L N O S1 W Z(i,k,l)
Emergency Action, Agency, Advocacy and Fixed Fee Interview undertaken
Ptr: Muirhead, Mr James MA . . . . Nov 1975

HEREFORD, Herefordshire

BEAUMONTS ‡
Beaumont House 1 Offa Street Hereford Herefordshire HR1 2LH
Tel: 01432 352345 *Fax:* 01432 263708 *Dx:* 17201 HEREFORD
List of partners: C H S Almond, R G P Clements, P H King, T D Treherne
Office: Bromyard
Work: A1 B1 C1 C3 D1 E J1 K1 L N O Q R1 S1 S2 T1 T2 V W Z(c,l,t)
Emergency Action, Agency, Advocacy and Legal Aid Franchise
Ptr: Almond, Mr Charles H S LLB(Leics). . . . . *Sep 1979
Clements, Mr Richard G P LLB . . . . *Oct 1984
King, Mrs Patricia Hunter LLB. . . . . Feb 2001
Treherne, Mr Timothy D LLB(L'pool). . . . . *Sep 1987
Asoc: Reid, Mrs Maxine . . . . May 2002
Con: Powell, Mr Christopher G MA; LLM(Cantab) Jurisprudence Prize . . . . *§Apr 1969

CALDICOTT GALLIMORE
21 Commercial Street Hereford Herefordshire HR1 2DE
Tel: 01432 261200 *Fax:* 01432 261213
E-mail: lawyers@caldicotts.com
Office: Leominster

CARVER JONES ‡
44 Bridge Street Hereford Herefordshire HR4 9DN
Tel: 01432 274301 *Fax:* 01432 352268 *Dx:* 17223 HEREFORD
E-mail: accounts@carverjones.co.uk
List of partners: J A Jones, L J R Rowberry
Work: K3 Q S1 S2 W
Ptr: Jones, Mr John Allan LLB. . . . . Nov 1972
Rowberry, Mrs Lucinda Jane Rosemary LLB; AKC . . Apr 1975
Ast: Stribling, Mr Christopher Richard Miles LLB . . . . . Jun 1980
Con: Nowell, Mr David R G LLB . . . . Jan 1977

COULSON READ LEWIS SOLICITORS ‡
St Peters Chambers 14a St Peters Street Hereford Herefordshire HR1 2LE
Tel: 01432 357005

ANTHONY M DAVIES SOLICITORS ‡
4 St Martins Street Hereford Herefordshire HR2 7RE
Tel: 01432 349004

GC LAW ‡
4b St Peters Street Hereford Herefordshire HR1 2LA
Tel: 01432 275397 *Fax:* 01432 275418
Emergency telephone 01432 275397
Languages: Italian
Work: B2 G H Z(g)
Agency, Advocacy, Fixed Fee Interview and Legal Aid undertaken
Ast: Divitantonio, Ms Marilena LLB. . . . . *Nov 2004

GABBS LLP ‡
14 Broad Street Hereford Herefordshire HR4 9AP
Tel: 01432 353481 *Fax:* 01432 353537 *Dx:* 17205 HEREFORD
Emergency telephone 01432 353481
E-mail: hereford@gabbs.biz
List of partners: J J Lee, E Phillips, J Stenner-Evans, J H Thacker, J E Wilding
Office: Hay-on-Wye, Leominster
Languages: French
Work: A1 A2 B1 C1 C2 C3 D1 D2 E F1 J1 K1 L M2 N O Q R1 S1 S2 T1 T2 W Z(d,l,o,p,q,r)
Emergency Action, Agency and Advocacy undertaken
Ptr: Lee, Mr James J BA . . . . *§Dec 1979
Phillips, Mrs Elaine . . . . Dec 1996
Wilding, Mr Jeremy J E MA(Oxon) Under Sheriff of Hertfordshire . . . . *§Oct 1987
Asoc: Whittall, Mrs Sarah C LLB(Warw) . . . . *§Dec 1989
Ast: Freeman, Mr Simon LLB . . . . Jan 1980
Grazier, Mrs Susan Nicola Jane LLB(Hons); DNP Notary Public . . . . Apr 2004

GARDNER DALLIMORE ‡
First Floor 52 Broad Street Hereford Herefordshire HR4 9AB
Tel: 01432 263535 *Fax:* 01432 263208 *Dx:* 17236 HEREFORD
Emergency telephone 07889 961663
List of partners: R J Dallimore, D H Gardner
Work: A1 B1 D1 E F1 G H J1 K1 L R1 S1 T1 T2 V W Z(c,l)
Emergency Action, Agency, Advocacy, Fixed Fee Interview and Legal Aid undertaken
Ptr: Dallimore, Mr Roger John LLB(Hons) . . . . *Nov 1989
Gardner, Mr Douglas Howard LLB(Hons) . . . . . . *§Feb 1975

GORDON LUTTON ‡
Wyevale Business Park Wyevale Way Hereford Herefordshire HR4 7BS
Tel: 01432 355345 *Fax:* 01432 278997 *Dx:* 17203 HEREFORD
E-mail: mail@gordonlutton.co.uk
List of partners: R N Beaumont, C D Gordon, M Hayes, C S Whittaker
Work: A1 B1 C1 C2 C3 D1 E F1 J1 K1 L N O P Q R1 S1 S2 T1 T2 W Z(l)
Emergency Action, Agency and Fixed Fee Interview undertaken
Ptr: Beaumont, Mr Robert N BA. . . . . *Oct 1989
Gordon, Mr Colin D BA . . . . *Oct 1978
Hayes, Mr Matthew LLB. . . . . Jan 2004
Whittaker, Mrs Clare S . . . . *Nov 1991
Ast: Goodwin, Mrs Alison LLB . . . . *Nov 2005
Greves, Mrs Melissa Katie LLB(Hons). . . . . Sep 2009
Middleton, Mrs Karen Elizabeth Curtis. . . . . *Jan 1982
Con: Hartwell, Mr David G . . . . *Dec 1975

HARRISON CLARK LLP
1st Floor Chambers 18 King Street Hereford Herefordshire HR4 9BX
Tel: 01432 267928 *Fax:* 01989 565961
E-mail: lawyers@harrison-clark.co.uk
Office: Cheltenham, Ross-on-Wye, Worcester (2 offices)

HUMFRYS & SYMONDS ‡
St John's Chambers 1 St Johns Street Hereford Herefordshire HR1 2ND
Tel: 01432 359261 / 276276 *Fax:* 01432 278726
Dx: 17202 HEREFORD
E-mail: dcampion@humfrys-symonds.co.uk
List of partners: D J Campion, S P Ferguson, A J Johnson, J A H Jones
Work: A1 B1 C1 D1 E F1 K1 K3 L M1 N P R1 S1 T1 V W
Emergency Action, Agency, Advocacy, Legal Aid undertaken, Legal Aid Franchise and Member of Accident Line
Ptr: Campion, Mr David J LLB. . . . . *§Apr 1982
Ferguson, Mr Stephen P BA . . . . *§Apr 1980
Johnson, Mr Andrew James BA. . . . . Nov 2001
Jones, Mr J A Huw BA . . . . *§Feb 1983
Asoc: Bracey, Mr Jeremy M LLB(Hons) . . . . *§Sep 1982
Bradshaw, Ms Beverley Joan LLB(Hons) . . . . . . May 2006
Tay-Lodge, Mrs Anna Louise LLB(Hons). . . . . . . *Feb 1991
Ast: Puri, Mrs Mira LLB(Hons) . . . . Oct 2002

KIDWELLS ‡
Phoenix Chambers 17 King Street Hereford Herefordshire HR4 9BX
Tel: 01432 278179 *Fax:* 01432 275795 *Dx:* 17216 HEREFORD
E-mail: info@kidwellssolicitors.co.uk

LAMBE CORNER ‡
36-37 Bridge Street Hereford Herefordshire HR4 9DJ
Tel: 01432 355301 *Fax:* 01432 356619 *Dx:* 17207 HEREFORD
E-mail: enq@lambecorner.co.uk
List of partners: H G M Bricknell, C R George, D M Halpern, L T Kidman, F H B Parsons, R J T Wooderson
Work: A1 A2 B1 C1 C2 D1 E F1 G J1 J2 K1 K2 K3 L M1 N O P Q R1 R2 S1 S2 T1 T2 V W X Z(c,h,l,q,r,t)
Agency, Advocacy and Fixed Fee Interview undertaken
Ptr: Bricknell, Mr H G Mark LLB(Wales) Deputy Coroner for Herefordshire . . . . *Oct 1983
George, Mr Charles R. . . . . *Jul 1980
Halpern, Mr David M LLB(Lond) H M Coroner of Herefordshire . . . . *Mar 1971
Kidman, Miss Lucy Therese BA(Hons); Attorney of Law Trinidad & Tobago . . . . *Mar 2000
Parsons, Ms Fiona H B BA . . . . *Sep 1998
Wooderson, Mr Roland J T LLB Assistant Coroner for Herefordshire . . . . *Oct 1987
Asoc: Cuncliffe, Mr Alexander P LLB . . . . Apr 2008

LANYON BOWDLER LLP
11 King Street Hereford Herefordshire HR4 9BW
Tel: 01432 378379 *Fax:* 01432 378383 *Dx:* 17255 HEREFORD
E-mail: enquiries@lblaw.co.uk
Office: Ludlow, Oswestry (2 offices), Shrewsbury, Telford, Wellington
Ptr: Lewis, Mr Peter Vaughan LLB. . . . . §Dec 1973

GUY LINLEY-ADAMS ‡
First Floor Offices 46 Bridge Street Hereford Herefordshire HR4 9DG
Tel: 01432 379093 *Fax:* 07837 881219
E-mail: guy@linley-adams.co.uk

MARCHES LAW
2 Offa Street Hereford Herefordshire HR1 2LJ
Tel: 01432 355366
E-mail: marcheslaw@hotmail.co.uk
Office: Tenbury Wells

T A MATTHEWS ‡
6 & 7 King Street Hereford Herefordshire HR4 9BS
Tel: 01432 352121 *Fax:* 01432 352700 *Dx:* 172041 HEREFORD
Emergency telephone 01432 352121
E-mail: m.speight@tamatthews.co.uk
List of partners: D M Backhouse, K E C Middleton, R C Smallwood, J Soderstrom, M R Speight
Office: Leominster
Work: A1 A3 B1 C1 D1 E F1 J1 K1 K2 K3 L N O Q S1 S2 T1 T2 W Z(c,d,l,q,r)
Agency, Fixed Fee Interview, Legal Aid undertaken, Legal Aid Franchise and Member of Accident Line
Ptr: Backhouse, Mr Derek M BSc . . . . *Nov 1990
Middleton, Mrs Karen Elizabeth Curtis. . . . . *Jan 1982
Smallwood, Mr Rodney Clive . . . . §Jan 1969
Soderstrom, Mr John-Berndt BSc(Hons). . . . . . . Oct 1993
Speight, Mr Malcolm R LLB . . . . *Oct 1970
Ast: Pryce, Mrs Gillian LLB(Hons) . . . . *Sep 1989

MORTIMERS
15 King Street Hereford Herefordshire HR4 9BX
Tel: 01432 355572 *Fax:* 01432 355923 *Dx:* 17217 HEREFORD
Office: Bridgnorth, Ludlow

MUNDY'S ‡
The Warehouse Gwynne Street Hereford Herefordshire HR4 9DP
Tel: 01432 265630 *Fax:* 01432 262799

GWYNETH O OWEN SOLICITOR ‡
Upper Haven Cottage Dilwyn Hereford Herefordshire HR4 8JE
Tel: 01544 318738
List of partners: G O Owen
Work: K1 S1 T2 W
Ptr: Owen, Miss Gwyneth O LLB . . . . *Sep 1978

THE WOODLAND DAVIES PARTNERSHIP LLP
Russell House 16 St Owen Street Hereford Herefordshire HR1 2PL
Tel: 01432 353727 *Fax:* 01432 353262
Office: Brecon, Hay-on-Wye, Kington, Talgarth

HERNE BAY, Kent

BULL & BULL
118a High Street Herne Bay Kent CT6 5JY
Tel: 01227 742660 *Fax:* 01227 742661
E-mail: hernebay@bullandbull.co.uk
Office: Canterbury, Faversham
Languages: French
Work: A1 C1 D1 E F1 J1 K1 L N Q S1 S2 T1 T2 V W Z(f,i,k,l,m,q,r)
Emergency Action, Agency, Advocacy, Fixed Fee Interview, Legal Aid undertaken, Legal Aid Franchise and Member of Accident Line
Ptr: Baldock, Mr Geoffrey . . . . *Jan 1987

DAVIS SIMMONDS DONAGHEY
91-95 High Street Herne Bay Kent CT6 5LQ
Tel: 01227 361690 *Fax:* 01227 363587
Office: Gillingham, Sittingbourne

ES LAW ‡
Lower Ground Floor 106 High Street Herne Bay Kent CT6 5LE
Tel: 01227 283388

FOSTERS LAW LIMITED ‡
67 High Street Herne Bay Kent CT6 5LQ
Tel: 01227 283634 *Fax:* 01227 283618 *Dx:* 32300 HERNE BAY
E-mail: info@fosters-law.co.uk
List of partners: E R Foster, C O'Mahoney
Office: Broadstairs
Languages: French
Work: A3 B1 C1 E F1 F2 J1 K1 K2 K3 K4 L N O Q R1 R2 S1 S2 W Z(c,h,r)
Agency and Fixed Fee Interview undertaken
Ptr: Foster, Mr Edward Richard LLB(Hons); DipLP. . . . *Aug 1997
O'Mahoney, Ms Catherine. . . . . Jan 2004
Ast: Skilbeck, Mr Jonathan. . . . . Jan 2008

GIRLINGS
39 William Street Herne Bay Kent CT6 5NR
Tel: 01227 367355 *Fax:* 01227 365348 *Dx:* 32303 HERNE BAY
E-mail: enquiries@girlings.com
Office: Ashford (2 offices), Canterbury, Margate
Work: D1 D2 K1 K2 K3 K4 S1 S2 T2 W
Advocacy, Fixed Fee Interview and Legal Aid Franchise
Ptr: Burrow, Mr Ian N LLB. . . . . *Apr 1976
Record, Mrs Susan E MA(Oxon) Winter Williams Law Prize 1979 . . . . *§Oct 1982
Neeve, Mr Chris FILEx . . . . NSP

LYONS SOLICITOR ‡
57 William Street Herne Bay Kent CT6 5NR
Tel: 01227 360801 / 07906 759286 *Fax:* 01227 741723
E-mail: michael@lyonssolicitor.co.uk
List of partners: M Lyons
SPr: Lyons, Mr Michael. . . . . Feb 2002

PARRY LAW
Lloyds Bank Chambers 144-146 High Street Herne Bay Kent CT6 5NJ
Tel: 01227 361131 *Fax:* 01227 373606 *Dx:* 32301 HERNE BAY
E-mail: info@parrylaw.co.uk
Office: Whitstable
Languages: German
Work: A1 C1 C2 D1 E F1 J1 K1 K3 L M1 O P Q R1 R2 S1 S2 T1 V W Z(c,d,e,f,l,o)
Agency and Fixed Fee Interview undertaken
Ptr: Goodwin, Mr Timothy P LLB(Hons); TEP Chairman of Age Concern, Whitstable . . . . *Oct 1994
Parry, Mr Stephen Lloyd LLB . . . . *Dec 1985
Sethna, Perveez . . . . Jan 1995
Teasdale, Miss Kate J LLB(Hons) . . . . *Oct 1990
Asoc: Stokoe, Miss Natalie LLB(Hons). . . . . *Oct 2002

HERTFORD, Hertfordshire

BETTERIDGES ‡
25a London Road Hertford Hertfordshire SG13 7LG
Tel: 01992 505406 *Fax:* 01992 512600 *Dx:* 57927 HERTFORD
E-mail: info@betteridges.com
List of partners: M A Betteridge
Work: D1 D2 K1 K3 Q S1 W
SPr: Betteridge, Mr Mark A BA(Hons) . . . . *Feb 1989

BREEZE & WYLES SOLICITORS LLP ‡
2nd Floor Stag House Old London Road Hertford Hertfordshire SG13 7LA
Tel: 01992 558411 *Fax:* 01992 582834 *Dx:* 57901 HERTFORD
List of partners: J M Appleton, M J Dismore, M Fraser, M Gupta, O McCarthy, B O'Brien, R J Thompson, A Toulson, P A Tunstill
Office: Bishop's Stortford, Cheshunt, Enfield
Work: A3 C1 C2 E J1 K1 K2 K3 L O Q R1 S1 S2 W Z(p)
Fixed Fee Interview, Legal Aid undertaken, Legal Aid Franchise and S.I.G
Dir: Dismore, Mrs Margaret Jane BEd(Cantab) . . . . . . *Oct 1995
McCarthy, Ms Olive . . . . *Jun 2000
Tunstill, Mr Peter A LLB(Lond); FCIArb . . . . *Apr 1972
Asoc: Gautam, Henal . . . . Jan 2004
Moore, Mr Andrew Kenneth. . . . . Oct 1990

HILARY A COURTNEIDGE ‡
53 The Avenue Bengeo Hertford Hertfordshire SG14 3DS
Tel: 01992 589120 *Fax:* 01992 504798
List of partners: H A Courtneidge
Work: S1 W
Ptr: Courtneidge, Mrs Hilary A LLB . . . . *Sep 1977

DUFFIELD HARRISON LLP
27-29 Fore Street Hertford Hertfordshire SG14 1DG
Tel: 01992 587065 *Fax:* 01992 585000 *Dx:* 57910 HERTFORD
Office: Hoddesdon
Agency undertaken

GARDEN HOUSE SOLICITORS ‡
23 London Road Hertford Hertfordshire SG13 7LG
Tel: 01992 422128 *Fax:* 01992 422129 *Dx:* 57905 HERTFORD
E-mail: patricia@gardenhousesolicitors.co.uk
List of partners: P Ling
Work: J1 N Q W
Agency, Fixed Fee Interview undertaken and Member of Accident Line
SPr: Ling, Patricia . . . . Jan 1998
Ast: Chopra, Miss Nidhi . . . . Sep 2010
Koon Koon, Mr David . . . . Mar 2009

JAMESON & HILL ‡
72-74 Fore Street Hertford Hertfordshire SG14 1BY
Tel: 01992 554881 *Fax:* 01992 551885 *Dx:* 57908 HERTFORD
E-mail: law@jamesonandhill.co.uk
List of partners: S J Battersby, N A Evans, R A Jameson, A P Singh
Office: Ware
Languages: French, German
Work: A1 B1 C1 C2 D1 E F1 F2 G H J1 K1 K2 L N O P Q R1 S1 S2 W X Z(l,r,t)
Emergency Action, Agency, Advocacy, Fixed Fee Interview, Legal Aid undertaken, Legal Aid Franchise and Member of Accident Line
Ptr: Battersby, Mr Stephen J LLB(Sheff) . . . . *Jun 1971
Jameson, Mr Robert A LLB(Sheff). . . . . *Oct 1971
Singh, Mr Andel Parthab LLB(Hons) ★ . . . . Oct 1997
Ast: Chapman, Mrs Anna Ruby LLB(Hons); LLM(Legal Practice) . . . . Aug 2003
Darwish, Mr Daniel BA . . . . *Jun 1997
Goodman, Mr Peter Wayne LLB(NZ) . . . . *Dec 1976
Johnson, Mr Philip . . . . *Aug 1991
Savva, Miss Maria LLB; LSF Sweet & Maxwell Law Prize 1990 . . . . *Jan 1996
Smith, Miss Katherine Ann FILEx University of Hertfordshire - Hawkins Russell Jones Prize - Employment Law . Oct 2005

JUDKINS SOLICITORS ‡
Prince of Wales House 3 Bluecoats Avenue Hertford Hertfordshire SG14 1PB
Tel: 01992 500456 *Fax:* 01992 505864 *Dx:* 57925 HERTFORD
List of partners: I C Judkins, P Judkins
Work: D1 J1 K1 K3 S1 S2
Agency and Advocacy undertaken
Ptr: Judkins, Mrs Irene Catherine BCL. . . . . Sep 1996
Judkins, Mr Paul BA . . . . Oct 1992

LEGAL MOVES (BRADDON & SNOW LIMITED) ‡
23a Fore Street Hertford Hertfordshire SG14 1DJ
Tel: 01992 536503 *Fax:* 01992 581314 *Dx:* 57911 HERTFORD
E-mail: legal.moves@btconnect.com
List of partners: S G Szolcek
SPr: Szolcek, Mrs Sara Gail LLB. . . . . *Jul 1985

LONGMORES ‡
24 Castle Street Hertford Hertfordshire SG14 1HP
Tel: 01992 300333 *Fax:* 01992 552662 *Dx:* 57900 HERTFORD
E-mail: advice@longmores-solicitors.co.uk
List of partners: A B Baptist, G J Field, E L Gallop, R Gvero, R M Horwood, C E Pease, R N Taylor
Languages: Polish, Serbo-Croat
Work: A1 A2 C1 C2 E F1 F2 J1 J2 K1 K3 K4 L O P Q R1 R2 S1 S2 T1 T2 W Z(b,c,d,j,n,p,q)
Agency, Advocacy and Fixed Fee Interview undertaken
Ptr: Baptist, Ms Anna B BA . . . . *§May 1979
Field, Mr Graham J BA . . . . *§May 1977
Gallop, Mrs Elizabeth Laura LLB . . . . *§Apr 1980
Gvero, Mr Richard BA. . . . . *§Dec 1991
Horwood, Mr Richard M LLB . . . . *§Sep 2001
Pease, Mr Christopher E LLB . . . . *§Oct 1986
Taylor, Mr Richard N . . . . *§Jun 1977
Ast: Ferreira, Mr Heinrich . . . . Jul 2006
France, Mr Robert . . . . *Sep 2004
Mills, Mrs Catrin BA(Hons); CPE; LLB. . . . . Jan 2000
Smith, Amy . . . . Jan 2009
Wiblin, Mr John Richard BA(Hons); LLB; LLM; FCIArb ♦ . . . . Mar 2004

MCKENZIES
Tooke House 20 Bull Plain Hertford Hertfordshire SG14 1DT
Tel: 01992 503344 *Fax:* 01992 501166 *Dx:* 57912 HERTFORD
E-mail: enquiries@mckenzies-solicitors.co.uk
Office: London N9
Ast: Genco, Giuseppina . . . . Feb 2011

See p112 for the Key to Work Categories & other symbols

Ricca, Alexandra . . . . Oct 2006
Shah, Zawar Hussain . . . . Jan 2002

MCLELLANS ‡
Old Cross House Old Cross Hertford Hertfordshire SG14 1RB
Tel: 01992 532000 *Fax:* 01992 534020 *Dx:* 57921 HERTFORD
E-mail: enquiries@mclellans.co.uk
List of partners: C M Eames, S A Locke
Work: C1 E F1 F2 J1 J2 L O Q S1 S2 Z(e,l,p,y)
Agency, Advocacy and Fixed Fee Interview undertaken
Ptr: Eames, Miss Clare Magaret LLB . . . . *Sep 1997
Locke, Mr Simon A LLB. . . . . *Dec 1989
Ast: Banwell, Ms Caroline LLB(Hons) . . . . Nov 1997
Connor, Mr Nigel William BA . . . . *Aug 1997

MANOR LAW FAMILY SOLICITORS ‡
27 Railway Street Hertford Hertfordshire SG14 1BA
Tel: 01992 306616 *Fax:* 01992 306617
E-mail: info@manorlawfamilysolicitors.co.uk
Languages: Bosnian, Croatian, Serbian
Work: K1
Fixed Fee Interview undertaken

MELDRUM YOUNG SOLICITORS
1st Floor Abbey Chambers 10 Bull Plain Hertford Hertfordshire SG14 1DT
Tel: 01992 535866 *Fax:* 01992 535867 *Dx:* 57919 HERTFORD
Office: St Albans, Watford

NICOLAOU SOLICITORS ‡
The Barn Studios Burnt Farm Ride Goffs Oak Hertford Hertfordshire EN7 5JA
Tel: 01707 877707 *Fax:* 01707 877708
E-mail: niclaw@tiscali.co.uk
List of partners: C Nicolaou
Languages: French
Work: C1 C3 I J1 M1 U2 Z(e,f,l,z,za)
Agency and Fixed Fee Interview undertaken
SPr: Nicolaou, Ms Constantina BA(Hons); LLM(Cantab) . . *Oct 1987

HESSLE, East Riding of Yorkshire

WELTON HARRISON ‡
Unit 1 2-6 Prestongate Hessle East Riding of Yorkshire HU13 0RE
Tel: 01482 627711 *Fax:* 01482 627703 *Dx:* 700072 HESSLE
E-mail: info@weltonlaw.co.uk
List of partners: P Harrison, T Welton
Work: E L R2 S1 S2 W
Ptr: Harrison, Mr Paul LLB. . . . . *Nov 1984
Welton, Mr Timothy LLB Andrew Marvell Jackson Prize (Hull University) . . . . *Oct 1986

HESWALL, Merseyside

C M BRAND ‡
The White House 7 The Paddock Heswall Merseyside CH60 1XJ
Tel: 0151 342 3081 *Fax:* 0151 342 5052
E-mail: cmbrandlaw@aol.com
List of partners: C M Brand
Work: R1
SPr: Brand, Mr Clive Maurice LLB . . . . *Dec 1975

LEES SOLICITORS LLP
90-92 Telegraph Road Heswall Merseyside CH60 0AQ
Tel: 0151 342 6273 *Fax:* 0151 342 8026 *Dx:* 14756 HESWALL
E-mail: info@lees.co.uk
Office: Birkenhead, West Kirby
Languages: Welsh
Work: B1 C1 C2 D1 E J1 K1 K2 K3 K4 L N O Q R1 R2 S1 S2 T1 T2 U2 W Z(c,d,l,m,q,r)
Agency, Fixed Fee Interview, Legal Aid undertaken and Member of Accident Line
Ptr: Broughton, Mr Mark William LLB . . . . *Sep 2002
Kingston-Davies, Ms Joanna . . . . .NSP
Ast: Wallace, Mr James . . . . Jan 2009

MAXWELL HODGE SOLICITORS
234 Telegraph Road Heswall Merseyside CH60 0AL
Tel: 0151 342 6447 *Fax:* 0151 342 7071 *Dx:* 14752 HESWALL
E-mail: info@maxweb.co.uk
Office: Formby, Huyton, Kirkby, Liverpool (2 offices), Maghull, West Kirby
Work: D1 E F1 F2 K1 K3 K4 N Q S1 S2 T2 W
Emergency Action, Agency, Advocacy, Fixed Fee Interview, Legal Aid undertaken and Legal Aid Franchise
Ptr: Dickinson, Mrs Christine A BA. . . . . *Jun 1982
Asoc: Jones, Mr Nigel Graham LLB(Hons). . . . . *May 2000
Morley, Ms Brenda LLB . . . . *Sep 1972

HEXHAM, Northumberland

ASH SOLICITORS ‡
7 Back Row Hexham Northumberland NE46 3PF
Tel: 01434 609829 *Fax:* 01434 607580
E-mail: ash_solicitors@btconnect.com

GIBSON & CO ‡
Saddlers Cottage Front Street Bellingham Hexham Northumberland NE48 2AA
Tel: 01434 602131 *Fax:* 01434 609365 *Dx:* 63201 HEXHAM
E-mail: melanie@gibsons-law.com
List of partners: D L Bawn, A G Gibson, D S C Gibson, J P Gibson, T J Gibson, M J Macgregor
Office: Newcastle upon Tyne
Languages: French
Work: A1 A2 E F1 J1 K1 K3 K4 L O Q S1 S2 T2 W Z(l,s)
Emergency Action, Agency and Advocacy undertaken
Ptr: Gibson, Mr Anthony Gair MA . . . . *Jan 1965
Gibson, Mr Derwent S C . . . . *Dec 1972
Gibson, Mr Toby J BA(Hons) ♦ . . . . *Oct 1995
Macgregor, Mr Michael James MA . . . . *§Feb 1985

MARSTONHARBOTTLE ‡
Orchard House Priestpopple Hexham Northumberland NE46 1PQ
Tel: 01434 602486 *Fax:* 01434 600229 *Dx:* 63204 HEXHAM
E-mail: reception@marstonharbottle.com
List of partners: R L Harbottle
Work: D1 D2 K1 K3 K4 L R2 S1 W
Emergency Action, Agency, Advocacy, Fixed Fee Interview, Legal Aid undertaken and Legal Aid Franchise
Ptr: Harbottle, Miss Ruth L LLB . . . . *§Nov 1983
Ast: Owens, Mrs Ann LLB(Hons). . . . . Feb 1994

NICHOLSON PORTNELL ‡
Priestpopple House Priestpopple Hexham Northumberland NE46 1PL
Tel: 01434 603656 *Fax:* 01434 608513 *Dx:* 63202 HEXHAM
E-mail: reception@nicholsonportnell.com
List of partners: P M Air, W R Best, R G Nelson
Languages: French
Work: A1 A2 C1 D1 E F1 J1 K1 K4 L N O P Q R1 S1 S2 T2 W Z(d,k,l)
Emergency Action, Agency, Fixed Fee Interview and Legal Aid undertaken
Ptr: Air, Miss Pamela M LLB. . . . . *§Oct 1982
Best, Ms Wendy R BSc . . . . *Jan 1985
Nelson, Mr Richard G LLB . . . . *§Oct 1984
Ast: Bragg, Mrs Alison M LLB . . . . *Dec 1987
Frost, Ms Sara Caroline LLB; TEP. . . . . *Oct 1986
Jewitt, Mr Simon Edward MA . . . . Sep 2005
Little, Miss Catherine Rose LLB. . . . . *Sep 2007
Murphy, Miss Laura Vivien LLB . . . . Sep 2010
Williams, Mr David LLB . . . . Sep 2010
Con: Humble, Mr John BA . . . . *§Mar 1984
Jewitt, Mr Peter A LLB . . . . *§Apr 1971

THE PROBATE FIRM ‡
Garden House Anick Hexham Northumberland NE46 4LL
Tel: 01434 600024
E-mail: john.halliday@theprobatefirm.com

RAMSEY ROBINSON SOLICITORS ‡
Mallan House Bridge End Industrial Estate Hexham Northumberland NE46 4DQ
Tel: 01434 610442 *Dx:* 63220 HEXHAM

STEMBRIDGE SOLICITORS ‡
Bishopside Allendale Hexham Northumberland NE47 9LR
Tel: 01434 618696 *Fax:* 01434 207534
E-mail: legal@stemshipping.com

SWINBURNE & JACKSON LLP
3 Orchard Place Hexham Northumberland NE46 1QQ
Tel: 01434 607035 *Fax:* 01434 608151 *Dx:* 63208 HEXHAM
E-mail: hexham@swinburnejackson.com
Office: Chester-le-Street, Gateshead, Ryton, Washington

WILLIAMSONS
40 Priestpopple Hexham Northumberland NE46 1PQ
Tel: 01434 602643 / 606308 *Fax:* 01434 608416 *Dx:* 63205 HEXHAM
E-mail: bjc@williamsons-solicitors.co.uk
Office: Whitley Bay
Work: A1 B1 C1 C2 C3 D1 E F1 G H J1 K1 L M1 M2 N P R1 S1 T1 T2 W
Agency, Advocacy, Fixed Fee Interview, Legal Aid undertaken and Member of Accident Line
Ptr: Craig, Mr E Graham BA. . . . . *Dec 1976

HEYWOOD, Greater Manchester

CARR HEWITT & CO ‡
1 Taylor Street Heywood Greater Manchester OL10 1EF
Tel: 01706 624240 *Fax:* 01706 691255
E-mail: carrhewitt@btconnect.com

HARDMAN & WHITTLES ‡
25 Market Place Heywood Greater Manchester OL10 1JY
Tel: 01706 369027 *Dx:* 13975 HEYWOOD
List of partners: D R Whittles, G G Whittles
Work: G J1 K1 N S1 W Z(j,o)
Fixed Fee Interview, Legal Aid undertaken and Member of Accident Line
Ptr: Whittles, Mr David R . . . . *Oct 1993

ISHERWOOD & HOSE ‡
6 Market Street Heywood Greater Manchester OL10 4NB
Tel: 01706 360032 / 368741 *Fax:* 01706 624222
Dx: 13973 HEYWOOD
E-mail: isherwoodandhose@btconnect.com
List of partners: C J Davidson, J C G Hulbert, M C McLachlan
Office: Rochdale
Languages: Punjabi, Urdu
Work: E F1 G H K1 K3 K4 L N Q S1 S2 V W
Emergency Action, Agency, Advocacy, Fixed Fee Interview, Legal Aid undertaken, Legal Aid Franchise and Member of Accident Line
Ptr: Davidson, Mr Colin J BA . . . . *Jan 1991
Hulbert, Mr John C G LLB. . . . . *§Dec 1968
McLachlan, Miss Moira C LLB. . . . . *Mar 1984
Ast: Begum, Miss Uzma Nasreen LLB . . . . *Apr 2006
Swientozielskyj, Miss Debbie LLB(Hons) . . . . . . *Apr 2006

LATIMER LEE LLP
59 York Street Heywood Greater Manchester OL10 4NR
Tel: 01706 628008 *Fax:* 01706 629761
E-mail: info@latimerlee.com
Office: Bolton, Bury, Prestwich
Work: C2 D1 E G H J1 K1 L N O P Q R1 S1 T1 T2 V W X Z(m)
Agency, Advocacy, Fixed Fee Interview undertaken and Member of Accident Line
Ptr: Latimer, Mrs Patricia M . . . . Oct 1974

CHRISTINE SHARP & CO ‡
13 York Street Heywood Greater Manchester OL10 4NN
Tel: 01706 623513 *Fax:* 01706 626800 *Dx:* 13972 HEYWOOD
E-mail: christinesharp@btconnect.com
List of partners: D J Midgley, C E Sharp
Work: B1 C1 D1 D2 E F1 J1 K1 K3 K4 L O P Q R1 S1 S2 W
Emergency Action, Agency, Advocacy and Fixed Fee Interview undertaken
Ptr: Midgley, Mr David J LLB . . . . May 1979
Sharp, Ms Christine E BA. . . . . *May 1981

TEMPERLEY TAYLOR LLP
Church Place Hartley Street Heywood Greater Manchester OL10 1LT
Tel: 01706 623511 *Fax:* 01706 625399 *Dx:* 13971 HEYWOOD
E-mail: im@temperleytaylor.co.uk
Office: Middleton
Work: C1 E J1 K1 K3 O Q S1 S2 W
Ptr: Mann, Mr Ian A LLB. . . . . *Oct 1981

WALDRON & SCHOFIELD ‡
25 York Street Heywood Greater Manchester OL10 4NN
Tel: 01706 624029 *Fax:* 01706 625628 *Dx:* 13976 HEYWOOD
E-mail: mail@waldronandschofield.com
List of partners: J A Schofield, J F Waldron
Work: B1 C1 C2 C3 D1 E F1 G H J1 K1 L M1 M2 N P R1 S1 T1 T2 V W Z(c,d,f,j,l,m,p,s,t)
Emergency Action, Agency, Advocacy, Fixed Fee Interview and Legal Aid undertaken
Ptr: Schofield, Mr James A LLM. . . . . *Dec 1970
Waldron, Mr James F LLB. . . . . *May 1977

2

HIGH WYCOMBE, Buckinghamshire

ALLAN JANES LLP ‡
21-23 Easton Street High Wycombe Buckinghamshire HP11 1NT
Tel: 01494 521301 *Fax:* 01494 442315 *Dx:* 4402 HIGH WYCOMBE
E-mail: enquiries@allanjanes.com
List of partners: P G Collier, R I Emanuel, C J G Hitchen, N Morrison
Work: A1 B1 C1 C2 C3 E F1 I J1 K1 L N O P Q R1 S1 S2 T1 T2 V W Z(c,k,m,o,t)
Emergency Action, Agency, Advocacy, Fixed Fee Interview undertaken and Member of Accident Line
Ptr: Emanuel, Mr Richard Iwan BA . . . . Nov 1994
Mem: Collier, Mr Peter G . . . . *Feb 1984
Hitchen, Mr Clive J G BA(Law) . . . . *Jan 1981
Morrison, Mr Nicholas LLB; Dip FR Law. . . . . *Feb 1996

BAILY GIBSON
30 High Street High Wycombe Buckinghamshire HP11 2AG
Tel: 01494 442661 *Fax:* 01494 525313 *Dx:* 4453 HIGH WYCOMBE 1
E-mail: wycombe@bailygibson.co.uk
Office: Beaconsfield
Languages: Hindi
Work: C1 C2 C3 E G H J1 K1 N Q S1 S2 T1 T2 W Z(e)
Agency, Legal Aid undertaken and Legal Aid Franchise
Ptr: Owen, Mr Lionel Peter Stephen Nicholls Prize. . . . *Sep 1974
Young, Mr Jeremy N BA(Law). . . . . *Mar 1986
Ast: Armitage, Miss Katie . . . . *Dec 2005
Bajwa, Miss Humaira Jabeen LLB; MA . . . . *Mar 2004
Crown, Mr Thomas Henry Robert LLB. . . . . *Sep 2007
Harper, Miss Jane. . . . . Sep 2006
Orman, Miss Elizabeth J . . . . *Sep 1998
Smith, Miss Rachel Louise LLB . . . . *Aug 2005
Wainman, Mr Richard J LLB. . . . . *Aug 1999

BARREA LLP ‡
85 Oxford Road High Wycombe Buckinghamshire HP11 2DX
Tel: 01494 537699 *Fax:* 01494 438612 *Dx:* 4455 HIGH WYCOMBE
E-mail: admin@barrea.co.uk
List of partners: A Barrea, P Macavoy
Languages: French, German, Italian
Work: B1 C1 D1 E F1 F2 G I J1 K1 L M1 N O Q R1 S1 S2 T2 W Z(c,d,e,f,g,i,q,w,z)
Agency and Fixed Fee Interview undertaken
Ptr: Barrea, Mr Angelo BA(Hons) . . . . *Feb 1997
Macavoy, Mr Patrick LLB(Hons). . . . . *Jul 1975

BERKLEYS ‡
19-20 Eston Street High Wycombe Buckinghamshire HP11 1NT
Tel: 0870 446 0704 *Fax:* 0870 446 0706
E-mail: advice@berkleyssolicitors.co.uk

BLASER MILLS ‡
Park House 31 London Road High Wycombe Buckinghamshire HP11 1BZ
Tel: 01494 450171 *Fax:* 01494 441815
Dx: 139590 HIGH WYCOMBE 6
List of partners: S Bennett, L K Benning, D E Herman, J Hutchison, D J A Kemp, A Kharbanda, A Kirk, J Lilley, S Manek, D J Matthews, J H Monk, A J Palmer, D J Rogers, C J Smith, M Thakrar, D A Tollinton
Office: Amersham, Aylesbury, Chesham, Harrow, Rickmansworth, Staines
Languages: French, Gujarati, Urdu
Work: C1 C3 D1 E F1 G H J1 K1 K3 L N O Q R1 S1 S2 Z(e,k,l,q)
Emergency Action, Agency, Advocacy, Fixed Fee Interview, Legal Aid undertaken, Legal Aid Franchise and Member of Accident Line
Ptr: Bennett, Mr Stephen BA . . . . *Mar 1979
Benning, Miss Louise Karina . . . . *Mar 2005
Hutchison, Miss Jolene . . . . *Sep 2005
Kemp, Mr David J A LLB . . . . *Nov 1985
Lilley, Mr Jonathan LLB . . . . *Oct 1990
Smith, Mr Colin James MA(Oxon). . . . . Sep 1998
Asoc: Ashford, Miss Abigail . . . . *Apr 2007
Ferro, Ms Anna Louisa Henrietta MMus . . . . *Oct 1995
French, Mr Barry Alan MA(Hons) . . . . Sep 2008
Gash, Mr Lloyd LLB(Hons) . . . . Sep 2008
Smith, Miss Joanne Patricia LLB(Hons) . . . . Sep 2004

JOHN S BREARLEY ‡
42 Rectory Avenue High Wycombe Buckinghamshire HP13 6HW
Tel: 01494 512775 *Fax:* 01494 464677
E-mail: johnbrearley@dsl.pipex.com
List of partners: J S Brearley
Work: P R1
Ptr: Brearley, Mr John Sebastian LLB; LARTPI; MA(Environmental Law) . . . . *Jun 1980

BROWNS
18 Crendon Street High Wycombe Buckinghamshire HP13 6LS
Tel: 01494 452211 *Fax:* 01494 450550 *Dx:* 141460 WYCOMBE 7
E-mail: wycombe@brownssolicitors.co.uk
Office: Amersham, Aylesbury, Beaconsfield, Bourne End, High Wycombe (2 offices), Maidenhead, Marlow, Princes Risborough, Thame

BROWNS
1a Penn Road Hazlemere High Wycombe Buckinghamshire HP15 7LN
Tel: 01494 716171 *Fax:* 01494 716616
Dx: 54804 HAZLEMERE (BUCKS)
E-mail: hazlemere@brownssolicitors.co.uk
Office: Amersham, Aylesbury, Beaconsfield, Bourne End, High Wycombe (2 offices), Maidenhead, Marlow, Princes Risborough, Thame
Work: C1 E S1 S2
Fixed Fee Interview undertaken

BUCHANANS SOLICITORS ‡
4 Suffolk House High Wycombe Buckinghamshire HP10 0EU
Tel: 01628 810707 *Fax:* 01628 810909
E-mail: office@buchanansonline.com
office@buchanansonline.com

BUCKS SOLICITORS ‡
Kelvin House Totteridge Avenue 1 Totteridge Avenue High Wycombe Buckinghamshire HP13 6XG
Tel: 01494 530303 *Fax:* 01494 530343
E-mail: info@buck-law.co.uk

BUSINESS LAWYERS LIMITED ‡
4 Bridle Gate High Wycombe Buckinghamshire HP11 2JH
Tel: 0845 130 6608 *Fax:* 0870 622 0702
E-mail: contactus@business-lawyers.org

P L ELLIOTT & CO ‡
Orchard House Hammersly Lane Tylers Green High Wycombe Buckinghamshire HP10 8EY
Tel: 01494 817599

FAIRWEATHER WHILLIS & TOGHILL SOLICITORS ‡
2 Amersham Mews Amersham Hill High Wycombe Buckinghamshire HP13 6NQ
Tel: 01494 445545
E-mail: mail@fwtlaw.co.uk

FENDOM DAWSON & PARTNERS ‡
6 Easton Street High Wycombe Buckinghamshire HP11 1NJ
Tel: 01494 450361 *Fax:* 01494 439282 *Dx:* 4414 HIGH WYCOMBE
E-mail: enquiries@fendomdawson.co.uk
List of partners: J N Dawson, K P J Haines, R Stafford, R N Towner
Office: Marlow
Work: A1 C1 C2 C3 D1 E F1 K1 K3 L M1 N P R1 S1 S2 T1 T2 V W Z(l)
Emergency Action, Agency, Advocacy, Fixed Fee Interview and Legal Aid undertaken
Ptr: Dawson, Mr Jeremy N LLB . . . *Dec 1974
Haines, Mr Keith P J . . . *§Jun 1976
Stafford, Mrs Rachel TEP . . . *Jan 2003
Ast: Asher, Miss Lucy . . . Aug 2008
Fisher, Miss Lucy . . . Aug 2008

GOLDMAN MARC LIMITED ‡
25 High Street High Wycombe Buckinghamshire HP11 2AG
Tel: 01494 478930 *Fax:* 01494 439093
E-mail: info@goldmanmarc.co.uk

HAZLEMERE
11 Penn Road Hazlemere High Wycombe Buckinghamshire HP15 7LN
Office: Amersham, Aylesbury, Beaconsfield, Bourne End, High Wycombe (2 offices), Maidenhead, Marlow, Princes Risborough, Thame

HERALD SOLICITORS ‡
Hawthorne Cottage 13 Amersham Road High Wycombe Buckinghamshire HP13 6QS
Tel: 0845 250 1778
E-mail: riz@heraldsolicitors.com

CATHERINE HERRIES-SMITH SOLICITOR ‡
Chaenomeles Bolter End Lane Bolter End High Wycombe Buckinghamshire HP14 3NB
Tel: 01494 880705 *Fax:* 01494 880705
E-mail: catherine@herries-smith.com

HODDERS
7 Castle Street High Wycombe Buckinghamshire HP13 6RZ
Tel: 01494 511345 *Fax:* 01494 521282 *Dx:* 4462 WYCOMBE 1
E-mail: enquiries@hodders.co.uk
Office: London NW10 (2 offices), London SW11, Wembley
Languages: Dutch, French, German, Greek, Gujarati, Hindi, Italian, Kanada, Polish, Punjabi, Sinhalese, Spanish
Work: D1 D2 K1
Legal Aid undertaken
Ast: Edwards, Ms Mary Ann BSc(Econ) . . . *Oct 1982
Preece, Ms Victoria Jane MSc . . . Sep 2002

KIDD RAPINET
2nd Floor Thane House Castle Street High Wycombe Buckinghamshire HP13 6RZ
Tel: 0845 017 9607 *Fax:* 01494 461291 *Dx:* 4406 HIGH WYCOMBE
E-mail: trichardson@kiddrapinet.co.uk
Office: Aylesbury, Farnham, London WC2, Maidenhead, Reading, Slough
Work: A1 B1 C1 D1 E F1 J1 K1 L N O Q R1 R2 S1 W X Z(b,c,d,e,f,g,h,i,j,k,l,m,n,o,p)
Emergency Action, Agency, Advocacy, Fixed Fee Interview, Legal Aid undertaken and Member of Accident Line
Ptr: Banks, Ms Catherine Simpson . . . Nov 1986
Bysshe, Mr Peter John Shelley LLB . . . Mar 1973
Rawlings, Mr Christopher John . . . *Feb 1970
Richardson, Mr Tim . . . *Jun 1983
Sehra, Ms Gurvinder . . . Jan 2003

BRUCE LANCE & CO ‡
87 Easton Street High Wycombe Buckinghamshire HP11 1NF
Tel: 01494 450494 *Fax:* 01494 441724 *Dx:* 4400 HIGH WYCOMBE
E-mail: kd@brucelance.co.uk
List of partners: K O Dixon, S P Gasper, A P Goss, A J Hawkins, C M Lancaster, D T D Widdowson
Office: Poole
Languages: French, German
Work: A1 B1 C1 C2 D1 D2 E F1 G J1 K1 L M1 M3 N R1 S1 S2 T1 T2 W Z(c,l,m,r,w)
Emergency Action, Agency, Advocacy, Legal Aid undertaken and Member of Accident Line
Ptr: Dixon, Mr Keith O LLB(Leics) . . . *Feb 1988
Gasper, Mr Stephen P. . . . *§Oct 1977
Hawkins, Mr Andrew J LLB(Leeds) . . . *§Oct 1987
Lancaster, Miss Claire Marie BA(Hons)(History of English Literature). . . . Aug 2003
Ast: Atkinson, Mrs Hazel. . . . Oct 1992
Con: George, Mr Arthur V. . . . *§Dec 1969

LAWRENCE HAMBLIN QUALITYSOLICITORS ‡
First Floor 2a Crendon Street High Wycombe Buckinghamshire HP13 6LW
Tel: 01494 838780 *Fax:* 01494 838785 *Dx:* 4419 HIGH WYCOMBE
E-mail: wycombe@lawrencehamblin.com

NUMBER ONE LEGAL LTD
The May House Widmoor Wooburn Common High Wycombe Buckinghamshire HP10 0JG
Tel: 01628 528555 *Fax:* 01628 528552
Office: Doncaster

OXFORD EMPLOYMENT LAW SOLICITORS
Aston Court Kings Mead Business Park High Wycombe Buckinghamshire HP11 1LA
Office: Oxford

REYNOLDS PARRY-JONES ‡
(in association with Lawnet Member Firm)
10 Easton Street High Wycombe Buckinghamshire HP11 1NP
Tel: 01494 525941 *Fax:* 01494 530701 *Dx:* 4407 HIGH WYCOMBE
E-mail: partners@rjp.uk.com
List of partners: R R Hill, G P Humphreys, G M King, R C M McCulloch, J R Scrace
Languages: Dutch, French
Work: C1 C2 C3 D1 E F1 J1 K1 L M1 N O P Q R1 S1 S2 T2 V W X Z(c,d,e,h,l,r)
Emergency Action, Agency, Advocacy, Fixed Fee Interview, Legal Aid undertaken and Legal Aid Franchise
Ptr: Hill, Mr Robert R LLB . . . *§Jun 1980
Humphreys, Miss Gillian P LLB . . . *§Apr 1972
King, Mr Graham M LLB(Bris). . . . *§Apr 1981
McCulloch, Mr Roderick C M LLB(Soton) . . . *Dec 1979
Scrace, Mr Julian R BA . . . *§Mar 1983
Asoc: Marshall, Mrs Margaret Wyn LLB . . . Jan 1986
Maunder, Ms Deborah Margaret LLB(Hons) . . . Nov 1984
Saville, Mrs Melanie C BA. . . . *Jun 1999
Yeates, Mrs Deborah J MA(Oxon). . . . *Nov 1990
Ast: Selby, Mr Carl William LLB . . . Sep 2008
Woodison, Miss Karen Lynn. . . . Sep 2010
Con: Hatton, Mr T Anthony . . . *§Dec 1970

SWL DISPUTE RESOLUTION ‡
Frederick Place Loudwater High Wycombe Buckinghamshire HP11 1LA
Tel: 01494 616007 *Fax:* 01494 616189

A M R WATTS ‡
South Cottage Chinnor Road Bledlow Ridge High Wycombe Buckinghamshire HP14 4AA
Tel: 01494 481576
E-mail: adrian@wattslegal.co.uk

HIGHAM FERRERS, Northamptonshire

WILSON BROWNE
Manor House 12 Market Square Higham Ferrers Northamptonshire NN10 8BT
Tel: 01933 410000 *Fax:* 01933 410401 *Dx:* 18964 RUSHDEN
Office: Kettering (2 offices), Leicester, Northampton, Wellingborough
Work: A1 B1 C1 D1 E F1 G H J1 K1 L M1 N P R1 S1 T1 V W Z(c,d,f,g,h,i,j,k,l,m,n,o,p,s,t)
Emergency Action, Agency, Advocacy, Fixed Fee Interview, Legal Aid undertaken, Legal Aid Franchise and Member of Accident Line
Ptr: Wicks, Mr Daniel P Notary Public . . . *§Sep 1972
Ast: Putnam, Mr P Sean. . . . *Jul 1979
Con: Daker, Mr John H LLB(B'ham). . . . *§Apr 1966

HIGHBRIDGE, Somerset

CASEYS ‡
21 Market Street Highbridge Somerset TA9 3BT
Tel: 01278 794495 *Fax:* 01278 765876
Dx: 7562 BURNHAM-ON-SEA
Emergency telephone 01278 445723
E-mail: caseysolicitors@btconnect.com
List of partners: S M Casey
Work: D1 G H K1
Agency, Advocacy and Legal Aid undertaken
SPr: Casey, Miss Siobhan M BA . . . *Oct 1985

HIGHCLIFFE, Dorset

DIXON STEWART SOLICITORS
374 Lymington Road Highcliffe Dorset BH23 5HB
Tel: 01425 279222 *Fax:* 01425 278512 *Dx:* 45353 HIGHCLIFFE
E-mail: enquiry@dixonstewart.com
Office: New Milton
Work: C1 C2 C3 D1 E F1 G J1 K1 L M1 M2 N P Q R1 R2 S1 T1 T2 W Z(c,e,h,l,q)
Emergency Action, Agency, Advocacy, Fixed Fee Interview and Legal Aid undertaken

HIGHWORTH, Swindon

COLLARD & CO ‡
40 High Street Highworth Swindon SN6 7AQ
Tel: 01793 765327 *Fax:* 01793 861117 *Dx:* 81050 HIGHWORTH
List of partners: I A Hare, J Williams
Work: K1 S1 V W
Emergency Action, Agency, Advocacy, Fixed Fee Interview, Legal Aid undertaken and Legal Aid Franchise
Ptr: Hare, Mr Ian A . . . *§Dec 1967
Williams, Mrs Jacqueline LLB(Hons) . . . *May 1995

SELBY & CO ‡
Red Lion House 6 Sheep Street Highworth Swindon SN6 7AA
Tel: 01793 762327 *Fax:* 01793 861277
List of partners: I C Selby
Work: A1 C1 E L S1 T1 W
Ptr: Selby, Mr Ian Charles LLB(B'ham). . . . *§May 1982

HILLINGDON, Middlesex

ZSA LAW ‡
Park Farm House Ducks Hill Road Northwood Hillingdon Middlesex HA6 2NP
Tel: 01923 834300 *Fax:* 01923 848613
E-mail: info@zsalaw.co.uk
List of partners: D Arya, S Arya
Work: B1 C1 E F1 I J1 O Q S1 S2 U1 Z(c,q)
Ptr: Arya, Mr Dhiren LLB(Hons) . . . Apr 1990
Arya, Miss Sangita LLB . . . Oct 1997

HINCKLEY, Leicestershire

ATKINS BASSETT ‡
16 Station Road Hinckley Leicestershire LE10 1AW
Tel: 01455 632685 *Fax:* 01455 619310 *Dx:* 716428 HINCKLEY
E-mail: info@atkinsbassett.co.uk
List of partners: M P Bassett, G D Pomfret, J M L Wheeler
Work: A1 C1 C2 D1 E F1 J1 K1 K3 K4 L N O Q R2 S1 S2 W Z(k,l,m,q,r)
Member of Accident Line
Ptr: Bassett, Mr Malcolm Patrick. . . . *Mar 1970
Pomfret, Mr Gareth D BA . . . *Oct 1978
Wheeler, Ms Judith M L . . . *Jan 1997

DAVID BENDELL & CO ‡
Catherine House Coventry Road Hinckley Leicestershire LE10 0JT
Tel: 01455 619322 *Fax:* 01455 619346 *Dx:* 716437 HINCKLEY
E-mail: enquiries@david-bendell.com
List of partners: D H T Bendell
Work: E F1 G H J1 K1 N Q S1 W Z(l)
Emergency Action, Agency, Advocacy and Fixed Fee Interview undertaken
SPr: Bendell, Mr David Harry Thomas MA(Cantab) . . . *Dec 1976

BRAY & BRAY
33 Station Road Hinckley Leicestershire LE10 1AP
Tel: 01455 639900 *Fax:* 01455 614331 *Dx:* 716434 HINCKLEY
Emergency telephone 07885 332421
E-mail: hinckley@braybray.co.uk
Office: Leicester, Market Harborough
Work: A1 B1 B2 C1 C2 D1 D2 E F2 G H J1 K1 K3 K4 L N O Q R2 S1 S2 T1 T2 W Z(c,e,j,l,p,q)
Emergency Action, Agency, Advocacy, Fixed Fee Interview, Legal Aid undertaken and Member of Accident Line
Ptr: Jefferson, Mr Duncan P BA(Hons). . . . *§Sep 1987
Knight, Mr Ian David LLB(Hons)(L'pool) . . . *Apr 1978
Ast: Gill, Ms Sarah Judith BA(Hons) . . . *Nov 1994

THOMAS FLAVELL & SONS ‡
Church Walk Hinckley Leicestershire LE10 1DN
Tel: 01455 610747 *Fax:* 01455 251006 *Dx:* 716424 HINCKLEY
E-mail: law@thosflavell.co.uk
List of partners: D J Boon, J W Connolly, M J Cowlard, G T Flavell, G W Hammond, S R Harrison, M B Healey, C J Stratford
Office: Earl Shilton, Market Bosworth
Work: A1 B1 C1 C2 C3 E F1 J1 J2 K1 K3 K4 L N O Q S1 S2 T1 T2 W Z(r)
Ptr: Boon, Mr David J LLB. . . . *Mar 1990
Connolly, Mr James William MA; BSc . . . *Jul 2003
Flavell, Mr G Thomas MA(Cantab) . . . *§Jun 1977
Harrison, Ms Susan R LLB . . . *May 1985
Healey, Mr Matthew B LLB . . . *§Oct 1991
Stratford, Mr Christopher John LLB . . . *Nov 1997
Con: Newton, Mr Christopher J. . . . *Nov 1977

GS SOLICITORS ‡
20 Station Road Hinckley Leicestershire LE10 1AW
Tel: 01455 618763

HALBORG & CO SOLICITORS ‡
17 Station Road Hinckley Leicestershire LE10 1AW
Tel: 01455 233323

HEADLEYS
15 Station Road Hinckley Leicestershire LE10 1AW
Tel: 01455 637815 *Fax:* 01455 612830 *Dx:* 716422 HINCKLEY
E-mail: reception@headleys.com
Office: Lutterworth
Work: A1 B1 C1 C2 C3 D1 E F1 G H J1 K1 L M1 M2 N O P Q R1 S1 T1 T2 V W Z(b,c,d,f,h,i,j,k,l,m)
Emergency Action, Agency, Advocacy, Fixed Fee Interview, Legal Aid undertaken and Member of Accident Line
Ptr: Broughton, Mr Robert A BA. . . . *Oct 1982
Headley, Mr John G A LLB . . . Jul 1965

GEOFFREY HILL & CO ‡
11 Station Road Hinckley Leicestershire LE10 1AW
Tel: 01455 637715 *Fax:* 01455 631718 *Dx:* 716423 HINCKLEY
List of partners: J W Cruickshank
Work: C2 E K1 L S1 W
Agency, Advocacy and Fixed Fee Interview undertaken
Ptr: Cruickshank, Mr John William LLB . . . *Sep 1970

LDJ SOLICITORS
Elizabeth House St Mary's Road Hinckley Leicestershire LE10 1EQ
Tel: 01455 637030 *Fax:* 01455 634264 *Dx:* 716426 HINCKLEY
Emergency telephone 01827 880167
E-mail: info.hinckley@ldjsolicitors.co.uk
Office: Nuneaton
Languages: French
Work: A1 B1 C1 C2 C3 D1 E F1 G H J1 K1 L M1 M2 N P R1 S1 T1 T2 V W Z(c,j,k,l)
Emergency Action, Agency, Advocacy and Legal Aid undertaken
Ptr: Daniels, Mr G H Ian. . . . *Sep 1978
Marlow-Ridley, Mr Simon BA . . . *Oct 1993
Ast: Jones, Mrs Andrea Mary Boswell LLB. . . . *Jul 1977

MANDER CRUICKSHANK SOLICITORS LLP
7a Leicester Road Hinckley Leicestershire LE10 1LW
Tel: 01455 614208 *Fax:* 01455 613824
Office: Coalville

PILGRIM & WEBSTER ‡
23 Station Road Hinckley Leicestershire LE10 1AW
Tel: 01455 634851 *Fax:* 01455 251224 *Dx:* 716425 HINCKLEY
E-mail: john.eaves@pilgrim-and-webster.co.uk
List of partners: J D Eaves
Work: E K1 K3 S1 W
Fixed Fee Interview undertaken
SPr: Eaves, Mr John D LLB . . . *Jul 1976

See p112 for the Key to Work Categories & other symbols

HINDHEAD, Surrey

KIDSON BRAY & LAWSON ‡
Beacon Hill Chambers Churt Road Hindhead Surrey GU26 6NW
Tel: 01428 605222 *Fax:* 01428 606844
E-mail: tamzin@braylaw.co.uk
List of partners: N D L Kidson, T P E Stileman
Office: London SE11
Work: C1 E S1 S2 T1 T2 W
Fixed Fee Interview undertaken
SPr: Stileman, Miss Tamzin Phillippa Emma BA(Hons) . . . Sep 1999
Con: Bray, Mr David Peter BTech . . . . *§Dec 1976

HITCHIN, Hertfordshire

BOWENS ‡
35 Bridge Street Hitchin Hertfordshire SG2 2DF
Tel: 01462 441443 *Fax:* 01462 441453
Work: K1 K3 K4 N Q S1 W Z(q)

CHAMBERLINS ‡
14-15 High Street Hitchin Hertfordshire SG5 1AT
Tel: 01462 623456 *Fax:* 01462 453413 *Dx:* 7103 HITCHIN
E-mail: chamberlins@btconnect.com
Web: www.chamberlins.co.uk
List of partners: A M F Chamberlin, G K Collin, T M Thurstan
Work: A1 C1 D1 E F1 G J1 K1 K3 N O Q S1 T2 W Z(l,m)
Agency, Advocacy and Fixed Fee Interview undertaken
Ptr: Chamberlin, Mr Arthur M F . . . . *May 1956
Collin, Mr George Kenneth BA(Law). . . . . *Jun 1980
Thurstan, Mr Timothy M LLB(Hull) Andrew Marvell Jackson Prize . . . . *Nov 1981

Particular areas of work include: Agricultural Law, Holdings and Property, Commercial, Child Care and Wardship, Commercial & Residential Property, Consumer Law - Agreements, Credit, Licensing, Sale, Wills, Probate, Trusts.

FOREMAN LAWS ‡
25 Bancroft Hitchin Hertfordshire SG5 1JW
Tel: 01462 458711 *Fax:* 01462 459242 *Dx:* 7102 HITCHIN
E-mail: lawyers@foremanlaws.co.uk
List of partners: S Cousins, J A Fairley, L Green, C L Whittaker
Work: A3 C1 C2 D2 E J1 K1 K2 K3 K4 L N O P Q R2 S1 S2 W Z(c,h,k,q)
Emergency Action, Agency, Advocacy, Fixed Fee Interview undertaken and Member of Accident Line
Ptr: Cousins, Ms Sarah . . . . *Sep 1999
Fairley, Mrs Judith Ann LLB(Lond). . . . . *Jul 1980
Green, Mrs Lisa. . . . . *Jan 1988
Whittaker, Mrs Cheryll L BA. . . . . *Oct 1983
Ast: Day, Mr Robert . . . . Sep 2007
Con: Halliday, Mr James G T MA. . . . . *Dec 1977
Hutchinson, Mr Richard. . . . . *Jan 1990
Newcombe, Mr David A Z. . . . . *Apr 1972

GROOM WILKES & WRIGHT LLP ‡
The Haybarn Upton End Farm Business Park Meppershall Road Hitchin Hertfordshire SG5 3PF
Tel: 01462 714300 *Fax:* 01462 714301

HRJ LAW LLP ‡
7-8 Portmill Lane Hitchin Hertfordshire SG5 1AS
Tel: 01462 628888 *Fax:* 01462 631233 *Dx:* 7100 HITCHIN
E-mail: enquiries@hrjlaw.co.uk
List of partners: D G Bruton, R M Cooper, C P M Duchenne, D R Howard, G C Kennedy, J E Marland, K E Mayes, F L Prince
Office: Welwyn Garden City
Languages: French, German
Work: A3 B1 C1 C2 C3 D1 E F1 F2 J1 K1 K3 K4 L N O Q S1 S2 T2 U2 V W Z(e,h,i,k,l,p,r)
Mem: Duchenne, Mr Charles P M LLB(Leeds) Deputy District Judge . . . . *§Jul 1974
Howard, Mr David R Notary Public . . . . *Dec 1972
Marland, Mrs Jane Elizabeth LLB(Anglia) . . . . Feb 1996
Dir: Kennedy, Mrs Geraldine C LLB(Leeds) . . . . *Dec 1979
Asoc: Johal, Mrs Parmjit LLB(Sheff) . . . . Sep 1995
Lobb, Mr Nicholas David BA. . . . . Jun 1999
Ast: Harding, Miss Gillian LLB(Soton) . . . . Sep 2002
Lawrence, Ms Melanie FILEx . . . . Jul 2006
Lutrario, Miss Emma LLB(Cardiff) . . . . Sep 2008
Maddah, Mrs Rebecca Edna Grace BA(Reading) . . . May 2005

SUSAN HALL & CO ‡
24-25 Market Place Hitchin Hertfordshire SG5 1DT
Tel: 01462 433800 *Fax:* 01462 420806 *Dx:* 7113 HITCHIN
E-mail: sue@susanhall.co.uk
Work: K1 N S1 W
Agency, Fixed Fee Interview undertaken and Member of Accident Line
Ast: White, Miss Jane BA(Jt Hons). . . . . *Dec 1990

LAW BRAND
8 Tilehouse Street Hitchin Hertfordshire SG5 2DU
Tel: 01462 457167 *Fax:* 01462 433155
Office: Stevenage
Ptr: Smith, Mrs Susan P. . . . . Jan 1998

MAXINE COX SOLICITORS ‡
57 High Street Kimpton Hitchin Hertfordshire SG4 8PU
Tel: 01438 833875 *Fax:* 07747 101871
E-mail: maxine@maxinecox.com

NEVES AND DYER SOLICITORS ‡
4 Tilehouse Street Hitchin Hertfordshire SG5 2DW
Tel: 01462 420978 *Fax:* 01462 434989
E-mail: info@nevesanddyer.co.uk

ROSS WILLIAMS ‡
Victoria House 26 Tilehouse Street Hitchin Hertfordshire SG5 2DY
Tel: 01462 636666 *Fax:* 01462 636666 / 624466 *Dx:* 7130 HITCHIN
E-mail: solicitors@rosswilliams-law.co.uk
Work: A1 B1 C1 C2 C3 D1 E F1 G J1 K1 L M1 M2 N O P Q R1 S1 T1 T2 V W Z(b,c,d,e,i,k,n,o,s)
Advocacy and Legal Aid undertaken

HOCKLEY, Essex

JEREMY DAVENPORT ‡
Montrose House 45 Southend Road Hockley Essex SS5 4PZ
Tel: 01702 205163 *Fax:* 01702 207970
E-mail: jeremy.davenport@btinternet.com
List of partners: J A Davenport
Languages: French
Work: A1 E L S1 S2 W
SPr: Davenport, Mr Jeremy A . . . . *Jul 1969

WELLS LEGAL SOLICITORS ‡
3 Spa Road Hockley Essex SS5 4AZ
Tel: 01702 203646 *Fax:* 01702 207642
E-mail: andrew@wellslegal.co.uk

HODDESDON, Hertfordshire

BRADDON & SNOW ‡
Montagu House 68 High Street Hoddesdon Hertfordshire EN11 8HA
Tel: 01992 464552 *Fax:* 01992 446367 *Dx:* 80650 HODDESDON

CURWENS
Estate House 19 High Street Hoddesdon Hertfordshire EN11 8SX
Tel: 01992 463727 *Fax:* 01992 708874 *Dx:* 80651 HODDESDON
E-mail: enquiries@curwens.co.uk
Office: Cheshunt, Enfield, Waltham Abbey
Languages: Italian
Work: A1 B1 B3 C1 D1 D2 E F1 G H J1 K1 L M1 N P R1 S1 S2 T1 V W Z(c,e,f,j,l,m)

DUFFIELD HARRISON LLP ‡
Rathmore House 56 High Street Hoddesdon Hertfordshire EN11 8EX
Tel: 01992 442911 *Fax:* 01992 462693 *Dx:* 80657 HODDESDON
List of partners: D P Citrine, A M Grant, D B Harris, R W Moore
Office: Hertford
Work: B1 C1 C2 D1 E F1 J1 K1 L N O Q R1 S1 W Z(k,p)
Agency, Advocacy, Fixed Fee Interview, Legal Aid undertaken and Member of Accident Line
Mem: Citrine, Mr David P BA . . . . *Jul 1978
Grant, Mr Alan M BA(Dunelm). . . . . *Oct 1981
Harris, Mr David Bruce . . . . Jan 1978
Moore, Mr Robert W . . . . Nov 1984
Con: Harrison, Mr Michael J W . . . . *Jun 1971

HOLBEACH, Lincolnshire

CALTHROPS
61 High Street Holbeach Lincolnshire PE12 7EA
Tel: 01406 422621 *Fax:* 01406 425095 *Dx:* 29521 HOLBEACH
Office: Spalding
Work: A1 B1 C1 D1 E F1 G H J1 K1 L M1 N P R1 S1 T1 V W Z(c,d,e,i,j,k,l,m)
Agency, Advocacy, Legal Aid undertaken and Member of Accident Line
Con: Molson, Mr F Brian . . . . *§Jul 1968

MOSSOP & BOWSER ‡
Abbot's Manor 10 Spalding Road Holbeach Lincolnshire PE12 7LP
Tel: 01406 422651 *Fax:* 01406 425177 *Dx:* 29522 HOLBEACH
E-mail: admin@mossops.co.uk
List of partners: R M Hill, J P Veasey, G J Wakefield
Office: Long Sutton
Languages: French
Work: A1 B1 C1 C2 E F1 J1 K1 K3 K4 L O P Q R1 S1 S2 T1 T2 W Z(q)
Emergency Action, Agency, Advocacy and Legal Aid Franchise
Ptr: Hill, Mr Richard M MA(Oxon) . . . . *Mar 1986
Veasey, Mr John Patrick BSc; LLB . . . . *Sep 1997
Wakefield, Mr Graham John BA. . . . . *Oct 1982
Ast: McGrath, Miss Emma LLB . . . . Apr 2008
Con: Brown, Mr Peter F S LLB . . . . *§May 1975

J C WOOLLEY ‡
Albion Chambers 1 West End Holbeach Lincolnshire PE12 7LW
Tel: 01406 423777 *Fax:* 01406 422909 *Dx:* 29529 HOLBEACH
List of partners: J C Woolley
Work: S1 S2 W
SPr: Woolley, Mr John C BA . . . . *Mar 1991

HOLMFIRTH, West Yorkshire

BAILEY SMAILES
38 Huddersfield Road Holmfirth West Yorkshire HD9 2JW
Tel: 01484 686000 *Fax:* 01484 688193 *Dx:* 708623 HOLMFIRTH
E-mail: mail@baileysmailes.co.uk
Office: Huddersfield
Work: A1 B1 C1 D1 E F1 G H J1 K1 L M1 N P R1 S1 T1 V W Z(c,d,i,k,l)
Agency, Advocacy, Fixed Fee Interview, Legal Aid undertaken and Member of Accident Line
Ptr: McNeil, Mr Alan LLB(Sheff) . . . . *Apr 1975
Ast: Green, Mr Richard Mark BA(Hons)(Law) . . . . Feb 1987
Palmer, Mrs Sarah Louise. . . . . *Jan 2003

HONLEY LAW PRACTICE ‡
24 Westgate Honley Holmfirth West Yorkshire HD9 6AA
Tel: 01484 667853 *Fax:* 01484 661220
E-mail: info@honleylaw.co.uk
List of partners: J N Taylor
Work: B1 F1 J1 K1 K3 K4 L Q S1 W
Agency, Advocacy and Fixed Fee Interview undertaken
SPr: Taylor, Mr Julian N LLB . . . . *Mar 1987

RAMSDENS SOLICITORS
102 Huddersfield Road Holmfirth West Yorkshire HD9 3AX
Tel: 01484 690040 *Fax:* 01484 685641
E-mail: info@ramsdens.co.uk
Office: Dewsbury, Elland, Halifax, Huddersfield (3 offices), Mirfield
Work: A1 A2 B1 C1 D1 D2 E G H J1 K1 K2 L N Q R1 S1 S2 V W Z(d,l)
Agency, Fixed Fee Interview and Legal Aid undertaken

HOLSWORTHY, Devon

KEVIN BODLEY ‡
Moorfield House Brandis Corner Holsworthy Devon EX22 7YD
Tel: 01409 221460 *Fax:* 01409 221065
E-mail: lawyer@kbodley.freeserve.co.uk
List of partners: K F Bodley
Work: A3 C1 C2 C3 F1 J1 M1 M2 M3 O Z(k,w)
SPr: Bodley, Mr Kevin F LLB(Hons); LLM; MSc Notary Public . . . . Mar 1979

COODES
4 Bodmin Street Holsworthy Devon EX22 6BB
Tel: 01409 253425 *Fax:* 01409 253439 *Dx:* 118657 HOLSWORTHY
E-mail: enquiries@coodes.co.uk
Office: Launceston, Liskeard, Newquay, Penzance, St Austell, Truro
Work: A1 E K1 L S1 S2 W
Fixed Fee Interview undertaken
Ptr: Johns, Mrs Pamela Jane . . . . Nov 1994
Ast: Williams, Miss Kate . . . . Sep 2010

PETER PETER & WRIGHT ‡
Fore Street Holsworthy Devon EX22 6ED
Tel: 01409 253262 *Fax:* 01409 254091 *Dx:* 118650 HOLSWORTHY
E-mail: info@ppwhol.co.uk
List of partners: A Bennett, P J Buckland, N J R Clark, D J Higgs, T J Rowland, C E S Smale, L Wakefield
Office: Bideford, Bude, Okehampton
Work: A1 A2 C1 E K1 K3 K4 L S1 S2 T2 V W Z(d)
Ptr: Clark, Mr Nigel J R . . . . *§Jun 1970
Wakefield, Ms Lorraine LLB. . . . . *Nov 1986
Ast: Miller, Mr Michael Justin Colleypriest MBA; FALA . . . *Nov 2009
Woolsey, Mrs Claire Joanne LLB(Hons); FILEx . . . . *Oct 2008
Con: Rowland, Mr James M MA(Cantab) . . . . *§Jul 1965

HOLT, Norfolk

BUTCHER ANDREWS
15 Market Place Holt Norfolk NR25 6BE
Tel: 01263 712023 *Fax:* 01263 711047 *Dx:* 31154 HOLT
E-mail: webmaster@butcherandrews.co.uk
Office: Fakenham
Languages: French
Work: A1 A2 B1 C1 D1 E F1 J1 J2 K1 K3 L N O P Q R1 S1 S2 T1 T2 V W Z(d,h,k,l,q)
Emergency Action, Agency, Advocacy, Fixed Fee Interview undertaken and Member of Accident Line
Ptr: Linthwaite, Mr Darren C LLB . . . . *§Apr 1996
Payne, Adney MA(Cantab) . . . . *§Jul 1980

HAYES & STORR
27 Bull Street Holt Norfolk NR25 6HP
Tel: 01263 712835 *Fax:* 01263 711056 *Dx:* 31151 HOLT
E-mail: law.holt@hayes-storr.com
Office: Fakenham, King's Lynn, Sheringham, Wells-next-the-Sea
Work: A1 B1 C1 C2 D1 E F1 J1 K1 K2 K3 L N O Q S1 S2 T2 V W Z(c,d,e,l,p,q,r)
Emergency Action, Agency, Advocacy and Fixed Fee Interview undertaken
Ptr: Pallister, Mr James Francis Timothy BA . . . . *Dec 2001
Ast: Fulcher, Katie . . . . Jul 2008

PAUL VEITCH SOLICITOR ‡
PO Box 23 Holt Norfolk NR25 7QR
Tel: 01263 741751 *Fax:* 01263 741751
E-mail: pnveitch@aol.com

MAX WILEY & CO ‡
13a Fish Hill Holt Norfolk NR25 6HN
Tel: 01263 711771 *Fax:* 01263 711709
E-mail: office@maxwileysolicitors.co.uk
List of partners: D M Wiley
Work: E S1 S2 T2 W Z(d)
SPr: Wiley, Mr David Max MA(Oxon) . . . . *Dec 1980

HOLYHEAD, Anglesey

T R EVANS HUGHES & CO ‡
Victoria Chambers Holyhead Anglesey LL65 1UR
Tel: 01407 762204 *Fax:* 01407 769266 *Dx:* 701792 HOLYHEAD
E-mail: sandra.treh@btconnect.com
List of partners: D E C Hughes, J R C Hughes, W R Williams
Office: Amlwch
Languages: Welsh
Work: A1 B1 C1 C2 C3 D1 E F1 G H J1 K1 L M1 M2 N P R1 S1 T1 T2 V W Z(l)
Emergency Action, Agency, Advocacy, Fixed Fee Interview and Legal Aid undertaken
Ptr: Hughes, Mr John R C LLB . . . . *Apr 1983
Williams, Mr William R LLB . . . . *§Aug 1973
Ast: Davies, Mrs Ann E C LLB. . . . . Jun 1976

H JENKINS & HUGHES ‡
Stanley House Market Square Holyhead Anglesey LL65 1UF
Tel: 01407 762301 *Fax:* 01407 769244 *Dx:* 701793 HOLYHEAD
Emergency telephone 01407 741012
E-mail: hjenkinshughes@tiscali.co.uk
List of partners: M P Jones, J T Williams
Languages: Welsh
Work: A1 B1 C1 D1 E F1 J1 K1 L M1 N P R1 S1 T1 V W
Emergency Action, Agency, Advocacy and Fixed Fee Interview undertaken
Ptr: Jones, Mrs Myra P . . . . *May 1980
Williams, Mr John Tyson LLB . . . . *Mar 1975

TUDUR OWEN ROBERTS GLYNNE & CO
6-8 Stanley Street Holyhead Anglesey LL65 1HG
Tel: 01407 762374 *Fax:* 01407 764891 *Dx:* 701790 HOLYHEAD
Office: Bangor (2 offices), Blaenau Ffestiniog, Caernarfon, Menai Bridge
Languages: French, Welsh
Work: A1 D1 E F1 G H J1 K1 K3 L N R1 S1 V W Z(l)
Emergency Action, Agency, Advocacy, Fixed Fee Interview, Legal Aid undertaken and Member of Accident Line
Ptr: Roberts, Mr Hywel G LLB. . . . . *Mar 1987
Ast: Jones, Mrs Frances P LLB . . . . *Jun 1980

HOLYWELL, Flintshire

GAMLINS
Vron Chambers High Street Holywell Flintshire CH8 7LB
Tel: 01352 714822 *Fax:* 01352 714240
E-mail: gamlins@gamlins.co.uk
Office: Bangor, Colwyn Bay (2 offices), Conwy, Llandudno, Rhyl

GREGSONS SOLICITORS ‡
49-51 High Street Holywell Flintshire CH8 7TF
Tel: 01352 871978 *Fax:* 0845 450 2336

GRIFFITHS & HUGHES PARRY ‡
7 Brynford Street Holywell Flintshire CH8 7RD
Tel: 01352 711815 / 711945 *Fax:* 01352 712974
Dx: 21726 HOLYWELL
E-mail: ghp@freeuk.com
List of partners: F Coaker, S G Jones
Work: A1 B1 C1 C2 C3 D1 D2 E F1 J1 K1 L N Q S1 S2 T1 T2 V W Z(l,p)
Emergency Action, Agency, Advocacy, Fixed Fee Interview, Legal Aid undertaken, Legal Aid Franchise and Member of Accident Line
Ptr: Coaker, Miss Faye BSc(Hons) . . . . *Feb 1992
Jones, Mr S Geraint MA. . . . . *Sep 1989

THE HUGHES PARRY PARTNERSHIP ‡
35 High Street Holywell Flintshire CH8 7TE
Tel: 01352 712422 *Fax:* 01352 719011 *Dx:* 21727 HOLYWELL
E-mail: shan@hughes-parry.co.uk
List of partners: S V Hughes-Parry, J D H Parry, T Wilson
Ptr: Hughes-Parry, Ms Shan Valmai BA(Hons); Cert MRS . Aug 2001
Wilson, Mr Timothy BA(Hons). . . . . Jan 1998

STEPHEN MULLARKEY SOLICITORS ‡
73 High Street Holywell Flintshire CH8 7TF
Tel: 01352 710657 *Fax:* 01352 715556 *Dx:* 21725 HOLYWELL
Emergency telephone 07885 194492
E-mail: sm.solicitors@btconnect.com
List of partners: S Mullarkey
Office: Flint
Work: D1 D2 G H K1 K2 K3 S1 W
Emergency Action, Agency, Advocacy, Fixed Fee Interview, Legal Aid undertaken and Legal Aid Franchise

PENELOPE J WINNARD ‡
The Hafod Halkyn Holywell Flintshire CH8 8BD
Tel: 01352 780229 *Fax:* 01352 781634
Emergency telephone 01352 780229
E-mail: pjwinnard@btinternet.com
List of partners: P J Winnard
Work: A1 B1 C1 C2 C3 D1 E K1 M1 M2 N P T1 T2 W
Ptr: Winnard, Miss Penelope J BA(Lond) . . . . *Dec 1980

HONITON, Devon

BEVISS & BECKINGSALE
Law Chambers The Manor House High Street Honiton Devon EX14 1DJ
Tel: 01404 548050 *Fax:* 01404 548051 *Dx:* 48803 HONITON
E-mail: enquiries@bevissandbeckingsale.co.uk
Office: Axminster, Chard, Seaton
Work: A1 C1 D1 E F1 J1 K1 K3 L N O P Q R1 S1 S2 T1 T2 V W Z(l,q)
Emergency Action, Advocacy and Fixed Fee Interview undertaken
Ptr: Gaitskell, Mrs Zoe LLB . . . . *Oct 2002
Ast: Collins, Ms Emma LLB . . . . Sep 2008
Curtis, Miss Karen-Lee LLB. . . . . Oct 2009
Fisher Crouch, Mr Stephen R MA(Cantab) . . . . . . *Apr 1981
Quinlivan, Mr Howard. . . . . Feb 2008

EVERYS ‡
130 High Street Honiton Devon EX14 1JR
Tel: 01404 41221 *Fax:* 01404 44976 *Dx:* 48800 HONITON
Emergency telephone 01404 822123
E-mail: law@everys.co.uk
List of partners: G C Bowen, G M Cherryson, J C Chesterton, C K Cuthbert, K Davies, C S J Dixon, J Griffin, J T Hawkins, M D N Izzett, S P Martin, F G Murray, A M Pearson, L J Powell, R A Scott, K J C Stamp, R W Stokes, K J Stradling, D L Wood
Office: Budleigh Salterton, Exeter, Exmouth, Honiton, Ottery St Mary, Seaton, Sidmouth, Taunton
Work: A1 A2 B1 B2 C1 C2 C3 D1 D2 E F1 F2 G H J1 J2 K1 L M1 N O P Q R1 R2 S1 S2 T1 T2 V W X Z(c,d,e,h,i,k,l,m,n,o,p,q,r,s,t,u,w,x,y)
Emergency Action, Agency, Advocacy, Fixed Fee Interview and Legal Aid undertaken
Ptr: Chesterton, Mr John Colin LLB . . . . *§Jul 1980
Griffin, Mr James LLB(Hons) . . . . *§Jun 1996

EVERYS
The Laurels 46 New Street Honiton Devon EX14 1BY
Tel: 01404 43431 *Fax:* 01404 45493 *Dx:* 48800 HONITON
Emergency telephone 01404 822123
E-mail: law@everys.co.uk
Office: Budleigh Salterton, Exeter, Exmouth, Honiton, Ottery St Mary, Seaton, Sidmouth, Taunton
Work: A1 A2 B1 B2 C1 C2 C3 D1 D2 E F1 F2 G H J1 J2 K1 L M1 N O P Q R1 R2 S1 S2 T1 T2 V W X Z(c,d,e,h,i,k,l,m,n,o,p,q,r,s,t,u,w,x,y)
Emergency Action, Agency, Advocacy, Fixed Fee Interview, Legal Aid undertaken and Legal Aid Franchise
Ptr: Davies, Mrs Karen BSc. . . . . *§Nov 1992
Martin, Mr Stephen P BA . . . . *§Oct 1988
Stamp, Mrs Katherine Jane Ceinwen . . . . *§Dec 1993
Wood, Mr David L LLB . . . . *§Jun 1973
Ast: Lovett, Mrs Claire Louise . . . . *§Sep 1999

FORD SIMEY LLP
118 High Street Honiton Devon EX14 1JP
Tel: 01404 540020 / 0800 169 3741 *Fax:* 01404 540021
Dx: 48807 HONITON
E-mail: info@fordsimey.co.uk
Office: Exeter, Exmouth, Sidmouth

NEIL GRIFFIN & CO ‡
Blackwater Chambers 114-116 High Street Honiton Devon EX14 1JP
Tel: 01404 42609 *Fax:* 01404 46499 *Dx:* 48804 HONITON
List of partners: N M Griffin
Work: D1 D2 K1 K2 K3 N
Agency and Legal Aid Franchise
SPr: Griffin, Mr Neil M BA . . . . *§Jun 1983

HOOK, Hampshire

BATES BRUNEL SOLICITORS
Regent House 123 High Street Odiham Hook Hampshire RG29 1LA
Tel: 01256 709900 *Fax:* 01256 701501 *Dx:* 121278 HOOK (OD)
E-mail: odiham@batesnvh.co.uk
Office: Fleet, Hook (2 offices), Leigh-on-Sea, London WC2

BATES NVH
Sanctuary House Barnwells Court Hartley Wintney Hook Hampshire RG27 8AY
Tel: 01252 844443 *Fax:* 01252 848731
E-mail: hw@batesnvh.co.uk
Office: Fleet, Hook (2 offices), Leigh-on-Sea, London WC2

BATES NVH
Phillips House Station Road Hook Hampshire RG27 9HD
Tel: 01256 760074 *Fax:* 01256 760726 *Dx:* 121278 HOOK
E-mail: hook@batesnvh.co.uk
Office: Fleet, Hook (2 offices), Leigh-on-Sea, London WC2
Work: C1 C2 E J1 K1 K3 L N Q S1 S2 W Z(l)
Ptr: Gibbons, Mr Geoffrey David. . . . . *Nov 1973
Knudsen, Miss Diana C BA . . . . *Apr 1980

LEONARD CRANE SOLICITORS ‡
Marralomeda Vicarage Lane Hook Hampshire RG27 8LF
Tel: 0118 932 6105
E-mail: leonard@lcrane.wanadoo.co.uk

WILLS CHANDLER BEACH
2 Station Road Hook Hampshire RG27 9HD
Tel: 01256 764646 / 764647 *Fax:* 01256 764648
Emergency telephone 01256 702650
E-mail: info@weblaw.co.uk
Office: Fleet
Languages: French, German
Work: A1 B1 C1 C2 C3 D1 E F1 F2 G H J1 K1 K3 K4 L N O P Q R1 R2 S1 S2 T1 T2 W Z(b,c,d,g,h,j,k,l)
Emergency Action, Agency, Advocacy and Fixed Fee Interview undertaken
SPr: Beach, Mr Piers Matthew . . . . *Feb 1980
Ast: Ennos, Mr Nicholas BA(French & German) . . . . . . Sep 2005

HORLEY, Surrey

BURSTOW LAW SOLICITORS ‡
Burstow Manor Rookery Lane Smallfield Horley Surrey RH6 9BD
Tel: 01342 844215 *Fax:* 0844 249 2821
E-mail: info@burstowlawsolicitors.co.uk

FRAME SMITH & CO ‡
First Floor 32 Victoria Road Horley Surrey RH6 7PZ
Tel: 01293 785885 *Fax:* 01252 331221
E-mail: info@framesmithsolicitors.co.uk

GOODALL BARNETT JAMES
7a High Street Horley Surrey RH6 7BE
Tel: 01293 414448 *Fax:* 01293 414449 *Dx:* 2004 HORLEY 10
Emergency telephone 07659 593926
E-mail: horley@gbj-crime.co.uk
Office: St Leonards-on-Sea
Work: G H V
Emergency Action, Agency, Advocacy, Fixed Fee Interview and Legal Aid undertaken
Ptr: Barnett, Mr Raymond BA ★. . . . . *Dec 1976
James, Mr Adam C ★. . . . . *Dec 1985
Con: Penny, Ms Jane ★ . . . . *Oct 1984

DAVID HOWES SOLICITORS ‡
Eton Chambers 95 Victoria Road Horley Surrey RH6 7QH
Tel: 01293 822280 *Fax:* 01293 775833
E-mail: info@davidhowessolicitors.co.uk

MAHANY & CO SOLICITORS LLP ‡
HSBC Bank Chambers 81 Victoria Road Horley Surrey RH6 7QH
Tel: 01293 772888 *Fax:* 01293 822223 *Dx:* 200417 HORLEY 1
E-mail: law@mahany.co.uk
List of partners: M G Barrell, D S Mahany, J Percy
Work: D1 K1 K3 S1 Z(l)
Emergency Action, Agency, Advocacy, Fixed Fee Interview, Legal Aid undertaken and Legal Aid Franchise
Ptr: Barrell, Mr Mark G . . . . *Mar 1984
Mahany, Mr David S. . . . . *Nov 1962
Percy, Miss Justina LLB(Hons) . . . . Dec 1996

NEWMANS SOLICITORS ‡
1 High Street Horley Surrey RH6 7BE
Tel: 01293 771521 *Fax:* 01293 820406
E-mail: reception@ranewman.co.uk
List of partners: S Babar, F Goodman
Languages: French, German, Urdu
Work: E L S1 S2 W
Ptr: Babar, Miss Saira . . . . *Jan 2003
Goodman, Mrs Farida LLB . . . . *Jan 1973
Asoc: Harrison-Obafemi, Mr James BSc(Hons) . . . . Jan 2003
James, Mr Raymond Martin MA(Cantab) . . . . . . *Mar 1979

ROSS & SON ‡
Eton Chambers 95 Victoria Road Horley Surrey RH6 7QH
Tel: 01293 782425 *Fax:* 01293 775833 *Dx:* 200401 HORLEY
E-mail: info@rossandson.co.uk
List of partners: D T Rae
Work: A1 B1 C1 E F1 J1 L R1 S1 S2 W Z(b,c)
Fixed Fee Interview undertaken
SPr: Rae, Mr David Thomas . . . . *§Jun 1972

SHEPPERSONS ‡
1 Massetts Road Horley Surrey RH6 7PR
Tel: 01293 772424 *Fax:* 01293 785642 *Dx:* 200402 HORLEY
E-mail: law@sheppersons.co.uk
List of partners: L M Elliott, S A Gandon, S H Shepperson, H Young
Office: Reigate
Languages: French
Work: A1 C1 D1 E F1 J1 K1 K2 L P R1 S1 V W Z(l)
Emergency Action, Agency, Advocacy, Legal Aid undertaken and Legal Aid Franchise
Ptr: Elliott, Mrs Louise Marion BA(Hons). . . . . *Jan 1995
Gandon, Miss Sally Ann. . . . . *May 1980
Shepperson, Mr Stephen H BA(Hons). . . . . *Jun 1979
Young, Mr Hamish LLB . . . . Oct 1980
Ast: George, Ms Leanne BA(Hons) . . . . Jun 2005
Shaw, Mr Richard LLB(Hons); BA(Hons) . . . . Oct 2006

GEOFF WHITE SOLICITORS ‡
83 Victoria Road Horley Surrey RH6 7QH
Tel: 01293 776916 *Fax:* 01293 782290 *Dx:* 200143 HORLEY
E-mail: criminal@geoffwhitesolicitors.co.uk

HORNCASTLE, Lincolnshire

CHATTERTONS SOLICITORS
5 South Street Horncastle Lincolnshire LN9 6DS
Tel: 01507 522456 *Fax:* 01507 522445 *Dx:* 29501 HORNCASTLE
E-mail: horncastle@chattertons.com
Office: Boston (2 offices), Grantham, Lincoln, Newark, Sleaford, Spalding, Stamford
Languages: French, German, Serbo-Croat
Work: A1 B1 C1 C2 D1 E F1 G H J1 K1 L M1 M2 N O P Q R1 S1 T1 T2 V W X Z(d,e,j,k,l,o)
Emergency Action, Agency, Advocacy, Fixed Fee Interview, Legal Aid undertaken, Legal Aid Franchise and Member of Accident Line
Ptr: Cordingley, Mr Patrick A B BA. . . . . *Dec 1979
Cox, Mr Stuart C . . . . *Dec 1977
Asoc: Parkinson, Mr Michael Christian Lennard LLB(Hons) . Mar 2002
Smith, Mr Robert H FILEx. . . . . *Mar 1985
Ast: Millen, Mrs Sylvia . . . . Jul 1980

WILKIN CHAPMAN GRANGE SOLICITORS
7 Bull Ring Horncastle Lincolnshire LN9 5HX
Tel: 01507 527521 *Fax:* 01507 526918 *Dx:* 29502 HORNCASTLE
E-mail: eboyd@wilkinchapman.co.uk
Office: Alford, Beverley, Grimsby (3 offices), Lincoln, Louth, Mablethorpe, Market Rasen, Sutton-on-Sea
Languages: French
Work: A1 A3 B1 B2 C1 C2 C3 D1 E F1 F2 G H J1 J2 K1 K2 L N O P Q R1 R2 S1 S2 T1 T2 V W X Z(b,e,g,i,k,l,m,p,q,r,s,y)
Emergency Action, Agency, Advocacy, Fixed Fee Interview, Legal Aid undertaken, Legal Aid Franchise and Member of Accident Line
Ptr: Parker, Mrs Claire Elizabeth. . . . . *Feb 1997

HORNCHURCH, Essex

G ADAMS & CO SOLICITORS ‡
Ground Floor Office Suite Swan House 54 Station Lane Hornchurch Essex RM12 6NB
Tel: 0844 800 0816 *Fax:* 0844 800 0817

MARK ELLIS & CO ‡
52 Station Lane Hornchurch Essex RM12 6NB
Tel: 01708 471808 / 471587 *Dx:* 51012 HORNCHURCH
List of partners: M Ellis
Work: A1 B1 C1 E K1 L M1 N P R1 S1 W
Agency, Advocacy and Legal Aid undertaken
Ptr: Ellis, Mr Mark. . . . . *Jul 1973

FISHER SANDS ‡
Estate Offices Coronation Drive Elm Park Hornchurch Essex RM12 5BL
Tel: 01708 474019

MOSS & COLEMAN ‡
170-180 High Street Hornchurch Essex RM12 6JP
Tel: 01708 446781 *Fax:* 01708 470341 *Dx:* 51003 HORNCHURCH
List of partners: G A Botwright, A E Foskett, G D Harrington
Work: A1 B1 C1 C2 C3 D1 E J1 K1 N O P Q R1 S1 W Z(d,k,l,m)
Emergency Action, Agency, Advocacy, Fixed Fee Interview, Legal Aid undertaken and Member of Accident Line
Ptr: Botwright, Ms Gillian A . . . . Dec 1991
Foskett, Mr Alan E . . . . Jan 1975
Harrington, Mr Gerald David LLB . . . . Oct 1980
Ast: Duke, Mrs Sheila . . . . Jul 1984
Jarvis, Miss Amanda . . . . Aug 1998
Con: Parker, Mr Ian A . . . . *Dec 1963

PINNEY TALFOURD LLP
Crown House 40 North Street Hornchurch Essex RM11 1EW
Tel: 01708 511000 *Fax:* 01708 511040 *Dx:* 51004 HORNCHURCH
E-mail: mail@pinneytalfourd.co.uk
Office: Brentwood, Upminster
Work: B1 C1 C2 C3 D1 E F1 F2 J1 J2 K1 L N O Q R1 R2 S1 S2 W Z(c,l,q,r)
Emergency Action, Advocacy, Fixed Fee Interview undertaken and Member of Accident Line
Ptr: Talfourd, Mr Peter Earl LLB . . . . *Dec 1975
Mem: Dean, Miss Adele LLB . . . . Sep 2002
Eccles, Mr Stephen Paul BA(Dunelm) ♦. . . . . *Oct 1986
Green, Mr Stephen FILEx. . . . . Oct 2000
Asoc: Bradley, Claire Louise. . . . . Aug 2006
Cannon, Sarah Ann. . . . . Feb 2010
Healy, Miss Nicola LLB . . . . Mar 2009
Rogers, Faye Margaret . . . . Aug 2008
Tsindides, Sarah Christina. . . . . Sep 2002
Ast: Hull, Kerry Elizabeth . . . . Oct 1994

SACKVILLES ‡
135 High Street Hornchurch Essex RM11 3YJ
Tel: 01708 446704 *Fax:* 01708 476018 *Dx:* 51005 HORNCHURCH
E-mail: law@sackvilles.co.uk
List of partners: R H Norrington, C Poole, P D Robins
Office: Rainham
Work: B1 C1 C2 D1 E F1 J1 K1 K3 K4 L O Q R1 S1 S2 V W Z(b,l)
Agency and Fixed Fee Interview undertaken
Ptr: Poole, Miss Carol BA(Law) . . . . *May 1982
Robins, Mr Paul D. . . . . *Nov 1973

See p112 for the Key to Work Categories & other symbols

HORNSEA, East Riding of Yorkshire

MMS SOLICITORS
5 Market Place Hornsea East Riding of Yorkshire HU18 1AN
Tel: 01964 537700 *Fax:* 01964 537711
E-mail: info@mmssolicitors.co.uk
Office: Withernsea

HORSFORTH, West Yorkshire

RICHMOND & CO ‡
(incorporating Wigin & Son)
105 New Road Side Horsforth West Yorkshire LS18 4QD
Tel: 0113 259 1188 *Fax:* 0113 258 4262
Emergency telephone 01924 458362
List of partners: R E Richmond
Agency undertaken
Ptr: Richmond, Mrs Robyn E LLB . . . . *Jul 1985

WELLS CONNOR & CO ‡
145-147 Town Street Horsforth West Yorkshire LS18 5BL
Tel: 0113 239 0088 *Fax:* 0113 258 2715
List of partners: C P Connor, T W T Wells
Emergency Action, Agency and Advocacy undertaken
Ptr: Connor, Mr Christopher P LLB . . . . *Dec 1979
Wells, Mr Thomas W T LLB . . . . *Oct 1983

WILSONS
New Road Side Horsforth West Yorkshire LS18 4QE
Tel: 0113 258 6888 *Fax:* 0113 258 1188
Office: Bradford (2 offices), Leeds, Pudsey
Work: A1 B1 D1 E F1 F2 J1 K1 K3 K4 L N O Q R2 S1 S2 Z(p,q,r)
Asoc: Hallam, Mr Francis . . . . *Dec 1989
Mawbey-Shaw, Mr James. . . . . Mar 2008

HORSHAM, West Sussex

OLIVER BEBB ‡
2nd Floor Afon Building Worthing Road Horsham West Sussex RH12 1TL
Tel: 0845 603 2808 *Fax:* 0870 124 7122
E-mail: mail@oliverbebb.com

DON BURSTOW SOLICITOR ‡
Great Ventors Farm Brighton Road Horsham West Sussex RH13 6JD
Tel: 01403 891660

COOLE & HADDOCK
14 Carfax Horsham West Sussex RH12 1DZ
Tel: 01403 210200 *Fax:* 01403 241275 *Dx:* 57600 HORSHAM
E-mail: info@coolelaw.co.uk
Office: Worthing
Work: A1 B1 C1 C2 C3 D1 E F1 F2 G H J1 K1 L M1 M2 N P R1 S1 T1 T2 V W Z(b,c,d,e,h,j,k,l,q,r)
Emergency Action, Agency, Advocacy, Legal Aid undertaken, Legal Aid Franchise and Member of Accident Line
Ptr: Bennett, Mrs Christina M . . . . *§Dec 1969
Descoutter, Mr Nigel A . . . . *Feb 1979
Lacy, Mr John G BA(Oxon) . . . . Sep 1977
Murphy, Mrs Jennifer Lesley. . . . . Jan 1996
Passmore, Mr Albert Edward . . . . May 1978
Ast: Barker, Mrs Penelope M BSc . . . . Jan 1981
White, Mrs Deborah A LLB(Hons). . . . . *Sep 1985

MARTIN C DALTON ‡
63 Hillside Horsham West Sussex RH12 1NF
Tel: 01403 266642 *Fax:* 01403 266642
E-mail: law@martindalton.plus.com
List of partners: M C Dalton
Languages: French, German
Work: G H K1 K3 N Q S1 Z(t)
Emergency Action, Agency, Advocacy and Fixed Fee Interview undertaken
SPr: Dalton, Mr Martin C BA(Hons)(Law). . . . . *Aug 1977

PAUL DAVIDSON TAYLOR ‡
Chancery Court Queen Street Horsham West Sussex RH13 5AD
Tel: 01403 262333 *Fax:* 01403 262444 *Dx:* 57617 HORSHAM
E-mail: law@pdt.co.uk
List of partners: J Clewlow, N C S Cook, M T Cremin, W J Keating, I M Robertson, N E Ruddy, G Timms
Languages: French, German
Work: B1 C1 C2 C3 E F1 I J1 L N O P Q R1 R2 S1 S2 U2 Z(b,c,e,f,l,p,w,z)
Ptr: Clewlow, Mr James BA; MSW. . . . . *Oct 1995
Cook, Mr Nigel C S BA(Oxon). . . . . *Jan 1977
Cremin, Mr Martyn T LLB . . . . *Dec 1982
Keating, Mr William J BA . . . . *§May 1982
Robertson, Mr Ian Massey . . . . *Apr 2001
Ruddy, Mr Noel Edward LLB . . . . *Oct 1990
Timms, Mr Gareth BA. . . . . *Jun 1999
Asoc: Burns, Mrs Ysanne C MA(Oxon) . . . . *Oct 1989
Butler, Mrs Claire LLB. . . . . *Nov 1994
Charity, Mrs Anne BA . . . . *May 1981
Rae, Mr Carlton Ashley BSc. . . . . Nov 2001
Shadwell, Miss Dawn A LLB. . . . . *Jun 2000
Smallman, Mr James Paul Bruno LLB. . . . . *Feb 1999

FLACKWOODS SOLICITORS ‡
22 Lintot Square Fairbank Road Southwater Horsham West Sussex RH13 9LA
Tel: 01403 738777
E-mail: flackwoods@btconnect.com

PETER G GATES ‡
Brook Cottage Loxwood Road Rudgwick Horsham West Sussex RH12 3BP
Tel: 01403 753636 *Fax:* 01403 753863
E-mail: pggates@aol.com
List of partners: P G Gates
Work: A1 E K1 Q S1 W Z(l)
SPr: Gates, Mr Peter George. . . . . *Jun 1973

MATTHEW JOHN GREEN ‡
14 Carfax Horsham West Sussex RH12 1DZ
Tel: 01403 210200 *Fax:* 01403 241275 *Dx:* 57600 HORSHAM
E-mail: matthew.green@coolelaw.co.uk
List of partners: M J Green
Languages: French
Work: E L S1 S2 W Z(o)
SPr: Green, Mr Matthew J MA(Oxon). . . . . *Mar 1959

HADDOCK & CO SOLICITORS ‡
The Office Walhurst Manor Picts Lane Horsham West Sussex RH13 8AW
Tel: 01403 865330

ROBERT MCLAREN SOLICITOR ‡
Cape Copse End Cape Copse Rudgwick Horsham West Sussex RH12 3HG
Tel: 01403 823440 *Fax:* 01403 823770
E-mail: mclarenlegal@btconnect.com
List of partners: R I McLaren
Work: C1 E R1
SPr: McLaren, Mr Robert I LLB. . . . . *Nov 1974

SUE PETRITZ ‡
Richmond Stud Farm Bognor Road Horsham West Sussex RH12 3PS
Tel: 01403 790218 *Fax:* 01403 790522
List of partners: S Petritz
Work: D1 D2 K1 K3 W
Emergency Action, Advocacy and Fixed Fee Interview undertaken
SPr: Petritz, Mrs Sue LLB(Hons) . . . . *Feb 1992

NICOLA PHILLIPS SOLICITORS ‡
1 Market Square Horsham West Sussex RH12 1EU
Tel: 01403 258965 / 0845 040 5901 *Fax:* 0845 040 5902
E-mail: nicola@nps-law.co.uk

D J QUELCH ‡
Owls Nest Orchard House Cowfold Horsham West Sussex RH13 8AL
Tel: 01403 865096

RW LAW ‡
19 The Marches Kingsfold Horsham West Sussex RH12 3SY
Tel: 01306 700021
E-mail: robin.williams@rwlaw.co.uk

RAWLISON BUTLER LLP
Ridgeland House 15 Carfax Horsham West Sussex RH12 1DY
Tel: 01403 252492 *Fax:* 01403 241545 *Dx:* 57602 HORSHAM
E-mail: info@rawlisonbutler.com
Office: Crawley, London W1
Work: A1 B1 D1 E F1 J1 K1 K2 L N Q R1 S1 T1 W Z(l)
Agency undertaken
Ptr: Matthews, Mrs Barbara . . . . .NSP
Strange, Mr Chris FILEx. . . . . .NSP
Mem: Armstrong, Mr Digby R . . . . *May 1978
Worthing, Mr Robert M BA(Hons) . . . . *Aug 1991
Asoc: Dixon, Mr Christ BA(Hons); DipLaw . . . . Sep 1998
Higgott, Ms Fiona LLB . . . . Jan 2005
Swain, Mr Danos BA(Hons)(French, German & Business); PGDipLaw; DipLP. . . . . Sep 2002
Ast: Carlin, Mrs Diane Wendy LLB. . . . . Nov 1995
Hulmes, Ms Kathryn LLB . . . . Aug 2006
Ng, Ms Kristine MChem; GDL; LPC . . . . Jan 2008
Wardrope, Mrs Emily LLB. . . . . Jan 2008
Winter, Mr Nigel Carr LLB. . . . . Nov 1994

SEYMOURS + SOLICITORS
10 The Courtyard 30 Worthing Road Horsham West Sussex RH12 1SL
Tel: 01403 839261
Emergency telephone 07788 555262
E-mail: info@seymoursolicitors.co.uk
Office: Brighton

AMANDA SHAW SOLICITORS ‡
1 Mill Lane Littleworth Partridge Green Horsham West Sussex RH13 8JU
Tel: 01403 710742 *Fax:* 01403 713081
E-mail: amanda@amandashaw.co.uk

SITTONS SOLICITORS ‡
44 Pollards Drive Horsham West Sussex RH13 5HH
Tel: 01403 267377 *Fax:* 01403 273399
E-mail: shalena@sittons-solicitors.co.uk

SMITH GADD & CO ‡
Courtyard Chambers 1 The Courtyard London Road Horsham West Sussex RH12 1AT
Est: 1992
Tel: 01403 271222 *Fax:* 01403 271999 *Dx:* 57635 HORSHAM
E-mail: horsham@smithgadd.co.uk
List of partners: P J Docking, N S Smith
Work: A1 D1 E F1 J1 K1 K3 K4 L N O Q S1 S2 W
Ptr: Docking, Mr Paul J MA(Cantab). . . . . *Sep 1989
Smith, Mr Nigel S LLB. . . . . *Feb 1987
Ast: Alison, Mr Peter George LLB . . . . *Oct 1982

HOUGHTON LE SPRING, Tyne & Wear

HODGSON COULTHARD & CO ‡
Glendale House 10 Church Street Houghton Le Spring Tyne & Wear DH4 4DN
Tel: 0191 584 3333 *Fax:* 0191 512 0154
Dx: 65305 HOUGHTON LE SPRING
E-mail: law@hodgsoncoulthard.com
List of partners: M Coulthard, R D Ford, R N Hodgson
Work: D1 G H K1 N Q S1 V
Emergency Action, Agency, Advocacy, Fixed Fee Interview, Legal Aid undertaken, Legal Aid Franchise and Member of Accident Line
Ptr: Coulthard, Mr Michael LLB(Newc). . . . . *§Nov 1984
Ford, Mr Robin David LLB(Hons) . . . . Jun 2000
Hodgson, Mr R Neil LLB(Sheff) . . . . *§May 1981
Ast: Buchanan, Mr Charles A LLB(Hons) Notary Public . . *Oct 1987

NICHOLSON MARTIN LEGGE & MILLER ‡
Scruton House 8 Newbottle Street Houghton Le Spring Tyne & Wear DH4 4AD
Tel: 0191 584 2841 *Fax:* 0191 584 0371
Dx: 65309 HOUGHTON LE SPRING
List of partners: D Abernethy, S Parsons
Office: Stanley
Work: D1 E K1 K2 K3 K4 S1 S2 W
Agency, Advocacy, Fixed Fee Interview and Legal Aid undertaken
Ptr: Abernethy, Miss Diane LLB(Manc). . . . . *Apr 1976
Ast: Dawkins, Miss Kelly LLB(Hons) . . . . *Aug 2005

SHERWOOD-SMITH TILLEY & CO ‡
Brittanic Chambers PO Box 4 92-94 Newbottle Street Houghton Le Spring Tyne & Wear DH4 4AJ
Tel: 0191 584 3186 *Fax:* 0191 512 0805
Emergency telephone 0191 528 1591
E-mail: dkss1@aol.com
List of partners: C A Maskell, D K Sherwood-Smith, C H Slater
Work: A1 B1 C1 D1 E F1 G H J1 K1 L M1 N P R1 S1 T1 V W Z(c,d,j,k,l,m,t)
Emergency Action, Agency, Advocacy, Fixed Fee Interview, Legal Aid undertaken and Member of Accident Line
Ptr: Maskell, Mrs Carole A LLB; LLM . . . . *Mar 1990
Sherwood-Smith, Mr David K . . . . *§Jan 1982

HOUNSLOW, Middlesex

AMR SOLICITORS ‡
8 Douglas Road Hounslow Middlesex TW3 1DA
Tel: 020 8622 3783 *Fax:* 020 8622 3784
E-mail: amr.solicitors@gmail.com

ASH SOLICITORS ‡
31 Cross Lances Road Hounslow Middlesex TW3 2AD
Tel: 020 8570 8588 *Fax:* 020 8570 0737 *Dx:* 3512 HOUNSLOW
E-mail: info@ashsolicitors.com

ASHTON PAGE SOLICITORS ‡
Craneshaw House 8 Douglas Road Hounslow Middlesex TW3 1DA
Tel: 020 8622 3671 *Fax:* 020 8622 3672 *Dx:* 3515 HOUNSLOW
E-mail: info@ashtonpage.com

ASTON CARTER SOLICITORS
50 Salisbury Road Hounslow Middlesex TW4 6JQ
Tel: 020 8538 0287 / 0288 *Fax:* 020 8538 0284
E-mail: london-enquiry@astoncartersolicitors.com
Office: Birmingham

BHOGAL PARTNERS ‡
51-53 High Street Hounslow Middlesex TW3 1RB
Tel: 020 8572 9867 *Fax:* 020 8572 9228 *Dx:* 3522 HOUNSLOW
Emergency telephone 07802 989960
E-mail: info@bhogalpartners.co.uk
List of partners: A Agyemang
Languages: Dari, Gujarati, Hindi, Kiswahili, Punjabi, Sinhalese, Tagalog, Urdu
Work: A1 B1 B2 C1 D1 E F1 J1 K1 K3 L N O Q S1 S2 V W Z(g,i,l,p)
Emergency Action and Advocacy undertaken
Ptr: Agyemang, Mr Augustus . . . . Jun 2000

BONNETTS SOLICITORS LLP ‡
33 Bath Road Hounslow Middlesex TW3 3BW
Tel: 020 8570 5286 *Fax:* 020 8570 8531 *Dx:* 3501 HOUNSLOW
E-mail: law@bonnetts.co.uk
List of partners: A Carroll, J F Mountford, S J Wareham
Office: Whitton
Languages: French, Greek
Work: E N S1 W Z(m)
Member of Accident Line
Ptr: Carroll, Mrs Angela LLB. . . . . *§Feb 1989
Wareham, Mr Steven J . . . . *§Oct 1983
Ast: Pilling, Ms Gillian M BA(Hons); LSF . . . . *Mar 1984

CL LAW ‡
138 The Crossways Hounslow Middlesex TW5 0JR
Tel: 020 8577 1222

RAYMOND CLARKE & CO SOLICITORS ‡
Building 208 Epsom Square Eastern Business Park Hounslow Middlesex TW6 2BG
Tel: 020 3250 0000 *Fax:* 020 8759 0931
E-mail: rclarke.lhrap@ukonline.co.uk

REENA GHAI SOLICITORS ‡
Stable Cottage 42 High Street Hounslow Middlesex TW5 9RU
Tel: 020 8759 9959 *Fax:* 020 8759 9958 *Dx:* 52251 SOUTHALL 2
Emergency telephone 07770 290000
E-mail: reena@ghaiandco.com
List of partners: R Ghai
Languages: Hindi, Punjabi, Urdu
Work: B2 D1 D2 G H K1 K3 V
Emergency Action, Agency, Advocacy, Fixed Fee Interview and Legal Aid undertaken
SPr: Ghai, Miss Reena LLB(Hons) • . . . . *Oct 1993

M K GILL SOLICITORS ‡
298a Bath Road Hounslow Middlesex TW4 7DN
Tel: 020 8572 4509 *Fax:* 020 8572 4609
E-mail: info@mkgillsolicitors.co.uk

GUMMER & SINGH ‡
5 Bell Parade Bell Road Hounslow Middlesex TW3 3NU
Tel: 020 8572 6905 *Fax:* 020 8577 7444 *Dx:* 3521 HOUNSLOW
E-mail: raminder@tslaw.co.uk
List of partners: C Haras-Gummer, J Singh
Languages: Hindi, Punjabi, Sinhalese, Urdu
Work: B1 C1 D1 E F1 G H J1 K1 L M1 N P S1 W Z(i,l,p)
Agency, Fixed Fee Interview and Legal Aid undertaken
Ptr: Haras-Gummer, Mr Cyril MBIM; AMIMI . . . . *§Jan 1981
Singh, Jaswant MA; LLB . . . . *§Oct 1983

HALLENS SOLICITORS ‡
Craneshaw House 8 Douglas Road Hounslow Middlesex TW3 1DA
Tel: 020 8622 3729
Emergency telephone 07780 601150
E-mail: msh@hallens.co.uk
List of partners: M S Hallen
Languages: Hindi, Punjabi
Work: J1 Q Z(p)
Emergency Action, Agency, Advocacy and Fixed Fee Interview undertaken
SPr: Hallen, Mr Manjit S LLB Part time Chairman of the Employment Tribunals . . . . *Aug 1989

HARIS ALI & CO SOLICITORS ‡
63a Kingsley Road Hounslow Middlesex TW3 1QB
Tel: 020 8570 8400 *Fax:* 020 8570 8400

HESTON LAW CHAMBERS ‡
(incorporating Hardial Singh & Co)
345 Vicarage Farm Road Hounslow Middlesex TW5 0DZ
Tel: 020 8577 4545 *Fax:* 020 8577 9009

JUSPROWESS SOLICITORS & ADVOCATES ‡
162d High Street Hounslow Middlesex TW3 1 BQ
Tel: 020 8814 0208 *Fax:* 020 8814 0187
E-mail: admin@jusprowess.com

KCP LAW ‡
77 Hanworth Road Hounslow Middlesex TW3 1TT
Tel: 020 8572 1212 *Fax:* 020 8572 9114 *Dx:* 3518 HOUNSLOW
Emergency telephone 07973 562448
E-mail: info@kcplaw.co.uk
List of partners: K C Pankhania
Languages: British Sign Language, Gujarati, Hindi, Punjabi
Work: B2 C1 E G H O Q S1 S2
Agency, Advocacy and Legal Aid undertaken
Ptr: Pankhania, Mr Kirit Chhagan LLB(Hons) . . . . Aug 1989

KS LAW ‡
30 Grosvenor Road Hounslow Middlesex TW3 3ER
Tel: 020 8569 6637

KAPOOR & CO ‡
6th Floor Vista Office Centre Hounslow Middlesex TW4 6JQ
Tel: 020 8538 2778
E-mail: satish@kapoors.co.uk
Work: C1 E J1 K1 K3 N O Q S1 S2 W Z(q,r)

A K KHULLAR & CO ‡
171 Martindale Road Hounslow Middlesex TW4 7EZ
Tel: 020 8569 4488 *Fax:* 020 8569 5156

LESLIE & CO ‡
40a High Street Hounslow Middlesex TW3 1NW
Tel: 020 8577 5491 / 8572 7252
List of partners: I K Ratnasekera, T D L Ratnasekera
Languages: Bengali, French, German, Gujarati, Hindi, Kiswahili, Punjabi, Sinhalese, Telugu, Urdu
Work: G K3 M2 Z(i)
Fixed Fee Interview and Legal Aid undertaken
Ptr: Ratnasekera, Mrs Indira K. . . . . *Dec 1983
Ratnasekera, Mr T Don Leslie. . . . . *Dec 1983

LOVELL CHOHAN & CO ‡
Tudor House 44-50 Bath Road Hounslow Middlesex TW3 3EB
Tel: 020 8814 7599 *Fax:* 020 8570 6639 *Dx:* 3537 HOUNSLOW 1

MB LAW LIMITED ‡
686 London Road Hounslow Middlesex TW3 1PG
Tel: 020 8863 3666
E-mail: mblawuk@googlemail.com
Con: Sharma, Himanshu . . . . Jan 2003

MPR SOLICITORS LLP ‡
8 Red Lion Court Alexandra Road Hounslow Middlesex TW3 1JS
Tel: 020 8607 4660 *Fax:* 020 8607 4661 *Dx:* 3535 HOUNSLOW
E-mail: enquiries@mprsolicitors.co.uk

MACKENZIE & CO ‡
64 Wellington Road North Hounslow Middlesex TW4 7AA
Tel: 020 8569 6289 *Fax:* 020 8569 6290 *Dx:* 3530 HOUNSLOW
List of partners: A S Bhachu, J K Mackenzie, H R Persaud
Ptr: Bhachu, Amarjit Singh LLB . . . . *Feb 1991
Mackenzie, Mr John K LLB . . . . Sep 1979
Persaud, Mr Harold R BA • Inner Temple Scholarship . *Jan 1988
Ast: Dhaliwal, Mrs Narmaljit Kaur LLB . . . . *§Apr 1996

MARTYNSROSE SOLICITORS ‡
Vista Centre 50 Salisbury Road Hounslow Middlesex TW4 6JQ
Tel: 020 8538 1397
E-mail: martynsrosesolicitors@yahoo.co.uk
Office: London E8

NP SOLICITORS ‡
1 Whitton Road Hounslow Middlesex TW3 2DB
Tel: 020 8577 7799 *Fax:* 020 8577 9788
E-mail: npsolicitors@yahoo.co.uk
List of partners: N Pasha
SPr: Pasha, Noor. . . . . Jul 2004

ORION SOLICITORS LLP ‡
1st and 2nd Floors 171-173 High Street Hounslow Middlesex TW3 1QR
Tel: 020 8577 7130 *Fax:* 020 8814 0177
E-mail: info@orionsolicitors.co.uk

OSMANS SOLICITORS ‡
Pinnacle House Cross Lances Road Hounslow Middlesex TW3 2AD
Tel: 020 8538 7666 *Fax:* 020 8538 7777 *Dx:* 3507 HOUNSLOW

OWEN WHITE & CATLIN
12 Bath Road Hounslow Middlesex TW3 3EB
Tel: 020 8570 5471 *Fax:* 020 8572 8494 *Dx:* 3504 HOUNSLOW 1
Emergency telephone 07860 806886 / 07973 212596
E-mail: hounslow@owenwhitecatlin.co.uk
Office: Addlestone, Ashford, Feltham, London W4, London W6, Shepperton
Work: D1 G H K1 K2 S1 S2 W Z(l)

RAJ & PILLAI ‡
686-692 London Road Hounslow Middlesex TW3 1PG
Tel: 020 8572 7245 *Fax:* 020 8572 7218 *Dx:* 3529 HOUNSLOW
Emergency telephone 020 8577 0602
E-mail: raj-pillai@btconnect.com
List of partners: R Anandanadarajah, M Kanapathipillai
Languages: Punjabi, Sinhalese, Tamil, Urdu
Work: B1 D1 E F1 G H J1 K1 L M1 N O Q R1 S1 V W Z(g,i,l)
Emergency Action, Agency and Fixed Fee Interview undertaken
Ptr: Anandanadarajah, Rajaratnam . . . . *Jan 1987
Kanapathipillai, Mangalambikai . . . . Jun 1989

RAVI SETHI SOLICITORS ‡
First Floor 26 High Street Hounslow Middlesex TW3 1NW
Tel: 020 8570 7450 *Fax:* 020 8814 1138
E-mail: info@ravisethisolicitors.com

REEMANS SOLICITORS ‡
Craneshaw House 8 Douglas Road Hounslow Middlesex TW3 1DA
Tel: 020 8622 3638 *Fax:* 020 8622 3641 *Dx:* 3502 HOUNSLOW
Emergency telephone 07904 961509
E-mail: mail@reemans-law.co.uk
List of partners: M Virdee
Languages: Hindi, Malayalam, Punjabi, Tamil, Urdu
Work: C1 E K1 K3 L S1 S2 Z(i,l)
Fixed Fee Interview undertaken
Ptr: Virdee, Mr Munpreet LLB(Hons). . . . . *Apr 2001

RISHI & CO SOLICITORS ‡
Unit 23 Bellview Court Hounslow Middlesex TW3 3TT
Tel: 020 8570 6862 *Fax:* 020 8570 6862
E-mail: info@rishiandcosolicitors.co.uk

SB LAW ‡
44 Montague Road Hounslow Middlesex TW3 1LD
Tel: 020 8570 4041 *Fax:* 0871 900 7191 *Dx:* 3519 HOUNSLOW

SBM SOLICITORS ‡
26a Bath Road Hounslow Middlesex TW3 3EB
Tel: 020 8577 2474 *Fax:* 020 8577 3424
E-mail: info@sbmsolicitors-hounslow.co.uk

SAMARS SOLICITORS ‡
79 Spring Grove Crescent Hounslow Middlesex TW3 4DA
Tel: 020 8570 4716 *Fax:* 020 8570 5542
Emergency telephone 020 8570 4716
E-mail: ssamaraweere@aol.com
List of partners: P S Samaraweera
Languages: Gujarati, Hindi, Portuguese, Punjabi, Sinhalese, Spanish, Urdu
Work: D1 F1 G H J1 K1 L N Q V Z(i,l)
Emergency Action, Fixed Fee Interview, Legal Aid undertaken and Legal Aid Franchise
SPr: Samaraweera, Miss Paphiranage Surya LLB . . . . *Mar 1992

N SHARMA & CO SOLICITORS ‡
50 Crestwood Way Hounslow Middlesex TW4 5EQ
Tel: 020 8569 5600 *Fax:* 020 8581 4235
E-mail: nidhiksharma@hotmail.com

SHERGILL & CO ‡
22 Bath Road Hounslow Middlesex TW3 3EB
Tel: 020 8570 2323 *Fax:* 020 8577 1211 *Dx:* 3534 HOUNSLOW
Emergency telephone 07774 969800
List of partners: G S Shergill
Languages: Gujarati, Punjabi
Work: C1 E F1 G H J1 K1 L N O Q R1 S1 V W Z(i,l)
Emergency Action, Agency, Advocacy, Fixed Fee Interview and Legal Aid undertaken
Ptr: Shergill, Gurnam S BA . . . . Feb 1989
Ast: Evans, Ms Debra Louise LLB(Hons). . . . . Oct 1997

SINGH KARRAN & CO ‡
480 Great West Road Hounslow Middlesex TW5 0TA
Tel: 020 8570 5776 *Fax:* 020 8572 2286 *Dx:* 3520 HOUNSLOW
E-mail: law@singhkarran.com
List of partners: J S Ahluwalia, K Singh
Languages: Gujarati, Hindi, Punjabi, Urdu
Work: B1 C1 D1 D2 E J1 K1 K3 L O Q R2 S1 S2 W Z(i,j,l,p,q,s)
Emergency Action undertaken
Ptr: Ahluwalia, Jagjit S BA(Sussex) ♦ . . . . *Dec 1979
Singh, Ms Kamaldeep ♦. . . . . *Jul 1994

SURIYA & CO ‡
412 Hanworth Road Hounslow Middlesex TW3 3SN
Tel: 020 8569 6352 *Fax:* 020 8581 0765
E-mail: zasslaw@hotmail.com

TALAT NAVEED SOLICITORS ‡
2nd Floor Pyramid House 1 Martindale Road Hounslow Middlesex TW4 7EW
Tel: 020 8577 6666 *Fax:* 020 8577 6699 *Dx:* 3511 HOUNSLOW

VIJAYAPALANS ‡
4 Shirley Close Hounslow Middlesex TW3 2HF
Tel: 020 8755 3239 *Fax:* 020 8893 3171
List of partners: Y Vijayapalan
Languages: Sinhalese, Tamil
Work: S1 W
Fixed Fee Interview undertaken
SPr: Vijayapalan, Mrs Yogeswary LLB(Hons); LLM(Lond). *May 1985
Ast: Vijayapalan, Mr Malavarayan Vijayasundaram. . . . . May 1985

WALKERS ‡
6 Red Lion House Alexandra Road Hounslow Middlesex TW3 1JS
Tel: 020 8572 2691 *Fax:* 020 8572 7364
Languages: Hindi, Punjabi
Work: B1 C1 C2 C3 D1 E F1 G H J1 K1 L N O Q R1 S1 V W Z(i,l)
Emergency Action, Agency and Advocacy undertaken

WEERAKOON SOLICITORS ‡
24 Gresham Road Hounslow Middlesex TW3 4BU
Tel: 020 8814 1883 *Fax:* 020 8230 5617
E-mail: thusita@thusita.freeserve.co.uk
List of partners: T Weerakoon
Languages: Hindi, Sinhalese
Work: B1 C1 E F1 J1 K1 K3 L Q S2 W Z(b,g,h,j,r)
SPr: Weerakoon, Mr Thusita BA . . . . Jan 1991

HOVE, Brighton & Hove

ACUMEN BUSINESS LAW ‡
Audley House Hove Street Hove Brighton & Hove BN3 2DE
Tel: 0845 867 8978 *Fax:* 0871 714 2698
Office: Burgess Hill

ARSCOTTS ‡
54 Lansdowne Place Hove Brighton & Hove BN3 1FG
Tel: 01273 735289 *Fax:* 01273 325091 *Dx:* 59281 HOVE
Emergency telephone 01273 735289
E-mail: enquiries@arscotts.com
List of partners: K J Arscott, P J Arscott, M K Ashton, K A Fenlon
Work: A1 B1 B2 C1 C2 C3 D1 E F1 J1 K1 K2 K3 K4 L M1 N O P Q R1 R2 S1 S2 T1 T2 V W Z(c,e,l,m,q,r,v)
Emergency Action, Agency, Advocacy, Legal Aid undertaken, Legal Aid Franchise and Member of Accident Line
Dir: Arscott, Mr Keith J LLB(Lond). . . . . *Jul 1974
Arscott, Mr Paul J. . . . . *Aug 1998
Ashton, Mr Mark Keighly . . . . May 2005
Fenlon, Mr Kevin A . . . . *Dec 1974
Ast: Bunting, Mrs Louise. . . . . May 2010

BISHOP & LIGHT ‡
Cambridge House Cambridge Grove Hove Brighton & Hove BN3 3ED
Tel: 01273 732733
E-mail: law@bishopandlight.co.uk

D S BOSHER & CO ‡
24-26 Blatchington Road Hove Brighton & Hove BN3 3YN
Tel: 01273 721913 *Fax:* 01273 775321
E-mail: info@dsbosher.co.uk
List of partners: D S Bosher, A A Parker
Office: Peacehaven
Work: B1 C1 D1 E F1 G H J1 K1 L N O P Q R1 S1 S2 T1 T2 V W X Z(c,l)
Emergency Action, Agency, Advocacy and Fixed Fee Interview undertaken
Ptr: Bosher, Mr Derek S. . . . . *Jun 1972
Parker, Mr Adrian Andrew BA(Hons)(Law) Sir George Fowler Prize 1990 . . . . Oct 1990

F E BURLINGHAM JOHNSON ‡
(incorporating H H Kemp & Co; J Hodges & Co)
9 Third Avenue Hove Brighton & Hove BN3 2PB
Tel: 01273 748555 *Fax:* 01273 735639
Emergency telephone 01273 735639
List of partners: F E Burlingham Johnson
Work: A1 C1 E L R1 S1 T1 W
Agency, Advocacy and Fixed Fee Interview undertaken

BURNAND BRAZIER TISDALL ‡
39 Church Road Hove Brighton & Hove BN3 2BU
Tel: 01273 734022 *Fax:* 01273 778760 *Dx:* 59253 HOVE
List of partners: A M E Hill, J M Latham, A J Potter, J M Sartin
Office: Worthing (2 offices)
Work: D1 E F1 J1 K1 K3 K4 L N Q S1 V W
Fixed Fee Interview undertaken
Ptr: Hill, Mrs Alison Mary Eleanor LLB(Hons) . . . . Dec 2004
Latham, Mrs Julie Mary Notary Public. . . . . *Sep 1988
Sartin, Mrs Judith Margaret . . . . *Feb 1984
Ast: Day, Mr Reginald James LLB . . . . *May 1971
Potter, Mr Anthony John LLB . . . . *Jul 1976

CROSBY & MOORE SOLICITORS ‡
Sussex House 75 Church Road Hove Brighton & Hove BN3 2BB
Tel: 01273 863295 *Fax:* 01273 863297 *Dx:* 59288 HOVE
E-mail: advice@crosbymooresolicitors.co.uk
List of partners: D B Crosby, W R Moore
Work: K1 K3 N Q Z(r)
Fixed Fee Interview undertaken
Ptr: Crosby, Mr David Baynon LLB; LPC. . . . . Nov 1997
Moore, Mr Warren Richard . . . . Feb 1996

STEPHANIE DALE & CO ‡
Curtis House 34 Third Avenue Hove Brighton & Hove BN3 2PD
Tel: 01273 748333 *Fax:* 01273 230124
Emergency telephone 07770 846680
List of partners: S Dale
Work: D1 G H K1
Agency, Advocacy, Fixed Fee Interview, Legal Aid undertaken and Legal Aid Franchise
SPr: Dale, Ms Stephanie ★. . . . . Nov 1993

ENGLEHARTS ‡
Vallance Hall Hove Street Hove Brighton & Hove BN3 2GL
Tel: 01273 204411 *Fax:* 01273 776267 *Dx:* 59252 HOVE
E-mail: david@englehart.co.uk
List of partners: D J Englehart
Languages: French
Work: E S1 S2 W Z(l)
Ptr: Englehart, Mr David J. . . . . *Jan 1966
Ast: Nari, Mr Philip R LLB . . . . *Dec 1975

GEORGE H COLES & CO ‡
3-4 Western Road Hove Brighton & Hove BN3 1AE
Tel: 01273 205101 *Fax:* 01273 204378 *Dx:* 59275 HOVE
E-mail: partners@coles-solicitors.co.uk
List of partners: J T Deacon, I Gilbert, S W Smithers
Work: E F1 J1 L N O S1 S2 W Z(l,q)
Emergency Action, Agency, Advocacy, Fixed Fee Interview, Legal Aid undertaken, Legal Aid Franchise and Member of Accident Line
Ptr: Deacon, Mr John Timothy LLB(Wales). . . . . *Sep 1981
Gilbert, Mr Ian LLB(Manc). . . . . *May 1981
Smithers, Mr Stuart W LLB(Wales) . . . . *Oct 1978

GIRASOL SERVICES ‡
30 Hove Street Hove Brighton & Hove BN3 2DN
Tel: 01273 701679

GRIFFITH SMITH CONWAY ‡
(incorporating Conway Benn & Co)
154a Church Road Hove Brighton & Hove BN3 2DL
Est: 1987
Tel: 01273 821577 *Fax:* 01273 203794 *Dx:* 59270 HOVE
Emergency telephone 01273 551040 / 01273 559680
E-mail: info@gsc.co.uk
List of partners: S Carrigan, S K R Conway, C J Martin
Languages: French, Hebrew
Work: B1 C1 C2 C3 D1 D2 E F1 F2 J1 J2 K1 K2 L N O Q R1 R2 S1 S2 T1 T2 V W X Z(d,l)
Emergency Action, Agency, Advocacy and Fixed Fee Interview undertaken
Ptr: Carrigan, Mr Steven LLB ♦ . . . . *Jan 1990
Conway, Mrs Susan K R John Marshall Prize; School Governor Farlington School. . . . . *Jan 1965
Martin, Mr Christopher John LLB . . . . *Sep 1977

HOWLETT CLARKE SOLICITORS
29 Boundary Road Hove Brighton & Hove BN3 4EF
Tel: 01273 419728 *Fax:* 01273 430193 *Dx:* 92704 PORTSLADE
E-mail: brighton@howlettclarke.co.uk
Office: Brighton
Work: B1 C1 C2 D1 E F1 J1 K1 K2 L N O Q S1 S2 W Z(q)
Emergency Action, Agency, Advocacy, Fixed Fee Interview, Legal Aid undertaken, Legal Aid Franchise and Member of Accident Line
Ptr: Edmonds, Mr Colin J LLB(Hons) . . . . *Nov 1986
Robertson, Mr Warren BA(Hons)(History) . . . . Mar 2000
Asoc: Rowe, Mrs Helen LLB(Hons) . . . . Jun 1998
Ast: Oram, Mrs Caroline. . . . . Sep 1997

See p112 for the Key to Work Categories & other symbols

ELIZABETH LANDY ‡
18 Saxon Road Hove Brighton & Hove BN3 4LE
Tel: 01273 415264 *Fax:* 01273 415264
E-mail: elandy@totalise.co.uk

BRIAN MACKRELL & CO LTD ‡
First Floor Office Western House Hove Brighton & Hove BN3 1FA
Tel: 01273 823456

I A MORCOWITZ ‡
11 Viceroy Lodge 143 Kingsway Hove Brighton & Hove BN3 4RA
Tel: 01273 251769 *Fax:* 0845 458 0742
E-mail: tony@morcolaw.net

OSMAN WARD & SONS ‡
37 Church Road Hove Brighton & Hove BN3 2BW
Tel: 01273 778787 / 778788 *Fax:* 01273 202726
E-mail: osmanward@aol.com
List of partners: J O Ward
Work: K4 S1 T2 W
Fixed Fee Interview undertaken
Ptr: Ward, Mr John Osman . . . . *Jul 1959

S M REED & CO ‡
6 The Drive Hove Brighton & Hove BN3 3JA
Tel: 01273 727351 *Fax:* 01273 737685 *Dx:* 59274 HOVE
E-mail: law@smreed.co.uk
List of partners: R H Crane, S M Reed
Languages: French
Work: C1 E L R1 S1 W Z(l)
Fixed Fee Interview undertaken
Ptr: Crane, Mr Ralph H BSc(Econ) . . . . . . *Dec 1978
Reed, Mr Stephen M . . . . *Jul 1971
Ast: Reed, Mrs Susan Andrea BA(Hons)(Business Studies)*Feb 2000

RIX & KAY SOLICITORS LLP
7 The Drive Hove Brighton & Hove BN3 3JS
Tel: 01273 329797 *Fax:* 01273 225609
Office: London W1, Seaford, Sevenoaks, Uckfield
Languages: Swedish
Work: A3 C1 C2 C3 D1 E F1 F2 J1 J2 K1 K2 K3 K4 L N O P Q R1 R2 S1 S2 T2 V W X Z(d,e,o,q,r,u)
Agency, Advocacy and Fixed Fee Interview undertaken
Ptr: Bates, Mr Richard LLB(Hons); PGDipLaw . . . . *Nov 2000
Dyson, Miss Julia E BA(Hons) . . . . *Sep 1997
Hayes, Mr Michael Niall LLB(Hons) . . . . . *Jul 1996
Peake, Mrs Sally Eunice Fage LLB(Hons); LSF . . . *Nov 1994
Wright, Mr Maxwell Benyon LLB . . . . . . *§Oct 1981
Asoc: Bourn, Mrs Jane Bridget Letitia LLB(Hons) . . . . Nov 1995
Ast: Fitch, Mrs Agneta Dagny . . . . *Sep 2002
Frisby, Miss Bridget Anne LLB . . . . *Dec 2009

MARTIN ROSS SOLICITOR ‡
61 Church Road Hove Brighton & Hove BN3 2NT
Tel: 01273 559128 *Fax:* 01273 617047

DERMOT SCULLY SOLICITORS ‡
19 Wilbury Gardens Hove Brighton & Hove BN3 6HQ

THEAKER LOADSMAN & REYNOLDS ‡
61 Church Road Hove Brighton & Hove BN3 2BP
Tel: 01273 229500 *Fax:* 01273 229515 *Dx:* 59284 HOVE
E-mail: solicitors@tlrlaw.uk.com
List of partners: C D Loadsman, A H Theaker
Languages: French, Swedish
Work: S1 S2 W
Ptr: Loadsman, Mr Christopher D . . . . Nov 1962
Theaker, Mr Andrew H LLB(Bris) . . . . . . Nov 1970

TREMLETTS ‡
Kingsway House 134-140 Church Road Hove Brighton & Hove BN3 2DL
Tel: 01903 214279 *Fax:* 01273 677782 *Dx:* 2728 BRIGHTON

WISDOM LAW ‡
45 Pembroke Crescent Hove Brighton & Hove BN3 5DF
Tel: 01273 272861
E-mail: sarah.mynard@wisdomlaw.co.uk

WOOLLEY BEVIS DIPLOCK
79 Church Road Hove Brighton & Hove BN3 2BB
Tel: 01273 722532 *Fax:* 01273 326347 *Dx:* 59263 HOVE
Office: Brighton
Ptr: Darby, Mr Andrew G LLB(Lond) . . . . . . *Dec 1974
Diplock, Mr David J E . . . . *§Jan 1968
Ellis, Mr Brian L MA(Cantab) . . . . *Dec 1968

HOWDEN, East Riding of Yorkshire

HEPTONSTALLS LLP
1 Vicar Lane Howden East Riding of Yorkshire DN14 7BP
Tel: 01430 430209 *Fax:* 01430 432101 *Dx:* 700844 HOWDEN
E-mail: legal@heptonstalls.co.uk
Office: Goole, Pontefract (2 offices), Scunthorpe
Work: A1 B1 C1 C2 C3 D1 E F1 G H J1 K1 L M1 M2 N O P Q R1 S1 T1 T2 V W Z(c,h,i,j,l,m,n,o,s,t)
Advocacy, Fixed Fee Interview, Legal Aid undertaken and Legal Aid Franchise
Ast: Wilson, Mrs Jennifer L LLB(Leeds) . . . . . *Jul 1974

SYMES BAINS BROOMER
55 Hailgate Howden East Riding of Yorkshire DN14 7ST
Tel: 01430 430230 *Fax:* 01430 431502 *Dx:* 700845 HOWDEN
E-mail: info@sbblaw.com
Office: Epworth, Goole, Grimsby, Scunthorpe

HUCKNALL, Nottinghamshire

ROBERT BARBER & SONS
35a Watnall Road Hucknall Nottinghamshire NG15 7LD
Tel: 0115 955 2299 *Fax:* 0115 878 9705 *Dx:* 28505 HUCKNALL
E-mail: reception@robertbarber.co.uk
Office: Eastwood, Nottingham
Work: A3 D1 E F1 J1 K1 K2 K3 L N O Q S1 S2 W
Emergency Action and Fixed Fee Interview undertaken
Ptr: Howard, Mr Donald C LLB . . . . *Feb 1980
Hussain, Mrs Samina LLB . . . . *Nov 2005

SHELTONS ‡
Belmont House Station Road Hucknall Nottinghamshire NG15 7UE
Tel: 0115 955 3444 *Fax:* 0115 955 3445 *Dx:* 28501 HUCKNALL
E-mail: info@sheltons-solicitors.co.uk
List of partners: J W Kujawinski, S J M Mannering, J C Smith, D E Tomlinson, B K Watkinson
Office: Nottingham (2 offices)
Work: C1 D1 D2 E F1 J1 K1 L N Q S1 S2 V W Z(l,r)
Agency, Advocacy, Legal Aid undertaken and Legal Aid Franchise
Ptr: Kujawinski, Mr Jerzy W BA . . . . *Feb 1983
Tomlinson, Mr David E LLB(Hons) Deputy District Chairman of the Appeals Service . . . . *Apr 1967
Ast: Tomlinson, Mrs Lesley Ann . . . . *Nov 2001

HUDDERSFIELD, West Yorkshire

ALI & CO SOLICITORS ‡
19a Westgate Huddersfield West Yorkshire HD1 1NP
Tel: 01484 517887 *Fax:* 01484 517883
E-mail: aliandco@btconnect.com
List of partners: K Hussain
Office: Bradford

AMAL SOLICITORS ‡
1 King Cliff Road Huddersfield West Yorkshire HD2 2RR
Tel: 01484 431999 *Fax:* 01484 431888
Emergency telephone 07699 753645
E-mail: info@amalsolicitors.co.uk
List of partners: I Amin, A Mahmood
Languages: Punjabi, Urdu
Ptr: Amin, Mr Ikram LLB(Hons) . . . . Mar 2001
Mahmood, Mr Amjid . . . . Aug 2004
Con: Younis, Mr Imran LLB . . . . Aug 2004

APPLEBYS SOLICITORS ‡
88a Westbourne Road Huddersfield West Yorkshire HD1 4LF
Tel: 01484 550944 *Fax:* 01484 432170
E-mail: enquiries@applebys-law.co.uk

APPLEYARD LEES
The Media Centre 7 Northumberland Street Huddersfield West Yorkshire HD1 1RL
Tel: 01484 483000 *Fax:* 01484 483100
E-mail: huddersfield@appleyardlees.com
Office: Burnley, Chester, Halifax, Harrogate, Leeds, Liverpool, Manchester, Preston, Sheffield, Stockton-on-Tees, York

ARMITAGE SYKES LLP ‡
72 & 74 New North Road Huddersfield West Yorkshire HD1 5NW
Tel: 01484 538121 *Fax:* 01484 518968
Dx: 711270 HUDDERSFIELD 9
E-mail: info@armitagesykes.co.uk
List of partners: B Ali, P Brewer, A M Iredale, V J Lewis, M H Thompson, R M Turner, D Walker, J Woodward
Office: Brighouse, Huddersfield
Languages: French, German
Work: A1 B1 C1 C2 C3 D1 D2 E F1 F2 J1 J2 K1 K3 K4 L M1 N O P Q R1 S1 S2 T1 T2 W Z(b,c,d,e,h,k,l,p,q)
Emergency Action, Advocacy, Legal Aid undertaken and Legal Aid Franchise
Ptr: Ali, Basharat LLB . . . . *Oct 1988
Iredale, Ashley M LLB . . . . *Oct 1988
Thompson, Mr Martin H LLB . . . . *Sep 1997
Turner, Mr Robert M LLB . . . . *Dec 1974
Walker, Mrs Diana LLB . . . . *Oct 1991
Asoc: Kelly, Mr Robert Daniel MA(Oxon) . . . . . . *Sep 2010
Sohpal, Mrs Kanika LLB . . . . *Sep 2004
Ude, Mr Alexander LLB . . . . *Apr 2001
Ast: Ahmed, Miss Aisha LLB . . . . *Jul 2008
Bannister, Mr Jason S LLB . . . . *Nov 2006
Hellawell, Mr Derek J LLB . . . . *Nov 2006
O'Leary, Dr Leanne PhD . . . . *Jan 2004

ARMITAGE SYKES LLP
4 Macaulay Street Huddersfield West Yorkshire HD1 2JW
Tel: 01484 344140 *Fax:* 01484 510055
Dx: 710087 HUDDERSFIELD 8
E-mail: info@armitagesykes.co.uk
Office: Brighouse, Huddersfield
Work: A1 B1 C1 C2 C3 D1 D2 E F1 F2 J1 J2 K1 K3 K4 L M1 N O P Q R1 S1 S2 T1 T2 W Z(b,c,d,e,h,k,l,p,q)
Emergency Action, Advocacy, Legal Aid undertaken and Legal Aid Franchise
Ptr: Woodward, Mr Jeffrey LLB . . . . *Dec 1975
Asoc: Miller, Ms Ruth LLB . . . . *Aug 1998
Skinner, Mr James LLB . . . . *May 1999
Ast: Thomas, Ms Sandra LLB . . . . *Sep 2009

AUSTIN KEMP SOLICITORS ‡
7 Northumberland Street Huddersfield West Yorkshire HD1 1RL
Tel: 01484 483033 *Fax:* 01484 741442
E-mail: mail@austinkemp.co.uk

BAILEY SMAILES ‡
6 New North Parade Huddersfield West Yorkshire HD1 5JP
Tel: 01484 435543 *Fax:* 01484 456190 *Dx:* 712959 HUDDERSFIELD
E-mail: mail@baileysmailes.co.uk
List of partners: J D G Crowther, R M Green, I R Holmes, A McNeil, D A Rycroft
Office: Holmfirth
Work: A1 B1 C1 C2 D1 E F1 H J1 K1 L N O Q S1 T1 T2 V W Z(i,l)
Emergency Action, Advocacy, Fixed Fee Interview, Legal Aid undertaken and Member of Accident Line
Ptr: Crowther, Mr John David Graham LLB . . . . . *Dec 1970
Green, Mr Richard Mark BA(Hons)(Law) . . . . . Feb 1987
Holmes, Mr Ian R . . . . *Oct 1973
McNeil, Mr Alan LLB(Sheff) . . . . *Apr 1975
Rycroft, Mr David A . . . . *Dec 1966
Ast: Ryan, Miss Charlotte Emerald LLB . . . . . . Jun 2007
Thubron, Miss Charlotte Hannah Sophie . . . . Apr 2006
Wells, Mr David Anthony BA(Hons) . . . . . . *§Mar 2004

BAXTER CAULFIELD ‡
13 Station Street Huddersfield West Yorkshire HD1 1LY
Tel: 01484 519519 *Fax:* 01484 518085 *Dx:* 712955 HUDDERSFIELD
E-mail: mail@baxlaw.co.uk
List of partners: P S S Booth, J H Coughlin, K E Donaldson, H J Garnett, R M Gillatt, S G Newman
Work: A1 B1 C1 C2 C3 E F1 F2 I J1 J2 L M1 M2 O P Q R1 R2 S1 S2 T1 T2 W Z(c,e,k,l,p,q,y,z)
Agency, Advocacy and Fixed Fee Interview undertaken
Ptr: Booth, Mr Paul S S LLB Maxwell Law Prize 1985 . . . *Nov 1989
Coughlin, Miss Jane H BA(Oxon) . . . . *Nov 1987
Donaldson, Ms Katherine Elizabeth BA . . . . . . *Oct 1995
Garnett, Miss Hilary J LLB . . . . *Sep 1992
Gillatt, Mr Richard M BA . . . . *Oct 1987
Newman, Mr Stephen G BA . . . . *§Oct 1986
Asoc: Metcalfe, Mr Nicholas Treloar BA(Hons) . . . . . *Aug 2002
Ward, Miss Sarah Louise BSc(Hons) . . . . . . Sep 2002
Ast: Beresford, Mr James Edward BA . . . . Jun 2008
Mann, Rachael . . . . Sep 2008
Spragg, Miss Emma Jayne BA(Hons)(Law with French) Oct 2005
Zarif, Mr Amar LLB . . . . Apr 2008
Con: Walkden, Mr W Ian BA(Cantab) . . . . *Apr 1973

ROBERT CAMPBELL ‡
94A Redcliff Road Golcar Huddersfield West Yorkshire HD7 4EZ
Tel: 01484 843323

CARR & CO ‡
1st Floor 3 Upperhead Row Huddersfield West Yorkshire HD1 2JL
Tel: 01484 467860 *Fax:* 01484 531688 *Dx:* 712963 HUDDERSFIELD
Emergency telephone 07659 106984 (CAR) / 07802 947957
E-mail: wainwrightj@carr-law.co.uk
List of partners: R A Carr, M W Sisson-Pell, J M Slawinski
Languages: Punjabi, Urdu
Work: G H
Emergency Action, Agency, Advocacy, Fixed Fee Interview, Legal Aid undertaken and Legal Aid Franchise
Ptr: Carr, Mr Robert A LLB(Hons) . . . . *§Aug 1978
Sisson-Pell, Mr Michael W ★ . . . . *Jan 1983
Slawinski, Mr Jonathan Mark BA(Hons) . . . . . *Nov 1995
Ast: Kidd, Mrs Sonia BSc(Hons); CPE; LPC . . . . . Jun 2003

CHADWICK LAWRENCE ‡
(incorporating Cartwright Cliffe & Co; Learoyd Sisson & Co; Mills Best & Wilson; Owen & Briggs)
13 Railway Street Huddersfield West Yorkshire HD1 1JS
Tel: 01484 519999 *Fax:* 01484 544099 *Dx:* 712953 HUDDERSFIELD
Emergency telephone 07850 315111
E-mail: enquiry@chadlaw.co.uk
Office: Halifax, Morley, Wakefield
Work: A3 C1 D1 E G H J1 K1 K2 L N O Q S1 S2 W X Z(g,r)

NEIL COOMBES SOLICITOR LTD ‡
25 Penistone Road Fenay Bridge Huddersfield West Yorkshire HD8 0AP
Tel: 01484 303585
E-mail: mail@ncoombes.co.uk

EAD SOLICITORS LLP
The Media Centre 7 Northumberland Street Huddersfield West Yorkshire HD1 1RL
Tel: 01484 437448 *Fax:* 01484 437453
E-mail: enquiry@eadsolicitors.co.uk
Office: Liverpool (2 offices)
Con: Thornley, Mr Jack LLB . . . . *Nov 1962

EATON SMITH LLP ‡
(incorporating Bruce & Co; Eaton Smith & Downey; Marshall Mills & Sykes)
14 High Street Huddersfield West Yorkshire HD1 2HA
Tel: 01484 821300 *Fax:* 01484 821333
Dx: 721870 HUDDERSFIELD 10
E-mail: mail@eatonsmith.co.uk
List of partners: J B Cooper, V L Heywood, J E Mahaffey, D A Melluish, N S J Murphy, A J Palmer, A E Pendlebury, S J Pollitt, J M Royle, J M Schofield, W A Sugden, M F Webb
Work: A1 A3 B1 C1 C2 C3 D1 D2 E F1 G H I J1 K1 K2 L N O Q R1 S1 S2 T1 T2 U2 V W Z(c,d,e,g,h,i,l,o,r)
Emergency Action, Agency, Advocacy, Fixed Fee Interview, Legal Aid undertaken, Legal Aid Franchise and Member of Accident Line
Ptr: Cooper, Mr J Benjamin BSc(Hons) . . . . *Oct 1984
Heywood, Miss Victoria L LLB . . . . *Oct 1991
Mahaffey, Ms Jane Elizabeth BA ♦ . . . . *Oct 1994
Melluish, Miss Deborah A . . . . *Sep 1991
Murphy, Mr Neil S J BA ★ . . . . *Oct 1987
Palmer, Mrs Alison Jane LLB(Hons) . . . . . . Oct 1990
Pendlebury, Ms Anne Elizabeth BSc ♦ . . . . . . *Mar 1993
Pollitt, Mr Steven J LLB ♦ . . . . *Nov 1974
Royle, Mr John M BA . . . . *Nov 1976
Schofield, Miss Judith M BA(Wales) ♦ . . . . . . *§Nov 1982
Sugden, Mr W Andrew MA(Cantab) Chairman of SSAT*Aug 1974
Webb, Mr Michael F . . . . *Jan 1982
Asoc: Birkbeck, Ms Rachel BA(Hons)(Cantab) . . . . . *Sep 1996
Crichton, Miss Sandra R LLB(Hons) . . . . . . *Oct 1998
Whitfield, Miss Adele Fiona LLB; FILEx . . . . . . Feb 2007
Ast: Booth, Miss Andrea Kate LLB . . . . Sep 2007
Byrne, Mrs Elizabeth Jayne LLB(Hons) . . . . . . Oct 2007
Coward, Mrs Amanda Jane BA(Hons); PGDipLaw; PGLPC . . . . Nov 2006
Dyson, Miss Magda Louise LLB(Hons); LLM . . . . *Mar 2009
Monkhouse, Miss Claire LLB(Hons) . . . . *Oct 2004
Mousavi, Miss Natalie Farah LLB(Hons); LPC; PGDip *Nov 2009
Taylor, Mr Christopher BSc(Hons) University Insolvency Prize 2002 . . . . Oct 2005
Walker, Ms Rosemary Jill LLB . . . . Dec 1999

GREENHEAD SOLICITORS ‡
125a Fitzwilliam Street Huddersfield West Yorkshire HD1 5PS
Tel: 01484 546022 *Fax:* 01484 546023

GRIEVES SOLICITORS ‡
Britannic Building 3 Upperhead Row Huddersfield West Yorkshire HD1 2JL
Tel: 01484 300192 *Fax:* 01484 352121
E-mail: helen.grieves@grieves-solicitors.co.uk
List of partners: H Grieves
Languages: French, German
Work: J2 N
SPr: Grieves, Miss Helen BA(Hons); LLM . . . . . . *Oct 1993

HW SOLICITORS ‡
81 New Street Huddersfield West Yorkshire HD1 2TW
Tel: 01484 518356 *Fax:* 01484 429819
E-mail: info@hwsolicitors.co.uk
Work: N Q S1
Agency, Advocacy, Fixed Fee Interview undertaken and Member of Accident Line

HAQ SOLICITORS ‡
Prospect House Prospect Business Centre Huddersfield West Yorkshire HD1 2NU
Tel: 01484 533759

HOLROYD & CO ‡
27 Market Street Milnsbridge Huddersfield West Yorkshire HD3 4ND
Tel: 01484 645464 *Fax:* 01484 460087
E-mail: info@holroydsolicitors.co.uk
List of partners: R J Bennett, D A Walsh
Office: Huddersfield
Work: C1 C2 D2 E F1 J1 K1 N O Q S1 S2 T1 T2 W Z(o,q)
Advocacy, Fixed Fee Interview undertaken and Member of Accident Line
Ptr: Bennett, Mr Richard J LLB . . . . *Oct 1984
Walsh, Mr David A Law Society Annual Prize for LPC *Nov 2000
Ast: Gibson, Natalie . . . . Jan 2007
Oldham, Mrs Lisa J LLB(Hons) . . . . *Feb 1994
Con: Morrell, Mr Mark A LLB(Hons)(L'pool) . . . . *Feb 1989

HOLROYD & CO
28 John William Street Huddersfield West Yorkshire HD1 1BG
Tel: 01484 645464 *Fax:* 01484 430670
Office: Huddersfield
Ast: Green, Mr Richard Mark BA(Hons)(Law) . . . . Feb 1987

KINGS SOLICITORS PRACTICE ‡
18 Burton Acres Lane Highburton Huddersfield West Yorkshire HD8 0QR
Tel: 01484 602218
E-mail: v.king156@btinternet.com

KINGSLEY BROOKES ‡
Estate Buildings Railway Street Huddersfield West Yorkshire HD1 1JY
Tel: 01484 302800 *Fax:* 01484 302870
Emergency telephone 01484 302800
E-mail: crime@kingsleybrookes.co.uk
List of partners: M Brookes, C Kingsley
Work: B2 G H
Agency, Fixed Fee Interview and Legal Aid undertaken
Ptr: Brookes, Mr Mark LLB(Nott'm) ★ . . . . *§Nov 1994
Kingsley, Mr Carl ★ . . . . *§Sep 1996
Ast: Watson, Miss Kathryn LLB(Hons); LawDip . . . . . . *Jan 2009

NORCLIFFE & CO ‡
New Street Chambers New Street Huddersfield West Yorkshire HD1 2AR
Tel: 01484 514907 *Fax:* 01484 435284
Dx: 712975 HUDDERSFIELD 1
E-mail: info@norcliffe-law.co.uk
List of partners: R C Dunn, J A Norcliffe
Languages: French
Work: B1 C1 C2 C3 D1 E F1 J1 K1 L M1 N O P Q S1 S2 T1 T2 W Z(e,f,l,q)
Emergency Action, Agency, Advocacy, Fixed Fee Interview undertaken and Member of Accident Line
Ptr: Dunn, Mr Roy C LLB . . . . *Nov 1992
Norcliffe, Mr John A LLB . . . . *Oct 1981
Ast: Robinson, Mr John Clive BA . . . . *Oct 1981

OAKS SOLICITORS ‡
26a Spaines Road Huddersfield West Yorkshire HD2 2QA
Tel: 01484 542754 *Fax:* 01484 545616

OATES HANSON ‡
(incorporating Howe Harrison Solicitors)
5 Market Street Huddersfield West Yorkshire HD1 2EH
Tel: 01484 300609 *Fax:* 01484 302322 *Dx:* 712970 HUDDERSFIELD
E-mail: oateshanson@ntlbusiness.com
List of partners: V P A Hanson, J Oates
Languages: Spanish
Work: A1 B1 C1 E F1 J1 K1 K4 L O Q R1 S1 S2 T1 T2 V W Z(c,d,h,l)
Agency, Advocacy and Fixed Fee Interview undertaken
Ptr: Hanson, Mr Victor P A BA . . . . *Mar 1978
Oates, Mr John MA(Cantab) . . . . *§Apr 1976

PARKER BIRD GARDNER ‡
24-28 Queen Street Huddersfield West Yorkshire HD1 2SP
Tel: 01484 825200 *Fax:* 01484 825205 *Dx:* 712969 HUDDERSFIELD
E-mail: enquiries@pbgardner.com
List of partners: R J Coneron, P R Gardner, S Hardman, R Uppal
Languages: French, Hindi, Punjabi, Urdu
Work: B1 C1 C2 C3 D1 D2 E F1 H J1 K1 K2 K3 M1 M2 N O P Q S1 S2 W Z(i,j,k,l)
Emergency Action, Agency, Advocacy, Fixed Fee Interview, Legal Aid undertaken, Legal Aid Franchise and Member of Accident Line
Ptr: Coneron, Mrs Ruth Joanna BSc(Econ); DipLaw; LLM . Jan 1999
Gardner, Mr Paul Ronald BA(Hons); LLM Deputy District Judge . . . . *Dec 1981
Hardman, Ms Sharron BA . . . . *Jun 1990
Uppal, Ranjit . . . . *Aug 1997
Ast: Layfield, Mr Allan Richard LLB(Hons) . . . . Jan 2004
McLay, Mr Ross Ian LLB(Hons) . . . . Apr 2004
Thapar, Miss Jaswinder LLB; MA; LLM . . . . Oct 2006
Con: Beckett, Mr John Graeme MA(Oxon) . . . . Oct 1981

PARKER BIRD WHITELEY ‡
Hammonds Yard 46/48 King Street Huddersfield West Yorkshire HD1 2QT
Tel: 01484 423300

RAMSDENS SOLICITORS ‡
Ramsden Street Huddersfield West Yorkshire HD1 2TH
Tel: 01484 821500 *Fax:* 01484 510446
Dx: 710094 HUDDERSFIELD 8
E-mail: info@ramsdens.co.uk
List of partners: D Amies, R C Bramall, J L Coen, J M C Cook, G Dolan, J M Fryer, D F Garsed, M A Hepworth, D Hofton, K D James, P R Joyce, D L Kaye, S Mills, J Murtagh, M G Parkinson, M J Roberts, S G Singh, G Swain, H E Thewlis, J Whitfield, P M Whitfield
Office: Dewsbury, Elland, Halifax, Holmfirth, Huddersfield (2 offices), Mirfield
Work: B1 C1 C2 D1 E F1 J1 K1 K2 K3 K4 L N O P Q R1 R2 S1 S2 T1 T2 V W Z(c,d,e,l,p,r,w)
Emergency Action, Agency, Advocacy, Fixed Fee Interview, Legal Aid undertaken, Legal Aid Franchise and Member of Accident Line
Ptr: Amies, Mr David . . . . *Feb 1997
Bramall, Mr Richard Charles LLB . . . . Oct 2003
Cook, Mr Jeremy M C LLB . . . . *Nov 1988
Dolan, Mr Greg BA(Hons); CPE; LPC; PSC . . . . . *Sep 1996
Fryer, Mr John M LLB; LLM; ALCM . . . . *Dec 1979
Garsed, Mr David Fowler . . . . *May 1977
Hepworth, Mr Mark Andrew . . . . *Oct 1985
Hofton, Mr David BA . . . . *Nov 1986
James, Miss Karen D LLB . . . . *Sep 1989
Joyce, Mr Paul R MA . . . . *Dec 1987
Kaye, Ms Deborah Louise LLB(Hons) . . . . *Jan 1996
Mills, Mr Simon . . . . *Nov 1989
Roberts, Mr Michael J LLB . . . . *Apr 1978
Singh, Mr Steven G LLB . . . . *Oct 1986
Thewlis, Miss Helen Elizabeth LLB(Hons)(Leeds); PGDip . . . . *Aug 1996
Whitfield, Mr Paul Mark BA(Hons) . . . . *Oct 1995
Asoc: Auty, Ms Alison Jane LLB . . . . *May 1997
Cornes, Mr Jonathan BSc Notary Public . . . . *Jul 1998
Dando, Mr Gareth . . . . *Oct 2000
Hancock, Miss Julia D LLB . . . . *Sep 1999
Ast: Barton, Mrs Linda LLB . . . . Apr 1973
Beevers, Miss Laura Claire . . . . *Apr 2008
Brown, Ms Joanne . . . . *Mar 2005
Frith, Lindsey . . . . *Dec 2008
Hirst, Mr Dan . . . . *Jul 2005
Mullins, Miss Veronica Jane LLB . . . . *Sep 2004
Nuttall, Ms Heather . . . . *Nov 1992
Scott, Ms Anne Margaret LLB . . . . *Jun 1996
Serjeant, Ms Emma . . . . *Aug 2005
Sheldrake, Ms Colette . . . . Sep 2009
Smith, Mrs Laura Naomi . . . . *Nov 2007
Sykes, Ms Rachael . . . . *May 2005
Walters, Jan . . . . *Oct 2005
Wharton, Miss Joanne LLB . . . . Aug 2007
Con: Gregory, Mr Timothy W BA(Leeds) . . . . *Jan 1977

RAMSDENS SOLICITORS
18 Lewisham Road Slaithwaite Huddersfield West Yorkshire HD7 5AL
Tel: 01484 844116 *Fax:* 01484 848984
Dx: 740960 HUDDERSFIELD 15
E-mail: info@ramsdens.co.uk
Office: Dewsbury, Elland, Halifax, Holmfirth, Huddersfield (2 offices), Mirfield
Work: S1 W

RAMSDENS SOLICITORS
Oakley House 1 Hungerford Road Edgerton Huddersfield West Yorkshire HD3 3AL
Tel: 01484 558066 *Fax:* 01484 558083
Dx: 740960 HUDDERSFIELD 15
E-mail: info@ramsdens.co.uk
Office: Dewsbury, Elland, Halifax, Holmfirth, Huddersfield (2 offices), Mirfield
Work: C1 E J1 S2 W

JOSEPH RAPHAEL SOLICITORS ‡
6 Middlemost Close Birkby Huddersfield West Yorkshire HD2 2PU
Tel: 01484 530003 *Fax:* 01484 530006
E-mail: jj@jrsolicitors.com

RIDLEY & HALL ‡
Queens House 35 Market Street Huddersfield West Yorkshire HD1 2HL
Tel: 01484 538421 *Fax:* 01484 533076
Dx: 710083 HUDDERSFIELD 8
E-mail: info@ridleyandhall.co.uk
List of partners: K D Ludgate, N J Priestley, D G Rhodes, S E Young
Languages: Punjabi, Urdu
Work: C1 D1 D2 E J1 K1 K3 L N Q S1 S2 V W X Z(l,r)
Emergency Action, Agency, Advocacy, Fixed Fee Interview, Legal Aid undertaken, Legal Aid Franchise and Member of Accident Line
Ptr: Ludgate, Mr Kevin D LLB(Hons) . . . . *Jul 1987
Priestley, Mr Nigel J LLB . . . . *Apr 1976
Rhodes, Mr David G LLB . . . . *Apr 1975
Young, Ms Sarah Elizabeth LLB . . . . *Oct 1994
Ast: Devenport, Mrs Julie LLB . . . . *Nov 1990
Ownsworth, Mrs Jolanta LLB(Hons) . . . . *Dec 1993
Wilson, Mr James BA(Hons) . . . . *Feb 2003

SWITALSKI'S
69 New Street Huddersfield West Yorkshire HD1 2BQ
Tel: 01484 821650 *Fax:* 01484 821651
Dx: 712964 HUDDERSFIELD 8
Office: Bradford, Dewsbury, Halifax, Leeds, Wakefield
Work: D1 G H J1 K1 K2 L Z(i,m,r)
Emergency Action, Agency and Legal Aid undertaken

TRINITY LAW SOLICITORS ‡
82 Trinity Street Huddersfield West Yorkshire HD1 4DS
Tel: 01484 300196 *Fax:* 01484 431754
E-mail: trinitylawsolicitors@hotmail.com

WILKINSON WOODWARD
22 Queen Street Huddersfield West Yorkshire HD1 2SP
Tel: 01484 483800 *Fax:* 01484 533490
Office: Halifax
Work: B1 D1 D2 G J1 K1 K2 K3 O R1 R2 S1 S2 Z(p)
Ast: Edge, Mr Richard LLB(Hons) . . . . *Nov 2010

HULL, Kingston upon Hull

AMBER SOLICITORS LLP ‡
171 High Street Hull Kingston upon Hull HU1 1NE
Tel: 01482 216799
E-mail: admin@ambersolicitors.co.uk

BARKER & CO ‡
Bury's Chambers 29 Scale Lane Hull Kingston upon Hull HU1 1LF
Tel: 01482 219966 *Fax:* 01482 589272 *Dx:* 11905 HULL
Emergency telephone 01482 219966
E-mail: pnb@barkerandco.karoo.co.uk
List of partners: L Kirk, T McCarthy, J P Seagrave
Work: B2 G H Z(l)
Emergency Action, Agency, Advocacy, Fixed Fee Interview, Legal Aid undertaken and Legal Aid Franchise
Ptr: Kirk, Lindsay-Anne . . . . Jan 2009
Seagrave, Mr John P MA(Oxon) ★ . . . . *Nov 1982
McCarthy, Toni . . . . NSP

BAXTERS ‡
2 Manor Street Hull Kingston upon Hull HU1 1YU
Tel: 01482 224011 *Fax:* 01482 224011
List of partners: R J Baxter
Languages: French
Work: D1 K1 L V W
Emergency Action, Agency, Advocacy, Legal Aid undertaken and Legal Aid Franchise
SPr: Baxter, Ms Rosemary Jane . . . . *Dec 1974

BRIDGE MCFARLAND
Suite 1 Marina Court Castle Street Hull Kingston upon Hull HU1 1TJ
Tel: 01482 320620 *Fax:* 01482 323642 *Dx:* 11135 HULL 1
E-mail: info@bmcf.co.uk
Office: Grimsby (3 offices), Lincoln, Louth, Mablethorpe, Market Rasen, Skegness
Work: N

BROOKE WILLIAMS
1 Parliament Street Hull Kingston upon Hull HU1 2AP
Tel: 01482 610886 *Fax:* 01482 22771
E-mail: hull@brookewilliams.co.uk
Office: Bridlington, Leeds, York
SPr: Walton Williams, Mrs Brooke Valerie Gail LLB(Hons) . *Jan 1992
Ast: Borgen, Ms Inga BA(Hons) . . . . *Feb 1994

JANE BROOKS LAW ‡
13 St Augustine's Gate Hedon Hull Kingston upon Hull HU12 8EU
Tel: 01482 893366 *Fax:* 01482 893930
E-mail: jmb@janebrookslaw.co.uk
List of partners: J M Brooks, N M Hudgell
Ptr: Brooks, Mrs Jane M LLB . . . . *Jun 1980
Hudgell, Mr Neil M MA; LLB(Hons) . . . . *Sep 1993

BURSTALLS ‡
Ocean Chambers 54 Lowgate Hull Kingston upon Hull HU1 1JF
Tel: 01482 621800 *Fax:* 01482 621819 *Dx:* 11903 HULL
E-mail: info@burstalls.co.uk
List of partners: H P Burstall, T Moore, D J Rosenberg
Work: A1 A2 C1 D1 E F1 J1 K1 K2 K3 K4 L N O Q S1 S2 T1 T2 W Z(q)
Agency, Advocacy, Legal Aid undertaken and Legal Aid Franchise
Ptr: Burstall, Mr Hugh Patrick . . . . *Jan 1968
Moore, Mr Terence LLB . . . . *Apr 1975
Rosenberg, Mr David Julian BA(Hons) . . . . *Aug 1996
Ast: Arnott, Mrs Prudence Sara LLB . . . . *Sep 2009
Moore, Mr Charles Hugo LLB . . . . *Oct 2006
Thomsen, Mrs Sarah Edith LLB(Hons) . . . . *Jan 2004
Weaver, Mr Marcus Simon LLB(Hons); FBDO . . . . *Oct 2003
Wilson, Mrs Anna Margaret LLB . . . . *Aug 2005

CARRICK READ SOLICITORS LLP ‡
Norwich House Savile Street Hull Kingston upon Hull HU1 3ES
Tel: 01482 211160 *Fax:* 01482 585798 *Dx:* 26955 HULL
List of partners: D W J Beresford, C C Garwood, J S Lupton
Work: B1
Agency and Advocacy undertaken
Ptr: Beresford, Mr David W J . . . . *Nov 1978
Garwood, Mr Christopher Charles MA(Oxon) . . . . *§Mar 1973
Lupton, Mr Jonathan S BSc(Hons); DipLaw . . . . . *Nov 1999
Asoc: McDonagh, Miss Caroline Rachel MA(Hons)(Edin) . *Dec 2004
Marham, Mr Adam Thomas MA . . . . *Sep 2003

COPEMAN MARKHAM SOLICITORS ‡
10 Parliament Street Hull Kingston upon Hull HU1 2AP
Tel: 01482 212979 *Fax:* 01482 211978 *Dx:* 11929 HULL
E-mail: enquiries@copemanmarkham.co.uk
List of partners: M Copeman, J L Markham
Work: G H
Agency, Legal Aid undertaken and Legal Aid Franchise
Ptr: Copeman, Mr Michael . . . . *Oct 1983
Markham, Miss Joanne Louise ★ . . . . *Oct 1993
Ast: Dann, Miss Emma BA . . . . *Sep 2003

DEVINE LAW ‡
54 Grammar School Yard Hull Kingston upon Hull HU1 1SE
Tel: 01482 212077 *Fax:* 01482 212260
E-mail: info@devinelaw.co.uk

GOSSCHALKS ‡
Queens Gardens Hull Kingston upon Hull HU1 3DZ
Tel: 01482 324252 *Fax:* 01482 590290 *Dx:* 11902 HULL
Emergency telephone 07770 576503
E-mail: info@gosschalks.co.uk
List of partners: W M Barlow, N J Beckwith, J S K Beharrell, C J Burton, Z S Carmichael, A D C Clark, N G Dean, R Gooch, R L Green, M C Johnson, N Johnson, I C Lanch, R Llewellyn, S W Lunt, R H Naylor, B H Raper, R F Taylor, M Teal, R O Thomson, A B Wilkie, H E Williamson, A J Woods
Languages: French, German, Italian
Work: A1 B1 C1 C2 C3 D1 E F1 G H J1 K1 L M1 M2 N O P R1 S1 T1 T2 V W Z(c,d,e,f,h,i,j,k,l,n,o,s)
Emergency Action, Agency, Advocacy, Legal Aid undertaken, Legal Aid Franchise and Member of Accident Line
Ptr: Barlow, Mr William M . . . . *Dec 1978
Beckwith, Mr Nigel J BA . . . . *Dec 1990
Beharrell, Mr Jonathan S K . . . . *Oct 1990
Burton, Mr Christopher J LLB(Manc) . . . . *§Oct 1987
Carmichael, Miss Zoe S LLB(Newc) . . . . *Feb 1991
Clark, Mr Anthony D C LLB; M Jur . . . . *Oct 1980
Dean, Mr Nicholas Gary LLB . . . . *Nov 1992
Gooch, Mr Richard . . . . *Oct 1988
Green, R Leslie LLB . . . . *Jan 1969
Johnson, Mrs M Clare BA(Sussex) . . . . *Nov 1981
Johnson, Mr Neil . . . . *May 1981
Lanch, Mr Ian C LLB(Leeds) . . . . *Apr 1976
Llewellyn, Mr Richard LLB . . . . *Oct 1973
Lunt, Mr Simon W LLB . . . . *Aug 1976
Naylor, Mr Robert H LLB(Lond) . . . . *Nov 1972
Raper, Mr Bruce H MA; LLB . . . . *§Nov 1963
Taylor, Mr Roy F LLB(Lond) . . . . *Oct 1973
Teal, Mr Mark LLB . . . . *Nov 1992
Thomson, Mr Robert O LLB(Newc) . . . . *Nov 1987
Wilkie, Mr A Bruce LLB(Leeds) . . . . *Mar 1976
Williamson, Mr Hugh E Notary Public . . . . *§Nov 1961
Woods, Mr Andrew J LLB . . . . *Oct 1989
Asoc: Brown, Mr Ian Martin LLB . . . . *Nov 1992
Hastie, Mr Robert David . . . . Nov 1994
Lamb, Mr Jonathan Stuart LLB . . . . *Nov 1992
Ast: Dunn, Miss Clare F . . . . Sep 1999
Fielding, Mr Stephen LLB; LLM . . . . Sep 1998
Houston, Mr James Andrew LLB . . . . Nov 1999
Johnson, Mr Andrew . . . . *Sep 1996
Taylor, Mr Richard J . . . . *Sep 1996
Walker, Mrs Mary LLB . . . . Sep 1996
Walker, Mr Stephen BA . . . . *Aug 1986

See p112 for the Key to Work Categories & other symbols

2

GRAHAM & ROSEN ‡
8 Parliament Street Hull Kingston upon Hull HU1 2BB
Tel: 01482 323123 *Fax:* 01482 223542 *Dx:* 11925 HULL
E-mail: law@graham-rosen.co.uk
List of partners: I Boyle, H P Drewery, A J Green, P Mounce, R F Palmer, A F Waller, M V Wilson
Work: A1 B1 C1 D1 E F1 J1 K1 K4 L N O Q R1 S1 S2 T1 T2 W Z(l,p,q)
Emergency Action, Agency, Advocacy, Fixed Fee Interview, Legal Aid undertaken, Legal Aid Franchise and Member of Accident Line
Ptr: Boyle, Mr Iain . . . . *Sep 1995
Drewery, Miss Helen P LLB(Newc) . . . . *Nov 1988
Green, Mr Alexander John LLB(Newc) . . . . *Oct 1984
Mounce, Mr Paul LLB . . . . Jan 2005
Palmer, Mr Richard F MA(Cantab) Clifford's Inn Prize *§Apr 1979
Waller, Mr Adam Francis LLB(Hons)(Law & German) . *Jan 2005
Wilson, Mr Martin V . . . . *Feb 1983
Asoc: Colley, Mrs Clair Louise BA . . . . *Jul 2000
Evans, Mr Philip . . . . *Nov 2007
Ast: Kitchman, Mrs Rachael . . . . Oct 2008
Rusling, Miss Dawn C BSc . . . . Sep 2010
Wood, Mr Philip A LLB . . . . *Sep 2009
Con: Mitchell, Mr Michael LLB(Sheff) . . . . *Jun 1969

HWP LIMITED ‡
110 Tranby Lane Anlaby Hull Kingston upon Hull HU10 7LA
Tel: 01482 629295
List of partners: R I Hairsine
Ptr: Hairsine, Mr Robert Ian LLB . . . . *Oct 1991

HALLMARK SOLICITORS ‡
158-159 Chandlers Court High Street Hull Kingston upon Hull HU1 1NQ
Tel: 01482 616616 / 0845 680 8251 *Fax:* 0845 680 8253
E-mail: enquiries@hallmarksolicitors.co.uk

HAMERS SOLICITORS ‡
5 Earls Court Priory Park East Hull Kingston upon Hull HU4 7DY
Tel: 01482 326666 *Fax:* 01482 324432
List of partners: P M Harris, L Howes, S Tomlinson, P J Worthy, J Wyatt
Languages: French, German
Work: A3 B1 C1 C2 D1 D2 E F1 F2 J1 J2 K1 K2 L N O P Q R1 R2 S1 S2 W Z(c,e,l,q,r)
Emergency Action, Agency, Advocacy, Fixed Fee Interview, Legal Aid undertaken, Legal Aid Franchise and Member of Accident Line
Mem: Harris, Mr Peter M BA . . . . *Oct 1982
Howes, Lynsey . . . . Aug 2003
Tomlinson, Mr Simon . . . . *Oct 2000
Worthy, Mr Paul J LLB(Hons) . . . . *Oct 1987
Wyatt, Mr James LLB . . . . *Apr 1976
Asoc: Hakes, Mr Anthony . . . . Sep 2004
Mckechnie, Mrs Diane LLB . . . . Oct 1985
Miller, Deborah . . . . Feb 1999
Moody, Emma . . . . Jan 2005
Rea, Mr Jeremy G BA . . . . *May 1987
Richardson, Mr Nigel J LLB . . . . *Jun 1977
Sonley, Ms Charlotte BA(Hons) . . . . Sep 1995
Ward, Amanda . . . . Jul 2006

HOWELLS LLP ‡
Hull CLAC Ground Floor Essex House Manor Street Hull Kingston upon Hull HU1 1YU
Tel: 01482 317420 *Fax:* 01482 221342 *Dx:* 728038 HULL 2
E-mail: enquiries@howellsllp.com

NEIL HUDGELL SOLICITORS ‡
530-532 Holderness Road Hull Kingston upon Hull HU9 3DT
Tel: 01482 787771 *Fax:* 01482 787887 *Dx:* 703343 HULL EAST
E-mail: info@neil-hudgell.co.uk
List of partners: N M Hudgell
Office: Hull
Work: N Z(r)
Fixed Fee Interview undertaken and Member of Accident Line
SPr: Hudgell, Mr Neil M MA; LLB(Hons) . . . . *Sep 1993

NEIL HUDGELL SOLICITORS
Interface House Ashcombe Road Kingswood Hull Kingston upon Hull HU7 3DD
Tel: 01482 787771 *Fax:* 01482 787887
E-mail: info@neil-hudgell.co.uk
Office: Hull

CHRIS HUTCHINSON & CO ‡
Shackles Chambers 7 Land of Green Ginger Hull Kingston upon Hull HU1 2ED
Tel: 01482 326404 *Fax:* 01482 214121 *Dx:* 11944 HULL 1

INGRAMS ‡
Estuary Business Park Henry Boot Way Priory Park East Hull Kingston upon Hull HU4 7DY
Tel: 01482 358850 *Fax:* 01482 353937 *Dx:* 716161 HULL 16
E-mail: enquiries@ingramssolicitors.co.uk
List of partners: D Bamforth, C L Copp, P Stott
Office: York
Languages: French, German, Hindi, Marathi, Polish, Punjabi, Urdu
Work: F1 J1 L N Q S1 S2 W Z(q,r)
Agency, Advocacy undertaken and Member of Accident Line
Ptr: Copp, Ms Catherine Louise . . . . *Nov 1993
Stott, Mr Paul LLB(Leics) Assistant Deputy Coroner . *Oct 1984
Asoc: Guest, Ms Natasha LLB . . . . Mar 2006

ANDREW JACKSON ‡
Essex House Manor Street Hull Kingston upon Hull HU1 1XH
Tel: 01482 325242 *Fax:* 01482 212974 *Dx:* 11920 HULL
E-mail: enquiries@andrewjackson.co.uk
List of partners: P R Barker, J I Dale, P A Duffus, A Fenton, W H Fisher, R M Foulkes, A Funnell, S C Gibson, K J E Habergham, R J Hoare, M Kell, S J Kell, R A Mays, A C Oliver, M A Pearson-Kendall, R P S Penrose, J E Rawlings, I A Robson, H E Smith, J I Swales, S J T Unwin, D J Ward, K S Webster, A J West, M R Whitehead, L M Whiting, S L Yates
Languages: French, German, Spanish
Work: A1 A3 B1 C1 C2 C3 D1 E F1 G J1 J2 K1 K2 K3 K4 L M1 M2 N O P Q R1 R2 S1 S2 T1 T2 U2 V W Z(a,c,d,e,h,i,j,l,o,t,y)
Emergency Action, Agency, Advocacy, Fixed Fee Interview, Legal Aid undertaken, Legal Aid Franchise and Member of Accident Line
Ptr: Barker, Mr Paul R BA . . . . *Apr 1983
Dale, Mr Jonathan I LLB(Hons) . . . . Jan 1989
Duffus, Mr Peter A LLB . . . . *Apr 1986
Fenton, Ms Amanda LLB . . . . Sep 1999
Fisher, Mr William H LLB(Manc) . . . . *§Mar 1978
Foulkes, Mrs Rachel Margaret LLB . . . . *Mar 1989
Funnell, Mr Andrew LLB(Hons) . . . . *Sep 1997
Gibson, Miss Sarah C LLB . . . . *Oct 1988
Habergham, Mr Kenneth John Ernest BA(L'pool) . . . *Oct 1994
Hoare, Mr Richard J LLB . . . . *May 1992
Kell, Mrs Marie . . . . Sep 2000
Kell, Mr Stephen J LLB(Hons) . . . . *Oct 1990
Mays, Mr Richard A MA . . . . *Mar 1986
Oliver, Mr Andrew C LLB(Hull) . . . . *Oct 1990
Pearson-Kendall, Mr Mark Andrew LLB . . . . *Sep 1998
Penrose, Mr Robert P S LLB(Nott'm) . . . . *Jul 1980
Rawlings, Miss Janice E LLB(B'ham) . . . . *§Jun 1975
Robson, Mrs Isobel A BA(Dunelm) . . . . *Nov 1986
Smith, Mr Hugh E LLB . . . . *Oct 1983
Swales, Mr Jeffrey Ian LLB(Nott'm) . . . . *Oct 1987
Unwin, Mr Stephen J T BA(Hons); LLM . . . . *Apr 1984
Ward, Mr Dominic J BA Notary Public . . . . *Oct 1987
Webster, Mr Kevin S LLB; ATII . . . . *Oct 1986
West, Mr Adrian John LLB . . . . Nov 1998
Whitehead, Mr Martin R . . . . *§Jan 1974
Whiting, Mr Lee M . . . . Sep 2000
Yates, Mr Scott Leroy LLB . . . . *Oct 1993
Asoc: Benson, Alison . . . . Sep 2003
Butterworth, Mr Iain . . . . May 2004
Coish, Mr Andrew J . . . . Jun 1999
Collingwood, Mr Martin B BA(Law); ACIArb . . . . *Jul 1981
Dixon, Mr David LLB . . . . Sep 2003
Rhodes, Mr David Craig BA(Hons) . . . . Sep 1998
Scott, Mr Nicholas James LLB; LLM . . . . Sep 2004
Sprakes, Mr Steven John LLB; LLM . . . . *§Dec 1989
Stephens, Mr Lee Dylan LLB; LPC . . . . *Apr 2003
Strickland, Ms Victoria . . . . Sep 2003
Tarbutt, Miss Claire Michelle LLB(Hons) . . . . Sep 1998
Ast: Crystal, Mrs Kirsty BA . . . . Sep 2002
Gordon, Ms Lindsey S . . . . Nov 2006
Hall, Mr David F . . . . Sep 1988
Hammond, Mr Daniel J LLB . . . . Sep 2001
Hansom, Miss Katy Jane LLB . . . . Sep 2005
Hobden, Mr Ben D . . . . Sep 2008
Labrom, Mrs Leanne LLB . . . . Sep 2005
Newbon, Mr Paul A B . . . . Sep 2006
Pether, Miss Sarah Jane LLB(Hons) . . . . Sep 2002
Phillips, Mr Geoff . . . . Sep 2007
Seward, Mrs Kate Elizabeth LLB . . . . May 2004
Simpson, Miss Elizabeth Rebecca LLB; LLM . . . . *Feb 2003
Southern, Ms Jenny LLB . . . . Sep 2005
Worthington, Mr James Mathew BA . . . . *Sep 2004
Con: Haines, Mr Andrew J . . . . *§Jan 1971
Taylor, Mrs Margaret J LLB; MA . . . . *Apr 1973
Taylor, Silas W LLB(Hull) Notary Public . . . . *Apr 1977

JAMES LEGAL SOLICITORS ‡
The Deep Business Centre Tower Street Hull Kingston upon Hull HU1 4BG
Tel: 01482 488000 *Fax:* 01482 488004
E-mail: info@jameslegal.co.uk
Office: Leeds

ANDREW KINGSTON & CO ‡
Ground Floor Lowgate House Lowgate Hull Kingston upon Hull HU1 1EL
Tel: 01482 216217 *Fax:* 01482 216218
E-mail: akingston@andrewkingston.co.uk
List of partners: A T Kingston-Splatt
Work: B1 F1 J1 K4 L O Q S1 S2 W
Agency undertaken
Ptr: Kingston-Splatt, Andrew T . . . . Dec 1978
Asoc: Gilyott, Mr Francis Howard LLB Notary Public . . . . Dec 1972
Ast: Adams, Mr Christopher Henry LLB . . . . Sep 2010

LOCKINGS ‡
St Marys Court Lowgate Hull Kingston upon Hull HU1 1YG
Tel: 0845 075 4197 *Fax:* 01482 225752 *Dx:* 11917 HULL
Emergency telephone 01482 45563
E-mail: info@lockings.co.uk
List of partners: R Allen, A P Cooney, P H Kirby, R A Locking, P W Rispin, P J Sainsbury
Office: Beverley, Hull
Work: A1 B1 C1 C2 C3 D1 E F1 G H J1 K1 L M1 M2 N P R1 S1 W Z(l,m,o)
Emergency Action, Agency, Advocacy, Fixed Fee Interview and Legal Aid undertaken
Ptr: Allen, Mr Richard LLB . . . . *Nov 1991
Cooney, Mr Andrew Patrick . . . . *Apr 1995
Kirby, Mr Paul H LLB . . . . *Apr 1979
Locking, Mr Robert A BA . . . . *Jan 1979
Rispin, Mr Paul W BA(Philosophy); BA . . . . *Apr 1978
Sainsbury, Mr Philip J BA(Hons)(Law) . . . . *Nov 1984
Ast: Railton, Miss Jane M LLB . . . . *Nov 1991

LOCKINGS
1 St Augustine's Gate Hedon Hull Kingston upon Hull HU12 8EU
Tel: 01482 300280 *Fax:* 01482 300289 *Dx:* 11917 HULL
Office: Beverley, Hull
Work: A1 B1 C1 D1 E F1 G H J1 K1 L M1 N P R1 S1 T1 W Z(l,m,o)
Advocacy, Fixed Fee Interview and Legal Aid undertaken

MMS SOLICITORS ‡
Marlborough House 99 Princes Avenue Hull Kingston upon Hull HU5 3QP
Tel: 01482 499199 *Fax:* 01482 498850
E-mail: info@mmssolicitors.co.uk

MASON & CO SOLICITORS ‡
Lowgate House Lowgate Hull Kingston upon Hull HU1 1EL
Tel: 01482 310170 *Fax:* 01482 310171
E-mail: roberta.mason@masonsolicitors.co.uk
List of partners: R Mason
Dir: Mason, Ms Roberta LLB . . . . Nov 1995

MAX GOLD LAW ‡
14 Scale Lane Hull Kingston upon Hull HU1 1LA
Tel: 01482 224900 *Fax:* 01482 240193 *Dx:* 11939 HULL
Emergency telephone 01482 655539
E-mail: law@maxgold.com
List of partners: W D C Boddy, M J Gold, S E M Lucatello, M Menato
Office: London E1
Languages: Bulgarian, Catalan, French, German, Hebrew, Hindi, Italian, Portuguese, Punjabi, Russian, Spanish, Urdu, Yiddish
Work: A1 B1 B2 C1 D1 E F1 G H J1 K1 M1 O P S1 W Z(c,g,l,p,w)
Emergency Action, Agency, Advocacy, Fixed Fee Interview, Legal Aid undertaken and Member of Accident Line
Ptr: Boddy, Mr W David C . . . . *Mar 1973
Gold, Mr Maxwell J . . . . *Dec 1970
Lucatello, Mr Stefano Enrico Mario LLB(Hons) . . . . *Feb 1988
Mem: Menato, Mr Michele QLTT . . . . Mar 2008
Asoc: Norton, Mr Paul Andrew James Edward LLB(Hons); LLM . . . . Feb 2002
Wharmby, Miss Shirley Margaret BA Notary Public . . *Jan 1982
Ast: Ahmad, Mr Hammad LLB(Hons) . . . . May 2006
Beckett, Mrs Jannina LLB(Hons) . . . . Apr 2008
Farr, Mr Michael David LLB . . . . *Nov 1996
Goodall, Mr Philip Andrew LLB(Hull) . . . . *Apr 1981
Nettleton, Mr Graham Ward BA; LLB Notary Public . . *Oct 1988
Pervazova, Mrs Miroslava LLB; LPC Lord Wilberforce Scholarship . . . . Sep 2007
Turner, Mr Karl William LLB . . . . Nov 2007

MYER WOLFF ‡
King William House Lowgate Hull Kingston upon Hull HU1 1YE
Tel: 01482 223693 *Fax:* 01482 225089 *Dx:* 11904 HULL 1
Emergency telephone 07626 415110
E-mail: info@myer-wolff.co.uk
List of partners: K L Barker, T F Durkin, A Easterbrook, M A Reeves, N L Stewart
Work: B2 D1 D2 G H J1 K1 K2 K3 K4 N O Q S1 S2 T2 W Z(k,m,q)
Emergency Action, Agency, Advocacy, Legal Aid undertaken and Legal Aid Franchise
Ptr: Barker, Ms Kerry Louise BA ♦ . . . . *Dec 2003
Durkin, Mr Timothy Francis LLB . . . . *Jul 1973
Easterbrook, Mr Ashley LLB . . . . *Sep 2004
Stewart, Miss Nathalie Louise BA; MA(Oxon) . . . . *Aug 2007
Reeves, Mr Mark Anthony . . . . NSP
Ast: Adams, Mrs Gemma Winifred LLB . . . . *Dec 2005
Draper, Mrs Fiona Heather LLB . . . . *Oct 1987
Garner, Miss Louise LLB . . . . *Nov 2006
Mason, Mrs Caroline Jane BA . . . . *Sep 2002
Quantick, Mr Gary BA ★ . . . . Mar 2003
Roberts, Miss Rebecca Michelle Linda LLB; LLM . . *Sep 2004
Sedgwick, Ms Susan LLB . . . . *Dec 2008
Smith, Mr Robin Graham ★ . . . . *Oct 1997
Walton-Jones, Mr Nicholas Paul BA . . . . *Feb 1986
Wasling, Mrs Sarah Louise LLB . . . . *Apr 2011

Holders of LSC Contracts for Crime and Family. We specialise in the following areas of work: Child Care, Crime - General and Motoring, Employment and Family Law, Agency Commissions gladly undertaken.

MYTON LAW LIMITED ‡
The Deep Business Centre Tower Street Hull Kingston upon Hull HU1 4BG
Tel: 01482 382080 *Fax:* 01482 382081
E-mail: scott.yates@mytonlaw.co.uk

PAYNE & PAYNE ‡
(incorporating Eustace Downs & Briggs)
Hanover House Alfred Gelder Street Hull Kingston upon Hull HU1 2AH
Tel: 01482 326446 *Fax:* 01482 210400 *Dx:* 11926 HULL
Emergency telephone 01482 326446
E-mail: enquiries@payneandpayne.co.uk
List of partners: M E Ashley, P E Craft, J A Knight, J P Seagrave, T J Wilson
Office: Hull
Work: B1 C1 C2 C3 D1 D2 E F1 F2 G H J1 K1 K2 L M1 M2 N O P Q R1 S1 T1 T2 W X Z(b,c,d,e,f,g,h,i,j,k,l,m,o,s,t)
Emergency Action, Agency, Advocacy, Fixed Fee Interview, Legal Aid undertaken, Legal Aid Franchise and Member of Accident Line
Ptr: Ashley, Miss Margaret E LLB . . . . *Dec 1973
Craft, Mr Patrick Ernest . . . . *Jul 1979
Knight, Miss Judith A LLB . . . . *Apr 1981
Wilson, Mr Timothy J . . . . *Jul 1976
Ast: Harvey, Sharan BA ♦ . . . . *Jan 1992
Quantick, Mr Gary BA ★ . . . . Mar 2003
Robson, Mr David W LLB . . . . *Feb 1987

PAYNE & PAYNE
1a Kingston Road The Square Willerby Hull Kingston upon Hull HU10 6AD
Tel: 01482 326446 *Fax:* 01482 658117 *Dx:* 11926 HULL
Emergency telephone 07778 216416
E-mail: enquiries@payneandpayne.co.uk
Office: Hull
Work: A1 B1 C1 C2 C3 D1 E F1 G H J1 K1 L M1 M2 N P R1 S1 T1 T2 V W Z(b,c,d,e,f,h,i,j,k,l,m,o,s,t)
Emergency Action, Agency, Advocacy, Fixed Fee Interview and Legal Aid undertaken
Ptr: Craft, Mr Patrick Ernest . . . . *Jul 1979
Seagrave, Mr John P MA(Oxon) ★ . . . . *Nov 1982

PEPPERELLS
(incorporating Ivesons)
100 Alfred Gelder Street Hull Kingston upon Hull HU1 2AE
Tel: 01482 326511
Office: Scunthorpe
Work: A3 B1 B2 C1 C2 D1 E F1 G H J1 K1 K2 K3 K4 L N O Q R1 S1 S2 T1 T2 V W Z(f,k,w)
Emergency Action, Agency, Advocacy, Fixed Fee Interview and Legal Aid undertaken
Ptr: Gardham, Mr John Raymond LLB(Hons) . . . . *§Jun 1971

DAVID PORTER & CO ‡
29 Bishop Lane Hull Kingston upon Hull HU1 1PA
Tel: 01482 325863 *Fax:* 01482 217642
E-mail: enquiries@davidporter.karoo.co.uk
List of partners: K Noble, D Porter
Languages: French
Work: D1 F1 G H J1 K1 N O Q S1 S2 V W Z(e,j,l)
Emergency Action, Agency, Advocacy and Fixed Fee Interview undertaken
Ptr: Noble, Miss Kellie . . . . Jul 2006
Porter, Mr David LLB(Hons); FCII; ACIArb; FRSA Part time Chairman of Social Security Appeals; Part time Chairman Yorkshire Rent Assessment Committee; Part time Chairman of Disability Appeals Tribunal . . . . *Oct 1971

RAPID RESPONSE SOLICITORS ‡
878 Beverley Road Hull Kingston upon Hull HU6 7DQ
Tel: 01482 345800 *Fax:* 01482 348924
E-mail: info@rapidsolicitors.co.uk

RAPID RESPONSE SOLICITORS ‡
65 New Cleveland Street Hull Kingston upon Hull HU8 7EX
Tel: 01482 475762
E-mail: info@rapidsolicitors.co.uk

JOHN ROBINSON & CO ‡
Kingston House 23 Parliament Street Hull Kingston upon Hull HU1 2AP
Tel: 01482 324818 *Fax:* 01482 589283 *Dx:* 11915 HULL
E-mail: contact@johnrobinsons.co.uk
List of partners: N Clay, B Hibbert
Work: B2 G H
Agency, Fixed Fee Interview and Legal Aid undertaken
Ptr: Clay, Mr Nicholas BA; DipLaw; DipLP . . . . Nov 1997
Hibbert, Mr Ben . . . . Oct 2000

ROBINSONS SOLICITORS ‡
58 Grammar School Yard Fish Street Hull Kingston upon Hull HU1 1SE
Tel: 01482 212401 *Fax:* 01482 212431
Ast: Robinson, Mr Michael LLB . . . . Oct 2004

ROLLITS LLP ‡
Wilberforce Court High Street Hull Kingston upon Hull HU1 1YJ
Tel: 01482 323239 *Fax:* 01482 326239 *Dx:* 715756 HULL 15
E-mail: info@rollits.com
List of partners: S L Ball, K J Benton, G E Coyle, G R Craft, M R Dixon, J Downing, C R Field, N R Franklin, R Frogson, R N Gilbert, C M Hardcastle, D Hextall, D E Ingleby, J R Lane, T W Morrison, D R Oliver, C Platts, N Sharf, R I Stirk, S J Trynka, J N Wild
Office: York
Languages: French, German, Spanish
Work: A1 A3 B1 C1 C2 C3 D1 E F1 F2 G I J1 J2 K1 K2 L M1 M2 N O P Q R1 S1 T1 T2 U2 W Z(a,b,c,d,e,f,h,j,k,l,n,o,p,q,s,t)
Agency and Advocacy undertaken
Ptr: Ball, Miss Sheridan Lesley BA . . . . *Oct 1992
Benton, Mr Keith James LLB Willis Mills Prize. . . . . *Oct 1991
Coyle, Mr George E BA . . . . *Jul 1976
Craft, Mr Glenn R LLB . . . . *§Jul 1980
Dixon, Mr Mark R . . . . Jun 1999
Downing, Mr John MA(Cantab) . . . . *Apr 1972
Field, Mr Charles R LLB. . . . . *§Oct 1987
Franklin, Mr Neil R LLB . . . . *Oct 1985
Gilbert, Mr Ralph N LLB. . . . . *§Sep 1990
Hardcastle, Mrs Caroline Mary BA(Jurisprudence). . . Sep 1999
Hextall, Mr David LLB. . . . . *Sep 1998
Ingleby, Miss Donna E LLB . . . . Oct 1988
Morrison, Mr Thomas William LLB. . . . . *Sep 2001
Platts, Mr Christopher BA . . . . *§Oct 1984
Sharf, Nasim BA . . . . Sep 1997
Trynka, Mr Stephen J LLB(B'ham). . . . . *§Apr 1978
Wild, Mr Julian Nicholas LLB(Exon) . . . . *May 1977
Asoc: Crystal, Mr Christopher Rex LLB(Hons) . . . . Jan 2003
Drinkall, Mr Christopher. . . . . Sep 2004
Flanagan, Mr John Paul LLB(Hons) . . . . Sep 2005
Jenneson, Mr Edward Charles LLB . . . . Oct 2004
Whittaker, Mr Richard John LLB(Hons) . . . . Nov 1997
Ast: Dixon, Kate Ann LLB . . . . Sep 2008
Douglas, Miss Claire Louise Dorothy LLB . . . . Sep 2009
Heppel, Mr Edward Peter John LLB . . . . Oct 2009
Latus, Mrs Rebecca BA; LPC . . . . Sep 2006
Myers, Mr David . . . . Sep 2008
Noton, Rachael Louise LLB . . . . Sep 2008
Peel, Mr James Derek LLB; BA . . . . Sep 2010
Pigg, Lottie . . . . Sep 2008
Sewell, Mrs Jennifer LLB(Hons). . . . . *Sep 2007
Sledmore, Miss Christina Rose LLB(Hons)(Law); LPC; DipLP . . . . *Sep 2011
Con: Dowson, Miss Lesley BA; FCIS . . . . *Feb 1986

SANDERSONS ‡
(incorporating D M Pontefract & Co)
17-19 Parliament Street Hull Kingston upon Hull HU1 2BH
Tel: 01482 324662 *Fax:* 01482 223110 *Dx:* 11938 HULL
E-mail: enquiries@sandersonssolicitors.co.uk
List of partners: E D Carson, P C Grimwood, D Hextall, M P O'Kane, D A Rann, D M Roberts, R A Thompson
Office: Beverley
Work: A1 B1 C1 C2 C3 D1 E F1 G H J1 K1 L M1 M2 N O P Q R1 S1 T1 T2 V W Z(a,e,l,m,o,w)
Agency, Advocacy, Legal Aid undertaken and Member of Accident Line
Ptr: Carson, Mrs Elaine D . . . . *Nov 1986
Grimwood, Mr Paul C LLB. . . . . *Sep 1988
Hextall, Mr David LLB. . . . . *Sep 1998
O'Kane, Mr Michael P LLB . . . . *Dec 1967
Rann, Mr Duncan Alistair LLB; LLM . . . . Jun 1994
Roberts, Mr David M LLB . . . . *Mar 1990
Thompson, Mr Richard Anthony LLB . . . . *May 1996
Ast: Ashton, Mr James Michael . . . . *May 1997
Con: Jackson, Mr M Rodney MA; LLM(Cantab) • Recorder *Nov 1962

STAMP JACKSON AND PROCTER ‡
5 Parliament Street Hull Kingston upon Hull HU1 2AZ
Tel: 01482 324591 *Fax:* 01482 224048 *Dx:* 11927 HULL
E-mail: ail@sjplaw.co.uk
List of partners: S T Burgess, S R T Gittings, N R Holland, A I Latham, I T Machin, A C T Procter, S J Ramshaw, C A L Robinson
Languages: French, Italian
Work: A1 A2 B1 C1 C2 C3 E J1 L M1 N O P R1 S2 T1 T2 W Z(c,d,e,o,r)
Fixed Fee Interview, Legal Aid undertaken, Legal Aid Franchise and Member of Accident Line
Ptr: Burgess, Mr Simon T LLB. . . . . *Nov 1990
Gittings, Mr Simon R T LLB . . . . *Oct 1984
Holland, Mr Neil R LLB; LLM(Hons) . . . . *Sep 1999
Latham, Mr Alistair I LLB(Hons). . . . . *Nov 1996
Machin, Mr Ian T LLB. . . . . *Jun 1977
Procter, Mr Andrew C T MA(Cantab) . . . . *§Oct 1983
Ramshaw, Mr Simon J LLB . . . . *Oct 1985
Robinson, Miss Claire A L LLB(Hons) . . . . *Sep 2001
Ast: Dixon, Miss Rebecca LLB(Hons) . . . . *Sep 2006
Kellett, Miss Sarah Jane LLB Bevan & Parry Prize 2003 . . . . *Apr 2008
Stevens, Miss Jane Lucy Elizabeth LLB. . . . . *Mar 2007
Con: Harne, Mr Michael V . . . . *Jun 1968

STAMPS FAMILY SOLICITORS ‡
3 Parliament Street Hull Kingston upon Hull HU1 2AP
Tel: 01482 323495 *Dx:* 728037 HULL 2
List of partners: D W Hudson, L N Lurie
Ptr: Hudson, Mr Dominic William . . . . *Apr 1999
Lurie, Mr Leon N LLB . . . . *Dec 1965

ANDREW TURNER SOLICITORS ‡
97 Spring Bank Hull Kingston upon Hull HU3 1BH
Tel: 01482 606151
Work: F2 J1 L Q
Agency and Advocacy undertaken

WARD SCOTT LLP ‡
Wyke Chambers 7 Silver Street Hull Kingston upon Hull HU1 1HT
Tel: 01482 489870 *Fax:* 01482 224905
E-mail: info@wardscottllp.co.uk
Office: Beverley

WILLIAMSONS ‡
Lowgate Hull Kingston upon Hull HU1 1EN
Tel: 01482 323697 *Fax:* 01482 328132 *Dx:* 11932 HULL
E-mail: bgc@williamsons-solicitors.co.uk
Office: Driffield
Work: C1 D1 D2 E F1 F2 G H K1 K2 K3 L N O P Q R1 S1 S2 T1 T2 V W Z(c,h,l,q,r,y)

HUNGERFORD, West Berkshire

JAMES S BARNETT ‡
The Pavilion 10 Inkpen Road Kintbury Hungerford West Berkshire RG17 9TU
Tel: 01488 658461 *Fax:* 01488 658461
Emergency telephone 01488 658450
List of partners: J S Barnett
Work: A1 C1 E J1 L M1 N O Q R1 S2 W Z(d,e,f,g,z)
Emergency Action, Agency and Fixed Fee Interview undertaken
Ptr: Barnett, Dr James S ♦. . . . . *§Mar 1967

DICKINS HOPGOOD CHIDLEY LLP ‡
The Old School House 42 High Street Hungerford West Berkshire RG17 0NF
Tel: 01488 683555 *Fax:* 01488 681919 *Dx:* 47107 HUNGERFORD
E-mail: dhc@dhc-solicitors.co.uk
List of partners: C J O Chidley, J G Dickins, V A Hopgood
Languages: French
Work: A1 B1 C1 E F1 J1 K4 L O Q R1 R2 S1 S2 T2 W
Ptr: Chidley, Mr Christopher J O LLB . . . . *Jun 1973
Dickins, Mr Julian G LLB . . . . *Oct 1983
Hopgood, Miss Victoria A LLB. . . . . *Nov 1988
Asoc: Drake, Mr Richard William Selwyn. . . . . *Jan 1975
Ast: Chidley, Miss Charlotte Alice LLB; BA . . . . *Nov 2008
May, Ms Amanda . . . . Jul 1977

CHARLES LUCAS & MARSHALL
28 High Street Hungerford West Berkshire RG17 0NF
Tel: 01488 682506 *Fax:* 01488 684824 *Dx:* 47102 HUNGERFORD
E-mail: ask@clmlaw.co.uk
Office: Newbury, Swindon, Wantage
Languages: French, Polish
Work: A1 C1 C2 C3 D1 E G J1 K1 K4 L M1 M2 N P Q R1 T2 W Z(c,l)
Agency, Advocacy undertaken and Member of Accident Line
Asoc: Davies, Mrs Ceri Rhian BSc(Hons) STEP President's Prize for Thesis . . . . Sep 1998
Sarnowski, Mr Mark T BA. . . . . *Jun 1978

MACAULEY & CO ‡
112 High Street Hungerford West Berkshire RG17 0LU
Tel: 01488 682348

DAVID SMALL ‡
(in association with The Merriman Partnership)
Crown Passage 23 High Street Hungerford West Berkshire RG17 0NF
Tel: 01488 684287 / 07713 094759 *Fax:* 01488 684287
E-mail: dagsmall@hotmail.com, david@dagsmall.co.uk

HUNSTANTON, Norfolk

SJP SOLICITORS ‡
Waverley House 37 Greevegate Hunstanton Norfolk PE36 6AB
Tel: 01485 532662 *Fax:* 01485 534802 *Dx:* 95250 HUNSTANTON
List of partners: K L Johnson, M W Procter, S A E Staveley
Agency, Advocacy, Fixed Fee Interview, Legal Aid undertaken and Legal Aid Franchise
Ptr: Johnson, Mr Kevin L LLB(Sheff). . . . . *§Dec 1983
Procter, Mr Mark W BA . . . . *§Apr 1987
Staveley, Mr Samuel A E . . . . *§Jan 1966
Ast: Guest, Mrs Tracey J LLB . . . . Sep 1999

CHRISTINA THAIN & CO ‡
Beamish 68 High Street Ringstead Hunstanton Norfolk PE36 5JU
Tel: 01485 525458 *Fax:* 01485 525605
List of partners: C Thain
Work: S1 W
Ptr: Thain, Mrs Christina. . . . . *Mar 1977

HUNTINGDON, Cambridgeshire

ADLAMS LLP
St Johns House 84 High Street Huntingdon Cambridgeshire PE18 6DP
Tel: 01480 458885 *Fax:* 01480 451817 *Dx:* 80903 HUNTINGDON
E-mail: info@adlams.co.uk
Office: St Neots
Work: A1 C1 C2 D1 E F1 J1 K1 L N O Q R1 S1 S2 W Z(l)
Emergency Action, Agency, Advocacy, Fixed Fee Interview, Legal Aid undertaken, Legal Aid Franchise and Member of Accident Line

COPLEYS
28 High Street Huntingdon Cambridgeshire PE29 3TH
Tel: 01480 456191 *Fax:* 01480 411386 *Dx:* 80902 HUNTINGDON
E-mail: huntingdon@copleys.net
Office: St Ives
Work: A1 B1 B2 C1 C2 D1 E F1 F2 G H J1 J2 K1 K2 K3 L M1 N P R1 S1 T1 V W Z(l,t,y)
Emergency Action, Advocacy, Legal Aid undertaken, Legal Aid Franchise and Member of Accident Line
Ptr: Langworthy, Mr Ian J LLB(Lond). . . . . *§Apr 1973
Ross, Mr Keith J BA. . . . . *Jul 1978
Trippitt, Mr Michael R LLB. . . . . *Feb 1988
Warboys, Mr Kevin R LLB. . . . . *Jun 1981
Ast: Dinsdale, Mrs Ann R LLB(Hons). . . . . *Feb 1983
Havord, Ms Elaine Collins LLB(Hons) University Mooting Prize (Aberystwyth) 1992 . . . . Nov 1995

FLEXPRO SERVICES LIMITED ‡
8 St Georges Close Brampton Huntingdon Cambridgeshire PE28 4US
Tel: 020 7060 2205
E-mail: contact@flexproservices.com

MARJORIE E GOWLETT ‡
Manor Farm Bull Lane Broughton Huntingdon Cambridgeshire PE28 3AP
Tel: 01487 822229 *Fax:* 01487 822990

LEEDS DAY
Godwin House George Street Huntingdon Cambridgeshire PE29 3ND
Tel: 01480 454301 *Fax:* 01480 408740 *Dx:* 96654 HUNTINGDON 2
E-mail: law@leedsday.co.uk
Office: St Ives, St Neots
Languages: Dutch, Finnish, French, German
Work: A1 A3 B1 C1 C2 C3 D1 D2 E F1 F2 J1 K1 K2 K3 K4 L N O P Q R1 S1 S2 T1 T2 W Z(c,d,e,h,i,j,k,l,o,p,q,r,t)
Emergency Action, Agency, Advocacy, Fixed Fee Interview undertaken and Member of Accident Line
Ptr: Dewdney, Mr Robert O LLB. . . . . *§Jun 1980
Dodd, Mr Christopher . . . . *May 2004
Glanvill, Ms Tamara LLB . . . . *Nov 1995
Hafiaz, Mr Mohammed . . . . Jul 2003
Metcalfe, Mr Ronald J BA; LLB . . . . *Jul 1976
Thomas, Mr Simon Roderick William LLB . . . . *Jun 2002
Ast: Burridge, Mr Stephen Robert BA(Hons)(Law) . . . . . *Jul 1984
Clark, Ms Claire. . . . . Nov 2005
Lawson, Mrs Sara Geraldine LLB(Hons); LLM. . . . *Feb 2002

POTTER SHELLEY & CO ‡
24 High Street Huntingdon Cambridgeshire PE29 3TD
Tel: 01480 459531 *Fax:* 01480 451907 *Dx:* 80915 HUNTINGDON
E-mail: dpotter@pottershelleyandco.co.uk
Con: Kirkpatrick, Mr John ★. . . . . Jan 1969

RPM LEGAL
Abacus House 93 High Street Huntingdon Cambridgeshire PE29 3DP
Tel: 01480 396396 *Fax:* 01480 455008
E-mail: v.perkins@rpmlegal.co.uk
Office: Kettering, Stratford-upon-Avon

TERRELLS LLP
Wykeham House Market Hill Huntingdon Cambridgeshire PE29 3NN
Tel: 01480 454987 *Fax:* 01480 412585 *Dx:* 80900 HUNTINGDON
E-mail: gh@terrells.co.uk
Office: Peterborough, Stamford
Work: D1 K1 K3 N S1 S2 W
Agency, Fixed Fee Interview, Legal Aid undertaken and Member of Accident Line
Ast: Hastewell, Miss Gemma LLB . . . . *Aug 2011

WARRENS BOYES & ARCHER ‡
20 Hartford Road Huntingdon Cambridgeshire PE29 3QH
Tel: 01480 411331 *Fax:* 01480 459012 *Dx:* 80901 HUNTINGDON
E-mail: wbalaw@wbalaw.co.uk
List of partners: G F Archer
Languages: French
Work: A1 B1 C1 D1 E G H J1 K1 K2 L N Q R1 S1 S2 T1 W Z(c,j,l)
Emergency Action, Agency, Advocacy and Fixed Fee Interview undertaken
SPr: Archer, Mr Gregory F . . . . *Dec 1973
Asoc: O'Beirne, Miss Jane Elisabeth. . . . . Nov 1993
Ast: Jacobsen, Mrs Eleanor . . . . Dec 1997
Con: Boyes, Mr C Robin . . . . *Jun 1963

HURSTPIERPOINT, West Sussex

CASTLES ‡
118 High Street Hurstpierpoint West Sussex BN6 9PX
Tel: 01273 836007 / 837107 *Fax:* 01273 832007
List of partners: B E V Castle, J R Castle
Work: C1 E L O Q S1 S2 W
Ptr: Castle, Mrs Branwen Elaine Valerie LLB(Lond) . . . *§Dec 1970
Castle, Mr John Robert . . . . *§Feb 1970

HUYTON, Merseyside

FORSTER DEAN LTD
69 Derby Road Huyton Merseyside L36 9UQ
Tel: 0151 203 2144 *Fax:* 0151 203 2145
E-mail: enquiries@forsterdean.co.uk
Office: Birkenhead, Bootle, Chorley, Crewe, Eccles, Ellesmere Port, Leigh, Liverpool (5 offices), Oldham, Preston, Rochdale, Runcorn, St Helens, Stockport, Warrington, Widnes (2 offices), Wigan

KEITH LEVIN & CO ‡
The Willows 2 Rupert Road Huyton Merseyside L36 9TF
Tel: 0151 480 5777 *Fax:* 0151 489 2514 *Dx:* 15454 HUYTON
Emergency telephone 0151 480 5833
E-mail: info@keithlevin.co.uk
List of partners: R J Flett, K S Levin
Work: B1 D1 E F1 G H J1 K1 L N O P Q W
Emergency Action, Agency, Advocacy, Fixed Fee Interview, Legal Aid undertaken and Legal Aid Franchise
Ptr: Flett, Mr Robin Jonathan LLB . . . . *Mar 1984
Levin, Mr Keith Steven LLB Deputy District Judge. . . *Jun 1974
Ast: Coghgan, Mr Michael Francis MA . . . . Jan 1980
Dugdale, Miss Helen Lydia LLB(Hons). . . . . *Oct 1994
Con: Leask, Mr Edwin LLB . . . . *Jun 1974

PATRICK MCLOUGHLIN & CO ‡
6 Rupert Road Huyton Merseyside L36 9TF
Tel: 0151 482 1236 *Fax:* 0151 482 1232 *Dx:* 15460 HUYTON

MAXWELL HODGE SOLICITORS
26 Sherborne Square Huyton Merseyside L36 9UR
Tel: 0151 489 6161 *Fax:* 0151 489 8685
E-mail: info@maxweb.co.uk
Office: Formby, Heswall, Kirkby, Liverpool (2 offices), Maghull, West Kirby
Work: D1 J2 K1 K3 N W
Emergency Action, Agency, Advocacy, Fixed Fee Interview, Legal Aid undertaken, Legal Aid Franchise and Member of Accident Line
Ptr: Banks, Mrs Claire Margaret . . . . *Nov 1997
Richardson, Mrs Victoria J LLB . . . . *Oct 1991

GORDON O'BRIEN ‡
5 Longview Drive Knowsley Huyton Merseyside L36 6DY
Tel: 0151 489 4899 *Fax:* 0151 480 3261
E-mail: gordonobrien@msn.com
List of partners: G O'Brien
Work: D1 G H N S1

 See p112 for the Key to Work Categories & other symbols

Advocacy, Legal Aid undertaken and Member of Accident Line
Ptr: O'Brien, Mr Gordon BA(Law); LSF. . . . . *Sep 1986

PORTERS SOLICITORS ‡
7 Sherborne Square Huyton Merseyside L36 9UR
Tel: 0151 489 9427 *Fax:* 0151 443 0656

HYDE, Greater Manchester

BOOTH INCE & KNOWLES
105 Market Street Hyde Greater Manchester SK14 1HL
Tel: 0161 368 2134 *Fax:* 0161 368 2774 *Dx:* 25910 HYDE
E-mail: janet@bikhyde.com
Office: Denton, Droylsden (2 offices)
Languages: French
Work: C1 E K4 L R1 R2 S1 S2 W
Ptr: Allen, Mr Wayne . . . . Oct 2000
Davies, Mrs Janet E BA. . . . . Sep 1982
Ast: Jones, Mrs Kathryn Susan BA . . . . Nov 1992

PAUL BRYSON SOLICITOR ‡
41 Stalybridge Road Mottram Hyde Greater Manchester SK14 6NF
Tel: 01457 763340
E-mail: scanuscript@lineone.net

CHRONNELL HIBBERT
4 Reynard Street Hyde Greater Manchester SK14 2HJ
Tel: 0161 368 3434 *Fax:* 0161 367 8830
Emergency telephone 0161 368 0022
Office: Stockport
Work: D1 E K1 L Q S1 W
Emergency Action, Agency, Advocacy, Fixed Fee Interview, Legal Aid undertaken and Legal Aid Franchise
Ptr: Jones, Mr Iain B LLB(B'ham) . . . . *Nov 1971
Ward, Mr Peter J BA . . . . *Dec 1980
Williams, Mr David G BA . . . . *Sep 1980

HT LEGAL LIMITED T/A HARRISON TOWNEND & ORMESHERS ‡
Clarendon Chambers 5a Market Place Hyde Greater Manchester SK14 2LX
Tel: 0161 368 1559 *Fax:* 0161 368 6219 *Dx:* 25901 HYDE
E-mail: mail@harrisontownend.co.uk
List of partners: D Kelly, D Nuttall
Office: Glossop
Work: C1 E J1 K1 K3 K4 L N O Q S1 S2 W Z(o,v)
Fixed Fee Interview undertaken
Ptr: Kelly, Mrs Debra FILEx; LPC . . . . *Jun 1998
Nuttall, Mr David BA . . . . *Aug 1980
Ast: Carter, Mr Anthony Mark LLB . . . . *Feb 1990

KEMPS SOLICITORS
40a Market Place Hyde Greater Manchester SK14 2QU
Tel: 0161 366 8181 *Fax:* 0161 368 7264
E-mail: lawyers@kemps-solicitors.com
Office: Oldham

KNOWLES & CO SOLICITORS ‡
7a The Square Hyde Greater Manchester SK14 2QR
Tel: 0161 366 8200 *Fax:* 0161 366 8300 *Dx:* 25920 HYDE

NORTON & CO
181 Market Street Hyde Greater Manchester SK14 1HF
Tel: 0161 366 8333 *Fax:* 0161 367 0007
Office: Denton
Work: D1 F1 G H K1 N Q S1 W Z(j)
Emergency Action, Agency, Advocacy, Fixed Fee Interview, Legal Aid undertaken and Member of Accident Line
Ptr: Abbott, Mr Harry LLB; ACII . . . . *May 1979
Penson, Mr Clive N LLB. . . . . *May 1983

MALCOLM PIMLOTT PROPERTY SOLICITOR ‡
104a Market Street Hyde Greater Manchester SK14 1ES
Tel: 0161 367 1044 *Fax:* 0161 367 9124
E-mail: info@mpsolicitors.co.uk

PLUCK ANDREW & CO ‡
(incorporating Hibbert Pownall & Newton)
6-16a Norfolk Street Hyde Greater Manchester SK14 1NB
Tel: 0161 368 6311 *Fax:* 0161 368 9494 *Dx:* 25907 HYDE
E-mail: reception@pluckandrew.com
List of partners: C J Allen, S J Andrew, M Lord, J G Rogers, T R Wild
Office: Ashton-under-Lyne
Languages: French
Work: D1 D2 G H J1 K1 K3 N S1 S2 W
Emergency Action, Agency, Advocacy, Fixed Fee Interview, Legal Aid undertaken, Legal Aid Franchise and Member of Accident Line
Ptr: Allen, Mr Christopher John LLB; LLM . . . . Mar 2003
Andrew, Mrs S Jill LLB Judge Jellinek Prize 1980 . . *Nov 1982
Lord, Mr Matthew BA(Hons). . . . . *Jan 1993
Rogers, Mr J Guy LLB . . . . *Apr 1972
Wild, Mr Thomas Russell LLB. . . . . *Jun 1993
Ast: Cox, Ms Rachael . . . . Jul 2008
Deaville, Ms Patricia . . . . Mar 2009
Rogers, Miss Catherine . . . . Sep 2008

HYTHE, Hampshire

ERIC ROBINSON SOLICITORS
(incorporating Dogherty & Towndrow)
Cooper House 9-10 New Road Hythe Hampshire SO45 6BP
Tel: 023 8084 4304 *Fax:* 023 8084 8192 *Dx:* 54953 HYTHE (HANTS)
Emergency telephone 0870 238 5687
E-mail: hythe@ericrobinson.co.uk
Office: Chandlers Ford, Southampton (4 offices)
Languages: French
Work: A1 A3 B2 C1 C2 D1 D2 E G H J1 K1 K2 K3 K4 L N O Q R1 R2 S1 S2 T1 T2 W Z(d,h,l,p,q)
Emergency Action, Agency, Advocacy, Fixed Fee Interview, Legal Aid undertaken and Legal Aid Franchise
Ptr: Bakewell, Mr Paul N . . . . *Mar 1979
Ast: Bakewell, Mrs Jenny LLB(Bris) . . . . *Apr 1979
Bird, Mr Christopher L. . . . . *§Jun 1973
Nicholas, Miss Joanna BA . . . . *Sep 2002

THE WARING PARTNERSHIP LLP ‡
8 Marsh Parade Hythe Hampshire SO45 6AN
Tel: 023 8084 9381
E-mail: paul.waring@the-waring-partnership.com

HYTHE, Kent

SHIRLEY GRIFFITHS ‡
Danehurst Lympne Hythe Kent CT21 4PD
Tel: 01303 266689 *Fax:* 01303 266484 *Dx:* 34458 HYTHE (KENT)
Emergency telephone 01303 266689
E-mail: enquiries@legallympne.co.uk
List of partners: S E F Griffiths
Languages: French, Italian
Work: D1 E F1 J1 K1 K3 K4 N O Q S1 S2 T2 W X Z(d,g,i,q,u)
Emergency Action and Advocacy undertaken
SPr: Griffiths, Miss Shirley E F LLB(Hons) . . . . *Oct 1960
Ast: Rushford, Miss Gillian LLB(Hons) . . . . *Oct 2005

T R S MILLER SOLICITORS
(incorporating Rootes & Alliott)
52 High Street Hythe Kent CT21 5JG
Tel: 01303 266861 *Fax:* 01303 269234 *Dx:* 34451 HYTHE (KENT)
E-mail: mail@trsmiller.co.uk
Office: Folkestone
Work: E L S1 S2 W
Ptr: Morrison, Mr James K LLB . . . . *Nov 1984
Ast: Garrard, Ms Sarah L BA . . . . *Oct 1995

HENRY MOORHEAD & CO ‡
2 Stade Street Hythe Kent CT21 6BD
Tel: 01303 262525 *Fax:* 01303 262922
List of partners: H C D Moorhead, R H V Moorhead
Ptr: Moorhead, Mr Henry C D . . . . *§Dec 1980

PERCIVAL ROSE & CO ‡
Shrine Barn Sandling Road Hythe Kent CT21 4HE
Tel: 01303 884964 *Fax:* 01303 884965 *Dx:* 34453 HYTHE
E-mail: susie@percivalrose.com

ROBSON & CO ‡
147 High Street Hythe Kent CT21 5JN
Tel: 01303 264581 / 267413 *Fax:* 01303 265157
Dx: 34452 HYTHE (KENT)
E-mail: post@robson-co.co.uk
List of partners: M J Dearden, C B G Doherty
Work: C1 E J1 K1 K3 K4 N Q S1 S2 W
Emergency Action, Agency, Advocacy, Fixed Fee Interview, Legal Aid undertaken and Legal Aid Franchise
Ptr: Dearden, Mr Malcolm John LLB LAFB. . . . . *§Jan 1985
Doherty, Mr Christopher B G LLB . . . . *Jan 1983
Ast: Fitzgerald, Mrs Lisa Elaine LLB . . . . *Dec 2003

ICKENHAM, Middlesex

CAMACOM LAW SOLICITORS LTD ‡
Panstar House 13-15 Swakeleys Road Ickenham Middlesex UB10 8DF
Tel: 01895 678314 *Fax:* 01895 634259
E-mail: camacom@aol.com

CATHCARTS ‡
2 Swakeleys Road Ickenham Middlesex UB10 8BG
Tel: 01895 631942 / 675631 *Fax:* 01895 678277
Dx: 42300 ICKENHAM
E-mail: cathcarts@cathcarts.co.uk
List of partners: J B Cathcart, P J Cathcart
Work: C1 C3 E J1 L M2 S1 S2 W
Ptr: Cathcart, Mr John B LLB(Lond) . . . . *Jul 1975
Cathcart, Mr Peter J LLB(Newc). . . . . *Dec 1977

J M CHARLES & CO ‡
Panstar House 13-15 Swakeleys Road Ickenham Middlesex UB10 8DF
Tel: 01895 634402 *Fax:* 01895 634402 *Dx:* 42305 ICKENHAM
List of partners: J M Charles
Agency, Fixed Fee Interview and Legal Aid undertaken
SPr: Charles, Mr Jon Marc . . . . Oct 1994

MAPLESTONES ‡
2 Glebe Avenue Ickenham Middlesex UB10 8PA
Tel: 01895 632255 *Fax:* 01895 679142 *Dx:* 42304 ICKENHAM
E-mail: rodney.flood@maplestones.com
List of partners: R C Flood, C E Maplestone
Advocacy and Fixed Fee Interview undertaken
Ptr: Flood, Mr Rodney C LLB(Lond) . . . . *May 1981

WORSDELL & VINTNER ‡
2 Ivy House Road Ickenham Middlesex UB10 8NE
Tel: 01895 672631 *Fax:* 01895 678270 *Dx:* 42303 ICKENHAM
E-mail: wandv@dial.pipex.com
List of partners: A C Barrett, N Crowther
Office: Harefield
Work: A1 C1 C2 E J1 K4 L P R1 S1 S2 T1 T2 W
Ptr: Barrett, Mrs Alison C LLB. . . . . *Jun 1985
Crowther, Mr Neil BA . . . . *Dec 1978
Con: Vintner, Mr Barry S . . . . *Jun 1972

ILFORD, Essex

AZ SOLICITORS ‡
279a Ilford Lane Ilford Essex IG1 2SD
Tel: 020 8553 1049 *Fax:* 020 8553 5326

ABDULLAH SOLICITORS ‡
56 Mansfield Road Ilford Essex IG1 3BD
Tel: 020 8554 6595 *Fax:* 020 8554 1083
E-mail: law@abdullahsolicitors.co.uk

ADVOCATES SOLICITORS ‡
6 Connaught Road Ilford Essex IG1 1QT
Tel: 020 8553 5656 *Fax:* 020 8478 6650 *Dx:* 124831 ILFORD 7
E-mail: info@advocatessolicitors.co.uk
List of partners: A Alabi
SPr: Alabi, Mr Anthony BA(Hons); LLB(Hons) . . . . *Mar 2002

AKAL SOLICITORS ‡
23a York Road Ilford Essex IG1 3AD
Tel: 020 8477 0280 *Fax:* 020 8477 0281
E-mail: akal_solicitors@btconnect.com

ALEXUS ASSOCIATES SOLICITORS ‡
119a Ilford Lane Ilford Essex IG1 2RN
Tel: 020 8911 9300 *Fax:* 020 8911 9314 *Dx:* 124843 ILFORD 7
E-mail: alexusassociates@yahoo.co.uk

ANDREWS ANGEL SOLICITORS ‡
First Floor 88 High Road Ilford Essex IG1 1DN
Tel: 020 8911 9289 *Fax:* 020 8911 9258 *Dx:* 60215 DURHAM
List of partners: P Angel
Ptr: Angel, Mr Paul . . . . Oct 1993

ARCHER FIELDS SOLICITORS ‡
259-261 Cranbrook Road Ilford Essex IG1 4TG
Tel: 020 8518 5600 *Fax:* 020 8518 5620 *Dx:* 8915 ILFORD
E-mail: info@archer-fields.com

ARNOLD GEORGE & CO ‡
Wellesley House 102 Cranbrook Road Ilford Essex IG1 4NH
Tel: 020 8554 5484 *Fax:* 020 8518 3486 *Dx:* 8930 ILFORD
List of partners: A George
Work: C1 E F1 J1 K1 K3 L N O Q S1 W
Ptr: George, Mr Albert BA . . . . *Apr 1981

ARORA ASHTON PATEL ‡
Premier House 190-192 Cranbrook Road Ilford Essex IG1 4LU
Tel: 020 8554 6263 *Fax:* 020 8554 6264
List of partners: N Arora, M Ashton
Languages: Gujarati, Hindi, Punjabi, Urdu
Work: D1 D2 F1 K1 K3 N O Q S1 S2 W
Emergency Action, Agency, Fixed Fee Interview, Legal Aid undertaken and Member of Accident Line
Ptr: Arora, Ms Nira LLB . . . . *Oct 1992
Ashton, Mr Mukesh . . . . Jan 1987

AVERY EMERSON SOLICITORS ‡
Gloucester House 335 Green Lane Ilford Essex IG3 9TH
Tel: 020 8215 0884 *Fax:* 020 8599 9442 *Dx:* 41908 GOODMAYES
E-mail: enquiry@ae-law.co.uk
List of partners: S Ahluwalia
Languages: Hindi, Punjabi, Urdu
Work: B1 D2 E F1 G J1 K1 K2 K3 O Q S2 W Z(i)
SPr: Ahluwalia, Mr Suki . . . . Jan 1997

BART-WILLIAMS & CO ‡
Second Floor 34-36 High Street Ilford Essex IG6 2QD
Tel: 020 8551 4747

S S BASI & CO ‡
153 Cranbrook Road Ilford Essex IG1 4TA
Tel: 020 8518 1236 *Fax:* 020 8518 1131 *Dx:* 8902 ILFORD
Emergency telephone 07654 578024
List of partners: S Basi, M Saimbhi
Languages: Hindi, Punjabi, Urdu
Work: C1 C2 D1 E F1 G H J1 K1 K3 L N O Q R1 S1 S2 V W Z(g,i,l,q,r)
Emergency Action, Agency, Advocacy, Legal Aid undertaken and Legal Aid Franchise
Ptr: Basi, Mr Satwinder MA; LLB . . . . *Sep 1993
Saimbhi, Miss Manjit . . . . *Jan 2009
Con: Caplan, Mr Geoffrey M LLB . . . . *Jan 1965

BEACON SOLICITORS LIMITED ‡
32 Bank Chambers Cranbrook Road Ilford Essex IG1 4NE
Tel: 020 8553 1893

C K SOLICITORS
144 Cranbrook Road Ilford Essex IG1 4LZ
Tel: 020 3285 8988 *Fax:* 020 3285 8989
E-mail: ilford@ck-solicitors.com
Office: London E11

CARTER DEVILE ‡
(incorporating Budd & Co; Carter & Co; Hargreaves & Co)
592 Green Lane Goodmayes Ilford Essex IG3 9SG
Tel: 020 8590 1066 *Fax:* 020 8597 0307 *Dx:* 41900 GOODMAYES
List of partners: J R Devile, I A Goldsmith
Office: Buckhurst Hill
Work: C1 D1 E F1 K1 L N O Q S1 S2 W Z(c,l)
Agency and Legal Aid undertaken
Ptr: Devile, Mr John R. . . . . *§Jun 1977
Goldsmith, Mr Ian Alexander BA(Law). . . . . *Nov 1975

CHANDARANA & CO ‡
297 High Road Ilford Essex IG1 1NR
Tel: 020 8503 4500 *Fax:* 020 8478 2475
E-mail: office@chandarana297.co.uk

CONIFER & PINES SOLICITORS ‡
1st Floor Wellesley House 102 Cranbrook Road Ilford Essex IG1 4NH
Tel: 020 8709 2077 *Fax:* 020 8709 2117
E-mail: info@coniferandpines.com

CUNNINGTONS
131 Cranbrook Road Ilford Essex IG1 4PU
Tel: 020 8553 0002 *Fax:* 020 8553 1003 *Dx:* 8929 ILFORD 1
E-mail: john.simpkin@cunningtons.co.uk
Office: Braintree (2 offices), Croydon, Solihull, Wickford
Work: D1 E G H K1 L Q S1 S2 W
Ptr: Simpkin, Mr John Robert . . . . *Jan 1980
Asoc: Chumber, Miss Neena LLB(Hons). . . . . Jul 2005

DAVIS & CO ‡
34-36 High Street Barkingside Ilford Essex IG6 2DQ
Tel: 020 8551 4228 *Fax:* 020 8550 6698 *Dx:* 99325 BARKINGSIDE
E-mail: info@davislegal.co.uk
List of partners: J R Davis
Work: D1 E F1 G H K1 N O Q S1 W
Emergency Action, Agency, Advocacy, Legal Aid undertaken and Member of Accident Line
Ptr: Davis, Mr John R . . . . *Dec 1977
Ast: O'Vel, Miss Jane A BA(Law) . . . . *Mar 1984

DAWAR & CO ‡
1 Stradbroke Grove Clayhall Ilford Essex IG5 0DN
Tel: 020 8550 4741 *Fax:* 020 8551 7443

List of partners: R Dawar
Ptr: Dawar, Ms Rita BA . . . . *Apr 1987

DHILLONS ‡
26 Cameron Road Seven Kings Ilford Essex IG3 8LB
Tel: 020 8262 6565 *Fax:* 020 8262 6566
E-mail: info@dhillons.com

ELS SOLICITORS ‡
Orion House 104-106 Cranbrook Road Ilford Essex IG1 4LZ
Tel: 020 8262 5010 *Fax:* 020 8262 1281 *Dx:* 8900 ILFORD
E-mail: info@elslaw.co.uk
Work: J1
Ast: Shuja, Miss Shiza. . . . . May 2008

EDWARD OLIVER & BELLIS ‡
19 Broadway Market Fencepiece Road Barkingside Ilford Essex IG6 2JW
Tel: 020 8500 4168 *Fax:* 020 8501 0021 *Dx:* 99326 BARKINGSIDE
List of partners: D C M Diamond, C M Rooney
Work: D1 E K1 L S1 W
Ptr: Diamond, Mr David C M LLB . . . . *Nov 1973
Rooney, Mr Crispin M BA . . . . *Jul 1978

EDWARD OLIVER & BELLIS ‡
City House 9 Cranbrook Road Ilford Essex IG1 4EG
Tel: 020 8553 1214 *Fax:* 020 8478 7762 *Dx:* 200857 ILFORD 4
E-mail: crooney@eobellis.co.uk

EDWARDS DUTHIE ‡
9-15 York Road Ilford Essex IG1 3AD
Tel: 020 8514 9000 *Fax:* 020 8514 9009 *Dx:* 200850 ILFORD 4
Emergency telephone 020 8471 8115
E-mail: allinfo@edwardsduthie.com
List of partners: P M Barton, R K Garvey, H A Green, J R Harrison, B Huber, P J Irvine, J E Life, S P Murphy, C F Newman, D Reeves, A P Wolton, B Wright, R S Yaqub
Office: London E13, London E6
Languages: French, Gujarati, Hindi, Punjabi, Urdu
Work: B2 C1 C2 D1 D2 E F1 G H J1 K1 K2 L N O Q R1 S1 V W X Z(g,h,i,k,l,p,t,w)
Emergency Action, Agency, Advocacy, Fixed Fee Interview, Legal Aid undertaken and Legal Aid Franchise
Ptr: Barton, Ms Philippa M BA. . . . . *Oct 1987
Green, Mrs Hilary A BA . . . . Feb 1987
Irvine, Mr Peter John BA(Hons) . . . . Mar 1993
Newman, Mr Charles F MA; LLM . . . . *Oct 1970
Wolton, Mr Anthony P LLB(Leics) . . . . *Nov 1984
Wright, Mr Bradley FILEx . . . . *Mar 1999
Yaqub, Ms Riffat Shaheen LLB(Hons). . . . . *Oct 1996
Ast: Landsberg, Ms Lesley. . . . . *Sep 2001
Lawrence, Mrs Ruth Annette LLB . . . . Sep 1993

C T EMEZIE SOLICITORS ‡
23a Sevenways Parade Gants Hill Ilford Essex IG2 6JX
Tel: 020 3489 9113 *Fax:* 020 3489 9113
E-mail: info@ctemeziesolicitors.com

ESSEX SOLICITORS ‡
170 Cranbrook Road Ilford Essex IG1 4LX
Tel: 020 8554 7123

EWAN & CO SOLICITORS ‡
33 York Road Ilford Essex IG1 3AD
Tel: 020 8514 5687 *Fax:* 0560 049 8338
Emergency telephone 020 8514 5687
E-mail: charles_ewan@btconnect.com
List of partners: C A Ewan
Work: B1 C1 E J1 K1 K3 L N O Q S1 S2 W Z(j,q,r)
Agency undertaken
SPr: Ewan, Mr Charles A LLB(Hons); LLM . . . . Jan 1998

EXCEL LAW ‡
Unit 8 Whilems Works Forest Road Ilford Essex IG6 3HJ
Tel: 020 8500 6476 *Fax:* 020 8500 6913 *Dx:* 99333 BARKINGSIDE
E-mail: info@excelaw.com

MARGARET M FRAME & CO ‡
68-70 Wanstead Lane Ilford Essex IG1 3SE
Tel: 020 8518 6767 *Fax:* 020 8518 3895 *Dx:* 200853 ILFORD 4
E-mail: rosemary.thompson@margaretmframe.co.uk
List of partners: R J Thompson
Languages: French
Work: C1 E R1 S1
Agency, Fixed Fee Interview undertaken and Member of Accident Line
Ptr: Thompson, Mrs Rosemary J LLB . . . . Jun 1981

GH CORNISH LLP ‡
One The Parade Monarch Way Newbury Park Ilford Essex IG2 7HR
Tel: 020 8090 0800 *Fax:* 020 8090 1234 *Dx:* 8957 GANTS HILL
E-mail: info@ghcornish.com
List of partners: P S Bosher, M T Cornish, H B Shulman
Office: London EC4
Languages: French, Spanish
Work: B1 C1 D1 E F1 H J1 L M1 N O P R1 R2 S1 S2 T1 W Z(e,f,h,i,l)
Emergency Action, Agency, Advocacy undertaken and Member of Accident Line
Ptr: Bosher, Mr Peter S . . . . *Dec 1977
Cornish, Mr Michael T. . . . . *Jul 1975
Shulman, Mr Harvey B LLM; LLB . . . . *Dec 1971
Ast: Coombs, Mr Gerard Edwin . . . . *Sep 1994
De Lausan, Ms Linda . . . . Oct 1986
Hicks, Mr Gareth J LLB . . . . *Mar 1982
Johnson, Mr Andrew . . . . Nov 1993
Rafe, Miss Meilee LLB(Chelmer) . . . . Apr 1992
Simmons, Ms Jennifer B LLB . . . . *Dec 1976
Con: Davies, Mr John B . . . . May 1962

GILL & CO ‡
Trevian House 422-426 Ley Street Ilford Essex IG2 7BS
Tel: 020 8554 8774 *Fax:* 020 8554 6698 *Dx:* 8908 ILFORD
Emergency telephone 07977 574471
E-mail: info@gillsolicitors.com
List of partners: G K Bhogal, A S Gill
Languages: Hindi, Kiswahili, Punjabi, Urdu
Work: B1 C1 D1 D2 E F1 G H J1 K1 K3 L N O Q R1 S1 S2 W Z(l,o)
Emergency Action, Agency, Advocacy, Fixed Fee Interview, Legal Aid undertaken and Legal Aid Franchise
Ptr: Bhogal, Mrs Gursharan Kaur LLB(Hons). . . . . . . *May 1981
Gill, Amrik S . . . . *Jul 1980
Ast: Beg, Miss Umbrena Shafaq LLB(Hons) . . . . Mar 2001
Gill, Mr Onkar Singh LLB(Hons). . . . . Mar 2006
Sanghera, Mrs Harsharan Kaur LLB; LLM. . . . . . *Nov 2006

GRAHAM CLAYTON SOLICITORS
103 Cranbrook Road Ilford Essex IG1 4PU
Tel: 020 8554 5525
Office: Chester-le-Street, Doncaster, Stafford

HKH KENWRIGHT & COX SOLICITORS ‡
202-212 High Road Ilford Essex IG1 1QB
Tel: 020 8553 9600 *Fax:* 020 8553 9995 *Dx:* 124836 ILFORD 7
Emergency telephone 07976 958248
E-mail: hkh.sol@tiscali.co.uk
List of partners: R Aravindan, K Mian
Languages: Bengali, French, Hindi, Punjabi, Urdu
Work: B2 D1 E G H K1 L O Q S1 V W Z(i,l)
Emergency Action, Agency, Advocacy, Fixed Fee Interview, Legal Aid undertaken and Legal Aid Franchise
Ptr: Aravindan, Mrs Renuka . . . . Jun 1986
Mian, Mr Khurram LLB; ACIOB ★ West Essex Committee Member; 2nd Vice President of West Essex Law Society . . . . . . *Apr 1997
Ast: Hussain-Akhtar, Mrs Samiera LLB(Hons) . . . . Feb 1995
Patch, Mr Mark John LLB(Hons) . . . . Apr 1994

HANSON WOODS SOLICITORS ‡
57 Goodmayes Road Goodmayes Ilford Essex IG3 9UD
Tel: 020 8590 9220 *Fax:* 020 8599 5527 *Dx:* 41910 GOODMAYES
E-mail: info@hansonwoods.com
List of partners: S Gyamfi
Mem: Gyamfi, Sally-Ann. . . . . Apr 2004

HARRIS WATERS SOLICITORS ‡
406-408 High Road Ilford Essex IG1 1TW
Tel: 020 8478 0888 *Fax:* 020 8478 8668 *Dx:* 97515 ILFORD 3
E-mail: roger@harriswaters.com

HILCREST SOLICITORS LLP ‡
277 Ilford Lane Ilford Essex IG1 2SD
Tel: 020 8911 9169 *Fax:* 020 8514 4878 *Dx:* 200872 ILFORD 4
E-mail: info@hilcrestsolicitors.co.uk

IFRAHIM & CO SOLICITORS ‡
468 Ilford Lane Ilford Essex IG1 2NF
Tel: 020 8911 9222 *Fax:* 020 8911 9333
Emergency telephone 07951 379922
List of partners: M Ifrahim
Languages: Hindi, Punjabi, Urdu
Work: K3 L S2 W Z(i,l)
SPr: Ifrahim, Mr Mohd . . . . Mar 2000

KAIHIVA & CO ‡
First Floor Offices 6 Clements Roads Ilford Essex IG1 1BA
Tel: 020 8553 0303

KAMAL SOLICITORS ‡
428 Ilford Lane Ilford Essex IG1 2NF
Tel: 020 8553 7733 *Fax:* 020 8553 7703

KHAKHAR & CO ‡
8a Cranbrook Road Ilford Essex IG1 4DJ
Tel: 020 8478 9881 *Fax:* 020 8478 9890 *Dx:* 200862 ILFORD
E-mail: khakhar@msn.com
List of partners: R R Khakhar
Work: C1 E F1 J1 K1 L O P Q R1 S1 W Z(c,d,i,l,o,s)
Agency and Fixed Fee Interview undertaken
Ptr: Khakhar, Rajesh R BA(Lond) . . . . Dec 1980

KHANS ‡
165 Ley Street Ilford Essex IG1 4BL
Tel: 020 8553 5995 *Fax:* 020 8553 0950
List of partners: M O Khan, S D Khan
Languages: Arabic, French, German, Gujarati, Hindi, Italian, Punjabi, Urdu
Work: B1 C1 D1 G H J1 K1 L N O Q S1 V W Z(g,i)
Emergency Action, Agency and Legal Aid undertaken
Ptr: Khan, Mr Muhammad Omar BA; LLB . . . . *Jan 2007
Khan, Mr Shahid Dastgir BSc; MBIM . . . . *Mar 1982

N S KUMAR ‡
151 Hamilton Avenue Barkingside Ilford Essex IG6 1AA
Tel: 020 8554 3393 *Fax:* 020 8220 7014
Emergency telephone 07939 133023
E-mail: nskumar@ntlworld.com
List of partners: N S Kumar
Languages: Sinhalese, Tamil
Work: L Q S1 S2 W Z(i,l)
SPr: Kumar, Mrs Nalayini Skanda . . . . Dec 1981

DAVID V LAWSON SOLICITORS ‡
315 Cranbrook Road Ilford Essex IG1 4UD
Tel: 020 8554 8848 *Fax:* 020 8554 5927 *Dx:* 200866 ILFORD 4
E-mail: dlawsonlegal315@aol.com
List of partners: D V Lawson
Ptr: Lawson, Mr David V. . . . . *Dec 1970

LEGAL EAGLES ‡
323 High Road Ilford Essex IG1 1NR
Tel: 0870 999 2911

LINKS LEGAL ‡
42 Redbridge Lane East Ilford Essex IG4 5EX
Tel: 020 8551 0999 *Fax:* 020 8551 2979 *Dx:* 8953 GANTS HILL
E-mail: info@linkslegal.co.uk
List of partners: M Dattani, J Patel, B Roopra
Languages: Gujarati, Hindi, Kiswahili, Punjabi, Urdu
Work: B1 C1 E F1 G H K1 K3 N O Q R1 S1 S2 W
Legal Aid undertaken
Ptr: Dattani, Mr Mayur. . . . . Jul 1992
Patel, Mr Jitesh . . . . Apr 2001
Roopra, Balwinder . . . . Sep 1992

LISS GULHANE INNES & CO
1 Chigwell Park Chigwell Ilford Essex IG7 5BE
Tel: 020 8501 0777
E-mail: info@lgi-solicitors.co.uk
Office: Romford

LORDS SOLICITORS LLP ‡
466 Cranbrook Road Ilford Essex IG2 6LE
Tel: 020 8518 2226 *Fax:* 020 8518 2244 *Dx:* 8905 ILFORD
E-mail: lordssolicitors@yahoo.co.uk

MACLEISH LITTLESTONE COWAN
269 Ilford Lane Ilford Essex IG1 2SD
Tel: 020 8514 3000 *Fax:* 020 8478 1548 *Dx:* 124839 ILFORD 7
Office: Barking, London E11, Sawbridgeworth
Languages: French, Gujarati, Hindi, Urdu
Work: D1 E J1 K1 L N O Q R1 S1 S2 Z(l)
Emergency Action, Agency, Advocacy, Fixed Fee Interview, Legal Aid undertaken and Member of Accident Line
Ptr: Bhambra, Ms Parmjeet . . . . Sep 2001
Cowan, Mr Brian BSc. . . . . *Dec 1979
Ast: Dumaka, Amelia . . . . Mar 2008

CARL MARTIN SOLICITORS ‡
Suite 511 3 Coventry Road Ilford Essex IG1 4QR
Tel: 020 8554 7764 / 07851 376156 *Fax:* 020 8518 5245
E-mail: cms@carlmartinsolicitors.com

MATWALA VYAS LLP ‡
3 Electric Parade Seven Kings Road Ilford Essex IG3 8BY
Tel: 020 8597 5097 *Fax:* 020 8599 4499 *Dx:* 41905 GOODMAYES
List of partners: G Matwala, A R Vyas
Languages: Gujarati, Hindi, Punjabi, Urdu
Work: D1 E G H J1 K1 L N O Q S1 S2 W
Emergency Action, Agency, Fixed Fee Interview and Legal Aid undertaken
Ptr: Matwala, Mr Gurcharan. . . . . Oct 1994
Vyas, Alkesh R . . . . Jan 2001

H MONTLAKE & CO ‡
Bank House 269-275 Cranbrook Road Ilford Essex IG1 4TG
Tel: 020 8532 4800 *Fax:* 020 8554 6100 *Dx:* 200870 ILFORD 4
E-mail: mail@montlake.co.uk
List of partners: M J Bonehill, A S Montlake
Work: B1 C1 C2 C3 E J1 L M3 N O R1 R2 S1 S2 T1 U1 W Z(c,d,e,l)
Emergency Action undertaken
Ptr: Bonehill, Mr Michael J LLB . . . . *Mar 1972
Montlake, Mr Andrew S BA . . . . *Sep 1982

MORGAN HALL SOLICITORS ‡
Westplan House 73-77 Ilford Hill Ilford Essex IG1 2DG
Tel: 020 8514 4448 *Fax:* 020 8514 2939 *Dx:* 200861 ILFORD 4
Emergency telephone 07961 105008
E-mail: info@morganhallsolicitors.co.uk
List of partners: A H Bhurawala
Work: B1 B2 C1 C2 C3 D1 D2 F1 F2 G J1 J2 K1 L N O Q R1 R2 S2 T1 V W Z(b,i,j,l,p,q)
Agency, Fixed Fee Interview and Legal Aid undertaken
Ptr: Bhurawala, Mr Altaf Husen LLB. . . . . *Aug 1993

MORGAN MARK SOLICITORS ‡
97a Ilford Lane Ilford Essex IG1 2RJ
Tel: 020 8553 0255 *Fax:* 020 8553 9368

NATHAN (KP) & CO ‡
80 Herent Drive Ilford Essex IG5 0HG
Tel: 020 8551 1661 *Fax:* 020 8550 0441

NATIONWIDE SOLICITORS ‡
Amanveer House 523-525 Green Lane Goodmayes Ilford Essex IG3 9RH
Tel: 020 8983 8944 *Fax:* 020 8590 7726 *Dx:* 41909 GOODMAYES
E-mail: info@nwsolicitors.com

PWC SOLICITORS ‡
253 Ilford Lane Ilford Essex IG1 2SB
Tel: 020 8478 8791 *Fax:* 020 8514 7535 *Dx:* 20086 ILFORD 4

A H PAGE ‡
640 Cranbrook Road Barkingside Ilford Essex IG6 1HQ
Tel: 020 8554 1985 *Fax:* 020 8554 2899
E-mail: richard@ahpage.com
List of partners: R A Bull
Work: B1 C3 D1 E F1 G H J1 K1 L N O Q R1 S1 W Z(c,d,e,l,m)
Emergency Action, Agency, Advocacy, Legal Aid undertaken and Member of Accident Line
Ptr: Bull, Mr Richard A BA. . . . . *Dec 1977
Ast: Butt, Miss Fariha BA(Hons)(Law & Spanish); PGDipLP*Sep 2005
Rewane, Miss Eyeulusan LLB(Hons); LLM . . . . . . Oct 2003

PATEL & JOACHIM LLP ‡
Balfour House 390-398 High Road Ilford Essex IG1 1TL
Tel: 020 8477 1399 *Fax:* 020 8477 1799 *Dx:* 124835 ILFORD 7
E-mail: mail@patelandjoachim.co.uk

PATTICHI HILL & CROQUES ‡
1 Roman Road Ilford Essex IG1 2NY
Tel: 020 8911 8233 *Fax:* 020 8911 8316
List of partners: F Croques, R Hill
Ptr: Croques, Fatima . . . . Dec 1998
Hill, Mr Richard . . . . Oct 1998

RATNAKUMAR & CO ‡
25 Crown Road Barkingside Ilford Essex IG6 1NF
Tel: 020 8551 1411 *Fax:* 020 8220 9604
List of partners: C Ratnakumar
Languages: Sinhalese, Tamil
Work: E S1 S2 Z(l)
Fixed Fee Interview undertaken
SPr: Ratnakumar, Mrs Chandrika LLB . . . . *Apr 1988

RAVALS LEGAL SERVICE ‡
124a Felbrigge Road Seven Kings Ilford Essex IG3 9XJ
Tel: 020 8590 3407 *Fax:* 020 8590 3407
E-mail: ravalslegal@aol.com

REGAL LAW SOLICITORS ‡
46 Ilford Lane Ilford Essex IG1 2JY
Tel: 020 8553 4420
E-mail: info@regallaw.co.uk
Languages: Hindi, Punjabi, Urdu

SA LAW CHAMBERS ‡
1st Floor Heraldic House 160-162 Cranbrook Road Ilford Essex IG1 4PE
Tel: 020 8554 0012 *Fax:* 020 8554 6619 *Dx:* 8938 ILFORD
Emergency telephone 07985 419788

 See p112 for the Key to Work Categories & other symbols

E-mail: info@salawchambers.com
List of partners: S Aboobaker, R Cashman, C Clements, P Tohani
Dir: Aboobaker, Siddik. . . . . Apr 1997
Cashman, Mr Robert . . . . . Jan 2001
Clements, Mr Charles. . . . . Jan 2000
Tohani, Pamela . . . . . Apr 1999

SAS SOLICITORS ‡
1st Floor 12 High Street Ilford Essex IG1 1BY
Tel: 020 8220 2900 *Fax:* 020 8220 2913

SJ SOLICITORS ‡
604 Green Lane Ilford Essex IG3 9SQ
Tel: 020 8548 3700

ST LAW SOLICITORS ‡
74 Ilford Lane Ilford Essex IG1 2LA
Tel: 020 8478 5599 *Fax:* 020 8478 7728 *Dx:* 200851 ILFORD 4
Languages: Punjabi, Urdu
Legal Aid undertaken

L SHARMA & CO SOLICITORS
96c Ilford Lane Ilford Essex IG1 2LD
Tel: 020 8478 0064 *Fax:* 020 8478 6664
Office: London E13

CHARLES SIMMONS ‡
31 York Road Ilford Essex IG1 3AD
Tel: 020 8514 0000 *Fax:* 020 8514 0222
E-mail: gurpal@csisolicitors.com
List of partners: N Uddin
Work: G
Ptr: Uddin, Nashir . . . . . Sep 1998
Ast: Oppal, Gurpal S. . . . . . May 1999

SOLOMONS SOLICITORS ‡
26 Cranbrook Road Ilford Essex IG1 4DL
Tel: 020 8514 7414 *Fax:* 020 8514 7222 *Dx:* 200856 ILFORD 4

SOODS SOLICITORS ‡
92 Goodmayes Road Goodmayes Ilford Essex IG3 9UU
Tel: 020 8597 0000 *Fax:* 020 8597 2666 *Dx:* 41907 GOODMAYES
Emergency telephone 07710 292342
E-mail: reception@soodssolicitors.co.uk
List of partners: A Sood
Languages: Hindi, Punjabi, Urdu, Yoruba
Work: B2 G H L N O Q R1 S1 S2 W Z(i)
Agency, Fixed Fee Interview and Legal Aid undertaken
SPr: Sood, Mr Anupam MA. . . . . Mar 1996

ST VALCHIKWE SOLICITORS ‡
729 High Road Ilford Essex IG3 8RL
Tel: 020 8597 7118 *Fax:* 020 8597 2992

STAINFORTH SOLICITORS ‡
16 Stainforth Road Newbury Park Ilford Essex IG2 7EH
Tel: 020 8510 1683 *Fax:* 020 8598 8544
E-mail: riffat@stainforthsolicitors.com

TAYLORS LEGAL ‡
184 Manor Road Chigwell Ilford Essex IG7 5PZ
Tel: 020 8501 4959 *Fax:* 020 8501 3008 *Dx:* 154760 CHIGWELL
E-mail: office@taylorslegal.com
List of partners: E Costa, N Taylor
Languages: French
Work: J1 K1 K3 N Q S1 S2 W
Member of Accident Line
Ptr: Costa, Mr Elliott. . . . . Jan 2001
Taylor, Miss Nicola . . . . . Jan 1999

TRIDENT LEGAL LIMITED ‡
392 Ilford Lane Ilford Essex IG1 2NB
Tel: 020 8478 5476 *Fax:* 020 8478 7347
E-mail: info@tridentlegal.com

VMD SOLICITORS ‡
Sherwood House 370 Ilford Lane Town Centre Ilford Essex IG1 2LZ
Tel: 020 8514 8703 *Fax:* 020 8514 8703
E-mail: info@vmdsolicitors.co.uk

A M WALTERS & CO ‡
118 Fairlop Road Ilford Essex IG6 2EN
Tel: 020 8551 5894 *Fax:* 020 8551 5894
List of partners: A M Walters
Languages: French, Punjabi, Urdu
Work: D1 D2 K1 K3 L Q S1 W
Agency, Advocacy and Fixed Fee Interview undertaken
SPr: Walters, Ms Ava Miriam BA(Hons) . . . . . *May 1983

WOODFORD WISE SOLICITORS ‡
9 Woodford Avenue Gants Hill Ilford Essex IG2 6UF
Tel: 020 8550 2506 *Fax:* 020 7504 8588 *Dx:* 8960 GANTS HILL

ILFRACOMBE, Devon

J F K ANNEAR ‡
Ding Dong Watermouth Berrynarbor Ilfracombe Devon EX34 9SJ
Tel: 01271 882239

BEACON LAW PRACTICE ‡
12 Montpelier Terrace Ilfracombe Devon EX34 9HR
Tel: 01271 867056

BREWER HARDING & ROWE
6-9 Market Square Ilfracombe Devon EX34 9AX
Tel: 01271 863495 *Fax:* 01271 865694 *Dx:* 82904 ILFRACOMBE
E-mail: lawyers@bhrlaw.co.uk
Office: Barnstaple (2 offices), Bideford, Braunton, Exeter
Work: A1 B1 C1 C2 C3 D1 E F1 G H J1 K1 K3 L N P R1 S1 W Z(k,l,m)
Emergency Action, Agency, Advocacy, Fixed Fee Interview, Legal Aid undertaken and Legal Aid Franchise
Ptr: Treasaden, Mr Nigel H LLB . . . . . *Mar 1984
Triggs, Mr Geoffrey John LLB(Exon) . . . . . §Oct 1978
Asoc: Preisner, Mr Nicholas F LLB(Manc Victoria) . . . . . *Jan 1987

TAYLORS SOLICITORS
8 Church Street Ilfracombe Devon EX34 8HA
Tel: 01271 864134 *Fax:* 01271 866088
E-mail: ilfracombe@taylors-law.co.uk
Office: Braunton

ILKESTON, Derbyshire

SHIRLEY FRETWELL ‡
42 Allendale Ilkeston Derbyshire DE7 4LE
Tel: 0115 932 3623 *Fax:* 0115 932 3623
E-mail: office@shirleyfretwell.co.uk
List of partners: S Fretwell
Languages: French, German
Work: S1 W
Ptr: Fretwell, Mrs Shirley. . . . . *Jul 1980

HORTON & MOSS ‡
4-5 East Street Ilkeston Derbyshire DE7 5JB
Tel: 0115 932 1431 / 930 8208 *Fax:* 0115 932 0731
Dx: 10303 ILKESTON
List of partners: A P Forman, R J Horton, R T Pumfrey
Work: C1 D1 E F1 J1 K1 L N Q R1 S1 W Z(l)
Agency, Advocacy and Fixed Fee Interview undertaken
Ptr: Forman, Mr Andrew P LLB(Manc). . . . . *Dec 1975
Horton, Mr Richard J LLB . . . . . *Jul 1986
Pumfrey, Mr Richard T LLB(Nott'm) . . . . . *Dec 1978

MACLAREN WARNER
129 Bath Street Ilkeston Derbyshire DE7 8AP
Tel: 0115 930 4994 *Fax:* 0115 944 1377 *Dx:* 10314 ILKESTON
Office: Beeston, Eastwood, Stapleford
Work: A1 C1 D1 E F1 G H J1 K1 L N P R1 S1 W Z(i,l)
Emergency Action, Agency, Advocacy, Fixed Fee Interview, Legal Aid undertaken and Member of Accident Line
Ptr: Kassell, Mr Simon C BA(Law). . . . . *Oct 1983

CHARLES NEWTON & CO
6-8 Bath Street Ilkeston Derbyshire DE7 8FB
Tel: 0115 930 5070 *Fax:* 0115 930 5071
E-mail: info@charlesnewton.co.uk
Office: Eastwood

ROBINSONS
21-22 Burns Street Ilkeston Derbyshire DE7 8AA
Tel: 0115 932 4101 *Fax:* 0115 944 6300 *Dx:* 10301 ILKESTON
Emergency telephone 07889 609992
E-mail: info@robinsons-solicitors.co.uk
Office: Derby
Work: A1 B1 C1 C2 C3 D1 E F1 J1 K1 L M1 M2 N O P Q R1 S1 T1 T2 V W Z(c,d,e,h,j,l,m,n,o,t)
Emergency Action, Agency, Advocacy, Legal Aid undertaken, Legal Aid Franchise and Member of Accident Line
Asoc: Ward, Mr Maurice. . . . . *Jan 1979
Ast: Spencer, Mrs Karen Nicola LLB(Hons) . . . . . *Nov 1989

J P STENT SOLICITOR ‡
38 Kniveton Park Ilkeston Derbyshire DE7 5FT
Tel: 0115 930 6099

VHS FLETCHERS SOLICITORS
66 South Street Ilkeston Derbyshire DE7 5QJ
Tel: 0115 944 1233 *Fax:* 0115 944 1220 *Dx:* 10309 ILKESTON
E-mail: ilkeston@vhsfletchers.co.uk
Office: Nottingham

WYKES O'DONNELL WILLIAMS
14 Queen Street Ilkeston Derbyshire DE7 5GT
Tel: 0115 932 8776 *Fax:* 0115 932 4474
E-mail: mail@wykesilkeston.co.uk
Work: D1 F1 G H J1 K1 L N O Q S1 S2 V W Z(l,r)
Emergency Action, Agency, Advocacy, Fixed Fee Interview, Legal Aid undertaken, Legal Aid Franchise and Member of Accident Line
Ptr: O'Donnell, Mr Kevin F. . . . . . *Dec 1969
Williams, Mr David J G . . . . . *Jun 1981

ILKLEY, West Yorkshire

BUTLER & KANDLER ‡
(incorporating Windle & Sullivan; Stephen Butler)
46 Kings Road Ilkley West Yorkshire LS29 9AT
Tel: 01943 816207 *Fax:* 01943 816198
Emergency telephone 01943 608 234
E-mail: smb@e-solicitors.co.uk
List of partners: S M Butler, R Kandler
Languages: German
Work: D2 J1 K1 K3 K4 L S1 W Z(i,l)
Emergency Action, Agency and Advocacy undertaken
Ptr: Butler, Mr Stephen Mark LLB(Vict); LLM. . . . . *§Jun 1977
Kandler, Dr Robert BA; MEd; DPhil . . . . . *May 1999

SUSAN CUTHBERTSON & CO ‡
Crescent Chambers 18a Leeds Road Ilkley West Yorkshire LS29 8DJ
Tel: 01943 602811 *Fax:* 01943 602822
List of partners: S Cuthbertson
Work: D1 F1 K1 L Q S1 V W Z(h)
Agency and Advocacy undertaken
Ptr: Cuthbertson, Miss Susan . . . . . Nov 1976

DAVENPORT LAW LIMITED ‡
PO Box 306 Ilkley West Yorkshire LS29 1EY
Tel: 01943 608226
E-mail: om@davenport-law.co.uk

HARD HAT LEGAL LIMITED ‡
26 Brodrick Drive Ilkley West Yorkshire LS29 9SN
Tel: 07545 347600
E-mail: enquiries@hardhatlegal.co.uk

ISON HARRISON
46a The Grove Ilkley West Yorkshire LS29 9EE
Tel: 01943 889100 *Fax:* 01943 262003 *Dx:* 28405 ILKLEY
E-mail: mail@isonharrison.co.uk
Office: Garforth, Guiseley, Leeds (3 offices)
Ptr: Bloomer, Mr James M. . . . . . Dec 1981
Ast: Essen, Mrs Andrea . . . . . Dec 2007
Con: Bloomer, Mr James M. . . . . . Dec 1981
Cuthbertson, Miss Susan . . . . . Nov 1976

LAST CAWTHRA FEATHER LLP
2 The Wells Walk Ilkley West Yorkshire LS29 9LH
Tel: 01943 601020 *Fax:* 01943 816372 *Dx:* 28404 ILKLEY
E-mail: enquiries@lcf.co.uk
Office: Baildon, Bradford, Leeds, Shipley
Languages: French
Work: A1 B1 C1 C2 C3 D1 E F1 G H J1 K1 L N O P Q R1 S1 T1 T2 V W Z(b,c,d,h,i,j,k,l,m,n,o)
Agency, Advocacy, Fixed Fee Interview, Legal Aid Franchise and Member of Accident Line
Ptr: Lee, Mrs Amanda. . . . . Jan 2001
Asoc: Gibbs, Mrs Carole D LLB(Hons). . . . . Oct 1991
Ast: Robinson, Mrs Simone . . . . . Aug 1997

READ DUNN CONNELL
9 New Brook Street Ilkley West Yorkshire LS29 8DQ
Tel: 01943 601173 *Fax:* 01943 604270
Office: Bradford
Work: E S1 W
Emergency Action, Agency, Advocacy, Fixed Fee Interview undertaken and Member of Accident Line
Con: Ward, Mr Nigel Henry. . . . . *Jan 1965

ADAM WALKER & CO ‡
PO Box 244 Ilkley West Yorkshire LS29 1AU
Tel: 07904 979879 *Fax:* 01274 347308
E-mail: adammwalker@btinternet.com

WALKER FOSTER WITH KENNEDY THOMPSON
27 Riddings Road Ilkley West Yorkshire LS29 9LX
Tel: 01943 609969 *Fax:* 01943 603550 *Dx:* 28411 ILKLEY
E-mail: info@walkerfoster.com
Office: Barnoldswick, Silsden, Skipton
Work: S1 S2 W
Ptr: Worrall, Mrs Maxine Susan LLB(Hons) . . . . . *Dec 2002
Asoc: Barton, Mr David Richard . . . . . Sep 2003
Coulter, Miss Janine-Leigh . . . . . Dec 2007

ILMINSTER, Somerset

BAKER & DUKE ‡
(in association with Poole & Co)
20 Silver Street Ilminster Somerset TA19 0DN
Tel: 01460 52293 *Fax:* 01460 57666 *Dx:* 95800 ILMINSTER
Emergency telephone 01460 53408
Work: A1 B1 C1 C2 C3 D1 D2 E F1 G H J1 K1 K3 K4 L N P Q R2 S1 S2 T1 T2 W Z(b,d,l,m,t)
Emergency Action, Agency, Advocacy, Fixed Fee Interview, Legal Aid undertaken, Legal Aid Franchise and Member of Accident Line

BROOMHEAD & SAUL
11 & 13 East Street Ilminster Somerset TA19 0AE
Tel: 01460 57056 *Fax:* 01460 54846 *Dx:* 95803 ILMINSTER
E-mail: enquiries@broomhead-saul.co.uk
Office: Taunton
Work: G H K1 K3 N Q S1 W
Emergency Action, Agency, Advocacy, Legal Aid undertaken, Legal Aid Franchise and Member of Accident Line
Ptr: Gayer, Mr William Peter. . . . . *Jan 1995
Peters, Mr Raymond O . . . . . *Nov 1976
Suffield, Ms Helena Anne BA(Hons)(Italian); CPE; LPC . . . . . *Nov 1996

MILFORD & DORMOR
Old Bank Building East Street Ilminster Somerset TA19 0AJ
Tel: 01460 55445 *Fax:* 01460 55443
E-mail: ilminster@milfordanddormor.co.uk
Office: Axminster, Chard, Seaton
Ast: Fowkes, Miss Nicola Elizabeth LLB(Hons). . . . . *Oct 2010

POOLE & CO
20 Silver Street Ilminster Somerset TA19 0DN
Tel: 01460 52293 *Fax:* 01460 57666
E-mail: enquiries@pooleandco.com
Office: Crewkerne, London WC1

IMMINGHAM, North East Lincolnshire

KEITH R THOMPSON & CO ‡
Craik Hill Chambers Craik Hill Avenue Immingham North East Lincolnshire DN40 1LP
Tel: 01469 510510 *Fax:* 01469 510555
E-mail: keithrthompson@btconnect.com
List of partners: K R Thompson
Work: G H J1 K4 L N Q S1
Agency and Legal Aid Franchise
Ptr: Thompson, Mr Keith Ronald LLB . . . . . *Sep 1992

INGATESTONE, Essex

LAWSON & CO ‡
Suite 3 The Limes Ingatestone Essex CM4 0BE
Tel: 01277 354515 *Fax:* 01277 356640
E-mail: info@lawsonsolicitors.co.uk
Languages: French
Work: B1 C1 C2 C3 E J1 O Q S1 S2 Z(e,q)
Agency undertaken

TERRY & CO ‡
23 Pemberton Avenue Ingatestone Essex CM4 0AG
Tel: 01277 354518 *Fax:* 020 7691 7359
E-mail: davidterry@terry.co.uk
List of partners: D A Terry
Work: K1
Ptr: Terry, Mr David A MA(Oxon) . . . . . Sep 1989

INGLETON, North Yorkshire

PEARSON & PEARSON
33 Main Street Ingleton North Yorkshire LA6 3EH
Tel: 01524 241368
Office: Kendal, Kirkby Lonsdale
Work: A1 E L N S1 S2 W
Agency, Fixed Fee Interview undertaken and Member of Accident Line

IPSWICH, Suffolk

ASHTON KCJ ‡
Waterfront House Wherry Quay Ipswich Suffolk IP4 1AS
Tel: 01473 232425 *Fax:* 01473 230505 *Dx:* 3221 IPSWICH
E-mail: enquiries.ipswich@ashtonkcj.co.uk
List of partners: R C Adam, D J Barnes, A M Brown, N S Cawthorn, R M Foyster, R J Gair, B M Head, T A P Kramers, J L E Long, M R Merriam, M Potter, I G Reed, A J Roe, P S Whittingham, S L Williams, I M Winterbone
Office: Bury St Edmunds (2 offices), Cambridge, Felixstowe, Norwich (2 offices), Thetford
Languages: Dutch, French, German, Spanish, Swedish
Work: A1 A2 A3 C1 C2 C3 D1 E F1 F2 G H J1 J2 K1 K2 L M1 M2 N O P Q R1 S1 S2 T1 T2 V W X Z(c,f,g,h,i,l,m,o,p,w)
Emergency Action, Advocacy, Fixed Fee Interview, Legal Aid undertaken, Legal Aid Franchise and Member of Accident Line
Ptr: Cawthorn, Mr Neil S LLB(Lond) . . . *Jul 1980
Gair, Mr Robert J LLB(Newc) . . . *Oct 1989
Head, Mrs Brenda M LLB(Lond) . . . *Nov 1988
Kramers, Mr Toby A P BSc(Hons) . . . *Oct 1992
Potter, Mr Matthew LLB(Hons) . . . *Sep 1996
Reed, Mr Ian G LLB(Leics) . . . *Jan 1978
Whittingham, Mr Paul S BSc(Econ); LSF . . . *Nov 1988
Williams, Mr Stephen L LLB; BA(Hons) . . . *Dec 1993
Ast: Barnard, Mr Ian John BA(Hons) . . . *Sep 2001
Kingsbury, Mrs Tina LLB(Hons) . . . Feb 2001
Outen, Mr Julian Alan BA(Hons) . . . *Oct 1994

ATTWELLS SOLICITORS ‡
Beacon House Whitehouse Road Ipswich Suffolk IP1 5PB
Tel: 01473 746000 *Fax:* 01473 466840
E-mail: info@attwells.com
List of partners: N Attwell, L Draper, W Oakes
Office: London NW8
Work: A1 B1 C1 C2 E J1 J2 L N O Q R1 R2 S1 S2 T1 T2 W Z(b,c,d,e,h,l,za)
Agency, Advocacy and Fixed Fee Interview undertaken
Ptr: Attwell, Mr Nicholas BA(Hons); LLM . . . Mar 2000
Draper, Mrs Lisa . . . Oct 2008
Oakes, Mr Will . . . Sep 2005

BARKER GOTELEE SOLICITORS ‡
41 Barrack Square Martlesham Heath Ipswich Suffolk IP5 3RF
Tel: 01473 611211 *Fax:* 01473 610560
Dx: 124722 MARTLESHAM HEATH
E-mail: bg@barkergotelee.co.uk
List of partners: K A Addison, N J Furmston, J A Nicholson, T J Pound, J J Skellorn, D P D Thomas
Languages: French
Work: A1 A2 A3 B1 C1 C2 C3 E F1 G J1 J2 K1 K2 K3 K4 L M1 M2 N O P Q R1 R2 S1 S2 T1 T2 W Z(c,d,g,j,m,n,o,q,t,y)
Agency undertaken
Ptr: Addison, Mrs Kerry Ann . . . Nov 2003
Furmston, Mrs Nicola Jane LLB . . . Oct 1992
Nicholson, Mr J Andrew . . . Nov 1993
Pound, Mr Toby J . . . Oct 1980
Skellorn, Mr James J BA(Oxon) . . . *Nov 1983
Thomas, Mr Dermott P D BA . . . *§Apr 1989
Asoc: Cracknell, Miss Emma LLB . . . Sep 1997
McKenzie, Mrs Sarah Joanna LLM; LLB . . . Mar 2003
Palmer, Mr Nicholas George LLB . . . Sep 2000
Richards, Miss Clare Margaret LLB . . . *Nov 1987
Whyman, Miss Suzanne Elizabeth LLB . . . *Oct 2009
Ast: Beaven, Miss Katie Jane LLB(Hons) . . . Sep 2006
Modasia, Mr Prasan LLB Lexis Nexis Student Associate Performance 08-09 . . . *Sep 2011
Con: Barker, Mr Richard E . . . *§Jan 1969
Gotelee, Mr Michael . . . *§Jun 1963

BARRICELLA HUGHES MARCHANT ‡
20 Butter Market Ipswich Suffolk IP1 1BP
Tel: 01473 226225 *Fax:* 01473 215828
Emergency telephone 07774 275292
E-mail: info@bhmsolicitors.co.uk
List of partners: D Barricella, J Hughes, C S G Marchant
Work: G H
Emergency Action, Advocacy, Legal Aid undertaken and Legal Aid Franchise
Ptr: Barricella, Mr Dino BA; MA ★ . . . Jul 1998
Hughes, Mr John BSc; Dip SW . . . *Jun 1995
Marchant, Mr Craig Stephen Glover BA(Law) ★ . . . *Mar 1986

BATES WELLS & BRAITHWAITE ‡
29 Lower Brook Street Ipswich Suffolk IP4 1AQ
Tel: 01473 219282 *Fax:* 01473 230804
E-mail: mail@bates-wells.co.uk

BIRKETTS LLP ‡
24-26 Museum Street Ipswich Suffolk IP1 1HZ
Tel: 01473 232300 *Fax:* 01473 230524 *Dx:* 3206 IPSWICH
E-mail: mail@birketts.co.uk
List of partners: M M C Atkins, J S J Austin, C J Barker, C R Boscawen, J Bristol, N J Burnett, N C Farthing, V V French, J S Hall, J W T Harbottle, R B Hayes, M A Henry, G E Kerr, W J Mabon, K J Palmer, R J Payne, R J Ruiz, C P Schwer, N J W Tavener, N H Thompson, W D R Turner, J A Whybrow, M T Wilson, R H Wollaston
Office: Cambridge, Chelmsford, Norwich
Languages: French, German, Italian
Work: A1 A2 A3 B1 C1 C2 C3 D1 E F1 I J1 J2 K1 K2 K3 K4 L M1 M2 N O P Q R1 R2 S1 S2 T1 T2 U1 U2 V W X Z(a,b,c,d,e,f,g,h,j,k,l,m,n,o,p,q,r,s,t,u,x,z,za)
Emergency Action, Agency, Advocacy, Legal Aid undertaken and Member of Accident Line
Ptr: Atkins, Mr Matthew M C LLB . . . *Oct 1988
Austin, Mr James St J BSc(Eng) . . . *Oct 1986
Barker, Mr Christopher J BA(Cantab) . . . *Nov 1982
Boscawen, Mr Charles R MA(Cantab) . . . *Nov 1984
Bristol, Mr Jeremy MA(Cantab) . . . *§May 1967
Farthing, Mr Nigel C LLB . . . *Mar 1979
French, Mrs Virginia V LLB(Exon) . . . *§Oct 1981
Hall, Mr James S MA(Cantab) Registrar & Bishops Legal Secretary to the Diocese of St Edmundsbury & Ipswich . . . *May 1979
Harbottle, Mr James W T BA(Hons) . . . *Nov 1994
Hayes, Mr Richard B MA(Cantab) . . . *Oct 1976
Henry, Mr Mark Andrew LLB . . . *Sep 1995
Mabon, Mr William J LLB(Manc) . . . *§Jun 1966
Schwer, Mr Christopher P LLB(Hons) . . . *Nov 1988
Tavener, Mr Nicholas J W MA(Cantab) . . . *§Jun 1974
Turner, Mr W Douglas R LLB(Soton) . . . *Dec 1985
Whybrow, Mrs J Annette LLB(Wales) . . . *§Apr 1976
Ast: Burkitt, Mr Ross LLB(Hons) . . . *Dec 1998
Cracknell, Miss Emma LLB . . . Sep 1997
Furmston, Mrs Nicola Jane LLB . . . Oct 1992
Gipson, Mr Mark Edward MA . . . *Sep 1997
Harris, Miss Victoria Mary T BA(Hons) . . . Aug 2001
Macdonald, Mrs Jane Victoria LLB(Hons) . . . Sep 1996
Raven, Mr Stuart James LLB(Hons) . . . Sep 2001
Con: Dodd, Mr Christian Henry LLB(Hons) . . . *May 1994
Sydenham, Mrs Pricilla Angela MA; LLB . . . *Jan 1965
Winn, Mr John P MA; LLM(Cantab) . . . *§Jun 1972

BLOCKS ‡
Arcade Chambers 2-6 Arcade Street Ipswich Suffolk IP1 1EL
Tel: 01473 230033 *Fax:* 01473 230150 *Dx:* 3207 IPSWICH
E-mail: info@blockslegal.co.uk
Web: www.blockslegal.co.uk
List of partners: F R Barker, M D Boast, G S Field, A R Fleming, G J Mead
Office: Felixstowe
Work: A1 A2 A3 B1 C1 C2 C3 E F1 F2 I J1 J2 K1 K3 K4 L O P Q R1 R2 S1 S2 T1 T2 W X Z(c,d,e,h,k,l,m,p,q)
Agency and Fixed Fee Interview undertaken
Ptr: Barker, Mrs Frances R LLB; AKC . . . *Oct 1987
Field, Mr Gerald S BA . . . *§Dec 1978
Fleming, Mr Andrew R MA(Oxon) . . . *§Mar 1985
Mead, Mr Graham Justin LLB(Hons) . . . *§Sep 1997
Asoc: Hoy, Mrs Julie Anne . . . *Sep 2005
Riddett, Mr John Digby Notary Public . . . *Jun 1981
Young, Mrs Victoria BA . . . *Sep 2007
Ast: Butler, Ms Demelza Christina LLB(Hons) . . . *Sep 2004
Buxton, Mrs Christine Jane LLB(Hons) . . . *Sep 2001
Con: French, Mr Benjamin G LLB(Lond) . . . *§Dec 1975

Other offices in Felixstowe. We specialise in the following areas of work Commercial and Company Law, Family Law, Wills, Trusts and Probate.

GRAEME CARMICHAEL ‡
PO Box 520 Churchgates House Cutler Street Ipswich Suffolk IP1 1ZF
Tel: 01473 252159 *Fax:* 01473 252163
List of partners: G Carmichael
Work: D1 D2 K1
Emergency Action, Agency, Advocacy, Legal Aid undertaken and Legal Aid Franchise
SPr: Carmichael, Mr Graeme LLB(Hons) . . . *Nov 1976

EVERSHEDS LLP
Franciscan House 51 Princes Street Ipswich Suffolk IP1 1UR
Tel: 0845 497 9797 *Fax:* 0845 497 2431 *Dx:* 3249 IPSWICH
E-mail: patrickfarrant@eversheds.com
Office: Birmingham, Cambridge, Cardiff, Leeds, London EC2, Manchester, Newcastle upon Tyne, Nottingham
Languages: French, German, Spanish
Work: A1 B1 C1 C2 C3 D1 E F1 G H I J1 K1 L M1 M2 N O P Q R1 S1 T1 T2 V W X Z(a,b,c,d,e,h,i,j,k,l,m,n,o,s,t)

FISON & CO ‡
Crown Hall Chambers Crown Street Ipswich Suffolk IP1 3LD
Tel: 01473 280900 *Fax:* 01473 288663
List of partners: G R Skippen
SPr: Skippen, Mr Graham R . . . *§Jan 1979

GIBBONS SOLICITORS ‡
133 High Street Hadleigh Ipswich Suffolk IP7 5EJ
Tel: 01473 822488

GORMAN HAMILTON
27 St Helens Street Ipswich Suffolk IP4 1HH
Tel: 01473 408073 *Fax:* 01473 400357 *Dx:* 3272 IPSWICH
E-mail: emma.crane@gordonhamilton.co.uk
Office: Leeds, Newcastle upon Tyne
Work: N
Member of Accident Line

GOTELEE ‡
31-41 Elm Street Ipswich Suffolk IP1 2AY
Tel: 01473 211121 *Fax:* 01473 230387 *Dx:* 3220 IPSWICH
E-mail: info@gotelee.co.uk
List of partners: C Abbott, H A Catherall, P R Crix, J E Fowles, M J Harnden, T J Humpage, V Judge, B Morron, I Radovic, J W Ripman, H R Rowland, H M Stuart, T C Thomas, R A West, M O Whitworth, E V Woollard
Office: Hadleigh
Languages: French, Italian
Work: B1 B2 C1 C2 C3 D1 D2 E G H I J1 J2 K1 K2 K3 K4 N O P Q R1 S1 S2 T1 T2 W Z(c,d,e,l,m,p,q,r,s,t,u)
Emergency Action, Agency, Advocacy, Fixed Fee Interview, Legal Aid Franchise and Member of Accident Line
Ptr: Abbott, Ms Catherine LLB; LSF . . . *Sep 1997
Catherall, Mr Howard A BA . . . Jan 2001
Crix, Mr Peter R LLB . . . *Nov 1982
Fowles, Mrs Jane E LLB(Hons) . . . *Jul 1998
Harnden, Mr Maxwell John LLB(Hons) . . . Feb 1988
Humpage, Mr Timothy J LLB . . . *Nov 1993
Judge, Mrs Victoria LLB Gossage Undergrad Scholarship (Liverpool University) 1995 . . . *Sep 2001
Morron, Mr Brian LLB; LLM . . . *Dec 1976
Radovic, Miss Ivana LLB . . . *Oct 2001
Ripman, Mr Jonathan W MA . . . *Jun 1981
Rowland, Mr Hugh R BA . . . *Oct 1987
Stuart, Miss Helen Marie LLB . . . *Oct 1993
Thomas, Ms Tanya Caroline MA . . . *Sep 1992
West, Mr R Andrew LLB(Hons) . . . *Jan 1996
Whitworth, Mr Martin O LLB(Hons) . . . *Oct 1983
Woollard, Mrs Emma Victoria BA(Hons) . . . *Dec 1999
Asoc: Allen, Ms Marie Louise LLB(Hons) . . . *Sep 2003
Infanti, Ms Diana BA(Hons) . . . *Jul 2002
Wardropper, Miss Susan Lesley BA(Hons) . . . *Oct 1994
Ast: Davies, Ms Sallie Jean BA(Hons); GDL . . . Sep 2007
Ray, Mr Oliver Philip . . . Jul 2007
Ripman, Mr Joshua LLB(Hons) Law Society JLD Pro-Bono Award 2008 . . . Sep 2009
Con: Wright, Mr Robert James MA . . . Jun 1975

HARVEY SON & FILBY ‡
231 Foxhall Road Ipswich Suffolk IP3 8LF
Tel: 01473 712962 *Fax:* 01473 721777
Dx: 124727 MARTLESHAM HEATH
E-mail: paul.harvey@harveysf.co.uk
List of partners: P Harvey, R Kong, S Kong
Office: Birmingham, London WC2
Languages: Chinese
Work: A1 C1 C2 E L R2 S1 S2 T2 W Z(d,i,x)
Ptr: Harvey, Mr Paul LLB(Hons) . . . *Jul 1973
Asoc: Vidgen, Mr Adrian David . . . Nov 1979
Ast: Chen, Ms Patricia LLB . . . Jul 2006

LAW OFFICES OF RICHARD HEMMINGS SOLICITOR ‡
Sandy Lane Barham Ipswich Suffolk IP6 0PB
Tel: 01473 833844 *Fax:* 01473 833230
Emergency telephone 07850 418032
E-mail: hemmings@dsl.pipex.com
List of partners: R A Hemmings
Work: J1 Z(p)
SPr: Hemmings, Mr Richard A LLM(Lond) Part time Chairman of Industrial Tribunals . . . *Mar 1974

HOLTS SOLICITORS ‡
11 Northgate Street Ipswich Suffolk IP1 3BX
Tel: 01473 217272

HULLOCK & CO SOLICITORS ‡
Brittanic House 28 Princes Street Ipswich Suffolk IP1 1RJ
Tel: 01473 286686

JACKAMANS ‡
(incorporating Nigel Steed & Co)
Oak House 7 Northgate Street Ipswich Suffolk IP1 3BX
Tel: 01473 255591 *Fax:* 01473 230796 *Dx:* 3229 IPSWICH
E-mail: mail@jackamans.co.uk
List of partners: J L Laband, P V McGrath, P J Nainthy, T Owers, M R Rowlands, P B Stevens
Office: Diss, Felixstowe, Harleston
Languages: French, German
Work: A1 B1 C1 C2 C3 D1 E G J1 K1 L M1 M2 N O P Q R1 R2 S1 S2 T1 T2 V W Z(a,c,l,o,r)
Agency, Advocacy, Fixed Fee Interview, Legal Aid undertaken, Legal Aid Franchise and Member of Accident Line
Ptr: McGrath, Mr Paul Vincent LLB Tom Ashton Memorial Prize . . . *Oct 1986
Stevens, Mr Paul Bridges . . . Apr 1978
Ast: Hendry, Mrs Helen . . . Feb 2007
Milton, Mr David Antony . . . Dec 1976
Con: Jenkins, Ms Ruth Caroline BA(Hons) . . . *§Oct 1985
Steed, Mr Nigel Harry Campbell . . . *§Jul 1971

KMA SOLICITORS ‡
25 St Margaret's Green Ipswich Suffolk IP4 2BN
Tel: 01473 760046 *Fax:* 01473 760058
E-mail: kem@kmasolicitors.co.uk

KERSEYS ‡
32 Lloyds Avenue Ipswich Suffolk IP1 3HD
Tel: 01473 213311 *Fax:* 01473 214874 *Dx:* 3231 IPSWICH 1
E-mail: info@kerseys-law.co.uk
List of partners: P F Awad, J Hayward, J E Riley, K Singh, G R Sutton, C F Thomas, E A Webb, A C Wooding
Work: A1 C1 C2 D1 D2 E F1 F2 I J2 K1 K3 K4 L N O Q R1 R2 S1 S2 T1 T2 U2 W X Z(d,e,g,h,i,l,p,q)
Emergency Action, Advocacy, Fixed Fee Interview, Legal Aid undertaken, Legal Aid Franchise and Member of Accident Line
Ptr: Awad, Mr Peter Frank BA(Hons) . . . *Nov 1994
Hayward, Mr James BA(Oxon) . . . *§Dec 1980
Riley, Mrs Jane E LLB(Hull) . . . *Oct 1988
Singh, Mr Kimat BA(Hons)(Econ & Law) . . . Sep 2003
Sutton, Mr Geoffrey R BA . . . *Oct 1993
Thomas, Mrs Clare Frances LLB(Hons) . . . *Sep 1996
Webb, Ms Elaine Ann BA(Hons)(Law) . . . *Oct 1992
Wooding, Mr Anthony C MA(Oxon) . . . *§Oct 1983
Asoc: Shaw, Miss Leila Nivette LLB(Hons) . . . *Sep 2004
Ast: Burkitt, Mr Ross LLB(Hons) . . . *Dec 1998
Parker, Mrs Laura Louise MA(Cantab) . . . *Aug 2009
Price, Mrs Caroline LLB(Hons) . . . Mar 1989
Thangavel, Miss Tharani LLB . . . *Feb 2007
Thom, Mr Iain R BA(Hons) . . . Apr 1989
Con: Bonham-Carter, Mr Nigel John MA(Cantab) . . . *May 1970
Carter, Ms Rosemary Elizabeth LLB(Hons) . . . *§Mar 1978
Nunn, Mr Graham R BSc; LLM; MEd . . . *Jan 1986
Reckitt, Miss Miranda H V LLB(Hons) . . . *§Dec 1966

OLIVER LEGAL ‡
14 St Peters Street Ipswich Suffolk IP1 1XB
Tel: 01473 359222 *Fax:* 0845 459 1032 / 01473 749673
E-mail: info@oliverlegal.com

IAN PERSAUD ‡
The Manor House 6-10 St Margarets Green Ipswich Suffolk IP4 2BS
Tel: 01473 281103

PRETTYS ‡
Elm House 25 Elm Street Ipswich Suffolk IP1 2AD
Tel: 01473 232121 *Fax:* 01473 230002 *Dx:* 3218 IPSWICH
E-mail: djohnson@prettys.co.uk
List of partners: A Bacon, P L G Blake, M Chasmer, M Cole, P J A Dickie, F McMutrie, J Schoop, R H Sharp, T Sleight, G Thompson, K J Vincent, I M Waine, M White
Office: Chelmsford
Languages: French, German, Italian, Urdu
Work: A3 B1 C1 C2 E F1 F2 I J1 J2 K1 K2 K3 K4 L M1 N O Q R1 R2 S1 S2 T2 U1 U2 W Z(a,b,c,d,e,h,j,k,l,o,p,q,r,t,w)
Emergency Action, Agency, Fixed Fee Interview undertaken and Member of Accident Line
Ptr: Bacon, Mr Alistair Licensed Insolvency Practitioner . . . Nov 1992
Blake, Mr Peter L G LLB . . . *Nov 1987
Cole, Mr Matthew LLB . . . *Nov 1995
Dickie, Mr Paul J A BA . . . *Dec 1988
Schoop, Mr Jonathan BA(Hons) . . . Oct 1985
Sharp, Mr Roland H LLB . . . *Jan 1986
Vincent, Mr Keith J LLB(Hons); LPC . . . *Nov 1998
Waine, Mr Ian M LLB . . . *Nov 1986
Asoc: Clemence, Mr Matthew Edward BA(Hons)(Law) . . . *May 2001
Hall, Ms Georgina R LLB . . . *May 1993
Hodge, Ms Zoe . . . Sep 2003
Hudson, Mr Guy John Kenyon LLB(Hons) . . . *Mar 2001
McBride, Miss Claire . . . *Sep 2000
O'Malley, Ms Lynn . . . *Jun 1996

See p112 for the Key to Work Categories & other symbols

Sayers, Ms Kelly . . . . *Aug 2002
Ast: Cain, Mr Luke. *Oct 2001
Cumberbatch, Mr Christopher LLB . . . . *Oct 2002
Rayment, Ms Georgina . . . . Oct 2006

QUANTRILLS ‡
The Peninsula Business Centre Wherstead Ipswich Suffolk IP9 2BB
Tel: 01473 688100 *Fax:* 01473 601466

ROSS COATES ‡
Unit 15 1 Bath Street Ipswich Suffolk IP2 8SD
Tel: 01473 695400 *Fax:* 01473 695500
List of partners: R F S Broughton, R M Coates, L Warren
Office: Ipswich (2 offices)
Work: C1 D1 E G J1 K1 K3 L N O Q R2 S1 S2 W Z(c,q)
Ptr: Coates, Mr Ross Michael MBE LLB. . . . . *Aug 1979
Warren, Lisa . . . . Feb 2005

ROSS COATES
139 Main Road Kesgrave Ipswich Suffolk IP5 2NP
Tel: 01473 621800 *Fax:* 01473 621900
Office: Ipswich (2 offices)
Languages: Polish
Work: E L S1 S2 W
Ptr: Broughton, Mr Richard Francis Stephen MA(Cantab) . *Jul 1973

ROSS COATES
15 High Street Ipswich Suffolk IP1 3JZ
Tel: 01473 222303 *Fax:* 01473 212806
Emergency telephone 01473 621800
E-mail: stephen.broughton@rosscoates.co.uk
Office: Ipswich (2 offices)
Languages: French
Work: L S1 W Z(d,m)
Agency, Fixed Fee Interview and Legal Aid undertaken

SAUNDERS GOODIN RIDDLESTON SOLICITORS ‡
32 Queen Street Ipswich Suffolk IP1 1SS
Tel: 01473 225600 *Fax:* 01473 230386 *Dx:* 3214 IPSWICH 1
Emergency telephone 07850 926588
E-mail: enquiries@sgr-solicitors.com
List of partners: C H Riddleston, N R Saunders, R B Thomson, M J Ward
Work: B2 D1 G H K1 K2 K3
Emergency Action, Agency, Advocacy, Legal Aid undertaken and Legal Aid Franchise
Ptr: Riddleston, Mr Charles H ★. . . . . *Nov 1982
Saunders, Mr Neil R ★ . . . . *Dec 1987
Thomson, Mr Roger Bullard BSc . . . . *Nov 1994
Ward, Mr Martin J LLB . . . . *Jul 1979

MICHAEL SMITH & CO ‡
Clarence House 21 St Margaret's Green Ipswich Suffolk IP4 2BN
Tel: 01473 226231 *Fax:* 01473 214515 *Dx:* 3277 IPSWICH
List of partners: M Smith
Work: B1 C1 E F1 G J1 L N O Q S1 W Z(i)
Agency, Advocacy and Fixed Fee Interview undertaken
SPr: Smith, Mr Michael LLB(Hons). . . . . *§Mar 1985

RICHARD STACE EMPLOYMENT LAW SERVICES ‡
Broom Cottage Lower Holbrook Ipswich Suffolk IP9 2RJ
Tel: 0844 800 8505 *Fax:* 01473 328301
E-mail: richard@stace-els.co.uk

TAYLOR HALDANE BARLEX LLP
Hubbard Way 2 Civic Drive Ipswich Suffolk IP1 2QA
Tel: 0845 293 7688 *Fax:* 0845 293 7686 *Dx:* 3210 IPSWICH
E-mail: mail@thblegal.com
Office: Benfleet, Braintree, Chelmsford, Southend-on-Sea

WATKINS STEWART & ROSS ‡
18 Lower Brook Street Ipswich Suffolk IP4 1AL
Tel: 01473 226266 *Fax:* 01473 230052 *Dx:* 3244 IPSWICH
Emergency telephone 01473 691535
E-mail: info@wsandr.co.uk
List of partners: S W Gilbey, D R Ross
Work: A1 B1 C1 D1 E F1 G H J1 K1 L M1 N O P Q R1 S1 T1 V W Z(e,j,l,m)
Emergency Action, Agency, Advocacy, Fixed Fee Interview and Legal Aid undertaken
Ptr: Gilbey, Mr Stephen William . . . . *Dec 1986
Ross, Mr David Robert Notary Public . . . . *Feb 1978
Ast: Anderson, Mr Michael G BA(Warw) . . . . *Sep 1990
Proctor, Mrs Rachel S. . . . . *Dec 1972
Simpson, Mrs Sarah LLB . . . . *Apr 2008

WILLIAM HINSHELWOOD ‡
Witnesham Hall Church Lane Ipswich Suffolk IP6 9JD
Tel: 01473 785359 *Fax:* 01473 785434
E-mail: billyhinshelwood@btconnect.com

WOLSEY PROBATE ‡
Fifth Floor Wolsey House 16-18 Princess Street Ipswich Suffolk IP1 1QT
Tel: 01473 230000 *Fax:* 01473 226683

MARK YOUNG & CO ‡
22 St Helens Street Ipswich Suffolk IP4 1HJ
Tel: 01473 226630 *Fax:* 01473 226640
E-mail: enquiries@myco-law.co.uk
List of partners: M Young
Work: E K1 N S1 S2 W Z(q)
Fixed Fee Interview undertaken
SPr: Young, Mr Mark LLB . . . . Mar 1990

IRLAM, Greater Manchester

BANNISTER PRESTON
180 Liverpool Road Irlam Greater Manchester M44 6FE
Tel: 0161 775 0444 *Fax:* 0161 777 9439
E-mail: info@bannisterpreston.co.uk
Office: Sale
Work: D2 J1 K1 N S1 S2
Emergency Action, Fixed Fee Interview and Legal Aid undertaken
Ptr: Baker, Mr William G C. . . . . *Dec 1974

W M FURNESS & SON
196 Liverpool Road Irlam Greater Manchester M44 6FE
Tel: 0161 775 9962 / 775 6765 *Fax:* 0161 775 8733
E-mail: info@wmfurness.co.uk
Office: Manchester, Marple, New Mills
Work: E F1 G H K1 P S1
Agency, Advocacy, Fixed Fee Interview and Legal Aid undertaken
Ptr: Skulnick, Mr Jonathan A BSc . . . . *Feb 1992
Con: Davies, Mr Malcolm C LLB(B'ham) . . . . *§Jan 1968

OGDEN LYLES & FOX
563 Liverpool Road Irlam Greater Manchester M44 5BE
Tel: 0161 775 3744 *Fax:* 0161 775 0153
Office: Eccles
Work: A1 B1 C1 D1 E F1 G H J1 K1 L M1 N P R1 S1 T1 V W Z(i,m,n)
Agency, Advocacy, Fixed Fee Interview, Legal Aid undertaken and Member of Accident Line
Ptr: Landey, Mr Howard S M BA(Law). . . . . *Jul 1980
Partington, Mr Albert D LLB(Reading) . . . . *Mar 1984

ISLEWORTH, Middlesex

BENNETT & RYAN SOLICITORS ‡
491 London Road Isleworth Middlesex TW7 4DA
Tel: 020 8568 2800 *Fax:* 020 8569 7480

GARNER & HANCOCK SOLICITORS LLP ‡
4 Church Street Isleworth Middlesex TW7 6BH
Tel: 020 8232 9560 *Fax:* 020 8560 0799 *Dx:* 53201 ISLEWORTH 2
E-mail: info@garner-hancock.co.uk
List of partners: A R T Hancock, J J E Hutson, S M Radcliffe
Languages: Arabic, French, German, Hindi, Serbo-Croat
Work: E F1 J1 L N O P Q S1 T1 T2 W Z(d,h,l)
Agency, Advocacy, Fixed Fee Interview, Legal Aid undertaken and Legal Aid Franchise
Ptr: Hancock, Mr A Richard T . . . . *§May 1970
Hutson, Mr Julian James Elliot BA(Dublin). . . . . . *Jun 1971
Radcliffe, Mrs Sarah M BA(Oxon). . . . . *Jun 1978

HKK LAW ‡
PO Box 511 Isleworth Middlesex TW7 4WN
Tel: 020 7060 1127 *Fax:* 020 7060 1128
E-mail: hkk@hkklaw.com

LAWVUE SOLICITORS ‡
9 Wighton Mews Isleworth Middlesex TW7 4DZ
Tel: 020 8568 6607 *Fax:* 020 7183 0898
E-mail: info@lawvue.co.uk

IVER, Buckinghamshire

DHANJU MCLEAN & ANWAR SOLICITORS ‡
DMA House 4 The Ridgeway Iver Buckinghamshire SL0 9HW
Tel: 01753 651743 *Fax:* 01753 653821 *Dx:* 42454 IVER
E-mail: middleton@dmasolicitors.co.uk
List of partners: P Dhanju, N L McLean
Languages: Punjabi, Urdu
Work: B2 G H
Advocacy, Fixed Fee Interview, Legal Aid undertaken and Legal Aid Franchise
Ptr: Dhanju, Mr Piara ★. . . . . *Jun 2001
McLean, Mr Nigel Lloyd BA(Hons) ★ . . . . *Jul 1999

IVYBRIDGE, Devon

CLARK & WEEKS
Westbeer House 50 Fore Street Ivybridge Devon PL21 9AE
Tel: 01752 698869 *Fax:* 01752 698808 *Dx:* 81468 IVYBRIDGE
E-mail: lbishop@clarkandweeks.co.uk
Office: Plymouth
Work: L S1

ERIC COWSILL SOLICITOR ‡
Kingsley Close East Way Lee Mill Industrial Estate Ivybridge Devon PL21 9GD
Tel: 01752 205202 *Fax:* 01752 205200
E-mail: eric.cowsill@swlaw.co.uk
List of partners: E Cowsill
Work: A1 B2 C1 D1 D2 E F1 F2 I J1 K1 K3 K4 L N O Q R1 R2 S1 S2 T1 T2 U2 W Z(c,d,j,k,l,o,p,q,r,za)
SPr: Cowsill, Mr Eric. . . . . *Nov 1979
Ast: Evans, Mrs Carolyn Mary . . . . *§Nov 1982
Stannard, Mr Nigel . . . . *Dec 1988

HOWARD & OVER (incorporating Paul Millband & Co)
61 Fore Street Ivybridge Devon PL21 9AE
Tel: 01752 690123 *Fax:* 01752 690589 *Dx:* 81452 IVYBRIDGE
Office: Plymouth (2 offices)
Work: B1 C1 D1 E F1 G H J1 K1 K3 K4 L N O P Q S1 V W Z(m)
Emergency Action, Advocacy, Fixed Fee Interview and Legal Aid undertaken
Ptr: Mossop, Mr C Paul . . . . Dec 1972
Ast: Millar, Mrs Janet . . . . Apr 2007

KINGS SOLICITORS ‡
24 Fore Street Ivybridge Devon PL21 9AB
Tel: 01752 895252 *Fax:* 01752 690770

WHITEFORD CROCKER
46 Fore Street Ivybridge Devon PL21 9AE
Tel: 01752 698488 *Fax:* 01752 698489
E-mail: mjc@whitefordcrocker.co.uk
Office: Plymouth, Plympton, Saltash
Work: A1 B1 C1 C2 C3 D1 E F1 G H J1 K1 L M1 M2 N P R1 S1 T1 T2 V W Z(a,b,c,d,e,f,h,j,k,l,m,n,o,p,s,t)
Agency, Advocacy, Legal Aid undertaken and Member of Accident Line
Ptr: Cox, Mr Anthony J LLB . . . . *Nov 1973

JARROW, Tyne & Wear

IAN CRUICKSHANK & CO ‡
10 Grange Road West Jarrow Tyne & Wear NE32 3JD
Tel: 0191 428 0900 *Fax:* 0191 428 0828 *Dx:* 60802 JARROW
E-mail: info@icsolicitors.co.uk
List of partners: A Cowley, I J Cruickshank
Work: C1 C2 D1 D2 E G H K1 K3 K4 L Q S1 S2 W Z(d,f,l)
Emergency Action, Agency, Advocacy, Fixed Fee Interview, Legal Aid undertaken and Legal Aid Franchise
Ptr: Cowley, Miss Andrea LLB . . . . Sep 2004
Cruickshank, Mr Ian James LLB(Hons)(Lond) . . . . *Oct 1978

GEOFFREY FORRESTER & CO ‡
4 Grange Road West Jarrow Tyne & Wear NE32 3JA
Tel: 0191 420 0820 *Fax:* 0191 420 0821 *Dx:* 60805 JARROW
Emergency telephone 07941 302269
E-mail: geoforrester@aol.com
List of partners: D L Forrester, G M Forrester
Office: South Shields
Work: D1 F1 G H J1 K1 K2 L S1 W
Emergency Action, Agency, Advocacy, Fixed Fee Interview, Legal Aid undertaken, Legal Aid Franchise and Member of Accident Line
Ptr: Forrester, Mr David Lewis. . . . . Nov 1998
Forrester, Mr Geoffrey M LLB . . . . *Jun 1974

DAVID C HATFIELD & CO ‡
73 Ellison Street Jarrow Tyne & Wear NE32 3JU
Tel: 0191 489 7639 / 489 9450 *Fax:* 0191 428 0079
Dx: 60801 JARROW
E-mail: david@hatfieldsolicitors.co.uk
List of partners: A E Hatfield, D C Hatfield
Work: C1 D1 E F1 G H J1 K1 L M1 P S1 W Z(l,m)
Emergency Action, Agency, Advocacy, Fixed Fee Interview, Legal Aid undertaken and Member of Accident Line
Ptr: Hatfield, Mr Anthony E BA . . . . *May 1980
Hatfield, Mr David C. . . . . *§Feb 1973

ANTHONY PATTEN SOLICITORS ‡
St Bedes Chambers Albert Road Jarrow Tyne & Wear NE32 5JB
Tel: 0191 423 3638

KEIGHLEY, West Yorkshire

AWB CHARLESWORTH LLP ‡
12-16 North Street Keighley West Yorkshire BD21 3SE
Tel: 01535 613678 *Fax:* 01535 613689 *Dx:* 21465 KEIGHLEY
E-mail: mail@awblaw.co.uk
List of partners: R H Armstrong, J E Bridgman, J A Broughton, D J Brown, A A Chamberlain, A J Davidson, D T M Hayes, A H Lane, D Tear, U Vietri, M B Wood
Office: Skipton
Work: B1 E F1 F2 K1 K3 K4 L O Q S1 S2 W Z(l)
Ptr: Vietri, Mr Umberto LLB(Hons). . . . . Oct 1991
Mem: Armstrong, Mr Roger H BA; MPhil. . . . . *Oct 1994
Bridgman, Ms Julie E BA . . . . *Jun 1984
Broughton, Mr John A LLM(Lond) . . . . *§Oct 1976
Chamberlain, Mrs April Alison BA(Hons)(Oxon); CPE; LPC . . . . Nov 1997
Tear, Mr David LLB(Hons). . . . . Sep 1999
Wood, Mr Martin B BA(Hons) . . . . *Nov 1979
Ast: O'Neill, Mr Liam TEP . . . . *Nov 2008

BLACKWELLS SOLICITORS ‡
19 Devonshire Street Keighley West Yorkshire BD21 2BH
Tel: 01535 600005
List of partners: A Khan
Languages: Punjabi, Urdu
Work: G H
Advocacy undertaken
Ptr: Khan, Amjid. . . . . Jan 2008

J E BROWN & CO ‡
51a Kirkgate Silsden Keighley West Yorkshire BD20 0AQ
Tel: 01535 653311

BURR SUGDEN ‡
23-27 Devonshire Street Keighley West Yorkshire BD21 2BQ
Tel: 01535 605407 *Fax:* 01535 602768 *Dx:* 21451 KEIGHLEY
E-mail: mail@burrsugden.com
List of partners: P I Foxall, T J Wilkinson
Work: A1 B1 C1 C2 E F1 J1 J2 K1 K3 L N O Q R1 R2 S1 S2 T1 T2 V W Z(c,j,l,q)
Emergency Action, Agency, Advocacy and Fixed Fee Interview undertaken
Ptr: Foxall, Mr Peter Ian LLB . . . . *Oct 1987
Wilkinson, Mr Timothy J. . . . . *§Feb 1972
Ast: Goodwin, Mr James. . . . . Mar 2004
Padgett, Mr Jonathan . . . . Oct 1985

JOHN HOLDEN ‡
23 Henry Street Keighley West Yorkshire BD21 3DR
Tel: 01535 667826 *Fax:* 01535 610316
List of partners: J C Holden
Languages: Punjabi, Urdu
Work: G H
Agency, Advocacy, Fixed Fee Interview, Legal Aid undertaken and Legal Aid Franchise
Ptr: Holden, Mr John C MA(Oxon). . . . . Nov 1976
Ast: Hussain, Mr Mohammed LLB . . . . Sep 1997

ANDREW HOLLAND LAW ‡
Suite 2 The Bakery Millennium Business Park Keighley West Yorkshire BD20 6RB
Tel: 01535 658274 *Fax:* 01535 655120
E-mail: mail@andrewhollandlaw.co.uk
Work: C1 C2 I J1 U2 Z(e,p)

MOHAMMED HUSSAIN SOLICITORS ‡
76b Cavendish Street Keighley West Yorkshire BD21 3RL
Tel: 01535 692999 *Fax:* 01535 692900
E-mail: mohammehussain@btconnect.com

JAMIESON FITZPATRICK SOLICITORS ‡
42 Devonshire Street Keighley West Yorkshire BD21 2AU
Tel: 01535 600657

MAKIN DIXON SOLICITORS
3rd Floor Provincial House 6-12 Cooke Street Keighley West Yorkshire BD21 3NW
Tel: 01535 605040 *Fax:* 01535 605565 *Dx:* 21454 KEIGHLEY
E-mail: enquiries@makindixon.co.uk
Office: Bradford, Halifax, Harrogate, Skipton, Todmorden
Ptr: Dixon, Mr Ian . . . . Sep 1997
Ast: Campbell, Jane . . . . Dec 2007

SOLICITORS PROPERTY SHOP KEIGHLEY ‡
34 North Street Keighley West Yorkshire BD20 3SE
Tel: 01535 608844 *Fax:* 01535 608822
E-mail: sps.admin@btconnect.com
List of partners: P J Brewer
Ptr: Brewer, Mr Peter J LLB . . . *Jun 1968

TURNER & WALL ‡
Phoenix House 22-24 Devonshire Street Keighley West Yorkshire BD21 2AU
Tel: 01535 607831 *Fax:* 01535 681117 *Dx:* 21453 KEIGHLEY
E-mail: info@turnerandwall.co.uk
List of partners: M S Bower, J A Brigg, M Handzji, A J H Waterhouse
Work: A1 C1 C2 D1 D2 E F1 J1 K1 K3 K4 L N O P Q R1 S1 S2 V W Z(c,d,j,o,q,r)
Emergency Action, Agency, Advocacy, Fixed Fee Interview, Legal Aid undertaken and Legal Aid Franchise
Ptr: Bower, Mr Michael S LLB . . . *Apr 1987
Brigg, Ms Jane Ann . . . *§Mar 1997
Handzji, Mr Myron . . . *§Oct 1982
Waterhouse, Mr Adrian J H . . . *§Dec 1976
Ast: Bates, Ms Hannah LLB . . . *Nov 2006

WADDINGTON WEBBER ‡
Yorkshire Bank Chambers 65 North Street Keighley West Yorkshire BD21 3RZ
Tel: 01535 662644 / 662647 *Fax:* 01535 600111
Dx: 21456 KEIGHLEY
List of partners: S Dworakowski, M A Hagyard
Languages: French, German, Polish
Work: A1 B1 C1 D1 E F1 G H J1 K1 L M1 N P R1 S1 T1 V W Z(b,c,d,e,f,h,j,k,l,m,n,o,p,r,s,t)
Emergency Action, Agency, Advocacy, Fixed Fee Interview, Legal Aid undertaken, Legal Aid Franchise and Member of Accident Line
Ptr: Dworakowski, Mr Stanley BA . . . *Jun 1978
Hagyard, Mr Mark Anthony LLB . . . *Sep 1995

SUSAN WEEDEN & COMPANY ‡
32 Kirkgate Silsden Keighley West Yorkshire BD20 0AL
Tel: 01535 658488 *Fax:* 01535 658288
Emergency telephone 01535 654928
E-mail: weedenco@msn.com
List of partners: S M Weeden
Work: J1 K1 L S1 S2 W
Agency and Fixed Fee Interview undertaken
SPr: Weeden, Mrs Susan Margaret LLM . . . Sep 1995

KEMPSTON, Bedfordshire

HILLIERSHRW SOLICITORS ‡
The Old Vicarage 132 Bedford Road Kempston Bedfordshire MK42 8BQ
Tel: 01234 858000 *Fax:* 01234 840816 *Dx:* 36758 KEMPSTON
Emergency telephone 0800 169 7877
E-mail: admin@hilliershrw.co.uk
List of partners: M K Addison, P A Hillier, P J Ivinson, P K Rimmer
Office: Stevenage
Work: A1 B1 C1 C2 D1 D2 E G H I J1 K1 K2 L M1 M2 N O P Q S1 S2 W Z(c,e,f,i,k,l)
Emergency Action, Agency, Advocacy, Fixed Fee Interview, Legal Aid undertaken, Legal Aid Franchise and Member of Accident Line
Ptr: Hillier, Mr Paul A BA; LLB . . . *Mar 1982
Rimmer, Mrs Paula K LLB . . . *Aug 1996
Ast: Standen, Mr Edward LLB(Hons) . . . *Nov 2002

KENDAL, Cumbria

ARNOLD GREENWOOD ‡
Exchange Chambers 8 & 10 Highgate South Lakeland Kendal Cumbria LA9 4SX
Tel: 01539 720049 *Fax:* 01539 726177 *Dx:* 63400 KENDAL
List of partners: A J Peel, S Pooley, B L Richardson
Office: Milnthorpe
Work: A1 C1 E F1 G J1 K1 K3 L N O Q S1 S2 T1 T2 W Z(d,h,l,o,r)
Emergency Action, Agency, Advocacy and Legal Aid Franchise
Ptr: Peel, Ms Alison J LLB . . . *Apr 1996
Pooley, Mr Stephen LLB(Nott'm) . . . *Oct 1982
Richardson, Miss Barbara Louise LLB(Hons) . . . *Oct 1995
Ast: Boyce, Ms Sylvia M BA(Hons); BEd(Hons) . . . *Nov 1993
Gorst, Mrs Lucy Anne BA(Hons) . . . *Sep 2005
Jackson, Mrs Bernadette Edna BSc(Hons); LLDip . . . *Sep 2008
Sparks, Mrs Jennifer LLB(Hons) . . . *Apr 2010
Walls, Mrs Danielle Maria BA(Hons) . . . *Nov 1998

THE BUNDLE BUSINESS LTD ‡
Mintsfeet Place Mintsfeet Road Kendal Cumbria LA9 6LL
Tel: 01539 729441
E-mail: sam.dawson@bundlebusiness.co.uk

CLARKSON HIRST
35a Stricklandgate Kendal Cumbria LA9 4LT
Tel: 01539 736916 *Fax:* 01539 742169
Office: Barrow-in-Furness, Lancaster
Work: G H J1 K1 K2 K3 L N O S2 W Z(c)

HAYTON WINKLEY ‡
Stramongate House 53 Stramongate Kendal Cumbria LA9 4BH
Tel: 01539 720136 *Fax:* 01539 733312 *Dx:* 63402 KENDAL
E-mail: alison.hine@hwlegal.co.uk
List of partners: P E S Briggs, N J Fell, J N Oldroyd
Office: Windermere
Languages: French
Work: A1 B1 C1 C2 D1 E F1 F2 J1 J2 K1 K2 K3 K4 L N O Q R1 S1 S2 T1 T2 V W Z(l,r)
Advocacy and Fixed Fee Interview undertaken
Ptr: Briggs, Mr Peter E S LLB . . . *May 1975
Fell, Mrs Naomi J LLB(Lond) . . . *Oct 1982
Oldroyd, Mr John N LLB . . . *May 1978
Ast: Adams, Mrs Rachel BA . . . *Sep 2010
Escolme, Mrs Sylvia Gail LLB . . . Jan 2003
Marwood, Miss Amanda . . . Dec 2006
Seymour, Mrs Kate LLB . . . Jan 1999
Steadman, Miss Nicola . . . Sep 2009

HOLDENS
Grosvenor House Stramongate Kendal Cumbria LA9 4BD
Est: 1855
Tel: 01539 720629 *Fax:* 01539 728203 *Dx:* 63503 LANCASTER
Emergency telephone 01524 263452
E-mail: info@holdens-solicitors.co.uk
Office: Lancaster
Work: G H K1

CHRISTOPHER HOYLE & CO ‡
Kentside Barn Burneside Road Staveley Kendal Cumbria LA8 9PQ
Tel: 01539 822078 *Fax:* 01539 822409
E-mail: c.hoyle@ndirect.co.uk
List of partners: C J Hoyle
Languages: French, Spanish
Work: D1 F1 G K1 L N O Q S1 W Z(c,i,l,m,o)
Emergency Action, Agency, Advocacy, Fixed Fee Interview, Legal Aid undertaken and Member of Accident Line
SPr: Hoyle, Mr Christopher John MA(Cantab) . . . *Oct 1985

NEIL E MANN
107 Highgate Kendal Cumbria LA9 4EN
Tel: 01539 729772 *Fax:* 01539 729772
E-mail: mail@neilemann.co.uk
Office: Prestwich

MILNE MOSER ‡
100 Highgate Kendal Cumbria LA9 4HE
Tel: 01539 729786 / 725582 *Fax:* 01539 723425 *Dx:* 63405 KENDAL
E-mail: solicitors@milnemoser.co.uk
List of partners: J R Allen, J P Davies, D J Emmett, H D Livesey, R E March, P G Williams
Office: Milnthorpe
Work: A1 C1 C2 D1 D2 E F1 G H J1 J2 K1 K3 L N O Q R1 R2 S1 S2 T2 V W Z(c,d,e,g,i,k,l,n,p,q,r,s,t)
Emergency Action, Agency, Advocacy, Fixed Fee Interview, Legal Aid undertaken, Legal Aid Franchise and Member of Accident Line
Ptr: Allen, Miss Justine Rebecca LLB(Hons) . . . *Jul 2004
Davies, Mr J Paul LLB . . . *Dec 1980
Emmett, Mr David J LLB . . . *Feb 1990
Livesey, Miss Helen Diane LLB . . . *Nov 1988
March, Mr Richard E BA(Law) . . . *Sep 1986
Williams, Mr Paul G BA . . . *Oct 1981
Ast: Birbeck, Mrs Judith H LLB(Hons) . . . *Jun 1979
Jenkinson, Mr Ian Michael LLB(Hons) . . . *Aug 2007
Ladell, Ms Rebecca Ann LLB(Hons) . . . *Jan 2007
Powell, Mrs Miriam BSc(Hons); DipLaw . . . *Sep 2004
Rose, Mr Simon J BA(Oxon) . . . *Nov 1989

PEARSON & PEARSON
98 Stricklandgate Kendal Cumbria LA9 4PU
Tel: 01539 729555 *Fax:* 01539 740279 *Dx:* 63418 KENDAL
Office: Ingleton, Kirkby Lonsdale
Work: A1 C1 C2 C3 D1 E F1 J1 K1 L M1 M2 P R1 S1 T1 T2 W
Agency, Advocacy, Fixed Fee Interview and Legal Aid undertaken
Ptr: Smith, Mr Paul W C BA . . . *Dec 1976

POOLE TOWNSEND
2 Market Place Kendal Cumbria LA9 4TN
Tel: 01539 734455 *Fax:* 01539 735706 *Dx:* 63466 KENDAL
Emergency telephone 0800 389 2939
E-mail: mbeecham@pooletownsend.co.uk
Office: Barrow-in-Furness, Dalton-in-Furness, Grange-over-Sands, Ulverston
Work: A1 B1 C1 C2 C3 D1 E F1 G H N O Q R1 S1 S2 T1 T2 U2 V W Z(c,g,j,l,o,r)
Emergency Action, Agency, Advocacy, Legal Aid undertaken and Member of Accident Line

RENSHAWS ‡
28a Finkle Street Kendal Cumbria LA9 4AB
Tel: 01539 740666 *Fax:* 01539 728334 *Dx:* 63403 KENDAL 1
List of partners: N Renshaw
Work: B2 G H S1 S2 W
Agency, Advocacy, Fixed Fee Interview and Legal Aid undertaken
SPr: Renshaw, Mr Nicholas . . . *Nov 1975

ANGELA ROGAN ‡
2 Captain French Lane Kendal Cumbria LA9 4HP
Tel: 01539 724140 *Fax:* 01539 736814
E-mail: angela@roganlaw.com
List of partners: A Rogan
Work: S1 W
SPr: Rogan, Miss Angela BA(Hons) . . . *May 1979
Con: Read, Mr Stephen MA . . . *Jun 1976

TEMPLE HEELIS LLP ‡
(incorporating Gatey Heelis; Whelan & Co)
Bridge Mills Stramongate Kendal Cumbria LA9 4UB
Tel: 01539 723757 *Fax:* 01539 727796 *Dx:* 730400 KENDAL 7
E-mail: post@templeheelis.co.uk
List of partners: R D Broady, J Hamilton, R J Moore, C J A Robinson, J A Sim
Office: Windermere
Work: A1 B1 C1 C2 C3 D1 E F1 G H J1 K1 L M1 M2 N O P Q R1 S1 S2 V W Z(c,i,j,o)
Emergency Action, Agency, Advocacy, Fixed Fee Interview, Legal Aid undertaken, Legal Aid Franchise and Member of Accident Line
Ptr: Broady, Mr Roger D MA(Oxon) . . . *Nov 1971
Hamilton, Mr Jamie LLB(Hons) . . . *Sep 1996
Moore, Mr Richard James LLB . . . *Oct 1992
Robinson, Mr Charles J A . . . *Jul 1988
Sim, Mr John A BA(Law) . . . *Feb 1986
Con: Townend, Mr J David BA(Hons) . . . *Dec 1973

THOMSON WILSON PATTINSON ‡
(incorporating Greenwood Kyle)
114-116 Stricklandgate Kendal Cumbria LA9 4QA
Tel: 01539 721945 *Fax:* 01539 740640 *Dx:* 63410 KENDAL
E-mail: kendal@twpsolicitors.com
List of partners: S L Barton, J W Cooke, I N Gunby, A D S Hill, D R Lavelle, S C Theobald
Office: Windermere
Work: A1 C1 D1 E F1 F2 G H J1 J2 K1 K3 K4 L M1 N O P Q R1 R2 S1 S2 T1 T2 V W Z(o,q)
Emergency Action, Agency, Advocacy, Fixed Fee Interview, Legal Aid undertaken and Legal Aid Franchise
Ptr: Barton, Mr Stuart L LLB . . . *Apr 1977
Cooke, Mr John W BA(Business Law) . . . *Mar 1987
Gunby, Mr Ian Nigel LLB(Leeds) . . . *Jul 1976
Hill, Mr Andrew D S LLB . . . *Oct 1992
Lavelle, Mr David Richard LLB . . . *Nov 1984
Theobald, Mr Simon Charles MA(Cantab) . . . *Jan 1993
Asoc: Dustan, Miss Joanna K BA(Hons) . . . *Aug 1997
Ferson, Mrs Aileen Elizabeth Emma BA(Law) . . . *Apr 2003
Hardiker, Mr Jonathan LLB . . . *Apr 1987
Hughes, Mrs Kathryn A LLB . . . *Nov 1990
Moore, Mrs Alison LLB . . . *Jan 1992
Con: Anthony, Mr Paul A E . . . *Jun 1980

KENILWORTH, Warwickshire

ACER SOLICITORS ‡
Warwick Corner 42 Warwick Road Kenilworth Warwickshire CV8 1HE
Tel: 01926 866644

HARRIS WILLIAMS SOLICITORS ‡
Broombank 33a Lower Ladyes Hills Kenilworth Warwickshire CV8 2GN
Tel: 01926 852000 *Fax:* 01926 852000
E-mail: elizabeth@harriswilliamslaw.co.uk

KEELERS ‡
Dunns Pitts Farm Hollis Lane Kenilworth Warwickshire CV8 2JY
Tel: 01926 853555 *Fax:* 01926 853919
E-mail: info@keelers.co.uk
List of partners: M S Keeler
Work: C1 E R1 S2
SPr: Keeler, Mr Michael S LLM(Lond) . . . *Oct 1975
Con: MacNamara, Mrs Siobhan LLB . . . Jun 2001

MILES PLANNING SOLICITORS ‡
10 Fennyland Lane Kenilworth Warwickshire CV8 2RS
Tel: 01608 661111
E-mail: lucy@milesplanning.com

PENMANS
30-32 Warwick Road Kenilworth Warwickshire CV8 1GW
Tel: 01926 858222 *Fax:* 01926 859527 *Dx:* 21402 KENILWORTH
Office: Coventry, Wellesbourne
Work: A1 B1 C1 C2 C3 D1 E F1 G H J1 K1 L N O P Q R1 S1 T1 T2 V W Z(i)
Emergency Action, Agency, Advocacy, Fixed Fee Interview, Legal Aid undertaken, Legal Aid Franchise and Member of Accident Line
Ptr: Aldridge, Mr Christopher J . . . *§Jul 1964
Chatham, Mr Timothy C LLB . . . *Jul 1980
Wyatt, Mrs Elizabeth Louise LLB . . . *May 1996

DAMIAN J PLANT & CO ‡
29b Warwick Road Kenilworth Warwickshire CV8 1HN
Tel: 01926 847741 / 854677 *Fax:* 01926 850667
List of partners: D J Plant, M P Shiels
Languages: French
Work: C1 C2 C3 E F1 J1 K1 L M1 N O Q S1 T1 T2 W Z(f)
Emergency Action, Agency, Fixed Fee Interview, Legal Aid undertaken and Member of Accident Line
Ptr: Plant, Mr Damian J LLB(Vict) Dauntesey Prize: R G Lawson Prize . . . *Oct 1982
Shiels, Mr Matthew P LLB(Hons) . . . *May 1995

SMITH JONES SOLICITORS
Park House 46 Park Road Kenilworth Warwickshire CV8 2GF
Est: 1984
Tel: 01926 859933 *Fax:* 01926 513859
Emergency telephone 01926 513859
E-mail: enquiries@sjlaw.co.uk
Office: Burnley
Work: J1 K1 N O Q Z(q)
Ptr: Bibby, Mr Craig LLB . . . Jan 2005
Graham, Mr Alexander J LLB(Manc) . . . *Apr 1977
Jones, Mr Peter Anthony Glyn BSc . . . *Oct 1984
Smith, Mr Paul J LLB . . . *Jun 1984
Woodhead, Mr Dermot C LLB . . . *Oct 1985
Con: Willoughby, Mr Robin LLB . . . *§Mar 1969

N R WILSON ‡
90a Warwick Road Kenilworth Warwickshire CV8 1HL
Tel: 01926 857631 *Fax:* 01926 850713 *Dx:* 21401 KENILWORTH
E-mail: nick@nrwilson.co.uk
List of partners: N R Wilson
Work: A1 E J1 K1 L S1 W
Agency and Advocacy undertaken
Ptr: Wilson, Mr Nicholas R BA . . . *§Jun 1976

KENLEY, Surrey

AWAN SOLICITORS ‡
32 Pondfield Road Kenley Surrey CR8 5JX
Tel: 020 8781 1838 *Fax:* 020 8781 1999
Emergency telephone 07949 660118
E-mail: info@awansolicitors.co.uk
List of partners: M A Awan, M A Awan
Office: Croydon
Languages: French, Italian, Punjabi, Spanish, Urdu
Work: B1 D1 F1 G J1 K1 K3 L N O Q S1 S2 Z(i,p,q)
Emergency Action, Agency, Advocacy and Fixed Fee Interview undertaken
SPr: Awan, Mr Mumtaz Ahmed LLB Justice of the Peace . . Nov 1993

KENTON, Middlesex

ALLIANCE SOLICITORS ‡
(incorporating The Radia Partnership)
Lincoln House 595 Kenton Road Kenton Middlesex HA3 9RT
Tel: 020 8204 3000 *Fax:* 020 8204 3333 *Dx:* 47516 KENTON
E-mail: pp@alliance-solicitors.com
List of partners: S K Radia, S K G Radia
Languages: Gujarati, Hindi
Work: C1 E F1 J1 K1 L N O Q R1 S1 S2 W Z(i,l)
Ptr: Radia, Mr Sunil Karsandas LLB . . . *Nov 1992
Radia, Mr Surendra K G BSc; LLB . . . *Sep 1989
Ast: Harding, Miss Karen A LLB . . . *§Jul 2000

CURRY POPECK
380 Kenton Road Kenton Middlesex HA3 8DP
Tel: 020 8907 2000 / 8907 8896 *Fax:* 020 8927 0499
Dx: 47504 KENTON
E-mail: cpinfo@currypopeck.com
Office: London W1
Languages: Farsi, Gujarati
Work: A3 B1 C1 C2 D1 E I J1 K1 K3 L M1 M2 N O P Q R1 R2 S1 S2 T1 U2 W Z(b,c,d,e,f,i,q,w)
Ptr: Lemon, Mr Jonathan Jerome . . . *Feb 1983
Popeck, Mr Philip I . . . *May 1979

See p112 for the Key to Work Categories & other symbols

Asoc: Valente, Neysan Haghshenas BA(Hons). . . . . *Oct 1998
Con: Moscow, Mr Neil Stephen . . . . *Nov 1979

MALCOLM DEAR WHITFIELD EVANS LLP ‡
279-299 Kenton Lane Kenton Middlesex HA3 8RR
Tel: 020 8907 4366 **Fax:** 020 8907 6143 **Dx:** 47508 KENTON
E-mail: post@mdwe-law.com
List of partners: M J Dear, N A Evans
Work: B1 C1 E K1 K3 K4 L O Q S1 S2 W Z(l,q)
Ptr: Dear, Mr Malcolm J BA . . . . *Sep 1980
Evans, Mr Neil A BA . . . . Apr 1980

ESS ESS BILAN SOLICITORS ‡
44 Draycott Avenue Kenton Middlesex HA3 0BU
Tel: 0844 800 1747 **Fax:** 0844 800 6102
List of partners: S S Bilan
SPr: Bilan, Sukhbir Singh LLB(Hons) . . . . *Mar 1990

MILLS CHODY LLP ‡
226-228 Kenton Road Kenton Middlesex HA3 8BZ
Tel: 020 8909 0400 **Fax:** 020 8907 0128 **Dx:** 47502 KENTON
E-mail: info@millschody.com
List of partners: K S Dulai, D J T Ford, H R Hodge, S S Johal
Office: Hatch End
Languages: Gujarati, Hindi, Punjabi
Work: C1 E J1 K1 L N Q R2 S1 S2 T1 T2 W Z(l,q)
Fixed Fee Interview, Legal Aid undertaken and Member of Accident Line
Ptr: Dulai, K S. . . . . May 2007
Hodge, Mr Hugo R BA . . . . *Jun 1974
Johal, Mr Shinder S BSc . . . . *May 1983
Ast: Brownson, Mr Raymond MA; BA(Hons) . . . . Sep 1997
Nyiri, Mr James Alexander LLB . . . . Jul 2006
Shah, Miss Kalpana LLB; LLM . . . . *Sep 1993

SHARIFF & CO ‡
8 Grenfell Gardens Kenton Middlesex HA3 0QZ
Tel: 020 8907 1817 **Fax:** 020 8933 6743
List of partners: S Shariff
Languages: French, Gujarati, Kachi
Work: E S1 W
Agency undertaken
SPr: Shariff, Mrs Saira BA(Hons). . . . . *Apr 1989

SOUTH ENGLAND SOLICITORS ‡
221 Kenton Lane Kenton Middlesex HA3 8RP
Tel: 0800 848 8991
E-mail: info@southenglandsolicitors.com

KESWICK, Cumbria

SCOTT DUFF & CO
32 St John's Street Keswick Cumbria CA12 5AS
Tel: 01768 774321 **Fax:** 01768 785725
E-mail: aduff@scottduff.co.uk
Office: Carlisle, Penrith
Languages: French, Italian
Work: E J1 J2 K1 K2 L N O Q S1 S2 W Z(q,r)
Emergency Action, Agency, Fixed Fee Interview and Legal Aid undertaken
Ast: McCallig, Miss Claire Louise . . . . Dec 2009
Sharman, Mr Ian Gerald. . . . . Nov 2001
Webster, Laura . . . . Aug 2008
Con: Duff, Mr Hugh Andrew Scott. . . . . *§Jul 1969

MIKE FANNING SOLICITORS ‡
Post Office Building Bank Street Keswick Cumbria CA12 5JJ
Tel: 01768 775454 **Fax:** 01768 775858

OGLETHORPE & BROATCH
(incorporating Brockbank Curwen Cain & Hall)
6 Borrowdale Road Keswick Cumbria CA12 5DB
Tel: 01768 772125 **Fax:** 01768 774678 **Dx:** 62951 KESWICK
E-mail: bt@brockbanks.co.uk
Office: Cockermouth, Maryport, Whitehaven, Workington
Work: A1 C1 E K4 L S1 S2 T2 W Z(d,l,o)
Fixed Fee Interview undertaken
Dir: Mendus, Mr Gareth W B LLB; TEP . . . . *§Jun 1976
Con: Moore, Mr Stephen J . . . . Oct 1974

KETTERING, Northamptonshire

ANDREW BODDY SOLICITORS ‡
The Old Fire Station School Lane Rothwell Kettering Northamptonshire NN14 6HZ
Tel: 01536 714900 **Fax:** 01536 418920
E-mail: andrew.boddy@andrewboddysolicitors.com

CROFTS ‡
4 School Lane Kettering Northamptonshire NN16 0DH
Tel: 01536 518742 **Fax:** 01536 416089 **Dx:** 12827 KETTERING
E-mail: gc@gcrofts.co.uk
List of partners: G F Crofts
Languages: French, German
Work: C1 C2 C3 E G K1 N S1 W Z(l)
Emergency Action, Agency, Advocacy and Fixed Fee Interview undertaken
Ptr: Crofts, Mr Glenn F BA . . . . *Sep 1980

GREENFIELD WHISTON ‡
Dalkeith House Dalkeith Place Kettering Northamptonshire NN16 0BS
Tel: 01536 410880 **Fax:** 01536 310076 **Dx:** 12832 KETTERING
Work: D1 K1 K3

GRAHAM HILL SOLICITORS ‡
PO Box 7413 Kettering Northamptonshire NN16 6GT
Tel: 01536 726381 / 07941 504346 **Fax:** 01536 726381
E-mail: ghill@grahamhillsolicitors.co.uk

HOSSACKS ‡
Ivy Cottage 89 Broadway Kettering Northamptonshire NN15 6DF
Tel: 01536 518638 **Fax:** 01536 516820
E-mail: info@hossackssolicitors.com
Work: J1 Z(g)

ISIS LEGAL LIMITED ‡
1a Horsemarket Kettering Northamptonshire NN16 0DG
Tel: 01536 485398 / 485888 **Fax:** 01536 417087
E-mail: enquiries@isis-legal.co.uk

LAMB & HOLMES ‡
West Street Kettering Northamptonshire NN16 0AZ
Tel: 01536 513195 **Fax:** 01536 410191 **Dx:** 12803 KETTERING
E-mail: enquiries@lamb-holmes.co.uk
List of partners: C M Atkinson, J N W Davies, J E Lamb, M P Reed, G D Robinson, D J Rose
Office: Corby
Work: A1 A3 B1 C1 C2 D1 E F1 F2 I J1 J2 K1 K2 K3 L N O Q R1 R2 S1 S2 W Z(c,d,l,p,q,r,t)
Agency, Advocacy, Fixed Fee Interview, Legal Aid Franchise and Member of Accident Line
Ptr: Atkinson, Mr Christopher Michael . . . . May 1992
Lamb, Mr J Edward Notary Public. . . . . *§Jan 1974
Reed, Mr Michael P Notary Public. . . . . *§Feb 1974
Robinson, Mr Glenn D . . . . *§Dec 1992
Rose, Dr Diana J BA(Hons); PhD . . . . *Feb 1996

MANN & COMPANY ‡
17 Station Road Kettering Northamptonshire NN15 7HH
Tel: 01536 520025 **Fax:** 01536 312251 **Dx:** 12821 KETTERING
Emergency telephone 07966 395866
E-mail: info@mannandcompany.co.uk
List of partners: B Mann
Languages: Punjabi
Work: B1 E K1 K3 L N Q S1 W Z(i)
Emergency Action, Agency, Fixed Fee Interview, Legal Aid undertaken and Member of Accident Line
Ptr: Mann, Birry LLB ♦. *Apr 1994

MARK NICHOLLS ‡
66 Windmill Avenue Kettering Northamptonshire NN16 0RD
Tel: 01536 502843 **Fax:** 01536 502843
Emergency telephone 07976 752817
E-mail: mark.nicholls4@ntlworld.com
List of partners: M A Nicholls
Languages: French
Work: G H
SPr: Nicholls, Mr Mark Anthony LLB . . . . Nov 1991

RPM LEGAL ‡
21 Heath Way Burton Latimer Kettering Northamptonshire NN15 5YF
Tel: 01536 722266 **Fax:** 01536 725553
E-mail: v.perkins@rpmlegal.co.uk
Office: Huntingdon, Stratford-upon-Avon

SEATONS SOLICITORS
4 Havelock Street Desborough Kettering Northamptonshire NN14 2LU
Tel: 01536 762773
E-mail: john.pridmore@seatons.co.uk
Office: Corby, Kettering

SEATONS SOLICITORS
38 Trafalgar Road Kettering Northamptonshire NN16 8DA
Tel: 01536 311690 **Fax:** 01536 511336
E-mail: info@seatons.co.uk
Office: Corby, Kettering

TOLLERS LLP
1 King's Court Kettering Parkway Kettering Northamptonshire NN15 6WJ
Tel: 01536 520111
E-mail: enquiries@tollers.co.uk
Office: Corby, Milton Keynes, Northampton
Work: A1 A3 B1 B2 C1 C2 D1 D2 E F1 J1 K1 K2 L M1 N O P Q R1 S1 S2 T2 V W Z(c,d,e,k,o,p,q,r)
Emergency Action, Agency, Advocacy, Legal Aid undertaken, Legal Aid Franchise and Member of Accident Line
Ptr: Fowler, Mr David C LLB. . . . . *§Jun 1974
Hill, Mr Martin T LLB . . . . *Oct 1987
Kings, Mr Thomas R LLB . . . . *§Oct 1984
Peck, Mr Alan T LLB . . . . *Oct 1989
Peck, Mrs Julie L LLB. . . . . *Oct 1989
Rogers, Mr Barry C. . . . . *Sep 1981
Asoc: Edmead, Ms Kirsti Jayne . . . . Sep 2003
Hill, Ms Nicola. Oct 2000
Ward, Ms Claire. . . . . Nov 1999
Webster, Ms Lindsay . . . . Oct 2005
Ast: Osborne, Mr Michael . . . . *Sep 2001

TURNER COULSTON
15 Station Road Kettering Northamptonshire NN15 7HH
Tel: 01536 523434 **Fax:** 01536 310138 **Dx:** 12820 KETTERING
E-mail: ketteringlaw@turner-coulston.co.uk
Office: Northampton
Languages: French
Work: B1 C1 C2 C3 D1 E F1 F2 G J1 J2 K1 K3 K4 L N O Q R1 S1 S2 T1 T2 W Z(e,k,l,p,q)
Emergency Action, Agency, Advocacy and Fixed Fee Interview undertaken
Ptr: Josephs, Mr John H LLB(Leeds) Deputy District Judge *Oct 1974

WILSON BROWNE ‡
PO Box 8 41 Meadow Road Kettering Northamptonshire NN16 8TN
Tel: 01536 410041 **Fax:** 01536 410444 **Dx:** 12802 KETTERING
E-mail: enquiries@wilsonbrowne.co.uk
List of partners: R M Arnold, A K Bergman, S R D Bridgens, M R Jackman, J M Laskey, K U Leslie, B R Matthews, F J Moore, D J Neuborn, P W Richards, J C Saynor, M O Sergeant, R J Smart, C J Smith, D P Wicks, M C Wilson, P J Wilson, J N Wright
Office: Higham Ferrers, Kettering, Leicester, Northampton, Wellingborough
Work: A1 B1 C1 D1 E F1 I J1 K1 L M1 N O P Q R1 S1 T1 V W X Z(c,d,e,f,g,h,i,j,k,l,m,n,o,p,q,s,t,y)
Emergency Action, Agency, Advocacy, Fixed Fee Interview, Legal Aid undertaken, Legal Aid Franchise and Member of Accident Line
Ptr: Bergman, Mr Andrew K LLB. . . . . *Jul 1979
Jackman, Mr Martin R BA. . . . . *Nov 1986
Matthews, Mr Barry R LLB(Lond) . . . . *§Jun 1978
Sergeant, Mrs Myra O LLB . . . . *§Nov 1981
Wilson, Mr Peter J LLB Clerk to Commissioner Notary Public . . . . *§Jan 1970
Wright, Mr James N BA. . . . . *§Jun 1973
Ast: Castka, Mrs Ika Anne LLB . . . . *Oct 1986
Chan, Mrs Sau Lay . . . . *§Sep 2001
Watkins, Deena Lynette. . . . . Oct 1992
Wilson, Ms Nina K . . . . *§May 2000

WILSON BROWNE COMMERICAL LAW
Kettering Park Way South Kettering Venture Park Kettering Northamptonshire NN15 6WN
Tel: 01536 410014 **Fax:** 01536 516805 **Dx:** 12811 KETTERING
Office: Higham Ferrers, Kettering, Leicester, Northampton, Wellingborough

KEW, Surrey

HAMMILL BURTON LLOYD ‡
5 High Park Road Kew Surrey TW9 4BL
Tel: 020 8392 6392 **Fax:** 020 8287 3049
E-mail: jmbham@aol.com
List of partners: S C Burton, J M Hammill
Work: E S1
Ptr: Burton, Ms Sarah Catrin BA. . . . . *Nov 1985
Hammill, Ms Jennifer Maria BA(Oxon). . . . . *Oct 1981

PHILIP MOODY & CO ‡
373a Sandycombe Road Kew Surrey TW9 3PR
Tel: 020 8948 6388 **Fax:** 020 8948 4254
E-mail: moodylaw@talk21.com
List of partners: R E Bourne, P R Moody
Work: D1 E J1 K1 L Q S1 W
Agency undertaken
Ptr: Bourne, Rachel Elizabeth BSc(Hons) . . . . *Oct 2008

KEYNSHAM, Bath & North East Somerset

FDC LAW
60A High Street Keynsham Bath & North East Somerset BS31 1DX
Tel: 0117 916 1088 **Fax:** 0117 916 1089
Dx: 42950 MIDSOMER NORTON
Office: Frome (2 offices), Radstock

WHITTUCK TAYLOR & CAINES ‡
16 High Street Keynsham Bath & North East Somerset BS31 1DJ
Tel: 0117 986 3504 **Fax:** 0117 986 0118 **Dx:** 30103 KEYNSHAM
E-mail: enquiries@whittucks.co.uk
List of partners: R A Hale, G G Poulter
Work: A1 C1 D1 E F1 G H J1 K1 K3 L N O Q R1 S1 S2 W Z(l)
Emergency Action, Agency, Advocacy and Fixed Fee Interview undertaken
Ptr: Hale, Mr Robert Alun LLB. . . . . *Oct 1973
Poulter, Mr Graham G. . . . . *Nov 1976

KIDDERMINSTER, Worcestershire

C&S SOLICITORS ‡
Scotland House 12 Comberton Hill Kidderminster Worcestershire DY10 1QG
Tel: 0845 272 0066 **Fax:** 0845 272 0067
E-mail: newclaim@cs-solicitors.com
Office: Bewdley

DBL TALBOTS LLP
30 Church Street Kidderminster Worcestershire DY10 2AX
Tel: 01562 749910 **Fax:** 01562 827601
Dx: 721543 KIDDERMINSTER 5
E-mail: info@talbotslaw.co.uk
Office: Codsall, Dudley (2 offices), Stourbridge (2 offices), Wolverhampton
Languages: French
Work: A3 B1 C1 C2 D1 D2 E F1 F2 G H J1 J2 K1 K3 K4 L N O P Q R1 R2 S1 S2 T1 V W Z(h,k,l,p,q,r)
Emergency Action, Agency, Advocacy, Fixed Fee Interview, Legal Aid undertaken, Legal Aid Franchise and Member of Accident Line
Ptr: Bowskill, Miss Gillian M BA . . . . *Oct 1982
Gwilliams, Mr James Edward LLB. . . . . *Sep 2003
Simmonds, Mr Derek John . . . . *Feb 1990
Trenchard, Ms Grace . . . . *Jan 1987
Ast: Moreton, Mrs Janet Margaret FILEx. . . . . *Dec 1992

DWT LEGAL LTD ‡
37 Worcester Street Kidderminster Worcestershire DY10 1EW
Tel: 0844 770 3799 **Fax:** 0844 770 3798
Dx: 16304 KIDDERMINSTER
E-mail: reception@dwt.co.uk
List of partners: M Abdulla, A G Gibb, R J Mason, G B Thompson
Languages: Hindi, Mirpuri, Punjabi, Urdu
Work: A1 A3 B1 C1 C2 D1 D2 E F1 F2 I J1 K1 K2 K3 L N O Q R1 R2 S1 S2 T1 U2 V W X Z(c,e,f,k,l,q,z)
Emergency Action, Agency and Advocacy undertaken
Dir: Abdulla, Mr Matloob GRSC; MSc . . . . *Sep 1996
Gibb, Mr Anthony George BA(Hons). . . . . *Jul 2003
Mason, Mr Robert J LLB(Hons) . . . . *Oct 1983
Thompson, Mr Gareth B LLB . . . . *Jan 1982
Asoc: Miller, Miss Shane. . . . . Nov 2008
Ast: Reardon, Mrs Marguerita LLB(Hons); LPC . . . . . . *Jan 2007

LEGAL ALLIANCES WORLDWIDE LTD ‡
3-4 The Ash Lane Centre Worcester Road Kidderminster Worcestershire DY10 1JR
Tel: 01562 756830 **Fax:** 01562 750908
E-mail: philip.morris@lawlimited.co.uk
List of partners: P S G Morris
Work: A3 C1 C2 E F1 J1 K1 O Q R2 S1 S2 W Z(c)
Emergency Action and Advocacy undertaken
SPr: Morris, Mr Philip Stephen George LLB(Hons) ♦ . . . *§Jan 1993

MFG SOLICITORS ‡
(incorporating Ivens & Morton)
Adam House Birmingham Road Kidderminster Worcestershire DY10 2SA
Tel: 01562 820181 **Fax:** 01562 820066 **Dx:** 16301 KIDDERMINSTER
E-mail: kidderminster@mfgsolicitors.com
List of partners: C Backler, S J Bishop, C J Bovey, M V Burton, R J F Connolly, S M Cooke, P B Copsey, S Coyne, F P G Hill, T M L Jones, S J Lee, P J MacKenzie, I Morrison, A J Neal, M H W Noble, J T Parker, M J Payne, J S C Quinn, K M Reynolds, P E H Rhodes, P L Simner, C G A Stanley, J Tougher, G S Trenchard
Office: Bromsgrove, Halesowen, Oswestry, Telford, Worcester
Work: A1 B1 C1 C2 C3 D1 E F1 G H J1 K1 L N O P Q R1 S1 T1 T2 V W Z(c,d,h,i,j,k,l,m,n,s)
Emergency Action, Agency, Advocacy, Fixed Fee Interview, Legal Aid undertaken, Legal Aid Franchise and Member of Accident Line
Ptr: Backler, Mrs Claire BA . . . . *§Oct 1982
Bovey, Mr Christopher J LLB . . . . *Jan 1981
Burton, Maynard V LLB(Hons). . . . . *Oct 1983
Copsey, Mr Peter B . . . . *§Sep 1979
Jones, Mr Timothy M L LLB(Hons); LLM. . . . . *§Oct 1989
Lee, Mrs Suzanne J. . . . . *Sep 1999
Parker, Mr Justin Trevelyn. . . . . *§Mar 1996

Quinn, Mr James S C LLB . . . . *§May 1964
Simner, Mr Peter L LLB(Hons) . . . . *§Dec 1983
Stanley, Mr Christopher G A BSc(Econ) . . . . *§Jun 1975
Tougher, Mr Jonathan . . . . Oct 1995
Asoc: Robinson, Mrs Valerie Myra . . . . Mar 1994
Warrilow, Miss Sarah . . . . *Dec 1999
Ast: Corbett, Miss Michelle Ann LLB . . . . Nov 1995
Kettle, Mr Geoffrey Ian Marshall . . . . Apr 2002
Morris, Miss Sally Ann . . . . Sep 2001
Phull, Ms Jespall . . . . Mar 2001
Shakespeare, Miss Maria Alana . . . . Mar 2001
Con: Morgan, Mr Terence . . . . *§Jul 1961

PAINTERS ‡
29 Church Street Kidderminster Worcestershire DY10 2AU
Tel: 01562 822295 *Fax:* 01562 820083
Dx: 721542 KIDDERMINSTER 5
E-mail: info@painters-solicitors.co.uk
List of partners: L R Baron, R J S Greig, A C Harling, C D Hobbs, D J Howarth, N A R Hughes, M Khosla, J R Painter, W R Painter
Office: Kidderminster, Stourport-on-Severn
Work: A1 B1 C1 C2 C3 D1 D2 E F1 G H J1 K1 K2 K3 K4 L M1 M2 N O P Q R1 S1 S2 T1 T2 V W Z(d,e,l,q)
Emergency Action, Agency, Advocacy, Fixed Fee Interview, Legal Aid undertaken and Legal Aid Franchise
Ptr: Baron, Mr Lee R BA . . . . Jan 1984
Harling, Mr Adrian C BA . . . . *Jul 1987
Hughes, Mr Nicholas A R BSocSc . . . . *Oct 1983
Khosla, Miss Meera LLB(Hons) . . . . *Nov 1992
Painter, Mr J Richard . . . . *§Mar 1971
Ast: Colley, Miss Laura LLB . . . . Oct 2004
Jagger, Miss Katie LLB . . . . Sep 2001
Williams, Louise . . . . Aug 2009
Con: Talbot, C E MA(Cantab) Town Clerk . . . . *Oct 1957

PAINTERS
11 Church Street Kidderminster Worcestershire DY10 2AH
Tel: 01562 822295 *Fax:* 01562 820083
Dx: 721542 KIDDERMINSTER
Emergency telephone 01905 772548
E-mail: info@painters-solicitors.co.uk
Office: Kidderminster, Stourport-on-Severn
Work: G H N
Emergency Action, Agency, Advocacy, Fixed Fee Interview and Legal Aid undertaken
Ptr: Hobbs, Mr Charles David LLB(Hons) . . . . *Nov 1988

PRESCOTTS ‡
4 Church Street Kidderminster Worcestershire DY10 2AD
Tel: 01562 829982 *Fax:* 01562 829555
E-mail: dtp@prescotts-sol.co.uk
List of partners: D T Prescott
Work: B1 C1 D1 E F1 G H J1 K1 L M1 N P R1 S1 T1 V W Z(c,d,e,f,h,i,j,k,l,m,o,p,s,t)
Agency, Advocacy, Fixed Fee Interview, Legal Aid undertaken and Member of Accident Line
Ptr: Prescott, Mr Derrick T . . . . *§Nov 1957

ROGERS & CO CRIMINAL LAW SOLICITORS ‡
2 Comberton Place Kidderminster Worcestershire DY10 IQR
Tel: 01562 861864 *Fax:* 01562 861873
E-mail: solicitors@rogerslaw.co.uk

STABLES & CO
27 New Road Kidderminster Worcestershire DY10 1AF
Office: Halesowen, Stourbridge

THURSFIELDS ‡
14 Church Street Kidderminster Worcestershire DY10 2AJ
Tel: 01562 820575 *Fax:* 01562 512496
Dx: 721541 KIDDERMINSTER 5
E-mail: info@thursfields.co.uk
List of partners: G M Banks, N W Davies, R E Edwards, J G Field, J F Forsyth, P N Gammon, A W Heaselgrave, S A Morrissy, N T O'Hara, M Pittaway, S F Pitts, D W Taylor, R A J Watkins
Office: Kidderminster, Stourport-on-Severn, Worcester
Languages: British Sign Language, French, German, Punjabi, Spanish, Urdu
Work: A1 A2 B1 C1 C2 C3 D1 D2 E F1 G H J1 K1 K2 L N O Q R1 S1 S2 T1 T2 V W Z(c,d,e,f,i,k,l,m,n)
Emergency Action, Agency, Advocacy, Fixed Fee Interview, Legal Aid undertaken, Legal Aid Franchise and Member of Accident Line
Ptr: Banks, Mr Gary Michael LLB . . . . *§Oct 1994
Davies, Mr Nigel W BA . . . . *§May 1980
Field, Mr Julian Gordon FILEx . . . . *§Apr 1994
Forsyth, Mr John F TEP . . . . *§Jul 1972
Heaselgrave, Mr A William LLB . . . . *§Nov 1967
Morrissy, Miss Susan Ann LLB Notary Public . . . . . *§Oct 1990
Pittaway, Mr Mark LLB(Wales) Maxwell Law Prize; Sir Samuel Evans Prize . . . . *Nov 1986
Pitts, Mr Stephen Francis LLB(Hull); TEP Honorary Secretary to Society for Computers & Law . . . . *§Jun 1977
Asoc: Mackie, Mrs Bernadette M LLB(Hons) . . . . *Oct 1990
Ast: Astbury, Miss Sarah Jane LLB(Hons) . . . . *Sep 2002
Brennan, Mrs Karen LLB(Hons) . . . . *Mar 2001
Johnson, Mrs Lisa . . . . Sep 2007
Jones, Mrs Katherine J LLB(Hons) . . . . *Nov 1993
Con: Grant, Mr Luke George Vincent . . . . *§Feb 1973

THURSFIELDS
27 Church Street Kidderminster Worcestershire DY10 2AT
Tel: 01562 820575 *Fax:* 01562 512496
E-mail: info@thursfields.co.uk
Office: Kidderminster, Stourport-on-Severn, Worcester

KIDLINGTON, Oxfordshire

LEIGH EDWARDS & CO ‡
41 Rutten Lane Yarnton Kidlington Oxfordshire OX5 1LN
Tel: 01865 378243

KEVIN GEANEY ‡
12 Poplar Close Kidlington Oxfordshire OX5 1HH
Tel: 01865 379498 *Fax:* 01865 379498
List of partners: K G P Geaney
Work: A1 E L S1 W
SPr: Geaney, Mr Kevin G P LLB(Reading) . . . . *§Nov 1982

ANGELA PORTER SOLICITORS ‡
10b Oxford Road Kidlington Oxfordshire OX5 1AA
Tel: 01865 841414 *Fax:* 01865 841515 *Dx:* 40556 KIDLINGTON
E-mail: mail@angelaportersolicitors.com
Work: B2 G H Z(t)
Agency, Advocacy and Legal Aid undertaken

SCOTT DIXON REILLY WILKES SOLICITORS ‡
14 Lakesmere Close North Oxford Business Centre Kidlington Oxfordshire OX5 1LG
Tel: 01865 594104
E-mail: mdixon@sdrwlaw.co.uk
Office: Witney

T M WARNER & CO ‡
Wesley House 7 High Street Kidlington Oxfordshire OX5 2ES
Tel: 01865 379311 *Fax:* 01865 378877
E-mail: info@tmwarner.co.uk
List of partners: T J Brown, T M Warner
Work: A1 B1 C1 D1 E F1 G H J1 K1 L N O Q S1 W Z(l)
Emergency Action, Agency and Advocacy undertaken
Ptr: Brown, Mr Timothy J BA(Cantab) . . . . *May 1976
Warner, Miss Tanya M . . . . *Oct 1995
Con: Pajak, Mr Stephen C BA . . . . *§Jan 1982

WHETTER DUCKWORTH FOWLER
1st Floor Sterling House 19-23 High Street Kidlington Oxfordshire OX5 2DH
Tel: 01865 842100 *Fax:* 01865 841006 *Dx:* 40553 KIDLINGTON
Emergency telephone 07767 416593
E-mail: kidlington@wdfsolicitors.co.uk
Office: Oxford
Languages: French, German
Work: A1 B1 C1 C2 C3 D1 D2 E F1 F2 G H J1 K1 K2 L M1 M2 N P R1 S1 T1 T2 V W Z(k,l,o)
Emergency Action, Agency, Advocacy, Fixed Fee Interview, Legal Aid undertaken and Legal Aid Franchise
Ptr: Duckworth, Mr John Peter . . . . *Jun 1970
Fowler, Mr Rod J LLB . . . . *May 1982
Whetter, Mr John McQ W LLB(Bris) . . . . *§Dec 1968

KIDSGROVE, Staffordshire

KENNETH JONES ‡
43 Liverpool Road Kidsgrove Staffordshire ST7 1EA
Tel: 01782 771113 *Fax:* 01782 776512
List of partners: K Jones
Work: E S1 W
SPr: Jones, Mr Kenneth . . . . *Oct 1976

KING'S LYNN, Norfolk

BERRY & WALTON SOLICITORS ‡
Chancery House 8 Kings Street King's Lynn Norfolk PE30 1ES
Tel: 01553 764398 *Fax:* 01553 819490 *Dx:* 57801 KING'S LYNN
E-mail: law@berryandwalton.co.uk
List of partners: D Berry, W Radford
Office: King's Lynn
Work: A1 B1 C1 C2 C3 E F1 J1 J2 K1 L N O P R1 S1 S2 T1 T2 W Z(b,c,q,t)
Agency, Advocacy undertaken and Member of Accident Line
Dir: Berry, Mr David LLB ♦ . . . . *Jun 1973
Radford, Mr William . . . . *Jul 1977

BERRY & WALTON SOLICITORS
8 High Street Heacham King's Lynn Norfolk PE31 7ER
Tel: 01485 571366 *Fax:* 01485 572466 *Dx:* 57801 KING'S LYNN
E-mail: law@berryandwalton.co.uk
Office: King's Lynn
Work: A1 B1 C1 C2 C3 E F1 J1 J2 K1 L N O P S1 S2 T1 T2 W Z(b,c,q,t)
Agency, Advocacy undertaken and Member of Accident Line
Dir: Berry, Mr David LLB ♦ . . . . *Jun 1973
Radford, Mr William . . . . *Jul 1977

KENNETH BUSH ‡
Evershed House 23-25 King Street King's Lynn Norfolk PE30 1DU
Tel: 01553 692737 *Fax:* 01553 691729 *Dx:* 57802 KING'S LYNN
E-mail: kingslynn@kennethbush.com
List of partners: S M Cambridge, P A J Croker, P B Denison, N D P Dodds, J P Eales, J Hallett, R Kowalski, D L Stafford, A J Williams
Office: King's Lynn
Languages: French, Polish
Work: A1 B1 D1 E F1 G H J1 K1 L N O P Q R1 S1 S2 V W Z(c,l,q,r,t)
Emergency Action, Agency, Advocacy, Fixed Fee Interview, Legal Aid undertaken, Legal Aid Franchise and Member of Accident Line
Ptr: Cambridge, Ms Sharon M FILEx . . . . *Apr 1996
Croker, Mr Paul Anthony James LLB . . . . Nov 1994
Denison, Mr Peter B LLB . . . . *Mar 1985
Dodds, Mr Nigel D P LLB(Lond) Clerk to Commissioner of the Inland Revenue . . . . *§Jun 1973
Eales, Mr Jonathan P BA(Law) . . . . *Oct 1983
Kowalski, Mr Roman LLB . . . . Jun 1976
Stafford, Mr Dennis L LLB(B'ham) . . . . *§Apr 1974
Ast: Webb, Miss Amanda Jane LLB(Hons) . . . . Jun 2001

KENNETH BUSH
11 New Conduit Street King's Lynn Norfolk PE30 1DG
Tel: 01553 692233 *Fax:* 01553 767318 *Dx:* 57802 KING'S LYNN
E-mail: ncs@kennethbush.com
Office: King's Lynn
Languages: French, Polish
Work: A1 B1 C1 C2 C3 D1 E F1 G H J1 K1 L M1 M2 N P R1 S1 T1 T2 V W Z(a,b,c,h,i,l,t)
Emergency Action, Agency, Advocacy, Fixed Fee Interview, Legal Aid undertaken, Legal Aid Franchise and Member of Accident Line
Ptr: Hallett, Mr Julian BSc(Lond)(Econ) . . . . *Oct 1985
Williams, Mr Anthony J MA(Cantab) . . . . *§Jun 1972

FRASER DAWBARNS
Chequer House 12 King Street King's Lynn Norfolk PE30 1ES
Tel: 01553 666600 *Fax:* 01553 767221 *Dx:* 57800 KING'S LYNN
Emergency telephone 01553 776999
E-mail: mail@fraserdawbarns.com
Office: Downham Market, March, Wisbech
Languages: French, German
Work: A1 B1 B2 C1 C2 C3 D1 D2 E F1 G H J1 J2 K1 K2 L M1 N O P Q R1 S1 S2 T1 T2 V W Z(c,d,e,k,l,m,q,t)
Emergency Action, Agency, Advocacy, Fixed Fee Interview, Legal Aid undertaken, Legal Aid Franchise and Member of Accident Line
Ptr: Allen, Mrs Deborah A BA . . . . *Apr 1981
Bailey, Mr Colin Stephen LLB . . . . *Jun 1979
Barratt, Mr Anthony J BA(Law) . . . . *May 1982
Meachem, Mr Neil Leslie BA . . . . *Jan 1988
Trevor, Mrs Silke . . . . *Oct 1993
Ast: Glazebrook, Mr Roger L BA(Hons); LLB(Hons) . . . . Oct 1997
Graham, Mr Ian David BSc(Hons); MSc; PGDipLaw . . Mar 2003
Hanson, Mrs Harleen LLB; LLM . . . . *Aug 2006
Hinchcliffe, Mr Michael Hilton LLB . . . . *Feb 2007
Mac Brayne, Mrs Barbara Lindis . . . . Feb 1975
Osborne, Mr David P MA(Cantab) . . . . *Nov 1990

HAWKINS SOLICITORS ‡
19 Tuesday Market Place King's Lynn Norfolk PE30 1JW
Tel: 01553 691661 *Fax:* 01553 691779 *Dx:* 57803 KING'S LYNN
E-mail: enquiries@hawkins-solicitors.com
Office: King's Lynn

HAWKINS SOLICITORS
Unit 2 St Nicholas' Court Dersingham King's Lynn Norfolk PE31 6GZ
Tel: 01485 501586 *Fax:* 01553 691779 *Dx:* 57803 KING'S LYNN
E-mail: enquiries@hawkins-solicitors.com
Office: King's Lynn

HAYES & STORR
The Old County Court County Court Road King's Lynn Norfolk PE30 5EJ
Tel: 01553 778900 *Fax:* 01553 768802 *Dx:* 57849 KING'S LYNN
E-mail: law.kingslynn@hayes-storr.com
Office: Fakenham, Holt, Sheringham, Wells-next-the-Sea
Ptr: Craig, Mrs Andrea Harvey LLB . . . . *Mar 1983
Morgan, Mr James Kenrick LLB; LSF(Hons) . . . . . *Nov 1995
Ni Charthaig, Ms Eileanora Mary . . . . Oct 1993
Taylor, Mrs Margaret Evelyn LLB(Lond) . . . . *§Dec 1979
Ast: Howliston, Mr Robert . . . . Sep 2009
Sparrow, Mrs Donna . . . . Nov 1998
Styles, Ms Amy LLB; BA(Hons) . . . . Jan 2011

MALLETTS SOLICITORS ‡
17 Tuesday Market Place Market Place King's Lynn Norfolk PE30 1JN
Tel: 01553 777744 *Fax:* 01553 776553 *Dx:* 57851 KING'S LYNN
Emergency telephone 01553 777744
E-mail: info@malletts.com
List of partners: J Macwhirter, R Mallett, S R Mallett
Office: London WC1
Work: B2 E G H K1 K3 L Q S1 S2 W Z(l,w)
Emergency Action, Agency, Advocacy, Fixed Fee Interview, Legal Aid undertaken and Legal Aid Franchise
Ptr: Macwhirter, Mr James LLB . . . . *Sep 1999
Mallett, Mr Richard . . . . *Nov 2000
Mallett, Mrs Sharon R LLB . . . . *Oct 1993
Ast: Meredith, Ms Tiffany . . . . Jan 2006
Whitworth, Mrs Sarah Frances BA(Hons) . . . . *Oct 1994

METCALFE COPEMAN & PETTEFAR
28-32 King Street King's Lynn Norfolk PE30 1HQ
Tel: 01553 778102 *Fax:* 01553 766807 *Dx:* 57811 KING'S LYNN
E-mail: info@mcp-law.co.uk
Office: Peterborough, Thetford, Wisbech
Languages: Portuguese
Work: A1 A3 B1 B2 C1 C2 C3 D1 E F1 F2 G H J1 J2 K1 K2 K3 K4 L M1 M2 N O P Q R1 R2 S1 S2 T1 T2 U2 V W Z(c,e,g,h,l,n,o,p,q,t,y,za)
Emergency Action, Agency, Advocacy, Fixed Fee Interview, Legal Aid undertaken, Legal Aid Franchise and Member of Accident Line
Ptr: Muir, Miss Alison M BA(Hons) . . . . *Sep 1990
Scott, Mr Simon BSc(Hons) . . . . *Nov 1995
Ast: Colwell, Mr Robert LLB . . . . *Mar 2007
Gillery, Mr Bryan Fred LLB Clements Inn Prize; Sheffield Prize; Edmund Thomas Child Prize . . . . *Apr 1976
Spence, Mr Andrew Michael MA(Hons); PGDipLaw; LPC . . . . *Feb 1999
Willis, Ms Karen Jane BA . . . . May 1999
Winchester, Miss Charlotte Lucy LLB . . . . *Apr 2002

P T RYAN & CO ‡
16 Portland Street King's Lynn Norfolk PE30 1RA
Tel: 01553 761741 *Fax:* 01553 767361
E-mail: jrq@ptryan.co.uk
List of partners: J R Gudgeon, D J Loasby
Languages: French
Work: A1 C1 E J1 K1 L O Q S1 S2 W Z(c,n)
Ptr: Gudgeon, Mr John R . . . . *Jun 1968
Loasby, Mr David J LLB . . . . *Jan 1977

SWANNS ‡
The Bungalow Old Manor Low Road Stowbridge King's Lynn Norfolk PE34 3PE
Tel: 01553 811747 *Fax:* 01553 811812
E-mail: swann.solicitors@btconnect.com
List of partners: F Swann
Work: E S1 S2 W
SPr: Swann, Ms Fiona LLB . . . . *Oct 1981

WARD GETHIN ‡
10-12 Tuesday Market Place King's Lynn Norfolk PE30 1JT
Tel: 01553 660033 *Fax:* 01553 766857 *Dx:* 57813 KING'S LYNN
E-mail: enquiries@wardgethin.co.uk
List of partners: C R Dewey, P Lees, C L Page, R W Pennington, S L Scott, S D Wilson
Office: Swaffham
Languages: French, Japanese, Spanish
Work: A1 A3 B1 B2 C1 C3 D1 D2 E F1 F2 G I J1 J2 K1 L M1 N O P Q R1 R2 S1 S2 T2 V W Z(c,d,e,g,j,k,l,o,p,q,s,t)
Emergency Action, Agency, Advocacy, Fixed Fee Interview undertaken and Member of Accident Line
Ptr: Dewey, Mr Christopher R BA . . . . *§Oct 1987
Lees, Miss Penelope LLB(Nott'm) . . . . *§Apr 1977
Page, Mrs Cheryl Lesley Notary Public . . . . *Oct 1995
Pennington, Mr Richard W LLB(Bris) . . . . *§Oct 1986
Scott, Miss Sarah Louise LLB(Hons) Notary Public . . *§Sep 1996
Wilson, Mr Simon Duncan . . . . *Jan 2004
Ast: Gaughan, Miss Lisa Keeley LLB(Hons) . . . . *Sep 2010
Gooden, Miss Michelle LLB . . . . *Sep 2000
Hall, Miss Anna Maria LLB(Hons) . . . . *Jan 2005
John, Mr Neil . . . . *Oct 1999
Matthews, Mrs Susan Gail MSc; PGDipLaw . . . . . . *Sep 2005
Payne, Mr Dean . . . . *May 2010
Phillips, Mr Marcus Beaumont MA(History) . . . . . . Sep 2006
Plummer, Miss Sara Louise . . . . *Sep 2006

See p112 for the Key to Work Categories & other symbols

KINGS NYMPTON, Devon

COPES SOLICITORS
Hammetts Kings Nympton Devon EX37 9ST
Tel: 01769 581581 *Fax:* 01769 581582

KINGSBRIDGE, Devon

BARTONS ‡
20 Fore Street Kingsbridge Devon TQ7 1NZ
Tel: 01548 855655 *Fax:* 01548 853955 *Dx:* 81402 KINGSBRIDGE
E-mail: kingsbridge@bartons.co.uk
List of partners: P J Albery, D C Hassall, L M Hassall, R C S Hayes, T J Walker
Office: Bristol, Plymouth, Salcombe, Totnes
Work: A1 A3 C1 C2 D1 E F1 K1 K3 K4 L N O R2 S1 S2 W Z(a,d,j,l)
Ptr: Hassall, Mr David Carl . . . Nov 1982

BEERS LLP ‡
29 Fore Street Kingsbridge Devon TQ7 1AA
Tel: 01548 857000 *Fax:* 01548 852101 *Dx:* 81401 KINGSBRIDGE
E-mail: info@beersllp.com
List of partners: M J Asharaf, M I J Hasler, P S L Housego
Office: Plymouth
Languages: Punjabi, Urdu
Work: A1 C1 C2 C3 D1 E F1 J1 K1 K3 L N O P Q R1 S1 S2 T1 T2 W Z(b,d,h,l,p)
Ptr: Hasler, Mr Michael I J LLB . . . *Dec 1979
Housego, Mr Paul S L MA; LLB . . . *§Oct 1978
Asoc: Ellis, Miss Elizabeth M LLB . . . *§May 1975
Ast: Cameron, Mrs Jenny LLB Cavendish Law Prize 2001 . *Sep 2007
Jones, Mr Richard LLB(Hons) . . . Jan 1996
Mitchell, Mrs Caroline Eva BSc(Life Sciences) . . . Sep 1996

GILLIAN FAZAN & CO ‡
Bank House Fore Street Kingsbridge Devon TQ7 1PG
Tel: 01548 856663 *Fax:* 01578 857071

WINDEATTS
48 Fore Street Kingsbridge Devon TQ7 1PE
Tel: 01548 852727 *Fax:* 01548 856216 *Dx:* 81400 KINGSBRIDGE
E-mail: kingsbridge@windeatts.co.uk
Office: Totnes
Work: A1 E L S1 S2 T2 W Z(d)
Ast: Bolt, Mrs Emily . . . Nov 2010
Hawker, Mr Peter . . . Feb 2010
Solanki, Miss Nyna . . . Apr 2006

KINGSTON UPON THAMES, Surrey

AVETOOM & COMPANY ‡
11 Cotswold Close Kingston Hill Kingston upon Thames Surrey KT2 7JN
Tel: 020 8547 0690 *Fax:* 0870 706 4235

BRIDGE BURKE SOLICITORS ‡
22-24 Thames Street Kingston upon Thames Surrey KT1 1PE
Tel: 020 8972 8018 *Fax:* 020 8972 8011
E-mail: cbj@bridgeburkesolicitors.co.uk

CARTER BELLS LLP ‡
Kings' Stone House 12 High Street Kingston upon Thames Surrey KT1 1HD
Tel: 020 8939 4000 *Fax:* 020 8939 4003
Dx: 31505 KINGSTON UPON THAMES
E-mail: mail@carterbells.co.uk
List of partners: M J Gale, E M Guy, F G Horder, R H F Norris, J Pinches, A N Thorne, M A Ward
Work: B1 C1 C2 D1 D2 E F1 J1 K1 K3 K4 L N O Q R1 R2 S1 S2 T1 T2 W Z(c,k,l)
Emergency Action, Agency and Advocacy undertaken
Mem: Gale, Ms Margaret J LLB . . . *Oct 1989
Guy, Mrs Elaine M . . . *Oct 1991
Horder, Mr Frank G BA(Law) . . . *May 1981
Norris, Mr Richard H F LLB(Soton); TEP . . . *§Jun 1980
Pinches, Mr Justin . . . *Oct 1997
Thorne, Mr Andrew N LLB(Lond) . . . *Nov 1977
Ward, Ms Monica A LLB . . . *Feb 1985
Ast: Crouch, Mr Roger . . . *Sep 2002
Hemus, Miss Frances LLB . . . *Dec 2007
Con: Field, Mr John P . . . *Jun 1976

CAYLAW ‡
96 Richmond Road Kingston upon Thames Surrey KT2 5EN
Tel: 020 8547 4422 *Fax:* 020 8547 4411

PAMELA CLEMO & CO ‡
146 Coombe Lane West Royal Borough GLC Kingston upon Thames Surrey KT2 7DE
Tel: 020 8949 8791 *Fax:* 020 8949 8792
List of partners: P Clemo
Work: C1 S1 W
SPr: Clemo, Miss Pamela LLB; LLM; MA(Econ); PhD . . . *Nov 1982

COLEMAN & BETTS ‡
85-87 Clarence Street Kingston upon Thames Surrey KT1 1RB
Tel: 020 8549 4402 *Dx:* 31514 KINGSTON UPON THAMES
List of partners: R J Coleman
Work: A1 B1 C1 E J1 M1 N P R1 S1 T1 W Z(c,e,k)
Ptr: Coleman, Mr Robin J . . . *Jul 1969
Ast: Studdert-Kennedy, Mr David A . . . *Dec 1988

COLEMANS - CTTS
25-29 High Street Kingston upon Thames Surrey KT1 1LL
Tel: 020 8296 9966 *Fax:* 020 8546 1400
Dx: 84864 KINGSTON UPON THAMES 1
E-mail: enquiries@colemans-ctts.co.uk
Office: Barnet, Manchester
Ptr: Fitzgerald, Ms Fiona Catherine LLB(Hons); DipLaw . . *Jul 1997
Roantree, Mrs Claire Elizabeth BA(Hons)(Law with English); LPC . . . *May 1997
Sutton, Mr Anthony P BA . . . *Jun 1979
Tarrant, Mr Nigel A LLB . . . *Jul 1980
Tilley, Mrs Janet Catherine BA(Hons) . . . *Oct 1982
Valcin, Mrs Lorna M . . . *May 1998
Asoc: Atkins, Mrs Sarah E LLB(Hons) . . . *Oct 1985
Mortimer, Nolan LLB(Hons) . . . Aug 2002

Trikha, Neelam BA(Hons) . . . Sep 2002
Ast: Fanning, Mr Patrick J LLB . . . *Jan 1976
Rankin, Ms Charlotte LLB . . . *Aug 2003
Simpson-Scott, Mr Geoffrey BA(Hons)(Law & Econ) . . *Sep 2002
Talwar, Satnam LLB . . . Aug 2003

CRISP & CO SOLICITORS
Parman House 30/36 Fife Road Kingston upon Thames Surrey KT1 1SY
Tel: 020 8546 7969 *Fax:* 020 8549 7071
Dx: 31503 KINGSTON UPON THAMES
E-mail: info@crispandco.com
Office: Guildford, London E14

DUNN & CO ‡
52 Fassett Road Kingston upon Thames Surrey KT1 2TF
Tel: 020 8541 1332 *Fax:* 020 8546 6108
List of partners: S R Dunn
Languages: French
Work: E L R2 S1 S2 W
SPr: Dunn, Mr Stephen R . . . *Oct 1980

STEPHANIE F GRIFFITHS ‡
27 Woodside Road Kingston upon Thames Surrey KT2 5AT
Tel: 020 8546 5986 *Fax:* 020 8547 2960
List of partners: S F Griffiths
Work: K1 K2 S1
SPr: Griffiths, Ms Stephanie Faye BA . . . *Jan 1981

GUILE NICHOLAS
Siddedly House 50 Canbury Park Road Kingston upon Thames Surrey KT2 6LX
Tel: 020 8549 4282 *Fax:* 020 8549 9615
Dx: 31536 KINGSTON UPON THAMES
E-mail: sols@gnlaw.co.uk
Office: London N12
SPr: Stokoe, Mr Anthony . . . *May 1981

HJ LEGAL ‡
KBC Kingston Exchange 12-50 Kingsgate Road Kingston upon Thames Surrey KT2 5AA
Tel: 020 8408 5299 *Fax:* 020 8547 1569
E-mail: info@hjlegal.co.uk

HOWELL-JONES LLP ‡
75 Surbiton Road Kingston upon Thames Surrey KT1 2AF
Tel: 020 8549 5186 *Fax:* 020 8549 3383 *Dx:* 57715 SURBITON
E-mail: kingston@howell-jones.com
List of partners: S A Addison, S A Carter, D C David, S A Forshaw, H L Hotten, C C Jackson, J B Petchey, I C Robertson, A Roper, C J Thorpe, P B H Trim
Office: Cheam, Leatherhead, London SW20, London WC2, Walton-on-Thames
Languages: Armenian, French
Work: B1 B2 C1 C2 C3 D1 E J1 K1 L M1 M2 N O Q R1 R2 S1 S2 T1 T2 U2 W Z(c,d,e,f,k,l,q,r)
Emergency Action, Advocacy undertaken and Member of Accident Line
Mem: Carter, Mr Simon Anthony . . . *Nov 2000
David, Mrs Domini Claire LLB . . . *Oct 1994
Forshaw, Mr Simon Alan . . . *Nov 1979
Hotten, Mrs Helen Lesley ARCO . . . *Mar 2003
Jackson, Mrs Claire Corrine LLB(Bris) . . . *§Apr 1976
Petchey, Mrs Juliet B LLB(Hons) . . . *Aug 1996
Roper, Mr Alan . . . *Nov 1973
Ast: Cullen, Ms Jo . . . *Sep 2006
Joyson, Clare . . . Sep 2009
Morris, Mr Stephen . . . Oct 1987

INFIELDS ‡
1 Old Bridge Street Hampton Wick Kingston upon Thames Surrey KT1 4DB
Tel: 020 8977 7633 / 8977 1149 *Fax:* 020 8977 9962
Dx: 31510 KINGSTON UPON THAMES
E-mail: law@infields.co.uk
List of partners: S J Burley, R E P Newhall
Work: A1 B1 C1 C2 C3 D1 E F1 J1 K1 K3 L M1 M2 N O P Q R1 S1 S2 T1 T2 V W Z(l)
Emergency Action, Agency, Advocacy, Fixed Fee Interview, Legal Aid undertaken and Member of Accident Line
Ptr: Burley, Mr Simon James BMus; LLB . . . *Dec 1995
Newhall, Mr Roger E P . . . *Dec 1972
Asoc: Armstrong, Ms Jane BA(Hons) . . . *Oct 1998
Ast: Loxton, Mrs Anna BA . . . *Jul 2005
Williams, Mrs Barbara H A BA . . . *Jun 1980

MACLAVERTY COOPER ATKINS ‡
25 Union Street Kingston upon Thames Surrey KT1 1RP
Tel: 020 8549 9994 *Fax:* 020 8549 1711
Dx: 31500 KINGSTON UPON THAMES
Emergency telephone 07956 261040 / 07770 582836
E-mail: enquiries@maclaverty.co.uk
List of partners: J A Cooper
Work: G H J1 K1 S1 W
Emergency Action, Agency, Advocacy, Fixed Fee Interview and Legal Aid undertaken
Ptr: Cooper, Ms Julie A . . . Oct 1990
Ast: Allman, Mr David . . . Nov 1999
Pearson, Ms Mary . . . Mar 2001

MATRIX LEGAL ‡
Surrey House 34 Eden Street Kingston upon Thames Surrey KT1 1ER
Tel: 020 8481 3727 *Fax:* 0845 280 9980
Dx: 31502 KINGSTON UPON THAMES
E-mail: info@matrix-legal.com

W H MATTHEWS & CO (incorporating Freeboroughs)
19 Penrhyn Road Kingston upon Thames Surrey KT1 2BZ
Tel: 020 8549 0264 *Fax:* 020 8549 8499 *Dx:* 57706 SURBITON
E-mail: kingston@whmatthews.com
Office: London EC1, Staines, Sutton
Work: C1 E J1 L N Q R2 S1 S2 Z(c,l)
Emergency Action, Agency, Advocacy and Fixed Fee Interview undertaken
Ptr: Howard, Mr Charles J LLB . . . *Dec 1975
Lanceley, Mr Ian Kenneth . . . *Feb 1971
Lawrence, Mr Richard LLB . . . *Oct 1988
Asoc: Spooner, Mrs Catharine Magdalen BA(Hons) . . . *Jun 1976

MEABY & CO (TRADING AS LEO AND STOCKTON) ‡
59a Eden Street Kingston upon Thames Surrey KT1 1DH
Tel: 020 8546 9074 *Fax:* 020 8546 9768
Dx: 31537 KINGSTON UPON THAMES
E-mail: mail@leoandstocktonsolicitors.com

2

PALMERS SOLICITORS ‡
89-91 Clarence Street Kingston upon Thames Surrey KT1 1QY
Tel: 020 8549 7444 *Fax:* 020 8547 2117
Dx: 31524 KINGSTON UPON THAMES
E-mail: enquiries@palmerssolicitors.co.uk
Web: www.palmerssolicitors.co.uk
List of partners: J J Horstman, J S Perry
Work: B1 C1 E F1 J1 K1 K3 K4 L N O Q S1 S2 T1 T2 W Z(c,d,l,m,q,r,s)
Agency, Advocacy and Fixed Fee Interview undertaken
Ptr: Horstman, Mr Jeffrey John TEP . . . *§Feb 1978
Perry, Mr John Sinclair BA . . . *§Jul 1978
Ast: Day, Mrs Lisa Kerry BSc; MSc . . . *Mar 2005
Hoyle, Miss Janet Barbara Notary Public . . . *Jan 1992
Lopez, Mr Arun Nicholas BSc Blackstone Press Prize . *Jan 2004
Rowe, Mrs Julie Amanda BA(Hons); GDL; LPC Russell Cooke Prize; College of Law Prize . . . *Nov 2008
Con: Palmer, Mr N John . . . *Jul 1953
Scott, Mr David J LLB . . . *Jan 1970

ROSE & ROSE SOLICITORS ‡
The Riverside Centre 40 High Street Kingston upon Thames Surrey KT1 1HL
Tel: 020 8974 7490 *Fax:* 020 8546 6823
Dx: 31516 KINGSTON UPON THAMES

RUSSELL-COOKE LLP
Bishop's Palace House Kingston Bridge Kingston upon Thames Surrey KT1 1QN
Tel: 020 8546 6111 *Fax:* 020 8541 4404
Dx: 31546 KINGSTON UPON THAMES
E-mail: helpdesk@russell-cooke.co.uk
Office: London SW15, London WC1
Languages: French, German
Work: A1 A3 B1 B2 C1 C2 D1 D2 E F1 G H J1 K1 K2 K3 K4 L N O Q R1 R2 S1 S2 T1 T2 V W Z(c,d,e,h,m,o,p,q,r,s,w)
Advocacy, Legal Aid undertaken and Member of Accident Line
Ptr: Ford, Mr Ian Roger LLB . . . *Oct 1981
Little, Ms Samantha LLB . . . *Oct 1993
Nichols, Mrs Therese M LLB . . . *Jul 1980
Ast: Akins, Ms Eva . . . Jan 1999
Bowe, Mr Kieran Vice President Surrey Law Society; Committee Member Surrey STEP branch . . . Jul 2006
Connolly, Ms Louise . . . Oct 1998
Dickson, Mr Andrew James Ross BA(Politics); LLB . . Sep 2011
Field, Ms Hannah . . . Jan 2007
Hall, Miss Lauren LLB; LPC . . . Sep 2008
Levi, Ms Frances Joy MA(Oxon); Dip Welfare Law . . *Dec 1974
MacDonald, Mrs Fiona BA . . . *Jun 1979
Richardson, Ms Sarah L LLB . . . Nov 2002
Sandiford, Mr James . . . Sep 2009
Williams, Ms Sarah . . . Sep 2008
Con: Higdon, Mr John . . . Oct 1971

Other offices in London and Putney. Charity, Children & Family, Conveyancing, Criminal, Commercial Litigation, Commercial Property, Company Law, Employment, French, IP, PI & Clinical Negligence, Regulation & Sports, Trusts, Wills, Probate & Tax

SHERIDAN & CO ‡
16 Princeton Mews 167-169 London Road Kingston upon Thames Surrey KT2 6PL
Tel: 020 8541 1181 *Fax:* 020 8549 7794 *Dx:* 200911 NEW MALDEN
E-mail: mail@sheridanlaw.co.uk
List of partners: I M Sheridan
Languages: French
Work: K4 M2 N O Q S1 W Z(q,r)
Agency, Fixed Fee Interview, Legal Aid undertaken and Legal Aid Franchise
Ptr: Sheridan, Mr Ian M LLB; Attorney at Law (New York) . *Dec 1971

SHERWOOD WHEATLEY ‡
48 High Street Kingston upon Thames Surrey KT1 1HW
Tel: 020 8546 0144 *Fax:* 020 8549 0783
Dx: 31517 KINGSTON UPON THAMES
E-mail: sherwood@btconnect.com
List of partners: D S Hawkins, R E Puttock, W J Webb
Work: G K1 S1 S2 W
Legal Aid undertaken
Ptr: Hawkins, Mr David S LLB . . . *Apr 1983
Puttock, Mr Roger E . . . *Nov 1966
Webb, Mr William J BA . . . *§Jun 1968
Asoc: Dorrington Ward, Miss Alix BA . . . *Jan 1979
Worgan, Mrs Rachel K BA(Hons) . . . Jun 1993

JOHN SMYTHE & CO ‡
Das House 20 Revell Road Kingston upon Thames Surrey KT1 3SW
Tel: 020 8546 1390
List of partners: F E D'Souza
SPr: D'Souza, Mr Frank E . . . Jul 1977

STUDIO LEGALE INTERNATIONAL LOMBARDO ‡
47 Old London Road Kingston upon Thames Surrey KT2 6NG
Tel: 020 3274 0016
E-mail: g.lombardo@lombardolawfirm.co.uk
Languages: Italian

KINGSWINFORD, West Midlands

AJR SOLICITORS ‡
Suite 19a Market Street Kingswinford West Midlands DY6 9JS
Tel: 0875 500 1201 *Fax:* 0875 500 1202
Dx: 15811 KINGSWINFORD
List of partners: A J Robson
Dir: Robson, Mrs Amanda Jayne LLB(Hons); LPC. . . . *Sep 2001

BLOUNT HEMMINGS ‡
Kingstone House 818 High Street Kingswinford West Midlands DY6 8AA
Tel: 01384 400565 *Fax:* 01384 401013 *Dx:* 15802 KINGSWINFORD
E-mail: jblount@blounthemmings.co.uk
List of partners: J L Banks, J Blount, R G Hemmings
Office: Kingswinford
Work: A1 C1 E K4 L R2 S1 S2 T2 W Z(f)
Dir: Banks, Mrs Jill Lesley. . . . . May 1982
Blount, Mr Julian . . . . *Dec 1975
Hemmings, Mr Robin Graham LLB . . . . *Dec 1975

BLOUNT HEMMINGS
The Cross Offices Summerhill Kingswinford West Midlands DY6 9JE
Tel: 01384 400565 *Fax:* 01384 401013 *Dx:* 15802 KINGSWINFORD
E-mail: jillbanks@blounthemmings.co.uk
Office: Kingswinford

HIGGS & SONS
1 Townsend Place Kingswinford West Midlands DY6 9JL
Tel: 01384 342100 *Fax:* 01384 342001 *Dx:* 15803 KINGSWINFORD
E-mail: law@higgsandsons.co.uk
Office: Brierley Hill
Work: A1 E F1 K2 L S1 T1 T2 V W Z(c,d,e,m)
Emergency Action, Agency, Advocacy, Fixed Fee Interview, Legal Aid undertaken and Member of Accident Line
Ptr: Higgs, Mr J Michael BA(Hons)(Law). . . . . *Oct 1984
Martin-Summers, Mr Philip BA(Hons) . . . . *Oct 1982
Asoc: Slater-Reay, Ms Rowena . . . . Apr 1996
Ast: Fletcher, Mrs Yvette S. . . . . Sep 1995

WALDRONS
(incorporating Richard Hobbs Solicitors)
813 High Street Kingswinford West Midlands DY6 8AD
Tel: 01384 811811 *Fax:* 01384 811855 *Dx:* 15801 KINGSWINFORD
E-mail: lawyers@waldrons.co.uk
Office: Brierley Hill, Dudley, Tipton, Walsall, Worcester
Languages: French, Italian
Work: A1 B1 C1 C2 D1 D2 E F1 F2 G H J1 K1 K2 L N O Q R1 R2 S1 S2 T1 T2 W Z(l,r)
Emergency Action, Agency, Advocacy, Fixed Fee Interview, Legal Aid undertaken, Legal Aid Franchise and Member of Accident Line
Ptr: Dawson, Ms Ada M LLB. . . . . *Feb 1969

KINGSWOOD, South Gloucestershire

BATCHELOR SHARP
377-379 Two Mile Hill Road Kingswood South Gloucestershire BS15 1AD
Tel: 0117 967 1772 *Fax:* 0117 935 2487 *Dx:* 43351 KINGSWOOD
Office: Bristol, Knowle
Work: C1 E L S1 W Z(l)
Fixed Fee Interview undertaken
Ptr: Batchelor, Mr Keith . . . . *Dec 1977

BRAIN SINNOTT & CO ‡
1 Moravian Road Kingswood South Gloucestershire BS15 8LY
Tel: 0117 960 6880 *Fax:* 0117 935 2523 *Dx:* 43362 KINGSWOOD
Emergency telephone 0117 960 6880
E-mail: kingswood@brainsinnott.co.uk
List of partners: J V Sinnott, L S Wilkes
Office: Bristol
Work: B1 D1 E F1 G H J1 K1 L N O Q R1 S1 S2 V W Z(c,k,l,w)
Emergency Action, Agency, Advocacy, Fixed Fee Interview, Legal Aid undertaken and Legal Aid Franchise
Ptr: Sinnott, Mr John V BA. . . . . *Dec 1977
Wilkes, Mrs Lisa S LLB . . . . *Nov 1987
Ast: Coates, Mr Richard Anthony BA. . . . . *Nov 1993
Griffiths, Mr Huw Rhoslyn LLB(Hons); DipLP; LLM Commercial Law. . . . . *Oct 1999
Woodman, Mr Daniel John BA(Hons) . . . . Oct 1997

KIRBY SHEPPARD ‡
(incorporating Kirby Fixsen & Godwin; Watson Sinnott)
111-117 Regent Street Kingswood South Gloucestershire BS15 2LJ
Tel: 0845 840 0045 *Dx:* 43350 KINGSWOOD
Emergency telephone 0117 961 1451
E-mail: info@kirbysheppard.co.uk
List of partners: J Bell, D B Curwen, I S Grant, J R Gridley, S R Parker, H Pennelegion, J C Reed, T M Sharkey, A G Willcocks, A E Wilson
Office: Bristol, Thornbury
Work: A1 B1 C1 C2 C3 D1 E F1 G H J1 K1 K4 L N O Q S1 W Z(l,m,p)
Emergency Action, Agency, Advocacy, Fixed Fee Interview, Legal Aid undertaken, Legal Aid Franchise and Member of Accident Line
Ptr: Grant, Mr Iain Stuart BA(Dunelm) . . . . *§Jul 1973
Parker, Mr Stephen R. . . . . Nov 1983
Reed, Mr John C . . . . *§Jul 1974
Sharkey, Mr Thomas Michael . . . . *Oct 2001
Wilson, Mrs Anna Elizabeth LLB(Hons); LPC . . . . *Aug 1997
Ast: Allen, Miss Joelle BA(Hons). . . . . Sep 2002
Gill, Ms Alison Rachel BA(Hons)(Psychology & Sociology); CPE; LPC. . . . . Jan 2003
Twose, Mr Simon Charles BA(Hons)(History with English); LPC; DipLaw . . . . Oct 2003

KINGTON, Herefordshire

E SMITH & CO ‡
46 Duke Street Kington Herefordshire HR5 3DR
Tel: 01544 231010 *Fax:* 01544 232718
E-mail: e.smithandco@btconnect.com
List of partners: P J Smith
Work: S1 S2 W
SPr: Smith, Mr Peter John LLB. . . . . *Sep 1968

THE WOODLAND DAVIES PARTNERSHIP LLP
Albion House Bridge Street Kington Herefordshire HR5 3DL
Tel: 01544 230841
Office: Brecon, Hay-on-Wye, Hereford, Talgarth
Work: A1 A2 D2 E K1 K2 K3 L N Q S1 S2 W Z(l)
Agency undertaken
Ptr: Davies, Miss E Ann . . . . *Nov 1979
Davies, Mr Peter G BSc(Econ) . . . . *Jan 1982
Asoc: Theobald, Miss Carolyn M LLB . . . . *Nov 1978

VAUGHAN & DAVIES ‡
32 Duke Street Kington Herefordshire HR5 3BW
Tel: 01544 230325 *Fax:* 01544 231379
List of partners: M P Miller, G M Parry
Office: Presteigne
Languages: Welsh
Work: A1 E F1 K4 L S1 S2 T1 T2 W
Ptr: Miller, Mr Michael P LLB . . . . *§Jun 1977
Parry, Mr Gareth M LLB. . . . . *§Dec 1988

KIRKBY, Merseyside

CANTER LEVIN & BERG
(incorporating Canter Levin & Co)
18 Newtown Gardens Kirkby Merseyside L32 8RR
Tel: 0151 546 4562 *Fax:* 0151 549 1209
Emergency telephone 0151 226 8552
E-mail: postmaster@canter-law.co.uk
Office: Liverpool, St Helens
Work: C1 C2 C3 D1 E F1 G H J1 K1 L M1 M2 N P R1 S1 V
Emergency Action, Agency, Advocacy, Fixed Fee Interview, Legal Aid undertaken and Member of Accident Line
Ptr: Flynn, Mr Mark Anthony William LLB . . . . *Jan 1988
Hughes, Mr Richard. . . . . Feb 1994
Jones, Mr Darren . . . . Nov 1999
Saunders, Mrs Elizabeth Anne LLB(Hons). . . . . . . *Jul 1997
Asoc: Mclaughlin, Mr Colm . . . . Dec 2007
Scott, Mr Philip . . . . Feb 2005

MAXWELL HODGE SOLICITORS
12 New Town Garden Kirkby Merseyside L32 8RR
Tel: 0151 548 7370 *Fax:* 0151 548 1414
Office: Formby, Heswall, Huyton, Liverpool (2 offices), Maghull, West Kirby
Work: N X Z(r)
Legal Aid undertaken
Ptr: Leyland, Mr Simon J BA; CPE. . . . . *Sep 1996
Lord, Ms Gillian BA(Hons); CPE. . . . . *Apr 2000
Newton, Mr Christopher H BA(Law) . . . . *Jul 1984
Ast: Stoddern, Miss Kristina LLB. . . . . Sep 2005

PAULINE REYNOLDS AND CO ‡
27-31 Admin Road Kirkby Merseyside L33 7TX
Tel: 0151 546 4583 *Fax:* 0151 546 4556
E-mail: paulinereynolds@btconnect.com
List of partners: P M Reynolds
SPr: Reynolds, Mrs Pauline Mary LLB(Hons). . . . . Feb 2000

KIRKBY LONSDALE, Cumbria

HUDSON AND ASSOCIATES SOLICITORS-ADVOCATES LTD ‡
65-67 Main Street Kirkby Lonsdale Cumbria LA6 2AH
Tel: 0800 019 9768
E-mail: info@hudson-solicitors.co.uk
List of partners: J E G Hudson
Work: K3 Q Z(y)
Emergency Action, Agency and Advocacy undertaken
Ptr: Hudson, Mr John Edward Gerard LLB. . . . . *May 1993

OGLETHORPE STURTON & GILLIBRAND
17 Main Street Kirkby Lonsdale Cumbria LA6 2AQ
Tel: 01524 271388 *Fax:* 01524 272996
E-mail: office@osg.co.uk
Web: www.osg.co.uk
Office: Lancaster
Work: A1 F1 J1 L S1 W
Legal Aid Franchise
Ptr: Miller, Miss Sarah Susan LLB(Hons) . . . . Sep 2005
Ast: Gregory, Mrs Fiona Susan LLB . . . . Jun 1995

PEARSON & PEARSON ‡
15 Market Square Kirkby Lonsdale Cumbria LA6 2AN
Tel: 01524 271222 *Fax:* 01524 272210
List of partners: I Fishwick, P J Haythornthwaite, P W C Smith
Office: Ingleton, Kendal
Work: A1 E F1 J1 K1 L N P S1 S2 V W
Agency, Fixed Fee Interview undertaken and Member of Accident Line
Ptr: Fishwick, Mr Ian MA(Cantab) . . . . *Oct 1996
Haythornthwaite, Mr Peter J. . . . . *§Jan 1974
Smith, Mr Paul W C BA. . . . . *Dec 1976

KIRKBY STEPHEN, Cumbria

FELL KILVINGTON & CO ‡
Westmorland House Market Square Kirkby Stephen Cumbria CA17 4QT
Tel: 01768 371495 *Fax:* 01768 371303
E-mail: info@kilvingtonsolicitors.co.uk
List of partners: W A S Kilvington
Work: A1 C1 C2 D1 E G H J1 K1 L P R1 S1 T1 V W Z(d)
Emergency Action, Agency, Advocacy, Fixed Fee Interview and Legal Aid undertaken
SPr: Kilvington, Mr William Anthony Shaw . . . . *Jan 1971

HEWITSON & HARKER LIMITED ‡
22 Market Street Kirkby Stephen Cumbria CA17 4QT
Tel: 01768 371534 *Fax:* 01768 371322
E-mail: harkerslaw@aol.com
List of partners: A D Birtles, P J Birtles
Languages: French
Work: A1 A2 B1 C1 E F1 G J1 K1 K3 K4 L N O P Q S1 S2 T1 T2 W X Z(d,f,g,i,l,r)
Agency undertaken
Ptr: Birtles, Dr Alexander Doyle BA; PhD . . . . *Aug 2001
Birtles, Mr Peter John. . . . . *Jul 1968

KIRKBY-IN-ASHFIELD, Nottinghamshire

FIDLER & PEPPER
(incorporating Spencer Hogg & Co; Vardy Wilson; Fuller Edwardson)
80 Station Street Kirkby-in-Ashfield Nottinghamshire NG17 7AP
Tel: 01623 451111 *Fax:* 01623 451133
Dx: 26102 KIRKBY-IN-ASHFIELD
Emergency telephone 01636 812856
E-mail: info@fidler.co.uk
Office: Mansfield, Sutton-in-Ashfield
Work: A1 B1 C1 C2 C3 D1 E F1 G H J1 K1 L N O P Q R1 S1 T1 T2 V W Z(c,j,l,m,n)
Emergency Action, Agency, Advocacy, Fixed Fee Interview, Legal Aid undertaken, Legal Aid Franchise and Member of Accident Line
Ptr: Dawes, Mr Christopher T LLB(Lond) . . . . *May 1979
Jones, Mr Russell LLB . . . . *Oct 1984
Slade, Mr Mark A LLB. . . . . *Feb 1989

MARCHANTS SOLICITORS
Wheatley House 3 Diamond Avenue Kirkby-in-Ashfield Nottinghamshire NG17 7GB
Tel: 01623 688400
Office: Mansfield

KIRKBYMOORSIDE, North Yorkshire

KITCHING WALKER ‡
8 Market Place Kirkbymoorside North Yorkshire YO62 6DD
Tel: 01751 431237 *Fax:* 01751 432822
Dx: 63741 KIRKBYMOORSIDE
E-mail: post@kitchingwalker.co.uk
List of partners: S R Harrison, K L Temple
Work: A1 D1 E F1 K1 L Q S1 T1 W
Agency, Advocacy, Fixed Fee Interview and Legal Aid undertaken
Ptr: Harrison, Ms Sally R LLB . . . . *Oct 1992
Temple, Mrs Kathleen Lesley . . . . *§Dec 1972
Ast: Melles-Sawyers, Miss Sallyann BA . . . . *May 1999
Temple, Mr Stuart Geoffrey LLB(Hons) . . . . *Apr 2006

KIRKHAM, Lancashire

CARTWRIGHT & CO ‡
108a Poulton Street Kirkham Lancashire PR4 2AH
Tel: 01772 683116 / 687010 *Fax:* 01772 671171
Dx: 24851 KIRKHAM
Emergency telephone 01772 683539
E-mail: cartwright.hill@btconnect.com
List of partners: M J Cartwright
Work: D1 E F1 G H J1 K1 N P S1 W
Emergency Action, Agency, Advocacy, Fixed Fee Interview and Legal Aid undertaken
SPr: Cartwright, Mr Malcolm J BA . . . . *Dec 1974

COUPE BRADBURY
48 Poulton Street Kirkham Lancashire PR4 2AH
Tel: 01772 683000 *Fax:* 01772 685060 *Dx:* 24852 KIRKHAM
Emergency telephone 01253 736909
Office: Lytham
Work: D1 E G H K1 N O Q S1 W
Emergency Action, Agency, Advocacy, Fixed Fee Interview and Legal Aid undertaken
Ptr: Coupe, Mr Simon Bruce LLB(Hons) . . . . *Apr 1977

DICKSON HASLAM ‡
12-14 Station Road Kirkham Lancashire PR4 2AS
Tel: 01772 685109 *Fax:* 01772 671064 *Dx:* 722392 KIRKHAM 2
Emergency telephone 01772 685109
E-mail: info@dicksonhaslam.co.uk
List of partners: G R Green, T A L Greensmith, E H Hall, J C H Mathews
Office: Lytham, Preston
Languages: French
Work: A1 A3 B1 C1 C2 C3 D1 E F1 J1 K1 L N Q S1 S2 W Z(l,o)
Emergency Action, Agency, Advocacy, Fixed Fee Interview undertaken and Member of Accident Line
Ptr: Greensmith, Mr T Andrew L BA . . . . *Feb 1986

SENIOR CALVELEY & HARDY
80 Poulton Street Kirkham Lancashire PR4 2AH
Tel: 01772 671177 *Fax:* 01772 671707
E-mail: dh@seniorslaw.co.uk
Office: Lytham, Poulton-le-Fylde
Work: A1 E K1 K3 K4 L N S1 S2 T2 W Z(d)
Agency, Advocacy and Fixed Fee Interview undertaken
Ptr: Hinchliffe, Mr J David G LLB(B'ham) . . . . *Oct 1986

KNARESBOROUGH, North Yorkshire

GREENWOODS ‡
90 High Street Knaresborough North Yorkshire HG5 0EA
Tel: 01423 862975 *Fax:* 01423 861327
E-mail: greenws@hotmail.com
List of partners: J N Greenwood, L D Greenwood
Work: E L S1 S2 W
Fixed Fee Interview undertaken
Ptr: Greenwood, Mr John N BA(Law) . . . . *Nov 1988
Greenwood, Mrs Lynda D LLB . . . . Aug 1983

STEEL & CO
Cranbourne House 36 Gracious Street Knaresborough North Yorkshire HG5 8DS
Tel: 01423 869977 *Fax:* 01423 860055
Dx: 29269 KNARESBOROUGH
E-mail: enquiry@steel-law.co.uk
Office: Wetherby
Work: A1 E K1 L S1 S2 T2 W
Fixed Fee Interview undertaken
Ptr: Curl, Mrs Lynn E R LLB(Leics) . . . . *May 1981
Steel, Mr C John . . . . *Dec 1975
Asoc: Brennan, Mrs Joanne Limbert LLB . . . . *Mar 1991

See p112 for the Key to Work Categories & other symbols

KNEBWORTH, Hertfordshire

BRIGNALLS BALDERSTON WARREN
117 London Road Knebworth Hertfordshire SG3 6ET
Tel: 01438 812374 *Fax:* 01438 815382 *Dx:* 6011 STEVENAGE
E-mail: enquiries@bbwlaw.biz
Office: Baldock, Biggleswade, Letchworth, Stevenage
Work: C1 E R1 S1 S2 W

KNIGHTON, Powys

MEDLICOTT SNOWS
7 Wylcwm Place Knighton Powys LD7 1AE
Tel: 01547 528332 *Fax:* 01547 520086
E-mail: solicitors@medlicottsnows.co.uk
Office: Bishops Castle
Work: A1 E J1 K1 K3 K4 L S1 S2 W
Fixed Fee Interview and Legal Aid undertaken
Ptr: Medlicott, Mr Peter James. . . . . *§Jul 1968

MORRIS & BATES
3 Broad Street Knighton Powys LD7 1BL
Tel: 01547 520130 *Fax:* 01547 520130 *Dx:* 92100 ABERYSTWYTH
E-mail: law@morrisbates.demon.co.uk
Office: Aberystwyth, Llandrindod Wells
Languages: Welsh
Work: A1 B1 C1 C2 D1 D2 E F1 F2 G H J1 K1 L N O P Q R1 R2 S1 S2 T1 T2 V W X Z(b,c,d,f,g,j,k,l,m,o,p,q,r,s)
Legal Aid undertaken and Legal Aid Franchise
Ptr: Morris, Mr W Gareth LLB(Wales) Under Sheriff of Ceredigion; Clerk to Tax Commissioners Notary Public . . . . *Sep 1970

PCB SOLICITORS LLP
Barclays Bank Chambers 8 Broad Street Knighton Powys LD7 1BL
Tel: 01547 520254
E-mail: info@pcblaw.co.uk
Office: Church Stretton, Ludlow, Shrewsbury, Telford
Work: A1 B1 C1 D1 E G H J1 K1 L N O Q S1 T2 W Z(d,l)
Emergency Action, Agency, Advocacy, Fixed Fee Interview and Legal Aid undertaken

KNOTT-END-ON-SEA, Lancashire

INGHAMS
18 Lancaster Road Knott-End-on-Sea Lancashire FY6 0AR
Tel: 01253 810547 *Fax:* 01253 812421
Office: Blackpool (2 offices), Fleetwood, Poulton-le-Fylde, Thornton Cleveleys
Work: A1 C1 E G H J1 K1 L M1 N P S1 W
Emergency Action, Agency and Legal Aid undertaken
Ptr: Hale, Mr Anthony T W. . . . . *Jan 1968

KNOWLE, Bristol

BATCHELOR SHARP
1 Redcatch Road Knowle Bristol BS4 2QB
Tel: 0117 977 0717 *Fax:* 0117 972 0791
Office: Bristol, Kingswood

COOKE PAINTER LIMITED
314 Wells Road Knowle Bristol BS4 2QG
Tel: 0117 977 7403 *Fax:* 0117 972 3658 *Dx:* 119404 KNOWLE
E-mail: knowle@cps-sols.co.uk
Office: Bristol (4 offices)
Work: L S1 S2 W
Ptr: Porter, Mr Stephen George . . . . *Jun 1981
Ast: Darr, Mr Wajid Hamid LLB; PGDip. . . . . *Apr 2002

DAVID LEES & CO ‡
319 Wells Road Knowle Bristol BS4 2QD
Tel: 0117 972 1261 *Fax:* 0117 972 3228
Dx: 119405 KNOWLE (BRISTOL)
E-mail: cmparker@davidlees.co.uk
List of partners: C M Parker
Work: A1 E K1 S1 W
Ptr: Parker, Mr Christopher M . . . . *Jun 1973

SANSBURY DOUGLAS
64 Leinster Avenue Knowle Bristol BS4 1NL
Tel: 0117 963 5044 *Fax:* 0117 963 5047
Emergency telephone 07659 105457
E-mail: trose@sansburydouglas.co.uk
Office: Bristol (2 offices)
Work: G H
Emergency Action, Agency, Advocacy and Legal Aid undertaken
Ptr: Fanson, Mr David J BA(Law) . . . . *Mar 1985
Rose, Mr Timothy J LLB(Bris). . . . . *Nov 1982
Ast: van Wely, Ms Anna M LLB . . . . *Feb 1979

KNOWLE, West Midlands

FENTIMANS ‡
1623 Warwick Road Knowle West Midlands B93 9LF
Tel: 01564 779459 *Fax:* 01564 779649
E-mail: nfentiman@fentimans.co.uk
List of partners: N P Fentiman
Work: C1 D2 E F1 F2 G J1 K1 L N O Q S1 S2 V W Z(p,q)
Emergency Action, Agency, Advocacy, Fixed Fee Interview, Legal Aid undertaken and Legal Aid Franchise
Ptr: Fentiman, Mr Nicholas P LLB(Lond). . . . . *Dec 1979
Ast: Biggs, Ms Susan LLB(Hons); LSF. . . . . *Apr 1987

SL & CO ‡
Chester Court 1673 High Street Knowle West Midlands B93 0LL
Tel: 01564 777250 *Fax:* 01564 777290 *Dx:* 18761 KNOWLE
E-mail: stephenlockwood@slandco.com
Work: B1 C1 C3 D1 E F1 I J1 K1 K2 L M1 M2 O Q S1 S2 U2 W Z(b,c,d,e,f,q,w)

STANDLEY & CO ‡
1612 High Street Knowle West Midlands B93 0JU
Tel: 01564 776287 *Fax:* 01564 778996 *Dx:* 18754 KNOWLE
E-mail: fosterc@standley.co.uk
List of partners: S P Gooden, J M Hunt
Work: B1 B2 C1 C2 C3 E F1 F2 G H J1 K1 L N O Q R1 S1 S2 T1 T2 W Z(c,d,e,l,t)
Agency, Advocacy and Fixed Fee Interview undertaken
Ptr: Gooden, Mr Stephen P LLB. . . . . *§May 1980
Hunt, Miss Judith M BA(Law) . . . . *Nov 1981

KNUTSFORD, Cheshire

BEESTON SHENTON
First Floor Suite 12 Princess Street Knutsford Cheshire WA16 6DD
Tel: 01565 754444
Office: Newcastle under Lyme, Sandbach

GRAHAM CREWE ‡
2 The Poplars Faulkners Lane Mobberley Knutsford Cheshire WA16 7PE
Tel: 07545 964984
E-mail: info@grahamcrewetep.co.uk

DELLAPINA & CO SOLICITORS ‡
Caledonian House Tatton Street Knutsford Cheshire WA16 6AG
Tel: 01565 634100 *Fax:* 01565 621300 *Dx:* 22967 KNUTSFORD
E-mail: info@dellapina.co.uk

FLETCHER & CO SOLICITORS ‡
Warford House 31 King Street Knutsford Cheshire WA16 6DW
Tel: 01565 755411 *Fax:* 01565 755896 *Dx:* 22972 KNUTSFORD
E-mail: johnfletcher@jfsolicitors.co.uk
List of partners: J G Fletcher
Office: Altrincham
Work: E S1 W
SPr: Fletcher, Mr John G LLB . . . . *Nov 1985

HAGUE LAMBERT ‡
(incorporating T M Fryer; Armstrongs)
131 King Street Knutsford Cheshire WA16 6EJ
Est: 1996
Tel: 01565 652411 *Fax:* 01565 653213 *Dx:* 22951 KNUTSFORD
E-mail: ts@hague-lambert.co.uk
Web: www.hague-lambert.co.uk
List of partners: E N Cooper, N G S Day, P J Horton, A C Pettitt, L C Robinson
Office: Macclesfield, Manchester, Urmston
Work: A1 C1 J1 K1 K3 L N S1 S2 T2 W
Fixed Fee Interview undertaken
Ptr: Pettitt, Mr Andrew C LLB(Hull) . . . . *Jan 1982
Asoc: McCluskey, Miss Beverley BA. . . . . *Oct 1995
Richardson, Mrs Sarah Louise LLB(Hons). . . . . . . *Mar 1990
Ast: Gosling, Mrs Samantha G LLB(Hons) . . . . *Jul 1987
Hayes, Miss Amy BA(Hons)(History) . . . . Nov 2005
Hudson, Ms Rachel Louise LLB(Hons) . . . . *Oct 2005

Offices in Manchester, Macclesfield & Urmston. Broad based firm offering a wide range of services to both the business & personal client.

NEXUS SOLICITORS
2 Swinton Square Knutsford Cheshire WA16 6HH
Tel: 01565 632152 *Fax:* 01565 632154 *Dx:* 22958 KNUTSFORD
E-mail: help@nexussolicitors.co.uk
Office: Manchester

WEIGHTMANS LLP
98 King Street Knutsford Cheshire WA16 6EP
Tel: 01565 634234 *Fax:* 01565 652711 *Dx:* 22959 KNUTSFORD
Office: Birmingham, Dartford, Leicester, Liverpool, London EC4, Manchester (2 offices)
Work: A1 C1 D1 D2 E F1 J1 K1 K2 L N O P Q R1 S1 S2 T2 W Z(k,l,q,r)
Agency, Advocacy, Fixed Fee Interview, Legal Aid undertaken, Legal Aid Franchise and Member of Accident Line
Mem: Collins, Ms Emma LLB . . . . *Oct 1994

LAMPETER, Ceredigion

ARNOLD DAVIES VINCENT EVANS ‡
33 High Street Lampeter Ceredigion SA48 7BB
Tel: 01570 422233 *Fax:* 01570 423244 *Dx:* 100950 LAMPETER
E-mail: post@adve.co.uk
List of partners: D P Evans, A W Lewis, M A Stewart
Office: Tregaron
Languages: Welsh
Work: A1 C1 D1 E F1 J1 K1 K3 K4 L N O Q R1 S1 S2 T1 T2 W Z(d)
Agency and Advocacy undertaken
Ptr: Evans, Mr Dafydd Peredur LLB . . . . *Apr 1980
Lewis, Mr Aled Wyn LLB . . . . *Sep 2001
Stewart, Mr Marc Alistair LLB . . . . *Sep 1991
Ast: Jenkins, Miss Gwyneth Eirlys LLB. . . . . *Aug 2010
Thomas, Miss Bethan Haf LLB; BSc. . . . . *Sep 2009
Con: Williams, Mr Clifford Charles LLB . . . . Jul 1977

ROSE THOMAS & CO ‡
19 College Street Lampeter Ceredigion SA48 7DY
Tel: 01570 423300 *Fax:* 01570 423223 *Dx:* 100951 LAMPETER
E-mail: mail@ruththomassolicitors.co.uk
List of partners: R L Thomas, C C Williams
Languages: Welsh
Work: B1 C1 D1 D2 E F1 G H J1 K1 L N O Q S1 S2 V W Z(c,l)
Agency, Advocacy and Legal Aid undertaken
Ptr: Thomas, Ms Ruth L BA . . . . *Oct 1987
Williams, Mr Clifford Charles LLB . . . . Jul 1977
Asoc: Mathias, Miss Kathryn Alison . . . . Oct 1996

LANCASTER, Lancashire

ALLAN GARRICK ‡
(incorporating Haytons)
6-8 Gage Street Lancaster Lancashire LA1 1UH
Tel: 01524 62985 *Fax:* 01524 847403
List of partners: A Garrick
Languages: French
Work: F1 G H K1 L N Q S1 W
Emergency Action, Agency, Advocacy, Fixed Fee Interview, Legal Aid undertaken and Member of Accident Line
Ptr: Garrick, Mr Allan LLB . . . . *Jun 1972

BLACKHURST SWAINSON GOODIER LLP ‡
3 & 4 Aalborg Square Lancaster Lancashire LA1 1GG
Tel: 01524 32471 *Fax:* 01524 386515 *Dx:* 63506 LANCASTER
E-mail: info@bsglaw.co.uk
List of partners: D R Bennetts, A K L Brown, M W Burrow, J O Goodier, G A Mercer, T P O'Neill, K G Parr
Office: Preston
Work: A1 B1 C1 C2 C3 D1 E F1 J1 K1 K2 K3 K4 L N O Q R1 S1 S2 T1 T2 V W X Z(d,l)
Emergency Action, Agency, Advocacy, Fixed Fee Interview, Legal Aid undertaken and Legal Aid Franchise
Ptr: Bennetts, Mr David R . . . . *§Jan 1973
Brown, Ms Andrea Katherine Lindsay LLB. . . . . . *Sep 1993
Burrow, Mr Mark W . . . . *Dec 1980
O'Neill, Mr Thomas Patrick LLB . . . . *Oct 1980
Ast: Butterfield, Miss Rebecca LLB. . . . . *Mar 2008
Catterson, Miss Rebecca Faye LLB. . . . . *Sep 2007
Owen, Mrs Amanda BA . . . . Oct 2003
Sutton, Mrs Helen Elizabeth LLB . . . . *Dec 1980
Con: Packer, Miss Phyllidia D LLB . . . . *Aug 1979

CLARKSON HIRST ‡
73 Church Street Lancaster Lancashire LA1 1ET
Tel: 01524 39760 *Fax:* 01524 67242 *Dx:* 63515 LANCASTER
Emergency telephone 01524 39760
E-mail: info@clarksonhirst.co.uk
List of partners: S P Farnsworth, R A Hirst, W M G Winder
Office: Barrow-in-Furness, Kendal
Work: A1 B1 C1 C2 C3 D1 E F1 G H I J1 K1 L M1 M2 N P R1 S1 T1 T2 V W Z(a,b,c,d,e,f,g,h,j,k,l,m)
Emergency Action, Agency, Advocacy, Fixed Fee Interview, Legal Aid undertaken, Legal Aid Franchise and Member of Accident Line
Ptr: Farnsworth, Mr Simon Paul LLB. . . . . *Jan 1996
Hirst, Mr Richard A LLB. . . . . *Jun 1977
Winder, Mr William Matthew Guy BA . . . . *Sep 1995

DOUGLAS CLIFT & CO ‡
25 Church Street Lancaster Lancashire LA1 1LP
Tel: 01524 32437 *Fax:* 01524 841135 *Dx:* 63528 LANCASTER
E-mail: info@douglasclift.co.uk
List of partners: M K G Bennett, I R Greenslade, P J Thornton
Work: D1 K1 K3 N S1 W
Emergency Action, Agency, Advocacy, Fixed Fee Interview, Legal Aid undertaken, Legal Aid Franchise and Member of Accident Line
Ptr: Bennett, Mr Mark K G LLB . . . . *Jan 1990
Greenslade, Mr Ian Robin LLB . . . . *Nov 1987
Thornton, Mr Peter J . . . . *Dec 1974
Ast: Garnett, Miss Joanna Clare BA(Hons). . . . . *Dec 1998
Houghton, Miss Lynsey Michelle LLB(Hons). . . . . . Sep 2005

LINDSAY HALEWOOD-DODD ‡
31 Church Street Lancaster Lancashire LA1 1LP
Tel: 01524 846024

HOLDENS ‡
2 Castle Hill Lancaster Lancashire LA1 1YR
Est: 1855
Tel: 01524 32484 *Fax:* 01524 35945 *Dx:* 63503 LANCASTER
Emergency telephone 01524 263452
E-mail: advice@holdens-solicitors.co.uk
Office: Kendal
Work: C1 D1 D2 E G H J1 K1 N O Q S1 S2 W Z(l,m,q)

JOBLING & KNAPE ‡
5 Aalborg Square Lancaster Lancashire LA1 1GG
Tel: 01524 598300 *Fax:* 01524 598339 *Dx:* 63529 LANCASTER
E-mail: mail@joblingandknape.com
List of partners: P J Bujakowski, I J N Gee, D Harrison, C N Hollingdrake
Office: Great Eccleston, Morecambe
Languages: Spanish
Work: A1 A2 B1 B2 C1 C2 D1 D2 E F1 F2 G H I J1 J2 K1 K2 K3 K4 L M1 M3 N O P Q R1 R2 S1 S2 T1 T2 U2 V W Z(c,e,f,g,h,j,k,l,n,o,p,q,r,t,u,w,za)
Emergency Action, Agency, Advocacy, Fixed Fee Interview, Legal Aid undertaken and Legal Aid Franchise
Ptr: Bujakowski, Mr Peter Jan LLB. . . . . *Jul 1974
Gee, Mr Ian J N LLB . . . . *§Jun 1979
Hollingdrake, Mr Craig N LLB . . . . *§Oct 1989
Asoc: Davey, Miss Clare Elizabeth LLB . . . . Nov 2003
Willey, Mr Michael C BA ●. . . . . Dec 1980
Willey, Miss Suzanne Margaret ♦ . . . . Sep 2003
Ast: Hughes, Mr Lee William. . . . . Nov 2010
Shawcross, Ms Kate Elizabeth . . . . Jan 2010
Snell, Ms Emma . . . . Sep 2008
Walling, Mrs Hannah Lynne . . . . *Mar 2011
Ward, Mrs Fiona Terese LLB . . . . *Apr 2010
Wilson, Mrs Anita LLB. . . . . Jul 2007
Con: Hardy, Mr David R . . . . *§Nov 1975

ANTHONY JONES ‡
Priory House Priory Lane Hornby Lancaster Lancashire LA2 8LE
Tel: 01524 221200 *Fax:* 01524 221200
Emergency telephone 07770 806486
Work: O Q Z(c)
Agency undertaken

JOSEPH A JONES & CO ‡
6 Fenton Street Lancaster Lancashire LA1 1TE
Tel: 01524 63371 *Fax:* 01524 65818 *Dx:* 63504 LANCASTER
E-mail: office@jajsolicitors.co.uk
List of partners: S E Hodgson, G F Rycroft
Work: A1 E L S1 S2 W
Ptr: Hodgson, Mrs Susan E . . . . *§Jun 1976
Rycroft, Mr Gary Francis LLB . . . . *Apr 1998
Con: Higgins, Mr Peter F D LLB . . . . §Jan 1966

MARSH & CO ‡
(incorporating Peter Sheard)
22 Sun Street Lancaster Lancashire LA1 1ER
Tel: 01524 68102 *Fax:* 01524 33126
E-mail: marshandco@btconnect.com
List of partners: S Pollard, P J Wilson
Work: D1 D2 E F1 J1 K1 K2 K3 L Q S1 W
Emergency Action, Agency and Advocacy undertaken
Ptr: Pollard, Mrs Shirley LLB Deputy District Judge . . . . *Nov 1971
Wilson, Mrs Pamela J LLB . . . . *Apr 1990

MARSHALL GLOVER LIMITED ‡
1 Middle Street Lancaster Lancashire LA1 1JZ
Tel: 0844 801 1422 *Fax:* 01524 298932

2

MAXWELL GILLOTT (MG LAW LTD) ‡
King's Yard High Street Lancaster Lancashire LA1 1LA
Tel: 0844 858 3900 *Fax:* 0844 858 3949
E-mail: office@mglaw.co.uk
List of partners: C R E Gillott, E M Maxwell
Languages: Hindi, Punjabi, Urdu
Work: X Z(g,r)
Legal Aid Franchise
Ptr: Gillott, Mr Charles R E BA(Oxon) . . . . *Oct 1986
Maxwell, Mrs Elaine Mary LLB . . . . *Dec 1991
Ast: Denver, Mrs Sarah BSc(Hons) . . . . Sep 1999
Gent, Ms Emily . . . . Mar 2005

OGLETHORPE STURTON & GILLIBRAND ‡
16 Castle Park Lancaster Lancashire LA1 1YG
Tel: 01524 846846 *Fax:* 01524 382247 *Dx:* 63500 LANCASTER
E-mail: office@osg.co.uk
Web: www.osg.co.uk
List of partners: E J Briggs, D L Gillibrand, R M N Gillibrand, A M Kinder, C L Love, S S Miller, D E Park, A D J Royce
Office: Kirkby Lonsdale
Work: A1 A2 A3 B1 C1 C2 C3 D1 E F1 J1 K1 K2 K3 L M1 M2 N O P Q R1 R2 S1 S2 T1 T2 W Z(c,d,e,h,j,l,o,q,r,s)
Emergency Action, Agency, Advocacy and Fixed Fee Interview undertaken
Ptr: Briggs, Miss Emma Jane LLB(Hons) . . . . *Nov 1994
Gillibrand, Mr David L BSc(Wales)(Econ) . . . . *Jul 1979
Gillibrand, Mr Richard M N MA(Cantab) . . . . *§Apr 1971
Kinder, Miss Alison M LLB . . . . *Sep 1993
Love, Mrs Clare Louise BA(Hons) . . . . *Sep 2003
Park, Mr David Edmund BA(Hons) . . . . *Sep 1997
Royce, Mr Andrew D J LLB(Hons)(B'ham) . . . . Sep 1989
Asoc: Grabowski, Mrs Jennifer Mary BA(Hons) . . . . Sep 2004
Mallaband, Miss Eleanor Kate MA . . . . Sep 2006
Ast: Alabaster, Mr Warwick BSc(Hons); PGDipLaw; LPC . . Aug 2004
Andrews, Mr Oliver Richard . . . . Sep 2010
Bates, Miss Hannah . . . . Sep 2010
Cross, Mrs Sarah Jane LLB(Hons) . . . . *Apr 1999
Labrum, Mr Timothy Hugh LLB(Hons) . . . . Sep 2009
Myers, Mr John Levison BSc(Hons) . . . . *Oct 2007

PATERSONS ‡
63a Scotforth Road Lancaster Lancashire LA1 4SD
Tel: 01524 843336 *Fax:* 01524 843334
E-mail: 63a@lineone.net
List of partners: C A Parker
Work: K4 S1 W
Ptr: Parker, Mr Colin Andrew . . . . *Jun 1971

RATCLIFFE & BIBBY
69-71 Church Street Lancaster Lancashire LA1 1ET
Tel: 01524 39039 *Fax:* 01524 36048 *Dx:* 63512 LANCASTER
E-mail: lancaster@rblegal.co.uk
Office: Carnforth, Morecambe
Work: C1 D1 E F1 J1 K1 L P R1 S1 W Z(l)
Agency, Legal Aid undertaken, Legal Aid Franchise and Member of Accident Line
Ptr: Drinkall, Mr Vernon R BA . . . . *Jun 1980
Asoc: Carr, Ms Sarah Anne . . . . *Nov 1966

STOCKDALE SOLICITORS ‡
1 Oubeck House Ellel Lancaster Lancashire LA2 0PU
Tel: 01524 753026 *Fax:* 01524 751261

DAVID SYKES SOLICITOR ‡
4 Castle Park Lancaster Lancashire LA1 1YQ
Tel: 01524 845849

LANCHESTER, Co Durham

BENNETT RICHMOND ‡
23 Front Street Lanchester Co Durham DH7 0LA
Tel: 01207 521843 *Fax:* 01207 529367 *Dx:* 61932 CONSETT
E-mail: info@bennett-richmond.co.uk
List of partners: P Aylmore, M G Davies, D S James
Office: Consett
Work: A1 B1 C1 D1 E F1 G H J1 K1 L M1 N P Q R1 S1 S2 T1 V W Z(a,b,c,d,e,f,g,h,i,j,k,l,m,n,o,p,q,s,t)
Emergency Action, Agency, Advocacy, Fixed Fee Interview, Legal Aid undertaken, Legal Aid Franchise and Member of Accident Line
Ptr: Aylmore, Mr Peter . . . . *§Dec 1978
Davies, Mr Mark G . . . . *Oct 1985
James, Mr David S BA(Cantab) . . . . *§Dec 1968

LANCING, West Sussex

GATES & MOLONEY ‡
13 South Street Lancing West Sussex BN15 8AH
Tel: 01903 766046 *Fax:* 01903 752950 *Dx:* 36703 LANCING
E-mail: reception@gatesandmoloney.com
List of partners: H J L Norton
Work: K1 K3 K4 L Q S1 S2 T2 W
Emergency Action, Agency, Advocacy, Fixed Fee Interview and Legal Aid undertaken
Ptr: Norton, Miss Helen Joanna Louise LLB . . . . *Sep 2002
Ast: Smee, Ms Alice Naomi BA . . . . *Mar 2008
Wagstaffe, Miss Gabrielle Katherine BA . . . . *Jan 2008

GREEN WRIGHT CHALTON ANNIS
28 North Road Lancing West Sussex BN15 9BQ
Tel: 01903 752918 *Fax:* 01903 814682 *Dx:* 36702 LANCING
E-mail: enquiries@gwca.co.uk
Office: Arundel, Rustington, Steyning, Worthing (2 offices)
Work: A1 B1 C1 C2 C3 D1 E F1 J1 K1 L M1 N O P Q R1 S1 S2 T1 T2 V W Z(c,l,q)

MALCOLM WILSON & COBBY
3 Station Parade South Street Lancing West Sussex BN15 8AA
Tel: 01903 765991 *Fax:* 01903 750595 *Dx:* 36700 LANCING
E-mail: nbrazier@netcomuk.co.uk
Office: Worthing (2 offices)
Work: E L S1 W
Ptr: Brazier, Mr Nigel P BSocSc . . . . *Feb 1991

WOOLACOTT & CO ‡
71 South Street Lancing West Sussex BN15 8AP
Tel: 01903 763011 / 764334 *Fax:* 01903 753216
Dx: 36709 LANCING
E-mail: info@woolacott.fsbusiness.co.uk
List of partners: G J Woolacott, M A Woolacott
Work: D1 E F1 J1 K1 L N Q S1 S2 V W
Emergency Action, Agency, Advocacy and Fixed Fee Interview undertaken
Ptr: Woolacott, Mr Graham J LLB . . . . *§Jul 1978
Woolacott, Mrs Margaret Ann BA . . . . *Dec 1992

LARKFIELD, Kent

J G RICHARDS ‡
787 London Road Larkfield Kent ME20 6DE
Tel: 01732 870377 *Fax:* 01732 847313
E-mail: mail@jgrichards.co.uk
List of partners: J G G Richards
Languages: French
Work: S1 W
SPr: Richards, Mr John G G . . . . Mar 1978

LAUNCESTON, Cornwall

COODES
8 Race Hill Launceston Cornwall PL15 9BA
Tel: 01566 770000 *Fax:* 01566 770001 *Dx:* 82700 LAUNCESTON
E-mail: enquiries@coodes.co.uk
Office: Holsworthy, Liskeard, Newquay, Penzance, St Austell, Truro
Languages: French
Work: A1 B1 C1 C2 C3 D1 E F1 G H J1 K1 L M1 M2 N O P Q R1 S1 T1 T2 V W Z(l)
Emergency Action, Agency, Advocacy, Fixed Fee Interview, Legal Aid undertaken, Legal Aid Franchise and Member of Accident Line
Ptr: Marshall, Mr Andrew S H LLB . . . . Nov 1996
Asoc: Robinson, Mrs Lisa J . . . . §Dec 1992
Ast: Garde-Evans, Miss Anna . . . . Apr 2011
Jordan, Mr Derek John LLB(Hons) . . . . *Nov 1996
Sampson, Mrs Gemma . . . . *Jul 2002

NICHOLAS HEWLITT FAMILY LAW PRACTICE ‡
11 High Street Launceston Cornwall PL15 8ER
Tel: 01566 777774 *Fax:* 01566 777775
E-mail: nicholashewlittfamilylaw@btconnect.com

PARNALLS SOLICITORS LIMITED ‡
13-19 Westgate Street Launceston Cornwall PL15 7AB
Tel: 01566 772375 *Fax:* 01566 772128 *Dx:* 82705 LAUNCESTON
E-mail: administrator@parnallsolicitors.co.uk
List of partners: J R B Parnall, K S Parnall, R M B Parnall
Work: A1 A2 B1 C1 C2 C3 D1 D2 E F1 F2 J1 J2 K1 K2 K3 K4 L N O P Q R1 R2 S1 S2 T2 U1 V W Z(c,d,h,i,k,l,m,p,r,s,t)
Emergency Action, Agency, Advocacy, Legal Aid undertaken and Legal Aid Franchise
Ptr: Parnall, Mr Jonathan R B . . . . *§Nov 1981
Parnall, Mrs Katherine Scott MA(Oxon) . . . . *§Sep 1993
Parnall, Mr R Mark B . . . . *§Oct 1980

Lexcel

PETERS LANGSFORD DAVIES ‡
Westgate Launceston Cornwall PL15 9AD
Tel: 01566 772451 *Fax:* 01566 774577 *Dx:* 82701 LAUNCESTON
E-mail: ag@peterslangsforddavies.com
Web: www.peterslangsforddavies.com
List of partners: H Davies, J K G de Ferrars, I J Langsford, T M Warne
Languages: French
Work: A1 D1 D2 E F1 G J1 K1 K3 K4 L N O P Q S1 S2 T1 T2 V W Z(c,d,l,q,t)
Emergency Action, Agency, Advocacy, Fixed Fee Interview, Legal Aid undertaken and Legal Aid Franchise
Ptr: Davies, Mrs Helen LLB; MA . . . . *§Oct 1989
de Ferrars, Mr James K G BA . . . . *Oct 1987
Langsford, Mr Ian James LLB(B'ham) . . . . *§Jul 1980
Warne, Mr Thomas Michael MA(Cantab) . . . . *§Dec 1976

JOHN WHITING & CO ‡
27 Westgate Street Launceston Cornwall PL15 7AD
Tel: 01566 777677 *Fax:* 01566 777688 *Dx:* 82702 LAUNCESTON
E-mail: reception@johnwhitingandco.com
List of partners: R J Whiting
Languages: French, German
Work: A1 E F1 J1 K1 K3 K4 L N Q R1 S1 S2 W Z(c,d,l)
Agency, Advocacy and Fixed Fee Interview undertaken
Ptr: Whiting, Mr R John BSc(Econ) . . . . *§Jun 1975
Ast: Chester, Mr Graham Christopher . . . . *§Dec 1977

LEAMINGTON SPA, Warwickshire

ALSTERS KELLEY ‡
Hamilton House 20-24 Hamilton Terrace Leamington Spa Warwickshire CV32 4LY
Tel: 0844 561 0100 *Fax:* 0844 561 0299
Dx: 11866 LEAMINGTON SPA
E-mail: enquiries@alsterskelley.com
List of partners: A C J Bannister, G W Brooke-Taylor, L C Harvey, S J Hunka, E J Kemp, T Mannion, N Raiseborough, H A Vedy, C J Wahlberg, K Wardley-Tipple, C J Witherall
Office: Coventry, Nuneaton
Languages: Afrikaans, French, Mirpuri, Punjabi, Urdu
Work: B1 C1 C2 C3 D1 E F1 G H J1 J2 K1 K2 K3 K4 L M1 N O Q R1 S1 S2 T2 W Z(c,d,e,h,i,k,l,p,q,r)
Emergency Action, Agency, Advocacy, Fixed Fee Interview, Legal Aid undertaken, Legal Aid Franchise and Member of Accident Line
Ptr: Brooke-Taylor, Mr Geoffrey W LLB(Sheff) . . . . . *Dec 1973
Kemp, Mrs Erica Jane BA . . . . Sep 2001
Raiseborough, Mr Neil LLB . . . . *Sep 2000
Vedy, Miss Haidee A BA . . . . *Jun 1989
Wahlberg, Miss Catherine Jane LLB(Hons) . . . . . *Oct 2000
Wardley-Tipple, Mrs Karen . . . . Oct 1998
Witherall, Mr Colin J . . . . *Jul 1977
Asoc: Frowd, Mr Colin James . . . . Dec 1995
Simister, Mr John . . . . Mar 1991
Ast: Fripp, Mrs Elizabeth Felicity . . . . Apr 2004
Piff, Ms Emma Jayne . . . . May 2005
Watts, Mr Andrew . . . . Sep 2000
Con: Fillmore, Mr Timothy M LLB . . . . *§Oct 1972

AMPHLETT CHATTERTON ‡
The Malthouse William Street Leamington Spa Warwickshire CV32 4HJ
Tel: 01926 311427 *Fax:* 01926 339681
Dx: 11875 LEAMINGTON SPA
E-mail: enquiries@amphlettchatterton.com
List of partners: G Eastgate, S A Hunter
Work: A1 B1 C1 E F1 K1 L M1 N O Q S1 S2 W X Z(d,j,l)
Agency, Advocacy and Fixed Fee Interview undertaken
Ptr: Eastgate, Mr Gareth LLB(Hons) . . . . Feb 1991
Hunter, Mr Stewart A BA(Hons) Notary Public . . . . . *Jun 1980

ASPELL & CO LTD ‡
29 Milverton Crescent Leamington Spa Warwickshire CV32 5NJ
Tel: 01926 337613 *Fax:* 01926 470095
E-mail: jayne.aspell@aspell-legal.com

BLAKEMORES
1 Clarendon Place Leamington Spa Warwickshire CV32 5QL
Tel: 01926 457300 *Fax:* 01926 457399
Dx: 11864 LEAMINGTON SPA
Emergency telephone 01926 457300
E-mail: leamington@blakemores.co.uk
Office: Birmingham
Work: K1 K3 S1

BLYTHE LIGGINS ‡
Edmund House Rugby Road Leamington Spa Warwickshire CV32 6EL
Tel: 01926 831231 *Fax:* 01926 831331
Dx: 11872 LEAMINGTON SPA
E-mail: rht@blytheliggins.co.uk
Languages: French, German, Polish
Work: A1 A3 B1 C1 C2 D1 E F1 I J1 K1 L M1 N O P Q R1 S1 V W Z(c,d,j,k,l,m,o,q,w)

DEVINE OKEEFFE SOLICITORS ‡
27 Regent Street Leamington Spa Warwickshire CV32 5EJ
Tel: 01926 888947 *Fax:* 01926 888948
E-mail: bethany@devineokeeffe.co.uk

EMPLOYMENT INTEGRATION ‡
The Old Barn Churchlands Business Park Leamington Spa Warwickshire CV33 9GX
Tel: 01926 612679

FIELD OVERELL ‡
42 Warwick Street Leamington Spa Warwickshire CV32 5JS
Tel: 01926 422101 *Fax:* 01926 450568
Dx: 11861 LEAMINGTON SPA
E-mail: leamington@fieldoverell.com
List of partners: R M Armitage, S C Homer, A P M McCusker
Office: Coventry
Work: A1 B1 D1 E F1 G H J1 K1 L N P R1 S1 V W Z(c,d,i)
Emergency Action, Agency, Advocacy, Legal Aid undertaken, Legal Aid Franchise and Member of Accident Line
Ptr: Armitage, Mr Richard M LLB(Lond) Notary Public . . . *Jun 1978
Homer, Mr Simon C LLB Notary Public . . . . *§Sep 1981
McCusker, Mr Andrew Patrick Michael LLB . . . . . *Sep 1992
Con: Lemberger, Mr Richard William . . . . *§Nov 1975

MARTIN GROVES SOLICITORS ‡
16 Cross Street Leamington Spa Warwickshire CV32 4PX
Tel: 01926 629007 *Fax:* 01926 882759
E-mail: mg@martingrovessolicitors.co.uk

LEGAL ESCROW & ARBITRATION SERVICES LIMITED ‡
29 Milverton Crescent Leamington Spa Warwickshire CV32 5NU
Tel: 0870 164 2264

DAVID LEIGH-HUNT ‡
Bedford House 76a Bedford Street Leamington Spa Warwickshire CV32 5DT
Tel: 01926 427400 *Fax:* 01926 335133
Dx: 11869 LEAMINGTON SPA
E-mail: info@davidleigh-hunt-solicitors.co.uk
List of partners: D R Leigh-Hunt
Languages: French, Spanish
Work: B1 C1 E J1 K3 N O Q S1 S2 W X Z(c,d,l,u,y)
Agency, Advocacy and Fixed Fee Interview undertaken
SPr: Leigh-Hunt, Mr David R LLB; LLM . . . . *Jun 1969
Asoc: Leigh-Hunt, Mrs Valerie I BA; LLB; AKC . . . . . . *Jun 1968

ROLLASONS ‡
114a Regent Street Leamington Spa Warwickshire CV32 4RE
Tel: 01926 883431 *Fax:* 01926 336832 *Dx:* 21957 DAVENTRY
E-mail: admin@rollasons.com

WITHERS & ROGERS
60 Holly Walk Leamington Spa Warwickshire CV32 4JE
Tel: 01926 336111 *Fax:* 01926 335519

WRIGHT HASSALL LLP ‡
Olympus Avenue Leamington Spa Warwickshire CV34 6BF
Tel: 01926 886688 *Fax:* 01926 885588
Dx: 742180 LEAMINGTON SPA
E-mail: enquiries@wrighthassall.co.uk
List of partners: N Q Abell, P C Beddoes, I R Besant, S S Bhandal, G D Blyth, J Bunting, G Davies, J E Forrester, P J Harris, P J Heath, L A Heizler, R D Koolhoven, R Lane, R J Lee, M V Lewis, C A Matthews, T C I McKenzie, R S Ogg, A C Payne, S J Perry, T J H Rowe, J A Senior, J L Whitby
Work: A1 A3 B1 C1 C2 C3 D1 E F1 F2 I J1 J2 K1 K2 L N O P Q R1 R2 S1 S2 T1 T2 U1 U2 W Z(c,d,e,f,g,h,j,k,l,p,q,r,s,u,w,z)
Agency, Advocacy and Fixed Fee Interview undertaken
Ptr: Abell, Mr Nicholas Q . . . . *Nov 1982
Beddoes, Mr Peter C BA(Hons) . . . . *§Oct 1979
Besant, Mr Ian R LLB . . . . *Oct 1982
Bhandal, Satvinder Singh BSc; LLB . . . . *Feb 1997
Blyth, Mr G David LLB . . . . *§Apr 1972
Bunting, Ms Julia LLB(B'ham) . . . . *Nov 1982
Davies, Mr Graham BA(Hons) . . . . *Jul 1998
Forrester, Mrs Judy E BA(Hons) . . . . *Aug 1989
Harris, Mr Philip Julian BA; MA(Cantab); FCIArb ♦ . . *Oct 1985
Heath, Mr Philip James LLB(Hons); MA; Former Barrister . . . . *Jan 2000
Heizler, Mr Laurence Anthony MA(Oxon) . . . . *Jan 1994
Koolhoven, Mr Robin Dick LLB(Hons) Hatchard Law Prize (Somerset Law Society) . . . . *Nov 1992
Lane, Mr Richard LLB . . . . *Oct 1985
Lee, Mr Robert J LLB . . . . *Oct 1992
Lewis, Mr Mark V MA(Oxon) . . . . *Nov 1985
McKenzie, Mr T Charles I LLB(Leics) Notary Public . *§Apr 1981

 See p112 for the Key to Work Categories & other symbols

Matthews, Miss Carol A BA . . . . *Oct 1980
Ogg, Mr Robin S MA(Cantab) Notary Public. . . . . *§Dec 1968
Payne, Mr Andrew C LLB(Wales) . . . . *Apr 1976
Perry, Mrs Sarah J LLB(Hons) Maxwell Law Prize . . *Nov 1991
Rowe, Mr Timothy J H BA(Cantab) . . . . *§Sep 1987
Senior, Ms Jane A LLB(Manc). . . . . *Nov 1988
Whitby, Mrs Julia L LLB(Lond). . . . . *Apr 1978
Asoc: Brooke-Taylor, Mr Geoffrey W LLB(Sheff) . . . . . . *Dec 1973
Burger, Mr Paul A. . . . . Oct 1987
Harrar, Ms Sukhpal Kaur LLB(Hons). . . . . *Apr 2000
Jakeman, Mrs Louisa Mary LLB(Hons) . . . . *Jun 1991
Jarman, Mr Anthony Rhys LLB(Hons) . . . . *Oct 1995
Loftus, Mr Stephen Roy BA(Hons). . . . . Apr 1985
Rouse, Mr John Alexander Ivan . . . . *Oct 1995
Worthington, Ms Gillian A LLB(Manc) . . . . *Oct 1987
Ast: Allen-Jones, Mr Christopher James . . . . *Oct 1996
Backhouse, Ms Ann BA(Hons)(Oxon); MSc . . . . . . *Oct 1997
Colville, Mr Iain James LLB(Hons). . . . . *Apr 1999
George, Mr Vinesh Shelton LLB(Hons) . . . . *Apr 2002
Hung, Mr Pak Kai BA(Hons). . . . . *Mar 1997
McVeigh, Mr James Michael MA(Hons) . . . . *Oct 2001
Sherriff, Ms Claire Alice LLB(Hons) . . . . *Sep 2000

LEATHERHEAD, Surrey

THE FAMILY LAW PARTNERSHIP LLP ‡
Thorncroft Manor Thorncroft Drive Leatherhead Surrey KT22 8JB
Tel: 01372 700890 *Fax:* 01372 700891 *Dx:* 7352 LEATHERHEAD
E-mail: info@familylawyers.co.uk
List of partners: S L Cloud, A Trier
Languages: French
Work: K1 K2
Ptr: Cloud, Ms Sharon Lee . . . . *May 1994
Trier, Mrs Anne BSc(Econ) . . . . *Oct 1982

FORTESCUE GRAHAM & LLOYD ‡
Bridge Chambers 37 Bridge Street Leatherhead Surrey KT22 8BN
Tel: 01372 374895 *Fax:* 01372 379391 *Dx:* 7308 LEATHERHEAD
E-mail: lh@fortescuegl.co.uk
List of partners: J M H Graham, P K Lloyd
Office: Great Bookham
Work: K1 K3 S1 W
Fixed Fee Interview undertaken and Member of Accident Line
Ptr: Graham, Mr John M H BDS(Lond) . . . . *Jul 1971
Lloyd, Mr Peter K LLB. . . . . *Jan 1969

HEDLEYS SOLICITORS LLP
Butler House Guildford Road Bookham Leatherhead Surrey KT23 4HB
Tel: 01483 284667 *Fax:* 01483 284817
Office: Croydon, East Horsley

HOWELL-JONES LLP
Flint House 52 High Street Leatherhead Surrey KT22 8AJ
Tel: 01372 860650 *Fax:* 01372 860659 *Dx:* 7305 LEATHERHEAD
E-mail: leatherhead@howell-jones.com
Office: Cheam, Kingston upon Thames, London SW20, London WC2, Walton-on-Thames
Languages: Armenian, French
Work: A1 B1 C1 E J1 K1 L M1 N P R1 S1 T1 W Z(c,e,f,j,k,l,o)
Mem: Hotten, Mrs Helen Lesley ARCO . . . . *Mar 2003
Ast: Coster, Ms Samantha. . . . . Apr 2005
Forshaw, Mr Simon Alan . . . . *Nov 1979
Jackson, Mrs Claire Corrine LLB(Bris). . . . . *§Apr 1976

JEPSEN & CO ‡
65 East Lane West Horsley Leatherhead Surrey KT24 6LR
Tel: 01483 281720 *Fax:* 01483 281721 *Dx:* 141173 EAST HORSLEY
List of partners: C R Jepsen
Languages: Cantonese, French
Work: E L S1 S2 W
SPr: Jepsen, Mrs Cecilia Rica LLB(Hons); ACIS . . . . . *Nov 1986

T I SHAWDON & CO ‡
17 Holtwood Road Oxshott Leatherhead Surrey KT22 0QL
Tel: 01372 200037 *Fax:* 01372 802873
E-mail: tis@tislaw.co.uk

TWM SOLICITORS LLP
Sweech House Gravel Hill Leatherhead Surrey KT22 7HF
Tel: 01372 374148 *Fax:* 01372 360628 *Dx:* 7319 LEATHERHEAD
E-mail: leatherhead.reception@twmsolicitors.com
Office: Cranleigh, Epsom, Guildford, London SW19, Reigate
Work: A1 B1 C1 C2 C3 D1 E F1 J1 K1 L M2 N O Q R1 S1 T1 T2 V W Z(c,d,e,k,l,o)
Ptr: McCullough, Mr Peter R BSocSc(Natal) . . . . *Dec 1980
Stevenson, Mr Mark Andrew LLB(Hons). . . . . *Aug 2000
Con: Benger, Mr Nicholas B H M Deputy Coroner of the County of Surrey . . . . *§Jul 1964

JULIE WEST SOLICITOR ‡
37 St Mary's Road Leatherhead Surrey KT22 8HB
Tel: 01372 383273 *Fax:* 0870 005 2048
E-mail: jw@juliewest.co.uk
List of partners: J West
Languages: French
Work: E K4 R1 R2 S1 S2 W
SPr: West, Mrs Julie MA(Cantab). . . . . *Oct 1985

S WINAYAK ‡
Ashyana Parkfields Oxshott Leatherhead Surrey KT22 0PW
Tel: 020 8941 6022 *Fax:* 020 8941 6022
E-mail: sheenawinayak@winayaksolicitors.co.uk
List of partners: S S Winayak
Languages: Hindi, Punjabi
Work: E S1 S2
Ptr: Winayak, Ms Sheena S LLB. . . . . *Mar 1985

LECHLADE, Gloucestershire

CROWDY & ROSE
High Street Lechlade Gloucestershire GL7 3AE
Tel: 01367 252644 *Fax:* 01367 252979
E-mail: lechlade@crowdyandrose.co.uk
Office: Faringdon
Work: A1 C1 E J1 K1 L N Q S1 T1 T2 W
Ptr: Clarke, Mr Stephen J BA(Hons). . . . . *Mar 1984

LEDBURY, Herefordshire

DF LEGAL LLP
13 The Southend Ledbury Herefordshire HR8 2LY
Tel: 01531 633222 *Fax:* 01531 631666 *Dx:* 27288 LEDBURY
E-mail: ljones@dflegal.com
Office: Tewkesbury
Work: A1 A3 B1 C1 C2 C3 E F1 F2 J1 K1 L O Q R1 R2 S1 S2 T1 T2 U1 U2 W Z(b,c,e,f,k,l,u,w,z)
Ast: Rees, Mr Malcolm LLB . . . . Aug 2008

MASEFIELD SOLICITORS LLP ‡
Worcester Road Ledbury Herefordshire HR8 1PN
Tel: 01531 632377 *Fax:* 01531 633904 *Dx:* 27282 LEDBURY
Emergency telephone 01531 660241
E-mail: law@masefield.co.uk
List of partners: F J Longstaff, C W Masefield
Work: A1 E J1 K1 K3 K4 L O Q S1 S2 W Z(d,l)
Fixed Fee Interview undertaken
Mem: Longstaff, Miss Fenella Jane . . . . *Sep 2004
Masefield, Mr Charles W BA . . . . *Oct 1984
Con: Brooks, Mr Richard J LLB Notary Public. . . . . . . *§Jun 1973

ORME & SLADE LTD ‡
National Westminster Bank Chambers The Homend Ledbury Herefordshire HR8 1AB
Tel: 01531 632226 *Fax:* 01531 632481
List of partners: C Greensmith, D A Rushton
Ptr: Greensmith, Mr Christopher LLB . . . . *Oct 1995
Rushton, Mr David A LLB(Newc) . . . . *Nov 1977
Ast: Neilson, Mrs Julie Dawn. . . . . *Nov 2001
Yeomans, Miss Lucy Charlotte LLB(Hons). . . . . . *Sep 2000

LEE-ON-THE-SOLENT, Hampshire

CHURCHERS
138 High Street Lee-on-the-Solent Hampshire PO13 9DG
Tel: 023 9255 1500 *Fax:* 023 9255 2796 *Dx:* 40807 FAREHAM
Emergency telephone 023 9252 6964
E-mail: solicitors@churchers.co.uk
Office: Fareham, Gosport, Portsmouth (2 offices), Ryde
Work: D1 E F1 G H J1 K1 L N P Q S1 V W Z(d,i,l)
Emergency Action, Agency, Advocacy, Fixed Fee Interview, Legal Aid undertaken, Legal Aid Franchise and Member of Accident Line
Ptr: Donnelly, Mr William S LLB(Lond). . . . . *Nov 1985

LEEDS, West Yorkshire

ADDLESHAW GODDARD
Sovereign House Sovereign Street Leeds West Yorkshire LS1 1HQ
Tel: 0113 209 2000 *Fax:* 0113 209 2060 *Dx:* 12004 LEEDS
Emergency telephone 0113 209 2000
Office: London EC1, Manchester
Languages: Dutch, French, German, Italian, Russian, Spanish, Welsh
Work: A1 A3 B1 C1 C2 C3 D1 E F1 F2 G I J1 K1 K2 L M1 N O P Q R1 R2 S1 S2 T1 T2 W X Z(b,c,d,e,f,h,j,l,o,q,r,s,w,z)
Advocacy and Legal Aid undertaken
Ptr: Bennett, Mr George Adam BA(Cantab) . . . . *Oct 1985
Bever, Mr Adrian . . . . Nov 1993
Bhaskaran, Ms Rachel Sarah LLB. . . . . *Sep 1996
Briggs, Mr Graham Micheal LLB. . . . . *Oct 1984
Butt, Miss Sally A LLB. . . . . *Sep 1992
Cockram, Mr Richard A MA(Cantab) . . . . *Oct 1973
Copley, Mr Dean Trent LLB . . . . *Sep 1988
Cromack, Ms Jennifer LLB . . . . Sep 1993
Dillon, Ms Paula M LLB(L'pool) . . . . *Nov 1990
Elliot, Mr Garry . . . . Mar 2001
Emerton, Mr John. . . . . May 1993
Fawcett, Mrs Judy Anne LLB . . . . *Oct 1993
Garrett, Ms Susan M BA . . . . *Sep 1991
Goodfellow, Mr Richard . . . . Sep 1998
Gray, Ms Amanda C LLB . . . . Sep 1993
Hardy, Mr Peter Justin BA(Cantab) . . . . *Oct 1991
Harvey, Mrs Margaret A LLB . . . . *Mar 1988
Hastings, Mr Ian Alexander W LLB . . . . *Oct 1985
Heffron, Mr David G. . . . . Sep 1993
Hilton, Mr Mark W LLB(Hons)(Leeds) . . . . *Oct 1982
Howell, Mr Paul Jonathan LLB . . . . *§Jun 1977
Humphrey, Ms Sandra A LLB . . . . *Oct 1983
Jagger, Mr Charles E LLB. . . . . Sep 1993
Jones, Mr David Mark BA(Cantab) . . . . *Apr 1979
Kamstra, Mr Simon P LLB(Manc) . . . . *Feb 1990
Kaur, Mr Pervinder . . . . Sep 1996
Kempner, Mr Richard Anthony BA. . . . . *Oct 1987
Leake, Mr A John LLB . . . . *Oct 1982
Lightbody, Mr Bruce R BA. . . . . *Sep 1987
Lowry, Mr Michael BA(Oxon) . . . . Sep 1994
McIntosh, Mr Ian William LLB . . . . Oct 1983
Middlemass, Ms Julie A LLB . . . . Nov 1991
Murray, Ms Jade . . . . Sep 1998
O'Loughlin, Mr Philip H MA(Cantab). . . . . Oct 1986
Palmer, Mr Simon D BA(Dunelm) . . . . Oct 1987
Papworth, Mr Richard Noel BA(Oxon) Christchurch, Oxford Open Scholarship; Norton Rose Prize for Company Law - 1986 . . . . *Nov 1989
Park, Mr Michael T . . . . *Jun 1989
Pettinger, Mr Andrew . . . . Oct 1995
Pike, Mr John Douglas MA(Cantab). . . . . *§Jun 1972
Porter, Mr Colin BA(Hons). . . . . *Nov 1984
Price, Mr Andrew B BA(Law) . . . . *Oct 1988
Rawnsley, Ms Rachel Mary MA . . . . Oct 1989
Reevey, Mr Michael Adrian MA(Oxon). . . . . *Oct 1982
Riley, Mr Robert BA. . . . . Nov 1994
Seedat, Mr Yunus LLB . . . . Nov 1994
Shankland, Mr Lee . . . . Sep 2000
Shaw, Mr David. . . . . Sep 1996
Snell, Ms Ruth E LLB . . . . Oct 1991
Stone, Mr James Francis LLB. . . . . *Apr 1981
Sturrock, Miss Lucy Francesca BA; CPE; LSF. . . . . *Oct 1995
Tolley, Mr Derek Neil MA . . . . *Dec 1989
Tweedie, Mr Colin J MA. . . . . *Oct 1978
Woolhouse, Mr Neil T LLB . . . . Oct 1988

ADDLESTONE KEANE SOLICITORS ‡
Carlton Tower 34 St Pauls Street Leeds West Yorkshire LS1 2QB
Tel: 0113 244 6700 *Fax:* 0113 244 6680 *Dx:* 26422 LEEDS
E-mail: brianaddlestone@aklaw.co.uk
List of partners: B D Addlestone, R Ashall, D J Evans
Work: B1 C1 E J1 N O Q S1 S2 T1
Agency and Advocacy undertaken
Ptr: Addlestone, Mr Brian D LLB. . . . . Oct 1984
Ashall, Mr Robert . . . . Jul 2003
Evans, Mr David James. . . . . Dec 1995

ADEL & HAQUE ‡
Lower Ground Floor 5 South Parade Leeds West Yorkshire LS1 5QX
Tel: 0844 871 1482 *Fax:* 0844 871 1482
E-mail: qasim@adelhaque.com

DAVID AKE & CO ‡
Falk House Westgate Leeds West Yorkshire LS1 2RA
Tel: 0113 244 8808 *Fax:* 0113 246 8303
Dx: 718022 LEEDS PARK SQUARE
E-mail: dja@davidake.co.uk
List of partners: D J Ake
Work: G H Z(m)
Agency, Advocacy and Legal Aid Franchise
SPr: Ake, Mr David J LLB . . . . *§Jul 1967
Ast: Guest, Miss Gail M PGDipLaw; FILEx. . . . . *Oct 2000

NASREEN AL-GAFOOR & CO SOLICITORS ‡
2nd Floor Sanderson House 22 Station Road Leeds West Yorkshire LS18 5NT
Tel: 0113 230 0083 *Fax:* 0113 230 0083
List of partners: N Al-Gafoor
SPr: Al-Gafoor, Ms Nasreen LLB(Hons) . . . . Aug 1999

APPLEYARD LEES ‡
5th Floor 8 St Paul's Street Leeds West Yorkshire LS1 2LE
Tel: 0113 246 5353 *Fax:* 0113 246 5472
E-mail: leeds@appleyardlees.com
Office: Burnley, Chester, Halifax, Harrogate, Huddersfield, Liverpool, Manchester, Preston, Sheffield, Stockton-on-Tees, York

ARENA LEGAL SOLICITORS ‡
Arena House 2 Pullan Way Howley Park Road Leeds West Yorkshire LS27 0BZ
Tel: 0800 599 9450 *Fax:* 0845 257 9998
E-mail: d.kelly@arenalegal.co.uk

ARNDALE SOLICITORS ‡
1 Kelsall Avenue Leeds West Yorkshire LS6 1RB
Tel: 0113 243 1280 *Fax:* 0113 243 1160
E-mail: info@arndalesolicitors.com

ASHTON BELL ‡
19 Hanover Square Leeds West Yorkshire LS3 1AP
Tel: 0113 243 8688 *Fax:* 0113 242 8379
Languages: French, German
Work: B1 C1 E F2 G J1 K1 L N O Q S1 S2 W Z(b,e,j,k,q,r)
Emergency Action, Agency and Advocacy undertaken

BARTON LEGAL ‡
1a Harrogate Road Rawdon Leeds West Yorkshire LS19 6HW
Tel: 0113 202 9550 *Fax:* 0113 202 9468 *Dx:* 700248 YEADON
E-mail: billbarton@bartonlegal.com

BEACHWOOD SOLICITORS ‡
Prestige Court Business Centre Beza Road Leeds West Yorkshire LS10 2BD
Tel: 0113 359 3067 / 200 8770 *Fax:* 0113 359 3057
E-mail: info@beachwoodsolicitors.co.uk

BENTLEYS SOLICITORS ‡
335 Burley Road Leeds West Yorkshire LS4 2JJ
Tel: 0113 274 0100 *Fax:* 0113 274 0300
E-mail: info@bentleyspersonalinjury.co.uk

BERRYMANS LACE MAWER
Park Row House 19-20 Park Row Leeds West Yorkshire LS1 5JF
Tel: 0113 236 2002 *Fax:* 0113 244 2002 *Dx:* 22149 LEEDS 1
E-mail: info@blm-law.com
Office: Birmingham, Bristol, Cardiff, Liverpool, London EC2, Manchester, Southampton, Stockton-on-Tees
Work: A3 J2 N O Q R2 Z(h,j,q,r)

BILLY HUGHES & CO SOLICITORS ‡
York Place Buildings 6-8 York Place Leeds West Yorkshire LS1 2DS
Tel: 0845 680 0863 *Fax:* 0845 680 0873

BLACKS ‡
Hanover House 22 Clarendon Road Leeds West Yorkshire LS2 9NZ
Tel: 0113 207 0000 *Fax:* 0113 242 1703 *Dx:* 720480 LEEDS 49
E-mail: hello@lawblacks.com
Office: Leeds
Work: A1 C1 E K1 K3 K4 N O Q S1 S2 W
Agency and Advocacy undertaken

BLACKS
Wade House The Merrion Centre Leeds West Yorkshire LS2 8NG
Tel: 0113 207 0000 *Fax:* 0113 227 9397 *Dx:* 721080 LEEDS 50
E-mail: hello@lawblacks.com
Office: Leeds

BLACKSTONE LAW SOLICITORS & ADVOCATES LLP ‡
Dunbar House Sheepscar Court Meanwood Road Leeds West Yorkshire LS7 2BB
Tel: 0113 247 3949 *Fax:* 0113 322 0430
E-mail: contact@blackstonelawllp.co.uk

BODNAR & CO ‡
Victoria House 228 Dewsbury Road Leeds West Yorkshire LS11 6ER
Tel: 0113 294 4944 *Fax:* 0113 294 4955
E-mail: john@bodlaw.co.uk

BOSCOS ‡
Vicarage Chambers 9 Leeds Parks Square East Leeds West Yorkshire LS1 2LH
Tel: 0113 209 1510

BRADWELL & CO SOLICITORS LIMITED ‡
30-38 Dock Street Leeds West Yorkshire LS10 1JF
Tel: 0113 242 1000 *Fax:* 0113 242 8577
E-mail: juliebradwell@bradwellsolicitors.co.uk
List of partners: J Bradwell
Languages: Arabic
Work: J2 L N O P Q R1 Z(h,q,u)

Emergency Action, Agency, Advocacy and Fixed Fee Interview undertaken
SPr: Bradwell, Ms Julie BA(Hons); LLB. . . . . Aug 1990

PETER BREARLEY & CO ‡
Sanderson House Station Road Horsforth Leeds West Yorkshire LS18 5NT
Tel: 0113 259 1761 *Fax:* 0113 281 9517 *Dx:* 713145 HORSFORTH 2
E-mail: enquiries@peterbrearley.com
List of partners: P Brearley
Languages: French, German
Work: N O Q Z(j)
SPr: Brearley, Mr Peter BA. . . . . *Jun 1981

BROOKE NORTH LLP ‡
Crown House Great George Street Leeds West Yorkshire LS1 3BR
Tel: 0113 283 2100 *Fax:* 0113 283 3999
Dx: 713100 LEEDS PARK SQUARE
E-mail: info@brookenorth.co.uk
List of partners: S A Frieze, N R Hoyle, G L Kaufman, H S W Middlemass, N S G Middlemass, R L Stockdale, G Watson
Office: London W1
Languages: French, Spanish
Work: A1 A3 B1 B2 C1 C2 C3 E F1 F2 I J1 L M1 M2 O P Q R1 R2 S1 S2 T1 T2 U1 U2 W Z(b,c,d,e,f,k,n,o,p,q,s,t,u,w,y,za)
Emergency Action, Agency, Advocacy and Fixed Fee Interview undertaken
Ptr: Frieze, Mr Steven A MA(Oxon) Notary Public . . . . *§Mar 1971
Hoyle, Mr Nigel R BA(Oxon) . . . . *§Oct 1982
Kaufman, Mrs Gillian Lucy BSc(Hons). . . . . Apr 2000
Middlemass, Mr Hugh S W LLB . . . . *§Jul 1978
Middlemass, Mr Nigel S G LLB(Nott'm) . . . . *§Apr 1980
Stockdale, Mr Richard L MA(Oxon) . . . . *§Oct 1983
Watson, Mr Gordon BA(Oxon) Notary Public . . . . *§Dec 1970
Asoc: Evans, Mr Andrew David LLB(Hons) . . . . Mar 2000
Hardy, Mr Benjamin P LLB(Hons). . . . . *Nov 1995
Pollock, Mrs Elizabeth Eve LLB(Hons). . . . . Oct 2003
Ast: Clark, Miss Lucy Victoria LLB(Hons). . . . . Sep 2011
Gill, Miss Manjot Kaur LLB(Hons). . . . . Sep 2010
Gyasi, Mr Koby LLB. . . . . Sep 2009
Jones, Ms Andrea D LLB(Hons). . . . . Sep 2006
Salvati, Miss Laura Michelle LLB(Hons) . . . . Sep 2010

BROOKE WILLIAMS
Suite 208d Enterprise House St Pauls Street Leeds West Yorkshire LS1 2LE
Tel: 0113 246 8400 *Fax:* 0113 246 8404
Office: Bridlington, Hull, York
Ptr: Grundell, Ms Carol BA(Hons) . . . . Apr 1997

BURTON BURTON & HO LLP ‡
Abtech House 18 Park Row Leeds West Yorkshire LS1 5JA
Tel: 0113 297 8787 *Fax:* 0113 297 8788
Emergency telephone 07768 063322
E-mail: info@bbho.co.uk
List of partners: W Y Ho, A S T Holroyd
Languages: Cantonese, Mandarin
Work: B1 C1 C2 E F1 J2 M2 O Q S1 S2 W Z(q)
Agency undertaken
Ptr: Ho, Mr William Yiu-Wah LLB(Hons) . . . . *§Aug 1989
Holroyd, Mr A Stephen T LLB(Hons). . . . . *§Dec 1975
Ast: Wan, Miss Macella Ming Yeng LLB . . . . Nov 2008

BURY & WALKERS LLP
4 Butts Court Leeds West Yorkshire LS1 5JS
Tel: 0113 244 4227 *Fax:* 0113 246 5965 *Dx:* 12048 LEEDS 1
E-mail: leeds@burywalkers.com
Web: www.burywalkers.com
Office: Barnsley, Wombwell
Work: A1 A3 B1 C1 C2 C3 D1 D2 E F1 G H I J1 K1 L M1 M2 N O P Q R1 R2 S1 S2 T1 T2 V W Z(c,d,e,h,k,l,n,o,q,r,s)
Emergency Action, Agency, Advocacy, Fixed Fee Interview and Legal Aid undertaken
Ptr: Burke, Mr Michael P LLB(Manc). . . . . *Oct 1986
Jones, Mr Richard O LLB . . . . *§May 1971
Nuttall, Mr Simon G LLB(Leeds). . . . . *Oct 1981
Ast: Archer, Mr Gareth J LLB(Law). . . . . Nov 1999
Colley, Mr David . . . . Sep 2005
Dickson, Mr Graham Howard LLB. . . . . May 2002

Other offices in Barnsley and Dearne Valley. We specialise in the following areas of work: Employment, Housing, Landlord & Tenant; Litigation and Commercial. Agency Commissions gladly undertaken.

CAMIDGE & CO ‡
14 Park Place Leeds West Yorkshire LS1 2SJ
Tel: 0113 245 7859

GARY CAPLAN SOLICITORS ‡
37 West Park Drive East Leeds West Yorkshire LS8 2EE
Tel: 0113 216 3118 *Fax:* 0113 217 5732
E-mail: info@garycaplan.co.uk
List of partners: G Caplan
Work: B1 C1 C2 E O Q S2 Z(i,l)
Agency, Advocacy and Fixed Fee Interview undertaken
Ptr: Caplan, Mr Gary . . . . Jan 1985
Asoc: Petrie, Mr George William LLB(Hons) . . . . *Oct 2003

CARRICK READ (LEEDS) SOLICITORS LLP ‡
12 Park Place Leeds West Yorkshire LS1 2RU
Tel: 0113 246 7878 *Fax:* 0113 243 9822
E-mail: enquiries@carrickread.com
List of partners: D J Barker, J Barnes, A M Laycock
Work: B1 C1
Ptr: Barker, Mr David J LLB(Leeds) . . . . *Aug 1998
Barnes, Ms Jo-Ann LLB(Hons) . . . . Sep 2003
Laycock, Mr Andrew M MA(Cantab). . . . . *Nov 1983

CASTLE SANDERSON ‡ (incorporating Spencer & Fisch; Kendrew Mellor & Marriott)
64-66 Austhorpe Road Crossgates Leeds West Yorkshire LS15 8DZ
Tel: 0113 232 1919 *Fax:* 0113 232 1913 *Dx:* 13902 CROSSGATES
E-mail: enquiries@castlesanderson.co.uk
List of partners: J H Kendrew, J A Leahy, P Shedlow
Office: Leeds
Languages: French
Work: A1 A3 B1 B2 C1 C2 C3 D1 D2 E F1 F2 G H J1 J2 K1 K2 L N O P Q R1 R2 S1 T1 T2 V W Z(c,e,f,i,j,k,l,o,q)
Emergency Action, Agency, Advocacy, Fixed Fee Interview, Legal Aid undertaken and Member of Accident Line
Ptr: Kendrew, Mr James H BSc . . . . *Jun 1979
Leahy, Mr John A LLB. . . . . *Dec 1977
Shedlow, Mr Philip LLB . . . . *Jan 1970
Asoc: Cowan, Mr Alastair LLB(Hons) Smalley Baker Prize for Jurisprudence. . . . . *Dec 1988

CHAPMAN DHILLON SOLICITORS ‡
147a Easterly Road Leeds West Yorkshire LS8 2RY
Tel: 0113 240 1041

CHILDRENS WORKFORCE AND DEVELOPMENT COUNCIL ‡
3rd Floor Friends Provident House 13-14 South Parade Leeds West Yorkshire LS1 5QS
Tel: 0113 244 6311 *Fax:* 0113 390 7744

CHINYOKA & CO ‡
19-20 Malmarc House 116 Dewsbury Road Leeds West Yorkshire LS11 6XD
Tel: 0113 276 8800 / 276 8801
Languages: Ndebele, Shona
Work: K1 Z(g,i)
Legal Aid Franchise

CLARION SOLICITORS LLP ‡
Britannia Chambers 4 Oxford Place Leeds West Yorkshire LS1 3AX
Tel: 0113 246 0622 *Fax:* 0113 246 7488
Dx: 26427 LEEDS PARK SQUARE
Emergency telephone 0113 246 0622 / 07850 899999
List of partners: D J Arundel, M R Burns, M Grange, C N R Hutton, C S Lawrence, R J Moran, R C Rode, S Rogers
Languages: French, German, Italian, Spanish
Work: A1 A2 A3 B1 B2 B3 C1 C2 C3 D2 E F1 F2 G H I J1 J2 K1 K2 L M1 M2 N O P Q R1 R2 S1 S2 T1 T2 U1 U2 W X Z(b,c,d,e,f,j,k,l,m,p,q,s,u,w,x,z)
Emergency Action, Agency, Advocacy, Legal Aid undertaken and Legal Aid Franchise
Ptr: Arundel, Mr David John LLB. . . . . *Oct 1992
Burns, Mr Mark Richard LLB . . . . *Sep 1990
Grange, Mr Martin. . . . . Apr 1997
Hutton, Mr C N Roger LLB; BA(Hons). . . . . *Dec 1991
Lawrence, Mr Clive Sydney MA(Cantab) . . . . *Nov 1993
Moran, Mr Richard John BA(Hons); LLB. . . . . *Aug 1996
Rode, Mr Robert Charles LLB(Hons) ★ . . . . Oct 1994
Rogers, Mrs Sara BA(Hons)(Law). . . . . *Apr 1976
Asoc: Hunt, Mr Christian Peter LLB . . . . Sep 2001
Kaufmann, Mrs Gillian. . . . . Apr 2000
Mackle, Mr John BA(Hons); MA . . . . *Apr 1997
Milmore, Mr Ryan LLB . . . . *Sep 2000
Milner, Mr Stephen BA(Oxon) . . . . *Sep 2000
Pratt, Miss Alice Victoria . . . . Sep 2003
Ast: Allen, Mr Keith . . . . Oct 2004
Batty, Mrs Alison . . . . Oct 2000
Byrne, Mr Peter. . . . . Feb 2003
Carey, Ms Beth . . . . Nov 2004
Dean, Mrs Rachel BA(Hons) . . . . Jul 2002
Dickinson, Miss Juile . . . . Oct 2005
Garfield, Mrs Rachael Francesca BA . . . . *Sep 2000
Gaul, Mr Stephen. . . . . Sep 2005
Harrison, Mrs Lynsey LLB(Hons) . . . . *Sep 2001
Hugill, Miss Lucie-Jane Pineau LLB . . . . *Jun 2002
Liddington, Mr Owen . . . . Aug 2005
Mills, Mr Jonathan LLB(Leeds) . . . . Oct 2005
Newman, Miss Victoria Alice BA(Hons) . . . . *Apr 2003
Pearson, Miss Juila . . . . Sep 2005
Power, Ms Elizabeth . . . . Jun 2002
Sadler, Mrs Deborah Elizabeth LLB . . . . *Jul 2002
Simms, Mr Jonathan . . . . Sep 2004
Spencer Robb, Mrs Rachel . . . . Nov 2002
Waters, Miss Kerry Louise LLB(Hons). . . . . Sep 2002

COBBETTS LLP
No1 Whitehall Riverside Leeds West Yorkshire LS1 4BN
Tel: 0845 404 2404 *Fax:* 0845 404 2424
Dx: 14085 LEEDS PARK SQUARE
E-mail: enquiries@cobbetts.com
Office: Birmingham, London WC1, Manchester
Languages: Danish, French, German, Spanish
Work: B1 C1 D1 E F1 I J1 K1 L M1 N O P R1 T1 W Z(b,c,e,g,k,l,o,p,s)

COGENT LAW ‡
Josephs Well Hanover Walk Leeds West Yorkshire LS3 1AB
Tel: 0844 245 4452
List of partners: N J S Addyman, J P Cure, M P O'Callaghan, S P Rodgers
Office: Croydon

COHEN CRAMER SOLICITORS ‡
St George House 40 Great George Street Leeds West Yorkshire LS1 3DL
Tel: 0800 542 9408 *Fax:* 0113 298 7363
Dx: 713108 LEEDS PARK SQUARE
E-mail: info@cohencramer.co.uk
List of partners: S A Baskind, H S Cohen, R G Cramer, J S Goodwin, J M Grant, M J McDonnell, J L Richards
Ptr: Baskind, Mr Simon A LLB. . . . . *Oct 1981
Cohen, Mr Howard S LLB. . . . . *Dec 1969
Cramer, Mr Richard Gary LLB. . . . . *Oct 1985
Goodwin, Mr John S BA. . . . . *Oct 1982
Grant, Mr John M LLB. . . . . *Feb 1986
McDonnell, Mr Michael J LLB . . . . Oct 1991
Richards, Mr John L LLB . . . . *Jan 1969
Asoc: Hardy, Ms Deborah E LLB. . . . . *Dec 1992
Menhennet, Ms Katia E BA . . . . *Dec 1997

DAVID COLLINS SOLICITORS ‡
21 Sedgegarth Thorner Leeds West Yorkshire LS14 3LB
Tel: 0113 289 2530 *Fax:* 0113 201 7192
E-mail: davidjmcollins@fsmail.net

ALEXANDER COUSINS CRIMINAL DEFENCE SOLICITORS ‡
Aspect Court 47 Park Square East Leeds West Yorkshire LS1 2NL
Tel: 0113 394 4175 *Fax:* 0113 394 4176
E-mail: simonalex@btconnect.com

COUSINS TYRER ‡
31 Oxford Row Leeds West Yorkshire LS1 3BE
Tel: 0113 247 0400 *Fax:* 0113 242 3691 *Dx:* 26413 LEEDS
Emergency telephone 07860 928404
E-mail: mail@cousins-tyrer.com
List of partners: H R Cousins, A Mazharuddin, D R G Tyrer
Work: G H
Emergency Action, Agency, Advocacy, Legal Aid undertaken and Legal Aid Franchise
Ptr: Cousins, Miss Helen Robina BA ★ Deputy District Judge (Crime) . . . . *Oct 1986
Mazharuddin, Miss Aysha LLB ★ . . . . *Apr 2004
Tyrer, Mr David R G BA ★. . . . . *Mar 1984
Ast: Woods, Mr Barry . . . . Sep 2009

MELANIE CRAIG SOLICITORS ‡
6 The Headrow Leeds West Yorkshire LS1 6PT
Tel: 0113 244 4081 *Fax:* 0113 244 5850
Emergency telephone 07770 780805
List of partners: M S Craig
Work: J1 K1 Q
Emergency Action and Agency undertaken
Ptr: Craig, Mrs Melanie S MA(Cantab). . . . . *Apr 1980

CROCKETT & CO ‡
260 Harehills Lane Leeds West Yorkshire LS9 7BD
Tel: 0113 226 0111 *Fax:* 0113 226 0110
Dx: 26434 LEEDS PARK SQUARE
Emergency telephone 07958 239090
E-mail: info@crockettsols.co.uk
List of partners: H Crockett
Languages: Punjabi, Urdu
Work: D1 K1 K3 W
Emergency Action, Agency, Advocacy, Fixed Fee Interview, Legal Aid undertaken and Legal Aid Franchise
SPr: Crockett, Mrs Helen BA(Hons)(Social Administration); CPE; LSF . . . . *Jan 1988
Ast: Brady, Ms Rosanne . . . . Apr 2007
Din, Sabeena . . . . Mar 2009
Doolan, Ms Helen. . . . . Feb 2009

DAC BEACHCROFT
7 Park Square East Leeds West Yorkshire LS1 2LW
Tel: 0113 251 4700 *Fax:* 0113 251 4900 *Dx:* 14099 LEEDS
Office: Birmingham, Bristol, London EC3 (3 offices), London EC4 (2 offices), Manchester (2 offices), Newcastle upon Tyne, Newport, Winchester
Languages: Arabic, French, German
Work: A1 B1 C1 E F1 G I J1 L M1 N O P R1 S1 W Z(b,c,e,j,l,n)
Emergency Action, Agency, Advocacy, Fixed Fee Interview, Legal Aid undertaken and Member of Accident Line
Ptr: Clegg, Miss Virginia E BA. . . . . *Nov 1991
Greenwood, Mr Duncan M LLB . . . . *Oct 1990
Hallatt, Ms Diane . . . . Oct 1983
Heenan, Ms Rachael . . . . Aug 2003
Larter, Ms Hilary C LLB . . . . Nov 1992
Lee, Mr Peter J Notary Public . . . . *Feb 1980
Marsh, Mr Andrew C M LLB. . . . . *Jun 1988
Rees, Mr Owen John . . . . *Nov 1989
Scott, Mr Andrew W H LLB . . . . Oct 1989
Sheikh Collins, Mrs Roohi LLB . . . . *Feb 1984
Sherwood, Mr Clive Frederick Simon . . . . Oct 1996
Suttie, Mr Frank I BA; LLB . . . . *Sep 1985
Wharton, Ms Suzanne . . . . Sep 1994
Willis, Mr F Michael MA(Cantab) . . . . *Nov 1985
Winterbottom, Ms Ruth . . . . Oct 1994

DLA PIPER UK LLP
Princes Exchange Princes Square Leeds West Yorkshire LS1 4BY
Tel: 0870 011 1111 *Fax:* 0113 369 2949 *Dx:* 12017 LEEDS 1
Emergency telephone 0870 011 1111
E-mail: info@dlapiper.com
Office: Birmingham, Liverpool, London EC2, Manchester, Sheffield
Languages: French, German
Work: A1 B1 C1 E F1 J1 N P R1 S1 T1 W Z(b,c,d,e,f,k,n,o,s)
Emergency Action, Agency, Advocacy undertaken and Member of Accident Line
Ptr: Ashford, Mr Colin I LLB . . . . *Nov 1993
Barraclough, Ms Helen R BA . . . . *Nov 1991
Bonnar, Mr Richard MA(Cantab) . . . . *Nov 1988
Bowler, Mr Iain William LLB(Manc) . . . . *Oct 1988
Burnley, Mr Paul A BA . . . . *Apr 1980
Chidley, Mr Mark A LLB(Soton) . . . . *Nov 1979
Clarke, Mr Andrew . . . . Oct 1995
Crosse, Mr Damian Gerard BA(Kent) . . . . Nov 1991
Da Costa, Mr Alastair John LLB. . . . . *Oct 1990
Davies, Mr Andrew . . . . Sep 1999
Davison, Mr Howard LLB . . . . Nov 1994
Day, Miss Sarah Jane BA(Hons)(Oxon); CPE; LSF . . Jan 1993
Dyson, Mr Andrew . . . . Feb 1999
Evans, Mr Hugh C LLB(B'ham) . . . . *§Oct 1982
Field, Mr Timothy Francis BA(Econ). . . . . Oct 1988
Hall, Mrs Kate LLB Chairman of the Law Society Planning & Environmental Law Committee . . . . *Oct 1989
Harrison, Mrs Wendy A LLB. . . . . *Oct 1991
Hartley, Mr Adam BA; CPE; LSF; MA . . . . *Oct 1996
Heylen, Mr Thomas. . . . . Sep 1998
Ibrahim, Mr Adam James LLB. . . . . Nov 1994
James, Mr Stewart . . . . Sep 1998
Kenyon, Mr Simon . . . . Sep 1997
Kittle, Mr John LLB . . . . *Oct 1992
Lamb, Mr Guy M LLB(Hons) . . . . May 1993
Lonergan, Mr Matthew Jason LLB. . . . . *Apr 1994
Lynch, Mr Mark . . . . *Oct 1993
McLean, Ms Neil M LLB. . . . . *§Apr 1977
Maltby, Mr Nicholas MA(Oxon) . . . . *Jan 1991
Massarano, Ms Vikki BA(Hons) . . . . Nov 1994
Mather, Ms Valerie F LLB . . . . *Oct 1990
Obank, Mr Richard C LLB(Manc) . . . . *Dec 1989
Page, Ms Allison . . . . Aug 1995
Payne, Ms Kate. Jun 1990
Procter, Ms Jonathan BA(Oxon)(Jurisprudence). . . . *Oct 1987
Smith, Mr Mark R BA(Oxon). . . . . §Mar 1984
Stone, Mr Paul B BA(Oxon). . . . . Apr 1986
Tulley, Mr Christopher T LLB . . . . *Nov 1985
Vipan, Mr Mark R A LLB(Hons) . . . . *Oct 1993

DWF
Bridgewater Place Water Lane Leeds West Yorkshire LS11 5DY
Tel: 0113 261 6000 *Fax:* 0870 094 0939 *Dx:* 728240 LEEDS 66
E-mail: enquiries@dwf.co.uk
Office: Liverpool, London EC4, Manchester, Newcastle upon Tyne, Preston
Work: J2 N Z(j)
Ptr: Lawson, Ms Helen Robina LLB . . . . *May 1993
Parker, Mr Richard BA(Hons) . . . . *Sep 1994

See p112 for the Key to Work Categories & other symbols

DAVIES GORE LOMAX ‡
63 Great George Street Leeds West Yorkshire LS1 3BB
Tel: 0113 242 2797 *Fax:* 0113 245 1117
Dx: 26437 LEEDS PARK SQUARE
Emergency telephone 0113 242 2797
E-mail: reception@dgllaw.co.uk
List of partners: P Gore, K Lomax
Work: D1 D2 K1 K3 K4 L Q V X Z(g)
Emergency Action, Agency, Advocacy, Fixed Fee Interview, Legal Aid undertaken and Legal Aid Franchise
Ptr: Gore, Ms Patricia BA Chairman of the Special Educational Needs Tribunal & Appeals Tribunal . . . . *Jun 1980
Lomax, Dr Keith BSc; PhD . . . . *Jan 1988
Ast: Burchell, Miss Sarah Elzabeth BA. . . . . *Feb 2000
Coughtrie, Mr Keith LLB. . . . . *Nov 2003
Goodyear, Ms Maria LLB . . . . *Apr 1999
Hirschhorn, Ms Clare BA; PGIP; LPC . . . . *Feb 2004
Lomax, Mr Tom BSc; MSc. . . . . *Aug 2009
Sherwood, Ms Sally LLB . . . . *Jul 2007
Todd, Mrs Elsia BA . . . . *Jan 2003

JOHN DELANEY & CO ‡
13 Bond Court Leeds West Yorkshire LS1 2JZ
Tel: 0113 246 8151 *Fax:* 0113 243 1342 *Dx:* 12082 LEEDS
Emergency telephone 0113 246 8151
List of partners: A Murphy, A Pollard
Work: D1 D2 G H K1 X
Emergency Action, Agency, Advocacy, Fixed Fee Interview, Legal Aid undertaken, Legal Aid Franchise and Member of Accident Line
Ptr: Murphy, Mr Anthony LLB(Hons). . . . . Jan 1998
Pollard, Mr Adrian LLB . . . . Dec 1989

DEVERS & CO SOLICITORS ‡
Devers House PO Box 84 Sherburn Leeds West Yorkshire LS25 9AS
Tel: 01977 783363 *Fax:* 01977 681888
E-mail: info@deverslaw.com

DIGWA COUSINS ‡
277 Roundhay Road Leeds West Yorkshire LS8 4HS
Tel: 0113 249 6661 *Fax:* 0113 249 6300
E-mail: digwa@btinternet.co.uk
List of partners: C T Cousins, R S Digwa
Languages: Hindi, Punjabi
Work: C1 E G H K1 S1 W
Ptr: Cousins, Mr Christopher T BA. . . . . *Feb 1984
Digwa, Mr Rajinder S BSc. . . . . *Oct 1989

DIXON LAW LIMITED ‡
The Round Foundry 8 Saw Mill Yard Leeds West Yorkshire LS11 5WH
Tel: 0113 204 2470
List of partners: C Dixon
Dir: Dixon, Mr Colin . . . . Apr 1993

EATONS
Aspect Court 47 Park Square East Leeds West Yorkshire LS1 2NL
Tel: 0845 660 0660
E-mail: enquiries@eatons-solicitors.co.uk
Office: Bradford, Otley

EBOR LAW LIMTED ‡
Calls Wharf 2 The Calls Leeds West Yorkshire LS2 7JU
Tel: 0113 237 2740 *Fax:* 0113 237 2741
E-mail: info@eborlaw.co.uk

RICHARD ELLIS & CO
41 Harrogate Road Chapel Allerton Leeds West Yorkshire LS7 3PD
Tel: 0113 228 4000 *Fax:* 0113 228 4001
Dx: 28878 CHAPEL ALLERTON
Office: Harrogate
Ptr: Ellis, Mr Richard Keith LLB . . . . *Dec 1976

ELMHIRST PARKER LLP
The Cross Kirkgate Sherburn-in-Elmet Leeds West Yorkshire LS25 6BH
Tel: 01977 682219 *Fax:* 01977 684454
Dx: 701452 SHERBURN-IN-ELMET
E-mail: sherburn@elmhirstparker.com
Office: Barnsley, Selby (2 offices)
Work: A1 C1 D1 E F1 J1 K1 K3 L N O P Q R1 S1 S2 T1 V W Z(d,i,l,m,r)
Emergency Action, Agency, Advocacy, Fixed Fee Interview undertaken and Member of Accident Line
Mem: Cox, Mr John Charles LLB . . . . *Dec 1977
Maxton, Miss Sarah Lucy . . . . *Oct 1995
Ast: Letby, Mrs Linda C . . . . *Jan 1978
Perkins, Mrs Emily LLB . . . . *Aug 2001

EMMOTT & CO ‡
1200 Century Way Thorpe Park Colton Leeds West Yorkshire LS15 8ZA
Tel: 0113 251 5008

EMSLEYS
Colton Mill Bullerthorpe Lane Leeds West Yorkshire LS15 9JN
Tel: 0113 232 1030 *Fax:* 0113 232 1040
E-mail: law@emsleys.co.uk
Office: Castleford, Crossgates, Garforth, Rothwell (2 offices)
Work: N Q
Ptr: Greenwood, Mr Andrew L BA(Law) . . . . Oct 1986
Serr, Mr Howard J LLB . . . . *Dec 1975
Asoc: Argyle, Miss Natalie Jane LLB(Hons) . . . . *Aug 2003
Davies, Mr Paul LLB(Hons) . . . . *Nov 1997
Hopton, Miss Jane Anne BA(Hons) . . . . *Sep 2001

EMSLEYS ‡
16 Cross Hill Kippax Leeds West Yorkshire LS25 7JP
Tel: 0113 232 0037 *Fax:* 0113 232 0327 *Dx:* 29761 GARFORTH
E-mail: law@emsleys.co.uk

EMSLEYS ‡
4 Wolsey Parade Sherburn in Elmet Leeds West Yorkshire LS25 6BQ
Tel: 01977 680088 *Fax:* 01977 680008
Dx: 70145 SHERBURN-IN-ELMET
E-mail: law@emsleys.co.uk

EVERSHEDS LLP
Bridgewater Place Water Lane Leeds West Yorkshire LS11 5DR
Tel: 0845 497 9797 *Fax:* 0845 498 4994 *Dx:* 12027 LEEDS 27
Office: Birmingham, Cambridge, Cardiff, Ipswich, London EC2, Manchester, Newcastle upon Tyne, Nottingham

FAIRFAX SOLICITORS LIMITED ‡
Fairfax House Merrion Street Leeds West Yorkshire LS2 8BX
Tel: 0113 823 3443 *Fax:* 0113 823 3898 *Dx:* 719041 LEEDS 45

FORBES
13/14 South Parade Leeds West Yorkshire LS1 5QS
Tel: 0113 244 6688 *Fax:* 0113 243 4546
Dx: 26417 LEEDS PARK SQUARE
Office: Accrington (2 offices), Blackburn (3 offices), Chorley, Manchester, Preston

FORD & WARREN ‡
Westgate Point Westgate Leeds West Yorkshire LS1 2AX
Tel: 0113 243 6601 *Fax:* 0113 242 0905
Dx: 706968 LEEDS PARK SQUARE
E-mail: clientmail@forwarn.com
List of partners: E V Brown, J Coen, J Colley, N D Collins, M C J Crabtree, B Daniel, I A Davison, J Flint, K Hearn, C Heppenstall, G Hodgson, B Mackenzie, M L Mathers, P McWilliams, P A Milligan, O Nelson, S A J Robinson, M Robson, B Smith, L C Staddon, F Sutcliffe, P J Taylor
Languages: French, German, Hindi, Mirpuri, Norwegian, Punjabi, Spanish, Urdu
Work: B1 B2 C1 C2 C3 D1 D2 E F1 F2 I J1 J2 K1 K2 K3 L M1 M2 N O P Q R1 R2 S1 S2 T1 T2 U2 W X Z(c,d,e,f,j,k,l,o,p,q,r,t,w)
Emergency Action, Agency, Advocacy, Fixed Fee Interview undertaken and Member of Accident Line
Ptr: Brown, Mr Edward V LLB(Leeds) . . . . *§Dec 1969
Coen, Mr John LLB . . . . *Jan 1991
Colley, Ms Janice LLB. . . . . Sep 1998
Collins, Mr Nicholas D LLB . . . . *§Jan 1988
Crabtree, Mr Mark C J LLB . . . . *Oct 1992
Daniel, Mr Ben BA . . . . Sep 1997
Davison, Mr Iain Alexander LLB. . . . . *Oct 1992
Flint, Mr John LLB . . . . Sep 1996
Hearn, Mr Keith LLB(Leeds); LLM(Leics) . . . . . . *§Apr 1973
Heppenstall, Mr Charles BA(Hons) . . . . Sep 1998
Hodgson, Mr Gary BA(Hons) . . . . *Dec 1977
Mackenzie, Mr Ben BA(Hons). . . . . Oct 1996
McWilliams, Mr Peter LLB. . . . . *Jan 1992
Mathers, Mrs Michelle Louise LLB Sweet & Maxwell Law Prize . . . . Sep 1999
Milligan, Mr Paul A BA . . . . *Oct 1984
Nelson, Mr Oliver LLB. . . . . Nov 1985
Robinson, Mr Simon A J LLB . . . . Mar 1998
Robson, Mr Mark LLB. . . . . *Sep 1998
Smith, Blaise LLB(Leeds) . . . . *Oct 1982
Staddon, Mrs Lindsay C LLB . . . . *Oct 1987
Sutcliffe, Mr Frank LLB . . . . Aug 1997
Taylor, Mr Philip J MA(Oxon) . . . . *Jan 1987
Asoc: Chant, Mr David CPE . . . . Sep 2000
Fallon, Mr Stephen Andrew LLB(Hons); LPC . . . . *Sep 2001
Felton, Mr Nick BA(Hons) . . . . Sep 2000
Lowe, Mr Benjamin BA; MA; LPC . . . . Oct 1997
Luscombe, Chris LPC; LLB . . . . *Jan 2006
Nuttman, Mr Edward LLB; LPC . . . . Apr 2004
Price, Mr Nigel C LLB. . . . . *Jul 1977
Wan, Ms Eleanor LLB. . . . . Sep 2000
Wilkinson, Mr Paul . . . . May 1999
Ast: Bailey-Gibbs, Mr Christopher James LLB; LPC . . . *Sep 2010
Beck, Miss Samantha BA(Hons); LLB . . . . Sep 2009
Clark, Miss Katherine . . . . Sep 2011
Crook, Miss Lyndsey Anne BA(Hons)(Political Studies); PGDipLaw; PGDipLP; LPC . . . . *Jan 2011
Dhanendran, Miss Marie BA; PGDipLaw. . . . . Sep 2010
Dufton, Miss Alice Lucy Barker LLB . . . . Nov 2009
Dunn, Mr James Alexander LLB(Hons); LPC . . . . . Oct 2006
Evans, Mr Benjamin BSc(Hons). . . . . Sep 2005
Gibbon, Mr Richard LLB. . . . . Sep 2008
Hutchison, Mr Ross LLB(Hons); BA(Hons) . . . . . . Sep 2009
James, Mr John William BA(Hons); LLB. . . . . *Mar 2011
McWilliams, Mr John Frances LLB(Hons); LSF . . . . *Dec 1995
Mahmood, Miss Farhat LLB; LLM . . . . Sep 2009
Newman, Mr Nick. . . . . Nov 2008
Paszek, Mr Nicholas . . . . Sep 2010
Weeks, Mr John Robert BA(Hons); CPE; LPC. . . . . Sep 2008
Wexler, Mr Robert. . . . . *Apr 2009
Willey, Mr Stephen Ernest John LLB. . . . . Mar 2011
Younis, Haroon . . . . Apr 2002

GSD LAW LTD ‡
West One Suite 5B Leeds West Yorkshire LS1 1BA
Tel: 0113 388 4897
E-mail: enquiries@gsdlaw.co.uk

GARTON & CO ‡
28 Town Street Armley Leeds West Yorkshire LS12 3AB
Tel: 0113 231 0766 *Fax:* 0113 202 2030

GODLOVES ‡
(incorporating Godlove Saffman; Pearlman Grazin & Co; Saffmans)
8-16 Dock Street Leeds West Yorkshire LS10 1LX
Tel: 0113 225 8811 *Fax:* 0113 225 8844
Dx: 14078 LEEDS PARK SQUARE
E-mail: mailbox@godloves.co.uk
List of partners: K Ali, P M Carvis, A Charuk, S L Hattersley, R G Holt, G S J Lachlan, K McNally, I Scobbie, T P Smith, E M Spencer
Office: Leeds (4 offices)
Languages: French, German, Urdu
Work: B1 C1 C2 C3 D1 E F1 I J1 K1 K2 L O Q R1 S1 W Z(c,e,h,k,l,m,r)
Emergency Action, Agency, Advocacy, Fixed Fee Interview, Legal Aid undertaken, Legal Aid Franchise and Member of Accident Line
Ptr: Ali, Kumer MA(Oxon) . . . . *Dec 1992
Carvis, Mr Paul M LLB . . . . *Oct 1972
Charuk, Mr Andrew LLB(Hons) . . . . *Nov 1995
Hattersley, Mr Stephen Leslie LLB(Hons) Notary Public*Oct 1994
Holt, Mr Robert G BA . . . . *§Oct 1979
Lachlan, Mr Guy St J BA . . . . *§Jan 1983
McNally, Miss Katherine BA(Law) . . . . *Nov 1987
Scobbie, Mr Ian LLB . . . . *Feb 1989
Spencer, Ms E Margaret LLM(Lond). . . . . *Oct 1980
Asoc: Nightingale, Miss Sarah Elizabeth BA . . . . Feb 2001
Ast: Brookes, Mr Mark David LLB . . . . Mar 2003
Kershaw, Mr Dominic P LLB. . . . . *Oct 2000
Con: Goldman, Mr Ian J LLB(Lond). . . . . *May 1971
Smith, Mr Terry P LLB. . . . . *Jul 1975
Utting, Mrs Evelyn LLB . . . . Jun 1980

GODLOVES
Beech House Willow Court Main Street Leeds West Yorkshire LS25 1HB
Tel: 0113 286 8822 *Fax:* 0113 232 0029 *Dx:* 29763 GARFORTH
Emergency telephone 0113 225 8811
E-mail: mailbox@godloves.co.uk
Office: Leeds (4 offices)
Work: A1 B1 C1 C2 C3 D1 E F1 I J1 K1 L M1 M2 N O P Q R1 S1 W Z(c,e,h,k,l,m,o,t)
Emergency Action, Agency, Advocacy, Fixed Fee Interview, Legal Aid undertaken, Legal Aid Franchise and Member of Accident Line
Ptr: McNally, Miss Katherine BA(Law) . . . . *Nov 1987
Con: Utting, Mrs Evelyn LLB . . . . Jun 1980

GODLOVES
258 Dewsbury Road Beeston Leeds West Yorkshire LS11 6JQ
Tel: 0113 225 8864 *Fax:* 0113 225 8866
Dx: 14078 LEEDS PARK SQUARE
Emergency telephone 0113 275 8378
E-mail: mailbox@godloves.co.uk
Office: Leeds (4 offices)
Work: D1 E F1 G H J1 K1 L N O P Q R1 S1 W Z(i,l,m)
Emergency Action, Agency, Advocacy, Fixed Fee Interview, Legal Aid undertaken, Legal Aid Franchise and Member of Accident Line
Ptr: Holt, Mr Robert G BA . . . . *§Oct 1979

GODLOVES
(incorporating Godlove Saffman; Pearlman Grazin & Co)
120 Harrogate Road Chapel Allerton Leeds West Yorkshire LS7 4NY
Tel: 0113 225 8874 *Fax:* 0113 225 8877
Dx: 28874 CHAPEL ALLERTON
E-mail: mailbox@godloves.co.uk
Office: Leeds (4 offices)
Work: D1 D2 E K1 K2 K3 K4 L N Q R1 S1 S2 V W Z(b,m,q,r)
Emergency Action, Agency, Advocacy, Fixed Fee Interview, Legal Aid undertaken, Legal Aid Franchise and Member of Accident Line
Ptr: Smith, Mr Terry P LLB. . . . . *Jul 1975

STUART GORDON SOLICITOR & ADVOCATE ‡
1 Oxford Place Leeds West Yorkshire LS1 3AX
Tel: 0113 244 4999 *Fax:* 0113 244 4800
E-mail: anne@stuart-gordon.com

GORDONS LLP
Riverside West Whitehall Road Leeds West Yorkshire LS1 4AW
Tel: 0113 227 0100 *Fax:* 0113 227 0113 *Dx:* 729680 LEEDS 68
E-mail: mail@gordonslegal.com
Office: Bradford
Languages: French, German, Italian
Work: A1 A3 C1 C2 D1 E F1 F2 I J1 J2 K1 K3 L N O Q R1 R2 S1 S2 V W Z(c,e,h,j,k,o,r,w,z,za)
Emergency Action, Agency, Advocacy, Fixed Fee Interview, Legal Aid undertaken, Legal Aid Franchise and Member of Accident Line
Ptr: Ayre, Mr Paul H LLB . . . . *Oct 1989
Barton, Mr Peter D . . . . Jun 1978
Chamberlain, Mr Nick J . . . . Sep 1998
Cross, Mr Tim D B . . . . Nov 1988
Davey, Mrs Victoria Louise LLB . . . . Oct 1995
Emmott, Mr Tony . . . . Jun 1975
Enderby, Mr Keith I . . . . Apr 1979
Errington, Mr Ian S . . . . Oct 1994
Foskett, Mr Peter W. . . . . Apr 1981
Foster, Mr John Matthew MA(Oxon). . . . . *Apr 1981
Frogson, Mr Richard J . . . . Sep 1999
Furniss, Mr Chris J . . . . Jun 1970
Hall, Mr John P . . . . Dec 1979
Holden, Mr John L BA. . . . . *May 1984
Howarth, Mr Charles M . . . . Oct 1994
Hudson, Mr Bill M. . . . . Dec 1970
Hudson, Ms Rachel . . . . Nov 1996
Jordan, Mr Andrew R MA(Cantab). . . . . Apr 1981
Leonard, Mr Simon B . . . . Oct 1979
Lewis, Mr Michael Paul MA; CPE; BA(Hons) . . . . . *Nov 1993
Linden, Mr Andrew J R LLB(Leeds) . . . . *§May 1979
Lister, Ms Julia R . . . . Sep 1990
Miller, Mrs Joanne T LLB . . . . *Oct 1993
Paget, Mr Philip J LLB(Hons) . . . . *Oct 1990
Piper, Mr Richard D S. . . . . Nov 1993
Pridmore, Mr David Andrew LLB . . . . *Sep 1994
Ratcliffe, Mr Tim H . . . . Apr 1976
Rollin, Ms Barbara . . . . Oct 1988
Singleton, Mr John LLB . . . . *§Oct 1982
Smyllie, Mr David A BA . . . . *Jun 1985
Spavin, Mrs Joanne Louise BA; LPC . . . . May 1997
Stakes, Mr John A LLB . . . . *§Jul 1971
Tunnicliffe, Mrs Rachel Shirley BA. . . . . *Oct 1993
Wooler, Mr Peter G . . . . *§Jan 1968
Young, Mr Paul S . . . . Nov 1995
Ast: Asquez, Mr Jonathan . . . . Mar 2005
Bateman, Ms Claire H. . . . . Sep 2003
Brian, Mr Andrew . . . . Sep 2005
Clossick, Mr Adrian Patrick LLB. . . . . *Sep 2003
Davies, Ms Frances R. . . . . Oct 1995
Dean, Mr Richard M. . . . . Sep 2001
Eaglesfield, Ms Janine L . . . . Oct 1990
Fawcett, Mr James LLB. . . . . Sep 2001
Gregory, Mr Philip. . . . . *Jan 2001
Hamilton-Hislop, Ms Ann . . . . Oct 1993
Hasyn, Mr Martin J . . . . Nov 1997
Hunt, Mr John R . . . . Sep 2002
Khan, Shamin A. Aug 2003
Leonard, Ms Gillian M. . . . . Oct 1983
Lester, Ms Angela P. . . . . Sep 2003
Lloyd, Ms Shereen J . . . . Sep 2003
Mackay, Ms Nicola J . . . . Oct 1993
Mcvey, Mr Stephen A . . . . Sep 2004
Malekotodjary, Ms Rebecca. . . . . Sep 2005
Mallik, Anjon . . . . Sep 1998
Markham, Ms Rachel E . . . . Apr 2002
Mathers, Ms Michelle L . . . . Sep 1999
Menham, Mr Paul C. . . . . Apr 2002
Miah, Babul . . . . Apr 2004
Mydlowski, Mr Simon T . . . . Oct 2003
Nicholas, Ms Anushka. . . . . Dec 2004
Owen, Mr John E . . . . Sep 1999
Pettingill, Miss Joan E LLB(Hons) . . . . Jun 1998
Preston, Mr Simon David LLB(Hons) . . . . *Oct 1994
Price, Mr Andrew W. . . . . Oct 1997
Raison, Ms Kelly-Louise. . . . . Oct 2005
Rooprai, Rashpal . . . . Jun 2003
Sellars, Ms Emma L. . . . . Sep 2001
Sohal, Mr Jasbinder Singh LLB . . . . *Sep 2002
Southby, Ms Katherine M . . . . Sep 1998
Stoker, Ms Suzanne. . . . . Nov 1996
Stokey, Mr Paul M. . . . . Sep 2001
Strickland, Mr Charles E S . . . . Sep 2004
Sussens, Ms Nicola J . . . . Nov 1998
Tear, Mr David A . . . . Sep 1999
Thompson, Miss Rachel LLB . . . . *Jul 2005
Young, Miss Louise LLB. . . . . Sep 2003
Con: Shuttleworth, Mr Ian R ACIArb . . . . *Dec 1975

GORMAN HAMILTON
2 Lisbon Square Leeds West Yorkshire LS1 4LY
Tel: 0113 386 2600 *Fax:* 0113 242 9662
Dx: 715140 NEWCASTLE UPON TYNE 19
Office: Ipswich, Newcastle upon Tyne

GRAHAME STOWE BATESON ‡
Portland House 5/7 Portland Street Leeds West Yorkshire LS1 3DR
Tel: 0113 246 8163 *Fax:* 0113 242 6682 *Dx:* 12022 LEEDS
Emergency telephone 07850 581691
E-mail: leeds@gsbsolicitors.com
List of partners: A J Bateson, H Cohen, A Glen, M Heath, R M Howard, M A Hurwood, S Page, R S Reed, G C Stowe, J S Thompson, A P Walker, R Walters
Office: Harrogate, Leeds (3 offices)
Work: C1 D1 E F1 G H J1 K1 L N Q R1 S1 V W Z(c,m)
Emergency Action, Agency, Advocacy, Fixed Fee Interview, Legal Aid undertaken and Legal Aid Franchise
Ptr: Bateson, Mr Arthur J ACIArb . . . . *Oct 1980
Glen, Ms Anne . . . . Dec 1990
Heath, Michael . . . . Aug 1997
Page, Stewart . . . . May 2005
Reed, Mr Richard Selby BA(Law) ★ . . . . *Feb 1985
Stowe, Mr Grahame C LLB; FCIArb ★ Chairman of Supply Benefit Appeals Tribunal & Mental Health Tribunal Yorkshire & Humberside; Chairman of MHRT . . . . . . *Oct 1974
Asoc: Woodhead, Ms Sarah-Jayne . . . . Sep 2006
Ast: Bates, Ms Hannah LLB . . . . *Nov 2006
Raj, Mr John . . . . Dec 2006
Tinning, Mr Andrew Roberts . . . . Apr 1998

GRAHAME STOWE BATESON
313 Town Street Bramley Leeds West Yorkshire LS13 3JT
Tel: 0113 255 8666 *Fax:* 0113 255 9851
Dx: 717651 BRAMLEY LEEDS
Emergency telephone 0113 269 2902
E-mail: bramley@gsbsolicitors.com
Office: Harrogate, Leeds (3 offices)
Work: D1 F1 G H J1 K1 L N
Emergency Action, Agency, Advocacy, Fixed Fee Interview, Legal Aid undertaken and Member of Accident Line
Ptr: Howard, Mr Richard Michael . . . . Nov 1992
Walters, Mr Richard . . . . Oct 1989
Ast: Porter, Elish . . . . Sep 1999

GRAHAME STOWE BATESON
10-14 Stonegate Road Meanwood Leeds West Yorkshire LS6 4HY
Tel: 0113 274 4611 *Fax:* 0113 230 4633 *Dx:* 12022 LEEDS
E-mail: meanwood@gsbsolicitors.com
Office: Harrogate, Leeds (3 offices)
Work: D1 E G H J1 K1 K2 L N S1 S2 W Z(m,r)
Emergency Action, Agency, Fixed Fee Interview, Legal Aid undertaken, Legal Aid Franchise and Member of Accident Line
Ptr: Cohen, Mr Howard LLB ● . . . . *Feb 1985

GRAHAME STOWE BATESON
87 Middleton Park Road Middleton Leeds West Yorkshire LS10 4LS
Tel: 0113 276 0044 *Fax:* 0113 277 4744
Dx: 12022 LEEDS (MIDDLETON)
E-mail: middleton@gsbsolicitors.com
Office: Harrogate, Leeds (3 offices)
Work: C1 G H J1 K1 L R1 S1 V W
Emergency Action, Agency, Advocacy, Fixed Fee Interview and Legal Aid undertaken
Ptr: Walker, Mr Andrew P . . . . Oct 1991
Ast: Hall, Adam . . . . Aug 2008
Hubbard, Mr David . . . . Jun 2009

GREEN WILLIAMSON SOLICITORS
Aspect Court 47 Park Square East Leeds West Yorkshire LS1 2NL
Tel: 0113 394 4120 *Fax:* 0113 394 4101
E-mail: jane.aldred@greenwilliamson.co.uk
Office: Wakefield

HGF LAW ‡
Belgrave Hall Belgrave Street Leeds West Yorkshire LS2 8DD
Tel: 0113 233 0148 *Fax:* 0113 233 0141
Emergency telephone 0778 818 4101
E-mail: law@hgf-law.com
Office: London WC2
Work: A3 C1 C3 I O U1 U2 Z(e,w,z,za)
Agency undertaken

HLW KEEBLE HAWSON LLP
Protection House 16-17 East Parade Leeds West Yorkshire LS1 2BR
Tel: 0113 244 3121 *Fax:* 0113 243 1100 *Dx:* 12043 LEEDS 1
E-mail: info@hlwkeeblehawson.co.uk
Office: Doncaster, Sheffield (2 offices)
Languages: Arabic, Brunei, Cantonese, French, German, Indonesian, Italian, Malay, Mandarin, Portuguese, Spanish
Work: A1 A3 B1 B2 C1 C2 C3 D1 D2 E F1 F2 G I J1 K1 K2 L M1 M2 N O P Q R1 R2 S1 S2 T1 T2 U1 U2 V W Z(b,c,d,e,f,g,h,i,j,k,l,m,n,o,p,q,r,s,w,x)
Emergency Action, Agency, Advocacy, Fixed Fee Interview, Legal Aid undertaken and Member of Accident Line
Ptr: Brown, Mr Robert A LLB Licensed Insolvency Practitioner . . . . *§Apr 1979
McKillop, H D LLB . . . . *§Mar 1984
Needle, Ms Sharon Lesley . . . . Aug 1998
Pliener, Mr Andrew M LLB Honorary Legal Counsel for Leeds Junior Chamber of Commerce . . . . Oct 1991
Ward, Ms Elizabeth Margaret . . . . Aug 1996
Ast: Ainsworth, Miss Ann Elizabeth LLB(Hons) . . . . . . Feb 2001
Drabble, Ms Josephine BSc(Hons) . . . . *Nov 1995

HALLAM SOLICITORS ‡
Lower Ground Floor 21 Otley Road Headingley Leeds West Yorkshire LS6 3AA
Tel: 0113 228 5306 *Fax:* 0113 217 4312
E-mail: frank@hallamsolicitors.co.uk

HAMILTONS ‡
20 Park Place Leeds West Yorkshire LS1 2SJ
Tel: 0113 244 6455 *Fax:* 0113 244 6189
Dx: 26430 LEEDS PARK SQUARE
List of partners: J S Hamilton
Work: E L S1 W
Ptr: Hamilton, Mr John S BA . . . . *Oct 1981

HARRIS & GREEN SOLICITORS ‡
The Old Library 116 Dewsbury Road Leeds West Yorkshire LS11 6XD
Tel: 0113 276 8866 *Fax:* 0113 276 8867
E-mail: info@harrisandgreensolicitors.com

HARRISON BUNDEY (incorporating Ruth Bundey & Co)
219-223 Chapeltown Road Chapeltown Leeds West Yorkshire LS7 3DX
Tel: 0113 200 7400 *Fax:* 0113 237 4685 *Dx:* 729240 LEEDS 67
E-mail: mail@harrisonbundey.co.uk
Office: Garforth, Guiseley, Ilkley, Leeds (2 offices)
Languages: Punjabi, Urdu
Work: D1 D2 G H K1
Emergency Action, Agency, Advocacy, Fixed Fee Interview, Legal Aid undertaken and Legal Aid Franchise
Ptr: Ahmed, Mrs Parveen LLB . . . . Jun 2005
Bundey, Ms Ruth Elizabeth Dobie BA Independent Governor . . . . *Apr 1980
Foley, Mr Mark G LLB ● . . . . *Jun 1979
Iqbal, Mr Mohammed Ghazanfar LLB; LLM . . . . . . Sep 2003
Message, Mr William R BA . . . . *Sep 1984
Ast: Banerjee, Miss Anita . . . . *Apr 2009
Collings, Rebecca . . . . Dec 2009
Frith, Kara . . . . Apr 2008
Hashim, Genan LLB . . . . Sep 2006
Taylor, Ms Frances K I LLB . . . . *Dec 1991
Con: Trythall, Mrs Joanna Mary BA(Hons) . . . . *Aug 1984

C W HARWOOD & CO ‡
Kimberley House 11 Woodhouse Square Leeds West Yorkshire LS3 1AD
Tel: 0113 245 7027 *Fax:* 0113 242 1329 *Dx:* 716923 LEEDS 39
E-mail: info@cwharwood.co.uk
List of partners: R K Addlestone, C W Harwood
Work: C1 C2 E F1 J1 K1 N O Q R1 R2 S1 S2 W Z(c,e,k,q)
Agency, Advocacy, Fixed Fee Interview undertaken and Member of Accident Line
Ptr: Addlestone, Mr Robert K LLB . . . . *Jun 1983
Harwood, Mr Christopher W LLB . . . . *Mar 1978

HASELTINE LAKE & CO ‡
West Riding House 67 Albion Street Leeds West Yorkshire LS1 5AA
Tel: 0113 233 9400 *Fax:* 0113 233 9401
Office: London WC1

HATCH LEGAL ‡
12 Park House Apartments 11-12 Park Row Leeds West Yorkshire LS1 5HB
Tel: 0113 234 6328 *Fax:* 0113 234 6328
E-mail: hilary@hcrook.orangehome.co.uk

HESLOP & PLATT ‡
Allerton House 75 Allerton Hill Leeds West Yorkshire LS7 3QB
Tel: 0113 393 1930 *Fax:* 0113 268 6544
E-mail: contact@heslop-platt.co.uk

HORROCKS & CO ‡
79 Otley Road Headingley Leeds West Yorkshire LS6 3PS
Tel: 0113 230 7944 *Fax:* 0113 230 7970 *Dx:* 713149 HORSFORTH 2
E-mail: enquiries@horrockssolicitors.co.uk
List of partners: S Horrocks
Work: B1 C1 E F1 J1 L N O Q S1 S2 W Z(j)
Emergency Action, Agency, Advocacy, Fixed Fee Interview undertaken and Member of Accident Line
SPr: Horrocks, Mr Stuart LLB(Hull) . . . . *Oct 1981
Ast: Harrison, Miss Louise Elizabeth . . . . Jan 2007

HENRY HYAMS ‡
7 South Parade Leeds West Yorkshire LS1 5QE
Tel: 0113 243 2288 *Fax:* 0113 246 0283 *Dx:* 12028 LEEDS 1
Emergency telephone 0113 383 7610
E-mail: info@henryhyams.com
List of partners: K Batty, C E Bergen, L A Bergen, M E Bush, J E Cooper, D C Hallam, D C H Nurse, G T Parkin, R Shedlow
Languages: French
Work: C1 D1 D2 E F1 F2 G H J1 K1 K2 L N O Q S1 S2 V W Z(f,i,l,m,p)
Emergency Action, Agency, Advocacy, Fixed Fee Interview, Legal Aid undertaken, Legal Aid Franchise and Member of Accident Line
Ptr: Batty, Mrs Kate ★ . . . . *Apr 2001
Bergen, Mr Clive E LLB(Manc) ★ . . . . *Mar 1980
Bergen, Mr Lloyd A LLB(Leeds) . . . . *Apr 1977
Bush, Mr Michael Elliot LLB . . . . *Nov 1994
Cooper, Miss Jane Elizabeth BA ★ . . . . *Dec 1995
Hallam, Mr Derek C LLB(L'pool) . . . . *Jul 1979
Nurse, Mr Dominic C H LLB(Leeds) . . . . *Oct 1993
Parkin, Mr Graham T LLB(Leeds) ★ . . . . *Nov 1982
Shedlow, Ms Ruth BA(Hons) . . . . *Mar 1999
Asoc: Jacobs, Mr Timothy MA(Cantab) . . . . *Oct 1997
Morrow, Mr Martin Joseph Robert LLB . . . . *Feb 1993
Ast: Bray, Miss Hannah . . . . May 2008
Cowans, Ms Katy . . . . *Mar 2004
Poli, Miss Davina LLB . . . . *Jul 2005
Richardson, Mrs Julie Ann . . . . *Sep 2002
Seedat, Rehana . . . . *Jun 2005
Walsh, Mr Michael BA(Hons) . . . . *Dec 2001

IBBOTSON BRADY ‡
1 City Square Leeds West Yorkshire LS1 2ES
Tel: 0113 366 3022 *Fax:* 0113 366 3082
Dx: 18020 LEEDS PARK SQUARE
Emergency telephone 0113 237 3011
E-mail: ibbotsonbrady@ibbotsonbrady.co.uk
List of partners: L S Brady, J M Ibbotson
Work: J2 N Q
Agency undertaken
Ptr: Brady, Mrs Lorraine Susan BA; ACII . . . . *Nov 1996
Ibbotson, Mr John Michael LLB(Hons) . . . . *Oct 1995

INCASSO LLP ‡
Trafalgar House 29 Park Place Leeds West Yorkshire LS1 2SP
Tel: 0845 404 1999

IRWIN MITCHELL LLP
Wellington Place Leeds West Yorkshire LS1 4BZ
Tel: 0870 150 0100 *Fax:* 0113 234 3322 *Dx:* 706951 LEEDS
E-mail: inquiries@irwinmitchell.co.uk
Office: Birmingham, Bristol, London EC1, Manchester, Newcastle upon Tyne, Sheffield
Languages: French, Italian, Punjabi
Work: A1 A3 B1 C1 C2 C3 D1 E F1 F2 G H I J1 K1 L M1 M2 N O P Q R1 R2 S1 T1 T2 W X Z(b,c,d,e,g,j,k,l,o,r,t,u,w)
Emergency Action, Agency, Advocacy, Legal Aid undertaken, Legal Aid Franchise and Member of Accident Line
Ptr: Coates, Mr Simon Cornelius LLB . . . . *Oct 1998
Cunningham, Mr Kevin Gerald BA . . . . *Aug 1979
Dapin, Mr Howard Lawrence LLB . . . . *Oct 1984
Gillott, Mr Charles R E BA(Oxon) . . . . *Oct 1986
Horton, Ms Jane A LLB(Hons) . . . . *Oct 1989
Hughes, Mr Richard William LLB(Hons) . . . . *Nov 1991
Knaggs, Mr David LLB(Hons) . . . . *Nov 1990
Love, Mr James Charles MA(Cantab); Dip Int Prop Law & Practice Member of the Institute of Trademark Agents and Chartered Institute of Patent Agents . . . . *Aug 1991
Taylor, Mrs Anne LLB . . . . *Oct 1990
Walker, Mrs Louise C LLB(Hons) . . . . *Nov 1991
Asoc: De Tute, Mrs Sara Louise LLB Hughes Scholar Leeds University 1983 . . . . *Oct 1996
Ast: Anderson, Miss Deborah S BA(Hons) . . . . *Nov 1995
Anderson, Miss Gillian LLB(Brunel) ♦ . . . . *Sep 1990
Aulton, Mrs Annaliese J BA; PhD(Econ); PD(Law); LPC . . . . *Sep 1998
Bailey, Mr Ian BA(German) . . . . *Oct 1994
Bentley, Mr Neil D BA(Hons); LPC; MA(Cantab) School Governor . . . . *Sep 1999
Brown, Mr Matthew LPC . . . . *Sep 1999
Brumpton, Mrs Sarah Christine . . . . *Mar 1994
Cuerden, Mr Simon Paul BA(Hons) . . . . *Oct 1998
Fallon, Mr Mark A . . . . *Sep 1991
Grimshaw, Ms Kate . . . . Nov 1997
Heaton, Miss Carolyn LLB(Hons) . . . . *Oct 1994
Henson, Miss Alison J LLB(Hons) . . . . *Sep 1997
Meehan, Ms Lorraine . . . . *Oct 1998
Perkins, Ms Julie LLB . . . . *Oct 1990
Ramage, Mr Christopher James BA(Hons) . . . . . . *Nov 1995
Rees, Ms Catherine H . . . . *Jul 1998
Slavin, Mr Robert . . . . *Sep 1996
Tonkinson, Ms Julie A LLB(Hons) . . . . *Sep 1997
Whysall, Ms Julia Victoria Firinne BA(Hons)(History); CPE; LPC . . . . *Feb 1998
Wilson, Mr Nigel M . . . . *Nov 1995
Wright, Ms Deirdre Ann BA(Hons) . . . . *Oct 1995
Con: Bell, Mr Peter Barrington LLB . . . . *§Nov 1972

ISON HARRISON ‡
Duke House 54 Wellington Street Leeds West Yorkshire LS1 2EE
Tel: 0113 284 5000 *Fax:* 0113 284 5150 *Dx:* 729240 LEEDS 67
E-mail: mail@isonharrison.co.uk
List of partners: P Ahmed, J M Bloomer, N Bowman, R E D Bundey, J Campbell, N R Fairbairn, S M Flint, R Flowers, M G Foley, S L Hattersley, J Hewardine, S Hills, M G Iqbal, D P S Mackenzie, W R Message, A F Munro, S M Neale, G L Nichol, I Oliver, M J Phillips, A Price, S R Purchas, J D Robson, R J Timperley, J L M Wearing
Office: Garforth, Guiseley, Ilkley, Leeds (2 offices)
Languages: Farsi, French, German, Gujarati, Hindi, Italian, Punjabi, Shona, Urdu
Work: C1 D1 D2 E J1 K1 K2 N O Q S1 S2 W Z(i,l,q,r)
Agency, Advocacy, Legal Aid undertaken, Legal Aid Franchise and Member of Accident Line
Ptr: Bowman, Mr Nigel ♦ . . . . *Oct 1989
Fairbairn, Ms Nancy Radford . . . . *Dec 1997
Flint, Mr Stephen M BA(Hons) . . . . *Sep 1999
Flowers, Mrs Ruth BA(Hons) . . . . *May 2000
Hattersley, Mr Stephen Leslie LLB(Hons) Notary Public *Oct 1994
Hewardine, Mr Jeremy . . . . *Oct 1993
Hills, Ms Sarah BA(Hons) . . . . *Oct 1996
Mackenzie, Mr Dominic Peter Stewart LLB . . . . . *Sep 1999
Munro, Miss Allison Fiona BA; LLB . . . . *Nov 1994
Neale, Mr Stephen M LLB . . . . *Nov 1989
Oliver, Mr Iain . . . . *Jan 1998
Price, Mr Andrew . . . . *Oct 1997
Purchas, Mr Simon R BA . . . . *Mar 1985
Robson, Mr Jonathan D LLB . . . . *Dec 1989
Timperley, Mr Richard J LLB(Hons) . . . . *Oct 1993
Wearing, Mr Jonathan L M BA; LLB . . . . *Oct 1996
Nichol, Gaynor Louise . . . . NSP
Asoc: Mayman, Sarah . . . . Jan 2007
Ast: Allen, Ms Debbie . . . . *Sep 2007
Beange, Dorota . . . . Jul 2009
Burns, Ms Claire . . . . Jul 2004
Carter, Mr Darren . . . . Apr 2005
Davison, Mr Ben . . . . *Feb 2008
Ellis, Miss Rebecca Helen . . . . Apr 2011
Hachemi, Mr Malcolm . . . . Apr 2003
Hatton, Mr David Peter LLB . . . . *Nov 1995
Lunat, Mr Yunas LLB(Hons) . . . . *Apr 1994
Macready, Miss Angela . . . . *Nov 2006
Rahman, Ms Tahira BA(Hons) . . . . *Jul 2005
Redfern, Mr Alastair . . . . Jan 2009
Russell, Miss Lisa . . . . *Jan 2008
Con: Bond, Ms Elizabeth . . . . *Nov 1982
Morley, Ms Christina . . . . Oct 1981
Warriner, Mr Gary . . . . Oct 1985

ISON HARRISON
48 Austhorpe Road Crossgates Leeds West Yorkshire LS15 8DX
Tel: 0113 232 6530 *Fax:* 0113 284 5140 *Dx:* 13904 CROSSGATES
E-mail: crossgates@isonharrison.co.uk
Office: Garforth, Guiseley, Ilkley, Leeds (2 offices)
Work: D1 D2 K1 K3 K4 S1 W
Emergency Action, Agency, Fixed Fee Interview, Legal Aid undertaken, Legal Aid Franchise and Member of Accident Line
Mem: Campbell, Ms Jade . . . . Sep 2009
Ast: Lorkins, Mr Geoffrey Alan LLB . . . . *Oct 1990

JBL LAW ‡
30 Park Cross Street Leeds West Yorkshire LS1 2QH
Tel: 0113 200 2000 *Fax:* 0113 200 2001
E-mail: info@jbllaw.co.uk

JWP SOLICITORS
Aspect Court 47 Park Square East Leeds West Yorkshire LS1 2NL
Tel: 0113 346 6030 *Fax:* 01924 379113
Office: Wakefield

PAUL R JACOBSON & CO ‡
3 Primley Park Garth Alwoodley Leeds West Yorkshire LS17 7LE
Tel: 0113 269 3925 *Fax:* 0113 368 0503
Emergency telephone 07710 463986
E-mail: prjacobson@hotmail.com
List of partners: P R Jacobson
Languages: French
Work: E L S1 W
Fixed Fee Interview undertaken
SPr: Jacobson, Mr Paul Robert LLB(Hons)(Lond) . . . . . . Jul 1980

See p112 for the Key to Work Categories & other symbols

JAMES LEGAL SOLICITORS
1 Whitehall Whitehall Road Leeds West Yorkshire LS1 4HR
Tel: 0113 390 6021 *Fax:* 0113 390 6100
E-mail: info@jameslegal.co.uk
Office: Hull

JONES MYERS LLP ‡
5th Floor St Paul's House 23 Park Square Leeds West Yorkshire LS1 2ND
Tel: 0113 246 0055 *Fax:* 0113 246 7446
Dx: 14080 LEEDS PARK SQUARE
E-mail: info@jonesmyers.co.uk
List of partners: S K Banerjee, P G Jones, R M Peaker
Work: D1 D2 K1 K2
Emergency Action, Agency, Advocacy, Legal Aid undertaken and Legal Aid Franchise
Ptr: Banerjee, Ms Kate . . . . . Oct 1990
Jones, Mr Peter G Former National Chairman of the Solicitors Family Law Association . . . . . *Dec 1980
Peaker, Mr Richard Matthew LLB(Hons) . . . . . *Nov 1993
Con: Taylor, Mr Norman S LLB(Newc) . . . . . *Jul 1975

JUST COSTS SOLICITORS
No1 City Square Leeds West Yorkshire LS1 2ES
Tel: 0113 366 3193 *Fax:* 0113 366 3194
Dx: 14094 LEEDS PARK SQUARE
Office: Chesterfield, London WC2, Manchester (2 offices)

KAMRANS SOLICITORS ‡
Waverley House 14 Woodhouse Square Leeds West Yorkshire LS3 1AQ
Tel: 0113 245 5000 *Fax:* 0113 245 1741 *Dx:* 71692 LEEDS 39
E-mail: mail@kamransolicitors.co.uk

KARIM & CO ‡
279 Roundhay Road Leeds West Yorkshire LS8 4HS
Tel: 0113 249 1662 *Fax:* 0113 249 1478 *Dx:* 17934 LEEDS

KELLY & CO ‡
49 St Pauls Street Leeds West Yorkshire LS1 2TE
Tel: 0113 244 2113 *Fax:* 0113 242 5395
Dx: 26445 LEEDS PARK SQUARE
E-mail: pkelly@kellyand.co.uk
List of partners: P G Kelly, S J Stanier
Work: A1 C1 E L M4 Q R1 S1 W Z(b,c,d,h,j,l)
Agency undertaken
Ptr: Kelly, Mr Patrick Gerald BA(Law) . . . . . *Oct 1981
Stanier, Mr Stephen John LLB(Hons) . . . . . Sep 1991

KEMPNER & PARTNERS ‡
Devonshire Hall Devonshire Avenue Leeds West Yorkshire LS8 1AW
Tel: 0113 393 1921 *Fax:* 0113 269 1512
E-mail: mail@kempnerandpartners.com

KHER SOLICITORS ‡
No2 Warehouse The Wharf Sowerby Bridge Leeds West Yorkshire HX6 2AG
Tel: 01422 836622 *Fax:* 01422 831144

LAKE LEGAL LLP ‡
Fountain House 4 South Parade Leeds West Yorkshire LS1 5QX
Tel: 0845 190 0001 *Fax:* 0845 190 0002
Dx: 26431 LEEDS PARK SQUARE
E-mail: enquiries@lakelegal.co.uk

LANDMARK SOLICITORS LLP ‡
Whitehall Waterfront 2 Riverside Way Leeds West Yorkshire LS1 4EH
Tel: 0113 244 0591 *Fax:* 0113 244 1459
E-mail: enquiries@landmarksolicitors.co.uk

LANSDOWNE & CO ‡
Park House 28 Park Square West Leeds West Yorkshire LS1 2PW
Tel: 0113 243 9270 *Fax:* 0113 245 5460

LAST CAWTHRA FEATHER LLP
Suite 24c Joseph's Well Hanover Walk Leeds West Yorkshire LS3 1AB
Tel: 0113 244 0876 *Fax:* 01274 390644 *Dx:* 716922 LEEDS 29
E-mail: enquiries@lcf.co.uk
Office: Baildon, Bradford, Ilkley, Shipley
Work: C1 E O W
Ptr: Abraham, Mr Charles . . . . . Sep 1999
McDonald, Mr Adrian Terence . . . . . Sep 1996
Shaw, Mr Neil . . . . . Oct 1984
Ast: Cooke, Miss Eleanor . . . . . Jan 2009
Troyna, Nicola . . . . . May 2003

LEE & PRIESTLEY LLP ‡
10-12 East Parade Leeds West Yorkshire LS1 2AJ
Tel: 0845 129 2300 *Fax:* 0845 129 2301 *Dx:* 14074 LEEDS
E-mail: info@leepriestley.com
List of partners: C A Burns, J R G Dale, A V Dyer, I Jenkins, A J Lawson, J M H Oxley, T G Williams
Work: A1 A3 B1 C1 C2 C3 D1 E I J1 K1 K2 K3 K4 L N O P Q R1 R2 S1 S2 T1 T2 U2 V W X Z(b,d,e,f,l,m,o,p,r,s)
Agency, Advocacy, Legal Aid undertaken and Legal Aid Franchise
Ptr: Burns, Mr Christopher Aubrey LLB . . . . . *Dec 1994
Dale, Mr James R G LLB . . . . . *Nov 1990
Dyer, Miss Andrea V BA . . . . . Oct 1992
Jenkins, Mr Iain LLB . . . . . *Oct 1985
Lawson, Mr Andrew John LLB(Hons) . . . . . Oct 1985
Oxley, Mr Jonathan M H LLB . . . . . *Oct 1986
Williams, Mr Timothy G LLB(Hons); LLM(Cantab) . . . *Sep 1990

LESTER MORRILL ‡
27 Park Square West Leeds West Yorkshire LS1 2PL
Tel: 0113 245 8549 *Fax:* 0113 242 1965
Dx: 14097 LEEDS PARK SQUARE
Emergency telephone 0113 245 8549
E-mail: info@lmlaw.co.uk
List of partners: S E Bartfield, F C Borrill, P M Goldberg, R E Lester, L A Lobley, J M Morrill
Languages: Punjabi, Urdu
Work: A1 B2 C1 D1 D2 E G H J1 K1 K2 N Q S1 S2 V W Z(g,l,r,y)
Emergency Action, Agency, Advocacy, Fixed Fee Interview, Legal Aid undertaken, Legal Aid Franchise and Member of Accident Line
Ptr: Bartfield, Ms Susan Eleanor LLB . . . . . *Oct 1995
Borrill, Ms Fiona C BA(Hons) . . . . . Nov 1986
Goldberg, Mr Philip Marshall LLB ★ Land Law Prize. . *Sep 1998
Lester, Mr Rodney E . . . . . *Dec 1971
Lobley, Miss Lindsey Ann LLB(Hons); PGDipLaw . . . Jun 2004
Morrill, Ms Julia M LLB Deputy District Judge . . . . . Nov 1983
Asoc: Barnes, Miss Kay E BA(Hons); CPE . . . . . *Sep 1997
Ast: Banks, Mrs Natalie BA; MSc . . . . . *Jun 2009
Bosley, Anna . . . . . Jul 2009
Smith, Mr Adrian DMS; DML . . . . . *Jul 1992
Wedlinscky, Ms Laura . . . . . Dec 2008
Con: Bowskill, Miss Elizabeth J BA; LLB . . . . . *Oct 1980
Gollott, Mr Charles Richard Edmund . . . . . Jan 1986

LEVI SOLICITORS LLP ‡
33 St Pauls Street Leeds West Yorkshire LS1 2JJ
Tel: 0113 244 9931 *Fax:* 0113 297 1872
Dx: 706957 LEEDS PARK SQUARE
E-mail: info@levisolicitors.co.uk
List of partners: J M Baum, D L Brown, H Cohen, I S Land, S Newdall, N Saunders, S J Spruce, J P Sykes, A C B Tai
Office: Bradford
Languages: Hindi, Punjabi, Urdu
Work: B1 C1 C2 C3 D1 E F1 J1 K1 K3 K4 L M1 M2 N O P Q R1 S1 S2 T1 T2 V W Z(c,j,l,p)
Emergency Action, Agency, Advocacy, Fixed Fee Interview, Legal Aid undertaken and Member of Accident Line
Ptr: Baum, Mr Jonathan Martyn LLB(Hons) ♦ . . . . . *Nov 1995
Brown, Mr Darren Lewis LLB(Hons) . . . . . *Sep 1995
Cohen, Mr Howard LLB ● . . . . . *Feb 1985
Land, Mr Ian S LLB ♦ . . . . . *Oct 1989
Newdall, Mr Steven BA ♦ . . . . . *Oct 1992
Saunders, Mrs Natalie MA . . . . . Sep 2000
Spruce, Mr Simon J ♦ . . . . . *Apr 1998
Sykes, Mr J Paul LLB ♦ . . . . . *Oct 1984
Tai, Mr Alan C B LLB ♦ . . . . . *Oct 1998
Asoc: Levin, Miss Michelle E BA ♦ . . . . . *Oct 2001
Rolston, Mrs Clare LLB . . . . . Sep 2001
Ast: Boardman, Miss Kelly LLB . . . . . *Sep 2005
Davies, Miss Catrin Mercrid LLB . . . . . Sep 2005
Wisnia, Mr Richard A . . . . . Sep 2003

MICHAEL LEWIN SOLICITORS ‡
376 Harrogate Road Leeds West Yorkshire LS17 6PY
Tel: 0113 393 0231 *Fax:* 0113 393 0176
E-mail: michaellewin@michaellewin.co.uk
List of partners: A Keech, M Lewin
Dir: Keech, Abbigail . . . . . Sep 2010
Lewin, Mr Michael BSc(Hons); FMAAT . . . . . Oct 1996

C T LEWIS & CO ‡
Basinghall Chambers No 47 Upper Basinghall Street Leeds West Yorkshire LS1 5HR
Tel: 0113 245 9726 *Fax:* 0113 243 6318
Emergency telephone 01943 601445
List of partners: C T Lewis
Languages: French
Work: A1 A2 B1 C1 C2 E F1 F2 J1 K4 L O P Q R1 R2 S1 S2 T1 T2 W Z(b,c,d,f,j,k,l,q)
Advocacy undertaken
Ptr: Lewis, Mr Christopher Thomas LLB . . . . . *Dec 1965

LUPTON FAWCETT ‡
Yorkshire House East Parade Leeds West Yorkshire LS1 5BD
Tel: 0113 280 2000 *Fax:* 0113 245 6782 *Dx:* 730000 LEEDS 70
E-mail: law@luptonfawcett.com
List of partners: N M Armitage, D W M Barraclough, L M Bland, A S Braithwaite, N J Broadbent, G J Clegg, D Corker, I D Coupland, A Cumming, P L Drazen, J C J Eaton, K H Emsley, T Forret, I C Furness, A Hackett, J R Harrap, J C Henderson, S P Houghton, R G Jones, S Ludlam, J R Marshall, E G McConnell, D Milwain, J M Norris, M A P Peacock, M Phillips, S C Pickard, H A Rutter, J R H Sykes, D M Whitaker
Office: Sheffield
Work: A1 A3 B1 C1 C2 D1 E F1 G H I J1 J2 K1 K2 L N O P Q R1 R2 S1 S2 T1 T2 U2 V W Z(b,c,d,e,h,j,k,l,o,p,q,r,w)
Emergency Action, Advocacy, Fixed Fee Interview, Legal Aid undertaken and Member of Accident Line
SPr: Ludlam, Ms Sara BSc; Dip LP . . . . . Dec 1996
Ptr: Armitage, Mr Nicholas M LLB . . . . . *Dec 1991
Barraclough, Mr David William Martin LLB(Hons) . . . Jun 1974
Bland, Miss Louise Mary MA . . . . . Jan 1993
Braithwaite, Miss Anne S MA(Cantab) . . . . . *Oct 1985
Broadbent, Mr Nigel J LLB . . . . . *Oct 1991
Coupland, Mr Ian David LLB(Hons) . . . . . *Oct 1988
Cumming, Mr Anthony . . . . . *§Jun 1965
Drazen, Mr Philip L BA(Hons)(Law) . . . . . *May 1995
Eaton, Mr John C J MA(Cantab) . . . . . *§May 1967
Emsley, Mr Kevin H BA; LLM . . . . . *§Apr 1979
Forret, Miss Tanya LLB . . . . . Jan 1995
Harrap, Mr J Robert MA(Cantab) . . . . . *§Mar 1975
Henderson, Mr Jeremy C LLB . . . . . *Jun 1980
Houghton, Mr Stephen P MA; LLB; DipLP . . . . . *Oct 1990
Jones, Mr Richard G LLB . . . . . *Jan 1976
McConnell, Mr Euan Graham LLB(Hons) . . . . . *Sep 1989
Marshall, Mr J Richard LLB . . . . . *Sep 1987
Norris, Mr John M . . . . . *§Jun 1963
Peacock, Mr Michael A P TD LLB . . . . . *§Apr 1978
Phillips, Miss Michele LLB . . . . . *Oct 1987
Rutter, Mr Howard A BA . . . . . *May 1980
Sykes, Mr John R H BA . . . . . *Oct 1984
Whitaker, Mr David M LLB . . . . . *Oct 1987
Mem: Clegg, Mr Giles J . . . . . *Sep 1996
Furness, Mr Ian C BA . . . . . *Dec 1986
Milwain, Mr Duncan . . . . . Mar 1995
Pickard, Mr Stephen C BA(Hons)(Business Law) . . . *Feb 1986
Asoc: Atkinson, Mr James LLB . . . . . *Sep 1991
Brodbent, Mrs Deborah LLB . . . . . Jul 1998
Davidson, Mr Andrew BA(Hons) . . . . . *Sep 1998
Francey, Mr Andrew . . . . . Sep 2000
Hart, Mr Douglas LLB . . . . . Oct 1998
Lumb, Mr Daniel James LLB(Hons) . . . . . Mar 2005
McFadyen, Mr Samuel S LLB . . . . . *Aug 1999
Markham, Ms Rachel E . . . . . Apr 2002
Simpson, Mrs Tracey Jane LLB . . . . . Oct 1994
Ast: Annett, Mr Richard Anthony LLB . . . . . Oct 2000
Buchanan, Mr Michael . . . . . Oct 2007
Dixon, Mr Brett LLB(Hons) . . . . . Nov 1999
Ferraro, Mr Giacomo Angelo LLB(Hons) . . . . . Nov 1998
Finn, Mrs Jane LLB . . . . . Oct 2001
Hunt, Mr Christian Peter LLB . . . . . Sep 2001
Johns, Miss Charlotte Louise LLB . . . . . Sep 2001
Johnson, Mr Andrew Colin LLB . . . . . *Sep 2001
Lang, Ms Zoe . . . . . Jun 2005
Laycock, Mr James Peter LLB . . . . . Sep 2003
McLean, Miss Georgina Mary . . . . . Sep 2003
Markhah, Miss Sarah Juliet Louise LLB . . . . . Nov 1992
Reed, Mr Jonathon . . . . . Apr 2001
Robertson, Mr Douglas Fan LLB . . . . . Sep 2002
Con: Dalton, Mr Rodney S . . . . . *§Jun 1970

LYONS DAVIDSON
St Martins House Britannia Street Leeds West Yorkshire LS1 2DZ
Tel: 0113 368 6161 *Fax:* 0113 368 6150
Dx: 26444 LEEDS PARK SQUARE
E-mail: info@lyondavidson.co.uk
Office: Bristol, Cardiff, New Malden, Plymouth, Solihull
Ptr: Kelbie, Ms Judith . . . . . Mar 1999

MB SOLICITORS LTD TRADING AS MB LAW ‡
Studio 3 The Quays Concordia Street Leeds West Yorkshire LS1 4ES
Tel: 0113 242 4444 *Fax:* 0113 246 7542
Emergency telephone 07753 740844
E-mail: advice@mb-law.co.uk
List of partners: R Adams, I R Hopkinson, C G Ingleby
Work: A3 B1 C1 C2 C3 F1 F2 J1 J2 M3 N O Q U2 Z(e,j,k,p,q,za)
Emergency Action, Agency, Advocacy, Fixed Fee Interview and Legal Aid Franchise
Dir: Adams, Mr Robin . . . . . *Oct 2002
Hopkinson, Mr Ian Robert . . . . . *Jul 1994
Ingleby, Ms Claire G LLB . . . . . *Oct 1990
Ast: Mitchell, Mr Thomas . . . . . *Jan 2009
Price, Mrs Emma . . . . . *Jan 2004
Tweddle, Mr Gary . . . . . *Apr 2004

MRN LEEDS ‡
17 Park Place Leeds West Yorkshire LS1 2SJ
Tel: 0113 247 1549 *Fax:* 0113 245 1091
Dx: 14083 LEEDS PARK SQUARE

MCARAS SOLICITORS LLP ‡
5 Park Place Leeds West Yorkshire LS1 2RU
Tel: 0113 243 4333 *Fax:* 0113 242 5626
Dx: 26432 LEEDS PARK SQUARE
Emergency telephone 0113 261 4084
E-mail: rjm@mcaras.com
List of partners: D E Hardy, J McAra, R J McAra, S L Smith
Work: D1 D2 K1 K2 K3 V
Emergency Action, Advocacy, Fixed Fee Interview, Legal Aid undertaken and Legal Aid Franchise
Ptr: Hardy, Ms Deborah E LLB . . . . . *Dec 1992
McAra, Mrs Judith BA . . . . . *Mar 1984
McAra, Mr Robert J BA . . . . . *Apr 1978
Smith, Miss Sarah L CPE; DL . . . . . *Nov 1998
Ast: Buxton, Miss Sarah LLB . . . . . *Dec 2005
Linden, Miss Clare LLB(Hons) . . . . . *Jul 2008
Penasar, Mrs Talvinder LLB(Hons) . . . . . *Feb 2002

MCILLMURRAYS SOLICITORS ‡
West One Wellington Street Leeds West Yorkshire LS1 1BA
Tel: 0113 322 7903 *Fax:* 0113 322 4677
E-mail: info@mcillmurrays.com
Office: St Albans

MCKAY LAW ‡
26 Park Square West Leeds West Yorkshire LS1 2PL
Tel: 0845 23 5571 *Fax:* 0845 123 5572
E-mail: info@mckaylaw.co.uk
List of partners: S A Mckay
Languages: French, German
Work: D1 J1 J2 K1 N O Q S1 W Z(f,g,k,q,w)
Advocacy and Fixed Fee Interview undertaken
Ptr: Mckay, Mr Simon A . . . . . Nov 2001

MARKS & CLERK
43 Park Place Leeds West Yorkshire LS1 2RY
Tel: 0113 389 5600 *Fax:* 0113 389 5601
Office: Birmingham, Cheltenham, Leicester, Liverpool, London WC2, Manchester, Oxford

VERONIQUE MAROT & CO ‡
(in association with HLW McCombie)
36 Newlay Lane Horsforth Leeds West Yorkshire LS18 4LE
Tel: 0113 258 2021 *Fax:* 0113 258 8079
Emergency telephone 07947 576886
E-mail: veronique@vmarot.lawlite.net
List of partners: M A C J Marot
Languages: French, German, Spanish
Work: C1 C2 C3 E I J1 M1 S1 S2 W Z(d,e,w)
Emergency Action and Fixed Fee Interview undertaken
SPr: Marot, Ms Marie-Veronique Antoinette C J BA(Hons) . *Mar 1992

MAVEN SOLICITORS ‡
1 City Square Leeds West Yorkshire LS1 2ES
Tel: 0113 366 3221 *Fax:* 0113 366 3222
E-mail: mail@mavensolicitors.com

METIS LAW LLP ‡
City Point King Street Leeds West Yorkshire LS1 2HL
Tel: 0113 242 4099 *Fax:* 0113 350 6678
E-mail: paul.cooper@metislaw.com

MILLS & REEVE
1 City Square Leeds West Yorkshire LS1 2ES
Tel: 0844 561 0011 *Fax:* 0113 388 8441 *Dx:* 713672 LEEDS 25
E-mail: david.salter@mills-reeve.com
Office: Birmingham, Cambridge, London EC3, Manchester, Norwich
Work: K1 Z(j)

MILNERS SOLICITORS ‡
Crown House 85-89 Great George Street Leeds West Yorkshire LS1 3BR
Tel: 0113 245 0852 *Fax:* 0113 242 0469 *Dx:* 12042 LEEDS
E-mail: office@milnerslaw.com
Office: Barnsley, Pontefract, Wakefield

MINTONS ‡
Minton Chambers 12 Heaton's Court Leeds West Yorkshire LS1 4LJ
Tel: 0113 245 7575 *Fax:* 0113 245 7577 *Dx:* 12012 LEEDS
E-mail: law@mintons.co.uk
List of partners: S J Minton
Languages: Gujarati, Urdu
Work: N Z(q,r)
Agency, Legal Aid undertaken and Legal Aid Franchise
SPr: Minton, Mr Simon J LLB . . . . . *Apr 1981

A A MIRSONS SOLICITORS LIMITED
103 Clarendon Road Leeds West Yorkshire LS2 9DF
Tel: 0845 050 5678 *Fax:* 0808 280 0880
Office: London EC4, London SE7

MORRISH SOLICITORS LLP ‡
Oxford House Oxford Row Leeds West Yorkshire LS1 3BE
Tel: 0113 245 0733 *Fax:* 0844 443 2679
E-mail: info@morrishsolicitors.com
List of partners: M A Bare, W D Gardiner, J E Hanley, T R Harris, J London, T W Morrish, R Rogerson, P A Scholey, I G Skirrow, I T Wharton, B A White, S G Wilson, J D Winn
Office: Bradford, Pudsey, Yeadon
Work: D1 G J1 K1 N Q S1 W
Agency, Fixed Fee Interview, Legal Aid undertaken and Member of Accident Line
Ptr: Bare, Mr Martin A BA(Oxon) . . . *Nov 1984
Gardiner, Mr William Duncan . . . *Sep 1994
Hanley, Mr Jamie Edmund LLB . . . Aug 1998
Harris, Mr Timothy Richard LLB(Warw) . . . *§Apr 1980
London, Mr Jason LLB(Leeds) . . . Oct 1993
Rogerson, Mr Richard LLB . . . Sep 1993
Scholey, Mr Paul Andrew LLB. . . . *§Sep 1989
Skirrow, Mr Ian George . . . *§Dec 1974
Wharton, Mr Iain Terence LLB(Leeds) . . . *§Sep 1989
White, Mr Bernard Arthur BA . . . *§Jun 1980
Wilson, Mr Simon George LLB . . . Sep 1995
Winn, Ms Julie Deborah BA(Accounting & Finance) . *Feb 1994
Asoc: Gallagher, Mr Stephen John LLB(L'pool) . . . *Jun 1981
Heath, Mrs Noelle Frances LLB(Hons) . . . Oct 1995
McGuire, Mr Joseph F LLB . . . *Sep 1992
Ast: Cook, Miss Laura Jane LLB; DipLP . . . Oct 2001
Mullan, Miss Sandra Elizabeth Theresa Claire BA(Hons) . . . *Nov 1998
Nabozny, Mr Matthew Adam LLB; DipLaw. . . . Oct 2001
Phillips, Miss Jayne LLB; LPC. . . . Sep 1999
Samaroo, Miss Sandra C D BA(Hons)(Soc Sci & Politics); CPE; CPC; Dip PI. . . . *Aug 1997
Simpson, Miss Fiona Jane . . . *Sep 2002
Sorensen, Mr David Paul BA(Hons) . . . Sep 2001
Worger, Mrs Amanda Louise LLB(Hons). . . . *Jun 1996
Con: Rigg, Mr Michael E LLB. . . . *§Jun 1977
Tidswell, Mr Thomas K BA(Law) . . . *May 1980

JEFFREY MYERS & CO ‡
Myers House 8 Blenheim Terrace Leeds West Yorkshire LS2 9HZ
Tel: 0113 242 2455 *Fax:* 0113 242 4796 *Dx:* 716928 LEEDS 39
E-mail: jeffrey@jeffrey-meyers.co.uk

NEEDHAMS SOLICITORS ‡
Haigh Hall Halifax Road Liversedge Leeds West Yorkshire WF15 6PG
Tel: 0800 731 0105
E-mail: info@needhamssolicitors.co.uk

THE NEEDLE PARTNERSHIP ‡
Suite 1E Gledhow Mount Mansion Roxholme Grove Leeds West Yorkshire LS7 4JJ
Tel: 0113 237 4008 *Fax:* 0113 262 6060

NESBIT LAW GROUP LLP
4th Floor Bann Suite 117 The Headrow Leeds West Yorkshire LS1 5JW
Tel: 0113 380 1631 *Fax:* 0113 320 0311
E-mail: mail@nesbitlawgroup.co.uk
Office: Bury, Liverpool, Wembley

NORTHONE SOLICITORS LLP ‡
279b Roundhay Road Leeds West Yorkshire LS8 4HS
Tel: 0845 863 0832 *Fax:* 0845 863 0833
Dx: 17932 ROUNDHAY LEEDS
E-mail: shahzad.ilyas@northonesolicitors.co.uk

O'GARRA'S ‡
(incorporating Warner Falk & Co)
32 Park Square Leeds West Yorkshire LS1 2PF
Tel: 0113 247 1477 *Fax:* 0113 247 1487
Dx: 26424 LEEDS PARK SQUARE
Emergency telephone 07693 413290
E-mail: info@osgsolicitors.com
List of partners: M J O'Garra, S M Smith
Work: B2 D1 G H K1 K2
Emergency Action, Agency, Advocacy, Fixed Fee Interview, Legal Aid undertaken and Legal Aid Franchise
Ptr: O'Garra, Mr Michael J LLB(Hons) . . . Oct 1992
Smith, Mr Sean M LLB(Hons) . . . Apr 1998
Asoc: Miller, Mr Michael LLB(Hons) . . . Aug 2000
Ast: Vickers, Mr Andrew LLB(Hons) . . . Jun 1994
Watson, Mr Charles. . . . Nov 1996
Con: Falk, Mr Warner William BA(Hons) . . . *§Oct 1976

O'ROURKE REID & CO ‡
17-19 York Place Leeds West Yorkshire LS1 2EX
Tel: 0113 245 7811 *Fax:* 0113 245 7879
Dx: 26450 LEEDS PARK SQUARE
E-mail: lex@orourkereid.co.uk
List of partners: M Purtill, J Reid
Work: B1 C1 E J2 L N O Q R2 S1 S2 Z(b,c,q,r)
Ptr: Purtill, Ms Mary. . . . Sep 2004
Reid, Mr John. . . . Jan 1998

PARAGON LAW LTD ‡
53 The Calls Leeds West Yorkshire LS2 7EY
Tel: 0113 391 7670 *Fax:* 0113 391 7679
E-mail: enquiries@paragonlaw.co.uk

PENSION & INVESTMENT PARTNERS LLP ‡
Suite 3 Realtex House Leeds Road Leeds West Yorkshire LS19 6AX
Tel: 0113 202 9529 *Fax:* 0560 114 0528
E-mail: bernard@pipllp.co.uk

PINSENT MASONS LLP
1 Park Row Leeds West Yorkshire LS1 5AB
Est: 2004
Tel: 0113 244 5000 *Fax:* 0113 244 8000 *Dx:* 26440 LEEDS 28
E-mail: enquiries@pinsentmasons.com
Office: Birmingham, Bristol, London EC2, Manchester
Languages: French, German, Italian, Spanish
Work: A1 B1 C1 C2 C3 E F1 F2 I J1 J2 L M1 M2 N O P Q R1 R2 S1 S2 T1 T2 U1 U2 W Z(b,c,d,e,f,h,k,l,n,o,p,q,u,za)
Emergency Action, Agency, Advocacy undertaken and Member of Accident Line
Ptr: Atkinson, Mr Peter R BA(Hons) . . . *Nov 1981
Barker, Mr Ian BA. . . . *Oct 1994
Barlow, Mr Adrian P. . . . *Oct 1989
Booth, Mr Christopher D LLB . . . *Nov 1987
Boyd, Mr Michael Philip LLB(Hons)(Leeds) . . . *Oct 1988
Brocklehurst, Mr Jonathan BA. . . . *Oct 1993
Chapman, Mr Stuart James BA(Nott'm) . . . *Dec 1991
Christian, Mr John M S MA(Cantab). . . . *Oct 1985
Cleland, Mr John LLM; MA(Cantab) . . . *Oct 1990
Daffern, Mr Richard BA(Hons)(Durham) . . . *Oct 1996
Dobson, Mr Nicholas BA(Hons); DipLLG . . . *Oct 1984
Goddard, Ms Victoria LLB(Bris) . . . *Nov 1995
Goldsborough, Mr Philip LLB(Hons)(L'pool) . . . *Nov 1995
Greaves, Ms Judith A BA(Cantab). . . . *Oct 1986
Harris, Mr Mark LLB(Essex); ACIArb . . . *Oct 1991
Hartley, Mr Keith LLB . . . *Sep 1982
Hoskin, Miss Janet S LLB(Wales) . . . *Oct 1991
Hutchings, Mr Robert MA . . . *Apr 1994
Jeffries, Mr Jonathan D LLB(Newc) . . . *Oct 1983
Kerr, Mr Andrew M BA . . . *Oct 1984
King, Mr Vincent LLB . . . Sep 1992
Kissack, Mr Nigel E J LLB(Sheff) . . . *Jun 1979
Larder, Mr Dean Maxwell BA . . . *Oct 1992
Lovitt, Mr Arthur M P LLB(Nott'm) . . . *Nov 1987
McClea, Mr Nigel P D BA(Cantab). . . . *§Apr 1975
Masterson, Mr Andrew LLB . . . *Nov 1991
Mordue, Mr Christopher BA . . . Oct 1993
Munro, Miss Pauline L . . . Nov 1993
Owen, Mr Mark R LLB . . . *Jul 1986
Parker, Mr Wayne M . . . *Dec 1987
Peeters, Mr Michael P D LLB . . . *Nov 1988
Quinlan, Mr Andrew LLB . . . *Nov 1986
Richards, Mr Mark D LLB; MSc . . . *Mar 1987
Shaw, Mr Martin LLB(Lond) . . . *§Mar 1969
Wallace, Miss Constance A L MA . . . *Nov 1986
Watkinson, Mr Richard LLB . . . *Oct 1993
Whitaker, Mr Neil Charles LLB . . . *Mar 1987
Wortley, Mr Stuart Sherbrooke LLB(Nott'm) . . . *Oct 1991

PLEXUS LAW (A TRADING NAME OF PARABIS LAW LLP)
Joseph's Well Hanover Walk Leeds West Yorkshire LS3 1AB
Tel: 0844 245 4100 *Fax:* 0870 832 5101 *Dx:* 716926 LEEDS 39
Office: Colchester, Croydon, Evesham, London EC2, London EC3, Manchester (2 offices)
Ptr: Allan, Lorraine . . . Sep 2002
Baker, Mr Anthony James LLB . . . Sep 1997
Bramall, Richard . . . Dec 2002
Dixon, Ms Jane L ♦ . . . *Nov 1988
Foulkes, Mr Christian Mark LLB(Hons); ACII; Dip PI Lit*Dec 1991
Hills, Mr Anthony Simon Alexander . . . Oct 1995
McDougall, Mr Andrew H LLB(Lond) . . . *Oct 1984
Metcalfe, Mr Douglas R LLB(Lond) Daniel Reardon Prize . . . *Apr 1972
Parker, Mr Jarrod William James . . . Jan 1999
Salvini, Mr Richard Marco LLB(Hons) . . . Oct 1995
Tetley, Mr Jonathon L B . . . Oct 1993
Watts, Mrs Lynn BSc(Hons); MSc . . . *Oct 1994
White, Ms A Rebecca N. . . . *Sep 1997
Whitfield, Mr Paul Mark BA(Hons). . . . *Oct 1995
Ast: Hussain, Bushra . . . Sep 2005

PORT & CO ‡
Lloyds Bank Chambers Vicar Lane Leeds West Yorkshire LS1 6PP
Tel: 0113 242 1212 *Fax:* 0113 242 2570
List of partners: J Port
Agency undertaken
Ptr: Port, Mr Joel LLB . . . Jan 1980

PROPERTYFAST CONVEYANCING SOLICITORS
(in association with Godloves)
Beech House Willow Court Main Street Leeds West Yorkshire LS25 1HB
Tel: 0113 287 2000 *Fax:* 0113 287 4153 *Dx:* 29763 GARFORTH
E-mail: info@propertyfast.co.uk
Office: Leeds (4 offices)
Work: S1 S2

RH SOLICITORS ‡
Suite 201 West One Leeds West Yorkshire LS1 1BA
Tel: 0113 203 1363 *Fax:* 0113 388 4764 *Dx:* 25173 LEEDS 4
E-mail: israr.malik@rhsolicitors.com

RADCLIFFES LE BRASSEUR
6-7 Park Place Leeds West Yorkshire LS1 2RU
Tel: 0113 234 1220 *Fax:* 0113 234 1573
Dx: 14086 LEEDS PARK SQUARE
E-mail: info@rlb-law.com
Office: Cardiff, London SW1
Work: A1 A3 B1 C1 C2 C3 D1 E F1 G I J1 K1 L M1 M2 N O P Q R1 R2 S1 S2 T1 T2 W Z(c,e,k,m,r,w)
Agency, Advocacy and Legal Aid undertaken
Ptr: Dixon, Mr Colin Peter LLB. . . . Mar 1993
Everett, Mr Stephen R BA. . . . *Dec 1973
Kernyckyj, Mr Simon M LLB. . . . *Oct 1989
Lynn, Miss Anne Elizabeth LLB(Hons). . . . *Sep 1997
Merchant, Mr Peter D BA(Hons). . . . *Nov 1984
Rawson, Mr Nicholas D A LLB . . . *Apr 1986
Thorniley-Walker, Mr Michael James MA(Oxon) Danish Vice-Consul for Leeds & Bradford . . . *Jun 1972
Williams, Miss Catherine J E MA(Oxon). . . . Jan 1985
Woodwark, Ms Sarah A RGN; BA. . . . *Oct 1990
Ast: Chapman, Miss Clare LLB . . . Sep 2000
Cooper, Mr Ian Robert LLB(Hons) . . . Aug 1999
Gilbert, Mrs Deborah Leigh BA(Hons) . . . Sep 1998
Pearson, Miss Hilda LLB . . . Oct 2001
Ward, Mr Timothy Jerome MSc; DipLaw. . . . Jun 2001
Watts, Miss Nichola LLB . . . Sep 2002

RAFIQ & CO ‡
291 Roundhay Road Leeds West Yorkshire LS8 4HS
Tel: 0113 240 7556 *Fax:* 0113 240 7557
Emergency telephone 07831 650433 / 07831 522132
List of partners: M Rafiq
Languages: Hindi, Punjabi, Urdu
Work: B1 C1 C2 C3 D1 E F1 G H J1 K1 L M1 M2 N O P Q R1 S1 T1 T2 V W Z(i,k,l,o)
Emergency Action, Agency, Advocacy, Fixed Fee Interview, Legal Aid undertaken and Member of Accident Line
Ptr: Rafiq, Mr Mohammed BA; Barrister . . . *May 1988

THE RE-MORTGAGE SOLICITORS ‡
4335 Park Approach Thorpe Park Leeds West Yorkshire LS15 8GB
Tel: 0845 053 1160 *Fax:* 0845 053 1161 *Dx:* 742131 LEEDS 17
E-mail: julianw@remortgagesolicitors.co.uk

REBIAN SOLICITORS ‡
City West 3 Gelderd Road Leeds West Yorkshire LS12 6LX
Tel: 0113 251 2251 / 250 6373 *Fax:* 0113 251 2001
E-mail: r.townsend@rebian.co.uk

RICHARDSON & CO ‡
Phoenix House 3 South Parade Leeds West Yorkshire LS1 5QX
Tel: 0113 243 1714 *Fax:* 0113 243 0984 *Dx:* 12005 LEEDS 1
Emergency telephone 0113 268 3775
E-mail: mail@richardsonlaw.co.uk
Office: York
Languages: French, German, Hebrew, Hindi, Mirpuri, Punjabi, Urdu
Work: B1 C1 C2 E J1 K1 L M1 N O Q R1 R2 S1 S2 T1 V W Z(c,h,i,q,r)
Agency and Advocacy undertaken

ROGERS & CO SOLICITORS ‡
6 Basinghall Buildings Upper Basinghall Street Leeds West Yorkshire LS1 5HR
Tel: 0113 246 9984 *Fax:* 0113 245 1587
Dx: 26449 LEEDS PARK SQUARE
E-mail: leeds@rogerssolicitors.com

SAMUELS & CO SOLICITORS
47 Park Square East Leeds West Yorkshire LS1 2NL
Tel: 0113 394 4117 *Fax:* 0844 507 0990
E-mail: info@samuels-solicitors.net
Office: London EC2
SPr: Samuels, Jacqueline . . . Nov 1998

SCHOFIELD SWEENEY
Springfield House 76 Wellington Street Leeds West Yorkshire LS1 2AY
Tel: 0113 220 6270 *Fax:* 0113 243 9326
Dx: 26409 LEEDS PARK SQUARE
E-mail: law@schoeys.com
Office: Bradford

BRIAN SELBY ‡
4 Primley Park Road Leeds West Yorkshire LS17 7HS
Tel: 0113 269 5102

SHULMANS ‡
120 Wellington Street Leeds West Yorkshire LS1 4LT
Tel: 0113 245 2833 *Fax:* 0113 246 7326 *Dx:* 729700 LEEDS 69
E-mail: mail@shulmans.co.uk
Web: www.shulmans.co.uk
List of partners: A P Bradley, I Dawson, R Edwards, J M Foster, T J Halstead, S M Jackson, A W Latchmore, M Lumley, V L Marshall, J I Shulman, E S Tasou, R C F Wadkin, M R Watson, R L Whitehead
Languages: French, German
Work: A1 A2 B1 B2 C1 C2 C3 D1 E F1 F2 G H I J1 J2 K1 K2 K3 L M1 M2 O P Q R1 R2 S1 S2 T1 T2 U2 V W X Z(b,c,d,e,f,g,h,j,k,l,m,n,o,p,r,s,t,za)
Emergency Action, Agency, Advocacy and Fixed Fee Interview undertaken
Ptr: Bradley, Mr Andrew P BA . . . Jan 1986
Dawson, Mr Ian LLB . . . Oct 1993
Edwards, Miss Rosemary LLB. . . . Nov 1991
Foster, Mr John Matthew MA(Oxon). . . . *Apr 1981
Halstead, Mr Timothy J LLB(Leeds) . . . *§Oct 1982
Jackson, Mr Simon M LLB . . . Oct 1988
Latchmore, Mr Andrew W LLB . . . Apr 1975
Lumley, Mr Mark LLB(Hons); LLM. . . . Dec 2000
Marshall, Miss Victoria Louise FILEx . . . Aug 2006
Shulman, Mr Jeremy I LLB(B'ham) Part time Chairman Employment Tribunals . . . *§Apr 1975
Tasou, Mrs Edwina Sharon LLB. . . . Oct 1998
Wadkin, Mr Richard C F LLB(B'ham) . . . Jan 1984
Watson, Mr Michael Richard TD LLB . . . Nov 1993
Whitehead, Mr Robert Lee LLB(Hons). . . . Jan 2000
Ast: Bagley, Mr Philip LLB(Hons) ★ . . . Jul 1998
Bateman, Mrs Jennifer Anne LLB(Hons). . . . Sep 2001
Chambers, Miss Jennifer Anne LLB(Hons) . . . Oct 2007
Dibb, Miss Rebecca Louise LLB; LPC. . . . Nov 2010
Hill, Miss Helen Elizabeth BA(Jt Hons); LLDip . . . Oct 2007
Hodge, Miss Sara LLB(Hons) . . . Nov 2009
King, Miss Cordelia Mary LLB. . . . Jan 2000
Lucas, Mr Robert Antony LLB. . . . Nov 1998
Stephens, Mr Lee Dylan BA(Education); LLB; LPC . May 2003
Wilkinson, Mr Kieran John LLB . . . Oct 2006
Wood, Miss Kathryn Anne MEng(Hons) . . . *Oct 2005

AGENCY WORK WILLINGLY UNDERTAKEN. CALL RICHARD WADKIN, HEAD OF COMMERCIAL LITIGATION.

ROBIN SIMON LLP
2 St David's Court David Street Leeds West Yorkshire LS11 5QA
Tel: 0333 010 0000 *Fax:* 0333 010 0003
Dx: 713115 LEEDS PARK SQUARE
E-mail: info@robinsimonllp.com
Office: Birmingham, London EC3, Manchester
Work: J1 Z(j,k,q)

SIMPSON MILLAR LLP ‡
27 St Paul's Street Leeds West Yorkshire LS1 2JG
Tel: 0844 858 3200 *Fax:* 0844 858 3299
Dx: 14098 LEEDS PARK SQUARE
E-mail: info@simpsonmillar.co.uk
List of partners: A L Davies, H R A F Davies, J A C Denham, J Dudson, A C Fawden, J A Harpur, J V Latimer, D Ross, P R Watson, A H Wontner-Smith
Office: Birmingham, Bristol, Cardiff, Gateshead, London EC1, London SW19, Manchester
Work: C1 C2 E F1 F2 J1 J2 K1 K2 K3 K4 L N O Q R1 R2 S1 S2 T1 T2 V W Z(c,o,p,q,r,za)
Agency, Legal Aid undertaken and Member of Accident Line
Ptr: Dudson, Ms Julie . . . Jan 1999
Watson, Mr Peter Richard BA; LLB . . . *§May 1992

SMITHSON HINDS MORRIS ‡
17 Park Row Leeds West Yorkshire LS1 5JQ
Tel: 0113 245 0456 *Fax:* 0113 200 1060
Dx: 706954 LEEDS PARK SQUARE
Emergency telephone 07831 316775
E-mail: stephen.welford@smithsonhindsmorris.com
List of partners: S Smithson
Languages: Spanish
Work: G H Z(l)
Emergency Action, Agency, Advocacy, Fixed Fee Interview, Legal Aid undertaken and Legal Aid Franchise
Ptr: Smithson, Mr Stephen ★ . . . *Mar 1983

 See p112 for the Key to Work Categories & other symbols

SOLICITORS ACTIVE ‡
2 Lambton Terrace Leeds West Yorkshire LS8 5PG
Tel: 0113 248 9805 *Fax:* 0113 249 2700
E-mail: enquiries@solicitorsactive.co.uk
List of partners: A M Alam, S S Sangra
Languages: Punjabi, Urdu
Work: E L O Q R2 S1 S2 Z(i)
Ptr: Alam, Mr Azair Mahmood LLB . . . Jul 2005
Sangra, Mr Sukhbir S LLB . . . *Feb 1986

SPENCER & FISCH (in association with Castle Sanderson)
64-66 Austhorpe Road Crossgates Leeds West Yorkshire LS15 8DZ
Tel: 0113 264 7603 *Fax:* 0113 260 6714 *Dx:* 13902 CROSSGATES
E-mail: j.doe@spencerfisch.co.uk
Office: Leeds
Work: D1 D2 F1 G H J1 J2 K1 K2 L N O Q S1 V W X Z(r)
Agency undertaken
Ptr: Leahy, Mr John A LLB . . . *Dec 1977
Shedlow, Mr Philip LLB . . . *Jan 1970

SQUIRE SANDERS (UK) LLP ‡
2 Park Lane Leeds West Yorkshire LS3 1ES
Tel: 0113 284 7000 *Fax:* 0113 284 7001 *Dx:* 26441 LEEDS
E-mail: enquiries@hammonds.com
List of partners: W Abraham, J C Alderton, A J P Allen, N P Allen, D W K Armitage, F Barker, D J Beswick, K M Brandt, P Bratt, T R Bridgford, C T Brigstocke, J Brown, L J Buckley, R Burns, G P Carney, M J Cassidy, A Clay, D J Colliver, R Cooke, J Cooper, E W H Coulson, J A Court, R C Cowen, N D Crocker, P M Crossley, L Dammone, M Danilunas, J D de Main, J Deacon, A B Dell, P Dillon, C M Donovan, J Doraisamy, W N Downs, J D L Edwards, C H Egan, R J Elvin, J A T H Emerton, M Evans, T Fisher, J S Forrest, F Fox, F S Garford, B D Gilbey, S G Glover, D Goodman, S M Gordon, R M Gravill, B R Green, N J Green, G N I Greenfield, I A Greenstreet, M Handley, P W Harling, K Harris, P Harris, J Haxby, M S Henley, J P Higton, M W Hilton, C J R Hodder, J P Hosie, C Hubbard, D J Hull, W Hunter, C N Hutton, T F Ingle, T H Jarvis, D M Jones, J J Jones, N A Jones, P Jones, R E Jones, S M Kelly, A J Korman, S P Levy, C P Lumley, G A Macaulay, A J MacCuish, C Marks, J Marsh, J M Marshall, N P Mason, C E May, C M P McKenna, S A Meek, C C Middleton-Smith, S Miller, J P Mitchell, P J Moorcroft, J F Moore, J E Morshead, D J Moss, S C Nickson, C Noblet, A M O'Meara, G J O'Neill, S M Owen, P A Oxnard, S D Palmer, S L Perraton, A Pike, A M Powell, S L Price, P R Rees, H S Roberts, A M Robertson, C A Rohsler, T L Saeedi, S A Sale, D J Savage, C Shepherd, M L Shepherd, R M Shrives, M C Simpson, D Singh, J Stephenson, G Stewart, J Tattersall, J Taylor, C J Terry, M K Thomas, S Townley, M R Trainer, A O Visintin, D Warburton, A J Watson, R J Weekes, R Wegenek, A M West, D H Whincup, D J Williams, N Williams, C A Willison, L M Winston, M D Woollard
Office: Birmingham, London EC2, Manchester
Languages: Cantonese, Dutch, French, German, Greek, Italian, Lithuanian, Malay, Portuguese, Punjabi, Russian, Serbo-Croat, Spanish, Turkish
Work: A1 A2 A3 B1 B2 B3 C1 E F1 I J1 J2 L M1 N O P Q R1 R2 S1 S2 T1 U1 U2 W Z(b,c,d,e,f,h,i,j,k,l,n,o,p,q,s,t,w,y,z)
Agency and Advocacy undertaken
Ptr: Alderton, Mr John C LLB . . . *Oct 1989
Armitage, Mr David W K MA(Cantab) . . . *Oct 1983
Clay, Mr Andrew BSc(Hons) . . . *Oct 1991
Coulson, Mr Edward W H MA(Cantab) . . . *Jan 1981
Crocker, Mr Nicolas D BSc(Econ) . . . *Oct 1986
Crossley, Mr Peter M BCom; LLB; MA(Cantab) . . . Sep 1989
de Main, Mr John Derek LLB(Manc) . . . *§Apr 1970
Emerton, Mr John Alan Thomas Haslam LLB . . . *Mar 1993
Glover, Mr Steven G LLB . . . Nov 1991
Goodman, Mr David LLB(Hons)(Sheff) . . . *Apr 1980
Green, Mr Brian R LLB . . . *Sep 1980
Greenfield, Mr G N Ian MA(Cantab) . . . *§Oct 1978
Harling, Mr Philip W LLB(Hons) . . . *§Oct 1974
Henley, Mr Michael S LLB . . . *§Oct 1985
Hilton, Mr Mark W LLB(Hons)(Leeds) . . . *Oct 1982
Hutton, Mr C Noel . . . *§Dec 1973
Jarvis, Mr Timothy Hugh BA . . . *Nov 1994
Jones, Mr Jonathan J LLB . . . Oct 1992
Lumley, Mrs Caroline Prew LLB(Hons) . . . Sep 1996
MacCuish, Mr Andrew James LLB(Auckland); Barrister & Solicitor High Court of NZ ♦ . . . *Dec 1987
McKenna, Miss Catherine M P LLB(Nott'm); LSF . . . *Sep 1989
Marks, Mr Christopher BA; LLM(Cantab) . . . *Mar 1984
Meek, Mr Simon Andrew LLB(Hons) . . . *Nov 1993
Miller, Mr Simon ♦ . . . Jan 1994
Mitchell, Mr J Patrick BA(Oxon) . . . *§Jun 1981
Owen, Mr Simon M LLB . . . Nov 1992
Palmer, Mr Simon D BA(Dunelm) . . . Oct 1987
Pike, Mr Andrew BA(Hons)(Cantab) . . . *Oct 1970
Roberts, Mr Howard Stephen LLB(Hons) . . . Mar 1993
Saeedi, Mrs Terry L BA(Hons); MSc . . . *Jun 1992
Shrives, Mr Robert Mark MA(Cantab); LLM(Cantab) . . . *Sep 1990
Simpson, Mr Mark C MA; LLB(Cantab) . . . *Oct 1985
Tattersall, Mr Jonathan LLB . . . Nov 1996
Williams, Mr David J BA(Hons)(Law) . . . *Jul 1985
Woollard, Mr Michael D LLB . . . Jul 1975
Asoc: Belcher, Mrs Penelope M MA . . . Mar 1993
Ast: Aaron, Miss Rachael Diane LLB . . . *Mar 2000
Aldred, Mr Adam LLB; LLM; MA(Cantab) . . . Jul 1991
Anson, Mrs Sally Elizabeth . . . May 2001
Bamford, Ms Alison Elisabeth . . . Sep 1999
Blakemore, Mrs Nicola Helen . . . May 2001
Blakey, Mr Jason Alexander . . . Jul 1999
Boneham, Ms Clare . . . Sep 1998
Boyle, Mrs Kerry A LLB . . . *Nov 1989
Bruce, Ms Julie Dawn . . . *Apr 1995
Bullock, Mr James Andrew Douglas . . . Sep 1998
Cameron, Mr Ian Scott . . . Sep 1999
Charmbury, Ms Rachael . . . Dec 1998
Clark, Ms Rebecca LLB(Hons) . . . Feb 1997
Clarke, Ms Rachel M LLB(Hons) Marron Dodds & Waite Law & Medicine Prize . . . Sep 1997
Cooper, Miss Tamsin C LLB . . . *Sep 1997
Dally, Mr Paul LLB . . . *Nov 1988
Duncan, Ms Sharon . . . Nov 1995
Fairman, Ms Susan Anita . . . Jun 1999
French, Mrs Karen LLB(Hons) . . . Oct 1986
Gledhill, Ms Charlotte Rose . . . Sep 1996
Glover, Mr Richard J BA(Hons); CPE; LSF . . . Sep 1993
Grange, Mr Martin . . . Apr 1997
Grant, Mrs Clare Anne LLB . . . *Nov 1988
Grayson, Ms Linda MA . . . *Oct 1995
Gupta, Ms Anita MA Evan Lewis Thomas Law Prize . . . Oct 1996
Hallows, Ms Janet R MA(Oxon) . . . Dec 1976
Hayre, Mr Harmajinder Singh . . . Sep 1997
Henson, Mr James Robert . . . Nov 1997
Johnson, Ms Charmain Elizabeth . . . Sep 1998
Jootla, Mr Jasvir Kaur . . . Sep 1997
Lawlor, Ms Sinead . . . Feb 2001
Ling, Miss Rebecca LLB . . . *Oct 1991
Lodge, Ms Sally . . . Oct 1995
Machin, Mr Andrew . . . *Nov 1998
Machin, Ms Elizabeth Anne-Marie . . . Apr 1994
Mulla, Mr Zakir LLB; MSc; ACIArb . . . *Jan 1992
Newberry, Mrs Claire A LLB . . . Oct 1993
Newman, Mr Alexander . . . Sep 1999
Nolan, Mr Richard T LLB . . . Nov 1992
O'Toole, Mr Ian Ward . . . Sep 1999
Oxtoby, Mr Ellie LLB . . . *Nov 1995
Plaw, Miss Sarah-Jane LLB . . . *Oct 1992
Poddington, Mr David Michael BA(Oxon) . . . *Sep 1998
Prosser, Miss Sharon . . . Sep 1999
Puvirajasingham, Mr Janani . . . Sep 1998
Rastrick, Mr John Simon . . . Sep 1997
Rawlinson, Mr Christopher John . . . Oct 2000
Redikin, Ms Louise Joanne . . . Sep 1999
Reeves, Mr Andrew Michael . . . May 2000
Reynolds, Mr Matthew John . . . Oct 1995
Ridler, Mr Mark P LLB . . . *Oct 1986
Rollin, Mrs Barbara . . . Oct 1988
Seed, Ms Helen R LLB(Hons) . . . Oct 1988
Smith, Mr Andrew David LLB(Hons); LSF . . . Sep 1998
Smith, Mr Martin Stockdale LLB(Hons) . . . *Sep 2000
Sprake, Mr Andrew David . . . Oct 1997
Sprenger, Mr Jason Antony Lee . . . Oct 2000
Thirsk, Mrs Joanna Louise BSc . . . §Nov 1997
Todd, Mr Andrew James . . . Sep 1998
Tullett, Miss Alison M D LLB . . . *May 1987
Uppal, Mr Charanjit Singh . . . Nov 2000
Waring, Ms Victoria . . . Sep 2000
Watkins, Miss Rowena Jane LLB(Hons) . . . *Oct 1998
Wilkinson, Mr Christopher CPE; LSF . . . *Sep 1996
Wilson, Mr David Lester LLB . . . Sep 1997
Wright, Ms Catherine M . . . Sep 1996
Young, Mr Simon David LLB . . . Oct 1994

STEWARTS LAW LLP
9 Bond Court Leeds West Yorkshire LS1 2JZ
Tel: 0113 222 0022 *Fax:* 0113 222 0044
Dx: 26428 LEEDS PARK SQUARE
E-mail: info@stewartslaw.com
Office: London EC4
Languages: Croatian, French
Work: A3 B2 C3 J1 K1 K2 K3 M1 M2 M3 N O Q Z(b,p,q,r)
Legal Aid undertaken, Legal Aid Franchise and Member of Accident Line
Ptr: Herman, Mr Daniel J LLB(Hons) . . . *Jul 1999
Pinch, Mr Frank Roger . . . *Oct 1993
Preston, Mr Simon David LLB(Hons) . . . *Oct 1994
Sinclair, Mr Jonathan BA(Oxon)(History) . . . *Jan 1987
Stringer, Mr Peter BA . . . *Nov 1999
Townsend, Mr Bennett Harry LLB . . . *Dec 1997
Asoc: Clossick, Mr Adrian Patrick LLB . . . *Sep 2003
Green, Mrs Angela Dawn . . . *Nov 1998
Kennedy, Mr Alistair Stuart . . . *Sep 2006
Maxwell, Mr Warren LLB(Hons) . . . *Jan 2002
Pollock, Ms Kate LLB(Hons); LPC . . . *Sep 1999
Ast: Cutts, Miss Mikaler LLB(Hons) . . . *Sep 2000
Dixon, Miss Rebecca LLB(Hons) . . . *Sep 2006
Ross, Miss Gabrielle Zoe LLB(Hons) . . . *Nov 2004
Tighe, Mr Matthew Robert LLB; LPC . . . *Oct 2010

STRADBROKES SOLICITORS ‡
1 Chapel Lane Armley Leeds West Yorkshire LS12 2DJ
Tel: 0113 279 0722 *Fax:* 0113 263 5012
E-mail: info@stradbrokes.com

STURGESS PERRING SOLICITORS ‡
20 Aberford Road Barwick in Elmet Leeds West Yorkshire LS15 4DZ
Tel: 07980 552942 *Fax:* 0118 979 4114 *Dx:* 742134 LEEDS 17
E-mail: johanna@sturgessperringsolicitors.com

SUGARE & CO ‡
36 Park Square Leeds West Yorkshire LS1 2NY
Tel: 0113 244 6978 *Fax:* 0113 245 5708
Emergency telephone 0113 269 6277
Work: B1 B2 C1 C2 C3 D1 D2 E F1 F2 G H J1 K1 L M1 M2 N O P Q R1 R2 S1 S2 V W Z(j,k,l,o,w)

SVARMSTRONG ‡
Precision House Ring Road Seacroft Leeds West Yorkshire LS14 1NH
Tel: 01904 520150
E-mail: stuart.armstrong@svarmstrong.com

SWITALSKI'S
St James House 28 Park Place Leeds West Yorkshire LS1 2SP
Tel: 0113 223 1400 *Fax:* 0113 223 1401
Dx: 14091 LEEDS PARK SQUARE
Office: Bradford, Dewsbury, Halifax, Huddersfield, Wakefield
Work: D1 G H J1 K1 K2 L Z(i,m,r)
Emergency Action, Legal Aid undertaken and Member of Accident Line

SYSTECH SOLICITORS
62 Wellington Street Leeds West Yorkshire LS1 2EE
Tel: 0113 388 8080 *Fax:* 0113 247 0741
Office: Liverpool, London SE1, Manchester

TATES SOLICITORS ‡ (incorporating Giles & Hammond)
2 Park Square East Leeds West Yorkshire LS1 2NE
Tel: 0113 242 2290 *Fax:* 0113 242 1282
Dx: 26439 LEEDS PARK SQUARE
Emergency telephone 07768 371512
E-mail: info@tates-solicitors.co.uk
List of partners: J M Batchelor, S P Cluderay
Languages: French, German
Work: B2 G H
Emergency Action, Agency, Advocacy, Fixed Fee Interview, Legal Aid undertaken, Legal Aid Franchise and Member of Accident Line
Ptr: Batchelor, Mr John M BA(Hons) . . . *Oct 1993
Cluderay, Mr Sean P . . . Jul 1987

ANDREW THOMPSON & CO ‡
Aspect Court 47 Park Square East Leeds West Yorkshire LS1 2NL
Tel: 0113 383 5314 *Fax:* 0113 383 5315
E-mail: andrew@agtlaw.co.uk
List of partners: A Thompson
Work: G
Ptr: Thompson, Mr Andrew . . . May 2002

THOMPSONS (FORMERLY ROBIN/BRIAN THOMPSON & PARTNERS)
17 Wellington Street Leeds West Yorkshire LS1 4DL
Tel: 0113 205 6300 *Fax:* 0113 234 2161
Dx: 26454 LEEDS PARK SQUARE
Office: Belfast, Birmingham, Bristol, Cardiff, Chelmsford, Dagenham, Derby, Harrow, Liverpool, London SW19, London WC1, Manchester, Middlesbrough, Newcastle upon Tyne, Nottingham, Plymouth, Sheffield, South Shields, Southampton, Stoke-on-Trent, Swansea, Wolverhampton
Work: G H J1 N Z(p,r)
Legal Aid undertaken, Legal Aid Franchise and Member of Accident Line
Ptr: Gledhill, Miss Judith LLB(Hons) . . . *Sep 1989
Towler, Mr David P LLB . . . *Apr 1979
Ast: Cook, Mr Sean LLB . . . Aug 1996
Hemsley, Ms Samantha . . . Oct 1995
Hewitt, Mr Alistair Scott BSc . . . Sep 1996
Smith, Miss Joanne Elizabeth LLB(Hons) . . . *Sep 1997
Wilson, Miss Susan Isobel BA(Hons) . . . *Oct 1995

TONKIN & CO ‡
32 Gledhow Wood Grove Leeds West Yorkshire LS8 1NZ
Tel: 0113 269 2058 *Fax:* 0113 269 2058
E-mail: tonkinandco@btconnect.com

TRAVLAW LLP ‡
2 Bachelor Lane Hordforth Leeds West Yorkshire LS18 5NA
Tel: 0113 258 0033 *Fax:* 0113 258 8833
E-mail: stephen@travlaw.co.uk

VAUGHAN & CO ‡
467a Otley Road Adel Leeds West Yorkshire LS16 7NR
Tel: 0113 261 1044 *Fax:* 0113 267 5349
E-mail: gen@vaughanlaw.co.uk
List of partners: I Brill
Work: B1 C1 E K1 N O Q S1 W
Member of Accident Line
SPr: Brill, Mr Ian LLB(Hons) . . . *Sep 1978
Ast: Marcus, Miss Victoria Helen LLB . . . Sep 2007

VELOCITY LEGAL ‡
90 Harrogate Road Leeds West Yorkshire LS7 4LZ
Tel: 0113 237 9940 *Fax:* 0113 318 8171
Dx: 28877 CHAPEL ALLERTON

VIRTUOSO LEGAL ‡
31 Harrogate Road Leeds West Yorkshire LS7 3PD
Tel: 0844 800 8871 *Fax:* 0113 262 2796
E-mail: liz@virtuosolegal.com

CLIVE WALKER ‡
40 High Ash Mount Leeds West Yorkshire LS17 8RW
Tel: 0113 268 4660 *Fax:* 0113 343 5056
E-mail: cliveccjs@hotmail.com
List of partners: C P Walker
Work: G I M2 Z(g,k)
Ptr: Walker, Prof Clive P LLB; PhD Maxwell Law Prize; Hughes Prizeman Professor of Criminal Justice Studies (University of Leeds) . . . *Apr 1978

WALKER MORRIS ‡
Kings Court 12 King Street Leeds West Yorkshire LS1 2HL
Est: 1998
Tel: 0113 283 2500 *Fax:* 0113 245 9412 *Dx:* 12051 LEEDS 24
Emergency telephone 01893 413290
E-mail: hello@walkermorris.co.uk
List of partners: I A Akitt, S P Anderson, A Beck, C Brook, C S Caisley, N B Cannon, P S Cantrill, S C Clark, S T Concannon, R Cowper, G Davies, P D Emmett, I M Gilbert, J J A Hamer, J Harwood, D W Hinchliffe, R H R Innes, D Jackson, D Jennings, A P Judson, J R Kelsall, D J Kilduff, N Lupton, A S Moodie, J D Moore, P J Mudd, J Muscroft, R Naish, T M Peel, J M Pike, M C Price, J F Roche, R M Sagar, M A Sanderson, R Sandford, M L Scott, J Seddon, M A Simpson, C Slater, P C Smart, D A Smedley, M Stevens, M Taylor, A D C Turnbull, A Uprichard, P L Walker, J Weaver, P Whur, A J Williamson, A Woods, C Woodthorpe
Languages: Afrikaans, Arabic, Danish, Dutch, French, German, Greek, Hausa, Italian, Japanese, Kanuri, Latin, Portuguese, Russian, Spanish, Swedish, Urdu
Work: A3 B1 B2 C1 C2 C3 E F1 F2 I J1 J2 L M1 M2 N O P Q R1 R2 S2 T1 T2 U1 U2 W X Z(b,c,d,e,h,j,k,l,m,n,o,p,q,r,s,u,w,za)
Emergency Action, Agency, Advocacy, Fixed Fee Interview and Legal Aid undertaken
Ptr: Akitt, Mr Ian Alasdair LLB(Sheff) . . . *Nov 1988
Anderson, Mr Simon Paul LLB . . . *Feb 1991
Beck, Mr Andrew BA . . . *Jan 1988
Brook, Ms Claire LLB . . . *Oct 1995
Caisley, Mr Christopher Stuart . . . *Feb 1978
Cannon, Mr Nicholas Barry LLB(Hons) . . . *Mar 1989
Cantrill, Mr Patrick Simon LLB . . . *Nov 1984
Clark, Mr Simon Charles LLB . . . *Sep 1992
Concannon, Mr Simon Terrence BA(Oxon) . . . *Oct 1990
Cowper, Ms Rachel LLB . . . Sep 2001
Davies, Miss Gwendoline LLB(Leics) . . . *Nov 1988
Emmett, Mr Paul David LLB . . . *Nov 1987
Gilbert, Mr Ian Michael LLB . . . *Oct 1981
Hamer, Mr John James Arthur LLB . . . Jun 1994
Harwood, Ms Jeanette . . . Oct 1996
Hinchliffe, Mr David Warwick LLB . . . *Sep 1989
Innes, Mr Richard Heath Robert BA . . . *§Oct 1984
Jackson, Mrs Debbie LLB . . . *Nov 1998
Jennings, Miss Dawn LLB . . . *Oct 1992
Judson, Mr Austin Peter . . . *Nov 1996
Kelsall, Mr John Robert LLB(Hull) . . . *Mar 1979
Kilduff, Mr David John BA . . . *Feb 1983
Lupton, Mr Neil . . . *Sep 1999
Moodie, Mr Andrew Shaun LLB . . . *May 1990
Moore, Mr Jeremy David BA(Law) . . . *§Oct 1986
Mudd, Mr Philip John LLB . . . *Dec 1983
Muscroft, Ms Julie BA(Dunelm) . . . *Aug 1987
Naish, Mr Richard LLB . . . Sep 1998
Peel, Mr Thomas Marc LLB; DipLP . . . Nov 1997
Pike, Mrs Judith Mary LLB . . . *Oct 1987
Price, Mr Martin Charles . . . *Nov 1992
Roche, Mr John Francis . . . *Nov 1995
Sagar, Mr Richard Mark LLB . . . *Sep 1991
Sanderson, Mr Mark Andrew . . . Nov 1992
Sandford, Mr Richard LLB . . . *Oct 1994
Scott, Mr Martin Leslie BA(Law) . . . *§Oct 1985
Seddon, Miss Jacqueline . . . Jan 2001
Simpson, Mr Malcolm Allan LLB(Hons); ACIArb . . . *Sep 1992
Slater, Mr Chris LLB . . . *Nov 1998
Smart, Mr Peter Charles BA . . . *Apr 1979

Smedley, Mr David Andrew LLB. . . . *Oct 1986
Stevens, Mr Michael BA(Hons); DipLaw; DipLP . . . *Nov 1997
Taylor, Mr Michael LLB . . . *Oct 1986
Turnbull, Mr Andrew Donald Charlton LLB. . . . *§May 1981
Uprichard, Mr Andrew BA(Lond). . . . *Feb 1989
Walker, Mr Paul Linsel LLB . . . Apr 1976
Weaver, Ms Jane LLB. . . . Oct 1992
Whur, Mr Patrick LLB . . . Oct 1991
Williamson, Mr Andrew James BA(Law); DipTP; MRTPI . . . *Jun 1983
Woods, Mr Andrew . . . Oct 1989
Woodthorpe, Mr Chris LLB . . . *Sep 1998
Asoc: Ahluwalia, Mr Marshal. . . . *Aug 1997
Anders, Mr Karl LLB . . . *Oct 1995
Auton, Mr Richard M LLB(Leeds) . . . Jun 1977
Babar, Ms Natasha . . . Nov 2003
Bulmer, Ms Melanie LLB(Hons) . . . *Nov 1993
Clark, Ms Samantha . . . Sep 2003
Crossley, Mr Robert. . . . Nov 1993
Crozier, Mr Roy LLB; MPhil . . . Sep 2001
Cullen, Ms Katy. . . . Oct 2002
Evans, Miss Claire A BA(Hons) . . . *Nov 1997
Evans, Mr Richard . . . *Nov 1993
Hagerty-Cross, Ms Siobhan. . . . Sep 1999
Hall, Mr Andrew. . . . Sep 1997
Harbage, Mr Julian James LLB . . . Sep 2002
Hardcastle, Mr Simon J. . . . *Sep 2000
Harris, Mrs Susan A. . . . *Feb 1992
Hartley, Ms Heloise . . . Sep 2002
Hartley, Mr Ian . . . Sep 2003
Hoath, Ms Donna . . . Nov 1996
Holmes, Mr Richard A BA(Hons) . . . *Sep 1997
Hornsey, Ms Susannah . . . Sep 2002
Howes, Mr Neil LLB. . . . Sep 1999
Hunter, Mrs Joanne Clare LLB . . . *Oct 1987
Jackman, Miss Rachel LLB(Hons). . . . Nov 2001
Larking, Mr Richard Patrick LLB(Hons); MCIPD . . . Nov 1998
Lole, Mr Duncan LLB . . . Oct 2001
Longfield, Ms Tracey . . . Sep 2000
Lowe, Dr Roger David BSc(Hons); PLD . . . *Jun 2001
McCall, Ms Rebecca . . . Sep 2002
McKeague, Mr Martin LLB. . . . *Sep 1999
Marsden, Mrs Emma J BA; LLB. . . . *Oct 1988
Moore, Mr Robert LLB . . . Sep 2002
Moran, Mr Julian . . . May 2002
Morrison, Ms Lyn . . . Sep 2003
Pope, Ms Bernadette . . . Nov 2001
Power, Mrs C Louise . . . *Oct 1993
Rayment, Mr Andrew S . . . *Mar 1998
Russell, Mrs Faye Louise LLB(Hons) . . . Jul 2002
Sheppard, Mr Ben David LLB . . . *Sep 2001
Smith, Ms Lynsey . . . Sep 2002
Strickland, Ms Victoria. . . . Sep 2003
Taylor, Mr Richard LLB(Hons) . . . Nov 2000
Wharton, Mr Hugo BSc(Hons)(Management Sciences)*Sep 1997
White, Mr Richard James LLB. . . . Oct 2002
Wilson, Ms Sarah . . . Sep 2001
Wood, Ms Elizabeth BA; CPE; LPC . . . *Mar 2002
Ast: Bailey, Mrs Lyndsay Anne LLB . . . Sep 2004
Carroll, Miss Emily Jane BA(Hons)(English Language & Literature); PGDipLaw; LPC; LLM. . . . Sep 2005
Dickinson, Miss Melaine BA(Hons); MA . . . Jun 2004
Hoyle, Mrs Vikki Leanne MA(Cantab) . . . Sep 2005
Khan, Ms Erfana LLB(Hons). . . . Nov 1999
McAdam, Mr Craig BSc; PGDipLaw. . . . Oct 2002
Outwaite, Mr Richard Jeffery LLB . . . Sep 2004
Pickersgill, Mr Mark David. . . . Sep 2004
Shedlow, Mr James Robert Oliver. . . . *Oct 2005
Wood-Robertson, Mr James LLB(Hons). . . . *Sep 2004

WALTON & CO ‡
2 Queen Street Leeds West Yorkshire LS1 2TW
Tel: 0113 245 8100 *Fax:* 0113 245 8133
E-mail: info@walton-co.co.uk

WARD HADAWAY ‡
1a Tower Square Wellington Street Leeds West Yorkshire LS1 4DL
Tel: 0113 205 6600 *Fax:* 0113 205 6700
E-mail: enquiries@wardhadaway.com

WATSON BURTON LLP
1 City Square Leeds West Yorkshire LS1 2ES
Tel: 0845 901 2100 *Fax:* 0845 901 2050 *Dx:* 12013 LEEDS
E-mail: enquiries@watsonburton.com
Office: London EC3, Newcastle upon Tyne
Work: A3 B1 B2 C1 C2 C3 D1 D2 E F1 F2 I J1 J2 L M1 M2 O P Q R1 R2 S1 S2 T1 T2 U1 U2 W X Z(b,c,d,e,f,h,j,n,o,p,q,u,w,za)
Ptr: Dalzell, Mr Matthew. . . . Sep 2003
Fahy, Mr Gearalt . . . Sep 2001
Lazenby, Mr Mark. . . . Nov 2001
Asoc: Nightingale, Mr James . . . Sep 2002
Whitehead, Miss Deborah. . . . Sep 2005

WATSONS ‡
4335 Park Approach Thorpe Park Leeds West Yorkshire LS15 8GB
Tel: 0845 053 1150 *Fax:* 0845 053 1151 *Dx:* 742130 LEEDS 17
E-mail: info@watsonslaw.com

WHITEROSE BLACKMANS SOLICITORS LLP ‡
Fryers House 146 Cardigan Road Leeds West Yorkshire LS6 1LU
Tel: 0113 216 5507 *Fax:* 0113 216 5508
E-mail: info@whiteroseblackmans.co.uk

ANDREW WILLIAMS SOLICITORS ‡
Spacemaker Business Centre 83 Roseville Road Leeds West Yorkshire LS8 5DT
Tel: 0113 244 1911 *Fax:* 0113 246 7119
E-mail: info@awsolicitors.co.uk
List of partners: A Williams
SPr: Williams, Mr Andrew . . . Jul 2004

WILSONS ‡
7-9 Austhorpe View Whitkirk Leeds West Yorkshire LS15 8NN
Tel: 0113 264 3444 *Fax:* 0113 264 3033
List of partners: J Wilson
Office: Bradford (2 offices), Horsforth, Pudsey
Work: A1 B1 D1 E F1 F2 J1 K1 K2 K3 K4 L N O Q R1 R2 S2 T1 T2 W X Z(o,p,q,r,t,u)
Emergency Action, Agency, Advocacy and Fixed Fee Interview undertaken
Ptr: Wilson, Mr John LLB; DipLG LP. . . . *Oct 1986
Asoc: Pollard, Miss Leanne LLB. . . . *Sep 2005

WINSTON SOLICITORS LLP ‡
Orchard View 112 Street Lane Leeds West Yorkshire LS8 2AL
Tel: 0113 320 5000 *Fax:* 0113 320 6000 *Dx:* 17944 ROUNDHAY
E-mail: info@winstonsolicitors.co.uk
List of partners: G M Caplan, R Lindley, M J Nolan, F O'Neill, J Winston
Work: C1 C2 E J1 K1 K2 K3 K4 N O Q S1 S2 W Z(e,l,p,q)
Fixed Fee Interview undertaken
Ptr: Caplan, Mr Gary Mark BA(Hons) . . . *Oct 1985
Mem: Lindley, Mr Richard MA(Oxon); DPhil(Oxon). . . . *§Oct 1992
Nolan, Martin John . . . NSP
O'Neill, Mr Francis . . . *§Feb 1992
Winston, Mr Jonathan LLB(Hons) . . . *§Oct 1993
Ast: Champaneri, Mr Anil . . . *Mar 2006
Clasper, Mrs Gabrielle Anne LLB . . . *Oct 1993
Conway, Mr Jeremy E LLB . . . *§Oct 1993
Fieldhouse, Miss Michelle LLB(Hons); LLM . . . *Apr 2004
Stephenson, Mr James . . . *Oct 2005
Walker, Mr Shaun Robert LLB(Hons) . . . Nov 1992
Con: Chadwick, Ms Lysbeth LLB(Hons). . . . *Jun 1974
Stewart, Mr Robert Shackleton . . . *Dec 1975

WRIGLEYS SOLICITORS LLP ‡
19 Cookridge Street Leeds West Yorkshire LS2 3AG
Tel: 0113 244 6100 *Fax:* 0113 244 6101 *Dx:* 12020 LEEDS 1
E-mail: thepartners@wrigleys.co.uk
List of partners: R M Ainscoe, J Attey, C M Billington, J E Boyes, L E Bradey, E A Bromet, A S Duchart, S Greaves, P G Greswold, M S Hamilton, L Holmes, V M James, M J Lynch, J Manfredi-Hamer, J McMullen, P S Nash, S A Nunn, G J Smallman, R M Sutton, E Wilson, A D Wriglesworth, W M Wrigley
Office: Sheffield
Work: A1 A2 E S1 S2 T2 W X Z(d,o,x)
Ptr: Ainscoe, Mr Raymond M MA; BCL(Oxon) . . . *Oct 1980
Attey, Mr Jonathan LLB(Hons). . . . *Oct 2000
Billington, Mr Christopher M LLB . . . *Nov 1993
Boyes, Miss Julia E LLB(Hons) CCH Editions Taxations Prize 1986 . . . *Oct 1989
Bromet, Mr Edward Anthony. . . . *Oct 1996
Duchart, A S LLB . . . *Apr 1981
Greswold, Mr Peter G BSc(B'ham) . . . *Apr 1985
Hamilton, Mrs Marie-Louise Spencer LLB . . . *Nov 1995
Holmes, Miss Leigh BA . . . *Nov 1994
James, Mrs Valerie M BA(Oxon) . . . *Jun 1980
Lynch, Mr Malcolm J LLB(B'ham); MPhil(Bradford) . *Mar 1983
Manfredi-Hamer, Josephine . . . Sep 1997
Nash, Mr Paul S LLB(Lond). . . . *Nov 1980
Nunn, Sylvie Aurelie LLB(Hons); TEP . . . Sep 2003
Sutton, Mr Richard Manners. . . . *Jun 1973
Wilson, Mrs Elizabeth LLB . . . Aug 2001
Wriglesworth, Mr Andrew D LLB. . . . *Nov 1994
Wrigley, Mr W Matthew MA(Cantab). . . . *§Dec 1972
Dir: McMullen, Dr John MA; PhD(Cantab); FRSA; FCIPD . Oct 1978
Asoc: Conway, Mrs Karen J LLB. . . . *Oct 1984
King, Mrs Susan BA(Hons)(Lond) . . . Sep 2005
Ast: Acomb, Miss Victoria Elisabeth MA . . . *Sep 2002
Busbridge, Mr Luke Benedict MA(Cantab); LLB . . . Sep 2009
Cooke, Ms Rebecca MA(Hons)(Cantab); LSF . . . Oct 1991
Edwards, Louise LLB; APMI. . . . Aug 2009
Gawthorp, Mrs Verity Ann BSc; PGDL. . . . Sep 2008
Glendinning, Miss Dawn C LLB . . . Nov 1987
Hallam, Mr Oliver Luke Hoyle MA(Hons)(Hist)(Edin); PGDL; LPC; TEP. . . . *Mar 2006
Hunter Smart, Mr Angus David Alastair . . . *Sep 2005
Johnson, Miss Natalie BA; LLB . . . Sep 2010
Kerr, Miss Sabine LLM; BSc. . . . Sep 2009
Kirk, Mrs Mary E BA(Dunelm). . . . *Oct 1983
McClory, Mrs Lisa Jane LLB(Hons)(ELS)(Durham) . . Sep 2006
Meredith, Miss Rachel LLB . . . Sep 2005
Nelson, Philip John BA(Hons). . . . Feb 2005
Sanderson, Mrs Joanna Elizabeth Louise BA; PGDL; LPC . . . May 2008
Thornton, Kate Elizabeth BA(Hons) . . . Aug 2006
Tweddle, Mrs Rosanne . . . Sep 2006
Wainman, Mrs Katherine Elaine BMus(Hons) . . . Sep 2006
Wainman, Thomas LLB . . . Mar 2007
Wray, Miss Helen Elaine LLB . . . Sep 2010
Wrigley, Mr Tim LLB. . . . Sep 2009
Con: Wightman, Mr David J MA(Oxon) . . . *§Apr 1968

YHM SOLICITORS ‡
271 Roundhay Road Oakwood Leeds West Yorkshire LS8 4HS
Tel: 0113 240 8781 *Fax:* 0113 240 8965
E-mail: enquiries@yhmsolicitors.co.uk

YASMIN AND SHAID SOLICITORS ‡
237 Dewsbury Road Leeds West Yorkshire LS11 5HZ
Tel: 0113 271 3939 *Fax:* 0113 271 4200
Dx: 14077 LEEDS PARK SQUARE
E-mail: info@yasminandshaidsolicitors.co.uk

ZERMANSKY & PARTNERS ‡
10 Butts Court Leeds West Yorkshire LS1 5JS
Tel: 0113 245 9766 *Fax:* 0113 246 7465 *Dx:* 12061 LEEDS
E-mail: admin@zermansky-solicitors.com
List of partners: C A Gallagher, J H Glynn, C J Preston
Languages: Hindi, Polish, Punjabi
Work: C1 C2 D1 E F1 F2 J1 K1 K2 K3 L N O P Q R1 R2 S1 S2 W Z(c,h,k,l,p,q)
Emergency Action, Agency, Advocacy, Fixed Fee Interview, Legal Aid undertaken and Legal Aid Franchise
Ptr: Gallagher, Mr Carl A BA(Hons) . . . *§Oct 1995
Glynn, Ms Judith H LLB(B'ham). . . . *§Mar 1984
Preston, Mr Christopher John BA . . . *§Nov 1996
Ast: Bajna, Miss Amandeep LLB. . . . *§Sep 2004
Chantrey, Miss Fiona J LLB. . . . *§Oct 1991
Horspool, Miss Vikki. . . . *§Nov 2003
Levison, Mrs Geraldine . . . *§Jun 2003
Payne, Miss Sarah . . . *§Nov 2000
Rhodes, Mr Christopher David . . . *§Oct 2003
Rhodes, Mrs Nicola Louise. . . . *§Jan 2010
Robertshaw, Mr Nicolas Alan . . . Oct 2008
Thompson, Mr Alex Douglas . . . Aug 2010
Con: Graham, Mr Russell N LLB(Manc). . . . *§Jul 1970
Zermansky, Mr Victor D LLB(Leeds) John Mackrell Prize . . . *§Nov 1953

LEEK, Staffordshire

BOWCOCK & PURSAILL ‡
54 St Edward Street Leek Staffordshire ST13 5DJ
Tel: 01538 399199 *Fax:* 01538 399362 *Dx:* 16352 LEEK
Emergency telephone 01538 382074
E-mail: info@bowcockpursaill.co.uk
List of partners: E L Curtis, T R Gregory, E W Hodkinson, I C Naylor, H J Stevenson, C A Whittles, T J Wolley
Office: Hanley
Languages: French, German
Work: A1 A2 A3 B1 C1 C2 D1 E J1 K1 K2 K3 K4 L N O Q R1 R2 S1 S2 T1 T2 W Z(b,e,l,q)
Ptr: Curtis, Miss Emma Louise. . . . *§Jan 2008
Gregory, Mr Thomas R LLB(Lond). . . . *§Mar 1976
Hodkinson, Mr Eric William . . . *§Jun 1971
Naylor, Mr Ian Christopher LLB . . . *§Mar 1971
Stevenson, Mr Howard J . . . *§Nov 1973
Whittles, Miss Catherine A BA(Law). . . . *§Oct 1985
Wolley, Mr Timothy John LLB(Hons). . . . *§Nov 1992
Ast: Bailey, Mr Timothy James LLB . . . *Jan 2011
Brown, Miss Julia . . . Sep 2007

A H BROOKS & CO ‡
(incorporating H G Terry & Co)
Derby House Derby Street Leek Staffordshire ST13 6JG
Tel: 01538 383201 *Fax:* 01538 387074 *Dx:* 16355 LEEK
Emergency telephone 01538 399201
E-mail: lawyers@ahbrooks.co.uk
List of partners: S D Chiverton, D A Hallen, G Williamson
Office: Cheadle
Languages: Spanish
Work: A1 B1 C1 C2 C3 D1 D2 E F1 F2 J1 K1 K3 K4 L M1 M2 N Q R1 S1 S2 T1 T2 V W Z(c,e,f,i,k,l,m,q,t)
Emergency Action, Agency, Advocacy, Fixed Fee Interview undertaken and Member of Accident Line
Ptr: Chiverton, Mr Simon David LLB . . . *May 1997
Hallen, Mr David A LLB . . . §Sep 1987
Williamson, Miss Greta LLB(Hons); LPC . . . *§Dec 1996
Con: Winter Morris, Mrs Elizabeth Anne BA. . . . *§May 1975

ROGER BROOKS & CO ‡
17 Russell Street Leek Staffordshire ST13 5JF
Tel: 01538 385656 *Fax:* 01538 385494 *Dx:* 16358 LEEK
E-mail: roger@rogerbrooks.demon.co.uk
List of partners: A R Brooks
Work: A1 L S1 S2 T2 W Z(l)
Agency undertaken
SPr: Brooks, Mr Arthur Roger . . . *Jun 1973

CARNEY SOLICITORS LTD
1-3 Dog Lane Leek Staffordshire ST13 5HQ
Tel: 01538 381444 *Fax:* 01538 381400 *Dx:* 20747 HANLEY
Office: Hanley

TINSDILLS
10 Derby Street Leek Staffordshire ST13 5AW
Tel: 01538 399332 *Fax:* 01538 399180 *Dx:* 16353 LEEK
Emergency telephone 01538 360900
E-mail: lawyers@tinsdills.co.uk
Office: Hanley, Newcastle under Lyme, Sandbach
Languages: French
Work: A1 A2 B1 B2 C1 C2 D1 D2 E F1 F2 H J1 K1 K2 K3 K4 L N O P Q R1 R2 S1 S2 T1 T2 V W Z(b,c,d,f,g,h,j,l,m,n,o,p,q,r,s,t)
Emergency Action, Agency, Advocacy, Fixed Fee Interview, Legal Aid undertaken and Legal Aid Franchise
Ptr: Burrows, Mr Andrew J LLB(Hons) Polytechnic of Wales Merit Award 1989 (Law FT). . . . *Oct 1992
Hawksworth, Mr Paul . . . Jun 1974

UPRIGHTS SOLICITORS ‡
12 Market Street Leek Staffordshire ST13 6HZ
Tel: 01538 388809 *Fax:* 01538 388810

LEICESTER

ACHARYAS ‡
2 Kensington Street Leicester LE4 5GL
Tel: 0116 251 7520 *Fax:* 0116 251 7530
E-mail: acharyasolicitors@hotmail.co.uk

ASHLEY ADAMS CONVEYANCING ‡
4 Thorpe Park Grove Park Leicester LE19 1YR
Tel: 0845 234 0241 *Fax:* 0116 281 6874

AFFINITY LAW LLP ‡
100 New Walk Leicester LE1 7EA
Tel: 0116 262 7292 *Fax:* 0116 255 2914
E-mail: enquiries@affinitylaw.co.uk

DIPAK ANCHARYA & CO SOLICITORS ‡
45a Melton Road Leicester LE4 6PN
Tel: 0116 266 0627

ASTILLS ‡
De Montfort House 1 De Montfort Square Leicester LE1 7ER
Tel: 0116 249 4450 *Fax:* 0116 247 0827 *Dx:* 28814 LEICESTER 2
E-mail: sjs@astills.co.uk
List of partners: R S Hamilton, S J Swanton
Languages: French
Work: A1 B1 C1 C2 C3 D1 E F1 G H J1 K1 K3 K4 L M2 N Q R1 S1 S2 T1 T2 W Z(b,c,i,k,l)
Agency, Advocacy and Fixed Fee Interview undertaken
Ptr: Hamilton, Mrs Rosemary S BSc. . . . *Jul 1980
Swanton, Mr Stephen J LLB. . . . *Oct 1976
Con: Berry, Miss Anne LLB. . . . *§Apr 1978

BHW COMMERCIAL SOLICITORS ‡
5 Grove Park Leicester LE19 1SA
Tel: 0116 289 6229

BARLOWS ‡
1 Berridge Street Leicester LE1 5JT
Tel: 0116 251 8295 *Fax:* 0116 253 7850 *Dx:* 10810 LEICESTER 1
E-mail: enquiries@barlowssolicitors.com
List of partners: R D Foxon, C D Gooch, J Hefford, R J Poyner
Office: Market Harborough
Work: C1 C2 D1 E F1 J1 K1 K3 K4 L N O Q S1 S2 T1 T2 W Z(l,r)
Emergency Action, Agency and Advocacy undertaken
Ptr: Foxon, Mr Roger D . . . *§Jun 1966
Gooch, Mr Colin D BA. . . . *Mar 1977
Poyner, Mr Richard Jonathan BA . . . *Mar 1985
Ast: Brown, Mr David Stephen LLB . . . *Jul 2002
Hughes, Mrs Christl A LLB(Leics) . . . *May 1980
Riley, Mrs Amanda Jane LLB . . . *Aug 2004

See p112 for the Key to Work Categories & other symbols

BHAVSAR PATEL SOLICITORS ‡
131a Evington Road Leicester LE2 1QJ
Tel: 0116 254 9477 *Fax:* 0116 254 9488

BILLSON & SHARP ‡
Belvoir Chambers 17 Bowling Green Street Leicester LE1 6AS
Tel: 0116 255 9911 *Fax:* 0116 255 9933 *Dx:* 10881 LEICESTER
List of partners: E A Hanson, T R G Heap
Office: Leicester
Languages: French, German, Spanish
Work: C1 C2 D1 E J1 K1 K3 L N O Q S1 S2 T1 T2 V W
Emergency Action, Agency, Advocacy, Fixed Fee Interview and Legal Aid undertaken
Ptr: Hanson, Mr Eric A . . . *Dec 1990
Heap, Mr Thomas R G . . . *Jan 1975
Ast: Morris, Ms Tara Marie LLB; LPC . . . *Feb 2005
Thornton, Ms Louise . . . Jul 2008
Whitfield, Mr Andrew Charles LLB(Hons) . . . *Oct 1994
Con: Cleaver, Mr Patrick F J . . . *Jan 1967

BILLSON & SHARP
104 Queens Road Leicester LE2 3AD
Tel: 0116 270 2260 *Fax:* 0116 244 8557 *Dx:* 10881 LEICESTER
Office: Leicester
Work: A1 C1 C2 E J1 K1 L N O Q S1 S2 T1 T2 V W
Agency, Advocacy and Fixed Fee Interview undertaken
Ast: Swift, Ms Shani Melinda . . . *Feb 1994

BINGHAM & CO ‡
19 Halford Street Leicester LE1 1JA
Tel: 0116 253 0091 *Dx:* 10855 LEICESTER 1
List of partners: A J Bingham, J O Cunningham
Ptr: Bingham, Mr Andrew J LLB(Manc) . . . *Jun 1967
Cunningham, Mr John O LLB . . . *Jun 1961

BLOXHAMS ‡
59 Princess Road West Leicester LE1 6TR
Tel: 0116 222 3302 *Fax:* 0116 222 3304
List of partners: J Bloxham
Work: E S1 S2 W
SPr: Bloxham, Mr John BSc . . . *Jan 1993

BOND ADAMS LLP ‡
Richmond House 105 London Road Leicester LE2 0PF
Tel: 0116 285 8080 *Fax:* 0116 285 8185 *Dx:* 17005 LEICESTER 2

BRADSHAW HOLLINGSWORTH SOLICITORS ‡
19 New Walk Leicester LE1 6TE
Tel: 0116 204 2500 *Fax:* 0116 204 2501 *Dx:* 17007 LEICESTER 2
E-mail: mail@bhlaw.co.uk
Work: A3 C1 F1 F2 I J1 O Q S1 U2 W Z(b,k,l,w)
Agency, Advocacy and Fixed Fee Interview undertaken
Asoc: Bradshaw, Mr Robin Peter . . . Nov 1994
Hollingsworth, Mr Gregory Michael . . . Sep 1994

BRAY & BRAY ‡
Spa Place 36-42 Humberstone Road Leicester LE5 0AE
Tel: 0116 254 8871 *Fax:* 0870 383 5023 *Dx:* 13657 LEICESTER 4
Emergency telephone 07885 332421
E-mail: info@braybray.co.uk
List of partners: D P Berridge, P Corrigan, A P Ganderton, M A Garvey, T M G Gladdle, P J Heseltine, M V T Hill, D P Jefferson, I W Johnson, I D Knight, I D Lewis, P D Trotter, J S C Tucker
Office: Hinckley, Market Harborough
Work: A1 A3 B1 B2 C1 C2 C3 D1 D2 E F1 G H I J1 J2 K1 K3 K4 L M1 N O Q S1 S2 T2 U2 W Z(b,c,e,l,o,q,r)
Emergency Action, Agency, Advocacy, Fixed Fee Interview, Legal Aid undertaken, Legal Aid Franchise and Member of Accident Line
Ptr: Berridge, Mr David Paul LLB(Hons) . . . *Sep 1990
Corrigan, Mr Peter . . . *Nov 1998
Ganderton, Mr Adrian P LLB(Hons) . . . *Oct 1989
Garvey, Mr Michael A LLB . . . *Oct 1987
Gladdle, Mr Timothy M G LLB . . . *Dec 1983
Heseltine, Mr Phillip John MA(Oxon) . . . *Jan 1990
Johnson, Mr Ian W LLB(Hons) . . . *Oct 1995
Lewis, Mr Ian D BA(Hons) . . . *Jan 1984
Trotter, Mr Paul D BA(Law) . . . *Nov 1987
Tucker, Mr Jeremy Spencer Charles BSc(Hons); ATII . *Oct 1994
Asoc: Thomas, Miss Eiran Delyth LLB; LPC . . . *Mar 2005
Ast: Bowen, Mrs Catherine Anne LLB Sweet & Maxwell Law Prize for Best Overall Performance 1998; Hydes Prize Best Performance in Commercial Law (1998); Law Society Prize (1999) . . . *Oct 2001
Evans, Mr Gavin Scott LLB . . . *Oct 2003
Maddy, Mrs Justine M LLB . . . *Sep 1999
Malone, Miss Ruth Louise MA(Oxon); BA . . . *Nov 2001
Preston, Mr Toby Benjamin LLB . . . *Sep 2004
Con: Hamylton, Mr Gordon S . . . *Dec 1979

DEREK A BURNHAM ‡
2a Ferneley Rise Thrussington Leicester LE7 4UA
Tel: 01664 424517 *Fax:* 01664 424517
List of partners: D A Burnham
Work: E K1 L N S1 W Z(l)
Fixed Fee Interview and Legal Aid undertaken
Ptr: Burnham, Mr Derek Abblett . . . *Aug 1969

CB LAW SOLICITORS ‡
98 London Road Leicester LE2 0QS
Tel: 0116 254 5566 *Fax:* 0116 254 0033

CARTWRIGHT KING
Permanent House 31 Horsefair Leicester LE1 5BU
Tel: 0116 253 9222 *Fax:* 0808 168 1500 *Dx:* 10825 LEICESTER
E-mail: admin@cartwrightking.co.uk
Office: Birmingham, Derby, Gateshead, Nottingham, Sheffield
Work: B2 F2 G H J2 P Z(m)
Legal Aid undertaken and Legal Aid Franchise
Ptr: Bouch, Mr Jeremy . . . Nov 1998
Boucher, Mr Richard Michael LLB . . . *Oct 1998
Cox, Miss Imogen Louise LLB . . . *Jul 1998
Hollingsworth, Mr Wayne K BA . . . *Jul 1981
Ast: Baptiste, Mr Clarkson . . . Feb 2005
Bhojani, Sital . . . Mar 2004
Bolc, Mr Andrew BA(Hons) . . . Oct 1995
Kaur, Kalminder . . . *Jul 2000
Lee, Ms Zoe . . . Mar 2010
McGlory, Ms Eve . . . Jan 2008
Pallett, Miss Hannah Elizabeth . . . *Oct 2008
Robinson, Ms Justine . . . Jun 1997
Sacranie, Farah . . . Dec 2007
Stanbanks, Emma Jane . . . *Apr 2002

OLIVER CHARLES ‡
534 Uppingham Road Leicester LE5 2GG
Tel: 0116 243 1166 *Fax:* 0116 243 3482
Emergency telephone 0116 243 1166
E-mail: oliver.charles@btinternet.com
List of partners: O P Charles
Work: C1 E F1 K1 N O Q Z(d,l)
Emergency Action, Agency, Advocacy and Fixed Fee Interview undertaken
SPr: Charles, Mr Oliver P BSc(Hons) Charity Director; Lecturer in Law . . . *Nov 1992

CHETTY & PATEL ‡
117 Evington Road Leicester LE2 1QH
Tel: 0116 254 6222 *Fax:* 0116 254 6333
Emergency telephone 0116 270 1598
List of partners: A Patel, U D Patel
Languages: Gujarati, Punjabi, Urdu
Work: B1 D1 E G H J1 K1 L M2 P Q R1 S1 V W Z(c,f,i,l,p)
Emergency Action, Agency, Advocacy and Fixed Fee Interview undertaken
Ptr: Patel, Arvind LLB . . . *Aug 1986
Patel, Umesh D LLB . . . *Mar 1997
Ast: Kotecha, Mrs Sushma . . . Jan 1994

PAUL COOPER & CO ‡
2 De Montfort Street Leicester LE1 7GA
Tel: 0116 255 4477 *Fax:* 0116 255 3905 *Dx:* 17017 LEICESTER 2
E-mail: paulcooperandco@tiscali.co.uk
List of partners: P R Cooper
Work: C1 E F1 L S1 S2 W Z(d)
SPr: Cooper, Mr Paul R BA(Law) . . . *Nov 1978

CRANE & WALTON
113-117 London Road Leicester LE2 0RG
Tel: 0116 255 1901 *Fax:* 0116 255 5864 *Dx:* 17012 LEICESTER 2
Emergency telephone 0116 281 1211
Office: Ashby-de-la-Zouch, Coalville
Work: A1 B1 C1 D1 E F1 G H J1 K1 L M1 N O P Q R1 S1 T1 V W Z(b,c,d,e,h,i,k,l,m,n,o,p)
Agency, Advocacy, Fixed Fee Interview, Legal Aid undertaken and Member of Accident Line
Ptr: Adkinson, Mr Richard F . . . *§Jul 1971
Klimowicz, Mr Andrew MA(Oxon) Exhibitioner (Oxford University) . . . *Aug 1989

DAVID CURTIS & CO ‡
425 Welford Road Leicester LE2 6BL
Tel: 0116 270 2402 *Fax:* 0116 270 6478
List of partners: D J Curtis
Work: E K1 N Q S1 W
Fixed Fee Interview undertaken
SPr: Curtis, Mr David John . . . *§Dec 1980

OLIVER D'SA SOLICITORS ‡
75-81 King Street Leicester LE1 6RP
Tel: 0116 275 5549 *Dx:* 10860 LEICESTER
List of partners: O A D'Sa
SPr: D'Sa, Mr Oliver A LLB(Leics) . . . Mar 1984
Ast: Collins, Ms Anne M LLB . . . *Apr 1990
Hallchurch, Mr Nigel Charles BA(Hons) . . . Jan 1990
Whittle, Mrs Marion P R BA(Hons) . . . *Jan 1986

DAVIS & CO ‡
3 Victoria Mews De Montfort Place Leicester LE1 7GZ
Tel: 0116 285 4774 *Fax:* 0116 255 1645 *Dx:* 17018 LEICESTER 2

DEWS WITCOMB ‡
87 London Road Leicester LE2 0PF
Tel: 0116 233 4499 *Fax:* 0116 233 7904 *Dx:* 17002 LEICESTER 2
List of partners: R J Dews
Languages: French
Work: C1 C2 C3 E L M1 M2 N P S1 T1 T2 W Z(c,d,i,l)
Ptr: Dews, Mr Robert J Clerk to Commissioner of Taxes . *§Nov 1970

DIXON COLES & GODDARD ‡
1 The Nook Anstey Leicester LE7 7AZ
Tel: 0116 236 4708 *Fax:* 0116 234 0529 *Dx:* 701140 ANSTEY
List of partners: G M North, J A Webb
Work: C1 D1 E K1 L N R1 S1 T1 V W
Emergency Action, Agency, Advocacy and Fixed Fee Interview undertaken
Ptr: North, Mr Graham M . . . *Feb 1972

DODDS & PARTNERS ‡
32 Friar Lane Leicester LE1 5RA
Tel: 0116 253 8585 *Fax:* 0116 253 0212 *Dx:* 10830 LEICESTER 1
Emergency telephone 0116 251 0000
E-mail: enquiries@dodds-solicitors.co.uk
List of partners: B J Dodds, S M Morris, M K Obhi, A Topiwala
Languages: British Sign Language, Gujarati, Hindi, Punjabi, Urdu
Work: B2 D1 E F1 G H J1 K1 K2 N O Q S1 W Z(e,g,i,l)
Emergency Action, Agency, Advocacy, Fixed Fee Interview and Legal Aid undertaken
Ptr: Dodds, Mr Brian J LLB . . . *Jan 1974
Morris, Mr Stephen M LLB . . . *Apr 1976
Obhi, Miss Manjit K LLB; LLM . . . *Nov 1987
Topiwala, Mr Ashwin . . . *Dec 1993
Asoc: Kavshal, S K . . . *Nov 1998
Ast: Spence, Mrs Sarah LLB . . . *Sep 1990

EDWARDS & GRANT SOLICITORS ‡
71 London Road Leicester LE2 0PE
Tel: 0116 255 2110

EMERY JOHNSON PARTNERSHIP ‡
3 & 5 Welford Road Leicester LE2 7AD
Tel: 0116 255 4855 *Fax:* 0116 255 5044
Emergency telephone 0116 255 4855
E-mail: legal@emeryjohnson.com
List of partners: K L Emery, H L Johnson, E C Mitchell
Languages: Gujarati, Hindi
Work: D1 D2 G H K1 K3
Agency, Advocacy and Legal Aid undertaken
Ptr: Emery, Ms Karen Lesley LLB ♦ . . . *Oct 1982
Johnson, Miss Helen Louise LLB ★ . . . *Nov 1990
Mitchell, Mrs Emma Catherine LLB . . . *Jan 1992

EMPLOYMENT LAW DIVERSITY & DISCRIMINATION SERVICE-ELIZABETH CARNEY ‡
14 Laytton Road Leicester LE2 1WH
Tel: 07900 212188 / 0116 212 1099
E-mail: info@lizcarneyemploymentlaw.co.uk

EQUITAS LAW LIMITED ‡
17 Wellington Street Leicester LE1 6HU
Tel: 0116 275 5054 *Fax:* 0116 254 7001
E-mail: zaida@equitaslaw.com

BARRIE FAIRBAIRN SOLICITORS ‡
57 Stoughton Road Leicester LE2 2EF
Tel: 0116 244 8272 *Fax:* 0116 290 1878
Emergency telephone 07973 139536
E-mail: barrie@bf-solicitors.co.uk
List of partners: B A Fairbairn
Work: G H
Agency, Advocacy and Legal Aid undertaken
SPr: Fairbairn, Mr Barrie A BSc . . . *May 1991

FAMILY LAW SOLICITORS ‡
10 Swallow Close Leicester Forest East Leicester LE3 3NY
Tel: 0116 239 5544 *Fax:* 0116 239 0845
E-mail: awisniewski@familylawsolicitors.net

CRAIG FERGUSON & CO LLP ‡
Queen Anne House 4-6 New Street Leicester LE1 5NR
Tel: 0116 270 5088 *Fax:* 0116 270 5089
E-mail: cf@craig-ferguson.co.uk

ANDREW M FORD SOLICITORS ‡
31 Lower Brown Street Leicester LE1 5TH
Tel: 0845 075 4059 *Fax:* 0116 247 0539
E-mail: leicester@qualitysolicitors.com
List of partners: A M Ford
Languages: French
Work: K1 N S1 S2 W
Ptr: Ford, Mr Andrew Michael LLB(Hons) . . . *Oct 1983

FOSSE LAW ‡
Witland House 23-25 Friar Lane Leicester LE1 5QQ
Tel: 0116 262 0290 *Fax:* 0116 262 0292 *Dx:* 10815 LEICESTER
E-mail: info@fosselaw.com
Office: Loughborough, Melton Mowbray

FREER & ARCHER ‡
24 Spencefield Lane Leicester LE5 6PS
Tel: 0116 241 3199
List of partners: A Archer, P R Freer
Languages: Gujarati, Hindi, Punjabi
Work: B1 C1 C2 C3 D1 E F1 G H J1 K1 L M1 M2 N P R1 S1 T1 T2 V W Z(b,c,h,i,j,k,l,m,s)
Emergency Action, Agency, Advocacy, Fixed Fee Interview, Legal Aid undertaken, Legal Aid Franchise and Member of Accident Line
Ptr: Archer, Mr Anthony MA . . . *Jan 1964
Freer, Mr Philip R LLB; ACII . . . *Dec 1975

FREETH CARTWRIGHT LLP
One Colton Square Leicester LE1 1QH
Tel: 0116 248 1100 *Fax:* 0845 634 2590 *Dx:* 744170 LEICESTER 41
E-mail: postmaster@freethcartwright.co.uk
Office: Birmingham, Derby, Manchester, Nottingham
Languages: French, Portuguese
Work: A1 B1 C1 C2 C3 E J1 L N O P Q R1 R2 S1 S2 T1 T2 V W Z(c,e,h,i,k,l,p,r)
Emergency Action, Agency, Advocacy, Legal Aid undertaken and Member of Accident Line
Ptr: Abbott, Mr Simon M BA . . . §Oct 1984
Cummins, Mr Mike . . . Mar 1998
Darby, Mr Charles J LLB . . . *§Oct 1986
Magdani, Mrs Rena . . . Sep 1996
Middleton, Mr Julian Matthew MA(Oxon) . . . *§Oct 1989
Osborn, Mr Richard . . . Sep 1997
Patel, Mukesh BA(Hons) . . . *Nov 1993
Philippon-Thomas, Ms Sophie . . . Sep 1992
Radcliffe, Mr Malcolm J . . . *§Feb 1972
Rowley, Mr Robert G LLB . . . *§Jul 1973
West, Mr David E LLB . . . *Apr 1977
Williams, Miss Jane LLB . . . *§Nov 1992
Asoc: Blank, Mrs Katherine S LLB; LLM . . . *Oct 1989

R G FRISBY & SMALL ‡
5 De Montfort Street Leicester LE1 7GT
Tel: 0116 233 5522 *Fax:* 0116 233 5810 *Dx:* 17001 LEICESTER 2
E-mail: enquiries@frisbysmall.co.uk
List of partners: A McNeil, R S Whiting, G Wright
Office: Leicester
Work: C1 C2 C3 D1 E F1 G J1 K1 L N O Q R1 S1 S2 W Z(h)
Emergency Action, Agency, Advocacy, Fixed Fee Interview and Legal Aid undertaken
Ptr: McNeil, Mr Andrew LLB . . . Oct 1995
Whiting, Mr Richard S LLB . . . *Apr 1978
Wright, Ms Glynis . . . Jan 2003
Ast: Fraser, Ms Fiona . . . Sep 1999
McCole, Mrs Susan G . . . Oct 1986

R G FRISBY & SMALL
72b Main Street Broughton Astley Leicester LE9 6RD
Tel: 01455 282832 *Fax:* 01455 282832 *Dx:* 17001 LEICESTER 2
E-mail: bastley@frisbysmall.co.uk
Office: Leicester
Work: C1 C2 C3 D1 E F1 G K1 L N O Q S1 W Z(h,l)
Emergency Action, Agency, Advocacy, Legal Aid undertaken and Member of Accident Line
Ptr: Whiting, Mr Richard S LLB . . . *Apr 1978
Wright, Ms Glynis . . . Jan 2003
Ast: Kotecha, Mrs Sushma . . . Jan 1994

GARRETT LONG SOLICITORS ‡
Florence Villa 5 Leicester Road Leicester LE7 7AT
Tel: 0116 236 4875

GATELEY LLP
Knightsbridge House Lower Brown Street Leicester LE1 5NL
Tel: 0116 285 9000 *Fax:* 0116 285 9001 *Dx:* 10829 LEICESTER 1
E-mail: info@gateleyuk.com
Office: Birmingham, London EC4, Manchester, Nottingham
Languages: French, German, Gujarati, Italian, Portuguese, Punjabi
Work: A1 B1 C1 C2 C3 E G J1 L N O P R1 S1 T1 T2 W Z(b,c,e,h,i,k,l,w)
Agency undertaken and Member of Accident Line
Ptr: John, Mr James Richard Gareth LLB(Hons) . . . *Apr 1990
Mitchell, Mr Craig L . . . *Feb 1973
Asoc: Gittus, Mr Colin M I LLB . . . Sep 1999
Hunt, Ms Emma . . . Sep 2000

HALBORG & CO (SOLICITORS) ‡
1 The Crescent King Street Leicester LE1 6RX
Tel: 0116 255 1010 *Fax:* 0116 254 0870 *Dx:* 17015 LEICESTER 2
E-mail: enquiry@halborg.com

PHILIP J HAMMOND & SONS ‡
47 Friar Lane Leicester LE1 5QX
Tel: 0116 251 7171 *Fax:* 0116 253 7370 *Dx:* 10820 LEICESTER 1
E-mail: enquiries@pjhammond.com
List of partners: R D Hammond, S Holland
Work: A1 B1 C1 C2 C3 D1 E F1 G H J1 K1 K3 L M1 M2 N O P Q R1 S1 S2 T1 T2 W Z(c,e,i,k,l,o)
Emergency Action, Agency, Advocacy, Fixed Fee Interview, Legal Aid undertaken and Member of Accident Line
Ptr: Hammond, Mr Richard D BA . . . *Feb 1987
Holland, Mrs Susan LLB . . . *Oct 1986
Ast: Cohoon, Miss Katherine Mary LLB . . . *May 1992
Taylor, Mr Ian James LLB . . . Jan 2007

HARVEY INGRAM LLP ‡
20 New Walk Leicester LE1 6TX
Tel: 0116 254 5454 *Fax:* 0116 255 4559 *Dx:* 17014 LEICESTER 2
E-mail: hio@hio.co.uk
List of partners: G D Arthur, S P Astill, D L Barker, K A Borneo, R Botterill, J Charlton, J E Clarke, C E Clay, H T Doyle, M K Dunkley, C V Finlay, V J Foley, K E A Hall, A E Hamblett, A J B Harris, R P Harris, S W Holmes, A G Hopgood, G H Humphrey, H E Johnstone, M J O Jones, P D Lane, J Lazard, D A Mansfield, R F Miller, D M Mills, D V M Mitchell, S P Moran, J Patel, P Perusko, S Phelan, R E Rose, P Saigal, C T Saul, J N Simon, I Slinger, J Soul, J Stobart, M Thompson, F R Whale, S H Woolfe
Office: Bedford, Birmingham, Milton Keynes, Newport Pagnell
Languages: French, German
Work: A1 B1 C1 E F1 G J1 K1 L M1 N O P Q R1 S1 T1 V W Z(b,c,d,e,h,i,j,k,l,o,s)
Emergency Action, Agency, Advocacy, Legal Aid undertaken and Member of Accident Line
Ptr: Arthur, Mr Gordon D MA(Cantab) . . . *§Apr 1976
Astill, Mr Simon Peter LLB . . . *Nov 1992
Botterill, Mr Roy BSc . . . *§Oct 1990
Doyle, Mr Henry T FILEx . . . *§Jul 1979
Dunkley, Mr Mark K LLB; TEP . . . *Oct 1984
Finlay, Mr Christopher V MA(Cantab) . . . *§Nov 1985
Hall, Mrs Katherine E A LLB . . . *Nov 1987
Harris, Mr Robert P LLB(Lond) . . . *§Jul 1969
Jones, Mr Martin J O LLB . . . *Oct 1988
Lane, Mr Phillip D LLB(Nott'm) . . . *§Apr 1974
Mansfield, Miss Debra A LLB(Leics) . . . *§Dec 1985
Miller, Mr Richard F LLB(Sheff) . . . *Jun 1978
Mitchell, Mr David V M . . . *§Dec 1967
Moran, Mr Sean P LLB . . . *Feb 1991
Rose, Mr Robert Edwin LLB . . . *Feb 1992
Saul, Mr Christopher T LLB . . . *§Apr 1978
Simon, Mr John N BA . . . *§Nov 1974
Slinger, Mr Ian BA . . . *§Dec 1981
Stobart, Mr John LLB . . . *Dec 1978
Whale, Mr Frank R . . . *§Jan 1983
Woolfe, Mr Stephen H LLB Notary Public . . . *§Apr 1979
Asoc: Clarke, Mrs Karen LLB . . . Sep 1997
Davies, Mrs L Margaret LLB(Hons) . . . *Apr 1974
Fear, Mr Jonathan C BSocSc . . . *Nov 1991
Hart, Mrs Kathryn Jane LLB . . . *Oct 1991
Hunt, Mr Paul . . . *Aug 1998
Munsey, Mrs Elizabeth Jane LLB . . . *Sep 1995
Patel, Mr Rafique LLB . . . *Oct 1996
Talbot, Mr Mathew BSc . . . *May 1998
Tucker, Mr Jeremy Spencer Charles BSc(Hons) . . . *Oct 1994
Wyvill, Mr Richard Mark LLB . . . *§Aug 1994
Ast: Anderson, Mrs Emma M LLB . . . *Oct 1990
Atterbury, Ms Lindsey Ann FILEx . . . *Oct 2000
Botham, Mr Andrew . . . *Sep 1999
Botterill, Mrs Lisa L LLB . . . *May 2001
Chase, Miss Verity LLB . . . *Sep 2001
Chaudhary, Miss Anita LLB . . . *Jun 1998
Clayton, Mr Neil LLB . . . *Jan 2001
Collier, Mrs Leenamari . . . *Aug 1997
Cook, Mrs Alison C MA . . . *Oct 1995
Dryden, Miss Georgia R . . . *Sep 2000
Hennell, Mr Lee Spencer . . . *Sep 1998
Holloway, Miss Michelle BA . . . *Feb 2001
Kaur, Miss Kirpal LLB(Hons) . . . *Dec 1996
Lyon, Mrs Elizabeth A D . . . *Apr 2001
McKittrick, Mr Scott W LLB(Hons) . . . *Oct 1999
Manley, Miss Katherine M J BA(Hons) . . . *Oct 1999
Matthews, Miss Louisa E LLB . . . *Jan 1998
Measures, Mr John . . . Nov 1998
Newton, Mrs Lucy Clare LLB(Hons) . . . *Sep 2000
Rani, Miss Nelum LLB First Prize Module Professional Skills . . . *Mar 1998
Rees, Mrs Lucy Jane . . . Oct 1998
Smith, Mr Darren Mark BA . . . *Sep 2002
Tuohy, Miss Kezia Elizabeth LLB; BCom . . . *Feb 2002
Unarkat, Mrs Shilpa Roopen LLB . . . *Oct 2002
Weston, Miss Rebecca Ann . . . *Sep 2001
White, Mr Jonathan William BA(Hons) . . . *Jun 1999
Whitehead, Miss Louise June LLB . . . *Sep 2002

R W HEMMINGS & CO ‡
40 Hinckley Road Leicester LE3 0RA
Tel: 0116 255 8500 *Fax:* 0116 254 0195
E-mail: rwhemmings@swanhill.co.uk
List of partners: S N Gangani, R W Hemmings
Languages: Gujarati, Hindi
Work: B1 C1 E F1 J1 K1 L N R1 S1 S2 W Z(c,d,i,j,s)
Emergency Action, Agency and Fixed Fee Interview undertaken
Ptr: Gangani, Mr Shakhar Narandas BA(Hons)(Law) . . . May 1987
Hemmings, R W . . . Jan 1963

HIGHCROSS LAW LLP ‡
5 Gower Street Leicester LE1 3LJ
Tel: 0116 262 0001 *Fax:* 0116 262 1110
E-mail: enquiries@highcrosslaw.co.uk

MICHAEL HILL PARTNERSHIP ‡
Top Hat Terrace 119 London Road Leicester LE2 0QT
Tel: 0116 254 1609 *Fax:* 0116 247 1084 *Dx:* 10846 LEICESTER
E-mail: info@michaelhill.co.uk
List of partners: J M T Hill, M I Hill, V Kumar, W G Welsh
Languages: Gujarati, Punjabi
Work: A1 B1 C1 D1 E F1 G H J1 J2 K1 L M1 N P Q R1 S1 S2 T1 V W Z(i,n)
Emergency Action, Agency, Advocacy, Fixed Fee Interview, Legal Aid undertaken and Member of Accident Line
Ptr: Hill, Mr Jeremy M T . . . Nov 1983
Hill, Mr Michael I . . . *Jun 1970
Kumar, Vijay . . . *Jan 1987
Welsh, Mr William G LLB . . . *May 1988
Asoc: Cook, Mr Richard J LLB . . . *Jan 1998

HOWELLS LLP ‡
60 Charles Street Leicester LE1 1FB
Tel: 0845 456 0074 *Fax:* 0116 251 8411
E-mail: enquiries@howellsllp.com

HOWES PERCIVAL LLP
No1 Bede Island Road Bede Island Business Park Leicester LE2 7EA
Tel: 0116 247 3500 *Fax:* 0116 247 3539 *Dx:* 17013 LEICESTER 2
Emergency telephone 0116 247 3500
E-mail: law@howespercival.com
Office: London WC2, Manchester, Milton Keynes, Northampton, Norwich
Languages: Hindi, Punjabi
Work: A1 B1 C1 C2 C3 E F1 I K1 L M1 M2 N O P Q R1 S1 T1 T2 W Z(b,c,d,e,f,g,h,i,j,k,l,o,p,q,s,t,w,y)
Emergency Action, Agency, Advocacy and Fixed Fee Interview undertaken
Mem: Bailey, Paula Kim . . . Sep 1999
Bennion, Mr Charles R MA(Cantab) . . . *Nov 1974
Davies, Mr Geraint Keith LLB(Hons) . . . *Nov 1991
Gilbert, Mr Keith LLB(Hons) . . . *Sep 1997
Herd, Mr John K C LLB . . . *Oct 1987
Singh, Mr Jit LLB . . . *Dec 1989
Asoc: Chayra, Satnam . . . Sep 2002
Steggles, Hannah . . . Sep 2005

IDRIS & CO ‡
186 Evington Road Leicester LE2 1HN
Tel: 0116 249 0100 *Fax:* 0116 249 0200
E-mail: a.idris@idrissolicitors.co.uk
Languages: Gujarati, Punjabi, Urdu
Work: K1 Q S2 W Z(i)

JOHAR & CO ‡
1st Floor Beckville House 66 London Road Leicester LE2 0QD
Tel: 0116 254 3345 *Fax:* 0116 254 2370 *Dx:* 28813 LEICESTER 2
Emergency telephone 07712 834585
E-mail: sunitamakwana@johars.com
List of partners: D K Johar, T R Johar
Languages: Gujarati, Hindi, Punjabi, Urdu
Work: B1 C1 D1 E G H K1 L M1 N O Q S1 S2 V W Z(b,c,d,e,g,i,j,k,p)
Emergency Action, Agency, Advocacy, Legal Aid undertaken and Legal Aid Franchise
Ptr: Johar, Mr Deepak K LLB(Lond) . . . May 1986
Johar, Tilak R . . . *§Jun 1975
Ast: Ahmad, Miss Maria LLB(Hons); LPC . . . *Apr 2001
Bailham, Mr Lee Stephen William . . . Nov 1995

JOHL & WALTERS SOLICITORS ‡
86 London Road Leicester LE2 0QR
Tel: 0116 255 7806 *Fax:* 0116 255 5693
E-mail: johlwalters@btconnect.com

JONES & DUFFIN SOLICITORS LLP ‡
142 Narborough Road Leicester LE3 0BT
Tel: 0116 222 1555 *Fax:* 0116 222 1560 *Dx:* 703052 LEICESTER 7
Emergency telephone 07773 237979
E-mail: iain@jonesduffin.co.uk
List of partners: K Dossani, P A Duffin, I R M B Jones
Languages: French, German, Gujarati, Hindi
Work: B1 C1 E K1 L N O Q R2 S1 S2 W Z(c,h)
Emergency Action, Agency, Advocacy, Fixed Fee Interview, Legal Aid undertaken, Legal Aid Franchise and Member of Accident Line
Mem: Dossani, Ms Kauser BA(Hons) . . . *May 1995
Duffin, Mr Peter A BA(Law); FILEx . . . *Jan 1987
Jones, Mr Iain R M B BA . . . *May 1981

JOSIAH HINCKS ‡
22 De Montfort Street Leicester LE1 7GB
Tel: 0116 255 1811 *Fax:* 0116 254 4870 *Dx:* 17010 LEICESTER 2
E-mail: info@josiahhincks.co.uk
List of partners: R A Eagle, N D Head, M Hill
Office: Blaby, Coalville
Languages: French, Hindi, Punjabi, Urdu
Work: A1 C1 C2 C3 D1 E G H J1 K1 K3 L M1 M2 N O P Q S1 T1 T2 W X Z(l,p)
Agency, Advocacy, Legal Aid undertaken and Legal Aid Franchise
Ptr: Eagle, Mr Ronald Andrew TEP . . . *Dec 1993
Head, Mr Neil David LLB(B'ham) . . . *Mar 1987
Hill, Mr Martin . . . *Feb 1981
Ast: Dowling, Mr Russell LLB(Hons) . . . Aug 2008
Jacobs, Miss Frances LLB . . . *Aug 2009
Jansari, Mr Asit D LLB(Hons) . . . *Mar 2002
Milk, Mr James LLB(Hons) . . . *May 2007
Sanghera, Miss Sandy LLB(Hons) . . . *Oct 2010

JASVIR JUTLA & CO ‡
99 London Road Leicester LE2 0PF
Tel: 0116 254 0809 *Fax:* 0116 254 3107
Emergency telephone 07984 424232
E-mail: jasvirjutla@hotmail.com
List of partners: J S Jutla
Languages: Gujarati, Hindi, Kiswahili, Punjabi, Urdu
Work: Z(i)
Emergency Action undertaken
SPr: Jutla, Mr Jasvir Singh BA . . . *Mar 1991
Ast: Bhavsar, Rajesh BA; LLM . . . *Dec 2000
Patel, Mr Mohammed . . . Dec 2004

K4 LAW ‡
100 New Walk Leicester LE1 7EA
Tel: 0116 216 0510 *Fax:* 0116 255 4316
E-mail: info@k4law.com

KELLY & CO SOLICITORS ‡
81 St Johns Enderby Leicester LE19 2BS
Tel: 0116 200 1998 *Fax:* 0116 275 2282
E-mail: enquiries@kellyandcosolicitors.co.uk

LAWSON WEST SOLICITORS LIMITED ‡
241 Uppingham Road Leicester LE5 4DG
Tel: 0116 212 1000 *Fax:* 0116 212 1051 *Dx:* 10884 LEICESTER 1
E-mail: mail@lawson-west.co.uk
List of partners: A S Dobson, J E Haworth, D Heys, J Hopkins, A M Hunt, V N Jones
Office: Market Harborough, Wigston
Work: C1 D1 E J1 K1 K2 K3 N S1 S2 W
Advocacy, Fixed Fee Interview, APIL and Member of Accident Line
Ptr: Dobson, Mr Alistair S LLB(Hons) . . . *Oct 1997
Heys, Mr David . . . *Dec 2005
Hunt, Mr Ashley Michael . . . *Oct 2000
Jones, Mrs Victoria Nova . . . *Jul 1999
Asoc: Cereghino, Ms Katherine . . . Feb 2007
Evans, Mr Mark Francis BA(Law) . . . *Aug 2003
Lawrenson, Ms Elizabeth . . . *Aug 2002

M&M SOLICITORS ‡
1st & 2nd Floors 24 King Street Leicester LE1 6RL
Tel: 0116 285 2300 *Fax:* 0116 285 2303
Emergency telephone 07958 720721
E-mail: mmsolicitors@btconnect.com
List of partners: A Mehta, R Morjana
Office: Loughborough
Languages: Gujarati, Hindi, Punjabi
Work: B2 G H
Agency, Advocacy, Fixed Fee Interview and Legal Aid undertaken
Ptr: Mehta, Ms Anita . . . Jan 2003
Morjana, Rakesh . . . Jan 1999

MHM SOLICITORS ‡
1 Francis Way Grove Park Enderby Leicester LE19 1SH
Tel: 0845 234 0230 *Fax:* 0116 281 5978 *Dx:* 724761 ENDERBY 2
List of partners: M H M Garton, C G Kelsey, L Mason
Ptr: Garton, Mr Michael Henry McRae BA . . . *Oct 1979
Kelsey, Mr Clive G . . . *Jun 1971
Mason, Mrs Linda Chairman of the DSS Appeals Tribunal . . . *§Jul 1978

MARKS & CLERK
144 New Walk Leicester LE1 7JA
Office: Birmingham, Cheltenham, Leeds, Liverpool, London WC2, Manchester, Oxford

MARRONS ‡
1 Meridian South Meridian Business Park Leicester LE19 1WY
Tel: 0116 289 2200 *Fax:* 0116 289 3733
Dx: 710910 LEICESTER MERIDIAN
E-mail: enquiries@marrons.net
List of partners: S D Andrews, J T S Edmond, P A Marron, L M Mee, P N Robinson, S P Stanion, K W Sumner, M E Thomson
Work: A1 C1 C2 E J1 L O P Q R1 R2 S1 S2 W Z(e,l,p,u)
Ptr: Andrews, Mr Stuart Daniel BA(Hons); DipLaw; MRTPI . . . *Jan 1997
Edmond, Mr John T S BA(Law); LARTPI . . . *Oct 1983
Marron, Mr Peter A LLB(L'pool) . . . *Jun 1970
Mee, Mrs Louise Marie LLB(Hons) . . . *Sep 1990
Robinson, Mr Paul Nicholas LLB(Newc) . . . *Mar 1978
Stanion, Mr Simon P DipML . . . *Oct 1986
Sumner, Mr Kevin W LLB(L'pool) . . . *Apr 1980
Thomson, Mrs Morag E LLB; LARTPI . . . *Dec 1982
Ast: Doyle, Miss Sarah Jane LLB(Hons) . . . *Jul 2001
Harries, Miss Bethan Mair LLB . . . *Mar 2002
Horton, Mr Baxter M BA(Hons) . . . *§Dec 1983
Sanders, Mr Ian James BA(Hons)(Modern History) . . . Sep 1999

LOUISE MEE LIMITED ‡
Meridian South Meridian Business Park Leicester LE19 1WY
Tel: 0116 289 2200

J B MOLONEY & CO ‡
146 Mountsorrel Lane Rothley Leicester LE7 7PW
Tel: 0116 230 1950 *Fax:* 0116 230 3531
E-mail: jbmoloney@supanet.com
List of partners: J B Moloney
Work: A1 E L S1 S2 W
Fixed Fee Interview undertaken
SPr: Moloney, Mr John Brian . . . Jul 1973

TREVOR F MOORE & CO ‡
The Cottage 71 High Street Ibstock Leicester LE67 6LH
Tel: 01530 261719 *Fax:* 01530 263378
List of partners: T F Moore
Emergency Action, Agency, Advocacy and Legal Aid undertaken
Ptr: Moore, Mr Trevor F FILEx Honorary Solicitor to Coalville & District CAB . . . *Jan 1983

MOOSA-DUKE ‡
213 London Road Leicester LE2 1ZE
Tel: 0800 952 0010 *Fax:* 0116 220 6432

NELSONS
Provincial House 37 New Walk Leicester LE1 6TU
Tel: 0116 222 6666 *Fax:* 0116 222 6650 *Dx:* 141220 LEICESTER 19
Office: Derby, Nottingham
Ptr: Coningsby, Mr James E R . . . Nov 1990
Dawkins, Miss Philippa Clare BA(Hons) . . . Oct 1995
Greenwell, Mr Christopher R LLB . . . Mar 1986
Holder, Mr Timothy M R LLB . . . *May 1983
McKinney, Mr Christopher P LLB . . . *Nov 1984
Oswin, Ms Melanie Stacey . . . Sep 1994
Rowell, Mr Andrew James BA(Law); LSF . . . *Nov 1991
Asoc: Watts, Mr David . . . Mar 1994
Ast: Bentley, Ms Jennifer . . . Dec 1998
Foreman, Mr Nicholas John LLB; MA . . . Dec 1995
Greenwell, Mrs Katrina Jayne BA(Law) . . . *§Jan 1986
Grover, Ms Elizabeth . . . Nov 1998
Holt, Mr Anthony J N Notary Public . . . *Jun 1974
Hubbard, Miss Deborah LLB(Hons) . . . *May 1996
Jarret, Mr Michael . . . Sep 1997
Raisbeck, Ms Joanne . . . Sep 2001
Scott, Mrs Louise LLB . . . *Oct 1993
Smith, Mr Stephen T J . . . *Nov 1992
Con: McLauchlan, Mr John Notary Public . . . *Jul 1964

PARMARS ‡
120 London Road Leicester LE2 0QS
Tel: 0116 255 5155 *Fax:* 0116 255 6490 *Dx:* 28801 LEICESTER 2
List of partners: D Parmar
Office: Loughborough
Languages: Gujarati, Hindi, Kiswahili, Punjabi
Work: E J1 L N O Q W Z(i)
Emergency Action, Agency and Fixed Fee Interview undertaken
Ptr: Parmar, Mr Dinesh BA(Law) . . . *May 1988

PARR & COMPANY ‡
1 Blaby Road Enderby Leicester LE19 4AR
Tel: 0116 284 8031 *Fax:* 0116 286 1621
E-mail: parrco@onetel.com

See p112 for the Key to Work Categories & other symbols

DAVID PHILLIPS & PARTNERS
2 De Montfort Street Leicester LE1 7GA
Tel: 0116 298 5525 *Fax:* 0116 298 5526
E-mail: info@dpp.law.com
Office: Birmingham, Bootle (2 offices), Chadwell Heath, Liverpool, London E1, London SE18, London W1, Manchester, Nelson, Wealdstone

PHOENIX SOLICITORS ‡
10 De Montfort Street Leicester LE1 7GG
Tel: 0116 254 2863 *Fax:* 0116 254 0391
E-mail: crystal@phoenixsolicitors.com
List of partners: C Andrade
SPr: Andrade, Crystal . . . . Feb 2001

PROPERTY LAWYERS DIRECT LIMITED ‡
108 Queens Road Leicester LE2 3FL
Tel: 0116 270 3000 *Fax:* 0116 270 6555
E-mail: office@propertylawyersdirect.com

QUEENS SOLICITORS ‡
8 Uppingham Road Leicester LE5 0QD
Tel: 0116 274 7927 *Fax:* 0116 274 7929 *Dx:* 13655 LEICESTER 4
E-mail: law@queens-solicitors.co.uk
List of partners: P Akhtar
Languages: French, Hindi, Punjabi, Urdu
Work: B1 E F1 K1 L N O Q S1 S2 Z(c,i,j,k,q)
Agency, Advocacy and Fixed Fee Interview undertaken
Dir: Akhtar, Ms Parvien LLB(Hons) . . . . *Dec 1998

RAKKANI SOLICITORS ‡
180 Melton Road Leicester LE4 5EE
Tel: 0116 299 2999 *Fax:* 0116 299 3999
Dx: 18466 LEICESTER BELGRAVE
Emergency telephone 07905 228555
E-mail: info@rakkani.com
List of partners: R J Patel
Languages: Gujarati, Hindi
Work: C1 E F1 F2 J1 K1 K3 L S1 S2 W Z(e,i,l)
Agency and Fixed Fee Interview undertaken
SPr: Patel, Mr Rakesh Jayant LLB(Hons). . . . . *Jun 1999

RICH & CARR FREER BOUSKELL ‡
Assurance House 24 Rutland Street Leicester LE1 9GX
Tel: 0116 253 8021 *Fax:* 0116 253 7427 *Dx:* 724400 LEICESTER 24
E-mail: enquiries@richandcarr.co.uk
List of partners: M Anastasiades, E J Barr, D M Charman, N M de Voil, J L Fowlds, J R Rixon, D M Roberts, A P Smith, M A Tildesley, P L Ward
Office: Blaby, Lutterworth, Oadby, Syston
Work: B1 C1 C2 C3 D1 E F1 F2 J1 J2 K1 L M1 M2 N O P Q R1 S1 S2 T1 T2 V W Z(b,c,d,e,f,h,i,l,p,w)
Emergency Action, Agency, Advocacy undertaken and Member of Accident Line
Ptr: Anastasiades, Mr Mario LLB Deputy Coroner . . . . *May 1988
Charman, Mr David M. . . . . *§Jun 1974
de Voil, Mr Neil M LLB(Nott'm) . . . . *§Jan 1965
Fowlds, Mr John L LLB(Sheff). . . . . *Jun 1975
Rixon, Mr James Robert . . . . *Jun 1973
Roberts, Mr David Mark LLB . . . . *§Jun 1980
Smith, Mr Anthony Peter . . . . Jan 1973
Tildesley, Mr Mark A LLB . . . . §Mar 1980
Ward, Mr Peter L MA; LLB(Cantab) Deputy Coroner. *§Feb 1965
Asoc: Coffee, Mr John Kenneth LLB. . . . . *Oct 1980
Ast: Drinkall, Verity. . . . . Jun 2005
Green, Mrs Ruth Elizabeth BA(Hons)(Law) . . . . . . *Jul 1979
Howkins, Miss Claire Louise. . . . . Jun 2005
Kalyanji, Geeta . . . . Sep 2004
Lyon, Ms Verity . . . . Feb 2008
Maini, Mrs Sabrina . . . . Jul 2004
Makan, Mrs Sukhbir LLB(Hons) . . . . *Nov 1991
Mann, Hardeep . . . . Jun 2007
Ridley, Ms Anne D LLB . . . . *Mar 1990

ROBERTS ROSE PARTNERSHIP ‡
10 Peacock Lane Leicester LE1 5PX
Tel: 0116 251 5120 *Fax:* 0116 251 4400

R P ROBINSON ‡
Imperial Buildings 2 Halford Street Leicester LE1 1JB
Tel: 0116 262 1462 *Fax:* 0116 251 6618 *Dx:* 10838 LEICESTER 1
List of partners: M G Robinson, R P Robinson
Work: D1 G H K1 K3 L W
Emergency Action, Agency, Advocacy and Legal Aid undertaken
Ptr: Robinson, Ms Margaret G LLB . . . . *May 1971
Robinson, Mr Roderick P BJuris. . . . . *Nov 1971

ROWLEY DICKINSON
Imperial House St Nicholas Circle Leicester LE1 4LF
Office: Manchester

SFS LEGAL LTD ‡
Barkby House Barkby Road Leicester LE4 9LG
Tel: 0845 257 6470 *Fax:* 0845 257 6471
Dx: 18459 LEICESTER BELGRAVE

SAKHI SOLICITORS ‡
12 Grey Friars Leicester LE1 5PH
Tel: 0116 253 6236 *Fax:* 0116 261 9689 *Dx:* 10814 LEICESTER
Emergency telephone 07790 903583
E-mail: enquiries@sakhisolicitors.com

SALUSBURYS HARDING & BARNETT ‡
14 New Street Leicester LE1 5NE
Tel: 0116 262 9033 / 262 6052 *Fax:* 0116 253 6587
Dx: 10821 LEICESTER
E-mail: law@salusburys.co.uk
List of partners: C R Cook, J A Hawkins, R I Hilton-Tapp, J S Hunt, S McCallister
Office: Leicester, Market Harborough
Ptr: Cook, Mr Clive R LLB. . . . . *Oct 1988
Hawkins, Mr James A. . . . . *§Feb 1983
Hilton-Tapp, Mr Robert Ian LLB . . . . *Feb 1992
Hunt, Mr John S LLB(L'pool) . . . . *§Apr 1974
McCallister, Mr Steven BA Notary Public . . . . . . *Sep 1995
Ast: Dunbar, Mrs Janice K BA . . . . *Oct 1987
Garner, Mrs Joanne S LLB . . . . *Oct 1989
Popat, Mrs Tushit Anant. . . . . *May 2000
Price, Miss Carly Anne LLB . . . . *Jul 2004
Young, Miss Sandra J LLB . . . . *Oct 1988
Con: Lander, Mrs Helen A M LLB(Lond) Notary Public . . *Dec 1973

SALUSBURYS HARDING & BARNETT
3 Wycliffe Street Leicester LE1 5LR
Tel: 0116 262 6052 *Fax:* 0116 251 5048
E-mail: law@salusburys.co.uk
Office: Leicester, Market Harborough
Work: B1 C1 D1 E F1 G J1 K1 L N Q S1 S2 T1 T2 V W Z(d,i,l,r,s)
Emergency Action, Agency, Advocacy, Fixed Fee Interview, Legal Aid undertaken and Member of Accident Line

SCUTT BEAUMONT SOLICITORS LTD ‡
102 New Walk Leicester LE1 7EA
Tel: 0116 254 4200 *Fax:* 0116 254 5511 *Dx:* 17016 LEICESTER 2
E-mail: info@sbs-solicitors.co.uk
List of partners: C Beaumont, J C Bouch
Office: Ashby-de-la-Zouch, Corby
Languages: Gujarati, Hindi, Punjabi
Work: G H K1 K2 S1 W
Emergency Action, Agency, Advocacy, Fixed Fee Interview and Legal Aid undertaken
Ptr: Beaumont, Mr Clive LLB(Hons) . . . . *Mar 1988
Bouch, Mr Jeremy Clive LLB(Hons). . . . . *Nov 1988
Asoc: Cox, Miss Imogen Louise LLB. . . . . *Jul 1998
Day, Mr Roger LLB . . . . *Sep 1996
Con: Wisniewski, Mr Andrew Christopher LLB; LLM. . . . . *Apr 1990

SHAKESPEARES
108 New Walk Leicester LE1 7EA
Tel: 0116 318 3711
E-mail: info@shakespeares.co.uk
Office: Birmingham, Moreton-in-Marsh, Nottingham, Shipston-on-Stour, Stratford-upon-Avon

SHIRES DEFENCE SOLICITORS ‡
24-26 Frair Lane Leicester LE1 5RA
Tel: 0116 262 6367 *Fax:* 0116 262 6372 *Dx:* 10809 LEICESTER 1
E-mail: info@shiresdefence.co.uk

THE SMITH PARTNERSHIP
10 Pocklingtons Walk Leicester LE1 6BN
Tel: 0116 255 6292 *Fax:* 0116 255 6294
E-mail: leicestercrime@smithpartnership.co.uk
Office: Burton-on-Trent (2 offices), Derby, Leicester, Stoke-on-Trent, Swadlincote
Ptr: McGrath, Mr Kevin T LLB Notary Public. . . . . Apr 1992
Newcombe, Mr Steven C LLB. . . . . *Oct 1984
Ast: Mehta, Ms Anita. . . . . Aug 2001
Morjaria, Rakesh . . . . Sep 1998

THE SMITH PARTNERSHIP
14 York Road Leicester LE1 5TS
Tel: 0116 247 2000 *Fax:* 0116 247 2007 *Dx:* 10831 LEICESTER 1
Emergency telephone 07802 542922
E-mail: leicester@smithpartnership.co.uk
Office: Burton-on-Trent (2 offices), Derby, Leicester, Stoke-on-Trent, Swadlincote
Work: A1 B1 C1 C2 D1 E G H J1 K1 K2 L N O Q R1 S1 S2 V W Z(i,l,m)
Emergency Action, Agency, Advocacy, Fixed Fee Interview, Legal Aid undertaken and Member of Accident Line
Ptr: Hart, Mr Gordon BA. . . . . *Aug 1976
Mansfield, Ms Esther A LLB. . . . . *Sep 1991
Neate, Miss Alison LLB . . . . Apr 1993
Ast: Herring, Mr Nicholas J LLB; LLM . . . . Nov 1987

SONA SOLICITORS ‡
221 Melton Road Leicester LE4 7AN
Tel: 0116 268 2300 *Fax:* 0116 3190 736
E-mail: enquiries@sonasolicitors.co.uk

SPEARING WAITE LLP ‡
41 Friar Lane Leicester LE1 5RB
Tel: 0116 262 4225 *Fax:* 0116 251 2009 *Dx:* 10837 LEICESTER 1
E-mail: info@spearingwaite.com
List of partners: L A Atterbury, A Badley, K S Blank, T W Bower, J C Foster, K L Herbert, M J Lawrence, A Mody, A J Rowell, T P Small, M S Smith, S Somaiya, J R C Wheeler, R M Wyvill
Languages: Catalan, French, German, Italian, Polish, Spanish
Work: A1 B1 C1 C2 C3 D1 D2 E F1 F2 J1 K1 K3 L M1 N O P Q R1 R2 S1 S2 T1 U2 W Z(b,c,d,e,f,h,j,k,l,m,p,q,r,s,u,w)
Fixed Fee Interview undertaken and Member of Accident Line
Ptr: Atterbury, Ms Lindsey Ann FILEx . . . . *Oct 2000
Badley, Ms Amanda. . . . . *Aug 2001
Blank, Mrs Katherine S LLB; LLM . . . . *Oct 1989
Bower, Mr Thomas W. . . . . *Oct 1989
Foster, Mr Jonathan C LLB . . . . *Oct 1989
Herbert, Mrs Karen L BA(Law) . . . . *Jan 1984
Lawrence, Mr Michael Jeremy BA(Hons)(German Language & Linguistics) . . . . Nov 1995
Mody, Mr Ashwin . . . . *Dec 1988
Rowell, Mr Andrew James BA(Law); LSF . . . . *Nov 1991
Small, Mr Timothy P BA. . . . . *Nov 1983
Smith, Mr Martin Stockdale LLB(Hons) . . . . *Sep 2000
Somaiya, Miss Swati BA(Hons) . . . . *Jan 1998
Wheeler, Mr Jonathan R Charles BA . . . . *Feb 1997
Wyvill, Mr Richard Mark. . . . . *Aug 1994
Asoc: Ali, Mr Jahid Ahmed LLB; LLM . . . . *Sep 2004
Ast: Burlinson, Mrs Katherine Ann LLB. . . . . *Aug 2006
Clarke, Miss Jodie LLB; LPC . . . . *Aug 2010
Clarke Janene, Miss Charlotte LLB . . . . *Aug 2009
Fisher, Miss Yvonne Lyn LLB . . . . *Jun 2007
Gohel, Mrs Nisha LLB(Hons) . . . . *Sep 1999
Harrod, Mrs Alison Margaret LLB(Hons). . . . . . . *Sep 2004
Parker, Miss Hannah Louise LLB Highest Degree in Year 2007 . . . . *Mar 2011
Ravalia, Mr Kishen LLB . . . . *Jun 2007
Con: McLauchlan, Mr John Notary Public. . . . . *Jul 1964

P M SUCHAK & CO ‡
1st Floor 1 Moores Road Leicester LE4 6QR
Tel: 0116 299 0007 *Fax:* 0116 299 0009
Emergency telephone 07710 311151
List of partners: P M Suchak
Office: Harrow
Languages: Gujarati, Hindi, Kiswahili
Work: B1 E F1 J1 K1 L N O Q S1 W Z(i,l,p)
Emergency Action, Agency, Advocacy undertaken and Member of Accident Line
SPr: Suchak, Prakash M LLB. . . . . Oct 1992

SUMAL CREASEY ‡
Carlton House 28 Regent Road Leicester LE1 6YH
Tel: 0116 275 5400 *Fax:* 0116 254 9100 *Dx:* 28803 LEICESTER 2

SUMAL CREASEY SOLICITORS ‡
26 High View Close Vantage Business Park Hamilton Leicester LE4 9LJ
Tel: 0116 274 3800 *Dx:* 18462 LEICESTER BELGRAVE
E-mail: sumal@blackberry.orange.co.uk

TANNA & CO ‡
7 Loughborough Road Leicester LE4 5LJ
Tel: 0116 268 2500 *Fax:* 0116 266 4070
Dx: 18463 LEICESTER BELGRAVE
Emergency telephone 07976 949774
E-mail: tannaco7@aol.com
List of partners: D N Tanna
Languages: Gujarati, Hindi, Punjabi
Work: E F1 K1 L N O Q S1 S2 W Z(i)
Emergency Action, Agency and Advocacy undertaken
SPr: Tanna, Mr Dushyant N BA(Law). . . . . *Nov 1988

TANNAS SOLICITORS ‡
91 Blaby Road South Wigston Leicester LE18 4PB
Tel: 0116 258 1560 *Fax:* 0116 258 1568

GEOFFREY TEW & CO ‡
Granby House 173 London Road Leicester LE2 1EG
Tel: 0116 255 6200 *Fax:* 0116 247 1579 *Dx:* 28808 LEICESTER 2
E-mail: geoffrey@geoffreytew.co.uk
List of partners: G H Tew
Work: E S1 S2 W Z(c)

THALIWAL BRIDGE SOLICITORS ‡
298 Welford Road Leicester LE2 6EG
Tel: 0116 274 5252 *Fax:* 0116 274 5254
E-mail: enquiries@thaliwalbridge.co.uk

P A TODD & CO ‡
142 Evington Road Leicester LE2 1HL
Tel: 0116 273 3091 *Fax:* 0116 249 0153 *Dx:* 17008 LEICESTER 2
Languages: Gujarati, Hindi, Punjabi

VADHER & COMPANY SOLICITORS ‡
27 Friar Lane Leicester LE1 5QS
Tel: 0116 261 9122 *Fax:* 0116 251 6410
E-mail: info@vadhersolicitors.co.uk

VEJA & CO SOLICITORS
58 London Road Leicester LE2 0QD
Tel: 0116 255 5557 *Fax:* 0116 255 5456 *Dx:* 17009 LEICESTER 2
E-mail: mail@vejaandco.com
Office: Hayes, Southall

J A WALKER SOLICITOR ‡
29 St Leonards Road Leicester LE2 1WS
Tel: 0116 270 1233

WEIGHTMANS LLP
Peat House 1 Waterloo Way Leicester LE1 6LP
Tel: 0116 253 9747 *Fax:* 0116 275 8912 *Dx:* 719592 LEICESTER 17
Office: Birmingham, Dartford, Knutsford, Liverpool, London EC4, Manchester (2 offices)
Work: F1 G J1 N O Q
Agency, Advocacy and Legal Aid undertaken
Mem: Cutts, Mr Daniel S LLB . . . . *Oct 1983
Ginvert, Mrs Gloria B BA . . . . *Aug 1992
Walsh, Mr Noel F LLB. . . . . *Oct 1985

DOUGLAS WEMYSS SOLICITORS ‡
18 Friar Lane Leicester LE1 5RA
Tel: 0116 299 9199 *Fax:* 0116 299 9099 *Dx:* 10888 LEICESTER
E-mail: info@d-w-s.co.uk
List of partners: L Clegg, D M Wemyss
Languages: French, Gujarati, Hindi, Punjabi
Work: B1 D1 E F1 G H J1 K1 L N O Q R1 S1 S2 T1 T2 V W Z(d,e,h,i,k,l,m,o,p)
Agency and Advocacy undertaken
Ptr: Clegg, Mrs Linda LLB(Leics) . . . . *May 1976
Wemyss, Mr Douglas Macduff LLB(Hons). . . . . . . Dec 1984

WILSON BROWNE
(incorporating Holyoak & Co; Sherman Sykes; Parker Daker)
Priory Chambers 6 Peacock Lane Leicester LE1 5PS
Tel: 0116 251 7181 *Fax:* 0116 251 3741 *Dx:* 10826 LEICESTER 1
Emergency telephone 0116 271 5611
E-mail: enquiries@wilsonbrowne.co.uk
Office: Higham Ferrers, Kettering (2 offices), Northampton, Wellingborough
Work: A1 A3 B1 C1 C2 C3 D1 D2 E F1 F2 I J1 J2 K1 K2 L N O P Q R1 S1 S2 U2 V W X Z(c,d,e,f,h,k,l,m,p,q,r,y)
Agency, Advocacy, Fixed Fee Interview, Legal Aid undertaken, Legal Aid Franchise and Member of Accident Line
Ptr: Leslie, Kennedy U. . . . . *§Jul 1968
Neuborn, Mrs Danuta J BA(Law) . . . . *Apr 1982
Richards, Mr Paul W . . . . *§Jul 1980
Smith, Mr Christopher J LLB . . . . *§Jun 1974
Ast: Rawlins, Mr Edward J LLB . . . . *Nov 1994

ZMS SOLICITOR ‡
11 Bowling Green Street Leicester LE1 6AS
Tel: 0116 247 0790 *Fax:* 0116 255 2713 *Dx:* 10812 LEICESTER
Emergency telephone 07973 757594
E-mail: parmjit.singh@zmslegal.co.uk
Languages: Bengali, Gujarati, Hindi, Punjabi, Urdu
Work: B1 B2 E F1 G H K1 L N Q S1 V W Z(d,i,j,p)
Agency, Advocacy, Fixed Fee Interview and Legal Aid undertaken

LEIGH, Greater Manchester

BUTCHER & BARLOW LLP
(incorporating Taberners)
34 Railway Road Leigh Greater Manchester WN7 4AU
Tel: 01942 674144 *Fax:* 01942 262217 *Dx:* 22510 LEIGH
E-mail: enquiries@butcher-barlow.co.uk
Office: Bramhall, Bury (2 offices), Frodsham, Northwich, Prestwich, Runcorn (2 offices), Sandbach, Tyldesley
Languages: German
Work: A1 B1 C1 C2 C3 D1 E F1 J1 K1 K3 K4 L M1 M2 N O P Q R1 R2 S1 S2 T1 T2 V W Z(c,d,e,j,l,m,o,p,q,r,t)
Emergency Action, Agency, Advocacy, Fixed Fee Interview, Legal Aid undertaken and Legal Aid Franchise
Ptr: Aldersley, Mr Jonathan Andrew Notary Public . . . . . *Aug 2000
Ast: Appleton, Ms Susan LLB(Hons). . . . . Dec 1994

Birch, Miss Rebecca Valerie LLB . . . . Jan 2010
Whalley, Miss Sarah LLB(Hons) . . . . Jan 2011

DOOTSONS LLP ‡
(incorporating Unsworths)
61-63 Church Street Leigh Greater Manchester WN7 1AY
Tel: 01942 673431 *Dx:* 22507 LEIGH
Emergency telephone 0800 092 4848
E-mail: lawyers@dootsons.co.uk
List of partners: I Howells, A D Stockton, M A Wright
Office: Atherton, Culcheth
Work: A1 C1 D1 E J1 K1 L O R1 S1 T1 W Z(l)
Ptr: Stockton, Mr Andrew D LLB. . . . . *Mar 1984
Wright, Mrs Michele A LLB . . . . *Oct 1986

FORSTER DEAN LTD
Portland House 31 Lord Street Leigh Greater Manchester WN7 1BY
Tel: 01942 604404 *Fax:* 01942 604228
E-mail: enquiries@forsterdean.co.uk
Office: Birkenhead, Bootle, Chorley, Crewe, Eccles, Ellesmere Port, Huyton, Liverpool (5 offices), Oldham, Preston, Rochdale, Runcorn, St Helens, Stockport, Warrington, Widnes (2 offices), Wigan

HEYMAN & CO ‡
44 Church Street Leigh Greater Manchester WN7 1AZ
Tel: 01942 604135 *Fax:* 01942 261539 *Dx:* 22511 LEIGH
E-mail: heymanco@cableinet.co.uk
List of partners: K Baker, M B Caplin
Languages: French
Work: B1 C1 C3 D1 E F1 G H J1 K1 L N O Q S1 W Z(l)
Emergency Action, Agency, Advocacy, Legal Aid undertaken and Legal Aid Franchise
Ptr: Baker, Mrs Karen . . . . *Nov 1996
Caplin, Mr Michael B LLB . . . . *Dec 1977

STEPHENSONS SOLICITORS LLP ‡
24 Lord Street Leigh Greater Manchester WN7 1AB
Tel: 01942 777777 *Fax:* 01942 774383 *Dx:* 22504 LEIGH
E-mail: enquiries@stephensons.co.uk
List of partners: D Baybut, N Boland, C M Carr, R Dawson-Gerrard, M D Devlin, N J Emo, A Harrison, R Holcroft, M D Jones, S H Lewtas, C J Malone, A J Rimmer, C J Stephenson, P Stott, E M Tait, M Taylor, B S Treanor, J A Wemyss, O L E Williams, N J Yates
Office: Bolton (2 offices), Leigh, Manchester, St Helens, Wigan (2 offices)
Work: A2 A3 B1 B2 C1 C2 C3 D1 D2 E F1 F2 G H I J1 J2 K1 K2 K3 K4 L N O P Q R1 R2 S1 S2 U1 U2 V W X Z(b,c,d,e,g,h,j,l,n,p,q,r,t,u,w,y,z,za)
Agency, Advocacy, Fixed Fee Interview and Legal Aid undertaken
Ptr: Dawson-Gerrard, Mr Richard LLB . . . . Oct 1995
Ast: Brown, Ms Hannah Beth BA(Hons) . . . . *Sep 2006
Litherland, Miss Gillian Marie LLB(Hons) . . . . . . Sep 2006
Love, Mr Grahame LLB(Hons) . . . . Jan 2003
Quinn, Mr Paul Alan LLB(Hons) . . . . Mar 2007
Redmond, Mr Michael William LLB . . . . Sep 2006

STEPHENSONS SOLICITORS LLP
26 Union Street Leigh Greater Manchester WN7 1AT
Tel: 01942 777777 *Fax:* 01942 774215 *Dx:* 22504 LEIGH
Emergency telephone 07836 574607
E-mail: enquiries@stephensons.co.uk
Office: Bolton (2 offices), Leigh, Manchester, St Helens, Wigan (2 offices)
Languages: Cantonese, French, German, Hindi, Urdu
Work: A1 B1 C1 C2 C3 D1 D2 E F1 G H J1 K1 K2 L N O P Q R1 R2 S1 S2 V W X Z(c,d,e,g,h,i,k,l,q,r,t)
Emergency Action, Agency, Advocacy, Fixed Fee Interview, Legal Aid undertaken, Legal Aid Franchise and Member of Accident Line
Ptr: Emo, Ms Nicola J LLB(Hons) . . . . *Oct 1995
Lewtas, Mr Stephen H BA . . . . *Jul 1978
Stephenson, Mr Christopher J LLB . . . . *Jun 1970
Tait, Ms Elizabeth M BA; MA(Cantab) . . . . *Nov 1990
Treanor, Mr Brendan Seamus BA(Econ) . . . . Sep 1984
Wemyss, Mr James A LLB . . . . *Dec 1967
Williams, Olwen L E BJuris . . . . *Sep 1974
Ast: Choudhuri, Mr Debapriya BSc; LLB CCH Award. . . . *Apr 1994
Dillon, Ms Jane LLB(Hons) . . . . *Sep 1997
Johnson, Ms Rowena L LLB . . . . *Oct 1995
Leakey, Mr Andrew LLB . . . . *Sep 1997

TQ SOLICITORS ‡
54 Church Street Leigh Greater Manchester WN7 1AZ
Tel: 01942 671166 *Fax:* 01942 671171 *Dx:* 22508 LEIGH
E-mail: info@tqsolicitors.com
Office: Northwich

WIDDOWS MASON ‡
18-20 King Street Leigh Greater Manchester WN7 4LR
Tel: 01942 673311 *Fax:* 01942 261760 *Dx:* 22502 LEIGH 1
E-mail: info@widdows.co.uk
List of partners: J M Barnes, J S Bullough, J L Edwards, S Ferguson, K Freer, G S Jackson, M J Stockton
Office: Warrington, Westhoughton, Wigan
Work: B1 C1 C3 D1 E F1 G H J1 K1 N S1 T1 T2 W Z(c,h)
Emergency Action, Agency, Advocacy, Fixed Fee Interview, Legal Aid undertaken, Legal Aid Franchise and Member of Accident Line
Ptr: Bullough, Mr John S ♦ . . . . *§Dec 1967
Ferguson, Mrs Sharon . . . . Sep 1990
Freer, Mr Keith BA . . . . Mar 1984
Stockton, Mr Michael John LLB(Hons)(L'pool) Liverpool Law Society Prize 1993; Timpron Martin Prize 1993 . . *Oct 1995
Ast: Driscoll, Mrs Rachel. . . . . Dec 2008
Con: Calvert, Mrs Janet Ann . . . . Oct 1982

LEIGH-ON-SEA, Essex

BATES BRUNEL SOLICITORS
Thames House 1528 London Road Leigh-on-Sea Essex SS9 2QQ
Tel: 01702 472222 *Fax:* 01702 712052
Dx: 39605 HADLEIGH ESSEX
E-mail: leigh@batesnvh.co.uk
Office: Fleet, Hook (3 offices), London WC2
Work: A1 C1 E K4 L R1 S1 S2 W
Agency and Fixed Fee Interview undertaken

COOPER LINGARD ‡
Watson House Broadway West Leigh-on-Sea Essex SS9 2DA
Tel: 01702 715411 *Fax:* 01702 470029 *Dx:* 52855 LEIGH-ON-SEA
E-mail: enquiries@cooperlingard.co.uk
List of partners: S D Lanaway, R J Phillips
Work: B1 C1 C2 C3 D1 E F1 J1 K1 L N Q S1 T1 T2 V W Z(c,d,e,i,k,l,m,o)
Emergency Action, Agency, Fixed Fee Interview, Legal Aid undertaken, Legal Aid Franchise and Member of Accident Line
Ptr: Lanaway, Ms Sandra D LLB. . . . . *Feb 1991
Phillips, Mr Richard James . . . . Nov 2003

FORBES MACLEAN ‡
(incorporating Fisher Lang Forbes Mclean; Maclean Harrhy)
Aton House 149 Leigh Road Leigh-on-Sea Essex SS9 1JF
Tel: 01702 472747 *Fax:* 01702 471559 *Dx:* 52853 LEIGH-ON-SEA
E-mail: solicitor@forbesmaclean.co.uk
List of partners: G J Hilbery
Work: B1 C1 E F1 J1 L S1 S2 W Z(c)
SPr: Hilbery, Mr Graham J FILEx. . . . . *Dec 1977

MICHAEL P REYNOLDS SOLICITOR ‡
27 Dale Road Leigh-on-Sea Essex SS9 2RQ
Tel: 01702 473548 *Fax:* 01702 473548
E-mail: michaelpreynolds@btinternet.com

ALICIA R F SEDGWICK SOLICITORS ‡
15 Gordon Road Leigh-on-Sea Essex SS9 3PW
Tel: 01702 476269 *Fax:* 01702 476269
Work: K1 K2 K3 K4 S1 W

FRANCIS THATCHER & CO ‡
Victoria Chambers 44/46 Broadway Leigh-on-Sea Essex SS9 1AH
Tel: 01702 471000 *Fax:* 01702 473651 *Dx:* 52856 LEIGH-ON-SEA
E-mail: an@ftandco.fsnet.co.uk
List of partners: K E Nehammer, M A F Nehammer
Languages: French, German
Work: A3 C1 D1 E F1 J1 K1 L N O Q S1 S2 T1 T2 V W Z(c,l,r,s)
Agency, Advocacy, Fixed Fee Interview and Legal Aid undertaken
Ptr: Nehammer, Mrs Karen Elizabeth BA(Hons) Notary Public . . . . *Nov 1986
Nehammer, Mr M Anthony F BA(Lond) . . . . *Jun 1989

GILES WILSON ‡
Sutherland House 1711 London Road Leigh-on-Sea Essex SS9 2SW
Tel: 01702 477106 *Fax:* 01702 470206 *Dx:* 52858 LEIGH-ON-SEA
E-mail: info@gileswilson.co.uk
List of partners: M Giles, P Giles
Office: Rochford
Work: D1 D2 E J1 K1 K3 K4 L N O Q S1 S2 T2 W Z(c,g,m,q)
Legal Aid undertaken
Ptr: Giles, Ms Melinda. . . . . Jun 1997
Giles, Mr Philip . . . . Nov 1995

THE WRITE WILL SERVICE ‡
2 Sheppard Close Leigh-on-Sea Essex SS9 5YR
Tel: 01702 713155
E-mail: alan@writewills.co.uk

LEIGHTON BUZZARD, Bedfordshire

MARK ANDREWS ‡
17 Leopold Road Linslade Leighton Buzzard Bedfordshire LU7 7QU
Tel: 01525 371616
List of partners: M Andrews
Ptr: Andrews, Mr Mark. . . . . *Dec 1978

AUSTIN & CARNLEY ‡
Albion Chambers High Street Leighton Buzzard Bedfordshire LU7 1DP
Tel: 01525 372140 *Fax:* 01525 851554
Dx: 90805 LEIGHTON BUZZARD
E-mail: office@austinandcarnley.co.uk
List of partners: D H Backhouse, R K Dhillon, S L Rogers
Languages: Hindi, Punjabi, Urdu
Work: A1 C1 C2 E F1 G H J1 L P R1 S1 S2 W Z(p)
Emergency Action, Agency, Advocacy, Fixed Fee Interview, Legal Aid undertaken and Legal Aid Franchise
Ptr: Backhouse, Mr David Hugh ★. . . . . *May 1997
Dhillon, Miss Ravanjit Kaur LLB ★. . . . . *Oct 1992
Rogers, Mr Stephen L MA(Cantab) . . . . *§Jun 1977
Asoc: Corcut, Mr Andrew ★ . . . . *Jan 2003
Curl, Mrs Kalpana BA(Hons) . . . . *Mar 1989
Sugrue, Mr James ★ . . . . *Jan 2001

CAMERON SOLICITORS ‡
144 Hockliffe Road Leighton Buzzard Bedfordshire LU7 3JU
Tel: 01525 300370 *Fax:* 01525 300371
E-mail: ivan@cameronlaw.co.uk

FRANKLINS ‡
Church House 11 Church Square Leighton Buzzard Bedfordshire LU7 1AE
Tel: 01525 376611 *Fax:* 01525 382790
Dx: 90807 LEIGHTON BUZZARD
E-mail: info@franklinslaw.co.uk
List of partners: I L Bacon, S C Clews
Emergency Action, Agency, Advocacy, Fixed Fee Interview and Legal Aid undertaken
Ptr: Bacon, Mr Ian Leslie . . . . Dec 1975
Clews, Mr Steven Charles LLB(Lond) . . . . *Oct 1981

GIFFEN COUCH & ARCHER ‡
(incorporating Barry Hibbert & Co)
Bridge House Bridge Street Leighton Buzzard Bedfordshire LU7 1EB
Tel: 01525 372681 *Fax:* 01525 850281
Dx: 90800 LEIGHTON BUZZARD
List of partners: J D Eklund, G P Lovelock, A M Taylor
Work: A1 B1 C1 C2 C3 D1 E F1 G H J1 K1 L M1 M2 N O P Q R1 S1 T1 T2 V W Z(l)
Emergency Action, Agency, Advocacy, Fixed Fee Interview, Legal Aid undertaken and Legal Aid Franchise
Ptr: Eklund, Mr John Dylan LLB(Hons). . . . . *Nov 1989
Lovelock, Mr Graham P BA . . . . *Oct 1988
Taylor, Mr Anthony M . . . . *May 1977

MADDISON-WARD & CO ‡
Foxley Tebworth Road Leighton Buzzard Bedfordshire LU7 9QH
Tel: 01525 873274

MILLGATES SOLICITORS ‡
Orchard House 36 Orchard Drive Leighton Buzzard Bedfordshire LU7 2PL
Tel: 01525 869616
E-mail: heather.millgate@millgatewoodbridge.com

OSBORNE MORRIS & MORGAN ‡
Danbury House West Street Leighton Buzzard Bedfordshire LU7 1EP
Tel: 01525 378177 *Fax:* 01525 851006
Dx: 90804 LEIGHTON BUZZARD
Office: Milton Keynes
Work: J1 N S1 S2 W Z(r)
Legal Aid undertaken

RAY NIXON BROWN ‡
4-6 Church Square Leighton Buzzard Bedfordshire LU7 1AE
Tel: 01525 372247 *Fax:* 01525 382548
Dx: 90803 LEIGHTON BUZZARD
E-mail: info@raynixonbrown.co.uk
List of partners: S De Nisi, S C Peacock, P A D Richardson
Languages: Italian
Work: A1 B1 C1 C2 D1 E G J1 K1 L N O Q R1 S1 T2 W Z(c,d,l,p,t)
Emergency Action, Agency, Advocacy and Legal Aid undertaken
Ptr: De Nisi, Mr Stefano . . . . *Jul 1978
Peacock, Mr Simon C BA . . . . *Oct 1986
Richardson, Mr Peter A D. . . . . *Jul 1965
Ast: Brown, Mr John S MA(Cantab) . . . . *Nov 1970
Nolan, Mrs Angela J LLB(Hons). . . . . Sep 1992

ROUTH CLARKE SOLICITORS ‡
PO Box 6324 Leighton Buzzard Bedfordshire LU7 6AU
Tel: 01296 662770 / 01525 373322
E-mail: richard@rcsolicitors.co.uk

MARTIN T SMITH ‡
The Old Coach House Old Road Linslade Leighton Buzzard Bedfordshire LU7 2RB
Tel: 01525 374183 *Fax:* 01525 374183
E-mail: martintsmith@btconnect.com
List of partners: M T Smith
Languages: French
Work: E S1 S2 W
SPr: Smith, Mr Martin Tanfield Notary Public . . . . *Jun 1975

USMANI KING SOLICITORS ‡
17a Market Square Leighton Buzzard Bedfordshire LU7 1EU
Tel: 01525 377911 *Fax:* 01525 377866
E-mail: usmaniking@hotmail.com

THE WHITE DALTON PARTNERSHIP ‡
Victor House Pitstone Green Business Park Westfield Road Leighton Buzzard Bedfordshire LU7 9GW
Tel: 0800 783 6191 *Fax:* 01296 661782
Dx: 90813 LEIGHTON BUZZARD
E-mail: mail@whitedalton.co.uk
List of partners: A J Dalton
Work: G J1 N Q Z(r)
Emergency Action, Advocacy and Fixed Fee Interview undertaken
Ptr: Dalton, Mr Andrew James LLB ● . . . . *Jan 1997

LEISTON, Suffolk

FAIRWEATHER STEPHENSON & CO ‡
Old Bank Chambers 51 High Street Leiston Suffolk IP16 4EL
Tel: 01728 832832 *Fax:* 01728 830305 *Dx:* 32655 LEISTON
E-mail: info@fairweatherstephenson.co.uk
List of partners: M P Fairweather
Office: Aldeburgh
Work: B1 C1 C2 D1 E G H I J1 K1 L N O Q R1 S1 V W Z(k,l,p)
Emergency Action, Agency, Advocacy, Fixed Fee Interview, Legal Aid undertaken and Legal Aid Franchise
Ptr: Fairweather, Mr Mark P MA(Oxon) . . . . *Oct 1984

G & M B READE ‡
17 Station Road Leiston Suffolk IP16 4HD
Tel: 01728 833495

LEOMINSTER, Herefordshire

CALDICOTT GALLIMORE ‡
10 South Street Leominster Herefordshire HR6 8JB
Tel: 01568 614168 *Fax:* 01568 611437 *Dx:* 27031 LEOMINSTER
Emergency telephone 01568 612343
E-mail: lawyers@caldicotts.com
List of partners: R M Caldicott, R J Edmonds, J D Gallimore
Office: Hereford
Languages: French, Spanish
Work: A1 B1 B2 C1 D1 E G H J1 K1 K3 L R1 S1 T1 W Z(l,y)
Agency, Advocacy, Fixed Fee Interview, Legal Aid undertaken and Legal Aid Franchise
Ptr: Caldicott, Mrs Rosslyn M ★ . . . . *Feb 1972
Edmonds, Ms Rebecca Jane LLM. . . . . Jan 1992
Gallimore, Mrs Janet Denise LLB . . . . *§Feb 1979

CORNELL & CO ‡
15 South Street Leominster Herefordshire HR6 8JA
Tel: 01568 612288 *Fax:* 01568 615843 *Dx:* 27035 LEOMINSTER
List of partners: P J Cornell
Work: G H
Emergency Action, Agency, Advocacy, Fixed Fee Interview and Legal Aid undertaken
Ptr: Cornell, Mr Philip J MA(Oxon) ★ . . . . *Jan 1983

GABBS LLP
26 Broad Street Leominster Herefordshire HR6 8BS
Tel: 01568 616333 *Fax:* 01568 614013 *Dx:* 27033 LEOMINSTER
E-mail: jthacker@gabbs.biz
Office: Hay-on-Wye, Hereford
Languages: French
Work: A1 C1 C2 C3 E G K1 M1 M2 N S1 W Z(c,e)
Emergency Action, Agency, Advocacy, Legal Aid undertaken and Member of Accident Line
Ptr: Thacker, Mr John H BSc(Tech) . . . . *Jun 1985
Asoc: Vincent, Miss Anne . . . . Oct 1986
Webb, Mrs Nansi May BA. . . . . *Dec 1996
Ast: Scott, Mr Giles LLB(Hons). . . . . Jan 2006
Con: Halliwell, Mr Thomas M BA Notary Public . . . . . . *§Jun 1969

See p112 for the Key to Work Categories & other symbols

J D GALLIMORE ‡
10 Burgess Street Leominster Herefordshire HR6 8DE
Tel: 01568 616345 *Fax:* 01568 615053

HUMFRYS & SYMONDS ‡
5a Broad Street Leominster Herefordshire HR6 8BT
Tel: 01568 613612 *Fax:* 01568 610929

LLOYDS & COOPER ‡
28 South Street Leominster Herefordshire HR6 8JB
Tel: 01568 613236 *Fax:* 01568 615417 *Dx:* 27036 LEOMINSTER
E-mail: enquiries@lloydsandcooper.co.uk
List of partners: P B Bayliss, J C Cutler, D B Francis, J M Haines
Work: A1 B1 E F1 J1 L N O P Q R1 S1 S2 T1 V W Z(c,d,l,m,r,s)
Emergency Action, Advocacy, Fixed Fee Interview and Legal Aid Franchise
Ptr: Bayliss, Mr Paul B . . . . *Jan 1969
Cutler, Mr John C . . . . *Mar 1969
Francis, Mr David B LLB(Manc) . . . . *Jul 1968
Haines, Mrs Judith M LLB(B'ham) . . . . *Oct 1986
Ast: Newbould, Miss Susan BA . . . . §Oct 1982
Pimblett, Mr Timothy Hugh Sutcliffe LLB . . . . *Jan 1996
Rudge, Mr Christopher Thomas LLB . . . . Oct 1997

T A MATTHEWS
National Westminster Bank Chambers 13a Broad Street Leominster Herefordshire HR6 8TZ
Tel: 01568 615905 *Fax:* 01568 611628 *Dx:* 27034 LEOMINSTER
E-mail: r.smallwood@tamatthews.co.uk
Office: Hereford
Work: A1 B1 C1 C2 C3 E F1 G H J1 K1 L M1 M2 N P R1 S1 T1 T2 V W Z(c,d,l)
Emergency Action, Agency, Advocacy, Fixed Fee Interview, Legal Aid undertaken and Member of Accident Line
Ast: Pryce, Mrs Gillian LLB(Hons) . . . . *Sep 1989

J P PALMER SOLICITOR ‡
4 Morris Mews Leominster Herefordshire HR6 8LZ
Tel: 01568 616253 *Fax:* 0870 803 2008 *Dx:* 27046 LEOMINSTER

LETCHWORTH, Hertfordshire

BRIGNALLS BALDERSTON WARREN
Broadway Chambers Letchworth Hertfordshire SG6 3AB
Tel: 01462 482248 *Fax:* 01462 480052 *Dx:* 31302 LETCHWORTH
E-mail: enquiries@bbwlaw.biz
Office: Baldock, Biggleswade, Knebworth, Stevenage
Work: C1 C2 E K1 L R2 S1 S2 W Z(c,h)
Agency, Advocacy, Fixed Fee Interview, Legal Aid undertaken and Legal Aid Franchise
Ptr: Atkins, Ms Deborah LLB . . . . *Dec 1995
Balsom, Mr Guy LLB Notary Public . . . . *Jan 1975
Elliott, Mr John B Y LLB . . . . *Dec 1976
Goodwin, Mr Alan W LLB Broderip & Easterbrook Prize . . . . *Oct 1984
Asoc: Elliott, Mrs Alison Lara LLB . . . . Dec 2006
Strachan, Mr Duncan Anthony . . . . *Jun 1979
Wilson, Mrs Eloise V LLB . . . . *Nov 2000
Ast: Chaffee, Miss Melissa Jane LLB(Hons) . . . . Aug 2008
Yates, Mr Andrew . . . . Oct 2009
Con: Garling, Mr Victor R H MA(Cantab) Notary Public . . . . Jul 1969

MICHAEL HALL ‡
Abbeyhill Broadway Letchworth Hertfordshire SG6 3PT
Tel: 01462 674767 *Fax:* 01462 486510
E-mail: michaelhall.sol@ntlworld.com
List of partners: R M Hall
Work: C1 E K1 S1 W
Fixed Fee Interview undertaken
Ptr: Hall, Mr R Michael LLB Notary Public . . . . *Jun 1970

HECKFORD NORTON
19 Leys Avenue Letchworth Hertfordshire SG6 3EB
Tel: 01462 682244 *Fax:* 01462 673433 *Dx:* 31301 LETCHWORTH
E-mail: law2@heckfordnorton.co.uk
Office: Saffron Walden, Stevenage
Work: A1 B1 B2 C1 D1 E F1 G H J1 K1 L N P Q S1 S2 V W Z(c,j,l,t)
Emergency Action, Agency, Advocacy, Fixed Fee Interview, Legal Aid undertaken, Legal Aid Franchise and Member of Accident Line
Ptr: Purser, Mr Brian L . . . . *Jul 1975
Taylor, Mr Alan Philip BA(Keele) . . . . *Dec 1982
Con: Jordan, Mr David . . . . *Dec 1964

MARSHALL HAINES ‡
351 Norton Way South Letchworth Hertfordshire SG6 1SZ
Tel: 01462 680955 *Fax:* 01462 680965
E-mail: info@marshallhaines.com

VALLELYS ‡
27 Leys Avenue Letchworth Hertfordshire SG6 3ED
Tel: 01462 483800 *Fax:* 01462 487878 *Dx:* 31306 LETCHWORTH
E-mail: law@vallelys.co.uk
List of partners: C Vallely
Work: D1 D2 F1 K1 L Q S1 V W
Emergency Action, Agency, Advocacy, Fixed Fee Interview, Legal Aid undertaken and Legal Aid Franchise
Ptr: Vallely, Mrs Christine LLB(Hons) . . . . *Oct 1995
Ast: Pate, Miss Alison Elizabeth BA(Hons) . . . . Jun 2001
Rai, Miss Sukhvinder LLB(Hons) . . . . Jun 2001

LEVENSHULME, Greater Manchester

MUSTAFA SOLICITORS ‡
899 Stockport Road Levenshulme Greater Manchester M19 3PG
Tel: 0161 248 0400 *Fax:* 0161 248 4044
List of partners: M I Mustafa
SPr: Mustafa, Mr Mohammed I BA . . . . *Apr 1990

LEWES, East Sussex

ADAMS & REMERS ‡
Trinity House School Hill Lewes East Sussex BN7 2NN
Tel: 01273 480616 *Fax:* 01273 480618 *Dx:* 3100 LEWES 1
E-mail: lewes@adams-remers.co.uk
List of partners: R S H Illingworth, S Midha, F Nation-Dixon, A J Pawlik, D J E Platt, M R Searle, C J R Walker
Office: London SW1
Languages: French
Work: A1 B1 C1 C2 C3 E F1 J1 K1 L M1 M2 N P Q R2 S1 S2 T1 T2 W Z(d,j,l,o,q,r)
Emergency Action, Agency, Advocacy undertaken and Member of Accident Line
Ptr: Illingworth, Mr Robin S H BA(Lond) . . . . *Sep 1985
Midha, Mrs Susan . . . . Jun 1986
Nation-Dixon, Mr Francis MA(Cantab) . . . . *Apr 1983
Pawlik, Mr Andrew J . . . . Nov 1978
Platt, Mr David Joseph Ellison MA(Oxon) . . . . *Nov 1982
Searle, Mr Matthew Richard MA(Cantab) . . . . *Jan 1991
Walker, Mr Christopher J R BA(Hons) . . . . *Oct 1983
Asoc: Hoar, Ms Catherine BA(Hons)(Leeds) . . . . *Jan 1999
Mitchell, Mr Simon Kingdon BA(Hons) . . . . *Sep 1998
Stewart, Mr Douglas BA(Hons) . . . . *Nov 2000
Ast: Bowman, Mrs Suzanne Jane LLB(Hons) . . . . *Oct 1988
Cain, Ms Deborah BA(Hons); CPE; LPC Blackstone Book Prize . . . . Nov 2000
Chaloner, Mr Paul Michael . . . . Oct 1984
Davis, Mrs Samantha . . . . *Jan 2002
Gage, Mrs Katherine Elizabeth BA(Hons) . . . . *Dec 1989
Gibbins, Miss Lisa Anne LLB . . . . Mar 2005
Janaway, Mr Simon . . . . Nov 2009
Kenny, Ms Fiona Grace MA(Legal Studies) . . . . Sep 2006
Marven, Miss Nichola MA . . . . Sep 2003
Passmore, Mr Albert Edward . . . . May 1978
Richardson, Ms Amy Victoria LLB; LPC . . . . Sep 2004
Rowland, Mr Philip Douglas BA(Hons) . . . . Aug 2004
Stone, Mr Darren Charles LLB(Hons); LLM . . . . . . Oct 1997

ASTBURYS ‡
Falcon Wharf Railway Lane Lewes East Sussex BN7 2AQ
Tel: 01273 405900 *Fax:* 01273 486383
E-mail: jastbury@astburys-law.co.uk
Work: A3 B1 C1 C3 E F1 F2 I J1 J2 K3 K4 L O P Q S1 S2 U1 U2 W X Z(c,d,e,f,j,k,q)
Agency, Advocacy and Fixed Fee Interview undertaken

SANDRA BANKS SOLICITOR ‡
2 Howard House 30-31 High Street Lewes East Sussex BN7 2LU
Tel: 01273 470434
E-mail: sandrabanks@mistral.co.uk

JOSEPH N BELL ‡
The Mallings 112 Malling Street Lewes East Sussex BN7 2RJ
Tel: 01273 897377 *Fax:* 01273 400088
E-mail: josephnbell@lawyersonline.co.uk
List of partners: J N Bell
Work: B1 F1 F2 J1 L N O Q S1 T2 W Z(k,q)
Agency, Advocacy and Fixed Fee Interview undertaken
SPr: Bell, Mr Joseph Norman BA Local Conciliation Officer Law Society . . . . *Jun 1994

BLAKER SON & YOUNG ‡
211 High Street Lewes East Sussex BN7 2NL
Tel: 01273 480234 *Fax:* 01273 485111 *Dx:* 3103 LEWES 1
E-mail: legal@bs-y.co.uk
List of partners: M E Barrett, N A P Walsh
Work: A3 C1 C2 D1 D2 E F1 G J1 J2 K1 L N Q S1 S2 W Z(c)
Emergency Action, Agency, Advocacy, Legal Aid undertaken and Legal Aid Franchise
Ptr: Barrett, Mr Mark E LLB; ACIArb . . . . *Feb 1989
Walsh, Mr Nicholas A P BA; ACIArb . . . . *Oct 1987
Ast: Glenton, Miss Anna LLB; MA; MEd; PhD . . . . *Mar 1987
Wright, Miss Holly BA; LPC; PGDipLaw . . . . *Dec 2004

SARAH EDMUNDS LEGAL ‡
Castle Works Westgate Street Lewes East Sussex BN7 1YR
Tel: 01273 407970 *Fax:* 01273 474788
E-mail: sarah@sarahedmundslegal.co.uk

HORSMAN SOLICITORS LTD ‡
163 Malling Street Lewes East Sussex BN7 2RB
Tel: 01273 474743 *Fax:* 01273 474896 *Dx:* 3113 LEWES
Emergency telephone 01424 812440
E-mail: enquiries@horsmanloader.co.uk
List of partners: A Horsman
Work: G H Z(l)
Agency, Advocacy, Fixed Fee Interview, Legal Aid undertaken, Legal Aid Franchise and Member of Accident Line
Ptr: Horsman, Mr Andrew ★ . . . . *Dec 1996
Ast: Loader, Mr Anthony James ★ President of Mental Health Review Tribunal . . . . *Jan 1977

LEWES SMITH ‡
First Floor Albion House Albion Street Lewes East Sussex BN7 2NF
Tel: 01273 483455 *Fax:* 01273 486427
E-mail: info@lewessmith.co.uk
List of partners: C A Smith
Languages: French
Work: S1 S2
SPr: Smith, Mr Clive A . . . . *May 1979

MAYO WYNNE BAXTER LLP
Dial House 221 High Street Lewes East Sussex BN7 2AE
Tel: 01273 477071 *Fax:* 01273 478515 *Dx:* 3101 LEWES
E-mail: lewes@mayowynnebaxter.co.uk
Office: Brighton, East Grinstead, Eastbourne, Seaford
Languages: British Sign Language, French, German, Italian, Portuguese, Spanish
Work: A1 A3 B1 C1 C2 C3 D1 E F1 G I J1 K1 K2 L M1 M2 N O P Q R1 R2 S1 S2 T1 T2 V W Z(a,b,c,d,e,f,g,h,i,j,k,l,m,o,r,s,t,x)
Emergency Action, Agency, Advocacy, Fixed Fee Interview, Legal Aid undertaken, Legal Aid Franchise and Member of Accident Line
Ptr: Dodds, Mrs Catrina F . . . . *May 1978
Johnston, Mr Roger Under Sheriff of East & West Sussex . . . . *Jun 1972
Le May, Mr Charles S BA(Law) . . . . *Jun 1985
Randall, Mr Christopher J MSc; BA . . . . *Oct 1991
Asoc: Beeson, Mr Glen K BA . . . . *May 1980
Ast: Baillie-Hamilton, Mr Simon J . . . . *Dec 1996
Evans, Mrs Mei H LLB . . . . Oct 1988
Healy, Miss Rosamund Anne BA(Hons)(Law) . . . . . *Feb 1988
Mulcare, Mr John ACIArb; CEDR Accredited Mediator . *Jun 1962
Rice, Mr Adam M BA(Lond) . . . . *Oct 1987
Roberts, Mrs Helen Claire LLB(Wales) . . . . *Mar 1981
Sanders, Mr Nicholas J BA . . . . *Sep 1986
Con: Hillman, Mr Bryan M G MA Deputy District Judge . . . *Jun 1962
Lear, Mr Nicholas C . . . . *Jul 1967
Thomas, Mr Andrew W L BA . . . . Dec 1976

PATRICK NEWMAN & CO ‡
3 Riverdale Church Lane Lewes East Sussex BN7 2JL
Tel: 01273 479991 *Fax:* 01273 473055
E-mail: patricknewman49@hotmail.co.uk
List of partners: P M Newman
Work: E S1 S2 W
Ptr: Newman, Mr Patrick Michael MA(Oxon) . . . . *Mar 1980

BEVERLEY OGDEN & CO ‡
Howard Cottage Broomans Lane Lewes East Sussex BN7 2LT
Tel: 01273 474159 *Fax:* 01273 474159
E-mail: beverley@beverleyogden.co.uk
List of partners: B A Ogden
Work: S1 W
Agency undertaken
Ptr: Ogden, Mrs Beverley A LLB(Lond) . . . . *Nov 1980

NIGEL WELLER & CO ‡
15 Market Street Lewes East Sussex BN7 2NB
Tel: 01273 487123 *Fax:* 01273 487122
List of partners: N J Weller
Languages: French
Work: G
Emergency Action, Agency, Advocacy, Fixed Fee Interview, Legal Aid undertaken and Legal Aid Franchise
SPr: Weller, Mr Nigel John LLB ★ . . . . *Nov 1977

LEYBURN, North Yorkshire

CRITCHLEY HALL SOLICITORS ‡
The Office Golden Lion Yard Leyburn North Yorkshire DL8 5AS
Tel: 01969 625526 *Fax:* 01969 625255 *Dx:* 61331 LEYBURN

RICHARD JOHNSON & PARTNERS
7 Railway Street Leyburn North Yorkshire DL8 5EH
Tel: 01969 625577 *Fax:* 01969 625588 *Dx:* 61333 LEYBURN
Emergency telephone 01969 624311
E-mail: enquiries@rjp-leyburn.co.uk
Office: Hawes
Work: A1 B1 C1 C2 C3 D1 E F1 G H J1 K1 L M1 M2 N P R1 S1 T1 T2 V
Emergency Action, Agency, Advocacy, Fixed Fee Interview and Legal Aid undertaken
Ptr: Mochrie, Mr Geoffrey C BA . . . . *Jul 1978

SCOTTS WRIGHT ‡
34 Market Place Leyburn North Yorkshire DL8 5AP
Tel: 01966 22227 *Fax:* 01969 624023 *Dx:* 61330 LEYBURN
E-mail: enquiries@scottswright.com
List of partners: I C Scott, M W Scott
Office: Catterick Garrison, Hawes
Work: A1 C1 D1 D2 E G H J1 K1 K3 K4 L N Q R1 S1 S2 T1 T2 W
Emergency Action, Agency, Advocacy, Fixed Fee Interview, Legal Aid undertaken and Legal Aid Franchise
Ptr: Scott, Mr Ian C BA . . . . *Dec 1974
Ast: Butterworth, Mrs Frances Amanda . . . . Nov 2010
Marsden, Miss Stephanie Kate LLB . . . . Sep 2009

LEYLAND, Lancashire

ASCROFT RAE ‡
67 Hough Lane Leyland Lancashire PR25 2SA
Tel: 01772 434488 *Fax:* 01772 453695 *Dx:* 20202 LEYLAND
E-mail: chrisrae06@aol.com
List of partners: C W Rae
Work: S1 W
SPr: Rae, Mr Christopher William BA . . . . *Jul 1979

BIRCHALL BLACKBURN LLP
4 Hough Lane Leyland Lancashire PR25 2SD
Tel: 01772 433775 *Fax:* 01772 427718 *Dx:* 20214 LEYLAND
Office: Chester, Chorley, Formby, Manchester, Morecambe, Preston (2 offices), Southport

CHADWICKS SOLICITORS ‡
9-11 Towngate Leyland Lancashire PR25 2EN
Tel: 01772 424080 *Fax:* 01772 424070 *Dx:* 20208 LEYLAND

G H LEE & CO ‡
The Croft 70 Moss Lane Leyland Lancashire PR25 4SH
Tel: 01772 424383 *Fax:* 01772 451061
E-mail: ghleeacb@aol.com

LEE RIGBY PARTNERSHIP ‡ (incorporating Wood Clayton & Lee; Mark Rigby & Co; Lee & Co)
Beech House Lancastergate Leyland Lancashire PR25 2EX
Tel: 01772 421748 *Fax:* 01772 457346 *Dx:* 20201 LEYLAND
Emergency telephone 07860 650364
E-mail: info@leerigby.co.uk
List of partners: J Kerrigan, S C Lloyd, M Rigby, J D Roberts
Work: B1 C1 C2 D1 E F1 G H J1 K1 K2 L N O Q R1 S1 S2 T1 T2 V W Z(l)
Emergency Action, Agency, Advocacy, Fixed Fee Interview, Legal Aid undertaken and Legal Aid Franchise
Ptr: Kerrigan, Mrs Jacqueline LLB; FILEx . . . . *Dec 1991
Lloyd, Mr Simon Christopher MSc; BSc(Hons) . . . . . *Jun 2000
Rigby, Mr Mark LLB . . . . §Jun 1977
Roberts, J D LLB(Lond) . . . . *Oct 1986
Asoc: Moss, Miss Julie Diane LLB; LPC . . . . *Feb 2009
Ast: Farry, Miss Geraldine LLB(Hons) . . . . Nov 1990
Kerrigan, Miss Amanda . . . . Sep 1998
McCormick, Mrs Allison LLB; BA(Hons) . . . . *Feb 2009

SOLICITOR DIRECT ‡
71 Hough Lane Leyland Lancashire PR25 2SA
Est: 1994
Tel: 01772 424999 *Fax:* 01772 433230 *Dx:* 20206 LEYLAND
Emergency telephone 01772 421582
E-mail: enquiries@solicitordirect.com
List of partners: D B Forrest, M Jones
Work: D1 G H K1 N S1 V W
Emergency Action, Agency, Advocacy and Fixed Fee Interview undertaken
Ptr: Forrest, Mr Derek Bradshaw LLB(Hons) ♦ . . . . *Nov 1972
Jones, Mr Matthew ♦ . . . . Jan 2005

LICHFIELD, Staffordshire

ADCOCKS SOLICITORS LTD ‡
Chancery House 27 Lombard Street Lichfield Staffordshire WS13 6DP
Tel: 0845 470 8081 *Fax:* 0845 470 8082 *Dx:* 19003 LICHFIELD
E-mail: info@adcocks.com
List of partners: M H Adcock
Office: West Bromwich
Languages: Hindi, Mirpuri, Punjabi, Urdu, Welsh
Work: C1 E L R1 S1 S2 W
Ptr: Adcock, Mr Mark H TEP Broderip & Easterbrook Prize . . . *§Dec 1985
Ast: Hardwick, Mr Roger Alistair BA(Hons)(History); GDL; LPC . . . Jun 2008

ANSONS LLP ‡
St Marys Chambers 5-7 Breadmarket Street Lichfield Staffordshire WS13 6LQ
Tel: 01543 263456 *Fax:* 01543 250942 *Dx:* 19004 LICHFIELD
List of partners: A Cooksley, S E A Heath, J F Helliwell, C P Kitto, B A Middlecote
Office: Cannock
Work: A1 B1 C1 C2 C3 D1 E F1 G H J1 K1 L M1 M2 N O P Q R1 S1 T1 T2 V W Z(c,h,i,l,m,p,q)
Emergency Action, Agency, Advocacy, Fixed Fee Interview, Legal Aid undertaken, Legal Aid Franchise and Member of Accident Line
SPr: Kitto, Mr Christopher Paul LLB Clerk to General Commissioner of Taxes . . . *§Jun 1972
Ptr: Cooksley, Mrs Amanda LLB(Hons) . . . *Oct 1995
Heath, Miss Sarah E A LLB . . . Sep 2000
Helliwell, Ms Jane F BA . . . *Aug 1984
Middlecote, Mr Brian A LLB . . . *Jun 1974
Ast: Cole, Mr Alan John BA; LLB School Governor . . . Mar 1990
Howdle, Mrs Nicola Jo . . . Jan 2006

BRADIN TRUBSHAW & KIRWAN SOLICITORS LLP ‡
Cathedral House 5 Beacon Street Lichfield Staffordshire WS13 7AA
Tel: 01543 421840

CARS SOLICITORS ‡
Bridge House Upper St John Street Lichfield Staffordshire WS14 9DT
Tel: 01543 303450 *Fax:* 01543 303460

COUNTRYWIDE CONVEYANCING DIRECT
4 Friary Court 13 St John Street Lichfield Staffordshire WS13 6NU
Tel: 01543 302223 *Fax:* 01543 302229
Office: Wirral

HCB SOLICITORS
Mill House 38 Dam Street Lichfield Staffordshire WS13 6AA
Tel: 01543 414426 *Fax:* 01543 250623 *Dx:* 19006 LICHFIELD
Office: Alcester, Redditch, Solihull, Stratford-upon-Avon, Walsall
Work: A1 B1 C1 C2 E F1 J1 K1 L N O Q R1 S1 S2 T1 T2 W
Emergency Action, Agency, Advocacy, Fixed Fee Interview and Legal Aid undertaken
Ptr: Dean, Ms Michelle S LLB(Leics) . . . *Sep 2002
Taylor, Mr Richard D LLB(Leeds) . . . *Dec 1966
Ast: Brown, Ms Sally Louise BA(Hons) . . . Aug 2004

HINCKLEY BIRCH & BROWN ‡
20 St John Street Lichfield Staffordshire WS13 6PD
Tel: 01543 262491 *Fax:* 01543 254986
E-mail: enquiries@hinckleybich.co.uk

KEELYS LLP ‡
28 Dam Street Lichfield Staffordshire WS13 6AA
Tel: 01543 420000 *Fax:* 01543 258469 *Dx:* 744930 LICHFIELD
E-mail: office@keelys.co.uk
List of partners: J A Chisholm, D J Keane, S Lawrence, J A W Parkes, M J G Phillips, J E Primmer, P K Roberts, D Williams, T Wright
Office: London EC2
Work: B1 B2 C1 C2 C3 E F1 F2 I J1 K1 K2 L M1 O Q R1 R2 S1 S2 T1 T2 W Z(b,c)
Agency and Fixed Fee Interview undertaken
Ptr: Chisholm, Mr James Alexander . . . Mar 1998
Keane, Mr Daniel J LLB . . . *Nov 1988
Lawrence, Ms Sharon . . . *Sep 1990
Parkes, Mr John A W BA(Cantab) . . . *§Dec 1980
Phillips, Mr Michael J G BA(Cantab) . . . *Oct 1986
Primmer, Mr John E LLB . . . *§Jan 1970
Roberts, Mr Paul Keeling . . . Sep 1999
Williams, Mr David . . . Mar 1984
Wright, Mr Trevor . . . May 1981
Asoc: McGauley, Mr Andrew J BA . . . *May 1978
Merry, Mrs Melissa Joy LLB . . . *Oct 1989
Spivey, Mr Justin Robert BA . . . Feb 1997
Ast: Pearshouse, Miss Jill LLB . . . *Jul 2001
Con: Keely, Mr Stephen M . . . *§Jan 1966
Smith, Mr John E MA(Cantab) . . . *§Oct 1967

MOSELEYS ‡
Compton House 18 Bore Street Lichfield Staffordshire WS13 6LL
Tel: 01543 414100 *Fax:* 01543 253721 *Dx:* 19025 LICHFIELD
Emergency telephone 01543 432002
E-mail: enq@moseleys.co.uk
List of partners: S A Atack, M B Cox, J F Cunningham, V J Ellis, A Hunter, J M W Smith
Work: A1 B1 C1 C2 D1 E F1 J1 K1 L N P Q R1 S1 S2 T1 V W Z(c,d,e,h,j,k,l,m,q,t)
Emergency Action, Agency, Advocacy, Fixed Fee Interview, Legal Aid undertaken, Legal Aid Franchise and Member of Accident Line
Ptr: Atack, Mrs Sarah A LLB . . . May 1998
Cox, Mr Martin Beaumont LLB . . . *Jul 1975
Cunningham, Mr Jonathan Frazer LLB . . . *Oct 2001
Ellis, Miss Victoria Jane LLB . . . Sep 2001
Hunter, Mrs Audrey LLB . . . *Mar 1984
Smith, Mr Jonathan M W LLB(B'ham) . . . *Dec 1979
Con: Heslop, Mr Robin M LLB(Lond) . . . *Jun 1969

G S SIRA ‡
33 Market Street Lichfield Staffordshire WS13 6LA
Tel: 01543 254382 / 254383 *Fax:* 01543 253713
List of partners: G S Sira
Languages: Hindi, Kiswahili, Punjabi, Urdu
Work: C1 E F1 G H K1 L M1 P S1 V W Z(i,j,p)
Agency and Legal Aid undertaken
Ptr: Sira, Gurmit S BA Notary Public . . . *Jul 1974

SOUTHWELL MOTT ‡
25 Lombard Street Lichfield Staffordshire WS13 6DP
Tel: 01543 252102 / 251484 *Fax:* 01543 253316
Dx: 19014 LICHFIELD
E-mail: jmott@southwellmott.co.uk
List of partners: E B J Mott, J C Mott
Work: A1 B1 C1 D1 E F1 J1 K1 K2 L N P Q S1 V W Z(c,d,i,j,l,m,t)
Emergency Action, Agency, Advocacy and Fixed Fee Interview undertaken
Ptr: Mott, Ms Elizabeth B J . . . *Dec 1970
Mott, Mr Jonathan Charles . . . *Dec 1973

LINCOLN, Lincolnshire

ADIE O'REILLY LLP ‡
3 The Landings Burton Waters Lincoln Lincolnshire LN1 2TU
Tel: 01522 577088 *Fax:* 01522 577099 *Dx:* 724523 LINCOLN 12

ANDREW & CO LLP ‡
St Swithin's Court 1 Flavian Road Nettleham Road Lincoln Lincolnshire LN2 4GR
Tel: 01522 512123 *Fax:* 01522 518913 *Dx:* 743960 LINCOLN 18
E-mail: info@andrew-solicitors.co.uk
List of partners: P J Armitage, J M Bailey, D J Hollingworth, C P Hoskins, C C G Hunter, H Newson, M J Pace, A C Short, C M A Wheeler
Office: Newark
Languages: French, German
Work: A1 A3 B1 C1 C2 C3 D2 E F1 F2 J1 J2 K1 K2 K3 K4 L N O P Q R1 S1 S2 T1 T2 U2 W X Z(c,d,e,h,l,q,t)
Emergency Action, Agency, Advocacy, Fixed Fee Interview undertaken and Member of Accident Line
Ptr: Bailey, Mrs Julie M LLB . . . Sep 1988
Hollingworth, Mr David J . . . *§Mar 1974
Hoskins, Mr Charles P LLB . . . *§Mar 1978
Hunter, Mr Charles C G . . . *§Feb 1973
Newson, Ms Helen LLB . . . *§Nov 1997
Pace, Mr Michael John DipLP . . . *§Oct 1994
Short, Mrs Alison Christine LLB . . . *Apr 1979
Wheeler, Miss Catriona Mary Ann LLB . . . *§Oct 1989
Ast: Barton, Helen . . . Feb 2007
Davidson, John . . . Dec 1973
Jolliff, Mrs Deborah C MA . . . *Oct 1990
Shaw, Helen . . . Nov 1993
Simson, Carrie . . . Oct 2005
Smith, Kathryn . . . Jun 2007
Con: Tilley, Ms Jessica . . . Oct 2001

BRIDGE MCFARLAND
1-9 Tentercroft Street Lincoln Lincolnshire LN5 7DB
Tel: 01522 518888 *Fax:* 01522 534728 *Dx:* 701683 LINCOLN 5
E-mail: info@bmcf.co.uk
Office: Grimsby (3 offices), Hull, Louth, Mablethorpe, Market Rasen, Skegness
Work: A1 A3 B1 B2 C1 C2 C3 D1 D2 E F1 F2 G H J1 K1 L M1 M2 M3 N O P Q R1 R2 S1 S2 T1 T2 V W X Z(a,c,l,m,p,q,r)
Emergency Action, Agency, Advocacy, Fixed Fee Interview, Legal Aid undertaken and Legal Aid Franchise
Ptr: Doughty, Mr Jonathan Charles BSc(Hons) . . . *Sep 1997
Parnell, Mr Richard John BA(Hons) . . . Sep 1999
Roebuck, Mrs Kathryn A E LLB . . . *Oct 1983
Skelton, Ms Jacqueline R LLB(Hons) . . . Nov 1990
Taylor, Mr Patrick J . . . *Oct 1996
Asoc: Harris, Mrs Bernadette A LLB(Hons) . . . Oct 1983

BURTON & CO LLP ‡
Stonebow Lincoln Lincolnshire LN2 1DA
Tel: 01522 523215 *Fax:* 01522 536902 *Dx:* 11003 LINCOLN 1
E-mail: inmail@burtonlaw.co.uk
List of partners: J E Brennan, R F Elmer, C Emery, P M Matthews, L J Robinson
Office: Sleaford
Work: A1 A2 A3 B1 B2 C1 C2 D1 D2 E F1 F2 G H J1 J2 K1 K2 L M1 N O P Q R1 R2 S1 S2 T2 U1 V W X Z(c,d,g,h,i,j,k,l,m,p,q,s,t,u,w,x)
Emergency Action, Agency, Advocacy, Fixed Fee Interview, Legal Aid undertaken and Member of Accident Line
Ptr: Brennan, Ms Judith E BA(Hons)(Law) ★ . . . *Oct 1987
Elmer, Mr Richard F . . . *§Jun 1974
Emery, Ms Carolyn LLB(Hons)(Law & Politics) . . . *Sep 1999
Robinson, Ms Lesley Jayne . . . Jan 1996
Asoc: Booth, Ms Nicola BA(Hons) . . . *Dec 2001
Elmer, Mrs Alison E . . . *Nov 1978
Gibbons, Mrs Claire Ellen . . . *Jan 2000
Kerrigan, Mr Andrew . . . May 2004

ANTHONY CARROLL & CO ‡
13 Beaumont Fee Lincoln Lincolnshire LN1 1UH
Tel: 01522 544017 *Fax:* 01522 532209 *Dx:* 716711 LINCOLN 9
E-mail: ajc@acarroll.co.uk
List of partners: A J Carroll
Agency, Legal Aid undertaken and Member of Accident Line
Ptr: Carroll, Mr Anthony J LLB . . . May 1980

CHATTERTONS SOLICITORS
2 Low Moor Road Lincoln Lincolnshire LN6 3JY
Tel: 01522 814600 *Fax:* 01522 814601
E-mail: lincoln@chattertons.com
Office: Boston (2 offices), Grantham, Horncastle, Newark, Sleaford, Spalding, Stamford
Languages: British Sign Language, French, German, Punjabi
Work: A1 B1 C1 C2 C3 D1 E F1 F2 G H J1 K1 L M1 M2 N O P Q R1 S1 S2 T1 T2 V W X Z(c,d,e,j,k,l,q)
Emergency Action, Advocacy, Fixed Fee Interview, Legal Aid undertaken, Legal Aid Franchise and Member of Accident Line
Ptr: Attfield, Ms Sophie . . . Nov 1993
Mockford, Ms Caroline F LLB . . . *Dec 1986
Speed, Miss Jane L BA . . . *Sep 1990
Wellman, Mr Derek M MA(Cantab) Notary Public . . . *Jun 1969
Ast: Clement, Ms Emma . . . Jan 2004

ANTHONY CLARK & CO ‡
16a Guildhall Street Lincoln Lincolnshire LN1 1TT
Tel: 01522 512321 *Fax:* 01522 538892 *Dx:* 701682 LINCOLN 5
Emergency telephone 01522 524287
List of partners: M Bentley, D J Ford, L M Kellett, C J Morgan, S W Paris, R Russell, W M Stevens
Work: A1 B1 C1 D1 E F1 G H J1 K1 K2 K3 L M1 N P R1 R2 S1 S2 T1 V W Z(b,c,d,j,l,m,o,s,t)
Emergency Action, Advocacy, Legal Aid undertaken, Legal Aid Franchise and Member of Accident Line
Ptr: Bentley, Mr Michael BA(Hons) . . . Aug 1996
Ford, Mr David J LLB . . . *Nov 1974
Kellett, Miss Lisa Margaret LLB . . . *Oct 1994
Morgan, Mrs Carole J BA . . . *Nov 1986
Paris, Mr Stuart W . . . *Jan 1972
Stevens, Ms Wendy Mary . . . *Dec 1997
Asoc: Marshall, Miss Alison LLB(Hons) . . . Dec 1999
Ast: Redman, Ms Sheila Elizabeth Marie LLB . . . Jul 2005

DALE & CO SOLICITORS LINCOLN ‡
(incorporating S E James)
11 Beaumont Fee Lincoln Lincolnshire LN1 1UH
Tel: 01522 513399 *Fax:* 01522 530589 *Dx:* 716710 LINCOLN 9
E-mail: mail@dale-law.co.uk
List of partners: G Corby, R A Dale
Languages: French, German
Work: B1 C1 D1 D2 E F1 G H J1 K1 K3 K4 O Q S1 S2 W Z(g,m)
Agency, Advocacy, Fixed Fee Interview and Legal Aid undertaken
Dir: Corby, Mrs Georgia LLB(Hons) . . . *Dec 2003
Dale, Mr Richard A BA(Essex) . . . *Mar 1982
Ast: Welbourn, Mrs Nicola Leanne BA(Hons) . . . *Nov 2008
Wise, Mr Nicholas M LLB(Hons) . . . *Jan 1972

DOWNES & SIDDALL ‡
16 West Parade Lincoln Lincolnshire LN1 1JT
Tel: 01522 543343 *Fax:* 01522 538893 *Dx:* 716712 LINCOLN 9
E-mail: reception@downes-siddall.co.uk
List of partners: P R C Downes
Work: A1 B1 C1 D1 D2 E F1 J1 K1 K3 L N O Q R1 S1 S2 V W X Z(c,h,q)
Emergency Action, Agency, Advocacy, Fixed Fee Interview, Legal Aid undertaken and Legal Aid Franchise
Ptr: Downes, Mr Peter Robert C LLB(Leeds) . . . *Jun 1983
Asoc: Brooks, Miss Sally Jane BA . . . *Sep 2005
Ast: Sanderson, Mrs Paula E BA(Hons)(Law) . . . *Apr 1978

DIANE GENDERS SOLICITORS ‡
Resolution House Crusader Road Lincoln Lincolnshire LN6 7AS
Tel: 01522 516500 *Fax:* 01522 516509
Dx: 700676 NORTH HYKEHAM
E-mail: enquiries@dianegenders.co.uk
Office: Nottingham

JGQC SOLICITORS ‡
The Chambers 22 The Green Lincoln Lincolnshire LN2 2NR
Tel: 01522 595441

JSP SOLICITORS ‡
1 Riseholme Road Lincoln Lincolnshire LN1 3SN
Tel: 01522 537353

ANDREW JAY & CO
8 West Parade Lincoln Lincolnshire LN1 3BN
Tel: 01522 539111 *Dx:* 716715 LINCOLN 9
Office: Gainsborough

LANGLEYS ‡
Olympic House Doddington Road Lincoln Lincolnshire LN6 3SE
Tel: 01522 888555 *Fax:* 01522 888556
Dx: 700678 NORTH HYKEHAM 2
E-mail: info@langleys.com
List of partners: S Baylis, H G Brown, F J M Buckton, J Conlon, T Cross, M Day, H M Edwards, A Fearn, R C Foyster, D A Garfitt, K Hindmarch, P J Horner, R Howitt, W Jones, A Kay, R Mackle, C R Price, R Ripley, S Robinson, K Saunders, G S Scott, J Scott, G Stenson, R Taylor, D J Thompson, D Tonge, J Towler, E Warner, D Wood
Office: Newark, York
Languages: Dutch, Norwegian
Work: B1 C1 E L N O Q
Agency undertaken
Ptr: Conlon, Mr John BA(Hons); LLM . . . *Apr 1997
Edwards, Mr Huw M LLB . . . *Feb 1990
Fearn, Mr Andrew . . . Mar 1976
Foyster, Mr Robin C . . . *Dec 1988
Hindmarch, Ms Kate . . . Oct 1995
Horner, Mr Peter J BA(Law) . . . *Oct 1986
Price, Mr Christopher R LLB . . . *Feb 1986
Robinson, Mrs Sally-Ann LLB . . . *Nov 1982
Saunders, Mrs Kathryn BA(Hons) . . . *Nov 1983
Stenson, Mr Graeme . . . Oct 1989
Tonge, Mr David LLB(Hons)(Business Law) . . . *Oct 1991
Wood, Mr David LLB . . . *Sep 1996
Asoc: Vandale, Ms Francoise LLB . . . Oct 1997

MCKINNELLS ‡
17-23 West Parade Lincoln Lincolnshire LN1 1NW
Tel: 01522 541181 *Fax:* 01522 513764 *Dx:* 716714 LINCOLN 9
E-mail: enquiries@mckinnells.co.uk
List of partners: V L Cohen, J L Costall, R G Hare, J Hazel, P D Smith, V A Watson
Languages: Polish, Swedish
Work: A1 B1 B2 C1 C2 C3 D1 D2 E F1 F2 G H J1 J2 K1 K2 K3 K4 L M1 M2 N O P Q R1 S1 S2 T1 T2 V W X Z(c,d,l,o,p,q)
Emergency Action, Agency, Advocacy, Fixed Fee Interview, Legal Aid undertaken and Legal Aid Franchise
Ptr: Cohen, Ms Victoria L LLB(Hons) . . . *Sep 1993
Costall, Miss Joanne Louise LLB(Hons) . . . *Sep 1997
Hare, Mr Richard G LLB(Hons) . . . *§Jun 1975
Hazel, Mr James . . . *Jan 2008
Smith, Mr Paul D LLB ★ Deputy Coroner . . . *Nov 1985
Watson, Mrs Valerie Anne FILEx . . . *Nov 2002
Asoc: Atkinson, Mr Justin Lee BA(Hons) ★ . . . *Apr 2002
Drakes, Mrs Cindy Ann LLB(Hons) . . . Oct 1995
Elkington, Mrs Lisa Marie LLB; LPC . . . Mar 2011
Freitas, Mr Anthony Adam Gerald LLB(Hons) . . . *Nov 2006
Jones, Miss Katherine Ann LLB(Hons) . . . Jul 2011
Lagergren, Miss Sofia Alexandra LLB(Hons) . . . Jan 2010
Roper, Mr John BA(Hons) . . . *Jan 2004
Soo, Miss Sarah Siew-Lin LLB(Hons) . . . Sep 2008
Con: Collingham, Mr Stuart J MA(Cantab) ● . . . *Jun 1976

N B LAW ‡
18 High Street Tattershall Lincoln Lincolnshire LN4 4LE
Tel: 01526 344858 *Fax:* 01526 345820

ON DEMAND LAWYERS LTD ‡
7 Marine Point Marine Approach Burton Waters Lincoln Lincolnshire LN1 2LW
Tel: 01522 806386 *Fax:* 020 8610 4800
E-mail: info@ondemandlawyers.co.uk

See p112 for the Key to Work Categories & other symbols

PAGE NELSON ‡
(incorporating Page & Co; Nelson Wright & Walker)
5 Lindum Road Lincoln Lincolnshire LN2 1NX
Tel: 01522 531741 *Fax:* 01522 529120 *Dx:* 11015 LINCOLN 1
E-mail: enquiries@pagenelson.co.uk
Work: A1 C1 D1 D2 E G H J1 K1 L N Q S1 S2 W Z(c,l)

THE RINGROSE LAW GROUP - RICHARD HARWOOD
(incorporating Adie Pickwell; Frost Gunning & Co; Grocock & Staniland)
Langton House Lindum Business Park Station Road Lincoln Lincolnshire LN6 3FE
Tel: 01522 814700 *Fax:* 01522 814799
Dx: 743380 NORTH HYKEHAM 2
E-mail: richard.harwood@ringroselaw.co.uk
Office: Boston, Grantham, Lincoln, Newark, Sleaford, Spalding
Languages: French, German, Hindi, Punjabi
Work: A1 A3 B1 B2 C1 C2 C3 D1 D2 E F1 F2 G H J1 J2 K1 K2 L M1 N O P Q R1 S1 S2 T1 T2 W X Z(c,d,g,h,i,j,k,l,m,n,p,q,r,s,t,z)
Emergency Action, Agency, Advocacy, Fixed Fee Interview, Legal Aid undertaken, Legal Aid Franchise and Member of Accident Line
Ptr: Clark, Mr Andrew John MA(Oxon). . . . . *§Apr 1976
Hanby, Mr Philip LLB(Lond) . . . . . *Dec 1974
Khanna, Mr Sunil LLB(Hons) . . . . . *Dec 1993
Pickwell, Ms Christine E BA . . . . . *Mar 1984
Stenson, Mr Graeme W BA(Hons). . . . . *Oct 1989
Asoc: Appleby, Mr Luke Justin LLB(Hons) . . . . . Mar 2002
Ast: Glover, Leanne . . . . . Nov 2006
Jackson, Miss Sarah Mary LLB(Hons). . . . . *Aug 2000
Willcox, Mr Robert F LLB . . . . . *Jan 1986

THE RINGROSE LAW GROUP
St Peter at Arches Silver Street Lincoln Lincolnshire LN2 1EA
Tel: 01522 561020 *Fax:* 01522 561049 *Dx:* 11006 LINCOLN 1
E-mail: sarah.jackson@ringroselaw.co.uk
Office: Boston, Grantham, Lincoln, Newark, Sleaford, Spalding
Ast: Welburn, Jane . . . . . Mar 2007

SILLS & BETTERIDGE LLP ‡
46 Silver Street Lincoln Lincolnshire LN2 1ED
Tel: 01522 542211 *Fax:* 01522 510463 *Dx:* 11025 LINCOLN 1
Emergency telephone 07766 110621 (CRIME & MENTAL HEALTH ONLY)
E-mail: info@sillslegal.co.uk
List of partners: I D Baker, K Bower-Brown, B Brickles, R Bussell, E Capes, I S Clarke, Y Clarke, H Derry, A Durkan, M Hayes, T Higham, A Hurton, S Jaehrig, C Johnson, E Lawler, R Maclean, R J Marshall, M McNeil, J E Mitchell, A G Payne, G I Phillips, E A Sharpe, W C Spalding-Siracusa, D P Stapleton, M K Straw, S W Swift, R Tinn, M Walsh, S R Wilson, A C Woods
Office: Boston, Coningsby, Gainsborough, Skegness, Sleaford, Spalding, Spilsby
Languages: French, Spanish
Work: A1 A2 B1 B2 C1 C2 C3 D1 D2 E F1 F2 G H I J1 J2 K1 K2 K3 K4 L M1 N O P Q R1 R2 S1 S2 T1 T2 U2 V W X Z(b,c,d,e,g,h,i,k,l,m,o,p,q,r,s,t,u,w,za)
Emergency Action, Agency, Advocacy, Fixed Fee Interview, Legal Aid undertaken, Legal Aid Franchise and Member of Accident Line
Ptr: Baker, Mr Ian D. . . . . *§Dec 1979
Bower-Brown, Mrs Karen BA; LLB. . . . . *Oct 1988
Bussell, Mr Richard LLB. . . . . *Feb 2001
Capes, Mr Edward LLB(Hons); Licence en Droit. . . . . Sep 2003
Derry, Mrs Helen LLB . . . . . *Nov 1994
Durkan, Mr Andrew BA(Hons). . . . . *Sep 1997
Higham, Mr Tim. . . . . Mar 2006
Hurton, Mrs Alison BA(Law). . . . . Feb 1999
Jaehrig, Mrs Shan FILEx; CPE . . . . . Jan 1994
Lawler, Mrs Emma LLB(Hons). . . . . *Jan 2005
McNeil, Mr Mark LLB(Hons). . . . . *Apr 2004
Marshall, Mr Richard J LLB; LLM Deputy District Judge; Assistant Deputy District Coroner . . . . . *Jun 1975
Mitchell, Mr John E BA(Oxon). . . . . *§Oct 1983
Payne, Mr Andrew G LLB(Leeds) . . . . . *§Mar 1978
Phillips, Mr Gary I MA(Oxon) Notary Public . . . . . *§Oct 1989
Sharpe, Mr Edward Adrian BSc(Hons); LLB(Hons) . . . Sep 2008
Spalding-Siracusa, Mrs Wendy Christina BA(Hons) . . . Nov 1991
Walsh, Mr Martin . . . . . Aug 1984
Wilson, Mr Stephen R BA Deputy District Judge. . . . *§Jul 1981
Woods, Mr Anthony C LLB . . . . . Sep 1984
Asoc: Brownless, Mr Dale Burt Cavell LLB(Hons) . . . . . Oct 2004
Wilson, Miss Anna Elizabeth BA(Hons)(Law & European Culture & Society). . . . . Aug 2008
Ast: Breeden, Mr Simon . . . . . Sep 2011
Curtis, Miss Jennifer. . . . . Sep 2010
McGill, Mr Malachy LLB. . . . . Dec 2006
McLaughlin, Mr Euan . . . . . Oct 2011
Miller, Mr William Frankton LLB(Nott'm) . . . . . Jan 1969
Milns, Mr Christopher David Arkley . . . . . *Oct 2009

Other offices in Boston, Coningsby, Gainsborough, Sleaford, Spalding, Spilsby. Holders of Franchise for Crime, Mental Health, Personal Injury, Family, Actions Against the Police. We conduct business in French, Spanish. We specialise in the following areas of work Commercial and Company Law, Family Law, Wills, Trusts and Probate.

WHITE & CO ‡
20 Cornhill Lincoln Lincolnshire LN5 7HB
Tel: 01522 548400 *Fax:* 01522 569227
E-mail: info@whiteandco.com

WILKIN CHAPMAN EPTON BLADES
The Maltings 11-15 Brayford Wharf East Lincoln Lincolnshire LN5 7AY
Tel: 01522 512345 *Fax:* 01522 545803 *Dx:* 11008 LINCOLN 1
E-mail: eboyd@wilkinchapman.co.uk
Office: Alford, Beverley, Grimsby (3 offices), Horncastle, Louth, Mablethorpe, Market Rasen, Sutton-on-Sea
Work: A1 A3 B1 B2 C1 C2 C3 D1 E F1 F2 G H J1 J2 K1 K2 L N O P Q R1 R2 S1 S2 T1 T2 V W X Z(b,e,g,k,l,m,p,q,r,s,y)
Emergency Action, Agency, Advocacy, Fixed Fee Interview, Legal Aid undertaken, Legal Aid Franchise and Member of Accident Line
Ptr: Blades, Mr Gilbert T ●. . . . . *§Jun 1964
Boileau, Mrs Lisa Michelle LLB(Hons). . . . . *Sep 1994
Burn, Mr Nigel M E LLB ★. . . . . *Jul 1977
Butcher, Mr Tean Miles BSc. . . . . *Apr 1993
Eke, Mr Russell John LLB Newsome Vaughan Prize. . *Dec 1992
Holt, Mr Andrew David LLB . . . . . *Nov 1990
Howes, Mrs Lisa-Jane BSc . . . . . *Sep 1996
Krick, Mr Peter S BA . . . . . *Oct 1985
Lloyd, Mr James MA(Cantab) . . . . . *Sep 1998
MacMillan, Mr Richard A S BA . . . . . *Dec 1979
Welch, Mr N Stuart LLB. . . . . *Apr 1980
Asoc: Taylor, Miss Rachel LLB. . . . . *Oct 2001
Ast: Clarke, Ms Anna . . . . . Mar 1997
Harris, Ms Catherine . . . . . Sep 2004
Taylor, Miss Louise Sarah LLB . . . . . *Aug 2002

LINGFIELD, Surrey

KATE LIMBERT SOLICITORS ‡
6 Godstone Road Lingfield Surrey RH7 6BW
Tel: 01342 837765 *Fax:* 01342 835744

LIPHOOK, Hampshire

BURLEY & GEACH
Index House Midhurst Road Liphook Hampshire GU30 7TN
Tel: 01428 722334 *Fax:* 01428 727413 *Dx:* 47852 LIPHOOK
E-mail: liphook@burley-geach.co.uk
Office: Grayshott, Haslemere, Petersfield
Languages: Italian
Work: A1 C1 C2 C3 D1 E F1 G H J1 K1 L N O P Q R1 S1 S2 T1 T2 W Z(c,d,e,l,m)
Emergency Action, Agency, Advocacy, Fixed Fee Interview, Legal Aid undertaken, Legal Aid Franchise and Member of Accident Line
Ast: Tozzi, Mr Robert P LLB(Hons); TEP. . . . . *Oct 1989

A DAPHNE DAVIDSON-KELLY ‡
Little Boarhunt Portsmouth Road Liphook Hampshire GU30 7EE
Tel: 01428 727978 *Fax:* 01428 724523 *Dx:* 47858 LIPHOOK
Emergency telephone 01428 724076
E-mail: addksolicitor@aol.com
Languages: French
Work: S1 W
Fixed Fee Interview undertaken

DIDLAW ‡
24 Longmoor Road Liphook Hampshire GU30 7NY
Tel: 01428 724685 *Fax:* 01428 723170
E-mail: info@didlaw.com

LISKEARD, Cornwall

CAUNTERS ‡
Lloyds Bank Chambers The Parade Liskeard Cornwall PL14 6AJ
Tel: 01579 343165 / 343484 *Fax:* 01579 342106
Dx: 81660 LISKEARD
E-mail: legal@caunters.co.uk
List of partners: J E Outten, L Z Vallance
Work: A1 C1 E F1 K1 K3 L N Q S1 S2 W Z(c,l)
Fixed Fee Interview undertaken
Dir: Outten, Mr James Edward LLB(Hons). . . . . *Aug 2006
Vallance, Mr Luke Z LLB(Hons) . . . . . *Dec 1999
Ast: Heaton, Ms Jennifer Margaret LLB(Hons); LPC . . . . *Mar 2011

COODES
10 Windsor Place Liskeard Cornwall PL14 4BH
Tel: 01579 347600 *Fax:* 01579 347947 *Dx:* 81653 LISKEARD
E-mail: enquiries@coodes.co.uk
Office: Holsworthy, Launceston, Newquay, Penzance, St Austell, Truro
Work: A1 B1 B2 C1 C2 C3 D1 D2 E F1 G H J1 K1 K2 L N O Q R1 S1 T1 T2 V W Z(c,d,l,m,q,r)
Agency, Advocacy, Legal Aid undertaken and Member of Accident Line
Ptr: Andrews, Mr Christopher Paul LLB ★ . . . . . May 1996
George, Mr Kevin G E LLB(Hons). . . . . *Nov 1991
Pollock, Mr Richard M MA(Oxon) . . . . . Oct 1997
Ast: Cornish, Mrs Sarah . . . . . Sep 2007
Evans, Miss Sarah . . . . . Oct 2010
Tomlinson, Mr Alex . . . . . Oct 2010

COX BURLEY SOLICITORS ‡
6 Windsor Place Liskeard Cornwall PL14 4BH
Tel: 01579 340020 *Fax:* 01579 349920
E-mail: sc@coxburley.co.uk

EARL & CROCKER ‡
6 West Street Liskeard Cornwall PL14 6BW
Tel: 01579 345304 *Fax:* 01579 347454 *Dx:* 81661 LISKEARD
Emergency telephone 01579 345304
E-mail: enquiries@earlandcrocker.co.uk
List of partners: J Crocker, A H Earl
Office: Looe
Work: A1 C1 D1 D2 E K1 K3 K4 L S1 S2 T1 T2 V W Z(c,d,l)
Emergency Action, Agency, Advocacy, Fixed Fee Interview, Legal Aid undertaken and Legal Aid Franchise
Ptr: Crocker, Mr John . . . . . *Jan 1980
Earl, Mr Anthony Howard LTCL; ALAM . . . . . *Oct 1984

LISS, Hampshire

HARVEYS ‡
96 Station Road Liss Hampshire GU33 7AQ
Tel: 01730 895000 *Fax:* 01730 893313 *Dx:* 118150 LISS
Emergency telephone 07831 127018
E-mail: law@harveys-solicitors.co.uk
List of partners: M R Harvey, S E Harvey
Work: B1 C1 D1 E F1 G H J1 K1 K2 L N O Q R1 S1 T1 V W Z(b,c,d,k,l,m,p,x)
Emergency Action, Agency, Advocacy and Fixed Fee Interview undertaken
Ptr: Harvey, Mr Mark R . . . . . *§May 1977
Harvey, Mrs Susan E LLB. . . . . *Oct 1977
Ast: Silk, Mr Adrian Michael LLB(Hons) . . . . . *Feb 1995

WATSON BRADY LTD ‡
Middle Oakshott Farm Hawkley Liss Hampshire GU33 6LP
Tel: 01730 827033
E-mail: markbrady100@btinternet.com

LITTLEBOROUGH, Greater Manchester

JOHN POYSER SOLICITORS
77 Church Street Littleborough Greater Manchester OL15 8AB
Tel: 01706 375968 *Fax:* 01706 376337
E-mail: mail@johnpoyser.co.uk
Office: Manchester

2

LITTLEHAMPTON, West Sussex

BRADBURY STEED ‡
20 High Street Littlehampton West Sussex BN17 5EA
Tel: 01903 717048 *Fax:* 01903 739389 *Dx:* 57402 LITTLEHAMPTON
E-mail: bradbury-steed@btconnect.com
List of partners: A Bradbury
Languages: French
Work: D1 D2 E J1 K1 K3 L N O Q R1 S1 S2 W Z(k,q,r)
Emergency Action, Agency, Advocacy, Fixed Fee Interview undertaken and Member of Accident Line
Ptr: Bradbury, Mr Arthur. . . . . *Jun 1996

CHAMBERLAIN MARTIN SOLICITORS
23 Goda Road Littlehampton West Sussex BN17 6AS
Tel: 01903 713814 / 716548 *Fax:* 01903 730551
Dx: 57404 LITTLEHAMPTON
E-mail: paul.bodkin@chamberlainmartin.com
Office: Bognor Regis
Work: C1 E F1 L R1 S1 T1 T2 W
Ptr: Bodkin, Mr Paul Martin BA(Hons) . . . . . *Jun 1979

EDWARD HAYES LLP
Ocean House 16-18 Beach Road Littlehampton West Sussex BN17 5HT
Tel: 01903 759024 *Fax:* 01903 759025
E-mail: info@edwardhayes.co.uk
Office: Bognor Regis, Chichester (2 offices), Havant, London EC2, London EC4, Worthing
Work: B2 D1 D2 G H J1 K1 K2 K3 L M2 N Q S1 S2 W Z(i,l,q,w)
Emergency Action, Agency, Advocacy, Legal Aid undertaken and Legal Aid Franchise

HENCHLEYS ‡
39a High Street Littlehampton West Sussex BN17 5EG
Tel: 01903 726477 *Fax:* 01903 726488 *Dx:* 57411 LITTLEHAMPTON
E-mail: henchleys@aol.com
List of partners: K F Henchley
Office: Worthing
Languages: French
Work: B1 E F1 F2 J1 K1 K3 L N O Q S1 S2 T2 W Z(g,k,l,m,q,r)
Agency and Fixed Fee Interview undertaken
SPr: Henchley, Mr Kevin F BA(Hons). . . . . *Mar 1984

GERARD MAYE LEGAL LIMITED
3 Arcade Road Littlehampton West Sussex BN17 5AP
Tel: 01903 734341 *Fax:* 01903 734342 *Dx:* 57416 LITTLEHAMPTON
Emergency telephone 07815 610178
E-mail: enquiries@gerardmaye.co.uk
Office: Brighton (2 offices)

E J MOYLE ‡
15 Beach Road Littlehampton West Sussex BN17 5HZ
Tel: 01903 725143 *Fax:* 01903 730569 *Dx:* 57407 LITTLEHAMPTON
E-mail: litmail@moyle.co.uk
List of partners: N R Byrnes, M F Kemp, T J Pitt, M A White
Office: Rustington
Work: D1 E F1 F2 J1 J2 K1 K3 K4 L N O Q R2 S1 S2 T2 V W Z(l,m,p,q)
Agency, Advocacy, Legal Aid undertaken and Legal Aid Franchise
Ptr: Byrnes, Ms Nadine Rosalind . . . . . *Oct 2006
Kemp, Mr Michael Frank BA . . . . . *Oct 1995
Pitt, Mr Timothy Julian Edis Prize for Conveyancing . . *Nov 1981
Ast: Harding, Mr Benjamin C BA(Hons) . . . . . *Jan 1975
Pain, Ms Allison Caroline . . . . . *Nov 2006

WANNOP FOX STAFFURTH & BRAY
(incorporating Peter C Careless)
36 High Street Littlehampton West Sussex BN17 5ED
Tel: 01903 721112 *Fax:* 01903 730860 *Dx:* 57408 LITTLEHAMPTON
E-mail: worthing@wfsblaw.com
Office: Bognor Regis, Chichester, Havant, Worthing (3 offices)
Languages: French, German, Greek
Work: A1 C1 C3 E F1 G J1 K1 K4 L M1 M2 N R1 R2 S1 S2 W Z(c,e,k,l)
Member of Accident Line
Ptr: Baker, Miss Sarah Elizabeth Notary Public . . . . . *§Jan 2003

LIVERPOOL, Merseyside

AS LAW ‡
8-10 Myrtle Parade Liverpool Merseyside L7 7EL
Tel: 0151 707 1212 *Fax:* 0151 707 2458
List of partners: D E Abrahamson, P Simm
Work: D1 D2 K1 Z(g,i)
Legal Aid undertaken and Legal Aid Franchise
Ptr: Abrahamson, Mr D Elkan LLB(Jerusalem); LLM(Lond). *Feb 1983
Simm, Mr Peter BA . . . . . *Feb 1986
Con: Johnstone, Mr Marcus Ashley LLB; PGCE. . . . . *Aug 2003

ABENSONS ‡
102 Allerton Road Liverpool Merseyside L18 2DG
Tel: 0151 733 3111 *Fax:* 0151 733 8999 *Dx:* 18901 ALLERTON
E-mail: reception@abensons.co.uk
List of partners: E S Abenson, G E Evans
Work: B1 C1 C2 D1 D2 E F1 J1 K1 K2 L N O Q R1 R2 S1 S2 T1 T2 V W X Z(k,l)
Emergency Action, Agency, Advocacy and Legal Aid undertaken
Ptr: Abenson, Mr Edward S LLB. . . . . *Nov 1971
Evans, Mrs George E LLB . . . . . *Dec 1972
Con: Davey, Mr Allastair C LLB. . . . . *Jun 1971

ANDERSON MIDDLETON ‡
135-137 Dale Street Liverpool Merseyside L2 2JH
Tel: 0151 236 5599 *Fax:* 0151 236 9749 *Dx:* 14119 LIVERPOOL
E-mail: reception@middletonsolicitors.co.uk

APPLEYARD LEES
Liverpool Science Park Innovation Centre 131 Mount Pleasant Liverpool Merseyside L3 5TF
Tel: 0151 331 5016
E-mail: liverpool@appleyardlees.com
Office: Burnley, Chester, Halifax, Harrogate, Huddersfield, Leeds, Manchester, Preston, Sheffield, Stockton-on-Tees, York

B J & CO SOLICITORS ‡
22 Stanley Street Liverpool Merseyside L1 6AF
Tel: 0151 227 7777 *Fax:* 0151 258 1112 *Dx:* 14139 LIVERPOOL
E-mail: help@bjandco.net

BMD LAW ‡
194 Picton Road Wavertree Liverpool Merseyside L15 4LL
Tel: 0151 222 5777 *Fax:* 0151 734 3449
Emergency telephone 07779 222708
E-mail: bmdlaw@blueyonder.co.uk
List of partners: B T McDonald
Work: C1 E F1 J1 L O R2 S2 W
Fixed Fee Interview undertaken
SPr: McDonald, Ms Bernadette Teresa LLB Sweet & Maxwell Law Prize 1997 . . . Feb 2003

JOANNE BALL SOLICITORS ‡
15 Vicarage Close Mossley Hill Liverpool Merseyside L18 7HU
Tel: 0151 724 6645 *Fax:* 0151 724 6645
E-mail: joanneball@joanneball.co.uk
List of partners: J Ball
Languages: French
Work: K4 S1 W Z(m)
SPr: Ball, Ms Joanne. . . . Sep 1999

BANNONS ‡
15b Sweeting Street Liverpool Merseyside L2 4TE
Tel: 0151 227 1818

BARTLETTS SOLICITORS ‡
Marldon Chambers 30 North John Street Liverpool Merseyside L2 9QN
Tel: 0151 227 3391 *Fax:* 0151 227 5017 *Dx:* 14108 LIVERPOOL
E-mail: info@bartlettslaw.co.uk
List of partners: P Aberdein, J A Bartlett, P N Bartlett, M C Burgess, A J Hunt, E J Latimer, T R Morris, E L Nelson
Office: Chester (2 offices), Liverpool (2 offices)
Languages: French
Work: A1 B1 C1 C2 C3 D1 E F1 J1 K1 L N P Q R1 S1 S2 T1 T2 V W Z(c)
Fixed Fee Interview undertaken and Member of Accident Line
Ptr: Bartlett, Mr John A . . . Jun 1965
Nelson, Ms Elizabeth L . . . Oct 1979
Ast: Bartlett, Mr Christopher D. . . . Apr 2009
Burch, Mr Jerome W . . . Jul 2009
Morse, Mr Stephen J . . . Jul 2009
Perry, Mrs Nicola . . . Apr 2001
Smith, Ms Catherine LLB(Hons). . . . Dec 1997
Smith, Mr Joseph S. . . . Aug 2002

BARTLETTS SOLICITORS
503 Prescot Road Old Swan Liverpool Merseyside L13 3BY
Tel: 0151 228 7730 *Fax:* 0151 220 7956 *Dx:* 700702 OLD SWAN
E-mail: newclaims@bartlettsos.co.uk
Office: Chester (2 offices), Liverpool (2 offices)
Work: N Q
Member of Accident Line
Ptr: Aberdein, Mr Paul LLB . . . *Oct 1989
Hunt, Mr Anthony James LLB(Hons) . . . *Nov 1995

BARTLETTS SOLICITORS
21 Walton Vale Liverpool Merseyside L9 4RE
Tel: 0151 521 7333 *Fax:* 0151 524 2300 *Dx:* 24702 WALTON VALE
E-mail: mb@bartlettwv.co.uk
Office: Chester (2 offices), Liverpool (2 offices)
Work: N Q
Ptr: Burgess, Mr Mark C. . . . *Oct 1986
Ast: Bloxham, Mr Andrew . . . *Mar 2003
Williams, Mr Gary. . . . Nov 1995

BEECH JONES DE LLOYD
4th Floor Exchange Court 1 Dale Street Liverpool Merseyside L2 2PP
Tel: 0151 236 2924 *Fax:* 0151 236 4425
E-mail: solutions@beechjones.com
Office: Cardiff

JOHN A BEHN TWYFORD & CO ‡
PO Box 19 1 Moorfields Liverpool Merseyside L69 2EJ
Tel: 0151 236 0367 *Fax:* 0151 255 0436
E-mail: behns@behns.co.uk
List of partners: D G Ashcroft, S E Graham, C D Knagg
Work: D1 F1 G H J1 K1 L M1 N P R1 S1 V W Z(a,t)
Agency, Advocacy, Fixed Fee Interview, Legal Aid undertaken and Member of Accident Line
Ptr: Ashcroft, Mr David G LLB. . . . §Jan 1979
Graham, Miss Suzanne E LLB . . . *§Apr 1979
Knagg, Mr Christopher D. . . . Dec 1993

BELL & CO ‡
(in association with Bellis Kennan & Gribble)
40 Crosby Road North Waterloo Liverpool Merseyside L22 4QQ
Tel: 0151 928 8686 *Fax:* 0151 928 3261 *Dx:* 13632 WATERLOO
E-mail: legal@bellandco.co.uk
List of partners: W A Gerrard
Work: C1 E J1 N Q S1 W
Agency, Advocacy, Legal Aid undertaken and Member of Accident Line
Ptr: Gerrard, Mr William Anthony LLB(Hons); LPC. . . . *Sep 1996
Con: Radam, Mrs Patricia R BA(Law). . . . *Mar 1984

BELL LAMB & JOYNSON ‡
(incorporating Rayner & Wade)
G15 Cotton Exchange Bixteth street Liverpool Merseyside L3 9LQ
Tel: 0844 412 4348 *Fax:* 0151 227 5937 *Dx:* 14110 LIVERPOOL
E-mail: mediation@bljsolicitors.co.uk
List of partners: B D Cooper, J C R Marshall, J D Rawson, R Scarisbrick
Office: Liverpool, Runcorn, Warrington, Weaverham
Work: A1 B1 C1 D1 E F1 G H J1 K1 K2 L M1 N O P Q R1 S1 S2 T1 V W Z(b,c,d,f,h,i,j,k,l,m,n,o,s)
Emergency Action, Agency, Advocacy, Fixed Fee Interview, Legal Aid undertaken, Legal Aid Franchise and Member of Accident Line

BELL LAMB & JOYNSON
39 Walton Vale Liverpool Merseyside L9 4ST
Tel: 0844 412 4348 *Fax:* 0151 474 8468 *Dx:* 24703 WALTON VALE
E-mail: walton@bljsolicitors.co.uk
Office: Liverpool, Runcorn, Warrington, Weaverham
Agency, Advocacy, Fixed Fee Interview, Legal Aid undertaken and Member of Accident Line
Ptr: Rawson, Mr Jeremy D LLB(Manc). . . . *§Sep 1983
Ast: Green, Mr Peter D LLB(Lancs) . . . Sep 1995
O'Donovan, Mrs Marion E B BA(Hons); LLB(L'pool) . . Jul 1993

BENNETT & CO ‡
11 Allerton Road Liverpool Merseyside L18 1LG
Tel: 0151 733 2372 *Fax:* 0151 734 4413 *Dx:* 18903 ALLERTON
List of partners: R A Billinge, A M Holmes
Work: E S1 W
Fixed Fee Interview undertaken
Ptr: Billinge, Mr Roger A LLB(Lond) . . . May 1974
Holmes, Mr Andrew M LLB . . . *Oct 1981

JAMES BENSON & CO ‡
Trident House 31-33 Dale Street Liverpool Merseyside L2 2HF
Tel: 0151 236 8755 *Fax:* 0151 258 1610 *Dx:* 14130 LIVERPOOL
Emergency telephone 07785 378 829 / 07771 658 863
E-mail: james.benson@jamesbensonsolicitors.co.uk
List of partners: J J Benson
Work: G H
SPr: Benson, Mr James J BA(Law). . . . *Jun 1979
Ast: Saxon, Mr Martin LLB(Hons); LLM . . . Mar 2005

BERKSON GLOBE PARTNERSHIP ‡
2nd Floor Granite Building 6 Stanley Street Liverpool Merseyside L1 6AF
Tel: 0151 236 1234 *Fax:* 0151 236 5678 *Dx:* 14132 LIVERPOOL
Emergency telephone 0151 727 2496
E-mail: info@berksonglobe.org
List of partners: V A Limont, C P Peter
Work: G H K1
Emergency Action, Agency, Advocacy, Fixed Fee Interview, Legal Aid undertaken and Legal Aid Franchise
Ptr: Limont, Mrs Valerie A LLB. . . . *Oct 1974
Peter, Mr Charles P LLB Part time Law Lecturer. . . . *Oct 1986

BERMANS LLP ‡
2nd Floor Lancaster House Mercury Court Liverpool Merseyside L2 2QP
Tel: 0151 224 0500 *Fax:* 0151 236 2107 *Dx:* 14116 LIVERPOOL
E-mail: info@bermans.co.uk
List of partners: N Benson, A Chapman, K Donovan, P A Farrelly, D B Gledhill, N Harvey, J Hunter, C McDermott, I R Munford, F R O'Cleirigh, P A Sinnett
Office: Manchester
Languages: Spanish
Work: A3 B1 B2 C1 C2 E F1 J1 L O Q R1 R2 S1 S2 U2 W Z(b,l,w)
Agency and Fixed Fee Interview undertaken
Ptr: Benson, Nicky. . . . Apr 1988
Chapman, Mr Alexander LLB . . . *Nov 1988
Donovan, Mr Kieran. . . . Sep 1999
Harvey, Mr Nicholas LLB(Hons) . . . *Jul 1997
Hunter, Miss Julie. . . . *Dec 2001
McDermott, Mr Charles . . . Feb 2004
O'Cleirigh, Mr Fergal R LLB. . . . *Oct 1986
Sinnett, Mr Peter A LLB; LLM ● . . . Jun 1991
Asoc: Ali, Mr Ansar . . . Oct 2002
Gill, Mr Robin. . . . Aug 2005
Jones, Ms Rachel. . . . May 2000
Pattison, Mr Guy . . . Nov 2006
Ast: Morris, Mrs Claire. . . . Mar 2008
Walker, Miss Sarah T LLB. . . . *Oct 1999
Con: Barrett, Mr Bernard LLB(Lond) . . . Dec 1973

BERRYMANS LACE MAWER
Castle Chambers 43 Castle Street Liverpool Merseyside L2 9SU
Tel: 0151 236 2002 *Fax:* 0151 236 2585 *Dx:* 14159 LIVERPOOL 1
E-mail: info@blm-law.com
Office: Birmingham, Bristol, Cardiff, Leeds, London EC2, Manchester, Southampton, Stockton-on-Tees
Work: A3 F2 J2 L N O Q Z(h,j,k,r)

ROBERT BINGHAM SOLICITORS ‡
Crescent House Liscard Crescent Wallasey Liverpool Merseyside CH44 1AE
Tel: 0151 630 7171 *Fax:* 0151 346 9966

DAVID BISHOP & CO ‡
14 Chapel Lane Formby Liverpool Merseyside L37 4DU
Tel: 01704 878421 *Fax:* 01704 878959

BOLTON-JONES & CO ‡
3 Menlove Avenue Allerton Liverpool Merseyside L18 1LS
Tel: 0151 733 2241 *Fax:* 0151 733 0407 *Dx:* 18914 ALLERTON
List of partners: S P Barton, R P Duggan
Languages: French
Work: C1 D1 E K1 L Q R1 S1 S2 T2 W
Fixed Fee Interview undertaken
Ptr: Barton, Mr Stephen P LLB(L'pool). . . . *Jul 1979
Duggan, Mr Robert P BA . . . *Jul 1978

MARK BONE SOLICITORS ‡
PO Box 64 Liverpool Merseyside L19 9WU
Tel: 0151 427 6380

BRABNERS CHAFFE STREET ‡
Horton House Exchange Flags Liverpool Merseyside L2 3YL
Tel: 0151 600 3000 *Fax:* 0151 227 3185 *Dx:* 14118 LIVERPOOL
Emergency telephone 0151 600 3000
E-mail: law@brabnerscs.com
List of partners: I B Alderson, D Bailey, R J Bate, M Bennett, D Bentham, M J Blood, D N Bowcock, J A Boydell, M G Brabner, C M Brandwood, S M Brodie, T M Burton, N D Campbell, E Canty, P Chamberlain, S T Chapple Gill, J Clarke, S Claus, A M Clearkin, C Couse, A J Cross, M Difelice, M Dobson, L T Edgar, M R Feeny, A Fitzmaurice, A Fletcher, R Gill, J A Gillbanks, M J Glenville, T M Goulden, I G Hardman, A J Harper, A D Holt, K Housley, J I'Anson, S Irons, R Jackson, K A James, R H Jones, J Lewis, S Lewis, C L Litchfield, J Lloyd, P G Lunt, S Mabon, M J Manley, D S Maples, H Marriott, P A R B Marsden, T J Marshall, N McBurney, T M Montague, P Morton, L D Mullan, A J O'Mahony, C Parkinson, J Purves, M E Rathbone, D I Renison, R Roberts, S Roper, C Round, A Ryan, J J Shelston, R Shine, J Smith, R H Street, D J Tournafond, D A Walker, R M Watkin, E M Watkins, N White, S Whitehead, N J Williams, J Withinshaw
Office: Manchester, Preston
Work: A1 A2 A3 B1 C1 C2 C3 D1 E F1 I J1 K1 L M2 N O P Q R1 R2 S1 S2 T1 T2 U2 V W Z(b,c,d,e,f,h,i,k,l,o,q)
Emergency Action, Agency and Fixed Fee Interview undertaken
Ptr: Alderson, Mr Ian B BA(Law) President of Disciplinary Commission of UIAA and IFSC . . . *Oct 1987
Bailey, Mr Duncan. . . . *Sep 2000
Brabner, Mr Michael G LLB . . . *§Oct 1974
Brodie, Mr Stephen M LLB(Hons) . . . *Mar 1988
Campbell, Mr Nicholas Damian LLB(Hons) . . . *Jan 1995
Chapple Gill, Mr Sandy T LLB(Hull) . . . *Sep 1982
Clarke, Mr James . . . *Sep 1999
Claus, Mr Stephen . . . *Aug 1992
Clearkin, Miss Angela M LLB . . . *Oct 1987
Cross, Mr Andrew J LLB . . . *Oct 1980
Feeny, Mr Mark R LLB . . . *Jun 1981
Fletcher, Mr Alistair BA(Oxon)(Jurisprudence). . . . *Dec 1981
Gill, Mr Rupert . . . *Oct 1999
Gillbanks, Mr Jeffrey A LLB. . . . *Nov 1991
Glenville, Mr Mark John LLB; LLM. . . . *Sep 1993
Goulden, Mr Timothy Morton . . . *Dec 1975
Hardman, Mr Ian Gerard BA(Hons); LPD; Dip(Comm Lit) . . . *Nov 1996
Holt, Mr Andrew D MA(Cantab) . . . *Nov 1978
Housley, Mr Keith LLB. . . . *§Apr 1970
I'Anson, Mr Jonathan . . . *Oct 1998
Jackson, Mr Rupert . . . *Jan 1996
Lewis, Mr Stephen LLB; LLM . . . Sep 2005
Lloyd, Mrs Jacqui LLB(L'pool) . . . *Nov 1985
Lunt, Mr Paul Graham LLB(Hons) . . . *Nov 1996
McBurney, Mr Neil LLB . . . *Nov 1985
Manley, Mr Mark J LLB . . . *Oct 1987
Maples, Mr David S LLB(Hons) . . . *Jan 1985
Marriott, Ms Helen . . . *Oct 1993
Marshall, Mr Timothy James . . . *Jan 1972
Montague, Mr Terence M BA . . . *Apr 1975
Mullan, Miss Lynn Donna LLB. . . . Sep 1999
O'Mahony, Mr Andrew James LLB(Hons); LPC . . . *Oct 1996
Parkinson, Chris . . . *Nov 1993
Rathbone, Mr Mark Edward MA. . . . *Nov 1996
Renison, Mr David Ian LLB . . . *§Apr 1968
Roberts, Mr Richard. . . . *Oct 2000
Roper, Mr Stephen LLB(Hons) . . . *Sep 1998
Ryan, Mr Adam LLB(Hons) . . . *Oct 2002
Shelston, Mr Joseph John BA; CPE; LPC; PGDL . . *Sep 2001
Tournafond, Mr David John LLB. . . . *Nov 1987
Walker, Mrs Denise A LLB . . . *Nov 1991
Watkin, Rachel Margaret LLB . . . Sep 1999
White, Nik. . . . *Oct 1997
Williams, Mr Nigel John LLB(Hons) . . . *Jun 1983
Withinshaw, Mr John MA(Cantab) . . . Dec 1976
Asoc: Bell, Mr Colin Philip MA(Cantab)(Classics); CPE; PGDipLaw; LPC; PGDip Commercial IP Law . . . Oct 2004
Brown, Ms Helen BA; PGDipLaw; LPC Prize for Meritorious Achievement 2002 . . . *Oct 2006
Emery, Mrs Lynn Ann LLB(Hons); TEP . . . *Aug 1988
Fagan, Mrs Jane L LLB . . . *Nov 1989
Livesey, Mrs Katherine Mary LLB . . . Mar 2001
McEvoy, Ms Caroline . . . *Oct 2003
Manley, Mr Kevin BA(Hons); DipLaw . . . *Nov 2001
Ngan, Mr William BA(Hons); ATT Slater Heelis Prize 1993-1994 . . . *Sep 1999
Owen, Mrs Carys Megan LLB . . . *Oct 1986
Paddock, Dewi LLB; LLM . . . *Sep 2004
Parker, Mr Phillip . . . *Oct 2004
Rogers, Mr Adrian. . . . *Oct 2004
Roseby, Mr Stephen . . . *Oct 2006
Spears, Ms Rebecca LLB; LLM . . . *Sep 2004
Thackeray, Ms Susan LLB(Hons); LPC Diploma. . . . *Oct 1998
Wheeler, Mr Nick . . . *Nov 2000
Ast: Barwick, Mr Darren LLB(Hons) Cavendish Prize for Academic Achievement . . . *May 2007
Bennett, Ms Susan . . . *Mar 2006
Brown, Mr Matt BSc; PGDipLaw. . . . *Jul 2002
Carlin, Mrs Dorothy BA(Hons); LLM(Law & Employment Relations). . . . *Oct 1987
Dickinson, Mr Tom Andrew . . . *Sep 2004
Foy, Miss Christine LLB . . . Dec 2005
Harper, Miss Rachel Elizabeth BA(Hons); GDL; LPC . Sep 2010
Hough, Mr Richard BSc(Hons); LLB(Hons) Cavendish Prize 2003 . . . *Sep 2007
Lancefield, Mr Glyn Michael LLB Simon Ball Memorial Prize for Contract Law 2001; Sir Basil Blackwell Prize for Law 2001 . . . *Sep 2008
Meadowcroft, Miss Natalie Ann LLB. . . . *Sep 2007
Parry, Miss Amy Margaret LLB(Hons) Atkinson Prize 2007 from Liverpool Law Soc; Bibby Scholarship 2005/6. . . Mar 2010
Rissbrook, Ms Alison LLB(Hons) . . . *Aug 2002
Roos, Mr Andrius BCom(Law); LLB; GDL . . . *Apr 2007
Starkey, Mr Thomas LLB(Hons) . . . *Sep 2005
Waddington, Ms Jan LLB(Hons). . . . *Nov 1991

BREENS SOLICITORS
34 Crosby Road North Waterloo Liverpool Merseyside L22 4QG
Tel: 0151 928 6544 *Fax:* 0151 949 0005 *Dx:* 13631 WATERLOO
Emergency telephone 0800 317 620
E-mail: js.breen@breensonline.co.uk
Office: Southport
Work: A1 B1 C1 E F1 J1 L N O P Q R1 S1 T1 V W Z(b,c,j,p)
Emergency Action, Agency, Advocacy and Fixed Fee Interview undertaken
Ptr: Breen, Mr John Stephen BA. . . . *Apr 1981
Ast: Charnley, Mrs Sarah Jane BA. . . . *Jul 2001
Wilkinson, Ms Jennifer LLB(Hons). . . . Aug 2009

STEPHEN D BRINE SOLICITORS ‡
24/26 Allerton Road Liverpool Merseyside L18 1LN
Tel: 0151 734 5000 *Fax:* 0151 734 3030
E-mail: enquiries@sdbsolicitors.co.uk
List of partners: M S Bracey, S D Brine
Ptr: Bracey, Mr Martin S BA . . . *Oct 1982
Brine, Mr Stephen D BA(Law). . . . Oct 1984

BROUDIE JACKSON CANTER
The Justice Partnership 24 Dale Street Liverpool Merseyside L2 2HD
Tel: 0151 227 1429 *Fax:* 0151 236 5161 *Dx:* 14156 LIVERPOOL
Emergency telephone 07860 554433
E-mail: mailbox@jacksoncanter.co.uk
Office: Liverpool
Work: E G H S1 S2 Z(i)
Emergency Action, Agency, Advocacy, Fixed Fee Interview, Legal Aid undertaken and Member of Accident Line
Ptr: Abrahamson, Mr Elkan LLB. . . . Jan 1985
Heckle, Mr Kenneth LLB . . . Dec 1998
Leach, Ms Esther LLB. . . . Apr 1999
Rogers, Mr Stephen J LLB(Leeds) . . . *Oct 1978
Thompson, Mr Paul BA(Law) . . . Dec 1983

See p112 for the Key to Work Categories & other symbols

Topping, Mr Christopher P LLB . . . . Oct 1988
Ast: Dagnall, Ms Victoria LLB . . . . Aug 2009
Hughes, Ms Lynne LLB . . . . *Dec 2004
Lieb, Mr Philip. . . . . *Apr 1996
Luces, Mrs Lyn Chrystelle Riah BA(Hons); CPE. . . . Sep 2006
McGreevy, Miss Mairaed LLB . . . . *Mar 2009
Templeman, Ms Rebecca LLB. . . . . Aug 2006
Walmsley, Mr Steven LLB. . . . . *Jun 2011

BROWN TURNER ROSS ‡
Granite Building 6 Stanley Street Liverpool Merseyside L1 6AF
Tel: 0151 236 2233 *Fax:* 0151 236 6208 *Dx:* 14184 LIVERPOOL
E-mail: law@brownturnerross.com
List of partners: K A Ross, M J Ross
Languages: Hindi
Work: B1 C1 C2 C3 D1 E F1 J1 K1 L N O Q R1 R2 S1 S2 V W Z(c,e,f,i,q)
Fixed Fee Interview undertaken
Ptr: Ross, Mr Kevin Alexander LLB; LPC . . . . *Sep 1998
Ross, Mr Malcolm J. . . . . *Jun 1970
Ast: Maginn, Mr Martin Saul LLB. . . . . *Apr 1996
Sharma, Ms Usha LLB(Hons) . . . . *Oct 2000

CFK LEGAL ‡
Suite 801 Executive Centre Liverpool Liverpool Merseyside L2 2LZ
Tel: 0151 708 6222 *Fax:* 0151 515 3001
E-mail: mark.forman@cfklegal.com

CANTER LEVIN & BERG ‡
1 Temple Square 24 Dale Street Liverpool Merseyside L2 5RU
Tel: 0151 239 1000 *Fax:* 0151 239 1001
E-mail: postmaster@canter-law.co.uk
List of partners: L Burns-Lunt, C Campbell, I Fitzpatrick, M A W Flynn, R Houghton, R Hughes, C Jansz, D Jones, R Krumins, M C Malone, P Mitchell, K C Pinkstone, H Roberts, E A Saunders, R Sibeon, I Smith, I J Troop
Office: Kirkby, St Helens
Work: A3 B1 B2 C1 C2 C3 D1 D2 E F1 G H J1 K1 K2 L M1 M2 N O P Q R1 S1 S2 T1 T2 W Z(h,j,l,m,r)
Emergency Action, Agency, Advocacy, Fixed Fee Interview, Legal Aid undertaken and Member of Accident Line
Ptr: Fitzpatrick, Mr Ian LLB . . . . Mar 1991
Krumins, Ms Rita BA . . . . Nov 1998
Malone, Mr Martin Christopher BA; CPE. . . . . *Oct 1993
Mitchell, Mr Peter BA . . . . Jan 1991
Pinkstone, Mr Kevin C LLB . . . . *Oct 1985
Roberts, Hazel . . . . Nov 2001
Sibeon, Mr Richard LLB. . . . . Aug 1998
Troop, Mr Ian James LLB(Hons). . . . . *Aug 2000
Burns-Lunt, Ms Louise . . . . .NSP
Asoc: Allanson, Ruth . . . . Jun 2009
Booth, Mr John . . . . Feb 2002
Budgen, Mr Rupert . . . . Apr 1999
Kelly, Katherine . . . . Apr 2008
Lee, Mr Robert . . . . Dec 2007
Polson, Mr Graham .Jul 1989
Sands, Joanne . . . . May 2007
Taylor, Jennifer . . . . Jun 2007
Valente, Ms Sheena LLB(Hons) . . . . *Jan 1994
Vickers, Mr Colin . . . . Dec 2007

CHEESMAN & CO ‡
5th Floor North House 17 North John Street Liverpool Merseyside L2 5QY
Tel: 0151 258 1212 *Fax:* 0151 236 1357 *Dx:* 14138 LIVERPOOL
Emergency telephone 0151 258 1212
E-mail: enquiries@cheesmanandco.com
List of partners: L E Cheesman
Languages: French
Work: C1 D1 E K1 L S1 W
Emergency Action, Agency, Advocacy, Fixed Fee Interview and Legal Aid undertaken
Ptr: Cheesman, Leslie E. . . . . *Dec 1981

COBLEYS LLP ‡
19-23 Sir Thomas Street Liverpool Merseyside L1 6BW
Tel: 0151 242 9000 *Fax:* 0151 236 2911 *Dx:* 14200 LIVERPOOL
Emergency telephone 07894 691666 / 691777
E-mail: cobleys.office@easylaw.co.uk
List of partners: N A Cobley, Z E Gascoyne, P J Killen, P F Martini, E W Williams
Work: B2 D1 G H K1 M1 N P Q
Emergency Action, Agency, Advocacy, Fixed Fee Interview, Legal Aid undertaken, Legal Aid Franchise and Member of Accident Line
Ptr: Cobley, Mr Neil A LLB(Hons)(Lond) ● . . . . *Jan 1980
Gascoyne, Ms Zoe Erin BA(Hons). . . . . *Jul 2002
Killen, Mr Peter James LLB(Hons). . . . . *Sep 1998
Martini, Mr Paolo F LLB(Hons) . . . . *Feb 1995
Williams, Mr Eric W BSocSc(Hons) . . . . *Mar 1984

CONNELL ASSOCIATES ‡
Union Marine Buildings 11 Dale Street Liverpool Merseyside L2 2SH
Tel: 0151 236 2011 *Fax:* 0151 236 2012 *Dx:* 14105 LIVERPOOL
List of partners: M J Connell
Work: B1 C1 E F1 J1 N O W Z(b,c,j)
Agency, Advocacy and Fixed Fee Interview undertaken
Ptr: Connell, Mr Michael J LLB(Hons) ★ . . . . *Oct 1982
Ast: McWilliams, Mr John Frances LLB(Hons); LSF . . . . *Dec 1995

COPE & CO SOLICITORS LIMITED
The Plaza 100 Old Hall Street Liverpool Merseyside L3 9QJ
Tel: 0151 600 5262 *Fax:* 0151 236 3028
E-mail: liverpool@copeandco.com
Office: Manchester

JANET M CORKE ‡
294 Aigburth Road Liverpool Merseyside L17 9PW
Tel: 0151 726 0443 *Fax:* 0151 726 0443
List of partners: J M Corke
Languages: Welsh
Work: L S1 W Z(d)
Agency undertaken
SPr: Corke, Mrs Janet M. . . . . *Jun 1960

CORNISH FORFAR & ALLEN ‡
Suite 4 Tower Building 22 Water Street Liverpool Merseyside L3 1BN
Tel: 0151 227 1831 *Fax:* 0151 236 3238 *Dx:* 14125 LIVERPOOL
E-mail: info@cornishforfar.co.uk
List of partners: C K Collins, J Manchett
Office: Wirral
Work: C1 C2 E F1 J1 K1 L N R1 S1 W Z(j)
Agency, Fixed Fee Interview and Legal Aid undertaken
Ptr: Manchett, Mr Julian LLB(Bris). . . . . *§May 1974

COYNE LEARMONTH ‡
135 Liverpool Road Great Crosby Liverpool Merseyside L23 5TE
Tel: 0845 602 0870 *Fax:* 0151 931 5422 *Dx:* 20404 CROSBY
E-mail: kcoyne@coynelearmonth.co.uk
List of partners: K J Coyne, A C Learmonth
Work: C1 E F1 G H J1 K1 P S1 T1 V W
Emergency Action, Agency, Advocacy, Fixed Fee Interview and Legal Aid undertaken
Ptr: Coyne, Mr Kevin J . . . . *§Dec 1974
Learmonth, Mr Anthony C LLB . . . . *Jun 1980

PAUL CROWLEY & CO ‡
Frank Crowley House 267 Breck Road Anfield Liverpool Merseyside L5 6SN
Tel: 0151 264 7363 *Fax:* 0151 263 4719 *Dx:* 702772 ANFIELD
Emergency telephone 07659 103666
E-mail: breck.road@paulcrowley.co.uk
Web: www.paulcrowley.co.uk
List of partners: P F Crowley, M Fogarty, J McKenna, T J Moran, P M Satchell
Office: Liverpool (2 offices)
Work: D1 G H K1 K3 N Q S1 S2 W
Emergency Action, Agency, Advocacy, Fixed Fee Interview and Legal Aid undertaken
Ptr: Crowley, Mr Paul F BA . . . . *Oct 1982
Fogarty, Mr Michael. . . . . Oct 2000
McKenna, Mr John . . . . May 2009
Moran, Mr Terry James . . . . Oct 2003
Satchell, Ms Paula Marie . . . . Jan 1998
Ast: Carter, Mr Michael P BA(Hons) . . . . *Dec 1977
Handel, Mrs Kate BSc(Hons) . . . . May 2009
Oakdene, Miss Rachel LLB(Hons). . . . . Nov 2001
Perischine, Ms Sara LLB(Hons). . . . . Jun 2010
Smith, Ms Emma LLB(Hons) . . . . Jun 2006
Williams, Mr Paul . . . . Oct 1993
Con: Higgins, Mr Peter M LLB . . . . *Dec 1970

PAUL CROWLEY & CO
257 Breck Road Anfield Liverpool Merseyside L5 6PT
Tel: 0151 264 7363 *Fax:* 0151 222 6458 *Dx:* 702772 ANFIELD
Emergency telephone 07659 103666
E-mail: breck.road@paulcrowley.co.uk
Office: Liverpool (2 offices)
Work: B2 G H
Agency and Legal Aid undertaken

PAUL CROWLEY & CO
86 County Road Walton Liverpool Merseyside L4 3QN
Tel: 0151 286 4515 *Fax:* 0151 286 4523 *Dx:* 70122 LIVERPOOL
E-mail: breck.road@paulcrowley.co.uk
Office: Liverpool (2 offices)

DLA PIPER UK LLP
India Buildings Water Street Liverpool Merseyside L2 0NH
Tel: 0870 011 1111 *Fax:* 0151 236 9208 *Dx:* 14103 LIVERPOOL 1
Emergency telephone 0870 011 1111
E-mail: phillip.rooney@dlapiper.com
Office: Birmingham, Leeds, London EC2, Manchester, Sheffield
Work: A1 B1 C1 C2 C3 E F1 F2 J1 J2 M1 N O P Q R1 R2 S1 T1 W X Z(a,b,c,d,e,f,j,k,l,n,o,p,u)
Ptr: Beardwood, Mr Mark P BA(Oxon). . . . . *Oct 1985
Bell, Ms Sarah . . . . Oct 1998
Brook, Mr Peter LLB(Hons); LPC . . . . Sep 1996
Cadwallader, Mr David H . . . . *Jan 1988
Goodwin, Mr Mark . . . . Mar 1992
Leach, Mr Mark LLB . . . . *Nov 1990
Lee, Mr Kevin Aidan LLB(Hons). . . . . *Nov 1990
Miller, Mr Benjamin . . . . Oct 1996
Mills, Ms Alison L LLB(Hons) . . . . *Oct 1992
Noon, Mr Andrew . . . . Sep 1997
O'Hanlon, Ms Mary LSF. . . . . *Dec 1992
Pinsent, Mr James LLB(L'pool) . . . . *§Jul 1977
Prince, Mr Michael J LLB . . . . *§May 1979
Roberts, Mr Andrew. . . . . Oct 1986
Rooney, Mr Philip J BA(Oxon). . . . . *§Jun 1980
Sweeney, Ms Sarah. . . . . Sep 1998
Vickery, Mr John . . . . Aug 1997
Wright, Mr David BA(Law). . . . . *Oct 1986

DWF ‡
5 St Paul's Square Old Hall Street Liverpool Merseyside L3 9AE
Tel: 0151 907 3000 *Fax:* 0151 907 3030 *Dx:* 14128 LIVERPOOL
E-mail: enquiries@dwf.co.uk
List of partners: D Astbury, P G Attwood, P C Barber, P A Berry, A D Blaquiere, A J J Bochenski, J S Bramley, C E Bruder, M C Burquest, C Chapman, D N Clay, G J Dagnall, D Davidson Lund, A R Davies, J C M Davies, M J Davies, S J Denyer, G D Dodds, D R C Evans, J L Evans, J Gemmell, C Graham, A J Green, A H Gregory, S Groch, S B Hackett, G D Halsall, M H Hudson, C M Lagar, K Lawrenson, H R Lawson, A Leatherland, I Macalister, R D Maguire, S M C Malia, S P Mather, I McCubbin, G T McIntegart, R J McKee, P G Moore, E A Needham, A Noce, P Park, R Parker, S K Parker, G R Perry, S Poole, M Poulston, S A C Prendergast, L P Pritchard, T Scott, M Selwyn, I Slater, J C Szerdy, I H Titchmarsh, G S J Wallis, K P Walshe, D R Waring, R H Wellman, A L Wild, C J Williams, S D Williamson, D L Wood, M J Yates, D A Young
Office: Leeds, London EC4, Manchester, Newcastle upon Tyne, Preston
Work: A1 A3 B1 B2 C1 C2 C3 E F1 F2 I J1 J2 L M1 N O P Q R1 R2 S1 S2 T1 T2 U2 W X Z(b,c,d,e,f,h,i,j,k,l,o,p,q,r,s,w,y)
Emergency Action, Agency, Advocacy and Fixed Fee Interview undertaken
Ptr: Attwood, Mr Paul G LLB . . . . *Nov 1982
Barber, Mr Peter C LLB(Hons) . . . . *Oct 1988
Berry, Mr Paul A BA. . . . . *Oct 1987
Blaquiere, Mr A David Notary Public. . . . . *§Dec 1977
Bramley, Mr Jonathan S LLB(Lond) . . . . *Jun 1976
Bruder, Mr Carl Edward LLB . . . . *Dec 1990
Burquest, Ms Maria C BA(Hons) . . . . *Feb 1986
Chapman, Ms Claire . . . . *Nov 1995
Clay, Mr David N LLB(Lond); LLM(L'pool John Moores) David Lobley Debating Prize. . . . . *Jul 1969
Dagnall, Mr Graham John LLB(Hons) . . . . *Oct 1990
Davies, Mr Andrew R . . . . Mar 1992
Davies, Mr James C M David Lobley Debating Prize . *§Mar 1971
Evans, Mr David R C LLB(Lond) . . . . *Jun 1991
Evans, Ms Jeanne Louise LLB; LSF. . . . . *Nov 1994
Graham, Mr Carl MA(Oxon). . . . . *Sep 1995
Green, Mr Andrew J BA(Dunelm) . . . . *Dec 1978
Halsall, Mr Guy D LLB(Hons) . . . . *Feb 1988
Hudson, Mr Michael Hugh BA. . . . . *May 1990
Macalister, Mr Ian LLB(Hons) . . . . *Oct 1987
McIntegart, Mr Gareth Thomas LLB(Hons) . . . . . . *Sep 1995

McKee, Mr Robert J LLB . . . . *Nov 1993
Noce, Ms Anita LLB Bibby Undergraduate Scholarship; Liverpool Undergraduate University Scholarship. . . . . . . *Dec 1992
Park, Mrs Paula LLB . . . . *Oct 1989
Perry, Mr Gavin R LLB . . . . *Oct 1994
Poole, Mr Stuart LLB . . . . *Oct 1992
Poulston, Mr Mark LLB; ACII; APMI Enoch Harvey Prize (Liverpool Law Society) . . . . *Dec 1997
Pritchard, Mr Laurence P LLB(Hons); LLM . . . . . . *Oct 1982
Scott, Mr Tim LLB(UCL). . . . . *Sep 1989
Selwyn, Mr Mark LLB . . . . *Sep 1984
Szerdy, Mr James C LLB . . . . *Dec 1989
Titchmarsh, Mr Ian H MA(Cantab). . . . . *Oct 1969
Wallis, Mr Guy St J . . . . *§Dec 1973
Waring, Mr David Russell LLB(Hons) . . . . Nov 1988
Mem: Young, Mr David A LLB . . . . *Sep 1990
Ast: Akaraonye, Miss Catherina LLB(Hons); LPC . . . . . *Oct 2000
Allen, Mr Timothy James BSc . . . . *Nov 1995
Ashton, Miss Karen Ann. . . . . *Jul 2001
Barker, Miss Nicola LLB(Hons); LPC . . . . *Jun 2000
Bell, Mr Gary Thomas BA . . . . *§Jul 1994
Bell, Ms Sarah LLB . . . . *Sep 1998
Biggs, Mr Richard J LLB(Hons) . . . . *Nov 1999
Burnet, Mr Mark Edward LLB(Hons); DipLP(Dist) . . . Aug 1996
Cavanagh, Mrs Karen BA(Hons)(Social Studies); CPE; LPC . . . . May 2000
Chambers, Dr James Philip BA; DPhil(Oxon) . . . . . Mar 1996
Donovan, Mr Kieran Paul LLB. . . . . *Sep 1999
Flynn, Miss Rebecca BA(Hons); CPE; LSF . . . . . . Nov 1993
Gorton, Ms Karen C LLB(Hons) . . . . *Oct 2001
Harvey, Ms Emma Louise BA(Hons); PGDipLaw. . . *Sep 2000
Horsewood, Mrs Heather Joan LLB(Hons). . . . . . . *Dec 1995
Hoy, Mr Timothy P LLB(Hons). . . . . *Nov 1988
Jeffs, Ms Amy Louise LLB Timperon Martin Prize (Liverpool Law Society) 1999. . . . . Oct 2001
Jones, Mr Barry N LLB . . . . Jul 2000
Knight, Mr Richard David LLB. . . . . *Oct 1995
Krumins, Ms Rita BA . . . . Nov 1998
Lester, Ms Vanessa Louise LLB; LPC . . . . Oct 1999
Liggett, Miss Angela. . . . . Sep 2001
Lloyd, Mrs Rachel LLB . . . . *Sep 1999
McLoughlin, Mr Tony LLB(Hons) . . . . *Jan 2000
Russell, Mrs Lesley Ruth LLB(Hons) . . . . Apr 1999
Scholes, Ms Louise LLB(Hons) . . . . *Nov 1993
Shortall, Miss Clare Louise LLB(Hons) Rupert Bremner Award 1995 (Liverpool Law Society) . . . . Nov 1998
Simpson, Mr Alan Martin LLB(Leics). . . . . *Oct 1994
Smirles, Ms Mary Christina LLB . . . . *Sep 1997
Stoll, Mr Matthew . . . . *Oct 1990
Thomas, Miss Helen LLB(Hons) Moses Ackah Prize 1995 . . . . Sep 2001
Tsai, Miss Rowena LLB . . . . *Oct 2001
Walsh, Mrs Christine Patricia BA(Hons) . . . . *Sep 1994
Whitehurst, Mr Philip Richard LLB. . . . . May 1997
Woolgar, Miss Katy Joanne LLB. . . . . Oct 2002

DERVAN SOLICITORS ‡
Third Floor The Corn Exchange Fenwick Street Liverpool Merseyside L2 7QL
Tel: 0151 225 0150 *Fax:* 0151 225 0151
E-mail: info@dervans.com

DOMINIC & CO SOLICITORS LTD ‡
67 Moss Pits Lane Childwall Wavertree Liverpool Merseyside L15 6XE
Tel: 0151 722 5540 *Fax:* 07879 675247
E-mail: dominic@dominicka.com

THE DURES PARTNERSHIP LLP ‡
21 Cheapside Liverpool Merseyside L2 2DY
Tel: 0151 242 5111 *Fax:* 0151 242 5112 *Dx:* 14181 LIVERPOOL
E-mail: enquiries@tdpsolicitors.co.uk
List of partners: F J Dures, P Fowler
Work: A3 B1 E F1 L N O Q R2 S1 S2 W Z(c,q)
Ptr: Dures, Mr Frederick Joseph LLB(Hons) . . . . Dec 1998
Fowler, Mr Paul LLB(Hons) . . . . Sep 1999
Ast: Moon, Ms Danielle Jacqueline LLB(Hons). . . . . . . Dec 2009
Myers, Mr Jeremy LLB(Hons); MBA. . . . . *Oct 1991
Con: Freeman, Mr Geoffrey Charles LLB(Hons) Notary Public . . . . *Jun 1972
Jones, Mr Christopher Leslie LLB(Hons). . . . . Jan 2003

EAD SOLICITORS LLP ‡
Prospect House Columbus Quay Liverpool Merseyside L3 4DB
Tel: 0151 291 2500 *Fax:* 0151 735 1000 *Dx:* 740875 LIVERPOOL 12
E-mail: enquiry@eadsolicitors.co.uk
List of partners: G M Abrams, C J Boulton, S J Campbell, S Cornforth, T Doherty, J D A Leith, G S Lesin-Davis, P J McCord
Office: Huddersfield, Liverpool
Ptr: Abrams, Mr Garry M BA. . . . . *Sep 1977
Boulton, Mr Charles J LLB(Leeds). . . . . Jun 1973
Campbell, Mr Steven J . . . . Nov 1984
Cornforth, Mr Stephen LLB(L'pool) . . . . *Apr 1980
Doherty, Mr Thomas BA. . . . . *Dec 1980
Lesin-Davis, Mr Gary S . . . . Oct 1986

EAD SOLICITORS LLP
125-131 Picton Road Liverpool Merseyside L15 4LG
Tel: 0151 734 4339 *Fax:* 0151 735 1000
E-mail: enquiry@eadsolicitors.co.uk
Office: Huddersfield, Liverpool
Ptr: Leith, Mr John D A . . . . *Nov 1976
McCord, Mr Paul J . . . . *Nov 1988
Ast: Cheadle, Mrs Catherine Jane . . . . Nov 1993
Collins, Mr Malcolm . . . . Jan 1979
Con: Sandiford, Mr David H MA; LLM; PhD Notary Public. . Oct 1982

EEI SOLICITORS ‡
1-27 Bridport Street Liverpool Merseyside L3 5QF
Tel: 0151 707 8004 *Fax:* 0151 707 8004
E-mail: eeisolicitors@googlemail.com
List of partners: I J Chohan, P McPartland
Languages: German, Punjabi, Urdu
Work: C1 F1 G J1 K1 N O Q R1 S2 W Z(e,f,i,w)
Ptr: Chohan, Mr Iqbal J . . . . *Oct 1998
McPartland, Mr Peter . . . . Apr 1999

EMERALD LAW SOLICITORS ‡
Lombard Chambers Ormond Street Liverpool Merseyside L3 9NA
Tel: 0800 804 8158
E-mail: info@emeraldlaw.co.uk

ESPLEY & CO ‡
15 St Georges Road Liverpool Merseyside L37 3HH
Tel: 01704 830200 *Fax:* 01704 830201 *Dx:* 15417 FORMBY
E-mail: alan@aespley.demon.co.uk
List of partners: A Espley
Work: C1 E L R2 S1 S2 W
Ptr: Espley, Mr Alan LLB. . . . . Dec 1977

FORSTER DEAN LTD ‡
Duxford House 5 Hurricane Court International Business Park Liverpool Merseyside L24 8RL
Tel: 0151 203 4300 *Fax:* 0151 427 6694
E-mail: enquiries@forsterdean.co.uk
List of partners: W E Betts, M Collins, P Forster Dean, M Hunter, A Hussain, G J Shields, R J Taylor, D Thompson
Office: Birkenhead, Bootle, Chorley, Crewe, Eccles, Ellesmere Port, Huyton, Leigh, Liverpool (4 offices), Oldham, Preston, Rochdale, Runcorn, St Helens, Stockport, Warrington, Widnes (2 offices), Wigan

FORSTER DEAN LTD
York House 35 Prescot Street Liverpool Merseyside L7 8UE
Tel: 0151 264 8822 *Fax:* 0151 264 8844
E-mail: enquiries@forsterdean.co.uk
Office: Birkenhead, Bootle, Chorley, Crewe, Eccles, Ellesmere Port, Huyton, Leigh, Liverpool (4 offices), Oldham, Preston, Rochdale, Runcorn, St Helens, Stockport, Warrington, Widnes (2 offices), Wigan

FORSTER DEAN LTD
6 Broadgreen Road Old Swan Liverpool Merseyside L13 5SG
Tel: 0151 228 5522 *Fax:* 0151 228 5566
E-mail: enquiries@forsterdean.co.uk
Office: Birkenhead, Bootle, Chorley, Crewe, Eccles, Ellesmere Port, Huyton, Leigh, Liverpool (4 offices), Oldham, Preston, Rochdale, Runcorn, St Helens, Stockport, Warrington, Widnes (2 offices), Wigan

FORSTER DEAN LTD
82 County Road Walton Liverpool Merseyside L4 3QN
Tel: 0151 524 2443 *Fax:* 0151 524 2445
E-mail: enquiries@forsterdean.co.uk
Office: Birkenhead, Bootle, Chorley, Crewe, Eccles, Ellesmere Port, Huyton, Leigh, Liverpool (4 offices), Oldham, Preston, Rochdale, Runcorn, St Helens, Stockport, Warrington, Widnes (2 offices), Wigan

FORSTER DEAN LTD
557 West Derby Road Liverpool Merseyside L13 8AD
Tel: 0151 259 1717 *Fax:* 0151 259 1718
E-mail: enquiries@forsterdean.co.uk
Office: Birkenhead, Bootle, Chorley, Crewe, Eccles, Ellesmere Port, Huyton, Leigh, Liverpool (4 offices), Oldham, Preston, Rochdale, Runcorn, St Helens, Stockport, Warrington, Widnes (2 offices), Wigan
Ptr: Hunter, Mr Mark. . . . . May 1996

FREEMANS SOLICITORS AND NOTARIES ‡
34 Castle Street Liverpool Merseyside L2 0NR
Tel: 0151 227 3435 *Fax:* 0151 227 1997 *Dx:* 14226 LIVERPOOL
E-mail: freemanlaw@btconnect.com

GK SOLICITORS ‡
PO Box 171 Liverpool Merseyside L12 2WU
Tel: 0151 220 2838 *Fax:* 07530 722231
E-mail: karen@gksolicitors.co.uk

GT LAW SOLICITORS ‡
Gores Road Knowsley Industrial Park Liverpool Merseyside L33 7XS
Tel: 0844 414 9771
E-mail: enquiries@gtlaw.co.uk

GAMON ARDEN & CO ‡
Church House 1 Hanover Street Liverpool Merseyside L1 3DW
Tel: 0151 709 2222 *Fax:* 0151 709 3095
E-mail: info@gamonarden.com
List of partners: G Arden, R H Arden
Languages: Welsh
Work: L R1 S1 S2 W X Z(d,x)
Ptr: Arden, Mrs Glenys LLB . . . . . §Jun 1973
Arden, Mr Roger H Diocesan Registrar Notary Public *§Jun 1968

GLOBE WAREING CROPPER ‡
96 Hillfoot Avenue Hunts Cross Liverpool Merseyside L25 0PF
Tel: 0151 486 8833 *Fax:* 0151 448 1397
Emergency telephone 0161 427 6108
E-mail: globe@globesolicitors.com
List of partners: D C Globe, M A Globe
Work: A1 C1 C2 D1 E F1 J1 J2 K1 K3 K4 L N O Q R1 S1 S2 T1 V W Z(b,c,d,j,k,l,m,q,s)
Emergency Action, Advocacy and Fixed Fee Interview undertaken
Ptr: Globe, Mr David Charles DipLaw . . . . . *Aug 1999

GOLDSMITH WILLIAMS ‡
Mersey Chambers 5 Old Churchyard Liverpool Merseyside L2 8TX
Tel: 0845 373 3737 *Fax:* 0845 373 6069 *Dx:* 14186 LIVERPOOL
E-mail: mrodman@goldsmithwilliams.co.uk
List of partners: S L Cottrell, E R Goldsmith, C G Williams
Work: N Q S1 S2 W
Agency, Advocacy, Fixed Fee Interview undertaken and Member of Accident Line
Ptr: Cottrell, Mr Simon L BA(Law) . . . . . *Jan 1982
Goldsmith, Mr Edward R LLB . . . . . *Sep 1977
Williams, Mr Christopher G LLB. . . . . *Oct 1979

GOODMAN GDP SOLICITORS LLP ‡
Goodman House 33 Rodney Street Liverpool Merseyside L1 9JF
Tel: 0151 707 0090 *Fax:* 0151 707 4600 *Dx:* 28955 LIVERPOOL 2
E-mail: info@goodmanlegal.co.uk

GREGORY ABRAMS DAVIDSON LLP ‡
(incorporating Dean Newman Green & Co)
20-24 Mathew Street Cavern Quarter Liverpool Merseyside L2 6RE
Tel: 0151 236 5000 *Fax:* 0151 330 2002 *Dx:* 14102 LIVERPOOL
E-mail: info@gadllp.co.uk
List of partners: G Abrams, B H Davidson, H Friend, P J Joseph, H M Mitchinson, C M Rumke
Office: Liverpool (2 offices), London NW11
Work: D1 E G H J1 K1 K2 L N Q S1 V W X Z(p)
Emergency Action, Agency, Advocacy, Fixed Fee Interview, Legal Aid undertaken, Legal Aid Franchise and Member of Accident Line
Ptr: Abrams, Mr Gregory. . . . . *Jul 1976
Davidson, Mr Barry H LLB. . . . . *Mar 1969
Friend, Mr Harold BA . . . . . *Oct 1982

GREGORY ABRAMS DAVIDSON LLP
3 Speke Road Garston Liverpool Merseyside L19 2LX
Tel: 0151 494 0777 *Fax:* 0151 282 8210 *Dx:* 18905 ALLERTON
E-mail: lawline@gregory-abrams.com
Office: Liverpool (2 offices), London NW11
Work: D1 K1 V
Emergency Action, Agency, Advocacy, Fixed Fee Interview, Legal Aid undertaken, Legal Aid Franchise and Member of Accident Line
Ptr: Abrams, Mr Gregory. . . . . *Jul 1976
Ast: Bacon, Miss Hazel Maxine LLB(Hons). . . . . *Oct 1991

GREGORY ABRAMS DAVIDSON LLP
(incorporating Dean Newman Green & Co)
123 Penny Lane Allerton Liverpool Merseyside L18 1DF
Tel: 0151 733 3353 *Fax:* 0151 282 8202 *Dx:* 18905 ALLERTON
E-mail: lawline@gregory-abrams.com
Office: Liverpool (2 offices), London NW11
Work: D1 E G H K1 N Q S1 V W X
Emergency Action, Agency, Advocacy, Fixed Fee Interview, Legal Aid undertaken and Legal Aid Franchise
Ptr: Mitchinson, Mrs Helena Mary LLB(Hons) . . . . . *Oct 1991
Ast: Shellien, Mr Martin LLB(Hons). . . . . Dec 1988
Con: Bennett, Mr Laurence J Part time Chairman of Rent Tribunal & Rent Assessment CTEC; Part time Chairman of SEN Tribunal. . . . . Nov 1972

GREGSONS ‡
(incorporating G Gerald Strong)
305 Century Buildings Brunswick Business Park Liverpool Merseyside L3 4BL
Tel: 0151 703 2550 *Fax:* 0151 703 2570 / 2560
Dx: 715711 LIVERPOOL 14
E-mail: gregson.ashton.sp@btconnect.com
List of partners: M C J Baden, I L Wright
Office: Liverpool
Work: B1 D1 E F1 G H J1 K1 L N O P Q R1 S1 S2 V W Z(d,l,p,q,r)
Emergency Action, Agency, Advocacy, Fixed Fee Interview, Legal Aid undertaken and Member of Accident Line
Ptr: Wright, Mr Ian L LLB . . . . . Oct 1985
Con: Grantham, Mr David R LLB . . . . . §Nov 1961

GREGSONS
56-58 Liverpool Road Great Crosby Liverpool Merseyside L23 5SG
Tel: 0151 924 6444 / 236 6120 *Fax:* 0151 932 2709
E-mail: enquiries@gregsonslaw.com
Office: Liverpool
Emergency Action, Agency, Advocacy, Fixed Fee Interview and Legal Aid undertaken
Ptr: Baden, Mr Michael C J LLB. . . . . *Dec 1977

GUY WILLIAMS LAYTON ‡
Pacific Chambers 11/13 Victoria Street Liverpool Merseyside L2 5QQ
Tel: 0151 236 7171 *Fax:* 0151 236 1129 *Dx:* 14202 LIVERPOOL 1
List of partners: J D A Clayton, D M Fieldhouse, J Hogg, C Sutton, A F Whittingham-Jones
Office: Wirral
Work: A1 B1 C1 C2 E F1 J1 K1 L N O Q S1 T1 T2 V W Z(h,t)
Emergency Action, Agency, Fixed Fee Interview and Legal Aid undertaken
Ptr: Fieldhouse, Mr David M LLB(B'ham) . . . . . *Jul 1976
Hogg, Miss Jane LLB . . . . . *Jan 1983
Sutton, Miss Christine BA(Hons) . . . . . *Nov 1983
Whittingham-Jones, Mr Andrew F. . . . . *Jan 1972

JOHN HALSON SOLICITORS ‡
24-26 Hope Street Liverpool Merseyside L1 9BX
Tel: 0151 708 8123

JOHN HALSON SOLICITORS ‡
2 Bedford Road Walton Liverpool Merseyside L4 5PU
Tel: 0151 524 4540 *Fax:* 0151 523 7475
E-mail: halson@rightsatwork.co.uk

HAMPSON HUGHES (HH LAW LTD) ‡
Hampson Hughes Cotton House Old Hall Street Liverpool Merseyside L3 9LQ
Tel: 0333 240 1234 *Fax:* 0151 236 0669
E-mail: info@hampsonhughes.com

HANDLEY LAW LIMITED ‡
Mersey House Matchworks 140 Speke Road Liverpool Merseyside L19 2PH
Tel: 0845 676 9228
E-mail: enquiries@handleylaw.co.uk

HARKIN LLOYD SOLICITORS ‡
Second Floor Suite 293 India Buildings Liverpool Merseyside L2 0QD
Tel: 0151 255 0740

HEALEY KENYON MCATEER SOLICITORS ‡
293 Breck Road Anfield Liverpool Merseyside L5 6PU
Tel: 0151 261 9857
E-mail: enquiries@motoringlawbarristers.co.uk
Office: Prescot

HEANEY WATSON ‡
44 Allerton Road Allerton Liverpool Merseyside L18 1LN
Tel: 0151 293 2936 *Fax:* 0151 293 2937 *Dx:* 18916 ALLERTON
E-mail: enquiry@heaneywatson.com
List of partners: S Heaney, R Kearns, L H Watson, T Winstanley
Office: Liverpool (2 offices), Manchester
Languages: Hindi, Potwari, Punjabi, Spanish, Urdu
Work: D1 D2 K1 K2 K3
Emergency Action, Agency, Advocacy, Fixed Fee Interview, Legal Aid undertaken and Legal Aid Franchise
Dir: Kearns, Miss Ruth BA(Hons) . . . . . *Aug 1999
Ast: Jones, Miss Jennifer LLB(Hons). . . . . *Feb 2011

HEANEY WATSON
6-8 Broadway Norris Green Liverpool Merseyside L11 1JS
Tel: 0151 256 7777 *Fax:* 0151 226 4044
E-mail: enquiry@heaneywatson.com
Office: Liverpool (2 offices), Manchester
Languages: Hindi, Potwari, Punjabi, Spanish, Urdu
Work: D1 D2 K1 K2 K3
Emergency Action, Agency, Advocacy, Fixed Fee Interview, Legal Aid undertaken and Legal Aid Franchise
Dir: Winstanley, Mrs Tracy BA(Hons) . . . . . *Mar 2002
Asoc: Ormrod, Mr Andrew LLB(Hons). . . . . *Jan 2007

HEANEY WATSON
9 York Street Liverpool Merseyside L1 5BN
Tel: 0151 282 5555 *Fax:* 0151 284 1955
E-mail: enquiry@heaneywatson.com
Office: Liverpool (2 offices), Manchester
Languages: French, Hindi, Potwari, Punjabi, Spanish, Urdu, Welsh
Work: D1 D2 K1 K2 K3
Emergency Action, Agency, Advocacy, Fixed Fee Interview and Legal Aid undertaken
Dir: Heaney, Mr Simon LLB(Hons) ♦. . . . . *Jan 1998
Watson, Ms Liza Helen LLB(Hons) . . . . . *Jul 1993
Asoc: Squires, Ms Emma L LLB(Hons) . . . . . Sep 2004
Stokes, Ms Kelly . . . . . *Jun 2004
Ast: Gomery, Ms Kate BA(Hons). . . . . *Apr 2011
Travis, Miss Rebecca LLB. . . . . *Nov 2009

HENLEY LAW ‡
PO Box 88 Liverpool Merseyside L17 5WA
Tel: 0151 726 0976 *Fax:* 0151 727 3266
E-mail: thea@henleylaw.co.uk

HERZOG & ASSOCIATES ‡
Charleston House 12 Rumford Place Liverpool Merseyside L3 9DG
Tel: 0844 499 5717 *Fax:* 0844 499 5727
E-mail: office@herzogandassociates.co.uk

CATHERINE HIGGINS LAW FIRM ‡
Suite 602 Cotton Exchange Liverpool Merseyside L3 9LQ
Tel: 0151 236 8840 *Fax:* 0870 738 6404
E-mail: enquiries@chigginslaw.co.uk

HILL DICKINSON LLP ‡
No1 St Paul's Square Liverpool Merseyside L3 9SJ
Tel: 0151 600 8000 *Fax:* 0151 600 8001 *Dx:* 14129 LIVERPOOL
E-mail: law@hilldickinson.com
List of partners: S Ahmed, A C Allen, G Archibald, S A Armstrong, A M Ashley Taylor, K E Ayres, P Baker, P Barlow, C N Batchelor, H A Baucher, J Berkson, M R Blakey, J Bleasdale, A Bogle, P F Bradbury, P W Bullivant, R H F Bullivant, A J Caddies, I Campbell, P A Campbell, W Chandler, E Charrot, E C Cheyney, D S Chinn, W J Clayton, N R Clift, D Conway, H Cornes, R F Coward, A Craggs, P D'Costa, R G L Dale-Jones, G R G Davidson, M N Davies, D Dowen, A C Dry, D J Dunne, E E Edwards, P Ellaby, M G Entwistle, A D Evans, N J Fagan, P Farrar, R A Farrell, S N Felce, I C Gardiner, R S J Gardner, P Garvey, A Gibbons, A P Gibson, A J Gillespie, D N Godfrey, A J Goldsmith, S A Grant, R B Green, V Green, L Grey, P Haddon, D J Halsall, J Hamilton, P Hanlon, P H Hawkins, R B Heanley, S C Hindmarsh, K Holuba, A Horne, A L Houghton, D M Hoyes, J R Hulmes, N Humphreys, J E Isaacs, P Jackson, P James, R A James, A Johnson, A Johnson, M K Jones, P Jones, R W Jones, L A Kelly, F M R Kenny, P Keown, F Konynenburg, S Lansdown, R J Lawrence, J E S Lawson, A D Leslie, C A Lewis-Ethelston, J D Lomax, C D Lucas, G J Lynch, A J W MacPhie, M F Mallin, A Marsh, L Martin, P C Mavroghonis, J M Maxwell, M C McDonald, A K McDonnell, J McGarva, D J McGinn, S J McGorian, M J McKenna, A Meads, P M Milburn, J B R Monck-Mason, M J Morrison, S K Morrison, A R Mowat, S J Naylor, B Nolan, J O'Sullivan, P Oakes, A Oliver, D R M Oram, R J Palmer, E Panayotopoulou, S H Parrington, A R Parry, R J Paton, M Penny, D N Phillips, D C Pitlarge, M Pittordis, G P Plunkett, R Pointon, J N Pople, J D Porter, P K Pourgourides, J Preece, A J Pugh, N G Pye, M J Quinn, D M Rabagliati, D J Rawlinson, H M Rooney, S J Russell, G M Ryan, D A Scott, J Seery, J Southworth, A W Speed, J Spencer, C Stanton, M P Stephens, T C Stephenson, D R Swaffield, M R Taylor, R M Taylor, J Trewin, W A Twemlow, J A Upton, C Walker, R H Wallis, P Walton, D Wareing, R C Watson, S Wightman, A J Williams, B M Williams, A E Wilson, S Wilson, P D Woods, M D Woolley
Office: Chester, London EC3, Manchester, Sheffield
Languages: Cantonese, Danish, French, German, Italian, Latin, Norwegian, Portuguese, Spanish, Swedish, Welsh
Work: A1 A3 B1 B2 B3 C1 C2 C3 D1 D2 E F1 F2 G H I J1 J2 K1 K2 L M1 M2 M3 N O P Q R1 R2 S1 S2 T1 T2 U1 U2 V W X Z(a,b,c,d,e,f,g,h,i,j,k,l,m,o,p,q,r,t,u,w,x,y)
Emergency Action, Agency, Advocacy, Fixed Fee Interview, Legal Aid undertaken, Legal Aid Franchise and Member of Accident Line
Ptr: Archibald, Mr Graham. . . . . Nov 1994
Baker, Mr Paul LLB . . . . . *Mar 1985
Barlow, Mr Peter LLB Bromley Prize. . . . . *Sep 1985
Berkson, Mr Jonathan LLB . . . . . *Oct 1990
Bleasdale, Mr Jason LLB . . . . . *Oct 1993
Bradbury, Mr Philip F LLB. . . . . *May 1992
Bullivant, Mr Peter W . . . . . *§Oct 1963
Bullivant, Mr Ralph H F LLB. . . . . *§Nov 1989
Campbell, Mr Peter A BA . . . . . *Oct 1987
Chandler, Mr William LLB . . . . . *§Sep 1996
Chinn, Mr David S LLB; FCIArb . . . . . *Nov 1990
Conway, Mr David. . . . . *Dec 1993
Coward, Mr Robert F LLB; LLM . . . . . *§Nov 1985
Craggs, Mr Andrew LLB. . . . . *Apr 2000
Dale-Jones, Mr R Glyn L MA; LLB(Cantab) . . . . . *Nov 1974
Davies, Mr Matthew Neil LLB(Hons). . . . . *Jun 1998
Dry, Miss Abigail Catherine LLB(Hons)(L'pool). . . . . §Sep 1997
Dunne, Mr David J BA(Law). . . . . *Dec 1987
Edwards, Elwyn E LLB . . . . . *Apr 1977
Evans, Mr Andrew David LLB(Hons); LPC. . . . . *Sep 2000
Fagan, Mr Noel J LLB(L'pool) . . . . . *Apr 1975
Farrar, Mr Philip LLB . . . . . Nov 1993
Farrell, Mr Ronald Arthur LLB(Hons); ACIArb . . . . . *Oct 1994
Felce, Mr Simon N LLB . . . . . *§May 1990
Gardiner, Mr Ian Christopher LLB(Hons). . . . . *Mar 1999
Gibbons, Mr Anthony LLB(Nott'm). . . . . *Apr 1972
Gillespie, Mr Alastair John LLB(Hons). . . . . *Nov 1994
Green, Mr Richard B LLB(Hons) E Rex Makin Prize; The Muir Mathews Prize . . . . . *Oct 1988
Green, Ms Victoria LLB . . . . . *Nov 1990
Grey, Ms Lisa. . . . . Jun 2002
Halsall, Mrs Deborah J LLB . . . . . *§Oct 1987
Hamilton, Mr Jamie LLB(Hons) . . . . . *Sep 1996
Hanlon, Ms Paula. . . . . Feb 1999
Holuba, Ms Kathy. . . . . Nov 1990
Houghton, Mr Anthony L LLB . . . . . *Oct 1988
Hulmes, Mr John R BA(Law) . . . . . *Nov 1982
Jackson, Mr Peter. . . . . Oct 1985
James, Mr Philip LLB(Hons). . . . . *Oct 1994
James, Mr Richard A LLB. . . . . *§Dec 1987
Johnson, Mr Alistair. . . . . Nov 1996
Jones, Mr Michael Kenneth LLB. . . . . Nov 1996
Jones, Miss Pamela. . . . . *§Nov 1977
Kelly, Miss Lisa Anne FILEx. . . . . *Nov 1999
Kenny, Miss Fionnuala Mary Rose LLB . . . . . *§Nov 1993
Lansdown, Mr Stephen LLB(Hons); LSF. . . . . *Nov 1994

See p112 for the Key to Work Categories & other symbols

Lawrence, Mrs Ruth J LLB . . . *Oct 1990
Leslie, Mr Andrew D LLB . . . *Nov 1999
Lomax, Mr John D LLB . . . *§Feb 1989
Lynch, Mr Graham J LLB . . . *Oct 1991
McDonald, Mr Martyn C BA . . . *§Mar 1986
McDonnell, Mr Anthony K LLB . . . *Oct 1984
McGinn, Mr Dominic John LLB . . . *Sep 1991
McGorian, Ms Susan J LLB . . . *§Oct 1986
Martin, Mr Lawford BA; LPC. . . . *Nov 1996
Maxwell, Mr John M LLB Notary Public . . . *Dec 1969
Mowat, Mr Allan R BA. . . . *Jul 1980
Naylor, Ms Sarah Jane BA; LLB. . . . *May 1991
Oliver, Mr Anthony LLB Sweet & Maxwell Law Prize. . *Sep 1994
Oram, Mr David Robert Michael BA(Hons) . . . *Oct 1986
Parry, Mr Anthony R . . . *§Nov 1997
Paton, Mr Richard J MA(Cantab) . . . *§Jun 1972
Plunkett, Mr Gregory P LLB(Hons) . . . *§Oct 1988
Pointon, Mr Roger LLB . . . *Nov 1996
Preece, Mr James. . . . Nov 1993
Pugh, Mr Alan John LLB(Hons) . . . *Sep 1996
Pye, Mr Nicholas G LLB. . . . *Oct 1982
Quinn, Mr Michael J MA(Cantab) . . . *Nov 1974
Rawlinson, Mr David J LLB . . . *§Apr 1976
Russell, Ms Susan J LLB . . . *Nov 1985
Scott, Mr David A BA(Law) . . . *Nov 1987
Southworth, Mr James . . . Feb 2000
Spencer, Mr Jason LLB . . . *Oct 1994
Stanton, Mr Christopher MA. . . . *§Sep 1997
Stephens, Mr Michael P. . . . *§Jun 1981
Swaffield, Mr David R MA(Cantab) Timpron Martin Prize; Atkinson Prize . . . *Jan 1979
Trewin, Ms Joanna LLB(Hons) Atkinson Prize Liverpool Law Society 1999 . . . *Sep 2001
Walker, Mr Craig LLB . . . *Oct 1993
Walton, Mr Paul LLB . . . *§Jun 1969
Watson, Mr Richard C LLB . . . *Oct 1990
Williams, Mr Andrew John LLB(Hons); BCL Maxwell Law Prize; Levi Law Prize . . . *Jan 1995
Wilson, Mr Anthony E LLB(Nott'm) ♦ . . . *Jan 1977
Wilson, Miss Sharon BA(Hons) . . . *May 1997
Dir: Twemlow, Mr William A MA(Cantab). . . . *§Sep 1968
Asoc: Herbert, Ms Nicola LLB . . . *§Jun 1990
Hilton, Mr Paul Robert FILEx . . . *Sep 2000
Hodges, Mr Philip Eric LLB(Hons). . . . Mar 2001
Smith, Mr Paul LLB . . . *§Apr 1977
Ast: Hodgkinson, Samantha . . . Sep 2004

HILL DICKINSON LLP ‡
The Corn Exchange Fenwick Street Liverpool Merseyside L2 7RB
Tel: 0151 236 5400
E-mail: law@hilldickinson.com

HOGAN BROWN ‡
1 Union Court Cook Street Liverpool Merseyside L2 4SJ
Tel: 0151 243 7500 *Fax:* 0151 243 7501 *Dx:* 14117 LIVERPOOL
E-mail: enquiries@hoganbrown.co.uk
Work: B2 G H Z(g)
Legal Aid Franchise

JOHN HUGHES & CO ‡
PO BOX 125 Formby Liverpool Merseyside L37 2WR
Tel: 01704 832244 *Fax:* 01704 832244

HUSBAND FORWOOD MORGAN ‡ (incorporating T D Morgan & Co; Husband Forwood Williams & Co)
26 Exchange Street East Liverpool Merseyside L2 3PH
Tel: 0151 236 9626 *Fax:* 0151 236 3934 *Dx:* 14173 LIVERPOOL
E-mail: hfmsols@btconnect.com
List of partners: P Crook, I A Fisher, C J Morton
Work: B1 C1 D1 D2 E F1 F2 J1 K1 K2 K3 K4 N Q R1 S1 S2 T1 T2 V W Z(d,m,q,v)
Agency and Advocacy undertaken
Ptr: Crook, Mr Peter. . . . *Jan 1970
Fisher, Mr Ian A LLB(St Andrews) Notary Public. . . *§Dec 1972
Morton, Mr Christopher John BA(Oxon) Notary Public *§Jun 1972

IMR SOLICITORS ‡
412-414 Longmoor Lane Fazakerley Liverpool Merseyside L9 9DB
Tel: 0151 521 0055 *Fax:* 0151 525 0337
E-mail: mail@imrlegal.com

IRVINGS ‡
45 Breck Road Anfield Liverpool Merseyside L4 2QS
Tel: 0800 954 0243 *Fax:* 0151 258 2000 *Dx:* 702773 ANFIELD
E-mail: info@irvingslaw.com
List of partners: A Irving, S T Irving
Office: Liverpool
Work: D1 E K1 L N Q V W Z(m)
Emergency Action, Advocacy, Fixed Fee Interview and Legal Aid undertaken
Ptr: Irving, Mrs Anne LLB; MBA Elizabeth James Scholarship; Liverpool University Award . . . *Sep 1984
Irving, Mr Stephen T LLB . . . *Apr 1977

IRVINGS
Mercury Court Tithe Barn Street Liverpool Merseyside L2 2QP
Tel: 0800 954 0243 *Fax:* 0151 258 2000 *Dx:* 14270 LIVERPOOL
E-mail: info@irvingslaw.com
Office: Liverpool
Work: B1 C1 C2 D1 E F1 K1 L N O P Q W Z(c,e,f,l,q,y)
Agency, Advocacy, Fixed Fee Interview and Legal Aid undertaken
Ptr: Irving, Mrs Anne LLB; MBA Elizabeth James Scholarship; Liverpool University Award . . . *Sep 1984
Irving, Mr Stephen T LLB . . . *Apr 1977
Ast: Carter, Miss Sarah V LLB(Hons); RGN Rupert Butler Prize . . . Nov 1997

JST LAWYERS ‡
Colonial Chambers Temple Street Liverpool Merseyside L2 5RH
Tel: 0151 282 2828 *Fax:* 0151 282 2848 *Dx:* 14278 LIVERPOOL 1
E-mail: info@jstmackintosh.co.uk
List of partners: J L Shield, H E Summers
Work: A3 B1 C1 C2 E I J1 L N O P Q R2 S1 S2 W Z(b,d,h,j,k,l,n)
Agency, Advocacy and Fixed Fee Interview undertaken
Ptr: Shield, Mr John L LLB. . . . *Mar 1971
Summers, Ms Heather E LLB . . . *Oct 1989

RICHARD JACKLIN & CO
Fraser House Rumford Court 8a Rumford Place Liverpool Merseyside L3 9BY
Tel: 0151 243 1313 *Fax:* 0151 243 1314
E-mail: sm@jacklin.co.uk
Office: Southport
Work: K4 T2 W
Ptr: Jacklin, Mr Richard LLB Notary Public. . . . *Jun 1971
Malthouse, Mrs Susan BA. . . . *Nov 1976

ANDREW JACKSON & CO ‡
Unit 7 Belle Vale Shopping Centre Childwell Valley Road Liverpool Merseyside L25 2RG
Tel: 0151 487 8426 *Fax:* 0151 708 5850
List of partners: M J Ellenbogen, A H James
Office: Liverpool
Work: D1 F1 G H J1 K1 L M1 P S1 V W Z(i,l)
Emergency Action, Agency, Advocacy, Fixed Fee Interview, Legal Aid undertaken and Member of Accident Line
Ptr: Ellenbogen, Mr Michael J . . . *Oct 1986

ANDREW JACKSON & CO
80 Lodge Lane Liverpool Merseyside L8 0QL
Tel: 0151 709 5816 / 488 1000
E-mail: andrew@larklaw.co.uk
Office: Liverpool
Work: K1 N Q S1 S2 W
Emergency Action, Fixed Fee Interview and Legal Aid Franchise
Ptr: Ellenbogen, Mr Michael J . . . *Oct 1986
James, Mr Andrew Henry LLB(Hons) . . . *Oct 1990

MARK JONES & PARTNERS ‡
19 Castle Street Liverpool Merseyside L2 4SX
Tel: 0151 286 9594 *Fax:* 0151 286 1661 *Dx:* 14254 LIVERPOOL 1
Emergency telephone 0800 131 3298
E-mail: justice@mjsolicitors.co.uk
List of partners: R A Code, M Ellis, P J Freckleton, N F Gunn, M H Jones, M J Lea, D J McNabb, S F Rae
Office: Birkenhead
Work: B2 G H N
Legal Aid Franchise
Ptr: Code, Mr Robert Andrew ★ . . . Sep 1998
Ellis, Mr Michael ★ . . . Oct 1996
Jones, Mr Mark Harold BA ★ . . . *§Apr 1983
Lea, Mr Michael John LLB(Hons) . . . *Mar 1985
McNabb, Mr Dominic James LLB . . . *Apr 1992
Rae, Mr Stuart Farquhar BA(Hons) ★ . . . Oct 1994

THOS R JONES & SON ‡
4 Sefton Road Litherland Liverpool Merseyside L21 7PG
Tel: 0151 928 0715 *Fax:* 0151 920 8765
List of partners: J G Smith
Work: A2 D2 E F1 J1 K1 L N S1 S2 V W Z(h,l)
Agency and Fixed Fee Interview undertaken
Ptr: Smith, Mr John G LLB(L'pool). . . . Nov 1974

KM TAMLIN ‡
11 Quickswood Close Woolton Liverpool Merseyside L25 4TT
Tel: 0151 428 2088

KEANEY WHITEHEAD PARTNERSHIP LLP (KWP) ‡
20-22 Mathew Street Liverpool Merseyside L2 6RE
Tel: 0151 255 1790 *Fax:* 0151 236 4121
E-mail: crime@kwpsolicitors.com

KIRWANS
6th Floor Martins Building Water Street Liverpool Merseyside L2 3SX
Tel: 0151 229 5600 *Fax:* 0151 229 5601 *Dx:* 14115 LIVERPOOL
Emergency telephone 07770 864 037
E-mail: info@kirwinssolicitors.co.uk
Office: Birkenhead, Moreton
Work: A1 B1 B2 C1 D1 E F1 F2 G H I J1 K1 K3 K4 L N O Q R1 R2 S1 S2 V W Z(e,k,l,p,q)
Emergency Action, Agency, Advocacy, Fixed Fee Interview, Legal Aid undertaken and Member of Accident Line
Ptr: Gibson, Mr Simon Keith LLB(Hons) . . . *Aug 2001
Murray, Mr Stephen John LLB. . . . *Feb 2003
Sandys, Mr Michael LLB; LLM. . . . *Mar 2002
Tuson, Mr John James Frederick BA . . . *Sep 1998
Ast: Armstrong, Miss Michelle . . . *Sep 2006
Lo, Miss Catherine LLB(Hons). . . . *Mar 2005
Nair, Mrs Mallika Arun. . . . *Jan 2006

KNOWLES SOLICITORS ‡
The Observatory 1 Old Haymarket Liverpool Merseyside L1 6EN
Tel: 0870 753 0850 *Fax:* 0870 753 0851

LAURENCE LEE & CO ‡
529 West Derby Road Liverpool Merseyside L13 8AA
Tel: 0151 259 1211 / 259 2824 *Fax:* 0151 259 5172
Dx: 14123 LIVERPOOL
Emergency telephone 07973 854095
E-mail: laurence.lee@laurenceleesolicitors.co.uk
List of partners: L M Lee
Languages: French, German
Work: B2 D1 D2 E F1 G H K1 L N P R1 S1 W
Emergency Action, Agency, Advocacy, Fixed Fee Interview, Legal Aid undertaken and Member of Accident Line
Ptr: Lee, Mr Laurence M LLB . . . *Jun 1976
Ast: Ablett, Mr John R. . . . Sep 1990

LEGAL RISK ‡
28 Bixteth Street Liverpool Merseyside L3 9UH
Tel: 0845 330 6791

LEI DAT & BAIG SOLICITORS ‡
2nd Floor 34 Stanley Street Liverpool Merseyside L1 6AL
Tel: 0151 258 1868

LEI DAT & BAIG SOLICITORS ‡
1st Floor Grand Central Chambers Liverpool Merseyside L1 2SF
Tel: 0151 708 8787 *Fax:* 0151 708 8781
E-mail: leidatbaigsolicitors@yahoo.com

J B LEITCH & CO ‡
71-72 Trade Winds Square Duke Street Liverpool Merseyside L1 5BG
Tel: 0151 708 2250 *Fax:* 0151 708 2251 *Dx:* 28953 LIVERPOOL 2
E-mail: mail@jbleitch.co.uk
List of partners: J B J Leitch
Work: B1 L O Z(b)
Advocacy and Fixed Fee Interview undertaken
SPr: Leitch, Mr Jonathan B J LLB(Hons) . . . *Nov 1991

LINSKILLS SOLICITORS ‡
6-8 Castle Street City Centre Liverpool Merseyside L2 0NB
Tel: 0151 236 2224 *Fax:* 0151 236 0151 *Dx:* 14215 LIVERPOOL 1
Emergency telephone 07836 711755
E-mail: stephanie.wilson@linskills.co.uk
List of partners: M J Lea, J S Linskill
Work: D1 F1 G H J1 K1 L N Q S1 V W Z(h,l,m,p)
Emergency Action, Agency, Advocacy, Fixed Fee Interview, Legal Aid undertaken, Legal Aid Franchise and Member of Accident Line
Ptr: Lea, Mr Michael John LLB(Hons) . . . *Mar 1985
Linskill, Mr Julian S LLB. . . . *Jul 1975
Ast: Beardwood, Mr Oliver J H LLB . . . *Feb 1988
Brunskill, Mr Michael John . . . *Oct 1998
Gunn, Mr Neil Fraser LLB(Hons) . . . *Dec 1998
Murphy, Mrs Julie BA(Hons). . . . *Jun 1996
Othen, Ms Victoria Jane BA. . . . *Sep 1997
Quinn, Miss Charlotte BA(Hons). . . . *Aug 1996
Sutton, Ms Miriam Louise LLB(Hons) . . . *Aug 1992
Whitelaw, Mr Roy LLB(Hons) . . . *Nov 1996

MJP JUSTICE LIMITED ‡
214 The Cotton Exchange Old Hall Street Liverpool Merseyside L3 9LQ
Tel: 0151 243 6700 *Fax:* 0151 243 6701 *Dx:* 14254 LIVERPOOL
E-mail: justice@mjpsolicitors.co.uk

MSB SOLICITORS LLP ‡
17 Allerton Road Allerton Liverpool Merseyside L18 1LG
Tel: 0151 281 9040 *Fax:* 0151 282 0164 *Dx:* 18906 ALLERTON
E-mail: enquiries@msbsolicitors.co.uk
List of partners: P S Bibby, E Carey, G P Dervan, S J E Sexton
Office: Liverpool (2 offices)
Work: C1 E F1 F2 G K1 L N O Q S1 S2
Ptr: Bibby, Mr Paul S LLB . . . *Nov 1986

MSB SOLICITORS LLP
20-22 Tapton Way Wavertree Business Village Liverpool Merseyside L13 1DA
Tel: 0151 281 9040 *Fax:* 0151 254 1652 *Dx:* 700701 WAVERTREE
E-mail: sean@msbsolicitors.co.uk
Office: Liverpool (2 offices)
Work: C1 E F1 F2 G H K1 L N O Q S1 W Z(f,m,q,w,x)
Agency, Advocacy, Legal Aid undertaken and Legal Aid Franchise
Ptr: Carey, Ms Emma . . . Jun 2000
Dervan, Mr Gerrard P. . . . Jan 1997
Sexton, Mr Sean J E BA(Dunelm) Honorary Secretary to Liverpool Law Society. . . . *Mar 1984

MSB SOLICITORS LLP
Silkhouse Court Tithebarn Street Liverpool Merseyside L2 2LZ
Tel: 0151 281 9040 *Fax:* 0151 236 6948
E-mail: enquiries@msbsolicitors.co.uk
Office: Liverpool (2 offices)

MWT SOLICITORS ‡
52 Penny Lane Mossley Hill Liverpool Merseyside L18 1DG
Tel: 0151 282 2615 *Fax:* 0151 734 5176
E-mail: info@mwtsolicitors.co.uk

MCKAYS SOLICITORS ‡
47 Seel Street Liverpool Merseyside L1 4AZ
Tel: 0151 702 4858 *Fax:* 0151 702 4868
List of partners: A Mckay
Dir: Mckay, Mr Adam LLB(Hons). . . . Dec 1998

MCKENNAS SOLICITORS ‡
49 Newsham Drive Liverpool Merseyside L6 7UQ
Tel: 07853 372037
E-mail: info@mckennasolicitors.eu

MACKRELL & THOMAS ‡
144 Liverpool Road Page Moss Liverpool Merseyside L36 3RG
Tel: 0151 480 3666 *Fax:* 0151 480 3677
Emergency telephone 07850 733625
E-mail: enquiries@mackrellandthomas.com
List of partners: J A Mackrell
Work: G H N
Emergency Action, Agency, Advocacy, Fixed Fee Interview, Legal Aid undertaken, Legal Aid Franchise and Member of Accident Line
Ptr: Mackrell, Mr Joseph Anthony LLB. . . . *Apr 1979
Asoc: Evans, Mrs Beverley A BA(Hons) . . . Oct 1995
Ast: Richardson, Mr Kevin LLB. . . . Nov 1994

E REX MAKIN & CO ‡
Leigh Street Whitechapel Liverpool Merseyside L1 1HQ
Tel: 0151 709 4491 *Fax:* 0151 708 8638
E-mail: mail@rexmakin.co.uk
List of partners: M W Green, E R Makin, R S G Makin, D Moss, J O'Leary, G H Scales
Work: B1 B2 C1 D1 D2 E F1 G H J1 K1 L M1 N O P Q R1 S1 S2 T1 W X Z(b,c,d,e,f,g,h,j,k,l,p,q,s,t)
Emergency Action, Agency, Advocacy, Fixed Fee Interview, Legal Aid undertaken, Legal Aid Franchise and Member of Accident Line
Ptr: Green, Mr Martin W ● . . . Jan 1969
Makin, Mr Robin S G LLB ● . . . Sep 1986
Moss, Mr Daniel LLB . . . Oct 1990
O'Leary, Mr John BCL. . . . Dec 1976
Scales, Miss Gillian Helen LLB . . . Dec 1996
Asoc: Edwards, Mr Richard LLB. . . . Apr 2005
Ast: Pinder, Mrs Naomi LLB . . . *Oct 1988
Con: Woodhams, Mr Brian D. . . . *§Dec 1964

MARKS & CLERK
Tower Building Water Street Liverpool Merseyside L3 1BA
Tel: 0151 243 5400 *Fax:* 0151 236 2244
Office: Birmingham, Cheltenham, Leeds, Leicester, London WC2, Manchester, Oxford

MAXWELL HODGE SOLICITORS ‡
9c Altway Old Roan Aintree Liverpool Merseyside L10 3JA
Tel: 0151 526 9321 *Fax:* 0151 526 1331
E-mail: info@maxweb.co.uk
List of partners: C M Banks, M P Danby, C A Dickinson, M L Gordon, D J Griffiths, A L F Langfeld, S J Leyland, G Lord, A D Newton, C H Newton, V J Richardson, D M Scoular, M B Unsworth, S E Veevers, F C Williams, M J Yates
Office: Formby, Heswall, Huyton, Kirkby, Liverpool, Maghull, West Kirby
Work: K4 S1 W
Fixed Fee Interview undertaken
Ptr: Scoular, Miss Denise Michelle Dip Prof Skills(Cantab) . *Oct 1996

MAXWELL HODGE SOLICITORS
14 Castle Street Liverpool Merseyside L2 0SG
Tel: 0151 227 4545 *Fax:* 0151 236 5067 *Dx:* 14192 LIVERPOOL
E-mail: info@maxweb.co.uk
Office: Formby, Heswall, Huyton, Kirkby, Liverpool, Maghull, West Kirby
Work: B1 C1 E F1 F2 J1 J2 N O Q S2 Z(q)

Agency and Fixed Fee Interview undertaken
Ptr: Griffiths, Mr David John . . . . *Jun 1975
Unsworth, Mr Martin B . . . . *§Dec 1969
Veevers, Mrs Sally Elisabeth . . . . *Mar 1992
Ast: Scott, Mrs Melissa Louise LLB(Hons) . . . . *Jun 2005

TRACEY MILLER FAMILY LAW ‡
7th Floor Silkhouse Court Tithebarn Street Liverpool Merseyside L2 2LZ
Tel: 0151 515 3036 *Fax:* 0151 515 3037
E-mail: info@traceymillerfamilylaw.com

MINARDS PAVLOU ‡
65-69 College Road Liverpool Merseyside L23 0RN
Tel: 0151 476 2000 *Fax:* 0151 476 2019 *Dx:* 13633 WATERLOO
E-mail: pp@mp-law.co.uk

MORECROFTS SOLICITORS LLP ‡
Tithebarn House 1-5 Tithebarn Street Liverpool Merseyside L2 2NZ
Tel: 0151 236 8871 *Fax:* 0151 236 8109 *Dx:* 14142 LIVERPOOL
E-mail: mail@morecroft.co.uk
List of partners: C A Brennan, H Broughton, R Burns, S P Davidson, A J Eaton, L A M Heseltine, B T Lawlor, B M Rimmer, J A Waring
Office: Birkenhead, Crosby, Liverpool
Languages: French
Work: A3 B1 B2 B3 C1 C2 C3 D1 D2 E F1 F2 J1 J2 K1 K2 K4 L M1 M2 N O P Q R1 R2 S1 S2 T1 T2 V W X Z(b,c,d,e,i,j,k,l,o,p,q,r,s)
Emergency Action, Agency, Advocacy, Fixed Fee Interview, Legal Aid undertaken, Legal Aid Franchise and Member of Accident Line
Ptr: Broughton, Miss Helen LLB . . . . *Apr 1981
Burns, Miss Rachel LLB(Hons) . . . . Oct 1993
Eaton, Miss Angela J LLB. . . . . *Nov 1985
Heseltine, Mrs Lesley Anne Mary LLB. . . . . Apr 1979
Lawlor, Mr Brian T LLB . . . . *Apr 1977
Rimmer, Miss Barbara M LLB . . . . *Apr 1978
Waring, Miss Julie Ann LLB(Hons) . . . . *Sep 2001
Asoc: Dring, Helen . . . . Jan 2006
Lamb, Mr Michael. . . . . Oct 2000
Lobb, Miss Alison LLB(Hons) . . . . *Oct 1993
Millet, Mr Charles Simon Giles LLB . . . . *Aug 2002
Ast: Brown, Angela . . . . Aug 2006
Carter, Miss Hannah Amy LLB . . . . *Jul 2007
Knewstubb, Catriona . . . . Apr 2004
Pool, Miss Eleanor LLB . . . . *Sep 2008
Stanway, Ms Sally. . . . . Sep 2010
Ware, Mr Robert Richard Herbert LLB. . . . . *May 2008
Con: Bark-Jones, Mr Richard MA. . . . . *§Nov 1968
Davidson, Mr G Crawford LLB Clerk to the Commissioner of Income Tax (Liverpool Division) . . . . Oct 1965
Freeman, Mr R N Godfrey LLB . . . . *§Dec 1971
Hugman, Mr John Melvin . . . . *Apr 1979

MORECROFTS SOLICITORS LLP
7 Church Road Woolton Liverpool Merseyside L25 5JE
Tel: 0151 428 1911 *Fax:* 0151 428 2065
E-mail: mail@morecroft.co.uk
Office: Birkenhead, Crosby, Liverpool
Work: A1 A3 B1 C1 C2 C3 D1 D2 E F1 G H J1 K1 K2 K4 L M1 M2 N O P Q R1 R2 S1 S2 T1 T2 V W X Z(l,o,q,r)
Emergency Action, Agency, Advocacy, Fixed Fee Interview, Legal Aid undertaken, Legal Aid Franchise and Member of Accident Line
Ast: Jarvis, Ms Michelle . . . . Sep 2007

SIMON J MURPHY ‡
Aintree Way Suite 8/9 Liverpool Merseyside L9 5AQ
Tel: 0151 559 9748 *Fax:* 0151 523 1490
E-mail: simon@sjmsolicitors.co.uk

JAMES MURRAY SOLICITORS
15 Cazneau Street Liverpool Merseyside L3 3AN
Tel: 0151 207 9910 *Fax:* 0151 207 9908
Emergency telephone 0151 222 3333
E-mail: info@jamesmurray.law.co.uk
Office: Bootle
Work: B2 D1 G H K1 N

NADIM ASSOCIATES SOLICITORS LIMITED
Unit 27 Inshops Kirby Liverpool Merseyside L32 8US
Tel: 0151 549 2522 *Fax:* 0151 548 0037
E-mail: info@solicitorslaw.com
Office: Birkenhead

NATIONAL LAWYER SERVICES- ASSAULT CLAIMS UK ‡
261 Ince Avenue Liverpool Merseyside L4 7UU
Tel: 0800 731 8344 *Fax:* 0151 434 4986
E-mail: info@assaultclaims.co.uk

NESBIT LAW GROUP LLP
Independence House 6 Tapton Way Wavertree Business Village Liverpool Merseyside L13 1DA
Tel: 0845 463 2836 *Fax:* 0844 412 7329
E-mail: mail@nesbitlawgroup.co.uk
Office: Bury, Leeds, Wembley

O'CONNORS LLP ‡
The Plaza 100 Old Hall Street Liverpool Merseyside L3 9QJ
Tel: 0151 906 1000 *Fax:* 0151 906 1001
E-mail: enquiries@oconnorsllp.co.uk

PCJ SOLICITORS (LLD) ‡
4th Floor 2 Moorfields Liverpool Merseyside L2 2BS
Tel: 0151 236 6400 *Fax:* 0151 236 4545 *Dx:* 14220 LIVERPOOL
E-mail: legal@pcjs.co.uk

PJW LEGAL ‡
34 Dulverton Road Liverpool Merseyside L17 6AR
Tel: 0151 427 0274 *Fax:* 0151 427 0274
E-mail: pjwlegal@btinternet.com

PARRY WELCH LACEY ‡
4 Gentwood Parade Liverpool Merseyside L36 2QB
Tel: 0151 480 4061 *Fax:* 0151 480 4330
E-mail: info@parrywelchlaceyllp.co.uk

THE PAUL ROONEY PARTNERSHIP ‡
19-23 Stanley Street Liverpool Merseyside L1 6AA
Tel: 0151 227 2851 *Fax:* 0151 255 0455 *Dx:* 14183 LIVERPOOL
Emergency telephone 0151 236 3031
List of partners: S A Brassington, T S Ireland, P O'Hare, C F M Rooney, P Rooney
Work: J1 N
Emergency Action, Agency, Advocacy, Fixed Fee Interview and Legal Aid undertaken
Ptr: Brassington, Ms Susan A . . . . Oct 1982
Ireland, Mr Tinothy Stephen LLB(Hons) ♦ . . . . *Apr 1987
O'Hare, Mr Paul LLB(Hons). . . . . Dec 2002
Rooney, Miss Claire F M LLB ♦ . . . . *Apr 1980
Rooney, Mr Paul LLB ♦ . . . . *Nov 1970
Ast: Evans, Mr Jonathon BA(Hons) . . . . Aug 2000
Stott, Mr Nick LLB(Hons) . . . . Jul 1997
Webster, Miss Mary Louise BSc(Hons)(Econ) . . . . . Aug 1998
Whitehurst, Mrs Helen LLB(Hons). . . . . Dec 1995

PEARSON FIELDING POLSON ‡
Trueman Court Trueman Street Liverpool Merseyside L3 2BA
Tel: 0151 236 3636 *Fax:* 0151 236 3630 *Dx:* 14277 LIVERPOOL
Emergency telephone 07703 348671
E-mail: enquiries@pearson-fielding.co.uk
List of partners: I Birch, J K Fielding, A J Pearson, A G Polson, S J Polson
Work: B2 G H
Emergency Action, Agency, Advocacy, Legal Aid undertaken and Legal Aid Franchise
Ptr: Birch, Mr Ian LLB(Hons). . . . . *Apr 1992
Fielding, Mr James K BA(Hons). . . . . *Apr 1981
Pearson, Mr Andrew Jonathan LLB(L'pool) . . . . . *Nov 1981
Polson, Mr Anthony G BA(Hons) . . . . *Jul 1989
Polson, Mr Stephen John BA . . . . Jul 1981
Ast: Christensen, Mr Adam LLB . . . . *May 2006
Con: Kilner, Mr David. . . . . *May 1967

DAVID PHILLIPS & PARTNERS
1st Floor Oriel Chambers 14 Water Street Liverpool Merseyside L2 8TD
Tel: 0151 236 3331 *Fax:* 0151 236 4447 *Dx:* 14113 LIVERPOOL
Emergency telephone 0151 236 3331
E-mail: info@dpp-law.com
Office: Birmingham, Bootle (2 offices), Chadwell Heath, Leicester, London E1, London SE18, London W1, Manchester, Nelson, Wealdstone
Work: B2 E G H N S2
Ast: Whatham, Mr Matthew BA . . . . Sep 2003

JOHN PICKERING & PARTNERS LLP
19 Castle Street Liverpool Merseyside L2 4SX
Tel: 0808 144 0958 *Fax:* 0151 258 1262 *Dx:* 14222 LIVERPOOL
E-mail: pg@johnpickering.co.uk
Office: Halifax, Manchester
Ast: Higgins, Ms Catherine. . . . . Oct 1989

PILKINGTONS SOLICITORS ‡
Roselands 3 Cross Green Formby Liverpool Merseyside L37 4BH
Tel: 01704 876624 *Fax:* 01704 873465
E-mail: mp@pilkingtonslaw.com

PRICE LAW ‡
174 Warbreck Moor Liverpool Merseyside L9 0HZ
Tel: 0151 222 0115
E-mail: info@price-partnership.com

QUALITYSOLICITORS JACKSON & CANTER ‡
88 Church Street Liverpool Merseyside L1 3HD
Tel: 0151 282 1700 *Fax:* 0151 282 1715 *Dx:* 14156 LIVERPOOL
Emergency telephone 07860 554433
E-mail: mailbox@jacksoncanter.co.uk
List of partners: E Abrahamson, D Choudhury, K Heckle, W A M Holroyd, E Leach, S J Rogers, M Sandys, P Thompson, C P Topping, P Widdison
Office: Liverpool
Languages: Bengali, Hindi
Work: D1 D2 G H K1 K3 K4 L N Q V W Z(g,i,m)
Emergency Action, Agency, Advocacy, Fixed Fee Interview, Legal Aid undertaken, Legal Aid Franchise and Member of Accident Line
Ptr: Choudhury, Dipanker . . . . Apr 1995
Holroyd, Mr W Andrew M CBE BA Former President of the Law Society . . . . *Dec 1974
Sandys, Mr Michael LLB; LLM. . . . . *Mar 2002
Widdison, Ms Paula LLB(Hons) . . . . *Oct 1993
Ast: Davidson, Mr Jonathan Garth BA(Hons)(Classics). . . Sep 2008
Gillespie, Mr Andrew N BA(Hons) . . . . *Oct 1982
Hims, Mrs Corine Eleanor BA Timpron Martin Prize 2001; Liverpool Law Society Achievement in Professional Exams . . . . *Jan 2004
Irving, Mr Gordon LLB. . . . . Jul 2005
Jones, Ms Teleri LLB . . . . *Aug 2009
Joyce, Ms Lisa LLB. . . . . *Sep 2010
Koucheksarai, Ms Nadia LLB . . . . Jul 2007
Leaker, Ms Anna LLM. . . . . *Sep 2004
Patel, Miss Niranjana LLB; BVC. . . . . *Sep 2004
Ryan, Mrs Rachel Marie LLB(Hons). . . . . *Dec 2004
Webster, Miss Catherine BA(Hons); PGDipLaw; LPC *Sep 2006
Whitelaw, Mr Roy LLB(Hons) . . . . *Nov 1996

QUINN MELVILLE ‡
15 Stanley Street Liverpool Merseyside L1 6AA
Tel: 0151 236 3340 *Fax:* 0151 255 0466 *Dx:* 14154 LIVERPOOL
Emergency telephone 0151 236 3340
E-mail: enquiries@quinn-melville.co.uk
List of partners: P B Barrow, P J Beck, M C Blackall, N Marray, N J Melville, P C Quinn
Languages: French, Spanish
Work: B2 C1 D1 E F1 G H J1 K1 L N O Q S1 V W Z(l,m)
Emergency Action, Agency, Advocacy, Fixed Fee Interview, Legal Aid undertaken and Member of Accident Line
Ptr: Barrow, Mr Paul B BSc . . . . *Mar 1985
Beck, Mr Paul Joesph LLB . . . . Nov 1994
Blackall, Miss Mary Catherine. . . . . May 1996
Marray, Mr Nicholas LLB . . . . Sep 1992
Melville, N J LLB . . . . *Feb 1986
Quinn, Mr Peter C LLB . . . . *May 1981
Asoc: Hughes, Mr John . . . . Oct 1985

REES-ROBERTS SOLICITORS ‡
4th Floor India Buildings Water Street Liverpool Merseyside L2 0QT
Tel: 0151 255 1300 *Fax:* 0151 236 3083
E-mail: info@rees-roberts.com
List of partners: P Rees-Roberts
Dir: Rees-Roberts, Phil . . . . Nov 1986

MARK REYNOLDS SOLICITORS LLP ‡
75 Walton Vale Liverpool Merseyside L9 4RQ
Tel: 0151 525 7222 *Fax:* 0151 525 9222
E-mail: mareynolds@markreynoldssolicitors.co.uk

ROBINSONS ‡
7 Queen Avenue Liverpool Merseyside L2 4TZ
Tel: 0151 227 2555 *Fax:* 0151 231 1934
List of partners: P J Hurst, D C Robinson
Work: B1 C1 D1 E F1 K1 L N Q S1 W Z(k)
Emergency Action, Agency, Advocacy and Legal Aid undertaken
Ptr: Hurst, Mr Peter James . . . . Jul 1974
Robinson, Mr David Christopher LLB . . . . *Jun 1968

SHARMAN & SON ‡
4 Coronation Road Crosby Liverpool Merseyside L23 3BJ
Tel: 0151 932 0333 *Fax:* 0151 932 0444
List of partners: L Pound, M D Sharman
Work: C1 E F1 G J1 K1 L M1 P S1 T1 W
Emergency Action, Agency, Advocacy, Fixed Fee Interview and Legal Aid undertaken
Ptr: Pound, Ms Lorna . . . . Aug 1988
Sharman, Mr Michael D. . . . . *Mar 1974

SHIPLEY SOLICITORS LIMITED ‡
2nd Floor 27 Lord Street Liverpool Merseyside L2 9SA
Tel: 0151 705 3440 *Fax:* 0151 705 3441
E-mail: markshipley@shipleysolicitors.com

LEONARD SIEVE & CO ‡
63 Wavertree Road Liverpool Merseyside L7 1PF
Tel: 0151 291 7700 *Fax:* 0151 291 7770
E-mail: 100127.141@compuserve.com
Languages: French, Portuguese, Spanish
Work: L S1 V W
Fixed Fee Interview and Legal Aid undertaken

SILVERBECK RYMER ‡
Dempster Building Atlantic Way Liverpool Merseyside L3 4UU
Tel: 0151 236 9594 *Fax:* 0151 227 1035 *Dx:* 14189 LIVERPOOL
E-mail: law@silverbeck-rymer.co.uk
List of partners: K I Hayes, C A Rymer, J Rymer
Languages: French
Work: B1 B2 C1 C2 E F1 J1 J2 L N O P Q R1 R2 S1 W Z(b,c,d,e,h,j,l,p)
Emergency Action, Agency, Advocacy, Fixed Fee Interview, Legal Aid undertaken and Member of Accident Line
Ptr: Hayes, Mr Kingsley Ian LLB. . . . . *Jul 1995
Rymer, Mr Charles A LLB . . . . *Oct 1986
Rymer, Mr James. . . . . *Feb 1976
Asoc: Bratherton, Mr Mark Robert. . . . . Sep 1994
Raeburn, Ms Sally LLB . . . . Dec 1994

J A SIMON & CO ‡
14 Mill Lane West Derby Liverpool Merseyside L12 7JB
Tel: 0151 256 6669 *Fax:* 0151 226 0286 *Dx:* 706971 TUEBROOK
E-mail: info@jasimon-law.co.uk
List of partners: J A Simon
Work: K1 K3 S1 S2 W
Agency and Fixed Fee Interview undertaken
Ptr: Simon, Mr Jonathan A LLB(L'pool) . . . . *Apr 1978

SINCLAIR SOLICITORS ‡
812-814 The Corn Exchange Fenwick Street Liverpool Merseyside L2 7RB
Tel: 0151 236 5377

STEINBERGS ‡
62 County Road Liverpool Merseyside L4 3QL
Tel: 0151 521 4491 *Fax:* 0151 525 4815 *Dx:* 701223 WALTON
E-mail: post@steinbergs.co.uk
List of partners: B H Steinberg
Work: B1 D1 F1 J1 K1 L N O Q S1 W Z(l)
Emergency Action, Agency, Advocacy, Fixed Fee Interview, Legal Aid undertaken and Member of Accident Line
SPr: Steinberg, Mr Barry Hugh LLB . . . . *Jun 1978

SWAIN & CO SOLICITORS ‡
Bulloch House 10 Rumford Place Liverpool Merseyside L3 9DG
Tel: 0808 168 0550 / 0151 255 2286 *Fax:* 0151 255 2287
E-mail: mail@swainandco.com

SYSTECH SOLICITORS
1st Floor The Observatory 1 Old Haymarket Liverpool Merseyside L1 6EN
Tel: 0151 707 1019 *Fax:* 0151 709 0154
Office: Leeds, London SE1, Manchester

DAVID TAYLOR SOLICITORS ‡
3rd Floor Muskers Building 1 Stanley Street Liverpool Merseyside L1 6AA
Tel: 0151 227 2557 *Fax:* 0151 227 2558

THOMPSONS (FORMERLY ROBIN/BRIAN THOMPSON & PARTNERS)
Martins Building 4 Water Street Liverpool Merseyside L2 3SX
Tel: 0151 224 1600 *Fax:* 0151 236 2141 *Dx:* 14153 LIVERPOOL 1
Office: Belfast, Birmingham, Bristol, Cardiff, Chelmsford, Dagenham, Derby, Harrow, Leeds, London SW19, London WC1, Manchester, Middlesbrough, Newcastle upon Tyne, Nottingham, Plymouth, Sheffield, South Shields, Southampton, Stoke-on-Trent, Swansea, Wolverhampton
Work: J1 N Z(p)
Legal Aid undertaken and Member of Accident Line
Ptr: Connolly, Ms Jacqueline A LLB . . . . Apr 1989
Davies, Mr Andrew D . . . . Jul 1991
Ast: Davies, Ms Sharron. . . . . Nov 1995
Slade, Mr Kenneth LLB(Hons); MSocSc; LPC. . . . *§Oct 1996
Wrigley, Ms Paula LLB . . . . Sep 2000

TOWER LAW ‡
PO Box 356 Liverpool Merseyside L15 6YR
Tel: 0844 745 2035 / 07850 030100
E-mail: reception@towerlawonline.com

VICTOR WELSH SOLICITOR & NOTARY ‡
66 Beech Lane Liverpool Merseyside L18 3ER
Tel: 0151 724 1855 / 07855 544259 *Fax:* 0151 724 1855
E-mail: info@victorwelshlegal.co.uk

WAFER-PHILLIPS ‡
54 Muirhead Avenue East Norris Green Liverpool Merseyside L11 1EL
Tel: 0151 256 7898 *Fax:* 0151 226 9817 *Dx:* 706975 TUEBROOK
Emergency telephone 0151 428 4152
E-mail: enquiries@waferphillips.co.uk
List of partners: M Wafer
Work: D1 F1 G H K1 L M1 P S1 V

See p112 for the Key to Work Categories & other symbols

Emergency Action, Fixed Fee Interview and Legal Aid undertaken
Ptr: Wafer, Mr Michael LLB . . . . *Feb 1988

H J WALKER SIBIA ‡
603/614 The Cotton Exchange Old Hall Street Liverpool Merseyside L3 9LQ
Tel: 0151 227 2600 *Fax:* 0151 255 1551
Languages: French, Punjabi
Work: B1 C1 E F1 J1 L Q R1 R2 S1 S2 W Z(c,h,l,p,q)

WALKER SMITH WAY
4th Floor Jack Jones House No 1 Islington Liverpool Merseyside L3 8EG
Tel: 0844 346 3100 *Fax:* 0844 346 3200
E-mail: enquiries@walkersmithway.com
Office: Ashton-under-Lyne, Birmingham, Chester, London SW11, Wrexham

WEIGHTMANS LLP ‡
India Buildings Water Street Liverpool Merseyside L2 0GA
Tel: 0151 227 2601 *Fax:* 0151 227 3223 *Dx:* 718100 LIVERPOOL 16
List of partners: C Atkinson, A Bannister, A C Blakemore, K Brannigan, L R Brenlund, T J Challis, E Collins, A J Cooper, R S Corran, S P Crotty, D S Cutts, F L Davidson, S W Dudley, F M East, K M Edwards, S M Ellington, I R Evans, D T Fagan, M J Forshaw, M M Garlick, P Gaul, G B Ginvert, M Green, R C Harris, M E J Hatfield, T M Henry, J M Holman, D A Holt, T K G Jackson, D Johnson, R Jolly, C E B Jones, G R E Jones, N W Jones, R Jones, G K Jump, C S V Kenyon, T T Lang, D L Lewis, S C Loveday, J R Macleod, V Maharaj, E J McBurney, V E Morris, M R Newman, S Peacock, N J Peel, D J Percival, J C Pinsent, P M Raftery, C B Robinson, K T Salmon, T B Salthouse, J A Schorah, J Shaer, N J Smith, T P A Smyth, S E Spriggs, P A Stephens, A Steventon, D Tabinor, A C Thompson, C Tomlinson, I S Vicary, N F Walsh, J Weatherly, L G Wilkin, B Williams, E B Williams, T R Williams, M D Yardley, A G Yeaman
Office: Birmingham, Dartford, Knutsford, Leicester, London EC4, Manchester (2 offices)
Ptr: Cooper, Mr Andrew J LLB(Nott'm). . . . . *Sep 1991
Mem: Atkinson, Miss Carole LLB . . . . *May 1979
Blakemore, Mr Anthony Craig LLB Margaret Bryce Smith Scholarship Prize . . . . *Oct 1982
Crotty, Mr Sean Paul LLB(Hons); LLM. . . . . *Jan 2001
Davidson, Miss Fiona L LLB(Hons) . . . . *Sep 1998
Edwards, Mr K Martin MA(Oxon); ACIArb . . . . *Apr 1980
Ellington, Ms Sarah M. . . . . Mar 1995
Evans, Mr Ian R LLB . . . . *§Oct 1975
Fagan, Mr David Thomas LLB. . . . . *May 1978
Forshaw, Mr Martin J . . . . *Nov 1992
Gaul, Mr Patrick BA(Oxon) . . . . *Jan 1987
Green, Mr Michael LLB . . . . Mar 1999
Hatfield, Mr Mark E J BA . . . . *Mar 1983
Holman, Mr James M LLB(L'pool) . . . . *Nov 1991
Holt, Mr David A LLB . . . . *Oct 1986
Jolly, Mr Richard . . . . Dec 1992
Jones, Mr Charles E B BSc. . . . . *Dec 1985
Jones, Mr Gary Robert Edmund LLB . . . . *Nov 1989
Jones, Mr Norman William BA(Hons) . . . . Oct 1978
Jump, Mr Graeme K Licensed Insolvency Practitioner. *Dec 1969
Lewis, Mr David L LLB . . . . *Oct 1987
McBurney, Mrs E Janet BA . . . . *Jun 1979
Morris, Miss Victoria E LLB . . . . Feb 1988
Peacock, Mr Stephen . . . . Oct 1992
Peel, Mr Nicholas J BA(Dunelm) . . . . *Oct 1985
Percival, Mr David John LLB(Hons) . . . . *Jan 1982
Pinsent, Mr John C BA . . . . *Nov 1988
Robinson, Mr C Bruce BSc . . . . *Nov 1994
Salthouse, Mr Timothy Bryan LLB. . . . . *Apr 1984
Schorah, Mr John A LLB . . . . *Oct 1990
Smith, Miss Nicola J LLB(L'pool) . . . . *Jan 1991
Smyth, Miss Tracy P A LLB . . . . *§Nov 1989
Stephens, Mr Paul A LLB . . . . *Oct 1988
Tabinor, Mr David . . . . Jul 1997
Vicary, Mr Ian S LLB . . . . *Oct 1990
Weatherly, Ms Janice . . . . Oct 1984
Wilkin, Ms Laura G LLB. . . . . *Nov 1991
Williams, Mr Emlyn Bryan LLB . . . . *Oct 1992
Asoc: Ball, Mr Christopher Charles LLB; LSF . . . . *Oct 1996
Chapman, Mrs Elaine Maria FILEx John Gilpen Award - Law of Contract . . . . *Oct 1994
Coleman, Miss Victoria E MA(Hons)(Oxon) . . . . . . Nov 1995
Collins, Mr Thomas James . . . . Sep 2000
Cox, Mr Andrew A BA(Dunelm) . . . . *Nov 1991
Hetherington, Mr Robert. . . . . *Oct 1996
Hutchins, Mr Roland . . . . Sep 1999
Jones, Mr Kieran Mark LLB(Hons). . . . . Oct 1994
Jones, Mr Stuart Alexander LLB. . . . . *Nov 1994
Lang, Mr Timothy Mark LLB(Hons) . . . . *Oct 1991
Marshall, Miss Penelope A BA(Hons) . . . . *Nov 1994
Tuck, Mr David Charles LLB. . . . . *Oct 1995
Whittle, Mr Stuart J BA; LSF. . . . . *Oct 1995
Williams, Mr Robert Lindsey LLB . . . . *Oct 1994
Ast: Darnell, Mr John M . . . . May 1998
Fox, Miss Michaela LLB. . . . . *Oct 1996
Leslie, Mr Richard Jeremy LLB; LLM . . . . *Jul 1996
Lim, Rachel. . . . . Jan 2003
Littlemore, Mrs Sarah J . . . . *Oct 1995
Quinn, Mr William A LLB . . . . *Jan 1996

WILSON COWIE & DILLON ‡
10 Duke Street Liverpool Merseyside L1 5AS
Tel: 0151 706 7000 *Fax:* 0151 706 7010 *Dx:* 14203 LIVERPOOL
E-mail: info@wcdlaw.com

WOOLWICH LANDER & SAVAGE ‡
56a Allerton Road Liverpool Merseyside L18 1LW
Tel: 0151 733 5807 *Fax:* 0151 734 5734
E-mail: alan.savage@wlslaw.co.uk

WWW.ELAWYERS.CO.UK ‡
59 Derby Road Liverpool Merseyside L36 9UQ
Tel: 0151 489 9900 *Fax:* 0151 489 9933
E-mail: info@porterssolicitors.co.uk

YAFFE JACKSON OSTRIN ‡
1 Temple Court Victoria Street Liverpool Merseyside L2 6PY
Tel: 0151 236 5555 *Fax:* 0151 236 2121 *Dx:* 14205 LIVERPOOL
Emergency telephone 0151 227 2598
List of partners: P J Bown, D R Hughes, R J Jones, D A J Lupton, A R Tidd
Office: Liverpool
Work: C1 E F1 G H J1 K1 L N O Q S1 V W X Z(l,m,t)
Emergency Action, Agency, Advocacy, Legal Aid undertaken and Member of Accident Line
Ptr: Bown, Mr Peter Jeremy BA(Law) . . . . *Apr 1979
Hughes, Mr David Ronald BA(Hons)(Law). . . . . . *Oct 1983
Jones, Mr Richard Jones LLB(Lond). . . . . *§Dec 1975
Lupton, Mr Daniel A J LLB(Wales). . . . . Oct 1981
Ast: Clements, Ms Susan Theresa LLB . . . . *Sep 1990

YAFFE JACKSON OSTRIN
659-661 West Derby Road Tuebrook Liverpool Merseyside L13 8AG
Tel: 0151 259 2666 *Fax:* 0151 228 0981 *Dx:* 706972 TUEBROOK
Emergency telephone 0151 227 2598
E-mail: enquiries@yjosolicitors.com
Office: Liverpool
Work: B1 C1 D1 E F1 G H J1 K1 L M1 N P R1 S1 T1 V W Z(b,c,d,e,f,i,j,k,l,m,o,p,s,t)
Emergency Action, Agency, Advocacy, Fixed Fee Interview, Legal Aid undertaken and Member of Accident Line
Ptr: Tidd, Mr Andrew R LLB . . . . *Oct 1985

LLANARTH, Ceredigion

BEVAN JONES ‡
Cilwenne Llanarth Ceredigion SA47 0QA
Tel: 01545 580746 *Fax:* 01545 581039
E-mail: bevan.jones@saqnet.co.uk
Languages: French, Welsh

LLANDEILO, Carmarthenshire

MOREB LIMITED ‡
Corner House 6 Carmarthen Street Llandeilo Carmarthenshire SA19 6AG
Tel: 01558 822215 *Fax:* 01558 822933 *Dx:* 44052 LLANDEILO
E-mail: j_owen@btinternet.com
List of partners: W J Owen
Languages: Welsh
Work: A1 A2 C1 D1 E F1 J1 K1 K2 K3 L N O P Q R1 S1 S2 T1 T2 V W Z(c,j,l)
Emergency Action, Advocacy, Fixed Fee Interview and Legal Aid undertaken
Ptr: Owen, Mr W John LLB(Lond) H M Coroner; Chairman of the Agricultural Land Tribunal (Wales). . . . . *Mar 1960
Ast: Mainwaring, Mrs Pauline LLB(Lond) H M Deputy Coroner . . . . *Sep 1996
Owen, Miss Amanda Elizabeth BA(Hons); PGDipLaw . *Nov 2005

HUGH WILLIAMS SON & CO ‡
81 Rhosmaen Street Llandeilo Carmarthenshire SA19 6HD
Tel: 01558 823417 *Fax:* 01558 823038 *Dx:* 44051 LLANDEILO
Emergency telephone 01558 685090
List of partners: E R Jones
Office: Llandovery
Languages: Welsh
Work: A1 B1 D1 E F1 G J1 K1 L N P Q R1 S1 T1 W Z(c,d,f,j,l)
Agency, Legal Aid undertaken and Legal Aid Franchise
Ptr: Jones, Mrs Eira R LLB . . . . *Dec 1970

LLANDOVERY, Carmarthenshire

IEUAN MORRIS & CO
18 Market Square Llandovery Carmarthenshire SA20 0AA
Tel: 01550 720300 / 720780 *Fax:* 01550 720933
Dx: 200052 LLANDOVERY
E-mail: im@morrissolicitors.co.uk
Office: Aberystwyth, Llandrindod Wells
Languages: Welsh
Work: A1 C1 D1 D2 F1 G H J1 K1 L M1 N P Q S1 S2 T1 V W Z(c,k,l,w)
Advocacy, Fixed Fee Interview and Legal Aid undertaken
Ast: Burton-Howell, Mrs Susan L BSc(Econ) . . . . *Jun 1998

HUGH WILLIAMS SON & CO
1 High Street Llandovery Carmarthenshire SA20 0PU
Tel: 01550 721500 *Fax:* 01550 721870 *Dx:* 44051 LLANDEILO
Office: Llandeilo
Languages: Welsh

LLANDRINDOD WELLS, Powys

DILWYNS ‡
Oxford Chambers Temple Street Llandrindod Wells Powys LD1 5DL
Tel: 01597 822707 *Fax:* 01597 824085
List of partners: R D Margrave-Jones, S R Margrave-Jones, P T Wilcox-Jones
Office: Aberystwyth, Llandovery
Work: A1 B1 C1 D1 E F1 G H J1 K1 L M1 N P R1 S1 T1 V W Z(l,t)
Emergency Action, Agency, Advocacy and Legal Aid undertaken
Ptr: Margrave-Jones, Mr Roy D LLB(Wales); LLM(Cantab) Hereford Brecon & Radnor Law Society Prize Under Sheriff of Bailiwick of Radnor Notary Public . . . . *Jun 1962
Margrave-Jones, Mr Simon R . . . . *Jul 1991
Wilcox-Jones, Mr Peter T LLB(Wales). . . . . *Oct 1983
Ast: Casaru, Mrs Jennifer Clare BSc(Hons); TEP. . . . . . Oct 1988

GERAINT JONES & CO
Temple Chambers South Crescent Llandrindod Wells Powys LD1 5DH
Tel: 01597 822244 *Fax:* 01597 825369
Dx: 200153 LLANDRINDOD WELLS
Emergency telephone 07808 093276
E-mail: legal@geraint-jones-solicitors.co.uk
Office: Newtown
Languages: Welsh
Work: B1 D1 D2 G H J1 K1 K3 N Q S1 S2 W X Z(i)
Agency undertaken
Asoc: Jenkins, Miss Cassie Lyn LLB. . . . . *Dec 2009

MARGRAVES ‡
Old Court Chambers Spa Road Llandrindod Wells Powys LD1 5EY
Tel: 01597 825565 *Fax:* 01597 825220 *Dx:* 200154 LLANDRINDOD
E-mail: law@margraves.co.uk
List of partners: C V Margrave-Jones
Work: A1 S1 S2 T1 T2 W
SPr: Margrave-Jones, Mr Clive V MA; LLM(Cantab); LLB(Wales); TEP Hereford Brecon & Radnor Law Society Prize Clerk to the Tax Commissioners (Radnor & Builth Wells) Notary Public. . . . . *Jul 1965
Asoc: Barlow, Ms Anne E BA . . . . *Oct 1983
Campbell, Mr Andrew . . . . *Oct 1991
Rodgers, Prof Christopher P LLM(Cantab); LLB(Wales)*Apr 1981

MORRIS & BATES
(incorporating Roberts & Evans; WABowen & Griffiths)
Ashby House Tudor Lane Llandrindod Wells Powys LD1 5ET
Tel: 01597 829055 *Fax:* 01597 829060 *Dx:* 92100 ABERYSTWYTH
E-mail: law@morrisbates.co.uk
Office: Aberystwyth, Knighton
Languages: Welsh
Work: A1 B1 C1 C2 D1 D2 E F1 F2 G H J1 K1 L N O Q R1 R2 S1 S2 T1 T2 V W X Z(b,c,d,f,g,j,k,l,m,o,p,q,r,s)
Agency, Advocacy, Legal Aid undertaken and Legal Aid Franchise
Ptr: Jones, Miss Annwen M LLB. . . . . *Dec 1992
Jones, Mr David R Hinton LLB(Wales); BA(Wales) . . *Oct 1988
Morris, Mr Richard John LLB(Nott'm) Deputy Under Sheriff of Ceredigion . . . . *Oct 1995

LLANDUDNO, Conwy

BONE & PAYNE LLP ‡
55 Madoc Street Llandudno Conwy LL30 2TW
Tel: 01492 876354 *Fax:* 01492 874531 *Dx:* 11354 LLANDUDNO
E-mail: enquiries@boneandpayne.co.uk
List of partners: G H Davies, H D Edwards, D R G Griffith, G Tierney-Jones
Office: Colwyn Bay, Old Colwyn
Languages: Welsh
Work: E G H J1 K1 K2 L N O Q S1 S2 W Z(l)
Emergency Action, Agency, Advocacy, Fixed Fee Interview, Legal Aid undertaken, Legal Aid Franchise and Member of Accident Line
Mem: Edwards, Mr Huw Dyfan LLB(Bris) Deputy District Judge (Magistrates Court) . . . . *Dec 1976
Griffith, Mr David R G BA . . . . *§May 1978
Tierney-Jones, Mr Gareth BA(Hons); CQSW . . . . . *Oct 1993
Asoc: Jones, Mr Brynden LLB . . . . *Oct 1991
Pari, Mr Owain Gwyndaf BA. . . . . *Apr 2001
Ast: Bray, Mrs Julie LLB . . . . Nov 1990
Kingsley, Mrs Lois. . . . . Apr 2010
Morgans, Miss Rhiannon LLB(Hons) . . . . Aug 2011

GAMLINS ‡
14-15 Trinity Square Llandudno Conwy LL30 2RB
Tel: 01492 860420 *Fax:* 01492 875296 *Dx:* 11357 LLANDUDNO
E-mail: llandudno@gamlins.com
List of partners: J P Brooke, J C Hoult, G Jones, G Morris, V Oliver, R D Petters, F N C Ranson, M P Salisbury, R A Salisbury, R H Williams
Office: Bangor, Colwyn Bay (2 offices), Conwy, Holywell, Rhyl
Work: D1 E F1 G H J1 K1 L N O Q R1 S1 T1 V W Z(c)
Emergency Action, Agency, Advocacy, Fixed Fee Interview and Legal Aid undertaken
Ptr: Brooke, Mr John P . . . . Oct 1994
Petters, Mr Robert D BA . . . . *Oct 1987
Salisbury, Mr Mark P LLB . . . . *Oct 1981
Williams, Mr Richard H LLB. . . . . *Apr 1980
Ast: Blakesley, Mr John F BA; MAIEx . . . . *Jun 1975
Carroll, Ms Debra A LLB . . . . *Oct 1987
Wright, Ms Ruth Salome BA(Dunelm) . . . . *Oct 1991

J W HUGHES & CO
27 Augusta Street Llandudno Conwy LL30 2AE
Tel: 01492 874774 *Fax:* 01492 879750 *Dx:* 11355 LLANDUDNO
E-mail: mailroom@jwhugheslaw.co.uk
Office: Conwy
Languages: French, Welsh
Work: B1 C1 C2 C3 D1 E F1 G H J1 K1 K2 L N Q R1 S1 S2 V W Z(r)
Emergency Action, Agency, Advocacy, Fixed Fee Interview, Legal Aid undertaken, Legal Aid Franchise and Member of Accident Line
Ptr: Kentish, Mr Philip B LLB(Leics); D'etudes Juridiques Francaises . . . . *Nov 1988
Thomas, Mr Alun W LLB . . . . *Jul 1980
Watters, Mr Phillip John LLB . . . . *May 1995
Ast: Carroll, Mrs Debra Ann LLB. . . . . Nov 1996
Longworth, Ms Julia Gail BA . . . . Apr 2004

DAVID JONES & CO ‡
22 Trinity Square Llandudno Conwy LL30 2RH
Tel: 01492 874336 *Fax:* 01492 860270 *Dx:* 11352 LLANDUDNO
E-mail: mail@davidjoneslaw.co.uk
List of partners: D I Jones, D R Moore
Languages: French, Welsh
Work: A1 B1 C1 C2 C3 E F1 I J1 K1 L O Q R1 S1 W Z(c,k,l,m)
Agency undertaken
Ptr: Jones, Mr David I LLB(Lond) . . . . *Dec 1976
Moore, Mr Dylan Richard LLB. . . . . *Apr 1991

KNOX INSOLVENCY ‡
Orme Hill Commercial Centre Pen y Ffridd Farm Great Orme Llandudno Conwy LL30 2JS
Tel: 0845 387 0105
E-mail: enquiries@knoxinsolvency.co.uk

SWAYNE JOHNSON SOLICITORS
17 Trinity Square Llandudno Conwy LL30 2RN
Tel: 01492 876271 *Fax:* 01492 876274 *Dx:* 11356 LLANDUDNO
E-mail: law@swaynejohnson.com
Office: Denbigh, Ruthin, St Asaph
Languages: Welsh
Work: A1 C1 D1 E F1 J1 K1 K2 L N O P Q R1 S1 T1 T2 V W Z(l,q)
Emergency Action, Agency, Fixed Fee Interview, Legal Aid undertaken and Member of Accident Line
Ptr: Williams, Mr D Rhys LLB ♦ Deputy District Judge . . . *Oct 1988
Ast: Vickers, Mr Jeffrey Howard LLB. . . . . Jan 1976
Con: Jones, Mr John O LLB ♦ . . . . *§Mar 1961

WATSONS SOLICITORS ‡
Augusta Chambers 23 Augusta Street Llandudno Conwy LL30 2AD
Tel: 01492 860006 *Fax:* 01492 560262
E-mail: atw@watsonssolicitors.co.uk

LLANDYSUL, Ceredigion

TEIFI LAW LIMITED ‡
12 Lincoln Street Llandysul Ceredigion SA44 4BU
Tel: 01559 362744 *Fax:* 01559 362021 *Dx:* 200250 LLANDYSUL
List of partners: C Mason-Watts
SPr: Mason-Watts, Mr Christopher LLM; MA . . . . Jan 1980

EIRIAN J WILLIAMS A'I GWMNI ‡
(incorporating Amphlett-Lewis & Evans)
4-5 Bridge Street Llandysul Ceredigion SA44 4BA
Tel: 01559 363244 *Fax:* 01559 363733 *Dx:* 200251 LLANDYSUL
E-mail: ejwilliams.aigwmni@btinternet.com
List of partners: E J Williams
Languages: French, Welsh
Work: A1 K4 S1 W
SPr: Williams, Eirian J BA; LLB; Solicitor Supreme Court of Alberta . . . . *Oct 1983

LLANELLI, Carmarthenshire

PHILIP AVERY & CO ‡
9 Murray Street Llanelli Carmarthenshire SA15 1AQ
Tel: 01554 746295 *Fax:* 01554 746324 *Dx:* 40329 LLANELLI
E-mail: philipaveryandco@aol.com
List of partners: S K Cartwright-Harwood, S J Lewis
Office: Ammanford
Work: E K1 N Q S1 S2 W Z(q)
Ptr: Cartwright-Harwood, Mrs S Katrina BA(Law) . . . . . *Oct 1984
Lewis, Miss Sarah J LLB . . . . *Sep 2002

BRINLEY MORRIS REES & JONES ‡
3 John Street Llanelli Carmarthenshire SA15 1UN
Tel: 01554 774241 *Fax:* 01554 774242 *Dx:* 40301 LLANELLI
E-mail: brinleymorris@tiscali.co.uk
List of partners: E R Davies, R L Jones
Work: A1 B1 C1 C3 D1 E F1 G H J1 K1 L N O P Q R1 S1 T1 V W Z(e,f,l,m,p,w)
Agency, Advocacy, Fixed Fee Interview, Legal Aid undertaken and Member of Accident Line
Ptr: Davies, Ms Elizabeth Ruth LLB . . . . Nov 1983
Jones, Mr Richard Lionel BSc; ACA. . . . . *Jun 1986

DAVIES PARSONS ALLCHURCH ‡
8-10 Queen Victoria Road Llanelli Carmarthenshire SA15 2TL
Tel: 01554 749144 *Fax:* 01554 774496 *Dx:* 40302 LLANELLI
Emergency telephone 07795 398249
E-mail: admin@daviesparsonssolicitors.co.uk
List of partners: J S Allchurch, M J Davey, A M Davies, N Richards
Office: Swansea
Work: A1 B1 C1 C2 D1 E F1 G H J1 K1 L M1 M2 N O P Q R1 S1 T1 T2 V W Z(c,h,j,k,l,m,n,o,p,t)
Emergency Action, Agency, Advocacy, Fixed Fee Interview, Legal Aid undertaken, Legal Aid Franchise and Member of Accident Line
Ptr: Allchurch, Mr John Stephen BA(Law) ● . . . . *Jan 1982
Davey, Mr Michael J BA. . . . . *Feb 1990
Davies, Mr Anthony M. . . . . *Mar 1976
Richards, Mr Neil LLB. . . . . Nov 1987
Ast: Adere, Mr Caesar LLB(Hons) . . . . *Jun 2006
Evans, Ms Gail . . . . Nov 2002
Hughes, Mrs Rachel LLB . . . . *Oct 2000
Isaac, Mr David Andrew LLB . . . . Mar 1998
Morris, Miss Sara Rhys LLB. . . . . *Nov 1994
Owens, Ms Lisa Elizabeth LLB(Hons); LPC . . . . . . Apr 2007
Thomas, Mr Leighton Rhodri . . . . Mar 1995
Wilkins, Miss Elizabeth T BA; LLB. . . . . *Aug 1999
Con: Hill, Mr Jonathan Nigel . . . . *Dec 1972

EVANS POWELL & CO ‡
Victoria House 17 Murray Street Llanelli Carmarthenshire SA15 1AQ
Tel: 01554 772632 *Fax:* 01554 754102 *Dx:* 40300 LLANELLI 1
E-mail: post@eplaw.demon.co.uk
List of partners: D G Bell, D R Evans, R N A B Powell
Languages: Welsh
Work: A1 B1 C1 D1 E F1 G H J1 K1 K3 L N O Q R1 S1 S2 V W Z(c,d,j,k,l,n,t)
Emergency Action, Agency, Advocacy and Fixed Fee Interview undertaken
Ptr: Bell, Mr Dafydd G BSc(Econ) . . . . *Mar 1980
Evans, Mr David R . . . . *Dec 1973
Powell, Mr Robert N A B LLB . . . . *Jul 1974
Ast: Edmunds, Mrs Laura Jayne LLB(Hons) . . . . Jan 2008

GOMER WILLIAMS & CO ‡
19 John Street Llanelli Carmarthenshire SA15 1UP
Tel: 01554 755101 *Fax:* 01554 775486 *Dx:* 40308 LLANELLI
E-mail: a.davies@gomerwilliams.co.uk
List of partners: A J Davies, M L Owen
Languages: Welsh
Work: A1 B1 D1 D2 E F1 G H J1 K1 L N Q S1 V W Z(h,l)
Emergency Action, Agency, Advocacy, Fixed Fee Interview, Legal Aid undertaken and Member of Accident Line
Ptr: Davies, Mr Andrew J LLB . . . . *Feb 1983
Owen, Mrs M Lee LLB . . . . *Jul 1978

JENNINGS ‡
17 Goring Road Llanelli Carmarthenshire SA15 3HF
Tel: 01554 772331 *Fax:* 01554 754549
Emergency telephone 01554 757004
E-mail: law@jennsols.demon.co.uk
List of partners: J Hogg, C L P Smith, C W Symons
Languages: Welsh
Work: B1 C1 C2 C3 D1 E F1 G H J1 K1 L M1 M2 N O P Q R1 S1 V W Z(l)
Emergency Action, Agency, Advocacy, Legal Aid undertaken, Legal Aid Franchise and Member of Accident Line
Ptr: Hogg, Mr James LLB(Essex) . . . . *§Feb 1987
Smith, Mrs Claire L P BSc. . . . . *Jan 1994
Symons, Mr Christopher W LLB(Wales) Clerk to the General Commissioners of Income Tax . . . . *Dec 1979

THE LAW PRACTICE ‡
15 John Street Llanelli Carmarthenshire SA15 1UH
Tel: 0800 612 9318 *Fax:* 01554 746877
E-mail: enquiries@thelawpracticeltd.co.uk

ANDREW MARKHAM & CO ‡
1 Carmarthan Road Cross Hands Llanelli Carmarthenshire SA14 6SP
Tel: 01269 842888 *Fax:* 01269 842050
E-mail: sue@carmarthentown.com

J M PARSONS & CO ‡
1st Floor Mallard House 1 Upper Park Street Llanelli Carmarthenshire SA15 3YN
Tel: 01554 779940 *Fax:* 01554 779949
E-mail: info@jmplaw.co.uk

PATON & CARPENTER ‡
5 Station Road Llanelli Carmarthenshire SA15 1AF
Tel: 01554 774760 / 751680 *Fax:* 01554 772306
Dx: 40314 LLANELLI
List of partners: P D L Carpenter, E J Godsell
Work: A1 B1 C1 C2 C3 D1 E K1 L N O P R1 S1 S2 T1 T2 W Z(c)
Agency, Fixed Fee Interview, Legal Aid undertaken and Member of Accident Line
Ptr: Carpenter, Mr Paul D L . . . . Mar 1997
Godsell, Mrs E Jayne LLB(Wales). . . . . Feb 1983
Ast: Carpenter, Mr Jonathan D. . . . . Sep 2001

RANDELL LLOYD & MARTIN ‡
23 Murray Street Llanelli Carmarthenshire SA15 1AQ
Tel: 01554 772149 *Fax:* 01554 774383 *Dx:* 40303 LLANELLI
Emergency telephone 01554 741701
List of partners: M Jenkins, S A Lloyd, P G Martin
Languages: Welsh
Work: A1 B1 C1 D1 E F1 G H J1 K1 L M1 N P S1 T1 W Z(c,i,j,k,l,m)
Emergency Action, Agency, Advocacy, Fixed Fee Interview, Legal Aid undertaken and Member of Accident Line
Ptr: Jenkins, Mr Mark LLB(L'pool) . . . . *Jun 1982
Lloyd, Mr Stephen A BA. . . . . Oct 1982
Martin, Mr Peter G BSc(Econ). . . . . Oct 1984
Ast: Cudd, Mrs Kathryn LLB . . . . *Jun 1979

RODERICKS ‡
8 Thomas Street Llanelli Carmarthenshire SA15 3JD
Tel: 01554 773424 *Fax:* 01554 774713
E-mail: rlewis@rodericks-solicitors.co.uk
List of partners: W R Lewis, L A Thorne
Languages: Welsh
Work: E K1 L Q S1 S2 T2 W Z(l)
Agency and Advocacy undertaken
Ptr: Lewis, Mr William Robert LLB. . . . . *Feb 1992
Thorne, Ms Lindsay Anne LLB . . . . Nov 1994
Con: Evans, Mr Richard M T MA(Oxon); MLitt . . . . . . *§Jun 1975

LINDSAY THORNE SOLICITORS ‡
Palm Grove House 144 Felinfoel Road Llanelli Carmarthenshire SA15 3JT
Tel: 01554 773146 *Fax:* 0871 503 3622
E-mail: lat@lindsaythornesolicitors.co.uk

LLANGEFNI, Anglesey

R GORDON ROBERTS LAURIE & CO ‡
Glandwr Chambers Llangefni Anglesey LL77 7EE
Tel: 01248 722215 / 723312 *Fax:* 01248 723470
Dx: 701773 LLANGEFNI
E-mail: rgrl@bt-connect.com
List of partners: D L Jones, H R Jones, R J L Morris, R Parry, E L Williams
Office: Beaumaris
Languages: Welsh
Work: A1 C1 D1 D2 F1 G H J1 K1 K2 K3 L M1 N P R1 S1 T1 V W Z(l,m,t)
Emergency Action, Agency, Advocacy, Fixed Fee Interview, Legal Aid undertaken and Member of Accident Line
Ptr: Jones, Mr Dylan Lloyd LLB(Hons)(Wales). . . . . . . Jan 2003
Jones, Mr Huw R . . . . Dec 2004
Morris, Mr Richard J L LLB(Wales) . . . . *Apr 1971
Parry, Mr Richard LLB(L'pool) . . . . *Dec 1976
Williams, Mr E Lloyd LLB(Wales) . . . . *Oct 1985
Ast: Owen, Miss Catrin E LLB . . . . Jun 2005

CARYS HUGHES ‡
29a High Street Gwenllys Llangefni Anglesey LL77 7NU
Tel: 01248 750941 *Fax:* 01248 723255

PARRY DAVIES CLWYD-JONES & LLOYD ‡
25 Church Street Llangefni Anglesey LL77 7DU
Tel: 01248 723106 *Fax:* 01248 724555 *Dx:* 701770 LLANGEFNI
List of partners: L R Davies, S Gwyn, G C Jones, N W Lloyd, G Parry
Office: Amlwch, Benllech, Caernarfon, Pwllheli
Languages: Welsh
Work: A1 A3 B1 B2 D1 D2 F1 G H J1 J2 K1 K2 L M1 N O P Q R1 R2 S1 S2 T1 T2 V W Z(g,h,j,q,t)
Emergency Action, Agency, Advocacy and Legal Aid undertaken
Ptr: Davies, Mrs Lena Rees ♦ . . . . Dec 1993
Gwyn, Mr Sion LLB . . . . Sep 1999
Jones, Mr Geraint C BA(Wales) ♦ Deputy District Judge . . . . *Dec 1982
Lloyd, Ms Nia W LLB(Wales) Deputy District Judge . *Nov 1982
Parry, Mr Gareth BA(Hons) ★ . . . . *Apr 1989
Ast: Jones, Mrs Winnifred Margaret LLB . . . . *Sep 2001

IEUAN WYN JONES ‡
Tynewydd Rhosmeirch Llangefni Anglesey LL77 7RZ
Tel: 01248 722261
Languages: Welsh
Work: A1 S1 T1 T2 W

LLANGOLLEN, Denbighshire

BARRY ASHTON ‡
21 Bridge Street Llangollen Denbighshire LL20 8PF
Tel: 01978 861140 *Fax:* 01978 860422
List of partners: B Ashton
Work: A1 B2 E G H N Q S1 S2 W Z(l)
Advocacy and Fixed Fee Interview undertaken
SPr: Ashton, Mr Barry Howard Watson Prize . . . . §Jan 1966

GHP LEGAL
The Malthouse Business Centre Regent Street Llangollen Denbighshire LL20 8HS
Tel: 01978 860313 *Fax:* 01978 860262
E-mail: llangollen@ghplegal.co.uk
Office: Oswestry, Wrexham
Work: A1 B1 C1 C2 C3 E F1 G J1 K1 L M1 M2 N P R1 S1 T1 T2 W Z(c,d,k,l)
Agency, Advocacy, Fixed Fee Interview and Legal Aid undertaken
Ast: Danvers, Mr Anthony BSc. . . . . Mar 2008
Con: Scott, Mr Christopher David BA(Hons). . . . . *Oct 1992

LLANIDLOES, Powys

MILWYN JENKINS & JENKINS LIMITED ‡
Mid Wales House Great Oak Street Llanidloes Powys SY18 6BN
Tel: 01686 412166 *Fax:* 01686 413580
E-mail: mail@mjandj.co.uk
List of partners: A Davies-Jones, M C Harvey
Languages: Arabic, Welsh
Work: A1 B1 D1 D2 G H J1 K1 L N O Q S1 S2 W X Z(c,g,l,r)
Emergency Action, Agency, Advocacy and Fixed Fee Interview undertaken
Ptr: Davies-Jones, Mrs Angela LLB . . . . *Jan 1986
Harvey, Mr Mark C LLB; BA. . . . . *Jan 1981

LLANRWST, Conwy

CYFRAITH JRL LAW ‡
Bank Buildings Watling Street Llanrwst Conwy LL26 0LS
Tel: 01492 641222 *Fax:* 01492 641820 *Dx:* 711490 LLANRWST
E-mail: law@jrl-law.co.uk
List of partners: R E Laing, G Price-Jones
Languages: French, German, Welsh
Work: A1 A2 B1 C1 C2 C3 D1 E F1 F2 G H J1 K1 L M1 M2 N O P Q R1 S1 S2 T1 T2 V W Z(c,d,e,f,j,k,m,q,s,t)
Emergency Action, Agency, Advocacy, Fixed Fee Interview, Legal Aid undertaken and Legal Aid Franchise
Ptr: Laing, Mr Robert E LLB(Hons) . . . . *Dec 1971
Price-Jones, Mrs Gwenno LLB(Wales) . . . . *Jul 1995
Asoc: Lewis, Mr Karl John LLB(Hons) . . . . *Oct 2004

HOWELL JONES & CO ‡
36 Station Road Llanrwst Conwy LL26 0DA
Tel: 01492 640277 *Fax:* 01492 640583 *Dx:* 711491 LLANRWST
E-mail: enquiries@howelljoneslaw.co.uk
List of partners: H Davies, D W P Hughes, N Hughes Parry, P McAlinden, N W Roberts
Office: Abergele
Languages: Welsh
Work: A1 A2 C1 C2 D2 E F1 G H J1 K1 K3 K4 L N O P Q R1 R2 S1 S2 T1 T2 V W Z(c,d,l,q)
Emergency Action, Agency, Advocacy, Fixed Fee Interview, Legal Aid undertaken and Member of Accident Line
Ptr: Davies, Mr Hywel LLB(Wales). . . . . *Oct 1984
Hughes, Mr David W P LLB(Wales) . . . . *Apr 1981
Hughes Parry, Ms Nia BA(Hons) . . . . *Oct 1984
McAlinden, Mr Paul LLB(Hons) . . . . *Nov 1994
Roberts, Mrs Nia W LLB(Wales). . . . . *Feb 1987
Asoc: Galloway, Mrs Carol Gail LLB(Hons) . . . . *Apr 2001
Jones, Mrs Eleri FILEx; TEP. . . . . *Oct 2005
Morris, Miss Rhonwen BA(Hons) . . . . *Sep 2003
Con: Evans, Mrs Janet P LLB . . . . *Jun 1975

LONGESPE & CO ‡
Cleveley House Abergale Road Llanrwst Conwy LL26 0NG
Tel: 01492 642363 *Fax:* 01492 642588
E-mail: longnges@aol.com

LLANTWIT MAJOR, Vale of Glamorgan

BIKELAWYER, MOTORCYCLE ACCIDENT SOLICITORS ‡
Commercial House Commercial Street Llantwit Major Vale of Glamorgan CF61 1RB
Tel: 01446 794199 *Fax:* 01446 796456 *Dx:* 50961 COWBRIDGE
E-mail: info@bikelawyer.co.uk

BARRIE Y JONES & CO ‡
1a Barons Close House East Street Llantwit Major Vale of Glamorgan CF61 1XY
Tel: 01446 793835 / 794542 *Fax:* 01446 796907
E-mail: jonesbarby@aol.com
List of partners: B Y Jones, P D Osborne
Office: Bridgend
Work: E K1 L N Q S1 W
Member of Accident Line
Ptr: Jones, Mr Barrie Y BSc(Econ). . . . . *Aug 1979
Osborne, Mr Philip D Notary Public . . . . *Aug 1991

VALE SOLICITORS
16 Poundfield Precinct Llantwit Major Vale of Glamorgan CF61 1DL
Tel: 01446 795456 *Fax:* 01446 795456 *Dx:* 38554 BARRY
E-mail: mail@valesolicitors.com
Office: Barry

LLANWRDA, Carmarthenshire

ERYL MATHIAS ‡
Tynwern Ffarmers Llanwrda Carmarthenshire SA19 8JX
Tel: 01588 650664 *Fax:* 01588 650557
List of partners: E W Mathias
Languages: Welsh
Work: S1 W
Ptr: Mathias, Eryl W LLB . . . . *Oct 1984

LODDON, Norfolk

CADGE & GILBERT
9 High Street Loddon Norfolk NR14 6EU
Tel: 01508 520361 / 520362 *Fax:* 01508 528703
Dx: 99100 LODDON
Office: Bungay
Work: A1 B1 C1 E F1 G H J1 K1 L N O Q S1 S2 W X Z(e,f,j,k,l,m,q,r,w,z)
Emergency Action, Agency and Advocacy undertaken
Ptr: Ferguson, Mr Barry LLM; BA . . . . *Nov 1987

See p112 for the Key to Work Categories & other symbols

LONG EATON, Derbyshire

CONSTANTINOU SOLICITORS ‡
28-32 Market Place Long Eaton Derbyshire NG10 1LT
Tel: 0115 849 8000 *Fax:* 0115 849 8001 *Dx:* 11622 LONG EATON
E-mail: costa@constantinousols.co.uk
List of partners: C Constantinou
Work: D1 D2 K1 S1 S2 W
Emergency Action, Agency, Advocacy and Fixed Fee Interview undertaken
Ptr: Constantinou, Mr Constantinos LLB . . . . Nov 1976

ELLIS-FERMOR & NEGUS
35 Derby Road Long Eaton Derbyshire NG10 1LU
Tel: 0115 972 5222 *Fax:* 0115 946 1152 *Dx:* 11607 LONG EATON
E-mail: longeaton@ellis-fermor.co.uk
Office: Beeston, Belper, Ripley
Work: A1 B1 B2 C1 C2 C3 D1 D2 E F1 G H J1 K1 K2 L N O P Q R1 R2 S1 S2 T1 T2 V W Z(c,d,g,l,o,p,x)
Emergency Action, Agency, Advocacy, Legal Aid undertaken, Legal Aid Franchise and Member of Accident Line
Ptr: Cobbett, Mr Michael S LLB Notary Public . . . . *Apr 1976
Macnab, Mr Murray A. . . . . Jan 1990
Asoc: Meredith, Mr Robert John LLB . . . . *Sep 2005
Ast: Wreford, Mrs Eleanor D LLB . . . . *Sep 2011
Con: Negus, Mr David P LLB. . . . . *Apr 1972

SHARP & PARTNERS
(incorporating E Willams & Son; L L B Lewis & Son; R L Morgan)
43 Market Place Long Eaton Derbyshire NG10 1JL
Tel: 0115 973 4111 *Fax:* 0115 946 2627
Emergency telephone 07817 454561
E-mail: long.eaton@sharpandpartners.co.uk
Office: Nottingham (3 offices)
Work: A1 B1 C1 C2 C3 D1 E F1 G H J1 K1 L M1 M2 N P R1 S1 T1 T2 V W Z(c,e,i,k,l,m)
Emergency Action, Agency, Advocacy, Fixed Fee Interview, Legal Aid undertaken and Member of Accident Line
Ptr: Evans, Mr Christopher J LLB . . . . *Jul 1979
Fyson, Mr Antony W BSocSc . . . . *Mar 1988
Ast: Close, Mr James LLB(Hons) . . . . *Apr 1998

STARKIE & GREGORY ‡
(incorporating Cruickshanks)
25 Derby Road Long Eaton Derbyshire NG10 1NA
Tel: 0115 849 9000 *Fax:* 0115 849 2350 *Dx:* 11601 LONG EATON
E-mail: enquiries@sgcsolicitors.co.uk
List of partners: R J Cliff, G P Holyoak, B W Kirk
Work: A1 B1 C1 C2 C3 E F1 J1 K1 L N P Q R1 S1 T1 T2 V W Z(c,l)
Emergency Action, Agency, Advocacy, Fixed Fee Interview undertaken and Member of Accident Line
Ptr: Cliff, Mr Richard J FILEx . . . . *Dec 1992
Holyoak, Mr Geoffrey P . . . . *Jul 1976
Kirk, Mr Bruce W BA . . . . *Oct 1983
Ast: Irving, Ms Elizabeth BA(Law) . . . . *Jan 1983
Spencer, Mrs Karen Nicola LLB(Hons) . . . . *Nov 1989

THOMAS SOLICITORS ‡
49 Derby Road Long Eaton Derbyshire NG10 1NB
Tel: 0115 946 1061 *Fax:* 0115 972 1314 *Dx:* 11602 LONG EATON
List of partners: G R Farries, F A Qureshi, D F Smith, S J Wrigley
Office: Loughborough
Work: A1 C1 D1 E F1 J1 K1 L O Q R1 S1 S2 V W
Advocacy, Fixed Fee Interview and Legal Aid Franchise
Ptr: Farries, Mr Graham Ramsay LLB(Lond). . . . . *Apr 1973
Smith, Mr David Foulkes LLB(Hons). . . . . *Nov 1971

LONG MELFORD, Suffolk

RUDLINGS & WAKELAM
Robins Row Hall Street Long Melford Suffolk CO10 9JB
Tel: 01787 464778
Office: Brandon, Bury St Edmunds, Thetford

LONG STRATTON, Norfolk

GREENLAND HOUCHEN POMEROY
The Plain Long Stratton Norfolk NR15 2XJ
Tel: 01508 530033 *Fax:* 01508 530088
E-mail: roger.percival@ghlaw.co.uk
Office: Attleborough, Norwich, Watton, Wymondham
Work: A1 E K1 K2 K3 S2 W
Agency, Advocacy, Fixed Fee Interview and Legal Aid undertaken
Ptr: Percival, Mr Roger MA(Cantab) . . . . *Jun 1971

LONG SUTTON, Lincolnshire

MOSSOP & BOWSER
30 Market Place Long Sutton Lincolnshire PE12 9JH
Tel: 01406 363212 *Fax:* 01406 363018
E-mail: gwebb@mossops.co.uk
Office: Holbeach
Work: A1 B1 C1 C2 E F1 J1 K1 K3 K4 L Q R1 S1 S2 T1 T2 W Z(q)
Con: Brown, Mr Peter F S LLB . . . . *§May 1975

LONGFIELD, Kent

MARTIN TOLHURST PARTNERSHIP LLP
61b Station Road Longfield Kent DA3 7QA
Tel: 01474 706168 *Fax:* 01474 703184 *Dx:* 51250 LONGFIELD
E-mail: mtpl@martintolhurst.co.uk
Office: Ashford, Gravesend
Work: E J1 K1 S1 W
Fixed Fee Interview undertaken
Ptr: Stewart, Ms Barbara Margaret LLB . . . . *Oct 1984
Williams, Mrs Jane LLB. . . . . *Nov 1995
Ast: Hobson, Mrs Julie. . . . . Jan 2006

LOOE, Cornwall

BROWNING & CO ‡
Fore Street Looe Cornwall PL13 1DN
Tel: 01503 262119 / 262129 *Fax:* 01503 262305
E-mail: law@brownings.freeserve.co.uk
List of partners: C P Browning, P M Grassam
Work: A1 E F1 L S1 S2 W
Ptr: Browning, Mr Christopher Patrick . . . . *Jan 1966
Grassam, Mr Peter Mark BA(Hons) . . . . Oct 1998
Ast: Kneebone, Ms Sarah Luise BA . . . . *May 1997

EARL & CROCKER
1st Floor Market House Higher Market Street Looe Cornwall PL13 1BP
Tel: 01503 265884 *Fax:* 01503 265887 *Dx:* 81661 LISKEARD
E-mail: enquiries@earlandcrocker.co.uk
Office: Liskeard
Work: A1 D1 E K1 K3 K4 L S1 S2 T1 T2 W Z(l)

LOSTWITHIEL, Cornwall

AP BASSETT SOLICITORS ‡
Saint Anthony Fore Street Lostwithiel Cornwall PL22 0BL
Tel: 01208 871485
E-mail: allsorts@apbassettsolicitors.co.uk
Office: Bodmin

LOUGHBOROUGH, Leicestershire

BIRD WILFORD & SALE ‡
20 Church Gate Charnwood Loughborough Leicestershire LE11 1UD
Tel: 01509 232611 *Fax:* 01509 239081
Dx: 19607 LOUGHBOROUGH
E-mail: reception@birdwilfordsale.co.uk
List of partners: J A Belderbos, R C Minifie, S J Roberts, J E Sale, K J Vaughan, R L Wilford
Work: A1 B1 C1 C2 C3 D1 E F1 G H I J1 K1 K2 K3 K4 L M1 M2 N O P Q R1 R2 S1 S2 T1 T2 V W Z(c,d,e,h,i,j,l,q,s,t)
Emergency Action, Agency, Advocacy, Fixed Fee Interview, Legal Aid undertaken and Member of Accident Line
Ptr: Belderbos, Mr James Anthony LLB(Hons). . . . . . . *Sep 1996
Minifie, Mr Richard C . . . . *Jun 1970
Roberts, Mr Stephen J BA . . . . *Dec 1985
Sale, Mr John Edwin LLB(Lond). . . . . *§Dec 1980
Vaughan, Mr Keith John LLB Pettit Prize . . . . *Apr 1979
Wilford, Mr R Lindsay LLB(Sheff) . . . . *Jun 1977

ELVIN & CO ‡
92 Main Street East Leake Loughborough Leicestershire LE12 6PG
Tel: 01509 852454 *Fax:* 01509 852195
Dx: 715235 LOUGHBOROUGH 3
E-mail: g.hills@elvinsolicitors.co.uk
List of partners: J M Elvin, M A S J Elvin, G S Hills
Work: A1 C1 E J1 J2 K1 O Q R2 S1 S2 W Z(q)
Agency and Advocacy undertaken
Ptr: Elvin, Mrs Julia M BA . . . . *Jun 1976
Elvin, Mr Michael A St J. . . . . *Dec 1974
Hills, Mr Graham S LLB(Leeds) • . . . . *Nov 1978

FOSSE LAW
The Advance Business Centre 10 Forest Road Loughborough Leicestershire LE11 3NP
Tel: 01509 231000 *Fax:* 0116 262 0292 *Dx:* 10815 LEICESTER
E-mail: info@fosselaw.com
Office: Leicester, Melton Mowbray

EDWARD HANDS & LEWIS ‡
3 Rectory Place Loughborough Leicestershire LE11 1UW
Tel: 01509 216161 *Fax:* 01509 216322
Dx: 19606 LOUGHBOROUGH
E-mail: ehandslewis@btinternet.com
List of partners: J McNab, A Roberts
Work: C1 C2 E F1 K1 K3 K4 N O R2 S1 S2 T2 W Z(d)
Agency, Advocacy, Fixed Fee Interview, Legal Aid undertaken and Legal Aid Franchise
Ptr: McNab, Mr John LLB . . . . *Jan 1969
Roberts, Mr Alan LLB . . . . *Oct 1978
Ast: Fuller, Miss Emma-Louise LLB(Hons) . . . . *Nov 1993

HAWLEY & RODGERS ‡
19-23 Granby Street Loughborough Leicestershire LE11 3DY
Tel: 01509 230333 *Fax:* 01509 239390
Dx: 19602 LOUGHBOROUGH
E-mail: l.office@hawleyandrogers.com
List of partners: P M Baker, S J Benson, V C Chamberlain, A S Forrest, E J Harlow, A V Mangham, C A Williams
Office: Bingham, Nottingham
Languages: Gujarati
Work: A1 B1 C1 C2 C3 D1 E F1 G H J1 K1 K3 K4 L M1 M2 N O P Q R1 R2 S1 S2 T1 T2 V W Z(c,d,h,i,k,l,p,q)
Emergency Action, Agency, Advocacy, Fixed Fee Interview, Legal Aid undertaken, Legal Aid Franchise and Member of Accident Line
Ptr: Baker, Mr Peter Michael BA(Hons); LLDip. . . . . Oct 2005
Chamberlain, Mrs Victoria Charlotte-Anne MA(Hons)(English); PGDipLaw; LPC . . . . *Sep 2000
Harlow, Mrs Elspeth J. . . . . *Feb 1985
Mangham, Mr Alan Victor MA(Cantab) . . . . *Oct 1995
Williams, Mrs Caroline Ann-Marie BA(Hons). . . . . . . Jan 2002
Ast: Duckitt, Mrs Jane E LLB . . . . *Feb 1989

LATHAM & CO
Charnwood House 2 Forest Road Loughborough Leicestershire LE11 3NP
Tel: 01509 238822 *Fax:* 01509 238833
Dx: 19614 LOUGHBOROUGH
Office: Melton Mowbray
Work: A1 B1 C1 D1 D2 E F1 J1 K1 L N O Q R1 S1 S2 T1 T2 V W X Z(c,d,e,h,j,l,p)
Emergency Action, Agency, Legal Aid undertaken and Legal Aid Franchise
Ptr: Hull, Miss Carolyn Lesley LLB. . . . . *§Dec 1984
Kirkman, Mr Trevor H MA(Cantab) Clerk to Commissioners of Taxes; H M Coroner; Diocesan Registrar and Bishop's Legal Secretary Notary Public. . . . . *§Jun 1976
Con: Davison, Miss Olivia M MA . . . . *Oct 1984

M&M SOLICITORS
18b Pinfold Gate Loughborough Leicestershire LE11 1BE
Tel: 01509 214262 *Fax:* 01509 217616
Office: Leicester

MOSS SOLICITORS LLP ‡
80-81 Wood Gate Loughborough Leicestershire LE11 2XE
Tel: 01509 217770 *Fax:* 01509 233698
Dx: 19605 LOUGHBOROUGH 1
E-mail: enquiries@moss-solicitors.co.uk
List of partners: T C Dunbar, S J Nottridge, D J Pagett-Wright, R Rathod
Office: Coalville
Languages: Hindi, Punjabi
Work: B1 B2 C1 C2 C3 D1 D2 E F1 F2 G H J1 J2 K1 K3 K4 L N O Q S1 S2 T1 T2 W X Z(c,e,f,h,j,k,l,m,n,p,q,t)
Emergency Action, Agency, Advocacy, Fixed Fee Interview, Legal Aid undertaken and Legal Aid Franchise
Dir: Dunbar, Mr Timothy Cospatrick LLB(Leics) . . . . . *§Oct 1987
Nottridge, Mr Stephen Jonathan LLB . . . . *§Dec 1990
Pagett-Wright, Mr David John LLB . . . . *§Nov 1989
Rathod, Mrs Rita LLB(Hons) . . . . *§Mar 1997
Ast: Benskin, Mr Anthony John LLB . . . . *§Jan 2003
Brassington, Mrs Julia Catherine BA ★ . . . . *§Sep 2005
Fantham, Mrs Lynne Marie LLB. . . . . *§Jun 1997
Gay, Mr Nicholas M LLB(Warw) . . . . *§Dec 1990
Greenwell, Mrs Katrina Jayne BA(Law) . . . . *§Jan 1986
Hinds, Mrs Jane Gabrielle LLB ★ . . . . *§Nov 1992
McGuiness, Ms Anne Maria BSc(Hons) . . . . *Nov 1992
Nelson, Mr James Waller Riley LLB. . . . . *§Feb 2006
Riozzi, Miss Carla Marie LLB . . . . *Oct 2009
Tarr, Miss Jayne Lesley BSc . . . . *§Oct 1993
Con: Cooper, Mr David P W BA(Leeds) John Mackrell Prize *§Jul 1970

PARMARS
Carfax Chambers 2 Woodgate Loughborough Leicestershire LE11 2TY
Tel: 01509 261823 *Fax:* 01509 610490 *Dx:* 28801 LEICESTER 2
Office: Leicester
Languages: Gujarati, Hindi, Kiswahili, Punjabi
Work: E L N O Q V W Z(i)
Emergency Action, Agency, Fixed Fee Interview and Legal Aid undertaken

PRUSINSKI SOLICITORS ‡
Unit 13 The Office Village North Road Loughborough Leicestershire LE11 1QJ
Tel: 01509 233622 *Fax:* 01509 610623
Dx: 19629 LOUGHBOROUGH
E-mail: enquiries@prusinkisolicitors.com
List of partners: A J Prusinski, M W Prusinski
Languages: Polish
Work: B1 C1 C2 C3 E F1 J1 K1 L N O Q S1 T1 T2 W
Emergency Action, Agency, Advocacy and Fixed Fee Interview undertaken
Ptr: Prusinski, Mr Andrew J LLB. . . . . *Oct 1983
Prusinski, Miroslaw W BA(Law) . . . . *Sep 1978

STERLING LAW ‡
30 Queen Street Loughborough Leicestershire LE11 1SG
Tel: 01509 263790
E-mail: info@sterlinglaw.org.uk

STRAW & PEARCE ‡
18 Rectory Place Loughborough Leicestershire LE11 1UU
Tel: 01509 268931 *Fax:* 01509 610217
Dx: 19601 LOUGHBOROUGH
Emergency telephone 07801 466811
E-mail: info@strawandpearce.co.uk
List of partners: J Brown, D T Leigh, D C Partridge, R E Severn, R A Thomas, M R Wardley
Languages: French, Gujarati, Italian
Work: A1 B1 B2 C1 C2 C3 D1 E F1 G H J1 K1 K3 L M1 N O P Q R1 S1 S2 V W Z(c,d,h,i,j,l,m,p,q,t)
Emergency Action, Agency, Advocacy, Fixed Fee Interview, Legal Aid undertaken and Member of Accident Line
Ptr: Brown, Miss Julie LLB(Hons) . . . . *Mar 1995
Leigh, Mr David T BA . . . . *Sep 1983
Partridge, Mr David C BA . . . . *Feb 1985
Severn, Mr Robert E LLB . . . . *Jun 1978
Thomas, Mrs Rosemary Ann . . . . *Jan 1992
Wardley, Mr Mark R LLB . . . . *Aug 1997
Ast: Gilmour, Miss Samantha LLB(Hons). . . . . *Oct 2001
Halliday, Nadia . . . . Sep 2008
Millward, Mr Peter L LLB . . . . *Jun 1978
Newcombe, Mrs Louise Margaret LLB(Hons) . . . . . *Aug 2005
Percival, Mr Jonathan. . . . . Sep 2008
Sayce, Mr Kevin BA(Hons); LPC; PGDipLaw . . . . . . Aug 2005
Swingler, Mr David LLB(Hons). . . . . *Sep 2000

THOMAS SOLICITORS
44 Church Gate Loughborough Leicestershire LE11 1UE
Tel: 01509 611061 *Fax:* 01509 611025
Dx: 19635 LOUGHBOROUGH
E-mail: loughborough@thomaslegal.co.uk
Office: Long Eaton
Work: B1 C1 C2 C3 D1 E F1 F2 J1 K1 L N O P Q S1 S2 W Z(c)
Emergency Action, Agency, Advocacy, Fixed Fee Interview, Legal Aid undertaken, Legal Aid Franchise and Member of Accident Line
Ptr: Qureshi, Fahrat A LLB(Hons) . . . . *Feb 2000
Wrigley, Mr Stephen J Deputy District Judge of the Midland Circuit. . . . . *Apr 1981

WEBSTERS ‡
Bridle House Nursery Lane Quorn Loughborough Leicestershire LE12 8BH
Tel: 01509 415116 *Fax:* 01509 413787
E-mail: bjw@webounsterslaw.co.uk
Work: C1 E J1 S1 S2 W

WOOLLEY BEARDSLEYS & BOSWORTH ‡
PO Box 22 Rectory Place Loughborough Leicestershire LE11 1UP
Tel: 01509 212266 *Fax:* 01509 232634
Dx: 19604 LOUGHBOROUGH
E-mail: services@woolleybees.co.uk
List of partners: K R Darby, D E Weston
Work: A1 E S1 T2 W Z(d)
Ptr: Darby, Mr Keith Ronald . . . . *Jun 1975
Weston, Ms Diane Elizabeth LLB(Hons). . . . . *Feb 2004

LOUGHTON, Essex

ALFANO & CO ‡
26 The Uplands Loughton Essex IG10 1NG
Tel: 020 8414 9271 *Fax:* 020 8418 7893
Emergency telephone 07930 574105
E-mail: alfanosolicitors@yahoo.co.uk
Languages: Italian
Work: G Q S1 Z(i)
Fixed Fee Interview undertaken

ATTWATERS ‡
147 High Road Loughton Essex IG10 4LY
Tel: 020 8508 2111 *Fax:* 0845 508 5909 *Dx:* 7900 LOUGHTON
E-mail: enquiries@attwaters.co.uk
List of partners: J C Clarke, D A M Flannagan, M K Henchie, T A Kenny, D G Kerry, L Mayhew, S B J Parsons, M Seibert, S E Tetlow, J E Westbrook, P Westbrook
Office: Harlow
Work: A1 B1 C1 C2 C3 D1 D2 E F1 J1 K1 K3 K4 L N O Q R1 S1 S2 T1 T2 V W Z(c,l,q,r)
Emergency Action, Advocacy, Fixed Fee Interview, Legal Aid undertaken and Legal Aid Franchise
Ptr: Flannagan, Mr David A M . . . . . *§Sep 1995
Tetlow, Mr Stephen E LLB. . . . . *Jan 1983
Asoc: Mizon, Miss Sheri-Anne LLB(Hons) . . . . . Jul 2003
Ast: Beekarry, Miss Devi LLB(Hons) . . . . . Jul 1999
Liddiard, Mr Alastair Peter John LLB(Hons) . . . . . Aug 2005

KIM BETTS & CO ‡
231a High Road Loughton Essex IG10 1AD
Tel: 020 8508 5505 *Fax:* 020 8508 9181
E-mail: betts231a@aol.com
List of partners: K J Betts
Work: C1 E S1 S2 W Z(l)
Ptr: Betts, Mrs Kim J BA(Law). . . . . *Apr 1987

FOSKETT MARR GADSBY & HEAD
106-108 High Road Loughton Essex IG10 4HN
Tel: 020 8502 3991 *Fax:* 020 8502 2261 *Dx:* 7901 LOUGHTON
E-mail: email@foskettmarr.co.uk
Office: Epping
Work: A1 B1 C1 C2 C3 E R1 S1 T1 T2 W

LE LAW SOLICITORS ‡
Vogel House 127 High Road Loughton Essex IG10 4LT
Tel: 020 8508 4691

LUCAS MCMULLAN JACOBS ‡
Law Chambers 258 High Road Loughton Essex IG10 1RB
Tel: 020 8418 3222

OP LAW ‡
188-192 High Road Loughton Essex IG10 1DN
Tel: 020 8418 8380 *Fax:* 020 8418 8381 *Dx:* 7953 LOUGHTON
E-mail: info@oplaw.co.uk

LYNNE V ROSEN ‡
56 Roundmead Avenue Loughton Essex IG10 1PZ
Tel: 020 8508 0804 *Fax:* 020 8281 7220
List of partners: L V Rosen
Work: S1
SPr: Rosen, Mrs Lynne Vivienne BA(History). . . . . *Jun 1978

STAPLEY & CO ‡
141a High Road Loughton Essex IG10 4LT
Tel: 020 8502 1934 *Fax:* 020 8508 6865 *Dx:* 7904 LOUGHTON
E-mail: solicitor@stapley.co.uk
List of partners: A P Mothew
Office: Woodford Green
Work: C1 E J1 K4 M3 R1 S1 S2 W Z(m)
SPr: Mothew, Mr Anthony Paul Dip Air & Space Law . . . . *Jan 1970
Ast: Mothew, Mr Ian Daniel Bentley MSc; BSc . . . . . *Jun 2004

LOUTH, Lincolnshire

JOHN BARKERS
11 Upgate Louth Lincolnshire LN11 9ES
Tel: 01507 604773 *Fax:* 01507 600040 *Dx:* 27556 LOUTH
E-mail: lth@jbarkers.co.uk
Office: Cleethorpes, Grimsby, Mablethorpe
Work: A1 B1 C1 C2 C3 D1 D2 E F1 F2 G H J1 K1 K2 K3 K4 L N O Q R1 S1 S2 T1 T2 V W Z(f,h,l,r,t)
Emergency Action, Agency, Advocacy, Fixed Fee Interview, Legal Aid undertaken, Legal Aid Franchise and Member of Accident Line
Ptr: Needley, Mr James L . . . . . *§Jan 1971
Ast: Brindle, Mr William Thomas Francis LLB . . . . . Apr 2005
Con: Brewer, Mr Paul S. . . . . . *§Dec 1980
Vamplew, Mr Terence J C. . . . . *§Jun 1977

BEETENSON & GIBBON
25a Northgate Louth Lincolnshire LN11 0LT
Tel: 01507 600610 *Fax:* 01507 600932 *Dx:* 27557 LOUTH
Office: Grimsby
Work: A1 C1 C2 C3 E F1 J1 K1 L N P Q S1 S1 T1 T2 W Z(o)
Member of Accident Line
Ptr: Braithwaite, Mr Peter R C MA; BCL(Oxon) . . . . . *Jul 1978
Ast: Swann, Mr Gary BA(Oxon) . . . . . *Oct 1990

BRIDGE MCFARLAND HADDON OWEN
9 Cornmarket Louth Lincolnshire LN11 9PY
Tel: 01507 605883 *Fax:* 01507 605708 *Dx:* 27554 LOUTH
Emergency telephone 01507 600340
E-mail: info@bmcf.co.uk
Office: Grimsby (3 offices), Hull, Lincoln, Mablethorpe, Market Rasen, Skegness
Work: A1 B1 C2 D1 E F1 G H J1 K1 L N Q R1 S1 S2 T1 T2 V W Z(c,e,i,l,m)
Emergency Action, Agency, Advocacy, Fixed Fee Interview, Legal Aid undertaken and Legal Aid Franchise
Ptr: Horne, Mr Anthony J MA(Oxon). . . . . *§Mar 1972
Lambert, Mr Stephen J BA . . . . . *Apr 1981
McFarland, Mr Patrick R E BA(Oxon) . . . . . *Jun 1971
Con: Moran, Mr Peter M LLB Atkinson Conveyancing Prize *Nov 1959

CHRISTIE SOLICITORS ‡
Suite 28 Fairfield Enterprise Centre Lincoln Way Louth Lincolnshire LN11 0LS
Tel: 01507 617716 *Fax:* 01507 617715
E-mail: mail@christiesolicitors.com

WILKIN CHAPMAN GRANGE SOLICITORS
17 Cornmarket Louth Lincolnshire LN11 9QA
Tel: 01507 606161 *Fax:* 01507 600015 *Dx:* 27551 LOUTH
E-mail: eboyd@wilkinchapman.co.uk
Office: Alford, Beverley, Grimsby (3 offices), Horncastle, Lincoln, Mablethorpe, Market Rasen, Sutton-on-Sea
Work: A1 A3 B1 B2 C1 C2 C3 D1 E F1 F2 G H J1 J2 K1 K2 K3 L N O P Q R1 R2 S1 S2 T1 T2 V W X Z(b,e,g,k,l,p,q,r,s,y)
Emergency Action, Agency, Advocacy, Fixed Fee Interview, Legal Aid undertaken, Legal Aid Franchise and Member of Accident Line
Ptr: Bennett, Mrs Flora M LLB. . . . . *Oct 1985
Day, Mr Philip D LLB(Leics) Notary Public. . . . . *§Mar 1975
Judge, Mr Jim LLB . . . . . *Jul 1997
Robinson, Mr Mark BA . . . . . *Apr 1993
Asoc: Vickers, Mrs Sally Marie BA(Hons); CPE . . . . . *Sep 1996
Ast: Horbury, Miss Caroline Patricia LLB. . . . . *Aug 2004

LOWESTOFT, Suffolk

CHAMBERLINS
Victoria Chambers Beach Road Waveney Lowestoft Suffolk NR32 1DT
Tel: 01502 573241 *Fax:* 01502 502361 *Dx:* 41211 LOWESTOFT
E-mail: debbie@chamberlinslowestoft.com
Office: Beccles, Caister-on-Sea, Great Yarmouth (2 offices)
Work: D1 D2 E K4 L S1 S2 W
Agency and Legal Aid undertaken
Ptr: Madgett, Mr Roger J G LLB. . . . . *Dec 1980

FOSTERS
(incorporating Bailey Crome & Gerard Dunne & Co)
17 Clapham Road South Lowestoft Suffolk NR32 1PG
Tel: 01502 573307 *Fax:* 01502 500614 *Dx:* 41209 LOWESTOFT
E-mail: lowestoft@fosters-solicitors.co.uk
Office: Bungay, Norwich, Wymondham
Work: A1 C1 E L R1 S1 S2 T1 T2 W Z(h,l)
Ptr: Dunne, Mr Martin F G. . . . . *Jul 1980
Mullender, Mr Michael J. . . . . *Dec 1973

GOODWIN COWLEY ‡
3 Regent Road Lowestoft Suffolk NR32 1PA
Tel: 01502 532700 *Fax:* 01502 532719 *Dx:* 41212 LOWESTOFT
List of partners: A G Cowley, E Locker, C Stockdale
Work: D1 D2 E K1 K3 L S1 W
Emergency Action, Agency, Advocacy, Legal Aid undertaken and Legal Aid Franchise
Ptr: Cowley, Mr Anthony G . . . . . *Jan 1981
Locker, Miss Emma LLB . . . . . *Jul 2005
Stockdale, Mrs Christine LLB . . . . . *Mar 1980

HKB WILTSHIRES
13 Surrey Street Lowestoft Suffolk NR32 1LJ
Tel: 01502 582338 *Fax:* 01502 501441 *Dx:* 41203 LOWESTOFT
E-mail: info@hkbw.co.uk
Office: Great Yarmouth
Work: B2 C1 C2 D1 G H J1 K1 L S1 V W
Emergency Action, Advocacy and Fixed Fee Interview undertaken
Ptr: Tuttle, Mr Philip Ian . . . . . *§May 1978
Ast: Lawrence, Mrs Helen LLB. . . . . Sep 1997

KHALAF & CO ‡
Unit 4 Riverside Business Centre Riverside Road Lowestoft Suffolk NR33 0TQ
Tel: 0845 601 9193 *Fax:* 01502 580738
List of partners: A Khalaf
Work: G J1 K3 Q S1 W
Ptr: Khalaf, Mrs Aisha LLB . . . . . *Apr 1987

LUCAS & WYLLYS
40 Alexandra Road Lowestoft Suffolk NR32 1PJ
Tel: 01502 500123 *Fax:* 01502 513009 *Dx:* 41201 LOWESTOFT
E-mail: lowestoft@lucasandwyllys.co.uk
Office: Great Yarmouth (3 offices)
Work: D1 F1 K1 L N Q S1 W
Emergency Action, Agency, Advocacy, Fixed Fee Interview, Legal Aid undertaken, Legal Aid Franchise and Member of Accident Line
Ptr: Benest, Miss Emma Charlotte LLB . . . . . *Nov 1992
Parsons, Mr Timothy James LLB(Hons) . . . . . *Oct 1993

MEARS HOBBS & DURRANT ‡
Somerset House 26 Gordon Road Lowestoft Suffolk NR32 1NL
Tel: 01502 583621 *Fax:* 01502 500473 *Dx:* 41207 LOWESTOFT
E-mail: mail@mearshobbs.co.uk
List of partners: P R Britten, A W Lyon, M J P Mears, J B Swanbury
Office: Beccles, Great Yarmouth
Work: A1 B1 C1 C2 C3 D1 E F1 G J1 J2 K1 L N O P Q R1 S1 S2 T1 T2 V W X Z(a,c,g,h,l,n)
Emergency Action, Agency, Advocacy, Fixed Fee Interview, Legal Aid undertaken, Legal Aid Franchise and Member of Accident Line
Ptr: Britten, Mr Peter Robert TD LLB(Lond) . . . . . *Oct 1982
Lyon, Mr Angus W . . . . . *Jul 1980

NICHOLSONS SOLICITORS LLP ‡
23 Alexandra Road Lowestoft Suffolk NR32 1PP
Tel: 01502 532300 *Fax:* 01502 568814 *Dx:* 41204 LOWESTOFT
E-mail: info@nicholsons-uk.com
List of partners: B J S Blower, G E Lamb, A Matthews, M J Nicholson, R J Nicholson, M A Rymarz
Work: A1 B1 C1 C2 C3 E F1 J1 K1 K3 K4 L M1 M2 N O P Q R1 S1 S2 T1 T2 W Z(a,c,d,e,f,j,l)
Emergency Action, Agency and Advocacy undertaken
Ptr: Blower, Mr Benjamin J S LLB . . . . . *Nov 1985
Lamb, Mr Gareth Edward . . . . . Sep 2005
Matthews, Ms Ann-Marie . . . . . *Sep 2004
Nicholson, Mr Mark J LLB Licensed Insolvency Practitioner . . . . . *May 1977
Nicholson, Mr Robert J LLB. . . . . *Oct 1972
Rymarz, Mr Mark Adam. . . . . *Sep 2004

NORTON PESKETT ‡
148 London Road North Lowestoft Suffolk NR32 1HF
Tel: 01502 533000 *Fax:* 01502 533001 *Dx:* 41200 LOWESTOFT
E-mail: enquire@nortonpeskett.co.uk
List of partners: A L Ambrose, R A Barley, J R Gibbons, J M Hartley, S A Knight, J M Loftus, D Spalding, A Stephenson
Office: Beccles, Great Yarmouth, Halesworth
Work: A1 C1 D1 E F1 G H J1 K1 L N O P Q R1 S1 T1 W Z(d,l,m)
Agency, Advocacy, Fixed Fee Interview, Legal Aid undertaken, Legal Aid Franchise and Member of Accident Line
Ptr: Ambrose, Mr Anthony L. . . . . *§Jan 1968
Barley, Mr Robert Anthony LLB(Hons). . . . . *Feb 1993
Hartley, Mr James M . . . . . Nov 1979
Knight, Mr Steven Allan . . . . . Nov 1998
Loftus, Mr John M BSc Clerk to General Commissioner of Taxes Notary Public . . . . . *§Dec 1977
Spalding, Mr David . . . . . Apr 1990
Ast: Blake, Ms Yvonne. . . . . Nov 2002
Thomas, Mrs Judy Margaret BA. . . . . *Nov 1983
Watson, Mr David. . . . . Jun 1999

COLIN PALMER & CO ‡
19 Regent Road Lowestoft Suffolk NR32 1PA
Tel: 01502 589277 *Fax:* 01502 500960
List of partners: C Palmer
Work: A1 C1 C2 C3 E F1 J1 L R1 S1 T1 T2 W
Ptr: Palmer, Mr Colin . . . . . *Jun 1980

POWLEYS ‡
17 Grove Road Lowestoft Suffolk NR32 1EB
Tel: 01502 581121 *Fax:* 01502 581122 *Dx:* 41221 LOWESTOFT
E-mail: powleys@btconnect.com
List of partners: W M Clarke, S H Crisp
Work: A1 B2 C1 D1 D2 E F1 G H J1 J2 K1 K3 L N O Q S1 S2 V W X Z(c,j,l,q,y)
Emergency Action, Agency, Advocacy, Legal Aid undertaken, Legal Aid Franchise and Member of Accident Line
Ptr: Clarke, Mr Wayne Morris LLB(Hons)(Lond) . . . . . *Dec 1978
Crisp, Mr Simon H . . . . . Apr 1975
Ast: Cattermole, Sarah. . . . . Oct 2010
Clarke, Mr Martin David Albert LLB . . . . . Aug 2004

PROFFITT & MANN ‡
Seaview House The Marina Lowestoft Suffolk NR32 1HH
Tel: 01502 538582 *Fax:* 01502 539242
List of partners: R Mann, E Proffitt
Ptr: Mann, Mr Richard BA . . . . . Apr 1999
Proffitt, Mr Edward LLB(Hons). . . . . Sep 1997

MARY SMITH SOLICITOR ‡
485 London Road South Lowestoft Suffolk NR33 0PD
Tel: 01502 511977 *Fax:* 01502 501097
E-mail: mary@marysmithsolicitor.co.uk
List of partners: J M Stevenson
Work: E L S1 W
Fixed Fee Interview undertaken
SPr: Stevenson, Mrs Jane Mary LLB . . . . . *Jun 1977

LUDLOW, Shropshire

GREENS ‡
18 Broad Street Ludlow Shropshire SY8 1NG
Tel: 01584 873918 *Fax:* 01584 876787 *Dx:* 26881 LUDLOW
E-mail: partners@greenssolicitors.com
List of partners: A C Whittle
Work: A1 C1 D1 E F1 J1 K1 K3 K4 L N O Q S1 S2 T1 T2 V W Z(c,d,l,q)
Agency and Advocacy undertaken
Ptr: Whittle, Mr Andrew C BA . . . . . *Sep 1991

LANYON BOWDLER LLP
12 The Business Quarter Eco Park Road Ludlow Shropshire SY8 1FD
Tel: 01584 872333 *Fax:* 01584 876459 *Dx:* 26883 LUDLOW 1
E-mail: enquiries@lblaw.co.uk
Office: Hereford, Oswestry (2 offices), Shrewsbury, Telford, Wellington
Ptr: Birtles, Ms Allison BA . . . . . *§Feb 1986
Goodwin, Mr Ian . . . . . Sep 2004
Spanner, Mr Colin M LLB President of Shropshire Law Society 2003-2004 . . . . . Oct 1987
Ast: Oxenham, Mr Andrew M LLB(Oxon). . . . . *§Nov 1984
Con: Taylor, Mr Roger O MA(Oxon). . . . . *Jul 1969

MORTIMERS
54 Broad Street Ludlow Shropshire SY8 1GZ
Tel: 01584 871000 *Fax:* 01584 871500
Office: Bridgnorth, Hereford
Ptr: Brake, Miss Karen Lynn BA. . . . . Oct 1987

PCB SOLICITORS LLP
Tolsey House 51 Bullring Ludlow Shropshire SY8 1AB
Tel: 01584 878456 *Fax:* 01584 874477
Emergency telephone 07703 486023
E-mail: info@pcblaw.co.uk
Office: Church Stretton, Knighton, Shrewsbury, Telford
Work: A1 B1 C1 D1 E G H J1 K1 L N O Q R1 S1 T2 W Z(d,l)
Emergency Action, Agency, Advocacy, Fixed Fee Interview, Legal Aid undertaken and Legal Aid Franchise
Ptr: Reedy, Mr Brendan J LLB. . . . . *Oct 1988

PHILLIPS & CO ‡
9 Corve Street Ludlow Shropshire SY8 1DE
Tel: 01584 873156 *Fax:* 01584 876686 *Dx:* 709052 LUDLOW 3
Emergency telephone 01584 872859
List of partners: G S Stephens, P J Stephens
Languages: French
Work: A1 C1 E F1 L S1 S2 T1 T2 W
Agency undertaken
Ptr: Stephens, Mr George S LLB . . . . . *§Dec 1963
Stephens, Mr Peter James LLB . . . . . *Feb 1996

LUTON, Luton

AKL SOLICITORS ‡
41 Adelaide Street Luton Luton LU1 5BD
Tel: 01582 454365 *Fax:* 01582 452847 *Dx:* 5911 LUTON
E-mail: info@akl.org.uk
List of partners: N Kulisra, S Lakhani
Ptr: Kulisra, Naresh BA(Dunelm) . . . . . *Jan 1979
Lakhani, Sherali. . . . . Nov 2002

See p112 for the Key to Work Categories & other symbols

ADAMS MOORE FAMILY LAW
105 Park Street Luton Luton LU1 3HG
Tel: 01582 481555 *Fax:* 01582 482211
E-mail: info@adamsmoore.co.uk
Office: Bedford, Bletchley, Corby, Daventry, Milton Keynes, Northampton

ALEXANDER SOLICITORS
146 Midland Road Luton Luton LU2 0BL
Tel: 01582 727888 *Fax:* 01582 728004 *Dx:* 5933 LUTON
E-mail: legal@alexandersolicitors.co.uk
Office: London EC4

AUDLEYS SOLICITORS ‡
51 Cardiff Road Luton Luton LU1 1PP
Tel: 01582 482999 *Fax:* 01582 412241

AUSTINS LLP ‡
36-40 Liverpool Road Luton Luton LU1 1RS
Tel: 01582 456222 *Fax:* 01582 401614 *Dx:* 130463 LUTON 10
E-mail: luton@austinslaw.com
List of partners: L Farrow, N G Frostick, R J Kissane, A G Pratt
Office: Berkhamsted
Languages: French
Work: D1 E J1 K1 K3 K4 L N O Q S1 S2 V W
Agency, Advocacy, Legal Aid undertaken and Member of Accident Line
Ptr: Kissane, Mr Robert J BA(Law) . . . . *Feb 1983
Pratt, Mr Anthony G LLB . . . . *Oct 1993
Ast: Morris, Mr H Richard M LLB(L'pool) . . . . *Sep 1984

BARNARD & TOMLIN
8 St Thomas Road Luton Luton LU2 7UY
Tel: 01582 453366 *Fax:* 01582 453397
E-mail: mark.lyon@barnard-tomlin.co.uk
Office: Luton
Work: S1 S2 W
Asoc: Lyon, Mr Mark . . . . Nov 1989

BEDFORDS SOLICITORS ‡
194 Dunstable Road Luton Luton LU4 8JJ
Tel: 01582 519736 *Fax:* 01582 519737
E-mail: mail@bedfordssolicitors.co.uk

BLAND & CO SOLICITORS ‡
29 King Street Luton Luton LU1 2DW
Tel: 01582 730544 *Fax:* 01582 429730
E-mail: blandoffice@blandsolicitors.co.uk

BUTT SOLICITORS ‡
21b George Street Luton Luton LU1 2AF
Tel: 01582 413471 *Fax:* 01582 726982 *Dx:* 5916 LUTON
E-mail: nadeembuttllb@hotmail.com

CHILTERN SOLICITORS ‡
110 Butterfield Great Marlings Luton Luton LU2 8DL
Tel: 01582 439795 *Fax:* 01582 439796
E-mail: philip.ivinson@chilternsolicitors.co.uk

CITY LAW CHAMBERS ‡
1st Floor Room 5/6 Courtney House Luton Luton LU2 0NT
Tel: 01582 418308 *Fax:* 01582 419702
E-mail: info@citylawchambers.com

DEEN SOLICITORS ‡
70-78 Collingdon Street Luton Luton LU1 1RX
Tel: 01582 484900 *Fax:* 01582 484901 *Dx:* 130464 LUTON 10
E-mail: law@deensolicitors.com
Languages: Gujarati, Hindi, Punjabi, Urdu
Work: E G H O Q S1 S2 Z(i)

DRUMMOND WALKER SOLICITORS ‡
69 Saturn Facilities 12-14 Park Street Luton Luton LU1 3EP
Tel: 0872 111 4336 *Fax:* 0845 504 9132
E-mail: info@dwslondon.com

ETON LAW ‡
25a Upper George Street Luton Luton LU1 2RD
Tel: 01582 726900 *Fax:* 01582 726909
E-mail: jilu@etonlaw.com
Languages: Bengali, Punjabi, Urdu
Work: B1 C1 D1 E F1 J1 K1 L M2 O Q R1 S1 S2 W Z(d,e,g,i,j,k,p)

GCA SOLICITORS (GIFFEN COUCH & ARCHER) ‡
Ground Floor Langham House West 29-37 Mill Street Luton Luton LU1 2NA
Tel: 01582 410041 *Fax:* 01582 401567
E-mail: solicitors@gcasolicitors.co.uk
List of partners: S Cousins, N S Donald, E C Halpin, S Singh-Takhar
Languages: Hindi, Punjabi
Work: A3 C1 D1 D2 E F1 J1 K1 K2 K3 K4 L N O Q R1 R2 S1 S2 V W Z(d,h)
Emergency Action, Agency, Advocacy, Fixed Fee Interview, Legal Aid undertaken and Legal Aid Franchise
Ptr: Cousins, Ms Sarah . . . . *Sep 1999
Donald, Mr Neil S . . . . *May 1993
Halpin, Ms Emma C . . . . *Sep 1998
Singh-Takhar, Santok Notary Public . . . . *Sep 2000
Asoc: Di-Donato, Miss Tatiana LLB University of Hertfordshire Prize for Excellent Performance 2008 . . . . Aug 2011
Ast: Chandler, Mr Graham Frederick . . . . *Apr 2004
Wallis, Mr Paul Henry BA . . . . *Jul 1986

HARVEYS ‡
74 George Street Luton Luton LU1 2BD
Tel: 01582 458567 *Fax:* 01582 456725
List of partners: M J Harvey
Work: B1 C1 E F1 G H J1 K1 L N O Q S1 W Z(b,j,l)
Agency, Advocacy and Legal Aid undertaken
SPr: Harvey, Mr Michael John BA(Hons) . . . . *May 1993

HEALEY COLBON ‡
Ground Floor Cannonkirk 64-66 Stuart Street Luton Luton LU1 2SW
Tel: 01582 405500

HUMA LAW ASSOCIATES ‡
27 Cardiff Road Luton Luton LU1 1PP
Tel: 01582 731330 *Fax:* 01582 415670
E-mail: humairashah05@hotmail.co.uk

INDUS SOLICITORS ‡
29 Cardiff Road Luton Luton LU1 1PP
Tel: 01582 431441 *Fax:* 01582 431872
E-mail: law@indussolicitors.co.uk

JL SOLICITORS ‡
AW House 6-8 Stuart Street Luton Luton LU1 2SJ
Tel: 01582 488688 / 020 8816 8106 *Fax:* 01582 380222
E-mail: contact@jlsolicitors.com

KNOWLES BENNING ‡
2 George Street West Luton Luton LU1 2BX
Tel: 01582 798000 *Fax:* 01582 457092 *Dx:* 5923 LUTON
E-mail: info@knowlesbenning.com
List of partners: S J Atkins, A Fallanca, T H Greensmith, C J Smith, R G Warfield, D R Welch
Office: Dunstable, Shefford
Languages: Italian
Work: B1 B2 C1 D1 E F1 G H J1 K1 L N O Q R1 S1 S2 V W X Z(c,k,l,m)
Emergency Action, Agency, Advocacy, Fixed Fee Interview, Legal Aid undertaken, Legal Aid Franchise and Member of Accident Line
Ptr: Fallanca, Mr Antonio . . . . *Jun 1978
Greensmith, Mr Trevor H LLB; DMA . . . . *Jun 1976
Smith, Mrs Catherine J . . . . Jun 1990
Warfield, Mr Royston G BA . . . . Dec 1974
Welch, Mr David R . . . . *§May 1971

LAWTONS SOLICITORS ‡
Station House Midland Road Luton Luton LU2 0HS
Tel: 01582 410111 *Fax:* 01582 484947 *Dx:* 5908 LUTON
E-mail: nick_titchener@yahoo.com

LEGAL SOLUTIONS PARTNERSHIP ‡
Maxet House Liverpool Road Luton Luton LU1 1RS
Tel: 01582 417208 *Fax:* 01582 485948 *Dx:* 130467 LUTON 1

G LEWIS AND CO SOLICITORS ‡
Britannia House Leagrave Road Luton Luton LU3 1RJ
Tel: 01582 486429 *Fax:* 0808 280 0672
E-mail: gxl@glewisandco.com

LUTON FAMILY LAW ‡
Business Competitiveness Centre Kimpton Road Luton Luton LU2 0SX
Tel: 01582 522385 *Fax:* 01582 522391

M & K SOLICITORS ‡
265 Dunstable Road Luton Luton LU4 8BS
Tel: 01582 732503 *Fax:* 01582 732533
List of partners: A Khan, M M Salim
Ptr: Khan, Ashrat . . . . Jan 2004
Salim, Mr Malik Mohammed . . . . Jan 1997

MA SOLICITORS ‡
4 Biscot Road Luton Luton LU3 1AT
Tel: 01582 431110 *Fax:* 01582 431110
E-mail: info@masolicitors.co.uk

MACHINS SOLICITORS LLP ‡
Victoria Street Luton Luton LU1 2BS
Tel: 01582 514000 *Fax:* 01582 535000 *Dx:* 5924 LUTON
E-mail: enquiries@machins.co.uk
List of partners: J Alvarez, R A J Bedford, N J Ginger, N D O'Callaghan, E A Oldham, P A Owen, M E Pelopida, S J Smith
Languages: Polish, Urdu
Work: A1 A3 B1 C1 C2 C3 D1 D2 E F1 F2 I J1 K1 K3 K4 L M3 N O P Q R1 R2 S1 S2 U2 V W Z(b,c,d,e,f,i,k,l,p,q,r,za)
Emergency Action, Agency, Advocacy, Fixed Fee Interview, Legal Aid undertaken, Legal Aid Franchise and Member of Accident Line
Ptr: Alvarez, Mr Jon BA . . . . *Oct 1998
Bedford, Mr Robert A J LLM . . . . *Apr 1979
Ginger, Mr Nicholas J LLB . . . . *Oct 1986
O'Callaghan, Mr Neil David BSc(Hons) . . . . *Nov 1995
Oldham, Mrs Elizabeth A LLB . . . . *Dec 1979
Owen, Mr Paul Anthony LLB(Hons) . . . . *Oct 1993
Pelopida, Mr Mark Ernest LLB . . . . *Jan 1991
Smith, Mr Stephen J LLB(Newc) . . . . *May 1981
Asoc: Beeley, Mr Hugh Wilfrid LLB . . . . *§Jun 1981
Gibson-Birch, Mr Nigel LLB(Hons) . . . . *Feb 1984
Melling, Mr Matthew B LLB; AKC . . . . *Nov 1988
Ast: Birnie, Mrs Josephine LLB . . . . *Sep 2003
Brown, Miss Siobhan Rose LLB; LPC; PSC Hertfordshire Law Society Student of the Year 2010 . . . . *Aug 2010
Denton-Masih, Mrs Nicki LLB; PGDip . . . . *Sep 2010
Dilley, Mrs Gemma . . . . *Mar 2007
Housden, Mrs Lydia LLB . . . . *Mar 2005
Jackson, Mr Martin LLB . . . . *Jul 2008
Jones, Ms Clare LLB(Hons) . . . . *Jan 1991
Liddiard, Mrs Sarah Jane . . . . *Nov 2005
McBean, Mr Wayne LLB(Hons) . . . . *Jan 2010
Pritchard, Mr Eugene LLB . . . . *Jan 2002
Rolfe, Mrs Shelley . . . . *Nov 2005
Rupping, Mrs Deborah Ann LLB(Hons); LPC . . . . . *Sep 2009
Walsh, Mr Kevin James LLB . . . . *Sep 2004
Con: Baggott, Mr David R . . . . *§Jul 1970

MENDIPS SOLICITORS ‡
Suite 3b Crystal House New Bedford Road Luton Luton LU1 1HS
Tel: 01582 720000 / 07981 000664 *Fax:* 01582 720000
E-mail: info@mendipssolicitors.co.uk

NEVES ‡
(incorporating Rylatt & McCaws; Rexworthy & Co)
8 George Street West Luton Luton LU1 2DA
Tel: 01582 725311 *Fax:* 01582 400972 *Dx:* 5900 LUTON
E-mail: info@neves-solicitors.co.uk
List of partners: S W S Clipstone, C Hume, J Joseph, P A T Kelly, S Matthews, M T McEvoy, A C Orriss, R I Simpson, E J Woodward
Office: Harpenden, Milton Keynes, Northampton
Work: A1 A3 C1 C2 D1 E F1 J1 K1 K2 K3 L M4 O Q R1 S1 S2 T1 T2 W Z(c,h,l,p)
Agency and Fixed Fee Interview undertaken
Ptr: Kelly, Mr Peter A T BA(Hons) . . . . *May 1981
McEvoy, Miss Mary T LLB Notary Public . . . . *Nov 1981
Orriss, Mr Andrew C LLB(Lond) . . . . *Oct 1983
Ast: Iqbal, Haqib . . . . *Jan 2007

NOBLE
50 Alma Street Luton Luton LU1 2PL
Tel: 01582 749490 *Fax:* 01582 749491 *Dx:* 5922 LUTON
Office: Shefford

NOBLE SOLICITORS ‡
3 High Town Road Luton Luton LU2 0BW
Tel: 01582 454083 *Dx:* 130461 LUTON 10
E-mail: admin@noblesolicitors.co.uk

PAUL NORTON & CO ‡
154 Marsh Road Luton Luton LU3 2QL
Tel: 01582 494970 *Fax:* 01582 494854
E-mail: reception@paulnorton.com
List of partners: P E Norton
SPr: Norton, Mr Paul Ernest . . . . Apr 1994

OWENS SOLICITORS ‡
Business Competitiveness Centre Kimpton Road Luton Luton LU2 0SX
Tel: 01582 451210 *Fax:* 01582 413914
E-mail: info@owenssolicitors.com

PICTONS SOLICITORS LLP ‡
28 Dunstable Road Luton Luton LU1 1DY
Tel: 01582 870870 *Fax:* 01582 870872 *Dx:* 144220 LUTON 14
E-mail: info@pictons.co.uk
List of partners: A Brall, N Drake, R J Fuller, J R King, G Meara, F Mills, S Saini, G C Sampson, R G Talbot, N H Terrell, J F Wardley, M C Wardrop, J R Webb, F A J Wilson
Office: Hemel Hempstead, Milton Keynes
Languages: Danish, Finnish, French, Gujarati, Hindi, Italian, Punjabi, Urdu
Work: B1 C1 C2 C3 D1 E F1 G H J1 K1 L N O Q S1 S2 T1 T2 U2 V W Z(f,l,r,w)
Emergency Action, Agency, Advocacy, Fixed Fee Interview, Legal Aid undertaken, Legal Aid Franchise and Member of Accident Line
Ptr: Brall, Mr Alexander . . . . Jun 1981
Drake, Mr Nigel LLB . . . . Sep 1991
Meara, Ms Gillian BA(Hons) . . . . Jun 1987
Mills, Ms Fiona LLB(Hons) . . . . *Aug 1997
Saini, Sukhdeep . . . . Sep 2000
Sampson, Mr Gerard C . . . . Dec 1972
Talbot, Mr Roger G MA(Cantab) . . . . May 1972
Terrell, Mr Neil H LLB(Nott'm) . . . . *Nov 1974
Wardley, Mr John F BA(Soton) . . . . Jun 1977
Webb, Ms Jacqueline Rachel BA(Law) . . . . *Jul 2000
Wilson, Mr Fabian Anthony John LLB(Hons) . . . . . . Nov 1990
Ast: Emmott, Ms Tracey BSocSc; LLB; LPC . . . . *Nov 2000
Pearson, Ms Jane Emma LLB(Hons) . . . . *Oct 1995

RODMAN PEARCE SOLICITORS ‡
54 Wellington Street Luton Luton LU1 2QH
Tel: 01582 424234 *Fax:* 01582 424235
E-mail: reception@rodmanpearce.com

SMITH BROWN & SPRAWSON
3-5 George Street West Luton Luton LU1 2BJ
Tel: 01582 876900 *Fax:* 01582 876966 *Dx:* 5970 LUTON
Emergency telephone 01582 650128 / 01462 435762
E-mail: luton@lawsbs.co.uk
Office: Dunstable
Work: D1 G H K1 S1 W Z(l)
Emergency Action, Agency, Advocacy, Fixed Fee Interview, Legal Aid undertaken and Legal Aid Franchise
Ptr: Brown, Mr Simon John . . . . *Jun 1982
Gentilella, Mr Michael . . . . *Jan 1997
Smith, Mr Andrew Charles . . . . *Nov 1988
Sprawson, Mr Stuart A BA(Law) . . . . *Jan 1984
Ast: Cestaro, Mrs Joanne Geraldine BA(Hons) . . . . . . *Jul 1997
Sohanpal, Miss Harveena LLB; LLM . . . . *Jan 1999

SOLOMON LEVY ‡
33 Alma Street Luton Luton LU1 2PL
Tel: 01582 425817 / 414948 *Fax:* 01582 402615
Dx: 130465 LUTON 10
E-mail: info@solomonlevy.com
List of partners: A A Levy, J Solomon
Work: B1 B2 C1 D1 E F1 G H J1 J2 K1 L M1 N O P Q R1 S1 S2 T1 T2 V W X Z(i,l,p,q,r,w,y)
Emergency Action, Agency, Advocacy, Fixed Fee Interview, Legal Aid undertaken, Legal Aid Franchise and Member of Accident Line
Ptr: Levy, Mr Alan A LLB . . . . *Oct 1978
Solomon, Mr Jeff BA(Law) . . . . *Nov 1978

STEPHENS WHEELER COOKE & SONS ‡
1 George Street West Luton Luton LU1 2BJ
Tel: 01582 720175 *Fax:* 01582 419820 *Dx:* 5904 LUTON
List of partners: N Barnard, A R Broughton, B B J Tomlin, A L Wheeler
Office: Luton
Work: S1
Agency, Advocacy and Legal Aid undertaken
Ptr: Barnard, Mr Nicholas . . . . Mar 1981
Broughton, Mr Alan R . . . . *Dec 1976
Tomlin, Mr Bernard B J . . . . *Jun 1982
Wheeler, Mr Alec L BA . . . . *Oct 1976

TAYLOR WALTON LLP ‡
28-44 Alma Street Luton Luton LU1 2PL
Tel: 01582 731161 *Fax:* 01582 457900 *Dx:* 130460 LUTON 10
E-mail: luton@taylorwalton.co.uk
List of partners: R J Atkins, J A Bartholomew, C O Borthwick, C M L Bowen, J N Brockis, D A Carey, J A Carpenter, A L Clarke, T Cook, H D Cowley, R Crocker, S W Griffiths, T K Harris, A P M Hartnett, J D Hobson, J S P James, R E Johnson, M P Kelly, A R Knight, P McGrath, I McLoone, M G Pettit, T M Shillabeer, A C Thomas, D von Hagen
Office: Harpenden, St Albans
Work: C1 C2 D1 I J1 K1 K2 K3 L O Q R2 S1 S2 U2 W Z(c,e,q)
Ptr: Bartholomew, Mr John A LLB(Lond) . . . . *Apr 1974
Borthwick, Mr Clive O MA(Oxon) . . . . *§Sep 1974
Bowen, Mr C Mark L . . . . *Sep 1976
Brockis, Mr Jeremy N LLB . . . . *§Oct 1988
Carey, Mr Dermot A LLB; AKC . . . . *§Oct 1987
Carpenter, Mr James A LLB(Nott'm Trent) . . . . Aug 1996
Clarke, Mr Anthony L LLB(Bris) . . . . *May 1967
Cook, Mr Tim . . . . *Oct 1999
Cowley, Ms Heather Doreen LLB . . . . *§Oct 1991
Griffiths, Mr Steven W LLB . . . . *§Dec 1980
Harris, Miss Tracy Kate LLB . . . . *Oct 1993
Hobson, Mr John D . . . . *§Jan 1970
Johnson, Mr Robert E BA . . . . Mar 1990
Kelly, Mr Michael P LLB . . . . *§Mar 1979
Knight, Mr Andrew R BA . . . . May 1987
McGrath, Mr Patrick . . . . Nov 1995
McLoone, Mr Ian LLB . . . . *Feb 1999
Pettit, Mr Michael G LLB . . . . *§Nov 1987
Thomas, Miss Angela C . . . . *§Nov 1986

von Hagen, Mr David . . . . . . *Nov 1990
Ast: Ali, Ms Sabahhit LLB(Hons) . . . . . . Sep 2000
Cooper, Ms Elena . . . . . . *Sep 2001
Dugal, Miss Surekha . . . . . . *Jul 1999
Evans, Ms Jane D . . . . . . *Oct 1990
Fitzpatrick, Mr Patrick John BA . . . . . . *Dec 1987
Fyfe, Mr Stewart . . . . . . *§Jan 1999
Greenhalgh, Mr Peter . . . . . . *Nov 1999
Knapman, Mrs Sandra B BA(Oxon) . . . . . . *Oct 1986
Lauder, Ms Alison J . . . . . . Sep 1999
O'Callaghan, Miss Helen M BSc . . . . . . *Mar 1996
Palmer, Mr Nicholas George LLB . . . . . . Sep 2000
Parmar, Ms Shetal . . . . . . Sep 2000
Plumbley-Jones, Ms Karen Mary LLB . . . . . . *Nov 1992
Roach, Ms Natalie . . . . . . *Sep 1998
Shuba, Mr Fraser Michael LLB(Hons) . . . . . . *Oct 1998
Thakyr, Ms Dipika . . . . . . Oct 2001
Voyce, Ms Alison Jayne MA(Oxon) . . . . . . *Oct 1991
Young, Ms Janice A LLB . . . . . . *Oct 1986

WHITMAN BREED ‡
960 Capability Green Luton Luton LU1 3PE
Tel: 01582 635077 *Fax:* 01582 842787
E-mail: enquiries@whitmanbreedlaw.com

WILLIAMS & CO ‡
(incorporating Gates Williams & Co)
22 King Street Luton Luton LU1 2DP
Tel: 01582 723322 *Fax:* 01582 455885 *Dx:* 5901 LUTON
List of partners: N Gibson-Birch, A P Morton, G A Richardson
Languages: French
Work: B1 C1 E F1 G H J1 K1 K3 L N O Q S1 S2 T1 T2 V W Z(c,l,o)
Emergency Action, Agency, Advocacy, Fixed Fee Interview and Legal Aid undertaken
Ptr: Gibson-Birch, Mr Nigel LLB(Hons) . . . . . . *Feb 1984
Morton, Mr Andrew P BA ★ . . . . . . *May 1981
Richardson, Mr Graham A LLB(Lond) . . . . . . *Oct 1962
Ast: Mashru, Ms Hita BA . . . . . . *Oct 1996

GORDON YOUNG SOLICITORS LTD ‡
AW House 6-8 Stuart Street Luton Luton LU1 2SJ
Tel: 01582 405577 *Fax:* 01582 452967 *Dx:* 5959 LUTON
Emergency telephone 01582 405577
List of partners: A Farr-Davies
Office: Welwyn Garden City
Work: G H
Emergency Action, Agency, Advocacy, Legal Aid undertaken and Legal Aid Franchise
Dir: Farr-Davies, Ms Alison LLB . . . . . . Sep 2001

ZAIDI SOLICITORS ‡
Suite 6b Crystal House New Bedford Road Luton Luton LU1 1HS
Tel: 01582 431333 *Fax:* 0845 890 1735
E-mail: info@zaidisolicitors.co.uk

LUTTERWORTH, Leicestershire

HALLETT EMPLOYMENT LAW SERVICES ‡
Liverpool House 15 South Avenue Ullesthorpe Lutterworth Leicestershire LE17 5DG
Tel: 01455 208886 *Fax:* 01455 208887
E-mail: john@hallett-els.co.uk

HEADLEYS ‡
39a Station Road Lutterworth Leicestershire LE17 4AP
Tel: 01455 554466 *Fax:* 01455 559048 *Dx:* 14855 LUTTERWORTH
E-mail: enquiries@headleys.com
List of partners: R A Broughton, J G A Headley
Office: Hinckley

JACKSON & CO ‡
10 Station Road Lutterworth Leicestershire LE17 4AP
Tel: 01455 556321
List of partners: A L Hall, M J Payne
Office: Birstall
Languages: Polish
Work: S1 S2 W
Agency undertaken
Ptr: Hall, Mr Anthony Louis BA(Law) . . . . . . *Oct 1982

MELKERTS SOLICITORS LIMITED ‡
12 Firtree Lane Swinford Lutterworth Leicestershire LE17 6BH
Tel: 01788 860088 *Fax:* 01788 860105
E-mail: enquiries@melkerts-solicitors.co.uk

RICH & CARR FREER BOUSKELL
Manor House 14 Market Street Lutterworth Leicestershire LE17 4EH
Tel: 0116 242 6048 *Fax:* 01455 550153 *Dx:* 14853 LUTTERWORTH
E-mail: enquiries@richandcarr.co.uk
Office: Blaby, Leicester, Oadby, Syston
Work: S1 S2 W
Ast: Crowle, Mr Julian . . . . . . Jan 2006

LYDNEY, Gloucestershire

FRANCIS LAW LLP ‡
Oakfield Hill Street Lydney Gloucestershire GL15 5HE
Tel: 01594 842242 *Fax:* 01594 841769 *Dx:* 92451 LYDNEY
E-mail: focus@francislaw.co.uk
List of partners: G J D Ellis, C A Mills
Work: A1 C1 D1 E G H J1 K1 L N Q R1 S1 U2 W Z(l)
Emergency Action, Agency, Advocacy, Fixed Fee Interview, Legal Aid undertaken, Legal Aid Franchise and Member of Accident Line
Ptr: Ellis, Mr Gary J D LLB . . . . . . *§Nov 1975
Mills, Mrs Carolyn Ann LLB(Hons) . . . . . . *Oct 1989

PITMAN BLACKSTOCK WHITE ‡
6 Cavendish Buildings Hill Street Lydney Gloucestershire GL15 5HD
Tel: 01594 842475 *Fax:* 01594 842225 *Dx:* 92450 LYDNEY
E-mail: pbwlydney@tiscali.co.uk
List of partners: G S C Blackstock, G C Pitman, R W H White
Office: Gloucester
Work: A1 C1 E F1 J1 K1 K3 L N O Q S1 S2 V W Z(l)
Emergency Action, Agency, Advocacy and Fixed Fee Interview undertaken
Ptr: Blackstock, Mr Gordon S C BA . . . . . . *Jun 1979
White, Mr Ross William Harvey BA(Hons) . . . . . . *Feb 1996
Dir: Pitman, Mr Glenn Craig BSc(Hons) . . . . . . *Mar 1992

LYME REGIS, Dorset

KITSON & TROTMAN
57-58 Broad Street Lyme Regis Dorset DT7 3QF
Tel: 01297 442580 *Fax:* 01297 442163
E-mail: lymeregis@kitsonandtrotman.co.uk
Office: Beaminster, Bridport
Work: A1 B1 C1 D1 E F1 G H J1 K1 L N O P Q R1 S1 T1 T2 V W Z(c,d,h,j,k,l,m,o)
Emergency Action, Agency, Advocacy, Fixed Fee Interview undertaken and Member of Accident Line
Ptr: Conroy, Mr Michael J Clerk to Commissioner of Taxes *Dec 1972
King, Mr Richard J BA(Hons) . . . . . . *Nov 1983
Scammell, Miss Tracy . . . . . . *Dec 1992

SCOTT ROWE
Raymond House 29 Broad Street Lyme Regis Dorset DT7 3QE
Tel: 01297 443777 *Fax:* 01297 445616
E-mail: enquiries@scottrowe.co.uk
Office: Chard
Work: E F1 G J1 K1 K2 K3 L N Q R1 S1 T1 T2 W
Agency, Advocacy and Legal Aid Franchise
Ptr: Trott, Mr Terence F BSc . . . . . . *§Jan 1976
Ast: Peters, Mr Gregory James Raymond BTh(Hons)(Oxon) . . . . . . *Nov 2004

LYMINGTON, Hampshire

ABRAMS COLLYER ‡
Twynham House 64 High Street Lymington Hampshire SO41 9AL
Tel: 01590 677888 *Fax:* 01590 673014 *Dx:* 34055 LYMINGTON
E-mail: law@abramscollyer.co.uk
List of partners: J M Collyer
Work: A1 C1 D1 E F1 G H J1 K1 K3 K4 L N O Q R1 S1 S2 T2 V W Z(d,h)
Emergency Action, Agency, Advocacy, Fixed Fee Interview and Legal Aid undertaken
Ptr: Collyer, Mrs Jennifer Margaret . . . . . . *Jun 1983
Ast: Bryant, Miss Christine R BMus; LRAM . . . . . . *§Jun 1977
Dew, Mr Michael P BA . . . . . . §Oct 1986
Dugdale, Mrs Vanessa Anne LLB(Hons) . . . . . . Jun 1999

SCOTT BAILEY ‡
63 High Street Lymington Hampshire SO41 9ZT
Tel: 01590 676933 *Fax:* 01590 679663 *Dx:* 34054 LYMINGTON
E-mail: law@scottbailey.co.uk
List of partners: I D S Davis, N P Jutton, S L Sutherland, S J Unsworth
Work: A1 B1 C1 C2 D1 E F1 J1 K1 L N O P Q R1 S1 T1 T2 V W Z(b,j)
Emergency Action, Agency, Advocacy, Fixed Fee Interview, Legal Aid Franchise and Member of Accident Line
Ptr: Davis, Mr Ian D S . . . . . . *Jul 1970
Jutton, Mr Nicholas Paul BSc . . . . . . *Oct 1987
Sutherland, Mrs Suzanne L BA(Kent) . . . . . . *Oct 1975
Unsworth, Miss Sarah Jane BA . . . . . . *Nov 1992

HEPPENSTALLS
75 High Street Lymington Hampshire SO41 9YY
Tel: 01590 689500 *Fax:* 01590 674434 *Dx:* 34053 LYMINGTON
E-mail: mail@heppenstalls-lymington.co.uk
Office: Lyndhurst, New Milton
Languages: French, German, Italian, Romanian
Work: D1 K1 K3 K4 L Q R1 S1 S2 T2 W Z(l,m)
Fixed Fee Interview and Legal Aid undertaken
Ptr: Bennett, Mr Christian William LLB . . . . . . *Oct 2003
Jennings, Mrs Alexandra Margaret LLB(Lond) . . . . . . *Jun 1980
O'Dea, Miss Catherine M LLB . . . . . . *§Nov 1972
Salt, Mr Philip Peter Maurice LLB . . . . . . *Jul 2002
Ast: Gurluk, Mr Ben . . . . . . *Sep 2006
Con: Pullan, Mrs Sheila Joan . . . . . . Feb 1985

MOORE BLATCH SOLICITORS ‡
48 High Street Lymington Hampshire SO41 9ZQ
Tel: 01590 625800 *Fax:* 01590 671224 *Dx:* 34050 LYMINGTON 1
List of partners: T Blackwell, C Cantoni, A Cassidy, M J Caton, M P V Duck, J R Hatchard, C L Haverfield, D P Horan, V J Hydon, P R Jeffery, K T Maxwell, M R Osgood, T D M Spring, D C Thompson, P A Walshe, P R A Whitaker
Office: Richmond upon Thames, Southampton (2 offices), Wickham
Languages: French, German
Work: A1 B1 C1 C2 C3 D1 E F1 G H I J1 K1 L M1 M2 N O P Q R1 S1 T1 T2 W Z(a,b,c,e,h,j,k,l,o,t)
Legal Aid Franchise
Ptr: Hatchard, Mr John Rayner . . . . . . *§Oct 1978

CLIVE SUTTON SOLICITOR ‡
Buckland Manor Southampton Road Lymington Hampshire SO14 8NP
Tel: 01590 672595 *Fax:* 01590 671466
E-mail: solicitor@clive-sutton.co.uk
Work: B1 B2 E G J1 N O Q S1 S2 W Z(a,g,k,q,x)
Emergency Action and Advocacy undertaken

LYMM, Warrington

HOWARD FITTON ‡
The Dingle Lymm Warrington WA13 0AE
Tel: 01925 757565 *Fax:* 01925 757535 *Dx:* 717890 LYMM
E-mail: office@hssols.co.uk
List of partners: H M Fitton
Work: C1 E F1 J1 K1 L N O Q S1 S2 T1 T2 W Z(l,q,r,w)
Fixed Fee Interview undertaken
SPr: Fitton, Mr Howard Michael LLB . . . . . . *Oct 1987

WILLIAM H LILL & CO
9 The Cross Lymm Warrington WA13 0HY
Tel: 01925 753170 / 755668 *Fax:* 01925 757714 *Dx:* 717893 LYMM
Office: Altrincham
Work: C1 E K1 N Q S1
Emergency Action, Agency, Advocacy, Fixed Fee Interview undertaken and Member of Accident Line
Ptr: Cooper, Mrs Gail LLB(Hons) . . . . . . *May 2003
Jackson, Mr Michael Rothwell BSc(Mech Eng) . . . . *§Jun 1966
Jackson, Mr Oliver BA; LPC . . . . . . *Sep 1996

LYNDHURST, Hampshire

HEPPENSTALLS
39-41 High Street Lyndhurst Hampshire SO43 7BE
Tel: 023 8028 2885 *Fax:* 023 8028 4137 *Dx:* 90652 LYNDHURST
E-mail: mail@heppenstalls-lyndhurst.co.uk
Office: Lymington, New Milton
Languages: French, German
Work: E F1 J1 K4 L S1 S2 W
Ast: Gurluk, Mr Ben LLB(Hons) . . . . . . Dec 2006

SMITH BATES ‡
101 High Street Lyndhurst Hampshire SO43 7BH
Tel: 023 8028 3414 *Fax:* 023 8028 3220 *Dx:* 90655 LYNDHURST
E-mail: justice@smithbates.co.uk
List of partners: R M J Smith
Work: C1 E J1 K1 N Q S1 S2 W Z(d,e,l)
Fixed Fee Interview undertaken
Ptr: Smith, Mr Richard M J LLB . . . . . . *May 1985
Con: Leatherdale, Mr Malcolm Charles John LLB(Lond); ACIS . . . . . . Jun 1976

TMS LEGAL COST CONSULTANTS ‡
Old School Grounds Southampton Road Cadnam Lyndhurst Hampshire SO40 2NF
Tel: 023 8081 6630 *Fax:* 023 8081 3796 *Dx:* 90653 LYNDHURST
E-mail: admin@t-ms.co.uk

LYTHAM, Lancashire

ACCESS EMPLOYMENT LAW LIMITED ‡
4A Clifton Square Lytham Lancashire FY8 5JP
Tel: 0845 121 2789 / 01253 731199 *Fax:* 01253 795252
E-mail: aj@accessemplaw.co.uk

APFEL CARTER ‡
28-30 Park Road St Annes-on-Sea Lytham Lancashire FY8 1PA
Tel: 01253 725265 / 712216 *Fax:* 01253 721235
Dx: 716861 ST ANNES ON SEA 2
E-mail: general@apfelcarter.co.uk
Work: E F1 K1 K2 K3 L N O Q S1 S2 W
Emergency Action, Agency, Advocacy, Fixed Fee Interview, Legal Aid undertaken and Member of Accident Line

BLACKLEDGE & CO ‡
33 Church Road Lytham Lancashire FY8 5LL
Tel: 01253 730070 *Fax:* 01253 731929 *Dx:* 28438 LYTHAM
E-mail: enquiries@blackledgeandco.co.uk
Work: E L N Q R2 S1 S2 T2 W
Agency and Fixed Fee Interview undertaken

BRADSHAWS HAMER PARK & HAWORTH ‡
298 Clifton Drive South St Annes-on-Sea Lytham Lancashire FY8 1LL
Tel: 01253 724251 / 728451 *Fax:* 01253 712006
Dx: 22901 ST ANNES 1
List of partners: C S Shillito, T J Wood
Office: Blackpool
Work: A1 A2 B1 C1 C3 D1 E F1 J1 K1 L N P Q R2 S1 S2 T1 T2 W Z(l,m)
Agency undertaken
Ptr: Wood, Mr T Jeffrey BA . . . . . . *§Dec 1976
Ast: Taylor, Miss Emma BA(Hons) . . . . . . *Nov 2007

CLONEY & CO ‡
34-36 Orchard Road St Annes-on-Sea Lytham Lancashire FY8 1PF
Tel: 01253 712116 *Fax:* 01253 721218 *Dx:* 716859 ST ANNES 2
E-mail: info@cloneyco.com
List of partners: V Cloney
Work: B1 C1 C2 C3 E L O Q R1 S1 T1 T2 W Z(m,q)
Ptr: Cloney, Mr Vincent LLB . . . . . . *Apr 1978

COUPE BRADBURY ‡
The Chapel House Bath Street Lytham Lancashire FY8 5ES
Tel: 01253 736670 *Fax:* 01253 794108 *Dx:* 28431 LYTHAM
Emergency telephone 01253 733563
E-mail: irene@coupe-bradbury.com
List of partners: D B S Coupe, S B Coupe, C D McGiue
Office: Kirkham
Languages: Gujarati, Hindi, Urdu
Work: A1 B1 C1 C2 D1 D2 E F1 G H J1 K1 K2 L N O Q R1 S1 S2 T1 T2 V W Z(d,i,k,l,m,q)
Emergency Action, Agency, Advocacy, Fixed Fee Interview, Legal Aid undertaken, Legal Aid Franchise and Member of Accident Line
Ptr: Coupe, Mr David B S . . . . . . *Nov 1968
Coupe, Mr Simon Bruce LLB(Hons) . . . . . . *Apr 1977
McGiue, Mr Colin D LLB(Hons) . . . . . . *Oct 1999
Asoc: Gadsden, Miss Emma LLB . . . . . . *Jul 2005
Hall, Mrs Rachel Louise LLB(Hons) . . . . . . Jun 2007
Lever, Mr Paul LLB(Hons) . . . . . . Apr 2000
Scott, Mr Matthew William Derek BSc(Hons) . . . . . . Jul 2006
Ast: Kernot, Ms Helen Marie LLB(Hons) . . . . . . Aug 2007
Pound, Ms Lorna . . . . . . Aug 1988

W H DARBYSHIRE & SON
51 Commonside Lytham Lancashire FY8 4EX
Tel: 01253 736134 *Fax:* 01253 733315
Office: Blackpool
Work: A1 B1 C1 D1 E F1 G H J1 K1 L M1 N P R1 S1 T1 V W Z(c,h,m)
Emergency Action, Agency and Fixed Fee Interview undertaken
Ptr: Darbyshire, Mr Rowland W Part time Chairman of TAS . . . . . . *§Oct 1965
Ast: Laszlo, Mr Martin George BA(Oxon) . . . . . . *Aug 2000

DICKSON HASLAM
(in association with Dickson Child & Green)
25 Park Street Lytham Lancashire FY8 5LU
Tel: 01253 730111 *Fax:* 01253 794627
Dx: 28435 LYTHAM ST ANNES
Emergency telephone 01772 684780
E-mail: info@dicksonhaslam.co.uk
Office: Kirkham, Preston
Languages: French
Work: A1 C1 D1 E F1 K1 L P S1 S2 W Z(d,l)
Emergency Action, Agency, Advocacy, Fixed Fee Interview, Legal Aid undertaken, Legal Aid Franchise and Member of Accident Line
Ptr: Hall, Mrs Elizabeth H . . . . . . May 1996

See p112 for the Key to Work Categories & other symbols

GLASSBROOKS LIMITED ‡
1 York Road St Annes-on-Sea Lytham Lancashire FY8 1HP
Tel: 0800 316 6484
E-mail: nick@glassbrooks.co.uk

LESLIE HARRIS SOLICITORS & ADVOCATES ‡
19 Park Road St Annes-on-Sea Lytham Lancashire FY8 1PP
Tel: 01253 724974 *Fax:* 01253 714951 *Dx:* 22909 ST ANNES
Emergency telephone 07626 949976
E-mail: mbland@leslieharristannes.co.uk
List of partners: M Bland, A Thompson, E A Wright
Work: D1 E F1 G H J1 K1 L M1 M2 N Q R1 S1 V W Z(c,j,l)
Emergency Action, Agency, Advocacy, Fixed Fee Interview, Legal Aid undertaken and Member of Accident Line
Ptr: Bland, Mr Martin LLB Deputy District Judge . . . . . . *Sep 1989
Thompson, Miss Anne LLB(Hons). . . . . *Sep 1998
Wright, Mr Eamonn A BA(Hons)(Law). . . . . *Jun 1979

MICHAEL A LECKEY ‡
284 Clifton Drive South Lytham Lancashire FY8 1LH
Tel: 01253 726100 *Fax:* 01253 721871

ROLAND ROBINSONS & FENTONS LLP
4 Church Road Lytham Lancashire FY8 5LH
Tel: 01253 734253
Office: Blackpool
Languages: French, Spanish
Work: A1 C1 E S1 S2 W Z(d,l)
Ptr: Batty, Mr Mark . . . . Jun 1978
Con: Crossley-Dawson, Mr Philip A LLB . . . . *Jun 1973

SARANGI COYLE SOLICITORS ‡
1st Floor 16 St George's Road Lytham Lancashire FY8 2AE
Tel: 01253 735919 *Fax:* 01253 711707

SENIOR CALVELEY & HARDY ‡
8 Hastings Place Lytham Lancashire FY8 5NA
Tel: 01253 733333 *Fax:* 01253 794430 *Dx:* 28440 LYTHAM
E-mail: enquiries@seniorslaw.co.uk
List of partners: G D Calderbank, R N Hardy, J D G Hinchliffe, D M Jefferies
Office: Kirkham, Poulton-le-Fylde
Work: A1 E K1 K3 K4 S1 S2 T2 W Z(d)
Ptr: Calderbank, Mr Grahame D BA(Law) . . . . *Jul 1981
Hardy, Mr Richard N LLB; TEP Notary Public . . . . . *Dec 1972
Hinchliffe, Mr J David G LLB(B'ham) . . . . *Oct 1986
Jefferies, Mr David M LLB; TEP. . . . . *Jun 1977
Ast: Barron, Mrs W Jane LLB . . . . *Dec 1990
Earnshaw, Mrs Sharon E LLB. . . . . *Sep 2003
Fleming, Mrs Zoe Jayne LLB . . . . *Aug 2006

THORNTON & CO ‡
325 Clifton Drive South Lytham Lancashire FY8 1HN
Tel: 01253 782808 *Fax:* 01253 782153 *Dx:* 22912 ST ANNES
E-mail: info@thorntonsolicitors.co.uk
List of partners: J M Bateson
Languages: French
Work: E G H J1 K1 N O Q S1 S2 W Z(l,q)
Emergency Action, Agency, Advocacy, Fixed Fee Interview and Legal Aid undertaken
Ptr: Bateson, Ms Janet M BA(Hons). . . . . *Oct 1996
Ast: Irving, Mr Andrew William . . . . Mar 2000

J WRIGHT ‡
101 Mayfield Road St Annes-on-Sea Lytham Lancashire FY8 2DR
Tel: 01253 727875 *Fax:* 01253 781142
E-mail: jwright@legal101.freeserve.co.uk
List of partners: J Wright
Work: J1 N O Q
Ptr: Wright, Mr John MA(Oxon) Regional Chairman for West Midlands and North West Region of Mental Health Review Tribunal. . . . . *§Dec 1970

MABLETHORPE, Lincolnshire

JOHN BARKERS
27 High Street Mablethorpe Lincolnshire LN12 1AF
Est: 1884
Tel: 01507 477673 *Fax:* 01507 478581
Office: Cleethorpes, Grimsby, Louth
Work: B1 C1 C2 D1 D2 E F1 F2 G H J1 K1 K3 K4 L N O Q R1 S1 S2 T1 T2 V W Z(h,l,r)
Emergency Action, Agency, Advocacy, Fixed Fee Interview, Legal Aid undertaken and Member of Accident Line
Ptr: Needley, Mr James L . . . . *§Jan 1971
Ast: Brindle, Mr William Thomas Francis LLB . . . . Apr 2005
Con: Brewer, Mr Paul S. . . . . *§Dec 1980
Vamplew, Mr Terence J C . . . . *§Jun 1977

BRIDGE MCFARLAND
16 Victoria Road Mablethorpe Lincolnshire LN12 2AQ
Tel: 01507 478285 *Fax:* 01507 477285
Emergency telephone 01507 600340
E-mail: info@bmcf.co.uk
Office: Grimsby (3 offices), Hull, Lincoln, Louth, Market Rasen, Skegness
Work: A1 B1 C1 D1 E F1 G H J1 K1 L M1 N P R1 S1 T1 V W Z(c,l)
Emergency Action, Agency, Advocacy, Fixed Fee Interview, Legal Aid undertaken and Member of Accident Line

WILKIN CHAPMAN GRANGE SOLICITORS
51 Victoria Road Mablethorpe Lincolnshire LN12 2AF
Tel: 01507 479824
E-mail: info@wilkinchapman.co.uk
Office: Alford, Beverley, Grimsby (3 offices), Horncastle, Lincoln, Louth, Market Rasen, Sutton-on-Sea

MACCLESFIELD, Cheshire

ALCOCK & SMALLEY ‡
147 Broken Cross Macclesfield Cheshire SK11 8TU
Tel: 01625 431530 *Fax:* 01625 501282
E-mail: mail@alcockandsmalley.co.uk
List of partners: P A Smalley
Work: K4 S1 W
SPr: Smalley, Mrs Pamela Anne BA(Hons). . . . . *Aug 1981
Con: Alcock, Ms Leonor A . . . . *Jun 1972

G A ARNOLD ‡
Royal Buildings 8 Pickford Street Macclesfield Cheshire SK11 6JD
Tel: 01625 615424 *Fax:* 01625 615424
Emergency telephone 07699 746220
List of partners: G A Arnold
Languages: French
Work: G H
Agency, Advocacy, Fixed Fee Interview, Legal Aid undertaken and Legal Aid Franchise
SPr: Arnold, Mr G Andrew LLB. . . . . *Jun 1975

BENNETTS ‡
37 Market Place Macclesfield Cheshire SK10 1DY
Tel: 01625 424666 *Fax:* 01625 511273 *Dx:* 25004 MACCLESFIELD
E-mail: jambler@btconnect.com
List of partners: J Ambler
Work: A1 B1 C1 C2 C3 D1 E F1 G H J1 K1 L M1 M2 N P R1 S1 T1 T2 V W
Emergency Action, Agency, Advocacy, Fixed Fee Interview, Legal Aid undertaken and Member of Accident Line
Ptr: Ambler, Ms Jane BA . . . . *Mar 1987

BOLLIN LEGAL ASSOCIATES LTD ‡
St Georges Chambers St Georges Place Macclesfield Cheshire SK11 8BT
Tel: 01625 667150

ABOUDI BRADLEY & CO ‡
35 Church Street Macclesfield Cheshire SK11 6LB
Tel: 01625 428749 *Fax:* 01625 611927 *Dx:* 19395 MACCLESFIELD
E-mail: ab@aboudi-bradley.fsnet.co.uk
List of partners: A Bradley
Work: A1 C1 E S1 W
Ptr: Bradley, Mr Alan LLB . . . . *Jun 1979

C M BROADBENT ‡
Close House Farm Bibby's Lane Macclesfield Cheshire SK10 2PJ
Tel: 01625 500038 *Fax:* 01625 501366
Emergency telephone 01625 500038
E-mail: cmb.law@zen.co.uk
List of partners: C M Broadbent
Work: A1 C1 E L O P Q R1 S1 S2 W Z(c,d)
Fixed Fee Interview undertaken
SPr: Broadbent, Mr Christopher M BA(Cantab). . . . . . . *Aug 1976

AMANDA CUNLIFFE SOLICITORS LTD ‡
St Georges Chambers St Georges Place Macclesfield Cheshire SK11 8BT
Tel: 01625 667166 *Fax:* 01625 667131
E-mail: info@amandacunliffesolicitors.co.uk

FEARNLEY & CO ‡
Roe Street House 67 Roe Street Macclesfield Cheshire SK11 6XD
Tel: 01625 427303 *Fax:* 01625 611397
Emergency telephone 01625 573067
E-mail: fearnleylaw@btconnect.com
List of partners: F T K Fearnley
Work: C1 E K1 L P R1 S1 T1 W Z(c)
Emergency Action and Advocacy undertaken
Ptr: Fearnley, Mr Frederick T K MA . . . . *Mar 1980

MARK FINDLOW & CO ‡
Sunrise House Hulley Road Hurdsfield Macclesfield Cheshire SK10 2LP
Tel: 01625 617306 *Fax:* 01625 430400
E-mail: mail@markfindlow.co.uk
List of partners: N M Findlow
Work: E K4 L Q R1 S1 S2 W
Ptr: Findlow, Mr Nicholas Mark LLB . . . . *Jul 1978

A D FIRTH & CO ‡
3 Oliver Close Bollington Macclesfield Cheshire SK10 5JS
Tel: 01625 261840 *Fax:* 01625 267597
E-mail: adfirth@btconnect.com
List of partners: A D Firth
Languages: French
Work: N S1 W
Agency and Fixed Fee Interview undertaken
SPr: Firth, Mr Alan D LLB(Sheff) . . . . *May 1977

DOREEN FREEAR SOLICITOR ‡
Brook House 122 Prestbury Road Macclesfield Cheshire SK10 3BN
Tel: 01625 611711 *Fax:* 0560 115 1899
E-mail: dfslaw@aol.com
List of partners: D E Freear
Languages: French
Work: K1 S1
Emergency Action, Agency and Fixed Fee Interview undertaken
SPr: Freear, Mrs Doreen E BA(Hons). . . . . *Nov 1991

HAGUE LAMBERT
36-38 Park Green Macclesfield Cheshire SK11 7NE
Tel: 01625 616480 *Fax:* 01625 610029 *Dx:* 19387 MACCLESFIELD 1
E-mail: lcr@hague-lambert.co.uk
Web: www.hague-lambert.co.uk
Office: Knutsford, Manchester, Urmston
Work: D1 E K1 K3 S1 T2 W Z(d)
Fixed Fee Interview undertaken
Ptr: Robinson, Mr Lawrence C BA. . . . . *Oct 1979
Ast: Bushell, Ms Sarah Caroline BA(English). . . . . *Oct 1990
Speed, Mrs Michelle BA(Hons)(Law) . . . . *Nov 1985

Offices in Manchester, Knutsford & Urmston. Broad based firm offering a wide range of services to both the business & personal client.

HERMANS SOLICITORS ‡
31 Great King Street Macclesfield Cheshire SK11 6PL
Tel: 01625 611224

WILLIAM HOOD & CO ‡
Victoria House Walker Street Macclesfield Cheshire SK10 1BH
Tel: 01625 611819 *Fax:* 01625 619623
E-mail: wh@williamhood.co.uk
List of partners: C W Hood
Work: A1 B1 C1 D1 E F1 J1 K1 L M1 N P Q R1 S1 S2 T1 V W Z(b,c,d,e,j,l,t)
Fixed Fee Interview and Legal Aid undertaken
Ptr: Hood, Mr C William . . . . *Jan 1968

HORNE & COMPANY ‡
34 Chester Road Macclesfield Cheshire SK11 8DG
Tel: 01625 820920

IMPERIUM LAW LLP ‡
Jordangate House Jordangate Macclesfield Cheshire SK10 1EQ
Tel: 01625 619062 *Fax:* 01625 616728 *Dx:* 19386 MACCLESFIELD

JB LAW ‡
Wesley Chapel 22 Sunderland Street Macclesfield Cheshire SK11 6JL
Tel: 01625 443190 *Fax:* 01625 443197

JOBLING GOWLER ‡
250 Park Lane Macclesfield Cheshire SK11 8AD
Tel: 01625 614250 *Fax:* 01625 614252 *Dx:* 25025 MACCLESFIELD 2
E-mail: info@jobling-gowler.co.uk
List of partners: S D L Gowler, M H Jobling, D F Mercer
Languages: French, German
Work: K4 N Q S1 W Z(q,r,w)
Agency, Fixed Fee Interview and Legal Aid undertaken
Ptr: Gowler, Mr Simon D L LLB . . . . *Sep 1988
Jobling, Mrs Margaret H BA. . . . . *Jun 1980
Mercer, Mr David F MA(Cantab). . . . . *Apr 1977
Ast: Acres, Miss Victoria Alexandra LLB . . . . *Nov 1993
Gaunt, Mrs Heather Kathleen LLB. . . . . *Nov 1994
Jacobs, Mrs Rebecca Mary LLB. . . . . *Mar 1991

LAW:MATIX ‡
43 Drummond Way Macclesfield Cheshire SK10 4XJ
Tel: 01625 828877 *Fax:* 0161 773 8000

LEWIS RODGERS SOLICITORS
Waters Green House Sunderland Street Macclesfield Cheshire SK11 6LF
Tel: 01625 429114 *Fax:* 01625 617915
Office: Winsford

THE OAKES PARTNERSHIP ‡
Oak House 3 Brunswick Street Macclesfield Cheshire SK10 1ER
Tel: 01625 422944 *Fax:* 01625 424111
E-mail: oakespartnership@btconnect.com

READ LAW ASSOCIATES ‡
2 King Edward Street Macclesfield Cheshire SK10 1AB
Tel: 01625 429131 *Fax:* 01625 511016 *Dx:* 19393 MACCLESFIELD
E-mail: info@readlaw.co.uk
List of partners: J Burke, N R Read
Work: C1 E S1 S2 W
Ptr: Burke, Mr John . . . . Apr 1978
Read, Mr Nigel R LLB(Hons) . . . . *Apr 1981

ROBERTS SOLICITORS ‡
42 Jordangate Macclesfield Cheshire SK10 1EW
Tel: 01625 431111 *Fax:* 01625 430033
E-mail: info@robertssolicitors.co.uk
List of partners: S C Bushell, W Roberts
Work: K1 N S1 W
Ptr: Bushell, Ms Sarah Caroline BA(English). . . . . *Oct 1990
Roberts, Mr Wayne . . . . Jan 1999

SAS DANIELS LLP
County Chambers 6 Chestergate Macclesfield Cheshire SK11 6BA
Tel: 01625 442100 *Fax:* 01625 615630
E-mail: help@sasdaniels.co.uk
Office: Bramhall, Chester, Congleton, Stockport
Work: A1 A3 B1 C1 D1 D2 E F1 J1 K1 K2 K3 K4 L N O P Q R1 R2 S1 S2 T2 V W Z(b,c,d,e,k,l,m,q,r,s,z)
Agency, Advocacy, Fixed Fee Interview, Legal Aid undertaken, Legal Aid Franchise and Member of Accident Line
Ptr: Bestley, Mr Mark R J MA(Cantab). . . . . *§Apr 1977
Browton, Miss Glenys MA; MSc. . . . . *Oct 1991
Hesford, Miss Shelley C LLB . . . . Sep 1991
Lomas, Mr Timothy R LLB(Manc) . . . . §Jun 1972
Thompson, Ms Helen Elizabeth . . . . Oct 1994
Tudin, Mr Alvin Lawrence BA . . . . Nov 1987
Wilson, Mrs Nicola Jane. . . . . Sep 1996
Asoc: Littlemore, Miss Justine Marie. . . . . Sep 2002
Con: Cutbill, Mr David A LLB . . . . §Mar 1977
Hodgkinson, Mr Philip J LLB(Lond) . . . . §Nov 1971

SHEPHERD EVANS SOLICITORS ‡
Mulberry House 10 Little Street Macclesfield Cheshire SK10 1AW
Tel: 01625 503909 *Fax:* 01625 500050
List of partners: C F Evans, S R Shepherd
Work: B1 C1 D1 E F1 G H J1 K1 L M1 M2 O Q S1 V W Z(m)
Emergency Action, Agency, Advocacy, Fixed Fee Interview, Legal Aid undertaken and Legal Aid Franchise
Ptr: Evans, Mr Christopher Frank . . . . Oct 1992
Shepherd, Mr Steven Ronald LLB. . . . . *Dec 1994

STRATFORD SOLICITORS ‡
Brook House 8 Willow Way Prestbury Macclesfield Cheshire SK10 4XB
Tel: 01625 820275 *Fax:* 01625 820335
E-mail: nick.stratford@stratford-solicitors.com
Office: Poynton

THORNEYCROFT SOLICITORS LTD ‡
Bridge Street Mills Bridge Street Macclesfield Cheshire SK11 6QA
Tel: 01625 503444 *Fax:* 01625 506600 *Dx:* 25022 MACCLESFIELD 2
E-mail: info@thorneycrofts.co.uk
List of partners: K Cockburn, M J Coghlan, R L Stow, R P Thorneycroft
Work: C1 E F1 J1 K1 L N Q S1 W Z(q)
Advocacy, Fixed Fee Interview undertaken and Member of Accident Line
Dir: Cockburn, Ms Kim . . . . Sep 2000
Coghlan, Mr Michael John. . . . . Aug 1995
Stow, Mrs Rachel Leonie BA(Hons) . . . . *Aug 1995
Thorneycroft, Mr Robert Patrick BA . . . . *Oct 1982
Asoc: Cooper, Ms Laura BA(Hons) . . . . Feb 2011
Farrow, Ms Sharon LLB. . . . . Jan 2004
Ast: Boardman, Mrs Kirsten LLB(Hons) . . . . *Jul 2010
Cartwright, Mrs Claire. . . . . Mar 2008
Ellis, Mr David Anthony LLB(Hons) . . . . Jun 2006
Nayee, Ms Usha . . . . Jun 2000
Phelps, Ms Susan. . . . . Jan 2000
Wilkinson, Mr Philip . . . . Jul 1980

WAINS ‡
39-43 Churchside Macclesfield Cheshire SK10 1HW
Tel: 01625 429511 *Fax:* 01625 511512 *Dx:* 19382 MACCLESFIELD
E-mail: reception@wainssolicitors.co.uk
List of partners: A M Dickinson, R E N Gough, A P Meachin
Office: Congleton
Work: A1 D1 E G H K1 K3 L Q S1 S2 W Z(l)
Agency, Advocacy, Fixed Fee Interview, Legal Aid undertaken and Legal Aid Franchise

Ptr: Dickinson, Miss Anne M BA(Hons)(Law). . . . . . *§Nov 1981
Gough, Mr Roger E N. . . . . *§Aug 1979
Meachin, Mr Andrew P . . . . *§Dec 1977
Asoc: Bartholomew, Miss Susan LLB . . . . *Oct 1982
Hughes, Mr Christopher BA(Hons) . . . . §Dec 2006
Worthington, Mr Kevin John LLB(Hons) . . . . *Mar 2000
Con: Biggs, Mr Philip A. . . . . *§Jan 1972
Dodson, Mr Christopher John MA; LLB(Cantab) . . . *Mar 1970

MACHYNLLETH, Powys

BRUNTON & CO
(incorporating D Emrys Williams & Co)
Maldwyn House Pentrehedyn Street Machynlleth Powys SY20 8AG
Tel: 01654 703110 / 703121 *Fax:* 01654 702514
Office: Aberystwyth
Languages: Welsh
Work: A1 B1 D2 E G J1 K1 L N R1 S1 S2 T2 W Z(l)
Agency, Advocacy and Fixed Fee Interview undertaken
Ptr: Brunton, Mr Peter L Coroner . . . . *Jul 1975
Davies, Miss Elizabeth M LLB H M Deputy Coroner . . *Apr 1975

EVANS-ROBERTS ‡
11 Penrallt Street Machynlleth Powys SY20 8AG
Tel: 01654 702335 / 702336 *Fax:* 01654 703742
Dx: 712240 MACHYNLLETH
Emergency telephone 01654 702524
List of partners: B Roberts
Languages: Welsh
Work: A1 A2 B2 C1 D1 E F1 G H J1 K1 L N O Q R1 S1 S2 T2 W Z(c,e,p)
Emergency Action, Agency, Advocacy, Fixed Fee Interview and Legal Aid undertaken
Ptr: Roberts, Mr Bryn LLB(Wales) . . . . Jul 1980
Ast: Rodgers, Mrs Judith Anne LLB . . . . *Nov 1980

MAESTEG, Bridgend

R L EDWARDS & PARTNERS
3 Church Street Maesteg Bridgend CF34 9AA
Tel: 01656 733297 *Fax:* 01656 737914
Office: Bridgend, Porthcawl, Treorchy
Work: B1 C1 D1 E F1 G H J1 K1 L M1 N P S1 W Z(d,l)
Emergency Action, Agency, Advocacy, Legal Aid undertaken and Member of Accident Line

KING DAVIES & PARTNERS ‡
Lloyds Bank Chambers 18 Talbot Street Maesteg Bridgend CF34 9BP
Tel: 01656 732911 *Fax:* 01656 738763 *Dx:* 55752 MAESTEG
E-mail: kingdavies@btconnect.com
List of partners: C H Morgan, B Shawe
Languages: Welsh
Work: A1 B1 C1 C2 D1 E G H J1 K1 L N R1 S1 S2 V W Z(c,d,j,l,m,s,t)
Emergency Action, Agency, Advocacy, Fixed Fee Interview, Legal Aid undertaken and Legal Aid Franchise
Ptr: Morgan, Mr Ceri H LLB(Leics). . . . . *§Apr 1981
Shawe, Bohdan BA. . . . . *§Jun 1976
Asoc: David, Mrs Philippa Glynis . . . . *Oct 1992

THOMAS & THOMAS SOLICITORS ‡
114 Commercial Street Maesteg Bridgend CF34 9DL
Tel: 01656 733265 *Fax:* 01656 736124
E-mail: melissa@thomasandthomassolicitors.co.uk

MAGHULL, Merseyside

BRIGHOUSE WOLFF
(incorporating Brighouse Jones & Co; Heald Wolff)
21 Liverpool Road North Maghull Merseyside L31 2HB
Tel: 0151 520 2717 *Fax:* 0151 526 6601 *Dx:* 708551 MAGHULL 2
E-mail: firm@brighouse-wolff.co.uk
Office: Ormskirk, Skelmersdale (2 offices)
Work: A1 D1 E F1 K1 K3 K4 L N O Q R1 S1 S2 W Z(d)
Emergency Action, Fixed Fee Interview, Legal Aid undertaken and Legal Aid Franchise
Ptr: Green, Mrs Jeanette Catherine . . . . *Nov 1988
Ast: Aitken, Ms Christine J BA . . . . *Apr 1980

HAL EMMETT & CO ‡
57 Liverpool Road North Maghull Merseyside L31 2HF
Tel: 0151 531 7666 *Fax:* 0151 520 1178 *Dx:* 708550 MAGHULL 2
List of partners: H Emmett
Work: E S1 S2 W
Ptr: Emmett, Mr Harold . . . . *Mar 1972

MAXWELL HODGE SOLICITORS
37-39 Liverpool Road North Maghull Merseyside L31 2HB
Tel: 0151 526 7131 *Fax:* 0151 531 0021 *Dx:* 708558 MAGHULL 2
E-mail: info@maxweb.co.uk
Office: Formby, Heswall, Huyton, Kirkby, Liverpool (2 offices), West Kirby
Work: D1 K1 K3 K4 N S1 W Z(q,r)
Fixed Fee Interview, Legal Aid undertaken and Legal Aid Franchise
Ptr: Danby, Mr Michael Phillip LLB. . . . . *Feb 1989
Ast: Boydell, Mrs Nuala A LLB(Hons) . . . . *Apr 1980

MAIDENHEAD, Windsor & Maidenhead

ABBOTT LLOYD HOWORTH ‡
(incorporating Staynors Solicitors; Harley & Co)
(in association with KK Moody Solicitors)
Minster Court 22-30 York Road Maidenhead Windsor & Maidenhead SL6 1SF
Tel: 01628 798800 *Fax:* 0871 210 0041 *Dx:* 6412 MAIDENHEAD
E-mail: lynette.abbott@lawyerline.co.uk
List of partners: L M Abbott, S D Harley
Languages: French, German, Gujarati, Hindi, Punjabi, Swedish, Urdu
Work: B1 C1 E J1 K1 K3 K4 L N O Q S1 S2 V W Z(l)
Emergency Action, Agency, Advocacy and Fixed Fee Interview undertaken
Ptr: Abbott, Mrs Lynette M BA(Hons) . . . . *May 1979
Harley, Mrs Susan Dorothy LLB. . . . . *§Nov 1970
Asoc: Tanner, Mr Malcolm John BSocSc. . . . . *§Nov 1972
Ast: Kharia, Mr Jeevan Sanjeet LLB . . . . *Aug 2007
Melville, Ms Tanya LLB; MA. . . . . *Mar 2000
Patel, Mrs Priya LLB . . . . *Jun 2004

ACKERS ‡
34a Queen Street Maidenhead Windsor & Maidenhead SL6 1HZ
Tel: 01628 622300 *Fax:* 01628 622455
E-mail: info@ackersclaytonreeve.co.uk

ANTINGHAMS SOLICITORS ‡
Hollywell Cannon Lane Maidenhead Windsor & Maidenhead SL6 3PH
Tel: 01628 825395 *Fax:* 01628 825819
E-mail: mark.antingham@zen.co.uk

BAYER SOLICITORS ‡
First Floor 5 High Street Maidenhead Windsor & Maidenhead SL6 1JN
Tel: 01628 770392 *Fax:* 01628 634593 *Dx:* 6403 MAIDENHEAD

BROWNS
16 Queen Street Maidenhead Windsor & Maidenhead SL6 1HZ
Tel: 01628 672767 *Fax:* 01628 672768 *Dx:* 148760 MAIDENHEAD 3
E-mail: maidenhead@brownssolicitors.co.uk
Office: Amersham, Aylesbury, Beaconsfield, Bourne End, High Wycombe (3 offices), Marlow, Princes Risborough, Thame

CLIFFORD JOSEPH ‡
Gatehouse Tiggers Hall Place Lane Maidenhead Windsor & Maidenhead SL6 6QY
Tel: 01628 823331 *Fax:* 01628 822716
List of partners: S Holmes
Languages: French, Portuguese
Work: A1 L R1 S1 T1 T2 W Z(h,s)
Ptr: Holmes, Ms Sheila . . . . *Jun 1968

CLIFTON OWEN SOLICITORS ‡
Park Chambers Unit 2 Havelock Business Centre Maidenhead Windsor & Maidenhead SL6 5FH
Tel: 01628 783891 *Fax:* 01628 783894
E-mail: paul.owen@clifton-owen.co.uk

COLEMANS SOLICITORS LLP ‡
21 Marlow Road Maidenhead Windsor & Maidenhead SL6 7AA
Tel: 01628 631051 *Fax:* 01628 622106 *Dx:* 6405 MAIDENHEAD
E-mail: clive.hollyer@colemans.co.uk
List of partners: M H R Cutler, M M Stone
Languages: French, Italian
Work: A1 B1 C1 C2 D1 D2 E G I J1 K1 L M1 N O P Q R1 R2 S1 S2 T1 V W Z(c,e,j,l,p,q)
Advocacy and Fixed Fee Interview undertaken
Ptr: Cutler, Mr Michael H R LLB(Lond); TEP. . . . . . . *§Jan 1980
Stone, Mr Michael M LLB . . . . *Oct 1981
Asoc: Jones, Mrs Susan J L MA(Cantab) . . . . *May 1979
Lennon, Mr John . . . . *Nov 1996
Newman, Mrs Karen Nadine LLB(Hons). . . . . . . *Mar 2002
Ast: Escott, Mr John R L. . . . . Oct 1994
Williams, Miss Kate LLB. . . . . Oct 2009
Con: Regler, Mr Brian Sidney BA(Durham) . . . . *Jul 1973

FUGLER & CO ‡
96 Queen Street Maidenhead Windsor & Maidenhead SL6 1HT
Tel: 01628 670935 *Fax:* 01628 781831 *Dx:* 6415 MAIDENHEAD
List of partners: M C Fugler
Work: E S1
Ptr: Fugler, Mr Mark C. . . . . Jun 1986

GORDONS SOLICITORS LLP
Marandaz House 1 Cordwallis Park Clivemont Road Maidenhead Windsor & Maidenhead SL6 7TL
Tel: 0870 777 1122 *Fax:* 0870 950 3606
Dx: 145321 MAIDENHEAD 4
E-mail: info@gordonspropertylawyers.co.uk
Office: Marlow
Languages: Hindi, Punjabi
Work: S1
Fixed Fee Interview undertaken
Ptr: Bhalla, Mr Sandeep Bob LLB(Hons). . . . . *Nov 1997

LOUISE GREER ‡
43 Switchback Road North Maidenhead Windsor & Maidenhead SL6 7QX
Tel: 01628 781693 *Fax:* 01628 781693
E-mail: lg@solace.demon.co.uk
Work: R1 S1 S2

HEATH BUCKERIDGE ‡
23 Queen Street Maidenhead Windsor & Maidenhead SL6 1NB
Tel: 01628 671636 *Fax:* 01628 671922 *Dx:* 6406 MAIDENHEAD
E-mail: richard.buckeridge@heathbuckeridge.com
List of partners: R H Buckeridge, D J Jackson
Languages: French, Hebrew
Work: C1 E I J1 K1 L O Q R1 R2 S1 S2 U1 U2 W Z(c,d,e,f,k,l,q)
Agency and Fixed Fee Interview undertaken
Ptr: Buckeridge, Mr Richard H BA. . . . . *§Jan 1980
Jackson, Mr David J LLB(L'pool) Notary Public . . . *Sep 1978
Con: Heath, Mr Edwin J . . . . *§Jul 1969

KIDD & CO ‡
Weir Bank Bray on Thames Maidenhead Windsor & Maidenhead SL6 2ED
Tel: 01628 762762 *Fax:* 01628 762763
E-mail: kiddco@weirbank.co.uk
List of partners: J D Kidd
Work: A1 B1 C1 C2 C3 D1 E F1 G H I J1 K1 L M1 M2 N O P Q R1 S1 T1 T2 V W X Z(e,o)

KIDD RAPINET
33 Queen Street Maidenhead Windsor & Maidenhead SL6 1ND
Tel: 0845 017 9608 *Fax:* 01638 783150 *Dx:* 6400 MAIDENHEAD
E-mail: jlett@kiddrapinet.co.uk
Office: Aylesbury, Farnham, High Wycombe, London WC2, Reading, Slough
Work: A1 B1 C1 C2 D1 E F1 I J1 K1 L N O P Q R1 S1 S2 T1 T2 V W Z(c,d,e,h,i,j,k,l,m,o)
Emergency Action, Advocacy, Fixed Fee Interview undertaken and Member of Accident Line
Ptr: Coyle, Miss Kathryn Anne. . . . . *Feb 1994
Haycock, Mr Karl Nicolas . . . . *Nov 1993
Lett, Mr James Reginald Joseph LLB . . . . *Jun 1976
Rhodes, Ms Claire . . . . *Jan 2002
Ast: McCabe, Mr Martin Kevin . . . . *Jan 2005
Norris, Mr Alexander . . . . Jan 2002

FRANCES LINDSAY & CO ‡
48 Broadway Maidenhead Windsor & Maidenhead SL6 1LU
Tel: 01628 643667

MAHER & CO ‡
19 York Road Maidenhead Windsor & Maidenhead SL6 1SQ
Tel: 01628 675239 *Fax:* 01628 638838
E-mail: patrickmaher@btinternet.com
List of partners: P R Maher
Work: L S1 S2 W Z(l)
Agency and Fixed Fee Interview undertaken
SPr: Maher, Mr Patrick Raphael LLB . . . . *Jul 1973

MASON-APPS SMALLMANS & CO ‡
The Old Post Office Old Post Office Lane High Street Maidenhead Windsor & Maidenhead SL6 1QY
Tel: 01628 636148 / 636149 *Fax:* 01628 624216
Dx: 6401 MAIDENHEAD
E-mail: law@masonapps.co.uk
List of partners: P W Mason-Apps
Languages: French
Work: A1 B1 C1 C2 C3 D1 E F1 J1 K1 K3 L N O P R1 S1 S2 T1 T2 W Z(i,l)
Advocacy and Fixed Fee Interview undertaken
Ptr: Mason-Apps, Mr Peter William . . . . *§Nov 1970

PAUL ANTHONY MILTON SOLICITORS ‡
Willen Coppice 67 Switchback Road South Maidenhead Windsor & Maidenhead SL6 7QF
Tel: 01628 670497 *Fax:* 01628 783707
E-mail: pamilton@btinternet.com
List of partners: P A Milton
SPr: Milton, Mr Paul A BA . . . . Feb 1983

PRODDOW MACKAY
The Cloisters Sun Lane Maidenhead Windsor & Maidenhead SL6 7XW
Tel: 01628 776847 *Fax:* 01628 776849 *Dx:* 6435 MAIDENHEAD
E-mail: enquiries@proddowmackay.co.uk
Office: Sheffield
Work: B1 E N S1 W Z(h,j)
Ptr: Mackay, Mr Donald J LLB. . . . . *§Oct 1981
Proddow, Mr Simon K LLB . . . . *§Dec 1980

J SCOTT & CO SOLICITORS ‡
7 High Street Maidenhead Windsor & Maidenhead SL6 1JN
Tel: 01628 777233

MAIDSTONE, Kent

ASB ASPIRE ‡
(incorporating Andrew Gardner Partnership)
Horizon House Eclipse Park Sittingbourne Road Maidstone Kent ME14 3EN
Tel: 0845 063 6465 *Fax:* 01622 356690 *Dx:* 153421 MAIDSTONE 18
E-mail: enquiries@asb-aspire.com
List of partners: R C Aylott, A H Gardner, C M Lodge
Languages: French, German
Work: C1 E F1 L N O Q S1 S2 W
Member of Accident Line
Ptr: Aylott, Mr Robert Christopher LLB(Hons) . . . . . . *Oct 1993
Gardner, Mr Andrew H . . . . *Apr 1971
Lodge, Mr Christopher M . . . . *Feb 1978
Ast: Muniandy, Miss Chantal Linlin. . . . . *Mar 2006

ASB LAW
Horizon House 1 Eclipse Park Sittingbourne Road Maidstone Kent ME14 3EN
Tel: 01622 656500 *Fax:* 01622 656690 *Dx:* 153420 MAIDSTONE 18
E-mail: maidstone@asb-law.com
Office: Crawley
Languages: Afrikaans, Danish, Dutch, French, German, Hebrew, Italian, Polish, Spanish, Turkish
Work: A1 B1 C1 D1 E F1 G H J1 K1 L M1 N O P Q R1 S1 T1 V W Z(b,c,d,e,f,h,i,j,k,l,m,n,o,s,t)
Emergency Action, Agency, Advocacy, Fixed Fee Interview, Legal Aid undertaken and Member of Accident Line
Ptr: Brown, Ms Michele Emily BSc(Hons) . . . . *Oct 1994
Catterick, Mr John W . . . . *Nov 1979
Cavell, Mr Jonathan Robert Brook BA(Hons); DipLP. *Nov 1995
Cowell, Mr Rex LLB. . . . . *Nov 1991
Curtis, Mr Roger M . . . . *Jun 1988
Cutler, Mr Michael William. . . . . *§Jun 1972
Danagher, Ms Ursula Mary Teresa . . . . Feb 1993
Harris, Mr Raymond C . . . . *§Dec 1968
King, Mrs Coralyn Ann . . . . *Jan 1970
Pawlik, Mr Andrew J . . . . Nov 1978
Simmons, Mr Jonathan K . . . . *Dec 1986
Thomas, Mr Stephen LLB; AKC ★. . . . . *Apr 1980
Trelfer, Mr Colin. . . . . *Jun 1979
Asoc: Judd, Ms Jackie LLB . . . . Feb 1985
Merriman, Mr Anthony R LLB(Hons). . . . . *Mar 1998
Miles, Mr Glen LLB(Hons); DipLP . . . . Aug 1999
Tyrer, Ms Lucienne Alexandra LLB(Hons) . . . . . . *Nov 1992
Ast: Foster, Mr Edward Richard LLB(Hons); DipLP. . . . *Aug 1997
Giles, Miss Karen BA(Hons); DipLaw . . . . Jan 2002
Graham, Ms Paula . . . . *Oct 1993
Harding, Ms Brenda. . . . . May 1979
Judd, Mrs Jacqueline . . . . *Feb 1985
McCourt, Ms Rebecca LLB(Hons). . . . . Mar 2001
Philips, Ms Anne . . . . May 1979
Phillips, Ms Anne BA(Hons). . . . . *May 1979
Rooke, Ms Elizabeth . . . . Sep 1998
Ryder, Mr Philip BA(Hons) . . . . Apr 2001

ADAN & CO ‡
Unit 10 The Old Brewery Buckland Road Maidstone Kent ME16 0DZ
Tel: 01622 600488 *Fax:* 01622 677477
E-mail: mail@adanandco.com
List of partners: M Lewis
Dir: Lewis, Mr Matthew . . . . Nov 2001
Ast: Mooruth, Navisha . . . . Dec 2006

DAVID BARTON SOLICITOR ADVOCATE ‡
13-17 Lower Stone Street Maidstone Kent ME15 6JX
Tel: 01622 695587

BENNETT & CO SOLICITORS ‡
Cornwallis House Pudding Lane Maidstone Kent ME14 1NY
Tel: 01622 682808 *Fax:* 01622 677808
E-mail: mail@bennettlegal.co.uk

See p112 for the Key to Work Categories & other symbols

BERRY & BERRY
Slencrest House 3 Tonbridge Road Maidstone Kent ME16 8RL
Tel: 01622 690777 *Fax:* 01622 662555
Dx: 400307 MAIDSTONE WEST
Emergency telephone 07528 270096
E-mail: mail@the-solicitors.co.uk
Office: Tonbridge, Tunbridge Wells
Languages: French, German, Spanish
Work: A1 B1 B2 C1 C2 C3 D1 D2 E F1 G H J1 K1 L M1 N O P Q R1 S1 S2 T1 T2 U1 V W Z(c,d,g,h,j,k,l,o,p,q,r)
Emergency Action, Agency, Advocacy, Fixed Fee Interview, Legal Aid undertaken, Legal Aid Franchise and Member of Accident Line
Ptr: Hawkins, Miss Sharon J LLB(Hons) . . . . Sep 1988
Reed, Mr Iain D BA(Newc)(Law) . . . . *§May 1988
Ast: Bennett, Mrs Claire LLB(Hons) . . . . *Sep 2004
Moore, Mr William BSc(Hons) . . . . Sep 2008
Sloane, Mrs Charlotte LLB(Jt Hons) . . . . *Feb 2002

BRACHERS ‡
Somerfield House 59 London Road Maidstone Kent ME16 8JH
Tel: 01622 690691 *Fax:* 01622 681430 *Dx:* 4806 MAIDSTONE 1
E-mail: info@brachers.co.uk
List of partners: H C Abraham, S P Alexander, K Baigent, C Daw, S K Gaines, S E Hart, J M Horton, M L Jones, J W Law, M Oatham, A S Palmer, R L Pegrum, M C Raymont, N Rennie, J C Sheath, A H G Wilson, J P Worby
Languages: French
Work: A1 A2 A3 B1 C1 C2 C3 D1 D2 E F1 F2 G I J1 J2 K1 K2 L M1 N O P Q R1 R2 S1 S2 T1 T2 V W X Z(c,d,e,g,h,i,j,k,l,m,o,p,q,r,t)
Emergency Action, Agency, Advocacy, Legal Aid undertaken, Legal Aid Franchise and Member of Accident Line
Ptr: Abraham, Mr Henry C LLB(Lond) . . . . *§May 1983
Alexander, Mr Scott Paterson . . . . Oct 1991
Baigent, Miss Katharine MA(Oxon) . . . . *§Oct 1985
Daw, Miss Catherine LLB(Hons) ♦ . . . . *Jun 1999
Hart, Miss Susan E BA . . . . *Apr 1978
Horton, Mr Jeremy M LLB . . . . *§Oct 1992
Jones, Miss Marita L LLB . . . . Jan 1989
Law, Ms Julia W LLB . . . . *Sep 1993
Oatham, Mr Michael BSc(Hons) . . . . *Sep 1996
Palmer, Mr Anthony S BA . . . . *§Nov 1988
Pegrum, Mr Robertson L LLB . . . . *§Apr 1973
Raymont, Ms Mary Catherine LLB . . . . *Nov 1992
Rennie, Mr Nicholas LLM Daniel Reardon Prize; Reginald Pilkington Prize . . . . *Sep 1979
Sheath, Mr John C LLB . . . . *§Jun 1976
Wilson, Mr Alexander H G LLB(Soton) . . . . *Apr 1982
Worby, Ms Joanna P LLB . . . . *Sep 1993
Mem: Gaines, Miss Sarah K LLB . . . . *Sep 1997
Ast: Byers, Miss Laura LLB . . . . *Sep 1994
Clarke, Mr Andrew Michael Richard BA . . . . *Mar 1994
Holland, Miss Hillary . . . . Jun 1992
Jilani, Mr Mahammad A BA; CPE Professor Wolfsun Prize . . . . *Mar 1995
Millis, Mr James LLB(Hons) . . . . *Sep 1999
Robson, Mr Stephen M LLB(Hons) ♦ . . . . *Dec 1993
Con: Dearing, Mr Geoffrey G . . . . *§Jun 1972

BURROUGHS ‡
Alliance House 38 King Street Maidstone Kent ME14 1BS
Tel: 01622 676976 / 676982 *Fax:* 01622 675111
Dx: 4809 MAIDSTONE
Emergency telephone 07808 404155
E-mail: tburrough@burroughs-solicitors.co.uk
List of partners: T J A Burrough
Languages: French
Work: B2 D1 E G H J1 K1 K2 K3 M3 N O Q S1 S2 V W Z(l,t)
Emergency Action, Agency, Advocacy, Legal Aid undertaken and Legal Aid Franchise
Ptr: Burrough, Mr Tobias J A . . . . Nov 1997
Ast: Sellahewa, Miss Sandra LLB . . . . Jan 2005
Con: Burrough, Mr Raymond J . . . . *Jun 1969

MALCOLM BUTLER & CO ‡
7 Copper Tree Court Loose Maidstone Kent ME15 9RW
Tel: 01622 749596 *Fax:* 01622 749022 *Dx:* 51951 MAIDSTONE 2
Emergency telephone 07836 360015
E-mail: mbutler2000@talktalk.net
List of partners: M J R Butler
Office: Walsall
Work: B1 C1 F1 Q
Agency and Advocacy undertaken
SPr: Butler, Mr Malcolm John Robert MA; LLB; FCIS Officer to the High Sheriff of Kent . . . . *§Sep 1997

ANTONY CLAPP ‡
Holly Bank Chambers Oasts Business Village Maidstone Kent ME18 5NN
Tel: 01622 815940 *Fax:* 01622 817872 *Dx:* 92851 WEST MALLING
E-mail: enquiries@antonyclapp.co.uk
List of partners: A E J Clapp
Ptr: Clapp, Mr Antony E J . . . . *Jun 1986

DUNDAS & DUCE ‡
9 Albion Place Maidstone Kent ME14 5DY
Tel: 01622 681867 *Fax:* 01622 678536 *Dx:* 4878 MAIDSTONE 1
E-mail: law@dundasandduce.co.uk
List of partners: C W Duce, R A S C Dundas
Languages: French, Italian
Work: E S1 Z(f,l)
Ptr: Duce, Mr Colin W . . . . *Dec 1989
Dundas, Mr Robert A S C BA(Law) . . . . *Jul 1977

EMB SOLICITORS ‡
49 Kingfisher Drive Chatham Maidstone Kent ME5 7NY
Tel: 01634 313002 *Fax:* 01634 313002
E-mail: eliza.saied@embsolicitors.co.uk

NIGEL EDWARDS & CO ‡
White Cottage 13 Ashford Road Maidstone Kent ME14 5DA
Tel: 01622 690575 *Fax:* 01622 691354
Emergency telephone 07718 536406
E-mail: nigeledwards@edwardslaw.co.uk
List of partners: N L Edwards
Work: B1 C1 C2 C3 D1 E F1 F2 G H J1 K1 L M1 M2 N O P Q R1 R2 S1 S2 T1 T2 V W X Z(h,i,k,l,o,p)
Agency, Advocacy and Fixed Fee Interview undertaken
SPr: Edwards, Mr Nigel L LLB . . . . *Apr 1977
Ast: Maunsell, Mrs Anne Catharine LLB . . . . *Jan 1990

DANIEL FRANCIS SOLICITORS ‡
5 Tonbridge Road Maidstone Kent ME16 8RL
Tel: 01622 669460 *Fax:* 01622 669461
Dx: 400305 MAIDSTONE WEST
E-mail: law@dfsolicitors.co.uk
Languages: Yoruba
Work: K1 K2 K3 S1 S2 W Z(i)

GILL TURNER TUCKER ‡
Colman House King Street Maidstone Kent ME14 1JE
Tel: 01622 759051 *Fax:* 01622 762192 *Dx:* 4804 MAIDSTONE 1
E-mail: info@gillturnertucker.com
List of partners: R G Green, M M Smith, M J Trigg
Languages: French
Work: A1 B1 C1 C2 D1 E F1 J1 K1 L O P Q R1 S1 S2 W Z(d,l,p)
Emergency Action, Agency, Advocacy, Fixed Fee Interview, Legal Aid undertaken and Legal Aid Franchise
Ptr: Green, Mr Robert G LLB . . . . *Apr 1975
Smith, Mr Michael M LLB . . . . *Apr 1978
Trigg, Mr Michael J BA(Law) . . . . *Jun 1985
Ast: Adourian, Miss Yester R BA(Hons) . . . . *Apr 1998
Donaldson, Mr Lachlan LLB . . . . *Aug 2009
Kent, Mr James LLB . . . . *Jul 2009
Lewis, Ms Julia . . . . *Feb 2004
Mangaroo, Miss Salena Elizabeth MA(Law) . . . . . . *Apr 2003
Miles, Miss Rebecca LLB . . . . *Sep 2009
Mooney, Miss Hannah Jane LLB(Hons) . . . . *Sep 2006
O'Grady, Ms Claire LLB . . . . Oct 1988

GREEN & CO ‡
5 Romney Place Maidstone Kent ME15 6LE
Tel: 01622 676769 *Fax:* 01622 762266
Emergency telephone 07768 700048
E-mail: fionagh@fionaghgreen.co.uk
List of partners: F J Green
Work: G H
Emergency Action, Agency, Advocacy, Fixed Fee Interview, Legal Aid undertaken and Legal Aid Franchise
SPr: Green, Mrs Fionagh Jean ★ Law Society Honours Judge Appeals Service (Social Entitlement Chamber 1996 & Tax Chamber 2009) . . . . *§Nov 1978

GULLANDS ‡
16 Mill Street Maidstone Kent ME15 6XT
Tel: 01622 678341 *Fax:* 01622 757735 *Dx:* 51973 MAIDSTONE 2
E-mail: mailbox@gullands.com
List of partners: A Astley, B L Bradley, D C Brown, P C Burbidge, R A J Cripps, P C Dimond, P W Grylls, A B Gulland, J L Roberts, T J Simmons
Languages: French, German, Gujarati, Hindi, Punjabi
Work: A1 A3 B1 C1 C2 D1 D2 E F1 G H I J1 J2 K1 K2 K3 L N O Q R1 R2 S1 S2 T1 T2 U2 W Z(c,d,e,k,l,q,r)
Emergency Action, Agency, Advocacy, Fixed Fee Interview, Legal Aid undertaken and Legal Aid Franchise
Ptr: Astley, Mr Alex BA; MA Notary Public . . . . *Oct 1998
Bradley, Mr Bernard Leroy . . . . *Nov 1993
Brown, Mr David C BA(Hons) RIBA - Professional Conduct Panel . . . . *Sep 1985
Burbidge, Mr Paul Christopher LLB(Hons) Member of the Honourable Solicitors Company . . . . *Jun 1985
Cripps, Mr Richard A J LLB . . . . *Oct 1991
Dimond, Mr Philip Charles . . . . *Feb 1976
Grylls, Mr Philip William LLB(Hons) . . . . *Oct 1983
Gulland, Mr Arthur Blair . . . . *Mar 1975
Roberts, Mr John Llewelyn BSc(Hons) . . . . *Oct 1992
Simmons, Mr Timothy John LLB(Hons) . . . . *Jan 1984
Asoc: Beadle, Miss Jacqueline Lesley . . . . *Oct 1999
Bligh, Mr Patrick ★ . . . . *§Jan 1975
Bond, Ms Catherine Louise LLB . . . . *Jul 2007
Claridge, Miss Laura LLB(Hons) . . . . *Nov 2010
Dhir, Mr Sunil Kumar BA(Hons) . . . . *Dec 2001
Finn, Mrs Amanda LLB(Hons) . . . . *Oct 1990
Golding, Mrs Anna Mayon BA(Hons)(English) . . . . . *Oct 2005
Markham, Mrs Melissa Grace BA(Hons) ♦ . . . . *Nov 2001
Westbrook, Mrs Alison Gail LLB(Hons) . . . . *Sep 2008
Williams, Mr Alan Martin LLB . . . . *Oct 1990
Con: Barrow, Mr John MA(Law)(Cantab) . . . . *§Apr 1971
Miller, Mr Andrew McKenzie LLB(Bris) . . . . *Nov 1973
Rice, Mr John Edward . . . . *§Oct 1978
Tomlinson, Mr Stephen S . . . . *Jan 1970

HESLING HENRIQUES ‡
Lyndean House 30 Albion Place Maidstone Kent ME14 5DZ
Tel: 01622 678877

HOLDEN & CO
4 Clarendon Place King Street Maidstone Kent ME14 1BQ
Tel: 01622 757665 *Fax:* 01622 757891 *Dx:* 4823 MAIDSTONE
Office: Ashford, Hastings

KENNEDYS
Victoria Court 17-21 Ashford Road Maidstone Kent ME14 5FA
Tel: 01622 625625 *Fax:* 01622 625600 *Dx:* 146120 MAIDSTONE 14
Office: Belfast, Birmingham, Cambridge, Chelmsford, London EC3, Manchester, Sheffield, Taunton

ANDREW LEE & CO ‡
93-95 High Street Maidstone Kent ME14 1SA
Tel: 01622 750101 *Fax:* 01622 751275 *Dx:* 133538 MAIDSTONE
E-mail: info@a-lee.com
Work: S1 S2

MORLINGS ‡
1, 2 & 3 Clarendon Place King Street Maidstone Kent ME14 1BQ
Tel: 01622 673081 *Fax:* 01622 691226 *Dx:* 4810 MAIDSTONE
Emergency telephone 01622 682221
E-mail: email@morlings.com
List of partners: J R Cripps, K S Middleton, B A Morling, N J Steele
Work: G H J1 K1 K3 N Q S1 S2 W
Emergency Action, Agency, Advocacy, Fixed Fee Interview, Legal Aid undertaken, Legal Aid Franchise and Member of Accident Line
Ptr: Cripps, Mr Julian R BSc . . . . *Jul 1978
Middleton, Mr Keith S LLB(Lond) . . . . *Jul 1987
Morling, Mr Brian A . . . . *Feb 1960
Steele, Mr Nicholas J . . . . *Jul 1975

REEVES & CO ‡
Preston House 15 Albion Place Maidstone Kent ME14 5DY
Tel: 01622 692220 *Fax:* 01622 692229 *Dx:* 4805 MAIDSTONE 1
List of partners: W A Burgess
Work: K1 Q
Agency, Advocacy, Fixed Fee Interview and Legal Aid undertaken
Ptr: Burgess, Ms Wendy A . . . . *Oct 1993

SHELLEY & CO ‡
Turkey Mill Ashford Road Maidstone Kent ME14 5PP
Tel: 01622 663060 *Fax:* 01622 766396
E-mail: shelleylaw@connectfree.co.uk
Work: C1 T1 T2

TAKK & COMPANY LIMITED ‡
25 County Road Maidstone Kent ME14 1HJ
Tel: 01622 661333 *Fax:* 01622 661380
E-mail: takkandcompany@btconnect.com

THORNELOE & CO ‡
22 High Street Lenham Maidstone Kent ME17 2QD
Tel: 01622 859416 *Fax:* 01622 859406
List of partners: H Thorneloe, M J Thorneloe
Work: E K4 S1 S2 W
Ptr: Thorneloe, Miss Harriet BA(Hons) . . . . *Sep 2005
Thorneloe, Mr Michael J . . . . *§Dec 1974

VYMAN SOLICITORS
G17 Innovation Centre Maidstone Road Maidstone Kent ME5 9FD
Tel: 01634 887282 *Fax:* 01622 671514
E-mail: admin@vyman.co.uk
Office: Gravesend, Harrow

WAI LEUNG SOLICITORS ‡
Kent House Kent Business Centre Romney Place Maidstone Kent ME15 6LH
Tel: 01622 772416 *Fax:* 01622 772417

WATSON NEVILL ‡
The College Tower College Road Maidstone Kent ME15 6YQ
Tel: 01622 661177 *Fax:* 01622 662244 *Dx:* 51952 MAIDSTONE 2
E-mail: legal@watsonnevill.co.uk
List of partners: Y Nevill, L J Watson
Work: C1 E K1 K3 L R2 S1 S2
Agency, Advocacy and Fixed Fee Interview undertaken
Ptr: Nevill, Miss Yvonne . . . . May 1981
Watson, Mrs Laura J . . . . Sep 1982
Ast: Higgins, Mr Robbie LLB . . . . *Jul 2000
Sculpher, Miss Margaret LLB(Hons) . . . . Oct 1995

WHITEHEAD MONCKTON ‡
Monckton House 72 King Street Maidstone Kent ME14 1BL
Tel: 01622 698000 *Fax:* 01622 690050 *Dx:* 4807 MAIDSTONE 1
E-mail: enquiries@whitehead-monckton.co.uk
List of partners: S Beck, R N J Coombe, J A Goode, D C Harrison, S K Holman, G K Jones, C A King, T C Monckton, A Robbins, R P Rogers, K L Speedie, P Still, R Stogdon
Office: Tenterden
Work: A1 B1 C1 C2 C3 D1 E F1 J1 K1 K2 L M1 M2 N O P Q R1 S1 S2 T1 T2 W Z(c,d,e,h,j,k,l,m,o,q,r,t)
Agency, Advocacy and Fixed Fee Interview undertaken
Ptr: Beck, Mr Stephen LLB Gards Solicitors Best Law Graduate 1991 H M Assistant Deputy Coroner . . . . *Nov 1994
Coombe, Mr Robert N J LLB(Newc) . . . . *§Nov 1984
Goode, Miss Janet A LLB; AKC Notary Public . . . . *§Oct 1990
Harrison, Miss Dawn C LLB . . . . *Oct 1987
Holman, Mr Stuart Keith BA(Hons)(Law) . . . . *Sep 1993
Jones, Mr Graham K LLB . . . . *Oct 1987
Monckton, Mr Timothy C MA(Cantab) . . . . *§Oct 1980
Robbins, Mr Adrian BJuris; LLB(Hons); LLM . . . . . *Dec 1989
Rogers, Mr Robin P Notary Public . . . . *§Jul 1971
Speedie, Miss Kerin L LLB(Hons); PGDip . . . . *Oct 1998
Still, Mr Peter FILEx . . . . *Nov 1995
Stogdon, Mr Richard LLB . . . . *Mar 1994
Asoc: King, Mrs Coralyn Ann . . . . *Jan 1970
Ast: Bell, Mr Michael Robert LLB; BA . . . . *Sep 2005
Davies, Mr Christopher Wyn . . . . Sep 2007
Fitz-Gibbon, Miss Sarah Louise LLB(Hons) . . . . . . Sep 2007
Fuller, Mr Graham Dean TEP . . . . *Sep 2005
Hills, Miss Michaela LLB . . . . Sep 2005
Longden, Mr Christopher LLB(European) . . . . *Nov 1997
Miller, Mr Jonathan L LLB(Hons) . . . . *Nov 1999
Patel, Amit . . . . *Feb 1998
Peri, Mr Haggai . . . . Oct 1998
Stallard, Mr Jonathan Harry LLB(Hons) . . . . Nov 2004

MALDON, Essex

BRIGHT & SONS ‡
(in association with Concha Compan Sala Alicante(Spain))
West House West Square Maldon Essex CM9 6HA
Tel: 01621 852323 *Fax:* 01621 859673 *Dx:* 41250 MALDON
List of partners: A J Bright, C J Hayward, G A Poulter, G E Stafford
Office: Witham
Languages: French, Spanish
Work: A1 B1 C1 C2 E F1 J1 K1 L N O Q R1 S1 S2 T1 T2 W Z(l)
Emergency Action, Agency, Advocacy, Fixed Fee Interview, Legal Aid undertaken and Member of Accident Line
Ptr: Bright, Ms Amanda Jane LLB(Hons) . . . . *Nov 1989
Hayward, Mr Christopher John LLB(Lond) Clerk to the Commissioners of Tax for Division of Maldon . . . *Apr 1982
Poulter, Mrs Gillian A BA(Hons); LLM . . . . *Oct 1984
Stafford, Mr Gary Earl LLB(Hons) . . . . Jan 1994
Ast: Fraser, Mrs Ann E LLB . . . . Jul 1984
Grayland, Ms Tracy Elizabeth LLB(Hons) . . . . *Aug 2002
Hickmott, Mrs Jennifer . . . . *Sep 2001
Martin, Miss Vidal Eulalie LLB(Hons) . . . . *May 2005
Sullivan, Ms Jane LLB(Hons); TEP . . . . Jan 1991
Tawn, Mrs Sharon C BA(Hons)(Law) . . . . *Oct 1986
Taylor, Ms Karen BSc(Hons) . . . . *Jan 1999

CRICK & FREEMAN ‡
1 & 3 Gate Street Maldon Essex CM9 5QW
Tel: 01621 852606 *Fax:* 01621 850945 *Dx:* 41252 MALDON
E-mail: info@crickandfreeman.co.uk
List of partners: R G Irvine
Work: A1 E L R1 S1 T2 W
Ptr: Irvine, Mr Robert G . . . . *Jan 1976

KEW LAW LLP ‡
1/3 Gate Street Maldon Essex CM9 5QW
Tel: 01621 843056 *Fax:* 01621 858127
E-mail: info@kewlaw.co.uk

THE MITCHELL PLAMPIN PARTNERSHIP ‡
Stonecroft 22 High Street Maldon Essex CM9 5PJ
Tel: 01621 852566 *Fax:* 01621 854904 *Dx:* 41251 MALDON
E-mail: ahunt@mitchellplampin.co.uk
List of partners: J R Dieffenthaller, A E Hunt

Languages: French, Gujarati, Spanish
Work: C1 D1 E F1 J1 K1 K3 K4 L N O Q S1 S2 T1 T2 V W
Agency, Advocacy and Fixed Fee Interview undertaken
Ptr: Dieffenthaller, Mr Jamie R LLB . . . . *Oct 1989
Hunt, Mr Allan E LLB . . . . *May 1980
Ast: Alter, Mrs Annette LLB . . . . *Sep 2001
Patel, Mr Bal-Krishna BA(Oxon). . . . . *May 2008
Wiseman, Mrs Judith M BA(Oxon). . . . . *Dec 1982

J R SLADE ‡
10 Howe Green Road Purleigh Maldon Essex CM3 6QA
Tel: 01621 828397 *Fax:* 01621 828397
Emergency telephone 01621 828397
E-mail: jrslade@talk21.com
List of partners: J R Slade
Languages: French, German
Work: B1 B2 D1 F1 G H J1 K1 K2 L N Q R1 S1 S2 T2 V W Z(c,j,k,l,m,p,r,y)
Emergency Action, Agency, Advocacy, Fixed Fee Interview, Legal Aid undertaken and Member of Accident Line
SPr: Slade, Mr John R Notary Public. . . . . Jul 1969

VACHAVIOLOS SOLICITORS ‡
2nd Floor 50 High Street Maldon Essex CM9 5PN
Tel: 01621 855516 *Fax:* 0560 126 9358

MALMESBURY, Wiltshire

FORRESTER & FORRESTER
59 High Street Malmesbury Wiltshire SN16 9AH
Tel: 01666 822671 *Fax:* 01666 823548 *Dx:* 47451 MALMESBURY
Office: Chippenham
Work: A1 B1 C1 D1 E F1 J1 K1 L N Q S1 T1 T2 V W Z(d,l)
Emergency Action, Agency, Advocacy, Fixed Fee Interview and Legal Aid Franchise
Ptr: Gill, Mr Andrew J Notary Public . . . . *§Feb 1965
Paterson, Mr Matthew James BA(Hons). . . . . *Sep 1995
Ast: Lester, Mr James M E LLB . . . . *Jul 1978

MALTON, North Yorkshire

MARGARET ADAMS LAW
Saxonfield Springfield Sherburn Malton North Yorkshire YO17 8QQ
Tel: 01944 711011 *Fax:* 01944 711994
E-mail: info@adamsscottlaw.co.uk
Office: Grimsby, Scarborough

CROMBIE WILKINSON
Forsyth House Market Place Malton North Yorkshire YO17 7LR
Tel: 01653 600070 *Fax:* 01653 600049 *Dx:* 63700 MALTON
E-mail: malton@crombiewilkinson.co.uk
Office: Selby, York
Work: A1 A2 A3 B1 C1 C2 C3 D1 D2 E F1 J1 K1 K2 K3 K4 L M1 N O P Q R1 R2 S1 S2 T1 T2 W Z(b,c,d,e,k,l,r,za)
Emergency Action, Agency, Advocacy, Fixed Fee Interview, Legal Aid undertaken, Legal Aid Franchise and Member of Accident Line
Dir: Bartram, Mrs Jennifer Ann LLB(Hons)(Lond) . . . . *Feb 1981
Broadbridge, Mr John N Assistant Deputy Coroner (North Yorks) . . . . *§Feb 1981
Asoc: Baines, Mr Anthony LLB . . . . *Jun 2003
Richardson, Miss Sarah Louise BA(Hons); LLM . . . . *Jan 2002

DRIVERS
5c Market Street Malton North Yorkshire YO17 7LY
Tel: 01653 600075 *Fax:* 01653 696479 *Dx:* 63701 MALTON
E-mail: sgt@drivers-solicitors.co.uk
Office: York
Languages: French
Work: A1 E F1 J1 K1 L N Q S1 S2 T2 W Z(h,l)
Fixed Fee Interview undertaken
Ptr: Thorn, Mr Stephen G MA(Cantab). . . . . *§Nov 1986
Ast: Dixon, Mr Peter Rex BA(Hons) . . . . *§Oct 1996

R D Y JENNINGS & CO ‡
47 York Road Malton North Yorkshire YO17 6AX
Tel: 01653 691515 *Fax:* 01653 691558
E-mail: mail@jenningslaw.co.uk
List of partners: R D Y Jennings
Work: C1 C2
SPr: Jennings, Mr Richard D Y MA(Oxon) . . . . May 1981

PEARSONS & WARD ‡
2 Market Street Malton North Yorkshire YO17 7AS
Tel: 01653 692247 *Fax:* 01653 600162 *Dx:* 63702 MALTON
E-mail: mail@pearslaw.co.uk
List of partners: E K Elwess, R P Scott, R I Tulloch
Work: A1 A2 B1 C1 E J1 K1 K3 K4 L N O Q R1 S1 S2 T1 T2 W Z(c,d,l)
Agency and Advocacy undertaken
Ptr: Elwess, Mrs Emma K BA . . . . *§May 1985
Scott, Mr Richard Peter BA . . . . Nov 1999
Tulloch, Mr Robert I. *§Jul 1978
Ast: Richardson, Ms Sarah L LLB . . . . Nov 2002

THORPE & CO
32 Yorkersgate Malton North Yorkshire YO17 7AB
Tel: 01653 694899 *Fax:* 01653 600217 *Dx:* 63705 MALTON
E-mail: malton@thorpeandco.com
Office: Filey, Scarborough, Whitby
Work: A1 C1 E S1 S2 T1 T2 W
Emergency Action, Agency, Advocacy, Legal Aid undertaken, Legal Aid Franchise and Member of Accident Line
Ptr: Mackinder, Mr Stephen MA . . . . *§Nov 1974

TOWNSEND HARRISON LTD ‡
13 Yorkersgate Malton North Yorkshire YO17 7AA
Tel: 01653 693259 *Fax:* 01653 600315

MALVERN, Worcestershire

CHARLSON SIMMONS ‡
8 Aldwyn Tower Malvern Worcestershire WR14 3HG
Tel: 01684 891385

EVANS + WEBB ‡
Sterling Lodge 287 Worcester Road Malvern Worcestershire WR14 1AB
Tel: 01684 562526 *Fax:* 01684 562711 *Dx:* 728563 MALVERN 4
E-mail: info@evans-webb.co.uk
List of partners: H M Evans, V Webb
Work: S1 S2 W
Ptr: Evans, Miss Hilary M BA . . . . *§Jan 1980
Webb, Mrs Vicki LLB . . . . *§Oct 1986

GAYNOR-SMITH OWEN & CO ‡
133-135 Barnards Green Road Malvern Worcestershire WR14 3LT
Tel: 01684 560771 *Fax:* 01684 560294 *Dx:* 17602 MALVERN
E-mail: info@gsolaw.com
Work: C1 C2 D1 E F1 G H J1 K1 K3 K4 L N O Q R1 S1 S2 T1 T2 V W Z(c,l,o)

HINCHLIFFES ‡
Byre Court Sandys Road Malvern Worcestershire WR14 1JJ
Tel: 01684 580900

M J PAYTON & CO ‡
112-118 Worcester Road Malvern Worcestershire WR14 1SS
Tel: 01684 563318 *Fax:* 01684 892760
E-mail: enquiries@paytons.co.uk
List of partners: M J Payton, J R Watts
Languages: French, German, Italian
Work: C1 D1 E F1 J1 K1 K2 L O Q S1 S2 V W Z(c,m)
Emergency Action, Agency, Advocacy, Fixed Fee Interview, Legal Aid undertaken and Legal Aid Franchise
Ptr: Payton, Ms Margaret J LLB . . . . *Jun 1976
Watts, Mr John R LLB. . . . . *Jun 1977

RUSSELL & CO ‡
Holland House 125 Church Street Malvern Worcestershire WR14 2AH
Tel: 01684 892000 *Fax:* 01684 892202 *Dx:* 17603 MALVERN
Emergency telephone 01684 572014
E-mail: law@russell-law.co.uk
List of partners: J S Croshaw, E C A Davis, N C Turner
Languages: French, Punjabi
Work: A1 B1 C1 C3 D1 E F1 G H J1 K1 L N O Q R1 S1 S2 T1 T2 V W Z(c,d,l)
Emergency Action, Agency, Advocacy, Fixed Fee Interview, Legal Aid undertaken and Legal Aid Franchise
Ptr: Croshaw, Mr Jeremy S BA . . . . *Nov 1978
Davis, Mr Edward C A LLB(B'ham) . . . . *Oct 1986
Turner, Mr Nicholas C BA. . . . . *§Feb 1989
Ast: Bird-Wood, Mrs Susannah LLB . . . . *§Jan 1970
Foskett, Mr Nigel LLB(B'ham) . . . . *Jul 1990
Phillips, Miss Shelagh C LLB . . . . *Dec 1982
Sandhu, Miss Baljeet LLB. . . . . Jan 2005
Con: Chetwood, Mr Denis C . . . . *§Jun 1966

MARTYN SLOCOMBE & CO ‡
Abbotsmead 3 Avenue Road Malvern Worcestershire WR14 3AG
Tel: 01684 574001 *Fax:* 01684 561002 *Dx:* 17628 MALVERN
E-mail: office@mslocombe.co.uk
List of partners: M Slocombe
Work: A1 C1 C2 E F1 F2 J1 J2 K1 K3 L N O Q R1 R2 S1 S2 W X Z(c,e,z)
Fixed Fee Interview undertaken
SPr: Slocombe, Mr Martyn LLB(B'ham). . . . . *Nov 1973
Ast: Ide, Mrs Fiona Margaret BA. . . . . *Jul 2000

SOPER & CO ‡
2 Graham Road Malvern Worcestershire WR14 2AQ
Tel: 01684 568495 *Fax:* 01684 564988
Emergency telephone 01684 573507
E-mail: soperandco@malvern255.fsnet.co.uk
List of partners: P D T Soper
Agency and Fixed Fee Interview undertaken

WHATLEY RECORDON ‡
12 Worcester Road Malvern Worcestershire WR14 4QU
Tel: 01684 892939 *Fax:* 01684 892327 *Dx:* 17604 MALVERN
List of partners: D R Parry, B Recordon, M Recordon
Languages: Dutch
Work: A1 D1 E F1 J1 K1 L N O Q S1 S2 T1 T2 W
Emergency Action, Agency, Advocacy, Legal Aid undertaken, Legal Aid Franchise and Member of Accident Line
Ptr: Parry, Mr David Rogerson BA(Law) . . . . *Nov 1985
Recordon, Mr Benedict LLB. . . . . *Sep 1996
Recordon, Miss Martha FILEx. . . . . *Nov 1996
Ast: Ashby, Mr Greg. . . . . Mar 1994
Con: Judge, Mr David Leslie MA(Oxon). . . . . *Jun 1967@

MANCHESTER, Greater Manchester

ADF LAW LLP ‡
Queens Chambers 5 John Dalton Street Manchester Greater Manchester M2 6ET
Tel: 0844 826 3670 *Fax:* 0844 826 3671
E-mail: info@adf-law.co.uk

AR SOLICITORS ‡
Adamson House Towers Buiness Park Wilmslow Road Manchester Greater Manchester M20 2YY
Tel: 0161 955 4206 *Fax:* 0161 955 4201

AST HAMPSONS
337 Hollinwood Avenue Moston Manchester Greater Manchester M40 0JA
Tel: 0161 681 1169 *Fax:* 0161 683 5712 *Dx:* 22810 ROCHDALE
Office: Rochdale
Work: E N S1 W
Agency, Advocacy and Fixed Fee Interview undertaken
Ptr: Taylor, Mr Franklyn D . . . . *Feb 1974

AARON & PARTNERS LLP SOLICITORS
3rd Floor 61-67 King Street Manchester Greater Manchester M2 4WQ
Tel: 0161 935 8334 *Fax:* 0161 935 8156
Dx: 14412 MANCHESTER 2
E-mail: manchester@aaronandpartners.com
Office: Chester
Ptr: Rowe, Mr Colin Notary Public . . . . *Feb 1978

ABACUS SOLICITORS ‡
Reedham House 31 King Street West Manchester Greater Manchester M3 2PN
Tel: 0161 833 0044 *Fax:* 0161 833 4004
E-mail: s.connor@abacus-law.co.uk
Office: Warrington

ABBEY SOLICITORS ‡
Brighton House 273-275 Wilmslow Road Fallowfield Manchester Greater Manchester M14 5JQ
Tel: 0161 835 9933 *Fax:* 0161 839 5553
Languages: Bengali, Gujarati, Hindi, Japanese, Punjabi, Spanish, Urdu
Work: B2 G H J1 K1 N O Q W Z(i)
Agency, Advocacy, Fixed Fee Interview and Legal Aid undertaken

ABBEYCROFT SOLICITORS ‡
35 Houldsworth Street Manchester Greater Manchester M1 1EB
Tel: 0161 235 5367 *Fax:* 0161 235 5367
E-mail: info@abbeycroftsolicitors.co.uk

ACKERS & COMPANY SOLICITORS ‡
223 Burnage Lane Burnage Manchester Greater Manchester M19 1FN
Tel: 0161 442 2656 *Fax:* 0161 443 2739

ADAM SOLICITORS ‡
479a Cheetham Hill Road Manchester Greater Manchester M8 9LR
Tel: 0161 795 6119 *Fax:* 0161 795 6118
E-mail: enquiries@adamsolicitors.co.uk
Work: E K3 N Q S1 S2 Z(i)

ADDLESHAW GODDARD
100 Barbirolli Square Manchester Greater Manchester M2 3AB
Tel: 0161 934 6000 *Fax:* 0161 934 6060 *Dx:* 14301 MANCHESTER
Emergency telephone 0161 934 6000
E-mail: info@addleshaw-booth.co.uk
Office: Leeds, London EC1
Languages: French, German, Italian, Spanish
Work: A1 A3 B1 C1 C2 C3 E F1 F2 I J1 K1 K2 L M1 M2 N O P Q R1 R2 S1 S2 T1 T2 U1 W X Z(b,c,d,e,f,j,l,o,p,q,r,t,w)
Emergency Action, Agency and Fixed Fee Interview undertaken
Ptr: Amsden, Mr Mark BEc; B Juris . . . . *Mar 1992
Anderson, Mr Grant. *May 1989
Barnes, Mr Gerard A LLB(Hons) . . . . *Oct 1996
Bee, Mr Tim J M . . . . Jan 1988
Bennett, Mr George Adam BA(Cantab) . . . . *Oct 1985
Bentham, Mr Paul J LLB . . . . *Dec 1989
Beresford, Ms Amanda LLB. . . . . Feb 1987
Bever, Mr Adrian . . . . Nov 1993
Birchall, Mr Michael J LLB. . . . . *Oct 1992
Briggs, Mr Graham Micheal LLB. . . . . *Oct 1984
Chamberlain, Mr Andrew M J BA . . . . *Nov 1988
Cockram, Mr Richard A MA(Cantab) . . . . *Oct 1973
Collins, Mr Adrian P LLB . . . . *Apr 1992
Conroy, Mr Paul LLB(Hons) . . . . *Sep 1994
Copley, Mr Dean Trent LLB . . . . *Sep 1988
Corner, Mrs Helen. . . . . *Nov 1985
Davey, Mr Jonathan W LLB(Manc) . . . . *Nov 1988
Davies, Ms Ruth . . . . Oct 1997
Delroy, Ms Justine . . . . Sep 1999
Devitt, Mr Paul LLB. *Oct 1988
Fleetwood, Mr Richard G BA . . . . Apr 1994
Garrett, Ms Susan M BA . . . . *Sep 1991
Gatenby, Mr John K MA; LLM(Cantab); FCIArb; MICM *Mar 1975
Goodstone, Mr Philip LLB. . . . . Nov 1992
Gosling, Mr John A BA(Dunelm). . . . . *Nov 1984
Hamilton, Mr Timothy G LLB(Manc) . . . . *Oct 1986
Handy, Mr David LLB(Hons). . . . . *Oct 1993
Harris, Mr Michael. . . . . Feb 1993
Hart, Mr Richard . . . . Oct 1996
Hastings, Mr Ian Alexander W LLB . . . . *Oct 1985
Hayes, Mr Richard W MA; LLB(Cantab). . . . . *§Sep 1972
Haywood, Mr Mark Bower BA. . . . . Apr 1991
Heffron, Mr David G. Sep 1993
Hiscock, Mr J John MA(Cantab). . . . . *Nov 1986
Houston, Mr Stephen BA . . . . *Dec 1985
Howell, Mr Paul Jonathan LLB . . . . *§Jun 1977
Humphrey, Ms Sandra A LLB . . . . *Oct 1983
Isaacs, Mr Michael Paul BA(Hons); Dip(Com Lit) . . *Nov 1994
Jansen, Mr Nathan . . . . Oct 1998
Jenkins, Mr Edmund G LLB. . . . . *Jul 1991
Johnston, Mr T Keith LLB . . . . *§Apr 1976
Jones, Mr David Mark BA(Cantab) . . . . *Apr 1979
Joyce, Mr John G LLB . . . . *Oct 1988
Kamstra, Mr Simon P LLB(Manc) . . . . *Feb 1990
Kelsall, Ms Nancy. . . . . Nov 1995
Kempner, Mr Richard Anthony BA. . . . . *Oct 1987
Kershaw, Mr Peter J LLB . . . . Dec 1989
Langley White, Mrs Jacqui . . . . *Jan 1983
Leake, Mr A John LLB . . . . *Oct 1982
Lee, Mr Paul A MA; LLB(Cantab) . . . . *Oct 1970
Lee, Mr Richard N F MA(Cantab) . . . . *Feb 1984
Leftley, Mr Michael A LLB(Warw); LLM . . . . *Nov 1993
Lightbody, Mr Bruce R BA. . . . . *Sep 1987
Lippell, Mr C Sean BA(Dunelm) . . . . *May 1979
McDonnell, Mr Philip BA(Oxon)(Jurisprudence) . . . *Nov 1988
McGuire, Miss Nancy J BA . . . . *Nov 1994
McIntosh, Mr Ian William LLB . . . . Oct 1983
Maskill, Mr Andrew Stuart Leslie LLB . . . . *Nov 1991
O'Connor, Mr Michael G BA(Dunelm) . . . . *Sep 1989
O'Loughlin, Mr Philip H MA(Cantab). . . . . Oct 1986
O'Shea, Mr Martin D BA(Hons) . . . . Sep 1997
Papworth, Mr Richard Noel BA(Oxon) Christchurch, Oxford Open Scholarship; Norton Rose Prize for Company Law - 1986 . . . . *Nov 1989
Pike, Mr John Douglas MA(Cantab). . . . . *§Jun 1972
Pike, Mr Malcolm J LLB . . . . *Oct 1984
Pilling, Mr Simon M LLB(Hons) . . . . Jun 1992
Proctor, Mr Nigel C BSc(Soton) . . . . *Sep 1990
Rawnsley, Ms Rachel Mary MA . . . . Oct 1989
Reevey, Mr Michael Adrian MA(Oxon). . . . . *Oct 1982
Sampson, Mr Ian Charles BA . . . . *Apr 1987
Shaw, Mr Nicholas J MA(Cantab) . . . . Apr 1981
Snell, Ms Ruth E LLB . . . . Oct 1991
Stone, Mr James Francis LLB. . . . . *Apr 1981
Sturrock, Mr Alan D LLB . . . . *Apr 1977
Tattersall, Mr Jonathan LLB . . . . Nov 1996
Thomas, Mr Richard . . . . Sep 2000
Tofalides, Mrs Margaret MA; LLB . . . . *Feb 1986
Tolley, Mr Derek Neil MA . . . . *Dec 1989
Toon, Mr John Terence LLB(Lond). . . . . *Oct 1991
Tully, Mr James M. . . . . *Dec 1993
Tweedie, Mr Colin J MA. . . . . *Oct 1978
Twigden, Mr Simon C H MA(Cantab) . . . . *Mar 1988
Wheeldon, Mr Richard A LLB . . . . *Oct 1985

See p112 for the Key to Work Categories & other symbols

Whittaker, Mr Quentin J . . . . Oct 1993
Woolhouse, Mr Neil T LLB . . . . Oct 1988
Woolley, Mr D P Karl LLB(Hons) . . . . *Nov 1983

AEQUITAS LEGAL ‡
Imperial Court Building 2 Exchange Quay Manchester Greater Manchester M5 3EB
Tel: 0161 358 0800 *Fax:* 0161 358 0805
E-mail: office@aequitaslegal.co.uk

AIM LEGAL LTD ‡
Office 30 The Tube Business Centre 86 North Street Manchester Greater Manchester M8 8RA
Tel: 0161 832 1770 *Fax:* 0161 819 5134

ALDERMAN PARTNERS ‡
81 King Street Manchester Greater Manchester M2 4ST
Tel: 0161 448 8451 *Fax:* 0161 445 0673
E-mail: info@aldermanpartners.co.uk

ALDERSON LEGAL ‡
1st Floor 1 Portland Street Manchester Greater Manchester M1 3BE
Tel: 0161 242 6859 *Fax:* 0161 850 1020

MICHAEL ALEXANDER & CO ‡
44-48 Oldham Road Manchester Greater Manchester M4 5EE
Tel: 0845 839 2011 *Fax:* 0161 237 3215
Emergency telephone 07774 637976
E-mail: mpa@michaelalexander.demon.co.uk
List of partners: M P Alexander
Work: B2 D1 D2 G H K1 N Q W
Emergency Action, Agency, Advocacy, Fixed Fee Interview and Legal Aid undertaken
SPr: Alexander, Mr Michael P LLB . . . . *Oct 1988

ALLIED SOLICITORS ‡
291 Slade Lane Manchester Greater Manchester M19 2HR
Tel: 0161 660 1505 *Fax:* 0161 660 1506
E-mail: info@alliedsolicitors.com

ALLISON & REILLY SOLICITORS ‡
Argyle House Park Road Middleton Manchester Greater Manchester M24 1AE
Tel: 0844 805 4735 / 0161 643 5923 *Fax:* 0161 654 7373

AMELANS ‡
Barlow House 708-710 Wilmslow Road Didsbury Manchester Greater Manchester M20 2FW
Tel: 0161 434 4545 *Fax:* 0161 445 3338 *Dx:* 23162 DIDSBURY
E-mail: law@amelans.co.uk
List of partners: M J Cockx, A Twambley
Work: E F1 J1 N O Q S1 W
Emergency Action, Agency, Advocacy, Fixed Fee Interview undertaken and Member of Accident Line
Ptr: Cockx, Mr Martin J BA(Law). . . . . *Jan 1987
Twambley, Mr Andrew BA(Law) . . . . *Oct 1982

AMICUS SOLICITORS LLP ‡
761 Wilmslow Road Didsbury Manchester Greater Manchester M20 6RN
Tel: 0161 434 4448 *Fax:* 0161 434 4449
E-mail: enquiries@amicussolicitors.co.uk

ANSARI SOLICITORS ‡
Liberty House 35-37 Slade Lane Manchester Greater Manchester M13 0QJ
Tel: 0161 225 2277

APPLEYARD LEES
Blackfriars House Parsonage Manchester Greater Manchester M3 2JA
Tel: 0161 835 9655 *Fax:* 0161 835 9654
E-mail: manchester@appleyardlees.com
Office: Burnley, Chester, Halifax, Harrogate, Huddersfield, Leeds, Liverpool, Preston, Sheffield, Stockton-on-Tees, York

ASHWOOD SOLICITORS LTD ‡
Suite S1 Kingsway Business Centre 140 Kingsway Manchester Greater Manchester M19 1BB
Tel: 0161 248 4444 *Fax:* 0161 248 4448
E-mail: info@ashwoodsolicitors.co.uk

ASUELIME SOLICITORS ‡
185a Dickinson Road Manchester Greater Manchester M13 0YN
Tel: 0161 224 7596

ATKINSONHODGSON LLP ‡
Peter House Oxford Street Manchester Greater Manchester M1 5AN
Tel: 0870 300 8790 *Fax:* 0870 300 8791
Emergency telephone 07970 900270
E-mail: sarah.hodgson@atkinsonhodgson.com
List of partners: S L Hodgson
Office: Nantwich
Work: L Q R1 R2 Z(h,u)
Fixed Fee Interview undertaken
Ptr: Hodgson, Ms Sarah Louise BA(Hons) . . . . *Jul 1996

ATTICUS LEGAL LLP ‡
Castlefield House Liverpool Road Manchester Greater Manchester M3 4SB
Tel: 0161 957 8888

AYMAN SOLICITORS ‡
961 Stockport Road Manchester Greater Manchester M19 3NP
Tel: 0161 225 8333 *Fax:* 0161 225 8666

BAKER ELLIS SOLICITORS ‡
880 Stockport Road Manchester Greater Manchester M19 3BN
Tel: 0161 225 2525

BARINGS SOLICITORS ‡
Dale House 35 Dale Street Manchester Greater Manchester M1 2HF
Tel: 0161 200 9960 *Fax:* 0161 425 8122
E-mail: info@baringslaw.com

BARLOW LYDE & GILBERT LLP
The merged firm of Barlow Lyde & Gilbert and Clyde & Co
Chancery Place 50 Brown Street Manchester Greater Manchester M2 2JT
Tel: 0161 829 6400 *Fax:* 0161 829 6401 *Dx:* 14448 MANCHESTER 2
Office: London EC3, Oxford
Ptr: Butchart, Ms Janet Patricia LLB(Law with French); LSF . . . . *§Oct 1990
Moon, Mr David LLB . . . . *§Oct 1991
Mullins, Mr Hugh K LLB. . . . . *Nov 1989
Murray, Chris . . . . *§Aug 1996
Mem: Dadge, Mr James William BA(Hons). . . . . *§Sep 2001
Finnigan, Mr Kevin P LLB(Hull) . . . . *§Sep 1978
Walmsley, Mr Peter LLB; LLM. . . . . §Sep 1999
Asoc: Field, Lucie . . . . Nov 2006
Gilligan, Rhian . . . . Sep 2003
Morgan-Barrett, Ms Ann-Marie BA(Kent) . . . . . . *§Nov 1992
Ast: Purrier, Mr Timothy J LLB(Hons) . . . . *§Apr 1978

BRIAN BARR SOLICITORS ‡
Enfield House Bury Old Road Manchester Greater Manchester M7 4QX
Tel: 0161 720 6700 *Fax:* 0161 721 4274
E-mail: info@brianbarr.co.uk
List of partners: B S Barr
Work: J1 N Z(q,r)
SPr: Barr, Mr Brian S LLB . . . . *Apr 1979
Ast: Cohen, Mr Phillip LLB Brigid Cotter Prize 2002 . . . . *Oct 2006
Ryan, Miss Lyndsey LLB(Law & Sociology) . . . . . . *Jul 2004

BEESLEY & CO ‡
736-740 Wilmslow Road Didsbury Manchester Greater Manchester M20 2DW
Tel: 0161 445 3678 *Fax:* 0161 445 3657 *Dx:* 23161 DIDSBURY
E-mail: mail@beesleysolicitors.co.uk
List of partners: M Lees
Work: B1 C1 E F1 J1 J2 L N O Q S1 S2 V W X Z(g,h,j,p,q,r,w)
Emergency Action, Agency, Advocacy, Fixed Fee Interview, Legal Aid undertaken and Member of Accident Line
Ptr: Lees, Mr Mark . . . . *Dec 1998
Ast: Bethell, Mr Colin . . . . May 2008

BERG LEGAL ‡
35 Peter Street Manchester Greater Manchester M2 5BG
Tel: 0161 833 9211 *Fax:* 0161 834 5566
E-mail: help@berg.co.uk
List of partners: R L Berg, G L Black, D M Carter, J P Dover, S A Foster, S Fulda, S Klass, A M Loveday, R J McKay, G Rechnitzer, P G Woolf
Work: A1 A3 B1 C1 C2 C3 E I J1 K1 K3 L N O Q R2 S1 S2 W Z(c,e,q)
Emergency Action and Advocacy undertaken
Ptr: Berg, Mr Reuben L LLB. . . . . *§Oct 1975
Black, Mr Gary Lee LLB(Hons) . . . . Mar 1996
Carter, Mr Damian Michael LLB . . . . *Sep 1997
Dover, Mr Jonathan Paul LLB(L'pool) . . . . *Nov 1989
Foster, Mr Stephen A MA(Cantab). . . . . *Oct 1985
Fulda, Sydney LLB . . . . *Oct 1988
Klass, Mrs Stephanie MA(Oxon) . . . . *§Dec 1974
Loveday, Mrs Alison Marie BA. . . . . *Oct 1992
McKay, Mr Richard J BA(Hons) . . . . *Sep 1999
Rechnitzer, Mr Gabriel LLB . . . . *Jun 1977
Woolf, Mr Peter G BA. . . . . *Sep 1978
Asoc: Daniels, Mr Stephen John BA(Hons)(Law). . . . . . . *Oct 1984
Jefcott, Mr Lee Jonathon BSc(Hons) . . . . *Oct 1996
Mendelsohn, Mr Ian C BA . . . . *Jul 1983
Ast: Forrest, Mrs Carly LLB . . . . Sep 1999
Bate, Mrs Victoria Alice LLB Watson Esam Prize . . . Sep 2003
Hyde, Miss Karen Lesley LLB . . . . Oct 2001
Ishaq, Ms Shabana LLB. . . . . Oct 2002
Kennedy, Mr Keith S G LLB(Hons) . . . . Sep 2001
Lister, Mr Elliot H BA(Hons); CPE; LPC . . . . *Aug 1997
McWilliams, Miss Helen LLB . . . . Sep 2004
Mason, Mrs Samantha BA . . . . Nov 2000
Perkins, Mr James Lawrence BSc. . . . . Sep 2003

BERMANS LLP
Cardinal House 20 St Mary's Parsonage Manchester Greater Manchester M3 2LY
Tel: 0161 827 4600 *Fax:* 0161 834 2402 *Dx:* 14365 MANCHESTER
E-mail: info@bermans.co.uk
Office: Liverpool
Work: A3 B1 B2 C1 C2 E F1 J1 L O Q R1 R2 S1 S2 U2 W Z(b,l,w)
Fixed Fee Interview undertaken
Ptr: Farrelly, Mr Philip A LLB. . . . . Oct 1986
Gledhill, Mr David B LLB . . . . *Oct 1986
Munford, Mr Ian R LLB(Sheff) . . . . *Apr 1978

BERRY & BERRY
174 Bury New Road Manchester Greater Manchester M45 6QF
Tel: 0161 796 7920 *Fax:* 0161 766 2453
E-mail: email.whitefield@berryberry.co.uk
Office: Eccles, Manchester, Walkden

BERRY & BERRY
496 Manchester Road East Little Hulton Manchester Greater Manchester M38 9NS
Tel: 0161 703 7300 *Fax:* 0161 703 7774
Emergency telephone 07074 237797
E-mail: email.lhulton@berryberry.co.uk
Office: Eccles, Manchester, Walkden
Work: G H K1
Legal Aid undertaken and Legal Aid Franchise
Ptr: James, Mr Michael A BA . . . . *Oct 1987

BERRYMANS LACE MAWER
King's House 42 King Street West Manchester Greater Manchester M3 2NU
Tel: 0161 236 2002 *Fax:* 0161 832 7956 *Dx:* 14302 MANCHESTER 1
E-mail: info@blm-law.com
Office: Birmingham, Bristol, Cardiff, Leeds, Liverpool, London EC2, Southampton, Stockton-on-Tees
Work: A3 C1 F2 J1 J2 L N O Q S1 W Z(h,q,r,t)

BETESH PARTNERSHIP ‡
Cardinal House 20 St Mary's Parsonage Manchester Greater Manchester M3 2LY
Tel: 0161 834 2623 *Fax:* 0161 832 2187 *Dx:* 14305 MANCHESTER 1
E-mail: enquiries@bpslaw.co.uk
List of partners: N Heywood, S E Kwasnik, H L Lipson
Office: Hale, Manchester
Work: C1 C2 D1 E J2 K1 L N O Q S1 S2 W Z(c)
Ptr: Heywood, Mr Nicholas BA(Hons) . . . . *Jan 1990
Kwasnik, Mr Sefton E BA . . . . *May 1981
Lipson, Mr Harry L LLB . . . . *Dec 1975
Con: Esterkin, Mr Nigel J LLB(Manc) . . . . *Jun 1980

BETESH PARTNERSHIP
71 Middleton Road Higher Crumpsall Manchester Greater Manchester M8 4JY
Tel: 0161 740 4918 *Fax:* 0161 795 9002 *Dx:* 14305 MANCHESTER 1
E-mail: enquiries@bpslaw.co.uk
Office: Hale, Manchester
Work: E S1 W

BINAS SOLICITORS ‡
765 Stockport Road Manchester Greater Manchester M19 3DL
Tel: 0161 257 0060 *Fax:* 0161 256 4695
Languages: Urdu
Work: N S1 Z(i)

BIRCHALL BLACKBURN LLP
20 Kennedy Street Manchester Greater Manchester M2 4BY
Tel: 0161 236 0662 *Fax:* 0161 236 0687
Dx: 718168 MANCHESTER 3
E-mail: info@birchallblackburn.co.uk
Office: Chester, Chorley, Formby, Leyland, Morecambe, Preston (2 offices), Southport
Languages: Bengali, Cantonese, French, Gujarati, Mandarin, Urdu
Work: B1 C1 C2 E L N O Q R2 S1 Z(c,g,l,q)
Agency and Fixed Fee Interview undertaken
Ptr: Foxford, Mr Michael John LLB. . . . . *May 1989
Hughes, Mr Graham Alexander MA; LLB; BSc; CTA(Fellow) John Allington Hughes Prize 1973; Sir Horatio Lloyd Prize 1973 Notary Public . . . . *Jun 1976
Nelson, Miss Amanda Patricia. . . . . Sep 2000
Patton, Mr Jamie LLB(Hons) ♦ . . . . *Sep 1996
Pickering, Mr Paul Edward ♦ LSC Cost Committee . . *Jan 1998
Woodcock, Mr Daniel James BA(Law & Criminology) . Sep 2002
Asoc: Birchall, Ms Deborah Catherine LLB(Hons) . . . . . . *Nov 1999
Coates, Mr Anthony John . . . . Sep 2005
Evans, Miss Susan Catherine LLB(Hons); BA(Hons) . Sep 2005
Fenton, Miss Theresa M LLB ♦ . . . . *Jul 1979
Ast: Altan, Mrs Halide Suzan LLB . . . . *Nov 2008
Lockwood, Miss Lesley Jane LLB(Hons). . . . . . . Feb 2007
Taylor, Miss Andrea Louise LLB(Hons) . . . . Mar 2010

BIRCHFIELDS ‡
10 Knowsley Street Cheetham Hill Road Manchester Greater Manchester M8 8GF
Tel: 0161 835 9865 *Fax:* 0161 839 4702
Dx: 718158 MANCHESTER 3
Office: Stoke-on-Trent
Asoc: Iqbal, Mr Ahmed BA(Hons) . . . . *Oct 1999

BLUE SKY LAW LIMITED ‡
Pall Mall Court 61-67 King Street Manchester Greater Manchester M2 4PD
Tel: 0161 618 1032 *Fax:* 0161 618 1130
E-mail: info@blueskylaw.co.uk

KEVIN BOLTON SOLICITOR ‡
Apartment 22 Northpoint House 5 Edgehill Street Manchester Greater Manchester M4 1BB
Tel: 0161 834 6776 *Fax:* 0161 834 6776
E-mail: kevinbolton@accident-claim-expert.co.uk

BOOTE EDGAR ESTERKIN ‡
7 St James Square Manchester Greater Manchester M2 6XX
Tel: 0161 832 7888 *Fax:* 0161 832 3597 *Dx:* 14375 MANCHESTER
E-mail: ebe@bootes.co.uk

BOUCHERS WITH ALLANSONS LLP
106-108 Reddish Lane Gorton Manchester Greater Manchester M18 7JL
Tel: 0161 220 8484 *Fax:* 0161 230 7508
Office: Bolton
Work: E K4 L S1 W
Fixed Fee Interview undertaken

BOWER HARRIS ‡
South Central 11 Peter Street Manchester Greater Manchester M2 5QR
Tel: 0161 832 9404 *Fax:* 0161 833 2174
List of partners: R Bower
Work: A1 B1 C1 D1 E F1 G H J1 K1 L M1 N P R1 S1 T1 W Z(c,i,j,o)
Emergency Action, Agency, Advocacy, Fixed Fee Interview, Legal Aid undertaken and Member of Accident Line
Ptr: Bower, Mr Roger BA(Law). . . . . *Jul 1979

BRABNERS CHAFFE STREET
55 King Street Manchester Greater Manchester M2 4LQ
Tel: 0161 836 8800 *Fax:* 0161 836 8801 *Dx:* 14431 MANCHESTER
Emergency telephone 0161 836 8800
E-mail: law@brabnerscs.com
Office: Liverpool, Preston
Languages: French, German, Spanish
Work: A1 A2 A3 B1 C1 C2 C3 D1 E F1 I J1 K1 L N O P Q R1 S1 S2 T1 T2 U2 W Z(b,c,d,e,f,h,k,o,q)
Emergency Action and Agency undertaken
Ptr: Bate, Mr Richard John LLB(Hons). . . . . *Oct 1994
Bentham, Mr David LLB. . . . . *Sep 2003
Blood, Mr Michael James BA(Hons). . . . . *§Mar 1994
Bowcock, Mr David Norman LLB(Hons); LSF Price Waterhouse Tax Prize, University of Birmingham 1989 . . . . . *Oct 1992
Brandwood, Mr C Mark BA(Dunelm). . . . . *Oct 1982
Burton, Mr Thomas M LLB(Manc) . . . . *Mar 1973
Canty, Mr Edward LLB . . . . *§Sep 2001
Chamberlain, Mr Paul. . . . . *Oct 1994
Couse, Ms Carol LLB(Law & Spanish). . . . . Sep 2003
Difelice, Mr Marcus . . . . *Sep 1996
Dobson, Mr Matthew . . . . *Sep 1997
Edgar, Mrs Lydia Therese LLB . . . . *Oct 1994
Fitzmaurice, Mr Anthony LLB(B'ham) . . . . *Oct 1984
Harper, Mr Anthony J LLB. . . . . *Oct 1983
Jones, Ms Ruth Helena . . . . *Apr 1996
Lewis, Mr Jeff. *Nov 1989
Litchfield, Miss Caroline Louise LLB(Hons) . . . . . *Oct 1997
Mabon, Sam . . . . *Sep 1999
Marsden, Mr Peter A R B MA(Cantab). . . . . *§Apr 1975
Morton, Mr Paul. . . . . *Mar 1991
Purves, Mr Jim . . . . *Nov 1995
Round, Ms Charlotte . . . . *Oct 1999
Smith, Mr Jason. . . . . *Jun 1996
Street, Mr Robert H LLB(L'pool). . . . . *Apr 1975
Watkins, Mr Edward Maurice LLM. . . . . *§May 1966
Whitehead, Mr Simon . . . . *Sep 1999
Asoc: Baird, Mr Stuart LLB . . . . Sep 2005
Leigh, Mr Simon John LLB . . . . *Oct 1999
Nicholls, Mr Paul LLB. . . . . *Nov 1986
Niven, Mr Mark Simon LLB(Hons)(B'ham). . . . . . . *Sep 2005
Partridge, Mr Jamie LLB(Hons) . . . . *Sep 2002
Soden, Miss Nicola Mary LLB. . . . . *Sep 2004
Ast: Agamian, Miss Emma Jane LLB. . . . . Oct 2007
Barnes, Mr Matthew MA(Oxon)(History); DipLaw . . . Sep 2004

Bennett, Mr Mark Stephen LLB(Hons); PGCert(Sports Law) . . . . Sep 2004
Morrell, Mr Mark LLB . . . . *Oct 2009
Parry, Ms Karen LLB Cavendish Law Prize 2002 . . *May 2007
Whalley, Mr Richard LLB; LPC . . . . *Feb 2008

BRODIE & COMPANY LIMITED ‡
64 Bridge Street Manchester Greater Manchester M3 3BN
Tel: 0161 829 3900 *Fax:* 0161 839 4839
Dx: 14309 MANCHESTER 1
E-mail: info@brodielegal.com

BROMLEYS SOLICITORS LLP
10th Floor 3 Hardman Street Spinningfields Manchester Greater Manchester M3 3HF
Tel: 0161 932 1572 *Fax:* 0161 932 1401
E-mail: bromleys@bromleys.co.uk
Office: Ashton-under-Lyne

ROBIN BURMAN & CO ‡
446 Barlow Moor Road Chorlton Manchester Greater Manchester M21 0BQ
Tel: 0161 860 7123 *Fax:* 0161 862 9548
Dx: 22404 CHORLTON CUM HARDY
E-mail: enquiries@robinburman.com
List of partners: P Citron, I P Hannam, J M T Monks
Office: Failsworth
Work: C1 C2 C3 E F1 I J1 K1 L N O Q S1 U2 W X Z(d,e,f)
Emergency Action, Agency, Advocacy and Fixed Fee Interview undertaken
Ptr: Citron, Mr Paul LLB . . . . *Nov 1982
Hannam, Mr Ian Paul LLB. . . . . Jan 1984
Monks, Mrs Jane Muriel Tildsley LLB; BSc(Hons) Diocesan Registrar . . . . *Apr 1981
Ast: Grantham, Mr Michael LLB(Manc). . . . . *Oct 1985
Myers, Mrs Donna Marie LLB(Hons); PGDipLP . . . . Sep 1999
Platts, Mrs Janet C B LLB. . . . . *Apr 1981
Con: Burman, Mr Robin B LLB . . . . *Jun 1978

BURROWS BUSSIN ‡
8 King Street Manchester Greater Manchester M2 6AQ
Tel: 0161 833 1411 *Fax:* 0161 819 1459 *Dx:* 14366 MANCHESTER
E-mail: enquiries@burrowsbussin.com

BURTON COPELAND LLP ‡
Astley House Quay Street Manchester Greater Manchester M3 4AS
Tel: 0161 827 9500 *Fax:* 0161 834 5941 *Dx:* 14362 MANCHESTER
Emergency telephone 0161 832 7834
E-mail: crime@burtoncopeland.com
List of partners: G Crossley, S Dooley, J A Kennerley, R S Lancaster, G R Lewis, M P Mackey, V J Oliver, M J Rainford, E A Ridgway, L V Straw, D R Weed
Office: Sale
Languages: French, German, Greek, Gujarati, Hindi, Italian, Punjabi, Spanish, Urdu
Work: B2 G H J2 P Z(g)
Emergency Action, Agency, Advocacy, Legal Aid undertaken and Legal Aid Franchise
Mem: Crossley, Miss Gillian LLB ★ . . . . *Apr 1979
Dooley, Miss Suzanne LLB; LPC; PSC . . . . Aug 2002
Kennerley, Mr John A LLB ★ . . . . Dec 1982
Lancaster, Mr Robert Simon. . . . . Jul 2004
Lewis, Gwynfor R LLB ★ . . . . *Feb 1986
Mackey, Mr Michael P LLB . . . . *Dec 1974
Oliver, Mr Victor John LLB. . . . . Nov 2003
Rainford, Mr Michael Joseph LLB . . . . *Apr 1981
Ridgway, Mrs Elizabeth Ann LLB . . . . *May 1996
Straw, Miss Louise V . . . . *Apr 1996
Ast: Bridge, Ms Lucy LLB . . . . Mar 2004
Kennaugh, Ms Gillian Anne LLB. . . . . Nov 2003
Moussalli, Mr Robert S LLB . . . . *May 1992
Mulcahy, Ms Victoria LLB . . . . Nov 2003
Vickers, Mr Adam John Tim LLB . . . . Jul 2004
Con: Milns, Mr John W . . . . *Jun 1968

BUSINESS PROPERTY LAW LLP ‡
Peters House Oxford Street Manchester Greater Manchester M1 5AN
Tel: 0161 209 3760 *Fax:* 0161 601 3511
E-mail: hello@bplawllp.co.uk

CM SOLICITORS ‡
13 St John Street Manchester Greater Manchester M3 4DQ
Tel: 0845 094 4544 *Fax:* 0845 034 4323
E-mail: info@cmsolicitors.co.uk

CALIBRE SOLICITORS LIMITED ‡
Orbit House Albert Street Manchester Greater Manchester M30 0BL
Tel: 0870 458 4418 *Fax:* 0870 458 4419
E-mail: info@calibresolicitors.co.uk
List of partners: J Clarke, E Johnson
Languages: French
Ptr: Clarke, Ms Joanne . . . . Nov 1998
Johnson, Mr Edward . . . . Oct 1999

CAMPBELL SYSTEMS LTD ‡
1st Floor Acre House Manchester Greater Manchester M22 4RW
Tel: 07770 123082 / 0161 495 2880
E-mail: neil.garvin@garvin-solicitors.com

CANTOR LAW SOLICITORS ‡
5th Floor Bracken House Charles Street Manchester Greater Manchester M1 7BD
Tel: 0161 273 7600

CARTER LAW ‡
The Point Suite 2-3 173-175 Cheetham Hill Road Manchester Greater Manchester M8 8LG
Tel: 0844 414 0667 *Fax:* 0844 414 0688
E-mail: info@carter-law.co.uk

CARTER MOORE SOLICITORS ‡
13 St John Street Manchester Greater Manchester M3 4DY
Tel: 0845 873 7333 *Fax:* 0845 873 7334
E-mail: info@cartermoore.com
Office: London EC4, Manchester

CARTER MOORE SOLICITORS
559 Barlow Moor Road Chorlton Manchester Greater Manchester M21 8AN.
Tel: 0845 873 7333 *Fax:* 0845 873 7334
E-mail: info@cartermoore.com
Office: London EC4, Manchester

CHANCE HUNTER SOLICITORS ‡
Portland House 431 Chester Road Manchester Greater Manchester M16 9HA
Tel: 0161 877 1200

CHANDLER HARRIS LLP ‡
25 Byrom Street Manchester Greater Manchester M3 4PF
Tel: 0161 834 2200 *Fax:* 0161 834 2206
Dx: 14335 MANCHESTER 1
E-mail: mail@chandlerharris.com
List of partners: S A L Chandler, D M Harris
Languages: German
Work: B1 C1 J1 L N O Q Z(k)
Agency undertaken
Ptr: Chandler, Mr Simon A L LLB . . . . *Oct 1988
Harris, Mr David M BA(Hons) . . . . *Oct 1986
Ast: Samuels, Mr Barry Louis MA(Oxon). . . . . *Oct 1995

D L CHAUDHRI & CO ‡
37a Wilmslow Road Rusholme Manchester Greater Manchester M14 5TB
Tel: 0161 224 6728 *Fax:* 0161 231 8991
Emergency telephone 07801 649557
Languages: Punjabi, Urdu
Work: L N V W
Agency and Legal Aid undertaken

CHINNERY & CO SOLICITORS ‡
53 Fountain Street Manchester Greater Manchester M2 2AN
Tel: 0161 233 7010 *Fax:* 0161 233 7011
E-mail: info@chinneryandcosolicitors.co.uk

CHUNG & PLATT ‡
58-60 George Street Manchester Greater Manchester M1 4HF
Tel: 0161 228 6777 *Fax:* 0161 228 7774
Emergency telephone 0161 228 6777
E-mail: chungandplattsolicitors@hotmail.com
List of partners: S J P Chung
Languages: Chinese, Mandarin
Work: B1 C1 E L R1 R2 S1 S2 T1 T2 W Z(b,i,j,l)
Emergency Action, Agency and Advocacy undertaken
SPr: Chung, Mr Stephen J P BA(Law) . . . . *Oct 1982

CLARKE WILLMOTT
10th Floor 3 Hardman Street Manchester Greater Manchester M3 3HF
Tel: 0845 209 1000 / 0117 305 6000 *Fax:* 0845 209 2005
Dx: 14351 MANCHESTER
Office: Birmingham, Bristol, London EC4, Southampton, Taunton

CLEAR LAW LTD ‡
7th Floor Paragon House 48 Seymour Grove Manchester Greater Manchester M16 0LN
Tel: 0870 850 8652

CLIFFORD JOHNSTON & CO ‡
434 Burnage Lane Burnage Manchester Greater Manchester M19 1LH
Tel: 0161 975 1900 *Fax:* 0161 443 2948
Emergency telephone 07974 316142
List of partners: N Doherty, P J Harris, P M Walsh
Office: Manchester
Work: B2 G H L N S1 S2 W Z(i,m,q)
Emergency Action, Agency, Advocacy, Fixed Fee Interview, Legal Aid undertaken and Legal Aid Franchise
Ptr: Harris, Mr Patrick John BA; MA ★. . . . . *Oct 1994
Walsh, Mr Philip Mark LLB ♦ . . . . *Nov 1994
Con: Johnston, Mr David S MSc ♦ . . . . *Apr 1980

CLIFFORD JOHNSTON & CO
326 Platt Lane Rusholme Manchester Greater Manchester M14 7DA
Tel: 0161 249 2700 *Fax:* 0161 249 2705
Emergency telephone 07974 316142
Office: Manchester
Work: A1 B2 D1 D2 G H K1 L N S1 W Z(g,j,l,m,q)
Emergency Action, Agency, Advocacy, Fixed Fee Interview, Legal Aid undertaken and Legal Aid Franchise
Ptr: Doherty, Ms Noreen. . . . . Nov 1997

CO-OPERATIVE GROUP LEGAL SERVICES ‡
PO Box 53 New Century House Manchester Greater Manchester M60 4ES
Tel: 0161 827 5296 *Fax:* 0161 834 3147
Dx: 700002 MANCHESTER 6
Emergency telephone 0161 827 5293

COBBETTS LLP ‡
58 Mosley Street Manchester Greater Manchester M2 3HZ
Tel: 0845 404 2404 *Fax:* 0845 404 2414
E-mail: enquiries@cobbetts.com
Office: Birmingham, Leeds, London WC1
Languages: French, German, Italian, Spanish
Work: A1 B1 C1 C2 C3 E F1 F2 I J1 J2 K1 K2 L M1 M2 N O P Q R1 R2 S1 S2 T1 T2 W Z(b,c,d,e,f,h,j,k,l,o,p,s,u,w,x,y,z)

GRAHAM COFFEY & CO ‡
First Floor Bank House Faulkner Street Manchester Greater Manchester M1 4EH
Tel: 0161 200 2440 *Fax:* 0161 200 2466
Emergency telephone 0161 819 6900
E-mail: mail@gcoffey.co.uk
List of partners: R S Bailey, I L Boni, G J Coffey, M S Mansfield, P J McCullough
Work: C1 J2 N O Q Z(j,q)
Agency and Fixed Fee Interview undertaken
Ptr: Bailey, Mr Richard S LLB . . . . *Oct 1995
Boni, Miss Isabel L LLB(Hons) . . . . *Aug 1998
Coffey, Mr Graham John LLB . . . . *Jan 1993
McCullough, Mr Peter James . . . . Sep 1996
Mansfield, Mr Michael S LLB . . . . May 1988

COLEMANS - CTTS ‡
100 Talbot Road Stretford Manchester Greater Manchester M16 0PG
Tel: 0161 876 2500 *Fax:* 0161 876 2501 *Dx:* 14380 MANCHESTER
E-mail: enquiries@colemans-ctts.co.uk
List of partners: M Burden, R J Coleman, G F Cox, D J Erwin, F C Fitzgerald, C E Roantree, S J Stanfield, A P Sutton, N A Tarrant, J C Tilley, L M Valcin
Office: Barnet, Kingston upon Thames
Languages: French, German, Hindi, Punjabi, Spanish
Work: C1 C3 E F1 J1 L N O Q S1 S2 W Z(c,j,p,q)
Agency, Advocacy, Fixed Fee Interview undertaken and Member of Accident Line
Ptr: Burden, Mrs Melanie BA; LLB. . . . . *Feb 2001
Coleman, Mr Roger J LLB; MBA . . . . *Nov 1982
Cox, Mr Gregory F LLB(Hons). . . . . *Sep 1998
Erwin, Mr David J BA(French & German); LSF . . . *Sep 1990
Stanfield, Mr Simon John . . . . Feb 2002
Asoc: Astley, Mr Steven BA(Hons). . . . . *Aug 2003
Hall, Mrs Helen A LLB(Hons) . . . . *Nov 1989
Krelle, Mrs Deborah Catherine . . . . Sep 1997
Rose, Miss Dawn LLB. . . . . *Feb 2003
Slack, Mr Jason LLB(Hons) . . . . *Apr 1998

THE CONNEXION PARTNERSHIP ‡
7th Floor Alberton House 30 St Mary's Parsonage Manchester Greater Manchester M3 2WJ
Tel: 0870 160 1160 *Fax:* 0870 197 5377 *Dx:* 727758 MANCHESTER
E-mail: infomanchester@cxp-law.com
Office: Birmingham

CONVEYANCING EXPERT LIMITED ‡
117 Chorley Road Swinton Manchester Greater Manchester M27 4AA
Tel: 0844 412 5857 *Fax:* 0161 794 9350 *Dx:* 28202 SWINTON
E-mail: enquiries@conveyancingexpert.co.uk

ANTHONY COOMBS ‡
18 Raynham Avenue Didsbury Manchester Greater Manchester M20 6BW
Tel: 0161 445 3789 *Fax:* 0161 445 4493
E-mail: info@anthonycoombs.co.uk

COOPER KENYON BURROWS ‡
196 Deansgate Manchester Greater Manchester M3 3WF
Tel: 0161 834 7374 *Fax:* 0161 839 3299
Dx: 14395 MANCHESTER 1
Emergency telephone 07836202448
E-mail: enquiries@c-k-b.com
Work: B2 G J2 O P Q T1
Fixed Fee Interview and Legal Aid undertaken

COPE & CO SOLICITORS LIMITED ‡
Centurion House 129 Deansgate Manchester Greater Manchester M3 3WR
Tel: 0161 214 7950 *Fax:* 0161 830 2196
E-mail: manchester@copeandco.com
Office: Liverpool

COTTRILL STONE LAWLESS ‡
International House 82-86 Deansgate Manchester Greater Manchester M3 2ER
Tel: 0161 835 3681 *Fax:* 0161 833 0556
Dx: 14310 MANCHESTER 1
E-mail: lawyers@cottrills.co.uk
List of partners: A T Irwin, C Lee, P J Mogg, I Walsh, R J Wilson
Work: E F1 F2 J1 L N O Q R1 R2 S1 S2 T1 T2 V W Z(j,q)
Emergency Action, Agency, Advocacy and Fixed Fee Interview undertaken
Ptr: Irwin, Ms Anne T LLB. . . . . *§Oct 1984
Lee, Miss Clare BA(Hons)(Accounting & Law). . . . . Sep 2001
Mogg, Mr Philip J BA . . . . *§Dec 1976
Walsh, Mr Ian. . . . . Jul 1999
Wilson, Mr Richard James . . . . Apr 2000
Ast: Sharp, Ms Rebecca. . . . . May 2003
Wise, Mr Daniel. Nov 2003

COUNTRYWIDE PROPERTY LAWYERS ‡
3rd Floor Lee House 90 Great Bridge Water Street Manchester Greater Manchester M1 5RR
Tel: 0870 380 9000 *Fax:* 0870 132 9020 *Dx:* 716870 MANCHESTER
Office: Cardiff
Work: S1

CROFTONS ‡
The Lexicon Mount Street Manchester Greater Manchester M2 5FA
Tel: 0161 214 6180 *Fax:* 0161 839 1743
Dx: 18572 MANCHESTER 7
E-mail: info@croftons.co.uk
List of partners: R Agnew, A Chapman, R J A Clarke, J Hampson, S T Leighton, J P Palmer
Work: C1 C2 C3 D1 D2 E F1 J1 J2 K1 L N O R1 S1 S2 T1 T2 W Z(c,d,h,l,q,r)
Emergency Action, Agency, Advocacy, Fixed Fee Interview, Legal Aid undertaken and Member of Accident Line
Ptr: Agnew, Mr Robert LLB(Hons) ♦ . . . . *Apr 1996
Chapman, Mr Arthur BA ♦. . . . . *Feb 1982
Clarke, Mr Richard J A BA ♦ . . . . *Jun 1976
Hampson, Mr John BA ♦ . . . . *Jun 1978
Leighton, Mr Simon Timothy LLB(Hons). . . . . . . *Nov 1994
Palmer, Mr Jeffrey P BA ♦. . . . . *Jan 1979
Ast: Slater, Mrs Victoria L LLB(Hons) . . . . *Jan 2001
Con: Bradley, Mr Stewart N TEP ♦ . . . . *§Nov 1971

CROSSMANS MTA
5 New York Street Manchester Greater Manchester M1 4JB
Tel: 01223 451442
E-mail: rachel.dunne@crossmansmta.com
Office: Cambridge, London EC4

CRUMPSALL SOLICITORS ‡
5 Delaunays Road Crumpsall Manchester Greater Manchester M8 4QS
Tel: 0161 492 0300 *Fax:* 0161 492 0900
Languages: Mirpuri, Urdu
Work: E S1 S2 Z(c,i)

CUNNINGHAMS ‡
4th Floor South Central 11 Peter Street Manchester Greater Manchester M2 5QR
Tel: 0161 833 1600 *Fax:* 0161 833 1060
Emergency telephone 07659 100768
E-mail: enquiries@cunninghamsolicitors.co.uk
List of partners: D Caplin
Work: G H
Agency, Advocacy, Legal Aid undertaken and Legal Aid Franchise
Ptr: Caplin, Mr David LLB . . . . *Nov 1993

CUTTLE & CO ‡
21 St Johns Street Manchester Greater Manchester M3 4DT
Tel: 0161 835 2050 *Fax:* 0161 831 7986
Emergency telephone 0161 835 2922

See p112 for the Key to Work Categories & other symbols

E-mail: cuttles@btconnect.com
List of partners: M B Cuttle, S Durham, M McQuillan, R G Williamson
Office: Oldham
Languages: French
Work: B1 C1 D1 E F1 G H J1 K1 L N O Q R1 S1 T1 W Z(j,k,l)
Emergency Action, Agency, Advocacy, Fixed Fee Interview, Legal Aid undertaken, Legal Aid Franchise and Member of Accident Line
Ptr: Cuttle, Mr Malcolm B . . . . Jan 1963
McQuillan, Mr Michael LLB . . . . Dec 1975
Williamson, Mr Richard G LLB . . . . *Jul 1980

DAC BEACHCROFT
3 Hardman Street Manchester Greater Manchester M3 3HF
Tel: 0161 934 3000 **Fax:** 0161 934 3288 **Dx:** 14341 MANCHESTER 1
Office: Birmingham, Bristol, Leeds, London EC3 (3 offices), London EC4 (2 offices), Manchester, Newcastle upon Tyne, Newport, Winchester
Languages: French, German, Italian, Spanish
Work: B1 C1 C2 C3 D1 E F1 I J1 K1 L M1 M2 N O P Q R1 S1 T1 T2 W Z(a,b,c,d,e,h,i,j,k,l,o,t)
Emergency Action, Advocacy, Legal Aid undertaken and Member of Accident Line
Ptr: Cole, Ms Paula M LLB(B'ham) . . . . *Oct 1986
Hely, Mrs Deborah BA . . . . *Aug 1990
Jenkins, Miss Susan Anne . . . . *Oct 1990
Key, Miss Alison Mary LLB(Hons) . . . . Oct 1997
Levinson, Mr Jan Matthew LLB(Hons); LSF . . . . *Nov 1992
McConkey, Mr Ian F BA(Dunelm) . . . . Nov 1992
Moore, Mr Iain C MA(Oxon) . . . . *Apr 1981
Moss, Mr Robert J LLB(Hull) . . . . *Sep 1985
Porter, Mrs Leila LLB(Leeds) . . . . *Nov 1983
Sinker, Ms Corrinne Louise LLB; Dip PI . . . . *Sep 1993
Wallbank, Mr Adrian . . . . Jan 1995
Ast: Legge, Mr Michael . . . . Jul 2008
Con: Birchall, Mr Stephen J MA(Cantab) . . . . *Oct 1982
Lindsay, Mr Peter S LLB . . . . *Oct 1983

DAC BEACHCROFT
60 Fountain Street Manchester Greater Manchester M2 2FE
Tel: 0161 839 8396 **Fax:** 0161 839 8309 **Dx:** 14363 MANCHESTER
Office: Birmingham, Bristol, Leeds, London EC3 (3 offices), London EC4 (2 offices), Manchester, Newcastle upon Tyne, Newport, Winchester
Languages: Afrikaans, Arabic, Catalan, Danish, Dutch, French, German, Greek, Gujarati, Hebrew, Hindi, Irish, Italian, Japanese, Latin, Norwegian, Portuguese, Punjabi, Russian, Spanish, Swedish, Welsh
Work: A3 B1 C1 C2 C3 E F1 I J1 L M1 M2 N O P Q R1 T1 Z(b,c,e,g,h,j,k,m)
Agency undertaken
Ptr: Hughes, Ms Lesley Anne . . . . *Oct 1990
Ast: Fleming, Miss Alison Marie LLB . . . . *§Oct 1994

DLA PIPER UK LLP
101 Barbirolli Square Bridgewater Manchester Greater Manchester M2 3DL
Tel: 0870 011 1111 **Fax:** 0161 235 4111 **Dx:** 14304 MANCHESTER
Emergency telephone 0870 011 1111
E-mail: roy.beckett@dlapiper.com
Office: Birmingham, Leeds, Liverpool, London EC2, Sheffield
Languages: French, Spanish
Work: A1 B1 C1 C2 C3 E F1 F2 J1 J2 L M1 M2 N O P Q R1 R2 S1 T1 W X Z(a,b,c,d,e,f,j,k,l,n,o,p,q,u)
Ptr: Arnison, Mr Robert W H . . . . *Jul 1999
Beckett, Mr Roy G LLB(Manc) . . . . *Oct 1983
Bowes, Mr Christopher G . . . . Sep 1997
Brierley, Mr Lee D LLB(Manc) . . . . *Nov 1988
Buckingham, Mr Timothy D LLB . . . . *Sep 1992
Christmas, Mr Matthew . . . . Sep 1999
Clarke, Ms Mary F BA(Oxon) . . . . *Feb 1985
Cowell, Mr Liam . . . . Oct 1996
Crossley, Mr Neil Andrew MA(Cantab) . . . . *Oct 1995
Devlin, Mr Stephen LLB(Hons) . . . . *Mar 1982
Dowle, Mr Paul William BA; BCL . . . . Sep 1996
Duffy, Mr Patrick LLB . . . . *Dec 1992
Eatough, Mr Jonathan Marcus LLB; DipLG . . . . *Jan 1993
Gray, Mr David J LLB . . . . *Nov 1986
Hall, Ms Helen . . . . Oct 1996
Hallam, Mr Martin C LLB . . . . *§Mar 1979
Harris, Mr Andrew D BSocSc(Keele); LLM(Bris) . . . . *§Nov 1985
Harris, Mr Jeremy J MA(Oxon); Jurisprudence Sweet & Maxwell Law Prize (Oxford University); Winter Williams Law Prize . . . . *Apr 1990
Hemsted, Mr Mark . . . . Oct 1999
Hyde, Mr W John A LLB(Lond) . . . . *Oct 1986
Jennings, Mr Steven P LLB; ACIArb . . . . *§Jan 1982
Keates, Mr Martin C LLB . . . . *Mar 1989
Kerrigan, Mr James Edward . . . . Jul 1994
Maka, Mr Yunus . . . . Sep 2000
Montorio, Ms Elia LLB(Hons) . . . . *Nov 1989
Morgan, Mr Matthew J . . . . Oct 1997
Muttock, Mr Robert M LLB(Hons) . . . . Nov 1991
Orchison, Mr Graeme W E LLB(Hons) . . . . *Feb 1988
Owen, Ms Polly . . . . Jan 1994
Pattinson, Mr Andrew E LLB . . . . *Nov 1989
Plant, Mr J Stewart F LLB(Hons) . . . . *Oct 1990
Rimmer, Mr Paul . . . . Oct 1995
Rout, Mr Peter J BA(Oxon) . . . . *Oct 1991
Scheiwiller, Mr Hans R BA(Dunelm) . . . . *Oct 1985
Shepherd, Mr Neal P LLB . . . . *Oct 1988
Smyth, Mr Richard BA . . . . *Dec 1977
Somekh, Mr Peter A N BA(Hons) . . . . *Nov 1992
Sweeney, Ms Liz . . . . Apr 2000
Thompson, Mr David BA(Oxon) . . . . *Nov 1992
Tinker, Mr Michael D LLB . . . . *Oct 1989
Watkins, Mr Jonathan . . . . Jan 1996
Weightman, Ms Anita LLB(Hons) . . . . *Oct 1989
Weightman, Mr Antony S LLB . . . . *Oct 1989

DRG SOLICITORS LLP ‡
3rd Floor Kenworthy Buildings 83 Bridge Street Manchester Greater Manchester M3 2RF
Tel: 0870 060 6075 **Fax:** 0161 834 4666

DWF
1 Scott Place 2 Hardman Street Manchester Greater Manchester M3 3AA
Tel: 0161 603 5000 **Fax:** 0161 603 5050 **Dx:** 14313 MANCHESTER
E-mail: enquiries@dwf.co.uk
Office: Leeds, Liverpool, London EC4, Newcastle upon Tyne, Preston
Work: A1 A3 B1 B2 C1 C2 C3 E F1 F2 G I J1 J2 L M1 N O P Q R1 R2 S1 S2 T1 T2 U2 W X Z(b,c,d,e,f,h,i,j,k,l,o,p,q,r,s,w,y)
Emergency Action, Agency, Advocacy and Fixed Fee Interview undertaken
Ptr: Astbury, Mr David BA(Dunelm) . . . . *Apr 1993
Bochenski, Mr Anthony J J LLB(Sheff) . . . . *Apr 1976
Davidson Lund, Mr David LLB . . . . *§Apr 1981
Davies, Mr James C M David Lobley Debating Prize . . . . *§Mar 1971
Davies, Mr Mark J LLB . . . . *Oct 1990
Denyer, Mr Simon J LLB . . . . *Oct 1984
Dodds, Mr Gareth David LLB . . . . *Oct 1996
Gregory, Mr Andrew H BA; LLB(L'pool) . . . . *Jul 1983
Groch, Mr Steffan LLB(Hons) . . . . Jul 1995
Lagar, Mr Christopher Michael . . . . Mar 1997
Lawrenson, Mrs Katharine LLB . . . . *Dec 1992
Leaitherland, Mr Andrew LLB(Hons); LLM; DipLaw . . . . *Oct 1995
Macalister, Mr Ian LLB(Hons) . . . . *Oct 1987
McCubbin, Mr Ian LLB(Hons) . . . . *Sep 1996
Maguire, Mr Roland D LLB(Hons) . . . . *Dec 1991
Malia, Ms Susan M C LLB . . . . *Oct 1986
Moore, Mr Peter G MCIArb . . . . *§Jan 1971
Needham, Mr E Andrew MA; LLB(Cantab) . . . . *§Jun 1975
Parker, Miss Susan K LLB . . . . Dec 1982
Prendergast, Mr Simon Anthony C MA(Hons) . . . . Nov 1994
Slater, Mr Ian LLB(Hons) ♦ . . . . *Oct 1992
Walshe, Mr Kieran Patrick . . . . Sep 1996
Wellman, Mr Ross H BA(Econ & Social History) . . . . *Oct 1987
Wild, Ms Andrea Louise LLB . . . . *Oct 1996
Williams, Mr Christopher James . . . . May 1994
Williamson, Ms Sharon Diane LLB . . . . *Nov 1990
Wood, Mr David L LLB(Leeds) . . . . *Oct 1983
Yates, Mr Matthew James BA(Hons) . . . . *Nov 1994
Asoc: Fusco, Miss Alexandra LLB(Lond) . . . . *§Sep 1998
Kapoor, Mrs Leena LLB; LLM . . . . Oct 1993
Olive, Mr David H LLB . . . . *§Jun 1983
Shuttleworth, Ms Catherine Wendy LLB(Hons) . . . . May 1993
Ast: Allsup, Mr Roger N LLB(Hons)(Manc) . . . . *Nov 1988
Asquith, Mr Marc LLB(Hons); BVC . . . . Oct 1999
Barrett, Miss Elizabeth LLB(Hons) . . . . Oct 2001
Carney, Mr Paul B BA(Hons); MPhil . . . . Sep 1999
Clark, Mr Michael A LLB(Hons) . . . . *Oct 2001
Clayton, Miss Sarah Frances BA; CPE . . . . Dec 1999
Colville, Mr Mitchell LLB(Hons) Solicitor of the Supreme Court of Northern Ireland . . . . *Nov 1990
Courtier, Ms Alison Jane MA(Hons) . . . . *Oct 1995
Foster, Mr Stephen James LLB . . . . *Sep 1999
Frew, Mr Joseph William . . . . Oct 2002
Fyles, Miss Helen Elizabeth BA(Hons); LLM(European Law) . . . . Nov 1998
Gelling, Mr Peter R MA(Oxon) . . . . *Jun 1970
Gidman, Mr Paul James BA(Hons) . . . . *Oct 2001
Gillis, Mr Ian F LLB Ede & Ravenscroft Prize . . . . *Sep 1999
Gummer, Mrs Alison Jane LLB(Hons); DipLP . . . . *Oct 1996
Hacking, Mr Steven Martin LLB . . . . Oct 2002
Higson, Mr Thomas Peter LLB(Hons) . . . . Oct 2002
Horsfall, Mr Peter BSc(Hons); PGDip . . . . *Sep 1998
Ingham, Miss Helen Alexandra LLB(Hons) . . . . *Feb 2001
Irving, Mr Neil BLC; LLB; LLM; South African Attorney . *Sep 2000
Jarman, Mr Stephen Anthony LLB(Hons) . . . . *Apr 1991
Jones, Mr Dominic BA(Hons) . . . . Sep 1997
Jones, Mr Michael LLB . . . . Aug 1996
Jones, Mr Peter Morgan LLB . . . . Oct 1993
Kenworthy, Mr Peter Robert BA(Hons) . . . . *Dec 1994
Knowles, Mr Timothy J BSc . . . . *Jan 1997
Laing, Mrs Neeta BA(Hons); CIPS . . . . Sep 2000
Lambe, Mr William John LLB(Hons); LLM . . . . Nov 2000
Luthra, Miss Sonia LLB(Hons); LLM University Prize for Best Law with French Graduate . . . . May 2002
Mason, Mr Paul Nicolas John LLB(Hull) . . . . *§Nov 1986
Pearce, Ms Joanne Catherine BA(Hons)(Cantab); LPC Nov 1999
Shearing, Miss Lynne T LLB . . . . *Oct 1999
Sherville-Payne, Mrs Kate LLB(Hons) . . . . *Mar 1997
Smith, Ms Paula Jane LLB . . . . Sep 1998
Sowerby, Miss Joanna Robyn LLB(Hons) . . . . Mar 1997
Truscott, Mr James C MA(Oxon) . . . . *Sep 1998
Venables, Mr Henry . . . . Sep 2005
Walsh, Mr John MA(Oxon) . . . . *Dec 1976

DAR & CO ‡
171 Wilmslow Road Rusholme Manchester Greater Manchester M14 5AP
Tel: 0161 225 3777 **Fax:** 0161 257 2375
E-mail: info@darsolicitors.co.uk
List of partners: J Benoy, M Z Dar
Languages: Malayalam, Punjabi, Urdu
Work: N S1 S2 W
Ptr: Benoy, Mr Jose . . . . Jan 2007
Dar, Mr Mohammed Zahid . . . . Mar 1990

PAUL DARNBOROUGH SOLICITORS ‡
125 Egerton Road South Chorlton Cum Hardy Manchester Greater Manchester M21 0XN
Tel: 0161 881 9479 **Fax:** 0161 881 9479 **Dx:** 22406 CHORLTON
E-mail: info@pdsolicitors.co.uk

GEORGE DAVIES SOLICITORS LLP ‡
8th Floor 1 New York Street Manchester Greater Manchester M1 4AD
Tel: 0161 236 8992 **Fax:** 0161 228 0030 **Dx:** 14316 MANCHESTER 1
E-mail: mail@georgedavies.co.uk
List of partners: S Barrett, P A Bibby, R C B Charrot, N S Collins, A P Fairhurst, A P Hall, C Hanratty, J E Hewison, M A Hovell, J E Kay, S Legge, A Lewis, S J McCann, S J Rearden, C Ross, Z I Siddiqui, C Wilkinson
Languages: French, German, Punjabi, Urdu
Work: B1 C1 C2 C3 D1 D2 E F1 I J1 K1 K2 K3 K4 L M1 M2 N O P Q R1 R2 S1 S2 T1 T2 U2 W X Z(b,c,d,e,f,k,l,o,p,q,r,w)
Emergency Action, Agency, Advocacy, Fixed Fee Interview and Legal Aid Franchise
Ptr: Barrett, Mrs Sara BA . . . . *Sep 1996
Bibby, Mr Paul Anthony . . . . Jan 1998
Charrot, Mr Robin Charles B LLB(Hons) . . . . Feb 1997
Collins, Ms Nicola Susan LLB . . . . Sep 1996
Fairhurst, Ms Anne P BA(Nott'm) Part time Chairman of SSAT . . . . *Mar 1982
Hall, Mr Anthony P MA(Cantab) . . . . *Nov 1986
Hanratty, Mrs Caroline LLB . . . . Sep 1994
Hewison, Mr John E LLB(Nott'm) . . . . *Apr 1973
Hovell, Mr Mark Andrew BSc(Hons) . . . . *Sep 1991
Kay, Mr Jonathan Edward LLB(Hons) . . . . *Oct 1994
Legge, Ms Shelagh LLB . . . . *Dec 1986
Lewis, Mr Alan . . . . *Jan 2002
McCann, Mr Stephen J LLB(Leics) . . . . *Apr 1978
Ross, Mr Christopher BA(Hons)(History); CPE; LPC . . . . Sep 2002
Siddiqui, Miss Zahra Itrat BA(Hons) . . . . *Sep 1997
Wilkinson, Mr Chris LLB(Hons) . . . . Jan 1990
Dir: Rearden, Mr Shaun James LLB Maxwell Law Prize . . . . *Dec 1979
Asoc: Aucott, Mrs Kimberley LLB(Hons) . . . . *Jan 1989
Banday, Mrs Zara LLB(Hons); LPC . . . . *Nov 2003
Fyles, Miss Helen Elizabeth BA(Hons); LLM(European Law) . . . . Nov 1998
Kay, Miss Catherine LLB . . . . Jan 1996
Lewis, Ms Jennifer BA(Hons)(English Lit/Philosophy); PGDipLaw; CPE; LPC . . . . Sep 2005
Morrison, Mrs Sandra LLB; Rechtsanwaltin . . . . Nov 1997
Parry, Mr Kelvin Thomas LLB . . . . Oct 2007
Robinson, Miss Louise LLB; LPC . . . . Sep 2003
Ast: Baxter, Mrs Helen LLB; LPC . . . . *Sep 2008
Burdett, Miss Nicole LLB . . . . Mar 2008
Chantler, Mr Matthew Jon Kenneth LLB . . . . Sep 2009
Chapman, Mr Michael LLB . . . . Apr 2005
Coyne, Mrs Deborah LLB; DIP . . . . *Sep 2004
Easdown, Mr David LLB(Hons) . . . . Sep 2007
Edwards, Miss Katie BA(Hons)(History); GDL; LPC . . Sep 2009
Farrelly, Mrs Lindsey . . . . Jan 2001
Goodman, Miss Fay LLB; PGDipLP . . . . Sep 2008
Hawkridge, Mr Richard Michael LLB . . . . Sep 2009
Khalid, Ms Tasnim LLB . . . . Jun 2009
Knowles, Mr James BA(Hons)(History & Politics); CPE; LPC . . . . Sep 2004
Lang, Mr Seb BSc(Psychology); LLB . . . . Sep 2010
Mason, Mrs Samantha Judith BA . . . . Nov 2000
Mongan, Miss Rachael BVC(Business with Law); BSc; GDL/LPC . . . . Sep 2009
Pinney, Ms Caroline . . . . Jan 1996
Sealy, Mr Alexander William PGDipLaw; LPC . . . . Aug 2002
Webb, Miss Louisa LLB(Hons) Hammonds LPC Prize for Business Law & Practice (Birmingham College of Law) 2004 . . . . *Sep 2006
Wirth, Ms Christina GDL; LPC . . . . *Sep 2010
Worrall, Mr Philip David BA(Law) . . . . Oct 1984
Yates, Mr Charlie BA; PGDipLP . . . . Sep 2008
Con: Howorth, Mr Charles R A . . . . *Jan 1974
Nicholls, Mr Walter . . . . Jan 1965

DAVIS BLANK FURNISS ‡
Church House 90 Deansgate Manchester Greater Manchester M3 2QJ
Tel: 0161 832 3304 **Fax:** 0161 834 3568 **Dx:** 14311 MANCHESTER
E-mail: manchester@dbf-law.co.uk
List of partners: K N Evans, M R Gee, R D Hamilton, J R C Litherland, T J McConnell, A E McNish, E K Oldfield, G R J Robson, A G Ryan, S Shadi, S L L Shalom, S Singh, K Witter, S Wood
Office: Glossop
Languages: French
Work: A1 A3 B1 C1 C2 E F1 J1 J2 K1 K2 K3 L N O Q R2 S1 S2 W Z(b,i,l,q)
Emergency Action, Advocacy, Fixed Fee Interview, Legal Aid Franchise and Member of Accident Line
Ptr: Hamilton, Mr Richard Domin LLB . . . . *Sep 2003
McConnell, Mr Timothy J LLB . . . . *§Jun 1980
McNish, Mr Andrew Edward LLB . . . . *Nov 1991
Oldfield, Miss E Kate LLB . . . . *Nov 1989
Robson, Mr Guy R J BA . . . . *§Jun 1973
Ryan, Mr Andrew G BSc . . . . *Dec 1992
Shadi, Miss Shiva LLB . . . . *Sep 1999
Shalom, Mr Stuart L L LLB . . . . *Jun 1978
Singh, Mr Sonio . . . . Mar 1999
Witter, Karen . . . . Sep 2005
Asoc: Bunting, Miss Anna LLB . . . . *Sep 2003
Ast: Reddington, Miss Claire LLB . . . . Jan 2006
Williams, Miss Caroline Sarah LLB . . . . May 2008
Con: Alcock, Mr John H MA(Oxon); ACIA . . . . *§Mar 1972
Heginbotham, Mr Peter OBE LLB . . . . *§Oct 1970
Hilton, Mr Robert Ian BA . . . . *Dec 1977
Jones, Mr Grahame M LLB . . . . *§Jun 1969
Walton, Mr Paul LLB . . . . *§Jun 1969
White, Mr Albert Joseph . . . . *Jan 1965

DENNISON GREER SOLICITORS ‡
Castlefield House Liverpool Road Manchester Greater Manchester M3 4SB
Tel: 0845 807 7788 **Fax:** 0845 807 8877 **Dx:** 14307 MANCHESTER
E-mail: info@dennisongreer.com

DIDSBURY FAMILY LAW ‡
833 Wilmslow Road Didsbury Manchester Greater Manchester M20 5WD
Tel: 0161 434 0600 **Fax:** 0161 434 1297
E-mail: info@didsburyfamilylaw.com

DONNS ‡
(incorporating Fitton & Bennett)
PO Box 41 The Observatory Chapel Walks Manchester Greater Manchester M60 1DZ
Tel: 0161 834 3311 **Fax:** 0161 834 2317 **Dx:** 14312 MANCHESTER 1
Emergency telephone 0161 834 3311
E-mail: lawyers@donnslaw.co.uk
List of partners: A Anson, A T Bradley, N M Close, A L De Vos, R L Donn, S B Forman, K Hopkins, C E Layfield, N A Lunt, A H Nayyar, A S Warchester
Work: N W Z(r)
Emergency Action, Legal Aid undertaken, Legal Aid Franchise and Member of Accident Line
Ptr: Anson, Miss Amanda LLB(Hons) . . . . *Mar 1998
Bradley, Miss Anne Teresa LLB(Hons) . . . . *Oct 1994
Close, Mr Nicholas Martin LLB . . . . Mar 1984
De Vos, Ms Adrienne Lesley LLB(Hons) . . . . Oct 1987
Donn, Mr Raymond L Chairman of the Royal British Legions Solicitors Referral Panel . . . . *Nov 1969
Forman, Mrs Stephanie B BA(Essex) . . . . *Jun 1988
Hopkins, Miss Katherine LLB(Hons) Councillor for the Borough of High Peak . . . . Feb 1998
Layfield, Mr Charles Edward BSc . . . . *Mar 1999
Lunt, Ms Nicola Anne FILEx; CPE; Dip PI Lit . . . . *Oct 2000
Nayyar, Mrs Ayesha Hannah LLB(Hons) . . . . *Oct 1999
Warchester, Ms Adele Susan BA(Hons)(Law) . . . . *Jun 1977

DRAYCOTT BROWNE SOLICITORS ‡
12 Oxford Court Manchester Greater Manchester M2 3WQ
Tel: 0161 228 2244 **Fax:** 0161 228 1144 **Dx:** 14376 MANCHESTER
Emergency telephone 0161 833 1333
E-mail: enquiries@draycottbrowne.co.uk
List of partners: M D Browne, S D Draycott, S Fagan, P A Gibbon, R H Mann, E M Riding, E Wright
Office: Sale
Languages: French, Russian, Spanish
Work: B2 G H K1 K3 N O Q
Emergency Action, Agency, Advocacy, Legal Aid undertaken and Legal Aid Franchise
Ptr: Browne, Mr Mark Damen LLB(Hons) . . . . *Feb 1990
Draycott, Mr Shaun Damian LLB ♦ . . . . *Jul 1996
Fagan, Mr Simon . . . . Jul 2001

Gibbon, Mr Paul Anthony LLB(Hons) . . . . *Sep 1985
Mann, Mr Robert H MA(Oxon). . . . . Feb 1965
Riding, Miss Elizabeth Mary LLB(Hons) . . . . *Oct 1991
Wright, Mr Evan. . . . . Jun 1997

KEITH DYSON & CO ‡
Northgate Chambers 39 Liverpool Road Castlefield Manchester Greater Manchester M3 4NQ
Tel: 0161 832 9933 *Fax:* 0161 839 1099
Dx: 728856 MANCHESTER 4
List of partners: K Dyson
Ptr: Dyson, Mr Keith. . . . . Oct 1976

E&K SOLICITORS & ESTATE AGENTS ‡
45 Wilmslow Road Manchester Greater Manchester M14 5TB
Tel: 0161 256 3915 *Fax:* 0870 382 1778 *Dx:* 28614 WITHINGTON
E-mail: info@eandksolicitors.co.uk
List of partners: A Egan, R Khurshid
Languages: Punjabi, Urdu
Work: G N Q S1 S2 W
Agency and Fixed Fee Interview undertaken
Ptr: Egan, Miss Andrea BA; DipLaw. . . . . *Jun 2001
Khurshid, Raza . . . . *Apr 2002

EDEN & CO ‡
34 Oxford Street Manchester Greater Manchester M1 5EL
Tel: 0161 237 1116 *Fax:* 0161 237 1099 *Dx:* 18576 MANCHESTER 7
List of partners: J W Eden, C A King
Work: M1 P S1
Fixed Fee Interview, Legal Aid undertaken and Member of Accident Line
Ptr: Eden, Mr Jack W LLB. . . . . *Oct 1975
King, Mr Colin A MA(Oxon) . . . . *Nov 1982
Ast: Gratton, Ms Elizabeth A LLB(L'pool). . . . . May 1979

ENDLARS ‡
86a Bury Old Road Cheetham Village Manchester Greater Manchester M8 5BW
Tel: 0161 795 4333 *Fax:* 0161 720 6656
E-mail: mail@endlars-solicitors.co.uk
List of partners: I D Endlar
Work: D1 E F1 G H K1 L N O Q S1 W
Emergency Action, Agency, Advocacy, Fixed Fee Interview and Legal Aid undertaken
Ptr: Endlar, Mr Ian D. . . . . *Nov 1984

ENTRUST PENSION RECOVERY LIMITED ‡
St James Court 30 Brown Street Manchester Greater Manchester M2 2JF
Tel: 0870 365 8000

ENVIRONMENTAL LAW CONSULTANCY ‡
23 Clarendon Road West Manchester Greater Manchester M21 0RN
Tel: 0845 860 0595
Emergency telephone 07712 661921
E-mail: kd@envsupport.com
Work: J2 P
Con: Davidson, Mr Keith LLB; LLM(Env) . . . . Dec 1995

EVERSHEDS LLP
Eversheds House 70 Great Bridgewater Street Manchester Greater Manchester M1 5ES
Tel: 0845 497 9797 *Fax:* 0161 831 8888
Dx: 14344 MANCHESTER 1
Office: Birmingham, Cambridge, Cardiff, Ipswich, Leeds, London EC2, Newcastle upon Tyne, Nottingham
Work: A1 E L R1 S1 Z(h)

EXPRESS SOLICITORS ‡
Hatro House 319 Palatine Road Manchester Greater Manchester M22 4HH
Tel: 0800 158 5274 *Fax:* 0161 945 2266
E-mail: advice@expresssolicitors.com

FARLEY DWEK LLP ‡
1st Floor Suite 1.2 1 Universal Square Manchester Greater Manchester M12 6JH
Tel: 0161 272 5222 *Fax:* 0161 272 5225
E-mail: andrew@farleydwek.com

FARLEYS SOLICITORS LLP
1st Floor North Parade Parsonage Gardens Manchester Greater Manchester M3 2NH
Tel: 0161 660 4254 *Fax:* 0161 839 9484
E-mail: info@farleys.com
Office: Accrington, Blackburn (3 offices), Burnley
Ptr: Bridge, Mr Jonathan D LLB(Hons). . . . . *Dec 1992
Ast: Kenyon, Miss Alexandra LLB(Hons). . . . . *Aug 2010
Skinner, Mr Mark LLB(Hons) . . . . *Mar 2004
Vine, Mrs Gemma LLB(Hons). . . . . *Jul 2010
Whittingham, Miss Ruth Margaret LLB(Hons); LPG; DipLaw . . . . *Oct 2001

FARRELL & HOBBS ‡
Xenon House 10 School Lane Didsbury Manchester Greater Manchester M20 6RD
Tel: 0161 445 1000 *Fax:* 0161 446 2243 *Dx:* 23154 DIDSBURY
Emergency telephone 07850 864 694
E-mail: info@farrellhobbs.co.uk
List of partners: F P T Farrell, D Hobbs
Work: B1 C1 C2 E G H J1 K1 L N O Q S1 V W Z(c,h,l)
Emergency Action, Agency, Advocacy and Legal Aid undertaken
Ptr: Farrell, Mr Fergal P T LLB. . . . . *Nov 1984
Hobbs, Mr David LLB . . . . *Nov 1983

FENTONS
5th Floor Trafford House Chester Road Manchester Greater Manchester M32 0RS
Tel: 0161 786 8320 *Dx:* 29222 STRETFORD
Office: Failsworth
Work: N
Ast: Ark, Mr Sukwinder. . . . . Mar 2003
Wilson, Ms Naomi Jade. . . . . Dec 1999

FENTONS SOLICITORS LLP ‡
Aurora Building 55 Princess Street Manchester Greater Manchester M2 4EW
Tel: 0161 238 6400 *Fax:* 0845 389 9525
Dx: 14445 MANCHESTER 2
E-mail: info@fentons.co.uk

JOAN FERGUSON & CO ‡
481 Cheetham Hill Road Cheetham Hill Manchester Greater Manchester M8 9LR
Tel: 0161 795 5866 *Fax:* 0161 740 4452
E-mail: jferguson@btconnect.com
List of partners: J M Ferguson
Languages: Cantonese, Gujarati
Work: D1 K1 K2 S1 V W
Emergency Action, Agency, Advocacy, Legal Aid undertaken and Legal Aid Franchise
Ptr: Ferguson, Miss Joan Margaret LLM; LLB(Hons). . . . *Jun 1970
Ast: Limbada, Miss Ayesha LLB . . . . *Nov 1997

FIELD CUNNINGHAM & CO ‡
St Johns Court 70 Quay Street Manchester Greater Manchester M3 3EJ
Tel: 0161 834 4734 *Fax:* 0161 834 1772

ANDREW FITZPATRICK ‡
349 Claremont Road Rusholme Manchester Greater Manchester M14 7NB
Tel: 0161 248 9799 *Fax:* 0161 248 5785 *Dx:* 813175 DUBLIN
Emergency telephone 07644 068510
E-mail: fitzpatrick.solicitors@virgin.net
List of partners: A J Fitzpatrick
Work: G Z(g)
Emergency Action, Agency, Advocacy, Fixed Fee Interview and Legal Aid undertaken
Ptr: Fitzpatrick, Mr Andrew J LLB ★. . . . . *Jan 1985

FORBES
Church House 90 Deansgate Manchester Greater Manchester M3 2GP
Tel: 0161 918 0000 *Fax:* 0161 918 0011 *Dx:* 14322 MANCHESTER
E-mail: andrew.ellis@forbessolicitors.co.uk
Office: Accrington (2 offices), Blackburn (3 offices), Chorley, Leeds, Preston

FORD BANKS IRWIN ‡
50 Stothard Road Manchester Greater Manchester M32 9HB
Tel: 0161 866 8999 *Fax:* 0161 866 8333
Emergency telephone 07901 910710
E-mail: info@fordbanksirwin.eclipse.co.uk
List of partners: M Afzal, T Hussain
Work: A3 C1 C2 C3 E M1 M2 M3 N O P Q R1 R2 S1 S2 U1 U2 Z(a,b,e,j,k,q,r)
Emergency Action, Agency, Advocacy, Fixed Fee Interview undertaken and Member of Accident Line
Ptr: Afzal, Mr Mohammed LLB(Hons) ♦ . . . . *Nov 1991
Hussain, Tassadaq LLB(Hons); DipLP ♦. . . . . Aug 1998

FOX WHITFIELD ‡
Adamson House Towers Business Park Wilmslow Road Manchester Greater Manchester M20 2YY
Tel: 0161 283 1276 *Fax:* 0161 210 2914
E-mail: info@foxwhitfield.com

FREECLAIM SOLICITORS
Alderman Gatley House Civic Centre Hale Top Manchester Greater Manchester M22 5RW
Tel: 0161 437 9999 *Fax:* 0161 436 3332
Office: Manchester, Stockport
Ptr: Barstow, Mr John . . . . Nov 1993
Fernie, Mr Alistair William. . . . . Jun 1996
Tranter, Mr Stephen BA . . . . Apr 1982

FREEMAN & CO ‡
8 Oxford Court Manchester Greater Manchester M2 3WQ
Tel: 0161 236 7007 *Fax:* 0161 236 0440
List of partners: N Freeman
Dir: Freeman, Mr Nicholas. . . . . Jun 1981

FREEMAN KEEP ON DRIVING LTD ‡
8 Oxford Court Bishopsgate Manchester Greater Manchester M2 3WQ
Tel: 0161 233 2130 *Fax:* 0161 233 2139
E-mail: enquiries@freemankeepondriving.com
List of partners: N Freeman
Dir: Freeman, Mr Nicholas. . . . . Jun 1981

FREETH CARTWRIGHT LLP
First Floor St James' Building 61-95 Oxford Street Manchester Greater Manchester M1 6FQ
Tel: 0845 634 2540 *Fax:* 0845 634 2541
E-mail: postmaster@freethcartwright.co.uk
Office: Birmingham, Derby, Leicester, Nottingham
Ptr: Byrne, Mr Joseph Oliver Gerard BBS . . . . Sep 1996
Calladine, Mr Paul . . . . Oct 1986
Jones, Mrs Patricia Ann LLB . . . . §Sep 1990
Whitton, Mrs Sheila May FILEx . . . . *Oct 1995

FRUHMAN DAVIES LIVINGSTONES ‡
Blackfriars House Parsonage Manchester Greater Manchester M3 2JA
Tel: 0161 833 0578 *Fax:* 0161 828 1500
Dx: 14306 MANCHESTER 1
E-mail: martyn.caplan@fdl-law.co.uk
List of partners: M L Abel, M B Caplan, H Cohen, J J Davies, S H Fruhman
Languages: French, German, Hebrew
Work: B1 C1 C2 D1 E F1 F2 I J1 K1 K3 L N O P Q R1 S1 S2 T1 T2 U1 U2 W Z(b,c,e,f,i,j,k,l,o,p,q,t,w,za)
Agency undertaken
Ptr: Abel, Mr Malcolm L LLB John Peacock Conveyancing Prize . . . . §Apr 1969
Caplan, Mr Martyn B LLB . . . . *Apr 1987
Cohen, Mr Harvey LLB Notary Public . . . . *Apr 1980
Davies, Mr Jonathan J LLB . . . . *Nov 1971
Fruhman, Mr Steven H LLB . . . . *May 1971
Asoc: Wong, Ann . . . . *Feb 1996
Ziskind, David. *Nov 2000
Ast: Hession, Ms Marlene . . . . *Apr 2000
Lee, Mei Ling . . . . *Jul 2008
Peeling, Zoe . . . . *Sep 2007
Con: Saperia, Martin . . . . *Mar 1991

FURNESS EVANS
Bank Chambers 90 Liverpool Road Cadishead Manchester Greater Manchester M44 5AN
E-mail: furnessevans@btconnect.com
Office: Irlam, Marple, New Mills
Ptr: Moore, Suzanne J. . . . . Jan 1998

GLP SOLICITORS ‡
85 Chapel Street Manchester Greater Manchester M3 5DF
Tel: 0161 834 6721 *Fax:* 0161 834 2015 *Dx:* 25593 MANCHESTER
List of partners: E Clifford, M J Cohen, S B N Fagelman, D H Foster, G S Leigh, J P Pfeffer, P A Wainwright
Office: Bury, Manchester (3 offices), Middleton, Prestwich
Languages: French, German
Work: B1 C1 C2 D1 E F1 G H J1 K1 L N O Q R1 S1 V W Z(c,d,e,f,g,k,p)
Emergency Action, Agency, Advocacy, Fixed Fee Interview, Legal Aid undertaken, Legal Aid Franchise and Member of Accident Line
Ptr: Leigh, Mr Graham S BA. . . . . *Dec 1981
Wainwright, Mr Paul A LLB . . . . *Sep 1990
Ast: Kelly, Mr Terence Andrew LLB(Hons) . . . . *Feb 1996

GLP SOLICITORS
672 Bolton Road Pendlebury Manchester Greater Manchester M27 8FH
Tel: 0161 793 0901 *Fax:* 0161 794 4779
E-mail: sf@glplaw.com
Office: Bury, Manchester (3 offices), Middleton, Prestwich
Work: C1 D1 E F1 J1 J2 K1 L N O P Q S1 V W Z(q,r)
Emergency Action, Agency, Advocacy, Fixed Fee Interview, Legal Aid undertaken, Legal Aid Franchise and Member of Accident Line
Ptr: Fagelman, Mr Sheldon B N LLB. . . . . *Sep 1988
Ast: Byrne, Mr James Joseph John LLB(Hons). . . . . . . Dec 1991

GLP SOLICITORS
100 Crumpsall Lane Crumpsall Manchester Greater Manchester M8 6SR
Tel: 0161 795 5531 *Fax:* 0161 721 4739
Office: Bury, Manchester (3 offices), Middleton, Prestwich
Work: E F1 G H K1 L M1 S1
Emergency Action, Agency, Advocacy, Fixed Fee Interview, Legal Aid undertaken, Legal Aid Franchise and Member of Accident Line
Ptr: Clifford, Mr Edward LLB. . . . . *Jan 1971
Cohen, Mr Martin J BA . . . . *Jun 1977
Pfeffer, Mr Jonathan P. . . . . *§Jun 1968

GLP SOLICITORS
15 Hulton District Centre Little Hulton Worsley Manchester Greater Manchester M38 0BA
Tel: 0161 703 8677 *Fax:* 0161 702 0190
E-mail: worsley@glplaw.com
Office: Bury, Manchester (3 offices), Middleton, Prestwich
Work: G H J1 K1 L N Q S1 V
Emergency Action, Agency, Advocacy, Legal Aid undertaken and Member of Accident Line
Ast: Woodhouse, Mr Graham . . . . Apr 1993

GR SOLICITORS ‡
489-493 Bolton Road Manchester Greater Manchester M27 8QT
Tel: 0161 793 6565 *Fax:* 0161 793 8866
E-mail: michael.regan@gr-solicitors.com

GARVINS SOLICITORS ‡
The Chambers New Acre House Shentonfield Road Manchester Greater Manchester M22 4RW
Tel: 0161 495 2880 *Fax:* 0161 495 2881
E-mail: info@garvins-solicitors.com
List of partners: N N P Garvin
Mem: Garvin, Mr Neil N P LLB(Hons) . . . . Apr 1997

GATELEY LLP
Ship Canal House 98 King Street Manchester Greater Manchester M2 4WU
Tel: 0161 836 7700 *Fax:* 0161 836 7701 *Dx:* 14317 MANCHESTER 1
E-mail: info@gateleyuk.com
Office: Birmingham, Leicester, London EC4, Nottingham
Ptr: Allen, Ms Janine E LLB . . . . *Sep 1989
Mem: Brown, Mr Nigel W LLB(Lond). . . . . *Dec 1989
Hassall, Miss Elizabeth J LLB. . . . . *May 1988
Rose, Mr Paul M A MA(Oxon). . . . . Apr 1973
Asoc: Maddox, Mr Simon . . . . Sep 2003
Ast: Barnes, Catherine. . . . . Sep 2003
Murrills, Mr Nicholas . . . . Aug 2008

CRAIG GEE ‡
616 Hyde Road Manchester Greater Manchester M18 7EE
Tel: 0161 666 9999 *Fax:* 0161 666 9988
Emergency telephone 07956 976431
E-mail: craig@craiggee.com
List of partners: C Gee
Work: B2 D1 D2 G H J1 K1 L N O Q W Z(p,q)
Emergency Action, Agency, Advocacy, Fixed Fee Interview and Legal Aid undertaken
SPr: Gee, Mr Craig BA(Hons); DipPl . . . . *Sep 1989
Ast: Brown, Miss Angela LLB(Hons) . . . . Apr 2003
Casson, Mr Peter. . . . . Oct 2000

GLAISYERS SOLICITORS LLP ‡
One St James's Square Manchester Greater Manchester M2 6DN
Tel: 0161 832 4666 *Fax:* 0161 832 1981 *Dx:* 14364 MANCHESTER 1
Emergency telephone 07850 554622
E-mail: info@glaisyers.com
List of partners: R M Arnall, J Bond, R W Brown, C J Bryan, C Budsworth, D J Burrows, M N Charlesworth, A J Connolly, E Freeman, N R Johnson, M Key, E Quirk, B E Taylor, E C Waddell
Office: Manchester
Languages: French, Hindi, Spanish, Urdu
Work: A1 A3 B1 C1 C2 D1 E F1 I J1 K1 K2 K3 K4 L M1 N O P Q R1 R2 S1 S2 T1 V W Z(b,c,e,h,i,j,n,p)
Emergency Action, Agency, Advocacy, Fixed Fee Interview, Legal Aid undertaken, Legal Aid Franchise and Member of Accident Line
Ptr: Arnall, Mr Raymond M LLB(Sheff). . . . . *Oct 1982
Bond, Mr Julian MA(Cantab) . . . . *May 1987
Brown, Mr Russell William BA(Hons)(Business Law) *Sep 2000
Burrows, Mr David J LLB(Hons). . . . . *May 1993
Charlesworth, Mr Michael N LLB . . . . *Jun 1981
Connolly, Miss Alison Jane LLB . . . . *Feb 1998
Johnson, Mr Nicholas R BA. . . . . *Oct 1985
Key, Mr Michael LLB(Hons) . . . . *Jun 1998
Quirk, Mr Eric LLB(Lond) . . . . *Mar 1975
Budsworth, Mr Craig . . . . NSP
Ast: Baines, Caroline Susan . . . . Sep 2010
Bentley, Mrs Kate Elizabeth. . . . . Sep 2008
Jenkinson, Miss Hannah Charlotte . . . . Sep 2009
Strangwood, Catherine . . . . *Sep 2004
Young, Miss Sarah Elizabeth . . . . Sep 2009

GLAISYERS SOLICITORS LLP
1st Floor 601 Stockport Road Longsight Manchester Greater Manchester M13 0RX
Tel: 0161 224 3311 *Fax:* 0161 257 3239
E-mail: cjb@glaisyers.com
Office: Manchester

See p112 for the Key to Work Categories & other symbols

Languages: Bengali, French, Punjabi, Urdu
Work: C1 D1 D2 E J1 K1 K2 K3 K4 L M1 O Q S1 S2 V W Z(g,i)
Emergency Action, Agency and Legal Aid undertaken
Ptr: Bryan, Mr Christopher John . . . . Feb 1982
Freeman, Mr Edward BA . . . . May 1979
Taylor, Mr Benedict Edward . . . . Mar 1994
Waddell, Ms Elena Clare LLB . . . . *Apr 1981
Ast: Bilous, Miss Caroline LLB . . . . Sep 2006
Casey, Ms Josephine Elizabeth . . . . Apr 2004
Daly, Miss Joanne Elizabeth . . . . Jan 2005
Donnelly, Miss Leanne . . . . Sep 2010
Exley, Miss Gillian . . . . Mar 2004
Gupta, Ms Sumita BA(Hons) . . . . *Jan 2000
Malik, Miss Sonia . . . . Sep 2008
Morton, Mr Richard David LLB . . . . Sep 1994
Rahman, Miss Sadia LLB; CPC . . . . Sep 2003
Shepherd, Miss Anita Mary BA . . . . May 1999
Theakston, Mr Anthony John BA(Law) . . . . Aug 2002
Vickerman, Miss Catherine A BA(Hons) . . . . *Oct 1980

GOODMAN HARVEY LLP ‡
Old Colony House 6 South King Street Manchester Greater Manchester M2 6DQ
Tel: 0161 819 6622 *Fax:* 0161 819 6644
E-mail: info@goodmanharvey.com

GRAY & CO ‡
3rd Floor Habib House 9 Stevenson Square Manchester Greater Manchester M1 1DB
Tel: 0161 237 3360 *Fax:* 0161 236 6717
Emergency telephone 07711 269939
E-mail: info@grayand.co.uk
List of partners: R A Kidd
Work: B1 C1 E I L O S2 U1 U2 W Z(d,e,f,k,w)
Agency and Fixed Fee Interview undertaken
Ptr: Kidd, Mr Rudolph Anthony HND; LLB(Hons) . . . . *Oct 1994

GREENWOODS
57 Spring Gardens Manchester Greater Manchester M2 2BY
Tel: 0161 245 6520 *Fax:* 0161 245 6550
E-mail: contact@greenwoods-solicitors.com
Office: Bristol, Fareham, London EC3, London WC1, Milton Keynes
Ast: Hardy, Ms Michele LLB(Hons) . . . . *§Jan 1999

HL INTERACTIVE ‡
76 King Street Manchester Greater Manchester M2 4NH
Tel: 0845 365 3869 *Fax:* 0845 365 3870
E-mail: info@hlinteractive.com

HSK SOLICITORS LLP ‡
474 Cheetham Hill Road Cheetham Manchester Greater Manchester M8 9JW
Tel: 0161 795 4818 *Fax:* 0161 740 0450
Dx: 743254 CHEETHAM HILL
E-mail: ged.singh@hsksolicitors.co.uk
List of partners: A Ali, M Dhokia, A Hussain, S Malik, G L Singh
Office: Bolton
Languages: Hindi, Punjabi, Urdu
Work: E J1 K3 N Q S1 S2 Z(i)
Ptr: Ali, Mr Asghar LLB(Hons) . . . . *Jan 2002
Dhokia, Mr Minesh LLB(Hons) . . . . *Nov 2003
Hussain, Mr Ansar LLB(Hons) . . . . *Nov 1983
Malik, Mr Sajid LLB(Hons) . . . . *Oct 2000
Singh, Mr Gurpralad Landa LLB(Hons) . . . . *May 1981
Ast: Landa, Kim Singh LLB(Hons) . . . . *Nov 2006
Malik, Mr Aseid LLB(Hons) . . . . Jan 2007
Patel, Mr Akhter Husain BA(Hons) . . . . Feb 2005
Riaz, Mrs Omera LLB(Hons) . . . . *Nov 2008
Shahbaz, Mrs Parveen Akhtar LLB(Hons) . . . . *Mar 2009

HAGUE LAMBERT
Artillery House 15 Byrom Street Manchester Greater Manchester M3 4PF
Tel: 0161 834 6066 *Fax:* 0161 832 6409 *Dx:* 14336 MANCHESTER 1
E-mail: dsl@hague-lambert.co.uk
Web: www.hague-lambert.co.uk
Office: Knutsford, Macclesfield, Urmston
Work: B1 C1 C2 C3 E F1 J1 L O S1 T1 T2 W X Z(d,e,x)
Fixed Fee Interview undertaken
Ptr: Day, Mr Nigel G S MA(Dundee) . . . . *May 1979
Horton, Mr Philip John . . . . *Mar 1972
Asoc: Jordan, Mr Paul Anthony . . . . *Feb 1971
Ast: Rajput-Driver, Mrs Mala . . . . Sep 2001
Sullivan, Miss Alicia . . . . Jul 2004
Wright, Miss Nicolette J BA . . . . Sep 1992
Con: Lambert, Mr David S LLB(Manc) . . . . *Apr 1973

Offices in Knutsford, Urmston and Macclesfield. Broad based firm offering a wide range of services to both the business and personal client.

HARGREAVES & CO ‡
516 Wilmslow Road Manchester Greater Manchester M20 4BS
Tel: 0161 445 6461 *Fax:* 0161 445 8667
E-mail: geraldpeacock@hargreavesandco.com
List of partners: G D Peacock
Work: E S1 S2 W
SPr: Peacock, Mr Gerald David MA(Oxon) . . . . *Jun 1972

HARGREAVES GILMAN ‡
(incorporating Gilman Wallwork & Tarran & Bale's)
512 Kingsway Didsbury Manchester Greater Manchester M19 1WW
Tel: 0161 443 1711 *Fax:* 0161 443 1839
Emergency telephone 07850 864694 (CRIME)
E-mail: hargreavesgilman@btconnect.com
List of partners: D Millington, F A Rogerson
Work: E G H N S1 S2 T2 W
Agency, Advocacy, Fixed Fee Interview, Legal Aid undertaken and Legal Aid Franchise
Ptr: Millington, Mrs Deborah LLB(Hons) . . . . *Nov 1992
Rogerson, Mr Frank A LLB(Hons) . . . . *Jan 1979
Con: Gilman, Mr Graham A . . . . Nov 1970
Wallwork, Mr Eric . . . . *Nov 1968

HARRISONS SOLICITORS ‡
The Triangle Exchange Square Manchester Greater Manchester M4 3TR
Tel: 0161 819 2511 *Fax:* 0161 819 2522
E-mail: partners@harrisonslawyers.co.uk
List of partners: M W Harrison, T A Harrison
Work: A3 C1 D2 F1 J1 K1 O Q Z(j)
Emergency Action, Agency and Advocacy undertaken
Ptr: Harrison, Mr Martin William MA(Oxon) . . . . *Apr 1984
Harrison, Mrs Teresa Ann MA(Oxon) . . . . Nov 1983

HEANEY WATSON
St John Chambers 2 St John Street Manchester Greater Manchester M3 4DA
Tel: 0800 567 7597 / 0161 359 3347 *Fax:* 0161 839 7234
Dx: 14329 MANCHESTER
E-mail: enquiry@heaneywatson.com
Office: Liverpool (3 offices)
Languages: Hindi, Potwari, Punjabi, Spanish, Urdu
Work: D1 D2 K1 K2 K3
Emergency Action, Agency, Advocacy, Fixed Fee Interview, Legal Aid undertaken and Legal Aid Franchise
Asoc: Fleming, Miss Felicity BA . . . . *Sep 2008

HEATH SONS & BROOME ‡
74-76 Old Church Street Newton Heath Manchester Greater Manchester M40 2JD
Tel: 0161 681 1933 *Fax:* 0161 684 7624 *Dx:* 703122 FAILSWORTH
E-mail: roger.w.lowe@btinternet.com
List of partners: M J Hayes, R W Lowe
Office: Failsworth
Work: B2 D1 E F1 G H K1 K2 N Q S1 S2 W Z(c,f,q)
Emergency Action, Agency, Advocacy, Fixed Fee Interview, Legal Aid undertaken and Member of Accident Line
Ptr: Lowe, Mr Roger W MA(Cantab) . . . . *Jun 1977
Ast: Ford, Mrs Verity M LLB . . . . *Jul 1981

HEATONS LLP ‡
5th Floor Free Trade Exchange 37 Peter Street Manchester Greater Manchester M2 5GB
Tel: 0161 835 8010 *Fax:* 0161 835 8015 *Dx:* 14477 MANCHESTER 2
List of partners: M E Beech, M D Fleetwood
Work: C1
Ptr: Beech, Mr Mark E LLB . . . . *Dec 1986
Fleetwood, Mr Matthew D LLB . . . . Aug 1997

HEMPSONS
14th Floor Portland Tower Portland Street Manchester Greater Manchester M1 3LF
Tel: 0161 228 0011 *Fax:* 0161 236 6734 *Dx:* 14482 MANCHESTER 2
E-mail: enquiries@hempsons.co.uk
Office: Harrogate, London WC2, Newcastle upon Tyne
Languages: French, German, Spanish
Work: B1 B2 C1 D1 E F1 G J1 J2 L N O P Q R1 R2 S2 Z(c,d,h,k,m,p,q,r)
Emergency Action, Agency and Advocacy undertaken
Ptr: Alderson, Mr Christopher J LLB(Hons) . . . . Aug 1997
Ball, Ms Anne P LLB . . . . Nov 1987
Bennett, Miss Sheila B LLB . . . . *Mar 1985
Blohm, Ms Kirsten E BA(Law) . . . . *Oct 1993
Bullbrook, Ms Jane LLB(Hons) . . . . *Jan 1993
Callaghan, Ms Amanda LLB(Hons) . . . . Oct 1990
Donnison, Mrs Jane LLB(Hons); MA . . . . *Feb 1988
Harrison, Miss Frances A BA ♦ . . . . *Jul 1978
Leason, Mr William A BA . . . . *Oct 1994
Meadowcroft, Ms Ann LLB . . . . *Mar 1983
Morris, Miss Racquelle LLB . . . . *Oct 1990
Taylor, Miss Margaret LLB . . . . Apr 1991
Ast: Davies, Mrs Siobhan Mary BSc . . . . *May 1997
Denver, Mrs Sarah BSc(Hons) . . . . Sep 1999
Draper, Miss Ann Charlotte BA; DLS . . . . Sep 2001
Fitzpatrick, Mr John . . . . Oct 1998
Freeman, Mrs Helen Melissa LLB(Hons) . . . . *Sep 1998
Goodwin, Miss Belinda BA . . . . *§Nov 1989
Graham, Ms Jane Louise LLB . . . . *Nov 1995
Hardy, Mr Paul LLB; LPC . . . . Oct 2001
Hay, Ms Kate E BA . . . . *Jan 1991
King, Miss Vanessa A LLB(Hons) . . . . *Oct 1997
Malpas, Ms Gillian BA; MA; CPE; LSF . . . . *Oct 1994
Reynolds, Mr Sean E BA(Hons) ♦ . . . . *Mar 1983
Rowley, Ms Georgina BA(Hons); DipLaw . . . . Jan 2001
Sealy, Mrs Lucy J LLB . . . . *Nov 1985
Sheldrick, Ms Katherine DPhil; BSc(Hons); CPE; LPE . Nov 2000
Spencer, Miss Deborah LLB(Hons)(Wales) . . . . *Jan 1990
Splaine, Ms Vanessa Ann LLB Conkerton Memorial Fund 1992 . . . . Oct 1996
Tyson, Miss Susan BA(Hons)(Law) . . . . *Nov 1994
Waheed, Taiyaba LLB . . . . *Apr 1991

HEYLIN LEGAL LIMITED ‡
215-217 Moston Lane Harpurhey Manchester Greater Manchester M9 4HE
Tel: 0161 205 2073 *Fax:* 0161 205 3987
E-mail: admin@heylins.co.uk

HILL DICKINSON LLP
50 Fountain Street Manchester Greater Manchester M2 2AS
Tel: 0161 817 7200 *Fax:* 0161 817 7201 *Dx:* 14487 MANCHESTER 2
E-mail: law@hilldickinson.com
Office: Chester, Liverpool, London EC3, Sheffield
Languages: Cantonese, Danish, French, German, Italian, Latin, Norwegian, Portuguese, Spanish, Swedish, Welsh
Work: A1 A3 B1 B2 B3 C1 C2 C3 D1 D2 E F1 F2 G H I J1 J2 K1 K2 L M1 M2 M3 N O P Q R1 R2 S1 S2 T1 T2 U1 U2 V W X Z(a,b,c,d,e,f,g,h,i,j,k,l,m,o,p,q,r,t,u,w,x,y,z)
Emergency Action, Agency, Advocacy, Fixed Fee Interview, Legal Aid undertaken, Legal Aid Franchise and Member of Accident Line
Ptr: Ahmed, Mr Saad . . . . Sep 1998
Ashley Taylor, Mr Andrew M . . . . Nov 1984
Batchelor, Miss Claire N LLB(Bris); LLM(Cantab) Deputy District Judge . . . . *Oct 1987
Blakey, Mr Michael R LLB . . . . Oct 1983
Bogle, Mr Andrew BA(Hons) . . . . *Jan 1982
Charrot, Ms Elaine . . . . Sep 2001
Clayton, Mr William J BSc(Hons) . . . . *Sep 1997
Cornes, Mr Howard LLM; MRICS; MCIOB; MCIArb . . Sep 1999
Davidson, Mr Gordon R G BA(Manc) . . . . *Jul 1987
Dowen, Ms Denise LLB . . . . *§Sep 1990
Ellaby, Mr Paul MA(Hons) . . . . *Nov 1990
Garvey, Miss Paula LLB(Hons) . . . . *Jul 1998
Grant, Ms Sarah A LLB(Exon) . . . . *§Jan 1985
Hindmarsh, Mr Stephen C LLB . . . . *Dec 1977
Keown, Mr Patrick . . . . Sep 2002
McKenna, Mr Michael J LLB Chairman of the FOIL's Special Interest Group on Rehabilitation . . . . *Oct 1984
MacPhie, Mr Alaisdhair John Wilkinson MA(Cantab) . . *Jun 1977
Marsh, Mr Adrian BA(Hons); CPE; LPC . . . . *Sep 1997
Morrison, Mr Michael J . . . . *Jun 1974
Morrison, Mrs Susan K LLB . . . . *Oct 1984
Nolan, Bobby . . . . Jul 1998
O'Sullivan, Ms Jane . . . . Jul 1979
Oakes, Mr Peter . . . . Oct 1998
Porter, Mr Jonathan D LLB; ACIArb . . . . *Sep 1991
Rooney, Miss Helen M LLB(Hons) . . . . *Sep 1996
Ryan, Ms Geraldine M LLB . . . . *Oct 1990
Seery, Ms Joanne LLB(Hons); BA(Hons) . . . . *Sep 1996
Upton, Mr James Andrew LLB(Hons) . . . . *May 2000
Wareing, Mr David . . . . May 1978
Woods, Mr Philip Dudley . . . . *§Dec 1974
Woolley, Mr Michael D . . . . *Feb 1987
Ast: Anwar, Parvez . . . . Apr 2008

HILLIS SOLICITORS ‡
1st Floor Colonnade House 163 Kingsway Manchester Greater Manchester M19 2ND
Tel: 0161 248 0500 *Fax:* 0161 248 0511
Emergency telephone 07885 941266
E-mail: law@hillis-solicitors.com
List of partners: T P Hillis
Work: N
Emergency Action, Agency, Advocacy and Fixed Fee Interview undertaken
Ptr: Hillis, Mr Thomas P . . . . Jul 1993

HILTON LAW ‡
10th Floor 3 Hardman Street Spinningfields Manchester Greater Manchester M3 3HF
Tel: 0161 932 1739
E-mail: info@hiltonlaw.co.uk

ANTONY HODARI & CO ‡
(incorporating Michael Kay & Co)
34 High Street Manchester Greater Manchester M4 1AH
Tel: 0161 832 4781 *Fax:* 0161 832 3319 *Dx:* 14419 MANCHESTER 2
E-mail: info@antonyhodari.co.uk
List of partners: G Cox, M H Y F Fong, G M Halon, A V Hodari, A J Jacobs, E Swainbank
Work: E L N S1 S2 W
Fixed Fee Interview undertaken and Member of Accident Line
Ptr: Cox, Mrs Gillian LLB(Hons) . . . . *Nov 1991
Fong, Mr Michael Hines Yun Fook LLB(Hons) R G Lawson Prize for Civil Liberties; R G Lawson Prize for Legal History . . . . *Nov 1991
Halon, Mr Gerald M BA(Oxon) . . . . *Apr 1976
Hodari, Mr Antony Victor LLB . . . . *Apr 1981
Jacobs, Mr Alan J LLB . . . . *Oct 1986
Swainbank, Miss Emma BA(Hons) . . . . *Sep 2000

HORWICH COHEN COGHLAN ‡
Quay House Quay Street Manchester Greater Manchester M3 3JE
Tel: 0161 830 4600 *Fax:* 0161 834 7382 *Dx:* 14352 MANCHESTER 1
E-mail: law@hccsolicitors.com
List of partners: B Coghlan, S E Cohen, A L C Dennison, J V Dwek, N Evans, A Farley, D J Horwich, M V Hymanson, I N Lewis, M J Lusher, I Rowe, A H Sacks, G P Small, J A Swarbrick
Office: London EC4
Work: C1 D1 E F1 F2 J1 K1 L N O P Q S1 V W Z(e,f,k,w)
Legal Aid undertaken, Legal Aid Franchise and Member of Accident Line
Ptr: Coghlan, Mr Brian . . . . Nov 1995
Cohen, Mr Simon E LLB . . . . Jun 1977
Dennison, Mr Anthony L C LLB . . . . *Mar 1985
Dwek, Mr Jonathan V LLB . . . . Nov 1991
Evans, Ms Nicola . . . . Dec 1993
Farley, Mr Andrew LLB . . . . *Oct 1992
Horwich, Mr David J BA(L'pool)(Law) . . . . *Oct 1987
Hymanson, Mr Michael V LLB(Hons) . . . . *Dec 1977
Lewis, Mr Ian N . . . . Oct 1985
Lusher, Mr Michael J LLB . . . . *Oct 1990
Rowe, Mr Ivor . . . . Mar 1984
Sacks, Mr Anthony H LLB . . . . *Apr 1980
Small, Mr Graham P BA(Hons) . . . . *Sep 1987
Swarbrick, Mr John Anthony . . . . Sep 1995
Asoc: Swerling, Mr Leon F LLB . . . . *Feb 1982
Woodall, Mr Mark C BA(Hons) . . . . Nov 1994
Ast: Cameron, Miss Alexandra BA(Hons); LPC; CPE . . . *Sep 1997
Kay, Mr Adrian H LLB(Hons) . . . . Jan 1998
McGarry, Mr Michael Gerard LLB(Hons) . . . . *Nov 1993
Myer, Mr Robert J LLB(Hons) . . . . Aug 1997
Sproston, Mr Robert J . . . . Apr 1997
Townsend, Mrs Lisa Y BA(Hons) . . . . *Aug 1993

HORWICH FARRELLY ‡
Alexander House 94 Talbot Road Manchester Greater Manchester M16 0SP
Tel: 0161 834 3585 *Fax:* 0161 834 3630
Dx: 743020 OLD TRAFFORD 5
E-mail: horwich@horwichfarrelly.co.uk
List of partners: R A Barrett, S Boylan, S Cowan, M J C Hudson, P O'Hagan, S Timmins, N J Yates
Work: C1 C2 C3 E F1 J1 K1 L M1 M2 N O P Q S1 S2 W Z(c,j,k)
Emergency Action, Agency, Advocacy, Fixed Fee Interview undertaken and Member of Accident Line
Ptr: Barrett, Mr Robert A BA . . . . Nov 1987
Boylan, Mr Stephen BA . . . . *Mar 1980
Cowan, Mrs Suzanne BA . . . . *Sep 1989
Hudson, Mr Mark Julian Charles LLB . . . . *Oct 1991
O'Hagan, Mr Philip BA(Law) . . . . Mar 1986
Timmins, Mr Stuart BA(Law) . . . . *§Oct 1985
Yates, Mr Nigel J BA . . . . *Dec 1976
Ast: Critchley, Mrs Nicola Petrina LLB(Hons) . . . . *Oct 1996

HOWARD SOLICITORS ‡
489 Chester Road Manchester Greater Manchester M16 9HF
Tel: 0800 876 6749 *Fax:* 0161 876 0489
Dx: 719205 OLD TRAFFORD 3
E-mail: info@howardssolicitors.com
List of partners: P Brooks, M C Davies
Work: E N O Q S1 S2 W Z(j)
Ptr: Brooks, Mr Phillip . . . . *Aug 1995
Davies, Mr Mark Charles LLB . . . . *Nov 1993

HOWARTH GOODMAN ‡
8 King Street Manchester Greater Manchester M60 8HG
Tel: 0161 832 5068 *Fax:* 0161 819 7878 *Dx:* 14308 MANCHESTER
E-mail: sb@howarthgoodman.com
List of partners: M S Baddiel, P Brogan
Languages: French
Work: B1 C1 C2 E F1 J1 K1 L N O Q R1 S1 W Z(d,h)
Emergency Action, Agency, Advocacy, Fixed Fee Interview, Legal Aid undertaken and Member of Accident Line
Ptr: Baddiel, Mr Martin S LLB . . . . *Jun 1979
Brogan, Mr Peter LLB . . . . *Oct 1973
Ast: Hesford, Mr Anthony LLB(Hons) . . . . Jul 2007

HOWES PERCIVAL LLP
Second floor 19 Spring Gardens Manchester Greater Manchester M2 1FB
Tel: 0161 259 0400 *Fax:* 0161 839 9953 *Dx:* 14398 MANCHESTER
E-mail: law@howespercival.com
Office: Leicester, London WC2, Milton Keynes, Northampton, Norwich

HUMD SOLICITORS ‡
115 Dickenson Road Manchester Greater Manchester M14 5HZ
Tel: 0161 225 5598 *Fax:* 0161 225 5598
E-mail: humdinfo@humdsolicitors.co.uk

IPS LAW LLP ‡
5 Ridgefield Manchester Greater Manchester M2 6EG
Tel: 0161 830 4710

IRVING M SHAPIRO ‡
New Maxdov House 130 Bury New Road Manchester Greater Manchester M25 0AA
Tel: 0161 798 8832 *Fax:* 0161 798 9251
E-mail: irving@mshapiro.co.uk

IRWIN MITCHELL LLP
Bauhaus Rossetti Place Quay Street Manchester Greater Manchester M3 4AW
Tel: 0870 150 0100 *Fax:* 0161 839 9804
Dx: 14368 MANCHESTER 1
E-mail: personalinjury@irwinmitchell.com
Office: Birmingham, Bristol, Leeds, London EC1, Newcastle upon Tyne, Sheffield
Ptr: Alexander, Miss Ann LLB; MBA . . . . *Jun 1978
Beadell, Mr Christian A LLB(L'pool) . . . . *§Oct 1997
Bell, Mr Andrew. . . . . Mar 2002
Castle, Miss Nicola Michelle. . . . . *Feb 1994
Griffiths, Miss Auriana. . . . . *Sep 1999
Harris, Mr David N LLB ♦ Deputy District Judge on the Northern Circuit. . . . . *Jul 1979
Herbertson, Miss Lesley D MA(Cantab) John Mackrell Prize; Howard Watson & Innes Prize President of Trafford Law Society . . . . *Sep 1990
Sit, Miss Yee F LLB(Hons) . . . . *Nov 1995
Wise, Ms Lindsay C. . . . . *Aug 1996
Mem: Lord, Mr John James LLB; MA . . . . *Sep 1996
Asoc: Annett, Mr Tim . . . . Sep 1998
Betts, Mr Jonathan LLB(Hons) . . . . Aug 2000
Binns, Mr Christopher Augustine PGDip; LPC. . . . . Nov 2002
Ast: Forsyth, Mrs Louise LLB(Hons); DipLP . . . . *Mar 1999
Gawne, Mr Christopher LLB(Hons) . . . . *Sep 2001
Gray, Mr Nicholas LLB . . . . *Sep 2001
Holmes, Mr Nicholas P MA(Oxon). . . . . *Nov 1995

JG SOLICITORS ‡
Conavon Court 12 Blackfriars Street Manchester Greater Manchester M3 5BQ
Tel: 0845 009 0975

JMS SOLICITORS ‡
Trafford Plaza Seymour Grove Old Trafford Manchester Greater Manchester M16 0LD
Tel: 0161 772 7927

JMW SOLICITORS ‡
1 Byrom Place Spinningfields Manchester Greater Manchester M3 3HG
Tel: 0845 872 6666 *Fax:* 0161 828 1827
Dx: 14372 MANCHESTER 1
Emergency telephone 0161 832 8087
E-mail: manager@jmw.co.uk
List of partners: J P Banfi, P Chape, I Gordon, P Grogan, W Jones, J McGoldrick, G S Tipton, P M Walker, G S Wilson
Work: B1 C1 D1 E F1 G H J1 K1 L M1 N P R1 S1 T1 V W Z(c,e,h,m,o)
Emergency Action, Agency, Advocacy, Fixed Fee Interview, Legal Aid undertaken, Legal Aid Franchise and Member of Accident Line
Ptr: Banfi, Mr James P BA. . . . . *Oct 1978
Chape, Mr Peter LLB . . . . Sep 1997
Gordon, Mr Ian LLB. . . . . *Oct 1990
Grogan, Mr Peter BA . . . . Sep 1982
Jones, Mr William. . . . . *Dec 1974
McGoldrick, Mr John BA . . . . Dec 1981
Tipton, Mr Gareth S. . . . . Oct 1988
Walker, Mr Paul M LLB(Manc). . . . . *Nov 1982
Wilson, Mr Gerard S . . . . Dec 1973
Ast: Burns, Mr Alan LLB(Hons) . . . . *Nov 1986
Eyre, Mr M Ian LLB . . . . *Oct 1990
Sands, Mr Scott Ben LLB . . . . *Jan 2003

JOHNSON YATES LIMITED ‡
Grampian House 144 Deansgate Manchester Greater Manchester M3 3EE
Tel: 0161 835 9977 *Fax:* 0161 835 3842

JONES FITZPATRICK SOLICITORS ‡
254 Wilmslow Road Manchester Greater Manchester M14 6LD
Tel: 0161 225 2070

JOYYA LAW ASSOCIATES ‡
426a Cheetham Hill Road Manchester Greater Manchester M8 9LE
Tel: 0161 795 5566 *Fax:* 0161 795 0888
E-mail: info@joyyalaw.com

JUDGE & PARTNERS ‡
78 Gartside Street Manchester Greater Manchester M3 3EL
Tel: 0161 819 5300 *Fax:* 0161 819 5599
E-mail: crime@judgeandpartners.co.uk

JUST COSTS SOLICITORS ‡
Trident One Trident Business Park Manchester Greater Manchester M22 5XB
Tel: 0161 435 6069 *Fax:* 0161 435 6172 *Dx:* 22355 CHEADLE
E-mail: info@justcosts.com
Office: Chesterfield, Leeds, London WC2, Manchester

JUST COSTS SOLICITORS
Pall Mall Court 61-67 King Street Manchester Greater Manchester M2 4PD
Tel: 0161 618 1095 *Fax:* 0161 618 1180 *Dx:* 22355 CHEADLE
Office: Chesterfield, Leeds, London WC2, Manchester

K H F SOLICITORS ‡
3 Wood Street Middleton Manchester Greater Manchester M24 4DH
Tel: 0161 654 6300 *Fax:* 0161 654 6310 *Dx:* 29064 MIDDLETON
E-mail: middleton@khfs.com

K H F SOLICITORS ‡
351 Moston Lane Moston Manchester Greater Manchester M40 9NB
Tel: 0161 205 3909 *Fax:* 0161 202 1209
E-mail: moston@khfs.com

KSG SOLICITORS ‡
150 Elliott Street Tyldesley Manchester Greater Manchester M29 8FL
Tel: 01942 896426 *Fax:* 01942 896406

KANGS SOLICITORS
Pall Mall Court 61-67 King Street Manchester Greater Manchester M2 4PD
Tel: 0161 618 1098
E-mail: enquiries@kangssolicitors.co.uk
Office: Birmingham (2 offices), London EC4

SAJJAD KARIM SOLICITORS ‡
442-444 Barlow Moor Road Manchester Greater Manchester M21 0BQ
Tel: 0161 860 7572 *Fax:* 0161 860 7582

KAUFMANLEGAL ‡
785 Rochdale Road Harpurhey Manchester Greater Manchester M9 5XD
Tel: 0161 205 3955 *Fax:* 0161 203 5559
Emergency telephone 07584 474164
E-mail: enquiries@kaufmanlegal.co.uk
List of partners: S A Kaufman
Languages: German
Work: G H Q
Emergency Action, Agency, Advocacy, Fixed Fee Interview, Legal Aid undertaken and Legal Aid Franchise
Ptr: Kaufman, Mr Stuart A MA(Cantab) . . . . *Jun 1981

SHIRLEY KELLY SOLICITORS ‡
320a Moseley Road Levenshulme Manchester Greater Manchester M19 2LH
Tel: 0161 248 5999 *Fax:* 0161 248 5666
E-mail: shirley.kelly@btconnect.com

KENNEDYS
44 Peter Street Manchester Greater Manchester M2 5GP
Tel: 0161 829 2599 *Fax:* 0161 819 2622 *Dx:* 14388 MANCHESTER
Office: Belfast, Birmingham, Cambridge, Chelmsford, London EC3, Maidstone, Sheffield, Taunton
Work: A3 B1 C1 J1 J2 K1 L N O Q Z(c,j,k,p,q,r)
Advocacy, Legal Aid undertaken, Legal Aid Franchise and Member of Accident Line
Ptr: Abbott, Mr Christopher David Kenneth LLB; PGDip Pl Lit . . . . *Oct 1978
Kershaw, Mrs Anne BA Tax Commissioner . . . . . *Dec 1974
Oldfield, Mr Christopher. . . . . Nov 1997
Asoc: Martin, Mrs Jo Anna. . . . . *Jan 2004
Ast: Conway, Miss Naomi BA(Hons) . . . . Jul 2006
Stanton, Miss Emma LLB(Hons) . . . . Apr 2007

KHAN SOLICITORS ‡
66 Dickinson Road Manchester Greater Manchester M14 5HF
Tel: 0161 256 2100
List of partners: S Dar, R A Schofield
Ptr: Dar, Mr Shaheen LLB(Hons) . . . . *Sep 1996
Schofield, Mr Robert Andrew LLB(Hons) . . . . . . *§Feb 1988

BRIAN KOFFMAN & CO ‡
Lloyds House 22 Lloyds Street Manchester Greater Manchester M2 5WA
Tel: 0161 832 3852 *Fax:* 0161 833 2547
Emergency telephone 07831 233542
E-mail: admin@briankoffman.co.uk
List of partners: B Koffman, C Mellor, H J Richardson
Work: G H K1 Z(i,j)
Emergency Action, Agency, Advocacy, Legal Aid undertaken and Legal Aid Franchise
Ptr: Koffman, Mr Brian. . . . . *Jan 1973
Mellor, Ms Carol LLB . . . . *Oct 1984
Richardson, Ms Helen Jane. . . . . *Sep 1995
Ast: Franks, Ms Wendy H LLB. . . . . *Jun 1980

KUIT STEINART LEVY ‡
3 St Marys Parsonage Manchester Greater Manchester M3 2RD
Tel: 0161 832 3434

LKS EMPLOYMENT LAW ‡
Adamson House Towers Business Park Wilmslow Road Manchester Greater Manchester M20 2YY
Tel: 0161 434 6446

LANE-SMITH & SHINDLER LLP ‡
Colwyn Chambers 19 York Street Manchester Greater Manchester M2 3BA
Tel: 0845 658 4848

LATITUDE LAW ‡
77 Lever Street Manchester Greater Manchester M1 1FL
Tel: 0161 234 6800 *Fax:* 0161 236 1493
E-mail: info@latitudelaw.com

LAVIN COPITCH ‡
552 Hyde Road Gorton Manchester Greater Manchester M18 7AA
Tel: 0161 223 5484 *Fax:* 0161 231 4360
Emergency telephone 0800 169 1796
List of partners: L M Copitch, T Lavin
Office: Altrincham
Work: D1 D2 K1 N Q S1 W
Emergency Action, Agency, Advocacy, Fixed Fee Interview, Legal Aid undertaken and Legal Aid Franchise
Ptr: Copitch, Mr Lawrence M LLB . . . . *Oct 1981
Lavin, Mr Thomas BA(Hons) . . . . *Feb 1985
Ast: Worthington, Mr Kevin John LLB(Hons) . . . . *Mar 2000

LAWSON COPPOCK & HART ‡
18 Tib Lane Cross Street Manchester Greater Manchester M2 4JA
Tel: 0161 832 5944 *Fax:* 0161 834 4409
Dx: 14370 MANCHESTER 1
E-mail: info@lawsons-uk.com
List of partners: S J Attree, D J Gallagher, E A Holloway, E G Kelly, P A Lochery, R Rawsthorn
Languages: French
Work: A1 B1 C1 C2 C3 E F1 F2 I J1 K1 K3 K4 L M1 M2 N O Q R1 R2 S1 S2 T2 U2 W Z(b,e,k,l,o,q,za)
Emergency Action, Agency and Advocacy undertaken
Ptr: Attree, Mr Stephen John LLB(Hons). . . . . *§Aug 2000
Gallagher, Mr David J. . . . . *§May 1981
Holloway, Miss Elizabeth A LLB(Manc) . . . . *§Nov 1981
Kelly, Mr Eamonn G LLB(Leeds) . . . . *§Nov 1983
Lochery, Mr Paul A . . . . *§Jun 1971
Rawsthorn, Mr Richard . . . . *§Jan 1974
Ast: Fox, Mr Paul Richard LLB. . . . . *Sep 2008
Howell, Mrs Michelle Elizabeth LLB . . . . *Oct 2006
Moores, Miss Catherine Maria BA. . . . . Nov 2007
Scott, Mrs Gemma Lee LLB(Hons) . . . . *Mar 2006

LAYTONS
(in association with Libralex; Gesica)
22 St John Street Manchester Greater Manchester M3 4EB
Tel: 0161 834 2100 *Fax:* 0161 834 6862
Dx: 14382 MANCHESTER 1
E-mail: manchester@laytons.com
Office: Guildford, London EC4
Work: A3 B1 C1 C2 C3 D1 D2 E F1 F2 I J1 J2 K1 K2 L M1 M2 N O P Q R1 R2 S1 S2 T1 T2 U1 W X Z(b,c,d,e,f,h,i,j,k,o,p,q,r,t,y,z)
Emergency Action, Agency, Advocacy and Legal Aid Franchise
Ptr: Barker, Mrs Christine Elizabeth LLB(Nott'm). . . . . *Dec 1978
Gavan, Mr John Vincent MA(Oxon) . . . . *Oct 1980
Sefton, Mr David Wiebe LLB(Hons) . . . . *Sep 1995
Spencer, Mr Paul LLB(Hons) . . . . *Oct 1989
Asoc: Powell, Mr Neil R BSc. . . . . Oct 1988
Scott-Goldstone, Mr Stuart James MA(Cantab) . . . *Sep 1997
Ast: Caddy, Mr Paul S LLB; PGDip; LPC. . . . . Sep 2000
Curtis, Mr Patrick Edward LLB . . . . *Mar 2000
Morrison, Miss Louise LLB(Hons) L G Lawson Prize (Manchester University). . . . . Sep 1998
Portsmouth, Miss Anna Lucy LLB(Hons) . . . . Sep 2002
Renison, Mr Michael Charles BA(Hons); DipLaw; DipLP . . . . *Oct 1997
Robinson, Miss Patricia Ann LLB(Hons). . . . . . . *Sep 1999

LEECH & CO ‡
Heron House Albert Square Manchester Greater Manchester M2 5HD
Tel: 0161 279 0279 *Fax:* 0161 279 1300
Dx: 716524 MANCHESTER 31
E-mail: peter.hartley@leech.co.uk
List of partners: A C Dow, P J Hartley, L Leckie, E J Leech, J E Morgan
Office: Bath
Languages: Hindi, Punjabi, Urdu
Work: A3 B1 C1 C2 E F1 J1 N O Q S1 S2 W Z(e,l,q,r)
Agency, Advocacy, Fixed Fee Interview and Legal Aid undertaken
Ptr: Dow, Mr Andrew Charles LLB(Hons) . . . . *Dec 1994
Hartley, Mr Peter Joseph LLB(Hons) . . . . *Dec 1994
Leckie, Miss Louise . . . . Dec 1996
Leech, Miss Emma Jane BA . . . . *Oct 1983
Morgan, Mrs Joyce E BA . . . . *Jul 1979
Asoc: Cunningham, Mrs Lynda Joyce LLB(Hons) . . . . . *Dec 1994
Ast: Bradley, Mr Andrew J LLB(Hons) . . . . *Sep 1998
Connery, Mr Matthew B LLB; CPE; LPC. . . . . . . *Apr 1998
Cowen, Miss Amy M LLB(Hons). . . . . *Nov 1995
Hadfield, Ms Christine LLB(Hons). . . . . Jan 1996

LEGALITY SOLICITORS ‡
Piccadilly House 49 Piccadilly Manchester Greater Manchester M1 2AP
Tel: 0161 212 1718 *Fax:* 0161 386 8794
E-mail: info@legality.biz

LEWIS HYMANSON SMALL SOLICITORS LLP ‡
Queens Chambers 5 John Dalton Street Manchester Greater Manchester M2 6ET
Tel: 0161 827 1800 *Fax:* 0161 839 8570 *Dx:* 14361 MANCHESTER
E-mail: law@lhs-solicitors.com

LICENSING LEGAL ‡
Barclay House 35 Whitworth Street West Manchester Greater Manchester M1 5NG
Tel: 0161 237 9961 *Fax:* 0161 237 9447
E-mail: sw@licensinglegal.co.uk

STEPHEN LICKRISH & ASSOCIATES LIMITED ‡
Portland Tower Portland Street Manchester Greater Manchester M1 3LD
Tel: 0161 237 1913 *Fax:* 0161 237 9251
E-mail: info@stephenlickrish.co.uk

LIEFMAN ROSE & CO ‡
94 Bury Old Road Cheetham Village Manchester Greater Manchester M8 5BW
Tel: 0161 740 7878 *Fax:* 0161 740 7279
List of partners: G Liefman, M S Rose
Work: E N P S1 T1 T2 W Z(d,j)
Agency, Advocacy and Fixed Fee Interview undertaken
Ptr: Liefman, Mr Gerald LLB(Vict) . . . . *Apr 1970
Rose, Mr Michael S LLB(Vict) . . . . *Oct 1974
Ast: Dytch, Mr Alvin LLB(Vict) . . . . *Jan 1983

LINCOLN SOLICITORS ‡
1110 Stockport Road Manchester Greater Manchester M19 2SU
Tel: 0161 442 2552 *Fax:* 0161 292 8705
E-mail: info@lincolnsolicitors.net

LINDER MYERS SOLICITORS ‡
(incorporating Bullock Worthington & Jackson)
Phoenix House 45 Cross Street Manchester Greater Manchester M2 4JF
Tel: 0844 984 6000 *Fax:* 0844 984 6200
Dx: 14360 MANCHESTER 1
Emergency telephone 0800 731 2511
E-mail: enquiries@lindermyers.co.uk
List of partners: D J Andrews, P A Bellamy, E T Bootland, J M Bridges, A Broadley, M W Brunert, A F Carr, C G Chapman, S Costello, J Crewe, N Crostan, A Cusworth, C Davies, J E Fleming, R G E Foster, M P Glancy, D Goodall, M R Grundy, C A Holdsworth, M D Horner, P S Kaye, A B Lewis, S C Lister, A B Mathias, P N Matthews, A C A McBride, W O'Neill, S Oxley, D J Rostron, A Rowlands, J D Sands, B F Seymour, M C Stewart, C Stratton, D Stratton, R Taylor, T Ward, P N D C Willan
Office: Manchester, Shrewsbury, Swinton
Languages: French, Russian
Work: A1 B1 C1 C2 C3 D1 D2 E F1 F2 G H I J1 K1 K2 L M1 M2 N O P Q R1 R2 S1 S2 T1 T2 U1 V W X Z(a,b,c,d,e,f,g,h,i,j,k,l,m,n,o,p,q,r,s,t,u,w,x,y,z)
Emergency Action, Agency, Advocacy, Fixed Fee Interview, Legal Aid undertaken, Legal Aid Franchise and Member of Accident Line
Ptr: Bootland, Mr Edward T LLB. . . . . Apr 1972
Bridges, Ms Julia Mary LLB . . . . *Oct 1994
Crewe, Mr Jeffrey LLB . . . . *Nov 1967
Cusworth, Mr Andrew LLB(Hons) . . . . Feb 1993
Davies, Mr Colin BA(Law). . . . . Oct 1985

See p112 for the Key to Work Categories & other symbols

Fleming, Mrs Janet E LLB . . . Oct 1985
Kaye, Mr Peter S BA(Hons) . . . *Oct 1985
Lewis, Mr Alan B BA . . . Sep 1992
McBride, Mr Andrew C A LLB . . . Feb 1985
Mathias, Mr Andrew Barry . . . Mar 1990
Seymour, Mr Bernard F LLB . . . *Apr 1981
Ward, Mr Trevor BA Maxwell Law Prize . . . *Oct 1986
Willan, Mr Paul N Di C LLB . . . Dec 1980
Asoc: Boyd, Mr Stephen . . . Jul 2001
Darlington, Ms Sue . . . Aug 1998
Lawson, Mr Richard . . . Nov 1997
Leadbetter, Ms Karen . . . Mar 1997
Leaman, Ms Sally BA(Hons) . . . Oct 1992
Robinson, Mr Anthony . . . Sep 1998
Wynne, Mr Sion BA(Econ) . . . *Oct 1994

LINDER MYERS SOLICITORS
3 York Street Manchester Greater Manchester M2 2RW
Tel: 0844 984 6400
Emergency telephone 07774 233986
E-mail: enquiries@lindermyers.co.uk
Office: Manchester, Shrewsbury, Swinton
Languages: French, Punjabi
Work: A1 B1 B2 C1 C2 D1 D2 E F1 G H J1 J2 K1 L M1 N O P Q R1 R2 S1 S2 T1 T2 V W X Z(c,h,j,l,o)
Emergency Action, Agency, Advocacy, Fixed Fee Interview, Legal Aid undertaken, Legal Aid Franchise and Member of Accident Line
Ptr: Andrews, Mr David J BA . . . *Sep 1992
Bellamy, Mr Philip A LLB(Leeds) . . . *§Jun 1971
Broadley, Mr Anthony ● . . . *May 1989
Brunert, Mr Michael W LLB(Vict) . . . *§Jul 1965
Carr, Mr Aidan F LLB . . . *§Jun 1980
Chapman, Mr Carl G BA . . . *Oct 1984
Costello, Ms Sheila . . . Nov 1997
Crostan, Ms Natalie . . . Nov 1998
Glancy, Ms Mary P LLB . . . *Apr 1974
Goodall, Mrs Dawn . . . *Jan 2001
Grundy, Mr Michael R LLB . . . *Apr 1978
Holdsworth, Miss Christine A LLB . . . *Jul 1979
Horner, Mr Malcolm D LLB . . . *Oct 1984
Matthews, Mr Paul N LLB . . . *Sep 1992
O'Neill, Mr William LLB . . . *Oct 1990
Oxley, Mr Sidney LLB . . . Nov 1971
Rostron, Miss Diane Julie LLB . . . *Jan 1993
Sands, Mr John D LLB John Peacock Broderip Prize; Stephen Heelis Prize; G H Charlesworth Scholarship . . . *§Jan 1965
Stewart, Mr Michael Craig LLB . . . *Aug 1995
Stratton, Mr Charles LLB . . . *Aug 2002
Stratton, Mr David LLB(Leeds) . . . *Jun 1971
Taylor, Mr Ronald LLB(Lond) . . . *§Dec 1973
Mem: Rowlands, Ms Amanda . . . Sep 2002
Asoc: Khan, Arslan Ali BA(Hons)(Law) ★ . . . *Aug 1996
Parry, James Edward Latham . . . Aug 2004
Wyles, Mrs Jean LLB . . . *Aug 1996
Ast: Brocklehurst, Mr Paul S . . . Dec 1992
Byrne, Mr Leo J LLB . . . *Oct 1972
Hardman, Ms Amanda . . . Aug 2002
Hawkins, Mr Stephen J BA(Dunelm) . . . *Apr 1981
Nutting, Mr Anthony Richard LLB . . . *Apr 1992
Parkington, Ms Catherine . . . Sep 1995
Willoughby-Foster, Ms Naomi . . . *Sep 2004

LIVINGSTONE & CO ‡
Blackfriars House Parsonage Manchester Greater Manchester M3 2JA
Tel: 0161 833 0578 *Fax:* 0161 721 4279
E-mail: harvey.cohen@fdl-law.co.uk
List of partners: H P Cohen
Languages: Hebrew, Yiddish
Work: A1 A3 B1 B2 C1 C2 D1 E F1 I J1 K1 L N O P Q R1 R2 S1 S2 V W X Z(b,c,d,e,g,j,k,l,q,r)
Emergency Action, Agency, Advocacy, Fixed Fee Interview, Legal Aid undertaken and Member of Accident Line
Ptr: Cohen, Mr Harvey Philip BA(Hons) Notary Public . . . *Apr 1980

ROBERT LIZAR ‡
159 Princess Road Moss Side Manchester Greater Manchester M14 4RE
Tel: 0161 226 2319 *Fax:* 0161 226 7985
Emergency telephone 07900 998999
E-mail: info@robertlizar.com
List of partners: A Foster, N J Hall, R S Lizar, C Micah
Office: Manchester (2 offices)
Work: D1 D2 G H K1 K3 L Z(g,h,i,m,p)
Emergency Action, Agency, Advocacy, Fixed Fee Interview and Legal Aid undertaken
Ptr: Foster, Mr Adam BA . . . May 1997
Hall, Ms Nicola J BA ★ . . . Jun 1989
Lizar, Mr Robert S LLB ♦ . . . *Jun 1974
Micah, Ms Carol BA . . . Feb 1991
Asoc: Hafezi, Mr Nasir LLB(Hons); MA . . . *Nov 2002
Ast: Andrews, Ms Rachel . . . *Jul 2003
Clark, Ms Joanna . . . *Nov 2003
Glynn, Ms Aoife . . . Apr 2003
Glynn, Miss Alison LLB(Hons) . . . *Jan 1998
Grant, Mr Adam . . . Aug 2004
Gupta, Ms Sumita . . . *Jun 2001
Harrison, Mr Michael BA(Hons) . . . *Nov 2002
McIndoe, Mr Gary . . . *May 2000
McKenna, Ms Catherine . . . *Apr 2005
Meades, Ms Alison . . . *Jun 1994
Moss, Mr James . . . *Nov 2001
Thomas, Ms Chelsea BA(Hons) . . . Nov 2002

ROBERT LIZAR
292 Barlow Moor Road Manchester Greater Manchester M21 8HA
Tel: 0161 860 7797 *Fax:* 0161 860 7739
E-mail: 292@robertlizar.com
Office: Manchester (2 offices)
Work: G H K1 Z(g,m)
Legal Aid undertaken

ROBERT LIZAR
101 Princess Road Moss Side Manchester Greater Manchester M14 4RB
Tel: 0161 227 7777 *Fax:* 0161 227 7788
Office: Manchester (2 offices)

LOCKETT LOVEDAY MCMAHON ‡
4 Oxford Court Manchester Greater Manchester M2 3WQ
Tel: 0161 237 3627 *Fax:* 0161 237 3621 *Dx:* 14345 MANCHESTER
E-mail: admin@llmsolicitors.co.uk
List of partners: E R Foulkes, J P Lockett, R E Loveday, T M McMahon, A J Mullen, M V Rhatigan
Work: A3 B1 C1 C2 E F1 F2 I J1 M1 O P Q R1 R2 S2 U2 W Z(b,c,d,e,f,k,q,za)
Ptr: Foulkes, Mr Edward R BA . . . *Oct 1996
Lockett, Mr J Paul . . . *Dec 1986
Loveday, Mr Robert E LLB . . . *Nov 1991
McMahon, Mr Terence Michael LLB(Hons) . . . *Jul 1992
Mullen, Mr Andrew J LLB . . . *Nov 1992
Rhatigan, Mr Michael Vernon LLB . . . *May 1977
Ast: Boulton, Mr Daniel . . . *Sep 2005
Davage, Mr Jonathan . . . *Nov 2002
Helliwell, Ms Susanne J LLB(Hons) . . . *Mar 1990
Lupton, Mr Mark . . . *Nov 2004

LOMAX GEDDES & CO ‡
441 Royal Exchange Manchester Greater Manchester M2 7FD
Tel: 0161 834 4722 *Fax:* 0161 832 9916 *Dx:* 14367 MANCHESTER 1
E-mail: office@lomaxgeddes.freeserve.co.uk
List of partners: P Brennand, R I Brown
Languages: French
Work: B1 C1 D1 E F1 G H J1 K1 L N O Q R1 S1 S2 T1 W Z(d,j,l)
Emergency Action, Agency, Advocacy, Fixed Fee Interview and Legal Aid undertaken
Ptr: Brennand, Mr Peter LLB(Nott'm) . . . *Jun 1979
Brown, Mr R Ian BA . . . *Dec 1972

LOPIAN WAGNER ‡
3rd Floor Maybrook House 40 Blackfriars Street Manchester Greater Manchester M3 2EG
Est: 1982
Tel: 0161 834 2324 *Fax:* 0161 835 2142 *Dx:* 14320 MANCHESTER 1
E-mail: mail@lopianwagner.co.uk
List of partners: C Bradley, M B Lopian, D S Lund, R H Stone, A W Wagner
Work: B1 C1 E F1 J1 K1 L N O P Q R1 R2 S1 S2 W Z(b,c,d,e,i,j,k,m,o,p,s)
Emergency Action, Agency, Advocacy, Fixed Fee Interview undertaken and Member of Accident Line
Ptr: Bradley, Ms Carin LLB . . . *Mar 1989
Lopian, Mr Michael B BA(Law) . . . *§May 1980
Lund, Mrs Davina Sharon LLB(Hons) . . . *Feb 1989
Stone, Mr Richard H BA(Hons) . . . *Dec 1996
Wagner, Mr Anthony W LLB(Hull) . . . *Sep 1978
Ast: Robertson, Mrs Morag BSc; LLB . . . *Apr 2002

LYONS WILSON ‡
Dickinson Chambers 1 Central Street Manchester Greater Manchester M2 5WR
Tel: 0161 830 7777 *Fax:* 0161 830 7778 *Dx:* 14353 MANCHESTER 1
E-mail: enquiries@lyonswilson.co.uk
List of partners: C D Rydeheard, I C Wilson
Languages: French, Spanish
Work: C1 C2 D1 E F1 F2 J1 K1 K2 L N O Q R1 S1 S2 W Z(e,f,h,j,k,q,w)
Agency and Advocacy undertaken
Ptr: Rydeheard, Miss Carole D LLB . . . *§Oct 1986
Wilson, Mr Ian C LLB . . . *§Nov 1969
Ast: Brown, Mr Owen BSc; MA . . . *Sep 1999
Cardwell, Miss Jennifer Anne LLB . . . *Aug 2001
Forster, Miss Katherine A LLB . . . *Jan 1991
Johnson, Miss Lucy K LLB . . . *Nov 2000
Tams, Mr Scott BA . . . *May 2004

MPH SOLICITORS ‡
86 Deansgate Manchester Greater Manchester M3 2ER
Est: 2004
Tel: 0161 832 7722 *Fax:* 0161 839 2329
Dx: 718178 MANCHESTER 3
E-mail: postbox@mphsolicitors.co.uk
List of partners: S P J Harrington, M A Havenhand, D Hemsi, G M McCool, F P Patterson
Office: Bury St Edmunds
Work: M3 N Z(r)
Legal Aid undertaken and Legal Aid Franchise
Dir: Harrington, Mr Simon Paul James LLB(Hons) Law Society Prize for Outstanding Performance on LPC 2003 . . . May 2004
Havenhand, Mr Mark Andrew LLB(Hons) . . . Sep 2001
Hemsi, Mr Dominic LLB(Hons) . . . *Mar 1996
McCool, Ms Geraldine M LLB(Nott'm) J D Marsden Prize President of Manchester Law Society 2002 - 2003 *Nov 1985
Patterson, Mr Frank P LLB(Manc) . . . *§Oct 1986
Ast: Grieveson, Miss Laura Jane . . . Sep 2010
Harris, Miss Gemma . . . Sep 2011
Logue, Miss Mealla Joy BA(Hons)(Sociology); CPE; LPC . . . Sep 2006
Patel, Mr Altaf LLB(Hons) . . . Aug 2008
Pearce, Mrs Emma BA(Law & Criminology) . . . Dec 2007
Sharrock, Ms Laura McDonald . . . Oct 2009
Con: Harrington, Mr Paul Alexander BA; MIExpE . . . Oct 1983

MS LAW LLP ‡
383 Bury New Road Prestwich Manchester Greater Manchester M25 1AW
Tel: 0161 772 4500 *Fax:* 0161 772 4501
E-mail: info@ms-law.co.uk

MWG SOLICITORS ‡
Suite 1 141 Cheetham Hill Road Manchester Greater Manchester M8 8LY
Tel: 0161 835 2446 *Fax:* 0161 850 2446
E-mail: admin@mwgsolicitors.co.uk

MCGRIGORS LLP
6th Floor The Pinnacle 73-78 King Street Manchester Greater Manchester M2 4NG
Tel: 0161 935 8337 *Fax:* 0161 935 8163 *Dx:* 14436 MANCHESTER 2
Office: Belfast, London EC4
Ptr: Blackmore, Mr Peter W . . . Jun 1993
Ogden, Mr Nicholas LLB . . . Aug 1991

MAGUIRES SOLICITORS ‡
334 Deansgate Manchester Greater Manchester M3 4LY
Tel: 0161 835 9872 *Fax:* 0161 819 1154
E-mail: ronanmaguire@maguiressolicitors.com

MALIK LEGAL SOLICITOR LIMITED ‡
Cheetham Hill Chambers 579 Cheetham Hill Road Cheetham Hill Manchester Greater Manchester M8 7JE
Tel: 0161 795 6217 *Fax:* 0161 740 9949

THOMAS MANSFIELD LLP
Barnett House 53 Fountain Street Manchester Greater Manchester M2 2AN
Tel: 0845 601 7756 *Fax:* 020 8681 8141
E-mail: info@thomasmansfield.com
Office: Birmingham, Croydon, London E1

MARKS & CLERK
Sussex House 83-85 Mosley Street Manchester Greater Manchester M2 3LG
Tel: 0161 233 5800 *Fax:* 0161 236 5846
Office: Birmingham, Cheltenham, Leeds, Leicester, Liverpool, London WC2, Oxford

MARTIN & CO ‡
St James's Buildings 79 Oxford Street Manchester Greater Manchester M1 6EJ
Tel: 0161 228 6195 *Fax:* 0161 228 7958
E-mail: info@martinandcosolicitors.co.uk

MASON HAYES ‡
3000 Manchester Business Park Aviator Way Manchester Greater Manchester M22 5TG
Tel: 0161 266 1129 *Fax:* 0161 266 1621
Office: London WC2

A S MATTHEWS & CO ‡
136 Park Lane Whitefield Manchester Greater Manchester M45 7PX
Tel: 0161 747 2262 *Fax:* 0161 747 0701
Emergency telephone 0161 747 2262
List of partners: C D Matthews
Languages: French
Work: C1 E L R1 S1 W Z(h)
Emergency Action, Agency and Fixed Fee Interview undertaken
Ptr: Matthews, Mr Clive D . . . *Jun 1966

ROBERT MEATON & CO ‡
Victoria Buildings 1 Princess Street Manchester Greater Manchester M2 4DF
Tel: 0845 634 9955 *Fax:* 0161 833 4251 *Dx:* 14424 MANCHESTER 2

MENDELL SOLICITORS ‡
Grove House 774-780 Wilmslow Road Manchester Greater Manchester M20 2DR
Tel: 0844 800 2427 *Fax:* 0870 836 2098
E-mail: enquiries@mendell-solicitors.co.uk

MERRICK SOLICITORS ‡
6th Floor Ship Canal House King Street Manchester Greater Manchester M2 4WU
Tel: 0161 838 5410 *Fax:* 0161 832 5050
E-mail: amanda.merrick@merrick-solicitors.com

MIDDLEWEEKS SOLICITORS ‡
1st Floor 18-20 Derby Street Manchester Greater Manchester M8 8RY
Tel: 0161 839 7255 *Fax:* 0161 839 7243
Emergency telephone 07760 174483
E-mail: law@middleweeks.com
List of partners: S Choudry, C Richmond, J L C Spencer
Languages: Punjabi
Work: B2 G H L V
Emergency Action, Agency, Advocacy, Legal Aid undertaken and Legal Aid Franchise
Ptr: Choudry, Shahid BA ● . . . *Dec 1998
Richmond, Mr Carl BA ● . . . *Oct 1995
Spencer, Mr Jeremy L C BA(Hons) ● . . . *Feb 1987

NEIL MILLAR & CO SOLICITORS ‡
No2 Universal Square Devonshire Street Manchester Greater Manchester M12 6JH
Tel: 0161 870 0177 *Fax:* 0161 870 0179
E-mail: neil@neil-millar.co.uk
List of partners: N M Millar
Work: C1 C2 E F1 J1 N O Q S1 S2 U2 W Z(b,p,q)
Agency undertaken
SPr: Millar, Mr Neil M LLB . . . *Oct 1984
Con: Aylward, Mr Joseph LLB . . . Jan 1997

MILLBANK EDGE LLP ‡
St Andrews House 62 Bridge Street Manchester Greater Manchester M3 3BW
Tel: 0161 725 7920 *Fax:* 0161 725 7939
E-mail: info@millbankedge.co.uk

MILLER GARDNER ‡
497 Chester Road Old Trafford Manchester Greater Manchester M16 9HF
Tel: 0161 877 4777 *Fax:* 0161 877 5777
Dx: 719207 OLD TRAFFORD 3
Emergency telephone 0161 877 4777
E-mail: law@millergardner.co.uk
List of partners: S Filton, R M Gardner
Work: B1 C1 E O Q S1 S2 T2
Advocacy and Legal Aid Franchise
Dir: Filton, Ms Shirley . . . Jan 1986
Gardner, Mr Rodney M . . . *Jun 1970

GEOFFREY MILLER SOLICITORS ‡
PO Box 748 Aeroworks Adair Street Manchester Greater Manchester M60 2YS
Tel: 0161 274 5580 *Fax:* 0161 274 5599 *Dx:* 14426 MANCHESTER 2

J S MILLER SOLICITORS ‡
Aeroworks 5 Adair Street Manchester Greater Manchester M1 2NQ
Tel: 0161 274 5588 *Fax:* 0161 274 5599

MILLS & REEVE
9th Floor 1 New York Street Manchester Greater Manchester M1 4HD
Tel: 0844 561 0011 *Fax:* 0161 235 5421 *Dx:* 14409 MANCHESTER 2
E-mail: info@mills-reeve.com
Office: Birmingham, Cambridge, Leeds, London EC3, Norwich
Asoc: Karow, Miss Wanda Marian LLB . . . *§Sep 1993
Con: Taylor, Miss Elisabeth L LLB(Bris) . . . *§Feb 1974

MOHINDRA MAINI SOLICITORS LLP ‡
14 Oxford Court Manchester Greater Manchester M2 3WQ
Tel: 0161 236 9833 *Fax:* 0161 233 6169 *Dx:* 18574 MANCHESTER 7
E-mail: post@mmsolicitors.co.uk
List of partners: S Burnett, M Maini, S Mohindra
Languages: Hindi, Punjabi, Urdu
Work: A3 B1 C1 E J2 N O Q R2 S2 Z(b,j,q)
Ptr: Maini, Ms Meera BA(Hons) . . . *May 1986
Mohindra, Sunil BSc; ARCS; ACII . . . *Apr 1980
Burnett, Sharon . . . NSP

JANE MONKS SOLICITORS ‡
Church House 90 Deansgate Manchester Greater Manchester M3 2QH
Tel: 0161 839 0092 ***Fax:*** 0161 839 0093

MORGAN BROWN & CAHILL SOLICITORS ‡
12 Victoria Avenue Blackley Manchester Greater Manchester M9 6QL
Tel: 0161 740 7468 ***Fax:*** 0161 795 2483
E-mail: info@mbcsolicitors.co.uk
Office: London WC2, Salford

C P MORLEY ‡
Horton House 2 Urmston Lane Stretford Manchester Greater Manchester M32 9BP
Tel: 0161 865 1771 ***Dx:*** 727852 STRETFORD 2

NK LEGAL SOLICITORS LIMITED ‡
255 Wilmslow Road Rusholme Manchester Greater Manchester M14 5LW
Tel: 0161 249 3994 ***Fax:*** 0161 249 3995
Dx: 730325 MANCHESTER 52
E-mail: info@nklegal.co.uk

NW LAW SOLICITORS ‡
Longfield Prestwich Manchester Greater Manchester M25 1XX
Tel: 0161 772 9922 ***Fax:*** 0844 443 1927
E-mail: naomi.wilson@nwlaw.co.uk

NEIL ROSS SUTCLIFFE & CO ‡
Grange House 27-31 John Dalton Street Manchester Greater Manchester M2 6FW
Tel: 0161 838 5454 ***Fax:*** 0161 832 4029
Dx: 14319 MANCHESTER 1
E-mail: nsutcliffe@nrslaw.co.uk

NEXUS SOLICITORS ‡
16-18 Albert Square Manchester Greater Manchester M2 5PE
Tel: 0161 819 4900 ***Fax:*** 0161 819 4901 ***Dx:*** 14355 MANCHESTER
E-mail: help@nexussolicitors.co.uk
List of partners: A S Brook, J Lloyd, C X Moran, B D O'Driscoll, T J Osborn, C C Pugh, P Turner, M Yeomans
Office: Knutsford
Languages: French, German, Spanish
Work: A1 A3 B1 C1 C2 E F1 F2 I J1 L M2 N O Q R2 S1 S2 T1 T2 U1 U2 W Z(c,e,f,j,k,p,q,w)
Fixed Fee Interview undertaken
Ptr: Brook, Mr Anthony S LLB . . . . . *Sep 1987
Lloyd, Mr James LLB . . . . . *Oct 1992
Moran, Mr Carl Xavier LLB(with French); LLM . . . . . Sep 1996
O'Driscoll, Mr Barry D LLB(Hons) . . . . . *Feb 1990
Osborn, Mr Terence J LLB . . . . . *Oct 1984
Pugh, Mr Christopher Charles LLB(Hons) . . . . . *Oct 1991
Turner, Mr Philip LLB(Hons) . . . . . Oct 1985
Yeomans, Miss Melanie LLB(Hons) . . . . . Oct 1996
Asoc: Illsley, Ms Debbie LLB(Hons) . . . . . *Oct 1999
Ast: Barnes, Miss Lesley Anna LLB . . . . . *Sep 2002
Mahajan, Miss Vaishali Hiraman LLB(Hons); LPC . . . Sep 2003
Martin, Mr Paul LLB(Hons) . . . . . *Jun 2006
Stylianou, Miss Helena LLB(Hons) . . . . . *Sep 2005
Tindal, Ms Caroline LLB . . . . . *Sep 2002
Walsh, Mr Alex Robert LLB . . . . . Jan 2006

NICHOLAS & PARTNERS ‡
Mount Pleasant House 164 Oldham Road Manchester Greater Manchester M4 6BG
Tel: 0161 202 4999 ***Fax:*** 0161 205 5558
Emergency telephone 07831 230999
List of partners: K M Nicholas
Work: D1 G H K1 N Q S1 S2 W Z(l)
Emergency Action, Agency, Advocacy, Fixed Fee Interview and Legal Aid undertaken
Ptr: Nicholas, Mr Kevin M LLB . . . . . Jun 1985

NIKOLICH & CARTER ‡
6th Floor Suite 602 Sunlight House Manchester Greater Manchester M3 3JZ
Tel: 0161 831 7044 ***Fax:*** 0161 819 1101

OCCASIO LEGAL ‡
Grampian House 144 Deansgate Manchester Greater Manchester M2 3EE
Tel: 0161 831 9961 ***Fax:*** 0161 831 7477
E-mail: philip.burgoyne@occasio-legal.com

OLLIERS ‡
Castlefield Chamber 11 Duke Street Manchester Greater Manchester M3 4NF
Tel: 0161 834 1515 ***Fax:*** 0161 839 0804 ***Dx:*** 727755 MANCHESTER
Emergency telephone 0161 834 1515
List of partners: D W Abbott, M J Claughton, R J Holliday, D Philpott, M Saffman
Work: B2 G H
Emergency Action, Agency, Advocacy, Fixed Fee Interview and Legal Aid undertaken
Ptr: Abbott, Mr David W LLB ★ . . . . . *Mar 1985
Claughton, Mr Matthew J LLB . . . . . *Mar 1990
Holliday, Mr Richard J BA(Law) ★ . . . . . *Feb 1990
Philpott, Mr David BA(Hons) . . . . . *Feb 1992
Saffman, Mr Max LLB ★ . . . . . *Nov 1994

OSBORN ABAS HUNT ‡
3 Oxford Court Bishopsgate Manchester Greater Manchester M2 3WQ
Tel: 0161 200 8450 ***Fax:*** 0161 236 6522 ***Dx:*** 727756 MANCHESTER
E-mail: theteam@oahlaw.com

OTTEN PENNA LTD
527 Stockport Road Longsight Manchester Greater Manchester M12 4JH
Tel: 0161 248 3660 ***Fax:*** 0161 256 4768 ***Dx:*** 29382 NORTHENDEN
E-mail: longsight@ottenpenna.co.uk
Office: Northenden
Languages: Punjabi, Urdu
Work: D1 D2 K1 K3 W Z(m)
Emergency Action, Agency, Advocacy, Fixed Fee Interview, Legal Aid undertaken and Legal Aid Franchise

OZON SOLICITORS ‡
The Lexicon 10-12 Mount Street Manchester Greater Manchester M2 5NT
Tel: 0161 832 0050 ***Fax:*** 0161 819 2063 ***Dx:*** 12211 MANCHESTER 2
E-mail: info@ozonlaw.com

PABLA & PABLA SOLICITORS ‡
Fourways House 57 Hilton Street Manchester Greater Manchester M1 2EJ
Tel: 0161 234 2650 ***Fax:*** 0161 228 2513
E-mail: enquiries@pablasolicitors.co.uk

PANNONE LLP ‡
123 Deansgate Manchester Greater Manchester M3 2BU
Tel: 0161 909 3000 ***Fax:*** 0161 909 4444
Dx: 14314 MANCHESTER 1
E-mail: law@pannone.co.uk
List of partners: R C M Ashworth, A P Barnfather, C A Brooks-Johnson, D J Carmichael, P A Chandler, A Clarke, A J Cohen, E C Cowell, R M R Dobson, C R F Fozard, R C Glithero, U M S Gould, S R Grant, D Healy, E E Holt, C G P Jackson, G O Jessop, C E Jones, H A S Jones, S L Jones, J M Kingsley, J M Kitchingman, C J B Leech, D J Leviten, S C Lintott, K J Lister, S W Lister, J McMuldroch, A Megaw, L J Morgan, A R Newbury, R J Pannone, S G Pedley, U G Pope, R J Price, A Rendell, R Scorer, A G Simpkin, C S R Tattam, P J Taylor, J L Urwin, S J Wallwork, B D Wilkins, A R Williamson, D B Woolfson, A Young, C J Young
Office: Altrincham
Languages: Danish, French, German, Swedish
Work: A3 B1 B2 C1 C2 C3 D1 D2 E F1 F2 I J1 J2 K1 K2 L M1 M2 N O P Q R1 R2 S1 S2 T1 T2 U2 V W Z(b,c,d,e,g,h,k,l,m,o,p,q,r,u,w,z)
Emergency Action, Agency, Advocacy, Legal Aid undertaken, Legal Aid Franchise and Member of Accident Line
Ptr: Ashworth, Mr Robert C M BA . . . . . *§Mar 1985
Barnfather, Mr Anthony P . . . . . Dec 1997
Brooks-Johnson, Mrs Carol Ann LLB(Hons) . . . . . *Oct 1988
Carmichael, Mr David J LLB . . . . . *Feb 1987
Chandler, Ms Pauline A LLB . . . . . *Jul 1974
Clarke, Miss Anne . . . . . *§Jun 1981
Cohen, Ms Andrea J LLB(Hons) . . . . . *Oct 1988
Cowell, Miss Elizabeth C LLB Deputy District Judge . . *Oct 1981
Dobson, Mrs Rachel Mary Ruth MA . . . . . *Nov 1994
Fozard, Mr C Robin F MA . . . . . *§Apr 1976
Glithero, Mr Richard C BA; DMS . . . . . *Oct 1986
Gould, Mrs Ursula M S LLB . . . . . *Apr 1990
Grant, Mr Steven R BA . . . . . *§Oct 1984
Healy, Ms Deirdre . . . . . Nov 1997
Holt, Mrs Emma Elisabeth LLB . . . . . *Apr 1994
Jackson, Ms Carol G P LLB . . . . . *Oct 1981
Jessop, Mr Gareth O LLB; MCIArb Notary Public . . *§Mar 1984
Jones, Mrs Catherine E . . . . . *§Dec 1977
Jones, Mr Hugh A S LLB . . . . . *Dec 1979
Jones, Mr Stephen L BA . . . . . *Nov 1986
Kingsley, Ms Joy M LLB . . . . . *§Jun 1980
Kitchingman, Mr John M LLB . . . . . *§Jun 1975
Leech, Ms Catherine J B LLB . . . . . *Nov 1987
Leviten, Mr David Jonathan BSc(Civ Eng) . . . . . *Feb 1988
Lintott, Mr Stephen Charles BA . . . . . *Nov 1995
Lister, Mr Kevin James LLB; FRSA . . . . . *Sep 1992
Lister, Mr S William MA(Oxon); AMITMA . . . . . *Jun 1987
McMuldroch, Mr John BA(Hons); LLM; MBA . . . . . *Oct 1982
Megaw, Mr Alexander Deputy District Judge . . . . . *Dec 1977
Morgan, Ms Laura J . . . . . *Sep 1997
Newbury, Mr Andrew Roger LLB . . . . . *Oct 1991
Pannone, Mr Rodger J DLitt(Hons); LLD(Hons); FRSA; FMMU President of Law Society of England & Wales 1993/94 . . . . . *§Jun 1969
Pedley, Mr Simon G . . . . . *Oct 1996
Pope, Mr Udo G BTech . . . . . *Nov 1991
Price, Mr Richard John MA . . . . . *§Oct 1992
Rendell, Miss Alicia LLB . . . . . *Sep 1987
Scorer, Mr Richard MA . . . . . *Nov 1994
Simpkin, Mr Andrew G . . . . . *Nov 1972
Tattam, Mr Charles Soren Robert BA Swedish Consul for Manchester; Chair Northern Chapter Swedish Chamber of Commerce for the UK . . . . . *§Jun 1978
Taylor, Mr Paul J LLB Chief Prosecution Solicitor . . *Feb 1980
Urwin, Ms Jenny Louise MA; LLM; LSF . . . . . *Oct 1995
Wallwork, Mr Simon John BA; LLB . . . . . Oct 1988
Wilkins, Mrs Beth D LLB . . . . . *Apr 1981
Williamson, Mr Andrew R LLB; MSc; MCIArb; Dip Com Lit CIA Annual Prize 1998 . . . . . *Oct 1993
Woolfson, Mrs Debra B LLB; MA . . . . . *Jan 1987
Young, Mr Andrew LLB(Hons) . . . . . *Nov 1996
Young, Miss Claire J BA . . . . . *Dec 1988
Ast: Alden, Miss Claire L BSc; CPE; LSF . . . . . Sep 1996
Attwell, Miss Kate Emily BA(Law); DipLP . . . . . Sep 2002
Bell, Mrs Amy Louise LLB(Hons) . . . . . *Dec 1999
Bell, Miss Lindsey Dawn LLB . . . . . *Sep 2001
Berry, Miss Vanessa LLB(Hons) . . . . . Sep 2001
Blackburn, Miss Samantha . . . . . *Nov 1998
Bonwick, Miss Sarah Ann LLB . . . . . Nov 2001
Brabin, Miss Melanie LLB . . . . . *Aug 2002
Brine, Ms Joanne LLB . . . . . Sep 1999
Brown, Mr Michael BA(Hons) . . . . . *Sep 1997
Brown, Mr Owen BSc; MA . . . . . *Sep 1999
Cassidy, Mr Michael Owen BA(Econ); CPE; LPC . . . Nov 1999
Chadwick, Miss Karen L BA . . . . . Nov 1999
Chadwick, Ms Louise LLB . . . . . *Feb 1997
Charrot, Mr Robin Charles B LLB(Hons) . . . . . Feb 1997
Edwards, Miss Gillian Barbara LLB(Hons); RGN . . . Sep 1997
Emslie, Miss Maia MA(History); CPE; LPC . . . . . Sep 1999
Fogerty, Mr Jonathan D BA(Hons); DipLaw . . . . . *Nov 1999
French, Mrs Patricia LLB(Hons) . . . . . Feb 1999
Gaudern, Miss Emma . . . . . *Sep 1999
Grainger, Miss Claire Marie PGDipLaw(CPE); PGLP; LPC . . . . . *Jul 2002
Grimes, Mr Mark . . . . . Nov 2001
Hamilton Ryan, Mrs Kathryn L MA . . . . . *Oct 1996
Hamor, Ms Fiona J . . . . . *Sep 1997
Hancock, Miss Claire . . . . . Nov 2001
Harrington, Mr John Gerard . . . . . *Mar 1998
Harris, Miss Victoria Kathryn LLB(Hons) . . . . . Nov 2000
Hawley, Mr Michael Richard LLB . . . . . *Sep 1996
Hope, Mr Brendan Local Councillor . . . . . Sep 2002
Howlett, Mrs Amanda J LLB . . . . . *Oct 1986
Ingham, Mr Jeremy David BA; PGDipLaw . . . . . Aug 2001
Inskip, Mr Kristofer BSc; PGDipLaw; LPC . . . . . *Nov 2000
Islam, Fokrul LLB(Hons) . . . . . Sep 2002
Jones, Ms Sarah Elizabeth Mounteney BA(Hons)(English Lit & Lang); CPE; LPC . . . . . *Sep 1998
Kerr, Ms Nadia J LLB . . . . . *Oct 1995
Kershaw, Ms Helen LLB; LAN; LPC . . . . . Feb 2001
Liyanearachchi, Miss Anushka LLB . . . . . Sep 2002
Lomas, Miss Emma Jane BA(Jt Hons); MA . . . . . *Sep 2001
Machell, Miss Estele BA(Hons); PGDipLaw; LPC . . . *Sep 2002
MacLennan, Miss Nicola LLB . . . . . *Nov 1999
Michael, Mr Steele LLB . . . . . Feb 1997
Miles, Ms Jennifer BA(Hons) . . . . . Nov 1988
Millar, Mr Carl James LLB(Hons) . . . . . *Jul 1998
Moore, Ms Rachel LLB(Hons); DipLP . . . . . *May 1998
O'Hara, Ms Lucy Catherine LLB; DipLP . . . . . Nov 2000
Oliver, Mr Richard M LLB(Hons) . . . . . *Sep 1998
Radiven, Mr Daniel Barry LLB; LPC; PSC . . . . . *Sep 2000
Rafiq, Miss Tahira LLB; LLM; LPC . . . . . *Sep 2001
Reilly, Ms Jean . . . . . May 1999
Sabzwari, Miss Raazia BA(Hons) . . . . . Oct 2002
Sahu, Miss Nina BA(Law & Accounting); LPC . . . . *Nov 2000
Saldanha, Dr Kathryn Eleanor MA(Oxon); PhD(Cantab) . . . . . *Nov 2000
Sandiford, Mr Paul LLB . . . . . Oct 2002
Short, Mrs Helen LLB . . . . . Sep 1997
Slater, Mrs Rachel E . . . . . *Nov 1997
Steele, Mr Michael John LLB . . . . . Feb 1997
Stewart, Mrs Claire LLB(Hons) . . . . . Nov 2001
Sutcliffe, Miss Jenny LLB(Hons) . . . . . Jul 2002
Sykes, Mrs Alison J MA(Hons)(Oxon); ALCM . . . . *Nov 1999
Teasdale, Miss Sara Therese LLB(Hons); LPC . . . *Sep 2000
Thomas, Miss Lucy A MA(Hons) . . . . . *Nov 1999
Whittall, Miss Molly Anna LLB(Hons); LPC . . . . . Apr 2002
Wilson, Miss Linzi . . . . . Sep 2002
Wood, Ms Fiona . . . . . *Apr 1997
Con: Payne, Mr Robert Gardiner MA . . . . . *§Jun 1961

GRAHAM PEART ‡
Essex House Essex Avenue Manchester Greater Manchester M20 6AN
Tel: 0161 434 9040

PEASEGOODS ‡
Bank Chambers 937/941 Rochdale Road Blackley Manchester Greater Manchester M9 8AE
Tel: 0161 205 2772 ***Fax:*** 0161 203 4218 ***Dx:*** 722020 BLACKLEY
E-mail: peasegoods@supanet.com
List of partners: N Chadwick, A McGurk, S P Mealand, R P Towers
Work: F1 L N O Q S1 W
Emergency Action, Agency, Advocacy, Fixed Fee Interview, Legal Aid undertaken, Legal Aid Franchise and Member of Accident Line
Ptr: Chadwick, Miss Nicola . . . . . *Mar 2001
McGurk, Mr Adrian . . . . . *Dec 2001
Mealand, Mr Steven P LLB . . . . . *Nov 1988
Towers, Mr Ramon P . . . . . Dec 1993
Asoc: Exley, Miss Gillian . . . . . Mar 2004
Leece, Miss Rebecca . . . . . Oct 2003

PENN FARADAY SOLICITORS ‡
116-118 Cheetham Hill Road Cheetham Hill Manchester Greater Manchester M4 4FG
Tel: 0161 832 7550 ***Fax:*** 0161 832 9551
E-mail: nyounis@pennfaraday.com

PENNINE KENNEDY SOLICITORS
450 Barlow Moor Road Chorlton Manchester Greater Manchester M21 0BQ
Tel: 0161 881 3133 ***Fax:*** 0161 881 4345
Dx: 22403 CHORLTON CUM HARDY
E-mail: info@penninekennedy.co.uk
Office: Rochdale
Languages: Farsi, French, Punjabi, Spanish, Urdu
Work: E L N O Q S1 S2 W Z(l)

DAVID PHILLIPS & PARTNERS
5a High Lane Chorlton Manchester Greater Manchester M21 9DJ
Tel: 0161 860 7354 ***Fax:*** 0161 862 9580
E-mail: info@dpp.law.com
Office: Birmingham, Bootle (2 offices), Chadwell Heath, Leicester, Liverpool, London E1, London SE18, London W1, Nelson, Wealdstone
Work: B2 G H
Ast: Coleman, Mr Jeremy Daniel BSc . . . . . Sep 2002

JOHN PICKERING & PARTNERS LLP
Old Exchange Buildings St Ann's Passage 29-31 King Street Manchester Greater Manchester M2 6BE
Tel: 0808 144 0957 ***Fax:*** 0161 834 1505
Dx: 14333 MANCHESTER 1
E-mail: pg@johnpickering.co.uk
Office: Halifax, Liverpool
Advocacy, Fixed Fee Interview, Legal Aid undertaken and Member of Accident Line
Ptr: Fisher, Mr Neil BSc(Lond) . . . . . *Oct 1980

PINSENT MASONS LLP
3 Hardman Street Manchester Greater Manchester M3 3AU
Est: 2004
Tel: 0161 234 8234 ***Fax:*** 0161 234 8235
Dx: 14490 MANCHESTER 2
E-mail: enquiries@pinsentmasons.com
Office: Birmingham, Bristol, Leeds, London EC2
Languages: French, German, Spanish
Work: A1 B1 C1 C2 C3 E F1 J1 L M1 M2 N O P R1 S1 Z(c,e,j)
Emergency Action, Agency, Advocacy and Fixed Fee Interview undertaken
Ptr: Alty, Mr Graham . . . . . Sep 1995
Clayton, Mr Peter Mark BA(Law) George Hadfield Prize . . . . . *Sep 1994
Davies, Mr Edward R LLB(Hons); MSc . . . . . *Nov 1982
Denton, Mr Andrew LLB(Hons) . . . . . *Oct 1996
Hopkins, Mr Michael D LLB . . . . . Oct 1989
Jay, Ms Rosemary P BA . . . . . Apr 1981
Job, Mr Mark LLB(Hons) . . . . . *Sep 1992
Kennedy, Mr Patrick C LLB . . . . . Apr 1990
Watson, Miss Angela M BA(Hons) . . . . . *Oct 1988
Ast: Birchall, Mr Phillip . . . . . Sep 2004

PLATT HALPERN
151 Dickenson Road Rusholme Manchester Greater Manchester M14 5HZ
Tel: 0161 224 2555 ***Fax:*** 0161 256 1253
Emergency telephone 07977 204040
E-mail: rusholme@platthalpern.co.uk
Office: Manchester, Oldham
Languages: Punjabi, Urdu
Work: D1 G H K1 L N
Emergency Action, Agency, Advocacy, Fixed Fee Interview, Legal Aid undertaken, Legal Aid Franchise and Member of Accident Line
Ptr: Deane, Ms Wilma A LLB(Manc) . . . . . *Oct 1980
Halpern, Mr Daniel J LLB . . . . . *Oct 1976
Asoc: Lee, Ms Ellen E PhD . . . . . *Apr 1992
O'Brien, Ms Marion . . . . . Nov 2000
Stringer, Mr John . . . . . Aug 1998
Yates, Ms Rebecca . . . . . Oct 2002
Ast: Younas, Shomaila . . . . . Dec 2002

See p112 for the Key to Work Categories & other symbols

PLATT HALPERN
Second Floor Grampian House Manchester Greater Manchester M3 3EE
Tel: 0161 834 3114 *Fax:* 0161 834 5198
Office: Manchester, Oldham
Work: D1 G H K1 L N Q S1 V W Z(i,l)
Emergency Action, Agency, Advocacy, Fixed Fee Interview, Legal Aid undertaken and Member of Accident Line
Ptr: Deane, Ms Wilma A LLB(Manc) . . . *Oct 1980
Halpern, Mr Daniel J LLB . . . *Oct 1976
Hopkinson, Mr Michael John BA . . . *Mar 1985
Potter, Mr John BA(Law) . . . *Jun 1987
Ast: Preston, Ms Alexandra J BA; MA . . . *Oct 1997

PLEXUS LAW (A TRADING NAME OF PARABIS LAW LLP)
Centurian House 129 Deansgate Manchester Greater Manchester M3 3WR
Tel: 0161 214 7933 *Dx:* 14391 MANCHESTER
Office: Colchester, Croydon, Evesham, Leeds, London EC2, London EC3, Manchester
Ptr: Burt, Mr Jason Drew . . . *Oct 1996
Wallace, Mr Craig LLB; LPC . . . Dec 2003

PLEXUS LAW (A TRADING NAME OF PARABIS LAW LLP)
21st Floor City Tower Piccadilly Plaza Manchester Greater Manchester M1 4BT
Tel: 0844 245 4100 *Dx:* 744610 MANCHESTER 72
Office: Colchester, Croydon, Evesham, Leeds, London EC2, London EC3, Manchester
Ptr: Gough, Mr Christopher BA . . . *Sep 1997
Shaw, Miss Lorraine . . . *Dec 1993
Short, Mr Timothy LLB . . . Sep 1997
Smith, Matthew . . . Feb 1998
Steel, Andrew . . . Oct 2003

POTTER REES (SERIOUS INJURY) SOLICITORS ‡
12 Commercial Street Manchester Greater Manchester M15 4PZ
Tel: 0161 237 5888 *Fax:* 0161 237 5999 *Dx:* 14342 MANCHESTER
Emergency telephone 0161 237 5888
E-mail: hughpotter@potterrees.co.uk
List of partners: H S Dolan, A E Hartley, J H C Potter, R S Rees
Languages: French, Italian
Work: J1 N V W Z(m,q,r)
Legal Aid undertaken and Legal Aid Franchise
Ptr: Dolan, Ms Helen Sarah ♦ . . . Aug 1996
Hartley, Ms Alison Elizabeth ♦ . . . Nov 1998
Potter, Mr Jonathan Hugh Conwy ♦ . . . Mar 1988
Rees, Ms Rachel Sian ♦ . . . Oct 1989
Asoc: Bledge, Ms Louise Fiona ♦ . . . Sep 1998
Davidson, Ms Janet Sally ♦ . . . Apr 1998
Lloyd-Ellis, Ms Sally ♦ . . . Nov 1998
Peterson, Ms Katherine Rosemary ♦ . . . Oct 1993
Renshaw, Mr Peter David Scott ♦ Legal Aid Peer Reviewer . . . Jan 1998
Seed, Ms Margaret ♦ . . . Dec 1983
Ast: Kushner, Mr Keith ♦ . . . Sep 1964
Mepstead, Ms Nicola ♦ . . . Nov 2004
Shaw, Ms Helen ♦ . . . Nov 1990
Smith, Mr Jeremy Michael ♦ . . . Nov 1991

JOHN POYSER SOLICITORS ‡
5a High Lane Chorlton Manchester Greater Manchester M21 9DJ
Tel: 0161 860 7354 *Fax:* 0161 862 9580
Emergency telephone 07778 472555
E-mail: mail@johnpoyser.co.uk
List of partners: J Poyser
Office: Littleborough
Languages: Punjabi, Urdu
Work: G K1 K3 K4 L N Q S1 W Z(q)
SPr: Poyser, Mr John LLB . . . Mar 1996
Ast: Williams, Ms Maria . . . Jul 1999
Con: Ali, Mrs Joanne LLB . . . Jan 2000
Shafqut, Miss Ayesha LLB . . . Sep 2009

Q & A SOLICITORS ‡
Adamson House Towers Business Park Wilmslow Road Manchester Greater Manchester M20 2YY
Tel: 0161 955 4440 *Fax:* 0161 955 4445
E-mail: info@qandasolicitors.co.uk

RHF SOLICITORS ‡
25 Cross Street Manchester Greater Manchester M2 1WL
Tel: 0161 839 9009 *Fax:* 0161 839 6009 *Dx:* 14309 MANCHESTER 1
E-mail: info@rhfsolicitors.co.uk

RH LAW LLP ‡
140 Kingsway Burnage Manchester Greater Manchester M19 1BB
Tel: 0161 286 1111 *Fax:* 0161 610 4411
E-mail: mail@yourfirstdefence.co.uk

RAIN GASKELL SOLICITORS ‡
78a Dickenson Road Longsight Manchester Greater Manchester M14 5HF
Tel: 0161 257 2933 *Fax:* 0161 248 6186
E-mail: info@raingaskell.com

RALLI SOLICITORS ‡
16-17 Ralli Courts West Riverside Manchester Greater Manchester M3 5FT
Tel: 0870 998 9000 *Fax:* 0870 998 9100 *Dx:* 14359 MANCHESTER 1
E-mail: beteshfox@beteshfox.co.uk
List of partners: M J Coyne, S H Fox, M J Rainford
Languages: French, German, Spanish
Work: B1 C1 C2 C3 E G H J1 M1 M2 N O P Q R1 S1 W Z(c,e,f,j,k,l,p)
Emergency Action, Agency, Advocacy, Fixed Fee Interview, Legal Aid undertaken and Member of Accident Line
Ptr: Coyne, Mr Martin J LLB . . . *May 1981
Fox, Mr Stephen H . . . *Dec 1973
Rainford, Mr Michael Joseph LLB . . . *Apr 1981

READ ROPER & READ ‡
(incorporating Merton Clarke & Co)
Alberton House St Mary's Parsonage Manchester Greater Manchester M3 2WJ
Tel: 0161 832 6905 *Fax:* 0161 832 7795 *Dx:* 14377 MANCHESTER 1
E-mail: law@readroper.co.uk
List of partners: A D Fairlie, A G Kay
Work: B1 C1 E F1 J1 K1 N O Q S1 S2 T2 W Z(b)
Emergency Action, Agency, Advocacy, Fixed Fee Interview and Legal Aid undertaken
Ptr: Fairlie, Mr Andrew D BA . . . *Dec 1980
Kay, Mr Andrew G BA . . . *Mar 1979
Asoc: Frost, Mr Dean Robert LLB(Hons) . . . Oct 1996

REGENTS SOLICITORS ‡
18 Whittles Croft 42 Ducie Street Manchester Greater Manchester M1 2DE
Tel: 0161 265 6975 *Fax:* 0161 273 3075
E-mail: enquiries@regents-lawyers.co.uk

RICHARD NELSON BUSINESS DEFENCE SOLICITORS
11th Floor 3 Piccadilly Place Manchester Greater Manchester M1 3BN
Tel: 0161 880 0040 *Fax:* 0161 880 4048
E-mail: defencemanch@richardnelsonllp.co.uk
Office: Bristol, Cardiff, Nottingham, Solihull

RICHARDSON LAW SOLICITORS ‡
3000 Aviator Way Manchester Business Park Manchester Greater Manchester M22 5TG
Tel: 0161 266 1114 *Fax:* 0161 266 1001
E-mail: info@richardsonlaw.org.uk

ROBERTS BUCKLEY ‡
46 Fountain Street Manchester Greater Manchester M2 2BE
Tel: 0161 835 1234 *Fax:* 0161 834 2352
List of partners: R Roberts
Work: C1 E S2
SPr: Roberts, Mr Raymond MA(Oxon) . . . *Dec 1976

PAUL ROSS & COMPANY ‡
Centurion House 129 Deansgate Manchester Greater Manchester M3 3WR
Tel: 0161 832 0706 *Fax:* 0161 832 2228
Emergency telephone 07808 473651
E-mail: pjr@paulrosslaw.co.uk
List of partners: P J Ross
Work: B1 B2 C1 C2 C3 E F1 G H I J1 K1 M1 M2 N O Q S1 Z(b,c,e,f,j,k,q)
Emergency Action, Agency, Advocacy, Fixed Fee Interview, Legal Aid undertaken and Legal Aid Franchise
Ptr: Ross, Mr Paul J BA; LLB . . . *Oct 1982

ROWLEY DICKINSON ‡
Halifax House 93-101 Bridge Street Manchester Greater Manchester M3 2GX
Tel: 0161 834 4215 *Fax:* 0161 834 5153 *Dx:* 14332 MANCHESTER 1
E-mail: info@rowleydickinson.com
List of partners: A J Fitzpatrick, A Hiett, J Tinman, D E Whipp
Office: Leicester
Languages: French, Japanese
Work: B1 C1 C2 E F1 J1 K1 L N O Q R1 R2 S1 S2 W Z(c,e,j,o,p,q,r)
Agency, Advocacy, Fixed Fee Interview, Legal Aid undertaken and Member of Accident Line
Ptr: Fitzpatrick, Mr Alan J . . . *Oct 1981
Hiett, Mr Andrew BA . . . *Nov 1992
Tinman, Mr Jonathan LLB . . . *Nov 1991
Whipp, Mr Daniel Edward LLB(Hons) . . . *Jul 2000
Ast: Barrow, Miss Lorna Louise LLB . . . Jan 2009
Coyle, Mr John C BA . . . *Jul 1979
Evans, Mrs Alison . . . Jan 2004
Lloyd, Mr Ian E . . . Jan 1980
Nield, Mrs Laura Elizabeth BSc(Psychology); PGDipLaw; LPC . . . Sep 2005
Ormes, Mrs Vicky . . . Dec 2006
Woodcock, Ms Beverly Helen LLB(Hons) . . . *Nov 1992

RUSSELL JONES & WALKER
1st Floor St James House 7 Charlotte Street Manchester Greater Manchester M1 4DZ
Tel: 0161 383 3500 *Fax:* 0161 383 3636 *Dx:* 14340 MANCHESTER 1
E-mail: enquiries@rjw.co.uk
Office: Birmingham, Bristol, Cardiff, London WC2, Newcastle upon Tyne, Sheffield, Wakefield
Work: G H J1 N Z(f,p,r)
Emergency Action, Fixed Fee Interview, Legal Aid undertaken, Legal Aid Franchise and Member of Accident Line
Ptr: Franey, Mr David Francis MA(Cantab) . . . Oct 1990
Holroyd, Mr Nicholas B BA(Law) . . . *Oct 1984
Kinsella, Mr Neil J LLB(Manc) . . . *Nov 1983
Ast: Barnard, Ms Alison . . . Oct 1991
Black, Mr Richard Anthony LLB(Cardiff) . . . Apr 1993
Cope, Ms Rachel . . . Nov 1998
Crabtree, Mr Richard Mark LLB(Hons); Dip Pl . . . *Sep 1993
Drinkwater, Ms Katie . . . Sep 1997
Ericsson, Ms Cara . . . Jan 2000
Frieze, Ms Jennie . . . Sep 1996
Gray, Ms Sally-Anne . . . Sep 1999
Harris, Ms Samantha . . . Mar 1999
Hedayati, Ms Amanda . . . Oct 2000
Hesketh, Mr Philip . . . *Nov 1991
Hoey, Ms Caroline . . . Apr 1999
London, Ms Katrina J LLB . . . *Nov 1989
Malik, Waseema . . . Feb 2000
Porter, Mr Craig BA(Hons) . . . *May 1997
Rafferty, M J . . . Nov 2000
Southcott, Mr William LLB . . . Nov 1997
Taylor, Mr Phillip . . . Sep 1997
Tonge, Ms Victoria . . . Sep 1999

RYAN SOLICITORS ‡
St James Building 79 Oxford Street Manchester Greater Manchester M1 6FQ
Tel: 0161 238 8668 *Fax:* 0161 238 8667 *Dx:* 14443 MANCHESTER 2
E-mail: mr@ryanm.co.uk

SALEHS LLP ‡
Didsbury House 748 Wilmslow Road Didsbury Manchester Greater Manchester M20 2DW
Tel: 0161 434 9991 *Fax:* 0161 434 9212 *Dx:* 23155 DIDSBURY
Emergency telephone 0161 434 9991
E-mail: enquiries@salehs.co.uk
List of partners: A R Koffman, H B Lever, M L Rothburn, R I Saleh
Languages: French, Hebrew, Russian
Work: C1 C2 E J1 O R2 S1 S2 T1 W Z(e)
Ptr: Koffman, Mr Andrew R MA(Oxon) . . . *Oct 1987
Lever, Mr H Brian MA(Cantab) . . . *§Oct 1978
Rothburn, Mrs Michelle L LLB . . . *Mar 1988
Saleh, Mr Richard I BA . . . *Jun 1979
Ast: Chanan, Ms Sara Yael . . . Nov 1995
Hilton, Mr Mark Joseph . . . Sep 1997
Lafinhan, Olajide . . . Jul 2004
Simpson, Mr Robert . . . Dec 1995
Stratton, Ms Nicola Sharon . . . Nov 1987
Walton, Mr David Conroy . . . Nov 1995

SANDHILL SOLICITORS ‡
First Floor 34-36 Wilmslow Road Manchester Greater Manchester M14 5TQ
Tel: 0161 249 2280 *Fax:* 0161 248 4885
Dx: 730324 MANCHESTER 52

SEDDON THOMSON ‡
207 Victoria Avenue Blackley Manchester Greater Manchester M9 0RA
Tel: 0161 720 8000 *Fax:* 0161 721 4280
E-mail: solicitors@seddonthomson.co.uk
List of partners: C A Seddon, C F Thomson
Work: D1 D2 G H K1 K2 K3 N Q S1 S2 W Z(l)
Emergency Action, Agency, Advocacy, Fixed Fee Interview, Legal Aid undertaken and Legal Aid Franchise
Ptr: Seddon, Miss Carol A BA . . . *Oct 1980
Thomson, Miss Clare F LLB . . . Dec 1987

SEMPLE FRASER LLP ‡
1 Portland Street Manchester Greater Manchester M1 3BE
Tel: 0161 907 3771 *Fax:* 0161 907 3776
E-mail: info@semplefraser.co.uk

SENTINELS SOLICITORS LTD ‡
792 Wilmslow Road Manchester Greater Manchester M20 6UG
Tel: 0161 998 2862 *Fax:* 0161 902 9097
E-mail: info@sentinelssolicitors.co.uk

SHAH & SONS SOLICITORS ‡
4a Albert Road Manchester Greater Manchester M19 3PJ
Tel: 0161 224 8444 *Fax:* 0161 224 2577
E-mail: shsale907@aol.com

SHAMMAH NICHOLLS LLP ‡
340 Deansgate Manchester Greater Manchester M3 4LY
Tel: 0161 832 9272 *Fax:* 0161 834 4727 *Dx:* 14328 MANCHESTER
E-mail: mail@shammahnicholls.com
List of partners: M Benjamin, M Dennis, R Furniss, S Hadlow, J J Johnston, T Jones, R A Rubin, L J Ryder, G R Sher
Languages: French
Work: B1 C1 C2 C3 D1 E F1 G J1 K1 L M1 M2 N O P Q R1 R2 S1 S2 T1 T2 W Z(b,c,d,e,j,k,l,o,s)
Emergency Action, Agency and Advocacy undertaken
Ptr: Benjamin, Mr Mark LLB . . . *Sep 1989
Dennis, Mr Mark . . . *Aug 1997
Furniss, Miss Rachel LLB . . . *Feb 2000
Hadlow, Mr Stephen LLB . . . Sep 2000
Johnston, Mr Joseph James LLB . . . *Oct 1992
Jones, Mr Thomas BSc; LLB . . . *§Feb 1975
Rubin, Mr Roger A LLB(Manc) Rylands Prize . . . *Oct 1990
Ryder, Miss Leanne Jane LLB . . . *Sep 2002
Sher, Mr Gregory Robert LLB . . . Jul 2000
Asoc: Crewe, Mr Peter Francis LLB . . . Sep 2005
Ast: Ducker, Mr Nick LLB . . . May 2008
Haigh, Mr James LLB . . . Sep 2008
Rich, Mr Darren Stuart LLB . . . *Jan 2002
White, Mrs Cherie LLB . . . *Sep 2003
Con: Shammah, Mr Joseph E BA . . . *§Jun 1975
Wish, Mr Ian . . . May 1987

SHANKLYS SOLICITORS LTD ‡
56 Bury New Road Manchester Greater Manchester M25 0JU
Tel: 0161 773 5222 *Fax:* 0161 773 9555
E-mail: abidghani@shanklys.com

SHOOSMITHS
3 Hardman Street Spinningfields Manchester Greater Manchester M3 3HF
Tel: 0370 086 5600 / 01604 543000 *Fax:* 0370 086 3001
Dx: 14393 MANCHESTER
E-mail: manchester@shoosmiths.co.uk
Office: Basingstoke, Birmingham, Fareham, London WC2, Milton Keynes, Northampton, Nottingham, Reading

RICHARD SILVER ‡
Lloyds House 18 Lloyd Street Manchester Greater Manchester M2 5WA
Tel: 0161 834 9494 *Fax:* 0161 834 8494
Emergency telephone 0161 834 9494
E-mail: mail@richardsilver.co.uk
List of partners: R Silver
Work: B2 G H J2
Emergency Action, Agency, Advocacy, Fixed Fee Interview, Legal Aid undertaken and Legal Aid Franchise
SPr: Silver, Mr Richard BA(Hons) ★ . . . *Oct 1986
Asoc: Mafham, Ms Alison Emily Ruth LLB ★ . . . Feb 2003

SILVERDALE SOLICITORS ‡
Silverdale House 404 Cheetham Hill Road Manchester Greater Manchester M8 9LE
Tel: 0161 740 0333 *Fax:* 0161 492 0308
E-mail: enquiries@silverdalelaw.co.uk

SIMON ADAMS SOLICITORS ‡
452a Bury Old Road Prestwich Manchester Greater Manchester M25 1PQ
Tel: 0161 773 2222 *Fax:* 0161 773 2322
E-mail: info@simonadams.info
Languages: French, Hebrew

ROBIN SIMON LLP
80 Mosley Street St Peter's Square Manchester Greater Manchester M2 3FX
Tel: 0333 010 0000 *Fax:* 0333 010 0006 *Dx:* 14435 MANCHESTER 2
E-mail: info@robinsimonllp.com
Office: Birmingham, Leeds, London EC3
Languages: French, Spanish
Work: O Z(c,j,q)
Ptr: Dally, Mr Paul LLB . . . *Nov 1988
Innes, Mr Niall . . . Sep 1997
MacLeod, Mr Andrew L . . . *Nov 1992
Mem: Jenkyn-Jones, Mr Mark MA(Hons) . . . *§Sep 1996

SIMPSON MILLAR LLP
Trafford House Chester Road Manchester Greater Manchester M32 0RS
Tel: 0844 858 3300 *Fax:* 0844 858 3399 *Dx:* 742100 STRETFORD 5
E-mail: info@simpsonmillar.co.uk
Office: Birmingham, Bristol, Cardiff, Gateshead, Leeds, London EC1, London SW19

Work: A1 A3 B1 C1 C2 D1 D2 E F1 F2 J1 J2 K1 K2 K3 K4 M2 M3 N O P Q R1 R2 S1 S2 T1 T2 U2 V W X Z(b,c,d,e,h,j,m,o,p,q,r,t,za)
Member of Accident Line

THE SKEMP PARTNERSHIP ‡
3rd Floor St James' Building 79 Oxford Street Manchester Greater Manchester M1 6FQ
Tel: 0800 040 7566 / 0161 238 5400 *Fax:* 0161 238 5401
Dx: 14400 MANCHESTER 2
Emergency telephone 0161 446 1000
E-mail: info@pisolicitors.com
List of partners: J M Kushnick
Work: K1 N S1
Legal Aid undertaken and Member of Accident Line
Ptr: Kushnick, Mr John M LLB. . . . . *Nov 1992

SMITHSONS ‡
Eagle Buildings 64 Cross Street Manchester Greater Manchester M2 4JQ
Tel: 0844 888 0551 *Fax:* 0844 888 0552
E-mail: alison@smithsonlaw.net

THE SOLOMON PARTNERSHIP SOLICITORS LLP
973 Stockport Road Manchester Greater Manchester M19 3NP
Tel: 0161 225 2555 *Fax:* 0161 224 0857
Dx: 22327 HEATON CHAPEL
E-mail: info@thesolomonpartnership.com
Office: Blackburn

SQUIRE SANDERS (UK) LLP
Trinity Court 16 John Dalton Street Manchester Greater Manchester M60 8HS
Tel: 0161 830 5000 *Fax:* 0161 830 5001 *Dx:* 14347 MANCHESTER 1
Office: Birmingham, Leeds, London EC2
Languages: French, German, Italian
Work: A2 A3 B1 B2 B3 C1 C2 C3 E F1 I J1 J2 K1 L M1 M2 N O P Q R1 R2 S2 T1 T2 U1 U2 W X Z(b,c,e,f,g,h,j,l,m,n,o,p,q,t,y,z)
Emergency Action, Advocacy, Fixed Fee Interview, Legal Aid undertaken, Legal Aid Franchise and Member of Accident Line
Ptr: Bratt, Mr Paul LLB(Hons) . . . . *Sep 1992
Bridgford, Mr Tom R LLB(Sheff). . . . . Nov 1994
Buckley, Mr Liam J LLB . . . . Dec 1987
Dammone, Mr Luciano LLB . . . . *Oct 1983
Downs, Mr William N MA(Cantab). . . . . *Nov 1982
Edwards, Mr Jonathan D L BA . . . . Oct 1991
Elvin, Mr Robert James LLB(Hons)(Sheff). . . . . . . *Oct 1995
Haxby, Ms Jane. . . . . Oct 1995
Jones, Mr Nicolas Alan LLB. . . . . *May 1993
Jones, Ms Patricia . . . . *Nov 1995
Kelly, Mrs Susan Mary BA. . . . . Nov 1988
Levy, Mr Stephen Peter LLB. . . . . Oct 1990
Moss, Mr David J LLB. . . . . *Oct 1986
Nickson, Ms Susan Carol MA(Cantab); BA William McNair Prize 1985; Tapp Postgraduate Scholarship Member of the Council of Salford University. . . . . Oct 1988
Shepherd, Ms Claire . . . . Nov 1990
Shepherd, Mr Michael Lloyd MA(Oxon) . . . . *Dec 1969
Warburton, Mr Darren LLB . . . . Oct 1991
West, Mr Andrew M LLB(Brunel) . . . . *Nov 1989
Ast: Barker, Mr John Mark. . . . . Jul 2001
Burtinshaw, Ms Catherine Frances . . . . Oct 1998
Byrne, Ms Juliet Katherine . . . . Sep 1997
Carmichael, Ms Samantha Joy . . . . Mar 1999
Connell, Mr Kevin John . . . . Dec 1999
Coutsavlis, Mr Stelio S LLB(Hons). . . . . Feb 1987
Donaldson, Mr Peter Wilson. . . . . Sep 2000
Elderton, Ms Sarah Louise . . . . Oct 1995
Firth, Mrs Judith Elizabeth LLB(Hons) . . . . *Oct 1992
Foulke, Mr Robert James BA . . . . Jul 1998
Hilton, Ms Caroline . . . . Oct 1997
Houghton, Mrs Fiona . . . . Sep 1997
Innes, Mr Niall . . . . Sep 1997
Joneja, Mr Sunil. . . . . Apr 2000
Lawrence, Ms Claire Alicia . . . . Jan 2000
McConnell, Ms Anita . . . . Sep 1999
McIlroy, Mr Bernard Patrick . . . . Feb 1999
Mason, Mr Jon . . . . Sep 2000
Munro, Mr Andrew R . . . . Sep 1998
Neary, Ms Julia M. . . . . Aug 1998
O'Reilly, Ms Carol L. . . . . Oct 1992
Ost, Mr Simon D . . . . Sep 2000
Page, Mr Andrew D S. . . . . Sep 2000
Patchett, Ms Emma Caroline Margaret . . . . *Sep 1999
Pickering, Ms Kathryn Fay. . . . . Sep 2000
Quaid, Ms Olivia Maria . . . . Jan 2001
Robbins, Mrs Louisa . . . . Oct 1994
Schmit, Ms Kathryn Frances Eugenie . . . . Sep 2000
Scott, Mr David Julian. . . . . Sep 1999
Shopland, Ms Emma Karoline. . . . . Sep 1998
Simpson, Ms Sarah . . . . Sep 1999
Southern, Mr Steven Mark LLB(Hons). . . . . *Oct 1996
Topham, Ms Amanda . . . . Nov 1990
Vayro, Mr David A BA. . . . . *Feb 1988
Warren-Jones, Mr Martin Paul. . . . . Apr 2000
Woodside, Ms Karen Jane . . . . Sep 1998

STEPHENSONS SOLICITORS LLP
City Wharf 30 New Bailey Street Manchester Greater Manchester M3 5ER
Tel: 0161 832 8844 *Fax:* 0161 832 8912 *Dx:* 13747 MANCHESTER
E-mail: enquiries@stephensons.co.uk
Office: Bolton (2 offices), Leigh (2 offices), St Helens, Wigan (2 offices)
Ptr: Devlin, Mr Michael D BSc(Econ) . . . . *Dec 1981
Jones, Mr Martin D BA . . . . *Mar 1982
Malone, Mr Campbell J LLB. . . . . *Jan 1969
Ast: Pizzey, Mr Martin S LLB. . . . . *Sep 1996
Roberts, Mrs Donna LLB . . . . *Mar 1992
Towey, Mr Gerald P LLB . . . . Jan 1986

STIRLING LAW COMMERCIAL LAW FIRM ‡
Westpoint 3-9 Duke Street Manchester Greater Manchester M3 4NF
Tel: 0161 241 5510 *Dx:* 14348 MANCHESTER 1

STOCKSLEGAL LTD ‡
Kingsway House 473 Kingsway Burnage Manchester Greater Manchester M19 1NR
Tel: 0800 988 9055
List of partners: J F Trick
Dir: Trick, Mr John F BA. . . . . Nov 1993

STOKOE PARTNERSHIP
Boatmans 40 City Road East Manchester Greater Manchester M15 4QF
Tel: 0161 237 5755 *Fax:* 0161 237 5700
Dx: 718152 MANCHESTER 3
E-mail: enquiries@stokoepartnership.com
Office: London E11, London WC2
Ptr: Babar, Mr Jawad LLB(Hons) . . . . *Mar 2000
Asoc: Kennaugh, Miss Gillian . . . . Nov 2002

STRIPES SOLICITORS ‡
Ship Canal House King Street Manchester Greater Manchester M2 4WU
Tel: 0161 832 5000 *Dx:* 709035 MANCHESTER 7

SYEDS SOLICITORS
366a Cheetham Hill Road Manchester Greater Manchester M8 9LS
Tel: 0161 795 2111 *Fax:* 0161 795 2444
E-mail: info@syedssolicitors.com
Office: Birmingham

SYSTECH SOLICITORS
7th Floor Mosley Street Manchester Greater Manchester M2 3FX
Tel: 0161 219 8008 *Fax:* 0161 219 8009
Office: Leeds, Liverpool, London SE1

TJL SOLICITORS ‡
3 Talbot Road Old Trafford Manchester Greater Manchester M16 0QL
Tel: 0800 634 0280 *Fax:* 0161 877 1066

TM FORTIS SOLICITOR ‡
131 Wilbraham Road Fallowfield Manchester Greater Manchester M14 7DS
Tel: 0161 220 6040 *Fax:* 0161 220 6041
E-mail: info@tmfortis.co.uk

TPC SOLICITORS ‡
Market Square Building 85 High Street Manchester Greater Manchester M4 1BD
Tel: 0161 832 8867 *Fax:* 0161 832 8070
E-mail: info@tpclaw.co.uk
Work: J1 N Z(p,r)
Emergency Action, Agency, Advocacy, Fixed Fee Interview, Legal Aid undertaken and Member of Accident Line
Ast: Robinson, Mr Brian LLB(Hons); Dip Pl Lit . . . . . . *Feb 1991

TAHIR SOLICITORS ‡
Feroz House 435 Cheetham Hill Road Manchester Greater Manchester M8 0PF
Tel: 0161 740 2333 *Fax:* 0161 740 2444
Emergency telephone 07979 078654
E-mail: team1@tahirsolicitor.com
Languages: Chinese, Hindi, Malay, Mirpuri, Punjabi, Urdu
Work: G J1 K3 N O Q S1 S2 V W Z(g,i,l)
Emergency Action, Agency, Advocacy and Fixed Fee Interview undertaken

TARRAN & CO ‡
Bridge Street Chambers 72 Bridge Street Manchester Greater Manchester M3 2RJ
Tel: 0161 834 3689 *Fax:* 0161 834 6340

ANGELA TAYLOR CRIMINAL SOLICITORS ‡
851-853 Stockport Road Manchester Greater Manchester M19 3PW
Tel: 0161 256 2233 *Fax:* 0161 256 2244
E-mail: angelamtaylor1@aol.com
Ast: Doherty, Mr Declan . . . . Nov 2005

MICHAEL TAYLOR & ASSOCIATES
3rd Floor 5 New York Street Manchester Greater Manchester M1 4JB
Tel: 0161 255 2700 *Fax:* 0161 255 2701
Dx: 709046 MANCHESTER 7
E-mail: info@mtasolicitors.com
Office: Bromley, Urmston

TAYLORS
Ninth Floor 80 Mosley Street Manchester Greater Manchester M2 3FX
Tel: 0844 800 0263 *Fax:* 0844 800 0264
E-mail: contact@taylors.co.uk
Office: Blackburn
Work: B1 C1 C2 C3 E I J1 J2 L M1 M2 O P Q R1 R2 S2 U2 Z(b,c,e,o,q)
Ptr: Bowers, Mr Christopher David BJuris(Oxon). . . . . *Aug 2000
Catterall, Mr Anthony R MA(Cantab) . . . . *§Jun 1978
Livesey, Mr Andrew J BA . . . . *Nov 1985
Niven, Mr Mark Simon LLB(Hons)(B'ham). . . . . . . *Sep 2005
Scott, Mr Christopher Granville BA(Brunel College) . . *Jan 1981
Asoc: Cowell, Mr James LLB(Hons) . . . . Mar 2001
Ast: Barron, Miss Charlotte LLB(Hons). . . . . Jul 2010
Daniels, Mrs Rebecca LLB(Hons) . . . . *Aug 2007

THOMPSONS (FORMERLY ROBIN/BRIAN THOMPSON & PARTNERS)
23 Princess Street Manchester Greater Manchester M2 4ER
Tel: 0161 819 3500 *Fax:* 0161 832 1676
Dx: 14357 MANCHESTER 1
Office: Belfast, Birmingham, Bristol, Cardiff, Chelmsford, Dagenham, Derby, Harrow, Leeds, Liverpool, London SW19, London WC1, Middlesbrough, Newcastle upon Tyne, Nottingham, Plymouth, Sheffield, South Shields, Southampton, Stoke-on-Trent, Swansea, Wolverhampton
Work: J1 J2 N Z(p)
Fixed Fee Interview, Legal Aid undertaken and Member of Accident Line
Ptr: Denham, Mr Alan LLB(Hons) . . . . Dec 1975
Strogen, Mr Christopher J LLB . . . . Oct 1991
Ast: Knaggs, Mr Spencer . . . . *Sep 1998
Osborn, Mrs Anne T LLB(Hons). . . . . *Feb 1993
Porter, Mrs Paula Jayne. . . . . *Sep 1998
Turnbull, Mr Mark Cameron . . . . *Nov 1995
Wetton, Ms Imogen J BA(Hons). . . . . Apr 1998
Wilson, Mr Alan A LLB(Hons) . . . . *Feb 1994
Yates, Ms Dianne M LLB(Hons); Dip PI . . . . *Mar 1990

THORNHILLS ‡
66 Oldham Road Manchester Greater Manchester M4 5EE
Tel: 0161 228 3003 *Fax:* 0161 228 1991

TOBINS SOLICITORS ‡
St Andrews Chambers 20-21 Albert Square Manchester Greater Manchester M2 5PE
Tel: 0161 884 0950 *Fax:* 0161 837 6255

TOTAL LAW ‡
Portland Tower 53 Portland Street Manchester Greater Manchester M1 3LF
Tel: 0161 238 4990 *Fax:* 0161 238 4991 *Dx:* 1441 MANCHESTER 2
E-mail: info@totallaw.co.uk

TOWNS NEEDHAM & CO ‡
(in association with John Redmond)
2nd Floor Kingsgate 51-53 South King Street Manchester Greater Manchester M2 6DE
Tel: 0161 832 3721 *Fax:* 0161 835 3792
Dx: 14369 MANCHESTER 1
List of partners: C Colburn, E Gilliland, A C Middleton, J M Towns
Work: B1 C1 C2 E F1 J1 L N O P Q R1 S1 S2 T2 V W Z(d,o,r,x)
Agency, Advocacy and Fixed Fee Interview undertaken
Ptr: Colburn, Mrs Carol LLB . . . . *Oct 1993
Gilliland, Mrs E LLB Part time Chairman of VAT and Duties Tribunals . . . . *Dec 1970
Middleton, Mr Andrew C LLB . . . . *Mar 1985
Towns, Mr J Michael LLB(Sheff). . . . . *Dec 1973
Ast: Carr, Mr John LLB(Hons) . . . . *Jul 1992
Higgs, Mr Simon Mark BA(Hons)(Econ) . . . . *Dec 1994
Jordan, Miss Carol Ann LLB. . . . . Oct 1990
Knott, Mrs Janet LLB . . . . *Dec 1979
Con: Oldham, Mr N Hartley LLB . . . . *Nov 1957

TRANTER CLEERE & CO ‡
210 Hollyhedge Road Wythenshawe Manchester Greater Manchester M22 4QN
Tel: 0161 428 1569 *Fax:* 0161 491 2789
Emergency telephone 01850 946315
List of partners: A P Cleere
Work: D1 G H J1 K1 L N Q V
Emergency Action, Agency, Advocacy, Fixed Fee Interview, Legal Aid undertaken and Member of Accident Line
Ptr: Cleere, Mr Anthony P BA(Law) . . . . Nov 1985

TRANTERS ‡
116-120 Sale Road Sale Circle Northern Moor Manchester Greater Manchester M23 0BX
Tel: 0161 998 9999 *Fax:* 0161 998 3399
Emergency telephone 0800 731 9042
List of partners: J Barstow, A W Fernie, S Tranter
Office: Manchester, Stockport
Work: G H N
Emergency Action, Advocacy and Legal Aid undertaken

TROWERS & HAMLINS
(in association with Singapore)
Heron House Albert Square Manchester Greater Manchester M2 5HD
Tel: 0161 211 0000 *Fax:* 0161 211 0001 *Dx:* 14323 MANCHESTER 1
E-mail: enquiries@trowers.com
Office: Exeter, London EC3
Work: B1 C1 E F1 J1 K1 L Q S1 T1 W Z(c,h)
Ptr: Bode, Mr Adrian F. . . . . *Apr 1978
Turner, Mr Graham F . . . . *Apr 1971
Winrow, Ms Janet A. . . . . *Oct 1982
Ast: Lake, Ms Jane . . . . *Jan 1991

AMIE TSANG & CO ‡
44 George Street Manchester Greater Manchester M1 4HF
Tel: 0161 236 8821 *Fax:* 0161 236 8388
Dx: 14449 MANCHESTER 2
E-mail: amie@amietsang.co.uk
List of partners: H A Tsang
Languages: Cantonese, Hakka
Work: G H K1 L N Q S1 W Z(i,l)
Emergency Action, Agency, Advocacy, Fixed Fee Interview, Legal Aid undertaken and Member of Accident Line
SPr: Tsang, Miss Hon-Ying Amie LLB . . . . Jul 1994

TUCKERS ‡
63-65 Mosley Street Manchester Greater Manchester M2 3HZ
Tel: 0161 233 4321 *Fax:* 0161 233 4333
Dx: 14451 MANCHESTER 2
Emergency telephone 0161 233 4321
List of partners: J J de Beauvoir Carey, R Egan, J E Meyer, F M Sinclair, P S Smith, B M Tucker, J Turner
Office: Birmingham, London SE5, London W1
Languages: French, German, Italian, Spanish
Work: D1 G H K1
Emergency Action, Agency, Advocacy, Fixed Fee Interview, Legal Aid undertaken and Legal Aid Franchise
Ptr: Sinclair, Mr Franklin M LLB(Hons). . . . . *Oct 1982
Asoc: Smith, Mr John Barry BA(Hons)(Law) . . . . *Nov 1994
Ast: Ahmed, Samina. . . . . Mar 2005
Ali, Asim . . . . Dec 2006
Johnstone, Mr William J I . . . . *Dec 1991
Sweetman, Ms Dawn . . . . Sep 2005
Watson, Joanne. . . . . Apr 2006

TURNER PARKINSON ‡
Hollins Chambers 64a Bridge Street Manchester Greater Manchester M3 3BA
Tel: 0161 833 1212 *Fax:* 0161 834 9098 *Dx:* 14373 MANCHESTER
E-mail: tp@tp.co.uk
List of partners: J D Blackburn, A W Booth, N F Davenport, D S Lund, R M Lund, A M J Openshaw-Blower, R C W Parkinson, A Sturge
Work: A1 A3 B1 C1 C2 C3 E F2 I J1 K1 K2 L M1 M2 O Q R1 R2 S1 S2 U2 W Z(b,c,e,f,k,p,q)
Agency, Advocacy and Fixed Fee Interview undertaken
Ptr: Blackburn, Mr J David LLB(Hons) . . . . Dec 1971
Booth, Mr Andrew William BA(Hons) . . . . Nov 1994
Davenport, Mr Nicholas F. . . . . Nov 1978
Lund, Mrs Davina Sharon LLB(Hons) . . . . *Feb 1989
Lund, Mr Richard M LLB(Manc); MABRP . . . . Oct 1987
Openshaw-Blower, Mr A Mark J MA(Hons) . . . . . . *Oct 1989
Parkinson, Mr Richard Christopher William LLB(Hons). Dec 1987
Sturge, Mr Andrew . . . . Aug 2000
Con: Johnson, Mrs Colette D LLB . . . . Feb 1990

UNITED SOLICITORS ‡
936-938 Stockport Road Manchester Greater Manchester M19 3NN
Tel: 0161 225 8181 *Fax:* 0161 249 0384
E-mail: enquiries@united-solicitors.co.uk

See p112 for the Key to Work Categories & other symbols

RHYS VAUGHAN ‡
382 Dickenson Road Longsight Manchester Greater Manchester M13 0WQ
Tel: 0161 224 1439 *Fax:* 0161 257 2779
List of partners: S L Lockwood, R H Vaughan
Work: B2 D1 F1 G H K1 L W
Emergency Action, Agency, Advocacy, Legal Aid undertaken and Legal Aid Franchise
Ptr: Lockwood, Miss Sandra L LLB(Wales) . . . . *Dec 1980
Vaughan, Mr Rhys H LLB; Dip Soc Admin ● . . . . . . *Dec 1975
Ast: Mitchell, Miss Lucy Elizabeth BA(Hons); DipLP . . . . Feb 2000

VERSUS LAW SOLICITORS ‡
Mercantile House 10 Lapwing Lane Manchester Greater Manchester M20 2WS
Tel: 0845 555 0606 *Fax:* 0845 555 0909 *Dx:* 23156 DIDSBURY
E-mail: info@versuslaw.co.uk

WE SOLICITORS LLP ‡
Ivy Mill Crown Street Failsworth Manchester Greater Manchester M35 9BG
Tel: 0870 165 9413 / 0161 684 3722

WEIGHTMANS LLP
First Floor Three Piccadilly Place Manchester Greater Manchester M1 3BN
Tel: 0161 233 7330 *Fax:* 0161 233 7331
Dx: 743520 MANCHESTER 65
Office: Birmingham, Dartford, Knutsford, Leicester, Liverpool, London EC4, Manchester
Mem: Garlick, Ms Michelle M LLB(Hons); LSF . . . . *§Oct 1992
Jones, Rachel . . . . Oct 1995
Macleod, Mr John R LLB . . . . *§Nov 1987

WEIGHTMANS LLP
Pall Mall Court 61-67 King Street Manchester Greater Manchester M2 4PD
Tel: 0161 233 7330 *Fax:* 0161 233 7331 *Dx:* 18564 MANCHESTER 7
Office: Birmingham, Dartford, Knutsford, Leicester, Liverpool, London EC4, Manchester
Work: A1 B1 C1 C2 C3 D1 E F1 G H I J1 K1 L M1 N O P Q R1 R2 S1 S2 T1 T2 U1 U2 W Z(b,c,e,k,l,o,p,q,r)
Emergency Action, Agency, Advocacy, Fixed Fee Interview, Legal Aid undertaken and Member of Accident Line
Mem: Corran, Mr Richard Stephen BSc . . . . *Dec 1993
Harris, Mr Robert C MA(Oxon) . . . . *Dec 1979
Jackson, Mr Thomas Karl G. . . . . *Oct 1989
Jump, Mr Graeme K Licensed Insolvency Practitioner . *Dec 1969
Maharaj, Varun . . . . *Jan 1991
Raftery, Mr Paul M LLB . . . . *Nov 1989
Salmon, Mr Kenneth T FILEx; MCIArb P J Lewis Prize . . . . *§Mar 1973
Steventon, Miss Andrea LLB(Hons) . . . . *Jul 1997
Thompson, Mr Alan C LLB . . . . *Feb 1974
Tomlinson, Mr Charles . . . . Jan 1997
Williams, Mr Timothy R . . . . *Nov 1967
Yardley, Mr Michael D LLB . . . . *Feb 1991
Ast: Vincent, Mr Martin. . . . . Mar 2008
Walton, Miss Sarah Vicki Louise LLB . . . . Mar 2002
Con: Denton, Mr Lewis A LLB . . . . *Nov 1971

WESTWOOD SOLICITORS ‡
Carlton House 16-18 Albert Square Manchester Greater Manchester M2 5PE
Tel: 0161 832 6178 *Fax:* 0161 832 6147 *Dx:* 14355 MANCHESTER
E-mail: info@westwood-solicitors.co.uk

WHITWORTH & GREEN SOLICITORS ‡
52 Bridge Street Manchester Greater Manchester M3 3BW
Tel: 0161 832 3547 *Fax:* 0161 832 4561
E-mail: claims@wgsolicitors.co.uk

R K WILCOCK ‡
Peter House Oxford Street Manchester Greater Manchester M1 5AN
Tel: 0161 602 3395
E-mail: kenwilcock@rkwlaw.co.uk
List of partners: R K Wilcock
Work: C1 E R2 S1 S2 W
SPr: Wilcock, Mr Robert Kenneth Notary Public . . . . . *§Jan 1966

WILSON GUNN PATENT AND TRADE MARK ATTORNEYS ‡
5th Floor Blackfriars House The Parsonage Manchester Greater Manchester M3 2JA
Tel: 0161 827 9400 *Fax:* 0161 832 4905
E-mail: manchester@wilsongunn.com
Work: Z(e)

WOLFSON & CO ‡
60 Talbot Road Manchester Greater Manchester M16 0PN
Tel: 0161 873 8999 *Fax:* 0161 877 9600
E-mail: info@wolfsonlaw.co.uk
List of partners: W Z Bergson, D A Wacks, L Wolfson
Languages: French, Hebrew
Work: C1 J1 K1 N O Q S1 W
Agency, Advocacy, Fixed Fee Interview and Legal Aid undertaken
Ptr: Bergson, Mr Warren Z LLB . . . . *Oct 1979
Wacks, Mr David A BA . . . . *Jan 1977
Wolfson, Mr Louis LLM; ACIArb . . . . *Dec 1990

DAVID YIP & CO SOLICITORS ‡
First Floor 59-61 Faulkner Street Manchester Greater Manchester M1 4FF
Tel: 0161 236 1880 *Fax:* 0161 850 1168
E-mail: info@dysolicitors.co.uk

YU & CO SOLICITORS ‡
111 Piccadilly Manchester Greater Manchester M1 2HY
Tel: 0161 638 0960 *Fax:* 0161 980 5594
E-mail: info@yusolicitors.co.uk

ZATMAN & CO ‡
1 The Cottages Deva Centre Trinity Way Manchester Greater Manchester M3 7BE
Tel: 0161 832 2500 *Fax:* 0161 834 4826 *Dx:* 14321 MANCHESTER 1
E-mail: mail@zatman.com
List of partners: D Berger, D Black, A N Haffner, A Shore, P Stedman, A B Zatman
Work: B1 C1 C2 C3 E G L M1 M2 N P S1 W Z(b,c,h)
Emergency Action, Agency, Advocacy, Legal Aid undertaken and Member of Accident Line
Ptr: Berger, Mr Daniel LLB. . . . . *Aug 1992
Black, Mr Dov LLB(Hons) . . . . Sep 1998
Haffner, Mr Andrew Nathan BA(Hons). . . . . Jul 1997
Shore, Anselm LLB . . . . *May 1974
Stedman, Mr Paul LLB . . . . *Oct 1992
Zatman, Mr Andrew B BA(Law); MBA . . . . *§Apr 1974
Ast: Beattie, Ms Victoria LLB(Hons) . . . . Nov 1999
Hackett, Miss Elaine LLB . . . . Nov 1987
Lucas, Mr John F BA(Law) . . . . §Jun 1981
Zatman, Mr Benjamin BA . . . . Feb 2007

MANNINGTREE, Essex

SPARLING BENHAM & BROUGH ‡
13 High Street Manningtree Essex CO11 1AQ
Tel: 01206 392201 *Fax:* 01206 396394
List of partners: R O Bartholomew
Work: A1 B1 C1 C2 C3 D1 E F1 G H J1 K1 L N O P R1 S1 T1 T2 W Z(c,d,j,k,l,m,o,s,t)
Agency, Advocacy, Fixed Fee Interview, Legal Aid undertaken and Member of Accident Line
Ptr: Bartholomew, Mr Robert O . . . . *§Dec 1977

MANSFIELD, Nottinghamshire

AGR SOLICITORS ‡
98 Nottingham Road Mansfield Nottinghamshire NG18 1BP
Tel: 01623 460444 *Fax:* 01623 460445 *Dx:* 10344 MANSFIELD
E-mail: bory@agr-solicitor.co.uk
List of partners: H A Hawkins, B C R Ory
Office: Shirebrook
Languages: Spanish
Work: C1 E F1 K1 K3 K4 L N O Q S1 S2 V W
Emergency Action, Agency, Advocacy, Fixed Fee Interview and Legal Aid undertaken
Ptr: Hawkins, Miss Harriet Ann LLB . . . . Mar 2001
Ory, Mr Bernard C R LLB . . . . *Oct 1970
Ast: Turner, Mr Marc LLB(Hons) . . . . *Aug 1995

BHATIA BEST
Halifax Buildings 39 Westgate Mansfield Nottinghamshire NG18 1RX
Tel: 01623 427944 *Fax:* 01623 427955 *Dx:* 10371 MANSFIELD
Office: Derby, Nottingham
Legal Aid Franchise

BILTON HAMMOND LLP ‡
(in association with Alfred Slack & Co)
The Corner House Union Street Mansfield Nottinghamshire NG18 1RP
Tel: 01623 675800 *Fax:* 01623 675863 *Dx:* 10348 MANSFIELD
Emergency telephone 01246 275448
E-mail: markbilton@biltonhammond.co.uk
List of partners: E Bilton, G Bilton, S M Bilton, R Davies, M Maiden
Office: Chesterfield
Languages: German
Work: C1 D1 E F1 G H J1 K1 L N R1 S1 W
Emergency Action, Agency, Advocacy, Fixed Fee Interview and Legal Aid undertaken
Ptr: Bilton, Miss Elizabeth LLB; Dip PI . . . . Nov 1993
Bilton, Mr Geoffrey LLB(Sheff). . . . . *Feb 1955
Bilton, Mr Stephen Mark LLB(Sheff); MBA. . . . . . . *Oct 1985
Davies, Mr Richard BA(Hons) . . . . Nov 2000
Maiden, Mr Matthew. . . . . Feb 2002
Ast: Bilton, Mr Paul ★ . . . . Feb 1984
Hoffman, Ms Melanie . . . . Nov 2008
Con: Hammond, Mr Julian C LLB(Newc) . . . . *Jun 1973

BROADBENTS
84 Nottingham Road Mansfield Nottinghamshire NG18 1BP
Tel: 01623 412870
Office: Alfreton, Chesterfield, Derby, Heanor, Sutton-in-Ashfield

BRYAN & ARMSTRONG ‡
The Old Meeting House Stockwell Gate Mansfield Nottinghamshire NG18 1LG
Tel: 01623 626039 *Fax:* 01623 635077 *Dx:* 10346 MANSFIELD
E-mail: enquiries@bryanandarmstrong.co.uk
Web: www.bryanandarmstrong.co.uk
List of partners: N E Croston, M F Dixon, A B L Donen, S Harrison, C J Perry
Office: Mansfield
Work: F1 J1 N O Q S1 S2 W Z(d)
Advocacy, Fixed Fee Interview, Legal Aid undertaken and Legal Aid Franchise
Ptr: Croston, Mr Nevil E LLB. . . . . *Oct 1977
Harrison, Mrs Susan LLB . . . . *Nov 1995

Other office in Mansfield. Holders of LA franchise for Matrimonial & Family, Employment and Criminal Law. All private client work carried out at this office.

BRYAN & ARMSTRONG
The New Meeting House Station Street Mansfield Nottinghamshire NG18 1EF
Tel: 01623 624505 *Fax:* 01623 623956 *Dx:* 10346 MANSFIELD
Emergency telephone 01733 604614 / 07779 428566
E-mail: enquiries@bryanandarmstrong.co.uk
Office: Mansfield
Work: D1 G H K1 K3
Emergency Action, Agency, Advocacy, Fixed Fee Interview, Legal Aid undertaken and Legal Aid Franchise
Ptr: Dixon, Mrs Mary Francesca BA(Hons); PGDipLaw. . . . *Aug 1998
Donen, Mrs Angela Barbara Lorraine LLB . . . . *Apr 1978
Perry, Mr Christopher Jason LLB(Hons) ★ . . . . *Jan 1998
Con: Bacon, Mr Gordon Paul ★. . . . . *Dec 1974

Holders of Franchise for Crime, Matrimonial / Family. We specialise in the following areas of work: Divorce and Matrimonial and Crime. One other office in Mansfield.

ELLIOT MATHER LLP
Westgate House 1 Chesterfield Road South Mansfield Nottinghamshire NG18 5NR
Tel: 01623 655666 *Fax:* 01623 659949 *Dx:* 10347 MANSFIELD
E-mail: admin@elliotmather.co.uk
Office: Chesterfield (2 offices), Matlock
Work: A1 B1 C1 C2 C3 D1 E F1 G H J1 K1 L M1 M2 N P R1 S1 T1 T2 V W Z(b,c,d,e,h,i,j,k,l,m,n,o,p,s,t)
Emergency Action, Agency, Advocacy, Fixed Fee Interview, Legal Aid undertaken and Member of Accident Line
Mem: Anderton, Mr Robert A LLB(Hons). . . . . *Jul 1979
Delgado-Bush, Miss Natalia Louise LLB(Hons) . . . . *Sep 2004
Froggatt, Ms Ruth LLB(Hons) . . . . *Aug 2000
Heppell, Mr Nicholas LLB . . . . *Nov 1992
Johnston, Mr Andrew T LLB. . . . . *Oct 1974
King, Mr Simon R J LLB. . . . . *Mar 1989
Ast: Goodall, Miss Emma Louise LLB(Hons) . . . . Dec 2009
Mahey, Miss Sangeeta LLB(Hons). . . . . *Dec 2009
Neale, Miss Sarah LLB(Hons); PGDip. . . . . Jul 2007

FIDLER & PEPPER
(incorporating Spencer Hogg & Co)
20-22 Queen Street Mansfield Nottinghamshire NG18 1JN
Tel: 01623 451111 *Fax:* 01623 656200 *Dx:* 10365 MANSFIELD
Emergency telephone 0115 987 7538
E-mail: info@fidler.co.uk
Office: Kirkby-in-Ashfield, Sutton-in-Ashfield
Emergency Action, Agency, Advocacy, Fixed Fee Interview, Legal Aid undertaken and Member of Accident Line
Ptr: Dawes, Mr Christopher T LLB(Lond) . . . . *May 1979

GLANSFIELDS ‡
29 St John Street Mansfield Nottinghamshire NG18 1QJ
Tel: 01623 627827 *Fax:* 01623 627739 *Dx:* 715326 MANSFIELD
E-mail: glansfields@lawyersweb.net
List of partners: R Glansfield
Work: D1 D2 G H K1 K3
Emergency Action, Agency, Advocacy, Fixed Fee Interview, Legal Aid undertaken and Legal Aid Franchise
SPr: Glansfield, Mr Robert LLB(Lond) . . . . *Jul 1975

HARMANS ‡
43 Albert Street Mansfield Nottinghamshire NG18 1EA
Tel: 01623 629224 *Fax:* 01623 627754 *Dx:* 10357 MANSFIELD
List of partners: B K E Harman
Work: B1 D1 D2 E F1 F2 G H J1 J2 K1 L N O Q R1 R2 S1 S2 V W Z(c,i,l,p,q,r,s)
Emergency Action, Agency, Advocacy, Fixed Fee Interview, Legal Aid undertaken and Member of Accident Line
SPr: Harman, Mr Barry K E. . . . . *Jun 1970

HARROP WHITE VALLANCE & DAWSON ‡
9-11 Albert Street Mansfield Nottinghamshire NG18 1EA
Tel: 01623 629221 *Fax:* 01623 420933 *Dx:* 10350 MANSFIELD
E-mail: info@harropwhite.co.uk
List of partners: C G Dawson, T J Lander
Work: E G H J1 K1 Q S1 T2 W Z(d)
Agency, Advocacy, Fixed Fee Interview, Legal Aid undertaken and Legal Aid Franchise
Ptr: Dawson, Mr Charles Geoffrey. . . . . *Jun 1977
Lander, Mr Treve J LLB. . . . . Jun 1979

HOPKINS ‡
Eden Court Crow Hill Drive Mansfield Nottinghamshire NG19 7AE
Tel: 01623 468468 *Fax:* 01623 466200 *Dx:* 10349 MANSFIELD 1
E-mail: info@hopkins-solicitors.co.uk
List of partners: I A Corbett, M C Knox, R R Pratt, R Siderfin, P J Todd, D W Winnett, C P Wright, P C Wright
Office: Mansfield, Nottingham
Work: A3 C1 C2 D1 E F1 F2 J1 K1 K2 K3 L N O Q R1 S1 S2 V W Z(c,d,e,h,i,k,l,p,q,r)
Emergency Action, Agency, Advocacy, Fixed Fee Interview, Legal Aid undertaken, Legal Aid Franchise and Member of Accident Line
Ptr: Corbett, Mr Ian Andrew LLB. . . . . Oct 1985
Knox, Mr Martyn C BA . . . . *Dec 1998
Siderfin, Mr Robert BA; LLB ♦. . . . . *Nov 1992
Ast: Pountney, Mrs Julie Ann LLB . . . . *Sep 2006
Stendall, Mr Tom . . . . *Feb 2008
Stevenson, Mr Andrew . . . . *May 2008
Webb, Mrs Amy Diane LLB . . . . Jul 2009
Con: Healey, Mr Roger LLB(Lond) . . . . *Dec 1969

HOPKINS
Waverley House 37 West Gate Mansfield Nottinghamshire NG18 1SH
Tel: 01623 460460 *Fax:* 01623 466170 *Dx:* 10349 MANSFIELD 1
E-mail: info@hopkins-solicitors.co.uk
Office: Mansfield, Nottingham
Work: C1 C2 C3 D1 D2 E F1 F2 J1 K1 K2 K3 L N O P Q R1 S1 S2 V W Z(c,d,h,i,k,l,q,r)
Emergency Action, Agency, Advocacy, Fixed Fee Interview, Legal Aid undertaken, Legal Aid Franchise and Member of Accident Line
Ptr: Todd, Mr Patrick J BA. . . . . *Jun 1992
Wright, Mr Carl Peter LLB. . . . . *Apr 2005
Ast: Ford, Miss Nicola . . . . Aug 2011
Hubbard, Mr Ross LLB . . . . *Nov 2003

J B JARVIS ‡
Mansfield Business Centre Ashfield Avenue Mansfield Nottinghamshire NG18 2AE
Tel: 01623 404360

J B JARVIS ‡
63 Main Street Mansfield Nottinghamshire NG20 8AN
Tel: 01623 747400 *Fax:* 01623 747400
E-mail: solicitors@jbjarvis.com

THE JOHNSON PARTNERSHIP
32-34 Rosemary Street Mansfield Nottinghamshire NG18 1QL
Est: 2007
Tel: 01623 427575 *Fax:* 01623 429463
Emergency telephone 01623 427575
E-mail: mail@jpmansfield.co.uk
Web: www.thejohnsonpartnership.co.uk
Office: Chesterfield, Derby, Nottingham
Work: B2 G H
Emergency Action, Agency, Advocacy, Fixed Fee Interview, Legal Aid undertaken and Legal Aid Franchise
Ptr: Treharne, Miss Louisa Jane LLB(Hons) . . . . *Jul 1998
Ast: Bostock, Mr Andrew LLB(Hons) . . . . *Aug 2005
Edwards, Mrs Abbie LLB(Hons). . . . . *Mar 2008
Wragg, Miss Yvonne LLB(Hons). . . . . *Jul 2010

Criminal Litigation, In-House Counsel, Specialist Fraud Panel Members, Higher Rights Advocate, Prison Law Specialists, Youth Court Specialists, Taxi Licensing.

MARTIN LEE & CO ‡
12 Queens Street Mansfield Nottinghamshire NG18 1JN
Tel: 01623 651886 *Fax:* 01623 651887 *Dx:* 10354 MANSFIELD
E-mail: swilliams@martin-lee.com
Languages: French, German
Work: E L N O Q S1 W Z(h,u)
Agency, Advocacy and Fixed Fee Interview undertaken

M H LEGAL ‡
PO Box 7826 Mansfield Nottinghamshire NG18 4ZL
Tel: 01623 620384 *Fax:* 01623 620384

MARCHANTS SOLICITORS ‡
Regent Chambers Regent Street Mansfield Nottinghamshire NG18 1SW
Tel: 01623 655111 *Fax:* 01623 654757 *Dx:* 10351 MANSFIELD
Emergency telephone 07973 970688
E-mail: legal@marchantsolicitors.co.uk
List of partners: N E Aspley, M C Cummins, J A Sullivan
Office: Kirkby-in-Ashfield
Languages: French
Work: A1 B2 C1 D1 D2 E F1 G H J1 K1 L N O Q R1 R2 S1 S2 T2 V W Z(c,h,l,o,q,r)
Emergency Action, Agency, Advocacy, Fixed Fee Interview, Legal Aid undertaken, Legal Aid Franchise and Member of Accident Line
Ptr: Aspley, Mr Nicholas E LLB . . . *Sep 1993
Cummins, Mr Michael C BA(Law) . . . *Dec 1980
Sullivan, Ms Jayne Annabel . . . Mar 1999
Ast: Calthrop, Mr Jonathan F G LLB(Hons)(Lond) . . . *Oct 1973

O H PARSONS & PARTNERS
42 St John Street Mansfield Nottinghamshire NG18 1QJ
Tel: 01623 274000
Office: London WC2

PHILLIPS ‡
6 Wood Street Mansfield Nottinghamshire NG18 1QA
Tel: 01623 658556 *Fax:* 01623 427530
Emergency telephone 07626 173838
List of partners: S Mansuri, M J Marriott
Languages: French
Work: D1 F1 G H K1 O Q S1 S2 V W Z(i,k,l)
Emergency Action, Agency, Advocacy, Fixed Fee Interview, Legal Aid undertaken and Legal Aid Franchise
Ptr: Mansuri, Ms Sulma . . . *Sep 2000
Marriott, Mr Mark James . . . *Feb 1996
Con: Phillips, Mr Daniel D. . . . *Dec 1969

SHACKLOCKS ‡
St Peter's House Bridge Street Mansfield Nottinghamshire NG18 1AL
Tel: 01623 626141 *Fax:* 01623 658633 *Dx:* 723580 MANSFIELD 10
E-mail: enquiries@shacklocks.co.uk
List of partners: C Parr, N R P Smith, M I Taylor, M E Vesey
Office: Belper, Derby, Ripley
Languages: French
Work: A3 B1 C1 C2 C3 D1 D2 E F1 F2 I J1 J2 K1 K2 K3 K4 L N O P Q R1 R2 S1 S2 T1 T2 U2 V W X Z(c,d,e,j,k,m,o,p,q,r,v,za)
Emergency Action, Agency, Advocacy, Fixed Fee Interview undertaken and Member of Accident Line
Ptr: Smith, Mr Nicholas R P LLB. . . . *§Apr 1973
Vesey, Ms Marion E BA; LLM . . . *Oct 1986
Asoc: Alvey, Mr Jeffrey BA(CNAA); LLM(Lond) . . . Sep 1982
Ast: Fox, Rebecca Susan . . . Oct 2010
Higgins, Mrs Debra Elaine. . . . *Nov 1994

TALLENTS SOLICITORS
28a Westgate Mansfield Nottinghamshire NG18 1RS
Tel: 01623 666700 *Fax:* 01623 621054 *Dx:* 10361 MANSFIELD
E-mail: info@tallents.co.uk
Office: Newark, Southwell
Work: D1 G H K1 K3 Q W Z(l)
Emergency Action, Agency, Advocacy, Fixed Fee Interview, Legal Aid undertaken and Legal Aid Franchise

TURNER ATKINSON & WARD
23 High Street Edwinstowe Mansfield Nottinghamshire NG21 9QP
Tel: 01623 823450 *Fax:* 01623 823450 *Dx:* 12201 WORKSOP
Emergency telephone 01777 870215
Office: Worksop
Work: S1 V W
SPr: Ward, Mr Peter James . . . *§Feb 1973

MARCH, Cambridgeshire

BOWSER OLLARD & BENTLEY
10 Market Square March Cambridgeshire PE15 9JQ
Tel: 01354 652606 *Fax:* 01354 656049 *Dx:* 30950 MARCH
Office: Wisbech
Work: D1 E J1 K1 L N Q S1 S2 V W Z(h)
Emergency Action, Agency, Advocacy, Fixed Fee Interview, Legal Aid undertaken and Legal Aid Franchise
Con: Orbell, Mr John H Notary Public. . . . *§Jul 1965

CHAPPLE & CO ‡
Jade Chambers 15 Dartford Road March Cambridgeshire PE15 8LA
Tel: 01354 652550 *Fax:* 01354 659537 *Dx:* 30951 MARCH
E-mail: david.chapple@chappleandco.net
List of partners: D A Chapple
Languages: French
Work: A1 B1 C1 D1 D2 E F1 G H J1 K1 K3 K4 L N O Q R1 S1 S2 V W X Z(l,t)
Emergency Action, Agency, Advocacy, Fixed Fee Interview, Legal Aid undertaken and Legal Aid Franchise
Ptr: Chapple, Mr David A LLB . . . *May 1978
Ast: Caley, Mrs Ann R LLB. . . . *§Jun 1978
Kirkman, Ms Alma BA. . . . *Sep 2000

GRAHAM DACK & COMPANY
36 Broad Street March Cambridgeshire PE15 8DG
Tel: 01354 661700 *Fax:* 01354 661737
E-mail: enquiries@grahamdack.com
Office: Chatteris

FRASER DAWBARNS
42 High Street March Cambridgeshire PE15 9JR
Tel: 01354 602880 *Fax:* 01354 602889 *Dx:* 30964 MARCH
E-mail: march@fraserdawbarns.com
Office: Downham Market, King's Lynn, Wisbech
Ptr: Ball, Mr Daniel Robert William. . . . Aug 2007
McGregor, Mr Stephen J . . . *Jun 1989
Ast: Summers, Mrs Stefanie Victoria LLB . . . Aug 2007

MARGATE, Kent

BARNES MARSLAND ‡
51 Hawley Square Margate Kent CT9 1NY
Tel: 01843 221466 *Fax:* 01843 290283 *Dx:* 30553 MARGATE
E-mail: enquiries@barnesmarsland.co.uk
List of partners: C Cagney, C J Chapman, J Mackenzie, J Miles
Office: Broadstairs
Languages: French
Work: C1 C2 D1 E F1 F2 J1 K1 K3 L N O Q R1 R2 S2 Z(c,e,k,q)
Agency, Advocacy and Fixed Fee Interview undertaken
Ptr: Cagney, Mr Christopher. . . . *§Mar 1970
Chapman, Mr Colin J LLB(Lond) . . . *Dec 1977
Ast: Hamer, Mrs Sarah. . . . *Mar 2005
Thomas, Ms Elaine Susan . . . *Oct 2000
Con: Horton, Mr Richard J . . . Jun 1974

BOYS & MAUGHAN ‡
India House Hawley Street Margate Kent CT9 1PZ
Tel: 01843 234000 *Fax:* 01843 234002 *Dx:* 30551 MARGATE
Emergency telephone 07721 432893
E-mail: margate@boysandmaughan.co.uk
List of partners: J Austin, R C A Bagley, A D J Baker, A G Cox, J Da Costa, R Durrant, M Insaidoo, A Michael, R C B Moulsdale, P L Reeves, P J Rodd, A Turnbull
Office: Birchington, Broadstairs, Ramsgate
Languages: Fanti, French, German, Italian, Spanish, Twi
Work: A1 A3 B1 C1 C2 D1 D2 E F1 J1 K1 K2 K3 K4 L M2 N O Q R1 R2 S1 S2 T1 T2 V W Z(c,d,h,l,o,s)
Emergency Action, Agency, Advocacy, Legal Aid undertaken, Legal Aid Franchise and Member of Accident Line
Ptr: Austin, Mr Jonathan BA(York); FCIArb. . . . *§Jun 1971
Da Costa, Mr Jonathan . . . *Nov 1998
Insaidoo, Ms Mary-Joyce LLB. . . . Oct 2006
Moulsdale, Mr Robert C B BA. . . . *§Dec 1984
Reeves, Mr Paul L HND; BA . . . *Nov 1981
Rodd, Mr Peter J LLB Notary Public. . . . *§Jun 1978
Turnbull, Mrs Angela . . . Oct 1996
Durrant, Mr Richard FILEx . . . NSP
Ast: Matloob, Mr Zaban BA; LLM . . . *May 2004

GIRLINGS
Crown Chambers Broad Street Margate Kent CT9 1BN
Tel: 01843 220274 *Fax:* 01843 297828 *Dx:* 30550 MARGATE
E-mail: enquiries@girlings.com
Office: Ashford (2 offices), Canterbury, Herne Bay
Languages: French
Work: D1 K1 K3 K4 S1 T1 T2 W Z(m)
Legal Aid undertaken and Legal Aid Franchise
Ptr: Browne, Mr Robin J R K LLB . . . *§Jun 1974
Trim, Mr Christopher Linton . . . *Sep 1976
Ast: Siddons, Mr Mark Adrian BA(Hons) . . . *Mar 1999

MARKET BOSWORTH, Leicestershire

THOMAS FLAVELL & SONS
20 Market Place Market Bosworth Leicestershire CV13 0LF
Tel: 01455 290203 *Fax:* 01455 291223 *Dx:* 716424 HINCKLEY
Emergency telephone 01455 610747
E-mail: law@thosflavell.co.uk
Office: Earl Shilton, Hinckley
Work: A1 E S1 S2 W
Ptr: Hammond, Mr Gavin William LLB . . . *Dec 1992

MARKET DEEPING, Lincolnshire

DOUBLE & MEGSON ‡
11 Market Place Market Deeping Lincolnshire PE6 8EA
Tel: 01778 341494 *Fax:* 01778 347663
Dx: 11451 MARKET DEEPING
E-mail: davids@deepings.doubleandmegson.co.uk
List of partners: P Double, J Megson, D Scotney, R R Wood
Office: Bourne
Work: A1 B1 C1 D1 E F1 G H J1 K1 L M1 N P R1 S1 T1 W
Emergency Action, Agency, Advocacy, Fixed Fee Interview and Legal Aid undertaken
Ptr: Double, Mr Paul. . . . *Feb 1969
Scotney, Mr David. . . . *Jun 1979

MARKET DRAYTON, Shropshire

ONIONS & DAVIES ‡
91 Cheshire Street Market Drayton Shropshire TF9 3AF
Tel: 01630 652405 *Fax:* 01630 658079
Dx: 26933 MARKET DRAYTON
E-mail: sols@onionsanddavies.co.uk
List of partners: C S Milne
Work: A1 E J1 K1 K3 K4 L N S1 S2 T2 W
Advocacy and Fixed Fee Interview undertaken
SPr: Milne, Mr Christopher Stuart BA(Hons); CPE; LPC . . *Jul 1996
Asoc: Balsom, Mr Derrick George LLB. . . . *Jan 1974
Con: Gomersall, Mr Roger V LLB. . . . *Jun 1971

GRAHAM WITHERS & CO ‡
(incorporating Warren Upton & Garside)
46 Cheshire Street Market Drayton Shropshire TF9 1PQ
Tel: 01630 657222 *Fax:* 01630 653452
Dx: 26931 MARKET DRAYTON
Emergency telephone 01694 724673
E-mail: robin.wilson@grahamwithers.co.uk
List of partners: S A Butter, G H Field, D J Forrester, M N J France, P Nutley, R N Wilson
Office: Shrewsbury
Work: A1 C1 E F1 K1 L S1 S2 T1 T2 W
Ptr: Butter, Miss Sally Ann BA(Oxon) LPC Law Society Prize 1995 . . . *§Sep 1995
Wilson, Mr Robin N MA(Cantab) . . . *§Apr 1971

MARKET HARBOROUGH, Leicestershire

BARLOWS
49a High Street Market Harborough Leicestershire LE16 7AF
Tel: 01858 410040 *Fax:* 01858 432772
Dx: 27309 MARKET HARBOROUGH
Emergency telephone 01858 410040
E-mail: jhefford@barlowssolicitors.com
Office: Leicester
Work: A1 K1 L S1 W
Emergency Action, Agency, Advocacy and Fixed Fee Interview undertaken
Ptr: Hefford, Mrs Janice LLB. . . . *§Jun 1971

BRAY & BRAY
51 High Street Market Harborough Leicestershire LE16 7AF
Tel: 01858 467181 *Fax:* 01858 434362
Dx: 27305 MARKET HARBOROUGH
E-mail: mvthill@braybray.co.uk
Office: Hinckley, Leicester
Work: A1 C1 C2 D1 E F1 J1 K1 K3 K4 L M1 N O Q S1 S2 T2 V W Z(l)
Emergency Action, Agency, Advocacy, Fixed Fee Interview, Legal Aid undertaken, Legal Aid Franchise and Member of Accident Line
Ptr: Hill, Mr Martin V T LLB; TEP; ATII. . . . *Mar 1985
Ast: Monro, Mr Christopher E S LLB. . . . *Dec 1981

BROWN & COMPANY ‡
4a Church Street Market Harborough Leicestershire LE16 7AA
Tel: 01858 434204 *Fax:* 01858 410178
Dx: 27308 MARKET HARBOROUGH
E-mail: office@brownsolicitors.co.uk
List of partners: E A Brown, K A Brown
Work: C1 E K4 R2 S1 S2 W Z(l,m)
Ptr: Brown, Mrs Elizabeth A MA(Cantab) . . . *Jan 1979
Brown, Mr Kenneth A LLB. . . . *Jun 1979
Ast: Gale, Mrs Rosemary Jean. . . . *Dec 1977

KEITH HARVEY & CO ‡
43 High Street Market Harborough Leicestershire LE16 7AQ
Tel: 01858 464327 *Fax:* 01858 410042
Dx: 27301 MARKET HARBOROUGH
E-mail: joe@keithharveyandcompany.co.uk
List of partners: K R Harvey
Work: E J1 L S1 W
Ptr: Harvey, Mr Keith R . . . *Jun 1981
Ast: Pryce, Mrs Penelope Jane BA(Hons) . . . *Nov 1982

CHARLES HENLEY ‡
17 Mill Lane Caldecott Market Harborough Leicestershire LE16 8RU
Tel: 01536 771811 *Fax:* 01536 772140
E-mail: charleshenley@sky.com
List of partners: C E Henley
Work: L S1 S2 W
SPr: Henley, Mr Charles E . . . *Nov 1972

CAROLINE KEMSLEY-PEIN ‡
Newbold Farm 4 Chapel Lane Market Harborough Leicestershire LE16 9RL
Tel: 01858 525639

LAWSON WEST SOLICITORS LIMITED
Portland House 1 Coventry Road Market Harborough Leicestershire LE16 9BX
Tel: 01858 445480 *Fax:* 01858 445481
Dx: 27326 MARKET HARBOROUGH
Emergency telephone 01858 445480
E-mail: harborough@lawson-west.co.uk
Office: Leicester, Wigston
Work: C1 D1 D2 E J1 K1 K2 K3 N S1 S2 W
Advocacy undertaken and Member of Accident Line
Ptr: Hopkins, Ms Janet . . . *Nov 1994
Asoc: Green, Ms Jodie . . . Nov 2007

DAVID MADAMS SOLICITOR ‡
Bank Cottage 4 Barlows Lane Wilbarston Market Harborough Leicestershire LE16 8QB
Tel: 01536 771077 *Fax:* 01536 771077

SALUSBURYS HARDING & BARNETT
44a Main Street Broughton Astley Market Harborough Leicestershire LE9 6RD
Tel: 01455 282757
E-mail: law@salusburys.co.uk
Office: Leicester (2 offices)

WARTNABYS ‡
44 High Street Market Harborough Leicestershire LE16 7AH
Tel: 01858 463322 *Fax:* 01858 410214
Dx: 27303 MARKET HARBOROUGH
E-mail: solicitors@wartnabys.co.uk
List of partners: R D Balme, M J Doody, R J Ilersic, J C W Wakefield
Work: A1 E J1 K1 L N Q S1 S2 T2 W
Legal Aid undertaken
Ptr: Balme, Mr Richard David MA(Cantab). . . . *§Dec 1979
Doody, Mr Michael J . . . *§Jul 1978
Ilersic, Mr Romilly J LLB. . . . *§May 1972
Wakefield, Mr Jeremy C W LLB. . . . *Feb 1988
Ast: Garvey, Mrs Sandra LLB(Hons) . . . §Oct 1987
Grocott, Miss Pauline A LLB . . . *§Apr 1977
Morris, Mrs Ursula Mary. . . . Oct 1985

MARKET RASEN, Lincolnshire

BRIDGE MCFARLAND
2 Mill Street Market Rasen Lincolnshire LN8 3BG
Tel: 01673 843723 *Fax:* 01673 843724 *Dx:* 28232 MARKET RASEN
Emergency telephone 01507 600340
E-mail: info@bmcf.co.uk
Office: Grimsby (3 offices), Hull, Lincoln, Louth, Mablethorpe, Skegness
Work: A1 B1 C1 D1 E F1 G H J1 K1 L M1 N P R1 S1 T1 V W Z(c,l)
Emergency Action, Agency, Advocacy, Fixed Fee Interview and Legal Aid undertaken
Ptr: McFarland, Mr Patrick R E BA(Oxon) . . . *Jun 1971

See p112 for the Key to Work Categories & other symbols

WILKIN CHAPMAN GRANGE SOLICITORS
17 Oxford Street Market Rasen Lincolnshire LN8 3AH
Tel: 01673 841300 *Fax:* 01673 844064 *Dx:* 28233 MARKET RASEN
E-mail: info@wilkinchapman.co.uk
Office: Alford, Beverley, Grimsby (3 offices), Horncastle, Lincoln, Louth, Mablethorpe, Sutton-on-Sea
Languages: French
Work: A1 A2 B1 C1 D1 E F1 J1 K1 L M1 N O P Q R1 R2 S1 S2 T1 T2 V W X Z(c,d,k,l,m,q,s)
Agency, Advocacy and Legal Aid undertaken

MARLBOROUGH, Wiltshire

AWDRY BAILEY & DOUGLAS
7 Woodstock Court Blenheim Road Marlborough Wiltshire SN8 4AN
Tel: 01672 518620 *Fax:* 01672 512798
E-mail: abd@awdrys.co.uk
Office: Calne, Devizes, Wootton Bassett
Work: A1 C1 D2 E F1 J1 K1 K3 K4 L N O Q S2 W Z(c,h,q)

BEECHMAST CONSULTANCY LIMITED ‡
61 High Street Burbage Marlborough Wiltshire SN8 3AF
Tel: 01672 810399

D GOLDSMITH & CO ‡
Unit 1 Frees Warehouse Angel Yard Marlborough Wiltshire SN8 1AG
Tel: 01672 512168 *Fax:* 01672 511797

HUTCHINSONS SOLICITORS LIMITED ‡
Barley Mead Aldbourne Road Marlborough Wiltshire SN8 2HZ
Tel: 01672 838216 *Fax:* 01672 540541

THE MERRIMAN PARTNERSHIP ‡
Hughenden House 107 High Street Marlborough Wiltshire SN8 1LN
Tel: 01672 512244 *Fax:* 01672 515871
Dx: 39450 MARLBOROUGH 3
E-mail: law@merriman-partnership.co.uk
List of partners: T G Cameron, V A Gist, L J Hughes, C J McGrorty, K M Tuckey
Languages: French
Work: E K1 K3 K4 S1 S2 W
Ptr: Cameron, Mr Timothy Graham BA(Hons) . . . . *Oct 1987
Gist, Mrs Vanessa Ann BA(Hons) . . . . *Dec 1987
Hughes, Mrs Louisa Jane . . . . *Sep 1996
McGrorty, Mr Christopher J . . . . *Dec 1973
Tuckey, Ms Katharine M LLB; LSF. . . . . *Nov 1989

DUNCAN MORRIS SOLICITORS LIMITED ‡
Eastholme Blowhorn Street Marlborough Wiltshire SN8 1BU
Tel: 01672 515193

MOSS FALLON LLP ‡
Carters Court North Farm Marlborough Wiltshire SN8 2JZ
Tel: 01672 542120 *Fax:* 01672 540873

R E O RUSSELL ‡
Main Office Highleaze House Oare Marlborough Wiltshire SN8 4JE
Tel: 01672 564352 *Fax:* 01672 564163 *Dx:* 118751 PEWSEY
Emergency telephone 01672 564352
E-mail: reorussell@lineone.net
Languages: French
Work: K4 S1 S2 T2 W

MARK TELFER ‡
Rudge Manor Farm Rudge Marlborough Wiltshire SN8 2HN
Tel: 01672 520517 *Fax:* 01672 521068

WITHY KING SOLICITORS
Aylesbury Court High Street Marlborough Wiltshire SN8 1AA
Tel: 01672 514781 *Fax:* 01672 515049 *Dx:* 39452 MARLBOROUGH
E-mail: enquiries@withyking.co.uk
Office: Abingdon, Bath (2 offices), Oxford, Swindon, Thame, Trowbridge
Languages: Cantonese, French, German, Italian
Work: A1 A3 B1 C1 C2 D1 D2 E F1 F2 G H I J1 J2 K1 K2 K3 L M1 N O P Q R1 R2 S1 S2 T1 T2 U2 V W Z(c,d,e,f,g,h,i,j,k,l,m,o,p,q,r,w,za)

MARLOW, Buckinghamshire

B LEGAL LIMITED ‡
Unit 1 Globeside Fieldhouse Lane Marlow Buckinghamshire SL7 1HZ
Tel: 01628 496687

BARRETT & ASSOCIATES ‡
290 Marlow Bottom Marlow Buckinghamshire SL7 3PT
Tel: 01628 476283 *Fax:* 01628 488961 *Dx:* 3009 MARLOW

SIMON BENNETT ‡
35 High Street Marlow Buckinghamshire SL7 1AU
Tel: 01628 478088 *Fax:* 01628 474441 *Dx:* 300915 MARLOW
Emergency telephone 01628 478088
E-mail: sarah@divorce-uk.com
List of partners: S A Bennett
Work: K1 W
SPr: Bennett, Mr Simon A LLB(Lond) Broderip & New Inn Prizes . . . . *Dec 1970

BROWNS ‡
Courtyard Offices 3 High Street Marlow Buckinghamshire SL7 1AU
Tel: 01628 476988 *Fax:* 01628 890857 *Dx:* 300913 MARLOW
E-mail: marlow@brownssolicitors.co.uk
List of partners: J P Bradley, J Brett, D C Hodges
Office: Amersham, Aylesbury, Beaconsfield, Bourne End, High Wycombe (3 offices), Maidenhead, Princes Risborough, Thame
Work: C1 E S1 S2
Fixed Fee Interview undertaken
Ptr: Bradley, Mr Justin Paul . . . . Jan 1994
Brett, Mr John. . . . . Nov 1985
Hodges, Mr David Charles . . . . Jan 1995

CHILTERN LEGAL SOLICITORS ‡
4 Chiltern Road Marlow Buckinghamshire SL7 2PP
Tel: 01628 472119

FENDOM DAWSON & TOWNER
65 High Street Marlow Buckinghamshire SL7 1AB
Tel: 01628 477808 *Fax:* 01628 477809 *Dx:* 300954 MARLOW
Office: High Wycombe
Ptr: Towner, Mr Roger N LLB . . . . *Mar 1979

A J FIELD & CO
11-13 Station Road Marlow Buckinghamshire SL7 1NG
Tel: 01628 488055 *Fax:* 01628 471247
Office: Gerrards Cross, Sheerness, Sittingbourne

GABBITAS ROBINS ‡
The Old House 27 West Street Marlow Buckinghamshire SL7 2LX
Tel: 01628 472600 *Fax:* 01628 484391 *Dx:* 300920 MARLOW
List of partners: J G Gabbitas, S J Robins
Work: A1 A3 B1 C1 C2 E F1 J1 J2 K1 K3 L N O P Q R1 R2 S1 S2 T1 T2 W X Z(c,d,e,l,q)
Emergency Action, Agency, Advocacy and Fixed Fee Interview undertaken
Ptr: Gabbitas, Mr John G LLB(B'ham) Clerk to General Commissioners for High Wycombe . . . . *§Oct 1967
Robins, Mr Stephen J. . . . . *§Nov 1978
Asoc: Furniss, Mrs Magaret A LLB; MA . . . . *Jun 2000
Con: Reback, Mr Myles Ingram LLB(Hons) . . . . *Nov 1992

GORDONS SOLICITORS LLP ‡
Winter Hill House Marlow Reach Station Approach Marlow Buckinghamshire SL7 1NT
Tel: 01628 487487 *Fax:* 01628 488884 *Dx:* 300905 MARLOW
E-mail: keithg@gordons-law.co.uk
List of partners: S B Bhalla, S M Brown, R J Gates, K W Gordon, D A Kempton, M R Santa-Olalla, G Skivington, M E Turpie
Office: Maidenhead
Work: B1 C1 C2 C3 E F1 I J1 L N O Q S1 W Z(b,c,f)
Ptr: Bhalla, Mr Sandeep Bob LLB(Hons). . . . . *Nov 1997
Brown, Ms Suzanne M . . . . *Aug 1999
Gates, Mr Robin J LSF . . . . *§Feb 1972
Gordon, Mr Keith W. . . . . *Jul 1977
Kempton, Mr David A . . . . *§Nov 1975
Santa-Olalla, Mr Mark R BA. . . . . *Jan 1979
Skivington, Mr Glenn . . . . Mar 1999
Turpie, Mr Mark E. . . . . Feb 1990
Ast: Craig, Jacqueline . . . . Jun 2006
Hylton, Mr Ian LLB(Hons) . . . . Mar 2006
Monfared, Sonna . . . . Sep 2005
Wilson, Mr Allen C BA; MA . . . . Feb 1990
Con: Dawson-Pick, Mrs Claire L LLB . . . . *Feb 1986

JULIA JACKSON SOLICITORS ‡
132a Marlow Bottom Marlow Buckinghamshire SL7 3PH
Tel: 01628 440582

ROBERT KYLE & CO ‡
15 South Place Marlow Buckinghamshire SL7 1PY
Tel: 01628 475751 *Fax:* 01628 474613
E-mail: robtkyleco@eclipse.co.uk
List of partners: R F A Page-Jones
Work: A1 C1 E S1 S2 T2 W
SPr: Page-Jones, Mr Richard Francis Antony MA(Oxon) . . *Feb 1965
Con: White, Ms Frances BA(Hons) . . . . *Jan 1997

LGP SOLICITORS ‡
Lacemaker House 5-7 Chappel Street Marlow Buckinghamshire SL7 3HN
Tel: 01628 404620 *Fax:* 01628 404630 *Dx:* 300907 MARLOW
E-mail: info@lgpsolicitors.co.uk

LAWSON ANTHONY SOLICITORS ‡
1 Buckingham Gate Medmenham Marlow Buckinghamshire SL7 2SA
Tel: 01628 472330 *Fax:* 01628 474311

MOORCROFTS LLP ‡
James House Mere Park Dedmere Road Marlow Buckinghamshire SL7 1FJ
Tel: 01628 470000 *Fax:* 01628 470001
E-mail: info@moorcrofts.com
List of partners: C Botham, T Hunter, A J S Katz, A R Phillips
Languages: French, German
Work: C1 C2 C3 E F1 I J1 R2 S2 U1 U2 Z(b,e,za)
Ptr: Botham, Mrs Charlotte . . . . Sep 1997
Hunter, Mrs Theresa . . . . Sep 1997
Katz, Mr Andrew James Stewart MA(Cantab) . . . . . Nov 1993
Phillips, Mr Adrian Roy MA(Cantab). . . . . Oct 1985
Ast: Eisenberg, Mrs Rosalie . . . . Oct 1999
Morris, Ms Rosalind BSc . . . . *Sep 2006
Picard, Mrs Alexandra. . . . . Sep 2002

THOMAS CHAYTOR ‡
The Courtyard 60 Station Road Marlow Buckinghamshire SL7 1NX
Tel: 01628 477889 *Fax:* 01628 488859

MARPLE, Greater Manchester

BISHOP & CO
87 Stockport Road Marple Greater Manchester SK6 6AA
Tel: 0161 427 1441 / 427 5543 *Fax:* 0161 449 7690
Dx: 23702 MARPLE
E-mail: marple@bishop-solicitors.co.uk
Office: New Mills
Work: A1 E F1 G H K1 N Q S1 S2 W
Agency, Advocacy, Fixed Fee Interview, Legal Aid undertaken and Member of Accident Line

JONES LAW PARTNERSHIP ‡
Vernon Chambers 11 Market Street Marple Greater Manchester SK6 7AA
Tel: 0161 426 0030 *Fax:* 0161 426 0402
List of partners: J M Hill, V L Jones
Work: N S1 S2 W
Ptr: Hill, Mr James Michael BA(Hons) . . . . *Jul 1989
Jones, Mrs Victoria Louise LLB(Hons). . . . . *May 1995

WHITING & MASON (incorporating Alan J Fidler & Co)
17-19 Stockport Road Marple Greater Manchester SK6 6BD
Tel: 0161 427 1040 *Fax:* 0161 426 0923 *Dx:* 23708 MARPLE
Office: Irlam, Manchester, New Mills
Work: B1 C1 D1 E F1 J1 K1 L N O Q S1 T1 W
Emergency Action, Agency, Advocacy, Fixed Fee Interview and Legal Aid Franchise

Ptr: Gunson, Mr Neil P LLB(Hons). . . . . *Jan 1986
Jones, Mr Richard D L LLB . . . . *Sep 1990
Con: Kay, Ms Patricia J BA(Law) . . . . *Sep 1983

2

MARTOCK, Somerset

RICHARD P KEMP BA SOLICITOR ‡
31 North Street Martock Somerset TA12 6DH
Tel: 01935 822572 *Fax:* 01935 826473
Emergency telephone 01460 241603
List of partners: R P Kemp
Work: A1 B1 C1 E F1 F2 G J1 K1 L M1 N P Q R1 S1 S2 T1 T2 V W
Emergency Action, Agency, Advocacy and Fixed Fee Interview undertaken
Ptr: Kemp, Mr Richard Peter BA(Oxon) . . . . *§Jul 1978

MARYPORT, Cumbria

BROCKBANK CURWEN CAIN & HALL
68 Curzon Street Maryport Cumbria CA15 6LH
Tel: 01900 813488 *Fax:* 01900 815877 *Dx:* 62832 MARYPORT
E-mail: bt@brockbanks.co.uk
Office: Cockermouth, Keswick, Whitehaven, Workington
Work: C1 D1 D2 E F1 J1 K1 K2 L M1 N P Q S1 T1 V W Z(l,r)
Emergency Action, Agency, Advocacy, Fixed Fee Interview and Legal Aid undertaken
Dir: Hall, Mr Charles Geoffrey BA . . . . *§Dec 1984
Con: Cain, Mr Michael F . . . . *§Mar 1955

MILBURNS SOLICITORS
Curzon House 45 Curzon Street Maryport Cumbria CA15 6LP
Tel: 01900 813541 *Fax:* 01900 818173 *Dx:* 62830 MARYPORT
E-mail: maryport@milburns.org
Office: Whitehaven, Workington
Work: A1 B1 C1 D1 E J1 K1 L N R1 S1
Emergency Action, Agency, Advocacy, Fixed Fee Interview and Legal Aid undertaken
Ptr: Moore, Mr John C LLB . . . . *Dec 1980
Telford, Mr David M LLB . . . . *Apr 1968
Ast: Gibson, Mr Darren T LLB . . . . *Nov 2003

MATLOCK, Derbyshire

JAMES BUTTON & CO ‡
7 Devonshire Drive Rowsley Matlock Derbyshire DE4 2HB
Tel: 01629 735566 *Fax:* 01629 735528
E-mail: james@jamesbutton.co.uk
List of partners: J T H Button
Work: J2 P R1 Z(g,l,u,y,za)
SPr: Button, Mr James T H BA; MCIArb; MIoL . . . . *Mar 1990
Con: Foxley, Mrs Jayne Melanie BA; DipLG. . . . . *Jan 1992

CARTER & CARTER SOLICITORS LTD ‡
Croft Cottage Start Lane High Peak Matlock Derbyshire SK23 7BR
Tel: 01663 735031

CHUBB & CO ‡
Bridge House 1 Dale Road Matlock Derbyshire DE4 3LT
Tel: 01629 581252 *Fax:* 01629 581373
E-mail: prd@chubblaw.co.uk
List of partners: P R Dalton
Work: A1 B1 C1 C2 K1 K3 L R2 S1 S2 T2 W Z(c,d,e,h,l,u)
Ptr: Dalton, Mr Paul Robert LLB(Hons) . . . . *Nov 1985
Ast: Bailey, Mrs Sara Ella BA(Hons) . . . . Mar 2003

CHUBBLAW LIMITED ‡
The Law Chambers The Archway Matlock Derbyshire DE1 3AT
Tel: 01629 581700

ELLIOT MATHER LLP
Sherwood House Holt Lane Matlock Derbyshire DE4 3LY
Tel: 01629 584885 *Fax:* 01629 584778 *Dx:* 27264 MATLOCK 1
E-mail: admin@elliotmather.co.uk
Office: Chesterfield (2 offices), Mansfield
Work: D1 E F1 G H J1 K1 L N O Q S1 V W
Agency, Advocacy and Legal Aid undertaken
Mem: Gill, Mrs Sally Anne FILEx . . . . *Nov 1998
Page, Miss Julie Louise LLB(Hons) . . . . *Dec 1994
Con: Mather, Mr Bertram J M. . . . . *Jul 1971

LOVEDAY & KEIGHLEY ‡
Crown Chambers 6 Bank Road Matlock Derbyshire DE4 3AQ
Tel: 01629 583142 / 56660 *Fax:* 01629 582515 *Dx:* 27251 MATLOCK
E-mail: law@lovedays-solicitors.co.uk
List of partners: C D Gale, R L Roberts
Languages: French
Work: A1 B1 C1 C2 C3 D1 E F1 G J1 K1 L M1 M2 N O P Q S1 S2 T1 T2 W Z(l,q)
Emergency Action, Advocacy and Fixed Fee Interview undertaken
Ptr: Gale, Mr Christopher David BSocSc(Law & Econ). . . *§Sep 1992
Roberts, Mr Richard Llewelyn BA(Law & Business) . . *Jul 1999
Ast: Coates, Mr James William LLB(Hons). . . . . Sep 2009
Wyles, Miss Amy Elizabeth BA(Law & French); LPC. . . Sep 2009
Con: Handforth, Mr M Christopher Notary Public . . . . . . *Jul 1977
Loveday, Mr Harry J C TD; DL BA(Cantab) . . . . . . *§Oct 1959

POTTER & CO ‡
Bridge Chambers 23 Dale Road Matlock Derbyshire DE4 3LT
Tel: 01629 582308 *Fax:* 01629 580357 *Dx:* 27255 MATLOCK
E-mail: a.cross@potterco-solicitors.co.uk
List of partners: R A Cross, C D Loeber
Office: Wirksworth
Work: A1 C1 D1 E F1 G H J1 K1 L N Q S1 S2 T2 V W Z(l)
Emergency Action, Agency, Advocacy, Fixed Fee Interview and Legal Aid Franchise
Ptr: Cross, Mr R Andrew LLB(Sheff). . . . . *§Feb 1980
Loeber, Mr Christopher D LLB(L'pool) . . . . *Apr 1978
Asoc: Park, Mr Christopher John LLB . . . . *§Apr 1981
Steer, Mr John LLB . . . . Oct 1971
Wood, Ms Barbara . . . . Dec 1979

VINES LEGAL LIMITED ‡
Speedwell Mill Old Coach Road Tansley Matlock Derbyshire DE4 5FY
Tel: 01629 761680 *Fax:* 01629 761681

MAYFIELD, East Sussex

MCKENZIE RICHARDS ‡
The Old Bank High Street Mayfield East Sussex TN20 6AB
Tel: 01435 872025 *Fax:* 0870 495 8010
E-mail: info@mckenzierichards.co.uk
List of partners: A E F Richards
Mem: Richards, Ms Amelia Ethelreda Florence BA . . . . . May 1993

MELBOURNE, Derbyshire

H PIPES & CO ‡
34 Market Place Melbourne Derbyshire DE73 8DS
Tel: 01332 862113 *Fax:* 01332 864531
List of partners: J E Lord, W Ramsbottom
Work: A1 E F1 J1 K1 L N S1 W Z(c)
Ptr: Lord, Mr John E BA(Nott'm) . . . . . *May 1973
Ramsbottom, Mr William LLB(Lond) . . . . . *Nov 1963

MELKSHAM, Wiltshire

GOUGHS
5 Bath Road Melksham Wiltshire SN12 6LN
Tel: 01225 703036 *Fax:* 01225 708544 *Dx:* 43902 MELKSHAM
E-mail: info@goughs.co.uk
Office: Calne, Chippenham, Corsham, Devizes, Trowbridge
Work: D1 E K1 S1 W
Emergency Action, Agency, Advocacy and Fixed Fee Interview undertaken
Ptr: Dobson, Mr Kevin George . . . . . Dec 1991
Pridmore, Mrs Jo LLB(Hons) . . . . . *Sep 1994

WANSBROUGHS
Oakwood House Spa Road Melksham Wiltshire SN12 7NP
Tel: 01225 703222 *Fax:* 01225 709547 *Dx:* 43900 MELKSHAM
E-mail: melksham@wansbroughs.com
Office: Devizes
Work: A1 B1 C1 C2 C3 D1 E F1 G H J1 K1 L M1 M2 N P R1 S1 T1 T2 V W Z(c,d,i,j,k,l,m,o,p,t)
Emergency Action, Agency, Advocacy, Fixed Fee Interview, Legal Aid undertaken and Legal Aid Franchise
Ptr: Clifford, Mr Stephen James LLB(Hons) . . . . . Sep 1992
Daymond, Mr Alex LLB . . . . . Sep 1995
Asoc: Bisgrove, Miss Esther LLB . . . . . May 1996
Clifford, Mrs Susan LLB(Hons) . . . . . Oct 1992
Eddy, Mr Andrew BA(Hons) . . . . . Sep 1985
Ost, Ms Jacqui LLB(Hons) . . . . . Jan 1981
Ast: Gwinnell, Ms Liz . . . . . Jan 2008
Hutchinson, Nicola . . . . . Jan 2009
Rudman, Amy . . . . . Jun 2009

MELTON MOWBRAY, Leicestershire

EDWARDS SOLICITORS ‡
Granary Chambers 37-39 Burton Street Melton Mowbray Leicestershire LE13 1AF
Tel: 01664 566606 *Fax:* 01664 566603
Dx: 26763 MELTON MOWBRAY
Emergency telephone 01664 566606
E-mail: law1@edwards-solicitors.com
List of partners: W G Hetherington, E S Hryniewiecki
Languages: French, Polish
Work: A1 C1 E F1 J1 J2 K1 K3 K4 L N O Q S1 S2 W Z(l,x)
Agency, Advocacy and Fixed Fee Interview undertaken
Ptr: Hetherington, Mr William Gary LLB(Hons) . . . . . *Jan 1974
Hryniewiecki, Mr Edward Stefan LLB(Hons) . . . . . *Mar 1994

FOSSE LAW
7 King Street Melton Mowbray Leicestershire LE13 1XA
Tel: 01664 500022 *Fax:* 01664 565600 *Dx:* 10815 LEICESTER
E-mail: info@fosselaw.com
Office: Leicester, Loughborough

ISIS LEGAL ‡
St Mary's Chambers Church Street Melton Mowbray Leicestershire LE13 0PN
Tel: 01664 560707 / 560708 *Fax:* 01664 410228
Dx: 26752 MELTON MOWBRAY
E-mail: david.irving@btconnect.com
Work: D2 K1 K3 L Q S1 S2 W
Agency undertaken

LATHAM & CO ‡
15 High Street Melton Mowbray Leicestershire LE13 0TX
Tel: 01664 563012 *Fax:* 01664 563014
Dx: 26753 MELTON MOWBRAY
List of partners: C L Hull, T H Kirkman
Office: Loughborough
Languages: French
Work: A1 B1 C1 C2 C3 D1 E F1 J1 K1 L N O Q R1 S1 T1 T2 V W Z(c,d,e,f,h,i,j,l,m,p,t)
Emergency Action, Agency, Advocacy, Fixed Fee Interview, Legal Aid undertaken and Member of Accident Line
Ptr: Hull, Miss Carolyn Lesley LLB . . . . . *§Dec 1984
Kirkman, Mr Trevor H MA(Cantab) Clerk to Commissioners of Taxes; H M Coroner; Diocesan Registrar and Bishop's Legal Secretary Notary Public . . . . . *§Jun 1976

PETER W MARSH & CO ‡
Pembroke Gardens 19 High Street Melton Mowbray Leicestershire LE13 0TZ
Tel: 01664 566471 *Fax:* 01664 410485
Dx: 26762 MELTON MOWBRAY
Emergency telephone 01664 454650
List of partners: P W Marsh
Work: A1 B1 C1 E F1 G H J1 L N P S1 T1 W Z(c,d,h,j,k,l,o)
Emergency Action, Agency, Advocacy, Legal Aid undertaken and Member of Accident Line
SPr: Marsh, Mr Peter W . . . . . *Jun 1974

OLDHAM MARSH PAGE FLAVELL ‡
The White House 19 High Street Melton Mowbray Leicestershire LE13 0TZ
Tel: 01664 563162 *Fax:* 01664 568815
Dx: 26758 MELTON MOWBRAY
List of partners: J O P Noonan, H P Partridge, N Pidgeon
Languages: French
Work: A1 C1 C2 C3 D1 E F1 G H J1 J2 K1 L N O P Q S1 S2 V W Z(g,i,q)
Agency, Advocacy, Fixed Fee Interview, Legal Aid undertaken and Member of Accident Line
Ptr: Noonan, Mr James O P LLB . . . . . *Oct 1990
Partridge, Mr Howard P LLB Justices Clerks Society Prize 1971 Clerk to Commissioner of Taxes . . . . . *Jun 1971
Pidgeon, Mr Neil LLB(Leeds) . . . . . *Dec 1983
Ast: Duddles, Mr Maxwell Roy LLB(Hons) . . . . . *§Nov 1995
Garvey, Mrs Sandra LLB(Hons) . . . . . §Oct 1987
Hewitt, Ms Kay FILEx; PGDipLP . . . . . *Nov 1999
Wan, Miss Oilen LLB(Hons) . . . . . *Mar 2000

YOUNG SWISTAK SOLICITORS ‡
56 Nottingham Street Melton Mowbray Leicestershire LE13 1NW
Tel: 01664 501801 *Fax:* 01664 501802
Dx: 26761 MELTON MOWBRAY
Emergency telephone 01644501801
List of partners: C Swistak, D Young
Languages: Polish
Work: G H J1
Agency, Advocacy, Fixed Fee Interview and Legal Aid undertaken
Ptr: Swistak, Mr Chris BA(Law) . . . . . Nov 1994
Young, Mr Darren . . . . . Dec 1999

MENAI BRIDGE, Anglesey

PATRICK BLACKMORE ‡
15 High Street Menai Bridge Anglesey LL59 5EE
Tel: 01248 715987 / 714987 *Fax:* 01248 713892
Emergency telephone 0800 587 2205
E-mail: law.pblackmore@zen.co.uk
List of partners: P N Blackmore
Work: N
Agency undertaken
Ptr: Blackmore, Mr Patrick Nicholas . . . . . *Feb 1972

SIS LAW ‡
1 Coronation Road Menai Bridge Anglesey LL59 5BD
Tel: 01248 800900

TUDUR OWEN ROBERTS GLYNNE & CO
London House 7 High Street Menai Bridge Anglesey LL59 5EE
Tel: 01248 712624 *Fax:* 01248 716537 *Dx:* 21622 MENAI BRIDGE
Office: Bangor (2 offices), Blaenau Ffestiniog, Caernarfon, Holyhead
Work: G H S1 W
Emergency Action, Agency, Advocacy, Fixed Fee Interview, Legal Aid undertaken and Member of Accident Line

MERE, Wiltshire

RUTTER & RUTTER
Newport House Salisbury Street Mere Wiltshire BA12 6HE
Tel: 01747 860295 *Fax:* 01963 32710 *Dx:* 48551 WINCANTON
Emergency telephone 01963 32224
Office: Wincanton
Emergency Action, Advocacy, Legal Aid undertaken and Member of Accident Line
Ptr: Rutter, Mr Charles Foster LLB . . . . . Jul 1976

MERTHYR TYDFIL

GEORGE & D'AMBRA
6-9 Glebeland Street Merthyr Tydfil CF47 8AU
Tel: 01685 371153
Office: Aberdare, Blackwood, Merthyr Tydfil, Ystradgynlais

THE GWYN GEORGE PARTNERSHIP
110 High Street Merthyr Tydfil CF47 8AP
Tel: 01685 377035 *Fax:* 01685 389841
E-mail: mail@ggplaw.co.uk
Office: Aberdare, Blackwood, Merthyr Tydfil, Ystradgynlais
Work: D1 D2 G H J2 K1 K2 K3 N S2 W Z(q)
Agency, Advocacy, Fixed Fee Interview and Legal Aid undertaken

JNP LEGAL ‡
12 Church Street Merthyr Tydfil CF47 0AY
Tel: 01685 350421 *Fax:* 01685 723654
Dx: 53406 MERTHYR TYDFIL
List of partners: E L Davies, H B Jenkins, I G Jenkins, J E Kellaway, M L Last, P A Newman, A D Williams
Office: Nelson
Languages: French, Welsh
Work: A1 A2 B1 B2 C1 D1 D2 E F1 F2 G H J1 J2 K1 K2 L M1 N O P Q R1 R2 S1 S2 V W Z(c,e,j,l,m,q,r,t)
Emergency Action, Agency, Advocacy and Legal Aid undertaken
Ptr: Davies, Eirian L LLB . . . . . *Jan 1982
Jenkins, Mr Huw B LLB(Wales) ★ . . . . . *Dec 1976
Jenkins, Mr Ifan G LLB(Wales) . . . . . *Jun 1981
Kellaway, Miss Jane Elizabeth LLB . . . . . *Oct 1998
Last, Miss Margaret Louise LLB . . . . . *Jul 1998
Newman, Miss Penelope A LLB . . . . . *Sep 1983
Williams, Mr Anthony Derek LLB . . . . . *Jul 1998

RJM SOLICITORS ‡
(in association with Layton & Co)
1st & 2nd Floors 34 Victoria Street Merthyr Tydfil CF47 8BW
Tel: 01685 373721 *Fax:* 01685 389679
Dx: 53400 MERTHYR TYDFIL
E-mail: janine@rgmsolicitors.co.uk
Work: B1 D1 E F1 G H J1 K1 L N Q R1 S1 V W Z(l)
Emergency Action, Agency, Advocacy, Fixed Fee Interview and Legal Aid undertaken

MEXBOROUGH, South Yorkshire

COWLINGS ‡
5-9 West Street Mexborough South Yorkshire S64 9HZ
Tel: 01709 587538 *Fax:* 01709 571803 *Dx:* 27703 MEXBOROUGH
List of partners: M Cowling
Office: Doncaster
Work: D1 G H K1 L N S1 W
Emergency Action, Agency, Advocacy, Fixed Fee Interview and Legal Aid undertaken
Ptr: Cowling, Mr Michael . . . . . *Nov 1973

HATTERSLEYS ‡
1 Hope Street Mexborough South Yorkshire S64 9HR
Tel: 01709 582434 *Fax:* 01709 584129 *Dx:* 27702 MEXBOROUGH
List of partners: N Priestley, T C Seal
Work: K1 N Q S1 S2 W
Legal Aid Franchise
Ptr: Priestley, Mr Neil FILEx; DipLP . . . . . Oct 1996
Seal, Mr Timothy C LLB . . . . . *Oct 1984

MIDDLESBROUGH

ABBOTT BAILEY SOLICITORS ‡
Vanguard Suite Broadcasting House Newport Road Middlesbrough TS1 5JA
Tel: 01642 246617 *Fax:* 01642 243634
E-mail: mail@abbottbailey.com
List of partners: P Humble
SPr: Humble, Mr Paul BA(Hons) . . . . . *Sep 1999

Appleby Hope & Matthews

APPLEBY HOPE & MATTHEWS ‡
35 High Street Normanby Middlesbrough TS6 0LE
Tel: 01642 440444 *Fax:* 01642 440342 *Dx:* 60040 NORMANBY
Emergency telephone 07659 100901
E-mail: info@ahmsolicitors.co.uk
Web: www.ahmsolicitors.co.uk
List of partners: J K S Askins, P J Graham, P J Lewis, A J Salmon, N A Turvey, S E Walker
Office: Stockton-on-Tees
Languages: French
Work: A1 C1 D1 E G H J1 K1 L N S1 S2 W Z(l,m)
Emergency Action, Agency, Advocacy, Fixed Fee Interview, Legal Aid undertaken and Legal Aid Franchise
Ptr: Askins, Mrs Julianne Kathryn Sarah LLB(Hons) . . . . Sep 2004
Graham, Mrs Philippa J Marshall & Strouts Prize; William Hutton Prize . . . . . *Oct 1985
Lewis, Mr Peter John LLB(Hons) ★ . . . . . *Aug 2004
Salmon, Mr Anthony J LLB(Newc) . . . . . *Jul 1971
Turvey, Mr Norman A LLB(B'ham) . . . . . *Mar 1979
Walker, Mr Simon Edward LLB ★ . . . . . *Jan 1994
Asoc: Fox, Mrs Laura . . . . . Jan 2005
Wood, Mr Gary LLB ★ . . . . . Jul 2009
Ast: Clark, Mrs Kate BA(Hons); DipLaw . . . . . May 2010
Crocker, Mr Paul LLB(Hons) ★ . . . . . Apr 1997
Rafiq, Ms Shazana LLB(Hons) . . . . . Dec 2007

Agency attendance at all Middlesbrough/Teesside Courts daily for Crime, Family, Child Care and Civil Matters.

ARMSTRONG FOULKES ‡
Cleveland Business Centre Watson Street Middlesbrough TS1 2RQ
Tel: 01642 231110 *Fax:* 01642 231153
Dx: 711702 MIDDLESBROUGH 11
List of partners: H Armstrong, P Foulkes
Work: Z(r)
Fixed Fee Interview, Legal Aid undertaken and Legal Aid Franchise
Ptr: Armstrong, Mr Hilton LLB . . . . . *§Oct 1982
Foulkes, Mr Peter MA(Cantab) . . . . . *Jun 1974
Ast: Dennison, Miss Joanne LLB . . . . . *Nov 2002
Holt, Mrs Ashleigh BA . . . . . Aug 2006

ASKEW BUNTING SOLICITORS LLP ‡
56-60 Borough Road Middlesbrough TS1 2JH
Tel: 01642 252555 *Fax:* 01642 253555
Dx: 60522 MIDDLESBROUGH
E-mail: askewbun@globalnet.co.uk
List of partners: D W Towler
Office: Guisborough
Work: A1 A3 C1 D1 D2 E F1 F2 J1 K1 K2 L N O Q R1 S1 V W Z(c,j,l,p,q)
Emergency Action, Agency, Advocacy, Legal Aid undertaken, Legal Aid Franchise and Member of Accident Line
Asoc: Bennett, Miss Janice Ann LLB(Hons) . . . . . §Apr 1996
Dixon, Mr Andrew John LLB(Hons) . . . . . Dec 1999
Doran, Mr Kieron LLB . . . . . Nov 1998
Hargreaves, Mr Paul LLB . . . . . *Oct 1988
Hart, Miss Karen LLB(Hons) . . . . . *Jun 1996
Pugsley, Mr Noel W LLB . . . . . Jul 1999

ASKEWS
92-94 Borough Road Middlesbrough TS1 2HJ
Tel: 01642 475252 *Fax:* 01642 211017
Dx: 60510 MIDDLESBOROUGH
E-mail: info@askews.com
Office: Redcar, Stockton-on-Tees

ATHA & CO ‡
165 Albert Road Middlesbrough TS1 2PX
Tel: 01642 222575 *Fax:* 01642 232037
Dx: 60504 MIDDLESBROUGH
E-mail: reception@atha.co.uk
List of partners: C A S Atha, T Atha, M R Demoily, A Guest, R F Maughan
Work: E J1 L N O S1 S2 W
Agency, Advocacy, Fixed Fee Interview undertaken and Member of Accident Line
Ptr: Atha, Mr Charles A S . . . . . *Mar 1987
Atha, Mr Tony . . . . . *Dec 1958
Demoily, Mr Martin Ronald LLB(Hons) . . . . . *Aug 1996
Guest, Ms Anna LLB . . . . . *Mar 1996
Maughan, Ms Rachel Frances BA; LLB Convocation Trust Award . . . . . *Oct 1995

See p112 for the Key to Work Categories & other symbols

BAILEY & BAILEY ‡
82 Borough Road Middlesbrough TS1 2JH
Tel: 01642 240991 *Fax:* 01642 240994
Dx: 60505 MIDDLESBROUGH
E-mail: enquiries@baileyandbailey.co.uk
Languages: French
Work: A1 C1 E K1 L S1 S2 T1 W
Agency, Advocacy and Fixed Fee Interview undertaken
Con: Bailey, Mr John K ACIArb; TEP . . . . *Jun 1974

DAVID BEADNALL ‡
5 Brass Wynd Nunthorpe Middlesbrough TS7 0QE
Tel: 01642 311635
List of partners: D S J Beadnall
Ptr: Beadnall, Mr David St J. . . . . .Jul 1978

BROWN BEER NIXON MALLON
153 Albert Road Middlesbrough TS1 2PS
Tel: 01642 254182 *Fax:* 01642 246330
Emergency telephone 07710 090 915
E-mail: enquiries@bbnm.co.uk
Office: Redcar
Ast: Boddy, Mr Nigel Frederick LLB(Newc Poly) . . . . . . Sep 2000

BRYAN & CO SOLICITORS ‡
98 The Grove Marton-in-Cleveland Middlesbrough TS7 8AP
Tel: 01642 322928 *Fax:* 01642 311193
E-mail: paulbryan.solicitor@tiscali.co.uk

C M SOLICITORS ‡
2nd Floor Vanguard Suite Broadcasting House Middlesbrough TS1 5JA
Tel: 01642 242996 *Fax:* 0560 205 6016

DOBSON & SLEEMAN ‡
29 Baker Street Middlesbrough TS1 2LF
Tel: 01642 231707 *Fax:* 01642 890833
E-mail: reception@dobsonsleeman.co.uk
List of partners: J S Dobson, C Sleeman
Work: D1 D2 F1 G H K1 L N Q S1 V W Z(i,l,m,q,r)
Emergency Action, Agency, Advocacy, Fixed Fee Interview, Legal Aid undertaken, Legal Aid Franchise and Member of Accident Line
Ptr: Dobson, Mr John S . . . . Jul 1980
Sleeman, Mr Colin . . . . Jan 1983

FREERS ‡
19-25 Baker Street Middlesbrough TS1 2LF
Tel: 01642 244666 *Fax:* 01642 246317
Dx: 60509 MIDDLESBROUGH
E-mail: reception@freers-solicitors.co.uk
List of partners: A Finn, D C McReddie, K Vaux, R Vaux
Work: B1 C1 C2 C3 D1 E F1 G H J1 K1 L M1 M2 N O P Q R1 S1 T1 T2 V W Z(c,k,l,m,r)
Emergency Action, Agency, Advocacy, Legal Aid undertaken and Member of Accident Line
Ptr: Finn, Mr Anthony LLB(Hons) . . . . *Mar 1989
McReddie, Mr Duncan Christopher LLB(Hons) . . . . . Jul 1997
Vaux, Mr Keith . . . . *Jul 1965
Vaux, Mr Richard . . . . *Nov 1996

MARTIN L GROVE
97 High Street Eston Middlesbrough TS6 9JD
Tel: 01642 456615 *Fax:* 01642 456615 *Dx:* 61720 SKELTON
Office: Saltburn-by-the-Sea
Work: E F1 J1 K1 L N R2 S1 S2 W Z(q)
Agency, Advocacy and Fixed Fee Interview undertaken
Ptr: Grove, Mr Martin L LLB . . . . *Jan 1979

GARY JOHNSON & CO ‡
14 Baker Street Middlesbrough TS1 2LH
Tel: 01642 222834 *Fax:* 01642 217354
Dx: 60557 MIDDLESBROUGH
E-mail: garyjohnson@garyjohnson-solicitors.co.uk
List of partners: G Johnson
Work: N S1 W Z(r)
Fixed Fee Interview undertaken and Member of Accident Line
Ptr: Johnson, Mr Gary LLB(Manc). . . . . *Oct 1982

LEIGH TURTON DIXON ‡
1st Floor Southlands Business Centre Ormsby Road Middlesbrough TS3 0HB
Tel: 01642 241101 *Fax:* 01642 230226
Emergency telephone 07815 935461
E-mail: ltdsols@yahoo.co.uk
List of partners: P Dixon, A Turton
Office: Stockton-on-Tees
Work: D1 F1 F2 G H K1 K2 L N Q S1 V W Z(i)
Emergency Action, Agency, Advocacy, Fixed Fee Interview and Legal Aid undertaken
Ptr: Dixon, Mr Paul BA(Hons) . . . . Feb 2000
Turton, Mr Andrew LLB . . . . *Oct 1990
Ast: McGee, Mr Andrew . . . . Feb 2011

MACKS SOLICITORS ‡
4 Woodland Road Middlesbrough TS1 3BE
Tel: 01642 252828 *Fax:* 01642 252622
Dx: 60588 MIDDLESBROUGH
E-mail: office@macksolicitors.com
List of partners: D J Graham, N Mack, A McCarthy
Office: Redcar
Dir: Graham, Mr David John LLB(Newc). . . . . *Oct 1986
McCarthy, Mr Anthony. . . . . Sep 2000
Mack, Mr Nicholas LLB . . . . Nov 1986
Asoc: Carey, Jane. . . . . Dec 2007
Montague, Rebecca. . . . . May 1999
Con: Shepherd, Miss Alison M BA . . . . Nov 1987

MILES HUTCHINSON & LITHGOW ‡ (incorporating W Stanley Smith)
68 Borough Road Middlesbrough TS1 2JH
Tel: 01642 242698 *Fax:* 01642 232488
Dx: 60516 MIDDLESBROUGH
Emergency telephone 01287 624852
List of partners: A J Gowans, F M Grant
Office: Saltburn-by-the-Sea
Work: B1 D1 E G H K1 K3 L N O Q R1 S1 S2 V W Z(g,i,l)
Emergency Action, Agency, Advocacy, Fixed Fee Interview and Legal Aid undertaken
Ptr: Gowans, Mr Alastair J LLB . . . . *Oct 1978
Grant, Mr Fergus M LLB(Lond) . . . . *Jun 1980

NEWBYS (incorporating Thomas Bingham & Spark)
100 Borough Road Middlesbrough TS1 2HJ
Tel: 01642 247717 / 247967 *Fax:* 01642 232630
Dx: 60517 MIDDLESBROUGH
E-mail: davidwilkinson@newbys.co.uk
Office: Guisborough, Stockton-on-Tees
Work: A1 B1 C1 C2 C3 D1 E F1 J1 K1 L N O P Q R1 S1 S2 T1 T2 V W Z(p)
Emergency Action, Agency, Advocacy, Fixed Fee Interview, Legal Aid undertaken and Legal Aid Franchise
Ast: Bingham, Mr Andrew David LLB. . . . . *Oct 1995
Harrison, Mr Thomas Michal LLB(Hons). . . . . . . Aug 2003
McDonald, Miss Clare Louise BA(Hons). . . . . . . Sep 2003

PUNCH ROBSON ‡
35 Albert Road Middlesbrough TS1 1NU
Tel: 01642 230700 *Fax:* 01642 233913
Dx: 60501 MIDDLESBROUGH
E-mail: mhealy@punchrobson.co.uk
List of partners: C Bailey, G Cruickshank, G Downs, D Greenwood, G R Tyler, P F W Walker, J Wilkin, S J Williamson
Office: Middlesbrough, Stockton-on-Tees
Work: A1 B1 C1 C2 D1 D2 E F1 F2 J1 K1 K2 K3 K4 L N O Q R1 S1 S2 T2 W X Z(c,d,h,k,l,m,q)
Emergency Action, Agency, Advocacy, Fixed Fee Interview, Legal Aid undertaken and Legal Aid Franchise
Ptr: Bailey, Miss Clare LLB(Hons) . . . . *Sep 1999
Cruickshank, Mr Geoffrey LLB. . . . . *§Dec 1979
Downs, Mr Graeme LLB. . . . . *Mar 2000
Greenwood, Ms Deborah BA(Hons). . . . . *May 1996
Tyler, Mr Graham R LLB . . . . *Nov 1994
Walker, Mr Peter F W LLB . . . . *§Apr 1970
Wilkin, Mr John LLB. . . . . *§Apr 1992
Williamson, Mr Stewart John . . . . *Jan 1979
Asoc: Haigh, Mr Stephen . . . . *Sep 1994
Ast: Brown, Mrs Julie LLB; DipLP . . . . *Aug 2004
Dorey, Mr Hugh MA. . . . . *May 1991
Gillson, Ms Jemma Louise . . . . *Sep 2010
Honchen, Mr Ben . . . . *Sep 2011
Wigham, Mrs Katie . . . . *Sep 2006
Con: Vaux, Mr Colin G LLB. . . . . *§Jun 1966

PUNCH ROBSON
Unit E Parkway Centre Coulby Newham Middlesbrough TS8 0TJ
Tel: 01642 298830 *Fax:* 01642 298840
Office: Middlesbrough, Stockton-on-Tees
Work: A1 B1 D1 D2 E F1 J1 K1 K3 L N O Q S1 S2 T2 W X Z(h,l,m)
Emergency Action, Agency, Advocacy, Fixed Fee Interview and Legal Aid undertaken
Ptr: Downs, Mr Graeme LLB. . . . . *Mar 2000

DAVID SCOURFIELD ‡
28 Baker Street Middlesbrough TS1 2LH
Tel: 01642 874999 *Fax:* 01642 874025
Dx: 60590 MIDDLESBROUGH
List of partners: D Scourfield
SPr: Scourfield, Mr David. . . . . Jan 1970

STOKESLEY FAMILY LAW ‡
17 The Acres Stokesley Middlesbrough TS9 5QA
Tel: 01642 714071

TAYLOR GOODCHILD SOLICITORS ‡
166 High Street Eston Middlesbrough TS6 9JA
Tel: 01642 430000 *Fax:* 01642 430011
E-mail: reception@taylorgoodchild.co.uk
Office: Middlesbrough

TAYLOR GOODCHILD SOLICITORS
10 Woodlands Road Middlesbrough TS1 3BE
Tel: 01642 430000 *Fax:* 01642 430011
E-mail: reception@taylorgoodchild.co.uk
Office: Middlesbrough

THOMPSONS (FORMERLY ROBIN/BRIAN THOMPSON & PARTNERS)
202-206 Linthorpe Road Middlesbrough TS1 3QW
Tel: 01642 554162 *Fax:* 0191 232 2324
Dx: 60545 MIDDLESBROUGH
Office: Belfast, Birmingham, Bristol, Cardiff, Chelmsford, Dagenham, Derby, Harrow, Leeds, Liverpool, London SW19, London WC1, Manchester, Newcastle upon Tyne, Nottingham, Plymouth, Sheffield, South Shields, Southampton, Stoke-on-Trent, Swansea, Wolverhampton
Ast: Gulliford, Miss Lydia Jane LLB . . . . *Nov 1994

PAUL J WATSON ‡
The Vanguard Suite Broadcasting House Newport Road Middlesbrough TS1 5JA
Tel: 01642 293427 *Fax:* 01642 293429
Emergency telephone 07949 186589
E-mail: admin@pauljwatson.com
List of partners: P J Watson
Languages: French
Work: B2 D1 D2 G H K1 K3 K4 N Q W
Emergency Action, Agency, Advocacy, Fixed Fee Interview, Legal Aid undertaken and Legal Aid Franchise
Ptr: Watson, Mr Paul J LLB . . . . *Apr 1980
Asoc: Phoenix, Miss Stacey . . . . *Jun 2010

WATSON WOODHOUSE ‡
York House 102 Borough Road Middlesbrough TS1 2HJ
Tel: 01642 247656 *Fax:* 01642 213481
Dx: 60502 MIDDLESBROUGH
E-mail: info@watsonwoodhouse.co.uk
List of partners: A R Brook, N A Douglas, J Watson, N J M Woodhouse
Office: Darlington, Stockton-on-Tees

MATTHEW WILKINSON SOLICITORS LTD ‡
39 Albert Road Middlesbrough TS1 1NS
Tel: 01642 218888 *Fax:* 01642 221222
Dx: 60574 MIDDLESBROUGH 1
E-mail: matthew_w@btconnect.com
List of partners: M B Wilkinson
Work: B1 C1 E F1 J1 J2 K1 K3 K4 L N O Q S1 S2 W Z(b,c,j,k,q,r)
Emergency Action and Agency undertaken
Dir: Wilkinson, Mr Matthew Bernard BA; PNLA William Hutton Prize 1981 . . . . *Oct 1983
Ast: Large, Mr Matthew William Leo LLB(Hons) . . . . . . Aug 1997

WILLIAMSON HILL ‡
The Co-Operative Building 251-255 Linthorpe Road Middlesbrough TS1 4AT
Tel: 01642 217961 *Fax:* 01642 231192
E-mail: info@williamsonhill.co.uk
List of partners: M Hill, A M Peirson, L N Wilkinson
Work: K1 L N S1 S2 W Z(l)
Fixed Fee Interview undertaken
Ptr: Hill, Mr Michael LLB. . . . . *Oct 1982
Peirson, Mr A Martin LLB . . . . *May 1992
Wilkinson, Mr Leonard N LLB(Leeds) . . . . *Feb 1985
Ast: Henderson, Mr Paul Jeremy DipLP . . . . *Mar 1999

WILSON & CO SOLICITORS ‡
9 Baker Street Middlesbrough TS1 2LF
Tel: 01642 222292 *Fax:* 01642 230934
Dx: 60519 MIDDLESBROUGH
Emergency telephone 07949 005665
List of partners: C Hughes, P Wilson
Languages: Punjabi, Urdu
Work: D1 G H K1 L N O Q
Emergency Action, Agency, Advocacy, Fixed Fee Interview and Legal Aid undertaken
Ptr: Hughes, Mrs Catherine LLB. . . . . Apr 1997
Wilson, Mr Paul BA . . . . Feb 1991
Ast: Boddy, Mr Nigel Frederick LLB(Hons) . . . . Sep 1999

MIDDLETON, Greater Manchester

GLP SOLICITORS
20a Lakeland Court Middleton Greater Manchester M24 5QJ
Tel: 0161 653 6295 *Fax:* 0161 655 4371
E-mail: post@fosterlaw.co.uk
Office: Bury, Manchester (4 offices), Prestwich
Languages: French
Work: D1 F1 G H J1 K1 L N Q S1 V W Z(l)
Emergency Action, Agency, Advocacy, Fixed Fee Interview, Legal Aid undertaken and Legal Aid Franchise
Ptr: Foster, Mr David H MA(Oxon). . . . . §Jun 1978

RUSSELL & RUSSELL
Colmar House Middleton Gardens Middleton Greater Manchester M24 4DB
Tel: 0161 653 6200 *Fax:* 0161 655 3379 *Dx:* 29054 MIDDLETON
Emergency telephone 0800 731 7555
E-mail: infomiddleton@russellrussell.co.uk
Office: Atherton, Bolton (4 offices), Bury
Work: K4 N S1 W
Emergency Action, Agency, Advocacy, Fixed Fee Interview, Legal Aid undertaken and Member of Accident Line
Ptr: Penman, Mrs Jane Alison BA(Hons). . . . . Aug 1999
Ast: Griffiths, Miss Nicola Jane LLB(Hons) . . . . Aug 2001

SEDGWICK PHELAN & PARTNERS ‡
1st Floor Royal London House 56-58 Long Street Middleton Greater Manchester M24 6UQ
Tel: 0161 653 5299 *Fax:* 0161 653 3161 *Dx:* 29052 MIDDLETON
E-mail: reception@sedgwick-phelan.co.uk
List of partners: J P Carey, J E Dennerly, R C Dennerly
Work: C1 C2 C3 E F1 J1 J2 K1 L N O P Q S1 W Z(h,l)
Emergency Action, Agency, Advocacy and Fixed Fee Interview undertaken
Ptr: Carey, Mr John P LLB. . . . . Mar 1986
Dennerly, Miss Judith E LLB(Lond) . . . . Mar 1979
Dennerly, Mr Roger C. . . . . May 1975
Ast: Boylan, Mr John Anthony GDL; LPC . . . . *Feb 2011

TEMPERLEY TAYLOR LLP ‡
Durham House Warwick Court Park Road Middleton Greater Manchester M24 1AE
Tel: 0161 643 2411 *Fax:* 0161 655 3015 *Dx:* 29051 MIDDLETON
E-mail: info@temperleytaylor.co.uk
List of partners: A J Cryne, I A Mann
Office: Heywood
Work: C1 D1 E G H J1 K1 L N O Q S1 S2 T2 W Z(c,d,q)
Emergency Action, Agency, Advocacy, Fixed Fee Interview, Legal Aid undertaken, Legal Aid Franchise and Member of Accident Line
Ptr: Cryne, Mr Alan J BA ♦ . . . . *Jun 1981
Ast: Early, Ms Rachel Anne . . . . Oct 1989
Finbow, Ms Nicola. Jan 2007
Murray, Ms Fiona Jane LLB. . . . . *Dec 1994
Con: Temperley, Mr Philip S LLB . . . . *May 1971

MIDDLEWICH, Cheshire

BMD LAW ‡
WPI House King Street Trading Estate Middlewich Cheshire CW10 9LF
Tel: 0800 6123 579

DIXON RIGBY KEOGH
Lex House Leadsmithy Street Middlewich Cheshire CW10 9BH
Tel: 01606 835736 *Fax:* 01606 834626
Office: Northwich, Sandbach, Winsford
Work: A1 B1 C1 C2 C3 D1 E F1 J1 K1 L N O Q R1 S1 T1 T2 W Z(c,d,l,m)
Ptr: Cowgill, Mr David Richard LLB(Hons)(Lond). . . . . . May 1972
Masters, Mr Simon J LLB(Hons)(Nott'm) . . . . *Nov 1986

FAMILY LEGAL ‡
Garden Cottage 78 St Ann's Road Middlewich Cheshire CW10 9BY
Tel: 01606 841273
E-mail: enquiries@famlegal.co.uk
Work: K1

MIDHURST, West Sussex

BEVIS ROWNTREE ‡ (incorporating Albery Lucas Raper & Co)
Sheep Lane Midhurst West Sussex GU29 9NS
Tel: 01730 812201 *Fax:* 01730 814922 *Dx:* 58401 MIDHURST
E-mail: mail@bevis-rowntree.co.uk
List of partners: M G Bevis, B M D M Davies, C H Rowntree
Work: A1 C1 E L S1 S2 T2 W Z(d)
Ptr: Bevis, Mr Michael G Notary Public . . . . *§Jun 1974
Davies, Mrs Bridget M D M LLB. . . . . *Nov 1990
Rowntree, Mr Clive Hilton LLB . . . . *§Oct 1980
Asoc: Cutler, Ms Heather A BA . . . . *Dec 1982

CAROLINE BUTLER ‡
Peachey House Bepton Road Midhurst West Sussex GU29 9LU
Tel: 01730 816782

JOHNSON & CLARENCE ‡
Market Place Midhurst West Sussex GU29 9NW
Tel: 01730 812244 *Fax:* 01730 814907 *Dx:* 58403 MIDHURST
List of partners: M A Asscher
Languages: French, German, Spanish
Work: B1 C1 D1 D2 E F1 G J1 J2 K1 L N O Q S1 S2 T1 T2 W Z(c,e,k,l,r)
Emergency Action, Agency, Advocacy, Fixed Fee Interview undertaken and Member of Accident Line
Ptr: Asscher, Mr Martin A LLB . . . *Oct 1988

MACDONALD OATES LLP
7-8 Knockhundred Row Midhurst West Sussex GU29 9DQ
Tel: 01730 816711 *Fax:* 01730 816016 *Dx:* 58400 MIDHURST
E-mail: midhurst@macdonaldoates.co.uk
Office: Petersfield
Languages: French
Work: A1 A3 B1 C1 C2 D1 D2 E J1 J2 K1 K2 K3 L N O Q R2 S1 S2 T1 T2 V W Z(d,p,r)
Emergency Action, Agency, Advocacy and Fixed Fee Interview undertaken
Ptr: Dunn, Mrs Andrea LLB . . . *Jul 2003
Melville-Walker, Mr Timothy David LLB(Hons) . . . *Sep 1998
Sawers, Mr James Alexander BSc . . . *Jan 1997
Asoc: Manktelow, Miss Hazel Elizabeth LLB . . . *Jan 2003
Ast: Chapman, Miss Felicity Jane Dale LLB . . . Sep 2009
Smith, Mr Karl Milan LLB . . . *Sep 2007

MIDSOMER NORTON, Bath & North East Somerset

THATCHER & HALLAM ‡
Island House The Island Midsomer Norton Bath & North East Somerset BA3 2HJ
Tel: 01761 414646 *Fax:* 01761 413754
Dx: 42951 MIDSOMER NORTON
E-mail: enquiries@th-law.co.uk
List of partners: C R Clarke, J G Macaulay, W G G Thomas, W A Weller
Work: A1 B1 C1 C2 C3 D1 E F1 G H J1 K1 L M1 M2 N O P Q R1 S1 T1 T2 V W Z(b,c,d,e,f,h,j,k,l,m,n,o,s,t)
Emergency Action, Agency, Advocacy, Fixed Fee Interview and Legal Aid undertaken
Ptr: Clarke, Mr Christopher Richard LLB(Hons) . . . *Oct 1996
Macaulay, Mr J Grahame MA(Oxon) . . . §Jun 1979
Thomas, Mr William Graeme Gwynne . . . *Jan 1983
Weller, Mr William A BA . . . Oct 1987
Asoc: Westlake, Mr Timothy N J LLB(B'ham) . . . *Jan 1980
Ast: Best, Miss Sally Ann BA(Hons)(Law) . . . *Oct 1986
Powell, Mrs Patricia Mary LLB . . . Aug 1973

MILDENHALL, Suffolk

BENDALL & SONS
Ashton House 13 Mill Street Mildenhall Suffolk IP28 7DW
Tel: 01638 712243 *Fax:* 01638 718592 *Dx:* 41554 MILDENHALL
E-mail: law@bendallandsons.co.uk
Office: Newmarket
Languages: French
Work: A1 B1 C1 C2 C3 D1 D2 E F1 J1 K1 K2 K4 L M1 M2 N O P Q R1 S1 S2 T1 T2 V W Z(b,c,d,i,j,k,l,m,o,q,t)
Emergency Action, Agency, Fixed Fee Interview, Legal Aid undertaken and Legal Aid Franchise

MILFORD HAVEN, Pembrokeshire

EAVES ‡
Barrallier House Milford Haven Pembrokeshire SA73 3AA
Tel: 01646 695785 *Fax:* 01646 699120
E-mail: sgriffiths@eaves.lawyersonline.co.uk
List of partners: S G Griffiths, S W Griffiths
Work: E K1 L O Q S1 S2 W Z(q)
Fixed Fee Interview undertaken
Ptr: Griffiths, Ms Sarah G BA(Hons) . . . *Nov 1995
Griffiths, Mr Simon W LLB . . . *Apr 1989

MORGANS
25 Hamilton Terrace Milford Haven Pembrokeshire SA73 3JJ
Tel: 01646 697039 *Fax:* 01646 696098
E-mail: info@morgans-sols.co.uk
Office: Cardiff (2 offices), Swansea

NOBLE HARBOUR SOLICITORS ‡
14 Cedar Court Haven's Head Business Park Milford Haven Pembrokeshire SA73 3LS
Tel: 01646 663991 *Fax:* 01646 663992 *Dx:* 98402 MILFORD HAVEN
E-mail: info@nobleharbour.co.uk
Office: Pembroke Dock

PRICE & KELWAY ‡
17 Hamilton Terrace Milford Haven Pembrokeshire SA73 3JA
Tel: 01646 695311 *Fax:* 01646 695848 *Dx:* 98400 MILFORD HAVEN
Emergency telephone 01646 692522
E-mail: enquiries@priceandkelway.co.uk
List of partners: E W F Davies, H C Thomas
Languages: French, Welsh
Work: A1 B1 C1 D1 E F1 G H J1 K1 L M1 N O P Q R1 S1 T1 V W X Z(a,b,c,d,e,f,h,j,k,l,m,n,o,p,s,t,w)
Emergency Action, Agency, Advocacy and Legal Aid undertaken
Ptr: Davies, Mr Eurian Wyn Francis LLB(Wales) . . . *Sep 1977
Thomas, Mr Harvey C Clerk to the Haverfordwest Income Tax Commissioner . . . *§Jul 1975
Asoc: Phillips, Mr Gareth D LLB . . . Oct 1980
Ast: Lewis, Mr Gareth Glyn LLB(Hons) . . . Dec 2003

RED KITE LAW
30 Hamilton Terrace Milford Haven Pembrokeshire SA73 3JJ
Tel: 01646 698008 *Fax:* 01646 699466 *Dx:* 98407 MILFORD HAVEN
Office: Carmarthen (2 offices), Haverfordwest, Pembroke, Pembroke Dock, Tenby
Work: A1 B1 C1 D1 D2 E F1 G H J1 K1 K3 K4 L N O Q S1 S2 T2 V W Z(c,l,m,t)
Emergency Action, Agency, Advocacy, Fixed Fee Interview, Legal Aid undertaken and Legal Aid Franchise
Ptr: Sangster, Mr David BSc(Hons); PGDipLaw . . . Jul 2002
Ast: Proctor, Ms Rebecca . . . Jul 1996
Redhouse, Mrs Sara . . . Jul 1997
Tudor, Mr Jonathan . . . Mar 2003

MARINA C VAN'T GOOR ‡
Northleigh Liddleston Milford Haven Pembrokeshire SA73 3PZ
Tel: 01646 697700
List of partners: M C Van't Goor
Languages: Dutch
Work: D1 D2 K1 W
Emergency Action, Agency and Advocacy undertaken
SPr: Van't Goor, Ms Marina Christiana BA(Hons) . . . *Oct 1991

MILFORD-ON-SEA, Hampshire

HUGH WHITLOCK ‡
44 High Street Milford-on-Sea Hampshire SO41 0QD
Tel: 01590 644777 *Fax:* 01590 645222
Emergency telephone 01590 644777
E-mail: legal@hwsolicitors.com
Work: E J1 L N Q S1 S2 W
Fixed Fee Interview undertaken

MILLOM, Cumbria

BROWN & MURRAY
Midland Bank Chambers Market Square Millom Cumbria LA18 4JA
Tel: 01229 772562 *Fax:* 01229 774289
Dx: 63902 BARROW-IN-FURNESS
Work: A1 C1 C2 C3 D1 E F1 G H J1 K1 L N O P Q R1 S1 T1 T2 V W Z(c,d,f,h,j,l,r)
Emergency Action, Agency, Advocacy, Fixed Fee Interview, Legal Aid undertaken, Legal Aid Franchise and Member of Accident Line
Ptr: Murray, Mr James R F BA Notary Public . . . *Jul 1975
Ast: Turner, Mr Martin Robert . . . *May 1996
Con: Marshall, Mr Michael A . . . *Jan 1976

THOMAS BUTLER & SON
41 Wellington Street Millom Cumbria LA18 4DG
Tel: 01229 772553 *Fax:* 01229 773890
Office: Broughton-in-Furness
Languages: French
Work: A1 C1 E F1 K4 L R1 S1 S2 T2 W Z(l)
SPr: Ilett, Mr William John LLB . . . *Oct 1974
Ast: Tattersall, Mr J Philip . . . *Sep 1971

MILNTHORPE, Cumbria

ARNOLD GREENWOOD
5 Church Street Milnthorpe Cumbria LA7 7DX
Tel: 01539 562424
Office: Kendal

IAN N GUNBY & CO ‡
4 Park Road Milnthorpe Cumbria LA7 7AB
Tel: 01539 562044 *Fax:* 01539 563500 *Dx:* 711171 MILNTHORPE
List of partners: L Bayles, J C Copeland, I N Gunby, M J Oates, S Pyne, T B Roberts, P J Yates
Work: A1 E L Q S1 T2 W
Agency and Fixed Fee Interview undertaken
Ptr: Bayles, Lindsey . . . *Dec 1992
Copeland, Mrs Joanne C . . . *Nov 1993
Gunby, Mr Ian Nigel LLB(Leeds) . . . *Jul 1976
Oates, Mr Martin J LLB . . . *Nov 1992
Pyne, Mrs Susan BSc(Hons); LPC . . . *Nov 1998
Roberts, Trystan Bleddyn LLB . . . *Nov 1995
Yates, Mr Peter J LLB . . . *§Jul 1975
Asoc: Thompson, Mr David M . . . *§Jan 1970

MILNE MOSER (incorporating Powell & Sykes)
7 Main Street Milnthorpe Cumbria LA7 7PN
Tel: 01539 562263 *Fax:* 01539 563976 *Dx:* 711170 MILNTHORPE
Office: Kendal
Work: D1 E F1 G H J1 K1 L N O Q S1 T2 W Z(d,l)
Emergency Action, Agency, Advocacy, Fixed Fee Interview undertaken and Member of Accident Line
Ast: Rose, Mr Simon J BA(Oxon) . . . *Nov 1989

MILTON KEYNES

ADAMS MOORE FAMILY LAW ‡
Ashton House West 409 Silbury Boulevard Milton Keynes MK9 2AH
Tel: 01908 201200 *Fax:* 01908 201777 *Dx:* 31423 MILTON KEYNES
Office: Bedford, Bletchley, Corby, Daventry, Luton, Northampton

ATLANTIC SOLICITORS
4th Floor Exchange House 494 Midsummer Boulevard Milton Keynes MK9 2EA
Tel: 01908 255560 / 255826 *Fax:* 01908 255571
E-mail: admin@atlanticsolicitors.com

AUSTIN RAY ‡
102 Queensway Bletchley Milton Keynes MK2 2RX
Tel: 01908 769648 *Fax:* 01908 633543
E-mail: reception@austinraylaw.co.uk
List of partners: E S Addison, S J Fuller
Ptr: Addison, Mr Edward Stephen BA(Hons)(Law) . . . *Nov 1981
Fuller, Miss Sarah Justine LLB(Hons)(Law with French) . . . *Oct 1990
Ast: Hamilton, Mrs Joanne Kate LLB(Hons) . . . *Oct 1992
Ritson, Mr Nicholas Charles . . . *Oct 1985
Con: Nixon, Mr Richard W Notary Public . . . *May 1978

BASTIAN LLOYD MORRIS SOLICITOR ADVOCATES ‡
Unit 7 Sovereign Court 209 Witan Gate East Milton Keynes MK9 2HP
Tel: 01908 546580 *Fax:* 01908 546589 *Dx:* 31429 MILTON KEYNES
E-mail: jab@blmsolicitors.co.uk

BEESONS ‡
196 Queensway Bletchley Milton Keynes MK2 2SW
Tel: 01908 271171 *Fax:* 01908 271179
E-mail: stuart@beesons.net
List of partners: S R Beeson
Work: E S1 S2 W
Fixed Fee Interview undertaken
SPr: Beeson, Mr Stuart R LLB . . . *Jun 1992

CAMPBELL LAW SOLICITORS ‡
Technology House 151 Silbury Boulevard Milton Keynes MK9 1LH
Tel: 0845 226 8118 *Fax:* 01908 545729
Dx: 84753 MILTON KEYNES 3
E-mail: mail@cambell-law.co.uk
List of partners: I C Campbell
Work: J1 K4 W Z(g,m,za)
Agency, Advocacy, Fixed Fee Interview, Legal Aid undertaken and Legal Aid Franchise
SPr: Campbell, Mr Ian Colin . . . Nov 1995

GRAHAM CARDONA ‡
39 King Edwards Street New Bradwell Milton Keynes MK13 0BG
Tel: 01908 225672

CARTWRIGHT CLARK SOLICITORS ‡
1st Floor Ashton House 403 Silbury Boulevard Milton Keynes MK9 2LJ
Tel: 01908 325600 *Fax:* 01908 325601 *Dx:* 31407 MILTON KEYNES

CITY LAW LIMITED ‡
5a Copperhouse Court Caldecotte Milton Keynes MK7 8NL
Tel: 01908 369333 *Fax:* 01908 369444 *Dx:* 54478 MILTON KEYNES

CRIMINAL DEFENCE MILTON KEYNES SOLICITORS ‡
62 Queensway Bletchley Milton Keynes MK2 2SA
Tel: 01908 379225 *Fax:* 01908 377851 *Dx:* 100006 BLETCHLEY

DAVID DOWNTON & CO ‡
Harefield Chambers 2 Brook Farm Northampton Road Milton Keynes MK19 7BB
Tel: 01908 563030 *Fax:* 01908 565252
Emergency telephone 01908 563030
E-mail: law@daviddowntonlaw.com
List of partners: D G Downton
Work: F1 F2 J1 L M1 O Q Z(b,c,j,p,q)
Emergency Action, Agency and Advocacy undertaken
SPr: Downton, Mr David Gareth LLB(Hons) . . . *Apr 1981

EMW ‡
Seebeck Place One Seebeck Place Knowlhill Milton Keynes MK5 8FR
Tel: 0845 070 6000 *Fax:* 0870 238 8098
Dx: 151620 MILTON KEYNES 18
E-mail: enquiries@emwllp.com
List of partners: E J Appleyard, P E Bevington, T R T Chamberlain, D J C Danskin, G Ferin, M Finn, R Goffman, M Hessel, W Hodrien, L Holder, S C Ingram, S J Kay, J M Lacey, N G Lloyd, I Mabbutt, I Morris, M Myers, M R d C Rondel, A C Stillman, J Taylor, D J Watt, G P W Willis, A Winfield, K A Young, I L Zant-Boer
Office: London WC2
Work: A3 B1 C1 C2 C3 E F1 I J1 L M1 N O Q R1 R2 S1 S2 U1 U2 W Z(b,c,e,g,i,q)
Ptr: Appleyard, Mrs Elizabeth J LLB(Hons) . . . *Oct 1989
Bevington, Mr Paul Edward CPE; LPC . . . *Sep 1996
Chamberlain, Mr Timothy R T BSc(Hons)(Genetics); DipLaw; STEP Diploma . . . Sep 1996
Danskin, Mr David J C LLB(Soton) . . . *Apr 1983
Ferin, Mr Giles . . . Jan 1978
Finn, Mr Mark LLB . . . Sep 1986
Goffman, Mr Rob LLB(Hons) . . . Sep 1984
Hodrien, Mrs Wendy BA . . . Nov 1995
Holder, Mrs Louise BA; PGDipLaw . . . Sep 2001
Ingram, Mr Simon C LLB . . . Dec 1976
Kay, Mr Stephen J LLB; LPC . . . *Sep 1999
Lacey, Miss Joanna M BA . . . Jan 1984
Lloyd, Mr Nicholas G LLB(Nott'm) . . . *Mar 1998
Mabbutt, Mr Ian LLB . . . *Sep 2000
Morris, Mr Ian BSc . . . *Oct 1985
Myers, Mrs Moira LLB(Hons)(Manc) . . . *Jun 1981
Stillman, Ms Anna Charlotte . . . Sep 1997
Taylor, Mr Jonathan LLB(Hons) . . . Jan 1993
Watt, Mr Damon James LLB . . . Oct 2001
Willis, Mr Geoffrey P W LLB; AKC . . . *Nov 1994
Winfield, Mr Andrew LLB . . . *Mar 1984
Young, Ms Karen A BA(Hons) . . . Sep 1997
Zant-Boer, Mr Ian L MA(Cantab) . . . *Feb 1984
Asoc: Arkell, Mr Simon LLB . . . Sep 2002
Barrable, Ms Aimee BA(Hons)(Law & Sociology) . . . Sep 2005
Bingham, Mr Jody BA . . . Sep 2005
Clarke, Miss Sophie BA(Hons) . . . Sep 2005
Robinson-Smith, Mr Matthew LLB . . . Sep 2001
Ast: Bradban, Mrs Lucy-Ann LLB(Hons) . . . *Mar 2007
Buckley, Miss Clare LLB . . . Sep 2006
Cooper, Mrs Kylie LPC . . . Sep 2011
Eden, Mr Jeremy BSc . . . Jun 2007
Facchiano, Miss Natalina Giovanna LLB . . . Oct 2010
Fletcher, Mr Antonio E V LLB; LPC . . . *Sep 2007
Harris, Miss Emily LLB . . . Sep 2009
Holman, Mr Matthew Martin James BA(Hons)(Law); PGDipLaw Sweet & Maxwell Law Prize; Best Graduate Performance 2004/2005 . . . Dec 2008
Ireland, Mr Mark Julian BA(Hons) . . . May 2001
Mauro, Mr Marco LLB; LPC . . . Feb 2007
Miller, Mrs Alexandra LLB(Hons) . . . Sep 2006
Norat, Miss Sajidah LPC . . . Sep 2011
O'Donoghue, Mr Gary Thomas LLB; LPC . . . *Sep 2011
Patel, Miss Amisa LLB . . . Jan 2009
Sanghera, Mr Gurpreet Singh BSc . . . Jan 2008
Con: Eyton-Jones, Mr Michael R . . . *Apr 1969
Rolfe, Mrs Derryn Penelope BSc(Hons); LLB(Hons); LPC . . . *May 2005
Thompson, Mr Peter LLB(Hons) Chairman of Employment Tribunals . . . Nov 1970

Commercial & Company, Property and Construction, Planning, Employment, Dispute Resolution, Insolvency, Mergers & Acquisitions, Banking, Intellectual Property, Competition, Technology, Property Finance and Private client.

STUART FANTHAM
Central Business Exchange CBX2 West Wing Milton Keynes MK9 2RG
Tel: 01908 250001 *Fax:* 01908 847401
Office: Aylesbury

See p112 for the Key to Work Categories & other symbols

FRANKLINS LLP
Silbury Court Silbury Boulevard Milton Keynes MK9 2LY
Tel: 01908 660966 *Fax:* 01908 690259 / 668769
Dx: 31409 MILTON KEYNES
E-mail: info@franklins-sols.co.uk
Office: Northampton
Languages: French, German
Work: A1 B1 C1 D1 E F1 G H J1 K1 L N O Q S1 V
Emergency Action, Agency, Advocacy and Legal Aid undertaken
Ptr: Franklin, Mr Michael L BA. . . . . *Apr 1977
Long, Mr Simon Anthony ♦ . . . . . *Sep 1990
Mem: Evans, Ms Sarah . . . . . Feb 2004
Smith, Ms Naomi . . . . . Nov 2003
Ast: Child, Ms Kimberley. . . . . May 2009
Hrydziuszko, Mrs Emma Claire LLB(Hons) . . . . . Sep 2002
Pusey, Joanne . . . . . Oct 2003
Watt, Mr Damon James LLB . . . . . Oct 2001

GREENWOODS
2 Eskan Court Campbell Park Milton Keynes MK9 4AN
Tel: 01908 298200 *Fax:* 01908 298298
E-mail: contact@greenwoods-solicitors.com
Office: Bristol, Fareham, London EC3, London WC1, Manchester
Ptr: Neuhoff, Ms Tanja BA(Hons) . . . . . Jul 1999
Parsons, Mr Paul T S BA(Dunelm) . . . . . *Jul 1982
Asoc: Barclay, Ms Elaine . . . . . *Jun 1997
Martin, Mr Simon LLB(Hons) . . . . . *Oct 1991
Ast: Kingsman, Ms Anita. . . . . Mar 2006
Lad, Bhrina . . . . . Apr 2011
Parekh, Sangita. . . . . Oct 2006
Con: Davies, Mr Paul. . . . . Nov 1983

HARVEY INGRAM BORNEOS
Chancery House 199 Silbury Boulevard Milton Keynes MK9 1JL
Tel: 01908 696002 *Fax:* 01908 677640
Dx: 84757 MILTON KEYNES 3
E-mail: mail@borneolinnells.co.uk
Office: Bedford, Birmingham, Leicester, Newport Pagnell
Work: C1 D1 E F1 G H J1 K1 L N O P Q S1 W Z(l,p,q)
Emergency Action, Agency, Advocacy, Legal Aid undertaken, Legal Aid Franchise and Member of Accident Line
Mem: Clay, Mr Charles E LLB . . . . . *Oct 1985
Hamblett, Mr Alan Edward BA(Hons) . . . . . *Apr 1981
Hopgood, Mr Antony G BA . . . . . *Apr 1981
Lazard, Mr Jason BA(Hons). . . . . Sep 1999
Patel, Miss Jyoti. . . . . Jun 1994
Perusko, Mr Patrick LLB . . . . . *Feb 1988
Saigal, Praveen LLB . . . . . *Mar 1990
Soul, Mr Joseph. . . . . Jul 2002
Ast: Asbery, Mrs Amanda FILEx . . . . . Sep 2000
Enstone, Mrs Rachel . . . . . Feb 2000
Gough, Mr David J LLB(Hons) . . . . . Sep 1999
Hardy, Mrs Jacqueline D S LLB(Hons). . . . . *Oct 1988
Steel, Miss Lynne FILEx . . . . . Nov 1998
Wardropper, Miss Susan Lesley BA(Hons) . . . . . *Oct 1994

HAWKINS SOLICITORS ‡
The Old Court House 19 Market Square Milton Keynes MK11 1BE
Tel: 01908 262680 *Fax:* 01908 262022

HEALD SOLICITORS ‡
Ashton House 471 Silbury Boulevard Milton Keynes MK9 2AH
Tel: 01908 662277 *Fax:* 01908 675667
Dx: 54459 MILTON KEYNES 1
E-mail: info@healdlaw.com
List of partners: M R Banham-Hall, N W Crook, S W Daw, D C Dees, G P Pobjoy, C Wilton
Work: B1 C1 C2 C3 D1 E I J1 K1 K2 K3 O Q S1 S2 U2 W Z(b,c,d,e,o,za)
Ptr: Banham-Hall, Mr Martin R LLB(Lond) . . . . . *Jun 1977
Crook, Mr Nicholas W MA(Oxon) . . . . . *May 1976
Daw, Mr Simon W. . . . . . *Dec 1982
Dees, Mr David Charles MA(Oxon); BCL Hardwicke Scholar . . . . . *May 1991
Pobjoy, Mr Gareth P Notary Public . . . . . *May 1979
Wilton, Ms Caroline LLB. . . . . *Jan 1989
Ast: Marchant, Ms Esther R BA . . . . . Jun 1985
Silverwood-Cope, Mr Tom. . . . . Mar 2008
Con: Banham-Hall, Mrs Mary A LLB . . . . . *Jul 1979

HEWITSONS
Exchange House 482 Midsummer Boulevard Milton Keynes MK9 2EA
Tel: 01908 247010 *Fax:* 01908 247020
E-mail: mail@hewitsons.com
Office: Cambridge, Northampton, Saffron Walden

HOWES PERCIVAL LLP
252 Upper Third Street Grafton Gate East Milton Keynes MK9 1DZ
Tel: 01908 672682 *Fax:* 01908 672638
Dx: 84750 MILTON KEYNES 3
Emergency telephone 01908 672682
E-mail: law@howespercival.com
Office: Leicester, London WC2, Manchester, Northampton, Norwich
Languages: French, German, Italian, Spanish
Work: A1 A2 A3 B1 B2 C1 C2 C3 D1 D2 E F1 I J1 L M1 M2 N O P Q R1 R2 S1 S2 T1 T2 U2 V W Z(b,c,d,e,f,i,j,k,l,o,p,q,r,t)
Emergency Action, Agency, Advocacy and Legal Aid Franchise
Asoc: Bloomer, Jane. . . . . Sep 2000
Ast: Clunie, Mr Peter John Holland. . . . . *Oct 1996

JONRO SOLICITORS ‡
56 OPD Old Stratford Milton Keynes MK19 6DP
Tel: 07734 318890 *Fax:* 01908 722458

KIMBELLS LLP ‡
Power House Harrison Close Knowlhill Milton Keynes MK5 8PA
Tel: 01908 668555 *Fax:* 01908 685085
Dx: 154900 MILTON KEYNES 20
E-mail: next.step@kimbells.com
List of partners: R D Brown, J L Hambleton, P A Holden, J Keeble, S E Kimbell, H Norris, L Skinner
Languages: French, German
Work: B1 C1 C2 C3 E O R2 S2 U2 Z(e,q)
Advocacy undertaken
Ptr: Brown, Mr Richard Devereux LLB(Hons) . . . . . *Nov 1987
Hambleton, Mr Jonathan L BA; MA(Oxon). . . . . *Oct 1990
Holden, Mr Peter A LLB. . . . . *Apr 1975
Keeble, Mr John LLB . . . . . *Sep 1997
Kimbell, Mr Stephen E BA. . . . . *§Jun 1979
Norris, Ms Hilary LLB . . . . . *Feb 1999
Skinner, Mr Leo BA . . . . . *Apr 1994
Ast: Ainsworth, Chris LLB . . . . . *Sep 2001
Brown, Mrs Karen BA. . . . . *Sep 2000

Lyon, Mr Neil MA . . . . . Oct 1994
Morgan, Miss Emma . . . . . *Sep 2004
Parker, Ms Jane. . . . . *Dec 1990
Smith, Mrs Amanda LLB . . . . . *Apr 1995
Warman, Ms Valerie C LLB(Bris) . . . . . *Sep 1987
Wilkinson, Mr Dino . . . . . *Apr 2002
Wood, Mr Richard LLB . . . . . *Oct 2000
Con: Clark, Mr Timothy W S MA(Cantab). . . . . *Feb 1979

KING PARTNERS SOLICITORS ‡
208 Queensway Bletchley Milton Keynes MK2 2ST
Tel: 01908 643122 *Fax:* 01908 367775
E-mail: jacob@kingpartnerssolicitors.com

KINGSLEY DAVID SOLICITORS LIMITED ‡
5 Whittle Court Knowlhill Milton Keynes MK5 8FT
Tel: 01908 325555 *Fax:* 01908 692488
Dx: 84770 MILTON KEYNES 3

GEOFFREY LEAVER SOLICITORS LLP ‡
251 Upper 3rd Street Bouverie Square Milton Keynes MK9 1DR
Tel: 01908 692769 *Fax:* 01908 692772
Dx: 54460 MILTON KEYNES 1
E-mail: legal@geoffreyleaver.com
List of partners: G P Brooks, T A B Coward, N Gill, A Maguire, J J McGarrity, R E Millard, M H Page, T R Roberts, N S Scott, S J Snelson, K M Stangoe, T D Warner, R E Willis
Languages: French, Polish, Punjabi, Urdu
Work: B1 C1 E F1 I J1 J2 L M1 N O P Q R1 S1 T1 W Z(c,d,e,f,h,l,o,r)
Advocacy undertaken
Ptr: Brooks, Mr Guy Peter. . . . . Nov 1980
Coward, Mr Trevor A B BL; LLB(Rhodesia) . . . . . *Jan 1984
Gill, Mr Navdip LLB . . . . . *Jul 1999
McGarrity, Mr James J LLB . . . . . *Sep 1984
Maguire, Mrs Anne LLB. . . . . Aug 1991
Millard, Mr Richard Edward LLB(Hons) . . . . . *Jan 1998
Page, Ms Melissa Hilary LLB . . . . . Oct 1993
Roberts, Mr Timothy R LLB . . . . . *Apr 1980
Scott, Mr Nicholas S LLB . . . . . *Feb 1983
Snelson, Mr Stuart John BA. . . . . *Sep 1999
Stangoe, Mr Kenneth Mckay LLB(Hons); LLM. . . . . Apr 1998
Warner, Mr Troy D BA. . . . . *Dec 1988
Willis, Mr Richard E BA; MA. . . . . *Feb 1987
Asoc: Mcerlean, Ms Mairead LLB . . . . . Sep 2005
Stuart, Mrs Paula Jane LLB. . . . . Aug 1996
Ast: Kulczykowska, Mrs Dagmara . . . . . Oct 2004
Seaford, Mr Samuel David LLB . . . . . Nov 2009

LEWINGTON LAW FOR BUSINESS ‡
17 Milton Road Willen Milton Keynes MK15 9AD
Tel: 01908 232226

MK LEGAL SOLICITORS ‡
14 Walker Avenue Stratford Office Village Wolverton Mill Milton Keynes MK12 5TW
Tel: 01908 577680 *Fax:* 01908 320938 *Dx:* 140234 WOLVERTON
E-mail: info@mk-legal.co.uk
List of partners: M Keeling
Dir: Keeling, Mr Martin LLB . . . . . Mar 1979

MCKEOWNS SOLICITORS LTD
35 Kelvin Drive Knowl Hill Milton Keynes MK5 8NH
Tel: 0800 032 8328 *Fax:* 01727 839118
Dx: 151053 MILTON KEYNES 17
E-mail: personalinjury@mckeowns.com
Office: St Albans

MALLETTS SOLICITORS ‡
1 Gardiner Court Blue Bridge Milton Keynes MK13 0LR
Tel: 01908 226138 *Fax:* 01908 320934

MATTHEW ARNOLD & BALDWIN LLP
401 Grafton Gate Milton Keynes MK9 1AQ
Tel: 01908 687880 *Fax:* 01908 687881
Dx: 84769 MILTON KEYNES 3
E-mail: info@mablaw.com
Office: London EC4, Watford
Ptr: Marsden, Mr David K TD LLB . . . . . *§May 1981
Power, Mr David M LLB. . . . . Nov 1994
Asoc: Fahy, Mr Robert. . . . . *Jan 2003

NC LAW LTD ‡
14 High Street Nash Milton Keynes MK17 0EP
Tel: 01908 520295

NEVES SOLICITORS
Kingsbridge House 702 South Seventh Street Milton Keynes MK9 2PZ
Tel: 01908 304560 *Fax:* 01908 304565 *Dx:* 31421 MILTON KEYNES
E-mail: info@neves-solicitors.co.uk
Office: Harpenden, Luton, Northampton
Work: A1 A3 C1 C2 D1 E F1 J1 K1 K2 K3 K4 L M4 O Q R1 R2 S1 S2 T1 T2 W Z(c,l)
Fixed Fee Interview undertaken
Ptr: Clipstone, Mr Simeon W S BA. . . . . *Mar 1990
Matthews, Mr Stewart. . . . . *Jul 2001
Woodward, Mrs Elizabeth Jane . . . . . *Dec 1995
Ast: Harvey, Mr James Robert Stephen LLB(Hons). . . . . *Jan 2009
McGlone, Miss Elizabeth May. . . . . *Sep 2009

NOVALEX SOLICITORS ‡
Midsummer Court 314 Midsummer Boulevard Milton Keynes MK9 2UB
Tel: 01908 440020 *Fax:* 07966 410984
E-mail: karen.mason@novalex.co.uk

OSBORNE MORRIS & MORGAN
216-220 Queensway Bletchley Milton Keynes MK2 2ST
Tel: 01908 373282 *Fax:* 01908 641367
Office: Leighton Buzzard

PICTONS SOLICITORS LLP
Moorgate House 201 Silbury Boulevard Milton Keynes MK9 1JL
Tel: 01908 663511 *Fax:* 01908 661800 *Dx:* 31411 MILTON KEYNES
E-mail: info@pictons.co.uk
Office: Hemel Hempstead, Luton
Languages: Danish, Finnish, French, Gujarati, Hindi, Italian, Punjabi, Urdu
Work: A3 B1 C1 C2 C3 D1 E F1 G H I J1 K1 L N O Q S1 S2 T1 T2 U2 V W Z(h,k,l,o,r,w)
Emergency Action, Agency, Advocacy, Fixed Fee Interview, Legal Aid undertaken, Legal Aid Franchise and Member of Accident Line
Ptr: Wardrop, Mr Mark C LLB . . . . . *Oct 1983

Ast: Biriah, Ms Jasvinder CPE; DipLaw; LPC; BA(Hons)(Business Admin); HND(Business & Finance) . . . . . *Jul 2001
Bryers, Mr John Richard Feneran . . . . . *Dec 1970
Howard, Mr Michael G LLB(Lond). . . . . *Dec 1977
Kent, Ms Katherine LLB(Hons); RSCN; RGN; HV Cert. *Jun 2001
Tomaszewska, Ms Jerewa M LLB(Hons) . . . . . Nov 2001
Wong, Mr Felix LLB. . . . . Nov 2000

PURCELL SOLICITORS ‡
Seckloe House 101 North 13th Street Milton Keynes MK9 3NX
Tel: 01908 693000 *Fax:* 01908 693008 *Dx:* 31417 MILTON KEYNES
E-mail: enquiries@purcellsolicitors.co.uk

RFB ASSOCIATE LIMITED ‡
Amberley House 2a Vicarage Road Milton Keynes MK17 0LU
Tel: 01908 410844

REYNOLDS & HAWKES ‡
(incorporating Wright & Bull)
3 Smabridge Walk Willen Milton Keynes MK15 9LT
Tel: 01908 366521 *Fax:* 01908 366629
List of partners: S L Reynolds
Work: B1 C1 C2 C3 D1 E F1 J1 K1 L M1 M2 N P R1 S1 W Z(d,e,f,i,j,k,m)
Agency, Advocacy, Fixed Fee Interview, Legal Aid undertaken and Member of Accident Line
SPr: Reynolds, Mrs Susan L . . . . . *Dec 1981

SKG SOLICITORS ‡
2 Lavender Grove Walnut Tree Milton Keynes MK7 7DB
Tel: 01908 528745 *Fax:* 01908 235524 *Dx:* 100002 BLETCHLEY
E-mail: surjit.gida@skgsolicitors.co.uk

SNR DENTON
The Pinnacle 170 Midsummer Boulevard Milton Keynes MK9 1FE
Tel: 01908 690260 *Fax:* 01908 668535 *Dx:* 84756 MILTON KEYNES
Office: London EC4
Languages: French, German
Work: B1 C1 E J1 L O Q R2 S2 Z(b,c,l,p,q,u)
Emergency Action, Agency and Advocacy undertaken
Ptr: Bowman, Mr Henry M H BSc(Hons). . . . . *§Oct 1994
Denny, Mr Christopher J . . . . . *May 1982
Fairbairn, Mr James E K BA. . . . . *Oct 1984
Ast: Foo, Ms Alicia LLB(Hons) . . . . . *Jan 1993

SHOOSMITHS
1st Floor Witan Gate Witan Gate House Milton Keynes MK9 1SH
Tel: 0370 086 8300 / 01908 488300 *Fax:* 0370 086 8301
Dx: 729360 MILTON KEYNES 15
E-mail: miltonkeynes@shoosmiths.co.uk
Office: Basingstoke, Birmingham, Fareham, London WC2, Manchester, Northampton, Nottingham, Reading
Work: A3 B1 B2 C1 C2 C3 E F1 F2 I J1 J2 K4 L M1 N O Q R1 R2 S1 S2 T1 T2 U2 W X Z(b,c,e,f,h,i,j,k,l,m,n,o,p,q,r,s,t,u,y,za)
Ptr: Assim, Mr Gary D BA(Hons) . . . . . *§Nov 1990
Bacon, Mr Timothy F BA(Dunelm). . . . . *Nov 1991
Brookshaw, Mr Oliver Chitty BA(Oxon) . . . . . *§Oct 1983
Burke, Mr Sean BA(Hons). . . . . *§Oct 1988
Chandler, Ms Heather. . . . . Nov 1993
Dard, Mr Satpaul . . . . . Jan 1998
Gordon Brown, Ms Deborah LLB(Hons) . . . . . *§Oct 1989
Howard, Mr William I LLB(Lond). . . . . *Jun 1980
Jess, Ms Helen . . . . . Apr 2001
Lehman, Ms Jill. . . . . Jun 1975
Mattis, Mr Colin. . . . . Oct 1998
Morley, Mr David A BA; CPE . . . . . Sep 1992
Pickin, Mr Andrew Jonathan BA; MSPI . . . . . *Oct 1983
Price, Mr Sebastian BA(Lond). . . . . *§Dec 1986
Seary, Mr W Peter LLB(Hons). . . . . §Dec 1991
Shakespeare, Ms Karen. . . . . Nov 1999
Sharma, Mr Sanjeev . . . . . Mar 2000
Simpson, Mr Graeme John . . . . . Mar 1997
Thompson, Mr David . . . . . Jan 1991
Williams, Ms Lisa . . . . . Mar 1997

TOLLERS LLP
Medina House 312-314 Silbury Boulevard Milton Keynes MK9 2AE
Tel: 01908 396230 *Fax:* 01908 237794 *Dx:* 31422 MILTON KEYNES
E-mail: enquiries@tollers.co.uk
Office: Corby, Kettering, Northampton
Ptr: Lord, Ms Lucy. . . . . Sep 2001
Niblock, Mr Andrew. . . . . May 1999
Smith, Ms Sally . . . . . Nov 1994

WATSON LAW SOLICITORS ‡
78 Walker Avenue Wolverton Mill Milton Keynes MK12 5GT
Tel: 01908 311366 *Fax:* 01908 222412 *Dx:* 14023 WOLVERTON

WINWARDS ‡
1 Waddon Hall High Street Waddon Milton Keynes MK17 0NA
Tel: 01908 502559 *Fax:* 01908 520433

WOODFINES LLP
226-228 Upper Fifth Street Regency Court Milton Keynes MK9 2HR
Tel: 01908 202150 *Fax:* 01908 202152 *Dx:* 54465 MILTON KEYNES
E-mail: mail@woodfines.co.uk
Office: Bedford, Bletchley, Cambridge, Sandy
Work: A1 A3 B1 C1 C2 C3 D1 E F1 F2 J1 K1 K2 K3 K4 L M1 M2 N O P Q R1 S1 S2 T1 T2 V W Z(c,d,e,i,j,k,l,m,n,o,p,x)
Emergency Action, Agency, Advocacy, Fixed Fee Interview, Legal Aid undertaken, Legal Aid Franchise and Member of Accident Line
Mem: Egan, Mr John . . . . . *Feb 1992
Gibbs, Mr Neil James. . . . . *Nov 1995
Hallsworth, Mr Christopher Charles ★. . . . . *Jul 1973
Asoc: Carter, Mr Andrew Michael BA(Hons) . . . . . *Oct 2002
Ast: Evans, Ms Carolyn ★ . . . . . *Jan 2004

MINEHEAD, Somerset

AMICUS SOLICITORS & ADVOCATES ‡
9 Parkhouse Road Minehead Somerset TA24 8AB
Tel: 01643 701888 *Fax:* 01643 704183

KINGS SOLICITORS ‡
PO Box 89 Minehead Somerset TA24 9BG
Tel: 01643 709600 *Fax:* 01643 797755
E-mail: kingssolicitors@btinternet.com

MAITLAND WALKER ‡
22 The Parks Minehead Somerset TA24 8BT
Tel: 01643 707777 *Fax:* 01643 700020 *Dx:* 117408 MINEHEAD
Emergency telephone 07977 465903
E-mail: office@maitwalk.co.uk
List of partners: H E Coles, R Croft, J H Maitland-Walker
Office: Cheltenham
Languages: Afrikaans, French
Work: A1 B1 C1 C2 C3 E F1 J1 K1 K2 L M1 M2 N O P R1 R2 S1 S2 T1 T2 U1 W Z(b,e,f,g,i,j,l)
Emergency Action, Agency, Advocacy, Fixed Fee Interview and Legal Aid undertaken
Ptr: Coles, Miss Hilary E. . . . . Feb 1999
Maitland-Walker, Mr Julian Henry Chairman of South West Dairies Tribunal . . . . *May 1974
Asoc: Eagle, Mrs Karen Heather Jane BA . . . . Jun 2003
Ast: Rowe, Mr Nick F LLB . . . . *Sep 2002
Slade, Mr Benjamin Jonathon Balham LLB . . . . Sep 2004
Con: Dyer, Mr John L LLB(B'ham) . . . . *§Jun 1962
Roach, Mr David M . . . . *Dec 1961

RISDON HOSEGOOD
(incorporating Risdons & Hosegood Burgess & Co; R G McLusky & Co)
6 Bancks Street Minehead Somerset TA24 5DF
Tel: 01643 703123 / 700008 *Fax:* 01643 705583
Dx: 117401 MINEHEAD
Emergency telephone 01643 703123
E-mail: minehead@risdonhosegood.com
Office: Dulverton, Taunton, Williton, Wiveliscombe
Work: A1 B1 D1 E F1 G H J1 K1 L N O Q R1 S1 V W Z(c,k,l)
Emergency Action, Agency, Advocacy, Legal Aid undertaken, Legal Aid Franchise and Member of Accident Line
Ptr: Needs, Mr Keith Leslie LLB(Manc) . . . . *Jun 1981

THORNE SEGAR ‡
3 Bancks Street Minehead Somerset TA24 5DE
Tel: 01643 703234 *Fax:* 01643 704697 *Dx:* 117403 MINEHEAD
E-mail: partners@thorneandthorne.co.uk
List of partners: J C J Barrington, I Milton-Jenkins, J E Mullis, D M Segar, J Tilley
Languages: French, Welsh
Work: A1 B1 C1 E F1 F2 G H J1 L N O Q R1 S1 S2 T1 T2 W Z(l,o,q,s)
Emergency Action, Agency, Advocacy and Fixed Fee Interview undertaken
Ptr: Barrington, Mr John C J LLB(Bris). . . . . *Jun 1985
Milton-Jenkins, Mr Iestyn MA(Oxon); LLB(Hons). . . . Oct 1996
Mullis, Mr John E Notary Public . . . . *Sep 1979
Segar, Mr David M BSc. . . . . *Nov 1972
Tilley, Miss Joanne LLB(Hons) . . . . *Oct 1992
Con: Hodges, Mr Crispin J LLB. . . . . *§Jun 1972

MIRFIELD, West Yorkshire

HELEN BINKS SOLICITOR ‡
Ledgard Bridge Mill Ledgard Bridge Mirfield West Yorkshire WF14 8NJ
Tel: 01924 497720

ROGER A CLAPHAM ‡
Spinners House 26 Spinners Way Lower Hopton Mirfield West Yorkshire WF14 8PU
Tel: 01924 521178

HAIGHS SOLICITORS ‡
116 Huddersfield Road Mirfield West Yorkshire WF14 8BQ
Tel: 01924 489197 *Fax:* 01924 489197

RAMSDENS SOLICITORS
7 King Street Mirfield West Yorkshire WF14 8AW
Est: 1870
Tel: 01924 499251 *Fax:* 01924 499324 *Dx:* 29642 MIRFIELD
E-mail: info@ramsdens.co.uk
Office: Dewsbury, Elland, Halifax, Holmfirth, Huddersfield (3 offices)
Work: A1 B1 C1 D1 E F1 G H J1 K1 L M1 N P R1 S1 T1 W Z(d,e,l)

MITCHAM, Surrey

BAKERS ‡
(incorporating Edward Isaacs & Co)
2 Upper Green East Mitcham Surrey CR4 2PF
Tel: 020 8648 0363 *Fax:* 020 8646 5387 *Dx:* 58653 MITCHAM
E-mail: bakers@bakerssolicitors.co.uk
List of partners: J P Ticktum
Work: B1 C1 C2 E J1 L N O Q R1 R2 S1 S2 T1 T2 W
Ptr: Ticktum, Mr Jeremy P LLB . . . . *Jan 1990

MCMILLAN WILLIAMS
8-10 Cricket Green Mitcham Surrey CR4 4LA
Tel: 020 8648 4044 *Fax:* 020 8640 4683
Dx: 88150 MITCHAM SOUTH
E-mail: mitcham@mcmillan-williams.co.uk
Office: Carshalton, Coulsdon, Croydon, South Croydon, Thornton Heath, Wallington
Ast: Kang, Ms Jasroop. . . . . Mar 2006
Kotecha, Deesha . . . . Sep 2008

PREUVENEERS & CO ‡
Elm House 103-105 London Road Mitcham Surrey CR4 2JA
Tel: 020 8646 4885 *Fax:* 020 8646 0191 *Dx:* 58650 MITCHAM
E-mail: legal@preuveneers.co.uk
List of partners: K Cirillo, B Preuveneers
Languages: Gujarati, Hindi, Punjabi, Urdu
Work: E J1 K1 K2 K3 M4 S1 S2 W Z(i)
Fixed Fee Interview undertaken
Ptr: Preuveneers, Mr Basil LLB Notary Public . . . . *§Jun 1973
Cirillo, Mrs Kelly. . . . . *Mar 2003

MOLD, Flintshire

ABRAHAM & CO SOLICITORS ‡
First Floor 23 Wrexham Street Mold Flintshire CH7 1ET
Tel: 01352 755595
E-mail: mail@abrahamsolicitors.co.uk

J G BUTTERWORTH ‡
Ty Coch Black Mountain Nercwys Mold Flintshire CH7 4BW
Tel: 07984 167453
List of partners: J G Butterworth
Languages: French
Work: D1 E F1 G K1 P S1 W Z(l,s)
Ptr: Butterworth, Mrs Joanne G BA(B'ham) . . . . *Jul 1973

CAPPER & JONES ‡
Old Bank Chambers 1 King Street Mold Flintshire CH7 1LA
Tel: 01352 752020 *Fax:* 01352 756967 *Dx:* 26555 MOLD
List of partners: R A Capper, B S Jones
Work: D1 E J1 K1 K2 K3 K4 S1 S2 W
Ptr: Capper, Mr Robert Arthur LLB. . . . . *Oct 1978
Jones, Mrs B Susan LLB . . . . *Oct 1983

RICHARD STEPHEN DAVIES ‡
62 New Street Mold Flintshire CH7 1NZ
Tel: 01352 754468 *Fax:* 01352 751616 *Dx:* 26558 MOLD
E-mail: rsdlaw@btconnect.com
List of partners: R S Davies
Work: A1 A2 C1 E F1 J1 L R1 S1 S2 W
Fixed Fee Interview undertaken
Ptr: Davies, Mr Richard S MA(Oxon) . . . . *Dec 1973

GEOFFREY MORRIS & ASHTON
Belgravia House Grosvenor Street Mold Flintshire CH7 1EJ
Tel: 01352 754711 *Fax:* 01352 754714 *Dx:* 26658 WREXHAM
E-mail: info@mold-solicitors.co.uk
Office: Wrexham
Work: D1 D2 E K1 K3 L N O Q R1 S1 S2 W Z(c,l)
Agency, Advocacy, Fixed Fee Interview, Legal Aid undertaken and Legal Aid Franchise
Ptr: Faulkner, Mr Keith LLB(Wales) . . . . *§Jul 1975

HALLOWS ASSOCIATES ‡
Abbey House Chester Street Mold Flintshire CH7 1EG
Tel: 01352 752773 / 758603 / 0800 525696 *Fax:* 01352 758604
Dx: 26559 MOLD
E-mail: hallows@hallowssol.co.uk
List of partners: R C Hallows, D H Lloyd
Work: A1 B1 C1 C2 C3 D1 D2 E F1 F2 J1 K1 L N O Q R1 S1 S2 V W Z(c,l)
Emergency Action, Agency, Advocacy, Fixed Fee Interview, Legal Aid undertaken and Legal Aid Franchise
Ptr: Hallows, Mr Richard C BSc . . . . *Sep 1983
Lloyd, Mr David Hugh LLB(Hons) . . . . *Dec 1993
Ast: Cotgreave, Ms Alison LLB(Hons) . . . . *Mar 1992

P LLOYD JONES & CO ‡
Cambrian Chambers Earl Road Mold Flintshire CH7 1AJ
Tel: 01352 758533 / 758534 *Fax:* 01352 758127 *Dx:* 26553 MOLD
Emergency telephone 01352 757369
E-mail: legalplj@btopenworld.com
List of partners: C Jesse, P L Jones
Office: Buckley
Work: A1 B1 C1 D1 E F1 G H J1 K1 L M1 N P R1 S1 T1 V
Emergency Action, Agency, Advocacy, Fixed Fee Interview and Legal Aid undertaken
Ptr: Jesse, Mr Christopher LLB . . . . *Oct 1980
Jones, Mr Philip L LLB . . . . §Dec 1977

THE JONES PARTNERSHIP ‡
St Marys Chambers 87 High Street Mold Flintshire CH7 1BQ
Tel: 01352 753388 *Fax:* 01352 750388
Emergency telephone 01352 753388
List of partners: C E Jones
Work: K1 N S1 W
Emergency Action, Agency, Advocacy, Fixed Fee Interview and Legal Aid undertaken
Ptr: Jones, Mrs Christine E BA(Hons) . . . . *Oct 1989
Ast: Jones, Ms Katherine Frances LLB. . . . . *Feb 1991

KEENE & KELLY ‡
(incorporating Keith Williams & Co)
The Limes 95 High Street Mold Flintshire CH7 1BJ
Tel: 01352 753882 *Fax:* 01352 758927 *Dx:* 26556 MOLD
E-mail: keeneandkelly@btconnect.com
List of partners: J R N Gregory, R J T Guest
Languages: Welsh
Work: A1 D1 D2 E F1 J1 K1 K3 K4 L O Q R1 S1 W Z(l,t)
Emergency Action, Agency, Advocacy, Fixed Fee Interview and Legal Aid undertaken
Ptr: Gregory, Mr John R N Under Sheriff. . . . . *§Nov 1970
Guest, Mr Robin J T BA. . . . . *Jun 1981
Asoc: Edwards, Miss Siwan Elen LLB; DipLG . . . . *Sep 1998
Jones, Mr Gareth E M LLB . . . . *Jun 1978
Woodward, Mr Philip D BA . . . . *Oct 1986

LLEWELLYN JONES & CO ‡
Victoria House Grosvenor Street Mold Flintshire CH7 1EJ
Tel: 01352 755305 *Fax:* 01352 755487 *Dx:* 26554 MOLD
List of partners: J D M Jones, D G Williams, D A G Williams
Office: Ruthin
Languages: Welsh
Emergency Action, Agency, Advocacy, Fixed Fee Interview and Legal Aid undertaken
Ptr: Jones, Mr John D M LLB(L'pool) Coroner for East Clwyd . . . . *Dec 1970
Williams, Mr Dion A G LLB . . . . *Jul 1980
Con: Davies, Mr Geoffrey A B LLB(Wales) . . . . *Jun 1963

MONKSEATON, Tyne & Wear

STOCKDALE & REID LTD
Grosvenor House 62 Front Street Monkseaton Tyne & Wear NE25 8DP
Tel: 0191 251 9494 *Fax:* 0191 251 8085 *Dx:* 67600 MONKSEATON
E-mail: law@stockdale-reid.co.uk
Office: North Shields
Work: C1 C2 E K1 L M1 N O Q S1 S2 W Z(c)
Agency and Advocacy undertaken
Dir: Amos, Mr Peter W LLB . . . . *§Jun 1978
Asoc: Vickers, Mr Philip David LLB . . . . *Jul 2007

TERRIE PRIDIE & CO SOLICITORS ‡
Woodburn House 9 The Grove Monkseaton Tyne & Wear NE25 8BH
Tel: 0191 289 4770 *Fax:* 0191 289 4771
E-mail: info@terriepridiesolicitors.co.uk

MONMOUTH, Monmouthshire

CHARLES BLACKLOCK & CO ‡
89 Monnow Street Monmouth Monmouthshire NP25 3EW
Tel: 01600 714444 *Fax:* 01600 716974 *Dx:* 44151 MONMOUTH
E-mail: mail@charlesblacklock.co.uk
List of partners: J C Blacklock
Work: D1 G H K1 L N O Q S1 W
Emergency Action, Agency, Advocacy, Fixed Fee Interview and Legal Aid undertaken
Ptr: Blacklock, Mr J Charles BSc . . . . *Apr 1979

ALAN CURTIS SOLICITORS ‡
78a Monnow Street Monmouth Monmouthshire NP25 3EQ
Tel: 01600 772288 *Fax:* 01600 715456
E-mail: alancurtislegal@compuserve.com
List of partners: A Curtis
Work: K1 L N O Q S1 W Z(c,d,f,k,l,p)
Emergency Action, Agency, Advocacy, Fixed Fee Interview, Legal Aid undertaken and Member of Accident Line
Ptr: Curtis, Mr Alan LLB(Hons) . . . . *Mar 1992

JACKLYN DAWSON
6 Priory Street Monmouth Monmouthshire NP25 3BR
Tel: 01600 716660 *Fax:* 01600 772007 *Dx:* 44157 MONMOUTH
Office: Newport
Languages: French, Welsh
Work: A3 B1 B2 C1 C2 C3 D1 D2 E F1 F2 J1 J2 K1 K2 K3 K4 L M1 N O P Q R1 R2 S1 S2 T1 T2 U1 V W Z(b,c,d,e,h,i,j,k,l,o,p,q,r,s,x)
Emergency Action, Agency, Advocacy and Fixed Fee Interview undertaken
Ast: O'Leary, Ms Hannah . . . . Nov 2005

R J MOSELEY LLP ‡
Singleton Court Business Park Wonastow Road Monmouth Monmouthshire NP25 5JA
Tel: 07785 518923 *Fax:* 01600 716744

TWOMLOWS
13 Monnow Street Monmouth Monmouthshire NP25 3EF
Tel: 01600 716200 *Fax:* 01600 716150 *Dx:* 44156 MONMOUTH
Office: Caldicot, Chepstow

GARETH WILSON ‡
Rome Farm Manson Lane Monmouth Monmouthshire NP25 5RB
Tel: 01600 772500
List of partners: G O Wilson
SPr: Wilson, Mr Gareth Owen BA(Oxon) . . . . *Feb 1982

MORDEN, Surrey

CRESCENT LAW ‡
81 London Road Morden Surrey SM4 5HP
Tel: 020 8640 2300

H K SOLICITORS ‡
111 London Road Morden Surrey SM4 5HP
Tel: 020 8646 7485 *Fax:* 020 8687 2438

MORDENS SOLICITORS ‡
7 London Road Morden Surrey SM4 5HT

JAMES O'NEILL ‡
64 London Road Morden Surrey SM4 5BD
Tel: 020 8648 1631 *Fax:* 020 8640 6530 *Dx:* 41651 MORDEN
E-mail: james.solicitors@virgin.net
List of partners: J O'Neill
Work: E L S1 W
SPr: O'Neill, Mr James. . . . . *Dec 1980

ROYDS LLP
18 Crown Lane Morden Surrey SM4 5BS
Tel: 020 8542 1067 *Fax:* 020 8544 0246 *Dx:* 41652 MORDEN
Office: London EC4
Work: S1 W
Member of Accident Line
Ptr: Buckland, Mr Jonathan M H LLB . . . . *Jun 1979
Davey, Mr Frank R LLB. . . . . *Jun 1981

STONE & STONE ‡
16 Crown Lane Morden Surrey SM4 5BP
Tel: 020 8540 2202 *Fax:* 020 8545 0380 *Dx:* 41657 MORDEN
E-mail: stoneandstone@btopenworld.com
List of partners: S F Stone
Work: E J1 K1 L O Q S1 T2 W
Fixed Fee Interview and Legal Aid undertaken
Ptr: Stone, Mr Stephen F . . . . *Jun 1979

MORECAMBE, Lancashire

BAINES BAGGULEY SOLICITORS ‡
15 Northumberland Street Morecambe Lancashire LA4 4AU
Tel: 01524 413294 *Fax:* 01524 831787
E-mail: office@bainesbagguley.co.uk
List of partners: R J Bagguley, D W Baines, G J Entwistle
Work: C1 D1 E K1 K3 K4 L S1 S2 T1 T2 W
Advocacy and Fixed Fee Interview undertaken
Ptr: Bagguley, Mr Richard J LLB. . . . . *Oct 1982
Baines, Mr David William LLM. . . . . *May 1965
Entwistle, Mr Glynn J LLB(Leeds) . . . . *Apr 1974

BANNISTER BATES PROPERTY LAWYERS ‡
(incorporating Edwards & Nevett)
12-22 Northumberland Street Morecambe Lancashire LA4 4AX
Tel: 01524 416300 *Fax:* 01524 831006
E-mail: mail@bannisterbates.co.uk
List of partners: P J Bates
Languages: French
Work: A1 B1 C1 C2 E F1 G J1 K1 L N O P Q R1 S1 T1 T2 W Z(c,k,l,o)
Emergency Action, Agency, Advocacy, Fixed Fee Interview undertaken and Member of Accident Line
Ptr: Bates, Mr Peter J BA(Law) . . . . *Nov 1983
Con: Miles, Mr Hugh R LLB(St Andrews) . . . . *§Dec 1969

See p112 for the Key to Work Categories & other symbols

BIRCHALL BLACKBURN LLP
45 Victoria Street Morecambe Lancashire LA4 4AF
Tel: 01524 833838 *Fax:* 01524 426479
Office: Chester, Chorley, Formby, Leyland, Manchester, Preston (2 offices), Southport

JOBLING & KNAPE
19 Northumberland Street Morecambe Lancashire LA4 4AZ
Tel: 01524 416960 *Fax:* 01524 402515
Office: Great Eccleston, Lancaster
Work: A1 A2 B1 B2 C1 C2 D1 D2 E F1 F2 G H I J1 J2 K1 K2 K3 K4 L M1 N O P Q R1 R2 S1 T1 T2 V W Z(b,c,d,e,h,k,l,m,n,o,p,q,t,za)
Emergency Action, Agency, Advocacy, Fixed Fee Interview, Legal Aid undertaken, Legal Aid Franchise and Member of Accident Line
Ptr: Harrison, Mr David LLB(L'pool) . . . . *§May 1971

THE PENHALE PRACTICE ‡
36 Northumberland Street Morecambe Lancashire LA4 4AY
Tel: 01524 401010 *Fax:* 01524 401011 *Dx:* 63612 MORECAMBE
E-mail: office@thepenhalepractice.co.uk
List of partners: P S Anderton, N J Codd, D Wilkinson
Work: B1 C1 E F1 J1 K1 K3 K4 L N O Q R1 R2 S1 S2 T1 T2 V W Z(c,i,q)
Emergency Action, Agency, Advocacy, Fixed Fee Interview undertaken and Member of Accident Line
Ptr: Anderton, Mr Paul Stephen . . . . Feb 1983
Codd, Ms Nicola Jayne . . . . Dec 2007
Wilkinson, Mr David. . . . . Sep 1992

RATCLIFFE & BIBBY
3 Northumberland Street Morecambe Lancashire LA4 4AT
Tel: 01524 410424 *Fax:* 01524 831783 *Dx:* 63603 MORECAMBE
E-mail: morecambe@rblegal.co.uk
Office: Carnforth, Lancaster
Work: A1 B1 C1 D1 E F1 J1 K1 L M1 N P Q R1 S1 V W Z(l)
Emergency Action, Agency, Legal Aid undertaken and Legal Aid Franchise
Ptr: Anderton, Mr Neil BA . . . . *Oct 1989
Gardner, Mr Ian S LLB(Vict). . . . . *Jul 1978
Ast: Brown, Miss Hilary LLB(Hons). . . . . *Jan 2004

WHITESIDE & KNOWLES LTD ‡
5-7 Skipton Street Morecambe Lancashire LA4 4AW
Tel: 01524 416315 *Fax:* 01524 831008 *Dx:* 63600 MORECAMBE
E-mail: chw@whiteside-knowles.co.uk
List of partners: A R Collinson, P George, C H Wilson
Work: A1 A2 C1 D1 D2 E F1 J1 J2 K1 K3 K4 L N O Q R1 S1 S2 T1 T2 V W Z(l,p,q)
Emergency Action, Agency, Advocacy, Fixed Fee Interview undertaken and Member of Accident Line
Ptr: Collinson, Mr Anthony Rickards . . . . *§Jun 1973
George, Mr Philip LLB. . . . . *Mar 1985
Wilson, Mr Charles H LLB. . . . . *Jun 1977
Ast: Pickles, Miss Antonia BSc(Hons); CPE; GDL; LPC . . *Aug 2007
Weeks, Mrs Melanie June Eileen BSc(Hons); GDL; LPC . . . . *Sep 2009

WRIGHT & LORD ‡
63 Victoria Street Morecambe Lancashire LA4 4AF
Tel: 01524 402050 *Fax:* 01524 402051 *Dx:* 63620 MORECAMBE
E-mail: info@wrightandlord.com
List of partners: C Gates, S H Lord, L Maring, K Murray, S N Wright
Office: Morecambe
Work: C1 E F1 J1 K1 K3 K4 L N O Q S1 S2 W Z(l,w)
Agency undertaken
Ptr: Gates, Mr Christopher LLB(Hons). . . . . *Aug 1998
Lord, Mr Simon H LLB(Hons) . . . . *Apr 1981
Maring, Miss Lynne LLB. . . . . *Nov 1983
Wright, Mr Stephen N LLB . . . . *§Nov 1990
Murray, Kay. . . . . .NSP
Asoc: Riley, Miss Zoe Leanne LLB(Hons) . . . . *Sep 2009

WRIGHT & LORD
53 Princes Crescent Morecambe Lancashire LA4 6BY
Tel: 01524 402050 *Fax:* 01524 402051 *Dx:* 63620 MORECAMBE
E-mail: info@wrightandlord.com
Office: Morecambe
Work: C1 E J1 K1 K3 K4 L N O Q S1 S2 W
Agency undertaken

MORETON, Merseyside

GROSSCURTH & CO ‡
174 Hoylake Road Moreton Merseyside CH46 8TQ
Tel: 0151 678 8212 *Fax:* 0151 605 0096 *Dx:* 18355 MORETON
E-mail: ellen@grosscurth.co.uk
List of partners: R D P Grosscurth
Work: B1 C1 E F1 K1 K3 K4 L O Q S1 S2 W
Ptr: Grosscurth, Mr R David P LLB . . . . *Dec 1973

KIRWANS
236-238 Hoylake Road Moreton Merseyside CH46 6AD
Tel: 0151 677 3433 *Fax:* 0151 641 8509 *Dx:* 18356 MORETON
Emergency telephone 07770 864 037
E-mail: info@kirwanssolicitors.co.uk
Office: Birkenhead, Liverpool
Work: A1 B1 B2 C1 D1 E F1 F2 G H I J1 K1 K3 K4 L N O Q R1 R2 S1 S2 V W Z(e,k,l,p,q)
Emergency Action, Agency, Advocacy, Fixed Fee Interview, Legal Aid undertaken, Legal Aid Franchise and Member of Accident Line
Ptr: Kirwan, Mr David Stanley LLB ♦. . . . . *Jul 1969
Asoc: Dennis, Mr John-Paul . . . . *Jun 2006
Ast: Thew, Mr Jonathan Richard LLB(Hons) . . . . *Nov 2007

MORETON-IN-MARSH, Gloucestershire

T S BARKES & SON ‡
Barklays House High Street Moreton-in-Marsh Gloucestershire GL56 0AX
Tel: 01608 650332 *Fax:* 01608 651648
Dx: 11482 MORETON-IN-MARSH
List of partners: H A Newell
Work: A1 B1 C1 D1 E G K1 L M1 P R1 S1 T1 W Z(l)
Agency, Advocacy, Fixed Fee Interview and Legal Aid undertaken
Ptr: Newell, Mr Harold A LLB(Dunelm). . . . . *§Nov 1963

KENDALL & DAVIES
Thurstan House Oxford Street Moreton-in-Marsh Gloucestershire GL56 0LF
Tel: 01608 650312 *Fax:* 01608 652971
Dx: 11481 MORETON-IN-MARSH
E-mail: moreton@kendallanddavies.co.uk
Office: Bourton-on-the-Water, Burford, Stow-on-the-Wold
Work: E S1 S2 T2 W
Dir: Draper, Mr Robert George LLB . . . . *Apr 1994
Ast: Warrington, Mrs Rowena . . . . *Jan 1976

PAUL ASHLEY HENRY ‡
Toy Cottage High Street Moreton-in-Marsh Gloucestershire GL56 0AD
Tel: 01608 651621 *Fax:* 01608 652527
E-mail: pahsolicitor@aol.com

SHAKESPEARES
Compton House High Street Moreton-in-Marsh Gloucestershire GL56 0AX
Tel: 0845 630 8833 *Fax:* 0845 630 8844
Dx: 11489 MORETON-IN-MARSH
E-mail: info@shakepeares.co.uk
Office: Birmingham, Leicester, Nottingham, Shipston-on-Stour, Stratford-upon-Avon
Work: A1 E R1
Ptr: Wellington, Mr Robert John LLB(Hons) . . . . Oct 1994

MORETONHAMPSTEAD, Devon

MANN JENKINS ‡
(in association with Helder Roberts & Co)
1 Lime Street Moretonhampstead Devon TQ13 8LT
Tel: 01647 440000 *Fax:* 01647 440430
E-mail: law@mannjenkins.co.uk
List of partners: D A Floyd-Walker, M E Jenkins, J W Mann
Office: Chagford
Languages: French, Spanish
Work: A1 B1 B2 C1 C2 C3 E I J1 L M1 M3 O Q S1 S2 U1 W Z(b,c,d,j,q)
Ptr: Floyd-Walker, Mr David Arnold . . . . *Sep 1970
Jenkins, Ms Maureen Elizabeth LLB(Scots Law); LLB(Exon) . . . . *Apr 1978
Mann, Mr John William MA(Oxon). . . . . *May 1987

MORLEY, West Yorkshire

CHADWICK LAWRENCE
29-31 Commercial Street Morley West Yorkshire LS27 8HX
Tel: 0113 252 3452 *Fax:* 0113 238 0590 *Dx:* 25705 MORLEY
E-mail: enquiry@chadlaw.co.uk
Office: Halifax, Huddersfield, Wakefield
Work: B1 C1 D1 E F1 G H J1 K1 K2 L M1 N O Q S1 S2 T1 V W Z(i,l,p,r)

SHAW GILLIS ‡
70a Queen Street Morley West Yorkshire LS27 9NP
Tel: 0113 252 0331 *Fax:* 0113 252 9415 *Dx:* 25702 MORLEY
E-mail: enquiries@shawgillis.co.uk
List of partners: S C I Shaw
Work: F1 G H J1 K1 L N P Q S1 S2 W Z(r)
Agency, Advocacy and Legal Aid undertaken
Ptr: Shaw, Mr Stewart C I LLB. . . . . *Oct 1972
Con: Bailey, Mr Allen J . . . . Jun 1982

STAPLETON GARDNER & CO ‡
(incorporating W R Ingle & Co)
Stoneleigh House Commercial Street Morley West Yorkshire LS27 8HN
Tel: 0113 253 8111 *Fax:* 0113 289 8482
E-mail: contact.us@stapleton-gardner.co.uk
List of partners: C K Blakey, D H Scott, J M Wadsworth
Work: D1 D2 E K1 N Q S1 W
Agency, Advocacy, Fixed Fee Interview undertaken and Member of Accident Line
Ptr: Blakey, Mr Christopher K . . . . *Dec 1977
Scott, Mr David Henry. . . . . *Jun 1975
Wadsworth, Mrs Jacqueline Mary FCA . . . . Feb 2009

MORPETH, Northumberland

DAVID AULD & CO ‡
22a Newgate Street Morpeth Northumberland NE61 1BA
Tel: 01670 505844 *Fax:* 01670 505848 *Dx:* 62513 MORPETH
Emergency telephone 01670 512552
E-mail: carole.burrell@david-auld.co.uk
List of partners: M D E Auld, M Lamond
Office: Bedlington
Work: D1 G K1
Emergency Action, Agency, Advocacy, Fixed Fee Interview and Legal Aid undertaken
Ptr: Auld, Mr M David E LLB. . . . . *Jun 1975
Lamond, Miss Michelle LLB . . . . *Mar 1998
Con: Auld, Mrs Valerie Lynn BA(Hons) . . . . *Dec 1981
Burrell, Miss Carole A LLB; MA Medical Law - Watson Burton Prize . . . . *Jul 1997

BRUMELL & SAMPLE ‡
15 Bridge Street Morpeth Northumberland NE61 1NX
Tel: 01670 512336 *Fax:* 01670 510471 *Dx:* 62501 MORPETH
E-mail: info@brumellandsample.s2s.com
List of partners: M A Gaunt, T H Horne
Work: L S1 S2 T1 T2 W
Ptr: Gaunt, Mr Michael A BA(Cantab) Clerk to the General Commissioners of Taxes . . . . *Nov 1974
Horne, Mr Thomas H . . . . *Feb 1959

CARR & CO
26 Newgate Street Morpeth Northumberland NE61 1BA
Tel: 01670 515182 *Fax:* 01670 505259
E-mail: morpeth@carrandcosolicitors.com
Office: Blyth, Gosforth
Work: K1 S1
Emergency Action, Agency, Fixed Fee Interview, Legal Aid undertaken and Legal Aid Franchise

R A W CLARK & CO ‡
47 Newgate Street Morpeth Northumberland NE61 1AT
Tel: 01670 512391 *Dx:* 62507 MORPETH
E-mail: law@rawclark.co.uk
List of partners: J T Robinson, V Usher
Work: G H J1 K1 L N P S1 V W
Agency, Advocacy, Fixed Fee Interview and Legal Aid undertaken
Ptr: Robinson, Mr John Trevor. . . . . *§Jan 1966
Usher, Mr Vernon LLB. . . . . *Jun 1974

JACQUELINE DUFF ‡
Lynnholm Thropton Morpeth Northumberland NE65 7JE
Tel: 01669 621987

HARDINGTON HOGG SOLICITORS
12 Manchester Street Morpeth Northumberland NE61 1HB
Tel: 01670 515955
Office: Alnwick

ROW & SCOTT
2-4 Wellwood Street Amble Morpeth Northumberland NE65 0EW
Tel: 01665 713544
Office: Consett, Newcastle upon Tyne

WHOLLEY GOODINGS LLP ‡
(incorporating Tocher Neal & Co)
Pethgate House Castle Square Morpeth Northumberland NE61 1YB
Tel: 01670 519714 *Fax:* 01670 514485 *Dx:* 62500 MORPETH
E-mail: rdw-kd@wholleygoodings.co.uk
List of partners: R G Goodings, R D Wholley
Office: Bedlington
Work: A1 B1 C1 C2 C3 D1 E F1 G H K1 L N O S1 T1 T2 V W Z(m,n,o)
Emergency Action, Agency, Advocacy, Fixed Fee Interview, Legal Aid undertaken and Legal Aid Franchise
Ptr: Wholley, Mr Richard D LLB . . . . *Apr 1980
Ast: Lane, Mrs Alice LLB. . . . . Feb 1996
Con: Tocher, Mr David Richard LLB. . . . . *Jul 1969

MORRISTON, Swansea

ARNOLDS
122 Woodfield Street Morriston Swansea SA6 8AR
Tel: 01792 533049 *Fax:* 01792 533039 *Dx:* 56765 MORRISTON
Office: Swansea

PETER LYNN & PARTNERS
109 Clase Road Morriston Swansea SA6 8DY
Tel: 01792 310731 *Fax:* 01792 310871 *Dx:* 56768 MORRISTON
E-mail: peterlynn6@aol.com
Office: Penarth, Swansea (2 offices)
Work: A1 B1 C1 C2 D1 D2 E F1 F2 G J1 J2 K1 K3 K4 L N O Q R1 R2 S1 S2 T1 T2 V W X Z(b,c,d,e,f,g,j,k,l,o,p,q,r,t,w)
Emergency Action, Agency, Advocacy, Fixed Fee Interview and Legal Aid undertaken
Ptr: Atherton, Mr Stuart . . . . *Oct 1993
Lynn, Mr Peter Alan BSc(Hons) . . . . *§May 1992
Pincott, Miss Sophie LLB . . . . *Jun 2005
Plant, Miss Sara Jane LLB(Hons) . . . . *Oct 1993
Ast: Broom, Mrs Lindsay Eileen . . . . Sep 2009
Bryant, Miss Jody Elizabeth LLB(Hons) . . . . May 2006
Cudd, Mr Jonathan Morgan James LLB(Hons) . . . . Sep 2009
Richards, Leslie J LLB(Wales). . . . . *Jun 1978
Con: Tymanowski, Mr Chris BSc; LPC . . . . Mar 2003

MOUNTAIN ASH, Rhondda Cynon Taff

GWILYM JONES & DAVIES WITH BRYANT & CO ‡
Bank Chambers Pryce Street Mountain Ash Rhondda Cynon Taff CF45 3NR
Tel: 01443 472206 *Fax:* 01443 474376 *Dx:* 54050 MOUNTAIN ASH
Emergency telephone 01443 477266
List of partners: A Bryant, D J Bryant, D J Bryant
Work: D1 G H K1 N S1 V W
Emergency Action, Agency, Advocacy, Fixed Fee Interview, Legal Aid undertaken, Legal Aid Franchise and Member of Accident Line
Ptr: Bryant, Mr Alexander LLB. . . . . *§May 1995
Bryant, Mr Denis J BSc; DPE; LLB . . . . *§Dec 1969
Bryant, Mr Denis Julian LLB. . . . . *§Sep 1998

MARCHANT HARRIES & CO
40 Oxford Street Mountain Ash Rhondda Cynon Taff CF45 3HB
Tel: 01443 476444 *Fax:* 01443 479475 *Dx:* 54052 MOUNTAIN ASH
Emergency telephone 07836 315738
Office: Aberdare (2 offices)
Languages: Italian
Work: A1 B1 C1 C2 C3 D1 D2 E F1 F2 G H J1 K1 L M1 M2 N O P Q R1 S1 T1 T2 V W Z(b,c,d,h,i,j,l,m,n,o,p,q,s,t)
Emergency Action, Agency, Advocacy, Fixed Fee Interview, Legal Aid undertaken, Legal Aid Franchise and Member of Accident Line
Asoc: Davies, Mrs Janine LLB. . . . . *§Oct 1996
Rabaiotti, Mr Stefano A F LLB. . . . . *Mar 1987

JOHN MORGAN & PARTNERS ‡
5-7 Oxford Street Mountain Ash Rhondda Cynon Taff CF45 3PG
Tel: 01443 473708 *Fax:* 01443 478171 *Dx:* 54051 MOUNTAIN ASH
List of partners: A D Morgan, J R D Morgan
Work: A1 E K1 K3 K4 L N Q R1 S1 W Z(l)
Emergency Action, Agency, Advocacy and Fixed Fee Interview undertaken
Ptr: Morgan, Mr Andrew D ♦. . . . . *Apr 1992

G SPILSBURY & CO ‡
49 Commercial Street Mountain Ash Rhondda Cynon Taff CF45 3PS
Tel: 01443 473213 *Fax:* 01443 477946 *Dx:* 54053 MOUNTAIN ASH
Emergency telephone 01443 412219
E-mail: gspilsburycosolicitors@hotmail.com
List of partners: S Samuel, G Spilsbury
Work: C1 D1 E F1 G H J1 K1 K3 L M1 N P S1 T1 V W Z(d,g,i,k)
Emergency Action, Agency, Advocacy, Fixed Fee Interview, Legal Aid undertaken and Legal Aid Franchise
Ptr: Samuel, Mr Stephen LLB(Hons). . . . . Jan 1998
Spilsbury, Glynne Griffiths Prize. . . . . Feb 1987

MUCH BIRCH, Herefordshire

JANET PICKERING ‡
Hollybush Lane Much Birch Herefordshire HR2 8HX
Tel: 01981 541264 *Fax:* 01981 541259

MUCH WENLOCK, Shropshire

FODENS ‡
58 High Street Much Wenlock Shropshire TF13 6AE
Tel: 01952 726111 *Fax:* 01952 726112
E-mail: info@fodens.co.uk
List of partners: S M Foden
Work: E O S1 S2 Z(c,q)
SPr: Foden, Mr Stephen M LLB(Hons) . . . . *Oct 1987

NAILSEA, North Somerset

BRADFORD & CO ‡
144 High Street Nailsea North Somerset BS48 1AP
Tel: 01275 856302 / 856303 *Fax:* 01275 810123
Dx: 48202 NAILSEA
E-mail: margaret@bradfordlaw.fsnet.co.uk
List of partners: M A Bradford
Office: Bristol
Fixed Fee Interview and Legal Aid undertaken
Ptr: Bradford, Mrs Margaret A LLB. . . . . *Oct 1987

SUSAN CHAPMAN ‡
Thornlea 17 Station Road Nailsea North Somerset BS48 4PD
Tel: 01275 401996 *Fax:* 01275 858941
E-mail: lady.law@btinternet.com
List of partners: S C Chapman
Work: S1 W
SPr: Chapman, Mrs Susan Christina . . . . *Dec 1982

M C HULLAH & CO ‡
116-120 High Street Nailsea North Somerset BS48 1AH
Tel: 01275 855561 *Fax:* 01275 851741 *Dx:* 48205 NAILSEA
E-mail: info@mchullah.co.uk
Work: S1

MURRAY ROACH SOLICITORS ‡
Clifford House 59 High Street Nailsea North Somerset BS48 1AW
Tel: 01275 858266 / 852705 *Fax:* 01275 810116 *Dx:* 48200 NAILSEA
E-mail: solicitors@murrayroach.co.uk
List of partners: P I Murray, D A Roach
Languages: French
Work: A1 B1 C1 C2 C3 D1 E F1 J1 K1 K3 L N O P Q R1 S1 S2 T1 T2 V W Z(l,w)
Emergency Action, Advocacy, Fixed Fee Interview undertaken and Member of Accident Line
Ptr: Murray, Mr Peter I. . . . . *§Feb 1967
Roach, Mr Dean A LLB Deputy District Judge . . . . *Dec 1979

WARDS SOLICITORS
(incorporating Westlake Solicitors)
The Courtyard 120 High Street Nailsea North Somerset BS48 1HA
Tel: 01275 858515 *Fax:* 01275 858055 *Dx:* 48215 NAILSEA
E-mail: info@wards.uk.com
Office: Bristol (2 offices), Clevedon, Portishead, Staple Hill, Weston-super-Mare (3 offices), Yate
Ptr: Westlake, Mr Clive J LLB . . . . *Jul 1979

NAILSWORTH, Gloucestershire

WINTERBOTHAM SMITH PENLEY LLP
Stokescroft Cossack Square Nailsworth Gloucestershire GL6 0DZ
Tel: 01453 832566 *Fax:* 01453 835441 *Dx:* 123329 NAILSWORTH
E-mail: mail@wspsolicitors.com
Office: Dursley, Stroud
Languages: Danish, French
Work: A1 D1 E F1 K1 K3 K4 L Q S1 S2 T2 V W Z(d)
Agency, Fixed Fee Interview, Legal Aid undertaken and Legal Aid Franchise
Asoc: Artaius, Mrs Samantha Sheila BA(English); PGDipLaw; LPC . . . . *Aug 2004
Ast: Adkin, Mr Timothy James LLB(Newc) . . . . *Jan 1981

NANTWICH, Cheshire

GEORGE S ASHWORTH ‡
2 Mayflower Road Nantwich Cheshire CW5 7DP
Tel: 01270 623723
List of partners: G S Ashworth
Work: R1 S1

ATKINSONHODGSON LLP
17 Alvaston Business Park Middlewich Park Nantwich Cheshire CW5 6PF
Office: Manchester

BOWCOCK CUERDEN LLP ‡
South Cheshire House Manor Road Nantwich Cheshire CW5 5LX
Tel: 01270 611106 *Fax:* 01270 610515 *Dx:* 22011 NANTWICH
E-mail: jfitton@bowcockcuerden.co.uk
List of partners: J P Cuerden, L C Smith, D C Thorp
Languages: French, German
Work: A1 A2 A3 B1 C1 C2 D1 D2 E F1 J1 J2 K1 K2 K3 K4 L N O P Q R1 R2 S1 S2 T1 T2 W Z(c,e,i,l,n,p,q)
Emergency Action, Agency, Advocacy and Fixed Fee Interview undertaken
Ptr: Cuerden, Mr James Philip BA. . . . . *Nov 1984
Smith, Mrs Lesley Carol LLB(Hons) . . . . *Nov 1986
Thorp, Mr David C LLB . . . . *Aug 1989
Asoc: Bevan, Mr David BA . . . . Mar 1984
Taylor, Ms Susannah LLB . . . . *Jun 1992
Ast: Pennant-Williams, Mrs Carina LLB . . . . *Jun 2009
Phillips, Rachel . . . . Sep 2008
Thompson, Mrs Mary BSc. . . . . Sep 2004
Con: Denton, Mr Lewis A LLB . . . . *Nov 1971

THE DENTAL LAW PARTNERSHIP ‡
Alvoston House Middlewich Nantwich Cheshire CW5 6PF
Tel: 01270 613320 *Fax:* 01270 613321
E-mail: info@dentallaw.co.uk
Work: Z(r)
Ast: Adams, Mr Edward BA(Hons); CPE; LPC . . . . Aug 1998
Coleman, Mrs Helen LLB(Hons). . . . . Sep 2001
Owen, Mr Jonathan LLB(Hons) . . . . Oct 2003
Robinson, Miss Nicola BA(Hons); CPE; LPC . . . . . Oct 2003
Stannard, Mr Dominic C BA(Hons); CPE; LPC . . . . Sep 1996

HALL SMITH WHITTINGHAM LLP ‡
1 Dysart Buildings Nantwich Cheshire CW5 5DP
Tel: 01270 610300 *Fax:* 01270 610443 *Dx:* 22002 NANTWICH
E-mail: law@hswsolicitors.co.uk
List of partners: C W Dodd, A K Masters, R J Morgan-Wynne, J C Percival, S J Wilson
Office: Crewe
Work: A1 B1 C1 C2 D1 E F1 J1 J2 K1 K2 K3 K4 L N O P Q R1 S1 S2 T1 T2 V W Z(d,j,l,o,p)
Emergency Action, Agency, Advocacy, Fixed Fee Interview, Legal Aid undertaken, Legal Aid Franchise and Member of Accident Line
Ptr: Dodd, Mr Christopher W. . . . . *Jun 1980
Masters, Mrs A Kay LLB • Deputy District Judge . . *Dec 1986
Morgan-Wynne, Mr Richard J LLB. . . . . *Nov 1983
Percival, Mr John C LLB . . . . *Dec 1975
Wilson, Mrs S Jane LLB • Leeds University Torts Prize 1976 . . . . *Mar 1980
Ast: Keanneally, Mr Simon Christopher LLB; LLM . . . . . Jul 2008
Lewis, Miss Angela BSc(Hons); LLDip; TEP. . . . . . Sep 2004
Con: Fox, Mr Charles R LLB • Deputy District Judge; Assistant Recorder . . . . *§Apr 1974

HIBBERTS LLP ‡
25 Barker Street Nantwich Cheshire CW5 5EN
Tel: 01270 624225 *Fax:* 01270 628065 *Dx:* 22004 NANTWICH
E-mail: enquiries@hibberts.com
List of partners: R Badman, S A Bailey, A S Dolphin, J Driver, S M Flood, S R Sorfleet, M A Ward, D Young
Office: Crewe, Ellesmere, Tarporley, Whitchurch
Languages: French, German
Work: A1 B1 C1 C2 D1 E F1 G H I J1 K1 L O P Q S1 T2 V W X Z(c,d,e,f,l)
Emergency Action, Agency, Advocacy, Fixed Fee Interview and Legal Aid undertaken
Ptr: Ward, Mr Michael Alexander . . . . Sep 1998
Young, Mr David MA(Oxon) Frederick Drinkwater Prize *Jul 1973
Asoc: Cutler, Mr Keith James . . . . Mar 1991
Platt, Mrs Nicky Amanda LLB(Hons). . . . . *Oct 1994
Ast: Carter, Mrs Juliette . . . . Jun 2005
Dale, Mr James Derek . . . . *Apr 1984
Sims, Mr Nigel . . . . Jul 1996
Thomas, Sarah . . . . Dec 1999
Walley, Anne . . . . Nov 1991
Worthington, Miss Gemma Louise LLB; BVC . . . . . Oct 2010
Young, Mr Michael E MA(Oxon). . . . . *Jul 1979
Con: Measures, Mr Martyn Harry . . . . *Dec 1981

POOLE ALCOCK
Mill House 14 Mill Street Nantwich Cheshire CW5 5ST
Tel: 01270 625478 *Fax:* 01270 624548 *Dx:* 22003 NANTWICH
E-mail: nantwich@poolealcock.co.uk
Office: Alsager, Chester, Congleton, Crewe (2 offices), Northwich, Sandbach, Warrington
Languages: French, German
Work: A1 C1 D1 D2 E F1 G J1 K1 K2 L N O Q R1 S1 S2 V W Z(j,k,l,q,r)
Emergency Action, Agency, Advocacy, Fixed Fee Interview, Legal Aid undertaken and Legal Aid Franchise
Ptr: Jarrett, Mrs Sarah Anne LLB(Hons) . . . . *Sep 1993
Markham, Mr Shane P LLB(Hons). . . . . Apr 1997
Roberts, Mr Andrew. . . . . *Nov 1996
Ast: Croot, Mr David John LLB(Hons) . . . . Jun 2003
Nash, Mrs Paula Helen BA(Hons). . . . . *Feb 1988

ZYDA LAW ‡
Old School House 44 Wellington Road Nantwich Cheshire CW5 7BX
Tel: 01270 620660 *Fax:* 01270 611170

NARBERTH, Pembrokeshire

DARWIN BOWIE LTD ‡
24 High Street Narberth Pembrokeshire SA67 7AR
Tel: 01834 860436 *Fax:* 01834 861383
E-mail: darwinbowie@btconnect.com
List of partners: N M Bowie
Languages: French, Spanish
Work: A1 B1 C1 E F1 K4 L R1 S1 S2 W Z(c,d,l)
Agency and Advocacy undertaken
Ptr: Bowie, Mrs Naomi M . . . . *§Nov 1975

HAINS & LEWIS LTD
Staunton House 7 St James Street Narberth Pembrokeshire SA67 7BZ
Tel: 0845 408 0125 *Fax:* 01834 861340
E-mail: law@hainsandlewis.co.uk
Office: Carmarthen, Haverfordwest
Languages: Welsh
Work: A1 D1 E F1 G H J1 K1 L N P R1 S1 V W Z(d,k,l)
Emergency Action, Agency, Advocacy, Fixed Fee Interview and Legal Aid undertaken

NEATH, Neath Port Talbot

HOWE & SPENDER
7 London Road Neath Neath Port Talbot SA11 1HG
Tel: 01639 881571 *Fax:* 01639 893137 *Dx:* 39253 PORT TALBOT
Emergency telephone 07789 798798
E-mail: administrator@howespender.co.uk
Office: Port Talbot
Work: C1 D1 D2 E G H K1 K2 Q R1 S1 S2 W
Emergency Action, Agency, Advocacy and Legal Aid undertaken
Ptr: Ambrose, Mr Richard Ivor. . . . . *§Jun 1974
Spender, Mr J Ian LLB . . . . *Dec 1991
Spender, Mr John R LLB(Wales) . . . . *Jan 1966
Wharmby, Mr Stephen Graham LLB. . . . . *Jun 1980
Ast: Hopkins, Ms Jayne BA(Hons)(Law) . . . . *Mar 1987
Lewis, Miss Felicity Anne . . . . *Jan 2011
McKenna, Mr James Lloyd LLB(Hons). . . . . *Aug 2009
Rees, Mr Hywel LLB . . . . *Oct 2000

HUTCHINSON THOMAS ‡
Pendrill Court 119 London Road Neath Neath Port Talbot SA11 1LF
Tel: 01639 645061 *Fax:* 01639 646792 *Dx:* 38351 NEATH
Emergency telephone 01639 625 639
E-mail: reception@hutchinsonthomas.com
List of partners: P J Bennett, S J Harrett, W H Jones, P R Morgan, R W A Morris, D Richards, S Thomas, L C P Williams, R Williams, R H P Williams
Languages: French, Welsh
Work: A1 B1 C1 C2 C3 D1 E F1 G H J1 K1 K3 L M1 M2 N O P Q R1 S1 S2 T1 T2 V W Z(c,d,e,i,j,k,l,m,n,o,r,s,t,w)
Emergency Action, Agency, Advocacy, Fixed Fee Interview, Legal Aid undertaken and Legal Aid Franchise
Ptr: Bennett, Mr Paul Jonathan LLB . . . . *§Aug 1987
Harrett, Mr Stephen James BA(Hons). . . . . *§Apr 1994
Jones, Mr William H LLB . . . . *§Oct 1983
Morgan, Mr Peter R LLB . . . . *§Sep 1999
Morris, Mr Roger W A MA(Cantab) Notary Public . . *§Jan 1979
Richards, Mrs Debbie BA . . . . *§Jul 1994
Thomas, Mr Simon LLB. . . . . *Feb 1995
Williams, Miss Louise C P. . . . . *Feb 2000
Williams, Ms Rhian MA(Oxon). . . . . *§Sep 2004
Williams, Mr Robert H P LLB . . . . *§Apr 1972
Ast: Griffiths, Mrs Fay Nicola LLB(Hons) . . . . *Oct 2000
Pudner, Mrs Rachel LLB(Hons) . . . . *Jan 2001
Con: Thomas, Mr Robert Mark Evan LLB Notary Public. . *§Nov 1971

JESTYN JEFFREYS ‡
Castle Buildings 23 Church Place Neath Neath Port Talbot SA11 3LP
Tel: 01639 635641 *Fax:* 01639 645665 *Dx:* 38352 NEATH
E-mail: reception@jestynjeffreys.co.uk
List of partners: I Jones, D W Phillips
Languages: Welsh
Work: A3 B1 C1 C2 C3 D1 D2 E F1 F2 G H J1 K1 L N O Q R1 S1 V W Z(j,k,l,q)
Emergency Action, Agency, Advocacy, Fixed Fee Interview, Legal Aid undertaken and Legal Aid Franchise
Ptr: Jones, Mr Ian . . . . Feb 1999
Phillips, Mr David W LLB(Wales) . . . . *Jan 1980
Con: Evans, Mr Richard E Deputy Coroner for West Glamorgan . . . . *Nov 1961

G HUW LEWIS ‡
8 Alfred Street Neath Neath Port Talbot SA11 1EF
Tel: 01639 637181 *Fax:* 01639 639064 *Dx:* 38369 NEATH
List of partners: C A B James, V J Murphy
Languages: French, Welsh
Work: A1 B1 C1 D1 E F1 G H J1 K1 L M1 M2 N O P Q R1 S1 V W Z(i,l,m,s,t)
Emergency Action, Agency, Advocacy, Fixed Fee Interview, Legal Aid undertaken and Legal Aid Franchise
Ptr: James, Mr Christopher Allyn Bowen BSc . . . . . . *Dec 1980
Murphy, Mr Vincent John BSc(Hons)(Econ) . . . . . *Jul 1999

T LLEWELLYN JONES ‡
Guildhall Chambers 2 Church Place Neath Neath Port Talbot SA11 3LL
Tel: 01639 643635 *Fax:* 01639 632904 *Dx:* 38350 NEATH
Emergency telephone 01656 58110
E-mail: law@tlj.demon.co.uk
List of partners: S E Llewellyn Jones, J A Lloyd, J D Lock, M G Pearn, M J Pearn
Office: Swansea
Emergency Action, Agency, Advocacy, Fixed Fee Interview, Legal Aid undertaken and Member of Accident Line
Ptr: Llewellyn Jones, Miss Sara E . . . . *§Jul 1969
Lloyd, Mr John A LLB(Wales) . . . . *Jun 1981
Lock, Mr Jeffrey D LLB . . . . *Oct 1985
Pearn, Mr Malcolm James LLB . . . . *Oct 1993
Ast: Harris, Ms Sian BA . . . . Mar 1984

PROBERT & GRAY ‡
21 Victoria Gardens Neath Neath Port Talbot SA11 3AY
Tel: 01639 643501 *Fax:* 01639 632193 *Dx:* 38358 NEATH
E-mail: mp@pglawyers.co.uk
List of partners: M Probert
Languages: Welsh
Work: B1 C1 C2 C3 D1 E F1 I J1 K1 M1 M2 R1 S1 T1 T2
Emergency Action, Agency, Advocacy and Legal Aid undertaken
Ptr: Probert, Mr Martin LLB(Wales) . . . . *Sep 1984

SHEEHANS SOLICITORS ‡
40-41a Alfred Street Neath Neath Port Talbot SA11 1EH
Tel: 01639 630844 *Fax:* 01639 630776 *Dx:* 38359 NEATH
List of partners: C G Davies, D Vickery
Office: Port Talbot
Work: A1 C1 C2 C3 E G H K1 L N Q S1 W Z(c,l)
Agency, Fixed Fee Interview, Legal Aid undertaken and Legal Aid Franchise
Ptr: Davies, Mr Ceri Gwyn LLB . . . . *Oct 1977
Vickery, Mr Dean LLB. . . . . Feb 2006

NELSON, Caerphilly

JNP LEGAL
1 High Street Nelson Caerphilly CF46 6EU
Tel: 01443 450561 *Fax:* 01443 451922
Emergency telephone 01633 400171
Office: Merthyr Tydfil
Languages: French, German, Welsh
Work: D1 E F1 G H K1 N O Q S1 V W Z(l)
Emergency Action, Agency, Advocacy, Legal Aid undertaken, Legal Aid Franchise and Member of Accident Line

NELSON, Lancashire

BUKHARI & CO SOLICITORS LIMITED ‡
14-16 Carr Road Nelson Lancashire BB9 7JS
Tel: 01282 611234 *Fax:* 01282 616648 *Dx:* 14666 NELSON
Emergency telephone 07973 640338 (MOBILE)
List of partners: N A S Bukhari, S Bukhari
Languages: Gujarati, Punjabi, Urdu
Work: F1 G H J1 K1 L N Q S1 W Z(i,m,q)
Emergency Action, Advocacy and Legal Aid undertaken
Ptr: Bukhari, Mr Nadeem Ali Shah BA. . . . . *May 1992
Bukhari, Mrs Selina BA . . . . *Mar 1994

CLIFFORD SMITH & BUCHANAN
79-81 Scotland Road Nelson Lancashire BB9 7UY
Tel: 01282 693182 *Fax:* 01282 603081 *Dx:* 14659 NELSON

See p112 for the Key to Work Categories & other symbols

E-mail: nelson@cs-b.co.uk
Office: Burnley, Colne
Ptr: Buchanan, Mr Ian Alexander . . . . *Jan 1968

CONCEPT LAW SOLICITORS ‡
35 Carr Road Nelson Lancashire BB9 7JS
Tel: 01282 700200 *Fax:* 01282 704000 *Dx:* 14652 NELSON
E-mail: enquiries@conceptlaw.co.uk

FARNWORTH ROSE ‡
First Floor Finance House 17 Kenyon Road Nelson Lancashire BB9 5SP
Tel: 01282 695400 *Fax:* 01282 691400

FARNWORTH SHAW
3 & 5 Carr Road Nelson Lancashire BB9 7JX
Tel: 01282 699996 *Fax:* 01282 698022 *Dx:* 14653 NELSON
E-mail: enquiries@farnworthshaw.co.uk
Office: Colne (2 offices)
Work: A1 B1 C1 C2 D1 E F1 G H J1 K1 K3 K4 L N O P Q S1 S2 T1 T2 V W Z(c,i,k,l,q)
Emergency Action, Agency, Advocacy, Fixed Fee Interview, Legal Aid undertaken, Legal Aid Franchise and Member of Accident Line
Ptr: Berry, Mr Anthony William LLB(Newc) . . . . *Jun 1981
Ennis, Mrs Elaine LLB . . . . *Dec 1979
Ast: Greenwood, Mr John Keith LLB(Manc) . . . . Jun 1972
Walmsley, Dawn . . . . Mar 2004

NIGEL HOLDEN & CO
97a Gisburn Road Barrowford Nelson Lancashire BB9 6DX
Tel: 01254 682424 *Fax:* 01282 606187
Emergency telephone 0800 716 997
E-mail: nigel@nigelholden.co.uk
Office: Blackburn, Burnley
Work: E N Q S1 S2 W

MARSDENS SOLICITORS ‡
20a-22a Manchester Road Nelson Lancashire BB9 7EG
Tel: 01282 611899 *Fax:* 01282 611988 *Dx:* 14662 NELSON
E-mail: info@marsdens.uk.com

DAVID PHILLIPS & PARTNERS
1st Floor Barclays Bank Annexe Carr Road Nelson Lancashire BB9 7JS
Tel: 01282 877244 *Fax:* 01282 606443
E-mail: info@dpp.law.com
Office: Birmingham, Bootle (2 offices), Chadwell Heath, Leicester, Liverpool, London E1, London SE18, London W1, Manchester, Wealdstone

ROBERTS & SMITH ‡
20 Carr Road Nelson Lancashire BB9 7LB
Tel: 01282 619000 *Fax:* 01282 617572
List of partners: J A Barrowclough, D Naylor
Languages: Punjabi, Urdu
Work: E L N Q R1 S1 S2 W
Agency and Fixed Fee Interview undertaken
Ptr: Barrowclough, Mr J Allan LLB . . . . *§Jun 1980
Naylor, Mr David BA . . . . *Jan 1980
Ast: Ahmed, Mr Nadeem LLB . . . . *Sep 2003

SOUTHERNS
17 & 23 Carr Road Nelson Lancashire BB9 7JS
Tel: 01282 603663 *Fax:* 01282 608340 *Dx:* 14656 NELSON
Emergency telephone 01282 603663
E-mail: carrroad@southernslaw.info
Office: Burnley (2 offices), Colne
Languages: Finnish, Punjabi, Swedish, Urdu
Work: E G H J1 K1 L S1 V W Z(i,l)
Emergency Action, Agency, Advocacy, Fixed Fee Interview, Legal Aid undertaken, Legal Aid Franchise and Member of Accident Line
Ptr: Rodwell, Mr Geoffrey . . . . *§Jun 1970
Rusius, Mr John H BA(Law) . . . . *§Apr 1979
Ast: Leach, Mr David P . . . . *§Jun 2001

STEELE FORD & NEWTON ‡
13-15 Carr Road Nelson Lancashire BB9 7JY
Tel: 01282 692531 *Fax:* 01282 617640 *Dx:* 14657 NELSON
Emergency telephone 07919 003535
E-mail: reception@steelefordnewton.com
List of partners: N Cassidy, L Hammond, M Irlam
Work: B1 C1 D1 D2 E G H J1 K1 L N Q S1 S2 W Z(j,l,q)
Emergency Action, Agency, Advocacy, Fixed Fee Interview, Legal Aid undertaken, Legal Aid Franchise and Member of Accident Line
Ptr: Cassidy, Mr Nicholas . . . . Jun 2004
Hammond, Mr Lee . . . . Dec 2003
Irlam, Mr Mark CPE; BA(Hons) . . . . *Jul 1999
Ast: Scott, Miss Nicola LLB(Hons) . . . . Apr 1999
Con: Irlam, Mr Brian C . . . . *§Jan 1970
We specialise in the following areas of work: Crime - General and Motoring. Agency Commissions gladly undertaken.

NESTON, Cheshire

BRAMHALLS ‡
Coombe House Cumbers Drive Neston Cheshire CH64 4AU
Tel: 0151 336 7616

FOSTERS SOLICITORS ‡
Hinderton Hall Coach House Neston Cheshire CH64 7TS
Tel: 0151 342 9828
E-mail: info@fosterssolicitors.com

RBM DAVIES & PARTNERS LLP ‡
13 The Cross Neston Cheshire CH64 9UB
Tel: 0151 336 6611 *Fax:* 0151 336 7123 *Dx:* 25054 NESTON
Emergency telephone 07785 374464
E-mail: web@rbmdavies.com
List of partners: R B M Davies, M Evans
Work: D1 D2 K1 K2 K3 K4 L S1 W
Emergency Action, Agency and Advocacy undertaken
Ptr: Davies, Mr Richard B M . . . . *§Jul 1979
Evans, Mr Matthew . . . . Sep 2005

WILDE & CO ‡
6 Bridge Street Neston Cheshire CH64 9UJ
Tel: 0151 353 1899 *Fax:* 0151 353 1899 *Dx:* 25065 NESTON
E-mail: wilde.co@btconnect.com
List of partners: A Fowler, S P R Wilde
Work: A1 B1 C1 C2 C3 D1 E F1 I J1 K1 L M1 M2 N O P Q R1 S1 T1 T2 W X Z(b,c,e,f,j,k,l,n,o,q,s,t)
Emergency Action, Agency undertaken and Member of Accident Line
Ptr: Fowler, Ms Angela BSc(Hons) . . . . Dec 2000
Wilde, Mr Stephen Paul Rathbone LLB . . . . *Dec 1974

NETHERTON, West Midlands

SILKS
(incorporating B H Bate & Co)
48-52 Halesowen Road Netherton West Midlands DY2 9QB
Tel: 01384 236101 *Fax:* 01384 239779 *Dx:* 10772 NETHERTON
E-mail: info@silks-solicitors.co.uk
Office: Oldbury, Smethwick
Work: A1 G H N Z(l)

NEW BRIGHTON, Merseyside

DAVID ROBERTS & CO ‡
Victoria House 96-98 Victoria Road New Brighton Merseyside CH45 2JF
Tel: 0151 639 9595 *Fax:* 0151 639 1434
Dx: 711290 NEW BRIGHTON
E-mail: david@davidroberts.co.uk
Work: E L N S1

NEW MALDEN, Surrey

ANTHONY CHAMBERS LIMITED ‡
206 West Barnes Lane New Malden Surrey KT3 6LT
Tel: 020 8942 2499
E-mail: ce@anthonychambers.net

HJ LEGAL ‡
25 Archdale Place New Malden Surrey KT3 3RW
Tel: 020 8241 8784

A C S HARDS & CO ‡
Bank Chambers 2 High Street New Malden Surrey KT3 4DA
Tel: 020 8942 2258 *Fax:* 020 8949 6128 *Dx:* 200903 NEW MALDEN
E-mail: hards@acshards.co.uk
List of partners: D N Hards, I D Lipscombe
Work: C1 D1 E F1 J1 K1 K2 L O Q S1 S2 V W Z(l)
Emergency Action, Agency, Advocacy and Fixed Fee Interview undertaken
Ptr: Hards, Mr David N BA . . . . *Jun 1976
Lipscombe, Mr Ian D LLB . . . . *Jun 1980

LYONS DAVIDSON
Park House 87 Burlington Road New Malden Surrey KT3 4QP
Tel: 020 8336 6900 *Fax:* 020 8949 4383
Dx: 154240 NEW MALDEN 3
E-mail: info@lyondavidson.co.uk
Office: Bristol, Cardiff, Leeds, Plymouth, Solihull
Work: J1 J2 N R2 S1 S2

MERCHANT LEGAL LLP
Milbourne House 66-70 Coombe Road New Malden Surrey KT3 4QW
Tel: 020 8949 5116 *Fax:* 020 8949 5016
E-mail: info@merchantlegal.com
Office: London EC4

V J NATHAN SOLICITORS ‡
220a Kingston Road New Malden Surrey KT3 3RJ
Tel: 020 8336 2226 *Fax:* 020 8336 0636

PEARSON MADDIN SOLICITORS ‡
Fountain House 2 Kingston Road New Malden Surrey KT3 3LR
Tel: 020 8949 9500 *Fax:* 020 8949 8011 *Dx:* 200900 NEW MALDEN
E-mail: sgraham@pearsonmaddin.co.uk
List of partners: T Browne, C Davies, A Earle, M C Kolapo, D F Morrison, H Mustafa, J C Pearson
Languages: Hindi, Italian, Turkish, Urdu
Work: B1 C1 C2 D1 E F1 I J1 K1 K3 L N O Q R1 S1 S2 W Z(c,m)
Emergency Action, Agency, Advocacy, Fixed Fee Interview, Legal Aid Franchise and Member of Accident Line
Ptr: Browne, Mr Tom MA . . . . Nov 1998
Davies, Mr Christopher BA . . . . *Dec 1976
Earle, Mrs Alison BSc(Hons) . . . . Nov 1999
Kolapo, Ms Michele Corrine BA(Hons) . . . . Nov 1997
Morrison, Mr Donald F LLB . . . . *Feb 1985
Mustafa, Ms Hatice LLB(Hons) . . . . *Jan 2000
Asoc: Gadd, Miss Patricia S LLB; LLM(Bris) . . . . *Apr 1981
Piliero, Ms Angela LLB(Hons) . . . . *Sep 1997
Ast: Bishop, Mrs Sarah Louise BA(Hons)(Media Studies) . Feb 2006
Halil, Mr Aliosman Hulusi LLB(Hons) . . . . Nov 2005
Mubarak, Mr Syed Tariq LLB(Hons); PGDip; LLM . . . Sep 2003
Obhrai, Mr Ajay . . . . Sep 2000

NEW MILLS, Derbyshire

BISHOP & CO ‡
45 Market Street High Peak New Mills Derbyshire SK22 4AA
Tel: 01663 746730 *Fax:* 01663 747726 *Dx:* 27452 NEW MILLS
Emergency telephone 07831 505603
E-mail: newmills@bishop-solicitors.co.uk
List of partners: A J Healey, H G Roe
Office: Marple
Work: D1 E G H K1 L N S1 W Z(c,l,t)
Emergency Action, Agency, Advocacy, Fixed Fee Interview, Legal Aid undertaken, Legal Aid Franchise and Member of Accident Line
Ptr: Healey, Mr Adrian John BA(Hons)(Law) . . . . *Jan 1979
Roe, Mr Howard G BA . . . . Jun 1989
Asoc: Kaufman, Mrs Victoria Jane LLB(Hons) . . . . . . Nov 1995

CHAFES
21-23 Union Road High Peak New Mills Derbyshire SK22 3EL
Tel: 01663 743344 *Fax:* 01663 746631 *Dx:* 27453 NEW MILLS
Office: Alderley Edge, Stockport, Wilmslow
Work: A1 B1 C1 C2 D1 D2 E F1 G H I J1 J2 K1 K2 L N O Q R1 R2 S1 S2 T2 V W Z(e,l,q,r)

WHITING & MASON ‡
24 Union Road High Peak New Mills Derbyshire SK22 3ES
Tel: 01663 742432 / 747958 *Fax:* 01663 741206
Dx: 27457 NEW MILLS
E-mail: info@whitingmason.co.uk
List of partners: N P Gunson, R D L Jones, S J Moore, J C Potts, J A Skulnick
Office: Irlam, Manchester, Marple
Work: D1 F1 K1 K4 L S1 W
Emergency Action, Agency, Advocacy and Fixed Fee Interview undertaken
Ptr: Potts, Miss Joanne C LLB . . . . *Mar 1987
Ast: Barden, Mrs Judith Lynn LLB; MSc . . . . *Feb 1996

2

NEW MILTON, Hampshire

BROOK OLIVER
(in association with Richard Griffths & Co)
10 Mallard Buildings Station Road New Milton Hampshire BH25 6HY
Tel: 01425 616809 *Fax:* 01425 611780 *Dx:* 46306 NEW MILTON
Emergency telephone 07774 448118
Office: Chippenham, Salisbury
Work: A1 B1 C1 C2 D1 D2 E F1 F2 G H J1 J2 K1 L N O Q R1 S1 S2 T1 T2 V W Z(b,c,p,q,t)

DIXON STEWART ‡
72 Station Road New Milton Hampshire BH25 6LF
Tel: 01425 621515 *Fax:* 01425 625009 *Dx:* 46307 NEW MILTON
E-mail: enquiry@dixonstewartwebb.com
List of partners: A J Dixon, B P Ryan, H A Stewart
Office: Highcliffe
Languages: French
Work: C1 D1 E F1 F2 G H J1 K1 L N O P Q R1 S1 S2 T1 V W Z(l)
Emergency Action, Agency, Advocacy, Fixed Fee Interview, Legal Aid undertaken and Legal Aid Franchise
Ptr: Dixon, Mr Andrew J BA . . . . *Dec 1977
Ryan, Mr Benedict Paul LLB . . . . *Mar 1995
Stewart, Ms Helen Anne LLB; Magisterial DipLaw . . . *Nov 1988

FRETTENS SOLICITORS
25 Old Milton Road New Milton Hampshire BH25 6DQ
Tel: 01425 610100 *Fax:* 01425 618143 *Dx:* 46310 NEW MILTON
Office: Christchurch

ANTHONY HARRIS & CO ‡
Elmhurst House 17 Elm Avenue New Milton Hampshire BH25 6HE
Tel: 01425 638288 *Fax:* 01425 622630
List of partners: A J Harris
Work: E K1 L Q R1 S1 W Z(e)
Fixed Fee Interview undertaken
SPr: Harris, Mr Anthony John BSc . . . . *Nov 1984

KARENA HARRISON SOLICITORS ‡
Canada House 1 Carrick Way New Milton Hampshire BH25 6UD
Tel: 01425 627187

HEPPENSTALLS ‡
82 Station Road New Milton Hampshire BH25 6LG
Tel: 01425 610078 *Fax:* 01425 619727 *Dx:* 46301 NEW MILTON
E-mail: mail@heppenstalls-newmilton.co.uk
List of partners: C W Bennett, A M Jennings, C M O'Dea, P P M Salt
Office: Lymington, Lyndhurst
Languages: French, Portuguese, Romanian
Work: D1 D2 E J1 K1 K3 K4 L Q R1 S1 S2 T2 V W Z(l)
Agency, Advocacy, Fixed Fee Interview, Legal Aid undertaken and Legal Aid Franchise
Ptr: Bennett, Mr Christian William LLB . . . . *Oct 2003
Jennings, Mrs Alexandra Margaret LLB(Lond) . . . . . *Jun 1980
Con: Pullan, Mrs Sheila Joan . . . . Feb 1985

LAMB & SMART ‡
44 Station Road New Milton Hampshire BH25 6JX
Tel: 01425 613434 *Dx:* 46303 NEW MILTON
Emergency telephone 01202 25294
List of partners: J R Smart
Languages: French
Work: C1 E L M1 S1 T1 W
Emergency Action, Agency, Advocacy, Fixed Fee Interview and Legal Aid undertaken
Ptr: Smart, Mr John R LLB . . . . *Mar 1981
Con: Lamb, Mr John J B . . . . *May 1967

NEW OLLERTON, Nottinghamshire

JAKES & CO ‡
Mayville Sherwood Drive New Ollerton Nottinghamshire NG22 9PP
Tel: 01623 860581 *Fax:* 01623 835721
List of partners: I R Jakes
Work: D1 E G H K1 L M1 M2 P S1 W Z(c,h,l)
Emergency Action, Agency, Advocacy, Fixed Fee Interview, Legal Aid undertaken, Legal Aid Franchise and Member of Accident Line
Ptr: Jakes, Mr Ian R ● . . . . *Jul 1979

NEW QUAY, Ceredigion

GWYNNE HUGHES
(incorporating Mark R Rishko)
Ina Lass 5 Gomer Crescent New Quay Ceredigion SA45 9NL
Tel: 01545 560525 *Dx:* 92400 ABERAERON
E-mail: gwynnehughes@ukgateway.net
Office: Aberaeron
Languages: Welsh
Emergency Action, Agency, Advocacy, Fixed Fee Interview and Legal Aid undertaken
Ptr: Gwynne-Hughes, Mr John Denys . . . . *Jan 1969
Asoc: Gwynne-Hughes, Mr John David LLB(Lond); LLM(Wales) . . . . *Oct 1996
Ast: Gawthorpe, Mr Barry John LLB . . . . *Nov 1991

NEW ROMNEY, Kent

HALLETT & CO
69 High Street New Romney Kent TN28 8AZ
Tel: 01797 362824 *Dx:* 30202 ASHFORD (KENT)
E-mail: info@hallettandco.co.uk
Office: Ashford (2 offices)
Languages: French
Work: A1 C1 C2 D1 E F1 G H J1 K1 L N O P Q R1 S1 T1 T2 V W X Z(c,d,h,k,l,o)
Emergency Action, Agency, Advocacy and Legal Aid undertaken

NELSON GUEST & PARTNERS
1st Floor 69 High Street New Romney Kent TH28 8AZ
Tel: 07870 497468
Office: Sidcup (2 offices)

NEWARK, Nottinghamshire

ANDREW & CO LLP
33 Kirkgate Newark Nottinghamshire NG24 1AD
Tel: 01636 673743 *Fax:* 01636 705506 *Dx:* 11807 NEWARK 1
E-mail: info@andrew-solicitors.co.uk
Office: Lincoln
Work: A1 A3 B1 C1 C2 C3 D1 D2 E F1 F2 J1 J2 K1 K2 K3 K4 L M1 M2 N O P Q R1 S1 S2 T1 T2 U2 W X Z(c,d,e,h,l,q,r,t)
Emergency Action, Agency, Advocacy undertaken and Member of Accident Line
Ptr: Armitage, Mr Philip J LLB . . . . *Sep 1991
Hollingworth, Mr David J . . . . *§Mar 1974

BIRD & CO
38 Kirkgate Newark Nottinghamshire NG24 1AB
Tel: 01636 650880 *Fax:* 01476 593235 *Dx:* 11815 NEWARK
E-mail: enquiries@birdandco.co.uk
Web: www.birdandco.co.uk
Office: Grantham
Work: D1 G K1 K3 S1 W
Agency, Fixed Fee Interview, Legal Aid undertaken and Legal Aid Franchise
Asoc: Clarson, Ms Vicky. . . . . *Nov 1993
Cobb, Mr Simon John LLB . . . . *Sep 1993
Rogerson, Mrs Mikaela . . . . *Jul 1996
Ast: Davies, Mrs Janet Louise LLB. . . . . *Dec 1993
Con: Thurston, Mr John M R LLB. . . . . *§Mar 1970

CHATTERTONS SOLICITORS
1 Trentside Business Village Farndon Road Newark Nottinghamshire NG24 4XB
Tel: 01636 673731 *Fax:* 01636 640631 *Dx:* 11802 NEWARK
E-mail: newark@chattertons.com
Office: Boston (2 offices), Grantham, Horncastle, Lincoln, Sleaford, Spalding, Stamford
Work: A1 C1 C2 D1 E F1 J1 K1 L M1 N O Q S1 S2 V W Z(c,d,e,l,q,r)
Emergency Action, Agency, Advocacy and Fixed Fee Interview undertaken
Ptr: Barnard, Miss Vanda L BA(Law). . . . . *Oct 1981
Dobbs, Mr Christopher LLB(Leics). . . . . Nov 1984
Rogerson, Mr David Simon LLB(Hons) Nottingham Law Society Council 2000-03 . . . . *Oct 1992

GLADSTONE SOLICITORS ‡
8 Albert Street Newark Nottinghamshire NG24 4BJ
Tel: 01636 640641
List of partners: J Ellis, J Ellis, J P Griffiths
Office: Derby, Nottingham (2 offices)

JBR LAW ‡
Northgate Business Centre 38 North Gate Newark Nottinghamshire NG24 1EZ
Tel: 01636 642842 *Fax:* 01636 642843
E-mail: jabbar@jbrlaw.co.uk

JACKSON QUINN
Queens Head Chambers Kirk Gate Newark Nottinghamshire NG24 1AB
Tel: 01636 610175 *Fax:* 01636 704923
Office: Worksop

LANGLEYS
Great North Road Newark Nottinghamshire NG24 1BY
Tel: 01636 706508 *Fax:* 01522 888556
Dx: 700678 NORTH HYKEHAM
Office: Lincoln, York

LARKEN & CO ‡
10 Lombard Street Newark Nottinghamshire NG24 1XE
Tel: 01636 703333 *Fax:* 01636 706649 *Dx:* 11803 NEWARK
E-mail: info@larken.co.uk
List of partners: P J Armitage, J A Bruce, J D Kitchen, S Roberts, C Rossin
Work: C1 D1 E G H J1 K1 K3 K4 L N O Q R2 S1 S2 V W Z(m,r)
Emergency Action, Agency, Advocacy, Fixed Fee Interview, Legal Aid undertaken, Legal Aid Franchise and Member of Accident Line
Ptr: Armitage, Mr Philip J LLB . . . . *Sep 1991
Bruce, Mr Julian A LLB . . . . *Mar 1984
Kitchen, Mr James D . . . . *§Sep 1968
Roberts, Miss Sheila BA . . . . *Mar 1987
Rossin, Mr Clive BA. . . . . *Mar 1980
Ast: Aston, Mrs Anika LLB. . . . . *Feb 2005
Hodgson, Miss Cara Mia BSc. . . . . Mar 2007
Long, Mr Basil LLB . . . . Feb 2006
Miles, Ms Sarah Marie LLB . . . . Oct 2003
Parkhill, Mr Jeremy A BA; LLB . . . . *Dec 1979
Ryan, Mrs Denise K LLB . . . . *Oct 1988
Smith, Mrs Kathryn Mary LLM; LLB . . . . Feb 1994
Whittington, Mrs Linda . . . . Nov 2000

PAYNE & GAMAGE ‡
(incorporating Colton & Franks)
48 Lombard Street Newark Nottinghamshire NG24 1XP
Tel: 01636 640649 *Fax:* 01636 640627 *Dx:* 11816 NEWARK
List of partners: M Gamage
Work: A1 A3 B1 B2 C1 D1 E F1 G H J1 K1 K2 L M1 N O P Q R1 S1 S2 T1 V W Z(d,g,j,k,l,o)
Emergency Action, Agency, Advocacy, Fixed Fee Interview, Legal Aid undertaken and Legal Aid Franchise
Ptr: Gamage, Mr Michael . . . . Jul 1978
Ast: Gamage, Mrs Elizabeth Louise LLB(Hons) . . . . . . Sep 2005
Con: Payne, Mr David Richard . . . . *Sep 1971

THE RINGROSE LAW GROUP- SALLY HUBBARD
2 & 2a Bargate Newark Nottinghamshire NG24 1ES
Tel: 01636 594460 *Fax:* 01636 691100
E-mail: sally.hubbard@ringroselaw.co.uk
Office: Boston, Grantham, Lincoln (2 offices), Sleaford, Spalding

TALLENTS SOLICITORS ‡
3 Middlegate Newark Nottinghamshire NG24 1AQ
Tel: 01636 671881 *Fax:* 01636 700148 *Dx:* 11801 NEWARK
E-mail: info@tallents.co.uk
List of partners: J D Blatherwick, P C Harding, F C Kelly, A J Millar
Office: Mansfield, Southwell
Work: A1 B1 C1 C2 C3 D1 E F1 F2 G H J1 K1 K3 K4 L M1 N O P Q R1 S1 S2 T1 T2 W Z(c,d,e,f,h,k,l)
Emergency Action, Agency, Advocacy, Fixed Fee Interview, Legal Aid undertaken, Legal Aid Franchise and Member of Accident Line
Ptr: Blatherwick, Mr Jeremy D BA Clerk to Commissioner of Taxes . . . . *Oct 1984
Harding, Mr Phillip C LLB . . . . *Jul 1978
Kelly, Mrs Frances C LLB . . . . *Dec 1973
Ast: Gouldingay, Ms Wendy LLB. . . . . Nov 1985
Con: Blatherwick, Mr Peter Notary Public. . . . . *Nov 1958
Lawrence, Mr John D LLB. . . . . *§Dec 1970

NEWBIGGIN-BY-THE-SEA, Northumberland

HELLAWELL & CO ‡
32 Front Street Newbiggin-by-the-Sea Northumberland NE64 6PT
Tel: 01670 817223 *Fax:* 01670 852142
Dx: 62441 NEWBIGGIN-BY-THE-SEA
Emergency telephone 01670 817223
List of partners: J E Darling, J Errington
Work: B1 D1 F1 G H J1 K1 L P S1 W
Emergency Action, Agency, Advocacy and Fixed Fee Interview undertaken
Ptr: Darling, Mrs Jane Ellen LLB. . . . . *Dec 1982
Errington, Mr James. . . . . *Nov 1973

NEWBURY, West Berkshire

CHARLES LUCAS & MARSHALL ‡
Radnor House 28 Bartholomew Street Newbury West Berkshire RG14 5EU
Tel: 01635 521212 *Fax:* 01635 37784 *Dx:* 30802 NEWBURY
E-mail: ask@clmlaw.co.uk
List of partners: H M Amin, M V Berrett, B Chandler, H M Ellins, P F Graham, S McMinn, L M C Parker, M S C Poynter, D J Thomas, P Trincas
Office: Hungerford, Swindon, Wantage
Languages: French, German, Polish, Urdu
Work: A1 B1 C1 C2 C3 D1 E F1 G I J1 K1 K3 K4 L M1 M2 N O P Q R1 R2 S1 S2 T1 T2 U2 W Z(b,c,d,e,i,k,l,m,o,p,r,s,t)
Agency, Advocacy, Fixed Fee Interview, Legal Aid Franchise and Member of Accident Line
Ptr: Amin, Mr Hemantkumar Manmohan LLB(Hons) . . . . Feb 1988
Graham, Mr Peter F. . . . . May 1978
McMinn, Mr Stewart. . . . . Feb 1972
Parker, Mr Lance Michael Charles LLB . . . . *May 1975
Poynter, Mr Malcolm S C . . . . May 1982
Trincas, Mr Paul LLB . . . . Jun 1981
Asoc: Hamshaw, Mrs Suzy LLB(Hons). . . . . Sep 1997
Mead, Mr Richard Graham LLB . . . . May 1987
Verney, Mrs Marie Claire BA(Hons)(Business & Law) . Oct 2002
Wharry, Mrs Nia LLB(Hons) . . . . *Sep 1998
Ast: Biggs, Mrs Nicole BA(Hons); CPE; LPC. . . . . . . *Jan 2005
Billyard, Mr Peter BA . . . . *Oct 2007
Marshall, Mrs Claire Suzanne LLB(Hons); LPC . . . . Sep 2000
Mee, Mr Simon BA . . . . Sep 2000
Walker, Mr Thomas Edward BA; PGDipLaw; LPC . . Sep 2006
Wilkinson, Mr Paul LLB; LLM . . . . Sep 2005

DAVID DUNWOODY & CO ‡
22 Lamtarra Way Newbury West Berkshire RG14 7WB
Tel: 01635 354333

THOMAS EGGAR LLP
Newbury House 20 King's Road West Newbury West Berkshire RG14 5XR
Tel: 01635 571000 *Fax:* 01635 523444 *Dx:* 30801 NEWBURY
E-mail: newbury@thomaseggar.com
Office: Chichester, Crawley, London EC4, Southampton, Worthing
Work: A3 D2 E J1 K1 K2 K3 K4 L N O Q S1 S2 T1 T2 W X Z(b,d,h,o,q,r,w)

ELM SOLICITORS ‡
Rothury House Graces Lane Chieveley Newbury West Berkshire RG20 8XG
Tel: 01635 248336 / 0118 907 1954

GARDNER LEADER LLP ‡
White Hart House 24 Market Place Newbury West Berkshire RG14 5BA
Tel: 01635 508080 *Fax:* 01635 521341 *Dx:* 30805 NEWBURY
E-mail: mail@gardner-leader.co.uk
List of partners: C M Bailey, J P Barton, J Buchanan, S R Durrant, C G Felton, A L Goggins, D J Goldsmith, G Humphreys, J D Jackson, S E C Myerscough, D Rodgers, R Tomlinson
Office: Thatcham
Languages: French
Work: A1 A3 B1 B2 C1 C2 D1 D2 E F1 G H J1 J2 K1 K2 K3 K4 L M1 N O P Q R1 S1 S2 T1 T2 V W Z(c,k,l,p,q,r,t,w,y)
Emergency Action, Agency, Advocacy, Fixed Fee Interview, Legal Aid undertaken and Member of Accident Line
Ptr: Bailey, Mrs Collette M LLB . . . . *Dec 1981
Barton, Jolyon P BA(Law). . . . . Nov 1981
Buchanan, Mrs Jennifer LLB . . . . Oct 1982
Durrant, Mr Stuart Robert LLB. . . . . Mar 1988
Felton, Mr Christopher George LLB(Hons). . . . . . Nov 1996
Goggins, Mr Alastair L LLB . . . . Nov 1998
Goldsmith, Mr David J LLB . . . . Mar 1990
Humphreys, Mr Greg . . . . Jan 2002
Jackson, Mr John D. . . . . *Jul 1980
Myerscough, Ms Seona E C LLB . . . . *§Oct 1987
Rodgers, Mr Derek LLB(Hons) . . . . Oct 1993
Tomlinson, Mr Robert LLB(Lond) . . . . Apr 1977
Asoc: Green, Mr Robert I . . . . *Jan 1971
Ast: Anns, Ms Charlotte . . . . Jan 2007
Drew, Ms Kathryn Louise LLB(Hons) . . . . Nov 1989
Jobson, Mr Robert P BA(Hons) . . . . *Apr 2000
Parsonson, Mr Robert John LLB . . . . Oct 2003
Taylor, Ms Julie . . . . Jan 2007
Tighe, Ms Fiona LLB . . . . *Oct 1983
Con: Child, Mr Derek S LLB(Lond) . . . . *§Jul 1969

ANTONY GORLEY & CO ‡
Wessex House London Road Newbury West Berkshire RG14 1PA
Tel: 01635 551321
Emergency telephone 07836 237780
List of partners: A A Gorley
Work: N Z(r)
Member of Accident Line
SPr: Gorley, Mr Antony A. . . . . *Dec 1971

CHARLES HOILE ‡
Wharf House Wharf Street Newbury West Berkshire RG14 5AP
Tel: 01635 45595 *Fax:* 01635 521964 *Dx:* 30803 NEWBURY
E-mail: enquiries@hoiles.co.uk
List of partners: I G R Campbell, A Cowdry, M J Davis, A Peace, A L R Scott-Malden, P J Stewart
Languages: French
Work: A1 B1 C1 D1 E F1 G H J1 K1 K2 L N O Q R1 S1 S2 T2 W Z(d,l)
Emergency Action, Agency, Advocacy, Fixed Fee Interview, Legal Aid undertaken, Legal Aid Franchise and Member of Accident Line
Ptr: Campbell, Mr Ian George Robert . . . . *Oct 1975
Cowdry, Ms Anna . . . . *Oct 1995
Davis, Mr Michael James LLB(L'pool) . . . . *Dec 1980
Scott-Malden, Miss Alexandra Lucy Rodney BSc(Exon); DipLaw . . . . *Oct 1999
Stewart, Mr Patrick J BA(Essex). . . . . *Apr 2000
Ast: Britton, Mr Anthony Charles LLB; BComm. . . . . . *Jun 2006

HORSEY LIGHTLY ‡
20 West Mills Newbury West Berkshire RG14 5HG
Tel: 01635 580858 *Fax:* 01635 582813 *Dx:* 30835 NEWBURY
E-mail: new@horseylightly.com
List of partners: S R Barrett, P Brooks, A J M Devlin, J Fitzgibbon, A Greenough, G A Horsey, C F J Popham, S Reed, M Reynolds, J D Trehearne, L C Wallis, R M Whitehead
Office: London SW1
Languages: French, German, Italian, Polish, Spanish
Work: A1 B1 C1 C2 D1 D2 E F1 F2 J1 K1 L M1 N O P Q R1 R2 S1 S2 T1 T2 V W X Z(d,j,l,n,p,q,r)
Emergency Action, Agency and Advocacy undertaken
Ptr: Barrett, Mr Simon Ralph Acting Coroner for West Berkshire . . . . *Nov 1977
Greenough, Miss Amanda. . . . . *Jan 2007
Horsey, Mr Guy Anthony LLB(Hons). . . . . *Apr 1998
Reynolds, Mr Martin MA(Hons)(Cantab). . . . . . . *Sep 1998
Trehearne, Mr John David LLB(Exon) . . . . *Nov 1991
Wallis, Mrs Lynn Christina LLM(Bris) . . . . *§Jul 1981
Whitehead, Mrs Rachel Marion DPhil . . . . *Dec 1993
Asoc: Jameson, Mr Barry . . . . Jan 1972
Thomas, Miss Kate . . . . *Jan 2004
Ast: Baldwin, Ms Emma . . . . *Jan 2007
Collyer, Mrs Mary . . . . Jan 2006
Edgington, Mrs Elianne . . . . Jan 2006
Con: Horsey, Mr John S N J . . . . *§Apr 1966
Horsey, Mrs Theresa P Deputy District Judge . . . . *§Jun 1972

CONOR MAGILL ‡
The Old Beer House Penwood Burghclere Newbury West Berkshire RG20 9EP
Tel: 01635 255217 *Fax:* 01635 250802
E-mail: conor.magill@ukgateway.net
Work: E L R1 R2 S2 Z(q)

MARCH SOLICITORS ‡
The Courtyard 2 London Road Newbury West Berkshire RG14 1JX
Tel: 0845 204 2020 *Fax:* 01635 33854
E-mail: mail@marchsolicitors.com

MILLS & BANN ‡
8 Cheap Street Newbury West Berkshire RG14 5DD
Tel: 01635 521545 / 32000 *Fax:* 01635 521920
Dx: 30808 NEWBURY
E-mail: a.milla@mills_and_bann.demon.co.uk
List of partners: P Bann, A H W Mills
Work: A1 B1 C1 D1 E F1 G H J1 K1 L M1 P S1 W
Emergency Action, Agency, Advocacy and Fixed Fee Interview undertaken
Ptr: Bann, Mr Philip MA(Cantab). . . . . *Oct 1975
Mills, Mr Andrew H W. . . . . *Nov 1979

IAN SPENCER & CO ‡
Top Floor Inch's Yard Market Street Newbury West Berkshire RG14 5DP
Tel: 01635 528424 *Fax:* 01635 522544
List of partners: I R Spencer
Work: A1 C1 E R1 S1 T1 T2 W
SPr: Spencer, Mr Ian Robin MA(Oxon) . . . . *Mar 1985

WINTON & WINTON ‡
Upper Cross Woodspeen Newbury West Berkshire RG20 8JY
Tel: 01635 814418

NEWCASTLE EMLYN, Carmarthenshire

RICHARD JAMES ‡
Bank Chambers Sycamore Street Newcastle Emlyn Carmarthenshire SA38 9AP
Tel: 01239 710455 *Fax:* 01239 711162
Dx: 92602 NEWCASTLE EMLYN
E-mail: rjames.solicitors@lineone.net
List of partners: R James
Languages: Welsh
SPr: James, Mr Richard LLB . . . . *May 1988

MASON-WATTS & CO ‡
Cavendish House Ebenezer Street Newcastle Emlyn Carmarthenshire SA38 9BN
Tel: 01239 711521 *Fax:* 01239 711110
Emergency telephone 01239 710250
Languages: French, German
Work: A1 C1 E F1 N O S1 W

See p112 for the Key to Work Categories & other symbols

ELERI THOMAS & CO LTD ‡
Cartrefle Bridge Street Newcastle Emlyn Carmarthenshire SA38 9DX
Tel: 01239 710942 *Fax:* 01239 711187
Dx: 92601 NEWCASTLE EMLYN
List of partners: A E Thomas
Languages: French, Welsh
Work: A1 C1 F1 G H J1 K1 L N Q S1 W Z(l)
Agency and Advocacy undertaken
SPr: Thomas, Mrs Ann Eleri LLB . . . . *Oct 1986
Con: Griffiths, Mr David G LLB . . . . Mar 1963

W EVANS GEORGE & SONS
(incorporating George Davies & Evans)
Sycamore Street Newcastle Emlyn Carmarthenshire SA38 9AJ
Tel: 01239 710228 *Fax:* 01239 711136
Dx: 92600 NEWCASTLE EMLYN
Office: Cardigan
Languages: Welsh
Work: A1 D1 D2 E F1 K1 L N O Q R1 S1 S2 T1 V W Z(i)
Emergency Action, Agency, Advocacy, Fixed Fee Interview, Legal Aid undertaken, Legal Aid Franchise and Member of Accident Line
Dir: Cole, Mrs Helen LLB . . . . *Oct 1987

NEWCASTLE UNDER LYME, Staffordshire

ATTICUS SOLICITORS ‡
Leeds House 79a High Street Newcastle under Lyme Staffordshire ST5 1PS
Tel: 01782 629840 *Fax:* 01782 628325
E-mail: admin@atticussolicitors.co.uk

BRIAN BAILES ‡
7 Kings Avenue Wolstanton Newcastle under Lyme Staffordshire ST5 8DA
Tel: 01782 626214
List of partners: B Bailes
SPr: Bailes, Mr Brian LLB . . . . *§Jul 1969

BEESTON SHENTON ‡
64 King Street Newcastle under Lyme Staffordshire ST5 1JB
Tel: 01782 662424
Office: Knutsford, Sandbach

BROWN & CORBISHLEY ‡
Queens Chambers 2/4 Queen Street Newcastle under Lyme Staffordshire ST5 1EE
Tel: 01782 717888 *Fax:* 01782 717042
Dx: 20951 NEWCASTLE UNDER LYME
E-mail: info@brownandcorbishley.co.uk
List of partners: K Carroll, C Drew, J Godwin
Office: Sandbach
Languages: French, Spanish
Work: A1 A3 B1 C1 D1 D2 E F1 G H J1 K1 K2 L M1 N O P Q R1 S1 S2 T1 V W Z(l)
Emergency Action, Agency, Advocacy, Legal Aid undertaken and Legal Aid Franchise
Ptr: Drew, Mr Colin LLB ★. . . . . Dec 1972
Godwin, Mr John BA(Law) . . . . *§Jun 1975
Asoc: Wiseman, Ms Emma . . . . Jan 2005
Ast: Drew, Miss Heather M LLB ★ . . . . Aug 2000
Knock, Mr Simon W BA . . . . Nov 1985
McCabe, Mrs L Ann MA. . . . . Oct 1993
Mason, Miss Rachel. . . . . Mar 2010
Wilson, Mrs Karen LLB . . . . Nov 1993

COOKS ‡
3 Fellgate Court Froghall Newcastle under Lyme Staffordshire ST5 2UA
Tel: 01782 611090 *Fax:* 01782 713675
Dx: 20955 NEWCASTLE UNDER LYME
Emergency telephone 01782 641608
E-mail: info@cooks-solicitors.co.uk
List of partners: N E Cook, D E Sumner
Work: K1 N S1
Emergency Action, Agency, Advocacy, Fixed Fee Interview undertaken and Member of Accident Line
Ptr: Cook, Mr Nigel E LLB(Lond). . . . . *Apr 1978
Sumner, Mrs Dianne E . . . . *§Jan 1980

DUTTON LAW LIMITED ‡
Lymedale Business Centre Lymedale Business Park Hooters Hall Road Newcastle under Lyme Staffordshire ST5 9QF
Tel: 01782 565900 / 07754 588302 *Fax:* 0845 280 0247
Dx: 700404 FENTON

JAMES A EVANS & CO SOLICITORS ‡
Hanover Street Newcastle under Lyme Staffordshire ST5 1HE
Tel: 01782 714007 *Fax:* 01782 714097
E-mail: jevans@jevans@jamesevanssolicitors.co.uk

HACKING ASHTON LLP ‡
Berkeley Court Borough Road Newcastle under Lyme Staffordshire ST5 1TT
Est: 1978
Tel: 01782 715555 *Fax:* 01782 715566 / 715577
Dx: 20954 NEWCASTLE UNDER LYME
E-mail: l.griffiths@hackingashton.co.uk
List of partners: M Akram, L A Griffiths, J Hickey, M R G P Rothwell, I R Wilson, C R Woolliscroft
Languages: French, Punjabi, Urdu
Work: A3 B1 C1 C2 E F1 J1 L M1 O P Q R1 R2 S1 S2 T1 W Z(c,e,l,q)
Emergency Action, Agency, Advocacy and Fixed Fee Interview undertaken
Mem: Akram, Mr Mohammed LLB; LPC . . . . *Jul 2003
Griffiths, Mr Lewis Alexander BSc. . . . . *Sep 1996
Hickey, Mr James. . . . . *Nov 1996
Rothwell, Mr Michael Richard George Pennington. . . *Oct 1980
Wilson, Mr Ian Robert LLB(Hons); LPC . . . . *Mar 1997
Woolliscroft, Mr Clive R . . . . *Aug 1999
Asoc: Barker, Mr Larry Dennis BEd(Hons); LLDip . . . . . . Sep 2003
Ast: Clarke, Mrs Kate Ellis LLDip; LLM; BSc . . . . Jul 2007
Kirkwood, Mrs Emma LLB. . . . . *Sep 2001
Nixon, Mrs Kahrine Helen LLB(Hons); LPC . . . . Jul 2001
Sereni, Mr Gian Carlo LLB . . . . Feb 1983
Wilkes, Mrs Hayley Teresa LLB; MA Best Business Law Profile 2005 . . . . Jul 2007

KNIGHTS SOLICITORS LLP ‡
The Brampton Newcastle under Lyme Staffordshire ST5 0QW
Tel: 01782 619225 *Fax:* 01782 620410
Dx: 711120 NEWCASTLE UNDER LYME 7
E-mail: mail@knightsllp.co.uk
List of partners: M A J Anton-Smith, A P Bailey, K R Bamford, A T Bruce, R G Coddington, J T Costello, A G F Davidson, C A Dyson, R F T Fearnley, I M Hancock, S V Honeyands, L G Howland, C Jones, R A Jones, R A Lashmore, C M Longshaw, G K H Miller, A S Rushton, C A Smith, Z T Theofilopoulos, C M Tierney, I C White, M R Whitehouse
Office: Alderley Edge, Cheltenham
Languages: French, German, Italian, Spanish
Work: A1 A2 A3 B1 C1 C2 C3 D1 E F1 F2 I J1 J2 K1 K3 K4 L M1 M2 N O P Q R1 R2 S1 S2 T1 T2 U1 U2 V W X Z(b,c,d,e,f,g,k,l,m,n,o,p,q,r,s,t,w)
Emergency Action, Advocacy, Fixed Fee Interview undertaken and Member of Accident Line
Ptr: Bailey, Mr Andrew Paul . . . . *Dec 1993
Bamford, Mr Karl R LLB. . . . . *§Oct 1988
Bruce, Mrs Andrea T BA . . . . *§Nov 1995
Costello, Ms Jessica Tuesday LLB(Hons) . . . . *Sep 2001
Davidson, Mr Andrew G F. . . . . *§Aug 1992
Dyson, Ms Christine A BA. . . . . *§Mar 1987
Fearnley, Mr Robert Frederick Thomas LLB . . . . . . *Sep 2001
Hancock, Ms Isabel M. . . . . *§Nov 1993
Honeyands, Mrs Susan V . . . . *§Oct 1991
Howland, Mrs Lindsey Gail LLB(Hons) . . . . *Mar 1981
Jones, Mr Charles BA. . . . . *§Nov 1983
Jones, Mr Richard A . . . . *§Oct 1984
Lashmore, Mr Richard A . . . . *§Oct 1985
Longshaw, Mrs Catherine Margaret . . . . Jun 2000
Miller, Mrs Glenda K H . . . . *§Apr 1981
Rushton, Mr Adrian S . . . . *§Sep 1999
Smith, Mrs Catherine A . . . . *§Nov 1993
Theofilopoulos, Mrs Zoe T. . . . . *§Apr 1984
Tierney, Miss Clare Marie . . . . *§Sep 1997
White, Mr Ian C . . . . *§Mar 1987
Whitehouse, Mr Mark Robert . . . . *§Jan 1999

MCHUGH SOLICITORS ‡
82 King Street Newcastle under Lyme Staffordshire ST5 1JB
Tel: 01782 628888
E-mail: advice@mchugh-solicitors.co.uk
List of partners: G McHugh
SPr: McHugh, Mr Gerald LPC . . . . Oct 1995

SALMONS ‡
20 High Street May Bank Newcastle under Lyme Staffordshire ST5 0JB
Tel: 01782 621266 *Fax:* 01782 717767
Dx: 20979 NEWCASTLE UNDER LYME
E-mail: lawyers@salmonssolicitors.net
List of partners: S A Brookes, N A Mason, J S Staff
Office: Stoke-on-Trent
Work: D1 K1 K2 K3 S1 S2 W
Emergency Action, Agency, Advocacy, Fixed Fee Interview, Legal Aid undertaken, Legal Aid Franchise and Member of Accident Line
Ptr: Mason, Mr Nicholas Anthony LLB . . . . *Nov 1990
Asoc: Boden, Miss Kerry. . . . . Feb 2007

TINSDILLS
15-19 Marsh Parade Newcastle under Lyme Staffordshire ST5 1BT
Tel: 01782 612311 *Fax:* 01782 717294
Dx: 20956 NEWCASTLE UNDER LYME
E-mail: lawyers@tinsdills.co.uk
Office: Hanley, Leek, Sandbach
Work: A1 A2 B1 B2 C1 C2 D1 D2 E F1 F2 J1 K1 K2 K3 K4 L N O P Q R1 R2 S1 S2 T1 V W Z(b,c,d,e,f,g,h,j,l,m,n,o,p,q,r,s,t)
Emergency Action, Agency, Advocacy, Legal Aid undertaken and Member of Accident Line
Ptr: Chadwick, Mr Neil. . . . . *§Jun 1974
Ast: Porter, Ms Nicola . . . . Jun 2008

WHITEHEADS ‡
6 Water Street Newcastle under Lyme Staffordshire ST5 1HR
Tel: 01782 615278 *Fax:* 01782 714637
Dx: 20972 NEWCASTLE UNDER LYME
E-mail: mail@whiteheads.uk.com
List of partners: C P Murphy, J A Murphy
Work: C1 E K1 N Q S1 S2 W
Emergency Action, Agency, Advocacy, Fixed Fee Interview and Legal Aid undertaken
Ptr: Murphy, Mr Christopher Paul BA . . . . Jul 1996
Murphy, Mr James A . . . . *§Jan 1965
Asoc: Murphy, Miss Suzanne Helen . . . . Aug 1999

WOOLLISCROFTS
19 Morris Square Wolstanton Newcastle under Lyme Staffordshire ST5 0EN
Tel: 01782 662545 *Fax:* 01782 713176 *Dx:* 20708 HANLEY
E-mail: mailbox@woolliscrofts.co.uk
Office: Alsager, Hanley, Stoke-on-Trent
Emergency Action, Agency, Advocacy, Fixed Fee Interview and Legal Aid undertaken
Ptr: Harrop, Mr William D LLB Deputy District Judge. . . *§Nov 1979

NEWCASTLE UPON TYNE, Tyne & Wear

ADAMS ‡
Clayton House 31 Bath Lane Newcastle upon Tyne Tyne & Wear NE4 5SP
Tel: 0191 261 0361 *Fax:* 0191 261 6699
E-mail: mail@adams-legal.com
List of partners: V W Adams
Languages: French
Work: L R1 Z(u)
Agency, Advocacy and Fixed Fee Interview undertaken
SPr: Adams, Mr Victor Williams FILEx; BA(Law); LARTPI; BA(Hons) . . . . *Jan 1984

THE ASSOCIATE LAW FIRM ‡
Cobalt Business Exchange Cobalt Park Way Newcastle upon Tyne Tyne & Wear NE28 9NZ
Tel: 0191 280 4110 *Fax:* 0191 280 5552

BHP LAW
Eldon Chambers 23 Quayside Newcastle upon Tyne Tyne & Wear NE1 3DE
Tel: 0191 221 0898 *Fax:* 0191 232 0930
Dx: 61085 NEWCASTLE UPON TYNE
E-mail: info@bhplaw.co.uk
Office: Darlington, Durham, Halifax, Newton Aycliffe, North Shields, Stockton-on-Tees
Work: A3 B1 C1 C2 C3 D1 D2 E F1 F2 G H J1 J2 K1 K2 K3 K4 L N O Q R1 R2 S1 S2 T1 T2 U1 U2 W X Z(c,e,o,p,q,r,u,w,x,za)
Legal Aid undertaken
Ptr: Hewitson, Mrs Andrea. . . . . Oct 1988
Moffitt, Mrs Margot S LLB. . . . . Jun 1978
Ritzema, Mr Graeme LLB . . . . *Oct 1983
Saxon, Mr Paul Sidney BSc; MSc. . . . . *Oct 1993
Wilson, Mr David J M LLB. . . . . *Dec 1972
Asoc: Fiddes, Mrs Jane LLB(Hons) . . . . Dec 2002
Hargreaves, Mr Paul . . . . Aug 2010
Monaghan, Mr Paul . . . . Dec 2009
Ast: Crumbley, Mr William Michael LLB . . . . Jul 1977
Ferguson, Miss Jane R G BSc . . . . Sep 1999
Lisgo, Miss Helen . . . . Oct 2009

BAKER GRAY & CO
3 Bigg Market Newcastle upon Tyne Tyne & Wear NE1 1UN
Tel: 0191 222 0203 *Fax:* 0191 261 0770
Emergency telephone 07860 526308
Office: Blaydon-on-Tyne
Work: D1 G H K1 S1 W
Emergency Action, Agency, Advocacy, Fixed Fee Interview, Legal Aid undertaken and Legal Aid Franchise
Ptr: Gray, Mr Cormac J P BA . . . . Oct 1983

DAVID BANKS SOLICITORS ‡
2a Forest Hall Road Forest Hall Newcastle upon Tyne Tyne & Wear NE12 9AJ
Tel: 0191 266 4776 *Fax:* 0191 266 7944 *Dx:* 65023 FOREST HALL
E-mail: db@davidbankssolicitors.co.uk

BEECHAM PEACOCK ‡
7 Collingwood Street Newcastle upon Tyne Tyne & Wear NE1 1JE
Tel: 0191 232 3048 *Fax:* 0191 261 7255
Dx: 61014 NEWCASTLE UPON TYNE
Emergency telephone 0191 285 1888
E-mail: genenquiries@beechampeacock.co.uk
List of partners: D G Lamb, C McCurley, M Quigley, K A Scott
Work: D1 F1 G H J1 K1 L N Q R1 S1 V W Z(i,m,q)
Emergency Action, Agency, Advocacy, Fixed Fee Interview, Legal Aid undertaken, Legal Aid Franchise and Member of Accident Line
Ptr: Lamb, Mr David G BA. . . . . *Jun 1979
McCurley, Ms Cris LLB . . . . *Sep 1990
Quigley, Mr Mark MA(Cantab). . . . . *Sep 1994
Scott, Ms Kirsten A LLB. . . . . *Nov 1985
Ast: Arullendran, Ms Pamela BA(Hons) . . . . *Dec 1998
Connell, Mr Neil Victor LLB(Hons). . . . . *Sep 1995
Jarrold, Ms Lucinda May LLB(Hons). . . . . *Aug 2000
MacDougall, Miss Ruth LLB(Hons) . . . . Sep 2001
Con: Beecham, Sir Jeremy H DL DCL; MA(Oxon) . . . . . *Mar 1968
Peacock, Mr Norman D . . . . *Dec 1974

BEN HOARE BELL & CO
Ouseburn Point 40 Shields Road Newcastle upon Tyne Tyne & Wear NE6 1DR
Tel: 0191 275 2626 *Fax:* 0191 275 2627
Emergency telephone 0191 565 3112
E-mail: advice@benhoarebell.co.uk
Office: Sunderland (3 offices)
Work: D1 D2 F1 G H J1 K1 L N V X Z(i,m)
Emergency Action, Agency, Advocacy, Fixed Fee Interview, Legal Aid undertaken, Legal Aid Franchise and Member of Accident Line
Ptr: Davies, Ms Clare Elizabeth BA(Hons); LSF(Hons). . . *Nov 1994

HARISH C BOURI ‡
54 St George's Terrace Jesmond Newcastle upon Tyne Tyne & Wear NE2 2SY
Tel: 0191 281 4860 *Fax:* 0191 281 9944
E-mail: hbouri2000@yahoo.co.uk
List of partners: H C Bouri
Languages: Hindi, Punjabi, Urdu
Work: A1 B1 C1 C2 C3 D1 E F1 G H J1 K1 L M1 M2 N P Q R1 R2 S1 S2 T1 T2 V W
Emergency Action, Agency, Advocacy, Fixed Fee Interview, Legal Aid undertaken and Member of Accident Line
Ptr: Bouri, Mr Harish C BA. . . . . *§Jul 1978

BRAR & CO ‡
240a Chillingham Road Heaton Newcastle upon Tyne Tyne & Wear NE6 5LP
Tel: 0191 276 6880 *Fax:* 0191 276 6882 *Dx:* 717422 BYKER 2
Emergency telephone 0191 240 2842
E-mail: enquiries@brar.co.uk
List of partners: B S Brar
Languages: Hindi, Punjabi, Urdu
Work: D1 D2 E J1 K1 L N Q S1 S2 W Z(i,l)
Emergency Action, Fixed Fee Interview, Legal Aid undertaken and Legal Aid Franchise
Ptr: Brar, Birinder S LLB. . . . . *Feb 1988

BROWELL SMITH & CO ‡
2nd Floor Commercial Union House 39 Pilgrim Street Newcastle upon Tyne Tyne & Wear NE1 6QE
Tel: 0871 474 3030 *Fax:* 0845 302 4755
Dx: 61084 NEWCASTLE UPON TYNE
E-mail: advice@browells.co.uk
Office: Ashington, Cramlington, Newcastle upon Tyne (2 offices), Stockton-on-Tees, Stoke-on-Trent, Sunderland

BROWELL SMITH & CO
1st Floor 6-8 Bell Villas Ponteland Newcastle upon Tyne Tyne & Wear NE20 9BE
Tel: 0871 474 3030 *Fax:* 0845 302 4755
E-mail: advice@browells.co.uk
Office: Ashington, Cramlington, Newcastle upon Tyne (2 offices), Stockton-on-Tees, Stoke-on-Trent, Sunderland

BROWELL SMITH & CO
679 West Road Denton Burn Newcastle upon Tyne Tyne & Wear NE15 7QQ
Tel: 0871 474 3030 *Fax:* 0845 302 4755
E-mail: advice@browells.co.uk
Office: Ashington, Cramlington, Newcastle upon Tyne (2 offices), Stockton-on-Tees, Stoke-on-Trent, Sunderland

GORDON BROWN ASSOCIATES
Hadrian House Higham Place Newcastle upon Tyne Tyne & Wear NE1 8AF
Tel: 0191 388 1778 *Fax:* 0191 340 0151
Office: Chester-le-Street

DAVID BRYSON SOLICITOR ‡
71 The Wills Building Newcastle upon Tyne Tyne & Wear NE7 7RH
Tel: 0191 209 3461

BURNETTS
12 Lansdowne Terrace Newcastle upon Tyne Tyne & Wear NE3 1HN
Tel: 0191 300 1833
Office: Carlisle (2 offices), Whitehaven

CARIS ROBSON LLP
2 Victoria Terrace Throckley Newcastle upon Tyne Tyne & Wear NE15 9EL
Tel: 0191 264 6664 *Fax:* 0191 264 6665
Dx: 727880 NEWCASTLE (THROCKLEY)
E-mail: enquiries@carisrobson.com
Office: Prudhoe
Work: B1 C1 D1 D2 E F1 J1 K1 L N O Q S1 S2 V W Z(l)
Emergency Action, Agency, Advocacy, Fixed Fee Interview, Legal Aid undertaken and Legal Aid Franchise
Ptr: Caris, Mrs Barbara BA . . . . . *Oct 1988
Caris, Mr Peter Lloyd . . . . . *Dec 1969
Robson, Miss Helen Kirsty MA . . . . . *Aug 2001

CARMICHAEL & HEATHFIELD ‡
16-18 Pink Lane Newcastle upon Tyne Tyne & Wear NE1 5DW
Tel: 0191 230 3010 *Fax:* 0191 232 5380
Emergency telephone 07930 180407
List of partners: N F Carmichael
Emergency Action, Agency, Advocacy, Fixed Fee Interview, Legal Aid undertaken, Legal Aid Franchise and Member of Accident Line
Ptr: Carmichael, Mr Neil Fraser BA(Law) . . . . . Apr 1999

CLARKE MAIRS ‡
Royal House 5-7 Market Street Newcastle upon Tyne Tyne & Wear NE1 6JN
Tel: 0845 111 0795 *Fax:* 0845 111 0794 *Dx:* 61057 NEWCASTLE
E-mail: law@clarkemairs.com

STEFAN CROSS SOLICITORS ‡
Buddle House Buddle Road Newcastle upon Tyne Tyne & Wear NE4 8AW
Tel: 0191 226 6686 *Fax:* 0191 226 6680
E-mail: enquiries@stefancross.co.uk
List of partners: S Cross
Dir: Cross, Mr Stefan LLB; LLM . . . . . Aug 1985

CROWE HUMBLE WESENCRAFT ‡
3 Addison Road Heaton Newcastle upon Tyne Tyne & Wear NE6 1SJ
Tel: 0191 287 2221 *Fax:* 0191 287 2221
Emergency telephone 07976 055602
Work: G H
Agency and Legal Aid undertaken

CRUTES ‡
Great North House Sandyford Road Newcastle upon Tyne Tyne & Wear NE1 8ND
Tel: 0191 233 9700 *Fax:* 0191 233 9701 *Dx:* 62553 JESMOND
E-mail: advice@crutes.co.uk
List of partners: H L Ager, P J Bell, G S Crute, D M Drewe, P M Earnshaw, D M Gibson, S Hamilton, S Howes, P M Hughes, N Hyam, G E Jones, R Matharu, A C McCulloch, K McKernan, S O'Neil, M K Robson, M K Robson, R Searl, T R Whitfield
Office: Carlisle, Stockton-on-Tees
Work: A1 A3 B1 C1 D1 E F1 G H J1 J2 K1 K3 L M1 N O P Q R1 V W Z(c,d,h,j,k,l,m,q,r,u)
Emergency Action, Agency, Advocacy, Fixed Fee Interview, Legal Aid undertaken and Member of Accident Line
Ptr: Ager, Mrs Helen L LLB . . . . . *Nov 1986
Bell, Mr Paul J LLB . . . . . *Oct 1989
Crute, Mr G Stephen LLB. . . . . *Jul 1978
Drewe, Mr David M LLB Chairman of the Newcastle FUSA Medical Services Committee . . . . . *Apr 1981
Earnshaw, Mr Paul M LLB(Hons) . . . . . *§Nov 1993
Gibson, Mr David M BA(Hons); MA . . . . . Oct 1997
Hamilton, Mr Stuart LLB; LLM. . . . . *Oct 1989
Hughes, Mr Paul M LLB. . . . . *Sep 1988
Hyam, Ms Nicola LLB(Hons) . . . . . *Sep 1996
McKernan, Mr Kevin . . . . . *Jun 1980
Matharu, Miss Ranj LLB(Hons); LLM . . . . . *Nov 1991
Robson, Mr Michael Kenneth BA(Hons); LLM Deputy District Judge. . . . . *Feb 1985
Searl, Mr Rod LLB(Hons) . . . . . *Feb 1992
Whitfield, Mr Thomas R LLB(Hons) . . . . . *Mar 1997
Mem: McCulloch, Ms Anne Catherine . . . . . Oct 1999
Asoc: Kingsland, Ms Joanne LLB . . . . . *Feb 1989
Ast: Searl, Mrs Christina Lesley LLB. . . . . *Oct 1992
Smith, Ms Claire Louise. . . . . Oct 2007
Con: Taylor, Mr David N LLB(Bris) . . . . . *Apr 1978

DAC BEACHCROFT
PO Box 1234 Time Central 32 Gallowgate Newcastle upon Tyne Tyne & Wear NE99 5AA
Tel: 0191 404 4000 *Fax:* 0191 404 4100
Dx: 61035 NEWCASTLE UPON TYNE
Office: Birmingham, Bristol, Leeds, London EC3 (3 offices), London EC4 (2 offices), Manchester (2 offices), Newport, Winchester

DWF
Cuthbert House All Saints Newcastle upon Tyne Tyne & Wear NE1 2ET
Tel: 0191 350 6173
E-mail: enquiries@dwf.co.uk
Office: Leeds, Liverpool, London EC4, Manchester, Preston

DAVIES BELL & REED ‡
27 Ridley Place Newcastle upon Tyne Tyne & Wear NE1 8LE
Tel: 0191 232 8058 *Fax:* 0191 222 1391
E-mail: law@daviesbellreed.co.uk
List of partners: A D Stokoe, C E Wilkie-Smith
Office: Whickham
Work: A1 B1 C1 D1 E F1 G H J1 K1 L M1 N P R1 S1 T1 V W
Emergency Action, Agency, Advocacy, Fixed Fee Interview and Legal Aid undertaken
Ptr: Wilkie-Smith, Mr Charles Edward BA . . . . . *§Jun 1978

DICKINSON DEES ‡
St Ann's Wharf 112 The Quayside Newcastle upon Tyne Tyne & Wear NE1 3DX
Tel: 0191 279 9000 *Fax:* 0191 279 9100
Dx: 61191 NEWCASTLE UPON TYNE
E-mail: law@dickinson-dees.com
List of partners: P Ashworth, G P Barnard, N D Bellis, J J Blair, R A Bloom, N E Braithwaite, M J Brown, G P Calvert, T J Care, A Dickinson, A E Downey, A A Fellows, P Fenwick, P A Finch, J Flynn, A C Gifford, A R Gray, I F Greenshields, C J Harker, G Harvey, N C Henderson, A J Hewitt, G Hockaday, S M Jackson, M H Jenkins, S Kirkup, D Kirtley, S J Lewis, K Lowthian, G Lyall, S Mantle, J P B Marshall, S T Nicolson, J S North Lewis, B J Painter, J H Pass, M D Pearce, J A Pennie, J D Ralph, D Rewcastle, C P Rogers, L M Rutherford, J D F Smith, J Smurthwaite, H Straker, H F Tavroges, I Ward, N K Warwick, S P Watts, J C Wilders, N T Williams, R M Wilson, W F Wilson, A G P Wright
Office: London EC4, Newcastle upon Tyne, Stockton-on-Tees, York
Languages: Arabic, French, German, Gujarati, Hindi, Kiswahili, Urdu
Work: A1 A3 B1 B2 C1 C2 C3 D1 E F1 I J1 J2 K1 L M1 M2 N O P Q R1 R2 S1 T1 T2 U2 V W X Z(b,c,d,e,f,g,h,i,j,k,l,m,n,o,p,q,r,s,t,u,w)
Emergency Action, Agency, Advocacy, Fixed Fee Interview, Legal Aid undertaken and Member of Accident Line
Ptr: Barnard, Mr Graham P LLB(Soton) . . . . . *§Jun 1978
Bellis, Mr Nigel D MA(Cantab). . . . . *§Apr 1977
Blair, Mr Jonathan J LLB . . . . . *§Oct 1989
Bloom, Mr Robin A . . . . . Jul 1979
Braithwaite, Mr Neil E MA(Cantab) . . . . . *§Apr 1978
Brown, Mr Mitchell J LLB(Newc). . . . . *§Dec 1987
Calvert, Mr Glenn P MA(Cantab) . . . . . *§Oct 1980
Care, Mr Timothy J BA(Dunelm). . . . . *§Oct 1985
Dickinson, Mr Alexander MA(Oxon) . . . . . *§Oct 1989
Downey, Ms Ashley E. . . . . Aug 1998
Fellows, Ms Alison A BA(Cantab) . . . . . *§Nov 1986
Fenwick, Mr Peter LLB(Newc). . . . . *§Oct 1985
Finch, Mr Paul A LLB(Newc) . . . . . *§Dec 1978
Flynn, Mr John LLB(Newc) . . . . . *§Dec 1983
Gifford, Mr Adrian C BSc . . . . . *§Jun 1977
Gray, Mrs Alison R BA . . . . . *§Oct 1988
Greenshields, Mr Ian F LLB. . . . . *Dec 1991
Harker, Mr Christopher J BA(Oxon) . . . . . *§Apr 1978
Harvey, Mr Guy . . . . . May 1976
Henderson, Mr Nick C. . . . . *§Feb 1993
Hewitt, Mr A Jonathan BA(Oxon) . . . . . *§Oct 1980
Hockaday, Mr Geoffrey LLB; LLM . . . . . *§Dec 1978
Jackson, Mr Stephen Mark BA . . . . . *Apr 1980
Jenkins, Mr Martin H . . . . . *§May 1992
Kirkup, Mr Simon . . . . . *§Oct 1992
Kirtley, Ms Deborah LLB . . . . . *§Sep 1991
Lewis, Mr Simon J LLM; LLB . . . . . *§Sep 1986
Lowthian, Ms Katharine LLB(Newc) . . . . . *§Sep 1989
Lyall, Mr George . . . . . *§Aug 1995
Mantle, Ms Susan BA(Law) . . . . . *§Jan 1986
Marshall, Mr John Philip Birkett BA Newcastle Law Society Prize 1989 . . . . . *§Nov 1991
Nicolson, Mr Sean T BA. . . . . *§Oct 1992
North Lewis, Mr John S . . . . . *§Oct 1967
Painter, Mrs Barbara J LLB . . . . . *Oct 1983
Pass, Mr James H MA . . . . . *§Nov 1988
Pearce, Mr Mark D BA(Oxon); DipLaw(Bris). . . . . *Oct 1993
Pennie, Mr John A MA(Cantab) . . . . . *§Oct 1981
Ralph, Mr John D LLB. . . . . *§Oct 1990
Rewcastle, Mr David BA(Manc) . . . . . *Nov 1994
Rutherford, Ms Lyn M LLB . . . . . *§Nov 1972
Smith, Mr Jeremy D F MA(Cantab) . . . . . *Oct 1992
Smurthwaite, Mrs Jennifer BEd . . . . . *§Feb 1986
Straker, Mr Henry BA . . . . . *§Nov 1975
Tavroges, Miss Helen F LLB(Newc) . . . . . *§Oct 1983
Ward, Mr Ian BA . . . . . *§Oct 1983
Warwick, Mr Neil K . . . . . *§Nov 1993
Watts, Mr Simon Paul LLB; LLM(Cantab) . . . . . *§Oct 1991
Wilders, Mr James C LLB. . . . . *§Sep 1987
Williams, Mr Nigel T LLB . . . . . *Oct 1991
Wilson, Mr Richard M . . . . . *§Oct 1969
Wilson, Mr W Frederick BA(Dunelm) . . . . . *§Jun 1972
Wright, Mr A Graham P MA(Cantab) . . . . . *§Jun 1972
Asoc: Babcock, Mr Michael . . . . . Nov 1994
Carrick, Mr Stephen BA. . . . . Nov 1995
Clark, Mr Peter . . . . . *§Nov 1994
Dallow, Ms Sarah E. . . . . *§Feb 1993
Emmerson, Mr Nigel James. . . . . *§Nov 1994
Griffen, Mr Bruce . . . . . Nov 1991
Harrison, Mr Neil . . . . . *§Nov 1995
Moncrieff, Miss Elspeth C MA. . . . . *Nov 1991
Ramshaw, Mrs Deborah LLB(Hons). . . . . *Sep 1995
Smith, Ms Lorraine . . . . . *§Jan 1992
Tompkins, Mr Phil BA. . . . . Sep 1996
Wood, Mr Malcolm . . . . . *§Nov 1995
Ast: Bainbridge, Mr Stefan R BA(Hons) . . . . . *Sep 1999
Broomfield, Mr Adrian. . . . . Oct 1998
Brown, Mr Michael Arthur . . . . . *§Nov 1994
Claire-Jane, Miss Nicol LLB. . . . . Oct 1997
Coleman, Mr Paul R BA(Oxon) . . . . . Nov 1995
Davies, Mr E Peter BA(Law) . . . . . *Feb 1983
Fellowes, Ms Kim. . . . . Oct 1997
Ferguson, Mr David S. . . . . Oct 1998
Fisher, Mr Duncan J LLB . . . . . *Oct 1993
Grogan, Mr Jonathan D. . . . . *Sep 1996
Lewis, Ms Heather C LLB. . . . . *§Oct 1991
Maxwell, Mr Peter L. . . . . Oct 1998
Nutley, Ms Nicola F LLB. . . . . Jul 1997
Parbery, Mr Lee A. . . . . Oct 1998
Poore, Mr Martin . . . . . *§Nov 1995
Whymant, Ms Helen. . . . . *§Nov 1995
Con: Kenny, Prof Phillip H LLB; Dip Crim; LLM . . . . . *Dec 1975

DICKINSON DEES
One Trinity Broad Chare Newcastle upon Tyne Tyne & Wear NE1 2HF
Tel: 0844 984 1500 *Fax:* 0844 984 1501
E-mail: law@dickinson-dees.com
Office: London EC4, Newcastle upon Tyne, Stockton-on-Tees, York

DOBERMAN DEEN
Second Floor Suite 1 The Exchange Newcastle upon Tyne Tyne & Wear NE2 2JA
Tel: 0191 281 7468 *Fax:* 0870 487 4939
E-mail: naren@dobermandeen.co.uk
Office: Newcastle upon Tyne

STEPHEN DOBERMAN SOLICITOR ‡
42 Mitchell Avenue Jesmond Newcastle upon Tyne Tyne & Wear NE2 3LA
Tel: 0191 281 0333 *Fax:* 0870 487 4937
E-mail: sd@stephendoberman.co.uk
Office: Newcastle upon Tyne

ELTRINGHAM & CO ‡
37 Station Road North Forest Hall Newcastle upon Tyne Tyne & Wear NE12 7AR
Tel: 0191 266 5878 *Fax:* 0191 266 1642 *Dx:* 65020 FOREST HALL
E-mail: eltringham@cosolicitor.wanadoo.co.uk
List of partners: M Eltringham
Work: S1 W
SPr: Eltringham, Miss Margaret LLB . . . . . *Jul 1976

EVERSHEDS LLP
Central Square South Orchard Street Newcastle upon Tyne Tyne & Wear NE1 3XX
Tel: 0845 497 9797 *Fax:* 0845 497 6499
Dx: 724340 NEWCASTLE 24
Emergency telephone 01632 812619
Office: Birmingham, Cambridge, Cardiff, Ipswich, Leeds, London EC2, Manchester, Nottingham
Languages: Danish, French, German, Hindi, Italian, Norwegian, Russian, Swedish
Work: A1 B1 C1 C2 C3 D1 E F1 G H J1 K1 L M1 M2 N P R1 S1 T1 T2 Z(a,b,c,d,e,f,g,h,i,j,k,l,m,n,o,p,s)

HELEN MARGARET FERGUSON ‡
45 Montague Avenue Newcastle upon Tyne Tyne & Wear NE3 4JJ
Tel: 0191 284 8844

FREEMANS ‡
7 St Mary's Place Newcastle upon Tyne Tyne & Wear NE1 7PG
Tel: 0191 222 1030 *Fax:* 0191 222 1819
E-mail: info@freemanssolicitors.co.uk
List of partners: K M Freeman, M G Ryans, H Thompson
Work: C1 D1 E F1 J1 K1 N O Q R1 S1 W Z(l,r)
Emergency Action, Agency, Advocacy, Fixed Fee Interview, Legal Aid undertaken, Legal Aid Franchise and Member of Accident Line
Ptr: Freeman, Mr Keith M LLB. . . . . *Oct 1982
Ryans, Mr Michael G BA(Hons) . . . . . *§Nov 1994
Thompson, Miss Helen LLB. . . . . *Nov 1988
Ast: Calder, Mr Caroline Anne BA(Hons). . . . . Dec 2005
McIvor, Mr Martin . . . . . *Dec 2006

GIBSON & CO
77-87 West Road Newcastle upon Tyne Tyne & Wear NE15 6PR
Tel: 0191 273 3817 *Fax:* 0191 273 3818
Dx: 743060 NEWCASTLE 45
E-mail: jane.gibson@gibsons-law.com
Office: Hexham
Work: A1 A3 B1 B2 E J1 L N O Q S1 S2 T2 W Z(d,k,q)
Emergency Action, Agency, Advocacy and Fixed Fee Interview undertaken
Ptr: Bawn, Mr David Lee LLB(Hons); LPC . . . . . *Sep 2003
Gibson, Mr Anthony Gair MA . . . . . *Jan 1965
Gibson, Ms Jane Phoebe MA(Hons). . . . . *Nov 1994
Gibson, Mr Toby J BA(Hons) ♦ . . . . . *Oct 1995
Asoc: Burke, Mr Jonathon Michael LLB(Hons); LPC . . . . . Feb 2010
Pringle, Miss Claire LLB; BA(Hons) Sue Watts IP Award 2006 . . . . . *Sep 2009
Reed, Mr Michael LLB(Hons) . . . . . *Aug 2005

GOLDWATERS ‡
Broadgarth House 25-27 Quayside Newcastle upon Tyne Tyne & Wear NE1 3DE
Tel: 0191 232 2653 *Fax:* 0191 222 0730
Dx: 61075 NEWCASTLE UPON TYNE
Emergency telephone 0191 284 9112
E-mail: info@goldwaters.co.uk
List of partners: A T Malik
Languages: Punjabi
Work: B1 B2 C1 C2 D1 E F1 F2 J2 K1 K3 L N O P Q R1 S1 S2 V W Z(j,l,q)
Emergency Action, Agency, Advocacy, Fixed Fee Interview undertaken and Member of Accident Line
Ptr: Malik, Amjed T BA; MIEX(Grad); MA . . . . . *Mar 1984
Ast: Liddle, Mrs Deborah J BA(Hons); Dip(International Law); LLM . . . . . *Feb 1998

GORMAN HAMILTON ‡
Percy House Percy Street Newcastle upon Tyne Tyne & Wear NE1 4PW
Tel: 0191 232 1123 *Fax:* 0191 221 1689
Dx: 715140 NEWCASTLE 19
Emergency telephone 0845 601 1262
E-mail: office@gormanhamilton.co.uk
List of partners: D R Auld, T Gorman, D A Hamilton, D J Johnson, S McCourt
Office: Ipswich, Leeds
Languages: French
Work: N
Agency undertaken and Member of Accident Line
Ptr: Auld, Mr Dean Robert LLB . . . . . *Sep 1993
Gorman, Mr Tim BA Vice Chair - MASS. . . . . *Mar 1987
Hamilton, Mr David A BSc. . . . . *Dec 1991
Johnson, Mr David James LLB; CQSW(Newc) . . . . . *Dec 1990
McCourt, Mr Stephen . . . . . *Jul 1994

DAVID GRAY SOLICITORS ‡
Old County Court 56 Westgate Road Newcastle upon Tyne Tyne & Wear NE1 5XU
Tel: 0191 232 9547 *Fax:* 0191 230 4149
Dx: 61036 NEWCASTLE UPON TYNE
E-mail: lawyers@davidgray.co.uk
List of partners: M R Bishop, S C Grebby, B Hegarty, L McGivern, L Monkhouse, B J Rest, C G Routledge, M C Shaw, E Thomson, C J Veitch
Work: D1 D2 F1 G H K1 K2 K3 K4 L N Q S1 S2 W Z(d,g,h,i,m,o,p)
Emergency Action, Agency, Advocacy, Fixed Fee Interview, Legal Aid undertaken, Legal Aid Franchise and Member of Accident Line
Ptr: Bishop, Mr Michael R BA; LLM ♦ . . . . . *Jun 1989
Grebby, Ms Susan Carol LLB(Hons). . . . . Nov 1996
Hegarty, Mr Brian BSc . . . . . Dec 1998
McGivern, Miss Lucy LLB(Hons) . . . . . Nov 2001
Monkhouse, Ms Lesley LLB. . . . . Nov 1991
Rest, Ms Bryony J LLB(Hons); LLM; LPC . . . . . Sep 1996
Routledge, Ms Clare G BA . . . . . Dec 1978
Shaw, Ms Mary Caroline BA. . . . . *Oct 1984
Thomson, Ms Elspeth BA; MA . . . . . Sep 1994
Veitch, Mr Clifford John LLB. . . . . *Oct 1990

Asoc: Metcalf, Mrs Julia LLB. . . . . . . Mar 1993
Ast: Charlton, Ms Joanne . . . . Nov 2009
Cousins, Mr Jonathan Tacime Mackay LLB; LLM . . . Oct 2005
Cramond, Mr Ian James BA(Hons); CPE . . . . . Oct 2006
Gibson, Mr Michael Jude LLB; LPC . . . . . Jan 2004
Hale-Burt, Ms Cara . . . . Apr 2009
Hall, Mrs Janice Catherine LLB; DipLP; QLTT . . . . Jan 2002
Holmes, Mrs Helen Catherine LLB; PG Professional Skills . . . . . . Mar 2007
Hunter, Miss Nicola Jane BA(Hons); CPE; LPC . . . . *Jun 2001
Jackson, Miss Lisa LLB . . . . . . Apr 2001
Nichols, Mr Peter BA . . . . . . *Jun 1980
Szoltysek, Mr Peter BA; PGDipLaw; LPC Law Society Prize 2001 & 2002 . . . . . . *Apr 2005
Wilkinson, Miss Jane Clair BA; CPE; LPC. . . . . . Nov 2005

HAQUE & HAUSMANN SOLICITORS AND COMMISSIONER FOR OATHS
1st Floor 149 Beaconsfield Street Newcastle upon Tyne Tyne & Wear NE4 5JQ
Tel: 0191 272 5197 *Fax:* 0191 272 0317

HARRISON & ASSOCIATES ‡
Commercial Law Office 124 Osborne Road Newcastle upon Tyne Tyne & Wear NE2 2TE
Tel: 0191 281 6221
E-mail: johnharrison@harrison-associates.com
johnharrison@harrison-associates.com

HART JACKSON HALL SMITH ‡
Watson House Pilgrim Street Newcastle upon Tyne Tyne & Wear NE1 6QE
Tel: 0191 261 5181 *Fax:* 0191 222 1694
Dx: 61018 NEWCASTLE UPON TYNE
E-mail: trevorsmith@hjhs.uk.com
List of partners: M N Brannan, P A Hall, T Smith
Work: A1 B1 C1 C2 C3 D1 E F1 J1 K1 L M1 M2 N P Q R1 S1 T1 T2 W Z(e,f,h,l,p,q)
Emergency Action, Agency, Advocacy, Fixed Fee Interview, Legal Aid undertaken and Legal Aid Franchise
Ptr: Brannan, Mrs M Nuala LLB . . . . . . *Nov 1975
Hall, Mr Peter A. . . . . . . *Jan 1974
Smith, Mr Trevor LLB . . . . . . *Jun 1977

HASWELL & CORNBERG ‡
262a Chillingham Road Heaton Newcastle upon Tyne Tyne & Wear NE6 5LQ
Tel: 0191 276 5300 *Fax:* 0191 276 5451 *Dx:* 717420 BYKER 2
Emergency telephone 07626 256065
List of partners: D M Cornberg, R M Haswell
Work: G H
Agency, Advocacy, Fixed Fee Interview, Legal Aid undertaken and Legal Aid Franchise
Ptr: Cornberg, Mr David Maxwell LLB . . . . . *Jun 1999
Haswell, Mr Richard Metcalf BA. . . . . . *Oct 1991

HAY & KILNER ‡
Merchant House 30 Cloth Market Newcastle upon Tyne Tyne & Wear NE1 1EE
Tel: 0191 232 8345 *Fax:* 0191 261 7704
Dx: 61019 NEWCASTLE UPON TYNE
E-mail: lawyers@hay-kilner.co.uk
List of partners: G W T Bass, D L M Bradshaw, K A Carlisle, N A Dwyer, E A Gallagher, M R Harrison, N A Harrold, R Hart, K Hately, B N Howorth, J N James, R W Jones, S C O'Neill, I M Padmore, C R Sim, J C Slater, R M Soloman, R K Sparrow, P J Taylor, A C Williams
Office: Wallsend
Languages: French, German
Work: A1 A3 B1 B2 C1 C2 C3 D1 D2 E F1 F2 G H I J1 J2 K1 K2 L M1 M2 N O P Q R1 S1 S2 T1 T2 U2 V W Z(b,c,d,e,f,h,i,j,k,l,m,n,o,p,q,r,s,t,z)
Emergency Action, Agency, Advocacy, Legal Aid undertaken, Legal Aid Franchise and Member of Accident Line
Ptr: Bradshaw, Mr David L M BA Consul for Belgium & Luxembourg . . . . . . *§Mar 1976
Dwyer, Mr Neil A LLB(B'ham) . . . . . *Oct 1986
Gallagher, Ms Elizabeth A MA(Oxon) . . . . *Nov 1988
Harrold, Mr Neil A LLB . . . . . *Apr 1991
Hately, Mr Keith LLB(Hons) . . . . . Jan 1987
Howorth, Mr Bruce N LLB. . . . . . *Oct 1988
James, Mr John Nicholas MA(Cantab). . . . . *§Oct 1987
Jones, Mr Rodney W BA . . . . . . Jun 1983
Padmore, Mr Ian M BA . . . . . . *§Mar 1991
Sim, Mr Colin R LLB(L'pool). . . . . . *§Jan 1979
Soloman, Mr R Martin BA(Law) . . . . . *Apr 1978
Sparrow, Miss Rosamund K BA(Bris) . . . . *Oct 1982
Taylor, Mr Paul J LLB . . . . . . *May 1979
Williams, Mr Alun C LLB . . . . . . §Apr 1979
Asoc: Bentley, Mr John T . . . . . . Nov 1989
Grogan, Mrs Fiona K . . . . . . Sep 1996
Luke, Mr John Y MA(Cantab) . . . . . *§Jan 1966
Maddock, Mr Christopher J LLB(Hons)(Law & French).*Sep 1997
Matthews, Miss Nicola J LLB . . . . . *Sep 1997
O'Leary, Miss Jane Clare LLB(Hons) . . . . *Oct 1995
Sutton, Mr Graham BA . . . . . . *Mar 1986
Whitfield, Mrs Joanne C LLB . . . . . Sep 1996
Wilkes, Dr Nicholas A J MA; DipLP . . . . Sep 1998
Ast: Monk, Miss Claire A BA. . . . . . Sep 2001
Waters, Mr Jonathan Straughan LLB . . . . Sep 2000
Con: Dickinson, Mr Colin LLB(Dunelm) . . . . *§Oct 1966
Kilner, Mr John K LLB(Dunelm) Newcastle upon Tyne Prize . . . . . . *§Oct 1961
Williams, Mrs Gail Deputy District Judge . . . . §Jan 1971

HEMPSONS
West One Forth Banks Newcastle upon Tyne Tyne & Wear NE1 3PA
Tel: 0191 230 0669 *Fax:* 0191 231 2669 *Dx:* 715141 TYNE 19
E-mail: newcastle@hempsons.co.uk
Office: Harrogate, London WC2, Manchester

HOUSEMANS ‡
First Floor Cathedral Buildings Dean Street Newcastle upon Tyne Tyne & Wear NE1 1PG
Tel: 0191 232 1307 *Fax:* 0191 222 1561
Dx: 61004 NEWCASTLE UPON TYNE
List of partners: M R J Appleby, G Davison, N M Davison, C D Wilkie
Office: London EC3
Languages: French
Work: A1 C1 C2 E J2 L N O P Q R1 R2 S1 T1 T2 W Z(c,l)
Ptr: Davison, Mr Nigel M . . . . . . Oct 1987
Wilkie, Mr Colin D BA(Oxon) . . . . . Dec 1971
Ast: Maxwell, Mr Paul . . . . . . Aug 1998

IRWIN MITCHELL LLP
Gainsborough House 34-40 Grey Street Newcastle upon Tyne Tyne & Wear NE1 6AE
Tel: 0870 150 0100 *Fax:* 0191 230 2478
Office: Birmingham, Bristol, Leeds, London EC1, Manchester, Sheffield

JACKSONS LAW ‡
Central Square Forth Street Newcastle upon Tyne Tyne & Wear NE1 3PJ
Tel: 0191 580 0183 *Fax:* 0191 231 3921
Dx: 720200 NEWCASTLE UPON TYNE
E-mail: asmith@jacksons-law.com

JAMIESON & CO ‡
West House 3 Holly Avenue West Jesmond Newcastle upon Tyne Tyne & Wear NE2 2AR
Tel: 0191 281 0063 *Fax:* 0191 281 0060
Emergency telephone 07780 791130
E-mail: n.borthwick@j-b-law.co.uk
Languages: French, German, Indonesian
Work: B1 B2 C1 E G H K1 K3 N O Q S1 S2 W Z(l)
Agency, Fixed Fee Interview and Legal Aid undertaken
Ast: Murphy, Mr James LLB . . . . . . Jul 1998

KK & CO SOLICITORS ‡
165 West Road Bandi Sirrah House Newcastle upon Tyne Tyne & Wear NE15 6PQ
Tel: 0191 273 5733 *Fax:* 0191 273 0006
E-mail: ash.admin@kksols.co.uk

KSH LAW FIRM ‡
Norfolk House 90 Grey Street Newcastle upon Tyne Tyne & Wear NE1 6AG
Tel: 0191 232 5232 *Fax:* 0191 232 5253 *Dx:* 62562 JESMOND
Emergency telephone 0800 068 0501
E-mail: enquiries@kshlawfirm.com
List of partners: D C Harper
Work: C1 C2 E J1 N O Q R2 S1 S2 W Z(p,q)
Emergency Action, Agency, Advocacy, Fixed Fee Interview, Legal Aid undertaken and Member of Accident Line
Ptr: Harper, Miss Diana Claire LLB . . . . . *Jun 1981
Ast: Stephenson, Mr James BA . . . . . . Oct 2003

KIDD & SPOOR
(incorporating Paul Mernin & Co)
29 West Road Newcastle upon Tyne Tyne & Wear NE4 9PU
Tel: 0191 273 9217 *Fax:* 0191 272 0617
Dx: 65176 NEWCASTLE UPON TYNE 4
Emergency telephone 07623 979115
E-mail: law@ncl.kidd-spoor-solicitors.co.uk
Office: Whitley Bay
Work: C1 D1 E F1 G H K1 K3 L M1 N P S1 W Z(h)
Emergency Action, Agency, Advocacy, Fixed Fee Interview and Legal Aid undertaken
Ptr: Dilks, Mr William N BA ♦ . . . . . . *Jun 1987
Miller, Mr Nigel P LLB(Hons) . . . . . *Sep 1989
Stobart, Mrs E Sheila BA ♦ . . . . . *Jul 1980
Asoc: Russell, Miss Julia BA ♦. . . . . . *Sep 1998

KINGSTONS SOLICITORS ‡
141-143 Benwell Lane Benwell Newcastle upon Tyne Tyne & Wear NE15 6RT
Tel: 0191 226 0333

KIRBYS SOLICITORS ‡
The Grainger Prestwick Park Newcastle upon Tyne Tyne & Wear NE20 9SJ
Tel: 01661 867010 *Fax:* 01661 822281
List of partners: M Kirby
SPr: Kirby, Miss Margaret LLB . . . . . . Mar 1993
Ast: Kelly, Mr Jonathon . . . . . . May 1990

SHARON LANGRIDGE EMPLOYMENT LAWYERS ‡
Milburn House Dean Street Newcastle upon Tyne Tyne & Wear NE1 1LE
Tel: 0191 222 1221 *Fax:* 0191 222 1551
E-mail: law@sharonlangridge.co.uk
List of partners: S E Langridge
SPr: Langridge, Ms Sharon Eleanor BA; DipLSIR; CPE R T Richardson Prize 1992 . . . . . . *§Jul 1994

LATIF SOLICITORS ‡
Floor 1 Adamson House 65 Westgate Road Newcastle upon Tyne Tyne & Wear NE1 1SG
Tel: 0191 230 0646

LOWTHIAN GRAY FAMILY LAW ‡
20 Portland Terrace Newcastle upon Tyne Tyne & Wear NE2 1QQ
Tel: 0191 281 0082 *Fax:* 0191 281 5013
E-mail: kl@lowthiangray.co.uk

LUNDSTRAMS SOLICITORS ‡
Brampton House 10 Queen Street Newcastle upon Tyne Tyne & Wear ST5 1ED
Tel: 01782 660050

GEOFFREY LURIE ‡
32 St Marys Place Newcastle upon Tyne Tyne & Wear NE1 7PS
Tel: 0191 232 1800 *Fax:* 0191 232 3006
Dx: 61052 NEWCASTLE UPON TYNE
E-mail: advice@geoffreylurie.com
List of partners: A J Lipman
Work: B1 C1 D1 E F1 G H J1 K1 K3 L N O Q R1 S1 S2 T1 W Z(r)
Emergency Action, Agency, Advocacy, Fixed Fee Interview and Legal Aid undertaken
SPr: Lipman, Ms Amanda Jane BSc; LLB . . . . . *Apr 1997

JOHN McCARTHY & CO ‡
184 Chillingham Road Newcastle upon Tyne Tyne & Wear NE6 5BU
Tel: 0191 276 9500 *Fax:* 0191 265 0532 *Dx:* 717425 BYKER 2
E-mail: john.mccarthy@john-mccarthy.co.uk
List of partners: J F McCarthy
Work: E S1 S2 W
Ptr: McCarthy, Mr John F . . . . . . *§Jul 1969

MCDANIEL & CO ‡
1 & 2 Osborne Road Jesmond Newcastle upon Tyne Tyne & Wear NE2 2AA
Tel: 0191 281 4000 *Fax:* 0191 281 4333

MARINE LAW SOLICITORS ‡
65 Westgate Road Newcastle upon Tyne Tyne & Wear NE1 1SG
Tel: 0191 261 1567 *Fax:* 0870 460 2020

MARK GILBERT MORSE ‡
Greys Building 53 Grey Street Newcastle upon Tyne Tyne & Wear NE1 6EE
Tel: 0191 261 0096 *Fax:* 0191 261 2325
Dx: 61056 NEWCASTLE UPON TYNE
E-mail: lawyers@mgmlaw.co.uk
List of partners: J B Morse, G Owen, A L Swatts
Work: B1 B2 C1 C3 E F1 F2 J2 L N O P Q R1 R2 S1 S2 W Z(e,g,k,l,p,q,r)
Emergency Action, Agency, Advocacy, Fixed Fee Interview undertaken and Member of Accident Line
Ptr: Morse, Mr John B BSc . . . . . . Oct 1981
Owen, Mr Geoffrey LLB(Lond). . . . . . Dec 1975
Swatts, Ms Andrea Louise. . . . . . Feb 2003
Ast: Crawley, Mr Paul . . . . . . Mar 2008
Farrow, Mr Christopher John . . . . . Sep 2006
Moir, Mr Philip. . . . . . Sep 2006
Wright, Mr Peter Hedley. . . . . . Dec 2002
Con: Mark, Mr John L . . . . . . Jan 1970

MARRONS ‡
58 Jesmond Road West Newcastle upon Tyne Tyne & Wear NE2 4PQ
Tel: 0191 281 1304 *Fax:* 0191 212 0080 *Dx:* 62555 JESMOND
E-mail: law@marrons.co.uk
List of partners: D R Allan, R Allbeson, E A Malcolm, S M Porteus
Work: N
Fixed Fee Interview undertaken and Member of Accident Line
Ptr: Allan, Mr David R LLB. . . . . . *§Apr 1981
Allbeson, Mr Richard LLB . . . . . *Nov 1987
Malcolm, Ms Elaine A BA . . . . . *Sep 1989
Porteus, Mr Stephen M . . . . . . *Jun 1976
Ast: Deritis, Ms Vittoria Saturnina Louise. . . . . *Feb 1988
Storey, Mr Alan LLB. . . . . . Feb 1992
Thompson, Mr David Gordon BA(Law) . . . . *Nov 1983

MARSHALL GLOVER LIMITED ‡
The Quadrus Centre Woodstock Way Boldon Business Park Newcastle upon Tyne Tyne & Wear NE35 9PF
Tel: 0191 519 7460 *Fax:* 0191 519 7461
E-mail: david@marshallglover.com

MILLS & CO ‡
Milburn House Dean Street Newcastle upon Tyne Tyne & Wear NE1 1LE
Tel: 0191 233 2222 *Fax:* 0191 233 2220
E-mail: law@mills-co.com
List of partners: J H Boaden, A B Brown, G M Clayton, G B Mills, M J Smith
Languages: French, German, Italian
Work: B1 C1 C2 E I J1 L M2 O P Q R2 S1 Z(a,b,c,e,j)
Ptr: Boaden, Mr Jonathan H MA(Cantab) . . . . *Nov 1990
Brown, Mr Alistdair Barclay LLB(LSE). . . . . *May 1991
Clayton, Mr G Mark BA(Dunelm) . . . . . *Oct 1990
Mills, Mr Guy B BA(Oxon). . . . . . *Jul 1991
Smith, Mr Michael J BA(Oxon) . . . . . Nov 1988
Ast: Hudson, Mr Emlyn MA . . . . . . Sep 2000
Tookey, Miss Clare Fenella BA(Oxon); MA . . . . Oct 1996

MINCOFFS SOLICITORS LLP ‡
5 Osborne Terrace Newcastle upon Tyne Tyne & Wear NE2 1SQ
Tel: 0191 281 6151 *Fax:* 0191 281 8069 *Dx:* 62550 JESMOND
Emergency telephone 0191 281 6151
E-mail: info@mincoffs.co.uk
List of partners: A J Ainsley, H G Cave, P Dean, H B Gold, P Hughes, N M I Kidwell, J P Nicholson, M Smith
Languages: French, German, Gujarati, Hindi, Polish, Punjabi, Urdu
Work: A1 J1 K1 O R1 S1 W Z(l,r)
Emergency Action, Agency, Advocacy, Fixed Fee Interview, Legal Aid undertaken, Legal Aid Franchise and Member of Accident Line
Ptr: Ainsley, Ms Alison J. . . . . . . *Oct 2002
Cave, Mr Henry Graham BA(Hons) . . . . . *Apr 1998
Dean, Phil. . . . . . . Jul 1997
Gold, Mr Howard B TEP Newcastle Upon Tyne Law Society Prize; Liverpool Board of Legal Studies Prize . . *§Apr 1969
Hughes, Mr Paul LLB(Hons). . . . . . *Jun 1991
Kidwell, Mr Nigel M I LLB(Nott'm) . . . . . *May 1990
Nicholson, Mr John Phillip LLB; LPC . . . . *Sep 1998
Smith, Mr Michael LLB(Hons) . . . . . *Dec 1974
Asoc: Keating, Miss Sara Louise. . . . . . Nov 1987
Smith, Mrs Mary E BA . . . . . . *Dec 1977
Ast: Foster, Mr Matthew BSc(Criminology); CPE; LPC . . . Sep 2005
Hall, Mr Anthony Michael LLB. . . . . . *Jan 2007
Loomba, Kumud BA. . . . . . *May 1986
Roberts, Ms Susan Ann BA(Hons); MBA; CPE; PGDipLaw; FETC. . . . . . *Sep 2003

MUCKLE LLP ‡
Time Central 32 Gallowgate Newcastle upon Tyne Tyne & Wear NE1 4BF
Tel: 0191 211 7777 *Fax:* 0191 211 7788
Dx: 61011 NEWCASTLE UPON TYNE
E-mail: enquiries@muckle-llp.com
List of partners: J Birkett, A Cawkwell, J W Combe, A J Craig, T R Craig, A J Davison, J R Devine, L Duffy, J P Dunkley, A S Grisedale, K Hately, A E Hill, S J Howe, G Hunter, S W Irvine, P A Johnstone, R Langley, N J C Loose, C J Maddock, W McKay, S T McNicol, A J N McPhillips, R J Phillips, P H Robinson, C R Swinhoe, K Turnbull, J B Wainwright, H B Welch
Languages: French, German, Spanish
Work: A1 B1 C1 C2 C3 D1 E F1 I J1 K1 K2 L M1 M2 O P Q R1 R2 S1 U2 W X Z(b,c,e,j,k,l,o,p,q,s,t,u,w,z)
Emergency Action, Agency, Advocacy and Fixed Fee Interview undertaken
Ptr: Birkett, Mrs Judith LLB(Hons) . . . . . Oct 1989
Cawkwell, Mr Andrew LLB(Hons) . . . . . Sep 2003
Combe, Mr Jonathan W LLB . . . . . *Nov 1989
Craig, Mrs Alexandra Jane MA(Hons); CPE; LPC . . . *Sep 2000
Craig, Mr Timothy Robert LLB(Hons); LSF. . . . . *Oct 1995
Davison, Mr Andrew John LLB . . . . . Oct 1985
Devine, Mr John Richard BA(Hons)(Law) . . . . *Mar 2001
Duffy, Ms Louise MA(Oxon); DipLaw Birmingham Law Society Prize (LPC Results). . . . . . *Sep 1996
Dunkley, Mr Jonathan P BA. . . . . . *§Jun 1979
Grisedale, Mr Alan Stuart LLB. . . . . . Aug 1997

Hately, Mr Keith LLB(Hons) . . . . Jan 1987
Hill, Mr Adrian Edward LLB . . . . *Oct 1983
Howe, Mrs Susan J LLB; CPE . . . . Nov 1989
Hunter, Mrs Gillian BA(Hons); CPE; LPC . . . . . . *Sep 1998
Irvine, Mr Stewart W BA(Hons); CPE; LPC . . . . . *Sep 1998
Johnstone, Mr Paul A LLB Price Waterhouse Dissertation Prize . . . . *Oct 1996
Langley, Mr Robert MA(Oxon); FCIArb . . . . *Oct 1979
Loose, Miss Nicola Jane Carrington BSc(Hons) . . . Sep 2004
McNicol, Mr Stephen T LLB(Hons) . . . . *§Oct 1995
McPhillips, Mr Anthony J N BA(Hons)(Law) . . . . . *Feb 1988
Maddock, Mr Christopher J LLB(Hons)(Law & French) *Sep 1997
McKay, Mr William BA(Hons) . . . . Nov 2002
Phillips, Mr Robert J LLB . . . . *Dec 1990
Robinson, Mr Peter Hume LLB(Hons) . . . . Nov 1995
Swinhoe, Mr Craig Robert LLB . . . . Sep 2001
Turnbull, Mr Kevin BA . . . . Sep 1998
Wainwright, Mr Jason Brian BA(Hons); CPE; LPC . . . Oct 1996
Welch, Mr Hugh B MA(Cantab) Evan Lewis Thomas Law Scholarship . . . . *Jan 1983

Asoc: Armstrong, Mr James John LLB . . . . Sep 2006
Clare, Mr Philip LLB . . . . *Sep 2005
Clegg, Mr Peter David BSc; CPE; LPC . . . . *Sep 2004
Davison, Mrs Joanne LLB . . . . *Sep 2004
Donabie, Mrs Jill Catherine BSc(Hons); CPE; LPC . . Sep 2003
Hewison, Miss Vicky LLB . . . . Sep 2006
Hicks, Mr Adrian Thomas . . . . May 1998
Hubbard, Mrs Aimee Victoria LLB; LLM; Diplome d'Etudes Juridiques Francaises . . . . Aug 2005
Maloney, Mr Kevin Simeon LLB(Hons); LPC . . . . . Sep 2000
Quayle, Ms Jennifer Robertson LLB(Hons) . . . . . Feb 2001
Sutton, Mrs Kate Samantha BA(Hons); CPE; LPC . . . Sep 2000

Ast: Bone, Mr Jonathan Paul LLB; LLM . . . . *Aug 2006
Cross, Miss Catherine BA(Hons); CPE; LPC . . . . . Nov 2001
Caddle, Miss Vanessa Jane BA(Hons) . . . . Nov 2009
Chesser, Miss Rachel Louise BA; CPE; LPC . . . . . Sep 2008
Cutmore, Ms Claire LLB(Hons) . . . . Jan 2001
Davies, Mr Tim BA(Hons); PGDipLaw; LPC . . . . . . Sep 2001
Forster, Miss Sarah Louise LLB(Hons) . . . . Oct 1999
Foxley, Miss Emma Rose LLB; BA(Hons) . . . . Sep 2011
Green, Mr Stephen Michael BA(Hons) . . . . Apr 2008
Greenwood, Mr Steven Peter LLB Irwin Mitchell International Pro Bono Scholarship 2007 . . . . Sep 2010
Hunter, Mrs Alexandra Helen LLB . . . . Sep 2005
McKay, Mrs Carolyn Jane LLB . . . . Jul 2004
Malik, Mr Imran Khalid LLB . . . . *Sep 2011
Nixon, Mr Richard LLB(Hons) . . . . Sep 2010
Pearson, Mr Anthony James BA(Jt Hons); LLB . . . . Sep 2010
Robinson, Mrs Deborah LLB(Hons) . . . . *Apr 2005
Ross, Mr Alan Hector BA . . . . Oct 2005
Rowe, Mrs Kathryn Julia BA; CPE; LPC . . . . Sep 2004
Sergison, Mrs Amy Natasha BA(Hons)(History); GDL; LPC Newcastle Law Society Prize for GDL - Best Performance by a Self-Funded Student 2005 . . . . Sep 2009
Smith, Mr Mark Robert MA(Hons) . . . . Oct 2002
Swansey, Miss Jennifer . . . . Sep 2006
Swindells, Mrs Jessica LLB(Hons) . . . . Apr 2007
Takiar, Mr Neville LLB(Hons) . . . . Sep 2009
Welch, Mr James William LLB . . . . Sep 2009
Wilson, Mr Martin LLB(Hons) . . . . *Sep 2008

NEIL MCQUEEN DUNCAN & EGNER ‡

Floor A Milburn House Dean Street Newcastle upon Tyne Tyne & Wear NE1 1LF
Tel: 0191 232 7469 *Fax:* 0191 222 1571
Dx: 716747 NEWCASTLE 20
E-mail: info@solicitorsupontyne.co.uk
List of partners: F G K Egner, M G K Egner
Work: A1 C1 C2 E F1 F2 J1 J2 K1 K2 K3 K4 L N O P Q R1 R2 S1 S2 W Z(c,e,f,j,k,l,p,q,r,w)
Agency, Advocacy and Fixed Fee Interview undertaken
Ptr: Egner, Mr F Giles K LLB ♦ . . . . *Dec 1968
Egner, Mr Mark Giles Kirtley LLB ♦ . . . . *Jul 2001

O'NEILL SOLICITORS ‡

23 Grey Street Newcastle upon Tyne Tyne & Wear NE1 6EE
Tel: 0191 232 9008 *Fax:* 0191 232 0961
Emergency telephone 07774 641062
E-mail: enquiries@stainsbyoneill.com
List of partners: K M J O'Neill
Work: B1 D1 G H K1 K3 Q
Agency, Advocacy, Fixed Fee Interview and Legal Aid undertaken
SPr: O'Neill, Mr Kieran M J LLB ● . . . . *Oct 1993

OPTIMA LEGAL SERVICES LIMITED

One Carliol Carliol Square Newcastle upon Tyne Tyne & Wear NE1 6UF
Tel: 0844 571 6700 *Fax:* 0191 211 1801
Dx: 61288 NEWCASTLE UPON TYNE 8
Office: Bradford

PATTERSON GLENTON & STRACEY

Milburn House Dean Street Newcastle upon Tyne Tyne & Wear NE1 1NR
Tel: 0191 232 8628 *Fax:* 0191 261 1306
Dx: 61007 NEWCASTLE UPON TYNE
E-mail: wjd@pgslaw.co.uk
Office: South Shields (2 offices)
Work: A1 C1 E F1 G H J1 K1 L N O Q S1 S2 V W Z(l,p)
Emergency Action, Agency, Advocacy, Fixed Fee Interview, Legal Aid undertaken, Legal Aid Franchise and Member of Accident Line
Ptr: Caisley, Leslie A BA(Hons) . . . . *§Jun 1981
Dryden, Mr William J BA(Dunelm) . . . . *§Oct 1989

PEARSON CAULFIELD ‡

Newgate Chambers 1 Newgate Street Newcastle upon Tyne Tyne & Wear NE1 5RE
Tel: 0191 261 8878 *Fax:* 0191 222 1259
Dx: 61067 NEWCASTLE UPON TYNE 1
Emergency telephone 0191 239 2418
List of partners: K L Graham, J P Oxnard, L F Pearson
Work: D1 E F1 G H J1 K1 L N Q R1 S1 V W Z(l)
Emergency Action, Agency, Advocacy, Fixed Fee Interview, Legal Aid undertaken and Member of Accident Line
Ptr: Graham, Ms Karen Lorraine LLB . . . . *Oct 1984
Oxnard, Mr John Paul LLB . . . . *Jun 1992
Pearson, Mr Lewis F BSc . . . . *Mar 1980
Ast: Kivlehan, Mr Kevin Michael LLB . . . . *Mar 1996

SAMUEL PHILLIPS LAW FIRM ‡

Gibb Chambers 52 Westgate Road Newcastle upon Tyne Tyne & Wear NE1 5XU
Tel: 0191 232 8451 *Fax:* 0191 232 7664
Dx: 61028 NEWCASTLE UPON TYNE
Emergency telephone 0191 279 8280 / 285 3101
E-mail: admin@samuelphillips.co.uk
List of partners: R M Gibson, J E Goldstein, S U Grant, E J Pybus, B N Speker
Languages: Cantonese, French, German
Work: A1 B1 C1 C2 C3 D1 D2 E F1 G H J1 K1 K2 L M1 M2 N O P Q R1 S1 T1 T2 V W Z(c,d,e,i,j,l,m,p,q,r)
Emergency Action, Agency, Advocacy, Fixed Fee Interview, Legal Aid undertaken, Legal Aid Franchise and Member of Accident Line
Ptr: Gibson, Mr Robert Maxwell LLB ♦ Deputy District Judge; ACAS Arbitrator . . . . *§Nov 1984
Goldstein, Mrs Jennifer E BA ♦ . . . . *Feb 1992
Grant, Mr Stuart U BA ★ . . . . *§Dec 1978
Pybus, Mr Edward John MA(Cantab) Harry Strouts Prize . . . . *§Aug 1973
Speker, Mr Barry Neil DL ● London University 2nd Year Prize Part time Chairman Industrial Tribunal; Past President Newcastle Law Society . . . . *§Jun 1971
Ast: Dick, Miss Kathryn Julia BA(Econ); CPE; LPC . . . . *Sep 2004
Gallagher, Ms Elizabeth A MA(Oxon) . . . . *Nov 1988
Gillespie, Ms Katharine A . . . . May 2004
Hunter, Ms Claire BA; CPE; LPC ● . . . . *Jul 1999
Lomas Fletcher, Miss Sally Louise LLB Part time Family Law Prize on LPC (Northumbria University) . . . . . . Sep 2002
Muir, Miss Gillian Morag Kirsten LLB ♦ . . . . *Oct 1997
Routledge, Miss Helen MA; CPE; LPC . . . . Sep 1997
Simmons, Miss Angela LLB . . . . *Sep 2004
Stobart, Mr Alan BA(Hons) . . . . Sep 1990
Storey, Mr Michael Antony LLB; BA(Hons) . . . . . . Aug 1997
Winter, Mr Rex Alexander . . . . Apr 2000

MORAG POLMEAR COMMERCIAL LAWYER ‡

89-91 Jesmond Road Jesmond Newcastle upon Tyne Tyne & Wear NE2 1NH
Tel: 0191 281 8050 *Fax:* 0191 281 5020
E-mail: morag@polmear.co.uk
List of partners: M Polmear
SPr: Polmear, Ms Morag LLB . . . . May 1991

MICHAEL PURDEN SOLICITOR ‡

Wards Building 31-39 High Bridge Newcastle upon Tyne Tyne & Wear NE1 1EW
Tel: 0191 232 1006

QUANTUM LAW LLP ‡

Dean Court 22 Dean Street Newcastle upon Tyne Tyne & Wear NE1 1PG
Tel: 0845 226 9008 *Fax:* 0191 247 8888
E-mail: info@quantumlawllp.co.uk

R TOBY RAIMES ‡

Churchill House 12 Mosley Street Newcastle upon Tyne Tyne & Wear NE1 1DE
Tel: 0191 230 8086
List of partners: R T Raimes
SPr: Raimes, Mr R Toby BA . . . . Jan 1987

RICHMONDS ‡

53 Westgate Road Newcastle upon Tyne Tyne & Wear NE1 1TS
Tel: 0191 232 2155 *Fax:* 0191 232 6156
Dx: 61020 NEWCASTLE UPON TYNE
E-mail: richmonds.solicitors@dial.pipex.com
List of partners: M G B Baker, C J Lowes, P Smith
Office: Newcastle upon Tyne
Languages: Cantonese, Mandarin
Work: C1 D1 E G H J1 K1 L S1 S2 T1 W Z(d,h,l,o)
Emergency Action, Agency, Advocacy, Fixed Fee Interview and Legal Aid undertaken
Ptr: Baker, Mr Michael G B . . . . *§Dec 1969
Lowes, Miss Christine J BA . . . . *Oct 1986
Smith, Mr Peter PhD . . . . *§Oct 1977
Ast: Chin, Kenny K L BSc . . . . Apr 1996
Short, Ms Corinne S LLB . . . . *Apr 1996

RICHMONDS

369 Benton Road Four Lane Ends Newcastle upon Tyne Tyne & Wear NE7 7EE
Tel: 0191 270 1711 *Fax:* 0191 270 0731 *Dx:* 61020 NEWCASTLE
E-mail: richmonds.solicitors@dial.pipex.com
Office: Newcastle upon Tyne
Work: E G H K1 M1 N P S1 W Z(a,l,o)
Emergency Action, Agency, Advocacy, Fixed Fee Interview and Legal Aid undertaken
Ptr: Smith, Mr Peter PhD . . . . *§Oct 1977

ROBINSON & MURPHY ‡

13 Grey Street Newcastle upon Tyne Tyne & Wear NE1 6EE
Tel: 0191 230 5023 *Fax:* 0191 230 2783
E-mail: staff@robinsonmurphy.co.uk
List of partners: J P Probert, N Robinson
Work: K1 N O Z(q)
Emergency Action, Agency, Advocacy, Fixed Fee Interview, Legal Aid undertaken and Member of Accident Line
Ptr: Probert, Mr John P BA(Hons) . . . . *Apr 1991
Robinson, Mr Nigel BSc(Econ) . . . . Jun 1980

ROW & SCOTT ‡

98 West Road Newcastle upon Tyne Tyne & Wear NE4 9QA
Tel: 0191 273 9929 *Fax:* 0191 272 3477
Dx: 65180 NEWCASTLE UPON TYNE 4
Emergency telephone 01665 711493
List of partners: B T Row, J R Scott
Office: Consett, Morpeth
Work: A1 B1 C1 C2 C3 D1 E F1 G H J1 K1 L M1 M2 N P R1 S1 T1 T2 V W
Emergency Action, Agency, Advocacy, Fixed Fee Interview and Legal Aid undertaken
Ptr: Row, Mr Barry T BA . . . . *Jul 1978
Scott, Mr J Richard . . . . Dec 1978
Ast: Docherty, Mr Peter Joseph LLB(Hons) . . . . *Mar 1997

RUSSELL JONES & WALKER

Block C Holland Park Holland Drive Newcastle upon Tyne Tyne & Wear NE2 4LD
Tel: 0191 323 3000 *Fax:* 0191 204 6001
Dx: 61275 NEWCASTLE UPON TYNE 1
E-mail: enquiries@rjw.co.uk
Office: Birmingham, Bristol, Cardiff, London WC2, Manchester, Sheffield, Wakefield
Work: G H N Z(r)
Emergency Action, Agency, Advocacy, Legal Aid undertaken, Legal Aid Franchise and Member of Accident Line
Ast: Buzzard, Ms Rowena . . . . Nov 1999
Duckworth, Mr Andrew S LLB; MA . . . . *Jan 1989
Leonard, Ms Samantha . . . . Dec 1994
Shakespeare, Miss Susan LLB; BA . . . . *Mar 1995

SN LAW ‡

Churchill House 12 Mosley Street Newcastle upon Tyne Tyne & Wear NE1 1DE
Tel: 0191 230 8119 *Fax:* 0191 230 8091
E-mail: sylvia@snlaw.co.uk

SHAW & CO ‡

3 Indian Kings House 31 The Quayside Newcastle upon Tyne Tyne & Wear NE1 3DE
Tel: 0800 019 1248
E-mail: info@shawandco.com
Office: Doncaster, Telford
Ast: Brown, James . . . . Feb 2004

SHORT RICHARDSON & FORTH LLP ‡

4 Mosley Street Newcastle upon Tyne Tyne & Wear NE1 1DE
Tel: 0191 232 0283 *Fax:* 0191 261 6956
Dx: 61037 NEWCASTLE UPON TYNE
E-mail: info@srflegal.co.uk
List of partners: T Berg, M T Green, T J Luckhurst-Matthews, D M Richardson, J Van Zyl, M D Winthrop
Languages: French, German
Work: A3 B1 B2 C1 C2 E F1 F2 G J1 J2 L O P Q R1 R2 S1 S2 T2 U2 Z(c,e,k,l,p,q,t,y)
Emergency Action, Agency and Advocacy undertaken
Ptr: Berg, Mr Timothy BSc(Hons); LLB ♦ . . . . *§Nov 1997
Green, Mr Mark Thomas LLB . . . . *§Jun 1999
Luckhurst-Matthews, Mr Timothy J LLB . . . . *Jan 1986
Richardson, Mr David M LLB . . . . *§Jun 1973
Van Zyl, Mr Jean-Pierre . . . . *§Mar 2003
Winthrop, Mr Max D BA; ACIArb . . . . *§May 1991
Asoc: Gibson, Mr Christopher . . . . Mar 2004
Swan, Mr Andrew LLB(Hons) . . . . Jul 2002
Ast: Choudry, Miss Azra LLB . . . . Nov 2007
Wilkinson, Miss Claire BA . . . . *Aug 2007

SINGLETON WINN MCDERMOTT SOLICITORS ‡

232 Shields Road Byker Newcastle upon Tyne Tyne & Wear NE6 1DQ
Tel: 0191 265 8817 *Fax:* 0191 276 0335 *Dx:* 60950 BYKER
Emergency telephone 07626 841203
E-mail: lawyers@swmcd.sagehost.co.uk
List of partners: F I McDermott, D H Singleton
Work: D1 D2 G H K1 V W Z(e,l,m)
Emergency Action, Agency, Advocacy, Fixed Fee Interview, Legal Aid undertaken and Legal Aid Franchise
Ptr: McDermott, Mr Frazer I LLB(Newc) ★ . . . . *Nov 1988
Singleton, Mr David H . . . . *Apr 1982
Ast: Bradbeer, Mrs Susan Jane . . . . *Jun 1996
Kilpatrick, Mr James C LLB . . . . *Dec 1980
Saunders, Mrs Kathryn Elizabeth Ruth LLB(Hons) . . *May 1995

SINTONS LLP ‡

The Cube Barrack Road Newcastle upon Tyne Tyne & Wear NE4 6DB
Tel: 0191 226 7878 *Fax:* 0191 226 7850
Dx: 715139 NEWCASTLE UPON TYNE 19
E-mail: law@sintons.co.uk
List of partners: A S J F Ashman, M R Collen, A G Dawson, J C Dias, M S Dobbin, A Evans, S J Freeman, T R Gray, K J Land, P A Liddle, F Matthewson, J C McCabe, H A Parker, M Quigley, K L Riddell, K Simms, S Smith, T Smith, A K Walker, C J Welch, L Winskell, C M Wood
Languages: French
Work: A1 B1 C1 C2 D1 E F1 I J1 J2 K1 K2 K3 K4 L M1 N O P Q R1 R2 S1 S2 T2 U2 W X Z(b,c,d,e,h,j,l,q,x,z)
Advocacy, Fixed Fee Interview undertaken and Member of Accident Line
Ptr: Ashman, Mr Angus S J F . . . . Nov 1992
Collen, Mr Matthew Robin BA(Hons) . . . . *Nov 1993
Dawson, Mr Alan G LLB(Hull) . . . . *§Oct 1982
Dias, Mr James C LLB(Leeds) . . . . *§Mar 1972
Dobbin, Mr Mark S BA . . . . Oct 1999
Evans, Mr Anthony . . . . Jan 1999
Freeman, Mr Steven J . . . . *Oct 1993
Gray, Mr Timothy R MA(Cantab) . . . . *§Jul 1978
Land, Mr Keith John BA(Hons)(Sheff) . . . . *Jan 1997
Liddle, Mr Paul Anthony LLB . . . . *§Apr 1980
McCabe, Mr James C LLB(Manc) Baker Ellis Law Prize . . . . *Nov 1991
Matthewson, Mr Frank LLB(Newc) . . . . *§Oct 1983
Parker, Mrs Hilary A LLB; LLM . . . . *Oct 1985
Quigley, Mr Mark BA; MA . . . . *Jan 1994
Riddell, Miss Kathryn Louise LLB; BA . . . . *Oct 1995
Simms, Mrs Karen BA . . . . *Oct 1995
Smith, Ms Sarah . . . . Jan 1994
Smith, Mr Timothy LLB(Hons) . . . . Sep 1991
Walker, Mr Andrew K LLB(Newc) . . . . *Oct 1984
Welch, Mr Christopher J LLB(Newc) . . . . *Oct 1989
Winskell, Ms Lucy LLB . . . . *Jan 1987
Wood, Mrs Catherine Mary LLB . . . . Jan 1986
Asoc: Aitken, Miss Phillipa LLB . . . . *Sep 2000
Burns, Mr Ian LLB . . . . *Nov 1997
Corcoran, Mr Jamie BSc(Hons) . . . . *Jan 2001
Garbutt, Ms Julie . . . . Sep 2000
Gray, Miss Emma LLB . . . . Jan 2003
Hennessey, Ms Susan BA . . . . *Oct 1984
Hutchinson, Miss Julie LLB . . . . Jan 2002
Lowdon, Mrs B Jane BA . . . . *Oct 1976
Maddison, Ms Suzanne Claire LLB . . . . *Nov 2002
Maskery, Miss Amanda . . . . Jan 2003
Peace, Miss Laura . . . . Jan 2004
Whitfield, Mrs Joanne C LLB . . . . Sep 1996
Willits, Mrs Joanne LLB . . . . Jan 1999
Winter, Mr Gavin . . . . Jul 1999
Ast: Campbell, Ms Elaine . . . . Mar 2008
Dye, Mr Adrian LLB . . . . Jan 2006
Loomba, Alok . . . . Sep 2004
Pandit, Mr Pawan Kumar LLB(Hons) . . . . *Oct 2002
Patton, Mr Christopher Neil . . . . Sep 2005
Williams, Mr Daniel Lloyd LLB . . . . *Sep 2007
Woodford, Mr Paul . . . . Aug 2004

SMITH & COPSEY

1st Floor 6 Market Street Newcastle upon Tyne Tyne & Wear NE1 6JF
Office: Wallsend

See p112 for the Key to Work Categories & other symbols

STANFORD & LAMBERT ‡
(incorporating C E Layne & Son)
4th Floor Abbey House 7-9 Bigg Market Newcastle upon Tyne Tyne & Wear NE1 1UN
Tel: 0191 232 6226 *Fax:* 0191 221 0392
Dx: 61053 NEWCASTLE UPON TYNE
Emergency telephone 0191 257 5160
E-mail: stanfordandlambert@tiscali.co.uk
List of partners: J F J Lambert
Work: B1 C1 D1 E F1 G H J1 K1 L N Q S1 W Z(l)
Emergency Action, Agency, Advocacy, Fixed Fee Interview, Legal Aid undertaken and Member of Accident Line
Ptr: Lambert, Mr John F J LLB(Newc) . . . . *§Jul 1969
Ast: Smith, Miss Brenda Anne MA(Oxon) . . . . *Feb 1987
Snowdon, Miss Lynn LLB . . . . *Sep 2008

STEPHENS MCDONALD & ROBSON ‡
8 Saville Row Newcastle upon Tyne Tyne & Wear NE1 8JE
Tel: 0191 232 0675 *Fax:* 0191 230 2790
Dx: 61269 NEWCASTLE UPON TYNE
Emergency telephone 07850 232067
List of partners: G B Stephens, J Taylor
Languages: French, German
Work: D1 E F1 G H J1 K1 L N Q S1 V W Z(l)
Emergency Action, Agency, Advocacy, Fixed Fee Interview, Legal Aid undertaken, Legal Aid Franchise and Member of Accident Line
Ptr: Stephens, Mr Gregg Bradley LLB . . . . *Oct 1990
Taylor, Mr Jeffrey LLB(Hons) . . . . *Jan 2002

TAIT FARRIER GRAHAM
73 Adelaide Terrace Benwell Newcastle upon Tyne Tyne & Wear NE4 8BN
Tel: 0191 272 3713 *Fax:* 0191 226 1795
E-mail: info@gatesheadsolicitors.co.uk
Office: Berwick-upon-Tweed, Gateshead
Work: B2 D1 G H J2 K1 K2 L N O Q S1 V X Z(q)
Emergency Action, Agency, Advocacy, Fixed Fee Interview and Legal Aid undertaken

THOMAS & MEIGHEN ‡
175 Kirkwood Drive Kenton Newcastle upon Tyne Tyne & Wear NE3 3BE
Tel: 0191 214 0355 *Fax:* 0191 214 5355
List of partners: A Meighen
Work: N
Emergency Action, Advocacy, Fixed Fee Interview, Legal Aid undertaken and Member of Accident Line
Ptr: Meighen, Mr Alan LLB . . . . *Sep 1979

C J THOMPSON ‡
20 Lansdowne Terrace Newcastle upon Tyne Tyne & Wear NE3 1HP
Tel: 0191 226 8998

THOMPSONS (FORMERLY ROBIN/BRIAN THOMPSON & PARTNERS)
St Nicholas Building St Nicholas Street Newcastle upon Tyne Tyne & Wear NE1 1TH
Tel: 0191 269 0400 *Fax:* 0191 232 2324 *Dx:* 68940 NEWCASTLE 9
Office: Belfast, Birmingham, Bristol, Cardiff, Chelmsford, Dagenham, Derby, Harrow, Leeds, Liverpool, London SW19, London WC1, Manchester, Middlesbrough, Nottingham, Plymouth, Sheffield, South Shields, Southampton, Stoke-on-Trent, Swansea, Wolverhampton
Work: J1 N Z(p)
Legal Aid undertaken and Member of Accident Line
Ptr: Allan, Ms Janet H LLB(Newc) . . . . *Oct 1982
Patten, Mr Keith LLB(Leeds) . . . . *Nov 1985
Prudham, Mr Bryan M LLB . . . . *Dec 1988
Ast: Bray, Mr Michael J LLB . . . . *Jul 1990
James, Mr Andrew BA(Hons) . . . . *Nov 1993
Laffey, Mr Michael LLB . . . . *§Oct 1996
McDonald, Mr Andrew J BA(Hons) . . . . *Sep 1990

WAKEEL PARTNERSHIP ‡
4 Fowberry Crescent Newcastle upon Tyne Tyne & Wear NE4 9XH
Tel: 0191 275 3777 *Fax:* 0191 275 3888
E-mail: rhussain@wakeelpartnership.co.uk

WALLERS ‡
30 Cloth Market Newcastle upon Tyne Tyne & Wear NE1 1EE
Tel: 0191 261 2281 *Fax:* 0191 232 1007
E-mail: wallerslaw@aol.com
List of partners: W L Brown, J M Gladders, J Sibbald, M J Smith
Work: B1 C1 E F1 J1 K1 L N O Q R1 R2 S1 S2 T1 U2 W Z(h,i,q,r)
Agency, Advocacy, Fixed Fee Interview undertaken and Member of Accident Line
Ptr: Brown, Mr William Leslie LLB(Hons). . . . . *Oct 1991
Gladders, Mr John M . . . . *May 1976
Sibbald, Mr John MA(Cantab) . . . . *Jul 1968
Smith, Mr Michael J BA . . . . *Mar 1984
Asoc: Capstaff, Mrs Hazel Ann . . . . Mar 1999
Ast: Moir, Mr Charles G . . . . *Aug 1977
Small, Ms Louise . . . . Apr 2001

WARD HADAWAY ‡
(incorporating Wheldon Houlsby & Scott; Keenlyside & Forster)
Sandgate House 102 Quayside Newcastle upon Tyne Tyne & Wear NE1 3DX
Tel: 0191 204 4000 *Fax:* 0191 204 4001
Dx: 730360 NEWCASTLE 30
E-mail: legal@wardhadaway.com
List of partners: R Atkin, J C Baker, D M Charlton, P Christian, I H Collinson, D Douglass, S K Elliott, S T Errington, A Facer, L A Fairclough, J M P Flower, D Glendinning, S T Graham, J Harrison, C T Hewitt, B K Hodgson, P Hornsey, M A Hulls, J A Keeble, N J Martin, K Myers, R J Nankervis, R O'Donnell, C N O'Loughlin, W P Reekie, N Robson, A Shiel, R A Thompson, J Thornhill, T Toomey, R Wrighton
Languages: French, German, Spanish
Work: A1 A2 A3 B1 B2 C1 C2 C3 D1 D2 E F1 F2 G I J1 J2 K1 K2 K3 L M1 M2 N O P Q R1 R2 S1 S2 T1 T2 U2 V W X Z(b,c,d,e,f,g,h,j,k,l,m,n,o,p,q,r,u,z,za)
Emergency Action, Agency, Advocacy, Fixed Fee Interview, Legal Aid undertaken and Legal Aid Franchise
Ptr: Atkin, Mr Robin LLB. . . . . Sep 1998
Baker, Ms Judith Christine BA; MSc. . . . . *Sep 1996
Charlton, Mr Damien M LLB(Hons) . . . . Oct 1998
Christian, Mr Paul MA. . . . . Nov 1998
Collinson, Mr Ian Howard LLB. . . . . §Sep 1981
Douglass, Mr David . . . . *Nov 1974
Elliott, Mr Stephen K LLB(Hons). . . . . *Sep 1998
Errington, Mr Simon Timothy LLB . . . . Dec 1992
Facer, Mr Andrew LLB; TEP. . . . . *Nov 1986
Fairclough, Ms Lesley Anne LLB . . . . *Nov 1992
Flower, Mr Jonathan Michael Peter LLB; LLM . . . . . *Oct 1994
Glendinning, Mr David LLB . . . . *Jun 1974
Graham, Mr Stephen T . . . . *Mar 1980
Harrison, Miss Julie BA . . . . *Feb 1984
Hewitt, Mr Colin Thompson LLB. . . . . *§Sep 1983
Hodgson, Mr Bernard K BA(Law & French) . . . . . *§Oct 1984
Hornsey, Mr Peter BA. . . . . *Dec 1991
Hulls, Mr Martin Ashley LLB. . . . . *Oct 1983
Keeble, Mr Jeffrey Alan LLB(Leeds). . . . . *Dec 1978
Martin, Mr N Jamie BA . . . . *§Jan 1980
Myers, Ms Kathryn LLB . . . . Aug 1995
Nankervis, Mr Roger J MA(Oxon) . . . . *Oct 1984
O'Donnell, Mr Roger LLB(Hons). . . . . *Apr 1992
O'Loughlin, Mr Christopher Nicholas MA . . . . . . *Oct 1982
Reekie, Mr W Paul . . . . *Oct 1983
Robson, Mr Neil. . . . . Dec 1977
Shiel, Mr Alex. Oct 1984
Thompson, Mr Robert Alfons LLB . . . . *Jun 1989
Thornhill, Mr Joe LLB . . . . *Sep 1993
Toomey, Mr Tim. . . . . May 1986
Wrighton, Mr Ralph . . . . Dec 1976
Asoc: Spence, Ms Deborah Ellen LLB . . . . *Nov 1994

ALASDAIR WATSON & CO ‡
139 Oakfield Road Whickham Newcastle upon Tyne Tyne & Wear NE16 5RZ
Tel: 0191 488 4521 *Fax:* 0191 488 7082
Emergency telephone 0191 488 4521
E-mail: awatson@elaw.org.uk
List of partners: A J P Watson
Work: D1 G H K1 S1 V W
Emergency Action, Agency, Advocacy, Fixed Fee Interview, Legal Aid undertaken and Legal Aid Franchise
Ptr: Watson, Mr Alasdair J P TD LLB Information Commissioner's North-East Agent . . . . *Dec 1980

WATSON BURTON LLP ‡
1 St James' Gate Newcastle upon Tyne Tyne & Wear NE99 1YQ
Tel: 0845 901 2100 *Fax:* 0845 901 2040 *Dx:* 61009 NEWCASTLE
E-mail: enquiries@watsonburton.com
List of partners: R Adams, R Arnot, A Brown, H Cave, N C D Craig, M Dalzell, G Fahy, R D Freeman-Wallace, B Frith, A Gardner, R C P R Gordon, C Graham, G M Hall, D Hardman, D Jenkins, D Jones, D M Jones, W Kemp, A Knight, M W Lawton, M Lazenby, E Meikle, R O' Donovan, R O'Donovon, M Ord, R J Palmer, G Parker-Fuller, D Reid, B Riley, S Scougall, C Storey, M Whitehead, S Wilson
Office: Leeds, London EC3
Work: A3 B1 B2 C1 C2 C3 D1 E F1 F2 I J1 J2 L M1 M2 N O P Q R1 R2 S1 S2 T1 T2 U1 U2 V W X Z(b,c,d,e,f,h,i,j,k,l,m,n,o,p,q,s,u,w,z,za)
Emergency Action, Agency, Advocacy, Fixed Fee Interview, Legal Aid undertaken, Legal Aid Franchise and Member of Accident Line
Ptr: Adams, Mr Robin . . . . Sep 1999
Arnot, Mr Richard. . . . . Oct 1992
Brown, Mr Anthony MA(Edin) . . . . *Nov 1993
Cave, Mr Henry. . . . . Apr 2009
Craig, Mr Nicholas C D . . . . *§Dec 1971
Freeman-Wallace, Mr Richard Dominic . . . . *Mar 1982
Frith, Mr Barney. . . . . Apr 1981
Gardner, Ms Andrea . . . . Sep 1998
Gordon, Mr Roderick C P R LLB; MCIArb . . . . . . *Feb 1988
Graham, Mr Christopher LLB . . . . *Jan 1993
Hall, Ms Gillian M MA(Cantab) . . . . *Oct 1985
Hardman, Mr David LLB. . . . . *§Apr 1978
Jenkins, Mr David. . . . . Sep 2001
Jones, Mr David M . . . . *May 1976
Kemp, Mr Warren. . . . . Aug 2002
Knight, Mrs Anne-Marie LLB; ACIArb . . . . Dec 1993
Lawton, Mr Mark W LLB . . . . *May 1988
Meikle, Mr Edward . . . . Sep 1999
Ord, Mr Michael. . . . . Nov 1982
Palmer, Mr Richard J LLB. . . . . Feb 1992
Parker-Fuller, Mr George LLB. . . . . Jan 2004
Reid, Mr Duncan . . . . Oct 1996
Riley, Mr Bryan LLB(Sheff) . . . . *Jun 1980
Scougall, Mr Simon . . . . Sep 2001
Storey, Mr Chris. . . . . Apr 1979
Whitehead, Mr Mark. . . . . Sep 1997
Wilson, Ms Sarah. . . . . Sep 2004
Dir: O'Donovan, Mr Robert . . . . Oct 1976
Asoc: Anderson, Mr Kevin. . . . . Sep 2001
Cambridge, Mr Eric . . . . Sep 1997
Clasby, Mr Nigel . . . . Nov 1994
Farrell-Knowles, Ms Julie . . . . Nov 2000
Harrison, Mr James. . . . . Feb 2003
Motherway, Ms Helena . . . . Jan 1996
Pickersgill, Mr Richard Newcastle upon Tyne Prize . *§Aug 1972
Spires, Mr David . . . . Mar 2000
Turner, Jacqueline . . . . Sep 2003
Ast: Applegarth, Miss Joanne . . . . Jan 2005
Barker, Mr Ian Blount BA . . . . Jun 1992
Barr, Mr Guy . . . . Oct 2006
Brady, Ms Katrina. . . . . Sep 2007
Campbell, Miss Amanda-Jayne BA(Hons); GDL; LPC . Aug 2006
Dalkin, Miss Jill . . . . Sep 2009
Kemp, Mr Patrick . . . . Sep 2005
Laird, Miss Roisin LPC . . . . Oct 2009
McCloud, Ms Sarah. . . . . Apr 2006
McLellan, Mr Stephen. . . . . Sep 2007
Milburn, Miss Helen Louise LLB; LPC . . . . Sep 2007
Rye, Ms Caroline . . . . Sep 2008
Scott, Ms Helen. . . . . Sep 2007
Shuker, Mr Michael . . . . Sep 2005
Stanwix, Ms Sara . . . . Mar 2008
Waller, Ms Claire . . . . Sep 2007
Wigham, Mr Paul . . . . Jan 2008
Wills, Mr Tom . . . . Sep 2008
Con: Sowler, Mr Thomas Richard Holland TD MA(Oxon); FTII Thesis Prize (CIOT) 1992 . . . . *May 1992

WAUGH MOODY & MULCAHY ‡
116 Pilgrim Street Newcastle upon Tyne Tyne & Wear NE1 6SQ
Tel: 0191 232 8107 *Fax:* 0191 230 4248
Dx: 61046 NEWCASTLE UPON TYNE
List of partners: M L Avery, J C Moody
Office: Blaydon-on-Tyne
Languages: French
Work: E K4 L S1 S2 T2 W Z(l)
Ptr: Avery, Mr Michael L LLB(Sheff) . . . . *Jun 1970
Moody, Miss J Carole LLB(Leeds). . . . . *Dec 1974

ALAN WILSON SOLICITORS ‡
Lynnwood Business Centre Lynnwood Terrace Newcastle upon Tyne Tyne & Wear NE4 6UL
Tel: 0191 273 2555 *Fax:* 0191 226 0876
E-mail: a.wilsonsolicitors@btconnect.com

WINN SOLICITORS LIMITED ‡
Brinkburn Street Byker Newcastle upon Tyne Tyne & Wear NE6 1PL
Tel: 0191 276 1000

NEWENT, Gloucestershire

MADGE LLOYD & GIBSON
22-24 Church Street Newent Gloucestershire GL18 1PP
Tel: 01531 820088 *Fax:* 01531 821120 *Dx:* 701391 NEWENT
Office: Gloucester (2 offices)
Languages: French
Work: A1 C1 D1 D2 E K1 K3 K4 L S1 S2 V W Z(d,x)
Agency, Fixed Fee Interview and Legal Aid undertaken
Ptr: Jones, Mr Robert D P . . . . *Jan 1981

NEWHAVEN, East Sussex

BARWELLS
19 High Street Newhaven East Sussex BN9 9PU
Tel: 01273 514213 *Fax:* 01273 516731 *Dx:* 39150 NEWHAVEN
E-mail: advice@barwells.com
Office: Eastbourne, Peacehaven, Seaford
Work: A1 B1 C1 C2 C3 D1 E F1 K1 L N O Q R1 S1 T1 T2 V W Z(c,l)
Emergency Action, Advocacy, Fixed Fee Interview, Legal Aid undertaken and Member of Accident Line
Ptr: Elliott, Mr William James . . . . *Nov 1978
Con: Harris, Mr David J LLB . . . . *Dec 1991

NEWMARKET, Suffolk

BENDALL & SONS ‡
23 High Street Newmarket Suffolk CB8 8LY
Tel: 01638 661116 *Fax:* 01638 561305 *Dx:* 50502 NEWMARKET
E-mail: law@bendallandsons.co.uk
List of partners: A J Geddes, J R Spencer
Office: Mildenhall
Languages: French
Work: A1 B1 C1 C2 C3 D1 D2 E F1 F2 J1 K1 K2 K4 L M1 M2 N O P Q R1 R2 S1 S2 T1 T2 V W Z(b,c,d,e,f,i,j,k,l,m,o,p,t)
Emergency Action, Agency, Fixed Fee Interview, Legal Aid undertaken and Legal Aid Franchise
Ptr: Geddes, Mr Andrew J. . . . . *§Oct 1967
Spencer, Mrs Jacqueline Rae . . . . *May 2000

EDMONDSON HALL ‡
25 Exeter Road Newmarket Suffolk CB8 8AR
Tel: 01638 560556 *Fax:* 01638 561656 *Dx:* 50521 NEWMARKET
Emergency telephone 07971 411345
E-mail: solicitors@edmondsonhall.com
List of partners: M A Edmondson, A Hall, D Hargreaves, S Watson
Languages: French, German, Spanish
Work: A2 B1 C1 C2 D1 E F1 J1 K1 K2 K3 L N O Q S1 S2 W Z(c,d,f,j,k,l,w)
Emergency Action, Agency, Advocacy and Fixed Fee Interview undertaken
Ptr: Edmondson, Mr Mark Andrew LLB . . . . *Mar 1991
Hall, Ms Anna-Marie LLB . . . . *Oct 1989
Hargreaves, Mrs Deborah LLB . . . . *Oct 2004
Watson, Miss Sarah LLB . . . . *Aug 1998
Asoc: Clemence, Mr Matthew Edward BA(Hons)(Law). . . *May 2001
Ast: Fotiou, Mr Adam Philios. . . . . Oct 2010
McGlennon, Miss Dominica . . . . *Sep 2011
Con: Wadham, Mr Justin John Wyndham BA(Hons) . . . . *Jun 1979

ROYTHORNES LLP
Agriculture House Willie Snaith Road Newmarket Suffolk CB8 7SN
Tel: 01638 561320 *Fax:* 01638 564139
E-mail: roythorne@roythorne.co.uk
Office: Nottingham, Peterborough, Spalding
Languages: Greek, Italian
Work: A1 A2 C1 C2 E F1 J1 J2 K1 K3 L M1 M2 O P Q R1 S2 T1 T2 W Z(l,n,o,p,q)
Agency, Advocacy and Fixed Fee Interview undertaken
Ptr: Smith, Mr Graham C H MA; LLB(Cantab) Notary Public . . . . *§Nov 1974

RUSTONS & LLOYD ‡
Beaufort House 136 High Street Newmarket Suffolk CB8 8JP
Tel: 01638 661221 *Fax:* 01638 661732 *Dx:* 50501 NEWMARKET
E-mail: mail@rustonsandlloyd.com
List of partners: M J Drake, J A Hatter, N F W Longford, C D Pitchers, A J Scott, B C Taylor
Work: A1 B1 C1 C2 C3 D1 E F1 G J1 J2 K1 L M1 N O P Q R1 S1 S2 T1 T2 V W Z(d,k,l,s)
Advocacy, Fixed Fee Interview, Legal Aid undertaken and Legal Aid Franchise
Ptr: Drake, Mr Michael John. . . . . *§Dec 1973
Hatter, Ms Julie Alexandria BA(Hons); CPE; LPC . . §Sep 2006
Longford, Mr Nicholas F W MA(Oxon). . . . . *§Apr 1979
Pitchers, Mr Christopher D BA . . . . *§Dec 1980
Scott, Mr Anthony James . . . . §Dec 2001
Taylor, Mr Barry C. . . . . *§Dec 1989

WHATLEY LANE ‡
13 High Street Newmarket Suffolk CB8 8LX
Tel: 01638 561133 *Fax:* 01638 669289 *Dx:* 50509 NEWMARKET
E-mail: mailbox@whatleylane.co.uk
List of partners: M C Whatley
Office: Bury St Edmunds
Languages: Chinese, Spanish
Work: F1 G H K1 N Q S1 W
Emergency Action, Agency, Advocacy, Fixed Fee Interview, Legal Aid undertaken and Member of Accident Line
SPr: Whatley, Mr Michael C . . . . *Nov 1971
Asoc: Chui, Karen. . . . . Aug 2006
Ast: England, Mr Alan . . . . Jun 1971

NEWPORT, Isle of Wight

ELDRIDGES ‡
36 St James Street Newport Isle of Wight PO30 1LF
Tel: 01983 524741 *Fax:* 01983 521421 *Dx:* 56356 NEWPORT (IOW)
E-mail: info@eldridges.co.uk
List of partners: D Burton, M J Friend, S B Gubbins, A P Jessup, G H Noble, W G Pimloit, S L Prince, P J Smith, J A Suggett
Office: Freshwater, Ryde
Languages: French
Work: A1 C1 E F1 F2 J1 K1 K3 K4 L N O Q R2 S1 S2 T1 T2 W Z(l)
Emergency Action undertaken
Ptr: Burton, Mr David . . . . . *§Jan 1985
Friend, Mrs Marian J BA(Hons)(Law) . . . . . *§Jun 1977
Gubbins, Miss Sandie Beverley . . . . . *§Dec 1991
Jessup, Mr Adam Peter . . . . . *§Dec 2001
Pimloit, Mr William Geoffrey . . . . . *§Jan 1971
Prince, Miss Sarah Louise . . . . . *§Nov 2001
Ast: Joyner, Mr Timothy R B LLB(Hons) . . . . . *§Jan 2003

GLANVILLES
(incorporating Buckell & Drew; Damant & Sons)
The Courtyard St Cross Business Park Monks Brook Newport Isle of Wight PO30 5BF
Tel: 01983 527878 *Fax:* 01983 821629 *Dx:* 56352 NEWPORT (IOW)
E-mail: newport@glanvilles.co.uk
Office: Fareham, Havant
Work: A1 B1 C1 C2 C3 D1 E F1 G H J1 K1 L M1 M2 N O P Q R1 S1 T1 T2 V W X Z(a,c,d,h,l)
Emergency Action, Agency, Advocacy, Fixed Fee Interview, Legal Aid undertaken, Legal Aid Franchise and Member of Accident Line
Ptr: Bateman, Mr Paul R . . . . . *Mar 1982
Lambie, Mr Graham J R LLB(B'ham) Notary Public . . *§Jul 1973
Ledger, Miss Susan E LLB . . . . . *Oct 1983
Samuelson, Mr Colin K LLB Notary Public. . . . . *Oct 1984

GURNEY-CHAMPION & CO
37 Quay Street Newport Isle of Wight PO30 5BQ
Tel: 01983 522665
E-mail: info@championlawyers.co.uk
Office: Portsmouth
Work: A1 B1 C1 D1 E F1 G H J1 K1 L M1 N P R1 S1 T1 V W Z(b,c,d,h,i,j,k,l,m,s)
Emergency Action, Agency, Advocacy and Fixed Fee Interview undertaken
Ptr: Gurney-Champion, Mr Nicholas C A LLB . . . . . *§Oct 1986

JEROMES ‡
98 High Street Newport Isle of Wight PO30 1BD
Tel: 01983 522664 *Fax:* 01983 527424 *Dx:* 56355 NEWPORT (IOW)
E-mail: clivewiggins@jeromelaw.co.uk
List of partners: A J Whittle, C L Wiggins
Office: Sandown, Shanklin
Work: A1 A3 B1 C1 C2 D1 D2 E F1 G H J1 K1 K2 K3 K4 L N O Q R1 S1 S2 V W Z(b,c,e,j,q)
Emergency Action, Agency, Advocacy and Legal Aid undertaken
Dir: Wiggins, Mr Clive L MA; FCIArb ★ Deputy District Judge . . . . . *Jun 1979
Ast: Spoors, Mr Michael LLB. . . . . Dec 2006

RJR SOLICITORS
19-21 Quay Street Newport Isle of Wight PO30 5BA
Tel: 01983 526924 *Fax:* 01983 821249 *Dx:* 56353 NEWPORT (IOW)
Emergency telephone 01983 526924
E-mail: newport@rjr.co.uk
Office: Freshwater, Ryde
Work: C1 D1 D2 E F1 G H J1 K1 K3 K4 N O Q S1 S2 T2 V W

ROACH PITTIS ‡
62-66 Lugley Street Newport Isle of Wight PO30 5EU
Tel: 01983 524431 *Fax:* 01983 525971 *Dx:* 56350 NEWPORT (IOW)
E-mail: aph@roachpittis.co.uk
List of partners: B W Arnett, A N Bradshaw, A P Holmes, P P Ledger, C A Prew, K Verrinder
Work: A1 A2 B1 B2 C1 C2 D1 D2 E F1 F2 G H J1 K1 L N O P Q R1 R2 S1 S2 T1 T2 V W Z(c,d,e,h,j,k,l,m,n,p,q,r,y)
Emergency Action, Agency, Advocacy, Fixed Fee Interview, Legal Aid undertaken, Legal Aid Franchise and Member of Accident Line
Ptr: Arnett, Mr Barry W BA(Hons)(Law) . . . . . *Apr 1978
Bradshaw, Mr Anthony N LLB. . . . . *Nov 1978
Holmes, Mr Anthony P BA(Business Law). . . . . *§Apr 1975
Ledger, Mr Philip P BA(Law) . . . . . *§Feb 1980
Prew, Mr Christopher A LLB. . . . . *Oct 1981
Verrinder, Mr Keith BSc(Econ) Deputy Coroner for Isle of Wight . . . . . Dec 1976
Ast: Bell, Mrs Janet Elizabeth BA(Leeds). . . . . Oct 1982
Peckham, Mr Lee Richard LLB(Hons) . . . . . Oct 2003
Ricks, Mr Peter John LLB District Judge (Tribunals) . *Dec 1976
Spoors, Mr Michael LLB. . . . . Dec 2006

KEITH TRAVES ‡
John Lamb House 66 Upper St James Street Newport Isle of Wight PO30 1LQ
Tel: 01983 525988 *Fax:* 01983 528265
Emergency telephone 01983 281117
E-mail: keith@keithtraves.fsnet.co.uk
List of partners: K Traves
Work: A1 A2 C1 E F1 F2 G J1 J2 L N P Q R1 S1 S2 W Z(c,e,j,l)
SPr: Traves, Mr Keith . . . . . Jun 1971

TWELL & CO ‡
3rd Floor 48 Lugley Street Newport Isle of Wight PO30 5HD
Tel: 01983 539999 *Fax:* 01983 539988
E-mail: rjp@twellandco.co.uk

VECTIS LAW SOLICITORS ‡
St Thomas House 17 St Thomas Square Newport Isle of Wight PO30 1SL
Tel: 01983 533006 *Fax:* 0845 833 8912 *Dx:* 56359 NEWPORT (IOW)
E-mail: info@vectislaw.com

PAUL WHEELER SOLICITOR ‡
69b High Street Newport Isle of Wight PO30 1BA
Tel: 01983 533938 *Fax:* 01983 527156

NEWPORT, Gwent

ATKINSON & CO ‡
Transport House 1 Cardiff Road Newport NP20 1EH
Tel: 01633 251118 *Fax:* 01633 262902
Dx: 33223 NEWPORT (GWENT)
Emergency telephone 01633 266524
E-mail: julie@atkinson-solicitors.com
List of partners: B E Atkinson, J P Couch
Work: D1 G H J1 K1 L N Q S1 V W
Emergency Action, Agency, Advocacy, Legal Aid undertaken and Legal Aid Franchise
Ptr: Atkinson, Ms Bridget E LLB . . . . . *Apr 1980
Couch, Miss Joanna P LLB(Hons). . . . . *Sep 1996

CITY LEGAL ‡
Summit House 5 Gold Top Newport NP20 4PG
Tel: 01633 259844 *Fax:* 01633 211190
E-mail: enquiries@citylegal.net

COLBORNE COULMAN & LAWRENCE ‡
Victoria Chambers 11 Clytha Park Road Newport NP20 4PB
Tel: 01633 264194 / 264196 *Fax:* 01633 841146
Dx: 33204 NEWPORT (GWENT)
List of partners: D T Bowen, W A James
Work: B1 C1 C2 C3 E F1 J1 K1 K3 L N P R1 S1 W Z(c,d,l,t)
Emergency Action, Agency, Advocacy and Fixed Fee Interview undertaken
Ptr: Bowen, Mr David Thomas Coroner; Under Sheriff . . *§Jul 1967
James, Ms Wendy A LLB Deputy Coroner; Deputy Under Sheriff . . . . . *Dec 1990

CONVEY UK SOLICITORS LIMITED ‡
Maxwell Chambers 34-36 Stow Hill Newport NP20 1JE
Tel: 01633 261223 *Fax:* 01633 261261
Dx: 151063 NEWPORT (GWENT)

DAC BEACHCROFT
Sovereign House Imperial Way Newport NP10 8UH
Tel: 0844 980 0400 *Fax:* 0844 980 0500
Dx: 743343 NEWPORT (GWENT) 16
Office: Birmingham, Bristol, Leeds, London EC3 (3 offices), London EC4 (2 offices), Manchester (2 offices), Newcastle upon Tyne, Winchester
Languages: Chinese, French, German, Icelandic, Italian, Mandarin, Welsh
Work: B1 C1 C3 E F1 I J1 M1 M2 O P Q Z(b,c,e,f,j,k,n,o,p,w)
Emergency Action, Agency, Advocacy, Fixed Fee Interview and Legal Aid undertaken

DARWIN GRAY
Merlin House No1 Langstone Business Park Newport NP18 2HJ
Tel: 01633 415440 *Fax:* 01633 415441
E-mail: bdarwin@darwingray.com
Office: Cardiff

DRISCOLL YOUNG SOLICITORS ‡
33 Stow Hill Newport NP20 1JH
Tel: 01633 266999 *Fax:* 01633 266888

T S EDWARDS & SON ‡
55 Bridge Street Newport NP20 4SR
Tel: 01633 257166 *Fax:* 01633 246731
Dx: 33219 NEWPORT (GWENT)
E-mail: mail@tsedwards.co.uk
List of partners: J M Bracey, M H Llewellyn-Jones, S G Neale, H L Thomas
Office: Hengoed
Emergency Action, Agency, Legal Aid undertaken and Member of Accident Line
Ptr: Bracey, Mr Jeremy M LLB(Hons) . . . . . *§Sep 1982
Llewellyn-Jones, Mr Michael H BA(Cantab) Chairman of the Social Security Tribunal; Chairman of the Child Support Appeal Tribunal. . . . . Mar 1965
Neale, Mr Stephen G LLB. . . . . *Jun 1981
Thomas, Mr Hugh L BA. . . . . Dec 1977

KEITH EVANS & COMPANY ‡
14 Clytha Park Road Newport NP20 4PB
Tel: 01633 257721 *Fax:* 01633 221066
Dx: 33213 NEWPORT (GWENT) 1
Emergency telephone 01633 221675
E-mail: office@keith-evans.co.uk
Office: Abergavenny, Cwmbran

EVERETT TOMLIN LLOYD & PRATT ‡
28-30 Stow Hill Newport NP20 1TL
Tel: 01633 251801 *Fax:* 01633 251840
Dx: 33210 NEWPORT (GWENT)
E-mail: newport@etlp.co.uk
List of partners: G W Edwards, A W Harkus, A C O'Brien, C R Pennant, G H Sandeman
Office: Pontypool
Ptr: Pennant, Mr Christopher Rogers MA(Cantab) Chapter Clerk to St Woolos Cathedral . . . . . *Jan 1969

FWD LAW ASSOCIATES ‡
Clifton Chambers 12-13 Clifton Road Newport NP20 4EW
Tel: 01633 660440 *Fax:* 01633 662070
E-mail: info@fwdlaw.com
List of partners: C R Williams
Languages: Hindi, Punjabi, Urdu, Welsh
Work: A3 B1 C1 D2 E J1 K1 K2 K3 L N O Q S1 S2 W Z(e,f,k,p)
Agency and Advocacy undertaken
Ptr: Williams, Mr Charles R . . . . . Feb 1998
Asoc: Dunn, Ms Catherine LLB . . . . . *Jul 1999
Ast: Goldsworthy, Miss Rebecca Jane LLB. . . . . *Nov 2004
Headford, Ms Cheryl LLB . . . . . *§Nov 1994
Stewart, Mr Darren Lee LLB. . . . . Oct 2004
Stolzenewbung, Ms Fiona Jane LLB. . . . . Feb 2007

GARTSIDES ‡
Brand House 2 Corn Street Newport NP20 1DJ
Tel: 01633 213411 *Fax:* 01633 266541
Dx: 148383 NEWPORT (GWENT) 11
E-mail: gglencross@gartsides.com
List of partners: C L Davies, H Knights, S Lewis, L A Rhead, M Thomas, S M Williams
Office: Abergavenny, Ebbw Vale
Work: B1 C1 D1 D2 E F1 G H J1 J2 K1 K2 K3 L M1 N O P Q R1 S1 S2 T1 V W X Z(i,m,q,r)
Emergency Action, Agency, Advocacy, Fixed Fee Interview, Legal Aid undertaken and Member of Accident Line
Ptr: Davies, Mr Christopher L LLB. . . . . *Jun 1973
Knights, Ms Hayley LLB(Hons) . . . . . Mar 2001
Lewis, Mrs Sian LLB . . . . . *Nov 1983
Rhead, Ms Lynda A LLB . . . . . Feb 1988
Thomas, Mr Matthew LLB. . . . . Jun 2001

GRANVILLE-WEST CHIVERS & MORGAN
Somerset Chambers 1 Tynewydd Terrace Newbridge Newport NP11 4LS
Tel: 01495 243268 *Fax:* 01495 248611 *Dx:* 86800 NEWBRIDGE
E-mail: newbridge@granville-west.co.uk
Office: Abertillery, Blackwood, Caldicot, Pontypool, Risca
Work: D1 D2 E F1 G H J1 K1 L M1 N P Q R1 S1 S2 V W Z(l,r)
Emergency Action, Agency, Advocacy, Fixed Fee Interview, Legal Aid undertaken and Legal Aid Franchise
Ptr: Harrison, Mr Colin. . . . . *Jun 1976
Ast: Jones, Mr David A LLB(Wales) . . . . . *Nov 1985
Roberts, Mrs Janet S LLB. . . . . May 1977

HARDING EVANS LLP ‡
Queens Chambers 2 North Street Newport NP20 1TE
Tel: 01633 244233 *Fax:* 01633 246453
Dx: 148380 NEWPORT (GWENT) 11
Emergency telephone 07966081992
E-mail: info@hevans.com
List of partners: R J Allison, G A S Bellavia, A J Christie, S L Edwards, M J Jenkins, P V Kent, C M Price, K M Thomas, D Wilde, W Williams
Languages: Welsh
Work: A1 A2 A3 B1 B2 C1 C2 C3 D1 D2 E F1 F2 G H I J1 J2 K1 K2 K3 K4 L N O P Q R1 R2 S1 S2 T1 T2 U1 U2 V W X Z(b,c,d,e,f,g,h,j,k,l,m,o,p,q,r,t,u,w,x,y,za)
Emergency Action, Agency, Advocacy, Fixed Fee Interview, Legal Aid undertaken, Legal Aid Franchise and Member of Accident Line
Ptr: Allison, Mr Richard John LLB . . . . . *Apr 1996
Bellavia, Mr Guiseppe A S LLB(Hons). . . . . *Oct 1986
Christie, Mr Andrew James BA(Hons). . . . . *Mar 1990
Edwards, Mrs Suzanne L LLB. . . . . *Dec 1980
Jenkins, Mr Michael John LLB. . . . . *Oct 1988
Kent, Mrs Pauline V LLB . . . . . *Apr 1976
Price, Miss Ceri M LLB(Wales) . . . . . *Apr 1984
Thomas, Mr Kenneth M LLB . . . . . *Nov 1994
Wilde, Daniel . . . . . *Sep 2004
Williams, Wyn. . . . . *Sep 2003
Asoc: Fletcher, Mrs Jayne Alison LLB . . . . . *Jan 1982
Georgious, Ms Samantha LLB. . . . . Jan 1993
Nash-Harding, Mrs Andrea . . . . . Aug 2005
Protheroe, Miss Angela Barbara LLB(Hons). . . . . *Jun 2000
Tudball, Ms Helen Claire LLB . . . . . *Dec 1991
Ast: Allen, Mrs Alia LLB . . . . . Oct 2009
Bettosi, Ms Francesca LLB . . . . . Sep 2007
Davies, Mr James Alexander LLB; LLM(Criminal Justice); LPC . . . . . Sep 2011
Downes, Ms Siobhan LLB. . . . . Mar 2010
Jenkins, Mr Benjamin LLB. . . . . Mar 2010
Kelly, Mr Dominic BA(Hons). . . . . Sep 1994
Lindsey, Mr Paul LLB . . . . . Mar 2006
Rhydderch, Ms Leah LLB . . . . . Sep 2007
Sage, Mr Michael . . . . . Jun 1979
Spedding, Miss Debra Jane LLB(Hons); LPC Dip . . *Sep 2006
Sprawson, Ms Emma LLB. . . . . Jun 2009
Strong, Miss Samantha Jane LLB(Hons); LPC Law Society LPC Prize - Outstanding Student. . . . . Aug 2006
Uren, Mrs Sara Haf BA(Hons). . . . . Mar 2010
Waters, Mr Ben LLB. . . . . Jul 2007
Watkins, Ms Lauren LLB . . . . . Sep 2010

HORNBY BAKER JONES & WOOD ‡
13 Clytha Park Road Newport NP20 4PB
Tel: 01633 262848 *Fax:* 01633 267847
Dx: 33209 NEWPORT (GWENT)
E-mail: nathanh@hbjwlaw.co.uk
List of partners: D C Coles, A C Collingbourne, N J Hennah, D A Trott
Office: Chipping Sodbury
Work: B2 D1 E F1 G H J1 J2 K1 K3 L N O Q S1 S2 V W Z(k,q,r)
Emergency Action, Agency, Advocacy, Fixed Fee Interview, Legal Aid undertaken and Legal Aid Franchise
Ptr: Coles, Mr David Charles LLB ★. . . . . *Oct 1986
Collingbourne, Mr Andrew C BA. . . . . *May 1989
Hennah, Mr Nathan John PGDipLaw . . . . . *Mar 2008
Trott, Mr David Alan. . . . . *Dec 1987

HOWELLS
29 Bridge Street Newport NP20 4BG
Tel: 01633 227960 *Fax:* 01633 227961
Dx: 33207 NEWPORT (GWENT)
E-mail: info@howellslegal.com
Office: Caerphilly, Cardiff, Swansea, Talbot Green
Work: C2 D1 E J1 K1 K3 N Q S1 S2 W
Agency, Fixed Fee Interview and Legal Aid undertaken

JACKLYN DAWSON ‡
Equity Chambers John Frost Square Newport NP20 1PW
Tel: 01633 262952 *Fax:* 01633 213924
Dx: 33201 NEWPORT (GWENT)
E-mail: enquiries@jacklyndawson.co.uk
List of partners: C J T Gwilliam, C J G Hill, J A James, M R Lane, T M S Russen, K L Smith, D N Whittaker
Office: Monmouth
Languages: French, Welsh
Work: A1 A2 A3 B1 B2 B3 C1 C2 C3 D1 D2 E F1 F2 G H I J1 J2 K1 K2 K3 K4 L M1 M2 M3 N O P Q R1 R2 S1 S2 T1 T2 U1 U2 V W X Z(a,b,c,d,e,f,g,h,i,j,k,l,m,n,o,p,q,r,s,t,w,x,y,z)
Emergency Action, Agency, Advocacy and Fixed Fee Interview undertaken
Ptr: Gwilliam, Miss Catherine J T LLB(Hons). . . . . *Oct 1989
Hill, Mr Christopher J G . . . . . *§Dec 1972
James, Mrs Julie Anita LLB . . . . . *Aug 1986
Lane, Mr Michael R LLB(Wales). . . . . *May 1979
Russen, Mr Timothy M S . . . . . *Apr 1981
Smith, Miss Karen L. . . . . *Dec 1979
Whittaker, Mr David Nigel . . . . . *Jun 1981
Ast: Davies, Miss Sioned W . . . . . *Sep 1998
Smith, Mr David LLB(Hons) . . . . . Oct 1988
Con: Davies, Mr Richard G LLB(Lond) . . . . . *Jun 1974
Williams, Mr Nigel C Diocesan Registrar. . . . . *Oct 1964

See p112 for the Key to Work Categories & other symbols

THE JOHN W DAVIES PARTNERSHIP ‡
27 Bridge Street Newport NP20 4BG
Tel: 01633 841773 *Fax:* 01633 841823
Dx: 33203 NEWPORT (GWENT)
List of partners: J D Hine, S E Kear, H K Thomas
Languages: French, Welsh
Work: B2 E F1 F2 G H J1 K1 K2 K3 L N O Q S1 S2 V W Z(l)
Emergency Action, Agency, Advocacy, Fixed Fee Interview and Legal Aid undertaken
Ptr: Hine, Mr Jonathan David LLB . . . . Apr 1991
Kear, Miss Sandra E BA . . . . *§Jul 1973
Thomas, Ms Helen K DipLP. . . . Sep 1997
Ast: Williams, Mr Gareth Rhys LLB . . . . Apr 2000

LEO ABSE & COHEN
12 Devon Place Gwent Newport NP20 4NN
Tel: 01633 224417 *Fax:* 01633 212991
Dx: 33212 NEWPORT (GWENT)
E-mail: law@leoabse.com
Office: Cardiff, Swansea

JON LEWIS & CO SOLICITORS ‡
38 Chepstow Road Newport NP19 8PT
Tel: 01633 256601 *Fax:* 01633 256602

DUNCAN MOGHAL ‡
9 Gold Tops Newport NP20 4UB
Tel: 01633 211600 *Fax:* 01633 211500
E-mail: reception@duncanmoghal.com
Office: Cardiff

PETERSONS ‡
Bank Chambers 110-112 Chepstow Road Maindee Newport NP19 8EE
Tel: 01633 255151 *Fax:* 01633 211144
Emergency telephone 07850 515144
List of partners: D Peterson, R Peterson
Languages: French
Work: B1 B2 C1 D1 D2 E F1 F2 J2 K1 L N Q R1 R2 S1 S2 T1 T2 W Z(e,h,j,k,o,q,r)
Emergency Action, Agency, Advocacy, Fixed Fee Interview undertaken and Member of Accident Line
Ptr: Peterson, Mr David LLB. . . . May 1979
Peterson, Mr Robert BA. . . . Jun 1982
Asoc: Miles, Miss Catrin S BA . . . . Feb 1999
Ast: Davies, Mrs Nicola Jane BA(Hons) . . . . *Apr 1992
Redmore, Ms Gaynor M BA. . . . Jan 1984

QUALITY SOLICITORS HPJV ‡
14 Baneswell Road Newport NP20 4PB
Tel: 01633 242526 *Fax:* 01635 252889
Dx: 148381 NEWPORT (GWENT) 11
Emergency telephone 07798 860310
E-mail: hpjv@qualitysolicitors.com
List of partners: P N Binnersley, P A Lewis, P Philpott, B P Rimola
Work: C1 D1 E F1 G H K1 K3 L N O Q S1 V W Z(c,l)
Emergency Action, Agency, Advocacy, Fixed Fee Interview, Legal Aid undertaken and Member of Accident Line
Ptr: Binnersley, Mr Peter N LLB(Wales) . . . . *Apr 1981
Lewis, Mr Paul Anthony BA(Hons). . . . *Feb 1991
Philpott, Mr Paul BA. . . . Nov 1989
Rimola, Mr Bruno P LLM; LLB. . . . *Nov 1986

THE ROBERT DAVIES PARTNERSHIP ‡
Wentwood House Langstone Business Village Priory Drive Newport NP18 2HJ
Tel: 01633 413500 *Fax:* 01633 413499
Dx: 88673 NEWPORT (GWENT)
E-mail: info@rdplaw.co.uk
List of partners: R H T Davies
Languages: French, German, Italian, Spanish
Work: A1 A2 B1 C1 C2 E F1 J1 O Q R1 R2 S1 S2 W Z(c,e)
Ptr: Davies, Mr Robert H T. . . . *Nov 1972
Con: Davies, Mr Philip H LLB(B'ham). . . . *Jun 1975

ROGER JAMES CLEMENTS & PARTNERS ‡
72 Bridge Street Newport NP20 4AQ
Tel: 01633 257844 *Fax:* 01633 244229
Dx: 33200 NEWPORT (GWENT)
List of partners: J S Clements, M R James, R S Mundy
Office: Newport, Risca
Work: A1 B1 C1 C2 C3 D1 E F1 G H J1 K1 L M1 M2 N P R1 S1 T1 T2 V W
Emergency Action, Agency, Advocacy, Fixed Fee Interview, Legal Aid undertaken and Member of Accident Line
Ptr: Clements, Mr John S BA . . . . Jun 1973
James, Mr M Roger LLB . . . . *Dec 1970
Ast: Fletcher, Mrs Alex LLB(Hons). . . . *Jul 1998
George, Mr David I LLB. . . . Feb 1995
Patience, Mr Iain W LLB . . . . *Feb 1997
Sturley, Ms Lynn Marie LLB. . . . *Sep 1990

ROGER JAMES CLEMENTS & PARTNERS (incorporating Robin H Jones & Co)
76 Caerau Road Newport NP20 4HJ
Tel: 01633 263316 / 663316 *Fax:* 01633 223088
Dx: 33200 NEWPORT (GWENT)
E-mail: joan@rjcp.co.uk
Office: Newport, Risca
Languages: Welsh
Work: C1 E G H K1 K3 K4 N O Q S1 S2 W Z(i,l)
Agency and Legal Aid undertaken
SPr: Mundy, Mr Robert S LLB(Wales) . . . . *May 1982
Con: Ferris, Mr Robert LLB(Lond). . . . *Dec 1972

SRB LEGAL LLP ‡
Alder House 5 Cedar Court Hazell Drive Newport NP10 8FY
Tel: 01633 817033 *Fax:* 01633 817099
E-mail: enq@srblegal.co.uk

SEARLE & BURGE (WITH HARDING EVANS) ‡
5 North Street Newport NP20 1JZ
Tel: 01633 267107 *Fax:* 01633 252364
Dx: 148380 NEWPORT (GWENT) 11
List of partners: I S Burge
Languages: French
Work: E L S1 W X
Fixed Fee Interview undertaken

WATKINS & GUNN
Sussex House 17 Gold Tops Newport NP20 4PH
Tel: 01633 262122 *Fax:* 01633 262192
E-mail: newport.office@watkinsandgunn.co.uk
Office: Pontypool
Work: D1 G H J1 K1 K3 N Q S2 W X Z(r)
Fixed Fee Interview and Legal Aid undertaken

PAUL L WILLIAMS SOLICITORS ‡
119-121 Chepstow Road Newport NP19 8BZ
Tel: 01633 213555 *Fax:* 01633 212359
E-mail: paul@plwsolicitors.co.uk

NEWPORT, Shropshire

CLARKES
21 High Street Newport Shropshire TF10 7AT
Tel: 01952 281060 *Fax:* 01952 405142 *Dx:* 27135 NEWPORT
Office: Shrewsbury, Telford (2 offices), Wellington

TERRY JONES SOLICITORS & ADVOCATES
64 Upper Bar Newport Shropshire TF10 7EJ
Tel: 01952 810307 *Fax:* 01952 820318
Dx: 27131 NEWPORT SALOP
Emergency telephone 01952 810307
E-mail: enquiries@terry-jones.co.uk
Office: Shrewsbury, Telford
Work: A1 B1 C1 D1 E F1 J1 J2 K1 K2 K4 L M1 N S1 V W Z(d,h,l,m,o,r,t)
Emergency Action, Agency, Advocacy, Fixed Fee Interview and Legal Aid undertaken
Ast: Roberts, Mrs Joanne Vivienne BA(Hons)(Financial & Legal Studies). . . . Nov 1999
Con: Fitzmaurice, Mr Nicholas F LLB(Hons) . . . . Nov 1983
Rees, Ms Linda BA . . . . *Dec 1978

CLARE THOMAS & CO ‡
Burgage House 23a High Street Newport Shropshire TF10 7AT
Tel: 01952 820050 *Fax:* 01952 820052
List of partners: C E Thomas
Work: E S1 S2 W
Ptr: Thomas, Ms Clare Elizabeth . . . . *Jul 1967

NEWPORT PAGNELL, Milton Keynes

HARVEY INGRAM BORNEOS
60 High Street Newport Pagnell Milton Keynes MK16 8AQ
Tel: 01908 613545 *Fax:* 01908 210654
Dx: 90905 NEWPORT PAGNELL
E-mail: mail@borneolinnells.co.uk
Office: Bedford, Birmingham, Leicester, Milton Keynes
Mem: Charlton, Mrs Jane BA(Hons). . . . Jun 1992
Clarke, Mrs Janet E BA(Law) . . . . *Aug 1984
Ast: Dales, Mrs Teresa E BA. . . . *Oct 1987
Jeffels, Mrs Suzanne D LLB. . . . Nov 1987

HENSHAW SOLICITORS ‡
Blair House 13 High Street Newport Pagnell Milton Keynes MK16 8AR
Tel: 01908 211202

RALLEY SOLICITORS ‡
Tickford House Silver Street Newport Pagnell Milton Keynes MK16 8EN
Tel: 01908 211234 *Fax:* 01908 211235
Dx: 90913 NEWPORT PAGNELL
E-mail: dralley@ralleysolicitors.com

NEWQUAY, Cornwall

BOWMAN & CO ‡
Towan Chambers 14 Beachfield Avenue Newquay Cornwall TR7 1DR
Tel: 01637 875065 *Fax:* 01637 851228
Emergency telephone 01637 874355
List of partners: M J Bowman
Work: C1 C2 C3 E G H K1 L M1 M2 P S1 W Z(c,j,l)
Emergency Action, Agency, Advocacy, Fixed Fee Interview, Legal Aid undertaken and Member of Accident Line
SPr: Bowman, Mr Martin J LLB. . . . *Jun 1971

BRIGHTLEY COMMERCIAL ‡
Lower Landrine Mitchell Newquay Cornwall TR8 5BB
Tel: 01872 519087 *Fax:* 01872 519086
Work: C1 E J1 S2 Z(e)

COODES
6 Cheltenham Place Newquay Cornwall TR7 1DQ
Tel: 01637 878111 *Fax:* 01637 874732 *Dx:* 81953 NEWQUAY
E-mail: enquiries@coodes.co.uk
Office: Holsworthy, Launceston, Liskeard, Penzance, St Austell, Truro
Work: B2 C1 D1 F1 G H J1 K1 N O Q S1 W Z(m)
Emergency Action, Agency, Advocacy and Legal Aid undertaken
Ptr: Bryant, Miss Lucy C P LLB . . . . *§May 1998
Gregson, Mr Michael John LLB ★. . . . *Oct 1980
Asoc: Tyson, Mr Julian . . . . *Oct 1993

GREENWAYS ‡ (incorporating Whitford & Sons)
19 St Michaels Road Newquay Cornwall TR7 1LL
Tel: 01637 872361 / 872251 *Fax:* 01637 877330
Dx: 81950 NEWQUAY
E-mail: greenwayslaw@btconnect.com
List of partners: A P Stephens
Work: A1 B1 C1 D1 E K1 K2 L R1 S1 S2 T2 W Z(c,d,h,l,o,q)
Advocacy undertaken
Ptr: Stephens, Mr A Paul Notary Public . . . . *§Nov 1974
Ast: Martin, Miss Angeline Kensa LLB(Hons). . . . *Nov 2001
Mattingley, Mr Norman R . . . . *Apr 1975

JENNERS CONVEYANCING ‡
19-21 East Street Newquay Cornwall TR7 1DN
Tel: 01637 850611

MURRELL ASSOCIATES LLP ‡
The Lodge Chapeltown Business Park Summercourt Newquay Cornwall TR8 5YA
Tel: 01872 511270 *Fax:* 01872 511270

NALDERS QUALITY SOLICITORS
11 Beachfield Avenue Newquay Cornwall TR7 1DP
Tel: 01637 871414 *Fax:* 01637 879414 *Dx:* 81951 NEWQUAY
E-mail: post@nalders.co.uk
Office: Camborne, Falmouth, Helston, Penzance, St Austell, Truro (2 offices)
Work: A1 B1 D1 E F1 G H J1 K1 L N O Q S1 V W Z(a,c,f,l)

RALPH & CO ‡
18-20 Cliff Road Newquay Cornwall TR7 1SG
Tel: 01637 872218 *Fax:* 01637 875523 *Dx:* 81952 NEWQUAY
E-mail: (initials)@ralphlaw.co.uk
List of partners: K A Clixby, N J Hall, D Wallis
Office: Wadebridge
Work: C1 C2 D1 D2 E F1 G H J1 K1 K3 K4 L N O Q R1 R2 S1 S2 T1 T2 V W Z(c,l)
Emergency Action, Agency, Advocacy, Fixed Fee Interview, Legal Aid undertaken and Legal Aid Franchise
Ptr: Clixby, Miss Katie Anne LLB(Hons) . . . . *Jan 1995
Hall, Mr Nicholas J MA(Oxon) • Recorder. . . . *Jun 1977
Wallis, Mr David LLB . . . . *Aug 2001
Ast: Calderwood, Tanya . . . . *Jan 2002
Harvey, Mr David S . . . . *Dec 1976
Lawer, Helen . . . . *Jan 1998
Con: Scawin, Mr Andrew LLB. . . . *May 1978

NEWTON ABBOT, Devon

IRENE HOGARTH CRIMINAL DEFENCE ‡
Ashcroft House 1 St Pauls Road Newton Abbot Devon TQ12 2HP
Tel: 01626 337373 *Fax:* 01626 337373 *Dx:* 59108 NEWTON ABBOT
Emergency telephone 01626 337373
E-mail: enquiries@ihlaw.co.uk
List of partners: I M Hogarth, T Huey-Smith
Work: G H
Fixed Fee Interview and Legal Aid undertaken
Ptr: Hogarth, Ms Irene Margaret BA(Hons); LLB . . . . *Dec 1992
Huey-Smith, Miss Tracee BA(Hons); CPE. . . . *Jul 2001

KELLOCK & JOHNSON (incorporating Pett & Co)
145 Queen Street Newton Abbot Devon TQ12 2BN
Tel: 01626 335454 *Fax:* 01626 332448
E-mail: newtonabbot@kellocks.co.uk
Office: Totnes
Work: A1 C1 C2 C3 E F1 J1 K1 L N Q S1 S2 T1 T2 W Z(c)
Agency, Fixed Fee Interview undertaken and Member of Accident Line

KITSONS LLP
14 Devon Square Newton Abbot Devon TQ12 2HR
Tel: 01626 203366 *Fax:* 01626 203360 *Dx:* 59118 NEWTON ABBOT
E-mail: advice@kitsons-solicitors.co.uk
Office: Exeter, Plymouth, Torquay
Languages: French
Work: A3 B1 B2 C1 C2 D1 E F1 G J1 J2 K1 K2 K3 L N O Q R1 R2 S1 S2 T1 T2 W Z(e,l,m,o,q,r)
Emergency Action, Agency, Advocacy, Legal Aid undertaken, Legal Aid Franchise and Member of Accident Line
Ptr: Boyne, Mr Peter James LLB . . . . *Jul 1977
Howell, Mr Jeremy Wynter . . . . Jun 1972
Asoc: Mulhern, Jane. . . . Sep 2005
Ritchie, Mrs Janet E M LLB; Mediator. . . . *Jan 1980
Con: Smith, Mr Michael Adrian LLB(Lond) . . . . *Aug 1980

LINNITTS SOLICITORS ‡
Suite 1 Wessex House Tuckers Maltings Newton Abbot Devon TQ12 4AA
Tel: 01626 333380

MCDERMOTT FRENCH ‡
112 Queen Street Newton Abbot Devon TQ12 2EU
Tel: 01626 200177 *Fax:* 01626 200178
Emergency telephone 01626 336418
E-mail: sarah@mcdermottfrench.co.uk
List of partners: S French, J McDermott
Work: G H K1 S1 W
Agency, Advocacy, Fixed Fee Interview and Legal Aid undertaken
Ptr: French, Ms Sarah BA . . . . *Dec 1987
McDermott, Miss Julie LLB(Sheff). . . . *Jun 1984

JAMES MASON TUCKER ‡
32 Devon Square Newton Abbot Devon TQ12 2HH
Tel: 01626 204060 *Fax:* 01626 204065 *Dx:* 59101 NEWTON ABBOT
List of partners: T W Roberton
Work: A1 B1 C1 D1 E F1 J1 K1 K2 L N Q R1 S1 S2 W Z(m)
Agency, Advocacy and Fixed Fee Interview undertaken
Ptr: Roberton, Mr Timothy W LLB(Lond). . . . *§Dec 1977
Ast: Regan, Mr Nicholas BA . . . . *Feb 1990
Warner, Miss Karen Ruth LLB(Hons) . . . . *Oct 1992

KAREN O'NEILL & CO ‡
47 Wolborough Street Newton Abbot Devon TQ12 1JQ
Tel: 01626 366399

PATTERSON LAW ‡
Tregenna 6 Rundle Road Newton Abbot Devon TQ12 2PJ
Tel: 01626 359800

TOZERS
10 St Paul's Road Newton Abbot Devon TQ12 4PR
Tel: 01626 207020 *Fax:* 01626 207019 *Dx:* 59102 NEWTON ABBOT
E-mail: p.towey@tozers.co.uk
Office: Exeter, Plymouth, Teignmouth
Work: A1 B1 C1 D1 D2 E K1 K2 L P R1 R2 S1 S2 T1 T2 W Z(c,o,s)
Emergency Action, Agency, Advocacy, Fixed Fee Interview, Legal Aid undertaken and Legal Aid Franchise
Ptr: Lambert, Mrs Tracy LLB. . . . *Oct 1989
Towey, Mr Patrick A LLB(Sheff) . . . . *Nov 1985
Wood, Mr Anthony LLB . . . . Jun 1988
Asoc: Hanbury, Mr Christopher J BA. . . . *§Jun 1978

WBW SOLICITORS ‡
Church House Queen Street Newton Abbot Devon TQ12 2QP
Tel: 01626 202404 *Fax:* 01626 202420 *Dx:* 59100 NEWTON ABBOT
E-mail: lawyer@wbw.co.uk
List of partners: R W A Barrett, J B Born, S A Bulman, S Colman, A Cooper, R S Coram, S J Couch, L Garrard, F Goddard, R W Lewis, F L Luscombe, M G Martin, D J Ogle, J Osborne, T J Pearce, D S Reed, N H Rowlinson, M A Setter, C E Strigner, M White, C M Williams, M N Williams, S M Witheridge, M C Zahara

Office: Bovey Tracey, Exeter, Torquay
Languages: French, German, Punjabi, Spanish, Urdu
Work: A1 A3 B1 B2 C1 C2 C3 D1 D2 E F1 F2 G H J1 K1 K2 K3 K4 L M1 M2 N O P Q R1 S1 S2 T1 T2 V W X Z(a,d,e,h,l,m,p,r)
Emergency Action, Agency, Fixed Fee Interview, Legal Aid undertaken, Legal Aid Franchise and Member of Accident Line
Ptr: Barrett, Mr Robin W A. . . . . . *Jul 1967
Born, Mr John B BA(Cantab) . . . . . *Oct 1983
Bulman, Mr Stephen Andrew LLB . . . . . *Jul 1995
Colman, Mr Simon LLB(Hons). . . . . . *Oct 1993
Couch, Mrs Sarah Jane BA . . . . . *§Nov 1994
Luscombe, Miss Fiona L LLB . . . . . *§Oct 1982
Osborne, Mr Justin LLB(Hons) . . . . . *Oct 1996
Reed, Mr Derek S LLB(L'pool). . . . . *§Aug 1971
Rowlinson, Mr Noel H Notary Public. . . . . *§May 1977
Setter, Mr Michael A LLB . . . . . *§Jun 1974
Strigner, Ms Catherine E LLB . . . . . *Aug 1993
Zahara, Mr Michael C LLB . . . . . *Jun 1984
Ast: Classon, Mrs Marie Therese LLB(Hons). . . . . *Oct 1992
Kelly, Ms Nuala BA(Hons); LPC . . . . . *Oct 1998
Melville-Shreeve, Mrs Alison M LLB. . . . . *Oct 1982
Thompson, Mr Robert C. . . . . . *Jun 1971
Con: Jervois, Mr David R W BA(Cantab) Chairman of Support Benefit Appeals Tribunal . . . . . *§Oct 1957

WOLLEN MICHELMORE SOLICITORS
15-21 Market Street Newton Abbot Devon TQ12 2RN
Tel: 01626 332266 *Fax:* 01626 883500 *Dx:* 59103 NEWTON ABBOT
Office: Dartmouth, Paignton, Torquay
Languages: Dutch, French, German, Italian
Work: A1 A2 A3 B1 C1 C2 C3 E F1 J1 J2 K1 K2 K3 K4 L M1 N O P Q R1 R2 S1 S2 T1 T2 U2 V W Z(c,d,e,h,j,k,l,p,q,r,za)
Emergency Action, Agency and Advocacy undertaken
Ptr: Cosgrave, Mr Michael B G LLB(Manc) . . . . . *§Nov 1971
Freeland, Mr Michael F LLB(Lond) . . . . . *§Jan 1975
Larbalestier, Miss Kerry J LLB(Soton) . . . . . *Oct 1989
Mudge, Miss Sarah Louise LLB . . . . . *May 2002
Tull, Mrs Shirley J LLB(Exon) . . . . . *Nov 1990
Williams, Miss Joanna Wendy. . . . . *Sep 1996
Williams, Mr Peter J B. . . . . *§Jan 1970
Asoc: Andrews, Mrs Kate LLB(Hons) . . . . . Jan 1993
Ast: Cooper, Mr Charles . . . . . *Aug 2008
Jarvis, Miss Helen Louise . . . . . *Sep 2001
Morgan-Wynne, Mr David Jeremy LLB . . . . . *Sep 1999
Scarrott, Mr David J. . . . . . *Sep 2003
Stacey, Mr David James . . . . . *Jan 1990
Thompson, Miss Samantha Jay . . . . . *Aug 2009
Wharmby, Mr Jonathan C LLB(Hons) . . . . . *May 1995
Con: Ager, Mr Robert S MA(Oxon) . . . . . *§Jul 1971
Spencer, Mr David J H . . . . . *§Mar 1965
Thomas, Mr Christopher N LLB(Nott'm) . . . . . *Apr 1975

NEWTON AYCLIFFE, Co Durham

BHP LAW
68 Beveridge Way Newton Aycliffe Co Durham DL5 4LD
Tel: 01325 312534 *Fax:* 01325 328419
Dx: 63801 NEWTON AYCLIFFE
E-mail: info@bhplaw.co.uk
Office: Darlington, Durham, Halifax, Newcastle upon Tyne, North Shields, Stockton-on-Tees
Work: A3 B1 C1 C2 C3 D1 D2 E F1 F2 G H J1 J2 K1 K2 K3 K4 L N O Q R1 R2 S1 S2 T1 T2 U1 U2 W X Z(c,e,o,p,q,r,u,w,x,za)
Legal Aid undertaken
Ast: Ablett, Mr Graham Thorpe BA(Hons) . . . . . *Mar 1984
Burgess, Mrs Cheryl LLB(Hons). . . . . . Jan 2002

HEWITTS
(incorporating Booth & Dixon; Marquis Penna; J R Waite & Alsop; Wager Turner; Cohens Hewitts)
1st Floor Suite 5 Avenue House Newton Aycliffe Co Durham DL5 4DH
Tel: 01325 316170 *Fax:* 01325 301407
Dx: 63802 NEWTON AYCLIFFE
E-mail: enquiries@hewitts.co.uk
Office: Bishop Auckland, Crook, Darlington, Stockton-on-Tees
Work: A1 A2 A3 B1 B2 C1 C2 D1 D2 E F1 G H J1 J2 K1 K2 L M1 N O P Q R1 S1 S2 U2 V W X Z(c,d,e,f,g,h,i,j,k,l,m,o,p,q,s,t)
Emergency Action, Agency, Advocacy, Fixed Fee Interview and Legal Aid undertaken
Ptr: Burnett, Mrs Gwendoline F BA(Hons) Part time DSS Tribunal Chairman. . . . . *Feb 1988
Green, Mr Alan Dennis DML; CPE Solicitor of the Supreme Court. . . . . *May 1987
Ast: Nelson, Ms Kirsty Ann LLB; LPC . . . . . Sep 2003
Oliver, Mr Michael L LLB . . . . . *Dec 1973
Parkin, Miss Helen L LLB . . . . . *Jun 1999

NEWTON-LE-WILLOWS, Merseyside

GRINDRODS ‡
25 Haydock Street Newton-le-Willows Merseyside WA12 9AD
Tel: 01925 221321 *Fax:* 01925 220431 *Dx:* 17752 WARRINGTON
Emergency telephone 0161 928 3309
E-mail: rv@fhsolicitors.com
List of partners: G W Barber
Work: D1 E F1 G H K1 L N O Q R1 S1 V W
Emergency Action, Agency, Advocacy, Fixed Fee Interview and Legal Aid undertaken
Ptr: Barber, Mr Gary W BA(Law). . . . . . *Nov 1987

MICHAEL W HALSALL ‡
2 The Parks Newton-le-Willows Merseyside WA12 0NZ
Tel: 01942 727000 *Fax:* 01942 717555
Dx: 713120 NEWTON-LE-WILLOWS 2
List of partners: N M Burke, M W Halsall, B V Higgins, D W McDermott, P J Stanton, S P Taylor
Work: N
Ptr: Burke, Mr Nial Martin . . . . . Oct 1995
Halsall, Mr Michael W. . . . . . *Mar 1973
Higgins, Mr Bernard V. . . . . . Oct 1986
McDermott, Mr David W. . . . . . Dec 1994
Stanton, Mr Paul John . . . . . Sep 1989
Taylor, Mr Stephen Paul LLB; LSF. . . . . . Feb 1994

A J PRESTON SOLICITORS ‡
Centrix House Crow Lane East Newton-le-Willows Merseyside WA12 9UY
Tel: 01925 273150 *Fax:* 01925 273151

WILSON BULLOUGH WALTON & KNOWLES ‡
42 Bridge Street Newton-le-Willows Merseyside WA12 9QT
Tel: 01925 224569 / 224560 *Fax:* 01925 229301
Dx: 720511 NEWTON-LE-WILLOWS 2
E-mail: wilsonbullough2@supanet.com
List of partners: G A Walton
Work: C1 E F1 K1 L N S1 W
Fixed Fee Interview undertaken
Ptr: Walton, Mr Geoffrey Alan LLB. . . . . . *Dec 1971

NEWTOWN, Powys

HANRATTY & CO ‡
The Eagles Shortbridge Street Newtown Powys SY16 2LW
Tel: 01686 626239 *Fax:* 01686 624052
Dx: 29235 NEWTOWN (POWYS)
Emergency telephone 01686 650387
E-mail: enquiries@hanrattylaw.com
List of partners: R G Hanratty, P A Inns
Languages: Welsh
Work: A1 A2 B2 C1 D1 E F1 F2 G H J1 J2 K1 K3 K4 L N O Q S1 S2 V W Z(d,l,p,q)
Emergency Action, Agency, Advocacy, Fixed Fee Interview, Legal Aid undertaken and Legal Aid Franchise
Ptr: Hanratty, Mr Robert G LLB(Hons) ★. . . . . *Jun 1981
Inns, Mr Paul Alfonso LLB(Hons) . . . . . *Aug 1996
Ast: Edwards, Ceri. . . . . . *Sep 2010
Joseph, Mr Oliver Stephen LLB(Hons). . . . . *Jun 2008
Nazar, Sophia. . . . . . *Jan 2006

Holders of Franchise for Crime, Family. We conduct business in Welsh. We specialise in the following areas of work Crime - General, Divorce and Matrimonial, Commercial Conveyancing.

HARRISONS SOLICITORS LLP
Unit 4 St Giles Business Park Pool Road Newtown Powys SY16 3AJ
Tel: 01686 625134 *Fax:* 01686 622040
Dx: 29234 NEWTOWN (POWYS)
Office: Welshpool
Languages: Welsh
Work: A1 B1 C1 D1 E F1 G H J1 K1 L M1 N P R1 S1 T1 V W Z(c,e,i,k,l)
Emergency Action, Agency, Advocacy, Fixed Fee Interview and Legal Aid undertaken
Asoc: Davies, Mrs Sian LLB. . . . . . *Nov 1983

SALLY HARVEY ‡
PO Box 66 Newtown Powys SY16 2WL
Tel: 01686 621033 *Fax:* 01686 621121
Dx: 29246 NEWTOWN (POWYS)
List of partners: S E Harvey
Work: C1 E O S1 S2 W
Ptr: Harvey, Miss Sally E LLB . . . . . *Sep 1985

GERAINT JONES & CO ‡
Bronwydd The Bank Newtown Powys SY16 2AA
Tel: 01686 627935 *Fax:* 01686 624257
Dx: 29240 NEWTOWN (POWYS)
Emergency telephone 07808 093276
E-mail: legalservices@geraint-jones-solicitors.co.uk
List of partners: G E Jones
Office: Llandrindod Wells
Languages: French, Welsh
Work: B1 D1 D2 F1 G H J1 K1 K3 N O Q S1 S2 V W Z(c,q)
Emergency Action, Agency, Advocacy, Fixed Fee Interview, Legal Aid undertaken and Member of Accident Line
Ptr: Jones, Mr Geraint E MA. . . . . . *Dec 1977
Ast: Ap Dafydd, Mr LLyr Gwion LLB . . . . . *Nov 1998
Jones, Mr Geraint Owain BA . . . . . *Feb 2008
Page, Mr Richard John LLB; BA. . . . . . *Dec 1976
Robinson, Miss Sarah Jane LLB . . . . . *Feb 2008
Sherrard, Mr Philip Paul Thomas MA . . . . . *Oct 2005

MILWYN JENKINS ‡
Cranford House 1 Severn Square Newtown Powys SY16 2AG
Tel: 01686 626218 *Fax:* 01686 610047
Dx: 29231 NEWTOWN (POWYS)
E-mail: enquiry@milwynjenkins.co.uk
List of partners: N P Jones, C Preece
Work: A1 C1 D1 E F1 J1 K1 K3 K4 L N P Q R1 R2 S1 S2 W Z(c,h,l,t)
Emergency Action, Agency, Advocacy and Fixed Fee Interview undertaken
Ptr: Jones, Mr Nicholas Paul LLB . . . . . *Oct 1995
Preece, Miss Christine LLB . . . . . *Sep 1988

RICHARD GEORGE & JENKINS ‡
Old Bank Chambers High Street Newtown Powys SY16 2NT
Tel: 01686 626210 *Fax:* 01686 629968
Dx: 29238 NEWTOWN (POWYS)
Emergency telephone 01686 413528
E-mail: info@midwales-legal.co.uk
List of partners: A M Davies, H D Evans
Work: A1 B1 C1 C2 C3 D1 E F1 G H J1 K1 K3 L M1 M2 N O P Q R1 S1 S2 T1 T2 V W Z(l,o,r)
Emergency Action, Agency, Advocacy, Fixed Fee Interview, Legal Aid undertaken, Legal Aid Franchise and Member of Accident Line
Ptr: Davies, Mr Alan M LLB Clerk to Commissioner of Taxes . . . . . *Feb 1978
Evans, Mr Huw D LLB. . . . . . *Nov 1981
Ast: Landers, Mr Geoffrey A BA(Hons)(Law). . . . . *Jun 1976

TOMLEYS ‡
31 Market Street Newtown Powys SY16 2PG
Tel: 01686 626641 *Fax:* 01686 628618
Dx: 29232 NEWTOWN (POWYS)
Emergency telephone 01686 650430
E-mail: wt@tomleys.co.uk
List of partners: J E C Tomley
Languages: Welsh
Work: A1 B1 C1 C2 D1 E F1 G H J1 K1 L M1 M2 N P R1 S1 T1 T2 V W Z(c,d,e,l)
Emergency Action, Agency, Advocacy, Legal Aid undertaken and Member of Accident Line
Ptr: Tomley, Mr J E Christopher Clerk to Commissioner of Taxes . . . . . *Nov 1972
Ast: Evans, Miss Sian Lynnette LLB(Hons); LLM. . . . . Apr 2005
Hughes, Ms Heather Elizabeth BA(Hons) . . . . . *Jun 1994
Joseph, Miss Emma BA(Hons) . . . . . *Aug 2002

NORTH FERRIBY, East Riding of Yorkshire

TM SOLICITORS ‡
Melton Court Gibson Lane Melton North Ferriby East Riding of Yorkshire HU14 3HH
Tel: 01482 638645

NORTH SHIELDS, Tyne & Wear

AMAKHALA LIMITED ‡
9 Hedley Court Orion Business Park North Shields Tyne & Wear NE29 7ST
Tel: 0191 293 1500 *Fax:* 0191 293 1501
E-mail: jburn@tlwsolicitors.co.uk

BHP LAW
11-12 Northumberland Square North Shields Tyne & Wear NE30 1PY
Tel: 0191 257 2213 *Fax:* 0191 296 3470
Dx: 62008 NORTH SHIELDS
E-mail: info@bhplaw.co.uk
Office: Darlington, Durham, Halifax, Newcastle upon Tyne, Newton Aycliffe, Stockton-on-Tees
Work: A3 B1 C1 C2 C3 D1 D2 E F1 F2 G H J1 J2 K1 K2 K3 K4 L N O Q R1 R2 S1 S2 T1 T2 U1 U2 W X Z(c,e,o,p,q,r,u,w,x,za)
Legal Aid undertaken
Ptr: Crawford, Mr George . . . . . Jan 1984
Con: Deas, Mr Richard . . . . . Jul 1974

BITTERMANN & WOOD ‡
(incorporating Bowman & Brown)
45-48 Howard Street North Shields Tyne & Wear NE30 1AJ
Tel: 0191 257 3211 / 259 6806 *Fax:* 0191 258 0926
Dx: 62001 NORTH SHIELDS
E-mail: administrator@bittermannwood.co.uk
List of partners: J Mayne, A G McDonald
Work: C1 C2 C3 D1 E G J1 K1 L M1 M2 N O S1 S2 W Z(d,l)
Agency, Advocacy and Fixed Fee Interview undertaken
Ptr: McDonald, Mr Alastair G LLB(Leeds) . . . . . *Oct 1983
Mayne, Mr James LLB(Newc). . . . . . *Jul 1977

BROWN HOLLIDAY & CLEMENTS ‡
50 Howard Street North Shields Tyne & Wear NE30 1PD
Tel: 0191 257 0431 *Fax:* 0191 257 4864
Dx: 62002 NORTH SHIELDS
List of partners: D R Keem
Work: E K1 K3 K4 L S1 T1 W
Ptr: Keem, Mr David R BA. . . . . . *Dec 1976

STANLEY M CALVERT ‡
7-8 Upper Norfolk Street North Shields Tyne & Wear NE30 1PT
Tel: 0191 258 1528 *Fax:* 0191 258 3811
Dx: 62005 NORTH SHIELDS
E-mail: stanleycalvert@dsl.pipex.com
List of partners: S M Calvert, J Mackenzie
Work: C1 E F1 K1 L M1 N P S1 W Z(e,i,l)
Emergency Action, Agency, Fixed Fee Interview and Legal Aid undertaken
Ptr: Mackenzie, Ms Julia BA. . . . . . *May 1988

HADAWAY & HADAWAY ‡
Midland Chambers 58 Howard Street North Shields Tyne & Wear NE30 1AL
Tel: 0191 257 0382 *Fax:* 0191 296 1904
Dx: 62003 NORTH SHIELDS
E-mail: info@hadaway.co.uk
List of partners: D M Dunn, C A Hall, N J Kincaid, J E Littlefield, A M Malia, L McGonnell
Work: A1 B1 C1 C2 C3 D1 E F1 G H J1 J2 K1 K3 K4 L N O P Q R1 S1 S2 V W Z(c,d,h,j,k,l,m,p,s,t)
Emergency Action, Agency, Advocacy, Fixed Fee Interview, Legal Aid undertaken, Legal Aid Franchise and Member of Accident Line
Ptr: Dunn, Mr D Michael LLB . . . . . *§Nov 1980
Hall, Ms Charlotte Ann LLB . . . . . *Oct 1995
Kincaid, Mr Nicholas J BA. . . . . . *§Oct 1984
Littlefield, Mrs Janet E LLB . . . . . *§Nov 1982
McGonnell, Ms Lynne LLB . . . . . *Nov 1991
Malia, Mr Anthony M LLB . . . . . *Nov 1983
Ast: Athey, Mr Stuart. . . . . . *Sep 2002
Brown, Ms Lynda LLB. . . . . . Nov 1989
Elliott, Mr Christopher. . . . . . Sep 2002
Forte, Ms Rose M LLB . . . . . Sep 1991
Grange, Ms Judith . . . . . Dec 2004
Horn, Mr Alan R LLB . . . . . *Jan 1978
Mann, Mr Len. . . . . . *Dec 1999
Singleton, Mr David H. . . . . . *Apr 1982

HINDLE CAMPBELL ‡
8 Northumberland Square North Shields Tyne & Wear NE30 1QQ
Tel: 0191 296 1777 *Fax:* 0191 257 9326
Dx: 62006 NORTH SHIELDS
Emergency telephone 07703 462191
E-mail: lawyer@hindle-campbell.co.uk
List of partners: D S Campbell, C M Hindle, C J Usher, E C Wilson
Languages: French, German, Italian
Work: A1 B1 C1 C2 C3 D1 D2 E F1 G H J1 K1 K3 L M1 M2 N O P Q R1 R2 S1 T1 T2 V W Z(c,e,g,i,j,k,l,m,o,p,q,s)
Emergency Action, Agency, Advocacy, Fixed Fee Interview and Legal Aid undertaken
Ptr: Campbell, Mr Duncan S BA. . . . . . *Oct 1982
Hindle, Mr Clive M LLB . . . . . *Jun 1973
Usher, Miss Clare Joanne MA(Cantab); CPE; LPC . *Aug 1997
Wilson, Miss Eileen Crawford . . . . . *Oct 1994
Asoc: Carroll, Miss Nicola . . . . . *Sep 2002

KIDD SPOOR TAYLOR ‡
(incorporating Rae Walton & Hogg)
25 Northumberland Square North Shields Tyne & Wear NE30 1PW
Tel: 0191 257 3101 *Fax:* 0191 258 5275
Dx: 62000 NORTH SHIELDS
Emergency telephone 07623 974636
E-mail: law@nsh.kidd-spur-solicitors.co.uk
List of partners: W N Dilks, T J Taylor
Work: C1 D1 E F1 G H K1 L N S1 V W Z(h)
Emergency Action, Agency, Advocacy, Fixed Fee Interview, Legal Aid undertaken and Member of Accident Line
Ptr: Dilks, Mr William N BA ♦ . . . . . *Jun 1987
Taylor, Ms Tracy J. . . . . . *Nov 1988

See p112 for the Key to Work Categories & other symbols

REED RYDER & MEIKLE ‡
19 Northumberland Square North Shields Tyne & Wear NE30 1QD
Tel: 0191 257 3222 *Fax:* 0191 257 3567
List of partners: W J Scott
Languages: French
Work: C1 E L S1 W
SPr: Scott, Mr William John TD; LLB; TEP . . . . *§Jul 1980

STOCKDALE & REID LTD ‡
52 Howard Street North Shields Tyne & Wear NE30 1AP
Tel: 0191 257 1341 *Fax:* 0191 258 2147
Dx: 62004 NORTH SHIELDS
E-mail: ns@stockdale-reid.co.uk
List of partners: P W Amos, J D Reid
Office: Monkseaton
Languages: French, German
Work: A1 A2 B2 C1 C2 C3 D1 D2 E F1 F2 G J1 K1 K3 K4 L M1 M2 N O P Q R1 R2 S1 S2 W Z(c,f,k,l,o,q,s,t,w,y)
Emergency Action, Agency, Advocacy, Fixed Fee Interview undertaken and Member of Accident Line
Ptr: Reid, Mr John D. . . . . *Jun 1970

TLW SOLICITORS ‡
9 Hedley Court Orion Business Park North Shields Tyne & Wear NE29 7ST
Tel: 0800 169 5925 *Fax:* 0191 293 1501
E-mail: info@tlwsolicitors.co.uk

NORTH WALSHAM, Norfolk

M J ELSDON ‡
63 Yarmouth Road North Walsham Norfolk NR28 9AU
Tel: 01692 403562 *Fax:* 01692 405401
Emergency telephone 01692 403562
E-mail: info@elsdons-solicitors.co.uk
List of partners: M J Elsdon
Office: Barnstaple
Languages: Italian, Maltese
Work: A1 B1 C1 C2 C3 D1 D2 E F1 J1 K1 K3 K4 L M1 M2 N O P Q R1 S1 S2 T1 T2 W Z(f,g,q,r)
Emergency Action, Agency and Advocacy undertaken
SPr: Elsdon, Dr Michael John . . . . *Jan 1986

HANSELLS
Canada House 4 Grammar School Road North Walsham Norfolk NR28 9JH
Tel: 01692 404351 *Fax:* 01692 406195
Dx: 31250 NORTH WALSHAM
E-mail: info@hansells.co.uk
Office: Aylsham, Cromer, Norwich (2 offices), Sheringham
Languages: French, German
Work: A1 B1 C1 C2 C3 D1 E F1 J1 K1 K2 K3 K4 L M2 N O P Q R1 S1 V W Z(c,h,k,l,o)
Advocacy, Fixed Fee Interview, Legal Aid undertaken and Member of Accident Line
Ptr: Seal-Coon, Mr R F Mark TD BA. . . . . *§Jul 1977
Sutherland, Mr Nick William. . . . . Apr 1975
Asoc: Care, Mr Jonathan Peter . . . . May 1978
Seal-Coon, Mrs Susan J LLB . . . . *§Jul 1973
Ast: Elsmore, Ms Felicity A BA. . . . . *§Apr 1980
Con: Stubbs, Mr Neil . . . . Dec 1991

NORTHALLERTON, North Yorkshire

COLES SOLICITORS ‡
Trinity House Thurston Road Northallerton North Yorkshire DL6 2NA
Tel: 01609 780717 *Fax:* 01609 779968
Dx: 61647 NORTHALLERTON
E-mail: info@coles-law.co.uk
List of partners: P A Gibson, A K Mortimer
Work: E J1 K4 N Q S1 S2 W
Agency and Fixed Fee Interview undertaken
Ptr: Mortimer, Mrs Angela K LLB . . . . *Jul 1980
Dir: Gibson, Mr Peter Alexander LLB(Newc). . . . . *Sep 2001
Asoc: Oldfield, Miss Joanne Elizabeth LLB. . . . . *Jul 2005
Con: Cole, Mr Andrew S P BA(Dunelm) Senior Litigator of College of Personal Injury Law. . . . . *Nov 1990
Ravalde, Mr John Colwil . . . . Jan 1974

FREEMAN JOHNSON
222 High Street Northallerton North Yorkshire DL7 8LX
Tel: 01609 772160 *Fax:* 0845 389 3204
Dx: 61646 NORTHALLERTON
E-mail: northallerton@freemanjohnson.co.uk
Office: Darlington, Durham, Spennymoor
Work: A1 C1 D1 E F1 J1 K1 L N R1 S1 T2 W Z(l)
Emergency Action, Agency, Advocacy, Fixed Fee Interview and Legal Aid undertaken
Ptr: Town, Mr Peter Francis LLB. . . . . Jun 1978
Wrigley, Mr Hugh Charles BA(Cantab). . . . . Dec 1975

HUNT & WRIGLEY ‡
Old Post Office 83 High Street Northallerton North Yorkshire DL7 8PX
Tel: 01609 772502 *Fax:* 01609 780644
Dx: 61640 NORTHALLERTON
List of partners: S A Lonsdale, S Woodall
Work: A1 D1 E F1 G H J1 K1 L N O P Q S1 S2 T1 T2 W Z(d,l,q,r)
Agency and Advocacy undertaken
Ptr: Lonsdale, Mr Stanley A . . . . Jan 1984
Woodall, Mr Stephen . . . . *§Mar 1968

PLACE BLAIR & HATCH ‡
The Old Grammar School 240 High Street Northallerton North Yorkshire DL7 8LU
Tel: 01609 780101 *Fax:* 01609 778099
Dx: 61641 NORTHALLERTON
E-mail: info@pbhsolicitors.co.uk
List of partners: E A Crawshaw, S P D Veakins
Work: A1 B1 D1 D2 E F1 G H J1 K1 K3 L N O P Q R1 S1 V W Z(c,l,m,s,t)
Emergency Action, Agency, Advocacy, Fixed Fee Interview, Legal Aid undertaken, Legal Aid Franchise and Member of Accident Line
Ptr: Crawshaw, Mrs Elizabeth Ann BA. . . . . *Jun 1980
Veakins, Mr Sean Patrick Denis LLB . . . . *Oct 1994

NORTHAMPTON, Northamptonshire

AMC LAW ‡
17 Albion Place Northampton Northamptonshire NN1 1UD
Tel: 01604 611980 / 01908 767014
E-mail: anne.coles@amc-law.co.uk

ADAMS MOORE FAMILY LAW
49-53 Hazlewood Road Northampton Northamptonshire NN1 1LG
Tel: 01604 633000
Office: Bedford, Bletchley, Corby, Daventry, Luton, Milton Keynes

ADDISON OLIVER MOORE
St Giles House St Giles Street Northampton Northamptonshire NN1 1JW
Tel: 01604 622331 / 07930 968578
Office: Watford

ASTONS ‡
The Stables Manor Road Staverton Northampton Northamptonshire NN11 6JD
Tel: 01327 706700 / 706705 *Fax:* 01327 706703
E-mail: rwa@astonssolicitors.co.uk

BORNEO HUGHES MARTELL LLP ‡
9 Notre Dame Mews Northampton Northamptonshire NN1 2BG
Tel: 01604 624822 *Fax:* 01604 638044
Dx: 703133 NORTHAMPTON 6
E-mail: mail@bhmllp.co.uk
List of partners: D Bacon, S J Beaumont, A T Devereux, S Hundal, P L Lindo, B Saigal
Work: A1 B1 C1 C2 C3 D1 D2 E F1 J1 K1 K3 L M1 M2 N O P Q R1 R2 S1 S2 T1 T2 V W Z(l)
Emergency Action, Agency, Advocacy, Fixed Fee Interview, Legal Aid undertaken and Legal Aid Franchise
Ptr: Bacon, Mr David BA . . . . *§Jun 1980
Beaumont, Mrs Sara J LLB(Nott'm) . . . . *§Dec 1976
Devereux, Mr Andrew Tony BA . . . . Oct 1986
Hundal, Ms Sharon LLB(Hons) . . . . *Sep 2005
Lindo, Miss Pauline L BA . . . . *Aug 2002
Saigal, Mrs Brona LLB . . . . *§Dec 1991

ALAN BUTHEE & CO ‡
9 Castilian Terrace Northampton Northamptonshire NN1 1LD
Tel: 01604 622301 *Fax:* 01604 622032
List of partners: A E Buthee
Work: C1 E J1 K1 N S1 S2 W
Ptr: Buthee, Mr Alan E . . . . *Feb 1975

CARTER SLATER & CO ‡
41 Harborough Road Kingsthorpe Northampton Northamptonshire NN2 7SH
Tel: 01604 717505 *Fax:* 01604 721165 *Dx:* 16051 KINGSTHORPE
Emergency telephone 07810 648398
List of partners: C Bennet, P I Carter, P B Harkins, S D Jeffery
Work: G H S1 W
Emergency Action, Agency, Advocacy, Legal Aid undertaken and Legal Aid Franchise
Ptr: Bennet, Mr Christopher LLB(Hons) . . . . *Dec 1991
Carter, Mr Paul I . . . . *Jun 1977
Harkins, Mr Paul Brian LLB(Hons). . . . . *Oct 1999
Jeffery, Mr Stuart David. . . . . *Feb 1993
Con: Carter, Mr Kevin R LLB . . . . *Apr 1981

NEIL CLARK ‡
65 Weedon Road Northampton Northamptonshire NN5 5BG
Tel: 01604 583684 *Fax:* 01604 754685
Dx: 15621 NORTHAMPTON 3
Emergency telephone 01604 409969
List of partners: N Clark
Emergency Action, Agency, Advocacy, Fixed Fee Interview and Legal Aid undertaken
Ptr: Clark, Mr Neil LLB. . . . . *Dec 1980

COUNTRYWIDE PROPERTY LAWYERS ‡
PO Box 100 Compton House Abington Street Northampton Northamptonshire NN1 2ZT
Tel: 01604 795208

CHRISTOPHER COX SOLICITORS ‡
Catherine House Harborough Road Brixworth Northampton Northamptonshire NN6 9BX
Est: 2005
Tel: 01604 882287 *Fax:* 01604 882247
Emergency telephone 07802 540977
E-mail: cjc@coxsolicitors.co.uk
Web: www.coxsolicitors.co.uk
List of partners: S C Calnan, C J Cox
Languages: French, Hindi, Italian, Punjabi, Urdu
Work: A3 B1 B2 C1 C3 E J1 O P Q U2 Z(b,c,n,q,w,y,za)
Agency undertaken
Ptr: Calnan, Mr Sebastian Charles BA Deputy District Judge . . . . *Jun 1977
Cox, Mr Christopher James BA; MSc; MCIArb. . . . . *Apr 1982
Ast: Minhas, Mrs Saranjit Kaur LLB . . . . *Apr 2006
Con: Taylor, Ms Angela Evelyn Llewellyn LLB. . . . . Apr 1976

We are a commercial law firm dealing predominantly with large commercial claims and are from either city law firms or in-house legal backgrounds. We believe in collaboration and consensus to close deals and solve disputes. We are experienced mediators and one partner is a deputy district judge.

DFA LAW LLP ‡
2 Waterside Way Northampton Northamptonshire NN4 7XD
Tel: 01604 609560 *Fax:* 01604 609561
Dx: 12472 NORTHAMPTON 1
E-mail: info@dfalaw.co.uk
List of partners: J Creek, P J Critchell, M F Fitzpatrick, J Keeble, A V Kiddle, R A Lynch, N A Martin, B Mcloughlin, M Sanders, C Towers, J A Walker
Office: Northampton
Work: A1 A3 B1 C1 C2 D1 D2 E F1 F2 J1 J2 K1 K2 K3 K4 L N O P Q R1 R2 S1 S2 T1 T2 V W Z(c,d,e,j,l,m,n,p,q,r,u)
Emergency Action, Agency, Advocacy, Fixed Fee Interview, Legal Aid undertaken, Legal Aid Franchise and Member of Accident Line
Ptr: Creek, Mr Jeffrey MA(Oxon). . . . . *§Oct 1971
Critchell, Mr Peter J BA . . . . *§Oct 1985
Fitzpatrick, Mr Michael F . . . . *Nov 1979
Keeble, Mr John LLB . . . . *Sep 1997
Kiddle, Mr Alan V LLB. . . . . *May 1981
Lynch, Mr Robert Anthony BA(Hons) . . . . *Sep 1993
Mcloughlin, Mr Barry LLB . . . . Jan 1989
Martin, Mr Nigel A BA. . . . . *Apr 1991
Sanders, Mr Michael . . . . *§Feb 1972
Towers, Ms Clare LLB. . . . . Jan 2000
Walker, Mr Jeremy A LLB(Lond). . . . . *Dec 1976
Asoc: Forskitt, Mr Richard David James LLB(Nott'm) . . . . *Nov 1995
Kitchen, Ms Jayne . . . . Sep 2003
Ast: Hayward, Mr David M LLB . . . . *Mar 1993
Lee, Mr Gary LLB. . . . . Jan 2002
Lo, Ms Elaine LLB. . . . . Jan 2006
Walker, Ms Rebecca . . . . Aug 2005

DFA LAW LLP
6 Cheyne Walk Northampton Northamptonshire NN1 5PT
Tel: 01604 609560 *Fax:* 01604 609561
Dx: 12472 NORTHAMPTON 1
E-mail: info@dfalaw.co.uk
Office: Northampton
Work: A1 A2 A3 B1 C1 C2 E F1 F2 J1 J2 L N O P Q R1 R2 S1 S2 Z(e,n,p,q)
Legal Aid undertaken

DW SOLICITORS ‡
262a Wellingborough Road Northampton Northamptonshire NN1 4EJ
Tel: 01604 624222 *Fax:* 01604 601123
E-mail: info@dwsolicitors.com
List of partners: D Ward
Languages: Bengali
Work: B1 C1 E J1 L O P R1 S1 S2 W Z(c,j,q)
SPr: Ward, Mr David LLB. . . . . Oct 1992
Ast: Begum, Miss Rena LLB(Hons) . . . . Nov 2005
Boehm, Miss Maria LLB(Hons) . . . . Sep 2006

DANBY & CO ‡
20 Market Square Northampton Northamptonshire NN1 2DL
Tel: 01604 604573 *Fax:* 01604 601577
List of partners: P A Danby
Work: A1 E L S1 W Z(l)
SPr: Danby, Mr Peter Arthur LLB(Nott'm). . . . . *May 1972

CLAIRE DELVES ‡
18 Church Lane Cold Higham Towcester Northampton Northamptonshire NN12 8LS
Tel: 01327 831050 *Fax:* 01327 830841
List of partners: M C Delves
Work: D1
Emergency Action, Agency, Advocacy, Fixed Fee Interview and Legal Aid undertaken
Ptr: Delves, Ms M Claire LLB . . . . *Jan 1976

ECKFORD RANDS ‡
Waterloo House 21 Market Square Northampton Northamptonshire NN1 2DL
Tel: 01604 621001 *Fax:* 01604 630506
Dx: 12414 NORTHAMPTON 1
E-mail: eckford.rands@virgin.net
List of partners: M J Cornelius, R Pleace
Work: A1 C1 C2 E K4 L R1 R2 S1 S2 T1 T2 W Z(c,l)
Ptr: Pleace, Mr Roger LLB(Manc) . . . . *Dec 1964

MAX ENGEL & CO LLP ‡
8 Hazelwood Road Northampton Northamptonshire NN1 1LP
Tel: 01604 887450 *Fax:* 01604 231465
Dx: 12411 NORTHAMPTON 1
E-mail: info@maxengel.co.uk
List of partners: R K Adamson, H Carville, R E Engel, R M Fowler, D Needham, R A Stewart
Work: A1 B1 C1 C2 D1 D2 E F1 F2 J1 K1 O Q R2 S1 S2 U2 W Z(l,p,q)
Agency and Fixed Fee Interview undertaken
Ptr: Adamson, Mr Richard K. . . . . *Feb 1974
Carville, Miss Helen LLB . . . . *Feb 2002
Engel, Mr Richard E LLB . . . . *Jun 1970
Fowler, Mrs Ruth M LLB . . . . *Apr 1977
Needham, Mr Duncan. . . . . *Jun 1976
Stewart, Miss Rachel Anne LLB. . . . . *Jun 1999
Ast: Finlay, Miss Debra Mary LLB . . . . Jul 2007
Con: James, Mrs Carolyn M . . . . Jun 1983

FIRST DEFENCE
23 Albion Place Northampton Northamptonshire NN1 1UD
Tel: 01604 745470 *Fax:* 01604 628816 *Dx:* 12410 NORTHAMPTON
E-mail: info@firstdefencesolicitors.co.uk
Office: Bedford, Wellingborough

SCOTT FOWLER ‡
(incorporating Hardman Cernik & Co)
Old Church Chambers 23-24 Sandhill Road St James Northampton Northamptonshire NN5 5LH
Tel: 01604 750506 *Fax:* 01604 750385
Dx: 15620 NORTHAMPTON 3
E-mail: law@scott-fowler.co.uk
List of partners: E R Fowler, R C Fowler, A M Horrell, T R Vaughan
Languages: Cantonese, French, Mandarin, Spanish
Work: A1 B1 B3 C1 C2 C3 D1 E F1 F2 G H J1 J2 K1 K2 K3 K4 L M1 M2 N O P Q R1 R2 S1 S2 T1 T2 V W Z(c,d,e,h,i,k,l,m,p,q,r)
Emergency Action, Agency, Advocacy, Fixed Fee Interview, Legal Aid undertaken and Member of Accident Line
Ptr: Fowler, Mr Edward Richard BA(Oxon). . . . . *Oct 1998
Fowler, Mr Richard Compton MA(Oxon). . . . . *Nov 1973
Horrell, Ms Anna Mari. . . . . *Nov 1998
Vaughan, Mr Timothy R LLB(Lond) . . . . *Apr 1975
Ast: Darby, Mrs Rebecca Kate BSc(Hons) . . . . *Oct 1995
Fowler, Miss Anna Edwina BA(Dunelm). . . . . *Nov 2005

McGowan, Ms Caroline BA(Hons). . . . . *Jan 2006
Moore, Miss Jennifer Ann . . . . Sep 2003
Wingfield, Mrs Helen Margaret LLB . . . . *May 1975
Con: Dawe, Mr Michael D A LLB(Lond). . . . . *Oct 1973
Vaughan, Mr Christopher James Notary Public Former President Notary Public . . . . *Dec 1973

FRANKLINS LLP ‡
14 Castilian Street Northampton Northamptonshire NN1 1JX
Tel: 01604 828282 *Fax:* 01604 609630 *Dx:* 12471 NORTHAMPTON
E-mail: info@franklins-sols.co.uk
List of partners: S J Canning, S Evans, M L Franklin, S A Long, N Smith, H P M Taylor
Office: Milton Keynes
Languages: French, German, Russian
Work: G S2 W
Emergency Action, Agency, Advocacy, Fixed Fee Interview, Legal Aid undertaken, Legal Aid Franchise and Member of Accident Line
Ptr: Canning, Mrs Sarah Jane . . . . Oct 1994
Franklin, Mr Michael L BA. . . . . *Apr 1977
Taylor, Ms Helen P M . . . . Aug 1998
Ast: Wright, Ms Rosemary . . . . Aug 2000

GILROY STEEL
32a Billing Road Northampton Northamptonshire NN1 5DQ
Tel: 01604 620890 *Fax:* 01604 629202 *Dx:* 12428 NORTHAMPTON
E-mail: kellysteel@gilroysteel.com
Office: Brackley, Buckingham

GUELLEC-DIGBY & CO ‡
Malsor House Gayton Road Northampton Northamptonshire NN7 3AB
Tel: 01604 878961

HEWITSONS
7 Spencer Parade Northampton Northamptonshire NN1 5AB
Tel: 01604 233233 *Fax:* 01604 627941 *Dx:* 12401 NORTHAMPTON
E-mail: mail@hewitsons.com
Office: Cambridge, Milton Keynes, Saffron Walden
Languages: French, German, Italian, Spanish
Work: A1 A3 B1 B2 C1 C2 C3 D1 E F1 G H I J1 K1 L M1 M2 N O P Q R1 R2 S1 S2 T1 T2 U2 W Z(b,c,d,e,f,h,i,j,k,l,m,o,p,q,r,s,u,y)
Agency, Advocacy, Fixed Fee Interview, Legal Aid undertaken and Legal Aid Franchise
Ptr: Bangor-Jones, Miss Clare L LLB . . . . *Oct 1990
Barnett, Mr Ian G MA(Oxon) Under Sheriff . . . . . *§Apr 1965
Browne, Mr David William LLB(Hons). . . . . *Mar 1990
Colacicchi, Mrs Clare E V MA(Oxon) . . . . *Nov 1983
Cooch, Mr Peter J MA(Cantab) . . . . *§Mar 1969
De Loynes, Mr Stephen J . . . . *§Jan 1979
Fletcher, Mr Kevin P W BA(Hons)(Law) . . . . *Oct 1980
Hall, Mr Nicholas . . . . Sep 1993
Hopkins, Mr Dominic A LLB ♦. . . . . *Oct 1989
Ingram, Mr Richard G MA(Cantab) Herbert Ruse Prize; Clabon Prize . . . . *Oct 1982
Legg, Mrs Mary E LLB . . . . *May 1976
Shephard, Mr John BA(Oxon). . . . . *§Jun 1976
Taylor, Mr Peter J A LLB . . . . *Oct 1985
White, Mr John A MA(Cantab) John Marshall Prize . *§Jan 1969
Asoc: Bullen, Mr Antony G S LLB(Soton) . . . . *§Nov 1972
Ast: Bell, Mrs Patricia LLB(Hons) . . . . *Oct 1993
Blezard, Mr Rodney John LLB(Hons) . . . . Dec 1987
Cole, Mr Stephen LLB(Hons); M Jur. . . . . *Nov 1995
Forde, Miss Christine LLB(Hons) . . . . *Sep 2000
Glynternick, Ms Neisha Caroline LLB(Hons). . . . . . Sep 2001
Hansford, Mr Charles Maurice BA. . . . . *Jul 1997
Harpham, Mr Neil T BA(Hons). . . . . *Oct 1994
Hayward, Ms Caroline Ann BA(Hons) . . . . *Feb 2000
Kay, Mr Stephen J LLB; LPC . . . . *Sep 1999
Lankester, Ms Judy Charlotte LLB. . . . . *Sep 2000
Nesbitt, Mr Guy Matthew BA(Hons); LSF . . . . . . *Sep 1999
Nutt, Mrs Catherine Elizabeth LLB. . . . . *Feb 1999
O'Hara, Ms Megan Grace LLB(Hons) . . . . *Sep 2000
Parry, Mr Stephen BSc(Sociology). . . . . *Sep 2001
Raval, Miss Kunjan LLB(Hons) . . . . Aug 1999
Roe, Mr Graham Philip BA; CTA . . . . Sep 2002
Stebbings, Miss Jane K LLB; TEP. . . . . *Oct 1989
Thomas, Ms Teresa L LLB(Hons) . . . . *Jun 1999
Wesley-Jones, Mrs Katharine Mary LLB(Hons) . . . *Nov 1995

HOWES PERCIVAL LLP ‡
Oxford House Cliftonville Northampton Northamptonshire NN1 5PN
Tel: 01604 230400 *Fax:* 01604 620956 *Dx:* 12413 NORTHAMPTON
E-mail: law@howespercival.com
List of partners: P K Bailey, A J Barnes, C R Bennion, R Colman, G M Couldrake, G K Davies, K Gilbert, T J Haskey, J Hayes, J P W Heal, R J Healey, J K C Herd, A Kirby, C S J Scott, J Singh
Office: Leicester, London WC2, Manchester, Milton Keynes, Norwich
Languages: French, German, Hindi, Norwegian, Punjabi, Spanish
Work: A1 A2 A3 B1 B2 C1 C2 C3 D1 D2 E F1 F2 I J1 L M1 M2 N O P Q R1 R2 S1 S2 T1 T2 V W Z(b,c,d,e,f,i,j,l,o,p,q,r,t)
Agency, Advocacy and Legal Aid Franchise
Mem: Couldrake, Mr Gerald M LLB . . . . *Feb 1985
Ast: Banner, Sarah. May 2007

HUNT & LISNERS ‡
7 Yew Tree Lane Spratton Northampton Northamptonshire NN6 8HL
Tel: 01604 846705 *Fax:* 01604 842884
E-mail: jhunt@onetel.com
List of partners: J F Hunt, J Lisners
Office: London NW4
Languages: French, German, Latvian
Work: A1 B1 C1 E F1 F2 J1 J2 K1 K3 L N O P Q R1 S1 S2 U1 W X Z(d,e,f,g,i,k,p,q,r,u,w,z)
Agency undertaken
Ptr: Hunt, Mr John Francis MA . . . . *Mar 1977
Lisners, Mr John LLB(Hons) Pattinson Brewer Prize in Employment Law . . . . *Jan 2004

M E JEFFERY ‡
Grosvenor House Chater Street Moulton Northampton Northamptonshire NN3 1UD
Tel: 01604 643241
Emergency telephone 01604 643241
List of partners: M E Jeffery
Work: G
Agency, Advocacy and Legal Aid undertaken

KING SOLICITORS ‡
2 St Giles Terrace Northampton Northamptonshire NN1 2BN
Tel: 01604 491939 *Fax:* 01604 820695 *Dx:* 12417 NORTHAMPTON

MACDONALD LAW ‡
19 Church Way Grendon Northampton Northamptonshire NN7 1JE
Tel: 01933 664827

MCGANNS LAW ‡
57 Norfolk Street Northampton Northamptonshire NN2 6HR
Tel: 0845 071 4393 *Fax:* 0845 071 4394
E-mail: caroline.mcgann@mcgannslaw.co.uk

J F MCMAHON ‡
Bluebell House 17 West Street Northampton Northamptonshire NN3 7SB
Tel: 01604 494340

MARTIN ADAMS & MCCOLL ‡
300 Wellingborough Road Northampton Northamptonshire NN1 4EP
Tel: 01604 634123 *Fax:* 01604 232282 *Dx:* 12415 NORTHAMPTON
E-mail: rah@adamsmccoll.com
List of partners: R A Haig, M Sharman
Work: E J1 K1 K3 K4 L N Q S1 S2 T2 V W Z(l)
Agency, Advocacy and Fixed Fee Interview undertaken
Ptr: Haig, Mr Rodney A Deputy Coroner for Northamptonshire . . . . *Jun 1971
Sharman, Mr Martin. . . . . *§May 1979

MASON BULLOCK SOLICITORS ‡
4 Albion Place Northampton Northamptonshire NN1 1UD
Tel: 01604 601575 *Fax:* 01604 603454
Dx: 12450 NORTHAMPTON 2
E-mail: info@masonb.co.uk
List of partners: A C Crisp, I S Mason
Work: B1 C1 E F1 I J1 L O Q S1 S2 W Z(d,e,g,p)
Agency undertaken
Ptr: Crisp, Mr Andrew Charles LPC . . . . *Sep 1999
Mason, Mr Ian Stuart MA(Oxon). . . . . *Jun 1977
Ast: Kennaird-Banner, Mrs Suzanne LLB. . . . . *Jul 2000

STEPHEN MOORE & CO
45 York Road Northampton Northamptonshire NN1 5QJ
Tel: 01604 601000 *Fax:* 01604 633017 *Dx:* 12486 NORTHAMPTON
E-mail: northampton@stephenmoore.ncounterus.co.uk
Office: Rugby

NEVES
Independent House Units 1-2 Wilks Walk Northampton Northamptonshire NN4 5DW
Tel: 01604 814500 *Fax:* 01604 765813
E-mail: info@neves-solicitors.co.uk
Office: Harpenden, Luton, Milton Keynes
Work: A1 A3 C1 C2 D1 E F1 J1 K1 K2 K3 L M4 O Q R1 S1 S2 T1 T2 W Z(c,h,l,p)
Fixed Fee Interview undertaken
Ptr: Hume, Mrs Caroline. . . . . *Aug 1999

R J OSBORNE & CO
Collingwood Business Centre Lower Harding Street Northampton Northamptonshire NN1 2JL
Tel: 01604 636279
E-mail: mail@rjo-corby.co.uk
Office: Corby, Wellingborough

PARK WOODFINE HEALD MELLOWS LLP
16 Castilian Street Northampton Northamptonshire NN1 1JX
Tel: 01604 233200 *Fax:* 01604 232593
Dx: 12418 NORTHAMPTON 1
E-mail: admin@pwhmllp.com
Office: Bedford, Rushden
Work: D1 F1 K1 L N O Q S1 T1 T2 V W Z(d,l)
Emergency Action, Agency, Advocacy, Fixed Fee Interview, Legal Aid undertaken and Member of Accident Line
Ptr: Pears, Mr Ian Geoffrey LLB(Hons) . . . . *§Jan 1986
Ast: Buys, Mr Pete. Mar 2000
Wilton, Mr Peter LLB . . . . Oct 2003

ANNE M C PEMBER ‡
300 Wellingborough Road Northampton Northamptonshire NN1 4EP
Tel: 01604 624732

PRESTER COLEMAN & CO ‡
327a Wellingborough Road Northampton Northamptonshire NN1 4EW
Tel: 01604 633133 *Fax:* 01604 639237
List of partners: P D Coleman
Work: D1 D2 K1 Z(m)
Emergency Action, Agency, Advocacy and Legal Aid undertaken
Ptr: Coleman, Prester D BA . . . . *Jun 1976

JANE E ROBERTS ‡
PO Box 5385 Northampton Northamptonshire NN6 0YT
Tel: 01604 494431 *Fax:* 01604 494431
List of partners: J E Roberts
Work: D1 K1
Agency, Advocacy and Legal Aid undertaken
SPr: Roberts, Mrs Jane Elizabeth LLB . . . . *Oct 1982

ROBIN ROSE ‡
12 Verdant Vale East Hunsbury Northampton Northamptonshire NN4 0SQ
Tel: 01604 760168 *Fax:* 01604 760168
Emergency telephone 07702 415185
E-mail: robinrose@btconnect.com
List of partners: R I L Rose
Languages: French
Work: G H
Agency, Advocacy and Legal Aid undertaken
SPr: Rose, Mr Robin I L . . . . Dec 1975

SP LAW ‡
133 Stimpson Avenue Northampton Northamptonshire NN1 4JN
Tel: 01604 638905 *Fax:* 01604 638548
Dx: 18509 NORTHAMPTON 2
E-mail: info@sp-law.co.uk

SHOOSMITHS ‡
The Lakes Bedford Road Northampton Northamptonshire NN4 7SH
Tel: 0370 086 3000 / 01604 543000 *Fax:* 0370 086 3001
Dx: 712280 NORTHAMPTON 12
E-mail: northampton@shoosmiths.co.uk
List of partners: Z Ahmed, P Andrews, S Angus, G D Assim, T F Bacon, C M Bagley, J A Bartley, G R Bennett, A Bishop, S A Boss, T Brookes, O C Brookshaw, O C Brookshaw, S Burke, H Chandler, D Clegg, A Corcoran, Y Dania, S Dard, J Davis, H Derbyshire, C Dewes, C P Dolan, R Donoghue, J Dorkins, D P Drew, P H Duff, A Farmery, V Farooq, R T Follis, C J Garnett, T George, C A Gibson, I Gilbey, D Gordon Brown, D Gordon-Brown, J Hadley, K L Harrison, J H Harvey, P J Heath, K Hewson, M J Higgin, J C Hill, W I Howard, D Jackson, J Jackson, J D Jackson, H Jess, J L Keates, M W J Kenwood, L Knight, S Knott, J N Kordan, S Law, J Lehman, S Little, S F Mallalieu, W Mannix, L J Marshall, O B Martin, A Mason, C Mattis, K McCavish, R McGuirk, S E Montgomery, D A Morley, N Murphy, M J Murray, D Parton, A Peet, G J C Perry, A J Pickin, S Porter, S Price, R F Reid, C M Rowe, A K Rusbridge, R Sawbridge, W P Seary, E Sfar-Gandoura, K Shakespeare, S Sharma, M Shepherd, N Shepherd, M Sherwood, E Shirtcliffe, G J Simpson, K Stewart, A E L Taylor, J C Temple, D Thompson, N M Thorne, M Upfold, G Willetts, L Williams, H Wilson, S A Wiltshire, E Wojciechowski, S Wright
Office: Basingstoke, Birmingham, Fareham, London WC2, Manchester, Milton Keynes, Nottingham, Reading
Languages: French, German
Work: A3 B1 B2 C1 C2 C3 E F1 F2 I J1 J2 K4 L M1 N O Q R1 R2 S1 S2 T1 T2 U2 W X Z(b,c,e,f,h,i,j,k,l,m,n,o,p,q,r,s,t,u,y,za)
Agency undertaken and Member of Accident Line
Ptr: Angus, Mr Stuart . . . . Jan 1998
Assim, Mr Gary D BA(Hons) . . . . *§Nov 1990
Bagley, Miss Carolyn Marjorie MA(Oxon) . . . . . . *§Oct 1985
Bartley, Mr Jonathan Adam LLB. . . . . *Nov 1997
Dorkins, Ms Judith LLB . . . . *§Dec 1989
George, Mr Trevor LLB(Lond). . . . . *§Apr 1977
Gibson, Mrs Catriona Ann LLB(Hons) . . . . *Nov 1993
Hill, Mr John Christopher BSc. . . . . *§Dec 1976
Mallalieu, Mrs Susan Frazer BA(Hons) . . . . *§Oct 1995
Mannix, Mr Waine LLB(Hons). . . . . *§Nov 1991
Marshall, Mr Laurence Jon LLB; ACIB. . . . . *§Feb 1986
Montgomery, Mr Stuart E . . . . Jan 1999
Murray, Mr Michael J . . . . *§Jul 1977
Parton, Mr David . . . . *§Nov 1991
Price, Mr Sebastian BA(Lond). . . . . *§Dec 1986
Reid, Mr Ronald F. . . . . *§Jan 1983
Rusbridge, Mrs Andrea Karen LLB(Hons) . . . . . . *§Dec 1989
Shepherd, Mr Nicholas BA(Hons) . . . . *Nov 1993
Stewart, Ms Karen . . . . *§Sep 1997
Taylor, Ms Angela Evelyn Llewellyn LLB. . . . . Apr 1976
Temple, Mr John C LLM(B'ham). . . . . *§Jun 1977
Upfold, Mr Malcolm . . . . *§Sep 1995
Wiltshire, Mr Stephen A LLB(Hons) . . . . *§Sep 1988
Asoc: Hibbett, Miss Jacqueline LLB(Leeds) . . . . *§Jan 1987
Ast: Burkitt, Mr Ross LLB(Hons) . . . . *Dec 1998

SUMMERS NIGH LAW LLP ‡
The Chapel Little Brington Northampton Northamptonshire NN7 4HX
Tel: 01604 771136 *Fax:* 01604 772330
E-mail: cheri@summersnighlaw.co.uk
List of partners: D Nigh, K C Summers
Mem: Nigh, Miss Deborah LLB . . . . Apr 1999
Summers, Mrs Katharine Claire LLB(Hons) . . . . . . *Oct 1992

ANDREW SUTTON LAW ‡
The Spinney 1 The Avenue Moulton Northampton Northamptonshire NN3 7TL
Tel: 07816 308265 *Fax:* 01604 644289

TMJ LAW SOLICITORS ‡
TMJ House 5 Notre Dame Mews Northampton Northamptonshire NN1 2BG
Tel: 01604 608111 *Fax:* 01604 628777
Emergency telephone 0845 230 8090
E-mail: info@tmjlaw.co.uk
List of partners: D R Peake, T Synnott
Languages: French, Hindi, Romanian, Russian, Spanish, Urdu
Work: C1 C2 E F1 F2 J1 K1 K3 L O Q R1 R2 S1 S2 Z(f,q,z)
Agency and Fixed Fee Interview undertaken
Ptr: Peake, Mr Darren R LLB . . . . *Oct 1987
Synnott, Mr Terry . . . . *Jul 2003

TOLLERS LLP ‡
2 Castilian Street Northampton Northamptonshire NN1 1JX
Tel: 01604 258558 *Fax:* 01604 258500
Dx: 12422 NORTHAMPTON 1
E-mail: enquiries@tollers.co.uk
List of partners: D Bisatt, D Boobyer, D M Boobyer, C Brooks, I Carson, P Felton, D C Fowler, J Gibney, K Herrod, M Hill, M T Hill, I Hunnings, T I M Hunnings, T R Kings, T Kings, L Lord, L E Lord, A Niblock, D Nicholson, A Peck, A T Peck, J L Peck, B Rogers, B C Rogers, A Rudkin, A M Rudkin, C Saunby, C C Saunby, C Scudamore, C B Scudamore, S Smith, S L Smith, G Tait, G R Tait
Office: Corby, Kettering, Milton Keynes
Ptr: Bisatt, Mr Duncan. . . . . Jan 1998
Boobyer, Mr David Michael LLB. . . . . *Oct 1993
Brooks, Mr Colin . . . . Jan 2001
Carson, Mr Ian BA(Cantab) . . . . *Nov 1993
Gibney, Mr John . . . . Jan 1995
Herrod, Ms Katie . . . . Jan 1997
Hill, Mr Martin. . . . . Jan 1987
Hunnings, Mr T Ingemar M LLB. . . . . *Nov 1992
Kings, Mr Tom . . . . Jan 1984
Lord, Ms Lucy Ellen. . . . . Sep 2001
Niblock, Mr Andrew . . . . May 1999
Nicholson, Mr Duncan. . . . . Jan 1996
Peck, Mr Alan. Jan 1989
Rogers, Mr Barry . . . . Jan 1981
Rudkin, Mr Andrew M BA . . . . *Dec 1975
Saunby, Chris. Jan 1977
Saunby, Mr Christopher C FCIArb. . . . . *§Jun 1977
Scudamore, Mrs Carol B LLB . . . . *Oct 1995
Smith, Miss Sally L LLB. . . . . *Nov 1994

See p112 for the Key to Work Categories & other symbols

Tait, Mr Gary R LLB. . . . . *Mar 1992
Dir: Felton, Ms Paula LLB(Hons); MBA Trustee of Age Concern Milton Keynes. Apr 2002
Asoc: Holdom, Mr Tristan . . . . Jan 1992
Markham, Ms Ruth . . . . Apr 2005
Ast: Barrett, Ms Emma. . . . . *May 1999
Cox, Miss Marie LLB . . . . Mar 2008
Gradus, Ms Erica . . . . Mar 2008
Hawkins, Ms Cheryl. . . . . Feb 1999
Tyrrell, Mrs Louise Mary LLB . . . . Apr 2003

TURNER COULSTON ‡
29 Billing Road Northampton Northamptonshire NN1 5DQ
Tel: 01604 622101 *Fax:* 01604 230829 *Dx:* 12405 NORTHAMPTON
E-mail: law@turner-coulston.co.uk
List of partners: R J Benneworth, J Cato, J H Josephs, K Turner
Office: Kettering
Work: B1 C1 C2 C3 D1 E F1 J1 K1 L N O P Q S1 T1 T2 W Z(c,e,h,i,k,l)
Emergency Action, Agency, Advocacy, Fixed Fee Interview, Legal Aid undertaken and Member of Accident Line
Ptr: Benneworth, Mr Roland JAMES. . . . . *Jul 1978
Cato, Mr John LLB . . . . *Feb 1989
Turner, Mr Keith ACIArb. . . . . *Dec 1972
Asoc: Franklin, Mrs Sarah Elizabeth LLB(Hons) . . . . . . *Nov 1998
Owens, Mrs Susan LLB(Hons); LPC. . . . . *Jun 1998
Ast: Ashton, Mr James Thomas . . . . *Oct 1980
Bhachu, Mrs Mandip . . . . *Feb 1998

WILSON BROWNE
4 Grange Park Court Roman Way Northampton Northamptonshire NN4 5EA
Tel: 01604 876697 *Fax:* 01604 768606
Dx: 719015 NORTHAMPTON 14
E-mail: enquiries@wilsonbrowne.co.uk
Office: Higham Ferrers, Kettering (2 offices), Leicester, Wellingborough
Languages: French
Work: A1 A3 B1 C1 C2 C3 D1 D2 E F1 F2 G I J1 J2 K1 K2 L M1 N O P Q R1 R2 S1 S2 T1 V W Z(d,h,l,m,r,t)
Emergency Action, Agency, Advocacy, Fixed Fee Interview, Legal Aid undertaken, Legal Aid Franchise and Member of Accident Line
Ptr: Arnold, Mr Richard M LLB. . . . . *§Apr 1974
Bridgens, Mr Simon R D LLB . . . . *Apr 1976
Laskey, Miss Jennifer Mary LLB. . . . . *Nov 1997
Saynor, Mr John Charles LLB(B'ham) . . . . *§Dec 1977
Wilson, Mrs Mary Christine LLB . . . . *§Jun 1977

WOODCOCK & THOMPSON ‡
121-123 St James Road St James Northampton Northamptonshire NN5 5LD
Tel: 01604 758855 *Fax:* 01604 750060
Dx: 15628 NORTHAMPTON 3
E-mail: cgreenwood@wtsolicitors.co.uk
List of partners: I Sanders
Office: Daventry
Languages: Russian
Work: A1 C1 E S1 S2 W Z(c,i)
Agency and Fixed Fee Interview undertaken
SPr: Sanders, Mr Ivan BA(Hons). . . . . *§Mar 1979

WOODFORD ROBINSON ‡
Williams House 4 Castilian Terrace Northampton Northamptonshire NN1 1LE
Tel: 01604 624926 *Fax:* 01604 231457
Dx: 12424 NORTHAMPTON 1
E-mail: info@woodford-robinson.co.uk
List of partners: N F Foster, B M J Lilley, R C Warren, J G Weaver
Work: A1 B1 C1 D1 D2 E G H K1 L N Q R1 S1 T1 W Z(l)
Emergency Action, Agency, Advocacy, Fixed Fee Interview, Legal Aid undertaken and Legal Aid Franchise
Ptr: Foster, Mr Neil F LLB(Lond). . . . . *§Sep 1978
Lilley, Mr Barry Martin James LLB(Bris) . . . . *Jun 1977
Warren, Mr Roy C. *Sep 1976
Weaver, Mr John G MA(Cantab) . . . . *May 1973

NORTHENDEN, Greater Manchester

MITCHELLS SOLICITORS ‡
392 Palatine Road Northenden Greater Manchester M22 4FZ
Tel: 0161 945 2299 *Fax:* 0161 945 2298
E-mail: mitchells.sols@btconnect.com

OTTEN PENNA LTD ‡
339 Palatine Road Northenden Greater Manchester M22 4HH
Tel: 0161 945 1431 *Fax:* 0161 946 0408 *Dx:* 29382 NORTHENDEN
E-mail: northenden@ottenpenna.co.uk
List of partners: V L Garner, S P Saunders, V Wright
Office: Manchester
Work: D1 D2 K1 K3 W Z(m)
Emergency Action, Agency, Advocacy, Fixed Fee Interview, Legal Aid undertaken and Legal Aid Franchise
Ptr: Garner, Miss V Louise BA. . . . . *Oct 1985
Saunders, Mr Simon Peter BA(Hons) . . . . Nov 1992
Wright, Mrs Victoria LLB(Hons) . . . . Oct 1997
Ast: Cragg, Ms Susan . . . . *Oct 1992
Edwards, Ms Ruth . . . . Oct 1985

NORTHOLT, Middlesex

HEBBAR & CO ‡
157 Mandeville Road Northolt Middlesex UB5 4LZ
Tel: 020 8423 8234

REGENT ASSOCIATES SOLICITORS ‡
1st Floor 171-175 Church Road Northolt Middlesex UB5 5AG
Tel: 020 8841 1100 *Fax:* 020 8841 1611
E-mail: regentsolicitors@aol.com

NORTHWICH, Cheshire

ACCIDENT ADVICE SOLICITORS ‡
Whitehall 75 School Lane Hartford Northwich Cheshire CW8 1PF
Tel: 0844 846 0499 *Fax:* 0844 846 0488
E-mail: info@accidentadvicesolicitors.co.uk

JOHN BLACK SOLICITORS ‡
27A High Street Northwich Cheshire CW9 5BY
Tel: 01606 330044 *Fax:* 01606 334401

BUTCHER & BARLOW LLP
Dane Bridge Chambers 3-5 London Road Northwich Cheshire CW9 5EY
Tel: 01606 47523 *Fax:* 01606 41289 *Dx:* 23804 NORTHWICH
E-mail: anorman@butcher-barlow.co.uk
Office: Bramhall, Bury (2 offices), Frodsham, Leigh, Prestwich, Runcorn (2 offices), Sandbach, Tyldesley
Work: A1 B1 C1 C2 C3 D1 E F1 J1 K1 K3 K4 L M1 M2 N O P Q R1 R2 S1 S2 T1 T2 V W Z(c,d,e,j,l,m,o,p,q,r,t)
Emergency Action, Agency, Advocacy, Fixed Fee Interview, Legal Aid undertaken, Legal Aid Franchise and Member of Accident Line
Ptr: Norman, Mrs Amy Susan . . . . *Sep 2002
Ast: Cockill-Guy, Mrs Caraoline BA(Hons) . . . . *Jan 1999
Porter, Mr Gregory Lee LLB(Hons) . . . . Jan 2010

CHAMBERS FLETCHER LLP ‡
20 Winnington Street Northwich Cheshire CW8 1AF
Tel: 01606 780400 *Fax:* 01606 782445 *Dx:* 23805 NORTHWICH
E-mail: info@chambersfletcher.co.uk
List of partners: D M Marks, M S Weston, P D Wilkinson
Work: A1 C1 C2 D1 D2 E F1 F2 J1 J2 K1 K3 L N Q R1 S1 S2 T1 T2 V W Z(q,r)
Agency, Advocacy, Fixed Fee Interview, Legal Aid undertaken and Legal Aid Franchise
Ptr: Marks, Mrs Danielle Marie LLB(Hons). . . . . *Aug 2000
Weston, Mr Martin S LLB . . . . *§Jun 1979
Wilkinson, Mr Peter D BA . . . . *§Nov 1987
Ast: Worrall, Mr Stephen LLB . . . . *§Nov 2001
Con: Lloyd, Mr Stephen F BA. . . . . *§Mar 1979
Lowe, Mr Timothy J. . . . . *§Jan 1969

DIXON RIGBY KEOGH
Old Bank Chambers 32 High Street Northwich Cheshire CW9 5BL
Tel: 01606 48111 *Fax:* 01606 41238 *Dx:* 23801 NORTHWICH
Office: Middlewich, Sandbach, Winsford
Work: C1 D1 D2 E F1 J1 K1 K3 K4 L N O Q S1 S2 W
Emergency Action, Agency, Advocacy and Fixed Fee Interview undertaken
Ptr: McMaster, Ms Linda Kay LLB(Hons). . . . . *Aug 1998
Parson, Mr Nicholas G LLB . . . . *May 1988
Sumner, Miss Melanie Kaye LLB(Hons) . . . . *Sep 1995

GAVIN EDMONDSON SOLICITORS ‡
90 Witton Street Northwich Cheshire CW9 5AE
Tel: 01606 43762
List of partners: G Edmondson
Dir: Edmondson, Mr Gavin LLB Welfare Law; Academic Excellence Prize . . . . Mar 2001

SUSAN HOWARTH & CO ‡
41 Chesterway Northwich Cheshire CW9 5JE
Tel: 01606 48777 *Fax:* 01606 49777 *Dx:* 23814 NORTHWICH
E-mail: info@susanhowarthsolicitors.co.uk
List of partners: S Howarth, J Williamson
Work: D1 D2 K1 K2 L N Q S1 S2 V W X Z(r)
Emergency Action, Agency, Advocacy, Legal Aid undertaken and Legal Aid Franchise
Ptr: Howarth, Mrs Susan BA(Hons)(Econ); DASS; LLB(Hons) . . . . *Oct 1993
Williamson, Ms Jane LLB Part time Chairman of Special Education Tribunal Needs. . . . . *May 1981

JONES ROBERTSON
County Court Building 27a High Street Northwich Cheshire CW9 5BY
Tel: 01606 331188 *Fax:* 01606 330099 *Dx:* 23812 NORTHWICH
E-mail: jonesrobertson@btconnect.com
Office: Runcorn, Widnes
Work: D1 G H J1 K1 L N Q S1 V W Z(o)
Emergency Action, Agency, Advocacy, Fixed Fee Interview, Legal Aid undertaken and Member of Accident Line

M&S LEGAL ‡
100 Witton Street Northwich Cheshire CW9 5AB
Tel: 01606 330202 *Fax:* 01606 46123

MOSSHASELHURST ‡
2 Castle Street Northwich Cheshire CW8 1AB
Tel: 01606 74301 *Fax:* 01606 871034 *Dx:* 23806 NORTHWICH
E-mail: reception@mosshaselhurst.co.uk
List of partners: C H Johnson, G M P Rooney
Office: Winsford
Work: A1 B1 D1 E F1 G H J1 K1 K3 L N Q S1 S2 T2 V W Z(l,t)
Agency, Advocacy, Fixed Fee Interview, Legal Aid undertaken, Legal Aid Franchise and Member of Accident Line
Ptr: Johnson, Mr Christopher H LLB Acting Stipendiary Magistrate . . . . *Mar 1975
Rooney, Mr Gerard M P LLB(L'pool). . . . . *Oct 1980
Ast: Bailey, Mrs Katie LLB; LPC . . . . *Jan 2006
Charles, Miss Joanne Claire LLB; LPC . . . . *Dec 2004
Hurley, Mr William Kenneth LLB(Hons); LPC . . . . . Mar 2007
McRae, Mr Kenneth Iain James LLB . . . . *Dec 1977
Con: Manning, Miss Diana Linda Vernon LLB; LSF . . . . *Jan 1980
Pickup, Mr John B Notary Public . . . . *§Mar 1961

PERSONAL INJURY PRACTICE LTD ‡
Citadel House Solvay Road Northwich Cheshire CW8 4DP
Tel: 01606 350000 *Fax:* 01606 350011
E-mail: info@piplaw.co.uk

POOLE ALCOCK
91-93a Brunner Court Witton Street Northwich Cheshire CW9 5DR
Tel: 01606 350445 *Fax:* 01606 350055 *Dx:* 23824 NORTHWICH
E-mail: northwich@poolealcock.co.uk
Office: Alsager, Chester, Congleton, Crewe (2 offices), Nantwich, Sandbach, Warrington
Work: S1 W

S E LAW ‡
443c London Road Davenham Northwich Cheshire CW9 8HP
Tel: 01606 333533 *Fax:* 01606 333963

TQ SOLICITORS
Walnut Barn Uplands Road Anderton Northwich Cheshire CW9 6AJ
Tel: 01942 671166 *Fax:* 01942 671171 *Dx:* 22508 LEIGH
E-mail: info@tqsolicitors.com
Office: Leigh

2

NORTHWOOD, Middlesex

BAVISI LEGAL LIMITED ‡
5 Reginald Road Northwood Middlesex HA6 1EG
Tel: 01923 835870 / 07811 439999
E-mail: info@bavisilegal.com

BLACKSTONES SOLICITORS ‡
Argyle House North Wing Joel Street Northwood Middlesex HA6 1NW
Tel: 01923 828244 *Fax:* 01923 828292 *Dx:* 35507 NORTHWOOD
E-mail: info@blackstoneslaw.com

DJ SOLICITORS ‡
116 Green Lane Northwood Middlesex HA6 1AW
Tel: 01923 828668

LINCOLNS SOLICITORS ‡
Lynx House Ferndown Northwood Middlesex HA6 1PQ
Tel: 01923 820909 *Fax:* 01923 241348
List of partners: R Lincoln, K J S Sohal
Work: E J1 K1 L S1 S2 Z(i,l)
Ptr: Lincoln, Mr Raj LLB(Hons) . . . . Sep 1996
Sohal, Mr Kanwal J S. . . . . *Feb 1986

NORTHWOOD LAW PRACTICE ‡
47-49 Green Lane Northwood Middlesex HA6 3AE
Tel: 01923 826208 *Fax:* 01923 835225 *Dx:* 35503 NORTHWOOD
E-mail: info@northwoodlaw.com
List of partners: N Tiwana
Work: D1 K1 L Q S1 W Z(q)
Emergency Action, Fixed Fee Interview, Legal Aid undertaken and Legal Aid Franchise
SPr: Tiwana, Mrs Noorani BSc(Hons) . . . . *Nov 1993

LAWRENCE C SAMUELS LLB SOLICITOR ‡
29 Farm Way Northwood Middlesex HA6 3EE
Tel: 01923 824708 *Fax:* 01923 824708
E-mail: lawrencesamuels29@hotmail.com
List of partners: L C Samuels
Work: E S1 S2 W
SPr: Samuels, Mr Lawrence C LLB. . . . . *Jun 1970

SEABOURNE LAWLEYS ‡
60-62 High Street Northwood Middlesex HA6 1BL
Tel: 01923 820639 *Fax:* 01923 821027 *Dx:* 35508 NORTHWOOD
Emergency telephone 01923 770629
List of partners: M Seabourne
Languages: French
Work: C1 C2 E F1 J1 K1 L O Q R2 S1 S2 W Z(m)
Fixed Fee Interview undertaken
Ptr: Seabourne, Mrs Megan LLB. . . . . *Oct 1989

TARBOX ROBINSON & PARTNERS ‡
25 Maxwell Road Northwood Middlesex HA6 2XY
Tel: 01923 836595 *Fax:* 01923 835315 *Dx:* 35500 NORTHWOOD
E-mail: law@trlaw.net
List of partners: J H Payne, M A H Robinson, J P Tarbox
Work: C1 D1 E F1 G I J1 K1 L M1 N O P Q R1 S1 T1 W
Agency, Fixed Fee Interview, Legal Aid undertaken and Member of Accident Line
Ptr: Payne, Mr John H LLB(Lond) . . . . *Dec 1976
Robinson, Mr Michael Alexander Henry BA . . . . . . *§Jun 1972
Tarbox, Mr Jeremy P . . . . *Jun 1976

LINDA S WARREN ‡
37 Nicholas Way Northwood Middlesex HA6 2TR
Tel: 01923 821213 *Fax:* 01923 827519
E-mail: lswarrensolicitor@btinternet.com
List of partners: L S Warren
Work: S1 S2 W
SPr: Warren, Mrs Linda S LLB . . . . *Apr 1974

NORWICH, Norfolk

ACT SOLICITORS ‡
25 St John Maddermarket Norwich Norfolk NR2 1DN
Tel: 01603 610611 *Fax:* 01603 230574
E-mail: info@actsolicitors.co.uk
List of partners: J Plummer, R Saunders
Mem: Plummer, Mr Jamieson LLB(Lond) Notary Public . . . *Nov 1977
Saunders, Rebecca. . . . . Sep 2003

ALLAN RUTHERFORD ‡
3 Woolgate Court St Benedicts Street Norwich Norfolk NR2 4AP
Tel: 01603 621722 *Fax:* 01603 625414
List of partners: I A G McNally, K M McNally
Work: D1 D2 E F1 G H K1 L N P Q R1 S1 S2 V W Z(i,q,r)
Emergency Action, Agency, Advocacy, Fixed Fee Interview, Legal Aid undertaken, Legal Aid Franchise and Member of Accident Line
Ptr: McNally, Mr Ian A G BA. . . . . *Nov 1988
McNally, Mrs Katherine Margaret . . . . *Dec 1998
Ast: Palihawadana, Mr Prasad BA. . . . . *Aug 1996
Rodger, Miss Lucinda J BA(Kent) . . . . *Oct 1981

ASHMOLES SOLICITORS ‡
Unthank Chambers 50 Unthank Road Norwich Norfolk NR2 2RF
Tel: 01603 629749
E-mail: info@ashmoles-law.co.uk

ASHTON KCJ
Trafalgar House Meridian Way Norwich Norfolk NR7 0TA
Tel: 01603 703070 *Fax:* 01603 703075 *Dx:* 138522 NORWICH 7
E-mail: enquiries.norwich@ashtonkcj.co.uk
Office: Bury St Edmunds (2 offices), Cambridge, Felixstowe, Ipswich, Thetford
Languages: French, German, Swedish
Work: A1 A2 A3 B1 C1 C2 C3 D1 E F1 F2 I J1 J2 K1 K2 K3 L M1 M2 N O P Q R1 R2 S1 S2 T1 T2 U2 V W Z(c,d,e,h,j,l,n,o,p,q,r,u,z)
Emergency Action, Agency, Advocacy, Fixed Fee Interview, Legal Aid undertaken and Member of Accident Line

BELMORES ‡
40 Crown Road Norwich Norfolk NR1 3DX
Tel: 01603 499999 *Fax:* 01603 499998 *Dx:* 5232 NORWICH
Emergency telephone 01603 499999
E-mail: info@belmores.co.uk
List of partners: D R M Foulkes, S J Nicholls
Languages: French
Work: G H
Agency, Fixed Fee Interview, Legal Aid undertaken and Legal Aid Franchise
Dir: Foulkes, Mr David R M LLB ★ . . . . *Oct 1990
Nicholls, Mr Simon J BA(Hons) ★ . . . . *Dec 1979
Ast: Gowland, Julie . . . . *Apr 2006
Taunton, Mr Alistair J LLB ★ . . . . *Jun 1979

BIRKETTS LLP
Kingfisher House 1 Gilders Way Norwich Norfolk NR3 1UB
Tel: 01603 232300 *Fax:* 01603 230533 *Dx:* 5230 NORWICH
Office: Cambridge, Chelmsford, Ipswich

CHAMBERS & CO ‡
Jonathan Scott Hall Thorpe Road Norwich Norfolk NR1 1UH
Tel: 01603 616155 *Fax:* 01603 616156

JOHN S CHINNERY SOLICITOR ‡
Loke Cottage The Croft Norwich Norfolk NR8 5DT
Tel: 01603 742141

COLE & CO ‡
23 Tombland Norwich Norfolk NR3 1RF
Tel: 01603 617018
List of partners: P A Brodie, D E Clarke, N J E Foster, R A G Temple
Ptr: Brodie, Ms Patricia Ann . . . . Dec 2004
Clarke, Mr David E BA . . . . *Mar 1984
Foster, Mr Nicholas James Edward LLB . . . . *Nov 1982
Temple, Mr Richard A G LLB(Hons) . . . . *§Feb 1983
Asoc: Eddy, Mr Carolyn Jane LLB . . . . *Nov 1987
Long, Mrs Beverley Jayne . . . . *Oct 1995
Ast: Illing, Mrs Caroline Lonsdale BSc . . . . Nov 2003
Smy, Miss Sarah Ruth LLB(Hons) . . . . *Nov 1990

COZENS-HARDY LLP ‡
Castle Chambers Opie Street Norwich Norfolk NR1 3DP
Tel: 01603 625231 *Fax:* 01603 627160 *Dx:* 5214 NORWICH
E-mail: lawyers@cozens-hardy.com
List of partners: J M Anderson, M Collins, C G Groves, S R Nunn, P Rudd, D J Short, A J Spencer, W S Whipp, I D White
Work: A1 B1 C1 C2 C3 D1 D2 E F1 J1 J2 K1 L N O P Q R1 S1 S2 T1 T2 V W Z(c,d,g,h,q,r)
Emergency Action, Advocacy, Fixed Fee Interview, Legal Aid undertaken, Legal Aid Franchise and Member of Accident Line
Ptr: Anderson, Mrs Jane M LLB(Hons) . . . . *Sep 1988
Collins, Mrs Michelle LLB . . . . *Jul 2007
Groves, Mr Christopher G LLB(L'pool) . . . . *§Jun 1975
Nunn, Miss Sandra R LLB(Hons) . . . . *Sep 1993
Rudd, Ms Philippa LLB(Hons) . . . . *Oct 1989
Short, Mr Damian J LLB(Hons) . . . . *Nov 1994
Spencer, Mr Andrew Jamie LLB(Hons) . . . . *Oct 1995
Whipp, Mr William Simon LLB . . . . *§Dec 1986
White, Mr Iain D LLB(Hons) . . . . *§Jan 1977
Asoc: Cross, Miss Janet Elizabeth BA(Law) . . . . *Nov 1977
Farquharson, Ms Anna LLB(Hons) . . . . *Jul 1996
Gilbert, Mrs Jane M LLB(Hons); MA . . . . *Oct 1987
Hunter, Mrs Charlotte LLB(Hons) . . . . *Sep 2002
Ast: Evans, Mr Daniel William BA(Hons) . . . . *Jul 2009
McCulloch, Mr James LLB(Hons) . . . . *Sep 2010
Sullivan, Miss Carly LLB(Hons) . . . . *Oct 2006
Watson, Miss Beth Caroline LLB . . . . *Sep 2010

DHP TRUSTEE CAMPANY ‡
Holland Court The Close Norwich Norfolk NR1 4DX

GORDON DEAN SOLICITORS ‡
16 Princes Street Norwich Norfolk NR3 1AE
Tel: 01603 767671 *Fax:* 01603 767688
E-mail: administration@gordondeansolicitors.co.uk
List of partners: N Austin, P C Bazley, G R Dean
Office: Great Yarmouth
Work: J1 K4 N Q W Z(q,r)
Fixed Fee Interview undertaken
Ptr: Bazley, Mr Phillip Colin BA(Hons); CPE; LPC . . . . *Nov 2001
Dean, Mr Gordon Richard . . . . *Dec 2001
Austin, Neil . . . . NSP

FACE TO FACE ‡
40 Rose Lane Norwich Norfolk NR1 1PN
Tel: 01603 625100 *Fax:* 01603 625101
E-mail: info@facetofacesolicitors.com

FAMILY LAW CONSULTANCY ‡
15 Charing Cross Norwich Norfolk NR2 4AX
Tel: 01603 664000 *Fax:* 01603 664006 *Dx:* 5321 NORWICH

FISHER COWE SOLICITORS ‡
44 Prince of Wales Road Norwich Norfolk NR1 1LL
Tel: 01603 878383

FOSTERS ‡
(incorporating Russell Steward)
William House 19 Bank Plain Norwich Norfolk NR2 4FS
Tel: 01603 620508 *Fax:* 01603 624090 *Dx:* 5225 NORWICH
Emergency telephone 01603 620508
E-mail: enquiries@fosters-solicitors.co.uk
List of partners: C R Brown, M F G Dunne, C A M Iliff, J R Ives, I S McClay, M J Mullender, A P Saul, L J Simpson
Office: Bungay, Lowestoft, Wymondham
Languages: French, German
Work: A1 B1 C1 C2 C3 D1 E F1 G H J1 K1 L N O P Q R1 S1 T1 T2 V W Z(c,i,l,m,p)
Emergency Action, Agency, Advocacy, Fixed Fee Interview, Legal Aid undertaken and Legal Aid Franchise
Ptr: Brown, Mr Christopher Roy . . . . Nov 1998
Iliff, Miss Catherine A M LLB . . . . *§Apr 1982
Ives, Mr Jeremy R LLB ♦ . . . . *§Jan 1987
McClay, Mr Iain S BA . . . . *Feb 1992
Saul, Mr Andrew P LLB(Lond) . . . . *§Dec 1980
Simpson, Ms Lucy Jane . . . . *Nov 1999
Ast: Green, Mr Stephen P BA . . . . *Oct 1991

RODNEY GOODSON ‡
50 Unthank Road Norwich Norfolk NR2 2RF
Tel: 01603 632832 *Fax:* 01603 763093
E-mail: rodlaw@btclick.com
List of partners: R Goodson
Work: E L S1 S2 W
SPr: Goodson, Mr Rodney . . . . *Jan 1970

GREENLAND HOUCHEN POMEROY ‡
36-40 Prince of Wales Road Norwich Norfolk NR1 1HZ
Tel: 01603 660744 *Fax:* 01603 610700 *Dx:* 5217 NORWICH
E-mail: mail@ghlaw.co.uk
List of partners: S N Carrel, P M Cook, A P Goldring, D J Harris, C E Heywood, J N Lightbown, K W Oelrichs, R Percival, J Walford, C D Wright
Office: Attleborough, Long Stratton, Watton, Wymondham
Languages: French, Spanish
Work: A1 B1 C1 D1 E F1 J1 K1 K2 K3 K4 L N O Q R1 S1 S2 T1 T2 V W Z(c,d,h,l,s,t,w)
Emergency Action, Agency, Advocacy, Fixed Fee Interview, Legal Aid undertaken, Legal Aid Franchise and Member of Accident Line
Ptr: Carrel, Mrs Sian Nicola BA . . . . *§Oct 1990
Harris, Mr David J LLB . . . . *§Oct 1987
Heywood, Mr Carl Eugene LLB . . . . *§Nov 1987
Lightbown, Mr John N BA . . . . *§Apr 1979
Oelrichs, Mr Kevin W LLB . . . . *§Apr 1974
Walford, Mrs Jane . . . . Sep 1999
Ast: Smith, Ms Sophie BA . . . . *Oct 2006
Ward, Mr Craig LLB . . . . Sep 2007
Ward, Mrs Lauren LLB . . . . May 2008

Other offices in Attleborough, Long Stratton, Watton, Wymondham. Holders of Franchise for Employment, Housing and Family. We conduct business in French & Spanish

NICHOLAS HANCOX SOLICITORS ‡
Cavell House St Crispins Road Norwich Norfolk NR3 1YE
Tel: 01603 821012 *Fax:* 01603 821001
E-mail: nick@nicholashancox.co.uk

HANSELLS ‡
13-14 The Close Norwich Norfolk NR1 4DS
Tel: 01603 615731 *Fax:* 01603 633585 *Dx:* 5204 NORWICH
E-mail: info@hansells.co.uk
List of partners: L J Cornish, T Eagle, J B Hardman, J N Harvey, K Hirst, P B Hoare, R S Holden, M Knott, H P Lansdell, S Mariscal, R M McGurk, P R Norton, R F M Seal-Coon, D R Sisson, M J Steward, J L Stockings, N W Sutherland
Office: Aylsham, Cromer, North Walsham, Norwich, Sheringham
Languages: French, German
Work: A1 B1 C1 C2 D1 E F1 J1 J2 K1 K2 L M3 N O P Q R1 S1 S2 V W Z(c,d,h,j,k,l,m,o,r)
Emergency Action, Agency, Advocacy, Fixed Fee Interview, Legal Aid undertaken, Legal Aid Franchise and Member of Accident Line
Ptr: Cornish, Miss Lisa Jane BA(Bris) . . . . *§Jun 1994
Eagle, Mr Timothy LLB . . . . *§Oct 1983
Hardman, Mr John Bernard . . . . *§Dec 1972
Hirst, Miss Kathryn LLB . . . . *§Sep 1999
Hoare, Mrs Pamela B BA . . . . *§Nov 1988
Holden, Mr Roger S LLB(Lond) . . . . *§Apr 1976
Knott, Mr Michael . . . . Nov 2000
McGurk, Ms Rachel M BA . . . . *§Mar 1984
Mariscal, Miss Shelyna LLB . . . . *§Sep 1996
Norton, Mr Philip R BA(Law) . . . . *§Oct 1984
Sisson, Mr David R BSc . . . . *§Dec 1977
Steward, Mr Michael J BA . . . . *§Jan 1980
Stockings, Miss Jane Louise . . . . *§Sep 1998
Asoc: Chiverton, Mr Timothy J LLB . . . . *§Nov 1986
Findlay, Mrs Denise Helen . . . . *§Oct 2001
White, Miss Melanie . . . . *§Sep 2003
Ast: Barnard, Miss Hayley Louise LLB; PGDipLP . . . . . *Sep 2008
Cordingley, Miss Helen Suzanne . . . . *§Mar 2006
Gowing, Ms Carla Mary . . . . May 1978
Parsley, Miss Julia Mary LLB . . . . Sep 2008
Vallgren, Mrs Mari Elisabeth . . . . *Sep 2005
Whitehead, Ms Lindsay Jane . . . . Sep 1998
Con: Betts, Mr Richard . . . . *§May 1979
Butcher, Mr Nicholas MA; LLM(Cantab) . . . . *§Mar 1971
Smith, Mr Graham Hinton Notary Public . . . . *§Dec 1970

HANSELLS
Cambridge House 26 Tombland Norwich Norfolk NR3 1RE
Office: Aylsham, Cromer, North Walsham, Norwich, Sheringham

HATCH BRENNER ‡
4 Theatre Street Norwich Norfolk NR2 1QY
Tel: 01603 660811 *Fax:* 01603 619473 *Dx:* 5237 NORWICH 1
List of partners: D J Bloomfield, J M Brock, R D Cassel, A M Dobbins, R C F Escott, M N Fitch, P Henderson, N J Horton, D P Parkes
Ptr: Bloomfield, Mr David J LLB . . . . *Dec 1976
Brock, Mr Jonathan M LLB(Warw) . . . . *Apr 1981
Cassel, Mr Richard D BA(Warw) Part time Chairman of Industrial Tribunals . . . . *§Jun 1980
Dobbins, Mr Alan M LLB(L'pool) . . . . *Dec 1974
Escott, Mrs Rosemary C F BA(Legal Studies) . . . . *Nov 1987
Fitch, Mr Mark Neil . . . . *Sep 1994
Horton, Mr Nathan John BA . . . . *Mar 1996
Parkes, Mrs Dawn P LLB . . . . *Oct 1986
Mem: Henderson, Mrs Penelope LLB . . . . Apr 1981
Asoc: Greenwood, Miss Susan Jane BA . . . . Feb 1982

TOM HIGGIN CHILDREN AND FAMILY SOLICITOR ‡
The Old Forge The Street Shotesham Norwich Norfolk NR15 1YL
Tel: 01508 558752 *Fax:* 01508 558104
E-mail: tom.higgin@homecall.co.uk

PHILIP HOOK ‡
26 Branksome Road Norwich Norfolk NR4 6SW
Tel: 01603 250050 *Fax:* 01603 250050
E-mail: philip.hook@btinternet.com
List of partners: P Hook
Languages: French
Work: E S1 S2 W
SPr: Hook, Mr Philip LLB . . . . *Oct 1977

HOWARD POLLOK & WEBB ‡
(in association with Pollok Webb & Gall)
7 Princes Street Norwich Norfolk NR3 1AZ
Tel: 01603 660051 *Fax:* 01603 760510 *Dx:* 5273 NORWICH
List of partners: G R Gall, C A Webb
Work: A1 A2 B1 B2 C1 C2 C3 D1 D2 E F1 F2 G H J1 K1 L N O P Q R1 S1 S2 T1 U1 V W Z(c,d,e,i,k,l,r,s)
Emergency Action, Agency, Advocacy and Fixed Fee Interview undertaken
Ptr: Gall, Mr Graham R ♦ . . . . *§Jul 1977
Webb, Ms Carole A . . . . *§Dec 1968

HOWES PERCIVAL LLP
The Guildyard 51 Colegate Norwich Norfolk NR3 1DD
Tel: 01603 762103 *Fax:* 01603 762104 *Dx:* 5280 NORWICH
E-mail: law@howespercival.com
Office: Leicester, London WC2, Manchester, Milton Keynes, Northampton
Languages: Cantonese, Farsi, French, German, Hindi, Italian, Punjabi, Romanian, Spanish, Urdu, Welsh
Work: A1 A2 A3 B1 B2 C1 C2 C3 D1 D2 E F1 I J1 L M1 M2 N O P Q R1 R2 S1 S2 T1 T2 U2 V W Z(b,c,d,e,f,g,h,i,j,l,o,p,q,r,t)
Emergency Action, Advocacy, Legal Aid undertaken, Legal Aid Franchise and Member of Accident Line
Mem: Barnes, Mr Andrew J LLB(Hons) . . . . *§Dec 1981
Colman, Mr Robert . . . . Sep 2003
Haskey, Ms Tessa J LLB . . . . *Oct 1996
Hayes, Mr Julian LLB(Hons) . . . . Oct 1991
Heal, Mr Jeremy P W MA; LLM(Cantab); ACIArb . . *§Oct 1967
Healey, Mr Richard J LLB(Hons) . . . . *Sep 1999
Kirby, Alison . . . . Jan 1998
Scott, Miss Catherine S J LLB . . . . *Oct 1996
Asoc: Bradshaw, Mr John LLB; LPC . . . . Mar 2000
Burroughes, Mr Jonathan T . . . . *Oct 1993
Disney, Cheryl . . . . Jan 1996
Frankland, Mr Edward John BA(Hons); CPE; LPC . . *Oct 1997
Nicholls, Miss Joanna Louise BA(Hons) . . . . Jan 2002
Shaw, Catherine . . . . Jan 2000
Shirley, Mr William . . . . Jan 2000
Ast: Balan, Anil . . . . *Oct 2003
Brewster, Antony . . . . Jan 2004
Bruford, Mr John Charles BSc; PGDipLaw . . . . . . *Oct 2001
Burrows, Jodie . . . . Jan 2006
Drake, Emily . . . . Jan 2005
Frankland, Mr James Alexander LLB . . . . *Sep 2001
Hammett, Susan . . . . Jan 1996
Lee, Sarah . . . . Jan 2009
McInnes, Harriet . . . . Jan 2008
Manning, Mr Patrick John Paul BA(Dunelm) . . . . . *Oct 1999
Rees, Ian . . . . Jan 2004
White, Nicholas . . . . Jan 2008

IEI SOLICITORS
The Royal 25 Bank Plain Norwich Norfolk NR2 4SF
Tel: 01603 283621 *Fax:* 01603 283622 *Dx:* 5260 NORWICH
E-mail: info@ieisolicitors.co.uk
Office: Birmingham, Edgware

IVES-KEELER & CO ‡
30 St Faiths Lane Norwich Norfolk NR1 1NN
Tel: 01603 219298 *Fax:* 01603 219403
E-mail: mail@iveskeeler.co.uk
List of partners: S R Ives-Keeler
Work: E L R2 S1 S2
SPr: Ives-Keeler, Mr Stephen R LLB(Lond) . . . . *Nov 1985

KENT & CO SOLICITORS ‡
3-4 Calthorpe Cottages The Green Acle Norwich Norfolk NR13 3QX
Tel: 01493 751351 *Fax:* 01493 751912
List of partners: S C Kent
Work: A1 C1 E K4 L S1 S2 T1 T2 W Z(c,d,m)
SPr: Kent, Mrs Susan Caroline BA(Hons) . . . . *Dec 1980

LD LAW
17 Cathedral Street Norwich Norfolk NR1 1LY
Office: Harlow
Mem: Wales, Mr Melvin E F . . . . *Jun 1977

LAKE JACKSON
The Lodge Buckenham Lane Lingwood Norwich Norfolk NR13 4NJ
Tel: 01603 715519 *Fax:* 01603 715395
E-mail: markjackson@lakejackson.org.uk
Office: London E1

LAMBERT PUGH ‡
19 Charing Cross Norwich Norfolk NR2 4AX
Tel: 01603 462796

DAVID LAWS SOLICITOR ‡
The Royal 25 Bank Plain Norwich Norfolk NR2 4SF
Tel: 01603 871126 / 07933 149810
E-mail: dal@davidlaws-solicitor.com
dal@davidlaws-solicitor.com

LEATHES PRIOR ‡
74 The Close Norwich Norfolk NR1 4DR
Tel: 01603 610911 *Fax:* 01603 610088 *Dx:* 5205 NORWICH
Emergency telephone 01603 700684
List of partners: M R Barlow, F Brumby, T J Cary, R J Chadd, D Chapman, H A Gill, M C Plowman, W R C Riley, R Sibley, R Thickett, P J Warman
Languages: Dutch, French, German
Work: A1 A3 B1 C1 C2 C3 D1 D2 E F1 F2 G H J1 K1 K2 K3 K4 L M1 M2 N O P Q R1 S1 S2 T1 T2 U2 V W Z(b,c,d,e,f,g,h,i,j,l,m,o,p,t,za)
Emergency Action, Agency, Advocacy, Fixed Fee Interview, Legal Aid undertaken, Legal Aid Franchise and Member of Accident Line
Ptr: Barlow, Mr Michael Robert BA(Hons) . . . . Sep 1997
Brumby, Mr Frank LLB(Hons)(Hull); BA(Hons); LPC(Notts) . . . . *Sep 1998
Cary, Mr Timothy J LLB(Lond) . . . . *Apr 1978
Chadd, Mr R Jonathan MA(Oxon) Notary Public . . . *Jun 1980
Chapman, Mr Daniel . . . . Sep 2002
Gill, Mrs Hazel Ann . . . . Sep 2002
Plowman, Mr Martin C MA(Cantab) . . . . *Oct 1987
Riley, William R C . . . . May 1979
Sibley, Mr Robert LLB(Hull) . . . . *Oct 1988
Thickett, Mrs Rosalyn LLB . . . . *Nov 1987
Warman, Mr Paul J BA . . . . *Nov 1988
Asoc: Challinor, Mrs Sally . . . . Jan 2003
Ast: Fox, Mr Richard Colin . . . . Oct 2003
Lawrence, Mr Thomas . . . . Oct 2005
Morgan, Miss Polly Elizabeth . . . . Oct 2005
Oldershaw, Mr Paul William . . . . Oct 2003
Con: Fahy, Ms Angela BA; MA; PhD . . . . Jan 1997

LINKED LAW ‡
1 Church Farm Barns Well Lane Sparham Norwich Norfolk NR9 5PY
Tel: 01362 688946 / 07833 332055 *Fax:* 01362 688946
E-mail: law@25am.co.uk

See p112 for the Key to Work Categories & other symbols

LONGE & CO ‡
2 Tombland Alley Norwich Norfolk NR3 1HL
Tel: 01603 660027 *Fax:* 01603 667666 *Dx:* 5234 NORWICH
E-mail: j.longe@longeandco.com

JOHN A MCDONNELL ‡
Wood Farm The Wood Swardeston Norwich Norfolk NR14 8DJ
Tel: 01508 570387 *Fax:* 01508 570387
Emergency telephone 01508 570387
List of partners: J A McDonnell
Work: W
SPr: McDonnell, Mr John A. . . . . *Dec 1970

MILLS & REEVE
1 St James Court Whitefriars Norwich Norfolk NR3 1RU
Tel: 01603 660155 *Fax:* 01603 633027 *Dx:* 5210 NORWICH
E-mail: info@mills-reeve.com
Office: Birmingham, Cambridge, Leeds, London EC3, Manchester
Work: A1 A2 A3 B1 C1 C2 C3 D1 E F1 F2 I J1 J2 K1 K2 L M1 M2 N O P Q R1 R2 S1 S2 T1 T2 U1 W X Z(b,c,d,e,f,g,h,j,k,l,m,n,o,p,q,r,s,t,u,x,y,z)
Emergency Action, Agency, Advocacy, Fixed Fee Interview, Legal Aid undertaken and Legal Aid Franchise
Ptr: Aizlewood, Mr Mark LLB . . . . *Nov 1991
Arrowsmith-Brown, Mr Matthew R BA. . . . . *Apr 1976
Barclay, Mr Jonathan R BA . . . . *§Oct 1971
Falkner, Mr James M G LLB. . . . . *May 1980
Fischl, Mr Nicolas J MA. . . . . *Oct 1979
Furnivall, Mr Peter W MA . . . . *Nov 1980
Herring, Mr John W F MA Registrar of the Diocese of Norwich . . . . *Dec 1971
Higgs, Ms Rachel J LLB; LLM. . . . . *Nov 1984
Hodgson, Mr Guy J. . . . . *Jun 1979
Hunter, Mr James Michael LLB . . . . *Nov 1995
Hutton, Mr Robert D MA . . . . *Apr 1977
Jack, Ms Susan MA. . . . . *Nov 1977
Jeffries, Mr R Mark MA . . . . *Apr 1981
King, Mr Stephen BA . . . . *§Oct 1986
Mayers, Mr Ian J LLB . . . . *Dec 1981
Ripman, Mr Justin J P MA(Cantab) . . . . *Feb 1988
Ryan, Mr Tim LLB. . . . . Oct 1984
Scott, Mr C J Harry MA(Cantab). . . . . *Apr 1980
Scoular, Mrs Gillian P L MA(Cantab) . . . . *Oct 1980
Stone, Mr Nicholas LLB. . . . . Jan 1995
Asoc: Abbott, Mr Nicholas LLB . . . . Nov 1994
Brown, Ms Philippa J A BA; PhD . . . . Feb 1988
Carriage, Mrs Rebecca R LLB(Law & French). . . . *Oct 1987
Collen, Ms Annette J LLB . . . . *Nov 1986
Garnier, Mrs Sarah M LLB . . . . *Dec 1975
Graham, Mrs Sally A LLB . . . . *Oct 1983
Howard, Ms Clare R . . . . Oct 1989
Ast: Allen, Miss Dawn Louise . . . . Sep 1999
Barrett, Mr Timothy L BA . . . . *Jan 1980
Bridges, Ms Angela V. . . . . *Nov 1992
Catchpole, Mr David . . . . Oct 1999
Dernie, Miss Nicola LLB. . . . . Nov 1994
Field, Mr Simon. . . . . Sep 2000
Garrood, Ms Sarah LLB. . . . . *Oct 1992
Girling, Ms Deborah LLB . . . . *Oct 1992
Henderson, Mr James Gordon BA. . . . . Sep 2002
Hesp, Ms Sinead M T. . . . . Oct 1999
Hipper, Mr Andrew Kenneth BA . . . . Nov 1993
Hunter, Mrs Sarah Pauline LLB(Hons) Lewenstein Prize . . . . *Nov 1995
Laming, Dr Gregory PhD; CPE; LPC Chester & North Wales Law Society Prize 1996 . . . . Nov 1999
Lever, Mrs Louisa Rachel . . . . Sep 1998
Rossell-Evans, Mr Simon LLB Treasurer of Norfolk & Norwich Inc Law Soc. . . . . *Jul 1999
Steed, Mr Julian PPE(Oxon) . . . . Nov 1994
Virgin, Mr Zak Ashley LLB. . . . . Sep 2001
Wagstaff, Mr Thomas R D MA(Oxon) . . . . *Sep 2001
Wells, Mrs Harriet A BSc . . . . *Nov 1980
Woollett, Mr Martyn Charles LLB . . . . Sep 2000

GODFREY MORGAN ‡
Roxley House 68 Yarmouth Road Norwich Norfolk NR7 0QZ
Tel: 01603 595700 *Fax:* 01603 595701
E-mail: admin@godfreymorgansolicitors.co.uk
List of partners: G H R Morgan
Work: B1 C1 D1 F1 J1 K1 L N O Q V W Z(b,j)
Emergency Action, Agency, Advocacy, Fixed Fee Interview, Legal Aid undertaken and Member of Accident Line
SPr: Morgan, Mr Godfrey H R LLB(Hons) . . . . *Oct 1990

MORGAN JONES & PETT ‡
Greyfriars House 18-20 Prince of Wales Road Norwich Norfolk NR1 1LB
Tel: 01603 877000 *Fax:* 01603 877007 *Dx:* 138514 NORWICH
E-mail: info@m-j-p.co.uk
List of partners: D J Jones, D R Pett, S Westwood
Work: J2 K1 N O S1 Z(q,r)
Fixed Fee Interview, Legal Aid undertaken and Legal Aid Franchise
Ptr: Jones, Mr David J. . . . . *Mar 1981
Pett, Mr David R BA(Hons) Trent Law Prize 1985 . . *Sep 1987
Westwood, Mrs Sara BA(Hons) . . . . *Feb 1998

OVERBURYS & RAYMOND THOMPSON ‡
3-5 Upper King Street Norwich Norfolk NR3 1RL
Tel: 01603 610481 *Fax:* 01603 632460 *Dx:* 5208 NORWICH
E-mail: info@overburys.co.uk
List of partners: R T G Bevan, N G Flower, H L George, B P G V Keane, A G Liddle, J M Liddle, A Maruca, G W Woolsey-Brown
Office: Diss
Languages: French, Spanish
Work: A1 B1 C1 C2 C3 D1 E F1 J1 K1 K3 L M1 M2 N O P Q R1 S1 T1 T2 W Z(c,d,e,g,l,o,p)
Emergency Action, Agency, Advocacy, Fixed Fee Interview, Legal Aid undertaken, Legal Aid Franchise and Member of Accident Line
Ptr: Bevan, Mr Richard Thomas Gareth . . . . *Oct 1995
Flower, Mr Nicholas G Law Society Annual Prize 1995 *Nov 1995
George, Ms Hayley Louise BA . . . . *Oct 2000
Keane, Mr Benedict P G V BA(Bris). . . . . *Jun 1984
Liddle, Mr Alisdair G . . . . *Jul 1995
Liddle, Mrs Jane M MA; LLB . . . . *Apr 1993
Maruca, Mrs Amanda LLB. . . . . *Oct 1992
Woolsey-Brown, Mr Geoffrey W MA(Cantab) . . . . *§Jul 1976
Ast: Biggs, Mrs Natalie LLB . . . . *Feb 2008
Henderson, Mr Thomas Lawrence BA(Hons) . . . . *Oct 1996
Jarvis, Mr Brian Hayward LLB. . . . . *§Jul 1964
Key, Miss Sophie Jane Simone Victoria LLB; MA . . *Sep 2003
Mitchell, Sophie. . . . . Sep 2006
Nixon, Ms Joanna E C . . . . Oct 1988
Ramsbottom, Mr David LLB. . . . . *Jun 1970
Thurston, Mrs Sophie LLB. . . . . *Oct 2008

Con: Nicoll, Miss Penelope J LLB(Nott'm). . . . . *Jun 1971
Rushmer, Mr John Stuart . . . . *§Jul 1967

ROGERS & NORTON ‡
(incorporating Crotch Partnership)
The Old Chapel 5-7 Willow Lane Norwich Norfolk NR2 1EU
Tel: 01603 666001 *Fax:* 01603 629663 *Dx:* 5226 NORWICH
Emergency telephone 01603 666001
E-mail: admin@roger-norton.co.uk
List of partners: R W J Etheridge, B W Faulkner, M C Greig, M Hambling, P N W Kerridge, D A Laws, T S Nobbs, N G Norton
Office: Norwich
Languages: French, Spanish
Work: A1 A3 B1 C1 C2 C3 D1 E F1 F2 J1 J2 K1 L M1 M2 N O P Q R1 R2 S1 S2 T1 T2 U2 V W Z(c,e,k,l,p,q,r,t)
Emergency Action, Agency, Advocacy, Fixed Fee Interview, Legal Aid undertaken and Member of Accident Line
Ptr: Etheridge, Mr Richard W J . . . . *Dec 1981
Faulkner, Mr Bruce W LLB . . . . *Nov 1989
Greig, Mr Marc C BA . . . . *Oct 1988
Hambling, Mr Mark . . . . *Oct 1998
Kerridge, Mr Philip N W LLB . . . . *Nov 1990
Laws, Mr David A. . . . . *Dec 1984
Nobbs, Mr Timothy S BA(Law) . . . . *Oct 1978
Norton, Mr Nicholas G . . . . *Sep 1981
Ast: Cole, Miss Lara. . . . . *Jun 2000
Hawdon, Ms Catherine . . . . *Nov 1974
Pyke, Mr Robert. . . . . *Sep 1998
Smith, Mrs Margaret . . . . *Jul 1984
Con: Crotch, Mr Andrew J M . . . . *Jul 1967

ROGERS & NORTON
2 Lansdowne Road Norwich Norfolk NR6 6NF
Tel: 01603 268910 *Fax:* 01603 268929 *Dx:* 5226 NORWICH
E-mail: ngn@rogers-norton.co.uk
Office: Norwich

RONALDSONS ‡
45 Dereham Road Norwich Norfolk NR2 4HY
Tel: 01603 618883 *Fax:* 01603 633426 *Dx:* 133142 NORWICH 12
E-mail: mail@ronaldsons.com
List of partners: R W Ronaldson
Work: D1 K1 K2 K3 S1 W
Emergency Action, Agency, Advocacy, Legal Aid undertaken and Legal Aid Franchise
SPr: Ronaldson, Mr Richard W LLB(Warw). . . . . *Feb 1982
Ast: Denny, Mrs Sarah. . . . . *Dec 2004
Rowell, Miss Kerry . . . . *Nov 2006

T J SHEPPERSON ‡
148 Unthank Road Norwich Norfolk NR2 2RS
Tel: 01603 763096
E-mail: info@landlordlaw.co.uk
List of partners: T J Shepperson
Work: L
Fixed Fee Interview undertaken
SPr: Shepperson, Ms Teresa Jeanette BA; LLB. . . . . . *§Jun 1990

STEELES ‡
3 The Norwich Business Park Whiting Road Norwich Norfolk NR4 6DJ
Tel: 0870 609 0200 *Fax:* 01603 598111 *Dx:* 138525 NORWICH 7
Emergency telephone 0870 609 0200
E-mail: info@steeleslaw.co.uk
List of partners: T J Addinell, R Bailey, E O Brabbins, S K Drake, M P Fahy, N Grearson, P Hastings, N C Lubbock
Office: Diss, London EC2
Languages: French, German
Work: A1 A3 B1 C1 C2 C3 D1 E F1 F2 I J1 K1 K2 K3 L M1 M2 N O P Q R1 R2 S1 S2 T1 T2 U2 V W Z(b,c,d,e,f,g,h,j,k,l,m,o,p,q,r,u,w,y)
Emergency Action, Agency, Advocacy, Fixed Fee Interview, Legal Aid undertaken, S.I.G and Member of Accident Line
Ptr: Addinell, Mr Timothy J MA(Cantab); LLB(Hons) . . . . *Mar 1986
Bailey, Mr Richard. . . . . Nov 1988
Brabbins, Mr Edric O . . . . *Apr 2001
Drake, Mr Stephen K . . . . *Jan 1984
Fahy, Mr Michael P LLB. . . . . *Oct 1987
Hastings, Mr Peter . . . . *Sep 2001
Lubbock, Mr Nigel C LLB(Bris) Notary Public . . . . . *Sep 1975
Asoc: Lewis, Miss Joy LLB . . . . *Aug 1995
Thomas, Ms Jean. . . . . Jun 1999
Ast: Cronin, Miss Rachel BA(Hons) . . . . *Sep 1994
Crossley, Mr Dominic . . . . *Mar 2000
Farman, Miss Rosemary A LLB . . . . *Mar 1986
Huckel, Mrs Sarah . . . . *Nov 1999
Pulham, Mr Christopher. . . . . *Sep 2000
Tarling, Mr James Paul . . . . Sep 2001
Townsend, Ms Lorna Anne BA(Lond) . . . . Jun 1993
Con: Davies, Ms Alison. . . . . *Sep 2003
Edmonds, MIss Cheryl . . . . *Nov 1998
Kalymnios, Triada. . . . . *Sep 2002
Lamb, Mr Norman P LLB . . . . *Oct 1984
Martins, Miss Sandra Fernandes . . . . *Sep 2001
Nicolaou, Ms Elena . . . . *Mar 1996
Swetman, Ms Victoria. . . . . *Sep 2002

MICHAEL J STIBBARD & CO ‡
14 Recorder Road Norwich Norfolk NR1 1NR
Tel: 01603 619845 *Fax:* 01603 619845
Languages: French
Work: E L S1 S2 W Z(l)

STORY & ROBISON ‡
24 Leopold Road Norwich Norfolk NR4 7AD
Tel: 01603 626355 *Fax:* 01603 627355
List of partners: B L Robison, J L Story
Work: D1 D2 K1 W
Fixed Fee Interview undertaken
Ptr: Robison, Mrs Belinda Louise BA . . . . *Feb 1989
Story, Ms Jaqueline Lesley . . . . Dec 1975

STORY & ROBISON ‡
Hingham House 1 Market Place Hingham Norwich Norfolk NR9 4AF
Tel: 01953 851125 *Fax:* 01953 851194
E-mail: storyrobison@btconnect.com

WILLCOX LEWIS LLP ‡
The Old Coach House Bergh Apton Norwich Norfolk NR15 1DD
Tel: 01508 480100 *Fax:* 01508 480001
E-mail: mdw@willcoxlewis.co.uk
List of partners: D Fisher, I G Lewis, M D Willcox, R J F Wortley
Languages: French
Work: A1 E L S1 S2 T1 T2 W Z(d)

Ptr: Fisher, Mrs Deborah LLB(Hons) Sweet & Maxwell Law Prize . . . . *May 1991
Lewis, Mr Ian G MA(Oxon) . . . . *§Jun 1972
Willcox, Mr Michael David LLB . . . . *§Dec 1970
Wortley, Mr Roger J F MA(Cantab) . . . . *Aug 1979

STEPHEN WOOD ‡
41 Cecil Road Norwich Norfolk NR1 2QL
Tel: 01603 766539
E-mail: swood@ultimate-law.com
List of partners: S Wood
SPr: Wood, Mr Stephen BA . . . . *Apr 1978

NOTTINGHAM

AM LAW LIMITED ‡
70 Exeter Road Forest Fields Nottingham NG7 6LS
Tel: 0115 960 3673
E-mail: contact@amlawsolicitors.co.uk

ACTONS ‡
20 Regent Street Nottingham NG1 5BQ
Tel: 0115 910 0200 *Fax:* 0115 910 0290
E-mail: enquiries@actons.co.uk
List of partners: C E Bell, J C Britten, N M Calthrop-Owen, G J Chadwick, S Dakin, A J Forster, A H Gordon, M M Kelly, S Lawson, R F Leman, C A Murratt, N D T Payne, P J Seymour, M J Spencer
Dir: Bell, Mrs Claire Elizabeth BA . . . . *Sep 1993
Britten, Mr John C. . . . . *§Jun 1971
Calthrop-Owen, Mrs Nicola M LLB . . . . *Oct 1990
Chadwick, Mr Gary J LLB. . . . . *Oct 1984
Dakin, Mr Simon . . . . Jan 2003
Forster, Mr Adrian J MA(Cantab) . . . . *§Oct 1982
Gordon, Ms Amanda H LLB. . . . . *Oct 1988
Kelly, Mrs Madeline M LLB . . . . *Dec 1988
Lawson, Mrs Susan LLB; PGDip . . . . *Nov 1989
Leman, Mr Richard F MA(Oxon) Licensed Insolvency Practitioner . . . . *§Dec 1965
Murratt, Mr Christopher A LLB. . . . . *§Nov 1992
Payne, Mr Nicholas David Thomas LLB . . . . *Oct 1996
Seymour, Mr Peter J . . . . *§Dec 1977
Spencer, Mr Michael J BSc . . . . *Nov 1983

ANDERSONS SOLICITORS ‡
40-42 The Ropewalk Nottingham NG1 5EJ
Tel: 0115 947 0641 *Fax:* 0115 950 4252 *Dx:* 10043 NOTTINGHAM
Emergency telephone 0115 947 0641
E-mail: info@andersonssolicitors.co.uk
List of partners: E K Dancer, A Kay, A M Kelly, S Laughton, A P Scott, P D Sutherland
Work: B1 C1 D1 D2 E F1 J1 K1 K3 K4 L M1 N O P Q R1 R2 S1 S2 U2 V W Z(c,g,l,p,q,r,t,w)
Emergency Action, Agency, Advocacy, Fixed Fee Interview, Legal Aid undertaken, Legal Aid Franchise and Member of Accident Line
Ptr: Dancer, Miss Emma K LLB . . . . *Sep 1995
Kay, Mr Anthony LLB(Hons). . . . . *Dec 2003
Kelly, Mr Andrew M . . . . *Jun 1976
Laughton, Miss Sally LLM. . . . . *Sep 2001
Scott, Mr Andrew P LLB. . . . . *Jun 1990
Sutherland, Mr Peter Douglas BA . . . . *Oct 1987
Ast: Brooke-Smith, Mr Alexander James LLB Derby Law Society Skills Triathlon Winner 2007 & 2008. . . . . *Jul 2009
Bunnell, Miss Victoria LLB. . . . . *Sep 2009
Forster, Miss Laura LLB. . . . . *Oct 2009
Perkins, Miss Sarah Jane . . . . *Jan 2008
Playle, Ms Alison LLB. . . . . *Nov 1986
Rodgers, Mrs Emma LLB . . . . Mar 2005
Scott, Mrs Louise LLB. . . . . Oct 1993
Con: Davies, Mr Malcolm G LLB . . . . *Jul 1973

ASHTON BOND GIGG ‡
Pearl Assurance House Friar Lane Nottingham NG1 6BX
Tel: 0115 947 6651 *Fax:* 0115 947 5244 *Dx:* 10002 NOTTINGHAM
E-mail: mailbox@abg-law.com
List of partners: C G A Gigg, S Goodacre, D E Hutchinson, K M Meir, W J Shaw, T Sisson, A J Sutton
Languages: French, German
Work: A1 A3 B1 C1 C2 C3 E I J1 L O Q R1 R2 S1 S2 T1 T2 W Z(c,d,e,j,o,q)
Ptr: Gigg, Mr Christopher G A LLB. . . . . *Apr 1981
Goodacre, Mrs Siobhan LLB(Hons) . . . . *Jan 1995
Hutchinson, Mrs Deborah E LLB . . . . *May 1979
Meir, Miss Kathryn Mary LLB(Hons). . . . . *Sep 2004
Shaw, Mrs Wendy Jane LLB . . . . Jun 1993
Sisson, Mr Tim LLB. . . . . *Oct 1987
Sutton, Mr Andrew John LLB . . . . *Dec 2001
Asoc: Hardstaff, Mr David Anthony LLB(Hons). . . . . . . *Jan 1975
Johal, Mrs Louise Claire LLB(Hons). . . . . *Jul 2004
Ast: Beggs, Miss Katherine BSc(Hons). . . . . Sep 2008

G A ATKINSON ‡
3 Matlock Court Nottingham NG1 4DT
Tel: 0115 969 3650 *Fax:* 0115 941 0947 *Dx:* 10139 NOTTINGHAM
List of partners: G A Atkinson
Work: S1
Ptr: Atkinson, Mr George Aidan LLB. . . . . *Oct 1978

ROBERT BARBER & SONS ‡
46 Bridgford Road West Bridgford Nottingham NG2 6AP
Tel: 0115 878 9000 *Fax:* 0115 878 9705
Dx: 719931 WEST BRIDGFORD
E-mail: reception@robertbarber.co.uk
List of partners: D C Howard, S Hussain, P Mullins, H A Tarran
Office: Eastwood, Hucknall
Work: A1 A3 D1 E F1 J1 K1 K2 K3 L N Q R1 S1 S2 W
Emergency Action undertaken
Ptr: Howard, Mr Donald C LLB . . . . *Feb 1980
Mullins, Mr Patrick LLB(Hons). . . . . *May 1980
Tarran, Mrs Hilary A LLB . . . . *§Nov 1981
Ast: Armstrong-Langley, Mrs Maria Antonietta . . . . . . *Sep 2003

BARKER EVANS PRIVATE CLIENT LAW ‡
PO Box 9982 Nottingham NG1 9GP
Tel: 0800 978 8582 *Fax:* 07810 733584

BARRATT GOFF & TOMLINSON ‡
3 Wheatcroft Business Park Landmere Lane Nottingham NG12 4DG
Tel: 0115 931 5171 *Fax:* 0115 931 5172
Dx: 719903 WEST BRIDGFORD
Emergency telephone 0800 435365

E-mail: mail@bgtsolicitors.co.uk
List of partners: J Y Barratt, A Brooks, M T A Goff, E E Myers, D A R Tomlinson
Work: J2 N Z(r,w)
Advocacy, Legal Aid undertaken, Legal Aid Franchise and Member of Accident Line
Ptr: Barratt, Mrs Jill Yvonne MA(Cantab) . . . *Oct 1982
Brooks, Miss Alison LLB . . . *Nov 1988
Goff, Mr Malcolm T A BA . . . *Feb 1984
Myers, Mr Edward E BA(Hons) President of Mental Health Review Tribunal; Legal Secretary of Nottinghamshire Medico Legal Society; Vice Chairman of Nottingham Headway . . . *Oct 1986
Tomlinson, Mr David A R LLB . . . *Oct 1984
Ast: Measures, Mr John . . . Nov 1998
Veasey, Ms Emma . . . *Jan 2005

JULIA T BETTS ‡
5 Milton Court Ravenshead Nottingham NG15 9BD
Tel: 01623 499080 ***Fax:*** 01623 490124
E-mail: julia@ravensheadlaw.com
List of partners: J T Betts
Work: A2 E K4 Q S1 S2 W
Ptr: Betts, Mrs Julia Theresa BA. . . . *§Jun 1981

BHATIA BEST ‡
12 Carrington Street Nottingham NG1 7FF
Tel: 0115 950 3231 ***Fax:*** 0115 941 3169 ***Dx:*** 702153 NOTTINGHAM
Emergency telephone 0115 950 3231
E-mail: nottingham@bhatiabest.co.uk
List of partners: S N Bell, M J Best, N S Bhandal, A K Bhatia, A J Driver, D J Hudson, J Jarvis, J C Lea, R H Posner, P S Samrai, R Todd, R J Wakefield, P N Wesson, J Whyley
Office: Derby, Mansfield
Languages: Hindi, Punjabi, Urdu
Work: B2 D1 D2 F1 G H J1 K1 K2 L N Q S1 S2 V W Z(g,i,k,m,p,q)
Emergency Action, Agency, Advocacy, Fixed Fee Interview, Legal Aid undertaken, Legal Aid Franchise and Member of Accident Line
Ptr: Bell, Mr Stuart N BA(Law). . . . *Dec 1985
Best, Mr Matthew J BA(Law) . . . *Sep 1988
Bhandal, Narotam Singh PhD . . . *Aug 1997
Bhatia, Ashish K BA. . . . *Sep 1985
Driver, Mr Adrian J LLB . . . *May 1995
Hudson, Mr David J LLB . . . Jan 1970
Jarvis, Ms Joanne LLB(Hons) . . . *Apr 1996
Lea, Mr John C BA . . . *Nov 1979
Posner, Mr Richard H LLB(Hons) Notary Public . . . *Sep 1995
Samrai, Parminder S LLB. . . . *Dec 1990
Todd, Mr Richard LLB. . . . *Nov 1996
Wakefield, Mr Richard J BA . . . *Oct 1987
Wesson, Mr Paul Nicholas LLB . . . *Mar 1991
Whyley, Mr James LLB . . . *Aug 1998
Asoc: Desai, Chaitanya BA; LLM . . . *Nov 1997
Ast: Cornwell, Miss Francesca Lucy LLB(Hons) . . . *Jun 2004
Cowley, Mrs Kirsty C T LLB. . . . Apr 1996
Deane, Miss Stephanie Amanda LLB . . . *Nov 2002
Dicks, Mr Nigel LLB. . . . *Dec 1989
Gill, Miss Lisa Maureen LLB. . . . *Jun 2003
Goodman, Miss Anita Lesley LLB . . . *Oct 2003
Grevatte, Mrs Katherine LLB . . . *Oct 2002
Hunt, Ms Sharon Martine LLB(Hons) . . . *Nov 2001
Jackson, Miss Donna Louise LLB(Hons). . . . *Jun 2004
Johnson, Miss Lucy LLB . . . *Oct 2003
Kabia, Miss Yazmin Celia BA(Hons). . . . *Oct 2003
McGarva, Miss Catherine Laura BA. . . . *Jun 2003
McLeod, Mr Paul LLB(Hons) . . . *Jul 2000
Major, Mr Mark Richard LLB. . . . *Oct 2003
Manan, Mr Rajesh LLB . . . *Nov 2002
Mandair, Miss Serena LLB . . . *Jun 2002
O'Sullivan, Miss Alison LLB . . . *Nov 1999
Rust, Ms Sarah BA . . . *Nov 1998
Vervoorts, Mrs Arwen Annabel LLB; MA. . . . *Sep 2001
Con: Macmillan, Mr Rory Duncan Hamilton BA . . . *Mar 1991

BRADY SOLICITORS ‡
1st Floor Imperial Buildings Victoria Street Nottingham NG1 2EX
Tel: 0115 985 3450
E-mail: success@bradysolicitors.com

JOHN BRITTEN LAW LIMITED ‡
16 Regent Street Nottingham NG1 5BQ
Tel: 0115 910 0200

BROWNE JACOBSON LLP ‡
(in association with DS Paris)
44 Castle Gate Nottingham NG1 7BJ
Tel: 0115 976 6000 ***Fax:*** 0115 947 5246
Dx: 718130 NOTTINGHAM 27
E-mail: info@brownejacobson.com
List of partners: M L Amphlett, C M M Ayre, D R Bambury, R G Barlow, E R J Benson, N J Blackwell, I P Blatherwick, N G Blundell, R V Brook, G G Cummings, J Daniels, R G L Davis, G Edwards, P J Ellis, P Giles, C J Green, P Hands, D S Hibbert, D Huddleston, P H Jenkins, M S Lodge, R H Metcalfe, N S Parsons, A H T Pirie, D W Potts, A J H Radford, G C Reed, R M Ridgwell, S T Robinson, R M Silverstein, M A Simpson, B M Smith, M A Snelgrove, P D Southby, S J W Tait, W J Thompson, D W Tilly, T P T Timson, G Wallis
Office: Birmingham, London EC3
Languages: French, German, Italian, Malay, Spanish, Welsh
Work: A1 A3 B1 C1 C2 C3 D1 E F1 F2 I J1 J2 K1 L M1 M2 N O P Q R1 R2 S1 S2 T1 T2 V W Z(b,c,d,e,f,g,h,i,j,k,l,m,n,o,p,q,r,s,t,u,w)
Emergency Action, Agency and Advocacy undertaken
Ptr: Ayre, Miss Carole M M BA(Dunelm)(Law) . . . *Apr 1981
Bambury, Mr Derek R LLB(Lond) . . . *Apr 1981
Barlow, Mr Richard G LLB(Sheff); DipLG . . . *Nov 1989
Benson, Mr Edward R J BA(Cantab) . . . *Jun 1980
Blackwell, Mr Nigel J LLB . . . *Nov 1988
Blatherwick, Mr Iain P LLB . . . *Oct 1991
Blundell, Mr Nigel G LLB . . . *Oct 1991
Brook, Mr Richard V MA(Cantab). . . . *§Dec 1967
Cummings, Mr Gavin George BA(Hons). . . . *Nov 1994
Daniels, Mr Jonathan LLB. . . . *Sep 1990
Davis, Mr Richard G L LLB(Leeds) . . . *§Jul 1977
Edwards, Mr Gareth LLB . . . Apr 1991
Ellis, Mr Peter J LLB(Lond) . . . *May 1976
Giles, Mr Paul BA(Oxon); ATII Judge Jellinek Prize . *Oct 1985
Green, Mrs Caroline J LLB(Exon) . . . *Dec 1984
Hands, Mr Peter MA(Oxon) . . . *§Jun 1975
Hibbert, Mr David S LLB(Lond) . . . *Apr 1974
Huddleston, Mr David . . . *§Jul 1971
Jenkins, Mr Paul H ACIB . . . *§Oct 1975
Lodge, Mr Michael S LLB(Hons). . . . *Oct 1987
Metcalfe, Mr Robin H LLB. . . . *Apr 1980
Parsons, Mr Nicholas S BA; MA. . . . Oct 1989
Pirie, Mr Andrew H T MA(Oxon). . . . *§Jan 1966
Potts, Mr David W BCL; MA(Oxon); MCIArb. . . . *Jun 1977
Radford, Mr Alan J H BA(Oxon). . . . *Nov 1982
Reed, Mr Geoffrey C Deputy District Judge . . . *Feb 1973
Ridgwell, Mr Robert M MA; LLM(Cantab) . . . *§Apr 1979
Robinson, Mr Simon T LLB(Hons). . . . *Oct 1987
Simpson, Mr Michael A BA(Law) . . . Jun 1983
Smith, Mr Brian M LLB(Manc) R G Lawson Prize . . . *Oct 1977
Snelgrove, Mr Mark A LLB . . . *Oct 1985
Southby, Mr Paul D LLB. . . . *Oct 1982
Tait, Mr Simon J W LLB . . . *Oct 1990
Thompson, Mrs Wenna J BA(Oxon). . . . *Nov 1986
Tilly, Mr David W BA(Dunelm). . . . *Nov 1987
Timson, Mr Timothy P T LLB(Leics). . . . *§Apr 1974
Wallis, Mr Gordon. . . . *Jul 1969
Asoc: Carter, Mrs Fiona M J LLB • . . . Oct 1982
Clarson, Mrs Susan M LLB(Nott'm) . . . *Dec 1977
O'Mahony, Mrs Maggie BA . . . *Mar 1992
Offord, Mr Dominic M N LLB(Hons) . . . Feb 1995
Webb-Jenkins, Mr Christian. . . . *Nov 1991
Wheldon, Mr Stephen J E LLB . . . *Oct 1974
Youldon, Ms Christine Anne BA . . . *May 1991
Ast: Aldrich, Mr Mark LLB; LSF . . . *Oct 1991
Alonzi, Mr Andrew G . . . *Sep 1997
Ashcroft, Miss Amanda Louise LLB(Hons). . . . Sep 1998
Atherton, Mrs Kathleen MA . . . *Oct 1993
Bagnall, Miss Frances Ruth LLB(Hons)(Manc). . . . Nov 1995
Baines, Mrs Carole MA(Oxon). . . . *Jun 1979
Blois, Mr Mark BA(Hons); LLM . . . *Oct 1998
Carle, Mr Nicholas N . . . Mar 1995
Cox, Mr Richard Charles BA(Hons) . . . *Oct 1996
Cutts, Ms Helen Kathryn LLB(Leics). . . . *Sep 1995
Davis, Mr Neil LLB . . . *Oct 1996
Deeming, Ms Melissa J LLB. . . . *Mar 1993
Driver, Mr James . . . Dec 1999
Eccleston, Miss Rachel . . . Oct 1995
Ekpenyoung, Mr Gary LLB . . . *Apr 1997
Erwin, Ms Sarah L . . . Nov 1993
Finney, Mr Christopher LLB . . . *Oct 1996
Freestone, Miss Heidi LLB; BSc. . . . *Jun 1997
Glendening, Dr John . . . *Sep 1997
Harris, Mr David A . . . Nov 1993
Hawkins, Ms Suzanne K LLB . . . Oct 1989
Holden, Miss Anne LLB(Oxon) . . . *Sep 1996
Jarman, Miss Jane BA(Hons) . . . Sep 1992
Jolin, Mr Simon A BA . . . May 1991
Jones, Mr Peter Melville BSc . . . *Oct 1990
Lockley, Miss Leanne . . . Oct 1998
Mabbot, Ms Susan . . . Jan 1998
Maggs, Mr David William LLB(Nott'm). . . . *Oct 1990
Place, Ms Alison Frances BA(Hons). . . . *Dec 1990
Shardlow, Mr Adrian BA. . . . Apr 1993
Sudbury, Ms Kay Louise LLB Maxwell Law Prize 1988; Trent Law Prize 1991 . . . *Oct 1994
Swift, Mr Dominic Mackenzie CPE; LSF. . . . *Jun 1991
Williamson, Miss Susan Anne BA(Hons)(Lancs). . . . Nov 1994
Worwood, Miss Lucy MA(Cantab) . . . *Sep 1997
Con: Huggon, Mr Thomas . . . *§Oct 1969

STEPHEN BURDON SOLICITORS ‡
13 Castle Gate Nottingham NG1 7AQ
Tel: 0115 950 0054 ***Fax:*** 0115 958 0808 ***Dx:*** 10059 NOTTINGHAM
Emergency telephone 0115 950 0054
E-mail: enquiries@stephenburdonsolicitors.co.uk
List of partners: W Bennett, S M Burdon, R Gowans
Languages: Punjabi
Work: G H
Agency, Advocacy and Legal Aid Franchise
Ptr: Bennett, Mr William LLB. . . . *Nov 1995
Burdon, Mr Stephen M BA . . . *Mar 1986
Gowans, Ms Rachel LLB . . . *Sep 1998
Ast: Wadhawa, Miss Avi BA(Hons). . . . *Apr 2005
Winter, Miss Karen LLB . . . *May 1987

BURTON & BURTON SOLICITORS LLP ‡
DBH House Carlton Square Nottingham NG18 1HR
Tel: 0845 094 2500 ***Fax:*** 0845 094 2600 ***Dx:*** 10013 NOTTINGHAM
Emergency telephone 0845 034 4062
E-mail: enquiries@burtonandburton.co.uk
List of partners: C S Burton
Office: Nottingham
Languages: French, Hebrew
Work: D1 F1 G H J1 K1 L N P S1 V W Z(i,l,m,p)
Emergency Action, Agency, Advocacy, Fixed Fee Interview, Legal Aid undertaken and Legal Aid Franchise
Asoc: Gallop, Mr Peter G B BA . . . *Jul 1979

BURTON & BURTON SOLICITORS LLP
15 Wheeler Gate Nottingham NG1 1NA
Office: Nottingham

CAMPION & CO ‡
45-49 Mansfield Road Nottingham NG1 3FH
Tel: 0115 947 6373 ***Fax:*** 0115 950 9171 ***Dx:*** 10132 NOTTINGHAM
E-mail: admin@campions.co.uk
List of partners: S C Campion, D Frempong, S Honeywood
Work: A1 B1 C1 D1 E F1 G H J1 K1 L M1 N P S1 V W Z(g,i,k,p)
Emergency Action, Agency and Advocacy undertaken
Ptr: Campion, Mr Stephen C BA. . . . *Jun 1976
Frempong, Miss Diana LLB . . . *Mar 1989
Honeywood, Miss Samantha BA . . . Nov 1999
Ast: Dougan, Mrs Keely LLB. . . . Nov 2000
Hennessy, Mr Finbarr LLB. . . . Jan 1996

CARRINGTONS SOLICITORS ‡
46 Carrington Street Nottingham NG1 7FG
Tel: 0115 958 3472 ***Fax:*** 0115 948 4913
Dx: 702158 NOTTINGHAM 6
Emergency telephone 0115 956 5000
E-mail: admin@carringtons-solicitors.co.uk

CARTWRIGHT KING ‡
Norwich Union House South Parade Nottingham NG1 2LH
Tel: 0115 958 7444 ***Fax:*** 0808 168 1500 / 0115 970 6220
Dx: 10032 NOTTINGHAM
Emergency telephone 0115 958 7444
E-mail: admin@cartwrightking.co.uk
List of partners: L Bleakley, J Bouch, R M Boucher, A Brammer, A J Cash, I L Cox, S J Gelsthorpe, J Hawkins, G E Heathcote, W K Hollingsworth, A Jones, R J Langton, T P Lumb, M Smith, M J Talbot, M G Thurston, K Waddingham, M S Wilson
Office: Birmingham, Derby, Gateshead, Leicester, Sheffield
Languages: Hindi, Punjabi
Work: B2 F2 G H J2 P Z(m)
Emergency Action, Agency, Advocacy, Fixed Fee Interview and Legal Aid undertaken
Ptr: Bleakley, Mrs Lynn BA; LLM(Lond) . . . *Sep 1986
Brammer, Mr Andrew BA . . . *May 1996
Gelsthorpe, Mr Stephen J BA(Hons) Former Co-Chairman of the Nottingham Duty Solicitor Committee . . . *Dec 1983
Hawkins, Ms Jill LLB . . . *Oct 1983
Heathcote, Mr Graham E. . . . Oct 1991
Hollingsworth, Mr Wayne K BA . . . *Jul 1981
Jones, Mr Alwyn BA ★ . . . *Nov 1984
Smith, Mr Matthew . . . *May 1995
Talbot, Miss Maria Jane LLB . . . *Feb 1992
Thurston, Mr Michael G BSc . . . *Jun 1974
Wilson, Mr Mark S LLB . . . *§Oct 1985
Ast: Bath, Satinder. . . . Mar 2007
Cant, Mr Andrew . . . Feb 2007
Gerrard, Ms Jenny . . . Sep 2001
Harvey, Ms Rachel . . . Jun 2008
Hopwell, Mr Mark LLB. . . . *Aug 2002
Kaur, Kalminder. . . . *Jul 2000
Kinchin-Smith, Mr David. . . . Sep 1989
Kirby, Mr Stephen. . . . Sep 2009
Malins, Ms Lucie . . . Jan 2006
O'Sullivan, Mr Neil LLB; LLM . . . *Apr 1996
Pallett, Miss Hannah Elizabeth . . . *Oct 2008
Pinkney, Ms Laura . . . Mar 2008
Riad, Mr Ahmed. . . . Sep 2007
Rutherford, Ms Victoria . . . Sep 2007
Shergill, Raminder . . . Jul 1998
Smith, Mr David K F MA . . . *Sep 1989
Soor, Mr Sundeep LLB . . . *May 2001
Stanbanks, Emma Jane. . . . *Apr 2002
Turner, Ms Rachel . . . Oct 2003
Usman, Ghuffar LLB(Hons) . . . *Oct 2001
Ward, Ms Alison Helen LLB(Hons) . . . *Sep 1998
Wright, Mr Paul. . . . Oct 2000
Con: Birkett, Mr Ron LLB. . . . *Jan 1971

CHALLINORS
The Wilkins Building Private Road No1 Colwick Nottingham NG4 2JQ
Tel: 0115 871 4510 ***Fax:*** 0115 940 3440 ***Dx:*** 10024 NOTTINGHAM
E-mail: info@challinors.co.uk
Office: Birmingham, Halesowen, West Bromwich, Wolverhampton

CHAMBERS & HIND (STAPLEFORD) ‡
194 Derby Road Stapleford Nottingham NG9 7BL
Tel: 0115 949 1141 ***Fax:*** 0115 949 0027 ***Dx:*** 11852 STAPLEFORD
E-mail: business@chambersandhind.co.uk
List of partners: H E Prins, W Skinner
Legal Aid undertaken
Ptr: Prins, Ms Helen E. . . . *Oct 1984
Skinner, Mr William . . . *Jan 1975

CLAYTON MOTT ‡
Milton Chambers 19 Milton Street Nottingham NG1 3EU
Tel: 0115 941 7422 ***Fax:*** 0115 948 3993 ***Dx:*** 10045 NOTTINGHAM
List of partners: H Barr, H F Lawton, S M Mott, C P Westlake
Office: Sutton-in-Ashfield
Work: A1 B1 C1 D1 E F1 G H J1 K1 K2 L O Q S1 S2 T1 T2 V W Z(c,d,h,i,j,l,m)
Emergency Action, Agency, Advocacy, Fixed Fee Interview, Legal Aid undertaken, Legal Aid Franchise and Member of Accident Line
Ptr: Barr, Mr Harry LLB(Manc). . . . *Jul 1967
Mott, Mrs Sheila Marian BA . . . *Jun 1980
Westlake, Mr Charles Paul . . . *Jul 1979
Asoc: Kent, Mr John Mervyn. . . . *Feb 1988
Con: Mott, Mr Robert M. . . . *Nov 1964

CLEGGS ‡
Apex Court Ruddington Lane Wilford Nottingham NG11 7DD
Tel: 0115 977 5877 ***Fax:*** 0115 977 5888 ***Dx:*** 10050 NOTTINGHAM
E-mail: mail@cleggssolicitors.com
List of partners: I Torr, D Vaughan-Birch, M K Williams
Work: C1 C2 E F1 F2 J1 N O P Q R1 R2 S1 T1 T2 V W Z(c,e,p,r)
Emergency Action, Agency, Advocacy, Fixed Fee Interview undertaken and Member of Accident Line
Ptr: Torr, Mr Ian BA . . . *Oct 1982
Vaughan-Birch, Mr David MSc(Eng). . . . *Nov 1991
Williams, Mr Mark K LLB; TEP. . . . *Oct 1990
Asoc: McSherry, Miss Leah Elizabeth LLB. . . . *May 2009
Ast: Evans, Mr Mark Francis BA(Law) . . . *Aug 2003
Williams, Mrs Fay LLB . . . *Nov 1990
Con: Hall, Mr Martin Francis FCA Trustee of Wellow School *Sep 1997
Sore, Miss Justine Millicent Charlotte LLB(Hons); LPC *Sep 2000

CRICHTONS SOLICITORS ‡
Sharkerdale Offices Fosse Road Nottingham NG13 8JB
Tel: 0845 331 2464

CURTIS PARKINSON ‡
96 Main Street Bullwell Nottingham NG6 8ET
Tel: 0115 931 7000 ***Fax:*** 0115 931 7003 ***Dx:*** 10112 NOTTINGHAM
E-mail: law@curtisparkinson.com
Office: Nottingham
Work: A2 D1 D2 E J1 K1 K2 K3 L N O Q S1 S2 W Z(q)
Agency, Advocacy, Fixed Fee Interview and Legal Aid undertaken
Ast: Attewell, Mr Paul BSc; PhD . . . *Aug 1985
Martin, Mr William A LLB . . . Feb 1982

CURTIS PARKINSON
160 Southchurch Drive Clifton Nottingham NG11 8AA
Tel: 0800 056 6042 ***Fax:*** 0115 931 7004
Dx: 709860 NOTTINGHAM 14
E-mail: law@curtisparkinson.com
Office: Nottingham
Work: D1 F1 J1 K1 K2 K3 N O Q S2 Z(q)
Agency, Advocacy undertaken and Member of Accident Line

DEVASSEY LEGAL ‡
15 Wheeler Gate Nottingham NG1 2NA
Tel: 0115 852 4710
Office: London W1

DONOVAN NEWTON LIMITED ‡
910 Woodborough Road Nottingham NG3 5QR
Tel: 0115 985 6600 ***Fax:*** 0115 962 6766
Emergency telephone 07977 114148
E-mail: admin@donovannewton.co.uk
List of partners: M Donovan, S Newton

See p112 for the Key to Work Categories & other symbols

Ptr: Donovan, Mr Malcolm . . . Feb 1980
Newton, Mr Simon . . . Sep 2000

ELEMENT LAW LIMITED ‡
35 Shaw Street Ruddington Nottingham NG11 6HF
Tel: 0115 984 5220 / 020 3239 4711
E-mail: sarahbird@elementlaw.co.uk

EVERSHEDS LLP
1 Royal Standard Place Nottingham NG1 6FZ
Tel: 0845 497 9797 *Fax:* 0845 497 7477 *Dx:* 10031 NOTTINGHAM
Office: Birmingham, Cambridge, Cardiff, Ipswich, Leeds, London EC2, Manchester, Newcastle upon Tyne
Work: A1 B1 C1 E F1 J1 L M1 O P Q R1 S1 T1 W Z(c,d,e,p,s)

FLINT BISHOP SOLICITORS
The Atrium 20 Wollaton Street Nottingham NG1 5FW
Tel: 0115 964 4450 *Fax:* 0115 950 8422 *Dx:* 10030 NOTTINGHAM 1
E-mail: info@flintbishop.co.uk
Office: Ashbourne, Derby
Work: A1 A3 B1 C1 C2 D1 E F1 J1 K1 K2 K3 L N O Q R1 R2 S1 S2 T1 T2 W Z(c,d,l,o,p,q,r)
Emergency Action, Agency undertaken and Member of Accident Line
Ptr: Jacobs, Mr Thomas Henry LLB; B Juris . . . Mar 1997
Sankey, Mr Barry . . . Jan 1983
Tyler, Miss Michelle L LLB(Hons) . . . Sep 1998
White, Mr Gavin . . . Jan 1996

FRASER BROWN ‡
(incorporating H J Hallam & Co; Whittingham; Bradwell & Mack; Buckley Quilliam & Matthews; Rutherfords; Rose & Co; Bernar)
84 Friar Lane Nottingham NG1 6ED
Tel: 0115 988 8777 *Fax:* 0115 947 3636
Dx: 722010 NOTTINGHAM 40
E-mail: info@fraserbrown.com
List of partners: C G Barnes, G M Green, P L T Jacks, D I Lucas, A B Palfreman, D G Peel, A C Ready, A C Russell, P A Thornley, P R Wood, R M Wright
Office: Bingham, Nottingham
Languages: French, German, Gujarati, Hindi
Work: A1 C1 C2 E J1 K1 K3 L N O S1 S2 W Z(d,e,l)
Fixed Fee Interview, Legal Aid undertaken and Legal Aid Franchise
Ptr: Barnes, Mr Christopher G BA . . . Oct 1984
Green, Mr Graham M BA(Hons) . . . *Mar 1978
Jacks, Mr Peter L T . . . *§Nov 1966
Lucas, Mr David Ian BA(Hons) . . . Dec 1980
Palfreman, Mr Anthony B MA(Cantab) . . . *§Oct 1971
Peel, Mr Donald George BSc(Chemistry with Law) . . *Apr 1998
Russell, Mr Anthony C BA(Hons) . . . *Nov 1979
Thornley, Mr Peter A LLB . . . Dec 1978
Wood, Mr Patrick R LLB . . . Aug 2000
Wright, Mr Robin M LLB(Hons) . . . *§Jun 1971
Ast: Beal, Miss Katie Elizabeth BA(Hons) . . . Sep 2004
Carr, Mr Ewan LLB(Hons) . . . Jan 2011
Chana, Mrs Kakhwinder BA . . . Sep 2008
Clark, Miss Laura Elizabeth LLB . . . Sep 2008
Davies, Miss Rhian Laura LLB; LPC . . . Aug 2009
Digva, Mrs Jasbinder LLB . . . Mar 2010
Ellis, Miss Joanna LLB(Hons) . . . Sep 2005
Hemingray, Mr Jamie John LLB(Hons) . . . Jul 2006
Lowe, Ms Claire . . . Oct 2007
Rathore, Mr Walaiti Singh PGDipLaw; BA; BSc; LPC . Sep 2005
Sargent, Mr M Michael BA(Law) . . . *Dec 1977
Soar, Ms Rebecca . . . Oct 2008
Whitmore, Mr Andrew Timothy LLB(Hons) . . . *Nov 1993
Con: Hodgson, Mr John S MA; LLM(Cantab) Broderip Prize*§Oct 1975

FRASER BROWN
The Old Police Station 24 Main Road Radcliffe-on-Trent Nottingham NG12 2FH
Tel: 0115 933 5311 *Fax:* 0115 933 4182 *Dx:* 10011 NOTTINGHAM 1
E-mail: radcliffe@fraserbrown.com
Office: Bingham, Nottingham
Work: A1 J1 K1 S1 S2 W
Agency undertaken
Ptr: Ready, Mr Andrew C LLB . . . *Dec 1975

FREETH CARTWRIGHT LLP ‡
Cumberland Court 80 Mount Street Nottingham NG1 6HH
Tel: 0115 936 9369 *Fax:* 0115 859 9600 *Dx:* 10039 NOTTINGHAM
E-mail: postmaster@freethcartwright.co.uk
List of partners: S M Abbott, P D Baigent, S C Baigent, P Balen, G K Berwick, R A Beverley, M S Bird, R Bullock, J O G Byrne, P Calladine, L Clifford, M G Copestake, C N Cullen, M Cummins, C J Darby, P A S Dempster, C Downhill, C D Golland, J Goulding, G M Greenfield, M D Grocock, P Hanson, J Hardy, N A Haynes, J Heaphy, C Holwell, D M Houghton, R A Hughes, K P Jansen, J D F Jefferies, P A Jones, R E Joyce, J L Kay, M A Keeley, A Khaliq, M B Mackintosh, A M Macnab, R Magdani, J P May, J H McLauchlan, J M Middleton, S M Miles, A Mills, A Morley, R Neal, R Osborn, M Patel, I P M Payne, S T Pearson, S Philippon-Thomas, K Pickup, D M J Potter, C Powell, M J Radcliffe, I J Radford, P M Raven, G R Reynolds, K E Reynolds, G Roberts, R G Rowley, I C Rowson, J A Smart, L Smith, J M Speed, M J Taplin, G E Taylor, S J Taylor, I J Tempest, M A Thomson, P D Thorogood, D J Tillcock, R Waite, J Walker, D E West, S M Whitton, D M Wilkins, J Williams, D Williamson, R E Wright
Office: Birmingham, Derby, Leicester, Manchester
Work: A1 C1 C2 E I J1 K1 K2 L N O P Q R1 S1 S2 T1 T2 U1 V W Z(b,c,e,f,g,h,j,o,q,r,w)
Ptr: Abbott, Mr Simon M BA . . . §Oct 1984
Baigent, Mr Philip D LLB . . . *Sep 1997
Baigent, Mr Simon Charles LLB . . . *Apr 1993
Balen, Mr Paul MA(Cantab) . . . *§Apr 1977
Berwick, Mr Guy K LLB; LLM . . . *§Nov 1982
Beverley, Mr Richard A LLB . . . *§Nov 1986
Bird, Mr Michael S BA . . . *Oct 1991
Bullock, Mr Richard MA(Oxon) Under Sheriff of Nottinghamshire . . . *§Nov 1971
Copestake, Mr Michael G LLB . . . *Apr 1976
Cullen, Mr C Nigel OBE; TD; DL Notary Public . . . *§Jan 1970
Darby, Mr Charles J LLB . . . *§Oct 1986
Dempster, Mrs Philippa A S LLB Trent Law Prize . . *§Sep 1991
Downhill, Mr Craig . . . Aug 1998
Golland, Mr Christopher D BA . . . *§Oct 1982
Goulding, Ms Jane BA . . . *§Apr 1986
Greenfield, Mr Graham M LLB . . . *§Oct 1987
Grocock, Mr Matthew David LLB . . . *Nov 1995
Hanson, Mr Peter . . . May 1993
Hardy, Ms Julie LLB . . . *Oct 1995
Haynes, Mr Nigel A LLB(Hons) Notary Public . . . *§Jun 1979
Heaphy, Mr John . . . *Oct 1992
Holwell, Mr Christopher LLB . . . *§Oct 1991
Houghton, Mr Deryck Martin LLB(Sheff) . . . May 1981
Hughes, Mr Robert A LLB . . . *§Mar 1973
Jansen, Mr Karl P BA; LLB . . . *§Oct 1990
Jefferies, Mr Jonathan D F LLB . . . *Jul 1989
Kay, Ms Joanne L LLB . . . *Nov 1993
Keeley, Mr Mark Arthur BA Nottingham Law Society Prize 1994 . . . *Sep 1996
Khaliq, Ms Atiyya . . . *Oct 1996
McLauchlan, Mr John H LLB . . . *§May 1979
Macnab, Mr A Murray LLB . . . *§Jun 1990
May, Mr John P LLB . . . Apr 1997
Middleton, Mr Julian Matthew MA(Oxon) . . . *§Oct 1989
Miles, Mrs Susan M LLB(Leeds) . . . *Jun 1971
Mills, Mr Andrew BEng . . . *Jul 1993
Morley, Mrs Amy . . . *Sep 1997
Neal, Mr Robert BA; MA . . . *Sep 1997
Payne, Mr Ian P M . . . *§Aug 1968
Pearson, Mr Stephen Thomas LLB(Hull); DipLGL . . *§Nov 1984
Pickup, Mrs Katherine BA; JD . . . *Aug 1998
Potter, D M J LLB; LLM . . . *§Nov 1989
Powell, Mr Charles . . . *Jun 1995
Radcliffe, Mr Malcolm J . . . *§Feb 1972
Radford, Mrs Isobel Jane . . . *Aug 1995
Raven, Mr Philip Miles LLB . . . *Apr 1993
Reynolds, Mr Gary R LLB . . . *§Apr 1976
Reynolds, Ms Karen E MA . . . *Oct 1993
Roberts, Ms Gillian . . . *Nov 1991
Rowley, Mr Robert G LLB . . . *§Jul 1973
Rowson, Mr Ian Christopher LLB(Hons) . . . *Jul 1982
Smart, Mr Jonathan Andrew MA(Cantab) . . . Nov 1995
Smith, Ms Laura . . . *Nov 1996
Speed, Miss Judith M LLB . . . *§Oct 1982
Taplin, Mr Michael John . . . *§Dec 1991
Taylor, Mr George E . . . *§Aug 1971
Taylor, Mr Simon J BA(Law) . . . *§Jun 1980
Tempest, Mr Ian J BA . . . *§Apr 1981
Thomson, Mr Mark Andrew . . . *Aug 1994
Thorogood, Mr Paul D LLB . . . *§Nov 1982
Tillcock, Mr David J LLB . . . *§Nov 1979
Waite, Mr Robert BA . . . Nov 1993
West, Mr David E LLB . . . *Apr 1977
Wilkins, Mr David M LLB(Manc) . . . *§Apr 1973
Williams, Miss Jane LLB . . . *§Nov 1992
Wright, Mr Roger E LLB . . . *§Aug 1973

FRENCH & CO ‡
6 Derby Terrace Nottingham NG7 1ND
Tel: 0115 955 1111 *Fax:* 0115 955 1187 *Dx:* 10098 NOTTINGHAM
E-mail: ian@frenchandco.co.uk
List of partners: J French, I R Hale
Languages: Hindi, Punjabi, Urdu
Work: B1 C1 D1 E F1 K1 K3 L N O Q S1 S2 V W X Z(g,i,p,q)
Legal Aid undertaken and Legal Aid Franchise
Ptr: French, Mrs Jacqueline BA . . . *May 1980
Hale, Mr Ian Reginald MA(Oxon) . . . *Feb 1996

GATELEY LLP
City Gate East Tollhouse Hill Nottingham NG1 5FS
Tel: 0115 983 8200 *Fax:* 0115 983 8201 *Dx:* 15491 NOTTINGHAM 1
E-mail: info@gateleyuk.com
Office: Birmingham, Leicester, London EC4, Manchester
Languages: French, German, Italian, Punjabi
Ptr: Matthews, Mr Andrew J LLB(Hons) . . . Oct 1986
Moore, Mr Austin John LLB Chairman of the Nottingham Multiple Sclerosis Society . . . *Sep 1988
Rutherford, Mr Mark James LLB . . . *Nov 1990
Tomasin, Miss Jill M LLB(Hons) . . . Nov 1984
Asoc: Mayfield, Miss Anna LLB; LPC . . . Oct 2001
Ast: Mather, Ms Beth . . . Sep 2005

GELDARDS LLP
The Arc Enterprise Way Nottingham NG2 1EN
Tel: 0115 983 3650 *Fax:* 0115 983 3761 *Dx:* 10010 NOTTINGHAM 1
E-mail: info@geldards.co.uk
Office: Cardiff, Derby
Languages: French, German
Work: A1 A3 B1 C1 C2 C3 E F1 F2 I J1 L M1 M2 N O P Q R1 R2 S1 T1 T2 U1 W Z(b,c,d,e,h,k,r,u,y)
Agency and Advocacy undertaken
Ptr: Butler, Mr Michael G LLB Part time Chairman of Industrial Tribunals . . . *Dec 1977
Dickens, Ms Penelope Joy . . . *Dec 1990
Gardner-Browne, Mr Ellis LLB . . . Sep 1997
Gordon, Mr Jamie Mark BA(Law) . . . *Oct 1986
Hacking, Mr Howard Mark MA(Oxon) . . . Nov 1992
Jenkins Jones, Ms Deborah . . . Feb 1997
Johnson, Mr Benjamin T LLB . . . *Oct 1988
Shock, Mr Timothy Guy BA(Dunelm)(Law) . . . *Oct 1982
Slater, Mr Adrian . . . Nov 1998
Strickland, Mr Hugh BSc(Hons)(Eng); CPE; LPC . . *Sep 1998
Tilly, Mr David W BA(Dunelm) . . . *Nov 1987
Tschentscher, Mr Frank . . . Jan 2000
Williams, Mr Ian Geoffrey LLB . . . *Nov 1989

DIANE GENDERS SOLICITORS
15 Wheeler Gate Nottingham NG1 2NA
Tel: 0115 852 4750 *Fax:* 0115 852 4001
Dx: 700676 NORTH HYKEHAM
E-mail: enquiries@dianegenders.co.uk
Office: Lincoln

PAUL GILES ‡
3 Richmond Drive Radcliffe-on-Trent Nottingham NG12 1BG
Tel: 0115 933 3275 *Fax:* 0115 933 3275
E-mail: paul.giles@paulgilestax.co.uk
Work: T1

GILL BOWNESS ‡
4 Kingston Hall Gotham Road Nottingham NG11 0DJ
Tel: 01509 674355

GLADSTONE SOLICITORS
100 Gregory Boulevard Hyson Green Nottingham NG7 5JE
Tel: 0115 978 1666
Office: Derby, Newark, Nottingham
Ptr: Griffiths, Mr Julian P BA(Law) . . . Jun 1981

GLADSTONE SOLICITORS
22 Market Place Arnold Nottingham NG5 6ND
Tel: 0115 955 5050
Office: Derby, Newark, Nottingham
Ptr: Ellis, Mrs Jeanette LLB . . . *Sep 1990
Ellis, Ms Jeanette . . . Sep 1990

GREGSONS ‡
11 Regent Street Nottingham NG1 5BS
Tel: 0115 941 1999 *Fax:* 0115 924 2450 *Dx:* 10046 NOTTINGHAM 1
List of partners: S M Gregson-Murray
Work: G H L Q S1 W Z(g,h,p)
Emergency Action, Agency, Advocacy, Legal Aid undertaken and Legal Aid Franchise
SPr: Gregson-Murray, Ms Susan M LLB(Hons) ★ . . . *Jan 1975
Ast: Short, Miss Theresa Ann BA(Hons) . . . *Oct 1999

GULL THOMPSON ‡
103 Davies Road West Bridgford Nottingham NG2 5HZ
Tel: 0115 966 5599

HR SOLICITOR ‡
6 Empingham Close Beeston Nottingham NG9 6FJ
Tel: 0115 946 2949
E-mail: info@hrsolicitor.co.uk

HANCOCKS SOLICITORS LTD ‡
1 Cottage Terrace Nottingham NG1 5DX
Tel: 0844 474 3377 *Fax:* 0844 474 2323
E-mail: enquiries@hancockslegal.com
List of partners: N A Harding
Work: J1
Fixed Fee Interview undertaken
SPr: Harding, Mrs Nichola Ann LLB . . . Mar 2002

HAWLEY & RODGERS
2 Clarendon Street Nottingham NG1 5JQ
Tel: 0115 955 9000 *Fax:* 0115 955 9001
Dx: 711340 NOTTINGHAM 16
E-mail: n.office@hawleyandrodgers.com
Office: Bingham, Loughborough
Work: C1 D1 D2 E F1 F2 G H J1 K1 K3 K4 L N O Q R1 S1 S2 T2 V W X Z(c,l)
Emergency Action, Agency, Advocacy, Fixed Fee Interview, Legal Aid undertaken, Legal Aid Franchise and Member of Accident Line
Ptr: Benson, Mrs Susan J . . . *Dec 1984
Forrest, Mrs Alison S LLB(Hons) . . . *Oct 1991
Ast: Baker, Mr Peter Michael BA(Hons); LLDip . . . Oct 2005
Williams, Mrs Caroline Ann-Marie BA(Hons) . . . Jan 2002

HEDLEYS ‡
(incorporating Hedley Rattenberry; Hetherington & Co)
6 Eldon Chambers Wheeler Gate Nottingham NG1 2NS
Tel: 0115 947 3506 *Fax:* 0115 941 1009 *Dx:* 15483 NOTTINGHAM 2
Emergency telephone 0115 928 5406
E-mail: legal@hedleys-law.co.uk
List of partners: A H Rattenberry
Work: B1 C1 D1 E F1 G H J1 K1 L M1 N P R1 S1 S2 T1 V W Z(b,c,h,s)
Emergency Action, Agency, Advocacy, Fixed Fee Interview, Legal Aid undertaken, Legal Aid Franchise and Member of Accident Line
Ptr: Rattenberry, Mr Alan H BA . . . *§Jun 1978

JOHN HOOPER & CO ‡
10 Regent Street Nottingham NG1 5BQ
Tel: 0115 941 5566 *Fax:* 0115 941 9977 *Dx:* 10048 NOTTINGHAM 1
Emergency telephone 0115 981 0885
E-mail: johnhooper@johnhooper.com
List of partners: J F Hooper
Work: K1
Ptr: Hooper, Mr John F LLB . . . Nov 1987

HOPKINS
27 Regent Street Nottingham NG1 5BS
Tel: 0115 910 5555 *Fax:* 0115 910 5530 *Dx:* 10052 NOTTINGHAM
E-mail: info@hopkins-solicitors.co.uk
Office: Mansfield (2 offices)
Work: C1 E F1 J1 K1 K2 K3 L N O Q S1 W Z(q)
Agency, Advocacy and Legal Aid undertaken
Ptr: Pratt, Mr Roger Richard . . . Apr 1981
Winnett, Mr David William LLB . . . Sep 1996
Wright, Miss Patricia Cheryl BA . . . *Jul 1995
Ast: Noblet, Mr Mark James LLB(Hons); LPC . . . Nov 2009
Smith, Mrs Alexandra LLB . . . Apr 2010

HUTCHINSONS EMPLOYMENT SOLICITORS ‡
9 College Street Nottingham NG1 5AQ
Tel: 0115 959 9700 *Fax:* 0115 959 9234
E-mail: info@hutchinsonssolicitors.co.uk

IVES & CO ‡
The Forge Main Road Plumtree Nottingham NG12 5NB
Tel: 0115 937 2408 *Fax:* 0115 937 6573
E-mail: viv@ivesandco.com
List of partners: V S Ives
Work: E S1 W
SPr: Ives, Mrs Vivienne S . . . *Jan 1981

THE JOHNSON PARTNERSHIP ‡
(incorporating Ian Boddy Solicitors)
Cannon Courtyard Long Row Nottingham NG1 6JE
Est: 1988
Tel: 0115 941 9141 *Fax:* 0115 947 0178 *Dx:* 10082 NOTTINGHAM
Emergency telephone 0115 941 9141
E-mail: mail@thejohnsonpartnership.co.uk
Web: www.thejohnsonpartnership.co.uk
List of partners: T Addae, I M Boddy, C A Brewin, V A Clayton, C E Coverley, E Eardley, A Graham, D I Henson, N Hornby, D M Johnson, R Keeble, A Parker, C M Saunders, T J Smith, W J E Soughton, L J Treharne, A Young
Office: Chesterfield, Derby, Mansfield
Languages: Spanish
Work: B2 G H
Emergency Action, Agency, Advocacy, Fixed Fee Interview, Legal Aid undertaken and Legal Aid Franchise
Ptr: Addae, Mr Theo LLB ★ . . . *Aug 2003
Boddy, Mr Ian M BA ★ . . . *Mar 1984
Brewin, Mr Christopher A LLB ★ . . . *Oct 1985
Clayton, Miss Victoria Ann LLB . . . *Jul 2001
Coverley, Miss Charlotte Emma LLB • . . . *Jan 2005
Eardley, Miss Emma LLB . . . *May 1999
Graham, Mrs Ashley LLB . . . *Jan 1998
Henson, Mr David I MA(Cantab) . . . *Oct 1974
Hornby, Miss Nicola BA(Hons) ★ . . . *Mar 1995
Johnson, Mr Digby M MA(Cantab) ★ . . . *Sep 1984
Keeble, Mr Robert LLB; LLM . . . *Oct 1995

Parker, Miss Amanda BA(Hons). . . . . *Nov 1992
Saunders, Mr Christopher M BA(Hons) . . . . *Jan 1986
Soughton, Mr William J E LLB(Nott'm). . . . . *Oct 1986
Young, Mr Alastair LLB(Hons). . . . . *Apr 2001
Ast: Ali, Mr Imran BA(Hons) . . . . *Dec 2010
Chad, Ms Jo LLB(Hons). . . . . *Oct 1994
Dunk, Miss Michaela Evonne LLB. . . . . *Jul 2006
Holland, Rosemary BSc(Econ) . . . . *Jul 2007
Johal, Mr Randheer LLB(Hons) . . . . *Jan 2010
Lau, Mr Denny LLB(Hons). . . . . *Sep 2007
Meadows, Miss Rebecca LLB(Hons) . . . . *Dec 2007
Rogers, Miss Jessica LLB(Hons) . . . . *Apr 2007
Rooks, Ms Helen Rebecca Vaughan BA(Hons) . . . . *Jan 1994
Turner, Mr John C LLB . . . . *Jul 1969
Watson-Weinberg, Mr Aaron . . . . *Jul 2007
Wyborn, Mrs Emma LLB(Hons) . . . . *Mar 2007

Criminal Litigation; In-house Counsel, Specialist Fraud Panel Members, Higher Rights Advocates. Prison Law Specialists, Youth Court Specialists, Taxi Licensing.

JOHN KENT SOLICITOR AND LICENSING CONSULTANT ‡
26-27 Huntingdon House 278-290 Huntingdon Street Nottingham NG1 3LY
Tel: 0115 993 4285

LEGAL DOMAIN LIMITED ‡
The Old Barn Church Lane Readmile Nottingham NG13 0GE
Tel: 01949 843125

LEXUS LAW ‡
664 Mansfield Road Nottingham NG5 2GA
Tel: 0800 032 1007 *Fax:* 0151 960 9022
E-mail: info@lexuslaw.co.uk

MCKINLEYS ‡
48 Wollaton Road Beeston Nottingham NG9 2NR
Tel: 0115 951 8010 *Fax:* 0115 922 9097

MACLAREN BRITTON ‡
Grosvenor Chambers 23 King Street Nottingham NG1 2AY
Tel: 0115 941 1469 *Fax:* 0115 947 6073 *Dx:* 10054 NOTTINGHAM
Emergency telephone 07714 094846
E-mail: sbritton@maclarenbritton.co.uk
List of partners: S M Britton, M Crow, E F Ford, D H MacLaren
Languages: French
Work: C1 D1 E G H J1 J2 K1 K3 K4 L N O Q R1 S1 S2 W Z(l,p)
Emergency Action, Agency, Advocacy, Fixed Fee Interview, Legal Aid undertaken and Legal Aid Franchise
Ptr: Britton, Mr Stephen M LLB . . . . *Jul 1988
Crow, Miss Melissa-Jane LLB . . . . *Mar 2001
Ford, Mrs Evelyn Frances LLB . . . . *Sep 1989
MacLaren, Mr Duncan H LLB . . . . *Jun 1972
Ast: Bridgwood, Miss Hannah LLB. . . . . Dec 2008
Charnley, Miss Lauren PGDipLaw. . . . . Jan 2003
Fuller, Mr Lynford R LLB(Hons) . . . . *Jun 1984
Hetherington, Mr Richard LLB. . . . . Sep 1974
Thomas, Mrs Susan J LLB . . . . Feb 1989
Wallace, Mrs Penelope . . . . *May 2002

MASSERS ‡
15 Victoria Street Nottingham NG1 2JZ
Tel: 0115 851 1666 *Fax:* 0115 851 1655 *Dx:* 10021 NOTTINGHAM 1
E-mail: law@massers.co.uk
List of partners: T J D Brooke, J P Carley, K E Flowerdew, R Gull, M F Hall, P D Johnson, M F Mason
Office: West Bridgford
Work: A1 B1 C1 C2 J1 K1 L N O Q S1 V W Z(d,e,j,l)
Emergency Action, Agency, Advocacy and Fixed Fee Interview undertaken
Ptr: Carley, Mr James Peter BA . . . . Sep 1996
Flowerdew, Ms Karon E LLB . . . . *Oct 1986
Gull, Ms Rachel. . . . . *Nov 1995
Hall, Mr Martin Francis FCA Trustee of Wellow School *Sep 1997
Johnson, Mr Peter David MA(Cantab). . . . . *Mar 1975
Mason, Mr Michael F LLB. . . . . *§Apr 1971
Asoc: Harrison, Mrs Claire. . . . . *Apr 2000
Ast: Bhalla, Ms Sonya LLB(Hons) . . . . *Apr 2001
Graham, Miss Julie LLB. . . . . *Oct 1993
Howland, Mrs Alyson LLB. . . . . Jan 1991
Loh, Mr Jason LLB; LLM(International Commercial Law) . . . . Nov 2002
Moothia, Mr Vic. . . . . *Sep 2003
Shaw, Miss Angela LLB . . . . *Oct 2002
Witherspoon, Mr Martin BA(Hons). . . . . Dec 2004

MITCHELL WILDE ‡
Mercury House Shipstones Business Centre Northgate Nottingham NG7 7FN
Tel: 0115 964 8236

TAMSIN MORRIS ‡
31 Private Road Nottingham NG5 4DD
Tel: 0115 962 1649 *Fax:* 0115 962 0209
E-mail: advice@tamsinmorris.co.uk
Languages: Punjabi
Work: J1 K1 L S2 W Z(i)

MOTORING LAWYERS ONLINE ‡
Icon Business Centre Lake View Drive Sherwood Park Nottingham NG15 0DT
Tel: 01623 726242 / 07799 383239 *Fax:* 01623 437256

NFLA LTD ‡
Albion House 5-13 Canal Street Nottingham NG1 7EG
Est: 2005
Tel: 0115 945 4555 *Fax:* 0115 945 4565 *Dx:* 10007 NOTTINGHAM
E-mail: mail@nflaw.co.uk
Web: www.nflaw.co.uk
List of partners: P J Bloomfield, A J Brown, N Flatt, J Gibbons, S D Leach, E Newbold
Office: Chesterfield, Rotherham, Sheffield, Wellingborough
Languages: French, Hindi, Punjabi, Spanish
Work: D1 K1 K3
Emergency Action, Advocacy and Legal Aid undertaken
Ptr: Bloomfield, Ms Paula J LLB(Hons) ♦ . . . . *Dec 1995
Flatt, Mr Nicholas LLB(Hons) . . . . *Mar 2006
Leach, Mr Simon D LLB(Hons) . . . . *Mar 1988
Brown, Amanda J FILEx . . . . NSP
Ast: Chahal, Mrs Rajvinder LLB(Hons). . . . . *Oct 2001
Chima, Mrs Sonia LLB(Hons) . . . . *Jul 2009

Clulee, Mr Benjamin LLM . . . . *Jan 2010
Rodgers, Mrs Emma LLB . . . . Mar 2005

NELSONS ‡
Pennine House 8 Stanford Street Nottingham NG1 7BQ
Tel: 0115 958 6262 *Fax:* 0115 958 4702 *Dx:* 10029 NOTTINGHAM 1
Emergency telephone 0115 958 7262
List of partners: C M Adams, L Bleakley, G B Buck, J A Carter, A J Cash, S P A Chaplin, J E R Coningsby, I T Copestake, P C Dawkins, C R Greenwell, R D Grosberg, T M Hastings, G E Heathcote, T M R Holder, S A Irish, A P Jamieson, A J Jefferies, M M Jenkinson, A Jones, C P McKinney, C Miller, M S Oswin, L Preece, J W V Roberts, A J Rowell, A Shipley, R Staniland, C Stansfield, J Sutherland, D J Taylor, J E Taylor, M A Walls, B H L Williams
Office: Derby, Leicester
Languages: French, German, Spanish, Swedish
Work: A3 B1 B2 C1 C2 C3 D1 D2 E F1 G H J1 J2 K1 K2 L M1 M2 N O P Q R1 S1 S2 T1 T2 U2 V W Z(c,e,i,k,l,o,p,q,r)
Emergency Action, Agency, Advocacy, Fixed Fee Interview, Legal Aid undertaken, Legal Aid Franchise, S.I.G and Member of Accident Line
Ptr: Adams, Mr Christopher M LLB . . . . *Oct 1984
Bleakley, Mrs Lynn BA; LLM(Lond) . . . . *Sep 1986
Buck, Mr Geoffrey B LLB . . . . *Oct 1982
Carter, Mr James A LLB; Dip Crim . . . . *Oct 1984
Chaplin, Mr Simon P A BA(Law). . . . . *Apr 1984
Grosberg, Mr Richard D LLB . . . . *Nov 1985
Hastings, Mr Timothy M LLB; MBA . . . . *Apr 1981
Heathcote, Mr Graham E . . . . Oct 1991
Holder, Mr Timothy M R LLB . . . . *May 1983
Jamieson, Mr Andrew P BA . . . . *Oct 1982
Jenkinson, Mr Mark M BA. . . . . *Jun 1976
Jones, Mr Alwyn BA ★ . . . . *Nov 1984
Miller, Mr Christopher LLB. . . . . *Jun 1976
Preece, Ms Lisa LLB . . . . *Sep 1992
Roberts, Mr Jonathan W V BA . . . . *Oct 1986
Shipley, Mr Andrew . . . . Nov 1983
Staniland, Mr Richard LLB(Hons) . . . . Nov 1975
Stansfield, Mr Christopher LLB . . . . *May 1988
Sutherland, Ms Jane . . . . *Oct 1991
Taylor, Mr Duncan J MA(Oxon); Jurisprudence . . . *Nov 1984
Walls, Ms Marie A FILEx . . . . *Nov 1996
Williams, Mr Bruce H L BA . . . . *Oct 1986
Asoc: Anderson, Mr James R D LLB. . . . . *Dec 1990
Atkinson, Mr John W LLB(Manc) . . . . Dec 1969
Davis, Ms Angela C. . . . . Oct 1991
Froggatt, Miss Helen P BA . . . . *Nov 1990
Lee, Mr Anthony J LLB . . . . *May 1990
Liptrot, Mrs Claire P LLB . . . . *Jul 1978
Pattison, Mr Andrew James LLB . . . . *Oct 1993
Talbot, Miss Maria Jane LLB . . . . *Feb 1992
Vandermark, Mr Stewart Neil LLB. . . . . *Nov 1994
Waterfield, Mr Simon L . . . . *Mar 1995
Ast: Adams, Mrs Angela L BA(Law) . . . . *Oct 1984
Bamford, Miss Sally LLB . . . . Dec 1999
Bell, Ms Audrey Janet. . . . . *Sep 1994
Creasey, Ms Barbara LLB. . . . . *Oct 1997
Eames, Ms Maria . . . . Nov 2001
Elson, Mr Sean A LLB. . . . . Nov 1994
Firmin, Ms Rebecca. . . . . Jul 1999
Gerrard, Ms Jenny . . . . Sep 2001
Gould, Mr Thomas LLB . . . . *Apr 1993
Hogg, Ms Angela . . . . Sep 2000
Jackson, Mr William R BA; ACBSI; Cert Ed . . . . . *Aug 1982
Kelly, Ms Faye . . . . Jul 1999
Kinman, Ms Jennifer . . . . Apr 1999
Lazzeri, Ms Lucy . . . . Sep 2001
O'Sullivan, Mr Neil LLB; LLM . . . . *Apr 1996
Rahman, Ziaur . . . . Aug 2001
Rees, Mr Christopher . . . . Sep 2000
Smith, Mr Matthew . . . . *May 1995
Stevenson, Miss Gillian L LLB. . . . . Sep 1999
Walker, Ms Karen. . . . . Sep 2001
Wright, Mr Paul. . . . . Oct 2000
Con: Smith, Mr David K F MA . . . . *Sep 1989

JOHN O'CONNOR SOLICITORS
Gothic House Barker Gate Nottingham NG1 1JU
Tel: 0115 958 6848 *Dx:* 10136 NOTTINGHAM
Office: Derby
Work: C1 E F1 K1 L M1 P S1 T1 W Z(l)
Emergency Action, Agency, Advocacy, Fixed Fee Interview and Legal Aid undertaken
Ptr: O'Connor, Mr John B BSc; ACIS . . . . *Apr 1985

PARAGON LAW ‡
Finelook Studios 7b Broad Street Nottingham NG1 3AJ
Tel: 0115 964 4123 *Fax:* 0115 964 4111
List of partners: T Vasishta
Office: London SW1
Dir: Vasishta, Thalej LLB . . . . *Sep 2000
Asoc: Lilley-Tams, Mark . . . . Mar 2010
Sheahan, Deidre . . . . Mar 2010
Ast: Becirevic, Aldijana . . . . Mar 2009
Bravery, Mr Steven LLB(Hons) . . . . Sep 1993
Tanner, Mr Kelvin . . . . Jan 2010

POPPLESTON ALLEN ‡
37 Stoney Street The Lace Market Nottingham NG1 1LS
Tel: 0115 953 8500 *Fax:* 0115 953 8501 *Dx:* 10100 NOTTINGHAM
Emergency telephone 0115 953 8500
E-mail: mail@popall.co.uk
List of partners: J R Allen, J R D Anderson, N P Arron, G J S Cushion, C M Eames, L Sharkey, J M Smith
Office: London WC2
Work: Z(l)
Agency undertaken
Ptr: Allen, Mr Jeremy R Honorary Companion CMBII . . . *Jun 1970
Anderson, Mr James Robert Duncan LLB . . . . . . *Jan 1990
Arron, Mr Nicholas Paul. . . . . *Nov 2006
Cushion, Mr Graeme John Stewart LLB. . . . . . . *Oct 1996
Eames, Miss Clare Magaret LLB . . . . *Sep 1997
Sharkey, Miss Lisa LLB(Hons). . . . . *Aug 1994
Smith, Mr Jonathan Mark LLB(Hons) Nottinghamshire Law Society Prize 1990 . . . . *Nov 1992

ERIC POTTER CLARKSON ‡
Park View House 58 The Ropewalk Nottingham NG1 5DD
Tel: 0115 955 2211 *Fax:* 0115 955 2201

PREMIER LEGAL LIMITED ‡
Cumberland House 35 Park Row Nottingham NG1 6EE
Tel: 0845 070 0505 *Fax:* 0845 675 7676
E-mail: info@premier-legal.co.uk

PRYOR JORDAN SOLICITORS ‡
PO Box 9540 Nottingham NG16 9DG
Tel: 0844 824 3117 *Fax:* 0844 824 3118
E-mail: info@pryorjordansolicitors.co.uk

QUANTUS LAW SOLICITORS ‡
513 Mansfield Road Sherwood Nottingham NG5 2JL
Tel: 0115 960 6565 *Fax:* 0800 121 4601
E-mail: info@quantuslawsolicitors.co.uk

RICHARD NELSON BUSINESS DEFENCE SOLICITORS ‡
Priory Court 1 Derby Road Nottingham NG9 2TA
Tel: 0115 986 3636 *Fax:* 0115 986 2626
Emergency telephone 07952 861868
E-mail: defencenottm@richardnelsonllp.co.uk
Office: Bristol, Cardiff, Manchester, Solihull
Languages: French, Greek, Gujarati, Hindi, Italian, Punjabi, Urdu
Work: B2 C3 F2 G I J2 P T1 T2 U2 V Z(y)

ROSLEYS ‡
1a Bridlesmith Gate Nottingham NG1 2GR
Tel: 0115 958 0584 *Fax:* 0115 950 0862 *Dx:* 10121 NOTTINGHAM
Emergency telephone 0500 454550
E-mail: rosleys@rosleys.co.uk
List of partners: J A Rosley, C Stevens
Work: D1 E F1 L M2 P S1 W X
Emergency Action, Agency, Advocacy, Legal Aid undertaken and Member of Accident Line
Ptr: Rosley, Mr John A BA; LLB Notary Public . . . . . . *Nov 1980
Stevens, Ms Claire . . . . Jul 2000
Asoc: McGrath, Mr David LLB; MA . . . . *Jan 1988
Ast: Noor, Ms Jasbir Kaur LLB; LLDip Shakespeare Prize for Obligations II . . . . *Dec 2004

ROTHERA DOWSON ‡
2 Kayes Walk Stoney Street The Lace Market Nottingham NG1 1PZ
Tel: 0115 910 0600 *Fax:* 0115 910 0800 *Dx:* 10028 NOTTINGHAM
E-mail: enquiries@rotheradowson.co.uk
List of partners: J D Allen, A J Balkitis, A Bowman, D G Brydon, P A Cobb, N J Etherington, M A Foulds, C J Fox, C J George, R B Hammond, A J Redgate, T C W Redgate, L K Sear, J E Smith
Office: Beeston, Nottingham (2 offices), West Bridgford
Languages: French, German, Italian, Japanese, Punjabi, Urdu
Work: A1 A3 B1 C1 C2 C3 D1 D2 E I J1 J2 K1 K2 K3 K4 L M1 M2 N O P Q R1 S1 S2 T1 T2 U2 W X Z(c,d,e,j,k,o,p,q,s,t,x)
Emergency Action, Agency, Advocacy, Fixed Fee Interview and Legal Aid undertaken
Ptr: Allen, Mr Jeremy D MA(Cantab). . . . . *Oct 1986
Balkitis, Mr Anthony J BA(Law & Politics) . . . . . . *Oct 1988
Bowman, Mrs Ann-Marie LLB . . . . *Oct 1999
Etherington, Mr Neil John LLB(Hons) . . . . *Oct 2000
Fox, Ms Carole J . . . . *Apr 1996
George, Mr Charles J LLB. . . . . *Oct 1983
Hammond, Mr Richard B LLB Notary Public. . . . . *Oct 1990
Redgate, Mrs Amanda J LLB . . . . *Mar 1990
Redgate, Mr Thomas C W. . . . . *Jan 2001
Sear, Ms Lorna K LLB; LPC. . . . . *Jan 1998
Asoc: Buchanan, Mr John Daniel . . . . *Oct 2002
Kirk, Miss Heather Ruth LLB(Hons) . . . . *Sep 2005
Wood, Mrs Lucy Jane. . . . . *Jul 2009
Ast: Gibbons, Mr Thomas Peter . . . . *Nov 2010
Harley, Mr Daniel . . . . *Jul 2008
Jinks, Miss Beth. . . . . *Jul 2009
Thurlby, Miss Emily Margaret . . . . *Apr 2009
Con: Boden, Mr J James LLB(Hons) . . . . *§Apr 1971

ROTHERA DOWSON
956 Woodborough Road Mapperley Nottingham NG3 5QS
Tel: 0115 952 0900 *Fax:* 0115 952 5575 *Dx:* 701408 MAPPERLEY
E-mail: enquiries@rotheradowson.co.uk
Office: Beeston, Nottingham (2 offices), West Bridgford
Languages: French, German, Italian, Japanese, Punjabi, Urdu
Work: A1 A3 B1 C1 C2 C3 D1 D2 E I J1 J2 K1 K2 K3 K4 L M1 M2 N O P Q R1 S1 S2 T1 T2 U2 W X Z(c,d,e,j,k,o,p,q,s,t,x)
Emergency Action, Agency, Advocacy, Fixed Fee Interview, Legal Aid undertaken and Legal Aid Franchise
Ptr: Foulds, Mr Martin A LLB(Hons) Notary Public . . . . *§Jul 1979

ROTHERA DOWSON
164a Bramcote Lane Wollaton Nottingham NG8 2QP
Tel: 0115 916 5200 *Fax:* 0115 916 5230 *Dx:* 743280 WOLLATON
E-mail: enquiries@rotheradowson.co.uk
Office: Beeston, Nottingham (2 offices), West Bridgford
Languages: French, German, Italian, Japanese, Punjabi, Urdu
Work: A1 A3 B1 C1 C2 C3 D1 D2 E F2 I J1 J2 K1 K2 K3 K4 L M1 M2 N O P Q R1 S1 S2 T1 T2 U2 W X Z(c,d,e,j,k,o,p,q,s,t,x)
Emergency Action, Agency, Advocacy, Fixed Fee Interview, Legal Aid undertaken and Legal Aid Franchise
Ptr: Smith, Mrs Jayne E BA . . . . *Oct 1984
Asoc: Ahmed, Mrs Smyia LLB(Hons) Runner Up Notts Law Society; Presidents Cup 2004 . . . . *Jul 2005

ROYTHORNES LLP
8-12 The Ropewalk Nottingham NG1 5DT
Tel: 0115 948 4555 *Fax:* 0115 945 4416 *Dx:* 10033 NOTTINGHAM
E-mail: roythorne@roythorne.co.uk
Office: Newmarket, Peterborough, Spalding
Languages: French, Polish, Spanish
Work: A1 A2 A3 B1 C1 C2 E F1 F2 G H J1 J2 K4 L M1 N O P Q R1 R2 S1 S2 W Z(c,l,n,q,r)
Agency, Advocacy, Fixed Fee Interview undertaken and Member of Accident Line
Ptr: Czajka, Mr Andrew M LLB(Hons) . . . . *Nov 1985
Fielding, Mr Mark W BA; TD. . . . . *§Jun 1982
Muldoon, Ms Fran MA(Cantab) . . . . *Dec 1998
Asoc: Robbins, Miss Kate LLB(Hons) . . . . *Nov 1997
Ast: Johnson, Mr Edward Charles LLB(Hons) . . . . . . Sep 2008

RUPERT BEAR MURRAY DAVIES ‡
32-36 High Pavement The Lace Market Nottingham NG1 1HN
Tel: 0115 924 3333 *Fax:* 0115 924 2255 *Dx:* 10015 NOTTINGHAM 1
E-mail: reception@rbmdlaw.com
List of partners: M J Davies, R I England, S E Heathcote
Work: D1 D2 K1 K2 S1 W
Agency undertaken
Ptr: Davies, Mr Murray J LLB . . . . *Jul 1978
England, Mrs Rachel I. . . . . *Dec 1979

See p112 for the Key to Work Categories & other symbols

Heathcote, Miss Sarah Elizabeth LLB Nottinghamshire Law Society Prize Winner Executive Committee of Nottinghamshire Relate . . . . *Nov 1992
Ast: Camidge, Mrs Helen E LLB; Diplome des Studies Juridiques Francaises . . . . *Oct 1990

SHAKESPEARES
Park House Friar Lane Nottingham NG1 6DN
Tel: 0115 945 3700 *Fax:* 0115 948 0234 *Dx:* 10004 NOTTINGHAM 1
E-mail: info@shakepeares.co.uk
Office: Birmingham, Leicester, Moreton-in-Marsh, Shipston-on-Stour, Stratford-upon-Avon
Languages: French, German
Work: A3 B1 C1 C2 C3 D1 D2 E F2 I J1 J2 K1 K2 K3 K4 L N O P Q R1 R2 S1 S2 T1 T2 U1 U2 W Z(b,c,d,e,f,h,j,k,o,p,q,r,w)
Agency, Fixed Fee Interview and Legal Aid Franchise
Ptr: Billyeald, Mr C Patrick MA(Cantab) . . . . . . *§Jun 1977
Brackenbury, Mr Richard MA(Cantab) . . . . . . *Apr 1980
Harvey, Miss Virginia Clare LLB(Hons) . . . . . . *Oct 1988
James, Mr Duncan A F LLB(Hons) . . . . . . *Oct 1990
Jarvis, Mr James Paul LLB . . . . . . *Nov 1993
Lewis, Mrs Jacqueline Louise LLB(Hons) . . . . . . *Sep 1999
Mifflin, Mr Carl LLB . . . . . . Mar 2004
Millband, Mr Alan LLB. . . . . . *Oct 1986
Pears, Mr John D LLB(B'ham); TEP. . . . . . *Oct 1986
Pope, Miss Julie BA(Hons) . . . . . . *Nov 1983
Robb, Mr Stephen John Grant BA(Hons) . . . . . . *Dec 1994
Selby, Mrs Cathryn Rachel LLB(Hons). . . . . . Nov 1995
Skiba, Mr Steven J LLB(Hons) . . . . . . *Apr 1993
Wright, Mr Gareth Edward LLB(Hons). . . . . . *Sep 1999
Mem: Harcourt, Mr Roger Stuart William BA(Jt Hons)(Law & Accountancy) . . . . . . Oct 1998
Asoc: Brentnall, Mrs Lesley FILEx. . . . . . *Nov 1996
Litherland, Kendal BA . . . . . . *Oct 1993
Sandhu, Harpreet LLB(Hons); LLM . . . . . . *Sep 2002
Con: Robinson, Mrs Anne E BSc . . . . . . *May 1980

SHARP & PARTNERS ‡
6 Weekday Cross Nottingham NG1 2GF
Tel: 0115 959 0055 *Fax:* 0115 959 0099 *Dx:* 10019 NOTTINGHAM 1
Emergency telephone 0845 733 3111 (PAGER REF 4570333)
E-mail: mail@sharpandpartners.co.uk
List of partners: R Calvert, C G Carlin, C J Evans, A W Fyson, D J V Godfrey, J A Hallam, E N J Halls, D P Morley, R P Oates, G J Tring, T P Wilkinson, V P Wilkinson
Office: Long Eaton, Nottingham (2 offices)
Languages: French
Work: A1 B1 C1 C2 C3 D1 E F1 G H J1 K1 L M1 M2 N P R1 S1 T1 T2 V W Z(c,e,h,i,j,k,l,m,o,p,t)
Emergency Action, Agency, Advocacy, Fixed Fee Interview, Legal Aid undertaken, Legal Aid Franchise and Member of Accident Line
Ptr: Calvert, Mr Roger. . . . . . *Dec 1971
Carlin, Mr Christopher G . . . . . . *Apr 1979
Godfrey, Mr Duncan J V BA. . . . . . *Nov 1984
Hallam, Mr John A LLB . . . . . . *§Jun 1975
Halls, Mrs Elisabeth N J LLB . . . . . . *Dec 1980
Morley, Mr David P LLB. . . . . . Jul 1975
Oates, Mr Robert P LLB. . . . . . *§Apr 1974
Tring, Mr Gregory J LLB. . . . . . *Oct 1988
Wilkinson, Mr Tony P LLB(Sheff) ★ . . . . . . *Apr 1982
Wilkinson, Mrs Valerie P BA. . . . . . *Dec 1982
Ast: Bates, Mr Richard D LLB . . . . . . *Apr 1995
Butt, Miss Joanne L LLB(Hons) . . . . . . Jan 1996
Jephson, Miss Elizabeth R LLB . . . . . . *Jul 1976
McCrery, Mrs Julie LLB . . . . . . *Oct 1995
Parmar, Mr Hashok LLB. . . . . . *Jan 1992
Perry, Mr Nicholas C LLB(Hons); BSc. . . . . . *Sep 1984
Tew, Mrs Heather E BA(Law) . . . . . . *Jul 1978
Witherspoon, Mr Martin John BA; PGDipLaw . . . . . . Aug 1997

SHARP & PARTNERS
69a Main Street Calverton Nottingham NG14 6FG
Tel: 0115 965 4881 *Fax:* 0115 965 5197
Emergency telephone 01345 333111
E-mail: calverton@sharpandpartners.co.uk
Office: Long Eaton, Nottingham (2 offices)
Work: A1 B1 C1 D1 E F1 G H J1 K1 L M1 N P R1 S1 T1 W Z(c,h,i,k,l,m,p)
Emergency Action, Fixed Fee Interview, Legal Aid undertaken and Member of Accident Line
Ptr: Wilkinson, Mrs Valerie P BA. . . . . . *Dec 1982

SHARP & PARTNERS
Byron House 140 Front Street Arnold Nottingham NG5 7EG
Tel: 0115 920 0020 *Fax:* 0115 926 9118
Emergency telephone 01345 333111
E-mail: arnold@sharpandpartners.co.uk
Office: Long Eaton, Nottingham (2 offices)
Work: A1 B1 C1 D1 E F1 G H J1 K1 L M1 N P R1 S1 T1 Z(c,h,i,j,k,l,m,o,p,t)
Emergency Action, Agency, Advocacy, Fixed Fee Interview, Legal Aid undertaken and Member of Accident Line

SHELTONS
388 Carlton Hill Carlton Nottingham NG4 1JA
Tel: 0115 955 3444 *Fax:* 0115 910 0410 *Dx:* 701414 MAPPERLEY
E-mail: info@sheltons-solicitors.co.uk
Office: Hucknall, Nottingham
Work: C1 D1 E F1 J1 K1 L N O Q S1 W Z(l)
Emergency Action, Agency, Advocacy, Legal Aid undertaken and Legal Aid Franchise
Ptr: Watkinson, Mr Brian K . . . . . . *Jun 1982
Ast: Robinson-Bradley, Mrs Nicola E LLB . . . . . . *Apr 1995

SHELTONS
299 Main Street Bulwell Nottingham NG6 8ED
Tel: 0115 955 3444 *Fax:* 0115 916 8515 *Dx:* 28501 HUCKNALL
E-mail: info@sheltons-solicitors.co.uk
Office: Hucknall, Nottingham
Work: C1 D1 D2 E F1 J1 K1 N O Q S1 S2 V W Z(l)
Agency, Advocacy, Legal Aid undertaken and Legal Aid Franchise
Ptr: Mannering, Mr Stephen J M BA(Law) . . . . . . *Jan 1982
Smith, Mr J Clive LLB(Hons) . . . . . . *May 1977
Ast: Millett, Miss Ella Louise LLB. . . . . . Sep 2007

SHOOSMITHS
Waterfront House 35 Station Street Nottingham NG2 3DQ
Tel: 0370 086 5000 / 0115 906 5000 *Fax:* 0370 086 5001
Dx: 10104 NOTTINGHAM 1
Office: Basingstoke, Birmingham, Fareham, London WC2, Manchester, Milton Keynes, Northampton, Reading
Work: A3 B1 B2 C1 C2 C3 E F1 F2 I J1 J2 K4 L M1 N O Q R1 R2 S1 S2 T1 T2 U2 W X Z(b,c,e,f,h,i,j,k,l,m,n,o,p,q,r,s,t,u,y,za)
Ptr: Andrews, Mr Peter . . . . . . Sep 1999
Brookshaw, Mr Oliver Chitty BA . . . . . . Jun 1972
Burke, Mr Sean BA(Hons). . . . . . *§Oct 1988
Duff, Mr Peter H. . . . . . *Oct 1995
Garnett, Mr Christopher J LLB. . . . . . *Oct 1985
Gordon-Brown, Mrs Deborah . . . . . . Oct 1989
Harrison, Mrs Karen Louise BA(Hons). . . . . . *Nov 1985
Morley, Mr David A BA; CPE . . . . . . Sep 1992
Pickin, Mr Andrew Jonathan BA; MSPI . . . . . . *Oct 1983
Seary, Mr W Peter LLB(Hons). . . . . . §Dec 1991
Shirtcliffe, Ms Elizabeth . . . . . . Jan 1997
Willetts, Mr Guy LLB; Diplome d'Etudes Juridiques Francaises . . . . . . Oct 1988

MARTIN SMALLEY & CO ‡
2a Cross Street Arnold Nottingham NG5 7BL
Tel: 0115 955 6555 *Fax:* 0115 955 6505 *Dx:* 29681 ARNOLD
Emergency telephone 07976 559609
E-mail: m.smalley@martinsmalley.co.uk
List of partners: M D Smalley, D Taylor
Work: D1 G H J1 K1 K3 S1 W
Emergency Action, Agency, Advocacy, Legal Aid undertaken and Legal Aid Franchise
Ptr: Smalley, Mr Martin D LLB. . . . . . *Dec 1976
Taylor, Ms Deanne LLB; PGDip Welfare Law . . . . . . *Dec 1993

THOMPSONS (FORMERLY ROBIN/BRIAN THOMPSON & PARTNERS)
4th Floor City Gate East Tollhouse Hill Nottingham NG1 5FS
Tel: 0115 989 7200 *Fax:* 0115 958 4700
Office: Belfast, Birmingham, Bristol, Cardiff, Chelmsford, Dagenham, Derby, Harrow, Leeds, Liverpool, London SW19, London WC1, Manchester, Middlesbrough, Newcastle upon Tyne, Plymouth, Sheffield, South Shields, Southampton, Stoke-on-Trent, Swansea, Wolverhampton
Work: G J1 N
Legal Aid undertaken and Member of Accident Line
Ast: Bainbridge, Mr Mark Johnathan LLB(Hons) . . . . . . Nov 1997
Baines, Mr Neil R LLB(Hons) . . . . . . *Nov 1995
Burgoyne, Mr David Edwin BA(Hons) . . . . . . Apr 1998
Fitchett, Ms Allison Jane LLB . . . . . . *Oct 1992
Greenwood, Mr Reuben James LLB(Hons); MA . . . . . . *Dec 1995
Magee, Mr Peter John Andrew LLB(Hons). . . . . . Nov 1996
Nolan, Miss Maria LLB(Hons). . . . . . *Dec 1997
Smith, Mr Robert H BA(Hons). . . . . . *May 1998
Snaith, Miss Nicola Jayne LLB . . . . . . *Jun 1998
Toft, Mr Ian Martin LLB . . . . . . *Nov 1990

UPPAL TAYLOR ‡
10 Bridgford Road West Bridgford Nottingham NG2 6AB
Tel: 0115 982 0770 *Fax:* 0115 981 0770

VHS FLETCHERS SOLICITORS ‡
111 Carrington Street Nottingham NG1 7FE
Tel: 0115 959 9550 *Fax:* 0115 959 9597 *Dx:* 10087 NOTTINGHAM
List of partners: J D Buckley, M B Hadley, T P Haines, J G Hullis, J A Siddall, A S Varley, N J Walsh, A D Wesley
Office: Ilkeston
Work: D1 D2 G H K1
Emergency Action, Agency, Advocacy, Fixed Fee Interview, Legal Aid undertaken and Legal Aid Franchise
Ptr: Buckley, Mr James D LLB(Hons) . . . . . . *Oct 1991
Hadley, Mr Martin B BA . . . . . . *Apr 1988
Haines, Mr Tim P . . . . . . Sep 1993
Hullis, Mr Jonathan Gorden . . . . . . *Oct 1997
Siddall, J Andrew . . . . . . Sep 1989
Varley, Mr A Steven LLB . . . . . . *Jul 1980
Walsh, Mr Nicholas J BA . . . . . . *Dec 1988
Wesley, Mr Andrew D LLB(Hons) . . . . . . *Oct 1994
Ast: Bower, Mr Alan Dean LLB. . . . . . Jul 1999
Carter, Mr Ian C S LLB . . . . . . Oct 1988
Green, Mrs Sarah Caroline LLB(Hons); LPC. . . . . . Sep 2001
Lees, Miss Helen Jane LLB . . . . . . *Oct 1995
Manuel, Ms Lauren LLB(Hons) . . . . . . Jan 2005
Moore, Ms Colette Laura LLB . . . . . . Sep 2003
Wilson, Mr Roger BSc(Hons) . . . . . . *Sep 1995

WOODTHORPE MEDICAL LAW ‡
2b Thackerays Lane Woodthorpe Nottingham NG5 4HP
Tel: 0115 966 1345 *Fax:* 0115 966 1456

YATES & CO ‡
St Peter's Chambers Bank Place St Peter's Gate Nottingham NG1 2JJ
Tel: 0115 947 4486 *Fax:* 0115 924 1686 *Dx:* 10056 NOTTINGHAM
Emergency telephone 07721 533316
E-mail: info@yatesandco.co.uk
List of partners: H S Pabla
Office: Nottingham
Work: D1 K1 K2 R1 S1 V W
Emergency Action, Agency, Advocacy, Fixed Fee Interview and Legal Aid undertaken
Ptr: Pabla, Harvinder Singh . . . . . . *Nov 1997
Ast: Cowley, Mrs Kirsty C T LLB. . . . . . Apr 1996

YATES & CO
530 Mansfield Road Sherwood Nottingham NG5 2FR
Office: Nottingham

HUGH YOUNG ‡
Cumberland House 35 Park Row Nottingham NG1 6EE
Tel: 0115 988 6050 *Fax:* 0115 988 6150 *Dx:* 10026 NOTTINGHAM
E-mail: hy@hughyoungsolicitor.co.uk
List of partners: H A Young
Work: K1 K3
Agency undertaken
SPr: Young, Mr Hugh A MA(Cantab) . . . . . . *Sep 1971

NUNEATON, Warwickshire

ALSTERS KELLEY
3 Dugdale Street Nuneaton Warwickshire CV11 5QQ
Tel: 0844 561 0100 *Fax:* 0844 561 0299 *Dx:* 16446 NUNEATON
E-mail: enquiries@alsterskelley.com
Office: Coventry, Leamington Spa
Languages: French, Spanish
Work: B1 B2 C1 C2 D1 D2 E G H J1 J2 K1 K2 K3 K4 N O Q R1 S1 S2 W Z(i,k,l,q,r)
Emergency Action, Agency, Advocacy, Fixed Fee Interview, Legal Aid undertaken and Legal Aid Franchise
Ptr: Bannister, Mr Adrian C J BA. . . . . . *Dec 1990
Mannion, Ms Teresa. . . . . . *Jun 1998
Raiseborough, Mr Neil LLB . . . . . . *Sep 2000
Ast: Fripp, Mrs Elizabeth Felicity. . . . . . Apr 2004
Vania, Mr Nazir Ahmed LLB. . . . . . *Oct 1997

JOHN BROMFIELD & COMPANY LTD ‡
120a Abbey Street Nuneaton Warwickshire CV11 5BY
Tel: 024 7638 2343 *Fax:* 024 7664 1994 *Dx:* 16471 NUNEATON
E-mail: enquiries@johnbromfield.co.uk
List of partners: J S Bromfield, C A Rhodes
Work: D1 J1 K1 S1 W
Emergency Action, Agency, Advocacy, Fixed Fee Interview, Legal Aid undertaken and Legal Aid Franchise
Dir: Bromfield, Mr John Simon BA(Hons) . . . . . . *§Dec 1982
Rhodes, Miss Charlotte Ann LLB(Hons) . . . . . . *Nov 2004

M M BYRNE SOLICITOR ‡
1 Church Terrace Church Road Barlestone Nuneaton Warwickshire CV13 0EF
Tel: 01455 292124 *Fax:* 01455 292104
E-mail: mmbyrnesolicitor@aol.com

COCKS LLOYD ‡
Riversley House Coton Road Nuneaton Warwickshire CV11 5TX
Tel: 024 7664 1642 *Fax:* 024 7664 1610 *Dx:* 16443 NUNEATON
E-mail: sol@cockslloyd.co.uk
List of partners: P K Aldridge, R C T Beech, D C Blood, K K Dosanj, A J Mathie, S Wilkinson, F J Wilson
Languages: Hindi, Punjabi, Urdu
Work: A1 B1 C1 C2 D1 E F1 G H J1 K1 L N O P Q R1 R2 S1 S2 T1 T2 V W Z(l)
Emergency Action, Agency, Advocacy, Fixed Fee Interview, Legal Aid undertaken and Member of Accident Line
Ptr: Aldridge, Mr Peter K MA(Cantab) . . . . . . *§Apr 1978
Beech, Mr Ronald C T LLB . . . . . . *§Jun 1969
Blood, Mr Daniel Charles BA(Hons) . . . . . . *Nov 2002
Dosanj, Mrs Kalvinder Kaur LLB Notary Public . . . . *Nov 1993
Mathie, Mr Andrew J LLB . . . . . . *Oct 1982
Wilkinson, Mrs Sharon LLB . . . . . . *Oct 1989
Wilson, Mrs Fiona Jane LLB(Hons) . . . . . . *Jul 1996
Ast: Blood, Mr Matthew James BA. . . . . . Sep 2003
Coyle, Mr David Joseph LLB(Hons); PGDip . . . . . . Oct 2002
Holmes, Mrs Michelle LLB. . . . . . *Aug 1990
Jones, Mr Mathew LLB . . . . . . Oct 2004
Con: Evans, Mr Steven R MA(Cantab); TEP . . . . . . *Jul 1984

IMPERIUM LAW LLP ‡
39 Church Street Nuneaton Warwickshire CV11 4AD
Tel: 024 7634 5060 *Fax:* 024 7637 5237

LDJ SOLICITORS ‡
29 Dugdale Street Nuneaton Warwickshire CV11 5QN
Tel: 024 7674 5000 *Fax:* 024 7674 5029 *Dx:* 16441 NUNEATON
E-mail: info.nuneaton@ldjsolicitors.co.uk
List of partners: M Bunney, K Burton, S J Chater, G H I Daniels, A Edgington, S Marlow-Ridley, G D Ridgway, B B Sheridan
Office: Hinckley
Languages: Gujarati, Urdu
Work: A1 C1 C2 C3 D1 E F1 G H J1 K1 L M1 M2 N O P Q S1 S2 T1 T2 V W Z(l)
Emergency Action, Agency, Advocacy, Legal Aid undertaken and Legal Aid Franchise
Ptr: Bunney, Mr Martin. . . . . . *Oct 1975
Burton, Ms Kate ♦. . . . . . *Jan 2001
Chater, Mrs Samantha Justine . . . . . . *Oct 1996
Edgington, Mr Alan Deputy District Judge . . . . . . *Nov 1975
Ridgway, Mr Graham D BA(Hons). . . . . . *Oct 1981
Sheridan, Mr Brian B . . . . . . *Jun 1974
Ast: Freeman, Mr Stewart John LLB . . . . . . *Sep 2005
Greenwell, Miss Nicola . . . . . . *Dec 2004
Jones, Mrs Andrea Mary Boswell LLB. . . . . . *Jul 1977

TUSTAIN JONES & CO ‡
Phoenix House 11-15 Coventry Street Nuneaton Warwickshire CV11 5TD
Tel: 024 7664 1222 *Fax:* 024 7664 2070 *Dx:* 16466 NUNEATON
List of partners: D N Hall, A Stanford, P Tustain
Office: Bedworth
Agency, Legal Aid undertaken and Legal Aid Franchise
Ptr: Hall, Mr David Nicholas . . . . . . *Jan 1993

WILLSON HAWLEY & CO ‡
George Eliot Building 4 Coventry Street Nuneaton Warwickshire CV11 5SZ
Tel: 024 7638 7821 *Fax:* 024 7664 1376 *Dx:* 16444 NUNEATON
Emergency telephone 01455 823695
E-mail: dhawley@whlitigation.co.uk
List of partners: D R Hawley, P J E Tracy, R W Willson, H L Wolfe
Languages: Farsi
Work: B1 C1 D1 F1 G H J1 K1 L N Q S1 V W
Emergency Action, Agency, Fixed Fee Interview, Legal Aid undertaken and Member of Accident Line
Ptr: Hawley, Mr David Robin LLB(Lond) . . . . . . *Feb 1983
Tracy, Mr Peter Jonathan Ernest LLB . . . . . . *Nov 1990
Willson, Mr Robert William . . . . . . *Nov 1978
Wolfe, Miss Heather Louise LLB . . . . . . *§Feb 1989
Ast: Ahark, Mrs Prem LLB. . . . . . Apr 2000
Marley, Mrs Alexandra BA. . . . . . *Feb 1988
Quinn, Miss Georgina LLB . . . . . . May 2001

OADBY, Leicestershire

RICH & CARR FREER BOUSKELL
49c The Parade Oadby Leicestershire LE2 5BB
Tel: 0116 242 6021 *Fax:* 0116 271 9590 *Dx:* 10989 OADBY
E-mail: enquiries@richandcarr.co.uk
Office: Blaby, Leicester, Lutterworth, Syston
Languages: French
Work: E F1 L Q S1 W Z(q)
Agency, Advocacy undertaken and Member of Accident Line

OAKHAM, Rutland

ALTMORE BUSINESS LAW ‡
30a High Street East Uppingham Oakham Rutland LE15 9PZ
Tel: 0845 094 9000

PAUL BROWNE ‡
20a Church Street Oakham Rutland LE15 6AA
Tel: 01572 757565 *Fax:* 01572 720555 *Dx:* 28349 OAKHAM
E-mail: enquiries@paulbrownesolicitors.co.uk

List of partners: P M Browne
Work: A1 C1 E R2 S1 S2 U1 W
SPr: Browne, Mr Paul M . . . . *§Dec 1979
Ast: Pepperdine, Alexandra . . . . Sep 2004

BUTLER & CO ‡
Church Street Wing Oakham Rutland LE15 8RS
Tel: 01572 737740 *Fax:* 01572 737780
E-mail: sean_butler@compuserve.com
List of partners: S C Butler
Languages: French, Spanish
Work: C1 Z(e)
Ptr: Butler, Dr Sean C MA(Oxon); LLM; CPGS(Cantab) . . *Jul 1980

CHATSWORTH LEGAL ‡
13 High Street Braunston Oakham Rutland LE15 8QU
Tel: 01572 759777

DALTONS
35 Market Place Oakham Rutland LE15 6DT
Tel: 01572 722002 / 724343 *Fax:* 01572 756384
Dx: 28331 OAKHAM
Emergency telephone 01572 755945
Office: Stamford
Work: A1 C1 D1 E K1 L S1 T1 T2 W Z(c,d,l)
SPr: Robson, Mr Philip LLB . . . . *Apr 1975
Ptr: Taylor, Mrs Rebecca Hannah BSc; LLB . . . . *Aug 2009

KEARNEYS ‡
1 Bear Yard Uppingham Oakham Rutland LE15 9RB
Tel: 01572 823605 *Fax:* 01572 824035
E-mail: kearneyssolicitors@kearney-rose.freeserve.co.uk

SIMMONDS GRANT ‡
4 Mill Street Oakham Rutland LE15 6EA
Tel: 01572 756866 *Fax:* 01572 755996 *Dx:* 28333 OAKHAM
List of partners: M S Grant, J F C Simmonds, J P Simmonds
Work: A1 C1 D1 E F1 G H J1 K1 L M1 N O Q S1 V W Z(d,l)
Emergency Action, Agency, Advocacy, Fixed Fee Interview, Legal Aid undertaken and Member of Accident Line
Ptr: Grant, Mrs Melanie Sinclair MA(Oxon). . . . . *Oct 1979
Simmonds, Mr Jeremy Frank Charles LLB. . . . . . *Nov 1997
Simmonds, Mr Jeremy Peter MA(Cantab) . . . . . . *Jul 1971
Ast: Weber, Mrs Julia Ann . . . . *Jun 1998

OKEHAMPTON, Devon

CLIFFORD HOWARD & CO ‡
Sprighill Farm Millaton Moor Bridestowe Okehampton Devon EX20 4QG
Tel: 01837 861455 *Fax:* 01837 861455
List of partners: C R Howard
Work: G N Q Z(t)
Agency and Advocacy undertaken
SPr: Howard, Mr Clifford R LLB . . . . *Jan 1974

PETER PETER & WRIGHT
1 West Street Okehampton Devon EX20 1HG
Tel: 01837 52379 *Fax:* 01837 53604 *Dx:* 82505 OKEHAMPTON
E-mail: mail@peterslaw.co.uk
Office: Bideford, Bude, Holsworthy
Languages: French
Work: A1 E K4 L R1 R2 S1 S2 W
Ptr: Higgs, Mr David John BA(Hons). . . . . *§Nov 1992
Ast: Betambeau, Mr Alexander LLB(Hons) . . . . *Sep 2010

STONES SOLICITORS LLP
21 Fore Street Okehampton Devon EX20 1AJ
Tel: 01837 650200 *Fax:* 01837 650201 *Dx:* 82500 OKEHAMPTON
E-mail: mail@stones-solicitors.co.uk
Office: Exeter
Work: A1 A3 B1 B2 C1 C2 D1 D2 E F1 G H J1 J2 K1 K2 K3 K4 L N O Q R1 R2 S1 S2 T1 W X Z(d,h,j,k,l,o,p,q)
Emergency Action, Advocacy, Legal Aid undertaken and Member of Accident Line
Ptr: Lugger, Mr Andrew BSc; DipLaw . . . . Aug 2001

ROBERT WILSON SOLICITORS ‡
Westhill Sampford Okehampton Devon EX20 2SR
Tel: 01837 55880 *Fax:* 01837 53195
Emergency telephone 01837 55880
List of partners: R E Wilson
Languages: French
Work: C1 E K3 K4 O Q S1 S2 W
SPr: Wilson, Mr Robert E LLB(Lond). . . . . *Oct 1970

OLD COLWYN, Conwy

BONE & PAYNE LLP ‡
Cadwgan Chambers 2 Cadwgan Road Old Colwyn Conwy LL29 9PU
Tel: 01492 515371 *Fax:* 01492 514198 *Dx:* 17909 CONWYN BAY
E-mail: george.price@boneandpayne.co.uk

GUEST PRITCHARD & CO
2 Cadwgan Road Old Colwyn Conwy LL29 9PU
Tel: 01492 515371 *Fax:* 01492 514198 *Dx:* 17909 COLWYN BAY
E-mail: guestpritchard@boneandpayne.co.uk
Office: Colwyn Bay, Llandudno
Languages: Welsh
Work: S1 S2 W
Fixed Fee Interview and Legal Aid undertaken
Asoc: Sandham, Mr Mark Stuart LLB Notary Public . . . . . Jun 2000
Con: Price, Mr George R LLB(Wales). . . . . *Jun 1981

OLDBURY, West Midlands

ARNOLD & CO ‡
148 Causeway Green Road Oldbury West Midlands B68 8LJ
Tel: 0121 552 2382 *Fax:* 0121 552 3048 *Dx:* 19237 OLDBURY 1
E-mail: info@arnoldsolicitors.com
List of partners: M D Arnold
Work: E S1 S2 W Z(l)
Ptr: Arnold, Mr Michael David LLB Notary Public. . . . . *§Mar 1956

HARBANS SINGH
17 Church Street Oldbury West Midlands B69 3AD
Tel: 0121 544 9100 *Fax:* 0121 544 9900 *Dx:* 24957 HANDSWORTH
Office: Birmingham
Languages: Hindi, Punjabi
Work: A1 B1 C1 D1 E F1 G H J1 K1 L M1 N P R1 S1 T1 V W Z(b,c,d,e,f,g,h,i,j,k,l,m,n,o,p,s,t)
Emergency Action, Agency, Advocacy, Fixed Fee Interview and Legal Aid undertaken

KAPASI & CO SOLICITORS ‡
1st Floor 17 Birmingham Street Oldbury West Midlands B69 4DT
Tel: 0121 544 8289

MIDDLETON DUMMER ‡
High Trees House 1-9 Pool Lane Oldbury West Midlands B69 4QX
Tel: 0121 544 4788 *Fax:* 0121 544 2494
E-mail: info@middletondummer.co.uk
List of partners: A R H Dummer, C H L Middleton
Languages: French, German, Spanish
Work: C1 E F2 J2 N O Q R2 S1 S2 W Z(l,q)
Agency and Advocacy undertaken
Ptr: Dummer, Mr Adam Reginald Hibberd . . . . *Nov 1979
Middleton, Mr Carl H L LLB . . . . *Jun 1974
Con: Ashton, Mr Robert C . . . . *Jun 1973
Burton, Mr Jonathan Richard LLB(Manc) . . . . Jun 1969
Mills, Mr Arthur Deryk. . . . . *§Mar 1959
Shingler, Mr Vivian . . . . *Dec 1968

RED LAW SOLICITORS LLP ‡
58 Birmingham Street Oldbury West Midlands B69 4DZ
Tel: 0121 010 8727 *Fax:* 0121 544 0569
E-mail: info@red-law.co.uk

SILKS ‡
Barclays Bank Chambers 27 Birmingham Street Oldbury West Midlands B69 4DY
Tel: 0121 511 2233 *Fax:* 0121 552 6322 *Dx:* 20876 OLDBURY 2
Office: Netherton, Smethwick
Languages: Hindi, Punjabi, Urdu
Work: B1 B2 C1 C2 C3 D1 E F1 G H I J1 J2 K1 K2 K3 L N O Q R1 R2 S1 S2 T1 T2 V W Z(c,g,i,k,l,m,o,p,q,t,za)

OLDHAM, Greater Manchester

ARNOLD BRIERLEY & ROBINSON ‡
14 Church Lane Oldham Greater Manchester OL1 3BP
Tel: 0161 678 1122 *Fax:* 0161 678 1133
E-mail: arnoldbrierley@btconnect.com
List of partners: R W England
Work: D2 K1 K3
Agency undertaken
Ptr: England, Mr Richard William LLB . . . . *Jun 1985

COLIN ASHWORTH & CO
Beal House Beal Lane Shaw Oldham Greater Manchester OL2 8PB
Tel: 01706 845002 *Fax:* 01706 843069 *Dx:* 13776 SHAW
Office: Rochdale
Work: K1 N O Q S1 S2 W
Ptr: Nagle, Mr Michael Antony. . . . . Jul 1975

JOHN BIRKBY & CO ‡
Hill Stores 150 Huddersfield Road Greenacres Oldham Greater Manchester OL4 2RD
Tel: 0161 626 5686 *Fax:* 0161 627 1789 *Dx:* 23627 OLDHAM
List of partners: F S Goode
Work: D1 E K1 K3 N O Q S1 S2 W
Emergency Action, Agency, Advocacy and Fixed Fee Interview undertaken
SPr: Goode, Miss Fiona Susan LLB(Hons) . . . . *§Oct 1986

BROADWAY SOLICITORS ‡
4 Howarth Court Gateway Crescent Chadderton Oldham Greater Manchester OL9 9XB
Tel: 0161 669 6179 *Fax:* 0161 683 3294

COUPLAND CAVENDISH SOLICITORS ‡
1st Floor Lancashire House 12 Church Lane Oldham Greater Manchester OL1 3AN
Tel: 0161 652 5689 *Fax:* 0161 622 0505
E-mail: enquiries@couplandcavendish.co.uk

CUTTLE & CO SOLICITORS
115 Union Street Oldham Greater Manchester OL1 1RU
Tel: 0161 678 7443 *Fax:* 0161 678 7841
Emergency telephone 0161 835 2922
E-mail: fc@cuttles.co.uk
Office: Manchester
Work: D1 G H K1 K3 K4 N Q W
Agency, Advocacy, Fixed Fee Interview and Legal Aid undertaken
Ptr: Durham, Mr Stephen LLB . . . . Nov 1997
Ast: Ahmad, Mr Kassim Rahman LLB(Hons). . . . . Nov 2003

DEEN WAHID ‡
370-372 Manchester Road Oldham Greater Manchester OL9 7PG
Tel: 0161 241 7676 *Fax:* 0161 633 1126
E-mail: personalinjury@deenwahid.co.uk

DIXON THOMASSON PARTNERSHIP ‡
25 Duchess Park Close Shaw Oldham Greater Manchester OL2 7YN
Tel: 01706 843230

EDENFIELD SOLICITORS ‡
PO Box 514 Oldham Greater Manchester OL1 9AU
Tel: 0161 345 7574

FA LAW ‡
102-104 Oxford Street Oldham Greater Manchester OL9 7SJ
Tel: 0161 665 0070

FORSTER DEAN LTD
14 Curzon Street Oldham Greater Manchester OL1 3AG
Tel: 0161 669 4940 *Fax:* 0161 669 4941
E-mail: enquiries@forsterdean.co.uk
Office: Birkenhead, Bootle, Chorley, Crewe, Eccles, Ellesmere Port, Huyton, Leigh, Liverpool (5 offices), Preston, Rochdale, Runcorn, St Helens, Stockport, Warrington, Widnes (2 offices), Wigan

HANSON & CO ‡
Valentine House 19 Jackson Pit Oldham Greater Manchester OL1 1LU
Tel: 0161 626 6116
E-mail: hansonco@compuserve.com

HEYLIN LEGAL LIMITED ‡
9 King Street Oldham Greater Manchester OL8 1DW
Tel: 0161 626 4561 *Fax:* 0161 620 4462
E-mail: admin@heylins.co.uk

HILLS (OLDHAM) ‡
9 Queen Street Oldham Greater Manchester OL1 1UD
Tel: 0161 652 3231 *Fax:* 0161 627 2360 *Dx:* 23604 OLDHAM
E-mail: stephen.parker@hillsoldham.co.uk
Work: D1 F1 G H J1 K1 L N Q S1 W Z(i,l,m)
Emergency Action, Agency, Advocacy, Fixed Fee Interview and Legal Aid undertaken

HILTON LEGAL ‡
Bowgreave Ball Grove Uppermill Oldham Greater Manchester OL3 6JG
Tel: 01457 830126 / 07771 725530

SCOTT HYMAN & CO ‡
Lancashire House 12 Church Lane Oldham Greater Manchester OL1 3AN
Tel: 0161 628 7018 *Fax:* 0161 627 5316
E-mail: info@scotthyman.co.uk
List of partners: K D Scott, G G Sladen
Languages: French, German
Emergency Action, Agency, Advocacy and Legal Aid undertaken
Ptr: Scott, Mr Kieran D LLB . . . . *Oct 1984
Sladen, Mr Geoffrey G LLB . . . . *Jul 1968

KEMPS SOLICITORS ‡
19-25 Union Street Oldham Greater Manchester OL1 1HA
Tel: 0161 633 0555 *Fax:* 0161 633 9905 *Dx:* 23622 OLDHAM
Emergency telephone 07785 501141
E-mail: lawyers@kemps-solicitors.com
List of partners: G M Kemp, S J Sullivan
Office: Hyde
Work: B2 G H
Agency and Legal Aid undertaken
Ptr: Kemp, Mr Gregory M LLB(Hons) . . . . *Apr 1991
Sullivan, Mr Steven John LLB(Hons) . . . . *Oct 1987
Asoc: Whitworth, Ms Justine LLB(Hons). . . . . *Jan 1995
Ast: Clarke, Ms Rebecca L BA(Hons); CPE; LPC . . . . *Aug 2000
Man, Ms Michelle LLB(Hons) . . . . *Nov 1999

STEPHEN KREBS & CO ‡
3 Retiro Street Oldham Greater Manchester OL1 1SA
Tel: 0161 652 0507 *Fax:* 0161 652 0050
List of partners: S M Krebs
Work: G H
Agency and Legal Aid undertaken
SPr: Krebs, Mr Stephen M BA(Law) . . . . *Jul 1990

SUSHMA LAL ‡
101 Windsor Road Coppice Oldham Greater Manchester OL8 1RP
Tel: 0161 627 2479
Languages: Urdu
Work: D1 G H K1 M1 P S1 Z(i)
Emergency Action, Agency, Advocacy, Fixed Fee Interview and Legal Aid undertaken

LEWIS & CO ‡
21 Queen Street Oldham Greater Manchester OL1 1RD
Tel: 0161 626 4444

LLOYDS SOLICITORS
41 Union Street Oldham Greater Manchester OL1 1HH
Tel: 0161 652 9996 *Fax:* 0161 652 4111
E-mail: oldhamoffice@lloydslaw.co.uk

LONGFORDS ‡
(in association with Mann & Co)
Pennine House 77 Union Street Oldham Greater Manchester OL1 1JZ
Tel: 0161 665 4400 *Fax:* 0161 665 4409
Dx: 710005 OLDHAM CIVIC CENTRE
Emergency telephone 07711 366606
E-mail: mail@longfords.net
List of partners: A Alam, T Shafiq
Languages: Bengali, Punjabi, Urdu
Work: E G H N O Q S1 S2 Z(i)
Emergency Action, Agency, Advocacy, Fixed Fee Interview, Legal Aid undertaken and Legal Aid Franchise
Ptr: Alam, Ashraful LLB(Hons); DipLP ★ Sweet & Maxwell Law Prize 1994 . . . . *Jul 1998
Shafiq, Tahir BA; LLM. . . . . *Jan 1990

MACFARLAINE ‡
1 Ivy Green Drive Springhead Oldham Greater Manchester OL4 4PR
Tel: 0161 624 2149 *Fax:* 0161 624 2149
E-mail: donna.macfarlaine@btinternet.com

MAYA SOLICITORS ‡
42a Horsedge Street Oldham Greater Manchester OL1 3SH
Tel: 0161 284 6907
E-mail: masoom@ntlworld.com

MEGSONS LLP ‡
7-9 Church Lane Oldham Greater Manchester OL1 3AN
Tel: 0161 633 6131 *Fax:* 0161 627 5251
List of partners: S Abbas, A D Cockburn, I P Hannam
Office: Bradford
Work: F1 J1 L N O Q R1 S1 W Z(l,r)
Emergency Action, Agency, Advocacy, Fixed Fee Interview, Legal Aid undertaken and Member of Accident Line
Ptr: Abbas, Mr Sajit . . . . *Dec 2000
Cockburn, Mr Alan D BA . . . . *§Sep 1983
Hannam, Mr Ian Paul LLB. . . . . *Jun 1984

MELLOR & JACKSON ‡
8 Church Lane Oldham Greater Manchester OL1 3AP
Tel: 0161 624 7081 *Fax:* 0161 627 4381 *Dx:* 23608 OLDHAM
E-mail: mail@mnj.co.uk
List of partners: M A Khan, T A Qureshi
Office: Royton
Languages: Mirpuri, Urdu
Work: E F1 G H N O Q S1 T2 W Z(l)
Emergency Action, Agency, Advocacy, Fixed Fee Interview and Legal Aid Franchise
Ptr: Khan, Mr Mohammed Afzal CBE LLB(Hons). . . . . *May 1996
Qureshi, Mr Tanvir Ahmed. . . . . Sep 2005
Asoc: Etherington, Mr Keith FILEx ♦. . . . . *Sep 2002
Ast: Wood, Mrs Rosemary Anne BA . . . . Oct 2002
Con: Edmondson, Mr John LLB. . . . . *§Mar 1975

See p112 for the Key to Work Categories & other symbols

MELLOR HARGREAVES SOLICITORS ‡
11 King Street Oldham Greater Manchester OL8 1DW
Tel: 0800 811 844 *Fax:* 0161 627 5156 *Dx:* 23603 OLDHAM
E-mail: enquiries@mellorhargreaves.co.uk
List of partners: S Hargreaves, D Mellor
Work: N
Member of Accident Line
Ptr: Hargreaves, Miss Susan LLB; MPA . . . . *Nov 1995
Mellor, Mr David BA(Hons) . . . . *Oct 1997

MULDERRIGS SOLICITORS LTD
29 King Street Oldham Greater Manchester OL8 1DP
Tel: 0161 665 0123
Office: Rawtenstall

NORCROSS LEES & RICHES ‡
19 Queen Street Oldham Greater Manchester OL1 1RD
Tel: 0161 624 6034 *Fax:* 0161 627 4284
Emergency telephone 07702 523938
E-mail: office@nlr-solicitors.co.uk
List of partners: D A Heap
Languages: French
Work: A1 B2 C1 D1 E F1 G H J1 K1 L N O P Q S1 S2 V W Z(c,f,j,k,l,m)
Emergency Action, Agency, Advocacy, Fixed Fee Interview, Legal Aid undertaken, Legal Aid Franchise and Member of Accident Line
Ptr: Heap, Mr David A LLB . . . . *§May 1979
Ast: Hughes, Mr Tim L BA(Dunelm) . . . . *Oct 1996
O'Brien, Miss Sonya E BA; LPC. . . . . *Oct 1999

NORTH AINLEY HALLIWELL ‡
(incorporating Malcolm Hurst & Co)
34-42 Clegg Street Oldham Greater Manchester OL1 1PS
Tel: 0161 624 5614 *Fax:* 0161 678 8380 *Dx:* 23605 OLDHAM
Emergency telephone 0161 620 3647
E-mail: law@northainley.co.uk
Work: A1 B1 C1 C2 D1 E F1 J1 K1 L N O Q R1 S1 S2 T1 T2 V W Z(d,l,p,w)

I J OWEN & CO ‡
9 Manchester Chambers Oldham Greater Manchester OL1 1LF
Tel: 0161 633 9999

PEARSON HINCHLIFFE ‡
Albion House 31 Queen Street Oldham Greater Manchester OL1 1RD
Tel: 0161 785 3500 *Fax:* 0161 624 2589 *Dx:* 23615 OLDHAM
E-mail: admin@pearson-hinchlif.co.uk
List of partners: C G Burke, M A Cox, R M Eastwood, G D Hinchliffe, R M Hinchliffe, A J Pearson, M Pitt, J M Pollitt, D T Prince, M H Talbot
Languages: French, German
Work: B1 C1 C2 D1 E F1 F2 G H J1 J2 K1 L M1 N O P Q R2 S1 S2 V W Z(c,e,q,r)
Emergency Action, Agency, Advocacy, Fixed Fee Interview, Legal Aid undertaken, Legal Aid Franchise and Member of Accident Line
Ptr: Burke, Mr Christopher G LLB ♦ . . . . *Oct 1990
Cox, Mr Matthew A BA ♦ . . . . *§Feb 1983
Hinchliffe, Mr George D LLB ● . . . . *Jun 1979
Hinchliffe, Mr Roger M ♦ . . . . *Dec 1971
Pearson, Mr A John LLB ♦ . . . . *§Apr 1975
Pitt, Mr Michael LLB ♦ . . . . Mar 1981
Pollitt, Mr John M LLB ♦. . . . . *§Apr 1981
Prince, Mr Daniel T LLB ♦. . . . . Jul 1991
Talbot, Mr Michael H LLB(Hons) ●. . . . . *§May 1990
Eastwood, Mr Richard Michael . . . . .NSP
Ast: Bowen, Mr Ian Richard LLB; BSc(Econ) ● . . . . . . *Nov 1994
Evans, Rebecca ♦. . . . . *§Jan 2007
Hanif-Ahmed, Ms Nazneem ♦ . . . . *§Jul 2004
Lees, Mr Kenneth. . . . . *Sep 2010
Mayall, Ms Susan ♦ . . . . *Jul 2004
Pearson, Ms Hannah ♦ . . . . *§Aug 2004
Pracy, Ms Laura ♦. . . . . *§Apr 2006
Tariq, Majidiah ♦ . . . . *§Mar 2004

PLATT HALPERN ‡
5 Union Street Oldham Greater Manchester OL1 1HA
Tel: 0161 626 4955 *Fax:* 0161 627 1672
List of partners: S Blakebrough, P E Bradbury, J Comyn-Platt, W A Deane, D J Halpern, M J Hopkinson, J Potter, A Preston
Office: Manchester (2 offices)
Languages: French, Punjabi, Urdu
Work: D1 G H K1 L N
Emergency Action, Advocacy and Legal Aid undertaken
Ptr: Blakebrough, Mr Simon . . . . Sep 1997
Bradbury, Mr Paul Edward BA; CQSW; Dip(Applied Soc Studies); LLB . . . . *Oct 1991
Comyn-Platt, Mr Jonathan LLB . . . . *Dec 1973
Preston, Mr Alex . . . . Oct 1997
Asoc: Iqbal, Mr Zaffar LLB(Hons) . . . . *Oct 1999
Ast: Burns, Ms Mary. . . . . *Oct 2005

QUALITYSOLICITORS GRUBER GARRATT ‡
King Street Buildings 39 Manchester Street Oldham Greater Manchester OL8 1DH
Tel: 0161 665 3502 *Fax:* 0161 665 4060 *Dx:* 23613 OLDHAM
Emergency telephone 07971 163241
E-mail: info@qshrubergarratt.co.uk
List of partners: D Cartledge, S J Garratt, H P Gruber, T M Hopley, T Machowski, T L Pearson, A Smith
Office: Ashton-under-Lyne, Radcliffe, Stalybridge, Worsley
Work: B1 C1 C2 C3 D1 D2 E F1 G H J1 K1 L N O P Q R1 S1 S2 T1 T2 W Z(e,k,l,m,p,q,r,s)
Emergency Action, Agency, Advocacy, Fixed Fee Interview, Legal Aid undertaken, Legal Aid Franchise and Member of Accident Line
Ptr: Cartledge, Ms Deborah LLB. . . . . *Feb 1997
Garratt, Mr Stephen J LLB . . . . *Apr 1981
Hopley, Mr Timothy Martin LLB(Hons). . . . . *Apr 1994
Machowski, Mr Tony MA . . . . *Mar 1992
Pearson, Mrs Tracey Lynne FILEx Commissioner for Oaths . . . . *Nov 1999
Smith, Angela LLB(Hons); TEP . . . . *Oct 2004
Asoc: Greenhalgh, Frances LLB(Hons) . . . . *May 2004
Hilditch, Mrs Dawn . . . . *Dec 2005

REDMONDS SOLICITORS ‡
Manchester House King Street Saddleworth Oldham Greater Manchester OL3 5DL
Tel: 01457 879500 *Fax:* 01457 879501
E-mail: info@redmonds-solicitors.co.uk
List of partners: C Holland
Work: N
Dir: Holland, Mrs Claire LLB(Hons) . . . . Apr 2000

IAN SIMPSON & CO ‡
Chapel House Chambers Business Centre Chapel Road Oldham Greater Manchester OL8 4QQ
Tel: 0161 622 4939 *Fax:* 0161 622 4938
E-mail: mail@iansimpson.co.uk
List of partners: I H Simpson
Languages: German
Work: B1 C1 C2 E R1 S1 T1 T2 W Z(c)
Ptr: Simpson, Mr Ian Hamilton LLB(Hons). . . . . *§Jun 1971

WRIGLEY CLAYDON ‡
29-33 Union Street Oldham Greater Manchester OL1 1HH
Tel: 0161 624 6811 *Fax:* 0161 624 3743 *Dx:* 23607 OLDHAM
E-mail: info@wrigleyclaydon.com
List of partners: G J Burns, W Connor, R L Damianou, P Gregory, A G Pickles, J A C Porter, V A Srivastava
Office: Todmorden
Work: A1 B1 C1 C2 C3 D1 E F1 G H J1 K1 L M1 M2 N O P Q R1 R2 S1 T1 T2 U2 V W Z(d,e,h,i,l,p,q,r,w)
Emergency Action, Agency, Advocacy, Fixed Fee Interview, Legal Aid undertaken and Legal Aid Franchise
Ptr: Burns, Mr Gary James LLB . . . . *May 2004
Connor, Mrs Wendy LLB . . . . *§Oct 1982
Damianou, Mrs Rachel Louise LLB . . . . *§Nov 1993
Gregory, Mr Paul LLB(Hons) . . . . *§Feb 1991
Porter, Mr John A C LLB . . . . *§Jan 1990
Srivastava, Vijay A LLB . . . . *§Dec 1989
Asoc: Mehta, Mr Shalish LLB . . . . *§Jun 2002
Swinscoe, Miss Martine Theresa LLB(Hons). . . . . . *Sep 1998
Taylor, Mrs Amanda Jane LLB. . . . . Jun 2011
Con: Haines, Mr David O LLB(Leeds). . . . . *§Jul 1965
Jolley, Mrs Frances Mary LLB Deputy District Judge. . *Apr 1980
Norcross, Mr Michael David LLB . . . . .Jul 1977
Postle, Mrs Ruth Mary LLB . . . . *Jun 1975
Smith, Mr Julian D LLB Notary Public . . . . *Jan 1970
Vincent, Mr Paul H BA(Manc) . . . . *§Apr 1973

YATES ARDERN
68 George Street Oldham Greater Manchester OL1 1LS
Tel: 0161 287 3331 *Fax:* 0161 287 3372
E-mail: yatesardernsolicitors@googlemail.com
Office: Ashton-under-Lyne

ZACHARIA & CO ‡
89 Union Street Oldham Greater Manchester OL1 1PF
Tel: 0161 620 8888

OLNEY, Milton Keynes

J GARRARD & ALLEN ‡
4 High Street Olney Milton Keynes MK46 4BB
Tel: 01234 711215 *Fax:* 01234 713391 *Dx:* 51300 OLNEY
E-mail: enquiries@jgarrardandallen.co.uk
List of partners: P F Gardener, B Hill, R Marchant, V P Schomberg
Work: A1 B1 C1 C2 C3 D1 E F1 J1 J2 K1 K2 K3 K4 L N O P Q R1 R2 S1 S2 T1 T2 W Z(c,j,k,l,n,q,r,t)
Agency and Advocacy undertaken
Ptr: Gardener, Mr Paul Francis . . . . Jan 2001
Hill, Mr Brent MA(Cantab). . . . . *Jun 1975
Marchant, Mr Robert LLB LSF. . . . . Oct 1987
Schomberg, Ms Vanessa P . . . . Oct 2001
Asoc: McCallum, Mrs Anne L LLB(Hons) . . . . *§Nov 1979
Satyanadhan, Richard. . . . . Sep 2004
Con: Perkins, Mr John D . . . . §Jun 1968

PARRISH SOLICITORS ‡
26 High Street South Olney Milton Keynes MK46 4AA
Tel: 01234 711701 *Fax:* 01234 711750 *Dx:* 51302 OLNEY
E-mail: cparrish@parrishsolicitors.co.uk
Work: D2 K1 K2 W
Fixed Fee Interview undertaken

ORMSKIRK, Lancashire

BRIGHOUSE WOLFF ‡
(incorporating Brighouse Jones & Co; Heald Wolff)
28 Derby Street Ormskirk Lancashire L39 2BY
Tel: 01695 573202 *Fax:* 01695 578922 *Dx:* 21253 ORMSKIRK
E-mail: firm@brighouse-wolff.co.uk
List of partners: J L Anderson, S G Brighouse, M Flynn, P A J Garside, J C Green, M G Hagerty, E E Jones, S Mossman
Office: Maghull, Skelmersdale (2 offices)
Work: A1 C1 D1 E G H J1 K1 K3 K4 L N O Q R1 S1 S2 T2 W Z(c)
Emergency Action, Advocacy, Fixed Fee Interview, Legal Aid undertaken and Legal Aid Franchise
Ptr: Anderson, Miss Jennifer Louise LLB. . . . . *Sep 2007
Brighouse, Mr Simon G. . . . . *Dec 1993
Garside, Mr Philip A J LLB . . . . *Apr 1977

JOHN CUNNINGHAM & ASSOCIATES ‡
44 New Court Way Ormskirk Lancashire L39 2YT
Tel: 01695 581007

DAVIES & GRIBBIN SOLICITORS ‡
Leyland House 16 Derby Street Ormskirk Lancashire L39 2BY
Tel: 01695 573433 *Fax:* 01695 573933
List of partners: S M Davies, B Gribbin
Ptr: Davies, Mr Stephen Mark LLB(Hons) . . . . Nov 1993
Gribbin, Mrs Barbara LLB(Hons) . . . . Jan 1993
Ast: Heath, Miss Sarah BSc(Hons). . . . . Jan 2002

DICKINSON PARKER HILL ‡
22 Derby Street Ormskirk Lancashire L39 2BZ
Tel: 01695 574201 *Fax:* 01695 579986 *Dx:* 21254 ORMSKIRK
E-mail: info@dphlaw.co.uk
List of partners: P A Clegg, A J Fowler, D H Lunn
Work: A1 C1 C2 D1 E J1 J2 K1 K3 L N O Q R1 R2 S1 S2 T1 T2 V W Z(l,o,t)
Emergency Action, Advocacy, Fixed Fee Interview, Legal Aid undertaken and Member of Accident Line
Ptr: Clegg, Mr Paul A LLB. . . . . *Dec 1982
Fowler, Mrs Alexandra Jane LLB. . . . . *Nov 1995
Lunn, Mr David Hamor LLB . . . . *Sep 1998
Ast: Greenwood, Miss Katherine Anne. . . . . *Nov 1998

ESPILON SOLICITORS ‡
New Sutch Farm Sutch Lane Lathom Ormskirk Lancashire L40 4BU
Tel: 01704 894945 *Fax:* 01704 894944
E-mail: eco@epsilonsolicitors.co.uk
List of partners: E C Ord
Work: J2 N O P Q R1 S1
Emergency Action, Agency, Advocacy and Fixed Fee Interview undertaken
Ptr: Ord, Miss Elizabeth Charlotte LLB; MA; LLM . . . . .*Sep 1988

ROWENA FOAT SOLICITORS ‡
57 Moor Street Ormskirk Lancashire L39 2AG
List of partners: R Foat
SPr: Foat, Rowena. . . . . Oct 1995

MOONEY EVERETT SOLICITORS ‡
30 Derby Street Ormskirk Lancashire L39 2BY
Tel: 01695 574111 *Fax:* 01695 581223

SCOTT DOYLE MOLYNEUX SOLICITORS ‡
4 Derby Chambers 2a Derby Street Ormskirk Lancashire L39 2BY
Tel: 01695 573555 *Fax:* 01695 574578
E-mail: info@scottdoylemolyneuxsolicitors.co.uk

ORPINGTON, Kent

ANJORIN & CO ‡
Suite 7 Safe Store Building Cray Avenue Orpington Kent BR5 3QF
Tel: 01689 891192 *Fax:* 01689 890967
E-mail: solicitor@anjorinsolicitors.co.uk
Languages: Igbo, Yoruba

T G BAYNES
Downe House 303 High Street Orpington Kent BR6 0NJ
Tel: 01689 886000 / 886042 *Fax:* 01689 886210
Dx: 31600 ORPINGTON
E-mail: johnw@tgbaynes.com
Office: Bexleyheath, Dartford
Work: D1 D2 K1 K3 K4 S1 W
Legal Aid Franchise
Ptr: Power, Ms Stephenie LLB(Hons) . . . . *Nov 2001
Wigginton, Mr John T LLB. . . . . *Jul 1985

BEYNONS ‡
113 Glentrammon Road Orpington Kent BR6 6DQ
Tel: 01689 861008 *Fax:* 01689 850160
List of partners: H M Beynon
Work: S1 S2 W
SPr: Beynon, Mrs Helen M LLB . . . . *Dec 1985

CLARKSON WRIGHT & JAKES LTD ‡
Valiant House 12 Knoll Rise Orpington Kent BR6 0PG
Tel: 01689 887887 *Fax:* 01689 887888 *Dx:* 31603 ORPINGTON
E-mail: cwj@cwj.co.uk
List of partners: W R Addis, N Androsov, J R Bowden, S J Chubb, A J Custis, P J Giblin, D J K Greenhalgh, J L Groeger Wilson, J N Lawton, B J Madden, A J Mehlin, C E Schneck, A J Wood, A C Wright
Languages: French, German, Russian, Spanish
Work: C1 C2 C3 D1 E F1 I J1 J2 K1 K2 M2 N O Q S1 S2 T1 T2 V W X Z(c,e,k,l,p,q,r)
Emergency Action, Agency, Advocacy, Fixed Fee Interview, Legal Aid undertaken, Legal Aid Franchise and Member of Accident Line
Ptr: Addis, Mr William Robert BA(Hons) . . . . Feb 2001
Androsov, Nicky. . . . . *Sep 1999
Bowden, Mr John R. . . . . *Oct 1982
Chubb, Mr Stephen J LLB(Hons)(NZ) . . . . *Sep 1989
Custis, Mrs Amanda J BA(York); ATII . . . . *Oct 1990
Giblin, Mr Peter J LLB(Lond) Notary Public . . . . . . *Jul 1978
Greenhalgh, Mr David J K LLB(Hons). . . . . *Jan 1989
Groeger Wilson, Mr Jeremy Laurence BA(Hons) . . . Dec 1988
Lawton, Miss Jill N LLB(Hons). . . . . *Sep 2005
Madden, Mr Benjamin J BSc(Accounting/German); CPE; LPC . . . . *Oct 1999
Mehlin, Miss Amanda J LLB(Hons) . . . . *Feb 1993
Schneck, Miss Claire E LLB. . . . . *Oct 2000
Wood, Mr Andrew John Outstanding Performance on LPC 2003 . . . . *Sep 2003
Wright, Mr Andrew Clarkson LLB(Hons) Notary Public *Oct 1987
Asoc: Ansary, Miss Nasima LLB(Hons) . . . . *Oct 2004
Bajaria, Mrs Pritti . . . . *Jan 2001
Brennan, Mrs Rosalie Eve BA; MA . . . . May 1998
Bristow, Mr Kevin John LLB(Hons); DipLP. . . . . . . Sep 1996
Denny, Miss Jo LLB. . . . . Oct 2003
Gupta, Mr Deepak BA(Hons) . . . . *Mar 2002
Wormald, Mr Alexander LLB; BVC; QLTT . . . . *May 2008
Ast: Awan, Miss Yasmin LLB; LPC. . . . . *Oct 2005
Ellingsworth, Ms Kate LLB . . . . *Mar 2010
Flagg, Mr Andrew LLB(Hons) . . . . Apr 2009
Kenward, Ms Louise LLB . . . . *Oct 2008
Lawrence, Mrs Claudine LLB(Business Law) . . . . . *Sep 2006
Smith, Mrs Helen LLB. . . . . Sep 2010
Thompson, Miss Laura Jane BA(Law & History). . . . . Jan 2006
Trinh, Miss Thuh Yao LLB. . . . . Oct 2008
Con: North, Mr Michael A MA(Oxon) Notary Public . . . . *§Jun 1972

CRAY VALLEY SOLICITORS LIMITED ‡
93 Cotmandene Crescent Orpington Kent BR5 2RA
Tel: 020 8302 4968

DILWORTH LAMB & CO ‡
International House Cray Avenue Orpington Kent BR5 3RS
Tel: 01689 821119 *Fax:* 01689 891422 *Dx:* 99302 ST MARY CRAY
Emergency telephone 020 7582 8543
E-mail: richardlamb@btconnect.com
List of partners: R M Lamb
Languages: French
Work: D1 G H K1 L N Q S1 W
Emergency Action, Agency, Advocacy, Fixed Fee Interview, Legal Aid undertaken and Member of Accident Line
Ptr: Lamb, Mr Richard M BA(Manc) ★ Crowther Shield Prize . . . . *Jan 1984
Ast: Reed, Miss Allison Joan LLB . . . . Sep 1993

DOBSONS ‡
Crown Building The Walnuts Orpington Kent BR6 0TN
Tel: 01689 886300 *Fax:* 0871 429 0048 *Dx:* 31611 ORPINGTON
Emergency telephone 0845 927 7378
E-mail: mail@dobsons.org.uk
List of partners: G E Dobson
Work: B2 F2 G H I J2
Emergency Action, Agency, Advocacy, Fixed Fee Interview, Legal Aid undertaken and Legal Aid Franchise

Ptr: Dobson, Mr Graham E BA(Hons) West London Law Society Prize Winner 1975 Chairman of the Legal Services Commission Funding Review Committee . . . . *§Mar 1977
Ast: Chudasama, Ms Bhavna LLB(Hons). . . . . Jan 1998
O'Leary, Ms Sarah . . . . *§Oct 1995
Payton, Mrs Vicky LLB(Hons). . . . . Jun 2001
Tuthill, Miss Katherine Helen . . . . *§Sep 2002

THOMAS DUNTON SOLICITORS ‡
217-219 High Street Orpington Kent BR6 0NZ
Tel: 01689 822554 *Fax:* 01689 839327 *Dx:* 31614 ORPINGTON
E-mail: enquiry@thomasdunton.co.uk
List of partners: T Bengo, M J Dunton, V F Hadida
Work: A3 B1 C1 C2 D1 E F1 F2 I J1 J2 K1 K2 K4 L M1 M2 N O Q R1 S1 S2 T2 U2 V W X Z(e,g,h,j,k,p,q,u)
Emergency Action, Agency, Advocacy, Fixed Fee Interview, Legal Aid undertaken, Legal Aid Franchise and Member of Accident Line
Ptr: Bengo, Ms Tessa LLB. . . . . *Oct 1990
Dunton, Miss Melanie J LLB. . . . . *Oct 1985
Hadida, Mr Vernon Francis BSc; C Phys; MInstP . . *Nov 1991
Asoc: Sardo, Mr Robert John BSc(Hons) . . . . *Oct 1992
Ast: Hendry, Miss Margaret C BA . . . . Jan 1980
Newton, Miss Lucy Jane LLB . . . . Sep 2009
Ryan, Miss Adrienne LLB(Hons). . . . . Aug 2000

LK SOLICITORS ‡
1 Woodcote Drive Orpington Kent BR6 8DB
Tel: 01689 878141

LEFEVRE & CO ‡
Alexandre House Crofton Road Locks Bottom Orpington Kent BR6 8NL
Tel: 01689 856835 / 856836 *Fax:* 01689 862913
Dx: 86855 LOCKS BOTTOM
List of partners: J C Bingham, B L Burton
Work: E S1 W
Ptr: Burton, Mrs Brenda L . . . . *Nov 1981

PUMFREY & LYTHABY ‡
(incorporating Attwater & Cope)
155-159 High Street Orpington Kent BR6 0LN
Tel: 01689 833657 *Fax:* 01689 825906 *Dx:* 31601 ORPINGTON
E-mail: enquiries@pumf.co.uk
List of partners: D Smith, C A Terry
Work: D1 D2 E K1 K2 K3 L N O Q S1 S2 V W
Emergency Action, Agency, Advocacy, Legal Aid undertaken and Legal Aid Franchise
Ptr: Smith, Mr David BA(Hons) . . . . *Oct 1983
Terry, Miss Caroline A LLB . . . . *Oct 1980
Ast: Bharaj, Mrs Anita LLB. . . . . *Jan 1994
Coventon, Mrs Elizabeth A LLB(Bris) . . . . Apr 1978
Margereson, Ms Janine Kristina LLB(Hons) . . . . . *Nov 1990

WADE STEVENS & CO ‡
32 Station Square Petts Wood Orpington Kent BR5 1NA
Tel: 01689 831122 *Fax:* 01689 876919
E-mail: pauls@wadestevens.com
List of partners: V A Gallier, P J Stevens
Work: B1 C1 E F1 J1 K1 K3 L O Q R1 S1 S2 T1 W Z(c,f,j,l,q)
Ptr: Gallier, Mrs Victoria A LLB . . . . *Oct 1992
Stevens, Mr Paul J . . . . Jun 1981
Ast: Kunz, Mrs Romilda LLB(Hons) . . . . May 2001

OSWESTRY, Shropshire

JEREMY CASE SOLICITOR ‡
The Willow Tree Willow Street Oswestry Shropshire SY11 1AJ
Tel: 01691 656563

CRAMPTON PYM & LEWIS ‡
The Poplars 47 Willow Street Oswestry Shropshire SY11 1PR
Tel: 01691 653301 *Fax:* 01691 658699 *Dx:* 26604 OSWESTRY
Emergency telephone 01691 670975
E-mail: info@crampton-pym-lewis.co.uk
List of partners: L M Croft, M H Woodward
Languages: Welsh
Emergency Action, Agency, Advocacy, Fixed Fee Interview, Legal Aid undertaken and Legal Aid Franchise
Ptr: Croft, Mrs L Mary BSc; MSc(Econ) . . . . *Nov 1984
Woodward, Mr Mark H . . . . *Oct 1967
Ast: Johnson, Miss Carole L MA(Oxon) . . . . *Jan 1992

GHP LEGAL
37-39 Willow Street Oswestry Shropshire SY11 1AQ
Tel: 01691 659194 *Fax:* 01691 652755 *Dx:* 26605 OSWESTRY
E-mail: oswestry@ghplegal.co.uk
Office: Llangollen, Wrexham
Languages: Welsh
Work: A1 B1 C1 C2 C3 D1 D2 E F1 G H J1 K1 K2 L N O Q R1 S1 S2 T1 T2 V W Z(c,k,l,m,q,r)
Emergency Action, Agency, Advocacy, Fixed Fee Interview, Legal Aid undertaken, Legal Aid Franchise and Member of Accident Line
Ptr: Hulme, Mr John A BA. . . . . *Jun 1985
Lloyd, Mr E Richard LLB(Wales) Clerk to the General Commissioners of Income Tax . . . . *Oct 1982
Ast: Lewis, Mr Karl LLB . . . . Oct 2004
Monaghan, Miss Alison Ann LLB . . . . Aug 2006
Wilson, Miss Victoria C LLB. . . . . *Nov 1999

GOUGH-THOMAS & SCOTT
31 Salop Road Oswestry Shropshire SY11 2NR
Tel: 01691 655600 *Fax:* 01691 655666
Dx: 701590 ELLESMERE SHROPSHIRE
E-mail: oswestry@gtssolicitors.co.uk
Office: Ellesmere
Work: A1 C1 D1 E F1 F2 J1 K1 L N O Q S1 S2 T1 T2 W Z(d)
Advocacy undertaken and Member of Accident Line
Ptr: Kendall, Mrs Christine LLB(Wales). . . . . *Oct 1984

SIMON JACKSON SOLICITORS ‡
The Office Tyn Celyn Llansilin Oswestry Shropshire SY10 7JW
Tel: 01691 791439 *Fax:* 01691 791583 *Dx:* 26602 OSWESTRY
E-mail: srbj@btconnect.com
List of partners: S R B Jackson
Work: L N O P Q
SPr: Jackson, Mr Simon Richard Braidwood BA(Hons) . . . Apr 1980

LANYON BOWDLER LLP
25 Church Street Oswestry Shropshire SY11 2SZ
Office: Hereford, Ludlow, Oswestry, Shrewsbury, Telford, Wellington

LANYON BOWDLER LLP
39-41 Church Street Oswestry Shropshire SY11 2SZ
Tel: 01691 652241 *Fax:* 01691 670074 *Dx:* 26603 OSWESTRY
Emergency telephone 07801 644107
E-mail: enquiries@lblaw.co.uk
Office: Hereford, Ludlow, Oswestry, Shrewsbury, Telford, Wellington
Languages: French, Welsh
Work: A1 A2 B1 B2 C1 C2 C3 D1 D2 E F1 F2 G H J1 K1 K2 K3 K4 L N O Q R1 R2 S1 S2 T1 T2 V W Z(c,d,l,q,t)
Emergency Action, Agency, Advocacy, Fixed Fee Interview, Legal Aid undertaken and Legal Aid Franchise
Ptr: Gittins, Mr Alan C LLB(Wales). . . . . *§Jul 1977
Glenister, Mr Ian LLB(Newc) . . . . *§Jun 1977
Thomas, Mr David K LLB . . . . *§Dec 1986
Wilde, Miss Emma May Louise LLB . . . . *Oct 1999
Asoc: Miles, Miss Bethan Jane LLB(L'pool) . . . . *Nov 1994
Ast: Burgess, Miss Anna LLB . . . . Jul 2004
Percival, Miss Kathryn LLB . . . . Jul 2004
Scott, Mrs Caroline Murray LLB . . . . Mar 2001
Yorke, Miss Caroline BA . . . . *§Nov 1990

MFG SOLICITORS
103 Beatrice Street Oswestry Shropshire SY11 1HL
Tel: 01691 684817
E-mail: oswestry@mfgsolicitors.com
Office: Bromsgrove, Halesowen, Kidderminster, Telford, Worcester

ROBERT MANN ‡
16 Salop Road Oswestry Shropshire SY11 2NU
Tel: 01691 671926 *Fax:* 01691 680994
List of partners: R Mann
Work: A1 C1 E F1 J1 K1 L N O Q R1 S1
Emergency Action, Agency, Advocacy, Fixed Fee Interview and Legal Aid undertaken
SPr: Mann, Mr Robert BA(Hons)(Law) . . . . *Oct 1986

MILTON FRANCIS & HUGHES SOLICITORS ‡
32-36 Willow Street Oswestry Shropshire SY11 1AD
Tel: 01691 654662 *Fax:* 01691 657623 *Dx:* 26606 OSWESTRY
E-mail: info@miltonfrancishughes.co.uk
List of partners: R E Hughes
Work: A1 A2 B1 C1 C2 C3 D1 D2 E F1 J1 L O P Q R2 S1 S2 T1 T2 W Z(b,c,d,e,h,l,s)
Ptr: Hughes, Mr Richard E LLB . . . . *§Jul 1978
Ast: Thomas, Mr Stephen M A LLB . . . . Oct 1981

STEVENS LUCAS
22 Upper Brook Street Oswestry Shropshire SY11 2TB
Tel: 01691 670999 *Fax:* 01691 662830 *Dx:* 712200 CHIRK
E-mail: enquiries@stevenslucas.co.uk
Office: Chirk
Work: A1 B1 C1 C2 D1 E F1 J1 J2 K1 L M2 N O P Q R1 S1 S2 T1 T2 U2 V W X Z(d,f,l,q)
Emergency Action, Agency, Advocacy and Fixed Fee Interview undertaken
Ptr: Davies, Mr Malcolm S BA(Hons) Deputy District Judge . . . . *§Nov 1986
Hill, Ms Linda LLB. . . . . *Jan 1995

PAUL WISEMAN INVESTIGATIONS ‡
PO Box 169 Oswestry Shropshire SY11 1WZ
Tel: 01691 655732
Emergency telephone 07855 691043
E-mail: paul@wisemaninvestigations.com
Work: B2 G J1 K1 K3 N Q
Emergency Action and Member of Accident Line

OTLEY, West Yorkshire

EATONS
49-51 Pegholme Wharfebank Business Centre Ilkley Road Otley West Yorkshire LS21 3JP
Tel: 0845 660 0660
Office: Bradford, Leeds

NEWSTEAD & WALKER ‡
Mercury House Mercury Row Otley West Yorkshire LS21 3HQ
Tel: 01943 461414 *Fax:* 01943 461068 *Dx:* 25651 OTLEY
E-mail: post@newsteadwalker.co.uk
Web: www.newsteadwalker.co.uk
List of partners: K J Baker, D W Louden, R J Meadows, H K Thornton
Languages: French, Spanish
Work: A1 A3 E F1 F2 J1 K1 K2 K3 K4 L N O Q R2 S1 S2 W
Ptr: Baker, Mrs Katharine Jane MA(Cantab); CPE; LSF . *Nov 1992
Louden, Mr David W LLB . . . . *Mar 1980
Meadows, Mr Robert J LLB . . . . *Jan 1991
Thornton, Ms Helen K MA(Oxon) . . . . *Jun 1978
Asoc: Armitage, Mrs Catherine BA. . . . . *Oct 1992

SAVAGE CRANGLE
Royal Oak House Manor Square Otley West Yorkshire LS21 3AZ
Tel: 01943 465050 *Fax:* 01943 466890
Office: Skipton
Ptr: Storah, Mr Christopher Mark BA. . . . . Nov 1993
Ast: Woolcott, Mr Andrew James BA. . . . . Dec 1998

OTTERY ST MARY, Devon

CHRISTINE ASHBY SOLICITORS ‡
61 Mill Street Ottery St Mary Devon EX11 1AB
Tel: 01404 814303
E-mail: mail@christineashby.co.uk
List of partners: C Ashby
Work: K4 T2 W
SPr: Ashby, Ms Christine. . . . . Feb 1996

EVERYS
The Old Manse Mill Street Ottery St Mary Devon EX11 1AA
Tel: 01404 813446 *Fax:* 01404 813046
Dx: 48752 OTTERY ST MARY
Emergency telephone 01404 822123
E-mail: law@everys.co.uk
Office: Budleigh Salterton, Exeter, Exmouth, Honiton (2 offices), Seaton, Sidmouth, Taunton
Work: A1 A2 B1 C1 C2 C3 D1 D2 E F1 F2 G H J1 K1 L M1 N O P Q R1 R2 S1 S2 T1 T2 V W X Z(c,d,e,h,i,k,m,n,o,p,q,r,s,t,u,w,x,y)
Emergency Action, Agency, Advocacy, Fixed Fee Interview, Legal Aid undertaken and Legal Aid Franchise

GILBERT STEPHENS
(incorporating Mossop & Whitham)
7 Broad Street Ottery St Mary Devon EX11 1BS
Tel: 01404 812228 *Fax:* 01404 815270
Dx: 48750 OTTERY ST MARY
E-mail: osmlaw@gilbertstephens.co.uk
Office: Exeter, Sidmouth
Work: A1 B1 C1 D1 E F1 F2 G J1 K1 L M1 N O Q R1 S1 T1 T2 V W X Z(b,c,d,l,o,p)
Agency, Advocacy and Fixed Fee Interview undertaken
Ptr: McKay, Mr Nigel I BSc(Hons) . . . . *Mar 1998
Ast: Govier, Miss Elizabeth Ann LLB; TEP . . . . Oct 1989

OUNDLE, Northamptonshire

HC SOLICITORS LLP
4 New Street Oundle Northamptonshire PE8 4ED
Tel: 01832 273506 *Fax:* 01832 273404 *Dx:* 716082 OUNDLE
E-mail: peter.izod@hcsolicitors.co.uk
Office: Peterborough
Work: A1 B1 C1 D1 E F1 G H J1 K1 L M1 N P R1 S1 T1 V W Z(b,c,d,e,h,i,j,k,l,m,n,o,p,s,t)
Emergency Action, Agency, Advocacy, Fixed Fee Interview, Legal Aid undertaken and Member of Accident Line
Ptr: Izod, Mr Peter L BA. . . . . *Oct 1983
Dir: Appleton, Mr Patrick J LLB . . . . *Oct 1985

JJ SOLICITORS ‡
2 Home Farm Close Wadenhoe Oundle Northamptonshire PE8 5TE
Tel: 01832 238088 *Fax:* 01832 238083

OVERTON, Hampshire

BARKER SON & ISHERWOOD LLP
25 High Street Overton Hampshire RG25 3HB
Tel: 01256 770211 *Fax:* 01256 771525 *Dx:* 90303 ANDOVER
E-mail: info@bsandi.co.uk
Office: Andover (2 offices), Whitchurch
Work: A1 B1 C1 E J1 J2 K1 K3 K4 L N O Q R2 S1 S2 T1 T2 W Z(c,j,q,r)

OXFORD, Oxfordshire

ABBOTT FORBES SOLICITORS ‡
Keble Court 26 Temple Street Cowley Oxford Oxfordshire OX4 1JS
Tel: 01865 794855
E-mail: help@afslaw.co.uk
List of partners: M N Khan
SPr: Khan, Mr Mohammed Nawaz LLB(Hons) . . . . Jul 1996

BARLOW LYDE & GILBERT LLP
The merged firm of Barlow Lyde & Gilbert and Clyde & Co
3140 Rowan Place Oxford Business Park South Oxford Oxfordshire OX4 2WB
Tel: 01865 336600 *Fax:* 01865 336611 *Dx:* 155700 OXFORD 12
Office: London EC3, Manchester
Ptr: Brett, Mr Clive MA(Oxon) . . . . *Nov 1997
Nurse-Marsh, Mr Anthony Roger . . . . Sep 1990

BLAKE LAPTHORN
Seacourt Tower West Way Oxford Oxfordshire OX2 0FB
Tel: 01865 248607 *Fax:* 01865 728445 *Dx:* 723000 OXFORD 5
E-mail: info@bllaw.co.uk
Office: Chandlers Ford, London EC1, Portsmouth
Languages: French, German, Italian, Polish, Spanish
Work: A1 A3 B1 C1 C2 C3 E F1 I J1 J2 K1 K2 K3 L N O Q R1 R2 S1 S2 T1 T2 U2 W X Z(b,c,d,e,g,l,p,q,r,z)
Agency, Advocacy, Legal Aid Franchise and Member of Accident Line
Ptr: Alder, Mr Christopher . . . . Sep 2000
Brook, Mr Niall . . . . Jul 1981
Brooks, Mrs Rachel LLB . . . . Nov 1995
Court, Mr Simon . . . . Nov 1993
Cowell, Mrs Anne M LLB . . . . *Jun 1975
Deech, Dr John S MA; DPhil . . . . *Mar 1979
Ellis, Mr Lindsay. . . . . Oct 1991
Graham, Mr Charles K C MA(Cantab) L Bentwich Prize 1997 . . . . Apr 1980
Hepworth, Mr Mark B BA . . . . *Oct 1979
Humphreys, Mr Richard E LLB . . . . *Oct 1988
Irwin-Singer, Mr Jeremy P T MA(Cantab); LLM . . . . *Jul 1978
Jarvis, Mrs Sue LLB. . . . . Oct 1990
Lee, Mr Edward Paul LLB. . . . . *Nov 1987
Lloyd-Jones, Mr Jonathan LLB . . . . *Oct 1979
McGruer, Mr Guthrie . . . . Jun 1980
Matthew, Miss Tamzin BA(Hons) . . . . *Sep 1996
Miscampbell, Mr Andrew I F LLB(Nott'm) . . . . *Jan 1985
Oster Warriner, Mrs Carol BA . . . . *Oct 1987
Plews, Mrs Christine BA(Hons) . . . . *Nov 1989
Potts, Mr Christopher David Charles BA. . . . . Nov 1998
Quigley, Mr Paul F LLB . . . . *Dec 1980
Saunders, Mr Jonathan S MA(Oxon) . . . . *Oct 1988
Smith, Mr Simon . . . . Dec 1994
Stansfield, Ms Judith M LLB(Leeds). . . . . *Feb 1983
Sutton, Mr Jamie P BA . . . . *Sep 1979
Talbot, Mrs Alison LPC . . . . *Sep 1998
Wade, Mr Richard Samuel Marlar LLB. . . . . *May 1994
Whiter, Mr James P LLB . . . . *Nov 1989
Asoc: Harte, Ms Michelle Catherine . . . . Jan 2002
Ast: Ahmed, Rabina . . . . Mar 2000
Antoniou, Mr James Michael BA(Hons) . . . . Apr 2003
Smith, Ms Suzy Elizabeth . . . . Sep 2003
Burt, Chris . . . . Sep 2006
Colbert, Miss Claire Louise LLB Family Law Prize; Private Client Prize 1999; Oxford Institute of Legal Practice 1999 Sep 2001
Cowley, Mr Jason. . . . . Aug 2006
Craggs, Miss Alison. . . . . *Oct 2004
Dawtrey, Jo. . . . . Sep 2006
Desmond, Mr Liam . . . . Jun 2006
Drummond, Miss Elizabeth . . . . Sep 2005
Dugdale, Miss Nicola . . . . Mar 2002
Evans, Mr David . . . . Sep 1997
Fillery, Ms Nicola . . . . Sep 1999
Graham, Mrs Melissa M. . . . . *Dec 1991
Haidermota, Mr Taha . . . . Mar 2006
Hathaway, Ms Kate . . . . Sep 2006
Ince, Mr Richard . . . . Feb 2005
Ingram, Ms Sarah. . . . . Sep 2002
Owens, Mr Nicholas David BA(Hons) . . . . Oct 2000
Pitman, Mr Scott . . . . Sep 2005

See p112 for the Key to Work Categories & other symbols

Rees, Ms Faye . . . . Sep 1998
Robinson, Miss Alexandra Kirsty LLB . . . . *Sep 2000
Robson, Mrs Lara. . . . . Sep 2007
Sadler, Mrs Deborah Jane BA(Hons); CPE; LPC . . . Aug 2003
Sales, Miss Rachel . . . . Sep 2007
Schollar, Ms Victoria Teresa. . . . . *Jun 2004
Somarakis, Mr Philip . . . . Oct 1990
Stodart, Ms Victoria. . . . . Mar 2004
Walsh, Ms Anna . . . . Mar 1997
Ward, Mr Michael. . . . . Nov 2002
Whiteford, Miss Louise . . . . Sep 2005
Wild, Ms Nicola MA(Cantab) . . . . *Oct 1982
Young, Ms Sophie. . . . . Sep 2006
Con: Linnell, Mr Michael J Notary Public . . . . *§Apr 1962
Milne-Day, Mr Trevor D MA(Oxon). . . . . *§Nov 1972
Rippon, Mr Paul Dudley William LLB(Hons) . . . . . . Jun 1972

BOODLE HATFIELD
6 Worcester Street Oxford Oxfordshire OX1 2BX
Tel: 01865 790744 *Fax:* 01865 798764 *Dx:* 4329 OXFORD 1
E-mail: bh@boodlehatfield.com
Office: London W1
Languages: French, German
Work: C1 C2 E J1 K1 K3 L Q R2 S1 T1 T2 U2 W Z(d)
Ptr: Hassall, Ms Natasha J D BA(Hons) . . . . *May 1995
Simpson, Ms Barbara M BA(Dunelm) . . . . *Jun 1974
Asoc: Graham, Ms Fiona . . . . *Mar 1997
Ast: Craggs, Miss Alison. . . . . *Oct 2004
Sepanski, Mrs Eleanor . . . . *Feb 1998

BOWER & BAILEY ‡
Anchor House 269 Banbury Road Summertown Oxford Oxfordshire OX2 7JF
Tel: 01865 311133 *Fax:* 01865 311722 *Dx:* 40669 SUMMERTOWN
E-mail: summertown@bowerandbailey.co.uk
List of partners: S E Bailey, D J Black, P Boardman, D J G Bower, R P Brookes, P D Cooksey, R E A Eden, D Falvert-Martin, D P S Hannam, T Harrhy, A J Hill, R M Jackson, D J Janata, J Lodge, R Millbourn, E Murphy, J H Newman, S A Norman, S T H Palmer, S J Porter, S P B C Read, J F Simms, J C Smith, S J L Smith, D C Spencer, G H Tucker, K E Went
Office: Banbury, Swindon, Witney
Work: B1 C1 C2 D1 E F1 G J1 K1 K2 K3 L N O P Q R1 S1 S2 T1 T2 V W Z(b,c,d,f,h,i,l,m,q,r)
Emergency Action, Advocacy, Fixed Fee Interview undertaken and Member of Accident Line
Ptr: Bailey, Miss Sally E BA(Law) . . . . *Oct 1983
Black, Mr David J LLB. . . . . *Oct 1990
Boardman, Mr Philip BA. . . . . *Oct 1991
Bower, Mr David J G . . . . *§Jan 1971
Eden, Mr Robert Edward Alister. . . . . *Jun 1998
Falvert-Martin, Mr David BA(Hons) . . . . *Nov 1987
Hannam, Mr Daniel Philip Stafford. . . . . *Nov 1998
Hill, Mrs Alison J BA . . . . *Oct 1986
Lodge, Mr Jonathan. . . . . *Aug 1995
Murphy, Mr Eugene. . . . . Jan 1999
Newman, Mr Jonathan Harker. . . . . *Jan 1999
Norman, Miss Susan Ann LLB Birmingham Law Society Gold Medal. . . . . *Dec 1979
Palmer, Mr Stuart T H BA . . . . *Jan 1998
Porter, Mr Stephen J BA(Law). . . . . *Jun 1979
Simms, Mr John Fraser LLB; BCL. . . . . *Apr 1969
Smith, Mr Julian C LLB(Hons). . . . . *Oct 1974
Smith, Mr Simon J L BA. . . . . *Nov 1984
Spencer, Mr David C MA(Cantab). . . . . *Apr 1981
Ast: Angwin, Mrs Kay Louise BA(Law) Notary Public. . . . *Oct 1990
Badcock, Mrs Angela LLB. . . . . Oct 1987
Hayward, Mr Gareth Steven James LLB. . . . . Sep 2008
Hulme, Mr James LLB . . . . *Sep 2006
Martin, Ms Joanna Louise LLB . . . . *Mar 2004
May, Miss Victoria LLB(Hons) . . . . Oct 2010
Stevens, Ms Brit Christine LLB . . . . *Sep 2006

CHALLENOR GARDINER ‡
29 New Inn Hall Street Oxford Oxfordshire OX1 2DH
Tel: 01865 721451 *Fax:* 01865 251804 *Dx:* 4316 OXFORD 1
E-mail: info@challenor-gardiner.co.uk
List of partners: N C Bingham
Work: A1 B1 C1 D1 D2 E F1 J1 K1 K3 K4 L N O Q S1 S2 T1 T2 V W Z(l)
Emergency Action, Agency, Advocacy, Fixed Fee Interview and Legal Aid undertaken
SPr: Bingham, Mr Nicholas C BSc(Hons). . . . . *§Feb 1985
Ast: Dewhurst, Mr Christopher Thomas LLB(Hons). . . . Jun 1997
Hodby, Mr Richard Andrew BA(Cantab) . . . . *Sep 2001
Con: Gardiner, Mr Nicholas G Coroner for Oxfordshire . . . *§Jul 1965

CHARLES RUSSELL LLP
7600 The Quorum Oxford Business Park North Oxford Oxfordshire OX4 2JZ
Tel: 0845 359 0090 *Fax:* 0845 359 0099 *Dx:* 45413 COWLEY
E-mail: enquiries@charlesrussell.co.uk
Office: Cambridge, Cheltenham, Guildford, London EC4
Work: C1 C2 J1
Ptr: Elliott, Mr Peter M MA(Cantab); Dip Comparative Legal Studies; Dip Superieur de Francais Des Affaires . . . . . . *Apr 1977
Ast: Scott, Mr Ian BA . . . . May 1998

CHASELAW SOLICITORS ‡
25 Beaumont Street Oxford Oxfordshire OX1 2NP
Tel: 01865 314800

CLAYDENLAW ‡
Prama House 267 Banbury Road Summertown Oxford Oxfordshire OX2 7HT
Tel: 01865 339640 *Fax:* 01865 339301

CLOVIS KHUJA SOLICITORS ‡
154a Cowley Road Oxford Oxfordshire OX4 1UE
Tel: 01865 200150 *Fax:* 01865 200149 *Dx:* 154783 OXFORD
E-mail: info@clovis-khuja.co.uk

CRESCO LEGAL SOLICITORS
Prama House 267 Banbury Road Oxford Oxfordshire OX2 7HT
Tel: 01865 339360 *Fax:* 01865 861915
Office: London NW1

DARBYS SOLICITORS LLP ‡
52 New Inn Hall Street Oxford Oxfordshire OX1 2DN
Tel: 01865 811700 *Fax:* 01865 811777 *Dx:* 145840 OXFORD 6
E-mail: info@darbys.co.uk
List of partners: J A Astle, R S Bell, M Bourne, D J Ceadel, M Geeson, J Harvey, N M Hedges, R L Hewitt, S Jeffrey, C Jones, S L Leigh, P R B Marsh, R F Money-Kyrle, H Niebuhr, D H Parry, W Selby-Lowndes, V L Smith, E E Taylor, M Taylor
Languages: Bengali, Danish, French, German, Gujarati, Hindi, Italian, Punjabi, Spanish, Swedish, Welsh
Work: A1 A2 A3 B1 B2 C1 C2 C3 D1 D2 E F1 F2 G H I J1 J2 K1 K2 K3 K4 L M1 M2 N O P Q R1 R2 S1 S2 T1 T2 U1 U2 V W X Z(b,c,d,e,f,g,h,i,j,k,l,m,o,p,q,r,s,t,u,w,y,z,za)
Emergency Action, Agency, Advocacy, Legal Aid undertaken, Legal Aid Franchise and Member of Accident Line
Ptr: Astle, Mr James A BA(Oxon) . . . . *§Mar 1977
Bell, Mr Richard S LLB(Exon) . . . . *Jun 1978
Bourne, Mr Martin BSc . . . . *Apr 1995
Ceadel, Mrs Deborah Jane MA(Oxon). . . . . *Nov 1977
Geeson, Mr Michael BA(Law) . . . . *Feb 1987
Harvey, Miss Jennifer . . . . *Nov 1994
Hedges, Mr Nicholas M BA . . . . *Apr 1979
Hewitt, Miss Rebecca Louise BSc. . . . . *Sep 2003
Jeffrey, Mrs Sian LLB(Hons). . . . . Oct 1996
Jones, Ms Claire LLB . . . . *Sep 1988
Leigh, Miss Samantha Louise BA; MA. . . . . *Sep 1997
Marsh, Mr Philip Richard Bruce BA(Hons)(History) . . *Jan 1998
Money-Kyrle, Mr Richard Francis BSc. . . . . *Sep 1996
Niebuhr, Mrs Helen . . . . *Nov 1994
Parry, Mr David H LLB . . . . *Nov 1989
Selby-Lowndes, Mr William MA . . . . *Oct 1995
Smith, Miss Victoria L LLB . . . . *Nov 1989
Taylor, Miss Elizabeth E MA(Oxon) . . . . *Oct 1992
Taylor, Mr Mark MA(Oxon) . . . . *Apr 1980
Asoc: Allred, Miss Katherine Alison LLB(Hons). . . . . . . *Oct 1995
Bacchus, Mr Simon K BA(Hons). . . . . *Dec 1989
Hall, Mr Graeme Clark . . . . *Feb 2002
Harris, Mr David LLB Judges Award Jurisprudence 1999 . . . . *Nov 2003
Kashti, Mrs Rebecca Mary BA(Hons)(Law) . . . . . *Jan 1992
Roberts, Mr Howard Stephen LLB(Hons) . . . . . . Mar 1993
Roberts, Miss Sian LLB; LPC . . . . *Mar 2007
Wright, Mr Nicholas John Gibson BSc. . . . . *Sep 1995
Wright, Ms Victoria MA(Oxon). . . . . Sep 2007
Ast: Aizlewood, Miss Jane M BSc(Hons)(Psychology) . . . *Feb 1997
Bennett, Mr Graham Mark LLB . . . . *Apr 1981
Cartwright-Terry, Mrs EF LLB . . . . Apr 2008
Chapman, Mr Mark BA(Hons). . . . . *Sep 2006
Foster, Ms Brigit BA. . . . . *Feb 2004
Foy, Miss Emily BA(Law & Criminology). . . . . . . *Sep 2008
Graham-Harrison, Mr Simon Andrew BA(Hons); CDE . *Sep 1998
Hedges, Mrs Jane H BSc . . . . *Nov 1979
Hopkin, Mr Edward Daniel BA(History); MA(History). . *Oct 2003
Hutchinson, Mr John BSc(Hons) . . . . *Sep 2003
Jones, Mr Mark Andrew LLB(Hons)(Law & French) . . *Sep 2005
Mendus, Mrs Kathryn Jane LLB(Hons) . . . . *Jun 1985
Phillips, Mr Jonathan LLB(Hons) . . . . *Sep 2007
Regan, Mr Andrew Neil BA(Hons); MA; MSc; PGDipLaw . . . . *Feb 2009
Sheikh, Mrs Resha BSc(Hons); LPC; PGDipLaw . . . *Mar 2007
Shotton, Mrs Emma J BSc; LPC . . . . *Nov 1999
Sullivan, Miss Gemma LLB . . . . *Sep 2008
Thacker, Miss Emma LLB(Hons) . . . . Feb 2007
Vernede, Mr Daniel BA(Hons)(Criminology & Sociology); GDL; LPC. . . . . *Sep 2008
Wadsworth, Mr Richard LLB. . . . . *Nov 2007
Wailoo, Miss Hannah BA(Hons)(Criminology/Sociology); LPC; PGDipLaw . . . . *Sep 2008
Williamson, Mr Jonathan Martin LLB(Hons) . . . . . *Sep 2003
Con: Eddy, Miss Catherine J LLB(B'ham). . . . . *§Sep 1970
Taylor, Mr Sturges C B . . . . *§Jan 1968

FERGUSON BRICKNELL ‡
(incorporating Bartram & Rogers; Ferguson Kemp & Co)
Chester House George Street Oxford Oxfordshire OX1 2AY
Tel: 01865 241814 *Fax:* 01865 791810 *Dx:* 4306 OXFORD 1
E-mail: oxford@ferguson-bricknell.co.uk
List of partners: C M Wallworth, S Whitehead
Office: Oxford
Languages: French, German
Work: C1 E J1 K1 K3 N O Q S1 S2 T2 W Z(l)
Advocacy undertaken
Ptr: Wallworth, Mr Christopher M LLB(Lond) Clerk to Commissioner of Taxes . . . . *May 1977
Whitehead, Miss Susan LLB(Lond) . . . . *§Mar 1974
Asoc: Ryman, Ms Julia C LLB. . . . . *Sep 2000

FERGUSON BRICKNELL
(incorporating Cecil Bartram & Roger)
Kingsway House London Road Headington Oxford Oxfordshire OX3 9AA
Tel: 01865 767567 *Fax:* 01865 744048 *Dx:* 42355 HEADINGTON
E-mail: headington@ferguson-bricknell.co.uk
Office: Oxford
Languages: French, German
Work: B1 E F1 J1 K1 K3 K4 L N O Q S1 S2 T1 T2 W Z(d)
Agency, Advocacy and Fixed Fee Interview undertaken
Ast: Angwin, Mrs Kay Louise BA(Law) Notary Public. . . . *Oct 1990
Clovis, Mrs Pauline Angela LLB. . . . . *Jun 2001

HMG LAW LLP ‡
126 High Street Oxford Oxfordshire OX1 4DG
Tel: 01865 244661 *Fax:* 01865 721263 *Dx:* 4321 OXFORD 1
E-mail: info@hmg-law.co.uk
List of partners: G S Baker, S E Ewens, R E Fuggle, S A Jackson
Office: Bicester
Languages: French, German
Work: A1 A3 B1 C1 C2 C3 D1 E F1 J1 K1 K3 K4 L O Q R1 S1 S2 T1 T2 W Z(b,c,d,f,k,l,q,t,w)
Agency and Advocacy undertaken
Ptr: Baker, Mr Gary Stephen LLB . . . . *Nov 1984
Ewens, Mr Stephen Edward LLB Notary Public . . . . *Mar 1985
Fuggle, Mr Roland Eric LLB; FCIArb . . . . *Dec 1976
Ast: Alesworth, Ms Julie A K BA(Lond); LLB . . . . *Nov 1990
Butterfield, Ms Christine. . . . . Sep 2004
Collier, Mrs Imogen Suzanne LLB(Hons) . . . . . . Sep 2011
Floyd, Mrs Susan Elizabeth BA(Nott'm) . . . . Nov 1985
Hollingbury, Mrs Isobel Ann LLB. . . . . Sep 2000
Jessop, Ms Catherine Elizabeth BA . . . . *Oct 1995

HENMANS LLP ‡
5000 Oxford Business Park South Oxford Oxfordshire OX4 2BH
Tel: 01865 781000 *Fax:* 01865 778504 *Dx:* 45418 COWLEY
E-mail: welcome@henmansllp.co.uk
List of partners: G Awty, A D Bowman, C A Cameron, P A Chadder, D C Crine, A M Crocombe, I R Davis, M Duncan, P J Evans, S A Foster, K Gregory, J A Iball, J M Maitland, R J McCullough, R M Oakes, L M Pollock, N P P Roots, M D Sadler, J F H Simpson, H J Taylor, P J Thompson, P W Whetter, A V S White
Languages: French, German, Polish, Spanish
Work: A1 A2 A3 B1 C1 C2 C3 D1 E F1 I J1 K1 K2 K3 L N O P Q R1 R2 S1 S2 T1 T2 W Z(c,d,e,f,h,i,j,k,l,n,o,p,q,r,s)
Emergency Action, Agency, Advocacy, Legal Aid undertaken, Legal Aid Franchise and Member of Accident Line
Ptr: Awty, Mr George . . . . *Nov 1997
Bowman, Miss Angela Dawn LLB; DipLP . . . . . . *Sep 1997
Cameron, Miss Cecily Anne BA(Hons); MEd . . . . *Oct 1995
Chadder, Mr Paul Andrew BA . . . . *Sep 1998
Crine, Mr Duncan C BA(Hons) . . . . *Oct 1991
Crocombe, Mr Andrew M BA(Hons) . . . . *Oct 1996
Davis, Mr Iain Robert . . . . *Oct 1997
Duncan, Ms Mary LLB(Exon) . . . . *Oct 1983
Evans, Mr Philip James LLB . . . . *Sep 2001
Foster, Mrs Sarah Ann LLB . . . . *Mar 1994
Gregory, Mrs Katherine BA(Durham); CPE; LPC . . . *Mar 1998
Iball, Mrs Julia A LLB . . . . *Nov 1987
McCullough, Mrs Rachel Jane LLB . . . . *Oct 1992
Maitland, Ms Jane M . . . . *Jun 1979
Oakes, Mrs Rachael Margaret LLB . . . . *Oct 1996
Pollock, Mrs Lesley Margaret BA(Hons). . . . . . . *Oct 1980
Roots, Mr Nigel Peter Patrick . . . . *Jan 2001
Sadler, Mr Malcolm D MA(Cantab) . . . . *Apr 1975
Simpson, Mr James Fraser Hamilton LLB(Hons) . . . *Sep 1993
Taylor, Mrs Helen Jane LLB. . . . . *Aug 2000
Thompson, Mr Paul Jeffrey BA(Hons). . . . . *Sep 1996
Whetter, Mr Patrick William . . . . *Sep 1998
White, Mr Adrian Victor Smith LLB; MA . . . . . . *Oct 1981
Asoc: Bellis, Miss Anna Clare MA(Cantab). . . . . *Nov 1993
Bendle, Ms Claire Diane LLB(Hons). . . . . *Nov 1992
Booker, Mrs Susan BA . . . . *Sep 2000
Carlisle, Ms Julie BA(Hons)(English & French Law) . . *Dec 1991
Cowdrey, Ms Veronica E . . . . *Apr 1979
Drasdo, Mr Mark Russell LLB(Hons) . . . . *Oct 1992
Ewen, Miss Melissa Mary BMus. . . . . *Sep 2001
Lightfoot, Miss Jane Katherine BA(Hons) . . . . . . *Sep 2003
Lowe, Mrs Carolyn LLB . . . . *Sep 1996
Maple, Mr Thomas James BA(Lancs); LPC . . . . . *May 2002
Riley, Mrs Katharine BA(Hons) . . . . *Dec 1993
Ross, Ms Helen Elizabeth. . . . . *Jan 1984
Rumary, Ms Phillipa Louise . . . . *Nov 1999
Stirling, Mrs Esther LLB(Hons) . . . . *Sep 2005
Ast: Brown, Miss Victoria . . . . *Jan 2011
Burchett, Mr Rupert . . . . *Jan 2011
Chavda, Mr Himesh BA(Hons)(Physiology & Biochemistry); PGDL; LPC. . . . . *Jan 2007
Chawla, Miss Dimple Kaur LPC . . . . *May 2011
Costello, Mrs Aimee Ann LLB(Hons) . . . . *Jan 2011
Duffy, Mrs Sarah Jane Louise LLB(Hons) . . . . . . *Mar 2007
Goodger, Mrs Sally LLB; LPC. . . . . *Sep 2005
Hallett, Mr Thomas BA(Hons)(UCL)(History); GDL; LPC . . . . *Jan 2011
Hindocha, Miss Shree. . . . . *Sep 2007
Hyland, Mrs Tamsin MA(Oxon) Parish Councillor . . . *Sep 2009
Kuenzel, Miss Avelina. . . . . *Jan 2011
Mark-Bell, Ms Lisa Annette BA . . . . *Sep 2007
Marsh, Miss Elizabeth Jean BA(Hons); PGDipLaw; LPC . . . . *Sep 2009
Morgan, Miss Michelle BA(Hons)(Law & Marketing Management) . . . . *Sep 2005
Nicholls, Miss Gemma Gabrielle LLB . . . . *Sep 2008
Randall, Mr Geoffrey Thomas LLM . . . . *Sep 1999
Rolfe, Mrs Catherine Clare Gabriel MA(Cantab). . . . May 1999
Schroedel, Miss Mona BA(Economics & Law); LLM(International Commercial Law) . . . . *Sep 2008
Sellars, Mrs Sarah MA; GDL; LPC . . . . Sep 2009
Thompson, Mr James BA(Hons)(English Lit) . . . . . Jan 2009
Walker, Mr Thomas Edward BA; PGDipLaw; LPC . . . *Sep 2006
Con: Foster, Mr Robert Edward BA . . . . *Oct 1985
Houston, Ms Alexandra M. . . . . *Nov 1973

HINE SOLICITORS
Prama House 267 Banbury Road Oxford Oxfordshire OX2 7HT
Tel: 01865 339660 *Fax:* 01865 339661 *Dx:* 40657 SUMMERTOWN
Office: Beaconsfield, Bracknell, Cheltenham, Gerrards Cross, Princes Risborough, Swindon, Yiewsley

ISAAC & CO ‡
15 Polstead Road Oxford Oxfordshire OX2 6TW
Tel: 01865 516449
E-mail: info@isaacandco.com

SIAN JEFFREY ‡
59 Sandfield Road Headington Oxford Oxfordshire OX3 7RW
Tel: 01865 920550
E-mail: sian@sianjeffrey.co.uk

MARK JOHNSON-WATTS ‡
31 Beaumont Street Oxford Oxfordshire OX1 2NP
Tel: 01865 302800 *Fax:* 01865 302809
E-mail: mark@pj-w.com
Work: B1 C1 E L Q R2 S1 S2 U1

LEWIS SILKIN LLP
King Charles House Park End Street Oxford Oxfordshire OX1 1JD
Tel: 01865 263070 *Fax:* 01865 724224 *Dx:* 4304 OXFORD
E-mail: info@lewissilkin.com
Office: London EC4
Work: J1
Ptr: Brimelow, Mr Russell A P BA(Oxon) Rowe & Maw Prize . . . . *Jan 1991
Carr, Mr Jonathan P LLB . . . . *Sep 1997
Ast: Price, Miss Hannah . . . . Sep 2003
Rome, Miss Paula Suzanne LLB . . . . *Sep 1993

ELIZABETH MCQUAY ‡
The Old Rectory Bletchingdon Oxford Oxfordshire OX5 3DH
Tel: 01869 351229 *Fax:* 01869 350231 *Dx:* 40560 KIDLINGTON
E-mail: law@elizabethmcquay.co.uk
List of partners: E M McQuay
Work: K1 K2
Ptr: McQuay, Miss Elizabeth M BA . . . . *Jun 1979

MANCHES LLP
9400 Garsington Road Oxford Business Park Oxford Oxfordshire OX4 2HN
Tel: 01865 722106 *Fax:* 01865 201012 *Dx:* 155710 OXFORD 13
E-mail: oxford@manches.co.uk
Office: London WC2, Reading
Work: B1 B2 C1 C2 C3 D1 E F1 F2 I J1 J2 K1 K2 L M1 O P Q R1 R2 S1 S2 T1 T2 U1 U2 V W X Z(b,c,d,e,f,h,k,l,m,o,p,s,z)
Emergency Action, Agency, Fixed Fee Interview, Legal Aid undertaken and Member of Accident Line
Ptr: Baddeley, Mr Patrick C M MA(Oxon) . . . . *Dec 1978

Blackburn, Ms Cathleen MA(Oxon) *Oct 1986
Bond, Miss Julie LLB(Wales) *Dec 1979
Clifford, Mr Giles BA(Hons) *Dec 1994
Kinner Nilson, Mr Jim BSc; MSc. *Dec 1987
Maier, Mr Steven A MA(Oxon). *Oct 1986
Mitchell, Ms Jane S BA *Nov 1988
Northwood, Mr Paul BA *Nov 1994
Reid, Ms Christine MA(Oxon) *Oct 1981
Richardson, Mr Daff MA(Oxon) *Oct 1989
Shaw, Mr Richard M MA(Cantab) *Dec 1968
Shelley, Mr Christopher J G BA *Nov 1986
Smith, Mr Richard Ashley LLB(Hons) *Feb 1989
Taylor, Mr Julian M A LLB *Nov 1990
Tighe, Mr David P BA(Cantab) Jul 1982
Ast: Bradshaw, Miss Catherine L MA(Cantab) *Jun 1989
Caldwell, Ms Deborah Kathleen Agnes *Apr 1998
Clayden, Mr Piers Beresford Carter *Sep 1998
Davies, Mrs Emma E BA(Hons) Sep 2003
Downing, Mr William James Linfield MA *Nov 1996
Evans, Mr David G MSc; CEng Veale Wasborough Law Prize *Oct 1997
Gibson, Ms Ursula BA(Hons) *Sep 1997
Gilman, Mr Thomas Edward BA Sep 2001
Hancock, Mrs Nicola Ann LLB Sep 1996
Hayes, Mr Robert J BA(Hons) Sep 2000
Hilton, Ms Susie PGDipLaw; LPC *Sep 2002
James, Mrs Ruth Jane BA; MA; LPC *Nov 2002
Lewis, Miss A Alexandra E BSc(Hons); CPE; LPC *Mar 1997
Lloyd, Mrs Amanda L LLB(Hons) *Oct 1990
Minns, Mr Mark Philip BSc(Hons) *Jul 1999
Mitchell, Mr James BA; LLM; DipIPLP Mar 1999
Morrison, Mr John James *Oct 1994
Rohll, Dr Catherine Louise PhD(Cantab); BA; MA Jan 2000
Stone, Mr A Paul MA(Oxon) *Jun 1996
Stratton, Mr Stephen P BA(Hons)(Exon) *Oct 1993
Taylor, Mr Alasdair James Robert LLB; MA Jan 2002
Went, Mr James Michael BA; LLM Oct 2000
Con: Angel, Mr Peter G LLB(Lond) *Mar 1970

MARKS & CLERK
4220 Nash Court Oxford Oxfordshire OX4 2RU
Tel: 01865 397900 *Fax:* 01865 397919
Office: Birmingham, Cheltenham, Leeds, Leicester, Liverpool, London WC2, Manchester

MORGAN COLE
Buxton Court 3 West Way Oxford Oxfordshire OX2 0SZ
Tel: 01865 262600 *Fax:* 01865 721367 *Dx:* 96200 OXFORD WEST
E-mail: info@morgan-cole.com
Office: Bristol, Cardiff, Reading (2 offices), Swansea
Languages: Farsi, Flemish, French, German, Spanish
Work: A1 B1 C1 C2 C3 D1 E G H I J1 K1 L M1 M2 N O P Q R1 S1 T1 T2 W X Z(b,c,d,e,f,j,k,l,o,s)
Agency and Legal Aid Franchise
Ptr: Ashtiany, Ms Sue BA *§Oct 1986
Buchanan, Mr Hugh C S BA *Dec 1980
Campbell, Mr Andrew M BA(Oxon) Oct 1975
Cater, Ms Sheila A M MA(Oxon) *Apr 1981
Chamberlain, Ms Emma J M BA; LRAM *Nov 1986
Cole, Mr John P O *§Jan 1970
Findley, Mr Christopher D LLB(Lond) *Jun 1979
Leadbitter, Mr Andrew H O *Jun 1970
Lewis, Mr Christopher G Jan 1968
Morgan, Ms Ruth LLB Nov 1990
Pillman, Mr Joseph C MA(Cantab) *§Dec 1977
Rouse, Mr Richard J BA; MPhil(Cantab) *Oct 1985
Russell, Mr Ronald D *§Jun 1963
Sarsfield-Hall, Mrs Alison B MA(Oxon) *Oct 1989
Walls, Ms Stephanie LLB(Bris); BCL(Oxon) *Oct 1986
Asoc: Redman, Mrs Heather LLB; LSF *Nov 1991
Ast: Allen, Mr Philip BA(Hons); DipLP Dec 1996
Ansell, Ms Judith L LLB(Hons) *Oct 1991
Badcock, Ms Angela Imogen LLB(Hons) Oct 1987
Baldock, Ms Kathryn BSc Oct 1991
Barnes, Mr Andrew LLB(Hons) Nov 1997
Brame, Mr Paul Frederick LLB(Hons) Nov 1995
Cheetham, Ms Georgina Nov 1993
Conder, Mr John H Nov 1994
Cripps, Ms Jill Alexandra BA *Oct 1993
Curry, Ms Gayle LLB Nov 1992
Elliott, Miss Elizabeth BA *Dec 1990
Fleetwood, Ms Bridget R Nov 1996
Khan, Sabeeha LLB Oct 1993
Richards, Mrs Eva BA; LLB Nov 1993
Snow, Miss Clara Nov 1995
Wharton, Ms Angela LLB(Hons) Nov 1997
Wood, Ms Allison LLB Nov 1994

NORTHWOOD REID ‡
Innovation House Mill Street Oxford Oxfordshire OX2 0JX
Tel: 01865 811101
E-mail: christine.reid@northwoodreid.com

OXFORD EMPLOYMENT LAW SOLICITORS ‡
7200 The Quorum Oxford Business Park North Oxford Oxfordshire OX4 2JZ
Tel: 01865 487136 *Fax:* 01865 481482
Emergency telephone 07711 606997
E-mail: martyburn@oxemplaw.co.uk
List of partners: M Burn, J D Godbolt
Office: High Wycombe
Work: A3 C1 J1 J2 O Q Z(p)
Agency undertaken
Ptr: Burn, Mr Martin MA Notary Public *Oct 1988
Godbolt, Mr Justin David BEng; CPE *Sep 2000

OXFORD LAW GROUP ‡
3 Frewin Chambers Frewin Court Off Cornmarket Street Oxford Oxfordshire OX1 3HZ
Tel: 01865 297300 *Fax:* 01865 202111 *Dx:* 82254 OXFORD 2
E-mail: kirstensmith@oxfordlawgroup.co.uk
List of partners: S L Hart, R Rouse, K Smith, P Westcott
Work: D1 D2 K1 K3 S1 V W Z(m)
Emergency Action, Agency, Advocacy, Fixed Fee Interview, Legal Aid undertaken and Legal Aid Franchise
Ptr: Hart, Ms Sarah L MA; BA(Hons) *Oct 1991
Rouse, Mr Richard BA(Hons); MA *Nov 1985
Smith, Mrs Kirsten BA(Hons) *Nov 1990
Westcott, Mr Phillip BA *Nov 1995
Ast: Armitage, Miss Katie *Dec 2005
Tan, Mr Khee Guan Jan 2006

PEARCE WEST SOLICITORS ‡
Innovation House Mill Street Oxford Oxfordshire OX2 0JX
Tel: 01865 812020 *Fax:* 01865 812018
List of partners: D W Pearce, J West
Office: Reading
Work: E J1 L N O Q S1 T2 W Z(k,p,q,w)
Agency, Fixed Fee Interview, Legal Aid undertaken and Member of Accident Line
Ptr: Pearce, Mr David W LLB(Hons) *Apr 1987
West, Mr Jonathan LLB(Hons) *Oct 1985

EDWARD PILLING & CO ‡
122 London Road Headington Oxford Oxfordshire OX3 9AG
Tel: 01865 741122 *Fax:* 01865 750478 *Dx:* 42351 HEADINGTON
E-mail: info@edwardpilling.co.uk
List of partners: E C H Pilling
Work: B1 E J1 N P R1 S1 S2 W
Agency and Advocacy undertaken
SPr: Pilling, Mr Edward C H *§Jun 1972
Ast: Calman, Miss Elisabeth J Jul 1979
Eaton, Mrs Catherine M LLB(Hons) *Apr 1981
Weaver, Mr John A LLB *Feb 1983

PLAINLAW LLP ‡
11a West Way Oxford Oxfordshire OX2 0JB
Tel: 01865 240202 *Fax:* 01865 247638 *Dx:* 96201 OXFORD WEST
E-mail: philip.horn@plainlaw.co.uk
List of partners: M A Horn, P J Horn
Ptr: Horn, Mr Michael Anthony BA(Bris) *Mar 1991
Horn, Mr Philip J LLB(Hons) *Nov 1982

REEDS SOLICITORS ‡
1 Cambridge Terrace Oxford Oxfordshire OX1 1RR
Tel: 01865 260230
List of partners: J Matthews, S Matthews
Dir: Matthews, Jan Feb 2008
Matthews, Stuart Jul 2000
Asoc: Reed, Mr Lee Mar 1989
Ast: Gotch, Mr Peter BSc(Hons)(Criminology) Jun 2010

CHRISTINE REID SOLICITOR ‡
49 Eynsham Road Botley Oxford Oxfordshire OX2 9BS
Tel: 01865 864195

W J SHORT & CO ‡
66 Elms Drive Oxford Oxfordshire OX3 0NL
Tel: 01865 724102 *Fax:* 01865 726378 *Dx:* 45414 COWLEY 1
E-mail: wjs@wjshort.co.uk
Work: S1 S2

STEEN & CO EMPLOYMENT SOLICITORS ‡
Magdalen Centre The Oxford Science Park Oxford Oxfordshire OX4 4GA
Tel: 01865 784101 *Fax:* 01865 784102
E-mail: simon@steenandco.co.uk
List of partners: S Steen
SPr: Steen, Mr Simon Nov 1998

STUART MALCOLM LLP ‡
The Dairy Chiswell Farm Boars Hill Oxford Oxfordshire OX1 5EP
Tel: 01865 601240 *Fax:* 01865 601241
E-mail: contact@stuartmalcolmllp.com

TAVENERS ‡
John Eccles House Robert Robinson Way Oxford Science Park Oxford Oxfordshire OX4 4GP
Tel: 0844 879 319
E-mail: simon.smith@tavenerslaw.co.uk

JULIAN TAYLOR SOLICITORS ‡
Hazel Cottage Studio Weston-on-the-Green Oxford Oxfordshire OX25 3QX
Tel: 01869 351833 *Fax:* 01869 351844

TESSA HENNESSY SOLICITOR ‡
27 Hugh Allen Crescent Marston Oxford Oxfordshire OX3 0HL
Tel: 01865 723727

TESSA HENNESSY SOLICITOR ‡
17 Hugh Allen Crescent Marston Oxford Oxfordshire OX3 0HL
Tel: 01865 723727 / 07773 991643

TURPIN & MILLER ‡
1 Agnes Court Oxford Road Oxford Oxfordshire OX4 2EW
Tel: 01865 770111 *Fax:* 01865 749099 *Dx:* 154780 OXFORD 11

USISKIN & CO ‡
Paddock Brow Jarn Way Boars Hill Oxford Oxfordshire OX1 5JF
Tel: 01865 322160 *Fax:* 01865 326359
Emergency telephone 07957 836167
E-mail: info@usisco.co.uk
List of partners: N S Usiskin
Languages: French, Hebrew, Italian
Work: C1 C2 E J1 M2 O Q S1 Z(e)
Advocacy and Fixed Fee Interview undertaken
SPr: Usiskin, Mr Nicholas S *Dec 1981

WHETTER DUCKWORTH FOWLER ‡
95 High Street Wheatley Oxford Oxfordshire OX33 1XP
Tel: 01865 872206 *Fax:* 01865 872473 *Dx:* 42357 HEADINGTON
E-mail: isheatly@wdfsolicitors.co.uk
List of partners: J P Duckworth, R J Fowler, J M W Whetter
Office: Kidlington
Languages: French
Work: A1 B1 C1 D1 E F1 K1 L M1 N P R1 S1 T1 V W
Emergency Action, Agency, Advocacy, Fixed Fee Interview, Legal Aid undertaken and Legal Aid Franchise

WILMERHALE
Park Gate 25 Milton Park Oxford Oxfordshire OX14 4SH
Tel: 01235 823000 *Fax:* 020 7645 2424
Office: London EC2, London W1
Work: A3 C1 C2 C3 J1 M2 M3 O T1 U1 U2 Z(e,o,za)

WILSONS SOLICITORS ‡
52 High Street Wheatley Oxford Oxfordshire OX33 1XT
Tel: 01865 874497 *Fax:* 01865 873793
Emergency telephone 01865 874497
E-mail: wilsonsolicitor@btconnect.com
List of partners: H J Wilson
Languages: French
Work: B2 D1 E G H J1 K1 K3 L N O Q S1 S2 V W X Z(q)
Emergency Action, Advocacy and Legal Aid undertaken
SPr: Wilson, Mr Howard John LLB(L'pool) ★ *Sep 1980
Ast: Wilson, Mr Laurence Feb 2009

WINCKWORTH SHERWOOD LLP
(incorporating Sherwood & Co)
16 Beaumont Street Oxford Oxfordshire OX1 2LZ
Tel: 01865 297200 *Fax:* 01865 726274 *Dx:* 145843 OXFORD 6
E-mail: info@wslaw.co.uk
Office: London SE1, London SW1
Work: L Z(d,x)
Agency and Fixed Fee Interview undertaken
Ast: Harrison, Mr Robert C LLB(B'ham) *Sep 1984

WITHY KING SOLICITORS
North Bailey House New Inn Hall Street Oxford Oxfordshire OX1 2EA
Tel: 01865 792300 *Fax:* 01865 793616 *Dx:* 4314 OXFORD 1
E-mail: enquiries@withyking.co.uk
Office: Abingdon, Bath (2 offices), Marlborough, Swindon, Thame, Trowbridge
Languages: Afrikaans, French, Italian, Portuguese, Spanish
Work: A1 C1 C2 C3 D1 E F1 G H J1 K1 L M1 M2 N O P R1 S1 T1 T2 W Z(d,h,i,j,l,m,o,p)

OXTED, Surrey

BALDWIN & ROBINSON LAW LLP ‡
4 Oxted Chambers 185-187 Station Road East Oxted Surrey RH8 0QE
Tel: 01883 708155 *Fax:* 01883 708156
E-mail: info@baldwinandrobinson.co.uk

TERESA M CORNWELL ‡
37 Station Road West Oxted Surrey RH8 9EE
Tel: 01883 712721 / 722594 *Fax:* 01883 723918 *Dx:* 39352 OXTED
List of partners: T M Cornwell
Languages: French, Italian
Work: E K1 L S1 W
Fixed Fee Interview undertaken
SPr: Cornwell, Ms Teresa M BA(Jt Hons) Apr 1981

HARROPS ‡
114 Station Road East Oxted Surrey RH8 0QA
Tel: 01883 712940 *Fax:* 01883 712996 *Dx:* 39361 OXTED
E-mail: solicitors@harropslaw.co.uk
List of partners: P C Harrop, V Harrop
Work: C1 E J1 K1 L N O Q S1 W
Fixed Fee Interview undertaken
Ptr: Harrop, Mr Peter C LLB Oct 1977
Harrop, Mrs Virginia Jul 1978
Ast: Sitton, Ms Shalena P E BA(Hons) *Jan 2001

HEPBURNS ‡
12 Station Road West Oxted Surrey RH8 9ES
Tel: 01883 723712 *Fax:* 01883 723757 *Dx:* 39360 OXTED
E-mail: advice@hepburns4law.co.uk
List of partners: D Hepburn, K S O'Sullivan
Work: C1 E F1 J1 K1 K3 L O Q S1 S2 W
Agency undertaken
Ptr: Hepburn, Mr David *Dec 1979
O'Sullivan, Mr Kevin S *Nov 1978
Asoc: Glibbery, Mr Peter John BA *Jul 1979

GLYNIS A JOHNSTONE ‡
Gallets High Street Limpsfield Oxted Surrey RH8 0DT
Tel: 01883 716894 *Fax:* 01883 715700
List of partners: G A Johnstone
Work: S1 S2 W
Ptr: Johnstone, Mrs Glynis A *§Apr 1976

NICHOLS & NICHOLS SOLICITORS ‡
Suite 3 157 Station Road East Oxted Surrey RH8 0QE
Tel: 01883 734751 *Fax:* 01883 722759 *Dx:* 39356 OXTED

ANGELA WILLIAMS ‡
17 Detillens Lane Oxted Surrey RH8 0DH
Tel: 01883 714618
List of partners: A Williams
Ptr: Williams, Ms Angela LLB(Lond) Nov 1970

PADDOCK WOOD, Kent

LAMBERTS
60 Commercial Road Paddock Wood Kent TN12 6DP
Tel: 01892 833456 *Fax:* 01892 836902 *Dx:* 55350 PADDOCK WOOD
E-mail: kc@lambertslaw.co.uk
Office: Sevenoaks
Work: C1 E F1 G J1 K1 L N O Q S1 S2 W
Agency and Advocacy undertaken
Ptr: Chapman, Mr Geoffrey K C *Aug 1977
Shireby, Mrs Claire Helen LLB Jun 1989

PADIHAM, Lancashire

SMITH SUTCLIFFE
White Horse Buildings 42 Burnley Road Padiham Lancashire BB12 8BN
Tel: 01282 778434 *Fax:* 01282 778311 *Dx:* 29301 PADIHAM
E-mail: padiham@smithsutcliffe.com
Office: Burnley
Work: A1 C1 C2 D1 E F1 J1 K1 K4 L N O Q R1 S1 S2 T2 V W Z(l)
Agency, Fixed Fee Interview, Legal Aid undertaken, Legal Aid Franchise and Member of Accident Line
Ptr: Wilkinson, Mr Peter *Dec 1977

WADDINGTON & SON
129-131 Burnley Road Padiham Lancashire BB12 8BA
Tel: 01282 778813 *Fax:* 01282 777426 *Dx:* 29304 PADIHAM
E-mail: enquiries@waddingtonandson.co.uk
Office: Burnley
Work: B1 D1 E F1 G H J1 K1 L N P Q R1 S1 V W Z(i,l,m,r)
Emergency Action, Agency, Advocacy, Fixed Fee Interview and Legal Aid undertaken

See p112 for the Key to Work Categories & other symbols

2

PAIGNTON, Torbay

EASTLEYS ‡
The Manor Office Victoria Street Paignton Torbay TQ4 5DW
Tel: 01803 559257 *Fax:* 01803 558625 *Dx:* 100603 PAIGNTON
E-mail: info@eastleys.co.uk
List of partners: C Fox, C A Hales, J Hopkins, C E Hudson, E Patterson, M G J Roddan, C Shute, I J Webb, S Willson, M O O Woloshak
Office: Brixham, Totnes
Languages: French
Work: A1 B1 C1 C2 D1 D2 E F1 G H J1 K1 K2 L N O Q R1 R2 S1 S2 T2 V W Z(c,d,l,m,o)
Emergency Action, Agency, Advocacy, Fixed Fee Interview, Legal Aid undertaken, Legal Aid Franchise and Member of Accident Line
Ptr: Fox, Ms Catherine BA(Hons) . . . . . *Oct 1989
Hales, Ms Carolyn Anne LLB . . . . . *Oct 1977
Hudson, Miss Clare Elizabeth LLB . . . . . *Mar 1997
Patterson, Miss Emma LLB . . . . . *Apr 1998
Shute, Mrs Christine LLB . . . . . *Oct 1986
Webb, Mrs Irene Jean PhD . . . . . *Jul 1989
Willson, Ms Stephanie BA(Hons) . . . . . *Oct 1996
Woloshak, Mr Mark O O BA(Hons) . . . . . *Oct 1990
Ast: Rowden, Mrs Wendy Helen BA(Hons) . . . . . *Jun 2001
Shropshall Clarke, Mrs Angela Elizabeth Dalgleish LLB . . . . . *Dec 2002
Shepard, Miss Ruth Deborah Louise LLB . . . . . *Jun 2006
Con: Pryce, Mr Andrew N MA(Oxon) . . . . . *§Apr 1975
Summers, Mr A Mark H . . . . . *§Dec 1966

GOWMANS ‡
65 Hyde Road Paignton Torbay TQ4 5BT
Tel: 01803 546100 *Fax:* 01803 528351 *Dx:* 100600 PAIGNTON
E-mail: lawyers@gowmans.co.uk
List of partners: R C T Hunton, R W Porritt
Work: C1 D1 G H K1 S1 S2 T2 W Z(l,m)
Emergency Action, Agency, Advocacy, Fixed Fee Interview and Legal Aid undertaken
Ptr: Hunton, Mr Robin C T MA(Cantab) Herbert Ruse Prize . . . . . *§Jun 1976
Porritt, Mr Richard W ● . . . . . *§Jun 1985
Asoc: Lister, Mr Mark Anthony BA(Hons)(History & Law) Student of the Year Staffs Law School . . . . . Sep 2002
Van Den Berg, Ms Sally BSc . . . . . *Aug 2004
Ast: Bellamy, Mr Philip J LLB . . . . . *Apr 1975
Dickson, Mr Jonathan . . . . . Apr 2008
Lewis, Miss Caroline J LLB(Lond) . . . . . *§Oct 1988
Con: Boddam-Whetham, Mr J David ♦ Cecil Karuth Prize . *§Nov 1966

KNAPMAN & CO ‡
Dendy House 16 Dendy Road Paignton Torbay TQ4 5DB
Tel: 01803 522700 *Fax:* 01803 524704 *Dx:* 100601 PAIGNTON
E-mail: knapman.co@btconnect.com
List of partners: D L Hoare, R Patterson
Work: E J1 L R1 S1 S2 T2 V W
Agency undertaken
SPr: Patterson, Mr Raymond . . . . . *Nov 1978
Ptr: Hoare, Mr David L . . . . . *Feb 1972

MICHAEL W PIPE ‡
Geneva House 10 Dendy Road Paignton Torbay TQ4 5DB
Tel: 01803 559746 / 529797 *Fax:* 01803 529121
Dx: 100611 PAIGNTON
E-mail: solicitors@mwpipe.co.uk
List of partners: N P Bonstow, M W Pipe
Work: A1 B1 C1 D1 E F1 G H J1 K1 L N R1 S1 W Z(l)
Agency, Advocacy and Fixed Fee Interview undertaken
Ptr: Bonstow, Mr Nicholas P . . . . . *Jun 1984
Pipe, Mr Michael W . . . . . *Dec 1980

ROGER RICHARDS ‡
10 Churston Broadway Dartmouth Road Churston Paignton Torbay TQ4 6LE
Tel: 01803 845191 *Fax:* 01803 846040
List of partners: C Foot
Office: Brixham
Work: C1 E G H J1 K1 L N O P Q R1 S1 W Z(a,c,f)
Emergency Action, Agency, Advocacy, Fixed Fee Interview, Legal Aid undertaken and Legal Aid Franchise
Ptr: Foot, Miss Caroline LLB; DipLP . . . . . *Jun 1999

WOLLEN MICHELMORE SOLICITORS
Belgrave House 2 Winner Street Paignton Torbay TQ3 3BJ
Tel: 01803 521692 *Fax:* 01803 550623 *Dx:* 100605 PAIGNTON
Office: Dartmouth, Newton Abbot, Torquay
Work: A1 C1 E F1 L R1 R2 S1 S2 W

PANGBOURNE, West Berkshire

RWP SOLICITORS ‡
Meadow House 22 Reading House Pangbourne West Berkshire RG8 7LY
Tel: 0118 984 2266 *Fax:* 0118 984 5133 *Dx:* 54650 PANGBOURNE
E-mail: pangbourne@rwp-solicitors.co.uk
List of partners: A P Beg, H N Messer, K M Tarry
Work: E J1 K1 K3 N O Q S1 S2 T2 W
Dir: Beg, Mrs Anjam P LLB(Hons) . . . . . *§Mar 1989
Messer, Mrs Hilary N LLB(Hons) . . . . . *§Jan 1991
Tarry, Ms Kathryn Mary LLB(Hons) . . . . . *Nov 1993
Ast: Winfield, Mrs Rowena J MA(Oxon) . . . . . *Oct 1987
Con: Thomas, Mr Richard J M . . . . . *§Jul 1968

PEACEHAVEN, East Sussex

BARWELLS
Bank House 238 South Coast Road Peacehaven East Sussex BN10 8JS
Tel: 01273 582271 *Fax:* 01273 582272 *Dx:* 39200 PEACEHAVEN
E-mail: advice@barwells.com
Office: Eastbourne, Newhaven, Seaford
Work: A1 C1 C3 E F1 K1 L N Q R1 S1 T1 T2 V W Z(c)
Advocacy, Fixed Fee Interview, Legal Aid undertaken and Member of Accident Line
Ptr: Jones, Nicola Christiane FILEx . . . . . NSP
Ast: McColl, Mr Rory Jonathan . . . . . Jan 2002
Con: Drake, Mr Paul Vincent . . . . . Dec 1980

D S BOSHER & CO
Central Chambers 226 South Coast Road Peacehaven East Sussex BN10 8JR
Tel: 01273 585771 *Fax:* 01273 582066
E-mail: bosher@mistral.co.uk
Office: Hove
Agency and Legal Aid undertaken

LAWSON LEWIS & CO
Meridian Chambers 10a Horsham Avenue Peacehaven East Sussex BN10 8LL
Tel: 01273 582680 *Fax:* 01273 588680
Office: Eastbourne
Work: J1 K1 K3 K4 S1 W
Legal Aid undertaken
Ast: Woodley, Mr Daniel BSc; PGDip . . . . . Apr 2001

PEMBROKE, Pembrokeshire

GREATHEAD & WHITELOCK ‡
3-5 Hamilton Terrace Pembroke Pembrokeshire SA71 4DF
Tel: 01646 682101 *Fax:* 01646 621248 *Dx:* 200654 PEMBROKE
Emergency telephone 01646 672452
E-mail: pg.gandw@btconnect.co.uk
List of partners: N J Fletcher, P G Griffiths, J B O Parsons
Languages: German, Welsh
Work: A1 B1 C1 C2 C3 D1 E F1 G H I J1 K1 L M1 M2 N O P Q R1 S1 T1 T2 V W Z(e,l,o,t)
Emergency Action, Agency, Advocacy, Legal Aid undertaken and Legal Aid Franchise
Ptr: Fletcher, Mr Nigel J LLB . . . . . Oct 1985
Griffiths, Mr Paul G BA . . . . . *Dec 1982
Parsons, Mr John B O LLB(Wales) . . . . . *Jun 1976
Ast: Anthony, Mr Charles Robert LLB(Hons); MSocSc; PhD *Mar 1974

RED KITE LAW ‡
Shaftesbury House 60 Main Street Pembroke Pembrokeshire SA71 4HJ
Tel: 01646 683222 *Fax:* 01646 682786 *Dx:* 200650 PEMBROKE
List of partners: P J Cowper, R Davies, D M Evans, J L Griffiths, K M Griffiths, T Haggar, J R Lewis, D M Lowless, D Sangster, L Smith, M J Subbiani, D I Williams
Office: Carmarthen (2 offices), Haverfordwest, Milford Haven, Pembroke Dock, Tenby
Languages: French, Spanish, Welsh
Work: A1 B1 C1 D1 D2 E F1 G H J1 K1 K3 K4 L N O P Q S1 S2 T2 V W Z(c,l,m,t)
Emergency Action, Agency, Advocacy, Fixed Fee Interview, Legal Aid undertaken and Legal Aid Franchise
Ptr: Haggar, Mr Timothy . . . . . Sep 2000
Lowless, Mr D Malcolm Associated Law Societies of Wales & West Wales Law Society . . . . . *Nov 1970
Ast: Escolme, Miss Helen . . . . . May 2005
Morgan, Mrs Deborah M MA(Oxon) . . . . . *§Apr 1981
Scourfield, Mrs Gemma LLB . . . . . Sep 2007
Con: Morgan, Mr Huw Geler LLB(Wales) . . . . . Jan 1967

PEMBROKE DOCK, Pembrokeshire

BISSMIRE FUDGE & CO
21 Laws Street Pembroke Dock Pembrokeshire SA72 6DJ
Tel: 01646 685501 *Fax:* 01646 687165
Dx: 98275 HAVERFORDWEST
E-mail: ian@ianfudge.com
Office: Haverfordwest
Work: A1 A2 A3 B1 C1 D1 E F1 G J1 K1 K2 K3 K4 L N O Q R1 S1 S2 W Z(c,l,n,q,r)
Agency and Advocacy undertaken
Ptr: Bissmire, Mr Michael J LLB(Lond) . . . . . Jun 1971
Fudge, Mr Ian G LLB(Lond) . . . . . *May 1979
Radford, Mr Peter J BA(Hons) . . . . . *Nov 1983
Scale, Mr Howard G BA(Law) . . . . . *Dec 1983

NOBLE HARBOUR SOLICITORS
5-6 Pier House Pier Road Pembroke Dock Pembrokeshire SA72 6TR
Tel: 01646 681559 *Fax:* 01646 683135
Office: Milford Haven

RED KITE LAW
18 Meyrick Street Pembroke Dock Pembrokeshire SA72 6UT
Tel: 01646 681529 *Fax:* 01646 680285
Dx: 120353 PEMBROKE DOCK
Office: Carmarthen (2 offices), Haverfordwest, Milford Haven, Pembroke, Tenby
Languages: Welsh
Work: A1 B1 C1 D1 D2 E F1 G H J1 K1 K3 K4 L N O Q S1 S2 T2 V W Z(c,l,m,t)
Emergency Action, Agency, Advocacy, Fixed Fee Interview and Legal Aid undertaken
Ptr: Subbiani, Mr Matthew J BSc . . . . . Aug 1996
Ast: Morgan, Mr Alun . . . . . Sep 2001

PHILIP ROACHE ‡
12 Meyrick Street Pembroke Dock Pembrokeshire SA72 6UT
Tel: 01646 682603 *Fax:* 01646 621011
E-mail: best@landlaw.co.uk
List of partners: P J Roache
Work: A1 E S1 S2 W
Ptr: Roache, Mr Philip J Notary Public . . . . . *Sep 1973

JOHN ROCHE ‡
Mediation House 74 Stockwell Road Pembroke Dock Pembrokeshire SA72 6TQ
Tel: 01646 622626 *Fax:* 01646 622252
E-mail: mail@mediationhouse.com
Work: A3

PEMBURY, Kent

BURTONS ‡
The Tyled House 23a High Street Pembury Kent TN2 4PH
Est: 1981
Tel: 01892 824577 *Fax:* 01892 822336
E-mail: burtons.solicitors@btconnect.com
List of partners: L W Trevor
Work: E K4 S1 S2 W
Fixed Fee Interview undertaken
SPr: Trevor, Mr Leslie Wilbraham BA(Hons) . . . . . *§Feb 1986
Particular areas of work include: Residential and Commercial Conveyancing, Wills, Trusts, Probate and Elderly Client.

PENARTH, Vale of Glamorgan

JONATHAN BRIERLY ‡
PO Box 2 Penarth Vale of Glamorgan CF64 5YL
Tel: 029 2071 2230 *Fax:* 029 2070 8760
Emergency telephone 07971 58776
E-mail: jonathanbrierley@tinyaline.co.uk
Work: B2 D1 G H I
Emergency Action, Agency, Advocacy, Fixed Fee Interview, Legal Aid undertaken and Legal Aid Franchise

CLARKE & HARTLAND SOLICITORS
5 Herbert Terrace Penarth Vale of Glamorgan CF64 2AH
Tel: 029 2071 1181 *Fax:* 029 2049 8377
Emergency telephone 07971 016070
E-mail: maria@clarkeandhartland.co.uk
Office: Cardiff
Work: B2 D1 D2 E F2 G H J2 K1 K2 K3 K4 R1 S1 S2 W Z(l,y)
Agency, Advocacy and Legal Aid undertaken

FIRST CONVEYANCING.CO.UK ‡
7 Bradham Place Penarth Vale of Glamorgan CF64 2AG
Tel: 029 2070 2449
Work: S1

J A HUGHES
7 Bradenham Place Penarth Vale of Glamorgan CF64 2AG
Tel: 029 2070 2449 *Fax:* 029 2070 1983 *Dx:* 52351 PENARTH
Emergency telephone 07831 509272
E-mail: jahughes@qualitysolicitors.com
Office: Barry, Cardiff
Work: A1 B1 D1 D2 E F1 G H J1 J2 K1 L N Q S1 S2 V W Z(h,l,q,r)
Emergency Action, Agency, Advocacy, Fixed Fee Interview, Legal Aid undertaken, Legal Aid Franchise and Member of Accident Line
Ptr: Davies, Mr Jeremy L LLB . . . . . *Sep 1986

KALEE LAU & CO ‡
PO Box 155 Penarth Vale of Glamorgan CF64 9AA
Tel: 029 2071 1400 *Fax:* 029 2071 1400
E-mail: info@kaleelausolicitors.co.uk

LUCAS LAW SOLICITORS ‡
Wayside Sully Road Penarth Vale of Glamorgan CF64 2TP
Tel: 029 2070 8963 *Fax:* 029 2070 8963
E-mail: info@lucaslaw.co.uk

PETER LYNN & PARTNERS
41 Ludlow Street Penarth Vale of Glamorgan CF64 1EX
Tel: 029 2071 3620
Office: Morriston, Swansea (2 offices)

WILLIAM MARSH SOLICITOR ‡
St Andrews Chambers PO Box 123 Penarth Vale of Glamorgan CF64 4ZR
Tel: 029 2051 5818 *Fax:* 029 2051 5818
E-mail: will.marsh.sol@hotmail.co.uk

MERRILS EDE SOLICITORS (incorporating T J Morgan & Co)
8 Herbert Terrace Penarth Vale of Glamorgan CF64 2AH
Tel: 029 2037 1131 *Fax:* 029 2070 5230 *Dx:* 52353 PENARTH
E-mail: central@merrilsede.co.uk
Office: Cardiff
Work: A1 C1 D1 E J1 K1 K4 L N R1 S1 S2 V W Z(l,m)
Emergency Action, Agency, Advocacy, Fixed Fee Interview, Legal Aid undertaken and Legal Aid Franchise
Ptr: Morris, Mr Andrew David LLB(Hons)(Wales) Maxwell Law Prize . . . . . *Nov 1984

MERYL EVANS CYFREITHWRAIG/SOLICITOR ‡
89 Westbourne Road Penarth Vale of Glamorgan CF64 3HD
Tel: 029 2019 5871

ALAN SIMONS & CO ‡
5 Bradenham Place Penarth Vale of Glamorgan CF64 2AG
Tel: 029 2070 3991 *Fax:* 029 2071 1615 *Dx:* 52359 PENARTH
E-mail: robwilcox@alansimons.co.uk
List of partners: G Lewis, R Wilcox
Work: D1 D2 E F1 J1 K1 L N O Q S1 S2 W Z(l)
Agency, Advocacy undertaken and Member of Accident Line
Ptr: Lewis, Mr Geoffrey BSc(Econ) . . . . . *§Nov 1971
Wilcox, Mr Robert LLB . . . . . *Feb 1992
Ast: Molinu, Mr Gianpiero LLB(Hons) . . . . . *Nov 2006

SINCLAIRS ‡
Windsor Chambers 36 Windsor Terrace Penarth Vale of Glamorgan CF64 1AB
Tel: 029 2070 6444 *Fax:* 029 2071 1199 *Dx:* 52361 PENARTH
E-mail: sinclairs@sinclairslaw.co.uk
List of partners: S M Charles, G S Evans
Office: Cardiff
Work: D1 D2 G K1 N Q S1 W X
Legal Aid undertaken
Ptr: Charles, Mr S Michael . . . . . Oct 1994

PENKRIDGE, Staffordshire

CHEETHAMS ‡
Church Farm Pinfold Lane Penkridge Staffordshire ST19 5AP
Tel: 01785 714761 *Fax:* 01785 712041 *Dx:* 29933 PENKRIDGE
E-mail: office@cheethamssolicitors.co.uk
List of partners: L C Cheetham, N R Cheetham
Work: A1 C1 E J1 K1 K3 K4 S1 S2 W
Ptr: Cheetham, Mrs Louise Catherine LLB . . . . . *Jan 2006
Cheetham, Mr Norman Roger LLB . . . . . *Dec 1975

TEDSTONE GEORGE & TEDSTONE ‡
Crown Bridge Penkridge Staffordshire ST19 5AA
Tel: 01785 712243 *Fax:* 01785 715529 *Dx:* 29931 PENKRIDGE
List of partners: N Lewis, A J A Tedstone

Work: A1 B1 C1 C2 C3 D1 E F1 G H J1 K1 L M1 M2 N P R1 S1 T1 T2 V W Z(c,d,h,j,m,o)
Emergency Action, Agency, Advocacy, Fixed Fee Interview, Legal Aid undertaken and Member of Accident Line
Ptr: Lewis, Ms Nicola . . . . Nov 1999
Tedstone, Mr Adam John Andrew . . . . . . *Sep 1992

PENMAENMAWR, Conwy

JOHN BELLIS & CO ‡
Llys Helyg Brynmor Terrace Penmaenmawr Conwy LL34 6AW
Tel: 01492 622377 *Fax:* 01492 622218 *Dx:* 22416 PENMAENMAWR
List of partners: B B Cunningham, C B Forfar, J M W Prichard
Office: Conwy
Languages: French, German, Welsh
Work: D1 D2 E F1 G H J1 K1 K2 K3 L N Q S1 S2 V W X Z(l)
Emergency Action, Agency, Advocacy, Fixed Fee Interview, Legal Aid undertaken and Legal Aid Franchise
Ptr: Cunningham, Mr Brian B LLB . . . . . . *Aug 1981
Forfar, Ms Carla B LLB . . . . . . *Oct 1984
Prichard, Mr John M W LLB. . . . . . *Jul 1970

PENRITH, Cumbria

ARNISON & CO SOLICITORS LIMITED ‡
1 St Andrews Place Penrith Cumbria CA11 7AW
Tel: 01768 862007 *Fax:* 01768 865156 *Dx:* 63301 PENRITH
E-mail: law@arnison.co.uk
List of partners: G D Hinckley, T P Price, B Richardson, C J Ryder, K G Walker
Work: A1 A2 B1 C1 D1 E G H J1 K1 L N O Q S1 T2 W Z(c,l,q)
Emergency Action, Agency, Advocacy, Fixed Fee Interview, Legal Aid undertaken, Legal Aid Franchise and Member of Accident Line
Ptr: Hinckley, Ms Gillian D. . . . . . . Dec 1987
Price, Mr Trevor P MA(Manc) . . . . . . *Nov 1985
Richardson, Mr Bruce BSc(Hons) . . . . . . *Oct 1993
Ryder, Mr Christopher J LLB . . . . . . *Oct 1989
Walker, Mr K Geyve MA(Oxon) . . . . . . *§Jun 1974
Ast: Brogden, Ms Lissa . . . . . . Aug 2002
Richardson, Mr Jonathan M LLB Notary Public . . . *Oct 1982
Sterling, Mr Michael C LLB . . . . . . *Dec 1975

BUTTERWORTHS
52 King Street Penrith Cumbria CA11 7AY
Tel: 01768 868989 *Fax:* 01768 863432 *Dx:* 63308 PENRITH
E-mail: info@butterworths-solicitors.co.uk
Office: Carlisle

CARTMELL SHEPHERD
Bishop Yards Penrith Cumbria CA11 7XS
Tel: 01768 862326 *Fax:* 01768 865255 *Dx:* 63300 PENRITH
E-mail: penrith@cartmells.co.uk
Office: Brampton, Carlisle (2 offices), Haltwhistle
Work: A1 B1 C1 C2 C3 D1 J1 K1 L M1 M2 N P R1 S1 V W Z(c,d,h,l,m,n,s)
Emergency Action, Agency, Advocacy, Fixed Fee Interview, Legal Aid undertaken and Member of Accident Line
Ptr: Hansford, Mr Charlie Maurice LLB. . . . . . Aug 1997
Wright, Ms Janet E Y BA(Hons)(Oxon) . . . . . *May 1995
Asoc: Marquis, Mr William Andrew BA. . . . . . Jul 1978
Ast: Boardman, Mr Tim . . . . . . Jan 2002
Calway, Ms Zoe Fawcett LLB . . . . . . Nov 2006

CUMBRIA EMPLOYMENT SOLICITORS ‡
Bownass Barn Lamonby Penrith Cumbria CA11 9SS
Tel: 01768 484938
E-mail: michael@cumbriaemploymentsolicitors.co.uk

SCOTT DUFF & CO ‡
40 King Street Penrith Cumbria CA11 7AY
Tel: 01768 865551 *Fax:* 01768 867003
Emergency telephone 01768 862286
E-mail: steven@scottduff.co.uk
List of partners: K Blue, C M Christian, S E Connell, F M Marsh, S J Marsh, K A Wright
Office: Carlisle, Keswick
Languages: French
Work: A1 B1 C1 D1 D2 E F1 G H J1 J2 K1 K2 L N O P Q S1 S2 V W Z(l,r)
Emergency Action, Agency, Advocacy, Fixed Fee Interview, Legal Aid undertaken and Legal Aid Franchise
Ptr: Blue, Mrs Katharine LLB . . . . . . *Dec 1983
Christian, Mrs Cheryl M LLB(Hons) . . . . . *Mar 1987
Marsh, Mrs Fiona M MA. . . . . . *Oct 1983
Marsh, Mr Steven J BA(York) . . . . . . *Oct 1983
Ast: Bell, Mr Alistair John . . . . . . *Apr 2009
Harding, Ms Philippa LLB . . . . . . *Nov 1994

GAYNHAM KING & MELLOR ‡
1-2 Mason Court Gillan Way Penrith 40 Business Park Penrith Cumbria CA11 9GR
Tel: 01768 864651 *Fax:* 01768 867487 *Dx:* 63302 PENRITH
E-mail: info@gkmsolicitors.co.uk
List of partners: M Graham, K A Lowther, K S Metcalfe
Office: Appleby
Work: D1 E K1 L S1 W Z(l)
Emergency Action, Agency, Advocacy, Fixed Fee Interview and Legal Aid undertaken
Ptr: Graham, Mr Mark PGDipLaw; LPC . . . . . . Dec 2004
Lowther, Mr Kevin A BA(Hons) . . . . . . *Aug 1986
Metcalfe, Miss Kathryn Sarah BA(Hons). . . . . *Nov 1998
Ast: Jackson, Mrs Bernadette Edna BSc(Hons); LLDip . . *Sep 2008
Mitchell, Mr Clive David LLB. . . . . . Oct 1985
Con: King, Mrs Julia BSc(Lond). . . . . . *Apr 1979

BRIAN LEAH EMPLOYMENT LAW SOLICITOR ‡
2 Church Street Skirwith Penrith Cumbria CA10 1RG
Tel: 01769 88640
E-mail: brian@brianleah.co.uk
Work: J1

PENRYN, Cornwall

CHRISTOPHER ROSE & CO ‡
24 Lower Market Street Penryn Cornwall TR10 8BG
Tel: 01326 372461 / 374430 *Fax:* 01326 376595
E-mail: notary@btconnect.com
List of partners: C A Rose
Languages: French
Work: K4 L S1 W
SPr: Rose, Mr Christopher Alan Notary Public . . . . . *§Jul 1965

PENTRE, Rhondda Cynon Taff

EDGAR CULE & EVANS ‡
213 Ystrad Road Pentre Rhondda Cynon Taff CF41 7PF
Tel: 01443 434179 *Fax:* 01443 438930 *Dx:* 115540 PENTRE
Emergency telephone 029 2089 0692
List of partners: D M Bartholomew
Work: K1 L N Q S1 W
Emergency Action, Agency, Advocacy, Fixed Fee Interview and Legal Aid undertaken
Ptr: Bartholomew, Mr David Michael BA . . . . . . *Oct 1974

DEBORAH REYNOLDS ‡
31 Gelli Road Pentre Rhondda Cynon Taff CF41 7LY
Tel: 01443 440888 *Fax:* 01444 434866
Emergency telephone 01443 440888
E-mail: drconveyancing@aol.com
List of partners: D J L Reynolds
Work: S1 S2 W
Fixed Fee Interview undertaken
SPr: Reynolds, Miss Deborah J L LLB(Bris) . . . . . . Oct 1984

PENZANCE, Cornwall

CVC SOLICITORS ‡
1st Floor Branwells Mill Penzance Cornwall TR18 2LQ
Tel: 01736 362313 *Fax:* 01736 364332 *Dx:* 151780 PENZANCE 5
E-mail: enquiries@cornishvenning.co.uk
List of partners: J Dunstan, M L B Evans, N W S Jones, D N Lush
Office: Hayle, St Ives
Languages: French, Welsh
Work: A1 C1 D1 E F1 J1 K1 K3 L N O P Q R1 S1 S2 V W Z(d,l,m,r,y)
Emergency Action, Agency, Advocacy, Legal Aid undertaken, Legal Aid Franchise and Member of Accident Line
Dir: Evans, Mostyn L B . . . . . . *Nov 1984
Lush, Mr David Norman LLB(B'ham) . . . . . . Jun 1974
Ast: Crewdson, Mrs Anita . . . . . . Oct 1994
Robinson, Mrs Lisa . . . . . . *Sep 2006
Sheridan, Mr Tony. . . . . . Mar 2010

COODES
49-50 Morrab Road Penzance Cornwall TR18 4EX
Tel: 01736 362294 *Fax:* 01736 363533 *Dx:* 81305 PENZANCE
E-mail: enquiries@coodes.co.uk
Office: Holsworthy, Launceston, Liskeard, Newquay, St Austell, Truro
Work: C1 D1 D2 E G H K1 L S1 S2 V W Z(c,d)
Agency, Fixed Fee Interview and Legal Aid Franchise
Ptr: Southwell, Miss Louise Antoinette BA(Hons) . . . . *Aug 1999
Stokes, Miss Heather A LLB(Lond) . . . . . *Jun 1977
Ast: Foote, Mr Nicholas John LLB . . . . . . Mar 2008
Sidgwick, Mr Benjamin John Benson . . . . . . Sep 2009

DB LAW
3a Alverton Street Penzance Cornwall TR18 2QH
Tel: 01736 364261 *Fax:* 01736 369114 *Dx:* 81301 PENZANCE
Emergency telephone 07693 424607 (PAGER)
E-mail: e-mail@vtjlaw.freeserve.co.uk
Office: Camborne, Falmouth, St Ives
Work: B1 B2 D1 D2 E F1 G H J1 K1 L N O Q S1 V W X Z(a,c,l)
Emergency Action, Agency, Advocacy, Fixed Fee Interview, Legal Aid undertaken and Legal Aid Franchise
Ptr: Calderwood, Mr Graham D ★ . . . . . . *§Dec 1968
Moore, Mr Elliott LLB(Hons). . . . . . *Jun 1996
Thomas, Mr Justyn . . . . . . Feb 2006
Timmis, Mr John M LLB(Hons) . . . . . . Apr 1986
Con: Jacoby, Mr James D . . . . . . *§Dec 1975

GILDENER BRETT ‡
4 Stewarts Buildings Penzance Cornwall TR18 2QU
Tel: 01736 332533 *Fax:* 01736 332522 *Dx:* 81316 PENZANCE
Emergency telephone 01736 332533
E-mail: enquiries@gildenerbrett.co.uk
List of partners: S S Brett, P Gildener
Work: C1 D1 E F2 J1 K1 K3 L N Q S1 S2 V W Z(l,q)
Agency and Advocacy undertaken
Ptr: Brett, Mr Sancho Sebastian . . . . . . *Jun 2007
Gildener, Mr Peter LLB(Hons). . . . . . *May 1964

NALDERS QUALITY SOLICITORS
104 Market Jew Street Penzance Cornwall TR18 2LF
Tel: 01736 364014 *Fax:* 01736 364054 *Dx:* 81317 PENZANCE
E-mail: post@nalders.co.uk
Office: Camborne, Falmouth, Helston, Newquay, St Austell, Truro (2 offices)
Work: B1 C1 D1 D2 E J1 K1 K3 K4 L N O P Q R1 R2 S2 V W Z(c,h,o,q,r)

PERIVALE, Middlesex

STEPHEN MURRAY & CO ‡
(incorporating Penzer & Co)
13 Medway Parade Perivale Middlesex UB6 8HN
Tel: 020 8997 9669 *Fax:* 020 8997 0931
List of partners: N C H Penzer
Languages: Hindi, Punjabi
Work: E S1 W Z(l)
Agency and Advocacy undertaken
SPr: Penzer, Mr Nigel C H MA(Cantab). . . . . . *Jul 1981
Con: Murray, Mr Stephen LLB . . . . . . *Oct 1981

PERRANPORTH, Cornwall

NIGEL S PULLEN ‡
The Old Station Business Park Station Road Perranporth Cornwall TR6 0LH
Tel: 01872 571046 *Fax:* 01872 572610
E-mail: info@cornwall-law.co.uk
List of partners: M S A O'Toole, N S Pullen
Office: Truro
Work: D1 E F1 G K1 K3 K4 L N O Q S1 S2 W Z(l,q)
Agency, Advocacy and Fixed Fee Interview undertaken
Ptr: Pullen, Mr Nigel S LLB . . . . . . *§Nov 1980
Ast: O'Toole, Mrs Mykal S A LLB(Hons) . . . . . . *Nov 1987

PERSHORE, Worcestershire

J F KIRBY ‡
The Old Saddlery Deer Park Pershore Worcestershire WR10 3DN
Tel: 01386 751760

PENNY RABY & CO ‡
Harmony House 7-9 Church Street Pershore Worcestershire WR10 1DT
Tel: 01386 555114 *Fax:* 01386 554091 *Dx:* 25933 PERSHORE
E-mail: penny@divorcefinance.co.uk
List of partners: P J Raby
Languages: French, Italian
Work: K1 K3
SPr: Raby, Mrs Penelope J LLB(Bris). . . . . . *Jan 1981

THOMSON & BANCKS LLP
37 High Street Pershore Worcestershire WR10 1AH
Tel: 01386 562000 *Fax:* 01386 562020 *Dx:* 25931 PERSHORE
E-mail: info@tblaw.co.uk
Office: Tewkesbury
Work: A1 C1 C2 D1 E F1 G H J1 J2 K1 K3 K4 L N O Q R1 R2 S1 S2 T1 T2 V W Z(h,l,p,q)
Emergency Action, Agency, Advocacy and Fixed Fee Interview undertaken
Ptr: Cook, Mr Stephen L D LLB . . . . . . *Jun 1977
Gillham, Ms Sylvia Alison LLB. . . . . . *Sep 2002
Greer, Mr David C LLB . . . . . . *Apr 1980
Johnson, Mr Paul N LLB . . . . . . *Oct 1986
Scott, Miss Angela J LLB . . . . . . *Nov 1988
Mem: Martin, Mr John Nicholas LLB(B'ham) . . . . . *§Apr 1978
Ast: Dale, Miss Zoe LLB . . . . . . Jan 2003
Phythian, Rachael. . . . . . Feb 2008

PETERBOROUGH

ANB LAW ‡
DHC Business Centre 226 Dogsthorpe Road Peterborough PE1 3PB
Tel: 01733 565900 *Fax:* 01733 565954
Dx: 123170 PETERBOROUGH 2
E-mail: amirbutt@anblaw.co.uk

THE A P PARTNERSHIP LTD ‡
Borough House Newark Road Peterborough PE1 5YJ
Tel: 01733 891081 *Fax:* 01733 557542
E-mail: info@appartnership.co.uk
Work: A3 J1 J2 Z(p)

AULEYS SOLICITORS ‡
Four Winds 11 Gaul Road March Peterborough PE15 9RF
Tel: 01354 650375 *Fax:* 01733 346369
E-mail: auleyssol@aol.com

BAL DHALIWAL SOLICITORS ‡
St Peters House Bishops Road Peterborough PE1 1YE
Tel: 01733 552000

BALFOUR LAW ‡
Balfour House 1110 Lincoln Road Peterborough PE4 6BP
Tel: 01733 324444 *Fax:* 01733 327999
E-mail: info@balfourlaw.co.uk

RICHARD BROWN & CO ‡
West Wing Broadway Court Broadway Peterborough PE1 1FR
Tel: 0870 850 3062 *Fax:* 01733 551922
Dx: 16868 PETERBOROUGH 2
List of partners: O S Barrett, R W Brown
Work: A1 G H
Advocacy undertaken
Ptr: Barrett, Mr Oliver Sebastian LLB . . . . . . *Mar 1997
Brown, Mr Richard W LLB(Bris) Secretary for Local Law Society . . . . . . *Nov 1985

BUCKLES SOLICITORS LLP ‡
Grant House 101 Bourges Boulevard Peterborough PE1 1NG
Tel: 01733 888888 *Fax:* 01733 888999
E-mail: enquiries@buckles-law.co.uk
List of partners: C J U Applegate, G Betts, M C Blank, P S Branch, L P Brisley, R E Clarke, J Coppinger, S M Duffy, C Gostick, D Jackson, J R Maxey, N E Moore, M C Rabbett, G Sykes
Office: Stamford
Work: A1 A3 B1 C1 C2 C3 D1 D2 E F1 I J1 K1 K2 K3 L M1 M2 N O P Q R1 R2 S1 S2 T1 T2 U2 W Z(b,c,d,e,i,k,l,m,o,q,z)
Emergency Action, Advocacy and Fixed Fee Interview undertaken
Ptr: Applegate, Mr Charles J U MA(Cantab) . . . . . *Dec 1979
Betts, Mr Giles LLB . . . . . . *Oct 1999
Blank, Mr Michael Charles LLB . . . . . . *Feb 1988
Branch, Mr Paul S BA; LLM. . . . . . *Nov 1987
Brisley, Mrs Lyn Penelope BA(Hons) Mediator. . . . *Nov 1995
Clarke, Mr Roger E LLB. . . . . . *Oct 1988
Coppinger, Mr James LLB(Hons); DipLaw Chairman of LAWNET Construction Group . . . . . . *Jan 1999
Duffy, Mr Stephen Martin LLB . . . . . . *Sep 2001
Gostick, Mrs Colleen LLB . . . . . . *§Oct 1985
Jackson, Mr Duncan LLB . . . . . . *Sep 1997
Maxey, Mr James Richard LLB; CEDR Mediator. . . *Sep 1994
Moore, Mr Nigel E BA. . . . . . *Oct 1985
Rabbett, Mr Michael Christopher LLB(Hons). . . . *Oct 1994
Sykes, Mrs Gail BA . . . . . . *Sep 1997
Asoc: Herson, Mr Martin BSc(Hons) Treasurer of Peterborough & District Law Society. . . . . . *Sep 1993
Westwood, Mrs Sarah. . . . . . *Sep 1997
Ast: Baker, Rebekkah . . . . . . *Jan 2010
Corrigan, Mr Peter . . . . . . *Nov 1998
Cotgrove, Joanna. . . . . . *Jan 2007
Patrick, Miss Kerry LLB; LLM . . . . . . *Sep 2008
Plummer, Ms Joy . . . . . . *Nov 1996
Porter, Mr Nick BSc. . . . . . *Apr 2002
Sandall, Mrs Donna LLB(Hons) . . . . . . *Jan 2002
Vernon, Mr Richard . . . . . . *Jan 1997

 See p112 for the Key to Work Categories & other symbols

CARTERS ‡
Third Floor Priestgate House Priestgate Peterborough PE1 1JN
Tel: 0845 075 4101
E-mail: info@carters-solicitors.com

CASEY LEGAL ‡
12 Earlswood Orton Brimbles Peterborough PE2 5UG
Tel: 01733 233301

CUTHBERT & CO ‡
(in association with Safe Systems at Work Health & Safety Consultants)
21 Fitzwilliam Street Peterborough PE1 2RU
Tel: 01733 564655 *Fax:* 01733 564655
E-mail: cuthbertg6@aol.com
List of partners: G V Cuthbert
Languages: German
Work: G H J1 J2 K1 L N O Q S1 V Z(c,l,p,q,r)
Emergency Action, Agency, Advocacy, Fixed Fee Interview and Legal Aid undertaken
SPr: Cuthbert, Mr Graham Vincent . . . . *Jul 1982

DEVAS KEOGH JAMES ‡
2 King Street (Off Cowgate) Peterborough PE1 1LT
Tel: 01733 340666 *Fax:* 01733 312757
Dx: 12333 PETERBOROUGH 1
E-mail: roy.james@devaskeoghjames.co.uk
List of partners: R James, R Keogh
Languages: Punjabi, Serbo-Croat, Urdu, Welsh
Work: G H
Agency, Advocacy, Fixed Fee Interview, Legal Aid undertaken and Legal Aid Franchise
Ptr: James, Mr Roy LLB ★. . . . . *Oct 1993
Keogh, Ms Rebecca BA(Hons) . . . . *Oct 1992

ELSEY & HODSON ‡
24-26 North Street Peterborough PE1 2RA
Tel: 01733 314064 *Fax:* 01733 565385
Dx: 16853 PETERBOROUGH 2
Emergency telephone 01733 266662 / 01780 782588
E-mail: email@elseyandhodsonsolicitors.co.uk
List of partners: A E Elsey, R D Hodson
Languages: Hindi, Punjabi
Work: A1 A2 B1 C1 C2 C3 D1 D2 E F1 J1 K1 K3 L M1 M2 N P R1 S1 T1 T2 V W Z(k,l,w)
Emergency Action, Agency, Advocacy, Fixed Fee Interview, Legal Aid undertaken, Legal Aid Franchise and Member of Accident Line
Ptr: Elsey, Mr Anthony E TD Deputy District Judge . . . . *Jul 1980
Hodson, Mr Robert D . . . . *Dec 1977
Asoc: Kumari, Miss Meena . . . . *Aug 2003

FUTTER CHAPMAN SOLICITORS ‡
The White House 59 Park Road Peterborough PE1 2TH
Tel: 0870 162 4499

GREENWOODS SOLICITORS LLP ‡
Monkstone House City Road Peterborough PE1 1JE
Tel: 01733 887700 *Fax:* 01733 887701
Dx: 12599 PETERBOROUGH 4
E-mail: mail@greenwoods.co.uk
List of partners: R Dillarstone, K A F Gilbertson, A Gunn, K E Horsley, S J Illingworth, J Macaulay, D F Morgan, D V Woods
Languages: French, German
Work: A1 A2 A3 B1 B2 C1 C2 C3 E F1 I J1 J2 L M1 M2 O P Q R1 R2 S1 S2 T1 T2 U1 U2 W X Z(c,d,e,f,h,i,k,l,o,p,q,s,u,w,z)
Mem: Dillarstone, Mr Robert LLB . . . . *Oct 1986
Gilbertson, Mrs Kathryn A F BSc(Hons) . . . . Nov 1994
Gunn, Mr Alastair LLB. . . . . *Mar 2003
Horsley, Ms Karin E LLB(Lond) . . . . *Oct 1979
Illingworth, Mr Stephen J LLB . . . . *Oct 1986
Macaulay, Mr John BA . . . . *Sep 1991
Morgan, Mr Darren F LLB. . . . . *Nov 1991
Woods, Mr David V MA(Cantab) Clements Inn Prize; Travers Smith Scholarship. . . . . *Oct 1982
Asoc: Cooper, Mr Graham Michael LLB(Hons). . . . . Mar 1995
Jinks, Mrs Lisa J BA(Hons) Arthur Andersen Tax Prize *Oct 1992
Scally, Mrs Joanna Rachel MA; CPE; LPC . . . . . . *Sep 2001
Starr, Mr Robert Leslie LLB . . . . Nov 2000
Whaley, Miss Adele Natalie LLB. . . . . *Sep 2001
Williams, Mr Keith Alan LLB(Hons) . . . . *Sep 2002
Ast: Lee, Mr Jeremy David BA. . . . . *Mar 1984
McCready, Mrs Cheryl LLB . . . . Feb 2006
Murphy, Miss Emma D LLB(Hons). . . . . *Jan 2003
Peck, Mrs Kelly Marie BA(Hons) . . . . *Sep 2001
Piper, Ms Louise LLB(Hons). . . . . Feb 2006

H & V SOLICITORS ‡
585 Lincoln Road Peterborough PE1 2PB
Tel: 01733 743743 *Fax:* 01733 743743
E-mail: info@hvsolicitors.co.uk

HC SOLICITORS LLP ‡
35 Thorpe Road Peterborough PE3 6AG
Tel: 01733 882800 *Fax:* 01733 552748
Dx: 12302 PETERBOROUGH 1
E-mail: info@hcsolicitors.co.uk
List of partners: H M Anstey, P J Appleton, L Ayres, A R Cave, D C Heming, J S Henson, P L Izod, S J Milburn, E J Owen, A E Spriggs, D W White, A Whitehead
Office: Oundle
Languages: French, Spanish, Urdu
Work: A1 B1 B2 C1 C2 C3 D1 D2 E F1 G H J1 K1 K2 L M1 N O P Q R1 R2 S1 S2 T1 T2 V W X Z(c,d,e,g,h,i,k,l,m,q,r,t,x)
Emergency Action, Agency, Advocacy, Fixed Fee Interview, Legal Aid undertaken, Legal Aid Franchise and Member of Accident Line
Ptr: Anstey, Mr Henry Michael LLB; TEP. . . . . *Feb 1992
Ayres, Miss Lynne LLB(Bris) . . . . *Mar 1971
Heming, Mr David C BA Deputy Coroner . . . . *Jan 1990
Henson, Mr John S LLB(B'ham). . . . . *Apr 1975
Izod, Mr Peter L BA. . . . . *Oct 1983
Milburn, Mr Simon J LLB . . . . *Oct 1991
Owen, Mr Edward J BA. . . . . *Apr 1981
Spriggs, Miss Anna Elizabeth LLB Assistant Deputy Coroner . . . . *Nov 1988
White, Mr Denis W LLB Chairman of the Diocese of East Anglia Child Protection Commission; Vice Chairman of Drinksense . . . . *May 1976
Dir: Cave, Mr Andrew Robert LLB ♦. . . . . *Sep 2002
Whitehead, Andrew. . . . . *Dec 1997
Asoc: Butt, Mrs Farhana LLB(Hons) . . . . *Feb 1999
Pighills, Robina Treasurer of SFE East Anglian Branch *Jan 1987
Turpin, Mrs Karen LLB NSPCC Business Support Group Committee . . . . *Nov 1996
Ast: Bassett, Mrs Gillian Margaret LLB(Hons) . . . . Nov 1994
Cookson, Reshma . . . . Aug 2002
Holland, Angela Nicole . . . . May 2000
Railton, Glynn LLB . . . . *Sep 2007
Sandbach, Catherine . . . . *Sep 2009
Sneddon, Mr Benjamin Member of the Board of Trustees for Peterborough CAB . . . . Nov 2005
Verdu De Haro, Mr Alejandro . . . . Jul 2007
Webb, Elizabeth. . . . . *Apr 2007

HEGARTY LLP ‡
48 Broadway Peterborough PE1 1YW
Tel: 01733 346333 *Fax:* 01733 562338
Dx: 16850 PETERBOROUGH 2
E-mail: email@hegarty.co.uk
List of partners: G R Baker, M D Bloom, A Heeler, R J Hegarty, H J H Nicholls, G J Peebles, S Rowcliffe, M B Sidebottom, K Singh, T A Thompson
Office: Stamford
Work: A1 A3 B1 B2 C1 C2 C3 D1 D2 E F1 G H I J1 K1 K2 K3 K4 L N O P Q R2 S1 S2 W Z(c,d,e,l,p)
Agency, Advocacy, Legal Aid undertaken and Legal Aid Franchise
Ptr: Baker, Mr Gregory Richard ACIB; TEP . . . . *Jul 1998
Bloom, Mr Martin D LLB Part time Environmental Tribunal Judge . . . . *§Oct 1981
Heeler, Mr Andrew LLB . . . . *Sep 1999
Hegarty, Mr Richard J LLB Member of the Solicitors Disciplinary Tribunal. . . . . *§Oct 1974
Nicholls, Mr Hugh Jonathan Harper LLB; MSc. . . . . *Jan 2001
Peebles, Mr Graham J LLB . . . . *Nov 1987
Rowcliffe, Mr Sean LLB . . . . *Oct 1995
Sidebottom, Mr Matthew B LLB . . . . *Oct 1988
Singh, Mr Kalbinder LLB . . . . *Nov 1992
Thompson, Mr Timothy A . . . . §Nov 1978
Asoc: Acres, Mrs Sarah LLB. . . . . *Sep 1997
Chilton, Vicki . . . . *Sep 1994
Grewer, Mrs Joanna Louise LLB(Hons); TEP . . . . . Sep 2003
Hornsby, Mr Andrew P LLB . . . . *Sep 1996
Ast: Beesley-Hewitt, Andrea. . . . . *Dec 2007
Carter, Miss Emma Jane BA(Hons) . . . . *Sep 1999
Dawson, Sarah . . . . *Sep 1997
Kidd, Miss Ashley LLB . . . . *Sep 2010
Murtagh, Ms Julie. . . . . *Oct 2001
Strong, Miss Rachel Teresa BA . . . . *Nov 1993
Tatlock, Ms Jane Elizabeth BSc(Hons); DipLaw . . . . *Nov 1997
Wild, Mrs Joanne LLB(Hons) . . . . *Sep 1992
Young, Ms Sara LLB . . . . *Jul 2001

RAYMOND HEMINGRAY ‡
4 Holywell Way Longthorpe Peterborough PE3 6SS
Tel: 01733 262523 *Fax:* 01733 330280
E-mail: rh@raymondhemingray.co.uk
List of partners: R Hemingray
Work: Z(x)
SPr: Hemingray, Rev Raymond LLB(Hons) Diocesan Registrar Notary Public. . . . . *Jun 1971

HUMBLE MUNSON LLP ‡
Websters Farm High Street Glinton Peterborough PE6 7LS
Tel: 01733 254815

IQBAL KHALIL & CO ‡
308 Lincoln Road Peterborough PE1 2ND
Tel: 01733 552772 *Fax:* 01733 554469
Dx: 21153 PETERBOROUGH 3
Emergency telephone 07956 181202
Languages: Punjabi, Urdu
Work: D1 E F1 G H J1 K1 L N Q S1 V W Z(i,p)
Emergency Action, Agency, Fixed Fee Interview and Legal Aid undertaken

LINCOLNS LAW SOLICITORS ‡
First Floor 254-256 Lincoln Road Peterborough PE1 2ND
Tel: 01733 897700 *Fax:* 01733 896700
Dx: 123173 PETERBOROUGH 2
E-mail: ai@lincolnslaw.co.uk

METCALFE COPEMAN & PETTEFAR
18 Priestgate Peterborough PE1 1JN
Tel: 01733 865880 *Fax:* 01733 895065
Dx: 12319 PETERBOROUGH 1
E-mail: info@mcp-law.co.uk
Office: King's Lynn, Thetford, Wisbech
Languages: Portuguese
Work: A1 A3 B1 B2 C1 C2 C3 D1 D2 E F1 F2 G H J1 J2 K1 K2 K3 K4 L M1 M2 N O P Q R1 R2 S1 S2 T1 T2 U2 V W Z(c,e,g,h,l,n,o,p,q,t,y,za)
Emergency Action, Agency, Advocacy, Fixed Fee Interview, Legal Aid undertaken, Legal Aid Franchise and Member of Accident Line
Ptr: Adlam, Miss Sarah LLB. . . . . *Oct 1992
Burton, Mr Jonathan R MA(Cantab) . . . . *Jun 1975
Hesketh, Mrs Jacqueline . . . . *Nov 1999
Newton, Mr Martin P LLB(Hons). . . . . *Oct 1993

MONDAIR SOLICITORS ‡
40 Peterborough Road Farcet Peterborough PE7 3BH
Tel: 01733 244459 *Fax:* 01733 244489
E-mail: boota@mondair.co.uk

PIRIE PALMANN ‡
Priestgate House 3-7 Priestgate Peterborough PE1 1JN
Tel: 01733 427799 *Fax:* 01733 427277 *Dx:* 12335 PETERBOROUGH
E-mail: mhenderson@movehomelegal.co.uk
List of partners: M I Palmann
Work: S1 W
Ptr: Palmann, Mrs Marion I LLB . . . . *Oct 1982

PRATCHETTS SOLICITORS ‡
555 Lincoln Road Peterborough PE1 2PB
Tel: 0870 350 8609 *Fax:* 01773 891118
Dx: 16863 PETERBOROUGH 2
E-mail: pratchett_law@btconnect.com

JEREMY ROBERTS & CO ‡
51 Park Road Peterborough PE1 2TH
Tel: 01733 343943 / 342172 *Fax:* 01733 313037
Dx: 16861 PETERBOROUGH 2
Emergency telephone 01733 576144
E-mail: jeremyroberts.co@btconnect.com
List of partners: J M Roberts
Languages: Punjabi, Urdu
Work: D1 F1 G H J1 K1 L M1 N P Q V W Z(f)
Emergency Action, Agency, Advocacy, Fixed Fee Interview, Legal Aid undertaken and Member of Accident Line
Ptr: Roberts, Mr Jeremy M LLB ★. . . . . *§Jan 1975

ROYTHORNES LLP
Dean's Court 10 Minster Precincts Peterborough PE1 1XS
Tel: 01733 558585 *Fax:* 01733 346868
Dx: 12311 PETERBOROUGH 1
E-mail: info@roythornes.co.uk
Office: Newmarket, Nottingham, Spalding
Work: A1 C1 E J1 J2 K3 L M2 P R2 S1 S2 T2 W Z(d,h)
Ptr: Cookson, Mr Phillip LLB. . . . . *§Nov 1995
Thompson, Mrs Catherine LLB(Hons) . . . . Feb 1979
Williams, Mr Jonathan M BA(Hons) . . . . *Jan 1983

SK LEGAL SOLICITORS ‡
213 Lincoln Road Peterborough PE1 2PL
Tel: 01733 565295 *Fax:* 01733 565277
Dx: 16858 PETERBOROUGH 2
E-mail: sajidkhan@sklegal.co.uk

SLOAN PLUMB WOOD ‡
Apollo House Isis Way Minerva Business Park Peterborough PE2 6QR
Tel: 01733 302410 *Fax:* 01733 390552 *Dx:* 118203 LYNCHWOOD 2

BELINDA SMITH & CO SOLICITORS ‡
Asset House 27/28 Thorpe Wood Peterborough PE3 6SR
Tel: 01733 267414 *Fax:* 01733 267408
E-mail: belinda@bscosolicitors.co.uk

GLENN SMITH & CO ‡
12 High Street Peterborough PE6 8EB
Tel: 01778 343272 *Dx:* 11457 MARKET DEEPING
E-mail: glenn.smithandco@tiscali.co.uk

SOLOMON LAW ‡
75 Broadway Peterborough PE1 1SY
Tel: 01733 312424 *Fax:* 01733 552877
Dx: 16867 PETERBOROUGH 2

TAYLOR ROSE LAW ‡
Midgate House Midgate Peterborough PE1 1TN
Tel: 01733 865600

TERRELLS LLP ‡
61 Lincoln Road Peterborough PE1 2SE
Tel: 01733 896789 *Fax:* 01733 890709
Dx: 16852 PETERBOROUGH 2
E-mail: enquiries@terrells.co.uk
List of partners: L Terrell, L Terrell, R Terrell
Office: Huntingdon, Stamford
Work: B1 C1 D1 E J1 K1 K3 N O P Q S1 S2 V W Z(l,w)
Emergency Action, Agency, Advocacy, Legal Aid undertaken, Legal Aid Franchise and Member of Accident Line
Ptr: Terrell, Mr Roger BA(Hons) . . . . *Feb 1980
Mem: Terrell, Miss Lucy LLB(Hons) . . . . *Aug 2009
Ast: Ayres, Mrs Lorna LLB(Hons) . . . . *May 2009
Farrar, Miss Rachael Louise LLB . . . . *Aug 2010
Fuller, Mrs Claire LLB(Hons) . . . . *Dec 2008
Howat, Ms Anna . . . . *Jul 2003
Roberts, Miss Louise LLB(Hons) . . . . *Aug 2009

JANET R THOMPSON ‡
Milton House 38a Cowgate Peterborough PE1 1NA
Tel: 01733 347247

WALLER NEEDHAM & GREEN ‡
Longueville 72 Broadway Peterborough PE1 1SU
Tel: 01733 311422 *Fax:* 01733 557570
Dx: 16854 PETERBOROUGH 2
Emergency telephone 01733 311422
List of partners: S H W Green, T P Needham, M G J Shelbourne, M J Trayford, C R d W Waller, D P C Willatt
Office: Peterborough
Work: A1 B1 C1 D1 E F1 G H J1 K1 L M1 N P Q R1 S1 T1 V W Z(c,e,h,l,s,t)
Emergency Action, Agency, Advocacy, Fixed Fee Interview, Legal Aid undertaken, Legal Aid Franchise and Member of Accident Line
Ptr: Green, Mr Stephen H W LLB . . . . *§Dec 1972
Needham, Mr Timothy P BA. . . . . *Jan 1982
Shelbourne, Mr Martin Graham John BA(Hons) . . . . *Sep 1994
Waller, Mr Christopher R de W LLB . . . . *Dec 1974
Willatt, Mr Damian P C LLB ★. . . . . *Oct 1990

WALLER NEEDHAM & GREEN
Rightwell East Bretton Peterborough PE3 8DS
Tel: 01733 262182 *Fax:* 01733 331520 *Dx:* 708490 BRETTON
Office: Peterborough
Work: B1 C1 D1 E F1 G H J1 K1 L M1 N O Q S1 V W Z(c)
Emergency Action, Agency, Advocacy, Fixed Fee Interview, Legal Aid undertaken and Member of Accident Line
Ptr: Trayford, Mr Martin J BA . . . . *Feb 1984

PETERLEE, Co Durham

C W BOOTH
3 Dean Terrace Horden Peterlee Co Durham SR8 4JF
Tel: 0191 586 7682
Office: Bishop Auckland

DONNELLY MCARDLE ADAMSON
9-11 Burnhope Way Peterlee Co Durham SR8 1BT
Tel: 0191 586 3581 *Fax:* 0191 518 0648 *Dx:* 60190 PETERLEE
E-mail: enquiries@macardles.co.uk
Office: Darlington, Hartlepool, Stockton-on-Tees, Sunderland (2 offices)
Ptr: Gething, Mr Hugh. . . . . *§Dec 1967

KIRKUP LASCELLES & CREED
1st Floor 25 Yoden Way Peterlee Co Durham SR8 1BP
Tel: 0191 586 8646 *Fax:* 0191 518 0784 *Dx:* 60194 PETERLEE
E-mail: kirkups@gmail.com
Office: Hartlepool
Work: A1 B1 C1 D1 D2 E K1 N O S1 S2 W
Emergency Action, Agency, Advocacy, Legal Aid undertaken and Legal Aid Franchise
Ptr: Brough, Mrs Diane . . . . *Dec 1990
Creed, Mr Terence BA(Law); LLM. . . . . *Oct 1981

NAUNTONS SOLICITORS
22 Seaside Lane Easington Colliery Peterlee Co Durham SR8 3PG
Tel: 0191 527 4050 *Fax:* 0191 527 4062
Office: Sunderland

SMITH & GRAHAM
6 Upper Yoden Way Peterlee Co Durham SR8 1AX
Tel: 0191 517 3393 *Fax:* 0191 518 3390 *Dx:* 60193 PETERLEE
Ptr: Townsend, Mr Alan LLB. . . . . *Nov 1991
Ast: Wright, Mrs Gillian LLB(Hons). . . . . *Oct 1993

TMJ LEGAL SERVICES LLP
14 Yoden Way Peterlee Co Durham SR8 1BP
Tel: 0191 586 5711 *Fax:* 0191 518 1178 *Dx:* 60191 PETERLEE
Emergency telephone 07793 201274
E-mail: legal@tmjlegal.co.uk
Office: Durham, Hartlepool, Wingate
Work: C1 D1 D2 E F1 J1 K1 K3 K4 L N O Q R1 S1 S2 W Z(p)
Emergency Action, Agency, Advocacy, Fixed Fee Interview, Legal Aid undertaken and Member of Accident Line

V G WAUGH ‡
31 Seaside Lane Easington Colliery Peterlee Co Durham SR8 3PG
Tel: 0191 527 2727 *Fax:* 0191 527 2348
List of partners: V G Waugh
Work: D1 G H K1 N S1
Emergency Action, Agency, Advocacy, Fixed Fee Interview, Legal Aid undertaken and Legal Aid Franchise
SPr: Waugh, Ms Vivian G BA. . . . . Aug 1980
Ast: Waites, Miss Helen BSc(Hons) . . . . Mar 1995

PETERSFIELD, Hampshire

BISCOES
Ingoldsby House 22 High Street Petersfield Hampshire GU32 3JL
Tel: 01730 264799 *Fax:* 01730 264913 *Dx:* 100420 PETERSFIELD
Office: Gosport, Portchester, Portsmouth, Waterlooville, Wickham
Work: C1 C2 E I J1 R1 R2 S1 S2 T1 T2 W Z(c,e,l)
Emergency Action, Agency, Advocacy, Fixed Fee Interview, Legal Aid undertaken, Legal Aid Franchise and Member of Accident Line
Ptr: Cover, Mr Marcus S MA(Cantab) . . . . *Apr 1980
Asoc: Wilson, Miss Joanna . . . . *Oct 2009

BURLEY & GEACH ‡
8 Swan Street Petersfield Hampshire GU32 3AE
Tel: 01730 262401 *Fax:* 01730 265182 *Dx:* 100402 PETERSFIELD
E-mail: petersfield@burley-geach.co.uk
List of partners: T J R Andrews, S R Bather, R J Baylis, H M Jennings, H M Jennings, A E Nellthorp, D A J Spirit
Office: Grayshott, Haslemere, Liphook
Work: A1 B1 C1 D1 E F1 G H J1 K1 L M1 N P Q R1 S1 T1 V W Z(c,d,h,i,j,k,l,m,p,s,t)
Emergency Action, Agency, Advocacy and Legal Aid undertaken
Ptr: Baylis, Mr Richard J BA. . . . . *§Jul 1976
Jennings, Mr Howard Michael. . . . . Jul 1983
Nellthorp, Mrs Alison E LLB(Exon) . . . . *Nov 1981
Spirit, Miss D Anna Jane BA . . . . *Dec 1985
Ast: Ireland, Mr Stephen C F LLB . . . . *Feb 1991

DONNA L CORBIN ‡
56 Heath Road East Petersfield Hampshire GU31 4HN
Tel: 01730 261288 *Fax:* 01730 261388
E-mail: donna.corbin@btopenworld.com
List of partners: D L Corbin
Work: B1 C1 D1 E J1 K1 L N Q S1 S2 W Z(e,i)
Agency and Advocacy undertaken
SPr: Corbin, Miss Donna L. . . . . *Sep 1987

DALTONS SOLICITORS ‡
Lyndum House 12 High Street Petersfield Hampshire GU32 3JG
Tel: 01730 262816 *Fax:* 01730 268725 *Dx:* 100408 PETERSFIELD
E-mail: enquiries@daltons-law.co.uk
List of partners: M Dalton, R E L Hawkins
Languages: French
Work: C1 C2 D1 E F1 F2 J1 K1 K2 K3 K4 L N O Q R1 R2 S1 S2 W Z(c,l,q,r)
Emergency Action, Agency, Advocacy and Fixed Fee Interview undertaken
Ptr: Dalton, Mr Michael . . . . *Oct 1982
Hawkins, Miss Rebecca E L BA(Hons) . . . . *Sep 1999
Ast: Jordon, Mrs Sarah LLB . . . . *Sep 2006
O'Flynn, Mr Paul LLB Notary Public. . . . . *Jul 2007

MC LAW ‡
55 Station Road Petersfield Hampshire GU32 3ES
Tel: 01730 261979 *Fax:* 01730 262375 *Dx:* 100410 PETERSFIELD
E-mail: reception@mclawmail.co.uk
List of partners: M P Crehan
Work: B1 C1 O
SPr: Crehan, Mr Michael Patrick LLB; LLM(Hons) . . . . *Sep 1999

MACDONALD OATES LLP ‡
Walltree Court St Peter's Road Petersfield Hampshire GU32 3HT
Tel: 01730 268211 *Fax:* 01730 261232 *Dx:* 100400 PETERSFIELD
E-mail: petersfield@macdonaldoates.co.uk
List of partners: A Dunn, P Jenkins, T D Melville-Walker, J A Sawers, R J Sawers, D G S Taylor
Office: Midhurst
Languages: French, German, Polish, Russian
Work: A1 A3 B1 C1 C2 D1 E F1 F2 I J1 J2 K1 K2 K3 L N O Q R1 R2 S1 S2 T1 T2 V W Z(c,d,j,k,o,q,r)
Emergency Action, Agency, Advocacy and Fixed Fee Interview undertaken
Ptr: Jenkins, Mr Patrick BA(Hons); PGDipLaw; LPC . . . *Sep 2004
Sawers, Mr Robert J BA . . . . *Mar 1988
Taylor, Mrs Deborah G S BSc. . . . . *Apr 1978
Asoc: Carter, Mrs Lisa Jane . . . . *Nov 1996
Dove, Mrs Clare LLB . . . . *Nov 1994
Smith, Mr Kevin Richard BSc(Hons); FCIArb; MRICS . *Jul 2002
Ast: Arneaud, Mr Simon James . . . . *Sep 2011
Davenport, Mrs Susan F BA(Hons) . . . . *Apr 1981
Nelson, Miss Kristy Emma LLB(Hons). . . . . *Jul 2007
Reid, Miss Rebecca Kelly BSc(Hons) . . . . *Mar 2008

MACKARNESS & LUNT ‡
16 High Street Petersfield Hampshire GU32 3JJ
Tel: 01730 265111 *Fax:* 01730 267994 *Dx:* 100401 PETERSFIELD
E-mail: mac@macklunt.co.uk
List of partners: S P R Mackarness, D Morrison, R K Petch, C S L Thompson
Work: A1 C1 E F1 J1 K1 K3 K4 L O Q R1 S1 S2 T1 T2 W Z(d)
Ptr: Mackarness, Mr Simon P R BA(Bris); TD . . . . . . *§Nov 1970
Morrison, Mr Dennis LLB(Sheff). . . . . *Jan 1976
Petch, Mr Roger K LLB(Sheff). . . . . *Jul 1976
Thompson, Mrs Claire Susan Louise BSc . . . . *Sep 2002
Ast: Hellyar, Ms Samantha Jane LLB; PGDip . . . . . . *Sep 2005
Hunter, Mr Patrick Andrew BA(Hons); MSc . . . . . . Feb 2006

ROBERT MCLAREN PLANNING & PROPERTY SOLICITORS ‡
Rogate Cross Cottage Rogate Petersfield Hampshire GU31 5HN
Tel: 01730 818202 *Fax:* 01730 818205
E-mail: mclarenlegal@btconnect.com

MEDIATION NOW LTD
Lyndum House 12 High Street Petersfield Hampshire GU32 3JG
Tel: 01730 266605 *Fax:* 01730 268725
E-mail: info@mediation-now.co.uk
Office: Emsworth, Fareham, Petersfield, Portsmouth

MEDIATION NOW LTD
Antrobus House 18 College Street Petersfield Hampshire GU31 4AD
Tel: 01730 266605
E-mail: rebecca@mediation-now.co.uk
Office: Emsworth, Fareham, Petersfield, Portsmouth

YVONNE MCGARRY SOLICITOR ‡
24 High Street Petersfield Hampshire GU32 3JL
Tel: 01730 265118

PETWORTH, West Sussex

ANDERSON LONGMORE & HIGHAM ‡
Wisteria House Market Square Petworth West Sussex GU28 0AJ
Tel: 01798 342391 *Fax:* 01798 343825 *Dx:* 49252 PETWORTH
E-mail: petw@alhlaw.co.uk
List of partners: A W Brooke, E W G Cooke, J C Dickerson, W J Stisted, C J D Wise
Office: Billingshurst, Chichester, Storrington
Work: A1 A3 C1 C2 C3 D1 E F1 J1 J2 K1 K2 K3 K4 L M2 N O P Q R1 S1 S2 T1 T2 W Z(d,k,l,p,q)
Ptr: Brooke, Mr Andrew W BA. . . . . *§Oct 1979
Dickerson, Mr John C. . . . . NSP
Ast: Armstrong, Mrs Holly LLB; BA(European Law & Languages) . . . . *Feb 2004
Lee, Mr Julian Mark LLB . . . . *Mar 2002
West, Mr Simon John LLB(Hons)(Hull) . . . . *Jan 2010
Con: Chadwell, Mr Stuart L. . . . . *§Jul 1971
Higham, Mr Anthony P . . . . *Jul 1965

WILLIAMS WOOLLEY ‡
Golden Square Petworth West Sussex GU28 0AP
Tel: 01798 342581 *Fax:* 01798 344022 *Dx:* 49251 PETWORTH
E-mail: solicitors@willamswoolley.co.uk
List of partners: P J Gardner, S J H Thorpe
Office: Haslemere (2 offices)
Work: A1 C1 E F1 L S1 W Z(d,l)
Ptr: Thorpe, Mr Steven John Howett BA(Hons) . . . . . *Dec 1998

PEVENSEY BAY, East Sussex

BARRY & CO ‡
Bay Terrace Pevensey Bay East Sussex BN24 6EE
Tel: 01323 766370 / 768382
List of partners: J Barry
Work: N S1 S2 W
Fixed Fee Interview undertaken
Ptr: Barry, Mr Jonathan . . . . *Jun 1979

PEWSEY, Wiltshire

MERRIMAN WAINE & CO
10 Market Place Pewsey Wiltshire SN9 5AD
Tel: 01672 563666 *Fax:* 01672 563898 *Dx:* 118752 PEWSEY
E-mail: mail@merrimanwaine.co.uk
Office: Tetbury
Work: A1 E K1 K3 L S1 S2 T2 W
SPr: Hodge, Mr Michael J BA(Oxon) . . . . *§Dec 1973
Con: Waine, Mr Peter Graham . . . . *§Jun 1972

PICKERING, North Yorkshire

ELLIS LAKIN & CO ‡
8 Hallgarth Pickering North Yorkshire YO18 7AP
Tel: 01751 472121 *Fax:* 01751 475132 *Dx:* 63720 PICKERING
E-mail: info@ellis-lakin.co.uk
List of partners: J M Ellis, D C FitzGerald
Work: A1 D1 E F1 F2 G H J1 K1 K2 K4 L N P Q R1 S1 S2 T2 V W Z(l)
Emergency Action, Agency, Advocacy, Fixed Fee Interview, Legal Aid undertaken and Legal Aid Franchise
Ptr: Ellis, Mr John M TEP . . . . *§Jan 1970
FitzGerald, Mr David C BSc. . . . . *§Nov 1977
Ast: Turner, Ms Lisa M LLB . . . . *§Oct 1991

HAGUE & DIXON
12 Smiddy Hill Pickering North Yorkshire YO18 7AN
Est: 1901
Tel: 01751 475222 *Fax:* 01751 474101 *Dx:* 63724 PICKERING
Emergency telephone 01751 472104
E-mail: adrian.morris@hague-dixon.co.uk
Office: York (2 offices)
Work: A1 E J1 K1 K3 L S1 S2 W Z(l)
Agency and Fixed Fee Interview undertaken
Ptr: Morris, Mr Adrian Charles BSc; LLM . . . . *Aug 2001
Asoc: Chappell, Mrs Mary Therese MBA. . . . . *Jan 1999

PINNER, Middlesex

ARTHUR & CO ‡
435 Rayners Lane Pinner Middlesex HA5 5ET
Tel: 020 8866 8282 *Fax:* 020 8429 2550 *Dx:* 48000 RAYNERS LANE
List of partners: A J Lemer, B D Sharma, C Withers
Languages: Hindi, Punjabi
Work: D1 E K1 K3 K4 L O Q S1 S2 W
Agency, Advocacy, Fixed Fee Interview and Legal Aid undertaken
Ptr: Lemer, Mr Alfred J LLB . . . . *Dec 1975
Sharma, Mr Braham D LLB . . . . *Mar 1985
Withers, Mr Christopher LLB . . . . *Nov 1978

AUSTIN EDWARDS SOLICITORS ‡
8 Lyndhurst Avenue Pinner Middlesex HA5 3XA
Tel: 020 8429 0741 *Fax:* 020 8429 0768
E-mail: fred.lamb@austinedwards.co.uk

BARNES & PARTNERS
38 Bridge Street Pinner Middlesex HA5 3JF
Tel: 020 8866 5566 *Fax:* 020 8866 7070 *Dx:* 35618 PINNER
E-mail: people@barnesandpartners.com
Office: Cheshunt, Enfield, Harlow, London E4, London N15, London N16, London N18, London N8, Ware
Work: C1 D1 E F1 J1 K1 L N O Q R1 S1 T1 T2 V W Z(f,h)

BEAUMONDE LAW PRACTICE ‡
Evans House 107 Marsh Road Pinner Middlesex HA5 5PA
Tel: 020 8868 1614 *Fax:* 020 8429 1940
Emergency telephone 07803 727 534
Languages: Hindi
Work: B2 G H I J1 K1 K2 Q Z(i,l,p)
Agency and Advocacy undertaken

BOTTRILL & CO ‡
10-12 Love Lane Pinner Middlesex HA5 3EF
Tel: 020 8429 1010 *Fax:* 020 8429 8444
E-mail: info@bottrill-familylaw.co.uk
List of partners: M D Bottrill
Work: D1 D2 K1 K3 Q
Emergency Action and Advocacy undertaken
SPr: Bottrill, Mr Michael D LLB . . . . *Jun 1975
Ast: Dhanota-Jones, Mrs Teena BA(Hons) . . . . Feb 1999

BULFIN & CO EMPLOYMENT LAW SOLICITORS ‡
203 Field End Road Eastcote Pinner Middlesex HA5 1QZ
Tel: 020 8866 0044 *Fax:* 020 8866 0244
Emergency telephone 020 8866 0044
E-mail: emplaw@bulfin.co.uk
List of partners: K J Bulfin
Work: J1 J2 Z(p)
Agency, Advocacy and Fixed Fee Interview undertaken
SPr: Bulfin, Mrs Karen J LLB. . . . . *May 1985

ROBERT CALLEN SOLICITORS ‡
Wakefield House 32 High Street Pinner Middlesex HA5 5PW
Tel: 020 8966 9777 *Fax:* 020 8866 8962
E-mail: robertcallen@btinternet.com

CHANDS & CO ‡
145 Cannonbury Avenue Pinner Middlesex HA5 1TR
Tel: 020 8933 8332 *Fax:* 020 8621 3809
E-mail: hinimme@aol.com
List of partners: N M Chandrasena
Work: E K1 S1 S2 Z(i)
SPr: Chandrasena, Mrs Nirmala M . . . . Mar 1983

E M COLLINS & CO ‡
Pinn House 2 High Street Pinner Middlesex HA5 5PW
Est: 1985
Tel: 020 8866 1820 *Fax:* 020 8429 4420 *Dx:* 35605 PINNER
E-mail: postbox@emcollins.co.uk
List of partners: A M Collins, E M Collins
Work: D2 K1 K3 K4 W
Emergency Action, Agency, Advocacy and Fixed Fee Interview undertaken
Ptr: Collins, Ms Aisling Mary BA; LLM . . . . *Sep 1972
Collins, Mrs Eline Mary BSocSc; HDipEd . . . . . . *Feb 1984

TANIA CORBETT ‡
Little Mead Cuckoo Hill Pinner Middlesex HA5 2BB
Tel: 020 8868 6100 *Fax:* 020 8429 0983
E-mail: tania.corbett@btinternet.com
List of partners: T E Corbett
Work: C1 E S1 S2 W
SPr: Corbett, Ms Tania E LLB . . . . *Dec 1984

KEITH FLOWER & CO ‡
62 Pinner Green Pinner Middlesex HA5 2AB
Tel: 020 8868 1277 *Fax:* 020 8868 1356 *Dx:* 35610 PINNER
E-mail: info@keithflower.com
List of partners: M V Derry, K D Flower
Work: D1 E K1 K3 L O Q S1 S2 W
Fixed Fee Interview and Legal Aid undertaken
Ptr: Derry, Mrs Mary Veronica LLB. . . . . *Dec 2003
Flower, Mr Keith D . . . . *Jul 1969
Ast: Chapman, Mr Paul . . . . Jan 2009

GARSON & CO ‡
Monument House 215 Marsh Road Pinner Middlesex HA5 5NE
Tel: 020 8429 4111 *Fax:* 020 8429 4333 *Dx:* 35611 PINNER
E-mail: greatlawyers@garson.co.uk
List of partners: J M Garson
Work: B1 E F1 J1 L O Q S1 W Z(c,l)
Agency and Advocacy undertaken
Ptr: Garson, Mr Jeremy M LLB . . . . *Aug 1985

GOLDENS ‡
343 Rayners Lane Pinner Middlesex HA5 5EN
Tel: 020 8429 8282 *Fax:* 020 8429 8261 *Dx:* 48006 RAYNERS LANE
E-mail: enquiries@goldens-solicitors.co.uk
List of partners: C M Golden
Work: N
Ptr: Golden, Mrs Caroline M BSc(Hons); CPE . . . . . . *Jan 1989
Ast: Hendron, Mr Geoffrey Paul LLb . . . . Dec 1996

HANNEY DAWKINS & JONES ‡
21 Bridge Street Pinner Middlesex HA5 3HX
Tel: 020 8866 2144 *Fax:* 020 8866 5070 *Dx:* 35600 PINNER
E-mail: reception@hdj-law.co.uk
List of partners: I H Archer, B K Davies, A J Fothergill, K E Roney
Work: A1 C1 C2 D1 E F1 G J1 K1 L N O P Q R1 S1 S2 T1 T2 W Z(c,l)
Agency, Fixed Fee Interview and Legal Aid undertaken
Ptr: Archer, Mr Ian H LLB . . . . *Jun 1978
Davies, Mr Brian K . . . . *Jun 1980
Fothergill, Mr Adrian J LLB(Lond) . . . . *Oct 1975
Roney, Mrs Karen E. . . . . *Nov 1982

See p112 for the Key to Work Categories & other symbols

JSK LAW ‡
201 Moss Lane Pinner Middlesex HA5 3BE
Tel: 020 8426 1750 *Fax:* 020 8426 1653

KAYE & CO ‡
6 Felden Close Hatch End Pinner Middlesex HA5 4PU
Tel: 020 8428 0010 *Fax:* 020 8428 0010
List of partners: L De Vere, T M Kaye
Office: St Albans
Work: S1
Ptr: Kaye, Mrs Theresa M . . . . Jan 1982

LEWIS GOLDSMITH SOLICITORS ‡
22 Chapel Lane Pinner Middlesex HA5 1AS
Tel: 020 8866 5989

A E MIZLER & CO SOLICITORS ‡
PO Box 270 Pinner Middlesex HA5 4WX
Tel: 020 8420 1175 *Fax:* 020 8420 1017
E-mail: aem@aemizler.com
List of partners: A E Mizler
Work: C1 J1 O Q Z(p)
SPr: Mizler, Mr Anthony E BA(Hons)(Kent)(Law) . . . . *Jan 1985

M J MURPHY ‡
Alma Cott The Chase Pinner Middlesex HA5 5QP
Tel: 020 8866 8929
List of partners: M J Murphy
Work: S1 W
Ptr: Murphy, Mr Michael J . . . . *Jan 1970

K RAVI SOLICITORS ‡
First Floor Suite 2 410-420 Rayners Lane Pinner Middlesex HA5 5DY
Tel: 020 8866 7800 *Fax:* 020 8866 4210 *Dx:* 48004 RAYNERS LANE

SINGLETONS ‡
The Ridge South View Road Pinner Middlesex HA5 3YD
Tel: 020 8866 1934 *Fax:* 020 8866 6912
E-mail: susan@singlelaw.com
List of partners: E S Singleton
Work: C1 C3 F1 I M1 O Z(e,f)
SPr: Singleton, Mrs E Susan LLB(Manc) Lydia Kemp Entrance Scholarship; R G Lawson Scholarship; R G Lawson Prize for Tax & Trade Competition . . . . . . *Oct 1985

WICK & CO SOLICITORS ‡
447 Rayners Lane Pinner Middlesex HA5 5ET
Tel: 020 8429 2950

PLYMOUTH

ACT FAMILY LAW ‡
8 The Crescent Plymouth PL1 3AB
Tel: 01752 226224 *Fax:* 01752 226213
E-mail: mail@actfamilylaw.co.uk
List of partners: I Downing
Work: K1 K3
Advocacy undertaken
Ptr: Downing, Mr Ian LLB(Hons) . . . . *Oct 1984
Ast: Wilson, Miss Rebecca Lindsay LLB(Hons) . . . . Jan 2000

ASHFORDS LLP
Princess Court 23 Princess Street Plymouth PL1 2EX
Tel: 01752 521500 *Fax:* 01752 526001 *Dx:* 8273 PLYMOUTH 2
E-mail: info@ashfords.com
Office: Bristol, Exeter, London W1, Taunton, Tiverton
Languages: French
Work: B1 C1 C2 E F1 J1 N O R2 X Z(d,e,o,r,u)
Agency, Advocacy and Fixed Fee Interview undertaken
Ptr: Beadel, Mr David P S LLB . . . . *Jul 1974
Gregson, Mr Christopher J MA(Cantab) . . . . *Mar 1984
Hattersley, Mr Charles William . . . . . . Feb 1988
Heard, Mr David J S LLB . . . . *Feb 1990
Lewis, Miss Rhiain Mary LLB(Hons) . . . . . *Oct 1990
Wilkinson, Mr George T N MA(Oxon) . . . . . *Apr 1979

BARTONS
10b The Crescent Plymouth PL1 3AB
Tel: 01752 675740 *Fax:* 01752 256852 *Dx:* 8255 PLYMOUTH 2
E-mail: plymouth@bartons-law.co.uk
Office: Bristol, Kingsbridge, Salcombe, Totnes
Ptr: Hassall, Mr Lee Maurice . . . . Nov 1991

BEERS LLP
2 Ensign House Parkway Court Longbridge Road Plymouth PL6 8LR
Tel: 01752 246000 *Fax:* 01752 246001 *Dx:* 98922 PLYMPTON
E-mail: info@beersllp.com
Office: Kingsbridge
Languages: Punjabi, Urdu
Work: J1 N Q S1 S2 W
Ptr: Asharaf, Musharaf Javid LLB . . . . . . *Oct 1994
Ast: Jones, Mr Richard LLB . . . . Aug 1996
Mitchell, Mrs Caroline Eva BSc(Life Sciences) . . . . Sep 1996

BOND PEARCE LLP ‡
Ballard House West Hoe Road Plymouth PL1 3AE
Tel: 0845 415 0000 *Fax:* 0845 415 7900 *Dx:* 8251 PLYMOUTH
E-mail: info@bondpearce.com
List of partners: W Ackerman, A J Askham, M Barley, N H Barwood, T M Beezer, S Briggs, L M Brocklebank, T Burbidge, R Challands, J E Chester, J E M Clarke, J Cooper, R J Davies, T L Davies, N Duncan, I H Dunn, N H Evans, L H Gabb, R D Guyatt, J S Hales, J C K Hamblin, C M Hanley, S P Hewes, I Holden, J E R Houghton, N Huddert, S J L Hughes, G D Jeffries, G Jones, M Jones, C G Kagan, A Kimble, C J M Kinsey, C A Leatt, S M Lister, A N MacKean, J D R Mallender, I A Martyn, G R Matthews, A Maxwell, P A McGoldrick, C Moore, K J Morrish, F T O'Kane, G Oldroyd, N J Page, E J Parry, N J Peacey, I D Peacock, S Pierce, J Rees, S Richardson, B A Rigg, A Robbins, J A Robins, C R Robson, H A Ross, J Rumley, D J Skelton, P J Stockley, P A Stone, N A Stuart, V S D Tettmar, N A Theyer, C E Tolvas-Vincent, N M Trayhurn, J Wall, A Walton, P Wetherall, M J Williams, T Woodward
Office: Bristol, London EC3, Southampton
Work: A1 A3 B1 C1 C2 C3 E F1 F2 I J1 J2 L M3 N O P Q R1 R2 S1 S2 T1 T2 U1 U2 W X Z(b,c,d,j,l,o,p,q,r,u,za)
Legal Aid Franchise
Ptr: Challands, Mr Richard LLB IBA . . . . . . *Apr 1975
Clarke, Ms Juliette E M . . . . May 1990
Cooper, Mr Jon . . . . Nov 1984
Duncan, Mrs Nikki LLB . . . . Oct 1979
Gabb, Mr Luke H . . . . *§May 1980
Hanley, Ms Christine M LLB(Bris) . . . . . . *Nov 1989
Huddert, Mr Nicholas . . . . Dec 1993
Kagan, Mr Christopher G . . . . Nov 1993
Leatt, Ms Charmian A BSocSc . . . . . . *§Nov 1985
Moore, Mr Craig LLB(Hull); LSF(York) . . . . . *Nov 1995
Rigg, Ms Bettina A LLB(Exon) . . . . *§Oct 1982
Skelton, Mr David J LLB(L'pool) . . . . . . *Sep 1992
Stuart, Mr Neil A BA(Oxon) . . . . *Nov 1980
Williams, Mr Michael J BA(Oxon); BCL . . . . . *§Oct 1975

BRIGHT (SOUTH WEST) LLP ‡
1st Floor Studio 5-11 5 Millbay Road Plymouth PL1 3LF
Tel: 01752 388884
E-mail: andy.price@brightllp.co.uk

C&C FAMILY LAW ‡
6 The Crescent Plymouth PL1 3AB
Tel: 01752 222211 *Fax:* 01752 227557
E-mail: info@candcfamilylaw.co.uk
List of partners: C I Charlton, S Cook
Work: K1 K3
Agency undertaken
Dir: Charlton, Ms Celia Irene LLB . . . . *Oct 1994
Cook, Ms Samantha LLB . . . . *Sep 2000

ANTHONY C CARTER ‡
38 Mannamead Road Plymouth PL4 7AF
Tel: 01752 255000 *Fax:* 01752 254044 *Dx:* 120172 MUTLEY PLAIN
List of partners: A C Carter
Work: E G H K1 L N O Q S1 W Z(l)
Emergency Action, Agency, Advocacy, Fixed Fee Interview and Legal Aid undertaken
SPr: Carter, Mr Anthony C LLB . . . . *Jun 1978

CLARK & WEEKS ‡
85-89 Ridgeway Plympton Plymouth PL7 2AA
Tel: 01752 345311 *Fax:* 01752 342360 *Dx:* 98904 PLYMPTON
E-mail: info@clarkandweeks.co.uk
List of partners: A M Clark, M J Weeks
Office: Ivybridge
Work: K1 K3 L S1 W
Legal Aid undertaken
Ptr: Clark, Mr Anthony M BEd . . . . *§Oct 1981
Weeks, Mr Martin J LLB . . . . *Oct 1982

CLEARWATER CONVEYANCING LIMITED ‡
26 Lockyer Street Plymouth PL1 2QW
Tel: 0870 700 0230

CHRISTINE COLLIER SOLICITOR ‡
44 Sutherland Road Plymouth PL4 6BN
Tel: 01752 666972 *Fax:* 01752 666913
E-mail: christinecollier@btconnect.com

MICHAEL CRUMLEY SOLICITOR ‡
The Business Centre 2 Cattedown Road Plymouth PL4 0EG
Tel: 01752 264474 *Fax:* 01752 264499
E-mail: admin@crumleylaw.co.uk

CURTIS ‡
87 & 89 Mutley Plain Mutley Plymouth PL4 6JJ
Tel: 01752 204444 *Fax:* 01752 600582 *Dx:* 120150 MUTLEY
E-mail: enquiries@curtissolicitors.co.uk
List of partners: S D Coles, R J Miller, E A Smith
Work: A1 A3 B1 C1 C2 C3 D1 D2 E F1 F2 I J1 J2 K1 L N O Q R1 S1 S2 T1 U2 W Z(b,c,d,e,g,h,i,l,p,q)
Emergency Action, Agency and Fixed Fee Interview undertaken
Ptr: Coles, Mr Steven D MA(Hons) . . . . Feb 1984
Miller, Mr Roger J . . . . *Dec 1986
Smith, Mrs Elizabeth Anne LLB . . . . . . *Sep 1995
Ast: Becker, Mr Matthew S . . . . Jan 2000
Con: Coish, Mr Stephen F . . . . *Jan 1983

DAVIES JOHNSON & CO (SHIPPING & COMMERCIAL SOLICITORS) ‡
The Old Harbour Office Guy's Quay Sutton Harbour Plymouth PL4 0ES
Tel: 01752 226020 *Fax:* 01752 225882 *Dx:* 8254 PLYMOUTH 2
Emergency telephone 01752 226020
E-mail: admin@djco.co.uk
List of partners: A N Fox, J M M Johnson, D J Ward
Languages: French, German, Norwegian, Russian
Work: A3 C1 N O Q Z(a,j,q)
Emergency Action, Agency and Fixed Fee Interview undertaken
Ptr: Fox, Mr Andrew Neil LLB(Hons) . . . . . . *Dec 1994
Johnson, Mr Jonathan M M LLB . . . . . . *Jul 1976
Ward, Mrs Diana Jane LLB . . . . *Apr 1977
Asoc: Kliarkina, Ms Nadia LLB . . . . *Sep 2003
Patterson, Mr Charles BSc; PGDipLaw . . . . . *Nov 2003
Ast: Clamp, Miss Jasmine MA(Oxon) . . . . . . Aug 2007
Gliddon, Miss Jennifer LLB; LPC . . . . . . Oct 2008
Con: McCunn, Mr Robert Alexander LLB . . . . . *Mar 1986

EASTLEYS DEFENCE SERVICE ‡
27 Marlborough Street Devonport Plymouth PL1 4AH
Tel: 01752 500281

EVANS HARVEY LAW ‡
34 & 39 Morshead Road Crownhill Plymouth PL6 5AH
Tel: 01752 785715 *Fax:* 01752 793355 / 786767

FOOT ANSTEY ‡
Salt Quay House 4 North East Quay Sutton Harbour Plymouth PL4 0BN
Tel: 01752 675000 *Fax:* 01752 675500 *Dx:* 118102 PLYMOUTH 2
E-mail: contact@footanstey.com
List of partners: R Bagwell, K M Biggs, M Bonner, J R Brimble, R H Brown, P J Carpanini, M H Chanter, T J Claridge, R G Coombs, N D Coveney, A Dunningham, J Evans, M Gay, S H Gregory, J P Guard, A J Hannam, A Hargreaves, C W Hattersley, D M Hincks, M S Horwood, P Howarth, A R Jaffa, M R L Lewis, J S A Lister, J M Loney, N H Lyons, A M McNicol, A W M Miller, J Pindard, G D Pinwell, V M L Priddis, E A W Probert, H Quantick, C A Rai, M Roberts, Y L Rooke, R J U Sands, N E Scott, C F Smith, G Smith, N J Sutcliffe, R P Sutton, D Sykes, C G Thorne, D Turner, J P Westwell, M V Whitehead, L Widley
Office: Exeter, Taunton, Truro
Languages: French, German
Work: A1 A3 B1 B2 C1 C2 C3 D1 D2 E F1 F2 G H I J1 J2 K1 K2 L M1 N O P Q R1 R2 S1 S2 T1 T2 U1 U2 V W X Z(a,b,c,d,e,f,g,h,j,k,l,n,o,p,q,s,t,u,w,y,z)
Emergency Action, Agency, Advocacy, Fixed Fee Interview, Legal Aid undertaken, Legal Aid Franchise and Member of Accident Line
Ptr: Bonner, Ms Margaret BA . . . . *§Mar 1985
Brown, Mr Robin H MA(Oxon) . . . . *Dec 1990
Carpanini, Mr Philip J LLB; LLM . . . . . . *Dec 1980
Coombs, Mr Richard G MA(Cantab) Harrison Exhibition . . . . *§Jun 1979
Coveney, Mr Nigel D BA(Hons) Notary Public . . . . §Oct 1988
Hattersley, Mr Charles William . . . . . . Feb 1988
Horwood, Mr Michael S . . . . *§Oct 1986
Howarth, Mr Patrick . . . . Oct 1996
Lewis, Mr Mark R L BA(Oxon) . . . . *Nov 1978
Lister, Mrs Jane S A Notary Public . . . . . . *§Nov 1976
Loney, Mr Jonathan M LLB . . . . *§Nov 1984
Lyons, Mr Nigel H . . . . *Feb 1990
Pindard, Mr John . . . . Apr 2008
Rai, Mrs Cindy A LLB . . . . *§May 1981
Rooke, Ms Yvette Louise MA(Hons)(English Lit); CPE; LPC . . . . Sep 1997
Sands, Mr Roger J U MA(Oxon) . . . . Oct 1986
Sutton, Mr Richard Paul BA . . . . *Oct 1987
Westwell, Mr John P LLB . . . . *Nov 1987
Widley, Miss Louise . . . . Sep 1999
Asoc: Axten, Ashley R BA(Law); MA . . . . . . *Jun 1988
Ast: Arnold, Ms Emma Jane LLB(Hons) . . . . . . *May 1996
Bligh, Ms Vicky J LLB . . . . *Oct 1988
Bonning, Mr Michael LLB(Hons) . . . . . . Sep 1999
Bull, Ms Helen . . . . *Oct 2000
Eddleston-Haynes, Mr Gary C . . . . *Sep 1995
Farmaner, Mr Kelvin Ian LLB(Hons) . . . . . . Oct 2000
Fowell, Mr Eoin Maurice . . . . Nov 2000
Gedge, Mrs Anne Elisabeth Schofield LLB . . . . Nov 1993
Goodman, Ms Joanna . . . . *Apr 1999
Grassam, Mr Peter Mark BA(Hons) . . . . . . Oct 1998
Meadows, Ms Fiona H BA . . . . *Oct 1984
Trahair, Mr Julian E R BSc(Wales) . . . . . . *Sep 1980
Turner, Ms Melanie . . . . *Oct 2000
Con: Dennerly, Mr Robert E BA Notary Public . . . . *§Jun 1973
Parsons, Mr James Ernest LLB(Hons) . . . . . Feb 1972
Welton, Mr Brian Notary Public . . . . . . *§Dec 1975

FURSDON KNAPPER ‡
308 St Levin Road Plymouth PL2 1JA
Tel: 01752 309090 *Fax:* 01752 309092 *Dx:* 120029 PLYMOUTH 12
E-mail: info@fklaw.co.uk
List of partners: K Fursdon, A Knapper, C Knapper
Office: Cambridge
Ptr: Fursdon, Ms Kate . . . . Sep 1997
Knapper, Ms Amanda . . . . Apr 1998
Knapper, Mr Charles . . . . Apr 1997
Ast: Gallagher, Mrs Margaret LLB . . . . . . Jun 2008

GARD & CO ‡
4 Bretonside Plymouth PL4 0BY
Tel: 01752 668246 *Fax:* 01752 222378 *Dx:* 8253 PLYMOUTH 2
E-mail: enquiries@gardandco.com
List of partners: T F Foss, S J Hudson, I G Taylor
Languages: Afrikaans, French
Work: A1 C1 C2 C3 D1 E K1 K3 K4 L N O Q R1 S1 S2 T2 V W Z(c,d,e,m,s)
Emergency Action, Agency, Advocacy, Fixed Fee Interview, Legal Aid undertaken and Member of Accident Line
Ptr: Foss, Mr Tony F . . . . *§Jun 1980
Hudson, Mr Steven J BSc . . . . *§Mar 1983
Taylor, Mr Ian G LLB(Wales) . . . . *Feb 1986
Asoc: Dusting, Mr Simon LLB(Hons) . . . . . . *Jul 2003
Gilding, Mrs Jane M LLB . . . . *Feb 1984
Longville, Mr Anthony Charles BA(Hons) . . . . Dec 1988
Shoheth, Ms Rachel Elizabeth BA(Hons) . . . . *Sep 1996
Whitaker, Mr Gary Gray LLB(Hons) . . . . . *Dec 2002
Ast: Shears, Miss Anne LLB; LPC . . . . . . *Sep 2007
Con: Prout, Mr Michael J . . . . *§Dec 1973

GILL AKASTER ‡
Gill Akaster House 25 Lockyer Street Plymouth PL1 2QW
Tel: 01752 203500 *Fax:* 01752 203503 *Dx:* 8284 PLYMOUTH 2
E-mail: enquiries@gillakaster.com
List of partners: S Allen, A J Cusack, M Grove, J J F Hall, R G Howard, P B Johnson, M J P Leech, S P Leigh, R H G Michelmore, P J Oke, S M Ramsden, M K Sheather, D M Stone, D Wallis
Languages: French
Work: A3 B1 C1 C2 D1 D2 E F1 F2 J1 K1 K2 K3 K4 L N O P Q R1 S1 S2 T2 W Z(c,l,r)
Legal Aid undertaken and Legal Aid Franchise
Ptr: Allen, Mr Stephen LLB(Nott'm) Hatchard Law Prize 1984 . . . . *Oct 1986
Cusack, Mr Anthony John . . . . Feb 2001
Grove, Ms Michelle . . . . *Sep 1997
Hall, Mr Jonathan James Foster LLB . . . . . *§Oct 1993
Howard, Mr Robert G LLB . . . . *Apr 1981
Johnson, Mr Paul B LLB . . . . Dec 1975
Leech, Mr Martin J P MA(Oxon) . . . . . . *§Oct 1987
Leigh, Mr Steven P MA(Oxon) . . . . *Mar 1979
Michelmore, Mr Richard H G . . . . *§Jul 1977
Oke, Mr Philip John LLB . . . . Oct 1992
Ramsden, Mr Stephen M LLB . . . . *May 1990
Sheather, Mr Matthew Keith . . . . Jan 2001
Stone, Mr David Matthew LLB . . . . Nov 1992
Wallis, Mr David LLB . . . . *Aug 2001
Ast: Bault, Mr Peter James . . . . Feb 1991
Brisley, Mrs Rebecca Ann . . . . Apr 2007
Clarke, Mr John Richard . . . . Apr 2007
Dodd, Jackie . . . . Apr 2008
Hall, Miss Lucy LLB . . . . Apr 2006
Peterson, Mr James . . . . Sep 2009
Yandle, Miss Isobel Louise Hanson BA(Hons)(Oxon); DipLaw . . . . *Oct 1997
Con: Pillar, Mr Malcolm G MA(Cantab) . . . . . . *§Dec 1975

GLANVILLE ROBINSON ‡
3rd Floor 3 The Crescent Plymouth PL1 3AB
Tel: 01752 500281 / 07530 625206 *Fax:* 01752 710567
E-mail: info@glanvillerobinson.co.uk

GOLDBERGS ‡
7 Ford Park Road Mutley Plymouth PL4 6QZ
Tel: 01752 660023 *Fax:* 01752 220032
Emergency telephone 01752 660023
E-mail: rlt@goldbergs-solicitors.co.uk
List of partners: R L Toms
Work: B1 C1 D1 F1 F2 J1 K1 K3 L N O Q W Z(c,k,q)
Emergency Action, Agency, Advocacy, Fixed Fee Interview, Legal Aid undertaken, Legal Aid Franchise and Member of Accident Line

Ptr: Toms, Mr Raymond L LLB. . . . *§Jun 1973
Ast: Hutchings, Mrs Janet M LLB . . . *Nov 1993
Quinn, Mr Timothy BA. . . . *Jun 1990
Smith, Mr Rory L MA(Oxon). . . . *Sep 1998

ALAN HARRIS ‡
1 St Andrew Street Plymouth PL1 2AH
Tel: 01752 223655 *Fax:* 01752 601081 *Dx:* 8236 PLYMOUTH
E-mail: office@alanharris-solicitors.co.uk
List of partners: A Harris, A Hill, K L B Papenfus
Work: G H Z(l)
Emergency Action, Agency, Advocacy, Fixed Fee Interview, Legal Aid undertaken and Legal Aid Franchise
Ptr: Harris, Mr Alan LLB. . . . *§Dec 1978
Hill, Mr Adrian. . . . *Sep 1995
Papenfus, Mr Kenneth Louis Bolitho LLB(Hons). . . . Jan 1997

HOWARD & OVER ‡
114 Albert Road Devonport Plymouth PL2 1AF
Tel: 01752 556606 *Fax:* 01752 607101 *Dx:* 120027 PLYMOUTH 12
List of partners: S M Dyer, C P Mossop
Office: Ivybridge, Plymouth
Work: C1 D1 F1 G H J1 K1 K4 L N Q R1 S1 T1 T2 W Z(m)
Emergency Action, Agency, Advocacy, Fixed Fee Interview, Legal Aid undertaken and Legal Aid Franchise
Ptr: Dyer, Ms Stella Marie LLB. . . . *Dec 1980
Ast: Randall, Mr Stephen . . . Apr 1998

HOWARD & OVER
254 Dean Cross Road Plymstock Plymouth PL9 7AZ
Tel: 01752 405774 *Fax:* 01752 482721
Office: Ivybridge, Plymouth
Work: K1 S1 S2 W
Ast: Brady, Mr Kevin BA(Hons) . . . *Oct 1989

ROBERT HOWARD ‡
1-3 Lifton Road Plymouth PL4 0NT
Tel: 01752 251851 *Fax:* 01752 254070
List of partners: R G Howard
Work: N O Q Z(r)
Agency and Advocacy undertaken
SPr: Howard, Mr Robert George . . . *§Dec 1970

JULIAN JEFFERSON ‡
St Andrew Street Solicitors' Chambers 2 St Andrew Street Plymouth PL1 2AH
Tel: 01752 250850 *Fax:* 01752 250770
Emergency telephone 01752 250850
List of partners: J M Jefferson
Languages: French
Work: G H
Emergency Action, Agency, Advocacy, Legal Aid undertaken and Legal Aid Franchise
Ptr: Jefferson, Mr Julian M MA(Cantab) ★. . . . *Jul 1975

M P JONES & CO ‡
97 Mutley Plain Plymouth PL4 6JJ
Tel: 01752 269007
List of partners: M Jones, K Zakharova
Languages: French, Polish, Russian
Ptr: Jones, Mr Michael. . . . Mar 1993
Zakharova, Ms Katrina . . . Jan 2008
Ast: Healy, Ms Dawn. . . . Jan 1995

CHRIS KALLIS SOLICITORS ‡
33 North Road East Plymouth PL4 6AY
Tel: 01752 225060

KITSONS LLP
55-57 Bretonside Plymouth PL4 5BD
Tel: 01752 603040 *Fax:* 01752 601090
E-mail: advice@kitsons-solicitors.co.uk
Office: Exeter, Newton Abbot, Torquay
Work: B1 C1 C2 C3 D1 D2 E F1 G H J1 K1 K2 K3 L M1 N O P Q R1 S1 S2 T2 V W Z(b,c,d,e,f,g,h,i,j,k,l,m,o,s,t)
Emergency Action, Agency, Advocacy, Fixed Fee Interview, Legal Aid undertaken and Legal Aid Franchise
Ptr: Lang, Mr James. . . . Jan 1981
Asoc: Willden, Mr Will . . . Mar 2005
Ast: Healy, Mrs Dawn Carol LLB(Hons) . . . Sep 1993
Maddocks, Mr Norman W LLB(Hons) . . . *Dec 1990
Newton, Mrs Kathryn . . . Jul 1992

OWEN LAWTON ‡
County House 12/13 Sussex Street Plymouth PL1 2HR
Tel: 01752 201169 *Fax:* 01752 301169 *Dx:* 118105 PLYMOUTH 2
Emergency telephone 07768 850355
E-mail: owen@owenlawton.fsbusiness.co.uk
List of partners: K O Lawton
Work: D1 G H K1
Emergency Action, Agency, Advocacy and Legal Aid undertaken
SPr: Lawton, Mr Kenneth Owen BA . . . *Jun 1989

LYONS DAVIDSON
1 Endeavour Street Parkway Court Marsh Mills Plymouth PL6 8LR
Tel: 01752 300530 *Fax:* 01752 214100 *Dx:* 98906 PLYMOUTH
E-mail: info@lyondavidson.co.uk
Office: Bristol, Cardiff, Leeds, New Malden, Solihull

MARSHALLS ‡
6 Drake Circus North Hill Plymouth PL4 8AQ
Tel: 01752 254555 *Fax:* 01752 250181
E-mail: marshallssols@aol.com
List of partners: D E Marshall
Work: K1 N
Agency, Legal Aid undertaken and Legal Aid Franchise
SPr: Marshall, Ms Denyse E BA . . . *Oct 1985

NASH & CO SOLICITORS LLP ‡
Beaumont House Beaumont Park Plymouth PL4 9BD
Tel: 01752 664444 *Fax:* 01752 667112 *Dx:* 8250 PLYMOUTH
E-mail: law@nash.co.uk
List of partners: A R Blackburn, K L Bussell, W M Giles, M R Shiers, G R J Walker, T Wright, J G Wyatt
Work: A1 A3 B1 C1 D1 D2 E F1 F2 I J1 K1 K2 K3 K4 L M3 N O Q R1 R2 S1 S2 T1 T2 W Z(a,c,d,e,j,k,l,p,q,r)
Emergency Action, Agency, Advocacy, Fixed Fee Interview, Legal Aid undertaken and Legal Aid Franchise
Ptr: Blackburn, Mr Austin Robert LLB . . . *Oct 1998
Bussell, Ms Karen Lesley BEd; PGDipLaw Foot & Bowden Best Diploma Student Rep 1998 . . . Jan 2002
Giles, Mr William Morgan LLB(Hons) . . . *§Dec 1994
Shiers, Mr Michael R LLB(Exon) . . . *Oct 1992
Walker, Mr Guy R J LLB(B'ham). . . . *§Nov 1975
Wright, Mrs Tracey LLB . . . Jun 2001
Wyatt, Mr John G LLB(Wales). . . . *Oct 1981
Ast: Cragg, Hilary . . . *Mar 2010
Holness, Miss Bridget E LLB Blackstone Prize-ELS; Highest 2nd Year Grades; Wolferstans Property Prize . . . *Aug 2001
Madge, Mr Jonathan LLB(B'ham)(Law with French) . *Nov 1997
Middleton, Mrs Lesley J BSc . . . *Jun 1978
Shaw, Mrs Laura Alwyn LLB . . . *Sep 2008
Con: Woodward, Mr Jeremy W MA(Cantab) . . . *§Jan 1979

PBW SOLICITORS ‡
12 Athenaeum Street Plymouth PL1 2RH
Tel: 01752 222206 *Fax:* 01752 228887
E-mail: pbw@solicitorsp.fsbusiness.co.uk
List of partners: J C Bradley, M A Plant
Work: B1 C1 E K4 R1 R2 S1 S2 W
Emergency Action and Fixed Fee Interview undertaken
Dir: Bradley, Mr John C . . . Jul 1971
Plant, Mr Michael A BSc . . . *Apr 1983

PARLBY CALDER SOLICITORS ‡
1st Floor 7 Whimple Street Plymouth PL1 2DH
Tel: 01752 600833 *Fax:* 01752 600933
Emergency telephone 07818 455864
E-mail: office@parlbycalder.co.uk
List of partners: P H Calder, G H Parlby
Work: G H
Agency, Advocacy and Legal Aid Franchise
Ptr: Calder, Miss Pamela H BSc(Hons) ★ . . . *Oct 1992
Parlby, Mr Geoffrey H BA ★. . . . *Jun 1981
Ast: Brookman, Mr Paul BSc(Hons); CPE; LPC . . . Oct 1999

T G READMAN ‡
The Copse Dixon Terr Yealmpton Plymouth PL8 2NB
Tel: 01752 880238 *Fax:* 01752 881187
List of partners: T G Readman
Work: E S1 S2
SPr: Readman, Mr Timothy G . . . *§Jul 1967

SITTERS & CO ‡
5 Windsor Villas Lockyer Street Plymouth PL1 2QE
Tel: 01752 220464 *Fax:* 01752 229220 *Dx:* 8258 PLYMOUTH 2
Emergency telephone 01752 220464
E-mail: info@sitters-solicitors.co.uk
List of partners: A J Parish
Work: D1 D2 E K1 K2 K3 K4 L N Q S1 S2 T2 V W Z(k,l,q,r)
Emergency Action, Agency, Advocacy, Fixed Fee Interview, Legal Aid undertaken and Legal Aid Franchise
Dir: Parish, Mr Anthony John . . . *§Dec 1972
Ast: Herns, Ms Hermione J LLB . . . *Jun 1975

JULIE SKITT SOLICITOR ‡
19 Lopwell Close Plymouth PL6 5BP
Tel: 01752 793572

R W STEBBINGS ‡
12-13 Sussex Street Plymouth PL1 2HR
Tel: 01752 202287 *Fax:* 01752 222678
E-mail: pamdale@blueyonder.co.uk
List of partners: R W Stebbings
Work: G H N S1
Agency, Advocacy, Legal Aid undertaken and Legal Aid Franchise
SPr: Stebbings, Mr Robert W LLB . . . Apr 1971

THE STROUD STITSON PARTNERSHIP ‡
North Hill House 119 North Hill Plymouth PL4 8JY
Tel: 01752 660066 *Fax:* 01752 206620
Emergency telephone 01752 660066
E-mail: enquiries@stroudstitson.co.uk
List of partners: R B Stitson, G B Stroud
Work: B1 C1 C2 D1 D2 E F1 J1 K1 K3 L N Q S1 S2 W Z(l,q)
Ptr: Stitson, Mr Robert B Notary Public . . . *§Mar 1979
Stroud, Mr Geoffrey B MA(Cantab) Notary Public . . *§Jun 1972

PAUL TAYLOR SOLICITORS ‡
Tamar House Thornbury Road Estover Plymouth PL6 7PT
Tel: 01392 811728
E-mail: paul@taylorsolicitors.co.uk

DAVID TEAGUE ‡
Plymouth Solicitors Chambers 2 St Andrews Street Plymouth PL1 2AH
Tel: 01752 600950 *Fax:* 01752 250770
Work: B2 G H
Advocacy and Legal Aid Franchise

THOMPSON & JACKSON ‡
(incorporating Dobells, Lipsons & Paul Tilden & Hill)
4 & 5 St Lawrence Road Plymouth PL4 6HR
Tel: 01752 665037 / 221171 *Fax:* 01752 670312
Dx: 8232 PLYMOUTH 1
E-mail: mail@thompsonandjackson.co.uk
List of partners: R H Barker, R Buscombe, J S Hill, N J Keatt, J H Petch, A P Stroud
Work: A1 B1 C1 D1 E F1 F2 J1 K1 K3 K4 L N O Q R1 S1 S2 T1 T2 W Z(d,h,l,q)
Emergency Action, Agency and Advocacy undertaken
Ptr: Barker, Mr Richard Hugh BSc. . . . *Jan 1997
Buscombe, Mr Rex LLB. . . . *§Jun 1976
Hill, Mrs Jillian S . . . *Dec 1987
Keatt, Mr Neil J LLB. . . . *Sep 1993
Petch, Mr Jonathan Heathcote LLB(Hons). . . . *Mar 2003
Stroud, Mr Adrian P LLB(Wales). . . . *Dec 1988
Ast: Fuller, Ms Julie Lily Victoria BSc; DipEngLaw; LPDip *Feb 2000
Gallington, Miss Piri Leigh LLB . . . *Jun 2005
Harman, Mr Stephen . . . Dec 1977
Con: Daniel, Mr W Anthony LLB(Hons) ★ Notary Public. . *Jan 1965

THOMPSONS (FORMERLY ROBIN/BRIAN THOMPSON & PARTNERS)
The New Union House 2 Harbour Avenue Plymouth PL4 0BJ
Tel: 01752 675810 *Fax:* 01752 603825
Office: Belfast, Birmingham, Bristol, Cardiff, Chelmsford, Dagenham, Derby, Harrow, Leeds, Liverpool, London SW19, London WC1, Manchester, Middlesbrough, Newcastle upon Tyne, Nottingham, Sheffield, South Shields, Southampton, Stoke-on-Trent, Swansea, Wolverhampton
Work: S1 W
Ptr: Allen, Mr Stephen P LLB . . . *Oct 1975
Andrews, Mr Patrick LLB; Dip IRTUS ● . . . *Dec 1992
Antoniw, Mr Michael LLB . . . *Oct 1982
Ballard, Mr Philip BA . . . *Jan 1980
Berry, Mr Mark J LLB . . . *Nov 1980
Cavalier, Mr Stephen BA; LSF. . . . *Oct 1986
Christie, Mr Douglas LLB . . . *Oct 1990
Cottingham, Mr Stephen W BA . . . *Oct 1981
Dandridge, Ms Nicola W BA. . . . Oct 1987
Davies, Ms Cathryn E LLB . . . *Oct 1988
Foy, Mr Francis . . . *Jan 1980
Goodman, Mrs Sarah J MA(Oxon) . . . *Jun 1980
Harris, Ms Susan J LLB(Hons) . . . *Oct 1991
Herbert, Mr Andrew F LLB . . . *Nov 1970
Jones, Mr Thomas P R . . . *Nov 1989
King, Mr Philip Norman Edward LLB(Hons) . . . *Feb 1992
Lawton, Mr Anthony C LLB . . . *Nov 1971
McIntyre Ross, Ms Katherine . . . Dec 1990
Mitchell, Ms Karen Margaret LLB(Lond) . . . *Apr 1982
Mulhern, Mr Peter A BSocSc; LLB . . . *Apr 1993
Nickson, Mr Jeremy H. . . . *§Apr 1972
O'Gorman, Ms Francine M LLB . . . *Aug 1981
Owen, Miss Gillian LLB . . . *May 1988
Pattern, Mr Keith . . . Nov 1985
Roberts, Mr Gavin D LLB . . . *Nov 1989
Ross, Ms Katherine M BA ♦. . . . *Dec 1990
Saunders, Mr Nigel BA(Hons). . . . *Nov 1989
Shears, Mr Geoffrey D LLB(Lond); MA(Warw). . . . *Jan 1975
Smith, Mr Phillip A BA. . . . *Nov 1988
Thompson, Mr David A BA . . . *Dec 1983
Tollitt, Mr Matthew J S LLB . . . Oct 1986
Toms, Mr Raymond L LLB. . . . *§Jun 1973
Wood, Miss Julie LLB. . . . *Sep 1987
Wood, Mr Robert A BA . . . *Jan 1989
Woolley, Mr Richard D LLB . . . *Oct 1986
Ast: Chapman, Miss Clare LLB(Hons) . . . *Sep 2000

THORNLEYS LIMITED ‡
247 Dean Cross Road Plymstock Plymouth PL9 7AZ
Tel: 01752 406977 *Fax:* 01752 493440 *Dx:* 140011 PLYMSTOCK
E-mail: thornleys@thornleys.com
List of partners: L Ainsworth, C M Horsey, T Pearce, M R Sherwood, S J Stevenson, P Thornley
Languages: French, German, Japanese, Spanish
Work: A1 B1 C1 D1 E F1 J1 K1 L M2 O Q S1 S2 V W Z(a,b,q)
Emergency Action, Agency, Advocacy, Fixed Fee Interview, Legal Aid undertaken, Legal Aid Franchise and Member of Accident Line
Ptr: Ainsworth, Ms Lynne . . . *Dec 1990
Horsey, Miss Catherine Mary BA(Hons); LSF . . . *Oct 1993
Pearce, Mr Tony. . . . *Dec 1990
Sherwood, Mr Michael R LLB . . . *Dec 1972
Stevenson, Mr Simon John LLB(Hons) . . . *May 1996
Thornley, Mr Peter . . . *Jul 1973
Ast: Meen, Mrs Sally BA. . . . *Nov 1982
Con: Murray-Jones, Mr Richard J. . . . *Dec 1975

TOZERS
9 The Crescent Plymouth PL1 3AB
Tel: 01752 206460 *Fax:* 01752 301662 *Dx:* 118106 PLYMOUTH 2
E-mail: j.shrimpton@tozers.co.uk
Office: Exeter, Newton Abbot, Teignmouth
Work: D1 D2 K1 K2 K3
Agency and Legal Aid undertaken
Ptr: Dodd, Mr Andrew James BA(Hons) . . . Dec 1995
Shrimpton, Ms Julie E W BA(Hons)(Business Law) . *Dec 1982
Asoc: Richardson, Mrs Annemarie Kelly MA(Dunelm) . . . *Sep 2001

TROBRIDGES ‡
1 Ford Park Road Mutley Plain Plymouth PL4 6LY
Tel: 01752 664022 *Fax:* 01752 223761
Emergency telephone 01752 707147
E-mail: mail@trobridgeslaw.co.uk
List of partners: C W G Matthews, T Waine
Office: Torpoint
Languages: German
Work: B1 B2 C1 C2 C3 D1 D2 E F1 G H J1 J2 K1 K2 K3 L M1 M2 N O P Q R1 R2 S1 S2 T1 T2 V W Z(a,j,l,q)
Emergency Action, Agency, Advocacy, Fixed Fee Interview, Legal Aid undertaken, Legal Aid Franchise and Member of Accident Line
Ptr: Matthews, Mr Christopher W G BA . . . *§Jun 1980
Waine, Mr Timothy BA . . . *Apr 1990
Ast: Cussen, Ms Teresa J BA(Hons). . . . *Apr 1988
Palmer, Ms Ingrid E. . . . *Jan 1992
Shamsolahi, Mr Ramin LLB . . . Mar 2009
Usher-Warren, Mrs Elizabeth Caroline Rahuom MSc; LLB(Hons) . . . *Mar 1978
Con: Matthews, Mr Andrew David LLB . . . *Dec 1977
Spatz, Mrs Angela LLB(Cardiff) . . . *Oct 1990

WALKER LAHIVE ‡
92 Devonport Road Plymouth PL3 4DF
Tel: 01752 551722 *Fax:* 01752 605489
Emergency telephone 07711 165252
List of partners: G Kinchin, W A Lahive
Work: G H
Emergency Action, Agency, Advocacy, Fixed Fee Interview, Legal Aid undertaken and Legal Aid Franchise
Ptr: Kinchin, Mr Graham BSc(Hons). . . . *Aug 1998
Lahive, Mr William Anthony BA(Hons)(Law) ★. . . . *Nov 1995
Con: Walker, Mr Stephen John Graham LLB . . . *Dec 1974

KATHLEEN WATKIN ‡
40 Mannamead Road Plymouth PL4 7AF
Tel: 01752 666715 *Fax:* 01752 666799
E-mail: watkin.solicitor@btopenworld.com
Work: E R1 S1 S2 W

WHITEFORD CROCKER ‡
(incorporating Bellingham & Crocker)
Park House 28 Outland Road Milehouse Plymouth PL2 3DE
Tel: 01752 550711 *Fax:* 01752 560029 *Dx:* 120025 PLYMOUTH 12
E-mail: ajc@whitefordcrocker.co.uk
List of partners: M J Clarke, A J Cox, P W Harker, A K Richardson
Office: Ivybridge, Plympton, Saltash
Work: A1 B1 C1 C2 D1 D2 E F1 F2 J2 K1 L N O Q R2 S1 S2 V W Z(c,d,l,p,q,w)
Emergency Action, Agency, Advocacy, Fixed Fee Interview, Legal Aid undertaken, Legal Aid Franchise and Member of Accident Line
Ptr: Clarke, Mr Matthew J BSc. . . . *Nov 1989
Cox, Mr Anthony J LLB . . . *Nov 1973
Harker, Mr Peter W BA . . . *Mar 1981
Richardson, Mrs Annemarie Kelly MA(Dunelm) . . . *Sep 2001
Ast: Burgess, Ms Julia Helen LLB; LLM; MPhil. . . . *Oct 1994

See p112 for the Key to Work Categories & other symbols

WOLFERSTANS ‡
Deptford Chambers 60-66 North Hill Plymouth PL4 8EP
Tel: 01752 663295 *Fax:* 01752 672021 *Dx:* 8206 PLYMOUTH 1
E-mail: info@wolferstans.com
List of partners: B J Bayley, S Buckthought, J T Chapman, N C Crump, W M Duncan, G P Hollinshead, A G Hunt, C C Magill, S W Parford, C A Rai, N J Roper, T J Roper, G Terrell, P M Thorneycroft, J J Walsh, A P Warlow, K H Westmacott, P L Woods, L J Woollams
Office: Plymouth
Languages: French, German, Spanish
Work: B1 B2 C1 D1 E F1 J1 K1 K2 L N O Q S1 S2 T1 V W Z(c,d,h,j,k,l,m,q,r,w)
Emergency Action, Agency, Advocacy, Fixed Fee Interview, Legal Aid undertaken, Legal Aid Franchise and Member of Accident Line
Ptr: Bayley, Mr Barry J BA. . . . . *§Oct 1986
Buckthought, Ms Samantha . . . . . Sep 2001
Chapman, Mr John T LLB. . . . . *Oct 1982
Crump, Mr Neale Clifford BA . . . . . Oct 1993
Duncan, Mr William M LLB . . . . . *Apr 1979
Hollinshead, Mrs Gillian P LLB . . . . . Mar 1972
Hunt, Mr Anthony Graham . . . . . Mar 1996
Magill, Miss Clare C BSc . . . . . *Dec 1991
Parford, Mr Simon W BA . . . . . *Oct 1983
Rai, Mrs Cindy A LLB. . . . . *§May 1981
Roper, Mr Nicholas J LLB(Manc) . . . . . *Oct 1985
Roper, Mr Timothy J LLB . . . . . *Sep 1998
Terrell, Mr Gregory LLB . . . . . *§Jun 1970
Thorneycroft, Mr Philip M LLB(Hull) . . . . . *Oct 1982
Walsh, Mr James J LLB. . . . . Sep 1998
Warlow, Mr Andrew P BA(Law) . . . . . *Dec 1979
Westmacott, Miss Kate H LLB. . . . . Dec 1993
Woods, Mr Paul L LLB . . . . . *§Feb 1975
Woollams, Miss Linda J LLB . . . . . Oct 1988
Asoc: Anning, Miss Pauline . . . . . Sep 2001
Hanbury, Mr Stephen . . . . . Dec 2005
Sands, Mr Roger J U MA(Oxon). . . . . Oct 1986
Ast: Allsop, Ms Julia M A BA. . . . . *Oct 1985
Bolton, Ms Michelle . . . . . Nov 2009
Burrows, Ms Jill. . . . . Nov 1993
Churchward, Mr Nicholas Lawrence Woodrow LLB . . Sep 1998
Ellerbeck, Mrs Rebecca LLB(Hons) . . . . . *Nov 1993
Eyre, Ms Rachel . . . . . Sep 2009
Foster, Mrs Gillian A . . . . . *Dec 1988
Fuller, Ms Julie Lily Victoria BSc; DipEngLaw; LPDip . *Feb 2000
Gill, Jennifer. . . . . Jul 2009
Hingston, Tammi . . . . . Aug 1999
James, Mr David LLB(Hons) . . . . . Sep 2001
Jenkins, Ms Natalie . . . . . Oct 2008
Kernohan, Ms Amy . . . . . Feb 2008
Lewis, Mr James . . . . . Oct 2007
Robertson, Miss Natalie Louise LLB(Hons) . . . . . Nov 2007
Rogers, Ms Natalie . . . . . Oct 2009
Twine, Mr James . . . . . Nov 2008
Williams, Mrs Alison Jane LLB . . . . . *Oct 2000
Willows, Miss Alisa J LLB(Hons) . . . . . Oct 1996
Con: Dennerly, Mr Robert E BA Notary Public. . . . . *§Jun 1973
Groves, Mr Neil K LLB . . . . . Nov 1978

WOLFERSTANS
7 Radford Park Road Plymstock Plymouth PL9 9DG
Tel: 01752 401515 *Fax:* 01752 401091 *Dx:* 8206 PLYMOUTH 1
E-mail: info@wolferstans.com
Office: Plymouth
Work: A1 B1 C1 C2 C3 D1 E F1 G H J1 K1 L N O P Q R1 S1 T1 T2 V W Z(c,e,k,l,m,q,r)
Emergency Action, Agency, Advocacy, Fixed Fee Interview, Legal Aid undertaken, Legal Aid Franchise and Member of Accident Line

WOOLLCOMBE YONGE ‡
63-65 Bretonside Plymouth PL4 0BD
Tel: 01752 660384 *Fax:* 01752 601071 *Dx:* 8200 PLYMOUTH
E-mail: info@woollcombeyonge.co.uk
List of partners: T Baker, J F H Haythorn, C S Parry
Work: D1 D2 E G H K1 K2 K3 K4 S1 S2 V W Z(l)
Emergency Action, Agency, Advocacy, Fixed Fee Interview, Legal Aid undertaken and Legal Aid Franchise
Ptr: Baker, Mrs Tracey. . . . . *Sep 1997
Haythorn, Mr John F H LLB. . . . . *Mar 1979
Parry, Mr Charles S LLB . . . . . *Mar 1983
Ast: Broom, Miss Rebecca Jane LLB(Hons) . . . . . Sep 2001
Page, Mr Roger John BA(Hons). . . . . §Feb 1981

PLYMPTON, Plymouth

HUDSON WEBB ‡
PO Box 135 Plympton Plymouth PL7 4WN
Tel: 01752 290447 *Fax:* 0870 900 3690
E-mail: info@hudson-webb.co.uk

RUSSELL WORTH ‡
Ashleigh Way Langage Park Office Campus Plymptom Plympton Plymouth PL7 5JX
Tel: 01752 334100 *Fax:* 01752 252113
List of partners: P J Russell, B E Worth
Work: N
Agency undertaken and Member of Accident Line
Ptr: Russell, Mr Peter John BA ♦ . . . . . *§Mar 1988
Worth, Mrs Bridgitte Elizabeth LLB ♦ . . . . . *Sep 1993
Ast: Christmas, Mr Simon John McAdam BSc(Hons); MA . Mar 2003
Wright, Mr Gary T LLB(Hons) ♦ . . . . . Nov 1997

WHITEFORD CROCKER
(incorporating Bellingham & Crocker)
Ridgeway House 111 Ridgeway Plympton Plymouth PL7 2AA
Tel: 01752 335994 *Fax:* 01752 348823 *Dx:* 98900 PLYMPTON
E-mail: mjc@whitefordcrocker.co.uk
Office: Ivybridge, Plymouth, Saltash
Work: A1 B1 C1 D1 E F1 K1 L N O Q S1 S2 V W Z(c,d,k,l,p)
Emergency Action, Agency, Advocacy, Fixed Fee Interview, Legal Aid undertaken and Member of Accident Line
Ast: Edgecombe, Mr Paul Stuart LLB . . . . . *§Jan 2005

POCKLINGTON, East Riding of Yorkshire

POWELL & YOUNG ‡
Market Place Pocklington East Riding of Yorkshire YO42 2AQ
Tel: 01759 302113 *Fax:* 01759 305037 *Dx:* 68530 POCKLINGTON
E-mail: pamela.precious@powellandyoung.co.uk
List of partners: M P A Hewitt, P J Precious, M R Short
Work: A1 C1 E G J1 K1 L N O Q S1 S2 T1 T2 W
Advocacy undertaken
Ptr: Hewitt, Mr Martin Peter Adrian BA(Hons) . . . . . *Nov 1979
Precious, Mrs Pamela Jane. . . . . *Oct 1998
Short, Mr Martin R LLB(Newc) . . . . . *Dec 1977
Asoc: Walker, Miss E . . . . . *Jun 2000

WOOD SHERWOOD & CO ‡
6-10 Railway Street Pocklington East Riding of Yorkshire YO42 2QZ
Tel: 01759 302791 *Fax:* 01759 305269 *Dx:* 68531 POCKLINGTON
E-mail: solicitors@woodsherwood.co.uk
List of partners: H E Coates, T Lawrence, J E Sherwood, J M Wood
Work: A1 A2 C1 D1 D2 E F1 J1 K1 K3 K4 L N O Q S1 S2 V W Z(l)
Emergency Action and Advocacy undertaken
Ptr: Coates, Miss Helen E LLB(Hons) . . . . . *§Sep 2001
Lawrence, Mr Tim LLB(Hons). . . . . *§Oct 1993
Sherwood, Mr John Edward. . . . . *§Dec 1979
Wood, Mr J Martin LLB Notary Public . . . . . *§Jun 1976

POLEGATE, East Sussex

DAVID DE MALLET MORGAN ‡
1 North Street Alfriston Polegate East Sussex BN26 5UG
Tel: 01323 871100

HART READE
55 High Street Polegate East Sussex BN26 6AL
Tel: 01323 487051 *Fax:* 01323 487724
E-mail: info@hartreade.co.uk
Office: Eastbourne, Hailsham
Work: S1 T2 W
Asoc: Hobden, Mrs Angela Victoria LLB(Hons). . . . . *Sep 2001

PONTARDAWE, Swansea

D R JAMES & SON ‡
3-4 Dynevor Terrace Pontardawe Swansea SA8 4HY
Tel: 01792 862334 *Fax:* 01792 865736
List of partners: W H Arthur, J E Perkins
Ptr: Arthur, Wynford H. . . . . *Jun 1976
Perkins, Ms Jan E. . . . . *Jun 1979
Ast: Booth, Miss Ceri-Lynne LLB; MBA . . . . . *Oct 1997
Con: James, Mr John R . . . . . *Nov 1958

PONTARDULAIS, Swansea

DAVID & ROY THOMAS & CO ‡
72 St Teilo Street Pontardulais Swansea SA4 8ST
Tel: 01792 882410 *Fax:* 01792 884502 *Dx:* 122511 GORSEINON
E-mail: robert.thomas@davidroythomas.co.uk
List of partners: R V Thomas
Languages: Welsh
Work: A1 E L S1 T2 W
SPr: Thomas, Mr Robert Vernon LLB(Wales). . . . . *Mar 1979

PONTEFRACT, West Yorkshire

CARTERS ‡
33 Ropergate Pontefract West Yorkshire WF8 1LE
Tel: 01977 703224 *Fax:* 01977 781333 *Dx:* 22251 PONTEFRACT
E-mail: anne.caswell@carterssolicitors.co.uk
List of partners: A Caswell, A P Mawdsley
Languages: French
Work: A1 A3 C1 C2 C3 D1 E F1 F2 J1 K1 K3 K4 L N O P Q R1 S1 S2 T1 T2 V W X Z(c,f,k)
Emergency Action, Agency, Advocacy, Fixed Fee Interview and Legal Aid undertaken
Ptr: Caswell, Mrs Anne LLB . . . . . *§Nov 1988
Mawdsley, Mr Andrew P BSc(Hons). . . . . *§Sep 1997
Ast: Manir, Miss Talat LLB(Hons). . . . . Feb 2010

CRIMINAL LAW SOLICITORS ‡
9 The Precinct Station Lane Pontefract West Yorkshire WF7 5BX
Tel: 01977 707999
E-mail: info@clssolicitors.co.uk
Office: Selby

J C HARRIS ‡
Long Lane Close High Ackworth Pontefract West Yorkshire WF7 7EY
Tel: 01977 795450 *Fax:* 01977 795470

HARTLEY & WORSTENHOLME
10 Gillygate Pontefract West Yorkshire WF8 1PQ
Tel: 01977 732222 *Fax:* 01977 600343 *Dx:* 22256 PONTEFRACT
E-mail: info@hartley-worstenholme.co.uk
Office: Castleford
Work: A1 C1 D1 D2 E J1 K1 K2 K3 L N O Q S1 S2 T1 T2 V W Z(l,q)
Emergency Action, Agency, Advocacy, Fixed Fee Interview, Legal Aid undertaken, Legal Aid Franchise and Member of Accident Line
Ptr: Gaythorpe, Mr David J LLB(Hons). . . . . *Oct 1987
Sharp, Mr Jonathan. . . . . Mar 2009
Wilton, Mr Christopher LLB(Hons) Notary Public. . . . *Jun 1979
Ast: Towell, Ms Victoria LLB(Hons). . . . . *Mar 2007
Con: Loynes, Mr David T LLB(Hons) . . . . . *Jun 1975

HEPTONSTALLS LLP
9-11 Ropergate End Pontefract West Yorkshire WF8 1JU
Tel: 01977 602804 *Fax:* 01977 602805 *Dx:* 22255 PONTEFRACT
E-mail: legal@heptonstalls.co.uk
Office: Goole, Howden, Pontefract, Scunthorpe
Work: C1 C2 D2 E J1 K1 K3 N O Q S1 S2 W
Member of Accident Line
Ptr: Hart, Ms Angele LLB(L'pool). . . . . *Oct 1992

HEPTONSTALLS LLP
Newgate House Jacksons Court Newgate Pontefract West Yorkshire WF8 1NB
Tel: 01977 602804 *Fax:* 01977 793560 *Dx:* 22265 PONTEFRACT
E-mail: legal@heptonstalls.co.uk
Office: Goole, Howden, Pontefract, Scunthorpe
Work: N Q
Ptr: Cawood, Mrs Clare LLB. . . . . *May 2002
Hensman, Mr Shane S LLB(Hons); LLM. . . . . *Oct 1997
Tilson, Mrs Sasha BA; PGDipLaw. . . . . Sep 2004
Ast: Bhatti, Miss Nabiha . . . . . Sep 2007

HEWISON & NIXON ‡
24 Station Lane Featherstone Pontefract West Yorkshire WF7 5BE
Tel: 01977 700705 *Fax:* 01977 704576
Emergency telephone 01924 254722
E-mail: hewisonnixon@tiscali.co.uk
List of partners: C Hewison, J Nixon
Work: B1 D1 E F1 G H J1 K1 L N Q S1 V W Z(f,l)
Emergency Action, Agency, Advocacy, Fixed Fee Interview, Legal Aid undertaken and Legal Aid Franchise
Ptr: Hewison, Mr Christopher LLB . . . . . *Jul 1977
Nixon, Mr John LLB. . . . . *May 1978
Ast: Plank, Ms Margaret BA . . . . . *Jun 1975

JOHN JONES & CO ‡
Becca House Market Street Hemsworth Pontefract West Yorkshire WF9 4JY
Tel: 01977 615522 *Fax:* 01977 615544

MILNERS SOLICITORS
9a High Street Upton Pontefract West Yorkshire WF9 1HR
Tel: 01977 644864 *Fax:* 0113 242 0469 *Dx:* 12042 LEEDS
E-mail: office@milnerslaw.com
Office: Barnsley, Leeds, Wakefield

MOXON & BARKER ‡
The Law Chambers Belks Court Pontefract West Yorkshire WF8 1DF
Tel: 01977 602999 *Fax:* 01977 602211 *Dx:* 22266 PONTEFRACT
E-mail: mjs@moxon-barker.co.uk
List of partners: A Y Firoz, E J Pearson, M J Scott
Work: A1 C1 C2 E F1 J1 K1 L R1 R2 S1 S2 T1 T2 W Z(c,j,l)
Ptr: Firoz, Mrs Abida Yakub LLB(Hons) . . . . . Apr 2007
Pearson, Mr Edwin James MA; LLB(Cantab) . . . . . Jul 1971
Scott, Mr Michael Joseph BA(Dunelm); LLM. . . . . May 1978

MOXONS ‡
(in association with Green Williamson)
49 Ropergate Pontefract West Yorkshire WF8 1JZ
Tel: 01977 703215 *Fax:* 01977 600115 *Dx:* 22253 PONTEFRACT
E-mail: ww@moxons.co.uk
List of partners: M W S Walters
Work: C1 D1 E F1 K1 L N O Q S1 V W
Emergency Action, Agency, Advocacy, Fixed Fee Interview, Legal Aid undertaken and Legal Aid Franchise
SPr: Walters, Mr Malcolm Ward S LLB(Lond). . . . . *Oct 1974
Asoc: Barlow, Mrs Mary Therese . . . . . *Mar 2000
Crofts-Turnbull, Mrs Delia Helen. . . . . *§Oct 1992

SHAW & ASHTON ‡
22a Ropergate Pontefract West Yorkshire WF8 1LX
Tel: 01977 703232 *Fax:* 01977 702298
List of partners: D Ashton
Work: E K1 L N Q S1 W
Emergency Action, Agency, Advocacy, Fixed Fee Interview and Legal Aid undertaken
SPr: Ashton, Mr David LLB(Exon) . . . . . *Jul 1967
Con: Shaw, Mr T Derrick LLB. . . . . *§Nov 1959

MAURICE SMITHS
Norwood House Stuart Road Pontefract West Yorkshire WF8 1BT
Tel: 01977 794395 *Fax:* 01977 600960 *Dx:* 22254 PONTEFRACT
Emergency telephone 07890 085688
E-mail: reception@mauricesmiths.co.uk
Office: Castleford
Work: C1 D1 D2 E G H J1 K1 L N O Q S1 S2 V W
Emergency Action, Agency and Legal Aid Franchise
Ptr: Gale, Mr Anthony LLB. . . . . *Feb 1990
Pinto, Mr Richard John BA(Law) . . . . . *Jan 1979
Warsop, Mrs Rachel Jane. . . . . *Sep 1997

THE SOLICITORS CHAMBERS ‡
9 Front Street Pontefract West Yorkshire WF8 1DA
Tel: 01977 599999 *Fax:* 01977 797999
E-mail: partners@solicitorschambers-yorks.co.uk

WOODS SOLICITORS ‡
1st Floor 21 Beastfair Pontefract West Yorkshire WF8 1SR

WRIGHT & CO ‡
Enterprise House Horsefair Pontefract West Yorkshire WF8 1RG
Tel: 01977 878130 *Fax:* 01977 600041
Emergency telephone 07710 010581
List of partners: G J Wright
Languages: French, German
Work: B1 C1 D1 E F1 H J1 K1 L N Q R1 S1 V W Z(c,h,j,l,m,t)
Emergency Action, Agency, Advocacy, Fixed Fee Interview, Legal Aid undertaken and Member of Accident Line
Ptr: Wright, Mr Gordon J BA. . . . . Oct 1988

PONTELAND, Northumberland

COLETTE STROUD SOLICITORS ‡
Abacus House Meadowfield Ponteland Northumberland NE20 9SD
Tel: 01661 820444 *Fax:* 01661 821771

MAJOR FAMILY LAW ‡
12 West Road Ponteland Northumberland NE20 9SU
Tel: 01661 824582 *Fax:* 01661 823529

NICHOLSON & MORGAN ‡
(incorporating Blackett & Co)
14 Bell Villas Ponteland Northumberland NE20 9BE
Tel: 01661 871012 / 823381 *Fax:* 01661 860042
Dx: 68923 PONTELAND 2
List of partners: J Heslop, A W Morgan, E M Nicholson
Work: E J1 K1 L M1 N P S1 W Z(c)
Agency, Advocacy, Fixed Fee Interview and Legal Aid undertaken
Ptr: Heslop, Mr Jonathon . . . . . *Oct 1986
Morgan, Mr Andrew W BA . . . . . *Oct 1986
Nicholson, Mr Eric M BA . . . . . *§Nov 1971

IAIN NICHOLSON & CO ‡
5 West Road Ponteland Northumberland NE20 9ST
Tel: 01661 823863 *Fax:* 01661 823724 *Dx:* 68921 PONTELAND 2
E-mail: law@iainnicholson.co.uk
List of partners: P J Dakin, I H Nicholson
Work: A1 C1 C2 C3 E J1 K1 L M1 M2 N P S1 T1 T2 W Z(c)

Emergency Action, Agency, Advocacy, Fixed Fee Interview, Legal Aid undertaken and Member of Accident Line
Ptr: Dakin, Mr Peter J LLB; TEP . . . . . *§Dec 1974
Nicholson, Mr Iain Harald MSI; TEP . . . . . *§May 1963
Ast: Stevenson, Mrs Victoria LLB . . . . . *Aug 2007

PONTYCLUN, Rhondda Cynon Taff

CLIVE ASHMAN ‡
15a Stuart Terrace Talbot Green Pontyclun Rhondda Cynon Taff CF72 8AA
Tel: 01443 231177 *Fax:* 01443 231208
List of partners: C Ashman
SPr: Ashman, Mr Clive . . . . . Apr 1996

EDWARD T DAVIES SONS & TILTMAN ‡
Rock Villa 6 Llantrisant Road Pontyclun Rhondda Cynon Taff CF72 9DQ
Tel: 01443 225446 *Fax:* 01443 223283
List of partners: E H Tiltman
Work: S1 W
Ptr: Tiltman, Mr Edward Harold . . . . . *§Jul 1980

ANDREW HOPPER QC ‡
PO Box 7 Pontyclun Rhondda Cynon Taff CF72 9XN
Tel: 01443 237788 *Dx:* 50952 COWBRIDGE
E-mail: andrewhopper@ahqc.com

PONTYPOOL, Torfaen

EVERETT TOMLIN LLOYD & PRATT
Clarence Chambers Clarence Street Pontypool Torfaen NP4 6XP
Tel: 01495 763333 *Fax:* 01495 750526 *Dx:* 44252 PONTYPOOL
Emergency telephone 01291 673883
E-mail: pontypool@etlp.co.uk
Office: Newport
Work: A1 B1 C1 C2 C3 D1 E F1 G H J1 K1 L N O P Q R1 S1 T1 T2 V W Z(c,d,k,l,m,q,t,y)
Emergency Action, Agency, Advocacy, Fixed Fee Interview, Legal Aid undertaken and Member of Accident Line
Ptr: Edwards, Mr Gareth W MA(Oxon) . . . . . *Nov 1973
Harkus, Mr Ashley William LLB(Hons) . . . . . *Nov 1996
O'Brien, Mrs Angela C LLB . . . . . *Jun 1977
Sandeman, Ms Gillian H . . . . . *Jul 1979
Ast: Campbell, Mr James Mervyn John LLB(Hons) . . . . . *Sep 1998
Doe, Mr Andrew Martin LLB(Wales) . . . . . *Jan 1985
Fifer, Mr Jeffrey I LLB . . . . . *Nov 1970
Tuck, Mrs Kirsten Louise . . . . . *Oct 1997

GRANVILLE-WEST ‡
23 Commercial Street Pontypool Torfaen NP4 6XT
Tel: 01495 751111 *Fax:* 01495 753858 *Dx:* 44250 PONTYPOOL
E-mail: pontypool@granville-west.co.uk
List of partners: J P Cox-Healey, J D Erasmus, C Harrison, G G M Sandercock, R Stark, W L Thomas
Office: Abertillery, Blackwood, Caldicot, Newport, Risca
Languages: French, Welsh
Work: B1 C1 C2 C3 D1 D2 E F1 J1 K1 L N Q R1 S1 S2 V W Z(c,d,l,m,q)
Emergency Action, Agency, Advocacy, Fixed Fee Interview, Legal Aid undertaken and Legal Aid Franchise
Ptr: Sandercock, Mr Geoffrey G M LLB(Wales) ♦ . . . . . *Mar 1973
Ast: Coward, Mrs Barbara Irene LLB(Hons) . . . . . *Feb 1996
Lewis, Miss Kelly LLB . . . . . *Jan 2005
Manners, Mrs Bethan T LLB . . . . . *Jun 1996
Wallace, Miss Jillian L LLB(Hons) . . . . . Mar 2001

WATKINS & GUNN ‡
Glantorfaen House Hanbury Road Pontypool Torfaen NP4 6XY
Tel: 01495 762244 *Fax:* 01495 758115 *Dx:* 44251 PONTYPOOL
E-mail: watkinsandgunn@hotmail.com
List of partners: A G Bolter, T J B Clancy, C R Thomas, D H Williams
Office: Newport
Languages: Welsh
Work: A1 B1 C1 C2 C3 D1 E F1 G H J1 K1 L M1 N O P Q R1 S1 T1 V W X Z(e,f,i,l)
Emergency Action, Agency, Advocacy, Fixed Fee Interview, Legal Aid undertaken, Legal Aid Franchise and Member of Accident Line
Ptr: Bolter, Mr Alan G . . . . . *Aug 1968
Clancy, Mr Thomas J B . . . . . *Jun 1972
Thomas, Mr Clive R LLB . . . . . *Oct 1991
Williams, Mr D Huw LLB . . . . . *Nov 1991
Ast: Gal, Miss Christina BSc(Hons); CPE . . . . . *Jun 2002
Con: Thomas, Mr Gareth R LLB . . . . . *Nov 1972

PONTYPRIDD, Rhondda Cynon Taff

IWAN DAVIES & CO ‡
1 Church Street Pontypridd Rhondda Cynon Taff CF37 2TH
Tel: 01443 485566 *Fax:* 01443 485717
List of partners: I M Davies
Languages: French, Welsh
Work: D1 G H K1 L N O Q S1 W
Emergency Action, Agency, Advocacy and Legal Aid undertaken
Ptr: Davies, Mr Iwan M LLB(Wales) . . . . . *Jun 1983

DEVONALDS ‡
York House Court House Street Pontypridd Rhondda Cynon Taff CF37 1JW
Tel: 01443 404700 *Fax:* 01443 404555
E-mail: pontypridd@devonalds.co.uk
List of partners: J G Evans, S D Evans, W E Griffiths, C J Lewis, L Murphy, P S Robinson
Office: Cardiff, Pontypridd, Talbot Green, Tonypandy
Ptr: Evans, Mr John G LLB . . . . . Jun 1979
Evans, Mr Stephen D . . . . . *Oct 1988
Griffiths, Mr Wayne E LLB(Wales) . . . . . Apr 1981
Murphy, Ms Lesley BA; LLB . . . . . *Oct 1983
Robinson, Mr Philip S . . . . . *Jul 1984

DEVONALDS
17 Gelliwastad Road Pontypridd Rhondda Cynon Taff CF37 2BW
Tel: 01443 404331 *Fax:* 01443 485299 *Dx:* 44361 PONTYPRIDD
emailpontypridd@devonalds.co.ukl
Office: Cardiff, Pontypridd, Talbot Green, Tonypandy
Work: A1 B1 C1 D1 D2 E F1 K1 K3 K4 L N Q R1 S1 S2 T1 V W
Emergency Action, Agency, Advocacy, Fixed Fee Interview, Legal Aid undertaken and Legal Aid Franchise
Ptr: Lewis, Mr Christopher J LLB . . . . . *Jun 1984

NEIL FOLEY & CO ‡
112 Broadway Pontypridd Rhondda Cynon Taff CF37 1BE
Tel: 01443 406085 *Fax:* 01443 406092
Emergency telephone 07712 078720
E-mail: neilfoley@btinternet.com
List of partners: N J Foley
Languages: Italian
Work: G H
Agency, Legal Aid undertaken and Legal Aid Franchise
Ptr: Foley, Mr Neil James LLB(Hons) ★ . . . . . *Feb 1987
Ast: Alonzi, Mr Tony LLB(Hons) . . . . . *Oct 1985
McKevitt, Miss Monique Ashley LLB . . . . . *May 2006

GLAMORGANLAW
15 Gelliwastad Road Pontypridd Rhondda Cynon Taff CF37 2BW
Tel: 01443 408455 *Fax:* 01443 485476 *Dx:* 44355 PONTYPRIDD
E-mail: jill@jpeterdavies.co.uk
Office: Cardiff, Cowbridge

DAVID W HARRIS & CO ‡
24-25 Gelliwastad Road Pontypridd Rhondda Cynon Taff CF37 2BW
Tel: 01443 486666 *Fax:* 01443 485715 *Dx:* 44353 PONTYPRIDD
Emergency telephone 029 2089 2127 / 01446 760480
E-mail: feeearner@dwharris.co.uk
List of partners: R A Hopkins, D A Mason, L Matthews, M A Newton, A M O'Callaghan, M R Pearce, G Treharne
Office: Bridgend, Talbot Green
Work: B1 D1 E F1 G H J1 J2 K1 K3 L N O Q S1 S2 V W Z(c,j,l,q)
Emergency Action, Agency, Advocacy, Fixed Fee Interview, Legal Aid undertaken and Legal Aid Franchise
Ptr: Hopkins, Mr Richard A BSc(Econ) . . . . . *Feb 1983
Mason, Mr David A LLB . . . . . *Oct 1985
Matthews, Mr Lee . . . . . Aug 2001
Newton, Mrs Michelle A DipLP Leo Abse & Cohen Prize . . . . . Sep 1995
O'Callaghan, Mr Anthony M . . . . . Dec 1988
Pearce, Mr Michael Ross BA(Hons) . . . . . Dec 1998
Treharne, Garan BSc . . . . . Sep 1998

ANTHONY JEWELL & CO ‡
Windsor Chambers 2 Penuel Lane Pontypridd Rhondda Cynon Taff CF37 4UF
Tel: 01443 493357 *Fax:* 01443 485316 *Dx:* 44356 PONTYPRIDD
E-mail: enquiries@anthonyjewell.com
List of partners: A Jewell
Languages: Welsh
Work: C1 D1 E F1 G H J1 K1 L M1 N O P S1 S2 W
Emergency Action, Agency, Advocacy, Fixed Fee Interview, Legal Aid undertaken and Legal Aid Franchise
SPr: Jewell, Mr Anthony LLB(Wales) . . . . . *Jan 1978
Ast: Preece, Mrs Llio Mererid LLB . . . . . *Nov 1992

JOHN HAMILTON LEYSHON SOLICITORS
6 Central Buildings Central Square Trallwn Pontypridd Rhondda Cynon Taff CF37 4PN
Tel: 01443 403666 *Fax:* 01443 403688
Office: Porth

KTP SOLICITORS
1 Gelliwastad Road Pontypridd Rhondda Cynon Taff CF37 2BW
Tel: 01443 485141 *Fax:* 01443 400335 *Dx:* 44370 PONTYPRIDD
E-mail: pontypridd@ktpsolicitors.net
Office: Bridgend (2 offices), Porth
Work: K2 Z(m)
Ptr: Kitchen, Mr Jeffrey LLB . . . . . *Jun 1994

PJE SOLICITORS ‡
115 Broadway Treforest Pontypridd Rhondda Cynon Taff CF37 1BE
Tel: 01443 408647 / 07970 269478 *Fax:* 01443 493580
E-mail: info@pjesolicitors.co.uk

R MILES RICHARDS & CO ‡
Main Road Church Village Pontypridd Rhondda Cynon Taff CF38 1RN
Tel: 01443 202237 *Fax:* 01443 208116
E-mail: office@happymiles.plus.com
List of partners: R M Richards
Languages: Welsh
Work: C1 C2 E L S1 S2 W Z(c)
Con: Lewis, Mr Ralph LLB(Wales) Associated Law Societies of Wales Prize . . . . . *§Mar 1961

ROBIN MORAN LLB (HONS) ‡
13 Castle Ivor Street Hopkinstown Pontypridd Rhondda Cynon Taff CF37 2PY
Tel: 01443 406801 *Fax:* 01443 406801

SPICKETTS BATTRICK LAW PRACTICE ‡
Gelliwastad House 3-4 Gelliwastad Road Pontypridd Rhondda Cynon Taff CF37 2AU
Tel: 01443 407221 *Fax:* 029 2048 7505 *Dx:* 44350 PONTYPRIDD
E-mail: enquiries@spickettsbattrick.co.uk
List of partners: R J Battrick, C J Cater, R Greenhough, L S Parish
Office: Cardiff (2 offices)
Work: D1 D2 J1 K1 K2 K3 L N S1 S2 W Z(h)
Emergency Action, Agency, Advocacy, Fixed Fee Interview, Legal Aid undertaken, Legal Aid Franchise and Member of Accident Line
Ptr: Cater, Mr Christopher J LLB . . . . . Oct 1985
Parish, Mrs Linda S BA . . . . . *Oct 1983
Asoc: Watkins, Ms Louise Ann LLB . . . . . *Nov 1992
Ast: Lewis, Mr Christopher LLB . . . . . *Jan 2006

DAVID WATKINS ‡
57 West Street Pontypridd Rhondda Cynon Taff CF37 4PS
Tel: 01443 409401 *Fax:* 01443 409522
List of partners: D T Watkins
Work: K1 L N S1 W
Fixed Fee Interview and Legal Aid undertaken
SPr: Watkins, Mr David Timothy LLB(Lond) . . . . . *Jan 1981

POOLE

M R BARROW ‡
73 Spur Hill Avenue Lower Parkstone Poole BH14 9PJ
Tel: 01202 737745 *Fax:* 01202 737745
E-mail: mrbarrow@compuserve.com
List of partners: M R Barrow
Work: C1 F1 F2
SPr: Barrow, Mr Michael R . . . . . Jun 1975

BOWMAN & CO ‡
203 Ashley Road Parkstone Poole BH14 9DL
Tel: 01202 716171 *Fax:* 01202 716032 *Dx:* 92902 PARKSTONE 2
E-mail: info@bowmanlaw.co.uk
Work: S1

CARO TAYLOR SOLICITORS ‡
18a High Street Poole BH15 1BP
Tel: 01202 678444 *Fax:* 0560 115 7952 *Dx:* 07606 POOLE
E-mail: info@carotaylor.com
List of partners: C F Taylor
Work: D1 K1 K2 K3 W
Agency and Advocacy undertaken
SPr: Taylor, Ms Carolyn Fiona LLB . . . . . Oct 1985

COLES MILLER SOLICITORS LLP ‡
44-46 Parkstone Road Poole BH15 2PG
Tel: 01202 673011 *Fax:* 01202 675868 *Dx:* 7609 POOLE
E-mail: office@coles-miller.co.uk
List of partners: N A R Andrews, A Cormack, C C Elliott, E Hamilton-Cole, A Howard, R H Kerley, F O Knight, R M Leedham, S Lines, D A Parfitt, D B C Simpson, S T Steele-Williams, C D Whittle
Office: Bournemouth (2 offices), Broadstone
Work: A1 B1 C1 C2 C3 D1 E F1 G H J1 J2 K1 K3 L M1 N O P Q R1 S1 S2 T1 T2 V W Z(a,c,d,e,h,l,m,p,q,r)
Emergency Action, Agency, Advocacy, Fixed Fee Interview, Legal Aid Franchise and Member of Accident Line
Ptr: Andrews, Mr Neil Anthony Robert BA; CPE; LSF . . . . . *Oct 1995
Cormack, Mr Adrian LLB(Hons) . . . . . *Sep 1991
Elliott, Mrs Carol C BA(Hons) . . . . . *Sep 1982
Leedham, Mr Roger M BA(Hons)(Law) . . . . . *Oct 1984
Lines, Miss Shauna LLB . . . . . *Oct 1993
Parfitt, Mr David A . . . . . *§Jun 1977
Simpson, Mr David Brian Charles LLB . . . . . Nov 1989
Ast: Cutmore, Mr Stephen LLB(Hons) Prince Delphus Prize 1966; Mackrell Prize 1967 Deputy District Judge . . . . . *§Apr 1970
Ellis, Mr Michael . . . . . Oct 2007
Lucy, Mr Ben Sterling LLB(Hons) . . . . . *Oct 2001
McDonnell, Mr Michael James . . . . . Jul 2006
McLean, Mr Graham BProc; South African Attorney . . . . . Jan 2004
Mitchell, Mr Colin LLB . . . . . Sep 1999
Richards, Miss Katie BSc(Hons); GDL; LPC . . . . . Dec 2008
Weber, Mr Anthony William . . . . . Sep 1996
Wright, Miss Lydia . . . . . Mar 2009
Con: Meldrum, Mr Neil J . . . . . *Nov 1975
Senior, Mr Roger F . . . . . *§Jun 1969

DICKINSON MANSER ‡
5 Parkstone Road Poole BH15 2NL
Tel: 01202 673071 *Fax:* 01202 680470 *Dx:* 7602 POOLE
E-mail: enquiries@dickinsonmanser.co.uk
List of partners: A J Carswell, G S Cox, M J Daniels, R Killer, J W Love, G M Pick, G E Yeoman
Office: Broadstone
Work: A1 B1 C1 C2 C3 D1 E F1 G H J1 K1 L N O P Q R1 S1 S2 T2 V W X Z(c,d,h,k,l,m,p,q)
Emergency Action, Agency, Advocacy, Fixed Fee Interview, Legal Aid undertaken, Legal Aid Franchise and Member of Accident Line
Ptr: Carswell, Mr Andrew James LLB Deputy Under Sheriff of Dorset . . . . . *Nov 1994
Cox, Mr Gary S LLB Under Sheriff of Dorset; Clerk to Talbot Village Trustees; Former President of Bournemouth Law Society . . . . . *§Jun 1975
Daniels, Mr Mark Jason LLB . . . . . *Oct 1986
Killer, Mr Richard LLB . . . . . *Jun 1981
Love, Mr James William BA(Hons) . . . . . Oct 2004
Pick, Mr Gary M LLB . . . . . *Nov 1983
Yeoman, Mr Gareth E . . . . . *Apr 1985
Ast: Balch, Mrs Helena LLB . . . . . *Oct 1993
Dudley, Ms Katharine . . . . . Sep 2003
Freeman, Miss Jane Maxine BA(Hons) . . . . . Jan 2000
Lake, Mr Verne . . . . . *Dec 1984
Nixon, Mrs Rebecca Jane LLB(Hons) . . . . . Sep 2009
Smith, Miss Susanna Jayne LLB(Hons) . . . . . Sep 2008
Con: Cake, Mr Richard W A . . . . . *Jan 1972

ELLIS JONES
14a Haven Road Canford Cliffs Poole BH13 7LP
Tel: 01202 709898 *Fax:* 01202 707871
Dx: 85300 CANFORD CLIFFS
E-mail: canford@ellisjones.co.uk
Office: Bournemouth, Ringwood, Swanage
Work: E S1 S2 T2 W
Agency undertaken and Member of Accident Line

J M FAIRHALL ‡
2a Alton Chambers 37 Church Road Parkstone Poole BH14 8UQ
Tel: 01202 735962 *Fax:* 01202 718248
Work: E S1

M D FURBER & CO ‡
6 Chester Road Poole BH13 6DD
Tel: 0870 766 1831

HUMPHRIES KIRK
15 Church Road Parkstone Poole BH14 8UF
Tel: 01202 715815 *Fax:* 01202 715511 *Dx:* 34802 PARKSTONE
E-mail: parkstone@hklaw.eu
Office: Bournemouth, Dorchester, Poole, Swanage, Wareham
Languages: French, German, Italian, Spanish
Work: D1 J1 K1 K3 K4 L N O Q R2 S1 S2 T2 V W Z(h)
Agency, Fixed Fee Interview, Legal Aid undertaken and Legal Aid Franchise
Ptr: Baker, Mrs Margaret Mary . . . . . *Nov 1997
Asoc: Davies, Mrs Rosemary L LLB(Lond) . . . . . *Oct 1983
Pearson, Mrs Victoria LLB . . . . . *Sep 2004
Ast: Bradford, Mr Stuart LLB . . . . . *Sep 2002
Cormack, Mrs Charlene Lucy LLB . . . . . *Mar 2006
Thake, Ms Marie-Claire . . . . . Oct 2008

HUMPHRIES KIRK
3 Acorn Business Park Ling Road Poole BH12 4NZ
Tel: 01202 725400 *Fax:* 01202 715877 *Dx:* 154880 POOLE 10
Emergency telephone 01202 725440
E-mail: poole@hklaw.eu
Office: Bournemouth, Dorchester, Poole, Swanage, Wareham
Languages: French, German, Italian, Spanish

See p112 for the Key to Work Categories & other symbols

Work: A1 A2 A3 B1 B2 C1 C2 C3 E F1 F2 I J1 J2 L M1 M2 N O P Q R1 R2 S1 S2 U2 Z(b,c,e,h,k,p,q,za)
Agency, Advocacy and Fixed Fee Interview undertaken
Ptr: Chittenden, Mr John W BA(Hons)(Law); MCIArb . . . *Sep 1998
Marrow, Ms Alison Louise LLB . . . *Oct 1993
Marrow, Mr Michael E. . . . *Jul 1965
Reeves, Mr Christopher James MCIOB . . . *Sep 2001
Selby Bennett, Mr James S TD . . . *Nov 1977
Stuart-Smith, Mr J Darrell LLB(Lond) . . . *Mar 1983
Asoc: Bartlett, Mrs Leigh LLB . . . *Sep 2001
Ast: Aram, Miss Helen Charlotte . . . Oct 2009
Dixon, Miss Michelle Esther . . . Oct 2009
Dollimore, Mrs Charlotte LLB(Hons) . . . *Sep 1997
Heath, Mr Julian James Martin LLB . . . Oct 1986
Henderson, Mr James . . . *Apr 2005
Holland, Miss Catherine L BA; MA(Oxon); DipLaw LP; PGDipLaw . . . *Sep 2002
Jourdan, Mr Marc LLB . . . Nov 2008
Kerr, Miss Amy Louise BA(Hons) . . . *Oct 2006
Martin, Miss Louise LLB(Hons) . . . Oct 2002
Spencer, Mrs Audrey Catherine BSc . . . *Sep 2007
Webster, Mrs Emma Charlotte LPC; LLB(Law) . . . *Dec 2004
Wood, Mr Robert Christopher . . . *Jun 1977

THE JMC PRACTICE ‡
4 Wilderton Road West Poole BH13 6EF
Tel: 01202 757435 *Fax:* 01202 759720
E-mail: jeancross@jmcpractice.co.uk

JACOBS & REEVES ‡
Beechurst 153 High Street Poole BH15 1AU
Tel: 01202 674425 *Fax:* 01202 681167 *Dx:* 7610 POOLE
E-mail: office@jacobsreeves.co.uk
List of partners: R H Boyce, R Dollimore, H S Henson, N P L Hyman, R S Nickless
Office: Poole, Wimborne
Languages: French, Spanish
Work: B1 C1 C2 C3 D1 E F1 G H J1 K1 L M1 M2 N O Q R1 R2 S1 S2 V W Z(i,l,r)
Emergency Action, Agency, Advocacy, Fixed Fee Interview, Legal Aid undertaken, Legal Aid Franchise and Member of Accident Line
Ptr: Dollimore, Mr Richard BSc(Econ) . . . *Sep 1997
Henson, Mrs Helen S BA(Hons) . . . *Nov 1998
Hyman, Mr Nicholas P L LLB . . . *Oct 1983
Ast: Del-Llano, Mr Marc . . . Sep 2002
Gibbs, Mr Paul Derek LLB . . . Sep 2006
Powell, Mrs Sophie . . . Jan 2009
Con: Dutton, Mr Rodney M LLB . . . *Sep 1984
Reeves, Mr Christopher P LLB . . . *Jun 1976

JACOBS & REEVES
3 Avon House 329 Ashley Road Parkstone Poole BH14 0AP
Tel: 01202 731849 *Fax:* 01202 736728 *Dx:* 92910 PARKSTONE 2
E-mail: office@jacobsreeves.co.uk
Office: Poole, Wimborne
Work: C2 D1 D2 E G K1 K3 N O Q S1 S2 W Z(q)
Emergency Action, Agency, Advocacy, Fixed Fee Interview, Legal Aid undertaken, Legal Aid Franchise and Member of Accident Line
Ptr: Nickless, Mr Robert Stephen LLB(Soton) . . . *Nov 1982
Ast: Watson, Ms Tracey Michelle LLB . . . *Mar 2000

KEVIN BROWN SOLICITOR ‡
52 Charborough Close Lytchett Matravers Poole BH16 6DH
Tel: 01202 620907 / 07977 191059 *Fax:* 01202 620908
E-mail: info@kevinbrownsolicitor.co.uk

LACEYS
(incorporating Allin & Watts)
257 Ashley Road Parkstone Poole BH14 9DY
Tel: 01202 743286 *Fax:* 01202 723156 *Dx:* 92900 PARKSTONE 2
E-mail: par@laceyssolicitors.co.uk
Office: Bournemouth (2 offices)
Languages: French
Work: A3 C1 C2 E F1 K1 K2 L O S1 S2 T1 T2 V W

BRUCE LANCE & CO
2 Winchester Place North Street Poole BH15 1NX
Tel: 01202 679379 *Fax:* 01202 677943 *Dx:* 7608 POOLE
E-mail: dw@brucelance.co.uk
Office: High Wycombe
Languages: French
Work: A1 B1 C1 C2 C3 D1 E J1 K1 L M1 M2 N O P Q R1 R2 S1 S2 T1 T2 W Z(b,c,d,e,h,j,l,o,p)
Emergency Action, Agency, Advocacy, Fixed Fee Interview, Legal Aid undertaken, Legal Aid Franchise and Member of Accident Line
Ptr: Goss, Mr Andrew Paul . . . *Nov 1995
Widdowson, Mr Dominic T D BSc(Cardiff)(Econ) . . . *Jun 1977

GILLIAN LINFORD SOLICITOR ‡
20 Doulton Gardens Parkstone Poole BH14 8RG
Tel: 01202 254090
E-mail: enquiries@gillianlinfordlaw.com

IAN NEWBERY & CO ‡
81-83 High Street Poole BH15 1AH
Tel: 01202 669986 *Fax:* 01202 669987
E-mail: mail@iannewbery.co.uk
List of partners: I R Newbery
Work: B1 C1 C2 C3 E F1 F2 I J1 K1 L N O P Q R1 R2 S1 S2 U2 W Z(c,d,e,g,h,j,l,q,r,u)
Agency, Advocacy and Fixed Fee Interview undertaken
Ptr: Newbery, Mr Ian R LLB . . . *Mar 1979

IAN PEARCE AND CO SOLICITORS ‡
7 Purbeck Avenue Poole BH15 4DN
Tel: 01202 681699

QUALITYSOLICITORS D'ANGIBAU
40 Haven Road Canford Cliffs Poole BH13 7LP
Tel: 01202 708634 *Fax:* 01202 709989
Dx: 85302 CANFORD CLIFFS
Office: Boscombe, Poole
Work: S1 T2 W
Ptr: Fielding, Mr Robert George Seymour . . . *Jun 2006
Asoc: Cake, Miss Caroline Louise LLB . . . *Jun 2005
Curtis, Mrs Lesley . . . *Jan 2001

QUALITYSOLICITORS D'ANGIBAU
15 New Fields 2 Stinsford Road Poole BH17 0UF
Tel: 01202 672598 *Fax:* 01202 680958 *Dx:* 134673 POOLE 8
Office: Boscombe, Poole
Work: C1 E S1 S2 W

Ptr: McArthur, Miss Fiona Elspeth . . . *Dec 1999
Turner, Mr Roger J . . . *§Mar 1968
Asoc: Stanton, Mr Daniel Neil LLB(Soton) . . . *Oct 2004
Con: Turner, Mrs Anastasia . . . *Jul 1968

RWPS LLP ‡
48-50 Parkstone Road Poole BH15 2PG
Tel: 01202 466669 *Fax:* 01202 668614 *Dx:* 07650 POOLE
List of partners: G H Perrins, J D Stevenson
Office: Poole
Ptr: Perrins, Mr George H LLB . . . *§Jun 1973
Stevenson, Mr John David LLB(Hons) . . . *Apr 1981

RWPS LLP
Salterns Court Lilliput Square Sandbanks Road Poole BH14 8HU
Tel: 01202 707897 *Fax:* 01202 737609
Office: Poole

SIMMONDS SOLICITORS ‡
Equity Chambers 247 High Street North Poole BH15 1DX
Tel: 01202 666417 *Fax:* 01202 666418
Emergency telephone 01202 709933
E-mail: simmondssols@btconnect.com
List of partners: R Simmonds
Languages: French, German
Work: D1 K1 L S1 S2 W
Emergency Action, Agency, Advocacy, Fixed Fee Interview, Legal Aid undertaken and Legal Aid Franchise
SPr: Simmonds, Miss Rosamond BA(Hons) . . . *Dec 1980

SHARON TAYLOR ASSOCIATES ‡
312 Bournemouth Road Parkstone Poole BH14 9AP
Tel: 01202 759769 *Fax:* 01202 764390 *Dx:* 34803 PARKSTONE
List of partners: S A Taylor
Work: B2 G H
Agency, Advocacy and Legal Aid undertaken
Ptr: Taylor, Ms Sharon Antoinette BA . . . *Dec 1992
Ast: Brooking, Ms Alison Mary . . . *Aug 1996

TOWNSEND SOLICITORS ‡
11 Branksome Park House Branksome Business Park Bourne Valley Road Poole BH12 1ED
Tel: 0800 876 6870 / 01202 540200

P A TWIST & CO ‡
7-9 Haven Road Canford Cliffs Poole BH13 7LE
Tel: 01202 709050
List of partners: P A Twist
Languages: French, German
Work: B1 E J1 K1 N Q R1 S1 T1 T2 W
Agency and Advocacy undertaken
SPr: Twist, Miss Pauline Anne LLB . . . *§Jul 1977

PORT ISAAC, Cornwall

SPROULL SOLICITORS LLP
The Rock Port Isaac Cornwall PL29 3RN
Tel: 01840 212315 *Fax:* 01840 212792 *Dx:* 81854 BODMIN
E-mail: camelford@sproulllp.co.uk
Office: Bodmin, Camelford
Work: A1 B1 C1 E F1 K1 K3 K4 L N O Q R2 S1 S2 W Z(j,q,r)
Agency, Advocacy and Fixed Fee Interview undertaken
Mem: Sproull, Dugald LLB . . . *Jun 1966

PORT TALBOT, Neath Port Talbot

BOWERMANS ‡
PO Box 28 1 Courtland Place Port Talbot Neath Port Talbot SA13 1WR
Tel: 01639 891892 *Fax:* 01639 891892 *Dx:* 39261 PORT TALBOT
Emergency telephone 07973 347390
List of partners: L C Bowerman, M R Bowerman
Work: D1 G H J1 K1 L N Q S1 V
Emergency Action, Agency, Advocacy, Legal Aid undertaken and Member of Accident Line
Ptr: Bowerman, Ms Lisa C LLB(Hons) . . . *Feb 1994
Bowerman, Mr Martyn R BA . . . Nov 1988

CAMERON JONES HUSSELL & HOWE ‡
1, 2 & 3 Grove Place Port Talbot Neath Port Talbot SA13 1HX
Tel: 01639 885261 *Fax:* 01639 887138 *Dx:* 39251 PORT TALBOT
Emergency telephone 07900 994449
E-mail: reception@cjhh.com
List of partners: R S Howe, J G Hussell, J E Hussell, S A Kingsbury
Languages: French, Welsh
Work: A1 A3 D1 D2 E F1 G H K1 K2 K4 L N Q R1 S1 S2 T1 T2 W Z(l)
Emergency Action, Agency, Advocacy, Fixed Fee Interview, Legal Aid undertaken and Legal Aid Franchise
Ptr: Howe, Mr Richard S BA(Exon) . . . Oct 1978
Hussell, Mr Julian Edward LLB . . . *Oct 1998
Hussell, Mr John Godfrey FCIArb Deputy District Judge; Chartered Arbitrator . . . *§Dec 1966
Kingsbury, Mrs Sally A LLB(Wales) Heather Meredith - Parry Prize University of Wales . . . *Oct 1983
Ast: Davies, Miss Joanne Clare LLB . . . Oct 2000
Hussell, Mr David Alexander LLB . . . Oct 2000

HOWE & SPENDER ‡
Courtland Chambers 38-42 Station Road Port Talbot Neath Port Talbot SA13 1JS
Tel: 01639 881571 *Fax:* 01639 893137 *Dx:* 39253 PORT TALBOT
Emergency telephone 07789 798798
E-mail: administrator@howespender.co.uk
List of partners: R I Ambrose, J I Spender, J R Spender, S G Wharmby
Office: Neath
Work: B1 C1 D1 D2 E G H K1 K2 K3 K4 R1 S1 S2 W Z(l)
Emergency Action, Agency, Advocacy, Legal Aid undertaken and Legal Aid Franchise
Ptr: Ambrose, Mr Richard Ivor . . . *§Jun 1974
Spender, Mr J Ian LLB . . . *Dec 1991
Spender, Mr John R LLB(Wales) . . . *Jan 1966
Wharmby, Mr Stephen Graham LLB . . . *Jun 1980
Ast: Hopkins, Ms Jayne BA(Hons)(Law) . . . *Mar 1987
Lewis, Mrs Jessica Mary . . . *Dec 2010
Rees, Mr Hywel LLB . . . *Oct 2000
Williams, Mr Vincent Russell . . . *Mar 1987

KEVIN LANE & CO ‡
10 & 11 Courtland Place Port Talbot Neath Port Talbot SA13 1JJ
Tel: 01639 893700 *Fax:* 01639 893744
E-mail: customer@kevinlane.co.uk
List of partners: R J Hardee, K A Lane
Languages: Welsh
Work: B1 C1 E J1 K1 L N O Q S1 W
Advocacy, Legal Aid undertaken and Legal Aid Franchise
Ptr: Hardee, Ms Rebecca Jane BA(Hons) . . . Jan 2005
Lane, Mr Kevin A LLB(Lond) . . . *§Jan 1983

SHEEHANS SOLICITORS
56 Station Road Port Talbot Neath Port Talbot SA13 1LZ
Tel: 01639 883237 *Fax:* 01639 871313
Office: Neath
Work: E G H J1 K1 L N Q S1 W Z(l)
Emergency Action, Agency, Advocacy, Fixed Fee Interview, Legal Aid undertaken and Member of Accident Line
Ptr: Davies, Mr Ceri Gwyn LLB . . . *Oct 1977
Vickery, Mr Dean LLB . . . Feb 2006

H MICHAEL SPRING ‡
2 Forge Road Port Talbot Neath Port Talbot SA13 1NU
Tel: 01639 897075 *Fax:* 01639 883369
Work: G H S1 W

PORTCHESTER, Hampshire

BISCOES
64-66 West Street Portchester Hampshire PO16 9UN
Tel: 023 9237 0634 *Fax:* 023 9238 3722
E-mail: bcg@biscoes-law.co.uk
Office: Gosport, Petersfield, Portsmouth, Waterlooville, Wickham
Work: A1 A3 B1 C1 D1 D2 E F1 G H I J1 J2 K1 L N O Q S1 S2 V W X Z(b,c,d,e,f,i,j,k,l,q,r)
Emergency Action, Agency, Advocacy, Fixed Fee Interview, Legal Aid undertaken, Legal Aid Franchise and Member of Accident Line
Ptr: Cloke, Miss Stephanie . . . *Mar 2010
Lee, Ms Alison . . . *Nov 1994
Asoc: Foulkes-Williams, Ms Margaret Theresa LLB(Wales) *May 1982

MOSSE SOLICITORS ‡
4 Russell Buildings 86 West Street Portchester Hampshire PO16 9UL
Tel: 0800 011 6462 *Fax:* 023 9238 8223
E-mail: enquiries@mossesolicitors.com

PORTH, Rhondda Cynon Taff

JOHN HAMILTON LEYSHON SOLICITORS ‡
73 Hannah Street Porth Rhondda Cynon Taff CF39 9PY
Tel: 01443 680000 *Fax:* 01443 680001
E-mail: info@jhlsolicitors.co.uk
Office: Pontypridd

KTP SOLICITORS
(incorporating Hammertons)
1 Williams Place Porth Rhondda Cynon Taff CF39 9RY
Tel: 01443 687222 *Fax:* 01443 681427 *Dx:* 54602 PORTH
Emergency telephone 01656 840497
E-mail: porth@ktpsolicitors.com
Office: Bridgend (2 offices), Pontypridd
Work: A1 B1 C1 D1 E F1 G H J1 K1 L M1 N P R1 S1 T1 V
Emergency Action, Agency, Advocacy, Fixed Fee Interview and Legal Aid undertaken
Ptr: Hinton, Mr Paul J . . . Jan 1992

PORTHCAWL, Bridgend

DAVID & SNAPE
4 Lias Road Porthcawl Bridgend CF36 3AH
Tel: 01656 782070 / 785038 *Fax:* 01656 785579
Dx: 55803 PORTHCAWL
E-mail: jonathan.chubb@davidandsnape.com
Office: Bridgend
Work: E K1 L N Q S1 W
Emergency Action, Agency, Advocacy, Legal Aid undertaken and Legal Aid Franchise
Ptr: Chubb, Mr Jonathan G LLM(Wales); TEP . . . *§Apr 1980
Ast: Jones, Mrs Sandra LLB . . . *Mar 1993

R L EDWARDS & PARTNERS
(incorporating Williams Simons & Thomas; Brinley Richards & Partners)
65 Mary Street Porthcawl Bridgend CF36 3YZ
Tel: 01656 784151 *Fax:* 01656 785532
Office: Bridgend, Maesteg, Treorchy
Work: C1 E F1 G H K1 L M1 P S1 W
Emergency Action, Agency, Advocacy, Fixed Fee Interview, Legal Aid undertaken and Member of Accident Line

GARY NEWBURY ‡
20 Austin Close Porthcawl Bridgend CF36 5SN
Tel: 01656 773590 *Fax:* 01656 773507

WHITTINGHAMS
16 Well Street Porthcawl Bridgend CF36 3BE
Tel: 01656 788823 *Fax:* 01656 786781
Office: Bridgend
Work: A1 B1 C1 D1 E F1 G H J1 K1 L N O Q R1 S1 T1 V W Z(l)
Emergency Action, Agency, Advocacy, Fixed Fee Interview, Legal Aid undertaken and Member of Accident Line
Ptr: Greenway, Mr Michael BA . . . *Mar 1980
Ast: Jones, Mrs Alison E LLB . . . Oct 1988

PORTHMADOG, Gwynedd

BREESE-GWYNDAF ‡
60 High Street Porthmadog Gwynedd LL49 9LL
Tel: 01766 512253 / 514227 *Fax:* 01766 514227
Dx: 711470 PORTHMADOG
Emergency telephone 01286 830075
E-mail: office@breesegwyndaf.fsnet.com
List of partners: T Griffiths, J B Williams
Office: Barmouth, Harlech
Languages: Welsh

Work: A1 C1 C2 C3 D1 D2 F1 F2 G H J1 K1 L M1 N O P Q R1 S1 S2 T1 T2 V W Z(c,d,j,k,l,q,r,t)
Emergency Action, Agency, Advocacy, Fixed Fee Interview, Legal Aid undertaken and Legal Aid Franchise
Ptr: Griffiths, Mr Talfryn LLB Deputy District Judge . . . *Jun 1972
Williams, Mr John B LLB . . . *Jun 1977
Con: Hughes, Mr David A LLB . . . *§Dec 1972
Roberts, Mr Ian M V BSc(Wales) . . . *§Jul 1978

WILLIAM GEORGE & SON ‡
(incorporating Lloyd George & George)
103 High Street Porthmadog Gwynedd LL49 9EY
Tel: 01766 512011 / 512474 ***Fax:*** 01766 514363
Dx: 711471 PORTHMADOG
E-mail: williamgeorgeandson@tiscali.co.uk
List of partners: P W George
Languages: Welsh
Work: A1 E L N Q R1 S1 S2 T2 W
Ptr: George, Mr Philip W LLB(Wales); LLM(Lond) . . . *Sep 1982

ROBYNS OWEN & SON
14 New Street Porthmadog Gwynedd LL49 9ED
Tel: 01766 514747 ***Fax:*** 01766 514848
E-mail: enq@robynsowen.co.uk
Office: Pwllheli
Languages: Welsh
Work: A1 J1 K1 N Q S1 W Z(l)
Ptr: Jones, Robyn Rees LLB . . . *Oct 1987
Owen, Mr Ieuan E LLB Notary Public . . . *Dec 1973

PORTISHEAD, North Somerset

CHARLES COOK AND COMPANY LIMITED ‡
Kestrel Court Harbour Road Portishead North Somerset BS20 7AN
Tel: 01275 390432 ***Fax:*** 01275 390439
E-mail: vicki.white@cookco.co.uk

KAYES SOLICITORS
PO Box 120 Portishead North Somerset BS20 7WZ
Tel: 01275 399933 ***Fax:*** 01275 399944
Office: Pudsey

DAVID PLAYFORD & CO ‡
11 Cabstand Portishead North Somerset BS20 7HW
Tel: 01275 840111 ***Fax:*** 01275 840222 ***Dx:*** 48053 PORTISHEAD
Emergency telephone 07802 822682
List of partners: J D Playford
Work: B2 D1 D2 G H I K1 S1 S2 W Z(l)
Emergency Action, Advocacy, Legal Aid undertaken and Legal Aid Franchise
Ptr: Playford, Mr John D BA . . . *§Mar 1990

QUALITY SOLICITORS BURROUGHS DAY
Combe House Combe Road Portishead North Somerset BS20 6BJ
Tel: 01275 843213 ***Fax:*** 01275 849232 ***Dx:*** 48050 PORTISHEAD
E-mail: contact@qsbdlaw.com
Office: Bristol
Languages: French, Spanish
Work: A1 D1 J1 K1 S1 T1 T2 V W Z(e,o,r)
Emergency Action, Agency, Advocacy, Fixed Fee Interview, Legal Aid Franchise and Member of Accident Line

WARDS SOLICITORS
2 Harbour Road Portishead North Somerset BS20 7EL
Tel: 01275 850460 ***Fax:*** 01275 845239 ***Dx:*** 48061 PORTISHEAD
E-mail: info@wards.uk.com
Office: Bristol (2 offices), Clevedon, Nailsea, Staple Hill, Weston-super-Mare (3 offices), Yate
Ptr: McCabe, Mrs Mandy BSc . . . *Oct 1989

PORTLAND, Dorset

PORTLAND LEGAL SERVICES ‡
6 Chiswell Portland Dorset DT5 1AN
Tel: 01305 866162 ***Fax:*** 01305 866163
List of partners: D C Cuff
Work: A3 C1 E F1 L O Q R1 R2 Z(c,q)
Agency undertaken
Ptr: Cuff, Mr Dennis Charles . . . Sep 2004

REDFERNS
15 Easton Street Portland Dorset DT5 1BS
Tel: 01305 823636 ***Fax:*** 01305 823737
E-mail: mail@redferns-solicitors.com
Office: Weymouth
Work: C1 D1 E J1 K1 N O Q S1 S2 W Z(l,o,q)
Agency, Advocacy and Legal Aid undertaken
Ptr: Mackenzie, Mr John R LLB(B'ham) . . . *§Oct 1971
Summerscales, Mr Damian J BA(Hons) . . . *§Feb 1988

GRENVILLE J WALKER
22 Easton Street Portland Dorset DT5 1BT
Tel: 01305 862211 ***Fax:*** 01305 862363
E-mail: office@grenvillejwalker.org.uk
Office: Blandford Forum, Bournemouth, Weymouth

PORTSLADE-BY-SEA, Brighton & Hove

DEIBEL & ALLEN ‡
Keasley House 10 Franklin Road Portslade-by-Sea Brighton & Hove BN41 1AN
Tel: 01273 430999 ***Fax:*** 01273 430640 ***Dx:*** 92708 PORTSLADE
E-mail: enquiries@da-law.co.uk
List of partners: P C Allen, J W Deibel
Languages: French, German
Work: C1 E F1 J1 K1 K3 L Q R2 S1 S2 W Z(l,w)
Fixed Fee Interview undertaken
Ptr: Allen, Mr Peter C Stokes Memorial Prize . . . *Oct 1984
Deibel, Mr John W LLB . . . *Oct 1978
Ast: Jones, Ms Dawn Caron . . . *Feb 2007

PORTSMOUTH

ALLENS ‡
(incorporating Allen Sons Ward & Blake; Edmonds & Bullin)
15 Landport Terrace Portsmouth PO1 2QS
Est: 1896
Tel: 023 9282 2411 ***Fax:*** 023 9229 3773 ***Dx:*** 2201 PORTSMOUTH
E-mail: nicolafoster@allens-law.co.uk
List of partners: D G Gresswell, R E Stone
Work: B1 C1 D1 E F1 J1 K1 K3 K4 L N O Q R1 S1 S2 T1 T2 W Z(d)
Emergency Action, Agency and Advocacy undertaken
Ptr: Gresswell, Mr Daniel G BA(Hons) . . . *Aug 1990
Stone, Mr Robert Edward LLB(Hons) Assistant Deputy Coroner Notary Public . . . *§Jul 1974
Ast: Russell, Mrs Carolyn Helga LLB(Hons); Cert Ed(FE) . Oct 1985

ANDREW & ANDREW SOLICITORS ‡
Atlantic House 114 Kingston Crescent Portsmouth PO2 8AL
Tel: 023 9266 1381 ***Fax:*** 023 9269 3052
Dx: 42404 PORTSMOUTH NORTH END
Emergency telephone 0800 243 877
E-mail: innes@innes.co.uk
List of partners: C Innes, A M Sears, A D Wisniewski
Languages: French, Italian
Work: B1 C1 C2 D1 E F1 J1 K1 L N Q R1 S1 S2 V W Z(h,s)
Emergency Action, Agency, Advocacy, Fixed Fee Interview, Legal Aid undertaken, Legal Aid Franchise and Member of Accident Line
Ptr: Innes, Mr Colin . . . *Jan 1980
Sears, Mr Andrew M . . . *Aug 1980
Wisniewski, Mr Andrew David LLB . . . *Dec 1994
Ast: Duncan, Mr Ryan BA(Hons)(Law & Sociology) . . . *Feb 1994
Rutherford, Mrs Nikki . . . Mar 2000

BISCOES ‡
Kingston Place 62-68 Kingston Crescent North End Portsmouth PO2 8AQ
Tel: 023 9266 0261 ***Fax:*** 023 9266 2970
Dx: 155730 PORTSMOUTH 17
E-mail: bcg@biscoes-law.co.uk
List of partners: R T Barnes, S Cloke, M S Cover, J Evans, J Hodge, A Lee, M A McCredie, R S Salvetti, M N S Smith, R P Williams
Office: Gosport, Petersfield, Portchester, Waterlooville, Wickham
Languages: French
Work: A1 A3 B1 B2 C1 C2 D1 D2 E F1 G H J1 J2 K1 K2 K3 K4 L N O Q R2 S1 S2 T1 T2 W Z(c,d,e,h,i,j,k,l,p,q,r,u)
Emergency Action, Agency, Advocacy, Fixed Fee Interview, Legal Aid undertaken and Legal Aid Franchise
Ptr: Barnes, Mr Richard T BA(Hons) . . . *Jan 1986
Evans, Mrs Jean BA . . . *Jan 1985
McCredie, Mr Michael Alexander BA . . . *Oct 1986
Williams, Mr Richard Philip . . . *Aug 1979
Asoc: Gamester, Mr Timothy . . . Mar 2007
Phillips, Mr Nicholas . . . *Apr 2011
Travis, Mrs Sara LLB(Hons) . . . *Apr 2007
Yates, Ms Joanna LLB(Hons) . . . *Sep 2007
Ast: Knight, Kate . . . Dec 1992
Stuart-Taylor, Sir Nicholas R . . . *Dec 1977
Con: Cobbett, Mr John R G LLB(Lond) Notary Public . . . *§Jun 1957

BLAKE LAPTHORN ‡
Harbour Court Compass Road North Harbour Portsmouth PO6 4ST
Tel: 023 9222 1122 ***Fax:*** 023 9222 1123
Dx: 124490 PORTSMOUTH 9
E-mail: info@bllaw.co.uk
List of partners: N R D Abbott, D Agnew, B Albuery, C Alder, N J Arnold, J Bainbridge, P W B Barber, K M Barrow, C S Blake, E P Boyd, M A Brandman, C C Brockman, N Brook, N P Brook, R Brooks, P D Broom, S N Burge, M J Burridge, D J Castle, W J B Cha, M L Chant, M Charter, T D Couldrick, S Court, A M Cowell, M C Craft, P B Crier, E J Davis, J S Deech, P D Diamond, J A H Dobson, C P Dolan, S J Dryden, L Ellis, W D Foot, P A Fretwell, D M P Gallaway, I W Gill, C K C Graham, R J Guttridge, A J Harlow, M B Hepworth, D R G Higham, R E Humphreys, L M T Inzani, J P T Irwin-Singer, S Jarvis, N Keitley, J I Kennedy, R M Labadie, G Leach, E P Lee, J Lloyd-Jones, E M C Marshland, M Martin, T Matthew, J N Mawhood, A McClure, C B McClure, N A McEwen, G McGruer, G E McGruer, S J Meadon, A I F Miscampbell, J Mitchell, P H C Moody, A C Morris, L E Munro, S H Munson, S E Murfitt, D C Oliver, C Oster Warriner, S G Palka, S A Palmer, A D Peck, B Penfold, P J Pennal, L S Phillips, C Plews, R A Portlock, C D C Potts, M D J Profit, P F Quigley, D Rayner, M C Riccio, D M Rose, D W Russell, C D Saunders, J S Saunders, C J Scragg, P M Shepherd, K J Shimmin, G A Short, D J Smith, S Smith, T R Southern, O Sowton, J M Stansfield, J R Steel, S J Stokes, G H Sturgess, J P Sutton, M O Tackley, A Talbot, R G M Tassell, C J Taunt, J F Taylor, M R Thurston, S G Treherne, R S M Wade, J P Whiter, P C Wilson, S J Woodhouse
Office: Chandlers Ford, London EC1, Oxford
Languages: French
Work: B1 C1 C2 D1 E F1 I J1 K1 L M1 N O P Q R1 S1 T1 T2 W X Z(b,c,d,e,h,i,j,k,l,o,r,s,t)
Emergency Action, Agency, Advocacy, Legal Aid undertaken, Legal Aid Franchise and Member of Accident Line
Ptr: Abbott, Mr Neil R D LLB . . . *Oct 1979
Boyd, Ms Elaine P LLB(Soton) . . . *Sep 1984
Burridge, Mr Michael J Clerk to Commissioner of Taxes . . . *§Nov 1962
Castle, Miss Deborah J BA . . . *§Dec 1983
Cha, Mr Walter J B BA . . . *Nov 1983
Davis, Mrs Elizabeth J . . . *Oct 1982
Fretwell, Mr Paul Anthony LLB . . . *Oct 1990
Gallaway, Mr David M P . . . *§Dec 1973
Gill, Mr Ian W LLB . . . *Jan 1974
Inzani, Miss Lisa M T LLB(Hons) . . . *Nov 1990
Labadie, Mr Robert M LLB . . . *May 1988
Leach, Mrs Gillian BA; LLB; FRSA . . . *Oct 1992
McGruer, Mr Guthrie E LLB(Hons) Legal Associate of the Royal Town Planning Institute . . . *Jun 1980
Palka, Mr Sean G LLB . . . *Oct 1990
Profit, Mr Michael D J LLB Notary Public . . . *§Jan 1968
Saunders, Mr Clive D MA(Cantab); TEP . . . *Jun 1973
Scragg, Mr Charles J MA(Oxon); TEP . . . *§Jun 1973
Tackley, Mr Michael O . . . *Jun 1976
Tassell, Mr Richard Guy Murray . . . *Dec 1972
Treherne, Mr Simon Grant BA(Law) Maxwell Law Prize . . . *Nov 1986
Ast: Anderson, Miss Elizabeth Louise BSc . . . *Oct 1994
Baker, Ms Claire D LLB(Hons) . . . *Sep 1997
Brooks, Mrs Rachel LLB . . . Nov 1995
Cornall, Miss Susan . . . Oct 1998
Easton, Miss Emma Kate BA(Hons) . . . Sep 2002
Gilpin, Miss Rachel Sara LLB(Hons) . . . Sep 2002
Hepworth, Mr Mark B BA . . . *Oct 1979
Hicks, Mrs Jennifer BA . . . *Nov 1985
Jagger, Miss Helen BA(Hons) . . . *Mar 1996
Kalman, Mr Jonathan Paul . . . *Jan 1996
Lawes, Miss Clare Hannah LLB(Hons) . . . Sep 2002
Levey, Mr Andrew David LLB(Wales) Deputy District Judge . . . *§Nov 1983
Miah, Mrs Gill Ruth LLB(Hons); HND; LSF; Dip Adv Litigation . . . *Nov 1995
Miah, Mr Sadak LLB . . . Jul 1994
Middleton, Miss Caroline Anne LLB(Hons)(Law) . . . Sep 2001
Mitchell, Mr Dominic James BA(Hons)(Law) . . . Sep 2001
O'Meara, Mr Jonathan Robert LLB(Hons)(Law) . . . Sep 2001
Oliver, Mr Nicholas Rhoderick LLB(Hons); PGDip . . . *Sep 1996
Peacock, Miss Sarah Vivien LLB(Hons) . . . Aug 2001
Prior, Ms Rachel LLB(Hons); DipLP . . . Apr 2000
Randall, Mr Jonathan Rupert LLB(Hons) . . . Sep 1997
Redgrave, Mr Peregrine Carlyle LLB(Hons) . . . *Feb 1998
Seevaratnam, Ms Tanya S LLB . . . *Mar 1995
Thorpe, Mr Martyn LLB . . . *Sep 1990
Wheeler, Mrs Lisa L . . . *Dec 1999
Winslade, Mr Graham R T George Rax Prize . . . *Dec 1991
Con: Collins, Mr David A LLB Notary Public . . . *§Feb 1962

BOLITHO WAY ‡
13-18 Kings Terrace Portsmouth PO5 3AL
Tel: 023 9282 0747 ***Fax:*** 023 9286 2831 ***Dx:*** 2205 PORTSMOUTH 1
E-mail: enquiries@bolithoway.com
List of partners: M J Cregan, D J Grinstead, S M Moger, N P Watkins, F P Worsley
Office: Ryde
Work: B1 C1 D1 E F1 G H I J1 K1 L M1 N P R1 S1 T1 W Z(e)
Agency, Advocacy, Fixed Fee Interview, Legal Aid undertaken and Legal Aid Franchise
Ptr: Cregan, Mr Michael John . . . Aug 1994
Grinstead, Mr David J LLB(B'ham) . . . *Oct 1987
Moger, Mr Simon M BA . . . *Apr 1987
Watkins, Mr Neville P . . . *Jun 1970
Worsley, Mr Francis P LLB(L'pool) . . . Oct 1984

CHURCHERS
60-62 Northern Road Cosham Portsmouth PO6 3DX
Tel: 023 9221 0170 ***Fax:*** 023 9221 0069
Dx: 94950 COSHAM (PORTSMOUTH)
E-mail: solicitors@churchers.co.uk
Office: Fareham, Gosport, Lee-on-the-Solent, Portsmouth, Ryde
Work: D1 F1 G H J1 K1 N S1 V W Z(m)
Emergency Action, Agency, Advocacy, Fixed Fee Interview, Legal Aid undertaken and Legal Aid Franchise
Ptr: Bryan, Mr Andrew LLB . . . *Dec 1995
Mackey, Mr Colin P LLB . . . *Apr 1972
Ast: Coates, Miss Sarah LLB . . . Jul 2006
Mackenzie, Mrs Jane Lindsey LLB . . . *Sep 2002

CHURCHERS
Enterprise House Isambard Brunel Road Portsmouth PO1 2AF
Tel: 023 9286 2424 ***Fax:*** 023 9286 1880 ***Dx:*** 2223 PORTSMOUTH
Emergency telephone 07708 285562
E-mail: solicitors@churchers.co.uk
Office: Fareham, Gosport, Lee-on-the-Solent, Portsmouth, Ryde
Languages: French
Work: G H K1 S1
Agency, Advocacy, Legal Aid undertaken, Legal Aid Franchise and Member of Accident Line
Ptr: O'Hagan, Miss Bridget LLB ★ . . . *Oct 1991
Robinson, Mr R Ian DML . . . *Sep 1987
Ast: Colmer, Miss Kristina LLB . . . Jun 2008
Dodd, Mr Adrian Lennox LLB(Hons) . . . *Oct 1983
Farley, Mr Henry Richard BA(Hons) . . . *Nov 1990
Hopley, Mr Graham John . . . *Dec 2002
Jones, Miss Hannah LLB . . . Mar 2007
Moger, Mr Simon M BA . . . *Apr 1987

COFFIN MEW & CLOVER
Bay House Compass Road North Harbour Business Park Portsmouth PO6 4RS
Tel: 023 9238 8021 ***Fax:*** 023 9221 0952
Dx: 124493 PORTSMOUTH 9
E-mail: portsmouth@coffinmew.co.uk
Office: Fareham, Gosport, Southampton
Work: D1 D2 G H K1 K2 S1 T2 V W Z(g,l,o,s)
Emergency Action, Agency, Advocacy, Fixed Fee Interview, Legal Aid undertaken, Legal Aid Franchise and Member of Accident Line
Ptr: Hansford, Miss Jane LLB; AKC . . . *Jan 1981
Johns, Ms Geraldine D LLB . . . *Feb 1988
Meads, Mr William A . . . *§Jul 1967
Yetman, Mr Philip J BA . . . *Dec 1976
Asoc: Busst, Ms Caroline Lisa . . . *Oct 1990
Ast: Reading, Mr Stephen BA(Hons) . . . *Mar 2001
Spanner, Ms Linda Jill FILEx; CPE; LPC . . . Nov 1998

GURNEY-CHAMPION & CO ‡
Champion House 104 Victoria Road North Southsea Portsmouth PO5 1QE
Tel: 023 9282 1100 ***Fax:*** 023 9282 0447
Dx: 117953 PORTSMOUTH CENTRAL
Emergency telephone 01983 522665
E-mail: info@championlawyers.co.uk
List of partners: J S C Gurney-Champion, N C A Gurney-Champion
Office: Newport
Work: B1 C1 D1 E F1 J1 K1 K3 K4 L N O P Q R1 R2 S1 S2 T2 W Z(c,d,g,i,l,p,q)
Emergency Action, Agency, Advocacy and Fixed Fee Interview undertaken
Ptr: Gurney-Champion, Mr Nicholas C A LLB . . . *§Oct 1986
Ast: Archer, Mr Matthew Attwood BA(Hons); LLB . . . Apr 2010
Green, Miss Sara Louise LLB . . . *Aug 2006
Howard, Mrs Anne-Marie LLB . . . *Sep 2006

LARCOMES LLP ‡
168 London Road North End Portsmouth PO2 9DN
Tel: 023 9266 1531 ***Fax:*** 023 9266 5701
Dx: 42401 PORTSMOUTH NORTH END
E-mail: enquiries@larcomes.co.uk
List of partners: J D Davis, L Davison, C J Gates, R P Hopgood, J M Quartermain, M Tooley, A C R Turner
Office: Waterlooville
Languages: French
Work: A1 C1 D1 D2 E J1 K1 K2 K3 L N O P Q R1 R2 S1 S2 W Z(o)
Emergency Action, Agency, Advocacy, Fixed Fee Interview, Legal Aid undertaken and Legal Aid Franchise
Ptr: Davis, Mrs Julia D . . . *Nov 1995
Davison, Ms Lynn . . . *Sep 1997

See p112 for the Key to Work Categories & other symbols

Gates, Mr Christopher John . . . . *Jun 1996
Hopgood, Mr Richard Paul LLB(Hons). . . . . *Jan 1999
Quartermain, Mr Julian M BA . . . . *Oct 1986
Tooley, Mr Mark LLB . . . . *Mar 1987
Turner, Mr Andrew C R BA(Lond) . . . . *§Dec 1974
Asoc: Beuzeval, Miss Lisa Jayne LLB . . . . *Aug 2006
Ast: Hayles, Mrs Christina Anne LLB. . . . . *Sep 1999
Shackleton, Miss Amanda-Jane LLB . . . . Aug 2009
Sumner, Mr David LLB . . . . *Jun 2006

M V LLOYD
404 Havant Road Portsmouth PO6 1NF
Tel: 023 9238 6757
Office: Fareham
Work: E L S1 S2 T2 W Z(l)

MEDIATION NOW LTD ‡
62-68 Kingston Crescent North End Portsmouth PO2 8AQ
Tel: 023 9262 6897 *Fax:* 023 9266 2970
E-mail: michael@mediation-now.co.uk
Office: Emsworth, Fareham, Petersfield (2 offices)

NELSON NICHOLS ‡
36a London Road North End Portsmouth PO2 0LN
Tel: 023 9265 0623 *Fax:* 023 9265 0608
E-mail: convey@nnlaw.co.uk
List of partners: I K Nelson
Work: E L N Q S1 S2 W
Ptr: Nelson, Mr Ian K . . . . *Dec 1985

RUTHERFORD SOLICITORS ‡
257 Milton Road Milton Portsmouth PO4 8PQ
Tel: 023 9273 5700 *Fax:* 023 9273 5551
E-mail: enquiries@rutherfordsolicitors.co.uk

STOKES SOLICITORS ‡
229 London Road Portsmouth PO2 9AL
Tel: 023 9266 1541 *Fax:* 023 9266 8221
Dx: 42400 PORTSMOUTH NORTH END
E-mail: mail@stokes-law.co.uk
List of partners: J A K Colville, S Harris, D S Hopkins, A P Jackson, M L R Long
Office: Portsmouth
Work: C1 D1 D2 E K1 S1 S2 W
Ptr: Colville, Mr James A K LLB(Hons). . . . . *Dec 1979
Harris, Mr Simon LLB(Hons) . . . . Mar 1990

STOKES SOLICITORS
(incorporating Huchlings Hollings & Son)
108 Victoria Road North Portsmouth PO5 1QQ
Tel: 023 9282 8131 *Fax:* 023 9281 1339 *Dx:* 2220 PORTSMOUTH 1
Emergency telephone 023 9246 6710
E-mail: mail@stokes-law.co.uk
Office: Portsmouth
Languages: French, Italian, Spanish
Work: A1 B1 B2 C1 C2 C3 D1 D2 E F1 F2 G H J1 K1 L M1 N O P Q R1 S1 S2 V W Z(c,d,f,g,i,j,k,l,p,q,r,s,t)
Emergency Action, Agency, Advocacy, Fixed Fee Interview, Legal Aid undertaken, Legal Aid Franchise and Member of Accident Line
Ptr: Hopkins, Mr Dudley S. . . . . *Jun 1972
Jackson, Mr Anthony P LLB(Hons) . . . . *§Dec 1974
Long, Mrs Maria L R BA. . . . . *Sep 1981
Ast: Chaudhry, Mr M Saleem BA(Hons) . . . . *Oct 1982
Manton, Mrs Caroline Elaine BA. . . . . Feb 1998
Metcalfe, Miss Christina Louise MA(Oxon); LLB(Hons) *Oct 1996
Mills, Mr Michael James LLB . . . . *Jul 1981
Strevens, Ms Caroline LLB(Hons). . . . . *Apr 1981
West, Mr John LLB . . . . *Jan 1972
Wilson, Mr Michael A BA(Hons). . . . . *Aug 1998
Con: Bateman, Mr Richard P TD . . . . *Mar 1979

TOLCHER & CO MARINE SOLICITORS ‡
Royal Naval Club 17 Pembroke Road Portsmouth PO1 2NT
Tel: 023 9273 7008 *Fax:* 023 9273 8723
E-mail: jt@tolchermarinelaw.com
Work: Z(d)

VERISONA SOLICITORS
1000 Lakeside North Harbour Portsmouth PO6 3EN
Tel: 023 9238 0112 *Fax:* 023 9231 2080
Office: Havant, Waterlooville

WARNER GOODMAN LLP
Coleman House 2-4 Landport Terrace Portsmouth PO1 2RG
Tel: 023 9275 3575 *Fax:* 023 9275 5094 *Dx:* 2210 PORTSMOUTH
E-mail: enquiries@warnergoodman.co.uk
Office: Fareham, Southampton
Languages: French, Italian, Spanish
Work: A1 B1 C1 C2 C3 D1 E F1 G H J1 K1 L M1 M2 N P R1 S1 T1 T2 V W Z(a,b,c,e,l)
Emergency Action, Agency, Advocacy, Fixed Fee Interview, Legal Aid undertaken, Legal Aid Franchise and Member of Accident Line
Mem: Grant, Mr Steven . . . . Sep 2003
Dir: Battye, Ms Claire . . . . Jul 1998
Grant, Mr Steven . . . . Sep 2003
Horn, Mr Kevin Barry Joseph . . . . Sep 1990
Winslade, Mr Paul John. . . . . Jun 1997
Asoc: Brennan, Mrs Zoe Claire . . . . Aug 2002
Bryson, Ms Elizabeth Jane . . . . Jan 2007
Legister, Mr Mark Percival Notary Public . . . . . . Jun 2008
Mills, Mrs Anne . . . . Mar 2000
Pennicott, Mrs Sarah Louise . . . . Sep 2003
Ast: Arnett, Mr Paul William . . . . Sep 2004

WESSEX SOLICITORS CHAMBERS LTD ‡
4 Highbury Buildings Portsmouth Road Cosham Portsmouth PO6 2SN
Tel: 023 9238 1114 *Fax:* 023 9238 1115 *Dx:* 94951 COSHAM
Emergency telephone 0808 033 3363 (CALL FREE DEFENCE)
E-mail: hugh@wessexsolicitors.co.uk
List of partners: H Barrington-Clark, H J Y Pringle, L Webster-Martin
Languages: French, German
Work: G H V Z(t)
Emergency Action, Agency, Advocacy, Fixed Fee Interview, Legal Aid undertaken and Legal Aid Franchise
Dir: Barrington-Clark, Mr Howard LLB ★. . . . . *Apr 1978
Pringle, Mr Hugh J Y LLB . . . . *§Jan 1979
Webster-Martin, Ms Lian . . . . *Oct 2008
Asoc: Taylor, Ms Kim F . . . . Sep 1976

GRENVILLE YOUNG SOLICITOR ‡
51 Woodfield Avenue Portsmouth PO6 1AN
Tel: 023 9237 2192 *Fax:* 023 9237 2192
E-mail: info@grenville-young.co.uk

POTTERS BAR, Hertfordshire

BATCHELOR MYDDELTON ‡
Brosnan House Darkes Lane Potters Bar Hertfordshire EN6 1BW
Tel: 01707 647088 *Fax:* 01707 647704
E-mail: robin@batchelor-myddelton.co.uk
List of partners: J A Batchelor, R H H Myddelton
Work: C1 C2 E F1 F2 I J1 L O Q R2 S1 S2 W Z(e,f,l,p,q,za)
Ptr: Batchelor, Mrs Jennifer A . . . . *Oct 1986
Myddelton, Mr Robin H H . . . . *Nov 1970
Asoc: Leite, Mrs Amy Louise LLB . . . . Mar 2010
Ast: Evans, Miss Christine Claire. . . . . Sep 2010
Con: Robinson, Mrs Claire LLB. . . . . *Aug 1984

OLIVER BRITTON ‡
16 Billy Lows Lane Potters Bar Hertfordshire EN6 1XN
Tel: 01707 660375 *Fax:* 01707 660375
E-mail: oliverbritton@aol.com
Work: J1

STANLEY DE LEON ‡
(in association with Williams & Rees)
45 Darkes Lane Potters Bar Hertfordshire EN6 1BJ
Tel: 01707 657277 *Fax:* 01707 651294 *Dx:* 135551 POTTERS BAR 3
E-mail: law@stanleydeleon.co.uk
List of partners: S J Acres, I Lock
Languages: French, German
Work: B1 C1 C2 C3 D1 E I J1 J2 K1 L O Q R2 S1 S2 T1 T2 U2 W Z(c,d,e,l,w)
Agency, Fixed Fee Interview and Legal Aid Franchise
Ptr: Acres, Mr Stephen J LLB . . . . Apr 1999
Lock, Mr Iain . . . . May 1997
Ast: Adefuve, Miss Olubunmi LLB . . . . Aug 2004
Henry, Miss Suzanne . . . . *Nov 2004
Con: McGovern, Ms Joanne LLB(Hons). . . . . *Jun 1996

DICKINS SHIEBERT ‡
Matthew House 45/47 High Street Potters Bar Hertfordshire EN6 5AW
Tel: 01707 851100 *Fax:* 01707 646627 *Dx:* 57950 POTTERS BAR
List of partners: M R A Bolton, T T Shiebert
Work: A1 C1 E L R1 S1 S2 W Z(c)
Ptr: Bolton, Mr Malcolm R A LLB(Nott'm) . . . . *§Dec 1970
Shiebert, Ms Tina T BA . . . . *Oct 1986
Ast: Bell, Miss Brona Margaret. . . . . Sep 2003

HEYDONS ‡
16 Carbone Hill Northaw Potters Bar Hertfordshire EN6 4PL
Tel: 01707 879646 *Fax:* 01707 888634
List of partners: G H Heydon
Work: T1 T2
Ptr: Heydon, Mr Gordon Howard. . . . . *Jun 1968

LAWRANCE & HOLDER ‡
82a High Street Potters Bar Hertfordshire EN6 5AB
Tel: 01707 645317 *Fax:* 01707 665590 *Dx:* 57954 POTTERS BAR
E-mail: lawrance-holder@btconnect.com
List of partners: C P Holder, J W Lawrance
Work: E S1 W
Fixed Fee Interview undertaken
Ptr: Holder, Mr Christopher Paul LLB(Lond) . . . . *Mar 1980
Lawrance, Mr John Wilfred LLB(Lond). . . . . *Jun 1976

E D C LORD & CO
Chasegate House 13-17 Southgate Road Potters Bar Hertfordshire EN6 5DR
Tel: 01707 659499 *Fax:* 01707 664277
Office: Hayes, London W13

MALE & WAGLAND ‡
4-8 Barnet Road Potters Bar Hertfordshire EN6 2QT
Tel: 01707 657171 *Fax:* 01707 646336 *Dx:* 57951 POTTERS BAR 1
E-mail: enquiry@mwlaw.co.uk
List of partners: M C Jones, R C Male, D A Saunders
Office: Barnet
Languages: French
Work: A1 B1 C1 C2 D1 E F1 G H I J1 J2 K1 K3 L N O Q R1 R2 S1 S2 T2 W Z(c,e,j,k,l,q,r)
Emergency Action, Advocacy undertaken and Member of Accident Line
Ptr: Jones, Mr Mark C LLB . . . . *§Aug 1981
Male, Mr Richard Chancellor . . . . *§Oct 1961
Saunders, Mr David A ♦. . . . . *§Dec 1976
Ast: Bayles, Miss Lindsay S BA(Hons); TEP . . . . *§Nov 1987
Begum, Miss Shamima LLB(Hons); LPC . . . . *Sep 2010
Gilmour, Ms Sarah E BA ♦ . . . . *Jul 1989
Ruckin, Mrs Hayley BA . . . . *Sep 2008

C PITTORDOU & CO ‡
Suite 32 The Enterprise Centre Cranbourne Road Potters Bar Hertfordshire EN6 3DQ
Tel: 01707 663760 *Fax:* 01707 654645
List of partners: C Pittordou
Languages: Greek
Work: C1 G H J1 K1 L M1 P T1 W Z(c,d,e,l,m)
Agency and Advocacy undertaken
SPr: Pittordou, Christakis LLB(Lond) . . . . *Jun 1980

SHAHIN & CO ‡
223 Darkes Lane Potters Bar Hertfordshire EN6 1BX
Tel: 01707 658722 *Fax:* 01707 652130
E-mail: dshahin123@aol.com
Languages: Turkish
Work: K1 K3 S1 S2 W
Fixed Fee Interview undertaken

WASON & CO ‡
60 High Street Potters Bar Hertfordshire EN6 5AB
Tel: 01707 664888 *Fax:* 01707 651785 *Dx:* 57953 POTTERS BAR
E-mail: info@wason-law.com
List of partners: P Karia, S Wason
Work: C1 E L S1 S2 W Z(l)
Ptr: Karia, Mrs Priya BA. . . . . *Jul 2003
Wason, Shamit BSc(Econ) . . . . *Oct 1983

POULTON-LE-FYLDE, Lancashire

ALKERS SOLICITORS ‡
Bancroft House 8 Hardhorn Road Poulton-le-Fylde Lancashire FY6 7SR
Tel: 01253 892237 *Fax:* 01253 892238
E-mail: mail@alkers.net

INGHAMS
12 Queens Square Poulton-le-Fylde Lancashire FY6 7BN
Tel: 01253 890545 *Fax:* 01253 893171
Dx: 703310 POULTON-LE-FYLDE
Office: Blackpool (2 offices), Fleetwood, Knott-End-on-Sea, Thornton Cleveleys
Work: C1 D1 E F1 G H J1 K1 L M1 P R1 S1 V W Z(l,p)
Emergency Action, Agency, Advocacy, Fixed Fee Interview, Legal Aid undertaken and Member of Accident Line
Ptr: Hale, Mr Anthony T W. . . . . *Jan 1968
Statham, Mr Richard J H BA(Law). . . . . *Apr 1981
Asoc: Jackson, Ms Helen BA(Law) . . . . Nov 1984

PAMELA K JOHNSON SOLICITOR ‡
7 Parrox Fold Preesall Poulton-le-Fylde Lancashire FY6 0QX
Tel: 01253 812400 *Fax:* 0560 204 3096
E-mail: pamela.pkjohnson@btconnect.com
List of partners: P K Johnson
Work: S1 W
Fixed Fee Interview undertaken
SPr: Johnson, Mrs Pamela Kay BA(Hons) . . . . *Oct 1981

PRESTONS ‡
15a Chapel Street Poulton-le-Fylde Lancashire FY6 7BQ
Tel: 01253 882426 *Fax:* 01253 893261
Dx: 703312 POULTON-LE-FYLDE
E-mail: jpreston@prestons-solicitors.co.uk
List of partners: J M Preston
Work: K1 Q S1 S2 W
Ptr: Preston, Mr John M BA. . . . . *Jun 1977
Ast: Care, Mrs Jayne Margaret LLB(Hons). . . . . Sep 1995

ROBINSON'S SOLICITORS ‡
Beckett House Sovereign Court Poulton-le-Fylde Lancashire FY6 8JX
Tel: 01253 882522 *Fax:* 01253 882599

ROWNTREE & BERRY
10a Tithebarn Street Poulton-le-Fylde Lancashire FY6 7DG
Tel: 01253 893599 *Fax:* 01253 899396 *Dx:* 18254 FLEETWOOD
Office: Fleetwood

SENIOR CALVELEY & HARDY
23 Hardhorn Road Poulton-le-Fylde Lancashire FY6 7SR
Tel: 01253 882883 *Fax:* 01253 794430
Office: Kirkham, Lytham

VINCENTS
26 Lancaster Road Knott End-on-Sea Poulton-le-Fylde Lancashire FY6 0AU
Tel: 01253 810643 *Fax:* 01253 812833
Emergency telephone 01995 601995
Office: Garstang
Work: H J1 K1 L N R1 S1 V W Z(l)
Emergency Action, Agency, Advocacy, Fixed Fee Interview and Legal Aid undertaken
Con: Brooks, Mr Roger W TD. . . . . *§Dec 1976

POYNTON, Cheshire

HENRYS SOLICITORS LTD
10 London Road North Poynton Cheshire SK12 1QZ
Tel: 01625 630880 *Fax:* 01625 871795
Emergency telephone 07770 816682
E-mail: reception@henryandcosolicitors.co.uk
Office: Stockport (2 offices)
Work: B2 G H I
Emergency Action, Agency, Advocacy, Legal Aid undertaken and Legal Aid Franchise

MANNERS PIMBLETT SOLICITORS ‡
4 London Road North Poynton Cheshire SK12 1QZ
Tel: 01625 850888 *Fax:* 01625 873888

NICHOLLS LINDSELL & HARRIS AND INGHAM & WAINWRIGHT ‡
34-36 Park Lane Poynton Cheshire SK12 1RE
Tel: 01625 876411 *Fax:* 01625 879947
E-mail: enquiries@nichollslindsellharris.co.uk
List of partners: J M Gibbons
Languages: French
Work: A1 B1 C1 E F1 K1 L N Q R1 S1 T2 W
Agency, Advocacy, Fixed Fee Interview, Legal Aid undertaken and Legal Aid Franchise
Ptr: Gibbons, Mrs Judith M BA . . . . *Jun 1977
Ast: Dawson, Ms Catherine M MA; LLB . . . . *Sep 1995
Lowe, Mrs Lorraine LLB. . . . . Apr 1976

STRATFORD SOLICITORS
Poynton Chambers 130 London Road South Poynton Cheshire SK12 1LQ
Tel: 01625 878204 *Fax:* 01625 878197
E-mail: enquiries@stratford-solicitors.com
Office: Macclesfield

PRESCOT, Merseyside

CE LAW ‡
Grange House 19-21 Grange Mount Prescot Merseyside CH43 4XN
Tel: 0151 670 0456 *Fax:* 0151 670 0678
E-mail: info@celawyers.com

DDE LAW ‡
53 Eccleston Street Prescot Merseyside L34 5QH
Tel: 0151 493 9993 *Fax:* 0151 493 9926
E-mail: info@ddelaw.com

DUNCAN GIBBINS SOLICITORS ‡
Forum House Tiger Court Kings Park Prescot Merseyside L34 1PJ
Tel: 0151 949 5757 *Fax:* 0151 949 5758
E-mail: info@duncangibbins.com

HEALEY KENYON MCATEER SOLICITORS
10 Derby Street Prescot Merseyside L34 3LG
Tel: 0151 261 9857
E-mail: enquiries@motoringlawbarristers.co.uk
Office: Liverpool

HOGANS ‡
10 Station Street Rainhill Prescot Merseyside L35 0LP
Tel: 0151 430 7529 *Fax:* 0151 430 6181 *Dx:* 15322 RAINHILL
E-mail: hogans@btinternet.com
List of partners: G Hogan, K A Lloyd, J O'Beirne
Work: D1 F1 G H K1 N Q S1 V W Z(l,m)
Agency and Legal Aid undertaken
Ptr: Hogan, Mr Gary BA . . . . . *Feb 1982
Lloyd, Mrs Katherine A LLB(Nott'm) . . . . . *Dec 1986
O'Beirne, Miss Johanne . . . . . Jul 1990

R JAMES HUTCHEON SOLICITORS ‡
Warburton Hey Rainhill Prescot Merseyside L35 4LF
Tel: 0151 431 0548 *Fax:* 0871 218 1082
E-mail: info@hutcheonlaw.co.uk
List of partners: R J Hutcheon
SPr: Hutcheon, Mr Ronald James LLB . . . . . *Dec 1993

NORTON & CO ‡
The Old Bank 499 Warrington Road Rainhill Prescot Merseyside L35 4LL
Tel: 0151 426 7001 *Fax:* 0151 426 8386 *Dx:* 15321 RAINHILL
E-mail: norton@sthelens-net.co.uk
List of partners: B A Evans, N Walker
Work: A1 B1 C1 D1 E F1 G H J1 K1 K3 L M1 N P Q R1 S1 T1 V W Z(c,l,m,q)
Emergency Action, Agency, Advocacy, Legal Aid undertaken and Member of Accident Line
Ptr: Evans, Mrs Beverley A BA(Hons) . . . . . Oct 1995
Walker, Mrs Nicala . . . . . *Dec 1995
Asoc: Cain, Mr Paul Alexander LLB(Hons) . . . . . Nov 1990
Ast: Coghlan, Mr Michael Francis MA(Cantab) . . . . . *Jan 1980
Con: Unsworth, Mr A Kenneth . . . . . *Dec 1967

PARRY & CO ‡
Dovecote Court Stanley Grange Knowsley Prescot Merseyside L34 4AR
Tel: 0870 380 4424 *Fax:* 0870 380 4425

PORTER ASSOCIATES ‡
1st Floor 3 High Street Prescot Merseyside L34 3LD
Tel: 0151 430 9160 *Fax:* 0151 431 1262 *Dx:* 24053 PRESCOT
E-mail: g.alderson@porter-law.co.uk
List of partners: D M Porter
Work: C1 D1 D2 E J1 K1 K3 K4 L N P Q R1 S1 S2 W Z(c,q)
Advocacy, Fixed Fee Interview, Legal Aid undertaken and Member of Accident Line
SPr: Porter, Mr David M LLB(Manc) . . . . . *§Jan 1970

TICKLE HALL CROSS
2 Derby Street Prescot Merseyside L34 3LJ
Tel: 0800 854379 *Fax:* 0151 430 8001 *Dx:* 24051 PRESCOT
Office: St Helens
Languages: French, German
Work: A1 B1 C1 D1 E F1 G H J1 K1 L M1 N P R1 S1 T1 V W Z(c,d,j,k,l,m,n,o,p,s)
Agency, Advocacy, Fixed Fee Interview, Legal Aid undertaken and Member of Accident Line
Ptr: Fitzpatrick, Mr Keith LLB . . . . . *Jul 1974

PRESTATYN, Denbighshire

CLEMENT HUGHES & CO ‡
4 Maes-y-Groes Prestatyn Denbighshire LL19 9DB
Tel: 01745 852121 *Fax:* 01745 852124 *Dx:* 14972 PRESTATYN
E-mail: david.sperring@clement-hughes.co.uk
List of partners: A M Ostanek, D Sperring, R M Sperring
Work: E K1 L Q S1 S2 W
Emergency Action, Agency and Fixed Fee Interview undertaken
Ptr: Ostanek, Mr Andrew M LLB . . . . . *Mar 1988
Sperring, Mr David LLB . . . . . *Dec 1974
Sperring, Miss Rachel Mary LLB . . . . . *Jul 2005
Ast: Sperring, Mr Ian LLB . . . . . *Jul 2010

G LLOYD JONES & CO ‡
83 High Street Prestatyn Denbighshire LL19 9AP
Tel: 01745 888666 *Fax:* 01745 888666
E-mail: gwynlloyd.jones@btconnect.com
List of partners: G L Jones
Languages: Welsh
Work: A1 E J1 K1 K3 K4 L S1 S2 W Z(l)
SPr: Jones, Gwyn Lloyd . . . . . *Jul 1971

D K MACBRYDE & CO ‡
4 Nant Hall Road Prestatyn Denbighshire LL19 9LH
Tel: 01745 856404 *Fax:* 01745 886154 *Dx:* 14971 PRESTATYN
E-mail: ajm@dkmacbryde.co.uk
List of partners: A J Macbryde, D K Macbryde
Work: C1 D1 D2 E F1 J1 K1 K3 L Q S1 S2 W Z(l)
Emergency Action, Agency, Advocacy, Legal Aid undertaken and Legal Aid Franchise
Ptr: Macbryde, Miss Amanda Jayne BA . . . . . *Nov 2001
Macbryde, Mr David K . . . . . *§Dec 1967

MACKENZIE JONES
Prior House 129 High Street Prestatyn Denbighshire LL19 9AS
Tel: 01745 852110 *Fax:* 01745 859727 *Dx:* 14975 PRESTATYN
E-mail: mailroom@macjones.com
Office: St Asaph

PURE CORPORATE SOLICITORS ‡
157 High Street Prestatyn Denbighshire LL19 9AY
Tel: 01745 888061 *Fax:* 0870 762 8059
E-mail: sch@purecorporate.com

PRESTEIGNE, Powys

VAUGHAN & DAVIES
5 Broad Street Presteigne Powys LD8 2AA
Tel: 01544 267731
Office: Kington

PRESTON, Lancashire

AMS SOLICITORS ‡
215-217 Ribbleton Lane Preston Lancashire PR1 5DY
Tel: 01772 653333

AYB LAW SOLICITORS ‡
93 Fishergate Hill Preston Lancashire PR1 8JD
Tel: 01772 250605 *Fax:* 01772 250615
List of partners: A Y Bodi
Work: F1 F2 N Z(q,r)
SPr: Bodi, Mr Asif Yunus LLB(Hons) . . . . . *Oct 1995

APPLEYARD LEES
Faraday Court Faraday Drive Fulwood Preston Lancashire PR2 9NB
Tel: 01772 884642
E-mail: preston@appleyardlees.com
Office: Burnley, Chester, Halifax, Harrogate, Huddersfield, Leeds, Liverpool, Manchester, Sheffield, Stockton-on-Tees, York

BARBER & CO ‡
Barber House 164 Deepdale Road Preston Lancashire PR1 1SA
Tel: 01772 203520 *Fax:* 01772 203620

BECKETT & CO ‡
First Floor 180-182 Station Road Bamber Bridge Preston Lancashire PR5 6TP
Tel: 01772 315200 *Fax:* 01772 315002
List of partners: D M Beckett
Work: N Q
SPr: Beckett, Mrs Donna M LLB(Hons) . . . . . *Oct 1996

BHAILOK FIELDING ‡
Church Court Buildings 111a Church Street Preston Lancashire PR1 3BS
Tel: 01772 202191 *Fax:* 01772 881600
E-mail: info@bfsols.co.uk
List of partners: A Bhailok, R M Fielding
Languages: Gujarati, Hindi, Mandarin, Punjabi, Urdu
Work: E J1 K1 L N Q Z(i)
Agency, Advocacy undertaken and Member of Accident Line
Ptr: Bhailok, Mr Ayub HND; DGD . . . . . *Oct 1993
Fielding, Mr Robert M BA(Nott'm)(Law) . . . . . *Oct 1988

BIRCHALL BLACKBURN LLP ‡
Merchant House 38-46 Avenham Street Preston Lancashire PR1 3BN
Tel: 01772 561663 *Fax:* 01772 202438 *Dx:* 713290 PRESTON 11
E-mail: info@birchallblackburn.co.uk
List of partners: M K Boyce, F Dillon, M J Foxford, C J Gallagher, C J Harris, G A Hughes, A M Leah, S V Liver, C R Lopez, C MacCracken, A P Nelson, J Patton, P E Pickering, R Rosenfield, A J Taylor, D J Woodcock
Office: Chester, Chorley, Formby, Leyland, Manchester, Morecambe, Preston, Southport
Languages: Gujarati, Spanish, Urdu
Work: A1 B1 C1 C2 C3 D1 E F1 G H J1 K1 L M1 M2 N O P Q R1 S1 T1 T2 V W X Z(b,c,e,f,i,l,m,o,q)
Emergency Action, Agency, Advocacy, Fixed Fee Interview, Legal Aid undertaken and Legal Aid Franchise
Ptr: Boyce, Mrs Moira K BA; MA . . . . . *Oct 1990
Foxford, Mr Michael John LLB . . . . . *May 1989
Hughes, Mr Graham Alexander MA; LLB; BSc; CTA(Fellow) John Allington Hughes Prize 1973; Sir Horatio Lloyd Prize 1973 Notary Public . . . . . *Jun 1976
Liver, Miss Susan Victoria LLB(Hons) . . . . . *Dec 1991
Lopez, Mr Carlos Ramon . . . . . *Jan 2000
MacCracken, Miss Catherine LLB(Hons) . . . . . *Jun 1994
Rosenfield, Mrs Rhonda LLB . . . . . *Mar 1992
Asoc: Birchall, Ms Deborah Catherine LLB(Hons) . . . . . *Nov 1999
Coates, Mr Anthony John . . . . . Sep 2005
Gallagher, Adele . . . . . Nov 1993
Harris, Mr Derrick Paul LLB(Hons) . . . . . *Nov 1994
Ranson, Mr Ian D BA . . . . . *Jun 1981
Ast: Bolton, Mr Christopher Neil LLB(Hons) • . . . . . Oct 2000
Evans, Mr Stephen Edward LLB(Hons) . . . . . Mar 2008
Garvey, Mrs Angela . . . . . Sep 2001
Hawker, Mrs Shelley Joanne LLB(Hons); LPC . . . . . Oct 2001
Lockwood, Miss Lesley Jane LLB(Hons) . . . . . Feb 2007
Malseed, Miss Leanne Keira LLB . . . . . Jan 2007
Marsden, Ms Fiona Jane . . . . . Oct 2000
Reid, Miss Alexandra Mary LLB . . . . . *Jan 2007
Con: Didsbury, Mr John C LLB . . . . . *Oct 1984
Waddingham, Mr Gerard J . . . . . *§Dec 1966

BIRCHALL BLACKBURN LLP
50c Liverpool Road Penwortham Preston Lancashire PR1 0DQ
Tel: 01772 744744 *Fax:* 01772 748888 *Dx:* 717441 PRESTON 15
Office: Chester, Chorley, Formby, Leyland, Manchester, Morecambe, Preston, Southport
Ptr: Gallagher, Mr Conal J LLB . . . . . *Apr 1992
Asoc: O'Neill, Mrs Joanne LLB(Hons) . . . . . Nov 1994

BLACKHURST SWAINSON GOODIER LLP
10 Chapel Street Preston Lancashire PR1 8AY
Tel: 01772 253841 *Fax:* 01772 201713 *Dx:* 714571 PRESTON 14
E-mail: info@bsglaw.co.uk
Office: Lancaster
Work: A1 A2 A3 B1 C1 C2 C3 D1 D2 E F1 F2 J1 J2 K1 K2 K3 K4 L M1 N O P Q R1 R2 S1 S2 T1 T2 V W Z(c,d,e,h,k,l,p,q,s,x)
Emergency Action, Agency, Advocacy, Fixed Fee Interview, Legal Aid undertaken and Legal Aid Franchise
Ptr: Goodier, Mr James O MA(Oxon) . . . . . *Nov 1982
Mercer, Mr George A BA(Law) . . . . . *Jun 1980
Parr, Mr Keith Geoffrey BA(Hons) Deputy District Judge . . . . . *Nov 1982
Ast: Chatburn, Miss Sarah Ellen LLB(Hons) . . . . . *Dec 1992
Glynn, Mr Malcolm Richard . . . . . *Apr 2004
Hayhurst, Miss Jennifer Claire . . . . . *Feb 2011
Hinks, Mrs Amanda Jane LLB(Hons) . . . . . *Jul 2004
Worcester, Mrs Jennifer Ann . . . . . *May 2000

BRABNERS CHAFFE STREET
7-8 Chapel Street Preston Lancashire PR1 8AN
Tel: 01772 823921 *Fax:* 01772 201918 *Dx:* 17118 PRESTON
Emergency telephone 01772 823921
E-mail: law@brabnerscs.com
Office: Liverpool, Manchester
Work: A1 A2 A3 B1 B2 C1 C2 C3 E F1 F2 I J1 J2 L M1 M2 N O P Q R1 R2 S1 S2 T1 T2 U2 W Z(c,d,e,f,g,k,l,o,p,q,r)
Agency, Advocacy and Legal Aid Franchise
Ptr: Boydell, Mr John A LLB . . . . . *Jun 1979
Irons, Mr Stuart BA(Hons)(Law) . . . . . *Apr 1988
James, Mr Kevin Anthony LLB . . . . . *Mar 1987
Shine, Mr Ross LLB . . . . . *Jun 1990
Asoc: Goulbourne, Ms Julie LLB . . . . . *Nov 1990
Ryan, Ms Helen Anne MA . . . . . *Sep 1998
Ast: Berry, Ms Jeanette LLB(Hons) Justice of the Peace . *Sep 2008
Dolan, Miss Amy Louise LLB Sweet & Maxwell Company Law Prize 2002 . . . . . *Nov 2005
Harper, Miss Rachel Elizabeth BA(Hons); GDL; LPC . Sep 2010
Holbrook, Ms Joanne . . . . . *Sep 2007

PHILIP H CUERDEN SOLICITORS ‡
107 Garstang Road Preston Lancashire PR1 1LD
Tel: 01772 203303 *Fax:* 01772 203603 *Dx:* 25410 FULWOOD 2
E-mail: phc@phclaw.co.uk

DWF
6 Winckley Square Preston Lancashire PR1 3JJ
Tel: 01772 556677 *Fax:* 0870 166 7161 *Dx:* 714570 PRESTON 14
E-mail: enquiries@dwf.co.uk
Office: Leeds, Liverpool, London EC4, Manchester, Newcastle upon Tyne
Work: A1 B1 C1 C2 C3 E F1 J1 J2 L M1 N O P Q R1 S1 T1 T2 W Z(b,e,h,j,l,o,p,q)
Emergency Action, Agency, Advocacy and Fixed Fee Interview undertaken
Ptr: Hackett, Mr Stephen B LLB . . . . . *Sep 1988
Mather, Mr Simon P LLB(Hons)(B'ham) . . . . . *Oct 1987
Ast: Ebenezer, Mrs Mary-Jane Ann LLB; LSF . . . . . *Oct 1993
Fearon, Miss Leisa Marie LLB(Hons) . . . . . *Sep 1999
Raghudati, Anand LLB; LLM . . . . . *Dec 1999
Teasdale, Mr Nigel . . . . . Mar 1999
Williams, Mr J Paul N BA . . . . . *§Nov 1985

DICKSON HASLAM
12 Chapel Street Preston Lancashire PR1 8BU
Tel: 01772 883100 *Fax:* 01772 883200 *Dx:* 714574 PRESTON 14
Emergency telephone 01772 684780
E-mail: info@dicksonhaslam.co.uk
Office: Kirkham, Lytham
Languages: French, German
Work: A1 A3 B1 C1 C2 C3 D1 D2 E F1 F2 G H J1 K1 K2 L M1 N O P Q R1 R2 S1 S2 T1 V W Z(e,h,k,l,o,p,q,r,t)
Emergency Action, Agency, Advocacy, Fixed Fee Interview undertaken and Member of Accident Line
Ptr: Green, Mr G Raymond LLB(Hons) Notary Public . . . *Apr 1974
Mathews, Mr John C H BA . . . . . *§Jul 1980

DOWSON BILLINGTON ‡
68 Stephenson Terrace Deepdale Road Preston Lancashire PR1 5AR
Tel: 01772 556807 *Fax:* 01772 250005 *Dx:* 17133 PRESTON 1
E-mail: enquiries@dowson-billington.co.uk
List of partners: C L Billington
Work: D1 E F1 J1 K1 K2 K3 K4 L N Q S1 S2 T1 T2 V W
Agency, Advocacy, Fixed Fee Interview, Legal Aid undertaken and Legal Aid Franchise
SPr: Billington, Mr Clive L BA(Hons) . . . . . *May 1980
Ast: Holmes, Ms Sara BA; CPE . . . . . *Nov 1993
Hothersall, Ms Gillian Louise LLB . . . . . *May 2006

ANDREW DOYLE & CO SOLICITORS ‡
Heatley Chambers Heatley Street Preston Lancashire PR1 2XB
Tel: 01772 561611 *Fax:* 01772 561551
Emergency telephone 01772 561611
E-mail: info@andrewdoylesolicitors.co.uk
Work: D1 D2 F1 F2 J1 K1 K3 K4 L N O P Q S1 V W X Z(f,h,i,k,q,r)
Agency, Advocacy and Fixed Fee Interview undertaken

ELLEN COURT PARTNERSHIP SOLICITORS ‡
25 Garstang Road Preston Lancashire PR1 1LA
Tel: 01772 882888 *Fax:* 01772 882555
E-mail: info@ellencourt.com
List of partners: A Burdett, M W R Wood
Work: N Q S1 W
Emergency Action, Agency, Advocacy and Fixed Fee Interview undertaken
Ptr: Burdett, Mr Alan . . . . . *Sep 1995
Wood, Mr Michael W R BA . . . . . *Feb 1986
Ast: Dawson, Mr Martin P LLB(Hons) . . . . . *Aug 1994

EMMETTS SOLICITORS ‡
54 Berry Lane Longridge Preston Lancashire PR3 3SL
Tel: 01772 785213 *Fax:* 01772 785300
E-mail: info@emmetts-solicitors.co.uk

EQUITAS SOLICITORS LIMITED ‡
Olivers Place Fulwood Preston Lancashire PR2 9WT
Tel: 01772 655196

FLETCHERS
13 Winckley Street Preston Lancashire PR1 2AA
Tel: 0871 971 1621 *Fax:* 01704 546918
E-mail: claims@fletcherssolicitors.co.uk
Office: Southport

FORBES
Ribchester House Lancaster Road Preston Lancashire PR1 2QL
Tel: 01772 220022 *Fax:* 01772 220166 *Dx:* 710059 PRESTON 10
Emergency telephone 01772 220022
E-mail: winston.mood@forbessolicitors.co.uk
Office: Accrington (2 offices), Blackburn (3 offices), Chorley, Leeds, Manchester
Work: A1 C1 D1 E F1 G H J1 K1 L M1 M2 N O P Q S1 V W
Emergency Action, Agency, Advocacy, Fixed Fee Interview, Legal Aid undertaken, Legal Aid Franchise and Member of Accident Line
Ptr: Baker, Mr Derek H LLB . . . . . Mar 1984
Earnshaw, Mr Gregory P LLB(B'ham) . . . . . *Mar 1984
Hood, Mr Winston J H LLB . . . . . *Apr 1980
Isherwood, Mr S Geoffrey . . . . . *§Jan 1972
Scholes, Mr Peter A . . . . . *§Feb 1964
Shorthouse, Mr Stuart T BA . . . . . *Mar 1980
Turner, Mr Peter B ★ . . . . . *§Oct 1968
Asoc: Wallace, Miss Mary Anne LLB(Hons) . . . . . Nov 1997
Ast: Baker, Mrs Dawn . . . . . *Nov 1986
Duxbury, Ms Carolynne LLB . . . . . *Oct 1998
Lee, Mr Ian LLB . . . . . Feb 2001
McCann, Mr Michael H LLB H M Coroner . . . . . *§Jul 1964
Parker, Mrs Elizabeth Ann LLB . . . . . *Sep 1996
Salter, Miss Zoe LLB(Hons) . . . . . *Sep 1998
Sarwar, Mr Abid Hussain BSc(Hons)(Econ) . . . . . Sep 2000
Williams, Mr Adrian LLB(Hons) . . . . . *Aug 1992
Wright, Ms Judith LLB(Hons) . . . . . Nov 1997

 See p112 for the Key to Work Categories & other symbols

FORSTER DEAN LTD
20 Orchard Street Preston Lancashire PR1 2EN
Tel: 01772 284643 *Fax:* 01772 284644
E-mail: enquiries@forsterdean.co.uk
Office: Birkenhead, Bootle, Chorley, Crewe, Ellesmere Port, Huyton, Leigh, Liverpool (5 offices), Oldham, Rochdale, Runcorn, St Helens, Stockport, Warrington, Widnes (2 offices), Wigan

GOWLINGS ‡
13 Lune Street Preston Lancashire PR1 2JU
Tel: 01772 251287 *Fax:* 01772 824329 *Dx:* 17141 PRESTON 1
E-mail: mail@gowlings.co.uk
List of partners: A Seddon, M L Taylor
Work: A1 B1 C1 D1 E F1 J1 K1 K3 K4 L N P Q R1 R2 S1 S2 T2 V W Z(e,l,m)
Agency, Advocacy, Fixed Fee Interview undertaken and Member of Accident Line
Ptr: Seddon, Mr Andrew LLB . . . . . *Nov 1992
Taylor, Mr Michael L. . . . . . *Nov 1972
Asoc: Haddleton, Mr Richard J BA. . . . . . *Jun 1979

DAVID G GREY SOLICITOR ‡
11 Calla Drive Garstang Preston Lancashire PR3 1JN
Tel: 01995 600190 *Fax:* 01995 600190 *Dx:* 63977 GARSTANG
E-mail: solicitor@davidgrey.co.uk

HANDLEY BROWN LLP ‡
Unit 6 Bluebell Way Millennium City Park Preston Lancashire PR2 5PY
Tel: 01772 652255

HARRISON DRURY & CO ‡
3 Fleet Street Preston Lancashire PR1 2UT
Tel: 01772 258321 *Fax:* 01772 258227 *Dx:* 714573 PRESTON 14
E-mail: enquiries@harrison-drury.com
List of partners: J G Chesworth, E A Hebden
Languages: French, German, Italian, Spanish
Work: A1 C1 C2 D1 E F1 J1 J2 K1 K3 K4 L M1 N O P R1 S1 S2 V W X Z(e,j,q,u,w)
Emergency Action, Agency, Advocacy and Fixed Fee Interview undertaken
Ptr: Chesworth, Mr John George BA(Hons); CPE; LPC . . Aug 1997
Hebden, Ms Elizabeth Anne. . . . . . Oct 1990
Asoc: Hesham, Mr Sabry . . . . . . Aug 2002
McKenna, Mr Owen. . . . . . Aug 2004
Con: Starkie, Mr John E LLB . . . . . . *Nov 1971

SIMON A HOLT & CO ‡
Fishergate Chambers 89 Fishergate Hill Preston Lancashire PR1 8JD
Tel: 01772 250871 *Fax:* 01772 201547
Dx: 710925 PRESTON COUNTY HALL
Emergency telephone 0800 387 815
E-mail: lawyer@personal-injury.co.uk
List of partners: S Ayre, C Marchbank-Caunce
Languages: French
Work: F1 J2 N P Q Z(j,q,r,w)
Emergency Action, Agency, Advocacy, Fixed Fee Interview, Legal Aid Franchise and Member of Accident Line
Ptr: Ayre, Ms Susan. . . . . . Oct 1996
Marchbank-Caunce, Mrs Caroline. . . . . . Oct 1995

KELLOCKS ‡
8 Cross Street Preston Lancashire PR1 3LT
Tel: 01772 828382 *Fax:* 01772 563500 *Dx:* 17140 PRESTON 1
Emergency telephone 07887 746697
E-mail: solicitors@kellocksonline.co.uk

LEIGH BAILEY SOLICITORS ‡
100 New Hall Lane Preston Lancashire PR1 4DT
Tel: 01772 744719
List of partners: P D P Flaherty
SPr: Flaherty, Mr Patrick D P LLB . . . . . . Nov 1993

MWRLAW LTD ‡
6 Cannon Street Preston Lancashire PR1 3PY
Tel: 01772 254201 *Fax:* 01772 202976 *Dx:* 17101 PRESTON 1
Emergency telephone 01995 640115
E-mail: info@mwrlaw.com
List of partners: C Blackburn, T J Booker, J A Greaves, A S Latham, P Meloy, W D Molyneux, S D Scott
Languages: French, Gujarati, Urdu
Work: B1 D1 E G H K1 N P S1 W
Emergency Action, Agency, Advocacy, Fixed Fee Interview, Legal Aid undertaken, Legal Aid Franchise and Member of Accident Line
Ptr: Blackburn, Mr Christopher BA(Law) . . . . . *Jun 1977
Booker, Mr T Jane . . . . . . Sep 1990
Greaves, Mr J Allan LLB; FCIl. . . . . . *Jan 1987
Latham, Ms Annette S LLB . . . . . . *Aug 1985
Meloy, Mr Peter BSc(Econ) . . . . . *§Jun 1978
Molyneux, Mr William D. . . . . . *§Jul 1969
Scott, Mr Stephen D LLB . . . . . . *Oct 1982
Ast: Moran, Mr Carl Xavier LLB(Hons)(with French) . . . Sep 1996
Patel, Altaf Yakub LLB(Hons) ♦ . . . . . . *Sep 1994

MARSDEN RAWSTHORN LLP ‡
(incorporating Marsdens Solicitors LLP & Rawsthorns)
Faraday Court Faraday Drive Fulwood Preston Lancashire PR2 9NB
Tel: 01772 799600 *Fax:* 01772 651831 *Dx:* 25404 FULWOOD 2
E-mail: info@marsdenrawsthorn.com
Web: www.marsdenrawsthorn.com
List of partners: S H Ahmed, R L Ainsworth, E P Gardner, P D Hine, S J Hodgson, P G Jolly, C W Maher, P Margey, C G McDonald, P A Ridehalgh, K J Wilson
Office: Chorley
Languages: French, German, Gujarati, Hindi, Urdu
Work: A1 A3 B1 B2 C1 C2 C3 D1 D2 E F1 F2 G H J1 J2 K1 K2 K3 K4 L N O Q R2 S1 S2 T1 T2 W Z(d,e,k,l,p,q,r)
Emergency Action, Agency, Advocacy, Fixed Fee Interview, Legal Aid undertaken and Legal Aid Franchise
Ptr: Ahmed, Mrs Sahida Hanif LLB(Hons) . . . . . *Mar 1998
Ainsworth, Mr Richard Len LLB(Hons). . . . . *Apr 1994
Gardner, Mr Eric P . . . . . . *Jan 1976
Hine, Mr Peter David MA(Oxon). . . . . *Oct 1983
Hodgson, Mr Stephen J BSc . . . . . . *Mar 1985
McDonald, Mr Charles G LLB(Hons) . . . . . *Nov 1978
Maher, Mr Charles W LLB. . . . . . *Jan 1983
Ridehalgh, Mr Paul Anthony LLB . . . . . *Nov 1985
Wilson, Mr Karl Jeffrey LLB; Dip PI . . . . . *Sep 1990
Asoc: Alexander, Mr Mark LLB(Hons) . . . . . *Nov 2005
Marshall, Mr Ashley Billington LLB(Hons); PGDip . . *Aug 2007
Ast: Clark, Miss Lisa LLB . . . . . . *Aug 2006
Daultrey, Miss Elizabeth LLB(Hons) . . . . . *Nov 1985
Gallagher, Miss Suzanne Marie LLB(Hons) . . . . *Nov 2004
Goral, Miss Amanda . . . . . . *Aug 2010
Haley, Miss Briony Michelle LLB; LPC. . . . . *Oct 2008
Hallett, Miss Laura . . . . . . *Apr 2010
Harrison, Mrs Sharon LLB(Hons) . . . . . Aug 2007
Madden, Caroline. . . . . . Nov 2011
Marshall, Mrs Margaret G LLB . . . . . *Dec 1976
Passi, Miss Sabita . . . . . . *Sep 2010
Con: Brown, Mr Derek Noel LLB(Hons). . . . . *Jul 1969
Fail, Mr Jonathan LLB(Lond) . . . . . *Dec 1973

BILL MEESON ‡
59 Village Drive Preston Lancashire PR2 6JH
Tel: 01772 796597

MOHAMMED & CO SOLICITORS ‡
St John's House 42 St John's Place Stoneygate Preston Lancashire PR1 3XX
Tel: 01772 888700 *Fax:* 01772 888345 *Dx:* 136096 PRESTON 16
Emergency telephone 01772 702161
E-mail: postmaster@m-co.demon.co.uk
List of partners: H Mohammed
Languages: Gujarati, Urdu
Work: B1 B2 D1 D2 E F1 F2 G H K1 L M2 N O Q S1 S2 V Z(g,i,l,p)
Agency, Advocacy, Fixed Fee Interview and Legal Aid undertaken
SPr: Mohammed, Mr Hanif LLB . . . . . . *Feb 1987
Asoc: Bell, Mr Stephen LLB(Hons); LLM. . . . . *Jun 1999
Jackson, Mr Anthony W J LLB . . . . . *Sep 1998
Tufail, Mr Farrukh LLB(Hons) . . . . . *Mar 1998

DYLAN NAIR SOLICITORS ‡
55 Garstangs Road Preston Lancashire PR1 1LB
Tel: 01772 254779

NAPTHENS LLP ‡
7 Winckley Square Preston Lancashire PR1 3JD
Tel: 01772 888444 *Fax:* 01772 257805 *Dx:* 714572 PRESTON 14
E-mail: preston@napthens.co.uk
List of partners: S R Ainsworth, J Allison, D A Barnes, D L Baron, C J Boyle, A D Clare, J M Crompton, J A Eatough, J A Ferguson, M J Fetherstone, S J Gledhill, T A S Griffin, K Harwood, W D Hawksworth, J Haymes, D Hill, M T Long, H Lucking, R J McDowell, K Melling, D P Sewell, A H Sumner, G R Tomlinson, J J Ward, J R Whittingslow, J M B Windle, J M Woosnam
Office: Blackburn, Blackpool, Chorley
Work: A1 A3 B1 C1 C2 D1 E F1 J1 K1 K2 L N O P Q R1 R2 S1 S2 W Z(c,d,f,j,k,l,m,n,o,p,r,s)
Emergency Action, Agency, Advocacy, Fixed Fee Interview undertaken and Member of Accident Line
Ptr: Ainsworth, Mr Simon R LLB. . . . . . *Nov 1995
Allison, Mr James. . . . . . Jan 2004
Barnes, Mr David Anthony BSc(Hons). . . . . *Oct 1993
Baron, Mr Damian L LLB Member of the Civil Legal Aid Appeal Tribunal. . . . . . *Sep 1990
Boyle, Mr Christopher James LLB(Hons) . . . . *Nov 2001
Ferguson, Mr J Andrew MA(Cantab) . . . . . *Nov 1971
Fetherstone, Mr Michael J LLB . . . . . *Oct 1986
Griffin, Mr Terence Anthony Stephen . . . . . *Feb 1989
Harwood, Mrs Kathryn BA(Dunelm) . . . . . *Nov 1987
Haymes, Jane. . . . . . Mar 1988
McDowell, Mr Richard J LLB . . . . . *Oct 1985
Melling, Mr Keith . . . . . . Oct 1997
Sewell, Mr David P LLB. . . . . . *Apr 1972
Sumner, Mr Allan H BA(Hons)(Oxon); Dip(Plan Env) . *Oct 1995
Tomlinson, Mr Geoffrey R BA(Dunelm) . . . . *May 1978
Ward, Mr John J . . . . . . *§Jun 1978
Whittingslow, Mr John R LLB . . . . . *Sep 1990
Woosnam, Mr John M BA(Oxon) . . . . . *Oct 1985
Ast: Baker, Kate. . . . . . Oct 2004
Barnes, Miss Sarah Elizabeth LLB; LPC. . . . . *Aug 2004
Bibby, Kate . . . . . . Jun 2009
Brice, Nikki . . . . . . Sep 2002
Cannon, Mr Mark . . . . . . Sep 2007
Carter, Stacey. . . . . . Aug 2009
Clutterbuck, Helen . . . . . . May 1997
Dobson, Mr Robert . . . . . . Sep 2005
England, Mr Simon . . . . . . Apr 2007
Holden, Mr Andrew BA(Hons)(with Business Information Systems); PGDipLP. . . . . . Apr 2005
Hutson, Janine . . . . . . May 2009
Macias Rial, Isabel . . . . . . Jan 2005
Newell, Mr Patrick. . . . . . Oct 2000
Spence, Mr Roger. . . . . . Sep 2001
Wright, Mr Philip . . . . . . Feb 1995
Con: Lord, Mr John R MA(Cantab) . . . . . Jul 1972

O'DONNELLS ‡
68 Glovers Court Preston Lancashire PR1 3LS
Tel: 01772 881000 *Fax:* 01772 883178 *Dx:* 17154 PRESTON 1
Emergency telephone 01772 881000
E-mail: office@odonnells-solicitors.co.uk
List of partners: J L Gale, J J O'Donnell, P S Roberts
Work: K1 K3 K4 W Z(m)
Emergency Action, Agency, Advocacy, Fixed Fee Interview, Legal Aid undertaken and Legal Aid Franchise
Ptr: Gale, Miss Jane L LLB . . . . . . *Oct 1990
O'Donnell, Mr John Joseph LLB(Leeds) Solicitor to the Preston Advocacy and Preston Chamber of Trade. . . . *Nov 1976
Roberts, Mr Peter S. . . . . . *Jan 1976
Asoc: Curran, Philippa. . . . . . Jul 2000

PARMAR & CO SOLICITORS ‡
151 Garstang Road Fulwood Preston Lancashire PR1 6AS
Tel: 0845 094 4646 *Fax:* 0845 094 4647
E-mail: pi@parmar-law.com

SEPHTON LEE WILKINSON SOLICITORS ‡
61 Friargate Preston Lancashire PR1 2AT
Tel: 01772 884144 / 07789 886 525 *Fax:* 01772 883910

ALISON TEECE SOLICITOR ‡
Maizefield 53 Cuerdale Lane Walton le Dale Preston Lancashire PR5 4BP
Tel: 01772 877238 *Fax:* 01772 877322
E-mail: aateece@blueyonder.co.uk
List of partners: A A Teece
Languages: French, German
Work: C1 C2 E J1 K1 R2 S1 S2 W
Fixed Fee Interview undertaken
Ptr: Teece, Mrs Alison A BA(Law) . . . . . *Oct 1984

THURNHILLS ‡
(incorporating Oakey Charnley & Thurnhill)
Charnley House 13 Winckley Square Preston Lancashire PR1 2JT
Tel: 01772 251762 *Fax:* 01772 561319 *Dx:* 17135 PRESTON
E-mail: marcus.thurnhill@thurnhills.co.uk
List of partners: A J Thurnhill, J A Thurnhill, M G Thurnhill
Office: Garstang
Languages: French
Work: A1 B1 C1 E F1 J1 K1 K3 K4 L N O Q R1 S1 S2 T1 W Z(c,j,k,l,p)
Emergency Action and Fixed Fee Interview undertaken
Ptr: Thurnhill, Mr Adam Joseph . . . . . . Dec 2001
Thurnhill, Mr Joseph A . . . . . . *Feb 1975
Thurnhill, Mr Marcus George . . . . . . Dec 2001

TURNER PEARSON ‡
29a Ribblesdale Place Preston Lancashire PR1 3NA
Tel: 01772 562222 *Fax:* 01772 203418 *Dx:* 17129 PRESTON 1
Emergency telephone 0800 132 383
E-mail: info@turnerslaw.co.uk
Office: Garstang
Work: A1 B1 D1 D2 E F1 J1 K1 K2 K3 L N O Q S1 S2 T2 W Z(l,r)

TURNER PEARSON ‡
72 Liverpool Road Penwortham Preston Lancashire PR1 0DQ
Tel: 01772 751775 *Fax:* 01772 751776 *Dx:* 717440 PRESTON 15
E-mail: sp@pearsonssolicitors.co.uk
List of partners: S Pearson
Work: E S1 S2 W
Ptr: Pearson, Mr Stephen LLB(Hons) . . . . . *Jan 1992

A D VARLEY & CO
15 Ribblesdale Place Preston Lancashire PR1 3NA
Tel: 01772 556777 *Fax:* 01772 887865 *Dx:* 17146 PRESTON 1
E-mail: mail@advarleyandco.co.uk
Office: Blackburn
Work: L N S1 S2 W

VINCENT LAVERYS ‡
(incorporating Shuttleworths & Branneys)
10 Camden Place Preston Lancashire PR1 3JL
Tel: 01772 555176 *Fax:* 01772 881233 *Dx:* 17111 PRESTON 1
E-mail: admin@laverys.co.uk
List of partners: J W Brailsford, C H Lavery, P M Lavery, J R Rimmer, R L Yates
Work: A1 C1 C2 D1 E G H K1 L N O Q S1 S2 T1 T2 W
Agency, Advocacy, Legal Aid undertaken, Legal Aid Franchise and Member of Accident Line
Ptr: Brailsford, Mr Jeffery W LLB • . . . . . *Jun 1973
Lavery, Mr Christopher H BA . . . . . *Jun 1972
Lavery, Mr Peter M BA . . . . . *Jun 1975
Rimmer, Mr John R BA; LLM • . . . . . *Oct 1984
Yates, Mr Richard L BA . . . . . *Dec 1979
Ast: Ellement, Mrs Nina Gudgeon LLB(Hons) . . . . *Mar 2003
Mercer, Miss Phillipa Jane. . . . . . *Sep 2001
Oates, Ms Helen Jane . . . . . . Jan 2003

WESTMINSTERS SOLICITORS ‡
Albert Edward House 6 The Pavilions Riversway Preston Lancashire PR2 2YB
Tel: 01772 833560 *Fax:* 01772 833561

JOHN WHITTLE ROBINSON ‡
13-14 Cross Street Preston Lancashire PR1 3LT
Tel: 01772 203000 *Fax:* 01772 257944 *Dx:* 17103 PRESTON
E-mail: enquiries@jwrlaw.co.uk

WORRALLS SOLICITORS ‡
(incorporating Georgina Worrall Solicitors)
147 Liverpool Road Preston Lancashire PR4 5AB
Tel: 01772 612494 *Fax:* 01772 615781
Dx: 706852 LONGTON (PRESTON)
E-mail: info@pworrall.co.uk
List of partners: G M Worrall, P Worrall
Work: D1 E K1 L S1
Agency, Advocacy, Fixed Fee Interview and Legal Aid undertaken
Ptr: Worrall, Mrs Georgina M BA(Hons) . . . . *Dec 1986
Worrall, Mr Philip LLB. . . . . . *Nov 1976

PRESTWICH, Greater Manchester

BUTCHER & BARLOW LLP
(in association with Platt Bodden & Co)
413 Bury New Road Prestwich Greater Manchester M25 1AA
Tel: 0161 773 2969 *Fax:* 0161 798 5718
E-mail: enquiries@butcher-barlow.co.uk
Office: Bramhall, Bury (2 offices), Frodsham, Leigh, Northwich, Runcorn (2 offices), Sandbach, Tyldesley
Work: A1 B1 C1 C2 C3 D1 E F1 J1 K1 K3 K4 L M1 M2 N O P Q R1 R2 S1 S2 T1 T2 V W Z(c,d,e,j,l,m,o,p,q,r,t)
Emergency Action, Agency, Advocacy, Fixed Fee Interview, Legal Aid undertaken, Legal Aid Franchise and Member of Accident Line
Ptr: Hopkins, Mr Christopher LLB . . . . . *Sep 2006
Ast: Ryles, Miss Claire LLB . . . . . *Sep 2005

GLP SOLICITORS
9 Fairfax Road Prestwich Greater Manchester M25 1AS
Tel: 0161 773 8626 *Fax:* 0161 798 8699
E-mail: prestwich@glplaw.com
Office: Bury, Manchester (4 offices), Middleton
Work: J1 K1 K3 N S1 W
Fixed Fee Interview, Legal Aid undertaken and Member of Accident Line
Ast: Williams, Ms Carol-Anne . . . . . . Dec 1996

AUBREY ISAACSON SOLICITORS ‡
3 Scholes Lane Prestwich Greater Manchester M25 0PD
Tel: 0161 959 5000 *Fax:* 0161 959 5001
E-mail: jeffrey@aubreyisaacson.co.uk
List of partners: J A Gilbert, P D Horridge, A Isaacson, S D Isaacson, J Rogerson, B B Simmonds
Office: Bury, Prestwich, Whitefield
Languages: French
Work: C1 C2 C3 D1 E F1 G H J1 K1 N O Q R1 S1 W
Agency and Advocacy undertaken
Ptr: Horridge, Mr Philip D BA(Law) . . . . . *Nov 1988
Isaacson, Aubrey LLB. . . . . . *May 1966
Isaacson, Mr Stephen Daniel LLB(Hons) . . . . *Nov 1995
Rogerson, Mrs Joanne LLB(Hons). . . . . *Aug 1999

AUBREY ISAACSON SOLICITORS
8 Scholes Lane Prestwich Greater Manchester M25 0BA
Tel: 0161 772 4000 *Fax:* 0161 772 4001
Office: Bury, Prestwich, Whitefield

JUST LAW SOLICITORS ‡
41a Bury New Road Prestwich Greater Manchester M25 9JY
Tel: 0161 798 6611 *Fax:* 0161 798 6699

LATIMER LEE LLP ‡
35 Bury New Road Sedgley Park Prestwich Greater Manchester M25 9JY
Tel: 0161 798 9000 *Fax:* 0161 773 6578
E-mail: info@latimerlee.com
List of partners: P M Latimer, S R Latimer, C Lee
Office: Bolton, Bury, Heywood
Languages: Greek
Work: B1 C1 D1 E G H J1 K1 K2 L N O Q R1 R2 S1 S2 T1 T2 V W Z(l,m,q,r)
Emergency Action, Legal Aid undertaken and Member of Accident Line
Ptr: Latimer, Mr Stephen R LLB Notary Public. . . . . . . May 1974
Lee, Mr Colin LLB; FCIArb; FRSA. . . . . *§Nov 1961
Con: Philbin, Mr Denis W. . . . . *§Jun 1962

NEIL E MANN ‡
513 Bury New Road Prestwich Greater Manchester M25 3AJ
Tel: 0161 832 8806 / 720 8199 / 773 1775 *Fax:* 0161 773 1774
E-mail: mail@neilemann.co.uk
List of partners: N E Mann
Office: Kendal
Emergency Action, Agency, Advocacy, Fixed Fee Interview, Legal Aid undertaken and Member of Accident Line
Ptr: Mann, Mr Neil E LLB . . . . *Jun 1976

REGAL SOLICITORS ‡
57a Bury Old Road Prestwich Greater Manchester M25 0FG
Tel: 0161 773 3183 *Fax:* 0161 637 9446
E-mail: info@regal-solicitors.co.uk

PRINCES RISBOROUGH, Buckinghamshire

BROWNS
The Gables Market Square Princes Risborough Buckinghamshire HP27 0AN
Tel: 01844 344123 *Fax:* 01844 275755
Dx: 54509 PRINCES RISBOROUGH
E-mail: risborough@brownssolicitors.co.uk
Office: Amersham, Aylesbury, Beaconsfield, Bourne End, High Wycombe (3 offices), Maidenhead, Marlow, Thame
Work: E J1 S1 W
Fixed Fee Interview undertaken
Asoc: Bradley, Mr Justin LLB . . . . *Nov 1994
Con: Watson, Mr David G MA(Oxon) . . . . *§Jun 1975

JOHN CODLING ‡
Grubbins Lane Princes Risborough Buckinghamshire HP27 0SE
Tel: 01494 488720

HINE SOLICITORS
First Floor Suite 2 The Malthouse Princes Risborough Buckinghamshire HP27 9AZ
Tel: 01844 274556 *Fax:* 01844 343009
Office: Beaconsfield, Bracknell, Cheltenham, Gerrards Cross, Oxford, Swindon, Yiewsley

READ COOPER
The Old Star Church Street Princes Risborough Buckinghamshire HP27 9AA
Tel: 01844 345788 *Fax:* 01844 343829
Dx: 54511 PRINCES RISBOROUGH
Office: Thame

PRUDHOE, Northumberland

CARIS ROBSON LLP ‡
7 Front Street Prudhoe Northumberland NE42 5HJ
Tel: 01661 836851 *Fax:* 01661 836853 *Dx:* 63230 PRUDHOE
E-mail: enquiries@carisrobson.co.uk
List of partners: B Caris, P L Caris, H K Robson
Office: Newcastle upon Tyne
Languages: British Sign Language, French
Work: B1 C1 D1 D2 E F1 J1 K1 K4 L N O Q S1 S2 V W X
Emergency Action, Agency, Advocacy, Fixed Fee Interview and Legal Aid undertaken
Ptr: Caris, Mrs Barbara BA . . . . *Oct 1988
Caris, Mr Peter Lloyd . . . . *Dec 1969
Robson, Miss Helen Kirsty MA . . . . *Aug 2001

PUDSEY, West Yorkshire

BENTLEY & CO ‡
7 Littlemoor Road Pudsey West Yorkshire LS28 8AF
Tel: 0113 236 0550 *Fax:* 0113 236 2511
List of partners: D J Bentley
Work: C1 C2
SPr: Bentley, Mr David J LLB. . . . . May 1990

CRABTREE CHADWICK ‡
Checker House Richardshaw Lane Pudsey West Yorkshire LS28 6BN
Tel: 0113 290 9499 *Fax:* 0113 290 9488
E-mail: info@crabtreechadwick.com
List of partners: C J Crabtree, W J O Crabtree
Work: A1 E L S1 S2 W Z(c)
Ptr: Crabtree, Mr Christopher J . . . . *Jan 1970
Crabtree, Mr William John Oakley BSc(Hons); MA . *Sep 2005

JOHN HOWE & CO ‡
(incorporating McCaul Saipe & Co)
Cooperative Chambers 4 Manor House Street Pudsey West Yorkshire LS28 7BH
Tel: 0113 236 3936 *Fax:* 0113 257 9891 *Dx:* 28573 PUDSEY 2
Emergency telephone 0113 236 3936
List of partners: J J Atkinson, J W Blake, A D Evans, J B Howe, P G Howell
Languages: Mandarin
Work: D1 E F1 G H J1 K1 L N O Q S1 S2 W Z(l)
Emergency Action, Agency, Advocacy, Fixed Fee Interview and Legal Aid undertaken
Ptr: Atkinson, Mr Jeremy John LLB(Hons). . . . . Sep 1994
Blake, Mr John W LLB; MA . . . . Feb 2003
Evans, Mr Andrew David LLB(Hons) . . . . Mar 2000
Howe, Mr John Barry LLB. . . . . *Oct 1988
Howell, Mr Phillip G. . . . . *Dec 1976
Con: Lyons, Mr John Trevor LLB . . . . *Dec 1969

KAYES SOLICITORS ‡
Trinity House 32 Church Lane Pudsey West Yorkshire LS28 7RF
Tel: 0113 290 0380 *Fax:* 0113 290 0389 *Dx:* 28577 PUDSEY 2
E-mail: info@kayessolicitors.co.uk
List of partners: P G Kaye
Office: Portishead
Work: N
Agency, Advocacy undertaken and Member of Accident Line
SPr: Kaye, Mr Paul Graham CPE; FILEx; Dip Advanced PI Lit; CPIL(Fellow) . . . . Sep 1997

LINDLEY CLOUGH
9 Lowtown Pudsey West Yorkshire LS28 7BQ
Tel: 0113 257 0523 *Fax:* 0113 257 1517
E-mail: info@morrishsolicitors.com
Office: Bradford, Leeds, Yeadon
Work: D1 E F1 G H K1 L N O Q S1 V W Z(d,l,m,t)
Emergency Action, Agency, Advocacy, Fixed Fee Interview, Legal Aid undertaken and Member of Accident Line
Con: Clough, Mr Charles G LLB . . . . *Oct 1976

THE LISTER CROFT PARTNERSHIP
2nd Floor Park Square House Park Square Pudsey West Yorkshire LS28 7RG
Tel: 0113 257 0526 *Fax:* 0113 239 3262 *Dx:* 28569 PUDSEY 2
Office: Wakefield
Work: D1 E G H J1 K1 L N O Q S1 S2 W Z(l,r)
Emergency Action, Agency, Advocacy, Fixed Fee Interview undertaken and Member of Accident Line
Ptr: Benstock, Mr Alan L BA H M Deputy Coroner of West Yorkshire East . . . . *§Oct 1982
Murray, Mr Stuart L . . . . *Oct 1984
Pattison, Mr Ian N. . . . . *Feb 1969

RYAN PROPERTY LAW LLP ‡
1 Church Lane Pudsey West Yorkshire LS28 7LD
Tel: 0113 236 2334
E-mail: neil.ryan@ryanpropertylaw.com

WILSONS
52 Town Street Farsley Pudsey West Yorkshire LS28 5LD
Tel: 0113 236 2333 *Fax:* 0113 255 4433
E-mail: postbox@lawoffice.co.uk
Office: Bradford (2 offices), Horsforth, Leeds
Work: A1 B1 D1 E F1 F2 J1 K1 K2 K3 K4 L N O Q R1 R2 S1 S2 T1 T2 W X Z(o,p,q,r,t,u)
Emergency Action, Agency, Advocacy and Fixed Fee Interview undertaken
Asoc: Murgatroyd, Mr Steven . . . . Jul 2007

PULBOROUGH, West Sussex

J E AIDIN ‡
The Old Rectory Wiggonholt Pulborough West Sussex RH20 2EL
Tel: 01798 872531 *Fax:* 01798 874129
E-mail: janetaidin@aol.com
List of partners: J E Aidin
SPr: Aidin, Ms Janet E MA(Oxon); LLM . . . . *Nov 1980

STUCKEY CARR & CO
62 Lower Street Pulborough West Sussex RH20 2BW
Tel: 01798 875358 *Fax:* 01798 875367 *Dx:* 85951 STORRINGTON
Office: Storrington
Work: A1 E S1 S2 T2 W Z(m)
Ptr: Carr, Mr George R D . . . . *Jul 1964
Asoc: Gyles, Mrs Nola J MA(Oxon) John Mackrell Prize; Charles Steel Prize; City of London Prize . . . . *Dec 1976

PURLEY, Surrey

STEPHEN MARSHALL ‡
21 Hillcrest Road Purley Surrey CR8 2JF
Tel: 020 8660 4141 *Fax:* 020 8668 8250
E-mail: srm@srmlaw.co.uk

RSE SOLICITORS
23 Whytecliffe Road South Purley Surrey CR8 2AY
Office: Wembley

STREETER MARSHALL
12 Purley Parade High Street Purley Surrey CR8 2AB
Tel: 020 8660 6455 *Fax:* 020 8668 3250 *Dx:* 59600 PURLEY
Office: Croydon, Warlingham
Work: C1 E S1 S2 W
Ptr: Cook, Mrs P Jane LLB Notary Public . . . . *§Dec 1974
Hopkins, Mr Gordon R . . . . *§Dec 1974
Pickering, Mr Andrew R. . . . . *§Jun 1970

PWLLHELI, Gwynedd

MARTIN & STRAIN ‡
Bank Place 33 High Street Pwllheli Gwynedd LL53 5RT
Tel: 01758 612042 *Fax:* 01758 613815 *Dx:* 711530 PWLLHELI
Emergency telephone 01758 701316
E-mail: legal@lawmn.com
List of partners: B Martin, W M Strain
Languages: French, Spanish, Urdu, Welsh
Work: A1 B1 D1 D2 E G H J1 K1 L M1 N O P Q R1 S1 S2 T1 W Z(i,l,q)
Emergency Action, Agency, Advocacy, Fixed Fee Interview, Legal Aid undertaken and Legal Aid Franchise
Ptr: Martin, Mr Bryn BSc(Econ) . . . . Mar 1981
Strain, Mr William Michael. . . . . *Feb 1992
Asoc: Evans, Mrs Mollie. . . . . Sep 1996

PARRY DAVIES CLWYD-JONES & LLOYD
22 Stryd Penlan Pwllheli Gwynedd LL53 5DE
Tel: 01758 703000 / 701155 *Fax:* 01758 701759
Dx: 711533 PWLLHELI
Office: Amlwch, Benllech, Caernarfon, Llangefni
Languages: Welsh
Work: K1 N R1 S1 W
Agency, Fixed Fee Interview and Legal Aid undertaken
Con: Jones, Gwynfor LLB(Wales). . . . . *Jun 1980

ROBERTS & ROBYNS ‡
26 Stryd Penlan Pwllheli Gwynedd LL53 5DE
Tel: 01758 612362 *Fax:* 01758 613914 *Dx:* 711538 PWLLHELI
List of partners: R O Robyns
Languages: Welsh
Work: A1 E F1 J1 K1 K4 L N Q R1 S1 S2 W
Advocacy and Fixed Fee Interview undertaken
SPr: Robyns, Mr Richard O LLB(Wales) . . . . *Nov 1970

ROBYNS OWEN ‡
36 High Street Pwllheli Gwynedd LL53 5RY
Tel: 01758 613177 *Fax:* 01758 613713 *Dx:* 711532 PWLLHELI
E-mail: robynsowen@f2s.com
List of partners: G T Jones, R R Jones, I E Owen
Office: Porthmadog
Languages: Welsh
Work: A1 A2 A3 B1 D1 E F1 G H J1 K1 K2 K3 L N O P Q R1 S1 S2 V W Z(h,k,l)
Emergency Action, Agency, Advocacy and Fixed Fee Interview undertaken
Ptr: Jones, Gwyn T LLB. . . . . *Jul 1970
Jones, Robyn Rees LLB . . . . *Oct 1987
Owen, Mr Ieuan E LLB Notary Public . . . . *Dec 1973
Asoc: Thomas, Miss Megan Mayall LLB(Hons). . . . . . *Aug 1999

RADCLIFFE, Greater Manchester

QUALITYSOLICITORS GRUBER GARRATT
110 Water Street Radcliffe Greater Manchester M26 4GR
Tel: 0161 724 0203 *Fax:* 0161 724 9552 *Dx:* 15753 RADCLIFFE
Emergency telephone 07971 163241
E-mail: info@qsgrubergarratt.co.uk
Office: Ashton-under-Lyne, Oldham, Stalybridge, Worsley
Work: A1 B1 C1 C3 D1 D2 E F1 G H J1 K1 L M1 M2 N O P Q R1 R2 S1 S2 T1 T2 V W Z(b,c,d,e,f,h,j,k,l,m,n,p,q,r,s)
Emergency Action, Agency, Advocacy, Fixed Fee Interview, Legal Aid undertaken, Legal Aid Franchise and Member of Accident Line

TYLERS SOLICITORS ‡
58 Church St West Radcliffe Greater Manchester M26 2SQ
Tel: 0161 723 1183 *Fax:* 0161 723 1183
E-mail: info@tylerssolicitors.co.uk

RADLETT, Hertfordshire

DEBENHAMS OTTAWAY
48 Watling Street Radlett Hertfordshire WD7 7NN
Tel: 01923 857171 *Fax:* 01923 854840 *Dx:* 89550 RADLETT
E-mail: pf@turnerdebs.co.uk
Office: St Albans
Work: E S1 S2
Agency undertaken
Ptr: Elgood, Mr Guy D A Notary Public . . . . *§Feb 1971
Ast: Holmstock, Mrs Ruth Michele LLB. . . . . *§Dec 1985
Mein, Mr Nicholas. . . . . *§Oct 1983
Con: Franks, Mr Morley L B. . . . . *§Jul 1971
Hayes, Mr Peter LLB Notary Public . . . . *§May 1968

LAURENCE KAYE SOLICITORS ‡
Wisley House Gills Hill Lane Radlett Hertfordshire WD7 8DD
Tel: 01923 352117

MOERANS
Osborne House Station Road Radlett Hertfordshire WD7 8JY
Office: Edgware

LAURENCE ROSS & ASSOCIATES ‡
Oak Chambers 34 Watling Street Radlett Hertfordshire WD7 7NN
Tel: 01923 850099 *Fax:* 01923 850585 *Dx:* 89553 RADLETT
E-mail: legal@rosslaw.co.uk
List of partners: L P Ross
Work: J1 K1 K3 L O Q W Z(p,q)
Emergency Action and Advocacy undertaken
SPr: Ross, Mr Laurence P LLB; LLM(Lond). . . . . *Jun 1976

RADSTOCK, Bath & North East Somerset

CROSSMANS ‡
1 The Shambles Wells Road Radstock Bath & North East Somerset BA3 3RH
Tel: 01761 431688 *Fax:* 01761 436838
E-mail: office@crossmans-solicitors.co.uk
List of partners: P V Crossman
Languages: French
Work: B2 D1 G H K1 K3 V
Emergency Action, Agency, Advocacy, Fixed Fee Interview, Legal Aid undertaken and Legal Aid Franchise
SPr: Crossman, Mr Patrick V MSc . . . . *Oct 1987
Asoc: Browne, Guen BA(Hons); PGDipLaw . . . . Aug 2005
Ast: Clarke, Ms Judith H LLB . . . . *Aug 1998
Martin, Ms Susan BSc(Hons) . . . . Jan 1993

FDC LAW
Norton House High Street Midsomer Norton Radstock Bath & North East Somerset BA3 2DF
Tel: 01761 417575 *Fax:* 01761 415528
Dx: 42950 MIDSOMER NORTON
E-mail: norton@fdc-law.co.uk
Office: Frome (2 offices), Keynsham
Work: A1 B1 C1 C2 D1 D2 E F1 J1 J2 K1 K2 K3 K4 L N O Q R1 S1 S2 T1 V W Z(c,d,o)

SOUTH WEST FAMILY LAW ‡
Kelson House Bakers Lane Chilcompton Radstock Bath & North East Somerset BA3 4EW
Tel: 01761 233289 *Fax:* 01761 233606
E-mail: enquiries@southwestfamilylaw.co.uk

 See p112 for the Key to Work Categories & other symbols

RAINHAM, Essex

DANIEL ARAMIDE SOLICITORS ‡
113 Upminster Road South Rainham Essex RM13 9AA
Tel: 01708 525961 / 07973 907417 *Fax:* 0870 762 2672
E-mail: lawyers@aramidesolicitors.co.uk

SACKVILLES
12 The Broadway Rainham Essex RM13 9YL
Tel: 01708 552804 *Fax:* 01708 520104
Dx: 91400 RAINHAM (ESSEX)
Office: Hornchurch
Languages: French
Work: A1 B1 C1 C2 D1 E F1 K1 L N O Q R1 S1 T2 W Z(l)
Agency, Fixed Fee Interview, Legal Aid undertaken and Legal Aid Franchise
Ptr: Norrington, Mr Roger H LLB(Hons)(Wales) Notary Public . . . *Apr 1979

SANDERS & CO ‡
18 The Broadway Rainham Essex RM13 9YW
Tel: 0844 353 3553 *Dx:* 91402 RAINHAM (ESSEX)
Emergency telephone 01277 216232
E-mail: enquiries@sanderssolicitors.co.uk
List of partners: P J Bostridge, D L Gearing, D Saunders
Office: Harold Wood
Languages: French, Italian
Work: A1 B1 C1 D1 E F1 G H J1 K1 L M1 N P S1 V
Emergency Action, Agency, Fixed Fee Interview and Legal Aid undertaken
Ptr: Bostridge, Mr Peter J . . . *Jun 1970
Saunders, Mr David BA; ACIArb. . . . *Mar 1984
Ast: Davies, Detlef C S LLB . . . *Dec 1976
Sanders, Mr Peter R B . . . Mar 1984

RAINHAM, Medway Towns

BIDDULPHS ‡
107 Station Road Rainham Medway Towns ME8 7SE
Tel: 01634 363535 *Fax:* 01634 363544
Work: S1 S2

GOLDRING & CO ‡
5 The Courtyard Holding Street Rainham Medway Towns ME8 7HE
Tel: 01634 260012 *Fax:* 01634 263586
E-mail: info@goldringandco.com
List of partners: S Goldring
Work: C1 T1 T2 W Z(d)
SPr: Goldring, Mr Simon CTA; ATT; TEP . . . Oct 1988

LOWES ‡
Hamilton House 84 High Street Rainham Medway Towns ME8 7JH
Tel: 01634 371111 *Fax:* 01634 377160 *Dx:* 7204 RAINHAM
List of partners: J C Foley, P M Lowe
Work: S1
Ptr: Foley, Mrs Judith C BSc. . . . *Dec 1987
Lowe, Mr Peter M BA(Law) . . . *Nov 1982

JOHN MORLEY & CO ‡
29-31 & 35 High Street Rainham Medway Towns ME8 7HX
Tel: 01634 375444 *Fax:* 01634 360006 *Dx:* 7200 RAINHAM
Emergency telephone 07669 018541 (CRIME)
E-mail: medway@morlaw.com
List of partners: S Davey-Holpin, J F Morley, S I Morley
Office: Chatham
Languages: French
Work: A1 B1 B2 C1 D1 E F1 G H J1 K1 K2 L M1 N P Q S1 S2 V W Z(l,r)
Emergency Action, Agency, Advocacy, Fixed Fee Interview, Legal Aid undertaken, Legal Aid Franchise and Member of Accident Line
Ptr: Davey-Holpin, Ms Sharon BA(Dunelm); DipLP. . . . Jun 1999
Morley, Mr John F. . . . *Jul 1968
Morley, Mr Simon I BA(Hons) . . . *Nov 1997
Asoc: Playford, Mr Geoffrey . . . Dec 1967
Rai, Ms Rajinder LLB(Hons); PGDipLPC; PSC . . . Mar 1997
Robinson, Mrs Yvonne Elizabeth . . . May 2001

V E WHITE & CO
10 Parkwood Green Rainham Medway Towns ME8 9PN
Tel: 01634 376555 *Fax:* 01634 376888 *Dx:* 7202 RAINHAM
E-mail: enquiries@vewhitesolicitors.co.uk
Office: Strood
Work: D1 D2 J1 K1 K3 N Q S1 S2 W X
Fixed Fee Interview undertaken

RAMSBOTTOM, Greater Manchester

ORBIS SOLICITORS ‡
Princes Court Silver Street Ramsbottom Greater Manchester BL0 9BJ
Tel: 01706 283610 *Fax:* 01706 827822
E-mail: info@orbissolicitors.co.uk

WOODCOCKS
52 Bolton Street Ramsbottom Greater Manchester BL0 9HX
Tel: 01706 824011 *Fax:* 01706 821709 *Dx:* 24451 RAMSBOTTOM
E-mail: tmb@woodcocks.co.uk
Office: Bacup, Bury, Haslingden, Rawtenstall
Work: A1 B1 C1 C2 D1 E F1 J1 K1 K3 L N O P Q R1 S1 S2 T1 T2 W Z(d,e,l,o,q)

RAMSEY, Cambridgeshire

SERJEANT & SON ‡
101 High Street Ramsey Cambridgeshire PE26 1DA
Tel: 01487 812325 *Fax:* 01487 812119 *Dx:* 88100 RAMSEY
E-mail: legal@serjeantandson.co.uk
List of partners: I G Caunt, J A R Chrisp, W A Wyers
Work: A1 B1 C1 D1 E F1 J1 K1 L N Q R1 S1 S2 T2 V W Z(d,l)
Emergency Action, Agency, Advocacy, Fixed Fee Interview, Legal Aid undertaken and Legal Aid Franchise
Ptr: Caunt, Mr Ian G BA. . . . *Jul 1978
Chrisp, Mr John Alexander Rodney . . . *§Jul 1973
Wyers, Mr William A LLB . . . *Oct 1977

RAMSGATE, Kent

BKRW LIMITED
87 High Street Ramsgate Kent CT11 9RJ
Tel: 01843 852953
E-mail: info@bkrwsolicitors.co.uk
Office: Dover, Folkestone

GEOFFREY BORG & CO ‡
22 King Street Ramsgate Kent CT11 8BJ
Tel: 01843 591378 *Fax:* 01843 590832 *Dx:* 30601 RAMSGATE
List of partners: B Hatton
Work: E S1 W
Fixed Fee Interview undertaken
SPr: Hatton, Miss Brenda BA. . . . May 1982

BOYS & MAUGHAN
57 Queen Street Ramsgate Kent CT11 9EJ
Tel: 01843 595990 *Fax:* 01843 852251 *Dx:* 30614 RAMSGATE
E-mail: ramsgate@boysandmaughan.co.uk
Office: Birchington, Broadstairs, Margate
Work: A1 C1 D1 D2 E G H J1 K1 K2 K4 N O Q R1 S1 S2 W Z(l,p,q)
Emergency Action, Agency, Advocacy, Fixed Fee Interview, Legal Aid undertaken, Legal Aid Franchise and Member of Accident Line
Ptr: Bagley, Mr Robert C A LLB . . . *Dec 1976
Baker, Mr Andrew David James LLB . . . *Oct 1995
Ast: Smith, Lorraine Dawn . . . Jan 1997

RICHARD CONNOR SOLICITORS ‡
PO Box 370 2 Brockenhurst Road Ramsgate Kent CT11 8WD
Tel: 01227 749777
E-mail: info@wills-on-wheels.co.uk

DANIEL & EDWARDS ‡
Thanet Chambers 44 & 46 Queen Street Ramsgate Kent CT11 9EG
Tel: 01843 594651 *Fax:* 01843 580194 *Dx:* 30602 RAMSGATE
List of partners: D A Cook, M R M Daniel, D B S Lawrie
Work: A1 D1 D2 E K1 K3 L Q S1 T2 V W Z(d)
Emergency Action, Agency, Advocacy, Legal Aid undertaken and Legal Aid Franchise
Ptr: Cook, Mr David Anthony LLB(L'pool) . . . *§Apr 1981
Daniel, Mr M Richard M Notary Public. . . . *§Jan 1966
Lawrie, Mr David B S . . . *§Nov 1970
Ast: McCoy, Mrs Andrea. . . . *Aug 2003
Wells, Miss Vanessa . . . Sep 2010

MACALISTER WHITE ‡
12 Cliff Street Ramsgate Kent CT11 9HS
Tel: 01843 572789 *Fax:* 01843 572780 *Dx:* 30606 RAMSGATE
E-mail: darryl.vas@mwllp.co.uk

MARSDEN DUNCAN
49-51 High Street Ramsgate Kent CT11 9AG
Tel: 01843 584500 *Fax:* 01843 852312 *Dx:* 30603 RAMSGATE
E-mail: info@marsdenduncan.co.uk
Office: Birchington, Cliftonville
Languages: French
Work: K1 K3 L S1 S2 W
Agency, Fixed Fee Interview and Legal Aid undertaken
Ast: Wild, Ms Claire M LLB . . . *Mar 1987

ROBINSON ALLFREE ‡
Cavendish House 17-25 Cavendish Street Ramsgate Kent CT11 9AL
Tel: 01843 592361 *Fax:* 01843 582774 *Dx:* 30604 RAMSGATE
E-mail: ramsgate@robinson-allfree.co.uk
List of partners: W A Burgess, C Easter, S J Harrison, M R Longdon, P J Moore, R J Owen, H Prettyjohn, J Robinson, E S Thomas, S Worth
Office: Broadstairs, Cliftonville
Languages: French
Work: B1 C1 D1 E F1 J1 J2 K1 K3 K4 L N O Q S1 S2 T1 T2 W Z(c,k,l,q,r)
Emergency Action, Agency, Advocacy, Fixed Fee Interview, Legal Aid undertaken, Legal Aid Franchise and Member of Accident Line
Ptr: Burgess, Ms Wendy A . . . *Oct 1993
Easter, Mr Crispin. . . . *Jun 1989
Harrison, Mr Steven J BA . . . *Mar 1984
Longdon, Mr Michael R . . . *Nov 1974
Moore, Mr Peter J. . . . *Oct 1974
Owen, Mr Robert J LLB. . . . *Jul 1977
Prettyjohn, Mrs Helen. . . . *Jun 1998
Robinson, Mr Julian. . . . *Aug 1998
Thomas, Ms Elaine Susan . . . *Oct 2000

THORN DRURY & SEARLES ‡
Meeting Street Chambers 76 High Street Ramsgate Kent CT11 9RS
Tel: 01843 593381 *Fax:* 01843 853194 *Dx:* 30605 RAMSGATE
E-mail: johnsearles@thorndrury.fsnet.co.uk
List of partners: J G Searles
Languages: French, German
Work: E F1 K1 L N O Q S1 S2 T2 W
Agency and Fixed Fee Interview undertaken
SPr: Searles, Mr John Gerard LLB . . . *Oct 1976

RAWTENSTALL, Lancashire

MULDERRIGS SOLICITORS LTD ‡
72 Bank Street Rawtenstall Lancashire BB4 8EG
Tel: 01706 222852
Office: Oldham

SUTCLIFFES ‡
90 Bank Street Rawtenstall Lancashire BB4 8EG
Tel: 01706 215107 *Fax:* 01706 212881
List of partners: R Battersby
Work: C1 E F1 G H J1 K1 L M1 P S1 T1
Emergency Action, Agency, Advocacy, Fixed Fee Interview, Legal Aid undertaken and Member of Accident Line
Ptr: Battersby, Mr Roy LLB Chairman of the Social Security and Disability Appeal Tribunals . . . *Aug 1971

WOODCOCKS
61 Bank Street Rawtenstall Lancashire BB4 7QN
Tel: 01706 225621 / 215018 *Fax:* 01706 830556
Dx: 26251 RAWTENSTALL
E-mail: info@woodcocks.co.uk
Office: Bacup, Bury, Haslingden, Ramsbottom
Work: A1 B1 C1 C2 C3 D1 D2 E F1 G H J1 K1 K3 L N O P Q R1 S1 S2 T1 T2 W Z(d,e,l,o,q)

RAYLEIGH, Essex

BARNES SARNEY & GAME ‡
(incorporating David Game & Hirsh)
7 High Street Rayleigh Essex SS6 7EU
Tel: 01268 773881 / 774785 *Fax:* 01268 745563
Dx: 50602 RAYLEIGH
E-mail: djg.bsgl@btinternet.com
List of partners: D J Game
Work: B1 C1 C2 C3 E J1 L N S1 S2 W Z(e,p)
Agency and Advocacy undertaken
SPr: Game, Mr David J LLB(Hons). . . . *Dec 1976

DAVE & CO SOLICITORS ‡
49 The Paddocks Rayleigh Essex SS6 8NE
Tel: 01268 773211

ELS & COLE SOLICITORS ‡
162-164 High Street Rayleigh Essex SS6 7BS
Tel: 01268 747006

PEARL BAKER ‡
Ivy House 13 High Road Rayleigh Essex SS6 7SA
Tel: 01268 745568 *Fax:* 01268 775111 *Dx:* 50619 RAYLEIGH
List of partners: P A Baker
Work: C1 E G K1 L M1 N P S1 W Z(c,l,s)
Fixed Fee Interview and Legal Aid undertaken
Ptr: Baker, Mrs Pearl A . . . *Jan 1986

RUDDS
81a High Street Rayleigh Essex SS6 7EJ
Tel: 01268 778152 *Fax:* 01268 771965 *Dx:* 50607 RAYLEIGH
Office: Westcliff-on-Sea
Work: J1 K1 K3 K4 L N Q S1 S2 T2 W Z(m)
Member of Accident Line
Ptr: Merrick, Mr David. . . . *Jun 1970
Philpott, Mr John W. . . . May 1976

ALAN SIMPSON & CO ‡
Mill Court 19 London Hill Rayleigh Essex SS6 7HW
Tel: 01268 745406 *Fax:* 01268 742299 *Dx:* 50626 RAYLEIGH
E-mail: ajs@alansimpson.com
List of partners: A J Simpson
Work: C1 D1 J1 K1 L N S1 S2 W
Fixed Fee Interview, Legal Aid undertaken and Legal Aid Franchise
SPr: Simpson, Mr Alan J. . . . *Nov 1981
Ast: Lodeto, Mrs Jane . . . Sep 2003

TODMANS SRE ‡
Barringtons Hockley Road Rayleigh Essex SS6 8EH
Tel: 01268 774073 *Fax:* 01268 747110 *Dx:* 50601 RAYLEIGH
E-mail: mail@todmans.co.uk
List of partners: S J H Jones, W H D Todman
Work: A1 B1 C1 C2 C3 E F1 J1 K4 L P R1 R2 S1 S2 T1 T2 U1 W Z(c,d,u)
Ptr: Jones, Mr Simon J H LLB. . . . *Nov 1988
Todman, Mr William H D LLB(Hons). . . . *Oct 1986
Ast: Fredericks, Ms Toni Frances LLB(Hons). . . . *Nov 2002

READING

ALBIN & CO ‡
46a West Street Reading RG1 1TZ
Tel: 0118 957 4018 *Fax:* 0118 950 7551 *Dx:* 40111 READING
List of partners: C Albin, R Jacques
Work: D1 D2 G H K1 V X Z(l,m)
Emergency Action, Agency, Advocacy, Fixed Fee Interview, Legal Aid undertaken and Legal Aid Franchise
Ptr: Albin, Mr Christopher . . . Sep 1997
Jacques, Mr Robert LLB . . . Oct 1993
Con: Cantrill, Mr Paul T BA(Oxon) . . . *Oct 1978

ARMSTRONG JAMES LLP ‡
39 Castle Street Reading RG1 7SL
Tel: 0800 169 2210 *Dx:* 146421 READING 21
E-mail: enquiry@claimscorporation.com

ARNOLD LAMBERT SOLICITORS ‡
16 Bridge Street Reading RG4 8AA
Tel: 0118 918 7610 *Fax:* 0118 947 6368 *Dx:* 84155 CAVERSHAM
E-mail: arnold.lambert@btconnect.com

ASTON BOND LLP
10 Southern Court South Street Reading RG1 4QS
Tel: 01889 596031 *Fax:* 0118 957 0556 *Dx:* 4012 READING
E-mail: info@astonbond.co.uk
Office: Slough

JOHN L BANKY SOLICITORS ‡
18a High Street Theale Reading RG7 5AN
Tel: 0118 930 4630 *Fax:* 0118 930 4640
E-mail: john@johnlbankysolicitors.co.uk
List of partners: J L Banky
Work: A1 B1 E K1 O Q S1 S2 W
Agency and Advocacy undertaken
Ptr: Banky, Mr John L LLB(B'ham). . . . *Feb 1989

BARRETT & CO SOLICITORS LLP ‡
Salisbury House 54 Queens Road Reading RG1 4AZ
Tel: 0118 958 9711 *Fax:* 0118 939 3605 *Dx:* 4033 READING
E-mail: info@barrettandco.co.uk
List of partners: S A Barrett, S H Buckle, J P Harrison
Office: Didcot
Work: A1 B1 C1 C2 C3 D1 E F1 F2 I J1 J2 K1 K2 K3 K4 L M1 O P Q R1 R2 S1 S2 W Z(c,e,p)
Advocacy, Fixed Fee Interview and Legal Aid Franchise
Ptr: Barrett, Mr Simon Anthony BSc. . . . *§Apr 1980
Buckle, Mrs Susan Hilary LLB(Lond) . . . *Nov 1982
Harrison, Mr John P. . . . Feb 2001
Asoc: Harris, Ms Janine Marie. . . . Mar 2006
Sadler, Mr Justin Roy LLB(Hons) . . . Aug 2002
Wild, Mr Paul Spencer BA(Hons); DipLaw; LPC. . . . *Sep 2001
Ast: Kurtz, Miss Emma-Jane Francesca BA; TEP . . . Jan 2004

DEBORAH BAXTER & CO ‡
9 Church Street Reading RG1 2SB
Tel: 0118 958 6855 *Fax:* 0118 958 5047 *Dx:* 4058 READING
Work: D1 D2 K1

BLANDY & BLANDY ‡
1 Friar Street Reading RG1 1DA
Tel: 0118 951 6800 *Fax:* 0118 958 3032 *Dx:* 4008 READING
E-mail: law@blandy.co.uk
List of partners: G E Benwell, D J Brett, N C Burrows, T J Clark, P B D'Arcy, S M Dimmick, A M W Don, S E Dowling, D J Few, K Fretwell, J B Gater, R G Griffiths, J E Gunnell, K Jones, B M Long, I G Sharman, J O Smith
Languages: French, German, Hindi, Punjabi, Spanish
Work: A1 A3 B1 C1 C2 C3 D1 D2 E F1 F2 I J1 K1 K2 K3 K4 L M1 M2 N O P Q R1 R2 S1 S2 T1 T2 U2 W X Z(c,d,e,h,j,k,l,o,p,q,t,u,y,z,za)
Emergency Action, Agency, Advocacy, Fixed Fee Interview, Legal Aid Franchise and Member of Accident Line
Ptr: Benwell, Mr Graham E BA(Hons) . . . . *Dec 1975
Brett, Miss Deborah Jane BA(Hons). . . . . *Sep 1999
Burrows, Mr Nicholas C LLB . . . . *Mar 1985
Clark, Mr Timothy J LLB. . . . . *Oct 1996
D'Arcy, Mr Philip B LLB Notary Public. . . . . *Feb 1981
Dimmick, Mr Simon M LLB . . . . *Apr 1977
Don, Mr Andrew M W LLB . . . . *Oct 1981
Dowling, Ms Susan E LLB(Business Law) . . . . *Oct 1988
Few, Mr David J LLB(Hons); CDipAF Notary Public . . *Oct 1982
Fretwell, Ms Kerry BA. . . . . Jun 1993
Gater, Mr Jonathan Brian LLB(Hons) . . . . *Oct 1993
Griffiths, Mr Richard G Notary Public . . . . *§Jun 1971
Gunnell, Ms Jane E BSc . . . . *Nov 1985
Jones, Miss Karen . . . . *Oct 1989
Long, Mrs Brenda M LLB . . . . Oct 1990
Sharman, Mr Ian Gerald. . . . . Nov 2001
Smith, Mr Jacques O LLB. . . . . *Feb 1989
Asoc: Banister Dean, Miss Emma . . . . *Feb 2002
Casagranda, Ms Caroline Katherine. . . . . *Sep 2003
Colby, Mrs Carli Samantha LLB . . . . *Mar 2002
Irwin, Ms Jessica Frances LLB; LPC . . . . Sep 2000
Wigham, Miss Katja Fau Elina LLB; LPC . . . . *Sep 1999
Woolley, Mr Peter. . . . . Oct 1999
Ast: Astley, Ms Charlotte. . . . . Sep 2007
Binnie, Ms Laura . . . . Sep 2007
Brass, Ms Rosie . . . . Oct 2008
Cameron, Ms Katherine. . . . . Sep 2007
Diamond, Miss Catharine . . . . *Feb 2006
Dyer, Miss Claire . . . . Jan 2006
Hales, Ms Lauren Josephine Ironmonger LLB . . . . . Jan 2008
Harris, Anna . . . . Sep 2004
Hill, Ms Rebecca . . . . Sep 2007
Jayes, Ms Nadine. . . . . Dec 1989
Matharoo, Mr Sukhpal. . . . . *Nov 2004
Reid, Miss Kate. . . . . Jan 2008
Spence, Mr Julian. . . . . Sep 2003
Con: Taylor, Ms Kate M BA. . . . . *Oct 1985

BOYES TURNER ‡
Abbots House Abbey Street Reading RG1 3BD
Tel: 0118 959 7711 *Fax:* 0118 957 3257 *Dx:* 54741 READING 2
E-mail: mail@boyesturner.com
List of partners: M J Appleton, C Branson, S E Brown, A D Chalkley, P J Daniel, A C A Desmond, S D Doyle, M J C Farrier, W R W Gornall-King, G I Mendelsohn, G Parkinson, R C Rice, M A Robinson, K E Smerdon, P J E Smith, B M A Stanton, C A Wallis, A J Wilkin
Languages: French, Italian
Work: B1 C1 C2 C3 D1 E F1 I J1 K1 K2 K3 L M1 M2 N O P Q R1 S1 S2 T1 T2 U1 W X Z(b,c,d,e,i,k,l,o,p,q,r,t)
Emergency Action, Agency, Advocacy, Legal Aid undertaken, Legal Aid Franchise and Member of Accident Line
Ptr: Appleton, Mr Mark J BA(Law) . . . . *Dec 1985
Branson, Mr Christopher BA(Hons) . . . . *Apr 1981
Brown, Mrs Susan Emma LLB . . . . *Nov 1992
Chalkley, Mr Andrew D . . . . *§Dec 1982
Daniel, Mr Peter James LLB(Wales). . . . . *May 1971
Desmond, Mr Adrian Clandillon Anthony BSc(Bris) . . *§Oct 1980
Doyle, Mr Simon D . . . . *Mar 1967
Farrier, Mr Michael J C BA(Hons)(Law) Polytechnic of Wales Prize 1981 . . . . *Mar 1985
Gornall-King, Mr William Richard Willis LLB(Exon). . *§Oct 1982
Mendelsohn, Mr Geoffrey Ian LLB(Leeds) . . . . . . *Oct 1987
Parkinson, Mr Gary LLB(Leeds). . . . . *Feb 1988
Rice, Mr Robert Charles LLB . . . . *Nov 1995
Robinson, Mr Michael Aidan MA(Cantab) . . . . *Jul 1980
Smerdon, Ms Kim Evelynn LLB; LSF Moniter Press Prize (University of Essex) . . . . *Apr 1994
Smith, Mr Phillip John Edney LLB. . . . . *Oct 1994
Stanton, Mr Barry M A LLB . . . . *Nov 1991
Wallis, Mrs Caroline A LLB . . . . *Oct 1985
Wilkin, Ashley James TD LLB(B'ham) . . . . *§Jun 1975
Asoc: Anstis, Mr Laurence John Edmund LLB . . . . *Sep 1997
Baker, Mr Stephen N BSc(Hons); CPE . . . . *Oct 1998
Blomfield, Mr David Richard BSc; CPE; LSF. . . . . . *Oct 1996
Carter, Ms Nichola LLB . . . . *May 1999
Clare, Mrs Joanne E LLB . . . . *Sep 1997
Kenyon, Mr Peter. . . . . *Oct 1999
Money-Kyrle, Mr Richard Francis BSc. . . . . *Sep 1996
Ast: Baily, Ms Tahlia Kate . . . . *Sep 2003
Bertrand, Mr Alistair LLB . . . . *Sep 2003
Blunden, Mr Mark. . . . . *Jan 2000
Crompton-Pell, Ms Helena Margaret. . . . . Mar 2000
Daniel, Mr Robert BA . . . . Sep 2003
Kaye, Ms Nancy. . . . . Sep 2004
Martin, Ms Sophie LLB(Hons) . . . . *Sep 2002
Meyer, Mrs Ruth M LLB; New York Bar . . . . *Oct 1990
Mytton, Mr David L LLB. . . . . *Oct 1989
Norton, Miss Lucy LLB . . . . *Feb 2002
O'Connor, Mrs Emma LLB . . . . Jan 2001
O'Dwyer, Ms Tracey. . . . . *Sep 2001
Preston, Mr Richard. . . . . Sep 2003
Rowan, Mr Allen . . . . Sep 2004
Singnagra, Mandeep . . . . Mar 2000
Smith, Miss Helen. . . . . Sep 2002
Thinzar, Thaung. . . . . Sep 2004
Walsh, Mr Patrick . . . . Jan 1971
Weeden, Ms Anna . . . . *Sep 2004
Williamson, Ms Sarah. . . . . Sep 2003
Yogadeva, Miss Arani LLB . . . . *Feb 2001

GRAHAM BRIDGMAN & CO ‡
1 Gordon Palmer Close Stratfield Mortimer Reading RG7 3PZ
Tel: 0118 933 1818 *Fax:* 0118 933 1808
Dx: 130158 BURGHFIELD COMMON
E-mail: bridgman.co@virgin.net
List of partners: G H Bridgman
Work: B1 O
SPr: Bridgman, Mr Graham H LLB(Lond); FICM . . . . . *Mar 1984

N C BROTHERS & CO ‡
47 London Street Reading RG1 4PS
Tel: 0118 958 9966 *Fax:* 0118 958 9408
List of partners: N C Brothers
Work: A1 B1 C1 E J1 K1 K3 L O Q S1 S2 T1 T2 W Z(b,c,i,q)
Agency undertaken
Ptr: Brothers, Mr Nigel Christopher LLB . . . . Jan 1983

CAVERSHAM SOLICITORS LTD ‡
Prospect House 1 Prospect Street Caversham Reading RG4 8JB
Tel: 0118 947 8638 *Fax:* 0118 946 1092 *Dx:* 84152 CAVERSHAM
E-mail: info@cavershamsolicitors.co.uk
List of partners: M Badenhorst, R A C Last, R Williams
Languages: Afrikaans, Hindi, Punjabi, Thai, Urdu
Work: B1 C1 D1 D2 E F1 F2 J1 K1 K3 K4 L N O Q S1 S2 W Z(k,l,q)
Emergency Action, Agency and Fixed Fee Interview undertaken
Ptr: Badenhorst, Mr Minnaar LLB . . . . *Aug 2007
Last, Mr Robert Arthur Charles BA . . . . *Oct 1994
Williams, Miss Rebecca LLB . . . . *Sep 2000
Asoc: Bains, Mrs Baljinder LLB . . . . *Sep 1996
Ord-Hume, Mr Ian Donald LLB . . . . *Oct 1974
Woodward, Mr David Alan LLB . . . . *Nov 2008
Ast: Wykes, Mrs Niraj LLB. . . . . *Nov 1990

CLARKSLEGAL LLP ‡
One Forbury Square The Forbury Reading RG1 3EB
Tel: 0118 958 5321 *Fax:* 0118 960 4611 *Dx:* 54700 READING 2
E-mail: contact@clarkslegal.com
List of partners: M Atwal, H L Beech, P K Byrne, D G Downes, R S Krol, S Lapthorne, D S Mills, A G L Morris, K Parker, D A J Rintoul, M A Sippitt, P J Stevens, C Tayton
Office: Cardiff, London WC2, Swansea
Languages: French, German, Welsh
Work: A3 C1 C2 E J1 J2 L N O P R1 R2 S1 T2 U2 W Z(c,e,l,o,u,za)
Advocacy and Fixed Fee Interview undertaken
Ptr: Atwal, Mrs Monica BSc . . . . *Sep 1997
Beech, Mrs Helen L LLB . . . . *Oct 1990
Byrne, Mr Peter Kevin. . . . . *Oct 1993
Mills, Mr David Stuart . . . . Jul 1994
Morris, Mr Antony G L MA(Cantab) . . . . *Oct 1988
Parker, Ms Kirstin BA(Hons)(Oxon) . . . . *Oct 1995
Rintoul, Mr David A J LLB. . . . . *Oct 1989
Sippitt, Mr Michael A LLB . . . . *§Jun 1975
Stevens, Mr Peter John LLB . . . . *Mar 1973
Tayton, Mr Christopher BA(Law); LPC CCH Business Law Prize 1997 . . . . Sep 1999
Asoc: Berry, Mr Simon Christopher BA(Law). . . . . *Oct 1988
Clayfield, Mrs Rachel J LLB. . . . . *Nov 1992
James, Mr Stephen . . . . *Sep 1999
Leyshon, Ms Claire . . . . Nov 1995
Rowe, Ms Julie . . . . *Mar 2002
Ast: Arif, Mr Ashan BSc; PGDipLaw; LPC . . . . *Sep 2004
Flaig, Miss Caroline Ann BSc(Hons); CPE; LPC. . . . Sep 2001
Higgs, Mr Richard Duncan LLB(Hons); PGDipLP CCH Business Law Prize 1998 . . . . Sep 2000
Jorgensen, Rebecca . . . . Sep 2006
Kanias, Natasha . . . . Aug 2005
Quinn, Mrs Rebecca Jane LLB . . . . Sep 2000
Rughani, Ms Claire Lara . . . . *Sep 2004
Sehmbi, Tanushree LLB(Hons) . . . . *Mar 2001

CLIFTON INGRAM LLP
(incorporating Sarjeant & Sheppard)
First Floor County House 17 Friar Street Reading RG1 1DB
Tel: 0118 957 3425 *Fax:* 0118 959 7302 *Dx:* 54705 READING 2
E-mail: info@cliftoningram.co.uk
Office: Wokingham
Languages: French
Work: C1 D1 D2 E F1 J1 K1 K2 K4 L Q R1 S1 S2 T1 T2 W Z(d,e)
Ptr: Grant, Ms Kathryn A E MA . . . . *Oct 1992
Martin, Mr Ian L LLB . . . . *May 1974
Read, Mr Timothy C. . . . . *§Mar 1982
Asoc: McCarthy, Mrs Emma Elizabeth Zwager BA(Hons) . . Jan 2001
Con: Lacey, Mr Hugh C BA(Soton) . . . . *Jul 1965
Thorowgood, Mr Nicholas J C. . . . . *§Jun 1968

CHARLES COLEMAN & CO ‡
14a Cross Street Reading RG1 1SN
Tel: 0118 958 1578 *Fax:* 0118 958 1588 *Dx:* 3809 WINDSOR
E-mail: law@charlescoleman.co.uk
List of partners: J L Martin, J A Thomas
Work: E K1 N S1 W
Ptr: Martin, Miss Jo L LLB; PSC. . . . . Aug 1996
Thomas, Miss J Ann BA(Dunelm) . . . . *Mar 1979

COMPLETE LAW LLP
Cockayne House 126-128 Crockhamwell Road Woodley Reading RG5 3JH
Tel: 0118 969 5514 *Fax:* 0118 969 7430 *Dx:* 5345 WOODLEY
Office: Southampton

DAVID CRAYFORD ‡
14 Harcourt Drive Earley Reading RG6 5TJ
Tel: 0118 931 1447 *Fax:* 0118 931 2725
E-mail: dcrayford@hotmail.co.uk

DALLAS & CO ‡
Old Lodge Whitchurch Hill Reading RG8 7NU
Tel: 0118 976 7500

DAWSON LLOYD & CO ‡
Eaglewood House 42 Church Road Earley Reading RG6 1HS
Tel: 0118 966 9238
List of partners: B Dawson, A Lloyd
Work: C1 E K1 O Q R1 S1 T2 W Z(c,k,q,s,x)
Agency undertaken
Ptr: Dawson, Mr Brian BA; Cert Ed . . . . *May 1980
Lloyd, Miss Andrea . . . . *Dec 1974

DEXTER MONTAGUE LLP ‡
105 Oxford Road Reading RG1 7UD
Tel: 0118 939 3999 *Fax:* 0118 959 4072
Dx: 40114 READING (CASTLE STREET)
E-mail: info@dextermontague.co.uk
List of partners: S M Alderwick, M Amjad, J F Elliott, M J Kelly, S Kinder, W H Montague
Languages: Bengali, French, Greek, Hindi, Punjabi, Spanish, Urdu
Work: C1 D2 E F1 J1 J2 K1 K2 K4 L N O Q R1 S1 S2 W X Z(c,g,i,l,m,p)
Emergency Action, Agency, Advocacy and Fixed Fee Interview undertaken
Ptr: Alderwick, Ms Stephanie M LLB. . . . . *Jun 1981
Amjad, Mr Mohammed LLB(Hons) . . . . Jun 1998
Elliott, Mrs Judith Fedilia LLB(Hons) ♦. . . . . *Jun 1996
Kelly, Mr Martin J MA(Oxon) . . . . *Oct 1985
Kinder, Mrs Sharon LLB(Hons) . . . . *Mar 1993
Montague, Mr William H LLB ♦ . . . . *Oct 1983
Ast: Bayliss, Miss Clare LLB; LPC . . . . *Sep 2007
De Carvalho, Ms Solange LLB; LLM. . . . . Sep 2006
Pall, Miss Selena LLB; LPC . . . . *Sep 2007

DOYLE CLAYTON SOLICITORS LIMITED
Sovereign House Vastern Road Reading RG1 8BT
Tel: 0118 959 6839 *Fax:* 0118 956 1749
E-mail: info@doyleclayton.co.uk
Office: London E14, London EC2
Work: J1 Z(i,p)
Ptr: Leigh-Pollitt, Mr Piers J BA(Hons). . . . . *Oct 1997
Wisener, Mrs Tina LLB(Hons); LPC Sweet & Maxwell Law Prize; Top Graduate Law Student . . . . *Sep 2001
Asoc: Anderson, Mr James BA(Oxon) . . . . *Jan 1991
McArthur, Mr Alistair LLB(Hons). . . . . *Sep 2004
Potter, Ms Vanessa BA(Hons). . . . . *Nov 1992
Ast: Harris, Ms Catherine LLB . . . . *Jun 2009
Saxon, Ms Verity Angela Li-Ying BA(Hons) . . . . . *Feb 2009
Strachan, Miss Angela . . . . Jul 2010

EMMERSON LAW LIMITED ‡
Davidson House Forbury Square Reading RG1 3EU
Tel: 0118 900 0980 *Fax:* 0845 384 9285
E-mail: simon.emmerson@emmersonlaw.co.uk

THE EMPLOYMENT LAW PRACTICE ‡
6 Dellwood Park Caversham Heights Reading RG4 7NX
Tel: 0118 375 9288
E-mail: sue@theemploymentlawpractice.co.uk

EXCELLO LAW LIMITED ‡
200 Brook Drive Green Park Reading RG2 6UB
Tel: 0845 257 9449
E-mail: info@excellolaw.co.uk

FARRINGTON & CO ‡
61 Kidmore End Road Emmer Green Reading RG4 8ST
Tel: 0118 947 8914 *Fax:* 07970 468853
E-mail: grahamfarrington@hotmail.com
List of partners: G Farrington
Languages: French
Work: E K1 S1 W Z(e,f)
SPr: Farrington, Mr Graham LLB . . . . *Jul 1980

FIELD SEYMOUR PARKES ‡
1 London Street Reading RG1 4QW
Tel: 0118 951 6200 *Fax:* 0118 950 2704 *Dx:* 4001 READING 1
E-mail: enquiry@fsp-law.com
List of partners: S B Baker, D J Bickford, J C A Burgess, B M Crossley, W R Dixon, M P Francis, J A Lott, M J Mann, J A McDermott, E R Mehdevy, J G Parkes, M C Pears, P R H Seymour, R Tozer, S E Vandersteen, I M Wood-Smith, S L Wray
Languages: Punjabi, Spanish
Work: A1 A2 A3 B1 B2 C1 C2 C3 D1 D2 E F1 F2 I J1 J2 K1 K2 K3 K4 L M1 M2 N O P Q R1 R2 S1 S2 T1 T2 U1 U2 V W X Z(b,c,d,e,f,h,j,k,l,m,n,o,p,q,r,s,t,w,z,za)
Emergency Action, Agency, Advocacy and Fixed Fee Interview undertaken
Ptr: Baker, Mrs Susan B BA(Lond). . . . . *§Feb 1991
Bickford, Mr Dean Justin BA . . . . *§Sep 1999
Burgess, Mr James Christopher Appleyard . . . . . *§May 1982
Crossley, Ms Bridget M LLB(Bris) . . . . *§Jan 1966
Dixon, Mr William Russell BA(Cantab). . . . . *Dec 1985
Francis, Mr Marcus P BSc . . . . *§Apr 2003
Lott, Mr Joseph A BA . . . . *Oct 2002
McDermott, Ms Jacqueline Anne . . . . *Oct 1998
Mann, Mrs Michelle Joanne LLB . . . . *§Nov 1994
Mehdevy, Mrs Elizabeth Rebecca LLB. . . . . Sep 2002
Parkes, Mr Jeremy G BA(Hons). . . . . *§Nov 1995
Pears, Mrs Mary Catherine LLB; PGDipLP. . . . . . *§Nov 1997
Seymour, Mr Philip R H . . . . *§Jan 1972
Tozer, Mrs Rachel LLB . . . . *§Mar 1999
Vandersteen, Mrs Susan E LLB . . . . *§Oct 1989
Wood-Smith, Mr Ian M BA(Exon) . . . . *§Oct 1984
Wray, Mrs Sarah L LLB(Hons). . . . . *§Oct 1986
Asoc: Child, Mr Timothy John Peto LLB(Hons). . . . . . . *Nov 1993
Clarke, Miss Mandy J LLB. . . . . *Oct 1991
Edwards, Miss Maria Anna LLB. . . . . *Oct 2005
Evans, Mr John Patrick BA . . . . *Sep 2003
Garden, Miss Penelope LLB. . . . . *Oct 2005
Illingworth, Mrs Alexandra Clare BA(Hons); CPE; LPC *Sep 2002
Kularia, Ms Kuljeet LLB . . . . *Apr 2009
Mactear, Mrs Julia M BA(Hons) . . . . *Sep 1996
Ripley, Mrs Cathrine Florence BA . . . . *Jan 1992
Roles, Mrs Philippa Jane LLB; PhD . . . . Sep 2005
Webb, Miss Hazel May MA(Oxon). . . . . *Nov 1984
Woodhouse, Mr Thomas R LLB . . . . *Oct 1987
Ast: Brightling, Mr Christopher Richard LLB . . . . Sep 2011
Chenery, Ms Rebekah BA(Hons)(English & Classical Studies); PGDipLaw; LPC . . . . Sep 2005
Davies, Mr James Kenneth Edward LLB. . . . . . . *May 2002
Few, Miss Catherine BA(Hons); GDL; LPC . . . . . . Sep 2011
Hitchman, Miss Claire Michelle BA; GDL; LPC . . . . *Oct 2008
Machray, Mr Ian Eric LLB . . . . Apr 2006
Moran, Mrs Ellen . . . . *Oct 2009
Morris, Miss Faye. . . . . *Sep 2010
Preisner, Mr Joseph LLB . . . . Sep 2006
Rees-Williams, Miss Luned . . . . *Oct 2009
Rowland, Mrs Jasmine Maria . . . . *Sep 2010
Smyth, Ms Louise Anne LLB . . . . *Aug 2006
Verma, Preetika. . . . . *Nov 2005
Whitaker, Ms Catherine Louisa Ellen MA; LLDip. . . . *Oct 2007
Williams, Ms Emma Marie LLB(Hons) . . . . *Oct 2006
Williams, Ms Laura BSc. . . . . *Jun 2010
York, Mr Daniel Jonathan PGDipLaw; LPC . . . . . . *Mar 2006
Con: Booth, Mrs Rachel LLB . . . . *§Jun 1992
Essenhigh, Miss Kelsie Amanda LLB . . . . *Nov 1996
Roberts, Mr Timothy Simon LLB(Hons) . . . . *Oct 1984
Watsham, Mr Robert J . . . . *§Oct 1967
Whyman, Mr Keith R LLB . . . . *Mar 1975
Williams, Mr David C H MA; LLB(Cantab) . . . . . . *§Jan 1965

 See p112 for the Key to Work Categories & other symbols

2

GQ EMPLOYMENT LAW
Davidson House Forbury Square Reading RG1 3EU
Tel: 020 3375 0331 *Fax:* 020 3375 0332
E-mail: gq@gqemploymentlaw.com
Office: London EC2

GRIFFITHS ROBERTSON ‡
1st Floor 7-11 Queen Victoria Street Reading RG1 1SY
Tel: 0118 958 5049 *Fax:* 0118 958 5659
Asoc: Candy, Tangiwai . . . . Nov 2005

LAWRENCE HAMBLIN
36 Queens Road Reading RG1 4AU
Tel: 0118 951 6180 / 951 6190 *Fax:* 0118 951 6188
Dx: 4053 READING
E-mail: reading@lawrencehamblin.com
Office: Henley-on-Thames
Languages: Hindi, Punjabi
Work: E N S1 Z(r)
Fixed Fee Interview, Legal Aid undertaken and Legal Aid Franchise
Asoc: Pollard, Mr Michael LLB(Hons) . . . . *Aug 2001

HARRISONS ‡
7 Castle Street Reading RG1 7SB
Tel: 0118 959 8974 *Fax:* 0118 959 8975
E-mail: enquiries@harrisonssolicitors.com
List of partners: A Harrison
Office: Reading
Work: J2 L N Q S1 W
Agency, Advocacy, Fixed Fee Interview undertaken and Member of Accident Line
SPr: Harrison, Ashley LLB . . . . *Aug 1997

HARRISONS
72 Headley Road Woodley Reading RG5 4JE
Tel: 0118 944 8898 *Fax:* 0118 969 4089
E-mail: enquiries@harrisonssolicitors.com
Office: Reading

THE HEAD PARTNERSHIP ‡
9 Chalfont Court Lower Earley Reading RG6 5SY
Tel: 0118 975 6622 *Fax:* 0118 975 6588
Dx: 80502 HENLEY-ON-THAMES
E-mail: office@thpsolicitors.co.uk
List of partners: J M Baggott, L J Dean, M V Fox, M A Head, R P Rodway
Office: Henley-on-Thames
Work: A1 C1 C2 C3 D1 E J1 K1 K2 K3 K4 L N S1 W Z(e,f,w)
Legal Aid Franchise
Ptr: Baggott, Mrs Judith M BA(Hons)(Econ) . . . . . Dec 2002
Dean, Mrs Linda J BA(Hons) . . . . Jul 1977
Fox, Ms Maureen Virginia . . . . Nov 1997
Head, Mr Malcolm A . . . . *§Dec 1978
Rodway, Mr Richard Peter LLB(Hons) . . . . . . *Sep 2000

HENNESSY & HAMMUDI ‡
44 Queens Road Reading RG1 4AU
Tel: 0118 939 3559 *Fax:* 0118 959 6167 *Dx:* 4009 READING

HEWETTS ‡
55-57 London Street Reading RG1 4PS
Tel: 0118 957 5337 *Fax:* 0118 939 3073 *Dx:* 4055 READING
E-mail: enquiries@hewetts.co.uk
List of partners: T C Butcher, R P Gambles, G A Kew
Work: A1 B1 C1 D1 E F1 I J1 K1 L N R1 S1 S2 W Z(c,d,j,k,l,p)
Emergency Action, Agency, Advocacy, Fixed Fee Interview, Legal Aid undertaken and Legal Aid Franchise
Ptr: Butcher, Mr Timothy Charles . . . . Oct 2002
Gambles, Mr Robin P LLB(Bris) . . . . *Apr 1973
Kew, Mr Geoffrey A . . . . *Nov 1984
Con: Josephi, Mr Christopher H . . . . *§Dec 1962
Kennedy, Mr Christopher N . . . . *Sep 1973

TREVOR JENKIN SOLICITOR ‡
56 Kennylands Road Sonning Common Reading RG4 9JT
Tel: 07798 686706
Work: B1 C2 E J1 K1 O S2

JOHNSONS SOLICITORS LLP ‡
Citygate Business Centre Southampton Street Reading RG1 2QW
Tel: 0118 922 7220 *Fax:* 0118 922 7299 *Dx:* 4066 READING
List of partners: I Johnson
Work: B1 J1 O
Ptr: Johnson, Mr Ian LLB . . . . Jul 1989

JUST EMPLOYMENT
20 High Street Theale Reading RG7 5AN
Tel: 0118 963 9328 *Fax:* 01483 459850
E-mail: info@justemployment.com
Office: Brighton, Guildford

KHAN SOLICITORS ‡
PO Box 2642 44 London Street Reading RG1 4XG
Tel: 0118 958 3615 *Fax:* 0118 959 8358

KIDD RAPINET
20 Cross Street Reading RG1 1SN
Tel: 0845 017 8750 *Fax:* 0118 950 8283 *Dx:* 54713 READING 2
E-mail: mbugg@kiddrapinet.co.uk
Office: Aylesbury, Farnham, High Wycombe, London WC2, Maidenhead, Slough
Work: B1 C1 D1 F1 J1 K1 L N O Q Z(c,k,l,p)
Emergency Action, Agency, Advocacy, Fixed Fee Interview, Legal Aid undertaken, Legal Aid Franchise and Member of Accident Line
Ptr: Bugg, Mr Michael A G S BA(Kent); MA(Brunel) . . . *Dec 1979

BELINDA KNIGHT SOLICITOR ‡
Reading Office Davidson House Forbury Square Reading RG1 3EU
Tel: 0118 900 1712 *Fax:* 0118 900 1711
Emergency telephone 07736 677626
E-mail: enquiries@belindaknightsolicitor.co.uk

LAMPORT BASSITT
Soane Point 6-8 Market Place Reading RG1 2EG
Tel: 0845 077 6600 *Fax:* 0845 077 6601
E-mail: info@lamportbassitt.co.uk
Office: Southampton
Work: A1 B1 C1 C2 D1 E J1 K1 K2 L N O Q S1 S2 W Z(b,f,l)

MPM LEGAL LLP ‡
Davidson House The Forbury Reading RG1 3EU
Tel: 0118 900 1880 *Fax:* 0118 900 1881
E-mail: mark@mpmlegal.co.uk

CHARLES S MAIDSTONE ‡
36 St Marys Butts Reading RG1 2LS
Tel: 0118 959 4545

MANCHES LLP
Reading Bridge House Reading Bridge Reading RG1 8LS
Tel: 0118 982 2640 *Fax:* 0118 982 2641
E-mail: reading@manches.com
Office: London WC2, Oxford

MILLICHAPS ‡
10 Heritage Court Castle Hill Reading RG1 7RP
Tel: 0118 959 9631 / 07866 704035 *Fax:* 0118 959 4688
E-mail: suzanne@millichaps.co.uk

MORGAN COLE
3rd Floor Kennet House 80-82 Kings Road Reading RG1 3BJ
Tel: 0118 982 2500 *Fax:* 0118 982 2577 *Dx:* 141260 READING
E-mail: info@morgan-cole.com
Office: Bristol, Cardiff, Oxford, Reading, Swansea

MORGAN COLE
Apex Plaza Forbury Road Reading RG1 1AX
Tel: 0118 955 3000 *Fax:* 0118 939 3210
Dx: 117878 READING APEX ROAD
E-mail: info@morgan-cole.com
Office: Bristol, Cardiff, Oxford, Reading, Swansea
Work: A1 B1 C1 C2 C3 E G H J1 K1 L M1 M2 N O P Q S1 T1 T2 W X Z(b,c,d,e,j,l,m,o)

MARTIN MURRAY & ASSOCIATES
31 Castle Street Reading RG1 7SB
Tel: 0118 950 8577 *Fax:* 0118 950 9151
Dx: 40131 READING (CASTLE STREET)
Emergency telephone 01753 600101
Office: Slough, West Drayton
Languages: Greek, Hindi, Urdu
Work: B2 G H
Emergency Action, Agency, Advocacy, Fixed Fee Interview, Legal Aid undertaken and Legal Aid Franchise
Ptr: Ahmed, Zahida LLB(Hons) ★ . . . . *Aug 1992
Ast: Cole-Marshall, Mrs Nicola . . . . *Jan 1991
Neighbour, Ms Sarah BA(Hons); LLM . . . . . . *Aug 2004

OLSWANG LLP
Apex Plaza Forbury Road Reading RG1 1AX
Tel: 020 7067 3000 *Fax:* 020 7071 7499 *Dx:* 54711 READING
E-mail: thamesvalley@olswang.com
Office: London WC1

OSBORNE CLARKE
Apex Plaza Forbury Road Reading RG1 1AX
Tel: 0118 925 2000 *Fax:* 0118 925 2005 *Dx:* 117882 READING
E-mail: info@osborneclarke.com
Office: Bristol, London EC2
Ptr: Barker, Mr John . . . . Nov 1992
Bowyer, Mr Russell BA(Dunelm) . . . . *§Nov 1998
Finnegan, Mr Angus J . . . . Jan 1998
Jebb, Mr Steven P MA(Oxon); FLD . . . . . . *Nov 1995
Kingdon, Miss Danielle J LLB . . . . Oct 1991
Leyshon, Mr Greg . . . . Oct 1994
Macpherson, Moray C L MA(Oxon) . . . . . . *§Nov 1985
Wilson, Mr Stephen Charles Notary Public . . . . *Aug 1997
Asoc: Antingham, Mr Mark A LLB . . . . *Sep 1990
Ast: Gowans, Mr Andrew J BA(Oxon); LLM(Cantab) . . . *Mar 1993
Leigh-Pollitt, Mr Piers J BA(Hons) . . . . *Oct 1997
Linton, Ms Roma L . . . . Apr 1998
Walsh, Mr Brian T . . . . Mar 1998

PEARCE WEST SOLICITORS
Regus Business Centre 200 Brook Drive Reading RG2 6UB
Tel: 0118 925 6218
Office: Oxford

PITMANS LLP ‡
47 Castle Street Reading RG1 7SR
Tel: 0118 958 0224 *Fax:* 0118 958 5097 *Dx:* 146420 READING 21
E-mail: marketing@pitmans.com
List of partners: D B Archer, C H Avery, S K Brooker, F J Choudri, T Clark, H Clarke, S V Crowther, A G Davies, R Devall, A F M Dowdney, D J Hosford, J C Hutchinson, N Kirk, P M Long, M B Lynch, D N L Mehouas, P Murray, S O'Brien, A D Peddie, S J Perry, S L Sharp, J N Summers, B M Symons, P Weaver
Office: London EC2, Reading
Languages: Afrikaans, Arabic, Dutch, Finnish, French, German, Gujarati, Hebrew, Hindi, Italian, Japanese, Polish, Portuguese, Punjabi, Spanish, Swedish, Urdu
Work: A1 A3 B1 C1 C2 C3 E F1 G I J1 K1 K2 K3 M2 N O P R1 R2 S1 S2 T1 T2 U1 U2 W Z(b,c,d,e,f,j,l,o,w,za)
Ptr: Archer, Mr David B LLB . . . . *Oct 1985
Avery, Mr Christopher H . . . . *Apr 1982
Brooker, Ms Suzanne Kay LLB(Hons); MIPA . . . . *Oct 1994
Choudri, Mr Ferhat Jehangeer LLB . . . . Feb 2002
Clark, Mr Timothy LLB . . . . Oct 1987
Clarke, Ms Helen LLB . . . . *Nov 2000
Crowther, Mrs Susan V BA(Hons) . . . . *Jun 1998
Davies, Mr Andrew G MA(Cantab) . . . . *Sep 1988
Devall, Mr Richard LLB(Hons); LSF . . . . . . *Apr 1996
Hosford, Mr David Jeremy LLB; APMI . . . . . . Feb 1995
Hutchinson, Mr John C BA . . . . *Nov 1990
Kirk, Ms Nicola LLB . . . . *Sep 1995
Long, Mr Patrick M BCL . . . . *Jul 1991
Lynch, Ms Marian B BA(Hons) Deputy District Judge . Oct 1985
Mehouas, Miss Delphine Natalie Lydie . . . . . Nov 1999
Murray, Mr Paul LLB(QUB) . . . . *Oct 1996
O'Brien, Miss Susan BA . . . . *Oct 1984
Peddie, Mr Andrew David BA(Hons)(History); CPE; LSF . . . . *Sep 1990
Perry, Ms Stephanie J LLB . . . . *Sep 1991
Sharp, Ms Sally L MA(Oxon) . . . . *May 1979
Symons, Mr B Mark LLB . . . . *Feb 1986
Weaver, Mr Philip . . . . *Nov 1996

RATCLIFFE DUCE & GAMMER LLP ‡
49-51 London Street Reading RG41 4PS
Tel: 0118 957 4291 *Fax:* 0118 939 3143 *Dx:* 4019 READING 1
E-mail: reading-enquiries@rdg-law.co.uk
List of partners: S B Benfield, R Cherry, M E Farnell, G A Powell, N J Rodriguez, R J Watts
Office: Wokingham
Languages: French, German, Russian
Work: A1 C1 D1 E J1 K1 L M1 N O P Q R1 S1 T1 T2 V W Z(c,k,l,o)
Emergency Action, Agency, Advocacy, Fixed Fee Interview, Legal Aid undertaken, Legal Aid Franchise and Member of Accident Line
Ptr: Benfield, Mrs Sarah B LLB(B'ham) . . . . . . *Oct 1984
Cherry, Mr Robert . . . . *Sep 1995
Farnell, Mr Mark E LLB(Lond) . . . . *May 1983
Watts, Mr Robert J LLB Clifford's Inn Prize; Winston Churchill Memorial Prize (Soton) . . . . *Apr 1974
Ast: Wylie, Ms Linda BA(Hons); CPE; LPC . . . . . May 2005

TONY ROE SOLICITORS ‡
5a Brewery Court Theale Reading RG7 5AJ
Tel: 0118 930 2360 *Fax:* 0118 930 6879
List of partners: A J Roe
Work: K1
Agency undertaken
SPr: Roe, Mr Anthony Joseph BA(Hons) . . . . . . *Oct 1990

ROWBERRY MORRIS ‡
(in association with Rowberry Morris(Gloucester))
17 Castle Street Reading RG1 7SB
Est: 1958
Tel: 0118 958 5611 *Fax:* 0118 959 9662
Dx: 40125 READING (CASTLE STREET)
List of partners: J Dail, R W Edwards, J Gallimore, N C Henson, R C Leathem, R E Preston, R E Preston, O D Reynolds, P B Reynolds
Office: Richmond upon Thames, Staines, Tadley
Languages: Italian, Urdu
Work: A3 B1 C1 C2 C3 D1 D2 E F1 I J1 K1 K2 L M1 N O P Q S1 S2 W Z(e,f,i,k,l,p,q,r,w)
Emergency Action, Agency, Advocacy, Fixed Fee Interview, Legal Aid undertaken, Legal Aid Franchise and Member of Accident Line
Ptr: Dail, Jasbinder LLB . . . . *Feb 1989
Edwards, Mr Rodney W BA . . . . *Jan 1979
Gallimore, Miss Julie . . . . *Jun 1996
Henson, Mr Neil C LLB(Hons) . . . . *Nov 1978
Leathem, Mr Richard C LLB Deputy District Judge; Part time Chairman of the Appeals Service . . . . *Nov 1970
Preston, Mr Robert Edwin LLB(Lond) . . . . . . *Jul 1975
Reynolds, Mr Owen D . . . . *Sep 1998
Reynolds, Mr Peter Bryan . . . . *Mar 1996
Asoc: Cutting, Ms Gaye . . . . *Jun 2001
Con: Rowberry, Mr Anthony L . . . . *§Jul 1961

ANTHONY SANDALL AND CO ‡
Brightwell House 40 Queens Road Reading RG1 4AU
Tel: 0118 958 5505 *Fax:* 0118 958 9977
List of partners: A V Sandall
SPr: Sandall, Mr Anthony Vincent BA . . . . *Mar 1979

SHOOSMITHS
Apex Plaza Forbury Road Reading RG1 1SH
Tel: 0370 086 8800 / 0118 965 8765 *Fax:* 0370 086 8801
Dx: 117879 READING APEX PLAZA
Office: Basingstoke, Birmingham, Fareham, London WC2, Manchester, Milton Keynes, Northampton, Nottingham
Languages: French, German, Spanish
Work: A3 B1 B2 C1 C2 C3 E F1 F2 I J1 J2 K4 L M1 N O Q R1 R2 S1 S2 T1 T2 U2 W X Z(b,c,e,f,h,i,j,k,l,m,n,o,p,q,r,s,t,u,y,za)
Emergency Action, Agency, Advocacy, Fixed Fee Interview, Legal Aid undertaken and Member of Accident Line
Ptr: Brookes, Mr Timothy . . . . Dec 1994
Corcoran, Mr Alan LLB . . . . Nov 1993
Drew, Mr Dean Patrick BA(Hons) . . . . §Nov 1990
Farmery, Mr Andrew . . . . Sep 1999
Harvey, Mr James H LLB . . . . *Oct 1985
Higgin, Mr Michael James BA(Oxon); LSF(Guildford) . *Nov 1993
Law, Mr Stephen . . . . Dec 1995
Little, Mr Stuart BA(Hons) . . . . *§Oct 1995
McCavish, Mr Kevin . . . . Jan 1991
Rowe, Miss Claire M LLB . . . . *§Nov 1986
Shepherd, Mr Mark . . . . Mar 1987
Thorne, Mr Nigel Martyn LLB(Hons) ♦ . . . . . . §Oct 1986
Wojciechowski, Mr Eugene . . . . Oct 1997

PETER A C SLOAN ‡
20 High Street Theale Reading RG7 5AN
Tel: 0118 930 5030 *Fax:* 0118 908 0685

ANDREW STORCH ‡
7 Barrington Way Reading RG1 6EG
Tel: 0118 958 4407 *Fax:* 0118 958 4407
Emergency telephone 07050 245800
E-mail: a@andrewstorch.co.uk
List of partners: A J Storch
Work: G H
Emergency Action, Agency, Advocacy, Fixed Fee Interview, Legal Aid undertaken and Legal Aid Franchise
SPr: Storch, Mr Andrew J MA(Cantab) ★ . . . . . . *Nov 1991

TSP LEGAL ‡
27 Harrington Close Lower Earley Reading RG6 3BU
Tel: 0118 907 6341 *Fax:* 0118 961 3600
E-mail: tsplegal@yahoo.co.uk

THOMPSON LEATHERDALE ‡
(incorporating Ellis & Fairbairn(Reading))
61 London Street Reading RG1 4PS
Tel: 0118 959 1773 *Fax:* 0118 958 6033 *Dx:* 4006 READING
E-mail: info@thompsonleatherdale.co.uk
List of partners: N J Hunt, M J Thompson, P V Tyson
Work: A1 C1 C2 E F1 J1 L P Q R1 R2 S1 S2 T1 T2 W Z(c)
Ptr: Hunt, Mr Nigel J LLB . . . . *Apr 1979
Thompson, Mr M John . . . . *§Jun 1973
Tyson, Mr Piers Valentine LLB . . . . *§Oct 1992
Con: Bradbury, Mr Peter Charles . . . . *Jan 1971

E J WINTER & SON ‡
St Laurence House 10-12 The Forbury Reading RG1 3EJ
Tel: 0118 957 4424 *Fax:* 0118 950 5417 *Dx:* 54710 READING 2
E-mail: sols@ejwinter.co.uk
List of partners: M J Chandler, T P C Clift, R Frost, P N Kilshaw, K Sethi
Languages: Gujarati, Hindi, Punjabi, Russian, Urdu
Work: B1 B2 D1 D2 E F1 F2 G H J1 K1 L M1 N O P Q S1 S2 V W Z(i,p,q)
Emergency Action, Agency, Advocacy, Fixed Fee Interview and Legal Aid undertaken

Ptr: Chandler, Mr Martin J LLB . . . . . . *§Oct 1985
Clift, Mr Timothy P C BA . . . . . . *Apr 1989
Frost, Mr Richard LLB . . . . . . *§Mar 1977
Kilshaw, Mr Paul Nicholas LLB . . . . . . *Jul 2004
Sethi, Kuldeep LLB . . . . . . *Jan 1984

J C WROE & CO ‡
24 Eldon Road Reading RG1 4DL
Tel: 0118 959 1496
List of partners: J C Wroe
Work: C1 E G H M1 N S1 W Z(m)
Emergency Action, Agency, Advocacy, Fixed Fee Interview and Legal Aid undertaken
Ptr: Wroe, Mr John C MA(Oxon) . . . . . . Oct 1974

REDBRIDGE, Essex

ALKAN & CO SOLICITORS ‡
314 Eastern Avenue Redbridge Essex IG4 5AA
Tel: 020 8554 9201 *Fax:* 020 8554 9201

KENNARDS WELLS
6 Roding Lane South Redbridge Essex IG4 5NX
Tel: 020 8550 5103 *Fax:* 020 8550 9148 *Dx:* 141023 WANSTEAD 3
E-mail: rcohen@kennardwells.co.uk
Office: Epping, London E11
Work: C1 C2 C3 G J1 L N P S1
Emergency Action, Fixed Fee Interview and Legal Aid undertaken
Ptr: Cohen, Mr Richard H LLB . . . . . . *Jun 1984

REDCAR, Redcar & Cleveland

ASKEWS ‡
4-6 West Terrace Redcar Redcar & Cleveland TS10 3BX
Tel: 01642 475252 *Fax:* 01642 211017 *Dx:* 60020 REDCAR
E-mail: info@askews.com
List of partners: D F Askew, P Askew, S H Askew, C J Buckland, D Clements, M Moran, M D J Robinson, T D Taylor
Office: Middlesbrough, Stockton-on-Tees
Work: B1 C1 C2 D1 E F1 J1 K1 K3 L N O P S1 T1 T2 V W Z(e,h,k,l)
Emergency Action, Agency, Advocacy, Legal Aid undertaken, Legal Aid Franchise and Member of Accident Line
Ptr: Askew, Mr David F . . . . . . *Jul 1967
Askew, Mr Philip . . . . . . Sep 2009
Askew, Mr Simon Hill LLB . . . . . . Jun 2001
Buckland, Mr Christopher J LLB . . . . . . Mar 1990
Clements, Mr Derek . . . . . . *Mar 1971
Moran, Mr Matthew . . . . . . Jan 2006
Robinson, Mr Michael D J LLB . . . . . . *Nov 1987
Taylor, Miss Teresa Dawn LLB . . . . . . §Oct 2001

ATHA STRONG & CO ‡
18 The Wynd Marske-by-the-Sea Redcar Redcar & Cleveland TS11 7LA
Tel: 01642 482421 *Fax:* 01642 481140 *Dx:* 61680 MARSKE
List of partners: N Strong
Work: B1 C1 D1 E F1 G H J1 K1 L M1 N P R1 S1 T1 V W Z(h,j,k,l,m)
Emergency Action, Agency, Advocacy, Fixed Fee Interview and Legal Aid undertaken
Ptr: Strong, Mr Nicholas LLB . . . . . . *Jan 1978

BOUSFIELD GASKIN MCGOIN ‡
Redcar Station Business Centre Station Road Redcar Redcar & Cleveland TS10 1RD
Tel: 01642 495717

BROWN BEER NIXON MALLON ‡
24 Cleveland Street Redcar Redcar & Cleveland TS10 1AP
Tel: 01642 490202 *Fax:* 01642 489187 *Dx:* 60029 REDCAR
Emergency telephone 01642 490202 / 01287 624422
E-mail: enquiries@bbnm.co.uk
List of partners: M C Beer, G T Brown, A L K Li, J N V Nixon, K E Petch
Office: Middlesbrough
Work: D1 G H K1 V
Emergency Action, Agency, Advocacy and Legal Aid undertaken
Ptr: Beer, Mr Martyn C BA(Law) . . . . . . *Dec 1980
Brown, Mr Graham T LLB(Hons)(Lond) . . . . . . *Apr 1979
Li, Ms Ann Lorraine Katherine FILEx; LPC; CPE . . . *Dec 1996
Nixon, Mr John N V . . . . . . *Jun 1977
Petch, Mrs Karen Elizabeth LLB(Hons) . . . . . . *Jul 1995
Asoc: Auton, Miss Janet Elizabeth LLB . . . . . . Sep 2010
Dixon, Mrs Amy Jessica LLB(Hons) . . . . . . Sep 2001
Lish, Mrs Sarah LLB . . . . . . Jul 2006

Agency commissions undertaken; Crime - General; Family; Child Care, Wardship; Daily attendance at Teesside (Middlesbrough) Crown and Magistrates' Courts.

R M FLETCHER & CO ‡
17-19 Cleveland Street Redcar Redcar & Cleveland TS10 1AR
Tel: 01642 490400 *Fax:* 01642 490400 *Dx:* 60034 REDCAR
List of partners: R M Fletcher
SPr: Fletcher, Mr Richard M MA(Cantab) . . . . . . *Jun 1972

GOODSWENS ‡
118 High Street Redcar Redcar & Cleveland TS10 3DH
Tel: 01642 482424 *Fax:* 01642 471475
E-mail: law@goodswens.co.uk
List of partners: M G Boyes, A G Eastwood
Work: A1 A2 B1 C1 D1 D2 E F1 F2 J1 J2 K1 K3 K4 L N O P Q R1 R2 S1 S2 W X Z(d,e,l,q,r)
Emergency Action, Agency, Advocacy, Fixed Fee Interview, Legal Aid undertaken, Legal Aid Franchise and Member of Accident Line
Ptr: Boyes, Mr Michael G LLB(Lond) . . . . . . *Mar 1970
Eastwood, Mr Anthony G LLB . . . . . . *Feb 1987
Ast: Owens, Miss Wendy LLB(Hons) . . . . . . Sep 2003

RICHARD J KNAGGS & CO ‡
119 High Street Redcar Redcar & Cleveland TS10 3DG
Tel: 01642 487011 *Fax:* 01642 487714 *Dx:* 60030 REDCAR
E-mail: enquiries@richardjknaggs.co.uk
List of partners: R J Knaggs, J C R Wilson
Work: A1 B1 C1 D1 E F1 J1 K1 L N O Q R1 S1 T1 T2 V W Z(b,c,f,h,j,k,l,p,s)
Emergency Action, Agency, Advocacy, Fixed Fee Interview, Legal Aid undertaken, Legal Aid Franchise and Member of Accident Line
Ptr: Knaggs, Mr Richard J . . . . . . *Dec 1978
Wilson, Mr John C R BA . . . . . . *Oct 1990
Asoc: Sullivan, Mrs Bernadette LLB(Hons) . . . . . . Dec 2002

MACKS SOLICITORS
12 Milbank Terrace Redcar Redcar & Cleveland TS10 1ED
Tel: 01642 252828 *Fax:* 01642 252622
Dx: 60588 MIDDLESBROUGH
Office: Middlesbrough

REDDITCH, Worcestershire

ASTWOOD LAW ‡
Astwood House 1262 Evesham Road Astwood Bank Redditch Worcestershire B96 6AD
Tel: 01527 892200 *Fax:* 01527 892380
E-mail: graham@grahamclark.co.uk
List of partners: G W Clark, B M Laird
Work: E K4 S1 W
Ptr: Clark, Mr Graham William . . . . . . *Jun 1971
Laird, Mr Bruce McGregor . . . . . . Jan 1981

BANK SOLICITORS ‡
1250 Evesham Road Astwood Bank Redditch Worcestershire B96 6AD
Tel: 0845 604 6504 *Fax:* 01527 893957
E-mail: info@banksol.co.uk

KENNETH CURTIS & CO
3 Alcester Street Redditch Worcestershire B98 8AE
Tel: 01527 61967 *Fax:* 01527 584365 *Dx:* 19109 REDDITCH
Office: Birmingham
Languages: French, German
Work: B1 D1 E F1 G H J1 K1 L M1 N P S1 V W Z(c,l)

DAVIS PRIEST & CO ‡
24 Church Green East Redditch Worcestershire B98 8DE
Tel: 01527 69231 *Fax:* 01527 584822
E-mail: post@davispriest.co.uk
List of partners: S L Priest
Work: D1 D2 K1 K3 K4 S1 W
Emergency Action, Agency, Advocacy, Fixed Fee Interview, Legal Aid undertaken and Legal Aid Franchise
Ptr: Priest, Mr Stephen L LLB(Lond) . . . . . . *Apr 1979
Con: Davis-Pipe, Mr Frederick J LLB(Lond) . . . . . . *Nov 1972

THE FIRM SOLICITORS LLP
M&P House 3 Church Green East Redditch Worcestershire B98 8BP
Tel: 0121 709 6506
E-mail: info@thefamilyfirm.co.uk
Office: Birmingham, Solihull

HCB SOLICITORS ‡
10 Market Place Redditch Worcestershire B98 8AA
Tel: 01527 62688 *Fax:* 01527 62347 *Dx:* 19101 REDDITCH
Office: Alcester, Lichfield, Solihull, Stratford-upon-Avon, Walsall
Work: C1 C2 D1 D2 E J1 J2 K1 K2 K3 L N O Q R1 R2 S1 S2 T1 T2 V W Z(e,i,l,r)

HL LEGAL & COLLECTIONS ‡
Grosvenor House Redditch Worcestershire B97 4DL
Tel: 01527 586500 *Fax:* 01527 63669
E-mail: info@hllc.co.uk
List of partners: R A Lavender
Work: F1 O Q
Ptr: Lavender, Ms Rhona Anne LLB . . . . . . *Nov 1994

ID LAW ‡
6 Bates Hill Redditch Worcestershire B97 4AN
Tel: 01527 596010 *Fax:* 01527 598433

KERWOODS ‡
7 Church Road Redditch Worcestershire B97 4AD
Tel: 01527 584444 *Fax:* 01527 584838 *Dx:* 19108 REDDITCH
E-mail: solicitors@kerwoods.co.uk
List of partners: R D Caley, I G Hughes, I L Powleson, T J Sidwell, J D Thompson
Work: A1 B1 C1 C2 C3 D1 D2 E F1 G H J1 J2 K1 K2 K3 K4 L N O Q R1 S1 S2 T1 T2 W Z(c,d,i,l,q)
Emergency Action, Advocacy, Legal Aid undertaken, Legal Aid Franchise and Member of Accident Line
Ptr: Caley, Mr Richard D LLB(Bris) . . . . . . *§Oct 1972
Hughes, Mr Ifor G BA . . . . . . *Oct 1983
Powleson, Mr Ian L LLB(Lond) . . . . . . *§Oct 1972
Sidwell, Mr Trevor J MA(Oxon) . . . . . . *§Nov 1971
Thompson, Ms Janet D BA . . . . . . *Nov 1984

IAN MCLACHLAN ‡
12 Church Green East Redditch Worcestershire B98 8BP
Tel: 01527 63883 *Fax:* 01527 584170
List of partners: I McLachlan
Work: S1 W
Agency, Advocacy and Fixed Fee Interview undertaken
SPr: McLachlan, Mr Ian LLB(Lond) . . . . . . *Jul 1972

SAMPSON & CO ‡
12 Church Green East Redditch Worcestershire B98 8BP
Tel: 01527 66221 *Fax:* 01527 584114
E-mail: sampson.j@btconnect.com
List of partners: A S Marshall, J B Sampson
Work: A1 C1 E F1 F2 K1 K3 K4 N O Q S1 S2 W Z(q)
Agency and Fixed Fee Interview undertaken
Ptr: Marshall, Ms Angela S LLB . . . . . . *Nov 1980

TAYLORS ‡
Mercury House 1 Mason Road Headless Cross Redditch Worcestershire B97 5DA
Tel: 01527 544221 *Fax:* 01527 544419
Dx: 12501 HEADLESS CROSS
Emergency telephone 01527 543411
E-mail: derek@taylorssolicitors.com
List of partners: D L Taylor
Languages: French, German
Work: E K1 K3 K4 S1 S2 T1 T2 V W

REDHILL, Surrey

MICHAEL BAKER SOLICITORS LIMITED
Kenty's 1 Batts Hill Redhill Surrey RH1 1DS
Tel: 01252 744600 *Fax:* 01737 774114
Office: Aldershot, Farnborough

BANCE COMMERCIAL LAW ‡
7 The Fairways Redhill Surrey RH1 6LP
Tel: 01737 226034

DOUGLAS SOLICITORS ‡
54 Station Road Redhill Surrey RH1 1PH
Tel: 01737 780295 *Fax:* 01737 780296 *Dx:* 100207 REDHILL
Emergency telephone 07973 173832
Languages: Chinese, French, German
Work: B1 C1 E F1 J1 K1 L N O Q S1 T2 V W
Emergency Action, Agency, Advocacy, Fixed Fee Interview and Legal Aid undertaken
Ast: Chapman, Mr Noel David LLB(Hons) . . . . . . Apr 1989
Young, Ms Shelley LLB(Hons) . . . . . . Nov 1997

FIELDHOUSE & CO LLP ‡
Abbey House 25 Clarendon Road Redhill Surrey RH1 1QZ
Tel: 01737 277668 *Fax:* 020 8181 6588

GOODHAND AND FORSYTH QUALITYSOLICITORS ‡
76 Station Road Redhill Surrey RH1 1PL
Tel: 01737 773533 *Fax:* 01737 761222 *Dx:* 100206 REDHILL
Emergency telephone 01883 743654
E-mail: reception@goodhandandforsyth.co.uk
Web: www.goodhandandforsyth.co.uk
List of partners: D R Forsyth, K F Goodhand
Work: G H J1 K1 K3 K4 L N Q S1 S2 W Z(l)
Emergency Action, Agency, Advocacy, Fixed Fee Interview, Legal Aid undertaken and Legal Aid Franchise
Ptr: Forsyth, Mr David R ★ . . . . . . *May 1981
Goodhand, Mr Keith F ★ . . . . . . *Aug 1977
Asoc: Connah, Miss Fiona Louise LLB . . . . . . *May 1999
Ast: Hulme, Miss Elizabeth BA(Hons) . . . . . . Aug 2009
Lane, Ms Diane . . . . . . May 2008
Laws, Miss Caroline . . . . . . Apr 1983

Agency work undertaken at Local Magistrates' / County Juvenile Courts.

GRAY HOOPER HOLT LLP ‡
Nash House 6 Linkfield Corner Redhill Surrey RH1 1BB
Tel: 01737 761004 *Fax:* 01737 764029 *Dx:* 100219 REDHILL
E-mail: robertgray@grayhooperholt.co.uk
List of partners: R Gray
Work: D1 G H K3 N Q S1 W Z(j)
Advocacy, Legal Aid undertaken and Member of Accident Line
Ptr: Gray, Mr Robert LLB . . . . . . *§May 1981

HOOPER HOLT & CO ‡
22 Station Road Redhill Surrey RH1 1NU
Tel: 01737 761111 *Fax:* 01737 768333 *Dx:* 100202 REDHILL
List of partners: K D Giles, G P Guerin
Languages: French
Work: B1 C1 D1 E F1 G H K1 L O Q S1 S2 V W X Z(l,q)
Emergency Action, Agency, Advocacy, Fixed Fee Interview and Legal Aid undertaken
Ptr: Giles, Mrs Karen D BA(Law) . . . . . . *Feb 1985
Guerin, Mr Graham P LLB . . . . . . *Jan 1979
Ast: Durcan, Miss Catherine LLB . . . . . . *May 1986

MORRISONS SOLICITORS LLP ‡
Clarendon House Clarendon Road Redhill Surrey RH1 1FB
Tel: 01737 854500 *Fax:* 01737 854596 *Dx:* 100201 REDHILL
E-mail: info@morrlaw.com
Web: www.morrlaw.com
List of partners: S I Calthrop-Owen, J C Forbat, A R Fowles, M A Goff, R J B Gravell, P A E Harvey, D G Humphreys, J E I Jupp, D C Kingham, K Lord, M Martin, P Mills, R A Rose, P Savage, J M O H Walker
Office: Camberley, London SW19, Woking
Work: A1 A3 B1 C1 C2 C3 D1 D2 E F1 J1 J2 K1 K2 K3 K4 L N O Q R1 R2 S1 S2 T1 T2 W X Z(c,d,e,l,r,za)
Agency, Advocacy, Fixed Fee Interview undertaken and Member of Accident Line
Ptr: Calthrop-Owen, Miss Stephanie Irene LLB . . . . . . *Oct 1990
Forbat, Mrs Jane C LLB . . . . . . *Nov 1979
Kingham, Mr David C MA(Cantab) . . . . . . *Mar 1991
Lord, Miss Karen . . . . . . *Oct 1998
Rose, Mr Richard A . . . . . . *May 1977
Asoc: Chantler, Miss Holly . . . . . . *Oct 2008
Fegan, Ms Louise . . . . . . *Mar 2004
Moore, Miss Emma A LLB(Hons); LPC; PSC . . . . . . *Mar 1998
Wilkes, Mr Stephen . . . . . . *Aug 1979
Wood, Ms Natalie . . . . . . *Mar 2002
Ast: Pearce, Miss Louise . . . . . . *Jan 2007
Waller, Ms Marina . . . . . . *Dec 2006

Agency Commissions gladly undertaken.

OWEN & CO ‡
47a Station Road Redhill Surrey RH1 1QH
Tel: 01737 760036 *Fax:* 01737 766883 *Dx:* 100209 REDHILL
E-mail: nickhodges@owenandco.co.uk
List of partners: N J Q Hodges, C A M Owen
Work: D1 E F1 J1 K1 K3 L O Q R1 S1 V W
Emergency Action, Agency, Advocacy and Fixed Fee Interview undertaken
Ptr: Hodges, Mr Nicholas James Quartermaine LLB(Hons) *Oct 1992
Owen, Mrs Cherrill A M LLB(Hons) . . . . . . *Aug 1976

REDRUTH, Cornwall

JOHN BOYLE & CO ‡
The Square 5 West End Redruth Cornwall TR15 2SB
Tel: 01209 213507 *Fax:* 01209 219470 *Dx:* 81758 REDRUTH
Emergency telephone 07626 313455
E-mail: info@johnboylesolicitors.com
List of partners: P J Gallagher, B S Jackson, J P Leaning, H M Thomas
Office: Truro
Languages: French
Work: D1 G H K1 K3 L S1 S2 V W
Emergency Action, Agency, Advocacy, Fixed Fee Interview, Legal Aid undertaken and Legal Aid Franchise
Ptr: Gallagher, Mr Paul Jerome LLB(Hons) . . . . . . *Jan 1993

See p112 for the Key to Work Categories & other symbols

Jackson, Mr Barry Stefan LLB. *Jul 1985
Leaning, Mr Jeremy Philip BA; Former Barrister *May 1992
Thomas, Ms Helen Marie LLB. *Jan 1996
Ast: Appleby, Mr David. *Jan 2001
Charnley, Mr Mark J BA(Hons) *Jun 1990
Smith, Mr Robin. Jan 1996
Con: Boyle, Mr Francis John BA(Oxon) ★. *Jun 1980

GRYLLS & PAIGE ‡
(incorporating Exelbys)
Bank House West End Redruth Cornwall TR15 2SD
Tel: 01209 215261 / 215357 *Fax:* 01209 219677
Dx: 81752 REDRUTH
E-mail: law@grylls-paige.co.uk
List of partners: O H Chappel, J A Ferguson
Work: A2 D1 D2 E K1 K3 L O Q S1 S2 W Z(q)
Emergency Action, Advocacy, Fixed Fee Interview, Legal Aid undertaken and Legal Aid Franchise
Ptr: Chappel, Mr Oliver Hugh LLB *Oct 1987
Ferguson, Mr J Aidan LLB. *Dec 1977

THURSTAN HOSKIN SOLICITORS ‡
Chynoweth Chapel Street Redruth Cornwall TR15 2BY
Tel: 01209 213646 *Fax:* 01209 210069 *Dx:* 81751 REDRUTH
E-mail: info@thurstanhoskin.co.uk
List of partners: D Appleby, D Farmer, T C Hoskin
Work: D1 D2 E K1 K3 S1 S2 W Z(d)
Emergency Action, Advocacy, Legal Aid undertaken and Legal Aid Franchise
Ptr: Appleby, Mr David LLB(Hons). Jan 2001
Farmer, Mr David BA(Hons)(Law) *Jul 1999
Hoskin, Mr Thurstan Charles BA §Dec 1975

REEPHAM, Norfolk

PURDYS ‡
Ivy House Market Place Reepham Norfolk NR10 4LZ
Tel: 01603 870606 *Fax:* 01603 871332 *Dx:* 118075 REEPHAM
Emergency telephone 01379 854455
E-mail: andrewgibb@purdysreepham.co.uk
List of partners: A Gibb, J M O Vertigan
Languages: French
Work: A1 A2 C1 E K4 L S1 S2 T2 W Z(l)
Ptr: Gibb, Mr Andrew *Sep 1975
Vertigan, Mr John M O *§Jul 1971

REIGATE, Surrey

BARLIN ‡
Millennium House 99 Bell Street Reigate Surrey RH2 7AN
Tel: 01737 231340 *Fax:* 01737 231341
E-mail: barlin@barlin.co.uk

CALOW & CO ‡
15 Beech Road Reigate Surrey RH2 9LS
Tel: 01737 248480

CARLTON CABRAL SOLICITOR ‡
1 Seale Hill Reigate Surrey RH2 8HZ
Tel: 01737 222717

ELGEE PINKS SOLICITORS
Priory House 45-51 High Street Reigate Surrey RH2 9AE
Tel: 01737 247554 *Fax:* 01737 247297
E-mail: info@elgeepinks.com
Office: Westerham

ROBERT M JUSTICE TAX & TRUST CONSULTANT ‡
Three Gables Beech Road Reigate Surrey RH2 9LS
Tel: 01737 222700 *Fax:* 01737 244502
Emergency telephone 020 7929 3144
List of partners: R M Justice
Work: T1 T2 W Z(j)
SPr: Justice, Mr Robert M FInstD; TEP; IRIB. *Nov 1968

ORMERODS
(incorporating Gray Marshall & Campbell; The Heap Partnership; Quirke & Wombwell & Coningsbys)
33 London Road Reigate Surrey RH2 9HZ
Tel: 020 8686 5000 *Fax:* 01737 223323
E-mail: enquiries@ormerods.co.uk
Office: Croydon, London SW19

PENDRIGH MAKIN ‡
Old Wheel House 31-37 Church Street Reigate Surrey RH2 0AD
Tel: 01737 221518 *Fax:* 01737 223446 *Dx:* 54110 REIGATE 2
List of partners: R A Healy, J W G Makin, N D G Pendrigh
Office: Sevenoaks
Work: D2 E J1 K1 K3 K4 S1 S2 T2 W
Ptr: Healy, Miss Rosamund Anne BA(Hons)(Law) *Feb 1988
Makin, Mr Justin W G BA(Hons). *Mar 1995
Pendrigh, Miss Naomi D G MA(Oxon). *Oct 1994

QUANTICKS ‡
40 Bell Street Reigate Surrey RH2 7BA
Tel: 01737 233555 *Fax:* 01737 233556 *Dx:* 30408 REIGATE

SHEPPERSONS
Pool House 1 Bancroft Road Reigate Surrey RH2 7RP
Tel: 01737 244987 *Fax:* 01737 248127 *Dx:* 200402 HORLEY
E-mail: law@sheppersons.co.uk
Office: Horley
Work: D1 K1 K2 K3
Fixed Fee Interview undertaken
Ptr: Gandon, Miss Sally Ann. *May 1980

SHERIDAN GOLD LLP ‡
Castle Court 41 London Road Reigate Surrey RH2 9RJ
Tel: 01737 735088 *Fax:* 01737 735001
E-mail: info@sheridangold.co.uk

TWM SOLICITORS LLP
40 West Street Reigate Surrey RH2 9BT
Tel: 01737 221212 *Fax:* 01737 240120 *Dx:* 54115 REIGATE 2
E-mail: reigate.reception@twmsolicitors.com
Office: Cranleigh, Epsom, Guildford, Leatherhead, London SW19
Languages: French, German, Spanish
Work: A1 B1 C1 C2 C3 D1 E F1 F2 J1 J2 K1 L M1 M2 N O P Q R1 S1 S2 T1 T2 W X Z(c,d,e,f,h,k,l,m,o,p,q)
Emergency Action, Agency and Advocacy undertaken
Ptr: Bradley, Mr Paul M LLB *Jan 1977
Cloud, Miss Sharon BA; JD(USA); Attorney at Law (Pennsylvania USA) J D Cum Laude 1986 *Jul 1994
Jones, Mr Michael C LLB *Mar 1976
Maberly, Mr Giles H P. *Jul 1967
Sharpe, Mr Christopher Coverdale *Jul 1971
Mem: Bosler, Mrs Wendy BA *Nov 1994
Patel, Mrs Tina Jan 1989
Patricio, Demelza. Jan 1999
Storer, Mr Andrew. Jan 1993
Asoc: Stagg, Mr Geoffrey P LLB. Oct 1987
Ast: Wrightson, Ms Melanie LLB(Hons) *Aug 2000

VENTERS SOLICITORS
7a West Street Reigate Surrey RH2 9BL
Tel: 01737 229610 *Fax:* 01737 244520 *Dx:* 30405 REIGATE
E-mail: reigate@venters.co.uk
Office: London SE5
Work: G H K1 K2 K3
Agency, Advocacy and Legal Aid undertaken
Ptr: Venters, Ms June Marion • Recorder *Jan 1984
Ast: Fiander, Mrs Carly LLB(Hons). *Jan 2005
Mundy, Miss Jennifer A LLB(Hons) *Jun 1983

RENDCOMB, Gloucestershire

ANTHONY ROSE & CO ‡
(in association with Amsterdam & Peroff(Canada); Hampden Legal PLC)
Knightsgate Law Offices Rendcomb Gloucestershire GL7 7ET
Tel: 01242 870040 *Fax:* 01285 870403
E-mail: ajwrose@aol.com
List of partners: A J W Rose
Languages: French
Work: C1 C2 C3 M1 Z(e,j)
Ptr: Rose, Mr Anthony J W *Jun 1970

RETFORD, Nottinghamshire

ATTEYS
19 Churchgate Retford Nottinghamshire DN22 6PF
Tel: 01777 713355 *Fax:* 01777 713377 *Dx:* 27156 RETFORD
Office: Barnsley, Doncaster, Sheffield, Wath-upon-Dearne
Work: A1 B1 C1 C2 D1 E F1 J1 K1 L N O Q R1 S1 T1 T2 V W Z(c,f,h,j,k,m,n,o,s)
Emergency Action, Agency, Advocacy, Fixed Fee Interview, Legal Aid undertaken, Legal Aid Franchise and Member of Accident Line
Ptr: Browne, Mr Michael E CBE; TD; DL Notary Public. *Apr 1966
Neeves, Mrs Marion F LLB *Oct 1989
Ast: Sweeney, Ms Susan LLB *Sep 1999

JONES & CO ‡
Cannon Square Retford Nottinghamshire DN22 6PB
Tel: 01777 703827 *Fax:* 01777 860710 *Dx:* 27154 RETFORD
Emergency telephone 07971 520334
E-mail: info@jonessolicitors.co.uk
List of partners: A M Green, A Hadfield, R K Jenkins, M Sharpe
Office: Bawtry
Work: D1 G H K1 L N Q S1 S2 W Z(l,m)
Agency, Advocacy, Fixed Fee Interview and Legal Aid undertaken
Ptr: Green, Mr Andrew M *Jul 1974
Hadfield, Mr Anthony *Jul 1980
Jenkins, Ms Rhona Kirsty LLB(Hons) *Aug 1993
Sharpe, Mr Matthew. Dec 1998

ROYCE MARSHALL & CO ‡
Gamston Airport Gamston Retford Nottinghamshire DN22 0QL
Tel: 07765 404753
E-mail: royce@retfordairport.co.uk
List of partners: R Marshall
Languages: Spanish
Work: B1 C1 D1 E F1 G H J1 K1 L N O Q R1 S1 V W X
Emergency Action, Agency, Advocacy, Fixed Fee Interview and Legal Aid undertaken
Ptr: Marshall, Mr Royce DipLP; FILEx; FILAM; AILCA *May 1996

PHILIP SENIOR & CO ‡
Exchange Buildings Exchange Street Retford Nottinghamshire DN22 6BL
Tel: 01777 869545 *Fax:* 01777 869627 *Dx:* 27153 RETFORD
List of partners: P Senior
Work: A1 C1 E R1 S1 W
SPr: Senior, Mr Philip *Dec 1974

DEAN THOMAS & CO
18 Grove Street Retford Nottinghamshire DN22 6JS
Tel: 01777 703100 *Fax:* 01777 709903 *Dx:* 27155 RETFORD
Emergency telephone 01909 500511
E-mail: dtcretford@aol.com
Office: Chesterfield, Worksop
Work: G H J1 K1 K3 L O Q S2 W Z(l)
Emergency Action, Agency, Advocacy, Fixed Fee Interview, Legal Aid undertaken and Legal Aid Franchise
Ptr: Morton, Mr Richard James *Dec 1976

TRACEY BARLOW FURNISS & CO
9 New Street Retford Nottinghamshire DN22 6EG
Tel: 01777 707677 *Fax:* 01777 709230 *Dx:* 27159 RETFORD
Emergency telephone 01623 794574
E-mail: michael@tbfsolicitors.co.uk
Office: Worksop
Work: A1 B2 D1 D2 E F1 F2 G H J1 K1 L N P Q R1 S1 S2 V W X Z(c,d,g,h,l,q,t)
Emergency Action, Agency, Advocacy, Fixed Fee Interview, Legal Aid undertaken and Legal Aid Franchise
Ptr: Pryor, Mr Michael David DML *Mar 1984
Ast: Newton, Ms Karen LLB(Hons). Sep 1998

RHAYADER, Powys

H VAUGHAN VAUGHAN & CO
(incorporating Marsden & Co)
South Street Rhayader Powys LD6 5BH
Tel: 01982 552331 *Fax:* 01982 552860 *Dx:* 100653 BUILTH WELLS
E-mail: david@hvaughan.co.uk
Office: Builth Wells
Work: A1 A2 D2 E K1 K3 L Q R1 R2 S1 S2 T1 T2 W
SPr: Lloyd, Mr David Thomas *§Apr 1975

2

RHYL, Denbighshire

MICHAEL A BROWN & CO ‡
25-27 Russell Road Rhyl Denbighshire LL18 3BS
Tel: 01745 332722

GAMLINS
31-37 Russell Road Sutton Associates Office Rhyl Denbighshire LL18 3DB
Tel: 01745 343500 *Fax:* 01745 343616 *Dx:* 17352 RHYL
E-mail: rhyl@gamlins.co.uk
Office: Bangor, Colwyn Bay (2 offices), Conwy, Holywell, Llandudno
Languages: French, German, Welsh
Work: A1 C1 C2 D1 D2 E F1 F2 G H J1 K1 K3 L N O P Q R1 S1 S2 W Z(e,l,p,q)
Emergency Action, Agency, Advocacy, Fixed Fee Interview, Legal Aid undertaken, Legal Aid Franchise and Member of Accident Line
Ptr: Hoult, Mr John C LLB *§Jul 1978
Jones, Mr Gwyn BA. *Oct 1984
Morris, Mr Gary LLB(L'pool). *Jun 1975
Salisbury, Mr Robert A LLB Notary Public *Jun 1973
Asoc: Wilkinson, Mrs Susan Catherine LLB(Hons) *Jan 1992
Ast: Reeve, Mr Andrew J LLB *Nov 1993
Rogers, Mrs Tracey Alexandra LLB(Hons). Jan 1998

GARNETT WILLIAMS POWELL ‡
18 Kinmel Street Rhyl Denbighshire LL18 1AL
Tel: 01745 334658 *Fax:* 01745 330764 *Dx:* 17355 RHYL
List of partners: J M Davies, A J Drake
Work: K1 K3 L S1 S2 V W
Agency, Fixed Fee Interview, Legal Aid undertaken and Legal Aid Franchise
Ptr: Davies, Ms Joanna M LLB(Wales). *Oct 1984
Drake, Mr Adrian J BA *Dec 1985

EDWARD HUGHES ‡
Canadian House 29-31 Kinmel Street Rhyl Denbighshire LL18 1AH
Tel: 01745 343661 / 344551 *Fax:* 01745 354962 *Dx:* 17359 RHYL
Emergency telephone 01745 350685
E-mail: edhughes@sols29.freeserve.co.uk
List of partners: E J L Evans, D M Jones, E S Parry, E R Thomas
Languages: Spanish, Welsh
Work: A1 B1 D1 D2 E F1 G H J1 K1 L N O Q R1 S1 S2 V W Z(c,d,f,h,l,o,p,t)
Emergency Action, Agency, Advocacy, Fixed Fee Interview, Legal Aid undertaken, Legal Aid Franchise and Member of Accident Line
Ptr: Evans, Miss Elizabeth Jane Louise LLB. *Oct 1992
Jones, Mr David Merfyn LLB ♦ *Oct 1993
Parry, Miss Elen S BSc(Hons)(Econ) *Sep 1990
Thomas, Mr E Roger LLB(L'pool) *May 1976

HUMPHRYS & CO ‡
(incorporating Dawsons)
52-54 Crescent Road Rhyl Denbighshire LL18 1PB
Tel: 01745 343158 *Fax:* 01745 342540 *Dx:* 17363 RHYL
Emergency telephone 01745 343158
E-mail: law@humphrys.co.uk
List of partners: C E H Dawson, N Dawson, C Humphrys, J C Humphrys, A C Hutchinson, A E Merigold, A N Newnes, J G Thomas, R A Vickery
Office: Colwyn Bay, Wrexham
Languages: Welsh
Work: D1 F1 G H K1 L Q S1 V W
Emergency Action, Agency, Advocacy, Legal Aid undertaken and Legal Aid Franchise
Ptr: Dawson, Mr Christopher E H LLB(Bris) *§Apr 1981
Dawson, Mrs Nia LLB. *Oct 1987
Humphrys, Ms Caroline BA(Leeds) *Apr 1978
Humphrys, Mr James C. *Oct 1978
Hutchinson, Mr Andrew Craig. Jul 1999
Merigold, Miss Annette E BA Mar 1987
Newnes, Mr Antony N BA Notary Public. *Dec 1979
Thomas, Mr John G. Jul 1976
Vickery, Mr Robert A BA *Jan 1983

KINGSLEY ROSE SOLICITORS ‡
14 Clwyd Street Rhyl Denbighshire LL18 3LA.
Tel: 01745 355535 *Fax:* 01745 355537

RUSHWORTH & GLYN OWEN ‡
16 Clwyd Street Rhyl Denbighshire LL18 3LG
Tel: 01745 343843 *Fax:* 01745 350180 *Dx:* 17353 RHYL
List of partners: G W Jones, M J Rushworth
Languages: Welsh
Work: C1 E F1 J1 K1 L N Q S1 W
Agency and Fixed Fee Interview undertaken
Ptr: Jones, Mr Gareth W LLB(Wales) *§Dec 1978
Rushworth, Mr Michael John BA(Law). *§Oct 1982

RICHMOND, North Yorkshire

HODGSONS & MORTIMER
Rosemary House Rosemary Lane Richmond North Yorkshire DL10 4DP
Tel: 01748 850950 *Fax:* 01748 823555
Dx: 65041 RICHMOND NORTH YORKS
E-mail: enquiries@hodgsons-mortimer.co.uk
Office: Darlington
Work: A1 B1 C1 D1 D2 E F1 J1 K1 K4 L N Q R1 S1 S2 T1 V W Z(c,l)
Emergency Action, Agency, Advocacy, Fixed Fee Interview, Legal Aid undertaken and Legal Aid Franchise
Ptr: Hodgson, Mr Nicholas J BA(Hons); TEP. *§Sep 1982
Hodgson, Mr Richard Anthony LLB Mar 1977
Asoc: Clark, Mr Alistair Callum LLB Oct 1976

HUDSONS HART & BORROWS ‡
18 Queens Road Chambers Richmond North Yorkshire DL10 4AQ
Tel: 01748 824333 *Fax:* 01748 850339
Dx: 65044 RICHMOND NORTH YORKS
List of partners: A Meehan
Work: A1 B1 C1 D1 E F1 G H J1 K1 L M1 P R1 S1 T1 W Z(l)
Emergency Action, Agency, Advocacy, Fixed Fee Interview and Legal Aid undertaken
Ptr: Meehan, Mr Alan LLB(Hull) Jan 1969

HUNTON & GARGET ‡
Burgage House 1 Millgate Richmond North Yorkshire DL10 4JL
Tel: 01748 850400 *Fax:* 01748 850217
Dx: 65042 RICHMOND NORTH YORKS
E-mail: law@huntonandgarget.co.uk
List of partners: S J Garget, S A Lawson
Work: A1 B1 C1 D1 E F1 J1 K1 K3 K4 L N O Q R1 S1 S2 T1 T2 V W Z(l,r)
Agency undertaken
Ptr: Garget, Mr Stephen John . . . *§May 1974
Lawson, Mr Stephen Allan BSc(Hons). . . *§Mar 1998
Ast: Potts, Miss Lisa Margaret LLB(Hons) . . . *Nov 2007

RICHMOND UPON THAMES, Surrey

W J H BROWN ‡
9 Friars Stile Road Richmond Hill Richmond upon Thames Surrey TW10 6NH
Tel: 020 8332 1566
Work: S1 S2 W

CALVERT SMITH & SUTCLIFFE ‡
Onslow House 9 The Green Richmond upon Thames Surrey TW9 1PU
Tel: 020 8940 0017 *Fax:* 020 8948 8498 *Dx:* 100250 RICHMOND 2
E-mail: enquiries@calvertslaw.co.uk
List of partners: J Davies, D C G Fellows, M E Kelley, R S Morton, J M L Williams
Languages: French
Work: C1 D1 E F1 G H J1 K1 L M1 N P R1 S1 T1 W Z(d)
Emergency Action, Agency, Advocacy, Fixed Fee Interview and Legal Aid undertaken
Ptr: Davies, Mrs Janette BSc . . . *Nov 1986
Fellows, Mr David C G LLB; AKC . . . *Dec 1976
Kelley, Mrs Mary E LLB(Wales) . . . *Nov 1982
Morton, Mr Robert S LLB . . . *Apr 1975
Williams, Mr Jeremy M L MA(Oxon). . . *May 1977
Ast: Aggett, Mrs Sarah LLB . . . *Oct 1997
Foster, Miss Mary H BA. . . *Oct 1984

DIXON WARD ‡
16 The Green Richmond upon Thames Surrey TW9 1QD
Tel: 020 8940 4051 *Fax:* 020 8940 3901 *Dx:* 100251 RICHMOND 2
List of partners: S J Davis, H A Eastwood, J R C Horler, K K Hundal, C L Nicholls, M D Prest, G B White
Office: Ham
Languages: French, German, Spanish
Work: B1 C1 C2 D1 E F1 J1 K1 K3 K4 L N O P Q S1 S2 T2 W Z(l)
Agency and Advocacy undertaken
Ptr: Davis, Mrs Sarah J LLB(Hons) . . . *May 1977
Eastwood, Ms Hazel A BA(Oxon) . . . *Jan 1980
Horler, Mr James Roderic Charles. . . *Nov 1991
Hundal, Ms Kulbir Kaur BA(Hons). . . *Jan 1989
Nicholls, Mrs Clare L LLB . . . *Feb 1989
Prest, Mr Mark D BA(Law) . . . *Feb 1986
White, Mr Gregory Ben BA; MPhil. . . *Jul 2003
Ast: Sales, Miss Vicki Natasha BA(Hons) . . . *Aug 1999
Thompson-Haughton, Miss Beverley LLB(Hons); LLM(Hons) . . . *Sep 1990

EDISON LAW ‡
7 Terrace House 128 Richmond Hill Richmond upon Thames Surrey TW10 6RN
Tel: 020 8406 0084 *Fax:* 020 7681 2102
E-mail: abi.will@edisonlaw.co.uk

FISHER MEREDITH
Parkshot House 5 Kew Road Richmond upon Thames Surrey TW9 2PR
Tel: 020 8334 7927 *Fax:* 020 8334 7940 *Dx:* 100265 RICHMOND 2
E-mail: info@fishermeredith.co.uk
Office: London SE11

GILES DIXON ‡
65 Kew Green Richmond upon Thames Surrey TW9 3AH
Tel: 020 8241 1059

GOLDMAN LAW ‡
Hogarth House 34 Paradise Road Richmond upon Thames Surrey TW9 1SE
Tel: 020 8332 2310 *Fax:* 020 8948 5629 *Dx:* 100260 RICHMOND 2
E-mail: enquiries@goldmanlaw.co.uk

GRAFF & REDFERN ‡
3a Spring Terrace Paradise Road Richmond upon Thames Surrey TW9 1LP
Tel: 020 8940 0860 / 8948 2815 *Fax:* 020 8940 5943
Dx: 100254 RICHMOND 2
E-mail: info@graffandredfern.co.uk
List of partners: S E Graff
Languages: French
Work: E K1 R2 S1 S2
SPr: Graff, Miss Sandra E . . . *Jul 1965

LXL LIMITED ‡
1 Blake Mews Richmond upon Thames Surrey TW9 3GA
Tel: 020 8439 8810 *Fax:* 020 8439 9868

THE LEGAL PARTNERS LIMITED ‡
Parkshot House 5 Kew Road Richmond upon Thames Surrey TW9 2PR
Tel: 020 8334 8049 *Fax:* 020 8334 8100
E-mail: info@thelegalpartners.com

MCCONNELL LAW ‡
98 Ennerdale Road Kew Richmond upon Thames Surrey TW9 2DL
Tel: 020 8255 9500 / 07726 794821
E-mail: charlotte@mcconnelllaw.co.uk

MACKINTOSH & CO ‡
21 Larkfield Road Richmond upon Thames Surrey TW9 2PG
Tel: 020 8332 2864 *Fax:* 020 8332 2867
E-mail: jmackintosh@hemscott.net
List of partners: J D M Mackintosh
Work: T2 W
SPr: Mackintosh, Mr James D M MA(St Andrews) . . . *Jun 1976

MOORE BLATCH SOLICITORS
3 Castle Yard Richmond upon Thames Surrey TW10 6TF
Tel: 020 8744 0766 *Fax:* 020 8332 8630
Office: Lymington, Southampton (2 offices), Wickham
Ptr: Cassidy, Ms Anne. . . Dec 1992
Ast: Stanton, Mrs Sarah Louise LLB(Hons). . . *Oct 1993

NEIRIZI SWAN SOLICITORS ‡
1 Princes Street Richmond upon Thames Surrey TW9 1ED
Tel: 020 8255 1013 *Fax:* 020 8401 1966 *Dx:* 100275 RICHMOND 2
E-mail: info@neiriziswan.com

PERRY HAY & CO ‡
(incorporating Peter Hay & Associates; John Perry & Co)
25 The Green Richmond upon Thames Surrey TW9 1LY
Tel: 020 8940 8115 / 8332 7532 *Fax:* 020 8948 8013
Dx: 100259 RICHMOND 2
E-mail: peterhay@perryhay.co.uk
Web: www.perryhay.co.uk
List of partners: N Green, P R Hay, H S Lynch, S K Testar
Languages: French
Work: A3 C1 C2 C3 E J1 K1 K2 K3 K4 L R2 S1 S2 T2 W Z(m,w)
Ptr: Green, Miss Nicole LLB. . . *Apr 2009
Hay, Mr Peter R. . . *§Jan 1973
Lynch, Mrs Henna Sultana LLB . . . *May 2001
Testar, Mrs Shelagh K BA(Hons) . . . *Jun 1979
Asoc: Smith, Mr Simon Vernon BSc(Hons). . . *Jun 2001
Ast: Byam-Cook, Mrs Philippa Michelle LLB . . . *Jan 2009

REDMANS SOLICITORS ‡
Parkshot House 5 Kew Road Richmond upon Thames Surrey TW9 2PR
Tel: 020 3397 3603 *Fax:* 020 3397 3609
E-mail: mailbox@redmans.co.uk

ROWBERRY MORRIS
Clockhouse Chambers 4a The Square Richmond upon Thames Surrey TW9 1DZ
Tel: 020 8334 4860 *Fax:* 020 8332 3021 *Dx:* 100276 RICHMOND 2
Office: Reading, Staines, Tadley

SAUNDERS & CO ‡
2 Friars Lane The Green Richmond upon Thames Surrey TW9 1NL
Tel: 020 8332 2995 *Fax:* 020 8940 0261
List of partners: C M Saunders
Work: E S1 S2 W
SPr: Saunders, Mr Christopher M BA; LLB . . . *Dec 1976

VAN BAAREN & WRIGHT ‡
237-239 Sandycombe Road Richmond upon Thames Surrey TW9 2EW
Tel: 020 8940 2525 *Fax:* 020 8940 3113 *Dx:* 36361 EAST SHEEN
E-mail: info@vbwsolicitors.com
List of partners: P Panayiotou, J Wright
Languages: Greek
Work: D1 D2 K1 K2 K3 N S1 W
Emergency Action, Agency, Advocacy and Legal Aid undertaken
Ptr: Panayiotou, Ms Paulena BA(Hons) . . . *Aug 1993
Wright, Ms Jane LLB(Hons). . . *Jan 1994
Asoc: Collins, Ms Laura LLB(Hons) . . . Oct 1982
Da Silva, Ms Laila Ann Fulmara. . . May 1976
Hammill, Ms Jenny BA(Hons). . . Jan 1981

WARAN SOLICITORS ‡
Clarence House Office Suite 2D 5 Dee Road Richmond upon Thames Surrey TW9 2JN
Tel: 020 7993 8403
E-mail: info@waransolicitors.co.uk

RICKMANSWORTH, Hertfordshire

ARCHER RUSBY LLP ‡
Cardinal Point Park Road Rickmansworth Hertfordshire WD3 1RE
Tel: 01923 432696 *Fax:* 01923 432601

BLASER MILLS
52 High Street Rickmansworth Hertfordshire WD3 1AJ
Tel: 01923 776211 *Fax:* 01923 775148
Dx: 38250 RICKMANSWORTH
Office: Amersham, Aylesbury, Chesham, Harrow, High Wycombe, Staines
Languages: Gujarati
Work: D1 E K1 K3 L N R1 S1 S2 W
Legal Aid undertaken, Legal Aid Franchise and Member of Accident Line
Ptr: Thakrar, Mr Minesh LLB(Hons) . . . *Jul 2001
Asoc: Durling, Mr Alan J. . . *§Dec 1974
Kiely, Mr Gary Robert LLB(Hons) . . . Nov 2006
Ronayne, Mr Richard . . . Nov 1998
Con: Turner, Mr David M . . . *Nov 1968

DARLINGTON HARDCASTLES ‡
28 Church Street Rickmansworth Hertfordshire WD3 1DD
Tel: 01923 774272 *Fax:* 01923 721177
Dx: 38258 RICKMANSWORTH
E-mail: info@dhsolicitors.co.uk
List of partners: H B Berwin, H D Schneider
Languages: French, German
Work: A3 B2 C1 E F1 J1 K1 K3 L N O Q R2 S1 S2 T1 T2 W Z(d,k,l)
Fixed Fee Interview undertaken
Ptr: Berwin, Mr Harold Brian. . . *Jun 1974
Schneider, Mr Howard Dennis. . . *§Nov 1967
Ast: Parkinson, Mr David Keith MA(Oxon). . . Jun 1975
Con: Darlington, Mr Christopher J V MA(St Andrews). . . *§Oct 1978
Pettit, Mr Kenneth John . . . *§Jul 1974
Reid, Mr Richard Norman BA . . . *Dec 1978

HARRISONS GARDENER ‡
1st Floor Windsor House Church Street Rickmansworth Hertfordshire WD3 1BX
Tel: 01923 776877

WACHTEL FOX & CO
165 New Road Croxley Green Rickmansworth Hertfordshire WD3 3HB
Tel: 01923 775651 *Fax:* 01923 711699
Dx: 38264 RICKMANSWORTH
E-mail: rickmansworth@chebsey.com
Office: Bath, Beaconsfield, Burnham, Windsor
Work: E F1 L S1 W
Ptr: Fox, Mr Michael C . . . *Jun 1972
Wachtel, Mr David M P MA(Cantab). . . *Dec 1980

WILLIAMSON EDWARDS ‡
First Floor Windsor House 13 Church Street Rickmansworth Hertfordshire WD3 1BX
Tel: 01923 718601 *Fax:* 01923 718904
Dx: 38260 RICKMANSWORTH
E-mail: law@williamsonedwards.co.uk

RINGWOOD, Hampshire

M C AFFLECK & CO ‡
Springfield Hangersley Ringwood Hampshire BH24 3JN
Tel: 01425 478502

DIXON & TEMPLETON
(incorporating Truman-Moore (Ringwood))
1 Pedlars Walk Ringwood Hampshire BH24 1EZ
Tel: 01425 476231 *Fax:* 01425 472955
E-mail: gw@dixon-templeton.com
Office: Fordingbridge
Languages: French
Work: A1 E S1 T2 W
Agency undertaken
Ptr: Wyatt, Mr Stephen John LLB(Exon); TEP . . . *Dec 1974
Ast: Moore, Mr John A. . . *Jan 1965
Welsby, Mr Graham A BA(Oxon) . . . *May 1981

ELLIS JONES
Monmouth Court Southampton Road Ringwood Hampshire BH24 1HE
Tel: 01425 484848 *Fax:* 01425 471588 *Dx:* 45701 RINGWOOD
E-mail: ringwood@ellisjones.co.uk
Office: Bournemouth, Poole, Swanage
Work: E K1 S1 S2 T2 W
Agency, Legal Aid Franchise and Member of Accident Line
Ptr: Naser, Mr Paul A . . . *§Dec 1976
Con: Dyer, Mr Paul N LLB . . . *Nov 1976

LETCHERS ‡
24 Market Place Ringwood Hampshire BH24 1BS
Tel: 01425 471424 *Fax:* 01425 470917 *Dx:* 45702 RINGWOOD
Emergency telephone 07767 457547
E-mail: mail@letchers.co.uk
List of partners: E G Holmes, M G A Stocken
Languages: Dutch, French
Work: A1 A3 B1 B2 C1 D1 D2 E F1 G H J1 J2 K1 K2 K3 K4 L M1 N O Q R1 R2 S1 S2 T1 T2 V W Z(b,c,d,e,h,j,l,m,n,o,p,q,r,s,w)
Emergency Action, Agency, Advocacy, Fixed Fee Interview, Legal Aid undertaken and Legal Aid Franchise
Ptr: Holmes, Mr Edward G BA(Hons) . . . *§Oct 1994
Stocken, Mr Michael G A LLB; ACIArb . . . *§Dec 1981
Asoc: Burt, Ms Pamela LLB . . . *§Mar 1977
Ast: Curtis, Mr Richard LLB . . . *§Nov 1975
Morris, Mrs Alison Grant MA; PGCE; PGDipLaw; LPC. Apr 2003
Uche, Miss Emmanuela BA(Hons) . . . *§Dec 2004
Con: Wingate-Saul, Mr Michael A MA(Cantab) Notary Public . . . *§Jan 1965

MEESONS ‡
New House Market Place Ringwood Hampshire BH24 1ER
Tel: 01425 472315 *Fax:* 01425 470912 *Dx:* 45700 RINGWOOD
Emergency telephone 01425 472315
List of partners: S L Bowen, M Quain
Office: Fordingbridge
Work: A1 C1 D1 E F1 F2 G J1 K1 K3 K4 L N O Q R1 S1 S2 T1 T2 V W Z(c,d,m)
Emergency Action, Agency, Advocacy, Fixed Fee Interview and Legal Aid undertaken
Ptr: Bowen, Miss Susan Linda. . . *Nov 2002
Quain, Mrs Meriel. . . *Nov 1983
Ast: Brian, Mrs Janet A . . . *Jan 1996
Con: Pratt, Mr Kevin R LLB(Wales). . . *Apr 1978
Turner, Mr Ian C LLB . . . *Apr 1980

PALKA DOWNTON SOLICITORS ‡
10 College Road Ringwood Hampshire BH24 1NX
Tel: 01425 479997

RIPLEY, Derbyshire

BRIGGS SAYER & CO
35 Grosvenor Road Amber Valley Ripley Derbyshire DE5 3JE
Tel: 01773 744011 *Fax:* 01773 821194 *Dx:* 16875 RIPLEY
E-mail: briggssayer@btconnect.com
Office: Belper
Work: Z(c,g,k,l)
Emergency Action, Agency, Advocacy, Legal Aid undertaken and Member of Accident Line
Ptr: Briggs, Mr Thomas E LLB(Sheff) . . . *Nov 1967
Sayer, Mr Michael B LLB(Sheff). . . *Jul 1980

EG LEGAL ‡
Unit G8 Rodin House 1 Ivy Grove Ripley Derbyshire DE5 3HN
Tel: 01773 749955

ELLIS-FERMOR & NEGUS ‡
5 Market Place Ripley Derbyshire DE5 3BS
Tel: 01773 744744 *Fax:* 01773 570047 *Dx:* 16873 RIPLEY
E-mail: ripley@ellis-fermor.co.uk
List of partners: M S Cobbett, S P Hale, D Kelly, D E Lyon, M A Macnab, R J Sinclair, S J Slack, R B Whiteley
Office: Beeston, Belper, Long Eaton
Languages: German
Work: A1 B1 C1 C2 C3 D1 D2 E F1 G H J1 K1 K2 L N O P Q R1 S1 S2 T1 T2 V W Z(c,d,g,h,j,k,l,m,n,o,r,w,x)
Emergency Action, Agency, Advocacy, Legal Aid undertaken, Legal Aid Franchise and Member of Accident Line
Ptr: Kelly, Mr Darren LLB(Hons) . . . *Sep 1999
Lyon, Mr Duncan E LLB. . . *Nov 1985
Sinclair, Mr Roderick J LLB(Wales) . . . *Nov 1980
Ast: Sallis, Mrs Patricia BSc(Hons). . . *Oct 1994
Sanders, Mrs Samantha . . . *Nov 1994

HARDY MILES TITTERTON ‡
16 Church Street Ripley Derbyshire DE5 3BW
Tel: 01773 747000 *Fax:* 01773 570798 *Dx:* 16881 RIPLEY
Emergency telephone 01332 513468
E-mail: enquiry@hmtlegal.com
List of partners: A Titterton
Office: Alfreton, Duffield

See p112 for the Key to Work Categories & other symbols

Work: A1 B2 C1 D1 D2 E F1 F2 G H J1 K1 L N O P Q R1 S1 T1 T2 V W Z(c,i,j,k,l,m,p,q,r,w)
Emergency Action, Agency, Advocacy, Fixed Fee Interview, Legal Aid undertaken, Legal Aid Franchise and Member of Accident Line

MILES & CASH
11a Grosvenor Road Ripley Derbyshire DE5 3JE
Tel: 01773 742222
Office: Heanor
Work: C1 D1 D2 G H K1 K2 K3 N O Q S1 Z(j)
Legal Aid undertaken

SHACKLOCKS
6 Chapel Street Ripley Derbyshire DE5 3DL
Tel: 01773 743513 *Fax:* 01773 570362 *Dx:* 16874 RIPLEY
E-mail: enquiries@shacklocks.co.uk
Office: Belper, Derby, Mansfield
Work: J1 S1 W Z(p)
Ast: McShane, Mrs Clare . . . . *Oct 2007
Stevens, Juliet Aia Calthrop . . . . Jan 2010

RIPON, North Yorkshire

CANAL LEGAL ‡
Danby House 10 Canal Street Ripon North Yorkshire HG4 1QN
Tel: 01765 606666

SIMON CROSFIELD & CO ‡
2 Duck Hill Ripon North Yorkshire HG4 1BL
Tel: 01765 692277 *Fax:* 01765 690057 *Dx:* 61415 RIPON
E-mail: sc@crosfields-solicitors.co.uk
List of partners: S Crosfield
Work: B1 D1 D2 E F1 G H J1 J2 K1 K3 K4 N O Q S1 S2 W Z(c,k,l,m,p,q)
Legal Aid undertaken
SPr: Crosfield, Mr Simon . . . . §Jun 1972
Asoc: Dow, Mr David LLB(Newc) . . . . Nov 1991
O'Mahony, Carolyn LLB(Lanc). . . . . Aug 1999
Virdee, Surinder LLB(Newc). . . . . Sep 1995

ECCLES HEDDON ‡
5 Westgate Ripon North Yorkshire HG4 2AT
Tel: 01765 601717 *Fax:* 01765 602920 *Dx:* 61402 RIPON
E-mail: ripon@eccles-heddon.com
List of partners: M Armstrong, A Clarke, M J Clarke, E S Kidd, D A Shackleton
Office: Bedale, Thirsk
Work: A1 A3 C1 C2 D1 D2 E F1 J1 K1 K2 K3 K4 L N O Q R1 R2 S1 S2 T1 T2 W Z(d,l)
Emergency Action, Agency and Advocacy undertaken
Ptr: Armstrong, Mr Michael BA . . . . *Jun 1971
Clarke, Mr Andrew LLB . . . . *Jun 1980
Clarke, Mr Martyn J LLB . . . . *Apr 1974
Kidd, Miss Elizabeth S BA. . . . . *Mar 1980
Shackleton, Mr David A BSc; MSc; LLM. . . . . . . *Oct 2001
Asoc: White, Mr Nicholas John LLB . . . . *Sep 2007

HUTCHINSON & BUCHANAN ‡
77 North Street Ripon North Yorkshire HG4 1DS
Tel: 01765 602156 *Fax:* 01765 690018 *Dx:* 61400 RIPON
E-mail: mail@hutchbuch.demon.co.uk
List of partners: K L Audsley, A M Hutchinson, S M Ord, A J Storey, R J Storey
Work: A1 A2 C1 D1 D2 E F1 G H J1 J2 K1 K3 K4 L N O P Q R1 R2 S1 S2 T1 T2 V W Z(c,d,l,m,q,r)
Emergency Action, Agency, Advocacy and Fixed Fee Interview undertaken
Ptr: Audsley, Mrs Katie Louise LLB . . . . *Sep 2004
Hutchinson, Mr Andrew Mark BA(Oxon). . . . . . . *May 1992
Ord, Mrs Sally Marie BA . . . . *Aug 2002
Storey, Mr Anthony J LLB. . . . . *Jul 1979
Storey, Mr Richard John BA. . . . . *Sep 2006
Asoc: Diedrick, Miss Jasmine Tracey . . . . *Feb 2008
Swinn, Miss Katherine Elizabeth LLB . . . . *Feb 2010

KINREAD SOLICITORS ‡
17 High Skellgate Ripon North Yorkshire HG4 1BD
Tel: 01765 607200

TUNNARD & CO ‡
Cathedral Chambers 4 Kirkgate Ripon North Yorkshire HG4 1PA
Tel: 01765 605629 *Fax:* 01765 690523 *Dx:* 61401 RIPON
E-mail: ctt@tunnardsolicitors.com
List of partners: N J Harding, C T Tunnard
Work: A1 C1 D1 D2 E K1 K3 L S1 W Z(d,x)
Agency, Advocacy, Legal Aid undertaken and Legal Aid Franchise
Ptr: Harding, Mrs Nicola Jane BA Diocesan Registrar for the Diocese of Ripon and Leeds . . . . *Jan 1991
Tunnard, Mr Christopher Timothy LLB Diocesan Registrar for the Diocese of Ripon and Leeds . . . . *Jul 1975

RISCA, Caerphilly

GRANVILLE-WEST CHIVERS & MORGAN
Central Chambers 50/51 Tredegar Street Risca Caerphilly NP11 6BW
Tel: 01633 612353 *Fax:* 01633 601426 *Dx:* 86700 RISCA
E-mail: risca@granville-west.co.uk
Office: Abertillery, Blackwood, Caldicot, Newport, Pontypool
Languages: Welsh
Work: A1 B1 C1 C3 D1 E F1 J1 K1 L N R1 S1 T2 V W Z(c,d,j,k,l,m,p,s,t)
Emergency Action, Agency, Advocacy, Fixed Fee Interview and Legal Aid undertaken
Ptr: Stark, Mr Robert . . . . *§Jun 1977
Thomas, Wyn L BA; LLB . . . . *Oct 1979
Ast: Stark, Miss Elise LLB(Hons). . . . . Oct 2003

ROGER JAMES CLEMENTS & PARTNERS
(incorporating Robin H Jones & Co)
72 Tredegar Street Risca Caerphilly NP11 6BW
Tel: 01633 614166 *Fax:* 01633 223088
E-mail: joan@rjcp.co.uk
Office: Newport (2 offices)
Languages: Welsh
Work: C1 E G H K1 K3 K4 N O Q S1 S2 W Z(i,l)
Legal Aid undertaken
Ptr: Mundy, Mr Robert S LLB(Wales) . . . . *May 1982

LOUISE STEPHENS & CO ‡
Equity House Tredegar Street Risca Caerphilly NP11 6BU
Tel: 01633 614005 / 601144 *Fax:* 01633 619797 *Dx:* 86702 RISCA
Emergency telephone 01633 612110
List of partners: L Stephens
Work: D1 F1 G H J1 K1 L N Q S1 V W Z(h)
Emergency Action, Agency, Advocacy, Fixed Fee Interview and Legal Aid undertaken
SPr: Stephens, Miss Louise LLB(Hons). . . . . *Oct 1991
Ast: Atkins, Mr Julian Michael LLB(Hons) . . . . *Jun 1992
Jones, Mrs Jill Elizabeth LLB . . . . *Aug 1980

ROBERTSBRIDGE, East Sussex

KELLYS SOLICITORS ‡
Gardener's Cottage New House Farm Robertsbridge East Sussex TN32 5EY
Tel: 01424 838151
E-mail: suelenier@yahoo.com

ROCHDALE, Greater Manchester

A2 ACCIDENT SOLICITORS ‡
Bull Brow Chambers 6 Baillie Street Rochdale Greater Manchester OL16 1JG
Tel: 01706 343322 *Fax:* 01706 342400 *Dx:* 22835 ROCHDALE
E-mail: paul@a2accidentsolicitors.co.uk

AST HAMPSONS ‡
7 South Parade Rochdale Greater Manchester OL16 1LR
Tel: 01706 522311 *Fax:* 01706 861326 *Dx:* 22813 ROCHDALE
Emergency telephone 07860 418994
List of partners: D C M Chad, W H Goodwin, I Hampson, H A Morris, F D Taylor, P L Taylor, P D Toomey, P J Watson
Office: Manchester
Work: C1 C2 C3 D1 E G H J1 K1 L M1 M2 P S1 W
Emergency Action, Agency, Advocacy, Fixed Fee Interview, Legal Aid undertaken and Member of Accident Line
Ptr: Chad, Mr David C M . . . . *Dec 1984
Goodwin, Mr William H LLB(L'pool) . . . . *Dec 1976
Hampson, Mr Ian . . . . Dec 1970
Morris, Mrs Helen Andrea LLB . . . . *Oct 1993
Taylor, Mr Peter Lyon LLB(Hull) . . . . .Jul 1980
Toomey, Mr Peter D MA(Oxon) . . . . *Mar 1970
Watson, Mr Paul J . . . . *Jan 1982
Ast: Watson, Mrs Sarah L LLB. . . . . Aug 1990

ALPHA SOLICITORS ‡
115a Drake Street Rochdale Greater Manchester OL16 1PZ
Tel: 01706 646111 *Fax:* 01706 646131
E-mail: mail@alphasolicitors.co.uk

DEAN SOLICITORS ‡
123 Drake Street Rochdale Greater Manchester OL16 1PZ
Tel: 01706 661400 *Fax:* 01706 715117 *Dx:* 719768 ROCHDALE
Languages: Gujarati, Punjabi, Urdu
Work: J1 N S1 Z(i)
Fixed Fee Interview undertaken

DIXON THOMASSON PARTNERSHIP ‡
61 Dale Street Milnrow Rochdale Greater Manchester OL16 3NJ
Tel: 01706 525253

FELD MCKAY & DONNER SOLICITORS ‡
160 Oldham Road Rochdale Greater Manchester OL11 1AG
Tel: 01706 645656 *Fax:* 01706 632722 *Dx:* 22815 ROCHDALE
E-mail: bradleyfeld@fmdsolicitors.co.uk
List of partners: R H Donner, B G Feld, D J McKay
Work: D1 E K1 L N S1 W
Agency, Advocacy, Legal Aid undertaken and Legal Aid Franchise
Ptr: Donner, Mr Ralph H LLB . . . . *Dec 1978
Feld, Mr Bradley G BA . . . . *Oct 1985
McKay, Mr Darren J BA; PGDip . . . . *Feb 1989

FORSTER DEAN LTD
99 Yorkshire Street Rochdale Greater Manchester OL16 1DW
Tel: 01706 390400 *Fax:* 01706 390401
E-mail: enquiries@forsterdean.co.uk
Office: Birkenhead, Bootle, Chorley, Crewe, Eccles, Ellesmere Port, Huyton, Leigh, Liverpool (5 offices), Oldham, Preston, Runcorn, St Helens, Stockport, Warrington, Widnes (2 offices), Wigan

HARTLEY THOMAS & WRIGHT ‡
Town Hall Chambers South Parade Rochdale Greater Manchester OL16 1LW
Tel: 01706 644118 *Fax:* 01706 647567 *Dx:* 22803 ROCHDALE
E-mail: par@htw-law.co.uk
List of partners: R G Addington, P A Riley, J P Wilson
Languages: French, German
Work: B1 D1 D2 F1 G H J1 K1 K2 K3 L M1 N O P Q R1 V Z(g,i,j,l,m,p,t)
Emergency Action, Agency, Advocacy, Fixed Fee Interview, Legal Aid undertaken and Legal Aid Franchise
Ptr: Addington, Mr Roger George BA(Hons)(Leeds) Hon Secretary of the Local Law Society. . . . . *Jun 1978
Riley, Mr Peter Anthony. . . . . *Dec 1973
Wilson, Mrs Janice Patrick BA(Hons) . . . . Oct 1995
Asoc: Walsh, Ms Pamela J LLB(Hons). . . . . *Nov 1999
Ast: Kidd, Mr Paul G BA. . . . . *§Feb 1981
Con: Tattersall, Mr J Philip . . . . *Sep 1971

HEALY CONNOR MULCAHY ‡
21a Drake Street Rochdale Greater Manchester OL16 1RE
Tel: 01706 718188

HUDSON & TAYLOR ‡
(in association with Colin Ashworth & Co)
19 Church Lane Rochdale Greater Manchester OL16 1NS
Tel: 01706 644525 *Fax:* 01706 711734 *Dx:* 22808 ROCHDALE
List of partners: P R Miller, M A Nagle, M A Nagle
Office: Oldham
Work: B1 C1 C2 E F1 J1 L N O Q R1 S1 S2 V W
Ptr: Miller, Mr Peter Richard LLB . . . . *Jan 1978
Nagle, Mr Michael Antony. . . . . *Jul 1975

ISHERWOOD & HOSE
138 Yorkshire Street Rochdale Greater Manchester OL16 1LD
Tel: 01706 359090 / 522225 *Fax:* 01706 713312
Dx: 13973 HEYWOOD
E-mail: isherwoodandhose@btconnect.com
Office: Heywood
Languages: Punjabi, Urdu
Work: K1 K4 L N Q S1 S2 V W
Fixed Fee Interview, Legal Aid undertaken and Member of Accident Line
Ptr: Hulbert, Mr John C G LLB. . . . . *§Dec 1968
Asoc: Mushtaq, Mr Amjed LLB(Hons) . . . . *Sep 2001
Ast: Bell, Miss Zoe Elizabeth LLB(Hons) . . . . Jun 2009

JACKSON BRIERLEY HUDSON STONEY ‡
(incorporating A H Sutcliffe & Co)
The Old Parsonage 2 St Marys Gate Rochdale Greater Manchester OL16 1AP
Tel: 01706 644187 / 649214 *Fax:* 01706 758600
Dx: 22804 ROCHDALE
Emergency telephone 01706 758600
E-mail: law@jbhs.co.uk
List of partners: F L Everett, M Rodak, S M Stoney, K M A Walker
Languages: German
Work: B1 C1 C2 E F1 J1 K1 K2 K3 K4 L N O Q R1 S1 S2 T1 T2 V W Z(d,i,j,l,q)
Emergency Action, Agency, Advocacy and Legal Aid undertaken
Ptr: Everett, Miss Fleur Louise LLB(Hons) . . . . *Oct 1997
Rodak, Mrs Mary LLB. . . . . *Apr 1981
Stoney, Miss Susan M LLB . . . . *Dec 1972
Walker, Mr Keith Malcolm Ashton . . . . *Jun 1970
Ast: Barrett, Ms Linda BA(Hons); MA; GDL; PGDipLP . . . *Feb 2007
Con: Ashley, Mr Colin BA(Law) . . . . *Jun 1976
Collins, Mr Edward G L OBE . . . . *May 1959

ALFRED LEDGER & SONS ‡
111 Drake Street Rochdale Greater Manchester OL16 1QA
Tel: 01706 645910 *Fax:* 01706 645910
List of partners: B A Ledger, H M Ledger
Work: S1 W

AMJAD MALIK SOLICITORS ‡
149 Drake Street Rochdale Greater Manchester OL11 1EE
Tel: 01706 346111 *Fax:* 01706 346012
E-mail: amsolicitors@aol.com

MOLESWORTHS BRIGHT CLEGG ‡
Octagon House 25-27 Yorkshire Street Rochdale Greater Manchester OL16 1RH
Tel: 01706 356666 *Fax:* 01706 354681 *Dx:* 22801 ROCHDALE
E-mail: mail@molesworths.co.uk
List of partners: A C Brannick, P F Dixon, K M Efthymiadis, G Haigh, D C H Owen, P Rhodes, C L Salisbury
Languages: French, German, Italian
Work: A1 B1 C1 C2 D1 D2 E F1 G H J1 K1 K3 L N O P Q R1 R2 S1 S2 W Z(c,i,j,k,l,n,o,p,q,r,t)
Emergency Action, Agency, Advocacy, Fixed Fee Interview, Legal Aid undertaken and Legal Aid Franchise
Ptr: Brannick, Mr Antony C MA(Cantab) President of British Junior Chamber Northampton 1994 . . . . *Oct 1983
Dixon, Mr Paul F BA(Law). . . . . *Nov 1982
Efthymiadis, Miss Kitsa M LLB . . . . *Dec 1981
Haigh, Mr Gordon. . . . . *Jun 1978
Owen, Mr Donald C H LLB(Manc). . . . . *Jun 1970
Rhodes, Mr Peter BA . . . . *§Oct 1975
Salisbury, Mrs Carolyn L LLB . . . . *Oct 1982
Ast: Benbow, Mr Ian Patrick LLB(Hons); LPC . . . . Jan 2006
Dunn, Mrs Judith LLB(Hons) . . . . *Nov 1991
Hashmi, Ms Afshan LLB(Hons); PGDipLP; QLTT . . . Mar 2007
Johnson, Ms Susan C LLB . . . . *Oct 1989
Mahmood, Mr Majid LLB(Hons) . . . . Nov 2004
Nuttall, Ms Anna LLB . . . . *Nov 2000
Rudd, Mr John LLB(L'pool) . . . . *Jun 1993
Shah, Zahira LLB . . . . Feb 2007
Con: Greenwood, Mr Richard S MBE LLB(Manc) . . . . . *§Feb 1962
Kay, Mr John F . . . . *§Jun 1971

PENNINE SOLICITORS ‡
136 Drake Street Rochdale Greater Manchester OL16 1PS
Tel: 01706 671434 *Fax:* 01706 671433 *Dx:* 719767 ROCHDALE
E-mail: info@penninesolicitors.co.uk
Office: Manchester
Languages: Bengali, Urdu
Work: B1 C1 J1 K1 O S1 W Z(r)
Agency, Fixed Fee Interview, Legal Aid undertaken and Legal Aid Franchise

PRICE MEARS & CO ‡
7 Church Lane Rochdale Greater Manchester OL16 1NR
Tel: 01706 653331 *Fax:* 01706 649072 *Dx:* 22805 ROCHDALE
E-mail: solicitors@pricemears.co.uk
List of partners: J A V Mears, S C Price
Work: E N O Q S1 W
Ptr: Mears, Mr James A V BA . . . . *Jun 1975
Price, Mr Steven C LLB(Lond). . . . . *May 1975

ROSS-BROWN & BIRTWISTLE ‡
12 Drake Street Rochdale Greater Manchester OL16 1LU
Con: Feingold, Mr David LLB(Manc) . . . . *Jan 1974

MICHAEL SALT ‡
South Parade Chambers 13 South Parade Rochdale Greater Manchester OL16 1LR
Tel: 01706 646655 *Fax:* 01706 630852 *Dx:* 22839 ROCHDALE
Emergency telephone 07770 611679
E-mail: michael@saltlaw.co.uk
Work: G H J2
Emergency Action, Agency, Advocacy, Fixed Fee Interview, Legal Aid undertaken and Legal Aid Franchise
Ast: Hall, Mrs Sarah Jane LLB(Hons) . . . . *May 2004

SHANLEY WRIGHT JUDGE PROPERTY LAWYERS ‡
28-30 St Mary's Gate Rochdale Greater Manchester OL16 1DZ
Tel: 01706 861188 *Fax:* 01706 710880 *Dx:* 22828 ROCHDALE
Work: S1 S2

DAVID K SWANN ‡
841a Bury Road Bamford Rochdale Greater Manchester OL11 4AA
Tel: 01706 366557 *Fax:* 01706 627477
List of partners: D K Swann
Work: E K1 S1 W
Ptr: Swann, Mr David Keith . . . . *Jan 1978

WHITESTONE SOLICITORS ‡
187 Yorkshire Street Rochdale Greater Manchester OL12 0DS
Tel: 01706 661591 *Fax:* 01706 661586 *Dx:* 22843 ROCHDALE 1

ROCHESTER, Medway Towns

HELEN BAKER SOLICITOR ‡
25 Gypsy Way High Halstow Rochester Medway Towns ME3 8DX
Tel: 01634 255265
E-mail: helenbaker@helenbakersolicitor.co.uk

BASSETS ‡
156 High Street Rochester Medway Towns ME1 1ET
Tel: 01634 400161 *Fax:* 01634 408251 *Dx:* 6500 ROCHESTER
Emergency telephone 07775 866527
E-mail: info.roch@bassetssolicitors.co.uk
List of partners: P N Ruse, M P Smith, P D J Sparks
Office: Gillingham
Work: A1 B1 D1 E F1 G H J1 K1 L N P Q R1 S1 T1 T2 V W Z(c,h,j,k,l,m,t)
Emergency Action, Agency, Advocacy, Fixed Fee Interview, Legal Aid undertaken, Legal Aid Franchise and Member of Accident Line

BORG KNIGHT EMPLOYMENT SOLICITORS
33 St Margaret's Street Rochester Medway Towns ME1 1UF
Tel: 01634 757001 / 020 7099 8135 *Fax:* 01634 757663
E-mail: info@borgknight.com
Office: Chatham

KING PRIOR MACDONALD BRIDGE
Forge House High Street Lower Stoke Rochester Medway Towns ME3 9RD
Tel: 01634 272720 *Fax:* 01474 569482
E-mail: reception@kingprior.co.uk
Office: Gravesend
Languages: French
Work: I U1 U2 Z(e,f,k,z,za)
SPr: MacDonald Bridge, Mr Richard BA; BSc. . . . . . . *Dec 1976

KENNETH W MELLOR ‡
30 Telegraph Hill Higham Rochester Medway Towns ME3 7NW
Tel: 01634 724951
List of partners: K W Mellor
Languages: French, German, Russian
Work: E K1 L S1 W
Ptr: Mellor, Mr Kenneth W. . . . . *Jun 1971

DAVID STINSON & CO ‡
Ditton Lodge 449 London Road Ditton Rochester Medway Towns ME20 6DB
Tel: 01622 711300 *Fax:* 01622 711306
E-mail: djs@davidstinson.co.uk
Work: N Z(r)
Member of Accident Line

ROCHFORD, Essex

GILES WILSON
5 Roche Close Rochford Essex SS4 1PU
Tel: 01702 477106 *Fax:* 01702 470206
E-mail: info@gileswilson.co.uk
Office: Leigh-on-Sea

ROMFORD, Essex

F BARNES & SON ‡
(incorporating Fenton & Hunwicks)
1-5 High Street Romford Essex RM1 1JU
Tel: 01708 745183 *Fax:* 01708 726257 *Dx:* 138122 ROMFORD 4
Emergency telephone 01277 213784
E-mail: romford@fbarnes.co.uk
List of partners: E V Hunwicks, T Juhanson, K Lewis, D J Oldham
Office: Romford
Work: B1 C1 D1 D2 E F1 J1 K1 K2 L N O Q R1 S1 S2 V W Z(b,l,q)
Emergency Action, Agency, Advocacy, Fixed Fee Interview, Legal Aid undertaken and Legal Aid Franchise
Ptr: Hunwicks, Mr Ellis V. . . . . *Dec 1970
Juhanson, Miss Tiina BA . . . . *§Jul 1986
Oldham, Mr David J LLB(Hons)(Lond) Deputy District Judge . . . . *§Oct 1974
Ast: White, Mr Jeffrey R C. . . . . *Sep 1994

F BARNES & SON
14 Chase Cross Road Collier Row Romford Essex RM5 3PS
Tel: 01708 743727 *Fax:* 01708 733194 *Dx:* 123400 COLLIER ROW
Emergency telephone 01277 73983
Office: Romford
Work: A1 E L N O Q S1 W
Ptr: Lewis, Mrs Katrina LLB . . . . *Mar 1987

BLOCK ASSOCIATES LIMITED ‡
16-20 Victoria Road Romford Essex RM1 2JH
Tel: 01708 723399

CAPSTICK-DALE & PARTNERS ‡
224 Main Road Gidea Park Romford Essex RM2 5HA
Tel: 01708 722466 *Fax:* 01708 725174 *Dx:* 123272 GIDEA PARK
E-mail: mkp@capstick-dale.com
List of partners: A N Liddell, P D Logue, M K Perry
Languages: French, German
Work: B1 C1 C2 C3 E F1 F2 J1 K1 L M1 N O Q R1 S1 T1 T2 W Z(c,e,f,k,l,p,q)
Agency and Advocacy undertaken
Ptr: Liddell, Mr Andrew Nicholas LLB(Hons) . . . . *Jun 1969
Logue, Mr Peter D . . . . *Jun 1970
Perry, Mr Michael K BA(Law) . . . . *May 1965

HAVILLANDS ‡
6 Atlanta Boulevard Romford Essex RM1 1TB
Tel: 01708 766559 *Fax:* 01708 761775
E-mail: staff@havillandsolicitors.co.uk
List of partners: O Adeniran, A Shokunbi
Work: B1 K1 L S1 S2 Z(i)
Fixed Fee Interview and Legal Aid undertaken
Ptr: Adeniran, Omolara . . . . Jan 2002
Shokunbi, Abiodun . . . . Jan 2001

HETHERINGTONS SOLICITORS LIMITED ‡
13 Athelstan Close Romford Essex RM3 0QJ
Tel: 01708 341500 *Fax:* 01708 507592
E-mail: hetheringtonssolicitorsltd@googlemail.com

HUGHES SOLICITORS ‡
5 Hamlet Road Collier Row Romford Essex RM5 2DS
Tel: 020 7566 8244
List of partners: K Hughes
SPr: Hughes, Miss K. . . . . Sep 2003

HUNT & HUNT ‡
Lambourne House No 7 Western Road Romford Essex RM1 3LT
Tel: 01708 764433 *Fax:* 01708 733613 *Dx:* 4606 ROMFORD
E-mail: enquiries@hunt-hunt.co.uk
Languages: French, German, Italian
Work: A1 B1 C1 C2 C3 D1 E F1 G H J1 K1 L M1 M2 N O P Q R1 S1 S2 T1 T2 W Z(b,c,d,e,f,h,i,j,k,l,m,o,s,t)

KENNETH ELLIOTT & ROWE ‡
Enterprise House 18 Eastern Road Romford Essex RM1 3PJ
Tel: 01708 757575 *Fax:* 01708 766674 *Dx:* 4602 ROMFORD
E-mail: law@ker.co.uk
List of partners: A M Carr, K E Darvill, C C Dixon, D Farr, N B Filar, K H Kassam, M B Sadler, S A Tuckett
Languages: Gujarati, Spanish
Work: B1 C1 C2 E F1 J1 K1 K2 K3 L M2 N O Q R1 R2 S1 S2 T1 T2 W Z(c,d,m,q,r)
Emergency Action, Fixed Fee Interview undertaken and Member of Accident Line
Ptr: Carr, Mr Adam Martin LLB(L'pool). . . . . *Jun 1988
Darvill, Mr Keith E. . . . . *Jan 1982
Dixon, Mr Christopher C LLB . . . . *Apr 1976
Farr, Mr David BA. . . . . *Oct 1985
Filar, Mr Neville B BA(Hons). . . . . *Jun 1984
Kassam, Mr Karim Hassanali MA(Cantab). . . . . . *Mar 1989
Sadler, Mr Mark Bernard LLB . . . . *Nov 1994
Tuckett, Mrs Stephanie A LLB(B'ham). . . . . *Jun 1974
Ast: Low, Miss Cheryl BA(Hons) . . . . *Jan 2002
McCormack, Mr Sean Anthony LLB(Hons) . . . . . . *Sep 1993
Rylah, Mr Frederick Henry Thomas LLB. . . . . . . *Aug 2008
Wahlhaus, Ms Nicola K LLB. . . . . *Oct 1981
Con: Ramsey, Mr Roger E LLB(Lond) Deputy District Judge Notary Public. . . . . *§Mar 1970

LELAND SWABY CLARKE & NORRIS ‡
209-211 South Street Romford Essex RM1 1QL
Tel: 01708 762227 *Fax:* 01708 732999 *Dx:* 4627 ROMFORD
E-mail: info@lelandscn.co.uk
List of partners: E Leland, E E Leland
Languages: French
Work: B1 E S1 S2 W Z(d)
Agency and Fixed Fee Interview undertaken
Ptr: Leland, Mr Edward . . . . Oct 2002
Leland, Mr Ernest E. . . . . *§Jul 1969

DUNCAN LEWIS & CO
1-3 Western Road Romford Essex RM1 3LD
Tel: 020 7923 4020 *Fax:* 020 7923 3320
E-mail: admin@duncanlewis.com
Office: Harrow, London E8, London SE14, London SW17, London W12

LIDDELL AND COMPANY ‡
20 Balgores Square Gidea Park Romford Essex RM2 6AU
Tel: 01708 775999 *Fax:* 01708 726675 *Dx:* 123275 GIDEA PARK
E-mail: info@liddell-solicitors.co.uk
List of partners: R Allen, J Elgar, K Groves, I D Liddell
Office: Benfleet, Billericay
Work: N
Agency undertaken and Member of Accident Line
Ptr: Groves, Mr Kevan. . . . . Mar 2006
Liddell, Mr Ian D LLB . . . . Aug 1979
Allen, Mr Richard . . . . NSP

LISS GULHANE INNES & CO ‡
1 Junction Road Romford Essex RM1 3QS
Tel: 01708 764440 *Fax:* 01708 767536
E-mail: info@lgi-solicitors.co.uk
List of partners: C D Innes, A R Liss, D P Schreiber
Office: Ilford
Ptr: Innes, Mr Calum D . . . . Oct 1984
Liss, Mr Anthony R LLB. . . . . *§Jan 1981
Schreiber, Mr David P LLB . . . . *Dec 1980

MCCORRY CONNOLLY SOLICITORS ‡
8 Holgate Court 4-10 Western Road Romford Essex RM1 3JS
Tel: 01708 727269 *Fax:* 01708 727458 *Dx:* 131529 ROMFORD 8
E-mail: info@mccorryconnolly.co.uk
List of partners: K M Connolly, R M McCorry
Work: D1 E F1 J1 K1 N O Q S1 W Z(c,l,p,q,t)
Emergency Action, Agency, Advocacy, Fixed Fee Interview, Legal Aid undertaken and Member of Accident Line
Ptr: Connolly, Mr Kevin M LLB(Lond) . . . . *May 1986
McCorry, Miss Roisin M BA(Hons); LLM. . . . . . . *Mar 1987

PAUL MARTIN & CO ‡
4th Floor 8-10 Eastern Road Romford Essex RM1 3PJ
Tel: 01708 380210 *Fax:* 01708 742787 *Dx:* 4610 ROMFORD

MEADOWS & MORAN ‡
Station Chambers 153-159 South Street Romford Essex RM1 1PL
Tel: 01708 753400 *Fax:* 01708 749339 *Dx:* 4617 ROMFORD
List of partners: R H Meadows, D S M Newhouse
Work: C1 E F1 J1 K1 L N R1 S1 S2 T1 W Z(c)
Emergency Action, Agency, Advocacy, Fixed Fee Interview and Legal Aid undertaken
Ptr: Meadows, Mr Roger H LLB . . . . *Jul 1977
Newhouse, Mr David S M. . . . . *Feb 1986
Ast: Reece, Ms Emma LLB(Hons) . . . . Oct 2003

MULLIS & PEAKE ‡
(incorporating A Martin & Co)
8-10 Eastern Road Romford Essex RM1 3PJ
Tel: 01708 784000 *Fax:* 01708 784099 *Dx:* 138126 ROMFORD 4
E-mail: office@mplaw.co.uk
List of partners: R P G Bell, P D Connell, A M Downes, A C W Emslie, D A J Fackler, A J Fidler, A J Lewis, J H Poulten, M M Shipton, M J W Trenerry
Office: Chadwell Heath
Languages: French, German
Work: B1 C1 C2 C3 D1 E F1 J1 J2 K1 L N O P Q R1 S1 S2 U2 V W Z(c,l,p,r)
Agency, Legal Aid Franchise and Member of Accident Line
Ptr: Bell, Mr Russell P G. . . . . *Jun 1977
Connell, Mr Peter D LLB . . . . *Dec 1975
Downes, Mr Adrian M LLB . . . . *Sep 1989
Emslie, Mr Alfred C W LLB(Wales) . . . . *Dec 1977
Fackler, Mr David A J. . . . . Dec 1977
Fidler, Mr Andrew J LLB(Hons) . . . . *Nov 1989
Lewis, Mr Alan J . . . . *Aug 1968
Poulten, Mr John H LLB. . . . . *§Mar 1969
Shipton, Mr Michael M BA. . . . . Mar 1987
Trenerry, Mr Martyn J W. . . . . Nov 1988
Asoc: Davies, Mr Jeremy BSc. . . . . Dec 1990
Ast: Chagger, Mrs Satinder . . . . Sep 2001
Clark, Mr Roger LLB(Hons) . . . . Nov 1984
Shelton, Miss Denise . . . . Jan 2006
Sherratt, Mr James . . . . Jan 1989
Taher, Mr Javed LLB . . . . *Jan 1996
Toloczko, Ms Joanna M MA(Cantab) . . . . *Aug 1987
Con: Martin, Mr Alan A . . . . *Dec 1960

B S O'CONNOR & CO ‡
147 Balgores Lane Gidea Park Romford Essex RM2 6BT
Tel: 01708 700042 *Fax:* 01708 704321
List of partners: B S O'Connor
Work: B1 B2 B3 E K1 K2 L N O S1 S2 W
Agency, Advocacy and Fixed Fee Interview undertaken
SPr: O'Connor, Mr Brian S LLB(Hons)(Lond) . . . . *Jun 1976

PENIEL SOLICITORS ‡
7a High Road Chadwell Heath Romford Essex RM6 6PU
Tel: 020 8590 2247 *Fax:* 020 8590 2267
E-mail: info@penielsolicitors.com

STERNBERG REED
(incorporating David Charnley & Co)
Phoenix House 102-106 South Street Romford Essex RM1 1RX
Tel: 01708 766155 *Fax:* 01708 730743 *Dx:* 4614 ROMFORD
Emergency telephone 01708 766155
E-mail: enquiries@sternberg-reed.co.uk
Office: Barking, Grays, London NW1
Languages: Dutch, French, Gujarati, Hindi, Punjabi, Russian
Work: B2 G H
Emergency Action, Agency, Advocacy, Fixed Fee Interview, Legal Aid undertaken and Legal Aid Franchise
Ptr: Anderson, Ms Frances Louise LLB(Hons) ★. . . . . *Nov 1994
St Prix, Ms Brenda ★ . . . . *Sep 1996
Taylor, Mr Christopher J BA ★. . . . . *Dec 1985
Thomas, Mr David Benedict Bryn MA(Cantab) ★ . . *Feb 1993
Asoc: Barbone, Mr David M BA ★ . . . . *Sep 1982
Davies, Miss Arlegh Jane LLB; LPC ★ . . . . *Apr 2002
Kaur, Ms Desho. . . . . Nov 2004
Kresner, Ms Yvette ★ . . . . Sep 1999
Shaw, Mr Gerard ★ . . . . May 2001
Ast: Sparkes, Mr Stephen . . . . Mar 2009
Wrightson, Miss Alexandra ★ . . . . Mar 2004
Con: Charnley, Mr David R LLB ★ Associated Law Societies of Wales Prize 1979 . . . . *Jun 1979

SYMONS & GAY ‡
91a South Street Romford Essex RM1 1PA
Tel: 01708 744211 *Fax:* 01708 727614 *Dx:* 131530 ROMFORD 8
E-mail: office@symons-gay.co.uk
List of partners: J W J Copeland, J Stringer, S J Wilson-McMahon
Work: A1 B1 D1 E F1 G H J1 L M1 N P R1 S1 S2 W
Emergency Action, Agency, Advocacy, Fixed Fee Interview, Legal Aid undertaken and Legal Aid Franchise
Ptr: Copeland, Mr John W J LLB(Exon) . . . . *Mar 1973
Stringer, Ms Jacqueline . . . . *Dec 1991
Wilson-McMahon, Mrs Suzanne J BA(Law) . . . . . *Oct 1983

ROMSEY, Hampshire

ASHER BROOMFIELD ‡
4 Brook Way Romsey Hampshire SO51 7JZ
Tel: 01794 501033 / 07799 551820 *Fax:* 01794 501033
E-mail: enquiries@asherbroomfield.com

BELLS ‡
5 Market Place Romsey Hampshire SO51 8XF
Tel: 01794 513328 *Fax:* 01794 515689 *Dx:* 45901 ROMSEY
E-mail: bells@bells-romsey-solicitors.co.uk
List of partners: H J Phillips, M L C Russell
Work: E J1 K1 K2 K3 K4 L O Q R1 R2 S1 S2 W Z(l)
Agency, Advocacy and Fixed Fee Interview undertaken
Ptr: Phillips, Miss Hayley J BA(Hons) . . . . *Apr 1998
Russell, Mr Martin L C LLB(Soton) . . . . *Nov 1972
Ast: Bradley, Miss Eleanor Jane FILEX; CPE . . . . . . *Oct 2008
Izzard, Mrs Julia Teresa MA(Classics); CPE; LPC . . *Sep 1999
Thomas, Ms Christine Linda LLB . . . . *Jul 1978
Con: Cox, Mr Peter Garnet . . . . *Apr 1975

FOOTNER & EWING
50 The Hundred Romsey Hampshire SO51 8XH
Tel: 01794 512345 *Fax:* 01794 522550 *Dx:* 45900 ROMSEY
Office: Southampton (2 offices), Totton
Work: A1 B1 C1 D1 E F1 J1 K1 L N O Q R1 S1 S2 T2 W Z(b,c,j,l)
Emergency Action, Advocacy, Fixed Fee Interview and Legal Aid undertaken
Ptr: Howorth, Mr Anthony J R LLB. . . . . *Jul 1981
McVean, Mr Peter J LLB . . . . *Apr 1981
Ast: Cox, Ms Caroline . . . . Oct 1995
Thomas, Mrs Julie D LLB . . . . *Oct 1986
Con: Robson, Mr Rodney M . . . . Dec 1967

HARPER LAW ‡
Manor Farm Plaitford Romsey Hampshire SO51 6EG
Tel: 01794 322364
E-mail: hilary@harperlaw.co.uk
List of partners: H K M Harper
Work: A2 J1 Q
SPr: Harper, Mrs Hilary K M LLB(Hons) . . . . *§Oct 1991

KIRKLANDS ‡
5 Abbey Walk Church Street Romsey Hampshire SO51 8JQ
Tel: 01794 513466 *Fax:* 01794 522378 *Dx:* 45903 ROMSEY
Emergency telephone 01794 514788
E-mail: pkirkland@kirklandssolicitors.co.uk
List of partners: M D Joy, P D M Kirkland
Office: Totton
Work: A1 B1 C1 C2 D1 E F1 J1 K1 L N O P Q R1 S1 S2 V W Z(c,d,j,l,m)

See p112 for the Key to Work Categories & other symbols

Ptr: Joy, Mr Michael D. . . . . *Jun 1969
Kirkland, Mr Philip D M . . . . *May 1974
Ast: Webb, Mrs Hafwen M BSc; MSc; PhD. . . . . Sep 2006

D E STURGESS ‡
Fernbrook House Middlebridge Street Romsey Hampshire SO51 8HL
Tel: 01794 830791 *Fax:* 01794 522861
Emergency telephone 023 8033 1453
E-mail: deborah.sturgess@megalith.plus.com
List of partners: D E Sturgess
Work: E S1 W
SPr: Sturgess, Mrs Deborah E LLB. . . . . *Jul 1980

ROSS-ON-WYE, Herefordshire

DAVID J BARRY ‡
Clytha House 44 New Street Ross-on-Wye Herefordshire HR9 7DA
Tel: 01989 564209 *Fax:* 01989 563253
E-mail: davidbarry@davidbarry.co.uk
List of partners: D J Barry
Work: K1 S1 W
Ptr: Barry, Mr David J . . . . *§Dec 1969

HARRISON CLARK LLP
6 High Street Ross-on-Wye Herefordshire HR9 5HL
Tel: 01989 562377 *Fax:* 01989 565961 *Dx:* 22485 ROSS-ON-WYE
E-mail: lawyers@harrison-clark.co.uk
Office: Cheltenham, Hereford, Worcester (2 offices)
Work: A1 B1 C1 C2 C3 D1 E F1 G H J1 K1 K2 L M1 M2 N O P Q R1 S1 S2 T1 T2 W Z(l,p,q)
Emergency Action, Agency, Advocacy, Fixed Fee Interview, Legal Aid undertaken and Legal Aid Franchise
Ptr: Perrett, Mr Andrew Lloyd BA(Hons) . . . . *Sep 1988
Shawcross, Mr Keith R Notary Public . . . . *§Nov 1968
Ast: Tristram, Mr Dion LLB. . . . . *§Sep 1996

OKELL & STEWART ‡
Church Row Ross-on-Wye Herefordshire HR9 5HR
Tel: 01989 762009 *Fax:* 01989 766899 *Dx:* 22481 ROSS-ON-WYE
E-mail: office@okellandstewart.com
List of partners: A D Morris, J P Watters
Work: A1 B1 C1 C2 C3 D1 E F1 J1 K1 L M1 M2 N O P Q R1 S1 T1 T2 W Z(c,d,e,f,i,k,l,q,r,s,t)
Ptr: Morris, Mr Andrew D . . . . Dec 1992
Watters, Mr J Phillip BA. . . . . *Jul 1980

ROSSENDALE, Lancashire

ASK SOLICITORS ‡
6 Beaconsfield Street Haslingden Rossendale Lancashire BB4 5TD
Tel: 01706 217774 *Fax:* 0560 114 6159

HAMERS ‡
6 Manchester Road Haslingden Rossendale Lancashire BB4 5ST
Tel: 01706 222260
List of partners: E A Hamer
SPr: Hamer, Mr Eric A LLB. . . . . *§Oct 1990

HOLT & LONGWORTH ‡
65 Bank Street Rawtenstall Rossendale Lancashire BB4 7QN
Tel: 01706 213251 / 229131 *Fax:* 01706 211331
Dx: 26253 RAWTENSTALL
E-mail: rawtenstall@holtandlongworth.co.uk
List of partners: I D F Bonney, J L Frain, P T Wilkinson
Work: A1 C1 C2 D1 E F1 G H J1 K1 L N O Q R1 S1 S2 T1 T2 V W Z(j,k,l,m)
Emergency Action, Agency, Advocacy, Fixed Fee Interview, Legal Aid undertaken, Legal Aid Franchise and Member of Accident Line
Ptr: Bonney, Mr Ian David Fletcher LLB . . . . *Sep 1998
Frain, Mr Jeremy Lloyd LLB. . . . . *Oct 1992
Wilkinson, Mr Peter T LLB . . . . *May 1980
Ast: Taylor, Mrs Janet Louise LLB . . . . *Sep 2001
Con: Longworth, Mr Ian P LLB . . . . *Mar 1970

TURNER MARCH LLP SOLICITORS ‡
501 Market Street Whitworth Rossendale Lancashire OL12 8QN
Tel: 01706 854167 *Fax:* 01706 852407
E-mail: info@turnermarch.co.uk

WALKERS ‡
574 Bacup Road Waterfoot Rossendale Lancashire BB4 7HB
Tel: 01706 213565 *Fax:* 01706 830245
List of partners: C S Foster, J Sime
Office: Burnley
Languages: French
Work: C1 D1 E G H J1 K1 N Q R1 S1 T1 W Z(c,g,l,n,o,s)
Emergency Action, Agency, Advocacy, Fixed Fee Interview, Legal Aid undertaken and Legal Aid Franchise
Ptr: Foster, Mr Colin S Notary Public. . . . . *§Jan 1980
Sime, Ms Janet . . . . Aug 1997
Ast: Farren, Ms Hilary . . . . Dec 1990
Graham, Mr David . . . . Jan 1980

ROTHERHAM, South Yorkshire

COLE & YOUSAF ‡
11 Effingham Square Rotherham South Yorkshire S65 1AT
Tel: 01709 367944 / 07982 884240 *Fax:* 01709 367947

MALCOLM C FOY & CO
2 Upper Millgate Rotherham South Yorkshire S60 1PF
Tel: 01709 836866 *Fax:* 01709 836755 *Dx:* 12607 ROTHERHAM
E-mail: info@malcolmcfoy.co.uk
Office: Doncaster
Languages: German, Spanish
Work: A1 B1 C1 C2 D1 D2 E F1 F2 J1 J2 K1 K3 L N O Q R1 S1 S2 V W X Z(l,m,p,q,r)
Emergency Action, Agency, Fixed Fee Interview, Legal Aid undertaken, Legal Aid Franchise and Member of Accident Line
Ptr: Foy, Mr Malcolm Clive LLB ♦ . . . . *Mar 1969
Ast: Mallinder, Mrs Shelley. . . . . *Nov 2001
Naylor, Miss Sarah . . . . May 2008

FOYS SOLICITORS
Church Steps All Saints Square Rotherham South Yorkshire S60 1QD
Tel: 01709 375561 *Fax:* 01709 828479 *Dx:* 12601 ROTHERHAM
E-mail: info@foys.co.uk
Office: Doncaster, Sheffield (2 offices), Worksop
Work: C1 D1 D2 E F1 F2 J1 J2 K1 L N O Q S1 S2 V W Z(k,p,q,r)
Emergency Action, Agency, Fixed Fee Interview, Legal Aid undertaken and Legal Aid Franchise
Ptr: Firth, Mr Andrew BA . . . . *Oct 1985
Ast: Gow, Mrs Stella M . . . . *May 1976

GICHARD & CO ‡
31-33 Doncaster Gate Rotherham South Yorkshire S65 1DF
Tel: 01709 365531 *Fax:* 01709 829752 *Dx:* 12612 ROTHERHAM
List of partners: B E Rhodes, C E R C Rhodes
Languages: French, Italian, Spanish
Work: A1 B1 C1 C2 C3 D1 E F1 G H J1 K1 K2 L M1 M2 N O P Q R1 S1 S2 T1 T2 V W Z(e,l,t)
Agency, Advocacy, Legal Aid undertaken and Legal Aid Franchise
Ptr: Rhodes, Mr Charles E R C LLB . . . . *Feb 1991

GRAYSON WILLIS BENNETT
Equity Chambers 22 Corporation Street Rotherham South Yorkshire S60 1NG
Tel: 01709 720287 *Fax:* 01709 375438
E-mail: help@gwbsol.co.uk
Office: Sheffield
Ptr: Jones, Mr Philip Nigel LLB(Hons) . . . . *Jan 1990
Ast: James, Mrs Suzanne LLB(Hons) . . . . *Sep 2005
Rowley, Ms Elizabeth LLB(Hons) . . . . *Oct 2004

HARTHILLS ‡
1a Effingham Street Rotherham South Yorkshire S65 1AQ
Tel: 01709 377399 *Fax:* 01709 839595 *Dx:* 12624 ROTHERHAM
Emergency telephone 01709 377399
E-mail: enquiries@harthills.co.uk
List of partners: J Bartlett, S L Hedley, D Lennox, H J Russell
Work: D1 D2 G H K1 V Z(m)
Emergency Action, Agency, Advocacy, Fixed Fee Interview, Legal Aid undertaken and Legal Aid Franchise
Ptr: Bartlett, Mr Joe LLB. . . . . *Nov 2003
Hedley, Mrs Sandra L . . . . *Dec 1990
Lennox, Mr Duncan LLB(Bris) . . . . *Nov 1982
Russell, Ms Hester Jane LLB . . . . *Jan 2001
Ast: Bertram, Miss Amy . . . . *Dec 2009
Clark, Mr Michael . . . . *Jul 2004
Giblin, Mrs Louisa. *Sep 1999
Robinson, Mrs Elizabeth LLB . . . . *Jan 2007
Shuttleworth, Miss Lucy. . . . . *Sep 2007

HOWELLS LLP
18-20 Ship Hill Rotherham South Yorkshire S65 1AJ
Tel: 01709 364000 *Fax:* 01709 370170 *Dx:* 12629 ROTHERHAM
Emergency telephone 01709 364000
E-mail: enquiries@howellsllp.com
Office: Barnsley, Sheffield
Work: D1 D2 F1 G H J1 K1 K3 L N Q V X Z(g,h,i,m,p,r)
Emergency Action, Agency, Fixed Fee Interview and Legal Aid undertaken
Ptr: Macadam, Ms Mary Rose. . . . . *Oct 1992
Ast: Leach, Mr George MSc; BSc(Hons) . . . . *Oct 2006
Lynch, Ms Sarah Jane BA(Oxon); MA(Keele) . . . . . *Oct 1989
McColgan, Mr Michael Anthony BA(Hons). . . . . . *Jun 1990
Patrick, Mr Christopher John LLB(Hons). . . . . . . *Oct 1994
Round, Ms Gemma LLB(Hons) . . . . *Sep 2004

ARTHUR JACKSON & CO ‡
4 Ash Mount Doncaster Gate Rotherham South Yorkshire S65 1DQ
Tel: 01709 363876 *Fax:* 01709 829928 *Dx:* 12608 ROTHERHAM
List of partners: J R Davison, N R Oliver, M A Thomas
Office: Rotherham
Work: B1 C1 C3 D1 D2 E F1 F2 G H J1 J2 K1 K2 L N O Q R1 R2 S1 S2 T1 T2 V W Z(c,i,j,k,l,m,p,q,r,t,w)
Emergency Action, Agency, Advocacy, Legal Aid undertaken and Member of Accident Line
Ptr: Davison, Mr John Robert LLB. . . . . *Jul 1978
Oliver, Mr Neil R LLB . . . . *Jun 1981
Thomas, Mr Mark A LLB . . . . *Oct 1980

ARTHUR JACKSON & CO
159 Bawtry Road Wickersley Rotherham South Yorkshire S66 2BW
Tel: 01709 547284 *Fax:* 01709 829928 *Dx:* 12608 ROTHERHAM
E-mail: mail@arthurjackson.co.uk
Office: Rotherham
Work: A3 B1 B2 B3 C1 D1 D2 E F1 F2 J1 J2 K1 K2 L N O Q R1 R2 S1 S2 V W X Z(l,m,w)
Emergency Action, Agency, Advocacy, Fixed Fee Interview, Legal Aid undertaken and Member of Accident Line
Ptr: Thomas, Mr Mark A LLB . . . . *Oct 1980

CHRIS MIDDLETON SOLICITOR ‡
Blandings Sitwell Grove Rotherham South Yorkshire S60 3AY
Tel: 01709 365020 *Dx:* 12625 ROTHERHAM
E-mail: cnmam@waitrose.com
Work: N Q
Agency undertaken

NFLA LTD
33 High Street Rotherham South Yorkshire S60 1PT
Tel: 01709 373000
Emergency telephone 0115 945 4555
E-mail: mail@nflaw.co.uk
Office: Chesterfield, Nottingham, Sheffield, Wellingborough
Work: D1 K1 K3
Ast: Naseem, Miss Adeeba LLB(Hons). . . . . May 2005

NORRIE WAITE & SLATER
69 Broad Street Rotherham South Yorkshire S62 6DU
Tel: 01709 523983 *Fax:* 01709 523994
Office: Sheffield (3 offices)
Work: B2 D1 D2 E G H K1 K2 K3 K4 L N O Q S1 S2 W Z(h)
Legal Aid undertaken
Asoc: Page, Ms Gillian M . . . . Dec 1991

OXLEY & COWARD SOLICITORS LLP ‡
34-46 Moorgate Street Rotherham South Yorkshire S60 2HB
Tel: 01709 510999 *Fax:* 01709 512999 *Dx:* 12600 ROTHERHAM
E-mail: mailbox@oxcow.co.uk
List of partners: M J Burdon, M R Chaudhary, R E Deadman, S J Jackson, B A Long, A J Ogley, S J Richmond-Sterry, K H Sadiq, S Scott, S R Sheppard, R C Stopford
Languages: French, Punjabi, Urdu
Work: A1 A3 B1 B2 C1 C2 D1 D2 E F1 G H J1 K1 K2 K3 K4 L N O Q R1 R2 S1 S2 W Z(c,e,k,l,p,q)
Emergency Action, Agency, Advocacy, Fixed Fee Interview, Legal Aid undertaken, Legal Aid Franchise and Member of Accident Line
Ptr: Burdon, Mr Matthew James LLB . . . . *Sep 2005
Chaudhary, Mamoon Rashid BA(Hons) . . . . *Sep 2000
Deadman, Mrs Rosemary Elizabeth BA(Hons). . . . . *Nov 1996
Jackson, Mrs Sandra J FILEx; PGDipLP. . . . . *Nov 2001
Long, Mr Barry A LLB. . . . . *Apr 1972
Ogley, Mr Anthony J . . . . *Sep 2004
Richmond-Sterry, Mrs Susan Jane LLB(Hons). . . . . *Nov 1992
Sadiq, Mr Khalid Hussain LLB(Hons) Price Waterhouse Prize 1992 . . . . *Oct 1995
Scott, Mr Sarah BA(Hons). . . . . *Sep 2004
Sheppard, Mr Simon Richard LLB. . . . . *Mar 1998
Stopford, Mrs Rebecca C BSc(Hons) . . . . *Sep 1997
Asoc: Burke, Ms Caroline M LLB . . . . *Jun 1992
Burtoft, Mr Adrian. *Jun 1974
Carter, Mrs Caroline Jane LLB(Hons) Herbert Ruse Prize; Clabon Prize . . . . *Oct 1983
Harris, Mrs Elizabeth Ann LLB Undergraduate Contract Law . . . . *Mar 2005
Smith, Mr Paul Andrew BA(Law & Criminology) . . . *May 2002
Ast: Cherry, Miss Dawn LLB . . . . *Sep 2008
Cusworth, Miss Amy Elizabeth LLB; BA . . . . *Sep 2010
Earnshaw, Mrs Amy Louise LLB; LPC. . . . . *Jul 2008
Ellami, Miss Ruksana LLB. . . . . *May 2007
Musgrave, Mr Colin Gibson BA(Hons); LPC; CPE . . *Sep 2005
Parker, Miss Rachael . . . . *Oct 2009

PARKER RHODES HICKMOTTS ‡
22 Moorgate Street Rotherham South Yorkshire S60 2DA
Tel: 01709 511100 *Fax:* 01709 371917 *Dx:* 12605 ROTHERHAM
E-mail: enquiries@parker-rhodes.co.uk
List of partners: J Hanson-Clerehugh, L Johnson, M F A C Shinner, D Tickle
Office: Rotherham
Languages: Arabic, French, Urdu
Work: D1 D2 E J1 K1 K3 K4 L N O Q S1 S2 V W Z(g,i,l,r)
Agency, Advocacy, Legal Aid undertaken, Legal Aid Franchise and Member of Accident Line
Ptr: Hanson-Clerehugh, Dr Julie PhD . . . . *Aug 2005
Johnson, Mr Lee . . . . *Apr 1999
Shinner, Mrs Margaret Fiona Ann Clarke BA(Hons) . *§Nov 1993
Tickle, Miss Debra BA(Hons) . . . . *Nov 1993
Asoc: Henshall, Ms Amie . . . . Dec 2008
Con: Stephen, Mr Ian J LLB . . . . *Oct 1967
Woffenden, Mr John P LLB . . . . *§Jan 1973

PARKER RHODES HICKMOTTS
Mansfield House 34 Mansfield Road Rotherham South Yorkshire S60 2DX
Tel: 01709 365116 *Fax:* 01709 363738 *Dx:* 12605 ROTHERHAM
E-mail: enquiries@hickmotts.co.uk
Office: Rotherham
Work: A1 C1 D1 E J1 K1 L N O Q S1 S2 W X Z(c,q,r)
Emergency Action, Agency, Advocacy, Fixed Fee Interview and Legal Aid undertaken
Con: Elmhirst, Mr Nigel D. . . . . *Dec 1971
Shaw, Mr Harold LLB . . . . *May 1976

PEACE REVITT
97a Houghton Road Thurnscoe Rotherham South Yorkshire S63 0JX
Tel: 01709 898454 *Fax:* 01709 880816
E-mail: law@peacerevitt.co.uk
Office: Barnsley
Work: D1 D2 E F1 G H J1 K1 L N Q R2 S1 S2 V W Z(m,q)
Emergency Action, Agency, Advocacy, Fixed Fee Interview, Legal Aid undertaken and Legal Aid Franchise
Ast: Flewitt, Mr Julian A LLB. . . . . *Jul 1998

PRAKTICE LEGAL ‡
13-15 Blyth Road Maltby Rotherham South Yorkshire S66 8HX
Tel: 01709 790403
E-mail: enquiries@prakticelegal.co.uk

TIERNEY & CO
137 Bawtry Road Wickersley Rotherham South Yorkshire S66 2BW
Tel: 01709 709000 *Fax:* 01709 709007 *Dx:* 29786 DINNINGTON
E-mail: adpt@tierneyandco.co.uk
Office: Dinnington
Work: C1 E F1 G J1 J2 K1 K3 K4 L N O Q R1 R2 S1 S2 W Z(l,q,r)
Emergency Action, Agency, Advocacy and Fixed Fee Interview undertaken
Ast: Clay, Mr Ian BA(Hons); BSc(Hons); GDL . . . . Feb 2009
Thorpe, Mrs Bridget. . . . . Sep 2004

WALKER & CO ‡
4-8 Tickhill Road Maltby Rotherham South Yorkshire S66 7BP
Tel: 01709 817112 *Fax:* 01709 818741 *Dx:* 27051 MALTBY
Emergency telephone 01709 817112
E-mail: enquiries@walkersolicitors.co.uk
List of partners: A P Walker
Office: Sheffield
Work: D1 E F1 G H J1 K1 K2 L N O Q S1 S2 V W Z(h)
Emergency Action, Agency, Advocacy, Fixed Fee Interview, Legal Aid undertaken, Legal Aid Franchise and Member of Accident Line
Ptr: Walker, Mr Andrew P . . . . *Nov 1979
Ast: Burns, Ms Catherine LLB . . . . Jul 2003
Dalowsky, Mr Paul M LLB. . . . . Jul 2003
Hall, Mrs Ruth Helen LLB . . . . *Nov 1992

WARING ASSOCIATES LLP ‡
354 Herringthorpe Valley Road Rotherham South Yorkshire S60 4LA
Tel: 01709 365286 / 07976 957125
E-mail: law@waringllp.com

WILFORD SMITH SOLICITORS ‡
22 Westgate Rotherham South Yorkshire S60 1AP
Tel: 01709 828044 *Fax:* 01709 829054 *Dx:* 12603 ROTHERHAM
List of partners: P R A Large, S D Smith, S F Wilford
Work: G H S2 W
Emergency Action, Agency, Advocacy, Fixed Fee Interview, Legal Aid undertaken, Legal Aid Franchise and Member of Accident Line
Ptr: Large, Mr Peter R A LLB . . . . *Mar 1985
Smith, Mr Stephen D MBE ★ . . . . Jul 1979
Wilford, Mr Steven F . . . . *Dec 1977
Ast: Cusworth, Miss Susanne Louisa LLB(Hons). . . . . . . Jul 2005
Raybould, Mr David. . . . . Jan 2009
Withers, Mr Darren BA(Hons) . . . . Dec 2007

ROTHWELL, West Yorkshire

EMSLEYS ‡
Viscount Court Leeds Road Rothwell West Yorkshire LS26 0JH
Tel: 0113 201 4900 *Fax:* 0113 201 4901 *Dx:* 715927 ROTHWELL
E-mail: law@emsleys.co.uk
List of partners: C J Bubb, A L Greenwood, I A McKinlay, J N Murray, H J Serr
Office: Castleford, Crossgates, Garforth, Leeds, Rothwell
Languages: French
Work: C1 E R1 S2 W
Ptr: McKinlay, Mr Ian Alistair BA(Hons) . . . . *Oct 1997
Asoc: Jarvis, Mrs Ailsa L LLB(Hons). . . . . *Apr 1978
Stephen, Mrs Liz . . . . *Sep 2003

EMSLEYS
65 Commercial Street Rothwell West Yorkshire LS26 0QD
Tel: 0113 282 4939 *Fax:* 0113 282 9216 *Dx:* 715927 ROTHWELL
E-mail: law@emsleys.co.uk
Office: Castleford, Crossgates, Garforth, Leeds, Rothwell
Work: B1 C1 D1 E J1 K1 L N P R1 S1 S2 W Z(h,l,m,n,p)

MARTIN GAFFNEY LEGAL SERVICES ‡
9-13 Commercial Street Rothwell West Yorkshire LS26 0AX
Tel: 0113 282 7988 *Fax:* 0113 282 1010
E-mail: mail@martingaffneysolicitors.co.uk

CHRISTOPHER J GREAVES ‡
9-13 Commercial Street Rothwell West Yorkshire LS26 0AW
Tel: 0113 282 7988 *Fax:* 0113 282 1010 *Dx:* 715926 ROTHWELL
List of partners: C J Greaves
Emergency Action, Agency, Advocacy, Fixed Fee Interview and Legal Aid undertaken
Ptr: Greaves, Mr Christopher J BTech(Hons) . . . . *Jan 1981

ROWLEY REGIS, West Midlands

JORDANS ‡
35 Payne Street Blackheath Rowley Regis West Midlands B65 0DH
Tel: 0121 559 2922 *Fax:* 0121 561 4244
Dx: 703070 ROWLEY REGIS 2
E-mail: jordans@jcjblackheath.plus.com
List of partners: J C Jordan
Languages: Punjabi
Work: E K1 K3 K4 L S1 S2 W
Emergency Action, Agency, Advocacy, Fixed Fee Interview and Legal Aid undertaken
SPr: Jordan, Mr John Craig LLB . . . . *Jun 1967
Asoc: Kaur Khara, Mrs Brinderpal LLB(Hons) Notary Public *Aug 1997

ROYSTON, Hertfordshire

C A W BLACKWELL ‡
28 Kneesworth Street Royston Hertfordshire SG8 5AB
Tel: 01763 243803 *Fax:* 01763 243803
List of partners: C A W Blackwell
Work: S1 T2 W
Fixed Fee Interview undertaken
Ptr: Blackwell, Mr Charles A W BA(Cantab) . . . . *Dec 1973

BUXLEYS SERVICES LIMITED ‡
61 Fowlmere Road Heydon Royston Hertfordshire SG8 8PZ
Tel: 01763 838471

LIMBACH BANHAM ‡
John Street Royston Hertfordshire SG8 9BG
Tel: 01763 242257 *Fax:* 01763 247019 *Dx:* 37310 ROYSTON
E-mail: info@limbach.co.uk
List of partners: S J Larcombe, P E R Parker
Work: A1 B1 C1 C2 D1 E F1 J1 K1 L M1 N O P Q R1 S1 S2 T1 V W Z(b,d,g,l)
Emergency Action, Agency and Fixed Fee Interview undertaken
Ptr: Larcombe, Mr Stephen J . . . . *Dec 1980
Parker, Mrs Pamela E R BA. . . . . *Dec 1976
Ast: Kerr, Mrs Susan E LLB(B'ham) . . . . *Oct 1987

PENN SASSOLI ‡
20a Market Hill Royston Hertfordshire SG8 9JG
Tel: 01763 245234 / 245957 *Fax:* 01763 245901
Dx: 37302 ROYSTON
E-mail: info@pennsassoli.com
List of partners: T J Penn, O N Sassoli
Languages: Italian
Work: A1 B1 C1 D1 E F1 G K1 L M1 N P S1 W Z(c,l)
Emergency Action, Agency, Advocacy, Fixed Fee Interview, Legal Aid undertaken and Legal Aid Franchise
Ptr: Penn, Mr Timothy J LLB. . . . . *Jun 1975
Sassoli, Mr Oscar N. . . . . *Dec 1980

THE WALKERS PARTNERSHIP ‡
1/3 Lower King Street Royston Hertfordshire SG8 5AJ
Tel: 01763 241121 / 248896 *Fax:* 01763 249096
Dx: 37303 ROYSTON
E-mail: info@walkerspartnership.co.uk
List of partners: T H Donnellan, S D Hughes
Office: Royston
Languages: French
Work: D1 E F1 G H J1 K1 L N S1 S2 V W Z(m)
Agency, Advocacy, Fixed Fee Interview, Legal Aid undertaken, Legal Aid Franchise and Member of Accident Line
Ptr: Donnellan, Mr Terence H BA . . . . *Feb 1988

THE WALKERS PARTNERSHIP
7 Angel Pavement Royston Hertfordshire SG8 9AS
Tel: 01763 248896 *Fax:* 01763 242660 *Dx:* 37303 ROYSTON
Office: Royston
Work: D1 E F1 G H J1 K1 L N O Q S1 S2 V W Z(m)
Agency, Advocacy, Fixed Fee Interview, Legal Aid undertaken and Member of Accident Line
Ptr: Donnellan, Mr Terence H BA . . . . *Feb 1988
Hughes, Mr Stuart David BSc(Hons) . . . . *Oct 1996

SIMON WILLANS & CO ‡
The Old Police Station 8 Priory Lane Royston Hertfordshire SG8 9DU
Tel: 01763 242454 *Fax:* 01763 246546 *Dx:* 37315 ROYSTON
Emergency telephone 07713 087630
E-mail: simon@willansco.fsnet.co.uk

ROYTON, Greater Manchester

MELLOR & JACKSON
Post Office Building Rochdale Road Royton Greater Manchester OL2 6QJ
Tel: 0161 624 0387 *Fax:* 0161 652 0195
E-mail: ah@mnj.co.uk
Office: Oldham
Work: C1 E G H K4 N O Q S1 T2 W Z(q)
Emergency Action, Agency, Advocacy and Fixed Fee Interview undertaken
Con: Darkwah, Mrs Abena Boatemaa. . . . . Aug 2003

RUGBY, Warwickshire

RICHARD BEST & CO ‡
5 Park Road Rugby Warwickshire CV21 2QU
Tel: 01788 571135 *Fax:* 01788 221509 *Dx:* 11697 RUGBY 1
Emergency telephone 01788 571135 (24HR)
E-mail: law@richardbest.net
List of partners: R L Best
Languages: French
Work: B1 D1 F1 G H J1 K1 L N O P Q V X Z(d,i,m,p,q,r)
Emergency Action, Agency, Advocacy, Fixed Fee Interview, Legal Aid undertaken, Legal Aid Franchise and Member of Accident Line
SPr: Best, Mr Richard Laurence LLB(Lond). . . . . *Jul 1974

BRETHERTONS LLP ‡
16 Church Street Rugby Warwickshire CV21 3PW
Tel: 01788 579579 *Fax:* 01788 570949 *Dx:* 11672 RUGBY 1
E-mail: enquiries@brethertons.co.uk
List of partners: M T Anderson, B C Auld, S G Craddock, R G Dawson, M P Dibben, T Dyer, J R Glenn, S M Jardine, L A Jones, R M Pell
Office: Banbury, Rugby (2 offices)
Languages: French, Spanish
Work: A1 B1 C1 C2 C3 D1 E F1 I J1 K1 L M1 M2 N O P Q R1 S1 T1 T2 V W Z(b,c,d,e,f,g,h,i,j,k,l,m,o,s,t)
Emergency Action, Agency, Advocacy, Fixed Fee Interview, Legal Aid undertaken, Legal Aid Franchise and Member of Accident Line
Ptr: Anderson, Mrs Mary Teresa LLB . . . . *Oct 1984
Auld, Mr Brian C LLB; Dip Eur Law . . . . *Oct 1983
Craddock, Mr Simon Geoffrey LLB . . . . *Nov 1990
Glenn, Mr Jeffery Richard BA(Dunelm)(Law) . . . . *Jan 1979
Jones, Miss Linda Ann . . . . *Oct 1998
Pell, Mr Richard Montague . . . . *Jan 1975
Dyer, Mr Trevor . . . . NSP
Ast: Bristow, Mrs Alison Jane LLB . . . . *§Dec 2000
Eyre, Mrs Sharon . . . . *Sep 2005
Hopkin, Mr Richard Timothy Buxton BA . . . . *Dec 1994
Kelsey, Miss Gemma . . . . Sep 2008
Lawrence, Miss Leanne Marie LLB . . . . *Mar 2006
Lawrence, Mr Tom Daniel. . . . . *Sep 2002
Virani-Bland, Mrs Nadyia . . . . *Sep 2007

BRETHERTONS LLP
26 Regent Street Rugby Warwickshire CV21 2PS
Tel: 01788 551611 *Fax:* 01788 551597 *Dx:* 11672 RUGBY 1
E-mail: enquiries@brethertons.co.uk
Office: Banbury, Rugby (2 offices)
Work: L S1
Ptr: Auld, Mr Brian C LLB; Dip Eur Law . . . . *Oct 1983
Dibben, Mr Michael Paul BA(Law). . . . . *Dec 1982
Ast: Gibbs, Mr Harvey William LLB. . . . . Dec 1981
Lawrence, Mr Tom Daniel. . . . . *Sep 2002
Con: Cooper, Mr Clifford Brian LLB(B'ham) . . . . *Apr 1972

BRETHERTONS LLP
The Robbins Building 25 Albert Street Rugby Warwickshire CV21 2SD
Tel: 01788 579579 *Fax:* 01788 552888 *Dx:* 11672 RUGBY 1
E-mail: enquiries@brethertons.co.uk
Office: Banbury, Rugby (2 offices)
Work: A1 B1 C1 E F1 J1 J2 M1 S2 T1 W Z(d,e)
Fixed Fee Interview undertaken
Ptr: Anderson, Mrs Mary Teresa LLB . . . . *Oct 1984
Glenn, Mr Jeffery Richard BA(Dunelm)(Law) . . . . *Jan 1979
Ast: Bristow, Mrs Alison Jane LLB . . . . *§Dec 2000
Eyre, Mrs Sharon . . . . *Sep 2005
Hodge, Mr David . . . . Nov 2003
Lawrence, Miss Leanne Marie LLB . . . . *Mar 2006
Lawrence, Mr Tom Daniel. . . . . *Sep 2002
Ollis, Miss Kathryn Mary LLB(Hons). . . . . *Oct 1999
Virani-Bland, Mrs Nadyia . . . . *Sep 2007
Con: Cooper, Mr Clifford Brian LLB(B'ham) . . . . *Apr 1972
Patel, Mr Jitendra. . . . . Sep 2009

FULLERS ‡
24 Albert Street Rugby Warwickshire CV21 2RT
Tel: 01788 542288 *Fax:* 01788 541039 *Dx:* 11683 RUGBY
Emergency telephone 01788 822910
List of partners: M A R King, V M King
Work: A1 B1 C1 D1 D2 E J1 K1 K3 N O Q S1 S2 T1 T2 W Z(c,j)
Emergency Action, Agency, Advocacy and Fixed Fee Interview undertaken
Ptr: King, Mr Michael A R LLB(B'ham). . . . . *May 1979
King, Mrs Victoria Mary BA . . . . Aug 1997
Con: Bailey, Mr Roger F Notary Public . . . . *Jan 1970

JH LAW LIMITED ‡
The Studio 16b Spring Street Rugby Warwickshire CV21 3HH
Tel: 0845 638 4440 *Fax:* 0844 264 0645
E-mail: office@jhlaw.co.uk
Work: A3 B1 B2 C1 F1 F2 J1 L O Q W Z(c,q)

JOHNS GILBERT & FRANKTON ‡
3 Regent Place Rugby Warwickshire CV21 2PJ
Tel: 01788 576384 *Fax:* 01788 540237 *Dx:* 11684 RUGBY
E-mail: enquiries@jgfsolicitors.co.uk
List of partners: J R Frankton, M R Gregory
Work: E K4 S1 S2 W
Ptr: Frankton, Mr James R LLB . . . . *§May 1977
Gregory, Mr Martin Richard LLB. . . . . *Sep 1999

LM SOLICITORS ‡
24 Warwick Street Rugby Warwickshire CV21 3DW
Tel: 01788 550016

LUPTON REDDISH ‡
9 Regent Place Rugby Warwickshire CV21 2PJ
Tel: 01788 542241 / 565163 *Fax:* 01788 547021 *Dx:* 11677 RUGBY
E-mail: lesley@luptonreddish.esbusiness.co.uk
List of partners: C P Sidey
Work: A1 D1 E K1 L M1 P S1 W Z(d,i,l)
Emergency Action and Fixed Fee Interview undertaken
Ptr: Sidey, Mr Christopher P LLB(Hons)(Lond). . . . . . *§Jun 1971

MILDWATERS CONSULTING LLP ‡
Walton House 25 Bilton Road Rugby Warwickshire CV22 7AG
Tel: 07867 970971 / 01788 560824
E-mail: drkcmildwaters@mildwatersconsulting.com

STEPHEN MOORE & CO ‡
34 Regent Place Rugby Warwickshire CV21 2PN
Tel: 01788 535127 *Fax:* 01788 542138
List of partners: C E Brockway, S P Moore
Office: Northampton
Work: C1 E G H S1 W
Agency, Advocacy and Legal Aid undertaken
Ptr: Brockway, Ms Catherine E LLB . . . . Mar 1991
Moore, Mr Stephen P LLB. . . . . Feb 1979

PRIME & CO ‡
5 Regent Place Rugby Warwickshire CV21 2PL
Tel: 01788 576289 *Fax:* 01788 573746 *Dx:* 29401 RUGBY
List of partners: A Stevenson, J E Stevenson
Work: C1 E F1 K1 L N O Q R1 S1 S2 T2 V W
Agency and Advocacy undertaken
Ptr: Stevenson, Mr Andrew . . . . *Feb 1980
Stevenson, Mrs Janet E. . . . . *Nov 1976

RATCLIFFE SOLICITORS ‡
The Old Rectory Main Street Harborough Magna Rugby Warwickshire CV23 0HS
Tel: 01788 833151 *Fax:* 01788 811783

RUGELEY, Staffordshire

GARDNER CHAMPION ‡
Brook House Brook Square Rugeley Staffordshire WS15 2DT
Tel: 01889 576121 / 582116 *Fax:* 01889 582119
Dx: 18053 RUGELEY
E-mail: gardnerchampion@tiscali.co.uk
List of partners: J A Ashley, P A G Ashley
Work: A1 E F1 G H J1 K1 L N S1 V W
Emergency Action, Agency, Advocacy, Fixed Fee Interview, Legal Aid undertaken, Legal Aid Franchise and Member of Accident Line
Ptr: Ashley, Mrs Julie A LLB. . . . . *Oct 1986
Ashley, Mr Peter A G BA . . . . *Mar 1987

HAND MORGAN & OWEN
(incorporating Denver Clarkson & Co; Lloyd & Robinson)
Albion House 3 Albion Street Rugeley Staffordshire WS15 2BY
Tel: 01889 583871 *Fax:* 01889 583777 *Dx:* 18054 RUGELEY
E-mail: info@hmo.co.uk
Office: Stafford
Work: A1 A3 B1 C1 C2 D1 D2 E F1 F2 J1 J2 K1 K2 K3 K4 L N O P Q S1 S2 T1 T2 W Z(c,d,k,l,p,q,t)
Emergency Action, Agency, Advocacy, Fixed Fee Interview undertaken and Member of Accident Line
Ptr: Carr, Mrs Shani Susan LLB . . . . *Oct 1986

PICKERING & BUTTERS
Market Square Rugeley Staffordshire WS15 2BN
Tel: 01889 803080 *Fax:* 01889 803081 *Dx:* 18051 RUGELEY
E-mail: info@pb4law.com
Office: Stafford
Languages: French, German, Russian, Spanish
Work: A1 B1 C1 C2 E F1 J1 K3 L N O P Q R1 S1 S2 T1 T2 V W Z(c,h,j,l,o,p,t)
Agency, Advocacy, Fixed Fee Interview, Legal Aid Franchise and Member of Accident Line
Ptr: Wallbank, Mr Martin C LLB . . . . *Dec 1982
Asoc: Pegg, Mr Daniel James BA(Law & Business) . . . . . Nov 2004
Con: Copley, Mr John S . . . . *Jun 1962

RUISLIP, Middlesex

ALBANY REED SOLICITORS ‡
Audit House 260 Field End Road Ruislip Middlesex HA4 9LT
Tel: 020 8429 7497 *Fax:* 020 8429 7498

BIRD & LOVIBOND
11 High Street Ruislip Middlesex HA4 7AV
Tel: 01895 636037 *Fax:* 01895 678958 *Dx:* 83100 RUISLIP
E-mail: ruislip@bird-lovibond.co.uk
Office: Greenford, Uxbridge
Work: E J1 K1 K3 L N Q S1 S2 W
Fixed Fee Interview undertaken and Member of Accident Line
Ptr: Everest, Ms Michelle C . . . . *Jan 2002

BUNCE SOLICITORS ‡
Canada House 272 Field End Road Ruislip Middlesex HA4 9NA
Tel: 020 8582 0150

DAVID DURN & CO ‡
Jebsen House 53-61 High Street Ruislip Middlesex HA4 7BD
Tel: 01895 612400 *Fax:* 01895 678768 *Dx:* 153480 EASTCOTE 2
E-mail: info@daviddurn.co.uk
List of partners: C W Artley, D Durn, A Nelson, J Sheldrick
Work: C1 C2 D1 E J1 K1 K3 L O Q S1 S2 W
Ptr: Artley, Mr Charles Winston . . . . Jun 1976
Durn, Mr David . . . . *Oct 1999
Sheldrick, Mr John . . . . *Aug 1990
Nelson, Amy FILEx . . . . NSP
Asoc: Guppy, Mrs Elizabeth Alexandra . . . . Jan 2004
O'Donovan, Ms Frances LLB(Hons). . . . . Sep 2000

ENEVER FREEMAN & CO ‡
48A High Street Ruislip Middlesex HA4 7AL
Tel: 01895 634031 *Fax:* 01895 621592 *Dx:* 80104 RUISLIP
List of partners: C F C G Bennett
Office: Ruislip
Languages: French
Work: A1 B1 C1 D1 E F1 J1 K1 K3 K4 L N O Q S1 S2 W Z(k,l,m,q)
Emergency Action and Fixed Fee Interview undertaken
Ptr: Bennett, Mr Christopher F C G BA . . . . *Oct 1975

See p112 for the Key to Work Categories & other symbols

ENEVER FREEMAN & CO
17 Victoria Road Ruislip Manor Ruislip Middlesex HA4 9AA
Tel: 01895 676385 / 676386 *Dx:* 80104 RUISLIP
Office: Ruislip
Work: B1 C1 D1 E F1 J1 K1 K3 K4 L N O Q R1 S1 S2 W Z(m,q,r)
Fixed Fee Interview undertaken

HOWMAN & CO ‡
College House 17 King Edward Road Ruislip Middlesex HA4 7AE
Tel: 01895 621777 *Dx:* 80118 RUISLIP
List of partners: M T Howman
Ptr: Howman, Mr Mark T. . . . . Jun 1980

THE MLT PARTNERSHIP ‡
1a Ickenham Road Ruislip Middlesex HA4 7BT
Tel: 01895 676251 *Fax:* 01895 621032
E-mail: office@mltpart.co.uk
List of partners: G N Sharpe, M J Treisman
Work: K4 W
Ptr: Sharpe, Mr Graham Neil BA. . . . . *Oct 1985
Treisman, Mr Michael J . . . . *Jun 1977

SOULSBY WILLIAMSON ‡
(in association with Williamson Edwards)
73 Parkway Ruislip Manor Ruislip Middlesex HA4 8NS
Tel: 01895 636999 *Fax:* 01895 678971 *Dx:* 83105 RUISLIP MANOR
E-mail: info@soulsbywilliamson.co.uk
List of partners: D S Williamson
Work: E F1 J1 K1 K3 K4 L S1 W Z(l)
Advocacy and Fixed Fee Interview undertaken
Ptr: Williamson, Mr David S LLB(Lond) . . . . *Oct 1975

WEBBERS SOLICITORS ‡
22 Bourne Avenue Ruislip Middlesex HA4 6TZ
Tel: 0845 604 5988 *Fax:* 020 8845 4718
E-mail: admin@webbersolicitors.co.uk

WILLS LINK ASSOCIATES LIMITED ‡
168 Victoria Road Ruislip Middlesex HA4 0AW
Tel: 01895 636573 *Fax:* 01895 636573

RUNCORN, Cheshire

BELL LAMB & JOYNSON
(incorporating Benjamin Kay & Co)
(in association with Rayner & Wade)
Grosvenor House Halton Lea Runcorn Cheshire WA7 2HF
Tel: 0844 412 4348 *Fax:* 01928 711709 *Dx:* 15201 RUNCORN 2
E-mail: runcorn@bljsolicitors.co.uk
Office: Liverpool (2 offices), Warrington, Weaverham
Work: D1 F1 G H K1 L S1 S2 V W Z(h,l)
Emergency Action, Agency, Advocacy, Fixed Fee Interview, Legal Aid undertaken, Legal Aid Franchise and Member of Accident Line
Ptr: Cooper, Mr Barry D LLB(Manc) Deputy District Judge . Jun 1975
Marshall, Mr James C R LLB . . . . *May 1976
Scarisbrick, Mrs Ruth BA . . . . *Nov 1985
Asoc: Green, Mr Peter D LLB(Lancs) . . . . Sep 1995

BUTCHER & BARLOW LLP
71 High Street Runcorn Cheshire WA7 1AH
Tel: 01928 572268 *Fax:* 01928 580498 *Dx:* 23453 RUNCORN 1
Office: Bramhall, Bury (2 offices), Frodsham, Leigh, Northwich, Prestwich, Runcorn, Sandbach, Tyldesley
Languages: French, German
Work: A1 B1 C1 C2 C3 D1 E F1 J1 K1 K2 L N O Q R1 S1 S2 T1 T2 V W Z(c,k,l,p)
Agency, Advocacy, Fixed Fee Interview, Legal Aid undertaken and Legal Aid Franchise
Ptr: Whitaker, Mr James Geoffrey LLB(Hons) . . . . May 1980
Ast: Charnock, Mr James Holt BCom(French); EMBs . . . Mar 2007
Lloyd, Miss Lynsey . . . . Jan 2010

BUTCHER & BARLOW LLP
66 High Street Runcorn Cheshire WA7 1AW
Tel: 01928 576056 *Fax:* 01928 580734 *Dx:* 23456 RUNCORN 1
E-mail: enquiries@butcher-barlow.co.uk
Office: Bramhall, Bury (2 offices), Frodsham, Leigh, Northwich, Prestwich, Runcorn, Sandbach, Tyldesley
Work: A1 B1 C1 C2 C3 D1 E F1 J1 K1 K3 K4 L M1 M2 N O P Q R1 R2 S1 S2 T1 T2 V W Z(c,d,e,j,l,m,o,p,q,r,t)
Emergency Action, Agency, Advocacy, Fixed Fee Interview, Legal Aid undertaken and Member of Accident Line
Ptr: Sandland, Mr Alexander G LLB(Hons). . . . . *Mar 2004
Ast: Gibson, Miss Amy LLB . . . . Jan 2011

FORSTER DEAN LTD
60 Devonshire Place Runcorn Cheshire WA7 1AW
Tel: 01928 590999 *Fax:* 01928 590666 *Dx:* 23454 RUNCORN 1
Emergency telephone 07702 111986
E-mail: enquiries@forsterdean.co.uk
Office: Birkenhead, Bootle, Chorley, Crewe, Eccles, Ellesmere Port, Huyton, Leigh, Liverpool (5 offices), Oldham, Preston, Rochdale, St Helens, Stockport, Warrington, Widnes (2 offices), Wigan
Languages: Hindi, Mirpuri, Punjabi
Work: D1 D2 K1 K2 N S1 W
Emergency Action, Agency, Advocacy, Fixed Fee Interview, Legal Aid undertaken and Legal Aid Franchise
Ptr: Collins, Mr Michael LPC. . . . . *Aug 2000
Forster Dean, Mr Peter BA . . . . *Apr 1981
Shields, Mr Gregory J LLB(Hons) . . . . *Mar 1999
Ast: Daniels, Mr Laurence LLB(Hons) . . . . *Jan 1994
Hammal, Mr Philip James LLB . . . . *Jan 2001
Hussain, Abid LLB(Hons) . . . . *Oct 1997
McCormack, Miss Alison . . . . *Apr 2002
O'Hara, Mrs Shauna LLB(Hons). . . . . *Nov 1998

JONES ROBERTSON
4-5 Rutland House Halton Lea Runcorn Cheshire WA7 2ES
Tel: 01928 711119 *Fax:* 01928 711801 *Dx:* 15203 RUNCORN 2
Emergency telephone 01928 732833
E-mail: cjones@jrlaw.co.uk
Office: Northwich, Widnes
Work: D1 E F1 G H J1 K1 L P S1 V W X Z(l)
Emergency Action, Agency, Advocacy, Fixed Fee Interview, Legal Aid undertaken, Legal Aid Franchise and Member of Accident Line
Ptr: De Haas, Mr Brian C BSc. . . . . *Jun 1977
Ferris, Mr Liam LLB(Hons) . . . . May 1995
Jones, Mr Christopher R BA. . . . . *Oct 1982
Weights, Mr Ian BA(Hons). . . . . Jun 1990

ROSE & DUNN ‡
58 High Street Runcorn Cheshire WA7 1AW
Tel: 01928 572030
Work: G
Advocacy undertaken

SILVERMAN LIVERMORE ‡
1 Rutland House Halton Lea Runcorn Cheshire WA7 2ES
Tel: 01928 714121 *Fax:* 01928 718135 *Dx:* 15204 RUNCORN 2
E-mail: lesley@silvermanlivermore.com
List of partners: D R Fraser, K M Wishart
Work: D1 D2 K1 K3 N Q W
Emergency Action, Agency, Advocacy, Fixed Fee Interview and Legal Aid undertaken
Ptr: Fraser, Mr Douglas R Deputy Coroner for Liverpool . . *Jun 1982
Wishart, Miss Karen M LLB . . . . *Feb 1987

RUSHDEN, Northamptonshire

HOBEN JOHNSON ‡
(incorporating Pilgrim Hales & Almond)
The Old Auction Rooms 8 West Street Rushden Northamptonshire NN10 0RT
Tel: 01933 411375 *Fax:* 01933 412690 *Dx:* 18959 RUSHDEN
E-mail: law@hobenjohnson.com
List of partners: L H Johnson
Office: Wellingborough
Work: E F1 G H J1 K1 L N O Q S1 T1 T2 V W Z(l,m)
Emergency Action, Agency, Fixed Fee Interview, Legal Aid undertaken and Legal Aid Franchise
Ptr: Johnson, Mr Leon Hoben LLB. . . . . *Mar 1985
Ast: Wood, Mr Stephen Paul LLB . . . . Jan 2002

PARK WOODFINE HEALD MELLOWS LLP
London House 16 High Street Rushden Northamptonshire NN10 0PR
Tel: 01933 397000 *Fax:* 01933 397010 *Dx:* 18953 RUSHDEN
E-mail: admin@pwhmllp.com
Office: Bedford, Northampton
Work: D1 F1 J1 K1 K3 K4 L N Q S1 W
Emergency Action, Agency, Advocacy, Legal Aid undertaken and Member of Accident Line
Ast: Izzard, Ms Jemma LLB . . . . Mar 2006
Quinlan, Ms Christine J LLB. . . . . *Nov 1984

C J SPOOR & CO ‡
121a High Street Rushden Northamptonshire NN10 0NZ
Tel: 01933 419499

RUSTINGTON, West Sussex

BENNETT GRIFFIN
62 The Street Rustington West Sussex BN16 3NR
Tel: 01903 777690 *Fax:* 01903 850162 *Dx:* 55107 RUSTINGTON
Emergency telephone 01903 229949
E-mail: recw@bennett-griffin.co.uk
Office: Ferring, Worthing
Work: K4 L S1 T1 T2 V W
Emergency Action, Agency, Advocacy, Fixed Fee Interview, Legal Aid Franchise and Member of Accident Line
Ptr: Kilby, Mr Patrick BSc(Hons). . . . . *Jan 1997
Macara, Mr Ian Stuart LLB . . . . *Sep 1996
Asoc: Woods, Mr Greg . . . . *Feb 2006

GREEN WRIGHT CHALTON ANNIS
Churchill Court 112 The Street Rustington West Sussex BN16 3DA
Tel: 01903 774131 *Fax:* 01903 778444 *Dx:* 55100 RUSTINGTON
Emergency telephone 01903 786672
E-mail: enquiries@gwca.co.uk
Web: www.gwca.co.uk
Office: Arundel, Lancing, Steyning, Worthing (2 offices)
Work: A1 B1 C1 C3 E F1 J1 K1 L M1 N O P Q R1 S1 S2 T1 T2 W Z(c,l)
Emergency Action, Advocacy, Fixed Fee Interview and Legal Aid undertaken
Ptr: Mason, Miss Elise LLB; IAC; MLIA(dip) . . . . *Sep 2000
Lewis, Mr Anthony James. . . . . NSP
Ast: Carter, Miss Katie. . . . . *Sep 2009
Con: Yates, Mr John T BA(Nott'm) . . . . *§Apr 1976

Particular areas of work include: Commercial and Company Law, Commercial Property, Probate & Wills, Court of Protection.

E J MOYLE
2a Broadmark Parade Rustington West Sussex BN16 2NE
Tel: 01903 784447 *Fax:* 01903 787822 *Dx:* 55112 RUSTINGTON
Emergency telephone 01903 715429
E-mail: rustmail@moyle.co.uk
Office: Littlehampton
Work: C1 C2 D1 E F1 J1 K1 L N P Q R1 S1 S2 T1 T2 W Z(l)
Agency, Advocacy, Fixed Fee Interview, Legal Aid undertaken, Legal Aid Franchise and Member of Accident Line
Ptr: White, Mr Martin Andrew BA . . . . *§Nov 1973

WARWICK & BARKER ‡
Woodlands Chambers 78 Woodlands Avenue Rustington West Sussex BN16 3EZ
Tel: 01903 775051 *Fax:* 01903 774932 *Dx:* 55105 RUSTINGTON
E-mail: info@warwickbarker.co.uk
List of partners: M G Barker, S F M Kenning
Work: C1 D1 E F1 J1 K1 L M1 P R1 S1 T1 W Z(c,d,k,l,m)
Agency, Advocacy, Fixed Fee Interview, Legal Aid undertaken and Member of Accident Line
Ptr: Barker, Mr Michael G . . . . *§Jan 1969
Kenning, Mr Simon F M. . . . . *§Aug 1978

RUTHIN, Denbighshire

GAMLINS ‡
16 St Peter's Square Ruthin Denbighshire LL15 1AD
Tel: 01824 702102 *Fax:* 01824 705909
E-mail: gamlins@gamlins.co.uk

LLEWELLYN JONES & CO
Barclays Bank Chambers Clwyd Street Ruthin Denbighshire LL15 1HW
Tel: 01824 704495 *Fax:* 01824 702535 *Dx:* 21831 RUTHIN
E-mail: post@lljsolicitors.co.uk
Office: Mold
Languages: Welsh
Work: A1 B1 D1 G J1 K1 L N Q S1 W
Emergency Action, Agency, Advocacy, Fixed Fee Interview, Legal Aid undertaken and Legal Aid Franchise
Ptr: Williams, Miss Delyth Geraint LLB(Hons) . . . . . . *May 1981

SWAYNE JOHNSON SOLICITORS
Llanrhydd Manor Ruthin Denbighshire LL15 1PP
Tel: 01824 703833 *Fax:* 01824 705071 *Dx:* 21833 RUTHIN
E-mail: law@swaynejohnson.com
Office: Denbigh, Llandudno, St Asaph
Languages: Welsh
Work: B2 E G K1 L N S1 S2 V W
Emergency Action, Agency and Advocacy undertaken
Ptr: Taylor, Mr Michael A H LLB(Lond). . . . . *Feb 1966

RYDE, Isle of Wight

BOLITHO WAY
13 Union Street Ryde Isle of Wight PO33 2DU
Tel: 01983 817060 *Dx:* 56655 RYDE (IOW)
Office: Portsmouth

CHURCHERS
16a Union Street Ryde Isle of Wight PO33 2DU
Tel: 01983 614541 *Fax:* 023 9286 1880
Office: Fareham, Gosport, Lee-on-the-Solent, Portsmouth (2 offices)

CORPORATE LEGAL ‡
Wightstones Thornton Manor Drive Ryde Isle of Wight PO33 1PQ
Tel: 0845 458 9448
E-mail: info@corporatelegal.co.uk

ELDRIDGES
17 Lind Street Ryde Isle of Wight PO33 2NS
Tel: 01983 562241 *Fax:* 01983 616867 *Dx:* 56653 RYDE (IOW)
E-mail: info@eldridges.co.uk
Office: Freshwater, Newport
Work: S1 W
Ptr: Noble, Mr Gareth H BSc(Hons) . . . . *§Oct 1994
Smith, Mr Peter John LLB. . . . . *§Jan 1971

WALTER GRAY & CO ‡
3-4 St Thomas Street Ryde Isle of Wight PO33 2ND
Tel: 01983 563765 *Fax:* 01983 617102 *Dx:* 56651 RYDE (IOW)
Emergency telephone 01983 616606
E-mail: ryde@waltergray.co.uk
List of partners: B M C Heptinstall, A J Norgate
Office: Cowes
Languages: French
Work: B1 E F1 K4 L O Q S1 S2 T2 V W Z(b,c,d,j,l,m,q)
Agency undertaken
Ptr: Heptinstall, Mr Brian Martin Casson LLB(Hull). . . . *§Dec 1970
Norgate, Mr Anthony John . . . . Jan 1979
Asoc: Blake, Mrs Mary LLB . . . . *§Apr 1975
Powe, Mrs Catherine E LLB(B'ham) Sheffield Prize; Sir George Fowler Prize; Child Pilkington Prizes . . . . *Nov 1985
Ast: Hardwicke, Ms Rosemary . . . . Aug 2004

HEYES SAMUEL ‡
67 Union Street Ryde Isle of Wight PO33 2LN
Tel: 01983 615615 *Fax:* 01983 612613 *Dx:* 56667 RYDE (IOW)
E-mail: admin@heyes-samuel.demon.co.uk
List of partners: S C Heyes, M A Samuel
Work: D1 F1 K1 L N Q Z(q)
Emergency Action, Agency, Fixed Fee Interview, Legal Aid undertaken and Member of Accident Line
Ptr: Heyes, Miss Serena C LLB(Hons). . . . . *Oct 1986
Samuel, Mr Mark A LLB(Hons) . . . . *Oct 1993
Ast: Chequer, Mr Jeremy Simon BSc . . . . *Aug 1991

JAMES KING ‡
9a Westwood Road Ryde Isle of Wight PO33 3BJ
Tel: 01983 564134
Work: C1 S2

MERRY & CO ‡
73 Union Street Ryde Isle of Wight PO34 2LN
Tel: 01983 811722 *Fax:* 01983 811243 *Dx:* 56665 RYDE (IOW)
E-mail: office@merryandco.co.uk
List of partners: B R Merry, I Merry
Work: D1 G H K1 K3 Q S1 S2 V W
Emergency Action, Agency, Advocacy, Fixed Fee Interview, Legal Aid undertaken and Legal Aid Franchise
Ptr: Merry, Mr Bernard Roger BA(Law) . . . . *Aug 1985
Merry, Mr Ian LLB. . . . . *Jul 2000

PLANE LEGAL LLP ‡
Tower House Quarr Road Ryde Isle of Wight PO33 4EL
Tel: 07774 847052 *Fax:* 01983 812011

RJR SOLICITORS ‡
18 Melville Street Ryde Isle of Wight PO33 2AP
Tel: 01983 562201 *Fax:* 01983 616602 *Dx:* 56652 RYDE (IOW)
Emergency telephone 01983 562201
E-mail: ryde@rjr.co.uk
Office: Freshwater, Newport
Languages: French, German
Work: A1 C1 C2 C3 D1 D2 E F1 G H J2 K1 K3 K4 N O P Q R1 S1 S2 T1 T2 V W Z(c,d,l,o)

PAUL WILKS & CO ‡
3 Garfield Road Ryde Isle of Wight PO33 2PS
Tel: 01983 614657
E-mail: paul@paulwilks.com

WILKS PRICE HOUNSLOW ‡
(incorporating Sherwin Price Hounslow Wilks)
9 Garfield Road Ryde Isle of Wight PO33 2PS
Tel: 01983 566241 *Fax:* 01983 616880 *Dx:* 56654 RYDE (IOW)
Emergency telephone 01983 614798
E-mail: postroom@wphiow.co.uk
List of partners: J H R Hounslow, R A Price
Work: A1 C1 C2 C3 D1 E F1 G H I J1 K1 K3 K4 L N O P Q R1 S1 S2 T1 T2 V W Z(c,h,j,k,l)
Emergency Action, Fixed Fee Interview, Legal Aid undertaken and Legal Aid Franchise
Ptr: Hounslow, Mr John H R. . . . . *Jun 1978
Price, Mr Robin A . . . . *Dec 1973

RYE, East Sussex

WILLIAM DAWES & CO ‡
Watchbell Chambers Watchbell Street Rye East Sussex TN31 7HB
Tel: 01797 223177 *Fax:* 01797 224851 *Dx:* 82001 RYE
E-mail: solicitors@williamdawes.co.uk
List of partners: R Parkes, J N Sperring
Work: A1 A2 C1 D1 D2 E F1 J1 K1 L N O P Q R1 R2 S1 S2 T1 T2 W Z(l,q)
Agency and Advocacy undertaken
Ptr: Parkes, Mr Rupert BA(Law) . . . . . *Oct 1984
Sperring, Mr John N BA(Kent) . . . . . *May 1979

HERINGTONS
Bank Chambers High Street Rye East Sussex TN31 7JR
Tel: 01797 222955 *Fax:* 01797 222236 *Dx:* 82000 RYE
E-mail: rfisher@heringtons.net
Office: Battle, Eastbourne, Hastings
Work: A1 B1 C1 D1 E F1 G H J1 K1 L N O Q R1 S1 S2 T1 T2 V W Z(l,m,q)
Emergency Action, Agency, Advocacy, Fixed Fee Interview, Legal Aid undertaken, Legal Aid Franchise and Member of Accident Line
Ptr: Fisher, Mr Richard A LLB(Leics) . . . . . *Nov 1990
Harding, Mr David LLB(Soton) . . . . . *Jun 1973
Ast: Cathcart, Miss Jane Elizabeth LLB . . . . . *Jun 2002

ELAINE PARKES SOLICITORS ‡
Steeplands Pottery Lane Rye East Sussex TN31 6HB
Tel: 01424 883183 *Fax:* 01424 882556
E-mail: info@elaineparkessolicitors.co.uk
List of partners: E Parkes
Work: D1 K1 K3
Agency and Legal Aid Franchise
Ptr: Parkes, Ms Elaine . . . . . Oct 1982

RYTON, Tyne & Wear

PATTERSON WOLF & CO ‡
Whitewall Chambers Lane Head Ryton Tyne & Wear NE40 3HF
Tel: 0191 488 7777 *Fax:* 0191 488 2072
E-mail: admin@pattersonwolf.co.uk
List of partners: A C Wolf
Work: A1 B1 C1 D1 E F1 G H J1 K1 L M1 N P R1 S1 T1 V W
Emergency Action, Agency, Advocacy, Fixed Fee Interview and Legal Aid undertaken
Ptr: Wolf, Mr Alastair C LLB . . . . . *May 1989

SWINBURNE & JACKSON LLP
1 Ashfield Terrace Ryton Tyne & Wear NE40 3LB
Tel: 0191 413 3468 / 413 2630 *Fax:* 0191 413 2630
E-mail: ryton@swinburnejackson.com
Office: Chester-le-Street, Gateshead, Hexham, Washington
Work: B1 C1 E F1 G H J1 K1 L M1 M2 N P S1 V W Z(m)
Emergency Action, Agency, Advocacy, Fixed Fee Interview, Legal Aid undertaken and Member of Accident Line
Ptr: Brennen, Mr Richard . . . . . *Oct 1977
Pescott, Miss Katrina Mary LLB(Hons) . . . . . *Oct 1998
Scott, Mrs Joanne Linda LLB(Hons) . . . . . Nov 1995
Swinburne, Mr Christian Hugh Stuart LLB(Hons)(Northumbria) . . . . . *§Sep 1996
Con: Swinburne, Mrs Rachel . . . . . Oct 1994

SAFFRON WALDEN, Essex

ADAMS HARRISON ‡
14-16 Church Street Saffron Walden Essex CB10 1JW
Tel: 01799 523441 *Fax:* 01799 526130
Dx: 200302 SAFFRON WALDEN
E-mail: enquiries@adams-harrison.co.uk
List of partners: P G Cammiss, J D Carpenter, S S R Goldhill, T B Harrison, M F Pratlett, R E Rees
Office: Haverhill, Sawston
Work: A1 B1 C1 C2 C3 D1 E F1 G H J1 K1 L M1 M2 N P R1 S1 T1 T2 V W Z(c,d,e,h,i,j,k,l,m,o,p,s)
Emergency Action, Agency, Advocacy, Fixed Fee Interview, Legal Aid undertaken and Legal Aid Franchise
Ptr: Carpenter, Miss Jennifer D . . . . . *Nov 2000
Goldhill, Ms Shoshana S R MA(Cantab) . . . . . *Nov 1986
Harrison, Mr Tom B LLB(Lond) . . . . . *Dec 1977
Pratlett, Miss Melanie F . . . . . *Dec 1988
Ast: Hutchings, Ms Julia . . . . . Nov 2005

HECKFORD NORTON
(incorporating Baily Williams & Lucas)
18 Hill Street Saffron Walden Essex CB10 1JD
Tel: 01799 522636 *Fax:* 01799 513282
Dx: 200304 SAFFRON WALDEN
E-mail: law@heckfordnorton.co.uk
Office: Letchworth, Stevenage
Languages: French
Work: A1 B1 C1 C2 C3 D1 D2 E F1 G H J1 J2 K1 K2 K3 K4 L O P Q R1 R2 S1 S2 W X Z(c,d,e,l,p,q,s,t,u)
Emergency Action, Agency, Advocacy, Fixed Fee Interview, Legal Aid undertaken and Legal Aid Franchise
Ast: Cobb, Mr Jonathan M . . . . . Jul 1992
Solanki, Miss Seema LLB(Hons) . . . . . *Sep 2005

HEWITSONS
53 High Street Saffron Walden Essex CB10 1AR
Tel: 01799 522471 *Fax:* 01799 524742
Dx: 200300 SAFFRON WALDEN
E-mail: mail@hewitsons.com
Office: Cambridge, Milton Keynes, Northampton
Languages: French, German, Italian, Spanish
Work: A1 A3 B1 B2 C1 C2 C3 D1 E F1 G H I J1 K1 L M1 M2 N O P Q R1 R2 S1 S2 T1 T2 U1 U2 W Z(b,c,d,e,f,g,h,i,j,k,l,m,o,p,q,r,s,u,y)
Agency, Advocacy, Fixed Fee Interview, Legal Aid undertaken and Legal Aid Franchise
Ptr: Hollest, Mr David E . . . . . *Jul 1969
Hughes, Ms Susanne M . . . . . *Jan 1989
Middleton, Mr Timothy S LLB . . . . . *Nov 1987
Ast: Birnage, Miss Susan Jane LLB . . . . . *Nov 1986

PELLYS SOLICITORS LIMITED ‡
12 Market Walk Saffron Walden Essex CB10 1JZ
Tel: 01799 514420 *Fax:* 01799 514421
Dx: 200303 SAFFRON WALDEN
E-mail: office@pellys.co.uk

STANLEY TEE LLP
68 High Street Saffron Walden Essex CB10 1AD
Tel: 01799 527299 *Fax:* 01799 525249
Dx: 200305 SAFFRON WALDEN
E-mail: law@teeslaw.co.uk
Office: Bishop's Stortford, Braintree, Great Dunmow
Work: C1 E S1 S2 W Z(d)
Ptr: Bricknell, Mr Peter Richard LLB . . . . . *Oct 1972
Hynard, Mr Stephen Richard LLB . . . . . *Nov 1989
Penney, Mr Paul James . . . . . *Feb 1983
Ast: Brett, Mrs M Henrietta BA(Hons) . . . . . *Sep 1996

STEVENS
Thorn House 11 Hill Street Saffron Walden Essex CB10 1EH
Tel: 01799 526849 *Fax:* 01799 524799
Dx: 200308 SAFFRON WALDEN
E-mail: info@stevens-law.co.uk
Office: Haverhill
Languages: Bengali, French, Hindi
Work: C1 D1 D2 E F1 G H J1 K1 K3 K4 O Q R1 S1 S2 W Z(l,p)
Emergency Action, Agency, Advocacy, Fixed Fee Interview, Legal Aid undertaken and Legal Aid Franchise
Ptr: Caldwell, Mr Alan BA(Hons) . . . . . *Dec 1989
Ast: Turner, Mrs Julia LLB; BComm(Hons) . . . . . Aug 2006

FIONA STRACHAN ‡
The Old Kiora London Road Saffron Walden Essex CB11 3SY
Tel: 01799 541331

SALCOMBE, Devon

BARTONS
Island Street Salcombe Devon TQ8 8DP
Tel: 01548 843005 *Fax:* 01548 843250 *Dx:* 81402 KINGSBRIDGE
E-mail: salcombe@bartons.co.uk
Office: Bristol, Kingsbridge, Plymouth, Totnes
Ptr: Hayes, Mr Raymond Charles Svend . . . . . Oct 1985

SALE, Greater Manchester

BANNISTER PRESTON ‡
30 Washway Road Sale Greater Manchester M33 7QY
Tel: 0161 973 2434 *Fax:* 0161 962 9562 *Dx:* 19269 SALE
E-mail: info@barristerpreston.com
List of partners: W G C Baker, D N Eccles, J G Heaton, L Willey, J L Wilson
Office: Irlam
Work: C1 E F1 G H K1 L N O Q S1 S2 W Z(c,t)
Agency, Advocacy, Fixed Fee Interview, Legal Aid undertaken and Member of Accident Line
Ptr: Eccles, Mr David N LLB . . . . . *Nov 1985
Heaton, Mr John Graham LLB(Hons) . . . . . *Jun 1981
Willey, Mr Lawrence LLB(L'pool) . . . . . *Jun 1977
Wilson, Miss Jeannette Louise LLB . . . . . *Oct 1985
Asoc: Blackhurst, Miss Kerry Jane MA(Hons) . . . . . *Jul 1999
Ast: Todd, Mrs Michele A LLB . . . . . *Oct 1986

JOHN BLACK SOLICITORS ‡
64 Cross Street Sale Greater Manchester M33 7AN
Tel: 0161 972 5999

BURTON COPELAND LLP
7 Washway Road Sale Greater Manchester M33 7AD
Tel: 0161 905 8530 *Fax:* 0161 905 8531 *Dx:* 19271 SALE
Emergency telephone 07659 109628
E-mail: trafford@burtoncopeland.com
Office: Manchester
Work: B2 G H J2 P Z(g)
Emergency Action, Agency, Advocacy, Legal Aid undertaken and Legal Aid Franchise
Mem: Weed, Mr Daniel Richard LLB . . . . . *Oct 2000
Ast: Atkinson, Mr Edward Paul . . . . . Feb 2004

DRAYCOTT BROWNE SOLICITORS
Charter Buildings 9a Ashton Lane Sale Greater Manchester M33 6WT
Tel: 0161 972 0999
Office: Manchester

LAWSMITHS ‡
1st Floor Dominion House Sibson Road Sale Greater Manchester M33 7PP
Tel: 0161 972 7700 *Fax:* 0161 972 7701
List of partners: G Smith
Languages: French, Spanish
Work: C1 E N O S1 S2
Ptr: Smith, Mr Geoffrey BA; ACIS Notary Public . . . . . *§Feb 1975
Asoc: Rowbotham, Ms Margaret Ann LLB(Hons) . . . . . Apr 2005

MAIDMENTS
27 Cross Street Sale Greater Manchester M33 7FT
Tel: 0870 403 4000 *Fax:* 0845 017 6633
Emergency telephone 0161 834 0008
E-mail: contact@maidments.co.uk
Office: Birmingham, Bolton, Salford
Work: B2 D1 G H J1 J2 K1 K2 N O Q Z(y)
Emergency Action, Agency, Advocacy, Fixed Fee Interview, Legal Aid undertaken and Member of Accident Line
Ptr: Williams, Mrs Stephanie LLB(Hons) . . . . . *Nov 1988

RICHARDSON MAIL SOLICITORS ‡
12 Washway Road Sale Greater Manchester M33 7QY
Tel: 0161 968 3400 *Fax:* 0161 969 8142
E-mail: enquire@richardsonmail.co.uk

ROTHWELL & EVANS
3 Claremont Road Sale Greater Manchester M33 1DZ
Tel: 0161 969 7341 *Fax:* 0161 969 3570
Emergency telephone 0161 799 5936
Office: Swinton
Languages: French, German
Work: C1 D1 E F1 G H J1 K1 L M1 N P R1 S1 V W Z(k,l,m)
Emergency Action, Agency, Advocacy, Fixed Fee Interview and Legal Aid undertaken
Ptr: McNamara, Mr John J M BA . . . . . *Feb 1983
Newton, Ms Kathryn J BA . . . . . *Oct 1990

SHEPHERD REYNOLDS SOLICITORS ‡
2nd Floor 6 Broad Road Sale Greater Manchester M33 2AL
Tel: 0161 969 6415 *Fax:* 0161 969 6326
E-mail: info@reynolds-solicitors.co.uk

SLATER HEELIS COLLIER LITTLER ‡
16 School Road Sale Greater Manchester M33 7XP
Tel: 0161 969 3131 *Fax:* 0161 973 1018 *Dx:* 19261 SALE 1
E-mail: enquiries@shcl.uk.com
Office: Sale
Languages: Dutch, French, German, Hindi, Punjabi, Ukrainian
Work: A1 A3 B1 B2 C1 C2 C3 D1 D2 E F1 F2 G H I J1 J2 K1 K2 K3 L M1 M2 N O P Q R1 R2 S1 S2 T1 T2 V W Z(b,c,d,e,g,h,i,j,k,l,m,o,p,q,r,s,t,u,w,za)

SLATER HEELIS COLLIER LITTLER
Commercial Office Dovercote House Off Old Hall Road Sale Greater Manchester M33 2HG
Tel: 0161 969 3131 *Fax:* 0161 975 3824 *Dx:* 19261 SALE 1
E-mail: intouch@slaterheelis.co.uk
Office: Sale
Work: C1 C3 E J1 O R2 S2 T1 W Z(h,o)

SALFORD, Greater Manchester

ALLWEIS & CO ‡
64 Leicester Road Salford Greater Manchester M7 4AR
Tel: 0161 792 1020 *Fax:* 0161 950 8177
List of partners: J A H Allweis
Work: B1 D1 E F1 G H J1 K1 L N Q S1 W X Z(b,l,r)
Emergency Action, Fixed Fee Interview, Legal Aid undertaken and Member of Accident Line
SPr: Allweis, Mr Jonathon Aubrey Howard LLB(Hons) . . . *Jul 1993
Asoc: Kornhauser, Mr David MA(Oxon) Rabbi . . . . . Nov 1978

AUGHTON AINSWORTH ‡
Furness House Furness Quay Salford Greater Manchester M50 3XZ
Tel: 0161 877 8555 *Fax:* 0161 877 8557
E-mail: info@aughtonainsworth.com
List of partners: T Ellis, A Williamson
Languages: Cantonese, Czech, German, Icelandic, Malay, Mandarin, Polish
Work: A3 B1 C1 C3 E F1 F2 J1 L M1 M2 N O P Q R1 R2 S1 S2 U2 W Z(c,d,e,g,i,j,k,p,q,u,w)
Agency and Fixed Fee Interview undertaken
Ptr: Ellis, Mr Tom . . . . . Jan 1984
Williamson, Mr Andrew . . . . . Jan 1993

BAYLEY LAW LTD (BYL) ‡
1st Floor The Bayley New Bailey Street Salford Greater Manchester M3 5AX
Tel: 0870 837 3300 *Fax:* 0870 837 3320 *Dx:* 727754 MANCHESTER
List of partners: L Goldstein
Work: B2 O
Legal Aid undertaken
Dir: Goldstein, Mr Lawrence . . . . . Oct 1994

BRANTON BRIDGE ‡
Second Floor Cloister House Salford Greater Manchester M3 5AG
Tel: 0161 834 2888

CHANCE HUNTER SOLICITORS LLP ‡
28 The Crescent Salford Greater Manchester M5 4PF
Tel: 0845 478 6354 *Fax:* 0161 877 1201
E-mail: info@chancehunter.co.uk

CLIFFORD POOLE & CO ‡
54 Fitzwarren Street Salford Greater Manchester M6 5JF
Tel: 0161 736 0160 *Fax:* 0161 736 2416
E-mail: jennydunlop@cliffordpoole.co.uk
List of partners: M J Poole
Work: D1 K1 N Q S1 W
Agency, Advocacy, Legal Aid undertaken, Legal Aid Franchise and Member of Accident Line
SPr: Poole, Mr Martin Joseph BSc . . . . . *Jun 1976
Ast: Dunlop, Ms Jennifer Mary LLB . . . . . *Apr 1975

GHUMAN SOLICITORS ‡
Technology House Lissadel Street Salford Greater Manchester M6 6AP
Tel: 0161 278 2562 *Fax:* 0161 278 2542
E-mail: enquiries@ghumansolicitors.co.uk

KRISTINA HARRISON
2 City Point 156 Chapel Street Salford Greater Manchester M3 6BF
Tel: 0161 832 7766 *Fax:* 0161 834 4393
E-mail: mail@kristinaharrisonsolicitors.co.uk

GARETH HUGHES & CO ‡
11 Blackfriars Road Salford Greater Manchester M3 7AG
Tel: 0161 832 3562 *Fax:* 0161 819 5255
Emergency telephone 0161 832 3562 / 01663 745683
Work: G H
Emergency Action, Agency, Advocacy, Fixed Fee Interview and Legal Aid undertaken

KHF SOLICITORS LIMITED ‡
208 Chapel Street Salford Greater Manchester M3 6BY
Tel: 0161 832 6677 *Fax:* 0161 839 3156 *Dx:* 719391 SALFORD
E-mail: mail@khfs.com

KLIEN & CO ‡
Room 6 399 Bury New Road Salford Greater Manchester M7 2BT
Tel: 0161 708 0815

HEIDI MAGUIRE ASSOCIATES ‡
1 The Malt House Deva Centre Salford Greater Manchester M3 7BD
Tel: 0161 828 3030

MAIDMENTS
River House 22 The Crescent Salford Greater Manchester M5 4PF
Tel: 0870 403 4000 *Fax:* 0845 017 6633
Emergency telephone 0870 403 4000
E-mail: serious@maidments.co.uk
Office: Birmingham, Bolton, Sale
Work: B2 G H J1 K1 K3 N Q

 See p112 for the Key to Work Categories & other symbols

Agency, Advocacy, Fixed Fee Interview, Legal Aid undertaken and Legal Aid Franchise
Ptr: Maidment, Mr Allan Leslie LLB(Hons) . . . . *Nov 1976
Sutton, Miss Lindsay Cathryn BA; CPE; LSF(York) . . *Oct 1994

A B MARSH SOLICITORS ‡
114 Chapel Street Salford Greater Manchester M3 5DW
Tel: 0161 839 2626 *Fax:* 0161 831 9162
Emergency telephone 0161 839 2626
E-mail: andrew.marsh@abmsolicitor.co.uk
List of partners: A B Marsh, D C P Mullarkey
Work: B2 C1 C2 D1 D2 E G H J1 K1 K3 M1 M2 N Q S1 S2 V Z(b,g,p)
Emergency Action, Advocacy, Fixed Fee Interview, Legal Aid undertaken and Legal Aid Franchise
Ptr: Marsh, Mr Andrew Baines LLB(Hons) . . . . *Feb 1990
Mullarkey, Mr Daimian C P . . . . *Nov 2001

MORGAN BROWN & CAHILL SOLICITORS
10 Bexley Square Salford Greater Manchester M3 6BZ
Tel: 0161 834 6662
Office: London WC2, Manchester

O'REILLY'S SOLICITORS LIMITED ‡
196 Chapel Street Salford Greater Manchester M3 6BY
Tel: 0161 819 5999 *Fax:* 0161 819 5900

ROSSLEGAL LLP ‡
9 Oakwell Drive Salford Greater Manchester M7 4PY
Tel: 0161 720 7200 / 0845 612 0222 *Fax:* 0161 278 0200

SALISBURY, Wiltshire

THE AUSTRENG PARTNERSHIP ‡
Wick Barn Salisbury Wiltshire SP3 6NW

WILLIAM BACHE ‡
The Clock Tower 4 Oakridge Office Park Whaddon Salisbury Wiltshire SP5 3HT
Tel: 01722 713370 *Fax:* 01722 711719 *Dx:* 124686 SALISBURY 3
Office: London EC1

BATT BROADBENT ‡
Minster Chambers 42-44 Castle Street Salisbury Wiltshire SP1 3TX
Tel: 01722 411141 *Fax:* 01722 411566 *Dx:* 58000 SALISBURY
E-mail: service@battbroadbent.co.uk
List of partners: S E de Candole, A T L Hart, A Johnson
Languages: French
Work: A1 B1 C1 C2 C3 D1 D2 E F1 J1 J2 K1 L N O Q R1 S1 S2 T1 T2 W Z(c,d,e,f,l,r,x)
Emergency Action, Agency, Advocacy and Fixed Fee Interview undertaken
Ptr: de Candole, Ms Susan E MA(Cantab) Deputy Diocesan Registrar . . . . *§Mar 1987
Hart, Mr Andrew T L LLB(Lond) . . . . *§Nov 1988
Johnson, Mr Andrew MA; LLB(Cantab) Diocesan Registrar; Bishop's Legal Secretary . . . . *§Jun 1974
Ast: Sutherland, Mr Phillip Wayne LLB. . . . . *Mar 1989
Con: Broadbent, Mr F Michael MA(Cantab) . . . . *§Jun 1963

BONALLACK & BISHOP ‡
Rougemont House Rougemont Close Manor Road Salisbury Wiltshire SP1 1LY
Tel: 01722 422300 *Fax:* 01722 422121 *Dx:* 58017 SALISBURY
E-mail: tim.bishop@bishopslaw.com
List of partners: T J Bishop, C D Carnegy
Office: Amesbury, Andover, Verwood
Languages: French
Work: A1 A2 A3 B1 B2 C1 C2 D1 D2 E F1 F2 G H I J1 J2 K1 K2 K3 K4 L N O P Q R1 R2 S1 S2 T1 T2 U2 W Z(c,e,h,k,l,o,p,q,r,z)
Emergency Action, Agency, Advocacy, Fixed Fee Interview, Legal Aid undertaken and Legal Aid Franchise
Ptr: Bishop, Mr Timothy John LLB. . . . . *Feb 1988
Carnegy, Mr Colin D MA(Oxon) Notary Public . . . . *§Dec 1968
Asoc: Broomfield, Miss Denise. . . . . Dec 1991
Jenner, Mr Alan LLB(Hons) . . . . *Nov 1986
Mills, Mr Nigel BA(Hons)(Philosophy) . . . . Mar 1983
Pownall, Mr Anthony LLB(Hons). . . . . Apr 1994
Ast: Bassett, Ms Gillian Alexandra BA(Hons). . . . . Oct 1995
Walters, Ms Georgina Mary LLB(Hons). . . . . Nov 2003
Con: Chudleigh, Mr Jonathan Paul . . . . Jan 1974
Trapnell, Mrs Laura K BA(Hons); CPE; LPC. . . . . . *Jul 1997

CATCHPOLE LAW ‡
Hill House Sixpenny Handley Salisbury Wiltshire SP5 5NT
Tel: 01725 552788 / 07920 585944
E-mail: michael@catchpolelaw.com

DAVID H N DAVIES ‡
(incorporating Nodder & Trethowan)
50 High Street Salisbury Wiltshire SP1 2NT
Tel: 01722 322272 *Fax:* 01722 333275 *Dx:* 58040 SALISBURY
E-mail: law@daviddavies.co.uk
List of partners: D H N Davies
Work: A1 E L R1 S1 W

NATALIE GAMBLE ASSOCIATES ‡
19 Glasshouse Studios Fryern Court Road Burgate Salisbury Wiltshire SP6 1QX
Tel: 0844 357 1602 *Fax:* 01425 656789
E-mail: hello@nataliegambleassociates.co.uk

RICHARD GRIFFITHS & CO ‡
86 Crane Street Salisbury Wiltshire SP1 2QD
Tel: 01722 329966 *Fax:* 01722 329988 *Dx:* 58011 SALISBURY
Emergency telephone 07659 136196
E-mail: info@richardgriffithsandco.com
List of partners: R L Griffiths, D J Lee, S D Pritchard, A J Stafford
Office: Chippenham, New Milton
Work: D1 D2 E F1 G H J1 K1 K2 K3 L S1 S2 W Z(g,l,m,p)
Emergency Action, Agency, Advocacy, Fixed Fee Interview and Legal Aid undertaken
Ptr: Griffiths, Mr Richard L MA(Oxon) . . . . *§Jul 1975
Ast: Baron, Miss Anne BSc(Hons) . . . . *Sep 1996
George, Mr Francis A LLB . . . . Aug 1999
Redhead, Mr Nicholas John BA(Oxon) . . . . Oct 1991
Tritschler, Mr Paul LLB . . . . *Apr 1975
Williams, Mr Richard LLB . . . . Jan 2000

HANNAFORDS ‡
126 The Borough Downton Salisbury Wiltshire SP5 3LT
Tel: 01725 514632

N C MORRIS & CO
Closegate House 47 High Street Salisbury Wiltshire SP1 2PB
Tel: 01722 415215 *Fax:* 01722 415216 *Dx:* 58046 SALISBURY 1
E-mail: charles.joly@ncmorris.co.uk
Office: London SW7
Work: E S1 S2
Ptr: Joly, Mr Charles R R . . . . Feb 1981

PARKER BULLEN ‡
45 Castle Street Salisbury Wiltshire SP1 3SS
Tel: 01722 412000 *Fax:* 01722 411822 *Dx:* 58001 SALISBURY
List of partners: G Bevan-Thomas, T J Crarer, I Deverill, P M Gower, P G Hatvany, R P Le Masurier, J M Lello, R W Sykes, N J Turner
Office: Andover
Languages: French
Work: A1 B1 C1 C2 D1 E F1 G H J1 K1 K2 K3 K4 L M1 N O Q R1 R2 S1 S2 T1 T2 V W X Z(b,c,d,e,f,i,j,k,l)
Agency and Advocacy undertaken
Ptr: Crarer, Mr Timothy J BA(Cantab) . . . . *Oct 1983
Gower, Mrs Patricia Maureen BSc(Hons) . . . . . . *§Nov 1979
Hatvany, Mr Peter G LLB . . . . *May 1991
Le Masurier, Mr Richard P LLB(Leics). . . . . *§Jul 1977
Lello, Mr John Mark LLB(Sheff) Notary Public . . . . . *Dec 1989
Sykes, Mr Robert W MA(Oxon) . . . . *Aug 1977
Turner, Mr Nicholas James . . . . *Oct 1984
Ast: Holyer, Miss Rosanne Teresa LLB; LPC. . . . . *Sep 2009
Le Masurier, Miss Olivia Jane BA(Hons); CPE; LPC. . *Nov 2010
Rundle, Ms Tamara . . . . Sep 2007
Tranah, Mr Nigel J BA(Oxon) . . . . *§Jun 1977
Wankling, Ms Stephanie Jane LLB . . . . *Feb 2008

PHILLIPS & CO ‡
36 High Street Salisbury Wiltshire SP1 2NT
Tel: 01722 321666 *Fax:* 01722 422258 *Dx:* 58027 SALISBURY
Emergency telephone 07733 880062
List of partners: D M Phillips, R Tan
Languages: French, Norwegian
Work: A1 B1 C1 C2 C3 D1 E F1 G H J1 K1 L M1 M2 N O P Q R1 S1 V W Z(b,c,i,j,k,l,m)
Emergency Action, Agency, Advocacy, Fixed Fee Interview, Legal Aid undertaken, Legal Aid Franchise and Member of Accident Line
Ptr: Phillips, Mr Derek M. . . . . *§Apr 1970
Tan, Mr Raymond LLB . . . . *Aug 1990
Asoc: Tier, Mr Jeremy Julian LLB(Hons); BSc(Hons). . . . . Dec 2005
Ast: Chapman, Mr David Paul MA . . . . *Sep 2000
Ritter, Mr Stephen BA(Hons)(Law) . . . . *Jan 1981
Sandu, Mr Lucian LLB . . . . *Sep 2009
Saunders, Mr John Charles MA(Oxon) . . . . *Nov 1991

RANSON HOUGHTON
(incorporating David G Bingham; Ranson and Walsh; Houghton Russell-Smith)
23 Brown Street Salisbury Wiltshire SP1 2AS
Tel: 01722 328871 *Fax:* 01722 323542 *Dx:* 58035 SALISBURY
Emergency telephone 01264 324172
E-mail: rh@rhsolicitors.co.uk
Office: Andover, Basingstoke
Work: A1 C1 D1 D2 E F1 K1 K3 M1 N O P Q S1 S2 V W
Emergency Action, Agency, Advocacy, Fixed Fee Interview, Legal Aid undertaken and Member of Accident Line
Ptr: Houghton, Mr Henry Fergus. . . . . *Dec 1973
Con: Russell-Smith, Mr Michael R . . . . *§Dec 1969

SAMPSON COWARD LLP ‡
2 St Thomas's Square Salisbury Wiltshire SP1 1BA
Tel: 01722 410664 *Fax:* 01722 410884 *Dx:* 58020 SALISBURY 1
E-mail: mail@sampsoncoward.co.uk
List of partners: D J Coward, T G M H Coward, V L Langdown, J R Sampson
Work: D1 F1 J1 K1 L Q S1 W
Emergency Action, Agency, Advocacy, Fixed Fee Interview and Legal Aid Franchise
Ptr: Coward, Mr David John . . . . *Oct 1986
Coward, Mrs Tina Gillian May Hatton . . . . Nov 1986
Sampson, Mr John Richard MA(Cantab). . . . . *Jun 1972
Langdown, Vicky Louise FILEx . . . . .NSP

STODDART & COMPANY ‡
Courtyard Chambers 21a New Street Salisbury Wiltshire SP1 2PH
Tel: 01722 417111 *Fax:* 01722 417113 *Dx:* 58006 SALISBURY
Work: K1 Q S1 S2

TRETHOWANS LLP ‡
London Road Office Park London Road Salisbury Wiltshire SP1 3HP
Tel: 01722 412512 *Fax:* 01722 411300 *Dx:* 1555610 SALISBURY 7
E-mail: info@trethowans.com
List of partners: R A J Chapman, R J Cook, K I Farmaner, N H Gent, D P Healy, G R Lane, J Loney, P Longman, C M MacRae, C E Matthews, A J Mercer, M J Messent, C M E Probert, S J Rhodes, N S Richards, J S Rogerson, Y L Rooke, K I Singleton, M J Tarrant-Smith, G Treagust, C Twaits, M W Watson, E R Webbe, C L Whiteley
Office: Southampton
Work: A1 C1 C2 C3 E F1 I J1 K1 K3 K4 L N O P Q R1 R2 S1 S2 T1 T2 U2 W X Z(e,l,o,p,q,r,x,za)
Advocacy, Fixed Fee Interview, Legal Aid undertaken, Legal Aid Franchise and Member of Accident Line
Ptr: Chapman, Mr Robert Arthur James LLB. . . . . Nov 1993
Healy, Mr David Paul BSc(Medical Physics); DipLaw; LPC . . . . *§May 1998
Mercer, Mr Andrew James LLB . . . . *Aug 1989
Probert, Ms Caroline M E MA(Cantab) . . . . *Oct 1987
Richards, Mrs Nicola Susan. . . . . *Oct 1995
Singleton, Mr Kimberley I BA . . . . *Nov 1985
Tarrant-Smith, Mrs Miriam Jane . . . . Oct 1995
Treagust, Mr Garry . . . . Nov 1992
Webbe, Mrs Elizabeth R LLB . . . . *Oct 1989
Whiteley, Mr Christopher Louis BA(Hons)(Law) . . . *Oct 1994
Asoc: Carter, Miss Clare MA. . . . . *Oct 1997
Foster, Miss Suzanne Jane LLB(Hons) . . . . Sep 2003
Higham, Mr Timothy John LLB Judges Prize - University of Hertfordshire . . . . Sep 1997
Jones, Mr David BA(Hons); CPE; LPC . . . . Sep 2000
Perugini, Mrs Karen Jane LLB. . . . . Dec 2001
Thorpe, Mr Marcus Somerled CPE . . . . Sep 2004
Ast: Culverhouse, Mrs Julie LLB(Hons) . . . . *Oct 1990
Freeman, Mr Matthew BA(Hons)(History); GDL; LPC . *Nov 2008
Gillett, Mrs Frances LLB. . . . . *Nov 2009

Hammersley, Mrs Johanna Maria LLB. . . . . May 2009
Hartigan, Mr Tom BA . . . . Apr 2007
Humphery, Mr James H Chairman of the General SYNOP . . . . *§May 1981
Smith, Miss Nicola Jayne GDL; LPC . . . . Sep 2007

WHITEHEAD VIZARD ‡
Close Gate Chambers 60 High Street Salisbury Wiltshire SP1 2PQ
Tel: 01722 412141 *Fax:* 01722 411177 *Dx:* 58007 SALISBURY
E-mail: enq@whitehead-vizard.co.uk
List of partners: E J Hendry, A J Hodder, S J Kenmir, C G Lush, P M Lush, C Parsons
Work: A1 A2 A3 B1 C1 C2 C3 E F1 I J1 K1 K3 K4 L M1 M2 N O P Q R1 R2 S1 S2 T1 T2 W X Z(k,l,q,r)
Emergency Action, Agency and Advocacy undertaken
Ptr: Hendry, Mrs Elizabeth Jean LLB. . . . . *Nov 2002
Hodder, Mr Andrew John . . . . *§Jun 1979
Kenmir, Mr Stephen John BSc(Hons) . . . . *Mar 1991
Lush, Mr Christopher G . . . . *§Dec 1972
Lush, Mrs Patricia M . . . . *§Nov 1971
Parsons, Miss Caroline LLB(Hons) . . . . *Jul 2000

WILSONS SOLICITORS LLP ‡
Steynings House Summerlock Approach Salisbury Wiltshire SP2 7RJ
Tel: 01722 412412 *Fax:* 01722 411500 *Dx:* 25003 SALISBURY 1
E-mail: enquiries@wilsonslaw.com
Office: London WC2
Languages: Dutch, French, German, Italian, Spanish
Work: A2 C1 C2 C3 E F1 F2 J1 K1 K2 K3 L O Q R1 R2 S1 S2 T1 T2 U2 W Z(d,e,l,n,q,w,za)

SALTASH, Cornwall

BLIGHT SKINNARD ‡
97-99 Fore Street Saltash Cornwall PL12 6AH
Tel: 01752 842141 *Fax:* 01752 843966 *Dx:* 82351 SALTASH
E-mail: enq@blightskinnard.co.uk
List of partners: D T Elson, K Pearson
Languages: French
Work: A1 D1 D2 E F1 K1 K3 L O Q S1 S2 V W Z(l)
Emergency Action, Agency, Advocacy, Fixed Fee Interview, Legal Aid undertaken and Legal Aid Franchise
Ptr: Elson, Miss Deborah T . . . . *Feb 2001
Pearson, Mr Kenneth LLB. . . . . *Nov 1974

NICHOLLS & SAINSBURY ‡
131-135 Fore Street Saltash Cornwall PL12 6AB
Tel: 01752 846116 *Fax:* 01752 844007 *Dx:* 82350 SALTASH
E-mail: n_and_s_uk@yahoo.co.uk
List of partners: C E Nicholls, J L Sainsbury
Work: D1 D2 E F1 J1 K1 L S1 S2 V W Z(l)
Emergency Action, Agency, Advocacy and Fixed Fee Interview undertaken
Ptr: Nicholls, Mr Christopher E. . . . . *§Aug 1979
Sainsbury, Ms Janet L BA(Hons) . . . . *§Oct 1987

WHITEFORD CROCKER
(incorporating Bellingham & Crocker)
165 Fore Street Saltash Cornwall PL12 6AG
Tel: 01752 843134 *Fax:* 01752 840017 *Dx:* 82360 SALTASH
E-mail: mep@whitefordcrocker.co.uk
Office: Ivybridge, Plymouth, Plympton
Work: A1 B1 C1 C2 E F1 J2 K1 K2 L N O Q R2 S1 S2 W Z(c,d,l,p,q,w)
Emergency Action, Agency, Advocacy, Fixed Fee Interview, Legal Aid undertaken, Legal Aid Franchise and Member of Accident Line
Ast: Pepper, Miss Michelle Erin LLB . . . . Jan 2011

SALTBURN-BY-THE-SEA, Redcar & Cleveland

MARTIN L GROVE ‡
81 High Street Skelton Saltburn-by-the-Sea Redcar & Cleveland TS12 2DY
Tel: 01287 650675 *Fax:* 01287 652187 *Dx:* 61720 SKELTON
E-mail: martin.grove1@virgin.net
List of partners: M L Grove
Office: Middlesbrough
Work: A1 B1 C1 D1 E F1 G H J1 K1 L M1 N P R1 S1 T1 V W Z(a,b,c,h,j,k,l,n,o,s)
Agency and Advocacy undertaken
Ptr: Grove, Mr Martin L LLB . . . . *Jan 1979

IMLAW ‡
136 Marshall Drive Brotton Saltburn-by-the-Sea Redcar & Cleveland TS12 2UW
Tel: 0870 720 3477

MILES HUTCHINSON & LITHGOW
(incorporating W Stanley Smith & Co)
27 Milton Street Saltburn-by-the-Sea Redcar & Cleveland TS12 1DJ
Tel: 01287 623049 / 622056 *Fax:* 01287 624406
Office: Middlesbrough
Work: B1 D1 E F1 G H K1 L N Q R1 S1 V W Z(g,i,l)
Emergency Action, Agency, Advocacy, Fixed Fee Interview, Legal Aid undertaken and Legal Aid Franchise
Ptr: Gowans, Mr Alastair J LLB . . . . *Oct 1978
Grant, Mr Fergus M LLB(Lond) . . . . *Jun 1980

SANDBACH, Cheshire

BEESTON SHENTON
Lea House 5 Middlewich Road Sandbach Cheshire CW11 1XR
Tel: 01270 750057
Office: Knutsford, Newcastle under Lyme

BROWN & CORBISHLEY
11 The Commons Sandbach Cheshire CW11 1EG
Tel: 01270 768033 *Fax:* 01270 768396 *Dx:* 15659 SANDBACH
Emergency telephone 01270 768033
E-mail: k.carroll@brownandcorbishley.co.uk
Office: Newcastle under Lyme
Languages: French
Work: B1 C1 C2 C3 E F1 G H J1 K1 L M1 M2 N O P Q R1 S1 S2 T1 T2 V W Z(l)

Emergency Action, Agency, Advocacy, Fixed Fee Interview, Legal Aid undertaken, Legal Aid Franchise and Member of Accident Line
Ptr: Carroll, Mr Kevin LLB . . . . *Mar 1985
Ast: Carroll, Mrs Susan LLB . . . . *Oct 1984

BUTCHER & BARLOW LLP
31 Middlewich Road Sandbach Cheshire CW11 1HW
Tel: 01270 762521 *Fax:* 01270 764795 *Dx:* 15655 SANDBACH
E-mail: enquiries@butcher-barlow.co.uk
Office: Bramhall, Bury (2 offices), Frodsham, Leigh, Northwich, Prestwich, Runcorn (2 offices), Tyldesley
Work: A1 B1 C1 C2 C3 D1 E F1 J1 K1 K3 K4 L M1 M2 N O P Q R1 R2 S1 S2 T1 T2 V W Z(c,d,e,j,l,m,o,p,q,r,t)
Emergency Action, Agency, Advocacy, Fixed Fee Interview, Legal Aid undertaken and Member of Accident Line
Ptr: Barlow, Mr Charles J M Notary Public . . . . *Nov 1982
Gleave, Miss Angela Simone BA(Hons) . . . . *Feb 2002
Hyatt, Mr John R . . . . *Oct 1984
Shelmerdine, Mr Jonathan M . . . . *Jan 1975
Walker, Mrs Le-Ann. . . . . *Nov 1999

DIXON RIGBY KEOGH ‡
34 Crewe Road Sandbach Cheshire CW11 4NF
Tel: 01270 766550 *Fax:* 01270 766471
List of partners: T H Caldecott, D R Cowgill, S J Masters, L K McMaster, A Page, P W Palmer, N G Parson, M K Sumner
Office: Middlewich, Northwich, Winsford
Work: A1 B1 C1 C2 D1 E F1 G H J1 K1 L N P Q R1 S1 T1 T2 W Z(c,d,l,n,t)
Emergency Action and Advocacy undertaken
Ptr: Palmer, Mr Philip W BA(Law) . . . . *§Jul 1979
Ast: Brown, Miss Julia . . . . Sep 2007
Eeles, Mrs Mandy BA. . . . . *Oct 1993

POOLE ALCOCK ‡
(incorporating Timperley & Co)
6 Middlewich Road Sandbach Cheshire CW11 1DL
Tel: 01270 762325 *Fax:* 01270 768075 *Dx:* 15651 SANDBEACH
Emergency telephone 01270 872994
E-mail: sandbach@poolealcock.co.uk
List of partners: P Boston, M C Bracegirdle, D M Gaut, G I Goodwin, D E Harrison, P R Harrison, S A Jarrett, S P Markham, A Roberts, I M Rose
Office: Alsager, Chester, Congleton, Crewe (2 offices), Nantwich, Northwich, Warrington
Languages: French, German
Work: A1 B1 C1 D1 E F1 G H J1 K1 L M1 N P R1 S1 T1 V W Z(a,b,c,d,e,f,g,h,i,j,k,p,s,t)
Emergency Action, Agency, Advocacy, Fixed Fee Interview, Legal Aid undertaken and Member of Accident Line
Ptr: Bracegirdle, Mr Michael C LLB(Warw). . . . . *Jun 1980
Harrison, Mr David E Chairman of the Social Security Tribunals Notary Public . . . . *Mar 1963
Harrison, Mr Philip R LLB. . . . . Oct 1990
Ast: Markham, Mr Shane P LLB(Hons). . . . . Apr 1997

TINSDILLS
47 High Street Sandbach Cheshire CW11 1FT
Tel: 01270 761111 *Fax:* 01270 768981 *Dx:* 15669 SANDBACH
E-mail: lawyers@tinsdills.co.uk
Office: Hanley, Leek, Newcastle under Lyme
Work: A1 A2 A3 B1 B2 C1 C2 D1 D2 E F1 F2 J1 K1 K2 K3 K4 L N O P Q R1 R2 S1 S2 T1 T2 V W Z(b,c,d,e,f,g,h,j,l,m,n,o,p,q,r,s,t)

SANDOWN, Isle of Wight

CARELESS & KEMP
2a Sandown Road Lake Sandown Isle of Wight PO36 9JP
Tel: 01983 400456 *Fax:* 01983 400440 *Dx:* 99225 VENTOR
E-mail: carelessandkemp@carelessandkemp.co.uk
Office: Ventnor
Work: D1 D2 E J1 K1 K4 L N Q S1 S2 W Z(d)
Emergency Action, Agency, Advocacy, Fixed Fee Interview and Legal Aid undertaken
Ptr: Kemp, Mrs Lesley Ann . . . . *Apr 1999
Ast: Brown, Miss Sandra LLB(Hons). . . . . Jan 1990

JEROMES
11 High Street Sandown Isle of Wight PO36 8DA
Tel: 01983 402026 *Fax:* 01983 407490 *Dx:* 56452 SANDOWN (IOW)
E-mail: jeanettecousins@jeromelaw.co.uk
Office: Newport, Shanklin
Work: C1 E J1 K4 L O Q R1 R2 S1 S2 W Z(l,q)
Dir: Whittle, Mr Adrian John LLB. . . . . *May 1981

LAWDIT SOLICITORS ‡
Bran Cottage Yaverland Road Sandown Isle of Wight PO36 8QN
Tel: 01983 402294

SANDWICH, Kent

EMMERSON BROWN & BROWN
1 Potter Street Sandwich Kent CT13 9DR
Tel: 01304 612444 *Fax:* 01304 614780 *Dx:* 200500 SANDWICH
Office: Deal, Dover
Work: A1 B1 C1 D1 E F1 G H J1 K1 L M1 N P R1 S1 T1 V W Z(k,l,s)
Agency, Advocacy, Fixed Fee Interview and Legal Aid undertaken
Ptr: Turner, Mr John A. . . . . *§May 1977

SANDY, Bedfordshire

MACKENZIE JOHNSON SOLICITORS ‡
1 Ivy Close Tempsford Sandy Bedfordshire SG19 2AU
Tel: 01767 641209 *Fax:* 01234 420359

WOODFINES LLP
6 Bedford Road Sandy Bedfordshire SG19 1EN
Tel: 01767 680251 *Fax:* 01767 691775 *Dx:* 47801 SANDY
E-mail: mail@woodfines.co.uk
Office: Bedford, Bletchley, Cambridge, Milton Keynes
Languages: French
Work: A1 A3 B1 C1 C2 C3 D1 E F1 F2 J1 K1 K2 K4 L M1 M2 N O P Q R1 S1 S2 T1 T2 V W Z(c,d,e,i,j,k,l,m,n,o,p,x)
Emergency Action, Agency, Advocacy, Fixed Fee Interview, Legal Aid undertaken, Legal Aid Franchise and Member of Accident Line
Ptr: Frost, Mr Adrian Nicholas BA(Hons). . . . . Apr 1981
Hall, Mr Brian Allan LLB(Lond) Under Sheriff of Bedfordshire, High Court Enforcement Officer Notary Public. . . . . *Nov 1972
Mount, Mr Peter J TD . . . . *§Jun 1971
Mem: Salter, Mr Ashley LLB. . . . . Nov 1990
Asoc: Bennett, Mr Brian Charles. . . . . *Oct 1980
Feeney, Ms Elizabeth BA . . . . Jan 1990
Quarmby, Mrs Lynne . . . . *Oct 1982
Con: Sills, Mr Timothy M DL Geoffrey Howard Watson Prize*Nov 1966

SAWBRIDGEWORTH, Hertfordshire

HAZELL & CO ‡
Churchgate Chambers 1a Church Street Sawbridgeworth Hertfordshire CM21 9AB
Tel: 01279 726604 *Fax:* 01279 726977
List of partners: S N Hazell
Languages: French
Work: N O P Q Z(c,j,q)
SPr: Hazell, Ms Sharon N LLB . . . . Nov 1982
Ast: Bruce, Mrs Kathleen Alexandra LLB. . . . . *Apr 1990

MACLEISH LITTLESTONE COWAN
36 Bell Street Sawbridgeworth Hertfordshire CM21 9AN
Tel: 01279 722453 *Fax:* 01279 600256
Office: Barking, Ilford, London E11
Work: B1 C1 E G H K1 M1 P S1 W
Agency, Fixed Fee Interview and Legal Aid undertaken

TWG LTD ‡
Allen House The Maltings Sawbridgeworth Hertfordshire CM21 9JX
Tel: 01279 600003
E-mail: johnmasfield@thewillgroup.co.uk

SAWSTON, Cambridgeshire

ADAMS HARRISON
43 High Street Sawston Cambridgeshire CB22 3BG
Tel: 01223 832939 *Fax:* 01223 837310 *Dx:* 91950 SAWSTON
E-mail: enquiries@adams-harrison.co.uk
Office: Haverhill, Saffron Walden

SAWTRY, Cambridgeshire

JEFFREY MILLS
(incorporating Merrick & Co)
The Green Sawtry Cambridgeshire PE28 5ST
Tel: 01487 832404 *Fax:* 01487 832659 *Dx:* 100302 ST NEOTS
E-mail: lawatlills@aol.com
Office: St Ives, St Neots
Work: B1 C1 E F1 G J1 K1 K3 L M1 M2 N P Q S1 S2 V W Z(r)
Agency, Fixed Fee Interview, Legal Aid undertaken and Member of Accident Line

SAXMUNDHAM, Suffolk

H T ARGENT & SON ‡
Old Bank House Market Place Saxmundham Suffolk IP17 1EL
Tel: 01728 602323 *Fax:* 01728 603660 *Dx:* 42000 SAXMUNDHAM
List of partners: A G Clarke
Office: Aldeburgh
Work: A1 C1 C2 E L S1 S2 T1 T2 W
Ptr: Clarke, Mr Alan Gerald . . . . *§Dec 1963
Ast: Mackinnon, Mrs Linda LLB . . . . *Apr 1974

PULHAM & CO ‡
Egmere House Market Place Saxmundham Suffolk IP17 1AG
Tel: 01728 602084 *Fax:* 01728 603739 *Dx:* 42002 SAXMUNDHAM
E-mail: jsp@pulham.co.uk
List of partners: J S Pulham
Languages: French, German
Work: B1 C1 C2 C3 E K4 L R2 S1 S2 T1 T2 W Z(c,d,l)
Fixed Fee Interview and Legal Aid Franchise
Ptr: Pulham, Mr John Sinclair LLB Clerk to General Commissioners . . . . *§May 1974

SCARBOROUGH, North Yorkshire

MARGARET ADAMS LAW
24 Alma Square Scarborough North Yorkshire YO11 1JR
Tel: 01723 372237 *Fax:* 01723 354346
E-mail: info@adamsscottlaw.co.uk
Office: Grimsby, Malton

APPLEBY & CO ‡
15 Whin Bank Scarborough North Yorkshire YO12 5LD
Tel: 01723 351994 / 07891 511152 *Fax:* 0560 315 2247
E-mail: info@applebyandco.com
info@applebyandco.com

B&C SOLICITORS - THE LAW SHOP ‡
26/28 Northway Scarborough North Yorkshire YO11 1JL
Tel: 01723 379777 *Fax:* 01723 379888 *Dx:* 61851 SCARBOROUGH
E-mail: lawshop@axis-connect.com
Work: D1 D2 E G H K1 N O Q S1 S2 W Z(l)

BEDWELL WATTS & CO ‡
32 Queen Street Scarborough North Yorkshire YO11 1HD
Tel: 01723 373356 / 363553 *Fax:* 01723 375347
Dx: 61802 SCARBOROUGH
E-mail: postmaster@bedwellwatts.co.uk
List of partners: R J C Creasey, H Watts
Work: A1 C1 D1 E F1 G H J1 K1 L M1 M2 N R1 S1 T2 W X Z(d,i,l,m,t)
Emergency Action, Agency, Advocacy, Fixed Fee Interview, Legal Aid undertaken and Legal Aid Franchise
Ptr: Creasey, Mr Richard J C LLB . . . . *Jun 1978
Watts, Mr Hilary MA(Cantab) . . . . *Apr 1978
Asoc: Maynard, Mr Peter A D LLB(Lond) . . . . *Feb 1979
Ast: Fountain, Mrs Jayne Taylor . . . . *Nov 1993
White, Mrs Susan V. . . . . *Oct 1993
Con: Bell, Mr Richard I BA(Dunelm) . . . . *Jun 1972

BIRDSALL & SNOWBALL ‡
(incorporating Moody Beanland & Co; Eagle-Clarke & Co; England & Co)
10 York Place Scarborough North Yorkshire YO11 2NU
Tel: 01723 351351 *Fax:* 01723 507987 *Dx:* 61800 SCARBOROUGH
E-mail: post@birdsall-snowball.co.uk
List of partners: T C Cathcart, D Leathard, P Richardson
Office: Filey
Work: E K1 K3 K4 L O Q S1 S2 W Z(l)
Agency, Fixed Fee Interview and Legal Aid undertaken
Ptr: Leathard, Mr David LLB. . . . . *§Dec 1976
Richardson, Mr Paul LLB . . . . *Jul 2002
Ast: Colley, Mr Andrew. . . . . *May 2007
Price, Mr John Christopher LLB. . . . . *Jun 1978

M J HARRISON ‡
Gallows Hill Brompton-by-Sawdon Scarborough North Yorkshire YO13 9QF
Tel: 01723 865578 *Fax:* 01723 862287
List of partners: M J Harrison
SPr: Harrison, Mr Michael J LLB(Hons). . . . . *Dec 1972

HILL DEHGHAN SOLICITORS ‡
16 York Place Scarborough North Yorkshire YO11 2NP
Tel: 01723 360500 *Fax:* 01723 360503
Work: B1 C1 E F1 F2 J1 K1 K3 K4 L N O Q S1 S2 W Z(l)
Agency, Advocacy and Fixed Fee Interview undertaken

JEPSON & CO ‡
58 High Street Scarborough North Yorkshire YO13 9AL
Tel: 01723 859249 *Fax:* 01723 850249 *Dx:* 61816 SCARBOROUGH
Office: Scarborough
Work: A2 D1 E F1 G H J1 J2 K1 K3 K4 L P Q S1 S2 W Z(c)
Emergency Action, Agency, Advocacy, Legal Aid undertaken and Legal Aid Franchise

JEPSON & CO
16 Victoria Road Scarborough North Yorkshire YO11 1SD
Tel: 01723 341340 *Fax:* 01723 377744
Office: Scarborough

LONGSTAFF & MIDGLEY ‡
PO Box 41 2 Vernon Road Scarborough North Yorkshire YO11 2NJ
Tel: 01723 351751 *Fax:* 01723 371429
E-mail: mail@longstaff-midgleyltd.co.uk
List of partners: W J Longstaff, J P Midgley
Work: A1 D2 K1 K3 K4 L S1 S2 W
Ptr: Longstaff, Mr William Joe LLB(Leeds) . . . . Jun 1974
Midgley, Mr J Paul BA. . . . . May 1981

JOHN P MARTIN & CO ‡
Bank Chambers Albion Road Scarborough North Yorkshire YO11 2BT
Tel: 01723 500922 *Fax:* 01723 500556 *Dx:* 61808 SCARBOROUGH
E-mail: johnpmartinandco@btconnect.com
List of partners: B J Martin, J P Martin
Work: E K3 K4 L S1 S2 W
Ptr: Martin, Mr Benedict J BSc. . . . . *Sep 2002
Martin, Mr John P MA(Oxon) . . . . *§Dec 1970

NORTH YORKSHIRE LAW ‡
Albemarle Chambers Albemarle Crescent Scarborough North Yorkshire YO11 1LA
Tel: 01723 360001 *Fax:* 01723 353973
Emergency telephone 01723 374957
E-mail: info@northyorkshirelaw.com
List of partners: R C Boyd, I Cocker, T J Martin, J R Newton
Office: Helmsley, Whitby
Languages: French, Spanish
Work: A1 A2 B1 C1 C2 C3 D1 D2 E F1 G H J1 K1 K2 L M1 M2 N P Q R1 R2 S1 S2 T1 T2 V W Z(l,m,o,r)
Emergency Action, Agency, Advocacy, Fixed Fee Interview, Legal Aid undertaken and Legal Aid Franchise
Ptr: Boyd, Mr Richard C BA . . . . Aug 1980
Cocker, Mr Ian LLB . . . . *Dec 1979
Martin, Mrs Tracy Jane LLB(Hons) . . . . Nov 1999
Ast: Murray, Ms Tracy . . . . Sep 2001
Truefitt, Ms H Susan . . . . *§Jun 1971
Webster, Mrs Catherine S LLB . . . . Sep 1999

PINKNEY GRUNWELLS LAWYERS LLP ‡
(incorporating Atha Summers & Co)
64 Westborough Scarborough North Yorkshire YO11 1TS
Tel: 01723 352125 *Fax:* 01723 500023 *Dx:* 61807 SCARBOROUGH
E-mail: solicitor@pinkneygrunwells.co.uk
List of partners: G N Barrett, T A Bennion, Z L Colling, R E Dean, R L Grunwell, A J Harvey, H E Jackson, K Morris
Office: Bridlington, Filey, Whitby
Languages: French, German
Work: A1 C1 C2 D1 D2 E F1 F2 J1 K1 K2 K3 K4 L N O P Q R1 R2 S1 S2 T1 T2 W Z(c,l,n,p)
Agency, Advocacy and Legal Aid undertaken
Mem: Bennion, Ms Teresa Ann . . . . *Sep 1999
Colling, Miss Zoe Louise . . . . *Dec 2006
Grunwell, Mr Richard Lincoln . . . . *Jan 1977
Jackson, Ms Helen Elizabeth LLB. . . . . *May 2005
Morris, Mrs Katie . . . . *May 2005
Ast: Kidd, Miss Helen Mary BA(Hons) . . . . Jan 2000
Moss, Ms Victoria Eloise . . . . *Dec 2006
Con: Glenday, Miss Fiona Margaret BA(Law) . . . . *Nov 1981
Summers, Mr Martin William . . . . *Nov 1971

THORPE & CO ‡
17 Valley Bridge Parade Scarborough North Yorkshire YO11 2JX
Tel: 01723 364321 *Fax:* 01723 500459
Dx: 61811 SCARBOROUGH 1
Emergency telephone 01723 364321
E-mail: info@thorpeandco.com
List of partners: I R Brabbs, C D Burnett, L E Burnett, M A C Jefferies, S Mackinder, C A McNeill, J C Nickson, N J Shaw, F J Wray
Office: Filey, Malton, Whitby
Work: A1 B1 C1 D1 D2 E F1 G H J1 K1 K2 K3 L N Q S1 S2 T1 T2 V W Z(l,m,q)
Emergency Action, Agency, Advocacy, Fixed Fee Interview, Legal Aid undertaken, Legal Aid Franchise and Member of Accident Line
Ptr: Brabbs, Mr Ian R LLB. . . . . *Apr 1978
Burnett, Mr Carl David . . . . *Sep 1997
Burnett, Mrs Lorraine E. . . . . *Oct 1998

 See p112 for the Key to Work Categories & other symbols

McNeill, Mrs Catherine A LLB . . . . *Oct 1991
Wray, Miss Fiona Johan LLB(Leics); LLM . . . . *Nov 1992

TUBBS & CO ‡
106 Victoria Road Scarborough North Yorkshire YO11 1SL
Tel: 01723 352666 *Fax:* 01723 353666 *Dx:* 61818 SCARBOROUGH
E-mail: nick@tubbsandco.com

SCUNTHORPE, North Lincolnshire

BRADBURY ROBERTS & RABY ‡
Wadsworth House Laneham Street Scunthorpe North Lincolnshire DN15 6PB
Tel: 01724 854000 *Fax:* 01724 856213 *Dx:* 14704 SCUNTHORPE
Emergency telephone 01724 762876
E-mail: reception@brrlaw.co.uk
List of partners: D G Bradbury, N Cavanagh, I P Horner, C J Raby, S A Rands, J W Roberts, R M Taylor
Work: A1 C1 D1 D2 E F1 J1 J2 K1 K3 K4 L N O Q R1 S1 S2 T1 T2 V W Z(c,l,p,q)
Emergency Action, Agency, Advocacy, Fixed Fee Interview, Legal Aid undertaken, Legal Aid Franchise and Member of Accident Line
Ptr: Bradbury, Mr David G . . . . *Nov 1972
Cavanagh, Mrs Nicole BSc(Genetics) . . . . *Mar 2005
Horner, Mr Ian Paul LLB . . . . *Aug 1999
Raby, Mr Christopher J LLB(Lond) . . . . *Jul 1979
Rands, Mrs Susan Alexandra LLB(Hons) . . . . *Nov 1993
Roberts, Mr John W LLB(Nott'm) . . . . *Apr 1975
Taylor, Mr Robert Michael . . . . *May 1984
Asoc: Chapman, Ms Helen BSc(Econ); LLB . . . . *Oct 2010
Hirst, Miss Sarah Elizabeth BA(History); LLB . . . . *Aug 2009
Inman, Mr Matthew LLB . . . . *Aug 2009
Watson, Miss Michelle LLB . . . . *Nov 2011

Situated near to the Magistrates' and County Courts, we are experienced and well qualified to advise on a broad range of matters and hold Legal Aid franchises in Matrimonial, Family, and Employment.

HEPTONSTALLS LLP
72 Mary Street Scunthorpe North Lincolnshire DN15 6LA
Tel: 01724 289959 *Fax:* 01724 289965 *Dx:* 14732 SCUNTHORPE
E-mail: legal@heptonstalls.co.uk
Office: Goole, Howden, Pontefract (2 offices)
Work: A1 C1 E N O Q S2 W Z(r)
Legal Aid Franchise
Ptr: Ward-Lowery, Dr Nicholas J L BA(Hons); PhD. . . . *Sep 1999
Ast: Smith, Miss Heather Marie LLB . . . . Oct 2010

HETTS ‡
(incorporating Hett Davy & Co)
11 Wells Street Scunthorpe North Lincolnshire DN15 6HW
Tel: 01724 843287 *Fax:* 01724 280004 *Dx:* 14705 SCUNTHORPE
List of partners: M S Connell, P E Stevenson
Office: Scunthorpe
Work: A1 B1 C1 C2 C3 D1 E F1 G H J1 K1 L M1 M2 N O P Q R1 R2 S1 S2 T1 T2 V W Z(c,d,e,g,h,i,k,l,m,o,q,r,t,w)
Emergency Action, Agency, Advocacy, Fixed Fee Interview, Legal Aid undertaken, Legal Aid Franchise and Member of Accident Line
Ptr: Connell, Mr Michael S BA(Law) Clerk to Commissioner of Taxes . . . . *Dec 1975
Stevenson, Mr Paul E LLB . . . . *Jun 1980

HETTS
(incorporating Hett Davy & Co)
35 Oswald Road Scunthorpe North Lincolnshire DN15 7PN
Tel: 01724 270290 *Fax:* 01724 270279 *Dx:* 14705 SCUNTHORPE
Office: Scunthorpe
Work: A1 B1 C1 C2 C3 D1 E F1 G H J1 K1 L M1 M2 N O P Q R1 R2 S1 S2 T1 T2 V W Z(c,d,e,g,h,l,m,o,q,r,t,w)
Emergency Action, Agency, Advocacy, Fixed Fee Interview, Legal Aid undertaken, Legal Aid Franchise and Member of Accident Line
Ptr: Connell, Mr Michael S BA(Law) Clerk to Commissioner of Taxes . . . . *Dec 1975
Asoc: Heathcote, Mr Martyn Robert LLB(Hons) . . . . *Jul 1998

JOHN HOULT & CO ‡
1st Floor 250/252 Ashby High Street Ashby Scunthorpe North Lincolnshire DN16 2SE
Tel: 01724 281312 *Fax:* 01724 281315 *Dx:* 29824 ASHBY
Emergency telephone 01724 763016
E-mail: johnhoult@btconnect.com
List of partners: J F Hoult
Work: A1 D1 E K1 K3 K4 L S1 S2 W
Agency and Fixed Fee Interview undertaken
Ptr: Hoult, Mr John F BA . . . . *§Jul 1973

MASON BAGGOTT & GARTON ‡
13-19 Wells Street Scunthorpe North Lincolnshire DN15 6HN
Tel: 01724 868611 *Fax:* 01724 280433 *Dx:* 14707 SCUNTHORPE
Emergency telephone 01724 868611
E-mail: scunthorpe@lawlincs.co.uk
List of partners: R Garton, E Johns, J P Mason, R J S Mason, S L Regan
Office: Brigg, Epworth
Work: A1 B1 C1 D1 E F1 G H J1 K1 K3 L M1 N P R1 S1 S2 T1 V W Z(a,b,c,d,e,h,i,j,k,l,m,n,o,p,s,t,w)
Emergency Action, Agency, Advocacy, Fixed Fee Interview, Legal Aid undertaken, Legal Aid Franchise and Member of Accident Line
Ptr: Garton, Mr Rex . . . . *Nov 1971
Johns, Ms Emma LLB. . . . . *Nov 1992
Mason, Sir John P CBE. . . . . *Oct 1964
Mason, Mr Richard J S LLB(Hons) . . . . Jul 1998
Regan, Miss Sarah Louise LLB(Hons). . . . . *Apr 1999
Ast: Carlile, Miss Eve . . . . Mar 2004

PARCTON LAW CHAMBERS SOLICITORS ‡
47-49 Laneham Street Scunthorpe North Lincolnshire DN15 6PB
Tel: 01724 847711 *Fax:* 01724 864880 *Dx:* 14721 SCUNTHORPE
Emergency telephone 07957 116587
E-mail: grahampressler@aol.com
List of partners: G J Pressler
Languages: French
Work: A1 C1 E F1 G H J1 K1 L M1 N P S1 W
Emergency Action, Agency, Advocacy, Fixed Fee Interview and Legal Aid undertaken
Ptr: Pressler, Mr Graham John LLM(Hull); ACIS • . . . . . *Apr 1980

PEPPERELLS ‡
(incorporating Ivesons)
40 Doncaster Road Scunthorpe North Lincolnshire DN15 7RQ
Tel: 01724 871999 *Fax:* 01724 280154 *Dx:* 14713 SCUNTHORPE
E-mail: office@pepperells.com
List of partners: S J Davies, J R Gardham, R A Houghton, B S Pepperell, S W Pepperell
Office: Hull
Work: A1 A2 A3 B1 B2 B3 C1 C2 C3 D1 D2 E F1 F2 G H J1 J2 K1 K2 K3 L M1 M2 N O P Q R1 R2 S1 S2 T1 T2 V W X Z(c,d,e,f,h,i,j,k,l,m,n,o,p,q,r,s,t,u,w)
Emergency Action, Agency, Advocacy, Fixed Fee Interview, Legal Aid undertaken and Legal Aid Franchise
Ptr: Davies, Mr Simon James . . . . *Jun 1998
Gardham, Mr John Raymond LLB(Hons) . . . . . . *§Jun 1971
Houghton, Ms Rosemary Anne . . . . *Sep 1995
Pepperell, Mr Ben Stewart . . . . *Jul 2005
Pepperell, Mr Stewart William . . . . *Oct 1981
Asoc: Beckett, Mrs Jannina LLB(Hons) . . . . Apr 2008
Hall, Mrs Gaynor LLB(Hons) . . . . Oct 1995
Kemshall, Mr David . . . . Aug 2008
Musgrave, Miss Jennifer . . . . *Sep 2006
Watterson, Mr Mark LLB(Hons) . . . . Aug 2000

RIX MCLAREN ‡
45 Frances Street Scunthorpe North Lincolnshire DN15 6ER
Tel: 01724 872038 *Fax:* 01724 864260 *Dx:* 14709 SCUNTHORPE
E-mail: andyford@rixmclaren.freeserve.co.uk
List of partners: D C W Rix
Work: B2 G H J1 K1 K3 L N O Q S1 S2 W Z(q)
Agency and Legal Aid undertaken
SPr: Rix, Mr David C W LLB . . . . *Jul 1978

SERGEANT & COLLINS ‡
25 Oswald Road Scunthorpe North Lincolnshire DN15 7PS
Tel: 01724 864215 *Fax:* 01724 280253
List of partners: A W Pascoe
Languages: French, German
Work: A1 C1 D1 D2 E F1 G H J1 K1 L N O P Q R1 S1 S2 V W X Z(h,i,j,l,m,p,s,t)
Emergency Action, Agency, Advocacy, Fixed Fee Interview and Legal Aid undertaken
Ptr: Pascoe, Mr Andrew W LLB(Manc) Deputy Stipendiary Magistrate . . . . *Apr 1975

SYMES BAINS BROOMER ‡
2 Park Square Laneham Street Scunthorpe North Lincolnshire DN15 6JH
Tel: 01724 281616 *Fax:* 01724 280678 *Dx:* 14701 SCUNTHORPE
E-mail: info@sbblaw.com
List of partners: C V Broomer, A S Horwich, L P Kirkby, R Price, A R Ramm, J P Smith
Office: Epworth, Goole, Grimsby, Howden
Languages: Urdu
Work: A1 A3 B1 B2 C1 C2 D1 D2 E F1 F2 J1 J2 K1 K2 K3 K4 L N O P Q R1 R2 S1 S2 T1 T2 V W X Z(c,e,g,h,i,j,k,l,o,p,q,r,s,t)
Emergency Action, Agency, Advocacy, Fixed Fee Interview, Legal Aid undertaken and Legal Aid Franchise
Ptr: Broomer, Mr Charles V LLB . . . . *§Nov 1986
Horwich, Mr Andrew Samuel LLB . . . . *Sep 1996
Kirkby, Mr Laurence P MA(Cantab) . . . . *Jun 1978
Price, Mr Rodger LLB(Hons) . . . . *Jun 1992
Ramm, Mr Andrew R . . . . *Nov 1980
Smith, Mr John P . . . . Apr 1971
Asoc: Akhtar, Mrs Yasmin . . . . *Jul 2008
Astley, Mr Roy . . . . *Jul 1977
Bell, Mrs Emma . . . . Oct 2007
Duncan, Laura . . . . Sep 2009
Holden, Mr David . . . . Sep 2009
Linford, Deborah . . . . *Mar 2001
Con: Wallis, Mr Richard T. . . . . *Dec 1972

Other offices in Epworth, Goole, Grimsby, Howden. Holders of Franchise for Debt, Family. We conduct business in Urdu. We specialise in the following areas of work Crime - General, Divorce and Matrimonial, Residential Conveyancing.

STEVEN WARNE SOLICITOR ‡
24 Laneham Street Scunthorpe North Lincolnshire DN15 6LJ
Tel: 01724 279449 *Fax:* 01724 279727
E-mail: stevenwarne@stevenwarnesolicitor.co.uk
Work: F1 K3 L N S1 W
Fixed Fee Interview undertaken

SEAFORD, East Sussex

BARWELLS
10 Sutton Park Road Seaford East Sussex BN25 1RB
Tel: 01323 899331 *Fax:* 01323 890108 *Dx:* 38900 SEAFORD
E-mail: advice@barwells.com
Office: Eastbourne, Newhaven, Peacehaven
Work: A1 B1 C1 C2 C3 D1 E F1 G H J1 K1 L N O Q S1 S2 T1 T2 W Z(c,d,e,l,r)
Emergency Action, Agency, Advocacy, Fixed Fee Interview, Legal Aid undertaken, Legal Aid Franchise and Member of Accident Line
Ptr: Ash, Mr Stephen . . . . Mar 2009
Woods, Mr Andrew S . . . . NSP
Ast: Chaloner, Mr Paul Michael . . . . Oct 1984
Hewitt, Miss Claire Susanne . . . . Aug 2008

FIELDINGS ‡
Firle Road Seaford East Sussex BN25 2HJ
Tel: 01323 492493

LINDA FILBY SOLICITOR ‡
PO Box 2151 Seaford East Sussex BN25 9DH
Tel: 01273 695321 *Fax:* 01273 695349
Emergency telephone 07623 791149
E-mail: lindafilby@btconnect.com
List of partners: L Filby
Work: D1 E F1 G H K1 L N O Q S1 W Z(k,l,m,p)
Emergency Action, Agency, Advocacy, Fixed Fee Interview and Legal Aid undertaken
SPr: Filby, Miss Linda BA . . . . *Mar 1992

MAYO WYNNE BAXTER LLP
Jubilee House 1 Warwick Road Seaford East Sussex BN25 1RS
Tel: 01323 891412 *Fax:* 01323 490016 *Dx:* 38903 SEAFORD
E-mail: seaford@mayowynnebaxter.co.uk
Office: Brighton, East Grinstead, Eastbourne, Lewes
Work: C1 C2 C3 D1 E F1 G H J1 K1 L N O Q S1 T1 T2 V W Z(c,d,h,k,l,p,t)
Emergency Action, Agency, Advocacy, Fixed Fee Interview, Legal Aid undertaken, Legal Aid Franchise and Member of Accident Line
Ptr: Clarke, Mr John R M BA(Hons) . . . . *Oct 1985
Thompson, Mr Richard P . . . . *§Jun 1968
Ast: Figgins, Ms Anne BA(Hons)(Lond); CPE; LSF. . . . . *Oct 1994

RIX & KAY SOLICITORS LLP
Paignton House Warwick Road Seaford East Sussex BN25 1RS
Tel: 0845 165 8178 *Fax:* 01323 490278
Office: Hove, London W1, Sevenoaks, Uckfield
Languages: French
Work: A1 C1 C2 C3 D1 E F1 J1 K1 K2 K3 L M1 M2 N O P Q R1 S1 S2 T1 T2 V W Z(c,e,f,j,l)
Agency, Advocacy, Fixed Fee Interview and Legal Aid Franchise
Ptr: Best, Mr Ian James LLB. . . . . *§Nov 1986
Ast: Edmunds, Mrs Sarah Betty . . . . *Dec 2004

SEAHAM, Co Durham

KENNETH M BARROW & CO ‡
15-16 Adelaide Row Seaham Co Durham SR7 7EF
Tel: 0191 513 0333 *Fax:* 0191 513 0949 *Dx:* 61730 SEAHAM
E-mail: kmb@kennethmbarrow.com
List of partners: K M Barrow, D Harbron
Work: G H K1 K3 L S1 S2 V W
Emergency Action, Advocacy, Fixed Fee Interview, Legal Aid undertaken and Legal Aid Franchise
Ptr: Barrow, Mr Kenneth Malcolm LLB(Hons) . . . . *Jul 1979
Harbron, Mr David LLB . . . . Jan 2003

SEATON, Devon

BEVISS & BECKINGSALE
Law Chambers 1 Major Terrace Seaton Devon EX12 2RF
Tel: 01297 626950 *Fax:* 01297 626951 *Dx:* 82300 SEATON
E-mail: enquiries@bevissandbeckingsale.co.uk
Office: Axminster, Chard, Honiton
Work: A1 C1 D1 E F1 K1 K3 L N P Q R1 S1 S2 T1 T2 V W Z(l,o)
Emergency Action, Advocacy and Fixed Fee Interview undertaken
Ptr: Ollier, Mr Mark E LLB . . . . *Oct 1984
Ast: Heron, Mrs Elizabeth MA(Oxon). . . . . Apr 2007
Watkins, Mr Paul LLB . . . . Oct 2006

EVERYS
2 Eyre Court Road Seaton Devon EX12 2QY
Tel: 01297 21105 *Fax:* 01297 20110 *Dx:* 82303 SEATON
Emergency telephone 01404 822123
E-mail: law@everys.co.uk
Office: Budleigh Salterton, Exeter, Exmouth, Honiton (2 offices), Ottery St Mary, Sidmouth, Taunton
Work: A1 A2 B1 B2 C1 C2 C3 D1 D2 E F1 F2 G H J1 J2 K1 L M1 N O P Q R1 R2 S1 S2 T1 T2 V W X Z(c,d,e,h,i,k,l,m,n,o,p,q,r,s,t,u,w,x,y)
Emergency Action, Agency, Advocacy, Fixed Fee Interview, Legal Aid undertaken and Legal Aid Franchise
Ptr: Stokes, Mr Richard W BA. . . . . *§Apr 1987

MILFORD & DORMOR
Seaton House Marine Place Seaton Devon EX12 2QJ
Tel: 01297 20528 *Fax:* 01297 20783
Emergency telephone 01297 33618
E-mail: seaton@milfordanddormor.co.uk
Office: Axminster, Chard, Ilminster
Work: A1 C1 D1 E F1 G H K1 L M1 P S1 T1 V W
Emergency Action, Agency, Advocacy and Legal Aid undertaken
Ptr: Fazio, Miss Domenica Tonina LLB. . . . . Nov 1998

SEDBERGH, Cumbria

DALTON & HAGUE ‡
7 Main Street Sedbergh Cumbria LA10 5BN
Tel: 01539 620365 *Fax:* 01539 620729
Emergency telephone 01539 625436
E-mail: office@daltonandhauge.co.uk
List of partners: G W Dalton
Work: A1 C1 E F1 G J1 K1 L N Q S1 T1 T2 W
Agency, Advocacy, Fixed Fee Interview, Legal Aid undertaken and Member of Accident Line
Ptr: Dalton, Mr Graham W LLB(Lond) . . . . *§Oct 1970

SEDGLEY, West Midlands

ELLIOTT & ALLEN ‡
(incorporating Elliot & Co; Kilroy Allen & Co)
3a Dudley Street Sedgley West Midlands DY3 1SA
Tel: 01902 677204 *Fax:* 01902 880255 *Dx:* 28901 SEDGLEY
E-mail: mail@elliott-allen.com
List of partners: S W Allen
Work: C1 D1 D2 E F1 G H J1 K1 Q S1 W X Z(l)
Emergency Action, Agency, Advocacy, Fixed Fee Interview, Legal Aid undertaken and Legal Aid Franchise
Ptr: Allen, Mr Stephen W LLB . . . . Jun 1980
Ast: Jane, Ms Tracey LLB . . . . Aug 2004

SELBY, North Yorkshire

BAILEY & HAIGH ‡
Abbey Chambers 5 The Crescent Selby North Yorkshire YO8 4PU
Tel: 01757 705191 *Fax:* 01757 210005 *Dx:* 27401 SELBY
Emergency telephone 01757 700587
List of partners: M J Gibson, V T Lindley, D G Newton
Office: Goole
Work: A1 B1 C1 D1 D2 E F1 F2 G H J1 K1 L N Q R1 S1 S2 T1 T2 V W Z(c,l,r)
Emergency Action, Agency, Advocacy, Fixed Fee Interview, Legal Aid undertaken, Legal Aid Franchise and Member of Accident Line
Ptr: Gibson, Mr Michael John LLB. . . . . *Oct 2003
Lindley, Mr Vaughan Terence LLB. . . . . *Oct 1987
Newton, Mr Derek G . . . . *Jul 1972
Ast: Blaza, Miss Rosalind Annmarie LLB. . . . . *Jan 1999
Dukes, Ms Nicola Ann LLB(Hons). . . . . *Aug 2006

CRIMINAL LAW SOLICITORS
No2 Market Lane Selby North Yorkshire YO8 4QA
Tel: 01757 241199
Office: Pontefract

CROMBIE WILKINSON
6 Park Street Selby North Yorkshire YO8 4PW
Tel: 01757 708957 *Fax:* 01757 210343 *Dx:* 27403 SELBY
E-mail: selby@crombiewilkinson.co.uk
Office: Malton, York
Languages: French, Mirpuri, Punjabi, Urdu
Work: A1 A2 A3 B1 C1 C2 C3 D1 D2 E F1 J1 K1 K2 K3 K4 L M1 N O P Q R1 R2 S1 S2 T1 T2 W Z(b,c,d,e,k,l,r,za)
Emergency Action, Agency, Advocacy, Fixed Fee Interview, Legal Aid undertaken, Legal Aid Franchise and Member of Accident Line
Dir: Norgate, Mr Darren LLB. . . . . *Jul 1999
Porter, Mr Neal R BA . . . . . *Oct 1983
Asoc: Ishaq, Miss Farzana LLB(Hons). . . . . *May 2007

ELMHIRST PARKER LLP
13 Finkle Street Selby North Yorkshire YO8 4DT
Tel: 01757 703602 *Fax:* 01757 708351 *Dx:* 27402 SELBY
E-mail: selby@elmhirstparker.com
Office: Barnsley, Leeds, Selby
Work: A1 B1 C1 C2 C3 D1 E F1 G H J1 K1 L N O P Q R1 S1 S2 T1 T2 V W Z(d,l)
Agency, Advocacy, Fixed Fee Interview undertaken and Member of Accident Line
Mem: Legg, Mr Martin P LLB . . . . . *Sep 1988
Ast: Forsyth, Miss Gillian LLB . . . . . *Apr 2004

ELMHIRST PARKER LLP
The Abbey Yard Selby North Yorkshire YO8 4PX
Tel: 01757 703895 *Fax:* 01757 213397 *Dx:* 27404 SELBY
Emergency telephone 01757 703895
E-mail: selby@elmhirstparker.com
Office: Barnsley, Leeds, Selby
Languages: French
Work: A1 C1 D1 D2 E G H J1 K1 K2 K3 K4 L N O Q R1 R2 S1 S2 T2 W Z(d,l,r)
Emergency Action, Agency, Advocacy, Fixed Fee Interview, Legal Aid undertaken and Legal Aid Franchise
Ptr: Bouvet, Mr J Pierre LLB. . . . . *Apr 1978
Haggerty, Mr Keith BA(Law). . . . . *Feb 1981
Rounding, Mr Simon L BA; TEP. . . . . *May 1981

SELSDON, Surrey

GORDON GRAY ‡
133 Addington Road Selsdon Surrey CR2 8LH
Tel: 020 8657 3444 *Fax:* 020 8657 8999
Work: S1

SELSEY, West Sussex

WINTLE & CO
138 High Street Selsey West Sussex PO20 0QE
Tel: 01243 605947 *Fax:* 01243 606221 *Dx:* 31201 BOGNOR REGIS
Emergency telephone 01243 603658
E-mail: wintle@selsey1.wanadoo.co.uk
Office: Bognor Regis (2 offices)
Languages: French
Work: D1 E F1 J1 K1 L N Q S1 T2 W
Advocacy undertaken and Member of Accident Line
Ptr: Pestelle, Mr Nigel BA . . . . . *Sep 1982
Seed, Mr Nigel R LLB(Leeds) . . . . . *§Dec 1972
Stanton, Mr Terence G Deputy District Judge . . . . *§Jun 1966

SETTLE, North Yorkshire

GOAD & BUTCHER ‡
Midland Bank Chambers Market Place Settle North Yorkshire BD24 9DR
Tel: 01729 823500 *Fax:* 01729 822023
Emergency telephone 01524 263095
E-mail: info@goadandbutcher.co.uk
List of partners: R T Bentley, D A Butcher
Work: A1 D1 D2 E K1 K2 K3 K4 S1 S2 W Z(d,l)
Emergency Action undertaken
Ptr: Bentley, Mr Richard T MA(Cantab) . . . . . *Dec 1987
Butcher, Mr David A LLB(Lond); MA. . . . . *Apr 1970
Ast: Clarke, Mrs Joanna LLB(B'ham). . . . . *Jun 1978
Verhagen, Ms Anne. . . . . *Mar 2009

DEREK M JORDAN ‡
Chapel Street Settle North Yorkshire BD24 9HT
Tel: 01729 823589 / 823514 *Fax:* 01729 822250
E-mail: jordandm@globalnet.co.uk
List of partners: D M Jordan
Office: Bentham
Work: A1 G K1 M1 P S1 T1 W
Emergency Action, Agency, Advocacy, Fixed Fee Interview and Legal Aid undertaken
SPr: Jordan, Mr Derek M. . . . . *Jun 1974
Ast: Glen, Miss Lilias LLB . . . . . Sep 1984

SEVENOAKS, Kent

BAKER MACDONALD ‡
3 The Square Riverhead Sevenoaks Kent TN13 2AA
Tel: 01732 457978 *Fax:* 01732 453495
List of partners: M J Baker, J E Whiting
Work: E F1 J1 K1 K3 L N O Q R1 R2 S1 S2 T2 W
Agency and Fixed Fee Interview undertaken
Ptr: Baker, Mr Michael J. . . . . *Nov 1992
Whiting, Ms Jane E. . . . . *Jun 1984

BAYHAM SOLICITORS
Greenacre House Comp Lane Platt Sevenoaks Kent TN15 8NR
Tel: 01732 882546 *Fax:* 01732 780178
Office: Tunbridge Wells

HELEN BLIGH EMPLOYMENT LAW SERVICES ‡
18 Witches Lane Sevenoaks Kent TN13 2AX
Tel: 01732 458302

BOWMAN & DREW LIMITED ‡
45 High Street Sevenoaks Kent TN13 1JF
Tel: 0845 221 1322 *Fax:* 0845 221 1322 *Dx:* 30013 SEVENOAKS
E-mail: mail@bdlaw.co.uk

DMB LAW ‡
144-146 St John's Hill Sevenoaks Kent TN13 3PF
Tel: 01732 228800 *Fax:* 01732 228818
E-mail: legal@dmblaw.co.uk
List of partners: D M Buckle, B T J Sharp
Work: A3 C1 D1 D2 E J1 K1 K2 K3 M2 N O Q S1 S2 W
Ptr: Buckle, Mr David Michael . . . . . Jan 1993
Sharp, Mr Barry T J. . . . . *Dec 1973
Ast: Arnold, Mrs Jacqueline . . . . . Oct 2008

ELLICOTTS & CO SOLICITORS ‡
Pond View House 6a High Street Otford Sevenoaks Kent TN14 5PQ
Tel: 01959 522442 *Fax:* 0560 113 3338

EVANS MAIN SOLICITORS ‡
82 High Street Sevenoaks Kent TN13 1LP
Tel: 01732 464848 *Fax:* 01732 460077 *Dx:* 30003 SEVENOAKS
List of partners: D Evans, A Main
Work: B2 D1 G H K1 K2 K3
Agency and Legal Aid undertaken
Ptr: Evans, Ms Diana . . . . . Sep 1984
Main, Mr Andrew . . . . . Nov 1991

FIELD MARTIN ‡
2 Holmesdale Road Sevenoaks Kent TN13 3XL
Tel: 01732 463934

C J HURRION ‡
The Spinney Underriver Sevenoaks Kent TN15 0SD
Tel: 01732 833997 *Fax:* 01732 833042
List of partners: C J Hurrion
Ptr: Hurrion, Mr Christopher J. . . . . *Jun 1973

JENNINGS IP & MEDIA SOLICITORS ‡
Lodge Farm Bitchet Green Seal Sevenoaks Kent TN15 0NE
Tel: 01732 762340 *Fax:* 01732 762055
E-mail: peterjennings@jenningsipandmedialaw.co.uk

KEYS SOLICITORS ‡
Unit 3 Pettings Court Farm Hodsell Street Sevenoaks Kent TN15 7LH
Tel: 01732 823110

KNOCKER & FOSKETT ‡
The Red House 50 High Street Sevenoaks Kent TN13 1JL
Tel: 01732 459931 *Fax:* 01732 459246 *Dx:* 30002 SEVENOAKS
E-mail: kfsols@knocker-foskett.co.uk
List of partners: D F Brazel, R J R Don, C J Hugo, S A J MacIntyre, F G B Williams
Languages: French
Work: A1 B1 C1 C2 D1 E F1 J1 J2 K1 K2 K3 K4 L N O P Q R1 R2 S1 S2 T1 T2 W Z(b,c,d,e,h,j,k,l,p,q,s,t)
Emergency Action, Agency, Advocacy and Fixed Fee Interview undertaken
Ptr: Brazel, Mr David F LLB . . . . . Nov 1983
Don, Mr Richard J R . . . . . *§Dec 1971
Hugo, Mr Christopher John BA(Hons); MA Law Society Bursary . . . . . *May 1994
MacIntyre, Mr Stuart A J BA(Dunelm) . . . . . *Jun 1980
Williams, Ms Felicity G B . . . . . Jan 1996
Asoc: Barnard, Mrs Marguerite G BA(Law). . . . . *Apr 1982
Ast: Campbell, Ms Sheila . . . . . Oct 1995
Con: Leathers, Mr Raymond L . . . . . *Oct 1974

LAMBERTS ‡
1 The Shambles Dorset Street Sevenoaks Kent TN13 1LL
Tel: 01732 460565 *Fax:* 01732 740258 *Dx:* 30005 SEVENOAKS
List of partners: G K C Chapman, C J Harvey, C H Shireby
Office: Paddock Wood
Work: A1 B1 C1 C2 C3 D1 E F1 I J1 K1 L M1 N O P Q R1 S1 T1 W Z(b,c,d,e,f,j,k,l,m,o)
Emergency Action, Agency, Advocacy and Fixed Fee Interview undertaken
Ptr: Harvey, Mr Clive J BA. . . . . *§Dec 1980
Con: Lambert, Mr John W . . . . . *§Aug 1966

PENDRIGH MAKIN
Estate House 2 Pembroke Road Sevenoaks Kent TN13 1XR
Tel: 01732 463030 *Fax:* 01732 460038 *Dx:* 30004 SEVENOAKS
E-mail: jmakin@pendrighmakin.com
Office: Reigate
Work: K1 K3 W

THE REECE-JONES PARTNERSHIP ‡
Epicurus House 1 Akehurst Lane Sevenoaks Kent TN13 1JN
Tel: 01732 457575 *Fax:* 01732 458646 *Dx:* 30000 SEVENOAKS
List of partners: W F Evershed, T M Henry, S P Reece-Jones
Languages: French
Work: A1 B1 C1 C2 D1 E F1 G H J1 K1 L N O R1 S1 S2 T1 T2 W Z(c,d,h,k,l,m)
Emergency Action, Agency, Advocacy and Legal Aid undertaken
Ptr: Evershed, Mr Wilfrid F MA(Cantab) . . . . . *§Jun 1967
Henry, Mr Thomas M LLB. . . . . *Oct 1982
Reece-Jones, Miss Sarah P LLB . . . . . *Oct 1986

RIX & KAY SOLICITORS LLP
6th Floor Suite E Tubs Hill House Sevenoaks Kent TN13 1BL
Tel: 01732 440855 *Fax:* 01732 440854
Office: Hove, London W1, Seaford, Uckfield

WALKER & WALKER ‡
35 High Street Sevenoaks Kent TN13 1JD
Tel: 01732 450699 *Fax:* 01732 452386 *Dx:* 30042 SEVENOAKS
E-mail: solicitors@walkerwalker.co.uk
List of partners: B M Walker, M V F Walker
Languages: Portuguese
Work: E K1 S1 S2 W
Fixed Fee Interview undertaken
Ptr: Walker, Mr Brian M . . . . . *Jun 1972
Walker, Mrs Marlene V F LLM(Lond) . . . . . *Nov 1984

DALE R WALKER SOLICITOR ‡
2nd Floor North Tower Tubs Hill House Sevenoaks Kent TN13 1BL
Tel: 020 8466 0967 *Fax:* 020 8466 0968 *Dx:* 30014 SEVENOAKS
List of partners: D R Walker
Work: B1 C1 E J1 K1 L N O Q R1 S1 W Z(h)
Ptr: Walker, Mr Dale R. . . . . *Aug 1985

WARNERS SOLICITORS
16 South Park Sevenoaks Kent TN13 1AN
Tel: 01732 747900 *Fax:* 01732 747919 *Dx:* 30017 SEVENOAKS
E-mail: general@warners-solicitors.co.uk
Office: Tonbridge
Work: A1 A3 B1 C1 C2 D1 E F1 F2 I J1 K1 K2 K3 L N O Q R1 R2 S1 S2 T1 T2 W Z(c,d,e,j,k,l,o,p,q,w)
Emergency Action, Advocacy and Fixed Fee Interview undertaken
Mem: Barratt, Mr Noel R M LLB Notary Public. . . . . *Oct 1999
Collins, Miss Rayma Louise LLB(Hons) . . . . . Oct 2002
Davis, Mr Mark O LLB. . . . . *Oct 1984
Manning, Mrs Claire Rosemary CPE . . . . . Nov 2005
Rosser, Mr Mark H MA; LLB(Cantab) . . . . . *§Jun 1979
Rowe, Mrs Angela J. . . . . *Mar 1998
Twining, Mr Robert P LLB. . . . . *Oct 1989
Ast: Aves, Mr Matthew Owen LPC . . . . . Dec 2005
Bohill, Mrs Jane Sylvia LLB . . . . . *Nov 2000
Connolly, Mrs Kim LLB . . . . . Oct 1990
Massam, Mrs Rebecca LLB(Hons) . . . . . Oct 2010
Philpot, Mr Darren James LLB . . . . . Nov 2008
Scrambler, Mrs Alice Rebecca LLB . . . . . Sep 2008
Sullivan, Mr Kevin Micheal LLB(Hons). . . . . Oct 2004
Tennant, Mr Charles D S LLB . . . . . Dec 2003

SHAFTESBURY, Dorset

BLANCHARDS BAILEY LLP
34 High Street Shaftesbury Dorset SP7 8JG
Tel: 01747 440447 *Fax:* 01747 855077 *Dx:* 46001 SHAFTESBURY
Emergency telephone 0845 271 0520
E-mail: shaftesbury@blanchardsbailey.co.uk
Office: Blandford Forum, Dorchester, Stalbridge
Work: A1 C1 C2 D1 E F1 F2 J1 K1 K2 K3 K4 L N O Q R1 S1 S2 T1 T2 V W X Z(d,h,k)
Agency, Advocacy, Fixed Fee Interview, Legal Aid undertaken and Legal Aid Franchise
Ptr: Holden, Ms Isobel Lisa . . . . . *Jan 1989
Lewis, Merlin D P BA . . . . . *Apr 1988
Asoc: Watson, Ms Jackie . . . . . *Mar 1990

C-REY CONVEYANCING ‡
Milestones Lower Blandford Road Compton Abbas Shaftesbury Dorset SP7 0NL
Tel: 01747 812263 *Fax:* 07808 961434
E-mail: info@c-reyconveyancing.co.uk

FARNFIELD & NICHOLLS
4 Church Lane Shaftesbury Dorset SP7 8JT
Tel: 01747 854244 *Fax:* 01747 851874 *Dx:* 46002 SHAFTESBURY
E-mail: info@farnfields.com
Office: Gillingham, Sturminster Newton, Warminster
Work: A1 B1 C1 C2 C3 D1 E F1 G H I J1 K1 L M1 M2 N O P Q R1 S1 T1 T2 V W X Z(c,d,e,k,l,p,t,w)
Emergency Action, Agency, Advocacy, Fixed Fee Interview, Legal Aid undertaken, Legal Aid Franchise and Member of Accident Line
Asoc: Muirhead, Mrs Claire Jane LLB; TEP . . . . . Sep 2005

RUTTERS ‡
2 Bimport Shaftesbury Dorset SP7 8AY
Tel: 01747 852377 *Fax:* 01747 851989 *Dx:* 46004 SHAFTESBURY
Emergency telephone 01747 852933
E-mail: enquiries@rutterslaw.co.uk
List of partners: S J Lewis, D J Rowntree, J G Wood
Office: Gillingham
Work: A1 C1 D1 D2 E F1 G H J1 J2 K1 K3 K4 L M1 N P Q R1 R2 S1 S2 T2 V W Z(d,h,l,o,s,u,x)
Emergency Action, Agency, Advocacy, Fixed Fee Interview undertaken and Member of Accident Line
Ptr: Lewis, Mrs Sharon Julia LLB; LLM . . . . . Nov 1986
Rowntree, Mr Derek J LLB(Lond) . . . . . *May 1979
Wood, Mr James G. . . . . Dec 1989
Ast: Arnold, Miss Claire LLB . . . . . Jan 2008
Biggs, Ms Tara FILEx . . . . . Oct 2006
Matthews, Helen Louise. . . . . Aug 2010

SHANKLIN, Isle of Wight

JEROMES
Steephill Chambers Steephill Road Shanklin Isle of Wight PO37 6AB
Tel: 01983 862643 *Fax:* 01983 867126 *Dx:* 56251 SHANKLIN
E-mail: sueterry@jeromelaw.co.uk
Office: Newport, Sandown
Work: A1 A3 C1 D1 D2 E K1 K2 K4 L O Q R1 S1 S2 W Z(q)
Emergency Action, Agency, Advocacy and Legal Aid undertaken
Ast: Daniel, Katie LLB(Hons). . . . . Jan 1994

SHAW, Greater Manchester

ANDREW THORNE & CO ‡
33 Market Street Shaw Greater Manchester OL2 8NR
Tel: 01706 290488 *Fax:* 01706 844976 *Dx:* 13780 SHAW
E-mail: andrew@andrewthorne.co.uk
List of partners: O A O Idowu, A J R Thorne
Office: Shaw
Languages: Spanish
Work: B1 C1 C2 D1 E F1 J1 K1 L N O Q R1 S1 V W Z(h,l,p)
Emergency Action, Agency, Advocacy, Fixed Fee Interview, Legal Aid undertaken and Legal Aid Franchise
Ptr: Idowu, Mr Olfunso Akinwale Omoyele BA(Hons); LLB(Hons) . . . . . *Feb 1992
Thorne, Mr Andrew J R LLB. . . . . *Mar 1972

ANDREW THORNE & CO
54 Market Street Shaw Greater Manchester OL2 8NH
Tel: 01706 841775 *Fax:* 01706 842688 *Dx:* 13780 SHAW
E-mail: andrew@andrewthorne.co.uk
Office: Shaw
Languages: Spanish
Work: B1 C1 C2 D1 E F1 J1 K1 L N O Q R1 S1 V W Z(c,h,l,p)
Agency, Advocacy, Fixed Fee Interview, Legal Aid undertaken and Legal Aid Franchise
Ptr: Idowu, Mr Olfunso Akinwale Omoyele BA(Hons); LLB(Hons) . . . . . *Feb 1992
Thorne, Mr Andrew J R LLB. . . . . *Mar 1972

See p112 for the Key to Work Categories & other symbols

SHEERNESS, Kent

PETER CLOUGH & CO ‡
13-15 Minster Road Halfway Sheerness Kent ME12 3JE
Tel: 01795 669299 *Fax:* 01795 669788
E-mail: enquiries@peterclougsolicitors.co.uk
List of partners: P J I Clough
Languages: French, German
Work: K3 L S1 W
SPr: Clough, Mr Peter John Illingworth BA(Lond) Notary Public . . . *§Jun 1971

JOHN COPLAND & SON ‡
77 High Street Sheerness Kent ME12 1TY
Tel: 01795 664431 *Fax:* 01795 580474 *Dx:* 59804 SHEERNESS
Emergency telephone 01795 872696
E-mail: jcoplands@aol.com
List of partners: J W D Bancroft, T J Bancroft
Languages: French, Slovak, Turkish
Work: A1 B1 C1 D1 D2 E F1 G H J1 K1 K3 K4 L M1 N O P Q S1 S2 T1 T2 V W Z(g,k,l,p,q,w)
Emergency Action, Agency, Advocacy, Fixed Fee Interview, Legal Aid undertaken, Legal Aid Franchise and Member of Accident Line
Ptr: Bancroft, Mr James W D BA(Dunelm) ★. . . *Oct 1991
Bancroft, Mr Timothy J BA(Dunelm) ♦ . . . *Oct 1988
Ast: Chetwynd, Mrs Karina Ruth BSc(Hons) . . . Jul 2004

A J FIELD & CO ‡
(incorporating Seviers & Ivor Jones & Co)
Britannia House 75 High Street Sheerness Kent ME12 1TX
Tel: 01795 580600 *Fax:* 01795 580029
List of partners: A J Field
Office: Gerrards Cross, Marlow, Sittingbourne
Work: A1 B1 C1 C2 C3 D1 E F1 J1 K1 L M1 M2 N O P Q R1 S1 S2 V W Z(b,c,j,k,l,m,o,r)
Emergency Action, Agency, Advocacy, Fixed Fee Interview, Legal Aid undertaken and Legal Aid Franchise
Ptr: Field, Mr Andrew J BA(Hons) . . . *Dec 1991

CHRISTOPHER HARRIS & CO ‡
202 High Street Sheerness Kent ME12 1UQ
Tel: 01795 661521 *Fax:* 01795 661487 *Dx:* 59801 SHEERNESS
E-mail: info@christopherharris.org.uk
List of partners: J H Steadman, P Summerbell
Office: Sittingbourne
Work: B1 B2 C1 D1 D2 E F1 F2 G H J1 J2 K1 K3 K4 L N O Q S1 S2 V W X Z(c,g,h,j,l,p,q,r)
Emergency Action, Agency, Advocacy, Fixed Fee Interview, Legal Aid undertaken, Legal Aid Franchise and Member of Accident Line
Ptr: Steadman, Ms Janice H BA ♦ . . . *Oct 1993
Summerbell, Mr Paul LLB(Hons) ♦ . . . *Dec 1994
Ast: Ormrod, Mr George Andrew LLB . . . *Dec 1977

H A UNDERWOOD SOLICITORS ‡
31 Broadway Sheerness Kent ME12 1AB
Tel: 01795 663555

SHEFFIELD, South Yorkshire

ACCIDENT SOLICITORS DIRECT ‡
275 Ecclesall Road Sheffield South Yorkshire S11 8NX
Tel: 0800 163 622 *Fax:* 0114 266 6006

ADAM LAW ‡
Ground Floor 759-761 Attercliffe Road Sheffield South Yorkshire S9 3RF
Tel: 0114 256 0111 *Fax:* 0114 256 0609

APPLEYARD LEES
Sheffield Technology Parks Cooper Buildings Arundel Street Sheffield South Yorkshire S1 2NS
Tel: 0114 270 0611 *Fax:* 0114 272 5046
E-mail: sheffield@appleyardlees.com
Office: Burnley, Chester, Halifax, Harrogate, Huddersfield, Leeds, Liverpool, Manchester, Preston, Stockton-on-Tees, York

ATHI LAW LLP
285 London Road Sheffield South Yorkshire S2 4NF
Tel: 0114 255 8001 *Fax:* 0114 250 7666
E-mail: info@athilaw.co.uk
Office: West Bromwich
Languages: Chinese, Hindi, Punjabi, Urdu
Work: C1 C2 C3 E G K1 L N Q S1 V W Z(c,e,j)
Emergency Action, Agency, Advocacy, Fixed Fee Interview, Legal Aid undertaken and Member of Accident Line
Ptr: Athi, Mr Hem Kumar LLB . . . *Jun 1978

ATTEYS
(incorporating Michael H Taylor & Co; Jean Blackwell Vickers & Co)
The Red Brick House 28-32 Trippet Lane Sheffield South Yorkshire S1 4EL
Tel: 0114 276 6767 *Fax:* 0114 273 1287 *Dx:* 10516 SHEFFIELD 8
Office: Barnsley, Doncaster, Retford, Wath-upon-Dearne
Languages: French
Work: B1 C1 C2 C3 D1 E F1 G H J1 K1 L M1 M2 N O P R1 S1 T1 T2 V W Z(b,c,e,o)
Emergency Action, Agency, Advocacy, Fixed Fee Interview undertaken and Member of Accident Line

BANNER JONES
3rd Floor 11 Leopold Street Sheffield South Yorkshire S1 2GY
Tel: 0114 275 5266 *Fax:* 0114 275 9786
E-mail: info@bannerjones.co.uk
Office: Chesterfield (4 offices), Dronfield
Work: A1 B1 C1 C2 C3 D1 D2 E F1 J1 K1 K2 K3 L M1 M2 N P R1 S1 T1 T2 V W Z(c,d,e,f,h,i,j,k,l,n,o,s)
Emergency Action, Agency, Advocacy, Fixed Fee Interview and Legal Aid undertaken
Ptr: Gordon, Mr Stephen LLB Notary Public . . . *Oct 1987
Joy, Mr Richard A BA . . . *Nov 1997
Ast: Fielder, Mr Andrew . . . *Sep 2007
Wheeldon, Ms Katheryn . . . *Sep 2008

BELL & BUXTON ‡
Telegraph House High Street Sheffield South Yorkshire S1 2GA
Tel: 0114 249 5969 *Fax:* 0114 249 3804 *Dx:* 10529 SHEFFIELD 1
E-mail: legals@bellbuxton.co.uk
List of partners: M S Butler, C B Neal, M E Rodgers, A D Ross
Languages: French
Work: A1 B1 B2 C1 C2 C3 D1 E F1 J1 K1 K2 K3 K4 L M1 M2 O P Q R1 S1 S2 T1 T2 U2 V W Z(d,e,l,o,s,za)
Emergency Action, Agency, Advocacy and Fixed Fee Interview undertaken
Ptr: Butler, Miss Mary S LLB(Bris) . . . *Oct 1984
Neal, Mr Charles Bernard LLB; JCL; PGDip . . . *Sep 2006
Rodgers, Mr Matthew Edward LLB(Hons) . . . *Aug 1998
Ross, Mr Alexander D LLB(Hons) . . . *Dec 1995
Asoc: Tudor, Mr Nicholas G . . . *Dec 1973
Ast: Bell, Ms Louise LLB . . . Jan 1997
Conlon, Mr James Michael LLB(Hons); LPC . . . *Nov 2002
Green, Mr John LLB; LPC . . . *Feb 2008
Con: Ibberson, Mr Charles D MA(Cantab) . . . *§Jul 1967

BEST SOLICITORS ‡
Regency House 2 Paradise Street Paradise Square Sheffield South Yorkshire S1 2DF
Tel: 0114 281 3636 *Fax:* 0114 281 3635
E-mail: info@bestsolicitorsonline.co.uk
Work: B1 B2 D1 G H J1 K1 K2 K3 L N O Q R1 R2 S1 V W Z(h,m,r,t)
Emergency Action, Agency, Advocacy, Fixed Fee Interview, Legal Aid undertaken and Member of Accident Line

CARTWRIGHT KING
4th Floor St James House Vicar Lane Sheffield South Yorkshire S1 2EX
Tel: 0114 321 1000 *Fax:* 0808 168 1500 *Dx:* 10561 SHEFFIELD
E-mail: admin@cartwrightking.co.uk
Office: Birmingham, Derby, Gateshead, Leicester, Nottingham
Ast: Stowers, Mr Daniel James LLB(Hons) . . . *Mar 1997
Woodfield, Mr Blake BA . . . *Aug 1999

COATES SOLICITORS ‡
38a High Street Mosborough Sheffield South Yorkshire S20 5AF
Tel: 0114 251 1111 *Fax:* 0114 251 1254
Work: S1 S2 W

COLLARDS SOLICITORS ‡
125 Devonshire Street Sheffield South Yorkshire S3 7SB
Tel: 0114 273 8149

CHRIS COOKE AND CO
Aizlewoods Mill Nursery Street Sheffield South Yorkshire S3 8GG
Tel: 0114 282 3433 *Fax:* 0114 282 3438
Emergency telephone 0114 282 3433
Office: Rotherham
Work: G H
Agency, Advocacy and Legal Aid Franchise

DLA PIPER UK LLP
1 St Pauls Place Sheffield South Yorkshire S1 1JX
Tel: 0870 011 1111 *Fax:* 0114 270 0568 *Dx:* 708580 SHEFFIELD 10
Emergency telephone 0870 011 1111
E-mail: paul.firth@dlapiper.com
Office: Birmingham, Leeds, Liverpool, London EC2, Manchester
Languages: French, German, Spanish
Work: A1 B1 C1 E F1 J1 L M1 N O P Q R1 S1 T1 V W Z(b,c,d,e,f,h,i,j,k,l,m,n,o,s,t)
Emergency Action, Agency, Advocacy, Fixed Fee Interview undertaken and Member of Accident Line
Ptr: Anson, Mr Peter M LLB; MA(Sheff) . . . *Jun 1976
Bentley, Mr Bruce LLB(B'ham) . . . *Apr 1971
Billing, Ms Petra . . . Oct 1994
Blacksell, Mr Stephen G LLB . . . *Nov 1987
Bradley, Mr David J LLB(Hons) . . . *Oct 1987
Chalmers, Mr Alan . . . Nov 1993
Craig, Mr Cameron . . . Sep 1996
Dury, Mr Alan LLB(Hons) . . . *Dec 1991
Firth, Mr Paul N BA(Law) . . . *May 1985
Gallen, Mr Gary . . . Jul 1995
Gough, Mr Roger LLB(Lond) . . . *Oct 1985
Hitchcock, Mrs Teresa Caroline BA(Hons) . . . *Oct 1993
Holland, Mr Martyn LLB . . . *Oct 1984
Howard, Mr Nigel Elliott LLB(Hons) . . . *Dec 1988
Kenworthy, Mr Jon . . . Sep 2000
Littler, Mr Tim . . . Apr 1989
May, Mr Richard . . . Sep 1997
Morris, Mr Andrew . . . Oct 1986
Morrissy, Ms Julie . . . Sep 1998
Mosley, Mr Duncan P BA(Law) . . . *Nov 1986
Moss, Ms Alison LLB(Hons) . . . Nov 1989
Mott, Ashley LSF . . . *Dec 1988
Norman, Mr Richard . . . Oct 1996
Slater, Mr Neil D LLB . . . Jun 1981
Sly, Mr Stephen LLB; ACIArb Deputy District Judge . . *Nov 1987
Staton, Mr Clive LLB . . . *Oct 1984
Stout, Ms Julia LLB . . . *Dec 1977

ESSENTIAL RIGHTS ‡
5 Gainsborough Road Sheffield South Yorkshire S11 9AJ
Tel: 0114 255 4526 *Fax:* 0114 255 4526
E-mail: essential.rights@legalisp.net
List of partners: S Ennals
Work: K4 V
Ptr: Ennals, Mr Simon LLB; CQSW Part time Chairman of the Social Security and Appeals Tribunals . . . *Dec 1995

DAVID EYRES
859 Gleadless Road Gleadless Sheffield South Yorkshire S12 2LG
Tel: 0114 249 3222 *Fax:* 0114 239 5270 *Dx:* 10524 SHEFFIELD
Office: Sheffield
Work: C1 E G H K1 N Q S1 W
Emergency Action, Agency, Advocacy, Fixed Fee Interview and Legal Aid undertaken
Ptr: Ibbotson, Mr Paul Clough Sidney Herbert Clay Prize *§Dec 1972

FAVELL SMITH & LAWSON SOLICITORS ‡
16 Bank Street Sheffield South Yorkshire S1 1DY
Tel: 0114 272 4381 *Fax:* 0114 276 1407 *Dx:* 10541 SHEFFIELD
E-mail: legal@favells.co.uk
List of partners: D A Lawson, C J Revitt, K Smith
Office: Hathersage
Work: A1 B1 D1 D2 E F1 G H J1 K1 L N P R1 S1 S2 T1 T2 V W Z(i,l,m)
Emergency Action, Agency, Advocacy, Fixed Fee Interview, Legal Aid undertaken, Legal Aid Franchise and Member of Accident Line
Ptr: Lawson, Mr David A LLB . . . *Dec 1978
Revitt, Mr Christopher J LLB . . . *Oct 1991
Smith, Mr Keith . . . *§Jun 1975
Ast: Bunting, Mrs Fay L LLB . . . *Nov 1992

FIRTH LINDSAY ‡
Refuge Assurance Buildings 41 Church Street Sheffield South Yorkshire S1 2GL
Tel: 0114 276 0586 *Fax:* 0114 272 4506 *Dx:* 10553 SHEFFIELD
Emergency telephone 0114 230 8240
E-mail: firth@netcomuk.co.uk
List of partners: R F Firth, A C Lindsay
Languages: German
Work: E G H L N O Q S1 W Z(c,i,l)
Emergency Action, Agency, Advocacy, Fixed Fee Interview, Legal Aid undertaken and Member of Accident Line
Ptr: Firth, Mr Robert Fred . . . *Apr 1972
Lindsay, Mr Andrew C LLB . . . *Jul 1979

FOYS SOLICITORS
102-112 Burncross Chapeltown Sheffield South Yorkshire S35 1TG
Tel: 0114 246 7609 *Fax:* 0114 240 2625 *Dx:* 19836 CHAPELTOWN
E-mail: info@foys.co.uk
Office: Doncaster, Rotherham, Sheffield, Worksop
Work: C1 D1 D2 E F1 F2 J1 J2 K1 L N O Q R1 S1 S2 V W Z(e,g,l,p,q)
Fixed Fee Interview, Legal Aid undertaken and Legal Aid Franchise
Ast: Davies, Miss Ann Hooton LLB . . . *Jun 1981
Makol, Mr Anuj LLB . . . *Aug 2003

FOYS SOLICITORS
Drake House Crescent Waterthorpe Sheffield South Yorkshire S20 7HT
Tel: 0114 251 1702 *Fax:* 0114 251 1750 *Dx:* 717230 SHEFFIELD 28
E-mail: info@foys.co.uk
Office: Doncaster, Rotherham, Sheffield, Worksop
Work: C1 C2 D1 D2 E F1 F2 J1 J2 K1 L N O Q S1 S2 V W Z(p,q)
Fixed Fee Interview, Legal Aid undertaken and Legal Aid Franchise
Asoc: Swannack, Ms Karen A BSc . . . *Oct 1995
Ast: Aslam, Mr Tahir LLB . . . Aug 2005

JOHN GAUNT & PARTNERS ‡
Omega Court 372-374 Cemetery Road Sheffield South Yorkshire S11 8FT
Tel: 0114 266 8664 *Fax:* 0114 266 0101
Emergency telephone 0114 266 3400
E-mail: post@john-gaunt.co.uk
List of partners: J R T Gaunt, M Hazlewood, K I Redford, T A Shield
Languages: French
Work: O Z(f,l)
Agency undertaken
Ptr: Gaunt, Mr John Richard Tom LLB(Sheff) . . . *Apr 1976
Hazlewood, Miss Michelle LLB . . . Sep 1992
Redford, Miss Katharine Isabel LLB . . . *Nov 1991
Shield, Mr Timothy Andrew LLB . . . *Oct 1992
Ast: Grunert, Mr Christopher Alan LLB . . . Nov 2002

GRAYSON WILLIS BENNETT ‡
7 North Church Street Sheffield South Yorkshire S1 1TD
Tel: 0114 290 9500 *Fax:* 0114 290 9501
Emergency telephone 07654 318616
E-mail: help@gwbsol.co.uk
List of partners: J A C Dalrymple, M Jones, P N Jones, M R Whitworth, M G Willis, C Z Wong
Office: Rotherham
Work: B2 G H
Emergency Action, Agency, Advocacy, Fixed Fee Interview, Legal Aid undertaken and Legal Aid Franchise
Ptr: Dalrymple, Mr J Andrew C MA(Cantab) . . . *Apr 1982
Jones, Mr Michael LLB . . . *Mar 1981
Whitworth, Mr Michael Robert LLB(Hons) . . . *Jun 1977
Willis, Mr Michael G LLB(Hons) ★ . . . *Mar 1984
Wong, Mr Christopher Zee LLB(Hons) . . . *Nov 1990
Ast: Jepson, Mr Richard Paul BA(Law); MA . . . *Jul 2005

GRAYSONS ‡
(incorporating Watson Esam)
4-12 Paradise Square Sheffield South Yorkshire S1 1TB
Tel: 0114 272 9184 *Fax:* 0114 279 6253 *Dx:* 10509 SHEFFIELD
E-mail: enquiries@graysons.co.uk
List of partners: P M Clark, D P Coffey, M Cooper, G N Dring, K M Fitzpatrick, C A Goodwin, J P Hatfield, B J Lancaster, E Newbold, J F West
Office: Chesterfield
Work: D1 D2 E K1 K3 K4 N S1 S2 W Z(r)
Emergency Action, Agency, Advocacy, Legal Aid undertaken, Legal Aid Franchise and Member of Accident Line
Ptr: Clark, Mr Peter M LLB Maxwell Law Prize . . . *Oct 1982
Coffey, Mr David Philip LLB(Sheff) Notary Public . . . Jan 1987
Cooper, Ms Michelle LLB(Hons) . . . *Oct 1998
Dring, Mr G Neil BA . . . *Nov 1985
Fitzpatrick, Ms Kathleen M BA ♦ . . . *Oct 1984
Goodwin, Mr Carl A LLB . . . *Dec 1986
Hatfield, Mr John P LLB . . . *Dec 1980
Lancaster, Ms Belinda J LLB . . . *Oct 1993
Newbold, Mrs Elizabeth . . . Sep 1990
West, Mr Jonathan F LLB . . . *Nov 1997
Asoc: Szabo, Mr Paul LLB; DipLP . . . *Nov 1998
Ast: Alder, Ms Helen . . . Sep 2002
Barton, Miss Leanne Kathleen LLB(Hons) . . . Sep 2009
Elliott, Ms Amy . . . Jul 2009
Fisher, Mr Mark Lee BA; LPC . . . Nov 2005
Hall, Ms Janet LLB . . . *Oct 1989
Heath, Mrs Petra LLB . . . *Sep 1998
Hubbard, Miss Emma LLB . . . *Jan 2007
Naseem, Miss Adeeba LLB(Hons) . . . May 2005
Toyn, Mr David Neil BA . . . Sep 2000
Whittle, Miss Marilyn Joan LLB(Hons); LPC . . . Jan 2008
Woodhouse, Miss Vicky LLB . . . *Sep 2007

HLW KEEBLE HAWSON LLP ‡
Old Cathedral Vicarage St James Row Sheffield South Yorkshire S1 1XA
Tel: 0114 272 2061 *Fax:* 0114 270 0813 *Dx:* 10527 SHEFFIELD
E-mail: info@hlwkeeblehawson.co.uk
List of partners: J Baker, A Birch, R A Brown, G Connell, A J Coombe, D R Cunliffe, M R Dixon, R K Dyson, E Eaton, J R Fergusson, V E Fox, J E P Gervasio, P V Goel, N Goulding, A H Gregory, P J Grindley, D M Guest, M K Harvey, V L Hilton, M W Hollinghurst, J R Holt, D A Jameson, S J Lockley, I P McCombie, A McKenzie Smith, H D McKillop, C A Moore, S L Needle, G R Owen, M T Pennington, P R Pennington, J E Pettingill, R W G Pickford, A M Pliener, D Rodgers, N J Rodwell, C E S Rothwell, J Rowden, R J Smith, P G Trudgill, G A Village, E M Ward, S Ward, B J Warne, R C Whitlam, R C Wilson, A M Wood
Office: Doncaster, Leeds, Sheffield
Languages: Arabic, Brunei, Cantonese, French, German, Hebrew, Indonesian, Malay, Mandarin, Portuguese, Spanish

Work: A1 B1 C1 C2 C3 D1 E F1 G H I J1 K1 K2 L M1 N O P Q R1 R2 S1 S2 T1 T2 U2 V W X Z(b,c,d,e,f,g,h,i,j,k,l,m,n,o,p,q,r,s,t,w,x)
Emergency Action, Agency, Advocacy, Fixed Fee Interview, Legal Aid undertaken, Legal Aid Franchise and Member of Accident Line
Ptr: Baker, Mrs Janet LLB(Hons); PGDip Personal Injury Litigation . . . *Apr 1974
Brown, Mr Robert A LLB Licensed Insolvency Practitioner . . . *§Apr 1979
Connell, Mr George . . . *May 1975
Coombe, Mr Andrew J FCA . . . *Sep 1976
Fergusson, Mr John R . . . Oct 1991
Fox, Ms Vanessa E MA(Cantab) . . . *Oct 1987
Gervasio, Mr James E P BSc(Econ); LLB . . . Jan 1984
Gregory, Mr Anthony H LLB(Leeds) Sidney Herbert Clay Prize . . . *Jun 1967
Grindley, Mr Paul J LLB . . . Sep 1990
Harvey, Mr Martin Kevin LLB(Hons) . . . *Mar 1987
Hilton, Miss Victoria Louise LLB(Hons) . . . *Nov 1996
Holt, Mr John R LLB; FCIArb . . . *Nov 1972
Moore, Miss Caroline A LLB . . . *Dec 1991
Owen, Mr Gareth R MA(Oxon) . . . *Dec 1977
Pickford, Mr Robert William Granville LLB Notary Public . . . May 1966
Rodgers, Mr Derek LLB(Hons) . . . Oct 1993
Rodwell, Mr Nicholas John BA(Nott'm)(Law) . . . *Dec 1977
Rothwell, Mr Charles Edward Shaw LLB Royal Bank of Scotland Prize for Banking Law Freeman of the City of London . . . *Nov 1993
Rowden, Mr Julian . . . *May 1986
Trudgill, Mr Paul Graham LLB . . . *Oct 1994
Ward, Mr Stuart LLB . . . *Oct 1993
Asoc: Woodward, Mr Darren . . . Dec 2000
Ast: Jones, Mr David N LLB . . . Nov 1994
Parsons, Mrs Deborah A LLB(Hons) . . . *Sep 1999

HLW KEEBLE HAWSON LLP
Commercial House Commercial Street Sheffield South Yorkshire S1 2AT
Tel: 0114 276 5555 *Fax:* 0114 276 8066 *Dx:* 10643 SHEFFIELD 1
E-mail: info@hlwkeeblehawson.co.uk
Office: Doncaster, Leeds, Sheffield
Languages: French, German
Work: A3 B1 C1 C2 C3 E F1 I J1 O Q R2 S1 S2 T1 U1 W Z(b,c,e,q)
Agency, Fixed Fee Interview and Legal Aid undertaken
Ptr: Birch, Mr Alaric BA . . . *Jun 1978
Dyson, Mr Roger Kenneth LLB . . . Jun 1978
Eaton, Mrs Emilda LLB(Hons) . . . *Dec 1993
Guest, Mr David Michael BA(Law) . . . Oct 1989
Jameson, Mr David Alan LLB(Hons) . . . *Jan 1985
Pettingill, Miss Joan E LLB(Hons) . . . Jun 1998
Smith, Mr Richard Jonathon . . . Sep 1997
Village, Mr Giles Alastair BA . . . *Dec 1979
Warne, Mr Barry John MA(Cantab) . . . Oct 1981
Whitlam, Mr Ronald Charles MA(Cantab) . . . *§Jun 1979
Wilson, Mr Robert Christopher LLB . . . *§Dec 1976
Wood, Mr Ashley Michael LLB . . . Mar 1994
Mem: Dixon, Mr Matthew R BSc(Econ) . . . *Jul 1998
Goulding, Mr Nicholas LLB(Hons) . . . *Oct 1997
Lockley, Mr Simon John LLB(Hons) . . . *Nov 1993
McCombie, Mr Ian Peter LLB(Hons) . . . Nov 1985
McKenzie Smith, Mr Andrew LLB(Hons) . . . *Mar 1992
Ast: Henwood, Elizabeth . . . Sep 2006
Con: Hartley, Mr Andrew James BA(Oxon) . . . *§Jun 1970

HILL DICKINSON LLP
City Plaza Pinfold Street Sheffield South Yorkshire S1 2GU
Tel: 0114 229 7907 *Fax:* 0114 229 8001 *Dx:* 10525 SHEFFIELD
E-mail: law@hilldickinson.com
Office: Chester, Liverpool, London EC3, Manchester
Ast: Bramley, Mr Gareth James LLB . . . Sep 2005

HOWELLS LLP ‡
15-17 Bridge Street Sheffield South Yorkshire S3 8NL
Tel: 0114 249 6666 *Fax:* 0114 279 9746 *Dx:* 10584 SHEFFIELD
Emergency telephone 0114 249 6666
E-mail: enquiries@howellsllp.com
List of partners: S M Colven, C Davey, J C Gibson, G J Hogarth, A P Kenworthy, D R Leach, M R Macadam, P J Mahy, J McSweeney, J A Seaborne, A L Siddall, D Simpson, J Whybrow
Office: Barnsley, Rotherham
Work: D1 F1 F2 G H J1 K1 K3 L N Q V X Z(g,i,m,q,r)
Emergency Action, Agency, Fixed Fee Interview and Legal Aid undertaken
Ptr: Colven, Ms Susan Mary . . . *Nov 1984
Davey, Ms Christine . . . *Dec 1987
Gibson, Mr John Christopher . . . *Oct 1988
Hogarth, Mr Graham John . . . *Jul 1993
Kenworthy, Ms Anne Pamela . . . *Mar 1982
Leach, Mr Douglas Robert . . . *Jun 1978
McSweeney, Mr John . . . *Nov 1994
Mahy, Mr Peter Julian . . . *Nov 1998
Seaborne, Ms Judith Ann ★ . . . *Feb 1988
Siddall, Ms Alyson Louise . . . *Oct 1987
Simpson, Mr Daniel ★ . . . *Nov 1984
Whybrow, Mr Jonathan . . . *Apr 1991
Asoc: Lloyd-Jones, Ms Isabel Anne . . . *Oct 1983
Ast: Ahmed, Mr Nadeem Ashraf LLB(Hons) . . . *Nov 2003
Bulmer, Mrs Julie Roxene BA(Hons) . . . *Sep 2005
Clegg, Mr John . . . Apr 2009
Copeland, Mr Martin BA(Hons) . . . *Aug 2006
Flemming, Mr Geoffrey Vincent LLB(Hons) . . . *Nov 1984
Forrest, Mrs Elizabeth Sarah LLB(Hons) . . . *Oct 1993
Gillott, Ms Sarah Lesley LLB(Hons) . . . *Jul 2000
Gyte, Ms Michelle . . . Sep 2001
Harrison, Ms Tania LLB(Hons) . . . *Sep 2005
Hogarth, Mrs Lucy BA(Hons) . . . *Dec 2002
Hudson, Miss Charlotte BA(Hons) . . . *Mar 2008
Kennaway, Miss Catriona LLB(Hons) . . . *Apr 2009
Leach, Ms Sarah Ann LLB(Hons) . . . *Aug 2006
Lockwood, Mrs Sharon LLB(Hons) . . . Sep 2003
Moxley, Mr Peter Jack BA(Hons) . . . *Nov 1995
Munday, Ms Julie BA(Hons) . . . *Jun 2002
Nieto, Mr Peter . . . *Oct 2008
Parveen, Ms Shazia BSc(Hons) . . . *Oct 2004
Peace, Ms Christine Ann BA(Hons) . . . *Nov 2002
Peart, Miss Sarah Elizabeth BA(Hons) . . . *Aug 2002
Rawson, Ms Lindsey Jane LLB(Hons) . . . *Apr 1999
Rinaldi, Ms Sharon . . . *Sep 2001
Rodgers, Ms Lucy . . . Sep 2001
Sim, Mr Iain Scott LLB . . . *Apr 2000
Steiner, Ms Katherine Jane LLB(Hons) . . . *Jun 1986
Swaby, Mr Andrew Admiral BA(Hons) . . . *Dec 2001
Thomas, Ms Carita . . . Oct 2008

IRWIN MITCHELL LLP ‡
(incorporating Braby & Waller)
Riverside House 2 Millsands Sheffield South Yorkshire S3 8DT
Tel: 0870 150 0100 *Fax:* 0114 275 3306
E-mail: enquiries@irwinmitchell.co.uk
List of partners: D M Adams, A Alexander, J L Atkinson, N D Baker, C A Beadell, A Bell, D M Billings, D I B Body, S A Booth, A P B Budgen, A J Burke, N M Castle, R M Clark, S C Coates, G R Codd, J P Crossland, H E Culley, K G Cunningham, H L Dapin, A J Darke, J A Davis, J De Lorenzo, K J Docherty, A M Eddy, C B Ettinger, A R Fernandes, J M Flathers, G V Flemming, R T Follis, C A W Garner, C R E Gillott, A Griffiths, D N Harris, P T Harris, S A Henderson, L D Herbertson, P S Hirst, M Holland, P Horner, J A Horton, R W Hughes, J M Jelly, L C Jordan, S Kingston, A R M Kirkpatrick, D Knaggs, A J H Lockley, J J Lord, J C Love, M P Loxley, S R Martin, S A Mewies, T M Napier, J Peacock, J Pickering, D N Prince, A P Reid, D J Revitt, M R Roberts, T I Roberts, K Robinson, K J Robinson, W Simpson, Y F Sit, A Somers, A A V Straw, C L Sykes, A Taylor, A Tucker, A Uprichard, D J Urpeth, L C Walker, G R Walters, J R Whiting, M R Whitworth, L C Wise, E J Wright, A Wylde, P R Wylde, M R W Zurbrugg
Office: Birmingham, Bristol, Leeds, London EC1, Manchester, Newcastle upon Tyne
Languages: Dutch, French, German, Italian, Punjabi, Spanish, Urdu
Work: A1 A3 B1 B2 C1 C2 C3 D1 E F1 G H I J1 J2 K1 K2 L M1 M2 N O P Q R1 R2 S1 S2 T1 T2 V W X Z(b,c,d,e,f,g,h,j,l,n,o,p,q,r,t,u,w)
Emergency Action, Agency, Advocacy, Fixed Fee Interview, Legal Aid undertaken, Legal Aid Franchise and Member of Accident Line
Ptr: Adams, Mr David M LLB(Hons) . . . *§May 1974
Atkinson, Miss Julie L LLB(Hons) . . . *Oct 1984
Baker, Mr Niall D LLB(Hons) . . . *Oct 1991
Body, Mr David I B MA(Oxon) . . . *§Jun 1981
Booth, Miss Sallie A BA(Hons) . . . *Nov 1987
Budgen, Mr Adrian P B BA(Hons) . . . *Nov 1988
Burke, Miss Andrea Jayne BA(Hons) . . . *Oct 1994
Clark, Mr Ross McKenzie BA; LLB; DipLP . . . *Sep 1993
Codd, Mr Grahame R . . . *Sep 1981
Crossland, Mr J Peter LLB(Hons) . . . *Oct 1985
Culley, Mr Howard E LLB . . . *Mar 1979
Darke, Mr Andrew J LLB(Hons) ● . . . *Feb 1991
Davis, Mr John A LLB(Hons) . . . *Apr 1983
Docherty, Mr Kevin J BA(Law) . . . *Jul 1980
Flemming, Mr Geoffrey V LLB(Hons) . . . *Nov 1984
Garner, Mr Clive Anthony Winston LLB; MA; LLM . . . *Nov 1992
Hirst, Mr Paul S BA(Law) . . . *Jan 1987
Holland, Mr Martyn LLB . . . *Oct 1984
Horner, Mr Peter MA(Cantab) . . . *Oct 1973
Jelly, Mr John M MA(Cantab) . . . *Mar 1968
Kingston, Mr Sion LLB . . . *Oct 1994
Lockley, Mr Andrew John Harold MA(Oxon) . . . Jul 1979
Loxley, Mr Martin P BA(Hons)(Law) . . . *Sep 1980
Martin, Mr Steven R LLB(Hons) . . . *Apr 1980
Napier, Mr T Michael LLB . . . *Mar 1970
Pickering, Mr John LLB . . . *Jun 1979
Prince, Mr David N LLB . . . *Oct 1982
Reid, Mr Alastair P LLB . . . *Oct 1983
Revitt, Mr Daniel J LLB(Hons) . . . *Oct 1990
Roberts, Mr Melvin R BA(Law) . . . *Oct 1987
Roberts, Mr T Ian MA(Oxon) Law Society Nominee on Court of Bradford University . . . *Oct 1982
Robinson, Mr Kevin J LLB . . . *Jun 1972
Somers, Mrs Amina LLB(B'ham) . . . *Feb 1989
Straw, Mrs Alison Ann Victoria LLB(Hons) . . . Oct 1991
Sykes, Ms C Louise LLB(Hons) . . . *Feb 1990
Tucker, Mr Andrew LLB . . . *Oct 1985
Uprichard, Mr Andrew BA(Lond) . . . *Feb 1989
Urpeth, Mr David John LLB(Hons)(Lond); DipLP . . . *Jul 1996
Whitworth, Mr Michael Robert LLB(Hons) . . . *Jun 1977
Wright, Ms E Jane BA . . . *Oct 1992
Ast: Abas, Ms Madeline N LLB(Hons) . . . *Dec 1996
Amin, Mr Yogendra LLB(Hons) . . . Apr 1999
Argyle, Miss Victoria Louise LLB(Hons) . . . *Oct 1997
Armstrong, Dr Nicholas James Buchanan LLB(Hons); PhD . . . *Oct 1998
Ashton, Ms Helen T BA; CPE; LPC . . . Dec 1998
Beahan, Mr Steven John LLB(Hons) . . . *Sep 1996
Beck, Ms Caroline . . . Aug 1998
Bentley, Mr Michael S LLB(Hons) . . . *Jun 1981
Bhabra, Ms Raminder K . . . *Mar 1998
Bowen, Ms A Gemma LLB(Hons) . . . *Oct 1998
Burch, Ms Jennifer J . . . *Oct 1998
Causier, Miss Karen Mary LLB . . . *Nov 1993
Coldicott, Mrs Rebecca L LLB . . . *Oct 1989
Delaney, Miss Caitlin Josephine Mary RGN(Hons); RM RNT; BSc(Hons); PGCEA; MSocSc . . . *Sep 1996
Fairclough, Miss Lisa C . . . *Mar 1999
Fenny, Mr James . . . *§Feb 1995
Gent, Mr Ben . . . Oct 1997
Gollaglee, Mr John BA . . . Nov 1996
Goulding, Mr Nicholas LLB(Hons) . . . *Oct 1997
Hadley, Miss Kerry Marianne . . . *Sep 1999
Hamilton-Hislop, Miss Ann LLB; LSF . . . *Oct 1993
Hardy, Mrs Simone Sarah LLB(Hons) . . . *Sep 1996
Harrison, Ms Lisa LLB(Hons) . . . *Oct 1995
Jenkins, Miss Louise Caroline . . . *Sep 1999
Malia, Ms Christine A BA . . . *Nov 1989
Marjoram, Ms Sally BA(Hons) . . . *Nov 1998
Matthewman, Miss Carole LLB . . . *May 1999
Mayes, Ms Francesca LLB(Hons) Herbert Clay Law Prize Secretary for Rotherham Headway . . . *Sep 1997
Meese, Miss Nicola . . . *Oct 1991
Meldrum, Mr Peter Llewellyn LLB . . . *Oct 1992
Mitchell, Miss Caroline E BA(Dunelm); CPE; LSF . . . *Oct 1995
Morgan, Ms Louise LLB . . . *Oct 1991
Nettleship, Mr Gregory R BA . . . *Nov 1984
Oldham, Mrs Lisa J LLB(Hons) . . . *Feb 1994
Owens, Mr Alan Jeffery LLB . . . *Sep 1997
Pape, Ms Felicity S BA . . . *Mar 1988
Phillips, Miss Jill Elizabeth LLB . . . *Oct 1991
Reid, Ms Julie Margot . . . *Oct 1983
Richardson, Mr Steven Graeme LLB . . . *Nov 1993
Russell, Ms Penelope BA . . . *Oct 1994
Russell, Mrs Sarah . . . *Nov 1998
Senior, Mr Jonathan Stuart LLB(Hons) . . . *Nov 1993
Smith, Mr Simon M LLB . . . *Dec 1996
Stowers, Mr Daniel James LLB(Hons) . . . *Mar 1997
Turner-Johnson, Mrs Madeleine LLB . . . *Oct 1993
Walker, Mr Andrew BA . . . *Oct 1994
Whitehouse, Mr Paul Ian LLB . . . *Oct 1995
Whiteley, Mr Neil Anthony LLB(Newc); LPC(Nott'm) . . . *Sep 1996
Wong, Mr Christopher Zee LLB(Hons) . . . *Nov 1990

KENNEDYS
Ventana House 2 Concourse Way Sheaf Street Sheffield South Yorkshire S1 2BJ
Tel: 0114 253 2000 *Fax:* 0114 253 2001 *Dx:* 10528 SHEFFIELD
Office: Belfast, Birmingham, Cambridge, Chelmsford, London EC3, Maidstone, Manchester, Taunton

LEVITEN THOMPSON & CO ‡
Wicker Chambers 19-21 Wicker Sheffield South Yorkshire S3 8JQ
Tel: 0114 276 9321 *Fax:* 0114 272 7111 *Dx:* 10569 SHEFFIELD
E-mail: ltandco@gotadsl.co.uk
List of partners: S Bennett, J M Thompson
Work: D1 E F1 G H J1 J2 K1 K2 K3 L N O W Z(l)
Emergency Action, Agency, Advocacy, Fixed Fee Interview and Legal Aid undertaken
Ptr: Bennett, Mr Sean BSocSc . . . *Jan 1986
Thompson, Mr John M LLB ● . . . Dec 1973
Ast: Dever, Mr Damien Michael LLB . . . *May 2009

LEWIS FRANCIS BLACKBURN BRAY ‡
14-16 Paradise Square Sheffield South Yorkshire S1 2DE
Tel: 0114 272 9721 *Fax:* 0114 275 4347 *Dx:* 10506 SHEFFIELD
List of partners: C P Bray, K B Exell, R S Francis, R Lewis
Work: C1 C2 E J1 K3 L S1 S2 T1 T2 W Z(e)
Ptr: Bray, Mr C Paul . . . *Jan 1983
Exell, Mr Kevin B LLB(B'ham) . . . *Jun 1971
Francis, Mr Richard Stephen LLB(Hons) . . . *Feb 1998
Lewis, Mr Roy . . . Jan 1972

SAM LODH ‡
643 Staniforth Road Sheffield South Yorkshire S9 4RD
Tel: 0114 243 5395
E-mail: babul@lodhlaw.co.uk

LUPTON FAWCETT
Velocity House 3 Solly Street Sheffield South Yorkshire S1 4DE
Tel: 0114 276 6607 *Fax:* 0114 276 6608 *Dx:* 10548 SHEFFIELD
E-mail: law@luptonfawcett.com
Office: Leeds
Ptr: Corker, Mr Daniel BA(Hons)(History) . . . Jan 2003
Hackett, Mr Adrian . . . Apr 2003

MAHMOOD MIRZA SOLICITORS ‡
371 Staniforth Road Sheffield South Yorkshire S9 3FP
Tel: 0114 256 1490 *Fax:* 0114 256 1491

F W MEGGITT & CO ‡
2 Broad Lane Sheffield South Yorkshire S1 4BT
Tel: 0114 272 7955 *Fax:* 0114 275 6961 *Dx:* 10560 SHEFFIELD
E-mail: helen@fwmeggitt.co.uk
List of partners: F W Meggitt
Languages: Gujarati, Kekchi, Kiswahili, Urdu
Work: B1 B2 B3 E K1 K3 Q R2 S1 S2 T1 T2 W Z(i)
Fixed Fee Interview undertaken
SPr: Meggitt, Mr Fred Wilkinson LLB(Manc) . . . *Apr 1970
Ast: Walji, Mr Barkatali Rajabali LLB(Hons); ASCA; FMAAT; FAIA Member of Valuation Tribunal for England . . . *Sep 2003

CAROLINE MOORE LAW ‡
8 Alexandra Gardens Sheffield South Yorkshire S11 9DQ
Tel: 0114 360 0035

MORTON PRICE ‡
Belmayne House 99 Clarkehouse Road Sheffield South Yorkshire S10 2LN
Tel: 0114 266 4141 *Fax:* 0114 266 9836 *Dx:* 709064 SHEFFIELD 12
E-mail: richard@mortonprice.demon.co.uk
List of partners: R Morton, S J Price
Work: B1 C1 C2 E I J1 L R1 R2 S1 S2 Z(e,f)
Ptr: Morton, Mr Richard LLB . . . *Oct 1986
Price, Mr Stephen J LLB . . . *Jan 1978
Ast: Newbould, Ms Fiona Alexandra LLB(Hons) . . . *Oct 1992

NFLA LTD
Northchurch Business Centre 84 Queen Street Sheffield South Yorkshire S1 2DW
Tel: 0114 213 3888 *Fax:* 0870 441 9145 *Dx:* 10864 SHEFFIELD
Emergency telephone 0115 945 4555
E-mail: mail@nflaw.co.uk
Office: Chesterfield, Nottingham, Rotherham, Wellingborough
Work: D1 K1 K3
Dir: Newbold, Mrs Elizabeth . . . Sep 1990
Asoc: Alder, Ms Helen . . . Sep 2002

NABARRO LLP
(in association with Key & Dixon; Livasiri & Co; Cabinet Lipworth(France))
1 South Quay Victoria Quays Sheffield South Yorkshire S2 5SY
Tel: 0114 279 4000 *Fax:* 0114 278 6123 *Dx:* 712550 SHEFFIELD 20
Office: London WC1
Work: A1 A3 B1 C1 C2 C3 E F1 F2 I J1 J2 L M1 M3 N O P Q R1 R2 S1 S2 T1 U1 W Z(b,c,d,e,f,j,k,n,o,p,q,r,s,u,w)
Ptr: Blackwell, Mr John LLB(Lond) . . . *§May 1972
Clarke, Mr Raymond G BA . . . *Jul 1987
Dray, Mr Carl G BA(Hons) . . . *Nov 1985
Fitzsimons, Mr Stephen MA(Oxon) . . . *Oct 1982
Goodwill, Mr Peter LLB . . . *Nov 1986
Grabiner, Mr Martin S MA(Cantab) . . . *Mar 1979
Logan, Mr Gordon Niall LLB(Leics) . . . *Apr 1981
McKenna, Ms Susan J BA . . . May 1978
Pointon, Mr Neil LLB(Hons)(Leics) . . . *Oct 1980
Pugh, Mr Keith W BA(Hons)(Manc) . . . Jan 1981
Renger, Mr Michael MA(Cantab) . . . *Apr 1980
Shaw, Mr Timothy J LLB(Hons)(Chester) . . . *Mar 1981
Watkins, Mr Gareth LLB(Hons)(Wales) . . . *Dec 1980
Williams, Mr Roger LLB(Wales) . . . *Nov 1971
Ast: Andrews, Miss Karen J BA(Manc) . . . Nov 1987

NATIONWIDE PROBATE SOLICITORS ‡
The John Banner Centre 620 Attercliffe Road Sheffield South Yorkshire S9 3QS
Tel: 0114 256 4774 *Fax:* 0114 256 4777
E-mail: info@nwprobate.co.uk

NETHER EDGE LAW ‡
PO Box 3439 Sheffield South Yorkshire S11 8NH
Tel: 0114 268 7638 *Fax:* 0114 268 7638
Dx: 701852 BANNER CROSS
E-mail: jss@netheredgelaw.co.uk

See p112 for the Key to Work Categories & other symbols

NORRIE WAITE & SLATER ‡
9-12 East Parade Sheffield South Yorkshire S1 2ET
Tel: 0114 276 6166 *Fax:* 0114 273 9311 *Dx:* 10559 SHEFFIELD
E-mail: info@norrie-waite.com
List of partners: M S Breislin, K Burgin, J F Darwin, S Ewbank, K Moxon-Smith, S Russell, D P Staniforth, P J M Stubbs, R B Wrigley
Office: Rotherham, Sheffield (2 offices)
Work: B2 C1 D1 D2 E F1 F2 G H J1 K1 K2 K3 K4 L M1 N O P Q S1 S2 W X Z(c,g,h,l,p,q,t,u)
Emergency Action, Agency, Advocacy, Fixed Fee Interview, Legal Aid undertaken, Legal Aid Franchise and Member of Accident Line
Ptr: Breislin, Mr Mark S BA . . . *§Dec 1980
Burgin, Ms Katy. . . . Sep 2003
Darwin, Mr Jonathan F LLB(Sheff) . . . Jun 1980
Ewbank, Ms Sarah LLB . . . *Oct 1986
Moxon-Smith, Ms Karen. . . . Dec 1997
Russell, Ms Sandra . . . Apr 1994
Staniforth, Mr David P BA(Law) . . . Nov 1991
Stubbs, Mr Peter J M BA . . . *Dec 1978
Wrigley, Mr R Brian BJuris; LLM. . . . *May 1972
Ast: Throup, Ms Hannah. . . . Oct 2007

Other offices in Rotherham, Sheffield (2). Holders of Franchise for Consumer / General Contract, Crime, Debt, Housing, Personal Injury, Family. We specialise in the following areas of work Crime - General, Housing, Landlord and Tenant, Residential Conveyancing.

NORRIE WAITE & SLATER
Criminal Department 72 Queen Street Sheffield South Yorkshire S1 1WR
Tel: 0114 276 5015 *Fax:* 0114 270 0681
E-mail: info@norrie-waite.com
Office: Rotherham, Sheffield (2 offices)
Work: G H

NORRIE WAITE & SLATER
21-23 Bridge Street Killamarsh Sheffield South Yorkshire S21 1AH
Tel: 0114 248 4890 *Fax:* 0114 248 4911
Office: Rotherham, Sheffield (2 offices)
Work: E G H K1 K3 L S1 S2
Legal Aid undertaken and Legal Aid Franchise

OAK TREE SOLICITORS ‡
Unit 2 Matrix Business Centre Nobel Way Sheffield South Yorkshire S25 3QB
Tel: 01909 547103

PENNINE LAW
Bank Chambers PO Box 259 Penistone Sheffield South Yorkshire S36 6HX
Tel: 01226 763551 *Fax:* 01226 767338
E-mail: mail@penninelaw.co.uk
Office: Barnsley
Work: A1 C1 E R2 S1 S2 W
Ptr: Hoyland, Mr William H M . . . *Jan 1986
Lofthouse, Mr Ian E. . . . Aug 1979

JAMES PETERS & CO ‡
Kendal House 41 Scotland Street Sheffield South Yorkshire S3 7BS
Tel: 0114 278 8900 *Fax:* 0114 275 6462 *Dx:* 10515 SHEFFIELD 1
E-mail: info@jamespeters.co.uk
List of partners: R W Ibbotson
Work: B1 O Q
SPr: Ibbotson, Mr Richard W BA(Hons)(Law). . . . *Jun 1980

PRODDOW MACKAY ‡
PM House 250 Shepcote Lane Sheffield South Yorkshire S9 1TP
Tel: 0114 249 3311 *Fax:* 0114 249 3440
E-mail: enquiries@proddowmackay.co.uk
List of partners: D J Mackay, S K Proddow
Office: Maidenhead

QUALITYSOLICITORS JORDANS
109 Wales Road Kiveton Park Sheffield South Yorkshire S26 6RD
Tel: 01909 773627
E-mail: info@jorsols.co.uk
Office: Doncaster
Languages: German, Gujarati, Hebrew
Work: A1 C1 E F1 G H J1 K1 L M1 N P R1 S1 T1 V W Z(d,e,h,i,j,k,l,m,o,s)
Emergency Action, Agency, Advocacy, Fixed Fee Interview, Legal Aid undertaken and Member of Accident Line
Ptr: Newby, Mr Mark LLB ★ . . . *§Sep 1993

RUSSELL JONES & WALKER
7th Floor The Fountain Precinct 1 Balm Green Sheffield South Yorkshire S1 2JA
Tel: 0114 276 6868 *Fax:* 0114 252 5600 *Dx:* 26078 SHEFFIELD 2
E-mail: enquiries@rjw.co.uk
Office: Birmingham, Bristol, Cardiff, London WC2, Manchester, Newcastle upon Tyne, Wakefield
Work: G H J2 N Z(p,r)
Emergency Action, Agency, Advocacy, Fixed Fee Interview, Legal Aid undertaken, Legal Aid Franchise and Member of Accident Line
Ptr: Allen, Mr Simon J N BA(Hons)(Law). . . . *Jan 1985
Ast: Bowers, Ms Anna. . . . Jan 1998
Cartwright, Ms Lorraine . . . Nov 1997
Clayton, Mr Rory G . . . Aug 1996
Duffy, Mr Shaun. . . . Oct 1999

SIMPSON SISSONS & BROOKE ‡
43 Townhead Street Sheffield South Yorkshire S1 2EB
Tel: 0114 241 3970 *Fax:* 0114 275 1879
E-mail: enquiries@simpsonsissonsandbrooke.co.uk

TAYLOR & EMMET LLP ‡
20 Arundel Gate Sheffield South Yorkshire S1 2PP
Tel: 0114 218 4000 *Fax:* 0114 218 4223 *Dx:* 10549 SHEFFIELD 1
E-mail: info@tayloremmet.co.uk
List of partners: P M Blower, R N Cooke, S Gaunt, V J Green, J Hawkins, M T Heathcote, R M King, P A Lennon, C A Moore, R W C Moore, J V Outram, C E Patton, D M Smart, J M Stittle, D Thompson, M R Ward, G A R Wilkinson
Office: Dronfield, Sheffield
Work: A3 B1 C1 C2 D1 D2 E F1 F2 J1 J2 K1 K2 K3 L N O Q R1 R2 S1 S2 T2 W Z(e,h,j,l,p,q,r,za)
Emergency Action, Agency, Fixed Fee Interview, Legal Aid undertaken and Member of Accident Line
Ptr: Blower, Mr Peter M LLB. . . . *Dec 1973
Cooke, Mr Robert Neil LLB . . . *Sep 1999
Green, Mr Vincent J BA(Law) . . . *May 1978
Hawkins, Mr John BA. . . . *Dec 1978
Heathcote, Mrs Michaela T LLB. . . . *Oct 1991
King, Mr Richard M LLB. . . . Aug 1997
Lennon, Miss Patricia A LLB . . . *Dec 1983
Moore, Ms Caroline A LLB . . . *Dec 1991
Moore, Mr Robert William Chaffey LLB . . . Nov 1991
Outram, Mr John V LLB. . . . *Nov 1982
Patton, Miss Channah E MA(Cantab) . . . *Sep 1997
Smart, Mrs Diana M LLB(Hons); CTA; TEP . . . *Dec 1989
Stittle, Mr Jonathan M MA(Oxon) . . . *Oct 1984
Thompson, Mrs Deborah LLB; BCL . . . *Apr 1993
Ward, Mr M Ross BA . . . *Oct 1983
Wilkinson, Mr George Antony Ryder LLB . . . *May 1972

TAYLOR & EMMET LLP
890-892 Ecclesall Road Sheffield South Yorkshire S11 8TP
Tel: 0114 218 4000 *Fax:* 0114 266 3713
Dx: 712922 BANNER CROSS
E-mail: info@tayloremmet.co.uk
Office: Dronfield, Sheffield
Work: E L S1 S2 Z(h)
Fixed Fee Interview and Legal Aid undertaken
Ptr: Gaunt, Ms Sarah LLB. . . . Sep 2000
Con: Burrows, Mr Randolph . . . Oct 1979

THOMPSONS (FORMERLY ROBIN/BRIAN THOMPSON & PARTNERS)
Arundel House 1 Furnival Square Sheffield South Yorkshire S1 4QL
Tel: 0114 270 3300 *Fax:* 0114 273 8519 *Dx:* 709070 SHEFFIELD 14
Office: Belfast, Birmingham, Bristol, Cardiff, Chelmsford, Dagenham, Derby, Harrow, Leeds, Liverpool, London SW19, London WC1, Manchester, Middlesbrough, Newcastle upon Tyne, Nottingham, Plymouth, South Shields, Southampton, Stoke-on-Trent, Swansea, Wolverhampton
Work: G H J1 J2 N V Z(p,q,r)
Legal Aid undertaken, Legal Aid Franchise and Member of Accident Line
Ptr: Stothard, Mr David I BA(Hons); BCL . . . *Nov 1991
Ast: Cooper, Ms Jane LLB(Hons) . . . *Jul 1995
Richmond-Sterry, Mr Tristram G LLB(Hons). . . . *Aug 1992
Rothwell, Ms Angela L ILEX; LPC. . . . *Oct 1995
Sharpe, Mrs Nicola ILEX; LPC . . . *Nov 1997
Wood, Ms Elizabeth BA(Hons); LPC. . . . *Oct 2001
Wood, Mr Simon P BA(Hons). . . . *Dec 1994

WAKE SMITH & TOFIELDS ‡
(incorporating Ronald England & Sons)
68 Clarkehouse Road Sheffield South Yorkshire S10 2LJ
Tel: 0114 266 6660 *Fax:* 0114 267 1253 *Dx:* 709061 SHEFFIELD 12
List of partners: J Baddeley, B P M Cashell, C M Doyle, M A Hayward, J C V Hunt, G L Jaques, J Knight, N T Lambert, R P Lees, N Salter, M R D Serby, E A Shaw, P R Thorn, M J Tunbridge, D W B Ware
Office: Sheffield
Languages: French, German
Work: A1 A3 B1 C1 C2 C3 D1 E F1 F2 I J1 J2 K1 K2 L M1 N O P Q R1 R2 S1 S2 T1 T2 U1 W X Z(b,c,d,e,f,h,l,m,o,p,q,r,s,t,y,z)
Agency, Fixed Fee Interview, Legal Aid undertaken, Legal Aid Franchise and Member of Accident Line
Ptr: Baddeley, Mr John LLB(Newc) . . . *Nov 1985
Cashell, Ms Breda P M LLB. . . . *Oct 1988
Hayward, Miss Michelle Anne LLB(Hons) . . . *May 1994
Hunt, Mr Jonathan C V OBE; TD; DL . . . *§Nov 1966
Jaques, Mr Glenn L LLB(Warw). . . . *Sep 1990
Knight, Mr Jonathan LLB(Hons)(Law). . . . *Oct 2002
Lambert, Mr Nicholas T LLB(Manc) . . . *Dec 1983
Lees, Mr Richard Patrick LLB(Hons); Dip PI Lit . . . *Feb 1990
Salter, Mr Neil LLB . . . *Feb 1988
Serby, Mr Mark R D BA. . . . *Nov 1988
Shaw, Miss Elizabeth A LLB(Hons) . . . *Nov 1992
Tunbridge, Mr Michael J TEP General Commissioner of Income Tax. . . . *Nov 1976
Ware, Mr David W B BA. . . . *§Jan 1981
Asoc: Shepherd, Mr Duncan G LLB(Hons). . . . *Sep 1997
Ast: Donnelly, Mr Damian . . . Oct 2001
Gibbon, Mr Paul A LLB(Hons). . . . Dec 1999
Glover, Miss Rachael Sarah LLB . . . *Sep 2004
Rawlinson, Mr Peter A LLB . . . *Oct 1996
Stopford, Mrs Rebecca C BSc(Hons). . . . *Sep 1997
Wilson, Mr Peter H BA(Hons). . . . May 1991

WAKE SMITH & TOFIELDS
(incorporating Ronald England & Sons)
6 Campo Lane Sheffield South Yorkshire S1 2EF
Tel: 0114 266 6660 *Fax:* 0114 267 1253 *Dx:* 10534 SHEFFIELD 1
Office: Sheffield
Work: D1 D2 K1 K2 N S1 W
Legal Aid Franchise
Ptr: Doyle, Mrs Carmel M BA . . . *Oct 1988
Thorn, Mr Paul R BA Deputy District Judge . . . *Oct 1982
Asoc: Canning, Lindsey M LLB(Hons) . . . *Oct 1992
Ast: Finn, Miss Rosemary LLB(Hons) . . . *Oct 1987

MICHAEL WARD ‡
67a Middlewood Road Hillsborough Sheffield South Yorkshire S6 4GX
Tel: 0114 233 6198 *Fax:* 0114 233 6198
List of partners: M R Ward
Work: D1 E G H K1 L N O Q S1 W Z(l)
Emergency Action, Agency, Advocacy, Legal Aid undertaken and Member of Accident Line
Ptr: Ward, Mr Michael R FILEx . . . *Jan 1983

ROSALIND WATCHORN ‡
10 Kenwood Park Road Sheffield South Yorkshire S7 1NF
Tel: 0114 229 0160 *Fax:* 0114 229 0170
E-mail: mail@rwatchorn.co.uk
List of partners: R S Linsell, R A Watchorn
Work: E K4 S1 S2 T2 W
Fixed Fee Interview undertaken
Ptr: Linsell, Ms Rebecca Sarah BA(Hons) . . . *Jul 1999
Watchorn, Ms Rosalind Ann BA(Hons); TEP. . . . *Apr 1989
Asoc: Warden, Mr James Stewart LLB. . . . Dec 1974
Ast: Buchan, Mr James Anthony LLB . . . Nov 2009
Saccaggi, Miss Anna Luise Maria LLB. . . . Sep 2010
Wright, Miss Annie LLB . . . Jun 2006

WOSSKOW BROWN ‡
620 Attercliffe Road Sheffield South Yorkshire S9 3QS
Tel: 0114 256 1560 *Fax:* 0114 243 3951 *Dx:* 700861 ATTERCLIFFE
E-mail: info@wosskowbrown.co.uk
List of partners: D E Brown, I D Brown, P C Ibbotson, S J Mallinson, M Wosskow
Office: Sheffield
Languages: Cantonese, French, German, Punjabi, Urdu
Work: B1 C1 D1 E F1 J1 K1 L N O Q S1 T1 T2 W Z(i)
Fixed Fee Interview undertaken and Member of Accident Line
Ptr: Brown, Mr David E LLB . . . *Oct 1989
Brown, Mr Ian David . . . *Jul 2000
Ibbotson, Mr Paul Clough Sidney Herbert Clay Prize *§Dec 1972
Mallinson, Miss Sally Jane LLB . . . *Jul 2003
Wosskow, Mr Michael MA(Oxon) . . . *§Mar 1972
Asoc: Nazir, Mr Mohammed LLB; MA . . . *Jul 2004
Ast: Gibson, Mr Matthew. . . . Apr 2010
Kennedy, Mr Alan LPC(Hons) . . . *Sep 2010
Khanam, Laki. . . . Jan 2010
Taff, Kerry. . . . Oct 2008
Tan, Mr Kiley Ban Teong LLB . . . *Aug 2003

WRIGLEYS SOLICITORS LLP
3rd Floor Fountain Precinct Balm Green Sheffield South Yorkshire S1 2JA
Tel: 0114 267 5588 *Fax:* 0114 276 3176
E-mail: thepartners@wrigleys.co.uk
Office: Leeds
Work: A1 T2 W Z(d)
Ptr: Bradey, Mrs Lynne Elizabeth . . . *Oct 2003
Greaves, Susan BA(Hons) . . . Sep 1998
Smallman, Mr Godfrey J MA(Oxon). . . . *Dec 1982
Ast: Buckley, Mrs Charlotte Lucie BA(Law & Criminology) . Jun 2010
Clark, Mrs Maria Dawn LLB(Hons) . . . Sep 2004
Clarkson, Mr Peter M BA(Hons)(Dunelm) . . . *Dec 1990
Irons, Emma . . . Sep 2005
Nelson, Miss Emma. . . . Sep 2011
Netting, Mrs Jane Helena LLB(Hons) . . . Sep 1997
Noreen, Miss Anjum LLB(Hons). . . . Jul 2011
Thornton, Austin James BA . . . Dec 1995
Watkinson, Mrs Julia Carolyn LLB(Hons) Vice President Sheffield Law Society . . . Dec 2002
Con: Allison, Miss Margaret LLB . . . Oct 1987

YOUNGS CRIMINAL DEFENCE SERVICES LIMITED ‡
10 Ellesmere Road Pitsmoor Sheffield South Yorkshire S4 7JB
Tel: 0114 249 5444 *Fax:* 0114 249 5442
Emergency telephone 07956 971461
E-mail: info@ycds.co.uk
List of partners: J C Young
Work: G H
Emergency Action, Agency, Advocacy, Legal Aid undertaken and Legal Aid Franchise
SPr: Young, Ms Janice C LLB(Hons) . . . *Apr 1990
Ast: Hale, Miss Nicola . . . Oct 2001

A ZACHARIA & CO SOLICITORS ‡
7a Page Hall Road Sheffield South Yorkshire S4 8GS
Tel: 0114 261 9203 *Fax:* 0114 261 9203
E-mail: info@azacharia.co.uk

SHEFFORD, Bedfordshire

KNOWLES BENNING
(incorporating Benning Hoare & Drew; Knowles Cave & Co)
32 High Street Shefford Bedfordshire SG17 5DG
Tel: 01462 814824 *Fax:* 01462 815188 *Dx:* 153443 SHEFFORD
E-mail: mavery@knowlesbenning.com
Office: Dunstable, Luton
Agency, Advocacy, Fixed Fee Interview and Legal Aid undertaken
Ptr: Atkins, Mr Stephen J BA . . . *Sep 1978
Ast: Cakebread, Mrs Marjorie E LLB(B'ham); BA. . . . *§May 1979

NOBLE ‡
21 High Street Shefford Bedfordshire SG17 5DD
Tel: 01462 814055 *Fax:* 01462 814155 *Dx:* 153444 SHEFFORD
Emergency telephone 07000 818283
List of partners: P S Millan, D F Noble, M Rajshakha
Office: Luton
Work: G H Z(m)
Advocacy, Fixed Fee Interview, Legal Aid undertaken and Legal Aid Franchise
Ptr: Millan, Pritpal S. . . . *Feb 1996
Noble, Mr David F LLB(Lond) . . . *Jul 1977
Rajshakha, Minal . . . *Feb 1994
Ast: Bellis, Mr Martin J. . . . *Aug 1968
Browne, Miss Jennifer Elaine . . . *Jun 2006
Dhillon, Narinder . . . *Jan 2004
Fox, Mr John N BA; BSc(Hons) . . . *Jan 2001
Gibson, Mrs Debbie LLB(Hons) . . . *Nov 2001
Iqbal, Mr Tariq. . . . *Mar 1998
Kaliari, Mr Jas LLB(Hons). . . . *Oct 2001
Lewis, Mr Ian . . . *Nov 1995
Musgreaves, Miss Jane LLB(Hons) . . . *May 2001
Staples, Mr Nicholas . . . *Apr 2006
Sugrue, Mr James . . . *May 2004

SHEPHERDSWELL, Kent

MARTYN HEWETT SOLICITOR ‡
The Chestnuts Eythorne Road Shepherdswell Kent CT15 7NU
Tel: 01304 831888 *Fax:* 01304 831771
List of partners: M L Hewett
Work: G H
Emergency Action, Agency, Advocacy, Fixed Fee Interview and Legal Aid undertaken
SPr: Hewett, Mr Martyn L LLB . . . *Mar 1980

SHEPPERTON, Surrey

OWEN WHITE & CATLIN
56 High Street Shepperton Surrey TW17 9AY
Tel: 01932 220451 *Fax:* 01932 240843 *Dx:* 41750 SHEPPERTON
E-mail: shepperton@owenwhitecatlin.co.uk
Office: Addlestone, Ashford, Feltham, Hounslow, London W4, London W6
Work: A1 B1 C1 C2 C3 D1 E F1 K1 K2 K4 S1 S2 T1 T2 V W Z(c,e,k,l)

JULIAN PHILIP & CO ‡
Paper Court Fairwater Drive Shepperton Surrey TW17 8AB
Tel: 01932 254354 *Fax:* 01932 254000 *Dx:* 41757 SHEPPERTON
E-mail: julianphilipco@btinternet.com

List of partners: J J N Philip
Work: C1 E S1 W
Ptr: Philip, Mr Julian James Nowell . . . . *Jul 1974

SHEPTON MALLET, Somerset

BARTLETT GOODING & WEELEN ‡ (incorporating Bartlett & Co; Austin & Bath; Robin Weelen & Co)
57 High Street Shepton Mallet Somerset BA4 5AQ
Tel: 01749 343091 ***Fax:*** 01749 345091
Dx: 43002 SHEPTON MALLET
Emergency telephone 01749 890248
E-mail: bill@bgw.uk.com
List of partners: B W Bartlett, D Nash, E Rae, G Reynolds, R A Weelen
Office: Castle Cary, Cheddar, Glastonbury
Languages: French
Work: A1 B1 C1 D1 E F1 G H J1 K1 K3 L N Q R1 S1 S2 T1 T2 V W Z(c,i,j,l,n)
Emergency Action, Agency, Advocacy, Fixed Fee Interview, Legal Aid undertaken and Member of Accident Line
Ptr: Bartlett, Mr Basil W . . . . *Apr 1967
Nash, Mrs Dervla LLB(Hons) . . . . *Sep 2002
Reynolds, Mr Gareth LLB . . . . *Oct 1985
Weelen, Mr Robin A. . . . . *Jun 1973

DYNE DREWETT SOLICITORS LTD
65 High Street Shepton Mallet Somerset BA4 5AH
Tel: 01749 342323 ***Fax:*** 01749 345016
Dx: 43003 SHEPTON MALLET
E-mail: info@dynedrewett.com
Office: Sherborne, Wincanton
Work: A1 B1 C1 C2 D1 E F1 J1 K1 K3 K4 L N O P Q R1 S1 S2 T2 V W Z(e,l)
Agency, Advocacy, Fixed Fee Interview and Legal Aid undertaken
Ptr: Foster, Mr Nicholas N LLB(Lond) . . . . *Apr 1977
Inch, Mrs Amanda . . . . *Dec 1991
Dir: Cheal, Mr Jonathan . . . . *Jun 1976
Asoc: Parsons, Mrs Andrea Jayne. . . . . *Nov 1998
Ast: Cudmore, Mrs Beth . . . . *Sep 2008
Hadley, Mr Richard James John. . . . . *Mar 1999
James, Mr Richard Stephen. . . . . *Aug 2005
Milton-Downes, Mrs Lucy Helen. . . . . *Jun 2008

LANCASTER PARR ‡
Pear Tree House Wanstrow Shepton Mallet Somerset BA4 4TF
Tel: 01749 850276 / 07976 710623 ***Fax:*** 01749 850276
E-mail: rhparr@lancasterparr.co.uk

SHERBORNE, Dorset

BATTENS
The Bank House Long Street Sherborne Dorset DT9 3BU
Tel: 01935 814811 ***Fax:*** 01935 816436 ***Dx:*** 49151 SHERBORNE
E-mail: webenquiry@battens.co.uk
Office: Dorchester, Weymouth, Yeovil
Languages: French
Work: A1 B1 C1 D1 E F1 G H J1 K1 L M1 N O P Q R1 S1 T1 V W Z(a,b,c,d,e,f,g,h,i,j,k,l,m,o,p,s,t)
Emergency Action, Agency, Advocacy, Fixed Fee Interview, Legal Aid undertaken and Member of Accident Line
Ptr: Christopher, Mr William D. . . . . *§Nov 1970
Davis, Mr Martin LLB . . . . *Jul 1994
Con: Traill, Mr Andrew B G. . . . . Nov 1977

DYNE DREWETT SOLICITORS LTD ‡
11 Cheap Street Sherborne Dorset DT9 3PU
Tel: 01935 813691 ***Fax:*** 01935 813091 ***Dx:*** 49152 SHERBORNE
E-mail: info@dynedrewettsherborne.com
List of partners: J N Arnot, R E Beresford, J Cheal, N N Foster, G R Godwin, A Inch, R G McFarlane, D R Morgan
Office: Shepton Mallet, Wincanton
Languages: French
Work: A1 C1 C2 C3 E F1 G J1 K1 L P R1 R2 S1 S2 T1 T2 W Z(d)
Agency, Advocacy, Fixed Fee Interview undertaken and Member of Accident Line
Ptr: Arnot, Mr J Nicholas Clerk to the Commissioner of Taxes (Wells Division) . . . . *§Jul 1969
Godwin, Mr Geoffrey R Clerk to Commissioner of Taxes (Wells Division) . . . . *Dec 1974
McFarlane, Mr Rory G . . . . *Jul 1999
Ast: Chaffey, Mr Martin Daniel LLB; DipLP. . . . . Jan 1999
Hunt, Mrs Amanda S L LLB. . . . . *Oct 1990
Lennon, Mr Thomas. . . . . Sep 1992
Thomas, Mr Street LLB . . . . Jan 2003

TOM LENON SOLICITOR ‡
4 Brecon House Long Street Sherborne Dorset DT9 3BY
Tel: 07981 500357
E-mail: t.lenon@dorsetlegal.co.uk

CORDELIA MCFARLANE SOLICITOR ‡
Avenue Cottage Nether Compton Sherborne Dorset DT9 4QE
Tel: 01935 817875

MACLACHLAN ‡
Long Street Sherborne Dorset DT9 3BS
Tel: 01935 817736 ***Fax:*** 01935 817798 ***Dx:*** 49158 SHERBORNE
Emergency telephone 01747 825927
E-mail: enquiries@maclachlansolicitors.co.uk
List of partners: T N Gawler, M Griffin, R J Snowdon
Office: Gillingham
Languages: French, German
Work: A1 A3 B1 C1 E G H J1 K1 L N O Q R2 S1 S2 W Z(b,h,k,l,q,r)
Emergency Action, Agency, Advocacy and Fixed Fee Interview undertaken
Ptr: Gawler, Mr Thomas Nairn LLB(Hons) . . . . Sep 2001
Griffin, Mr Mark BSc . . . . *Sep 1995
Snowdon, Mr Roger J LLB . . . . Dec 1981
Ast: Bennetts, Miss Nicola Ann LLB . . . . Sep 2004
Con: Hoskinson, Ms Joanna LLB . . . . *Sep 1981
Traill, Mr Andrew B G. . . . . Nov 1977

PORTER DODSON
The Abbey Close Sherborne Dorset DT9 3LH
Tel: 01935 813101 ***Fax:*** 01953 814024 ***Dx:*** 49150 SHERBORNE
E-mail: porterdodson@porterdodson.co.uk
Office: Dorchester, Taunton, Wellington, Yeovil
Work: A1 B1 C1 C2 C3 D1 E F1 G H I J1 K1 M1 M2 N O P Q R1 S1 T1 T2 V W Z(b,c,d,h,i,j,l,p,t)

SHERINGHAM, Norfolk

CLAPHAM & COLLINGE
The Point 1 Augusta Street Sheringham Norfolk NR26 8LA
Tel: 01263 823398 ***Dx:*** 31651 SHERINGHAM
E-mail: sheringham@qualitysolicitors.com

HANSELLS
Waterbank House Station Approach Sheringham Norfolk NR26 8RA
Tel: 01263 822176 ***Fax:*** 01263 824159 ***Dx:*** 31652 SHERINGHAM
E-mail: info@hansells.co.uk
Office: Aylsham, Cromer, North Walsham, Norwich (2 offices)
Languages: French, German
Work: A1 B1 C1 C2 D1 E F1 J1 K1 K2 K3 L M3 N O Q R1 S1 S2 W Z(c,d,l,o,r)
Agency, Advocacy, Fixed Fee Interview, Legal Aid undertaken and Legal Aid Franchise
Ptr: Harvey, Mr J Nicholas LLB . . . . *§Dec 1975

HAYES & STORR
Burnham House 57-63 Station Road Sheringham Norfolk NR26 8RG
Tel: 01263 825959 ***Fax:*** 01263 824282 ***Dx:*** 31650 SHERINGHAM
E-mail: law.sheringham@hayes-storr.com
Office: Fakenham, Holt, King's Lynn, Wells-next-the-Sea
Work: A1 E F1 K1 L P S1 T1 V W Z(c,d,f)
Emergency Action, Agency, Advocacy, Fixed Fee Interview, Legal Aid undertaken, Legal Aid Franchise and Member of Accident Line
Ptr: Abel, Mrs Christine Rosemary Harvey LLB Harbour Commissioner of the Port of Wells Norfolk. . . . *Nov 1996
Hewitt, Mr Richard Paul LLB; LARTPI . . . . *Oct 1983
Ast: Lonsdale, Mr David LLB. . . . . Sep 2006
Widdall, Ms Hilary. . . . . Sep 2007

SHIFNAL, Shropshire

MARTIN EDWARDS ‡
Idsall Chambers 20 Bradford Street Shifnal Shropshire TF11 8AU
Tel: 01952 462118 ***Fax:*** 01952 461555
Emergency telephone 01952 257767
E-mail: enquiries@martin-edwards.co.uk
List of partners: H M Edwards
Work: C1 D1 E G J1 K1 K3 K4 O Q R1 S1 S2 W Z(l)
Agency and Advocacy undertaken
Ptr: Edwards, Mr H Martin LLB Notary Public . . . . . . *§Oct 1971
Ast: Strangwood, Miss Jill BA(Hons). . . . . Sep 2009

SHILDON, Co Durham

SMITH RODDAM
18 Church Street Shildon Co Durham DL4 1DX
Tel: 01388 772661 ***Fax:*** 01388 776269
Dx: 60150 BISHOP AUCKLAND
Office: Bishop Auckland, Crook
Work: C1 C2 C3 D1 E G H K1 L N S1 W Z(l,m)
Emergency Action, Agency, Advocacy, Fixed Fee Interview and Legal Aid undertaken

SHILLINGFORD, Oxfordshire

ANDERSON & COMPANY ‡
76 Wallingford Road Shillingford Oxfordshire OX10 7EU
Tel: 01865 858878 ***Fax:*** 01865 858900
E-mail: markanderson@andersonsolicitors.com
List of partners: M S Anderson
Languages: French
Work: C1 C3 F1 I J1 L M1 M2 O P T1 T2 U2 Z(c,d,e)
SPr: Anderson, Mr Mark Stephen BA(Dunelm); Former Barrister Company Secretary for Imperial College Innovations Ltd . . . . *Jun 1990
Asoc: Maclennan, Mr Paul BSc(Hons). . . . . Jan 2008
Warner, Mr Victor BSc; MBA Notary Public . . . . . *Mar 1999

SHIPLEY, West Yorkshire

ATKINSON & FIRTH ‡
Fenix House New Kirkgate Shipley West Yorkshire BD18 3QY
Tel: 01274 584305 ***Fax:*** 01274 531355 ***Dx:*** 20902 SHIPLEY
List of partners: H M Atkinson, A C Brocklehurst, F J Hedar
Work: D1 E K1 M2 S1 S2 V W
Emergency Action, Agency, Advocacy, Fixed Fee Interview and Legal Aid undertaken
Ptr: Atkinson, Mrs Helen Margaret BA . . . . *Mar 1984
Brocklehurst, Mrs Angela Carol BA(Dunelm) . . . . . *Oct 1994
Hedar, Mrs Fiona J LLB(Leeds) . . . . *Feb 1980

BIRD & DANIELS ‡
34 Westgate Shipley West Yorkshire BD18 3QX
Tel: 01274 580999 ***Fax:*** 01274 595715 ***Dx:*** 20903 SHIPLEY
Emergency telephone 07000 580999
E-mail: deb@birdanddaniels-sols.co.uk
List of partners: C J Bird, D E Daniels
Languages: French
Work: C1 C2 D1 E F1 G H J1 K1 N O Q S1 V W X Z(c,m,q)
Emergency Action, Agency, Advocacy, Fixed Fee Interview, Legal Aid undertaken and Legal Aid Franchise
Ptr: Bird, Mr Christopher J LLB Notary Public . . . . . . *Oct 1973
Daniels, Mrs Deborah E LLB(Lond) . . . . *Sep 1986

BROOKS SOLICITORS ‡
Kirkgate House Kirkgate Shipley West Yorkshire BD18 3QN
Tel: 01274 596724 ***Fax:*** 01274 597365
List of partners: I M Brook
SPr: Brook, Mr Ian M LLB . . . . *Apr 1981

LAST CAWTHRA FEATHER LLP
11-19 Westgate Shipley West Yorkshire BD18 3QX
Tel: 01274 585459 ***Fax:*** 01274 390644 ***Dx:*** 20901 SHIPLEY
E-mail: enquiries@lcf.co.uk
Office: Baildon, Bradford, Ilkley, Leeds
Languages: German, Spanish
Work: B1 C1 C2 D1 E F1 G H J1 K1 L N O Q S1 S2 T1 T2 V W Z(c,e,f,k,l,m)
Emergency Action, Agency, Advocacy and Fixed Fee Interview undertaken
Ptr: Mordey, Mr Simon D LLM . . . . *Jan 1990
Wright, Mr Jonathan Hedley MBE. . . . . *Feb 1973
Ast: Appleton, Mr Steven . . . . Oct 2006
Ingham, Miss Katie . . . . Jul 2009

SOVEREIGN SOLICITORS ‡
11 Market Street Shipley West Yorkshire BD18 3QD
Tel: 01274 809696 ***Fax:*** 01274 809697
E-mail: info@sovereignsolicitors.co.uk

SHIPSTON-ON-STOUR, Warwickshire

BROOKS ‡
11 Sheep Street Shipston-on-Stour Warwickshire CV36 4AE
Tel: 01608 664406 ***Fax:*** 01608 664407
Dx: 25135 SHIPSTON-ON-STOUR
E-mail: brookslaw@btconnect.com
List of partners: D C Brooks
Work: B1 C1 D2 E F1 J1 J2 K1 K3 L N O P Q S1 S2 V W Z(c,h,q,r)
Emergency Action, Agency, Advocacy, Fixed Fee Interview, Legal Aid undertaken and Legal Aid Franchise
SPr: Brooks, Mr David Charles LLB(Leics) . . . . *Apr 1973

DAVID M D MILLS ‡
Darlingscott Hill Darlingscote Road Shipston-on-Stour Warwickshire CV36 4JA
Tel: 0870 753 7700 ***Fax:*** 01608 662434
E-mail: adam@mstj.com
Languages: French, Italian
Work: C1 Z(b)

SHAKESPEARES
The Assembly Rooms Church Street Shipston-on-Stour Warwickshire CV36 4AT
Tel: 0845 630 8833 ***Fax:*** 0845 630 8818
Dx: 25131 SHIPSTON-ON-STOUR
E-mail: info@shakepeares.co.uk
Office: Birmingham, Leicester, Moreton-in-Marsh, Nottingham, Stratford-upon-Avon

SHIREBROOK, Derbyshire

AGR SOLICITORS
211 Station Road Shirebrook Derbyshire NG20 8AF
Tel: 01623 748522 ***Fax:*** 01623 748005
E-mail: jjeffery@agr-solicitors.co.uk
Office: Mansfield
Work: A1 C1 E F1 J1 K1 K4 L N Q S1 S2 W
Emergency Action, Agency, Advocacy, Fixed Fee Interview, Legal Aid undertaken, Legal Aid Franchise and Member of Accident Line
Ast: Jeffery, Mr John Walter Notary Public . . . . *Dec 1973

SHOEBURYNESS, Southend-on-Sea

ROBINSONS ‡
61 Ness Road Shoeburyness Southend-on-Sea SS3 9DB
Tel: 01702 298282 ***Fax:*** 01702 298559
Dx: 141404 SHOEBURYNESS
E-mail: emailcjr@bconnect.com
List of partners: J C R Monod, C J Robinson
Work: C1 E L S1 W Z(m)
Ptr: Monod, Mr Jeremy C R LLB. . . . . *Oct 1986
Robinson, Mr Christopher John . . . . *Nov 1975

SHOREHAM-BY-SEA, West Sussex

FITZHUGH GATES
23-25 High Street Shoreham-by-Sea West Sussex BN43 5EE
Tel: 01273 461381 ***Fax:*** 01273 465332
Dx: 59751 SHOREHAM-BY-SEA
E-mail: mail@fitzhugh.co.uk
Office: Brighton
Work: B1 C1 C2 C3 D1 E F1 J1 K1 K2 L M1 M2 N O P Q R1 R2 S1 T1 T2 V W Z(b,c,d,e,h,j,k,l,m,o,q,r,s,t)
Emergency Action, Agency, Advocacy, Legal Aid undertaken, Legal Aid Franchise and Member of Accident Line
Ptr: Hill, Mrs Patricia Marianne FILEx . . . . *Dec 1993
Hunt, Mr Hugo P BSc Notary Public. . . . . *Jun 1979
Ast: Blakey, Ms Carol . . . . Aug 1990
Cioffi, Mr Julian C LLB . . . . Oct 1992

ROBERT SIMON & CO ‡
4-6 East Street Shoreham-by-Sea West Sussex BN43 5ZE
Tel: 01273 452333 ***Fax:*** 01273 452434
Work: E L S1 T2 W

WENDY HOLMES SOLICITORS ‡
Little High Street Shoreham-by-Sea West Sussex BN43 5HG
Tel: 01273 455015 ***Fax:*** 01273 455015
E-mail: wendyholmeslaw@hotmail.com

SHOTTON, Flintshire

E A HARRIS & CO LTD ‡
Transport House 54 Chester Road East Shotton Flintshire CH5 1QA
Tel: 01244 822555 ***Fax:*** 01244 813167 ***Dx:*** 24372 SHOTTON
E-mail: solicitors@eaharris.com
List of partners: G Connah, K A Jones
Office: Buckley
Work: D1 E F2 J1 J2 K1 K2 K3 K4 L N O Q S1 S2 W
Dir: Connah, Mr Gary BSc(Hons)(Econ) . . . . *§Oct 1988
Jones, Mr Keith A LLB(Lond) . . . . *§Sep 1972
Ast: Jones, Ms Alison Victoria LLB. . . . . *Nov 2006

 See p112 for the Key to Work Categories & other symbols

JACOBS SOLICITORS
(incorporating De Cordova Alis & Filce)
46-48 Chester Road West Shotton Flintshire CH5 1BY
Tel: 01244 816211 *Fax:* 01244 814505 *Dx:* 24371 SHOTTON
E-mail: info@jacobslaw.co.uk
Office: Ellesmere Port
Work: D1 F1 G H J1 K1 L N Q S1 V W Z(l)
Emergency Action, Agency, Advocacy, Fixed Fee Interview and Legal Aid undertaken
Ptr: Alis, Mr Steven P BA . . . . *Nov 1986

CYRIL JONES & CO
89 Chester Road West Shotton Flintshire CH5 1BZ
Tel: 01244 812109 *Fax:* 01244 811633 *Dx:* 24373 SHOTTON
E-mail: gareth.jones@cyril-jones.co.uk
Office: Wrexham (2 offices)
Languages: Polish
Work: A1 C1 C2 C3 D1 E F1 F2 G H J1 J2 K1 K2 K3 K4 L M1 M2 N P Q R1 S1 S2 T1 T2 W
Emergency Action, Agency, Advocacy, Fixed Fee Interview, Legal Aid undertaken and Legal Aid Franchise
Ptr: Cunnah, Mr Michael LLB . . . . *Oct 1981
Ast: Byram, Mr Timothy S LLB. . . . . Jul 1992
Jones, Ms Alison Victoria LLB. . . . . *Nov 2006

PSR SOLICITORS ‡
Shotton Villa 36 Chester Road West Deeside Shotton Flintshire CH5 1BY
Tel: 0800 321 3239 / 07737 137358

SHREWSBURY, Shropshire

EDWARD AUSTIN ‡
Old Bank Buildings Bellstone Shrewsbury Shropshire SY1 1HU
Tel: 01743 236222 *Fax:* 01743 236333
List of partners: E Austin
SPr: Austin, Mr Edward . . . . Jan 1988

BENNETTS LEGAL ‡
Suite 1 Rural Enterprise Centre Stafford Drive Shrewsbury Shropshire SY1 3FE
Tel: 0844 472 2378 *Dx:* 148563 SHREWSBURY 14

BLACKBOURN ANDREWS LIMITED ‡
12 Belmont Shrewsbury Shropshire SY1 1TE
Tel: 01743 233255

CLARKES
Kingston House St Alkmunds Place Shrewsbury Shropshire SY1 1UL
Tel: 01743 231531 *Fax:* 01743 351860 *Dx:* 19730 SHREWSBURY
Emergency telephone 01743 231432
E-mail: shrewsbury@clarkeslaw.co.uk
Office: Newport, Telford (2 offices), Wellington
Work: D1 E F1 F2 G H J1 J2 K1 L N O Q S1 W Z(c,k,l,q,r)
Emergency Action, Agency, Advocacy, Fixed Fee Interview, Legal Aid undertaken, Legal Aid Franchise and Member of Accident Line
Ptr: Harrison, Mr Paul LLB(Exon) . . . . *Dec 1980

ENGLAND JOHN SOLICITORS ‡
Beaconsfield House Meadow Terrace Shrewsbury Shropshire SY1 1PE
Tel: 01743 233700

FBC MANBY BOWDLER LLP
Rowan House South 1 The Professional Quarter Sitka Drive Shrewsbury Shropshire SY2 6LG
Tel: 01743 241551 *Fax:* 01743 241623
Dx: 741103 SHREWSBURY 17
E-mail: info@fcbmb.co.uk
Office: Bridgnorth, Telford, Willenhall, Wolverhampton
Work: A1 A2 C1 C2 D1 D2 E F1 F2 I J1 K1 K3 N O Q S1 S2 T1 T2 U2 W Z(e,l)
Ptr: Hughes, Miss Jane BA . . . . *Apr 1978
Lucas, Mr David William BA. . . . . *Nov 1995
Rea, Mr Stuart A LLB(Hons) . . . . *§Jun 1989
Shepherd, Mr David A LLB(B'ham) . . . . *§Mar 1975
Asoc: Bowen, Mr John. . . . . *Mar 2006
Ast: Burroughs, Ms Sally. . . . . Dec 1992

FIRMLEGAL SOLICITORS ‡
Roushill Shrewsbury Shropshire SY1 1PQ
Tel: 01743 273777

GARRARDS ‡
Swinson Chambers 3a The Square Shrewsbury Shropshire SY1 1LA
Tel: 01743 341140

HATCHERS SOLICITORS LLP ‡
25 Castle Street Shrewsbury Shropshire SY1 1DA
Tel: 01743 248545 *Fax:* 01743 242979
Dx: 722160 SHREWSBURY 10
E-mail: mail@hatchers.co.uk
List of partners: M Bowering, A D Cross, V A Edwards, A E Fisher, P M Gittins, N Harrison, A L Holland, R Kerry, M R Munro, D M Ryder, D Saunders, J N Y Walmsley, C D N Wilson
Office: Shrewsbury, Whitchurch
Languages: French, German
Work: A1 A2 A3 B1 C1 C2 C3 D1 E F1 G H J1 K1 L N O P Q R1 R2 S1 S2 T1 T2 V W Z(c,e,l,o,p,q,t,x)
Agency, Advocacy, Fixed Fee Interview, Legal Aid undertaken, Legal Aid Franchise and Member of Accident Line
Ptr: Bowering, Mr Matthew . . . . Sep 1999
Cross, Mr Andrew D LLB(Leeds) . . . . §Apr 1975
Edwards, Mrs Valerie Anne LLB. . . . . Oct 2000
Fisher, Mrs Ann Elizabeth MSc; GDL Deputy Lieutenant . . . . *Sep 2000
Gittins, Mr Patrick M LLB . . . . *Oct 1988
Harrison, Mr Nigel. . . . . *Sep 1998
Holland, Mr Andrew Leslie LLB . . . . Oct 1995
Kerry, Mr Richard . . . . Nov 1993
Saunders, Mr David MA; LLB(Lond); Dip(Env Law); ACIB . . . . *§Jun 1980
Walmsley, Mrs Jacinta N Y LLB . . . . *Jul 1985
Wilson, Mr Christopher D N BA . . . . *Apr 1981
Asoc: Cowley, Ms Helen. . . . . Nov 2006
Dalby, Miss Clare Marisa LLB(Hons) . . . . *Aug 1998
Thompson, Mrs Valerie S BA(Hons). . . . . *Oct 1989
Ast: Leighton-Jones, Ms Gina . . . . Jan 2007

HATCHERS SOLICITORS LLP
6-7 Harlescott Lane Harlescott Shrewsbury Shropshire SY1 3AH
Tel: 01743 467641 *Fax:* 01743 462384
E-mail: mail@hatchers.co.uk
Office: Shrewsbury, Whitchurch
Work: A1 B1 D1 D2 K1 K2 K3 K4 L N S1 S2 W
Emergency Action, Advocacy, Fixed Fee Interview and Legal Aid undertaken
Ptr: Munro, Mr Mark Reginald LLB. . . . . *Sep 1988

HOWELLS WILLIAMS ‡
Hollings House 35 Hills Lane Shrewsbury Shropshire SY1 1QU
Tel: 01743 241429 *Fax:* 01743 360336
Emergency telephone 01743 233461
List of partners: P W F Howells
Office: Telford
Work: B1 D1 F1 F2 G H J1 K1 L N Q R1 S1 S2 V W X Z(l,m)
Emergency Action, Agency, Advocacy, Fixed Fee Interview, Legal Aid undertaken and Member of Accident Line
Ptr: Howells, Mr Peter W F LLB . . . . *Jul 1974

TERRY JONES SOLICITORS & ADVOCATES ‡
Abbey House Abbey Foregate Shrewsbury Shropshire SY2 6BH
Tel: 01743 285888 *Fax:* 01743 285900
Dx: 724600 SHREWSBURY 12
Emergency telephone 01743 356815
E-mail: enquiries@terry-jones.co.uk
List of partners: C S Fitzmaurice, T H L Jones
Office: Newport, Telford
Work: A1 A2 A3 B1 B2 C1 C2 C3 D1 D2 E F1 F2 G H J1 J2 K1 K2 K3 K4 L N O Q R1 R2 S1 S2 W X Z(c,e,g,h,k,l,m,p,q,t,y)
Emergency Action, Agency, Advocacy, Fixed Fee Interview, Legal Aid undertaken and Legal Aid Franchise
Ptr: Fitzmaurice, Mrs Carolyn S . . . . *Oct 1984
Jones, Mr Terence H L ★ . . . . *§Feb 1975
Asoc: Durant, Mr Ian LLB . . . . *Nov 1991
Mitchell, Mr Ian M LLB(L'pool). . . . . *Sep 1980
Ast: Awty, Sarah. . . . . Jun 2007
Charlton, Mr Jeremy Craig BA(Hons) . . . . Feb 1981
Hall, Rachel. . . . . Jun 2007
Hand, Mr James LLB(Hons); BA(Hons) . . . . Jun 2011
Howarth, Mr Andy BA(Hons) . . . . Nov 2004
Lyon-Small, Mrs Kate Julie LLB(Hons) . . . . Jun 2011
Nicholas, Mr Paul William LLB . . . . Jul 2003
Rogerson, Mr Martin BCL ★. . . . . *Apr 1970
Con: Parry, Mr Geoffrey Allen LLB(Hons)(Wales) . . . . . *Nov 1975

LANYON BOWDLER LLP ‡
Chapter House North Abbey Lawn Abbey Foregate Shrewsbury Shropshire SY2 5DE
Tel: 01743 280280 *Fax:* 01743 282340
Dx: 144320 SHREWSBURY 11
E-mail: enquiries@lblaw.co.uk
List of partners: D K Battisby, A Birtles, A M Evans, R B Evans, P J Flint, A C Gittins, I Glenister, I Goodwin, P V Lewis, N R T Lorimer, J G Merry, R Murrall, P H Nash, E G Rees, A C Roberts, C M Spanner, D K Thomas, E M L Wilde
Office: Hereford, Ludlow, Oswestry (2 offices), Telford, Wellington
Work: A1 A2 A3 B1 B2 C1 C2 C3 D1 D2 E F1 F2 G H I J1 J2 K1 K2 L M1 N O P Q R1 R2 S1 S2 U2 W X Z(c,e,h,k,l,p,q,r,t,w,y)
Emergency Action, Agency, Advocacy, Fixed Fee Interview, Legal Aid undertaken, Legal Aid Franchise and Member of Accident Line
Ptr: Evans, Mr Andrew M BA(Hons)(Law) . . . . *§Dec 1980
Flint, Mr Peter J MCFM . . . . *§Jul 1972
Lorimer, Mr Neil R T LLB . . . . *§Oct 1989
Nash, Ms Paula Helen LLB . . . . Feb 1988
Rees, Mr Edward Guy MA(Hons) . . . . *Oct 2000
Roberts, Mr Adrian C BA(Law) . . . . *§Oct 1985
Asoc: Broomfield, Ms Emma. . . . . Feb 1991
Humphries, Mrs Debbie LLB(Hons) . . . . Mar 2000
Pegg, Mr Andrew . . . . Oct 2003
Vale, Miss Claire LLB . . . . *§Oct 1991
Ast: Cater, Ms Lynsey . . . . Sep 2010
Easthope, Mr Dean LLB(B'ham). . . . . *Sep 2000
Haylock, Ms Suzanne LLB . . . . *Nov 1986
Hodgson, Sue. . . . . Sep 1997
Humphries, Ms Dawn Fay. . . . . Jul 1994
Kealy, Lucy . . . . Mar 2006
Swallow, Lucy. . . . . Jan 2002
Weaver, Kathryn . . . . Sep 2004
Whittaker, Rebecca . . . . Mar 2008
Woodhead, Miss Rowena LLB(Hons) . . . . *Sep 2001

LINDER MYERS SOLICITORS
Ireland's Mansion High Street Shrewsbury Shropshire SY1 1SQ
Tel: 0844 984 6002 *Fax:* 0844 984 6350
Dx: 19708 SHREWSBURY 1
E-mail: enquiries@lindermyers.co.uk
Office: Manchester (2 offices), Swinton
Languages: French
Work: A1 C1 D1 D2 E F1 F2 G H J1 J2 K1 L M1 N O P Q R1 R2 S1 S2 W Z(l,m,p,q,r)
Emergency Action, Agency, Advocacy, Fixed Fee Interview, Legal Aid undertaken and Member of Accident Line
Ptr: Foster, Mr Reginald G E LLB(Lond) . . . . *Dec 1974
Ast: Newsome, Mr Timothy John LLB(Hons). . . . . *Jul 2005
Sedgwick, Mr Duncan K LLM; MSc . . . . *Oct 1991

GAVIN MCKENZIE ‡
Meole Cottage Mill Road Meole Brace Shrewsbury Shropshire SY3 9JT
Tel: 01743 235957 *Fax:* 01743 356137
Emergency telephone 07654 327844 (PAGER)
E-mail: mckenzie0449@hotmail.com
List of partners: G N McKenzie
Work: G H
Emergency Action, Agency, Advocacy, Legal Aid undertaken and Legal Aid Franchise
SPr: McKenzie, Mr Gavin Neil . . . . Nov 1972

MCLOUGHLIN & COMPANY LLP ‡
Telford House 1 Claremont Bank Shrewsbury Shropshire SY1 1RW
Tel: 01743 272272 *Fax:* 01743 341050
List of partners: R M Dugan, P A McLoughlin
Office: London WC2
Work: A3 B1 J1 J2 L O P Z(c,j,q)
Ptr: Dugan, Mr Roger M LLM Sweet & Maxwell Law Prize . *Oct 1991
McLoughlin, Mr Peter A LLB . . . . *§Oct 1985

M A MORRISON ‡
The Poplars Hanley Lane Bayston Hill Shrewsbury Shropshire SY3 0JN
Tel: 01743 874986 *Fax:* 01743 873975
List of partners: M A Morrison
Work: S1 W
SPr: Morrison, Ms Margaret A LLB . . . . Apr 1979

MOSS & POULSON ‡
4 Claremont Bank Shrewsbury Shropshire SY1 1RS
Tel: 01743 350571 *Fax:* 01743 232184 *Dx:* 19715 SHREWSBURY
E-mail: law@mossandpoulson.co.uk
List of partners: R Ashton, K J Bond, M S Limbrey
Work: A1 B1 C1 E F1 J1 L O P R1 S1 T2 W X Z(c,d,e,l,n)
Ptr: Ashton, Mr Richard LLB. . . . . *Apr 1997
Bond, Mr Kieran J BA Chairman of the Special Education Needs & Disability Tribunal. . . . . *Dec 1980
Limbrey, Mr Michael S LLB(B'ham) . . . . *Apr 1971

PCB SOLICITORS LLP ‡
(incorporating Clarke & Son; Shay & Lingford Hughes; Corser & Co)
Cypress Centre Shrewsbury Business Park Sitka Drive Shrewsbury Shropshire SY2 6LG
Tel: 01743 248148 *Fax:* 01743 363917
Dx: 741100 SHREWSBURY 17
Emergency telephone 07703 486023
E-mail: info@pcblaw.co.uk
List of partners: J I Burrowes, E W J Coxhead, E M Freeman, R E Hughes, L M Morris-Jones, B J Reedy, M H Surzyn
Office: Church Stretton, Knighton, Ludlow, Telford
Languages: French
Work: A1 B1 C1 D1 E G H J1 K1 K3 L N O S1 T2 W Z(d,j,l,m,q,r)
Emergency Action, Agency, Advocacy, Fixed Fee Interview, Legal Aid undertaken and Legal Aid Franchise
Ptr: Burrowes, Mr John Irvine . . . . Dec 1978
Coxhead, Mr Edmund W J BA . . . . *Jul 1984
Ast: Campbell, Mrs Christine. . . . . *Oct 1996
Davenport, Mrs Rachel LLB(Hons) . . . . *Oct 1994
Davies, Miss Pauline Mary LLB . . . . *Nov 1998
Dobson, Mrs Amanda Jane-Marie LLB . . . . Nov 1991
Edwards, Mrs Sandra Karen LLB(Hons). . . . . Sep 2000
Gray, Miss Katie . . . . *Dec 2007
Russell, Mr Trevor. . . . . *Mar 1992
Smith, Miss Sarah-Jane LLB(Hons) . . . . Nov 1992
Vowles, Miss Lynn . . . . Jul 1998
Con: Fowler, Mr Paul F C MA(Cantab) . . . . *Oct 1978
McKenzie, Mr Gavin Neil . . . . Nov 1972
Nye, Mr Marc. . . . . Jan 1975

HOWARD SHAH SOLICITORS ‡
24 St John's Hill Shrewsbury Shropshire SY1 1JJ
Tel: 0800 092 5523 *Fax:* 01743 272952
E-mail: enquiries@howardshah.co.uk

THORNTONS SOLICITORS ‡
Willow House East Shrewsbury Business Park Shrewsbury Shropshire SY2 6LG
Tel: 01743 341770 *Fax:* 0560 116 3554
E-mail: shrewsbury@thorntonssolicitors.co.uk
Office: Telford

TURNBULL GARRARD ‡
24 The Crescent Town Walls Shrewsbury Shropshire SY1 1TJ
Tel: 01743 350851 / 351332 *Fax:* 01743 351844
Dx: 19705 SHREWSBURY 1
E-mail: solicitors@turnbullgarrard.co.uk
List of partners: A H R Brierley, A James, C S Leaman, B A Marshall, S A Sutcliffe
Work: A1 B1 C1 C3 D1 E F1 J1 K1 L M1 N O P Q R1 S1 T1 T2 V W Z(c,d,j,l,m)
Emergency Action, Agency, Advocacy, Fixed Fee Interview, Legal Aid undertaken and Legal Aid Franchise
Ptr: Brierley, Mr Alastair H R BA(Cantab) . . . . *§Nov 1987
James, Mrs Anna BA . . . . *§Oct 1982
Leaman, Mr Charles S . . . . *Dec 1977
Marshall, Mrs Bridget A LLB(L'pool) Daniel Reardon Prize . . . . *§Nov 1975
Sutcliffe, Mrs Sandra A BA(Law) . . . . *Dec 1980
Ast: Baker, Mr Christopher George Bowron BSc . . . . . . *Nov 1993

WACE MORGAN ‡
(in association with Forces Law; The Forces Legal Network)
1-2 Belmont Shrewsbury Shropshire SY1 1TD
Est: 1800's
Tel: 01743 280100 *Fax:* 01743 280111 *Dx:* 19718 SHREWSBURY
Emergency telephone 07823 777774
E-mail: help@wmlaw.co.uk
Web: www.wace-morgan.co.uk
List of partners: M Butcher, C J Detheridge, D U Gittins, K Hirst, V J McKenzie, S O'Byrne, Z D Oliver, D N Packwood, J P Taylor
Office: Shrewsbury (2 offices)
Work: A1 B1 C1 C2 D1 D2 E F1 J1 K1 K2 K3 K4 L N O P Q R1 R2 S1 S2 T2 V W Z(d,e,h,l,m,n,p,q,r,t)
Emergency Action, Agency, Advocacy, Fixed Fee Interview, Legal Aid undertaken, Legal Aid Franchise and Member of Accident Line
Ptr: Butcher, Mrs Madeleine MA. . . . . *§Mar 1973
Detheridge, Mr Christopher John BSc. . . . . May 1999
Gittins, Miss Deborah U BA . . . . *§Nov 1984
Hirst, Mr Keir BA . . . . *Jul 2000
McKenzie, Mrs Victoria Jane . . . . Sep 1996
O'Byrne, Mrs Sallie-Anne . . . . Oct 1994
Oliver, Mrs Zara Dawn . . . . Nov 1998
Packwood, Ms Diana N BA(Law); LLB. . . . . *Mar 1983
Taylor, Mr Jeremy P LLB(Newc). . . . . *§Oct 1985
Ast: Cains, Miss Rhian Sonile LLB. . . . . May 2006
Corcoran, Mrs Louisa Alice Elizabeth Jones BA(Hons) Sep 2007
Edwards, Miss Katherine Anne LLB . . . . Sep 2010
Evans, Mrs Rachelle E BA(Hons) . . . . Nov 1982

McGee, Miss Tania LLB. . . . . Sep 2000
Peddar-Adams, Mr Robert LLB(Hons). . . . . *Apr 1981
Swan, Mrs Catherine E BA(Durham) . . . . *Oct 1984
Wilkinson, Miss Amanda Jayne LLB; DipSW. . . . . . Nov 2010
Con: Holdsworth, Mrs Elizabeth A BA; TEP. . . . . *§Feb 1986
Wheatley, Mr Trevor N P LLB(Bris); MCIArb. . . . . *§Apr 1971

WACE MORGAN
19 College Hill Shrewsbury Shropshire SY1 1LY
Tel: 01743 280100 *Fax:* 01743 280144
Office: Shrewsbury (2 offices)

WACE MORGAN
3 High Street Shrewsbury Shropshire SY1 1SP
Tel: 01743 266866 *Fax:* 01743 266868
Office: Shrewsbury (2 offices)

GRAHAM WITHERS & CO
7 The Square Shrewsbury Shropshire SY1 1LA
Tel: 01743 236345 *Fax:* 01743 241333 *Dx:* 19712 SHREWSBURY
E-mail: enquiries@grahamwithers.co.uk
Office: Market Drayton
Work: B1 C1 D1 D2 E J1 K1 L N O Q R1 R2 S1 S2 V W Z(c,l,q)
Emergency Action, Agency, Advocacy, Fixed Fee Interview, Legal Aid undertaken, Legal Aid Franchise and Member of Accident Line
Ptr: Field, Mr Godfrey H LLB . . . . *Oct 1979
Forrester, Mrs Diana J . . . . *Jun 1979
France, Mr Martin N J LLB(Lond) . . . . *Jun 1980
Nutley, Mr Paul MA(Cantab). . . . . Dec 1978
Ast: Hughes, Jesse MA(Oxon). . . . . Feb 1981

SIDCUP, Kent

BRAUND & FEDRICK
10 Hatherley Road Sidcup Kent DA14 4BQ
Tel: 020 8300 6515 *Fax:* 020 8300 7710 *Dx:* 31701 SIDCUP
E-mail: bandfsidcup@btconnect.com
Work: F1 K1 L N P S1 W
Fixed Fee Interview undertaken
Ptr: Coulson, Mr Geoffrey A LLB(Soton). . . . . *§Jul 1969
Grove, Mr Richard C . . . . *Oct 1973

T R IRELAND ‡
17 Barton Road Sidcup Kent DA14 5LU
Tel: 020 8300 6487 *Fax:* 020 8306 2358
Work: S1 T2 W Z(m)

LAWBRIDGE SOLICITORS ‡
Roxby House 20-22 Station Road Sidcup Kent DA15 7EJ
Tel: 020 8308 3610 *Fax:* 020 8338 3070
E-mail: mpope@lawbridgesolicitors.com

NELSON GUEST & PARTNERS ‡
4th & 5th Floors Roxby House 20-22 Station Road Sidcup Kent DA15 7EJ
Tel: 020 8309 5010 / 8309 0558 *Fax:* 020 8309 6045
Dx: 31723 SIDCUP 1
Emergency telephone 01850 933663
E-mail: enquiries@nelson-guest.co.uk
List of partners: S Nelson, A S Rumistrzewicz
Office: New Romney, Sidcup
Languages: Czech, French, Polish
Work: B1 B2 C1 E F1 F2 G H J1 L Q R1 S1 S2 V W Z(g)
Emergency Action, Agency, Advocacy, Fixed Fee Interview, Legal Aid undertaken and Legal Aid Franchise
Ptr: Nelson, Mr Stephen ★. . . . . *Dec 1986
Rumistrzewicz, Andrzej S. . . . . *Jun 1974
Ast: Dickson, Mr Alistair Ian MA . . . . *Oct 1994

NELSON GUEST & PARTNERS
80 High Street Sidcup Kent t DA14 6DS
Tel: 020 8309 5010 *Fax:* 020 8309 6045 *Dx:* 31723 SIDCUP 1
Office: New Romney, Sidcup

RG SOLICITORS ‡
25 High Street Sidcup Kent DA14 6ED
Tel: 020 8269 9900 *Fax:* 0844 414 5136 *Dx:* 31703 SIDCUP
E-mail: sidcup@rgsolicitors.co.uk
Office: York

TUMMINGS SOLICITORS ‡
9 Christopher Close Sidcup Kent DA15 8PU
Tel: 020 8850 4465

WOOLSEY MORRIS & KENNEDY ‡
100 Station Road Sidcup Kent DA15 7DT
Tel: 020 8300 9321 *Fax:* 020 8300 0443 *Dx:* 31700 SIDCUP
E-mail: mail@wmk-law.com
Work: A1 B1 C1 C2 C3 D1 E F1 F2 J1 J2 K1 L N O P Q R1 S1 S2 T1 T2 U2 V W Z(c,d,e,h,j,k,l,m,o,p,r)

SIDMOUTH, Devon

EVERYS
104 High Street Sidmouth Devon EX10 8EF
Tel: 01395 577983 *Fax:* 01395 578189 *Dx:* 48701 SIDMOUTH
Emergency telephone 01404 822123
E-mail: law@everys.co.uk
Office: Budleigh Salterton, Exeter, Exmouth, Honiton (2 offices), Ottery St Mary, Seaton, Taunton
Work: A1 A2 B1 B2 C1 C2 C3 D1 D2 E F1 F2 G H J1 J2 K1 L M1 N O P Q R1 R2 S1 S2 T1 T2 V W X Z(c,d,e,h,i,k,l,m,n,o,p,q,r,s,t,u,w,x,y)
Emergency Action, Agency, Advocacy, Fixed Fee Interview, Legal Aid undertaken and Legal Aid Franchise
Ptr: Bowen, Mr Giles Christopher LLB . . . . *§Mar 1993
Ast: Molyneux, Mr Richard J MA(Cantab) . . . . *§Jun 1977

FORD SIMEY LLP
Warwick House 30 High Street Sidmouth Devon EX10 8EA
Tel: 01395 577061 / 0800 169 3741 *Fax:* 01395 578206
Dx: 48703 SIDMOUTH
Emergency telephone 01395 577585
E-mail: info@fordsimey.co.uk
Office: Exeter, Exmouth, Honiton
Languages: French
Work: A1 B1 C1 D1 E F1 G H J1 K1 L N O Q R1 S1 T1 T2 W Z(c,d,h,j,k,l,o)
Emergency Action, Agency, Advocacy, Fixed Fee Interview, Legal Aid undertaken, Legal Aid Franchise and Member of Accident Line
Ptr: Holdich, Mr Alec J LLB . . . . *Apr 1980
Horwood, Mr Michael G. . . . . *Jan 1970
Wheaton, Mr A David MA(Oxon) . . . . *§Feb 1980
Ast: Brazier, Mr Ian Faraday LLB . . . . Feb 1993

GILBERT STEPHENS
(incorporating Mossop & Whitham)
Albion House 36 High Street Sidmouth Devon EX10 8ED
Tel: 01395 512443 *Fax:* 01395 515007 *Dx:* 48700 SIDMOUTH
E-mail: sidlaw@gilbertstephens.co.uk
Office: Exeter, Ottery St Mary
Work: A1 C1 E J1 K1 L N O Q S1 S2 T2 W Z(l,o)
Fixed Fee Interview and Legal Aid Franchise
Ptr: Bates, Mr Alastair J MA(Cantab) . . . . *Mar 1984
Heron, Mr R Alistair LLB(Reading) . . . . *§Nov 1980
Ast: Govier, Miss Elizabeth Ann LLB; TEP . . . . Oct 1989

MICHELMORES LLP
Harston Church Street Sidmouth Devon EX10 8LT
Tel: 01395 512515 *Fax:* 01395 578422 *Dx:* 48704 SIDMOUTH
E-mail: enquiries@michelmores.com
Office: Exeter, London W1
Languages: French, German
Work: A1 D1 E K1 K3 K4 L S1 S2 T2 V W Z(d)
Emergency Action and Advocacy undertaken
Ptr: Hedger, Mr Richard Michael BA(Hons); LSF; FPC Trustee of Kennaway House . . . . *Oct 1995
Ast: Coram, Mr Robert LLB; MA . . . . *Jan 1975
Dowen, Mrs Susan N LLB(Hons) . . . . *Dec 1982

SHIRLEY MAY YARD ‡
Sidford Legal Centre Church Street Sidford Sidmouth Devon EX10 9RL
Tel: 01395 577199 *Fax:* 01395 516163
E-mail: smylaw@btinternet.com
List of partners: S Yard
Work: A1 D1 D2 F1 F2 J1 K1 K2 K3 K4 L Q S1 S2 W Z(l)
Emergency Action and Agency undertaken
SPr: Yard, Mrs Shirley-May. . . . . *Mar 1984

SILSDEN, West Yorkshire

JOHN J HALLIWELL & CO ‡
53 Kirkgate Silsden West Yorkshire BD20 0AQ
Tel: 01535 653094 *Fax:* 01535 653094
List of partners: J J Halliwell
Work: A1 C1 D1 E G H J1 K1 L M1 S1 T1 V W Z(m)
Agency, Advocacy, Fixed Fee Interview, Legal Aid undertaken and Member of Accident Line
Ptr: Halliwell, Mr John J BA; AKC Chairman of the Independent Tribunal Service. . . . . *§Jun 1974

WALKER FOSTER
63 Kirkgate Silsden West Yorkshire BD20 0PB
Tel: 01535 653408 *Fax:* 01535 655127 *Dx:* 702810 SILSDEN
E-mail: info@walkerfoster.com
Office: Barnoldswick, Ilkley, Skipton
Languages: Italian
Work: E K4 S1 S2 T2 W
Ptr: Binns, Mr David R LLB. . . . . *Jun 1974
Rowland, Mr Stuart William . . . . Sep 2005

SITTINGBOURNE, Kent

DUDLEY CRAMP & CO ‡
42 High Street Sittingbourne Kent ME10 4PB
Tel: 01795 420024 *Fax:* 01795 420014
Dx: 30508 SITTINGBOURNE 1
E-mail: lawyers@dudleycramp.co.uk
List of partners: D W Cramp
Work: B1 C1 C2 E J1 R1 S1 S2 T1 T2 W
Ptr: Cramp, Mr Dudley William Notary Public . . . . . . *Nov 1970

DAVIS SIMMONDS DONAGHEY
123-125 High Street Sittingbourne Kent ME10 4AQ
Tel: 01795 599931 *Fax:* 01795 424552
Office: Gillingham, Herne Bay

A J FIELD & CO
(incorporating Seviers & Ivor Jones & Co)
15a Station Street Sittingbourne Kent ME10 3DU
Tel: 01795 436363 *Fax:* 01795 472955
Office: Gerrards Cross, Marlow, Sheerness
Work: A1 B1 C1 C2 C3 D1 E F1 J1 K1 L M1 M2 N O P Q R1 S1 S2 V W Z(b,c,j,k,l,m,o,r)
Emergency Action, Agency, Advocacy, Fixed Fee Interview and Legal Aid undertaken
Ptr: Field, Mr Andrew J BA(Hons) . . . . *Dec 1991

FORDLITTLE ‡
14 Park Road Sittingbourne Kent ME10 1DR
Tel: 01795 436111 *Fax:* 01795 436222
Dx: 30520 SITTINGBOURNE 1
E-mail: law@fordlittle.co.uk
List of partners: G C Ford, W J Little
Work: A1 B1 C1 C2 E J1 L N O Q R1 R2 S1 S2 T1 T2 W Z(b,c,e,j,l,q,s)
Agency and Advocacy undertaken
Ptr: Ford, Mr Giles C LLB . . . . *Nov 1986
Little, Mr William J . . . . *Sep 1981

CHRISTOPHER HARRIS & CO
20 West Street Sittingbourne Kent ME10 1AB
Tel: 01795 437268 *Fax:* 01795 473183
E-mail: info@christopherharris.org.uk
Office: Sheerness
Work: B1 B2 C1 D1 D2 E F1 F2 G H J1 J2 K1 L N O Q S2 X Z(c,g,h,j,l,r)
Emergency Action, Agency, Advocacy, Fixed Fee Interview, Legal Aid undertaken and Member of Accident Line
Ptr: Steadman, Ms Janice H BA ♦. . . . . *Oct 1993
Summerbell, Mr Paul LLB(Hons) ♦ . . . . *Dec 1994
Ast: Pratt, Miss Julia LLB(Hons) . . . . *Jan 2004

ANDREW MCCOOEY & CO ‡
3 London Road Sittingbourne Kent ME10 1NQ
Tel: 01795 470686 *Fax:* 01795 424497
Emergency telephone 01795 478047
E-mail: amccooey@aol.com
List of partners: A E McCooey
Work: A3 G H N Z(g)
Emergency Action, Agency, Advocacy and Fixed Fee Interview undertaken
SPr: McCooey, Mr Andrew E BA ★. . . . . *Nov 1979

P GANZ & CO ‡
Hawks Hill Studio Bexon Cottage Hawks Hill Lane Sittingbourne Kent ME9 8HE
Tel: 01795 830009 *Fax:* 01795 830195
E-mail: pennyganz@ganzlegal.com

POPE & CO ‡
71 High Street Sittingbourne Kent ME10 4AW
Tel: 01795 474004 *Fax:* 01795 474454
Dx: 30523 SITTINGBOURNE 1
E-mail: admin@popeandco.co.uk
List of partners: D J Milan, J D Way
Work: C1 C3 D1 E F1 J1 K1 K3 L N O Q S1 S2 V W X
Emergency Action, Legal Aid undertaken and Legal Aid Franchise
Ptr: Milan, Mr Daniel John LLB . . . . *Mar 2001
Way, Mr Justin Darren LLB(Lond). . . . . *Sep 1993
Ast: Heywood, Mr James BA(Hons) . . . . *Aug 2006

RATCLIFFES SOLICITORS ‡
22 Park Road Sittingbourne Kent ME10 1DR
Tel: 01795 477505 *Fax:* 01795 430505 *Dx:* 30500 SITTINGBOURNE

SKEGNESS, Lincolnshire

AA LAW SOLICITORS ‡
Skegness Business Centre Heath Road Skegness Lincolnshire PE25 3SJ
Tel: 01754 896970 / 07733 228081 / 07900 913830
Fax: 07900 913830
Fax:
E-mail: info@aalaw.co.uk

BAILEY MORGAN & CO ‡
34 Algitha Road Skegness Lincolnshire PE25 2AJ
Tel: 01754 768383 / 763007 *Fax:* 01754 610356
List of partners: M E Bailey
Work: E J1 L R2 S1 S2 T1 T2 W
SPr: Bailey, Mr Martyn Edward LLB . . . . *Dec 1977

BRIDGE MCFARLAND
9 Lumley Avenue Skegness Lincolnshire PE25 2EH
Tel: 01754 762266 *Fax:* 01754 767010 *Dx:* 27502 SKEGNESS
E-mail: info@bmcf.co.uk
Office: Grimsby (3 offices), Hull, Lincoln, Louth, Mablethorpe, Market Rasen

BROUGH HALL & CO ‡
The Shrubberies 28 Lumley Avenue Skegness Lincolnshire PE25 2AT
Tel: 01754 768641
List of partners: P R Brough, C J Hall
Work: A1 B1 C1 E F1 F2 J1 J2 K1 L N O Q S1 S2 W Z(l)
Agency and Advocacy undertaken
Ptr: Brough, Mr Peter R LLB. . . . . *Jan 1980
Hall, Mrs Clare Joanne LLB(Hons) . . . . *Apr 1998

EAGER & CO ‡
33 Algitha Road Skegness Lincolnshire PE25 2AJ
Tel: 01754 766688 *Fax:* 01754 610049 *Dx:* 27514 SKEGNESS 1
Emergency telephone 07740 248727
E-mail: davideager@btconnect.com
Work: G H
Agency, Advocacy, Fixed Fee Interview, Legal Aid undertaken and Legal Aid Franchise

G M FARMER ‡
13 Ridley Avenue Skegness Lincolnshire PE25 3LD
Tel: 01754 763767 *Fax:* 01754 763767

FREARSONS ‡
50 Algitha Road Skegness Lincolnshire PE25 2AW
Tel: 01754 897600 *Fax:* 01754 610074 *Dx:* 27504 SKEGNESS
E-mail: mail@frearsons.com
List of partners: P W Downing, H D Fisher, M R Phelps, C N H Seymour
Work: C1 C2 D1 D2 E J1 K1 K2 K3 K4 L N O Q S1 S2 W Z(f,k,l)
Emergency Action, Agency, Advocacy, Fixed Fee Interview, Legal Aid undertaken, Legal Aid Franchise and Member of Accident Line
Ptr: Downing, Mr Peter W LLB(Hons) . . . . *§Oct 1973
Fisher, Miss Helen Dawn LLB(Hons) . . . . *Oct 1988
Phelps, Mr Michael R BA(Hons). . . . . *Sep 1986
Seymour, Mr Colin N H BA . . . . *Jul 1979
Ast: Berriman, Miss Catherine Ann LLB(Hons). . . . . . Oct 2005
Burge, Miss Pamela Helen LLB(Hons). . . . . Dec 1995
Connolly, Mrs Lesley Ann LLB(Hons); BA . . . . . Jan 2002
Dales, Miss Anne V LLB(Hons) . . . . *Jul 1996
Downing, Miss Emma Kate LLB(Hons) . . . . *Dec 1997
Phelps, Mrs Caroline B BA(Law) . . . . *Apr 1988

HODGKINSONS SOLICITORS ‡
The Bracings 7 Heath Road Skegness Lincolnshire PE25 3ST
Tel: 01754 897150 *Fax:* 01754 897199 *Dx:* 27506 SKEGNESS 1
Emergency telephone 01754 897150
E-mail: csli@hodgkinsons.co.uk
Work: A1 B1 C1 C2 D1 E F1 F2 G H J1 J2 K1 L N O P Q R1 S1 V W Z(c,e,i,l,p,q,t)

JSP SOLICITORS ‡
10-12 Algitha Road Skegness Lincolnshire PE25 2AG
Tel: 01754 762252 / 01522 537353 *Fax:* 01754 610369
Dx: 27501 SKEGNESS
E-mail: jamessmith@jsp-skeg.demon.co.uk
List of partners: J A Smith
Work: D1 E K1 N R1 S1 W Z(l)
Emergency Action, Agency, Advocacy, Fixed Fee Interview, Legal Aid undertaken, Legal Aid Franchise and Member of Accident Line
Ptr: Smith, Mr James Anthony LLB; MBA . . . . *Jan 1982

MARIANNE JOHNSON FAMILY LAW PRACTICE ‡
22 High Street Burgh le Marsh Skegness Lincolnshire PE24 5JT
Tel: 01754 812812 *Fax:* 01754 811001
E-mail: marianne@mjohnsonfamilylaw.co.uk

See p112 for the Key to Work Categories & other symbols

SILLS & BETTERIDGE LLP
45 Algitha Road Skegness Lincolnshire PE25 2AJ
Tel: 01754 610101 *Fax:* 01754 761268 *Dx:* 27507 SKEGNESS 1
Office: Boston, Coningsby, Gainsborough, Lincoln, Sleaford, Spalding, Spilsby
Work: D1 G H K1 K3 N Q
Emergency Action, Agency, Advocacy, Fixed Fee Interview, Legal Aid undertaken and Legal Aid Franchise
Ast: Theofanous, Ms Chrystal . . . . Mar 2008

Holders of LA franchise. We specialise in the following areas of work: Child Care and Family, Crime - General and Motoring, Litigation General. Agency commissions gladly undertaken.

SKELMERSDALE, Lancashire

BRIGHOUSE WOLFF
(incorporating Brighouse Jones & Co; Heald Wolff)
Whelmar House Southway Skelmersdale Lancashire WN8 6NX
Tel: 01695 722577 *Fax:* 01695 727147 *Dx:* 22203 SKELMERSDALE
E-mail: firm@brighouse-wolff.co.uk
Office: Maghull, Ormskirk, Skelmersdale
Work: B2 D1 F1 G H J1 K1 K2 K3 N O P Q V X Z(k,l,q)
Emergency Action, Advocacy, Fixed Fee Interview, Legal Aid undertaken and Legal Aid Franchise
Ptr: Flynn, Mr Michael LLB(Hons) ★ . . . . *Oct 1994
Hagerty, Mr Michael G BA(Oxon) ★ . . . . *Feb 1990
Mossman, Mr Stephen LLB . . . . *Apr 1981
Con: Lloyd, Mr David . . . . *Jan 1969
Lloyd, Ms Sheila A . . . . *Jun 1970

BRIGHOUSE WOLFF
(incorporating Brighouse Jones & Co; Heald Wolff)
82 Sandy Lane Skelmersdale Lancashire WN8 8LQ
Tel: 01695 717000 *Fax:* 01695 717111 *Dx:* 22203 SKELMERSDALE
E-mail: firm@brighouse-wolff.co.uk
Office: Maghull, Ormskirk, Skelmersdale
Work: E K3 L R2 S1 S2 W
Ptr: Jones, Mr E Eric LLB . . . . *Nov 1972

GREENHALGHS SOLICITORS ‡
Olympic House Maple Court Maple View Skelmersdale Lancashire WN8 9TW
Tel: 0333 200 5200 *Fax:* 0333 200 5201
E-mail: info@greenhalghs.net

DAVID LACIDE & CO ‡
Office Suite 1 48 Westgate Skelmersdale Lancashire WN8 8AZ
Tel: 01695 722444

SCOTT REES & CO ‡
Centaur House Gardiners Place Skelmersdale Lancashire WN8 9SP
Tel: 01695 722222 *Fax:* 01695 733333 *Dx:* 22201 SKELMERSDALE
E-mail: info@scottrees.co.uk
List of partners: T J Allen, D J Byrne, D A Rees, P A Scott, R F Smith, S Tansey
Languages: Bengali, Cantonese, French, German, Gujarati, Hindi, Italian, Mirpuri, Polish, Portuguese, Punjabi, Spanish, Urdu
Work: J1 N O S1 S2 W
Agency, Fixed Fee Interview, Legal Aid undertaken and Member of Accident Line
Ptr: Allen, Mr Timothy James BSc . . . . *Nov 1995
Byrne, Mr David J LLB . . . . *Dec 2000
Rees, Mr Daniel A LLB . . . . *Dec 1983
Scott, Mr Peter A LLB . . . . *§Jun 1970
Smith, Mr Royston Francis . . . . *Feb 1997
Tansey, Mr Simon LLB . . . . Sep 2000
Asoc: Ahmed, Ms Nigat . . . . *Jun 2004
Kingston, Ms Karla LLB . . . . *Oct 2003
Lomax, Ms Catherine LLB . . . . *Mar 1998
Ast: Akhtar, Mrs Nasreen LLB . . . . Apr 2004
Ali, Mr Yasar . . . . Jan 2006
Begum, Ms Saida LLB . . . . *Oct 2005
Driscoll, Mr James LLB . . . . *Dec 2003
Duckworth, Mr Andrew S LLB; MA . . . . *Jan 1989
Durosholа, Mr Ayinde . . . . Jan 2000
Harvey, Ms Claire . . . . Oct 2004
Illingworth, Ms Lucie . . . . Aug 2006
Kartikapallil, Mr Dominic LLB . . . . Jun 2006
Lester, Ms Vanessa Louise LLB; LPC . . . . Oct 1999
Lloyd-Jones, Mrs Catherine LLB . . . . *Dec 2002
Masters, Miss Amy LLB . . . . Jul 2007
Ramzan, Ms Rusbana . . . . Oct 2004
Smith, Ms Catherine . . . . Jun 2006

SKELTON-IN-CLEVELAND, Redcar & Cleveland

BARTONS
93-95 High Street Skelton-in-Cleveland Redcar & Cleveland TS12 2DY
Tel: 01287 651521 *Fax:* 01287 650881 *Dx:* 61722 SKELTON
E-mail: enquiries@bartons-solicitors.co.uk
Office: Guisborough
Work: D1 D2 E F1 F2 G H J1 K1 L N Q S1 S2 V W Z(r)
Agency undertaken
Ptr: Barton, Mr Richard S LLB . . . . *May 1988
Gent, Miss Clare L LLB . . . . *Nov 1997

SKIPTON, North Yorkshire

AWB CHARLESWORTH LLP
23 Otley Street Skipton North Yorkshire BD23 1DY
Tel: 01756 793333 *Fax:* 01756 794434 *Dx:* 21753 SKIPTON
E-mail: info@cwb.uk.com
Office: Keighley
Work: A1 B1 C1 C2 D1 D2 E F1 F2 J1 K1 K3 L N O Q R2 S1 S2 T1 T2 W Z(c,d,l)
Emergency Action, Agency, Advocacy, Fixed Fee Interview, Legal Aid undertaken and Legal Aid Franchise
Ptr: Brown, Mrs Debra Jane LLB(Hons) . . . . *Oct 1998
Davidson, Mr Alan J LLB(Hons) . . . . *Oct 1989
Hayes, Mr Declan Thomas Matthew BSc(Hons) . . . . *Oct 1998
Lane, Mr Andrew Hardingham LLB . . . . *Aug 1981
Con: Chambers, Mrs Nicola BA(Dunelm) . . . . *Jun 1972

ARMSTRONG LUTY SOLICITORS ‡
Kipling House 24 Otley Street Skipton North Yorkshire BD23 1EW
Tel: 01756 799977 *Fax:* 01756 797888
List of partners: A S Armstrong, N P Luty
Work: N
Ptr: Armstrong, Mr Andrew S LLB(L'pool) . . . . *Jul 1978
Luty, Mr Nicholas Paul LLB . . . . *Jul 1996

FOSTERLAW SOLICITORS ‡
The Clock House Watermill Park Broughton Hall Skipton North Yorkshire BD23 3AG
Tel: 01756 700110 *Fax:* 01756 795310
E-mail: mail@fosterlawsolicitors.com

MAKIN DIXON SOLICITORS
High Street House Newmarket Street Skipton North Yorkshire BD23 2HU
Tel: 01756 797284 *Fax:* 01756 798397 *Dx:* 21760 SKIPTON
E-mail: enquiries@makindixon.co.uk
Office: Bradford, Halifax, Harrogate, Keighley, Todmorden
Ptr: Makin, Caroline . . . . Oct 2002

QUALITY SOLICITORS MEWIES ‡
Clifford House Keighley Road Skipton North Yorkshire BD23 2NB
Tel: 01756 799000 *Fax:* 01756 700101 *Dx:* 21754 SKIPTON
Emergency telephone 07973 473750
E-mail: mewies@qualitysolicitors.com
List of partners: J R Birch, M J Crossley, C C Jackson, J C Mewies
Work: A1 D1 D2 G H J1 K1 K3 L N O S1 S2 T2 W
Emergency Action, Agency, Advocacy, Fixed Fee Interview, Legal Aid undertaken, Legal Aid Franchise and Member of Accident Line
Ptr: Birch, Mr Justin Rupert LLB(Hons) . . . . *Dec 1990
Crossley, Mr Martin J LLB; PGDip Pl Lit . . . . *Feb 1989
Jackson, Mr Christopher C BA(Oxon) . . . . *Oct 1985
Mewies, Mr John C . . . . *Jun 1980
Ast: Worger, Mrs Amanda Louise LLB(Hons) . . . . *Jun 1996

SAVAGE CRANGLE ‡
15 High Street Skipton North Yorkshire BD23 1AJ
Tel: 01756 794611 *Fax:* 01756 791395 *Dx:* 21751 SKIPTON
E-mail: law@savage-crangle.co.uk
List of partners: P J Crangle, J M Eyre, J R Leach, T P G Manock, C M Storah
Office: Otley
Languages: French, German
Work: A1 B1 C1 C2 C3 D1 E F1 G H J1 K1 L M1 M2 N P R1 S1 T1 T2 V W
Emergency Action, Agency, Advocacy, Fixed Fee Interview undertaken and Member of Accident Line
Ptr: Crangle, Mr Peter J LLB(Lond) Notary Public . . . . . *Mar 1977
Eyre, Mr John M LLB . . . . *May 1984
Leach, Mr Jonathan R LLB(Wales) . . . . *Jun 1980
Manock, Mr Timothy P G LLB . . . . *Oct 1988
Asoc: Hallam, Mr Stephen . . . . Jan 1989
Ast: Mour, Miss Linzi Jane LLB . . . . Jul 2003

STERRATT & CO
43 Otley Street Skipton North Yorkshire BD23 1EL
Tel: 01756 795069 *Fax:* 01756 798343 *Dx:* 21755 SKIPTON
E-mail: enquiries@sterratt.co.uk
Office: Barnoldswick
Work: K4 L S1 S2 W
Ptr: Sterratt, Mr Malcolm C LLB(Bris) . . . . *§Apr 1971

WALKER FOSTER ‡
3 High Street Skipton North Yorkshire BD23 1AA
Tel: 01756 700200 *Fax:* 01756 700186 *Dx:* 21752 SKIPTON
E-mail: info@walkerfoster.com
List of partners: D R Binns, K Hardington, A D D Keighley, J C Phillip, S W Rowland, C J Varley, P C Walker, M S Worrall
Office: Barnoldswick, Ilkley, Silsden
Work: A1 A3 C1 D1 E F1 J1 K1 K4 L N O P Q R1 R2 S1 S2 T1 T2 V W Z(q,r)
Emergency Action, Agency, Advocacy and Fixed Fee Interview undertaken
Ptr: Hardington, Mr Keith BA . . . . *§Aug 1995
Keighley, Mr Alister D D LLB . . . . *May 1974
Phillip, Mr Julian C . . . . *Feb 1981
Varley, Mr Christopher J LLB . . . . *Dec 1975
Ast: Swindells, Mr Tom . . . . Sep 2009

WEIR & CO SOLICITORS ‡
13 Otley Street Skipton North Yorkshire BD23 1DY
Tel: 01756 701300

SLEAFORD, Lincolnshire

ARNOLD DEACON GREENE & CO ‡
18 Eastgate Sleaford Lincolnshire NG34 7DP
Tel: 01529 414414 *Fax:* 01529 306653 *Dx:* 26908 SLEAFORD
E-mail: reception@adgreene.biz
List of partners: J H Baines
Work: A1 C1 E L S1 S2 W
Ptr: Baines, Mr John Hewley . . . . *Jun 1963

BURTON & CO LLP
7-8 Market Place Sleaford Lincolnshire NG34 7SH
Tel: 01529 306008 / 306009 *Fax:* 01529 413028
Dx: 26905 SLEAFORD
Emergency telephone 01529 306008
E-mail: inmail@burtonlaw.co.uk
Office: Lincoln
Work: A1 B1 C1 C2 D1 D2 E F1 G H J1 K1 K2 K3 K4 L N O Q R1 S1 S2 V W Z(h,m,p,q)
Emergency Action, Agency, Advocacy, Fixed Fee Interview, Legal Aid undertaken, Legal Aid Franchise and Member of Accident Line
Ptr: Matthews, Mrs Patricia M BA . . . . *Oct 1984
Asoc: Sheen, Mr Julian H BA . . . . *Jan 1982

CHATTERTONS SOLICITORS
5 Market Street Sleaford Lincolnshire NG34 7SQ
Tel: 01529 411500 *Fax:* 01529 414236 *Dx:* 26903 SLEAFORD
E-mail: sleaford@chattertons.com
Office: Boston (2 offices), Grantham, Horncastle, Lincoln, Newark, Spalding, Stamford
Work: A1 B1 B2 C1 C2 D1 D2 E F1 F2 G H J1 K1 L N O Q R1 S1 S2 T2 W X Z(c,d,e,l,o,p,q)
Emergency Action, Advocacy, Fixed Fee Interview, Legal Aid undertaken, Legal Aid Franchise and Member of Accident Line
Ptr: Alcock, Mr Robert Edward LLB(Hons) . . . . *Sep 1995
Ellis, Mr Benjamin M LLB(Hons) . . . . *Oct 1997
Freeman, Mr Roland . . . . Apr 2004
Thornton, Mrs Eleanor S LLB(Hons) . . . . *Apr 1980
Ast: Cragg, Mr Andrew Christopher LLB(Hons) CCH Prize for Company Law . . . . Sep 2003

2

THE RINGROSE LAW GROUP - NERINA FARMER
(incorporating Frost Gunning & Co; Grocock & Staniland; Adie Pickwell)
Pride Parkway Sleaford Lincolnshire NG34 8GL
Tel: 01529 301300 *Fax:* 01529 301399 *Dx:* 26902 SLEAFORD
Emergency telephone 01529 302775
E-mail: nerina.farmer@ringroselaw.co.uk
Office: Boston, Grantham, Lincoln (2 offices), Newark, Spalding
Languages: French, German, Hindi, Punjabi
Work: A1 A3 B1 B2 C1 C2 D1 D2 E F1 F2 G H J1 J2 K1 K2 L N O P Q R1 S1 S2 T1 T2 V W Z(c,d,h,i,j,k,l,m,p,q,r,t)
Emergency Action, Agency, Advocacy, Fixed Fee Interview, Legal Aid undertaken, Legal Aid Franchise and Member of Accident Line
Ptr: Harwood, Mr Richard James LLB(Hons) . . . . *Nov 1996
Hitchcock, Mr David W LLB(Lond) . . . . *§Jan 1970
Knight, Mr John Antony Philip LLB(Hons) . . . . . . Nov 1995
Asoc: Appleby, Mr Luke Justin LLB(Hons) . . . . Mar 2002
Ast: Green, Mrs Amanda J LLB . . . . Feb 1994

SILLS & BETTERIDGE LLP
(incorporating Godsons)
27-31 Northgate North Kesteven Sleaford Lincolnshire NG34 7BW
Tel: 01529 302800 *Fax:* 01529 413703 *Dx:* 26901 SLEAFORD
E-mail: info@sillslegal.co.uk
Office: Boston, Coningsby, Gainsborough, Lincoln, Skegness, Spalding, Spilsby
Work: A1 A2 A3 B1 B2 C1 C2 C3 D1 E F1 F2 G H I J1 J2 K1 K2 K3 K4 L M1 M2 N O P Q R1 R2 S1 S2 T1 T2 V W Z(b,c,d,e,f,g,h,i,j,k,l,m,o,p,q,r,s,t,u,w,za)
Emergency Action, Agency, Advocacy, Fixed Fee Interview, Legal Aid undertaken, Legal Aid Franchise and Member of Accident Line
Ptr: Clarke, Mrs Isabel Scott . . . . May 2001
Maclean, Mrs Rachel LLB(Hons) . . . . *Oct 1996
Straw, Mr Martin Keith LLB . . . . *§Oct 1983
Swift, Mr Stephen W BA . . . . *§Jan 1982

Holders of Franchise for Crime, Mental Health, Personal Injury, Family, Actions Against the Police. We specialise in the following areas of work Family Law, Litigation, Accidents, Injury, Criminal Injury Com, Wills, Trusts and Probate.

SLOUGH

ASGHAR & CO
1st Floor 112-114 High Street Slough SL1 1JQ
Tel: 01753 535577 *Fax:* 01753 529334 *Dx:* 42261 SLOUGH WEST
E-mail: info@asghar-solicitors.co.uk
Office: Southall

ASTON BOND LLP ‡
135-139 High Street Slough SL1 1DN
Tel: 01753 486777 *Fax:* 01753 517180 *Dx:* 42257 SLOUGH WEST
E-mail: info@astonbond.co.uk
List of partners: P J Payne
Office: Reading
Ptr: Payne, Mr Philip J . . . . *Jun 1981
Con: Khatter, Gurdeep S BA . . . . Apr 1993

AZHAR & CO ‡
12 Buckingham Avenue East Slough SL1 3EA
Tel: 01753 779637 *Fax:* 01753 748909
E-mail: azhar@webstar.co.uk
List of partners: A M Ghose
Languages: Punjabi, Urdu
Work: D1 E K1 L N Q S1 S2 W Z(i)
Emergency Action, Agency, Advocacy, Fixed Fee Interview and Legal Aid undertaken
SPr: Ghose, Mr Azhar M LLB(Hons) . . . . *Oct 1994

BARRETT & THOMSON ‡
Buckingham Court Buckingham Gardens Slough SL1 1TQ
Tel: 01753 437416 *Fax:* 01753 777590
E-mail: info@barrettandthomson.com
List of partners: C A Fitzgerald, C A Lang, D Thomson
Languages: Hindi, Punjabi, Urdu
Work: A1 A3 B1 C1 C2 C3 D1 E F1 J1 K1 L M1 M2 N O P Q R1 S1 T1 T2 V W Z(b,c,d,e,f,g,h,k,l,o,p,q,r)
Emergency Action, Agency, Advocacy, Fixed Fee Interview, Legal Aid undertaken, Legal Aid Franchise and Member of Accident Line
Ptr: Fitzgerald, Miss Claire A BA(Dunelm) . . . . *§Nov 1984
Lang, Mrs Catherine A . . . . *Dec 1994
Thomson, Mr Duncan LLB . . . . *Dec 1994
Ast: Reynolds, Miss Amanda . . . . *Nov 1996

CSL ASSOCIATES ‡
Regal Court 42-44 High Street Slough SL1 1EL
Tel: 01753 245546
E-mail: csl.associates@tiscali.co.uk

CHAMBERS SOLICITORS
124a High Street Slough SL1 1JE
Tel: 01753 522204 *Fax:* 01753 524876 *Dx:* 42274 SLOUGH WEST
Work: B1 F1 K1 L O Q Z(b)
Ptr: Uppal, Ms Surinder Singh . . . . Mar 1996
Con: Lall, Aqbal S LLB . . . . *Oct 1987

CHARSLEY HARRISON LLP
4 Burlington Court Burlington Road Slough SL1 2JS
Tel: 01753 517600 *Fax:* 01753 518440 *Dx:* 42265 SLOUGH WEST
E-mail: slough@charsleyharrison.com
Web: www.charsleyharrison.com
Office: Windsor
Work: E K1 S1 W
Ptr: Barr, Mr Steven J . . . . *Sep 2001
Asoc: Shangari, Mr Sumeet LLB(Hons) . . . . *Jul 2008

Particular areas of work include: Residential Conveyancing, Commercial Conveyancing, Wills Trusts & Probate, Employment Law

FAMILY LAW SOLUTIONS ‡
268 Bath Road Slough SL1 4DX
Tel: 0845 603 2237

FITZ SOLICITORS ‡
Chappell House The Green Slough SL3 9EH
Tel: 01753 592000

FORT & CO ‡
6 & 7 Kingfisher Court 281 Farnham Road Slough SL2 1JF
Tel: 01753 691224

H&M SOLICITORS LTD ‡
36 Carlton Road Slough SL2 5PZ
Tel: 01753 524128

HSBS LAW LIMITED ‡
50 Farnham Road Slough SL1 3TA
Tel: 01753 475400 *Fax:* 01753 691798
E-mail: balwant@hsbslaw.com

HARRIS CARTIER LLP ‡
Windsor Crown House 7 Windsor Road Slough SL1 2DX
Tel: 01753 810710 *Fax:* 01753 810720 *Dx:* 42268 SLOUGH WEST
E-mail: enquiries@hclaw.co.uk
List of partners: G P Bee, L I Cartier, S J Fuller, C J Gooderidge, K J McCarthy, G A McDonagh, J C Neal, D C Nicholls, K Pattinson
Office: London WC2
Languages: French, German, Hindi, Punjabi, Urdu
Work: A3 B1 C1 C2 C3 D1 E F1 J1 K1 K2 K3 L M1 N O Q R1 R2 S1 S2 T1 T2 U1 U2 W Z(c,d,e,h,o,p,q,r)
Advocacy undertaken and Member of Accident Line
Ptr: Bee, Mr Gregory P . . . Aug 1997
Gooderidge, Mr Christopher J ACIArb. . . . *§Jul 1967
McCarthy, Miss Karen Jennifer LLB(Hons). . . . Feb 1997
Neal, Mr Justin Charles BSc; LSF. . . . Sep 1995
Asoc: Denham, Ms Katherine LLB . . . Sep 1997
Hills, Miss Vanessa LLB(Hons) . . . Sep 1999
Ast: Haider, Mr Alexander K LLB; RGN . . . *Mar 2001
Kurtz, Miss Emma-Jane Francesca BA; TEP . . . Jan 2004
O'Connor, Mr Sean BSc(Hons) . . . *Oct 2003
Patankar, Miss Sadia . . . Sep 2007
Powlesland, Mrs Deborah. . . . Sep 2009
Sakaria, Mr Sandeep . . . Apr 2003

J R HOBBS & CO ‡
Maple House 95 High Street Slough SL1 1DH
Tel: 01753 524466 *Fax:* 01753 550347 *Dx:* 42258 SLOUGH WEST
Emergency telephone 07767 833873
List of partners: A M Everatt, D M Todd
Work: B1 B2 D1 F1 G H J1 K1 Q S1 W
Emergency Action, Agency, Advocacy, Fixed Fee Interview and Legal Aid undertaken
Ptr: Everatt, Miss Andrea M LLB. . . . *Jul 1980
Todd, Mr David Maitland BSc . . . *Oct 1994

IE LAW ‡
1 Mill Court 51 Mill Street Slough SL2 5DA
Tel: 01753 554040 *Fax:* 01753 576757

KIDD RAPINET
Parliament House St Laurence Way Slough SL1 2BW
Tel: 0845 017 9638 *Fax:* 01753 820501 *Dx:* 42269 SLOUGH WEST
E-mail: pastles@kiddrapinet.co.uk
Office: Aylesbury, Farnham, High Wycombe, London WC2, Maidenhead, Reading
Work: A1 B1 C1 C2 C3 D1 E F1 G H J1 K1 L M1 M2 N O P Q R1 R2 S1 T1 T2 V W Z(a,b,c,d,e,f,g,h,i,j,k,l,m,n,o,p,s,t)
Emergency Action, Agency, Advocacy, Legal Aid undertaken, Legal Aid Franchise and Member of Accident Line
Ptr: Astles, Mr Philip John Goolden . . . *Sep 2000
Comley, Mr Christopher Michael. . . . Dec 1976
Williams, Ms Teresa Jane LLB(Hons) . . . *Oct 1982
Ast: Choudhery, Miss Fozia LLB . . . *Sep 2008

LYONS SOLICITORS ‡
1st Floor Elmshott Lane Slough SL1 5QS
Tel: 01628 661999 *Fax:* 01628 669287

FRANCIS MOSTYN & CO ‡
242 High Street Langley Slough SL3 8LL
Tel: 01753 545322 *Fax:* 01753 544018
E-mail: mail@francismostyn.co.uk
List of partners: F E T Mostyn
Ptr: Mostyn, Mr Francis E T LLB. . . . *Dec 1973

MARTIN MURRAY & ASSOCIATES
1 The Pavilions Stoke Gardens Slough SL1 3QD
Tel: 01753 551313 *Fax:* 01753 552237 *Dx:* 3401 SLOUGH
Emergency telephone 01753 600101
Office: Reading, West Drayton
Languages: Greek, Hindi, Urdu
Work: D1 G H K1 S1
Emergency Action, Agency, Advocacy, Fixed Fee Interview, Legal Aid undertaken and Legal Aid Franchise
Ptr: Asghar, Mr Amer . . . Jul 2006
Burns, Miss Danielle BA. . . . Aug 2004
Hughes, Miss Kate Juliette LLB(Hons) ★ . . . *Aug 2001
Rai, Ms Manjit. . . . *Oct 2003
Turnbull, Mr Paul Leslie BA(Hons) ★ . . . *Jul 1990
Ast: Alam, Mr Fiaz. . . . *Feb 2005
Choudhry, Miss Nadira LLB . . . *Sep 2006
Duncan, Miss Monique . . . *Nov 2006
Loftus, Carly . . . Sep 2009
Taylor, Miss Eloise . . . *Jun 2009
Uddin, Mr Mohammed LLB . . . Sep 2006
Walker, Mr Alan. . . . Nov 2006

OWEN WHITE ‡
Senate House 62-70 Bath Road Slough SL1 3SR
Tel: 01753 876800 *Fax:* 01753 876876 *Dx:* 3409 SLOUGH
E-mail: law@owenwhite.com
List of partners: N G H Barnard, C E Beidas, S R Bishop, C Cowley, A J Devlin, R Ford, A Hayward, R J Keen, P J Lawrence, J E Masih
Languages: French, Hindi, Punjabi
Work: A1 A3 B1 C1 C2 C3 E F1 F2 I J1 J2 L M1 M2 N O P Q R1 S1 S2 U2 W Z(c,d,e,f,h,j,k,p,q)
Advocacy undertaken
Ptr: Barnard, Mr Nicholas G H. . . . *§Dec 1977
Beidas, Mrs Caryn Elizabeth LLB . . . *Mar 2000
Bishop, Miss Stephanie Rose LLB. . . . *Jan 1999
Cowley, Ms Caroline LLB(Hons). . . . *Oct 1992
Devlin, Mr Anthony John LLB; BA. . . . Mar 2008
Ford, Mr Russell LLB(Hons). . . . *Oct 1993
Hayward, Mr Andrew LLM. . . . *Apr 1993
Keen, Mr Richard J BA . . . *Nov 1980
Lawrence, Mr Philip J LLB. . . . *Oct 1991
Masih, Mrs Jane E BA . . . *Oct 1987
Ast: Anderson, Mr William Whiteford LLB . . . Sep 2009
Bashir, Mrs Shazia LLB . . . Sep 2003
Eustace, Ms Victoria BA; CPE; LPC. . . . Sep 2010
Hindes, Mrs Pamela LLB(Hons). . . . Nov 2001
King, Miss Nicola LLB. . . . *Mar 2006
Martin, Miss Emma-Jane Steven BA(Hons) . . . Jul 2002
Smith, Miss Lynsey Sarah LLB . . . Sep 2007
Smith, Mr Michael David LLB . . . *Sep 2003

PHILLIPS OSBOURNE ‡
Beech Court 31 Summer Road Slough SL1 7EP
Tel: 01628 663344 *Fax:* 01628 664465
E-mail: mark@phillipsosborne.com
Ast: Wiggett, Claire . . . Jan 2008

RAI SOLICITOR ‡
72 Stoke Road Slough SL2 5AP
Tel: 01753 576800 *Fax:* 01753 576801
Emergency telephone 07790 040522
E-mail: railegal@gmail.com
List of partners: Z S Rai
Languages: French, German, Punjabi, Urdu
Work: A3 B1 C1 D1 E F1 G J1 K1 K3 L N O Q S1 S2 V W Z(d,i)
Agency and Fixed Fee Interview undertaken
SPr: Rai, Mr Zoraber Singh BA(Hons) . . . Feb 1998

RAYAT & CO SOLICITORS ‡
3 High Street Chalvey Slough SL1 2RU
Tel: 01753 736815 *Fax:* 01753 792693
E-mail: pashi@familylaw.fsnet.co.uk

S & V SOLICITORS ‡
Abbey Business Centre 18-24 Stoke Road Slough SL2 5AG
Tel: 01753 722130 / 07767 637582 *Fax:* 01753 722133
E-mail: info@svsolicitors.co.uk

SLOUGH SOLICITORS ‡
24 High Street Slough SL1 1EQ
Tel: 01753 535422 / 0800 051 7624 *Fax:* 0870 762 8815
E-mail: enquiries@sloughsolicitors.co.uk

TEMPLARS SOLICITORS ‡
98a High Street Slough SL1 1HL
Tel: 01753 550476 *Fax:* 01753 534896 *Dx:* 42251 SLOUGH WEST
E-mail: info@templarssolicitors.co.uk

SMETHWICK, West Midlands

KHAN & CO ‡
47 Cape Hill Smethwick West Midlands B66 4SF
Tel: 0121 565 4292 *Fax:* 0121 555 5813 *Dx:* 22559 SMETHWICK

NICHOLLS BRIMBLE & CO ‡
(incorporating Bryan Davies & Co)
427 Bearwood Road Smethwick West Midlands B66 4DF
Tel: 0121 429 8016 *Fax:* 0121 429 5025 *Dx:* 22562 SMETHWICK
E-mail: info@nicholsbrimble.com
List of partners: N C Brimble, P M Davies
Languages: Hindi, Punjabi
Work: B1 C1 E F1 G H J1 K1 L N Q R1 S1 W
Agency undertaken
SPr: Brimble, Mr Nicholas C LLB. . . . *May 1975
Ptr: Davies, Mr Philip M . . . Mar 1983

SAHNI & CO ‡
104 High Street Smethwick West Midlands B66 1AA
Tel: 0121 558 5222
E-mail: hardevsahni@ukonline.co.uk
List of partners: H S Sahni
Languages: Hindi, Punjabi, Urdu
SPr: Sahni, Hardev S MA; LLB(Lond) Notary Public . . . *Apr 1974

SILKS
368 High Street Smethwick West Midlands B66 3PG
Tel: 0121 558 1147 *Fax:* 0121 565 4586 *Dx:* 22551 SMETHWICK
E-mail: info@silks-solicitors.co.uk
Office: Netherton, Oldbury
Work: G H R1 S1 W

SOLIHULL, West Midlands

DAVID ACTON & CO ‡
143 Dorridge Road Dorridge Solihull West Midlands B93 8BN
Tel: 01564 730028 *Fax:* 01564 730028
List of partners: D E Acton
Work: C1 E L R1 R2 S1 S2 W Z(s)
SPr: Acton, Mr David E. . . . *Dec 1979

ALLSOPP & CO ‡
42a Poplar Road Solihull West Midlands B91 3AB
Tel: 0121 705 9020 *Fax:* 0121 711 1019 *Dx:* 714011 SOLIHULL 1
E-mail: ppty@alsoppandco.co.uk
List of partners: E T M Allsopp, L A Szostek
Office: Solihull
Ptr: Allsopp, Mr Edward T M. . . . *Feb 1974
Szostek, Leslie A LLB(Warw) . . . *Dec 1977

ALLSOPP & CO
46 High Street Solihull West Midlands B91 3TB
Tel: 0121 704 4282 *Fax:* 0121 711 2087 *Dx:* 714001 SOLIHULL 1
Office: Solihull
Work: A1 C1 E G H J1 K1 L N O Q S1 S2 W
Ptr: Allsopp, Mr Edward T M. . . . *Feb 1974

ERIC BOWES & CO ‡
Marlborough House 139 Stratford Road Shirley Solihull West Midlands B90 3AY
Tel: 0121 744 3691 *Fax:* 0121 733 1487 *Dx:* 20653 SHIRLEY 1
E-mail: enquiries@ericbowesandco.co.uk
List of partners: D P Wade
Languages: Hindi, Punjabi, Urdu
Work: C1 K1 K3 K4 L N O Q S1 S2 W Z(h)
Emergency Action, Agency, Advocacy, Fixed Fee Interview, Legal Aid undertaken and Legal Aid Franchise
Ptr: Wade, Mr David P LLB . . . *Feb 1988

Ast: Cordon, Ms Anne Collette LLB . . . *Jul 2009
Gill, Gurbinder Singh LLB. . . . *May 1996

AGNES CROMPTON-ROBERTS SOLICITOR ‡
Petersfield House 9 Greyfreirs Close Solihull West Midlands B92 7DR
Tel: 0121 707 2309 *Fax:* 0121 707 2309
E-mail: asm@acr-solicitors.com

CUNNINGTONS
Northampton House Poplar Road Solihull West Midlands B91 3AP
Tel: 0121 705 6868 *Fax:* 0121 705 9800 *Dx:* 714005 SOLIHULL 1
E-mail: aymer.hutton@cunningtons.co.uk
Office: Braintree (2 offices), Croydon, Ilford, Wickford
Work: E L S1 W
Ptr: Hutton, Mr Aymer Jan Patrick BA . . . Nov 1991

DRAYSON LAW LIMITED ‡
Blythe Valley Innovation Centre Central Boulevard Blythe Valley Park Solihull West Midlands B90 8AJ
Tel: 0845 643 9800
E-mail: charles@draysonlaw.com

EXCALIBUR SOLICITORS ‡
Old Bank House 50 St John's Close Knowle Solihull West Midlands B93 0JU
Tel: 01564 774480
E-mail: info@excalibursolicitors.co.uk

THE FIRM SOLICITORS LLP
2 Station Road Solihull West Midlands B91 3SB
Tel: 0121 709 6506
E-mail: info@thefamilyfirm.co.uk
Office: Birmingham, Redditch

FORUM LAW LIMITED ‡
Avon House 435 Stratford Road Shirley Solihull West Midlands B90 4AA
Tel: 0844 335 8456 *Fax:* 0121 210 7547
E-mail: contact@forumlaw.co.uk

HCB SOLICITORS
691-693 Warwick Road Solihull West Midlands B91 3DA
Tel: 0121 705 2255 *Fax:* 0121 705 0202 *Dx:* 714006 SOLIHULL 1
Office: Alcester, Lichfield, Redditch, Stratford-upon-Avon, Walsall
Languages: French, Portuguese
Work: C1 C2 C3 E F1 J1 K1 L M1 M2 N O P Q S1 T1 T2 W Z(c)
Agency, Advocacy undertaken and Member of Accident Line
Ptr: Cashmore, Mr Gary LLB; ACIArb . . . *§Apr 1974
Harris, Mr Anthony L LLB . . . *Jul 1980
Walsh, Ms Georgina H LLB . . . *Feb 1987
Asoc: Bawa, Ms Kay. . . . Jan 1996
Da Silva, Mr Daniel LLB(Hons) . . . Feb 1996
Power, Ms Lesley J . . . *Jan 1986
White, Miss Claire LLB(Hons) . . . Apr 1999
Williams, Mr G Rhys . . . *Jun 1976

HEAVEN & CO ‡
Hanoby House 18 Lady Byron Lane Solihull West Midlands B93 9AU
Tel: 01564 770598

HILL HOFSTETTER LLP ‡
Trigen House Central Boulevard Blythe Valley Park Solihull West Midlands B90 8AB
Tel: 0121 210 6000 *Fax:* 0121 210 6499 *Dx:* 714138 SOLIHULL 18
Emergency telephone 020 7403 2900
List of partners: R A Chalkley, L Coltman, C A Hill, J M Hofstetter, N G Watkins
Languages: French, German
Work: A1 B1 C1 E J1 L M1 N O P Q R1 T1 Z(b,c,e,i,j,p,y)
Agency, Advocacy and Fixed Fee Interview undertaken
Ptr: Chalkley, Mr Richard A LLB . . . *Apr 1971
Coltman, Mr Larry LLB(Leics); FICM; ACIArb . . . *Apr 1984
Hill, Mr Christopher A BA; LPC . . . *Jul 1984
Hofstetter, Mr Jonathan M BA(Oxon) . . . *Jan 1988
Watkins, Mr Nigel G LLB . . . *§Apr 1970
Asoc: Reynolds, Mrs Dawn LLB . . . Mar 2001
Smith, Mr Darren LLB; LPC . . . *Oct 1993
Thomas, Ms Jane. . . . *Oct 1999

CARLA HULL SOLICITORS LIMITED ‡
458 Warwick Road Solihull West Midlands B91 1AG
Tel: 0845 466 4333 *Fax:* 0845 466 4300
E-mail: enquiries@carlahull.com

KAREN LAYLAND SOLICITORS ‡
Central Boulevard Blythe Valley Business Park Solihull West Midlands B90 8AG
Tel: 0800 328 8841
E-mail: karen.layland@blueyonder.co.uk

RICHARD LUDLOW & CO
186 Stratford Road Shirley Solihull West Midlands B90 3BQ
Tel: 01789 552872
Office: Stratford-upon-Avon

LYONS DAVIDSON
Westbury House 701-705 Warwick Road Solihull West Midlands B91 3DA
Tel: 0121 683 8310 *Fax:* 0121 683 8311 *Dx:* 14043 SOLIHULL 2
E-mail: info@lyondavidson.co.uk
Office: Bristol, Cardiff, Leeds, New Malden, Plymouth
Ptr: Davies, Mr Ian . . . Aug 1999
Walsh, Mr Mark. . . . Oct 2002

MAJELLA O'NEILL SOLICITORS ‡
Priest House 1624 High Street Knowle Solihull West Midlands B93 0JU
Tel: 01564 739298

MERIDIAN PRIVATE CLIENT LLP ‡
Corner Oak 1 Homer Road Solihull West Midlands B91 3QG
Tel: 0121 711 4800 *Fax:* 0121 711 4853
E-mail: info@meridianprivateclient.co.uk

MILLICHIPS
4 The Courtyard Warwick Road Solihull West Midlands B91 3DA
Tel: 0121 624 4000 *Fax:* 0121 624 8400 *Dx:* 14041 SOLIHULL 2
Emergency telephone 0121 233 4700
Office: West Bromwich
Languages: Chinese, Danish, French, German, Punjabi, Urdu
Work: B1 C1 C2 D1 E F1 J1 K1 L N P R1 S1 V W Z(b,c,d,e,f,l,o)

See p112 for the Key to Work Categories & other symbols

Emergency Action, Agency, Advocacy, Fixed Fee Interview and Legal Aid undertaken
Ptr: Boyars, Mr Alan L. . . . . Jun 1970
Brien, Mr Michael J LLB(Wales). . . . . *Sep 1983

PEARCELEGAL LLP ‡
2 The Square Solihull West Midlands B91 3SX
Tel: 0844 412 7899 *Fax:* 0121 777 9210 *Dx:* 714021 SOLIHULL
E-mail: enquiries@pearcelegal.co.uk
List of partners: G M Pearce
Work: C1 C2 D1 E F1 J1 K1 K3 N O P Q R1 S1 S2 T1 T2 W X Z(c,d,p,q,r)
Fixed Fee Interview undertaken
Ptr: Pearce, Mr Graham M BA(Hons) . . . . *§Dec 1977
Ast: Sohal, Mrs Sharad . . . . Jul 2003

RICHARD NELSON BUSINESS DEFENCE SOLICITORS
8 The Courtyard 707 Warwick Road Solihull West Midlands B91 3DA
Tel: 0121 707 7666 *Fax:* 0121 707 7999
Emergency telephone 07739 349557
E-mail: defencebham@richardnelsonllp.co.uk
Office: Bristol, Cardiff, Manchester, Nottingham
Work: B2 F2 G P
Agency, Advocacy and Legal Aid undertaken

SCHOFIELD & ASSOCIATES ‡
Milverton Villas 6 Wilsons Road Knowle Solihull West Midlands B93 0HZ
Tel: 01564 739103 *Fax:* 01564 776404
E-mail: eileen.schofield@schofieldandassociates.co.uk

SOLOMONS LEGAL ‡
Central Boulevard Blythe Valley Business Park Solihull West Midlands B90 8AG
Tel: 01564 711101 *Fax:* 01564 711258 *Dx:* 714137 SOLIHULL 18
E-mail: info@solomonslegal.com

SYDNEY MITCHELL
Chattock House 346 Stratford Road Shirley Solihull West Midlands B90 3DN
Tel: 0121 746 3300 *Fax:* 0121 745 7650 *Dx:* 13856 SHIRLEY 2
E-mail: enquiries@sydneymitchell.co.uk
Office: Birmingham (2 offices)
Work: A1 B1 C1 C3 D1 E F1 F2 J1 K1 N O Q R1 R2 S1 S2 T2 V W Z(c,l,p,q)
Emergency Action, Agency, Advocacy, Fixed Fee Interview, Legal Aid undertaken and Member of Accident Line

S V WADSWORTH & CO ‡
325 Stratford Road Shirley Solihull West Midlands B90 3BL
Tel: 0121 745 8550 *Fax:* 0121 745 5380 *Dx:* 20656 SHIRLEY
List of partners: S V Wadsworth
Work: E J1 L N Q S1 W Z(q,r)
Fixed Fee Interview, Legal Aid undertaken and Member of Accident Line
Ptr: Wadsworth, Mr Stephen V LLB; DMA . . . . . . *§Jun 1976
Ast: Cramp, Ms Charlotte . . . . Oct 2001
Makhani, Karima . . . . Sep 2002
Tait, Miss Alexandra. . . . . Nov 2008
Wadsworth, Mrs Emma Louise . . . . Sep 2008
Wadsworth, Mr John . . . . Sep 2005

WALLACE ROBINSON & MORGAN ‡
(incorporating Bond Lassen)
4 Drury Lane Solihull West Midlands B91 3BD
Tel: 0121 705 7571 *Fax:* 0121 705 9512 *Dx:* 714015 SOLIHULL 1
E-mail: enquiries@wallacerobinson.co.uk
List of partners: K L Ferris, R P Hughes, T R Langford, S M Stewart, M L Thompson, V S Warner
Office: Solihull
Work: A1 B1 C1 C2 C3 E F1 J1 K1 K3 L O Q R1 R2 S1 S2 T1 T2 W Z(d,l,p,q)
Agency undertaken
Ptr: Ferris, Mrs Kathryn Louise LLB(Hons). . . . . . *Sep 2000
Hughes, Mr Robert P LLB. . . . . *Jun 1981
Langford, Mr Timothy Richard LLB . . . . . . *Nov 1992
Stewart, Mr Stephen Michael BA(Law) . . . . . *Oct 1986
Thompson, Mrs Mary Louisa LLB . . . . . . *Nov 1996
Warner, Mrs Valerie Stella LLB(Hons); TEP . . . . *Jun 1980
Ast: Bluck, Miss Lucy Ann LLB. . . . . Sep 2009
Fisher, Mrs Marta MA. . . . . Mar 2009
Gower, Miss Ruth Barbara LLB National Law Society Prize for LPC. . . . . *Sep 2005
Nicholls, Miss Hannah Elizabeth LLB . . . . . . Sep 2010
Tungate, Miss Wendy Jane BA(Law & Criminology) . . Mar 2011
Zakis, Mr Daniel Mark LLB(Hons); LPC . . . . . Oct 2007
Con: Fordham, Mr Denys Eric . . . . *§Mar 1958
Woodhead, Mr Eric LLB(Leeds). . . . . *§Nov 1959

WALLACE ROBINSON & MORGAN
17-19 Station Approach Dorridge Solihull West Midlands B93 8JA
Tel: 01564 779393 *Fax:* 01564 778809 *Dx:* 714015 SOLIHULL1
E-mail: enquiries@wallacerobinson.co.uk
Office: Solihull
Work: J1 K1 O Q S1 S2 W Z(l)

WHITING & PURCHES ‡
Northampton House Poplar Road Solihull West Midlands B91 3AP
Tel: 0121 605 5050 *Fax:* 0121 605 5055
Emergency telephone 07774 794491
E-mail: whitingandpurches@gmail.com
List of partners: N Purches, D N Whiting
Work: F2 G H J2 P Z(l,m,y)
Emergency Action, Agency, Advocacy, Fixed Fee Interview, Legal Aid undertaken and Legal Aid Franchise
Ptr: Purches, Miss Nicola BA ★ . . . . *Sep 1990
Whiting, Mr David N LLB(Hull). . . . . *Oct 1982

SALLY WILCOCK & CO SOLICITORS ‡
PO Box 11229 Shirley Solihull West Midlands B90 2WT
Tel: 0121 270 6289 *Fax:* 0121 243 6208 *Dx:* 13861 SHIRLEY 2

WILLIAMSON & SODEN ‡
Stanton House 54 Stratford Road Shirley Solihull West Midlands B90 3LS
Tel: 0121 733 8000 *Fax:* 0121 733 3322 *Dx:* 20652 SHIRLEY 1
Emergency telephone 0121 778 5000
E-mail: law@williamsonandsoden.co.uk
List of partners: J J R Briars, J A Bryce, G J P Cusack, C Fletcher, S Rowe, J S Soden, F Warman, I P Williamson
Office: Birmingham
Work: B1 B2 C1 C2 D1 E F1 G H J1 K1 K3 K4 L N O P Q R1 R2 S1 S2 U1 V W Z(c,f,h,l,m,r,w)
Emergency Action, Agency, Advocacy, Fixed Fee Interview, Legal Aid undertaken, Legal Aid Franchise and Member of Accident Line
Ptr: Briars, Mr Jeremy J R BA . . . . *Dec 1976
Cusack, Mr Gerard J P BA . . . . *Jan 1989
Fletcher, Mrs Clare BA Maxwell Law Prize 1982. . . *Nov 1985
Rowe, Mr Stephen MA . . . . *Nov 1993
Soden, Mr John S BA. . . . . *Dec 1975
Warman, Ms Fiona LLM. . . . . Oct 1980
Williamson, Mr Ian P LLB . . . . *Apr 1972
Asoc: Jakeman, Mrs Louisa Mary LLB(Hons) . . . . . *Jun 1991
Middleton, Miss Alison Irene Evelyn LLB . . . . *§Jul 2000
Stephens, Mr Adrian Charles BA(Hons) ★. . . . . *Mar 1994
Ast: Adams, Ms Natasha Louisa LLB . . . . . . Nov 2004
Attride, Ms Catriona FILEx . . . . *Oct 2005
Forrester, Miss Kirstie Scott LLB(Hons) . . . . . *Nov 2002
Holden, Ms Amanda Jane LLB . . . . *Dec 1995
Holland, Ms Eleanor Ruth LLB(Hons) . . . . . . *Nov 2006
Lee, Miss Helen Louise LLB. . . . . *May 2004
Peggs, Regan LLB(Hons); PGDipLP. . . . . . . *Oct 2003
Seeney, Miss Joanne HND . . . . *Dec 1992
Wiseman, Ms Clare J LLB(Hons) . . . . *Nov 1994
Con: Doyle, Mr Colin Richard LLB ★ . . . . *Jul 1990
Scott, Mrs Allison G. . . . . *Sep 1979

THE WOOD GLAISTER PARTNERSHIP ‡
(incorporating Chattock & Hatton)
Homer House 8 Homer Road Solihull West Midlands B91 3QQ
Tel: 0121 705 8151 *Fax:* 0121 704 0061 *Dx:* 709160 SOLIHULL 5
List of partners: A N Atkinson, M R Richmond
Work: A1 B1 B2 C1 C2 D1 E F1 G H J1 K1 L M1 N P R1 R2 S1 S2 T1 T2 W Z(c)
Agency and Advocacy undertaken
Ptr: Atkinson, Mr Andrew N LLB. . . . . *Dec 1973
Richmond, Mr Martin R BA . . . . *Dec 1980
Ast: Arstall, Ms Susan Lynn LLB. . . . . *May 1976
Sinnett, Mr Alan J BA(Law) . . . . *May 1987

SOMERTON, Somerset

BARNEY & COMPANY SOLICITORS ‡
Somerton Somerton Somerset TA11 7NQ
Tel: 01458 270296 / 07766 095865
E-mail: david@barneysolicitors.co.uk

BEDFORDS ‡
Chimney Cottage Compton Street Compton Dundon Somerton Somerset TA11 6PS
Tel: 01458 888153 *Fax:* 01458 888153
List of partners: R Bedford
Work: K1 L N O Q S1 W
Fixed Fee Interview undertaken and Member of Accident Line
Ptr: Bedford, Mr Rupert BA; MA. . . . . *Mar 1993

CHUBB BULLEID
Langler House Market Place Somerton Somerset TA11 7LZ
Tel: 01749 836100 *Fax:* 01458 274019
E-mail: solicitors@chubb-bulleid.co.uk
Office: Street, Wells
SPr: Walton, Mr Alan R. . . . . *Dec 1978

ROGER GAY & CO ‡
Brunel House Brunel Precinct Somerton Somerset TA11 7PY
Tel: 01458 273137 *Fax:* 01458 274432
E-mail: roger@rogergay.co.uk
List of partners: R W Gay
Work: E S1 S2 W
SPr: Gay, Mr Roger Wyn LLB(Hons); BSc(Hons); CEng; MICE . . . . *Oct 1986

GEORGE HAWKS SOLICITOR ‡
Gingers Acre Foddington Somerton Somerset TA11 7EL
Tel: 01963 240409

ADRIAN STABLES ‡
Westover Chambers Willows Business Park Westover Somerton Somerset TA10 9RB
Tel: 0845 873 6180 *Fax:* 0845 873 6181
E-mail: adrian@adrianstables.com
Languages: French
Work: E F1 J1 N O Q S1 W
Emergency Action, Agency, Advocacy, Fixed Fee Interview, Legal Aid undertaken and Member of Accident Line
Ast: Haines, Mr Peter H . . . . Jun 1972

SOUTH CROYDON, Surrey

BOND & CO SOLICITORS ‡
34 Kersey Drive South Croydon Surrey CR2 8SX
Tel: 020 8405 0596

EDRIDGES & DRUMMONDS ‡
4 Crossways Parade Selsdon Park Road South Croydon Surrey CR2 8JJ
Tel: 020 8651 1218 *Fax:* 020 8651 6055
List of partners: M C Cauter, R Dench
Work: E K1 L S1 W
Ptr: Cauter, Mr Martin C. . . . . *Aug 1977
Dench, Mr Richard LLB . . . . Jul 1980

PETER LOCK & COMPANY SOLICITORS ‡
1st Floor Offices 5-7 Selsdon Road South Croydon Surrey CR2 6PU
Tel: 020 8688 2208 *Fax:* 020 8760 9899
E-mail: peter-lock@btconnect.com

MCMILLAN WILLIAMS
104 South End South Croydon Surrey CR0 1DQ
Tel: 020 8253 7600 *Fax:* 020 8253 7601
Dx: 38452 SOUTH CROYDON
Emergency telephone 020 8660 3383
E-mail: southcroydon@mcmillan-williams.co.uk
Office: Carshalton, Coulsdon, Croydon, Mitcham, Thornton Heath, Wallington
Languages: Afrikaans, Bengali, Greek, Hindi, Urdu
Work: N S1 S2 Z(r)
Fixed Fee Interview and Legal Aid undertaken
Ptr: Channer, Mr Terence Nathaniel LLB(Hons) . . . . *Jun 1996
Ast: Hooker, Mr Jason . . . . Oct 2002
Mooney, Ms Nicola . . . . Oct 1985
Philips, Ms Lauren . . . . Sep 2004
Serwanga, Mrs Grace. . . . . Jan 2002

MANCHESTERS ‡
21 Limpsfield Road Sanderstead South Croydon Surrey CR2 9LA
Tel: 020 8651 3118
List of partners: A J Durman, J R G Manchester
Work: K4 S1 T1 T2 W
Fixed Fee Interview undertaken
Ptr: Durman, Mr Andrew John LLB . . . . *Dec 1997
Manchester, Mr James Richard George MA; LLB . . *Nov 1996
Con: Manchester, Mr Richard G . . . . *§Jan 1969

ROWE RADCLIFFE ‡
6 Dornton Road South Croydon Surrey CR2 7DP
Tel: 020 8680 2070 *Fax:* 020 8680 3013 *Dx:* 2637 CROYDON
List of partners: E J Radcliffe
Work: E F1 K1 K3 L Q S1 S2 W Z(l)
Advocacy and Fixed Fee Interview undertaken
Ptr: Radcliffe, Mrs Elizabeth Jane LLB(Manc) . . . . *§Apr 1976
Con: Garland, Mrs Deborah Harrison LLB(Soton). . . . *Dec 1981
Ireland, Mr Terence Richard. . . . . *Jan 1984
Watts, Mrs Geraldine Marguerite LLB(Wales) . . . . *Nov 1982

SANDOM ROBINSON ‡
Triumph House Station Approach Sanderstead Road South Croydon Surrey CR2 0PL
Tel: 020 8651 7020 *Fax:* 020 8651 9146
Dx: 38461 SOUTH CROYDON
E-mail: nick.robinson@sandomrobinson.co.uk
List of partners: P J Nichols, N R Robinson
Work: A3 C1 E L R2 S1 S2 W Z(d,w)
Ptr: Nichols, Mrs Penelope Jane BA. . . . . *Feb 1981
Robinson, Mr Nicholas R FCIArb . . . . *Mar 1977

G M WATTS ‡
2a Ridge Langley South Croydon Surrey CR2 0AR
Tel: 020 8657 0391 *Fax:* 020 8657 0391

SOUTH MOLTON, Devon

CROSSE WYATT VERNEY & AYRE ‡
7 East Street South Molton Devon EX36 3BX
Tel: 01769 572157 *Fax:* 01769 573457 *Dx:* 33951 SOUTH MOLTON
Emergency telephone 01271 43716
E-mail: enquiries@crossewyatt-solicitors.co.uk
List of partners: N D Ayre, S E Gowing, C F J Punt, J C S White
Work: A1 A2 B1 C1 D1 D2 E F1 F2 G H J1 J2 K1 L N O Q R1 S1 S2 V W X Z(c,g,h,l,m,t,u,y)
Emergency Action, Agency and Legal Aid undertaken
Ptr: Ayre, Mr Nigel D BA(Law). . . . . *§Apr 1981
Gowing, Mr Stephen E . . . . *Apr 1982
Punt, Mr Christopher F J LLB(Newc) . . . . . . *§Jun 1971
White, Mr John Charles Spencer BA(Hons); DipLaw. . *Aug 1997
Asoc: Phillips, Mr Jeremy D BA(Hons). . . . . *Aug 1995

FURSE SANDERS & CO ‡
(incorporating Furse Sanders & Taylor, South Molton)
13-14 Broad Street South Molton Devon EX36 3AF
Tel: 01769 572251 *Fax:* 01769 574972 *Dx:* 33952 SOUTH MOLTON
Emergency telephone 01769 572251
E-mail: info@fursesanders.co.uk
List of partners: M Barnes
Work: A1 C1 E F1 L R1 S1 S2 T1 T2 W Z(d,l)
SPr: Barnes, Mrs Maxine LLM; TEP . . . . *Oct 2001
Ast: Checkley, Mr Raymond Harvey LLB(Hons) . . . . *Oct 1963
Meek, Mr Paul William David LLB; BSc Hart Prize - Public Law (University of London) 1996/7. . . . . . . *Jun 2004

SLEE BLACKWELL
(incorporating Riccard & Son)
2 Lime Court Pathfields Business Park South Molton Devon EX36 3LH
Tel: 01769 573771 *Fax:* 01769 574207 *Dx:* 33950 SOUTH MOLTON
E-mail: southmolton@sleeblackwell.co.uk
Office: Barnstaple, Bideford, Braunton, Exeter
Languages: French
Work: A1 E G K1 L N O R1 S1 W Z(l,o)
Agency, Advocacy, Fixed Fee Interview and Legal Aid undertaken
Ptr: Pearn, Mr John A G LLB(Wales) . . . . *§Nov 1974

SOUTH SHIELDS, Tyne & Wear

TERENCE CARNEY
Law Court Chambers Coronation Street South Shields Tyne & Wear NE33 1AP
Tel: 0191 456 3201 *Fax:* 0191 454 4761
Office: Hebburn
Work: D1 F1 G H J1 K1 M1 S1
Emergency Action, Agency, Advocacy, Fixed Fee Interview, Legal Aid undertaken and Member of Accident Line

G E DOWNS ‡
Tedco Business Works Henry Robson Way South Shields Tyne & Wear NE33 1RF
Tel: 0191 427 4745 *Fax:* 0191 427 4751
E-mail: george.downs@ymail.com

GEOFFREY FORRESTER & CO
301a Sunderland Road South Shields Tyne & Wear NE34 6RB
Tel: 0191 456 2255 *Fax:* 0191 427 6409
Dx: 60792 SOUTH SHIELDS
Emergency telephone 07626 241216
Office: Jarrow
Asoc: Van der Velde, Mrs Elaine LLB(Hons) . . . . . . *Oct 1987

HANNAYS SOLICITORS AND ADVOCATES ‡
(incorporating Hannay & Hannay Solicitors)
3 Beach Road South Shields Tyne & Wear NE33 2QA
Tel: 0191 456 7893 / 455 5361 *Fax:* 0191 455 1610
Dx: 60851 SOUTH SHIELDS 4
Emergency telephone 0191 455 3320
E-mail: info@hannayslaw.co.uk
List of partners: C H A Brown, G M Cook, P G Cresswell, D Logg, K C Rainford
Languages: French, German
Work: A1 B1 C1 D1 E F1 G H J1 K1 K3 K4 L R1 R2 S1 S2 T1 T2 V W Z(c,d,j,k,l,m,q)

Emergency Action, Agency, Advocacy, Fixed Fee Interview, Legal Aid undertaken and Legal Aid Franchise
Ptr: Brown, Mr Christopher Hugh Anthony LLB . . . . . *Dec 1987
Cook, Mr Graeme M LLB . . . . . *Oct 1985
Cresswell, Mr Peter G LLB . . . . . *Jan 1986
Logg, Mr Derek BA(Hons); LLB . . . . . Aug 1992
Rainford, Mr Kim C BA(Hons) . . . . . *Feb 1984
Ast: Hood, Mrs Angela Mary BA(Hons) . . . . . Aug 2001
Kennedy, Mr Paul LLB . . . . . Nov 2003
Waddell, Mr Charles Quentin Osborne LLB(Hons) . . . Sep 2006
Con: Lees, Mrs Julie N A BA(Hons) . . . . . *Oct 1986
Smallcombe, Mr Alan Kevin BSc(Econ) . . . . . Jul 1996

THE LETTING GROUP ‡
40 Dean Road South Shields Tyne & Wear NE33 4DZ
Tel: 0191 497 5333 *Fax:* 0191 427 6853
Office: Darlington

MARSHALL HALL & LEVY ‡
Saville Chambers Fowler Street South Shields Tyne & Wear NE33 1NS
Tel: 0191 455 3181 *Fax:* 0191 456 0201
Dx: 60753 SOUTH SHIELDS
E-mail: mhl@marshallhalllevy.co.uk
List of partners: M G Puech, K B Turnbull
Work: A1 A2 A3 B1 C1 C2 C3 D1 D2 E F1 F2 I J1 J2 K1 K2 L M3 N O P Q R1 R2 S1 S2 T1 T2 V W X Z(c,d,e,f,g,h,j,k,l,o,p,q,r,s,u,w)
Emergency Action, Agency, Advocacy, Fixed Fee Interview, Legal Aid undertaken, Legal Aid Franchise and Member of Accident Line
Ptr: Puech, Mr Michael Gerard LLB . . . . . Feb 1994
Turnbull, Mr Keith Burn BA(Hons) . . . . . Jul 1978
Ast: Kelly, Mr Terence Joseph BA . . . . . *Oct 1977

PATTERSON GLENTON & STRACEY ‡
Law Court Chambers 22 Waterloo Square South Shields Tyne & Wear NE33 1AW
Tel: 0800 011 6487 *Fax:* 0191 455 7380
Dx: 60750 SOUTH SHIELDS
E-mail: waw@pgslaw.co.uk
List of partners: L A Caisley, W J Dryden, C E Potts, K Swan, D W Walker, W A Ward
Office: Newcastle upon Tyne, South Shields
Work: A1 B1 B3 C1 C2 C3 D1 E F1 J1 K1 L M1 M2 N P R1 S1 T1 T2 V W X Z(b,c,e,f,h,i,j,k,l,m,n,o,p,s,t)
Emergency Action, Agency, Advocacy, Fixed Fee Interview, Legal Aid undertaken, Legal Aid Franchise and Member of Accident Line
Ptr: Walker, Mr Derek W LLB; AKC . . . . . *§Jul 1974
Ward, Mr William A LLB . . . . . *Nov 1986

PATTERSON GLENTON & STRACEY
Coronation Chambers 10 Coronation Street South Shields Tyne & Wear NE33 1AZ
Tel: 0800 011 6487 *Fax:* 0191 455 7381
Dx: 60750 SOUTH SHIELDS
E-mail: ks@pgslaw.co.uk
Office: Newcastle upon Tyne, South Shields
Work: C1 E J1 K4 N S1 S2 W
Ptr: Potts, Mr Christopher E . . . . . *§Nov 1979
Swan, Mr Keith . . . . . Jan 1996
Asoc: Hargreaves, Mr Paul Matheson BA(Hons); DipLaw . *Aug 2001

ROBSON PALMER ‡
(incorporating Tindle & Bullen)
Tindle House 31 Beach Road South Shields Tyne & Wear NE33 2QU
Tel: 0191 455 4561 *Fax:* 0191 455 2954
Dx: 60752 SOUTH SHIELDS
E-mail: legal@robsonpalmer.co.uk
List of partners: H E J Palmer, D L Robson
Work: C1 C2 E F1 L M3 N O Q R1 R2 S1 S2 V W Z(c,d,f,i,k,l,r,u,y)
Agency and Fixed Fee Interview undertaken
Ptr: Palmer, Mrs Heather E J BSc; DipLS . . . . . *May 2001
Robson, Mr Derrick L . . . . . *Apr 1975
Con: Sutton, Mr Stephen LLB Gregg Memorial Prize . *Apr 1978

SOUTHERN STEWART & WALKER ‡
Georgian House 15 Beach Road South Shields Tyne & Wear NE33 2QA
Tel: 0191 427 0770 *Fax:* 0191 455 3296
Dx: 60857 SOUTH SHIELDS 4
E-mail: legal@ssandw.co.uk
List of partners: G G Hindson, I Stewart
Office: South Shields
Work: D1 K1 L N Q S1 S2 W Z(l)
Emergency Action, Agency, Advocacy and Legal Aid undertaken
Ptr: Hindson, Mr Geoffrey George LLB(Hons) . . . . . *Jan 1990
Ast: Bowery, Mrs Mary . . . . . Oct 1999
Glass, Mrs Christine LLB . . . . . Feb 2004
Con: Walker, Mrs Frances Mary LLB(Newc) . . . . . *Jan 1975

SOUTHERN STEWART & WALKER
(incorporating Small Hindson & Co)
157 Prince Edward Road South Shields Tyne & Wear NE34 8PL
Tel: 0191 456 7788 *Fax:* 0191 427 1167
Dx: 60790 SOUTH SHIELDS 2
E-mail: legal@ssandw.co.uk
Office: South Shields
Work: D1 E K1 N S1 S2 W
Emergency Action, Agency, Advocacy, Fixed Fee Interview and Legal Aid undertaken
Ptr: Stewart, Mr Ian . . . . . *Jan 1983
Ast: Langers, Mr John James LLB . . . . . Nov 2007

AILEEN TALLINTIRE SOLICITORS ‡
2a Prince George Square South Shields Tyne & Wear NE33 2BE
Tel: 0191 454 1101 *Fax:* 0191 454 0966
Dx: 60853 SOUTH SHIELDS 4
Work: D1 D2 F1 G H K1 L N Q S1 V
Emergency Action, Agency and Legal Aid undertaken

THOMPSONS (FORMERLY ROBIN/BRIAN THOMPSON & PARTNERS)
60 Fowler Street South Shields Tyne & Wear NE33 1PG
Tel: 0191 497 4440 *Fax:* 0191 427 6966
Office: Belfast, Birmingham, Bristol, Cardiff, Chelmsford, Dagenham, Derby, Harrow, Leeds, Liverpool, London SW19, London WC1, Manchester, Middlesbrough, Newcastle upon Tyne, Nottingham, Plymouth, Sheffield, Southampton, Stoke-on-Trent, Swansea, Wolverhampton

WATSON & BROWN ‡
Crest House 99a Fowler Street South Shields Tyne & Wear NE33 1NU
Tel: 0191 455 0251 *Fax:* 0191 454 5669

SOUTH WOODHAM FERRERS, Essex

PALMERS
1/3 Brickfields Road South Woodham Ferrers Essex CM3 5XB
Tel: 01245 322111 *Fax:* 01245 324363
Dx: 53555 SOUTH WOODHAM FERRERS
E-mail: enquiries@palmerslaw.co.uk
Office: Basildon, Grays
Work: C1 C2 D1 E F1 J1 K1 K2 K4 L M1 O P Q R1 R2 S2 T1 T2 W Z(c,h,r)
Fixed Fee Interview undertaken
Ptr: Steele, Mr Timothy C LLB . . . . . *Oct 1993
Ast: Fothergill, Mr Simon David MA(Hons)(Cantab) . . . . Jun 1986
Taylor, Mrs Jennifer LLB . . . . . *Aug 2001

SOUTHALL, Middlesex

ADEN & CO ‡
84b High Street Southall Middlesex UB1 3DB
Tel: 020 8574 0114 *Fax:* 020 8574 5857

ARANI & CO ‡
43a South Road Southall Middlesex UB1 1SW
Tel: 020 8893 5000 *Fax:* 020 8893 5506 *Dx:* 42051 SOUTHALL
Emergency telephone 07092 386816
E-mail: arani@aranisolicitors.com
List of partners: M Arani
Languages: Gujarati, Hindi, Kiswahili, Punjabi, Urdu
Work: B2 D1 D2 G H K1 K2 Q
Emergency Action, Agency, Fixed Fee Interview and Legal Aid undertaken
SPr: Arani, Ms Muddassar LLB(Hons) • . . . . . *Sep 1993

ASGHAR & CO ‡
112-114 The Broadway Southall Middlesex UB1 1QF
Tel: 020 8843 0010 *Fax:* 020 8843 0080 *Dx:* 119576 SOUTHALL 3
E-mail: info@asghar-solicitors.co.uk
List of partners: M Asghar, N Kadri
Office: Slough
Languages: Arabic, Dari, Farsi, French, Punjabi, Urdu
Work: D1 F1 G H K1 L N O Q S1 W Z(i)
Emergency Action, Fixed Fee Interview and Legal Aid undertaken
Ptr: Asghar, Mr Mohammed BA(Hons) ★ . . . . . *Apr 1993
Kadri, Naseem . . . . . Apr 2003
Ast: Bijlani, Rajendra . . . . . Oct 2002

ASHER & TOMAR ‡
118a The Broadway Southall Middlesex UB1 1QF
Tel: 020 8867 7737 *Fax:* 01895 549688
E-mail: info@asherandtomar.co.uk

BANSAL & CO ‡
Second Floor 92a The Broadway Southall Middlesex UB1 1QF
Tel: 020 3118 2063 *Fax:* 020 3118 2064
List of partners: R T Bansal
Languages: Hindi, Punjabi, Urdu
Work: B1 C1 E J1 L S1 S2 T1 T2 W Z(i,l)
SPr: Bansal, Mr Ram Tirath LLB; LLM(Lond) Notary Public *Mar 1986

CHHOKAR & CO ‡
29a The Broadway Southall Middlesex UB1 1JY
Tel: 020 8574 2488 *Fax:* 020 8574 2752
E-mail: law@chhokar.com
List of partners: J S Chhokar, S S Chhokar, S Thomas
Languages: Hindi, Malayalam, Punjabi, Urdu
Work: B1 E F1 K1 K3 L O Q S1 S2 W Z(d,e,g,i,j,k,l,q)
Legal Aid Franchise
Ptr: Chhokar, Mr Jaspal Singh LLB(Hons) . . . . . *Jun 2007
Chhokar, Mr Santokh Singh BSc . . . . . *Aug 1994
Thomas, Mr Sajo LLM; LLB . . . . . *May 2003
Ast: Fegbemi, Mr Olabode Olatunde LLB; BL . . . . . *Jul 2005
Mann, Ms Kirrendip Kaur LLB(Hons) . . . . . Jun 2010
Randhawa, Ms Kuldeep Kaur LLB . . . . . Feb 2010

DASH SOLICITORS ‡
First Floor 41 North Road Southall Middlesex UB1 2JL
Tel: 07813 506291 *Fax:* 020 8574 8290
E-mail: mandip@dashsolicitors.co.uk

EDWARD DE SILVA & CO ‡
(incorporating J A Phillips & Co)
281 The Broadway Southall Middlesex UB1 1NG
Tel: 020 8571 2299 *Fax:* 020 8893 6287 *Dx:* 119585 SOUTHALL 3
Emergency telephone 020 8571 2299
E-mail: edslawyer@btconnect.com
List of partners: K W E De Silva, V Lazar
Languages: French, Hindi, Malayalam, Punjabi, Tamil
Work: D1 F1 G K1 L N O Q S1 V W Z(i)
Emergency Action, Agency, Advocacy and Fixed Fee Interview undertaken
Ptr: De Silva, Mr K W Edward LLB(Hons)(Lond) . . . . . *May 1983
Lazar, Mr Vincent LLB . . . . . *Jul 2005

DOGRA & CO ‡
112b The Green Southall Middlesex UB2 4BQ
Tel: 020 8571 7741 *Fax:* 020 8571 0144
List of partners: M Dogra
Languages: Hindi, Punjabi
SPr: Dogra, Minni . . . . . Dec 1989

INDIRA FERNANDO ‡
22 Enmore Road Southall Middlesex UB1 2PG
Tel: 020 8575 6544 *Fax:* 020 8578 9162
List of partners: I Fernando
Work: E K1 L Q W Z(i)
SPr: Fernando, Mrs Indira LLB . . . . . *Jul 1991

JUNG & CO ‡
41 North Road Southall Middlesex UB1 2JL
Tel: 020 8813 8996 *Fax:* 020 8813 8559 *Dx:* 52258 SOUTHALL 2
E-mail: law@jungsolicitors.com
List of partners: V Jung
Languages: Gujarati, Hindi, Punjabi
Work: B2 D2 G H K1 W
Emergency Action, Advocacy, Legal Aid undertaken and Legal Aid Franchise
SPr: Jung, Viney . . . . . *Jul 1995

H S KANG & CO
1a Beaconsfield Road Southall Middlesex UB1 1BA
Tel: 020 8571 7258 *Fax:* 020 8574 9349
Office: Barking

KING SOLICITORS ‡
91 Western Road Southall Middlesex UB2 5HH
Tel: 020 8571 2239 *Fax:* 020 8090 3709
Emergency telephone 07931 919799 (Mobile)
E-mail: king.solicitors@yahoo.co.uk
List of partners: P King
Languages: Bengali, Hindi, Punjabi, Swedish, Tamil, Urdu
Work: B1 D2 E F1 J1 K1 L N S1 S2 V W Z(d,g,i,j,p)
Fixed Fee Interview undertaken
Ptr: King, Ms Preeti MA; LLB . . . . . *Feb 2002
Asoc: Saiyed, Mr Tahir LLB . . . . . Feb 2002

KRISH RATNA ‡
61a-2 King Street Southall Middlesex UB2 4DQ
Tel: 020 8574 6303 *Fax:* 020 8574 1096 *Dx:* 52255 SOUTHALL 2
List of partners: D Ratnasingham, V Ratnasingham
Languages: Tamil
Ptr: Ratnasingham, Mr Durairajasingham . . . . . *Nov 1987
Ratnasingham, Vijayaluxmy . . . . . Feb 1989

KRISH SOLICITORS ‡
86a High Street Southall Middlesex UB1 3DP
Tel: 020 8893 6661 *Fax:* 020 8917 9091 *Dx:* 119580 SOUTHALL 3
List of partners: N Krishnarajah, V Ratnam
Languages: Tamil
Work: S1 S2 Z(i)
Ptr: Krishnarajah, Nadarajah . . . . . *Nov 1986
Ratnam, Vijayasakthy . . . . . *Mar 2000

LATIF ADAMS SOLICITORS ‡
2 Gladstone Cottages Wimborne Avenue Southall Middlesex UB2 4HD
Tel: 020 8574 2255

LONDON LEGAL SOLICITORS ‡
37-39 King Street Southall Middlesex UB2 4DQ
Tel: 020 8571 6889

M H LAW SOLICITORS ‡
41 Wentworth Road Southall Middlesex UB2 5TT
Tel: 020 7096 5056 / 07504 599737 *Fax:* 0871 918 4103
E-mail: m.h.lawsolicitors@inbox.com

MIDDLESEX LAW CHAMBERS ‡
First Floor 5 South Road Southall Middlesex UB1 1SU
Tel: 020 8843 1172 *Fax:* 020 8843 9332
E-mail: hinaandfarooq@aol.com

NOORI RASHID & CO SOLICITORS ‡
31a South Road Southall Middlesex UB1 1SW
Tel: 020 8893 6787 *Fax:* 020 8893 6797

PINIDIYA SOLICITORS ‡
83a South Road Southall Middlesex UB1 1SQ
Tel: 020 8571 3535
Languages: Punjabi, Sinhalese, Urdu

POLPITIYA & CO ‡
1st Floor 66 King Street Southall Middlesex UB2 4DD
Tel: 020 8813 9282 *Fax:* 020 8571 0362
Emergency telephone 07930 943949
E-mail: polpitiya@hotmail.co.uk
List of partners: P Polpitiya
Languages: Hindi, Punjabi, Sinhalese
Work: G H K3 L N Q V Z(h,i)
Emergency Action, Fixed Fee Interview, Legal Aid undertaken and Legal Aid Franchise
Dir: Polpitiya, Mrs Pemila LLM . . . . . Jun 1992
Ast: Warnapala, Mr Sampath LLM . . . . . Jul 2004

S Z SOLICITORS ‡
10 Park Avenue Southall Middlesex UB1 3AQ
Tel: 020 8574 1794 *Fax:* 020 8571 5139
E-mail: enquiries@szsolicitors.co.uk

DAVID SHINE & KHARBANDA ‡
8a South Road Southall Middlesex UB1 1RT
Tel: 020 8571 6001 / 8571 6002 *Fax:* 020 8571 2647
Dx: 42059 SOUTHALL
E-mail: info@dsandk.com
List of partners: S K Kharbanda, D Shine
Languages: Gujarati, Hindi, Punjabi, Urdu
Work: D1 E G K1 M1 N S1 W Z(l,m)
Emergency Action, Fixed Fee Interview and Legal Aid undertaken
Ptr: Kharbanda, Satish K LLB . . . . . *Sep 1980
Shine, Mr David LLB . . . . . *Feb 1964

SHUTTARI PAUL & CO ‡
33-35 South Road Southall Middlesex UB1 1SW
Tel: 020 8574 7151 *Fax:* 020 8571 6097 *Dx:* 42057 SOUTHALL
E-mail: paulshuttari@yahoo.co.uk
List of partners: F A Shuttari, A Yaqoob
Languages: French, Hindi, Punjabi, Urdu
Work: D1 E F1 G H J1 K1 L M1 N P R1 S1 T1 V W Z(h,i,j,k,m)
Emergency Action, Agency, Advocacy, Fixed Fee Interview and Legal Aid undertaken
Ptr: Shuttari, Ms Fawzia A-H BA . . . . . Nov 1984
Yaqoob, Mr Asif . . . . . Feb 2000

SIMON & CO ‡
28 South Road Southall Middlesex UB1 1RR
Tel: 020 8571 3883 *Fax:* 020 8813 8235 *Dx:* 119578 SOUTHALL 3
E-mail: info@simonandco.net
List of partners: K S Dhaliwal, S Hsu
Languages: Chinese, Hindi, Punjabi
Work: B1 E F1 J1 K1 L N O Q S1 S2 T2 V W Z(i,k,l)
Fixed Fee Interview undertaken
Ptr: Dhaliwal, Mr Kulwinder Singh LLB(Wales) . . . . . *Feb 1988
Hsu, Mr Simon LLB . . . . . *Sep 1990
Asoc: Hothi, Yadevinder S . . . . . Sep 2000

SRIHARANS ‡
223 The Broadway Southall Middlesex UB1 1ND
Tel: 020 8843 9974 *Fax:* 020 8574 1766 *Dx:* 119583 SOUTHALL 3
E-mail: sriharans.solicitors@virgin.net
List of partners: A Sriharan, R S Sriharan
Languages: Hindi, Nepalese, Pashto, Punjabi, Tamil, Urdu
Work: E L S1 S2 V W Z(i)

See p112 for the Key to Work Categories & other symbols

Emergency Action, Agency, Advocacy, Fixed Fee Interview and Legal Aid undertaken
Ptr: Sriharan, Mr Ariyaratnarajah . . . . Nov 1983
Sriharan, Mr Renuka S . . . . .Jul 1987

THAKRAR & CO ‡
38a-38b The Broadway Southall Middlesex UB1 1PT
Tel: 020 8571 5851 / 8843 1599 *Fax:* 020 8843 2480
E-mail: jitesh@thakrarlaw.com
List of partners: J Thakrar
Work: B1 C1 E F1 G J1 K1 L N O Q S1 V W Z(i,k,l)
Emergency Action, Fixed Fee Interview and Legal Aid undertaken
Ptr: Thakrar, Jitesh . . . . .Jul 1979

VEJA AND CO SOLICITORS
91 South Road Southall Middlesex UB1 1SH
Tel: 020 8574 2626 *Fax:* 020 8571 3118 *Dx:* 42052 SOUTHALL
Emergency telephone 020 8574 7711
E-mail: mail@vejaandco.com
Office: Hayes, Leicester
Languages: Hindi, Punjabi, Urdu
Work: D1 G H J1 K1 K3 L Q W Z(g,i,p)
Emergency Action, Agency, Advocacy, Fixed Fee Interview, Legal Aid undertaken and Legal Aid Franchise
SPr: Marks, Mr David J MA(Oxon) . . . . *May 1981
Ast: Mann, Ms Parmjit Kaur LLB(Hons) . . . . *Nov 1999
Mbeledogu, Miss Oge Azuka . . . . *Jul 2002
Rai, Mr Ramandeep Singh LLB(Hons). . . . . *Nov 2003
Seema, Mrs Suji LLB(Hons). . . . . *Jul 1997

VINCENT SOLICITORA ‡
First & Second Floor 11-13 South Road Southall Middlesex UB1 1SU
Tel: 020 8574 0666 *Fax:* 020 8574 8439
E-mail: info@vincentsolicitors.com

WARNAPALA & CO LTD ‡
14a Norwood Road Southall Middlesex UB2 4DL
Tel: 020 8571 1823 *Fax:* 020 8571 9597
List of partners: H U Warnapala, N K Warnapala
Work: B1 L O Q S1 V Z(g,h,i)
Legal Aid Franchise
Dir: Warnapala, Mr Hemantha U. . . . . *Aug 1991
Warnapala, Nishanti K . . . . *Sep 1993

SOUTHAM, Warwickshire

NUALAW LIMITED ‡
Brewsters Corner Pendicke Street Southam Warwickshire CV47 1PN
Tel: 01926 888953
E-mail: nuala@nualaw.co.uk

SOUTHAMPTON

ABELS ‡
6-7 College Place London Road Southampton SO15 2XL
Tel: 023 8022 0317 *Fax:* 023 8033 5245
Dx: 38500 SOUTHAMPTON 3
Emergency telephone 023 8076 9499
E-mail: enquiries@abels.co.uk
List of partners: M A Harper, P A Humphris, R K Kirby, N S Roberts, J C Titt
Languages: French
Work: A1 B1 C1 D1 E F1 G H J1 K1 L M1 N O Q R1 S1 S2 T1 T2 V W Z(a,c,d,h,i,j,l,q,r,t)
Emergency Action, Agency, Advocacy, Fixed Fee Interview, Legal Aid undertaken and Legal Aid Franchise
Ptr: Harper, Mr Malcolm Alan LLB . . . . *§Oct 1980
Humphris, Mr Peter Andrew LLB(UEA) . . . . *Oct 1987
Kirby, Rebecca Kay BA . . . . Sep 2004
Roberts, Mr Noel Simon LLB . . . . Jun 1998
Titt, Mr Julian Christopher BA . . . . *§Nov 1990
Ast: Guelfi, Lisa LLB. . . . . Sep 2008
Con: Caplen, Mr Andrew Howard Arthur LLB Notary Public *§Oct 1982
Hawkins, Mr Nigel John LLB . . . . *Sep 1994

ACCESS LAW ‡
14-24 Cannon Street Shirley Southampton SO15 5PQ
Tel: 023 8087 8600 *Fax:* 023 8087 8611
Dx: 54856 SOUTHAMPTON 4
E-mail: law@accesslaw.co.uk

BASTOWS DIVORCE SOLICITORS ‡
The Old House The Square Southampton SO31 4LS
Tel: 023 8045 5366 *Fax:* 023 8045 7572
Dx: 151803 SOUTHAMPTON 44
E-mail: enquiries@bsdivorcesolicitors.co.uk
Work: K1 K3 S1 W

BEETON EDWARDS ‡
Unit C Drivers Wharf Business Park Northam Road Southampton SO14 0PF
Tel: 023 8038 2850 *Fax:* 023 8038 2851
E-mail: info@beetonedwards.co.uk

BERNARD CHILL & AXTELL ‡
24 The Avenue Southampton SO17 1XL
Tel: 023 8022 8821 *Fax:* 023 8021 1300
Dx: 38508 SOUTHAMPTON 3
Emergency telephone 07885 201495 / 201496
E-mail: admin@bcasol.co.uk
List of partners: J G W Coppen, P C Harvey, S J Jones, G E Strange
Office: Eastleigh
Work: A1 B1 C1 C2 C3 D1 E F1 G H J1 K1 K3 L M1 N P R1 S1 S2 T1 T2 V W Z(a,b,c,e,f,h,j,k,l,m,o,s,t)
Emergency Action, Agency, Advocacy, Fixed Fee Interview, Legal Aid undertaken, Legal Aid Franchise and Member of Accident Line
Ptr: Coppen, Mr Jonathan G W LLB(Lond) Deputy District Judge . . . . *Apr 1977
Jones, Mr Simon J BA . . . . *§Jan 1978
Strange, Ms Gail Elizabeth LLB . . . . Jun 1998
Ast: Coad, Mr Greg . . . . Nov 2004

BERRYMANS LACE MAWER
2 Charlotte Place Southampton SO14 0TB
Tel: 023 8023 6464 *Fax:* 023 8023 6117
Dx: 96880 SOUTHAMPTON 10
E-mail: info@blm-law.com
Office: Birmingham, Bristol, Cardiff, Leeds, Liverpool, London EC2, Manchester, Stockton-on-Tees
Work: A3 B2 F2 J1 J2 N O P Q Z(h,j,k,q,r)

BOND PEARCE LLP
Oceana House 39-49 Commercial Road Southampton SO15 1GA
Tel: 0845 415 0000 *Fax:* 0845 415 8200
Dx: 38517 SOUTHAMPTON 3
E-mail: info@bondpearce.com
Office: Bristol, London EC3, Plymouth
Work: A1 A3 B1 C1 C2 C3 E F1 F2 I J1 J2 L M3 N O P Q R1 R2 S1 S2 T1 T2 U1 U2 W X Z(b,c,d,e,j,l,n,o,p,q,r,u,za)
Legal Aid Franchise
Ptr: Ackerman, Mr William. . . . . Sep 1997
Askham, Mr Anthony J Notary Public . . . . *§Feb 1968
Barley, Mr Mark MA(Oxon) . . . . *Dec 1989
Barwood, Mr Nicholas H LLB . . . . *Nov 1988
Beezer, Mr Thomas Mathew BA(Hons); LPC . . . . . *Oct 1996
Briggs, Mr Sebastian . . . . Nov 1994
Brocklebank, Miss Lea M LLB. . . . . *Oct 1991
Burbidge, Mr Timothy . . . . Oct 1992
Davies, Mr Robert J LLB Notary Public . . . . *§Jun 1973
Hales, Mr Jon S. . . . . *Nov 1998
Hamblin, Mr Julian C K MA(Cantab). . . . . *§Mar 1987
Holden, Mr Ian LLB(Hons). . . . . May 1993
Jeffries, Mr Graham D BA(Oxon) . . . . *Dec 1989
Kimble, Mr Andrew . . . . *§Sep 1997
MacKean, Mr Andrew N LLB . . . . *§Feb 1983
Matthews, Mr Gavin R LLB . . . . *§Nov 1987
Page, Mr Nicholas J LLB . . . . *§Apr 1981
Pierce, Mr Stephen . . . . *§Nov 1994
Richardson, Mr Simon. . . . . *Jan 1983
Robbins, Ms Anna . . . . Mar 1998
Robins, Mr James A LLB(Soton) Swords Prize . . . . *Nov 1991
Tolvas-Vincent, Mrs Christina Elisabeth LLM(Finland) *§Feb 1995
Wall, Mr Jonathan. Jan 2000
Walton, Mr Alistair LLB . . . . *Jul 1998

CGM ‡
2-5 College Place London Road Southampton SO15 2UT
Tel: 023 8063 2733 *Fax:* 023 8033 0954
Dx: 38504 SOUTHAMPTON 3
E-mail: enquiries@c-g-m.co.uk
List of partners: S P Brandes, J H G Driver, S Massey, A Scouller, C M I Stennett, R H M Stennett, J T Taylor, A D E Waring, J P Waring
Office: Southampton
Languages: French, Swedish
Work: B2 C1 D1 D2 E G H J1 K1 M1 N O Q S1 S2 W Z(l,m,p,q)
Emergency Action, Agency, Advocacy, Fixed Fee Interview, Legal Aid undertaken and Legal Aid Franchise
Ptr: Brandes, Mr Stephen P LLB(Wales). . . . . Apr 1981
Driver, Mr Jonathan H G LLB . . . . Oct 1988
Massey, Mr Stephen LLB . . . . *§Jun 1971
Scouller, Miss Angela LLB(Exon); Dip EU Law & Practice . . . . *§Apr 1977
Stennett, Mrs Caroline M I MA(Oxon) . . . . *Feb 1986
Stennett, Mr Richard H M BA . . . . *§Apr 1985
Taylor, Mr James T LLB. . . . . *Jun 1970
Waring, Mrs Andrea D E . . . . *Oct 1998
Waring, Mr J Paul BA(Hons) . . . . *Nov 1989
Ast: Appleby, Mrs Karen Elizabeth LLM . . . . Jan 1983
Cude, Miss Diana J LLB. . . . . *§Apr 1981

AMANDA CAPON SOLICITORS ‡
180e Bridge Road Sarisbury Green Southampton SO31 7EH
Tel: 01489 574778 *Fax:* 01489 574772

CARLTON PLACE LAW ‡
9 Carlton Place Southampton SO15 2EA
Tel: 023 8048 0007 *Fax:* 023 8048 0006
Dx: 385223 SOUTHAMPTON 3
E-mail: mail@carltonplacelaw.com

CHARTER HOUSE CONVEYANCING ‡
79 Bedford Place Southampton SO16 2DF
Tel: 023 8022 8714

CLARKE WILLMOTT
Burlington House Botleigh Grange Business Park Hedge End Southampton SO30 2AF
Tel: 0845 209 1000 / 0117 305 6000 *Fax:* 0845 209 2003
Dx: 49665 SOUTHAMPTON 2
E-mail: info@clarkewillmott.com
Office: Birmingham, Bristol, London EC4, Manchester, Taunton
Work: A1 A2 A3 B1 C1 C2 C3 E F1 F2 I J1 J2 K1 K3 L M2 N O P Q R1 R2 S1 S2 T1 T2 U2 W X Z(b,c,d,e,h,j,k,l,o,p,q,r,t,u,w,za)
Ptr: Barker, Mr Matthew James Machen BA . . . . *Dec 1995
Evans, Mr Roderick BA . . . . *Nov 1981
Grigg, Mr Jonathan . . . . *Oct 1996
Hyde, Mr Thomas W L ARICS. . . . . *Aug 1999
Ingram, Mr Stephen C. . . . . *May 1976
Mohindra, Mr Ravi . . . . Sep 1999
Mundy, Mr Michael P . . . . *May 1982
Norcross Webb, Mrs Sally MA; LLM(Cantab) . . . . *§Dec 1980
Russell, Mr John E LLB . . . . *Oct 1985
Stephens, Mr John L BA . . . . Oct 1977
Thair, Mr Stephen Sydney William LLB . . . . *§Jul 1973
West, Mr Andrew LLB(Hons) . . . . *Apr 1984
Wilson, Mr Michael BA . . . . *Oct 1991
Wiltshire, Mrs Jessica Mary LLB. . . . . *Nov 1986
Young, Mr Lee . . . . Sep 1996

CAROLINE COATS SOLICITORS ‡
Marston House Blackfield Road Southampton SO45 1WD
Tel: 023 8089 0919 *Fax:* 023 8089 2826
E-mail: caroline@carolinecoats.co.uk
List of partners: C M Coats, F L Heald
Work: K4 S1 T2 V W
Ptr: Coats, Mrs Caroline Mary FILEx. . . . . *Nov 1997
Heald, Miss Fiona Louise AAT. . . . . *Sep 1993

COFFIN MEW & CLOVER
Kings Park House 22 Kings Park Road Southampton SO15 2UF
Tel: 023 8033 4661 *Fax:* 023 8033 0956
Dx: 38505 SOUTHAMPTON 3
E-mail: southampton@coffinmew.co.uk
Office: Fareham, Gosport, Portsmouth
Work: B1 C1 C2 C3 D1 D2 E F1 F2 G H I J1 J2 K1 K2 L M1 M2 N O P Q R1 R2 S1 S2 T1 T2 U2 V W Z(c,e,f,g,h,i,j,k,l,m,o,r,s)
Emergency Action, Agency, Advocacy, Fixed Fee Interview, Legal Aid undertaken, Legal Aid Franchise and Member of Accident Line
Ptr: Brockwell, Mrs Amanda Jane LLB(B'ham). . . . . . *§Oct 1992
Gross, Mr Nicholas M LLB . . . . *Nov 1985
Johnson, Miss Pauline E LLB(Lond) Herbert Ruse Prize . . . . *§Apr 1977
Neil, Mr Donald M LLB(Bris) Notary Public . . . . . *§Jul 1969
Asoc: Byfield, Mr Peter G . . . . May 1979
Harris, Mrs Jennifer Susan LLB; BA. . . . . *Feb 1992
Pike, Miss Sally Georgina BA; CPE; LPC . . . . Oct 1996
Ast: Chesney, Miss Katrina Emmy LLB; LPC. . . . . *Sep 2001
Regan, Mr Michael James LPC . . . . *Nov 1995

COMPLETE LAW LLP ‡
First Floor Mitchell House Southampton SO31 9HN
Tel: 01489 885788
Office: Reading

DC EMPLOYMENT SOLICITORS ‡
29 Carlton Crescent Southampton SO15 2EW
Tel: 0844 800 7072 *Fax:* 0844 800 6682

JOSEPH DARIOS SOLICITORS ‡
15 College Place Southampton SO15 2FE
Tel: 023 8023 7575 *Fax:* 023 8063 6058
List of partners: J Darios
SPr: Darios, Mr Joseph LLB . . . . Oct 1985
Ast: Day, Sally. . . . . Jul 1995
Con: Adams, Mr David . . . . Aug 1991

DENT ABRAMS SOLICITORS
Enterprise House Ocean Village Southampton SO14 3XB
Tel: 0845 833 2318 *Fax:* 0845 833 2319
E-mail: info@dentabramslondon.co.uk
Office: London W6

DRIVER BELCHER SOLICITORS
3 St Johns Road Hedge End Southampton SO30 4AA
Tel: 01489 785737 *Fax:* 01489 788779 *Dx:* 95101 HEDGE END
Office: Bishop's Waltham
Work: C1 E F1 G H J1 K1 L N O Q S1 W
Emergency Action, Agency, Advocacy, Fixed Fee Interview and Legal Aid undertaken
Ptr: Belcher, Mrs Patricia Dawn . . . . *Dec 1991
Ast: Bury, Miss Joanna J BA(Hons) Associated Law Societies of Wales Prize 1989. . . . . §Oct 1990
Storry, Mr David Austin Wynn BA . . . . *Jan 1990

DUTTON GREGORY
Ambassador House 8 Carlton Crescent Southampton SO15 2EY
Tel: 023 8022 1344 *Fax:* 023 8021 2132
Dx: 49653 SOUTHAMPTON 2
E-mail: contact@duttongregory.co.uk
Office: Bournemouth, Winchester
Languages: French
Work: A1 A3 B1 B2 B3 C1 C2 C3 D1 D2 E F1 F2 G H I J1 J2 K1 K2 K3 K4 L M1 M2 N O P Q R1 R2 S1 S2 T1 T2 U1 U2 V W Z(b,c,d,e,h,i,j,k,l,n,o,p,q,r,s,z)
Emergency Action, Agency, Advocacy, Fixed Fee Interview, Legal Aid undertaken, Legal Aid Franchise and Member of Accident Line
Ptr: Breese, Mr Roger David. . . . . *§Dec 1976
Brown, Mr Jonathan. Jan 1990
Brown, Mr Richard Simon LLB . . . . Oct 1986
Kirkconel, Mr Andrew Holland Deputy District Judge. *§May 1980
Lucas, Mr Martin . . . . *§Oct 1974
Ast: Andrews, Mrs Karen L . . . . *Feb 1994
Everett, Miss Joanne Louise LLB . . . . Feb 2005
Singh, Mr Amarjit BSc(Politics & Law). . . . . *Sep 2006
Con: Alexandre, Mr Stephen Robert LLB(Lond) Deputy District Judge . . . . *§Jun 1984

ENT LAW ‡
Grange Farm Business Park Sandy Lane Southampton SO32 2HD
Tel: 01329 834100

DAVID EBERT & CO ‡
44 High Street West End Southampton SO30 3DR
Tel: 023 8047 7625 *Fax:* 023 8046 6394
E-mail: david@davidebert.co.uk
List of partners: D H Ebert
Work: K1 S1 S2 W
Ptr: Ebert, Mr David H LLB(Lond) . . . . *Mar 1977

THOMAS EGGAR LLP
Brunel House 21 Brunswick Place Southampton SO15 2AQ
Tel: 023 8083 1100 *Fax:* 023 8083 1199 *Dx:* 2003 SOUTHAMPTON
E-mail: southampton@thomaseggar.com
Office: Chichester, Crawley, London EC4, Newbury, Worthing
Work: C1 C2 D2 E F1 J1 J2 K1 K2 K3 K4 L N O Q R1 R2 S1 S2 T1 T2 W X Z(b,c,d,h,j,o,q,r,w)

ELLIOTTS SOLICITORS ‡
81 London Road Southampton SO15 2AA
Tel: 023 8063 1540

ERIC ROBINSON SOLICITORS ‡
359 Bitterne Road Bitterne Southampton SO18 1DN
Tel: 023 8042 5000 *Fax:* 023 8042 5025 *Dx:* 52750 BITTERNE
Emergency telephone 0870 238 5687
E-mail: bitterne@ericrobinson.co.uk
List of partners: P N Bakewell, M W Dyer, R D Evans, A C Hampshire, D P Lawrence, C E E Maxfield, G O Onoufriou, G P W Payne, P Sams, J Swaby
Office: Chandlers Ford, Hythe, Southampton (3 offices)
Work: B1 B2 C1 C2 D1 E F1 G H J1 K1 L N O Q S1 S2 V W Z(i,l,q)
Emergency Action, Agency, Advocacy, Fixed Fee Interview, Legal Aid undertaken, Legal Aid Franchise and Member of Accident Line
Ptr: Lawrence, Mr David P FILEx . . . . Dec 1991
Swaby, Jennifer. . . . . Jan 2004

ERIC ROBINSON SOLICITORS
18 West End Road Southampton SO18 6BU
Tel: 023 8042 5000 *Fax:* 023 8042 6231 *Dx:* 52750 BITTERNE
Emergency telephone 0870 238 5687
E-mail: bitterne@ericrobinson.co.uk
Office: Chandlers Ford, Hythe, Southampton (3 offices)
Work: A1 B1 C1 D1 E F1 G H J1 K1 L M1 N P R1 S1 T1 V W Z(c,d,i,l,m,p)
Emergency Action, Agency, Advocacy, Fixed Fee Interview and Legal Aid undertaken
Ptr: Dyer, Mr Michael W LLB . . . . *May 1984

ERIC ROBINSON SOLICITORS
5a St Johns Road Hedge End Southampton SO30 4AA
Tel: 01489 788922 *Fax:* 01489 786348 *Dx:* 95100 HEDGE END

Emergency telephone 0870 238 5687
E-mail: hedgeend@ericrobinson.co.uk
Office: Chandlers Ford, Hythe, Southampton (3 offices)
Work: D1 G H K1 N O Q S1 W
Emergency Action, Agency, Advocacy, Fixed Fee Interview, Legal Aid undertaken and Member of Accident Line
Ptr: Hampshire, Miss Allison Catherine LLB(Hons). . . . . Sep 1997

ERIC ROBINSON SOLICITORS (incorporating Waller Chesshire)
4 Carlton Crescent Southampton SO15 2EY
Tel: 023 8022 6891 *Fax:* 023 8022 0699
Dx: 38546 SOUTHAMPTON 19
Emergency telephone 0870 238 5687
E-mail: southampton@ericrobinson.co.uk
Office: Chandlers Ford, Hythe, Southampton (3 offices)
Languages: Cantonese, French, German, Greek, Spanish
Work: B1 C1 C2 C3 D1 E F1 F2 G H J1 K1 K2 K3 K4 L N O Q R1 S1 S2 W Z(i,k,l,q,r)
Emergency Action, Agency, Advocacy, Fixed Fee Interview, Legal Aid undertaken, Legal Aid Franchise and Member of Accident Line
Ptr: Evans, Mr Russell David LLB . . . . *Oct 1989
Onoufriou, Mr Geoffrey Onoufrios LLB(Soton). . . . *May 1975
Sams, Mr Paul LLB . . . . Nov 2003

FOOTNER & EWING ‡
19 Brunswick Place Southampton SO15 2SZ
Tel: 023 8033 2991 *Fax:* 023 8033 0483
List of partners: A J R Howorth, P J McVean
Office: Romsey, Southampton, Totton

FOOTNER & EWING
33 Portsmouth Road Southampton SO19 9RE
Tel: 023 8044 8266 *Fax:* 023 8044 6876
Office: Romsey, Southampton, Totton

GAMMON PIERCY & GAIGER
14-24 Cannon Street Shirley Southampton SO15 5PQ
Tel: 023 8065 8180 *Fax:* 023 8077 7119
Dx: 54851 SOUTHAMPTON 4
E-mail: enquiries@gpglaw.co.uk
Office: Eastleigh

BEVERLEY GOLDEN ‡
Holly Cottage Trotts Lane Eling Southampton SO40 4UE
Tel: 023 8086 7137 *Fax:* 023 8066 8671
E-mail: bevgolden@enterprise.net
List of partners: B J Golden
Work: D1 D2 K1
Advocacy and Legal Aid undertaken
SPr: Golden, Miss Beverley J LLB ♦ . . . . *Dec 1982

CHRISTOPHER GREEN MCCARRAHERS
2a High Street Hythe Southampton SO45 6YW
Tel: 023 8084 2765 *Fax:* 023 8084 6732 *Dx:* 54952 HYTHE (HANTS)
E-mail: enquiries@cgm2.demon.co.uk
Office: Southampton
Work: D1 E K1 N O Q S1 S2 V W
Emergency Action, Advocacy, Fixed Fee Interview, Legal Aid undertaken, Legal Aid Franchise and Member of Accident Line
Ptr: Waring, Mrs Andrea D E . . . . *Oct 1998
Asoc: Knight, Mr Matthew I BA(Oxon); LLB . . . . Aug 1998
Snabaitis, Ms Justine Angela . . . . *May 1999
Ast: Williams, Mr Sion . . . . Sep 2006

HANNIDES HEWSTONE & CO ‡
43-45 High Street Shirley Southampton SO15 3UN
Tel: 023 8078 6770 *Fax:* 023 8070 2624
Dx: 54852 SOUTHAMPTON 4
E-mail: law@hhsolicitors.co.uk
List of partners: N M Hannides, W J Hewstone
Languages: Greek
Work: C1 F1 J1 K1 L N Q R1 S1 S2 V W
Emergency Action, Agency, Advocacy, Fixed Fee Interview, Legal Aid undertaken and Legal Aid Franchise
Ptr: Hannides, Mr Nicholas M LLB. . . . . *Oct 1984
Hewstone, Mrs Wendy J LLB . . . . *Oct 1986

IDICULLLA SOLICITORS ‡
8 Portland Street Southampton SO14 7EB
Tel: 023 8063 0905

JASPER & VINCENT ‡
39 Botley Road Park Gate Southampton SO31 1AY
Tel: 01489 885788 *Fax:* 01489 885546
List of partners: H Vincent, M T Vincent
Languages: French, German
Work: B1 C1 E J1 K1 N O Q S1 S2 W Z(q)
Emergency Action, Agency, Advocacy, Fixed Fee Interview, Legal Aid undertaken and Legal Aid Franchise
Ptr: Vincent, Mrs Helen BA . . . . *Sep 1995
Vincent, Mr Michael T. . . . . *§Mar 1959

KITELEYS SOLICITORS LIMITED
Southampton General Hospital 4 Hollybrook Arcade Tremona Road Southampton SO16 6YD
Tel: 023 8090 9091 *Fax:* 023 8090 4181
Office: Bournemouth

LAMPORT BASSITT ‡
46 The Avenue Southampton SO17 1AX
Tel: 023 8083 7777 *Fax:* 023 8083 7788
Dx: 38529 SOUTHAMPTON 3
E-mail: info@lamportbassitt.co.uk
Office: Reading
Work: C1 N Q

LAWDIT SOLICITORS ‡
No1 Brunswick Place Southampton SO15 2AN
Tel: 023 8023 5979

LEONARD & CO ‡
First Floor Oakwood Court 62a The Avenue Southampton SO17 1XS
Tel: 023 8023 4433 *Fax:* 023 8022 0460
Dx: 54863 SOUTHAMPTON 4
List of partners: C F Jones, G M Leonard, G M Leonard, E B Pritchard
Office: Southampton
Work: D1 D2 G H J1 K1 K2 K3 L N O Q Z(g,i)
Emergency Action, Agency, Advocacy, Fixed Fee Interview, Legal Aid undertaken and Legal Aid Franchise
Ptr: Leonard, Mr Gary Michael BA(Hons)(Law) . . . . . *Dec 1983
Pritchard, Mrs Elizabeth Barbara BA(Hons)(Law) . . . May 2000
Ast: Elcombe, Ms Michelle LLB . . . . Sep 2003

LEONARD & CO
126 Shirley Road Shirley Southampton SO15 3FF
Tel: 023 8023 3242 *Fax:* 023 8023 3450
Dx: 54863 SOUTHAMPTON 4
Office: Southampton
Work: B2 D1 D2 F1 G H K1 K2 L N O P Q X Z(i,p,q,r)
Emergency Action, Agency, Advocacy, Fixed Fee Interview, Legal Aid undertaken, Legal Aid Franchise and Member of Accident Line
Ptr: Jones, Miss Caroline Frances LLB(Hons)(Nott'm) . . *Nov 1983
Leonard, Mr Gary Michael BA(Hons) . . . . *Dec 1983
Ast: Palmer, Ms Sally . . . . Oct 2006

LESTER ALDRIDGE LLP
Alleyn House Carlton Crescent Southampton SO15 2EU
Tel: 023 8082 0400 *Fax:* 023 8082 0410
Dx: 96882 SOUTHAMPTON 10
E-mail: online.enquiry@la-law.com
Office: Bournemouth (2 offices), London WC2

MKS SOLICITORS ‡
93 Romsey Road Shirley Southampton SO16 4DD
Tel: 023 8039 6952 *Fax:* 023 8039 6941
E-mail: mkssolicitors@aol.com
List of partners: M Sidhu
Languages: Punjabi
Work: S1 W Z(i)
Fixed Fee Interview and Legal Aid undertaken
Ptr: Sidhu, Ms Mandip LLM . . . . May 2000

MOORE BLATCH SOLICITORS
London Court 64 London Road Southampton SO15 2AH
Tel: 023 8071 8000 *Fax:* 023 8033 3104
Dx: 38524 SOUTHAMPTON 3
Office: Lymington, Richmond upon Thames, Southampton, Wickham
Ptr: Blackwell, Mr Timothy. . . . . May 2004
Horan, Mr Damian Patrick LLB . . . . *Aug 1995
Hydon, Mrs Victoria Jane BA . . . . *Nov 1988
Spring, Mr Timothy Donald Morley LLB(Hons) Notary Public . . . . *May 1982
Thompson, Mr David Clinton BSc . . . . *Dec 1978
Ast: Hedley, Mr John Anthony LLB. . . . . *Dec 1997
Mayhew, Amy. Mar 2010
Monnington, Mr James Evelyn Thomas MA(Cantab). *Dec 1991

MOORE BLATCH SOLICITORS
11 The Avenue Southampton SO17 1XF
Tel: 023 8071 8000 *Fax:* 023 8033 2205
Dx: 38507 SOUTHAMPTON 3
Office: Lymington, Richmond upon Thames, Southampton, Wickham
Languages: French, German
Work: A1 B1 C1 C2 E J1 J2 K1 L M1 N O P R1 S1 T2 W Z(b,c,d,e,h,j,k,l,p,r,t)
Emergency Action, Agency, Advocacy and Fixed Fee Interview undertaken
Ptr: Cantoni, Mr Charles. . . . . *Dec 1977
Caton, Mr Michael John LLB Notary Public . . . . . . *Oct 1974
Duck, Mr Martin Patrick Victor. . . . . Jul 1999
Haverfield, Miss Claire Louise LLB; LLM . . . . Nov 1996
Jeffery, Mr Peter Robin . . . . *Oct 1989
Maxwell, Miss Katherine Theresa . . . . Nov 1996
Osgood, Mr Mark Richard. . . . . Sep 1997
Walshe, Mr Paul Anthony . . . . May 1997
Whitaker, Mr Paul Robert Allan BA . . . . *Mar 1985
Ast: Agnew, Ms Dorothy BA(Hons). . . . . Jan 2003
Clifton, Helen . . . . Mar 2011
Over, Mr Jeremy David Noel . . . . Mar 2006
Sturdy, Mr Justin William MA(Cantab). . . . . *Nov 1993
Con: Barrington, Mr William John Redding Notary Public . . Oct 1957

PAGE GULLIFORD & GREGORY LIMITED ‡
9 Cumberland Place Southampton SO15 2WL
Tel: 023 8022 5821 *Fax:* 023 8022 2332
Dx: 49651 SOUTHAMPTON 2
E-mail: mail@pagegulliford.co.uk
List of partners: E C Coulter, F I Coulter
Languages: French
Work: E J1 K1 K3 K4 L O Q S1 S2 W
Emergency Action, Agency and Advocacy undertaken
Dir: Coulter, Mr Edward C LLB. . . . . *Nov 1970
Coulter, Ms Fiona I . . . . *May 1982
Ast: Clifton, Mr Steven LLB . . . . Sep 2009
Williams, Ms Lucy Clare Stuart BA; PGDipLaw . . . . *Nov 2007

PARIS SMITH LLP ‡
1 London Road Southampton SO15 2AE
Tel: 023 8048 2482 *Fax:* 023 8063 1835
Dx: 38534 SOUTHAMPTON 3
E-mail: info@parissmith.co.uk
List of partners: S C Allen, D I Bird, R H A Burnett, D A Cooper, N L Davies, S P Davies, C M Dick, C Dobbin, D E Eminton, P J Gammie, A T Georgiou, A E Heathcock, M H Howarth, C D C Jameson, J J Mansell, J C May, J McNeil, G H Miles, M W Moore, S V Passemard, F Prior, D S Roath, J P Roy, R Saint, J E Snaith, P A B Taylor, C H Thomson, N J Vaughan, M Withers
Languages: French, German
Work: A1 A3 B1 B2 C1 C2 C3 D1 E F1 F2 I J1 J2 K1 K2 K3 L M2 N O P Q R1 R2 S1 S2 T1 T2 U2 V W X Z(b,c,d,e,g,h,j,k,l,o,p,q,r,s,t,u,w)
Emergency Action, Advocacy, Fixed Fee Interview and Legal Aid undertaken
Ptr: Allen, Mr Stuart Charles LLB(Hons) . . . . *Apr 2003
Bird, Mr David I . . . . Jan 1994
Burnett, Mrs Rachel Hilary Ann BA . . . . Jan 1980
Cooper, Mr Douglas Anthony BA . . . . *§Feb 1982
Davies, Mr Neil L BA(Law) Committee Member of Hampshire SFLA. . . . . *§Oct 1986
Davies, Mr Sean Paul LLB . . . . *§Dec 1992
Dick, Mr Crispin Mathew BSc; MA. . . . . *Nov 1999
Dobbin, Mr Clive BA; MA . . . . *§Sep 1997
Eminton, Mr David E BA(Law). . . . . *§Oct 1988
Gammie, Mr Peter John BA. . . . . *May 1986
Georgiou, Mr Anastasios Thomas LLB(Hons) . . . . *§Oct 1995
Heathcock, Mr Andrew Edward LLB(Bris) . . . . *§May 1977
Howarth, Mr Mark Henry LLB(Soton) . . . . *§Apr 1981
Jameson, Mr Crispin D C LLB(Soton) . . . . *§Jun 1975
McNeil, Mr James. . . . . Sep 2001
Mansell, Mr John James LLB(Bris) . . . . *§Aug 1987
May, Miss Janet C . . . . *Dec 1990
Miles, Mr Geraint Huw LLB . . . . *§Oct 1997
Passemard, Ms Sarah Victoria LLB . . . . *§Oct 1995
Prior, Mr Frank LLB(Hons) . . . . *Aug 1999
Roath, Mr David Stuart LLB. . . . . Dec 1995
Roy, Mr Jonathon Peter BA . . . . Sep 1997
Saint, Miss Rachel BSc(Hons). . . . . *§Dec 1994
Snaith, Mr James Edward LLB(Wales) . . . . *§Oct 1982
Taylor, Mr Peter A B BSc(Econ). . . . . *§Mar 1985
Thomson, Mr Clive H LLB(Exon) . . . . *§Dec 1978
Vaughan, Mr Nicholas John LLB(Leeds). . . . . *§Jul 1982
Withers, Mr Mark BA(Hons). . . . . Sep 1996
Mem: Moore, Mr Michael William LLB(Hons); DipLP . . . . . Apr 1998
Asoc: Atcherley, Mr Richard Alan LLB . . . . *Sep 2004
Brainsby, Ms Julianne E LLB . . . . *Sep 1996
Lee, Mrs Clare Ann LLB. . . . . Sep 2002
Morris, Mr Clifford George LLB . . . . *§Nov 1995
Onoufriou, Miss Victoria BA(Hons) . . . . *Jan 1999
Osgood, Mrs Rachel Barbara LLB(Hons); LPC; Dip Advanced Litigation . . . . Apr 2000
Power, Mr Edward Ronald LLB . . . . *Nov 2002
Spittles, Ms Joanne LLB . . . . *§Sep 1997
Swain, Mr Richard Anthony MA . . . . Sep 2000
Takhar, Mr Jin LLB(Hons) . . . . Oct 2000
Wheadon, Mrs Sarah . . . . Oct 1993
Ast: Baldwin, Mr Phillip LLB . . . . Nov 2011
Bansal, Miss Bindu LLB(Hons) . . . . Sep 1995
Biddlecombe, Mrs Jane Elizabeth BA; MA(Cantab) . *Sep 2002
Bray, Miss Lisa Michelle LLB . . . . Feb 2007
Busby, Miss Lisa Marie LLB(Hons) . . . . *Nov 2003
Casey-Evans, Kathryn . . . . Jul 2007
Clays, Mr Jonathan Mark . . . . Oct 2007
Cort, Miss Helen Jane LLB . . . . Oct 2008
Foster, Miss Emma Louise LLB . . . . Oct 2009
Horne, Miss Lucy Jane LLB. . . . . Nov 2011
McCauley, Mrs Clare LLB(Hons) . . . . *Oct 1998
McNaughton, Mr Gavin Stuart. . . . . Oct 2009
Merritt, Claire . . . . Oct 2009
Merritt, Ms Stephanie Janet LLB . . . . Aug 2001
Pearce, Diane. Apr 2006
Perry, Mrs Susy Alice LLB. . . . . Apr 2003
Power, Mrs Elizabeth Julia-Ann LLB; LLM . . . . Feb 2004
Price, Mr Darren . . . . Oct 2005
Roberts, Miss Jennifer LLB; LPC . . . . Nov 2010
Sadler, Mrs Emily Louisa LLB; LPC . . . . Sep 2007
Sanders, Mr Daniel Shane . . . . Sep 2005
Scally, Ms Amanda Claire LLB(Hons); LPC . . . . . . Oct 1998

PAUL PAVELEY ‡
Peterscroft House 16 Peterscroft Avenue Ashurst Southampton SO40 7AB
Tel: 023 8029 2123 *Fax:* 023 8029 2123
E-mail: paul@paulpaveleysolicitors.co.uk

PAYNE MARSH STILLWELL ‡
6 Carlton Crescent Southampton SO15 2EY
Tel: 023 8022 3957 *Fax:* 023 8022 5261
Dx: 96886 SOUTHAMPTON 10
E-mail: enquiries@pms.gs
List of partners: S Aston, A W Silvestro, K Stillwell, L E Whitfield, H E Wright
Languages: Italian
Work: A3 B1 B2 C1 C3 E F1 I J1 K1 N O Q S1 S2 T1 T2 W Z(e,k,l,q,r)
Emergency Action, Agency, Advocacy undertaken and Member of Accident Line
Ptr: Aston, Mrs Sheena . . . . *Dec 2000
Silvestro, Mr Antony W LLM. . . . . *Mar 1983
Stillwell, Mr Kevin LLB . . . . *Jun 1979
Whitfield, Mrs Lorraine Elizabeth LLB(Hons). . . . . *Jan 1985
Wright, Miss Hannah Elisabeth LLB . . . . Oct 2006
Ast: Corcoran, Mr Adam John LLB. . . . . Sep 2008
Gregory, Mr Chris BA(Hons). . . . . *Aug 2003
Con: Marsh, Mr Christopher G . . . . *Jun 1976

PEACH GREY & CO ‡
14 College Place Southampton SO15 2FE
Tel: 023 8033 4695 *Dx:* 38501 SOUTHAMPTON 3
Emergency telephone 07850 735413
E-mail: enq@peachgrey.co.uk
List of partners: J Chester, J Grey, R C Harris, R A Peach
Work: B2 G H
Emergency Action, Agency, Advocacy, Fixed Fee Interview and Legal Aid undertaken
Ptr: Chester, Mrs Joanne LLB(Hons) ★ . . . . *Nov 1995
Grey, Miss Janet LLB ★. . . . . *Dec 1974
Harris, Mr Richard C LLB ★. . . . . *Dec 1976
Peach, Mr Roger A ★. . . . . *Oct 1963

PLACIDI & CO ‡
31 Middle Road Southampton SO31 7GH
Tel: 01489 579804 *Fax:* 01489 576259
E-mail: info@placidi.co.uk
List of partners: S L Placidi
Work: A3 B1 B2 C1 E F1 F2 J1 L M2 N O Q S1 S2 U2 W Z(c,e,i,j,k,q)
Agency and Advocacy undertaken
Ptr: Placidi, Mr Sandro L ♦. . . . . Oct 1988
Asoc: Lakin, Mr Ian Michael LLB; LLM. . . . . Dec 1989

RM LEGAL SOLICITORS ‡
15 Carlton Place Southampton SO15 2DY
Tel: 023 8092 6060 *Fax:* 023 8092 6061
Dx: 38514 SOUTHAMPTON 3

ROCHFORD & CO ‡
Ferryside The Green Southampton SO31 4JB
Tel: 023 8045 8268 *Fax:* 023 8045 8268

ROWE SPARKES PARTNERSHIP
16 College Place Southampton SO15 2FE
Tel: 023 8021 3890 *Fax:* 023 8021 1880 *Dx:* 96881 SOUTHAMPTON
E-mail: office@rowe-sparkes.co.uk
Office: Havant, Southsea

CATHERINE SOUSA SOLICITORS ‡
16 College Place Southampton SO15 2FE
Tel: 023 8071 3060 *Fax:* 023 8022 5283
Dx: 49659 SOUTHAMPTON 2
E-mail: enquiries@catherinesousasolicitors.co.uk

SWAIN & CO ‡
Oakwood Court 62a The Avenue Southampton SO17 1XS
Tel: 023 8063 1111 *Fax:* 023 8023 3181
Dx: 49662 SOUTHAMPTON 2
Emergency telephone 023 8063 1111

 See p112 for the Key to Work Categories & other symbols

E-mail: mail@swainandco.com
List of partners: S A Lee, G F Swain, H C A Syms
Office: Havant
Work: B2 D1 D2 G H J1 J2 K1 K2 L N O P Q V X Z(g,h,i,m,q,r)
Emergency Action, Agency, Advocacy, Fixed Fee Interview, Legal Aid undertaken, Legal Aid Franchise and Member of Accident Line
Ptr: Swain, Mr Graeme Frederick LLB . . . . . . *Sep 1980
Syms, Mr Henry Charles Adrian BSc(Hons); LLM; DipLP . . . . *Oct 1996
Ast: Rayner, Miss Angela BA(Hons) . . . . *Sep 2000
Walsh, Ms Nina LLB . . . . May 2005
Wright, Miss Victoria Jane BMus(Hons); LLM . . . . Dec 1996

THOMPSONS (FORMERLY ROBIN/BRIAN THOMPSON & PARTNERS)
Queens Keep 1-4 Cumberland Place Southampton SO15 2NP
Tel: 023 8021 2040 *Fax:* 023 8063 3691
Dx: 118630 SOUTHAMPTON 19
Office: Belfast, Birmingham, Bristol, Cardiff, Chelmsford, Dagenham, Derby, Harrow, Leeds, Liverpool, London SW19, London WC1, Manchester, Middlesbrough, Newcastle upon Tyne, Nottingham, Plymouth, Sheffield, South Shields, Stoke-on-Trent, Swansea, Wolverhampton
Ast: Hall, Mr John N LLB; MA . . . . *Feb 1994

TRETHOWANS LLP
15 Rockstone Place Southampton SO15 2EP
Tel: 023 8032 1000 *Fax:* 023 8032 1001
Dx: 154120 SOUTHAMPTON 48
E-mail: info@trethowans.com
Office: Salisbury
Work: A1 A3 C1 C2 C3 E F1 I J1 J2 K1 K3 K4 L N O P Q R1 R2 S1 S2 T1 T2 U2 W X Z(d,e,l,o,p,q,r,x,za)
Advocacy, Fixed Fee Interview, Legal Aid undertaken, Legal Aid Franchise and Member of Accident Line
Ptr: Cook, Mr Richard J BA(Oxon). . . . Feb 1983
Farmaner, Mr Kelvin Ian LLB(Hons) . . . . Oct 2000
Gent, Mr Nicholas Henry LLB(Hons). . . . Oct 1994
Lane, Mr Gavin Robert LLB . . . . Oct 1991
Loney, Mr Jonathan LLB(Hons) . . . . *Sep 1985
Longman, Mr Paul LLB . . . . Aug 2001
MacRae, Miss Catherine M LLB. . . . *Nov 1978
Matthews, Mrs Caroline Elizabeth LLB . . . . Dec 1996
Messent, Mr Michael J LLB . . . . *Apr 1971
Rhodes, Mr Simon James BA(Jt Hons) . . . . *Sep 1995
Rogerson, Miss Jennifer Sarah LLB; LPC; Diploma in Land Registration Law . . . . Nov 2003
Rooke, Ms Yvette Louise MA(Hons)(English Lit); CPE; LPC . . . . Sep 1997
Twaits, Mr Christopher . . . . Sep 2000
Watson, Mr Michael W LLB . . . . Oct 2000
Asoc: Blamire, Miss Bethany Louise BA(Jt Hons); PGDip; CPE; LPC Sir George Fowler Prize - Devon Law Society. . . . Sep 2005
Cudbill, Ms Holly BA(Hons)(Jurisprudence) . . . . Oct 2003
Sclater, Mr William Patrick BA(Hons)(History) . . . . Sep 1997
Ast: Bowes, Mrs Jennifer Louise LLB . . . . Nov 2011
Boyle, Miss Louise Charlotte LLB(Hons). . . . *Sep 2009
Braund, Mr James Guthrie MA . . . . Nov 2009
Christie, Miss Laura LLB . . . . *Nov 2009
Forbes, Ms Marie LLB. . . . Nov 2006
Grimshaw, Mr Ian David BSc . . . . Oct 2006
Irvine, Mr Matthew James LLB . . . . Nov 2001
Newport, Miss Carly Victoria BA(Hons); PGDipLaw; LPC Former Chair of the Southampton Trainee Solicitors Group Nov 2007
Rowe, Mrs Laura LLB; LPC . . . . Nov 2003
Stevenson, Miss Crystal LLB; LPC . . . . Nov 2010
Stocker, Miss Emily Clare BA(Hons)(History); GDL; LPC . . . . Nov 2008
Thompson, Miss Louise LLB . . . . Sep 2008
Con: Parsons, Mr James Ernest LLB(Hons). . . . Feb 1972

WALTON MILLS & CO ‡
PO Box 140 Hedge End Southampton SO18 3ZA
Tel: 023 8047 7221 *Fax:* 023 8047 7004 *Dx:* 45260 PARK GATE
E-mail: enquiries@walton-mills.co.uk
List of partners: A J Mills, S Mills, L Walton
Work: N O Z(q,r,t,y)
Member of Accident Line
Ptr: Mills, Miss Alison J LLB. . . . *§Mar 1990
Mills, Miss Sarah LLB. . . . *§Oct 1989
Walton, Mr Leslie . . . . *§Jul 1979

WARNER GOODMAN LLP
8-9 College Place Southampton SO15 2FF
Tel: 023 8063 9311 *Fax:* 023 8022 6423
Dx: 38542 SOUTHAMPTON 3
E-mail: enquiries@warnergoodman.co.uk
Office: Fareham, Portsmouth
Languages: French
Work: A1 B1 B2 C1 C2 D1 D2 E F1 F2 G H I J1 J2 K1 K2 K3 K4 L N O Q R1 R2 S1 S2 T1 T2 V W Z(a,b,c,d,e,i,j,m,o,q)
Emergency Action, Agency, Advocacy, Fixed Fee Interview, Legal Aid undertaken, Legal Aid Franchise and Member of Accident Line
Dir: Barclay, Mr Graham Scott. . . . Jul 2006
Miles, Mrs Samantha Jane . . . . Nov 2004
Munden, Mr Andrew John. . . . Mar 2002
Oatham, Ms Denise Yvette . . . . Mar 2007
Robson, Mr Howard. . . . *Feb 2002
Sheerin, Mrs Clare . . . . Dec 2004
Thompson, Mr Daniel E LLB Law Society LPC Prize 1997 . . . . *Aug 1997
Voller, Mr Edward BA . . . . *Aug 1987
Whitemore, Ms Sarah J LLB Ford Prize. . . . *Sep 1992
Asoc: Chun, Mr David . . . . Oct 2006
Foundling, Mrs Deborah J LLB(Hons). . . . *Sep 1992
Lee, Mr Howard. . . . Feb 2010
Porter, Ms Helen . . . . Feb 2008
Ralls, Ms Catriona Louise. . . . Sep 2000
Whitaker, Ms Caroline Mary. . . . Apr 2008
Ast: Cook, Ms Polly . . . . Nov 2004
Cook, Miss Tabitha Jane Elisabeth . . . . Sep 2008
D'Aguilar, Ms Lana . . . . Dec 2002
Seaman, Miss Nicole Louise . . . . Sep 2008

WELBURN & CO ‡
1 Howard Road Southampton SO15 5BB
Tel: 023 8023 0500 *Fax:* 023 8022 4091
Emergency telephone 07768 005050
E-mail: peterwelburn@btconnect.com
List of partners: P Welburn
Work: C1 E J1 M2 U2
SPr: Welburn, Mr Peter BA; LSF Secretary for British/Hungarian Law Association . . . . *Jan 1983

WILFRED LIGHT & REID ‡
89a Shirley High Street Southampton SO15 3TU
Tel: 023 8077 7817 *Fax:* 023 8077 7817
Dx: 54853 SOUTHAMPTON 4
List of partners: D J Brocken
Work: E K4 S1 S2 T2 W
SPr: Brocken, Mr David James. . . . *Jul 1974

D YOUNG & CO ‡
Britton House Briton Street Southampton SO14 3EB
Tel: 023 8071 9500 *Fax:* 023 8071 9800
Office: London EC1

SOUTHBOURNE, Bournemouth

MATTHEW & MATTHEW LIMITED ‡
194 Seabourne Road Southbourne Bournemouth BH5 2JD
Tel: 01202 431943 *Fax:* 01202 420054 *Dx:* 50554 SOUTHBOURNE
E-mail: enquiries@mm4law.co.uk
List of partners: D Carroll, S R Matthew, L Vermeulen, D R Webb
Work: A1 B1 C1 C2 E J1 K4 L R2 S1 S2 W Z(h,m)
Dir: Carroll, Mr Dean . . . . *Dec 2006
Matthew, Mr Stephen R BSc(Lond) . . . . *Dec 1979
Vermeulen, Ms Louise. . . . *May 2006
Webb, Mr David Ross. . . . *Feb 1988
Asoc: Monk, Mr David T LLB(Lond) . . . . *Jun 1975
Ast: Eddy, Mrs Alex . . . . *Oct 2002
Con: Clayton, Mrs Meliane . . . . *Jan 2001
Matthew, Mr Richard A BSc(Econ) . . . . *Jun 1975
Merritt, Mr James Charles BA. . . . *Nov 1976

SOUTHEND-ON-SEA

BTMK SOLICITORS LLP ‡
19 Clifftown Road Southend-on-Sea SS1 1AB
Tel: 01702 339222 *Fax:* 01702 331563 *Dx:* 2821 SOUTHEND
Emergency telephone 01702 339168
E-mail: enquiries@btmk.co.uk
List of partners: A J Bacon, B A Briscoe, S M Callaghan, S J Caplan, M A Clark, R Cooper, Y Hume, N K Khandhia, I S Powell, M R Warren
Office: Southend-on-Sea
Languages: French, Gujarati, Hindi, Indonesian, Japanese, Malay, Malayalam, Punjabi, Spanish, Tamil
Work: B1 B2 C1 C2 D1 D2 E F1 G H J1 K1 K3 L N Q R2 S2 W Z(l,q,r)
Emergency Action, Agency, Advocacy, Fixed Fee Interview, Legal Aid undertaken, Legal Aid Franchise and Member of Accident Line
Mem: Bacon, Mr Alan J . . . . *May 1982
Briscoe, Mr B Anthony BA. . . . *Oct 1987
Callaghan, Mr Sean M BA(Hons) Deputy District Judge . . . . *Feb 1986
Caplan, Mr Saul J BSc(Hons). . . . *Oct 1993
Clark, Mr Matthew Adam . . . . Mar 1996
Cooper, Mr Richard. . . . Nov 1998
Hume, Miss Yvonne. . . . *Dec 1997
Khandhia, Mr Nitin Kishor. . . . *Sep 2003
Powell, Mr Ian S LLB . . . . *Sep 1992
Warren, Mr Michael R BA(Hons) . . . . *Jun 1994
Asoc: McAnaw, Miss Fiona . . . . *Jan 2002
Wilcockson, Mr Lee M LLB . . . . *Oct 1997
Ast: Burrell, Mr Gavin LLB. . . . *Aug 2000
Fleming, Adam . . . . Sep 2008
Haine, Miss Rachael LLB . . . . *Sep 2008
Hemingway, Miss Ruth BA(Hons) . . . . *Oct 1995
Neild, Mr Roger J. . . . *Jan 2002
Pidgeon, Antony. . . . Sep 2006
Powell, Joanna . . . . Sep 2009
Robertson, Miss Victoria H . . . . *Jan 2000
Con: Cherry, Mr Clive T LLB . . . . *Apr 1972

BTMK SOLICITORS LLP
Madison House, 100 Alexandra Road Southend-on-Sea SS1 1HQ
Tel: 01702 339222 *Fax:* 01702 331563 *Dx:* 2821 SOUTHEND
Emergency telephone 01702 339168
E-mail: email@btmk.co.uk
Office: Southend-on-Sea
Work: G H
Advocacy, Legal Aid undertaken and Legal Aid Franchise

BARNES & TAYLOR ‡
4 Nelson Street Southend-on-Sea SS1 1EF
Tel: 01702 347300 *Fax:* 01702 460922 *Dx:* 2804 SOUTHEND
E-mail: barnestaylor@btinternet.com
List of partners: R A Carlile
Work: B1 C1 D1 D2 E F1 G H J1 K1 L N O Q R1 S1 V W Z(c,d,i,j,k,l,p)
Emergency Action, Agency, Advocacy, Fixed Fee Interview, Legal Aid undertaken and Legal Aid Franchise
Ptr: Carlile, Mr Robin A MA(Oxon). . . . Oct 1990

MARCUS BAUM ‡
Madison House 100-102 Alexandra Road Southend-on-Sea SS1 1HQ
Tel: 01702 346677 *Fax:* 01702 354246 *Dx:* 2807 SOUTHEND
E-mail: enquiries@marcusbaum.co.uk
List of partners: C Baum
Work: C1 C2 C3 E F1 L M1 M2 P R1 S1 S2 T1 T2 W Z(e,j,q)
Ptr: Baum, Mr Colin BA . . . . Jun 1981

BEECHAM FISHER RIDLEY ‡
26 Clifftown Road Southend-on-Sea SS1 1AH
Tel: 01702 348384 *Fax:* 01702 433424 *Dx:* 2810 SOUTHEND
E-mail: enquiries@beechamfisherridley.co.uk
List of partners: P H Fisher, M H Ridley, F M White, B J R Withecombe
Work: A1 B1 C1 D1 D2 E F1 F2 J1 K1 K2 L N O Q S1 S2 T1 T2 V W X Z(d,h,r)
Emergency Action, Agency, Advocacy, Fixed Fee Interview and Legal Aid undertaken
Ptr: Fisher, Mr Peter H . . . . *Dec 1969
Ridley, Mrs Margaret H LLB. . . . *Jun 1969
White, Miss Frances M ATII; LLB . . . . *Apr 1978
Withecombe, Mr Brian J R . . . . *May 1987

ANN BLYTH-COOK & CO ‡
Southchurch Chambers 3 Chase Road Southend-on-Sea SS1 2RE
Tel: 01702 462999 *Fax:* 01702 462988
Emergency telephone 07771 752047
E-mail: abcsolicitors@hotmail.co.uk
List of partners: A M Blyth-Cook, M Breindel
Languages: French, German, Italian
Work: G H
Emergency Action, Agency, Advocacy, Fixed Fee Interview, Legal Aid undertaken and Legal Aid Franchise
Ptr: Blyth-Cook, Mrs Ann Margaret BEd(Hons) ★ . . . . *Oct 1994
Breindel, Miss Michelle BA(Hons) ★. . . . *Jul 1998

2

THOMAS LINDSEY BROWN & CO ‡
Gordon House 819/821 Southchurch Road Southchurch Southend-on-Sea SS1 2PP
Tel: 01702 466266 *Fax:* 01702 466867
Dx: 141400 SHOEBURYNESS
E-mail: info@tlb-law.co.uk
List of partners: T L Brown
Work: D1 G J1 K1 L S1 S2 W Z(l)
Agency and Advocacy undertaken
Ptr: Brown, Mr Thomas Lindsey LLB. . . . *Jul 1980

BURKETTS SOLICITORS ‡
Suite 4 4a Southchurch Road Southend-on-Sea SS1 2NE
Tel: 01702 462 323 / 07957 241939 *Dx:* 2833 SOUTHEND
E-mail: burketts@btconnect.com

ADRIAN DANN & COMPANY ‡
Admirals House 18 Nelson Street Southend-on-Sea SS1 1EF
Tel: 01702 348802 *Fax:* 01702 348856 *Dx:* 2836 SOUTHEND
E-mail: adrian.dann@btconnect.com

DHILLON & CO
37 Clarence Street Southend-on-Sea SS1 1BH
Tel: 01702 393022
Office: London E13

DRYSDALES ‡
Cumberland House 24-28 Baxter Avenue Southend-on-Sea SS2 6HZ
Tel: 01702 423400 *Fax:* 01702 423408 *Dx:* 2808 SOUTHEND
E-mail: law@drysdales.net
Web: www.drysdales.net
List of partners: J A Grimes, A D Murrell, M A Robertson
Languages: French
Work: B1 C1 D1 D2 E F1 J1 K1 K2 K3 K4 L N O P Q R1 R2 S1 S2 W Z(c,d,e,k,l,o,q)
Emergency Action, Agency, Advocacy, Fixed Fee Interview undertaken and Member of Accident Line
Ptr: Grimes, Mr John Adrian LLB(Bris). . . . *Jun 1974
Murrell, Mr Andrew David LLB(Hons); PGCE; LLM . . *Oct 1996
Robertson, Mr Mark Andrew LLB(Hons). . . . *Jan 2006
Ast: Adams, Miss Kelly Louise LLB . . . . *May 2010
Bannister, Ms Catherine Jeanette FILEx. . . . *Nov 2008
Roberts, Miss Kelly LLB(Hons) . . . . *Feb 2008

JOHN L ESCOTT ‡
12 Devereux Road Southend-on-Sea SS1 1DR
Tel: 01702 433110
Work: S1 S2 W

JORGE IGUACEL SPANISH LAWYERS ‡
36 Clarence Street Southend-on-Sea SS1 1BD
Tel: 01702 333341

JERMAN SIMPSON PEARSON & SAMUELS ‡
4a Southchurch Road Southend-on-Sea SS1 2NE
Tel: 01702 610071 *Fax:* 01702 613124 *Dx:* 2803 SOUTHEND
Emergency telephone 07717 798373
List of partners: M Bone, M C Jerman, M Pearson, S Samuels
Office: Basildon
Ptr: Bone, Mr Matthew LLB . . . . Sep 1999
Samuels, Mr Simon BA(Hons). . . . Jan 1987
Ast: Jones, Danielle . . . . May 2010
Werry, Miss Laura Jane. . . . Sep 2002

KLOOSMANS ‡
706 Southchurch Road Southend-on-Sea SS1 2PS
Tel: 01702 600090 *Fax:* 01702 600115 *Dx:* 2841 SOUTHEND
E-mail: mail@kloosmans.com
List of partners: G A Kloosman, E D Lee
Work: L S1 S2 W
Ptr: Kloosman, Mr George A. . . . *Nov 1979
Lee, Mr Edward D DipLG Law Society Prize Winner Legal Executives 1971 President of Southend-on-Sea and District Local Law Society 2002/2003. . . . *Jul 1977

LINDOPS ‡
(incorporating Malcolm Pratt Baker)
35 Clarence Street Southend-on-Sea SS1 1BH
Tel: 01702 431791 *Fax:* 01702 436141 *Dx:* 2839 SOUTHEND
E-mail: info@lindops.com
List of partners: J W Lindop, M J Pratt, H J Skinner
Work: B1 C1 C2 E F1 J1 K1 L M1 M2 N O Q
Emergency Action, Agency, Advocacy and Legal Aid undertaken
Ptr: Lindop, Mr John W . . . . Jun 1975
Pratt, Mr Malcolm J. . . . Dec 1972
Skinner, Ms Helen J LLB . . . . Jul 1988

CHRISTOPHER PINNION & CO ‡
11th Floor Maitland House Southend-on-Sea SS1 2JS
Tel: 01702 338218
List of partners: C P Pinnion
Ptr: Pinnion, Mr Christopher P. . . . *Jan 1982

TAYLOR HALDANE BARLEX LLP
23 Weston Road Southend-on-Sea SS1 1BB
Tel: 01702 339168 *Fax:* 0845 658 7990 *Dx:* 2805 SOUTHEND
E-mail: mail@thblegal.com
Office: Benfleet, Braintree, Chelmsford, Ipswich

TOLHURST FISHER LLP ‡
Trafalgar House 8-10 Nelson Street Southend-on-Sea SS1 1EF
Tel: 01702 352511 *Fax:* 01702 348900 *Dx:* 2811 SOUTHEND
E-mail: info@tolhurstfisher.com

List of partners: R Bain, C Bard, S Blake, J Cuthbert, M Francis, N Holdcroft, C D Latham, A O'Donogue, G Provan, P Tolhurst
Office: Chelmsford
Work: A1 B1 C1 C2 D1 E F1 F2 J1 K1 L M1 N O P Q R1 S1 S2 T1 T2 W Z(c,d,e,f,k,o,q)
Agency, Advocacy undertaken and Member of Accident Line
Ptr: Bain, Mr Robin . . . . Dec 1985
Bard, Chris . . . . *Jun 1979
Blake, Ms Susan . . . . Dec 1991
Francis, Mr Mark . . . . Nov 1994
Holdcroft, Mr Nigel . . . . Sep 1983
Latham, Mr Charles D. . . . . *Mar 1984
O'Donogue, Mr Aidan . . . . Nov 1981

ALISTAIR J WHIPPS ‡
327 Southchurch Road Southend-on-Sea SS1 2PE
Tel: 01702 616516 *Fax:* 01702 612100
E-mail: ajw@ajwhipps.lawyersonline.co.uk
List of partners: A J Whipps
Work: B1 C1
Agency undertaken
SPr: Whipps, Mr Alistair J BA(Law) . . . . *Dec 1986

WHITE & CO ‡
51 Alexandra Street Southend-on-Sea SS11 1BW
Tel: 01702 340340 *Fax:* 01702 349564 *Dx:* 2801 SOUTHEND
E-mail: info@whitesolicitors.co.uk

SOUTHMINSTER, Essex

M A PLANT ‡
Bank House Station Road Southminster Essex CM0 7EW
Tel: 01621 773185 / 772794 *Fax:* 01621 772398
List of partners: M A Plant
Work: C1 J1 K1 Q S1 W
Agency, Fixed Fee Interview and Legal Aid undertaken
Ptr: Plant, Mrs Margaret Anne LLB; AKC . . . . *Jul 1973
Ast: Reid, Mrs Carol A LLB . . . . *Jul 1977

SOUTHPORT, Merseyside

ALB LAW ‡
33 Hoghton Street Southport Merseyside PR9 0NS
Tel: 01704 500771 *Fax:* 01704 500303
Emergency telephone 07770 808904
E-mail: alb@alblaw.co.uk
List of partners: A L Blackhurst
SPr: Blackhurst, Mr Arthur Linton ★ . . . . Mar 1959

BARNETTS ‡
Southport Business Park Wight Moss Way Southport Merseyside PR8 4HQ
Tel: 0870 787 3600 *Fax:* 0870 111 8688
List of partners: P T Bright
Ptr: Bright, Mr Philip T LLB . . . . *§Apr 1981

BELLIS KENNAN GRIBBLE & CO ‡
(in association with Bell & Co)
40 Hoghton Street Southport Merseyside PR9 0PQ
Tel: 01704 532217 *Fax:* 01704 500079 *Dx:* 20120 SOUTHPORT
E-mail: attwood@bellis.lawlite.net
List of partners: D G Attwood
Work: C1 D1 E K1 L N O Q R1 S1 S2 W Z(l,o)
Agency, Advocacy undertaken and Member of Accident Line
Ptr: Attwood, Mr David George . . . . Apr 1977

BIRCHALL BLACKBURN LLP
180 Cambridge Road Churchtown Southport Merseyside PR9 7LW
Tel: 01704 232323 *Fax:* 01704 229745 *Dx:* 20129 SOUTHPORT
Office: Chester, Chorley, Formby, Leyland, Manchester, Morecambe, Preston (2 offices)
Ptr: Dillon, Miss Fiona ILEX; CPE; LPC . . . . *Sep 2003
Leah, Mr Andrew Martin LLB; MBA . . . . Feb 1994

ANDREA BLEACKLEY & CO ‡
26 Bridge Street Southport Merseyside PR8 1BW
Tel: 01704 500297 *Fax:* 01704 531666 *Dx:* 720943 SOUTHPORT
E-mail: andreableakley@btconnect.com
Work: K1 K3 N Q S1 W
Fixed Fee Interview undertaken

BREENS SOLICITORS ‡
30 Hoghton Street Southport Merseyside PR9 0PA
Tel: 01704 532890 *Fax:* 01704 547799 *Dx:* 20123 SOUTHPORT
Emergency telephone 0800 317 620
E-mail: js.breen@breensonline.co.uk
List of partners: J S Breen, K S McKno
Office: Liverpool
Work: B1 C1 E F1 F2 J1 J2 N O Q S1 S2 T1 T2 W
Advocacy and Fixed Fee Interview undertaken
Ptr: Breen, Mr John Stephen BA . . . . *Apr 1981
McKno, Miss Kirsty Susan LLB(Hons) . . . . *Nov 2000

BRIGHOUSES ‡
Clarendon House St Georges Place Lord Street Southport Merseyside PR9 0AJ
Tel: 01704 534101 / 500151 *Fax:* 01704 548318
Dx: 20105 SOUTHPORT
Emergency telephone 01704 563665
List of partners: D C J Barr, M P Braham, G E Cheetham, M Collins, R M Ratcliffe, J A Stanley
Work: A1 B1 C1 C2 D1 D2 E F1 G H J1 J2 K1 L N O Q S1 S2 T2 V W Z(c,l,m,o,p,q,r)
Emergency Action, Agency, Advocacy, Fixed Fee Interview, Legal Aid undertaken and Legal Aid Franchise
Ptr: Barr, Mr David Christopher James. . . . . *§Nov 1975
Braham, Mr Michael P. . . . . *§Jan 1981
Cheetham, Miss Gillian E BA(Law) . . . . *Feb 1989
Collins, Ms Margaret . . . . *Apr 1997
Ratcliffe, Mr R Michael MA(Oxon) . . . . *Jun 1979
Stanley, Mr James A LLB . . . . *Apr 1976
Ast: Howard, Ms Karen P LLB . . . . *Dec 1992

BROMILEY HOLCROFT & CO ‡
143-149 Bispham Road Southport Merseyside PR9 7BL
Tel: 0870 236 0000 *Fax:* 0870 236 0019 *Dx:* 20132 SOUTHPORT
E-mail: bromilyholcroft@btinternet.com
List of partners: R M Holcroft
Agency, Fixed Fee Interview, Legal Aid undertaken and Member of Accident Line
Ptr: Holcroft, Mr Roger M BA(Law) . . . . *Mar 1981
Ast: Aspinall, Mr John LLB. . . . . Dec 1976

BROWN TURNER ROSS ‡
11 St Georges Place Lord Street Southport Merseyside PR9 0AL
Tel: 01704 542002 *Fax:* 01704 543144 *Dx:* 20104 SOUTHPORT
Emergency telephone 01704 877949
E-mail: law@brownturnerross.com
List of partners: D T Bushell, J N K Colas, I R Knifton, A M Otto, P A Wright
Languages: French, Polish, Spanish
Work: B1 C1 C2 C3 D1 E F1 G H J1 K1 L M1 M2 N O P Q S1 S2 V W Z(d,i,k,l)
Emergency Action, Agency, Advocacy, Fixed Fee Interview, Legal Aid undertaken, Legal Aid Franchise and Member of Accident Line
Ptr: Bushell, Mr David T LLB . . . . *Jul 1977
Colas, Mr Julian N K BA . . . . *Feb 1988
Knifton, Mr Ian R LLB. . . . . *Oct 1985
Otto, Mr Andrew M LLB(Lond). . . . . *Dec 1977
Wright, Mr Phillip A LLB. . . . . *Feb 1995
Ast: Bushell, Miss Samantha Jayne LLB(Hons) . . . . *Sep 2002

BYRNE & CO ‡
42 Hoghton Street Southport Merseyside PR9 0PQ
Tel: 01704 545912 *Fax:* 01704 540892
E-mail: claims@byrneandco.com

COCKSHOTT PECK LEWIS ‡
24 Hoghton Street Southport Merseyside PR9 0PA
Tel: 01704 534034 *Fax:* 01704 540570 *Dx:* 20107 SOUTHPORT
List of partners: A J G Cottrell, A H Ford, D G Holt, V A Hulton, W J Tyson, C K Watson
Office: Ainsdale, Southport
Work: A1 B1 C1 D1 D2 E F1 J1 K1 K4 L N Q R1 S1 S2 T2 W Z(d,l,m)
Ptr: Cottrell, Mr Arthur John Geoffrey LLB . . . . *§Jun 1975
Ford, Mr Alistair H BA. . . . . *Dec 1980
Holt, Mr David Graham . . . . *§Jun 1975
Hulton, Ms Valerie A BA. . . . . *Jan 1986
Tyson, Mrs Wendy Joan LLB(Hons). . . . . *Oct 1992
Watson, Mr C Keith . . . . *§Oct 1959
Asoc: Lawrence, Mrs Fleur V LLB . . . . *Oct 1999

COCKSHOTT PECK LEWIS
143 Cambridge Road Churchtown Southport Merseyside PR9 7LN
Tel: 01704 211649 *Fax:* 01704 506616
Office: Ainsdale, Southport
Work: A1 B1 C1 C2 C3 D1 E F1 G H J1 K1 L N O P Q R1 S1 T2 W Z(d,h,j,k,l,m)
Emergency Action, Agency, Advocacy, Fixed Fee Interview and Legal Aid undertaken
Ptr: Tyson, Mrs Wendy Joan LLB(Hons). . . . . *Oct 1992

COOK & TALBOT ‡
St Georges Place 140 Lord Street Southport Merseyside PR9 0AH
Tel: 01704 535216 *Fax:* 01704 546915 *Dx:* 20113 SOUTHPORT
E-mail: enquiries@cookandtalbot.co.uk
List of partners: A H A Cook, M L Cook
Languages: French
Work: A1 E F1 J1 K1 L N S1 S2 T1 T2 W
Ptr: Cook, Mr Alfred Henry Ainsworth LLB Deputy Coroner*Nov 1963
Cook, Mrs Margaret L LLB Clerk to Commissioner of Taxes . . . . *Nov 1963
Ast: Cook, Miss Lucinda Frances LLB . . . . *Dec 2007
Ind, Mrs Rebecca C LLB(Hons) . . . . *Feb 1996
Lloyd, Mr Mark Andrew LLB(Hons) . . . . *Nov 1992
Rostamlou, Miss Sarah Natalie BA . . . . *Jan 2008
Williamson, Mrs Joan M Notary Public. . . . . *Dec 1973

FLETCHERS ‡
160-162 Lord Street Southport Merseyside PR9 0QA
Tel: 01704 546919 *Fax:* 01704 545588 *Dx:* 20126 SOUTHPORT
E-mail: enquiries@fletcherssolicitors.co.uk
List of partners: E B Fletcher, R A Fletcher, P A McNamara, S D Threlfall
Office: Preston
Languages: French, Italian, Spanish
Work: K1 K3 N O Q W
Emergency Action, Agency, Advocacy, Fixed Fee Interview, Legal Aid undertaken, Legal Aid Franchise and Member of Accident Line
Ptr: Fletcher, Mr Edward B LLB . . . . *Oct 1998
Fletcher, Mr Robert A BA Deputy District Judge . . . *Mar 1979
McNamara, Miss Pauline A LLB. . . . . *Oct 1985
Threlfall, Mr Stephen D LLB. . . . . *Dec 1989
Asoc: Higham, Ms Andrea LLB . . . . *Nov 1994
Ast: Airnes, Miss Tracy LLB . . . . *Sep 2003
Clark, Mr Andrew FILEx. . . . . *Jul 2000
Fletcher, Lucy. . . . . Sep 2001
Green, Mrs Sarah LLB(Hons) . . . . Sep 1998
Kane, Miss Janet LLB. . . . . *Mar 2003
Morgan, Ms Helen J LLB . . . . *Oct 1989
Pilkington, Mr Michael William BA(Hons)(Law with Psychology) . . . . Jun 1998
Roberts, Miss Lucy LLB. . . . . *Sep 2001
Spence, Mrs Adele S LLB. . . . . *Oct 2000

GOFFEYS ‡
(incorporating Hurtley Mills & Co; Adler Sumner Moore)
1 London Street Southport Merseyside PR9 0UF
Tel: 01704 531755 *Fax:* 01704 536646 *Dx:* 20101 SOUTHPORT
E-mail: goffeys@btopenworld.com
List of partners: J A P Flanagan, T J Mills
Work: C1 C2 E F1 J1 L R1 S1 S2 W Z(l)
Emergency Action undertaken
Ptr: Flanagan, Mr James A P Deputy District Judge . . . . Jan 1986
Mills, Mr Thomas J LLB Chairman of the Social Security Appeal Tribunal. . . . . *Dec 1971

HODGE HALSALL ‡
18 Hoghton Street Southport Merseyside PR9 0PA
Tel: 01704 531991 *Fax:* 01704 537475 *Dx:* 20102 SOUTHPORT
E-mail: info@hhlegal.co.uk
List of partners: J A Bond, G Hatton, M Robinson
Office: Ainsdale
Work: B1 C1 D1 D2 E F1 F2 J1 J2 K1 K3 K4 L N O Q R2 S1 S2 T2 W X Z(e,k,l,p,q)
Emergency Action, Agency, Advocacy, Fixed Fee Interview, Legal Aid undertaken and Legal Aid Franchise
Ptr: Bond, Ms Judith A ♦. . . . . *Jan 2002
Hatton, Mr Gordon LLB . . . . *Nov 1971
Robinson, Mr Mark LLB. . . . . *Oct 1983

Asoc: Dootson, Mr Geoffrey J LLB(Hons) . . . . *Nov 1990
Leadsom, Mr Paul . . . . *Jan 2008
Ast: Connolly, Miss Sinead LLB(Hons) . . . . *Apr 2010

RICHARD JACKLIN & CO ‡
38 Hoghton Street Southport Merseyside PR9 0PQ
Tel: 01704 500024 *Fax:* 01704 500075
E-mail: rj@jacklin.co.uk
List of partners: R Jacklin, S Malthouse
Office: Liverpool
Work: K4 T2 W
Ptr: Jacklin, Mr Richard LLB Notary Public. . . . . *Jun 1971
Malthouse, Mrs Susan BA. . . . . *Nov 1976
Ast: Foggin, Mrs Elizabeth Sarah BA . . . . *Apr 2009

MAWDSLEYS ‡
152 Lord Street Southport Merseyside PR9 0QB
Tel: 01704 537676 *Fax:* 01704 500020 *Dx:* 20110 SOUTHPORT
E-mail: mail@152law.co.uk
List of partners: A Burns, C J H Lawrence
Work: D1 K1 K4 L Q S1 S2 T2 W
Emergency Action, Advocacy, Fixed Fee Interview, Legal Aid undertaken and Legal Aid Franchise
Ptr: Burns, Mr Anthony MA(Oxon) . . . . *Oct 1989
Lawrence, Mr Charles J H BA(Hons) . . . . *Jun 1998
Ast: Murphy, Mr Peter . . . . *Feb 1986

J O'NEILL & CO ‡
11 Cheriton Park Southport Merseyside PR8 6QB
Tel: 0800 234 6173

PETERSON SOLICITORS ‡
Suite 2 Hesketh Mount 92-96 Lord Street Southport Merseyside PR8 1JR
Tel: 01704 504350

GRAHAM M RILEY & CO ‡
Norman House 14-16 Hoghton Street Southport Merseyside PR9 0PA
Tel: 01704 532229 *Fax:* 01704 544224 *Dx:* 20145 SOUTHPORT
E-mail: rta@rta-solicitors.co.uk
List of partners: G M Riley
Work: N O
Agency undertaken and Member of Accident Line
Ptr: Riley, Mr Graham Mark LLB. . . . . *Sep 1999
Asoc: Weaver, Mrs Jennifer Margaret LLB(Hons) . . . . Aug 2003
Ast: Martland, Ms Carol Louise LLB(Hons). . . . . *Dec 2004

ROSETTA THOMAS SOLICITORS ‡
15 Hoghton Street Southport Merseyside PR9 0NS
Tel: 01704 543344 / 07883 302770 *Fax:* 01704 513917
E-mail: enquiries@rosettathomas.co.uk

J ROSTRON ‡
1 Hartley Crescent Birkdale Southport Merseyside PR8 4SG
Tel: 01704 551414 *Fax:* 01704 568432
E-mail: info@jrostron.co.uk

CHRIS SALTRESE SOLICITORS ‡
13 Scarisbrick New Road Southport Merseyside PR8 6PU
Tel: 01704 535512 *Fax:* 01704 533056
E-mail: law@saltrese.fsbusiness.co.uk
List of partners: C J Saltrese
Work: C1 G J1 O Z(e)
Agency and Legal Aid undertaken
SPr: Saltrese, Mr Christopher J. . . . . Dec 1992

SILVERMITHS ‡
53 Hoghton Street Southport Merseyside PR9 0PG
Tel: 01704 542490 *Fax:* 01704 547710 *Dx:* 20135 SOUTHPORT

MS DENISE WATLING ‡
47 Windsor Road Southport Merseyside PR9 9DB
Tel: 01704 500055
E-mail: denise@cpims.com

GUY WIGMORE SOLICITOR ‡
9 Mill Lane Churchtown Southport Merseyside PR9 7PL
Tel: 01704 222277 *Fax:* 01704 228905
Emergency telephone 07941 322898
E-mail: guywigmore@yahoo.com
List of partners: G Wigmore
Work: E S1 S2 W
Fixed Fee Interview undertaken
Ptr: Wigmore, Mr Guy . . . . *Oct 1994

SOUTHSEA, Portsmouth

BRAMSDON & CHILDS ‡
141 Elm Grove Southsea Portsmouth PO5 1HR
Tel: 023 9282 1251 *Fax:* 023 9289 3777 *Dx:* 2224 PORTSMOUTH
E-mail: legalservices@bramsdonandchilds.com
List of partners: C Innes, A J Rafferty, R N E Rixon, A L White
Languages: French, German, Italian
Work: A1 B1 B2 C1 D1 D2 E F1 F2 G H J1 K1 K2 L M1 N O P Q R1 S1 S2 T1 V W X Z(a,b,c,e,g,i,j,k,l,m,o,p,q,r,s)
Emergency Action, Agency, Advocacy, Fixed Fee Interview, Legal Aid undertaken and Member of Accident Line
Ptr: Innes, Mr Colin . . . . *Jan 1980
Rafferty, Mr Andrew John LLB(Hons) . . . . *Sep 1990
Rixon, Mr Roger N E . . . . *Jan 1981
White, Mr Andrew L LLB . . . . *Oct 1980
Ast: Ashton, Mr Will . . . . *Apr 2000
Bartlett, Miss Amanda. . . . . Oct 2010
Woods, Miss Charlotte . . . . Oct 2009

HARRIS & CO ‡
(incorporating Wilkinson & Co)
Albermarle House Osborne Road Southsea Portsmouth PO5 3LB
Tel: 023 9278 5757 *Fax:* 023 9278 8866 *Dx:* 2289 PORTSMOUTH
List of partners: M A P Harris
Ptr: Harris, Mr Michael A P MA(Oxon). . . . . *Jan 1965

LARGE & GIBSON ‡
Kent House 49 Kent Road Southsea Portsmouth PO5 3EJ
Est: 1899
Tel: 023 9229 6296 *Fax:* 023 9282 6134 *Dx:* 2248 PORTSMOUTH
E-mail: reception@largeandgibson.co.uk
List of partners: P M Dymock, R I M Wootton
Work: C1 D1 E G H J1 K1 K3 K4 L N O Q S1 S2 W Z(l,q)
Emergency Action, Agency and Legal Aid undertaken

See p112 for the Key to Work Categories & other symbols

Ptr: Dymock, Mr Peter M LLB . . . . *Oct 1984
Wootton, Mr Richard Ivor Maynard TEP . . . . *Jun 1974
Asoc: King, Mrs Nicolette . . . . *May 2007
Rowland, Mr Michael Leslie LLB(Hons) . . . . *Feb 1992
Twiney, Mrs Ruth F LLB(Reading). . . . . *Apr 1981
Ast: Bradley-Shaw, Mrs Vivien Elaine LLB(Hons); TEP Maxwell Law Prize . . . . *Oct 1989

ROWE SPARKES PARTNERSHIP
First Floor The Old Treasury No7 Kings Road Southsea Portsmouth PO5 4DJ
Tel: 023 9248 6886 *Fax:* 023 9275 2368 *Dx:* 2217 PORTSMOUTH
E-mail: office@rowe-sparkes.co.uk
Office: Havant, Southampton

SAULET & CO ‡
Froddington House Cumberland Business Centre Northumberland Road Southsea Portsmouth PO5 1DS
Tel: 023 9281 9442 *Fax:* 023 9229 6067 *Dx:* 2247 PORTSMOUTH
E-mail: info@saulet.co.uk
List of partners: J R Saulet, R N I Townsend
Languages: French
Work: C1 D1 E F1 G H J1 K1 K3 K4 L N O P Q R1 S1 S2 T2 V W X Z(j,l,r)
Emergency Action, Agency, Advocacy, Fixed Fee Interview, Legal Aid undertaken, Legal Aid Franchise and Member of Accident Line
Ptr: Saulet, Mr John R Notary Public. . . . . *Jan 1973
Townsend, Mr Robin N I LLB . . . . *Dec 1980
Ast: Egremont, Mr Nicholas J LLB . . . . *Jun 1972
Knight, Mr Robin R A MA(Cantab). . . . . *Oct 1961
Con: Pyne, Mr A Roger J MA(Oxon) ♦ . . . . *Feb 1963

WOODGATE & CO ‡
95-97 Palmerston Road Southsea Portsmouth PO5 3PR
Tel: 023 9283 5790 *Fax:* 023 9229 1413
E-mail: kwoodgate@woodgateandco.co.uk

SOUTHWELL, Nottinghamshire

KIRKLAND & LANE ‡
(in association with Freeth Cartwright)
North Muskham Prebend Church Street Southwell Nottinghamshire NG25 0HQ
Tel: 01636 813128 / 812180 *Fax:* 01636 815135
Dx: 11630 SOUTHWELL
E-mail: kirklandlane@hotmail.com
List of partners: C S Beaumont, J L Carpenter, V J Hood-Williams
Languages: French
Work: A1 A2 C1 D1 E F1 J1 K1 L M2 N Q S1 T1 W Z(c,d,e)
Fixed Fee Interview undertaken
Ptr: Beaumont, Mr Charles S BA . . . . *§Feb 1987
Carpenter, Mrs Joanna Louise LLB . . . . *Sep 1991
Hood-Williams, Ms Vanessa Jane BA . . . . *Mar 1984
Con: Clarke, Mr Barrie . . . . Jan 1969
Gouldingay, Ms Wendy E . . . . *Oct 1985

TALLENTS SOLICITORS
2 Westgate Southwell Nottinghamshire NG25 0JJ
Tel: 01636 813411 *Fax:* 01636 815314 *Dx:* 11631 SOUTHWELL
E-mail: info@tallents.co.uk
Office: Mansfield, Newark
Work: A1 C1 C2 C3 D1 E F1 G J1 K1 L M1 M2 N P S1 T1 T2 W Z(d,k,l)
Emergency Action, Agency, Advocacy, Fixed Fee Interview, Legal Aid undertaken and Member of Accident Line
Ptr: Millar, Mr Alistair John LLB(Hons); PGDip . . . . . . *Oct 1996
Ast: Farnill, Mrs Ann. . . . . Aug 2004
Watts, Mrs Jacqueline Ruth BSc; DipLaw Notary Public*Oct 2003

SOUTHWICK, West Sussex

PB LAW ‡
Bank House Southwick Square Southwick West Sussex BN42 4EY
Tel: 01273 592624 *Fax:* 01273 595487
E-mail: office@pblaw.co.uk
Work: A1 B1 C1 C2 D1 E F1 J1 K1 L N O P Q R1 S1 S2 V W Z(d,q,r,u)
Emergency Action, Agency, Advocacy, Legal Aid undertaken and Legal Aid Franchise

SOUTHWOLD, Suffolk

MANTINS SOLICITORS & NOTARIES ‡
82 High Street Southwold Suffolk IP18 6DP
Tel: 01502 724750 *Fax:* 01502 797930
E-mail: enquiries@mantins.co.uk

MARGARY & MILLER
73-73a High Street Southwold Suffolk IP18 6DS
Tel: 01502 723308 *Fax:* 01502 723430
E-mail: info@margary-miller.co.uk
Office: Felixstowe, Woodbridge (2 offices)
Languages: German
Work: A1 C1 E K4 S1 S2 T2 W Z(d)
Fixed Fee Interview undertaken and Member of Accident Line
Ptr: Gaffney, Mr David John LLB; LLM. . . . . Jun 1976

SPALDING, Lincolnshire

CCW SOLICITORS ‡
Manorcrown Business Centre 5a Sheepmarket Spalding Lincolnshire PE11 1BE
Tel: 01775 718669 *Fax:* 01775 714735
E-mail: andrew.cogan@ccwsolicitors.co.uk

CALTHROPS ‡
11 Market Place Spalding Lincolnshire PE11 1SP
Tel: 01775 724381 *Fax:* 01775 722286 *Dx:* 26704 SPALDING
List of partners: K Pallister, J A Sutton, B K Tatnall
Office: Holbeach
Work: A1 B1 C1 D1 E F1 G H J1 K1 L M1 N P R1 S1 V W Z(c,d,e,i,j,k,l,m)
Emergency Action, Agency, Advocacy, Fixed Fee Interview, Legal Aid undertaken and Member of Accident Line
Ptr: Pallister, Mr Kevin LLB . . . . *Mar 1987
Sutton, Mr James A LLB(Nott'm) . . . . *Mar 1986
Tatnall, Mr B Keith . . . . *Jul 1976
Ast: Bowker, Mr Robert H . . . . *Dec 1976
Stringfellow, Miss Belinda J LLB. . . . . *Nov 1988
Con: Frost, Mr Peter G FCIArb . . . . *§Apr 1964

CHATTERTONS SOLICITORS
(incorporating Knipe Miller & Co Solicitors LLP)
Dembleby House 12 Broad Street Spalding Lincolnshire PE11 1ES
Tel: 01775 768774 *Dx:* 26705 SPALDING
E-mail: post@chattertons.com
Office: Boston (2 offices), Grantham, Horncastle, Lincoln, Newark, Sleaford, Stamford
Work: A1 C1 C2 E J1 L S1 S2 T1 T2 W Z(d,o)
Legal Aid Franchise
Ptr: Burns, Mr Peter J BSc; PhD. . . . . *Oct 2000
Cunnington, Mrs Caroline E LLB . . . . *Oct 1988
Hopkins, Mrs Elizabeth Mary LLB(Hons). . . . . . . *Oct 1988
Knipe, Mr Richard A LLB; LLM; MSc(L'pool). . . . . *§Sep 1973
Miller, Mrs Dianne L LLB(Leics) . . . . *§Nov 1980
Con: Start, Mr Peter . . . . *§Apr 1971

MAPLES SOLICITORS LLP ‡
23 New Road Spalding Lincolnshire PE11 1DH
Tel: 01775 722261 *Fax:* 01775 767525 *Dx:* 26706 SPALDING
E-mail: enquiries@maplessolicitors.com
List of partners: D Hicken, J Mawer, C McGregor, D J Naghen, M H Pepper, G Shackleston, A L Toal, J J W Turner
Languages: French, German
Work: A1 A2 B1 B2 C1 C2 C3 D1 D2 E F1 F2 G H J1 J2 K1 K3 K4 L M1 M2 N O P Q R1 R2 S1 S2 T1 T2 V W X Z(c,d,e,g,i,j,k,l,m,o,p,q,r,s,t,u,w,y)
Emergency Action, Agency, Advocacy, Fixed Fee Interview, Legal Aid undertaken, Legal Aid Franchise and Member of Accident Line
Ptr: Naghen, Mr Daven James LLB; LPC . . . . *Sep 2003
Mem: Hicken, Mr David LLB(Sheff) . . . . *Oct 1984
McGregor, Ms Catherine . . . . *Sep 1999
Mawer, Miss Jane LLB . . . . *Sep 2002
Pepper, Mr Michael H MA(Cantab) . . . . *Apr 1981
Shackleston, Mr Grant LLB . . . . *§Oct 1995
Toal, Mrs Anita Lorraine LLB(Hons) . . . . *Oct 1991
Turner, Mr James Jonathon W . . . . *Sep 1996
Con: Lewis, Mr Richard W LLM(Lond) . . . . *Dec 1974

P J LEGAL ‡
Coubro Chambers 11 West End Holbech Spalding Lincolnshire PE12 7LW
Tel: 01406 420023 *Fax:* 01406 423496
E-mail: info@pjlegal.com
List of partners: P J Enstone
SPr: Enstone, Miss Philippa Jane LLB(Hons). . . . . . . *Feb 1991

THE RINGROSE LAW GROUP- CHRISTINE PICKWELL
24 The Crescent Spalding Lincolnshire PE11 1AF
Tel: 01775 662662 *Fax:* 01775 712316
E-mail: christine.pickwell@ringroselaw.co.uk
Office: Boston, Grantham, Lincoln (2 offices), Newark, Sleaford

ROYTHORNES LLP ‡
Enterprise Way Pinchbeck Spalding Lincolnshire PE11 3YR
Tel: 01775 842500 *Fax:* 01775 725736 *Dx:* 744230 SPALDING 6
E-mail: roythorne@roythorne.co.uk
List of partners: C P Bennett, P J Brewster, D J Brown, P Cookson, A M Czajka, S J Disley, M W Fielding, T G Foottit, C M Gumbrell, J J Ladds, V Mortlock, F Muldoon, P R Osborne, A J Plummer, G C H Smith, V A R Stevenson, C Thompson, J M Williams, J Wright
Office: Newmarket, Nottingham, Peterborough
Languages: French
Work: A1 A2 A3 B1 B2 C1 C2 C3 D1 E F1 F2 G H J1 J2 K1 K2 K3 K4 L M1 M2 N O P Q R1 R2 S1 S2 T1 T2 U1 V W Z(c,d,e,h,j,k,l,n,o,p,q,r,s,t,y,z,za)
Agency, Advocacy, Fixed Fee Interview undertaken and Member of Accident Line
Ptr: Bennett, Mr C Peter. . . . . *§Jul 1976
Brewster, Mr Philip J MA(Cantab) . . . . *§Jun 1974
Brown, Mrs Deborah Jane MA(Hons); PGDipLaw . . . Mar 2004
Disley, Mr Simeon J BCom(Hons). . . . . *Sep 1997
Foottit, Mr Thomas G LLB(Leeds). . . . . *§Nov 1986
Gumbrell, Mrs Caroline Marie BA(Hons). . . . . . . *Feb 1998
Ladds, Miss Johan Jamieson BA . . . . *Sep 1997
Mortlock, Ms Vember . . . . *Oct 1995
Osborne, Mr Paul R BA. . . . . *§Apr 1980
Plummer, Mr Alan J BSc(Edin) . . . . *§Jun 1979
Stevenson, Ms Victoria Alexandra Rower BA(Hons). . *§Apr 1994
Wright, Mr Jarred . . . . *Sep 2000
Asoc: Banks, Miss Sally Anne . . . . *Sep 2000
Hallmark, Mrs Rachel LLB. . . . . *Sep 2003
Lazell, Mr Adrian John BA. . . . . *Dec 1994
Ast: Barker, Ms Emily LLB(Hons) . . . . Mar 2006
Boon, Mr John Anthony LLB . . . . Jul 2008
Cooper, Mrs Ruth LLB . . . . *Sep 2008
Dempsey, Mr Robert John MA(Hons)(Law) . . . . . . *Sep 2004
Hines, Miss Nicola LLB . . . . Jun 2007
Hodgetts, Ms Laura. . . . . Sep 2006
Hope, Miss Victoria Caroline LLB . . . . Sep 2004
Whitmore, Mr Michael S BA(Hons) . . . . *Oct 1983

SILLS & BETTERIDGE LLP
Welland Workspace 10 Pinchbeck Road Spalding Lincolnshire PE11 1PZ
Tel: 01775 714874 *Fax:* 01775 710996
E-mail: info@sillslegal.co.uk
Web: www.sillslegal.co.uk
Office: Boston, Coningsby, Gainsborough, Lincoln, Skegness, Sleaford, Spilsby
Ptr: Johnson, Mrs Caroline LLB(Hons). . . . . *Sep 1999

SPENNYMOOR, Co Durham

EVANS & CO ‡
33a Cheapside Spennymoor Co Durham DL16 6QF
Tel: 01388 815317 *Fax:* 01388 811605
E-mail: spennymoor@evansco.co.uk
List of partners: C M Bond, R G Evans, D A Swinburn
Office: Ferryhill
Work: C1 D1 E F1 G K1 K3 L N S1 S2 T1 T2 W Z(d,l,m)
Emergency Action, Agency, Advocacy, Fixed Fee Interview and Legal Aid undertaken
Ptr: Bond, Mrs Christina M LLB(Leeds) . . . . *Apr 1977
Evans, Mr Robert G LLB; LLM; TEP. . . . . *Nov 1975
Swinburn, Mrs Debra A LLB. . . . . *§Oct 1992

FREEMAN JOHNSON
(incorporating Clinton Clarke & Coia)
11-12 Whitworth Terrace Spennymoor Co Durham DL16 7LD
Tel: 01388 814389 *Fax:* 0845 389 3202 *Dx:* 60451 SPENNYMOOR
E-mail: spennymoor@freemanjohnson.co.uk
Office: Darlington, Durham, Northallerton
Work: B1 C1 D1 D2 F1 F2 G H J1 K1 L M1 P Q S1 V W Z(l,r)
Emergency Action, Agency, Advocacy, Fixed Fee Interview, Legal Aid undertaken and Member of Accident Line
Asoc: Blakey, Miss Lorraine LLB. . . . . Nov 1999
Swan, Mr Andrew LLB(Hons) . . . . Jul 2002
Ast: Nunn, Ms Natalie Jane . . . . Oct 2004

MEIKLES
2 Clyde Terrace Spennymoor Co Durham DL16 7SE
Tel: 01388 814336 *Fax:* 01388 420612 *Dx:* 60450 SPENNYMOOR
E-mail: enquiries.spennymoor@meikles-solicitors.co.uk
Office: Barnard Castle, Bishop Auckland, Ferryhill, Stockton-on-Tees
Work: D1 D2 F1 G H J1 K1 L N Q S1 V W
Emergency Action, Agency, Advocacy, Fixed Fee Interview and Legal Aid undertaken
Ptr: Steinberg, Miss Lyanne Melissa. . . . . Oct 1996
Con: Welsh, Miss Karin E LLB . . . . *Oct 1984

SPILSBY, Lincolnshire

SILLS & BETTERIDGE LLP
1 Ashby Road Spilsby Lincolnshire PE23 5DT
Tel: 01790 752277 *Fax:* 01790 754229 *Dx:* 27953 SPILSBY
Emergency telephone 01790 752173
E-mail: info@sillslegal.co.uk
Web: www.sillslegal.co.uk
Office: Boston, Coningsby, Gainsborough, Lincoln, Skegness, Sleaford, Spalding
Work: A1 E L S1
Emergency Action, Agency, Advocacy, Fixed Fee Interview, Legal Aid undertaken and Member of Accident Line
Ptr: Stapleton, Mr David P. . . . . *Aug 2000

TINN CRIDDLE & CO
6 High Street Spilsby Lincolnshire PE23 5JH
Tel: 01790 756810 *Fax:* 01790 756807
E-mail: enquiries@tinncriddle.co.uk
Office: Alford, Sutton-on-Sea
Work: A2 C1 D1 E F1 J1 K1 K2 K3 L O Q R1 S1 S2 U1 W Z(c)

ST AGNES, Cornwall

DAVIES PARTNERSHIP
6 Vicarage Road Carrick St Agnes Cornwall TR5 0TJ
Tel: 01872 553131 *Fax:* 01872 553860
E-mail: davies.partnership@virgin.net
Office: Helston
Work: E K4 L S1 S2 T1 T2 W
Legal Aid Franchise
Ptr: Martin, Mr Keith LLB Tribunal Judge. . . . . *Mar 1974

ST ALBANS, Hertfordshire

ADB LAW ‡
3 Kenton Gardens St Albans Hertfordshire AL1 1JS
Tel: 01727 842586
E-mail: andrew@adblaw.co.uk

BEST SOLICITORS LLP ‡
Fountain Court Victoria Square Victoria Street St Albans Hertfordshire AL2 3EB
Tel: 01727 884688
E-mail: family@bestsolicitorsllp.co.uk
Work: K1

BLAVO & CO SOLICITORS
Phoenix House Suites 2 & 3 63 Campfield Road St Albans Hertfordshire AL1 5FL
Tel: 01727 732800 *Fax:* 01727 835344
E-mail: enquiries@legalblavo.co.uk
Office: Enfield, Guildford, London EC2, London N3, London WC1, Uxbridge

BRETHERTON LAW ‡
1st Floor Alban Row 27-31 Verulam Road St Albans Hertfordshire AL3 4DG
Tel: 01727 869293 *Fax:* 01727 853767
E-mail: info@brethertonlaw.co.uk
List of partners: S M Bradley
Ptr: Bradley, Mrs Sandra M LLB. . . . . *Oct 1982
Ast: Cantaris, Mr Costa LLB . . . . *Jun 2006
Humphrey, Mr Paul LLB; DMS . . . . Jul 2002
Larkins, Mrs Louise LLB; PGDip. . . . . Sep 2001
Prince, Miss Debra LLB(Hons) . . . . *May 2008
Stuart, Ms Alison BA(Hons). . . . . Sep 2003
White, Miss Suzanne LLB. . . . . Jun 2006
Con: Kent, Mr Bruce S BA . . . . Apr 1979
Thomas, Mr Edward G LLB Deputy Coroner. . . . . . Jun 1972

BRYAN & MERCER ‡
(incorporating Bryan & Gordon)
59 London Road St Albans Hertfordshire AL1 1LJ
Tel: 01727 861414 *Fax:* 01727 834518 *Dx:* 6147 ST ALBANS
E-mail: enquiries@bryanandmercer.co.uk
List of partners: R A Bryan, G D Mercer
Work: C1 E L R1 S1 W
Ptr: Bryan, Mr Rex A . . . . *Feb 1967
Mercer, Mr Graeme D LLB . . . . *Jul 1981

CARR & CO ‡
103 Dunstable Road Redbourn St Albans Hertfordshire AL3 7PR
Tel: 01727 866155 *Fax:* 01727 836908 *Dx:* 1495 ST ALBANS 23
E-mail: susan@carr-co.net
List of partners: S S Carr
Work: C1 E S1 S2
Agency undertaken
SPr: Carr, Mrs Shani Susan LLB . . . . *Oct 1986

CITY LAWYERS ‡
5 Woodland Court Soothouse Spring St Albans Hertfordshire AL3 6NR
Tel: 01727 739774

CLAYTONS ‡
Holywell Lodge 41 Holywell Hill St Albans Hertfordshire AL1 1HD
Tel: 01727 865765 *Fax:* 01727 844736 *Dx:* 133337 ST ALBANS 14
E-mail: dcheetham@claytonssolicitors.co.uk
List of partners: D N Cheetham, A P Stovin
Work: E L S1 Z(d,x)
Ptr: Cheetham, Mr David N Diocesan Registrar; Legal Secretary to Bishop . . . *§Jul 1971
Stovin, Mr Andrew P LLB(Lond) . . . *Oct 1980

COPLEY DAVIES ‡
45 Battlefield Road St Albans Hertfordshire AL1 4DB
Tel: 01727 764978 *Fax:* 01727 764829
List of partners: J C P Copley
Work: J1 O Q Z(p)
Agency undertaken
SPr: Copley, Mrs Joanna C P LLB . . . Oct 1989

GORDON DE VERE
99 Gurney Court Road St Albans Hertfordshire AL1 4QX
Tel: 01727 758126 *Fax:* 01727 758126
Office: Pinner
Work: S2
Ptr: De Vere, Miss Lauren LLB(Hons) . . . Nov 2000

DEBENHAMS OTTAWAY ‡
Ivy House 107 St Peters Street St Albans Hertfordshire AL1 3EW
Tel: 01727 837161 *Fax:* 01727 830506 *Dx:* 6105 ST ALBANS
E-mail: lawyers@turnerdebs.co.uk
List of partners: L Attrup, B A Brennan, K E Carroll, S P Chadwick, C J Debenham, R E Debenham, G D A Elgood, J D Foy, S Glenholme, B Hillman, D D Keegan, H J Kent, N A G Turner, H Young
Office: Radlett
Languages: French, German, Greek, Italian, Punjabi
Work: A3 C1 D1 E J1 K1 K3 N O Q S1 S2 W Z(j,q)
Emergency Action, Agency, Advocacy, Fixed Fee Interview, Legal Aid Franchise and Member of Accident Line
Ptr: Attrup, Mrs Louise . . . Sep 1998
Brennan, Mrs Brigid A LLB(Nott'm) . . . *§Apr 1979
Carroll, Mrs Kate Elizabeth . . . *Jan 1988
Chadwick, Mr Stephen P BA . . . *§Jun 1979
Debenham, Mr Christopher J . . . *§Jun 1977
Debenham, Mr Richard E . . . *§Feb 1970
Foy, Mr Jonathan Dominic BA(Hons)(European Finance & Accounting) Notary Public . . . *§Jul 1997
Glenholme, Mrs Susan LLB . . . *§Oct 1998
Hillman, Mrs Bernadette . . . Apr 1990
Keegan, Mr Denis Damian . . . *§Jun 1985
Kent, Mr Howard James . . . *Oct 1984
Turner, Mr Nicholas A G LLB(Hons)(Lond) . . . *§Apr 1981
Young, Miss Helen . . . *Dec 1989
Asoc: Gilbert, Mr Richard Michael LLB(Hons) . . . *§Sep 1996
Ast: Anstis, Ms Caroline LLB . . . *Sep 2006
Bailey, Mrs Anna M . . . *§Oct 1997
Bridel, Miss Victoria LLB . . . *§Sep 2005
Brooks, Mr Richard . . . *Jul 1973
Hall, Mrs Sacha LLB . . . *§Sep 1996
Harding, Miss Karen A LLB . . . *§Jul 2000
Harrison, Mr Luke Tucker LLB . . . *Sep 2006
Harvey, Mrs Janet BA(Hons) . . . *Sep 2003
Henry, Ms Amanda LLB . . . *Sep 2006
Mendham, Mr Stephen . . . Oct 1983
Mulley, Mr Hugh LLB . . . Oct 1990
Rajaratnam, Miss Mrinalini . . . *Dec 1992
Sharp, Ms Claire LLB . . . *§Sep 2005
Smith, Miss Angela . . . *Oct 1988
Stevens, Mr Mark LLB . . . Sep 2007
Tucker, Mr Simon . . . Oct 1983
Whiteley, Miss Helen . . . *Jan 1981
Williams, Miss Susannah BA(Hons) . . . Sep 2007
Wilson, Mrs Rachel . . . Jun 2008
Con: Raine, Mr Douglas . . . *Jun 1970

EDMONDSONS ‡
181 Ridgeway St Albans Hertfordshire AL4 9XE
Tel: 01727 866497 *Fax:* 01727 866497
E-mail: edmondsons.solicitors@btinternet.com
List of partners: S D Edmondson
Work: D2 J1 K1 O Q S1 S2 W
Fixed Fee Interview undertaken
SPr: Edmondson, Mr Stephen David BA(Law) . . . *Oct 1986

FINANCIAL MARKETS LAW INTERNATIONAL ‡
Netherley House 18 Watford Road St Albans Hertfordshire AL1 2AJ
Tel: 01727 845897 *Fax:* 01727 855838
E-mail: info@fmli.co.uk

HSCO SOLICITORS ‡
1-7 Victoria Street St Albans Hertfordshire AL1 3JG
Tel: 01727 738538

RALPH HARING SOLICITORS ‡
1 Stonecross St Albans Hertfordshire AL1 4AA
Tel: 01727 843576 / 07831 110528
E-mail: ralph@ralaw.co.uk

LINDA HOLLOWAY & CO ‡
97b Sandpit Lane St Albans Hertfordshire AL1 4BN
Tel: 01727 841651 *Fax:* 01727 835494
E-mail: linda.holloway@ntlworld.com
List of partners: L H Holloway
Work: K4 S1 W
SPr: Holloway, Mrs Linda Helene LLB(Lond) . . . *Oct 1977

JCS SOLICITORS ‡
Hill House 1 St Albans Road Codicote St Albans Hertfordshire SG4 8UT
Tel: 01438 820946 *Fax:* 01438 821340
E-mail: info@jcssolicitors.co.uk

JONES CLARKE LIMITED ‡
14 Damson Way St Albans Hertfordshire AL4 9XU
Tel: 01727 845101

LABRUMS ‡
New Barns Mill Cotton Mill Lane St Albans Hertfordshire AL1 2HA
Tel: 01727 858807 *Fax:* 01727 841827
E-mail: gec@labrums-sols.co.uk
List of partners: J C Harrison, M J Labrum
Languages: Spanish
Work: C1 C2 E F1 J1 K1 K3 L N O Q S1 S2 W Z(q)
Fixed Fee Interview undertaken
Ptr: Harrison, Mr John C BA . . . *Nov 1981
Labrum, Mr Michael John LLB(Hons) . . . *Jun 1980
Ast: Darbyshire, Miss Karen E LLB(Hons); LSF . . . *Feb 1992

MCILLMURRAYS SOLICITORS
Suite 4 Arquen House 4-6 Spicer Street St Albans Hertfordshire AL3 4PQ
Tel: 01727 221655 *Fax:* 01727 220814
E-mail: info@mcillmurrays.com
Office: Leeds

MCKEOWNS SOLICITORS LTD ‡
8 The Parkway Porters Wood St Albans Hertfordshire AL3 6PA
Tel: 0800 032 8328 *Fax:* 01727 838118 *Dx:* 153940 ST ALBANS
E-mail: personalinjury@mckeowns.com
List of partners: D McKeown
Office: Milton Keynes
Work: N Z(r)
Ptr: McKeown, Mr Diarmuid BA . . . *Dec 1990
Ast: Burns, Ms Helen . . . Dec 2006
Campion, Mr Kieron . . . May 2008
Carter, Mr John BA . . . Apr 1991
Dillon, Mr John-Paul . . . Jun 2008
Doran, Mr Stephen . . . Jun 2007
Ejikeme, Ms Isabelle . . . Feb 2004
Harris, Mr Geraint James LLB . . . *Mar 1992
Hayes, Mr Sean . . . Jul 2007
Lawrence, Mr Daniel . . . Apr 2010
McKinney, Mr Stephen Joseph . . . Jul 2008
Matthews, Ms Suzanne . . . Jan 2005
Sanders, Ms Anne . . . Feb 1999

ALAN MANN & CO ‡
80a Victoria Street St Albans Hertfordshire AL1 3XH
Tel: 01727 833281 / 846012 *Fax:* 01727 840116
List of partners: A R Mann
Work: E L S1 S2 W
SPr: Mann, Mr Alan R BA . . . *Jun 1980

MELDRUM YOUNG SOLICITORS ‡
Trident House 42-48 Victoria Street St Albans Hertfordshire AL1 3HZ
Tel: 01727 840333 *Fax:* 01727 845137 *Dx:* 6165 ST ALBANS
Emergency telephone 07699 113300 (REF 767428)
List of partners: A Kerry, A R J Meldrum
Office: Hertford, Watford
Work: B2 G H
Emergency Action, Agency, Advocacy and Legal Aid undertaken
Ast: Hobdell, Mr Andrew LLB . . . *Nov 1996

I A MORCOWITZ ‡
2 Corringham Court Lemsford Road St Albans Hertfordshire AL1 3PA
Tel: 01727 840570

ONHAND COUNSEL LIMITED ‡
114a Old London Road St Albans Hertfordshire AL1 1PU
Tel: 01727 867289
E-mail: andrew.james@onhandcounsel.co.uk

PHOTIADES ‡
Longmire House 36-38 London Road St Albans Hertfordshire AL1 1NG
Tel: 01727 833134 *Fax:* 01727 841074 *Dx:* 6106 ST ALBANS
E-mail: postmaster@photiades.com
List of partners: J M Cox, W J Harvey, K R Parsons, J G P Photiades, D A Shiebert
Office: Harpenden
Work: C1 D1 E I J1 K1 K2 K3 L N O Q S1 S2 T1 T2 U2 W
Ptr: Harvey, Mr William J LLB . . . *Nov 1990
Parsons, Mr Kevin R BA(Law) . . . *May 1981
Shiebert, Mr David A BA(Cantab) . . . *Apr 1986

RAYDEN SOLICITORS ‡
21 Victoria Street St Albans Hertfordshire AL1 3JJ
Tel: 020 7112 1453 *Fax:* 020 7112 2399 *Dx:* 122734 ST.ALBANS 10
E-mail: info@raydensolicitors.co.uk

REXTON LAW LLP ‡
The Old Post Office 38 South Riding Bricket Wood St Albans Hertfordshire AL2 3NE
Tel: 020 8819 5899 *Fax:* 01923 674776 *Dx:* 89559 RADLETT
E-mail: admin@rextonlaw.co.uk

SA LAW ‡
Keystone 60 London Road St Albans Hertfordshire AL1 1NG
Tel: 01727 798000 *Fax:* 01727 798002 *Dx:* 122730 ST ALBANS 10
Emergency telephone 07666 731894
E-mail: marketing@pictons.co.uk
List of partners: P W Baines, M Bell, C Brown, R E J Ryall, S J Ryan, C Wilks
Languages: French, German
Work: B1 C1 C2 C3 D1 E F1 G H J1 K1 K2 L N O Q R1 S1 T1 T2 U2 V W Z(c,e,f,j,k,l,p,r,s,t,w)
Emergency Action, Agency, Advocacy, Fixed Fee Interview, Legal Aid undertaken, Legal Aid Franchise and Member of Accident Line
Ptr: Baines, Mr Peter W . . . *Jan 1969
Bell, Mrs Marilyn BSc(Hons) University of Hertfordshire Ottaways Prize 1992 . . . *Nov 1995
Brown, Mr Christopher LLB . . . *Jun 1969
Ryall, Mr Robert Edward Joseph LLB . . . *Dec 1994
Ryan, Mr Stephen J LLB . . . *Oct 1983
Wilks, Mr Christopher BA(Law) . . . *Oct 1983
Ast: Dunne, Ms Caroline LLB(Hons); LLM . . . Aug 1995
McDonald, Mr Glenn BSc; CPE; LPC . . . Apr 1999
Thirlway, Ms H Margaret W BA . . . *Nov 1989
Con: Knight, Mr Robert John John Mackrell Prize; Charles Steele City of London Solicitors Co Prize 1969 . . . *Jan 1969

DEBORAH A SABALOT REGULATORY CONSULTING ‡
24 Harvesters Jersey Farm St Albans Hertfordshire AL4 9QU
Tel: 01727 859434
E-mail: dsabalot@netcomuk.co.uk
List of partners: D Sabalot
Languages: German
Work: C1 U2 Z(b)
Ptr: Sabalot, Ms Deborah BA(Louisiana) . . . Nov 1992

SHALLCROSS & CO ‡
25 Verulam Road St Albans Hertfordshire AL3 4DG
Tel: 01727 847804 *Fax:* 01727 841117 *Dx:* 6152 ST ALBANS
E-mail: r.shallcross@btopenworld.com
List of partners: R A Shallcross
Work: B1 C1 C2 C3 E L O Q S1 S2 W Z(c,j)
Ptr: Shallcross, Mr Robert A . . . *Jul 1976

SHERRARDS ‡
45 Grosvenor Road St Albans Hertfordshire AL1 3AW
Tel: 01727 832830 *Fax:* 01727 832833 *Dx:* 141853 ST ALBANS 17
E-mail: law@sherrards.com
List of partners: A V L Drake, T E Fendt, G P Lunnon, P D Marmor, A P McMillin, M A Peters, D S Staal, R J Staal
Office: London W1
Languages: Dutch, French, German, Hebrew, Italian, Spanish
Work: A3 B1 B2 C1 C2 C3 E F1 F2 I J1 J2 K4 L M1 M2 O P Q R1 R2 S1 S2 T2 U1 U2 W X Z(b,c,e,f,g,h,k,l,p,w,z,za)
Ptr: Drake, Ms Alexandra V L BA(Durham) . . . *Apr 1989
Fendt, Mr Terence Edward LLB(Hons) . . . *Sep 1989
Lunnon, Mr Gregory P LLB(Exon) . . . *Apr 1978
McMillin, Mr Alasdair P LLB . . . *Dec 1988
Marmor, Mr Paul David LLB . . . *Dec 1990
Peters, Mr Mark Andrew LLB(Hons) . . . *§Apr 1980
Ast: Dobson, Mrs Karen Patricia FILEx . . . *Oct 2004
Laurence, Mr Barnaby James LLB(Hons) . . . *Oct 2004
Stanley, Mrs Helen M BA(Hons) . . . *Oct 1988
Thompson, Miss Nicola BSc(Hons) . . . *Jul 1999
Wright, Miss Kelly-Lee LLB; LLM . . . *Nov 2002
Con: Ishani, Mr Manzoor Guliam Hussein Kassam MA . . . *Jun 1976

SONY SADAF HAROON SOLICITORS ‡
222 Hatfield Road St Albans Hertfordshire AL1 4LW
Tel: 01727 568353 *Fax:* 01727 834270
E-mail: info@sonylaw.com

ST ALBANS SOLICITORS ‡
Fountain Court 3 Victoria Court Victoria Street St Albans Hertfordshire AL1 3TF
Tel: 01727 884658 *Fax:* 01727 884800

JOHN STEPHENSON & CO ‡
Suite 2 7 French Row St Albans Hertfordshire AL3 5DU
Tel: 01727 847983 *Fax:* 01727 844337 *Dx:* 6136 ST ALBANS
E-mail: johnstephenson@globalnet.co.uk
List of partners: J M Stephenson
Languages: Hindi, Kiswahili, Punjabi, Urdu
Work: E F1 G H J1 K1 L N O Q S1 S2 V W Z(r)
Emergency Action, Agency, Advocacy, Fixed Fee Interview and Legal Aid undertaken
SPr: Stephenson, Mr John Mark BA(Law) . . . *Oct 1982

TAYLOR WALTON LLP
10 Bricket Road St Albans Hertfordshire AL1 3JA
Tel: 01727 845245 *Fax:* 01727 864970 *Dx:* 122713 ST ALBANS 9
E-mail: ian.riches@taylorwalton.co.uk
Office: Harpenden, Luton
Work: A1 B1 C1 C2 C3 D1 E F1 I J1 K1 L M1 M2 N O P Q R1 S1 T1 T2 W X Z(b,c,d,e,f,h,i,j,k,l,m,o,s)
Emergency Action, Advocacy, Fixed Fee Interview, Legal Aid undertaken, Legal Aid Franchise and Member of Accident Line
Ptr: Atkins, Mr Richard J LLB . . . *§Oct 1982
Crocker, Mr Richard BA . . . *Oct 1989
James, Mr John S P LLB(Wales) . . . *§Apr 1981
Shillabeer, Mr Trevor M BA . . . *§Dec 1977
Ast: Cox, Ms Kathryn . . . *Jan 1997
Haines, Mrs Hilary Frances MA(Cantab) . . . *Oct 1992
Stevens, Ms Sarah L BA . . . *Oct 1978

TILLEY & CO ‡
36 Holywell Hill St Albans Hertfordshire AL1 1BT
Tel: 01727 840467 *Fax:* 01727 863210 *Dx:* 133336 ST ALBANS 14
List of partners: D F Tilley
Work: B1 D1 E F1 G H J1 K1 L N P R1 S1 V W Z(k,l,m,p)
Emergency Action, Agency, Advocacy, Fixed Fee Interview, Legal Aid undertaken, Legal Aid Franchise and Member of Accident Line
Ptr: Tilley, Mr David F BA(Dunelm) . . . *Nov 1976

TOUCHSTONE LEGAL SERVICE ‡
199 Camp Road St Albans Hertfordshire AL1 5NB
Tel: 07787 283749
E-mail: sarah@touchstonels.com

WELLS BURCOMBE LLP
5 Holywell Hill St Albans Hertfordshire AL1 1EU
Tel: 01727 840900 *Fax:* 01727 840005 *Dx:* 6108 ST ALBANS
E-mail: info@wellsburcombe.co.uk
Office: West Drayton

WILLANS & CO LIMITED ‡
20 London Road St Albans Hertfordshire AL1 1NP
Tel: 01727 840549 *Fax:* 01727 843179
E-mail: philip@willansp.freeserve.co.uk
List of partners: P J Willans
Languages: German
Work: A3 C1 D1 E J1 K1 L N O Q S1 W Z(c,l,p)
Advocacy undertaken
Ptr: Willans, Mr Philip J • Part time Chairman Employment Tribunals . . . *Nov 1970

ANNE WOODCOCK & CO ‡
20 London Road St Albans Hertfordshire AL1 1NP
Tel: 01727 861212 *Fax:* 01727 864966 *Dx:* 6125 ST ALBANS
Emergency telephone 07990 574249
List of partners: A E Woodcock
Work: G H
Emergency Action, Agency and Legal Aid undertaken
SPr: Woodcock, Ms Anne E BA . . . Apr 1986

ST ASAPH, Denbighshire

TUDOR H DAVIES ‡
Barclays Bank Chambers High Street St Asaph Denbighshire LL17 0RF
Tel: 01745 583806 *Fax:* 01745 582613 *Dx:* 18230 ST ASAPH
List of partners: T H Davies
Work: E R1 S1 W
Agency and Legal Aid undertaken

See p112 for the Key to Work Categories & other symbols

JOSEPH LLOYD ‡
Elwy Grove The Roe St Asaph Denbighshire LL17 0LY
Tel: 01745 583648 *Fax:* 01745 583523
E-mail: joelloyduk@aol.com

MACKENZIE JONES ‡
26 St Asaph Business Park St Asaph Denbighshire LL17 0LJ
Tel: 01745 536030 *Fax:* 01745 536040 *Dx:* 18235 ST ASAPH
E-mail: mailroom@macjones.com
List of partners: J J Burnett, A P Foley Jones, R D Jones
Office: Prestatyn
Languages: Welsh
Work: B1 C1 C2 E F1 J1 K1 K2 K3 L N O Q R2 S1 S2 Z(c,e,l,r)
Agency, Advocacy and Fixed Fee Interview undertaken
Dir: Burnett, Mr John Joseph LLB(Hons). . . . . *Nov 1997
Foley Jones, Mr Andrew Paul LLB(Hons) . . . . Oct 1997
Jones, Mr Richard D LLB(Hons). . . . . *Oct 1988
Ast: Evans, Miss Anna Jane LLB(Hons) . . . . *Dec 2002
Owens, Miss Karen Morris LLB(Hons). . . . . Jan 2006

JOHN OWENS SOLICITOR ‡
Hanover House The Roe St Asaph Denbighshire LL17 0LT
Tel: 01745 582333 *Fax:* 01745 582777
E-mail: john.owens.solicitor@ic24.net
List of partners: J T E Owens
Languages: Welsh
Work: B1 C1 E F1 J1 K1 K3 L N O Q S1 S2 W Z(k)
SPr: Owens, Mr John T E LLB(Wales) . . . . *§Jan 1979

SWAYNE JOHNSON SOLICITORS
Church House High Street St Asaph Denbighshire LL17 0RD
Tel: 01745 582535 *Fax:* 01745 584504 *Dx:* 18231 ST ASAPH
E-mail: law@swaynejohnson.com
Office: Denbigh, Llandudno, Ruthin
Languages: Welsh
Work: A1 C1 C3 D1 E F1 J1 K1 L N O P Q S1 S2 T1 T2 V W Z(c,d,k,l,q,r,x)
Emergency Action, Agency, Advocacy and Legal Aid undertaken
Dir: Chamberlain, Mr Richard C LLB(Lond) . . . . *Jun 1980
Lloyd, Mr Edward T A BA . . . . *Feb 1983
Con: Hooson, Mr David J LLB(Lond) Diocesan Registrar . *May 1967

ST AUSTELL, Cornwall

BRAINS ‡
Sydney House 44 South Street St Austell Cornwall PL25 5BN
Tel: 01726 68111 *Fax:* 01726 61433 *Dx:* 81252 ST AUSTELL
Emergency telephone 01726 68111
E-mail: info@brainssolicitors.co.uk
List of partners: J F Evans, M J Evans, S F Rogers
Office: Truro
Work: A1 B1 C1 D1 D2 E F1 F2 J1 J2 K1 K2 K3 K4 L N O Q R1 R2 S1 S2 T1 T2 W Z(c,d,h,l,q)
Emergency Action, Agency, Advocacy, Fixed Fee Interview, Legal Aid undertaken and Legal Aid Franchise
Ptr: Evans, Mrs Julie F LLB(Hons); TEP; CTAPS . . . . *Dec 2002
Evans, Mr Martyn Jonathan LLB(Hons); FABRP. . . . *Nov 1986
Ast: Symons, Miss Leanne LLB(Hons) Best European Law Student . . . . *Feb 2008
Wood, Mr Thomas Joseph LLB(Hons). . . . . *Nov 2009

COODES ‡
8 Market Street St Austell Cornwall PL25 4BB
Tel: 01726 874700 *Fax:* 01726 874799 *Dx:* 81250 ST AUSTELL
Emergency telephone 01726 874700
E-mail: enquiries@coodes.co.uk
List of partners: E G Alma, C P Andrews, L C P Bryant, A I Bunney, J Eade, L G Ford, K G E George, M J Gregson, J D Harvey, C J Hunter, P J Johns, P Lamble, A S H Marshall, R M Pollock, L A Southwell, H A Stokes, I Taylor, K Theophilus, A J Whyte, C Wilson
Office: Holsworthy, Launceston, Liskeard, Newquay, Penzance, Truro
Work: A1 C1 D1 E F1 G H J1 K1 L N P Q S1 S2 T1 T2 U2 V W Z(d,l,m,n,q,r)
Emergency Action, Agency, Advocacy, Fixed Fee Interview, Legal Aid undertaken and Legal Aid Franchise
Ptr: Alma, Ms Elise G LLB(Warw) . . . . *Oct 1987
Harvey, Mr Jeremy D LLB(Nott'm). . . . . *Apr 1981
Hunter, Mr Colin Joseph LLB(Hons). . . . . *Mar 1994
Taylor, Mr Ian LLB Honorary Solicitor to St Austell CAB . . . . *Nov 1991
Theophilus, Mrs Kate LLB. . . . . §Apr 1986
Eade, Mr Jonathan . . . . NSP
Ast: Griffin, Emma. . . . . Feb 2001
Theobald, Miss Lucy . . . . Sep 2004

CORNWALL DEFENCE SOLICITORS ‡
Unit 15 Victoria Trading Estate Victoria Business Park St Austell Cornwall PL26 8LX
Tel: 01726 892842 *Fax:* 01726 892850
E-mail: office@cornwalldefencesolicitors.co.uk
Office: Truro

FAMILY LAW IN CORNWALL ‡
PO Box 268 St Austell Cornwall PL25 9ES
Tel: 0845 604 2985
E-mail: cornlaw@live.com

NALDERS QUALITY SOLICITORS
Cannis House Chapmans Way St Austell Cornwall PL25 4QU
Tel: 01726 879333 *Fax:* 01726 67401
E-mail: post@nalders.co.uk
Office: Camborne, Falmouth, Helston, Newquay, Penzance, Truro (2 offices)

STEPHENS & SCOWN
3 Cross Lane St Austell Cornwall PL25 4AX
Tel: 01726 74433 *Fax:* 01726 68623 *Dx:* 81251 ST AUSTELL
E-mail: solicitors@stephens-scown.co.uk
Office: Exeter, Truro
Languages: French, German, Spanish
Work: A1 A3 B1 C1 C2 C3 D1 D2 E F1 J1 J2 K1 K2 L M1 M2 N O P Q R1 R2 S1 S2 T1 T2 V W X Z(a,b,c,d,e,h,i,j,k,l,m,n,q,r,s,t)
Emergency Action, Agency, Advocacy, Fixed Fee Interview, Legal Aid undertaken, Legal Aid Franchise and Member of Accident Line
Ptr: Atkins, Mr Timothy R LLB(Hons) . . . . *Oct 1998
Bassett, Mr Alan Paul LLB(Lond) . . . . *Apr 1981
Beadel, Mr Michael J S LLB. . . . . *Oct 1984
Jones, Mr Richard P MA(Oxon) . . . . *Apr 1971
Lamond, Mr Ian Douglas MA(Dundee). . . . . *§Jul 1978
Lowry, Mr Michael P BA(Law) . . . . *May 1983
Marshall, Mr Peter Grant LLB . . . . *Apr 1990
Mitchell, Mr Scott BA(Hons). . . . . *§Oct 1995
Nicholls, Mrs Alison H L LLB Notary Public . . . . . . *§Oct 1990
Reed, Mr Philip Henry Under Sheriff of Cornwall. . . *§Oct 1995
Snell, Mr Philip G LLB(Lond) . . . . *§Jan 1979
Ast: Cahill, Miss Deborah LLB . . . . *Nov 1989
Cavell, Mrs F H LLB . . . . *Oct 1993
Cogar, Mr Richard Martin BA(Hons). . . . . *Feb 1999
Doble, Ms Emma LLB. . . . . Apr 2005
Fitzgerald, Ms Sarah LLB . . . . *Oct 1997
Hancock, Ms Sharon LLB . . . . *Jan 2005
Ware, Mrs Deborah Jayne LLB . . . . Nov 1987
Con: Church, Mr Jonathan F . . . . *Jan 1969
Evans, Mr John R P LLB Sir George Fowler Prize. . . *Jun 1968
Newbery, Mr James A. . . . . *Jan 1965

ST CLEARS, Carmarthenshire

LEWIS LEWIS & COMPANY LTD ‡
County Chamber Pentre Road St Clears Carmarthenshire SA33 4AA
Tel: 01994 231044 *Fax:* 01994 230791 *Dx:* 98375 ST CLEARS
E-mail: info@lewislewis.co.uk
List of partners: E G Lewis, J D R Lewis
Office: Carmarthen, Tenby
Work: A1 B1 C1 D1 E F1 G H J1 K1 L M1 N O P Q R1 S1 W
Emergency Action, Agency, Advocacy, Fixed Fee Interview and Legal Aid undertaken
Ptr: Lewis, Mr Edward G BA. . . . . *Dec 1983
Lewis, Mr James D R. . . . . *Mar 1986
Ast: Phillips, Mrs Anthea LLB . . . . Sep 1998
Phillips, Miss Catrin BA . . . . *Nov 1997
Williams, Mr Haydn LLB. . . . . *Nov 1978

ST HELENS, Merseyside

BARROW & COOK ‡
5-7 Victoria Street St Helens Merseyside WA10 1HH
Tel: 01744 23271 *Dx:* 19452 ST HELENS
Work: C1 E J1 K1 K2 K3 K4 L N O Q S1 S2 W Z(l,p)
Agency and Legal Aid undertaken

BARWISE & CO ‡
71 North Road St Helens Merseyside WA10 2TU
Tel: 0151 292 7800
E-mail: barwiselawfirm@tiscali.co.uk

CANTER LEVIN & BERG
Century House Hardshaw Street St Helens Merseyside WA10 1QW
Tel: 01744 634141 *Fax:* 01744 634146
E-mail: enquiries@canter-law.co.uk
Office: Kirkby, Liverpool
Emergency Action, Agency, Advocacy, Fixed Fee Interview, Legal Aid undertaken and Member of Accident Line
Ptr: Campbell, Claire . . . . Sep 2000
Houghton, Miss Romilly . . . . *Aug 1996
Jansz, Miss Claire LLB . . . . *Apr 2000
Smith, Mr Ian BA . . . . *May 1998
Asoc: Brown, Miss Rebecca P BA(Hons) . . . . *Feb 1999
Choudhuri, Debapriya. . . . . Apr 1994
Greenhalgh, Georgina. . . . . Dec 2008
Koucheksarai, Nadia . . . . Jul 2006
Logan, Samantha. . . . . Sep 2003
Steel, Cheryl . . . . Jun 2001
Templeton, Mr Steven. . . . . Aug 2003
West, Mrs Michele . . . . Sep 2001

FORSTER DEAN LTD
9 Hardshaw Street St Helens Merseyside WA10 1QX
Tel: 01744 755577 *Fax:* 01744 755588 *Dx:* 19464 ST HELENS 1
E-mail: enquiries@forsterdean.co.uk
Office: Birkenhead, Bootle, Chorley, Crewe, Eccles, Ellesmere Port, Huyton, Leigh, Liverpool (5 offices), Oldham, Preston, Rochdale, Runcorn, Stockport, Warrington, Widnes (2 offices), Wigan
Work: N S1 W
Fixed Fee Interview undertaken
Ast: Campbell, Mr Colin James DipLaw; LPC . . . . Jun 2000
Shields, Mr Gregory J LLB(Hons) . . . . *Mar 1999

FRODSHAMS ‡
(incorporating Charles E Harrison & Co)
19 Hardshaw Street St Helens Merseyside WA10 1RB
Tel: 01744 626600 *Fax:* 01744 626641
E-mail: info@frodshams.co.uk
List of partners: Y Hughes, H M Morris, M J Teinert, A Woods
Work: C1 E K4 L R2 S1 S2 W Z(h)
Ptr: Hughes, Mrs Yvonne LLB(Hons) . . . . *Jan 2008
Morris, Mr Howard M LLB. . . . . *Jun 1969
Teinert, Mr Michael John LLB(Hons). . . . . *Jul 2007
Woods, Miss Amanda LLB(Hons) . . . . *Aug 2002

HATTONS SOLICITORS ‡
Prudential Buildings 3 Victoria Square St Helens Merseyside WA10 1HQ
Tel: 01744 744400
Office: Widnes

HAYGARTH JONES ‡
66 Claughton Street St Helens Merseyside WA10 1SN

IAIN MACDONALD SOLICITORS ‡
89 Corporation Street St Helens Merseyside WA10 1SX
Tel: 01744 612549 *Fax:* 01744 733575
E-mail: enq@imslaw.co.uk

J KEITH PARK & CO ‡
Claughton House 39 Barrow Street St Helens Merseyside WA10 1RX
Tel: 01744 636000 *Fax:* 01744 451442 *Dx:* 19451 ST HELENS
List of partners: D S Achillies, I J Bates, N J Hall, J K Park
Languages: French, German, Russian
Work: A1 B1 C1 D1 E F1 G H K1 L N Q R1 S1 T1 V W Z(c,k,l,m,q,r)
Emergency Action, Agency, Advocacy, Fixed Fee Interview, Legal Aid undertaken, Legal Aid Franchise and Member of Accident Line
Ptr: Achillies, Mr David S LLB. . . . . *Jun 1987
Bates, Mr Ian J BA(Law) . . . . *Jun 1977
Hall, Mr Nicholas J MBA . . . . *Dec 1990
Park, Mr James K LLB(L'pool). . . . . *Nov 1970
Asoc: Williams, Ms Alison Jane . . . . Dec 2004
Ast: Crook, Mr Steven LLB. . . . . *Jun 1993
Moore, Miss Diane Louise BA; LPC . . . . Jan 2003
O'Neill, Miss Jennifer Clare LLB. . . . . Jul 2006
Parry, Miss Michaela LLB(Hons). . . . . Jul 2005
Price, Mr Stephen T LLB . . . . Mar 1980
Quigley, Mr Derek L LLB . . . . *Apr 1972
Wheeler, Miss Susie LLB(Hons). . . . . Jun 2006
Con: Shaw, Mr Geoffrey LLB . . . . *Apr 1970

POTTER JONES & CO ‡
7 George Street St Helens Merseyside WA10 1DA
Tel: 01744 730376 *Fax:* 01744 730397
List of partners: H M C Jones, P H Potter
Ptr: Jones, Mr Haydn M C LLB . . . . *§Jun 1990
Potter, Mr Paul Howard LLB. . . . . Sep 1994

FRANK ROE SOLICITORS ‡
Prudential Buildings 60 Claughton Street St Helens Merseyside WA10 1SN
Tel: 01744 24218 *Fax:* 01744 28851 *Dx:* 19459 ST HELENS
Emergency telephone 07710 482439
List of partners: F A Roe
Work: D1 G H K1
Emergency Action, Agency, Advocacy, Legal Aid undertaken and Legal Aid Franchise
Ptr: Roe, Mr Francis A LLB . . . . *Mar 1974

RUSHTON HINCHY SOLICITORS ‡
Unit 1 Mill Brook Business Park Mill Lane St Helens Merseyside WA11 8LZ
Tel: 0845 054 0564 *Fax:* 0845 054 0565
E-mail: info@rushtonhinchy.com
List of partners: C Allen, H Cliffe, C Hinchy, S Rushton
Dir: Allen, Mr Christopher . . . . Mar 2006
Cliffe, Hilary. Oct 2004
Hinchy, Carl. . . . . Feb 2003
Rushton, Mr Steven LLB; MA . . . . Aug 1997
Ast: Noonan, Lisa . . . . Oct 2006

SBW LAWYERS ‡
Cross House Sutton Road St Helens Merseyside WA9 3DR
Tel: 01744 762070 *Fax:* 01744 732328
E-mail: admin@sbwlawyers.com
Ast: Wake, Alison . . . . Mar 2000

P R SCULLY & CO SOLICITORS ‡
Cross House Sutton Road St Helens Merseyside WA9 3DR
Tel: 01744 755800 *Fax:* 01744 755885
E-mail: admin@prscully.com
List of partners: A J Brown, P Scully
Ptr: Brown, Mr Alasdair James LLB . . . . *Dec 1991
Scully, Patricia . . . . Dec 1994
Ast: Ryan, Mr Sean Francis . . . . Feb 2001

ST HELENS LAW LIMITED ‡
5 Hardshaw Street St Helens Merseyside WA10 1QX
Tel: 01744 454433 *Fax:* 01744 737347 *Dx:* 19485 ST HELENS
List of partners: K Chisnall, B A Moffat, D A Murphy, H J Nulty
Work: E L N S2 W Z(q)
Ptr: Chisnall, Ms Katherine . . . . May 2002
Moffat, Ms Barbara Ann. . . . . Nov 1998
Murphy, Ms Deborah Ann . . . . Sep 2002
Nulty, Mr Howard James LLB . . . . *Apr 1981

STEPHENSONS SOLICITORS LLP
95-101 Corporation Street St Helens Merseyside WA10 1SX
Tel: 01942 777777 *Fax:* 01744 451381 *Dx:* 19475 ST HELENS
Emergency telephone 07836 574607
E-mail: enquiries@stephensons.co.uk
Office: Bolton (2 offices), Leigh (2 offices), Manchester, Wigan (2 offices)
Work: A1 B1 C1 C2 C3 D1 E F1 G H J1 K1 L N P Q R1 S1 V W Z(c,e,h,i,k,l,m,s,t)
Emergency Action, Agency, Advocacy, Fixed Fee Interview, Legal Aid undertaken, Legal Aid Franchise and Member of Accident Line
Asoc: Welch, Mr Andrew BA(Hons) . . . . Nov 1994
Ast: Collier-Jones, Ms Bridget LLB(Hons) . . . . *Mar 1997
Morris, Mr Ian. *Oct 1993

TICKLE HALL CROSS ‡
Carlton Chambers 25 Hardshaw Street St Helens Merseyside WA10 1RP
Tel: 0800 854379 *Fax:* 01744 746001 *Dx:* 19455 ST HELENS
E-mail: he@ticklehallcross.co.uk
List of partners: H A Evans, K Fitzpatrick, R J Hatton, D E Wood
Office: Prescot
Work: B1 C1 C2 C3 E F1 F2 J1 K1 L M1 M2 N O P Q R1 S1 S2 T1 T2 W Z(l,q)
Agency, Advocacy, Fixed Fee Interview, Legal Aid undertaken, Legal Aid Franchise and Member of Accident Line
Ptr: Evans, Miss Helen Alyson LLB . . . . *Oct 1994
Fitzpatrick, Mr Keith LLB . . . . *Jul 1974
Hatton, Mr Roger John . . . . *Apr 1992
Wood, Mr David E LLB . . . . *Jan 1975
Ast: La Rocca, Mr Frank. . . . . Jun 1998
Van, Mr Garry. *Mar 2002
Con: Blackledge, Mr Peter L Clerk to General Commissioner of Income Taxes. . . . . *Dec 1969

ST IVES, Cambridgeshire

COPLEYS ‡
Red House 10 Market Hill St Ives Cambridgeshire PE27 5AW
Tel: 01480 464515 *Fax:* 01480 467171
Dx: 46402 ST IVES (CAMBRIDGE)
E-mail: legal@copleys-stives.co.uk
List of partners: G W Brook, I J Langworthy, K J Ross, M R Trippitt, K R Warboys
Office: Huntingdon
Work: A1 B1 C1 D1 E F1 G H J1 K1 L N O Q R1 S1 V W Z(c,d,h,i,j,l)
Emergency Action, Agency, Advocacy, Fixed Fee Interview, Legal Aid undertaken and Member of Accident Line
Ptr: Brook, Dr Graham W BA; PhD(Cantab) . . . . *Mar 1984
Langworthy, Mr Ian J LLB(Lond). . . . . *§Apr 1973

EATON & FEW ‡
8 The Meadow Meadow Lane St Ives Cambridgeshire PE27 4LG
Tel: 01480 301558 *Fax:* 01480 497674
Dx: 46403 ST IVES (CAMBRIDGE)
List of partners: M W S Eaton, J E Few, L S B Leader
Languages: Polish
Work: B1 C1 E J1 K1 K3 L N O Q R1 S1 S2 W Z(l)
Agency, Advocacy and Legal Aid undertaken

Ptr: Eaton, Mr Martin W S BA(Hons) Commissioner for Oaths . . . . *Dec 1975
Few, Mr John E Commissioner for Oaths Notary Public . . . . *Sep 1973
Leader, Miss Lisa Sylvia Byford LLB. . . . . *Dec 1999

LEEDS DAY
11 Station Road St Ives Cambridgeshire PE27 5BH
Tel: 01480 464600 *Fax:* 01480 408720
Dx: 46401 ST IVES (CAMBRIDGE)
E-mail: law@leedsday.co.uk
Office: Huntingdon, St Neots
Languages: French, German
Work: A1 A3 B1 C1 C2 C3 D1 D2 E F1 J1 K1 K2 K3 K4 L M1 N O P Q R1 S1 S2 T1 T2 W Z(c,d,e,h,i,j,k,l,o,p,t)
Emergency Action, Agency, Advocacy, Fixed Fee Interview undertaken and Member of Accident Line
Ptr: Roberts, Mr Andrew J. . . . . *Jan 1983
Ast: Goodwin, Mr Stephen B BA. . . . . *Dec 1979

JEFFREY MILLS
1 Free Church Passage St Ives Cambridgeshire PE27 5DU
Tel: 01480 495616 / 494810 / 465757 *Fax:* 01480 492638
Dx: 100302 ST NEOTS
E-mail: lawatmills@aol.com
Office: Sawtry, St Neots
Work: B1 E F1 J1 K1 K3 L M1 M2 N O P Q S1 T1 T2 V W
Agency, Advocacy and Fixed Fee Interview undertaken
Ptr: Mills, Mr Jeffrey Thomas . . . . *Jul 1966

MOVE WITH US ‡
Sterling House 10b Harding Way St Ives Cambridgeshire PE27 3WR
Tel: 01480 356058 / 0800 074 0242

WINTERS ‡
3 The Sheep Market St Ives Cambridgeshire PE27 5AJ
Tel: 01480 377377 *Fax:* 01480 377379
Dx: 46413 ST IVES (CAMBRIDGE)
List of partners: P L Burrows, S Featherstone, S J Lowe
Work: A1 E S1 S2 W
Ptr: Burrows, Mr Paul Leonard BA(Kent). . . . . *Dec 1978
Featherstone, Miss Sarah-Jane BA(Hons). . . . . *Apr 2000
Lowe, Mr Steven John BA(Hons)(Lond) . . . . *Dec 1971

ST IVES, Cornwall

CVC SOLICITORS
6-7 Fernlea Terrace St Ives Cornwall TR26 2BJ
Tel: 01736 795456 *Fax:* 01736 797075
Dx: 81800 ST IVES (CORNWALL)
E-mail: enquiriesives@cvc-solicitors.co.uk
Office: Hayle, Penzance
Languages: French
Work: A1 B1 C1 C2 C3 D1 E F1 J1 K1 L M1 M2 N O P Q R1 S1 S2 T1 T2 W Z(b,c,d,f,h,i,j,k,l,m,n,o,t)
Agency, Advocacy, Fixed Fee Interview, Legal Aid undertaken and Member of Accident Line
Dir: Dunstan, Mr John President of Cornwall Law Society *§Jun 1974
Ast: Simpson, Mr Nicholas A LLB(Lond) . . . . *Jul 1975
Thorp, Mr Oliver. . . . . Sep 2009

DB LAW
Poldhu High Street St Ives Cornwall TR26 1RR
Tel: 01736 793883 *Fax:* 01736 793883
Dx: 81802 ST IVES (CORNWALL)
Emergency telephone 07693 424607 (PAGER)
Office: Camborne, Falmouth, Penzance
Work: D1 D2 E F1 G H J1 K1 L N O Q S1 V W
Emergency Action, Agency, Advocacy, Fixed Fee Interview and Legal Aid undertaken
Ptr: Calderwood, Mr Graham D ★ . . . . *§Dec 1968

ROBINSON LE GRICE ‡
(incorporating R A Spouse & Co)
Royal Square Chambers Chapel Street St Ives Cornwall TR26 2ND
Tel: 01736 797973 *Fax:* 01736 798989
Dx: 81805 ST IVES (CORNWALL)
List of partners: T C Le Grice, A W S Robinson
Languages: French
Work: A1 A2 K4 L N Q S1 S2 W Z(d,n,q)
Agency and Fixed Fee Interview undertaken
Ptr: Le Grice, Mr Timothy C BA . . . . *Jan 1971
Robinson, Mr Andrew W S MA(Cantab); Cert Ed(FE) Notary Public. . . . . *§Jun 1974

VINGOE LLOYD SOLICITORS
5 Fernlea Terrace St Ives Cornwall TR26 2BH
Tel: 01736 797335
Office: Hayle, Helston

ST LEONARDS-ON-SEA, East Sussex

RICHARD BODY & CO ‡
66 Bohemia Road St Leonards-on-Sea East Sussex TN37 6RQ
Tel: 01424 201301 *Fax:* 01242 201302
E-mail: crimedept@richardbodyandco.com
List of partners: R Body
Agency and Fixed Fee Interview undertaken
SPr: Body, Mr Richard BA(Hons); DipLaw . . . . *Jan 1995

CONVEYANCING DIRECT LTD ‡
Windmill Road St Leonards-on-Sea East Sussex TN38 9BY
Tel: 0845 788 8666
E-mail: enquiries@cdpll.co.uk
Work: D1 K1 S1 W
Emergency Action, Agency, Advocacy, Fixed Fee Interview, Legal Aid undertaken and Legal Aid Franchise
Ast: Holman, Miss Ann BA(Hons) . . . . *Jan 1985

EMD LAW LLP ‡
13 Warrior Square St Leonards-on-Sea East Sussex TN37 6BA
Tel: 01424 420261 *Fax:* 01424 203853
List of partners: E M Dumbleton
Languages: French
Work: A1 D1 D2 E F1 F2 G H J1 K1 L N O Q S1 V W Z(d,h,i,j,k,l,m,o,q,r)
Agency, Advocacy, Fixed Fee Interview and Legal Aid undertaken
Ptr: Dumbleton, Mrs Elizabeth M LLB(Hons). . . . . Apr 1999

FITZGRAHAMS ‡
399 London Road St Leonards-on-Sea East Sussex TN37 6PH
Tel: 01424 446666 *Fax:* 01424 721536 *Dx:* 7033 HASTINGS
List of partners: F A Graham
Work: B1 C1 D1 E F1 G J1 K1 L M1 P S1 W Z(i,k,l,p)
Agency, Advocacy, Fixed Fee Interview and Legal Aid undertaken
Ptr: Graham, Mr Fitzmorris Augustus LLB(Hons)(Lond) . *Dec 1980

GOODALL BARNETT JAMES ‡
59 London Road St Leonards-on-Sea East Sussex TN37 6AY
Tel: 01424 444475 *Fax:* 01424 444080
Dx: 33113 ST LEONARDS-ON-SEA
Emergency telephone 07659 593925
E-mail: hastings@gbj-crime.co.uk
List of partners: R Barnett, K Goodall, A C James
Office: Horley
Work: G H
Emergency Action, Agency, Advocacy, Legal Aid undertaken and Legal Aid Franchise
Ptr: Goodall, Mr Kim ★ . . . . *Dec 1989
Ast: Wingfield, Miss Samantha. . . . . *Sep 2001

MENNEER SHUTTLEWORTH
28-29 Grand Parade St Leonards-on-Sea East Sussex TN37 6DR
Tel: 01424 720044 *Fax:* 01424 722221
Dx: 33100 ST LEONARDS-ON-SEA
E-mail: legalhast@menneershuttleworth.co.uk
Office: Bexhill
Work: A1 B1 C1 D1 D2 E F1 G H J1 K1 L N O Q R1 S1 S2 T1 T2 V W Z(c,k,l,m)
Emergency Action, Agency, Advocacy, Fixed Fee Interview undertaken and Member of Accident Line
Ptr: Collins, Mr David J MA(Oxon). . . . . *Apr 1980
Harrison, Mr Richard J F LLB . . . . *Dec 1975
Howlett, Mr Richard BA(Hons); PGDipLaw Trustee of Bexhill CAB . . . . *Jan 2007
Reid, Mr Alastair G . . . . *§Jan 1970
Wilson, Mrs Amanda Jane LLB . . . . *Sep 2004
Asoc: Daniels, Miss Gemma LLB(Hons). . . . . Sep 2008
Con: Craze, Mr Alan R LLB Clerk to Commissioner for Taxes; Coroner for East Sussex Notary Public . . . . *§Nov 1970

ST MAWES, Cornwall

SHARP & RIMMER ‡
Hillhead St Mawes Cornwall TR2 5AL
Tel: 01326 270291 *Fax:* 01326 270882
Emergency telephone 01872 580512
E-mail: law@sharp-rimmer.co.uk
List of partners: E B Rimmer, R V G Sharp
Work: A1 C1 E F1 J1 K1 L R1 S1 W Z(d,l)
Emergency Action, Agency and Fixed Fee Interview undertaken
Ptr: Rimmer, Mr Edward B LLB; MA . . . . *Oct 1997
Sharp, Mr Richard V G MA(Cantab). . . . . *Jan 1969

ST NEOTS, Cambridgeshire

ADLAMS LLP ‡
First Floor 37B Market Square St Neots Cambridgeshire PE19 2AR
Tel: 01480 474061 *Fax:* 01480 474959 *Dx:* 100300 ST NEOTS
E-mail: info@adlams.co.uk
List of partners: A J Burden, L J Eaton, J E Lowther, P Lowther
Office: Huntingdon
Work: A1 A3 B1 C1 D1 D2 E F1 J1 K1 K2 K3 K4 L N O Q S1 S2 T1 T2 V W Z(l,r)
Agency, Fixed Fee Interview, Legal Aid undertaken and Legal Aid Franchise
Ptr: Burden, Mrs Alison J LLB . . . . *Oct 1986
Eaton, Mrs Linda J BA . . . . *Oct 1985
Lowther, Mrs Janice E. . . . . *Jan 1982
Lowther, Mr Paul . . . . Oct 2006
Ast: Brace, Grace . . . . Oct 2008
Cunningham, Ruth . . . . Jul 2005
Olley, Mr Andrew . . . . Jun 2009

KING LAWES LEGAL ‡
4 The Highway Great Staughton St Neots Cambridgeshire PE19 5DA
Tel: 01480 860299
E-mail: enquiries@kinglawes.co.uk

LEEDS DAY ‡
1a South Street St Neots Cambridgeshire PE19 2BW
Tel: 01480 474661 *Fax:* 01480 408710 *Dx:* 100305 ST NEOTS
E-mail: law@leedsday.co.uk
List of partners: D L Coombs, R O Dewdney, C Dodd, T Glanvill, M Hafiaz, R J Metcalfe, J A Ollett, A J Roberts, S R W Thomas
Office: Huntingdon, St Ives
Languages: Dutch, Finnish, French, German
Work: A1 B1 C1 C2 C3 D1 D2 E F1 J1 K1 K3 K4 L M1 N O P Q R1 S1 T1 T2 V W Z(e,i,j,k,l,q,t)
Emergency Action, Agency, Advocacy, Fixed Fee Interview undertaken and Member of Accident Line
Ptr: Coombs, Miss Deborah Lesley . . . . *Nov 2004
Ollett, Mrs Jane Alison LLB(Hons). . . . . *Nov 1991

SIMON MERCHANT PROPERTY SOLICITOR ‡
14 The Highway Great Staughton St Neots Cambridgeshire PE19 5DA
Tel: 01480 860808

JEFFREY MILLS ‡
26 Market Square St Neots Cambridgeshire PE19 2AF
Tel: 01480 475871 / 219699 *Fax:* 01480 475451
Dx: 100302 ST NEOTS
E-mail: lawatmills@aol.com
List of partners: P S Clark, J T Mills
Office: Sawtry, St Ives
Work: B1 C1 C2 C3 D1 E F1 G J1 K1 L M1 M2 N O P Q S1 V W Z(e,i)
Agency, Advocacy and Fixed Fee Interview undertaken
Ptr: Clark, Mr Peter Stephen. . . . . *Jan 1981
Mills, Mr Jeffrey Thomas . . . . *Jul 1966
Asoc: Byatt, Mrs Hannah Elizabeth BA(Hons) . . . . May 2007

SCRIVENGER SEABROOK ‡
Vernon House 26 New Street St Neots Cambridgeshire PE19 1XB
Tel: 01480 214900 *Fax:* 01480 474833 *Dx:* 100315 ST NEOTS
E-mail: email@sslaw.co.uk
List of partners: M S Folgate, S M Newcombe, M J Scrivenger, V Seabrook
Languages: French
Work: N Z(r)
Fixed Fee Interview and Legal Aid undertaken
Ptr: Folgate, Mr Marc Steven BA(Hons) . . . . *Sep 1992
Newcombe, Ms Sarah May MA . . . . *Aug 1991
Scrivenger, Mr Mark J LLB(Melbourne) . . . . *Jan 1977
Seabrook, Miss Vicki LLB . . . . *Jun 1979
Ast: Hillson, Ms Helen Jane LLB. . . . . *Apr 1999

WILKINSON & BUTLER ‡
Peppercorn House 8 Huntingdon Street St Neots Cambridgeshire PE19 1BH
Tel: 01480 219229 *Fax:* 01480 472651 *Dx:* 100301 ST NEOTS
E-mail: law@wbsols.demon.co.uk
List of partners: D P Camwell, C W C Dawson, P R M Vialls, J L Watson
Work: A1 C1 C2 D1 E F1 G H J1 K1 K3 L N O P Q S1 S2 V W Z(c,l,m)
Emergency Action, Agency, Advocacy, Fixed Fee Interview, Legal Aid undertaken and Legal Aid Franchise
Ptr: Camwell, Mr David P LLB. . . . . *§Oct 1989
Dawson, Mr Clive W C LLB(St Andrews) . . . . *§Jul 1975
Vialls, Mr Peter R M LLB . . . . *Oct 1988
Watson, Mrs Jane Louise BA . . . . *§Oct 1990
Ast: Davies, Mr James LLB(Sheff) . . . . Nov 2005
Parker, Ms Sarah BA(De Montfort) . . . . Sep 2003
Sheehan, Ms Emma-Jayne MA; LLM(Cantab). . . . . Sep 2000
Watkins, Mr David E LLB(Wales) . . . . *§Dec 1970
Con: Keyworth, Mr Roger M LLB(Leeds) . . . . *§Jan 1969

S D YOUNG ‡
5 Dairy Court 97 Huntingdon Street St Neots Cambridgeshire PE19 1DU
Tel: 01480 470411 *Fax:* 01480 406091
E-mail: stuartyoung@sdyoungsol.co.uk
List of partners: S D Young
Work: K1 K3 L N
Emergency Action, Agency, Advocacy and Fixed Fee Interview undertaken
Ptr: Young, Mr Stuart D BA(Hons). . . . . *Oct 1984

STAFFORD, Staffordshire

1ST SOLICITORS ‡
14 Park Street Stafford Staffordshire ST17 4AL
Tel: 01785 213234 *Fax:* 01785 218351
E-mail: enquiry@1st-solicitors.co.uk
List of partners: N P Rostance
Dir: Rostance, Mr Nigel P LLB(Hons) . . . . *Oct 1980

GARY CHRISTIANSON ‡
The Stables Radford Lane Lower Penn Stafford Staffordshire WV3 8JT
Tel: 01902 763971 / 07733 895565
E-mail: enquiries@gc-legal.co.uk

CHRIS CLARK SOLICITORS & ESTATE AGENTS ‡
25 Eastgate Street Stafford Staffordshire ST16 2LZ
Tel: 01785 241842 / 241944 *Fax:* 01785 213143
Dx: 14566 STAFFORD 1
Emergency telephone 07802 364741
E-mail: chrisclarksol@hotmail.com
List of partners: C A Clark, P M Hemming
Office: Cannock
Work: G H R1 S1 S2 V W Z(g,l)
Emergency Action, Agency, Advocacy, Legal Aid undertaken and Legal Aid Franchise
Ptr: Clark, Mr Christopher A FILEx ★ R T Richardson Prize 1977 Chairman of the Registered Duty Solicitors Committee . . . . Dec 1979
Hemming, Mr Peter Mark LLB(Hons) ★ . . . . *Oct 2002

FRISBY & CO ‡
26-28 Eastgate Street Stafford Staffordshire ST16 2LZ
Tel: 01785 244114 *Fax:* 01785 251508 *Dx:* 14564 STAFFORD
E-mail: enquiries@frisbysolicitors.co.uk
List of partners: R Barber, S Belfield, A W Broome, T Cleary, K Downes
Office: London EC4, Stafford
Work: B1 B2 C1 C2 D1 E F1 G H J1 J2 K1 K3 L N O P Q R1 S1 S2 V W Z(e,l,q)
Emergency Action, Agency, Advocacy, Fixed Fee Interview and Legal Aid undertaken
Dir: Barber, Ms Ruth LLB(Hons). . . . . *Dec 1996
Belfield, Mr Simon BA. . . . . *Aug 2001
Broome, Mr Andrew W LLB. . . . . *Sep 1990
Cleary, Mr Tom . . . . *Dec 2007
Downes, Mr Kevin LLDip . . . . *Oct 1997
Asoc: Thompson, Miss Elizabeth A LLB . . . . *Jun 1981
Walton, Mr Simon BA(Hons) . . . . Dec 1990
Ast: Bayliss, Mr David A BA(Hons). . . . . Jul 2002
Bell, Mrs Moira LLB. . . . . *§Jan 1975
Cook, Mr Nathan . . . . *Nov 1998
Ladwa, Miss Veena . . . . Jul 2008
Lester, Mr Andrew. . . . . Sep 2008
McCreath, Miss Katie Louise . . . . Mar 2010
Matthew, Ms Fiona . . . . Oct 2010
Peckmore, Mrs Sarah. . . . . Sep 2008
Con: Ashworth, Mr Harry First Tier Tribunal Judge . . . . Nov 1978
Benn, Miss Rosamunde. . . . . Aug 2005

Other offices in London EC4Y, Stafford. We specialise in the following areas of work Crime - General, Litigation - General, Residential Conveyancing.

GCS PROPERTY SOLICITORS ‡
12 Winsford Crescent Hillcroft Park Stafford Staffordshire ST17 0PH
Tel: 01785 604820 *Fax:* 01785 604881
E-mail: gillsquire@gcspropertysolicitors.co.uk

GRAHAM CLAYTON SOLICITORS
Jarvis House 96 Stone Road Stafford Staffordshire ST16 2RS
Tel: 01785 244129
Office: Chester-le-Street, Doncaster, Ilford

See p112 for the Key to Work Categories & other symbols

HAND MORGAN & OWEN ‡
(incorporating Lloyd & Robinson)
17 Martin Street Stafford Staffordshire ST16 2LF
Tel: 01785 211411 *Fax:* 01785 248573 *Dx:* 14554 STAFFORD
E-mail: info@hmo.co.uk
List of partners: S S Carr, P M M Farrington, S P Harris, J A W James, P D S Slater
Office: Rugeley
Languages: Hindi, Punjabi
Work: A1 A2 B1 B2 C1 C2 C3 D2 E F1 G J1 J2 K1 K2 K3 K4 L N O P Q R2 S1 S2 T1 T2 W Z(c,d,e,k,l,p,q,t)
Emergency Action, Agency, Advocacy, Fixed Fee Interview undertaken and Member of Accident Line
Ptr: Farrington, Mr Patrick M M LLB Secretary for Staffs District Law Society . . . *Jun 1990
Harris, Mr Stewart Peter BA(Lond); LLM; ATII Notary Public . . . *Dec 1981
James, Mr John A W Under Sheriff; Deputy Coroner; Clerk to the Commissioner of Taxes . . . *Aug 1967
Slater, Mr Paul D S MA(Oxon) . . . *Nov 1984
Asoc: Cammock, Mrs Catherine Anne . . . *Mar 2002
Carr, Mr James E BSc(Wales)(Econ) . . . *Nov 1984
Nelson, Mr Patrick W BSc(Econ); MBA . . . *Sep 2003
Woodyard, Ms Jennifer . . . *Jul 1994
Con: Pepper, Mr Nigel R LLB . . . *Apr 1978

HUTSBY MEES ‡
(incorporating Kendrick Mees & Co)
5, 6 & 7a St Mary's Grove Stafford Staffordshire ST16 2AT
Tel: 01785 259211 *Fax:* 01785 224745 *Dx:* 14555 STAFFORD
Emergency telephone 07860 121501
E-mail: post@hutsbymees.co.uk
List of partners: H Hutsby, D J Mees
Work: A1 B1 E J1 K1 L O Q R2 S1 S2 T1 T2 V W Z(l,q)
Emergency Action, Agency, Advocacy, Fixed Fee Interview, Legal Aid undertaken and Legal Aid Franchise
Ptr: Hutsby, Mr Henry LLB(Nott'm) . . . *May 1979
Mees, Mr David J LLB . . . *Jun 1976
Ast: Skilton, Ms Nina LLB(Hons) . . . *Apr 2000
Con: Grundy, Ms Janet K LLB(Nott'm) . . . *Jul 1978

JEWELS SOLICITORS ‡
Victoria Chambers 15 Victoria Road Stafford Staffordshire ST16 2BY
Tel: 01785 602030 *Fax:* 01785 222455 *Dx:* 25305 STAFFORD 2
E-mail: enquiry@jewlssolicitors.co.uk
List of partners: M A Jewels, C G Seville
Office: Cannock
Work: D1 D2 E G H J2 K1 N S1 S2 W Z(l,m,r)
Emergency Action, Agency, Advocacy, Fixed Fee Interview, Legal Aid undertaken and Legal Aid Franchise
Ptr: Jewels, Mr Mark A LLB Notary Public . . . *Jun 1975
Dir: Seville, Mrs Cathie Ginette LLB(Hons) . . . Aug 2005
Ast: Carnes, Ms Caroline H LLB . . . *Aug 1987
Genner, Mrs Sarah Ann BA(Hons) . . . Sep 2002
Sargent, Mrs Helen Vera . . . *Nov 1993
Seabridge, Marian . . . *Jan 2003

JACQUELINE MCCABE LIMITED ‡
Bethany 2 Salisbury Drive Stafford Staffordshire ST16 3SS
Tel: 01785 212521 *Fax:* 020 7726 3972
E-mail: jmac22@hotmail.co.uk

NOWELL MELLER SOLICITORS LIMITED ‡
7 & 8 St Mary's Grove Stafford Staffordshire ST16 2AT
Tel: 01785 252377 *Fax:* 01785 273122 *Dx:* 14557 STAFFORD
List of partners: A J Hall, S P Kirwan, J A Matthewman, P S Sherratt
Office: Stoke-on-Trent (2 offices)
Work: A3 D1 D2 E K1 K2 K3 K4 Q S1 S2 W Z(m)
Emergency Action, Agency, Advocacy, Fixed Fee Interview, Legal Aid undertaken and Legal Aid Franchise
Dir: Hall, Mr Andrew J LLB(Hons) . . . *Jul 1994
Kirwan, Mr Stephen P MA(Oxon); LLM; FILCA . . . *Oct 1988
Matthewman, Ms Jane Alison LLB(Hons) . . . *Oct 1992
Sherratt, Mr Paul Slater LLB(Bris) . . . *Apr 1975
Ast: Boydon, Ms Robina Zoe BA(Hons) . . . *Mar 1989
Buckley, Mrs Caroline Jane BA(Hons) . . . *Mar 1984
Campbell, Ms Barbara Claire . . . *Jun 1977
Hackney, Mrs Deborah F LLB Staffordshire University Law School Joint Prize for Part-time Course . . . *Jul 2000
Roberts, Mrs Julie Ann BA(Hons) . . . *Nov 1995
Robinson, Mr Neil MA(Oxon) President of the Mental Health Tribunal . . . *Apr 1980

ORJ SOLICITORS LLP ‡
Queensville House 49 Queensville Stafford Staffordshire ST17 4NL
Tel: 01785 223440 *Fax:* 01785 223410 / 247888
Dx: 14556 STAFFORD
E-mail: ian.tullett@orj.co.uk
Languages: French, Spanish
Work: B1 C1 C2 C3 E F1 F2 J1 J2 K1 L N O Q S1 S2 T1 T2 W Z(c,e,j,l,q)

PICKERING & BUTTERS ‡
19 Greengate Street Stafford Staffordshire ST16 2LU
Tel: 01785 603060 *Fax:* 01785 607500 *Dx:* 14551 STAFFORD 1
E-mail: info@pb4law.com
List of partners: J Boulter, W G Johnson, W P Rigg, M C Wallbank, D J J White, D J Worrall
Office: Rugeley
Work: A1 A2 B1 C1 C2 D1 E F1 I J1 K1 K3 K4 L N O P Q R1 R2 S1 S2 W X Z(c,h,l,p,q,t)
Agency, Advocacy, Fixed Fee Interview undertaken and Member of Accident Line
Ptr: Boulter, Mrs Jan LLB . . . *Sep 1993
Johnson, Mr William G LLB . . . *Nov 1994
Rigg, Mr Warren P LLB R G Lawson Prize . . . *Oct 1984
White, Mr Donald J J LLB . . . *Oct 1983
Worrall, Mr David J LLB(Lond) . . . *Dec 1976
Asoc: Bedford, Mrs Amy Louise LLB(Hons); GDL; LPC . . . *Sep 2009
Pyatt, Miss Tracy LLB . . . *Dec 2001
Spinetto, Mr Sean Austin LLB . . . Oct 2007
Con: Price, Mr Roger A LLB(Lond) . . . *Apr 1977

MARK REDLER & CO ‡
23 Greengate Street Stafford Staffordshire ST16 2HS
Tel: 01785 256445 *Fax:* 01785 240971

RODERICK RAMAGE ‡
Copehale Coppenhall Stafford Staffordshire ST18 9BW
Tel: 01785 223030 / 07785 707111 *Fax:* 01785 228281
E-mail: roderick.ramage@law-office.co.uk

SHEPPARDS SOLICITORS LTD ‡
1st Floor 28 Salter Street Stafford Staffordshire ST16 2JU
Tel: 01785 257155 *Fax:* 01785 257128 *Dx:* 14579 STAFFORD 1
Emergency telephone 07699 747336
Work: G H
Emergency Action, Agency, Advocacy, Fixed Fee Interview and Legal Aid undertaken

STEVENS
Bank Passage off Market Square Stafford Staffordshire ST16 2JR
Tel: 01785 250908 *Fax:* 01785 251370 *Dx:* 14577 STAFFORD 1
Emergency telephone 07659 111000
E-mail: admin@stafford.stevenssolicitors.co.uk
Office: Stoke-on-Trent (2 offices), Wolverhampton
Work: G H
Emergency Action, Agency, Advocacy, Fixed Fee Interview, Legal Aid undertaken and Legal Aid Franchise
Ptr: Buckley, Mr Carl LLB ★ . . . *Sep 2004
Asoc: Bell, Mr Nicholas ★ . . . *Apr 2006
Jhawar, Mr Harpreet . . . Jan 2010
Steele, Mrs Natasha . . . Feb 2010

STAINES, Middlesex

BLASER MILLS
(incorporating Fancy & Jackson)
19 High Street Staines Middlesex TW18 4QY
Tel: 01784 462511 *Fax:* 01784 456592 *Dx:* 90400 STAINES
Office: Amersham, Aylesbury, Chesham, Harrow, High Wycombe, Rickmansworth
Ptr: Kharbanda, Miss Alka LLB . . . *Oct 1988
Matthews, Mr David John BA(Hons) . . . *Oct 1996
Monk, Mr Julian Harvey LLB . . . Apr 1990
Asoc: Almond, Mrs Lesley Eleanor . . . Mar 1984
Laxman, Miss Nisha Kishorbhai . . . Nov 2008
Wou, Mr Thomas Tai-Son . . . May 1989
Con: Jackson, Mr Anthony Paul Charles . . . Nov 1969

CLAYTON ‡
100 Church Street Staines Middlesex TW18 4DQ
Tel: 01784 227590 *Fax:* 01784 227591 *Dx:* 90401 STAINES
E-mail: mail@claytonlaw.co.uk
List of partners: A Clayton
Languages: French
Work: E
Ptr: Clayton, Miss Anne LLB(Hons)(B'ham) . . . *Feb 1984

CREIGHTON & PARTNERS
No2 The Courtyard 57a Church Street Staines Middlesex TW18 4XS
Tel: 01784 426710 *Fax:* 01784 452389 *Dx:* 90407 STAINES
Office: London WC1

DALE & NEWBERY LLP ‡
Clarence House 31 Clarence Street Staines Middlesex TW18 4SY
Tel: 01784 464491 *Fax:* 01784 463004 *Dx:* 90402 STAINES
E-mail: info@daleandnewbery.co.uk
List of partners: G W J Burton, P Cotran, S B Duncombe, S Pegler, S J Tame, C Taylor
Work: A1 A3 B1 C1 C2 C3 D2 E F1 F2 J1 J2 K1 K2 K3 K4 L N O P Q R1 R2 S1 S2 W Z(c,k,q,r)
Emergency Action, Agency, Advocacy, Fixed Fee Interview, Legal Aid undertaken and Member of Accident Line
Ptr: Burton, Mr Graham Walter John BA . . . *§Jul 1980
Cotran, Mr Patrick LLB . . . *Sep 1991
Duncombe, Mr Stephen B LLB . . . *May 1975
Pegler, Miss Sharon BA(Hons)(Law); FRSA; TEP . . . *Feb 1986
Tame, Mr Stephen J BA . . . *Nov 1981
Taylor, Mr Craig LLB . . . *Sep 1994
Ast: Chapman, Mr Noel David LLB(Hons) . . . Apr 1989
Khak, Mr Balraj Singh LLB(Hons) . . . *Dec 1994
King, Mrs Lynda Susan BA; LLB . . . Jan 1995
Mardarescu, Miss Ilinca BA(Hons) . . . Jun 2002
Rahi, Mrs Kulbir K LLB . . . *Oct 1989

W H MATTHEWS & CO
31 Church Street Staines Middlesex TW18 4EN
Tel: 01784 453154 *Fax:* 01784 460537 *Dx:* 90404 STAINES
Office: Kingston upon Thames, London EC1, Sutton
Languages: French, German, Spanish
Work: A1 B1 C1 C2 C3 D1 E F1 G H J1 K1 L M1 M2 N O P Q S1 S2 T1 T2 W Z(c,i,k,l)
Agency, Fixed Fee Interview, Legal Aid undertaken and Member of Accident Line
Ptr: Lovering, Ms Kirsty Maria . . . Nov 1997
Lowry, Ms Eleanor M . . . Sep 1992
Tribick, Mr Alex . . . Oct 1999

ROWBERRY MORRIS
15 Clarence Street Staines Middlesex TW18 4SU
Tel: 01784 457655 *Fax:* 01784 465114 *Dx:* 90408 STAINES
Office: Reading, Richmond upon Thames, Tadley
Work: C1 D1 E F1 J1 K1 L N O Q S1 W Z(l)
Agency, Advocacy undertaken and Member of Accident Line
Ptr: Edwards, Mr Rodney W BA . . . *Jan 1979
Preston, Mr Robert Edwin LLB(Hons) . . . Jul 1976

STALBRIDGE, Dorset

BLANCHARDS BAILEY LLP
High Street Stalbridge Dorset DT10 2LH
Tel: 01963 363593 *Fax:* 01963 362214
E-mail: stalbridge@blanchardsbailey.co.uk
Office: Blandford Forum, Dorchester, Shaftesbury
Work: E K1 S1 W
Con: Foster-Pegg, Mr John . . . *Jul 1978

STALHAM, Norfolk

CAPRON & HELLIWELL ‡
West View High Street Stalham Norfolk NR12 9AN
Tel: 01692 581231 *Fax:* 01692 580620 *Dx:* 85100 STALHAM
List of partners: E A Collyer, N R Harries, L D Little
Office: Wroxham
Work: A1 C1 E K1 L Q S1 S2 T1 T2 W Z(c,d,l,m)
Ptr: Collyer, Mrs Elizabeth Alexandra BA . . . *Sep 1992
Harries, Mr Neil R BA . . . *§Oct 1982
Ast: Kemp, Mr Roderick John BA(Hons) . . . *Jun 1977
Smith, Miss Margaret Anne . . . *Jul 1984
Con: Coleman, Mr Richard John . . . *§Oct 1976

STALYBRIDGE, Greater Manchester

QUALITYSOLICITORS GRUBER GARRATT
Cheethams House 96 Market Street Stalybridge Greater Manchester SK15 2AB
Tel: 0161 303 2328 *Fax:* 0161 338 4201 *Dx:* 15576 STALYBRIDGE
Emergency telephone 07971 163241
E-mail: info@qsgrubergarratt.co.uk
Office: Ashton-under-Lyne, Oldham, Radcliffe, Worsley
Work: B1 C1 C2 C3 E F1 G H K1 M1 N P S1 S2 W Z(m)
Emergency Action, Agency, Advocacy, Fixed Fee Interview, Legal Aid undertaken, Legal Aid Franchise and Member of Accident Line
Asoc: Goodall, Mr Richard LLB . . . *Jul 1987

THOMPSON & COOKE LLP ‡
12 Stamford Street Stalybridge Greater Manchester SK15 1LA
Tel: 0161 338 2614 *Fax:* 0161 303 8967 *Dx:* 15571 STALYBRIDGE
E-mail: peter.holden@thompsonandcooke.co.uk
List of partners: N J Ashworth, P E Holden, C E Maher, J H Maltby
Office: Stalybridge
Work: A3 B1 C1 C2 C3 D1 D2 E F1 J1 J2 K1 K3 K4 L N O Q R1 R2 S1 S2 T1 T2 V W X Z(c,l,m,o,q,x,za)
Emergency Action, Agency, Advocacy, Fixed Fee Interview undertaken and Member of Accident Line
Ptr: Holden, Mr Peter Edward BA(Dunelm); Dip PI Lit; Dip(Family Law) ★ Notary Public . . . *Oct 1982
Maltby, Mr John H LLB(Lond) . . . *Apr 1975
Ast: Moore, Mr Roger . . . *Oct 1993
Con: Buckley, Mr V Rufus LLB(B'ham) . . . *Feb 1972
Davis, Mr John Keith LLB(Manc) . . . *Jun 1981

THOMPSON & COOKE LLP
100 Market Street Stalybridge Greater Manchester SK15 2AB
Tel: 0161 338 2614 *Fax:* 0161 338 2616 *Dx:* 15571 STALYBRIDGE
Emergency telephone 0161 330 2675
E-mail: peter.holden@thompsonandcooke.co.uk
Office: Stalybridge
Work: A1 A3 B1 C1 C3 D1 E F1 J2 K1 L N P S1 V W Z(c,d,h,j,k)
Emergency Action, Agency, Advocacy, Fixed Fee Interview, Legal Aid undertaken and Member of Accident Line
Ptr: Ashworth, Mr Nigel J BA . . . *Oct 1981
Holden, Mr Peter Edward BA(Dunelm); Dip PI Lit; Dip(Family Law) ★ Notary Public . . . *Oct 1982
Maher, Mr Craig E BA . . . *Oct 1987

STAMFORD, Lincolnshire

BUCKLES SOLICITORS LLP
3 St Mary's Hill Stamford Lincolnshire PE9 2DW
Tel: 01780 484570 *Fax:* 01780 484571
E-mail: stamford@buckles-law.co.uk
Office: Peterborough
Work: E K1 K2 K3 S1 S2 T1 T2 W

CHATTERTONS SOLICITORS
9 Broad Street Stamford Lincolnshire PE9 1PY
Tel: 01780 764145 *Fax:* 01780 766413 *Dx:* 26001 STAMFORD
E-mail: stamford@chattertons.com
Office: Boston (2 offices), Grantham, Horncastle, Lincoln, Newark, Sleaford, Spalding
Languages: Danish
Work: A1 B1 C1 C2 C3 D1 E F1 G J1 J2 K1 L M2 N O P Q R1 S1 S2 T1 T2 W Z(c,d,h,j,l,o,q)
Emergency Action, Agency, Advocacy and Fixed Fee Interview undertaken
Con: Small, Mr David C MA(Cantab) . . . *§Jul 1977
Vipan, Mr Robert F M Notary Public . . . *§Nov 1965

DALTONS ‡
29 St Marys Street Stamford Lincolnshire PE9 2DL
Tel: 01780 762526 *Fax:* 01780 764955 *Dx:* 26002 STAMFORD
E-mail: philip.robson@daltonssolicitors.co.uk
List of partners: P Robson, R H Taylor
Office: Oakham
Work: A1 D1 E K1 K4 L S1 T1 T2 W Z(d,l)
Ptr: Robson, Mr Philip LLB . . . *Apr 1975
Ast: Rose, Mrs Lynda A . . . *Dec 1991
Con: Williams, Mr Anthony J . . . *Jun 1972

DICKINSON & CO ‡
34 Broad Street Stamford Lincolnshire PE9 1PJ
Tel: 01780 752581 *Fax:* 01780 480918 *Dx:* 26012 STAMFORD
E-mail: m_dickinson@hotmail.co.uk
List of partners: R M Dickinson
SPr: Dickinson, Mr Robin M BA . . . *Jun 1981

GARNERS SOLICITORS ‡
1 Oxford Road Stamford Lincolnshire PE9 1BT
Tel: 01780 751196 *Fax:* 01780 482848 *Dx:* 26011 STAMFORD
E-mail: garners_law@btinternet.com
Work: C1 E S1 S2 W

HEGARTY LLP
10 Ironmonger Street Stamford Lincolnshire PE9 1PL
Tel: 01780 752066 *Fax:* 01780 762774 *Dx:* 26006 STAMFORD
E-mail: email@hegarty.co.uk
Office: Peterborough
Work: A1 A3 B1 B2 C1 C2 D1 D2 E F1 G H J1 K1 K2 K3 L M1 N O Q R2 S1 S2 W Z(e,l)
Agency, Advocacy, Legal Aid undertaken and Legal Aid Franchise
Ptr: Peebles, Mr Graham J LLB . . . *Nov 1987
Ast: Strong, Miss Rachel Teresa BA . . . *Nov 1993
Wild, Mrs Joanne LLB(Hons) . . . *Sep 1992

PJH LAW ‡
16 Wharf Road Stamford Lincolnshire PE9 2EB
Tel: 0870 350 5805 *Fax:* 0870 350 5806
E-mail: mail@pjhlaw.co.uk

STAPLETON & SON ‡
1 Broad Street Stamford Lincolnshire PE9 1PD
Tel: 01780 751226 *Fax:* 01780 766407 *Dx:* 26003 STAMFORD
E-mail: enquiries@stapletons.co.uk
List of partners: J A Buxton, N P Fluck

For a range of specialised Legal Services please refer to Section 20

Languages: French
Work: A1 B1 C1 C2 D1 E F1 J1 K1 K2 K3 K4 L O Q R1 R2 S1 S2 T1 T2 U1 U2 V W X Z(c,d,h,o,p,s,t)
Emergency Action and Legal Aid undertaken
Ptr: Buxton, Mr James A MA(Cantab) . . . . *Oct 1979
Fluck, Mr Nicholas P BA . . . . *§Oct 1984
Ast: McAuliffe, Miss Moira BA . . . . *Jun 1986

TERRELLS LLP
Sheepmarket Stamford Lincolnshire PE9 2QZ
Tel: 01780 481129 *Fax:* 01780 482496
E-mail: lt@terrells.co.uk
Office: Huntingdon, Peterborough
Work: D1 K1 K3 N S1 S2 W
Agency, Fixed Fee Interview, Legal Aid undertaken and Member of Accident Line
Mem: Terrell, Miss Lucy LLB. . . . . Aug 2007

STANFORD-LE-HOPE, Thurrock

PENMANS ‡
Stanhope House High Street Stanford-le-Hope Thurrock SS17 0HA
Tel: 01375 677777 *Fax:* 01375 641107
Dx: 34603 STANFORD-LE-HOPE
E-mail: stanford@penmanslaw.co.uk
List of partners: G J Buggle, M D Hornby
Office: Corringham
Work: A1 B1 C1 C2 C3 D1 E F1 G H J1 K1 L M1 M2 N P R1 S1 T1 T2 V W Z(a,b,c,d,e,f,g,h,i,j,k,l,m,n,o,s,t)
Emergency Action, Agency, Advocacy, Fixed Fee Interview, Legal Aid undertaken, Legal Aid Franchise and Member of Accident Line
Ptr: Buggle, Mr Gerard Joseph LLB(Hons). . . . . *Jun 1978
Hornby, Mr Michael D. . . . . May 1987

SCANNELL EVANS ‡
(incorporating Shaen Roscoe & Swift)
Lingwood House 4-5 The Green Stanford-le-Hope Thurrock SS17 0EX
Tel: 01375 642240 *Fax:* 01375 360061
Dx: 34601 STANFORD-LE-HOPE
E-mail: chris.bailey@scannell-solicitors.co.uk
List of partners: E A Scannell
Languages: French
Work: J1 K1 K4 L N Q S1 W Z(p)
Fixed Fee Interview undertaken
Ptr: Scannell, Mrs Elizabeth Anne BA . . . . *§Jul 1968
Ast: Evans, Mrs Paula Louise LLB(Hons) . . . . Sep 2001

STANHOPE, Co Durham

HODGSON & ANGUS ‡
62 Front Street Stanhope Co Durham DL13 2UD
Tel: 01388 528517 *Fax:* 01388 527683
E-mail: gkrobinson@hodgsonandangus.co.uk
List of partners: G K Robinson, I Shuttleworth
Work: A1 B1 C1 D1 D2 E F1 G H J1 K1 K3 K4 L N O Q S1 S2 T2 V W Z(d,g,l,n)
Emergency Action, Agency, Advocacy and Fixed Fee Interview undertaken
Ptr: Robinson, Mr George Kenneth . . . . *Mar 1973
Shuttleworth, Mr Ian. . . . . *§Dec 1990

STANLEY, Co Durham

NICHOLSON MARTIN LEGGE & MILLER
11 Thorneyholme Terrace Stanley Co Durham DH9 0BL
Tel: 01207 232277 *Fax:* 01207 230844 *Dx:* 62052 STANLEY
Office: Houghton Le Spring
Work: D1 E K1 K2 K3 K4 S1 S2 W
Agency, Advocacy, Fixed Fee Interview and Legal Aid undertaken
Ptr: Parsons, Mrs Susan MA . . . . *Oct 1983

POWER SCOTT SOLICITORS ‡
16 Clifford Road Stanley Co Durham DH9 0AB
Tel: 01207 230125 *Fax:* 01207 290027 *Dx:* 62050 STANLEY
E-mail: info@power-scott.co.uk
List of partners: A W Power, R H Scott
Work: D1 F1 G H J1 K1 K3 L N S1 S2 V W Z(l,q)
Emergency Action, Advocacy, Fixed Fee Interview, Legal Aid undertaken and Legal Aid Franchise
Ptr: Power, Mr Anthony W BA(Law) . . . . Mar 1981
Scott, Mr Robert H BA . . . . *Jan 1986

STANMORE, Middlesex

CHAPLIN & CO ‡
The Firs Valencia Road Stanmore Middlesex HA7 4JL
Tel: 020 8954 8202 *Fax:* 020 8954 7477 *Dx:* 48909 STANMORE
E-mail: chaplinco@aol.com
List of partners: M P Chaplin
Work: B1 C1 C2 E I J1 K1 K3 L N O Q R2 S1 S2 W Z(b,c,e,f,i,l,q)
Emergency Action, Agency and Fixed Fee Interview undertaken
Ptr: Chaplin, Mr Melvin Perry LLB . . . . *Feb 1987

SIMONE COLLINS & CO ‡
Hunters Moon Priory Drive Stanmore Middlesex HA7 3HL
Work: C1 C2

THE COMPENSATION LAWYERS ‡
Jubilee House Merrion Avenue Stanmore Middlesex HA7 4RY

CRICKHOLLOW SOLICITORS ‡
55 Morley Crescent West Stanmore Middlesex HA7 2LL
Tel: 020 8907 3535

FELTON & CO ‡
30 Fauna Close Stanmore Middlesex HA7 4PX
Tel: 01923 839599 *Fax:* 0845 056 9822
Emergency telephone 07850 484769
List of partners: K H Felton
Work: E L S1 S2 W
Agency and Fixed Fee Interview undertaken
SPr: Felton, Ms Karen H . . . . Oct 1990

KIRKWOODS ‡
41a Church Road Stanmore Middlesex HA7 4AB
Tel: 020 8954 8555 *Fax:* 020 8954 4124 *Dx:* 48901 STANMORE
E-mail: kirkwoods.stanmore@lineone.net
List of partners: R D Bridges, B P Kramer
Languages: Gujarati, Hindi
Work: C1 C2 E F1 K1 L Q S1 T1 T2 W
Emergency Action undertaken
Ptr: Bridges, Mr Richard D BA(Lond) . . . . *§Dec 1979
Kramer, Mr Bradley Paul LLB . . . . *Apr 1975

LEVINE MELLINS KLARFELD ‡
24-26 Church Road Stanmore Middlesex HA7 4AW
Tel: 020 8954 7474 *Fax:* 020 8954 8098 *Dx:* 48907 STANMORE
E-mail: adaniels@lmklaw.co.uk
List of partners: A R Daniels, M A Levine, G A Mellins, R Sthalekar, E H Sulkin
Languages: Gujarati, Hindi
Work: C1 C2 D1 E F1 J1 K1 K3 L N O Q S1 S2 W Z(c,d,k,l)
Agency undertaken
Ptr: Daniels, Mr Anthony R . . . . *Nov 1978
Levine, Mr Michael A BA(Econ) . . . . *Dec 1977
Mellins, Mr Godfrey A LLB . . . . *Apr 1975
Sthalekar, Mr Rohit LLB(Hons) . . . . *Nov 1989
Sulkin, Ms Elizabeth H LLB . . . . *Oct 1984
Asoc: Bernstein, Ms Lorraine LLB . . . . *Apr 1994
Robinson, Mrs Lynn B LLB(Hons) . . . . *Oct 1985
Con: Klarfeld, Mr Stanley B. . . . . *Jun 1962

MILLER CLAYTON ‡
1st Floor Suite 1 Fountain House Stanmore Middlesex HA7 4AU
Tel: 020 8954 5280 *Fax:* 020 8954 5785 *Dx:* 48912 STANMORE
E-mail: law@millerclayton.co.uk
List of partners: A D Miller, J C Miller
Work: C1 E J1 K1 L Q R2 S1 S2 W Z(c)
Ptr: Miller, Mr Anthony D LLB . . . . Jun 1970
Miller, Mr John C . . . . Mar 1962

PEARL & CO
15 Court Drive Stanmore Middlesex HA7 4QH
Tel: 020 8958 4889 *Fax:* 020 8958 4982
Office: London N15, London NW4
Work: C1 E F1 K1 K4 S1 S2 W
Fixed Fee Interview undertaken
Con: Cowan, Mrs Janice A LLB. . . . . *Jan 1980

PINDORIA SOLICITORS
1st Floor 502 Honeypot Lane Stanmore Middlesex HA7 1JR
Tel: 020 8951 6959 *Fax:* 020 8951 6951
Office: London EC2

SLP SOLICITORS ‡
51-53 The Broadway Stanmore Middlesex HA7 4DJ
Tel: 020 8420 7950 *Fax:* 020 8416 0911 *Dx:* 146882 STANMORE 3
E-mail: info@slp.uk.com
List of partners: P S Elliston, M Goldwater, J Holder
Work: B1 C1 E K1 L Q R1 S1 W Z(c,i,l)
Agency, Advocacy, Legal Aid undertaken and Member of Accident Line
Ptr: Elliston, Mr Peter S MA(Cantab). . . . . *Apr 1972
Goldwater, Mr Mark LLB . . . . *Sep 1988
Holder, Mr Joseph LLB(Hons). . . . . *Oct 1988

DAVID R SAFFRIN ‡
116 Stanmore Hill Stanmore Middlesex HA7 3BY
Tel: 020 8954 3090

SIMMONS STEIN ‡
Compass House Pynnacles Close Stanmore Middlesex HA7 4AF
Tel: 020 8954 8080 *Fax:* 020 8954 8900 *Dx:* 48904 STANMORE
E-mail: info@simmons-stein.co.uk
List of partners: G S Simmons, J H Stein
Languages: French, German
Work: B1 E L O Q S1 S2 W
Ptr: Simmons, Mr Gary S BA . . . . *Oct 1982
Stein, Mr Jeffrey H LLB(Manc) . . . . *Jun 1985
Con: Alton, Mr Jeremy BA(Hons) . . . . Jun 1972

SURJJ LEGAL LIMITED ‡
1 St Andrews Drive Stanmore Middlesex HA7 2LY
Tel: 020 3278 8849
E-mail: info@surjjlegal.co.uk

VP THAKRAR & CO ‡
110 Portland Crescent Stanmore Middlesex HA7 1NA
Tel: 020 8905 0021 *Fax:* 020 8905 0021

A S TIBBER & CO SOLICITORS ‡
First Floor Buckingham House West Stanmore Broadway Stanmore Middlesex HA7 4EB
Tel: 020 8954 4705 *Fax:* 020 8954 0387

YUGIN & PARTNERS ‡
Jubilee House Stanmore Middlesex HA7 4RY
Tel: 020 8954 2410 *Fax:* 020 8954 2411 *Dx:* 148803 STANMORE 5
E-mail: info@yuginlaw.com
List of partners: J I Sheril, M L Yugin
Work: C1 C2 E J1 N S1 S2 W Z(b)
Legal Aid undertaken
Ptr: Sheril, Mr Jonathan Ian . . . . Oct 1987
Yugin, Mr Murray L . . . . *Aug 1970
Ast: Shah, Mr Kamran BA(History). . . . . Sep 2003

STANSTED MOUNTFITCHET, Essex

SOLUTIONS LEGAL SOLICITORS ‡
The Exchange 9 Station Road Stansted Mountfitchet Essex CM24 8BE
Tel: 020 8166 0700

STAPLE HILL, South Gloucestershire

RICHARD HERNE & CO SOLICITORS ‡
113 High Street Staple Hill South Gloucestershire BS16 5HF
Tel: 0117 957 4508 *Fax:* 0117 957 4688 *Dx:* 31852 STAPLE HILL
E-mail: enquiries@richardhernesolicitors.co.uk
List of partners: R J Herne
Work: D1 F1 J1 K1 L M1 P S1 V W Z(h,l,o,p)
Agency and Advocacy undertaken
Ptr: Herne, Mr Richard James BSocSc; MSc(Econ) . . . *Dec 1992

WARDS SOLICITORS
Hynam Court Eclipse Office Park 20 High Street Staple Hill South Gloucestershire BS16 5EL
Tel: 0117 943 4800 *Fax:* 0117 970 1220 *Dx:* 31850 STAPLE HILL
E-mail: info@wards.uk.com
Office: Bristol (2 offices), Clevedon, Nailsea, Portishead, Weston-super-Mare (3 offices), Yate
Work: D1 K1 K3 K4 L N S1 T2 V W Z(r)
Emergency Action, Agency, Advocacy, Fixed Fee Interview, Legal Aid undertaken and Legal Aid Franchise
Ptr: Simon, Mr Philip J LLB(L'pool) . . . . *Apr 1981
Underhill, Ms Alison R LLB . . . . *Oct 1989

STAPLEFORD, Nottinghamshire

MACLAREN WARNER ‡
50 Nottingham Road Stapleford Nottinghamshire NG9 8AA
Tel: 0115 939 5252 *Fax:* 0115 949 1299 *Dx:* 11855 STAPLEFORD
List of partners: R M Bevan, S C Kassell, S J Warner
Office: Beeston, Eastwood, Ilkeston
Work: A1 C1 C2 C3 D1 E F1 G H J1 K1 L M1 M2 P R1 S1 W Z(i,l)
Emergency Action, Agency, Advocacy, Fixed Fee Interview and Legal Aid undertaken
Ptr: Bevan, Mr Robert M LLB . . . . *Sep 1988
Kassell, Mr Simon C BA(Law). . . . . *Oct 1983
Warner, Mr Stephen J BA(Law) . . . . *Aug 1981
Ast: Ballantyne, Ms Jane Rosemary BA; MPhil. . . . . . *Nov 1994

STAVELEY, Derbyshire

KIERANCLARKEGREEN
2 Barnfield Walk Staveley Derbyshire S43 3UN
Tel: 01246 280099 *Fax:* 01246 476238 *Dx:* 12352 CHESTERFIELD
E-mail: enquiries@kieranclarke.co.uk
Office: Chesterfield (2 offices)
Work: D1 D2 G H K1 K3 N S1 W Z(m)
Agency, Advocacy, Fixed Fee Interview, Legal Aid undertaken, Legal Aid Franchise and Member of Accident Line
Ptr: Dewson, Mrs Siobhan Mary. . . . . *Jun 1984

STEVENAGE, Hertfordshire

DAVID BARNEY & CO ‡
31a Queensway Stevenage Hertfordshire SG1 1DA
Tel: 01438 314281 *Fax:* 01438 222330
E-mail: davidbarney@ukonline.co.uk
List of partners: R G Amos, M T Feely, D R Tough
Work: A1 C1 D1 E G H L S1
Ptr: Amos, Mr Robert G LLB(Lond) . . . . *§Jun 1981
Feely, Mr Mark Thomas LLB(Hons) . . . . Dec 2002
Tough, Mr David R MA(Cantab). . . . . *§Nov 1981

BRIGNALLS BALDERSTON WARREN ‡
Forum Chambers The Forum Stevenage Hertfordshire SG1 1EL
Tel: 01438 359311 *Fax:* 01438 740127 *Dx:* 6011 STEVENAGE
Emergency telephone 01438 820339
E-mail: enquiries@bbwlaw.biz
List of partners: D Atkins, G Balsom, T P Brain, J B Y Elliott, A W Goodwin, A J H Laing, B C Lendrum, J M Nicholls, A J Nickels, M J Quieros, D J Stott, R G Watson, D S J Whiddett
Office: Baldock, Biggleswade, Knebworth, Letchworth
Work: B1 C1 C2 E G H J1 K1 N O Q S1 S2 W Z(q)
Emergency Action, Agency, Advocacy, Fixed Fee Interview, Legal Aid undertaken and Legal Aid Franchise
Ptr: Lendrum, Mr Bruce C LLB Director of the Stevenage Business Initiative. . . . . *Jan 1980
Nicholls, Mr Jonathan M LLB(Bris) . . . . *May 1980
Quieros, Mr Maurice J. . . . . *§Jun 1978
Stott, Mr David J LLB . . . . *§Apr 1974
Watson, Mr Richard G LLB . . . . *Dec 1980
Ast: Fletcher, Mr Steven BA . . . . *Dec 1998
Harding, Miss Leanne Amy LLB(Hons) . . . . Sep 2005

FRIIS & RADSTONE ‡
Hertlands House Primett Road Stevenage Hertfordshire SG1 3EE
Tel: 01438 741001 *Fax:* 01438 360060
Dx: 122191 OLD STEVENAGE
E-mail: mail@friislaw.co.uk
List of partners: L J Friis
Languages: French
Work: E L S1 S2 W
SPr: Friis, Ms Linda J BA. . . . . *Nov 1973

GRIGSBY EDDLESTON & CO ‡
11a Market Place Stevenage Hertfordshire SG1 1DH
Tel: 01438 742525 *Fax:* 01438 740777
List of partners: M E Eddleston, G Grigsby
Work: E S1 S2 W
Ptr: Eddleston, Mrs Margaret E BSc. . . . . *Apr 1980
Grigsby, Mr Gerald LLB . . . . *Jan 1978

HALDANES ‡
Wye Lodge 66 High Street Stevenage Hertfordshire SG1 3EA
Tel: 01438 312525 *Fax:* 01438 312526
Dx: 122196 OLD STEVENAGE
E-mail: partners@haldanes-uk.com
List of partners: G R Miles
Office: London W1

HAMILTON DAVIES ‡
(incorporating Hazel Jones Solicitors)
28 High Street Stevenage Hertfordshire SG1 3HF
Tel: 01438 315898 *Fax:* 01438 740084
Dx: 122185 OLD STEVENAGE
E-mail: law@hamiltondavies.co.uk
List of partners: P B Davies, I D Hamilton, H Jones
Languages: French, German
Work: B1 C1 C2 D2 E F1 F2 J1 J2 K1 K3 K4 L N O Q S1 S2 T1 T2 V W Z(d,f,l,m,p,q,w)
Emergency Action, Agency, Advocacy and Fixed Fee Interview undertaken
Ptr: Davies, Mr Paul B LLB(L'pool) Council Member of the Hertfordshire Law Society. . . . . *Oct 1986

See p112 for the Key to Work Categories & other symbols

Hamilton, Mr Ian D BA(Bris). . . . . *Nov 1974
Jones, Ms Hazel . . . . *Jan 2001
Con: Pearson, Mrs Elisabeth I BA; LAMRTPI . . . . . . *§Dec 1974

HECKFORD NORTON ‡
Tudor House 2 Letchmore Road Stevenage Hertfordshire SG1 3HU
Tel: 01438 312211 *Fax:* 01438 740805
Dx: 122180 OLD STEVENAGE
E-mail: law1@heckfordnorton.co.uk
List of partners: D M Pidgeon, B L Purser, A P Taylor
Office: Letchworth, Saffron Walden
Work: A1 B1 C1 C2 C3 E F1 G H J1 J2 K3 L M1 N O Q R1 S1 S2 T1 T2 W Z(d,l,q,r)
Emergency Action, Agency, Advocacy, Legal Aid undertaken and Legal Aid Franchise
Ptr: Pidgeon, Mr David M LLB(Lond) H M Deputy Coroner of Hertfordshire . . . . *Jun 1979
Asoc: Cooke, Mrs Julia Elizabeth BA . . . . *Mar 1993
Ast: Kilbane, Mr Michael Edward BA(Hons) . . . . *Jan 2003
Phillips, Mr Tariq LLB(Hons). . . . . Jan 2003
Yates, Ms Marian LLB(Hons)(Herts); BA; ILCA Dip . . *Apr 2006

HILLIERSHRW SOLICITORS
Mindenhall Court High Street Stevenage Hertfordshire SG1 3UN
Tel: 01438 346000 *Fax:* 01438 721866
Dx: 122183 STEVENAGE OLD TOWN
Emergency telephone 0800 169 7877
E-mail: admin@hilliershrw.co.uk
Office: Kempston
Work: A1 B1 C1 C2 C3 D1 E F1 G H J1 K1 L M1 M2 N O P Q R1 S1 T1 T2 U2 V W Z(e,k,l,o,p)
Emergency Action, Agency, Advocacy, Fixed Fee Interview, Legal Aid undertaken and Member of Accident Line
Ptr: Addrison, Mr Martin K BA. . . . . *May 1980
Ivinson, Mr Philip Jonathan LLB(Hons) . . . . *Dec 1992
Ast: Manikam, Mr Baskaran . . . . *Jan 2001
Martin, Miss Tracey LLB . . . . *May 2002
Plane, Mrs Janet BSc(Hons) . . . . *May 1997

LAW BRAND ‡
Business & Technology Centre Bessemer Drive Stevenage Hertfordshire SG1 2DX
Tel: 01438 367373 *Fax:* 01438 368900
List of partners: C G Smith, S P Smith
Office: Hitchin
Work: B1 C1 E J1 L R2 S1 W Z(c)
Ptr: Smith, Mr Charles G . . . . Dec 1977

TYNAN SOLICITORS ‡
1st Floor Suites 1-2 Southgate House Stevenage Hertfordshire SG1 1HG
Tel: 01438 356333
E-mail: tynansolicitors@btconnect.com

STEYNING, West Sussex

GREEN WRIGHT CHALTON ANNIS
60 High Street Steyning West Sussex BN44 3RD
Tel: 01903 814190 *Fax:* 01903 814682 *Dx:* 86001 STEYNING
E-mail: enquiries@gwca.co.uk
Office: Arundel, Lancing, Rustington, Worthing (2 offices)
Work: A1 B1 C1 C2 C3 D1 E F1 K1 L N O Q R1 S1 S2 T2 V W Z(c,l)
Emergency Action, Agency, Advocacy and Fixed Fee Interview undertaken
Ptr: Chatwell, Ms Emma Jane . . . . *Oct 1996
Ast: Collins, Mr Gareth Edward . . . . Sep 2009
Con: Baker, Mr Nigel Gordon . . . . *§May 1971

MORTIMER CLARKE SOLICITORS LIMITED ‡
2 The Courtyard Shoreham Road Steyning West Sussex BN44 3BJ
Tel: 0845 370 9280 *Fax:* 01903 817909 *Dx:* 86002 STEYNING
E-mail: info@mortimerclarke.co.uk

STOCKBRIDGE, Hampshire

HELEN M BRADLEY ‡
Anstey House Winchester Street Chilbolton Stockbridge Hampshire SO20 6BQ
Tel: 01264 860200 *Fax:* 01264 860200
E-mail: helen.bradley@btinternet.com
List of partners: H M Bradley
Work: S1 W
SPr: Bradley, Mrs Helen Margaret MA(Cantab) . . . . *Nov 1978

BROCKMANS ‡
3 Clarendon Terrace Stockbridge Hampshire SO20 6EY
Tel: 01264 810910 *Fax:* 01264 810977 *Dx:* 134321 STOCKBRIDGE
E-mail: inmail@brockmanlaw.com
List of partners: A P Brockman, J A Docherty, A E L Ford
Languages: French, German
Work: B1 C1 C2 E F1 J1 J2 K1 K3 L O Q S1 S2 W Z(e,q)
Fixed Fee Interview undertaken
Ptr: Brockman, Mrs Alison Patricia BSc German Law First Cert Prize . . . . *Oct 1988
Docherty, Ms Julie Anita LLB . . . . *Jan 1987
Ford, Mr Anthony E L. . . . . *Jul 1980
Con: Hargreaves, Mrs Hilary Jane LLB . . . . Mar 1986
Stone, Mrs Susan Gertrude BA . . . . Jun 1976

MCPHERSONS ‡
The Long Barn Winchester Road Kings Somborne Stockbridge Hampshire SO20 6NZ
Tel: 01794 389002 *Fax:* 01794 389006 *Dx:* 134328 STOCKBRIDGE
E-mail: mcphersons@longbarn.org
List of partners: G C Rowe
Work: A1 A2 E S1 W
SPr: Rowe, Miss Gillian C LLB . . . . *Oct 1980
Con: Strudwick, Mrs Caroline LLB . . . . *Jan 1984

STOCKPORT, Greater Manchester

ADDISON LEGAL ‡
117 Stockport Road Marple Stockport Greater Manchester SK6 6AG
Tel: 0161 660 9232 *Fax:* 0161 660 9233
E-mail: info@addisonlegal.co.uk
List of partners: G Yates
SPr: Yates, Mr Gregory. . . . . Mar 1993

AYRES WATERS ‡
5 St Petersgate Stockport Greater Manchester SK1 1EB
Tel: 0161 480 5229 *Fax:* 0161 476 2549 *Dx:* 19665 STOCKPORT 1
E-mail: mail@ayreswaters.co.uk
List of partners: A Ayres, P Waters
Work: D1 K1 S1 V W
Emergency Action, Agency, Advocacy, Fixed Fee Interview, Legal Aid undertaken and Member of Accident Line
Ptr: Ayres, Mr Andrew LLB . . . . *Apr 1979
Waters, Mr Paul LLB . . . . *Apr 1990
Ast: Flannery, Mr Shane Michael. . . . . *Jul 1997
Smith, Miss Rachel Ann LLB . . . . *Sep 2000

BELSHAWS SOLICITORS LIMITED ‡
27 Greek Street Stockport Greater Manchester SK3 8AX
Tel: 0161 477 5377 *Fax:* 0161 477 5334 *Dx:* 22633 STOCKPORT 2
Emergency telephone 0161 477 5377
E-mail: mailbox@belshawlaw.com
Languages: Spanish
Work: B2 G H J1 J2 K1 K3 N Q W Z(q,r)
Agency, Advocacy, Fixed Fee Interview, Legal Aid undertaken and Legal Aid Franchise

SIMON BERGIN ‡
335 Wellington Road North Heaton Chapel Stockport Greater Manchester SK4 4QG
Tel: 0161 432 9945 *Fax:* 0161 432 1111
Dx: 22321 HEATON CHAPEL
E-mail: sdb@simonbergin.com
List of partners: S D Bergin
Languages: Hebrew
Work: B1 C1 E S1 S2 W Z(d)
Ptr: Bergin, Mr Simon David. . . . . *Feb 1971

CHAFES ‡
20 Market Place Stockport Greater Manchester SK1 1EY
Tel: 0161 477 1525 *Fax:* 0161 480 3731 *Dx:* 19655 STOCKPORT
E-mail: mail@chafes.co.uk
Office: Alderley Edge, New Mills, Wilmslow
Languages: Spanish
Work: A1 B1 B2 C1 C2 C3 D1 D2 E F1 G H J1 J2 K1 L M1 M2 N O P Q R1 S1 T1 T2 W Z(g,h,i,j,l,p,q,t,w,y,z)

CHRONNELL HIBBERT ‡
11 Hyde Road Woodley Stockport Greater Manchester SK6 1QG
Tel: 0161 494 6085 *Fax:* 0161 494 8280
List of partners: I B Jones, P J Ward, D G Williams
Office: Hyde
Work: C1 D1 E G H J1 K1 L N O P Q S1 W Z(m)
Emergency Action, Agency, Advocacy, Fixed Fee Interview, Legal Aid undertaken and Member of Accident Line
Ptr: Jones, Mr Iain B LLB(B'ham) . . . . *Nov 1971
Williams, Mr David G BA . . . . *Sep 1980
Ast: Cookson, Miss Helena J LLB . . . . *Dec 1990

THE CLARKE PARTNERSHIP ‡
1 Waterloo Court Waterloo Road Stockport Greater Manchester SK1 3DU
Tel: 0161 474 6600 *Fax:* 0161 474 6601 *Dx:* 19680 STOCKPORT
E-mail: info@theclarkepartnership.co.uk
List of partners: I W J Clarke, M W Gough
Work: N
Agency undertaken
Ptr: Clarke, Mr Ian W J . . . . *Dec 1979
Gough, Mr Michael William LLB. . . . . *Jan 1999
Ast: Axton, Mrs Catherine . . . . *Jan 1996
Jones, Mr Michael Ivan BA; MSc; CPE; LPC . . . . . *Apr 2005
Thorpe, Mr Andrew BA . . . . *Jan 1999
Con: Clarke, Mrs Sheenagh M BA(Hons); MSc . . . . *Aug 1983

MARTIN CUNNINGHAM SOLICITORS ‡
PO Box 395 12 Egerton Court Egerton Road Stockport Greater Manchester SK3 8WZ
Tel: 0161 456 5857
E-mail: martincunningham@martincunninghamsolicitor.co.uk
List of partners: M S Cunningham, J Naylor
Work: B2 G
Legal Aid undertaken
Ptr: Cunningham, Mr Martin S LLB(Hons)(Lond) Supervisor of the Specialist Fraud Panel . . . . Jul 1982
Naylor, Ms Judith . . . . Jul 2002

DAVIES & COMPANY ‡
Grand Central Central House 17 Grand Central Square Stockport Greater Manchester SK1 3TA
Tel: 0161 355 5500 *Fax:* 0161 355 5515 *Dx:* 22637 STOCKPORT 2
E-mail: philipd@dcsolicitors.com
List of partners: P H Davies
Languages: Gujarati, Punjabi, Urdu
Work: N
Ptr: Davies, Mr Philip H LLB. . . . . *§Apr 1972
Ast: Barrowcliff, Mr Nigel Paul LLB(Hons) . . . . *Apr 1995
Salim, Mr Imran LLB(Hons) . . . . Feb 2001

DELTA LEGAL ‡
1 Riverview The Embankment Stockport Greater Manchester SK4 3GN
Tel: 0870 350 5101 *Fax:* 0870 350 5109 *Dx:* 23166 DIDSBURY
E-mail: solicitors@deltalegal.co.uk
List of partners: D J Ismay
Languages: French, Mirpuri, Punjabi, Urdu
Work: N Q
Ptr: Ismay, Mr Daren John LLB(Hons) . . . . *Jan 1993

BRIAN DREWITT ‡
1 Levens Road Newby Road Hazel Grove Stockport Greater Manchester SK7 5DL
Tel: 0845 260 0855
E-mail: brian.drewitt@briandrewitt.co.uk
List of partners: B A Drewitt
Work: A3 C1 E I J1 O Q R1 R2 S2 U2 Z(b,c,e,j,za)
SPr: Drewitt, Mr Brian A MA(Cantab); MCIArb . . . . *Jan 1970

FORSTER DEAN LTD
71 Princes Street Stockport Greater Manchester SK1 1RW
Tel: 0161 870 3585 *Fax:* 0161 870 3586
E-mail: enquiries@forsterdean.co.uk
Office: Birkenhead, Bootle, Chorley, Crewe, Eccles, Ellesmere Port, Huyton, Leigh, Liverpool (5 offices), Oldham, Preston, Rochdale, Runcorn, St Helens, Warrington, Widnes (2 offices), Wigan

FRANCIS ALEXANDER SOLICITORS ‡
Alexander House 476 Didsbury Road Heaton Mersey Stockport Greater Manchester SK4 3BS
Tel: 0161 432 3633
E-mail: alex.speed@francisalexandersolicitors.co.uk
List of partners: A Speed
SPr: Speed, Mr Alexander . . . . Jan 1998

NIGEL GLASSEY SOLICITOR ‡
Houldsworth House 13 Leamington Road Reddish Stockport Greater Manchester SK5 6BD
Tel: 0161 443 1395 *Fax:* 0161 443 2094 *Dx:* 702792 REDDISH
List of partners: N J A Glassey, J V Woods
Ptr: Glassey, Mr Nigel J A BA(Oxon) Notary Public . . . *§Mar 1969
Woods, Mr J Vincent LLB . . . . *Apr 1977

GLOBAL SOLICITORS ‡
5 Winston Close Marple Stockport Greater Manchester SK6 6HW
Tel: 0161 427 0553

GORVINS ‡
Dale House Tiviot Dale Stockport Greater Manchester SK1 1TA
Tel: 0161 930 5151 *Fax:* 0161 930 5252 *Dx:* 719421 STOCKPORT 7
E-mail: enquiries@gorvins.com
Work: A3 B1 B2 C1 C2 C3 D1 D2 E F1 F2 G I J1 J2 K1 K2 K3 K4 L N O P Q R2 S1 S2 T1 T2 U2 V W X Z(b,c,d,e,f,j,l,m,o,p,q,r,t,w,za)

GREGORYS SOLICITORS
8-10 Commercial Road Hazel Grove Stockport Greater Manchester SK7 4AA
Tel: 0161 456 8125 *Fax:* 0161 483 7950 *Dx:* 15105 HAZEL GROVE
E-mail: enquiries@gregoryssolicitors.co.uk
Office: Altrincham
Work: D1 D2 K1 K3 K4 L S1 W
Advocacy, Legal Aid undertaken and Legal Aid Franchise
Ptr: Gorner, Mr John S LLB . . . . *Jun 1984
Jones, Jenny Hannah. . . . . Apr 2004
Knight, Miss Linda M . . . . Jun 1981
Pinto, Miss Lorna M. . . . . Nov 1982
Sandler, Mr Michael H. . . . . *Sep 1979
Yasser, Mr Mohammed LLB. . . . . Feb 1979
Asoc: Thompson, Mrs Helen J BA(Hons) Committee Member of Stockport Law Society. . . . . *Oct 1993

HALE SOLICITORS ‡
Octagon House 8a Fir Road Stockport Greater Manchester SK7 2NP
Tel: 0161 439 0999

HARGREAVES MOUNTENEY SOLICITORS ‡
Errwood House 212 Moss Lane Bramhall Stockport Greater Manchester SK7 1BD
Tel: 0161 440 9901 *Fax:* 0161 439 4207
E-mail: info@mounteney.com

HARVEY ROBERTS ‡
92-94 Gorton Road Reddish Stockport Greater Manchester SK5 6AN
Tel: 0161 443 2828 *Fax:* 0161 432 8079 *Dx:* 702790 REDDISH
E-mail: john@harveyroberts.co.uk
List of partners: N R Bolton, J Burgess, J H Roberts, D J Smith
Languages: French, Spanish
Work: E F1 J1 K1 N O Q S1 V W Z(l)
Emergency Action, Agency, Advocacy, Fixed Fee Interview undertaken and Member of Accident Line
Ptr: Bolton, Mr Neil R LLB. . . . . Nov 1986
Burgess, Mr Jeffrey LLB. . . . . Nov 1991
Roberts, Mr John H BA . . . . Nov 1987
Smith, Mr David John LLB(Lond) . . . . *Jul 1976

HENRYS SOLICITORS LTD ‡
72-74 Wellington Road South Stockport Greater Manchester SK1 3SU
Tel: 0161 477 8558 *Fax:* 0161 474 7667
E-mail: reception@henrysolicitors.co.uk
List of partners: K J Henry
Office: Poynton, Stockport
Ptr: Henry, Mr Kieran J LLB(Hons). . . . . *Oct 1992
Ast: Kerrigan, Mr Stephen . . . . Jan 1975
Sadiq, Tarick . . . . *Sep 2002

HENRYS SOLICITORS LTD
Kendal House Rear Market Street New Mills Stockport Greater Manchester SK22 4BS
Tel: 01663 742222 *Fax:* 01663 742222
Emergency telephone 07074 816682
E-mail: henryco@cwcom.net
Office: Poynton, Stockport
Work: B2 G H W
Emergency Action, Agency, Advocacy, Fixed Fee Interview, Legal Aid undertaken and Legal Aid Franchise

THE HOWE PRACTICE ‡
2 Waterloo Court Waterloo Road Stockport Greater Manchester SK1 3DU
Tel: 0161 480 2629 *Fax:* 0161 480 0015 *Dx:* 22619 STOCKPORT 2
List of partners: J E Howe
Work: E F1 K1 L N S1 W Z(l)
Agency undertaken
SPr: Howe, Mr John E LLB(Hons) . . . . *Oct 1978
Asoc: Marsden, Mr Roger L. . . . . *Dec 1977

JONES GOUGH LLP SOLICITORS ‡
Unit 5 The National Trading Estate Bramhall Moor Lane Stockport Greater Manchester SK7 5AA
Tel: 0845 373 2585 *Fax:* 0845 373 2586
E-mail: info@jonesgough.com

JONES KNOWLES WARBURTON ‡
48 Middle Hillgate Stockport Greater Manchester SK1 3DG
Tel: 0161 474 1992 *Fax:* 0161 474 1993
Emergency telephone 07641 104689 / 01459 122780
List of partners: D G Jones, N R Warburton
Work: G H
Emergency Action, Agency, Advocacy, Fixed Fee Interview, Legal Aid undertaken and Legal Aid Franchise
Ptr: Jones, Mr David G BA . . . . *Dec 1975
Warburton, Mr Neville R BA. . . . . *Sep 1982

HUGH JOSEPH SOLICITORS ‡
102 Heaton Moor Road Stockport Greater Manchester SK4 4NZ
Tel: 0161 975 0600

LEA & CO ‡
(in association with Alex Trappeniers-Advokaat(Belgium))
Bank Chambers Market Place Stockport Greater Manchester SK1 1UN
Tel: 0161 480 6691 *Fax:* 0161 480 0904 *Dx:* 19651 STOCKPORT 1
E-mail: mail@lealaw.com
List of partners: A Berry, S H Q Lea
Work: C1 C2 E L M1 M2 N O P Q R2 S1 S2 W Z(c,e,f)
Legal Aid undertaken
Ptr: Berry, Mr Alan LLB . . . *Oct 1990
Lea, Mr Stephen H Q . . . *§Jun 1979

MLS SOLICITORS LLP ‡
Unit 14-15 International House Bredbury Park Way Stockport Greater Manchester SK6 2SN
Tel: 0161 968 7037 *Fax:* 0161 968 7030
E-mail: info@mortgagelegal.co.uk
List of partners: S Jenden, I S Mason, J A White
Work: S1
Mem: Jenden, Miss Susan BA. . . . Nov 1983
Mason, Mr Ian Stuart MA(Oxon). . . . *Jun 1977
White, Mr John A . . . *Jul 1974

B J MCKENNA & CO SOLICITORS ‡
182a Heaton Moor Road Heaton Moor Stockport Greater Manchester SK4 4DU
Tel: 0161 432 5757 *Fax:* 0161 431 5123
Emergency telephone 07763 195868
E-mail: bj.mckenna@zen.co.uk
List of partners: B J McKenna, R W Schirmer
Languages: German
Work: D1 J1 K1 K3 K4 N S1 W
Emergency Action, Agency, Fixed Fee Interview and Legal Aid undertaken
Ptr: McKenna, Mr Bernard Joseph LLB(Hons) . . . *Dec 1996
Schirmer, Mr Richard Werner BProc; LLB . . . *Apr 2002
Ast: Harold, Mrs Sinead Catherine LLB(Hons) . . . *Jun 2004
Missenden, Miss Karen Lorraine LLB(Hons). . . . *Dec 1998
Neill, Miss Amanda . . . *Oct 2007

MORTONS ‡
22 Middle Hillgate Stockport Greater Manchester SK1 3AY
Tel: 0161 477 1121 *Fax:* 0161 477 0708 *Dx:* 22614 STOCKPORT 2
Emergency telephone 0161 477 1121
List of partners: S E Morton
Work: G H
Emergency Action, Agency, Advocacy, Fixed Fee Interview, Legal Aid undertaken and Legal Aid Franchise
Ptr: Morton, Mr Simon E ★ . . . Jun 1995

ALFRED NEWTON & CO ‡
(incorporating Olliers; Davies & Jackson)
49-51 Wellington Road South Stockport Greater Manchester SK1 3RX
Tel: 0161 480 6551 / 480 1245 *Fax:* 0161 429 9316
Emergency telephone 0161 406 8726
List of partners: R A Fleming, A Penman, S A Penman
Office: Stockport, Wilmslow
Work: A1 B1 B2 D1 D2 E F1 F2 G H J1 K1 K3 L M1 N O P Q R1 S1 S2 T1 T2 V W Z(c,h,i,l,m)
Emergency Action, Agency, Advocacy, Fixed Fee Interview, Legal Aid undertaken, Legal Aid Franchise and Member of Accident Line
Ptr: Fleming, Mr Robert Alastair LLB(Manc) . . . *Dec 1977
Penman, Mr Anthony . . . *Feb 1970
Penman, Mrs Sarah A BA(Law) . . . *Oct 1982
Ast: Owen, Mr Peter R BA. . . . *Jul 1977
Con: Allsager, Mr William J F. . . . *§Feb 1952

ALFRED NEWTON & CO
231 George Lane Bredbury Stockport Greater Manchester SK1 1DJ
Tel: 0161 430 8831 *Fax:* 0161 430 6636
Office: Stockport, Wilmslow
Work: B1 D1 G H K1 L M1 M2 Q S1 W
Emergency Action, Agency, Fixed Fee Interview, Legal Aid undertaken, Legal Aid Franchise and Member of Accident Line
Ptr: Penman, Mrs Sarah A BA(Law) . . . *Oct 1982
Ast: Penman, Miss Jennifer Joy LLB(Hons) . . . Aug 2010
Tysall, Miss Danielle Louise LLB(Hons) . . . Jun 2010

NIGHTINGALES SOLICITORS LIMITED ‡
(incorporating John Nightingale Knott & Castle; Withington & Petty)
127 Buxton Road High Lane Stockport Greater Manchester SK6 8DX
Tel: 01663 764038 *Fax:* 01663 763540
E-mail: ptaylor@nightingalessolicitors.co.uk
Web: www.nightingalessolicitors.co.uk
List of partners: N J Harney, R B Houlker, P P Taylor
Work: A1 B1 C1 C2 D1 D2 E F1 G H J1 K1 K2 L M1 N O P Q R1 R2 S1 S2 T1 T2 V W Z(a,b,c,d,e,f,h,i,j,k,l,m,n,o,p,q,r,s)
Emergency Action, Agency, Advocacy, Fixed Fee Interview, Legal Aid undertaken, Legal Aid Franchise and Member of Accident Line
Dir: Harney, Mr Nicolas J LLB Notary Public. . . . *§Nov 1973
Houlker, Mr Roger B Notary Public . . . *§May 1977
Taylor, Mr Peter Philip BA(Law) . . . *Dec 1980

NUTTALL HOGG ‡
11-13 Lower Hillgate Stockport Greater Manchester SK1 1JQ
Tel: 0161 480 0901 *Fax:* 0161 477 7508 *Dx:* 19659 STOCKPORT 1
List of partners: D Hogg
Work: C1 C2 E J1 N R1 S1 W

O'NEILL MORGAN SOLICITORS LIMITED ‡
Prudential Buildings 63 St Petersgate Stockport Greater Manchester SK1 1DH
Tel: 0161 429 8383 *Fax:* 0161 480 4574 *Dx:* 195656 STOCKPORT 1
E-mail: oneill.morgan@oneill-morgan.co.uk
List of partners: M E Morgan, D Ward
Work: B1 C1 D1 D2 E J1 K1 K3 L N Q R2 S1 S2 W Z(b,r)
Emergency Action, Agency, Advocacy, Fixed Fee Interview undertaken and Member of Accident Line
Dir: Morgan, Mr Michael E LLB . . . *§Sep 1981
Ward, Ms Deborah LLB(Hons) . . . *Aug 1999

O'NEILL PATIENT ‡
Chester House Hazel Grove Stockport Greater Manchester SK7 5NT
Tel: 0161 483 8555 *Fax:* 0161 483 0333
E-mail: enqs@oneillpatient.co.uk
List of partners: S E Ashton, S Brown, R J C Higham, L J Patient, L M Stenson
Work: C1 C2 E F1 F2 I J1 L N O Q R2 S1 S2 U2 W Z(b,f,j,w,z)
Ptr: Ashton, Mr Simon E BA(Law) . . . *Oct 1984
Higham, Mr Robin J C LLB . . . *Mar 1980
Patient, Mr Leslie J LLB. . . . *May 1988
Stenson, Mr Lee M LLB. . . . *Apr 1979
Brown, Sue . . . NSP

Asoc: Kaye, Mr Warren Elliot LLB(Hons). . . . *Jan 2006
Moore, Mrs Suzanne C LLB. . . . *Nov 1994
Parker, Mrs O Jane LLB(Hons) . . . *Oct 1983
Thomas, Mr Steven LLB . . . *Jan 1998
Ast: Bourke, Mr Martin LLB . . . *Sep 2004
Frost, Mr Stephen BA. . . . *Jun 2004
Heppell, Mr Mark Michael LLB(Hons) . . . *Feb 2008
Kime, Miss Laura LLB. . . . *Jun 2008

PARKERS ‡
33 Wellington Road South Stockport Greater Manchester SK1 3RP
Tel: 0161 477 9451 *Fax:* 0161 477 9452
List of partners: M G Parker, S K Parker, J J Pegna
Languages: Italian
Work: C1 E F1 K1 N O Q S1
Agency, Advocacy and Legal Aid undertaken
Ptr: Parker, Mr Michael Graham BSc; LRIC . . . *Dec 1979
Parker, Miss Susan K LLB . . . Dec 1982
Pegna, Mr Julian J . . . *May 1982
Asoc: Parker, Mrs O Jane LLB(Hons) . . . *Oct 1983

PRICKETTS ‡
30 Great Underbank Stockport Greater Manchester SK1 1NB
Tel: 0161 429 8000 *Fax:* 0161 480 0968 *Dx:* 19666 STOCKPORT 1
E-mail: nick.seymour@pricketts.co.uk
List of partners: E A Ince, N J Seymour, A Shackleton, B M Wragg
Office: Buxton
Work: B1 C1 C2 C3 D1 E F1 J1 J2 K1 K3 K4 L N O P Q R1 R2 S1 S2 W Z(c,d,e,j,k,l,q,r)
Emergency Action and Advocacy undertaken
Ptr: Seymour, Mr Nicholas J LLB(Manc). . . . *§Jun 1974

REYNARDS SOLICITORS ‡
Hilton House Lord Street Stockport Greater Manchester SK1 3NA
Tel: 0161 217 7000 / 217 7002
E-mail: info@reynardslaw.co.uk

SAS DANIELS LLP ‡
30 Greek Street Stockport Greater Manchester SK3 8AD
Tel: 0161 475 7676 *Fax:* 0161 475 7677
E-mail: help@sasdaniels.co.uk
List of partners: M R J Bestley, E A Bottrill, A E Brown, G Browton, S J Chesworth, J C Cook, A C Dowd, N R C Haddon, S C Hesford, T R Lomas, M D Ridings, R Simpson, S Sinclair, C R J Smith, P M Smith, H E Thompson, A L Tudin, J M Whittaker, N J Wilson
Office: Bramhall, Chester, Congleton, Macclesfield
Work: A1 A3 B1 C1 C2 C3 D1 D2 E F1 F2 J1 J2 K1 K2 L N O P Q R1 S1 S2 W Z(c,l,p,q,r)
Emergency Action, Agency, Advocacy, Fixed Fee Interview undertaken and Member of Accident Line
Ptr: Bottrill, Ms Elizabeth Anne LLB . . . Sep 1992
Brown, Mrs Angela Elizabeth LLB. . . . *Dec 1991
Chesworth, Mrs Shelley Jane . . . *Nov 1991
Cook, Mr John Charles LLB. . . . *Sep 1995
Dowd, Mr Andrew Christopher LLB(Hons). . . . *Oct 1991
Haddon, Mr Nigel Richard Charles LLB; ACIArb. . . . *Oct 1981
Sinclair, Ms Sandra LLB(Hons) . . . *Oct 1985
Smith, Mr Charles Richard Julian LLB. . . . *May 1977
Smith, Mr Philip M LLB . . . *Feb 1975
Whittaker, Mr Jonathan Michael LLB(Hons) . . . *Jun 1980
Asoc: Taylor, Ms Maria Theresa LLB(Hons) . . . *Oct 1993
Ast: Bennett, Mrs Lorna Allan . . . *Aug 2002
McColl, Mrs Pamela Mary Rose LLB(Hons) . . . *Apr 2005
Waugh, Ms Sarah Louise BA(Hons). . . . *Apr 2000
Wong, Miss Janet Bik-ki. . . . Jan 2006
Con: Leach, Mrs Karen Heather LLB . . . *Oct 1985
Neary, Mr Nigel Howard LLB . . . *Jun 1978

SGM SOLICITORS ‡
10 Riverview The Embankment Heaton Mersey Stockport Greater Manchester SK4 3GN
Tel: 0161 947 4990
E-mail: info@sgmsolicitors.com

S J LEGAL LIMITED ‡
119-123 Wellington Road South Stockport Greater Manchester SK1 3TH
Tel: 0845 658 0142 *Fax:* 0845 659 5912

SOHAN RABHERU SERVICES LIMITED ‡
Brookfield House 193-195 Wellington Road South Stockport Greater Manchester SK2 6NG
Tel: 0845 241 1299 *Fax:* 0845 241 0868

THE THRASHER WALKER PARTNERSHIP ‡
The Old Bank 112 Heaton Moor Road Heaton Moor Stockport Greater Manchester SK4 4AN
Tel: 0161 442 6240 *Fax:* 0161 442 6292
E-mail: post@twpsolicitors.co.uk
List of partners: C Gartland, J D Walker
Work: B1 C1 D1 D2 E F1 F2 K1 K3 N O Q S1 S2 W
Emergency Action, Agency, Fixed Fee Interview, Legal Aid undertaken and Legal Aid Franchise
Ptr: Gartland, Miss Caroline LLB. . . . Oct 2006
Walker, Ms Jean D LLB(Hons) . . . *Jun 1979

TRANTERS
29-31a Middle Hillgate Stockport Greater Manchester SK1 3AY
Tel: 0161 480 9999 *Fax:* 0161 480 9993
Office: Manchester (2 offices)

WEBSTER O'BRIEN LLP ‡
Broadstone House Broadstone Road Reddish Stockport Greater Manchester SK5 7DL
Tel: 0161 283 3750 *Fax:* 0161 291 1860
List of partners: P M O'Brien, J D Webster
Ptr: O'Brien, Ms Peta Mary . . . Nov 1993
Webster, Mr John David. . . . Dec 1993

CLIVE G WOOD & CO ‡
49 Middle Hillgate Stockport Greater Manchester SK1 3DL
Tel: 0161 480 1000 *Fax:* 0161 429 0211 *Dx:* 22631 STOCKPORT 2
E-mail: mail@cgwlaw.co.uk
List of partners: M Higgins, C G Wood
Work: D1 D2 E K1 K3 Q S1 S2 V W
Emergency Action, Agency, Advocacy, Fixed Fee Interview and Legal Aid undertaken
Ptr: Higgins, Mr Mark LLB. . . . *Nov 1993
Wood, Mr Clive Graham BA. . . . *Sep 1982
Ast: Miller, Miss Sarah LLB . . . *Nov 2007
Wells, Mrs Patricia E LLB. . . . *Oct 1984

STOCKTON-ON-TEES

APPLEBY HOPE & MATTHEWS
24a High Street Stockton-on-Tees TS18 1SP
Tel: 01642 617000 *Fax:* 01642 616995
Office: Middlesbrough
Work: G H K1 K2 S1
Agency, Advocacy, Fixed Fee Interview, Legal Aid undertaken and Legal Aid Franchise

APPLEYARD LEES
NETPark Incubator Thomas Wright Way Sedgefield Stockton-on-Tees TS21 3FD
Tel: 0191 301 7191 *Fax:* 0191 301 7192
E-mail: durham@appleyardlees.com
Office: Burnley, Chester, Halifax, Harrogate, Huddersfield, Leeds, Liverpool, Manchester, Preston, Sheffield, York

ARCHERS LAW LLP ‡
Lakeside House Kingfisher Way Stockton-on-Tees TS18 3NB
Tel: 01642 636500 *Fax:* 01642 636501 *Dx:* 721030 STOCKTON 3
E-mail: enquiries@archerslaw.co.uk
List of partners: D A Collier, R G Irons, R A Porter, J Richardson, A K Smith, C D Todd, A K Torrance
Work: A1 B1 C1 D1 E F1 G H J1 K1 K3 K4 L M1 N O P Q R1 R2 S1 S2 T1 T2 W Z(c,d,e,f,i,k,l,m,o,p,q,r,s)
Emergency Action, Advocacy, Fixed Fee Interview, Legal Aid undertaken and Legal Aid Franchise
Ptr: Collier, Mr David A LLB Clerk to Commissioner of Taxes . . . *Mar 1983
Irons, Mr Robert G BA(Hons) Notary Public . . . *May 1983
Porter, Mr Raymond A MA(Cantab) William Hutton Prize . . . *Jul 1979
Richardson, Mr John LLB(Leeds) . . . Jun 1974
Smith, Mr Alistair Kellett LLB; BSc. . . . Sep 1994
Todd, Mr Christopher David LLB. . . . Nov 1993
Torrance, Miss Angela K . . . *Sep 1997
Ast: Barnes, Mrs Sara Dominique F LLB. . . . *Sep 2002
Cox, Mrs Irene M MA; TEP . . . *Oct 1991
Dunn, Miss Claire LLB; FILEx. . . . Nov 2005
Foreman, Ms Elizabeth LLB(Hons) . . . May 1999
Mclaine, Ms Elaine . . . *Oct 2006
Pope, Mrs Ann C LLB. . . . *Dec 1976
Turner, Miss Helen Fiona BA . . . Jun 2004
Con: Crute, Mr Geoffrey T LLB; FFA; FIMgt; TEP. . . . *Jun 1967

ASKEWS
Dunedin House Columbia Drive Thornaby Stockton-on-Tees TS17 6BJ
Tel: 01642 475252 *Fax:* 01642 211017
Dx: 723017 STOCKTON-ON-TEES 10
E-mail: info@askews.com
Office: Middlesbrough, Redcar
Work: B1 C1 C2 D1 E F1 J1 K1 K3 L N O P S1 T1 T2 V W Z(e,h,k,l)
Emergency Action, Agency, Advocacy, Legal Aid undertaken and Member of Accident Line

BHP LAW
Kingfisher House 2 Kingfisher Way Preston Farm Stockton-on-Tees TS18 3EX
Tel: 01642 672770 *Fax:* 01642 660288 *Dx:* 65001 THORNABY
E-mail: info@bhplaw.co.uk
Office: Darlington, Durham, Halifax, Newcastle upon Tyne, Newton Aycliffe, North Shields
Work: A3 B1 C1 C2 C3 D1 D2 E F1 F2 G H J1 J2 K1 K2 K3 K4 L N O Q R1 R2 S1 S2 T1 T2 U1 U2 W X Z(c,e,o,p,q,r,u,w,x,za)
Legal Aid undertaken
Ptr: Baker, Mr Richard. . . . Jun 1977
Birks, Mr David LLB(Hons) . . . Oct 2005
Lucas, Mr David. . . . Mar 2003
Robinson, Mr Simon MA(Cantab) Notary Public . . . Nov 1986
Wood, Mrs Helen . . . Nov 2000
Ast: Wood, Mrs Helen . . . Nov 2000

BERRYMANS LACE MAWER
Innovation House Yarm Road Stockton-on-Tees TS18 3TN
Tel: 01642 661630 *Fax:* 01642 661631
Dx: 715799 STOCKTON-ON-TEES 8
E-mail: info@blm-law.com
Office: Birmingham, Bristol, Cardiff, Leeds, Liverpool, London EC2, Manchester, Southampton
Work: J2 N Z(j)

BROWELL SMITH & CO
Unit 16 Halegrove Court Cygnet Drive Stockton-on-Tees TS18 3DB
Tel: 0871 474 3030 *Fax:* 0845 302 4755
E-mail: advice@browells.co.uk
Office: Ashington, Cramlington, Newcastle upon Tyne (3 offices), Stoke-on-Trent, Sunderland

CRUTES
Crutes House University Boulevard Teesdale Park Stockton-on-Tees TS17 6EN
Tel: 01642 623400 *Fax:* 01642 623401
Dx: 723018 STOCKTON-ON-TEES 10
Emergency telephone 01642 781045
E-mail: advice@crutes.co.uk
Office: Carlisle, Newcastle upon Tyne
Work: A3 C1 D1 E F1 G H J1 J2 K1 K3 L N O Q R1 R2 S1 S2 V W Z(c,h,j,k,l,o,q,r,u)
Emergency Action, Agency, Advocacy, Fixed Fee Interview, Legal Aid undertaken and Member of Accident Line
Ptr: Howes, Miss Sue . . . Oct 2002
Jones, Mr Gareth E LLB(Hons) . . . Oct 1993
Ast: Hutchinson, Ms Sarah Jane LLB . . . Sep 2006
Nickalls, Mr Paul . . . Nov 1997
Taylor, Ms Ysanne M . . . Nov 1984

SIMON DALY SOLICITORS ‡
Unit 7/8 1 Brunswick Street Stockton-on-Tees TS18 1DW
Tel: 01642 604074 *Fax:* 01642 604084
Emergency telephone 01642 604074
E-mail: sdalysol@btconnect.com
List of partners: S N Daly
Languages: French, German
Work: B1 C1 C3 F1 J1 M1 O Q Z(b,za)
Agency, Advocacy and Fixed Fee Interview undertaken
SPr: Daly, Mr Simon N BA(Hons) ♦. . . . *Nov 1984

See p112 for the Key to Work Categories & other symbols

DICKINSON DEES
Camden House Prince's Wharf Teesdale Stockton-on-Tees TS17 6QY
Tel: 0844 984 1500 *Fax:* 0844 984 1501
E-mail: law@dickinson-dees.com
Office: London EC4, Newcastle upon Tyne (2 offices), York

DONNELLY MCARDLE ADAMSON
Unit 115 Stockton Business Centre 70 Brunswick Street Stockton-on-Tees TS18 1DW
Tel: 01642 345151 *Fax:* 01642 345152
E-mail: enquiries@macardles.co.uk
Office: Darlington, Hartlepool, Peterlee, Sunderland (2 offices)

THE ENDEAVOUR PARTNERSHIP LLP ‡
Westminster St Marks Court Teesdale Business Park Stockton-on-Tees TS17 6QP
Tel: 01642 610300 *Fax:* 01642 610330 / 610348
Dx: 723015 STOCKTON 10
E-mail: enquiries@endeavourpartnership.com
List of partners: P L Bennett, L C Bramley, J Brown, J D Bruce, J P Bury, J Smith, S Wake
Languages: Dutch, Flemish, French, German
Work: A1 B1 C1 C2 E J1 O Q R1 S2 T1 Z(b,e,q)
Mem: Bennett, Mr Paul Lloyd . . . *Nov 1975
Bramley, Mr Lee Carl . . . *Sep 2000
Brown, Mr Jamie . . . *Oct 2002
Bruce, Ms Julie Dawn . . . *Apr 1995
Bury, Mr John Paul . . . *May 1979
Smith, Miss Joanna . . . *Sep 1997
Wake, Mr Simon . . . *Oct 1988
Ast: Burbidge, Miss Vivienne . . . Sep 2011
Devereux, Ms Catherine . . . *Dec 2003
Gibbon, Mrs Fiona . . . *Sep 2005
Ketchley, Mrs Alexander . . . Sep 2009
McPhie, Miss Katy . . . Sep 2011
Pandal, Satpal . . . *Nov 2006
Smith, Mr Alexander Frey . . . *Mar 2008

GIBBENS SOLICITORS ‡
Newport House Teesdale South Stockton-on-Tees TS17 6SE
Tel: 01642 702481 *Fax:* 01642 702480
E-mail: sjgibbens@gibbens-solicitors.co.uk
List of partners: S J Gibbens
SPr: Gibbens, Mr Stephen James LLB(Hons) . . . *Sep 2001

HAWKINS ROSS LIMITED ‡
PO Box 49 6 Finkle Street Stockton-on-Tees TS18 1AR
Tel: 01642 613647 / 678888 *Fax:* 01642 612338
Dx: 60607 STOCKTON-ON-TEES
E-mail: hawkinsross@qnetadsl.com
List of partners: N Capstick, A N Ross
Work: B1 C1 C2 D1 D2 E F1 G H J1 K1 L N O Q R1 R2 S1 S2 W X Z(c,e,j,k,l,q,t)
Agency and Advocacy undertaken
Dir: Capstick, Mr Nicholas . . . *Dec 1978
Ross, Mr Alastair N LLB(Hons) . . . *Jun 1980

HEWITTS
(incorporating Cohens)
1 Yarm Lane Stockton-on-Tees TS18 3DR
Tel: 01642 673701 *Fax:* 01642 675428
Dx: 60606 STOCKTON-ON-TEES
E-mail: enquiries@hewitts.co.uk
Office: Bishop Auckland, Crook, Darlington, Newton Aycliffe
Work: D1 D2 E K1 L N O Q S1 S2 Z(q)
Emergency Action, Agency, Advocacy, Fixed Fee Interview, Legal Aid undertaken, Legal Aid Franchise and Member of Accident Line
Ptr: Fountain, Mr Christopher J L LLB . . . *Jun 1975
Hole, Mr Michael . . . *Sep 1995

LEIGH TURTON DIXON
Unit 112 Stockton Business Centre 70-74 Brunswick Street Stockton-on-Tees TS18 1DW
Tel: 01642 345230 *Fax:* 01642 345231
Emergency telephone 07815 935461
E-mail: ltdsols@yahoo.co.uk
Office: Middlesbrough
Ast: Clancy, Alexandra . . . Feb 2009

MEIKLES
(incorporating Dawson Arnott & Pickering; Hardesty Elleanor)
7 High Street Sedgefield Stockton-on-Tees TS21 3AS
Tel: 01740 620255 *Fax:* 01740 620713
Office: Barnard Castle, Bishop Auckland, Ferryhill, Spennymoor
Work: D1 E G H K1 L N Q S1 V W Z(l,m)
Emergency Action, Agency, Advocacy, Fixed Fee Interview, Legal Aid undertaken and Legal Aid Franchise
Ptr: Forrest, Miss Elizabeth LLB(Hons) . . . *Oct 1995
Ast: Schofield, Jacquelyn . . . May 2008
Con: Wilson, Mr Michael G LLB . . . *Apr 1977

NEWBYS ‡
(incorporating Thomas Bingham & Spark)
10 Finkle Street Stockton-on-Tees TS18 1AS
Tel: 01642 673733 / 676666 *Fax:* 01642 676666
Dx: 60600 STOCKTON-ON-TEES
Emergency telephone 01388 721675
E-mail: johnpacey@newbys.co.uk
List of partners: S J Bosomworth
Office: Guisborough, Middlesbrough
Work: A1 B1 C1 C2 C3 D1 E F1 J1 K1 L N O Q R1 S1 T1 T2 V W Z(i,l,m,o,p)
Emergency Action, Agency, Advocacy, Fixed Fee Interview, Legal Aid undertaken and Member of Accident Line
Ptr: Bosomworth, Mr Stephen John . . . *Jan 1979
Ast: Juggins, Miss Lindsey LLB(L'pool) . . . *Dec 1989
Owens, Miss Alexandra LPC . . . *Nov 1996
Con: Pacey, Mr F John LLB(Lond) Notary Public . . . *§Aug 1964

P B BRADLEY ‡
40-42 Dryburn Road Stockton-on-Tees TS19 8JN
Tel: 01642 672220 *Fax:* 01642 672220
E-mail: pbbradley@btinternet.com

PUNCH ROBSON
34 Myton Road Ingleby Barwick Stockton-on-Tees TS17 0WG
Tel: 01642 754050 *Fax:* 01642 754060
Office: Middlesbrough (2 offices)
Work: K1 K3 K4 S1 W
Emergency Action, Agency, Advocacy, Fixed Fee Interview, Legal Aid undertaken and Legal Aid Franchise
Asoc: Tansley, Miss Zoe LLB(Hons) . . . *Sep 2003

Ast: Clark, Ms Joanne . . . *Nov 2004
Eaton, Ms Kathryn BA . . . *Sep 2001

JOHN TILLOTSON ‡
8 Silver Street Stockton-on-Tees TS18 1SX
Tel: 01642 676000 *Fax:* 01642 671364
Dx: 60605 STOCKTON-ON-TEES
List of partners: J Tillotson
Work: F1 G J1 K1 L M1 P S1 W
Emergency Action, Agency, Advocacy, Fixed Fee Interview and Legal Aid undertaken
Ptr: Tillotson, Mr John . . . Dec 1975
Ast: Rathmell, Mrs Anne Caroline Notary Public . . . *Nov 1981

TILLY BAILEY & IRVINE LLP
Castle House 11 Bridge Road Stockton-on-Tees TS18 3AD
Tel: 01642 673797 *Fax:* 0845 302 2991
Dx: 60624 STOCKTON-ON-TEES
E-mail: info@tbilaw.co.uk
Office: Barnard Castle, Billingham, Hartlepool
Work: D1 D2 K1 K3 K4 L N S1 T2 V W Z(r)
Emergency Action, Agency, Advocacy, Fixed Fee Interview, Legal Aid undertaken, Legal Aid Franchise and Member of Accident Line
Ptr: Brown, Mr Martin Leigh LLB(Newc) William Hutton Prize . . . *Mar 1978
Moreton, Ms Victoria Jane Suzanne LLB(Hons) Deputy District Judge . . . *Oct 1995
Wilsdon, Mr Timothy J LLB . . . *Dec 1978
Ast: Elstob, Miss Helen Mary . . . *Dec 2007
Nelson, Mrs Emma Linsey LLB . . . *Mar 2010
Samuels, Miss Rebecca LLB(Hons) . . . *Sep 2005

VICKERS CHISMAN & WISHLADE ‡
33 Silver Street Stockton-on-Tees TS18 1SX
Tel: 01642 615439 *Fax:* 01642 615014
Dx: 60617 STOCKTON-ON-TEES
E-mail: info@vcwsolicitors.co.uk
List of partners: D Chisman, T Vickers, B C Wildbridge, P Wishlade
Work: B2 D1 G H K1 L Q S1 V W Z(g)
Emergency Action, Agency, Advocacy, Fixed Fee Interview and Legal Aid undertaken
Ptr: Chisman, Mr Denis ★ . . . *Apr 1975
Vickers, Mr Trevor . . . Oct 1980
Wildbridge, Mr Brett Charles LLB(Hons) . . . *Jul 1972
Wishlade, Mr Peter ★ . . . *§Jun 1969

WATSON WOODHOUSE
7-9 Yarm Lane Stockton-on-Tees TS18 3DR
Tel: 01642 247656 *Fax:* 01642 213418 *Dx:* 60602 STOCKTON
Office: Darlington, Middlesbrough
Work: D1 G H J1 K1 L N V Z(m)
Emergency Action, Agency, Advocacy, Legal Aid undertaken and Legal Aid Franchise
Ptr: Brook, Mr Andrew R LLB(Sheff) . . . *Oct 1985
Douglas, Mr Neil A . . . *Oct 1988
Watson, Mr James LLB(Newc) . . . *May 1982
Woodhouse, Mr Nicolas J M LLB . . . Nov 1980

WREN MARTIN ‡
8 Nelson Terrace Stockton-on-Tees TS18 1NH
Tel: 01642 603609 *Fax:* 01642 614026
Dx: 60633 STOCKTON-ON-TEES
E-mail: wren.martin@btconnect.com
List of partners: P R Martin
Work: K1 S1 W
SPr: Martin, Mr Paul Ronan . . . *Dec 1977

STOKE-ON-TRENT

ATTWOOD SOLICITORS ‡
5-7 Hartshill Road Stoke-on-Trent ST4 1QH
Tel: 01782 608420 / 0800 145 5105
E-mail: enquiries@attwoodsolicitors.co.uk

BAILEY WAIN & CURZON ‡
Springfield House Baker Street Fenton Stoke-on-Trent ST4 3AF
Tel: 01782 847934 *Fax:* 01782 413272 *Dx:* 700401 FENTON
E-mail: acurzon@bwc-solicitors.co.uk
List of partners: R Bailey, A F Curzon, D C Moore
Work: D1 D2 E F1 J1 K1 L N O Q S1 S2 V W Z(c,l,q)
Emergency Action, Agency, Advocacy, Fixed Fee Interview and Legal Aid undertaken
Ptr: Bailey, Mr Robert LLB(Manc) . . . *Apr 1976
Curzon, Mr Anthony F Deputy Coroner for Staffordshire North . . . *Jan 1972
Moore, Mr David C LLB(Manc) Deputy District Judge . *Apr 1977

BESWICKS ‡
Sigma House Lakeside Festival Way Stoke-on-Trent ST1 5TD
Tel: 01782 205000 *Fax:* 01782 285986
List of partners: T Bailey, F Craig, H C Heath, P J Howland, J McGuiness, G N Mellor, G Neyt, N D Phillips, R Preston, A Scheland, M J Stephenson, S Taylor, A Turnock, S Woodings
Office: Hanley
Ptr: Neyt, Mr Graham . . . Oct 1989
Phillips, Mr Nicholas David LLB . . . *Sep 1999
Preston, Mr Richard . . . Jan 2004
Scheland, Mrs Anne ICSA . . . *Jan 1999
Taylor, Mr Stephen . . . *Oct 1997
Woodings, Mr Simon LLB . . . *Oct 1991
Asoc: Howle, Ms Rebecca . . . Oct 2004
Mellor, Ms Sarah . . . Jun 2005
Morris, Miss Jaqueline . . . Dec 1994
Simmonds, Mr Matthew . . . Sep 2002
Simmonds, Mr Richard . . . Nov 2008
Smith, Miss Elayna . . . Nov 2008
Ast: Shufflebottom, Ms Kate . . . Jan 2010

BIRCHFIELD
6 Bagnall Street Hanley Stoke-on-Trent ST1 3AQ
Tel: 01782 216888 *Fax:* 01782 286213
E-mail: enquiries@birchfields.co.uk
Office: Manchester

ARTHUR BOULTON SOLICITORS
24 Market Place Burslem Stoke-on-Trent ST6 4AX
Tel: 01782 813315 *Fax:* 01782 835782 *Dx:* 22307 BURSLEM
Emergency telephone 01782 610972
E-mail: enquiries@arthurboulton.com
Office: Stafford, Stoke-on-Trent
Work: D1 D2 E K1 K3 L S1 S2 W Z(d)

Emergency Action, Agency, Advocacy, Fixed Fee Interview, Legal Aid undertaken and Legal Aid Franchise

A F BROOKS & CO ‡
Valley House 12 Hartshill Road Stoke-on-Trent ST4 7QU
Tel: 01782 415007 *Fax:* 01782 845600
List of partners: A F Brooks
Languages: Welsh
Work: B1 D1 E F1 G H J1 K1 L M1 N P S1 V W
Emergency Action, Agency, Advocacy, Fixed Fee Interview and Legal Aid undertaken
Ptr: Brooks, Mr Alwyn F . . . *Dec 1976

BROWELL SMITH & CO
Park Road Burslem Stoke-on-Trent ST6 1EG
Tel: 0871 474 3030 *Fax:* 0845 302 4755
E-mail: advice@browells.co.uk
Office: Ashington, Cramlington, Newcastle upon Tyne (3 offices), Stockton-on-Tees, Sunderland

CHESWORTHS ‡
37 Trentham Road Longton Stoke-on-Trent ST3 4DQ
Tel: 01782 599992 *Fax:* 01782 599415 *Dx:* 21851 LONGTON
E-mail: mjrigby@chesworths.co.uk
List of partners: M Earl, M J Rigby
Office: Stoke-on-Trent
Work: C1 C2 C3 D1 E F1 G H J1 K1 L N O S1 S2 W Z(q,r)
Agency, Advocacy undertaken and Member of Accident Line
Ptr: Rigby, Mr Michael J BA . . . *§May 1981

CHESWORTHS
80 Weston Road Meir Stoke-on-Trent ST3 6RU
Tel: 01782 599993 *Fax:* 01782 333351 *Dx:* 22451 MEIR
E-mail: chesworths@chesworths.co.uk
Office: Stoke-on-Trent
Work: E S1 S2 W
Ptr: Earl, Mr Mark LLB(Leics) . . . *Dec 1973
Ast: Hewitt, Ms Laura Elizabeth LLB(Hons) . . . *Feb 2007

CLYDE CHAPPELL & BOTHAM ‡
97/99 Weston Road Meir Stoke-on-Trent ST3 6AJ
Tel: 01782 599577 *Fax:* 01782 599728
E-mail: solicitors@clydechappellandbotham.com
List of partners: R J Clarke, A E Whitmore
Work: A1 D1 E K1 K3 K4 L S1 S2 V W
Emergency Action, Agency, Advocacy, Fixed Fee Interview and Legal Aid Franchise
Ptr: Clarke, Mr Robert James BA . . . *Jul 1980
Whitmore, Mr Alan E . . . *Jan 1980

DE CONINCK SOLICITORS ‡
161 Sandbach Road North Alsager Stoke-on-Trent ST7 2AX
Tel: 01270 883484
List of partners: R De Coninck
SPr: De Coninck, Mr Robert BA(Hons) . . . *Aug 1983

DICKSONS SOLICITORS LTD ‡
Gordon Chambers 30-36 Cheapside Hanley Stoke-on-Trent ST1 1HQ
Tel: 01782 262424 *Fax:* 01782 684001 *Dx:* 20701 HANLEY 1
E-mail: help@dicksonssolicitors.co.uk
List of partners: J Bereford, P B Beresford, A W Grace, C J Hopkin, S P Marsden, A E Martin
Office: Cheadle, Stoke-on-Trent
Work: C1 D1 E F1 K1 K3 L N O Q R1 S1 S2 V W Z(i,l,q,r)
Emergency Action, Agency, Advocacy, Fixed Fee Interview, Legal Aid undertaken, Legal Aid Franchise and Member of Accident Line
Dir: Bereford, Mr Jonathan . . . *Dec 2001
Beresford, Mr Peter B . . . *§Dec 1970
Grace, Mr Andrew W BA(Law) . . . *§Oct 1980
Marsden, Mr Stephen Paul BA(Hons)(Law) . . . *Apr 1983
Martin, Mr Andrew Edwin LLB(Hons) . . . *§Sep 1995
Ast: Horton, Miss Jane G LLB(Hons) . . . *Apr 1990

DICKSONS SOLICITORS LTD
7-9 The Boulevard Tunstall Stoke-on-Trent ST6 6BD
Tel: 01782 262424 *Fax:* 01782 575261 *Dx:* 21551 TUNSTALL
E-mail: help@dicksonssolicitors.co.uk
Office: Cheadle, Stoke-on-Trent
Work: C1 D1 D2 E F1 K1 K3 L N O Q R1 S1 S2 V W Z(i,l,q,r)
Emergency Action, Agency, Advocacy, Fixed Fee Interview, Legal Aid undertaken, Legal Aid Franchise and Member of Accident Line
Dir: Hopkin, Mr Christopher J . . . *Dec 1977

FARROW SOLICITORS ‡
777 Lightwood Road Stoke-on-Trent ST3 7HA
Tel: 01782 341121 *Fax:* 01782 463947
E-mail: john.farrow@farrowsolicitors.co.uk

GRINDEYS LLP ‡
Glebe Court Stoke-on-Trent ST4 1ET
Tel: 01782 846441 *Fax:* 01782 416220
Dx: 21053 STOKE-ON-TRENT
E-mail: enquiries@grindeys.com
List of partners: S Campbell, S Doherty, S Grocott, D James, S Lewis, J G McGettigan, D G Rushton, A J Smith, D A Trevitt
Office: Stoke-on-Trent (2 offices), Stone
Work: A1 A3 B1 C1 C2 C3 D1 D2 E F1 F2 I J1 J2 K1 K2 K3 K4 L M1 M2 N O P Q R1 R2 S1 S2 T1 T2 U2 W X Z(b,c,d,e,h,j,l,n,p,q,r,t,z)
Emergency Action, Agency, Advocacy, Fixed Fee Interview, Legal Aid Franchise and Member of Accident Line
Ptr: Doherty, Mrs Suzanne LLB . . . *§Oct 1985
Grocott, Mr Stephen LLB(Sheff) . . . *Oct 1986
James, Mr David . . . *Nov 1980
Lewis, Ms Susan LLB . . . *Sep 1989
Rushton, Mr Daniel Giles LLB(Hons) . . . *Dec 1994
Smith, Mr Andrew J MA(Cantab) . . . *Oct 1993
Trevitt, Miss Denise A LLB(Manc) . . . *§Apr 1976
Asoc: Washington, Mr Jason . . . Nov 2000
Washington, Ms Katy . . . *Sep 2000
Ast: Freakley, Ms Rachel . . . *Nov 2005
Goel, Ms Rita . . . *Jul 2004
Hayward, Michael . . . *Apr 2001
Millington, Ms Emma . . . Jul 2006
Con: Hill, Mr Graham . . . *Oct 1975

GRINDEYS LLP
5-6 Brook Street Stoke-on-Trent ST4 1JN
Tel: 01782 846441 *Fax:* 01782 411918
Dx: 21057 STOKE-ON-TRENT
E-mail: enquiries@grindeys.com
Office: Stoke-on-Trent (2 offices), Stone

Languages: French, German, Italian, Spanish
Work: B1 C1 C2 C3 D1 E F1 F2 G H I J1 J2 K1 K2 L M1 N O Q R1 R2 S1 S2 T1 T2 V W Z(b,c,e,h,i,j,l,o,p,q,r,t,u,w)
Agency, Legal Aid undertaken and Member of Accident Line
Ptr: Campbell, Mrs Susannah LLB. . . . . *Nov 1992
McGettigan, Mr John Gerard LLB; ACII; PGDip ♦ . . . *Jan 1999

GRINDEYS LLP
Swift House Glebe Street Stoke-on-Trent ST4 1HG
Tel: 01782 846441
E-mail: enquiries@grindeys.com
Office: Stoke-on-Trent (2 offices), Stone
Ast: Simmonds, Ms Carole. . . . . May 2006
Tizley, Ms Cathy. . . . . Dec 2005

JL LAW ‡
16b Market Street Stoke-on-Trent ST3 1BX
Tel: 01782 328171

KJD ‡
Churchill House Regent Road Stoke-on-Trent ST1 3RQ
Tel: 01782 202020 *Fax:* 01782 202041 *Dx:* 20727 HANLEY 2
E-mail: dispute.resolution@kjd.co.uk
List of partners: P G Atkinson, M J Cork, P T Ellis, P Gavin, T Graham, S W Hadley, D H Jones, J G Moore, D M Morris, P M R Owen, A A Reeves, M S Servian
Languages: French, German, Italian
Work: A1 B1 C1 C2 C3 E I J1 L M1 O P Q R1 R2 S1 S2 T1 T2 U2 W Z(b,c,e,f,h,j,n,o,q)
Emergency Action, Agency, Advocacy and Fixed Fee Interview undertaken
Ptr: Atkinson, Mr Philip G LLB. . . . . *Mar 1990
Cork, Mr Martin J LLB. . . . . *Dec 2001
Ellis, Mr Peter T MA(Cantab) . . . . *Nov 1987
Gavin, Mr Peter LLB(Hons) . . . . *Oct 1996
Graham, Mr Thomas BA . . . . *Mar 1984
Hadley, Mr Stephen W LLB; LLM; LSF. . . . . *Oct 1990
Jones, Mr David H LLB(Hons). . . . . *Nov 1986
Moore, Mr James G BA(Cantab) . . . . *§Aug 1969
Morris, Mr Derek M LLB(L'pool) . . . . *§Oct 1973
Owen, Mr Paul Michael Robin LLB; LLM Frederick Drinkwater Prize; Sir Horatio Lloyd Prize . . . . *Nov 1993
Reeves, Mr Anthony A . . . . *§Mar 1965
Servian, Dr Michael S BA; PhD(Kent) . . . . *Oct 1990
Asoc: Calloway, Mr Tim . . . . Jan 1977
Garner, Claire. . . . . Sep 2005
Holmes, Mr Richard. . . . . Jan 2002
Milan, Mr Julian. . . . . Jan 2001
Ast: Bury, Mr Phillip LLM. . . . . Sep 2002
Hodgkinson, Gemma . . . . Jan 2008
Jones, Sarah . . . . Sep 2009
Vandrewala, Zalena. . . . . Mar 2009
Con: Levy, Ms Kate LLB(Hons) . . . . *Nov 1995
Ramage, Mr Roderick W BSc(Econ). . . . . *§Jan 1966

LEADBEATER & KAY ‡
1 Birch Terrace Hanley Stoke-on-Trent ST1 3JN
Tel: 01782 201933 *Fax:* 01782 265602
E-mail: debbie@leadbeaterkay.co.uk
List of partners: P M Kay, D J Leadbeater
Work: B2 D1 D2 E G J1 K1 K3 L N Q R1 S1 S2 W Z(l)
Emergency Action, Agency, Advocacy and Fixed Fee Interview undertaken
Ptr: Kay, Mr Paul M LLB ●. . . . . *Jan 1989
Leadbeater, Miss Deborah J LLB . . . . *Oct 1987

LICHFIELD REYNOLDS ‡
7-9 Commerce Street Longton Stoke-on-Trent ST3 1TU
Tel: 01782 313212 *Fax:* 01782 598130 *Dx:* 21858 LONGTON
Emergency telephone 07659 172997
E-mail: longton@lichfield-reynolds.co.uk
List of partners: G K Alcock, M S Bromley, E M James, R A Lichfield, J Phillipson, G C Reynolds, I D Rose, M Walsh
Office: Stoke-on-Trent (2 offices)
Work: B2 C1 D1 D2 E F1 G H J1 K1 K2 K3 L N O Q S1 S2 W Z(l)
Emergency Action, Agency, Advocacy, Fixed Fee Interview, Legal Aid undertaken, Legal Aid Franchise and Member of Accident Line
Ptr: James, Mrs Emma Michele LLB. . . . . Sep 2000
Phillipson, Mrs Jane MA; BA . . . . Oct 1996
Reynolds, Mr Geoffrey C . . . . *Mar 1979
Rose, Mrs Isobel Diana LLB. . . . . May 1986
Walsh, Mrs Marilyn LLB. . . . . *Jun 1992
Asoc: Sherratt, Mr John R BA(Hons). . . . . Dec 1984

LICHFIELD REYNOLDS
6 Pall Mall Hanley Stoke-on-Trent ST1 1HG
Tel: 01782 289122 *Fax:* 01782 201486 *Dx:* 20706 HANLEY
Emergency telephone 07659 172997
E-mail: hanley@lichfield-reynolds.co.uk
Office: Stoke-on-Trent (2 offices)
Work: B2 D1 D2 E F1 G H K1 K3 K4 L N Q S1 S2 W X Z(g,h,k,l,m,p,s,t)
Emergency Action, Agency, Advocacy, Fixed Fee Interview, Legal Aid undertaken and Legal Aid Franchise
Ptr: Lichfield, Mr Robin A LLB ★. . . . . *§Mar 1977

LICHFIELD REYNOLDS
81 Weston Road Meir Stoke-on-Trent ST3 6AJ
Tel: 01782 595599 *Fax:* 01782 593061
Emergency telephone 07659 172997
E-mail: meir@lichfield-reynolds.co.uk
Office: Stoke-on-Trent (2 offices)
Ptr: Alcock, Mr Graham K BA . . . . *Oct 1984
Bromley, Mr Mark Stephen BA . . . . *Oct 1987

MYERS & CO ‡
33-43 Price Street Stoke-on-Trent ST6 4EN
Tel: 01782 577000 *Fax:* 01782 575634

NOWELL MELLER SOLICITORS LIMITED
Yorke House Furlong Lane Burslem Stoke-on-Trent ST6 3LF
Office: Stafford, Stoke-on-Trent

SMK SOLICITORS ‡
First Floor 31-33 Albion Street Stoke-on-Trent ST1 1QF
Tel: 01782 213666 *Fax:* 01782 728018
E-mail: smk554@yahoo.com

SALMONS
336 Hartshill Road Hartshill Stoke-on-Trent ST4 7NX
Tel: 01782 639827 *Fax:* 01782 712793
Dx: 20979 NEWCASTLE UNDER LYME
E-mail: solicitors@salmonssolicitors.net
Office: Newcastle under Lyme
Languages: French
Work: D1 J1 K1 K2 K3 N Q S1 W Z(r)
Emergency Action, Agency, Advocacy, Fixed Fee Interview, Legal Aid undertaken, Legal Aid Franchise and Member of Accident Line
Ptr: Brookes, Mr Stephen Arthur LLB(Hons) . . . . *Oct 1987
Staff, Mrs Jane Susan BA(Hons)(Law) . . . . *Jul 1981
Asoc: Farrell, Mrs Patricia BA(Hons). . . . . *Nov 1993
Slater-Williams, Mrs Julie LLB. . . . . Sep 2005

THE SMITH PARTNERSHIP
88-90 The Strand Longton Stoke-on-Trent ST3 2PB
Tel: 01782 324454 *Fax:* 01782 332448 *Dx:* 21862 LONGTON
E-mail: longton@smithpartnership.co.uk
Office: Burton-on-Trent (2 offices), Derby, Leicester (2 offices), Swadlincote
Work: D1 F1 G H J1 K1 L N S1 V Z(i,j,m,p)
Emergency Action, Agency, Advocacy, Fixed Fee Interview, Legal Aid undertaken, Legal Aid Franchise and Member of Accident Line
Ptr: Brealey, Mr Martin O BA . . . . Oct 1981
Oldroyd, Mr D Richard BA. . . . . Oct 1985
Asoc: Kimberley, Mr Michael J BA . . . . *Jul 1986
Ast: Bradbury, Mr Martin J LLB. . . . . *Dec 1985
Kellett, Mr Shaun . . . . Jul 2000
Molloy, Mrs Sharon Elleen LLB(Leics) . . . . Jul 1980

STEVENS ‡
Union House Uttoxeter Road Longton Stoke-on-Trent ST3 1NX
Tel: 01782 343353 *Fax:* 01782 599321 *Dx:* 21860 LONGTON
Emergency telephone 07659 111000
E-mail: admin@stevenssolicitors.co.uk
List of partners: D G Bell, D C Bratt, C Buckley, R G Davies, J B Holt, R Moreland, S Muldoon, D Shackson, D C Starrs
Office: Stafford, Stoke-on-Trent, Wolverhampton
Work: G H
Emergency Action, Agency, Advocacy, Fixed Fee Interview, Legal Aid undertaken and Legal Aid Franchise
Ptr: Bell, Mr D Geoffrey . . . . *May 1987
Holt, Mr Jason Brian LLB(Hons) ★ . . . . *Sep 1999
Muldoon, Mr Stuart ★. . . . . *Nov 2001
Shackson, Mrs Dianne BA(Law) ★ . . . . *Feb 1986
Asoc: Corbett, Mr Gary . . . . Mar 2008
Green, Mr David John LLB . . . . *Jul 2007
Morris, Mr James . . . . Feb 2010
Thompson, Miss Rachel LLB . . . . *Jul 2005

STEVENS
22 Market Place Burslem Stoke-on-Trent ST6 4AT
Tel: 01782 813200 *Fax:* 01782 837937 *Dx:* 22312 BURSLEM
Emergency telephone 07659 111000
E-mail: admin@stevenssolicitors.co.uk
Office: Stafford, Stoke-on-Trent, Wolverhampton
Work: G H
Emergency Action, Agency, Advocacy, Fixed Fee Interview, Legal Aid undertaken and Legal Aid Franchise
Ptr: Davies, Mr Rees Garath LLB(Hons) ★. . . . . *Feb 1999
Moreland, Mr Raymond MA(Cantab) . . . . *Jun 1978
Asoc: Davies, Mr Simon. . . . . Feb 2010
Dykes, Mr Simon . . . . Mar 2008
Lee, Mr Stephen David BA(Hons); PGCE; CPE; LLM; LPC . . . . *Apr 2009
Meredith, Miss Emma. . . . . *May 2005

THOMPSONS (FORMERLY ROBIN/BRIAN THOMPSON & PARTNERS)
(in association with Thompsons McClure; The Thompson Partnership)
Bethesda Chambers Lower Bethesda Street Hanley Stoke-on-Trent ST1 3TA
Tel: 01782 406200 *Fax:* 01782 201244 *Dx:* 20748 HANLEY
Office: Belfast, Birmingham, Bristol, Cardiff, Chelmsford, Dagenham, Derby, Harrow, Leeds, Liverpool, London SW19, London WC1, Manchester, Middlesbrough, Newcastle upon Tyne, Nottingham, Plymouth, Sheffield, South Shields, Southampton, Swansea, Wolverhampton
Work: G J1 N Z(p,r)
Legal Aid undertaken and Member of Accident Line
Ptr: Jones, Mr Stephen LLB. . . . . *Sep 1995
Ast: Attwood, Mr Ashley Peter Barry LLB . . . . *Dec 1998
Hassiall, Mr Mark LLB; LPC. . . . . *Jul 2000
Leonard, Ms Dawn . . . . *Jul 1999
Liptrot, Mr Philip William BSc(Hons). . . . . *Aug 1998
Mitchell, Mr Stephen LLB . . . . *Oct 1991
Moll, Miss Christina E LLB(Hons) . . . . *§May 1991
Patterson, Mr Ian David BA(Hons). . . . . *Aug 1998
Tyson, Miss Susan BA(Hons)(Law) . . . . *Nov 1994
Uppal, Mrs Kashmir LLB(Hons) . . . . Oct 1993

WALTERS & PLASKITT ‡
Bews Corner 2 Westport Road Burslem Stoke-on-Trent ST6 5AW
Tel: 01782 819611 *Dx:* 22306 BURSLEM
List of partners: J M Allen, J Bloor, S A Leech, M Plaskitt, R E J Raby
Office: Stoke-on-Trent (2 offices)
Languages: French
Work: C1 D1 E F1 G H J1 K1 L M1 N P S1 W Z(l)
Emergency Action, Agency, Advocacy, Fixed Fee Interview and Legal Aid undertaken
Ptr: Allen, Mr John M ● . . . . May 1987
Bloor, Miss Jayne LLB ♦. . . . . *Mar 1993
Leech, Mr Simon A LLB ●. . . . . *Oct 1990
Plaskitt, Mr Michael LLB ●. . . . . *Jul 1978
Raby, Mr Robert E J BA(Law) ● . . . . Nov 1983
Ast: Biddulph-Smith, Mr Neil R LLB . . . . *Feb 1989

WALTERS & PLASKITT
124 Ford Green Road Smallthorne Stoke-on-Trent ST6 1PG
Tel: 01782 830038 *Fax:* 01782 818671 *Dx:* 701051 SMALLTHORNE
Emergency telephone 01782 249061
Office: Stoke-on-Trent (2 offices)
Work: C1 D1 E F1 G H J1 K1 L M1 N P S1 W Z(l)
Emergency Action, Agency, Advocacy and Legal Aid undertaken
Ptr: Plaskitt, Mr Michael LLB ●. . . . . *Jul 1978

WALTERS & PLASKITT
712 London Road Oakhill Stoke-on-Trent ST4 5NP
Tel: 01782 844500 *Fax:* 01782 848149
Emergency telephone 01782 680631
Office: Stoke-on-Trent (2 offices)
Work: K1 N Q S1 V W
Emergency Action, Agency, Fixed Fee Interview and Legal Aid undertaken

WALTERS & PLASKITT ‡
19 Glebe Street Stoke-on-Trent ST4 1JG
Tel: 01782 845807 *Fax:* 01782 744663
Dx: 21052 STOKE-ON-TRENT
List of partners: W M Cantlay, R E J Raby
Work: B1 C1 C2 C3 D1 E F1 G H J1 K1 L M1 M2 N P Q R1 S1 V W Z(c,d,e,j,l,n,p)
Emergency Action, Agency, Advocacy, Fixed Fee Interview, Legal Aid undertaken and Member of Accident Line
Ptr: Cantlay, Mr W Murray. . . . . *Jun 1980
Raby, Mr Robert E J BA(Law) ● . . . . Nov 1983

WOOLLISCROFTS
Hollinshead Chambers Butterfield Place Tunstall Stoke-on-Trent ST6 6BA
Tel: 01782 577246 *Fax:* 01782 577359 *Dx:* 21554 TUNSTALL
E-mail: annette@edwardhollinshead.co.uk
Office: Alsager, Hanley, Newcastle under Lyme
Work: D1 E F1 J1 K1 K3 L M1 M2 N R1 S1 S2 W Z(c,e,i,l,m)
Emergency Action, Agency, Advocacy, Fixed Fee Interview and Legal Aid undertaken

YOUNG & CO ‡
Edward House Uttoxeter Road Longton Stoke-on-Trent ST3 1NZ
Tel: 01782 339200 *Fax:* 01782 339201 *Dx:* 21854 LONGTON
Emergency telephone 0845 733 3111
E-mail: info@youngandco.com
List of partners: J R Bott, P J Connolly, D Lockett
Languages: French, German, Italian
Work: B1 D1 D2 E F1 G H K1 K3 L N O Q R2 S1 S2 T2 V W Z(m,q,r)
Emergency Action, Agency, Advocacy, Legal Aid undertaken and Legal Aid Franchise
Ptr: Bott, Mr Jonathan Richard LLB . . . . *Jul 1994
Connolly, Miss Phillipa J BA(Law). . . . . *Dec 1987
Lockett, Miss Denise LLB . . . . *Jan 1989
Asoc: Abbotts, Mrs Alison LLB(Hons) . . . . Apr 2000
Cooke, Mr Antony J LLB(Hons) ★. . . . . *Feb 2003
Forrester, Mrs Nadine LLB . . . . *Dec 1992
Ast: Brittain, Miss Sarah LLB. . . . . *Mar 2008
Downs, Mrs Alison J LLB(Hons) ★ . . . . *Sep 1996
Hartley, Mr Philip James . . . . Dec 2008
Hussain, Mr Tacarat LLB(Hons). . . . . *Nov 2005
Newby, Miss Clare E LLB. . . . . *Oct 1988
West, Mr Robert . . . . Mar 2008

STOKESLEY, North Yorkshire

STOREY & CO ‡
10 Bridge Road Stokesley North Yorkshire TS9 5AA
Tel: 01642 712132 *Fax:* 01642 712709 *Dx:* 60071 STOKESLEY
E-mail: marias@swallco.co.uk
List of partners: M P Storey
Work: K1 S1 W
Fixed Fee Interview undertaken
SPr: Storey, Mrs Maria Pina LLB(Hons) . . . . *Oct 1985

THORP PARKER LLP ‡
Martin House High Street Stokesley North Yorkshire TS9 5AD
Tel: 01642 711354 *Fax:* 01642 711257 *Dx:* 60061 STOKESLEY
E-mail: enquiries@thorp-parker.co.uk
List of partners: R H Parker, A C Rathmell
Work: C1 E K1 K3 S1 S2 W
Agency and Fixed Fee Interview undertaken
Ptr: Parker, Mr Richard Hartley BA . . . . *Nov 1986
Rathmell, Mrs Anne Caroline Notary Public . . . . . *Nov 1981
Ast: Warburton, Mrs Paula M MA(Oxon) . . . . *Oct 1988

STONE, Staffordshire

JOHN BURTON SOLICITORS ‡
Temple Chambers Market Square Stone Staffordshire ST15 8AT
Tel: 01785 814818 *Fax:* 01785 812489 *Dx:* 23405 STONE
Emergency telephone 01785 811437
List of partners: J G Burton
Work: A1 C1 E N O S1 T1 T2 W Z(l)
Ptr: Burton, Mr John G . . . . *Mar 1978

CRICK & MARDLING ‡
51 High Street Stone Staffordshire ST15 8AF
Tel: 01785 812650 / 812434 *Fax:* 01785 812117 *Dx:* 23402 STONE
Emergency telephone 01785 814505
E-mail: trmardling@crickandmardling.co.uk
List of partners: T R Mardling, R J Scholes
Work: A1 B1 C1 C2 C3 D1 E F1 G H J1 K1 L M1 M2 N P R1 S1 T1 T2 V W Z(l,m,t)
Agency, Advocacy, Fixed Fee Interview undertaken and Member of Accident Line
Ptr: Mardling, Mr Trevor R. . . . . *§Oct 1969
Scholes, Mr Richard Julian LLB. . . . . *Oct 1992

GRINDEYS LLP
Christchurch House Christchurch Way Stone Staffordshire ST15 8BZ
Tel: 01785 810780 *Fax:* 01785 810789 *Dx:* 23407 STONE
E-mail: enquiries@grindeys.com
Office: Stoke-on-Trent (3 offices)
Work: A3 C1 C2 D2 E G J1 K1 K3 L N R1 S1 S2 W X Z(d,e,r,t)
Agency and Fixed Fee Interview undertaken
Mem: Lewis, Ms Susan LLB. . . . . *Sep 1989
Ast: Jones, Ms Henrietta. . . . . Nov 2008

MITRE CONSULTANCY ‡
Stone Heath Stone Staffordshire ST15 8SH
Tel: 01889 505678 *Fax:* 01889 505679

STONEHOUSE, Gloucestershire

GLRS PHOENIX LLP
40 High Street Stonehouse Gloucestershire GL10 2NA
Tel: 01453 825151 *Fax:* 01453 826103 *Dx:* 99125 STONEHOUSE
Office: Dursley, Stroud (2 offices)
Work: A1 C1 C2 E L S1 S2 T1 T2 W Z(c,l)
Ptr: Langley, Mrs Amanda Jane . . . . Jul 2002
Read, Mr Hugh . . . . *Jun 1972

See p112 for the Key to Work Categories & other symbols

STONY STRATFORD, Milton Keynes

GIFFEN COUCH & ARCHER ‡
7 Market Square Stony Stratford Milton Keynes MK11 1BE
Tel: 01908 563911 *Fax:* 01908 562944
List of partners: P J Harrison
Work: A1 C1 E L R1 S1 S2 W
Ptr: Harrison, Mr Peter J LLB Notary Public . . . . *Apr 1975

RAY BORLEY & DUNKLEY ‡
79 High Street Stony Stratford Milton Keynes MK11 1AU
Tel: 01908 563232 *Fax:* 01908 560466
Dx: 56901 STONY STRATFORD
E-mail: reception@rayborleydunkley.co.uk
List of partners: R Dunkley, D S Jagatia
Work: A1 B1 C1 C2 E F1 G H J1 K1 K3 L N O Q R1 R2 S1 S2 T1 T2 V W Z(c,j,l,r)
Emergency Action, Agency, Advocacy, Fixed Fee Interview, Legal Aid undertaken, Legal Aid Franchise and Member of Accident Line
Ptr: Dunkley, Mr Richard. . . . . *Oct 1978
Jagatia, Miss Darshana Shantilal LLB(Hons) . . . . . *Jan 1992
Ast: Addison, Mrs Joanna M LLB . . . . *Jun 1981
Muggeridge, Mr Terence Charles BA(Hons)(Law) . . . *Jan 1984

STORRINGTON, West Sussex

AKERMANS
33 West Street Storrington West Sussex RH20 4EB
Tel: 01903 745353 *Fax:* 01903 743310 *Dx:* 85950 STORRINGTON
E-mail: storrington@akermanssolicitors.co.uk
Office: Worthing
Work: K1 K4 S1 W
Ptr: Hammock, Mr Andrew J LLB(Nott'm) . . . . *Mar 1968
Kerslake, Mrs Rosalind J BA . . . . *Apr 1978

ANDERSON LONGMORE & HIGHAM
5 The Square Storrington West Sussex RH20 4DJ
Tel: 01903 745666 *Fax:* 01903 744618 *Dx:* 85952 STORRINGTON
E-mail: storr@alhlaw.co.uk
Office: Billingshurst, Chichester, Petworth
Work: A1 C1 D1 D2 E F1 J1 K1 K2 K3 K4 L N O Q S1 S2 T2 W
Ptr: Wise, Mr Christopher J D LLB. . . . . *Jun 1979
Ast: Chambers, Mrs Rachel LLB; PGDipLP. . . . . *Dec 2005

STUCKEY CARR & CO ‡
Mulberry House 8 The Square Storrington West Sussex RH20 4DJ
Tel: 01903 743201 *Fax:* 01903 746757 *Dx:* 85953 STORRINGTON
E-mail: scstorrington@tiscali.co.uk
List of partners: G R D Carr, P M Jones, A Wright
Office: Pulborough
Work: A1 C1 E R1 S1 W
Ptr: Jones, Mr Peter Malcolm LLB(B'ham). . . . . *§Aug 1969
Wright, Mr Andrew LLB(Leeds) . . . . *§Apr 1975

STOURBRIDGE, West Midlands

ANDREW BURN SOLICITORS ‡
Woodlands Leys Close Stourbridge West Midlands DY9 0UL
Tel: 01384 826361 *Fax:* 01384 826498
E-mail: andrew-burn@virginmedia.com

DBL TALBOTS LLP ‡
63 Market Street Stourbridge West Midlands DY8 1AQ
Tel: 01384 445850 *Fax:* 01384 378461 *Dx:* 710675 STOURBRIDGE
E-mail: info@talbotslaw.co.uk
List of partners: G M Bowskill, L Colesby, J E Gwilliams, P W A Hill, M K Hodgson, D E Jones, L M Jones, K E Maynereid, M E Mocklow, M P Morgan, D J Simmonds, G Trenchard, A E Wakeman, J Wetherall
Office: Codsall, Dudley (2 offices), Kidderminster, Stourbridge, Wolverhampton
Languages: French
Work: A3 B1 C1 C2 D1 D2 E F1 F2 G H J1 J2 K1 K2 K3 K4 L N O P Q R1 R2 S1 S2 T1 V W Z(h,i,k,l,p,q,r,za)
Emergency Action, Agency, Advocacy, Fixed Fee Interview, Legal Aid undertaken, Legal Aid Franchise and Member of Accident Line
Ptr: Hodgson, Mr Mark K LLB . . . . *Feb 1988
Morgan, Mr Martyn Peter LLB Birmingham Law Prize .*Nov 1977
Colesby, Liz. . . . . .NSP
Mocklow, Mary Elizabeth . . . . .NSP
Asoc: Mapstone, Ms Melanie . . . . *Jun 2001
Reeve, Mrs Nicola E . . . . *Dec 1997
Ast: Adams, Ms Lorraine. . . . . *Nov 2004

DEAN & CO ‡
Church Chambers 9 Church Street Stourbridge West Midlands DY8 1LT
Tel: 01384 352525 *Fax:* 01384 352526 *Dx:* 710679 STOURBRIDGE
E-mail: jd@deanandco.com
List of partners: A G Dean, J Dean
Office: Dudley
Work: C1 E J1 K1 K4 L R1 S1 S2 W Z(d)
Ptr: Dean, Mr Anthony Graham MSc; PhD. . . . . *Jun 1978
Dean, Mrs Janet LLB . . . . *Nov 1971

HOLLIES SOLICITORS AND ADVOCATES LIMITED
111a High Street Wordsley Stourbridge West Midlands DY8 5QR
Tel: 01384 402211
Office: Bromsgrove

LUNN GROVES ‡
Sterling House 158 Hagley Road Stourbridge West Midlands DY8 2JL
Tel: 01384 397355 *Fax:* 01384 397356

JOHN MCCORMACK SOLICITOR & ADVOCATE ‡
1 The Paddock Stourbridge West Midlands DY9 0YE
Tel: 0560 343 7516
E-mail: mail@johnmccormacksolicitor.co.uk

MORGAN & CO ‡
62 Bridgnorth Road Wollaston Stourbridge West Midlands DY8 3PA
Tel: 01384 440069 *Fax:* 01384 392202
E-mail: smm@morgansolicitors.com
List of partners: S M Morgan
Work: D1 D2 E K1 L S1 S2 W
Emergency Action and Fixed Fee Interview undertaken

Ptr: Morgan, Mrs Susan Mary BA . . . . *Feb 1987
Ast: Dorr, Mr Andrew W . . . . Nov 1982

REGULATORY LEGAL SOLICITORS ‡
Brindley House Engine Lane Lye Stourbridge West Midlands DY9 7AQ
Tel: 01384 426400 *Fax:* 01384 894807
E-mail: info@regulatorylegal.co.uk

SANDERS & CO ‡
10 Hagley Road Stourbridge West Midlands DY8 1PS
Tel: 01384 375437 / 378991 *Fax:* 01384 393739
Dx: 710677 STOURBRIDGE
Emergency telephone 01384 375437
E-mail: sandersandco@btconnect.com
List of partners: M J Davies
Work: D1 D2 F1 G H J1 K1 K3 L N Q S1 S2 W Z(l)
Emergency Action, Agency, Advocacy, Fixed Fee Interview, Legal Aid undertaken and Legal Aid Franchise
Ptr: Davies, Mr Michael J BA . . . . *May 1986
Asoc: Sharma, Mrs Jenny LLB. . . . . *Aug 2003
Con: Billingham, Mr Roger BA . . . . *May 1974
Wilkins, Mr David C N LLB(Bris). . . . . *Dec 1982
Willetts, Mr Nicholas P BA . . . . *Apr 1990

BRIAN L SENTER ‡
15 New Road Stourbridge West Midlands DY8 1PQ
Tel: 01384 375649 *Fax:* 01384 371296
E-mail: brian.senter@btconnect.com
List of partners: B L Senter
Languages: French
Work: B1 C1 E F1 G H J1 K1 L N O Q S1 W Z(c,i,l)
Emergency Action, Agency and Advocacy undertaken
SPr: Senter, Mr Brian L. . . . . *Dec 1967

STABLES & CO
The Old Drapers House 138 High Street Stourbridge West Midlands DY8 1DW
Tel: 01384 390581 *Fax:* 01384 442383
Office: Halesowen, Kidderminster
Work: B1 C1 D1 E F1 G H J1 K1 L M1 N P R1 S1 T1 V W Z(b,c,e,f,i,j,k,l,m,o,p,s,t)
Emergency Action, Agency, Advocacy, Fixed Fee Interview and Legal Aid undertaken
Ptr: Jordan, Mr Nigel LLB(Hons). . . . . *Aug 1989

TALBOTS LEGAL ADVICE CENTRE
2nd Floor 124 High Street Stourbridge West Midlands DY8 1DT
Tel: 01384 445850 / 447777 *Fax:* 01384 447799
Dx: 710675 STOURBRIDGE
E-mail: info@talbotslac.co.uk
Office: Codsall, Dudley (2 offices), Kidderminster, Stourbridge, Wolverhampton
Languages: Gujarati, Hindi, Punjabi, Urdu
Work: C1 D1 E G H J1 K1 K2 K3 N O Q S1 S2 V W Z(k)
Emergency Action, Agency, Advocacy, Fixed Fee Interview, Legal Aid undertaken and Member of Accident Line
Ptr: Maynereid, Ms Katherine E . . . . Jan 2001
Morgan, Mr Martyn Peter LLB Birmingham Law Prize .*Nov 1977
Wakeman, Mr Andrew E LLB . . . . Oct 1992
Ast: Jagatia, Sunil P . . . . Jun 2003
Patel, Miss Mamata BA(Hons) . . . . May 2000
Tompkins, Ms Amanda S . . . . Mar 2004

JULIA TOLSON FAMILY SOLICITOR ‡
57 Westwood Avenue Norton Stourbridge West Midlands DY8 3EQ
Tel: 01384 346467 *Fax:* 01384 377038
E-mail: info@juliatolsonfamilysolicitor.co.uk

TREVOR CLARKE (THE PENSION LAWYER) ‡
6 Pedmore Court Road Stourbridge West Midlands DY8 2PH
Tel: 01384 396339 *Fax:* 01384 376535
E-mail: trevorclarke@thepensionlawyer.com

WALL JAMES CHAPPELL ‡
15-23 Hagley Road Stourbridge West Midlands DY8 1QW
Tel: 01384 371622 *Fax:* 01384 374057 *Dx:* 710678 STOURBRIDGE
E-mail: post@wjclaw.co.uk
Web: www.wjclaw.co.uk
List of partners: J Beale, J M Browne, J M Cockling, S E Griffiths, C Hamlyn, R Latham, J Rousell, T A Stepien
Work: B1 C1 C2 C3 D1 E F1 J1 K1 K3 K4 L O P Q R1 S1 S2 T1 T2 W Z(c,q)
Ptr: Beale, Ms Jane ♦ . . . . *Oct 1989
Browne, Mr Jonathan M LLB(Wales) ♦ . . . . *Oct 1978
Cockling, Mr John M BA ♦. . . . . *§Nov 1988
Griffiths, Mrs Susannah E LLB(Hons) ♦ . . . . *Nov 1995
Hamlyn, Mr Christopher TEP ♦ . . . . *May 1977
Latham, Ms Ruth ♦ . . . . *Dec 1999
Rousell, Mr James ♦ . . . . *Nov 2004
Stepien, Miss Teresa A ♦ . . . . *Jul 1988
Ast: Chapman, Mr Philip Richard BA(Hons); PGDL; LPC. . *Mar 2007
Con: Beddow, Mr Simon J LLB ♦ . . . . *§May 1980

Particular areas of work include: Commercial and Company Law, Tax Planning, Planning Law, Family, Litigation (including employment), Conveyancing.

STOURPORT-ON-SEVERN, Worcestershire

BINNION LINDSAY-VEAL LLP ‡
2 High Street Stourport-on-Severn Worcestershire DY13 8DJ
Tel: 01299 827860 *Fax:* 01299 829679
Dx: 21001 STOURPORT-ON-SEVERN
Emergency telephone 07918684137
E-mail: blvsolicitors@btinternet.com
List of partners: L A Binnion, C Lindsay-Veal
Office: Worcester
Work: D1 K1 K3 N S1 W Z(j,q,r,w)
Agency undertaken and Member of Accident Line
Ptr: Binnion, Miss Lisa Annette LLB(Hons). . . . . *Dec 1995
Lindsay-Veal, Ms Cozette . . . . Jan 1998

BRYAN COLLEY & CO ‡
16 New Street Stourport-on-Severn Worcestershire DY13 8UW
Tel: 01299 871066

LUMSDONS SOLICITORS LLP ‡
Salford House 29 Bridge Street Stourport-on-Severn Worcestershire DY13 8UR
Tel: 01299 827766 *Fax:* 01299 827251
Dx: 21003 STOURPORT-ON-SEVERN
List of partners: B Colley, J W A Rogers, K A Yates
Office: Worcester
Work: A1 E K1 L N Q R2 S1 W
Agency, Fixed Fee Interview and Legal Aid undertaken
Ptr: Colley, Mr Bryan . . . . Dec 1991
Rogers, Mr James W A LLB. . . . . *Sep 1985
Yates, Mr Keith A FILEx. . . . . .NSP
Ast: Harris, Kathryn . . . . Apr 1980
Shrimpton, Mrs Katy Jane. . . . . Jan 2007

PAINTERS
1 New Street Stourport-on-Severn Worcestershire DY13 8UN
Tel: 01299 822033 *Fax:* 01299 878888
Dx: 21005 STOURPORT-ON-SEVERN
E-mail: info@painters-solicitors.co.uk
Office: Kidderminster (2 offices)
Work: A1 C1 C2 C3 D1 E G H J1 K1 K3 L N O P Q S1 S2 W Z(l,q,r)
Emergency Action, Agency, Advocacy, Fixed Fee Interview, Legal Aid undertaken and Legal Aid Franchise
Ptr: Greig, Miss Rosalind J S LLB . . . . *Oct 1986
Howarth, Mr David J BA. . . . . *Feb 1979
Painter, Mr William R LLB. . . . . *§Mar 1979
Ast: Begum, Romi . . . . Aug 2006
Poole, Mrs Stephanie . . . . Sep 2008
Randle, Mrs Rebecca . . . . Sep 2006

THURSFIELDS
The Old Inspector's House York Street Stourport-on-Severn Worcestershire DY13 9EE
Tel: 01299 827517 *Fax:* 01299 878070
Dx: 21002 STOURPORT-ON-SEVERN
E-mail: info@thursfields.co.uk
Office: Kidderminster (2 offices), Worcester
Languages: British Sign Language, French, German, Hindi, Kiswahili, Polish, Punjabi
Work: C1 D1 D2 E F1 J1 K1 K2 L N O Q R1 S1 S2 W
Emergency Action, Agency, Advocacy, Fixed Fee Interview, Legal Aid undertaken, Legal Aid Franchise and Member of Accident Line
Ptr: O'Hara, Mr Nicholas T BA. . . . . *§May 1981
Ast: Circus, Mrs Tina Kathleen LLB . . . . *Sep 2007
Underwood, Mrs Anita G FILEx; TEP . . . . *Dec 1991
Ward, Miss Nicola LLB(Hons) . . . . *Sep 2000

STOW-ON-THE-WOLD, Gloucestershire

KENDALL & DAVIES
Cheltenham House The Square Stow-on-the-Wold Gloucestershire GL54 1AB
Tel: 01451 830295 *Fax:* 01451 831604
Dx: 23332 STOW-ON-THE-WOLD
E-mail: stow@kendallanddavies.co.uk
Office: Bourton-on-the-Water, Burford, Moreton-in-Marsh
Work: E L S1 S2 T2 W
Ast: Redman, Mrs Heather LLB; LSF. . . . . *Nov 1991
White, Miss Jane Elizabeth LLB(Hons) . . . . *Oct 1980

STOWMARKET, Suffolk

HARRIET BURGE SOLICITORS ‡
Broadview Debenham Road Stowmarket Suffolk IP14 5LP
Tel: 01449 710308

GUDGEONS PRENTICE ‡
Buttermarket Stowmarket Suffolk IP14 1ED
Tel: 01449 613101 *Fax:* 01449 615087 *Dx:* 35902 STOWMARKET
E-mail: info@gudgeons-prentice.co.uk
List of partners: G M Beresford, S J L Burt, D C Clark
Work: A1 C1 D1 E F1 K1 L Q R1 S1 S2 T1 V W Z(l)
Advocacy and Fixed Fee Interview undertaken
Ptr: Beresford, Mr Geoffrey Michael LLB. . . . . *§Mar 1981
Burt, Mr Simon J L LLB(Nott'm) . . . . *§Oct 1983
Clark, Mr David Charles BA(Hons)(Law). . . . . . . *Feb 1988
Ast: Dyke, Miss Rhian BA(Hons); TEP. . . . . *Jan 2005
Jackson, Mr Robert Michael LLB(Hons) . . . . *§Aug 2000
Lewis, Ms Susan LLB; LLM . . . . *Sep 1997
Murray-Lacey, Mrs Kathryn Ann BA(Hons); TEP. . . . *Mar 2007
Con: Prentice, Mr Martin P M BA(Cantab) . . . . *§Jan 1967

HAYWARDS ‡
7-9 Tavern Street Stowmarket Suffolk IP14 1PJ
Tel: 01449 613631 *Fax:* 01449 613851 *Dx:* 35900 STOWMARKET
E-mail: enquiries@haywards-solicitors.co.uk
List of partners: F J Bailey, L E Goodenough
Work: D1 D2 E K1 S1 S2 W
Emergency Action, Agency, Advocacy, Fixed Fee Interview, Legal Aid undertaken and Legal Aid Franchise
Ptr: Bailey, Mrs Fiona J LLB . . . . *Sep 1988
Goodenough, Louise Ellen . . . . .NSP
Ast: Dove, Miss Pollyanna Jessie LLB(Hons). . . . . . . Oct 2007
Con: Wiltshear, Mr Robert Guy . . . . *Jul 1975

MCCARTHY STEWART & BOOTY SOLICITORS
Beverley House Market Place Stowmarket Suffolk IP14 1DP
Tel: 01449 612343 *Fax:* 01449 673018 *Dx:* 35906 STOWMARKET
Emergency telephone 07899 960751
E-mail: enquiries@mccarthyandbooty.co.uk
Office: Bury St Edmunds
Languages: French
Work: G H K1 Z(l)
Emergency Action, Agency, Advocacy, Legal Aid undertaken and Legal Aid Franchise
Ptr: Stewart, Mr David M C . . . . . . *Jul 1980

OSLERS SOLICITORS
99 Ipswich Street Stowmarket Suffolk IP14 1BB
Tel: 01449 774670 *Fax:* 01449 774640
Emergency telephone 07711 654033
E-mail: mail@oslers.co.uk
Office: Cambridge
Languages: French
Work: G H
Emergency Action, Agency, Advocacy, Fixed Fee Interview, Legal Aid undertaken and Legal Aid Franchise
Ptr: Lockwood, Miss Claire Rose LLB . . . . *Nov 1998
Yardy, Mr James Sidney LLM . . . . *Dec 2002
Ast: Kendall, Mr Jeremy I BA(Hons) . . . . *Oct 1993

STRATFORD-UPON-AVON, Warwickshire

BONELL & CO ‡
2 Chestnut Walk Stratford-upon-Avon Warwickshire CV37 6HG
Tel: 01789 299115 *Fax:* 01789 295826
Dx: 700742 STRATFORD-UPON-AVON 2
E-mail: bonellaw@aol.com
List of partners: A P Bonell, E C Talbot
Work: A1 C1 C2 E J1 K1 K3 L N Q S1 S2 W Z(c)
Ptr: Bonell, Mr Andrew Paul . . . . *Nov 1978
Talbot, Ms Elizabeth C MA; LLB Deputy District Judge. May 1985

DAVIES MURRAY-WHITE & CO ‡
1 Mansell Street Stratford-upon-Avon Warwickshire CV37 6NR
Tel: 01789 295544 *Fax:* 01789 415236
Dx: 16209 STRATFORD-UPON-AVON
List of partners: J W H Davies, R B Davies, N J Murray-White
Work: A1 C1 C2 E F1 J1 L N R1 S1 T1 T2 W Z(l)
Fixed Fee Interview undertaken
Ptr: Davies, Mr Jonathan William Howard LLB. . . . *Sep 1988
Davies, Mr Robert B . . . . *May 1981
Murray-White, Mr Nicholas J BA(Lond) . . . . *Jun 1979

GPB SOLICITORS LLP ‡
11 Elm Court Ardem Street Stratford-upon-Avon Warwickshire CV37 6PA
Tel: 01789 261131 *Fax:* 01789 265750
Dx: 16214 STRATFORD-UPON-AVON
E-mail: webmarketing@gpbsolicitors.co.uk
List of partners: S A C Newbold, A M Organ, G Roy
Work: A1 B1 C1 C2 D1 E F1 G J1 K1 K3 L N O Q R1 S1 S2 W Z(c,h,l,q,r)
Emergency Action, Agency, Advocacy, Fixed Fee Interview undertaken and Member of Accident Line
Dir: Newbold, Mr Simon A C BSc(Econ) . . . . *Oct 1988
Organ, Mr Adrian M. . . . . *Dec 1977
Roy, Mr George LLB(Hons); PGDipLaw . . . . Mar 2005
Ast: Khalid, Miss Zakia. . . . . Aug 2008
Peak, Ms Holly . . . . Jan 2008

HCB SOLICITORS
Unit 7 The Court Yard Timothy's Bridge Road Stratford-upon-Avon Warwickshire CV37 9NP
Tel: 01789 270452
Office: Alcester, Lichfield, Redditch, Solihull, Walsall

JACKSON WEST ‡
The Old Pump House Clifford Chambers Stratford-upon-Avon Warwickshire CV37 8HR
Tel: 01789 204020 *Fax:* 01789 297373
Dx: 700740 STRATFORD-UPON-AVON
E-mail: gw@jacksonwest.co.uk
List of partners: D A Jackson, G West
Work: D1 K1 K3 S1
Agency and Legal Aid undertaken
Ptr: Jackson, Miss Deborah Ann LLB . . . . *Oct 1984
West, Mrs Gillian Notary Public . . . . *May 1978

LODDERS SOLICITORS LLP ‡
Number Ten Elm Court Arden Street Stratford-upon-Avon Warwickshire CV37 6PA
Tel: 01789 293259 *Fax:* 01789 268093
Dx: 16201 STRATFORD-UPON-AVON
E-mail: lawyers@lodders.co.uk
List of partners: S J Baker, J R S Bird, S R Brignull, N East, A Frew, M P Green, S Lapidge, M Lee, F M Lees, D S D Lodder, V G F Matts, R W Ollis, P A Samworth, M J Wakeling, D M G Williams
Office: Cirencester, Henley-in-Arden
Languages: Polish
Work: A1 B1 C1 C2 C3 E F1 J1 K4 L N O P Q R1 R2 S1 S2 T1 T2 W Z(c,d,e,l)
Ptr: Baker, Mr Steven J LLB. . . . . *Nov 1987
Bird, Mr Jonathan R S LLB(B'ham) . . . . *§Feb 1978
Brignull, Mr Stephen R LLB . . . . *Nov 1995
East, Mr Nicolas LLB . . . . *Oct 1982
Frew, Mr Alastair BA(Hons) . . . . *Sep 1996
Green, Mr Martin P LLB. . . . . *§Sep 1980
Lee, Mr Mark BSc(Hons); MRICS . . . . *Sep 2000
Lees, Miss Frances M LLB . . . . *§Oct 1985
Lodder, Mr David S D LLB . . . . *§Nov 1973
Matts, Mr Victor G F LLB . . . . *Oct 1979
Ollis, Mr Richard W LLB Notary Public . . . . *§Jun 1971
Wakeling, Mr Michael J BA . . . . *Oct 1988
Williams, Mr Dale Mark Glyn . . . . *Sep 1999
Asoc: Ausden, Mr Anthony M MA(Oxon); MBA. . . . . *Feb 1973
Bartlett, Mrs Ruth A LLB(B'ham) . . . . *Apr 1976
Igoe, Mrs Louise Rebecca LLB . . . . *Oct 2005
Mourton, Mr Paul . . . . *Oct 2005
Scott, Miss Ruth Mary LLB . . . . *Nov 1990
Strong, Mrs Helen D BA(Hons) . . . . *Mar 1996
Tayton, Mrs Sophia L BA(Hons). . . . . *Oct 2003
Ast: Beddows, Miss Kim Elizabeth LLB(Hons) . . . . *Oct 2009
Ditchfield, Ms Catrin. . . . . *Nov 2003
Eaves, Miss Laura BA(Hons)(Law and Business); LPC*Dec 2008
Forrester, Mrs Judy E BA(Hons). . . . . *Aug 1989
Gough, Miss Helen LLB(Hons) . . . . *Aug 2006
Kang, Miss Sandeep Sonia LLB. . . . . *Jul 2009
Patrick, Miss Jennie. . . . . *Apr 2010
Smith, Mrs Margaret Anne LLB(Hons). . . . . *Apr 1976
Steemson, Miss Anna Jane LLB; LPC. . . . . *Dec 2008
Vaqueiro, Mrs Emma Jane . . . . *Jan 2004
Waldron, Mr Anthony John . . . . *Jan 1972
Con: Bridges, Miss Karen BA. . . . . *Jun 1983
Orlik, Mr Michael Frederick MA(Oxon). . . . . *Nov 1970

RICHARD LUDLOW & CO ‡
16 The Willows Stratford-upon-Avon Warwickshire CV37 9QJ
Tel: 01789 552872 *Fax:* 01789 549540
E-mail: richard@ludlowsolicitors.co.uk
List of partners: E R Ludlow
Office: Solihull
Work: C1 E J1 L S1 S2 W
Fixed Fee Interview undertaken
SPr: Ludlow, Mr Ernest Richard BA(Hons) . . . . Nov 1983

JOHN ONIONS ‡
4 Brewery Street Stratford-upon-Avon Warwickshire CV37 0BQ
Tel: 01789 269899
Work: G H
Agency, Advocacy and Legal Aid undertaken

PARIS & CO ‡
Hansell Farm Cottage Lane Stratford-upon-Avon Warwickshire CV37 9RL
Tel: 01789 298177 *Fax:* 01789 295104
E-mail: steveparis@msn.com
List of partners: S W Paris
Work: C1 C2 C3 E J1 J2 K1 M1 M2 M3 N O P Q T1 T2 W Z(b,c,j,m,q,r,w)
Emergency Action, Agency and Advocacy undertaken
Ptr: Paris, Mr Steven W LLB; ACII. . . . . Nov 1975

RPM LEGAL
24 Ryland Street Stratford-upon-Avon Warwickshire CV37 6BT
Tel: 01789 295656
E-mail: v.perkins@rpmlegal.co.uk
Office: Huntingdon, Kettering

RAWSTORNE HERAN SOLICITORS ‡
27a Windsor Street Stratford-upon-Avon Warwickshire CV37 6NL
Tel: 01789 267646 *Fax:* 01789 415335
Dx: 16212 STRATFORD-UPON-AVON 1
Emergency telephone 07663 761013
E-mail: jrawstorne@rawstorneheran.co.uk
List of partners: D Heran, J R Rawstorne
Work: D1 G H J1 K1 L Q S1 V Z(m)
Emergency Action, Agency, Advocacy, Fixed Fee Interview, Legal Aid undertaken and Legal Aid Franchise
Ptr: Heran, Daljit. . . . . Nov 2006
Rawstorne, Mr Julian R MA(Oxon) . . . . *§Jul 1971

ROBERT LUNN & LOWTH ‡
2 Sheep Street Stratford-upon-Avon Warwickshire CV37 6EJ
Tel: 01789 292238 *Fax:* 01789 298443
Dx: 700741 STRATFORD-UPON-AVON 2
List of partners: P I Hardy, E C Jeffery
Work: A1 B1 C1 C3 D1 E F1 G H J1 K1 L N O P Q R1 S1 S2 T1 T2 V W Z(c,d,e,l,m,r,u,x)
Emergency Action, Agency, Advocacy, Fixed Fee Interview, Legal Aid undertaken and Legal Aid Franchise
Ptr: Hardy, Mr Paul I LLB; AKC . . . . *§Apr 1978
Jeffery, Mr Edward C BA . . . . *Apr 1985
Ast: Murray, Mrs Hannah Bridget Ruth BA; LLB . . . . Jan 2010
Siemonek, Mrs Lesley Catherine FILEx . . . . Oct 2006

SHAKESPEARES
Bridgeway House Bridgeway Stratford-upon-Avon Warwickshire CV37 6YY
Tel: 0845 630 8833 *Fax:* 0845 630 8844
Dx: 16202 STRATFORD-UPON-AVON
E-mail: info@shakespeares.co.uk
Office: Birmingham, Leicester, Moreton-in-Marsh, Nottingham, Shipston-on-Stour
Languages: French, German, Spanish
Work: A1 B1 C1 C2 C3 D1 E F1 G H J1 K1 L M1 M2 N O P Q R1 S1 S2 T1 T2 W Z(b,c,d,e,h,j,l,m,o,q,s,u,w)
Emergency Action, Agency and Advocacy undertaken
Ptr: Allen, Mrs Finula M BA(Oxon). . . . . *Oct 1985
Andrews, Mr Herbert LLB(Newc) . . . . *Apr 1976
Archer, Mrs Susan R LLB . . . . Oct 1983
Cox, Mr Richard Neal LLB. . . . . Nov 1991
Drayson, Mrs Nichola Annette LLB . . . . *Oct 1993
Dudley, Mr Andrew P LLB(Wales). . . . . *Oct 1981
Huggins, Mr Paul Anthony BA(Hons) . . . . Sep 1996
James, Mrs Janet C D LLB . . . . *Oct 1988
Simpson, Ms Victoria . . . . Jan 1994
Snodgrass, Mr Peter Mark MA(Cantab) . . . . Nov 1994
Walker, Mrs Catherine A LLB . . . . *Oct 1989
Webb, Mr Kevin Richard LLB . . . . *Oct 1996
Asoc: Dark, Mr Alan Philip LLB . . . . Sep 2002

STREET, Somerset

CHUBB BULLEID
Strode House 10 Leigh Road Street Somerset BA16 0HA
Tel: 01749 836100 *Fax:* 01458 440640 *Dx:* 45200 STREET
E-mail: solicitors@chubb-bulleid.co.uk
Office: Somerton, Wells
Languages: French, Russian
Work: A1 B1 D1 E F1 G H J1 K1 L N P Q R1 S1 T1 T2 V W Z(c,e,l,m)
Emergency Action, Advocacy, Fixed Fee Interview, Legal Aid undertaken and Member of Accident Line
Dir: Chalfont-Griffin, Mr Matthew BA. . . . . Jan 2001
Fowles, Mr Anthony J C. . . . . *Nov 1977
Medlicott, Mr Paul S BA(Wales). . . . . *Aug 1977
Ast: Jones, Mrs Caroline A. . . . . May 1981
Siggs, Miss Kylie LLB. . . . . Mar 2005

GOULD & SWAYNE ‡
Cranhill House Cranhill Road Street Somerset BA16 0BY
Tel: 01458 442433 *Fax:* 01458 446028 *Dx:* 45202 STREET
E-mail: c.haskins@gouldandswayne.co.uk
List of partners: J G Cann, S T Clark, C J Culshaw, S J Taylor
Office: Burnham-on-Sea, Glastonbury, Wells
Work: A1 B1 C1 E F1 J1 K4 L O Q S1 S2 T1 T2 W Z(d,l,m)
Dir: Culshaw, Mr Charles J BA(Law). . . . . *§Nov 1984
Ast: Fletcher, Miss Caroline Louise LLB . . . . *Sep 2005

STRETFORD, Greater Manchester

M I BANKS ‡
1080 Chester Road Stretford Greater Manchester M32 0HF
Tel: 0161 864 1961 *Fax:* 0161 864 1080
E-mail: reception@mibanks.co.uk
List of partners: M I Banks
Work: D1 F1 G H K1 M1 P S1
Agency, Advocacy, Fixed Fee Interview, Legal Aid undertaken and Member of Accident Line
Ptr: Banks, Miss Margaret I LLB. . . . . *Apr 1981

CRANGLE EDWARDS ‡
15 Edge Lane Stretford Greater Manchester M32 8HN
Tel: 0161 865 2993 / 865 7816 / 865 5875 *Fax:* 0161 864 4833
E-mail: crangleedwards@yahoo.co.uk
List of partners: G R Edwards
Office: Cheadle
Work: D1 K1 N Q S1 W Z(l)
Advocacy and Legal Aid undertaken
Ptr: Edwards, Mr Gareth Rhys. . . . . *Oct 1986
Asoc: Lister, Mrs Andrea BA(Hons) . . . . *Feb 1998
Smith, Mrs Angela Claire LLB(Hons) . . . . *§Nov 1991
Con: Morram, Ms Isabel BA . . . . Jan 1996

ELLISON & THOMAS ‡
10 Dorset Street Stretford Greater Manchester M32 8HB
Tel: 0161 865 3827 *Fax:* 0161 865 1437
List of partners: C C Rolfe, D G Thomas
Work: E J1 K1 L N P R1 S1 W
Ptr: Rolfe, Mr Clive Charles LLB. . . . . *Jun 1980

J ARNOLD HANCOCK & CO ‡
166 Barton Road Stretford Greater Manchester M32 8DP
Tel: 0161 865 2267 *Fax:* 0161 864 1362 *Dx:* 727851 STRETFORD 2
List of partners: R G Thorpe
Ptr: Thorpe, Mr Robert George . . . . *§Jul 1975

STROOD, Medway Towns

DAKERS MARRIOTT SOLICITORS ‡
First Floor Michael Gill Building Tolgate Lane Strood Medway Towns ME2 4TG
Tel: 01634 813300 *Fax:* 01634 813344 *Dx:* 6505 ROCHESTER
E-mail: mail@dakersmarriott.co.uk
List of partners: M J Dakers, M S Marriott
Languages: French, German
Work: B1 C1 C2 D2 E J1 J2 K1 K3 L M1 O P Q R1 R2 S1 S2 T1 T2 W Z(e,l,q,s,t,u,w)
Agency and Advocacy undertaken
Ptr: Dakers, Mr Michael John LMRTPI. . . . . *Jul 1967
Marriott, Mr Mark Sean LLB(Hons) . . . . *Nov 2001
Ast: Forrow, Miss Lindsey LLB(Hons) . . . . *May 2009
Mayston, Mr William Henry BProc. . . . . *Apr 2004

V E WHITE & CO ‡
118 High Street Strood Medway Towns ME2 4TT
Tel: 01634 739195 *Fax:* 01634 714024 *Dx:* 7202 RAINHAM
E-mail: enquiries@vewhitesolicitors.co.uk
List of partners: V E White
Office: Rainham
Languages: French
Work: C1 D1 D2 E F1 F2 J1 J2 K1 K3 L N O Q S1 S2 W X Z(e,f,l,p,r)
Agency, Advocacy and Fixed Fee Interview undertaken
Ptr: White, Ms Veronica Eleana . . . . Sep 1996

STROUD, Gloucestershire

GLRS PHOENIX LLP ‡
1 & 2 Rowcroft Stroud Gloucestershire GL5 3BB
Tel: 01453 763433 *Fax:* 01453 763434 *Dx:* 58805 STROUD
List of partners: A J Langley, C M Morgan, K G Penna, S F Pikett, H Read, J M Russell, R F Wicks, L Young
Office: Dursley, Stonehouse, Stroud
Languages: Danish, French, German
Work: A1 B1 C1 D1 E F1 J1 K1 L N O Q S1 W Z(c,d,h,l)
Emergency Action, Agency, Advocacy and Legal Aid undertaken
Ptr: Russell, Mr John M LLB. . . . . *Jun 1975
Mem: Pikett, Mr Stephen F LLB(Hons). . . . . *Sep 1991
Wicks, Mr Robert F LLB. . . . . *Jun 1976

GLRS PHOENIX LLP
Cotswold Chambers John Street Stroud Gloucestershire GL5 2HB
Tel: 01453 757381 *Fax:* 01453 752704 *Dx:* 58802 STROUD
Office: Dursley, Stonehouse, Stroud
Work: C1 C2 D1 E F1 J1 K1 L N O Q S1 V W
Emergency Action, Agency, Legal Aid undertaken and Member of Accident Line
Ptr: Morgan, Ms Christine M BA. . . . . *May 1981
Penna, Mr K Graham . . . . *Feb 1971

LEIGH YOUNG SOLICITORS ‡
The Old Court Offices Beeches Green Stroud Gloucestershire GL5 4BJ
Tel: 01453 762114 *Fax:* 01453 764495

MD SOLICITORS ‡
3 Crown Cottages Paganhill Stroud Gloucestershire GL5 4AZ
Tel: 01453 752015 *Fax:* 0870 131 2492
E-mail: md@mdsolicitors.co.uk

J G NASH ‡
Blackberry Hill Horsley Stroud Gloucestershire GL6 0PS
Tel: 01453 833652 *Fax:* 01453 835772
List of partners: J G Nash
Work: S1
Ptr: Nash, Mrs Julia Gay LLB(Lond). . . . . *Jun 1980

See p112 for the Key to Work Categories & other symbols

ROBERT SMITH & CO ‡
3-4 Lansdown Stroud Gloucestershire GL5 1BB
Tel: 01453 757435 *Fax:* 01453 759375 *Dx:* 58811 STROUD
E-mail: property@rsmithsolicitors.co.uk
List of partners: R J Smith
Languages: French
Work: S1 S2 W
SPr: Smith, Mr Robert J LLB . . . . . *§Dec 1974

FRANCES J WALSH ‡
12 Bowbridge Lock Stroud Gloucestershire GL5 2JZ
Tel: 01453 755092 *Fax:* 01453 753545 *Dx:* 58821 STROUD
E-mail: fjwalshsol@aol.com
List of partners: F J Walsh
Work: S1
Ptr: Walsh, Miss Frances J LLB; Dip Land Registration Law & Practice. . . . . *Jun 1975

WINTERBOTHAM SMITH PENLEY LLP ‡
3-7 Rowcroft Stroud Gloucestershire GL5 3BJ
Tel: 01453 847200 *Fax:* 01453 751997 *Dx:* 58800 STROUD
E-mail: mail@wspsolicitors.com
List of partners: J B Bonham, S A James, D G Knight, M J Lambert, P R Mardon, J A Penley, N J H Sherwood
Office: Dursley, Nailsworth
Work: A3 C1 C2 C3 D1 D2 E G H J1 J2 K1 K3 K4 L N O Q R2 S1 S2 T1 T2 W Z(c,d,e,q,r)
Emergency Action, Agency, Advocacy, Fixed Fee Interview, Legal Aid undertaken, Legal Aid Franchise and Member of Accident Line
Ptr: Bonham, Mrs Judi Barbara LLB . . . . . *Oct 1996
James, Mr Simon Andrew LLB . . . . . *§Jun 1972
Lambert, Mr Michael John BSc(B'ham) . . . . . *Jul 1974
Mardon, Mr Peter Robert LLB(Sheff) Wolverhampton Law Society Prize . . . . . *Oct 1990
Sherwood, Mr Nigel John Herbert. . . . . *Jun 1979
Asoc: Evans, Mrs Beth Louise BA(Hons) . . . . . Nov 2007
Goaziou, Ms Christiane Marie BA(Hons)(Law); Licence Es Lettres . . . . . Oct 1992
Green, Mrs Catherine Joanna. . . . . Sep 1998
Mortimer, Ms Clare . . . . . *Jul 2005
Ast: Highams, Ms Elizabeth Rachel . . . . . Dec 2006
Pratt, Ms Kirsten Louise. . . . . Apr 2005
Selwood, Mr Robert Mark. . . . . *Nov 2003
Thornton, Miss Fiona Margaret LLB . . . . . *Dec 2006

STUDLEY, Warwickshire

THOMAS GUISE
Haydon House Alcester Road Studley Warwickshire B80 7AN
Tel: 01527 852600 *Fax:* 01527 854394 *Dx:* 29921 STUDLEY
Office: Worcester
Work: A1 B1 C1 D1 E F1 G H J1 K1 L N Q R1 S1 T1 V W Z(l,w)
Agency, Fixed Fee Interview and Legal Aid undertaken

STURMINSTER NEWTON, Dorset

FARNFIELD & NICHOLLS
Sturminster House Bath Road Sturminster Newton Dorset DT10 1AS
Tel: 01258 474270 *Fax:* 01258 473762
E-mail: info@farnfields.com
Office: Gillingham, Shaftesbury, Warminster
Ptr: Gundry, Claire. . . . . Sep 2002
Asoc: Preece, Mr Mark Robert LLB(Hons); LLM(Hons). . . . *Oct 2008

SUDBURY, Suffolk

MICHAEL AVES PLANNING CONSULTANT ‡
Mill Cottage Yeldham Road Belchamp Walter Sudbury Suffolk CO10 7BB
Tel: 01787 237911 *Fax:* 01787 238504
E-mail: enquiries@michaelaves.co.uk

PRECISION LAW ‡
Ancient House Boxford Sudbury Suffolk CO10 5HP
Tel: 01787 211778 *Fax:* 07918 665531

STEED & STEED LLP ‡
6 Gainsborough Street Sudbury Suffolk CO10 2ET
Tel: 01787 373387 *Fax:* 01787 880287 *Dx:* 41303 SUDBURY
E-mail: lawyers@steed-and-steed.co.uk
List of partners: K A Goulding, S R Jarlett, A Peachey
Office: Braintree
Languages: French
Work: A1 B1 C1 D1 D2 E F1 G H K1 K3 L S1 S2 V W Z(d)
Emergency Action, Advocacy, Fixed Fee Interview and Legal Aid undertaken
Ptr: Goulding, Karen Ann FILEx . . . . . NSP
Ast: Jenkins, Mrs Janet Clare . . . . . *Oct 1980
Jerram, Mrs Philippa J LLB . . . . . *Oct 1984
Matherson, Ms Pauline LLB(Hons) . . . . . *Dec 1997
Con: Sneezum, Mr David F BA(Lond) Clerk to Commissioner of Taxes Notary Public . . . . . *§Dec 1974

TOMLINSON & DICKINSON
23 Friars Street Sudbury Suffolk CO10 2AA
Tel: 01787 375189 / 376820 *Fax:* 01787 373494
Dx: 41305 SUDBURY
E-mail: tandd@waymanandlong.co.uk
Office: Sudbury
Work: A1 B1 C1 C2 C3 E F1 G J1 K1 L N P R1 S1 T1 T2 V W
Agency and Fixed Fee Interview undertaken
Ptr: Dickinson, Mr Alan E LLB(Sheff) . . . . . *Dec 1976
Wallace, Mr Ross I LLB . . . . . *Nov 1970

WAYMAN & LONG ‡
27 High Street Clare Sudbury Suffolk CO10 8NZ
Tel: 01787 277375 *Fax:* 01787 278319
E-mail: enquiries@waymanandlong.co.uk
List of partners: A E Dickinson, P R Wade, R I Wallace
Office: Sudbury
Languages: French
Work: A1 E K1 K3 K4 L S1 S2 T2 W
Ptr: Wade, Mr Peter R. . . . . *§Dec 1980

SUNBURY-ON-THAMES, Middlesex

RIGBY GOLDING
57 Staines Road West Sunbury Cross Sunbury-on-Thames Middlesex TW16 7AU
Tel: 01932 765741 *Fax:* 01932 765720
Dx: 100350 SUNBURY-ON-THAMES
E-mail: reception@heflip.co.uk
Office: Egham
Work: J1 K1 Q S1 W
Ptr: Webster, Miss Susan Notary Public . . . . . Jan 1976
Asoc: Gelshinan, Mr Eric BSc(Hons). . . . . *Nov 1991

SETHI & CO ‡
79 Staines Road West Sunbury-on-Thames Middlesex TW16 7AH
Tel: 01932 772121 *Fax:* 01932 761221 *Dx:* 100359 SUNBURY
E-mail: privateclient@sethilaw.co.uk
List of partners: R Sethi, S Sethi
Languages: Hindi, Punjabi
Work: E F1 K1 K2 L O Q S1 S2 W
Ptr: Sethi, Mrs Rashmee BA. . . . . *Mar 1984
Sethi, Sehdev BA . . . . . Mar 1985

SUNDERLAND, Tyne & Wear

GERALD ARMSTRONG & CO ‡
24 Frederick Street Sunderland Tyne & Wear SR1 1LT
Tel: 0191 514 0966 *Fax:* 0191 564 2887 *Dx:* 60744 SUNDERLAND
List of partners: G K K Armstrong, S Grey
Work: D1 F1 G H K1 S1 V W
Emergency Action, Agency, Advocacy, Fixed Fee Interview, Legal Aid undertaken and Legal Aid Franchise
Ptr: Armstrong, Mr Gerald K K BA. . . . . *§Jan 1980
Grey, Mrs Susan LLB . . . . . *Apr 1981

JAMES E BAIRD ‡
37 Frederick Street Sunderland Tyne & Wear SR1 1LN
Tel: 0191 514 5888 *Fax:* 0191 514 2888 *Dx:* 60707 SUNDERLAND
List of partners: J E Baird
Languages: French
Work: B1 C1 E J1 K1 N O Q R1 S1 W Z(c,l,q,r)
Ptr: Baird, Mr James Edward ♦ Deputy District Judge; Former Chairman of Employment Tribunal . . . . . *§Jan 1976

BEN HOARE BELL & CO ‡
47 John Street Sunderland Tyne & Wear SR1 1RD
Tel: 0191 565 3112 *Fax:* 0191 510 9122 *Dx:* 60704 SUNDERLAND
Emergency telephone 0191 565 3112
E-mail: advice@benhoarebell.co.uk
List of partners: N G Barnes, M R Bell, A Dalton, C E Davies
Office: Newcastle upon Tyne, Sunderland (2 offices)
Languages: French, Greek, Spanish
Work: D1 D2 F1 G H K1 L N P V X Z(g,i,m,q,r)
Emergency Action, Agency, Advocacy, Fixed Fee Interview, Legal Aid undertaken, Legal Aid Franchise and Member of Accident Line
Ptr: Dalton, Mr Adrian BA . . . . . Aug 1992
Ast: Kinsley, Mr Oliver LLB. . . . . Aug 1999

BEN HOARE BELL & CO
2-3 South Terrace Southwick Sunderland Tyne & Wear SR5 2AW
Tel: 0191 516 0466 *Fax:* 0191 516 0230 *Dx:* 60704 SUNDERLAND
E-mail: advice@benhoarebell.co.uk
Office: Newcastle upon Tyne, Sunderland (2 offices)
Work: D1 D2 G H K1 L N Q V X Z(g,i,m,r)
Legal Aid Franchise
Ptr: Bell, Mr Martin R BA(Oxon)(Jurisprudence) . . . . . *Jan 1980

BEN HOARE BELL & CO
58 John Street Sunderland Tyne & Wear SR1 1QH
Tel: 0191 565 3112 *Fax:* 0191 570 9122 *Dx:* 60704 SUNDERLAND
Emergency telephone 0191 565 3112
E-mail: advice@benhoarebell.co.uk
Office: Newcastle upon Tyne, Sunderland (2 offices)
Languages: French, Russian
Work: Z(i,m)
Emergency Action, Agency and Legal Aid undertaken
Ptr: Barnes, Mr Nigel G MA . . . . . *Nov 1987

BROWELL SMITH & CO
22 John Street Sunderland Tyne & Wear SR1 1JG
Tel: 0871 474 3030 *Fax:* 0845 302 4755 *Dx:* 60732 SUNDERLAND
E-mail: advice@browells.co.uk
Office: Ashington, Cramlington, Newcastle upon Tyne (3 offices), Stockton-on-Tees, Stoke-on-Trent

MARK COOK SOLICITORS ‡
1st Floor 32 Frederick Street Sunderland Tyne & Wear SR1 1LN
Tel: 0191 567 7244 *Fax:* 0191 567 7255

CULLEN HAMMOND ‡
Regus House 4 Admiral Way Doxford International Business Park Sunderland Tyne & Wear SR3 3XW
Tel: 0191 501 8062 *Fax:* 0191 501 8563 / 0845 833 8892
E-mail: admin@cullenhammond.co.uk

DONNELLY MCARDLE ADAMSON ‡
26 Frederick Street Sunderland Tyne & Wear SR1 1LT
Tel: 0191 510 9911 *Fax:* 0191 567 7666 *Dx:* 60733 SUNDERLAND
E-mail: enquiries@macardles.co.uk
List of partners: G Adamson, N Bennett, G H Cardwell, M J Cook, C W M Donnelly, H Gething, J I Mathieson, P G Mitchell, A C Morris, J Phillips, J Relton, A C Russell
Office: Darlington, Hartlepool, Peterlee, Stockton-on-Tees, Sunderland
Ptr: Cook, Mr Mark J BA. . . . . Dec 1986
Phillips, Mr James. . . . . Sep 1980

DONNELLY MCARDLE ADAMSON
15 Norfolk Street Sunderland Tyne & Wear SR1 1EA
Tel: 0191 510 3020 *Fax:* 0191 510 1223 *Dx:* 60733 SUNDERLAND
E-mail: enquiries@macardles.co.uk
Office: Darlington, Hartlepool, Peterlee, Stockton-on-Tees, Sunderland

PETER DUNN & CO ‡
20 Athenaeum Street Sunderland Tyne & Wear SR1 1DH
Tel: 0191 568 9000 *Fax:* 0191 568 9018 *Dx:* 60739 SUNDERLAND
List of partners: B L Chapman, J S Cosgrove, P Dunn, S E McCabe, A M Tilbury
Languages: French
Work: B1 C1 C2 D1 E F1 G H J1 K1 L O P Q R1 R2 S1 S2 V W Z(c,d,i,l,m,r)
Agency, Advocacy, Fixed Fee Interview, Legal Aid undertaken and Legal Aid Franchise
Ptr: Chapman, Mr Brian L BA; LLB . . . . . *Jun 1996
Cosgrove, Mr John Stephen MA. . . . . *Aug 1983
Dunn, Mr Peter LLB. . . . . *Jul 1976
McCabe, Ms Susan Elizabeth LLB . . . . . Apr 1998
Tilbury, Mr Andrew M . . . . . *Nov 1997
Con: Worthy, Mr David Paxton . . . . . *Jun 1955

2

EMMERSONS SOLICITORS ‡
52 John Street Sunderland Tyne & Wear SR1 1QN
Tel: 0191 567 6667
List of partners: D M Emmerson, J Emmerson, A M Robinson
Office: Gosforth
Ptr: Emmerson, Mr Duncan M LLB . . . . . *Jun 1976
Emmerson, Miss Jacqueline. . . . . *Oct 1991

HARDING SWINBURNE JACKSON & CO ‡
58 Frederick Street Sunderland Tyne & Wear SR1 1NF
Tel: 0191 565 8194 *Fax:* 0191 510 0334
Emergency telephone 0191 565 8194
List of partners: C D Hughes, B Robson
Work: A1 C1 E H K1 L M1 R1 S1 W Z(i,l,m)
Emergency Action, Agency, Advocacy, Fixed Fee Interview, Legal Aid undertaken, Legal Aid Franchise and Member of Accident Line
Ptr: Hughes, Mr Charles David . . . . . May 1992
Robson, Mr Brian. . . . . Oct 2005
Asoc: Askins, Mr Jonathan . . . . . Apr 2006

HEDLEYS & CO ‡
Alliance House 20 Fawcett Street Sunderland Tyne & Wear SR1 1RZ
Tel: 0191 567 0101 *Fax:* 0191 514 7212 *Dx:* 60702 SUNDERLAND
E-mail: legal@hedleyssolicitors.com
List of partners: L M Johnston, C L Truscott
Work: B1 C1 E F1 J1 K1 K3 K4 L N O Q R1 S1 S2 T1 T2 W Z(c,d)
Emergency Action, Agency, Advocacy and Fixed Fee Interview undertaken
Ptr: Johnston, Mr Leo M LLB(Lond) . . . . . *Apr 1978
Truscott, Ms Claire L . . . . . Aug 2001
Asoc: Brown, Ayesha Katy. . . . . Nov 2007

HEDLEYS & CO ‡
78 Sea Road Sunderland Tyne & Wear SR6 9DB
Tel: 0191 548 2323 *Fax:* 0191 548 8292
E-mail: legal@hedleyssolicitors.com

LONGDEN WALKER & RENNEY ‡
14 John Street Sunderland Tyne & Wear SR1 1HZ
Tel: 0191 567 7024 *Fax:* 0191 510 9049 *Dx:* 60718 SUNDERLAND
List of partners: J Clark, R A Ebdon, D H Kirkwood, D Nesbitt, K A Stenger
Work: E F1 L N S1 S2 W Z(r)
Emergency Action, Agency, Advocacy, Fixed Fee Interview, Legal Aid undertaken, Legal Aid Franchise and Member of Accident Line
Ptr: Clark, Mr Julian LLB(Hons) . . . . . *Jan 1991
Ebdon, Mr Richard A LLB(Newc) . . . . . *§Apr 1976
Kirkwood, Mr Dermot H LLB. . . . . *§Mar 1984
Nesbitt, Mr David LLB. . . . . *Jan 1984
Stenger, Mr Kenneth A BA . . . . . *§Jun 1980

BRIAN MACKENOW & CO ‡
38 West Sunniside Sunderland Tyne & Wear SR1 1BU
Tel: 0191 565 6262 *Fax:* 0191 514 5247
E-mail: bm@bmackenowandco.com
List of partners: B A Mackenow, J R Mackenow
Work: B1 C1 E J1 K4 L O Q R1 R2 S1 S2 T1 T2 W Z(c,d,h,l,za)
Agency undertaken
Ptr: Mackenow, Mr Brian Anthony . . . . . *§Jun 1972
Mackenow, Ms Judith Rosemary LLM . . . . . *§Nov 1975

MCKENZIE BELL SOLICITORS ‡
19 John Street Sunderland Tyne & Wear SR1 1JG
Est: 1822
Tel: 0191 567 4857 *Fax:* 0191 510 9347 *Dx:* 60719 SUNDERLAND
Emergency telephone 07885 274508
E-mail: enquiries@mckenzie-bell.co.uk
List of partners: M P Brown, D Dixon, T F Greenshields, P R Heron, S F Lincoln, B McNeany, D E Pearson, J S G Sword, P W Taylor
Office: Washington
Languages: French, German
Work: A1 B1 C1 D1 E F1 G H J1 K1 L M1 N P R1 S1 T1 W Z(c,d,e,k,l)
Emergency Action, Agency, Advocacy, Fixed Fee Interview, Legal Aid undertaken, Legal Aid Franchise and Member of Accident Line
Ptr: Brown, Mr Michael P LLB(Bris) . . . . . *May 1973
Dixon, Miss Deborah LLB . . . . . *§Apr 1998
Greenshields, Mr T Francis LLB(Dunelm) . . . . . *§May 1967
Heron, Mr Paul R LLB(Dunelm) . . . . . *Jan 1969
Lincoln, Mr Steven F LLB . . . . . *§Dec 1983
McNeany, Mr Brendan . . . . . Mar 2002
Pearson, Mr David E . . . . . *May 1981
Sword, Mr John S G LLB; MA. . . . . *§Jan 1985
Taylor, Mr Peter W MA; LLM William Hutton Prize . . . *§Jun 1972
Con: Pearson, Mr Geffory LLB(Hons) ★ Tribunal Chairman *§Jan 1982

MORTONS ‡
110-112 High Street West Sunderland Tyne & Wear SR1 1TX
Tel: 0191 514 4323 *Fax:* 0191 514 8100 *Dx:* 60721 SUNDERLAND
Emergency telephone 0191 527 2597
E-mail: reception@mortons-solicitors.com
List of partners: F Aitken, A Ashcroft, J A Hobson, D J Place, D Winter
Work: D1 D2 E F1 J1 K1 K3 K4 L N O Q S1 S2 V W Z(l)
Emergency Action, Agency, Advocacy, Fixed Fee Interview, Legal Aid undertaken and Legal Aid Franchise
Ptr: Aitken, Mrs Fiona BA(Law). . . . . *Sep 1984
Ashcroft, Mrs Angela LLB . . . . . *Oct 1996
Hobson, Ms Janine A . . . . . Oct 1987
Place, Mr David J LLB . . . . . *Sep 1998
Winter, Mr Derek LLB(Hull) ♦ . . . . . *Feb 1983

NAUNTONS SOLICITORS ‡
25 Ryhope Street South Ryhope Sunderland Tyne & Wear SR2 0RW
Tel: 0191 521 3047 *Fax:* 0191 521 3625
E-mail: enquiries@nauntons.co.uk
Office: Peterlee

STANLEY J POTTS ‡
45 Frederick Street Sunderland Tyne & Wear SR1 1NF
Tel: 0191 510 3880 *Fax:* 0191 510 3898 *Dx:* 67758 SUNDERLAND

RICHARD REED ‡
3-6 Frederick Street Sunderland Tyne & Wear SR1 1NA
Est: 1949
Tel: 0191 567 0465 *Fax:* 0191 510 9013 *Dx:* 60726 SUNDERLAND
E-mail: ar@richardreed.co.uk
List of partners: S J Reid, G S Wellham
Work: B1 D1 E F1 K1 K3 K4 L N O P Q R1 S1 S2 T2 V W Z(q)
Emergency Action, Agency, Advocacy, Fixed Fee Interview, Legal Aid undertaken, Legal Aid Franchise and Member of Accident Line
Ptr: Reid, Mrs Sarah Jane LLB . . . . *Jan 2003
Wellham, Mr Gordon S LLB; TEP . . . . *§Jan 1979
Ast: Grimes, Miss Laura Mary BA . . . . *Sep 2006
Moir, Mr Alexander Phillip BA . . . . Sep 2006
Mullen, Miss Janine LLB . . . . *Jun 2005
Wormald, Mr Peter Leathard . . . . Nov 1972

We will undertake Agency commissions. Gordon Wellham is a member of STEP. Sarah J. Reid is a member of the Law Society Family Law Panel.

SCANLANS ‡
23 John Street Sunderland Tyne & Wear SR1 1JG
Tel: 0191 565 2565 *Fax:* 0191 510 9327 *Dx:* 60711 SUNDERLAND 1
Emergency telephone 07850 233832
E-mail: ashley@scanlans.co.uk
List of partners: H Bolton, W T Scanlan
Work: D1 D2 G H K1 S1 S2 W
Emergency Action, Agency, Advocacy, Fixed Fee Interview and Legal Aid undertaken
Ptr: Bolton, Ms Heather . . . . *Mar 2002
Scanlan, Mr William T BA . . . . *Dec 1977

SNOWBALL WORTHY LOWE ‡
51 John Street Sunderland Tyne & Wear SR1 1QN
Tel: 0191 565 3221 *Fax:* 0191 514 0166 *Dx:* 60728 SUNDERLAND
E-mail: johnlowe@swlsols.co.uk
List of partners: J W Lowe
Work: B1 C1 C2 E F1 J1 O S1 S2 W Z(c,l)
Agency and Advocacy undertaken
Ptr: Lowe, Mr John W . . . . *§Feb 1969
Asoc: Wilford, Mrs Marian LLB(Hons) . . . . *Nov 1978
Ast: Barron, Mr Graeme LLB(Hons) . . . . *Jan 2007

SWEENEY MILLER ‡
Mowbray Villas Mowbray Road Sunderland Tyne & Wear SR2 7EA
Tel: 0191 568 2050 *Fax:* 0191 568 2051
List of partners: P Miller, P J Sweeney
Work: E J1 J2 L N O Q R2 S1 S2 W
Ptr: Miller, Mr Paul . . . . Sep 1996
Sweeney, Mr Peter J LLB . . . . *Oct 1984
Ast: Augu, Miss Lindsey Samantha LLB . . . . Nov 2005
Hennessy, Miss Melanie Marie LLB . . . . May 2007
Lowery, Mr Robert James BA(Hons) . . . . Feb 2006
Veall, Miss Melanie Dinah LLB . . . . Oct 2006

THOMPSON & CO ‡
9 Green Terrace Sunderland Tyne & Wear SR1 3PZ
Tel: 0191 565 6290 *Fax:* 0191 565 6291 *Dx:* 60705 SUNDERLAND
Emergency telephone 0800 731 3985
E-mail: pthompson@thompson.co.demon.co.uk
List of partners: P C Thompson
Work: N Z(r)
Legal Aid Franchise
Ptr: Thompson, Mr Philip C BA . . . . *Nov 1986
Ast: Rafferty, Ms Jacqueline . . . . *Oct 1993
Thompson, Mr Mark Gordon LLB(Hons). . . . . . . *Nov 1999

PETER THUBRON & CO ‡
53 John Street Sunderland Tyne & Wear SR1 1QH
Tel: 0191 510 1221 *Fax:* 0191 510 1881 *Dx:* 60700 SUNDERLAND
Emergency telephone 0191 510 1221
E-mail: info@peterthubron.co.uk
List of partners: P Thubron
Languages: French, Italian, Spanish
Work: G H
Emergency Action, Agency, Advocacy, Fixed Fee Interview, Legal Aid undertaken and Legal Aid Franchise
Ptr: Thubron, Mr Peter. . . . . *§Dec 1972

TREANORS ‡
25 John Street Sunderland Tyne & Wear SR1 1JG
Tel: 0191 565 7395 *Fax:* 0191 514 1793 *Dx:* 60738 SUNDERLAND
Work: N

WESTGARTHS ‡
18 Fredrick Street Sunderland Tyne & Wear SR1 1LT
Tel: 0191 565 5000

DAVID PAXTON WORTHY ‡
38 Barnes View Sunderland Tyne & Wear SR4 7QA
Tel: 0191 522 7977
E-mail: davidworthy@fsmail.net

WRIGHT & MORTON ‡
32 Frederick Street Sunderland Tyne & Wear SR1 1LN
Tel: 0191 567 4289 *Fax:* 0191 510 0731 *Dx:* 60724 SUNDERLAND
Emergency telephone 07815 181486
E-mail: wrightmorton@btinternet.com
List of partners: M Wright
Work: E G H K1 L Q S1 W X
Emergency Action, Agency, Advocacy, Fixed Fee Interview and Legal Aid undertaken
Ptr: Wright, Mr Martyn LLB . . . . *Dec 1982

SUNNINGDALE, Windsor & Maidenhead

CAMPBELL HOOPER & CO LLP ‡
Apex House 116 London Road Sunningdale Windsor & Maidenhead SL5 0DJ
Tel: 01344 622141 *Fax:* 01344 291371 *Dx:* 119901 SUNNINGDALE
List of partners: S W Aldred, A E Vaughan
Work: D1 K1 K3 K4 S1 W
Agency, Fixed Fee Interview and Legal Aid undertaken
Ptr: Aldred, Mr Stephen W LLB(Lond) . . . . *Jun 1979
Vaughan, Ms Annabelle E BSc . . . . *Nov 1988

CHRIS LYNAM ‡
9 Station Road Sunningdale Windsor & Maidenhead SL5 0QQ
Tel: 01344 628863 / 07860 590456 *Fax:* 01344 628864
E-mail: chris.lynam@dsl.pipex.com

SUNNINGHILL, Windsor & Maidenhead

MYLLES & CO ‡
14 High Street Sunninghill Windsor & Maidenhead SL5 9NE
Tel: 01344 623388 *Fax:* 01344 874339
E-mail: pc@mylles.co.uk
List of partners: I T Colquhoun, R A Furness
Work: C1 D1 D2 E G H J1 K1 K3 O Q R2 S1 S2 W Z(e,h,k,l)
Emergency Action, Agency and Advocacy undertaken
Ptr: Colquhoun, Mr Iain T LLB(Lond) . . . . *Jun 1968
Furness, Mr Roy A LLB(St Andrews) . . . . *Jun 1968
Con: Carne, Miss Penelope A S ★ Stokes Memorial Prize; Daniel Reardon Prizes . . . . *Oct 1983

SURBITON, Surrey

AHM LAW ‡
81 Portsmouth Road Surbiton Surrey KT6 5PT
Tel: 020 8339 9195 *Dx:* 57700 SURBITON

S ABRAHAM SOLICITORS ‡
290a Ewell Road Surbiton Surrey KT6 7AQ
Tel: 020 8390 0044 *Fax:* 020 8241 0601
List of partners: S Abraham
Languages: Hindi, Malay, Malayalam, Tamil
Work: J1 K1 L N O Q S1 W Z(q)
Emergency Action, Agency, Advocacy and Fixed Fee Interview undertaken
SPr: Abraham, Mrs Sushila LLB; LLM(Lond) . . . . Dec 1994

ABSOLUTE LEGAL ‡
Claremont Business Centre 6-8 Claremont Road Surbiton Surrey KT6 4QU
Tel: 020 8390 5222 *Fax:* 020 8399 4219
E-mail: info@absolute-legal.com

P CHEVALIER & CO ‡
298 Ewell Road Surbiton Surrey KT6 7AQ
Tel: 020 3393 8217 *Fax:* 020 8391 3476 *Dx:* 57503 TOLWORTH
List of partners: P I Chevalier
SPr: Chevalier, Mr Paul I. . . . . *May 1974

CHIVERS EASTON BROWN ‡
420-424 Ewell Road Tolworth Surbiton Surrey KT6 7EH
Tel: 020 8390 0081 *Fax:* 020 8390 8651 *Dx:* 57505 TOLWORTH
E-mail: email@chiverseb.co.uk
List of partners: D J Brown, S Goldberg, P Johns, K S Osborne
Office: Surbiton
Work: B1 D1 E F1 J1 K1 L N O Q R1 S1 W
Emergency Action, Agency, Advocacy, Fixed Fee Interview, Legal Aid undertaken and Legal Aid Franchise
Ptr: Brown, Mr Duncan J . . . . *Jul 1980
Osborne, Mrs Katy Simson . . . . *Oct 1993

CHIVERS EASTON BROWN
381 Ewell Road Tolworth Surbiton Surrey KT6 7DF
Tel: 020 8390 6155 *Fax:* 020 8390 6603 *Dx:* 57505 TOLWORTH
E-mail: email@chiverseb.co.uk
Office: Surbiton
Work: C1 E L S1 S2 W
Ptr: Goldberg, Ms Shelley BA(Law) . . . . Jan 1990
Johns, Mr Philip LLB(Leeds); TEP. . . . . *Jun 1980
Asoc: Stark, Mr William A LLB(Warwick). . . . . *Nov 1988
Williams, Mr David Michael LLB(Hons) . . . . Jul 2001

ROBERTA DAVIDSON ‡
66 Kings Drive Berrylands Surbiton Surrey KT5 8NH
Tel: 020 8399 6704 *Fax:* 020 8399 6704
List of partners: R W Davidson
Work: S1
Ptr: Davidson, Mrs Roberta W LLB(Lond) . . . . *Feb 1978

M H FILES & CO ‡
32 Sugden Road Long Ditton Surbiton Surrey KT7 0AE
Tel: 020 8398 3646
Languages: French, German
Work: A1 E F1 L S1 Z(c)

HILL JOHNSON ‡
Suite 1 59 Victoria Road Surbiton Surrey KT6 4NQ
Tel: 020 8390 0185 *Fax:* 020 8390 8000

BRETT HOLT SOLICITORS
308a Ewell Road Surbiton Surrey KT6 7AL
Tel: 020 8399 1195
E-mail: bretthollt@qualitysolicitors.com
Office: Epsom, Worcester Park

MALCOLM JOHNSON & CO ‡
Suite 13 Claremont House 22-24 Claremont Road Surbiton Surrey KT6 4QU
Tel: 020 8399 5272 *Fax:* 020 8399 1152 *Dx:* 57714 SURBITON

J LIM LEGAL LIMITED ‡
150 Elgar Avenue Berrylands Surbiton Surrey KT5 9JT
Tel: 020 8149 6341 *Fax:* 020 8399 1987
E-mail: j.lim198@btinternet.com

MAGNE & CO SOLICITORS ‡
2nd Floor 23 Victoria Road Surbiton Surrey KT6 4JZ
Tel: 020 8399 3939 *Fax:* 020 8399 0202
E-mail: post@magne.co.uk
List of partners: D Magne
Languages: French, Spanish
Work: Z(i)
Fixed Fee Interview undertaken
SPr: Magne, Mr Dominic. . . . . Jan 2001

MILLAR KINGSLEY ‡
77a Victoria Road Surbiton Surrey KT6 4NS
Tel: 020 8390 8727 *Fax:* 020 8390 6248

D R SCEATS SOLICITOR ‡
3 Manor Court Manor House Surbiton Surrey KT6 4SH
Tel: 020 8399 5457 *Fax:* 0871 989 6093
E-mail: mail@drsceats-solicitors.co.uk
List of partners: D R Sceats
Languages: French
Work: J1 K1 L N O Q Z(g,q)
Advocacy and Fixed Fee Interview undertaken
SPr: Sceats, Mr David Roger MA(Oxon) . . . . *Dec 1979

SURBITONLAW LLP ‡
16A Isabel House 46 Victoria Road Surbiton Surrey KT6 4JL
Tel: 020 8399 8900 *Fax:* 020 8399 8909

SUTTON, Surrey

BWTLAW LLP
6 High Street Sutton Surrey SM1 1HN
Tel: 020 8643 5311 *Fax:* 020 8643 0109 *Dx:* 56461 SUTTON 1
E-mail: contact@bwtlaw.co.uk
Office: Epsom

WILLIAM BARTON ‡
23 Mead Crescent Sutton Surrey SM1 3QS
Tel: 020 8642 4858
List of partners: W Barton
SPr: Barton, Mr William LLB(Lond); LMRTPI ♦ Notary Public . . . . *Mar 1958

BELL & CO
5 Mulgrave Chambers 26-28 Mulgrave Road Sutton Surrey SM2 6LE
Tel: 020 8661 8611 *Fax:* 020 8661 6574 *Dx:* 56402 SUTTON
E-mail: info@bellsolicitors.com
Office: Cheam (2 offices)
Languages: Gujarati
Work: B1 C1 C2 C3 E F1 J1 K1 K2 K3 K4 L O Q R1 R2 S1 S2 W Z(e,l,p,q)
Ptr: Mill, Mr John C . . . . *Jun 1975
Patel, Mr Deepesh Chandubhai LLB(Hons) . . . . . *Feb 1992
Asoc: Lunn, Mr David . . . . Nov 2001
Ast: Goodship, Mr Roy Leonard BA . . . . *Jul 1980

CHARLES BROWN SOLICITORS ‡
Quorin House Alfred Road Sutton Surrey SM1 4RR
Tel: 020 8722 8868

CRM LAW LLP ‡
186 High Street Sutton Surrey SM1 1NL
Tel: 020 8661 1177

CHAPMANS SOLICITORS ‡
152-154 Epsom Road Sutton Surrey SM3 9EU
Tel: 020 8337 3801 *Fax:* 020 8330 4432
Dx: 42750 SUTTON STONECOT HILL
List of partners: C C L Blori, A G Findlay, R D J McNair, J Throp
Languages: French
Work: B1 C1 D1 E F1 J1 K1 L M1 N O P Q S1 S2 V W Z(k,l,m)
Fixed Fee Interview and Legal Aid undertaken
Ptr: Blori, Mrs Christine Choon Lian LLB. . . . . *Dec 1995
Findlay, Mr Andrew G BA . . . . *Nov 1986
McNair, Mr Robin D J . . . . *Jun 1971
Throp, Mr Jonathan LLB . . . . *Nov 1985

A K GULATI & CO ‡
White House Chambers 84 Lind Road Sutton Surrey SM1 4PL
Tel: 020 8770 7979 *Fax:* 020 8770 7961 *Dx:* 37265 SUTTON 2
E-mail: law@akgulati.co.uk
List of partners: A K Gulati
Work: D1 D2 K1 K2 K3 L O Q S1 S2 T2 W
Fixed Fee Interview, Legal Aid undertaken and Legal Aid Franchise
Ptr: Gulati, Anand K LLB . . . . *§Oct 1970
Ast: Waldon, Mr Julian Peter LLB ★ . . . . *Feb 1988

HOGANCO ‡
3-4 Mulgrave Court Mulgrave Road Sutton Surrey SM2 6LF
Tel: 020 8642 9999 *Fax:* 020 8642 7582 *Dx:* 56413 SUTTON

DAVID ISAACS
Barlin House 50 Throwley Way Sutton Surrey SM1 4BF
Tel: 020 8770 1901 *Fax:* 020 8770 3578
Office: Henley-on-Thames

MARRIOTT DAVIES YAPP ‡
St Nicholas House St Nicholas Road Sutton Surrey SM1 1EL
Tel: 020 8643 9794 *Fax:* 020 8770 9184
E-mail: mdy@crownagents.co.uk
List of partners: L C Davies, R R Marriott, T Yapp
Office: London SW1
Languages: French, German, Spanish, Welsh
Work: C1 C2 C3 F1 I J1 M1 M2 O P T1 U1 U2 Z(b,c,d,e,f,j,k,u)
Ptr: Davies, Mr Liam Craig LLB(Bris) . . . . *Dec 1988
Marriott, Mr Robin R BA(Law). . . . . *Dec 1980
Yapp, Mr Timothy LLB(Hons) . . . . *Feb 1990
Ast: Bryan, Ms Kirsten. . . . . Sep 2005
Harris, Miss Diane Elizabeth . . . . Apr 2004
Kennedy, Mr Tom . . . . Sep 2008
Kirk, Mr Angus James Kelton BA(Hons). . . . . . . *Sep 1998
Williamson, Mr Neil Henry Thomas CPD; LPC; BA(History) . . . . *Feb 2001
Con: Thorne, Mr James Henry BA(Hons) . . . . *Apr 1992
Wagland, Mr Nigel Cleevley LLB(Hons) . . . . Nov 1980

W H MATTHEWS & CO
(incorporating A D Perriman & Co)
11-13 Grove Road Sutton Surrey SM1 1DS
Tel: 020 8642 6677 *Fax:* 020 8643 3428 *Dx:* 56406 SUTTON 1
E-mail: sutton@whmatthews.com
Office: Kingston upon Thames, London EC1, Staines
Work: A1 B1 C1 C2 E F1 F2 G H J1 K1 K2 K3 L N O P Q R1 S1 S2 T1 T2 W Z(c,h,j,k,l,p,q,r)
Emergency Action, Agency, Advocacy and Fixed Fee Interview undertaken
Ptr: Guy, Mr David Jonathan LLB(Hons). . . . . *Oct 1987
Mangnall, Mrs Deborah M A LLB . . . . *Jun 1981
Perriman, Mr Richard Dale LLB(Hons). . . . . *May 1985
Quinney, Mr Nigel J LLB . . . . *Dec 1984
Asoc: Hughes, Mrs Margaret Ann BCL; DipLP. . . . . *Oct 1999
Ast: MacLeod, Miss Heather LLM . . . . *Sep 2008
Wilson, Mr Daniel James LLB. . . . . *Sep 2006

See p112 for the Key to Work Categories & other symbols

DAVID RUBIE MITCHELL & CO ‡
53 The Market Rose Hill Sutton Surrey SM1 3HE
Tel: 020 8641 0575 *Fax:* 020 8644 9740
Dx: 98875 ROSEHILL SUTTON
Emergency telephone 020 8641 0575
E-mail: reception@davidrubie.com
List of partners: W H Mitchell, D A Rubie
Languages: Chinese, Gujarati, Punjabi, Urdu
Work: B2 D1 D2 E G H K1 K3 N O Q S1 W Z(g,l)
Emergency Action, Agency, Advocacy, Fixed Fee Interview, Legal Aid undertaken and Legal Aid Franchise
Ptr: Mitchell, Mr Warren H BA; LLB(NZ) . . . . Mar 1993
Rubie, Mr David A . . . . *Jul 1971
Ast: Bruce, Mr Rod LLB . . . . Aug 2004
Burrell, Ms Domonique . . . . Jan 2004
Jhalla, Mrs Parol Shaylesh LLB(Hons) ♦ . . . . *May 1984
Mitchell, Miss Sara Charlotte LLB(Hons) . . . . Nov 2002
Phelan, Ms Patricia M BA; MA(Cantab) . . . . Apr 1979
Sinnett, Miss Katie Ruth LLB(Hons) . . . . May 2005
Stevens, Mr Paul LLB . . . . Jul 2005
Con: Ambridge, Mr Alan . . . . Jan 1983
Lowe, Mr Martin C . . . . *Dec 1967

OUVRY GOODMAN & CO ‡
65 Carshalton Road Sutton Surrey SM1 4LH
Tel: 020 8642 7571 *Fax:* 020 8643 2217 *Dx:* 56410 SUTTON 1
E-mail: sb@ouvrygoodman.co.uk
List of partners: S Brierley, C N Green
Languages: French
Work: A1 B1 C1 C2 C3 D1 E F1 G H J1 K1 L M1 M2 N O P Q R1 S1 T1 T2 V W Z(b,c,d,e,i,j,k,l,m,o,s)
Advocacy, Fixed Fee Interview, Legal Aid undertaken, Legal Aid Franchise and Member of Accident Line
Ptr: Brierley, Mr Stuart LLB . . . . Apr 1974
Green, Mr Christopher N LLB . . . . *Dec 1986
Ast: Fawcett, Miss Elizabeth M . . . . *Mar 1967
Forman, Mr John Benjamin . . . . Jul 2004
Pearson, Mr John B BA(Oxon) . . . . *Aug 1972

PORTER & CO ‡
40 Benhill Avenue Sutton Surrey SM1 4DA
Tel: 020 8643 5111 *Fax:* 020 8770 0771 *Dx:* 37254 SUTTON 2
E-mail: solicitors@portersol.co.uk
List of partners: P D E Long, A R M Porter
Work: C1 D1 E F1 G H J1 K1 L M1 N P R1 S1 T1 W
Emergency Action, Agency, Advocacy, Fixed Fee Interview, Legal Aid undertaken and Member of Accident Line
Ptr: Long, Mr Peter D E FCIArb; MBIM . . . . *Nov 1978
Porter, Mr Anthony R M Notary Public . . . . *Jul 1965

QUALITY SOLICITORS COPLEY CLARK ‡
36 Grove Road Sutton Surrey SM1 1BS
Tel: 020 8643 7221 *Fax:* 020 8643 5265 *Dx:* 56401 SUTTON 1
E-mail: info@copleyclark.co.uk
List of partners: R A Brigham, A J Coady, N A Hughes, M J Lawrence, D W Thompson, D C Thompstone, G A T Wildig
Office: Banstead
Languages: French, Spanish
Work: B1 C1 C2 C3 D1 E F1 J1 K1 L O Q R1 S1 S2 T1 T2 W Z(c,l,p,q)
Emergency Action, Agency, Advocacy, Fixed Fee Interview undertaken and Member of Accident Line
Ptr: Coady, Ms Andrea Jane LLB . . . . Jan 1996
Thompson, Mr Derek W LLB(Hons) . . . . Oct 1991
Thompstone, Mr David C LLB . . . . *§Dec 1976
Wildig, Mr Graeme A T BA . . . . *§Apr 1978
Con: Jones, Mr David P . . . . *§Nov 1970

CHARMINI RAVINDRAN & CO ‡
8 Lind Road Sutton Surrey SM1 4PJ
Tel: 020 8770 7874 *Fax:* 020 8643 9549 *Dx:* 56407 SUTTON 1
Emergency telephone 07932 946280
E-mail: charmini@charmini-ravindran.com
List of partners: C Ravindran
Languages: Tamil
Work: D1 K1 K3 S1 S2 W
Emergency Action, Fixed Fee Interview, Legal Aid undertaken and Legal Aid Franchise
SPr: Ravindran, Mrs Charmini . . . . Apr 1990

ROBINSON & KINRADE ‡
69 Carshalton Road Sutton Surrey SM1 4LH
Tel: 020 8770 2020 *Fax:* 020 8642 5218
E-mail: robinsonkinrade@aol.com
List of partners: W F Kinrade, D Robinson
Work: C1 E J1 L N Q S1 W
Ptr: Kinrade, Mr William Fletcher BSc(Econ) . . . . *Apr 1981
Robinson, Mr David LLB . . . . *May 1989

SAM SOLICITORS ‡
288 High Street Sutton Surrey SM1 1PQ
Tel: 020 8770 7143 *Fax:* 020 8643 9245

JOHN D SELLARS & CO ‡
1st Floor Aldgate House 72-74 Grove Road Sutton Surrey SM1 1BT
Tel: 020 8661 7014 *Fax:* 020 8643 3335 *Dx:* 56414 SUTTON
Emergency telephone 01372 376310
List of partners: J D Sellars
Work: D1 G H K1 M1 P S1 W Z(m)
Emergency Action, Agency, Advocacy, Fixed Fee Interview, Legal Aid undertaken, Legal Aid Franchise and Member of Accident Line
Ptr: Sellars, Mr John D . . . . *Dec 1976

STUART V SHOWELL & CO ‡
8 John Marshall House 246-254 High Street Sutton Surrey SM1 1PA
Tel: 020 8661 7605 *Fax:* 020 8661 0799
Emergency telephone 020 8741 1221
List of partners: S V Showell
Work: S1
SPr: Showell, Mr Stuart V MA(Cantab) . . . . Jun 1975

SUTTON COLDFIELD, West Midlands

AEW LITIGATION ‡
462 Chester Road North Sutton Coldfield West Midlands B73 6RG
Tel: 0121 354 8640 *Fax:* 0121 355 1169
E-mail: andrewwylde@aewltigation.co.uk
List of partners: A Wylde
Dir: Wylde, Mr Andrew LLB . . . . *Nov 1991

ACTIVE LEGAL ‡
The Gate House 27 Gate Lane Sutton Coldfield West Midlands B73 5TR
Tel: 0121 355 4700 *Fax:* 0121 355 4704
E-mail: info@activelegal.co.uk

BELL LAX LITIGATION ‡
New Bank House 21 Maney Corner Sutton Coldfield West Midlands B72 1QL
Tel: 0121 355 0011 *Fax:* 0121 355 0099
Dx: 15736 SUTTON COLDFIELD 1
Emergency telephone 07973 122485
E-mail: heather.bell@belllax.com
List of partners: H Bell, C D Bowman, R M Cooper, P A Lax
Languages: French, German, Italian
Work: A3 B1 B2 F1 F2 J1 J2 M3 N O Q W Z(b,c,e,j,k,m,p,q,r,z)
Emergency Action, Agency, Advocacy, Fixed Fee Interview undertaken and Member of Accident Line
Ptr: Bell, Ms Heather BA(Hons) Sweet & Maxwell Law Prize . . . . *§Mar 1978
Bowman, Mr Christopher David BA(Hons); CPE . . . . *Feb 1998
Cooper, Mr Richard Michael . . . . *Sep 2002
Lax, Mr Peter A BA(Dunelm) Stokes Memorial Prize . . *Nov 1982
Asoc: Andrews, Mr Stuart Martin MA(Cantab) . . . . *Apr 1999
Garrett, Miss Kate MBA; BSc(Econ) . . . . Sep 2005
Ast: Denton, Mr Adrian BSc(Hons); PGDipLaw . . . . Sep 2008
Dickens, Miss Michelle Ann Louise BMedSci(Hons) . . Sep 2008
Rees, Mr Morgan LLB . . . . Sep 2007
Thomas, Mr Nicholas Andrew LLB . . . . *Sep 2007

KEITH B BRIGHT ‡
30 Walmley Road Walmley Sutton Coldfield West Midlands B76 1QN
Tel: 0121 351 6296 *Fax:* 0121 313 1948
List of partners: B K Bright
Work: E G H N S1 W
Agency and Advocacy undertaken
Ptr: Bright, Mr B Keith LLM ★ . . . . *Jun 1972

COTTERHILL HITCHMAN LLP ‡
Arthur House 21 Mere Green Road Sutton Coldfield West Midlands B75 5BL
Tel: 0121 323 1860 *Fax:* 0121 323 1865 *Dx:* 20856 FOUR OAKS
E-mail: mail@cotterhillhitchman.co.uk
List of partners: M W Cotterhill, D L Hitchman
Work: C1 C2 E J1 N O Q S1 S2 W Z(p,q)
Ptr: Cotterhill, Mr Michael W LLB . . . . *Sep 1982
Hitchman, Mr David L LLB . . . . *Aug 1997
Ast: Danks, Miss Melissa BA . . . . *Jul 2004
Mann, Miss Brinder LLB . . . . *Feb 2005
Pancholi, Miss Trisha LLB . . . . *Feb 2005
Zulfiqar, Miss Saima LLB(Hons) . . . . *Oct 2001

DAVISONS
254 Lichfield Road Four Oaks Sutton Coldfield West Midlands B74 2UH
Tel: 0121 323 2525 *Fax:* 0121 323 2929 *Dx:* 20852 FOUR OAKS
E-mail: lawyers@oak.davisons-solicitors.co.uk
Office: Birmingham (3 offices)
Work: E S1 S2 W
Ast: Jones, Mr Nigel . . . . Nov 1975
Con: Mason, Mr Andrew David . . . . *Sep 1968

EDDOWES PERRY & OSBOURNE ‡
Sadler House 44 High Street Sutton Coldfield West Midlands B72 1UL
Tel: 0121 686 9444 *Fax:* 0121 686 9333
Dx: 12715 SUTTON COLDFIELD 1
Emergency telephone 07880 541354
E-mail: info@e-p-o.co.uk
List of partners: J Berg, E M Hayton, A P M McLarney, L W Mounce, K Osbourne
Office: Sutton Coldfield (2 offices)
Work: B2 D1 E F1 G H J1 K1 L N O Q R1 S1 S2 W Z(g,k,l,m,r)
Emergency Action, Agency, Advocacy, Fixed Fee Interview, Legal Aid undertaken, Legal Aid Franchise and Member of Accident Line
Ptr: Berg, Mr Julian . . . . *Mar 1976
Hayton, Miss Elizabeth M LLB . . . . *Oct 1995
McLarney, Mr Anthony P M LLB . . . . *Apr 1981
Mounce, Miss Leigh W BSc . . . . *Dec 1977
Osbourne, Mr Kerry LLB . . . . *Jun 1972
Ast: Stockton, Miss Jolene BA . . . . Jul 2003
Con: McGuire, Mr Anthony M LLB . . . . *Oct 1972
Wheadon, Mrs Alexandra Mary LLB . . . . *May 1973

EDDOWES PERRY & OSBOURNE
26 Lichfield Road Sutton Coldfield West Midlands B74 2NJ
Tel: 0121 686 9444 *Dx:* 12715 SUTTON COLDFIELD 1
Emergency telephone 07880 541354
E-mail: info@e-p-o.co.uk
Office: Sutton Coldfield (2 offices)
Work: B2 D1 E F1 G H K1 L N O Q R1 S1 S2 W Z(g,l,m,r)
Emergency Action, Agency, Advocacy, Fixed Fee Interview, Legal Aid undertaken and Member of Accident Line

EDMUNDS & CO ‡
420 Birmingham Road Wylde Green Sutton Coldfield West Midlands B72 1YJ
Tel: 0121 350 0987 *Fax:* 0121 377 7283 *Dx:* 22852 WYLDE GREEN
E-mail: sutton@edmunds-co.com
List of partners: K Edmunds
Office: Walsall
Ptr: Edmunds, Mr Keith BA(Law) . . . . *Dec 1977

FERDINAND KELLY ‡
Westwing Yew House Freasley Sutton Coldfield Staffordshire B78 2EY
Tel: 01827 893526 *Fax:* 01827 895039
E-mail: info@ferdinandkelly.co.uk
List of partners: S C I Ferdinand, J C Tracy Kelly
Languages: French, Greek, Italian, Russian
Work: A3 B1 C1 C3 E F1 J1 L M1 O Q S1 S2 Z(f,j,p)
Legal Aid Franchise
Ptr: Ferdinand, Mrs Sarah C I MA . . . . *Jun 1979
Tracy Kelly, Mr John C . . . . *Jan 1996

FRENCH & CO SOLICITORS LTD ‡
247a Jockey Road Boldmere Sutton Coldfield West Midlands B73 5XE
Tel: 0121 362 7330 *Fax:* 0121 355 6299 *Dx:* 14532 BOLDMERE
Emergency telephone 07860 630450
E-mail: info@frenchcosol.co.uk
List of partners: D V French, D I French
Work: D1 E K1 K3 K4 S1 S2 W
Emergency Action, Agency, Advocacy and Fixed Fee Interview undertaken
Ptr: French, Mr Derek I LLB ★ . . . . *Jan 1979
French, Mrs Denise Veronica LLB . . . . *May 1979

GARNER CANNING VICKERY
2 Hill Village Road Four Oaks Sutton Coldfield West Midlands B75 5BA
Tel: 0121 323 2646 *Fax:* 0121 323 2412 *Dx:* 20851 FOUR OAKS
Emergency telephone 07625 101671
Office: Atherstone, Birmingham, Tamworth
Work: A1 C1 C2 D1 D2 E J1 K1 K3 L O Q R1 R2 S1 S2 T1 T2 W Z(c,d,l)
Agency and Legal Aid undertaken
Ptr: Mills, Mr Terence M . . . . Sep 1997

NICHOLAS GEE ‡
1 Loxton Close Little Aston Sutton Coldfield Staffordshire B74 4HY
Tel: 0121 353 3543
E-mail: nick@ngeesolicitor.com

WILL HARRINGTON & CO ‡
Quality House 41 High Street Sutton Coldfield West Midlands B72 1UH
Tel: 0121 321 1999 *Fax:* 0121 321 1911
Dx: 720164 SUTTON COLDFIELD
Emergency telephone 0121 321 1999
List of partners: A R Bannister, W M Harrington
Office: Tamworth
Languages: Punjabi, Urdu
Work: B2 D1 G H K1 K3 Z(l)
Agency, Advocacy, Fixed Fee Interview and Legal Aid undertaken
Ptr: Bannister, Mr Austin Richard LLB . . . . *Nov 1996
Harrington, Mr William M LLB . . . . *Sep 1989
Asoc: Ricketts, Mr Peter M C BA(Hons) . . . . *Aug 1989

M R HEPBURN ‡
The Bungalow 2a Hollyfield Road Sutton Coldfield West Midlands B75 7SG
Tel: 0121 378 0440 *Fax:* 0121 329 3838
List of partners: M R Hepburn
Work: E K3 S1 S2
Agency, Advocacy and Legal Aid Franchise
SPr: Hepburn, Mr Michael R LLB . . . . *Jul 1980

HUBBALL & CO ‡
12 Cressington Drive Four Oaks Sutton Coldfield West Midlands B74 2SU
Tel: 0121 323 4822 *Fax:* 0121 323 4822
List of partners: D J Hubball
Work: F1 G N O Q Z(b,k,l,y)
Advocacy undertaken
SPr: Hubball, Mr David J MA(Oxon) Deputy District Judge; Part time Immigration Adjudicator . . . . Dec 1975

ANTHONY LEA & CO ‡
390 Boldmere Road Sutton Coldfield West Midlands B73 5EZ
Tel: 0121 382 5550 *Fax:* 0121 382 5554

LIN & CO SOLICITORS
95 Chester Road Sutton Coldfield West Midlands B73 5BA
Tel: 0121 244 2300 *Fax:* 0121 244 2200
Dx: 711807 BIRMINGHAM 28
E-mail: linsolicitors@aol.com
Office: Birmingham
Work: K1 K3 N Q S1 S2 Z(i)
SPr: Lin, Miss Callie K L LLB . . . . *Dec 1992
Asoc: Varachhia, Mr Abdul Rehman LLB . . . . *Sep 1992

J MCGRATH ‡
15 Monkseaton Road Wylde Green Sutton Coldfield West Midlands B72 1LB
Tel: 0121 355 4749 *Fax:* 0121 321 2222
List of partners: J A McGrath
Work: S1 W
Legal Aid undertaken
Ptr: McGrath, Mrs Judith A Herbert Willison Prize 1973 . . *Dec 1977

HARVEY MCKIBBIN SOLICITORS ‡
32 Beeches Walk Sutton Coldfield West Midlands B73 6HN
Tel: 0121 240 9115 *Fax:* 0121 241 0467
Dx: 12703 SUTTON COLDFIELD
E-mail: info@harveymckibbin.co.uk
List of partners: H McKibbin, R A Plane
Work: E L Q S1 S2 W Z(h)
Ptr: McKibbin, Harvinder . . . . Nov 2002
Plane, Mr Robert A . . . . *Feb 1975

PENNY MACMILLAN EMPLOYMENT LAW SOLICITORS LIMITED ‡
12 Saracen Drive Sutton Coldfield Staffordshire B75 7HF
Tel: 0121 311 2758 *Fax:* 0121 378 0636

MOSELEY CHAPMAN & SKEMP ‡
4 Trinity Place Midland Drive Sutton Coldfield West Midlands B72 1DX
Tel: 0121 355 4537 *Fax:* 0121 355 7438
Dx: 12712 SUTTON COLDFIELD 1
E-mail: mcs@moseleychapman.co.uk

N LEGAL ‡
Charter House 1 High Street Sutton Coldfield West Midlands B72 1XH
Tel: 0121 355 8885 *Fax:* 0121 355 6315
Dx: 12702 SUTTON COLDFIELD
List of partners: K Kong
Work: B1 C1 C2 E K4 L R2 S1 S2 W Z(b,l)
Agency and Legal Aid undertaken
SPr: Kong, Miss Kimberley LLB; LLM . . . . Jan 1990
Asoc: Parkinson, Mr David John Matthew LLB . . . . *Nov 1990

THOMAS O'GORMAN SOLICITORS ‡
9 Boldmere Road Sutton Coldfield Staffordshire B73 5UY
Tel: 0121 321 2820 *Fax:* 0121 355 3820 *Dx:* 14536 BOLDMERE
E-mail: tom@thomasogorman.co.uk

PARISI TAX LLP ‡
6 Kingsleigh Croft Four Oaks Sutton Coldfield Staffordshire B75 5TL
Tel: 07747 100141 / 07958 233827
E-mail: lisa.stevenson@parisitax.co.uk

JAMES PEARCE & CO
34a Walmley Road Walmley Sutton Coldfield West Midlands B76 1QN
Tel: 0121 351 5575 *Fax:* 0121 351 4222 *Dx:* 22859 WYLDE GREEN
Emergency telephone 0121 784 1886
Office: Birmingham (3 offices)
Work: C1 E F1 K1 N R2 S1 W
Ptr: Pearce, Mr Edward James Frederick LLB(Hons) . . . *Jan 1995

POWELL & CO ‡
9-11 Coleshill Street Sutton Coldfield West Midlands B72 1SD
Tel: 0121 355 1001 *Fax:* 0121 354 8325
Dx: 12714 SUTTON COLDFIELD 1
E-mail: powellandco@onetel.com
List of partners: N M Humphrey
Work: E F1 G K1 L S1 T1 W
Agency undertaken
Ptr: Humphrey, Mr Nicholas M BA(Law) . . . . *Nov 1985
Ast: Carpenter, Mrs Susan M Herbert Willison Prize 2000 *Aug 2003

WATKIN & CO ‡
229 Birmingham Road Wylde Green Sutton Coldfield West Midlands B72 1EA
Tel: 0121 321 2200 *Fax:* 0121 321 2221
E-mail: neil-watkin@hotmail.com
List of partners: N E A Watkin
Work: C1 E F1 J1 K1 L N O Q S1 W Z(c,d)
Agency and Legal Aid undertaken
Ptr: Watkin, Mr Neil Edwin Austin LLB(B'ham) . . . . . . *Sep 1983

R R WILLIAMS & SON ‡
(incorporating Conway & Co)
Warwick House 9 High Street Sutton Coldfield West Midlands B72 1XP
Tel: 0121 354 7870 *Fax:* 0121 355 0956
Dx: 12701 SUTTON COLDFIELD
E-mail: mail@rrwilliams.co.uk
List of partners: D J Williams, R J Williams
Work: E K4 L S1 S2 T2 W
Agency and Fixed Fee Interview undertaken
Ptr: Williams, Mr David John . . . . *Jul 2007
Williams, Mr Richard John . . . . *§Jun 1971

WOODHOUSE & COMPANY
Oculus House 16 Mill Street Sutton Coldfield West Midlands B72 1TJ
Tel: 0121 355 5601 *Fax:* 0121 321 3720
Dx: 12710 SUTTON COLDFIELD 1
Office: Walsall, Wolverhampton

WOOLLASTONS ‡
331 Jockey Road Boldmere Sutton Coldfield West Midlands B73 5XE
Tel: 0121 355 5516 *Fax:* 0121 355 1983 *Dx:* 14533 BOLDMERE
Emergency telephone 0121 354 6430
E-mail: enquiries@woollastonssolicitors.co.uk
List of partners: F I Woollaston
Work: F1 J1 K1 L N Q S1 S2 W
Emergency Action, Agency, Advocacy, Fixed Fee Interview undertaken and Member of Accident Line
SPr: Woollaston, Mrs Frances Irene . . . . *Dec 1992

WOOLLASTONS ‡
64 Walsall Road Sutton Coldfield West Midlands B74 4QY
Tel: 0121 308 4030 *Fax:* 0121 308 4717 *Dx:* 14533 BOLDMERE
E-mail: enquiries@woollastonssolicitors.co.uk

SUTTON-IN-ASHFIELD, Nottinghamshire

BROADBENTS
Opas House Market Street Sutton-in-Ashfield Nottinghamshire NG17 1AG
Tel: 01623 441123 *Fax:* 01623 559211
Dx: 24814 SUTTON-IN-ASHFIELD
Office: Alfreton, Chesterfield, Derby, Heanor, Mansfield
Work: G H K1 K2 N W Z(g,q)
Agency, Advocacy and Legal Aid undertaken
Ptr: Robbins, Mr Quentin LLB . . . . *Sep 1989
Ast: Stocks, Mr Mark . . . . Oct 1997

CLAYTON MOTT & LAWTON
(in association with Clayton Mott)
Market Chambers Market Place Sutton-in-Ashfield Nottinghamshire NG17 1AQ
Tel: 01623 556601 *Fax:* 01623 557500
Dx: 24809 SUTTON-IN-ASHFIELD
E-mail: advice@claytonmottandlawton.co.uk
Office: Nottingham
Work: K1 K3 S1 W
Fixed Fee Interview undertaken
Ptr: Lawton, Mrs Helen F LLB(Hons) . . . . *Dec 1986
Mott, Mrs Sheila Marian BA . . . . *Jun 1980

FIDLER & PEPPER ‡
(incorporating Spencer Hogg & Co; Vardy Wilson; Fuller Edwardson)
1 Low Street Sutton-in-Ashfield Nottinghamshire NG17 1DH
Tel: 01623 451111 *Fax:* 01623 451122
Dx: 24801 SUTTON-IN-ASHFIELD
E-mail: info@fidler.co.uk
List of partners: C T Dawes, R Jones, C J Limb, A C Lord, A T Slade, M A Slade
Office: Kirkby-in-Ashfield, Mansfield
Work: C1 C2 C3 E F1 J1 K1 L S1 W Z(c,l)
Agency, Advocacy, Fixed Fee Interview, Legal Aid undertaken and Member of Accident Line
Ptr: Limb, Christie J . . . . Jan 1998
Lord, Mr Anthony C MA(Oxon) Associated Law Societies of Wales Prize 1965 . . . . *§Dec 1965
Slade, Mr Anthony T Notary Public . . . . *§Jun 1968

HOLLIS & CO ‡
Market View Market Place Sutton-in-Ashfield Nottinghamshire NG17 1AQ
Tel: 01623 443344 *Fax:* 01623 442201
Emergency telephone 07973 636880
List of partners: D J Bell, A J Hollis
Work: D1 F1 G H K1 N S1 V W Z(l)
Emergency Action, Agency, Advocacy, Fixed Fee Interview and Legal Aid undertaken
Ptr: Bell, Miss Deborah Jayne LLB(Hons) ★ . . . . *Dec 1998
Hollis, Mr Andrew John BA(Hons) . . . . *Sep 1988
Ast: Pollen, Mrs Rachel LLB . . . . *Jan 1999

SUTTON-ON-SEA, Lincolnshire

TINN CRIDDLE & CO
(in association with Brough Hall & Co(Skegness))
31 High Street Sutton-on-Sea Lincolnshire LN12 2EY
Tel: 01507 443043 *Fax:* 01507 442710 *Dx:* 29741 ALFORD
E-mail: enquiries@tinncriddle.co.uk
Office: Alford, Spilsby
Work: A1 E J1 K1 L N Q S1 T1 T2 W
Fixed Fee Interview undertaken
Ptr: Allen, Mr Geoffrey . . . . *Jan 1989
Brough, Mr Peter R LLB . . . . *Jan 1980
Hall, Mrs Clare Joanne LLB(Hons) . . . . *Apr 1998
Hynes, Mr John BA(Hons) . . . . *Jul 2001
Ast: Briggs, Mrs Ann BSc(Hons)(Econ) . . . . *§Aug 1993
Brooks, Mrs Pamela Joan Leeds LLB(Leeds) . . . . *Jan 1977
Con: Criddle, Mr Peter M MA(Oxon) . . . . *Dec 1967
Forman, Mr John W S LLB(Lond) . . . . *Mar 1963

WILKIN CHAPMAN LLP
44 High Street Sutton-on-Sea Lincolnshire LN12 2HB
Tel: 01507 440400 *Fax:* 01507 442895 *Dx:* 29742 ALFORD
E-mail: stn@grangewintringham.com
Office: Alford, Beverley, Grimsby (3 offices), Horncastle, Lincoln, Louth, Mablethorpe, Market Rasen
Work: A1 K1 N S1 S2 T2 W Z(l)
Member of Accident Line
Ptr: Houltby, Mr Richard W B LLB Notary Public . . . . . *§Jul 1982

SWADLINCOTE, Derbyshire

FISHERS
74 High Street Swadlincote Derbyshire DE11 8HS
Tel: 01283 217193 *Fax:* 01283 550324 *Dx:* 23906 SWADLINCOTE
E-mail: swadlincote@fisherslaw.co.uk
Office: Ashby-de-la-Zouch
Work: A1 D1 J1 K1 K3 L S1 T1 T2 W Z(c)

THE SMITH PARTNERSHIP
22 High Street Swadlincote Derbyshire DE11 8HY
Tel: 01283 226444 *Fax:* 01283 550319 *Dx:* 23904 SWADLINCOTE
E-mail: swadlincote@smithpartnership.co.uk
Office: Burton-on-Trent (2 offices), Derby, Leicester (2 offices), Stoke-on-Trent
Languages: French
Work: D1 F1 G H J1 K1 L M1 P S1 V Z(i,j,p)
Emergency Action, Agency, Advocacy, Fixed Fee Interview, Legal Aid undertaken and Legal Aid Franchise
Ast: Bridgen, Mrs Melanie Jane . . . . Oct 2002

TIMMS SOLICITORS
Empire Buildings 23 West Street Swadlincote Derbyshire DE11 9DG
Tel: 01283 214231 *Fax:* 01283 222272 *Dx:* 23903 SWADLINCOTE
E-mail: legal@timmssol.co.uk
Office: Burton-on-Trent, Derby
Work: A1 C1 D1 D2 E F1 G H J1 K1 K2 L O Q S1 S2 V W Z(m)
Agency, Advocacy, Fixed Fee Interview, Legal Aid undertaken, Legal Aid Franchise and Member of Accident Line

SWAFFHAM, Norfolk

W F SMITH LLP
95 Market Place Swaffham Norfolk PE37 7AQ
Tel: 01760 336083 *Fax:* 01760 720949 *Dx:* 31753 SWAFFHAM
E-mail: jakki.upton@wfsmith.co.uk
Office: Dereham, Watton

WARD GETHIN
11 London Street Swaffham Norfolk PE37 7BW
Tel: 01760 721992 *Fax:* 01760 724937 *Dx:* 31752 SWAFFHAM
E-mail: enquiries@wardgethin.co.uk
Office: King's Lynn
Work: A1 B1 C1 C2 C3 D1 E F1 I J1 K1 K4 L M1 M2 N O P Q R1 S1 S2 T2 V W Z(c,d,e,g,k,l,m,p,s,t)
Emergency Action, Agency, Advocacy, Fixed Fee Interview undertaken and Member of Accident Line
Ast: Leman-Bunkall, Gemma . . . . *Jul 2006

SWANAGE, Dorset

ROBIN BELLIS ‡
Lark Rise 17 Russell Avenue Swanage Dorset BH19 2ED
Tel: 01929 425722 *Fax:* 01929 425722
Languages: French, German
Work: M1 M2

ELLIS JONES
55 High Street Swanage Dorset BH19 2LT
Tel: 01929 422233 *Fax:* 01929 425729 *Dx:* 49756 SWANAGE
E-mail: swanage@ellisjones.co.uk
Office: Bournemouth, Poole, Ringwood
Work: S1 W
Ptr: Wells, Mr Craig . . . . Sep 1996
Con: Pond, Mrs Janice J LLB . . . . Jun 1976

HUMPHRIES KIRK
4 Rempstone Road Swanage Dorset BH19 1DP
Tel: 01929 423301 *Fax:* 01929 427163 *Dx:* 49751 SWANAGE
E-mail: swanage@hklaw.eu
Office: Bournemouth, Dorchester, Poole (2 offices), Wareham
Languages: Dutch, Finnish, French, German, Italian, Spanish
Work: K1 K3 K4 S1 W
Emergency Action, Agency, Advocacy, Fixed Fee Interview, Legal Aid undertaken and Legal Aid Franchise
Ast: Mason, Miss Natalie Janne LLB . . . . *Sep 2003
Mount, Mr J Derek LLB(B'ham) . . . . *Jul 1971

TINA MACINNES ‡
48 Ulwell Road Swanage Dorset BH19 1LN
Tel: 01929 427227 *Fax:* 01929 427227
E-mail: tina.macinnes@virgin.net
List of partners: C M MacInnes
Work: K4 W Z(m)
Fixed Fee Interview undertaken
SPr: MacInnes, Mrs Christina M BA ♦ . . . . *Dec 1986

NEVILLE-JONES & CO
(incorporating Stevens & Griffin; Guy Williams Green & Co; Neville Jones & Howie; Janice J Pond)
52-54 Station Road Swanage Dorset BH19 1AF
Tel: 01929 422666 / 423761 *Fax:* 01929 424393
Dx: 49750 SWANAGE
E-mail: info@neville-jones.co.uk
Office: Wareham
Work: E F1 K1 K2 K3 K4 L N Q R1 S1 S2 T2 W Z(r)
Emergency Action and Fixed Fee Interview undertaken
Ptr: Griffin, Mr Paul LLB(Lond) Notary Public . . . . . . *§Jun 1979
Stevens, Mr Peter Henry Hadden Commissioner for Oaths . . . . *§Nov 1957

SWANLEY, Kent

BISHOP AKERS & CO ‡
Haven House 193 Swanley Lane Swanley Kent BR8 7LA
Tel: 01322 660617 *Fax:* 01322 664550
E-mail: info@bishopakers.co.uk
List of partners: J M Hardy
Office: Swanley
Work: K1 K3 S1 S2 W
SPr: Hardy, Mrs Jennifer M BA . . . . Mar 1983
Ast: Adams, Mr Christopher J LLB(Hull) Deputy District Judge . . . . *§Jun 1972

BISHOP AKERS & CO
Imperial House 46 High Street Swanley Kent BR8 8BQ
Tel: 01322 666766 *Fax:* 01322 666817
E-mail: lizh@bishopakers.co.uk
Office: Swanley
Work: J1 K1 K3 Q S1 S2 W

LONSDALE & MAYALL SOLICITORS ‡
40 High Street Swanley Kent BR8 8BQ
Tel: 01322 660880 *Fax:* 01322 660887 *Dx:* 56503 SWANLEY

SWANSEA

ARNOLDS ‡
80 Mansel Street Swansea SA1 5TY
Tel: 01792 418094 *Fax:* 01792 418098
Office: Morriston

AVERY NAYLOR ‡
35-36 Walter Road Swansea SA1 5NW
Tel: 01792 463276 *Fax:* 01792 458842 *Dx:* 39560 SWANSEA
Emergency telephone 07850 646864
E-mail: enquiries@averynaylor.co.uk
List of partners: L Naylor, J L Scannell, P Wilson, G Wynter
Languages: Welsh
Work: B1 C1 C3 D1 E F1 G H J1 K1 M1 P Q R1 S1 W X Z(l,p)
Emergency Action, Agency, Advocacy, Fixed Fee Interview, Legal Aid undertaken and Legal Aid Franchise
Ptr: Naylor, Miss Lynne BSc(Econ) . . . . *Jul 1979
Scannell, Ms Jayne Louise LLB . . . . *Mar 1996
Wilson, Mr Paul LLB(Wales) . . . . *Oct 1977
Wynter, Mrs Gail . . . . Mar 1997
Asoc: Hopkins, Mr Ian Howard BSc; CPE . . . . *Oct 1995
Tarrant, Mr Jonathan Nicholas LLB(Cardiff) . . . . *Apr 1996
Ast: McCarthy, Mrs Rachael M LLB(Hons) . . . . May 1998
White, Mr David Iwan BA(Hons); LLB(Hons) . . . . . *Jun 1998

ROY THOMAS BEGLEY & CO ‡
117 Walter Road Swansea SA1 5RH
Tel: 01792 643797 / 643798 *Fax:* 01792 646838
Dx: 39590 SWANSEA
E-mail: roy.thom117@virgin.net
List of partners: P G David, D A Thomas
Work: D1 D2 E F1 F2 J1 J2 K1 K2 L N Q R1 R2 S1 S2 T1 T2 V W Z(c,k,r)
Emergency Action, Agency, Advocacy, Fixed Fee Interview, Legal Aid undertaken and Legal Aid Franchise
Ptr: David, Mrs Philippa Glynis . . . . *Oct 1992
Thomas, Mr David Andrew . . . . Nov 1991

BENSON WATKINS ‡
(incorporating Glass & Co)
4 Tawe Business Village Phoenix Way Llansamlet Swansea SA7 9LA
Tel: 01792 704320 *Fax:* 01792 797374 *Dx:* 82811 SWANSEA 2
E-mail: mail@benwat.co.uk
List of partners: M J Benson, A G Stephens, D M Watkins
Office: Swansea
Work: D1 E G H J1 K1 L N R1 S1 T1 V W
Emergency Action, Agency, Advocacy, Fixed Fee Interview and Legal Aid undertaken
Ptr: Benson, Mr Michael J BA(Wales) . . . . Jul 1968
Watkins, Mr David M BA(Hons) . . . . Jun 1993
Ast: Carter, Ms Virginia LLB(Hons) . . . . *Feb 1993

BENSON WATKINS
108 Walter Road Swansea SA1 5QQ
Tel: 01792 464564 *Fax:* 01792 475797
Office: Swansea
Ptr: Stephens, Mr Andrew G BA . . . . Jun 1979

See p112 for the Key to Work Categories & other symbols

BEOR WILSON LLOYD ‡
Calvert House Calvert Terrace Swansea SA1 6AP
Tel: 01792 655178 *Fax:* 01792 467002 *Dx:* 39550 SWANSEA
E-mail: post@bwl-law.co.uk
List of partners: P L Bevan, G B A Rees, R J Taylor
Work: A1 C1 C2 E K4 L N O Q R1 S1 S2 T2 V W Z(q)
Agency, Advocacy, Fixed Fee Interview undertaken and Member of Accident Line
Ptr: Bevan, Mr Paul Lewis LLB . . . . *Nov 1993
Rees, Mr Geoffrey B A LLB(Exon) Deputy Clerk to the Commissioners of Taxes . . . . *Apr 1981
Taylor, Mr Robert J . . . . Jun 1978

CLARKSLEGAL LLP
Cefnmor Panmaen Gower Swansea SA3 2HQ
Tel: 0118 958 5321 *Fax:* 0118 960 4611
Office: Cardiff, London WC2, Reading

JOHN COLLINS & PARTNERS LLP ‡
Venture Court Waterside Business Park Valley Way Swansea SA6 8QP
Tel: 01792 773773 *Fax:* 01792 774775 *Dx:* 82804 SWANSEA 2
E-mail: law@johncollins.co.uk
List of partners: C W Davies, C M Gilroy, C S Goldsworthy, R K Hutchings, S J Jackson-Thomas, G Llewellyn Williams, L Morgan, K O'Brien, S R Penny, A J Rees, K Thomas
Work: A1 A2 A3 B1 C1 C2 E J1 O P R1 S1 S2 U2 Z(e,q)
Ptr: Davies, Mr Christopher W LLB . . . . Oct 1992
Gilroy, Mr Christopher Mark . . . . Sep 1999
Goldsworthy, Mrs Claire S LLB . . . . *Sep 1992
Hutchings, Mr Rory Kerr LLB(Hons) Gamlen Law Prize*Nov 1994
Jackson-Thomas, Miss Sali J BA(Keele) . . . . *Apr 1989
Llewellyn Williams, Mr Gareth MA. . . . . *Dec 1992
Morgan, Miss Lynne LLB . . . . Sep 1996
O'Brien, Mr Kevin LLB . . . . Sep 1998
Penny, Mr Stephen R LLB(B'ham) Jurisprudence Prize *Jun 1979
Rees, Miss Amanda J LLB(Wales) . . . . *Jun 1988
Thomas, Mr Keith LLB(Wales). . . . . *Jun 1982
Asoc: Davies, Ms Meinir Megan BA(Hons)(Law) . . . . . . *Oct 1993
King, Ms Lynda . . . . *Sep 1995
Thomas, Mr Nicholas Vaughan LLB . . . . Sep 2004
Con: Burniston, Mr Bruce Humphrey . . . . *Dec 1981
Evans, Mr Robert Kelvin LLB(Vict) . . . . Apr 1975
Jacobi, Mr Neil David DipLP; LLB(Hons) . . . . . . *Nov 1999
Kent, Mrs Allison LLB . . . . Sep 1998

DAVIES INGRAM & HARVEY ‡
(incorporating R S Gething & Co; F H Edwards & Co)
Cornhill Chambers 7/8 Christina Street Swansea SA1 4ES
Tel: 01792 653764 *Fax:* 01792 651690 *Dx:* 39557 SWANSEA
Emergency telephone 01792 207010
E-mail: colin@daviesingram.com
List of partners: J E Davies, C I G Phillips
Work: C1 E K4 S1 S2 W
Ptr: Davies, Mr John E . . . . *Apr 1961
Phillips, Mr Colin I G BSc(Econ). . . . . Oct 1980
Con: Rogers, Mr Philip MA(Cantab) City Coroner & Under Sheriff of West Glamorgan . . . . *May 1981

DAVIES PARSONS ALLCHURCH
2 De La Beche Street Swansea SA1 3EY
Tel: 01792 461146 *Fax:* 01792 477886
Office: Llanelli

DOUGLAS-JONES MERCER ‡
16 Axis Court Mallard Way Swansea Vale Swansea SA7 0AJ
Tel: 01792 650000 *Fax:* 01792 656500 *Dx:* 742500 SWANSEA 19
E-mail: post@djm.law.co.uk
List of partners: M J Snowdon
Languages: Welsh
Work: B1 C1 C2 D1 E F1 G H J1 K1 K2 L N O Q R1 S1 S2 W Z(c,e,h,k,l,q)
Emergency Action, Agency, Advocacy, Fixed Fee Interview, Legal Aid undertaken, Legal Aid Franchise and Member of Accident Line
Ptr: Snowdon, Mr Michael J BSc(Econ) . . . . Jun 1980
Asoc: Llewelyn, Mr Nicholas Paul BA(Hons). . . . . *Sep 1999
Ast: Evans, Dorian. Apr 2003
Con: Jones, Mr Martin L M LLB(Lond) . . . . *Dec 1966

GRAHAM EVANS & PARTNERS ‡
Moorgate House 6 Christina Street Swansea SA1 4EW
Tel: 01792 655822 *Fax:* 01792 645387 *Dx:* 39573 SWANSEA
List of partners: J P Clayton, G Dickens, A N Evans, F C Griffiths, S G Howell, G D James, D A R John, B Lewis
Languages: Welsh
Work: A1 B1 C1 C2 C3 D1 E F1 G H J1 K1 L N O Q R1 S1 W Z(b,c,i,j,k,l)
Emergency Action, Agency, Advocacy, Legal Aid undertaken, Legal Aid Franchise and Member of Accident Line
Ptr: Clayton, Mr Jeremy P LLB . . . . Dec 1975
Dickens, Mrs Gaynor LLB(Wales). . . . . *Nov 1987
Evans, Mr Andrew N LLB . . . . *Jun 1992
Griffiths, Miss Fiona C LLB . . . . *Jun 1987
Howell, Mr Simon G BSc(Econ). . . . . Oct 1981
James, Mr Geoffrey D LLB(Wales) . . . . §Jun 1972
John, Mr David A R LLB . . . . Jan 1971
Lewis, Mr Brian LLB. . . . . *Dec 1967
Ast: Burnell, Mr Steven J LLB . . . . *Mar 1990
Kreppel, Ms Wendy J LLB. . . . . Jun 1992
Lee, Mrs Fiona J LLB(Hons) . . . . *May 1997
Con: Evans, Mr Graham L LLB(Lond). . . . . Apr 1961

GEE & EDWARDS ‡
98 Walter Road Swansea SA1 5QJ
Tel: 01792 465806 / 464937 *Fax:* 01792 645914
Dx: 39583 SWANSEA
Emergency telephone 01792 290341 / 01792 477254
E-mail: law@gee-ed.freeserve.co.uk
List of partners: G D Owen
Work: B1 C1 C2 C3 D1 D2 E F1 G H J1 K1 L M1 M2 N P S1 V W Z(i,j,k,l,m,r)
Emergency Action, Agency, Advocacy, Legal Aid undertaken, Legal Aid Franchise and Member of Accident Line
Ptr: Owen, Mr Geoffrey D LLB. . . . . *Jan 1980

SALLY GOLDSTONE FAMILY LAW ‡
114 Walter Road Swansea SA1 5QQ
Tel: 01792 456139 *Fax:* 01792 456283
E-mail: law@sallygoldstone.co.uk
List of partners: S R Goldstone
SPr: Goldstone, Miss Sally Ruth LLB(Hons) . . . . Apr 1991

GOLDSTONES ‡
10 Walter Road Swansea SA1 5NF
Tel: 01792 643021 *Fax:* 01792 469614 *Dx:* 52951 SWANSEA
Emergency telephone 01554 62258
E-mail: law@goldstones.co.uk
List of partners: R A Cookson, D W Hutchison, C A Stewart
Languages: Welsh
Work: D1 D2 F1 G H J1 K1 K2 L N Q S1 V W Z(l)
Emergency Action, Advocacy, Fixed Fee Interview, Legal Aid undertaken, Legal Aid Franchise and Member of Accident Line
Ptr: Cookson, Mrs Rosemary A BSc Sweet & Maxwell Law Prize . . . . *Oct 1989
Hutchison, Mr David W BA Sweet & Maxwell Law Prize*Oct 1986
Stewart, Mrs Catherine A ACIArb . . . . *Jul 1979
Asoc: Bateman, Mrs Pamela LLB . . . . Oct 1979
Pritchard, Mr Jonathan LLB(Hons) . . . . Nov 1993
Ast: Jones, Mrs Sandra LLB . . . . *Mar 1993
Vosper, Mrs Ann P LLB . . . . *Dec 1980

EDWARD HARRIS SOLICITORS ‡
Tredegar Fawr Llangyfelach Swansea SA5 7LS
Tel: 01792 772505 *Fax:* 01792 772553
E-mail: eh@ehlaw.co.uk

HOWELLS
4 Langdon House Langdon Road SA1 Waterfront Swansea SA1 8QY
Tel: 01792 410016 *Fax:* 01792 412728 *Dx:* 39571 SWANSEA
E-mail: info@howellslegal.com
Office: Caerphilly, Cardiff, Newport, Talbot Green
Work: C2 D2 E J1 K1 K3 N Q S1 S2 W
Agency, Fixed Fee Interview and Legal Aid undertaken

HUGHES GRIFFITHS PARTNERSHIP ‡
150 St Helens Road Swansea SA1 4DF
Tel: 01792 458275 *Fax:* 01792 456834 *Dx:* 39570 SWANSEA
E-mail: info@hughes-griffiths.co.uk
List of partners: P J F Hughes
Work: C1 C2 E J1 O Q R1 S1 W Z(c)
Ptr: Hughes, Mr Peter J F BSc(Econ) . . . . *Jul 1965

HUW JAMES SOLICITOR ‡
21 Mansel Street Swansea SA1 5SG
Tel: 01792 643476 / 411600 *Fax:* 01792 411601
E-mail: enquiries@lawofficeuk.co.uk
List of partners: P H B James
Work: B1 E F1 G H K1 K3 L Q S1 S2 V W Z(i)
Emergency Action, Agency and Fixed Fee Interview undertaken
Ptr: James, Mr Phillip H B BSc(Econ) . . . . Jul 1972

JEFFREYS SOLICITORS ‡
Cheriton Chambers 81 St Teilo Street Pontarddulais Swansea SA4 8SS
Tel: 01792 886899 / 07966 220535 *Fax:* 01792 886691
E-mail: jeffreys@keithjeffreys.co.uk

T G JONES & ASSOCIATES ‡
9 St James Crescent Uplands Swansea SA1 6DZ
Tel: 01792 469717 *Fax:* 01792 472355 *Dx:* 39555 SWANSEA
List of partners: T G Jones
Work: A1 B1 C1 D1 E F1 G H J1 K1 L M1 N P R1 S1 T1 V W Z(b,c,i,l,p)
Emergency Action, Agency, Advocacy, Legal Aid undertaken and Member of Accident Line
Ptr: Jones, Mr Timothy G LLB(Wales) . . . . *§Dec 1977

T LLEWELLYN JONES
22 Station Road Swansea SA9 1NT
Tel: 01639 842235 *Fax:* 01639 844290
E-mail: elizabeth.parcell@tllewellynjones.co.uk
Office: Neath
Work: D1 G H J1 K1 L M1 N Q S1 S2 V W Z(h,l,q,r)
Emergency Action, Agency, Advocacy, Fixed Fee Interview, Legal Aid undertaken and Member of Accident Line
Ptr: Pearn, Mr Malcolm G BA(Oxon) Associated Law Societies of Wales Prize. . . . . *Dec 1963

KEARNS & CO ‡
Llys Kearns Jersey Marine Swansea SA1 8QL
Tel: 01792 463111 *Fax:* 01792 463888 *Dx:* 39552 SWANSEA 1

LEO ABSE & COHEN
Conwy House Phoenix Way Swansea SA7 9LA
Tel: 01792 762030 *Fax:* 01792 762031 *Dx:* 82802 SWANSEA 2
E-mail: law@leoabse.com
Office: Cardiff, Newport

PETER LYNN & PARTNERS ‡
2nd Floor Langdon House 130 Port Tennant Road Swansea SA1 8QY
Tel: 01792 450010 *Fax:* 01792 462881 *Dx:* 56768 MORRISTON
E-mail: info@peterlynnandpartners.co.uk
List of partners: S Atherton, R A Howe, P A Lynn, S Pincott, S J Plant
Office: Morriston, Penarth, Swansea
Work: A1 B1 C1 C2 D1 E F1 F2 J1 J2 K1 K3 K4 L M3 N O Q R1 R2 S1 S2 T1 T2 V W X Z(b,c,e,f,g,j,k,l,p,q,t,u,w)
Emergency Action, Agency, Advocacy, Fixed Fee Interview and Legal Aid undertaken
Ptr: Howe, Mr Richard A LLB . . . . Jan 1996
Lynn, Mr Peter Alan BSc(Hons) . . . . *§May 1992
Plant, Miss Sara Jane LLB(Hons) . . . . *Oct 1993
Con: Stephens, Miss Catrin Anne BA(Hons); CertEd . . . . *Apr 1995

PETER LYNN & PARTNERS
21 Holly Street Pontardawe Swansea SA8 4ET
Tel: 01792 863633 *Fax:* 01792 863693
Office: Morriston, Penarth, Swansea

MORGAN COLE
(incorporating Geo L Thomas; Nettleship & Co; John Hope & Co; Collins; Wood)
Llys Tawe Kings Road Swansea SA1 8PG
Tel: 01792 634634 *Fax:* 01792 634500 *Dx:* 141063 SWANSEA 11
E-mail: info@morgan-cole.com
Office: Bristol, Cardiff, Oxford, Reading (2 offices)
Languages: Bemba, French, German, Hebrew, Italian, Mandarin, Polish, Portuguese, Punjabi, Spanish, Welsh
Work: B1 C1 C2 C3 D1 E F1 G H J1 L M1 M2 N O P Q R1 S1 T1 T2 V W Z(b,c,d,e,f,j,l,m,o)

MORGAN LAROCHE ‡
PO Box 176 Bay House Tawe Business Village Swansea SA7 9YT
Tel: 01792 776756 *Fax:* 01792 776777 *Dx:* 82808 SWANSEA 2
E-mail: info@morganlaroche.com

MORGANS
105a Walter Road Swansea SA1 5QQ
Tel: 01792 479150 *Fax:* 01792 479159
E-mail: swansea.info@morgans-sols.co.uk
Office: Cardiff (2 offices), Milford Haven

MORGANS ‡
86 Gower Road Sketty Swansea SA2 9BZ
Tel: 01792 512403 *Fax:* 01792 512402
E-mail: info@morgans-sols.co.uk

JOHN MORSE SOLICITORS ‡
St Helen's House 156 St Helen's Road Swansea SA1 4DG
Tel: 01792 648111 *Fax:* 01792 648028 *Dx:* 39598 SWANSEA
E-mail: mail@johnmorse.co.uk
List of partners: J F Morse, A P Sivertsen
Languages: French, Italian
Work: B1 B2 C1 C2 D1 E F1 G J1 K1 K3 L N O Q S1 S2 T1 W Z(f,l)
Emergency Action, Advocacy undertaken and Member of Accident Line
Ptr: Morse, Mr John F. . . . . *Nov 1967
Sivertsen, Mr Andrew P LLB; LPC. . . . . *Oct 2002
Ast: Johnson, Miss Laura . . . . *Jan 2007
Con: Harrop-Griffiths, Mr Brian . . . . Jan 1961

PJW SOLICITORS ‡
11 Alexandra Road Gorseinon Swansea SA4 4NW
Tel: 01792 897654 *Fax:* 01792 898050

W PARRY & CO ‡
(in association with Kearns & Co(London W1))
37 Walter Road Swansea SA1 5NW
Tel: 01792 470037 *Fax:* 01792 464539 *Dx:* 39553 SWANSEA
E-mail: law@wparry.com
List of partners: B J Cornelius, K G Kirby, P O'Brien, W T Parry, D A Seal
Work: A1 B1 C1 C2 C3 D1 E F1 F2 G J1 K1 L N O Q S1 S2 W Z(l,t)
Emergency Action, Agency, Advocacy and Fixed Fee Interview undertaken
Ptr: Cornelius, Mr Benjamin Jason. . . . . Apr 2006
Kirby, Mr Kenneth G President of Swansea District Law Society 2002/2003 . . . . *Jul 1969
O'Brien, Mr Patrick LLB; LLM . . . . *Sep 1998
Parry, Mr William T LLB(Brunel). . . . . *Oct 1986
Seal, Mr David A LLB. . . . . *Aug 1996

PHILLIPS GREEN & MURPHY ‡
120 Walter Road Swansea SA1 5RF
Tel: 01792 468684 *Fax:* 01792 468685
E-mail: enquiries@phillipsgreenmurphy.com
List of partners: P M Murphy
Dir: Murphy, Mrs Paula Marie . . . . *Feb 1993

CLIVE REES SOLICITOR ‡
10 Metropole Chambers Salubrious Passage Wind Street Swansea SA1 3RT
Tel: 01792 474201 *Dx:* 92055 SWANSEA 3
E-mail: clive@clivereessolicitor.com

REES DAVIES & PARTNERS ‡
29 Alexandra Road Swansea SA1 5DQ
Tel: 01792 645962 *Fax:* 01792 646383 *Dx:* 39580 SWANSEA

SALTER REES & KELLY ‡
18 Walter Road Swansea SA1 5NQ
Tel: 01792 470707 *Fax:* 01792 466489 *Dx:* 39593 SWANSEA
List of partners: P A Kelly, K M Salter
Office: Ammanford
Emergency Action, Agency, Advocacy, Fixed Fee Interview, Legal Aid undertaken and Member of Accident Line
Ptr: Kelly, Mr Phillip A BA(Law) . . . . *Jun 1980
Salter, Mrs Katherina M LLB(Wales). . . . . *Jun 1990
Ast: Allgood, Ms Margaret H. . . . . Mar 1989

SIMMONDS HURFORD ‡
113 Walter Road Swansea SA1 5QQ
Tel: 01792 462729 / 641070 *Fax:* 01792 646560
Dx: 39584 SWANSEA
E-mail: law@simmondsco.co.uk
List of partners: H M Hurford, M O Simmonds
Languages: French, German, Welsh
Work: A1 B1 C1 C2 C3 D1 E F1 G H J1 K1 L N O Q R1 S1 W
Emergency Action, Agency, Advocacy, Fixed Fee Interview, Legal Aid undertaken and Member of Accident Line
Ptr: Hurford, Mrs Helen M BSc . . . . *Oct 1981
Simmonds, Mr Michael O LLB. . . . . *Dec 1973
Ast: Evans, Mr David E BA; LLB. . . . . *§Jan 1979
Hoskins, Mr Julian Richard LLB; PGDipLaw. . . . . *Sep 2006

SMITH LLEWELYN PARTNERSHIP ‡
18 Princess Way Swansea SA1 3LW
Tel: 01792 464444 *Fax:* 01792 464726 *Dx:* 92051 SWANSEA 3
E-mail: enquiries@smithllewelyn.com
List of partners: S L Bennett, A D Davies, G S Jones, P J M Smith
Languages: Mandarin, Welsh
Work: B1 C1 D1 D2 E F1 K1 K2 K3 K4 N O P Q S1 S2 W Z(m,r)
Emergency Action, Agency, Advocacy, Fixed Fee Interview, Legal Aid undertaken and Legal Aid Franchise
Ptr: Bennett, Miss Susan L LLB . . . . *Jul 1985
Davies, Mrs Amanda D LLB(Hons) . . . . *Nov 1989
Jones, Mr Graham S BSc ♦. . . . . *Nov 1985
Smith, Mr Peter J M Associated Law Societies of Wales Prize . . . . *Nov 1972
Asoc: Jones, Mrs Janine. . . . . *Dec 1998
Li, Miss Mei Y LLB(Hons). . . . . Jun 1998
Ast: Davies, Miss Claire . . . . *Nov 2005
Dunn, Miss Rebecca Emily BSc; GDL; LPC . . . . . Sep 2011
Phillips, Miss Joanne LLB . . . . Mar 2008
Walker, Mr Ian James BA(Hons); DipLaw . . . . . . *Mar 2002
Con: Struel, Mr Malcolm . . . . Nov 1958

STRICK & BELLINGHAM ‡
2 Princess Way Swansea SA1 3ND
Tel: 01792 641201 *Fax:* 01792 653012 *Dx:* 92050 SWANSEA 3
E-mail: strickbellingham@btconnect.co.uk
List of partners: J D B Moses, A G Robins
Work: C1 E L S1 S2 T1 T2 W
Agency undertaken
Ptr: Moses, Mr John D B LLB(Bris) . . . . *Dec 1963
Robins, Mr Anthony G. . . . . Mar 1971

THOMPSONS (FORMERLY ROBIN/BRIAN THOMPSON & PARTNERS)
30-31 Castle Street Swansea SA1 1HY
Tel: 01792 484920 *Fax:* 01792 301971 *Dx:* 92054 SWANSEA
Office: Belfast, Birmingham, Bristol, Cardiff, Chelmsford, Dagenham, Derby, Harrow, Leeds, Liverpool, London SW19, London WC1, Manchester, Middlesbrough, Newcastle upon Tyne, Nottingham, Plymouth, Sheffield, South Shields, Southampton, Stoke-on-Trent, Wolverhampton

TONNER JOHNS RATTI ‡
48 Walter Road Swansea SA1 5PW
Tel: 01792 643296 *Fax:* 01792 652572 *Dx:* 39561 SWANSEA
E-mail: law@tonnerjohns.co.uk
List of partners: D Johns, S L Ratti
Work: A1 B1 C1 C2 D1 D2 E F1 G H J1 K1 L N O P Q S1 T1 T2 W X Z(b,c,f,h,l,m)
Emergency Action, Agency, Advocacy, Fixed Fee Interview, Legal Aid undertaken, Legal Aid Franchise and Member of Accident Line
Ptr: Johns, Mr David BA(Law) . . . . Nov 1982
Ratti, Mr Stuart L LLB. . . . *Sep 1989
Con: Tonner, Mr James H LLB(Bris) . . . . *Jun 1966

TREVOR THOMAS SCOTT & JENKINS ‡
Central Chambers Clydach Swansea SA6 5HB
Tel: 01792 843821 *Fax:* 01792 846180
List of partners: D C Hughes, D M Jenkins, G L Powell
Emergency Action, Agency, Advocacy, Fixed Fee Interview, Legal Aid undertaken and Member of Accident Line
Ptr: Hughes, Mr David C LLB . . . . Jun 1975
Jenkins, Mr David M Notary Public . . . . *Oct 1966
Powell, Mr Gareth L. . . . . Jun 1977

TY ARIAN ‡
Alexandra House 1 Alexandra Road Swansea SA1 5ED
Tel: 01792 484200

PETER WILLIAMS & CO ‡
Ethos Kings Road Swansea SA1 8AS
Tel: 01792 465597 *Fax:* 01792 467390 *Dx:* 743462 SWANSEA
E-mail: mail@peterwilliamscolaw.co.uk
List of partners: J D Jones, D I Norton
Languages: Welsh
Work: B1 C1 C2 D1 E F1 G H J1 K1 L N O Q R1 S1 S2 T1 T2 V W Z(d,l,m)
Emergency Action, Agency, Advocacy, Fixed Fee Interview, Legal Aid undertaken, Legal Aid Franchise and Member of Accident Line
Ptr: Jones, Mr James D LLB. . . . *§Feb 1982
Norton, Mr David I . . . . *§Jan 1980

WILSON DEVONALD LTD ‡
38 Walter Road Swansea SA1 5NW
Tel: 01792 484566 *Fax:* 01792 484566 *Dx:* 52976 SWANSEA
Emergency telephone 07850 646864
E-mail: enquiries@wilsondevonald.co.uk
List of partners: N Devonald, J Tarrant, P Wilson
Languages: Welsh
Work: G H
Legal Aid undertaken and Legal Aid Franchise
Dir: Devonald, Mr Nick . . . . Mar 1992
Tarrant, Mr John . . . . Apr 1996
Wilson, Mr Paul. . . . . Oct 1977

SWINDON

ANDREWS MARTIN ‡
6 Little London Court Old Town Swindon SN1 3HY
Tel: 01793 641707 *Fax:* 01793 495950 *Dx:* 6216 SWINDON
E-mail: solicitors@andrewsmartin.co.uk
List of partners: P A Martin, R A Martin
Languages: French
Work: A1 C1 E J1 K4 L O R1 R2 S1 S2 W Z(l,m)
Ptr: Martin, Mrs Patricia A BA(Hons) Notary Public . . . *May 1981
Martin, Mr Richard A Panel Deputy (Court of Protection) Notary Public. . . . *Jun 1971

BLB SOLICITORS
54-57 Commercial Road Swindon SN1 5NX
Tel: 01793 615011 *Fax:* 01793 613842 *Dx:* 38635 SWINDON 2
Emergency telephone 01225 769787
E-mail: solicitors@swindon.blandb.co.uk
Office: Bath, Bradford-on-Avon, Trowbridge
Languages: French
Work: A1 B1 D1 E F1 G H J1 K1 L N P R1 S1 T1 V W Z(l,m,t)
Emergency Action, Agency, Advocacy, Fixed Fee Interview, Legal Aid undertaken, Legal Aid Franchise and Member of Accident Line
Ptr: Dunkerley, Mrs Angeli T W LLB . . . . *Feb 1989
Smyth, Mr Christopher J W BA ★ . . . . *Feb 1983
Asoc: Bishop, Mr Stephen Andrew LLB(Hons) . . . . *Sep 1992
Jennings, Ms Nicola LLB(Hons) . . . . *Jul 1999
Long, Miss Debra Anne LLB; LPC. . . . *Nov 1998
Vale, Miss Caroline Frances LLB . . . . Jan 1996
Ast: Mott, Mr Lee Arthur . . . . Apr 2001
Tawn, Mr Mark A LLB. . . . *Oct 1994

BEVIRS ‡
36 Regent Circus Swindon SN1 1UQ
Tel: 01793 532363 *Fax:* 01793 619585 *Dx:* 400916 SWINDON 6
List of partners: D F Brown, J Hunt, S A McNeil, N J Sewell, E A Spearey, S L Woolnough
Office: Calne, Wootton Bassett
Work: A1 B1 C1 C2 C3 D1 E F1 G H J1 K1 K2 K3 K4 L N O Q R1 R2 S1 S2 T2 W Z(d,m,q,r)
Emergency Action, Agency, Advocacy, Fixed Fee Interview, Legal Aid undertaken and Member of Accident Line
Ptr: Hunt, Mr John. . . . . Dec 1973
McNeil, Mr Stuart A LLB . . . . *Oct 1984
Sewell, Mr Nicholas John LLB(Hons) . . . . *Oct 1990
Asoc: Locke, Miss Kathryn LLB(Hons) . . . . Oct 1994
Ast: Kurtz, Miss Emma-Jane Francesca BA; TEP . . . . Jan 2004
Strong, Mrs Janet LLB . . . . *Nov 1990

BOWER & BAILEY
Cambridge House 4 College Court Regent Circus Swindon SN1 1PJ
Tel: 01793 610466 *Fax:* 01793 511505 *Dx:* 400901 SWINDON 6
Emergency telephone 01793 610466
E-mail: swindon@bowerandbailey.co.uk
Office: Banbury, Oxford, Witney
Work: B1 C1 C2 D1 E F1 F2 J1 K1 K3 L N O Q S1 S2 W Z(c,l,r)
Emergency Action, Advocacy, Fixed Fee Interview undertaken and Member of Accident Line
Ptr: Hannam, Mr Daniel Philip Stafford. . . . *Nov 1998
Hill, Mrs Alison J BA . . . . *Oct 1986
Janata, Mr David J BSc. . . . *Nov 1988
Millbourn, Mr Robert . . . . *Sep 1992
Murphy, Mr Eugene . . . . Jan 1999
Read, Mr Simon P B C BA . . . . *Oct 1982
Smith, Mr Simon J L BA. . . . *Nov 1984
Went, Ms Katie Emma . . . . *Jul 1996
Ast: Cutts, Ms Mary Louise BSc . . . . Apr 2005

ANDREW C N BRAND ‡
Little Foxes Marston Meysey Swindon SN6 6LQ
Tel: 01285 810328 *Fax:* 01285 810138
E-mail: andrew.c.n.brand@btinternet.com
List of partners: A C N Brand
Work: C1 E L S1 W
SPr: Brand, Mr Andrew C N . . . . *§May 1964

CARTER READ & DOVE ‡
Commerce House 34-35 Commercial Road Swindon SN1 5PL
Tel: 01793 617617 *Fax:* 01793 511249 *Dx:* 38608 SWINDON 2
E-mail: admin@crdlaw.co.uk
List of partners: R A Carter, S H Dove
Work: A1 B1 C1 E J1 L R1 S1 S2 W
Ptr: Carter, Mr Robert A BA . . . . *§Dec 1980
Dove, Mr Stephen H LLB(Lond) . . . . *§Jun 1980
Asoc: Andrews, Miss Kirstie Michelle LLB . . . . Sep 1999
Martin, Mr Steven Charles BA(Hons)(History) . . . . Jun 1999

CHARLES LUCAS & MARSHALL
Eastcott House 4 High Street Old Town Swindon SN1 3EP
Tel: 01793 511055 *Fax:* 01793 610518 *Dx:* 131296 SWINDON 13
E-mail: ask@clmlaw.co.uk
Office: Hungerford, Newbury, Wantage
Work: A1 B1 C1 D1 E F1 F2 G H J1 K1 L M1 N O P Q R1 S1 S2 V W Z(c,e,i,k,l,p,q,s,t)
Emergency Action, Agency, Advocacy, Fixed Fee Interview undertaken and Member of Accident Line
Ptr: Chandler, Ms Brigitte LLB Solicitor of the Supreme Court . . . . *Apr 1977
Ellins, Mr Hugh M. . . . . *§Dec 1971
Asoc: Egan, Mr Andrew James BEc; LLB . . . . Sep 1996
Overend, Mr Michael C . . . . *§Oct 1986
Ast: Lloyd, Miss Julie Iris BA; PGDipLaw. . . . Nov 2003
McCabe, Mr Philip LLB(Hons); BA(Hons)(Econ). . . . *May 2005

CLARK HOLT ‡
Hardwick House Prospect Place Swindon SN1 3LJ
Est: 1995
Tel: 01793 617444 *Fax:* 01793 617436 *Dx:* 38606 SWINDON 2
E-mail: richardc@clarkholt.com
List of partners: J M C Ashbridge, M J Bazen, R A Clark, J M Holt, P M G Humphreys, P R James, J G Jenkins, A R M Kirkpatrick, K L Whitter
Work: A1 C1 C2 C3 E I J1 L R1 R2 S2 U2 Z(b,e,f,za)
Ptr: Ashbridge, Mr Jonathan M C LLB. . . . *Nov 1989
Bazen, Mr Martin J BSc; BA. . . . *Nov 1993
Clark, Mr Richard A . . . . *Oct 1973
Holt, Mr Jeremy Martin MA(Oxon). . . . *Sep 1980
Humphreys, Mr Philip M G LLB . . . . *Jan 1991
James, Mr Peter Robin . . . . *Oct 1984
Jenkins, Mr Jeffrey G LLB. . . . *Nov 1985
Kirkpatrick, Mr Alasdair Robert Moore LLB R W Stead Memorial Scholarship 1982 . . . . *Oct 1986
Mem: Whitter, Ms Karron Louise LLB . . . . Oct 1993
Ast: Eldridge, Miss Fleur Polly Mary Rose BA(Hons); LPC; PGDL . . . . May 2007
Houlston-Hope, Mr James Thomas BA . . . . *Feb 2006
Smith, Mr Stuart William Blaiklock DipLaw. . . . Sep 2007
Thorpe, Mr James Alexander . . . . Oct 2001
Con: Maitland-Walker, Mr Julian H . . . . *Jun 1974

S J EDNEY ‡
Alexander House 19 Fleming Way Swindon SN1 2NG
Tel: 0800 421234 *Fax:* 01793 610959
Emergency telephone 01285 644383
E-mail: office@sjedney.co.uk
List of partners: S J Edney
Work: N Z(r)
Legal Aid undertaken and Legal Aid Franchise
SPr: Edney, Mr Seamus J LLB . . . . *Nov 1985

EMPORIKO DIKAIO LEGAL SERVICES ‡
19 Thresher Drive Abbeyfields Swindon SN25 4AE
Tel: 01793 701864
E-mail: manassutzi@aol.co.uk

FAMILY AFFAIRS ‡
87 Commercial Road Swindon SN1 5PD
Tel: 0333 240 1040 *Fax:* 0333 240 1049

FULLAGARBROOKS ‡
4 Cricklade Court Cricklade Street Swindon SN1 3EY
Tel: 01793 777007 *Fax:* 01793 777006 *Dx:* 131293 SWINDON 13
Emergency telephone 07768 892715
E-mail: vaughanf@fullagarbrooks.com
List of partners: D J Brooks, J V S Fullagar
Work: B1 C1 E F1 J1 K1 L N O Q S1 V W Z(c,e,f,p)
Emergency Action, Agency, Advocacy and Fixed Fee Interview undertaken
Ptr: Brooks, Mr David James LLB(Hons). . . . *Feb 1994
Fullagar, Mr Julian Vaughan Shearer BA . . . . *§Feb 1986

GREAT WESTERN SOLICITORS ‡
10 Commercial Road Swindon SN1 5NF
Tel: 01793 436007

HALE & HOPKINS ‡
43 Victoria Road Old Town Swindon SN1 3AY
Tel: 01793 522277 *Fax:* 01793 431428 *Dx:* 6223 SWINDON 1
E-mail: info@haleandhopkins.co.uk
List of partners: P C James
Work: S1
Fixed Fee Interview undertaken
Ptr: James, Mr Philip Clive LLB(Bris) . . . . *§Oct 1981
Ast: Dol, Mrs Hardeep LLB . . . . Nov 2007

HENRY & COMPANY ‡
The Farm Office South Marston Farm South Marston Swindon SN3 4RX
Tel: 01793 832000 *Fax:* 01793 834166
E-mail: info@henryandco.co.uk
List of partners: D A Cook
Work: S1
Ptr: Cook, Mr Darren Anthony LLB(Hons) . . . . Sep 1988

THE HILLMAN PARTNERSHIP ‡
72 Victoria Road Swindon SN1 3BB
Tel: 01793 642100 *Fax:* 01793 512480 *Dx:* 6210 SWINDON
Emergency telephone 01793 782669
E-mail: enquiries@hillmanpart.co.uk
List of partners: J C Fernandes, T F Hillman
Work: E F1 G H J1 K1 L S1 W Z(l)
Agency, Advocacy, Fixed Fee Interview and Legal Aid undertaken
Ptr: Fernandes, Mr J Conleth LLB(Hull) . . . . §Feb 1981
Hillman, Mr Thomas F LLB(Nott'm) . . . . §Apr 1975

HINE SOLICITORS
Park House Business Centre Church Place Swindon SN1 5ED
Tel: 01793 698027
Office: Beaconsfield, Bracknell, Cheltenham, Gerrards Cross, Oxford, Princes Risborough, Yiewsley

HOFFMAN MALE & CO ‡
First Floor 8 Bath Road Old Town Swindon SN1 4BA
Tel: 01793 538198 *Fax:* 01793 613804

JEARY & LEWIS
46 Commercial Road Swindon SN1 5NX
Tel: 01793 435577 *Fax:* 01793 979456
Office: Chippenham

JOHN LATHAM & CO ‡
77-78 Bridge Street Swindon SN1 1BT
Tel: 01793 430133 *Fax:* 01793 431009 *Dx:* 120129 SWINDON 11
Work: G H Z(g)
Agency, Advocacy, Fixed Fee Interview, Legal Aid undertaken and Legal Aid Franchise

LEMON & CO ‡
34 Regent Circus Swindon SN1 1PY
Tel: 01793 527141 *Fax:* 01793 614168 *Dx:* 400912 SWINDON 6

MORGAN & CO ‡
Regus House Windmill Hill Business Park Whitehill Way Swindon SN5 6QR
Tel: 01793 512982 *Fax:* 01793 495653
E-mail: solicitors@morgan-co.co.uk
List of partners: N U Morgan
Work: J1 Q S1 S2 W
SPr: Morgan, Mr Nigel Urquhart . . . . *Jul 1982

MORRISON & MASTERS LIMITED ‡
17-20 Commercial Road Swindon SN1 5NS
Tel: 01793 526601 *Fax:* 01793 520977 *Dx:* 132171 SWINDON 2
E-mail: fet@mnm2.co.uk
List of partners: A D Gascoigne, T P Hartshorn, C Riddle, P N Riddle, F E Tucker
Languages: French, Italian
Work: A1 B1 C1 E F1 G H J1 J2 K1 K3 L N O Q R1 S1 V W Z(c,e,i,k,l,p,q)
Emergency Action, Agency, Advocacy, Fixed Fee Interview, Legal Aid undertaken and Member of Accident Line
Dir: Gascoigne, Mr Andrew D LLB. . . . *§Dec 1985
Hartshorn, Mr Thomas P . . . . *§Dec 1977
Riddle, Mrs Catherine LLB . . . . *§Sep 1990
Riddle, Mr Peter N . . . . *§Jan 1969
Tucker, Mr Frederick Edward LLB. . . . *§Dec 1980
Ast: Pipe, Mr Steven Francis. . . . *Jan 2004
Tucker, Ms Kim . . . . Jan 2005

POOLEY DALE & CO ‡
Bristol & West House 10-15 Regent Circus Swindon SN1 1PP
Tel: 01793 488848 *Fax:* 01793 511209 *Dx:* 400903 SWINDON 6
List of partners: N J J Buckley, A G Dale, M R S de Bertodano
Languages: Cantonese
Work: A1 B1 C1 C2 C3 D1 E G H J1 K1 K2 L M1 M2 N P R1 S1 T1 T2 W Z(l)
Emergency Action, Agency, Advocacy, Fixed Fee Interview and Legal Aid undertaken
Ptr: Buckley, Mr Nicholas J J LLB(L'pool) . . . . *§Mar 1977
Dale, Mr Anthony G MA(Oxon) . . . . *§Jun 1968
de Bertodano, Mr Martin R S . . . . *§Jun 1963
Ast: Wong-Robinson, Mrs Brenda W S. . . . . Feb 1987

ROSS SOLICITORS LTD ‡
40 Victoria Road Old Town Swindon SN1 3AS
Tel: 01793 512960 *Fax:* 01793 432962 *Dx:* 400919 SWINDON 6
List of partners: G J Hotson, R B Ross
Languages: Urdu, Welsh
Work: G H
Legal Aid undertaken and Legal Aid Franchise
Dir: Hotson, Mr Gordon J LLB(Hons) . . . . *Dec 1992
Ross, Mr Robert B LLB(Warw) ★ . . . . *Feb 1986
Ast: Hall, Mr Philip D LLB(Wales) . . . . *§Oct 1980
Mott, Mr Lee Arthur . . . . Apr 2001
Sambreen, Ms Arif LLB(Hons); LPC. . . . Jun 2003

THRINGS LLP
6 Drakes Meadow Penny Lane Swindon SN3 3LL
Tel: 01793 410800 *Fax:* 01793 539040 *Dx:* 6204 SWINDON
E-mail: solicitors@thrings.com
Office: Bath, Bristol, London SW1
Languages: French, German
Work: A1 A3 B1 C1 C2 C3 D1 D2 E F1 I J1 J2 K1 K2 L M1 M2 N O P Q R1 S1 S2 T1 T2 U1 U2 V W X Z(b,c,d,e,f,g,h,i,j,k,l,n,o,p,q,w,x)

STEPHEN WEIGHELL & CO ‡
Alexander House 19 Fleming Way Swindon SN1 2NG
Tel: 01793 600724
List of partners: S N Weighell
SPr: Weighell, Mr Stephen N DMS . . . . Nov 1970

WINTON RAYNES & CO ‡
(incorporating Warren-Green & Broughton)
Canford House 13 Devizes Road Swindon SN1 4BH
Tel: 01793 522688 *Fax:* 01793 513812 *Dx:* 6222 SWINDON 1
E-mail: wintonraynes@legalisp.net
List of partners: P J Winton
Languages: French
Work: A1 C1 C2 E L S1 S2 W Z(l)
Ptr: Winton, Mr Peter John LLB(L'pool) . . . . *§Nov 1972

See p112 for the Key to Work Categories & other symbols

WITHY KING SOLICITORS
(incorporating Chalk Smith Brooks)
Vectis Court 4-6 Newport Street Old Town Swindon SN1 3DX
Tel: 01793 536526 *Fax:* 01793 618140
E-mail: enquiries@withyking.co.uk
Office: Abingdon, Bath (2 offices), Marlborough, Oxford, Thame, Trowbridge
Work: A1 A3 B1 C1 C2 D1 D2 E F1 F2 G H I J1 J2 K1 K2 L M1 N O P Q R1 R2 S1 S2 T1 T2 V W Z(c,d,e,f,g,h,i,j,k,l,m,p,q,r,w)

SWINTON, Greater Manchester

LINDER MYERS SOLICITORS
97-101 Chorley Road Swinton Greater Manchester M27 4AB
Tel: 0161 794 5957 *Fax:* 0161 794 0431 *Dx:* 28201 SWINTON
E-mail: enquiries@lindermyers.co.uk
Office: Manchester (2 offices), Shrewsbury

MARY MONSON SOLICITORS LTD ‡
87 Chorley Road Swinton Greater Manchester M27 4AA
Tel: 0161 794 0088 / 0808 155 4870 *Fax:* 0161 794 5333
Dx: 23515 BIRMINGHAM 3
Emergency telephone 0161 794 0088
E-mail: info@marymonson.co.uk
List of partners: M Monson
Languages: Farsi, French, Gujarati, Hindi, Iranian, Polish, Punjabi, Russian, Slovak, Urdu
Work: B2 G H
Advocacy, Legal Aid undertaken and Legal Aid Franchise
Dir: Monson, Miss Mary LLB. . . . . Dec 1975
Ast: Davin, Mr James . . . . . Oct 2007
McCallan, Ms Mary . . . . . Jul 2005

ROTHWELL & EVANS ‡
The Old Brewery House 1 Station Road Swinton Greater Manchester M27 6AH
Tel: 0161 794 1830 *Fax:* 0161 794 5423
List of partners: J Baker, G L Hall, J J M McNamara, K J Newton, K S Taylor
Office: Sale
Languages: French, German
Work: C1 C2 C3 D1 E F1 G H J1 K1 L M1 M2 N P R1 S1 V W Z(k,l,m)
Emergency Action, Agency, Advocacy, Fixed Fee Interview, Legal Aid undertaken, Legal Aid Franchise and Member of Accident Line
Ptr: Baker, Ms Jacqueline MA(Cantab) . . . . . Nov 1987
Hall, Mr Gary L . . . . . May 1998
Taylor, Mr K Stephen LLB. . . . . *Jun 1979

SYSTON, Leicestershire

BABYLAW SOLICITORS ‡
Orchard House 1044 Melton Road Syston Leicestershire LE7 2NN
Tel: 0844 561 1161
E-mail: jo.robson@babylaw.co.uk
Work: J1

RICHARD KNIGHT & CO ‡
1331 Melton Road Syston Leicestershire LE7 2EP
Tel: 0116 260 0021 *Fax:* 0116 269 7017 *Dx:* 17373 SYSTON
E-mail: info@richardknight.co.uk
List of partners: R H Knight
Work: A1 C1 D1 E F1 G H J1 K1 L M1 N P R1 S1 V W Z(c,d,e,l)
Emergency Action, Agency, Advocacy, Fixed Fee Interview and Legal Aid undertaken
Ptr: Knight, Mr Richard H LLB(L'pool) . . . . . *Jun 1979

RICH & CARR FREER BOUSKELL
1172 Melton Road Syston Leicestershire LE7 2HB
Tel: 0116 242 6036 *Fax:* 0116 264 0655 *Dx:* 724400 LEICESTER 24
E-mail: enquiries@richandcarr.co.uk
Office: Blaby, Leicester, Lutterworth, Oadby
Work: C1 E F1 J1 K1 L M1 N P Q S1 W
Agency, Advocacy undertaken and Member of Accident Line
Asoc: Coffee, Mr John Kenneth LLB. . . . . *Oct 1980

TADCASTER, North Yorkshire

BROMETS JACKSON HEATH ‡
Kirkgate House Tadcaster North Yorkshire LS24 9AD
Tel: 01937 832371 *Fax:* 01937 835666 *Dx:* 29661 TADCASTER
E-mail: legal@brometsjacksonheath.co.uk
List of partners: D J Creasey, J F Harbottle, R W W Jackson
Work: A1 E F1 J1 K1 K3 L N Q S1 S2 W Z(l,q)
Agency, Advocacy, Fixed Fee Interview undertaken and Member of Accident Line
Ptr: Creasey, Mr David Julian MA; LLB . . . . . *Oct 1996
Harbottle, Mr John J . . . . . *Jan 1968
Jackson, Mr Richard William Wilson LLB . . . . . *Aug 1977

NORTH STAR TAX ‡
Commer House Station Road Tadcaster North Yorkshire LS24 9JF
Tel: 01937 830065
E-mail: info@northstartax.co.uk

TADLEY, Hampshire

ROWBERRY MORRIS
Sherfield House Mulfords Hill Tadley Hampshire RG26 3XJ
Tel: 0118 981 2992 *Fax:* 0118 981 7946 *Dx:* 100552 TADLEY
Office: Reading, Richmond upon Thames, Staines
Work: A1 D1 E F1 I J1 K1 L N O Q S1 S2 W Z(p,q,r)
Agency, Advocacy and Legal Aid undertaken
Ptr: Gallimore, Miss Julie . . . . . *Jun 1996
Henson, Mr Neil C LLB(Hons). . . . . *Nov 1978
Asoc: Hodges, Ms Diane LLB . . . . . Jun 1973

TADWORTH, Surrey

BARRCO LIMITED ‡
20 Green Lane Lower Kingswood Tadworth Surrey KT20 6TB
Tel: 01737 833850 *Fax:* 01737 833850
E-mail: m.trench@barrco.org.uk

DEBORAH BEARHAM & CO ‡
The Haven 73 Breech Lane Tadworth Surrey KT20 7SJ
Tel: 01737 812707 *Fax:* 01737 812707
List of partners: D Y Bearham
SPr: Bearham, Ms Deborah Y . . . . . Sep 1996

TALBOT GREEN, Rhondda Cynon Taff

DEVONALDS
46 Talbot Road Talbot Green Rhondda Cynon Taff CF72 8AF
Tel: 01443 223888 *Fax:* 01433 238516
E-mail: talbotgreen@devonalds.co.uk
Office: Cardiff, Pontypridd (2 offices), Tonypandy

FRANCIS-TROWE SOLICITORS ‡
56 Talbot Road Talbot Green Rhondda Cynon Taff CF72 8AF
Tel: 01443 231555 *Fax:* 01443 231777 *Dx:* 52610 TALBOT GREEN
E-mail: reception@francis-trowe.co.uk
Languages: Welsh
Work: S1 S2 W Z(h)

DAVID W HARRIS & CO
Grove House 21-25 Talbot Road Talbot Green Rhondda Cynon Taff CF72 8AD
Tel: 01443 223265 *Fax:* 01443 229875 *Dx:* 52606 TALBOT GREEN
Office: Bridgend, Pontypridd
Work: D1 F1 G H J1 K1 L M1 N P Q S1 V W
Emergency Action, Agency, Advocacy, Fixed Fee Interview, Legal Aid undertaken and Member of Accident Line
Ptr: Hopkins, Mr Richard A BSc(Econ). . . . . *Feb 1983

HOWELLS
First Floor 83 Talbot Road Talbot Green Rhondda Cynon Taff CF72 8AE
Tel: 01443 230411 *Fax:* 01443 230414 *Dx:* 52611 TALBOT GREEN
E-mail: info@howellslegal.com
Office: Caerphilly, Cardiff, Newport, Swansea
Work: C2 D1 E J1 K1 K3 L N Q S1 S2 W
Agency, Fixed Fee Interview and Legal Aid undertaken

TALGARTH, Powys

THE WOODLAND DAVIES PARTNERSHIP LLP
Enig Chambers The Square Talgarth Powys LD3 0BW
Tel: 01874 711744
Office: Brecon, Hay-on-Wye, Hereford, Kington
Work: A1 A2 D2 E K1 K2 K3 L N Q S1 S2 W Z(l)
Agency undertaken
Ptr: Davies, Miss E Ann. . . . . *Nov 1979
Davies, Mr Peter G BSc(Econ) . . . . . *Jan 1982
Asoc: Theobald, Miss Carolyn M LLB . . . . . *Nov 1978

TAMWORTH, Staffordshire

ARGYLES ‡
43 Albert Road Tamworth Staffordshire B79 7JS
Tel: 01827 56276 *Fax:* 01827 66628 *Dx:* 12656 TAMWORTH
Emergency telephone 07801 882048
E-mail: enquiries@argylessolicitors.co.uk
List of partners: D H Ford, C T Lorton, T Wilkinson, G Willoughby
Languages: German
Work: A1 A3 B1 B2 C1 D1 E F1 G H J1 K1 L M1 N O P Q R1 R2 S1 S2 T1 T2 V W Z(b,c,d,h,i,j,k,l,m,n,o,p,r,s,t)
Emergency Action, Agency, Advocacy, Fixed Fee Interview, Legal Aid undertaken, Legal Aid Franchise and Member of Accident Line
Ptr: Ford, Mr David H LLB(B'ham). . . . . *Jan 1965
Lorton, Mr Charles T LLB(Lond). . . . . *Jun 1977
Wilkinson, Mr Terence LLB(Lond); FCIArb. . . . . *May 1976
Willoughby, Miss Gail LLB; MA . . . . . Nov 1998

BAXTERS
51 Bridge Street Polesworth Tamworth Staffordshire B78 1DR
Tel: 01827 899059 *Fax:* 01827 892321 *Dx:* 12652 TAMWORTH
E-mail: davidjfoster@btconnect.com
Office: Tamworth
Work: D1 J1 K1 S1 S2 V W
Emergency Action, Agency and Legal Aid undertaken
Ptr: Ashman, Mr Lance H BSc. . . . . *Jun 1974
Foster, Mr David J LLB(B'ham) . . . . . *May 1981
Con: Rowley, Mr Malcolm BA. . . . . Aug 1981

DEWES LLP ‡
2 Bolebridge Street Tamworth Staffordshire B79 7PA
Tel: 01827 58391 *Fax:* 01827 54313
E-mail: info@dewesllp.com
List of partners: R Eddowes, J C O'Connor, P D Sketchley, J P Walsh
Work: A1 B1 C1 D1 E F1 G H J1 K1 L M1 N P R1 S1 T1 V W Z(d,i,l,m)
Emergency Action, Agency, Advocacy, Legal Aid undertaken and Member of Accident Line
Ptr: Eddowes, Mr Roger LLB . . . . . Jun 1976
O'Connor, Mr John C . . . . . *Jan 1983
Sketchley, Mr Peter D LLB . . . . . *Jun 1978
Walsh, Mr John P LLB . . . . . Nov 1974

DAVID J FOSTER & CO ‡
3 Albert Road Tamworth Staffordshire B79 7JN
Tel: 01827 58333 / 58334 *Fax:* 01827 52116
Dx: 12652 TAMWORTH 1
E-mail: davidjfoster@btconnect.com
List of partners: L H Ashman, D J Foster
Office: Tamworth
Work: D1 D2 E F1 G J1 K1 L N Q S1 S2 V W
Emergency Action, Agency, Advocacy, Legal Aid undertaken and Legal Aid Franchise
Ptr: Ashman, Mr Lance H BSc. . . . . *Jun 1974
Foster, Mr David J LLB(B'ham) . . . . . *May 1981
Ast: Martin, Mr Phillip BA . . . . . *Mar 1997
Con: Rowley, Mr Malcolm BA. . . . . Aug 1981

GARNER CANNING ‡
11 Aldergate Tamworth Staffordshire B79 7DL
Tel: 01827 314004 *Fax:* 01827 60327 *Dx:* 12667 TAMWORTH
E-mail: enquiries@garnercanning.co.uk
List of partners: M P Canning, D J Lewis, T M Mills, E Rymell, R M Taylor, I L U Webster
Office: Atherstone, Birmingham, Sutton Coldfield
Work: A1 C1 C2 D1 D2 E J1 K1 K2 K3 L O Q R1 R2 S1 S2 T1 T2 W Z(d,l)
Agency, Fixed Fee Interview and Legal Aid undertaken
Dir: Webster, Mr Ian Leslie Urquhart. . . . . Jun 1980
Ast: Rigby, Ms Vanessa . . . . . Jan 2008
Con: Garner, Mr Kevin Notary Public . . . . . Apr 1974
Other offices in Atherstone, Birmingham, Sutton Coldfield. We specialise in the following areas of work Commercial Property, Family Law, Residential Conveyancing.

2

GLAISYERS ‡
4 Bolebridge Street Tamworth Staffordshire B79 7PA
Tel: 01827 61011 *Fax:* 01827 61827 *Dx:* 12655 TAMWORTH
E-mail: sue@glaisyers.net
List of partners: R P Bonsall, P Brinkley
Languages: French
Work: E F1 K1 K3 S1
Ptr: Bonsall, Mr Richard Paul LLB(Hons) . . . . . *Oct 1999
Brinkley, Mr Paul LLB . . . . . *Feb 1991
Con: Hope, Mr Kenneth A LLB . . . . . *May 1976

MCGREGORS ‡
7 College Lane Tamworth Staffordshire B79 7LP
Tel: 01827 313999 *Fax:* 01827 315551 *Dx:* 12675 TAMWORTH
E-mail: mh@mcgregors-solicitors.co.uk
List of partners: J R McGregor
Languages: German
Work: G H K3
Ptr: McGregor, Mr John Ramsey BA. . . . . *May 1989
Ast: Tait, Ms Joanne LLB(Hons) . . . . . Jan 2006

MARK MATTHEWS & CO ‡
Bank House 16-21 Church Street Tamworth Staffordshire B79 7DH
Tel: 01827 65765 *Fax:* 01827 53207 *Dx:* 12666 TAMWORTH
Emergency telephone 01827 830523
E-mail: post@markmatthewssolicitors.co.uk
List of partners: G M A Matthews
Work: C1 D1 E F1 G H J1 K1 L M1 N P R1 S1 T1 V W
Emergency Action, Advocacy, Fixed Fee Interview and Legal Aid undertaken
Ptr: Matthews, Mr Godfrey M A . . . . . *Dec 1976

MERCIAN LAW LIMITED ‡
PO Box 15245 Tamworth Staffordshire B77 9HE
Tel: 0844 736 1980 *Fax:* 0844 736 1975
E-mail: complaints@mercianlaw.com

MORAN & CO ‡
40 Upper Gungate Tamworth Staffordshire B79 8AA
Tel: 01827 54631 *Fax:* 01827 68905 *Dx:* 12659 TAMWORTH
E-mail: solicitors@moranlaw.co.uk
List of partners: P G Isherwood, D C Lines, P G Moran
Work: A3 B1 E F1 J1 L N O Q S1 S2 Z(b,q)
Advocacy undertaken
Ptr: Isherwood, Mr Paul G BA. . . . . *Jan 1985
Lines, Mr David Christopher BA. . . . . *Aug 1978
Moran, Mr Patrick G LLB . . . . . *Apr 1981

PICKERINGS LLP ‡
Etchell House Etchell Court Bonehill Road Tamworth Staffordshire B78 3HQ
Est: 1997
Tel: 01827 317070 *Fax:* 01827 317080 *Dx:* 12651 TAMWORTH
E-mail: mail@pickerings-solicitors.com
List of partners: S M Albini, C Davies, S C King, G L Pegg
Languages: Afrikaans, French, Gujarati
Work: A1 A3 B1 C1 C2 D1 D2 E F1 J1 K1 K3 K4 L M1 O P Q R1 R2 S1 S2 T1 T2 W X Z(c,d,e,j,l,m,o,p,q,t)
Advocacy, Fixed Fee Interview and Legal Aid Franchise
Mem: Albini, Dr Susan M BSc; MSc; PhD; LPC . . . . . *Sep 1997
Davies, Mr Craig LLB(Hons). . . . . *Jun 1997
King, Mr Simon C BA . . . . . *Jan 1982
Pegg, Mr Graham L LLB . . . . . *Apr 1974
Ast: Clifford, Mr Martin MA(Management)(St Andrews). . . *Mar 2008
England, Mr Richard John. . . . . Nov 2007
Head, Miss Rebecca LLB; LPC . . . . . *Sep 2004
Makhani, Miss Taslim LLB; LPC. . . . . *Apr 2005
Mason, Mr Ben LLB. . . . . *Oct 2008
Napier, Miss Elizabeth Ann BA(Hons); PGDipLaw . . *Sep 2008
Pearce, Mrs Kate BA(Hons)(History); LLB; LPC . . . *Sep 2000
Roberts, Miss Katie LLB. . . . . *Oct 2008

RUTHERFORDS ‡
6-9 Ladybank Tamworth Staffordshire B79 7NB
Tel: 01827 311411 *Fax:* 01827 311666 *Dx:* 12654 TAMWORTH
E-mail: enquiries@rutherfordssolicitors.co.uk
Office: Birmingham, Tamworth
Languages: German
Work: A1 B1 C1 C2 C3 D1 E F1 G H I J1 J2 K1 L M1 M2 N O P Q R1 S1 T1 T2 U2 V W Z(c,d,e,g,h,j,k,l,m,q,r,t)

RUTHERFORDS
Residential Letting Centre 5 Victoria Road Tamworth Staffordshire B79 7HL
Tel: 01827 310410 *Fax:* 01827 67428 *Dx:* 12654 TAMWORTH
E-mail: properties@rutherfords-law.co.uk
Office: Birmingham, Tamworth
Work: A1 B1 C1 C2 C3 D1 E F1 G H J1 K1 M1 M2 N P R1 S1 T1 T2 V W Z(a,b,c,d,e,f,g,h,i,j,k,l,m,n,o,p,s,t)

WILL HARRINGTON
64 Albert Road Tamworth Staffordshire B79 7JN
Tel: 0844 846 1999 *Fax:* 01827 66868
Office: Sutton Coldfield

TANKERTON, Kent

COATES ALLBUTT EDMONDSON & TAYLOR ‡
(in association with Elliot Allard Edmondson & Taylor)
113a Tankerton Road Tankerton Kent CT5 2AN
Tel: 01227 272617 / 262813 *Fax:* 01227 274714
Dx: 45650 TANKERTON
Emergency telephone 01227 272208
List of partners: D W L Edmondson, W D B Edmondson
Work: B1 E F1 L R1 S1
Agency, Fixed Fee Interview and Legal Aid undertaken
Ptr: Edmondson, Mr William D B . . . . . *Dec 1978

TARPORLEY, Cheshire

HIBBERTS LLP
Avenue Buildings High Street Tarporley Cheshire CW6 0AZ
Tel: 01829 733338 *Fax:* 01829 733055
E-mail: enquiries@hibberts.com
Office: Crewe, Ellesmere, Nantwich, Whitchurch
Work: A1 C1 E F1 L R1 S1 W Z(l)
Ptr: Driver, Mr John Notary Public . . . . *Mar 1969
Ast: Querelle, Mr Richard E LLB(Hons) . . . . Jun 1998

LEBRETON TOWELL SOLICITOR ‡
4 Clemley Close Kelsall Tarporley Cheshire CW6 0RD
Tel: 01829 751459 *Fax:* 01829 752556
List of partners: S Lebreton-Towell
Languages: Hindi, Punjabi, Urdu
Work: B1 K1 K3 K4 N Q S1 W
Agency undertaken
SPr: Lebreton-Towell, Mrs Susan LLB . . . . *Nov 1994
Ast: O'Donovan, Mrs Marion E B BA(Hons); LLB(L'pool) . . Jul 1993

TAUNTON, Somerset

ACORN SOLICITORS ‡
1st and 2nd Floors 41 High Street Taunton Somerset TA1 3PN
Tel: 01823 273010

AMICUS SOLICITORS AND ADVOCATES ‡
Powlett House 34 High Street Taunton Somerset TA1 3PN
Tel: 01823 353111

ASHFORDS LLP
Ashford Court Blackbrook Park Avenue Taunton Somerset TA1 2PX
Tel: 01823 232300 *Fax:* 01823 232301
Dx: 97179 TAUNTON (BLACKBROOK)
E-mail: info@ashfords.co.uk
Office: Bristol, Exeter, London W1, Plymouth, Tiverton
Languages: French
Work: A1 A3 C1 E J1 K1 N O S1 W Z(e,o,q,u)
Emergency Action, Agency, Advocacy, Fixed Fee Interview, Legal Aid undertaken, Legal Aid Franchise and Member of Accident Line
Ptr: Blackburn, Mr J Darren LLB. . . . . *Dec 1991
Channer, Mr Gervase John Osborn . . . . *Oct 1974
Edwards, Ms Rachel J LLB(Hons). . . . . *§Nov 1990
Fox, Ms Michelle LLB . . . . *Nov 1993
Fox, Mr Peter Richard LLB . . . . *Jun 1980
Lomas, Miss Sarah Anne MA(Hons). . . . . Oct 1981
Mason, Mr Anthony . . . . *§Dec 1975
Squire, Mr Jason Steven LLB; LPC Law Society LPC Prize Winner 1995 . . . . *Sep 1997

BAILHACHE SHAW MARSDEN ‡
2 Church Square Taunton Somerset TA1 1SA
Tel: 01823 351122 *Fax:* 01823 335701 *Dx:* 96114 TAUNTON
E-mail: enquiries@bailhachesolicitors.com
Work: B1 C1 C2 D1 D2 E J1 K1 L N O Q R1 R2 S1 S2 W Z(d,l,q,r)
Agency and Advocacy undertaken
Asoc: Bailhache, Mr Edmund . . . . Nov 1992
Ast: Leyland, Mr Bruce. . . . . Jan 1991

BOYCE & CO SOLICITORS ‡
1 Church Square Taunton Somerset TA1 1SA
Tel: 01823 210670 *Fax:* 01823 334738
E-mail: enquiries@boycesolicitors.co.uk

BROOMHEAD & SAUL ‡
11 Hammet Street Taunton Somerset TA1 1RZ
Tel: 01823 288121 *Fax:* 01823 333486 *Dx:* 32102 TAUNTON
E-mail: enquiries@broomhead-saul.co.uk
List of partners: P N Brierley, J E Clegg, W P Gayer, A P M Lewis, R O Peters, H A Suffield, P Sykes
Office: Ilminster
Work: D1 G H J2 K1 K2 K3 L N Q S1 S2 V W
Emergency Action, Agency, Advocacy, Legal Aid undertaken, Legal Aid Franchise and Member of Accident Line
Ptr: Brierley, Mr Paul N MA(Cantab). . . . . *Apr 1975
Clegg, Mrs Julia E BA(Law). . . . . *Jun 1976
Lewis, Mr Andrew P M BA(Law). . . . . *Oct 1983
Sykes, Mr Paul MA(Oxon)(Law). . . . . *Oct 1986
Ast: Banks, Miss Eleanor Rachel LLB . . . . *Aug 2009

BUTLER & CO ‡
2a Church Square Taunton Somerset TA1 1SA
Tel: 01823 323665 *Fax:* 01823 323536
E-mail: office@butler-solicitors.co.uk

CLARKE WILLMOTT
Blackbrook Gate Blackbrook Park Avenue Taunton Somerset TA1 2PG
Tel: 0845 209 1000 / 0117 305 6000 *Fax:* 0845 209 2004
Dx: 97175 TAUNTON (BLACKBROOK)
E-mail: info@clarkewillmott.com
Office: Birmingham, Bristol, London EC4, Manchester, Southampton
Work: A1 A2 A3 B1 C1 C2 C3 E F1 F2 I J1 J2 K1 K3 L M2 N O P Q R1 R2 S1 S2 T1 T2 U2 W X Z(b,c,d,e,h,j,k,l,o,p,q,r,t,u,w,za)
Advocacy, Fixed Fee Interview, Legal Aid undertaken and Legal Aid Franchise
Ptr: Fairweather, Mr Anthony Charles . . . . *Mar 1997
Farren, Mr Miles C LLB(Hons). . . . . Sep 1994
Francombe, Mr Nicholas D LLB(Soton) . . . . *Oct 1984
Hayden, Mr Timothy LLB(Cardiff) . . . . *Apr 1981
Kennedy, Mr Kevin . . . . Sep 1998
Lloyd Jones, Mr Rodyon Owen . . . . Dec 1995
Nellist, Mr Peter LLB(Bris). . . . . *Oct 1973
Russ, Mr Timothy LLB Notary Public . . . . *Nov 1988
Smeath, Mr Robert J LLB(B'ham) . . . . *Oct 1994
Thorne, Mr Stuart LLB(Soton). . . . . *§Apr 1980
Walker, Mr Timothy LLB(Bris) . . . . *Apr 1980

DAVITT JONES BOULD ‡
15 The Crescent Taunton Somerset TA1 4EB
Tel: 01823 279279 *Fax:* 01823 279111 *Dx:* 32129 TAUNTON
E-mail: general@djblaw.co.uk
List of partners: S R A Bould, M F Davitt, T J Sylvester Jones
Work: A1 E L O P R1 R2 S2 Z(h)
Dir: Bould, Mr Stuart R A MA(Oxon). . . . . *§Apr 1979
Davitt, Miss Madeleine F LLB . . . . *Nov 1987
Sylvester Jones, Mr Timothy J . . . . *Dec 1974
Asoc: Alison, Mrs Diane LLB(Exon) . . . . *Oct 1990
Bottle, Mr Stephen . . . . *Feb 1985
Boyland, Mr Benjamin Garth BA(Hons); LLM . . . . *Mar 2005
Bulman, Mr Sean Christopher LLB . . . . *Oct 1993
Close, Mrs Dinah Mary BA; LLM . . . . *Oct 1986
Cooper, Mr Michael V LLB . . . . *Feb 1976
Dancey, Mr Edward James LLB. . . . . *Apr 1990
Dolley, Mrs Mary Anne Josephine LLB . . . . *Dec 1978
Exley, Mr Simon David Hartnell LLB(Hons) . . . . . *May 1998
Forrester, Mr Terry . . . . *Jul 1971
Francis, Mr Kevin Murray . . . . *Jan 1970
Hair, Mr Malcolm J MA(Cantab). . . . . *May 1975
Heal, Miss Rebecca Abigail LLB(Hons) CCH Company Law Prize 1994 . . . . *Sep 1996
Hildreth, Miss Frances Gail BA(Hons). . . . . *Oct 1988
Howe, Mr Timothy LLB(Lond) . . . . *Jul 1976
Lowe, Mr Peter John LLB(Hons) . . . . *Oct 1984
Morrison, Mr Andrew Richard LLB. . . . . *Jun 1983
Palmer, Mrs Elizabeth Jane BA(Hons)(Law) . . . . . *Oct 1987
Prior, Mr Anthony W TD LLB(Hons) . . . . *Jun 1972
Spencer, Mr Colin. . . . . *Dec 1965
Verity, Mr Michael Dalton LLB(Hons) . . . . *Feb 1970
Webb, Mr Jonathan Roderick Giles . . . . *Dec 2000
Wilkes, Mr Brian John. . . . . *Feb 1972
Con: Stephenson, Ms Helen LLB . . . . *Jun 1981

DENLEYS ‡
12 Long Street Williton Taunton Somerset TA4 4QN
Tel: 01643 707998

EVERYS
(incorporating Kites)
12 Hammet Street Taunton Somerset TA1 1RL
Tel: 01823 337636 *Fax:* 01823 334106 *Dx:* 32107 TAUNTON
E-mail: law@everys.co.uk
Office: Budleigh Salterton, Exeter, Exmouth, Honiton (2 offices), Ottery St Mary, Seaton, Sidmouth
Languages: French, Italian
Work: A1 B1 C1 D1 D2 E F1 F2 J1 K1 L N O Q S1 S2 T1 T2 V W Z(c,j,m,o,q)
Emergency Action, Agency, Advocacy and Fixed Fee Interview undertaken
Ptr: Murray, Mr Francis G . . . . *§Jun 1974
Ast: Dabbs, Ms Janet Kathryn LLB(Soton) . . . . *§Dec 1975

FOOT ANSTEY
The Quad Blackbrook Park Avenue Blackbrook Business Park Taunton Somerset TA1 2PX
Tel: 01823 625600 *Fax:* 01823 625678
Dx: 97177 TAUNTON (BLACKBROOK)
E-mail: contact@footanstey.com
Office: Exeter, Plymouth, Truro
Work: A1 B1 C1 D1 D2 E F1 G H J1 K1 K2 L N O P Q S1 S2 T2 W Z(h,l,q,r)
Emergency Action, Agency, Advocacy, Fixed Fee Interview, Legal Aid undertaken and Legal Aid Franchise
Ptr: Brimble, Mr John R LLB. . . . . *§Apr 1981
Dunningham, Mr Andrew LLB . . . . Oct 1988
Gay, Mr Michael. . . . . *Oct 1996
Hannam, Mr Andrew J LLB(Exon). . . . . *Oct 1982
Hargreaves, Mr Alastair. . . . . Sep 2001
Hincks, Mr David M MA. . . . . *§Dec 1977
Quantick, Mrs Hilary LLB(Hons). . . . . *§Nov 1989
Roberts, Mrs Maggie . . . . Sep 1991
Scott, Mr Neil E LLB J F Hatchard Memorial Prize. . *§Oct 1987
Sutcliffe, Mr Nicholas J LLB(Sheff) . . . . *§Apr 1971
Thorne, Mr Christopher Gordon LLB. . . . . *§Oct 1985
Asoc: Morgan, Mr Richard W LLB . . . . *§Nov 1971

GARBETTS ‡
2 Coleford Water Lydeard St Lawrence Taunton Somerset TA4 3QP
Tel: 01984 667506 *Fax:* 01984 667277
List of partners: S M Garbett
Work: E S1 S2
SPr: Garbett, Miss Sarah M BA(Hons); LLB . . . . *Nov 1988

HARRIS FOWLER ‡
6-7 Hammet Street Taunton Somerset TA1 1RZ
Tel: 01823 251515
List of partners: S Baker
Work: J1 J2 N Q Z(r)
Ptr: Baker, Mr Stephen . . . . Oct 1993
Asoc: Taylor, Ms Ceri-Ann. . . . . Oct 2003

R W HEMMINGS & CO ‡
(in association with R W Hemmings & Co(Leicester))
Lloyds Bank Chambers 3 Hammet Street Taunton Somerset TA1 1RZ
Tel: 01823 325090 *Fax:* 01823 325100
E-mail: hemsol@talktalkbusiness.net
List of partners: R W Hemmings
Languages: French
Work: B1 C1 C2 E F1 J1 K1 K3 L N O R2 S1 S2 U1 W Z(i)
Fixed Fee Interview undertaken
Ptr: Hemmings, Mr Reginald Walter MA(Oxon) . . . . . *§Oct 1963

KSFLP ‡
The Post House Church Square Taunton Somerset TA1 1SA
Tel: 01823 256494 *Fax:* 01823 279414 *Dx:* 32109 TAUNTON
E-mail: mail@ksflp.co.uk

KENNEDYS
Monmouth House Blackbrook Business Park Taunton Somerset TA1 2PX
Tel: 01823 692600 *Fax:* 01823 692601
Dx: 97187 TAUNTON (BLACKBROOK)
Office: Belfast, Birmingham, Cambridge, Chelmsford, London EC3, Maidstone, Manchester, Sheffield

ALISON MCVAY ‡
Old Bartletts Fore Street Milverton Taunton Somerset TA4 1JX
Tel: 01823 401118
E-mail: alison_mcvay@btinternet.com

PARDOES
Chandos House Heron Gate Office Park Taunton Riverside Taunton Somerset TA1 2LR
Tel: 01823 446200 *Fax:* 01823 444614
Dx: 97182 TAUNTON (BLACKBROOK)
Office: Bridgwater, Yeovil
Languages: French, Japanese
Work: C1 C2 E J1 N O Q S1 S2 W Z(e,f)
Emergency Action, Agency, Advocacy, Legal Aid undertaken and Legal Aid Franchise
Ptr: Fitzgerald, Mr Richard C LLB; JD . . . . Jan 1992
O'Brien, Mrs Kit BA(Hons). . . . . *Oct 1991
Asoc: Wickett, Mr James Richard Charles LLB(Hons) . . . . Sep 2001
Ast: Gorman, Mr Damian Joseph LLB(Hons). . . . . Oct 2008

PORTER DODSON
The Quad Blackbrook Park Avenue Taunton Somerset TA1 2PX
Tel: 01823 625800 *Fax:* 01823 625812
Dx: 97176 TAUNTON (BLACKBROOK)
E-mail: porterdodson@porterdodson.co.uk
Office: Dorchester, Sherborne, Wellington, Yeovil
Languages: French
Work: A1 B1 C1 C2 C3 D1 D2 E F1 F2 G H J1 J2 K1 K2 L M1 N O P Q R1 R2 S1 T1 T2 V W Z(b,c,d,e,f,h,i,j,k,l,m,p,q,t,w)

RISDON HOSEGOOD
1 Chartfield House Castle Street Taunton Somerset TA1 4AS
Tel: 01823 251571 *Fax:* 01823 336152 *Dx:* 32106 TAUNTON
Emergency telephone 01984 656635
E-mail: taunton@risdonhosegood.com
Office: Dulverton, Minehead, Williton, Wiveliscombe
Work: A1 B1 C1 D1 E G J1 K1 L M2 N O Q R1 S1 S2 T2 W Z(i,l,t,x)
Emergency Action, Agency, Advocacy, Fixed Fee Interview, Legal Aid undertaken, Legal Aid Franchise and Member of Accident Line
Asoc: Orme, Mr David John LLB. . . . . *Oct 1974

ANDREW RUGG ‡
5 Hammet Street Taunton Somerset TA1 1RZ
Tel: 01823 326822 *Fax:* 01823 326833 *Dx:* 32140 TAUNTON
E-mail: andrew.rugg@btinternet.com
List of partners: A J Rugg
Work: A1 C1 E L R2 S1 S2 W Z(d)
SPr: Rugg, Mr Andrew John LLB. . . . . *Dec 1971

SHAW MARSDEN ‡
50 North Street Taunton Somerset TA1 1LX
Tel: 01823 330944 *Fax:* 01823 330966 *Dx:* 32148 TAUNTON
E-mail: info@shawmarsden.com
List of partners: P J Marsden
Languages: Japanese
Work: C1 C2 C3 E J1 R2 S1 S2 W Z(e,o,za)
Ptr: Marsden, Mr Philip J . . . . *Dec 1980

J TEHRANI SOLICITORS ‡
Cannonsgrove House Staplehay Taunton Somerset TA3 7HP
Tel: 0845 257 4007

TAVISTOCK, Devon

BROWNER MILNE-DAVIDSON ‡
First Floor 13 Duke Street Tavistock Devon PL19 0BA
Tel: 01822 617666

CHILCOTTS ‡
10 Plymouth Road Tavistock Devon PL19 8AY
Tel: 01822 612535 / 614242 *Fax:* 01822 618004
Dx: 82403 TAVISTOCK
E-mail: dmw@chilcotts.co.uk
List of partners: H C T Cornford, D M Wilde
Work: A1 A2 C1 D1 E F1 F2 J1 K1 K3 L N O Q R1 S1 S2 W Z(c,l)
Emergency Action, Agency, Advocacy, Fixed Fee Interview, Legal Aid undertaken, Legal Aid Franchise and Member of Accident Line
Ptr: Cornford, Mr Hugh C T Deputy District Judge . . . . . *Oct 2007
Wilde, Mr David Michael LLB(Hons) Notary Public. . *Nov 1996
Asoc: Petch, Mr Jonathan Heathcote LLB(Hons). . . . . . *Mar 2003
Con: Willetts, Mr Peter G. . . . . *Feb 1974

GOODMAN KING ‡
12 Plymouth Road Tavistock Devon PL19 8AY
Tel: 01822 615510 *Fax:* 01822 615520
Emergency telephone 01822 615510
List of partners: A F Goodman, J M King
Work: E J1 K1 S1 S2 W Z(p)
Fixed Fee Interview undertaken
Ptr: Goodman, Miss Amanda Frances BA(Hons). . . . . *Oct 1992
King, Miss Jacqueline Mary BA(Exon). . . . . *Oct 1993

ANN POINTER ‡
26 King Street Tavistock Devon PL19 0DT
Tel: 01822 614882 *Fax:* 01822 617271
E-mail: enquiries@annpointersolicitor.co.uk
List of partners: A Pointer
Work: E S1 S2 W
SPr: Pointer, Mrs Ann LLB; LLM . . . . *§Apr 1980
Ast: Dingle, Mrs Lesley Jane LLB(Hons). . . . . *Oct 1982

SLEEP & CO ‡
(incorporating A. Craig Mooney & Co)
4 Plymouth Road Tavistock Devon PL19 8AY
Tel: 01822 618850 *Fax:* 01822 618878 *Dx:* 82404 TAVISTOCK
E-mail: peter.sleep@care4free.net
Work: A1 E L S1 S2 W

WILLS & PROBATE COUNTRYWIDE ‡
Suite 9 Tavy Business Centre Tavistock Devon PL19 0NU
Tel: 01626 334455
List of partners: W M Douglas
Work: A1 E F1 J1 K1 K3 K4 L O Q S1 S2 T2 W
Agency and Fixed Fee Interview undertaken
Ptr: Douglas, Mr Warren Mathew . . . . *§Nov 1993
Ast: Major, Mrs Gillian Mavis LLB . . . . *Dec 1995
Stacey, Mr David James . . . . *Jan 1990

TEDDINGTON, Middlesex

J W BARTLETT & CO ‡
56 Hampton Road Teddington Middlesex TW11 0JX
Tel: 020 8943 9831 *Fax:* 020 8977 1080
E-mail: bartlett.sols@virgin.net
List of partners: J W Bartlett
Work: C1 E S1
Fixed Fee Interview undertaken
SPr: Bartlett, Mr Jasper W BA . . . . *Nov 1982

BRUCE MCGREGOR & CO SOLICITORS ‡
8 The Course Way Teddington Middlesex TW11 0HE
Tel: 020 8977 4435

See p112 for the Key to Work Categories & other symbols

CORBETT & CO INTERNATIONAL CONSTRUCTION LAWYERS LTD ‡
George House 2 Claremont Road Teddington Middlesex TW11 8DG
Tel: 020 8614 6200 *Fax:* 020 8614 6222
E-mail: mail@corbett.co.uk
List of partners: E C Corbett, S J Mangan, N Mathru, A G Tweeddale, V M Tyson
Languages: French, Spanish
Work: A3 O Z(c)
Dir: Corbett, Mr Edward Christopher MA(Oxon); MSc(KCL); FCIArb . . . *Oct 1988
Mangan, Mr Stephen John BA; MSc. . . . *Oct 1994
Matharu, Miss Natalie BSc(Hons) . . . Feb 2007
Tweeddale, Mr Andrew Gavin MSc(Prop); LLB(Hons); DipArb; FCIArb . . . Nov 1998
Tyson, Miss Victoria Margaret BSc(Hons)(Building Management); CIOB . . . *Sep 1998
Ast: Culatto, Mr Nicholas LLB; LLM . . . *Sep 2009
Con: Helps, Mr Dominic BA(Cantab) . . . *Jan 1984
Rosenberg, Mr George H LLB(Hons); FCIArb • . . . *Aug 1987
Slattery, Mrs Elizabeth LLB . . . *Nov 1987

COZENS MOXON & HARTS ‡
(incorporating Graham Whitworth & Co.)
24 The Causeway Teddington Middlesex TW11 0HD
Tel: 020 8977 8486 / 8977 4424 *Fax:* 020 8977 5116
Dx: 35251 TEDDINGTON
E-mail: teddington@cmhlaw.co.uk
List of partners: R E G Farrer, L R Munby, G Whitworth
Office: Hampton
Work: B1 C1 E F1 G J1 K1 K3 L N O Q R1 S1 S2 T1 T2 V W Z(d,l)
Ptr: Munby, Mrs Lesley Ruth LLB . . . *Jul 1977
Whitworth, Mr Graham LLB . . . *Jul 1979
Ast: Morris, Mr Richard John LLB; TEP Notary Public . . . *Oct 1988

KAGAN MOSS & CO ‡
22 The Causeway Teddington Middlesex TW11 0HD
Tel: 020 8977 6633 *Fax:* 020 8977 0183 *Dx:* 35250 TEDDINGTON
E-mail: maralyn.hutchinson@kaganmoss.co.uk
List of partners: M D Garson, P J Hodges, M L Hutchinson
Languages: French, Spanish
Work: A3 C1 E O Q R2 S1 S2 T1 T2 W
Ptr: Garson, Mr Michael D LLB; TEP Council of Law Society . . . *May 1973
Hodges, Mr Philip J LLB; AKC; TEP. . . . *May 1968
Hutchinson, Mrs Maralyn Louise. . . . *Jun 1977

RICHARD STEER & CO ‡
72 High Street Teddington Middlesex TW11 8JD
Tel: 020 8977 8621 *Fax:* 020 8943 1509 *Dx:* 35254 TEDDINGTON
E-mail: advice@steerlaw.com
List of partners: R A Steer
Work: C1 E J1 K1 K3 L O Q S1 S2 W
Emergency Action and Fixed Fee Interview undertaken
Ptr: Steer, Mr Richard A LLB; FCIArb . . . *Jun 1976

TEIGNMOUTH, Devon

AQUILA LAW ‡
33a Teignmouth Road Teignmouth Devon TQ14 8UR
Tel: 01626 870280 / 07799 773567 *Fax:* 01752 451939
E-mail: robinbarrett@aquilalaw.co.uk

SCOTT RICHARDS ‡
Newfoundland House 4 Regent Street Teignmouth Devon TQ14 8SL
Tel: 01626 772441 *Fax:* 01626 779718
E-mail: law@scottrichards.co.uk
List of partners: S J Dayment, P R Dyson, P Lennon
Work: B1 C1 C2 D1 E F1 K1 L M1 M2 N P R1 S1 V W Z(c,l)
Emergency Action, Agency, Advocacy, Legal Aid undertaken, Legal Aid Franchise and Member of Accident Line
Ptr: Dayment, Ms Susan Jane. . . . *May 1995
Dyson, Mr Paul R BA(Sheff). . . . *§Mar 1986
Lennon, Miss Penelope LLB. . . . *Nov 1994
Ast: Lamb, Lucy . . . Sep 1999

TOZERS
2-3 Orchard Gardens Teignmouth Devon TQ14 8DR
Tel: 01626 772376 *Fax:* 01626 770317 *Dx:* 82051 TEIGNMOUTH
E-mail: r.king@tozers.co.uk
Office: Exeter, Newton Abbot, Plymouth
Languages: French
Work: A1 E L S1 S2 T1 W Z(c,d)
Emergency Action, Agency, Advocacy, Fixed Fee Interview, Legal Aid undertaken, Legal Aid Franchise and Member of Accident Line
Ptr: King, Mr A Richard G BA(Keele) . . . *§Jun 1979

TELFORD, Shropshire

AKD SOLICITORS ‡
3 Badhan Court Castle Street Telford Shropshire TF1 5QX
Tel: 01952 260777 *Fax:* 01952 260776

ELLIOTT BRIDGMAN ‡
67-70 Court Street Madeley Telford Shropshire TF7 5EB
Tel: 01952 684544 *Fax:* 01952 684559 *Dx:* 27586 MADELEY
Emergency telephone 07831 828629
E-mail: info@elliottbridgman.com
List of partners: M N E Bridgman
Languages: Punjabi
Work: B2 D1 D2 G H J1 K1 K3 L M1 Q S1 S2 V W Z(g,j,m,t)
Emergency Action, Agency, Advocacy, Fixed Fee Interview, Legal Aid undertaken and Legal Aid Franchise
Dir: Bridgman, Mr Mark N E LLB(Hons); LLM • Notary Public . . . *Oct 1985
Ast: Chester, Mrs Gabi. . . . Apr 2007
Hira, Ms Suneet Kaur LLB. . . . Feb 2011
Meredith, Mrs Jackie LLB . . . Nov 2003

Other offices in Telford. Holders of Franchise for Crime, Mental Health, Family. We specialise in the following areas of work Crime - General, Family Law, Mental Health, Conveyancing, Notary, Children Law

CLARKES ‡
(incorporating Mitchells of Wellington)
Hazledine House Telford Town Centre Telford Shropshire TF3 4JL
Tel: 01952 291666 *Fax:* 01952 291331 *Dx:* 28075 TELFORD
Emergency telephone 07626 514566
E-mail: law@clarkessolicitors.co.uk
List of partners: P Harrison, W E D Lewis, J M Mason, P E Roberts
Office: Newport, Shrewsbury, Telford, Wellington
Work: A1 B1 B2 C1 C2 C3 D1 E F1 F2 G H I J1 J2 K1 K2 L N O Q R1 R2 S1 S2 U2 V W Z(c,e,f,j,k,l,p,q,r,w)
Emergency Action, Agency, Advocacy, Fixed Fee Interview, Legal Aid undertaken, Legal Aid Franchise and Member of Accident Line
Ptr: Lewis, Mr Warren E D BSc . . . *Nov 1979
Mason, Mr Jonathan Michael . . . *Feb 1988
Roberts, Mr Paul E LLB. . . . *Feb 1983

CLARKES
Lloyds Bank House 30 Market Street Oakengates Telford Shropshire TF2 6ED
Tel: 01952 618787 *Fax:* 01952 616298 *Dx:* 27884 OAKENGATES
Emergency telephone 01952 607270
E-mail: oakengates@clarkeslaw.co.uk
Office: Newport, Shrewsbury, Telford, Wellington
Work: D1 G H K1 N O Q R1 S1 V W Z(l)
Emergency Action, Agency, Advocacy, Fixed Fee Interview, Legal Aid undertaken and Member of Accident Line

COOPER ROLLASON SOLICITORS ‡
Suite 9b Pemberton House Stafford Park 1 Telford Shropshire TF3 3BD
Tel: 01952 204242

FBC MANBY BOWDLER LLP
Routh House Hall Court Hall Park Way Telford Shropshire TF3 4NJ
Tel: 01952 292129 *Fax:* 01952 291716 *Dx:* 707201 TELFORD 4
E-mail: info@fbcmb.co.uk
Office: Bridgnorth, Shrewsbury, Willenhall, Wolverhampton
Work: C1 C2 D1 D2 E F2 I J1 K1 K3 L O P Q R1 S1 S2 U2 Z(c,d,e,h,n)
Ptr: Blackie, Mr Niall A C LLB . . . *§Apr 1981
Dixon, Mrs Alison J LLB(Hons) . . . *Feb 1990
Horton, Mr Paul James . . . *Nov 1999
Lloyd, Mr Matthew. . . . *Sep 2004
Shaw, Mr David Thomas LLB . . . *Jul 1979
Sower, Mr Graham D H BSc . . . *Jul 1978
Thomson, Ms Anne E BA. . . . *§Jan 1986
Asoc: Tinsley, Miss Jane. . . . *Oct 2003
Ast: Macey, Mr David . . . *Sep 2007
Morton, Miss Sara Leanne . . . *Sep 2006
O'Brien-Quinn, Mrs Helen LLB . . . *§Nov 1990
Sargent, Mrs Alison LLB(Hons) . . . Mar 2006
Tucker, Ms Suzanne . . . Mar 2008

HOWELLS WILLIAMS
71 High Street Madeley Telford Shropshire TF7 5AH
Tel: 01952 582631 *Fax:* 01952 582952
Emergency telephone 01743 233461
Office: Shrewsbury
Work: B1 C1 D1 F1 G H J1 K1 L M1 M2 N O P Q R1 S1 V W Z(c,e,h)
Emergency Action, Agency, Advocacy, Fixed Fee Interview, Legal Aid undertaken and Member of Accident Line
Ptr: Howells, Mr Peter W F LLB . . . *Jul 1974

TERRY JONES SOLICITORS & ADVOCATES
7 Hollinswood Stafford Park 1 Telford Shropshire TF3 3DE
Tel: 01952 297979 *Fax:* 01952 297980
Dx: 724600 SHREWSBURY 12
Emergency telephone 07921 694246
E-mail: enquiries@terry-jones.co.uk
Office: Newport, Shrewsbury
Work: A1 A2 A3 B1 B2 C1 C2 C3 D1 D2 E F1 F2 G H J1 J2 K1 K2 K3 L N O Q R1 R2 S1 S2 W X Z(c,e,g,h,k,l,m,o,p,q,t,y)
Emergency Action, Agency, Advocacy, Fixed Fee Interview and Legal Aid undertaken
Asoc: McNeish, Ms Christine Diane BA(Hons); LLB(Hons); Dip Ed . . . Dec 1995
Oakley, Miss Rachel BA(Hons) . . . Apr 1999
Opperman, Mr Adam . . . Sep 1997
Ast: Meredith, Mr Steven LLB(Hons). . . . Nov 2007
Reynolds, Mrs Sarah BA(Hons) . . . Nov 2008
Wade, Mr Jamie LLB(Hons). . . . *Jan 2008

LANYON BOWDLER LLP
Brodie House Town Centre Telford Shropshire TF3 4DR
Tel: 01952 291222 *Fax:* 01952 292585 *Dx:* 28071 TELFORD
E-mail: enquiries@lblaw.co.uk
Office: Hereford, Ludlow, Oswestry (2 offices), Shrewsbury, Wellington
Work: A1 A2 A3 B1 B2 C1 C2 C3 D1 D2 E F1 F2 G H I J1 J2 K1 K2 L M1 N O P Q R1 R2 S1 S2 U2 W X Z(c,e,h,k,l,p,q,r,t,w,y)
Emergency Action, Agency, Advocacy, Fixed Fee Interview, Legal Aid undertaken, Legal Aid Franchise and Member of Accident Line
Ptr: Evans, Mr Robert Brian MA(Cantab) . . . *§Sep 1994
Lorimer, Mr Neil R T LLB . . . *§Oct 1989
Merry, Mr John Gerard LLB(Hons). . . . *Sep 1999
Murrall, Mr Richard LLB. . . . *Sep 1989
Asoc: Chaudhari, Mr Praveen . . . Aug 2005
Ast: Gibson, Ms Jennifer Elizabeth LLB . . . May 2008
Grimmett, Miss Lisa Jayne LLB(Hons); LPC. . . . §Sep 1996
Jones, Ms Bethan. . . . Sep 2010

MFG SOLICITORS
Padmore House Hall Court Hall Park Way Telford Shropshire TF3 4LX
Tel: 01952 641651 *Dx:* 707204 TELFORD 4
E-mail: telford@mfgsolicitors.com
Office: Bromsgrove, Halesowen, Kidderminster, Oswestry, Worcester
Work: A1 B1 C1 C2 C3 D1 E F1 G H J1 K1 L M1 M2 N P R1 S1 T1 T2 V W Z(c,d,e,f,i,l,m,n)
Emergency Action, Agency, Advocacy, Fixed Fee Interview, Legal Aid undertaken, Legal Aid Franchise and Member of Accident Line
Ptr: Payne, Mr Michael J FILEx . . . *§Jan 1983
Rhodes, Mr Paul E H . . . *§Jan 1970
Asoc: Baugh, Ms Sarah J LLB(Hons) . . . *Sep 1997
Jones, Ms Irfana Zia BA; LLB . . . *Nov 1992
Ast: Ahmed, Mr Saeed LLB(Hons) . . . *Sep 2001
Campbell-Castle, Mrs Krystyna Yvonne BA(Hons); CPE; LSF . . . *Oct 1994
Timson, Mrs Helen E LLB. . . . Dec 1980
Con: Kenny, Mr Philip J. . . . *§Jul 1969

MCKENZIE LAW LIMITED ‡
e-Innovation Centre Priorslee Telford Shropshire TF2 9FT
Tel: 01952 288390

martinkaye LLP

Lexcel

MARTIN-KAYE LLP ‡
The Foundry Euston Way Telford Shropshire TF3 4LY
Tel: 01952 272222 *Fax:* 01952 272223 *Dx:* 725100 TELFORD 10
E-mail: law@martinkaye.co.uk
Web: www.martinkaye.co.uk
List of partners: A L Carter, G W Davies, N Davis, A J L Green, S J Haynes, S E R Heath, J Mehtam, N Patel, S P Wagner
Languages: French, Gujarati, Punjabi, Urdu
Work: B1 C1 C2 C3 D1 D2 E F1 I J1 K1 K2 K3 K4 L M1 M2 N O P Q R1 R2 S1 S2 U2 V W Z(c,e,p,q)
Emergency Action, Agency, Advocacy, Fixed Fee Interview, Legal Aid undertaken, Legal Aid Franchise and Member of Accident Line
Ptr: Carter, Mrs Alison Louise BA(Hons). . . . Oct 1995
Davies, Mr Graham William . . . *Dec 1984
Davis, Ms Nadia LLB(Hons). . . . *Oct 1995
Green, Mr Andrew J L. . . . *Jun 1980
Haynes, Mr Stuart J BA(Law) . . . *Oct 1982
Heath, Miss Sarah Elizabeth Rosemary LLB(Hons) . . Sep 2000
Mehtam, Mr John LLB. . . . *Sep 1995
Patel, Mrs Nita LLB . . . *Jan 1997
Wagner, Mr Simon P BA(Hons) . . . *Jan 1999
Ast: Ahsan, Mr Mohammed LLB(Hons) . . . *Mar 2005
Chander, Miss Ashima Rani LLB(Law with Psychology); MSc(Clinical Criminology); LLM(Advanced Legal Practice); Barrister (Non-practising) . . . Sep 2008
Clowes, Mrs Elizabeth Louise Alexandra PGDipLaw; LLM; BSc . . . Sep 2006
Hawley, Mrs Janet Ann LLB. . . . *Sep 2002
Thornton, Mrs Alison LLB(Hons) . . . Oct 2000

Holders of Franchise for Personal Injury, Family. We conduct business in French, Gujarati, Punjabi, Urdu. We specialise in the following areas of work Commercial and Company Law, Commercial Property, Employment Law.

PCB SOLICITORS LLP
35 High Street Dawley Telford Shropshire TF4 2EX
Tel: 01952 403000 *Fax:* 01952 403331 *Dx:* 27234 DAWLEY
Emergency telephone 07890 576117
E-mail: info@pcblaw.co.uk
Office: Church Stretton, Knighton, Ludlow, Shrewsbury
Work: B1 C1 D1 E F1 J1 K1 L N O Q S1 T1 T2 V W Z(c,h,j,l)
Emergency Action, Agency, Advocacy, Fixed Fee Interview and Legal Aid undertaken
Ptr: Freeman, Mr Edward Michael LLB ★ . . . *Jul 1979
Morris-Jones, Ms Lisa Maria LLDip . . . Oct 2007
Surzyn, Mr Michael Henry LLB . . . *Feb 1987
Ast: Brigman, Ms Sarah . . . Jul 2002
Nicholas, Mr Oliver . . . Nov 2004
O'Reilly, Miss Joyce. . . . Aug 2009
Smith, Danny . . . Jan 2007
Tutchener-Ellis, Mr Julian . . . Dec 1998
Wright, Ms Susan Elizabeth BA; DipLaw. . . . Mar 2000

PARRY CARVER
(incorporating Espley & Co)
23 High Street Dawley Telford Shropshire TF4 2ET
Tel: 01952 504757 *Fax:* 01952 247232 *Dx:* 27233 DAWLEY
Office: Wellington
Work: A1 C1 D1 E F1 J1 K1 K3 K4 L N Q S1 S2 W Z(i,l,p)

SHAW & CO
Grosvenor House Central Park Telford Shropshire TF2 9TW
Tel: 0800 019 1248
E-mail: info@shawandco.com
Office: Doncaster, Newcastle upon Tyne

THORNTON SOLICITORS
5 Ainsdale Drive Priorslee Telford Shropshire TF2 9QJ
Tel: 0845 438 7795 *Fax:* 0560 116 3554
E-mail: telford@thorntonssolicitors.co.uk
Office: Shrewsbury

WRIGHT & MCMILLAN BENNETT ‡
Kingsland House Stafford Court Telford Shropshire TF3 3BD
Tel: 01952 291100 *Fax:* 01952 291821 *Dx:* 28074 TELFORD
Emergency telephone 07659 100487
E-mail: info@wmblaw.co.uk
List of partners: F E Wright
Work: B2 D1 D2 E G H J2 K1 N Q S1 S2 W X Z(l,q)
Emergency Action, Agency, Advocacy, Fixed Fee Interview, Legal Aid undertaken and Legal Aid Franchise
Ptr: Wright, Mrs Fay E LLB . . . *Mar 1983
Ast: Cooper, Miss Sarah J LLB(Hons); DipLP Blackstone Prize 1993/94; Staffordshire University Prize 1997 . . . *Feb 2000
Griffiths, Miss Sarah Jane LLB(Hons); DipLP . . . Sep 2000
Heal, Mrs Miranda LLB(Hons); LLM . . . Apr 2002
McMillan, Mr John R LLB . . . *Jul 1973

TENBURY WELLS, Worcestershire

MARCHES LAW ‡
34 Teme Street Tenbury Wells Worcestershire WR15 8AA
Tel: 01584 819535
E-mail: marcheslaw@hotmail.co.uk
Office: Hereford

NORRIS & MILES ‡
6 Market Square Tenbury Wells Worcestershire WR15 8BW
Tel: 01584 810575 *Fax:* 01584 811759 *Dx:* 27633 TENBURY WELLS
E-mail: post@norrismiles.co.uk
List of partners: H R Griffiths, N E Walker
Work: A1 B1 C1 C2 C3 D1 D2 E F1 F2 G H J1 J2 K1 L N O P Q R1 R2 S1 S2 T1 T2 V W Z(b,c,d,e,h,j,l,q,r,s,t,x,y)
Emergency Action, Agency, Advocacy, Fixed Fee Interview, Legal Aid undertaken and Legal Aid Franchise
Ptr: Griffiths, Mr Harvey R LLB . . . *Nov 1990
Walker, Mr Nicholas E MA. . . . *Jun 1981

Asoc: Reynolds, Mrs Rosalind Isabella LLB(B'ham) . . . . . *Oct 1983
Ast: Pearson, Ms Philippa Alexandra Prescott BA(Hons)(Oxon) . . . . . *Oct 1988

TENBY, Pembrokeshire

LEWIS LEWIS & COMPANY LTD
County Chambers Warren Street Tenby Pembrokeshire SA70 7JS
Tel: 01834 844844 *Fax:* 01843 845775
Office: Carmarthen, St Clears
Ptr: Lewis, Mr Edward G BA. . . . . *Dec 1983
Lewis, Mr James D R . . . . . *Mar 1986
Ast: Mathias, Mr Clive LLB. . . . . *Oct 1981
Williams, Mr Haydn LLB. . . . . *Nov 1978

RED KITE LAW
Lorne Chambers Warren House Warren Street Tenby Pembrokeshire SA70 7JP
Tel: 01834 842122 *Fax:* 01834 842223 *Dx:* 85403 TENBY
Office: Carmarthen (2 offices), Haverfordwest, Milford Haven, Pembroke, Pembroke Dock
Languages: Spanish, Welsh
Work: A1 B1 C1 D1 D2 E F1 G H J1 K1 K3 K4 L N O Q R1 S1 S2 T2 V W Z(c,l,m,t)
Emergency Action, Agency, Advocacy, Fixed Fee Interview, Legal Aid undertaken and Legal Aid Franchise
Ptr: Cowper, Mr Paul J LLB(Lond) . . . . . *Sep 1983
Ast: Irvine, Miss Louise LLB(Hons). . . . . Apr 2005
McMillan, Miss Emma BA(Hons) . . . . . Nov 1997
Rees, Mr Ian BA(Hons) . . . . . Jan 1998
Con: Rogers, Mrs Sally. . . . . Mar 1997

TENTERDEN, Kent

NELSONS ‡
Bell House Bells Lane Tenterden Kent TN30 6ES
Tel: 01580 767100 *Fax:* 01580 767101 *Dx:* 39004 TENTERDEN
E-mail: mail@nelsonslegal.co.uk
List of partners: J P H Nelson
Work: C1 E S1 S2 W
Fixed Fee Interview undertaken
SPr: Nelson, Mr Justin P H. . . . . *§Nov 1979
Ast: Jirbandey, Ms Jasmine LLB . . . . . Mar 2009

PENGELLY & RYLANDS ‡
(in association with Justin Nelson)
39-41 High Street Tenterden Kent TN30 6BJ
Tel: 01580 762248 / 763008 *Fax:* 01580 763307
Dx: 39001 TENTERDEN
E-mail: mail@pengelly-rylands.co.uk
List of partners: R Bell, R K Johnson, K Rylands
Work: A1 E F1 J1 K1 L N R1 S1 S2 T1 T2 W
Fixed Fee Interview undertaken
Ptr: Bell, Ms Rebecca BA(Hons). . . . . *Mar 2002
Johnson, Mrs Rosalind K LLB. . . . . *Apr 1977
Rylands, Mr Keith LLB . . . . . *Jun 1975
Asoc: Bassett, Mr Malcolm R LLB . . . . . *Jun 1978

WHITEHEAD MONCKTON
37 High Street Tenterden Kent TN30 6BJ
Tel: 01580 765722 *Fax:* 01580 765180 *Dx:* 39003 TENTERDEN
E-mail: enquiries@whitehead-monckton.co.uk
Office: Maidstone
Work: A1 B1 C1 C2 C3 D1 E F1 G H J1 K1 L M1 M2 N O P Q R1 S1 T1 T2 V W Z(a,b,c,d,e,f,g,h,i,j,k,l,m,n,o,p,q,s,t)
Legal Aid Franchise
Ptr: King, Mrs Coralyn Ann . . . . . *Jan 1970
Monckton, Mr Timothy C MA(Cantab) . . . . . *§Oct 1980
Ast: Houston, Miss Andrea Elizabeth LLB(Hons); BVC . . . Feb 2003

WYKEHAM HURFORD SHEPPARD & SON LLP
151 High Street Tenterden Kent TN30 6JT
Tel: 01580 762251 *Fax:* 01580 761952
E-mail: kent@whss.co.uk
Office: Battle, Chislehurst
Con: Honey, Mr Michael G . . . . . *§Jan 1969
Miller, Mr Ian N . . . . . *§Oct 1959

TETBURY, Gloucestershire

RICHARD T BATE & CO ‡
Deron House 20 Market Place Tetbury Gloucestershire GL8 8DD
Tel: 01666 503722 *Fax:* 01666 503672
Emergency telephone 07759 417394
E-mail: richard.bate@richardbate.com
List of partners: R T Bate
Work: A1 A2 A3 B2 C1 C2 C3 E F1 F2 G H I J1 J2 K1 K2 K3 K4 L M1 M2 M3 N O P Q R1 R2 S1 S2 T1 T2 U1 U2 W X Z(b,c,e,f,g,i,j,k,l,m,n,o,p,q,r,s,t,u,w,y,z,za)
Emergency Action, Agency, Advocacy and Fixed Fee Interview undertaken
SPr: Bate, Mr Richard T LLB ● . . . . . *Dec 1980

OUVRY CREED SOLICITORS ‡
15 Long Street Tetbury Gloucestershire GL8 8AA
Tel: 01666 504005 *Fax:* 01666 503818 *Dx:* 50650 TETBURY
E-mail: mail@ouvrycreed.co.uk
List of partners: M J Hodge
Office: Pewsey
Languages: French, Italian
Work: A2 C1 C2 C3 E G J1 L M1 N P Q R1 S1 W Z(e,k,l,t)
Emergency Action, Agency and Advocacy undertaken
Ptr: Hodge, Mr Michael J BA(Oxon) . . . . . *§Dec 1973
Asoc: Bennett, Miss Elizabeth BA . . . . . *Dec 1978
Con: Arnold, Mr Anthony J MA(Cantab). . . . . *§Dec 1966
Creed, Mr Richard D MA(Oxon). . . . . *§Aug 1965

TEWKESBURY, Gloucestershire

DAVID BILLINGHAM & PARTNERS
39 Church Street Tewkesbury Gloucestershire GL20 5SN
Tel: 01684 276469
Office: Cheltenham

DF LEGAL LLP ‡
Avonside 63 High Street Tewkesbury Gloucestershire GL20 5BJ
Tel: 01684 850750 *Fax:* 01684 297717 *Dx:* 11405 TEWKESBURY
E-mail: aavery@dflegal.com
List of partners: J G Daniels, D J Ferraby, L A Jones
Office: Ledbury
Languages: French, German
Work: A1 A3 B1 C1 C2 C3 D1 E F1 F2 J1 K1 L M1 O Q R1 R2 S1 S2 T1 T2 U1 U2 W Z(c,e,f,k,l,u,w)
Emergency Action, Agency, Advocacy and Fixed Fee Interview undertaken
Ptr: Daniels, Mr John G LLB. . . . . *May 1975
Ferraby, Mr David J LLB . . . . . *Jun 1979
Jones, Miss Lorraine Anne . . . . . *Sep 2001
Ast: Rees, Mr Malcolm LLB . . . . . Aug 2008

MOORE BROWN & DIXON LLP ‡
69-70 High Street Tewkesbury Gloucestershire GL20 5LE
Tel: 01684 292341 *Fax:* 01684 295147
List of partners: P R Hemelryk, I Hughes, B M Lawler, J V Moss
Office: Upton-upon-Severn
Languages: French, German, Kiswahili
Work: A1 C1 D1 E F1 J1 K1 L M1 N P Q R1 S1 T1 W Z(b,c,d,e,f,g,h,j,l,n,r,s,t,w)
Emergency Action, Agency and Advocacy undertaken
Ptr: Hemelryk, Mr Paul R LLB(Lond). . . . . *Jun 1973
Hughes, Ms Ingrid BA. . . . . *Jun 1987
Lawler, Mr Brendan Martin LLB(Soton) Honorary Solicitor to Gloucestershire Football Association . . . . . *May 1981
Moss, Miss Julie V LLB . . . . . *Jun 1976
Con: Otter, Mr Robert G MA(Oxon). . . . . *Nov 1966

THOMSON & BANCKS LLP ‡
27 Church Street Tewkesbury Gloucestershire GL20 5RH
Tel: 01684 299633 *Fax:* 01684 851633 *Dx:* 11401 TEWKESBURY
E-mail: info@tblaw.co.uk
List of partners: D C S Bloxham, S C Cook, S L D Cook, S A Gillham, D C Greer, P N Johnson, J N Martin, J Roberts, A J Scott, J S Smith
Office: Pershore
Work: A1 B1 C1 D1 D2 E F1 J1 K1 K2 K3 K4 L N O P Q R1 S1 S2 T1 T2 W Z(c,d,l,m,p,q)
Emergency Action, Agency, Advocacy and Fixed Fee Interview undertaken
Ptr: Bloxham, Mr David C S BA . . . . . *May 1985
Cook, Mr Simon C LLB; TEP . . . . . *Nov 1993
Martin, Mr John Nicholas LLB(B'ham). . . . . *§Apr 1978
Roberts, Ms Julie-Anne . . . . . Dec 1989
Smith, Mr Jeremy S LLB . . . . . *Mar 1985
Ast: Phythian, Rachael. . . . . Feb 2008
Pipe, Miss Philippa BA . . . . . Apr 2000
Sherahilo, Mr John I. . . . . Jan 1985

THAME, Oxfordshire

BENHAMS ‡
The Sanderum Centre 30a Upper High Street Thame Oxfordshire OX9 3EX
Tel: 020 7581 5636 *Dx:* 80563 THAME

BIRCH REYNARDSON & CO ‡
Adwell House Thame Oxfordshire OX9 7DQ
Tel: 01844 281184

BROWNS
Adelaide House 17 High Street Thame Oxfordshire OX9 2BZ
Tel: 01844 260800 *Fax:* 01844 216662
Office: Amersham, Aylesbury, Beaconsfield, Bourne End, High Wycombe (3 offices), Maidenhead, Marlow, Princes Risborough

J P CAVE & CO ‡
112 High Street Thame Oxfordshire OX9 3DZ
Tel: 01844 216208 *Fax:* 01844 261142 *Dx:* 80551 THAME
List of partners: J P Cave
Work: A1 B1 C1 C2 C3 D1 E F1 G H J1 K1 L M1 M2 N P R1 S1 T1 T2 V W Z(c,d,i,k,l,o,t)
Agency, Advocacy, Legal Aid undertaken and Member of Accident Line
SPr: Cave, Mr John Peter . . . . . May 1974

HONNIBALL & CO ‡
98 High Street Thame Oxfordshire OX9 3EH
Tel: 01844 261484 *Fax:* 01844 261403 *Dx:* 80577 THAME
E-mail: info@honniball.co.uk
List of partners: M P Honniball
Work: A1 C1 E J1 L R1 S1 W Z(c)
Fixed Fee Interview undertaken
SPr: Honniball, Mr Michael P LLB . . . . . May 1974

LIGHTFOOTS LLP ‡
1-3 High Street Thame Oxfordshire OX9 2BX
Tel: 01844 212305 *Fax:* 01844 214984 *Dx:* 80550 THAME
Emergency telephone 01844 212305
E-mail: info@lightfoots.co.uk
List of partners: M A L Havers, H Lovell, J Middleton, I M Norman, J H Ovens, N Summerfield, G G Wright
Languages: French, German, Hungarian, Polish, Portuguese, Punjabi
Work: A1 C1 C2 D1 D2 E F1 J1 K1 K2 K3 K4 L O Q R1 S1 S2 T1 T2 W Z(b,c,d,e,l,q)
Ptr: Havers, Mrs Monica Alice Louise BA(Hons) . . . . . *Apr 1999
Middleton, Mr Joe LLB(Hons) . . . . . *§Sep 2001
Norman, Mr Ian Mark LLB(Law & French) . . . . . Mar 2008
Ovens, Mr John Henry . . . . . *§May 1980
Summerfield, Mr Neil LLB. . . . . *§Jan 1985
Wright, Ms Gillian G. . . . . *§Dec 1981
Lovell, Hilary . . . . . NSP
Ast: Biggs, Mr Christopher Mark LLB. . . . . *Aug 2004
Cave, Mr John Peter . . . . . May 1974
Clift, Ms Caroline Patricia LLB. . . . . Dec 2002
Jamieson, Mrs Catherine Anne BA(Hons) . . . . . Dec 2006
Lewis, Mrs Louise Margaret LLB . . . . . Sep 2005
Moran, Mr Eamonn Anthony BSc(Econ); LLB . . . . . Mar 2008
Nunn, Mrs Louise Jane FILEx. . . . . Dec 2007
Parker, Mr Anthony Graeme BA(Hons) . . . . . *Nov 1983
Preston, Mr Timothy J N BA(Cantab) . . . . . *§Nov 1995
Thiara, Mr Ranjit Singh LLB; LPC . . . . . Aug 2009
Winter, Ms Eiluned Sian BA; PGDipLaw. . . . . Feb 2006
Wragg, Mr Michael James. . . . . Mar 2008

READ COOPER ‡
Dorchester House 15 Dorchester Place Thame Oxfordshire OX9 2DL
Tel: 01844 260038 *Fax:* 01844 218923 *Dx:* 80572 THAME
E-mail: law@readcooper.com
List of partners: P J Read
Office: Princes Risborough
Work: A2 E L S1 S2 W
Ptr: Read, Mr Peter J BA . . . . . *Oct 1983
Con: Cooper, Mr Colin S . . . . . *Mar 1973

STOCKER & CO ‡
10a Buttermarket Thame Oxfordshire OX9 3EW
Tel: 01844 216995 *Fax:* 01844 213227 *Dx:* 80552 THAME
E-mail: stocker@solicitors55.freeserve.co.uk
List of partners: C H R Stocker
Work: A1 B1 E F1 K1 L S1 W
Fixed Fee Interview undertaken
Ptr: Stocker, Mr Christopher H R LLB . . . . . *Jun 1976

R F TANSEY ‡
6a The Buttermarket Thame Oxfordshire OX9 3EW
Tel: 01844 218000 *Fax:* 01844 260407 *Dx:* 80555 THAME
Emergency telephone 01844 218000
E-mail: mail@tansey-solicitors.co.uk
List of partners: R F Tansey
Languages: French, Spanish
Work: D1 D2 K1 K3
Emergency Action, Agency, Advocacy and Legal Aid undertaken
SPr: Tansey, Mrs Rosemary Flynn MA(Hons) Deputy District Judge . . . . . §Jan 1987
Ast: Richardson, Mrs Sally LLB . . . . . Oct 1983
Con: Harrison, Mrs Sophie MA . . . . . May 1994

WITHY KING SOLICITORS
7 The Buttermarket Thame Oxfordshire OX9 3EW
Tel: 01844 261966 *Fax:* 01865 793616 *Dx:* 4314 OXFORD 1
E-mail: enquiries@withyking.co.uk
Office: Abingdon, Bath (2 offices), Marlborough, Oxford, Swindon, Trowbridge
Work: E J1 K1 K2 L S1 S2 V W Z(l,q)

THATCHAM, West Berkshire

BURTON STANCLIFFE & CO ‡
17 High Street Thatcham West Berkshire RG19 3JG
Tel: 01635 867967 *Fax:* 01635 871001 *Dx:* 41851 THATCHAM
E-mail: mail@burtonstancliffe.co.uk
List of partners: E A Stancliffe
Work: B1 E K1 L N O Q S1 S2 W
Agency and Legal Aid undertaken
Ptr: Stancliffe, Mr Edward A LLB . . . . . *Jun 1974

RICHARD CRUMLY ‡
The Old Courthouse 31 The Broadway Thatcham West Berkshire RG19 3HX
Tel: 01635 866166 *Fax:* 01635 874096 *Dx:* 41856 THATCHAM
E-mail: richard.crumly@btconnect.com
List of partners: R J Crumly
Work: F1 K1 K3 L S1 V W Z(q)
Emergency Action, Agency, Advocacy, Fixed Fee Interview, Legal Aid undertaken and Legal Aid Franchise
SPr: Crumly, Mr Richard J BA(History) . . . . . *§Jul 1973

GARDNER LEADER LLP
Winbolt House The Broadway Thatcham West Berkshire RG19 3HX
Tel: 01635 508080 *Fax:* 01635 521341 *Dx:* 41852 THATCHAM
E-mail: mail@garner-leader.co.uk
Office: Newbury
Work: B1 C1 C2 C3 D1 E F1 G H J1 K1 M1 M2 N O P Q S1 V W Z(l)
Emergency Action, Agency, Advocacy, Fixed Fee Interview, Legal Aid undertaken, Legal Aid Franchise and Member of Accident Line
Ptr: Tomlinson, Mr Robert LLB(Lond) . . . . . Apr 1977

THETFORD, Norfolk

ACT (NORFOLK) LLP ‡
2 White Hart Street Thetford Norfolk IP24 1AD
Tel: 01842 765577 *Fax:* 01842 764028 *Dx:* 100918 THETFORD

ASHTON KCJ
Fairstead House 7 Bury Road Thetford Norfolk IP24 3PL
Tel: 01842 752401 *Fax:* 01842 753555 *Dx:* 124810 THETFORD 2
E-mail: enquiries.thetford@ashtonkcj.co.uk
Office: Bury St Edmunds (2 offices), Cambridge, Felixstowe, Ipswich, Norwich (2 offices)

GERALD JONES & CO ‡
23 Old Market Street Thetford Norfolk IP24 2AY
Tel: 01842 754466 / 754467 *Fax:* 01842 762707
Dx: 100904 THETFORD
List of partners: G A Jones
Work: S1 S2 W
Ptr: Jones, Mr Gerald A MA(Oxon) . . . . . *Mar 1965

METCALFE COPEMAN & PETTEFAR
Red Cross Building Cage Lane Thetford Norfolk IP24 2DT
Tel: 01842 756100 *Fax:* 01842 752818 *Dx:* 100902 THETFORD
E-mail: info@mcp-law.co.uk
Office: King's Lynn, Peterborough, Wisbech
Languages: Portuguese
Work: A1 A3 B1 B2 C1 C2 C3 D1 D2 E F1 F2 G H J1 J2 K1 K2 K3 K4 L M1 M2 N O P Q R1 R2 S1 S2 T1 T2 U2 V W Z(c,e,g,h,l,n,o,p,q,t,y,za)
Emergency Action, Agency, Advocacy, Fixed Fee Interview, Legal Aid undertaken, Legal Aid Franchise and Member of Accident Line
Ptr: Coller, Miss Dawn F LLB . . . . . *Oct 1987
Davies, Mr Andrew P C LLB(Hons) . . . . . *Sep 1989
Dures, Mr Benjamin BA(Hons) . . . . . *Jul 1997
Stevenson, Mr Timothy W MA(Cantab) . . . . . *Feb 1976
Ast: Ivory, Ms Priscilla MA(Oxon) . . . . . *§Dec 1978
Marsh, Miss Aimee LLB. . . . . Jan 2009

RUDLINGS & WAKELAM ‡
1 Well Street Thetford Norfolk IP24 2BL
Tel: 01842 754151 *Fax:* 01842 766143 *Dx:* 100903 THETFORD
Emergency telephone 01842 754151
E-mail: info@rudlings-wakelam.co.uk
Office: Brandon, Bury St Edmunds, Long Melford
Languages: French, German

See p112 for the Key to Work Categories & other symbols

Work: A1 C1 D1 D2 E F1 J1 J2 K1 K2 K3 L N O Q S1 S2 T2 V W X Z(l,m,p,q)

SALENA DAWSON & CO ‡
20 Thetford Road Watton Thetford Norfolk IP25 6BS
Tel: 01953 883535 *Fax:* 01953 881719

THIRSK, North Yorkshire

ECCLES HEDDON
Barclays Bank Chambers 24a Market Place Thirsk North Yorkshire YO7 1LF
Tel: 01845 522324 *Fax:* 01845 525045 *Dx:* 61624 THIRSK
E-mail: thirsk@eccles-heddon.com
Office: Bedale, Ripon
Work: A1 E K4 S1 S2 T1 T2 W
Ptr: Armstrong, Mr Michael BA . . . . *Jun 1971
Clarke, Mr Andrew LLB . . . . *Jun 1980
Asoc: Brown, Mr Matthew BSc(Hons)(Agriculture); GDL . . . *Jul 2009

HILEYS ‡
17 Finkle Street Thirsk North Yorkshire YO7 1DB
Tel: 01845 522278 *Fax:* 01845 522799 *Dx:* 61620 THIRSK
E-mail: info@hileys.co.uk
List of partners: P D Hannam, C L Moore
Office: Easingwold
Work: A1 E L S1 S2 T2 W
Fixed Fee Interview undertaken
Ptr: Moore, Mr Colin Leslie MBA; BSc RT Richardson Prize 1999 (Durham & N Yorks Law Society); National Legal Practice Course Prize 1999 . . . . *Oct 2000
Con: Hiley, Mr John D BA(Cantab) . . . . *§Jul 1967

SHIRTCLIFFE & RESTON SOLICITORS ‡
1 Finkle Street Thirsk North Yorkshire YO7 1DA
Tel: 01845 526222 *Fax:* 01845 526222 *Dx:* 61627 THIRSK
E-mail: sol@shirtcliffelaw.co.uk
List of partners: C S Shirtcliffe
Languages: French, Italian
Work: A1 B1 B2 C1 D1 F1 G H J1 K1 K3 K4 L N O Q S1 S2 T1 T2 W Z(k,l,m,p)
Agency, Advocacy, Legal Aid undertaken and Legal Aid Franchise
Ptr: Shirtcliffe, Mr Charles S MA(Cantab) . . . . *May 1985
Ast: Markland, Mrs Gillian FILEx. . . . . Nov 2003

THORNBURY, South Gloucestershire

DAVID CROSS & CO ‡
52 High Street Thornbury South Gloucestershire BS35 2AN
Tel: 01454 419696 *Fax:* 01454 281880 *Dx:* 48365 THORNBURY
E-mail: legal@davidcross.co.uk
List of partners: D Cross
Languages: French, German
Work: C1 C3 E F1 J1 S2 W
Ptr: Cross, Mr David LLB . . . . *May 1977

CROSSMANS SOLICITORS LIMITED ‡
12 The Plain Thornbury South Gloucestershire BS35 2BE
Tel: 01454 412278 / 412004 *Fax:* 01454 419744
Dx: 48350 THORNBURY
E-mail: info@crossmanssolicitors.co.uk
List of partners: D T Hodsman, D W Hodsman
Work: A1 K4 S1 S2 T2 W
Ptr: Hodsman, Mr David Timothy . . . . *Sep 1975
Hodsman, Mrs Dilys Wynne LLB(L'pool). . . . . *Mar 1975

KIRBY SHEPPARD
(incorporating Watson Sinnott)
36 High Street Thornbury South Gloucestershire BS35 2AJ
Tel: 0845 840 0045 *Dx:* 48352 THORNBURY
Emergency telephone 0117 961 1451
E-mail: info@kirbysheppard.co.uk
Office: Bristol, Kingswood
Work: A1 B1 C1 C2 C3 D1 E F1 G H J1 K1 L M1 M2 N O P Q S1 T1 T2 V W X Z(h,l,p)
Emergency Action, Agency, Advocacy, Fixed Fee Interview, Legal Aid undertaken, Legal Aid Franchise and Member of Accident Line
Asoc: Hale, Ms Kirsten Rhiannon LLB . . . . Aug 2003
Thomas, Ms Angela Elizabeth LLB; TEP. . . . . . . *Nov 1986

MCCARTHY & WHITE ‡
34 High Street Thornbury South Gloucestershire BS35 2AJ
Tel: 01454 413696 *Fax:* 01454 414474 *Dx:* 48362 THORNBURY
E-mail: felicity@mcwhite.lawlite.net
List of partners: F A McCarthy, I J White
Work: S1 V W Z(m)
Agency, Advocacy, Fixed Fee Interview and Legal Aid undertaken
Ptr: McCarthy, Ms Felicity A. . . . . Oct 1980
White, Mr Ian J. . . . . Dec 1971

SIMS COOK & TEAGUE ‡
40 High Street Thornbury South Gloucestershire BS35 2AJ
Tel: 01454 414342 *Fax:* 01454 281276 *Dx:* 48361 THORNBURY
E-mail: info@simscookteague.com
List of partners: J D Evans, M C H Nimmo, B A Sims, G R Teague
Office: Bristol
Work: A1 B1 C1 C2 C3 E F1 J1 K1 L N O Q R1 S1 T1 T2 W Z(c,d,e,l)
Agency undertaken
Ptr: Evans, Mr Jonathan David LLB . . . . *Nov 1992
Nimmo, Mr Martin C H BA. . . . . *Dec 1979
Sims, Mr Basil A . . . . *§Sep 1968

THORNE, South Yorkshire

BRIDGE SANDERSON MUNRO
3 Farriers Court Horsefair Green Thorne South Yorkshire DN8 5EE
Tel: 01405 814136 *Fax:* 01405 740367 *Dx:* 13921 THORNE
E-mail: info@bsmlaw.co.uk
Office: Doncaster, Wath-upon-Dearne
Work: B1 C1 C2 C3 D1 D2 E F1 F2 G H J1 K1 L N O P Q R1 R2 S1 T1 T2 V W Z(b,c,f,g,h,j,k,l,m,o,p,q,s,t)
Emergency Action, Agency, Advocacy, Fixed Fee Interview, Legal Aid undertaken, Legal Aid Franchise and Member of Accident Line

THORNTON CLEVELEYS, Lancashire

BLACKBURN & CO
7 The Crescent Thornton Cleveleys Lancashire FY5 3LN
Tel: 01253 853101 *Fax:* 01253 853145 *Dx:* 27905 CLEVELEYS
Emergency telephone 01253 853101
E-mail: douglas@blackburnsolicitors.com
Office: Fleetwood
Languages: Flemish, French
Work: C1 E F1 G H J1 K1 L N R1 S1 T1 T2 V W
Emergency Action, Agency, Advocacy, Fixed Fee Interview and Legal Aid undertaken
Ptr: Green, Mr Douglas R BA . . . . *Dec 1979
Ast: Curtis, Miss Patricia LLB(Hons) . . . . *Jan 1996

HAWORTH BROTHERTON ‡
6 Crescent East Thornton Cleveleys Lancashire FY5 3LX
Tel: 01253 852356 *Fax:* 01253 827783 *Dx:* 27909 CLEVELEYS
E-mail: info@haworthbrotherton.co.uk
List of partners: A M Brotherton, C R Haworth, T P Haworth
Work: A1 C1 E K1 L R1 R2 S1 S2 W Z(l)
Ptr: Brotherton, Mr Andrew Michael LLB(Hons) . . . . . . *Oct 1989
Haworth, Mr Christopher R . . . . *Dec 1968
Haworth, Mr Timothy P LLB(Soton) . . . . *Feb 1971
Con: Haworth, Mr Leonard A . . . . *Jan 1943

HOLDEN SON & ULLOCK ‡
10 Crescent East Thornton Cleveleys Lancashire FY5 3LP
Tel: 01253 852613 / 862606 *Fax:* 01253 861000
List of partners: J S Holden, J E R Ullock
Work: K3 K4 L S1 S2 T2 W
Agency undertaken
Ptr: Holden, Mr John S LLB(L'pool) . . . . *Jul 1975
Ullock, Mr John E R LLB(B'ham) . . . . *Nov 1977

INGHAMS
(incorporating Irving Harris & Co)
8 The Crescent Thornton Cleveleys Lancashire FY5 3LW
Tel: 01253 824111 *Fax:* 01253 827747 *Dx:* 27901 CLEVELEYS
Office: Blackpool (2 offices), Fleetwood, Knott-End-on-Sea, Poulton-le-Fylde
Work: B1 C1 D1 E F1 G H J1 K1 L M1 N O P Q R1 S1 T1 V W Z(l)
Emergency Action, Agency, Advocacy, Fixed Fee Interview, Legal Aid undertaken and Legal Aid Franchise
Asoc: Killey, Miss Diane Marie LLB . . . . *May 1996
Con: Band, Mr Christopher J . . . . *§Dec 1960
Roberts, Mr Frank MA(Oxon) . . . . *Nov 1962

ORMRODS SOLICITORS & ADVOCATES ‡
19a Marsh Mill Village Fleetwood Road North Thornton Cleveleys Lancashire FY5 4JZ
Tel: 01253 850777
E-mail: info@ormrods.co.uk

PALMER HODGSON & HEYES ‡
York House York Avenue Thornton Cleveleys Lancashire FY5 2UQ
Tel: 01253 824216 *Fax:* 01253 823671 *Dx:* 27908 CLEVELEYS
E-mail: cjp@palmerhodgsonheyes.co.uk
List of partners: G Heyes, M T Hodgson, C J Palmer
Office: Fleetwood
Work: A1 B1 C1 D1 D2 E F1 G H J1 K1 L M1 N P R1 S1 S2 T1 W Z(a,b,c,j,k,l,m,o,q)
Emergency Action, Agency, Advocacy, Legal Aid undertaken and Member of Accident Line
Ptr: Hodgson, Mrs Moira T BA. . . . . Dec 1976
Palmer, Mr Christopher J MA(St Andrews). . . . . . *Nov 1980

THORNTON HEATH, Surrey

CHARLES ALLOTEY ‡
1st Floor 791 London Road Thornton Heath Surrey CR7 6AW
Tel: 020 8664 8155 *Fax:* 020 8683 1771
List of partners: C Allotey
Ptr: Allotey, Mr Charles . . . . Nov 1994

DEYGOO & CO SOLICITORS ‡
50 Foxley Road Thornton Heath Surrey CR7 7DT
Tel: 020 8664 9224 *Fax:* 020 8664 9224
List of partners: E S Deygoo
Work: E F1 J1 K1 K3 K4 L Q R1 S1 S2 V W Z(c,l,q)
Fixed Fee Interview undertaken
SPr: Deygoo, Miss Eleanor Sheila LLB(Lond). . . . . *§Jul 1980

E & J LAW LLP ‡
69-71 High Street Thornton Heath Surrey CR7 8RY
Tel: 020 8684 5515 *Fax:* 020 8683 4012
Dx: 59153 THORNTON HEATH

MCMILLAN WILLIAMS
(in association with Odhams)
1 Heath Road Thornton Heath Surrey CR7 8NF
Tel: 020 8653 8844 *Fax:* 020 8771 7036
Dx: 59154 THORNTON HEATH
Emergency telephone 020 8660 3383
E-mail: thorntonheath@mcmillan-williams.co.uk
Office: Carshalton, Coulsdon, Croydon, Mitcham, South Croydon, Wallington
Languages: German, Kurdish, Turkish, Twi
Work: D1 D2 K1 K2 K3 S1
Emergency Action, Advocacy, Fixed Fee Interview, Legal Aid undertaken and Legal Aid Franchise
Ptr: Perot, Mr Neil Simon BA . . . . *Nov 1995
Ast: Phillips, Miss Anna . . . . *Sep 2005
Con: Sherwin, Mr Michael M . . . . *Jul 1970

MANIS ‡
3 Thornton Road Thornton Heath Surrey CR7 6BD
Tel: 020 8239 7111 *Fax:* 020 8239 7117
Dx: 59150 THORNTON HEATH
E-mail: manissols@aol.com
List of partners: A M Patel
Languages: Gujarati, Hindi, Urdu
Work: E F1 J1 K1 K3 L N O Q S1 S2 W Z(i,l)
Agency undertaken
SPr: Patel, Mr Amit Manibhai BA(Hons)(Law). . . . . *Aug 1988

PRAGESH & MCKENZIE SOLICITORS ‡
791a London Road Thornton Heath Surrey CR7 6AW
Tel: 020 8689 0089 *Fax:* 020 8684 1840
E-mail: ramnarine@btconnect.com
List of partners: R S Mungol, H Ramnarine
Work: B1 C1 D1 F1 G H J1 K1 K3 L N O Q S1 S2 W Z(i,k,l)
Agency and Advocacy undertaken
Ptr: Mungol, Ms Roma S LLB . . . . *Jan 1990
Ramnarine, Mr Harold. . . . . *Nov 1975

TILBURY GODDARD ‡
792-794 London Road Thornton Heath Surrey CR7 6YQ
Tel: 020 8684 5581 *Fax:* 020 8684 5511
Dx: 59156 THORNTON HEATH 1
E-mail: tilburygoddard@btconnect.com
List of partners: R T Dryland, S N Williams
Work: E J1 K1 K3 K4 L N Q S1 S2 W
Ptr: Dryland, Mr Roy Thomas . . . . *Jul 1976
Williams, Mr Stephen N BA . . . . *Mar 1984
Con: Ramnarine, Mr Harold. . . . . *Nov 1975

WIMAL & CO ‡
Sowjana House 727b London Road Thornton Heath Surrey CR7 6AU
Est: 1981
Tel: 020 8689 7503 *Fax:* 020 8689 4023
Dx: 59151 THORNTON HEATH
E-mail: wimalandco@btconnect.com
List of partners: P Sockanathan, W Sockanathan
Languages: Gujarati, Hindi, Malayalam, Sinhalese, Tamil, Telugu
Work: E F1 K1 K3 L S1 S2 W Z(i,l)
Ptr: Sockanathan, Mrs Pathma . . . . *Dec 1976
Sockanathan, Wimal . . . . *Dec 1976

THORPE BAY, Southend-on-Sea

ANDREW HURRELL SOLICITORS
(incorporating Francis Thatcher & Ray)
198 The Broadway Thorpe Bay Southend-on-Sea SS1 3EU
Tel: 01702 582211 / 582030 *Fax:* 01702 587870
Dx: 39617 HADLEIGH ESSEX
E-mail: andrewh@andrewhurrell.com
Office: Benfleet
Languages: French
Work: C1 E F1 L S1 T1 T2 W Z(l)

THRAPSTON, Northamptonshire

VINCENT SYKES & HIGHAM LLP ‡
Montague House Chancery Lane Thrapston Northamptonshire NN14 4LN
Tel: 01832 732161 *Fax:* 01832 733701 *Dx:* 701612 THRAPSTON
E-mail: mail@vshlaw.co.uk
List of partners: J R Davies, L M Davies, S M Green, S J Knowles, R M Rowland
Work: A1 C1 C2 D1 D2 E J1 J2 K1 K3 K4 L N O Q R2 S1 S2 T1 T2 W Z(c,d,e,p,t)
Fixed Fee Interview undertaken
Ptr: Davies, Mr John R BSc; MSc(Lond); DipLaw(Bris); MIEE . . . . *Aug 1991
Davies, Mrs Louise M BA . . . . *Oct 1986
Knowles, Mrs Susan Janet BSc; LLB . . . . *Jul 2006
Rowland, Mrs Rhona Margaret LLB(Hons) President of Northamptonshire Law Society 2011-2012. . . . . *Apr 2001
Green, Mrs Sally Margaret . . . . NSP
Asoc: Williams, Mrs Sarah Lucy LLB(Hons) . . . . *Oct 2003
Ast: Maurice, Miss Elizabeth Ann BA; MPhil . . . . *Sep 2005

TILBURY, Thurrock

STEPHEN ROBERTS & CO ‡
14 Bermuda Road Tilbury Thurrock RM18 7DA
Tel: 01375 841841 *Fax:* 01375 857676
Emergency telephone 01375 841841
List of partners: S J Roberts
Work: D1 G H K1 S1 W
Emergency Action, Agency, Advocacy, Fixed Fee Interview and Legal Aid undertaken
Ptr: Roberts, Mr Stephen J . . . . *Sep 1984

TILEHURST, Reading

BERRYS ‡
66 School Road Tilehurst Reading RG31 5AW
Tel: 0118 942 2333 *Fax:* 0118 945 1608 *Dx:* 90551 TILEHURST
E-mail: postmaster@berryssolicitors.demon.co.uk
List of partners: M W Jones
Work: C1 E F1 G J1 K1 L N O S1 S2 W
Emergency Action, Agency, Advocacy and Fixed Fee Interview undertaken
Ptr: Jones, Mr Michael W . . . . *Jun 1977

COLLINS DRYLAND & THOROWGOOD LLP
81-83 School Road Tilehurst Reading RG31 5AT
Tel: 0118 942 2448 *Fax:* 0118 945 1224 *Dx:* 90550 TILEHURST
E-mail: collinsdryland@btclick.com
Office: Henley-on-Thames
Work: A1 B1 C1 D1 E F1 G H J1 K1 K3 L M1 N O P Q R1 S1 T1 V W Z(l,p,q)
Emergency Action, Agency, Advocacy, Fixed Fee Interview, Legal Aid undertaken and Legal Aid Franchise
Ptr: Fursman, Mr William LLM(Bris) Notary Public . . . . . *Mar 1977
Ast: Fursman, Mr Paul LLB; MBA . . . . Oct 2010
Stevens, Mrs Jenny LLB(Hons) . . . . *Sep 2006
Stone, Mr Andrew J LLB(Exon) . . . . *Oct 1983

HAYES CLIFFORD & CO ‡
16a Norcot Road Tilehurst Reading RG30 6BU
Tel: 0118 941 8416 *Fax:* 0118 943 1259 *Dx:* 90552 TILEHURST
E-mail: jhayes@hayesclifford.co.uk
List of partners: J Hayes, P R Ongley
Work: B1 D1 E G J1 K1 N O Q S1 S2 W
Emergency Action, Agency, Advocacy, Fixed Fee Interview, Legal Aid Franchise and Member of Accident Line
Ptr: Hayes, Ms Joanna BA . . . . *Nov 1980
Ongley, Mr Peter R . . . . *Jun 1980

TIPTON, West Midlands

BAINS & CO SOLICITORS ‡
Brook House Business Centre Brook Street Tipton West Midlands DY4 9DD
Tel: 0121 520 9990 *Fax:* 0121 520 9959
E-mail: bainsr@aol.com

DENNINGS LLP ‡
12-15 Unity Walk Tipton West Midlands DY4 8QL
Tel: 0121 520 3599 *Fax:* 0121 520 4300
E-mail: enquiry@denningsllp.co.uk

HAYRE GEORGIOU & HAYRE LIMITED ‡
Bank Chambers 1 Owen Street Tipton West Midlands DY4 8HB
Tel: 0121 557 7766

MANN & CO ‡
Unit 38 Owen House 17 Unity Walk Tipton West Midlands DY4 8QL
Tel: 0121 555 7000 *Fax:* 0121 555 7080 *Dx:* 22561 SMETHWICK

WALDRONS
22 & 27 Brook House Brook Street Tipton West Midlands DY4 9DD
Tel: 01384 811811 *Fax:* 01922 426252 *Dx:* 12760 DUDLEY
E-mail: lawyers@waldrons.co.uk
Office: Brierley Hill, Dudley, Kingswinford, Walsall, Worcester

TIVERTON, Devon

ALEXANDER PAUL ‡
Portia House 54B Bampton Street Tiverton Devon EX16 6AH
Tel: 01884 252361 *Fax:* 01884 253461
E-mail: peterbuechel@alexanderpaul.com
List of partners: P M M Buechel
Languages: German
Ptr: Buechel, Mr Peter Martin Mark . . . . Nov 1986

ASHFORDS LLP
Gotham House Tiverton Devon EX16 6LT
Tel: 01884 203000 *Fax:* 01884 203001 *Dx:* 49002 TIVERTON
E-mail: info@ashfords.co.uk
Office: Bristol, Exeter, London W1, Plymouth, Taunton
Languages: French, German, Welsh
Work: A1 G J1 K1 N O Q S1 T2 W Z(d,e,g,h,u)
Emergency Action, Agency, Advocacy, Fixed Fee Interview, Legal Aid undertaken, Legal Aid Franchise and Member of Accident Line
Ptr: Barton, Mr Peter Lawrence BA(Hons) . . . . *Sep 1999
Cruwys, Mr Guy A L LLB(Exon) . . . . *Jun 1972
Dodd, Mr Andrew James BA(Hons) . . . . Dec 1995
Howells, Mr Timothy LLB . . . . Apr 1980
Smith, Mr John Stanley MA(Oxon) . . . . *§Dec 1977
Walker, Mr Stephen John LLB. . . . . *§Nov 1990
Wood, Miss Flora Christian BA(Hons); Dip(Hons); CPE*Oct 1995
Asoc: Harvey, Ms Sarah. . . . . Oct 1992

HOLE & PUGSLEY ‡
6 St Peter Street Tiverton Devon EX16 6NX
Tel: 01884 252827 *Fax:* 01884 256553 *Dx:* 49000 TIVERTON
E-mail: charles@hole-pugsley.co.uk
List of partners: C F Pugsley, I L Pugsley, M J Pugsley, R J L Pugsley
Work: A1 A3 E L S1 S2 W Z(d)
Ptr: Pugsley, Mr Charles F. . . . . *§Jun 1974
Pugsley, Mr Ian L . . . . *§Nov 1970
Pugsley, Miss Morwenna J LLB(Hons)(Bris) . . . . . . Feb 2004
Pugsley, Mr Richard J L LLB(Hons)(Open) . . . . . . Mar 2010

NICHOLAS HUBER & CO ‡
23 Newport Street Tiverton Devon EX16 6NL
Tel: 01884 255515 *Fax:* 01884 256272
E-mail: law@hubers.eclipse.co.uk
List of partners: N J Huber
Work: B1 E F1 J1 K1 K3 L N O Q S1 S2 W
Agency and Fixed Fee Interview undertaken
SPr: Huber, Mr Nicholas J BSc. . . . . *§Dec 1977

TODMORDEN, West Yorkshire

JAYNE BREARLEY & CO SOLICITORS ‡
2 White Hart Fold Todmorden West Yorkshire OL14 7BD
Tel: 01706 812926 / 817755 *Fax:* 01706 839923
E-mail: enq@jaynebrearleyandco.co.uk

MAKIN DIXON SOLICITORS
Johns House 32 Halifax Road Todmorden West Yorkshire OL14 5QG
Tel: 01706 839787 *Fax:* 01706 812996 *Dx:* 29624 TODMORDEN
E-mail: enquiries@makindixon.co.uk
Office: Bradford, Halifax, Harrogate, Keighley, Skipton

WRIGLEY CLAYDON
31-33 Water Street Todmorden West Yorkshire OL14 5AB
Tel: 01706 815712 *Fax:* 01706 815684 *Dx:* 29621 TODMORDEN
E-mail: info@wrigleyclaydontod.com
Office: Oldham
Work: A1 C1 E F1 G H J1 K1 L M1 N P R1 S1 T1 V W Z(c,h,l)
Emergency Action, Agency, Advocacy, Fixed Fee Interview, Legal Aid undertaken, Legal Aid Franchise and Member of Accident Line
Ptr: Pickles, Mr A Godfrey. . . . . *§Jun 1977
Asoc: Brannick, Mr Antony Charkes MA . . . . Oct 1983

TONBRIDGE, Kent

BAILEY & COGGER ‡
139 High Street Tonbridge Kent TN9 1DG
Tel: 01732 353305 *Fax:* 01732 359678 *Dx:* 5504 TONBRIDGE
E-mail: rh@baileycogger.co.uk
List of partners: G A Beach, R Holland, J P Woodford
Work: A1 B1 C1 C2 C3 E F1 J1 J2 K1 L N O Q R1 S1 S2 T1 T2 V W Z(c,j,l,q)
Emergency Action, Agency, Advocacy, Fixed Fee Interview, Legal Aid undertaken and Legal Aid Franchise
Ptr: Beach, Mr Graham A LLB. . . . . *§Apr 1979
Holland, Mr Robert . . . . *§Dec 1974
Woodford, Mr Jeremy P. . . . . *May 1981
Ast: Biggerstaff, Mrs Helen Louise . . . . *Nov 1998
Vallis, Mr Harvey A . . . . *Jun 1971

BERRY & BERRY
185 High Street Tonbridge Kent TN9 1BX
Tel: 01732 355911 *Fax:* 01732 355191 *Dx:* 5500 TONBRIDGE
Emergency telephone 07528 270096
E-mail: mail@the-solicitors.co.uk
Office: Maidstone, Tunbridge Wells
Languages: French, German, Spanish
Work: A1 B1 B2 C1 C2 C3 D1 D2 E F1 G H J1 K1 L M1 M2 N O P Q R1 S1 S2 T1 T2 V W Z(b,c,d,e,f,g,h,j,k,l,m,o,p,q,r,w)
Emergency Action, Agency, Advocacy, Fixed Fee Interview, Legal Aid undertaken, Legal Aid Franchise and Member of Accident Line
Ptr: Herman, Mr Anthony BSc(Econ) . . . . *Mar 1965
Masoliver, Mr Yashin Juan-Ramon BSc(Hons) British Gas Prize . . . . *Jun 1995
Nickolls, Mr Matthew Lewis BSc(Hons) . . . . *Nov 1999
Reed, Mr Iain D BA(Newc)(Law) . . . . *§May 1988
Ast: Allan, Miss Katie Louise LLB . . . . *Aug 2010
Cranfield, Miss Emma LLB . . . . *Sep 2009
Hollingum, Ms Laura LLB . . . . *Aug 2006
Johnson, Mr Andrew L R . . . . §Dec 1980
Noble, Mrs Helen M BA(Hons) . . . . *Sep 1990
Philips, Miss Sarah PGDipLaw . . . . *Sep 2007

BOWER CONLON ‡
Goose Green Farmhouse Hadlow Tonbridge Kent TN11 0JJ
Tel: 01732 850318

BRINDLES SOLICITORS ‡
11 Bell Cottages Three Elm Lane Tonbridge Kent TN11 0BB
Tel: 01732 852688
E-mail: debra@brindleslaw.co.uk

CLARKE KIERNAN ‡
2-4 Bradford Street Tonbridge Kent TN9 1DU
Tel: 01732 360999 *Fax:* 01732 773355 *Dx:* 5537 TONBRIDGE
E-mail: info@clarkekiernan.com
List of partners: C McCarthy
Office: Tonbridge
Work: B2 D1 G H K1 K3 L Q Z(g)
Agency, Fixed Fee Interview, Legal Aid undertaken and Legal Aid Franchise
Ptr: McCarthy, Miss Catherine LLB(Hons) . . . . *Jan 1992
Ast: Alexander, Sacha . . . . Mar 2005
Barford, Mrs Bridget C LLB . . . . Feb 1989
Colquhoun, Mr Edward S . . . . Jul 1976
Fraser, Mr Glen . . . . Jan 1999
Gregory, Mr Liam . . . . Jul 2007
Hill, Miss Sara Corinne BA . . . . Oct 2003
Penny, Mr Timothy . . . . Apr 2004
Wawiye, Lydia . . . . Dec 2008

CLARKE KIERNAN
Lamberts Yard Tonbridge Kent TN9 1ER
Tel: 01892 537999 *Fax:* 01892 531536
Office: Tonbridge

DENNIS MORRIS SOLICITOR ‡
Beale Farm Goudhurst Road Tonbridge Kent TN12 9LT
Tel: 01622 833048 *Fax:* 01622 833048
E-mail: denmorr@btinternet.com

LONGS SOLICITORS ‡
12 Stacey Road Tonbridge Kent TN10 3AR
Tel: 01732 360895 *Fax:* 01732 360896
E-mail: longs@longssolicitors.co.uk
List of partners: R L H Long, T A Long
Languages: French, Norwegian
Work: C1 C2 C3 E J1 S2 Z(c,d,e)
Ptr: Long, Mr Richard L H TD TD; MA. . . . . Nov 1991
Long, Mrs Tina A BA(Hons). . . . . Dec 1993

JANE MOORE SOLICITORS ‡
Pauls Farm Enfield Road Leigh Tonbridge Kent TN11 8RX
Tel: 01732 835555
E-mail: jane@janemoorelaw.com

SEAN O'CONNOR ‡
2 River Walk Tonbridge Kent TN9 1DT
Tel: 01732 365378 *Fax:* 01732 360144
E-mail: seanoconnorco@aol.com
List of partners: S O'Connor
Languages: French, Spanish
Work: C1 S1 W
Emergency Action and Agency undertaken
SPr: O'Connor, Mr Sean MA(Oxon) . . . . *§Dec 1972

SIMMONS & CO ‡
Orchard House Sheephurst Lane Tonbridge Kent TN12 9LY
Tel: 01622 831823 *Fax:* 01622 832951
E-mail: jks@simmonsco.eu

WARNERS SOLICITORS ‡
Bank House Bank Street Tonbridge Kent TN9 1BL
Tel: 01732 770660 *Fax:* 01732 362452 *Dx:* 5501 TONBRIDGE
E-mail: general@warners-solicitors.co.uk
List of partners: N R M Barratt, R L Collins, S W Colville, M O Davis, E A Dolding, M P Galvin, C R Manning, J P McAuliffe, D S Millis, J M Roberts, M H Rosser, A J Rowe, P A Smith, R P Twining, W B S Wass, D S Wilson
Office: Sevenoaks
Work: A1 A3 B1 C1 C2 D1 E F1 F2 I J1 K1 K2 K3 L N O Q R1 R2 S1 S2 T1 T2 W Z(c,d,e,j,k,l,o,p,q,w)
Emergency Action, Advocacy and Fixed Fee Interview undertaken
Mem: Colville, Mr Stephen William. . . . . Oct 1999
Dolding, Miss Elizabeth A BCS . . . . *Jan 1990
Galvin, Mr Martin P . . . . *§Dec 1981
McAuliffe, Mr John Peter . . . . Sep 1999
Millis, Mr Darren S LLB(Hons); DipLP . . . . *Jan 1998
Roberts, Mr Jonathan Mark LLB(Hons) . . . . Oct 2003
Smith, Mr Patrick Andrew LLB Notary Public . . . . . *Oct 1993
Wass, Mr William B S LLB . . . . *§Feb 1974
Wilson, Mr David S LLB. . . . . *§Apr 1979
Ast: Barker, Mrs Suzanne Jane LLB(Hons). . . . . Apr 1996
Bradburne, Mrs Samantha Ruth MA(Cantab) . . . . *Sep 1999
Brinkhurst, Mr Russell James LLB. . . . . Oct 2007
Eriksson-Lee, Mr Christopher BA(Hons). . . . . . . *Sep 2007
Lock, Miss Ann-Marie Barbara LLB; LPC . . . . Mar 2011
Morris, Mrs Amy Laura LLB . . . . Sep 2009
Sabine, Mr Matthew David LLB(Hons). . . . . Apr 2007
Tague, Miss Estelle LLB(Hons) . . . . May 2009
Taylor, Mrs Fiona R LLB(Hons) . . . . *Oct 1998
Winnett, Ms Barbara A LLB . . . . *Nov 1985
Con: Warner, Mr Charles J MA(Cantab) Notary Public . . *§Jun 1976

TONYPANDY, Rhondda Cynon Taff

DEVONALDS
135 Dunraven Street Tonypandy Rhondda Cynon Taff CF40 1QD
Tel: 01443 434343 *Fax:* 01443 437130 *Dx:* 55901 TONYPANDY
Emergency telephone 07801 561557
E-mail: tonypandy@devonalds.co.uk
Office: Cardiff, Pontypridd (2 offices), Talbot Green
Work: B1 C1 D1 D2 E F1 G H J1 K1 L M1 N P R1 S1 T1 V W Z(c,k,l,m,w)
Emergency Action, Agency, Advocacy, Fixed Fee Interview and Legal Aid undertaken

EMERY HOGG ‡
3 Dunraven Street Tonypandy Rhondda Cynon Taff CF40 1QE
Tel: 01443 433317 *Fax:* 01443 434181 *Dx:* 55908 TONYPANDY
E-mail: hoggandco@btconnect.com

GRAEME JOHN SOLICITORS
(in association with Berwyn Davies & A F Brooks)
44 Dunraven Street Tonypandy Rhondda Cynon Taff CF40 1AL
Tel: 01443 423797 *Fax:* 01443 432798 *Dx:* 55900 TONYPANDY
E-mail: info@graemejohn.co.uk
Office: Aberdare (3 offices), Ystradgynlais
Languages: Welsh
Work: C1 C2 D1 E F1 G H J1 K1 L N O Q R1 S1 V W Z(l,t)
Emergency Action, Agency, Advocacy, Fixed Fee Interview, Legal Aid undertaken and Member of Accident Line
Ptr: Henderson, Mr Michael Rylan LLB . . . . *Nov 1985

TORPOINT, Cornwall

RICHARD HARRIS SOLICITORS ‡
4 Coombe Park Close Practice Cawsand Torpoint Cornwall PL10 1PW
Tel: 01752 822224

TROBRIDGES
24 Fore Street Torpoint Cornwall PL11 2AD
Tel: 01752 812787 *Fax:* 01752 815428
Emergency telephone 01752 812036
Office: Plymouth
Languages: German
Work: A1 B1 C1 C2 C3 D1 E F1 G H J1 K1 L M1 M2 N O P Q R1 S1 T1 T2 V W Z(a,l,q)
Emergency Action, Agency, Advocacy, Fixed Fee Interview, Legal Aid undertaken, Legal Aid Franchise and Member of Accident Line
Ptr: Matthews, Mr Christopher W G BA . . . . *§Jun 1980
Asoc: Isaac, Mr Geoffrey Francis Warwick. . . . . *§Jul 1973
Ast: Lentell, Mrs Jennifer LLB(Hons). . . . . Dec 2007

TORQUAY, Torbay

ALMY & THOMAS ‡
71 Abbey Road Torquay Torbay TQ2 5NL
Tel: 01803 299131 *Fax:* 01803 200399 *Dx:* 59015 TORQUAY 1
Emergency telephone 07738 637720
E-mail: enquiries@almythomas.co.uk
List of partners: P J Dentith, O M Evans, A M Parsons
Work: B2 B3 G H J1 K1 K3 K4 L N Q S1 W Z(q)
Agency and Advocacy undertaken
Ptr: Dentith, Mr Paul John LLB . . . . *Sep 2005
Evans, Mr Owen M LLB. . . . . *Apr 1986
Parsons, Mr Alan M MA(Cantab) . . . . *Sep 1983
Ast: Brooks, Mr Niall. *Jun 2007

BAY ADVOCATES CRIMINAL DEFENCE LAWYERS ‡
238 Union Street Torquay Torbay TQ2 5QS
Tel: 01803 408290 *Fax:* 01803 405689 *Dx:* 59004 TORQUAY 1
E-mail: enquiries@bayadvocates.co.uk
Languages: Spanish
Work: G H
Agency, Fixed Fee Interview and Legal Aid undertaken

BOYCE HATTON ‡
(incorporating Carter Fisher & Co)
12 Tor Hill Road Castle Circus Torquay Torbay TQ2 5RB
Tel: 01803 403403 *Fax:* 01803 214876 *Dx:* 59000 TORQUAY 1
E-mail: mail@boycehatton.co.uk
Languages: French
Work: A1 A3 B1 C1 C2 C3 D1 D2 E F1 G I J1 J2 K1 K2 L M1 M2 N O P Q R1 R2 S1 S2 T1 T2 U1 V W X Z(a,b,c,d,e,f,g,h,i,j,k,l,o,p,q,r,s,t,u,w,y,z)

BYNES ‡
Court Chambers 186 Union Street Torquay Torbay TQ2 5QP
Tel: 01803 295692 *Fax:* 01803 298048 *Dx:* 59002 TORQUAY 1
E-mail: enquiries@bynes.co.uk
List of partners: J C Byne, M J Hayman, A D James
Work: B1 B2 C1 C2 D1 E F1 F2 G H J1 J2 K1 K2 K3 K4 L M1 N O Q R1 R2 S1 S2 V W Z(c,e,g,h,k,l,q,r)
Emergency Action, Agency, Advocacy, Fixed Fee Interview, Legal Aid undertaken, Legal Aid Franchise and Member of Accident Line
Ptr: Byne, Mr John C . . . . *§Jun 1974
Hayman, Mr Michael J LLM . . . . *Oct 1982
James, Mr Alasdair D LLB. . . . . *Mar 1987

DARBY & DARBY ‡
(incorporating Moriarty & Co)
Tudor Chambers Fore Street St Marychurch Torquay Torbay TQ1 4PR
Tel: 01803 313656 *Fax:* 01803 313460 *Dx:* 83000 TORQUAY 3
Emergency telephone 01803 312321
E-mail: info@darbylaw.co.uk
List of partners: J E Darby
Work: D1 E G H K1 L M1 R1 S1 T1 W
Emergency Action, Agency, Advocacy, Fixed Fee Interview, Legal Aid undertaken and Member of Accident Line
Ptr: Darby, Mr John E . . . . *§Jun 1970

EWA DAVIS SOLICITORS & NOTARY PUBLIC ‡
10 Court Road Torquay Torbay TQ2 6SE
Tel: 01803 607662 *Fax:* 01803 231144
E-mail: edavis@blueyonder.co.uk

FAMILY MATTERS SOLICITORS ‡
52 Fore Street St Marychurch Torquay Torbay TQ1 4LX
Tel: 01803 328577 *Fax:* 01803 329132

See p112 for the Key to Work Categories & other symbols

E-mail: solutions@familylawmatters.co.uk
List of partners: S G Childs
Work: K1 K3 W
Agency undertaken
SPr: Childs, Mrs Susan Gillian . . . . Sep 1996

KITSONS LLP ‡
Minerva House Orchard Way Edginswell Park Torquay Torbay TQ2 7FA
Tel: 01803 202020 *Fax:* 01803 299831 *Dx:* 744650 TORQUAY 8
E-mail: advice@kitsons-solicitors.co.uk
List of partners: P J Boyne, J M G Cross, R Davey, E Davy, P M Gaskins, D Hollingsworth, J W Howell, R J Hutchings, N Johnson, J Lang, R D Newman, A S Perkins, A Smith, L Smith
Office: Exeter, Newton Abbot, Plymouth
Languages: French, German, Polish
Work: A1 B1 C1 C2 C3 D1 D2 E F1 G H J1 K1 K2 K3 L N O P Q R1 S1 S2 T1 T2 V W Z(k,l,m,q)
Emergency Action, Agency, Advocacy, Fixed Fee Interview, Legal Aid undertaken and Legal Aid Franchise
Ptr: Cross, Mr James M G BA . . . . *Oct 1992
Davey, Mr Rhodri . . . . Sep 1999
Gaskins, Mr Patrick Micheal BA(Hons) . . . . Sep 1997
Hollingsworth, Mr Dominic BSc(Hons) . . . . Nov 1999
Hutchings, Mr Richard J . . . . *§Jan 1972
Johnson, Mr Nick . . . . Jan 1990
Newman, Mr Robert D MA(Oxon) Deputy Coroner . . *§Dec 1976
Smith, Ms Lynn LLB . . . . *Dec 1988
Asoc: Weare, Rebecca . . . . Dec 2003
Con: Forward, Mr Graham A Notary Public . . . . *§Jan 1972

LEE-BARBER GOODRICH & CO ‡
St Johns Chambers 22 The Terrace Torquay Torbay TQ1 1BP
Tel: 01803 295535 *Fax:* 01803 294446 *Dx:* 59205 TORQUAY 2
List of partners: M G Goodrich, P A Goodrich, P F V White
Work: A1 B1 C1 D1 E F1 G J1 K1 L N O Q S1 S2 T1 T2 W Z(i,j,k,l)
Agency, Advocacy and Fixed Fee Interview undertaken
Ptr: Goodrich, Mr Michael G . . . . *§Jun 1970
Goodrich, Mr Peter A . . . . *§Jun 1963
White, Mr Philip F V . . . . *§Apr 1970

PERRY MASON SOLICITORS ‡
44 The Terrace Torquay Torbay TQ1 1DE
Tel: 01803 299000 *Fax:* 01803 299004 *Dx:* 59222 TORQUAY 2
E-mail: lawyer@perrymason.co.uk
List of partners: P J P Mason
Languages: Polish
Work: E L S1 S2 Z(l)
Agency and Fixed Fee Interview undertaken
Ptr: Mason, Mr Peter John Perry LLB(Hons) . . . . *§Sep 1986
Ast: Bradbury, Mr Ian . . . . *May 1986

PHOENIX SOLICITORS & ADVOCATES LIMITED ‡
272 Union Street Torquay Torbay TQ2 5QY
Tel: 01803 219220
E-mail: crime@phoenixadvocates.co.uk

SOMERVILLE & SAVAGE ‡
Alderbourne Greenway Road St Marychurch Torquay Torbay TQ1 4NJ
Tel: 01803 312700 *Fax:* 01803 316790 *Dx:* 83001 TORQUAY 3
E-mail: office@somsav.co.uk
List of partners: M S J French
Office: Torquay
Work: E K1 S1 S2 T2 W
Fixed Fee Interview undertaken
Ptr: French, Mr Michael St John BA(Oxon) . . . . *§Jun 1967
Ast: Keen, Mr Antony Paul Clow LLB . . . . *Sep 1972
Osborne, Miss Lisa Marie HND; FILEx . . . . Jan 2011

SOMERVILLE & SAVAGE
16a Fore Street St Marychurch Torquay Torbay TQ1 4NA
Tel: 01803 324500 *Fax:* 01803 316790 *Dx:* 83001 TORQUAY 3
E-mail: convey@allensconveyancing.co.uk
Office: Torquay
Work: S1 S2 W
Fixed Fee Interview undertaken
SPr: French, Mr Michael St John BA(Oxon) . . . . *§Jun 1967
Ast: Keen, Mr Antony Paul Clow LLB . . . . *Sep 1972

HAMISH TURNER ‡
1 Palk Street Torquay Torbay TQ2 5EL
Tel: 01803 213806 *Fax:* 01803 213806
Work: K4 W Z(d,i)

WBW SOLICITORS
24 Tor Hill Road Torquay Torbay TQ2 5RD
Tel: 0870 701 4321 *Fax:* 01803 407666
E-mail: lawyer@wbw.co.uk
Office: Bovey Tracey, Exeter, Newton Abbot
Languages: French
Work: A1 A3 B1 B2 C1 C2 D1 D2 E F1 G H J1 K1 K2 L N O Q R1 S1 S2 T1 T2 V W Z(e,g,h,l,r)
Emergency Action, Agency, Advocacy, Fixed Fee Interview, Legal Aid undertaken, Legal Aid Franchise and Member of Accident Line
Ptr: Cooper, Mr Andrew LLB . . . . *Jun 1976
Garrard, Mr Laird BSc(Econ); LLB . . . . *§Aug 1983
Lewis, Mr Roderic W BA . . . . *§Jun 1980
Pearce, Mrs Tracey J BA . . . . *§Dec 1986
Williams, Mr C Mark LLB(Hons) . . . . *Jan 1992
Williams, Mr Mervyn N LLB . . . . *§Nov 1974
Ast: Blair, Mr Richard J G LLB(Hons) . . . . *Feb 1989
Silk, Mr Adrian LLB(Hons) . . . . *Feb 1995

WOLLEN MICHELMORE SOLICITORS ‡
Carlton House 30 The Terrace Torquay Torbay TQ1 1BS
Tel: 01803 213251 *Fax:* 01803 296871 *Dx:* 59204 TORQUAY 2
Office: Dartmouth, Newton Abbot, Paignton
Languages: French, German
Work: A1 B1 B2 C1 C2 C3 D1 D2 E F1 F2 I J1 K1 K2 K3 K4 L M1 N O P Q R1 R2 S1 S2 T1 T2 V W Z(a,c,d,e,g,h,i,j,k,l,m,o,p,q,r,t,w)

TOTNES, Devon

BARTONS
9 Townquay The Plains Totnes Devon TQ9 5DW
Tel: 01803 864705 *Fax:* 01803 865904 *Dx:* 81509 TOTNES
E-mail: totnes@bartons.co.uk
Office: Bristol, Kingsbridge, Plymouth, Salcombe
Work: D1 K1 K2 L Q S1 Z(a)
Fixed Fee Interview and Legal Aid undertaken
Ptr: Walker, Miss Tracey Jean . . . . Jan 1991

EASTLEYS
(incorporating Cornish & Co)
Courtyard Chambers 46 Fore Street Totnes Devon TQ9 5RP
Tel: 01803 864888 *Fax:* 01803 867488 *Dx:* 81502 TOTNES
E-mail: totnes@eastleys.co.uk
Office: Brixham, Paignton
Work: A1 D1 D2 S1 T2 W
Emergency Action, Agency, Advocacy, Fixed Fee Interview, Legal Aid undertaken, Legal Aid Franchise and Member of Accident Line
Ptr: Roddan, Mr Matthew Garnett John LLB . . . . *Nov 1995
Asoc: Merrison, Miss Ida LLB . . . . Mar 2005

KELLOCK & JOHNSON ‡
8 High Street Totnes Devon TQ9 5SA
Tel: 01803 862414 *Fax:* 01803 866552
E-mail: totnes@kellocks.co.uk
List of partners: J H J K Pett
Office: Newton Abbot
Work: A1 B1 C1 C2 C3 E F1 G H J1 K1 L N P Q S1 W Z(c,d,q)
Agency, Fixed Fee Interview undertaken and Member of Accident Line
Asoc: Northam, Mr Barry F BA(Law) . . . . May 1967

RECOMPENSE SOLICITORS LTD ‡
Waterleat House Burke Road Totnes Devon TQ9 5XL
Tel: 0800 037 5817
E-mail: claims@recompense.co.uk
List of partners: C Hales
Dir: Hales, Carolyn . . . . May 1977
Ast: Larner, Elizabeth . . . . Apr 2008
Con: Stockdale-Garbutt, Mr John W . . . . Mar 1983

WINDEATTS ‡
19 High Street Totnes Devon TQ9 5NW
Tel: 01803 862233 *Fax:* 01803 863950 *Dx:* 81500 TOTNES
E-mail: totnes@windeatts.co.uk
List of partners: N P Butt, N Campbell, W Harris, F Hughes, C Kendall, A J Osborne
Office: Kingsbridge
Languages: French
Work: A1 B1 C1 D1 E F1 G H J1 K1 K3 K4 L N O P Q R1 S1 S2 T1 T2 V W Z(d,h,l)
Emergency Action, Agency, Advocacy, Fixed Fee Interview, Legal Aid undertaken and Member of Accident Line
Ptr: Butt, Mr Nigel P LLB . . . . *Feb 1989
Campbell, Mrs Nicola . . . . *Jul 1990
Hughes, Mrs Fiona . . . . Sep 2002
Kendall, Mr Christopher LLB . . . . *Nov 1995
Osborne, Mr Anthony J . . . . *Dec 1974
Harris, Mrs Wendy . . . . NSP

TOTTON, Hampshire

PETER CLARKE SOLICITORS ‡
63a Commercial Road Totton Hampshire SO40 3AH
Tel: 023 8066 6636 *Fax:* 023 8057 3939 *Dx:* 44969 TOTTON
E-mail: enquiries@peterclarkesolicitors.co.uk
List of partners: P A Clarke
Work: B2 D1 G H K1 S1
Agency, Advocacy and Legal Aid undertaken
SPr: Clarke, Mr Peter A LLB(Warw) . . . . *Oct 1980

FOOTNER & EWING
14a Water Lane Totton Hampshire SO40 3ZB
Tel: 023 8086 3493 *Fax:* 023 8086 2674
Office: Romsey, Southampton (2 offices)

KIRKLANDS
26-28 Commercial Road Totton Hampshire SO40 3BY
Tel: 023 8066 3313 *Fax:* 023 8087 1127 *Dx:* 44953 TOTTON
Emergency telephone 01794 514788
E-mail: pkirkland@kirklandssolicitors.co.uk
Office: Romsey
Work: A1 B1 C1 C2 D1 E F1 J1 K1 L M1 N O P Q R1 S1 S2 V W Z(c,d,j,l)
Ptr: Kirkland, Mr Philip D M . . . . *May 1974

UNDERWOOD & CO ‡
15 Junction Road Totton Hampshire SO40 9HG
Tel: 023 8087 1479 / 8086 0827 *Fax:* 023 8086 9563
Dx: 44952 TOTTON
E-mail: underwoodsols@aol.com
List of partners: G J Porter
Languages: French
Work: C1 E K1 N S1 S2 W Z(l)
Agency and Fixed Fee Interview undertaken
Ptr: Porter, Mr Graham J . . . . *Jul 1977

TOWCESTER, Northamptonshire

ARNOLD THOMSON LIMITED ‡
(in association with D N Bromwich)
205 Watling Street West Towcester Northamptonshire NN12 6BX
Tel: 01327 350266 *Fax:* 01327 353567 *Dx:* 16932 TOWCESTER
E-mail: enquiries@arnoldthomson.com
List of partners: M M J Hawkins, M A Thomson
Languages: French, German
Work: A1 A2 E L O P Q R1 S1 S2 T1 T2 W Z(d,x)
Dir: Hawkins, Mr Matthew Michael John BSc(Hons); LLB . *Apr 2004
Thomson, Mr Michael A BA . . . . *§Apr 1981
Asoc: Hibbett, Miss Jacqueline LLB(Leeds) . . . . *§Jan 1987
Ast: Alton Honeywell, Mr K Maurice S MA(Oxon); FTII Notary Public . . . . *§Dec 1978
Fursey, Mr Michael J LLB . . . . *Jan 1989
Love, Mr Jon . . . . *Jul 2008
Simkins, Mrs Christine A LLB . . . . *Oct 1981
Walker, Miss Victoria H LLB . . . . *Mar 2005

HUNTERS
The Old Rectory Litchborough Towcester Northamptonshire NN12 8JF
Tel: 01327 830895 *Fax:* 01327 830044
Office: London WC2
Work: A1 E S1 T2 W
Ptr: Sykes, Ms Patricia A . . . . *§Nov 1976
Particular areas of work include: Agricultural Law, Holdings and Property, Commercial Property, Residential Conveyancing, Taxation - Personal, Wills, Trusts and Probate.

SHEPHERD & CO ‡
184 Watling Street East Towcester Northamptonshire NN12 6DB
Tel: 01327 350185 *Fax:* 01327 359010 *Dx:* 16933 TOWCESTER
E-mail: rps@shepherdandco.com
Languages: Punjabi
Work: A1 C1 D1 E F1 G H J1 K1 K3 L N O Q S1 S2 T2 W Z(d,k,l)

TOWCESTER FAMILY LAW PRACTICE ‡
First Floor Victoria House 138 Watling Street East Towcester Northamptonshire NN12 6BT
Tel: 01327 358321 *Fax:* 01327 358460 *Dx:* 16934 TOWCESTER
E-mail: law@tflp.co.uk

TREDEGAR, Blaenau Gwent

ROGER EDWARDS & CO ‡
22 Commercial Street Tredegar Blaenau Gwent NP2 3DH
Tel: 01495 722865 *Fax:* 01495 717755 *Dx:* 92552 TREDEGAR
Emergency telephone 01495 722940
E-mail: jenn@rogeredwards.fsnet.co.uk
List of partners: R B S Edwards
Languages: French
Work: C1 D1 E F1 G H J1 K1 L M1 N P R1 S1 S2 V W Z(l,m)
Emergency Action, Agency, Advocacy, Fixed Fee Interview, Legal Aid undertaken and Legal Aid Franchise
Ptr: Edwards, Mr Roger B S . . . . *§Dec 1966

MACQUILLAN & CO
14 Commercial Street Tredegar Blaenau Gwent NP2 3DH
Tel: 01495 725031 *Fax:* 01495 711687
Emergency telephone 01873 77985
Office: Ebbw Vale
Work: A1 B1 C1 D1 E F1 G H J1 K1 L M1 N P R1 S1 T1 V
Emergency Action and Legal Aid undertaken
Ptr: MacQuillan, Ms Juliet A V LLB . . . . May 1972
Williams, Mr Jonathon A J LLB . . . . Apr 1982

TREGARON, Ceredigion

ARNOLD DAVIES VINCENT EVANS
Manyrafon Chapel Street Tregaron Ceredigion SY25 6HA
Tel: 01974 298816 *Fax:* 01974 298779
E-mail: post@adve.co.uk
Office: Lampeter
Languages: Welsh
Work: A1 K1 K4 L S1 S2 T1 W
Agency undertaken
Ptr: Evans, Mr Dafydd Peredur LLB . . . . *Apr 1980
Lewis, Mr Aled Wyn LLB . . . . *Sep 2001
Ast: Thomas, Miss Bethan Haf LLB; BSc . . . . *Sep 2009

TREORCHY, Rhondda Cynon Taff

R L EDWARDS & PARTNERS
13 High Street Treorchy Rhondda Cynon Taff CF42 6AA
Tel: 01443 775000 *Fax:* 01443 775007
Office: Bridgend, Maesteg, Porthcawl
Languages: French, Spanish
Work: A1 A2 B1 B2 C1 C2 D1 D2 E F1 F2 G H I J1 K1 L N O Q R1 R2 S1 S2 V Z(d,h,i,k,l,m,n,q,r,t,w,y)
Emergency Action, Agency, Advocacy, Fixed Fee Interview, Legal Aid undertaken, Legal Aid Franchise and Member of Accident Line

DAVID EDWARD REES & CO ‡
Plas Medi 160 Bute Street Treherbert Treorchy Rhondda Cynon Taff CF42 5PE
Tel: 01443 776361 *Fax:* 01443 776878
Emergency telephone 01443 776489
List of partners: D E Rees
Work: D1 F1 G H J1 K1 M1 P S1 V
Emergency Action, Agency, Advocacy, Fixed Fee Interview and Legal Aid undertaken
Ptr: Rees, Mr David E LLB . . . . Mar 1984

TRING, Hertfordshire

HUGHES & COMPANY ‡
Orchard Mews High Street Tring Hertfordshire HP23 5XA
Tel: 01442 891717 *Fax:* 01442 890772 *Dx:* 80755 TRING
E-mail: peter@hughesand.co.uk
List of partners: A J Alldred, P S Hughes, R J A Hughes, N A King
Languages: French
Work: E K1 K3 K4 N S1 S2 T2 W Z(r)
Ptr: Alldred, Mr Andrew John LLB(Hons) . . . . *Apr 1978
Hughes, Mr Peter Saville Commissioner for Oaths . . *Dec 1976
Hughes, Mr Richard James Asplin . . . . *Jan 1969
King, Mrs Nicola Ann LLB(Hons) . . . . Aug 1997

SWATTON TAYLOR DUTTON ‡
11 High Street Tring Hertfordshire HP23 5AL
Tel: 01442 825566 *Fax:* 01442 827865 *Dx:* 80750 TRING
List of partners: A A Dutton
Work: E J1 K3 L N O Q S1 S2 W
Ptr: Dutton, Mr Andrew A Chairman of the London & Eastern Rent Assessment Panels . . . . *Nov 1981

MATTHEW WAITE & CO ‡
Ariel House Frogmore Street Tring Hertfordshire HP23 5AU
Tel: 01442 890111 *Fax:* 01442 890955 *Dx:* 80753 TRING
E-mail: info@matthewwaite.com
List of partners: M D Waite
Work: C1 F1 J1 K1 K3 L N O Q S1 S2 W
Fixed Fee Interview undertaken
Ptr: Waite, Mr Matthew Douglas LLB(Hons) . . . . *Mar 1986

TROWBRIDGE, Wiltshire

BLB SOLICITORS ‡
Rodney House 5 Roundstone Street Trowbridge Wiltshire BA14 8DH
Tel: 01225 755656 *Fax:* 01225 753266 *Dx:* 43106 TROWBRIDGE
E-mail: solicitors@trowbridge.blandb.co.uk
List of partners: G Bagnall, T A Bishop, A T W Dunkerley, D R Morison, D A Palmer, C J W Smyth

Office: Bath, Bradford-on-Avon, Swindon
Work: A1 B1 C1 D1 E F1 G H J1 K1 L N P R1 S1 T1 V W Z(l,m)
Emergency Action, Agency, Advocacy, Fixed Fee Interview, Legal Aid undertaken, Legal Aid Franchise and Member of Accident Line
Ptr: Bishop, Mr Terence A . . . . . *§Feb 1962
Palmer, Mr David A . . . . . *§Feb 1972
Asoc: Bennett, Miss Claire BSc(Hons)(Politics) . . . . . Oct 2002
Ast: Cooper, Mr Martin Frederick. . . . . Nov 1980

GOUGHS
2 Fore Street Trowbridge Wiltshire BA14 8HX
Tel: 01225 762683 *Fax:* 01225 760555 *Dx:* 43103 TROWBRIDGE
Emergency telephone 01225 752673 / 313344
E-mail: info@goughs.co.uk
Office: Calne, Chippenham, Corsham, Devizes, Melksham
Work: A1 B1 C1 C2 C3 D1 E F1 J1 K1 L N Q R1 S1 W Z(c,d,e,h,m,r)
Emergency Action, Agency, Advocacy and Fixed Fee Interview undertaken
Ptr: Moir, Mrs Dawn-Marie BA(Hons)(Financial Services); PGDipLaw; LPC . . . . . §Sep 2000
Vingoe, Mr Paul G . . . . . *§Jul 1975
Ast: Mortimor, Miss Louise Frances BA; PGDipLaw . . . . Sep 2005

SYLVESTER MACKETT ‡
Castle House Castle Street Trowbridge Wiltshire BA14 8AX
Tel: 01225 755621 *Fax:* 01225 769055 *Dx:* 43101 TROWBRIDGE
E-mail: solicitors@sylvestermackett.co.uk
List of partners: M P Cavalla, J C Frayling, N E Godsiffe, S N K Guinness, G McGlynn, J D Riley, H V Venables
Office: Warminster
Work: C1 C2 E J1 K1 K3 K4 L N O Q S1 S2 W Z(l)
Emergency Action, Agency, Advocacy, Fixed Fee Interview, Legal Aid undertaken, Legal Aid Franchise and Member of Accident Line
Ptr: Cavalla, Mr Michael P LLB(Hons); TEP . . . . . *Oct 1997
Frayling, Mr Jonathan Charles LLB(Hons). . . . . *Aug 2000
Godsiffe, Mr Nigel E BSc(Econ) . . . . . *Oct 1979
Guinness, Mr S Nicholas K BA . . . . . *Oct 1985
McGlynn, Mr Gerard LLB . . . . . *Jul 1975
Riley, Mr John David BA; MA . . . . . *Jan 2002
Venables, Mr Howard V BA(Hons)(Wales). . . . . *Jan 1983
Ast: Bryant, Miss Claire LLB(Hons)(Law & French); Licence de Droit . . . . . *Sep 2009
Fitzgerald, Ms Marie Christine PGDipLaw; LPC . . . *Feb 2003
Hood, Miss Elizabeth Anne BA(Hons); LPC . . . . . *Mar 2007
Jetwani, Miss Sarika LLB . . . . . Mar 2005
McCabe, Mr Philip LLB(Hons); BA(Hons)(Econ). . . *May 2005

ANTHONY D WILKIN ‡
1st Floor 11 Silver Street Trowbridge Wiltshire BA14 8AA
Tel: 01225 765526

WITHY KING SOLICITORS
(incorporating Chalk Smith Brooks)
Bryer Ash Business Park Bradford Road Trowbridge Wiltshire BA14 8AW
Tel: 01225 777464 *Fax:* 01225 405115 *Dx:* 190498 TROWBRIDGE 3
E-mail: enquiries@withyking.co.uk
Office: Abingdon, Bath (2 offices), Marlborough, Oxford, Swindon, Thame
Work: A1 A3 B1 C1 C2 D1 D2 E F1 F2 G H I J1 J2 K1 K2 L M1 N O P Q R1 R2 S1 S2 T1 T2 V W Z(c,d,e,f,g,h,i,j,k,l,m,p,q,r,w)

TRURO, Cornwall

@ CORNWALL LAW ‡
36 Lemon Street Truro Cornwall TR1 2NR
Tel: 01872 222688 / 222712 *Fax:* 01872 222740
Emergency telephone 01872 222688
Languages: French
Work: B2 D1 D2 G H K1 V W Z(l)
Emergency Action, Agency, Advocacy, Fixed Fee Interview, Legal Aid undertaken and Legal Aid Franchise
Ast: Furness, Ms Karen LLB(Hons) . . . . . *Jan 1983

JOHN BOYLE & CO
(incorporating Thrall Ryder)
10-11 Edward Street Truro Cornwall TR1 3AR
Tel: 01872 272356 *Fax:* 01872 222316 *Dx:* 81226 TRURO
Emergency telephone 01872 242067
E-mail: mail@thrallryder.com
Office: Redruth
Languages: French
Work: A1 A3 B1 C1 D1 E F1 F2 J1 K1 K2 L M1 N O Q R1 S1 S2 T1 V W Z(c,d,h,k,l,p,q,r)
Emergency Action, Agency, Advocacy, Fixed Fee Interview, Legal Aid undertaken and Legal Aid Franchise
Ptr: Gallagher, Mr Paul Jerome LLB(Hons) . . . . . *Jan 1993
Jackson, Mr Barry Stefan LLB. . . . . *Jul 1985
Leaning, Mr Jeremy Philip BA; Former Barrister. . . *May 1992
Thomas, Ms Helen Marie LLB. . . . . *Jan 1996
Ast: Hosking, Ms Heather . . . . . *Jan 1978
Con: Davey, Ms Melanie . . . . . Jan 1985
Hosking, Ms Heather Alison BA(Hons) . . . . . *Jun 1978

BRAINS
29 Lemon Street Truro Cornwall TR1 2LS
Tel: 01872 276363 *Fax:* 01872 276364 *Dx:* 81220 TRURO
E-mail: info@brainssolicitors.co.uk
Office: St Austell
Work: A1 B1 C1 D1 D2 E F1 K1 K3 K4 L N O Q R1 R2 S1 S2 T1 T2 W Z(b,c,d,h,q)
Emergency Action, Agency, Fixed Fee Interview and Legal Aid undertaken
Ptr: Evans, Mrs Julie F LLB(Hons); TEP; CTAPS . . . . *Dec 2002
Evans, Mr Martyn Jonathan LLB(Hons); FABRP. . . *Nov 1986
Rogers, Mr Simon Felix LLB(Hons) . . . . . *May 2004

BRAY & DILKS ‡
33 & 34 Lemon Street Truro Cornwall TR1 2NR
Tel: 01872 271717 *Fax:* 01872 272717 *Dx:* 81205 TRURO
E-mail: office@braydilks.co.uk
List of partners: N J Fenton, J F Healey, R L A Warner
Office: Falmouth
Work: A1 B1 C1 D1 E F1 F2 G H J1 K1 K2 K3 L N O Q R1 S1 S2 W Z(l,q)
Emergency Action, Agency, Advocacy and Fixed Fee Interview undertaken
Ptr: Fenton, Mr Nigel J BA. . . . . *Nov 1982
Healey, Mr Jonathan F BA . . . . . *Feb 1982
Warner, Mr Robert L A LLB . . . . . *§Jul 1980

Ast: Major, Miss Kathryn Elizabeth BA . . . . . *Oct 1994
Con: Rundle, Mr Colin A LLB(Lond). . . . . *Dec 1978

CARLYON & SON ‡
(in association with John Rabey & Co)
78 Lemon Street Truro Cornwall TR1 2PZ
Tel: 01872 278641 *Fax:* 01872 272073 *Dx:* 81231 TRURO
E-mail: info@carlyonandson.co.uk
List of partners: M P Granville, R J Rabey
Work: E J1 K3 L N O Q S1 S2 W
Fixed Fee Interview undertaken
Ptr: Granville, Mr Maurice Paul LLB . . . . . *Dec 1984
Rabey, Mr Richard John. . . . . *§Jun 1975
Ast: Williams, Mr David Rees LLB . . . . . Mar 2009

CONROYS SOLICITORS ‡
4-5 Old Bridge Street Truro Cornwall TR1 2AQ
Tel: 01872 272457
E-mail: benconroy@conroys.gb.com

COODES
Elizabeth House Castle Street Truro Cornwall TR1 3AP
Tel: 01872 246200 *Fax:* 01872 241122 *Dx:* 81202 TRURO
E-mail: enquiries@coodes.co.uk
Office: Holsworthy, Launceston, Liskeard, Newquay, Penzance, St Austell
Work: A1 B1 C1 D1 E F1 G H J1 K1 L N O P Q R1 S1 T1 V W Z(a,b,c,e,l,m,n,o)
Emergency Action, Agency, Advocacy, Fixed Fee Interview, Legal Aid undertaken and Member of Accident Line
Ptr: Bunney, Miss Allison Irene . . . . . Oct 2000
Ford, Mr Lawrence Gerald . . . . . Oct 1987
Lamble, Mr Peter . . . . . *Dec 1992
Whyte, Mr Alistair J LLB. . . . . *Oct 1985
Wilson, Mr Christian. . . . . *Jun 2004
Ast: Higginson, Mr Darren . . . . . Sep 2001

CORNWALL DEFENCE SOLICITORS
The Old Chapel Greenbottom Truro Cornwall TR4 8QP
Tel: 01872 561201 *Fax:* 01872 561361
E-mail: office@cornwalldefencesolicitors.co.uk
Office: St Austell

FOLLETT STOCK LLP ‡
Truro Business Park Truro Cornwall TR4 9NH
Tel: 01872 241700 *Fax:* 01872 245980 *Dx:* 81225 TRURO
E-mail: info@follettstock.co.uk
List of partners: C D Lingard, M J Pearse
Office: Exeter
Languages: French, German, Italian, Portuguese, Spanish
Work: A1 A2 A3 B1 C1 C2 E F1 F2 I J1 J2 K1 K2 K3 L M1 N O P Q R1 R2 S1 S2 T1 T2 U1 U2 V W X Z(b,c,d,e,f,g,h,k,l,m,n,o,p,q,r,w,x,za)
Emergency Action, Agency, Advocacy, Fixed Fee Interview, Legal Aid undertaken and Legal Aid Franchise
Ptr: Lingard, Mr Christopher David LLB(Hons) Maxwell Law Prize; Calcott-Price Law Prize . . . . . *Sep 1993
Pearse, Mr Martin J BA(Hons). . . . . *Sep 1996
Asoc: Bramley, Miss Emma Clare LLB(Hons); BVC; QLTT . . Jan 2004
De Lacey, Mr Slade Liam LLB(Hons) . . . . . May 2004
Dell, Ms Sarah Louise. . . . . *Oct 2003
Morgan, Ms Lucy Harriet MA . . . . . Aug 1998
Paddle, Ms Penny. . . . . Nov 1994
Scrase, Mr Richard Stuart BA(Hons) . . . . . *Sep 2001
Slater, Miss Verity LLB(Hons) ♦ . . . . . *Sep 2002
Stephens, Mr Christopher George CPE; LPC . . . . . May 2005
Ast: Haywood, Ms Lisa . . . . . Sep 2009
Higgins, Ms Fiona BA(Cantab); MBA . . . . . *Jul 2004
Jones, Mr Ashley LLB(Hons) . . . . . Nov 2007
Lea, Mr Jonathan Michael BSc; GDL . . . . . *Sep 2006
Martin, Mrs Rebecca . . . . . Mar 2008
Matthias, Ms Barbara . . . . . Jun 2006
Negus, Mrs Donna Marie BA(Hons)(Business & Law) . Mar 2009
Piper-Thompson, Ms Jessica . . . . . Aug 2008
Swift, Miss Chloe BA(Hons). . . . . Sep 2006

FOOT ANSTEY
High Water House Malpas Road Truro Cornwall TR1 1QH
Tel: 01872 243300 *Fax:* 01872 242458 *Dx:* 81200 TRURO
E-mail: contact@footanstey.com
Office: Exeter, Plymouth, Taunton
Ptr: Chanter, Mr Mark H LLB . . . . . *Dec 1981
Claridge, Mr Tobias J BSc(Hons) . . . . . Dec 1992
Ast: Dugdale, Ms Erika LLB . . . . . *§Nov 1993

CHARLES FRENCH & CO ‡
Second Floor Landrian House 59-60 Lemon Street Truro Cornwall TR1 2PE
Tel: 01872 263813 *Fax:* 01872 264786 *Dx:* 81218 TRURO
E-mail: info@charlesfrenchlaw.co.uk
List of partners: R C Bailey

CHRIS HARRISON LAW ‡
High Cross Truro Cornwall TR1 2AJ
Tel: 01872 241408 *Fax:* 01872 273848 *Dx:* 81212 TRURO
E-mail: rjp@chrisharrisonlaw.com
List of partners: R J Pender
Work: A1 B1 C1 C2 C3 E L N R2 S1 S2 T1 T2 W Z(c,i,r)
Emergency Action, Agency, Advocacy, Fixed Fee Interview undertaken and Member of Accident Line
Ptr: Pender, Mr Robin J BA . . . . . *Dec 1992

HARTNELL SOLICITORS ‡
Trevorva Farmhouse Probus Truro Cornwall TR2 4HN
Tel: 01872 520630 *Fax:* 01872 520318
E-mail: marchartnell@hartnell-solicitors.co.uk

MURRELL ASHWORTH LLP ‡
14 High Cross Truro Cornwall TR1 2AJ
Tel: 01872 226990 *Fax:* 01872 278669

NALDERS QUALITY SOLICITORS ‡
(incorporating Stewart & Knight; Rishworths)
Farley House Falmouth Road Truro Cornwall TR1 2HX
Tel: 01872 241414 *Fax:* 01872 242424 *Dx:* 81204 TRURO
Emergency telephone 01872 864094
E-mail: post@nalders.co.uk
Office: Camborne, Falmouth, Helston, Newquay, Penzance, St Austell, Truro
Languages: French, German, Spanish
Work: A1 B1 C1 C2 C3 D1 E F1 G H J1 K1 L M1 M2 N P R1 S1 T1 T2 W Z(l)

NALDERS QUALITY SOLICITORS
38-39 Lemon Street Truro Cornwall TR1 2NS
Tel: 01872 241414 *Fax:* 01872 271019
E-mail: post@nalders.co.uk
Office: Camborne, Falmouth, Helston, Newquay, Penzance, St Austell, Truro

NIGEL S PULLEN
18 Castle Street Truro Cornwall TR1 3AF
Tel: 01872 274404 / 276456 *Fax:* 01872 274434
E-mail: info@cornwall-law.co.uk
Office: Perranporth
SPr: O'Toole, Mrs Mykal S A LLB(Hons) . . . . . *Nov 1987
Ast: O'Toole, Mrs Mykal S A LLB(Hons) . . . . . *Nov 1987

STEPHENS & SCOWN
Osprey House Malpas Road Truro Cornwall TR1 1UT
Tel: 01872 265100 *Fax:* 01872 279137 *Dx:* 81203 TRURO
E-mail: solicitors@stephens-scown.co.uk
Office: Exeter, St Austell
Languages: French, German, Spanish
Work: A1 A3 B1 C1 C2 C3 D1 D2 E F1 I J1 J2 K1 L M1 M2 N O P Q R1 R2 S1 S2 T1 T2 W X Z(a,b,c,d,e,h,i,j,k,l,m,n,q,r,s,t)
Agency, Advocacy, Legal Aid undertaken and Legal Aid Franchise
Ptr: Evans, Mr Martyn Jonathan LLB(Hons); FABRP. . . *Nov 1986
Murdoch, Mr Graham I LLB; LLM(Cantab) Notary Public . . . . . *Nov 1988
Stone, Mr Jonathan P LLB(Hons) . . . . . *Nov 1998
Stubbs, Mr Mark BA. . . . . *Mar 1980
Welford, Mr Anthony R H LLB; MA Council Member of the Bristol Chamber of Commerce & Initiative . . . . *§Oct 1981
Wright, Mr Keith LLB . . . . . *Oct 1989
Ast: Bell, Ms Sarah LLB . . . . . *Apr 2003
Cross, Mr Matthew E LLB . . . . . *Apr 1989

WALSH & COMPANY ‡
Chancery House Visicks Yard Perranarworthal Truro Cornwall TR3 7NR
Tel: 01872 870923 *Fax:* 01872 865058 *Dx:* 81239 TRURO
E-mail: enquiries@walshlaw.co.uk
List of partners: T Walsh
Work: B1 C1 E F1 F2 J1 K1 K3 K4 L M1 N O Q R2 S1 S2 W Z(b,c,e,f,h,j,k,l,p,q,r,s,w)
Emergency Action, Agency, Advocacy and Fixed Fee Interview undertaken
SPr: Walsh, Mr Thomas . . . . . *Apr 1980
Ast: Painter, Mrs Sarah Louise. . . . . Sep 2001

KATHRYN WHITFORD SOLICITOR ‡
Alexandra House 18 St George's Road Truro Cornwall TR1 3JD
Tel: 01872 275300 *Fax:* 01872 275300
List of partners: K A Whitford
Work: B1 F1 N O Q Z(b,c,j,q)
Emergency Action, Agency, Advocacy, Fixed Fee Interview and Legal Aid undertaken
SPr: Whitford, Miss Kathryn A LLB. . . . . *Oct 1991

WILDE LAW ‡
Charles House 18-21 Charles Street Truro Cornwall TR1 2PQ
Tel: 01872 321070 *Fax:* 01872 309507
E-mail: info@wildelaw.co.uk

TUNBRIDGE WELLS, Kent

AITKEN LAW ‡
Shernfold Meadow Cottage Wadhurst Road Frant Tunbridge Wells Kent TN3 9EH
Tel: 01892 750049 / 07771 674379 *Fax:* 01892 750049
E-mail: neil.aitken@aitkenlaw.co.uk

AWKLAW ‡
17 College Drive Tunbridge Wells Kent TN2 3PN
Tel: 01892 533999

MAX BARFORD & CO ‡
16 Mount Pleasant Road Tunbridge Wells Kent TN1 1QU
Tel: 01892 539379 *Fax:* 01892 521874
Dx: 3918 TUNBRIDGE WELLS
E-mail: reception@maxbarford.co.uk
List of partners: M T Barford, V J Fytch, M A Leeson, D Miller
Languages: French
Work: B1 B2 C1 D1 E F1 F2 J1 J2 K1 K2 K3 L N O Q S1 S2 V W X Z(g,h,k,l,p,q,r)
Emergency Action, Agency, Advocacy, Fixed Fee Interview, Legal Aid undertaken, Legal Aid Franchise and Member of Accident Line
Ptr: Barford, Mr Max T Member of the Area Committee of LAB . . . . . *§Jan 1971
Fytch, Miss Verity Jane LLB. . . . . *Nov 1994
Leeson, Mr Mark A LLB. . . . . *§Nov 1990
Miller, Ms Deborah . . . . . *§Nov 1973
Ast: Phillips, Mr David Layton . . . . . *May 1977
Tennant, Mr Charles D S LLB . . . . . Dec 2003
Uttridge, Ms Liz S J BA(Hons); LLM. . . . . *Nov 1993

BAYHAM SOLICITORS LLP ‡
The Bell House Bayham Abbey Lamberhurst Tunbridge Wells Kent TN3 8BG
Tel: 01892 891999 *Fax:* 01892 890049
E-mail: mva@bayhamsolicitors.com
List of partners: M V Athey, J G Gore
Office: Sevenoaks
Languages: French
Work: A3 B1 C1 E F1 F2 J1 O Q R2 S1 S2 W Z(c,e,q)
Ptr: Athey, Mr Martin V BA. . . . . *§Jul 1980
Gore, Mr Jonathan Grant . . . . . Jun 2006

BERRY & BERRY ‡
11 Church Road Tunbridge Wells Kent TN1 1JA
Tel: 01892 526344 *Fax:* 01892 511223
Dx: 3908 TUNBRIDGE WELLS
Emergency telephone 07528 270096
E-mail: mail@the-solicitors.co.uk
List of partners: S J Hawkins, A Herman, Y J Masoliver, R Moseley, M L Nickolls, P Reader, I D Reed, N Stratton, I M Tysh
Office: Maidstone, Tonbridge
Languages: French, German, Spanish
Work: B1 C1 C2 C3 D1 D2 E F1 G H J1 K1 L M1 N O P Q R1 S1 S2 T1 T2 V W Z(b,c,d,f,g,k,l,o,p,q)
Emergency Action, Agency, Advocacy, Fixed Fee Interview, Legal Aid undertaken, Legal Aid Franchise and Member of Accident Line
Ptr: Herman, Mr Anthony BSc(Econ) . . . . . *Mar 1965

See p112 for the Key to Work Categories & other symbols

Masoliver, Mr Yashin Juan-Ramon BSc(Hons) British Gas Prize *Jun 1995
Moseley, Mr Robert LLB *Jan 2007
Nickolls, Mr Matthew Lewis BSc(Hons) *Nov 1999
Reader, Mr Paul LLB(Hons) *Sep 2000
Stratton, Mr Nigel LLB *Oct 1979
Tysh, Mr Ian Michael BA(Oxon) *Oct 1988
Asoc: Douglas, Mrs Catherine M LLB(Hons) *May 1976
Fuller, Miss Rebbecca LLB(Hons) *Sep 1998
Thomas, Miss Dianne *Dec 2002
Ast: Monham, Miss Amy BSc(Hons) *Dec 2009
Moore, Mr William BSc(Hons) Sep 2008
Noble, Mrs Helen M BA(Hons) *Sep 1990
Phillips, Ms Sarah Jan 2007
Samy, Miss Lucy LLB(Hons) Oct 2009

BUSS MURTON LLP ‡
Wellington Gate 7-9 Church Road Tunbridge Wells Kent TN1 1HT
Tel: 01892 510222 *Fax:* 01892 510333
Dx: 3913 TUNBRIDGE WELLS
E-mail: buss@bussmurton.co.uk
List of partners: C L Browne, J N Cherrill, R M Sedgwick, M V Shaw, P P W Smith
Office: Cranbrook, Dartford
Work: A1 B1 C1 C2 C3 D1 E F1 I J1 K1 L M1 M2 O P Q R1 S1 S2 T1 T2 V W Z(c,d,e,f,h,j,l,m,o,p,q,s,t)
Emergency Action, Agency, Advocacy and Fixed Fee Interview undertaken
Ptr: Cherrill, Mr John Nicholas MA(Cantab) *May 1967
Sedgwick, Mr Robert Mannering LLB(Lond) *Jun 1973
Shaw, Ms Mary V MA *Oct 1982
Smith, Mr Peregrine P W *Jul 1967
Asoc: Edwards, Mr Graham LLB Jan 1980
Ast: Bourn, Mrs Caroline LLB Jan 2004
Cooper, Mr Robin A *Aug 2001
Evans, Mrs Margaret BA Jan 2003
Field, Reshma Dileep *Sep 2001
Hitch, Mrs Stephanie May 1996
Jaswal, Ms Daldeep Oct 2003
Linton, Mr Andrew J C *Oct 1997
McCormick Paice, Mrs Rosemary BA(Hons)(Dunelm) Sep 1996

GRAHAM CHARLES & CO ‡
134 London Road Tunbridge Wells Kent TN4 0PL
Tel: 01892 511766 *Fax:* 01892 511769
List of partners: G P Charles
Work: E L R1 R2 S1 S2 W Z(l)
SPr: Charles, Mr Graham P *§Jun 1976

COOPERBURNETT ‡
Napier House 14-16 Mount Ephraim Road Tunbridge Wells Kent TN1 1EE
Tel: 01892 515022 *Fax:* 01892 515088
Dx: 3905 TUNBRIDGE WELLS
E-mail: jmo@cooperburnett.com
List of partners: R S Buckland, N J Burnett, G W Daughtrey, T A Lumsden, J M Oates, L A Reeves-Perrin, J B Rowe, V L Sampson, J R S Smithers
Languages: French, German
Work: A1 B1 C1 C2 C3 D1 E F1 G H J1 K1 L M1 M2 N P R1 S1 T1 T2 V W Z(c,d,e,h,i,k,l,m)
Emergency Action, Agency, Advocacy and Fixed Fee Interview undertaken
Ptr: Buckland, Mr Richard Sydney LLB(Hons) *Aug 1999
Burnett, Mr Nigel J LLB(Lond) *Nov 1979
Daughtrey, Mr Geoffrey W LLB Part Chairman of the Appeal Tribunal SSAT *Dec 1976
Lumsden, Mr Thomas Anthony BA(Hons) *Nov 1993
Oates, Mr Joseph M MSc(Econ) *Aug 1998
Reeves-Perrin, Mr Lee Anthony BSc *Apr 1996
Rowe, Mr Jonathan Barton BSc(Hons) *Oct 1997
Sampson, Miss Victoria Louise LLB(Hons) *May 1998
Smithers, Mr Jonathan R S LLB *Oct 1986
Asoc: Ansell, Mrs Victoria Jane BSc *Sep 2008
Barnett, Miss Teresa Ophelia BA(Hons) *Mar 2008
Gillam, Miss Katie Jane LLB(Hons) *Feb 2008
Theobald, Mr Richard John BA *Oct 2009

CRIPPS HARRIES HALL LLP ‡
Wallside House 12 Mount Ephraim Road Tunbridge Wells Kent TN1 1EG
Tel: 01892 515121 *Fax:* 01892 544878
Dx: 3954 TUNBRIDGE WELLS
E-mail: reception@crippslaw.com
List of partners: P R Ashford, C R Broadie, R S Byard, G T Carney, J M Denny, M F Ellis, A P L Fermor, P S Garry, S M R Green, C N Hyland, P Jennings, C J Langridge, S D Leney, L A Leporte, A E Lewis, P A Lintott, W G Mackie, F E McIntosh, M S McIntosh, R F Penticost, P J Raymond, K Robinson, M Rowlands, H J Ryland, M L Scott, P J M Scott, B R Simpson, M F Stevens, J O Towell, G T Tyler, M S Vos, C A Wakeford, E J S Weeks, S R Williams
Office: London WC2
Languages: French, German, Italian, Japanese, Russian
Work: A1 A3 B1 B2 C1 C2 C3 D1 E F1 F2 I J1 J2 K1 L M1 N O P Q R1 R2 S1 S2 T1 T2 U1 U2 W Z(b,c,d,e,f,h,j,k,l,m,n,p,q,s,t,u)
Emergency Action, Agency, Advocacy undertaken and Member of Accident Line
Ptr: Ashford, Mr Peter R BSc *Oct 1986
Broadie, Mr Charles R MA; LLM *Jun 1969
Byard, Mr Roger Stephen LLB *Nov 1979
Carney, Mr George Trevor *§Oct 1965
Denny, Mr Jonathan M LLB *Apr 1977
Ellis, Mr Michael F *Mar 1979
Fermor, Mr Andrew P L LLB; AKC *Apr 1974
Garry, Mr Peter S LLB(Reading) *Dec 1981
Green, Mrs Samantha M R BA *Nov 1990
Hyland, Miss Clare N LLB *Oct 1990
Jennings, Mr Peter BA; MA(Hons) *Apr 1981
Langridge, Mr Christopher J BA Notary Public *Oct 1984
Leney, Mr Simon D Notary Public *§May 1977
Leporte, Mr Lawrence A BA; JD(USA Lawrence/North Western) *Mar 1996
Lewis, Mrs Anne E LLB; AKC; ATII; TEP *Oct 1983
Lintott, Mr Peter A *Jan 1965
McIntosh, Mrs Fiona Elizabeth LLB *Oct 1996
McIntosh, Mr Myles S LLB *Nov 1995
Mackie, Mr William G MA *Dec 1977
Penticost, Mr Richard F LLB Notary Public *Sep 1971
Raymond, Mr Peter J Notary Public *§Dec 1969
Robinson, Ms Kate BA(Lond) *Oct 1988
Rowlands, Mr Michael BA *Mar 1988
Ryland, Miss H Jane MA(Cantab) Paul Wareham Prize *Oct 1991
Scott, Mr Michael Langston BA(Hons) *Oct 1996
Scott, Mr Peter J M MA(St Andrews) *Apr 1978
Simpson, Mr B Russell LLB *May 1986
Stevens, Mr Michael F LLB *Dec 1975
Towell, Mr Jason O LLB *Nov 1993
Tyler, Mr Gavin T LLB *May 1986
Vos, Mr Michael S BSc *§Jan 1981
Wakeford, Mrs Carol Ann LLB *Oct 1985
Weeks, Mr Edward J S BA *Nov 1994
Williams, Mr Stephen R MA(Oxon); BA *Apr 1981
Asoc: Edgar, Mrs Penelope S BA(Hons) *Oct 1993
Gribbon, Mrs Mary-Anne MA *Dec 1977
Jennings, Mrs Sarah LLB(Hons) *Nov 1992
Law, Miss Kirstie Alison LLB *Sep 1997
Mayor, Mrs Kathleen Louise LLB Notary Public *Nov 1989
Roots, Mr Ivan Alexander LLB(Hons) *Oct 1992
Rowe, Mr Nicholas David BA *Nov 1986
Stephen, Ms Jane LLB *Oct 1994
Stoodley, Ms Victoria BA *Nov 1998
Thomas, Mr Christopher M MA(Cantab) *Jun 1995
Ward, Mrs Alison BSc(Hons); CPD; LSF *Nov 1993
Ast: Duxbury, Miss Wendy J BSc; MBA *Nov 2000
Ferguson, Miss Sarah J LLB *Oct 1988
Firby, Miss Sally BA *Oct 2000
Gardiner-Hill, Mr Edward *Oct 2001
Garrett, Miss Sarah Louise BA(Hons) *Oct 2001
Grainge, Miss Kirstin Victoria LLB *Oct 2001
Halton, Mr John S BA(Hons) *Aug 1999
Hawkeswood, Mr James LLB *Oct 2000
Higbee, Mrs Janet Valentine BA; MA Governor of Skinners School Tunbridge Wells *Jun 1977
Hill-Smith, Mrs Leslie BA *Feb 2000
Laws, Mr Jeremy P BSc Best Performance on LPC *Oct 1999
Raper, Mr Andrew John BA *Dec 1997
Roberts, Mr Stephen Daniel *Oct 2001
Teale, Mrs Sarah BA(Hons) *Oct 1999
Terrell, Mrs M Susan LLB *Oct 1991
Wells, Miss Jessica Isabel BA *Oct 1997
Westbrook, Ms Alison LLB *Oct 2000
Young, Mr Lee BA; CPE; LPC; PSC *Sep 1996
Con: Shankland, Mr M David BA(Cantab) *Jun 1967

DUXBURYS SOLICITORS ‡
3 Buckingham Road Tunbridge Wells Kent TN1 1TQ
Tel: 01892 538762 *Fax:* 01892 538762
E-mail: wjd@duxburyssolicitors.co.uk

BRIAN FERRIS ‡
8 Ferndale Point Tunbridge Wells Kent TN2 3RN
Tel: 01892 518609 *Fax:* 01892 518701
Emergency telephone 07973 139358
E-mail: brian@brianferris.co.uk
List of partners: B J P J Ferris
Work: G H
Agency, Advocacy, Legal Aid undertaken and Legal Aid Franchise
SPr: Ferris, Mr Brian J P J BA(Hons) *Jul 1978

ROBERT HAGGER & CO ‡
32 Church Road Tunbridge Wells Kent TN1 1JP
Tel: 01892 515795 *Fax:* 01892 515819
List of partners: R O Hagger
Work: C1 C2
SPr: Hagger, Mr Robert O *§May 1966

KEENE MARSLAND ‡
6 Clanricarde Gardens Tunbridge Wells Kent TN1 1PH
Tel: 01892 526442 *Fax:* 01892 510486
Dx: 3906 TUNBRIDGE WELLS
E-mail: djd@keenemarsland.co.uk
List of partners: J C P Barratt, J A Franklin, P K Jelly, S E Jelly
Work: E K1 K2 K3 K4 L R1 S1 S2 T2 W Z(c)
Emergency Action, Agency, Advocacy and Fixed Fee Interview undertaken
Ptr: Barratt, Mr James Christopher Paul LLB(Hons) Jan 1980
Jelly, Mr Peter Keith May 1978
Jelly, Mrs Sarah E *Apr 1978
Mem: Franklin, Miss Juliet Anne *Dec 1992

KEOGH CAISLEY ‡
Kenwood House 1 Upper Grosvenor Road Tunbridge Wells Kent TN1 2EL
Tel: 01892 548411 *Fax:* 01892 534155
Dx: 3974 TUNBRIDGE WELLS
E-mail: gina.tarr@keoghcaisley.com
List of partners: A G Caisley, S J F Judd
Work: C1 C2 C3 E J1 M2 O S1 S2 W
Ptr: Caisley, Mr Alastair G BA(Law) Notary Public *Jan 1986
Judd, Mr Simon J F BA(Cantab) *Jun 1978

KNIGHTS ‡
Regency House 25 High Street Tunbridge Wells Kent TN1 1UT
Tel: 01892 537311 *Fax:* 01892 526141
Dx: 3919 TUNBRIDGE WELLS
Emergency telephone 01892 537311
E-mail: knights@knights-solicitors.co.uk
List of partners: G J Dorman, M D M Knight, M P McNally, T J Ryan
Work: A1 A2 G J1 J2 N O P Q R1 S1 W Z(d,k,q,r,w,za)
Emergency Action, Agency and Advocacy undertaken
Ptr: Dorman, Mr Graham John *Jun 1983
Knight, Mr Matthew D M LLB(Newc) ♦ *Nov 1982
McNally, Mr Michael Patrick BA ♦ *Aug 1991
Ryan, Mr Timothy John LLB(Hons) ★ *Jul 2006
Ast: Gooch, Miss Nicola LLB(Hons) Sep 2010
Con: Hall, Mr Christopher Sandford LLB ♦ Notary Public *Jun 1963

LOCH ASSOCIATES
Oxford House 15-17 Mount Ephraim Road Tunbridge Wells Kent TN1 1EN
Tel: 01892 773970
E-mail: info@lochassociates.co.uk
Office: London EC1

PAUL G MURRELLS ‡
Spa House 18 Upper Grosvenor Road Tunbridge Wells Kent TN1 2EP
Tel: 01892 528333 *Fax:* 01892 614637
E-mail: si@pmurrells.freeserve.co.uk

A J POWELL & CO ‡
60 St James Park Tunbridge Wells Kent TN1 2LL
Tel: 01892 548784 / 07919 336790
E-mail: apowell@lawdisputes.co.uk

JULIE REYNOLDS SOLICITORS ‡
39 Mount Pleasant Road Tunbridge Wells Kent TN1 1PN
Tel: 01892 673418

ROBERT C SEECKTS ‡
Thorpe House 18-20 London Road Tunbridge Wells Kent TN1 1DA
Tel: 01892 537615 *Fax:* 01892 533717
Dx: 3910 TUNBRIDGE WELLS
E-mail: robertseeckts@btconnect.com
List of partners: S R Children, R C Seeckts
Work: C1 E L S1 S2 W
Ptr: Children, Mr Simon R LLB *Jul 1979

STEADMANS ‡
6 Dudley Road Tunbridge Wells Kent TN1 1LF
Tel: 01892 511102 *Fax:* 01892 511105
Dx: 3937 TUNBRIDGE WELLS
E-mail: gs@steadmans.com
List of partners: G A C Steadman
Work: A1 C1 E L S1 S2 W Z(c,h)
Ptr: Steadman, Mrs Geraldene A C *Jul 1979

THOMSON SNELL & PASSMORE ‡
3 Lonsdale Gardens Tunbridge Wells Kent TN1 1NX
Tel: 01892 510000 *Fax:* 01892 549884
Dx: 3914 TUNBRIDGE WELLS 1
E-mail: info@ts-p.co.uk
List of partners: K K Aggarwal, R J Beard, G Bell, S M Brown, A R Dickins, E Fardell, P A Fearnley, J Gallagher, S W Goodbody, F G Green, A E Harris, A C Harvey, J R Harwood, N D Hobden, N J Horton, S E Judd, J I Malcolm, W M J Partridge, J C Passmore, M Politz, P J Radula-Scott, J A Reid, M J Sugden, S E Sullivan, R C Taylor, M P Varley, P T Viner, F Warran-Smith, A S Watson, C M Whittington, R Willis, B J Wright
Office: Dartford
Languages: French, German
Work: A1 A3 B1 B2 C1 C2 C3 D1 E F1 F2 I J1 J2 K1 K2 K3 K4 L N O P Q R1 R2 S1 S2 T1 T2 U2 W Z(c,d,e,h,i,k,l,m,p,q,r,u,z,za)
Agency, Advocacy, Legal Aid undertaken and Legal Aid Franchise
Ptr: Beard, Mr Raymond J LLB(Lond) *Oct 1979
Bell, Mr Graham LLB Oct 1993
Brown, Mr Simon M MA *Apr 1984
Dickins, Mr Alan R MA(Cantab) *§Dec 1972
Fardell, Mr Edward *Dec 1990
Fearnley, Mrs Patricia A *Dec 1993
Gallagher, Mrs Joanne LLB *§Dec 1994
Goodbody, Mr Stuart W MA(Edin) *Oct 1990
Green, Mr F Gilbert BA(Cantab) Notary Public *§Dec 1978
Harris, Miss Anne Elizabeth LLB *§Apr 1975
Harvey, Mr Alastair C BA *Sep 1988
Harwood, Mrs J Ruth LLB(Nott'm) *Sep 1983
Hobden, Mr Nicholas David LLB(Hons) §Feb 1989
Horton, Mr Nicholas James BA; CPE; LSF *Nov 1995
Judd, Miss Sarah E BA *Jun 1973
Malcolm, Mrs Jane I BA(Hons) *Dec 1980
Partridge, Mr W M James TD BA(Cantab) *Oct 1983
Passmore, Mr Jeremy C MA(Cantab) *§Oct 1977
Politz, Mr Mark *Sep 1992
Radula-Scott, Mr Peter J BA *Dec 1980
Reid, Mr John A MA(Oxon) *§Sep 1974
Sugden, Mr Michael J LLB Notary Public *Oct 1974
Sullivan, Miss Susan E LLB *Nov 1982
Taylor, Miss Rachel C LLB *Oct 1983
Varley, Mr Martin P LLB *Oct 1985
Viner, Mr Paul T LLB *Apr 1981
Warran-Smith, Mrs Felicity BA; LLM *Nov 1980
Watson, Mr Andrew S MA(Oxon) *§Feb 1976
Whittington, Mr Christopher Michael MA(Cantab) *§Apr 1982
Willis, Mr Roy BA(Hons) Oct 1998
Wright, Mrs Barbara J LLB *Jun 1979
Asoc: Androsov, Nicky *Sep 1999
Durdant-Hollamby, Mr Guy LLB *Oct 1981
Flory, Mr Peter A RGN; LLB; DipLP Sep 1999
Gabay, Mr Nicholas J BA; LLM Sep 1999
Gage, Mrs Katherine Elizabeth BA(Hons) *Dec 1989
Gough, Mr Richard D LLB(Bris) *Mar 1972
Holland, Miss Hillary Jun 1992
Lister, Miss Sue MA(Hons); DipLaw Sep 2001
Mackenzie, Ms Caroline Kirsty MA *Mar 1999
Manning, Miss Sandra Feb 2000
Mooney, Ms Nicola BA Sep 1999
O'Donnell, Mr Desmond BA Dec 1985
Pierce, Ms Frances *Sep 1997
Pratt, Miss Joanna L LLB Dec 1993
Smith, Mrs Susan L LLB(Hons) *§Jul 1975
Stewart, Miss Helen LLB(Hons) Mar 1999
Swain, Miss Rebecca A LLB(Hons)(Hull) Jul 1999
Willis, Mr James Michael Sep 2001
Ast: Cashman, Mrs Jane Ellen MA(Oxon) *Sep 1998
Donoghue, Ms Kirstie LLB Sep 2004
Edwards, Ms Jennifer Nov 2003
Furnish, Ms Catherine BA(Hons) Oct 1994
Gohil, Ms Bhavna LLB(Hons) May 2003
Jennings, Ms Dominique LLB Sep 2005
Keily, Ms Sarah Sep 2006
Robinson, Ms Mary BA(Hons) Sep 2003
Skilton, Mr Douglas Sep 2006
Spence, Mr John LLB Sep 2001
Steggles, Mr Mark LLB Sep 2005
Vernon, Ms Rebecca Sep 2005
West, Ms Heather Sep 2005
Con: Cairns, Ms Elizabeth BA(Hons); LLB Nov 1979

WHITFIELD & CO SOLICITORS ‡
33 Mount Ephraim Tunbridge Wells Kent TN4 8AA
Tel: 01892 529500
E-mail: info@whitfieldandco.com

ROBIN WILLIAMS ‡
Lodge Etherton Stockland Park Road Speldhurst Tunbridge Wells Kent TN3 0TX
Tel: 01892 863057 *Fax:* 01892 863057
List of partners: R H Williams
Work: S1 T2 W
SPr: Williams, Mr Robin H MA(Cantab) *§Jul 1966

WOWLAW SOLICITORS ‡
3 Montacute Gardens Tunbridge Wells Kent TN4 8HG
Tel: 01892 511066 *Fax:* 01892 511066

TWICKENHAM, Middlesex

ANSELM ELDERGILL ‡
3 Powers Court Twickenham Middlesex TW1 2JJ
Tel: 07971 198742 *Fax:* 020 8744 1056
Emergency telephone 07971 198742
E-mail: medicolegal@email.com
List of partners: A C Eldergill
Work: Z(m)
SPr: Eldergill, Prof Anselm Charles BSc(Econ) Alexander Maxwell Law Scholar; David Hallett Prize for Government Mental Health Commissioner; President of Appeals Tribunal; Assistant Coroner; Legal Director of African Regional Council for Mental Health; President of Mental Health Lawyers Association; President of Institute of Mental Health Act Practitioners . . . . . Nov 1987

BARON GREY ‡
Langtry House 441 Richmond Road Twickenham Middlesex TW1 2EF
Tel: 020 8891 4311 *Fax:* 020 8891 2058 *Dx:* 100264 RICHMOND 2
E-mail: info@barongrey.co.uk
List of partners: V J Hambleton-Grey
Work: B1 C1 E F1 J1 K1 L M1 N O P Q R1 S1 S2 T1 T2 W Z(e,i,k,l,q,r)
SPr: Hambleton-Grey, Mr Vincent J. . . . . . *Oct 1990
Ast: Grant, Mr Duncan J. . . . . . *Nov 2004
Whitern, Mr Clive R. . . . . . *Dec 1978
Con: Starck, Mr Jonathan Charles Edmonds LLB(Hons) . . Oct 2008

BATHURST BROWN DOWNIE & AIREY LLP ‡
6 The Mews Bridge Road Twickenham Middlesex TW1 1RE
Tel: 020 8892 1537 *Fax:* 020 8891 4205 *Dx:* 200035 TWICKENHAM
E-mail: mail@bbda-llp.co.uk
List of partners: A Airey, R Downie
Work: B1 C1 E J1 K1 L N O Q S1 S2 W Z(b,q,r)
Agency and Fixed Fee Interview undertaken
Ptr: Airey, Ms Amanda. . . . . . *Sep 1996
Downie, Mr Robert LLB(Hons). . . . . . *Apr 1997
Con: O'Hagan, Mr Richard BA(Hons) . . . . . Apr 1999

CHRISTINE E BOWER ‡
17 Wellesley Road Strawberry Hill Twickenham Middlesex TW2 5RR
Tel: 020 8898 1615
Emergency telephone 020 8893 3133
List of partners: C E Bower
Work: S1 W
Ptr: Bower, Miss Christine E LLB(Leics); LLB . . . . *Jul 1979

FORMAN WELCH & BELLAMYS ‡
23 London Road Twickenham Middlesex TW1 3SX
Tel: 020 8892 8907 / 8892 7733 *Fax:* 020 8744 2046 / 8892 8162
E-mail: mail@fwblaw.co.uk
List of partners: P M Arnstein, T James
Work: C1 E L Q S1 W
Ptr: Arnstein, Mr Peter M LLB(Hons). . . . . *Dec 1977
James, Mr Timothy . . . . . *Jun 1972

ANN GIBBON & CO ‡
62 Crown Road Twickenham Middlesex TW1 3EH
Tel: 020 8891 2707 *Fax:* 020 8891 2707
E-mail: anngibbon@f25.com

GILLMAN-SMITH LEE SOLICITORS ‡
Suites D-F 52-64 Heath Road Twickenham Middlesex TW1 4BX
Tel: 020 8744 0909 *Fax:* 020 8744 1155
E-mail: kencwlee@aol.com

SANDRA GOLDSTONE ‡
3 Short Way Twickenham Middlesex TW2 7NU
Tel: 020 8287 3635 *Fax:* 020 8287 3273
List of partners: S H Goldstone
Work: S1 W
SPr: Goldstone, Mrs Sandra H MA(Arts) . . . . . Jun 1988

HORNSBY DE GRAY SOLICITORS LLP
8 Richmond Mansions Denton Road Twickenham Middlesex TW1 2HH
Tel: 07808 585586
Office: Brecon

KEPPE & PARTNERS SOLICITORS ‡
33 Candler Mews Amyand Park Road Twickenham Middlesex TW1 3JF
Tel: 020 8891 4488 *Fax:* 020 8892 8171 *Dx:* 200007 TWICKENHAM
Emergency telephone 07957 382765
E-mail: info@keppe.co.uk
List of partners: T Firdose, G E Keppe, Z Khatun, M Mandelli
Languages: Hungarian, Italian
Work: B1 B2 C1 C2 C3 D1 D2 E F1 G H J1 K1 K3 L N O P Q R1 R2 S1 S2 T1 V W X Z(b,c,e,f,j,k,l,m,o,p,r)
Emergency Action, Agency, Advocacy, Fixed Fee Interview, Legal Aid undertaken and Legal Aid Franchise
Ptr: Firdose, Mr Tariq BSc. . . . . *Sep 1999
Keppe, Mr George E . . . . . *May 1979
Khatun, Zeba . . . . . *Nov 1999
Mandelli, Mr Marco . . . . . *Dec 1995
Asoc: McNulty, Ms Sharon. . . . . *Jul 2004
Shenton, Mrs Anne . . . . . *Jan 2006
Waskett, Mr Julian Davies BA. . . . . *Jun 1981

AVRIL MCDOWELL ‡
25 Erncroft Way Twickenham Middlesex TW1 1DA
Tel: 020 8891 1566 *Fax:* 020 8891 1566
E-mail: avril.mcdowell@btclick.com
List of partners: A J McDowell
Work: S1
SPr: McDowell, Mrs Avril Joan LLB Notary Public. . . . *Mar 1985

MERRONY WALL ‡
82 Hampton Road Twickenham Middlesex TW2 5QS
Tel: 020 8898 4700 *Fax:* 020 8898 4701 *Dx:* 200018 TWICKENHAM
E-mail: enquiries@merronywall.com
List of partners: A Wall
Languages: Spanish
Work: A3 C1 D1 E F1 J1 K1 K2 K3 K4 O Q S1 S2 W
Emergency Action, Agency, Advocacy and Fixed Fee Interview undertaken
Ptr: Wall, Mrs Anne-Lise BA. . . . . *Jun 1980
Ast: Cotterell, Miss Victoria LLB . . . . . *Nov 2003
Keady Smith, Mrs Anne-Marie LLB(Law & French) . . Oct 2002
Con: Marquis, Mr Antony Richard BA(Hons)(Law & English) Jan 1990
Wright, Ms Jane LLB(Hons). . . . . *Jan 1994

READ & CO ‡
Sherland House 108 Sherland Road Twickenham Middlesex TW1 4HD
Tel: 020 8892 8063 *Fax:* 020 8891 2475 *Dx:* 200010 TWICKENHAM
List of partners: M Neville, P A Read
Work: B1 C1 C2 C3 D1 D2 E F1 J1 K1 L M1 M2 N O P Q R1 S1 S2 T1 T2 V W Z(i,k,l,p,q)
Ptr: Read, Mr Peter A. . . . . *Jun 1975

SCULLY & SOWERBUTTS SOLICITORS
Suite G 52-64 Heath Road Twickenham Middlesex TW1 4BX
Tel: 020 8892 2463 *Fax:* 020 8892 6403
E-mail: info@ssplaw.co.uk
Office: Brentford, London N3

STONE ROWE BREWER LLP ‡
Stone House 12-13 Church Street Twickenham Middlesex TW1 3NJ
Tel: 020 8891 6141 *Fax:* 020 8744 1143 *Dx:* 200006 TWICKENHAM
E-mail: info@srb.co.uk
Web: www.srb.co.uk
List of partners: J M Andrews, J E Brewer, P J Holt, I M Leslie, P L McNutt
Work: C1 E J1 K1 L N O S1 S2 T1 T2 W Z(r)
Emergency Action, Legal Aid Franchise and Member of Accident Line
Ptr: Andrews, Mr John M LLB . . . . . *Oct 1991
Brewer, Miss Jennifer E. . . . . *Jan 1976
Holt, Mr Philip James LLB. . . . . Mar 2000
Leslie, Mr Iain M LLB . . . . . *Jan 1982
McNutt, Mr Paul Leonard LLB. . . . . Oct 1983
Ast: Broddle, Ms Lisa J . . . . . *Feb 1988
Cobb, Elizabeth. . . . . Mar 2007
Diton, Christina . . . . . Aug 2003
Grimm, Karen. . . . . Aug 2004
Parker, Mr Nigel McDowell LLB . . . . . *§Apr 1971

UPSTREAM LAW ‡
14 Spencer Road Twickenham Middlesex TW2 5TH
Tel: 020 8894 9528

CHRISTOPHER WRIGHT & CO ‡
6th Floor Regal House 70 London Road Twickenham Middlesex TW1 3QS
Tel: 020 8607 9666 *Fax:* 020 8607 9777
E-mail: info@cwrightandco.co.uk

TWYFORD, Wokingham

ACKERS CLAYTON REEVE ‡
9 Church Street Twyford Wokingham RG10 9DN
Tel: 0118 982 8800 *Dx:* 148723 TWYFORD 2
E-mail: info@ackersclaytonreeve.co.uk

TYLDESLEY, Greater Manchester

BUTCHER & BARLOW LLP
132 Elliott Street Tyldesley Greater Manchester M29 8FJ
Tel: 01942 883669 *Fax:* 01942 897480
E-mail: enquiries@butcher-barlow.co.uk
Office: Bramhall, Bury (2 offices), Frodsham, Leigh, Northwich, Prestwich, Runcorn (2 offices), Sandbach
Work: D1 K1 K3 S1 W Z(e)
Emergency Action, Agency, Fixed Fee Interview, Legal Aid undertaken and Legal Aid Franchise
Ptr: Cryan, Miss Rachel LLB(Hons) . . . . . Sep 2003
Ast: Isaacs, Mr Martin Russell LLB. . . . . Jul 1973

TYWYN, Gwynedd

ALWENA JONES & JONES
Bryn Llewellyn High Street Tywyn Gwynedd LL36 9AD
Tel: 01654 711499 *Fax:* 01654 711568
E-mail: alwena_jones@btconnect.com
Office: Blaenau Ffestiniog
Languages: Welsh
Work: A1 C1 K1 L N S1 S2 W
Agency and Advocacy undertaken
SPr: Jones, Miss Alwena W LLB(L'pool) . . . . . *§Mar 1990
Ast: Dorr, Mr Andrew. . . . . *Jan 1981

UCKFIELD, East Sussex

JULIET BELLIS & CO ‡
Isfield Place Isfield Uckfield East Sussex TN22 5XR
Tel: 01825 750811 *Fax:* 01825 750703 *Dx:* 133965 UCKFIELD 2
E-mail: jmb@julietbellis.co.uk
List of partners: J M S Bellis, P J Solomon
Work: E L O Q S1 S2
Ptr: Bellis, Ms Juliet M S LLM(Lond). . . . . Apr 1979
Solomon, Mr Patrick John. . . . . *§Jun 1972
Asoc: Andrews, Mr Michael Jon LLB(ELS). . . . . *Sep 2003
Cowell, Mr Rex Jonathan LLB(Hons) . . . . . Nov 1991
Ast: Kilbane, Mr Michael Edward BA(Hons) . . . . . *Jan 2003
Rosser, Ms Catherine BSc . . . . . *Jan 2000

DAWSON HART ‡
The Old Grammar School Church Street Uckfield East Sussex TN22 1BH
Tel: 01825 762281 *Fax:* 01825 767811 *Dx:* 39050 UCKFIELD
E-mail: info@dawson-hart.co.uk
List of partners: M Abey, D Dhinsa, P C Edwards, J M Hardaway, J S Kavanagh, L M Manton, D C Marshall, J V Osborne, K T A Rosling, A Rustemeyer
Languages: French
Work: A1 A2 A3 B1 C1 C2 D1 E F1 J1 J2 K1 K2 K3 K4 L N O P Q R1 R2 S1 S2 T1 T2 W Z(d,p,q,r)
Emergency Action, Agency, Advocacy and Fixed Fee Interview undertaken
Ptr: Abey, Mr Mahie BA(Cantab). . . . . *May 2004
Dhinsa, Miss Dalvinder . . . . . *Oct 2002
Edwards, Miss Petra Caroline LLB(Hons) Notary Public . . . . . *Aug 2000
Hardaway, Mrs Jacqueline Margaret. . . . . *Apr 1996
Kavanagh, Mrs Joanne Susan BA(Hons) . . . . . *Nov 1998
Manton, Mrs Laura Michelle LLB; TEP. . . . . *Aug 1998
Marshall, Mr David C BSc(Sussex) . . . . . *Jun 1981
Osborne, Mrs Joelle V MA(Oxon) . . . . . *Jun 1978
Rosling, Ms Kim Tracey Amanda BA(Hons) . . . . . *Oct 1993
Rustemeyer, Mr Alistair LLB. . . . . Nov 1994
Ast: Horn, Ms Vanessa Marion BA(Hons); PGDipLaw . . *Sep 2004
Mayhew, Mrs Jenny Susan LLB. . . . . *Oct 1988
Wilson, Miss Larissa . . . . . *Nov 2007

RIX & KAY SOLICITORS LLP ‡
The Courtyard River Way Uckfield East Sussex TN22 1SL
Tel: 01825 700177 *Fax:* 01825 764172
List of partners: R Bates, I J Best, J E Dyson, A C Foster, M N Hayes, B N F Hayter, L Jones, S E F Peake, F N Wallace, M B Wright
Office: Hove, London W1, Seaford, Sevenoaks
Languages: French, German
Work: A1 B1 C1 C2 C3 D1 D2 E F1 J1 J2 K1 K2 K3 K4 L M1 M2 N O P Q R1 R2 S1 S2 T1 T2 V W Z(c,d,e,h,j,k,l,q,w)
Emergency Action, Agency, Advocacy and Fixed Fee Interview undertaken
Ptr: Foster, Mr Alan Charles BA . . . . . *Apr 1980
Hayter, Mr Bruce N F BA . . . . . *Jul 1982
Jones, Mrs Lisa LLB(Hons); BA(Hons) . . . . . *Oct 1999
Wallace, Mr Francis N LLB(Bris). . . . . *Oct 1982

SWANBOROUGHS LLP ‡
Cygnet House Hurstwood Road High Hurstwood Uckfield East Sussex TN22 4BJ
Tel: 01825 733334 *Fax:* 01825 733302
E-mail: info@swanboroughs.com

ULVERSTON, Cumbria

DENBY & CO
(incorporating Hampson & Scott & Jobling & Knape)
Ellers House Market Street Ulverston Cumbria LA12 7LT
Tel: 01229 582283 *Fax:* 01229 581129 *Dx:* 63951 ULVERSTON
Emergency telephone 01229 822807
Office: Barrow-in-Furness
Work: A1 B1 C1 D1 E F1 G H J1 K1 L N O Q S1 S2 T2 V W Z(c,d,h,j,k,l)
Emergency Action, Agency, Advocacy, Fixed Fee Interview, Legal Aid undertaken, Legal Aid Franchise and Member of Accident Line
Ptr: Denby, Mr Richard Mark LLB(Hons). . . . . *Dec 1993
Gallagher, Mr Andrew LLB(Hons) . . . . . *May 2000
Sadler, Mr Michael LLB(Hons). . . . . *§Jun 1974
Scott, Mr John Philip LLB(Hons). . . . . *Dec 1993
Asoc: Hollins Gibson, Mr Andrew James BA(Hons) . . . . *Jan 1977
Ast: Brown, Miss Hilary Georgina . . . . . Jan 2004

HART JACKSON & SONS ‡
8-10 New Market Street South Lakeland Ulverston Cumbria LA12 7LW
Tel: 01229 583291 *Fax:* 01229 581136 *Dx:* 63952 ULVERSTON
Emergency telephone 01229 585878
E-mail: enquiries@hartjackson.co.uk
List of partners: S E Clarke, J M Going, D H Jackson, G G Jackson, R F H Jackson, R A N Pearson, J D Tennyson
Work: A1 B1 C1 D1 E F1 G H J1 K1 L N O Q R1 S1 S2 T1 V W Z(c,d,l,n,t)
Emergency Action, Agency, Advocacy, Fixed Fee Interview, Legal Aid undertaken and Member of Accident Line
Ptr: Clarke, Ms Sharon E LLB. . . . . *Mar 1979
Going, Mr James M BA Chairman of the Rent Assessment Committee . . . . . *Oct 1980
Jackson, Mr David Hart BA; MA; PhD. . . . . *Sep 1996
Jackson, Mr Graham G . . . . . Nov 1976
Jackson, Mr Rowland F H BA(Cantab) . . . . . *Jul 1964
Pearson, Mr Rodney A N LLB(Lond) . . . . . *Jul 1979
Tennyson, Mr Jeremy David BA(Hons) . . . . . *Aug 1999

LIVINGSTONS ‡
9 Benson Street Ulverston Cumbria LA12 7AU
Tel: 01229 585555 *Fax:* 01229 584950 *Dx:* 63950 ULVERSTON
E-mail: enquiries@livingstons.co.uk
List of partners: K A Chambers, L J Dacre, S J Hollis, S Walker
Office: Barrow-in-Furness, Dalton-in-Furness
Work: C1 C2 C3 D1 D2 E J1 K1 K2 N O Q R2 S1 S2 T2 W Z(l,p,q,r)
Emergency Action, Agency, Advocacy, Fixed Fee Interview, Legal Aid undertaken and Legal Aid Franchise
Dir: Chambers, Mrs Kim Alexandra MA . . . . . *Nov 1998
Hollis, Mr Simon J LLB(Hons) . . . . . *Oct 1990
Walker, Mr Steve . . . . . *Nov 1999
Ast: Marsden, Mr Steven J BA. . . . . *Oct 1978

POOLE TOWNSEND
County Square Ulverston Cumbria LA12 7LZ
Tel: 01229 588111 *Fax:* 01229 580662 *Dx:* 63954 ULVERSTON
Emergency telephone 0800 389 2939
E-mail: daviddawson@pooletownsend.co.uk
Office: Barrow-in-Furness, Dalton-in-Furness, Grange-over-Sands, Kendal
Work: B1 C1 C2 C3 D1 E F1 F2 G H J1 J2 K1 L M1 M2 N O P Q R1 R2 S1 S2 T1 T2 V W X Z(c,i,k,l,m,o,q,r)
Emergency Action, Agency, Advocacy, Legal Aid undertaken and Member of Accident Line

PROGRESSION SOLICITORS ‡
11 Queen Street Ulverston Cumbria LA12 7AF
Tel: 01229 580956 *Fax:* 01229 484383
E-mail: info@progressionsolicitors.com

UMBERLEIGH, Devon

JANE KNEIL & CO ‡
Dobbs Cottages Atherington Umberleigh Devon EX37 9HY
Tel: 01769 560557

UPMINSTER, Essex

JOHNSON CRILLY SOLICITORS LLP ‡
26 Grosvenor Gardens Upminster Essex RM14 1DJ
Tel: 01708 228069 *Fax:* 01708 226576 *Dx:* 35553 UPMINSTER
E-mail: info@johnsoncrilly.co.uk

PINNEY TALFOURD LLP ‡
52 Station Road Upminster Essex RM14 2TU
Tel: 01708 229444 *Fax:* 01708 228163 *Dx:* 35555 UPMINSTER
List of partners: P T Cockram, A Dean, S P Eccles, S Green, C H Polli, P E Talfourd

 See p112 for the Key to Work Categories & other symbols

Office: Brentwood, Hornchurch
Work: C1 D1 E J1 K1 K2 L N O Q S1 S2 T1 T2 W Z(b,l,m,p)
Fixed Fee Interview undertaken and Member of Accident Line
Mem: Polli, Catherine Helen . . . Jul 2005
Asoc: Croad, Mr Kristian . . . Sep 2006
Joseph, Rhiannon Lucinda . . . Sep 2008

STANTON & DORAN ‡
79 Corbets Tey Road Upminster Essex RM14 2AJ
Tel: 01708 641781 *Fax:* 01708 641792 *Dx:* 35561 UPMINSTER
E-mail: diane@stantondoran.co.uk
List of partners: D F Doran, J J Stanton
Work: E L S1 S2 W
Ptr: Doran, Mr David Francis BA(Hons) . . . *Jan 1987
Stanton, Miss Jennifer Jane . . . *Jun 1981

UPPINGHAM, Rutland

ABEL-BROWN SOLICITORS ‡
18a Orange Street Uppingham Rutland LE15 9SQ
Tel: 01572 822945

UPTON-UPON-SEVERN, Worcestershire

MOORE BROWN & DIXON LLP
Rear of 4 High Street Upton-upon-Severn Worcestershire WR8 0HB
Tel: 01684 592675 *Fax:* 01684 295147
Office: Tewkesbury
Languages: French, German
Work: A1 C1 C2 C3 D1 E F1 J1 K1 L M1 N O Q R1 S1 S2 T1 T2 W Z(b,c,d,e,f,g,h,j,k,l,n,o,r,s,t,w)
Emergency Action, Agency and Advocacy undertaken
Ptr: Lawler, Mr Brendan Martin LLB(Soton) Honorary Solicitor to Gloucestershire Football Association . . . *May 1981

URMSTON, Greater Manchester

HAGUE LAMBERT
2 Primrose Avenue Urmston Greater Manchester M41 0TY
Tel: 0161 747 7321 *Fax:* 0161 746 7043 *Dx:* 29078 URMSTON
E-mail: enc@hague-lambert.co.uk
Web: www.hague-lambert.co.uk
Office: Knutsford, Macclesfield, Manchester
Work: C1 E J1 K1 N Q S1 W
Fixed Fee Interview undertaken
Ptr: Cooper, Mr Edward N LLB(Nott'm) . . . *Jun 1976
Ast: Emmett, Mrs Bernadette . . . *Aug 2003
Stanley, Mr Jason . . . *Jan 2001

Offices in Manchester, Knutsford and Macclesfield. Broad based firm offering a wide range of services to both the business and personal client.

MICHAEL TAYLOR & ASSOCIATES
Fernacre House 38 Croftsbank Road Urmston Greater Manchester M41 0TQ
Tel: 0161 746 7776 *Fax:* 0161 747 1086 *Dx:* 29075 URMSTON
E-mail: info@mtasolicitors.com
Office: Bromley, Manchester
Work: D1 E G K1 L N O Q S1 V W
Emergency Action, Agency, Advocacy, Fixed Fee Interview, Legal Aid undertaken, Legal Aid Franchise and Member of Accident Line
Ptr: Taylor, Mr Michael BA . . . May 1983

USK, Monmouthshire

JONATHAN STEPHENS & CO ‡
Ty Cornel 11 Castle Parade Usk Monmouthshire NP15 1AA
Tel: 01291 673344 *Fax:* 01291 673575 *Dx:* 32552 USK
E-mail: js@agrilaw.co.uk
List of partners: J M H Stephens
Work: A1 E L M1 R1 S1 T2 W Z(l)
Emergency Action, Agency, Advocacy, Fixed Fee Interview and Legal Aid undertaken
Ptr: Stephens, Mr Jonathan Marten Henry Maurice Norden Prize . . . *Jun 1970

UTTOXETER, Staffordshire

COWLISHAW & MOUNTFORD ‡
90 High Street Uttoxeter Staffordshire ST14 7JD
Tel: 01889 565211 *Fax:* 01889 565212 *Dx:* 28051 UTTOXETER
Emergency telephone 01782 396264
E-mail: mail@cowlishawandmountford.co.uk
List of partners: J Blake, D Hopkins, P Hopkins
Work: B1 C1 D1 D2 E F1 J1 L N O Q S1 S2 V W Z(c,j)
Emergency Action, Agency, Advocacy, Fixed Fee Interview, Legal Aid undertaken and Legal Aid Franchise
Ptr: Blake, Jemma . . . Jan 2007
Hopkins, Mr David . . . Jan 2009
Hopkins, Mr Paul LLB . . . Dec 1976

GLANDFIELD & CRUDDAS ‡
Highgate House 17 Carter Street Uttoxeter Staffordshire ST14 8EY
Tel: 01889 565657 *Fax:* 01889 568688 *Dx:* 28056 UTTOXETER
E-mail: glandas.sols@btconnect.com
List of partners: I C Cruddas, J E Glandfield
Work: A1 D1 D2 E F1 G H K1 K3 L Q S1 T2 V W Z(k,l)
Emergency Action, Agency, Advocacy and Fixed Fee Interview undertaken
Ptr: Cruddas, Mr Ian Clive . . . *§Jul 1971
Glandfield, Mr John E . . . *Dec 1970
Ast: Cruddas, Mr Martin Ian LLB . . . *Aug 1997

WILKINS & THOMPSON ‡
9-11 Carter Street Uttoxeter Staffordshire ST14 8HB
Tel: 01889 562875 *Fax:* 01889 564143 *Dx:* 28053 UTTOXETER
E-mail: mwhitaker@wtsols.co.uk
List of partners: S B H Herbert, P Taylor, M D Whitaker
Work: A1 C1 D1 E F1 J1 K1 K3 L N Q S1 S2 T2 W Z(l,m)
Agency and Advocacy undertaken
Ptr: Herbert, Mr Stephen B H . . . *§Dec 1970
Taylor, Mr Philip MA; LLB(Cantab) . . . *Apr 1979
Whitaker, Mr Michael D LLB . . . *Mar 1980
Ast: Brumwell, Mrs Sara L B LLB . . . Aug 2003

UXBRIDGE, Middlesex

BANA VAID & ASSOCIATES ‡
(incorporating Male Wagland & Davis)
5 Marlborough Parade Uxbridge Road Uxbridge Middlesex UB10 0LR
Tel: 01895 272481 *Fax:* 01895 810207
Dx: 146921 HAYES MIDDLESEX 7
Emergency telephone 01753 882391
List of partners: M J O'Toole, M J Treisman
Office: Hayes
Work: B1 C1 C2 C3 D1 E F1 G H J1 K1 L M1 M2 N O P Q S1 T1 T2 V W Z(i,l)
Emergency Action, Agency, Advocacy, Fixed Fee Interview, Legal Aid undertaken and Member of Accident Line
Ptr: O'Toole, Mr Michael John LLB . . . *Dec 1978
Treisman, Mr Michael J . . . *Jun 1977

BIRD & LOVIBOND ‡
3 Vine Street Uxbridge Middlesex UB8 1RP
Tel: 01895 256151 *Fax:* 01895 274668 *Dx:* 45103 UXBRIDGE
E-mail: info@bird-lovibond.co.uk
List of partners: G Bennett, M C Everest, C W Matthews-Stroud, S G Nash, A C Neocleous, D P Trood
Office: Greenford, Ruislip
Work: B1 C1 D1 E J1 K1 K3 K4 L N O P Q S1 S2 W Z(l)
Agency, Advocacy, Fixed Fee Interview undertaken and Member of Accident Line
Ptr: Bennett, Mr Gary . . . Feb 1988
Nash, Mr Simon G BA(Oxon) . . . *Apr 1977
Neocleous, Mr Anthony C . . . *Oct 1997
Trood, Mr David Peter BA(Oxon) . . . *Dec 1997
Ast: Dhaliwal, Mrs Amandip LLB; LPC . . . Nov 2007
Minihane, Ms Niamh Charlotte . . . Nov 2002
Con: Brind, Ms Zoe A LLB . . . *Nov 1991
Shale, Mr Charles A BA(Hons) Geoffrey Howard Watson 1975; Robert Innes 1975; Reginald Pilkington 1976 . . . *Sep 1978

BLAVO & CO SOLICITORS
Affinity Point 8 Arundel Road Uxbridge Middlesex UB8 2RR
Tel: 01895 204848
E-mail: enquiries@legalblavo.co.uk
Office: Enfield, Guildford, London EC2, London N3, London WC1, St Albans

CAPITAL LEGAL SOLICITORS ‡
Regus Building Highbridge Estate Oxford Road Uxbridge Middlesex UB8 1HR
Tel: 01895 876534 *Fax:* 01895 876434

CURTIS DAVIS GARRARD ‡
Waterview House 1 Roundwood Avenue Stockley Park Uxbridge Middlesex UB11 1AU
Tel: 020 8734 2800 *Fax:* 020 8734 2820
E-mail: cdg@cdg.co.uk
List of partners: W Cecil, S R Curtis, D A Gardner, P H Measures, R Platt
Languages: French, German, Norwegian, Spanish
Work: A3 C1 O Z(a)
Ptr: Cecil, Mr William . . . *Dec 1994
Curtis, Mr Simon R MA(Oxon); BCL . . . Jan 1982
Gardner, Mr David A . . . *Aug 1994
Measures, Mr Peter H LLB(B'ham) . . . *Dec 1980
Platt, Mr Robert . . . *Mar 1998
Asoc: McGladdery, Mr Joe MSc; MA . . . Sep 2000
Waters, Miss Fiona LLB(Hons) . . . *Nov 1999
Ast: Jardine-Brown, Mr Robert A . . . *Oct 1996
Mateo, Miss Maria . . . *Mar 1998

HAL-SOLICITORS ‡
8-9 High Street Uxbridge Middlesex UB8 1JN
Tel: 01895 270907 / 270908 *Fax:* 01895 237569
Dx: 45115 UXBRIDGE
List of partners: P E P Honke, J L Olliffe
Office: Uxbridge
Languages: French
Work: D1 G H K1 L M1 N S1 S2 W
Advocacy and Legal Aid undertaken
Ptr: Honke, Mr Paul E P . . . *Jan 1980
Olliffe, Ms Jane L . . . *Nov 1987

HAL-SOLICITORS
400a Long Lane Hillingdon Uxbridge Middlesex UB10 9PG
Tel: 01895 251700 *Fax:* 01895 251136
Office: Uxbridge

IBB SOLICITORS ‡
Capital Court 30 Windsor Street Uxbridge Middlesex UB8 1AB
Est: 1994
Tel: 0845 638 1381 *Fax:* 0845 638 1351 *Dx:* 45105 UXBRIDGE
E-mail: enquiries@ibblaw.co.uk
List of partners: J Almond, S Booth, P Brampton, T Brownlow, P Burnett, D Clark, J Elphee, E Fitzpatrick, J Galloway, J Gibbons, J Govier, R Humphries, R Johnstone, P Kite, M Lewis, P Mason, S Mawson, J Mowbray, G Murray, A Olins, G Outram, A Rajani, V Rimmer, D Silva, M Silverman, V Stokes, M D Underhill, J Wodzianski
Office: Chesham
Languages: French, Gujarati, Hindi, Punjabi
Work: A3 B2 C1 D1 D2 E G H J1 J2 K1 K3 O R2 T2 W Z(d)
Emergency Action, Agency, Advocacy, Fixed Fee Interview, Legal Aid undertaken and Legal Aid Franchise
Ptr: Brampton, Mr Paul . . . Sep 1996
Brownlow, Mr Thomas . . . *May 1983
Burnett, Mr Peter . . . *Oct 1972
Clark, Mr David . . . Oct 1983
Elphee, Mr Jeff . . . *Sep 1990
Fitzpatrick, Ms Elizabeth . . . *Oct 1985
Gibbons, Ms Joanne . . . *Jun 1996
Govier, Mr Justin . . . Sep 1998
Humphries, Mr Ross . . . *Mar 1988
Johnstone, Mr Ross LLB(Glasgow) . . . *Jan 1990
Kite, Mr Paul . . . *Sep 1996
Lewis, Mr Mark . . . Nov 1986
Mason, Mr Paul . . . *Jun 1980
Mawson, Mrs Susan . . . *Apr 1977
Mowbray, Mr John . . . Mar 1998
Olins, Mr Andrew . . . *Feb 1989
Rajani, Mr Anil . . . *Oct 1988
Rimmer, Mrs Vivien . . . *Oct 1984
Silva, Mr David Sweet & Maxwell Law Prize . . . *Nov 1990
Stokes, Ms Victoria . . . Sep 1998
Underhill, Mr Malcolm D . . . Dec 1992
Wodzianski, Mr Juliusz . . . Oct 1984
Asoc: Busfield, Mr Julian . . . *Jul 1989
Fromont, Miss Sally . . . Apr 1999
McWatt, Miss Rachel . . . *Nov 2001
Rutherford, Mr Timothy . . . *§Sep 1998
Ast: Bankes, Mr Ralph . . . *Sep 2003
Davern, Miss Catherine . . . *Nov 2003
DeBiase, Ms Joanna . . . May 1992
Esien, Miss Ingrid . . . *Mar 2002
Fernandez, Mr Iskander . . . Nov 2004
Fuller, Mrs Alexander . . . Nov 2005
Greenwood, Mrs Karen . . . *Nov 1994
Kerai, Miss Hemlata . . . *Dec 1999
Kerr, Miss Joanna . . . Oct 2003
McKay, Ms Lorna . . . Mar 2005
Masih, Bez-A-Leel . . . May 2007
Sampat, Ms Shreena . . . Nov 2007
Varaitch, Mr Kam . . . Jan 1995
Vora, Ms Bhavna . . . Jul 2005
Walsh, Ms Nicola . . . Aug 2008
Wynds, Miss Liz . . . *Sep 2000

INJURY SPECIALISTS SOLICITORS LIMITED ‡
Sheraton House 2 Rockingham Road Uxbridge Middlesex UB8 2UB
Tel: 01895 207150 *Fax:* 01895 207160
E-mail: info@isslaw.co.uk

ALUN JAMES & CO ‡
20 Windsor Street Uxbridge Middlesex UB8 1AB
Tel: 01895 811511 *Fax:* 01895 254546
List of partners: J Ure
Ptr: Ure, Mr Jonathan BA . . . Jun 1980

F E JOHNSON & CO ‡
Old Bank Chambers 32 Station Parade Uxbridge Middlesex UB9 5EW
Tel: 01895 821818 *Fax:* 01895 821819 *Dx:* 42460 IVER
E-mail: frazinejohnson@lawyer.com
Work: J1 K4 L R1 S1 S2 W Z(d,u)

MASKELL EDWARDS & ASSOCIATES ‡
Bungalow to the rear of 71 Oxford Road Uxbridge Middlesex UB9 4DB
Tel: 01895 272226
E-mail: info@bucksconveyancing.com
Work: S1 W

NICHOLLS CHRISTIE & CROCKER ‡
130 High Street Uxbridge Middlesex UB8 1JX
Tel: 01895 256216 *Fax:* 01895 252102 *Dx:* 45112 UXBRIDGE
List of partners: R E J Hansom
Office: Harrow
Work: B2 D1 D2 G H K1 K3
Emergency Action, Agency, Advocacy, Fixed Fee Interview and Legal Aid undertaken
Ptr: Hansom, Mr Richard E J LLB(Sheff) . . . *Jun 1974
Asoc: Kurth, Mrs Sandra L . . . *Jun 1979
Con: Berry, Mr William J C LLB . . . *Jul 1975

TURBERVILLES ‡
Hill House 118 High Street Uxbridge Middlesex UB8 1JT
Tel: 01895 201700 *Fax:* 01895 273519 *Dx:* 45116 UXBRIDGE
E-mail: solicitors@turbervilles.co.uk
List of partners: J S Clement, R P Dixon, R H Hallam, K Healy, R J Ronayne, S Sigre, D C Smith, D C Smith
Office: Chorleywood, Uxbridge
Languages: Arabic, French, German, Gujarati, Hindi, Punjabi, Urdu
Work: A2 B1 C1 C2 C3 D1 E G J1 J2 K1 L N O Q R1 R2 S1 S2 T1 T2 U1 W Z(c,l,r)
Emergency Action, Agency, Fixed Fee Interview, Legal Aid undertaken and S.I.G
Ptr: Clement, Mr John Simon LLB(Hons) . . . *Sep 1993
Dixon, Mr Robert P MA(Cantab) School Governor . . . *Dec 1976
Healy, Mr Kevin LLB . . . *Aug 1995
Ronayne, Mr Richard J LLB . . . *Nov 1986
Sigre, Mr Sylvain BA . . . *Jan 1980
Smith, Mr David C LLB . . . *Jul 1981
Smith, Mr David C . . . Jul 1981
Asoc: Addlestone, Ms Karen . . . *Apr 1976
Denham, Miss Sarah Jane . . . *Oct 1999
Ast: Cameron, Mr Andrew J . . . Apr 1972
Gordon, Mr Glenn C BA . . . Aug 2000
Healy, Mr Kevin LLB . . . Aug 1995
Hobbs, Ms Marilyn BA . . . *Jun 1993
O'Sullivan, Ms Annabel Margaret LLB(Hons) . . . *Dec 1995
Patel, Miss Neesha LLB . . . *Oct 2001

TURBERVILLES
11 Crescent Parade Hillingdon Uxbridge Middlesex UB10 0LG
Tel: 01895 231311 *Fax:* 01895 256527
E-mail: solicitors@turbervilles.co.uk
Office: Chorleywood, Uxbridge (2 offices)
Languages: Arabic, French, German, Gujarati, Hindi, Punjabi
Work: A2 B1 C1 C2 C3 E G J1 J2 R1 R2 S1 T1 T2 W Z(i,l,r)
Emergency Action, Fixed Fee Interview, Legal Aid undertaken and S.I.G
Ptr: Hallam, Mr Russell H LLB . . . *Oct 1985

VENTNOR, Isle of Wight

CARELESS & KEMP ‡
Old Bank Chambers 19 Church Street Ventnor Isle of Wight PO38 1SN
Tel: 01983 852626 *Fax:* 01983 855600 *Dx:* 99225 VENTNOR
E-mail: tony.careless@carelessandkemp.co.uk
List of partners: A J Careless, L A Kemp
Office: Sandown
Work: D1 D2 E J1 K1 K3 L N O Q S1 S2 W Z(d)
Emergency Action, Agency, Advocacy, Fixed Fee Interview and Legal Aid undertaken
Ptr: Careless, Mr Anthony John LLB(Wales) . . . . *May 1981
Kemp, Mrs Lesley Ann . . . . *Apr 1999
Ast: Thorn, Mr James Edwin LLB(Hons) . . . . *Jan 1999

VERWOOD, Dorset

BONALLACK & BISHOP
Bank Court Manor Road Verwood Dorset BH31 6DY
Tel: 01202 834450
E-mail: verwood@bishopslaw.com
Office: Amesbury, Andover, Salisbury

FOREST EDGE LEGAL PRACTICE ‡
41 Foxes Close Verwood Dorset BH31 6JZ
Tel: 01202 376787 *Fax:* 01202 823041
E-mail: enquiries@fe-legal.co.uk

HAROLD G WALKER
27 Vicarage Road Verwood Dorset BH31 6DR
Tel: 01202 823308 *Fax:* 01202 827710 *Dx:* 54900 VERWOOD
Office: Bournemouth, Broadstone, Christchurch, Wimborne
Work: K1 K3 S1 S2 W

MJP LAW ‡
4 Ringwood Road Verwood Dorset BH31 7AQ
Tel: 01202 823666 *Fax:* 01202 827091 *Dx:* 54902 VERWOOD
E-mail: mp@mjplaw.co.uk

TRUMAN-MOORE ‡
4 Restynge House 11/13 Ringwood Road Verwood Dorset BH31 7AA
Tel: 01202 824677 *Fax:* 01202 824677 *Dx:* 54901 VERWOOD
E-mail: trumanmoore@btconnect.com
List of partners: P J C Durant, R A Field
Office: Christchurch
Work: A1 B1 C1 C2 C3 D1 E F1 G H J1 K1 L M1 M2 N P R1 S1 T1 T2 V
Agency, Fixed Fee Interview, Legal Aid undertaken and Member of Accident Line
Ptr: Durant, Mr Peter J C LLB . . . . §Nov 1981
Field, Mr Richard A LLB. . . . . *Jul 1973
Con: Coombs, Mr Ian LLB . . . . *Jul 1966
Moore, Mr John A. . . . . *Jan 1965

VIRGINIA WATER, Surrey

SEAKENS SOLICITORS ‡
18 Station Approach Virginia Water Surrey GU25 4DW
Tel: 01344 843666 *Fax:* 01344 844584 *Dx:* 94650 VIRGINIA WATER
E-mail: ks@kseakens.co.uk
List of partners: K Seakens
Languages: French
Work: C1 E K4 S1 S2 W
Fixed Fee Interview undertaken
SPr: Seakens, Mr Kenneth. . . . . *§Jun 1971

WADEBRIDGE, Cornwall

CHISHOLMS ‡
58 Molesworth Street Wadebridge Cornwall PL27 7DR
Tel: 01208 812470 / 814205 *Fax:* 01208 815673
Dx: 81703 WADEBRIDGE
Emergency telephone 01208 814308
E-mail: mail@chisholmswade.plus.com
List of partners: W C Rushforth
Languages: French, Spanish
Work: A1 E K1 K3 K4 L R1 S1 S2 T2 W Z(c)
SPr: Rushforth, Mr Wilfred Charles. . . . . *§Dec 1980

MACMILLANS ‡
Manor House Wadebridge Cornwall PL27 6BS
Tel: 01208 812415 *Fax:* 01208 812271 *Dx:* 81702 WADEBRIDGE
E-mail: info@macmillans-solicitors.co.uk
List of partners: S G G Ambrose, A K Martin, T A Paget
Work: A1 A2 B1 D1 D2 E F1 F2 J1 K1 K3 K4 L N O Q S1 S2 V W Z(k,q)
Emergency Action, Agency, Advocacy and Fixed Fee Interview undertaken
Ptr: Ambrose, Mr Simon Gerald Gunning LLB; TEP . . . *Dec 1978
Martin, Miss Angeline Kensa LLB(Hons). . . . . *Nov 2001
Paget, Miss Terri Ann LLB. . . . . *Oct 2007
Ast: Casaru, Mrs Jennifer Clare BSc(Hons); TEP. . . . . . Oct 1988

MERRICKS FORMERLY MERRICK KELLEHER ‡
Cross Street Wadebridge Cornwall PL27 7DT
Tel: 01208 812068 / 813104 *Fax:* 01208 814186
Dx: 81701 WADEBRIDGE
Emergency telephone 01872 52407
E-mail: richard@merricks-law.co.uk
List of partners: C L Facey, R F Merrick
Work: A1 B1 C1 D1 E F1 G H J1 K1 K2 L M1 N P S1 T1 W
Emergency Action, Agency, Advocacy, Fixed Fee Interview and Legal Aid undertaken
Ptr: Facey, Mr Clifford Leonard . . . . *Jan 1966
Merrick, Mr Richard Foster LLB . . . . *§May 1976
Asoc: Merrick, Mr Timothy Foster BA(Hons) . . . . *Dec 2007

RALPH & CO
(incorporating Richardson & Scawin)
52 Molesworth Street Wadebridge Cornwall PL27 7DR
Tel: 01208 812277 *Fax:* 01208 814829 *Dx:* 81700 WADEBRIDGE
E-mail: (initials)@ralphlaw.co.uk
Office: Newquay
Work: A1 C1 E K4 L S1 S2 T1 T2 W
Emergency Action, Fixed Fee Interview, Legal Aid undertaken and Member of Accident Line
Ptr: Wallis, Mr David LLB . . . . *Aug 2001

WADHURST, East Sussex

LAGES & CO ‡
The Old Forge Offices Sparrows Green Road Wadhurst East Sussex TN5 6SL
Tel: 01892 784419 *Fax:* 01892 784512
List of partners: P R Lages
Work: A1 E L R1 S1 S2 T1 T2 W Z(d,m)
Fixed Fee Interview undertaken
Ptr: Lages, Miss Pamela R MA(Dublin) . . . . *§Jul 1976

WAKEFIELD, West Yorkshire

ARMITAGE & GUEST ‡
4 Bond Terrace Wakefield West Yorkshire WF1 2HW
Tel: 01924 371877 *Fax:* 01924 200031
E-mail: armitageandguest@btconnect.com
List of partners: M A Guest
Work: C1 K1 S1 W
Ptr: Guest, Mr Michael A LLB . . . . *Nov 1972

BBT LAW ‡
PO Box 605 Wakefield West Yorkshire WF1 9GU
Tel: 0845 833 3351 *Fax:* 0845 833 3352
E-mail: info@bbtlaw.co.uk

BEAUMONT LEGAL ‡
Beaumont House 1 Paragon Avenue Wakefield West Yorkshire WF1 2UF
Tel: 0845 122 8100 *Fax:* 0845 122 8101
E-mail: enquiries@beaumont-legal.co.uk
List of partners: M E Atkinson, N A Castle, R Cusworth, D J Hilton, P M Smith
Work: C1 E J1 L N O Q S1 W Z(l)
Ptr: Atkinson, Mr Michael E LLB(B'ham). . . . . *§Jun 1970
Castle, Mr Nicholas A BA(Hons). . . . . *Dec 1987
Cusworth, Mr Roy BSc . . . . *§Mar 1977
Hilton, Mr Daniel J LLB(Hons); PI Dip. . . . . *Nov 1995
Smith, Mr Philip Martyn BA(Hons). . . . . *Dec 1983

CATTERALLS ‡
(incorporating Catterall Pell & Moxon & Co; Higgins Mason & Co)
PO Box 43 15 King Street Wakefield West Yorkshire WF1 2SL
Tel: 01924 291122 *Fax:* 01924 290953 *Dx:* 15016 WAKEFIELD
List of partners: J Burgess, E L Cornell, P Kininmonth, P Lisle
Work: A1 B1 D1 E F1 J1 K1 L N O Q R1 S1 V W Z(c,e,f,j,k,l,n,o,p)
Emergency Action, Agency, Advocacy, Fixed Fee Interview, Legal Aid undertaken and Legal Aid Franchise
Ptr: Burgess, Miss Julie LLB. . . . . *Nov 1996
Cornell, Mrs Emma Louise LLB . . . . *Aug 2004
Kininmonth, Mr Paul LLB(Hull) . . . . *Oct 1983
Lisle, Mr Philip . . . . *Apr 1981
Asoc: Knee, Miss Danielle LLB Commercial Law (2009); Business Law & Practice (2009). . . . . Jul 2011
Con: McKiddie, Mr Dennis J . . . . *Jul 1967
Spink, Mr Michael A. . . . . *§Jul 1973

CHADWICK LAWRENCE
(incorporating Dickinson & Wainwright)
2a Red Hill Crescent Paragon Business Village Wakefield West Yorkshire WF1 2DF
Tel: 01924 379078 *Fax:* 01924 383373 *Dx:* 743303 WAKEFIELD 15
E-mail: howardw@chadlaw.co.uk
Office: Halifax, Huddersfield, Morley
Work: B1 C1 C2 C3 D1 E F1 G H J1 K1 L M1 M2 N O P Q R1 S1 T1 T2 V W Z(b,c,d,g,i,j,l,m,n,o,r,t)

DIXON COLES & GILL ‡
Bank House 1 Burton Street Wakefield West Yorkshire WF1 2DA
Est: 1785
Tel: 01924 373467 *Fax:* 01924 366234 *Dx:* 15030 WAKEFIELD
E-mail: info@dixon-coles-gill.com
List of partners: L M Box, J S Gill, J H Wilding
Office: Wakefield
Work: B1 C1 E F1 J1 L N Q R1 S1 W Z(d,i,l,r,x)
Emergency Action, Agency, Advocacy, Legal Aid undertaken and Member of Accident Line
Ptr: Box, Mrs Linda Mary LLB Chancellor of the Diocese of Southwell & Nottingham Notary Public . . . . . *Dec 1973
Gill, Mr Julian S LLB Joint Diocesan Registrar. . . . . *Apr 1977
Wilding, Mrs Julia Helen LLB Joint Diocesan Registrar Notary Public. *Jul 1997
Ast: Allen, Mrs Sindy Michelle LLB. . . . . *Apr 2006
Knox, Mr Stuart Jonathan LLB . . . . *Apr 2006
Smith, Mr Philip Martyn BA(Hons). . . . . *Dec 1983

DIXON COLES & GILL
22 Westfield Road Horbury Wakefield West Yorkshire WF4 6HP
Tel: 01924 263166 / 263899 *Fax:* 01924 264244
Dx: 15030 WAKEFIELD
E-mail: info@dixon-coles-gill.com
Office: Wakefield
Work: B1 C1 D1 E K1 K3 K4 L N O Q S1 S2 T2 W Z(c,d,i,l,q,x)
Agency and Fixed Fee Interview undertaken
Ast: Allen, Mrs Sindy Michelle LLB. . . . . *Apr 2006

GREEN WILLIAMSON SOLICITORS ‡
7-13 King Street Wakefield West Yorkshire WF1 2SJ
Tel: 01924 291400 *Fax:* 01924 290373 *Dx:* 15013 WAKEFIELD
E-mail: enquiries@greenwilliamson.co.uk
List of partners: M N Bradley, J A Denison, R Dennett, A Gait
Office: Leeds
Work: A1 B1 C1 C3 E F1 G H J1 K1 L M1 N O P Q R1 S1 T1 V W Z(b,c,d,e,f,g,h,i,j,k,l,m,n,o,p,s,t)
Emergency Action, Agency, Advocacy, Fixed Fee Interview, Legal Aid undertaken and Member of Accident Line
Ptr: Bradley, Mr Michael Norman BSc(Econ). . . . . Jun 1973
Denison, Mr John Andrew. . . . . Jul 1973
Dennett, Mr Richard. . . . . May 1992
Gait, Mrs Amanda LLB Advocate of the Year 1996 . . Oct 1992

HAWKSWELL KILVINGTON LLP ‡
17 Navigation Court Calder Park Wakefield West Yorkshire WF2 7BJ
Tel: 01924 258719 *Fax:* 01924 257666
E-mail: enquiries@thkp.co.uk
Work: A3 O Z(c)

HENSHAW PRATT SOLICITORS ‡
Raines House Denby Dale Road Wakefield West Yorkshire WF1 1HR
Tel: 01924 882405

JWP SOLICITORS ‡
9 Cheapside Wakefield West Yorkshire WF1 2SD
Tel: 01924 387171 *Fax:* 01924 379113 *Dx:* 15031 WAKEFIELD
List of partners: W P Campbell, J M Curnin, J R Wilkinson, J C Wood
Office: Leeds
Ptr: Campbell, Miss Wendy P . . . . *Feb 1999
Curnin, Miss Jane M . . . . *Sep 1988
Wilkinson, Mr John R ★. . . . . *Dec 1996
Wood, Mr John C BA . . . . *Oct 1986
Asoc: Simpson, Miss Fiona C . . . . *Apr 1999
Smith, Mr Daniel J . . . . *Sep 2002
Ast: Steele, Miss Amanda LLB. . . . . Nov 1996

CLAIRE JONES & ASSOCIATES ‡
32 Cheapside Wakefield West Yorkshire WF1 2TF
Tel: 01924 290029 *Fax:* 01924 290240 *Dx:* 15029 WAKEFIELD
Emergency telephone 01924 290029
E-mail: clairejones@clairejonesandassociates.co.uk
List of partners: S C Jones
Work: D1 K1 S1 W
Emergency Action, Agency, Fixed Fee Interview and Legal Aid undertaken
Ptr: Jones, Ms S Claire LLB . . . . *Dec 1980
Asoc: Thornton, Miss Clare Louise BA(Hons)(Law) . . . . *Sep 1995

JORDANS
18 King Street Wakefield West Yorkshire WF1 2SQ
Tel: 01924 387110 *Fax:* 01924 387112 *Dx:* 15033 WAKEFIELD
E-mail: enquiries@jordanssolicitors.co.uk
Office: Castleford, Dewsbury
Work: A3 B1 C1 D1 D2 E F1 F2 G H J1 J2 K1 K2 K3 K4 L N O Q R1 R2 S1 S2 V W Z(c,h,l,p,q,s,t)
Emergency Action, Agency, Advocacy, Fixed Fee Interview and Legal Aid undertaken
Ptr: Lewis, Miss Susan . . . . *Oct 2001
Mactaggart, Miss Deborah J LLB(B'ham) . . . . . . *Mar 1984
Proctor, Mr Stephen Thomas LLB. . . . . *Nov 1993
Shergill, Mrs Sukhbeer BA . . . . *May 1998
Ast: Batten, Miss Helen Louise Ruth LLB . . . . *Sep 2010
Cook, Ms Catherine Emma . . . . *Oct 1995
Jones, Mr Gareth Robert George BA(Hons). . . . . . *Jul 2006
Moorby, Miss Laura Jayne LLB . . . . *Mar 2010

KING STREET SOLICITORS ‡
6 Chancery Lane Wakefield West Yorkshire WF1 2SS
Tel: 01924 332395 *Fax:* 01924 366656
E-mail: fg@kingstreetsolicitors.co.uk

LR SOLICITORS ‡
Stowe House 34 Blacker Lane Crigglestone Wakefield West Yorkshire WF4 3EW
Tel: 01924 257896 *Fax:* 01924 257896

LARGO LAW ‡
10 Silkwood Business Park Fryers Way Wakefield West Yorkshire WF5 9TJ
Tel: 01924 886555 *Fax:* 01924 886556 *Dx:* 702449 OSSETT

LAWSONS SOLICITORS ‡
2nd Floor Central Buildings Wakefield West Yorkshire WF1 1HB
Tel: 01324 202000

LIDDYS PROPERTY SOLICITORS
20 Wood Street Wakefield West Yorkshire WF1 2ED
Office: Wakefield

LIDDYS SOLICITORS ‡
2 King Street Wakefield West Yorkshire WF1 2SQ
Tel: 01924 780753
List of partners: M N Khallil, K M Liddy
Office: Wakefield
Work: J1 N Q
Agency and Advocacy undertaken
Ptr: Khallil, Mr Mohammed N . . . . Jan 2002
Liddy, Mr Kevin M LLB . . . . *Oct 1993

THE LISTER CROFT PARTNERSHIP ‡
(in association with Lister Croft)
Victoria Chambers 40 Wood Street Wakefield West Yorkshire WF1 2HL
Tel: 0871 220 1333 *Fax:* 0871 220 3111 *Dx:* 762680 WAKEFIELD 11
Emergency telephone 0113 266 2212
List of partners: A L Benstock, N R Macleod, S L Murray, I N Pattison
Office: Pudsey
Work: C1 E F1 J1 K1 N Q S1 S2 T1 T2 W Z(r)
Agency, Advocacy, Fixed Fee Interview undertaken and Member of Accident Line
Ptr: Benstock, Mr Alan L BA H M Deputy Coroner of West Yorkshire East . . . . *§Oct 1982
Macleod, Mr Neil R LLB. . . . . *Apr 1981
Ast: Durgan, Mrs Nasreen LLB. . . . . *May 1981
Hartley, Mr David J LLB(Newc) . . . . *Jan 1970
Steele, Ms Susan J LLB(Manc) . . . . *Oct 1989

LORDS ‡
30 Cheapside Wakefield West Yorkshire WF1 2TF
Tel: 01924 380830 *Fax:* 01924 380816
Emergency telephone 07785 901264
List of partners: J M Allott, M P Lord
Work: G H
Agency, Advocacy and Legal Aid undertaken
Ptr: Allott, Ms Julie Margaret BA(Hons); LLB. . . . . . . *Feb 1993
Lord, Mr Martyn P LLB . . . . *Jun 1980

See p112 for the Key to Work Categories & other symbols

MCALINNEYS SOLICITORS ‡
Suite 4 6 South Parade Wakefield West Yorkshire WF1 1LR
Tel: 01924 377017 *Fax:* 01924 377018
E-mail: info@mcalinneys.co.uk
List of partners: D McAlinney
SPr: McAlinney, Mr Damian BA . . . . Jul 1998

MILNERS SOLICITORS
5a Wood Street Wakefield West Yorkshire WF1 2EL
Tel: 01924 386111 *Fax:* 01924 386609 *Dx:* 15012 WAKEFIELD
E-mail: office@milnerslaw.com
Office: Barnsley, Leeds, Pontefract

MINSTER LAW LIMITED
Kingfisher House Calder Park Wakefield West Yorkshire WF2 7UA
Tel: 0845 600 3272
E-mail: info@minsterlaw.co.uk
Office: York

REEDS FAMILY LAW SOLICITORS ‡
19a Cheapside Wakefield West Yorkshire WF1 2SD
Tel: 01924 201001
E-mail: dstevens@reeds-solicitors.co.uk

RUSSELL JONES & WALKER
2nd Floor Unit 6b Benton Office Park Wakefield West Yorkshire WF4 5RA
Tel: 01924 234300 *Fax:* 01924 234343 *Dx:* 702458 OSSETT
E-mail: enquiries@rjw.co.uk
Office: Birmingham, Bristol, Cardiff, London WC2, Manchester, Newcastle upon Tyne, Sheffield
Languages: Ukrainian
Work: G H J1 N Z(l,p,t)
Emergency Action, Agency, Advocacy, Legal Aid undertaken, Legal Aid Franchise and Member of Accident Line
Ast: Innes, Ms Susan . . . . Aug 1999
Kelly, Mr Damian Gerard LLB(Hons) . . . . *Apr 1994
Merrick, Miss Kirsten Anne LLB(Hons); LSF . . . . . . *Apr 1995

SKELLERN & CO ‡
Room 7 1 Chancery Lane Crown Court Wakefield West Yorkshire WF1 2SS
Tel: 01924 298780 *Fax:* 01924 200024
Work: G H
Agency and Advocacy undertaken

SWITALSKI'S ‡
19 Cheapside Wakefield West Yorkshire WF1 2SX
Tel: 01924 882000 *Fax:* 01924 290333 *Dx:* 15017 WAKEFIELD
Emergency telephone 07850 582427
E-mail: help@switalskis.com
List of partners: A S Bridger, L J Law, S J T Switalski
Office: Bradford, Dewsbury, Halifax, Huddersfield, Leeds
Work: D1 G H J1 K1 K2 L Z(i,m,r)
Emergency Action, Agency and Legal Aid undertaken
Ptr: Law, Ms Lorrette Joy BA(Hons) . . . . *Oct 1989
Switalski, Mr Stephen Jan Thomas BA(Law) . . . . . . *Apr 1981
Asoc: Casey, Mr Robert James LLB(Hons) . . . . *Nov 1995
Ast: Davidson, Ms Lorna LLB . . . . *Apr 1993

G M WILSON ‡
1 Crown Court Wakefield West Yorkshire WF1 2SU
Tel: 01924 291111 *Fax:* 01924 386700 *Dx:* 15020 WAKEFIELD
Emergency telephone 01424 291111
E-mail: davidbrooke@gmwilson.co.uk
List of partners: D R Brooke
Office: Barnsley
Work: E F1 G J1 K1 L N O Q S1 V W
Agency, Advocacy, Fixed Fee Interview and Legal Aid undertaken
Ptr: Brooke, Mr David R LLB(Hons) . . . . *Oct 1982

WALKDEN, Greater Manchester

ABBOTT & CO ‡
5 The Old Co-op Buildings High Street Walkden Greater Manchester M28 3JH
Tel: 0161 799 8003 *Fax:* 0161 703 8013 *Dx:* 721413 WALKDEN 2
List of partners: S M Batchelor, J A King
Work: D1 F1 K1 L Q S1 W
Emergency Action, Agency, Advocacy, Fixed Fee Interview, Legal Aid undertaken and Legal Aid Franchise
Ptr: Batchelor, Mrs Susan M LLB . . . . *Aug 1978
King, Miss Jill A LLB . . . . *Nov 1984

BERRY & BERRY ‡
1-5 Longley Road Walkden Greater Manchester M28 3JB
Tel: 0161 790 1411 *Fax:* 0161 790 1971 *Dx:* 721410 WALKDEN 2
E-mail: email.walkden@berryberry.co.uk
List of partners: M A James, P C Regan
Office: Eccles, Manchester (2 offices)
Work: A1 B1 C1 D1 E F1 G H J1 K1 L M1 N P R1 S1 T1 V W Z(l)
Emergency Action, Agency, Advocacy, Fixed Fee Interview, Legal Aid undertaken and Member of Accident Line

WIDDOWS PILLING & CO ‡
The Manse 2b Memorial Road Walkden Greater Manchester M28 3AQ
Tel: 0161 790 1825 *Fax:* 0161 703 8251 *Dx:* 706990 WALKDEN
E-mail: enquiries@widdows-pilling.co.uk
List of partners: J R Parker, N Pattichis, D C S Pilling
Languages: French, Greek
Work: A1 B1 C1 C2 C3 D1 E F1 J1 K1 K2 K3 K4 N O P Q S1 S2 V W
Emergency Action, Agency, Advocacy, Fixed Fee Interview, Legal Aid Franchise and Member of Accident Line
Ptr: Parker, Mr Jeremy R LLB . . . . *Dec 1983
Pattichis, Mr Nicholas BSc . . . . *Mar 1997
Pilling, Mr Donald C S . . . . *Jun 1973
Ast: Pilling, Miss Claire Jane LLB . . . . Oct 2007

WALLASEY, Merseyside

BECKETT BEMROSE HAGEN (incorporating Somerfield & Parkhouse)
96 Wallasey Road Wallasey Merseyside CH44 2AE
Tel: 0151 630 1206 *Fax:* 0151 691 2539
Office: Wirral
Languages: French
Work: A1 B1 C1 D1 E F1 G H J1 K1 L M1 N P R1 S1 T1 V W

BERKSON WALLACE SOLICITORS ‡
106 Wallasey Road Wallasey Merseyside CH44 2AE
Tel: 0151 691 6900 *Fax:* 0151 691 6901
E-mail: solicitors@berksonwallace.co.uk
List of partners: N G Edwards, J S Mather, P D F Morris
Office: Ellesmere Port
Work: C1 E F1 J1 J2 L N O Q R2 S1 S2 V W Z(c,e,m,q,r)
Emergency Action, Agency, Fixed Fee Interview, Legal Aid undertaken and Member of Accident Line
Ptr: Edwards, Mr N Gareth BA(Hons) . . . . *Jan 1993
Mather, Mr James Stuart . . . . Aug 2006
Morris, Mr Peter D F . . . . *Oct 1979
Asoc: Mitchell, Ms Joanne . . . . Apr 2007
Ast: Entwistle, Mr Richard Ronald . . . . Oct 2007

BURD WARD SOLICITORS ‡
23-25 Seaview Road Wallasey Merseyside CH45 4QT
Tel: 0151 639 8273

VALENTINE DUGGINS ‡
101 Wallasey Road Wallasey Merseyside CH44 2AA
Tel: 0151 638 4844 *Fax:* 0151 638 4805 *Dx:* 20066 WALLASEY
E-mail: val@valentineduggins.co.uk
List of partners: V P Duggins, D C Kendall
Work: E L S1 S2 W
Ptr: Duggins, Mr Valentine Patrick BA(Hons) . . . . *§Mar 1983
Kendall, Mr Derek C . . . . *§Dec 1964

HAWORTH & GALLAGHER (incorporating Swancott Morgan Hannaford & Taggart)
37-39 Wallasey Road Wallasey Merseyside CH45 4NN
Tel: 0151 638 5457 / 638 6088 *Fax:* 0151 639 0914
Dx: 20053 WALLASEY
Office: Birkenhead
Work: B1 D1 E F1 J1 K1 L N P R1 S1 V W Z(i,j,k)
Emergency Action, Agency, Advocacy, Fixed Fee Interview, Legal Aid undertaken, Legal Aid Franchise and Member of Accident Line
Ptr: Kehoe, Mrs Catherine M LLB(Hons) . . . . *Oct 1984
Nelson, Mr Anthony J . . . . Jun 1984
Ast: Neal, Mr Quentin Mark BA(Wales) . . . . *Nov 1990

THOMAS HIGGINS & CO ‡
Capitol Buildings 10 Seaview Road Wallasey Merseyside CH45 4TH
Tel: 0151 630 8006 *Fax:* 0151 630 8005 *Dx:* 20063 WALLASEY
List of partners: T Higgins
Work: O
Ptr: Higgins, Mr Thomas . . . . *Sep 1976
Ast: McIver, Mrs Tracey Anne . . . . Oct 2003
Rea, Ms Gillian . . . . Dec 1984

WALLINGFORD, Oxfordshire

HEDGES ‡
16 Market Place Wallingford Oxfordshire OX10 0AE
Tel: 01491 839839 *Fax:* 01491 833396 *Dx:* 39851 WALLINGFORD
E-mail: info@hedgeslaw.co.uk
List of partners: M E Buxton, A S Hatt, N Y Poole
Office: Didcot
Languages: French, Welsh
Work: A1 C1 D1 E K1 K2 K3 L R1 S1 S2 T1 W
Legal Aid undertaken
Ptr: Hatt, Mr Adrian S MA(Cantab) . . . . *§Oct 1975
Poole, Mrs Nicola Yvette LLB(Hons) . . . . Sep 1993

SLADE LEGAL
7 St Martin's Street Wallingford Oxfordshire OX10 0AN
Tel: 01491 839346 *Fax:* 01491 832191 *Dx:* 39850 WALLINGFORD
E-mail: enquiries@slade-legal.co.uk
Office: Abingdon, Didcot
Work: A1 B1 C1 C2 D1 E F1 J1 K1 L N O Q R1 S1 S2 T2 W Z(l,m)
Advocacy, Fixed Fee Interview and Legal Aid Franchise
Ptr: Slade, Mr David H BSc(Civ Eng) . . . . *Dec 1978
Smith, Mr Stephen H BA(Oxon) . . . . *Dec 1977

WALLINGTON, Surrey

CARPENTER & CO ‡
46 Woodcote Road Wallington Surrey SM6 0NW
Tel: 020 8669 5145 *Fax:* 020 8773 3585 *Dx:* 59950 WALLINGTON
Emergency telephone 020 8773 5172
E-mail: mail@carpenterssolicitors.co.uk
List of partners: G J Cooper, D A Greenfield, P Hogg, P Verlander
Languages: Sinhalese
Work: D1 E J1 K1 K3 K4 L N O Q S1 S2 T2 W Z(r)
Agency, Advocacy and Fixed Fee Interview undertaken
Ptr: Greenfield, Mr David Alan BA; TEP . . . . *Oct 1983
Hogg, Ms Patricia . . . . Feb 1997
Verlander, Mr Paul BA . . . . *§Feb 1991
Cooper, Mr Gavin J . . . . NSP
Ast: O'Dowd, Mr Richard BA . . . . Sep 2008
Con: Nilaweera, R Harshadeva W . . . . May 1976

MCMILLAN WILLIAMS
9 Beddington Gardens Wallington Surrey SM6 0HU
Tel: 020 8669 4962 *Fax:* 020 8763 2016 *Dx:* 59952 WALLINGTON
Emergency telephone 020 8660 3383
E-mail: wallington@mcmillan-williams.co.uk
Office: Carshalton, Coulsdon, Croydon, Mitcham, South Croydon, Thornton Heath
Languages: Turkish
Work: G H K4 S1 S2 W
Fixed Fee Interview, Legal Aid undertaken and Legal Aid Franchise
Ast: Amartey, Miss Helena . . . . Oct 1997
Fell, Mr Glen BA(Hons) . . . . May 1998
Mander, Ms Katherine . . . . Sep 2006
Wilson, Mr Christopher . . . . *Dec 1973

JOHN NASH & CO SOLICITORS ‡
38 Stafford Road Wallington Surrey SM6 9AA
Tel: 020 8647 1148 *Fax:* 020 8254 7611
E-mail: ajn@johnnashsolicitors.co.uk

CHRISTIAN PAUL SOLICITORS ‡
1 Milton Road Wallington Surrey SM6 9RP
Work: B1 K3 Z(l)

R E PEARCE & CO ‡ (incorporating Spencer Gibson)
23 Ross Parade Wallington Surrey SM6 8QF
Tel: 020 8652 3574 *Fax:* 020 8669 3788 *Dx:* 59955 WALLINGTON
Emergency telephone 020 8669 0663
List of partners: R E Pearce
Work: B1 C1 D1 E F1 G H J1 K1 L M1 N P S1 W Z(i,l)
Emergency Action, Agency, Advocacy, Fixed Fee Interview and Legal Aid undertaken
Ptr: Pearce, Mr Robert E BA . . . . Nov 1983

WALLSEND, Tyne & Wear

BRENNANS SOLICITORS ‡
44-52 Station Road Wallsend Tyne & Wear NE28 6TB
Tel: 0191 262 5133 *Fax:* 0191 263 1015 *Dx:* 62202 WALLSEND
Emergency telephone 0191 281 5431 (EXT 67)
E-mail: janeh@the-jbp.demon.co.uk
List of partners: J M Hucknall, J Kirkham
Work: D1 E F1 G H J1 K1 L M1 N P S1 V W
Emergency Action, Agency, Advocacy, Fixed Fee Interview, Legal Aid undertaken and Legal Aid Franchise
Ptr: Hucknall, Ms Jane M . . . . Oct 1993
Kirkham, Mr John . . . . Oct 1988
Ast: Melvin, Ms Susan BSc; LLB . . . . Oct 1986

PAUL DODDS SOLICITORS ‡
70 High Street East Wallsend Tyne & Wear NE28 7RH
Tel: 0191 263 6200 *Fax:* 0191 234 0898 *Dx:* 62206 WALLSEND
Emergency telephone 07860 887583
E-mail: office@pauldodds.co.uk
List of partners: P R Dodds, D J Dollimore
Work: B1 D1 E F1 G H J1 K1 L N Q S1 V W X Z(k)
Emergency Action, Agency, Advocacy and Legal Aid undertaken
Ptr: Dodds, Mr Paul R LLB . . . . *Jun 1979
Dollimore, Mr Duncan J BA(Hons) . . . . *Dec 1995
Asoc: Cassidy, Mr Dominic Martin LLB . . . . *Nov 1989
Simpson, Mr Paul LLB(Hons) . . . . Dec 2003
Ast: Mason, Mr Stephen LLB . . . . Feb 1991

HAY & KILNER
16 High Street West Wallsend Tyne & Wear NE28 8HU
Tel: 0191 262 8231 *Fax:* 0191 234 0538 *Dx:* 62201 WALLSEND
Office: Newcastle upon Tyne
Work: C1 D1 D2 E F1 G H J2 K1 N Q S1 S2 V X Z(l,m)
Emergency Action, Agency, Advocacy, Fixed Fee Interview, Legal Aid undertaken and Legal Aid Franchise
Ptr: Bass, Mr Gerald W T BA(Econ) . . . . *§May 1967
Harrison, Mr Mark R . . . . *Aug 1997
Hart, Mr Robert LLB . . . . Feb 1985
Slater, Ms Jacqueline C . . . . *Oct 1991
Ast: Barratt, Miss Sarah L . . . . *Sep 1999
Elliott, Mr Christopher Paul LLB; DipLP . . . . *Sep 2002

SMITH & COPSEY ‡
42 High Street East Wallsend Tyne & Wear NE28 8PQ
Tel: 0191 262 4428 *Fax:* 0191 263 0273 *Dx:* 62200 WALLSEND
Emergency telephone 07831 165837
List of partners: R B Copsey, F J Smith
Office: Newcastle upon Tyne
Work: B2 D1 D2 F1 G H K1 K3 L Q S1 V
Emergency Action, Agency, Advocacy, Fixed Fee Interview and Legal Aid undertaken
Ptr: Copsey, Mr Richard B BA ★ . . . . *Oct 1987
Smith, Mr F Jeffrey LLB . . . . *Oct 1988
Ast: Cameron, Mrs Jill BA(Hons) . . . . Jan 1993

WALSALL, West Midlands

A S SOLICITORS ‡
6-8 Mayou Court No32 High Street Pelsall Walsall West Midlands WS3 4LX
Tel: 01922 682822 *Fax:* 01922 693614 *Dx:* 12133 WALSALL
E-mail: info@as-solicitors.co.uk

ADDISON O'HARE ‡
Kelvin House 23 Lichfield Street Walsall West Midlands WS1 1UL
Tel: 01922 725515 *Fax:* 01922 616998 *Dx:* 12102 WALSALL
E-mail: mail@addisonohare.co.uk
List of partners: A P Hunt, D M Milne, A R Ward, D R Wilton
Work: D1 D2 E J1 K1 K3 K4 L N O Q S1 S2 T2 V W Z(q)
Emergency Action, Agency, Advocacy, Fixed Fee Interview, Legal Aid undertaken, Legal Aid Franchise and Member of Accident Line
Ptr: Hunt, Mr Andrew Peter . . . . *§Aug 1988
Milne, Mr David Mearns MA . . . . *Dec 1995
Ward, Mrs Anne R BA . . . . *Dec 1982
Wilton, Mr Dixon R LLB(Manc) . . . . *Apr 1978
Ast: Ford, Mr Paul . . . . *Oct 1988
Thomas, Mr Richard . . . . Jan 1988
Whyte, Mr Jordan . . . . Apr 2011
Holders of Franchise for Family. We specialise in the following areas of work Employment Law, Family Law, Litigation, Childcare.

AKTHER & DARBY ‡
Corporate House 65 Bradford Street Walsall West Midlands WS1 3QD
Tel: 01922 634175 *Fax:* 01922 634842

ASPECT LAW ‡
3 Bradford Place Walsall West Midlands WS1 1PL
Tel: 0871 288 3212
E-mail: info@aspectlaw.com

BEASLEY JOHNSON LOYNS ‡
60a Lichfield Road Walsall West Midlands WS4 2BX
Tel: 01922 644433 *Fax:* 01922 746888
List of partners: S Beasley, C W Loyns
Work: N Q
Emergency Action, Agency, Advocacy, Legal Aid Franchise and Member of Accident Line
Ptr: Beasley, Mr Steven LLB . . . . *Dec 1979
Loyns, Mr Clive W BA(Hons) . . . . *Jun 1982

BURGOYNE & CO ‡
Victoria House 11a Vicarage Place Walsall West Midlands WS1 3NA
Tel: 01922 616916 *Fax:* 01922 616922 *Dx:* 12134 WALSALL
E-mail: paul@burgoynesolicitors.co.uk
List of partners: P R Burgoyne
Work: C1 E L Q S1 S2 W
Agency and Fixed Fee Interview undertaken
SPr: Burgoyne, Mr Paul Roy FILEx. *Dec 1988

MALCOLM BUTLER & CO
1st Floor Tameway Tower 48 Bridge Street Walsall West Midlands WS1 1JZ
Tel: 01922 704048 *Fax:* 07922 638654 *Dx:* 12143 WALSALL
Office: Maidstone
Work: Q
Ast: Kaur, Ms Amritpal. Jan 2005

CMHT SOLICITORS ‡
55-56 Bradford Street Walsall West Midlands WS1 3QD
Tel: 01922 646400 *Fax:* 01922 646469 *Dx:* 717086 WALSALL 7
Emergency telephone 01922 646425
E-mail: barbara.evans@cmht.co.uk
List of partners: P A Bellshaw, V A Cox, M E Hughes, D J McQueen
Office: Brownhills, Walsall
Languages: Bengali, French, Hindi, Punjabi, Urdu
Work: A1 C1 D1 D2 E F1 G H J1 K1 L N Q S1 S2 V W Z(i,m)
Emergency Action, Agency, Advocacy, Legal Aid undertaken, Legal Aid Franchise and Member of Accident Line
Ptr: Bellshaw, Mr Philip A LLB. *Oct 1987
Cox, Mrs Valerie A LLB Sweet & Maxwell Law Prize; Birmingham Law Society Bronze Medal *Oct 1984
Hughes, Mr Mark E LLB; LLM. *Sep 1984
McQueen, Mr David J LLB • Deputy District Judge *May 1978
Asoc: Haynes, Mr Patrick A BA *Mar 1991
Ast: Fox, Mr Stephen LLB Mar 1999
Khan Hussain, Mrs Shazia LLB; LPC Jan 2001
McFarlane, Ms Kirstine Fiona Sep 2000
Perry, Mr Rupert L BA. Jan 1998
Con: Blakemore, Mrs Jean LLB. *Apr 1981
Gray, Mr Sidney C LLB(Lond) *Mar 1979
Hollinshead, Miss Wendy BA(Hons)(Law) *Aug 1983

CMHT SOLICITORS
41 Anchor Road Aldridge Walsall West Midlands WS9 8PT
Tel: 01922 743525 *Fax:* 01922 743164 *Dx:* 29192 ALDRIDGE
Emergency telephone 01922 646425
E-mail: david.mcqueen@cmht.co.uk
Office: Brownhills, Walsall
Work: D1 E F1 G H J1 K1 L M1 N O P Q R1 S1 V W Z(l,m)
Emergency Action, Agency, Advocacy, Legal Aid undertaken and Legal Aid Franchise
Ptr: McQueen, Mr David J LLB • Deputy District Judge *May 1978

EDMUNDS & CO
The Jerome Building 30a Bradford Street Walsall West Midlands WS1 1PN
Tel: 0845 260 5050 *Fax:* 0845 260 4040 *Dx:* 717084 WALSALL 7
E-mail: walsall@edmunds-co.com
Office: Sutton Coldfield

ENOCH EVANS LLP ‡
St Pauls Chambers 6-9 Hatherton Road Walsall West Midlands WS1 1XS
Tel: 01922 720333 *Fax:* 01922 720623 *Dx:* 12125 WALSALL
Emergency telephone 07836 289425
E-mail: ee@enoch-evans.co.uk
List of partners: E L Birch, S K Comrie, J G Cooke, D J Evans, B S Guest, C T Loach, A L P Pointon, L Richards, S Shemar
Work: A1 B1 B2 C1 C2 D1 E F1 F2 G H J1 J2 K1 L M1 N O P Q R1 R2 S1 S2 T1 T2 W V Z(c,e,f,h,i,j,k,l,m,n,o,q,r,s,t)
Emergency Action, Agency, Advocacy, Fixed Fee Interview, Legal Aid undertaken and Legal Aid Franchise
Ptr: Birch, Mrs Emma L LLB. *Oct 1992
Comrie, Mrs Susan Kinsey LLB *§Feb 1988
Cooke, Mr Jeremy G *§Nov 1977
Evans, Mr David J LLB *§Nov 1985
Guest, Mr Barry S BA(Econ) *§Jun 1978
Loach, Mr Christopher T LLB(B'ham) *§Apr 1981
Pointon, Mr Andrew L P LLB *§Oct 1989
Richards, Miss Leighann LLB(Hons). *Oct 2004
Shemar, Miss Sukhvira BA *Sep 2002
Asoc: Gough, Miss Laura LLB. *Nov 2011
Hayden, Mr Simon Brian LLB(Hons); LSF *Aug 1996
Jarrett, Mr Michael *Sep 1997
McTigue, Mrs Catherine BA. *Sep 2003
Neea, Mr Richard F. *May 2009
Nixon, Mr Stephen *Jul 2010
Patel, Miss Anita LLB *Oct 2001
Patel, Mr Nayan T BSc *Aug 1998
Venables, Patricia. *Nov 2009
Con: Meere, Mr Richard LLB(Sheff) Notary Public *§Oct 1971

FAWCETT & PATTNI ‡
150 Lichfield Street Walsall West Midlands WS1 1SE
Tel: 01922 640424 *Fax:* 01922 721661
E-mail: clients@fp-law.com
List of partners: N E Fawcett, B S Pattni
Office: Birmingham
Languages: French, Gujarati, Hindi
Work: D1 K1 K3 N Q S1 S2
Emergency Action, Agency, Advocacy, Fixed Fee Interview, Legal Aid undertaken and Legal Aid Franchise
Ptr: Fawcett, Mr Neil Edward Nov 1969
Pattni, Ms Bharti S LLB. Jun 1981
Ast: Bloodworth, Mr Adam. Jan 2008
Longhurst, Mr Robin Nicholas LLB Jan 2010
Westley, Mr Richard John LLB Jan 2010

Accident Advice; Divorce; Family Law; Legal Aid; Personal Injury. County Court and Magistrates' Court Agency work.

FOUNTAIN SOLICITORS LIMITED ‡
Alexander House 52 Bradford Street Walsall West Midlands WS1 3QD
Tel: 01922 645429 *Fax:* 01922 612947
E-mail: info@fountainsolicitors.com
List of partners: R Sharif
Work: J1 K1 K2 K3 N W Z(g,i)
Fixed Fee Interview and Legal Aid undertaken
Dir: Sharif, Mr Ramzan LLB(Hons) ♦. *Jul 2002

GILLESPIES ‡
Darwall Street Walsall West Midlands WS1 1DD
Tel: 01922 627474 *Fax:* 01922 720165 *Dx:* 12116 WALSALL
E-mail: djl@gillespies.entadsl.com
List of partners: A Dewsbury, D J Longmore
Work: C1 C2 D1 E J1 K1 K3 K4 L Q R1 S1 S2 W Z(c,l)
Agency, Advocacy and Fixed Fee Interview undertaken
Ptr: Dewsbury, Mr Adrian *Jan 1989
Longmore, Mr David J LLB(Hull) *Jun 1978

HCB SOLICITORS
20 Lichfield Street Walsall West Midlands WS1 1TJ
Tel: 01922 720000 *Fax:* 01922 720023 *Dx:* 12122 WALSALL
Office: Alcester, Lichfield, Redditch, Solihull, Stratford-upon-Avon
Work: B1 C1 C2 C3 D1 E F1 J1 K1 L N O Q R1 S1 T1 T2 W X Z(c,d,e,f,h,k,l,p)
Emergency Action, Agency, Advocacy and Legal Aid Franchise
Ptr: Buckle, Mr John. Jan 1994
Dawson, Mr Robert G H LLB *Dec 1982
Elliott, Mrs Catherine LLB. *Feb 1990
Underwood, Mr Charles LLB *§Dec 1978
Asoc: Astbury-Crimes, Mr Miles Oct 1994
Ensor, Ms Michelle Dec 2005
Leonard, Mr Adrian BA(Hons). *Jun 2002
Nicol, Mrs Maria Rita BSc. Oct 2004
Ast: Haycock, Bethany. Jan 2010
Hunter, Mr John. Aug 1979
Jarvis, Ms Katharine Verity BA Apr 1985
Jevon, Ms Jane Kathryn LLB Nov 1991
Malhi, Rita Jan 2007
Con: Griffiths, Mr Donald H. *Jun 1973
Wilson, Mr Peter John LLB *Jun 1977

JENNINGS PERKS & CO ‡
Lloyds House Chambers 3 High Street Aldridge Walsall West Midlands WS9 8LX
Tel: 01922 459000 *Fax:* 01922 459001 *Dx:* 29204 ALDRIDGE
E-mail: solicitors@jenningsperks.co.uk
List of partners: K Golestani, S P Jennings, T J Perks
Languages: Farsi, French, German
Work: C1 D1 E K1 L S1 S2 W Z(d)
Agency and Fixed Fee Interview undertaken
Ptr: Golestani, Mr Kian BA(Hons) *Nov 1988
Jennings, Mr Stephen Paul BA *Dec 1981
Perks, Mr Timothy James. *Dec 1986

LANE & CO ‡
24-26 Broadway North Walsall West Midlands WS1 2AJ
Tel: 01922 721259 *Fax:* 01922 724000 *Dx:* 12106 WALSALL 1
List of partners: M J Edwards, J A Pitt
Work: O Q
Agency, Advocacy and Fixed Fee Interview undertaken
Ptr: Edwards, Mr Mark Julian BA(Hons) *Mar 1988
Pitt, Mr John Anthony LLDip. Feb 2005

STUART J MANDER & CO ‡
36 Bradford Street Walsall West Midlands WS1 3QA
Tel: 01922 642018 *Fax:* 01922 724586
Emergency telephone 07956 506989
E-mail: aweisha.chandia@stuartjmander.co.uk
List of partners: S J Mander
Languages: Hindi, Punjabi, Urdu
Work: D1 G H K1 K2 S1 V W Z(i,j,k)
Emergency Action, Agency, Advocacy, Fixed Fee Interview, Legal Aid undertaken and Legal Aid Franchise
Ptr: Mander, Mr Stuart J LLB *Nov 1970

OWEN NASH & CO ‡
44 Bradford Street Walsall West Midlands WS1 3QA
Tel: 01922 746746 *Fax:* 01922 746777 *Dx:* 717088 WALSALL 7
Emergency telephone 01922 746746
E-mail: office@owennash.co.uk
List of partners: B S Chaudhry, D B Nash, R K Owen
Languages: Punjabi
Work: B2 G H
Emergency Action, Agency, Advocacy, Fixed Fee Interview and Legal Aid undertaken
Ptr: Chaudhry, Brijinder Singh LLB(Hons) *Feb 1996
Nash, Mr David B BA. *§Jan 1982
Owen, Mr Roger K LLB *§Sep 1990

ROSIE OWEN SOLICITOR ‡
PO Box 4497 Walsall West Midlands WS1 9BJ
Tel: 01922 712440 *Fax:* 01922 492842
E-mail: rosieowen@talktalk.net

PARTRIDGE ALLEN & CO ‡
Portland Buildings Anchor Road Aldridge Walsall West Midlands WS9 8PR
Tel: 01922 452860 *Fax:* 01922 452452 *Dx:* 29196 ALDRIDGE
E-mail: rodallen@partridgeallen.co.uk
List of partners: R A Allen, E Toon
Work: B1 C1 D1 D2 E F1 F2 J1 K1 K2 L Q R1 R2 S1 S2 W Z(l,q,r)
Advocacy and Fixed Fee Interview undertaken
Ptr: Allen, Mr Roderick A *Dec 1985
Toon, Ms Emma BA(Hons) Feb 2006
Ast: Bourbonnux, Miss Lisa Ann LLB. Jul 2007

PEARMAN SMITH ‡
35 Lichfield Street Walsall West Midlands WS1 1TJ
Tel: 01922 624164 *Fax:* 01922 620708 *Dx:* 12119 WALSALL
E-mail: mail@pearmansmith.encadsl.com
List of partners: J V Lawrence
Work: A1 C1 C2 E L R1 S1 W
Ptr: Lawrence, Mr Jeremy Vernon *May 1984

CLIVE SHEPHERD & CO ‡
25 Station Street Walsall West Midlands WS2 9JZ
Tel: 01922 647797 *Fax:* 01922 641284 *Dx:* 717085 WALSALL 7
Emergency telephone 07831 636673
List of partners: S M Hicklin, C J Shepherd, M D Shepherd
Work: D1 F1 G H K1 L P S1 V W
Emergency Action, Agency, Advocacy, Fixed Fee Interview, Legal Aid undertaken and Legal Aid Franchise
Ptr: Hicklin, Ms Sheila M Aug 1997
Shepherd, Mr Clive J BA Nov 1980
Shepherd, Mr Mark D. Aug 1998

WALDRONS
38 Lichfield Street Walsall West Midlands WS1 1UP
Tel: 01384 811811 *Fax:* 01922 426249 *Dx:* 12107 WALSALL
E-mail: lawyers@waldrons.co.uk
Office: Brierley Hill, Dudley, Kingswinford, Tipton, Worcester
Work: B1 C1 E F1 J1 K1 L N O Q R1 S2 T1 T2 W
Agency and Advocacy undertaken
Ptr: Andrews, Mr Trevor J. *Jun 1979
Harrison, Mr Laurence Simon *Nov 1998
Whitehouse, Mr Nicholas H *Oct 1968
Ast: Dean, Ms Stephanie J. *Jan 1972

WALKER & CO ‡
206a-212 Stafford Street Walsall West Midlands WS2 8DW
Tel: 01922 639080 *Fax:* 01922 639196 *Dx:* 12117 WALSALL
Languages: Gujarati, Hindi, Punjabi, Urdu
Work: D1 D2 G H K2 S1 S2 W

WOODHOUSE & COMPANY
(incorporating Watt & Morgan Sutton)
25 Lichfield Street Walsall West Midlands WS1 1TJ
Tel: 01922 612523
Office: Sutton Coldfield, Wolverhampton
Work: M1 S1 W
Emergency Action, Agency, Advocacy, Fixed Fee Interview, Legal Aid undertaken and Member of Accident Line

WALTHAM ABBEY, Essex

CURWENS
(incorporating Trefor R James; Jessop & Gough; Curwen Carter & Evans)
29 Highbridge Street Waltham Abbey Essex EN9 1BZ
Tel: 01992 712549 *Fax:* 01992 769987
Dx: 54301 WALTHAM ABBEY
E-mail: enquiries@curwens.co.uk
Office: Cheshunt, Enfield, Hoddesdon
Work: A1 B1 C1 D1 E F1 G H J1 K1 L N O S1 T1 V W Z(e,f)

DJK SOLICITORS ‡
30 Howard Business Park Farm Hill Road Waltham Abbey Essex EN9 1XE
Tel: 01992 718880 *Fax:* 01992 716908
Dx: 54300 WALTHAM ABBEY
E-mail: info@djk-solicitors.co.uk
List of partners: D J King
Work: C1 E R2 S1 S2 W Z(l)
SPr: King, Miss Debra J LLB(Soton) *Oct 1983

TOWNSEND FAMILY LAW ‡
Willowdene Epping Road Nazeing Waltham Abbey Essex EN9 2DH
Tel: 01992 892214 *Fax:* 01992 892627

WALTHAM CROSS, Hertfordshire

BOULTER & CO
105a High Street Waltham Cross Hertfordshire EN8 7AN
Tel: 01992 787811 *Fax:* 01992 787822
Dx: 133983 WALTHAM CROSS 3
Office: London N8

PERRY CLEMENTS SOLICITORS ‡
58 High Street Waltham Cross Hertfordshire EN8 7BU
Tel: 01992 655930 *Fax:* 01992 655931
E-mail: info@perryclementssolicitors.com

SHEPHERD HARRIS & CO
Springfield House 99-101 Crossbrook Street Waltham Cross Hertfordshire EN8 8JR
Office: Enfield

WALTON-ON-THAMES, Surrey

FRIEND & CO ‡
14 Church Street Walton-on-Thames Surrey KT12 2QS
Tel: 01932 242962 *Fax:* 01932 224935
Dx: 80002 WALTON-ON-THAMES
E-mail: info@friendandco.co.uk
List of partners: M D Curley, J C Read
Work: B2 E G H J1 K1 K3 K4 L N O Q S1 S2 W Z(j,l,q,r)
Emergency Action, Agency and Advocacy undertaken
Ptr: Curley, Mr Martin D BA(Law) Jul 1975
Read, Mr John C BA(Oxon) *Jul 1969

HOWELL-JONES LLP
68 High Street Walton-on-Thames Surrey KT12 1DT
Tel: 01932 234500 *Fax:* 01932 234501
Dx: 80007 WALTON-ON-THAMES
E-mail: walton@howell-jones.com
Office: Cheam, Kingston upon Thames, Leatherhead, London SW20, London WC2
Languages: Armenian, French, Italian
Work: A3 B1 C1 C2 C3 D1 D2 E F1 I J1 J2 K1 K2 L M1 M2 N O P Q R1 R2 S1 S2 T1 T2 U2 W Z(c,e,f,j,k,l,q,r)
Agency, Advocacy, Fixed Fee Interview undertaken and Member of Accident Line
Ptr: Roper, Mr Alan *Nov 1973
Mem: David, Mrs Domini Claire LLB. *Oct 1994
Ast: Kalsi, Miss Simi LLB(Hons) *Jan 2004

TREVOR MUNN ‡
Easterly Boathouse The Towpath Manor Road Walton-on-Thames Surrey KT12 2PF
Tel: 01932 269153 *Fax:* 01932 247961
E-mail: info@trevormunn.co.uk
List of partners: T Munn
Work: E R2 S1 S2 W
SPr: Munn, Mr Trevor LLB(Hons). *Jan 1979

NICHOLS MARCY DAWSON ‡
77 High Street Walton-on-Thames Surrey KT12 1DR
Tel: 01932 219500 *Fax:* 01932 220549
Dx: 80001 WALTON-ON-THAMES
List of partners: E C Coller, R E Dawson, C G Hadfield, C J H Mitchell
Work: C1 E L S1 S2 W

 See p112 for the Key to Work Categories & other symbols

Ptr: Coller, Mr Edward C. . . . . *Jan 1972
Dawson, Mr Richard E LLB . . . . *Dec 1979
Hadfield, Mr Christopher G . . . . *May 1982
Mitchell, Mr Christopher J H. . . . . *Jan 1983
Ast: Hunt, Mr Andrew Philip BA(Manc). . . . . *Jan 1984
Khaira, Mrs Harinder Kaur LLB . . . . Nov 1999
Con: Nichols Marcy, Miss Carole A . . . . *Aug 1963

RANSONS ‡
Lynwood House 10 Eastwick Road Walton-on-Thames Surrey KT12 5AW
Tel: 01932 269448 *Fax:* 01932 269449
E-mail: mail@ransons.com
List of partners: C S Ranson
Languages: French, German
Work: C1 C2 I J1 Z(e,w,z)
Ptr: Ranson, Mr Charles S LLB(Hons). . . . . *Apr 1979

CRISPIAN SHEPLEY ‡
79 High Street Walton-on-Thames Surrey KT12 1DN
Tel: 01923 221122
E-mail: crispian.shepley@btconnect.com
List of partners: C R Shepley
Work: J1
SPr: Shepley, Mr Crispian R . . . . *Jul 1973

WALTON-ON-THE-NAZE, Essex

POWELLS ‡
21 New Pier Street Walton-on-the-Naze Essex CO14 8ED
Tel: 01255 675698 *Fax:* 01255 679372
Dx: 54401 FRINTON-ON-SEA
E-mail: powellssolicitors@btconnect.com
List of partners: C A Powell
Work: B1 D1 G J1 K1 L N S1 S2 W Z(h,l)
Fixed Fee Interview and Legal Aid Franchise
SPr: Powell, Mr Christopher A LLB . . . . *Jun 1983

WANTAGE, Oxfordshire

ANGEL WILKINS ‡
The Woolpack Church Street Wantage Oxfordshire OX12 8BL
Tel: 01235 775100 *Fax:* 01235 775101
E-mail: neil@angelwilkins.co.uk

CHARLES LUCAS & MARSHALL
Brooklands 48 Newbury Street Wantage Oxfordshire OX12 8DF
Tel: 01235 771234 *Fax:* 01235 772234 *Dx:* 40752 WANTAGE
E-mail: ask@clmlaw.co.uk
Office: Hungerford, Newbury, Swindon
Work: A1 C1 E L S1 W Z(d,r)
Emergency Action, Agency, Advocacy undertaken and Member of Accident Line
Ptr: Berrett, Mr Michael V Deputy District Judge . . . . . . *Jun 1986
Thomas, Mr David J LLB . . . . *§Oct 1982
Asoc: Angel, Mr Neil Russell LLB; LSF. . . . . Nov 1995
Ast: Thomas, Michelle LLB. . . . . Apr 1984
Con: Ball, Mr Christopher J . . . . *§Mar 1968

ELIZABETH A HUGHES ‡
Autumn Earth Charney Bassett Wantage Oxfordshire OX12 0EN
Tel: 01235 868438 *Fax:* 01235 868438
E-mail: elizabeth_hughes163@hotmail.com
Work: L S1 W

JOHN MANT SOLICITORS ‡
Unit 5 Manor Farm Manor Road Wantage Oxfordshire OX12 8NE
Tel: 01235 762900 *Fax:* 01235 762898 *Dx:* 40761 WANTAGE
E-mail: jmant@johnmantsolicitors.co.uk
List of partners: J C Mant
Work: A1 E L S1 W
SPr: Mant, Mr John C MA(Cantab). . . . . *Jun 1979

PATRICK SMITH & CO ‡
18 Newbury Street Wantage Oxfordshire OX12 8DA
Tel: 01235 772212 *Fax:* 01235 769633 *Dx:* 40757 WANTAGE
E-mail: patrick@patricksmithandco.com
List of partners: S H Robinson, P J Smith
Work: A1 B1 C1 C2 C3 D1 E F1 G H J1 K1 L M1 M2 N P Q R1 S1 T1 T2 V W Z(j)
Emergency Action, Agency, Advocacy, Fixed Fee Interview, Legal Aid undertaken and Member of Accident Line
Ptr: Robinson, Mr Scott H LLB. . . . . Feb 1990
Smith, Mr Patrick J BA(Oxon) . . . . *Aug 1978

WARE, Hertfordshire

BAILEY NICHOLSON GRAYSON
Unit T9 The Maltings Ware Hertfordshire SG12 8UU
Tel: 0844 939 6889
Office: Woodford Green

BARNES & PARTNERS
Baldock House 15 Baldock Street Ware Hertfordshire SG12 9DH
Tel: 01920 460823 *Fax:* 01920 460817 *Dx:* 48463 WARE 1
E-mail: people@barnesandpartners.com
Office: Cheshunt, Enfield, Harlow, London E4, London N15, London N16, London N18, London N8, Pinner
Work: A1 B1 C1 C2 D1 E F1 F2 J1 J2 K1 L N O P Q R1 S1 S2 U1 W Z(b,c,d,h,l,q,r)

CORBETTS SOLICITORS ‡
60 The Maltings Stanstead Abbots Ware Hertfordshire SG12 8HN
Tel: 01920 872929 *Fax:* 01920 870810 *Dx:* 48456 WARE
E-mail: info@corbettssolicitors.com

HUMAN LAW ‡
74 Millacres Station Road Ware Hertfordshire SG12 9PU
Tel: 01920 462202

JAMESON & HILL
(incorporating John A G Royce)
60-62 High Street Ware Hertfordshire SG12 9DA
Tel: 01920 460531 *Fax:* 01920 465142 *Dx:* 48452 WARE
Emergency telephone 01920 465142
E-mail: as@jamesonandhill.co.uk
Office: Hertford
Work: A1 B1 C1 C2 D1 E F1 G H J1 K1 L N O Q R1 S1 S2 T2 W Z(l,q)
Emergency Action, Agency, Advocacy and Fixed Fee Interview undertaken
Ptr: Evans, Mr Nicholas A LLB. . . . . *Oct 1985
Singh, Mr Andel Parthab LLB(Hons) ★ . . . . Oct 1997
Ast: Chapman, Mrs Anna Ruby LLB(Hons); LLM(Legal Practice) . . . . Aug 2003

WINTERS & CO ‡
3 Baldock Street Ware Hertfordshire SG12 9DH
Tel: 01920 466696 *Fax:* 01920 465113 *Dx:* 48451 WARE
List of partners: R E Winters, S M Winters
Languages: French
Work: C1 C2 C3 D1 E F1 G H J1 K1 L N P R1 S1 V W Z(c)
Emergency Action, Agency, Advocacy, Fixed Fee Interview, Legal Aid undertaken, Legal Aid Franchise and Member of Accident Line
Ptr: Winters, Mr Richard E. . . . . *Jan 1980
Winters, Mrs Siva Marie. . . . . *May 1982

WAREHAM, Dorset

HUMPHRIES KIRK ‡
Glebe House North Street Wareham Dorset BH20 4AN
Tel: 01929 552141 *Fax:* 01929 556701 *Dx:* 49700 WAREHAM
Emergency telephone 01929 552426
E-mail: wareham@hklaw.eu
List of partners: M M Baker, C Carretta, J W Chittenden, S D Cross, R F Hedger, K Jones, K E Levene, A L Marrow, M E Marrow, C J Reeves, R C Rowland, J S Selby Bennett, J D Stuart-Smith, H W Yarnold
Office: Bournemouth, Dorchester, Poole (2 offices), Swanage
Languages: French, German, Italian, Spanish
Work: D1 E K1 K3 K4 L S1 S2 T2 V W
Fixed Fee Interview, Legal Aid undertaken and Legal Aid Franchise
Ptr: Rowland, Mr Robin C BA(Dunelm) . . . . *Dec 1978

NEVILLE-JONES & CO ‡
(incorporating Stevens & Griffin; Guy Williams Green & Co; Neville Jones & Howie; Janice J Pond.)
19-21 North Street Wareham Dorset BH20 4AJ
Tel: 01929 552471 *Fax:* 01929 554600 *Dx:* 49702 WAREHAM
E-mail: info@neville-jones.co.uk
List of partners: P Griffin, P H H Stevens
Office: Swanage
Work: E F1 K1 K2 K3 K4 L N Q R1 S1 S2 T2 W Z(r)
Emergency Action and Fixed Fee Interview undertaken
Ptr: Stevens, Mr Peter Henry Hadden Commissioner for Oaths . . . . *§Nov 1957
Ast: Eaves, Mrs Pauline . . . . *Nov 2010
Oliver, Miss Rosalind Jane Charlton LLB(Hons) . . . *May 1981

WARLINGHAM, Surrey

STREETER MARSHALL
416 Limpsfield Road Warlingham Surrey CR6 9LA
Tel: 01883 622433 *Fax:* 01883 624080 *Dx:* 53352 WARLINGHAM
E-mail: warlingham@streetermarshall.com
Office: Croydon, Purley
Work: E F1 K1 L P S1 T1 T2 W Z(h)
Agency, Fixed Fee Interview, Legal Aid undertaken and Member of Accident Line
Ptr: Bowness, Lord P S CBE; DL Notary Public . . . . . *§Oct 1966

WARMINSTER, Wiltshire

BEASHEL SOLICITORS ‡
3 Station Road Warminster Wiltshire BA12 9BR
Tel: 01985 220680 *Fax:* 01985 214232
List of partners: R Beashel
Work: D1 D2 K1
SPr: Beashel, Ms Rosaleen BA(Hons) . . . . Jan 1993

FARNFIELD & NICHOLLS
37 High Street Warminster Wiltshire BA12 9AJ
Tel: 01985 214661 *Fax:* 01985 218314 *Dx:* 43603 WARMINSTER
E-mail: info@farnfields.com
Office: Gillingham, Shaftesbury, Sturminster Newton
Languages: French, German, Spanish
Work: A1 C1 D1 E J1 K1 K2 K4 S1 S2 T1 T2 W Z(d)
Legal Aid undertaken and Legal Aid Franchise
Asoc: Hamer, Mrs Fiona Anne BA . . . . *Nov 1994
Kerin, Mrs Sarah Maxine BSc(Econ) . . . . *Sep 2000
Weir, Mr Duncan Peter BA; GDL . . . . *Sep 2006

MICHAEL HUTCHINGS ‡
Sandhayes Deep Lane Corsley Warminster Wiltshire BA12 7QQ
Tel: 07768 105777
E-mail: mbh@dircon.co.uk
List of partners: M B Hutchings
Languages: French, German
Work: C3 M1
SPr: Hutchings, Mr Michael B BA. . . . . *Jun 1973

MIDDLETON & UPSALL LLP ‡
94 East Street Warminster Wiltshire BA12 9BG
Tel: 01985 214444 *Fax:* 01985 213426 *Dx:* 43600 WARMINSTER
Emergency telephone 01985 214444
E-mail: cgoodbody@mulaw.co.uk
List of partners: C J B Goodbody, H I Hindle
Languages: French
Work: A1 C1 D1 E J1 K1 L Q R1 S1 S2 W
Emergency Action, Advocacy, Fixed Fee Interview and Legal Aid Franchise
Ptr: Goodbody, Mr Charles J B BA(Law). . . . . *§Jan 1978
Hindle, Mrs Helen Ingrid BA(Hons) Gamlen Law Prize (Holborn Law Society) Notary Public . . . . *Jul 1992
Con: Vine, Mr Richard H W Notary Public. . . . . *§Nov 1972

SYLVESTER MACKETT
(incorporating Piper & Co)
1 Weymouth Street Warminster Wiltshire BA12 9NP
Tel: 01985 217464 / 217114 *Fax:* 01985 216587
Dx: 43605 WARMINSTER
Emergency telephone 01985 215514
E-mail: johnriley@sylvestermackett.co.uk
Office: Trowbridge
Work: C1 E J1 K1 K2 L N O Q S1 S2 W Z(q)
Agency and Fixed Fee Interview undertaken
Ptr: Riley, Mr John David BA; MA . . . . *Jan 2002

WARRINGTON, Warrington

ABACUS SOLICITORS
100 London Road Stockton Heath Warrington WA4 6LE
Tel: 01925 210999 *Fax:* 01925 210777
Dx: 28184 STOCKTON HEATH
Office: Manchester

ALBINSON NAPIER & CO ‡
(incorporating Willett Bullough & Boadman(John Marote))
20 Bold Street Warrington WA1 1HP
Tel: 01925 634681 *Fax:* 01925 230253 *Dx:* 17751 WARRINGTON
E-mail: law@albinson-napier.co.uk
List of partners: A J S Albinson, N D C Davis, R J Napier, R M Napier
Work: B1 C1 E J1 K1 K3 N O Q S1 S2 W Z(e,g,l,q,r)
Emergency Action, Agency, Advocacy and Fixed Fee Interview undertaken
Ptr: Albinson, Mr Adrian J S. . . . . *Jul 1968
Davis, Mr Nicholas D C BA(Hons); DipLP . . . . *Dec 1997
Napier, Mr Richard J . . . . Jan 2000
Napier, Mr Richard M LLB(Manc) . . . . *Dec 1963

AVALON SOLICITORS ‡
Avalon House 47 Museum Street Warrington WA1 1LD
Tel: 01925 232111 *Fax:* 01925 236200
Emergency telephone 01925 232111
E-mail: info@avalonlaw.co.uk
Work: N

BELL LAMB & JOYNSON
Mayfield House 84 Sankey Street Warrington WA1 1SG
Tel: 0844 412 4348 *Fax:* 01925 232088
E-mail: warrington@bljsolicitors.co.uk
Office: Liverpool (2 offices), Runcorn, Weaverham

BROOKSON LEGAL SERVICES ‡
Brunel House 340 Firecrest Court Centre Park Warrington Warrington WA1 1RG
Tel: 0845 058 1500 / 01925 235704 *Fax:* 0845 058 1250
E-mail: customerservices@brookson.co.uk

FIONA BRUCE & CO LLP ‡
Justice House 3 Grappenhall Road Stockton Heath Warrington WA4 2AH
Tel: 01925 263273 *Fax:* 01925 217077
Dx: 28189 STOCKTON HEATH
E-mail: legal@fionabruce.co.uk
List of partners: F C Bruce, S C Gray, S J Hayes, P A Porter
Work: A1 C1 D1 D2 E F1 J1 K1 K3 K4 N O Q R1 R2 S1 S2 W Z(c,d,r,x)
Emergency Action, Agency, Advocacy, Fixed Fee Interview, Legal Aid undertaken and Legal Aid Franchise
Ptr: Bruce, Mrs Fiona C LLB Councillor . . . . *§Nov 1981
Gray, Mr Stephen C. . . . . *Jul 1999
Hayes, Mr Stephen J Deputy District Judge . . . . . *Nov 1993
Porter, Mr Philip Anthony LLB(Hons) . . . . *Nov 1995
Asoc: Ashby, Mr John P LLB . . . . *§Nov 1971
Ast: Grainger, Mr Timothy David LLB. . . . . *Jun 2009
Harkness, Mrs Melanie Jane LLB . . . . *Aug 2009
Keegan, Mrs Rachel Clare LLB . . . . *Jan 2010
Langham, Mr Gareth Denbigh LLB . . . . *Apr 2004
Seaton, Mr Jonathan William BSc(Hons); MA . . . . . Sep 2011
Turner, Mrs Danielle LLB . . . . *Jul 2006
Worth, Mrs Hannah Ruth LLB(Hons) . . . . *Jan 2007

CANNING & CO ‡
Stanley Chambers 27 Stanley Street Warrington WA1 1EZ
Tel: 01925 630012 *Fax:* 01925 415046 *Dx:* 17756 WARRINGTON
E-mail: law@canningandco.com
List of partners: L R Canning
Work: K1 S1 W
Emergency Action, Advocacy, Fixed Fee Interview and Legal Aid undertaken
SPr: Canning, Mr Leslie R LLB. . . . . *Feb 1977

DSM LEGAL SOLICITORS ‡
Proud House 19 Bold Street Warrington WA1 1DG
Tel: 0845 009 0863 *Fax:* 0845 053 2350
E-mail: info@dsmlegal.co.uk
List of partners: D S Massey
Work: C1 F1 J1 J2 K3 N Q S1 Z(p,q)
Agency and Fixed Fee Interview undertaken
SPr: Massey, Ms Diane Susan . . . . Oct 1994

DALGARNO SOLICITORS ‡
Lovell House 412 The Quadrant Birchwood Park Warrington WA3 6AT
Tel: 0870 444 1501 *Fax:* 0870 444 1502
E-mail: info@dalgarnosolicitors.co.uk
List of partners: F Dalgarno, A Mills
Work: J1 N
Ptr: Dalgarno, Mr Fergus . . . . Jan 2000
Mills, Mr Anthony LLB. . . . . Jul 1997

DEAKIN & CO ‡
19 Hudson Grove Lowton Warrington WA3 2LJ
Tel: 01942 738580

DICKENSON MARTIN ‡
23 Museum Street Warrington WA1 1JA
Tel: 01925 574748
List of partners: G W Dickenson, D A Hughes, S M Martin
Work: J1 K1 M1 S1 W
Agency, Fixed Fee Interview and Legal Aid undertaken
Ptr: Dickenson, Mr George W . . . . *Jan 1978
Hughes, Mr David A LLB . . . . Nov 1974
Martin, Mr Stephen M. . . . . *May 1983

FORSHAWS DAVIES RIDGWAY LLP ‡
1-5 Palmyra Square Warrington WA1 1BZ
Est: 1878
Tel: 01925 230000 *Fax:* 01925 230616
Dx: 743430 WARRINGTON 15
E-mail: info@forshaws.co.uk
List of partners: C A N Agar, N L Banner, A Brown, V J Coulthurst, M Evans, G P Heaven, R C Hetherington, D A Hodd, J Hodd, T F C Jordan, J J King, S P Lawson, S M Poyner, J Roulston, C A Royle, G Schooler, E J Stride, A E Venables, S Woodall
Office: Frodsham, Warrington (3 offices)
Languages: French
Work: A1 A3 B1 B2 C1 C2 C3 D1 D2 E F1 F2 G H J1 J2 K1 K2 K3 L M1 M2 N O P Q R1 S1 S2 T1 T2 V W Z(c,d,e,h,l,q,r,w)
Agency, Advocacy, Legal Aid undertaken and Legal Aid Franchise
Ptr: Heaven, Mr Gary P LLB. . . . . *Jan 1982
Jordan, Mr Timothy Francis Comyn LLB. . . . . *Jan 1986
King, Mr John J LLB . . . . . *Oct 1986
Schooler, Mr Gary LLB . . . . . *Oct 1992
Venables, Miss Audrey E LLB(Hull) . . . . . *Apr 1981
Asoc: Bunglawala, Parveen . . . . . May 2005
McGuinness, Jennifer. . . . . Sep 2004
Mckenna, Mr Peter Edward LLB(Hons) . . . . . Dec 1973
Ast: Dyke, Emma . . . . . Jun 2007
Howarth, Nova . . . . . Aug 2006

FORSHAWS DAVIES RIDGWAY LLP
16 Walton Road Stockton Heath Warrington WA4 6NL
Tel: 01925 604713 *Fax:* 01925 604889
Dx: 28183 STOCKTON HEATH
E-mail: info@forshaws.co.uk
Office: Frodsham, Warrington (3 offices)
Languages: French, Spanish
Work: B1 F1 J1 M1 Q R1 S1 Z(c,e,k,l)
Legal Aid undertaken
Ptr: Roulston, Jennifer. . . . . Apr 2004
Stride, Ms Emma Jane . . . . . Jan 1990
Con: Spittle, Mr John B MA(Cantab) . . . . . *§Oct 1969

FORSHAWS DAVIES RIDGWAY LLP
21 Palmyra Square Warrington WA1 1BW
Tel: 01925 230000 *Fax:* 01925 416527 *Dx:* 17757 WARRINGTON
E-mail: info@forshaws.co.uk
Office: Frodsham, Warrington (3 offices)
Work: A1 B1 C1 D1 E F1 G H J1 K1 K2 L M1 N O P Q R1 S1 S2 T1 W Z(h,j,l,q)
Emergency Action, Agency, Advocacy, Fixed Fee Interview, Legal Aid undertaken and Member of Accident Line
Ptr: Agar, Mr Charles A N LLB. . . . . *Nov 1981
Banner, Mr Norman L BA Clerk to Commissioner of Taxes . . . . . *Jun 1973
Coulthurst, Mrs Vicki J . . . . . *Oct 1989
Royle, Mr Christopher A Mellersh Prize Notary Public *Mar 1962
Asoc: Fisher, Miss Michelle C LLB. . . . . Mar 1999
Holcroft, Miss Phillippa Ashley BSc(Hons); LSF(Hons). *Oct 1994
Ast: Kelly, Gemma. . . . . Nov 2006

FORSHAWS DAVIES RIDGWAY LLP
21 Bold Street Warrington WA1 1DG
Tel: 01925 230000 *Fax:* 01925 416527 *Dx:* 17757 WARRINGTON
E-mail: info@forshaws.co.uk
Office: Frodsham, Warrington (3 offices)
Work: A1 B1 C1 C2 C3 D1 D2 E F1 J1 K1 K2 L N O P Q R1 R2 S1 S2 W Z(c,e,f,k,l,q,r)
Emergency Action, Agency, Advocacy, Legal Aid undertaken, Legal Aid Franchise and Member of Accident Line
Ptr: Brown, Mr Alastair LLB(Newc). . . . . *Jul 1975
Evans, Margaret . . . . . Jan 1999
Hodd, Mrs Deborah A. . . . . *Jan 1982
Hodd, Mr John . . . . . *Dec 1981
Poyner, Mr Stephen M LLB R G Lawson Prize 1984. *Sep 1987
Woodall, Mr Stephen . . . . . Oct 1984
Asoc: Marks, Mr Peter. . . . . Sep 2000
Ast: Courtney, Jane . . . . . Jan 2007

FORSTER DEAN LTD
11 Suez Street Warrington WA1 1EF
Tel: 01925 575566 *Fax:* 01925 419530 *Dx:* 17816 WARRINGTON 1
E-mail: enquiries@forsterdean.co.uk
Office: Birkenhead, Bootle, Chorley, Crewe, Eccles, Ellesmere Port, Huyton, Leigh, Liverpool (5 offices), Oldham, Preston, Rochdale, Runcorn, St Helens, Stockport, Widnes (2 offices), Wigan
Work: N S1
Advocacy and Fixed Fee Interview undertaken
Ast: Leadbetter, Mr Andrew LLB(Hons) . . . . . *Nov 1988
Rathe, Mr Stuart M LLB(Hons) . . . . . *Sep 1996

GWS SOLICITORS ‡
22 Marlborough Crescent Grappenhall Warrington WA4 2EE
Tel: 0330 123 9011 *Fax:* 0844 335 1084

GRACE & CO ‡
Aztec House 20 Froghall Lane Warrington WA2 7JR
Tel: 01925 242488 *Fax:* 01925 242487
List of partners: J Grace
SPr: Grace, Miss Joanne LLB(Hons) . . . . . Mar 1991
Asoc: Massey, Mrs Diane Susan LLB(Hons). . . . . *Oct 1994
Ast: Avraam, Mrs Despina. . . . . Aug 2001
Birchall, Miss Deborah Catherine LLB(Hons) . . . . . Nov 1999

HALL & CO ‡
141 Orford Lane Warrington WA2 7AZ
Tel: 01925 245858 *Fax:* 01925 245939
List of partners: I T Hall
Work: D1 G J1 K1 K2 N Q S1 W Z(r)
Ptr: Hall, Mr Ian T. . . . . May 1994

HOBSONS ‡
79 High Street Golbourne Warrington WA3 3BU
Tel: 01942 725111 *Fax:* 01942 726111
E-mail: ken.fairclough@hobsonlaw.com

FRANK HOWARD ‡
(incorporating Freeman Wilkes & Co; DGR Newman; Langsdales; Grindrods; DT Lloyd)
10 Winmarleigh Street Warrington WA1 1NB
Tel: 01925 653481 *Fax:* 01925 418115 *Dx:* 17752 WARRINGTON
Emergency telephone 01925 740426
E-mail: enquiries@fhsolicitors.co.uk
List of partners: R Birtles, F Howard, J D Morris, D S Robb, H E Sadler, G Stokes
Languages: French, Spanish
Work: A1 B1 C1 C2 C3 D1 E F1 G H J1 K1 L M1 M2 N O P Q R1 S1 T1 T2 V W Z(c,l,t)
Emergency Action, Agency, Advocacy, Fixed Fee Interview, Legal Aid undertaken, Legal Aid Franchise and Member of Accident Line
Ptr: Birtles, Ms Roma LLB(Hons) . . . . . *Nov 1992
Howard, Mr Frank LLB Notary Public . . . . . *Aug 1969
Morris, Mr John D LLB . . . . . Jun 1979
Robb, Mr David Stuart . . . . . *Jan 1996
Sadler, Mrs Helen Elizabeth LLB(Hons) . . . . . Feb 1997
Stokes, Mr Geoffrey. . . . . *Jan 1984
Ast: Harrison, Mrs Laura Dionne. . . . . *Mar 1995

HUGHES CARLISLE LAW ‡
7500 Daresbury Park Daresbury Warrington WA4 4BS
Tel: 0845 519 2699 *Fax:* 0845 519 2688
E-mail: info@hughescarlislelaw.com

JMP SOLICITORS
The Genesis Centre Garrett Field Birchwood Science Park Warrington NG31 9RT
Tel: 0845 680 1895 *Fax:* 0845 680 1896
Dx: 701650 BIRCHWOOD WARRINGTON
E-mail: enquiries@jmp-solicitors.com
Office: Grantham
Asoc: Rudd, Mr Christopher LLB(Hons) . . . . . Oct 1994

KLS LAW ‡
Lawshield House Ibis Court Warrington WA1 1RL
Tel: 01925 428198 *Fax:* 01925 635209
Dx: 723604 WARRINGTON 11
Office: London EC1

KIRKHAM EDWARDS SOLICITORS ‡
Patton House Moulders Lane Warrington WA1 2BA
Tel: 01925 414614 *Fax:* 01925 414014
Work: E R1 R2 S1 S2 W

LONGLANDS SOLICITORS ‡
Burtfield House 23 Wilson Patten Street Warrington WA1 1PG
Tel: 01925 634277 *Fax:* 01925 659980 *Dx:* 17759 WARRINGTON
E-mail: info@longland.co.uk
List of partners: I D Burton-Baddeley
Work: C1 E L N Q S1 S2 W
Agency, Advocacy and Fixed Fee Interview undertaken
SPr: Burton-Baddeley, Mr Ian D BA . . . . . *Sep 1980

ORTOLAN LEGAL LIMITED ‡
The Genesis Centre Birchwood Warrington WA3 7BH
Tel: 01925 830895 *Fax:* 01925 851516
E-mail: info@ortolangroup.com
Office: London W1

POOLE ALCOCK
1D Warrington Business Centre Gilbert Wakefield House Bewsey Street Warrington WA2 7JQ
Tel: 01925 573447
E-mail: warrington@poolealcock.co.uk
Office: Alsager, Chester, Congleton, Crewe (2 offices), Nantwich, Northwich, Sandbach

RESTON'S SOLICITORS LIMITED ‡
Arpley House 59 Wilson Patten Street Warrington WA1 1NF
Tel: 0870 755 8998 *Fax:* 01925 417517 *Dx:* 17770 WARRINGTON
E-mail: cjr@restons.co.uk
List of partners: N P Coe, C J Reston, S C Reston
Languages: French, Russian, Spanish
Work: O S2 Z(b)
Agency undertaken
Ptr: Coe, Mr Nigel P BA; ACIArb. . . . . *Feb 1989
Reston, Mr Christopher J MA(Oxon). . . . . *§Jun 1976
Reston, Mrs Sara C LLB . . . . . *§Oct 1976
Ast: Bouchier, Mr Jeremy BA(Hons)(Law) . . . . . *Jul 1991

JEFFREY H RILEY CONSULTANT SOLICITOR ‡
Old Hall Farm Runcorn Road Warrington WA4 6UB
Tel: 01925 740862 *Fax:* 01925 740862

THE SPECTER PARTNERSHIP
Ibis Court Lakeside Drive Centre Park Warrington WA1 1RL
Tel: 01925 428360 *Fax:* 01925 428361
Dx: 723603 WARRINGTON 11
Office: Birkenhead, London EC1

STEELS ‡
17 Bold Street Warrington WA1 1DH
Tel: 01925 632676 *Fax:* 01925 444658 *Dx:* 17753 WARRINGTON
E-mail: general@steels-solicitors.co.uk
List of partners: J D Culleton, D S Hannah, C A Levitt, P Ness
Office: Warrington
Languages: French
Work: A1 C1 C2 C3 E G K1 L P S1 T1 T2 W Z(l)
Emergency Action, Agency, Advocacy and Fixed Fee Interview undertaken
Ptr: Culleton, Mr John D LLB . . . . . *Sep 1985
Ness, Mr Phillip . . . . . *Feb 1982

STEELS
Pembroke House 1 Victoria Road Stockton Heath Warrington WA4 2AL
Tel: 01925 261354 *Fax:* 01925 860034
Dx: 28181 STOCKTON HEATH
E-mail: enquiries@steels-solicitors.co.uk
Office: Warrington
Work: A1 E K1 L P R1 S1 S2 W
Fixed Fee Interview undertaken
Ptr: Hannah, Mr David S LLB(Hons) Councillor . . . . . *May 1977
Levitt, Miss Catriona Anne BA; PGDipLaw Graham Turnbull Prize - Criminal Law. . . . . *Oct 2004
Asoc: Lockley, Mr Michael G LLB . . . . . *Jul 1975

WATSON SOLICITORS ‡
13 Bold Street Warrington WA1 1DJ
Tel: 01925 571212 *Fax:* 01925 444323 *Dx:* 17755 WARRINGTON
E-mail: enquiries@watsonssolicitors.com
List of partners: J E Banasko, C J H Hanratty, D Hudson, S M Martin, C Parry
Work: B1 B2 C1 D1 E F1 G H J1 J2 K1 K2 K3 K4 L N O Q R2 S1 S2 T1 T2 V W Z(c,j,l,q)
Emergency Action, Agency, Advocacy, Fixed Fee Interview, Legal Aid undertaken, Legal Aid Franchise and Member of Accident Line
Ptr: Banasko, Mr John E LLB . . . . . *Dec 1976
Hanratty, Mr Christopher J H LLB Deputy District Judge . . . . . *Apr 1981
Hudson, Mr Daniel LLB(Hons); LPC. . . . . *Apr 2004
Martin, Mr Stephen M. . . . . *May 1983
Parry, Miss Catrin BSc . . . . . *Mar 1990
Ast: Mitchell, Ms Alexandra . . . . . *Mar 2005
Taylor, Miss Sally Anne . . . . . *Dec 1992

WIDDOWS MASON
Arundel House 12 Rylands Street Warrington WA1 1EP
Tel: 01925 632267 *Fax:* 01925 445148 *Dx:* 17796 WARRINGTON
Office: Leigh, Westhoughton, Wigan
Work: D1 G H K1 L N O Q R1 S1 S2 V W
Emergency Action, Agency, Fixed Fee Interview, Legal Aid undertaken and Member of Accident Line
Ptr: Barnes, Mr John M . . . . . *Jun 1970
Edwards, Mr James Lindsay LLB(Hons). . . . . *Dec 1989
Asoc: Cosgrove, Mrs Melanie Claire BA . . . . . Feb 2001
Ast: Ireland, Mr Paul Michael LLB(Hons). . . . . Jan 2000
Chadwick, Mr Christopher. . . . . Dec 1974
Thompson, Mr Geoffrey. . . . . Dec 1968

WILLETTS MARSDEN ‡
51 Wilson Patten Street Warrington WA1 1PG
Tel: 01925 230020 *Fax:* 01925 231492 *Dx:* 17771 WARRINGTON
E-mail: peter.marsden@willettsmarsden.co.uk
List of partners: P Marsden
Work: E F1 K1 K3 K4 N O Q S1 S2 T1 T2 W
SPr: Marsden, Mr Peter BA(Hons) . . . . . *May 1982

WARWICK, Warwickshire

BIDDLE MASON & CO - NOTARY PUBLIC ‡
Close Tower Brownley Green Lane Beausale Warwick Warwickshire CV35 7PD
Tel: 01926 484264 *Fax:* 01926 484424
E-mail: bidmasco@btinternet.com
Work: J1 S1 W

SARAH CAMPBELL SOLICITORS ‡
The Old Stores Yard 2a Banbury Street Kineton Warwick Warwickshire CV35 0JS
Tel: 01926 691110 *Fax:* 01926 641388

EVANS DERRY BINNION
5 Church Hill Coleshill Warwick Warwickshire B46 3AD
Tel: 01675 464400
E-mail: info@evansderry.com
Office: Birmingham

HAMILTON PRATT ‡
Franchise House 3A Tournament Court Tournament Fields Warwick Warwickshire CV34 6LG
Tel: 01926 838900 *Fax:* 01926 258799
E-mail: john.pratt@hplaw.co.uk
Languages: French, Punjabi
Work: C1 C3

HEATH & BLENKINSOP ‡
42 Brook Street Warwick Warwickshire CV34 4BL
Tel: 01926 492407 *Fax:* 01926 401424 *Dx:* 18109 WARWICK
E-mail: heath.blekinsop@btopenworld.com
List of partners: J M P Hathaway
Work: S1 S2 T2 W Z(d)
Ptr: Hathaway, Mr John M P. . . . . *§Dec 1975
Ast: Martin, Mrs Amy Louise LLB(Hons) . . . . . *Jul 2005

KW LAW ‡
First Floor Gervayne House 20-22 Market Place Warwick Warwickshire CV34 4SL
Tel: 01926 498981 *Fax:* 0800 066 4335
E-mail: contact@kw-law.co.uk

MACNAMARA KING SOLICITORS ‡
Coten House 61 Coten End Warwick Warwickshire CV34 4NU
Tel: 01926 499889 *Fax:* 01926 499552 *Dx:* 18107 WARWICK
E-mail: mail@macnamaraking.com
List of partners: M King, S Magnamara
Office: Coventry
Work: E F1 F2 J1 K4 L N O Q R2 S1 S2 W Z(k,q,r)
Agency and Fixed Fee Interview undertaken
Ptr: King, Mrs Marcella . . . . . Jan 2006
Magnamara, Mrs Siobhan. . . . . Jan 2001

MOORE & TIBBITS ‡
34 High Street Warwick Warwickshire CV34 4BE
Tel: 01926 491181 *Fax:* 01926 402692 *Dx:* 18102 WARWICK
E-mail: email@moore-tibbits.co.uk
List of partners: P R Freeman, C E R Houghton, J V Pike, A Woodruff, K A Wright
Languages: French
Work: D1 G H K1 L M2 P S1 Z(c,d,h,i,l,m,p,s)
Emergency Action, Agency, Advocacy, Fixed Fee Interview, Legal Aid undertaken and Member of Accident Line
Ptr: Freeman, Mr Peter R LLB ★ . . . . . *§Apr 1975
Houghton, Mr Christopher E R . . . . . *§Jul 1969
Pike, Mr John V. . . . . *§Jun 1970
Woodruff, Mrs Angela LLB . . . . . *§Jun 1969
Wright, Mr Keith Alan. . . . . *Jan 1983

O'GORMAN & CO ‡
1 Church Street Warwick Warwickshire CV34 4AB
Tel: 01926 409900 *Fax:* 01926 419900 *Dx:* 18111 WARWICK
Emergency telephone 07770 605577
E-mail: mail@ogormanandco.com
List of partners: K C O'Gorman, D A B Twigg
Work: C1 E G H J1 L M3 O Q S1 S2 Z(l,r)
Emergency Action, Agency, Advocacy, Legal Aid undertaken and Legal Aid Franchise
Ptr: O'Gorman, Mr Kevin Christopher LLB . . . . . *Nov 1994
Twigg, Mr David A B LLB(Manc). . . . . *Dec 1976

DUNCAN WATTS LLP ‡
26 Market Place Warwick Warwickshire CV34 4SL
Tel: 01926 493485 *Fax:* 01926 493517 *Dx:* 18116 WARWICK
E-mail: email@duncanwatts.co.uk
List of partners: J E Connor, M J Croom
Work: K1 K2 K3
Ptr: Connor, Miss Joanne Elizabeth BSc(Econ) . . . . . *Sep 1995
Croom, Mr Martin John . . . . . *Sep 1987
Ast: Patrick, Miss Lindsey Samantha LLB(Hons). . . . . Mar 2008

See p112 for the Key to Work Categories & other symbols

WOOLLEY & CO ‡
Warwick Enterprise Park Wellsbourne Warwick Warwickshire CV35 9EF
Tel: 01789 267377 *Fax:* 0871 661 5207
Emergency telephone 07768 096725
E-mail: admin@family-lawfirm.co.uk
Work: D1 K1 K3

WASHINGTON, Tyne & Wear

K BOSWELL SOLICITORS ‡
Arndale House Concord Washington Tyne & Wear NE37 2SW
Tel: 0191 417 6471

JOHN DONKIN & CO
Unit 53 The Galleries Washington Tyne & Wear NE38 7SD
Tel: 0191 416 9444 *Fax:* 0191 416 9111
E-mail: johndonkin@btconnect.com
Office: Gateshead
Work: B2 C1 D2 E F1 G H J1 K1 K3 L Q S1 S2 W Z(l)
Agency undertaken
Ptr: Langlands, Mr Graeme . . . . Jun 2002

MICHAEL HENDERSON & CO ‡
6 Victoria Road Washington Tyne & Wear NE37 2SY
Tel: 0191 415 1158 *Fax:* 0191 419 4054
E-mail: michaelhendersonandco@btconnect.com

MCKENZIE BELL SOLICITORS
The Galleries Washington Tyne & Wear NE38 7SD
Tel: 0191 416 2605 *Fax:* 0191 415 5175 *Dx:* 60905 WASHINGTON
E-mail: washingtonenquiries@mckenzie-bell.co.uk
Office: Sunderland
Languages: French, German
Emergency Action, Agency, Advocacy, Fixed Fee Interview, Legal Aid undertaken and Member of Accident Line
Ptr: Dixon, Miss Deborah LLB. . . . . *§Apr 1998
Sword, Mr John S G LLB; MA. . . . . *§Jan 1985

GEORGE MILLS ‡
Washington Town Centre 46 The Galleries Washington Tyne & Wear NE38 7SD
Est: 1962
Tel: 0191 416 2182 *Fax:* 0191 417 6088 *Dx:* 60900 WASHINGTON
Emergency telephone 0191 416 2182
E-mail: admin@georgemills.co.uk
List of partners: L Mann, I D Mills
Work: A1 C1 C2 C3 D1 D2 E F1 F2 J1 J2 K1 K3 L N O P Q R1 R2 S1 S2 T1 T2 V W Z(c,d,e,j,l,m,o,q,r,t,w)
Emergency Action, Agency, Advocacy, Fixed Fee Interview, Legal Aid undertaken, Legal Aid Franchise and Member of Accident Line
Ptr: Mann, Mr Leonard . . . . *Nov 1999
Mills, Mr Ian Donald William Hutton Prize . . . . . . *§Mar 1961

SWINBURNE & JACKSON LLP
(incorporating Armstrong Rose & Appleby)
56-57 The Galleries Washington Tyne & Wear NE38 7SD
Tel: 0191 416 0004 *Fax:* 0191 415 4822 *Dx:* 60907 WASHINGTON
E-mail: washington@swinburnejackson.com
Office: Chester-le-Street, Gateshead, Hexham, Ryton
Work: A1 B1 D1 E F1 G H J1 K1 L N P Q R1 R2 S1 S2 V W Z(c,d,h,j,l,m,p,s,t,w)
Emergency Action, Agency, Advocacy, Fixed Fee Interview, Legal Aid undertaken and Legal Aid Franchise
Ptr: Scott, Mrs Joanne Linda LLB(Hons). . . . . Nov 1995
Swinburne, Mr Christian Hugh Stuart LLB(Hons)(Northumbria) . . . . *§Sep 1996
Ast: Graham, Mr Alistair . . . . Jul 1977
Jackson, Mrs Rebecca Jayne . . . . Sep 2008

WATERLOO, Merseyside

GOODMANS ‡
Wellington House 4-6 St Johns Road Waterloo Merseyside L22 9QG
Tel: 0151 257 6000 *Fax:* 0151 257 6001 *Dx:* 13640 WATERLOO
E-mail: enquiries@goodmanslaw.co.uk

WATERLOOVILLE, Hampshire

BISCOES
15a Somerset House Hussar Court Waterlooville Hampshire PO7 7SG
Tel: 023 9225 1257 *Fax:* 023 9226 3314
Dx: 40719 WATERLOOVILLE
E-mail: bcg@biscoes-law.co.uk
Office: Gosport, Petersfield, Portchester, Portsmouth, Wickham
Work: A1 B1 C1 D1 E F1 G H J1 K1 L N O Q S1 V X Z(b,c,j,k,l)
Emergency Action, Agency, Advocacy, Fixed Fee Interview, Legal Aid undertaken, Legal Aid Franchise and Member of Accident Line
Ptr: Smith, Mr Mathew Nicholas Simon BA(Hons) . . . . . *Sep 1996
Ast: Webb, Mrs Franca . . . . *Nov 1986

CHANGING-HOMES.COM ‡
Appletree House 17 St Georges Walk Waterlooville Hampshire PO7 7TU
Tel: 023 9224 6699 *Fax:* 023 9224 6692
Dx: 40701 WATERLOOVILLE
E-mail: enquiries@changing-homes.com
Work: S1

HENTYS LLP ‡
Wellesly House 202 London Road Waterlooville Hampshire PO7 7AN
Tel: 023 9224 6710 *Fax:* 023 9224 1597
E-mail: hentys@hentys.com
List of partners: N S Craig, J J L Taylor
Work: C1 J1 Z(p)
Ptr: Craig, Mr Nigel S BA . . . . *Oct 1981
Taylor, Mr John J L BA . . . . *Oct 1990

LARCOMES LLP
Appletree House 17 St Georges Walk Waterlooville Hampshire PO7 7TU
Tel: 023 9224 6666 *Fax:* 023 9226 9144
Dx: 40701 WATERLOOVILLE
Office: Portsmouth
Languages: French
Work: C1 D1 D2 E J1 K1 K2 L N O Q R1 S1 T1 W
Emergency Action, Agency, Advocacy, Fixed Fee Interview, Legal Aid undertaken and Legal Aid Franchise

O'HARA SOLICITORS ‡
69-71 London Road Waterlooville Hampshire PO7 7EX
Tel: 023 9225 9822 *Fax:* 023 9224 0481
Dx: 40702 WATERLOOVILLE
E-mail: enquiries@oharasolicitors.co.uk
List of partners: K J O'Hara
Work: A1 B1 C1 D1 E F1 G H J1 K1 L M1 N P R1 S1 T1 V
Agency, Advocacy, Fixed Fee Interview and Legal Aid undertaken
Ptr: O'Hara, Mr Kevin J . . . . *Dec 1974

RCN LEGAL SERVICES LIMITED ‡
31a Queens Road Waterlooville Hampshire PO7 7SB
Tel: 023 9236 0914 *Fax:* 023 9298 4783
E-mail: rcnls@me.com

VERISONA SOLICITORS ‡
(incorporating MacDonald & Co)
Wellesley House 202 London Road Waterlooville Hampshire PO7 7AN
Tel: 023 9226 5251 *Fax:* 023 9226 5251 *Dx:* 50002 HAVANT
Emergency telephone 023 9223 2316
E-mail: admin@graypurdue.co.uk
List of partners: S J Ball, N J Cole, A L Collins, A J Cox, R A Downie, M J Dyer, M C Purdue, T G Reynolds, C Webb
Office: Havant, Portsmouth
Languages: French
Work: C1 C2 C3 D1 E F1 G H I J1 K1 L M1 N O P Q R1 S1 S2 T1 T2 V W X Z(c,d,e,h,i,l,m,p,q,r,y)
Emergency Action, Agency, Advocacy, Fixed Fee Interview, Legal Aid undertaken and Member of Accident Line
Ptr: Collins, Mr Alan L LLB(Wales). . . . . *Aug 1990
Dyer, Mr Michael J . . . . *Dec 1977
Reynolds, Mr Timothy G LLB(Cardiff) . . . . *Dec 1984
Dir: Ball, Mrs Susan Jane LLB(Hons) . . . . *Oct 1995
Cole, Mr Nigel J LLB . . . . *Jul 1980
Cox, Mrs Andrea J BA . . . . *Oct 1985
Downie, Mrs Ruth Alexandra LLB(Hons). . . . . . . *Jan 2003
Purdue, Mr Malcolm C Serjeants Inn Prize . . . . . *Nov 1977
Webb, Mrs Claire . . . . Mar 1998
Ast: Holden, Mr Benjamin BA(Hons); PGDipLaw; LPC . . *Nov 2006
Southwell, Mr Nicholas Edward BA(Hons); PGDipLaw; LPC . . . . Jul 2006

WATFORD, Hertfordshire

ADDISON OLIVER MOORE ‡
Parade House 135 The Parade Watford Hertfordshire WD17 1NA
Tel: 07930 968578 / 01268 833020
Office: Northampton

ANDELLS SOLICITORS ‡
Suite 10 Leaford Court Leaford Cresent Watford Hertfordshire WD24 5JF
Tel: 01923 682328

ARKRIGHTS SOLICITORS ‡
15 Exchange Road Watford Hertfordshire WD18 0JD
Tel: 01923 233477

E M BALL & CO ‡
17 Clarendon Road Watford Hertfordshire WD1 1JR
Tel: 01923 213456 *Fax:* 01923 254451

BROWN & EMERY ‡
153 The Parade Watford Hertfordshire WD17 1NA
Tel: 01923 225255 *Fax:* 01923 228922 *Dx:* 4511 WATFORD 1
E-mail: johnkillington@brownandemery.com
List of partners: J R Killington, J T Sinclair
Work: C2 E G H R1 S1 T1 T2 V W
Emergency Action, Agency, Advocacy, Fixed Fee Interview, Legal Aid undertaken and Legal Aid Franchise
Ptr: Killington, Mr John Richard BA . . . . *Jan 1983
Sinclair, Mr James T BA(Hons) . . . . *May 1987
Ast: Al-Wakeel, Mrs Duha LLB(Hons) . . . . Jun 2004

CHO & CO ‡
CP House Otters Pool Way Watford Hertfordshire WD25 8HP
Tel: 01923 650377

COLLINS SOLICITORS ‡
20 Station Road Watford Hertfordshire WD17 1AR
Tel: 01923 223324 *Fax:* 01923 211399 *Dx:* 51516 WATFORD 2
E-mail: collins@collinslaw.co.uk
List of partners: L F Collins, W D Collins, W Collins, D Holliday, P McGinley
Languages: French, German, Gujarati, Hebrew
Work: D1 J1 K1 L M3 N O Q S1 S2 V W Z(q,r)
Emergency Action, Agency, Advocacy, Fixed Fee Interview, Legal Aid undertaken and Legal Aid Franchise
Ptr: Collins, Mrs Lesley F BA . . . . May 1977
Collins, Mr William BSc(Hons). . . . . Oct 2008
Collins, Mr W Desmond BA; LLB . . . . *Apr 1975
Holliday, Miss Danielle LLB . . . . Mar 2009
McGinley, Mr Paul BA. . . . . Sep 2001
Ast: Cathcart, Miss Karen LLB; LPC . . . . Apr 2010
Downes, Miss Donna BA(Hons). . . . . Feb 2001
Gershuny, Mrs Rebekah M BA(Oxon) . . . . *Nov 1984

PAUL FALLON & CO ‡
(incorporating Samuel J Weaver & Tabor)
87-89 Market Street Watford Hertfordshire WD18 0PT
Tel: 01923 226795 *Fax:* 01923 231445
E-mail: j.jackson@paulfallonlaw.co.uk
List of partners: J A Jackson
Work: A1 B1 C1 D1 E F1 G J1 K1 L M1 N O P Q R1 S1 S2 T1 V W Z(b,c,e,f,g,h,j,k,l,m,n,o,p,r,s)
Emergency Action, Agency, Advocacy, Fixed Fee Interview and Legal Aid undertaken
Ptr: Jackson, Mr Jeffrey A LLB . . . . *Mar 1987

HANCOCK QUINS ‡
22-26 Station Road Watford Hertfordshire WD17 1ER
Tel: 01923 650850 *Fax:* 01923 250787 *Dx:* 51502 WATFORD 2
E-mail: law@hancockquins.co.uk
Work: B1 B2 C1 D1 D2 E G H J1 K1 K3 K4 L N O Q S1 S2 W Z(l,p,q)

HINES & CO ‡
54 Clarendon Road Watford Hertfordshire WD17 1DU
Tel: 01923 431714 *Fax:* 01923 431868
E-mail: info@lghines.co.uk

JANIS-ZAHEER ‡
24 The Harebreaks Watford Hertfordshire WD24 6NG
Tel: 01923 448138

JEFFREY DOCTORS & MARCHANT ‡
34a Market Street Watford Hertfordshire WD18 0PY
Tel: 01923 231250 *Fax:* 01923 220504 *Dx:* 4521 WATFORD 1
List of partners: J Doctors, J L Marchant
Work: A1 C1 E F1 L N R1 S1 W Z(c)
Legal Aid undertaken
Ptr: Doctors, Mr Jeffrey . . . . *Nov 1970
Marchant, Mr John Laurence . . . . *Jun 1980

JANE KAIM-CAUDLE & CO ‡
9 Devereux Drive Watford Hertfordshire WD17 3DD
Tel: 01923 219061 *Fax:* 01923 219062
E-mail: jane@kaimcaudle.com
List of partners: P J Kaim-Caudle
Languages: Gujarati, Hindi
Work: D1 K1
Emergency Action, Agency, Advocacy, Fixed Fee Interview, Legal Aid undertaken and Legal Aid Franchise
SPr: Kaim-Caudle, Mrs Priscilla Jane. . . . . *Jun 1977
Ast: Dodhia, Daksha. . . . . *Nov 1992

PAUL LINTON & CO ‡
17 King Street Watford Hertfordshire WD18 0BW
Tel: 01923 230478 *Fax:* 01923 818159
E-mail: info@paul-linton.co.uk
List of partners: P D Linton
Work: C1 E S1 W
Ptr: Linton, Mr Paul D . . . . *Jul 1973

LLOYDS PR SOLICITORS
73 Clarendon Road Watford Hertfordshire WD17 1DS
Tel: 01923 201717 *Fax:* 01923 201727 *Dx:* 57654 HARLESDEN
E-mail: info@lloydspr.com
Office: London NW10

EDWARD MCCOURT & CO ‡
225 St Albans Road Watford Hertfordshire WD24 5BH
Tel: 01923 448401 / 448402 *Fax:* 01923 448403 *Dx:* 42561 BUSHEY
List of partners: E C McCourt
Work: E K1 L S1 S2 W
Ptr: McCourt, Mr Edward Christopher BA(Law) . . . . . . *Nov 1987

MAFFEY & BRENTNALL ‡
149 The Parade Watford Hertfordshire WD17 1NB
Tel: 01923 234607 *Fax:* 01923 818500 *Dx:* 4512 WATFORD
List of partners: J P Cox, P S Cox, J Hurrell
Work: A1 C1 C2 D1 E F1 J1 K1 L N O P Q S1 S2 T1 T2 W X Z(c,h)
Ptr: Cox, Mr Jeremy P LLB . . . . *Nov 1988
Hurrell, Miss Jennifer LLB. . . . . *Oct 1995

MATTHEW ARNOLD & BALDWIN LLP ‡
(in association with MAB Ltd)
21 Station Road Watford Hertfordshire WD17 1HT
Tel: 01923 202020 *Fax:* 01923 215050 *Dx:* 4508 WATFORD
E-mail: info@mablaw.com
List of partners: T Brittain, M J Delaney, I C Donaldson, P Gerschlick, K S Holt, R H John, J Kwok, D K Marsden, A Melton, S P Mills, R A Phillips, D M Power, R Raja, W A Ramsey, L M Seaman, T C Stothard, M P Tempest, M W Tudor, M Weston
Office: London EC4, Milton Keynes
Languages: Farsi, French, Hindi, Punjabi, Spanish
Work: A1 B1 C1 C2 C3 D1 D2 E F1 F2 I J1 J2 K1 L M1 M2 N O P Q R1 R2 S1 S2 T1 T2 U2 W Z(b,c,d,e,f,j,k,l,m,o,p,q,r,s,w)
Emergency Action, Agency, Advocacy, Fixed Fee Interview undertaken and Member of Accident Line
Ptr: Delaney, Mr Michael J BA(Hons) . . . . *Nov 1984
Donaldson, Mr Iain C LLB; TEP. . . . . *§Jan 1988
Gerschlick, Mr Paul LLB. . . . . Jul 1999
Holt, Mrs Karin S FILEx University Prize. . . . . . . *§Oct 1997
John, Mr Richard H LLB; BSc(Econ/Accounts) . . . . *Sep 1998
Kwok, Mr Joseph BA . . . . *§Sep 1998
Melton, Amanda . . . . Jan 2008
Mills, Mr Steven P LLB . . . . *§Mar 1987
Raja, Mrs Reshma . . . . Nov 1999
Ramsey, Mr William A LLB . . . . *§May 1981
Seaman, Ms Laura Mary LLB . . . . *Oct 1991
Stothard, Ms T Clare LLB. . . . . *§Oct 1990
Tempest, Mr Mark P LLB; PGDip . . . . *Oct 2000
Tudor, Mr Mark William LLB. . . . . *Aug 1991
Weston, Mr Mark LLB(Hons) . . . . *Mar 1997
Asoc: Messenger, Danielle . . . . Sep 2002
Santra, Ms Krishna . . . . Oct 1999
Wiper, Rachel. Mar 2001

MELDRUM YOUNG SOLICITORS
2nd Floor Suite Hannay House 39 Clarendon Road Watford Hertfordshire WD17 1JA
Tel: 01923 231598 *Fax:* 01923 231599 *Dx:* 51539 WATFORD 2
Office: Hertford, St Albans
Ptr: Kerry, Mr Andrew BA(Hons) ★. . . . . *Sep 1998
Meldrum, Mr Alistair R J ★ . . . . *Dec 1980

MOERAN OUGHTRED & CO ‡
Monmouth House 87 The Parade Watford Hertfordshire WD17 1LL
Tel: 01923 256263 *Fax:* 01923 228374 *Dx:* 4522 WATFORD 1
E-mail: general@molaw.co.uk
List of partners: W G Bennett, J A Earl
Languages: French
Work: C1 E J1 K1 L N Q S1 W Z(i)
Fixed Fee Interview undertaken
Ptr: Bennett, mr Walter G . . . . *Jul 1975
Earl, Ms Judith A . . . . *Dec 1980

MURPHY & CO ‡
Langley Place 99 Langley Road Watford Hertfordshire WD17 4BF
Tel: 01923 288043 *Fax:* 01923 288025
List of partners: M J Murphy
Work: B1 O Q Z(q)
SPr: Murphy, Mr Michael Joseph LLB. . . . . *Nov 1983

PENMAN JOHNSON ‡
5 George Street Watford Hertfordshire WD18 0SQ
Tel: 01923 225212 / 239566 *Fax:* 01923 223522
Dx: 4509 WATFORD 1
List of partners: J M Alderton, I M Avent, P R Butler, D Harris, J Y Windsor
Work: B1 C1 C2 C3 D1 E F1 J1 K1 L N O P Q R1 S1 S2 T1 T2 U2 W X Z(c,d,g,i,k,l,m,p,q,r)
Emergency Action, Agency, Advocacy, Fixed Fee Interview, Legal Aid undertaken, Legal Aid Franchise and Member of Accident Line
Ptr: Alderton, Miss Jacqueline M LLB; BCL Goldie Award 1985; Senior Scholarship Prize - Gray's Inn 1986 . . . *Jan 1990
Avent, Mr Ian M BA . . . *Mar 1984
Butler, Mr Paul R MA . . . *Nov 1979
Harris, Mrs Deborah MA(Cantab) . . . *Apr 1991
Windsor, Ms Julie Y LLB . . . *Oct 1984
Asoc: Browne, Mr Anthony Richard . . . *Dec 1975
Ast: Godwin, Miss Martha Elizabeth LLB(Hons) . . . *Dec 1991
Whiteley, Miss Helen . . . *Jan 1981

PULVERS ‡
Rigby House 34 The Parade Watford Hertfordshire WD17 1EA
Tel: 01923 240666 *Fax:* 01923 245405
List of partners: A R Pulver
Work: B1 C1 E J1 L O Q R1 S1 W Z(c,e,g,l,p,q,u)
Agency, Advocacy, Fixed Fee Interview and Legal Aid undertaken

SEDGWICK KELLY LLP ‡
Watford Place 27 King Street Watford Hertfordshire WD18 0BY
Tel: 01923 228311 *Fax:* 01923 228626 *Dx:* 4507 WATFORD 1
E-mail: mail@sedgwickkelly.co.uk
List of partners: A J Clark, C J Kernanec, C J Miller, G F Whyte
Work: C1 E F1 J1 K1 K3 K4 O Q R1 R2 S1 S2 T2 W
Agency, Advocacy and Legal Aid undertaken
Mem: Clark, Ms Amanda J LLB(Hons) . . . *Nov 1986
Kernanec, Mrs Caroline J . . . *Oct 1995
Miller, Mrs Claire J LLB . . . *Sep 1994
Whyte, Mr Gavin Fraser MA(Hons) . . . *Dec 1986
Ast: Barton, Deborah . . . *Apr 1999
Chipping, Mrs Elspeth Margaret BA(Hons)(Law) . . . *Jan 1987
Foster, Mr Robert Charles Hardcastle LLB . . . *Nov 1988
Merifield, Ms Frances LLB . . . *Nov 2000

JEREMY SIMON & CO ‡
St Mary's House 72a St Mary's Road Watford Hertfordshire WD18 0WQ
Tel: 01923 219292 *Fax:* 01923 219293 *Dx:* 4537 WATFORD 1
E-mail: jeremysimon@btconnect.com
List of partners: J E Ottman
Work: B1 E F1 L O Q S1 Z(b,l)
Ptr: Ottman, Mr Jeremy E MA(Oxon) . . . *Nov 1984

SIMPLY LAW ‡
Malvern House Croxley Business Park Watford Hertfordshire WD18 8YF
Tel: 01923 426600

GRAHAM SMITH PROPERTY LAWYERS ‡
St Johns House 304-310 St Albans Road Watford Hertfordshire WD24 6PW
Tel: 01923 227212 *Fax:* 01923 239345
List of partners: G Gibbons, G Q Smith
Work: E S1
Ptr: Gibbons, Mr Gary . . . Dec 1981
Smith, Mr Graham Q LLB . . . Nov 1981

WATH-UPON-DEARNE, South Yorkshire

ATTEYS
9 High Street Wath-upon-Dearne South Yorkshire S63 7QQ
Tel: 01709 872106 *Fax:* 01709 760328 *Dx:* 713436 ROTHERHAM 8
Office: Barnsley, Doncaster, Retford, Sheffield
Work: A1 D1 E F1 G H K1 L N Q S1 V W
Agency, Advocacy, Fixed Fee Interview, Legal Aid undertaken, Legal Aid Franchise and Member of Accident Line
Ptr: Buckley, Mr James W LLB . . . *§Apr 1969
Ast: Maylard, Mrs Victoria Jayne LLB(Hons) . . . *Oct 1995

BRIDGE SANDERSON MUNRO
42 High Street Wath-upon-Dearne South Yorkshire S63 7QE
Tel: 01709 873321 *Fax:* 01709 878637 *Dx:* 713435 ROTHERHAM 8
E-mail: info@bsmlaw.co.uk
Office: Doncaster, Thorne
Work: A1 B1 C1 C2 C3 D1 E F1 J1 K1 L N O Q R1 S1 S2 T1 T2 V W Z(i,k,l,m,o,q,r)
Emergency Action, Agency, Advocacy, Fixed Fee Interview, Legal Aid undertaken and Legal Aid Franchise
Ptr: Davies, Mr Paul D LLB . . . *Dec 1976

WATLINGTON, Oxfordshire

MCFARLANE WATTS & COMPANY SOLICITORS ‡
The Old Bishops House 44 Brook Street Watlington Oxfordshire OX49 5JH
Tel: 0700 077 7529 *Fax:* 0700 077 7329
E-mail: solicitors@ppslaw.com
List of partners: N H McFarlane-Watts
Work: C1 I O Q Z(e)
SPr: McFarlane-Watts, Mr Nicholas Henry BA(Hons)(Law) *Dec 1978

STEFANIE O'BRYEN SOLICITOR ‡
20 Shirburn Street Watlington Oxfordshire OX49 5BT
Tel: 01491 614700 *Fax:* 01491 612424
E-mail: sobfamlaw@hotmail.com
List of partners: S A O'Bryen
Languages: French
Work: E K1 K2 K3 K4 S1 S2 W
Emergency Action, Agency, Advocacy and Fixed Fee Interview undertaken
Ptr: O'Bryen, Miss Stefanie A BA(Hons) . . . *Jan 1982
Con: Dunn, Mrs Nuzhat Nazir BSc(Hons); GDL . . . *Apr 2000

WATTON, Norfolk

GREENLAND HOUCHEN POMEROY
40 High Street Watton Norfolk IP25 6AE
Tel: 01953 882864 *Fax:* 01953 883035 *Dx:* 31552 WATTON
E-mail: adrian-goldring@ghlaw.co.uk
Office: Attleborough, Long Stratton, Norwich, Wymondham
Work: B1 C1 E F1 F2 J1 K1 K3 L N O Q R1 S1 S2 W
Agency, Advocacy, Fixed Fee Interview, Legal Aid undertaken and Member of Accident Line
Ptr: Goldring, Mr Adrian P BA(Hull) . . . *§Jan 1980
Particular areas of work include: Bankruptcy, Commercial and Company Law, Commercial Property, Consumer Law - Agreements, Credit, Licensing, Sale, Consumer Protection

W F SMITH LLP ‡
The Manor House 8 Dereham Road Watton Norfolk IP25 6ER
Tel: 01953 880800 *Fax:* 01953 884258 *Dx:* 31551 WATTON
E-mail: marie.dickens@wfsmith.co.uk
List of partners: P S Lane, R Molony, A G H Stokes, J A Upton
Office: Dereham, Swaffham
Work: J1 J2 K1 K3 K4 N Q S1 V W
Emergency Action, Advocacy, Fixed Fee Interview, Legal Aid undertaken, Legal Aid Franchise and Member of Accident Line
Ptr: Lane, Mr Peter S BA(Law) . . . *Jul 1981
Upton, Mrs Jaqueline Anne . . . *Nov 1998

WEALDSTONE, Middlesex

GARSIDE & HOY ‡
21-23 The Bridge Wealdstone Middlesex HA3 5AG
Tel: 020 8427 5656 *Fax:* 020 8427 1121 *Dx:* 30452 HARROW 3
List of partners: B Hoy
Work: D1 E F1 J1 K1 L M1 N O P Q R1 S1 W
Emergency Action, Agency, Advocacy, Fixed Fee Interview, Legal Aid undertaken and Member of Accident Line
Ptr: Hoy, Ms Bernadette LLB . . . *Nov 1993

HARROW LAW PARTNERSHIP ‡
159 High Street Wealdstone Middlesex HA2 0DU
Tel: 020 8863 7888 *Fax:* 020 8861 2033
Emergency telephone 07974 004980
List of partners: E Meade-King, H Patel
Work: B2 G H
Advocacy, Fixed Fee Interview, Legal Aid undertaken and Legal Aid Franchise
Ptr: Meade-King, Mr Edward MA(Oxon) . . . *§Oct 1975
Patel, Hiten . . . Jan 1997

HARROW SOLICITORS & ADVOCATES ‡
5-7 Masons Avenue Wealdstone Middlesex HA3 5BQ
Tel: 020 8863 0788 *Fax:* 020 8420 9998 *Dx:* 80403 WEALDSTONE
Emergency telephone 07977 068809
E-mail: info@harrowsolicitors.org
List of partners: E Blades, S Down, R Herath, G Simpson
Languages: Gujarati, Hindi, Punjabi, Urdu
Work: B2 B3 D1 E F1 G H J1 K1 K3 L N O Q S1 S2 V W Z(g,h,i,l,m)
Emergency Action, Agency, Advocacy, Fixed Fee Interview and Legal Aid undertaken
Ptr: Blades, Mr Elvin . . . Sep 2001
Down, Mr Stephen Notary Public . . . Jan 1998
Herath, Mr Ranjan . . . Feb 1992
Simpson, Mr Gavin . . . Jan 1997

DAVID PHILLIPS & PARTNERS
130 High Street Wealdstone Middlesex HA3 7AL
Tel: 020 8861 3800 *Fax:* 020 8861 3332 *Dx:* 80404 WEALDSTONE
E-mail: info@dpp.law.com
Office: Birmingham, Bootle (2 offices), Chadwell Heath, Leicester, Liverpool, London E1, London SE18, London W1, Manchester, Nelson

ATUL SHAH ‡
75 High Street Wealdstone Middlesex HA3 5DQ
Tel: 020 8861 5000 *Fax:* 020 8863 2772
List of partners: A Shah
Languages: Gujarati, Hindi, Kiswahili
Work: C1 E F1 J1 K1 K3 L N O Q S1 S2 W X
Fixed Fee Interview undertaken
SPr: Shah, Mr Atul LLB(Hons) . . . *Mar 1991

WEAVERHAM, Cheshire

BELL LAMB & JOYNSON
26 High Street Weaverham Cheshire CW8 3HB
Tel: 0844 412 4348 *Fax:* 01606 854090 *Dx:* 711580 WEAVERHAM
Emergency telephone 01928 732936
E-mail: weaverham@bljsolicitors.co.uk
Office: Liverpool (2 offices), Runcorn, Warrington
Work: D1 F1 G H K1 M1 P S1 V W Z(h,l)
Emergency Action, Agency, Advocacy, Fixed Fee Interview, Legal Aid undertaken and Member of Accident Line
Ptr: Cooper, Mr Barry D LLB(Manc) Deputy District Judge . Jun 1975

WEDMORE, Somerset

JOHN HODGE SOLICITORS
(incorporating Burrough & Co)
Cheddar Road Wedmore Somerset BS28 4EH
Tel: 01934 713030 / 712431 *Fax:* 01934 713424
Dx: 8403 WESTON-SUPER-MARE
E-mail: mailbox@johnhodge.co.uk
Office: Bristol, Clevedon, Weston-super-Mare (2 offices), Yatton
Work: A1 B1 C1 E F2 J1 K1 K3 L N P Q R1 S1 S2 W Z(p,q,r)
Emergency Action and Legal Aid undertaken

WEDNESBURY, West Midlands

MOORE SOLICITORS ‡
PO Box 4778 Wednesbury West Midlands WS10 1AL
Tel: 0121 531 0442 *Fax:* 0121 531 0443

WELLESBOURNE, Warwickshire

PENMANS
(incorporating Wilkins & Co)
The Precinct Wellesbourne Warwickshire CV35 9NL
Tel: 01789 470022 *Fax:* 01789 470077
Dx: 708982 WELLESBOURNE
E-mail: wellesbourne@penmanssolicitors.co.uk
Office: Coventry, Kenilworth
Work: E K1 L S1 S2 T2 V W
Emergency Action, Agency, Advocacy, Fixed Fee Interview, Legal Aid undertaken, Legal Aid Franchise and Member of Accident Line
Ptr: Griffiths, Mr Robert R G BA . . . *Dec 1978

WELLING, Kent

GOUGH CLINTON & BROOM ‡
104 Bellegrove Road Welling Kent DA16 3QD
Tel: 020 8301 9000 *Fax:* 020 8301 9009 *Dx:* 50204 WELLING
List of partners: N W Broom, K D Clinton, J C Guillen, C M Walters
Work: B1 C1 C2 C3 D1 E F1 G H J1 K1 L N O P Q R1 R2 S1 S2 T1 T2 W Z(c,j,k,l,q)
Emergency Action, Agency, Advocacy, Fixed Fee Interview, Legal Aid undertaken and Member of Accident Line
Ptr: Broom, Mr Neil W . . . *Dec 1973
Clinton, Mr Keith D . . . *Nov 1972
Guillen, Mr John C BA(Hons) . . . *Nov 1992
Walters, Mr Clive M MA(Cantab) . . . *Nov 1979

HADFIELD & CO ‡
1 Central Avenue Welling Kent DA16 3AX
Tel: 020 8301 0808 *Fax:* 020 8301 0060 *Dx:* 50205 WELLING
E-mail: lawyer@hadfieldsolicitors.co.uk
List of partners: M T Hadfield, K Sampson
Work: A3 B1 C1 C2 D1 E F1 F2 I J1 K1 K2 K3 K4 L M1 O Q R2 S1 S2 T1 T2 W Z(c,d,e,i,l)
Fixed Fee Interview undertaken
Ptr: Hadfield, Mr Michael Thomas BA; HNC(Business Studies) . . . *Jan 1984
Sampson, Mrs Karen . . . *Nov 1995

WELLINGBOROUGH, Northamptonshire

BAINS SOLICITORS ‡
71 Midland Road Wellingborough Northamptonshire NN8 1LU
Tel: 01933 440000 *Fax:* 01933 225400
Dx: 12870 WELLINGBOROUGH 1
Emergency telephone 07720 597407
E-mail: bains.solicitors@btconnect.com
List of partners: A S Bains
Languages: Punjabi
Work: G H
Advocacy and Legal Aid undertaken
SPr: Bains, Ammolak Singh LLB . . . *Jan 1993
Ast: Garcha, Mrs Baljit . . . Apr 1998

EVANS COOK SOLICITORS ‡
62 Broad Green Wellingborough Northamptonshire NN8 4LQ
Tel: 01933 278259 *Fax:* 01933 278140

FIRST DEFENCE
4 Sheep Street Wellingborough Northamptonshire NN8 1BL
Tel: 01933 442666 *Fax:* 01933 442707
Office: Bedford, Northampton

HOBEN JOHNSON
1 High Street Wellingborough Northamptonshire NN8 4HS
Tel: 01933 277666 *Fax:* 01933 272666
Dx: 12881 WELLINGBOROUGH
E-mail: law@hobenjohnson.com
Office: Rushden
Work: E F2 J1 J2 K1 K3 K4 N O Q S1 S2 W
Agency, Advocacy, Fixed Fee Interview and Legal Aid Franchise

LAWRENCES ‡
32a Sheep Street Wellingborough Northamptonshire NN8 1BZ
Tel: 01933 442324 *Fax:* 01933 442178
Dx: 12874 WELLINGBOROUGH
Emergency telephone 07789 867354
List of partners: J Smith-Wilds
Work: G H Q
Emergency Action, Agency, Advocacy, Legal Aid undertaken and Legal Aid Franchise
Ptr: Smith-Wilds, Mr James . . . Dec 2003
Asoc: Nicholls, Mr Mark . . . Jan 1991
Ast: Eaton, Mr Russell . . . Apr 1981
Lockwood, Ms Shona . . . Aug 2006

NFLA LTD
17 Sheep Street Wellingborough Northamptonshire NN8 1BL
Tel: 01933 222700 *Fax:* 01933 222646
Dx: 12896 WELLINGBOROUGH
E-mail: mail@nflaw.co.uk
Web: www.nflaw.co.uk
Office: Chesterfield, Nottingham, Rotherham, Sheffield
Work: D1 K1 K3
Emergency Action, Agency, Advocacy and Legal Aid undertaken
Ptr: Leach, Mr Simon D LLB(Hons) . . . *Mar 1988
Ast: Cooper, Mr Daniel LLB(Hons); PGDipLaw . . . Jul 2010
Gallacher, Ms Marie LLB(Hons) . . . Sep 2004

R J OSBORNE & CO
59 Midland Road Wellingborough Northamptonshire NN8 1HF
Tel: 01933 273400
E-mail: mail@rjo-corby.co.uk
Office: Corby, Northampton
Ptr: Gibson, Andrew . . . Jul 2007

SHERWOOD DUNHAM ‡
3 Sheep Street Wellingborough Northamptonshire NN8 1BL
Tel: 01933 276147 *Fax:* 01933 440275
Dx: 12853 WELLINGBOROUGH
E-mail: bbrown@sherwooddunham.com
List of partners: D W Dunham, M Fraiser, A R Sherwood
Work: B1 C1 D1 E F1 G H J1 K1 L N Q S1 S2 V W X Z(l)

See p112 for the Key to Work Categories & other symbols

Emergency Action, Agency, Advocacy, Fixed Fee Interview, Legal Aid undertaken and Member of Accident Line
Ptr: Dunham, Mr David W LLB . . . . Jan 1978
Fraiser, Miss Michelle LLB . . . . *Jul 1998
Sherwood, Mr Anthony R LLB . . . . Jun 1973

SMITH CHAMBERLAIN ‡
Regent House 61-62 Oxford Street Wellingborough Northamptonshire NN8 4JL
Tel: 01933 224971 *Fax:* 01933 228608
Dx: 12858 WELLINGBOROUGH
E-mail: enquiries@smithchamberlain.co.uk
List of partners: A E Frost, M D Ridout, W K Ryan, H E York
Work: A1 B1 B2 C1 C2 C3 D1 D2 E F1 F2 G H J1 J2 K1 K3 L N O P Q R1 R2 S1 S2 T1 T2 V W Z(c,e,j,k,l,o,p,q,r,s)
Emergency Action, Agency, Advocacy, Legal Aid undertaken, Legal Aid Franchise and Member of Accident Line
Ptr: Frost, Ms Ann E Notary Public . . . . *May 1987
Ridout, Mr Michael D . . . . *Dec 1971
Ryan, Mr William Keith BSc; MA . . . . *Aug 1995
York, Mrs Helen E LLB . . . . *Oct 1985

WILSON BROWNE
(incorporating Holyoak & Co; Sharman Sykes; Parker Daker)
60b Oxford Street Wellingborough Northamptonshire NN8 4JJ
Tel: 01933 279000 *Fax:* 01933 227350
Dx: 12855 WELLINGBOROUGH
E-mail: enquiries@wilsonbrowne.co.uk
Office: Higham Ferrers, Kettering (2 offices), Leicester, Northampton
Work: A1 A3 B1 C1 C2 C3 D1 D2 E F1 F2 I J1 J2 K1 K2 L N O P Q R1 R2 S1 S2 U2 V W Z(c,d,e,f,g,h,l,m,p,q,r,u,y)
Advocacy, Fixed Fee Interview, Legal Aid undertaken, Legal Aid Franchise and Member of Accident Line
Ptr: Moore, Miss Fiona J LLB . . . . *Oct 1984
Smart, Mr Richard J LLB . . . . *Jun 1975

WELLINGTON, Shropshire

BHAKAR TOMLINSON ‡
The Manor House 26 Vineyard Road Wellington Shropshire TF1 1HB
Tel: 01952 270555 *Fax:* 01952 270556
List of partners: G S Bhakar
Languages: Punjabi
Work: B1 C1 C2 C3 E F1 J1 L N O Q R1 S1 S2 T1 T2 W Z(e,q)
Emergency Action, Agency, Advocacy and Fixed Fee Interview undertaken
Ptr: Bhakar, Mr Gurcharan Singh BA(Hons) . . . . *Jan 1988
Con: Halstead, Mr Ian H . . . . Jun 1978

CLARKES
(incorporating Newillson & Barrowclough; R F Mitchell & Co; Revell Phillips)
7 Landau Court Tanbank Wellington Shropshire TF1 1DG
Tel: 01952 223548 *Fax:* 01952 222042 *Dx:* 23108 WELLINGTON
Emergency telephone 01952 254340
E-mail: law@clarkessolicitors.co.uk
Office: Newport, Shrewsbury, Telford (2 offices)
Work: D1 F1 G H J1 K1 L N Q S1 W
Emergency Action, Agency, Advocacy, Fixed Fee Interview, Legal Aid undertaken and Member of Accident Line

DIXON LEWIS SOLICITORS ‡
7 Queen Street Wellington Shropshire TF1 1EH
Tel: 01952 245700 *Fax:* 01952 245770 *Dx:* 23105 WELLINGTON
Emergency telephone 01952 550506
E-mail: dixoncarol@btconnect.com
List of partners: C Dixon-Lewis, J Taylor
Office: Craven Arms
Work: B1 C1 D1 K1 K3 N O Q S1 S2 W Z(l)
Emergency Action, Agency, Fixed Fee Interview, Legal Aid undertaken and Legal Aid Franchise
Ptr: Dixon-Lewis, Miss Carol . . . . Nov 1991
Taylor, Mr Jeremy BSc . . . . Nov 1991

GRINDROD & CO ‡
11 Queen Street Wellington Shropshire TF1 1EH
Tel: 01952 243064 *Fax:* 01952 222453
List of partners: S L Grindrod
Languages: Welsh
Work: A1 C1 E L S1 S2 T1 T2 W
SPr: Grindrod, Mrs Susan L LLB . . . . *Oct 1988

LANYON BOWDLER LLP
49 Church Street Wellington Shropshire TF1 1DA
Tel: 01952 244721 *Fax:* 01952 222418 *Dx:* 23101 WELLINGTON
E-mail: enquiries@lblaw.co.uk
Office: Hereford, Ludlow, Oswestry (2 offices), Shrewsbury, Telford
Work: A1 A2 A3 B1 B2 C1 C2 C3 D1 D2 E F1 F2 G H I J1 J2 K1 K2 L M1 N O P Q R1 R2 S1 S2 U2 W X Z(c,e,h,k,l,p,q,r,t,w,y)
Emergency Action, Agency, Advocacy, Fixed Fee Interview, Legal Aid undertaken, Legal Aid Franchise and Member of Accident Line
Ptr: Battisby, Mr David K LLB(L'pool) . . . . *§Dec 1978
Lewis, Mr Peter Vaughan LLB . . . . §Dec 1973
Merry, Mr John Gerard LLB(Hons) . . . . *Sep 1999
Asoc: Grimmett, Lisa . . . . Sep 1996
Ast: Hill, Miss Rebecca BA(Hons) . . . . Sep 2005
James, Ruth . . . . Sep 2003
Marston-Jones, Mr David . . . . Sep 2008
Con: Smith, Mr Peter Neville . . . . *§Dec 1967

GEOFFREY MILNE ‡
28 Church Street Wellington Shropshire TF1 1DS
Tel: 01952 223300 / 223381 *Fax:* 01952 244334
Dx: 23106 WELLINGTON
E-mail: geoffreymilne@hotmail.co.uk
List of partners: G Milne
Office: Wolverhampton
Work: A1 J1 K1 K3 L S1 S2 W
Advocacy and Fixed Fee Interview undertaken
Ptr: Milne, Mr Geoffrey . . . . *Jan 1982

NICHOLAS MOORE SPECIALIST EMPLOYMENT LAWYERS ‡
One Ruggin Place Wellington Shropshire TA21 9LL
Tel: 01823 421556 *Fax:* 01823 421474

MURRAY CAIRNS & CO ‡
29-31 Church Street Wellington Shropshire TF1 1DG
Tel: 01952 261650 *Fax:* 01952 261433 *Dx:* 23112 WELLINGTON
E-mail: info@murraycairns.co.uk
List of partners: S J Cairns, J M Murray
Ptr: Cairns, Mr Stuart J BA(Law) . . . . *Feb 1985
Murray, Miss Judith M LLB(Lond) . . . . *Jul 1976

PARRY CARVER ‡
(incorporating Espley & Co)
7 Church Street Wellington Shropshire TF1 1BX
Tel: 01952 641291 *Fax:* 01952 257519 *Dx:* 23116 WELLINGTON
List of partners: S J Carver, S J Hoyle, R M Prigg, C J Thomas
Office: Telford
Languages: Hindi, Punjabi, Urdu
Work: A1 C1 D1 E F1 J1 K1 K3 K4 L N Q S1 S2 W Z(i,l,p)
Emergency Action, Agency, Advocacy, Fixed Fee Interview, Legal Aid undertaken and Legal Aid Franchise
Ptr: Carver, Mr Stephen John BSc . . . . *Apr 1979
Hoyle, Miss Samantha Jane BA(Hons) . . . . *Oct 2002
Prigg, Mr Robert Michael LLB(Hons) . . . . *Oct 1995
Thomas, Miss Catharine Jane LLB(Hons) . . . . *Jan 2002
Ast: Khaira, Miss Parmjit LLB(Hons); LLM . . . . Apr 2005

WELLINGTON, Somerset

PORTER DODSON
15 High Street Wellington Somerset TA21 8QR
Tel: 01823 666622 *Fax:* 01823 665712
Dx: 49201 WELLINGTON SOMERSET
E-mail: porterdodson@porterdodson.co.uk
Office: Dorchester, Sherborne, Taunton, Yeovil
Work: A1 A3 B1 C1 C2 C3 D1 E F1 G H J1 J2 K1 K2 L M1 N O P Q R1 S1 S2 T1 T2 V W X Z(b,c,d,g,h,j,l,p,q,r,s,t)

WELLS, Somerset

CHUBB BULLEID ‡
7 Market Place Wells Somerset BA5 2RJ
Tel: 01749 836100 *Fax:* 01749 676300 *Dx:* 44902 WELLS
E-mail: solicitors@chubb-bulleid.co.uk
List of partners: M Chalfont-Griffin, R J Cussell, A J C Fowles, P S Medlicott, B J W Scobie, A R Walton
Office: Somerton, Street
Languages: French, Russian
Work: A1 B1 C1 D1 E F1 J1 K1 L N Q R1 S1 T1 T2 W Z(d,l,m,t)
Emergency Action, Advocacy, Legal Aid undertaken, Legal Aid Franchise and Member of Accident Line
Dir: Cussell, Mr Richard J BA(Legal Studies) . . . . *Sep 1987
Scobie, Mr Bruce J W LLB(Lond) . . . . *Oct 1985

GOULD & SWAYNE
21 Broad Street Wells Somerset BA5 2DJ
Tel: 01749 675535 *Fax:* 01749 686909 *Dx:* 44910 WELLS
Office: Burnham-on-Sea, Glastonbury, Street
Work: A1 B1 C1 E F1 J1 K4 L O Q S1 S2 T1 T2 W Z(d,l,m)
Dir: Taylor, Ms Sarah Jane LLB(Hons) . . . . *Apr 2005
Ast: Floris, Mr Giancarlo BA(Hons) . . . . Aug 2008

HARRIS & HARRIS
25 Market Place Wells Somerset BA5 2RF
Tel: 01749 674747 *Fax:* 01749 834060
E-mail: reception@harris-harris.co.uk
Office: Frome

MILLER LYONS SOLICITORS ‡
Melbourne House Chamberlain Street Wells Somerset BA5 2PJ
Tel: 01749 674150 *Fax:* 01749 674049
E-mail: paul.lyons@millerlyons.co.uk

T G POLLARD & CO ‡
Avenue House 64 High Street Wells Somerset BA5 2RS
Tel: 01749 674722 *Fax:* 01749 676296 *Dx:* 44903 WELLS
E-mail: law@tgpollard.co.uk
List of partners: J F Boucher, S R Lewis, I W F Tetley, R J Wright
Languages: French, Italian, Welsh
Work: A1 B1 C1 D1 E F1 J1 K1 K4 L N Q R1 S1 S2 T1 T2 V W Z(c,d,k,l,q,t)
Emergency Action, Advocacy, Fixed Fee Interview, Legal Aid undertaken and Legal Aid Franchise
Ptr: Boucher, Mr John F MA(Oxon) . . . . Jan 1977
Lewis, Mr Stephen R BA . . . . *Mar 1981
Tetley, Mr Ivor W F BA(Oxon) . . . . *Oct 1978
Wright, Mr Richard J LLB . . . . *Jan 1977

SIRIUS BUSINESS LAW LTD ‡
St Lawrence Lodge 37 Chamberlain Street Wells Somerset BA5 2PQ
Tel: 0844 209 8500 *Fax:* 0844 209 8510
E-mail: enquiries@siriusbusinesslaw.co.uk

WELLS-NEXT-THE-SEA, Norfolk

HAYES & STORR
Chancery Lane The Buttlands Wells-next-the-Sea Norfolk NR23 1ER
Tel: 01328 710210 *Fax:* 01328 711261
E-mail: law.wells@hayes-storr.com
Office: Fakenham, Holt, King's Lynn, Sheringham
Work: A1 C1 E F1 J1 K1 K3 K4 L N O Q R1 S1 S2 T1 T2 V W Z(d,l)
Ptr: Marshall, Miss Miranda Lucy MA(Oxon); TEP Notary Public . . . . *§Apr 1991
Ast: Connor, Miss Stephanie Anne . . . . Jan 2003
Newham, Mr Walter John Lisle . . . . Nov 2007

WELSHPOOL, Powys

EMRYS JONES & CO ‡
8 Broad Street Welshpool Powys SY21 7RZ
Tel: 01938 552510 *Fax:* 01938 555241 *Dx:* 29211 WELSHPOOL
E-mail: info@emrysjones.co.uk
List of partners: B W Thistlethwaite
Office: Bishops Castle
Work: A1 B1 C1 D1 E F1 G H J1 K1 K3 L N O P Q R1 S1 S2 T1 W Z(c,j,k,l,q,s,t)
Emergency Action and Advocacy undertaken
Ptr: Thistlethwaite, Mr Bennett W . . . . *May 1971

GILBERT DAVIES & PARTNERS ‡
(incorporating Gilbert Davies & Roberts)
(in association with Milwyn Jenkins & Jenkins)
18 Severn Street Welshpool Powys SY21 7AD
Tel: 01938 552727 *Fax:* 01938 555350 *Dx:* 29212 WELSHPOOL
E-mail: lisabrown@gilbert-davis.com
List of partners: N E Jones, D G Thomas
Languages: Welsh
Work: B2 D1 E F1 G J1 J2 K1 K2 L O Q S1 S2 W Z(k,l,p,r)
Emergency Action, Agency, Advocacy, Fixed Fee Interview and Legal Aid undertaken
Ptr: Jones, Mrs Nerys E BA Clerk to the Advisory Committee of the Tax Commissioners & Secretary to the Advisory Committee . . . . *Nov 1987
Thomas, Mr David G LLB(Wales) . . . . *§Mar 1958

HARRISONS SOLICITORS LLP ‡
11 Berriew Street Welshpool Powys SY21 7SL
Tel: 01938 552545 *Fax:* 01938 552970 *Dx:* 29215 WELSHPOOL
E-mail: enquiries@harrisonsllp.com
Web: www.harrisonsllp.com
List of partners: L P Ingram, A Jones, A J Smith, D H W Williams
Office: Newtown
Languages: Welsh
Work: A1 A2 A3 B1 B2 C1 C2 C3 D1 D2 E F1 G H J1 J2 K1 K2 K3 L N O P Q R1 R2 S1 S2 T1 T2 W Z(c,e,k,l,p,t)
Emergency Action, Agency, Advocacy, Legal Aid undertaken and Legal Aid Franchise
Ptr: Ingram, Mr Lee Paul . . . . *Sep 1999
Jones, Mr Alun LLB Clerk to Commissioner of Taxes . *Apr 1978
Smith, Ms Anne J BSc . . . . *Oct 1995
Williams, Mr D Huw W LLB ● . . . . *Mar 1987
Asoc: Easthope, Rebecca . . . . Sep 2004
Hibbert, Mr Eliot BA . . . . Jul 2006
Powell, Miss Charlotte E . . . . Jan 2008
Rees, Mrs Lowri Wyn BA; LLB . . . . Sep 2004
Ast: Bruce, Mr David E C . . . . *May 1979

WELWYN GARDEN CITY, Hertfordshire

CARR & KAYE SOLICITORS
30a The Avenue Welwyn Garden City Hertfordshire AL6 0PP
Tel: 0845 241 5136 *Fax:* 020 8711 5742
Office: London NW3

CRANE & STAPLES ‡
Longcroft House Fretherne Road Welwyn Garden City Hertfordshire AL8 6TU
Tel: 01707 329333 *Fax:* 01707 331194
Dx: 30051 WELWYN GARDEN CITY
E-mail: law@crane-staples.co.uk
List of partners: G Ainscough, D W Bird, E Ismay, S Montgomery, D L Peters, I P Smith
Work: B1 C1 C2 D1 D2 E J1 K1 K2 K3 N O Q R1 S1 S2 T1 T2 V W Z(r)
Emergency Action, Agency, Advocacy, Legal Aid undertaken and Legal Aid Franchise
Ptr: Ainscough, Mr Gregory . . . . *§Dec 1978
Bird, Mr David W BA(Hons) Secretary and Treasurer of Hertfordshire Law Society . . . . *Nov 1995
Ismay, Miss Eileen BA; LLM(Lond) . . . . *Apr 1976
Montgomery, Ms Sharon BA(Law) . . . . *Apr 1986
Peters, Mrs Danielle L LLB . . . . *Nov 1999
Smith, Mr Ian P . . . . *§May 1978
Ast: Brewis, Mr Christopher Robert LLB . . . . Sep 2008
Twiggs, Mrs Bonnie Lorraine LLB(Hons) LPC Law Society Prize 2005 - Most Outstanding Student . . . . *Sep 2007
Webb, Ms Samantha . . . . Jun 2009

EWART PRICE ‡
(in association with Ewart Price & Primhak)
1st Floor 16-18 Church Road Welwyn Garden City Hertfordshire AL8 6PS
Tel: 01707 332383 *Fax:* 01707 372846
Dx: 30058 WELWYN GARDEN CITY
List of partners: M B Bottomley, J M Briscoe, M G Steel
Office: London NW3
Work: B1 C1 E J1 K1 L N O Q S1 T1 T2 W Z(c,j)
Emergency Action, Agency, Advocacy, Fixed Fee Interview, Legal Aid undertaken and Member of Accident Line
Ptr: Bottomley, Mr Michael B BA . . . . *Dec 1977
Briscoe, Mr John M . . . . *Jan 1980
Steel, Mr Michael G LLB(Lond) . . . . *Jul 1977
Ast: Lowe, Ms Zoe Ann . . . . *Nov 1995

HRJ LAW LLP
Gate House Fretherne Road Welwyn Garden City Hertfordshire AL8 6RD
Tel: 01707 887700 *Fax:* 01707 887701
Dx: 30050 WELWYN GARDEN CITY
E-mail: enquiries@hrjlaw.co.uk
Office: Hitchin
Languages: Cantonese, Hindi, Punjabi, Urdu
Work: B1 C1 C2 D1 E F1 F2 J1 J2 K1 K3 K4 L N O Q S1 S2 T2 U2 V W Z(e,h,i,k,l,p,r)
Mem: Bruton, Mr David G TEP . . . . *Dec 1970
Cooper, Mr Robin M LLB(Lond) . . . . Dec 1977
Mayes, Miss Karen E LLB(Bris) . . . . *May 1979
Prince, Mrs Fiona Lesley LLB(Northumbria); TEP . . . . Sep 1996
Ast: Bearne, Ms Abigail . . . . Dec 2010

NOBLE
5-7 Stonebank Welwyn Garden City Hertfordshire AL8 6NQ
Tel: 01707 326241 *Dx:* 30053 WELWYN GARDEN CITY

PREMIER LAW ‡
Suite 3 Fretherne Chambers Fretherne Road Welwyn Garden City Hertfordshire AL8 6NY
Tel: 01707 830030 *Fax:* 020 3014 7654

R A SAVAGE & CO ‡
Gate House Fretheme Road Welwyn Garden City Hertfordshire AL8 6NS
Tel: 01707 373037 *Fax:* 01707 326961
Dx: 30064 WELWYN GARDEN CITY
E-mail: legal@rasavage.co.uk
List of partners: C J Perry, R A Savage
Office: London NW3
Work: D1 D2 K1 K2 S1

Emergency Action, Agency, Advocacy, Legal Aid undertaken and Legal Aid Franchise
Ptr: Perry, Mr Christopher John LLB Deputy District Judge. Jul 1973
Savage, Mrs Rosemary A LLB(Hons)(Leeds) . . . . *Jul 1971
Ast: Savage, Mr Dominic LLB; LLM . . . . *May 2000

SWIFT PROPERTY LAWYERS ‡
5 Swallow Court Swallow Fields Welwyn Garden City Hertfordshire AL7 1SB

GORDON YOUNG SOLICITORS LTD
Purley Cottage Pottersheath Road Welwyn Garden City Hertfordshire AL6 9SU
Tel: 01582 405577 *Fax:* 01582 452967 *Dx:* 5959 LUTON
Office: Luton

WEM, Shropshire

PAUL F HARFITT & CO ‡
Tudor House 47 High Street Wem Shropshire SY4 5DG
Tel: 01939 232775 *Fax:* 01939 232775 *Dx:* 27385 WEM
Emergency telephone 01939 260114
E-mail: pfh@wemsolicitors.fsbusiness.co.uk
List of partners: P F Harfitt
Languages: French, German
Work: A1 C1 E K1 L N Q S1 S2 T1 T2 W Z(c,l)
Agency undertaken
SPr: Harfitt, Paul F BA . . . . *Jun 1976

WEMBLEY, Middlesex

AB SOLICITORS ‡
Trinity House Heather Park Drive Wembley Middlesex HA0 1FU
Tel: 020 8900 2099 *Dx:* 80231 WEMBLEY CENTRAL

AMAN SOLICITORS ADVOCATES (LONDON) LTD ‡
295 Harrow Road Wembley Middlesex HA9 6BD
Tel: 020 8782 3776 *Fax:* 020 8782 3778
List of partners: R Latif
Office: Birmingham
Dir: Latif, Mr Raheel BA(Law) . . . . Dec 2002
Ast: Saeed, Saad . . . . Mar 2008

J M AMIN & CO ‡
Premier House 45 Ealing Road Wembley Middlesex HA0 4BA
Tel: 020 8903 3766 *Fax:* 020 8903 1449
E-mail: jmamin@nomail.co.uk
List of partners: J M Amin
Languages: Gujarati, Kiswahili, Punjabi, Urdu
Work: B1 F1 G J1 K1 L N Q S1 W Z(i,l,r)
Agency, Advocacy and Fixed Fee Interview undertaken
SPr: Amin, Jayendra Manubhai LLB . . . . *Jan 1990
Ast: Koritsas, Miss Xenia Helen Kay LLB. . . . . . . *May 1992

AMORY GLASS & CO ‡
784 Harrow Road Wembley Middlesex HA0 3EA
Tel: 020 8904 8236 *Fax:* 020 8904 2695 *Dx:* 43256 SUDBURY HILL
List of partners: D R Young
Work: E L S1 S2 W
SPr: Young, Mr David R LLB . . . . *Jun 1974

AVERTON WALLACE & CO ‡
13th Floor York House Wembley Middlesex HA9 0PA
Tel: 020 8902 9440

BIRDY & CO ‡
606 High Road Wembley Middlesex HA0 2AF
Tel: 020 8900 9112 *Fax:* 020 8900 9113
Emergency telephone 07802 436120
E-mail: sols@birdylaw.co.uk
List of partners: L R Birdy
Languages: Gujarati, Hindi, Punjabi, Urdu
Work: B1 D1 D2 E J1 K1 K3 L N O Q S1 S2 W Z(d,i,l,q)
Emergency Action undertaken
SPr: Birdy, Lekh R LLB. . . . . *Oct 1979
Ast: Naz, Miss Farzana . . . . *Apr 2004
Popat, Mrs Dee LLB . . . . *Apr 2003

BUNCE-LINSELL ‡
(incorporating J A Bunce & Co)
235 Preston Road Wembley Middlesex HA9 8PE
Tel: 020 8904 2229 *Fax:* 020 8904 1948
List of partners: J A Bunce-Linsell
Languages: French, Italian
Work: W
SPr: Bunce-Linsell, Miss Jacqueline A LLB(Hons) Notary Public . . . . Jul 1967

CITY LAW SOLICITORS ‡
1 Olympic Way Wembley Middlesex HA9 0NP
Tel: 020 7663 8030 *Fax:* 020 7663 8035

GEORGE DANIELS ASSOCIATES ‡
Fulton House Fulton Road Wembley Middlesex HA9 0TF
Tel: 020 8728 8726

DE MELLO KAMATH & CO ‡
297 Harrow Road Wembley Middlesex HA9 6BD
Tel: 020 8902 5284 *Fax:* 020 8903 4816

DIVINE LEGAL PRACTISE ‡
Empire House Empire Way Wembley Middlesex HA9 0EW
Tel: 020 8970 2198

DON SOLICITORS ‡
1 Olympic Way Wembley Middlesex HA9 0NP
Tel: 020 8782 1130

JACK FRIEND & CO ‡
11 Sudbury Hill Close Wembley Middlesex HA0 2QR
Tel: 020 8904 4281

GPT SOLICITORS ‡
799 Harrow Road Sudbury Town Wembley Middlesex HA0 2LP
Tel: 020 8904 6495 / 8904 6598 *Fax:* 020 8904 5239
Dx: 43253 SUDBURY HILL
E-mail: mail@pateltejani.com
List of partners: S K Goel, N D Patel, F B Tejani
Languages: Gujarati, Hindi, Urdu
Work: B1 C1 E J1 K1 L N O Q S1 S2 W Z(i,l,q)
Emergency Action, Agency and Advocacy undertaken
Ptr: Goel, Miss Sukhneel Kaur LLB(Hons). . . . . . . Jan 1992
Patel, Nish D LLB. . . . . *Nov 1984
Tejani, Farid B LLB(Hons). . . . . *Apr 1985

GENGA & CO ‡
1st Floor 588 High Road Wembley Middlesex HA0 2AF
Tel: 020 8795 5020 *Fax:* 020 8795 5030
Dx: 80210 WEMBLEY CENTRAL
Emergency telephone 07956 569559
E-mail: genga@co.wembley.k24.net
List of partners: M Gengatharan
Languages: Gujarati, Sinhalese, Tamil
Work: B2 G H V Z(i)
Emergency Action, Agency, Advocacy, Fixed Fee Interview, Legal Aid undertaken and Legal Aid Franchise
Ptr: Gengatharan, Manickavasagar . . . . Sep 1992

CLIVE GOMES SOLICITORS ‡
Continental House 497 Sunleigh Road Alperton Wembley Middlesex HA0 4LY
Tel: 020 8904 2614 *Fax:* 020 8423 8832
E-mail: gomessolicitors@aol.com
List of partners: C T Gomes
Work: G H
Emergency Action, Agency, Advocacy, Legal Aid undertaken and Legal Aid Franchise
Ptr: Gomes, Mr Clive T BA . . . . *Jul 1984
Ast: Rao, Miss Sumitra LLB . . . . *Jul 1998

GURUSINGHE & CO ‡
427b High Road Wembley Middlesex HA9 7AB
Tel: 020 8903 5349 *Fax:* 020 8903 5239
Emergency telephone 01956 282450
List of partners: S C K P Gurusinghe
Languages: Hindi, Punjabi, Sinhalese, Spanish
Work: D1 E G K1 L N Q S1 V Z(i)
Emergency Action, Fixed Fee Interview and Legal Aid undertaken
Ptr: Gurusinghe, Mrs Suhasini C K P . . . . *Apr 1987

HACKMAN SOLICITORS ‡
City Bank Chambers 562a High Road Wembley Middlesex HA9 8YT
Tel: 020 8902 6282 *Fax:* 020 8903 7216
Dx: 80212 WEMBLEY CENTRAL

CHARLES HARDING & CO ‡
553a High Road Wembley Middlesex HA0 2DW
Tel: 020 8795 0990 *Fax:* 020 8795 0991
Dx: 80227 WEMBLEY CENTRAL
E-mail: 114175.2523@compuserve.com
List of partners: C E K D Harding
Work: B1 D1 F1 G H J1 K1 L N O Q S1 S2 V W Z(e,f,g,h,i,j,p,r)
Emergency Action, Agency and Advocacy undertaken
SPr: Harding, Mr Charles Emile Kwesi Desmond LLB; BSc .*Apr 1992
Ast: Klinger, Mr Ian Martin LLB(Hons) . . . . *Nov 1973

ALAN HARRISON & CO ‡
6 Park Lane Wembley Middlesex HA9 7RP
Tel: 020 8900 0262 *Fax:* 020 8900 0084
Dx: 80223 WEMBLEY CENTRAL
E-mail: mail@alanharrison.co.uk
List of partners: A S Harrison
Work: S1 W
Ptr: Harrison, Mr Alan Stewart. . . . . *Dec 1977

HINDOCHA & CO ‡
1st Floor Premier House 45 Ealing Road Wembley Middlesex HA0 4BA
Tel: 020 8903 1120 *Fax:* 020 8903 1099
List of partners: K K Hindocha
Languages: Gujarati, Hindi
Work: E L S1 W
SPr: Hindocha, Mr Kantilal Kurji . . . . *Jan 1976

HODDERS
The Triangle 311 Harrow Road Wembley Middlesex HA9 6BD
Tel: 020 8902 9604 *Fax:* 020 8903 4906
Dx: 51154 WEMBLEY PARK
E-mail: enquiries@hodders.co.uk
Office: High Wycombe, London NW10 (2 offices), London SW11
Languages: Dutch, French, German, Greek, Gujarati, Hindi, Italian, Kanada, Polish, Punjabi, Sinhalese, Spanish
Work: C1 E R1 S1 S2 T1 T2 W Z(l)

HORACE WRIGHT SOLICITORS ‡
9 Dickens Court 7 Byron Road Wembley Middlesex HA0 3PF
Tel: 020 8908 1804

JOSEPH & WHITE ‡
558 High Road Wembley Middlesex HA0 2AA
Tel: 020 8795 2020 *Dx:* 80225 WEMBLEY CENTRAL
E-mail: info@jwsolicitors.com

KOTHALA & CO ‡
423b High Road Wembley Middlesex HA9 7AB
Tel: 020 8902 4932 *Fax:* 020 8902 4958

F A LEE & CO CRIMINAL DEFENCE SOLICITORS ‡
Room 12 13 Quad Road East Lane Business Park Wembley Middlesex HA9 7NB
Tel: 020 8904 0700

THE LEGAL PRACTICE SOLICITORS ‡
(incorporating Craig & Co)
100 Wembley Park Drive Wembley Park Wembley Middlesex HA9 8HR
Tel: 020 8903 7017 *Fax:* 020 8900 1686
List of partners: E J M M Craig
Languages: Gujarati, Hindi, Tamil
Work: C1 C2 E J1 L R1 S1 W Z(c,d)
Agency undertaken
Ptr: Craig, Miss Elizabeth J M M. . . . . *Jul 1956
Asoc: Klinger, Mr Ian Martin LLB(Hons) . . . . *Nov 1973

LINCOLN HARFORD SOLICITORS LLP ‡
713 Harrow Road Wembley Middlesex HA0 2LL
Tel: 020 8903 1750 *Fax:* 020 8902 1526
E-mail: info@lincolnharford.com

LAWRENCE LUPIN ‡
2nd Floor Dexion House 2-4 Empire Way Wembley Middlesex HA9 0EF
Tel: 020 8733 7200 *Fax:* 020 8733 7250
Dx: 51165 WEMBLEY PARK
E-mail: enquiries@lawrencelupin.co.uk
List of partners: L P R Lupin
Languages: Albanian, Finnish, French, Hindi, Italian, Portuguese, Punjabi, Russian, Spanish, Swedish, Ukrainian, Urdu
Work: K1 K3 Z(g,i)
Emergency Action, Legal Aid undertaken and Legal Aid Franchise
SPr: Lupin, Mr Lawrence P R LLB(Hons). . . . . *Dec 1992
Ast: Aziz, Ms Tamana BA(Hons); CPE. . . . . Apr 2007
Barrett, Ms Jane BA; MSc; LLB . . . . *Nov 2010
Bettiga, Gabriella . . . . Jan 2006
Bhullar, Mrs Pardeep LLB. . . . . Mar 2009
Booker, Mr Michael LLB; LLM . . . . Mar 1996
Davin, Miss Sian Jenny BA(Eng Lit); MA(Intl Relations); CPE; GDL; LPC. . . . . Feb 2011
Dodo, Miss Tanya BA(Hons) . . . . Jul 2006
Freeman, Ms Sophie BA; LLB. . . . . Oct 2009
Olmos-Serrano, Miss Natalia . . . . Dec 2009
Parkar, Mrs Farah LLB; LPC . . . . May 2009
Vnuk, Mr Stefan Chad LLB(Hons); BSc(Jurisprudence) . . . . *Aug 1996

MNS LAW ‡
107a Ealing Road Wembley Middlesex HA0 4BP
Tel: 020 8902 0083 *Fax:* 020 8903 7768
E-mail: mnslaw@btconnect.com

CHRISTOPHER MATHEW SOLICITORS ‡
1 Olympic Way Wembley Middlesex HA9 0NP
Tel: 020 8782 1142 / 1146 *Fax:* 020 8782 1134
E-mail: solicitors@christophermathew.com

NATHAN SURESH & AMIRTHAN ‡
150a Ealing Road Wembley Middlesex HA0 4PY
Tel: 020 8574 1058 *Fax:* 020 8571 1610
List of partners: G Kathirgamanathan, J A Rajakariyar, P Suresh
Languages: French, Polish, Punjabi, Sinhalese, Tamil
Work: B1 E G K1 L N O S1 V W Z(d,i,l)
Ptr: Kathirgamanathan, Mrs Gaithirdevi . . . . *Sep 1983
Rajakariyar, Mr Jebaram Amirthanayagam . . . . . Dec 1994
Suresh, Mrs Pavaleswary . . . . Jun 1987

NESBIT LAW GROUP LLP
Office 202 11 Courtenay Road East Lane Business Park Wembley Middlesex HA9 7ND
Tel: 020 8901 9820 *Fax:* 020 3137 2013
E-mail: mail@nesbitlawgroup.co.uk
Office: Bury, Leeds, Liverpool

NICHOLAS SOLICITORS ‡
Wembley Point 1 Harrow Road Wembley Middlesex HA9 6DE
Tel: 07869 259049
E-mail: chimannadi@hotmail.com

OAKS SOLICITORS ‡
Suite 205 Empire House 1 Empire Way Wembley Middlesex HA9 0EW
Tel: 020 8970 2159 *Fax:* 020 8970 2164
E-mail: info@oakssolicitors.com
List of partners: V Balakumar
SPr: Balakumar, Ms Venuka . . . . Aug 1997

J C PATEL ‡
23 The Dene Wembley Middlesex HA9 7QS
Tel: 020 8903 3519 *Fax:* 020 8900 2319
List of partners: J C Patel
Languages: Gujarati, Hindi
Work: E S1 S2 W Z(i)
SPr: Patel, Mr Jayantilal C . . . . *Dec 1975

PINNACLE SOLICITORS ‡
Suite 120 Empire House Empire Way Wembley Middlesex HA9 0EW
Tel: 020 8970 2132 *Fax:* 020 8970 2152

RAFINA SOLICITORS ‡
795 Harrow Road Wembley Middlesex HA0 2LR
Tel: 020 8908 6742 *Fax:* 020 8904 6353
Emergency telephone 07956 564042
E-mail: rafina@rafina.uk.com
List of partners: B R Rahaman-Rahim
Office: Purley
Languages: Gujarati, Hindi, Urdu
Work: B1 C1 C2 C3 E G I J1 K1 K2 K3 L M2 N O Q S1 V W X Z(e,i,m,p)
Emergency Action, Agency, Advocacy and Fixed Fee Interview undertaken
Ptr: Rahaman-Rahim, Mrs Bibi R LLB . . . . Apr 1990
Asoc: Ibe, Mr Bertrum LLB; LPC. . . . . Apr 2006
Japal, Mr Trevor LLB; LPC . . . . Oct 2010

SHAH LAW CHAMBERS ‡
1st Floor 604 High Road Wembley Middlesex HA0 2AF
Tel: 020 8900 9529 *Fax:* 020 8900 1864
Dx: 80201 WEMBLEY CENTRAL
E-mail: shah@slchambers.co.uk

K SIVA & CO ‡
30 Saunderton Road Wembley Middlesex HA0 2NE
Tel: 020 8904 2577
Languages: Sinhalese, Tamil
Work: B1 G K1 L Q V W Z(i,l)

SRI KANTH & CO ‡
557 High Road Wembley Middlesex HA0 2DW
Tel: 020 8795 0648 *Fax:* 020 8795 0649
Dx: 80230 WEMBLEY CENTRAL
Emergency telephone 07831 195979 / 07958 356055
E-mail: srikanthsolicitors@hotmail.com
List of partners: S Srikanthalingam, M Umasuthan
Languages: German, Gujarati, Hindi, Krio, Limba, Sinhalese, Tamil, Themne, Urdu
Work: F1 G J1 K1 L N Q S1 V W Z(g,i)
Emergency Action, Legal Aid undertaken and Legal Aid Franchise
Ptr: Srikanthalingam, Mr Subramaniam BA . . . . *Jan 1992
Umasuthan, Mrs Malarvili . . . . *Mar 1994

See p112 for the Key to Work Categories & other symbols

STANLEY & CO ‡
SKL House 18 Beresford Avenue Wembley Middlesex HA0 1YP
Tel: 020 8903 7864 *Fax:* 020 8903 7128
E-mail: stanleyandco18@aol.com
List of partners: S C A Obeyesekere
Languages: French, Gujarati, Hindi, Punjabi, Sinhalese, Somali, Urdu
Work: C1 D1 E J1 K1 K3 L M2 N Q S1 S2 V W Z(g,i,p,q)
Emergency Action, Agency, Legal Aid undertaken and Legal Aid Franchise
SPr: Obeyesekere, Mr Stanley C A LLM(Cantab) ♦ . . . . *May 1989
Ast: Gorsia, Mrs Sheila LLB . . . . *Nov 2006

TANN & TANN SOLICITORS ‡
2nd Floor 604 High Road Wembley Middlesex HA0 2AF
Tel: 020 8902 6810 *Fax:* 020 8902 6811
E-mail: alex_tann@hotmail.com
List of partners: A Tann, S P L R Tann
Office: Harrow
Work: F1 F2 J1 K1 K3 L Q S1 S2 W Z(i)
Ptr: Tann, Mr Alex LLB(Hons)(Lond) . . . . Sep 1995
Tann, Mrs Samy P L Reynard LLB(Hons) . . . . Jun 2000

TOUSSAINT & CO ‡
451-453 High Road Wembley Middlesex HA9 7AF
Tel: 020 8903 6111 *Fax:* 020 8903 6234
Dx: 80220 WEMBLEY CENTRAL
Emergency telephone 07956 136121
E-mail: toussaintco@hotmail.co.uk
List of partners: R A Hepburn, A M Toussaint
Work: G H
Emergency Action, Advocacy, Fixed Fee Interview, Legal Aid undertaken and Legal Aid Franchise
Ptr: Hepburn, Ms Roselyn Ann BA. . . . . *Mar 2001
Toussaint, Mr Andonio Matthew . . . . *Oct 1990

TRIVEDY SOLICITORS ‡
8 Coniston Gardens Wembley Middlesex HA9 8SD
Tel: 020 8904 5615 *Fax:* 020 8904 5616
E-mail: vtrivedy@btinternet.com
List of partners: V Trivedy
Languages: Gujarati, Hindi
Ptr: Trivedy, Vipool LLB(Hons). . . . . *Oct 1989

VERMA & CO ‡
429a High Road Wembley Middlesex HA9 7AB
Tel: 020 8903 0309 *Fax:* 020 8903 9191
E-mail: info@vermasolicitors.co.uk
List of partners: P Verma
Languages: Gujarati, Hindi, Kiswahili, Punjabi
Work: C1 C2 C3 E L S1 W Z(i)
Agency undertaken
SPr: Verma, Parveen LLB(Newc); MA(Lond) . . . . . . *Jan 1978

WEMBLEY LAW SOLICITOR ‡
Suite 8 Stanley House Stanley Avenue Wembley Middlesex HA0 4JB
Tel: 020 8902 0202 *Fax:* 020 8900 1134
Dx: 80214 WEMBLEY CENTRAL
E-mail: wembleylaw@btconnect.com

WENDOVER, Buckinghamshire

D C KAYE & CO
10a High Street Wendover Buckinghamshire HP22 6EA
Tel: 01296 620443 *Fax:* 01296 620612 *Dx:* 141430 PRESTWOOD
E-mail: office@dc-kaye.co.uk
Office: Great Missenden
Languages: Czech

WEST BRIDGFORD, Nottinghamshire

COXONS ‡
6 Highfield Road West Bridgford Nottinghamshire NG2 6DT
Tel: 0115 981 2000 *Fax:* 0115 981 1237
E-mail: law@coxonssolicitors.co.uk
List of partners: E C G Coxon
Work: C1 E K4 S1 S2 T2 W
SPr: Coxon, Mrs Elizabeth C G LLB . . . . *§Jan 1987

MASSERS
Rossell House Tudor Square West Bridgford Nottinghamshire NG2 6BT
Tel: 0115 851 1666 *Fax:* 0115 851 1614
Dx: 719902 WEST BRIDGFORD
E-mail: law@massers.co.uk
Office: Nottingham
Work: D1 D2 E K1 K2 N Q S1 S2 W
Emergency Action, Agency, Advocacy, Fixed Fee Interview, Legal Aid undertaken, Legal Aid Franchise and Member of Accident Line
Ptr: Brooke, Mr Timothy J D. . . . . *Nov 1995
Ast: Goodall, Mrs Marian K LLB(Hons). . . . . . . *Jan 1980

NICHOLSON DAVIS SOLICITORS ‡
128 Melton Road West Bridgford Nottinghamshire NG2 6EP
Tel: 0333 577 0977 / 0115 933 8636
E-mail: enquiries@nicholsondavis.co.uk

ROTHERA DOWSON
52 Rectory Road West Bridgford Nottinghamshire NG2 6BU
Tel: 0115 914 0077 *Fax:* 0115 914 1777
Dx: 719915 WEST BRIDGFORD
E-mail: enquiries@rotheradowson.co.uk
Office: Beeston, Nottingham (3 offices)
Languages: French, German, Italian, Japanese, Punjabi, Urdu
Work: A1 A3 B1 C1 C2 C3 D1 D2 E F2 I J1 J2 K1 K2 K3 K4 L M1 M2 N O P Q R1 S1 S2 T1 T2 U2 W X Z(c,d,e,j,k,o,p,q,s,t,x)
Emergency Action, Agency, Advocacy, Fixed Fee Interview, Legal Aid undertaken and Legal Aid Franchise
Ast: Adcock, Miss Emma Victoria LLB(Hons). . . . . . . *Jul 2000
Mcauley, Ms Suzanne Louise . . . . *Feb 2010

WEST BROMWICH, West Midlands

ADCOCKS SOLICITORS LTD
5 St Michaels Court West Bromwich West Midlands B70 8ET
Tel: 0845 470 8181 *Fax:* 0845 470 8082
E-mail: info@adcocks.com
Office: Lichfield
Work: B1 C1 C2 C3 E F1 J1 K4 L R1 S1 S2 T1 T2 W Z(d,e,q)
Agency undertaken

ATHI LAW LLP ‡
(incorporating G R Smith & Co)
388 High Street West Bromwich West Midlands B70 9LB
Tel: 0121 553 5555 *Fax:* 0121 553 5557
Dx: 14612 WEST BROMWICH
Emergency telephone 07774 181111
E-mail: info@athilaw.co.uk
List of partners: H K Athi
Office: Sheffield
Languages: Chinese, Hindi, Punjabi, Urdu
Work: C1 E G H K1 L N O Q R1 S1 V W Z(c,e,i,j,l)
Emergency Action, Agency, Advocacy and Legal Aid undertaken
Ptr: Athi, Mr Hem Kumar LLB . . . . *Jun 1978

BACHES ‡
Lombard House Cronehills Linkway West Bromwich West Midlands B70 7PL
Tel: 0121 553 3286 / 553 7076 *Fax:* 0121 500 5204
Dx: 14604 WEST BROMWICH 1
E-mail: info@baches.co.uk
List of partners: J M Darbyshire, J T Johnson, A E Simonds, J S Styler, N A Sutton
Languages: Hindi, Punjabi, Urdu
Work: C1 C2 D1 E G H K1 L R1 S1 T1 T2 W Z(d,l,m,s)
Agency, Advocacy, Fixed Fee Interview, Legal Aid undertaken and Legal Aid Franchise
Ptr: Darbyshire, Mrs Jill M LLB Recorder. . . . . . . *Oct 1973
Johnson, Ms Joanne Theresa. . . . . *Nov 2001
Simonds, Mrs Ann E BA(Wales). . . . . *§Jul 1974
Styler, Mrs Jennifer S LLB(Manc) . . . . *May 1974
Sutton, Mr Nicholas A. . . . . *Dec 1977

CHALLINORS ‡
Guardian House Cronehills Linkway West Bromwich West Midlands B70 8SW
Tel: 0121 553 3211 *Fax:* 0121 553 2079
Dx: 713650 WEST BROMWICH
Emergency telephone 0121 200 2717 (EXT 200)
E-mail: info@challinors.co.uk
List of partners: H Ashworth, R Bannister, R Billingham, R H Bishop, A J Bowen, G W Brady, J L Chapple, A A A Chowdhury, R D R Corser, F Debney, P Debney, M I Follis, P F Griffiths, M J Harris, A M Houston, E Howe, P C Jordan, B S Kang, S T Kelsall, J M D Kerrigan, N Lewis, P T Lowe, P J McHugh, F M O'Sullivan, R E Price, N P Sellar, G N Sohail, M M Turner, J P Walker, P J L White
Office: Birmingham, Halesowen, Nottingham, Wolverhampton
Languages: Bengali, French, German, Hindi, Mandarin, Punjabi, Urdu
Work: B1 C1 C2 C3 D1 E F1 G H J1 K1 L M1 M2 N P Q S1 S2 T1 T2 V W Z(c,e,i,l,m,q,r)
Emergency Action, Agency, Advocacy, Legal Aid undertaken, Legal Aid Franchise and Member of Accident Line
Ptr: Ashworth, Mr Harry First Tier Tribunal Judge . . . . Nov 1978
Bishop, Mr Roger H. . . . . *Feb 1974
Bowen, Mr Andrew J . . . . Dec 1990
Brady, Mr Gerard W LLB . . . . *Mar 1991
Chowdhury, Mr Andrew A A. . . . . *Apr 1996
Debney, Mr Paul LLB . . . . Oct 1991
Griffiths, Mr Paul F MA . . . . *Oct 1982
Harris, Malford J BA. . . . . *Jun 1974
Jordan, Mr Peter C LLB. . . . . *Apr 1972
Lowe, Mr Peter T Notary Public . . . . *Jul 1978
Sohail, Ghulam Naeem . . . . *Oct 1994
Turner, Mr M Milo LLB . . . . *Jan 1984
Asoc: Allchin, Mr John. . . . . *Sep 1998
Greaves, Miss Dee F M LLB(Hons) . . . . Oct 1993
Kelly, Miss Susan. . . . . *Sep 1997
Shaw, Mr Richard P G LLB(Hons). . . . . *Sep 1999
Trott, Mrs Lindsey. . . . . *Aug 1999
Ast: Clennel-White, Mrs Johanna E BA(Hons)(Law) . . . *Nov 1986
Cotterill, Ms Pauline Valerie . . . . Oct 1971
Nixon, Mrs Ann Eva FILEx . . . . Nov 1998
O'Malley, Mr Shaun Patrick Joseph LLB; DipLPC . . . Sep 2001
Oliver, Mr Martin BSc. . . . . Sep 2001
Owen, Mrs Rosemary M LLB(Hons). . . . . . . *Jan 1988
Ribchester, Mr Edward LLB . . . . *May 1996
Rowley, Mr Stephen N . . . . Jul 1972

CLARK BROOKES ‡
2 Lombard Street West West Bromwich West Midlands B70 8EH
Tel: 0121 553 2576 *Fax:* 0121 500 5021
Dx: 14606 WEST BROMWICH
Emergency telephone 0121 308 0709
List of partners: P Breen, J R Edwards, R J Pinning
Languages: Punjabi
Work: B1 C1 C2 C3 D1 E F1 G H J1 K1 L M1 M2 N P Q R1 S1 T1 T2 W Z(e,h,i,l,o,p)
Emergency Action, Agency, Advocacy, Fixed Fee Interview, Legal Aid undertaken and Legal Aid Franchise
Ptr: Breen, Mr Paul BSc(Hons) . . . . *§Oct 1994
Edwards, Mr John R LLB Notary Public . . . . . . *§Jan 1968
Pinning, Mr Richard J LLB. . . . . *§Oct 1984
Asoc: Pinning, Ms Helen Mary. . . . . Dec 1993
Ast: Banks, Mrs Sara Michelle . . . . Nov 2001

Holders of Franchise for Crime, Family. We conduct business in Punjabi. We specialise in the following areas of work Fraud, Crime - General, Crime - Juvenile.

GANGAR & CO ‡
323 High Street Sandwell West Bromwich West Midlands B70 8LU
Tel: 0121 553 4166 *Fax:* 0121 553 2957
Dx: 14614 WEST BROMWICH 1
Emergency telephone 07941 061399
E-mail: info@gangar-solicitors.co.uk
List of partners: S S Gangar, B Sumon
Languages: Hindi, Punjabi, Urdu
Work: B1 D1 F1 G H J1 K1 L M1 M2 N P S1 V W Z(i,j,l)
Emergency Action, Agency, Advocacy, Fixed Fee Interview, Legal Aid undertaken and Legal Aid Franchise
Ptr: Gangar, Surjit S BA(Hons) ● . . . . *Jan 1983
Sumon, Mr Baljinder BA(Hons) . . . . *Sep 2000
Ast: Momi, Ms Angela . . . . Jan 2007

H&V SOLICITORS ‡
79 Birmingham Road West Bromwich West Midlands B70 6PX
Tel: 0121 525 2555

KHIRRI SOLICITORS ‡
2nd Floor Kinder House Lombard Street West Bromwich West Midlands B70 8RT
Tel: 0121 500 4020 *Fax:* 0121 500 4029
E-mail: rkhan@khirrisolicitors.com

MILLICHIPS ‡
317-319 High Street West Bromwich West Midlands B70 8LU
Tel: 0121 500 6363 *Fax:* 0121 553 1519
Dx: 14601 WEST BROMWICH
List of partners: A L Boyars, M J Brien, M E Hall, M Hartshorn, M Sharma, C G Viner
Office: Solihull
Languages: Punjabi, Urdu
Work: B1 C1 C2 D1 E K1 K3 L N O Q R1 S1 S2 V W Z(l,q,r)
Emergency Action, Agency, Advocacy, Fixed Fee Interview, Legal Aid undertaken and Legal Aid Franchise
Ptr: Hall, Mr Matthew E LLB(B'ham). . . . . *Jul 1983
Hartshorn, Mrs Michelle LLB . . . . *Oct 1995
Sharma, Madhur . . . . Jan 2006
Viner, Mr Colin G LLB(Leeds) . . . . *Apr 1975
Ast: Beeley, Mr Christopher Alexander BA(Hons). . . . . Sep 1995
Lines, Mr Nicholas C BA(Law). . . . . Apr 1981

RAI LEGAL ‡
380 High Street West Bromwich West Midlands B70 9LB
Tel: 0121 580 0511 / 07976 926156 *Fax:* 0121 580 2064
E-mail: jrai@railegal.co.uk

TURNER CARY PARTNERSHIP SOLICITORS ‡
Bank Chambers 313 High Street West Bromwich West Midlands B70 8LU
Tel: 0121 553 3017 / 07900 216284 *Fax:* 0121 553 2254
Dx: 14602 WEST BROMWICH
E-mail: gclements@turnercary.co.uk

WEST BYFLEET, Surrey

LARKIN & JAMES ‡
Newland House 31 High Road West Byfleet Surrey KT14 7QH
Tel: 01932 355433 *Fax:* 01932 336414 *Dx:* 52917 WEST BYFLEET
List of partners: C D James, A Larkin
Office: Guildford
Work: S1 S2 W
Ptr: James, Mr Colin D . . . . Jan 1971
Larkin, Mr Adrian LLB. . . . . *§Oct 1979

STUART Q MURPHY ‡
15 Station Approach West Byfleet Surrey KT14 6NF
Tel: 01932 355755 *Fax:* 01932 352208 *Dx:* 52912 WEST BYFLEET
E-mail: stuart@sqmurphy.co.uk
List of partners: S Q Murphy
Languages: French
Work: K3 S1 S2 W
Fixed Fee Interview undertaken
SPr: Murphy, Mr Stuart Quail BA(Business Law) . . . . . *Jun 1981

WEST DRAYTON, Middlesex

BURCH PHILLIPS & CO ‡
63a Station Road West Drayton Middlesex UB7 7LR
Tel: 01895 442141 *Fax:* 01895 421231 *Dx:* 47652 WEST DRAYTON
E-mail: admin@burchphillips.co.uk
List of partners: D C S Burch, S H Phillips
Languages: French, Hebrew
Work: G J1 K1 L O Q S1 S2 W Z(q)
Emergency Action, Agency, Advocacy and Fixed Fee Interview undertaken
Ptr: Burch, Mr David C S . . . . Jun 1975
Phillips, Mr Stephen H . . . . *Nov 1976

MARTIN MURRAY & ASSOCIATES ‡
Chapel House 152-156 High Street Yiewsley West Drayton Middlesex UB7 7BE
Tel: 01895 431332 *Fax:* 01895 448343 *Dx:* 47658 WEST DRAYTON
Emergency telephone 01753 600101
List of partners: Z Ahmed, A Asghar, N J R Ashby, D Burns, A Cosma, K J Hughes, I N Paul, J Phull, M Rai, P L Turnbull
Office: Reading, Slough
Languages: Greek, Punjabi, Urdu
Work: B2 G H K1 S1
Emergency Action, Agency, Advocacy, Fixed Fee Interview, Legal Aid undertaken and Legal Aid Franchise
Ptr: Ashby, Mr Nicholas J R BSc ★ . . . . *Jun 1998
Cosma, Mr Andrew LLB(Hons) . . . . *Sep 1990
Paul, Mr Iain N BA(Hons)(Oxon) . . . . *Dec 1998
Phull, Mr Jagdeep LLB . . . . *Feb 2003
Ast: Ali, Mr Mohammed LLB . . . . Aug 2004
Speed, Ms Jenny Sarah. . . . . Sep 2008
Tamana, Ms Gurbinder . . . . May 2003
Yaqub, Mr Shahnawaz . . . . May 2008

SHERRARDS
Abbey House 450 Bath Road Longford West Drayton Middlesex UB7 0EB
Tel: 020 8757 5670 *Fax:* 020 8757 8619
E-mail: advice@harrysherrard.com
Office: Haywards Heath

WELLS BURCOMBE LLP ‡
7 The Green West Drayton Middlesex UB7 7PL
Tel: 01895 449288 *Fax:* 01895 449726 *Dx:* 47654 WEST DRAYTON
E-mail: info@wellsburcombe.co.uk
Office: St Albans

WEST KIRBY, Merseyside

IAN C FREE ‡
11a Banks Road West Kirby Merseyside CH48 0QX
Tel: 0151 625 0000 *Fax:* 0151 625 3537
Emergency telephone 0151 625 8318
List of partners: I C Free
Work: E L S1 W Z(f)
SPr: Free, Mr Ian Clifford BA(Hons) . . . . Jun 1981

LEES SOLICITORS LLP
52a Grange Road West Kirby Merseyside CH48 4EF
Tel: 0151 625 9364 *Fax:* 0151 625 5576 *Dx:* 24653 WEST KIRBY
E-mail: info@lees.co.uk
Office: Birkenhead, Heswall
Languages: French
Work: B1 C1 C2 D1 E F1 J1 K1 K2 K3 K4 L N O Q R2 S1 S2 T1 T2 U2 W Z(c,d,l,m,r)
Agency, Advocacy, Fixed Fee Interview, Legal Aid undertaken, Legal Aid Franchise and Member of Accident Line
Ptr: Fisher, Mr Thomas B LLB(Lond). . . . . *Dec 1975
Read, Mr Michael J BA(Law) . . . . *Jul 1976
Kingston-Davies, Ms Joanna . . . . NSP
Ast: Cucchi, Miss Amanda LLB . . . . Oct 2003

MAXWELL HODGE SOLICITORS
34 Grange Road West Kirby Merseyside CH48 4EF
Tel: 0151 625 9154 *Fax:* 0151 625 1662 *Dx:* 24652 WEST KIRBY
E-mail: info@maxweb.co.uk
Office: Formby, Heswall, Huyton, Kirkby, Liverpool (2 offices), Maghull
Work: D1 E F1 J1 K1 K3 K4 N O Q S1 S2 T2 W
Emergency Action, Agency, Advocacy, Fixed Fee Interview, Legal Aid undertaken and Legal Aid Franchise
Ptr: Gordon, Miss Margaret L LLB(Nott'm). . . . . *Apr 1980
Newton, Mr Andrew David LLB . . . . *Oct 1990
Scoular, Miss Denise Michelle Dip Prof Skills(Cantab) . *Oct 1996
Ast: Bridson, Ms Daphne M LLB(Hons) . . . . *Apr 1981

REX TAYLOR & MEADOWS ‡
Midland Bank Building Grange Road West Kirby Merseyside CH48 4EB
Tel: 0151 625 6414 *Fax:* 0151 625 7757 *Dx:* 24654 WEST KIRBY
E-mail: rextaylormeadows@hotmail.co.uk
List of partners: C W Johnson, A D Tickell
Work: B1 C1 C2 C3 D1 E F1 G H J1 K1 L M1 M2 N P R1 S1 T1 T2 V W
Emergency Action, Agency, Advocacy, Fixed Fee Interview, Legal Aid undertaken and Member of Accident Line
Ptr: Johnson, Mr Christopher W Coroner. . . . . *§Dec 1971
Tickell, Mr Alan D BA Deputy Coroner. . . . . *Dec 1982

WEST MALLING, Kent

HAFTKE LIMITED ‡
Suite 2 30 Churchill Square West Malling Kent ME19 4YU
Tel: 020 7193 5371

KL PROPERTY LAWYERS ‡
Town House 74-80 High Street West Malling Kent ME19 6LU
Tel: 01732 873041 *Fax:* 01732 875738

KASLERS SOLICITORS LLP ‡
Suite 3 10 Churchill Square Kings Hill West Malling Kent ME19 4YU
Tel: 0845 270 2511 *Fax:* 0845 270 2513 *Dx:* 92863 WEST MALLING
Emergency telephone 07900 195195
List of partners: M D Breeze, S M Scott
Office: London E14
Languages: French, German
Work: B1 C1 C2 D2 E F1 I J1 J2 K1 K3 K4 L N O Q R1 S1 S2 U2 W Z(c)
Emergency Action, Advocacy and Fixed Fee Interview undertaken
Ptr: Breeze, Mr Michael D LLB . . . . *Jun 1977
Scott, Mr Simon McCree LLB(Hons). . . . . *Feb 2005

SPAINWILLIAMS LLP ‡
Suite 15 70 Churchill Square Business Centre Kings Hill West Malling Kent ME19 4YU
Tel: 01732 523590 *Fax:* 01732 523591 *Dx:* 92850 WEST MALLING

STEPHEN THOMAS LAW ‡
8 Grassmere Leybourne West Malling Kent ME19 5QP
Tel: 01732 321114 / 07774 612651 *Fax:* 01732 321078
E-mail: st@stephenthomaslaw.co.uk

VERTEX LAW ‡
23 Kings Hill Kings Hill West Malling Kent ME19 4UA
Tel: 01732 224000 *Fax:* 01732 224001
Dx: 155770 WEST MALLING 2

WEST MERSEA, Essex

D W GALLIFANT ‡
2 Barfield Road West Mersea Essex CO5 8QT
Tel: 01206 383050 *Fax:* 01206 382998
E-mail: dwgsol@aol.com
List of partners: D W Gallifant
Work: K4 S1 S2 W
SPr: Gallifant, Mr David William MA(Oxon) . . . . *Jul 1971

WEST WICKHAM, Kent

ALLEN BARFIELDS
Gainsford House 115 Station Road West Wickham Kent BR4 0PX
Tel: 020 8654 2706 *Fax:* 020 8654 0963
Dx: 37552 WEST WICKHAM
E-mail: mail@allenbarfields.co.uk
Office: Croydon
Languages: French
Work: C1 C2 E J1 L R1 S1 S2 W Z(l,p)
Agency and Fixed Fee Interview undertaken
Ptr: Colman, Mr Peter N BA(Hons) . . . . *Feb 1988
Miller, Mr Ian H BA . . . . *Oct 1982
Ast: Coutts, Ann. . . . . Oct 2004
O'Dwyer, Ms Samantha. . . . . May 1997

GILLAN & CO ‡
1a Red Lodge Road West Wickham Kent BR4 0EL
Tel: 020 8777 4600

THACKRAY WILLIAMS
73 Station Road West Wickham Kent BR4 0QG
Tel: 020 8777 6698 *Fax:* 020 8777 7306
Office: Beckenham, Bromley
Legal Aid undertaken and Member of Accident Line
Ptr: Thomas, Mr Paul M LLB . . . . Jun 1979

WESTBOURNE, Bournemouth

BUCHANAN & LLEWELLYN
52a Poole Road Westbourne Bournemouth BH4 9EP
Tel: 01202 752525 *Fax:* 01202 752997 *Dx:* 89300 WESTBOURNE
Office: Ferndown
Work: A3 C1 E K1 K3 K4 N S1 S2 W Z(l)
Fixed Fee Interview undertaken
Ptr: Holmes, Mr Andrew F BA. . . . . *Oct 1982
Asoc: Harding, Mr Adrian Kenneth BA(Hons); FCIArb . . . *§Aug 1985

WESTBURY, Wiltshire

PINNIGER FINCH & CO ‡
35-37 Church Street Westbury Wiltshire BA13 3BZ
Tel: 01373 823791 *Fax:* 01373 858012 *Dx:* 43501 WESTBURY
Emergency telephone 01380 830256
E-mail: info@pinnigerfinch.co.uk
List of partners: M R Wieck
Languages: French, Spanish
Work: A1 B1 D1 E F1 G H J1 K1 L N P Q S1 S2 T1 T2 V W Z(d,h,k,l,m)
Emergency Action, Agency, Advocacy, Fixed Fee Interview, Legal Aid undertaken, Legal Aid Franchise and Member of Accident Line
Ptr: Wieck, Mr Malcolm R Clerk to Commissioners. . . . *§Jun 1970
Asoc: White, Mr William H LLB(Hons) . . . . Feb 1998

WESTBURY-ON-TRYM, Bristol

THE DIVORCE PRACTICE ‡
52a High Street Westbury-on-Trym Bristol BS9 3DZ

LYONS ROUNSFELL ‡
Old Police Station 49 High Street Westbury-on-Trym Bristol BS9 3ED
Tel: 0117 950 6506 *Fax:* 0117 950 6041
Dx: 33350 WESTBURY-ON-TRYM
E-mail: enquiries@lyonsrounsfell.co.uk
List of partners: C A Lyons, E P J F Lyons, D G Shaw
Office: Bristol
Work: A1 D1 D2 F1 J1 K1 K2 K4 L M1 M2 N O P Q S1 W Z(l,q,t)
Emergency Action, Agency, Advocacy undertaken and Member of Accident Line
Ptr: Lyons, Mr Edward P J F. . . . . *Dec 1976
Shaw, Mr Duncan G. . . . . *Dec 1994
Ast: Westlake, Mrs Joyce . . . . Jul 1979

PRITCHETTS ‡
The Moat 1a Rosery Close Westbury-on-Trym Bristol BS9 3HF
Tel: 0117 307 0266 / 07722 714650 *Fax:* 0117 330 8614
E-mail: info@pritchettslaw.com

WESTCLIFF-ON-SEA, Southend-on-Sea

CHENNELLS ‡
583-585 London Road Westcliff-on-Sea Southend-on-Sea SS0 9PJ
Tel: 01702 349971 / 352195 *Fax:* 01702 430415
Dx: 100804 WESTCLIFF-ON-SEA 1
Emergency telephone 01268 759861
E-mail: ckb@chennells.co.uk
List of partners: C K Byford
Work: E K1 K3 N O Q S1 S2 W Z(j,q)
Emergency Action, Agency and Fixed Fee Interview undertaken
Ptr: Byford, Mr Colin Kenneth BA . . . . *§Mar 1979
Ast: Brown, Ms Ruth Elizabeth BA(Hons)(Oxon) . . . . . . Jul 1994
Kerrigan, Ms Margaret Anne LLB . . . . *Aug 2003

CONWAY & CONWAY ‡
867 London Road Westcliff-on-Sea Southend-on-Sea SS0 9SZ
Tel: 01702 710373 *Fax:* 01702 471715
Dx: 100807 WESTCLIFF-ON-SEA 1
E-mail: jlc@conwayandconway.co.uk
List of partners: A D Conway, J L Conway
Work: A1 B1 C1 E R1 S1 W
Ptr: Conway, Mr Andrew D . . . . Jun 1977
Conway, Mr Jeffrey L . . . . *Dec 1977

HUNTERS ‡
116 Hamlet Court Road Westcliff-on-Sea Southend-on-Sea SS0 7LP
Tel: 01702 353093 *Fax:* 01702 431462
Dx: 39704 WESTCLIFF-ON-SEA 2
E-mail: greghunter@hunterssolicitors.co.uk
List of partners: G R A Hunter
Work: E K3 Q S1 S2 W
Ptr: Hunter, Mr Gregor Roland Ayers . . . . *Jun 1969

JEFFERIES ESSEX LLP ‡
Courtway House 129 Hamlet Court Road Westcliff-on-Sea Southend-on-Sea SS0 7EW
Tel: 01702 332311 *Fax:* 01702 332807 *Dx:* 39705 WESTCLIFF 2
Emergency telephone 07659 107829
E-mail: info@essexlaw.co.uk
List of partners: G Bartlett, R Daby, A H Gershlick, S J Mitchell, D G Travell, S M Young
Languages: French, German
Work: A1 B1 B2 C1 C2 D1 D2 E F1 G H J1 J2 K1 K2 L N O P Q R2 S1 S2 T1 T2 V W X Z(a,c,k,l,m,p,q,r,s)
Emergency Action, Agency, Advocacy, Fixed Fee Interview, Legal Aid undertaken, Legal Aid Franchise and Member of Accident Line
Ptr: Bartlett, Mr Glen BA(Law) ♦. . . . . *May 1981
Daby, Mr Roy ♦ . . . . *Jun 2003
Gershlick, Mr Alan H . . . . *Jul 1967
Mitchell, Miss Sarah Jane BA(Hons); CPE; LSF. . . . Sep 1993
Travell, Mr Dennis G . . . . Sep 1975
Young, Ms Stella Marie . . . . *Nov 1993
Asoc: Hidveghy, Mr Mark . . . . Mar 1986
Holland, Katrina. . . . . Sep 2004
Ast: Alavi, Susanne ★ . . . . *Oct 2007
Bennington, Mr Duncan. . . . . Aug 2009
Deacon, Christine. . . . . Nov 2010
Diver, Mr John . . . . Jan 1970
Dovaston, Miss Karen. . . . . Sep 1995
Hayes, Amelia . . . . Sep 2006
Hills, Danielle . . . . Sep 2009
Lewzey, Mr George ★. . . . . *Jul 2001
O'Connor, Kathleen . . . . *Aug 2008
Redrup, Naomi . . . . Sep 2010
Shoeb, Shahid . . . . Sep 2010

LAW HURST & TAYLOR ‡
153 Hamlet Court Road Westcliff-on-Sea Southend-on-Sea SS0 7EL
Tel: 01702 337864 *Fax:* 01702 435052
Dx: 39700 WESTCLIFF-ON-SEA 2
Emergency telephone 07641 124521
List of partners: A A Hurst, R E Liebeschuetz, P Whight
Languages: German
Work: D1 E G H K1 L M1 M2 S1 W Z(l,m)
Emergency Action, Agency, Advocacy, Fixed Fee Interview, Legal Aid undertaken, Legal Aid Franchise and Member of Accident Line
Ptr: Hurst, Mr Alan A BA. . . . . *Jun 1975
Liebeschuetz, Miss Rachel E LLB. . . . . *Dec 1983
Whight, Mr Paul. Dec 1980

LLOYD JONES & CO ‡
8-10 Southbourne Grove Westcliff-on-Sea Southend-on-Sea SS0 9UR
Tel: 01702 710338 *Fax:* 01702 473169
Dx: 100802 WESTCLIFF-ON-SEA
List of partners: G O Jones, M D Jones
Languages: French
Work: A1 C1 C2 E F1 J1 K1 L N R1 S1 S2 T1 T2 V W Z(c,d,m,o)
Ptr: Jones, Mr Graham O MA(Oxon). . . . . *Jun 1973
Jones, Mr Malcolm D MA(Oxon). . . . . *Dec 1991

MNS SOLICITORS & COMPANY ‡
31 Ailsa Road Westcliff-on-Sea Southend-on-Sea SS0 8BJ
Tel: 01702 352971
E-mail: mnssolicitors@googlemail.com

PARK LEGAL SERVICES ‡
645a London Road Westcliff-on-Sea Southend-on-Sea SS0 9PD
Tel: 01702 346641 *Fax:* 01702 346645
E-mail: yvonne@parklegalsevices.co.uk
Work: C1 E L R2 S1 S2 W

PAUL ROBINSON SOLICITORS ‡
The Old Bank 470-474 London Road Westcliff-on-Sea Southend-on-Sea SS0 9LD
Tel: 01702 338338 *Fax:* 01702 354032
Dx: 100808 WESTCLIFF-ON-SEA 1
Emergency telephone 01702 342525
E-mail: info@paulrobinson.co.uk
List of partners: S Agasee, G A Chetland, W E Cole, S Molineaux, P A Robinson, S P Robinson
Languages: French
Work: A1 B1 C1 C2 C3 D1 E F1 G H J1 K1 K2 L M1 M2 N O P Q R1 S1 S2 T1 T2 V W Z(c,l,m,o,r,t)
Emergency Action, Agency, Advocacy, Fixed Fee Interview, Legal Aid undertaken and Legal Aid Franchise
Ptr: Agasee, Ms Sybilla . . . . May 2000
Chetland, Mr Glenn A. . . . . *Jan 1983
Cole, Miss Wendy Elizabeth LLB(Hons) . . . . *Nov 1995
Molineaux, Miss Samantha LLB(Hons) . . . . *Apr 1992
Robinson, Mr Paul A . . . . *Nov 1971
Robinson, Mr Samuel Paul . . . . *Aug 1998
Ast: Bolt, Ms Louise . . . . *Sep 2004
Colwell, Miss Fiona LLB(Hons); LPC; PSC . . . . . . *Jun 2001
Deans, Mr Mark S. . . . . *Oct 1999
Joseph, Mr David LLB. . . . . *Sep 2001
Vickers, Mr Paul . . . . Nov 2002

RUDDS ‡
350 London Road Westcliff-on-Sea Southend-on-Sea SS0 7JL
Tel: 01702 347853 *Fax:* 01702 343872
Dx: 39702 WESTCLIFF-ON-SEA 2
E-mail: jphilpott@rudds.co.uk
List of partners: R Cohen, D Merrick, J W Philpott
Office: Rayleigh
Work: A1 C1 E K1 K3 N Q R1 S1 S2 W Z(c,d)
Ptr: Cohen, Mr Richard . . . . Jul 1998
Philpott, Mr John W. . . . . May 1976
Ast: MacBean, Mr James I N LLB . . . . Dec 1986

ELIZABETH SHAER SOLICITOR ‡
38 Kenilworth Gardens Westcliff-on-Sea Southend-on-Sea SS0 0BH
Tel: 01702 348710

DAVID WEBB & CO ‡
492 London Road Westcliff-on-Sea Southend-on-Sea SS0 9LD
Tel: 01702 392939 *Fax:* 01702 349770 *Dx:* 100822 WESTCLIFF 1
E-mail: david@davidwebb.co.uk
List of partners: D A Webb
Office: Westcliff-on-Sea
Work: B1 C1 E F1 F2 K1 K3 L N O Q S1 S2 W Z(q,r)
Emergency Action, Agency, Advocacy and Fixed Fee Interview undertaken
SPr: Webb, Mr David Alan LLB(Hons) . . . . *Dec 1977
Con: Thornes, Mr John Angus . . . . *Feb 1974

DAVID WEBB & CO
48 The Ridgeway Westcliff-on-Sea Southend-on-Sea SS0 8NU
Office: Westcliff-on-Sea

WESTERHAM, Kent

BRUNSWICK LAW ‡
16 The Green Westerham Kent TN16 1AU
Tel: 01959 561515 / 563163 *Fax:* 01959 561919
Dx: 83515 WESTERHAM
E-mail: email.brunswick@gmail.com
List of partners: D D Reynolds
Work: E F1 J1 K1 K3 K4 L O Q S1 S2 W
Fixed Fee Interview undertaken
SPr: Reynolds, Mrs Debra Denise LLB(Hons) . . . . *Dec 1999

 See p112 for the Key to Work Categories & other symbols

COWELLS SOLICITORS ‡
Wolfelands High Street Westerham Kent TN16 1RQ
Tel: 01959 563420 *Fax:* 01959 565354 *Dx:* 83502 WESTERHAM
E-mail: info@cowells-solicitors.com

ELGEE PINKS SOLICITORS ‡
Wolfelands High Street Westerham Kent TN16 1RQ
Tel: 01959 568100 *Fax:* 01959 568110 *Dx:* 83506 WESTERHAM
E-mail: info@elgeepinks.com
List of partners: J E Elgee, N H Pinks
Office: Reigate
Ptr: Elgee, Mr John E BA; LLB . . . . *May 1984
Pinks, Mr Nicholas H BA(Kent) . . . . *§Oct 1981

SHARRATTS (LONDON) LLP ‡
1 The Old Yard Rectory Lane Brasted Westerham Kent TN16 1JP
Est: 1999
Tel: 01959 568000 *Fax:* 01959 568001 *Dx:* 83512 WESTERHAM
E-mail: mail@sharratts-london.co.uk
List of partners: S Jarvis, R W Locke, G Metcalf, N Wookey
Work: C1 E L R1 R2 S1 S2 Z(b,c,d,h,u)
Mem: Jarvis, Sarah . . . . Aug 2005
Locke, Mr Richard W BA(Law) . . . . *Mar 1985
Metcalf, Mrs Gillian LLB(Hons) . . . . *Nov 1987
Wookey, Mr Nicholas . . . . *Sep 2001
Asoc: Hicks, Kerry. . . . . Nov 2005

WESTHOUGHTON, Greater Manchester

FIELDINGS PORTER
St Andrews House 58 Market Street Westhoughton Greater Manchester BL5 3AZ
Tel: 01942 814089 *Fax:* 01942 812383
Dx: 18933 WESTHOUGHTON
E-mail: westhoughton@fieldingsporter.co.uk
Office: Bolton
Work: E F1 G H J1 K1 L M1 P S1 W Z(k,l)
Agency, Fixed Fee Interview and Legal Aid undertaken

WIDDOWS MASON
(incorporating Martin & Co)
63 Market Street Westhoughton Greater Manchester BL5 3AG
Tel: 01942 816515 *Fax:* 01942 819152
Dx: 18932 WESTHOUGHTON
Office: Leigh, Warrington, Wigan
Work: A1 B1 C1 C2 C3 D1 E F1 G H J1 K1 M2 N O P Q R1 S1 T1 T2 V W Z(c,h,k,l,m,o,p)
Emergency Action, Agency, Advocacy and Fixed Fee Interview undertaken
Ptr: Freer, Mr Keith BA . . . . Mar 1984
Asoc: Longworth, Mr Peter William Simon BA . . . . Jun 1981
Ast: Tahir, Miss Arouge . . . . Jul 2008

WESTON-SUPER-MARE, North Somerset

BERRY REDMOND & ROBINSON ‡
(incorporating Moore Murray & Co)
115-121 High Street Worle Weston-super-Mare North Somerset BS22 6HB
Tel: 01934 513963 *Fax:* 01934 512865 *Dx:* 47300 WORLE
E-mail: terrl.blackhurst@bbr.co.uk
List of partners: R M S Berry, D P Bird, R K F Burdock, I Coules, C Georgiou
Office: Weston-super-Mare, Winscombe
Languages: French, Greek
Work: A1 C1 C3 D1 E G H J1 K1 L N O Q S1 W
Emergency Action, Agency, Advocacy, Fixed Fee Interview, Legal Aid undertaken and Legal Aid Franchise
Ptr: Berry, Ms Ruth Marianne Sian BA. . . . . *Oct 2000
Burdock, Mr Roger K F LLB(Lond) . . . . *Mar 1975
Coules, Mr Ian LLB . . . . *Oct 1990
Georgiou, Mr Christopher . . . . *Dec 2000
Asoc: Bailey, Jan . . . . Jun 2006
Boyd, Mr Nicholas J W Commissioner for Oaths. . . . *Jul 1967
Ast: Mehlig, Ms Anne . . . . *Dec 1988
Con: Charnley, Mr Francis B D LLB(Lond) . . . . *Jul 1976
Curnow, Mrs Gillian E. . . . . *Oct 1964
Robinson, Mr Alan W R LLB(Lond) . . . . *§Dec 1976
Whicher, Mr Peter G LLB . . . . *Nov 1974

BERRY REDMOND & ROBINSON
19 The Boulevard Weston-super-Mare North Somerset BS23 1NR
Tel: 01934 619000 *Fax:* 01934 614148
Dx: 8401 WESTON-SUPER-MARE
Emergency telephone 01934 619000
Office: Weston-super-Mare, Winscombe
Languages: French
Work: A1 B1 C1 D1 E F1 G H J1 K1 L M1 N P R1 S1 T1 V W Z(o)
Emergency Action, Agency, Advocacy, Fixed Fee Interview, Legal Aid undertaken, Legal Aid Franchise and Member of Accident Line
Ptr: Bird, Mr David P. . . . . *§Jan 1981
Ast: Strickland, Mr Owen C L LLB . . . . *§Nov 1974

BRITTON & CO ‡
Clarence House 186 High Street Worle Weston-super-Mare North Somerset BS22 6JD
Tel: 01934 522000 *Fax:* 01934 522111 *Dx:* 47307 WORLE
E-mail: enquiries@brittonandco.co.uk
List of partners: C M Britton
Work: E L S1 S2 W
Legal Aid undertaken
Ptr: Britton, Mrs Cathryn Mary LLB(Hons) . . . . *Aug 1980

CHAWNER GREY & CO ‡
(incorporating Brian Chawner & Co; Grey & Co)
Grove Chambers Grove Road Weston-super-Mare North Somerset BS23 2AA
Tel: 01934 417768 / 623541 *Fax:* 01934 635411
Dx: 8412 WESTON-SUPER-MARE
E-mail: enquiries@chawnergrey.co.uk
List of partners: T C Hannah, A M Roost
Work: A1 B1 C1 C3 D2 E F1 J1 P R1 S1 S2 T1 T2 V W Z(l,m)
Ptr: Hannah, Mr Timothy C . . . . *Apr 1982
Roost, Mr Anthony M LLB(Lond) . . . . *§Jan 1976
Ast: Dawson, Miss Kay BA(Hons); PGDipLaw . . . . *Aug 2009

THE FAMILY SOLICITOR ‡
Parkhead 3b Montpelier Weston-super-Mare North Somerset BS23 2RQ
Tel: 01934 625551 / 07837 797427
E-mail: macdonaldfraser@aol.com

GORDON & PENNEY ‡
48 Boulevard Weston-super-Mare North Somerset BS23 1NF
Tel: 01934 414161 *Fax:* 01934 626512
Dx: 8419 WESTON-SUPER-MARE
E-mail: gorpen@lawyers37.freeserve.co.uk
List of partners: J A Mills, J P Penney
Work: D1 D2 G H K1
Emergency Action, Agency, Advocacy, Fixed Fee Interview, Legal Aid undertaken and Legal Aid Franchise
Ptr: Mills, Mrs Judith A BSc . . . . *Jun 1988
Penney, Mr J Paul BSc . . . . *Jul 1980

HALL WARD & FOX ‡
3 Walliscote Road Weston-super-Mare North Somerset BS23 1UZ
Tel: 01934 626656 / 626657 *Fax:* 01934 614154
Dx: 8406 WESTON-SUPER-MARE
E-mail: solicitors@hwflaw.co.uk
List of partners: C J Carter, G J Wilkins
Languages: French
Work: A1 C1 E F1 F2 J2 K1 K3 L R1 R2 S1 S2 W Z(c,l)
Ptr: Carter, Mr Christopher J. . . . . *§Jan 1979
Wilkins, Mr Graham J. . . . . *§Jul 1971

JOHN HODGE SOLICITORS ‡
10-11 Morston Court Aisecome Way Weston-super-Mare North Somerset BS22 8NG
Tel: 01934 623511 *Fax:* 01934 418210
Dx: 8403 WESTON-SUPER-MARE
E-mail: mailbox@johnhodge.co.uk
List of partners: J Banks, J L Stevenson, A J J Topham
Office: Bristol, Clevedon, Wedmore, Weston-super-Mare, Yatton
Work: A1 B1 C1 C2 C3 D1 E F1 F2 J1 K1 K3 K4 L M1 M2 N O P Q R1 S1 S2 T1 T2 V W Z(i,p,q,r)
Advocacy, Fixed Fee Interview undertaken and Member of Accident Line
Ptr: Banks, Ms Jane. . . . . *Sep 2004
Stevenson, Mrs Jennifer L LLB . . . . Sep 1997
Topham, Mr Alan Jonathan James BSc ♦ . . . . *Sep 1996
Asoc: Mackie, Mr Stephen. . . . . Jan 1990
Ast: Dury, Miss Lesley . . . . Sep 2010
Kenyon, Ms Joanna. . . . . *Sep 2004
Robertson, Miss Lesley . . . . *Sep 1989
Woodman, Mrs Denise . . . . Feb 1983
Wright, Mr Mark. Feb 2005

JOHN HODGE SOLICITORS
33 Boulevard Weston-super-Mare North Somerset BS23 1PD
Tel: 01934 425999 *Fax:* 01934 418114
Dx: 8416 WESTON-SUPER-MARE
E-mail: mailbox@johnhodge.co.uk
Office: Bristol, Clevedon, Wedmore, Weston-super-Mare, Yatton
Work: A3 C1 D1 D2 E F2 J1 J2 K1 K2 K3 K4 L N O Q S1 S2 W Z(p,q,r)
Fixed Fee Interview undertaken

JOHN KIRKHOPE & CO ‡
33 Clarence Road North Weston-super-Mare North Somerset BS23 4AW
Tel: 01934 644647 *Fax:* 0870 800 4115
E-mail: john@jkirkhope.co.uk

HUW LANGLEY ‡
9 Laurel Drive Uphill Weston-super-Mare North Somerset BS23 4SN
Tel: 07718 354074

OXLEY & WALSH ‡
13 Milton Road Weston-super-Mare North Somerset BS23 2SH
Tel: 01934 517500 *Fax:* 01934 521245
E-mail: oxley.walsh@btconnect.com
List of partners: G A Oxley
Work: D1 E F1 G H J1 K1 N O P Q S1 W
Agency, Advocacy, Fixed Fee Interview and Legal Aid undertaken
Ptr: Oxley, Mr Graham A LLB . . . . *Mar 1986

POWELLS ‡
7-13 Oxford Street Weston-super-Mare North Somerset BS23 1TE
Tel: 01934 623501 *Fax:* 01934 635036
Dx: 8405 WESTON-SUPER-MARE
List of partners: P R Addison, G S Evans, R A Ferrari, S G Hopkin, I D Shipton, S J Soper
Languages: Hindi, Italian, Punjabi, Urdu
Work: A1 A2 A3 B1 B2 C1 C2 D1 D2 E F1 F2 G H I J1 J2 K1 L M1 N O P Q R1 S1 S2 T1 T2 V W X Z(c,d,f,g,h,i,j,k,l,o,p,q,r,s,t,u,w)
Emergency Action, Agency, Advocacy, Fixed Fee Interview, Legal Aid undertaken and Legal Aid Franchise
Ptr: Addison, Mr Paul R LLB Robert Innes and Howard Maxwell Prizes (1985) . . . . *Aug 1987
Evans, Mr Glyn Stephen LLB . . . . *Aug 1983
Ferrari, Mrs Roberta A LLB . . . . *Oct 1985
Hopkin, Miss Sian Gwyneth BSc(Econ) Notary Public . Oct 1985
Shipton, Mr Ian D LLB(L'pool). . . . . *May 1979
Soper, Mr Stephen John LLB(Hons). . . . . *Oct 1997
Ast: Ahmed, Ms Rabina LLB(Hons) . . . . Mar 2000
Brading, Miss Jennifer Helen LLB(Hons); TEP. . . . . Sep 1995
Oberoi, Jay LLB. *Jan 1998

WARDS SOLICITORS
37 Boulevard Weston-super-Mare North Somerset BS23 1PE
Tel: 01934 413535 *Fax:* 01934 635899
Dx: 8404 WESTON-SUPER-MARE
E-mail: info@wards.uk.com
Office: Bristol (2 offices), Clevedon, Nailsea, Portishead, Staple Hill, Weston-super-Mare (2 offices), Yate
Languages: French, German
Work: A1 B1 D1 E F1 F2 J1 K1 K2 L N O P Q R1 R2 S1 S2 T2 W Z(b,c,d,k,l,m,n,p,q,r)
Emergency Action, Advocacy, Fixed Fee Interview, Legal Aid undertaken, Legal Aid Franchise and Member of Accident Line
Ptr: Brentnall, Mr John N LLB President of Weston-Super-Mare RFU . . . . *Apr 1973
Peacock, Miss Georgina LLB . . . . *Oct 1991

WARDS SOLICITORS
195-197 High Street Worle Weston-super-Mare North Somerset BS22 6JS
Tel: 01934 428811 *Fax:* 01934 515759 *Dx:* 47302 WORLE
E-mail: info@wards.uk.com
Office: Bristol (2 offices), Clevedon, Nailsea, Portishead, Staple Hill, Weston-super-Mare (2 offices), Yate
Work: E F1 J1 K1 L N O Q S1 T2 W
Fixed Fee Interview, Legal Aid undertaken and Legal Aid Franchise

WARDS SOLICITORS (FAMILY LAW ENQUIRIES)
5a-7a Waterloo Street Weston-super-Mare North Somerset BS23 1LA
Tel: 01934 428800 *Fax:* 01934 614381
Dx: 8404 WESTON-SUPER-MARE
E-mail: info@wards.uk.com
Office: Bristol (2 offices), Clevedon, Nailsea, Portishead, Staple Hill, Weston-super-Mare (2 offices), Yate
Work: C1 L S1 S2 W
Ptr: Parkman, Mrs Rebecca E E LLB . . . . *Oct 1992
Peacock, Miss Georgina LLB . . . . *Oct 1991

WETHERBY, West Yorkshire

ALEXANDERS SOLICITORS LIMITED ‡
1st Floor Equinox 1 Wetherby West Yorkshire LS22 7RD
Tel: 01937 543350

FREEMAN & CO SOLICITORS ‡
12a-16 North Street Wetherby West Yorkshire LS22 6NN
Tel: 01937 583111
E-mail: freemanandco@btconnect.com
List of partners: M Freeman
Work: K1
Fixed Fee Interview undertaken
SPr: Freeman, Mrs Maureen LLB. . . . . *Nov 1990

HARTLAW LLP ‡
St James Street Wetherby West Yorkshire LS22 6RS
Tel: 01937 547000 *Fax:* 01937 547030 *Dx:* 16802 WETHERBY
E-mail: info@hartlaw.co.uk
List of partners: P Brown, D Burke, N R Dyson, J S Pickworth, M J Seldon, M J Storey
Languages: French, German
Work: A1 B1 C1 C2 D1 E F1 J1 K1 K2 K3 L N O Q R1 R2 S1 S2 T1 T2 U2 W Z(d,j,l,m,o,q)
Emergency Action, Agency, Advocacy, Fixed Fee Interview, Legal Aid undertaken, Legal Aid Franchise and Member of Accident Line
Mem: Brown, Mr Philip BA(Hons); LLB. . . . . *Apr 2005
Burke, Mrs Dianne BSc(Hons); LLB. . . . . *Jul 1999
Dyson, Mr Nicholas Ralph LLB Notary Public . . . . *Oct 1972
Pickworth, Mr Jeremy S MA(Cantab) . . . . *Apr 1981
Seldon, Mr Mathew John LLB(Hons) . . . . *Jan 2003
Storey, Miss Marie J LLB . . . . *May 1981
Ast: McNally, Mr Stephen V LLB. . . . . *Apr 1978
Robinson, Miss Kate LLB . . . . Jan 2010
Smith, Ms Rebecca . . . . *May 2004

HOWARTH & CO ‡
20 Bank Street Wetherby West Yorkshire LS22 6NQ
Tel: 01937 584020 *Fax:* 01937 584091 *Dx:* 16806 WETHERBY
Emergency telephone 07808 722243
E-mail: n.howarth@btconnect.com
List of partners: N G Howarth
Work: B1 C1 E F1 F2 J1 K1 K3 L N O Q S1 S2 W Z(c,e,k,l,q)
SPr: Howarth, Mr Nicholas Glenn. . . . . *Apr 1988

STEEL & CO ‡
Highfield House 179 High Street Boston Spa Wetherby West Yorkshire LS23 6AA
Tel: 01937 845539 *Fax:* 01937 843198
E-mail: enquiries@steel-law.co.uk
List of partners: L E R Curl, C J Steel
Office: Knaresborough
Work: A1 C1 E K1 K3 L N S1 S2 T2 W Z(r)
Ptr: Steel, Mr C John . . . . *Dec 1975
Asoc: Brennan, Mrs Joanne Limbert LLB . . . . *Mar 1991
Ast: Henderson, Mrs Amanda Jane LLB . . . . Oct 1986

WARE & KAY LLP
The Manor House North Street Wetherby West Yorkshire LS22 6NU
Tel: 01937 583210 *Fax:* 01937 587556 *Dx:* 16805 WETHERBY
E-mail: law@warekay.com
Office: York
Languages: Mandarin
Work: A1 C1 C2 D1 D2 E F1 J1 K1 K3 K4 L N O P Q R2 S1 S2 T1 T2 V W Z(l,q)
Emergency Action, Agency, Advocacy, Fixed Fee Interview undertaken and Member of Accident Line
Ptr: Boreham, Mr Roger W BSc. . . . . *Apr 1980
Peach, Mr Michael Neil LLB; MBA. . . . . *§Oct 1986
Asoc: Leftwich, Mrs Catherine . . . . Jul 2007
Reid, Ms Harriet Kate LLB(Hons) . . . . Oct 1993
Ast: Wilkinson, Mrs Gillian Ann BA(Hons)(Hispanic Studies); GDL; LPC. . . . . Aug 2009

FRANCINA WHELAN & CO ‡
New Barn House Hall Mews Clifford Road Wetherby West Yorkshire LS23 6DT
Tel: 01937 534022 *Fax:* 01937 541902
E-mail: info@francinawhelan.com

WEYBRIDGE, Surrey

CRELLINS CARTER SOLICITORS ‡
111 Queens Road Weybridge Surrey KT13 9UW
Tel: 01932 858833 *Fax:* 01932 857249 *Dx:* 30914 WEYBRIDGE
E-mail: admin@crellinscarter.co.uk
List of partners: B F Carter, V Cooper, D E Crellin, J A Fitzwater
Ptr: Carter, Mr Bryan Frank . . . . Jun 1963
Cooper, Miss Valerie LLB . . . . *Aug 1981
Crellin, Mr Derek E LLB. . . . . *Jun 1969
Fitzwater, Ms Julie Alison LLB. . . . . Dec 2001
Ast: Fitzwater, Ms Julie Alison LLB. . . . . Dec 2001

GUILLAUMES SOLICITORS ‡
50 Church Street Weybridge Surrey KT13 8DS
Tel: 01932 840111 *Fax:* 01932 841182 *Dx:* 30901 WEYBRIDGE
E-mail: info@guillaumes.com
Web: www.guillaumes.com
List of partners: M I Betts, R T C Guilfoyle, T Hansom, E L Newman, N Sapsed, C A L Tan
Office: Weybridge
Languages: French
Work: C1 E K1 K3 K4 L O Q R1 R2 S1 S2 T1 T2 W Z(m)
Legal Aid Franchise
Ptr: Betts, Mr Martin Ide. . . . . *Nov 1981
Guilfoyle, Mr Robert T C . . . . *§Oct 1984
Hansom, Mr Tom . . . . *Apr 2004
Newman, Miss Emma Louise . . . . *Apr 1999
Sapsed, Mr Neil. . . . . *Oct 2004
Tan, Ms Carolynn Ann Louise BA; CPE . . . . *Oct 1994
Asoc: Buttaci, Ms Giuseppina . . . . Jul 2003
Slavin, Ms Jemma . . . . *Jul 2005
Ast: Hunjan, Mrs Rupinder LLB . . . . Sep 2002
Con: Bowen, Mr Roger J LLB(Wales); Barr & Solicitor Sup Ct New Zealand. *§Apr 1973

GUILLAUMES SOLICITORS
Ibex House 61-65 Baker Street Weybridge Surrey KT13 8AH
Tel: 01932 840111 *Fax:* 01932 858092 *Dx:* 30901 WEYBRIDGE
Office: Weybridge
Work: C1 E K1 K3 K4 L O Q R1 R2 S1 S2 T1 T2 W Z(m)
Ptr: Newman, Miss Emma Louise . . . . *Apr 1999
Sapsed, Mr Neil. . . . . *Oct 2004

ERNA MCKENNA DONELLY ‡
2 Southwood Court Pine Grove Weybridge Surrey KT13 9AT
Tel: 01932 844651 *Fax:* 01932 844651

MCNAMARA RYAN ‡
(incorporating Beauvoisin & Burgess)
Ashburton House 3 Monument Green Weybridge Surrey KT13 8QR
Tel: 01932 846041 *Fax:* 01932 857709 *Dx:* 30904 WEYBRIDGE
Emergency telephone 01932 846041
E-mail: email@mrsolicitors.co.uk
List of partners: M A Beauvoisin, J C A Flood
Work: B1 C1 C2 C3 D1 E F1 J1 K1 K2 K3 K4 L M1 M2 N O P Q R2 S1 S2 T1 T2 W X Z(b,d,j,q)
Agency undertaken
Ptr: Beauvoisin, Mr Michael Anthony. . . . . *Dec 1970
Flood, Mr John C A. . . . . *§Dec 1972
Ast: Dell, Ms Gabrielle LLB; TEP. . . . . *Oct 1972
Gooding, Miss Anne E BA(Hons) . . . . *May 1981

MEADOWS FRASER LLP ‡
56 Church Street Weybridge Surrey KT13 8DP
Tel: 01932 852057 *Fax:* 01932 857177
List of partners: P H C Fraser, M W B McCulloch, F E P Meadows
Work: A1 C1 C2 E L R1 S1 T1 T2 W Z(c)
Ptr: Fraser, Mr Peter H C . . . . *Jun 1964
McCulloch, Mr Malcolm W B BA. . . . . *Jan 1980
Meadows, Mr Francis E P. . . . . *Dec 1970

JUDITH PARISH SOLICITOR ‡
Monkmoor Beechwood Avenue Weybridge Surrey KT13 9TE
Tel: 01932 842022 *Fax:* 01932 828645
List of partners: J B Parish
Work: E L S1 W
SPr: Parish, Mrs Judith Barbara LLB . . . . *Jun 1971

ANDREW SMITH ‡
21 Oakwood Grange Weybridge Surrey KT13 9RY
Tel: 07852 132420

WEYMOUTH, Dorset

BATTENS
26 St Thomas Street Weymouth Dorset DT4 8EJ
Tel: 01305 774666 *Fax:* 01305 760423 *Dx:* 8753 WEYMOUTH
Emergency telephone 01305 775609
E-mail: webenquiry@battens.co.uk
Office: Dorchester, Sherborne, Yeovil
Work: A1 A2 A3 B1 C1 C2 C3 D1 D2 E F1 F2 J1 K1 K2 L M1 N O P Q R1 R2 S1 T1 T2 V W X Z(a,b,c,d,e,f,h,j,k,l,m,o,p,q,r,s,t,u,w,x)
Emergency Action, Agency, Advocacy, Fixed Fee Interview, Legal Aid undertaken and Member of Accident Line
Ptr: Thompson, Mr Christopher I. . . . . *§Jul 1970

THE COMMERCIAL LAW PRACTICE ‡
Second Floor 9 Westham Road Weymouth Dorset DT4 8NP
Tel: 01305 779545 *Fax:* 01202 884812

SIMON LACEY LAW ASSOCIATES ‡
9a St Marys Street Weymouth Dorset DT4 8PB
Tel: 01305 777711 *Fax:* 01305 776222 *Dx:* 8775 WEYMOUTH
E-mail: simon.lacey@simonlacey.co.uk
List of partners: S C Lacey
Work: G H K1 K3
Fixed Fee Interview and Legal Aid undertaken
Ptr: Lacey, Mr Simon Compton LLB(Hons). . . . . *Oct 1986
Asoc: Cole, Ms Cheryl. . . . . *Oct 1995

MUSTOE SHORTER ‡
6-8 Frederick Place Weymouth Dorset DT4 8HQ
Tel: 01305 752700 *Fax:* 01305 778928 *Dx:* 8755 WEYMOUTH
E-mail: info@mustoeshorter.co.uk
Office: Dorchester
Work: C1 D1 D2 E F1 G H J1 K1 K2 K3 K4 L M1 N P S1 S2 V W Z(c,k,l,m)

NANTES
69 The Esplanade Weymouth Dorset DT4 7AJ
Tel: 01305 771000 *Fax:* 01305 767422 *Dx:* 8758 WEYMOUTH
Office: Bridport, Dorchester
Ast: Neill, Ms Hilary Frances LLB . . . . *Oct 1989

PENGILLYS LLP ‡
Post Office Chambers 67 St Thomas Street Weymouth Dorset DT4 8HB
Tel: 01305 768888 *Fax:* 01305 768777 *Dx:* 8756 WEYMOUTH 1
E-mail: contact@pengillys.co.uk
List of partners: C M Berry, M J Edmonds, T Guppy, S Jones, E J Lilley, C F Lousley, G P Meakins, J T P W Walkington
Office: Dorchester
Languages: French, German
Work: A1 B1 C1 C2 C3 D1 E F1 J1 K1 K2 L M1 M2 N P Q R1 S1 T1 T2 V W Z(a,c,i,k,l,m,s)
Emergency Action, Agency, Advocacy, Fixed Fee Interview, Legal Aid undertaken and Legal Aid Franchise
Ptr: Berry, Mr Christopher Michael LLB . . . . *§Apr 1981
Edmonds, Mr Michael J LLB(Wales). . . . . *Jul 1981
Guppy, Mr Timothy . . . . *Sep 1984
Jones, Mr Stephen LLB(Hons) . . . . *§Oct 1986
Lilley, Mr Edward J LLB. . . . . *Jun 1978
Lousley, Mr Christopher F MA(Oxon) . . . . *§Jun 1976
Meakins, Mr Geoffrey P LLM . . . . *§Oct 1980
Walkington, Mr John T P W LLB. . . . . *Nov 1991
Ast: Sanders, Mrs Jennifer Kathleen BA(Hons). . . . . . *Oct 1988
Turner, Miss Rachel Louise LLB. . . . . Sep 2008
Con: Whitehouse, Mr Graham LLB . . . . *Sep 2004

REDFERNS ‡
34a St Thomas Street Weymouth Dorset DT4 8EJ
Tel: 01305 781401 / 782704 *Fax:* 01305 788175
Dx: 8763 WEYMOUTH
E-mail: jrm@redferns-solicitors.com
List of partners: J R Mackenzie, D J Summerscales
Office: Portland
Work: A1 B1 C1 D1 E F1 J1 K1 K3 L N O Q R1 S1 S2 T1 W X Z(c,l)
Emergency Action, Agency, Fixed Fee Interview, Legal Aid undertaken and Member of Accident Line
Ptr: Mackenzie, Mr John R LLB(B'ham) . . . . *§Oct 1971

GRENVILLE J WALKER
18-20 Park Street Weymouth Dorset DT4 7DQ
Tel: 01305 759090 *Fax:* 01305 759091
E-mail: office@grenvillejwalker.org.uk
Office: Blandford Forum, Bournemouth, Portland
Work: B1 D1 D2 G H K1 K3 Q S1 S2 W Z(l)
Agency, Advocacy, Legal Aid undertaken and Legal Aid Franchise

WHALEY BRIDGE, Derbyshire

LEATHEMS SOLICITORS ‡
12 Market Street Whaley Bridge Derbyshire SK23 7LP
Tel: 01663 733431 *Fax:* 01663 735488 *Dx:* 28468 WHALEY BRIDGE
E-mail: enquire@leathems.com
List of partners: C W Leathem
Work: A1 S1 S2 T1 T2 W
Ptr: Leathem, Mr Christopher William . . . . *§May 1983
Asoc: Gaskell, Miss Lesley Christine BA(Hons)(Law) . . . . Mar 1984

WHEATHAMPSTEAD, Hertfordshire

BURN & CO ‡
12 Beech Way Blackmore End Wheathampstead Hertfordshire AL4 8LY
Tel: 01438 833446 *Fax:* 01438 832774 *Dx:* 80471 HARPENDEN
E-mail: burnandco@hotmail.com
List of partners: G Burn, R Burn
Work: B1 C1 D2 E F1 J1 K1 K3 L N O Q S1 S2 V W Z(e)
Agency, Advocacy and Fixed Fee Interview undertaken
Ptr: Burn, Mrs Gillian LLB(B'ham) . . . . *Dec 1979
Burn, Mr Richard LLB(Lond). . . . . *§Jun 1978

WHICKHAM, Tyne & Wear

MICHAEL ANDERSON & CO
(in association with Davies Bell & Reed)
8 Fellside Road Whickham Tyne & Wear NE16 4JU
Tel: 0191 488 1221 *Fax:* 0191 488 2013 *Dx:* 60406 WHICKHAM
Office: Newcastle upon Tyne
Work: E S1 W
Ptr: Stokoe, Mr Andrew Donald . . . . *§Dec 1993
Wilkie-Smith, Mr Charles Edward BA . . . . *§Jun 1978
Ast: Robson, Mrs Susan LLB . . . . *Jul 1979

BINDMAN & CO ‡
22 Front Street Whickham Tyne & Wear NE16 4DW
Tel: 0191 488 4950 *Fax:* 0191 420 0485 *Dx:* 60401 WHICKHAM
E-mail: manthony@bindman-solicitors.co.uk
List of partners: S L Bindman
Work: B1 D2 E G H J1 K1 M1 N P Q S1 S2 W Z(j,k,l)
Emergency Action, Agency, Advocacy, Fixed Fee Interview, Legal Aid undertaken, Legal Aid Franchise and Member of Accident Line
Ptr: Bindman, Mr Simon Leslie BA(Newc) . . . . *§Jan 1976

THOMAS MAGNAY & CO
(incorporating Williamson & Jackson (Whickham))
8 St Marys Green Whickham Tyne & Wear NE16 4DN
Tel: 0191 488 7459 / 488 7766 *Fax:* 0191 488 8682
Dx: 60400 WHICKHAM
Office: Gateshead
Work: A1 C1 C2 C3 D1 E F1 G H J1 K1 K4 L N O Q R1 S1 T1 T2 W Z(b,c,d,j,k,l,m,s)
Agency and Advocacy undertaken
Ptr: Magnay, Mr Peter DL. . . . . *§Jun 1972
Ast: Spark, Mrs Victoria Jane BA(Hons) . . . . Jul 2010

WHITBY, North Yorkshire

COLIN BROWN & KIDSON ‡
Wellington House 5 Wellington Road Whitby North Yorkshire YO21 1BH
Tel: 01947 603391 *Fax:* 01947 820546 *Dx:* 61752 WHITBY
Emergency telephone 01947 603647
E-mail: law@cbk.uk.com
List of partners: P I L Bastiman, M A Crossling, R G B Evans
Work: A1 B1 C1 D1 E F1 G H J1 K1 L M1 N P Q R1 S1 V W
Emergency Action, Agency and Advocacy undertaken
Ptr: Bastiman, Mr Paul I L. . . . . *Dec 1963
Crossling, Mr Michael Anthony LLB(Hons). . . . . . . *Jul 1995
Evans, Mr Richard G B . . . . *May 1976

NORTH YORKSHIRE LAW
23 Baxtergate Whitby North Yorkshire YO21 1BW
Tel: 01947 602131 *Fax:* 01947 606165 *Dx:* 61751 WHITBY
E-mail: info@northyorkshirelaw.com
Office: Helmsley, Scarborough
Languages: French, Spanish
Work: A1 E H L S1 W
Ptr: Cocker, Mr Ian LLB . . . . *Dec 1979
Newton, Mr John R . . . . Nov 1977
Ast: Carter, Mr Michael . . . . *Dec 1970
Coxon, Mr John G . . . . *Dec 1963
Naylor, Mr David M . . . . Feb 1976
Thomas, Ms Catherine . . . . Mar 1997
Truefitt, Ms H Susan . . . . *§Jun 1971

PINKNEY GRUNWELLS LAWYERS LLP
Lion Chambers 2 Golden Lion Bank Whitby North Yorkshire YO21 3BS
Tel: 01947 601122 *Fax:* 01947 829850 *Dx:* 61750 WHITBY
E-mail: solicitors@pinkneygrunwells.co.uk
Office: Bridlington, Filey, Scarborough
Work: A1 E J1 K1 K3 Q R1 S1 S2 W
Mem: Barrett, Mr Geoffrey Noel . . . . Nov 1987
Ast: Sullivan, Mrs Bernadette LLB(Hons). . . . . Dec 2002

THORPE & CO
3 Bagdale Whitby North Yorkshire YO21 1QL
Tel: 01947 603465 *Fax:* 01947 600068 *Dx:* 61754 WHITBY
Emergency telephone 01947 810010 / 880757 / 895590
E-mail: whitby@thorpeandco.com
Office: Filey, Malton, Scarborough
Languages: French
Work: A1 B1 C1 C3 D1 E F1 G H J1 K1 L N O P Q R1 S1 T1 T2 V W Z(b,c,d,i,j,k,l,m,o,s,t)
Emergency Action, Agency, Advocacy, Fixed Fee Interview, Legal Aid undertaken, Legal Aid Franchise and Member of Accident Line
Ptr: Jefferies, Mr Mark A C LLB . . . . *Feb 1983
Asoc: Burnett, Mr Carl David . . . . *Sep 1997

WHITCHURCH, Hampshire

BARKER SON & ISHERWOOD LLP
2 Newbury Street Whitchurch Hampshire RG28 7DN
Tel: 01256 896262 *Fax:* 01256 895550 *Dx:* 90303 ANDOVER
E-mail: info@bsandi.co.uk
Office: Andover (2 offices), Overton
Work: A1 B1 C1 D1 E F1 J1 J2 K1 K4 L N O P Q R1 R2 S1 S2 T1 T2 V W Z(b,c,d,e,h,j,l,m,o,q,r,t)
Ptr: Holland, Mr Clive R . . . . *§Dec 1978

WHITCHURCH, Shropshire

HATCHERS SOLICITORS LLP
45 Green End Whitchurch Shropshire SY13 1AD
Tel: 01948 663361
E-mail: mail@hatchers.co.uk
Office: Shrewsbury (2 offices)
Work: A1 B1 C1 E F1 K1 L N O Q S1 T1 T2 W
Emergency Action, Agency, Advocacy, Fixed Fee Interview and Legal Aid undertaken
Ptr: Ryder, Mr David M LLB . . . . Dec 1979
Ast: McRae, Mr Kenneth Iain James LLB . . . . *Dec 1977
Con: Kynaston, Mr Clive . . . . Jun 1975

HIBBERT LUCAS BUTTER
29 St Marys Street Whitchurch Shropshire SY13 1RA
Tel: 01948 662231 *Fax:* 01948 666364 *Dx:* 27731 WHITCHURCH
Emergency telephone 07710 541156
Office: Crewe, Ellesmere, Nantwich, Tarporley
Work: A1 K1 L S1 S2 W Z(d,h,l)
Ptr: Dolphin, Mrs S Alison BA(Law) . . . . *Mar 1983
Sorfleet, Mr Stephen R MA(Cantab). . . . . *Jan 1977
Ast: Collins, Wynford F BA Clerk to Commissioner of Taxes *Jul 1981

SWEETMANS SOLICITORS ‡
Yew Tree Lodge Bickley Moss Whitchurch Shropshire SY13 4JE
Tel: 0800 141 2620 / 01829 770903 *Fax:* 01829 720794
E-mail: info@sweetmanssolicitors.co.uk

WHITEFIELD, Greater Manchester

SHELDON DAVIDSON SOLICITORS ‡
219 Bury New Road Whitefield Greater Manchester M45 8GW
Tel: 0161 796 5445 *Fax:* 0161 767 9770
E-mail: srd@sds-solicitors.com
List of partners: S R Davidson
Work: N Q
SPr: Davidson, Mr Sheldon Rene LLB(Hons) . . . . *Mar 1994

AUBREY ISAACSON SOLICITORS
66 Bury Old Road Whitefield Greater Manchester M45 6TL
Tel: 0161 959 6000 *Fax:* 0161 959 6001
E-mail: jeffrey@aubreyisaacson.co.uk
Office: Bury, Prestwich (2 offices)
Languages: Hebrew
Work: E F1 G H J1 K1 L N Q S1 W
Agency, Advocacy, Fixed Fee Interview, Legal Aid undertaken and Member of Accident Line
Ptr: Gilbert, Mr Jeffrey Aaron LLB . . . . *Sep 1993
Simmonds, Mr Benjamin B LLB . . . . *Oct 1990

KHATTAK SOLICITORS ‡
279 Bury New Road Whitefield Greater Manchester M45 7SE
Tel: 0161 796 5800 *Fax:* 0161 796 5011
Emergency telephone 0161 796 5800
List of partners: S A Khattak
Languages: Pashto, Punjabi, Urdu
Work: G H N
Advocacy undertaken
Ptr: Khattak, Mr Shabir Ahmed . . . . Nov 1996

THOMAS SAUL & CO ‡
6 Bury Old Road Whitefield Greater Manchester M45 6TF
Tel: 0161 773 2833 *Fax:* 0161 773 0003
List of partners: T J Saul
Work: B1 C1 E N O S1 T1 W X Z(c)
Ptr: Saul, Mr Thomas J LLB. . . . . *Nov 1982
Asoc: May, Miss Lesley A LLB(Hons) . . . . *Nov 1992

See p112 for the Key to Work Categories & other symbols

2

WHITEHAVEN, Cumbria

BLEASDALE & CO ‡
14 Scotch Street Whitehaven Cumbria CA28 7NQ
Tel: 01946 692165 *Fax:* 01946 691128 *Dx:* 62901 WHITEHAVEN
E-mail: cathy.dodd@bleasdales.com
Work: A1 B1 C1 D1 E F1 G H J1 K1 K2 L N Q R1 S1 S2 T1 V W X Z(k,l,n,p,r,s,t)

BROCKBANK CURWEN CAIN & HALL ‡
PO Box 1 44 Duke Street Whitehaven Cumbria CA28 7NR
Tel: 01946 692194 *Fax:* 01946 62686 *Dx:* 62902 WHITEHAVEN
Emergency telephone 01946 692008
E-mail: bt@brockbanks.co.uk
List of partners: C J Bevan, J W Dugan, J M W Dunn, L Greenwood, C G Hall, V M Hendren, T Hill, G W B Mendus, M Owen, R P Taylor, M J Woolaghan
Office: Cockermouth, Keswick, Maryport, Workington
Work: A1 B1 C1 D1 D2 E F1 G H J1 K1 K2 K3 K4 L M1 N P Q R1 S1 S2 W Z(a,c,d,f,h,i,j,k,l,m,n,p,r,s)
Emergency Action, Agency, Advocacy, Fixed Fee Interview, Legal Aid undertaken, Legal Aid Franchise and Member of Accident Line
Dir: Dugan, Mr John W BA ★ . . . . *§Mar 1978
Hendren, Mrs Valerie M BSc(Econ) . . . . *Jan 1979
Owen, Miss Mary . . . . *§Sep 2004
Ast: Fitzsimmons, Mr Michael LLB(Hons) . . . . Mar 2009
Rowell, Mr Michael LLB. . . . . *§Oct 1996

BURNETTS
Samuel Lindow Building Westlakes Science & Technology Park Moor Row Whitehaven Cumbria CA24 3JY
Tel: 01946 550250
Office: Carlisle (2 offices), Newcastle upon Tyne

K J COMMONS & CO
76 Lowther Street Whitehaven Cumbria CA28 7RB
Tel: 01946 66699 *Fax:* 01946 66688 / 518380
Dx: 62916 WHITEHAVEN
E-mail: law@kjcommons.co.uk
Office: Carlisle, Workington
Work: B2 D1 G H J1 K1 L N Q S1 S2 W X Z(i,r)
Emergency Action, Agency, Advocacy, Fixed Fee Interview and Legal Aid undertaken
Ptr: Nickson, Mr Marcus P LLB . . . . *§Nov 1977

H F T GOUGH & CO ‡
38-42 Lowther Street Whitehaven Cumbria CA28 7JU
Tel: 01946 692461 *Fax:* 01946 692015 *Dx:* 62900 WHITEHAVEN
Emergency telephone 01900 823547
E-mail: admin@goughs-solicitors.com
List of partners: M A Little, C S G Madden, R T Reed, D L Roberts, E C Sandelands, J C Taylor, S P P Ward
Work: A1 B1 C1 C2 C3 D1 E F1 F2 G H J1 J2 K1 K3 L N O P Q R1 S1 S2 T1 T2 V W Z(d,l,m,q)
Emergency Action, Agency, Advocacy, Fixed Fee Interview, Legal Aid undertaken and Legal Aid Franchise
Ptr: Little, Mr Michael A LLB. . . . . *Mar 1986
Madden, Ms Claire St G LLB Clerk to the Commissioners of Non-Exec of North Cwmbran NHS Trust . . . . *Jun 1975
Reed, Mr Ryan T LLB. . . . . *Jul 1999
Roberts, Mr David L LLB(Manc) Deputy Coroner . . . *Apr 1980
Sandelands, Mrs Elizabeth C LLB. . . . . *Nov 1995
Taylor, Mr John C Coroner . . . . *Jan 1970
Ward, Mr Simon P P LLB Assistant Deputy Coroner. . *Dec 1989
Ast: Holliday, Mrs Michelle. . . . . Oct 2007
Hughes, Mrs Stephanie . . . . Jun 2004
Sandelands, Mr Michael Thomas . . . . Mar 2007

MILBURNS SOLICITORS
25-26 Church Street Whitehaven Cumbria CA28 7EB
Tel: 01946 694818 *Fax:* 01946 64273 *Dx:* 62905 WHITEHAVEN
E-mail: whitehaven@milburns.org
Office: Maryport, Workington
Languages: French, German
Work: A1 B1 C1 D1 E F1 G H J1 K1 L M1 N P R1 S1
Emergency Action, Agency, Advocacy, Fixed Fee Interview and Legal Aid undertaken
Ptr: Atkinson, Mrs Emma Louise LLB . . . . *Oct 1996
Tupman, Mr Piers Nigel LLB . . . . *§May 1994

WHITLEY BAY, Tyne & Wear

HIPKIN & CO ‡
130-132 Park View Whitley Bay Tyne & Wear NE26 3QN
Tel: 0191 253 3509 *Fax:* 0191 297 0269 *Dx:* 62106 WHITLEY BAY
E-mail: law@hipkin.co.uk
List of partners: J H W Bishop, M D Hipkin
Work: B1 C1 C2 C3 D1 D2 E F1 J1 J2 K1 K3 K4 L N O Q S1 S2 V W Z(p,q,r)
Emergency Action, Agency, Advocacy and Fixed Fee Interview undertaken
Ptr: Bishop, Mr Jonathan H W LLB(Newc). . . . *Dec 1990
Hipkin, Mr Mark D LLB . . . . *Oct 1982
Ast: Nicholson, Ms Maureen Julie LLB. . . . *Mar 1995

KIDD & SPOOR ‡
(incorporating Briggs Peart & Easdon; Paul Mervin & Co)
7 Marden Road Whitley Bay Tyne & Wear NE26 2JN
Tel: 0191 297 0011 *Fax:* 0191 297 0022 *Dx:* 62100 WHITLEY BAY
Emergency telephone 07623 979115
List of partners: W N Dilks, N P Miller, E S Stobart
Office: Newcastle upon Tyne
Work: D1 D2 E F1 G H K1 L N P Q S1 W Z(h,l,m,q)
Emergency Action, Agency, Advocacy, Fixed Fee Interview and Legal Aid undertaken
Ptr: Miller, Mr Nigel P LLB(Hons) . . . . *Sep 1989
Stobart, Mrs E Sheila BA ♦ . . . . *Jul 1980
Asoc: English, Mr Kris LLB . . . . Oct 2007
Robinson, Miss Sharon-Ann LLB(Hons) Cavendish Law Prize 2000 . . . . *May 2005
Ward, Mr Richard ♦. . . . . *Sep 1976

MITCHELL DODDS & CO ‡
(incorporating Adamson & Adamson)
208-210 Park View Whitley Bay Tyne & Wear NE26 3QS
Tel: 0191 252 2396 / 252 9557 *Fax:* 0191 297 0305
Dx: 62107 WHITLEY BAY
E-mail: mitchelldodds1@btconnect.com
List of partners: P Sanderson
Work: C1 C2 E K1 K3 L N O Q S1 T2 W Z(c,d,m)
SPr: Sanderson, Mr Peter . . . . *§Nov 1978

IAN ROSE & FIRTH ‡
285 Whitley Road Whitley Bay Tyne & Wear NE26 2SP
Tel: 0191 252 0113 *Fax:* 0191 253 3555 *Dx:* 62110 WHITLEY BAY
E-mail: firthsolicitors@btconnect.com
List of partners: I G Firth
Work: C1 E S1 S2 T2 W Z(d)
Ptr: Firth, Mr Ian G LLB(Leeds) . . . . *§Apr 1973

WILLIAMSONS ‡
240 Whitley Road Whitley Bay Tyne & Wear NE26 2TF
Tel: 0191 252 7711 *Fax:* 0191 297 0686 *Dx:* 62103 WHITLEY BAY
E-mail: dianewilliams@btconnect.com
List of partners: E G Craig, A I Douglas, A Ross
Office: Hexham
Work: B1 C1 C2 C3 D1 E F1 J1 K1 L N O P Q S1 V W
Ptr: Douglas, Mr Alan I BA . . . . *§Apr 1975
Ross, Mr Alan LLB . . . . *Oct 1980

YARWOOD STIMPSON & CO ‡
(incorporating M H Hardy)
5 Marden Road Whitley Bay Tyne & Wear NE26 2JL
Tel: 0191 297 0123 *Fax:* 0191 252 9627 *Dx:* 62119 WHITLEY BAY
Emergency telephone 0191 297 0123
E-mail: mail@yarwood-stimpson.co.uk
List of partners: A A Crosby, M H Hardy, D Kelly
Work: A1 C1 D1 E F1 G H J1 K1 L N O P Q S1 S2 T1 T2 V W X Z(e,j,l,m)
Emergency Action, Agency, Advocacy, Fixed Fee Interview, Legal Aid undertaken and Legal Aid Franchise
Ptr: Crosby, Mr Anthony Allan LLB(Hons) . . . . *Aug 1995
Hardy, Mr Michael H LLB . . . . *Jul 1980
Kelly, Mr Dominic BA(Law) . . . . *Feb 1984

WHITSTABLE, Kent

FURLEY PAGE LLP
52-54 High Street Whitstable Kent CT5 1BG
Tel: 01227 274241 *Fax:* 01227 275704 *Dx:* 32352 WHITSTABLE
E-mail: info@furleypage.co.uk
Office: Canterbury, Chatham, London EC3
Work: E S1 W Z(p)
Ptr: Addis, Mr Paul F OBE LLB . . . . *§Jun 1974
McDonagh, Mrs Myfanwy . . . . *Oct 1985

PARRY LAW ‡
12-14 Oxford Street Whitstable Kent CT5 1DE
Tel: 01227 276276 *Fax:* 01227 265507 *Dx:* 32350 WHITSTABLE
E-mail: info@parrylaw.co.uk
List of partners: D Alp, P Chandra, T P Goodwin, S L Parry, P Sethna, K J Teasdale
Office: Herne Bay
Work: C1 C2 E J1 K1 K3 K4 L O R1 R2 S1 S2 T2 W Z(d,l,q)
Agency and Fixed Fee Interview undertaken
Ptr: Alp, Mr David . . . . Jan 1998
Chandra, Mr Prashanth . . . . Jan 2005
Goodwin, Mr Timothy P LLB(Hons); TEP Chairman of Age Concern, Whitstable . . . . *Oct 1994
Parry, Mr Stephen Lloyd LLB . . . . *Dec 1985
Asoc: Fuller, Mr Graham Dean TEP . . . . *Sep 2005
Rider, Mr Michael Edward. . . . . Sep 1971
Stokoe, Miss Natalie LLB(Hons). . . . . *Oct 2002
Thomson, Miss Elizabeth LLB. . . . . Mar 2003
Ast: Perry, Ms Emma Jane. . . . . Apr 2010

POCOCKS SOLICITORS OF WHITSTABLE ‡
Elizabeth House 63 Oxford Street Whitstable Kent CT5 1DA
Tel: 01227 770222 *Fax:* 01227 266877 *Dx:* 32354 WHITSTABLE
E-mail: mail@pococklaw.com

SUNLEY SOLICITORS ‡
46 Nelson Road Whitstable Kent CT5 1EA
Tel: 01227 274455 *Fax:* 01227 273894
E-mail: enquiries@sunley-solicitors.co.uk

WHITTON, Middlesex

BONNETTS SOLICITORS LLP
(incorporating Partridge & Mountford)
HSBC Bank Chambers High Street Whitton Middlesex TW2 7LF
Tel: 020 8898 2022 *Fax:* 020 8898 9169 *Dx:* 43050 WHITTON
E-mail: law@bonnetts.co.uk
Office: Hounslow
Work: B1 C1 E F1 L O Q S1 S2 W Z(l)
Agency undertaken
SPr: Mountford, Mr John F. . . . . *Jun 1970

T A DEEGAN ‡
136 High Street Whitton Middlesex TW2 7LL
Tel: 020 8755 2574 *Fax:* 020 8755 2737
E-mail: tadeegansolicitor@btconnect.com
List of partners: T A Deegan
Work: S1 S2 W
SPr: Deegan, Mr Thomas A . . . . Dec 1976

WICKFORD, Essex

CHRIS ALNUTT ‡
Ground Floor Broadway House 1-7 The Broadway Wickford Essex SS11 7AD
Tel: 01268 561541 *Fax:* 01268 561585
E-mail: alnutt12@btconnect.com

BRIAN RUFF ANGUS & JEWERS ‡
(incorporating Hatten Jewers & Mepham)
The Old Bank 2-8 The Broadway Wickford Essex SS11 7AL
Tel: 01268 761126 *Fax:* 01268 764369 *Dx:* 50801 WICKFORD
E-mail: brianruffs@aol.com
List of partners: A S Angus, R H Jewers
Work: A1 B1 C1 D1 D2 E F1 F2 J1 J2 K1 K2 L N O P Q R1 R2 S1 S2 T1 T2 W Z(c,g,i,l,o,q,r)
Emergency Action, Agency, Advocacy and Fixed Fee Interview undertaken
Ptr: Angus, Mr Alexander S LLB(Lond) . . . . *Sep 1980
Jewers, Mr Robert H LLB . . . . *Oct 1980
Ast: MacBean, Mr James I N LLB . . . . Dec 1986
O'Brien, Mr Andrew LLB . . . . *Jan 1980

CUNNINGTONS
13 London Road Wickford Essex SS12 0AW
Tel: 01268 732268 *Fax:* 01268 732274 *Dx:* 50800 WICKFORD
E-mail: quotes@cunningtons.co.uk
Office: Braintree (2 offices), Croydon, Ilford, Solihull
Work: E L S1 W
Ptr: Parsons, Ms Fiona Sara LLB(Hons). . . . . *Jan 2004
Asoc: Hayre, Miss Sukhbi LLB(Hons) . . . . Jan 2006
Hunt, Ms Kate LLB(Hons). . . . . *Mar 2006

HARVEY COPPING & HARRISON ‡
De Burgh House Market Road Wickford Essex SS12 0BB
Tel: 01268 733381 / 763211 *Fax:* 01268 739462
Dx: 50802 WICKFORD
Emergency telephone 01268 733381
E-mail: wickford@hchsolicitors.co.uk
List of partners: V A Copping, N C Harrison, S J Shepard, S J Shepard
Office: Chelmsford
Work: D1 E J1 K1 L O Q S1 S2 W Z(l)
Emergency Action, Fixed Fee Interview and Legal Aid undertaken
Ptr: Copping, Mr Victor A . . . . *Jun 1982
Harrison, Mr Nicholas C LLB(Nott'm) . . . . *Jul 1980
Shepard, Mrs Susan J LLB(Hons). . . . . *Nov 1993
Ast: Harrison, Ms Gillian. . . . . Oct 1980

WICKHAM, Hampshire

BISCOES
Boyces Cottage The Square Wickham Hampshire PO17 5JN
Tel: 01329 833249 *Fax:* 01329 833701 *Dx:* 40818 FAREHAM
E-mail: bcg@biscoes-law.co.uk
Office: Gosport, Petersfield, Portchester, Portsmouth, Waterlooville
Languages: French
Work: A1 A2 A3 B1 C1 D1 D2 E F1 G H I J1 J2 K1 K2 L N O Q S1 S2 V W X Z(b,c,d,e,f,j,k,l,q,r)
Emergency Action, Agency, Advocacy, Fixed Fee Interview, Legal Aid undertaken, Legal Aid Franchise and Member of Accident Line
Ptr: Salvetti, Mr Roger Steven. . . . . *Jun 1974
Asoc: Hansford, Miss Jane LLB; AKC . . . . *Jan 1981
Ast: Cleverly, Mrs Nicola LPC . . . . *Oct 1995
Hetzel, Miss Katharine BA(Hons). . . . . *Jan 1999

MOORE BLATCH SOLICITORS
Turnberry House 4400 Parkway Whiteley Wickham Hampshire PO15 7FJ
Tel: 01489 884100 *Fax:* 01489 880683
Office: Lymington, Richmond upon Thames, Southampton (2 offices)

WIDNES, Cheshire

BYRNE FRODSHAM & CO ‡
1 Deacon Road Widnes Cheshire WA8 6EB
Tel: 0151 424 5601 *Fax:* 0151 495 2297 *Dx:* 15956 WIDNES 2
E-mail: mail@burnefrodsham.co.uk
List of partners: C W Asbury, B J M Cashman, C R Rees
Work: A1 C1 D1 E F1 G H J1 K1 L N O P Q R1 S1 T2 V W Z(w)
Emergency Action, Agency, Advocacy, Fixed Fee Interview, Legal Aid undertaken and Legal Aid Franchise
Ptr: Asbury, Mr Charles W BA. . . . . *Oct 1980
Cashman, Mr Barry J M BA . . . . *Dec 1977
Rees, Mr Ceri R LLB . . . . *Jun 1971
Ast: Dodd, Ms Caroline E LLB . . . . *Nov 1992

FORSTER DEAN LTD
57-59 Albert Road Widnes Cheshire WA8 6JS
Tel: 0151 422 0982 *Fax:* 0151 422 0983 *Dx:* 15957 WIDNES 2
Emergency telephone 07702 111986
E-mail: enquiries@forsterdean.co.uk
Office: Birkenhead, Bootle, Chorley, Crewe, Eccles, Ellesmere Port, Huyton, Leigh, Liverpool (5 offices), Oldham, Preston, Rochdale, Runcorn, St Helens, Stockport, Warrington, Widnes, Wigan
Work: D1 D2 K1 K2 N S1
Emergency Action, Agency, Advocacy, Fixed Fee Interview and Legal Aid undertaken
Ptr: Betts, Mr William Edward LPC . . . . Jul 2000
Ast: Gamble, Miss Donna M BA(Hons). . . . . *Nov 1998
Labor, Miss Samantha A LLB(Hons). . . . . *Apr 1999

FORSTER DEAN LTD
32-34 Widnes Road Widnes Cheshire WA8 6AS
Tel: 0151 495 3270 *Fax:* 0151 495 3271 *Dx:* 24307 WIDNES 1
E-mail: enquiries@forsterdean.co.uk
Office: Birkenhead, Bootle, Chorley, Crewe, Eccles, Ellesmere Port, Huyton, Leigh, Liverpool (5 offices), Oldham, Preston, Rochdale, Runcorn, St Helens, Stockport, Warrington, Widnes, Wigan
Work: D1 G H K1 N Q S1 W Z(l,r)
Emergency Action, Agency, Advocacy, Fixed Fee Interview, Legal Aid undertaken, Legal Aid Franchise and Member of Accident Line
Ptr: Forster Dean, Mr Peter BA . . . . *Apr 1981
Thompson, Mr Daniel. . . . . Oct 1998
Ast: Hunter, Mr John Mark LLB(Hons) . . . . *Sep 1996
Taylor, Mrs Rachel Jane LLB . . . . *Oct 1995

HATTONS SOLICITORS
78 Victoria Road Widnes Cheshire WA8 7RA
Tel: 0151 495 2228 *Fax:* 0151 495 2227
Office: St Helens

KEITH M HURST ‡
3 Denton Street off Albert Road Widnes Cheshire WA8 6LR
Tel: 0151 420 0900 *Fax:* 0151 420 0685

JONES ROBERTSON ‡
131 Albert Road Widnes Cheshire WA8 6LF
Tel: 0151 423 3661
List of partners: B C De Haas, L Ferris, C R Jones, D W Jones, T M Murphy, M Robertson, I Weights
Office: Northwich, Runcorn
Emergency Action and Fixed Fee Interview undertaken
Ptr: De Haas, Mr Brian C BSc. . . . . *Jun 1977
Jones, Mr Christopher R BA. . . . . *Oct 1982
Jones, Mr David W LLB. . . . . *Apr 1975
Murphy, Mr Thomas M LLB . . . . *Mar 1984
Robertson, Mr Mark LLB . . . . *Apr 1981
Ast: Aynsley, Ms Catherine Ann . . . . Sep 1994

NYLAND & BEATTIE ‡
63 Albert Road Widnes Cheshire WA8 6JS
Tel: 0151 424 5656 *Fax:* 0151 424 6716 *Dx:* 15953 WIDNES 2
E-mail: info@nylandandbeattie.co.uk
List of partners: B A Hill, M J Verdin
Languages: French
Work: C1 D1 E F1 G H J1 K1 K3 L N O Q R1 S1 S2 W Z(g,l,r)
Emergency Action, Agency, Advocacy, Fixed Fee Interview and Legal Aid undertaken
Ptr: Hill, Mr Barry A MA(Oxon) ● . . . . *Jun 1980
Verdin, Mr Mark J BA(Law) ● . . . . *Oct 1987
Asoc: Balmford, Mr Colin R LLB . . . . Aug 1980
Ast: Birch, Mrs Stephanie BA . . . . Sep 1995
Cadman, Mrs Louise Victoria LLB(Hons) . . . . . . *Sep 2004
Majid, Mr Imran . . . . Feb 2004

JOHN ROBERTSON ‡
Number One Frederick Street Widnes Cheshire WA8 6PF
Tel: 0151 423 6500 *Fax:* 0151 420 3765 *Dx:* 15954 WIDNES 2
Emergency telephone 01925 722582
List of partners: K L Porter
Work: D1 G H K1 S1 W
Emergency Action, Agency, Advocacy, Fixed Fee Interview, Legal Aid undertaken and Legal Aid Franchise
Ptr: Porter, Mr Keith L LLB . . . . *May 1977

SPEEDING SOLICITOR / MAJ LAW SOLICITORS ‡
1st Floor 55 Widnes Road Widnes Cheshire WA8 6AZ
Tel: 0151 422 8020 / 07810 804464 *Fax:* 0151 424 1149

WIGAN, Greater Manchester

ALKER & BALL ‡
29-33 King Street Wigan Greater Manchester WN1 1EG
Tel: 01942 246241 *Fax:* 01942 820086 *Dx:* 19315 WIGAN
E-mail: roger.alker@alkerandball.co.uk
List of partners: R L Alker, A R Bowden, S A Dean, S A Magrath, K Whitehead, J E Wood, J J Wroblewski
Work: A1 B1 C1 C2 C3 D1 D2 E F1 F2 J1 J2 K1 K2 K3 K4 L O P Q R1 S1 S2 W Z(c,k)
Agency, Advocacy and Fixed Fee Interview undertaken
Ptr: Alker, Mr Roger Lloyd BA(Law) . . . . *Apr 1973
Bowden, Mr Alan Richard LLB(Vict) . . . . *May 1974
Dean, Mr Stephen A MA(Oxon) . . . . *Dec 1975
Magrath, Mr Stephen A LLB . . . . Jun 1978
Whitehead, Mr Keith BA(Law) . . . . Oct 1985
Wood, Mrs Janette E LLB(L'pool) . . . . *May 1981
Wroblewski, Mr John Joseph BA(Hons) . . . . *Oct 1995
Ast: Thompson, Mr Karl James LLB . . . . *Sep 2008

ARTHUR SMITHS ‡
(incorporating Arthur Smith & Broadie-Griffith & Rhodes & Swalwel)
30-32 King Street Wigan Greater Manchester WN1 1DA
Tel: 01942 242815 *Fax:* 01942 820020 *Dx:* 19337 WIGAN
E-mail: info@arthursmith.co.uk
List of partners: G J Fairhurst, P Higgins, L Porter
Work: C1 D1 E J1 J2 K1 N O Q S1 S2 W Z(q)
Emergency Action, Agency, Advocacy, Fixed Fee Interview, Legal Aid undertaken, Legal Aid Franchise and Member of Accident Line
Ptr: Fairhurst, Mr Gerald J LLB(Sheff) . . . . *Jan 1968
Higgins, Miss Patricia LLB . . . . Nov 1990
Porter, Miss Lesley LLB(Hull) . . . . Feb 1990
Ast: Burke, Mr Robert John BA(Wales)(Law) . . . . May 2002
Fairhurst, Mr Christopher John FILEx . . . . Sep 2003
Prescott, Mr Liam LLB(Staffs) . . . . Aug 2004
Con: Appleton, Mr John LLB(L'pool) . . . . Oct 1974

FORSTER DEAN LTD
15 Mesnes Street Wigan Greater Manchester WN1 1QP
Tel: 01942 366365 *Fax:* 01942 366366
E-mail: enquiries@forsterdean.co.uk
Office: Birkenhead, Bootle, Chorley, Crewe, Eccles, Ellesmere Port, Huyton, Leigh, Liverpool (5 offices), Oldham, Preston, Rochdale, Runcorn, St Helens, Stockport, Warrington, Widnes (2 offices)

HEALDS ‡
Moot Hall Chambers 8 Wallgate Wigan Greater Manchester WN1 1JE
Tel: 01942 241511 *Fax:* 01942 826639 *Dx:* 19313 WIGAN
E-mail: mail@healds.co.uk
List of partners: J G Byrne, A J Foden, J Larkin, G B Peet, G Shepherd
Work: A1 B1 C1 C2 D1 E F1 J1 J2 K1 K3 K4 N O Q R1 S1 S2 W Z(c,h,l,p,q)
Agency, Advocacy, Legal Aid undertaken and Legal Aid Franchise
Ptr: Byrne, Mr J Graham LLB(L'pool) Clerk to Commissioner of Taxes . . . . *§Jun 1968
Foden, Mr Andrew J LLB; LLM . . . . *Sep 1991
Larkin, Miss Janet LLB; Adv Dip Counselling . . . . . *Oct 1983
Peet, Mr Geoffrey B LLB . . . . *§Jul 1974
Shepherd, Mr Gary FILEx . . . . *Nov 1993

HILTON NORBURY ‡
6-8 Upper Dicconson Street Wigan Greater Manchester WN1 2AD
Tel: 01942 241424 *Fax:* 01942 324188 *Dx:* 702074 WIGAN
List of partners: V S Hilton, I Ranson
Work: D1 D2 E K1 K3 K4 Q S1 S2 W
Emergency Action, Agency, Advocacy, Fixed Fee Interview, Legal Aid undertaken and Legal Aid Franchise
Ptr: Hilton, Miss Victoria S LLB . . . . *Oct 1989
Ranson, Mr Ivan LLB(Hons) . . . . *Nov 1997
Ast: Atkinson, Miss Vivienne Sharon LLB . . . . *Dec 2007

HOUGHTON PIGOT & CO ‡
(incorporating G Raymond Pigot & Co)
25 Bridgeman Terrace Wigan Greater Manchester WN1 1TD
Tel: 01942 241288 / 824424 *Fax:* 01942 282154
Dx: 702062 WIGAN 2
E-mail: enquiries@houghtonpigot.co.uk
List of partners: S E Houghton, F M Lawlor, M J Randall
Office: Ashton-in-Makerfield
Languages: French, Spanish
Work: A1 C1 C2 E F1 J1 K1 K4 L N O Q S1 T2 W
Emergency Action, Agency, Advocacy and Fixed Fee Interview undertaken
Ptr: Houghton, Miss Susan Elizabeth LLB Notary Public . . *Jan 1994
Lawlor, Mrs Frances M BA . . . . *Oct 1983
Randall, Mr Mark J LLB(UWIST) . . . . *Oct 1986

MCCARTHY BENNETT HOLLAND ‡
26 Bridgeman Terrace Wigan Greater Manchester WN1 1TD
Tel: 01942 206060 *Fax:* 01942 200505 *Dx:* 702061 WIGAN 2
E-mail: mbh@wigansolicitors.com
List of partners: P D Aynsley, M T Boon, J R Holland, J M Long
Work: C1 C2 D1 E F1 J1 K1 K3 L N O Q S1 S2 W Z(c,l)
Emergency Action, Agency, Advocacy and Fixed Fee Interview undertaken
Ptr: Aynsley, Mr Paul D LLB . . . . *Sep 1991
Boon, Mr Mark T BSc(Econ) . . . . *Jun 1983
Holland, Mr John Richard LLB(Bris) . . . . *§Jan 1969
Long, Mrs Janet Maria LLB . . . . *Nov 1997

MALCOLM PEET & CO ‡
36 High Street Standish Wigan Greater Manchester WN6 0HL
Tel: 01257 427867 *Fax:* 01257 423561
List of partners: M Peet, S J Rudd
Office: Atherton
Work: E S1 W
Ptr: Peet, Mr Malcolm . . . . *Apr 1971

PLATT & FISHWICK ‡
The Old Bank 47 King Street Wigan Greater Manchester WN1 1DB
Tel: 01942 243281 *Fax:* 01942 495522 *Dx:* 19318 WIGAN 1
List of partners: R I Armstrong, L A Davies, S A Finch, M A Richardson
Office: Wigan
Work: A1 B1 C1 D1 E F1 J1 K1 K3 K4 L N O Q R1 R2 S1 S2 T1 T2 V W X Z(c,l,m,n)
Emergency Action, Agency, Advocacy, Fixed Fee Interview, Legal Aid undertaken, Legal Aid Franchise and Member of Accident Line
Ptr: Armstrong, Mr Robert Ian LLB(L'pool) . . . . *Dec 1982
Davies, Mrs Lesley Anne LLB(Hons) . . . . *Apr 2004
Finch, Miss Sandra Anne LLB . . . . *Oct 1989
Richardson, Mr Mark Alan LLB . . . . *Oct 1986
Ast: Collette, Ms Louise . . . . *Aug 2006
Wade, Miss Jacqueline Susan . . . . *Aug 2006

PLATT & FISHWICK
11 Preston Road Standish Wigan Greater Manchester WN6 0HR
Tel: 01257 402430 *Fax:* 01257 402431
E-mail: satherton@plattandfishwick.co.uk
Office: Wigan
Work: E K1 K3 K4 N O Q R2 S1 S2 W

SIMPSON HEALD PEARSON ‡
17 Bridgeman Terrace Wigan Greater Manchester WN1 1SX
Tel: 01942 495999 *Fax:* 01942 491888 *Dx:* 19312 WIGAN

STEPHENSONS SOLICITORS LLP
Wigan Investment Centre Waterside Drive Wigan Greater Manchester WN3 5BA
Tel: 01942 777777 *Fax:* 01942 774178
E-mail: enquiries@stephensons.co.uk
Office: Bolton (2 offices), Leigh (2 offices), Manchester, St Helens, Wigan

STEPHENSONS SOLICITORS LLP
10-14 Library Street Wigan Greater Manchester WN1 1NN
Tel: 01942 777777 *Fax:* 01942 821262 *Dx:* 19319 WIGAN
Emergency telephone 07836 574607
E-mail: enquiries@stephensons.co.uk
Office: Bolton (2 offices), Leigh (2 offices), Manchester, St Helens, Wigan
Work: A1 B1 C1 C2 C3 D1 E F1 G H I J1 K1 K2 L M1 N O P Q R1 S1 S2 V W Z(c,d,e,h,l,o,q,r,s,t)
Emergency Action, Agency, Advocacy, Fixed Fee Interview, Legal Aid undertaken, Legal Aid Franchise and Member of Accident Line
Ptr: Baybut, Mr David BSc(Hons) . . . . *Feb 1996
Boland, Mr Neal BA(Hons) . . . . *Nov 1983
Carr, Mr Christopher M LLB . . . . *Oct 1987
Harrison, Ms Ann . . . . Nov 1983
Holcroft, Ms Rosemary . . . . *Dec 1985
Rimmer, Ms Amanda J LLB(Hons) . . . . Nov 1993
Stott, Mr Peter BA . . . . *Jun 1981
Taylor, Mr Malcolm . . . . *Jul 1978
Yates, Mr Nicholas J LLB . . . . *Jan 1985
Asoc: Baron, Mrs Kate LLB . . . . *Sep 1996
Platt, Ms Corenna LLB; MSc . . . . *Jan 1996
Sweeney, Ms Kate LLB(Hons) . . . . *Sep 1996
Ast: Fergusson, Mr Mark BSc . . . . Jul 1998
Flynn, Ms Linda LLB(Hons) . . . . *Aug 1997
Joyce, Mr Sean Adrian . . . . *Jul 1998
McMahon, Ms Jacynta Elizabeth BA(Hons); CPE . . *Mar 1997
Waddington, Miss Kay LLB . . . . *Sep 1998

STOCK MORAN SWALWELL ‡
Nationwide Chambers 30 Market Place Wigan Greater Manchester WN1 1PJ
Tel: 01942 771771 *Fax:* 01942 771777
Emergency telephone 01942 771771
Work: G H

UNSWORTH & WOOD ‡
23 King Street Wigan Greater Manchester WN1 1EQ
Tel: 01942 242400 *Fax:* 01942 242857
E-mail: jm@uwlaw.co.uk
List of partners: J B McAreavey
Work: E K1 K3 K4 L R2 S1 S2 W
SPr: McAreavey, Mr Jonathan Bede BA(Hons) Notary Public . . . . *Nov 1991

VINCENT & CO ‡
13 Bridgeman Terrace Wigan Greater Manchester WN1 1SX
Tel: 01942 241421 *Fax:* 01942 241421 *Dx:* 702069 WIGAN 2
E-mail: info@vincentswigan.co.uk
List of partners: D B Beardsmore, K J D Keyho
Office: Wigan
Work: C1 D1 E F1 G H K1 L M1 N S1 T1 V W Z(c,l)
Emergency Action, Agency, Advocacy, Fixed Fee Interview, Legal Aid undertaken and Member of Accident Line
Ptr: Beardsmore, Mr David B LLB . . . . Mar 1973
Keyho, Miss Karen J D . . . . *Oct 1981

VINCENT & CO
24 High Street Standish Wigan Greater Manchester WN6 0HL
Tel: 01257 425121 *Fax:* 01257 472899 *Dx:* 702170 STANDISH
Office: Wigan
Work: E F1 K1 K3 K4 L N O Q R1 S1 S2 T1 T2 V W
Emergency Action, Agency, Advocacy, Fixed Fee Interview undertaken and Member of Accident Line
Ptr: Keyho, Miss Karen J D . . . . *Oct 1981

WIDDOWS MASON
Prudential Buildings 16 Library Street Wigan Greater Manchester WN1 1NZ
Tel: 01942 244294 *Fax:* 01942 821673 *Dx:* 19314 WIGAN
Emergency telephone 07739 446805
E-mail: info@widdows.co.uk
Office: Leigh, Warrington, Westhoughton
Work: D1 D2 E K1 N O Q S1 W
Agency, Advocacy, Fixed Fee Interview, Legal Aid undertaken, Legal Aid Franchise and Member of Accident Line
Ptr: Jackson, Mr Gary S . . . . Dec 1993
Ast: Cadman, Mrs Louise Victoria LLB(Hons) . . . . . . *Sep 2004
Con: Toppin, Mr Robert E LLB ★ . . . . Aug 1975

WIGSTON, Leicestershire

LAWSON WEST SOLICITORS LIMITED
44 Long Street Wigston Leicestershire LE18 2Ah
Tel: 0116 212 1080 *Fax:* 0116 212 1081 *Dx:* 29842 WIGSTON
E-mail: mail@lawson-west.co.uk
Office: Leicester, Market Harborough
Work: D1 D2 E K1 K2 K3 N S1 S2 W
Emergency Action, Agency, Advocacy, Fixed Fee Interview undertaken and Member of Accident Line
Ptr: Haworth, Mr James E LLB . . . . *Jan 1990

WIGTON, Cumbria

ATKINSON RITSON
(incorporating Atkinson & North; Hetherington Ritson & Co; Saul & Lightfoot; J A Coupland & Co; Karen Messenger)
39 High Street Wigton Cumbria CA7 9PE
Tel: 01697 343241 *Fax:* 01697 344820 *Dx:* 714666 WIGTON
Emergency telephone 01697 344415
Office: Carlisle
Work: A1 C1 D1 E K1 L N P Q S1 S2 T1 T2 W Z(l,r)
Emergency Action, Agency, Advocacy, Fixed Fee Interview, Legal Aid undertaken, Legal Aid Franchise and Member of Accident Line
Ptr: Fitzgerald, Mr Hugh James Brown Under Sheriff of Cumberland . . . . §Jun 1971

BEATY & CO ‡
1 Victoria Place High Street Wigton Cumbria CA7 9PJ
Tel: 01697 342121 *Fax:* 01697 344697 *Dx:* 714665 WIGTON
E-mail: info@beatysolicitors.co.uk
List of partners: C M Harrod, E J Hawks, P R Johnston, M P Wright
Work: A1 A2 B1 C1 E F1 J1 K4 L N Q R1 R2 S1 S2 T1 T2 W Z(d,h,n,q)
Emergency Action, Advocacy, Fixed Fee Interview undertaken and Member of Accident Line
Ptr: Hawks, Mr Edward J LLB Notary Public . . . . *§Apr 1973
Johnston, Mr Peter R MA(Cantab) . . . . *§Dec 1969
Wright, Mrs Maria Patricia LLB . . . . *Aug 2001
Harrod, Mrs Catherine Mary . . . . NSP
Ast: Steel, Miss Dorothy Sarah LLM . . . . Sep 2010
Con: Hart, Sir David M OBE FRSA Herbert Ruse Prize . . . *Jun 1963

CHRIS TOMS SOLICITOR ‡
Creek House Kirkbride Wigton Cumbria CA7 5HX
Tel: 01697 352931 *Fax:* 01697 352932
E-mail: chris.toms@btconnect.com

WILLASTON, Cheshire

BLAIN BOLAND & CO
The Green Neston Road Neston Willaston Cheshire CH64 1RA
Tel: 0151 327 1301 *Fax:* 0151 327 8360
E-mail: nicholas.thomas@blainboland.co.uk
Office: Ellesmere Port
Work: C1 E L S1 T1 T2 W Z(d,x)
Agency undertaken
Dir: Blain, Mr Michael John Heygarth LLB . . . . *Jul 1969
Boland, Mr Bernard David LLB . . . . *Jul 1974
Thomas, Mr Nicholas D W BA; LLM(Canon Law) . . *§Jan 1982

WILLENHALL, West Midlands

AVERY KNIGHTS SOLICITORS LIMITED ‡
West Midlands House Gipsy Lane Willenhall West Midlands WV13 2HA
Tel: 0121 609 7240 *Fax:* 0121 609 7241 *Dx:* 24408 WILLENHALL
Office: Willenhall

AVERY KNIGHTS SOLICITORS LIMITED
2 Isis Grove Willenhall West Midlands WV13 1JD
Tel: 0845 458 6293 *Fax:* 0845 458 6294 *Dx:* 24408 WILLENHALL
Office: Willenhall

FBC MANBY BOWDLER LLP
11-12 New Road Willenhall West Midlands WV13 2BL
Tel: 01902 366566 *Fax:* 01902 636455 *Dx:* 24404 WILLENHALL
E-mail: info@fbcmb.co.uk
Office: Bridgnorth, Shrewsbury, Telford, Wolverhampton
Work: D1 D2 E F1 G H K1 K2 K3 N O Q R1 S1 S2 Z(l)
Ptr: Gray, Mr Timothy C LLB . . . . *§Mar 1989
Robinson, Mr David S BSc(Econ); LLB . . . . *§Apr 1977
Asoc: Tawana, Mrs Jaswinder Kaur . . . . *Dec 2005
Ast: Hodson, Mr Adam . . . . Mar 2009

IAN HENRY & CO SOLICITORS ‡
Quickjay Buildings Bilston Street Willenhall West Midlands WV13 2AW
Tel: 01902 366615

JD SOLICITORS ‡
Malthouse Chambers 30 Walsall Street Willenhall West Midlands WV13 2ER
Tel: 01902 632123

See p112 for the Key to Work Categories & other symbols

MH SOLICITORS ‡
117 Lower Lichfield Street Willenhall West Midlands WV13 1PU
Tel: 01902 605083

ROWLAND TILDESLEY & HARRIS ‡
1 Rose Hill Willenhall West Midlands WV13 2AR
Tel: 01902 366571 *Fax:* 01902 608097 *Dx:* 24405 WILLENHALL
List of partners: J J Easter, S Kumar, J N Richards
Languages: Punjabi
Work: C1 D1 E F1 G H J1 K1 K3 L S1 S2 W Z(l,m,p)
Emergency Action, Agency, Advocacy, Fixed Fee Interview and Legal Aid undertaken
Ptr: Easter, Mr John J . . . . . *May 1977
Kumar, Surbjit LLB(Hons) Notary Public. . . . . *Aug 2002
Richards, Mr Jonathan N BA . . . . . *Apr 1979
Ast: Lala, Mitesh LLB(Hons) . . . . . *Dec 2006

SUNDIP MURRIA SOLICITORS LIMITED ‡
2-3 Walsall Road Willenhall West Midlands WV13 2EH
Tel: 0844 567 4999 *Fax:* 01902 637090 *Dx:* 24410 WILLENHALL

LYNN M WAINWRIGHT ‡
4 Haley Street Willenhall West Midlands WV12 4JU
Tel: 01902 609842
List of partners: L M Wainwright
SPr: Wainwright, Mrs Lynn Marion . . . . . Oct 2002

WILLITON, Somerset

RISDON HOSEGOOD ‡
18 Fore Street Williton Somerset TA4 4QD
Tel: 01984 632277 *Fax:* 01984 632192 *Dx:* 117700 WILLITON
E-mail: williton@risdonhosegood.com
List of partners: E G Kidner, K L Needs, J P Sunderland
Office: Dulverton, Minehead, Taunton, Wiveliscombe
Work: A1 C1 D1 E F1 G H J1 K1 K2 L N O Q S1 S2 V W Z(r)
Emergency Action, Agency, Advocacy, Fixed Fee Interview, Legal Aid undertaken and Legal Aid Franchise
Asoc: Bensley, Mr Andrew W LLB . . . . . *Nov 1980
Ast: Capper, Mr Peter D . . . . . *Oct 1979
Hallett, Ms Angela Mary. . . . . *Sep 1998

WILMSLOW, Cheshire

ANTROBUS SOLICITORS ‡
Suite 167 Courthill House 60 Water Lane Wilmslow Cheshire SK9 5AJ
Tel: 07919 561266
E-mail: info@antrobussolicitors.co.uk

BOTT & COMPANY ‡
St Ann's House Pasonage Green Wilmslow Cheshire SK9 1HG
Tel: 01625 415800 *Fax:* 01625 415900
List of partners: D Bott
Work: Z(j)
Ptr: Bott, Mr David BSc(Hons); CPE; LPC . . . . . *Sep 1996

CHAFES
Hesketh House 16 Alderley Road Wilmslow Cheshire SK9 1JX
Tel: 01625 531676 *Fax:* 01625 529401 *Dx:* 20816 WILMSLOW
Emergency telephone 01625 582461
E-mail: wilmslow@chafes.co.uk
Office: Alderley Edge, New Mills, Stockport
Work: A1 B1 C1 D1 E F1 G H J1 K1 L M1 N P R1 S1 T1 V W Z(b,c,e,f,h,i,j,k,l,t)
Emergency Action, Agency, Advocacy, Fixed Fee Interview and Legal Aid undertaken
Ptr: Lee, Mrs Susan LLB . . . . . *Sep 1989
Roberts, Mr Jonathan P LLB . . . . . *Oct 1982
Welton, Mr John C LLB . . . . . *Apr 1970
Williams, Mr John F. . . . . . Oct 1968
Asoc: Battersby, Mr M John . . . . . *§Jun 1972
Con: Haig, Mr Robin M LLB. . . . . . *§Jun 1972
Rawsthorn, Mr Michael LLB(Lond). . . . . *Nov 1967

EB LEGAL SOLICITORS ‡
Astute House Wilmslow Road Wilmslow Cheshire SK9 3HP
Tel: 01625 544753
E-mail: info@eblegal.co.uk

MARK GOODWIN & CO ‡
90 Water Lane Wilmslow Cheshire SK9 5BB
Tel: 01625 526495 *Fax:* 01625 523459
E-mail: enqs@goodwinlaw.co.uk
List of partners: M Goodwin
Ptr: Goodwin, Mr Mark BA. . . . . . Apr 1985

JACKSON BARRETT & GASS ‡
(incorporating New Homes Legal Helpline)
Smithy Annexe 112 Adlington Road Wilmslow Cheshire SK9 2LN
Tel: 01625 523988 *Fax:* 01625 525851
E-mail: mail@jbgass.com
List of partners: S C J Barrow
Work: A3 S1 W
Legal Aid Franchise
Ptr: Barrow, Mr Sean C J LLB . . . . . *Dec 1978

JAMES MAGUIRE & CO ‡
Blackbox Beech Lane Wilmslow Cheshire SK9 5ER
Tel: 01625 529456 / 07739 247630 *Fax:* 01625 838501
E-mail: james.maguire@family-law.co.uk

HILARY MEREDITH SOLICITORS ‡
Churchgate House 25-27 Water Lane Wilmslow Cheshire SK9 5AR
Tel: 01625 539922 *Fax:* 01625 539944 *Dx:* 20805 WILMSLOW
E-mail: enq@hmsolicitors.co.uk
List of partners: D Edwards, H Meredith
Work: N Z(r)
Fixed Fee Interview, Legal Aid undertaken and Legal Aid Franchise
Ptr: Edwards, Mr David . . . . . Oct 1986
Meredith, Ms Hilary Executive Council Member of Association of Personal Injury Lawyers. . . . . *Oct 1994

ALFRED NEWTON & CO
32 Alderley Road Wilmslow Cheshire SK9 1JX
Tel: 01625 523647 *Fax:* 01625 522068
Emergency telephone 0161 406 8726
Office: Stockport (2 offices)
Work: B1 D1 G H K1 L M1 M2 N Q S1 W
Emergency Action, Agency, Advocacy, Fixed Fee Interview, Legal Aid undertaken, Legal Aid Franchise and Member of Accident Line
Ptr: Penman, Mr Anthony . . . . . *Feb 1970
Penman, Mrs Sarah A BA(Law). . . . . *Oct 1982

ROBERTS JACKSON SOLICITORS ‡
Blackbox Business Centre Beech Lane Wilmslow Cheshire SK9 5ER
Tel: 01625 522215 *Fax:* 01625 546629

CHARLES STANSFIELD ‡
24 Altrincham Road Wilmslow Cheshire SK9 5ND
Tel: 01625 539695

LAURA STANSFIELD & CO ‡
24 Altrincham Road Wilmslow Cheshire SK9 5ND
Tel: 01625 529409 *Fax:* 01625 539310

WIMBORNE, Dorset

THE COMMERCIAL LAW PRACTICE ‡
Redcott House 1 Redcotts Lane Wimborne Dorset BH21 1JX
Tel: 01202 843976 *Fax:* 01202 884812

DIBBENS ‡
3 West Borough Wimborne Dorset BH21 1LU
Tel: 01202 882456 *Fax:* 01202 89200 *Dx:* 45306 WIMBORNE
E-mail: wimborne@dibbens.co.uk
List of partners: G H Evans, R B R Fleet, A P D Mellowes
Work: A1 B1 C1 C2 C3 D1 E F1 J1 J2 K1 L M1 N O Q R1 S1 S2 T1 T2 V W Z(b,c,e,h,i,j,k,l,o,t)
Emergency Action, Agency, Advocacy, Fixed Fee Interview, Legal Aid undertaken, Legal Aid Franchise and Member of Accident Line
Ptr: Evans, Mr Graham H Maurice Nordon Prize. . . . . *Nov 1967
Fleet, Miss Rachel B R LLB. . . . . *Oct 1986
Mellowes, Mr Anthony P D . . . . . *Jan 1981
Ast: Craig, Miss Lucy Harriett LLB . . . . . Oct 2006

PETER J FOWLER ‡
Marshall House 1 East Borough Wimborne Dorset BH21 1PA
Tel: 01202 849242 *Fax:* 01202 842098 *Dx:* 45317 WIMBORNE
E-mail: p_fowler@lds.co.uk
List of partners: J S Filleul, P J Fowler
Work: C1 C2 E L M2 S1 S2 W Z(e)
Ptr: Filleul, Mrs Joanna S . . . . . Jan 1978
Fowler, Mr Peter John BA. . . . . *Jun 1974

HAROLD G WALKER
1 The Square Wimborne Dorset BH21 1PS
Tel: 01202 881454 *Fax:* 01202 841715 *Dx:* 45301 WIMBORNE
E-mail: wimborne@hgwalker.co.uk
Office: Bournemouth, Broadstone, Christchurch, Verwood
Work: K1 K3 S1 S2 W
Fixed Fee Interview undertaken
Ptr: Lowe, Mrs Nicola Anne LLB(Hons) . . . . . *Jan 2003
Con: Phillips, Mr David Andrew MA(Cantab) . . . . . *Jan 1990

JCP LAW ‡
Potterne Farm Cottage Potterne Way Three Legged Cross Wimborne Dorset BH21 6RS
Tel: 01202 813658 *Fax:* 01202 820478
E-mail: julia.palmer@jcplaw.co.uk

JW LAW ‡
21 Beacon Hill Lane Corfe Mullen Wimborne Dorset BH21 3RU
Tel: 01202 690658 *Fax:* 0870 005 2069
E-mail: juliawylie@jw-law.co.uk
List of partners: J A Wylie
Work: C1 E I U2 Z(d,e)
SPr: Wylie, Mrs Julia Ann LLB(Hons). . . . . Sep 1996
Ast: Ledger, Miss Tamsin Ruth LLB . . . . . Sep 2003

JACOBS & REEVES
25 East Street Wimborne Dorset BH21 1DU
Tel: 01202 880382 *Fax:* 01202 842602 *Dx:* 45302 WIMBORNE
E-mail: office@jacobsreeves.co.uk
Office: Poole (2 offices)
Work: C1 C3 D1 D2 E F1 F2 G H J1 K1 K3 L N O Q S1 S2 T1 T2 V W Z(d,l,r)
Agency, Advocacy, Fixed Fee Interview, Legal Aid undertaken, Legal Aid Franchise and Member of Accident Line
Ptr: Boyce, Mr Robert H G Howard-Watson & R Innes Prizes . . . . . *§May 1983

MJP LAW ‡
22a West Borough Wimborne Dorset BH21 1NF
Tel: 01202 842929 *Fax:* 01202 842493 *Dx:* 45300 WIMBORNE
E-mail: mp@mjplaw.co.uk

THERESA O'HARE SOLICITOR ‡
4 Cobbs Road Colehill Wimborne Dorset BH21 2RL
Tel: 01202 840153 *Fax:* 01202 841180
E-mail: ohare.theresa@btinternet.com
List of partners: T A O'Hare
Work: L S1 S2 W
SPr: O'Hare, Mrs Theresa A BA; DipLG . . . . . *Sep 1987

RICHARD FILLEUL SOLICITOR ‡
1 East Borough Wimborne Dorset BH21 1PA
Tel: 01202 849484 *Fax:* 01202 849454 *Dx:* 45317 WIMBORNE
E-mail: richard@filleul.net

WINCANTON, Somerset

DYNE DREWETT SOLICITORS LTD
Market Place Wincanton Somerset BA9 9AB
Tel: 01963 32374 *Fax:* 01963 33490 *Dx:* 48550 WINCANTON
E-mail: info@dynedrewett.com
Office: Shepton Mallet, Sherborne
Languages: French
Work: A1 C1 E R1 S1 T1 T2 W
Ptr: Beresford, Mrs Rebecca Eleanor Notary Public . . . . *Sep 1996
Morgan, Mr David R LLB . . . . . *Jun 1974
Con: Fenton, Mr Christopher P . . . . . *Jul 1978
We conduct business in French. We specialise in the following areas of work Residential Conveyancing, Commercial Conveyancing, Wills, Trusts and Probate.

RUTTER & RUTTER ‡
St Audreys South Street Wincanton Somerset BA9 9DR
Tel: 01963 32224 *Fax:* 01963 32710 *Dx:* 48551 WINCANTON
List of partners: D G R Carnegie, C F Rutter, J F Rutter
Office: Mere
Languages: French
Work: A1 B1 C1 E J1 K1 K3 L Q R1 S1 S2 T2 V W Z(j,k,l,m)
Ptr: Carnegie, Mr David G R BA. . . . . *Oct 1990
Rutter, Mr Charles Foster LLB. . . . . Jul 1976

WINCHCOMBE, Gloucestershire

JACKMAN WOODS ‡
Lloyds Bank Chambers Abbey Terrace Winchcombe Gloucestershire GL54 5LL
Tel: 01242 602378 *Fax:* 01242 604370 *Dx:* 118776 WINCHCOMBE
E-mail: jan@jackmanwoods.com
List of partners: D C Jackman, J Y Woods
Work: A1 E K4 S1 S2 T2 W Z(d)
Ptr: Jackman, Mr David Charles BA . . . . . *Jul 1978
Woods, Ms Janet Yvonne . . . . . *Sep 1994

WINCHESTER, Hampshire

CAJ SOLICITORS ‡
6 Eastcliffe East Hill Winchester Hampshire SO23 0JB
Tel: 01962 877100
Work: K1 K2 K3 Q S1

PENNY CATCHPOLE SOLICITORS ‡
Southgate Chambers 37-39 Southgate Street Winchester Hampshire SO23 9EH
Tel: 01962 866522
List of partners: P J Catchpole
SPr: Catchpole, Mrs Penelope J BA(Law) . . . . . Sep 1986

DAC BEACHCROFT
Winton House St Peter Street Winchester Hampshire SO23 8BW
Tel: 01962 705500 *Fax:* 01962 705510 *Dx:* 2540 WINCHESTER 1
Office: Birmingham, Bristol, Leeds, London EC3 (3 offices), London EC4 (2 offices), Manchester (2 offices), Newcastle upon Tyne, Newport
Work: A3 B1 B2 B3 C1 C2 C3 E F1 F2 I J1 J2 L M1 N O P Q R1 S2 T1 T2 U1 U2 W X Z(c,d,e,h,j,l,n,o,p,q,r,s,u,w,y,z)
Ptr: Durston-Hillyer, Ms Heather LLB . . . . . Nov 1995
McGrath, Mr Matthew J LLB. . . . . Aug 1993
Rutter, Mr Duncan S BA . . . . . *Oct 1988

DUTTON GREGORY ‡
Trussell House 23 St Peters Street Winchester Hampshire SO23 8BT
Tel: 01962 844333 *Fax:* 01962 863582 *Dx:* 2515 WINCHESTER
E-mail: contact@duttongregory.co.uk
List of partners: S R Bowden, R D Breese, M D Broad, J Brown, J T Brown, R S Brown, I L Campbell, J H Dyson, R G Egglestone, J H Grice, K J Hawkins, N M Kingsford, A H Kirkconel, P J E Lloyd, R B Loughridge, M Lucas, A J Sydney, A C Tilley, C A Wallis, A L Webb
Office: Bournemouth, Southampton
Languages: French
Ptr: Bowden, Mr Stephen R BA(Hons) Chairman of the Governors of Romsey School; Part time Chairman of the Special Education Needs Tribunal. . . . . *Mar 1975
Broad, Mr Mark David BA(Hons) ♦ . . . . . *Mar 1997
Brown, Mr Jonathan T LLB(Hons). . . . . *Oct 1990
Brown, Mr Richard Simon LLB . . . . . Oct 1986
Campbell, Ms I Lorne LLB. . . . . *Aug 1979
Dyson, Mrs Jane H BA . . . . . *Jun 1979
Egglestone, Mr Richard G. . . . . . *May 1977
Grice, Mr Jeremy H. . . . . . *Jul 1970
Hawkins, Mr Keith J. . . . . . *Dec 1974
Kingsford, Mr Nicholas M . . . . . *Jan 1980
Lloyd, Mr Peter J E LLB Governor of Peter Symonds 6th Form College Winchester . . . . . *§Oct 1973
Loughridge, Mr Robert B LLB(Hons). . . . . *Oct 1978
Sydney, Mr Alan J LLB . . . . . *Oct 1980
Tilley, Mr Andrew Charles LLB . . . . . *Oct 1984
Wallis, Mrs Caroline A LLB . . . . . *Oct 1985
Webb, Mr Andrew L LLB . . . . . *§Dec 1975
Ast: Le Vay, Miss Jane L M BSc Notary Public. . . . . *Feb 1988
Rivers, Miss Emma LPC . . . . . *Nov 1997
Shaw, Mrs Maria Anne LLB; TEP . . . . . *Jan 1989

EDGERLEY HARRIS SOLICITORS ‡
Chalk Hill Rectory Lane Itchen Abbas Winchester Hampshire SO21 1BW
Tel: 01962 779861 *Fax:* 01962 779051
List of partners: A A Edgerley Harris, G J Edgerley Harris
Work: S1
Ptr: Edgerley Harris, Mrs Adrienne A LLB(Lond) . . . . . *Aug 1980
Edgerley Harris, Mr Gavin J. . . . . . May 1989

THE ENGLISH COGGER PARTNERSHIP ‡
5a Charlecote Mews Staple Gardens Winchester Hampshire SO23 8SR
Tel: 01962 858800
E-mail: tecp@tecp.co.uk

GILL STEEL LAW PRACTICE ‡
Rose Cottage Woodman Lane Sparsholt Winchester Hampshire SO21 2NS
Tel: 01962 776442 *Fax:* 01962 776525
E-mail: gill.steel@lawskills.co.uk

GODWINS ‡
12 St Thomas Street Winchester Hampshire SO23 9HF
Tel: 01962 841484 *Fax:* 01962 841554 *Dx:* 2502 WINCHESTER 1
E-mail: info@godwins-law.co.uk
List of partners: C A Carden, A Cowgill, F G Leeson, R J M Morton-Curtis, A L Spencer, N S Spicer
Languages: French
Work: A1 C1 C2 E F1 J1 K1 K2 K3 K4 L N O Q R1 S1 S2 T2 W Z(c,d,h,l,s,x)
Ptr: Carden, Ms Carolyn A LLB; MA. . . . . *Jan 1982
Cowgill, Mr Alan LLB(Bris) . . . . . *§Nov 1984
Leeson, Mrs Fiona G LLB. . . . . *Oct 1998
Morton-Curtis, Mr Rupert James Morton BA(Law) . . *Nov 1984
Spencer, Miss Anna Louise MA(Cantab). . . . . *Nov 1995
Spicer, Mr Nigel Shaw. . . . . *Nov 1981
Ast: Neal, Mr Andrew John Kennety BA(Dunelm) . . . . *Sep 2010
Stroud, Mrs Margaret Mary BA . . . . . *Apr 1981
Thompson, Mr Rupert Alexander Robert Neale BA(Hons) . . . . . *Sep 2002

Con: Lawrenson, Mr Keith Raymond LLB First Tier Judge Tribunal Service . . . . *§Dec 1973
Nichols, Mr Christopher Dearmer Notary Public . . . . Jan 1972
Russell, Mr James Cecil Cumine CBE. . . . . *Jul 1969

KNIGHT POLSON
Southgate Chambers 37/39 Southgate Street Winchester Hampshire SO23 9EH
Tel: 01962 706243
E-mail: enquiries@knightpolson.co.uk
Office: Eastleigh, Fareham

LITTLE & CO ‡
The Tower House Micheldever Station Winchester Hampshire SO21 3AL
Tel: 01962 774222 *Fax:* 01962 774742
E-mail: michaellittle@hotmail.com

VIVIEN MANFIELD ‡
6 Branksome Close Winchester Hampshire SO22 5PZ
Tel: 01962 853930 *Fax:* 01962 853930

MARSDEN & CO ‡
52 Fairfield Road Winchester Hampshire SO22 6SG
Tel: 01962 841550
E-mail: ilm@sky.com

PENFOLD & MCPHERSON ‡
7a Southgate Street Winchester Hampshire SO23 9DY
Tel: 01962 840310 *Fax:* 01962 859492 *Dx:* 2516 WINCHESTER
E-mail: info@penmac.co.uk

SHENTONS ‡
Star Lane House Staple Gardens Winchester Hampshire SO23 9AD
Tel: 01962 844544 *Fax:* 01962 844501 *Dx:* 2503 WINCHESTER 1
E-mail: main@shentons.co.uk
List of partners: N W Bell, L J Hollely, R C Kerr, E L Pollard, S D Underhill
Work: A1 A3 B1 C1 C2 C3 D1 E F1 G H J1 K1 K2 K3 K4 L N O Q R1 S1 S2 T1 T2 W Z(c,d,e,k,l,m,s)
Emergency Action, Agency, Advocacy, Fixed Fee Interview, Legal Aid undertaken and Legal Aid Franchise
Ptr: Bell, Mr Nicholas W LLB . . . . *§Apr 1979
Hollely, Miss Louisa Jane LLB. . . . . *Jan 1994
Kerr, Mr Robert C MA. . . . . *§Jan 1985
Pollard, Mrs Elisabeth Lucy . . . . Oct 2003
Underhill, Mr Shaun David BA(Hons) Costs Appeals Assessor; LSC Funding & Costs Review Committee . . . . *§Feb 1991
Ast: Batten, Miss Sarah BSc(Hons) . . . . Oct 2007
Carey, Miss Corrinne Amber FILEx . . . . Nov 2007
Chawner, Ms Jayne BA(Hons); LLB . . . . Jan 1989
Cull, Mr Simon M LLB. . . . . *Dec 1986
Morse, Mrs Nicola Jane LLB(Hons) . . . . Apr 2007
Richards, Mrs Karen Louise LLB(Hons) . . . . Apr 2007

SPENCERS LAWYERS LIMITED ‡
Lambs Hill Southdown Road Winchester Hampshire SO21 2BY
Tel: 01962 850171

THOMAS SIMPSON SOLICITORS LTD ‡
Southgate Chambers 37-39 Southgate Street Winchester Hampshire SO23 9EH
Tel: 01962 820228 *Fax:* 01962 865225

WARNER & RICHARDSON ‡
29 Jewry Street Winchester Hampshire SO23 8RR
Tel: 01962 868366 *Fax:* 01962 840607 *Dx:* 2511 WINCHESTER
E-mail: lawyers@wandr.co.uk
List of partners: G Chapman, C I Duncan, R Goodchild, R S Robson, N S Spicer
Work: A1 A2 B1 C1 C2 C3 D1 E F1 G H J1 K1 L M1 M2 N P R1 S1 T1 T2 V W Z(a,b,c,d,e,f,g,h,i,j,k,l,m,n)
Emergency Action, Agency and Advocacy undertaken
Ptr: Chapman, Mr Garth. . . . . *§Jun 1980
Duncan, Mrs Claire I LLB(Glasgow) Secretary for Winchester District Housing Association. . . . . *Feb 1980
Goodchild, Mr Robert LLB; TEP. . . . . *Oct 1990
Robson, Mr Richard S. . . . . *Dec 1981
Spicer, Mr Nigel Shaw. . . . . *Nov 1981

WINCHESTER LEGAL ‡
The Cavendish Centre Winnall Close Winchester Hampshire SO23 0LD
Tel: 01962 841041 *Fax:* 01962 864852

WINDERMERE, Cumbria

HAYTON WINKLEY
Regent House 25 Crescent Road Windermere Cumbria LA23 1BJ
Tel: 01539 446585 *Fax:* 01539 446778 *Dx:* 711230 WINDERMERE
Office: Kendal

PEARSON & PEARSON
27 Main Road Windermere Cumbria LA23 1DX
Tel: 01539 447825 *Fax:* 01539 488640

STEPHENSON REYNELL ‡
Windermere Business Centre Oldfield Court Windermere Cumbria LA23 2HJ
Tel: 01539 488622 *Fax:* 01539 488622 *Dx:* 711232 WINDERMERE
List of partners: J C Stephenson
Languages: French
Work: E F1 L N Q S1 S2 W Z(l)
Agency and Fixed Fee Interview undertaken
SPr: Stephenson, Mr Jonathan Charles MA(Cantab) . . . . *Oct 1991

TEMPLE HEELIS LLP
(incorporating Whelan & Co)
47 Crescent Road Windermere Cumbria LA23 1BL
Tel: 01539 442455 *Fax:* 01539 442042
Office: Kendal
Work: A1 B1 C1 D1 E G H J1 K1 L M1 N P R1 S1 S2 W Z(c,i,j,l)
Emergency Action, Agency, Advocacy, Fixed Fee Interview, Legal Aid undertaken and Member of Accident Line
Ptr: Sim, Mr John A BA(Law) . . . . *Feb 1986

THOMSON WILSON PATTINSON
Stonecliffe Lake Road Bowness-on-Windermere Windermere Cumbria LA23 3AR
Tel: 01539 442233 *Fax:* 01539 488810 *Dx:* 711234 WINDERMERE
E-mail: windermere@twpsolicitors.com
Office: Kendal
Work: D1 E G K1 K3 K4 Q S1 S2 T2 W Z(o)
Legal Aid undertaken
Asoc: Dawson, Mr Alan M LLB . . . . *Nov 2003
Con: Crompton, Mr John R M MA(Oxon) Notary Public . . . *Jun 1969
Whittaker, Mr Brian Gordon . . . . *Jan 1986

WINDLESHAM, Surrey

SAVILL & CO ‡
39 Chertsey Road Windlesham Surrey GU20 6EW
Tel: 01276 451292 *Fax:* 01276 451298

WINDSOR, Windsor & Maidenhead

A'COURT & CO ‡
Suite 3 5-6 High Street Windsor Windsor & Maidenhead SL4 1LD
Tel: 01753 857146 *Fax:* 01753 830589 *Dx:* 3827 WINDSOR
Emergency telephone 01753 857146
E-mail: acourtchantelle@btinternet.com
List of partners: L A A'Court, P M A'Court
Work: D1 E J1 K1 K2 K3 L N Q R2 S2 W Z(r)
Emergency Action, Agency, Advocacy and Fixed Fee Interview undertaken
Ptr: A'Court, Mrs Lynette A FILEx . . . . *Jun 1999
A'Court, Mr Peter M DMA Mellersh Prize . . . . . . *§Sep 1972

ALLWYN SANGER SOLICITORS ‡
St Stephens House Arthur Road Windsor Windsor & Maidenhead SL4 1RU
Tel: 0845 217 1377 *Fax:* 0844 443 8982
E-mail: enquiries@allwynsanger.com
Work: F1 J1 K1 K2 K3 O Q W Z(o,q)
Advocacy undertaken

APPLEBY SHAW ‡
Trinity House 15a Trinity Place Windsor Windsor & Maidenhead SL4 3AS
Tel: 01753 860606 *Fax:* 01753 860620 *Dx:* 3830 WINDSOR
E-mail: info@applebyshaw.com
Web: www.applebyshaw.com
List of partners: R U Shah, M M Younus
Languages: Bengali, Hindi, Polish, Punjabi, Urdu
Work: D2 E G H K1 K3 M4 O Q R1 S1 S2 W Z(i)
Ptr: Shah, Mr Razi Ul-Abbas. . . . . Jun 1997
Younus, Mr Muhammad Munir. . . . . Jan 2006

We conduct business in Bengali, Hindi, Polish, Punjabi, Urdu. We specialise in the following areas of work Crime - General, Family Law, Divorce and Matrimonial.

LESLEY P BARRY ‡
Hallam Pines 30 Dower Park St Leonards Hill Windsor Windsor & Maidenhead SL4 4BQ
Tel: 01753 860061
List of partners: L P Barry
Work: G
Emergency Action, Advocacy and Legal Aid undertaken
Ptr: Barry, Miss Lesley P. . . . . *Jul 1969

BOSWELLS ‡
The Lodge 66 St Leonards Road Windsor Windsor & Maidenhead SL4 3BY
Tel: 01753 620888 *Fax:* 01753 620999 *Dx:* 3801 WINDSOR

CHARLES COLEMAN LLP ‡
28 Beaumont Road Windsor Windsor & Maidenhead SL4 1JP
Tel: 01753 861115 *Fax:* 01753 861113 *Dx:* 3809 WINDSOR
E-mail: law@charles-coleman.com
List of partners: J O Humphreys, L Wall
Work: K3 S1 W
Ptr: Humphreys, Mr John O LLB ♦. . . . . *§May 1981
Wall, Mrs Louise ♦ . . . . *§Nov 1995
Asoc: Richardson, Ms Marsha Louise LLB(Hons) ♦ . . . . *§Nov 2003
Ast: Barlow, Mr Guy Jonathan LLB ♦. . . . . *Nov 1991
Lewis, Miss Abigail Zoe BA(Hons); PGDip. . . . . . *§Nov 2008
Con: Mitchell, Mr Charles R MA(Oxon); Jurisprudence; BA ♦ . . . . *§Jul 1978

CHARSLEY HARRISON LLP ‡
Windsor House Victoria Street Windsor Windsor & Maidenhead SL4 1EN
Tel: 01753 851591 *Fax:* 01753 832550 *Dx:* 3800 WINDSOR
E-mail: reception@charsleyharrison.com
Web: www.charsleyharrison.com
List of partners: S J Barr, V E Ives, P H Jones, B Leach, P R Owen, P A Spooner
Office: Slough
Work: C1 C2 C3 D1 E J1 K1 K2 K3 K4 M1 M2 N O Q R1 R2 S1 S2 T1 T2 V W Z(c,e,h,l,t)
Advocacy undertaken
Ptr: Ives, Miss Victoria Elizabeth LLB . . . . *Jan 2008
Jones, Mr Phillip H Notary Public . . . . *§Mar 1971
Leach, Mr Bartholomew LLB . . . . *Oct 2002
Owen, Mr Paul Robert BA(Hons)(Law) . . . . *Apr 1981
Spooner, Mr Paul A BA . . . . *Dec 1975
Asoc: Burgess, Mrs Amy Leigh Victoria LLB(Hons) . . . . *Sep 2007
Hussain, Ms Assmiea Humeria LLB(Hons); DipLP. . . *Apr 2005
Jolliffe, Miss Samantha Anne LLB. . . . . *Sep 2009
Toms, Mr Graeme Andrew MPhil; MA . . . . *Aug 2002

Particular areas of work include: Trust & Probate, Residential Property, Commercial & Company Law, Mergers & Acquisitions, Commercial Property, Family, Employment, Personal Injury and Notarial.

CHEBSEY & CO
(incorporating Ashley Perkins & Co)
Suite 2 5/6 High Street Windsor Windsor & Maidenhead SL4 1LD
Tel: 01753 833737 *Fax:* 01753 833131
Office: Bath, Beaconsfield, Burnham, Rickmansworth
Work: S1 S2 W

GOLDSTEIN LEGAL ‡
Thames Court 1 Victoria Street Windsor Windsor & Maidenhead SL4 1YB
Tel: 01753 865165

LOVEGROVE & ELIOT ‡
Fountain Court 32 Princes Road Windsor Windsor & Maidenhead SL4 3AA
Tel: 01753 851133 *Fax:* 01753 850812 *Dx:* 3808 WINDSOR
List of partners: K B Bull, D J P Carroll, B S McInerney, C F Schnadhorst, P A Simpson
Work: A1 B1 C1 C2 D1 D2 E F1 J1 K1 K2 L M3 N O P Q R1 R2 S1 S2 T1 V W Z(l)
Emergency Action and Advocacy undertaken
Ptr: Bull, Mr Keith Brian LLB(Hons)(Law) . . . . *Nov 1990
Carroll, Mr Douglas J P LLB. . . . . *Dec 1979
McInerney, Mr Barry Sinclair. . . . . *Jul 1970
Schnadhorst, Mr Colin F. . . . . *§Jul 1965
Ast: Doyle, Mrs M Patricia LLB(Lond) . . . . *Jun 1968
Con: Edwards, Mrs Gillian J LLB . . . . *Dec 1974

WINGATE, Co Durham

TMJ LEGAL SERVICES LLP
Gladstone Chambers Wingate Co Durham TS28 5DA
Tel: 01429 838225 *Fax:* 01429 838035
E-mail: legal@tmjlegal.co.uk
Office: Durham, Hartlepool, Peterlee
Languages: German, Spanish
Work: A1 B1 C1 D1 D2 E F1 J1 J2 K1 K3 K4 L N O P Q R1 S1 S2 W Z(l,q)
Emergency Action, Agency, Advocacy, Fixed Fee Interview, Legal Aid undertaken, Legal Aid Franchise and Member of Accident Line
Ptr: Claxton, Miss Kate L LLB . . . . *Sep 2005
Morgan, Mr Keith I LLB . . . . *Dec 1984
Turner, Miss Catherine J A BA . . . . *May 1978
Ast: Dunkerley, Miss Clair LLB. . . . . *Nov 2003
Greggs, Mrs Amanda J LLB. . . . . *Nov 2001
Liddle, Mrs Helen BA . . . . *Nov 1994
Ryan, Mrs Lyn Marie LLB . . . . *Feb 1997
Stannard, Mr Christopher LLB. . . . . *Dec 2007

WINSCOMBE, North Somerset

BERRY REDMOND & ROBINSON
10 Woodborough Road Winscombe North Somerset BS25 1AA
Tel: 01934 842811 *Fax:* 01934 842903
Dx: 8401 WESTON-SUPER-MARE 3
Office: Weston-super-Mare (2 offices)
Languages: French, Italian
Work: A1 C1 E G H J1 K1 K2 K3 L Q S1 T1 W
Emergency Action, Agency, Advocacy, Fixed Fee Interview, Legal Aid undertaken and Legal Aid Franchise
Ptr: Berry, Ms Ruth Marianne Sian BA. . . . . *Oct 2000
Burdock, Mr Roger K F LLB(Lond) . . . . *Mar 1975
Asoc: Boyd, Mr Nicholas J W Commissioner for Oaths. . . . *Jul 1967
Con: Berry, Mr P George LLB(Lond) . . . . *Oct 1961

JUDITH TAYLOR LLB ‡
Brooklands Hillyfields Way Winscombe North Somerset BS25 1AE
Tel: 01934 843353

WINSFORD, Cheshire

CLULEY & CO ‡
G7 Verdin Exchange High Street Winsford Cheshire CW7 2AN
Tel: 01606 553719 *Fax:* 0872 115 7500
E-mail: margaretc@bdgassoc.com
List of partners: M Cluley
Work: D1 D2 K1 N S1 W
Emergency Action, Agency, Advocacy, Fixed Fee Interview, Legal Aid undertaken and Legal Aid Franchise
SPr: Cluley, Mrs Margaret BSc; LLB; PGCE Methodist Local Preacher . . . . *Feb 1992

DIXON RIGBY KEOGH
402 High Street Winsford Cheshire CW7 2DP
Tel: 01606 557211 *Fax:* 01606 861002 *Dx:* 26459 WINSFORD
Office: Middlewich, Northwich, Sandbach
Work: D1 D2 E F1 J1 K1 K3 K4 L N O Q S1 S2 W
Emergency Action, Agency, Advocacy and Fixed Fee Interview undertaken
Ptr: Caldecott, Mr Trevor Harry MA(Oxon). . . . . Dec 1978
Page, Ms Anita LLB. . . . . Apr 1981
Ast: Pursglove, Miss Sian Marie LLB. . . . . Sep 2005

FLETCHERS ‡
374 High Street Winsford Cheshire CW7 2DP
Tel: 01606 556322 / 556324 *Fax:* 01606 861472
Emergency telephone 01270 764268
List of partners: J M Fletcher
Languages: French
Work: B1 E F1 G H J1 K1 L M1 P R1 S1 T1 V W
Emergency Action, Agency, Advocacy, Fixed Fee Interview, Legal Aid undertaken and Member of Accident Line
Ptr: Fletcher, Mr Jeffrey M. . . . . *Dec 1973

LEWIS RODGERS SOLICITORS ‡
372a High Street Winsford Cheshire CW7 2DP
Tel: 01606 861858 *Fax:* 01606 861859 *Dx:* 26461 WINSFORD
Office: Macclesfield

See p112 for the Key to Work Categories & other symbols

MOSS & HASELHURST
Grange House Grange Lane Winsford Cheshire CW7 2DH
Tel: 01606 592159 *Fax:* 01606 861381 *Dx:* 26458 WINSFORD
E-mail: mh@winsfordfsbusiness.co.uk
Office: Northwich
Work: D1 F1 G H J1 K1 L N O Q S1 T2 V W Z(l)
Emergency Action, Agency, Advocacy, Fixed Fee Interview, Legal Aid undertaken and Legal Aid Franchise
Ast: Holdway, Mrs Sally LLB . . . . *Sep 1999
Manning, Miss D Linda V LLB(Manc) . . . . Jan 1980
Con: Johnson, Mr Christopher H LLB Acting Stipendiary Magistrate . . . . *Mar 1975

WINSLOW, Buckinghamshire

CHANDLER RAY
10 High Street Winslow Buckinghamshire MK18 3HG
Tel: 01296 712204 / 712729 *Fax:* 01269 712077
Dx: 39950 BUCKINGHAM
Office: Buckingham (2 offices)
Work: A1 B1 C1 E F1 G J1 K1 L M1 N O P Q S1 T1 V W Z(c,l,m)
Agency, Advocacy, Fixed Fee Interview and Legal Aid undertaken
Ptr: Guse, Mr Victor T H LLB(Soton). . . . . *§Jan 1980

WINTERBOURNE, South Gloucestershire

HENRIQUES GRIFFITHS
107 High Street Winterbourne South Gloucestershire BS36 1RD
Tel: 01454 854000 *Fax:* 01454 773954 *Dx:* 122076 BRISTOL 11
E-mail: info@henriquesgriffiths.com
Office: Bristol (3 offices)
Languages: French, German, Greek, Italian
Work: B1 C1 C2 C3 D1 E F1 G H J1 K1 L M1 M2 N O P S1 W Z(b,c,d,i,j,k,l,m,t)
Emergency Action, Agency, Advocacy, Fixed Fee Interview, Legal Aid undertaken, Legal Aid Franchise and Member of Accident Line
Ptr: Griffiths, Mr Mark R W LLB . . . . *Jun 1977
Woodburn, Mr U Antony Deputy District Judge; Assistant Deputy H M Coroner . . . . *Nov 1981
Asoc: Hickinbotham, Mrs Sarah . . . . Oct 1994
Horne, Mrs Pauline . . . . *Jan 1965
Ast: Vitagliano, Mr Theodore Benjamin. . . . . *Aug 1998

WIRKSWORTH, Derbyshire

ANDREW MACBETH CASH & CO
The Old Savings Bank 6 St Johns Street Wirksworth Derbyshire DE4 4DR
Tel: 01629 822553 *Fax:* 01629 825641
E-mail: amacash@aol.com
Office: Matlock
Work: A1 E F1 G K1 L N Q S1 V W Z(d,l,n)
Emergency Action, Agency, Advocacy, Fixed Fee Interview, Legal Aid undertaken, Legal Aid Franchise and Member of Accident Line
Ast: Austin, Mr Terence J BA . . . . *Jun 1979

WIRRAL, Merseyside

A HALSALL & CO
(incorporating Thompson Rigby & White)
(in association with J P Almond & Co)
41 Greasby Road Greasby Wirral Merseyside CH49 3NF
Tel: 0151 678 9090 *Fax:* 0151 604 0304
Office: Birkenhead, Wirral (2 offices)
Work: C1 E K3 Q S1 S2 T2 W
Ptr: Davies, Mr Richard Wynne BA; LLB Morgan Owen Law Prize . . . . *Apr 1979

A HALSALL & CO
507 Pensby Road Thingwall Wirral Merseyside CH61 7UQ
Tel: 0151 648 7111 *Fax:* 0151 648 7113
Office: Birkenhead, Wirral (2 offices)

AEGIS LAW LTD ‡
3 The Row Market Street Hoylake Wirral Merseyside CH47 3BB
Tel: 0845 270 2093

J P ALMOND & CO
(in association with A Halsall & Co)
23 Market Street Hoylake Wirral Merseyside CH47 2BG
Tel: 0151 632 2336 *Fax:* 0151 632 4577 *Dx:* 27182 HOYLAKE
Emergency telephone 0151 632 2336
E-mail: amf@halsalls.co.uk
Office: Birkenhead, Wirral (2 offices)
Work: E J1 K1 R2 S1 S2 T2 W
Fixed Fee Interview undertaken
Ptr: Almond, Mr Andrew J LLB(L'pool). . . . . *§May 1967
Fountain, Mr Alexander M LLB(Hons) . . . . *Oct 1995

BTW SOLICITORS ‡
228 Holyrake Road Wirral Merseyside CH46 6AD
Tel: 0151 677 3333

BECKETT BEMROSE HAGEN ‡
Eastern Hall Eastern Village Wirral Merseyside CH62 0AF
Tel: 0151 326 2340 *Dx:* 725320 LITTLE SUTTON 2
Office: Wallasey

CHAMBERLAIN THOMAS & CO ‡
91 Market Street Hoylake Wirral Merseyside CH47 5AA
Tel: 0151 633 2800 *Fax:* 0151 633 2805 *Dx:* 715105 HOYLAKE 2
List of partners: K Chamberlain
Office: Lichfield
Work: E J1 L N S1 S2 W
Agency, Fixed Fee Interview, Legal Aid undertaken and Member of Accident Line
Ptr: Chamberlain, Mr Keith . . . . *Dec 1980

CORNISH FORFAR & ALLEN
283 Wallasy Village Wallasy Wirral Merseyside CH45 3HA
Tel: 0151 630 4343 *Fax:* 0151 691 0784 *Dx:* 14125 LIVERPOOL
E-mail: info@cornishforfar.co.uk
Office: Liverpool
Work: E K4 L N Q S1 S2 W
Fixed Fee Interview undertaken

DGB SOLICITORS ‡
Brow Lane House Brow Lane Heswall Wirral Merseyside CH60 0DT
Tel: 0151 342 2211 *Fax:* 0151 342 2233

PETER EDWARDS LAW ‡
Ventura House Market Street Hoylake Wirral Merseyside CH47 2AE
Tel: 0151 632 6699 *Fax:* 0151 632 0090
E-mail: law@peteredwardslaw.com
List of partners: J I Edwards, P C Edwards
Languages: French, German, Polish, Russian
Work: K4 Z(g,m)
Ptr: Edwards, Jolanta Iwona. . . . . Dec 2002
Edwards, Mr Peter Charles . . . . Nov 1975

ALYSON FRANCE & CO ‡
125 Brimstage Road Heswall Wirral Merseyside CH60 1XF
Tel: 0151 348 4400

GRAYSTONS ‡
The Orchard 71 The Village Bebbington Wirral Merseyside CH63 7PL
Tel: 0151 645 0055 *Fax:* 0151 645 0056
E-mail: enquiries@graystons.net
List of partners: J A Grayston
Work: N Z(q,r)
Legal Aid undertaken
Ptr: Grayston, Ms Julie Anne ♦ . . . . Oct 1989
Ast: Price, Miss Jennifer MA; BSc(Hons); RGN; PGDipLP . .Jul 2002

GUY WILLIAMS LAYTON
(incorporating JM Quiggin & Son And Kendall & Rigby)
87 Telegraph Road Heswall Wirral Merseyside CH60 0AU
Tel: 0151 342 1831 / 342 6144 *Fax:* 0151 342 7991
Dx: 14751 HESWALL
E-mail: jdac@guywilliams.uk.com
Office: Liverpool
Work: C1 C2 E K1 L O Q S1 T2 W Z(o)
Agency undertaken
Ptr: Clayton, Mr John David A. . . . . *May 1990
Con: Shepherd, Mr John A . . . . *Jul 1971

THE HETHERINGTON PARTNERSHIP ‡
32 Market Street Hoylake Wirral Merseyside CH47 2AF
Tel: 0151 632 3411 *Fax:* 0151 632 1284
List of partners: M B Hetherington, P C Hetherington
Work: A1 C1 E G H L P S1 W
Emergency Action, Agency, Fixed Fee Interview and Legal Aid undertaken
Ptr: Hetherington, Ms Margaret B LLB(Hons) . . . . Nov 1994
Hetherington, Mr Patrick C LLB(Lond). . . . . *Oct 1986

JACKSONS ‡
56 Market Street Hoylake Wirral Merseyside CH47 3BQ
Tel: 0151 632 3386 *Fax:* 0151 632 6517 *Dx:* 27184 HOYLAKE
List of partners: R A Jackson, J B Salmon
Languages: French, German
Work: E K1 L R1 S1 S2 W
Emergency Action and Agency undertaken
Ptr: Jackson, Mr Robin A . . . . Apr 1972
Salmon, Mr John Barry LLB. . . . . *Jul 1994
Con: Mann, Mr Thomas G . . . . *§Dec 1972

LAMB & CO ‡
8 Market Street Wirral Merseyside CH47 3BB
Tel: 0808 252 8001
E-mail: enquiry@lamb-law.co.uk

MATRIX SOLICITORS ‡
Station Approach Pasture Road Wirral Merseyside CH46 8SD
Tel: 0151 677 3999

ROONEY & CO ‡
3 The Quadrant Hoylake Wirral Merseyside CH47 2EE
Tel: 0151 632 4175 *Fax:* 0151 632 1400
E-mail: paul@rooneyandco.com

SOLICITORHELP ‡
230 Hoylake Road Moreton Wirral Merseyside CH46 6AD
Tel: 0151 522 3410 *Fax:* 0151 522 3411
E-mail: legalteam@solicitorhelp.com

C A SPARKES SOLICITORS ‡
6 The Quadrant Hoylake Wirral Merseyside CH47 2EE
Tel: 0151 625 3777 *Fax:* 0151 625 2888 *Dx:* 27181 HOYLAKE

WISBECH, Cambridgeshire

BOWSER OLLARD & BENTLEY ‡
15 South Brink Wisbech Cambridgeshire PE13 1JL
Tel: 01945 583194 *Fax:* 01945 463218 *Dx:* 41353 WISBECH
E-mail: helpdesk@bowsers.co.uk
List of partners: B R Bowser, R Ruston
Office: March
Work: A1 B1 C1 C2 C3 E F1 J1 K1 K3 L N O Q R1 S1 T1 T2 V W Z(c,d,l,t)
Emergency Action, Advocacy, Fixed Fee Interview and Legal Aid undertaken
Ptr: Bowser, Mr Brian R Clerk to Commissioner of Taxes *§May 1978
Ruston, Mr Ronald LLB . . . . *§Oct 1994
Asoc: Pearson, Mrs Susan M BA; MBA . . . . Oct 1997
Con: Orbell, Mr John Henderson Notary Public . . . . *Jul 1985

HUGH A CAUTHERY ‡
6 Queens Road Wisbech Cambridgeshire PE13 2PD
Tel: 01945 464692 *Fax:* 01945 464692
Emergency telephone 01945 464692
E-mail: hughcauthery@hotmail.com
List of partners: H A Cauthery
Languages: French
Work: G H
Agency and Advocacy undertaken
SPr: Cauthery, Mr Hugh Alexander LLB ★ . . . . *Jun 1970

FRASER DAWBARNS ‡
1-3 York Row Wisbech Cambridgeshire PE13 1EA
Tel: 01945 461456 *Fax:* 01945 461364 *Dx:* 41351 WISBECH
Emergency telephone 01945 461456
E-mail: info@fraserdawbarns.com
List of partners: J M Aitken, D A Allen, C S Bailey, D R W Ball, D Ball, A J Barratt, A H Charlton, R A Cheetham, I R Grimes, J Jones, S J McGregor, N L Meachem, W R Morris, M Smith, S Trevor
Office: Downham Market, King's Lynn, March
Languages: French, German
Work: A1 B1 B2 C1 C2 C3 D1 D2 E F1 G H J1 J2 K1 K2 L M1 N O P Q R1 S1 S2 T1 T2 V W Z(c,d,e,k,l,m,q,t)
Emergency Action, Agency, Advocacy, Legal Aid undertaken, Legal Aid Franchise and Member of Accident Line
Ptr: Aitken, Mr John M. . . . . *§Jun 1975
Ball, Mr David. . . . . Nov 1978
Cheetham, Mr Richard Antony LLB; Diplome d'Etudes Juridiques Francaises . . . . *May 1984
Jones, Ms Jacqueline LLB(Nott'm) . . . . *Aug 1987
McGregor, Mr Stephen J . . . . *Jun 1989
Morris, Mr William R LLB(Bris) H M Coroner. . . . . *§Jun 1972
Smith, Ms Melinda . . . . Nov 2006
Ast: John, Mr Neil . . . . *Oct 1999
Rushmer, Mrs Jennifer Jayne LLB; PG DipLP . . . . . Nov 2009
Con: Morris, Mrs Elizabeth C LLB(Lond) . . . . Jun 1974

METCALFE COPEMAN & PETTEFAR ‡
8 York Row Wisbech Cambridgeshire PE13 1EF
Tel: 01945 464331 *Fax:* 01945 476695 *Dx:* 41350 WISBECH
E-mail: info@mcp-law.co.uk
List of partners: S Adlam, J R Burton, R R Carlson, D F Coller, A P C Davies, B Dures, P Garner, J Hesketh, A M Muir, M P Newton, S Scott, T W Stevenson, S J Welcomme
Office: King's Lynn, Peterborough, Thetford
Languages: Portuguese
Work: A1 A3 B1 B2 C1 C2 C3 D1 D2 E F1 F2 G H J1 J2 K1 K2 K3 K4 L M1 M2 N O P Q R1 R2 S1 S2 T1 T2 U2 V W Z(c,e,g,h,l,n,o,p,q,t,y,za)
Emergency Action, Agency, Advocacy, Fixed Fee Interview, Legal Aid undertaken, Legal Aid Franchise and Member of Accident Line
Ptr: Carlson, Mr Richard R . . . . *Jul 1971
Garner, Mr Paul BA. . . . . *Jan 1984
Welcomme, Mr Stephen John LLB . . . . Nov 1988
Ast: Clarke, Mr John F LLB; AKC . . . . *Dec 1973

PEARSON SOLICITORS ‡
6 South Brink Wisbech Cambridgeshire PE13 1JA
Tel: 01945 467053 *Fax:* 01945 580293

WITHAM, Essex

BAWTREES LLP ‡
65 Newland Street Witham Essex CM8 1AB
Tel: 01376 513491 *Fax:* 01376 510713 *Dx:* 33400 WITHAM
E-mail: mail@bawtrees.co.uk
List of partners: D P Clancy, J M Clarke, C H Gill, S J Hodges, J Jenkinson
Work: A1 A3 B1 B2 C1 C2 D1 D2 E F1 F2 J1 K1 K2 K3 L N O Q R2 S1 S2 V W Z(c,g,k,l,q,r)
Emergency Action, Agency, Advocacy, Fixed Fee Interview, Legal Aid undertaken, Legal Aid Franchise and Member of Accident Line
Ptr: Clancy, Mr Damian Philip LLB. . . . . *Dec 2000
Clarke, Mr John M LLB . . . . *May 1993
Gill, Mr Christopher H BA . . . . *Apr 1983
Hodges, Mr Stephen J LLB . . . . *Nov 1978
Jenkinson, Mrs Jeanne LLB(Manc) . . . . *Jun 1979
Ast: Hastings, Mr William John LLB . . . . Aug 2004
Sharman, Ms Katrina LLB. . . . . Dec 2003
Shirley, Mr Adam Edward LLB. . . . . Apr 2005

THE BEAVIS PARTNERSHIP
2 Freebourne Court Newland Street Witham Essex CM8 2BL
Tel: 01376 500255 *Fax:* 01376 502236
Office: Chelmsford
Work: D1 K1 S1 W
Emergency Action, Agency, Advocacy, Fixed Fee Interview and Legal Aid undertaken
Ptr: Wayman, Mr Trevor J LLB . . . . *Oct 1988
Con: Beavis, Mr Kenneth F MA(Oxon) . . . . *Jun 1965

BRIGHT & SONS
(in association with Concha Compan Sala Alicante(Spain))
87-91 Newland Street Witham Essex CM8 1AD
Tel: 01376 512338 *Fax:* 01376 519763 *Dx:* 33401 WITHAM
Office: Maldon
Languages: Afrikaans, Fanti, Ga, Spanish
Work: A1 A2 C1 C2 D1 E F1 I J1 J2 K1 K3 K4 L N O Q S1 S2 T1 T2 W X Z(p,y)
Emergency Action, Advocacy, Fixed Fee Interview, Legal Aid undertaken, Legal Aid Franchise and Member of Accident Line
Ptr: Hayward, Mr Christopher John LLB(Lond) Clerk to the Commissioners of Tax for Division of Maldon . . . *Apr 1982
Ast: Bright, Ms Amanda Jane LLB(Hons). . . . . *Nov 1989
Grayland, Ms Tracy Elizabeth LLB(Hons) . . . . *Aug 2002
Hickmott, Mrs Jennifer . . . . *Sep 2001
Johnson, Mr Paul Douglas . . . . *Oct 2001
Martin, Miss Vidal Eulalie LLB(Hons) . . . . *May 2005
Nel, Mrs Stacy BA(Hons) . . . . *Jul 2005
Stobirski, Ms Emma BA(Hons) . . . . *Nov 2003
Taylor, Ms Karen BSc(Hons) . . . . *Jan 1999

COUNTRYWIDE PLC ‡
Countrywide House Witham Essex CM8 3SX
Tel: 01376 533700 *Fax:* 01376 520758 *Dx:* 140680 WITHAM 4
Work: C1 F1 F2 J1 J2 O Q Z(j,o)

KEW LAW LLP ‡
121 Newland Street Witham Essex CM8 1BE
Tel: 01376 500049 *Fax:* 01376 500959
E-mail: info@kewlaw.co.uk

LEVY & CO SOLICITORS LLP ‡
St Georges House 31 Bridge Street Witham Essex CM8 1DY
Tel: 01376 511819 *Fax:* 01376 511781
E-mail: mail@levysolicitors.co.uk
List of partners: E Hicks, S Levy
Office: Braintree
Ptr: Hicks, Mrs Evelyn LLB(Hons) . . . . Feb 2005
Levy, Mr Steven LLB . . . . Oct 1999
Ast: Austin, Ms Laura LLB; LLM . . . . *May 2002
Hunter, Mr Gareth. . . . . Jan 2007
Con: Young, Mr Peter. . . . . Jan 1977

SALMONWORKS LIMITED ‡
87-91 Newlands Street Witham Essex CM8 1AD
Tel: 07748 962350
E-mail: simon@simonmorganandco.com

WITHERNSEA, East Riding of Yorkshire

MMS SOLICITORS ‡
187 Queen Street Withernsea East Riding of Yorkshire HU19 2JR
Tel: 01964 612318 *Fax:* 01964 613058
E-mail: office@davidmacnamara.com
List of partners: D R MacNamara, C J Moore, V W Shore
Office: Hornsea
Work: D1 F1 G H L N P S1 V W Z(l,r)
Agency, Advocacy, Fixed Fee Interview undertaken and Member of Accident Line
Ptr: MacNamara, Mr David R BA; LLB. . . . . *Oct 1984
Moore, Mr Christopher J LLB . . . . *May 1991
Shore, Mr Vincent W BA(Hons) . . . . *Sep 1998

WITHINGTON, Greater Manchester

HARRY BOODHOO & CO ‡
21 Copson Street Withington Greater Manchester M20 3HE
Tel: 0161 445 0588 *Fax:* 0161 445 4949 *Dx:* 28608 WITHINGTON
Emergency telephone 07860 272119
E-mail: clerks@harryboodhoo.co.uk
List of partners: H D Boodhoo, C A O'Donoghue
Work: B2 D1 E G H K1 K3 L S1 S2 V W Z(g)
Emergency Action, Agency, Advocacy, Fixed Fee Interview, Legal Aid undertaken and Legal Aid Franchise
Ptr: Boodhoo, Mr Harry D LLB. . . . . *Apr 1981
O'Donoghue, Miss Cecilia A LLB . . . . *Oct 1985
Ast: Parkes, Mr David LLB. . . . . *Oct 2006

ROZITA HUSSAIN SOLICITORS ‡
2a Egerton Crescent Withington Greater Manchester M20 4PN
Tel: 0161 448 8222 *Fax:* 0161 448 8333 *Dx:* 28605 WITHINGTON
E-mail: law@rozitahussain.co.uk
List of partners: R Hussain
Languages: Farsi, Punjabi, Urdu
Work: D1 E K1 L N Q S1 W Z(i)
Emergency Action, Fixed Fee Interview and Legal Aid undertaken
Ptr: Hussain, Miss Rozita BSc(Hons) Trustee of RELATE *Feb 1992

KRELLS ‡
Palatine Court 84 Palatine Road Withington Greater Manchester M20 9JW
Tel: 0161 445 8649
List of partners: S G Krell
Work: E S1 Z(o)
Ptr: Krell, Mr Stuart G LLB(Manc) . . . . *May 1980

WITNEY, Oxfordshire

ARNOTTS ‡
28a High Street Witney Oxfordshire OX28 6HG
Tel: 0844 372 1333 *Fax:* 0844 372 1334 *Dx:* 40205 WITNEY
E-mail: john@arnottslaw.co.uk
List of partners: J D Arnott
Work: D1 K1 K3
Ptr: Arnott, Mr John David. . . . . Jul 1978

BCC SOLICITORS
The Chambers 61a High Street Witney Oxfordshire OX28 6JA
Tel: 01993 770778
E-mail: crawley@barnescampling.co.uk
Office: Brackley

BOWER & BAILEY
2 Heynes Place Station Lane Witney Oxfordshire OX28 4YN
Tel: 01993 705095 *Fax:* 01993 776554 *Dx:* 40203 WITNEY
E-mail: witney@bowerandbailey.co.uk
Office: Banbury, Oxford, Swindon
Work: B1 C1 C2 D1 E J1 K1 K2 K3 L N O Q R2 S1 S2 W
Emergency Action, Advocacy, Fixed Fee Interview undertaken and Member of Accident Line
Ptr: Bailey, Miss Sally E BA(Law) . . . . *Oct 1983
Palmer, Mr Stuart T H BA. . . . . *Jan 1998
Smith, Mr Julian C LLB(Hons). . . . . *Oct 1974
Tucker, Mr Gareth H BA(Hons) . . . . *Jan 1999
Harrhy, Mr Trevor . . . . NSP
Ast: Hancock, Mrs Francesca LLB(Hons) . . . . Nov 2005
Staunton, Miss Clara Joan BA . . . . Sep 2009
Taylor, Mrs Louise Elizabeth LLB . . . . Jan 2005

LEE CHADWICK & CO ‡
14 Market Square Witney Oxfordshire OX28 6BE
Tel: 01993 703272 *Fax:* 01993 776073 *Dx:* 40202 WITNEY
E-mail: dh@lee-chadwick.co.uk
List of partners: J Cowley, D Hillman
Languages: German
Work: B1 E F1 J1 L O Q S1 W Z(d,m)
Fixed Fee Interview undertaken
Ptr: Cowley, Jason . . . . Nov 2007
Hillman, Mr David LLB . . . . *§Nov 1971
Ast: Dickinson, Mr John W. . . . . Dec 1977

EVERYMAN LEGAL LTD ‡
IG Network Point Range Road Windrush Park Witney Oxfordshire OX29 0YN
Tel: 0845 868 0960 *Fax:* 0845 868 0961
E-mail: everyman@everymanlegal.com

YVONNE KEARNEY ‡
9 Harvest Way Madley Park Witney Oxfordshire OX28 1AW
Tel: 01993 776018 *Fax:* 01993 776042
E-mail: solicitor@yvonnekearney.co.uk
List of partners: Y M Kearney
Work: S1 S2 W
SPr: Kearney, Miss Yvonne M . . . . May 1991

LEGAL ADVICE DIRECT SOLICITORS ‡
Holdan House 26 Bridge Street Witney Oxfordshire OX28 1HY
Tel: 01993 700434

RIDLEY'S ‡
39 Corn Street Witney Oxfordshire OX28 6BT
Tel: 01993 776341 *Fax:* 01993 778101
E-mail: ridleysconvey@legaltx.com
List of partners: R J Ridley
Work: E L S1 S2
SPr: Ridley, Mr Raymond John MA(Cantab) . . . . May 1979

SCOTT DIXON REILLY WILKES
37 High Street Witney Oxfordshire OX28 6HP
Tel: 01295 201210
Office: Kidlington

STANGER STACEY & MASON ‡
35a High Street Witney Oxfordshire OX28 6HP
Tel: 01993 776491 *Fax:* 01993 702059 *Dx:* 40201 WITNEY
E-mail: mws@stanger-stacey.co.uk
List of partners: W T Mason, L D Stacey, M W Stacey
Work: D1 D2 E K1 K3 L N O Q S1 S2 V W
Emergency Action, Agency, Advocacy and Fixed Fee Interview undertaken
Ptr: Mason, Mr William Tomas LLB; MPRE . . . . *Nov 1992
Stacey, Mrs Lorraine D BA . . . . *May 1983
Stacey, Mr Martyn W BA . . . . *Dec 1980

JOHN WELCH & STAMMERS ‡
24 Church Green Witney Oxfordshire OX8 6AT
Tel: 01993 703941 *Fax:* 01993 776071 *Dx:* 40204 WITNEY
E-mail: glavelle@johnwelchandstammers.co.uk
List of partners: G T Alty, K E Joels, G J C Lavelle
Languages: French
Work: B2 D1 D2 E F1 G H J1 K1 K2 K3 K4 L N O Q R1 S1 S2 T2 W Z(c,d,h,k,l,q,r)
Emergency Action, Agency, Advocacy, Fixed Fee Interview undertaken and Member of Accident Line
Ptr: Alty, Mr Gareth T LLB. . . . . *Nov 1989
Joels, Miss Kerry E LLB. . . . . *Nov 1985
Lavelle, Mr Gabriel J C MA(Oxon). . . . . *Nov 1973
Ast: Noble, Mrs Grace Myfanwy LLB(Hons) . . . . *Sep 2002
Robertson, Mrs Katherine J LLB(Hons) . . . . *§Oct 1994

WIVELISCOMBE, Somerset

RISDON HOSEGOOD
17 High Street Wiveliscombe Somerset TA4 2JX
Tel: 01984 623203 *Fax:* 01984 623711
E-mail: wiveliscombe@risdonhosegood.com
Office: Dulverton, Minehead, Taunton, Williton
Work: A1 B1 C1 D1 E G H J1 K1 L N Q R1 S1 T1 T2 V W
Emergency Action, Agency, Advocacy, Fixed Fee Interview and Legal Aid undertaken
Ptr: Kidner, Mr Eric G . . . . *Jun 1977

WOBURN SANDS, Milton Keynes

ASHOKA & CO ‡
Barclays Bank Chambers 8-10 High Street Woburn Sands Milton Keynes MK17 8RN
Tel: 01908 288120 *Fax:* 01908 584753
List of partners: S S Ashoka
Work: E S1 S2
SPr: Ashoka, Mr Shyam Sunder BA . . . . *Jun 1988

ALAN SMEATH & CO ‡
6 High Street Woburn Sands Milton Keynes MK17 8RL
Tel: 01908 584307 / 584331 *Fax:* 01908 585380
Dx: 45804 WOBURN SANDS
List of partners: E T Maybaum, G M Smeath
Languages: French, German
Work: A1 C1 E F1 J1 K1 L N R1 S1
Agency, Advocacy, Legal Aid undertaken and Legal Aid Franchise
Ptr: Maybaum, Mrs Elisabeth T MA . . . . *Aug 1981
Smeath, Mrs Gillian M LLB(Lond) . . . . Dec 1961

WOKING, Surrey

AJR SOLICITORS ‡
Whyte Gables Pyrford Road Woking Surrey GU22 8UQ
Tel: 01932 342107 / 07979 241761
E-mail: alistair@ajrlegal.com

ANNA ARTHUR ASSOCIATES ‡
Fieri Facias House High Street Ripley Woking Surrey GU23 6AF
Tel: 01483 222499 *Fax:* 01483 222766
E-mail: aarthur@arthurlegal.co.uk
List of partners: A M Arthur
Languages: French, Italian
Work: A3 B1 C1 D1 D2 J1 K1 K2 K3 K4 N Q S1 S2 T2 W X Z(q)
Agency and Advocacy undertaken
Ptr: Arthur, Mrs Anna M BA . . . . *Dec 1978
Ast: Nagle, Miss Sarah LLB . . . . *Jul 2009

BARLOW ROBBINS LLP
Concord House 165 Church Street East Woking Surrey GU21 6HJ
Tel: 01483 748500 *Fax:* 01483 729933
E-mail: woking@barlowrobbins.com
Office: Godalming, Guildford (2 offices)
Languages: French, Spanish
Work: A3 C1 C2 D1 E F1 F2 I J1 J2 K1 K2 K3 L N O Q R1 R2 S1 S2 U2 W Z(b,e,i,k,p,r,za)
Ptr: Archibald, Mrs Helen J LLB . . . . *Oct 1987
Ludlow, Mr David C H BA(Hons) ♦ . . . . *Nov 1989
Wilson, Mr Graham LLB. . . . . *Apr 1980
Asoc: Andrews, Ms Clare . . . . *Jul 2003
Flashman, Mrs Caroline J LLB . . . . *Apr 1982
Hailey, Mrs Elizabeth Ann LLB(Hons) . . . . *Sep 2003
McGrigor, Mr Rhoderick Ian LLB(Hons) . . . . *Sep 1996
Ast: Andrews, Mr Michael Jon LLB(ELS). . . . . *Sep 2003
Bayley, Ms Karen . . . . *Nov 1993
Collingwood, Mr Benjamin Douglas . . . . *Sep 2009
Fitzgerald, Ms Kathleen Maria LLB . . . . *Aug 1996
Flanagan, Mrs Angela Jane BSc(Econ) Norton Rose Prize 1997 . . . . *Oct 2003
Hughes, Mr Amira LLB(Hons). . . . . *Apr 2006
McDonagh, Mrs Victoria LLB(Hons). . . . . *Sep 1998
Peters, Mr Andrew Neil . . . . *Jan 2004
Underwood, Mr Stephen Geoffrey. . . . . *Nov 2007
Con: England, Mr Michael J LLM . . . . *Apr 1973
Smith, Mr Roger Gordon LLB . . . . *Dec 1974
Wright, Ms Barbara M LLB . . . . *Feb 1989

We conduct business in French, Spanish. We specialise in the following areas of work Commercial and Company Law, Commercial Property, Employment Law.

BLACKFORDS LLP
Cleary Court 169 Church Street East Woking Surrey GU21 6HJ
Tel: 01483 723331 *Fax:* 01483 724441 *Dx:* 2958 WOKING
Emergency telephone 07786 550640
E-mail: woking@blackfords.com
Office: Cardiff, Croydon, London EC4
Ptr: Francis, Mr Trevor. . . . . *Apr 1998

BUGLEAR BATE & CO ‡
(incorporating Milford Conveyancers)
31 Guildford Road Woking Surrey GU22 7QQ
Tel: 01483 715527 / 724246 *Fax:* 01483 723237 *Dx:* 2906 WOKING
List of partners: J R S Bate, B O Buglear
Work: B1 C1 D1 E F1 J1 K1 L N O Q S1 W Z(k,q)
Emergency Action, Agency, Advocacy, Fixed Fee Interview and Legal Aid undertaken
Ptr: Bate, Mr Jeremy R S BA Amphlett Prize Notary Public *Oct 1986
Buglear, Mr Bruce O LLB . . . . *Dec 1981

THE CASTLE PARTNERSHIP
20a High Street Woking Surrey GU21 6BW
Tel: 01483 730062 *Fax:* 01483 729862
Emergency telephone 07973 943111
E-mail: enquiries@castlepartnership.co.uk
Office: Guildford
Work: G H
Ptr: Castle, Mr David T LLB ★. . . . . Oct 1984

W DAVIES ‡
Acorn House 5 Chertsey Road Woking Surrey GU21 5AB
Tel: 01483 744900 *Fax:* 01483 744901 *Dx:* 2903 WOKING
E-mail: wds@wdavies.com
List of partners: C Batko, A E Cohen, F J Lawson, A K Milton, G R Mott, S J G Oxley, S E Solomon
Work: A1 A3 B1 C1 C2 D1 E F1 J1 K1 L N O P Q R1 R2 S1 S2 U2 V W Z(b,c,d,e,f,g,h,j,k,l,m,n,o,s,v,z)
Advocacy undertaken
Ptr: Batko, Mr Craig LLB . . . . Oct 2001
Cohen, Mr Andrew E BA(Reading) . . . . *Oct 1985
Lawson, Mr Frederick John BA . . . . Feb 1998
Milton, Mrs Alexandra Kirsty LLB(Hons); DipLaw . . . *Jul 2003
Mott, Mr Graham R . . . . Dec 1977
Oxley, Mr Simon J G . . . . *Jul 1965
Solomon, Mr Stephen E LLB(Manc). . . . . *Jun 1973
Ast: Bird, Miss Caroline LLB . . . . Apr 2006
Black, Mr Graeme Rory BSc(Hons)(Geography). . . . Feb 2007
Gould, Miss Fiona Elizabeth Anne MA(Cantab) . . . Jan 1986
Mistry, Ms Ayesha Porus BA(Hons) . . . . May 2004
Molla Mohieddin, Ms Sanaz LLB(Hons) . . . . Jan 2007
Williams, Mr Mark Ian LLB(Hons) . . . . Jul 1996
Con: Davies, Ms Carolynn S LLB(Hons) . . . . *Oct 1991
Main, Mr David LLB(Hons) . . . . Jun 1976
Risbridger, Mr John A H MA(Oxon) . . . . Nov 1957
Solomon, Mrs Maureen D BA . . . . *Dec 1976

J P A DEVANE SOLICITOR ‡
59 Lane End Drive Knaphill Woking Surrey GU21 2QQ
Tel: 01483 472760 *Fax:* 01483 486625
E-mail: devane@easynet.co.uk
List of partners: J P A Devane
Ptr: Devane, Mr James P A . . . . Feb 1980

FULCHERS ‡
8 Chertsey Road Woking Surrey GU21 5AB
Tel: 01483 885522 *Fax:* 01483 755630 *Dx:* 2918 WOKING
E-mail: david@fulchers.co.uk
List of partners: D S Fulcher, D Norris
Work: D1 D2 E F1 J1 K1 K2 K3 L N O P Q S1 S2 W Z(p)
Emergency Action, Agency, Advocacy, Legal Aid undertaken and Legal Aid Franchise
Ptr: Fulcher, Mr David S BSc . . . . *Sep 1978
Norris, Mr Damian LLB . . . . *Nov 1995
Asoc: Kingston, Mr Andrew Malcolm LLB(Hons) . . . . Jun 2003

See p112 for the Key to Work Categories & other symbols

HART BROWN SOLICITORS
7 Guildford Road Woking Surrey GU22 7PX
Est: 1919
Tel: 0800 068 8177 *Fax:* 01483 887753 *Dx:* 2900 WOKING
E-mail: lawyers@hartbrown.co.uk
Office: Cobham, Cranleigh, Godalming, Guildford, London SW19
Work: A1 B1 C1 C2 C3 D1 D2 E F1 F2 I J1 J2 K1 K2 L M1 M2 N O P Q R1 R2 S1 T2 V W Z(b,c,d,e,i,k,l,m,o,p,q,r,s,z)
Emergency Action, Agency, Advocacy, Fixed Fee Interview, Legal Aid undertaken, Legal Aid Franchise and Member of Accident Line
Ptr: Knapp, Mr David S BA(Law) . . . . . *Oct 1984
Ast: Beeharry, Mrs Rajani LLB(Hons) . . . . . *Jan 2004
Dearsall, Mrs Catherine BA; LLB . . . . . *Mar 2003

LINDSAY SAIT & TURNER ‡
Kingfield House Kingfield Road Woking Surrey GU22 9RE
Tel: 01483 604033
List of partners: A M Lindsay, W E Sait, J L Turner
Work: K1 Q S1 S2 W
Ptr: Lindsay, Mr Allen M LLB . . . . . *Nov 1975
Sait, Mr William E. . . . . . *Mar 1968
Turner, Mr John Leonard . . . . . *Jul 1972

MACKRELL TURNER GARRETT
(in association with Mackrell International)
8 Anchor Crescent Knaphill Woking Surrey GU21 2PD
Tel: 01483 476022 *Fax:* 01483 473049
Dx: 42202 WOKING (KNAPHILL)
Office: Addlestone, London WC2, Woking
Work: A1 B1 C1 C2 C3 E F1 J1 K1 L M1 M2 N O P Q R1 S1 T1 T2 W Z(e,i,k,l,t)
Agency, Fixed Fee Interview and Legal Aid undertaken
Ptr: Appleyard, Mr Christopher J LLB . . . . . *Dec 1974

MACKRELL TURNER GARRETT
(in association with Mackrell International)
Church Gate 21-25 Church Street West Woking Surrey GU21 6DJ
Tel: 01483 755609 *Fax:* 01483 755818 *Dx:* 2912 WOKING
Office: Addlestone, London WC2, Woking
Languages: French, Italian, Spanish
Work: A1 B1 C1 C2 C3 E F1 J1 K1 L M1 M2 N O P Q R1 S1 T1 T2 W Z(e,i,k,l,t)
Agency, Fixed Fee Interview and Legal Aid undertaken
Ptr: Cox, Mr David. . . . . . Apr 1961
Cummins, Miss Mary W BSc(Econ) . . . . . Dec 1980
Dudley, Mr John A BA. . . . . . *Apr 1983
Parrott, Mr Philip Alan. . . . . . *Jan 1980
Slorick, Mr Michael A LLB. . . . . . *§Nov 1963
Asoc: Denley, Miss Gillian LLB(Hons) . . . . . *Jul 1999
Ast: McDermott, Miss Claire L LLB(Hons); DipLP. . . . . *Oct 1999
Sall, Dharmender Singh LLB(Hons)(Lond). . . . . *Jan 1996
Scott, Mr Duncan J M BA; CPE; LPC . . . . . May 1999
Smith, Mr Simon Vernon BSc(Hons). . . . . . *Jun 2001

MARSHALLS
Waterside Chambers Bridge Barn Lane Woking Surrey GU21 1NL
Tel: 01483 730531 *Fax:* 01483 728618
Office: Godalming
Languages: French
Ptr: Kilburn, Mr Barry LLB . . . . . *Dec 1979

MORRISONS SOLICITORS LLP
2nd Floor Cleary Court 169 Church Street East Woking Surrey GU21 6HJ
Tel: 01483 726146 *Fax:* 01483 755293 *Dx:* 2917 WOKING
E-mail: info@morrlaw.com
Office: Camberley, London SW19, Redhill
Work: C1 E L S1 S2 T1 T2 W Z(d)
Ptr: Goff, Ms Margaret A . . . . . *Jun 1979
Jupp, Mr Jeremy Edwin Ian . . . . . *Nov 1992
Mills, Mr Peter. . . . . . *Apr 1981
Savage, Mr Peter. . . . . . *Sep 2003
Walker, Mr J Mark O'Hara BA(Soton) . . . . . *Oct 1987
Asoc: Greenhall, Mrs Jessica . . . . . *Sep 2006
Perryman, Mr Andrew Michael . . . . . *Oct 2004
Syed, Ms Sofia . . . . . *Sep 1999
White, Mrs Hannah Margaret . . . . . *Jan 2005
Con: Kirtley, Mr Michael J BSc . . . . . *Jan 1976

MULLENDERS ‡
Griffin House West Street Woking Surrey GU21 6BS
Tel: 01483 771733 *Fax:* 01483 727425 *Dx:* 2911 WOKING
Emergency telephone 07917 823000
E-mail: office@mullenderlaw.com
List of partners: R G Mullender
Work: B2 G H J1 K1 K3 S1
Emergency Action, Agency, Advocacy, Fixed Fee Interview, Legal Aid undertaken and Legal Aid Franchise
Ptr: Mullender, Mr Roger Gerald LLB(Hons) . . . . . *Nov 1997
Ast: Russell, Miss Joanne LLB. . . . . . Apr 2006

O'KEEFFE & CO ‡
5 Penhurst Woking Surrey GU21 4HP
Tel: 01483 740734 *Fax:* 01483 761731
Dx: 42209 WOKING (KNAPHILL)
List of partners: M A O'Keeffe
Work: E R2 S1 S2 W
Ptr: O'Keeffe, Miss Marian A BA(Law). . . . . . *Jun 1980

M PENDER ‡
St Mary's Ridgway Road Pyrford Woking Surrey GU22 8PR
Tel: 01932 352653 *Fax:* 01932 351779
Dx: 52919 WEST BYFLEET
List of partners: M Pender
Work: E S1 W
SPr: Pender, Miss Margaret LLB . . . . . *Dec 1975

PROPERTY LAW PARTNERS ‡
No 1 Crown Square Woking Surrey GU21 6HR
Tel: 01483 768629 *Fax:* 01483 755533
List of partners: D Sledge
Ptr: Sledge, Mr David . . . . . Mar 1991

TRG LAW ‡
Lyndhurst Guildford Road Woking Surrey GU22 7UT
Tel: 01483 730303 *Fax:* 01483 776706
E-mail: info@trglaw.com

WOKINGHAM

BIGGS & CO ‡
8 Broad Street Wokingham RG40 1AB
Tel: 0118 989 4511 *Fax:* 0118 978 9801 *Dx:* 33518 WOKINGHAM
E-mail: mail@biggs.co.uk
List of partners: G M Fordham
Work: C1 E K1 L N Q S1 W
Emergency Action, Agency, Advocacy and Fixed Fee Interview undertaken
SPr: Fordham, Mr Gregory M Church Warden for St Lukes (Southwark). . . . . . *Jul 1977
Con: Biggs, Mr Christopher I W BA . . . . . *Feb 1965

CLIFTON INGRAM LLP ‡
22-24 Broad Street Wokingham RG40 1BA
Tel: 0118 978 0099 *Fax:* 0118 977 1122 *Dx:* 33500 WOKINGHAM
E-mail: info@cliftoningram.co.uk
List of partners: W J Annan, C J Baggs, T E Crow, J R Davis, J H P Dyson, I A Graham, K A E Grant, I L Martin, P D McGeown, T C Read, S A Rose, M A Young
Office: Reading
Languages: French, German
Work: A1 B1 C1 C2 C3 D1 D2 E F1 F2 I J1 K1 L N O P Q R1 R2 S1 S2 T1 W Z(b,c,d,e,h,j,k,l,o,w)
Emergency Action, Fixed Fee Interview, Legal Aid undertaken and Legal Aid Franchise
Ptr: Annan, Mr William J MA(Oxon) . . . . . *Dec 1978
Baggs, Mr Christopher J LLB(B'ham) . . . . . *Apr 1981
Crow, Miss Tina E LLB(Hons) . . . . . *Nov 1985
Davis, Mr Jonathan R MA(Cantab) . . . . . *Oct 1978
Dyson, Mr James H P. . . . . . *Dec 1975
Graham, Mr Ian A LLB(Hons) . . . . . *Dec 1985
McGeown, Mr Peter Dominic BA; TEP. . . . . . *Sep 2001
Rose, Miss Stephanie Anne. . . . . . *Mar 2001
Young, Mrs Marilyn A . . . . . *Dec 1992
Asoc: Andrews, Mrs Helen M LLB . . . . . *Oct 1983
Deller, Miss Anne Marie BA(Hons) . . . . . *Nov 1995
Gair, Mrs Alison BA(Law); LLM . . . . . *Feb 2001
Joshi, Mrs Rekha . . . . . *Mar 2004
Lindon-Morris, Mrs Caroline A BA(Oxon) . . . . . *Jun 1979
Niven, Mr Barry William . . . . . *Apr 2003
Prymak, Miss Anita Eve BA(Hons)(Law). . . . . . Jun 1989
Rae, Mr Carlton Ashley BSc. . . . . . Nov 2001
Tufail, Ms Rubeena BA(Hons). . . . . . Jan 2003
Ast: Adams, Mr Stuart Antony BA(Hons)(Accounting); LLB. *Jan 2010
Goddard, Mr David Andrew LLB. . . . . . Sep 2008
Morris, Ms Rosalind BSc . . . . . *Sep 2006
Con: Eyriey, Mr Dennis G. . . . . . *§Mar 1960

C J GILES & CO ‡
63 Peach Street Wokingham RG11 1XP
Tel: 0118 978 1017 *Fax:* 0118 977 2773
List of partners: A Dobson, C J Giles
Languages: French
Work: E K1 N O Q S1 W
Legal Aid undertaken
Ptr: Dobson, Mrs Ann BA . . . . . *Jul 1980
Giles, Mr Charles J LLB(Lond) . . . . . *Jul 1981

HM LAW ‡
Albany House 14 Shute End Wokingham RG40 1BJ
Tel: 0118 977 1718 *Fax:* 0118 977 3252
Languages: Punjabi
Work: C1 E J1 S1

HERRINGTON & CARMICHAEL LLP
Market Chambers 3 & 4 Market Place Wokingham RG40 1BL
Tel: 0118 977 4045 *Fax:* 0118 977 4560 *Dx:* 33504 WOKINGHAM
E-mail: info@herrington-carmichael.com
Office: Camberley
Languages: French, German
Work: A1 B1 C1 C2 C3 D1 E F1 I J1 K1 L N O P Q R1 S1 T1 T2 W Z(c,e,k,l,t)
Agency, Fixed Fee Interview, Legal Aid undertaken, Legal Aid Franchise and Member of Accident Line
Ptr: Brar, Yavin . . . . . *Sep 1999
Eatwell, Mr James W LLB. . . . . . *Apr 1974
Holden, Ashley D B BA(Law) . . . . . *§Dec 1987
Ast: Bishop, Miss Laura Anne LLB. . . . . . Apr 2010
Coppins, Mr Christopher L LLB . . . . . *Jul 1979
Isbell, Ms Rosemary FILEx . . . . . *Oct 1994
Vaughan, Miss Rhianne LLB(Hons) . . . . . *Sep 2008
Woolhouse, Caroline . . . . . Dec 1982

MM SOLICITORS ‡
393 Reading Road Winnersh Wokingham RG41 5LT
Tel: 0118 989 3788

CHARLES PLATEL SOLICITORS ‡
Guildgate House Shute End Wokingham RG40 1BJ
Tel: 0118 978 4866 *Fax:* 0118 977 4291
E-mail: mail@lawyersforlife.co.uk
List of partners: M Machin-Jefferies, L Pashen, C D Platel
Work: C1 C2 E F1 J1 K1 K3 K4 L O Q R1 R2 S1 S2 T2 W Z(c,e,l)
Fixed Fee Interview and Thames Law Group
Ptr: Machin-Jefferies, Ms Michelle LLB(Hons) . . . . . *Feb 1997
Pashen, Mr Lee LLB(Hons) . . . . . *Sep 2000
Platel, Mr Charles D. . . . . . *Dec 1978
Ast: Eccles, Miss Janine Leigh BSc(Hons) . . . . . *Sep 2004

RATCLIFFE DUCE & GAMMER LLP
86 Rose Street Wokingham RG40 1XU
Tel: 0118 978 3681 *Fax:* 0118 977 4260 *Dx:* 33505 WOKINGHAM
E-mail: wokingham.enquiries@rdg-law.co.uk
Office: Reading
Work: D1 D2 E F1 J1 K1 K2 K3 K4 N O Q S1 S2 W Z(q)
Emergency Action, Agency, Advocacy, Fixed Fee Interview, Legal Aid undertaken and Legal Aid Franchise
Ptr: Powell, Mrs Gillian Ann BA . . . . . *Apr 1993
Rodriguez, Mr Nicholas J BA . . . . . *Feb 1990

WOLVERHAMPTON, West Midlands

BSB SOLICITORS LIMITED ‡
Regent House Bath Avenue Wolverhampton West Midlands WV1 4EG
Tel: 01902 810114 *Fax:* 01902 810115
E-mail: b.bagri@bsbsolicitors.co.uk

MICHAEL J CARLESS SOLICITOR ‡
Maypole House Maypole Street Wolverhampton West Midlands WV5 9JB
Tel: 01902 897743 *Fax:* 01902 897702
E-mail: solicitor@mjcarless.co.uk

CHALLINORS
47 Queen Street Wolverhampton West Midlands WV1 3BJ
Tel: 01902 428121 *Fax:* 01902 424373
Dx: 10416 WOLVERHAMPTON
E-mail: info@challinors.co.uk
Office: Birmingham, Halesowen, Nottingham, West Bromwich
Ast: Najran, Mr Jaisheel LLB(Hons) . . . . . Jan 2004
Con: Caddick, Mr Peter J LLB . . . . . *§Jan 1980
Hingley, Mr David LLB(Lond) . . . . . *§Dec 1976
Hingley, Mr Peter MA(Oxon). . . . . . *§Jan 1968

CHAMBA & CO ‡
177 Dudley Road Wolverhampton West Midlands WV2 3DR
Tel: 01902 454749 *Fax:* 01902 454610
Emergency telephone 07956 512540
Languages: Hindi, Punjabi, Urdu
Work: E G H J1 K1 L S1 V W Z(i,l)
Emergency Action, Agency, Advocacy, Fixed Fee Interview, Legal Aid undertaken and Legal Aid Franchise

CHOPRA & GILL SOLICITORS ‡
337 Dudley Road Wolverhampton West Midlands WV2 3JY
Tel: 01902 621277 *Fax:* 01902 621276
Dx: 70244 WOLVERHAMPTON 5
E-mail: chopraandgillsolicitors@btconnect.com

CONNOLLEY & COMPANY ‡
2 Walkers Way Wombourne Wolverhampton West Midlands WV5 9DP
Tel: 01902 326000 *Fax:* 01902 326838 *Dx:* 13958 WOMBOURNE
E-mail: sharon@connolleyandcompany.co.uk

DBL TALBOTS LLP
Denning House George Street Wolverhampton West Midlands WV2 4DP
Tel: 01902 427561 *Fax:* 01902 420787 / 429788
E-mail: info@dbltalbots.co.uk
Office: Codsall, Dudley (2 offices), Kidderminster, Stourbridge (2 offices)
Languages: French
Work: B1 C1 D1 E G H J1 K1 K2 L N O Q S1 S2 T1 W Z(c,h,j,k,l)
Emergency Action, Agency, Advocacy, Legal Aid undertaken, Legal Aid Franchise and Member of Accident Line
Ptr: Hill, Mr Peter W A BA. . . . . . *§Dec 1983
Jones, Ms Louise Mary LLB. . . . . . *Sep 1994
Wetherall, Mr John BA . . . . . *Dec 1975
Ast: Kettle, Mr Paul J . . . . . Sep 2005
Monnes, Miss Michelle Marie LLB(Hons) . . . . . Dec 2007

DALLOW & DALLOW ‡
23 Waterloo Road Wolverhampton West Midlands WV1 4TJ
Tel: 01902 420208 *Fax:* 01902 428982
E-mail: solicitors@dallowanddallow.co.uk
List of partners: H V Hilton, S Hilton
Languages: French
Work: B1 E F1 J1 K1 L N O Q S1 S2 W Z(d)
Agency, Advocacy and Fixed Fee Interview undertaken
Ptr: Hilton, Mr Harold V LLB(Lond); ACIS . . . . . *§Jun 1966
Hilton, Ms Sarah LLB . . . . . *Oct 1992

DAWSON SOLICITORS ‡
8 Mount Road Tettenhall Wood Wolverhampton West Midlands WV6 8HT
Tel: 01902 759944 *Fax:* 01902 747494
E-mail: m.dawson@dawsonsolicitors.co.uk

ELLIOTT & CO ‡
The Corner House High Street Wombourne Wolverhampton West Midlands WV5 9DN
Tel: 01902 894020 *Fax:* 01902 326770
E-mail: info@elliottco.co.uk

FBC MANBY BOWDLER LLP ‡
George House St John's Square Wolverhampton West Midlands WV2 4BZ
Tel: 01902 578000 *Fax:* 01902 311886
Dx: 727920 WOLVERHAMPTON 22
E-mail: info@fbcmb.co.uk
List of partners: B W Aikman, G J Birkett, N A C Blackie, S H Bowdler, J Burn, K K Carr, E A Cleverley, P D Collins, S G Corfield, P H Cowell, A J Dixon, I R Fallon, T C Gray, D Grove, A G M Hobbs, P J Horton, J Hughes, K Johal, J L Knight, J Kynnersley, M Lloyd, D W Lucas, S A Rea, C D Ridge, D S Robinson, F Rothery, J E Sage, D T Shaw, D A Shepherd, G A L Southall, G D H Sower, K A Styles, A E Thomson, S Todhunter, A C Vernon, T K Worthington, A Wynne
Office: Bridgnorth, Shrewsbury, Telford, Willenhall
Languages: French, Spanish
Work: A3 B1 C1 C2 C3 D1 D2 E F1 J1 J2 K1 K2 K3 K4 L N O Q R1 R2 S1 S2 T1 T2 U2 W Z(c,e,h,l,p)
Ptr: Aikman, Mr Brian William LLB Deputy District Judge. . *Oct 1982
Birkett, Mr Guy Jonathan . . . . . *Nov 1995
Bowdler, Mr Simon H . . . . . *§Jul 1975
Carr, Mrs Kim K LLB . . . . . *§Jan 1986
Cleverley, Mrs Elizabeth Anne LLM . . . . . *Oct 1997
Collins, Mr Peter David BA(Hons) . . . . . *Aug 2003
Fallon, Mr Ian R MA(Cantab) . . . . . *§Oct 1975
Grove, Mr David LLB . . . . . *§Nov 1993
Hobbs, Mr Alasdair Grant Mackenzie LLB(Hons) . . . *Aug 1993
Johal, Miss Kamaljit LLB(Hons)(with Business Law). . . *Jun 2003
Knight, Mr James L LLB(Hons) . . . . . *Nov 1990
Ridge, Mr Craig Duncan. . . . . . *Sep 2002
Rothery, Ms Fay. . . . . . *Jul 1999
Sage, Mr James Emmet BSc. . . . . . *Jan 1996
Southall, Mr Gavin A L LLB . . . . . *§Dec 1974
Styles, Mr Kevin A BA. . . . . . *§Oct 1984
Todhunter, Ms Susan LLB. . . . . . *Jun 1991
Vernon, Mr Andrew C LLB. . . . . . *§Oct 1988

Worthington, Ms Tracy K LLB . . . . . *Nov 1988
Wynne, Mr Andrew LLB . . . . . *§Sep 1996
Asoc: Bohanna, Ms Lindsey Denise LLB . . . . . *Sep 2002
Campbell, Mr David LLB . . . . . *Feb 1999
Consiglid, Miss Leanne Faye LLB(Hons) . . . . . *Sep 2005
Grimshaw, Mrs Karen Elizabeth LLB . . . . . *Apr 1990
Thiara, Ms Charanjit LLB(Hons) . . . . . *Oct 1993
Ast: Angus, Ms Kimberly . . . . . Sep 2010
Clode, Miss Charlotte . . . . . Mar 2009
Davies, Ms Maxine Louise . . . . . *Feb 2007
Downes, Mr Stuart . . . . . Jan 2006
Glover, Miss Elisabeth BA(Hons)(Oxon) . . . . . *Sep 2006
Hoskin, Ms Liz . . . . . Jan 2001
Massey, Ms Rebecca . . . . . Sep 2008
Preece, Mr David . . . . . Sep 2010
Pugh, Ms Charlotte . . . . . *Jan 2008
Ruddock, Mr Gareth John . . . . . *Mar 2007
Taylor, Miss Rebecca . . . . . Mar 2009
Vernon, Miss Joanne Lesley LLB(Hons) . . . . . Sep 2000
Wilkes, Ms Lara . . . . . Sep 2010
Con: Hayes, Mr James LLB(Hons) . . . . . *Dec 1989

MR M FAQUIR ‡
12 Alderdale Wolverhampton West Midlands WV3 9JF
Tel: 01902 424887

FISH & CO ‡
96-98 Cannock Road Wolverhampton West Midlands WV10 8PW
Tel: 01902 826464 *Fax:* 01902 826466
Emergency telephone 07958 584649
List of partners: D G Fish
Languages: Gujarati, Hindi, Punjabi, Urdu
Work: D1 D2 K1 Z(m)
Emergency Action, Agency, Advocacy, Fixed Fee Interview and Legal Aid undertaken
Ptr: Fish, Mr David G LLB . . . . . Jun 1987
Ast: Patel, Miss Mamata . . . . . May 2000

R S GOUGH & CO ‡
Wolverhampton Science Park Glaisher Drive Wolverhampton West Midlands WV10 9RU
Tel: 01902 420200 *Fax:* 01902 420220
E-mail: rsg@rsgoughlaw.co.uk

KALE & CO ‡
85-86 Darlington Street Wolverhampton West Midlands WV1 4EX
Tel: 01902 772500 *Fax:* 01902 771900
Dx: 722202 WOLVERHAMPTON 15
E-mail: kaleandco@aol.com
List of partners: R S Kale
Languages: Hindi, Punjabi
Work: B1 C1 D1 D2 E F1 J1 K1 K3 S1 S2 W Z(i,l)
Emergency Action, Agency, Advocacy, Fixed Fee Interview, Legal Aid undertaken and Legal Aid Franchise
SPr: Kale, Mrs Rabinder Sandhu LLB(Hons); LSF . . . . . May 1989

KHAN & CO ‡
19a Chapel Ash Wolverhampton West Midlands WV3 0TZ
Tel: 01902 424477 *Fax:* 01902 425523
List of partners: S A Khan
Languages: Pashto, Punjabi, Urdu
Work: S1 S2 T1 T2 Z(i)
SPr: Khan, Mr Sher A BCom; MA; LLB; LLM . . . . . Oct 2007

KUMARI-BANGA SOLICITORS ‡
179 Newhampton Road East Whitmore Reans Wolverhampton West Midlands WV1 4PQ
Tel: 01902 423651 *Fax:* 01902 420882
E-mail: info@kumari-banga.co.uk

GEOFFREY MILNE
Post Office Building Station Road Albrighton Wolverhampton West Midlands WV7 3QH
Tel: 01902 373000 *Fax:* 01902 373390
Office: Wellington
Work: A1 J1 K1 K3 K4 L S1 S2 W
Advocacy and Fixed Fee Interview undertaken
SPr: Milne, Mr Geoffrey . . . . . *Jan 1982
Ast: Lott, Mrs Susanne Lilian . . . . . *Nov 1973

MORRIS READ & CO ‡
(incorporating Edward Marston & Co; A Denis Morris & David L Read)
Wulfrun House 51 Waterloo Road Wolverhampton West Midlands WV1 4QQ
Tel: 01902 420973 / 710004 *Fax:* 01902 685152
List of partners: R A Morris
Work: C1 E F1 G K1 L N O Q S1 W Z(i,l)
Emergency Action, Agency, Advocacy and Legal Aid undertaken
Ptr: Morris, Mr Richard A LLB . . . . . *Dec 1978
Con: Thompson, Mr Roger D LLB(B'ham) . . . . . *Mar 1965

VINCENT OAKLEY SOLICITOR ‡
Neville Lodge 53 Newbridge Crescent Tettenhall Wolverhampton West Midlands WV6 0LH
Tel: 01902 743333 *Fax:* 01902 744435

REES PAGE ‡
(incorporating Darbey Scott Rees; Pages & Skidmore Hares & Co)
8-12 Waterloo Road Wolverhampton West Midlands WV1 4BL
Tel: 01902 577777 *Fax:* 01902 577735
Dx: 10405 WOLVERHAMPTON
E-mail: info@reespage.co.uk
List of partners: P Dougall, R J Ennis, P C Horsley, S D Hughes, A Lund, I C Macpherson, J Murphy, J A Tennant, N S Wynn-Williams
Office: Bilston
Languages: French
Work: A1 B1 C1 C2 D1 D2 E F1 I J1 K1 K3 L N O Q R1 S1 S2 T1 T2 U2 W Z(c,d,h,j,l,q)
Emergency Action, Agency, Advocacy, Fixed Fee Interview, Legal Aid undertaken, Legal Aid Franchise and Member of Accident Line
Ptr: Ennis, Mr Richard Jonathan LLB . . . . . *§Sep 1995
Lund, Mr Andrew LLB . . . . . *§Mar 1986
Macpherson, Mr Ian C BA . . . . . *§Mar 1985
Murphy, Mr James BA . . . . . *§Mar 1994
Tennant, Mrs Julia A LLB(Wales) . . . . . *§Nov 1986
Wynn-Williams, Mr Nicholas S LLB . . . . . *§Nov 1992
Ast: Kearns, Miss Samantha Jane LLB . . . . . *Feb 2010
Neale, Miss Rebecca Louise LLB(Hons) . . . . . *Sep 2006
Peniket, Miss Samantha Joanne LLB . . . . . Sep 2010
Rose, Mrs Kirsty Anne LLB . . . . . *Nov 2008

Con: Kilvert, Mr Michael J . . . . . *§Nov 1971
Tomlinson, Mr Michael . . . . . *§Jul 1973

RILEY HAYES & CO ‡
24 Waterloo Road Wolverhampton West Midlands WV1 4BL
Tel: 01902 773666 *Fax:* 01902 713187
Dx: 10432 WOLVERHAMPTON
Emergency telephone 07733 304383
List of partners: A S Johal, S V Misra, H S Suthi
Office: Bilston
Work: D1 G H K1 K3
Emergency Action, Agency, Advocacy and Legal Aid undertaken
Ptr: Johal, Amritpal Singh LLB . . . . . Oct 1999
Suthi, Mr Hocknam Singh . . . . . *Mar 2001
Ast: Aston, Ms Isabel LLB(Hons) . . . . . *Sep 2002
Kumar, Mrs Nishi LLB(Hons) . . . . . Dec 2004

ROGERS & CO ‡
57 Victoria Street Wolverhampton West Midlands WV1 3NX
Tel: 01902 310312 *Fax:* 01902 310089
Dx: 10412 WOLVERHAMPTON
Emergency telephone 01902 310312
E-mail: info@rogerslaw.co.uk
Languages: Punjabi, Urdu
Work: G H
Agency, Advocacy, Fixed Fee Interview, Legal Aid undertaken and Legal Aid Franchise
Asoc: McNamara, Mr Martin C LLB(Hons) . . . . . Oct 1996

SHARRATTS FAMILY LAW LIMITED ‡
Rock House Old Hill Tettenhall Wolverhampton West Midlands WV6 8QB
Tel: 01902 759500 *Fax:* 01902 759779
E-mail: info@sharratts.com

GEOFFREY T SMITH & CO ‡
32 Waterloo Road Wolverhampton West Midlands WV1 4BN
Tel: 01902 426961 *Fax:* 01902 313127
Dx: 722231 WOLVERHAMPTON 15
List of partners: D T Williams
Work: E F1 G H J1 K1 L S1 S2 V W Z(i,l,o)
Emergency Action, Agency, Advocacy, Fixed Fee Interview, Legal Aid undertaken and Legal Aid Franchise
Ptr: Williams, Mr David T BA(Law) . . . . . *Dec 1979

STEVENS
21 Waterloo Road Wolverhampton West Midlands WV1 4DJ
Tel: 01902 772776 *Fax:* 01902 772778
Dx: 10429 WOLVERHAMPTON 1
Emergency telephone 07659 111000
E-mail: admin@stevenssolicitors.co.uk
Office: Stafford, Stoke-on-Trent (2 offices)
Work: G H
Emergency Action, Agency, Advocacy, Fixed Fee Interview, Legal Aid undertaken and Legal Aid Franchise
Ptr: Bratt, Mr David C BA ★ . . . . . *Sep 1989
Starrs, Mrs Debbie C LLB ★ . . . . . *Oct 1990
Asoc: Hiatt, Mr Paul LLB ★ . . . . . *Nov 2001
Con: Amos, Mrs Caroline . . . . . *Oct 1982

THOMPSONS (FORMERLY ROBIN/BRIAN THOMPSON & PARTNERS)
St Johns House St John's Square Wolverhampton West Midlands WV2 4BH
Tel: 01902 771551 *Fax:* 01902 773636
Office: Belfast, Birmingham, Bristol, Cardiff, Chelmsford, Dagenham, Derby, Harrow, Leeds, Liverpool, London SW19, London WC1, Manchester, Middlesbrough, Newcastle upon Tyne, Nottingham, Plymouth, Sheffield, South Shields, Southampton, Stoke-on-Trent, Swansea

THORNES ‡
Lich Gates Wolverhampton West Midlands WV1 1UA
Tel: 01902 313311 *Fax:* 01902 423454
Dx: 10407 WOLVERHAMPTON 1
E-mail: mike_kelly@thornessolicitors.co.uk
List of partners: T M Davis, B J Gaudion, K E Grimshaw, M J Kelly, G A Thorne
Work: C1 D1 E G H K1 S1 S2 W Z(l)
Emergency Action, Agency, Advocacy and Legal Aid undertaken
Ptr: Davis, Miss Tracy Marie . . . . . *§Nov 1998
Gaudion, Mr Bruce James . . . . . Jun 2001
Grimshaw, Mrs Karen Elizabeth LLB . . . . . *Apr 1990
Kelly, Mr Michael J LLB . . . . . *§Dec 1975
Thorne, Mr Gerald A . . . . . *§Nov 1979
Con: Crofts, Mr Donald A LLB(B'ham) . . . . . *§Jun 1961

UNDERHILL LANGLEY & WRIGHT ‡
7 Waterloo Road Wolverhampton West Midlands WV1 4DW
Tel: 01902 423431 *Fax:* 01902 711696
Dx: 10402 WOLVERHAMPTON
List of partners: R C Alderson, W S C Carter, S G Davies, A C Smillie, A C P Thompson
Office: Bridgnorth, Wolverhampton
Work: A1 C1 E J1 K1 K3 L Q S1 S2 W Z(l)
Agency and Advocacy undertaken
Ptr: Alderson, Mr Richard Charles LLB(Leics) . . . . . *§Jun 1979
Carter, Mr W Stephen C LLB(B'ham) . . . . . *§Nov 1976
Davies, Mr Samuel G BA(Law) . . . . . *Oct 1986
Smillie, Mr Angus C LLB Deputy Assistant Coroner for Wolverhampton . . . . . *Oct 1980
Thompson, Mr Alexander Charles Piers . . . . . Sep 2000
Ast: Martin, Mrs Sarah Anne Margaret BA(Hons) . . . . . Sep 1999
Con: Dakin, Mrs Clare Louise . . . . . *May 1988
Nock, Mr Kevin Jonathan . . . . . Nov 1966

UNDERHILL LANGLEY & WRIGHT
(incorporating Owen & Co)
460 Stafford Road Oxley Wolverhampton West Midlands WV10 6AN
Tel: 01902 782606 *Fax:* 01902 781799
Office: Bridgnorth, Wolverhampton
Work: C1 D1 E F1 G H J1 K1 L N S1 T1 W Z(j)
Emergency Action, Agency, Advocacy, Fixed Fee Interview and Legal Aid undertaken
Ast: Davies, Mr Samuel G BA(Law) . . . . . *Oct 1986

VKM SOLICITORS ‡
Suite 1 Talisbrook House Castle Street Wolverhampton West Midlands WV1 3AD
Tel: 01902 311155 *Fax:* 01902 311159
Dx: 702435 WOLVERHAMPTON 5
E-mail: vkmsolicitors@aol.com
List of partners: V Momi, A Puri
Languages: Hindi, Punjabi, Urdu
Work: E Q S1 S2 Z(i)
Agency, Advocacy and Fixed Fee Interview undertaken
Ptr: Momi, Vijay . . . . . Jan 1998
Puri, Aman LLB(Hons) Middle Temple Scholarship Offer . . . . . May 2005

R N WILLIAMS & CO LIMITED ‡
53 Waterloo Road Wolverhampton West Midlands WV1 4QQ
Tel: 01902 429051 *Fax:* 01902 313435
Dx: 10406 WOLVERHAMPTON
E-mail: enquiries@rnwilliams.com
List of partners: A F Randle, C J Richards, R N Williams
Work: B1 B2 C1 D1 E F1 G H J1 K1 K2 K3 K4 L N O Q S1 S2 T1 V W Z(l,q,r)
Emergency Action, Agency, Advocacy, Fixed Fee Interview, Legal Aid undertaken and Legal Aid Franchise
Ptr: Randle, Mr Anthony Frank . . . . . *Jan 2000
Richards, Miss Charlotte Jane . . . . . *Nov 1997
Williams, Mr Roderick Norman LLB . . . . . *§Jan 1970
Ast: Clark, Mr Anthony Stephen John LLB . . . . . *Aug 1978
Romney, Mr John LLB(Hons) . . . . . *Mar 2009
Vandaele, Mr Mark LLB . . . . . *Aug 2006
Willets, Mrs Kathryn LLB(Hons) Law Diversity Access Award Scholarship 2004 . . . . . Dec 2007

ROSE WILLIAMS & PARTNERS ‡
Blossoms Fold Wolverhampton West Midlands WV1 4HJ
Tel: 01902 710822 *Fax:* 01902 717813
E-mail: conveyancing@roselaw.co.uk
List of partners: C J Hugheston-Roberts, A N M Mitchinson, M S Williams
Languages: French, German
Work: S1
Ptr: Hugheston-Roberts, Mr Charles Justin ★ . . . . . *Dec 1986
Mitchinson, Mr Andrew N M LLB ★ . . . . . *Oct 1982
Williams, Mr Michael Shawn ★ . . . . . *Jan 1986
Asoc: Good, Mr Kevin D C LLB(Hons) . . . . . Dec 1985

WOODHOUSE & COMPANY ‡
22 Waterloo Road Wolverhampton West Midlands WV1 4BL
Tel: 01902 773616 *Fax:* 01902 423297
List of partners: A W Major, R J L Pass, A J Woodhouse
Office: Sutton Coldfield, Walsall
Work: A1 B1 C1 E F1 J1 K1 L M1 N S1 S2 T1 W
Fixed Fee Interview undertaken
Ptr: Major, Mr Anthony W LLB(Hons) . . . . . Jun 1978
Pass, Mr Robert J L . . . . . *Mar 1982
Woodhouse, Mr Anthony J . . . . . Dec 1975

WOMBOURNE, Staffordshire

STEPHENSONS
The Cottage High Street Wombourne Staffordshire WV5 9DN
Tel: 01902 894187
E-mail: info@stephensons-wombourne.co.uk
Office: Brierley Hill
Work: B1 C1 D1 E F1 G H J1 K1 L N O Q S1 W
Emergency Action, Agency, Advocacy, Fixed Fee Interview and Legal Aid undertaken

WOMBWELL, South Yorkshire

BURY & WALKERS LLP
Watford House Church Street Wombwell South Yorkshire S73 0DG
Tel: 01226 753433 *Fax:* 01226 340294
Emergency telephone 01226 733533
E-mail: wombwell@burywalkers.com
Office: Barnsley, Leeds
Work: A1 B1 C1 D1 E F1 G H J1 K1 L M1 N P R1 S1 T1 W Z(c,d,l,m,n,o,p)
Emergency Action, Advocacy, Fixed Fee Interview, Legal Aid undertaken and Legal Aid Franchise
Ptr: Walden, Mr John . . . . . *Sep 1981
Ast: Booth, Mr Nigel BA . . . . . Dec 1981
Wilkinson, Mr John P de Garr LLB . . . . . May 1998

Holders of Franchise for Crime, Family. We specialise in the following areas of work Family Law, Residential Conveyancing, Wills, Trusts and Probate.

WOODBRIDGE, Suffolk

GROSS & CURJEL ‡
15 Thoroughfare Woodbridge Suffolk IP12 1AB
Tel: 01394 383436 *Fax:* 01394 386936 *Dx:* 41408 WOODBRIDGE
List of partners: J K Winton
Languages: French, German
Work: A1 C1 E K1 L S1 W
Fixed Fee Interview undertaken
SPr: Winton, Mr John K . . . . . Apr 1970

LIGHTFOOT O'BRIEN WESTCOTT ‡
Barton House 84 The Thoroughfare Woodbridge Suffolk IP12 1AL
Tel: 01394 386336 *Fax:* 01394 380098 *Dx:* 41402 WOODBRIDGE
E-mail: mail@lightfoot-obrien.co.uk
List of partners: J C E Lightfoot, B R O'Brien, W J Westcott
Office: London W1
Languages: French
Work: A1 B1 C1 D1 D2 E F1 J1 K1 K3 L N O Q S1 S2 T2 W Z(c)
Emergency Action and Fixed Fee Interview undertaken
Ptr: Lightfoot, Mr James C E MA(Oxon) . . . . . *Jan 1979
O'Brien, Mr B Rory MA(Cantab) . . . . . *Jun 1985
Westcott, Mr Walter Jeremy BA(Hons)(Dunelm) . . . . . *Nov 1984

See p112 for the Key to Work Categories & other symbols

MCTERNANS ‡
The Old Dairy Cowslip House Long Green Woodbridge Suffolk IP13 7JD
Tel: 01728 627929
E-mail: sean@mcternans.co.uk

MARGARY & MILLER
19 Deben Mill Business Centre Old Maltings Approach Melton Woodbridge Suffolk IP12 1BL
Tel: 01394 388605 *Fax:* 01394 386287
Office: Felixstowe, Southwold, Woodbridge

MARGARY & MILLER
19 Church Street Woodbridge Suffolk IP12 1DS
Tel: 01394 382777 *Fax:* 01394 380424 *Dx:* 41401 WOODBRIDGE
E-mail: info@margary-miller.co.uk
Office: Felixstowe, Southwold, Woodbridge
Languages: French, German
Work: A1 B1 C1 D1 E F1 J1 K1 K3 K4 L N O Q S1 S2 T1 T2 W Z(c,j,l,q)
Emergency Action, Agency, Advocacy, Fixed Fee Interview undertaken and Member of Accident Line
Ptr: Leach, Mr Stephen M J Notary Public . . . . *Jun 1973
Ast: Duckworth, Mrs Lindsay J LLB(Sheff) . . . . Jul 1978

MARSHALL HATCHICK ‡
The Ancient House 22 Church Street Woodbridge Suffolk IP12 1DH
Tel: 01394 388411 *Fax:* 01394 387616 *Dx:* 41413 WOODBRIDGE
Emergency telephone 07889 119463
List of partners: K A Hatchick, N J Marshall, J O'Connor, J N Robbins, M G Sparrow
Office: London W1
Languages: French, German, Italian
Work: A1 B1 C1 C2 C3 E I J1 K1 K4 L R1 R2 S1 S2 T2 V W Z(b,c,d,e,f,h)
Agency undertaken
Ptr: Hatchick, Mr Keith Andrew LLB . . . . *Oct 1981
Marshall, Mr Nicholas John . . . . *Nov 1977
O'Connor, Mr James . . . . Jul 1990
Robbins, Mr James Nathan . . . . *Nov 1995
Sparrow, Mr Michael George LLB . . . . Apr 1974
Ast: Church, Mrs Jennifer Denise Marina Oxtoby LLB . . . Nov 1974
Con: Thew, Mr Michael Adrian LLB(Hons)(Lond) . . . . . . Mar 1975

MAYLAND PORTER ‡
29 New Street Woodbridge Suffolk IP12 1DZ
Tel: 01394 615795 *Fax:* 01394 610290

MITCHELL & CO ‡
7a Cumberland Street Woodbridge Suffolk IP12 4AH
Tel: 01394 386421 *Fax:* 01394 380826
Emergency telephone 01394 387149
E-mail: mitchell.co@talk21.com
List of partners: A H Mitchell
Work: A1 B1 C1 E L S2 W
Emergency Action undertaken
Ptr: Mitchell, Mr Anthony Hewittson . . . . *§Jan 1982

WOODFORD, Essex

BURNEY LEGAL SOLICITORS ‡
6 Bourne Court Southend Road Woodford Essex IG8 8HD
Tel: 020 8551 2211 *Fax:* 020 8551 6600
E-mail: info@burneylegal.co.uk

MUNRO SOLICITORS
69 Princes Avenue Woodford Essex IG8 0LW
Tel: 020 8503 1718 *Fax:* 020 8503 0990 *Dx:* 52105 FOREST GATE
Office: London E7

WHISKERS
445 High Road Woodford Essex IG8 0XE
Tel: 020 8505 4777 *Fax:* 020 8506 1294
Dx: 110164 WOODFORD GREEN
E-mail: woodford@whiskers.co.uk
Office: Bishop's Stortford, Epping, Harlow
Work: S1 S2 W Z(l)

WOODFORD GREEN, Essex

BAILEY NICHOLSON GRAYSON ‡
15 Bourne Court Southend Road Woodford Green Essex IG8 8HD
Tel: 020 8418 2900 *Fax:* 020 8418 2901 *Dx:* 8968 GANTS HILL
Emergency telephone 020 8518 3999
E-mail: mail@bnglaw.co.uk
List of partners: M Bailey, J D Grayson, D M Nicholson
Office: Ware
Work: B2 G H
Agency, Advocacy and Legal Aid undertaken
Ptr: Bailey, Mr Mark LLB(Hons) . . . . *Jun 1995
Grayson, Mr Jose David LLB . . . . Sep 1990
Nicholson, Mr David Michael . . . . Sep 1994

CARTWRIGHT CUNNINGHAM HASELGROVE & CO
13-13a The Broadway Woodford Green Essex IG8 0HL
Tel: 020 8506 5200 *Fax:* 020 8505 1563
Dx: 40453 BUCKHURST HILL
Office: London E17
Work: A1 C1 C2 C3 D1 E F1 G H J1 K1 L M1 M2 N P R1 S1 T1 T2 V W Z(c,d,e,h,i,j,k,l,m,o,s)
Agency, Legal Aid undertaken and Member of Accident Line
Ptr: Gayer, Mr Geoffrey I LLB . . . . *Oct 1973
Smith, Mr Nigel P . . . . *Jan 1983
Ast: Murphy, Mr Sean ★ . . . . Mar 1992
Tarring, Mr Brian W LLB . . . . *Nov 1960

FORBES HALL LLP ‡
3 Johnston Road Woodford Green Essex IG8 0XA
Tel: 020 8498 0080 *Fax:* 020 8504 9078
Dx: 110165 WOODFORD GREEN
E-mail: info@forbeswheater.co.uk
List of partners: J D Carroll, R D P Paganuzzi, P T Wheater
Office: London EC2
Work: B1 C1 C2 C3 E F1 J1 K1 L M1 M2 N O Q R1 S1 S2 W Z(b,c,j,l)
Agency undertaken
Ptr: Carroll, Mr John D MA(Cantab) . . . . *Nov 1983
Paganuzzi, Renzo D P BA . . . . *Jan 1985
Wheater, Mr Phillip T LLB . . . . *Mar 1978
Ast: Teng, Mrs Eva Georgia . . . . Jul 2005
Con: Hall, Mr Brian William LLB(Hons) . . . . *Jan 1968

MICHAELS & CO ‡
1 Churchwood Gardens Woodford Green Essex IG8 0PL
Tel: 020 8245 1138 *Fax:* 020 8245 1138 *Dx:* 99341 BARKINGSIDE
E-mail: michaelscosolicitors@gmail.com
List of partners: M Michaels
SPr: Michaels, Mr Martin BA(Law) . . . . Jun 1984

A V A MITCHELL & CO ‡
39 Forrest Approach Woodford Green Essex IG8 9BP
Tel: 020 8504 7766 *Fax:* 020 8504 9907
List of partners: J V Bohuszewicz
Work: L S1 S2 W
Ptr: Bohuszewicz, Mr John V LLB(Lond) . . . . Jun 1976

SCUDAMORES ‡
132 Snakes Lane East Woodford Green Essex IG8 7HZ
Tel: 0844 880 2323 *Fax:* 0844 880 2322
Dx: 110156 WOODFORD GREEN
Emergency telephone 07801 494894
E-mail: admin@scudamores4solicitors.co.uk
Work: E G H S2 Z(i,l)
Emergency Action, Agency, Advocacy, Fixed Fee Interview and Legal Aid undertaken

STAPLEY & CO
82 Snakes Lane East Woodford Green Essex IG8 7QQ
E-mail: solicitors@stapley.co.uk
Office: Loughton
Work: K4 M3 S1 S2 W

WOOTTON BASSETT, Wiltshire

AWDRY BAILEY & DOUGLAS
Stafford House 57 High Street Wootton Bassett Wiltshire SN4 7AQ
Tel: 01793 853200 *Fax:* 01793 853710
Dx: 40352 WOOTTON BASSETT
E-mail: abd@awdrys.co.uk
Office: Calne, Devizes, Marlborough
Languages: French, German
Work: A1 B1 C1 C2 D1 E F1 J1 K1 K3 L N O P Q R1 S1 S2 T1 T2 W Z(c,d,h,j,k,l,o,q,r)
Emergency Action, Agency, Advocacy, Fixed Fee Interview, Legal Aid undertaken, Legal Aid Franchise and Member of Accident Line
Ptr: Awdry, Mr G Antony. . . . . *§Dec 1978
Douglas, Mr Andrew J BA(Law) . . . . *§Oct 1983
Everett, Mr Alistair Munro . . . . *§Nov 1992
Robinson, Mr Nicholas LLB(Hons). . . . . *Nov 2000
Shah, Mr Peter Vipin LLB . . . . *Dec 1992
Ast: Strickland, Mrs Corynne L BSc(Hons) . . . . *Dec 1976
Tomlinson, Ms Halina . . . . Feb 2003

BEVIRS
141 High Street Wootton Bassett Wiltshire SN4 7AZ
Tel: 01793 848900 *Fax:* 01793 853191
Dx: 40350 WOOTTON BASSETT
Office: Calne, Swindon
Languages: Greek
Work: A1 B1 C1 C2 C3 D1 E F1 G H J1 K1 L M1 M2 N O P R1 S1 T1 T2 W Z(c)
Emergency Action, Agency, Advocacy, Legal Aid undertaken and Member of Accident Line
Ptr: Brown, Mr Derek F LLB . . . . *Mar 1983
Woolnough, Mrs Sonyia L BA(Dunelm)(Law) . . . . . Oct 1984
Ast: Pithouse, Miss Gemma LLB(Hons); LPC . . . . *Apr 2008

D R HUGHES ‡
115 High Street Wootton Bassett Wiltshire SN4 7AU
Tel: 01793 840077 *Fax:* 01793 840099
Dx: 40360 WOOTTON BASSETT
List of partners: D R Hughes
Work: S1 S2 W
SPr: Hughes, Mr Douglas Robert. . . . . *Nov 1972

DAVID JEACOCK ‡
41 Church Street Wootton Bassett Wiltshire SN4 7BQ
Tel: 01793 854111 *Fax:* 01793 853600
E-mail: jeacock@lineone.net
List of partners: D Jeacock
Languages: French
Work: B1 C1 C2 C3 O Q S1 S2 Z(e,w)
SPr: Jeacock, Mr David MA(Oxon) . . . . *§May 1970

WORCESTER, Worcestershire

ABBOTTS SOLICITORS ‡
11-13 St Johns Worcester Worcestershire WR2 5AE
Tel: 01905 339181

ANNING LAW ‡
Hallow Park Hallow Worcester Worcestershire WR2 6PG
Tel: 01905 641934 *Fax:* 01905 641934
E-mail: pa@anninglaw.co.uk

BINNION LINDSAY-VEAL LLP
1st and 2nd Floors 46 Foregate Street Worcester Worcestershire WR1 1EE
Tel: 01905 747809
Office: Stourport-on-Severn

THOMAS GUISE ‡
5 Foregate Street Worcester Worcestershire WR1 1DB
Tel: 01905 723131 *Fax:* 01905 723312 *Dx:* 716284 WORCESTER
E-mail: info@thomasguise.co.uk
List of partners: S G J Bailey, P J Guise, P W Thomas
Office: Studley
Work: A1 B1 C1 C2 C3 E F1 J1 K1 L M1 M2 N O P Q R1 R2 S1 S2 W Z(f,l,p,w,y)
Emergency Action, Agency, Advocacy, Fixed Fee Interview, Legal Aid undertaken and Member of Accident Line
Ptr: Bailey, Mr Stuart G J LLB . . . . *Aug 2000
Guise, Mr Philip J LLB(B'ham) . . . . *Jul 1976
Thomas, Mr P Wayne BA(Econ). . . . . *Oct 1979
Ast: Bartley-Smith, Mr Thomas BA(Oxon) . . . . *Sep 2005
Bonney, Mrs Shelley Anne . . . . *May 2008
Ellis, Mr Geoffrey A J LLB. . . . . *Sep 1983
Holmes, Mr Edward Antony LLB(Hons) . . . . Sep 2003
Strickland, Miss Suzannah Jane. . . . . Oct 2006

HALLMARKHULME ‡
4-5 Sansome Place Worcester Worcestershire WR1 1UQ
Tel: 01905 726600 *Fax:* 01905 743366 *Dx:* 716252 WORCESTER
E-mail: enquiries@hallmarkhulme.co.uk
List of partners: L Y Bartlett, T A F Sherwood, M A Thomas, R Widdowson, R J Wilkes
Work: A1 B1 C1 C2 C3 D1 E F1 G H J1 K1 K3 L M1 M2 N O P Q R1 S1 T1 T2 V W Z(d,g,h,l,m,s)
Emergency Action, Agency, Advocacy, Fixed Fee Interview, Legal Aid undertaken and Legal Aid Franchise
Ptr: Bartlett, Ms Lesley Y . . . . *May 1978
Sherwood, Mr Timothy A F LLB Deputy Coroner. . . . *Apr 1975
Thomas, Mr Martin A LLB. . . . . *§May 1981
Widdowson, Ms Rebecca . . . . *Jul 1996
Wilkes, Mr Richard John . . . . *Sep 1997
Ast: Leyland, Mr James Francis . . . . *Sep 2002
Webley, Miss Lucy Catherine . . . . *Nov 1997
Williams, Laura . . . . *Mar 2010
Con: Hallmark, Mr David J S LLM. . . . . *§Jan 1970
Pugh, Mr Ian C LLB(Lond) . . . . *§Dec 1975
Stafford, Mr Paul Thomas LLB . . . . *Apr 1981

HAMER CHILDS ‡
58 The Tything Worcester Worcestershire WR1 1JT
Tel: 01905 724565 *Fax:* 01905 21002 *Dx:* 716273 WORCESTER
E-mail: info@hamerchilds.demon.co.uk
List of partners: A M Childs, R H Macrory, M Turnbull
Work: G H
Agency and Advocacy undertaken
Ptr: Childs, Mr Andrew M BA(Exon) . . . . *Mar 1980
Macrory, Mr Robert H LLB. . . . . *May 1997
Turnbull, Mr Mark DipSW; PGDipLaw . . . . *Jul 2006
Asoc: Harper, Mr Gary Stephen BSc(Hons)(Econ) . . . . . . Nov 1994
Patel, Mr Jason David LLB(Hons) . . . . *Jan 2002

HARRISON CLARK LLP ‡
5 Deansway Worcester Worcestershire WR1 2JG
Tel: 01905 612001 *Fax:* 01905 744899 *Dx:* 716260 WORCESTER 1
E-mail: lawyers@harrison-clark.co.uk
List of partners: A L Bateman, C A Bexfield, J Brew, A Caldicott, R M Capper, M A Cave, R Green, C J Irvine, A M James, B G Jordan, R C Morgan, D E Oliver, A L Perrett, P Savage, K R Shawcross, B V Spain, R Thomas, C J Thornton-Smith, J R Whitbread
Office: Cheltenham, Hereford, Ross-on-Wye, Worcester
Languages: Malay, Mirpuri, Punjabi, Tamil, Urdu
Work: A1 A2 A3 B1 C1 C2 C3 D1 D2 E F1 F2 I J1 J2 K1 K2 K3 K4 L M1 N O P Q R1 R2 S1 S2 T1 U2 V W X Z(b,c,d,e,h,j,l,m,o,p,q,r,s,u)
Emergency Action, Agency, Advocacy, Fixed Fee Interview, Legal Aid undertaken, Legal Aid Franchise and Member of Accident Line
Ptr: Bexfield, Ms Cindy April BA(Hons) . . . . *Jan 1988
Brew, Mr Jonathan LLB . . . . *§Oct 1980
Caldicott, Mr Andrew . . . . *Feb 1994
Capper, Mr Robert Matthew LLB . . . . *Sep 1997
Cave, Mr Michael A. . . . . Sep 1987
Green, Mr Richard BA . . . . *Jan 1983
Irvine, Miss Caroline Jane BA(Hons) . . . . *Oct 1990
James, Mr Andrew M BA(Oxon). . . . . *Oct 1990
Morgan, Mr Richard Charles . . . . *Mar 1984
Oliver, Miss Dawn E LLB(Hons). . . . . *Oct 1992
Savage, Mr Peter. . . . . *Mar 1997
Spain, Mrs Brenda V BA . . . . *Nov 1987
Thomas, Mr Rod . . . . *Aug 1998
Thornton-Smith, Miss Charlotte Jane . . . . *Oct 2003
Whitbread, Mr Jonathan R . . . . *Sep 1999
Asoc: Baker, Ms Ruth . . . . Jan 2007
Cambridge, Mr Daniel. . . . . *Jan 2004
Dhillon, Miss Arpinder LLB . . . . *Oct 1999
Emery, Miss Clare Elizabeth BA(Hons)(Jurisprudence) Jan 1998
Gilhooly, Miss Suzzane Jane . . . . Oct 2005
Goodwin, Mr Michael BA . . . . *Sep 1999
Hodgetts, Ms Joanne . . . . *Jan 2006
Leask, Rebecca. . . . . *Oct 2007
Lowe, Ms Tracey . . . . Jan 2006
Priest, Ms Emma . . . . *Jan 2002
Scott, Ms Alison. . . . . *Jan 2001
Small, Miss Lucinda LLB . . . . *Nov 1996
Thompson, Ms Claire . . . . *Jan 1998
Tipple, Ms Lorna . . . . *Jan 2004
Waddington, Mr Mathew Nicholas George. . . . . . . *Oct 2003
Ast: Berry, Constantine . . . . *Jan 2006
Grove, Mr Simon Leslie LLB . . . . Oct 2009
Haq, Ms Suraiya . . . . May 1994
Morgan, Mr Daniel MEng(Civil & Structural Engineering)Apr 2008
Phelps, Mr James LLB(Hons); LPC . . . . Aug 2008
Thornton, Miss Rachael Sarah LLB . . . . Apr 2009
Wathen, Ms Mary. . . . . Jul 2008

HARRISON CLARK LLP
5 College Yard Worcester Worcestershire WR1 2LD
Tel: 01905 612001 *Fax:* 01905 619690
E-mail: lawyers@harrison-clark.co.uk
Office: Cheltenham, Hereford, Ross-on-Wye, Worcester
Languages: French
Work: A1 B1 C1 C2 D1 D2 E F1 F2 J1 J2 K1 K2 K3 K4 L N O P Q R1 S1 S2 U2 V W X Z(c,d,e,h,l,q,r)
Emergency Action, Agency, Advocacy, Fixed Fee Interview, Legal Aid undertaken, Legal Aid Franchise and Member of Accident Line
Ptr: Bexfield, Ms Cindy April BA(Hons) . . . . *Jan 1988
Brew, Mr Jonathan LLB . . . . *§Oct 1980
Caldicott, Mr Andrew . . . . *Feb 1994
Capper, Mr Robert Matthew LLB . . . . *Sep 1997
Cave, Mr Michael A. . . . . Sep 1987
Green, Mr Richard BA . . . . *Jan 1983
Irvine, Miss Caroline Jane BA(Hons) . . . . *Oct 1990

James, Mr Andrew M BA(Oxon). . . . . *Oct 1990
Morgan, Mr Richard Charles . . . . . *Mar 1984
Oliver, Miss Dawn E LLB(Hons) . . . . . *Oct 1992
Savage, Mr Peter . . . . . *Mar 1997
Spain, Mrs Brenda V BA . . . . . *Nov 1987
Thomas, Mr Rod . . . . . *Aug 1998
Thornton-Smith, Miss Charlotte Jane . . . . . *Oct 2003
Whitbread, Mr Jonathan R . . . . . *Sep 1999
Asoc: Baker, Ms Ruth . . . . . Jan 2007
Cambridge, Mr Daniel. . . . . *Jan 2004
Dhillon, Miss Arpinder LLB . . . . . *Oct 1999
Gilhooly, Miss Suzzane Jane . . . . . Oct 2005
Goodwin, Mr Michael BA . . . . . *Sep 1999
Hodgetts, Ms Joanne . . . . . *Jan 2006
Leask, Rebecca. . . . . *Oct 2007
Lowe, Ms Tracey . . . . . Jan 2006
Priest, Ms Emma . . . . . *Jan 2002
Scott, Ms Alison. . . . . *Jan 2001
Thompson, Ms Claire . . . . . *Jan 1998
Tipple, Ms Lorna . . . . . *Jan 2004
Waddington, Mr Mathew Nicholas George. . . . . *Oct 2003
Ast: Berry, Constantine . . . . . *Jan 2006
Haq, Ms Suraiya . . . . . May 1994
Wathen, Ms Mary . . . . . Jul 2008

HARWOOD & CO ‡
102 Hallow Road Worcester Worcestershire WR2 6DD
Tel: 01905 420855 *Fax:* 01905 420855
List of partners: M D Harwood
Work: L S1 W
Fixed Fee Interview undertaken
SPr: Harwood, Mr Michael D LLB. . . . . *Aug 1987

DUNCAN KENNEY ‡
Restdale House 32-33 Foregate Street Worcester Worcestershire WR1 1EE
Tel: 01905 25221 *Fax:* 01905 23221
E-mail: info@duncankenney.co.uk

KIERAN & CO ‡
First Floor Anbrian House Worcester Worcestershire WR1 1HD
Tel: 01905 28635 *Fax:* 01905 21803 *Dx:* 716310 WORCESTER
List of partners: J P Kieran
Work: A1 B1 C1 D1 E F1 G H J1 K1 L M1 N P R1 S1 T1 V W Z(c,e,h,i,k,l,m,p,t)
Emergency Action, Agency, Advocacy, Fixed Fee Interview and Legal Aid undertaken
Ptr: Kieran, Mr Joseph P LLB . . . . . *Dec 1972
Asoc: Leek, Mrs Emma LLB. . . . . *Aug 2001
Ast: Roberts, Mr Nicholas J LLB . . . . . Dec 1988

LISTER BRADY ‡
Second Floor 54-55 Foregate Street Worcester Worcestershire WR1 1DX
Tel: 01905 20010 *Fax:* 01905 20050
E-mail: kenneth.lister@btconnect.com

LUMSDONS SOLICITORS LLP
(incorporating Bryan Colley & Co)
9-10 The Tything Worcester Worcestershire WR1 1HD
Tel: 01905 730670 *Fax:* 01905 613112 *Dx:* 716258 WORCESTER
Office: Stourport-on-Severn
Work: D1 D2 E F1 J1 K1 K3 L N O Q S1 S2 T1 T2 V W
Emergency Action, Agency, Advocacy, Fixed Fee Interview, Legal Aid undertaken and Member of Accident Line

MFG SOLICITORS
20-21 The Tything Worcester Worcestershire WR1 1HD
Tel: 01905 610410 *Fax:* 01905 610191 *Dx:* 716306 WORCESTER
E-mail: worcester@mfgsolicitors.com
Office: Bromsgrove, Halesowen, Kidderminster, Oswestry, Telford
Work: A1 B1 C1 D1 E F1 J1 K1 L N O Q S1 T1 V W Z(i)
Emergency Action, Agency, Advocacy, Fixed Fee Interview, Legal Aid undertaken, Legal Aid Franchise and Member of Accident Line
Ptr: Connolly, Mr Richard John Frederick . . . . . *§Nov 1993
Coyne, Mrs Sarah. . . . . *§Oct 1992
Hill, Mr F Peter G. . . . . *Oct 1972
MacKenzie, Ms Patricia J LLB; DipLP. . . . . *§Jun 1991
Morrison, Mr Iain . . . . . *§Oct 1995
Quinn, Mr James S C LLB . . . . . *§May 1964
Reynolds, Mrs Karen M BA(Law) . . . . . *§Nov 1985
Asoc: Holland, Ms Maureen BA . . . . . *§Jul 1976
Ast: Gowling, Mrs Serena . . . . . Aug 2001
Karim, Miss Safter LLB(Hons); LPC. . . . . *§May 1998
Leyland, Mr James Francis . . . . . *Sep 2002

PARKINSON WRIGHT LLP ‡
Haswell House St Nicholas Street Worcester Worcestershire WR1 1UN
Tel: 01905 726789 *Fax:* 01905 21363 *Dx:* 716257 WORCESTER
E-mail: worcester@parkinsonwright.co.uk
List of partners: C E Arridge, M A Blake, J R Gardner, D L Green, M Heath, D Houghton, P S Lewis, J R Newton, S Penn, J F Redfern, P G Scott, S A Smith
Office: Droitwich, Evesham
Work: A1 B1 C1 C2 C3 D1 D2 E F1 F2 J1 K1 K2 L M1 N O P Q R1 S1 S2 T1 T2 V W Z(b,c,d,e,h,i,j,k,l,m,o,p,q,r)
Emergency Action, Agency, Advocacy, Fixed Fee Interview, Legal Aid undertaken and Legal Aid Franchise
Ptr: Arridge, Mr Cyril E LLB . . . . . *Apr 1991
Blake, Mr Mark Andrew BA . . . . . *Jun 1989
Gardner, Miss Joanna R BSocSc . . . . . *Sep 2001
Green, Mr D Laurence . . . . . *Nov 1978
Heath, Mr Mark . . . . . Nov 1991
Lewis, Mr Peter S BA Deputy District Judge. . . . . *Nov 1983
Newton, Mrs Jean R LLB . . . . . *Apr 1980
Redfern, Mr Jeremy F LLB . . . . . *Oct 1987
Scott, Mr Peter G BA(Oxon). . . . . Mar 1971
Smith, Ms Sheila A . . . . . *May 1987
Asoc: Wilson, Miss Florence Sarah Russell LLB . . . . . Sep 2000
Ast: Cooper, Miss Dawn Katherine LLB . . . . . Apr 2002
Kelly, Miss Joanne LLB(Hons). . . . . *Jun 1998

PENSION PARTNERS ‡
The Old Rectory Church Lane Worcester Worcestershire WR2 6PF
Tel: 0845 050 6222 *Fax:* 01905 507800
E-mail: email@pensionpartners.co.uk

NEIL PRICE LAW ‡
Suite 9B Malvern Gate Bromwich Road Worcester Worcestershire WR2 4BN
Tel: 01905 422911 *Fax:* 01905 422914
E-mail: nprice@neilpricelaw.co.uk

QUANTUM SOLICITORS ‡
4 The Triangle Wildwood Drive Worcester Worcestershire WR5 2QX
Tel: 01905 673311 *Fax:* 01905 363533
E-mail: law@quantumsolicitors.co.uk
List of partners: J Wickstead
SPr: Wickstead, Mr John LLB . . . . . Mar 1976

SCAIFF LLP ‡
23 Foregate Street Worcester Worcestershire WR1 1DN
Tel: 01905 727700 *Fax:* 01905 29038 *Dx:* 716254 WORCESTER
E-mail: mail@scaiff.co.uk
List of partners: M J Bayliss, E H Rimell, P C Scaiff, S J Shaw, A J Wright
Work: B1 C1 C2 C3 D1 E J1 K1 L N P S1 T2 V W Z(c,e,r)
Emergency Action, Agency, Advocacy, Legal Aid undertaken and Member of Accident Line
Ptr: Bayliss, Mr Mervyn J BA . . . . . *Jun 1981
Rimell, Mrs Elizabeth Helen LLB(Hons) . . . . . *Aug 2002
Scaiff, Mr Peter C BSc . . . . . *May 1971
Shaw, Mr Simon J BSc . . . . . *Dec 1992
Wright, Mrs Amanda Jane BSc(Hons); LSF . . . . . *Nov 1995
Ast: Shaw, Mrs Juliette Margaret BA. . . . . *Nov 1995

STALLARD MARCH & EDWARDS ‡
8 Sansome Walk Worcester Worcestershire WR1 1LW
Tel: 01905 723561 *Fax:* 01905 723812 *Dx:* 716253 WORCESTER
E-mail: info@smesolicitors.co.uk
List of partners: P M H Beeching, T J Burt, M G Huskinson, J P Lewis, P Mucklow, B J N O'Connell, J O'Hora, S A Owen, R F W Stallard, W B Stallard, I R Stirzaker
Office: Worcester (2 offices)
Ptr: Huskinson, Mr Michael G LLB Notary Public. . . . . *Dec 1971
O'Connell, Mr Brian J N BSc . . . . . *Jul 1978
Stirzaker, Mr Ian Robert LLB ♦ . . . . . *Sep 1989
Asoc: Mullins, Mr Philip Michael BSc; CPE; LPL. . . . . *Oct 1996
Salter, Mr Guy Charles LLB . . . . . *Aug 1991
Ast: Richmond, Mrs Eileen. . . . . *Dec 1993

STALLARD MARCH & EDWARDS
2 & 3 Pierpoint Street Worcester Worcestershire WR1 1TD
Est: 1845
Tel: 01905 613404 *Fax:* 01905 726668 *Dx:* 716268 WORCESTER
E-mail: info@smesolicitors.co.uk
Office: Worcester (2 offices)
Work: A1 C1 C2 C3 D1 E F1 G H J1 K1 L M1 N O Q R1 R2 S1 S2 T2 V W Z(c,d,j,k,l,q,r)
Emergency Action, Agency and Advocacy undertaken
Ptr: Beeching, Mrs Patricia M H MA(Oxon) . . . . . *Oct 1981
Burt, Mr Timothy James LLB . . . . . Jan 1990
Lewis, Mr Jonathan P LLB . . . . . *Feb 1988
Mucklow, Mr Peter MA(Oxon). . . . . *Dec 1975
O'Hora, Ms Jasminka. . . . . Apr 1999
Owen, Mr Shaun A LLB. . . . . *Oct 1986
Stallard, Mr Richard Francis William LLB . . . . . *Jan 1992
Stallard, Mr William B MA; LLM(Cantab). . . . . Mar 1965
Asoc: Bendall, Mrs Ann E LLB(Hons) . . . . . *Jul 1980
Lawrence, Mrs Claire Jane Macrae LLB(Hons) . . . *Sep 1998
Ast: Miah, Mr Shazu LLB(Hons) . . . . . Mar 2006
Con: McGowan, Mrs Alyson Jean LLB(Hons). . . . . *Nov 1989

STALLARD MARCH & EDWARDS
19 Foregate Street Worcester Worcestershire WR1 1DS
Tel: 01905 613404 *Fax:* 01905 25772
E-mail: info@smesolicitors.co.uk
Office: Worcester (2 offices)

THURSFIELDS
42 Foregate Street Worcester Worcestershire WR1 1EF
Tel: 01905 730450 *Fax:* 01905 730499 *Dx:* 716251 WORCESTER
E-mail: info@thursfields.co.uk
Office: Kidderminster (2 offices), Stourport-on-Severn
Languages: British Sign Language, French, German, Hindi, Polish, Punjabi
Work: A1 B1 C1 C2 C3 D1 D2 E F1 G H J1 K1 K2 L N O Q R1 R2 S1 S2 T1 T2 V W Z(c,h,i,k,l,m,s,t)
Emergency Action, Agency, Advocacy, Fixed Fee Interview, Legal Aid undertaken, Legal Aid Franchise and Member of Accident Line
Ptr: Edwards, Mrs Ruth Edwina LLB. . . . . *§Dec 1990
Gammon, Mr Paul Nicholas LLB . . . . . *Apr 1979
Taylor, Mr David W LLB ★. . . . . *Oct 1982
Watkins, Mr Richard A J LLB . . . . . *Oct 1980
Asoc: Humes, Ms Susan Iona LLB(Hons); LSF. . . . . *Nov 1995
Humphreys, Mr Robin Harold LLB(Hons) . . . . . *Apr 1981
Wright, Mr Christopher James BA(Politics with History); LLB Notary Public . . . . . Oct 1998
Ast: Bonegal, Ms Judith Margaret LLB. . . . . Oct 1977
Hetheridge, Miss Michelle S LLB(Hons) . . . . . *Jul 2001
Mason, Miss Sarah A LLB(Hons) . . . . . *Oct 2001
Sheward, Mr Mark LLB(Hons). . . . . *Jan 2000
Terry, Miss Fiona LLB. . . . . *Oct 2001

WALDRONS
County House St Mary's Street Worcester Worcestershire WR1 1HB
Tel: 01384 811811 *Fax:* 01384 811833
Dx: 701422 BRIERLEY HILL 4
E-mail: lawyers@waldrons.co.uk
Office: Brierley Hill, Dudley, Kingswinford, Tipton, Walsall

WHATLEY WESTON & FOX ‡
15-16 The Tything Worcester Worcestershire WR1 1HD
Tel: 01905 731731 *Fax:* 01905 22347 *Dx:* 716264 WORCESTER
E-mail: office@wwf.co.uk
List of partners: A G Duncan, N B Horner, S M Lewis, R J P Musgrave, N Snowball, D J H Wotherspoon
Work: A1 B1 C1 C2 C3 D1 D2 E F1 J1 K1 K3 L N O P Q R2 S1 S2 T1 T2 U1 W Z(b,c,d,e,j,q,r)
Agency undertaken and Member of Accident Line
Ptr: Duncan, Mr Andrew G Deputy Lieutenant of Worcestershire; Under Sheriff of Worcester and Hereford; Clerk to General Commissioners of Income Tax; High Court Enforcement Officer . . . . . *§Mar 1970
Horner, Mr Nigel B LLB(Nott'm) Under Sheriff (City); Deputy Clerk to General Commissioners of Income Tax; High Court Enforcement Officer. . . . . *§Jun 1973
Lewis, Mrs Susan M BA(Hons) . . . . . *Oct 1990
Musgrave, Mr Richard J P LLB(Bris) Deputy District Judge . . . . . *§Sep 1978
Snowball, Mr Norman . . . . . *Jan 1983
Wotherspoon, Mr Douglas J H LLB(Hons). . . . . *Feb 1990
Ast: Vickery, Mr Charles R L BA(Hons). . . . . Sep 2002

THE WORCESTER FAMILY LAW PRACTICE ‡
34-35 Foregate Street Worcester Worcestershire WR1 1EE
Tel: 01905 730900 *Fax:* 01905 611621 *Dx:* 716274 WORCESTER
List of partners: P A Kemp
Work: D1 D2 K1 K2
Emergency Action, Agency, Advocacy, Fixed Fee Interview and Legal Aid undertaken
Ptr: Kemp, Mr Paul A LLB. . . . . *Mar 1977
Ast: Miles, Mrs Elizabeth BA(Hons) . . . . . *Sep 2004
Con: Andrew, Mrs Penelope BA(Hons) . . . . . *Jun 1992
Wright, Mr David G . . . . . *Jun 1966

WORCESTER PARK, Surrey

BRETT HOLT SOLICITORS ‡
138a Central Road Worcester Park Surrey KT4 8HW
Tel: 020 8337 0174 *Fax:* 020 8337 8305
Dx: 200800 WORCESTER PARK
E-mail: brettholt@qualitysolicitors.com
List of partners: R J Sudweeks, A L Woolford
Office: Epsom, Surbiton
Work: E J1 K1 L N O P Q S1 W
Agency undertaken
Ptr: Sudweeks, Mr Richard J . . . . . *§Jun 1971
Woolford, Mr Andrew L . . . . . Jun 1986

VIVASH HUNT ‡
(incorporating Gilling & Hounsome)
19-21 Central Road Worcester Park Surrey KT4 8EH
Tel: 020 8330 1961 *Fax:* 020 8330 7735
Dx: 200804 WORCESTER PARK
E-mail: arthur-barron@vivash-hunt.freeserve.co.uk
List of partners: A H Barron, M J Rowe, A W Saunders
Languages: French, Italian
Work: C1 C2 E J1 J2 K1 L N P R1 S1 S2 T1 T2 W Z(c,h,m)
Ptr: Barron, Mr Arthur H. . . . . *Oct 1972
Rowe, Mr Michael J. . . . . *Nov 1977
Saunders, Mr Andrew W . . . . . *Jan 1973
Ast: Boyd, Ms Catherine Elizabeth LLB . . . . . Sep 2002

WORKINGTON, Cumbria

BROCKBANK CURWEN CAIN & HALL
4 Portland Square Workington Cumbria CA14 4BH
Tel: 01900 603563 *Fax:* 01900 601239 *Dx:* 62851 WORKINGTON
E-mail: bt@brockbanks.co.uk
Office: Cockermouth, Keswick, Maryport, Whitehaven
Work: C1 D1 D2 G H J1 J2 K1 K2 K3 L N R1 S1 S2 V W Z(g,r)
Agency, Advocacy and Fixed Fee Interview undertaken
Dir: Hill, Ms Trudy LLB . . . . . *§Aug 2002
Taylor, Mr Richard P. . . . . *§Nov 1975
Woolaghan, Mr Michael Joseph LLB . . . . . *§Sep 1996
Ast: Foley, Mr Ryan LLB. . . . . *Jul 2006
Moffatt, Miss Hayley LLB . . . . . *Aug 2006
Con: Bailey, Mr Peter W MA(Oxon). . . . . *Jan 1976

K J COMMONS & CO ‡
2 Upper Jane Street Workington Cumbria CA14 4AY
Tel: 01900 604698 *Fax:* 01900 609439 *Dx:* 62855 WORKINGTON
E-mail: law@kjcommons.co.uk
List of partners: M P Nickson
Office: Carlisle, Whitehaven
Work: B1 D1 E G H J1 K1 L N O Q S1 W Z(j,k,l,r)
Emergency Action, Agency, Advocacy, Fixed Fee Interview, Legal Aid undertaken and Legal Aid Franchise
Ptr: Nickson, Mr Marcus P LLB . . . . . *§Nov 1977

MILBURNS SOLICITORS ‡
Oxford House 19 Oxford Street Workington Cumbria CA14 2AW
Tel: 01900 67363 *Fax:* 01900 65552 *Dx:* 62852 WORKINGTON
E-mail: workington@milburns.org
List of partners: E L Atkinson, R Atkinson, B Earl, N M Molyneaux, J C Moore, J E Shaw, D M Telford, P N Tupman
Office: Maryport, Whitehaven
Languages: French
Work: A1 B1 B3 C1 C2 C3 D1 D2 E F1 J1 K1 L M1 N O P Q R1 S1 V Z(c,h,j,l)
Emergency Action, Agency, Advocacy, Fixed Fee Interview, Legal Aid undertaken and Member of Accident Line
Ptr: Atkinson, Mrs Emma Louise LLB . . . . . *Oct 1996
Atkinson, Mr Richard . . . . . *Oct 1977
Earl, Mr Barry MA(Cantab) . . . . . *§Apr 1980
Molyneaux, Mr Nicholas M LLB . . . . . *Sep 1981
Moore, Mr John C LLB . . . . . *Dec 1980
Shaw, Ms Jane Elizabeth . . . . . Oct 1993
Telford, Mr David M LLB . . . . . *Apr 1968
Tupman, Mr Piers Nigel LLB . . . . . *§May 1994
Ast: Gibson, Mr Darren . . . . . Jan 2003
Nicholson, Mr Paul LLB. . . . . Oct 2007
Rothery, Ms Courtney LLB . . . . . May 2007
Stainton, Ms Tracy BA(Hons)(Durham) . . . . . *Jun 2005

PAISLEYS ‡
31 Jane Street Workington Cumbria CA14 3BN
Tel: 01900 602235 *Fax:* 01900 65766
E-mail: enquiries@paisleys.co.uk
List of partners: J Cooper, J S Kelly, D E Martin

See p112 for the Key to Work Categories & other symbols

Work: A1 C1 E F1 G H L N P R1 S1 S2 W Z(l)
Emergency Action, Advocacy, Legal Aid undertaken, Legal Aid Franchise and Member of Accident Line
Ptr: Cooper, Mr John . . . . . Oct 2005
Kelly, Mr Joseph S LLB(Hons) ★ Chairman of SSAT. . *Jun 1974
Martin, Mr David Edward BA . . . . . *Aug 2004
Ast: Twyford, Mr Paul . . . . . Dec 1980

MIKE POPE SOLICITOR ‡
22a Finkle Street Workington Cumbria CA14 2BB
Tel: 01900 608363 *Fax:* 01900 608363
List of partners: M Pope
SPr: Pope, Mr Michael . . . . . Feb 2001

WORKSOP, Nottinghamshire

FOYS SOLICITORS
102 Bridge Street Worksop Nottinghamshire S80 1HZ
Tel: 01909 473560 *Fax:* 01909 482760 *Dx:* 12207 WORKSOP
E-mail: info@foys.co.uk
Office: Doncaster, Rotherham, Sheffield (2 offices)
Work: C1 C2 D1 D2 E F1 F2 G H J1 J2 K1 L N O P Q R1 S1 S2 V W Z(e,k,l,p,q,r)
Emergency Action, Agency, Advocacy, Fixed Fee Interview, Legal Aid undertaken and Legal Aid Franchise
Ptr: Evans, Mr Paul DMA . . . . . *Oct 1976
Kite, Mr Gareth David Anthony BA(Hons) . . . . . *Aug 1999
Verity, Mr David A LLB . . . . . *Sep 1982
Ast: Lawson, Mr Hugh LLB . . . . . Jul 1998
Parlett, Mrs Michelle LLB . . . . . *Feb 2003
Reid, Mr Wayne. . . . . . *Nov 1994

ILETT & CLARK SOLICITORS ‡
86 Bridge Street Worksop Nottinghamshire S80 1JF
Tel: 01909 500544 *Fax:* 01909 505200 *Dx:* 12203 WORKSOP
E-mail: law@ilettclark.co.uk
List of partners: S F Fairweather, M E Murphy
Work: A1 A2 A3 C1 C2 C3 D1 D2 E F1 F2 J1 J2 K1 K2 K3 K4 L N O P Q R1 R2 S1 S2 T1 T2 U2 V W X Z(c,d,f,h,l,n,o,q,t,u,w)
Agency, Advocacy and Fixed Fee Interview undertaken
Ptr: Fairweather, Mr Simon F BA(Hons) . . . . . *Oct 1982
Murphy, Mr Matthew Edward LLB(Hons). . . . . *Jul 1989
Ast: Fairweather, Ms Hannah Jane LLB(Hons); MA . . . . . Jul 2010
Sorby, Mr Thomas David LLB(Hons) . . . . . *Jul 2005
Con: Clark, Mr Richard J . . . . . *Nov 1973

JACKSON QUINN
38 Potter Street Worksop Nottinghamshire S80 2AQ
Tel: 01909 480066 *Fax:* 01909 501033 *Dx:* 12209 WORKSOP
Office: Newark

DEAN THOMAS & CO ‡
120 Bridge Street Worksop Nottinghamshire S80 1HU
Tel: 01909 500511 *Fax:* 01909 500624 *Dx:* 12204 WORKSOP
Emergency telephone 01909 500511
List of partners: W J Dean, S Dixon, R J Morton, P E Tillcock
Office: Chesterfield, Retford
Work: A1 D1 G H J1 K1 L N P S1 W Z(k,l)
Emergency Action, Agency, Advocacy, Fixed Fee Interview, Legal Aid undertaken and Legal Aid Franchise
Ptr: Dean, Mr William John LLB(Sheff). . . . . *Jun 1976
Tillcock, Mrs Pauline E MA(Oxon). . . . . *Dec 1977
Asoc: Jones, Mr Peter LLB(Hons) . . . . . *Mar 1998

TRACEY BARLOW FURNISS & CO ‡
68-78 Bridge Street Worksop Nottinghamshire S80 1JE
Tel: 01909 472355 *Fax:* 01909 480193 *Dx:* 12205 WORKSOP
Emergency telephone 01623 794574
E-mail: michael@tbfsolicitors.co.uk
List of partners: D Grant, J Holt, M D Pryor
Office: Retford
Languages: French, German
Work: A1 B1 C1 D1 E F1 G H J1 K1 L N O Q R1 S1 S2 T1 T2 V W X Z(c,d,e,j,k,l,m,n,o,q,r,t)
Emergency Action, Agency, Advocacy, Fixed Fee Interview, Legal Aid undertaken, Legal Aid Franchise and Member of Accident Line
Ptr: Grant, Mr David LLB . . . . . *Dec 1974
Holt, Mrs Jane BA(Hons) . . . . . *Sep 1992
Pryor, Mr Michael David DML . . . . . *Mar 1984
Con: Barlow, Mr John K LLB . . . . . *Jun 1970

TURNER ATKINSON & WARD ‡
39 Potter Street Worksop Nottinghamshire S80 2AE
Tel: 01909 473489 *Fax:* 01909 478664 *Dx:* 12201 WORKSOP
Emergency telephone 01777 870215
List of partners: P J Ward
Office: Mansfield
Languages: French
Work: S1 W
Ptr: Ward, Mr Peter James . . . . . *§Feb 1973

WORMLEY, Surrey

ROUTLEDGE QUILL & CO ‡
Paddock Woods Wormley Surrey GU8 5TR
Tel: 01428 682589
List of partners: M A M Quill, A R Routledge
Work: C1 C2 E N S1 T1 T2 Z(b,e,f,j)
Emergency Action and Agency undertaken
Ptr: Quill, Ms Margaret Ann Mary LLB(Hons)(Lond) . . . . *Apr 1979
Routledge, Mr Allen Ronald . . . . . *Apr 1971

WORSLEY, Greater Manchester

PMN LAW ‡
168-170 Chaddock Lane Worsley Greater Manchester M28 1DF
Tel: 0161 799 0768 *Fax:* 0161 880 0345

QUALITYSOLICITORS GRUBER GARRATT (incorporating Vinings)
7 Barton Road Worsley Greater Manchester M28 2PD
Tel: 0161 794 7479 *Fax:* 0161 728 5198
Emergency telephone 07971 163241
E-mail: info@qsgrubergarratt.co.uk
Office: Ashton-under-Lyne, Oldham, Radcliffe, Stalybridge

LISA TONGE SOLICITORS ‡
Lower New Row Worsley Greater Manchester M28 1BE
Tel: 0161 241 6118 *Fax:* 0161 241 6738
E-mail: info@lisatongesolicitors.com
List of partners: L Tonge
Work: S1 S2 W
SPr: Tonge, Ms Lisa . . . . . *May 2000

WORTHING, West Sussex

AKERMANS ‡
Whitley House 32 Rowlands Road Worthing West Sussex BN11 3JP
Tel: 01903 820413 *Fax:* 01903 230075 *Dx:* 3714 WORTHING
List of partners: J H Akerman, A J Hammock, J M Jenkins, R J Kerslake
Office: Storrington
Work: B1 C1 D1 E F1 F2 G H J1 J2 K1 L N O Q S1 S2 T2 W Z(d,l,q)
Advocacy undertaken
Asoc: Ward, Mr Samuel LLB; LLM. . . . . *Jul 1992
Ast: Fairbank, Mrs Megan E BA . . . . . *Oct 1986

BENNETT GRIFFIN ‡
Shelley House 23 Warwick Street Worthing West Sussex BN11 3DG
Tel: 01903 229925 *Fax:* 01903 229166 *Dx:* 3706 WORTHING 1
Emergency telephone 01903 229949
E-mail: sjh@bennett-griffin.co.uk
List of partners: T E Barrett, P G Bennett, R Fawcett, S J Hollamby, C Kemp, P Kilby, I S Macara, E Smith
Office: Ferring, Rustington
Languages: French
Work: A1 A3 B1 B2 C1 C2 C3 D1 D2 E F1 F2 G H K1 K2 K3 L M1 M2 N O P Q R1 S2 T1 T2 Z(c,d,g,h,j,k,p,q)
Emergency Action, Agency, Advocacy, Fixed Fee Interview, Legal Aid Franchise and Member of Accident Line
Ptr: Barrett, Mr Tobias Ernest LLB. . . . . *Oct 1994
Hollamby, Mr Stephen James . . . . . *Jan 1987
Kemp, Chris. . . . . NSP
Asoc: Hind, Mr Nicholas Anthony BA . . . . . *Nov 1999
Mensah, Miss Jacqueline Nina BA(Law & Anthropology) . . . . . *Sep 1998

BRIGHTLAW LIMITED ‡
4 Longlands Spinney Worthing West Sussex BN14 9NU
Tel: 0345 652 2201 *Fax:* 0345 652 0013
E-mail: alex@brightlaw.biz

A R BROWN & CO ‡
Rivoli Chambers 77/79 Chapel Road Worthing West Sussex BN11 1HU
Tel: 01903 237118 *Fax:* 01903 231657 *Dx:* 3736 WORTHING
Emergency telephone 01903 247909
List of partners: A R Brown
Work: A1 C1 E F1 G K1 L M1 P R1 S1 W Z(c,l,s)
Emergency Action, Agency, Advocacy, Fixed Fee Interview, Legal Aid undertaken and Member of Accident Line
Ptr: Brown, Mr Alan R LLB(Lond) . . . . . *Jun 1971

BURNAND BRAZIER TISDALL
4-5 Aldsworth Parade Goring-by-Sea Worthing West Sussex BN12 4UA
Tel: 01903 502155 *Fax:* 01903 506731
Dx: 400503 GORING-BY-SEA 3
E-mail: law@bbt-goring.co.uk
Office: Hove, Worthing
Work: C1 C2 C3 D1 E F1 J1 K1 L N P Q S1 S2 T1 T2 V W Z(l,m)
Agency, Advocacy, Fixed Fee Interview and Legal Aid undertaken
Ptr: Latham, Mrs Julie Mary Notary Public. . . . . *Sep 1988
Sartin, Mrs Judith Margaret . . . . . *Feb 1984

BURNAND BRAZIER TISDALL
72 Broadwater Street West Worthing West Sussex BN14 9DH
Tel: 01903 235002 *Fax:* 01903 830636
Dx: 400503 GORING-BY-SEA 3
E-mail: law@bbt-bw.co.uk
Office: Hove, Worthing
Work: C1 E K1 N Q S1 T2 W
Emergency Action, Agency, Advocacy, Fixed Fee Interview, Legal Aid undertaken and Member of Accident Line
Ptr: Potter, Mr Anthony John LLB . . . . . *Jul 1976

BURT BRILL & CARDENS ‡
8 High Street Worthing West Sussex BN11 1NU
Tel: 01903 235196 *Fax:* 01273 570837

COOLE & HADDOCK ‡
5 The Steyne Worthing West Sussex BN11 3DT
Tel: 01903 213511 *Fax:* 01903 237053 *Dx:* 3717 WORTHING
E-mail: info@coolelaw.co.uk
List of partners: C M Bennett, W P Burke, N A Desoutter, F N F Haddock, S M Jones, J G Lacy, S P Loosemore, J L Murphy, A E Passmore, I M Swalwell
Office: Horsham
Work: A1 B1 C1 D1 E F1 G H J1 K1 L M1 N P Q R1 S1 T1 V W Z(b,c,d,h,j,k,l,p)
Emergency Action, Agency, Advocacy, Legal Aid undertaken and Legal Aid Franchise
Ptr: Burke, Mr W Paul. . . . . *Dec 1969
Jones, Mr Steven M. . . . . . Nov 1987
Loosemore, Mr Stephen P MA(Cantab) . . . . . Jun 1978
Swalwell, Mr Iain M MA. . . . . *Jun 1980

COOPERS SOLICITORS ‡
10 Marshall Avenue Findon Valley Worthing West Sussex BN14 0ES
Tel: 01903 872130
E-mail: info@coopers-solicitors.co.uk

CORCORANS ‡
113 South Street Tarring Worthing West Sussex BN14 7ND
Tel: 01903 824428 *Fax:* 01903 821085 *Dx:* 3711 WORTHING 1
Emergency telephone 01903 824428
E-mail: jac@corcorans.com
List of partners: J A Corcoran
Languages: French, German, Italian
Work: S1 W Z(l)
Emergency Action, Agency, Advocacy and Fixed Fee Interview undertaken
Ptr: Corcoran, Mr J Anthony MA(Cantab) . . . . . *§Apr 1982

THOMAS EGGAR LLP (in association with Avrio; The Bridge Group; Lexcel)
Arundel House 1 Liverpool Gardens Worthing West Sussex BN11 1SL
Tel: 01903 234411 *Fax:* 01903 207566 *Dx:* 3704 WORTHING
E-mail: worthing@thomaseggar.com
Office: Chichester, Crawley, London EC4, Newbury, Southampton
Work: A1 A2 A3 B1 B2 C1 C2 C3 D1 D2 E F1 F2 J1 J2 K1 K2 L M2 N O P Q R1 R2 S1 S2 T1 T2 U2 W X Z(b,c,d,e,g,m,o,p,q,r,s,t,x,y)

FINLAY SOLICITORS ‡
148 George V Avenue Worthing West Sussex BN11 5RX
Tel: 07976 371743 *Fax:* 01903 245041
E-mail: richardfinlay@finlaysolicitors.co.uk

GREEN WRIGHT CHALTON ANNIS ‡
13-14 Liverpool Terrace Worthing West Sussex BN11 1TQ
Tel: 01903 234064 *Fax:* 01903 200743 *Dx:* 3722 WORTHING
Emergency telephone 01903 234064
E-mail: enquiries@gwca.co.uk
Web: www.gwca.co.uk
List of partners: G J W Adams, E J Chatwell, J C F Ennis, A J Lewis, T Lewis, E Mason, C D Nestor, T L Parsons, J Rogers
Office: Arundel, Lancing, Rustington, Steyning, Worthing
Work: A1 B1 C1 C2 C3 D1 E F1 J1 K1 L N O Q R1 S1 S2 T2 V W Z(c,l,q)
Emergency Action, Agency, Advocacy and Fixed Fee Interview undertaken
Ptr: Adams, Mr Glyn John William LLB . . . . . *Jun 1983
Chatwell, Ms Emma Jane . . . . . *Oct 1996
Ennis, Mr Jerome C F. . . . . . *Jan 1978
Mason, Miss Elise LLB; IAC; MLIA(dip) . . . . . *Sep 2000
Nestor, Miss Christine D LLB(Hons). . . . . *Oct 2000
Parsons, Mr Timothy Leslie . . . . . *§May 1986
Rogers, Mr Jonathon . . . . . *Sep 2002
Lewis, Mr Tony . . . . . NSP
Ast: Carter, Miss Katie. . . . . . *Sep 2009
Clark, Mr Gavin LLB(Hons) . . . . . *Nov 2004
Collins, Mr Gareth Edward . . . . . Sep 2009
Dickson, Mr Malcolm James Neale . . . . . Jul 2011
Hoare, Ms Katie Louise . . . . . *Nov 2001
Smallman, Mr James Paul Bruno LLB. . . . . *Feb 1999
Con: Yates, Mr John T BA(Nott'm) . . . . . *§Apr 1976

Other offices in Rustington, Lancing, Worthing, Goring, Arundel and Steyning. Agency Commissions undertaken.

GREEN WRIGHT CHALTON ANNIS
305-7 Goring Road Goring-by-Sea Worthing West Sussex BN12 4NX
Tel: 01903 700220 *Fax:* 01903 505093 *Dx:* 3722 WORTHING
E-mail: enquiries@gwca.co.uk
Office: Arundel, Lancing, Rustington, Steyning, Worthing
Work: A1 C1 C2 C3 D1 E F1 J1 K1 L N O Q R1 S1 S2 T1 T2 V W Z(c,e,f,h,k,l,o)
Emergency Action, Agency, Advocacy, Fixed Fee Interview undertaken and Member of Accident Line
Ptr: Adams, Mr Glyn John William LLB . . . . . *Jun 1983

EDWARD HAYES LLP
11 Liverpool Terrace Worthing West Sussex BN11 1TA
Tel: 01903 215999 *Fax:* 01903 210310 *Dx:* 3749 WORTHING
Emergency telephone 0800 080 8596
E-mail: info@edwardhayes.co.uk
Office: Bognor Regis, Chichester (2 offices), Havant, Littlehampton, London EC2, London EC4
Work: B2 D1 D2 G H K1 K3
Legal Aid undertaken
Ast: Gozzett, Mr Neal LLB . . . . . *Mar 2007
Minns-Davies, Ms Louise ★. . . . . *May 2007
Rogers, Sonja. . . . . . May 2003

HENCHLEYS
196-198 Findon Road Worthing West Sussex BN14 0EJ
Tel: 01903 877657 *Fax:* 01903 874136 *Dx:* 57411 LITTLEHAMPTON
E-mail: henchleys@aol.com
Office: Littlehampton
Languages: French
Work: B1 E F1 F2 J1 K1 K3 L N O Q S1 S2 T2 W Z(g,k,l,m,q,r)
Agency and Fixed Fee Interview undertaken
Ast: Henchley, Miss Stephanie LLB(Hons) . . . . . Feb 2011

ROSEMARY E HENSBY ‡
20 Mulberry Lane Goring-by-Sea Worthing West Sussex BN12 4NS
Tel: 01903 244953 *Fax:* 01903 700338 *Dx:* 49802 GORING BY SEA

E B HURST ‡
63 Aldsworth Avenue Goring-by-Sea Worthing West Sussex BN12 4XG
Tel: 01903 246818 *Fax:* 01903 506968
Emergency telephone 01903 246818
List of partners: E B Hurst
Languages: French, Spanish
Work: E J1 K1 L N R1 S1 W X
Emergency Action, Agency and Fixed Fee Interview undertaken
SPr: Hurst, Mr Edward B LLB(Leeds). . . . . *Jan 1978

PETER KINGSHILL & CO ‡
7 Liverpool Terrace Worthing West Sussex BN11 1TA
Tel: 01903 218210 *Fax:* 01903 218211 *Dx:* 3707 WORTHING
E-mail: info@pkco.co.uk
List of partners: C M Sheffield
Work: E L N O Q S1 S2 W
Fixed Fee Interview undertaken
Ptr: Sheffield, Mr Christopher Michael BA(Oxon). . . . . *Nov 1980

LAWMOBILITY ‡
5 Lansdowne Place Worthing West Sussex BN11 5HD
Tel: 01903 500896 *Fax:* 01903 500818
Work: K1 S1 W

LINGS SOLICITORS ‡
110 George V Avenue Worthing West Sussex BN11 5RR
Tel: 01903 700303 *Fax:* 01903 700311
E-mail: john@lingssolicitors.co.uk
List of partners: J P Ling
Languages: French
Work: E L S1 W
Ptr: Ling, Mr John Patrick BA . . . . *Dec 1980

MALCOLM WILSON & COBBY ‡
Highworth 3 Liverpool Terrace Worthing West Sussex BN11 1TA
Tel: 01903 237581 *Fax:* 01903 200624 *Dx:* 3720 WORTHING
E-mail: sgt@mwcsolicitors.co.uk
List of partners: E J Alderson, N P Brazier, N C O Gifford, R J Wilson
Office: Lancing, Worthing
Languages: French
Work: L S1 S2 T2 W Z(l)
Ptr: Gifford, Mr Nigel C O LLB(Soton) . . . . *Nov 1985
Ast: Wells, Mr Michael John MA(Cantab). . . . . *Dec 1989

MALCOLM WILSON & COBBY
First Floor 74 Goring Road Worthing West Sussex BN12 4AF
Tel: 01903 244973 *Fax:* 01903 700018 *Dx:* 49808 GORING-BY-SEA
E-mail: ngifford@idnet.co.uk
Office: Lancing, Worthing
Work: L S1 S2 W
Agency undertaken
Ptr: Alderson, Mr Eric J . . . . *Dec 1968

MILLER PARRIS ‡
3-9 Cricketers Parade Broadwater Street West Worthing West Sussex BN14 8JB
Tel: 01903 205771 *Fax:* 01903 235402 *Dx:* 130135 WORTHING 5
E-mail: enquiries@millerparris.co.uk
List of partners: M J W Metters, C I Rockwood, M D Troy, V M Voakes
Work: B1 C1 C2 D1 E F1 J1 K1 L N Q R1 R2 S1 S2 T2 V W Z(j,q,r)
Emergency Action, Agency, Advocacy, Fixed Fee Interview, Legal Aid undertaken and Member of Accident Line
Ptr: Metters, Mr Michael J W LLB(Leics). . . . . *§Mar 1992
Rockwood, Ms Christina Isobel . . . . *§Dec 2000
Troy, Mr Martin D MA . . . . *§Apr 1992
Voakes, Miss Valerie M LLB. . . . . *§Jan 1982
Asoc: Fadoju, Mrs Nicola LLB . . . . Nov 1992
Fuhrmann, Mrs Carolyn BA; PGDipLaw . . . . Jun 2002

MYERS SOLICITORS ‡
10 Blackwater Street West Worthing West Sussex BN14 9DA
Tel: 01903 211088 *Fax:* 01903 236837
E-mail: arminius30k@googlemail.com

ANDREW MYERSON & CO ‡
40 Compton Avenue Boring By Sea Worthing West Sussex BN12 4UF
Tel: 01903 700961 *Fax:* 01903 536078
E-mail: andrewmyerson@compuserve.com
List of partners: A A J Myerson
Work: C1 E F1 J1 K1 L N Q S1 V W
Agency, Advocacy, Fixed Fee Interview and Legal Aid undertaken
Ptr: Myerson, Mr Alastair Andrew Jonathan LLB(Hons)(Lond); LLM(Lond) . . . . *Oct 1986

REAL ESTATE LAW LIMITED ‡
Columbia House Columbia Drive Worthing West Sussex BN13 3HD
Tel: 01903 263721 *Fax:* 01903 691727 *Dx:* 49803 GORING BY SEA
E-mail: brv@real-estate-law.co.uk

RICHARDSON SOLICITORS ‡
Columbia House Columbia Drive Worthing West Sussex BN13 3HD
Tel: 01903 831000 *Fax:* 01903 831000
E-mail: sohierichardson@btconnect.com

SPENCER HOWARD ‡
117 Shandon Road Worthing West Sussex BN14 9EA
Tel: 01903 538869 *Fax:* 01903 216679
Emergency telephone 07899 728176
E-mail: info@spencerhoward.org

SUMNER & MAIN ‡
Ashdown 123a Dominion Road Worthing West Sussex BN14 8LG
Tel: 01903 239420 *Fax:* 01903 239423 *Dx:* 130136 WORTHING 5
E-mail: info@summerandmain.co.uk
List of partners: L C Main, R L Sumner
Work: S1 W
Ptr: Main, Miss Laurenda Constance . . . . *Jan 1991
Sumner, Mrs Rosemary Lorna. . . . . *Jan 1983

SUSSEX DEFENCE SOLICITORS ‡
5 Selden Parade Salvington Road Worthing West Sussex BN13 2HL
Tel: 01903 261127 *Fax:* 01903 260282

SIMON TAYLOR SOLICITOR ‡
22 Upton Gardens Worthing West Sussex BN13 1DA
Tel: 01903 261580 *Fax:* 01903 261414
E-mail: simonntaylor@tiscali.co.uk

WANNOP FOX STAFFURTH & BRAY
Southfield House 11 Liverpool Gardens Worthing West Sussex BN11 1SD
Tel: 01903 228200 *Fax:* 01903 228201 *Dx:* 3701 WORTHING
E-mail: worthing@wfsblaw.com
Office: Bognor Regis, Chichester, Havant, Littlehampton, Worthing (2 offices)
Work: C1 E K1 K3 L R2 S1 S2 T2 W
Fixed Fee Interview undertaken
Ptr: Osborne, Mr Christopher BA(Hons) . . . . *Oct 1995
Seear, Mr Philip J. . . . . *Jan 1975
Asoc: Tutt, Ms Joanne Claire LLB(Hons). . . . . *Nov 1992
Con: Kent, Mr Robin Hilary Notary Public. . . . . *Nov 1970

WANNOP FOX STAFFURTH & BRAY
(incorporating Lynch Hall; Naunton & Bradley; Dixon Holmes & Cushing; Stuckey Carr & Piper Edis (Worthing Practice))
1 Chapel Road Worthing West Sussex BN11 1LJ
Tel: 01903 228200 *Fax:* 01903 228201 *Dx:* 3701 WORTHING
E-mail: worthing@wfsblaw.com
Office: Bognor Regis, Chichester, Havant, Littlehampton, Worthing (2 offices)
Languages: French, German, Punjabi
Work: B1 C1 D1 D2 E F1 F2 I J1 K1 K3 K4 L R1 R2 S1 S2 T2 U2 W Z(d,e,za)
Emergency Action, Agency, Advocacy, Fixed Fee Interview and Legal Aid undertaken
Mem: Dahill, Mrs Jane LLB(Hons) . . . . *Jun 1988
Fletcher, Miss Carol LLB(Hons) . . . . *Nov 1984
Asoc: Ursell, Mrs Lisa E LLB(Hons) . . . . *Oct 1992
Ast: Hothi, Miss Berinder LLB(Hons). . . . . *Oct 2008
Massie, Miss Kate LLB . . . . *Oct 2007
Smith, Mrs Alexandra LLB. . . . . *Feb 2007
Con: Edwards, Mrs Alison G BSc. . . . . *Dec 1997

WANNOP FOX STAFFURTH & BRAY
77 Portland Road Worthing West Sussex BN11 1QG
Tel: 01903 201120 *Fax:* 01903 200213
E-mail: wendyholmeslaw@hotmail.com
Office: Bognor Regis, Chichester, Havant, Littlehampton, Worthing (2 offices)
Work: E G H K1 K3 S1 S2 W
Emergency Action, Agency, Advocacy, Legal Aid undertaken and Legal Aid Franchise
Ptr: Albon, Mr Christopher. . . . . Sep 2000
Collett, Mr Stephen . . . . Nov 1995
Morgan, Mr Gareth . . . . Oct 1996

DENNIS J WEBB ‡
41 Longlands Worthing West Sussex BN14 9NW
Tel: 01903 236006 *Fax:* 01903 539979 *Dx:* 130140 WORTHING 5
E-mail: enquiries@denniswebb.co.uk
List of partners: D J Webb
Work: C1 E S1 S2
Fixed Fee Interview undertaken
SPr: Webb, Mr Dennis J . . . . Jun 1980

ALAN WHEATLEY ‡
40-41 New Broadway Tarring Worthing West Sussex BN11 4HS
Tel: 01903 216116 *Fax:* 01903 216027
List of partners: A Wheatley
Work: F1 J1 K3 N O Q S1 S2 W Z(q,r)
SPr: Wheatley, Mr Alan LLB . . . . *Jul 2001

WILLIAMS MACDOUGALL & CAMPBELL ‡
24 Liverpool Gardens Worthing West Sussex BN11 1RY
Tel: 01903 214186 *Fax:* 01903 215776 *Dx:* 3740 WORTHING 1
List of partners: A Bishop, C E Campbell, J Macdougall
Work: D1 D2 G H K1 K2 V
Emergency Action, Agency, Advocacy, Fixed Fee Interview, Legal Aid undertaken and Legal Aid Franchise
Ptr: Bishop, Mr Antony BA. . . . . *Oct 1994
Campbell, Ms Christine E BA; MSc . . . . *Apr 1984
Macdougall, Miss Jane LLB . . . . *Dec 1982
Ast: Blunden, Mrs Wendy . . . . *Nov 1978
Brown, Miss Margaret Joan LLB. . . . . *Nov 1994
Dray, Ms Fiona . . . . Oct 2006
Elves, Mrs Christine LLB . . . . *Apr 2000

WOTTON-UNDER-EDGE, Gloucestershire

RICHARD ERRIDGE & CO ‡
Bishops Farm Baden Hill Road Tytherington Wotton-under-Edge Gloucestershire GL12 8UG
Tel: 01454 418615 *Fax:* 01454 417365
Emergency telephone 01454 418615
E-mail: law@richarderridge.co.uk
List of partners: R Erridge
Work: A1 E K4 R2 S1 S2 W
SPr: Erridge, Mr Richard BA(Hons). . . . . *Mar 1989

LOXLEY LEGAL SERVICES LLP ‡
The Byre Woodend Farm Woodend Lane Wotton-under-Edge Gloucestershire GL12 8AA
Tel: 01453 700620 *Fax:* 01453 700183

STAFFORD EALES ‡
12 Turnpike Gate Wickwar Wotton-under-Edge Gloucestershire BS1 4PS
Tel: 0117 370 0500 *Fax:* 01454 294956
E-mail: peter@bristol.stafford-eales.co.uk
List of partners: P S Eales
Work: E L R2 S1 S2 W
Ptr: Eales, Mr Peter Stafford. . . . . *Feb 1971

WREXHAM

ABRAHAM & CO SOLICITORS ‡
55 King Street Wrexham LL11 1HR
Tel: 01978 291600 *Fax:* 01978 291602 *Dx:* 26678 WREXHAM
E-mail: mail@abrahamsolicitors.co.uk

ALLINGTON HUGHES ‡
10 Grosvenor Road Wrexham LL11 1SD
Tel: 01978 291000 *Fax:* 01978 290493 *Dx:* 26651 WREXHAM
Emergency telephone 07644 067157
E-mail: enquiriesw@allingtonhughes.co.uk
List of partners: J A Clayton, J A Partington
Office: Chester
Languages: Welsh
Work: A1 B1 B2 C1 C2 C3 D1 D2 E F1 G H J1 J2 K1 L M1 N O P Q R1 S1 S2 T1 T2 V W Z(c,d,e,h,l,m,p,q)
Emergency Action, Agency, Advocacy, Fixed Fee Interview, Legal Aid undertaken and Legal Aid Franchise

THOMAS ANDREWS & PARTNERS ‡
31 High Street Wrexham LL13 8HY
Tel: 01978 291506 *Fax:* 01978 358793 *Dx:* 26653 WREXHAM
List of partners: P Andrews, C L McGuire, R J M Thomas
Office: Bala
Languages: Welsh
Work: A1 B1 C1 C2 D1 E F1 G H J1 K1 L N P R1 S1 T1 V W
Emergency Action, Agency, Advocacy, Fixed Fee Interview, Legal Aid undertaken, Legal Aid Franchise and Member of Accident Line
Ptr: Andrews, Mr Paul LLB(Wales). . . . . Dec 1975
McGuire, Miss Caroline L LLB(Wales). . . . . Sep 1980
Thomas, Mr Robert J M LLB . . . . Jun 1976

DAVID BIGMORE & CO ‡
(in association with Goodman Derrick LLP)
Thornton Grange Chester Road Gresford Wrexham LL12 8NU
Tel: 01978 855058 *Fax:* 01978 854623 *Dx:* 26673 WREXHAM
E-mail: db@dbigmore.co.uk
List of partners: D Bigmore
Languages: French
Work: C1 Z(e)
Ptr: Bigmore, Mr David BA(Oxon) Sole Practitioner of the Year - Welsh Law Awards November 2004. . . . . *Apr 1972

GHP LEGAL ‡
(incorporating Charles Richards & Sons; Edmund Pickles & Upton; Brown & Lloyd)
26-30 Grosvenor Road Wrexham LL11 1BU
Tel: 01978 291456 *Fax:* 01978 291716 *Dx:* 26663 WREXHAM
E-mail: wrexham@ghplegal.co.uk
List of partners: P J Butler, J S P Edwards, J A Hulme, E H Jones, J A Lancaster, E R Lloyd, J Marshall, P R Whitley, A V Williams, R D Williams
Office: Llangollen, Oswestry
Languages: Welsh
Work: A1 C1 D1 E F1 F2 G H J1 K1 L M1 M2 N O P Q R1 S1 S2 W Z(c,d,e,l,m)
Emergency Action, Agency, Advocacy, Fixed Fee Interview, Legal Aid undertaken, Legal Aid Franchise and Member of Accident Line
Ptr: Butler, Mr Peter J LLB(Cantab); LLB(Wales) ♦. . . . . *Oct 1978
Edwards, Mr J Stephen P LLB ★ . . . . *Oct 1982
Jones, Mr Euros Huw LLB. . . . . Apr 2003
Lancaster, Mr John A LLB(Law & Politics) ♦. . . . . . *Apr 1984
Marshall, Mr John BA . . . . Aug 2001
Whitley, Miss Pamela R LLB(Hons) . . . . *Dec 1979
Williams, Mr Alun Vaughan LLB ★. . . . . *Mar 1995
Williams, Mr Robert David BSc(Hons). . . . . Feb 1993
Ast: Blakemore, Mr Peter John. . . . . Sep 2009
Davies, Miss Anne LLB; MA. . . . . Aug 1989
Hughes, Mrs Christine Roberta . . . . Mar 2002
Kenny, Mrs Elzbeth BA . . . . Jul 2004
Lewis, Mrs Ceri-Anne . . . . Jan 2007
Marles, Mrs Wendy P LLB. . . . . Mar 1998
Shearer, Miss Amy Claire . . . . Jul 2009
Talog Davies, Mr Robert Idris LLB(Hons); CIArb. . . *§Nov 1996
Thomas, Mr Stuart Phillip . . . . Mar 2009
Waters, Mr Rodney BA . . . . *Oct 1989
Wright, Mr Nathan LLB . . . . Apr 2007

GEOFFREY MORRIS & ASHTON ‡
39 King Street Wrexham LL11 1HR
Tel: 01978 291322 *Fax:* 01978 295700 *Dx:* 26658 WREXHAM
Emergency telephone 07950 030105
E-mail: enquiries@wrexhamsolicitors.co.uk
List of partners: R M Davies, K Faulkner, A Holmes, C L Hulmes
Office: Mold
Languages: Welsh
Work: A1 B1 C1 D1 D2 E F1 G H J1 K1 K3 L M1 N P Q R1 S1 S2 T1 W Z(c,m,u,y)
Emergency Action, Agency, Advocacy, Fixed Fee Interview, Legal Aid undertaken, Legal Aid Franchise and Member of Accident Line
Ptr: Davies, Mr R Mark LLB(Wales); ACIArb ★. . . . . . *§Mar 1985
Holmes, Mr Andrew LLB . . . . *Jan 1981
Hulmes, Ms Ceri Lynne . . . . *Feb 2003
Ast: Edwards, Berwyn LLB. . . . . *Jun 1975
Con: Prosser, Mr Dafydd LLB. . . . . *Jun 1963

GITTINS MCDONALD ‡
Marbel House Overton Arcade High Street Wrexham LL13 8LL
Tel: 01978 291662 *Fax:* 01978 362893 *Dx:* 26675 WREXHAM
Emergency telephone 01829 271457
E-mail: post@gittins-mcdonald.co.uk
List of partners: K Champaneria, B Gittins, J A Gittins, K M McDonald
Languages: Gujarati
Work: B1 D1 D2 E F1 F2 G H J1 J2 K1 K3 L N O Q R2 S1 S2 V W Z(f,l,r,u)
Emergency Action, Agency, Fixed Fee Interview, Legal Aid undertaken and Legal Aid Franchise
Ptr: Champaneria, Mr Kirit BA(Law) . . . . *May 1989
Gittins, Bharti . . . . *Oct 1989
Gittins, Mr John A Deputy Coroner . . . . *Oct 1988
McDonald, Ms Kathryn M LLB. . . . . *Oct 1986

HILLYER MCKEOWN LLP
The Racecourse Wrexham Football Club Mold Road Wrexham LL11 2AH
Tel: 01978 229346
Office: Bebington, Chester

HOPLEY PIERCE & BIRD ‡
5 King Street Wrexham LL11 1HF
Tel: 01978 315100 *Fax:* 01978 315101 *Dx:* 26659 WREXHAM
E-mail: jl@hpblaw.co.uk
List of partners: D N Bird, J P Marsland, C P Ridgway
Work: D2 E F1 J1 K1 K4 L Q S1 S2 T2 W
Emergency Action and Agency undertaken
Ptr: Bird, Mr David Nigel MA(Oxon) . . . . *Nov 1987
Marsland, Ms Jacqueline Patricia LLB. . . . . *Jul 1998
Ridgway, Mr C Peter LLB . . . . *Dec 1972

HUMPHRYS & CO
26 Chester Street Wrexham LL13 8BG
Tel: 01978 313399 *Fax:* 01978 266200
Emergency telephone 01978 266366
E-mail: law@humphrys.co.uk
Office: Colwyn Bay, Rhyl
Work: D1 D2 G H K1 N Q
Emergency Action, Advocacy, Legal Aid undertaken and Legal Aid Franchise
Ptr: Humphrys, Ms Caroline BA(Leeds) . . . . *Apr 1978
Humphrys, Mr James C. . . . . *Oct 1978
Newnes, Mr Antony N BA Notary Public. . . . . *Dec 1979

CYRIL JONES & CO ‡
19 Grosvenor Road Wrexham LL11 1DE
Tel: 01978 367830 *Fax:* 01978 367831 *Dx:* 26661 WREXHAM
Emergency telephone 01978 832001
E-mail: glen.murphy@cyril-jones.co.uk
List of partners: M Cunnah, S Fisher, G Jones, G V Kelly, G V Murphy, S Williams
Office: Shotton, Wrexham
Languages: Polish, Urdu, Welsh
Work: A1 B1 C1 D1 E F1 J1 K1 K4 L N Q R2 S1 S2 T2 W Z(e)
Agency undertaken
Ptr: Jones, Mr Gareth BA . . . . *Nov 1976
Kelly, Mr Gareth V LLB; LLM . . . . *§Dec 1986
Williams, Mrs Sali LLB . . . . *Apr 1973
Fisher, Sian FILEx . . . . .NSP

CYRIL JONES & CO
17 Egerton Street Wrexham LL11 1NB
Tel: 01978 263131 *Fax:* 01978 290530 *Dx:* 26661 WREXHAM
Emergency telephone 01978 263083 / 354256
E-mail: glen.murphy@cyril-jones.co.uk
Office: Shotton, Wrexham
Languages: Polish
Work: D1 E F1 G H J1 J2 K1 L N Q R1 S1 S2 V W Z(h,j,l,n,o,p,q,r)
Emergency Action, Agency, Advocacy, Fixed Fee Interview and Legal Aid undertaken
Ptr: Murphy, Mr Glen V BA . . . . *§Jun 1981

BARRY MACLOSKEY SOLICITORS ‡
Thornton Grange Chester Road Gresford Wrexham LL12 8NU
Est: 1985
Tel: 01978 852485 *Fax:* 01978 854612 *Dx:* 26660 WREXHAM
Emergency telephone 01978 852485
E-mail: macloskey@mac.com
List of partners: B M Macloskey
Work: F1 K1 K3 K4 N O Q S1 S2 W
Fixed Fee Interview undertaken
SPr: Macloskey, Mr Barry M MA(Cantab). . . . . *Dec 1981
Con: Macloskey, Mr Mark C L LLB . . . . *Feb 1985

DAVID SPALDING SOLICITORS ‡
Weston House Narrow Lane Gresford Wrexham LL12 8EN
Tel: 01978 851688 *Fax:* 01978 851724
E-mail: david@davidspalding.co.uk

TUDOR WILLIAMS & CO ‡
27 Chester Street Wrexham LL13 8BG
Tel: 01978 362006 *Fax:* 01978 356635
E-mail: tudorwilliams@micro-plus-web.net
List of partners: T Williams
Languages: Welsh
Work: J1 J2 M1 P R1 S1 W X Z(d,g,p)
Agency and Advocacy undertaken
Ptr: Williams, Mr Tudor LLB; MSc; MCIArb ● . . . . *Nov 1972

WALKER SMITH WAY
23 Chester Street Wrexham LL13 8BG
Tel: 0844 346 3100 *Fax:* 0844 346 3200 *Dx:* 721920 WREXHAM 4
E-mail: enquiries@walkersmithway.com
Office: Ashton-under-Lyne, Birmingham, Chester, Liverpool, London SW11
Languages: French, Welsh
Work: A1 D1 E F1 G H J1 K1 K2 K3 K4 L N O P Q R1 S1 S2 T2 W Z(c,k,n,p,q,r)
Emergency Action, Agency, Advocacy, Fixed Fee Interview, Legal Aid undertaken and Legal Aid Franchise
Ptr: Denholm, Mr Mark G LLB. . . . . *May 1992
Elliott, Mr Martyn Andrew LLB(Hons) . . . . *Sep 2000
Lewis, Mr Ian Brynmor LLB(Wales) . . . . *Oct 1984
Lewis, Mr J Martin LLB(Wales) . . . . *§Oct 1978
Rudd, Mr David C LLB(L'pool). . . . . *§Jun 1977
Sharples, Mr Jonathon LLB(Hons). . . . . *Jan 1994
Turnbull, Mr Neil Harper LLB . . . . *§Oct 1993
Vasmer, Mrs Rachael Mary LLB. . . . . *Oct 1989
Wynn-Jones, Ms Rachel LLB . . . . *Nov 1995
Ast: Hughes, Mr Darren . . . . *Sep 2003
Hughes, Mrs Patricia F LLB. . . . . Mar 1984
Jones, Miss Lisa Marie . . . . *Sep 2003
Lowe, Miss Jennifer Louise . . . . *Jul 2004
Watling, Mr Stephen John. . . . . *Dec 2002

WHITEHEAD WOODWARD & CO ‡
Gleniffer House Hoseley Lane Marford Wrexham LL12 8YE
Tel: 01978 855478 *Fax:* 01978 856817 *Dx:* 26677 WREXHAM
E-mail: fwhitehead@wwsolicitors.co.uk
List of partners: F Whitehead
Work: J1 L S1 S2 W
Ptr: Whitehead, Mr Francis BA(Hons) . . . . *Nov 1993

WRINGTON, North Somerset

BENNETTS SOLICITORS ATTORNEYS & NOTARIES ‡ (in association with Fryer Collett)
High Street Wrington North Somerset BS40 5QB
Tel: 01934 862786 *Fax:* 01934 862404 *Dx:* 96357 YATTON
E-mail: info@bennettlaw.co.uk
List of partners: K M Burke, L Hamer, F G D Montagu, F I Pearce, A R Reed, A G Reed
Languages: French, Spanish
Work: A1 A2 B1 C1 C2 C3 E F1 F2 J1 K1 K3 K4 L M2 N O P Q R1 R2 S1 S2 T1 T2 W X Z(c,d,e,i,k,l,o,p,q)
Agency and Advocacy undertaken
Ptr: Burke, Mr Kevin M Dr Jur(USA); AMF; AMO Notary Public . . . . *Mar 1999
Hamer, Mr Lee LLB(Hons); PGDip . . . . *May 2004
Montagu, Mr Francis Gerard Drogo MA(Cantab). . . . *Jun 1978
Pearce, Mrs Florence Isabel BSc(Hons); PGDip. . . . Mar 2003
Reed, Ms Alison G . . . . *Dec 1974
Reed, Mr Alan R Hampshire Law Prize 1970 Deputy District Judge. . . . . *Dec 1970
Ast: Wallington, Miss Hannah Lucy. . . . . *Jul 2007
Whittaker, Miss Sara LLB(Hons); LPC. . . . . Jan 2009

WROXHAM, Norfolk

CAPRON & HELLIWELL
Broads Centre Wroxham Norfolk NR12 8AJ
Tel: 01603 783818 *Fax:* 01603 784083 *Dx:* 85150 WROXHAM
Office: Stalham
Work: A1 C1 E L S1 T1 T2 V W Z(c,l)
Ptr: Little, Miss Lindsay Dianne BA . . . . *Oct 1985
Ast: Clarke, Mr Brynley R BA . . . . *Oct 1982
Con: Lucking, Miss Nicola A L LLB . . . . *§Sep 1974

LAWRENCE WOOD ‡
Old Mill The Bridge Wroxham Norfolk NR12 8DA
Tel: 01603 783711 *Fax:* 01603 784105 *Dx:* 85151 WROXHAM
E-mail: legal@paston.co.uk
List of partners: J S Lawrence, T K Quint
Work: E L S1 S2 W
Ptr: Lawrence, Mr John S . . . . *Jun 1977
Quint, Mr Timothy K LLB . . . . *Jul 1988

WYMONDHAM, Norfolk

FOSTERS (incorporating Russell Steward)
1 Middleton Street Wymondham Norfolk NR18 0AB
Tel: 01953 607724 *Fax:* 01953 607845 *Dx:* 43152 WYMONDHAM
E-mail: enquiries@fosters-solicitors.co.uk
Office: Bungay, Lowestoft, Norwich

GREENLAND HOUCHEN POMEROY
5-7 Church Street Wymondham Norfolk NR18 0PP
Tel: 01953 606351 *Fax:* 01953 601268
Office: Attleborough, Long Stratton, Norwich, Watton
Work: A1 C1 E J1 K1 K2 K3 K4 O Q R1 S1 S2 W
Agency, Advocacy, Fixed Fee Interview and Legal Aid undertaken
Ptr: Cook, Mr Peter Miles LLB(Manc) . . . . *Jun 1980

MORONEYS
10-12 Damgate Street Wymondham Norfolk NR18 0BQ
Tel: 01953 607042 *Fax:* 01953 607511 *Dx:* 44001 ATTLEBOROUGH
Emergency telephone 01953 603234
E-mail: moroneysolicitor@aol.com
Office: Attleborough
Work: A1 C1 D1 F1 G K1 N P Q S1 W
Emergency Action, Agency and Advocacy undertaken
Ptr: Moroney, Mr Lawrence A J . . . . *§Jan 1971

YARM, Stockton-on-Tees

FORTH & CO ‡
21 High Street Yarm Stockton-on-Tees TS15 9BW
Tel: 01642 784000 *Fax:* 01642 788500 *Dx:* 60082 YARM
E-mail: info@forths.co.uk
List of partners: T E Forth
Work: A1 A3 B1 C1 C2 E F1 J1 L N O Q S1 S2 W Z(l)
Ptr: Forth, Mr T Edward LLB. . . . . *Feb 1980
Asoc: Ivanec, Mr Roman J BSocSc . . . . *Oct 1988
Jenyns, Mr Hugh B . . . . *§Dec 1976
Con: Harvard, Mr John Clive de Jersey MA(Cantab) . . . *May 1966

MERRITT & CO ‡
Manor House 83 High Street Yarm Stockton-on-Tees TS15 9BG
Tel: 01642 885555 *Fax:* 01642 875174 *Dx:* 60080 YARM
E-mail: jab@merritts-solicitors.co.uk
List of partners: H Baxter, N Coward, A Goncalves, D M Holtham, P W Johnstone, G Moran
Work: A1 B1 C1 E F1 J1 K1 L M1 N O P Q R1 S1 S2 T1 W Z(d,h,i,k,l,q,t)
Emergency Action, Agency, Advocacy undertaken and Member of Accident Line
Ptr: Baxter, Mrs Helen LLB . . . . *Oct 1991
Coward, Mr Noel MA(Cantab). . . . . *May 1967
Goncalves, Mrs Alison LLB . . . . *Feb 2000
Holtham, Mr David M LLB. . . . . *Jun 1973
Johnstone, Mr Paul William LLB. . . . . *Nov 1982
Moran, Mr Gerard LLB . . . . *Dec 1979

YATE, South Gloucestershire

WARDS SOLICITORS
19 West Walk Yate South Gloucestershire BS37 4AX
Tel: 01454 316789 *Fax:* 01454 316333 *Dx:* 47266 YATE
E-mail: info@wards.uk.com
Office: Bristol (2 offices), Clevedon, Nailsea, Portishead, Staple Hill, Weston-super-Mare (3 offices)
Work: C1 C2 D1 E F1 F2 J1 K1 K3 K4 L N O Q S1 S2 W Z(d,e)
Emergency Action, Agency, Fixed Fee Interview and Legal Aid undertaken
Ptr: Murray, Mr Nigel J LLB(Lond) . . . . *Oct 1975

YATELEY, Hampshire

EVE COLLMANS ‡
72a Reading Road Yateley Hampshire GU46 7UH
Tel: 01252 404456 *Fax:* 01252 860397 *Dx:* 94352 YATELEY

DAVIES BLUNDEN & EVANS
68a Reading Road Yateley Hampshire GU46 7UJ
Tel: 01252 872617 *Fax:* 01252 874999 *Dx:* 94351 YATELEY
Emergency telephone 07973 408686
E-mail: yateley@dbande.co.uk
Office: Farnborough
Work: B2 D1 E G H J1 K1 L N S1 S2 W
Agency, Advocacy, Legal Aid undertaken and Member of Accident Line

LGFL LLP ‡
Top Floor Saddlers Court 94 Reading Road Yateley Hampshire GU46 7RX
Tel: 01252 877327 *Fax:* 01252 873048
E-mail: enquiries@lgfamilylawyers.co.uk
List of partners: R Gupta, A Leiper
Ptr: Gupta, Rita . . . . Jan 1995
Leiper, Anne . . . . Jan 1986

YATTON, North Somerset

JOHN HODGE SOLICITORS
50 High Street Yatton North Somerset BS49 4HJ
Tel: 01934 833208 *Fax:* 01934 876261 *Dx:* 96350 YATTON
E-mail: mailbox@johnhodge.co.uk
Office: Bristol, Clevedon, Wedmore, Weston-super-Mare (2 offices)
Languages: French
Work: A1 B1 C1 C3 E F1 J1 K1 K3 K4 L M1 O P Q S1 S2 W Z(p,q,r)
Fixed Fee Interview undertaken

YEADON, West Yorkshire

MORRISH SOLICITORS LLP
61 High Street Yeadon West Yorkshire LS19 7SP
Tel: 0113 250 7792 *Fax:* 0113 250 0289
E-mail: info@morrishsolicitors.com
Office: Bradford, Leeds, Pudsey
Work: K4 S1 W
Agency undertaken and Member of Accident Line
Ptr: Morrish, Mr Thomas Wade MA(Cantab) . . . . *May 1992

YEOVIL, Somerset

BPL SOLICITORS LTD
First Floor Mansion House Princes Street Yeovil Somerset BA20 1EQ
Tel: 0845 345 3131 *Fax:* 0845 072 3162 *Dx:* 100511 YEOVIL
E-mail: info@bplaw.co.uk
Office: Dorchester

BANNISTER & CO ‡
90 Huish Yeovil Somerset BA20 1AQ
Tel: 01935 433133 *Fax:* 01935 410253
E-mail: info@bannisterandco.co.uk
List of partners: J P Bannister
Work: G H Z(l)
Emergency Action, Agency, Advocacy, Fixed Fee Interview, Legal Aid undertaken and Legal Aid Franchise
SPr: Bannister, Mr Jeffrey Paul BA. . . . . *Dec 1981

BATTENS ‡
Mansion House Princes Street Yeovil Somerset BA20 1EP
Tel: 01935 846000 *Fax:* 01935 846001 *Dx:* 100503 YEOVIL
E-mail: webenquiry@battens.co.uk
List of partners: S R Allen, D H C Batten, D M Bell, M R Blackmore, W D Christopher, M Davis, R M Edwards, J E P Haran, J Hayes, G J Hughes, C M May, R A Paul, D C Stephens, A H Thompson, C I Thompson, W R C Unwin, R J Vaughan
Office: Dorchester, Sherborne, Weymouth
Languages: French, German
Work: A1 A2 B1 C1 C2 C3 D1 D2 E F1 F2 J1 J2 K1 K2 L M1 M2 N O P Q R1 R2 S1 S2 T1 T2 V W X Z(b,c,d,e,f,h,j,k,l,m,o,p,q,r,s,t,u,w,x)
Emergency Action, Agency, Advocacy, Fixed Fee Interview, Legal Aid undertaken, Legal Aid Franchise and Member of Accident Line
Ptr: Allen, Mr Stuart R MA(Oxon) . . . . *§Oct 1981
Batten, Mr David H C Clerk to Commissioner of Taxes *Nov 1976
Edwards, Mr Raymond M BA(Law) . . . . *§Jun 1972
Haran, Mr J E Patrick . . . . *Jul 1966
Hayes, Mr Julian LLB(Lond). . . . . *Apr 1981
Hughes, Mr Graham J. . . . . *§May 1977
May, Mr Christopher M LLB . . . . *Oct 1983
Paul, Mr Roger A LLB. . . . . *Sep 1987
Stephens, Mr David C LLB(Wales) . . . . *Jun 1977
Thompson, Mrs Angela H BA . . . . *Oct 1983
Unwin, Mr W Robert C MA(Oxon) Deputy District Judge . . . . *§Dec 1975
Vaughan, Mr Rupert J. . . . . *§Nov 1978
Asoc: Bridge, Mr David . . . . *Dec 1994
Ast: Ager, Mr David G BA(Hons). . . . . *§Jun 1977
Bovell, Mr John P A LLB . . . . Sep 1999
de Quidt, Mrs Elizabeth J LLB. . . . . Nov 1983
Reeves, Mr Christopher James MCIOB . . . . *Sep 2001
Stephens, Ms Ceri Ann . . . . Sep 2000
Weatherill, Ms Leanne M . . . . *Nov 1996
Con: Bogaardt, Ms Jean M . . . . *Dec 1979

MORNEMENTS SOLICITORS ‡
Burton Cottage Farm East Coker Yeovil Somerset BA22 9LS
Est: 1999
Tel: 01935 863333 *Fax:* 01935 863323
E-mail: mornements@bcfcoker.co.uk
Work: K1 L Q S1 S2 W Z(b,d,h)

MORTON LAW ASSOCIATES ‡
Court Ash House Court Ash Yeovil Somerset BA20 1HG
Tel: 01935 310500 *Fax:* 01935 310501 *Dx:* 100517 YEOVIL
E-mail: susan.may@mortonlaw.co.uk

PARDOES
Glenthorne House Princes Street Yeovil Somerset BA20 1EJ
Tel: 01935 382680 *Fax:* 01935 476150 *Dx:* 100500 YEOVIL
Office: Bridgwater, Taunton
Ptr: Hughes, Mr Michael D BA(Keele) ★. . . . . *Dec 1973
Middle, Mr Keith E LLB(Leeds) . . . . *Jun 1979
Rich, Mr Jonathan. . . . . Jan 1992
Ast: Driscoll, Miss Sarah LLB . . . . Sep 2009

PORTER DODSON ‡
Central House Church Street Yeovil Somerset BA20 1HH
Tel: 01935 424581 *Fax:* 01935 706063 *Dx:* 100501 YEOVIL
E-mail: porterdodson@porterdodson.co.uk
Office: Dorchester, Sherborne, Taunton, Wellington
Languages: French, German, Portuguese, Spanish
Work: A1 A3 B1 B2 C1 C2 C3 D1 D2 E F1 F2 G H I J1 J2 K1 K2 L M1 M2 N O P Q R1 R2 S1 S2 T1 T2 V W Z(b,c,d,e,f,h,i,j,k,l,m,o,p,q,s,w)

SLATER RHODES SOLICITORS ‡
Abbey Manor Business Centre The Abbey 200 Preston Road Yeovil Somerset BA20 2EN
Tel: 01935 848595 *Fax:* 01935 848594
E-mail: mail@slater-rhodes.com

GARETH WEBB & CO SOLICITORS ‡
5 Church Terrace Yeovil Somerset BA20 1HX
Tel: 01935 428885

JEREMY WOOD & CO ‡
1a Princes Street Yeovil Somerset BA20 1EN
Tel: 01935 426047 *Fax:* 01935 427890 *Dx:* 100508 YEOVIL
E-mail: yeovil@jeremywood.co.uk
List of partners: H L Wishart, C J Wood
Work: E K1 L N Q S1 S2 W Z(k)
Emergency Action, Agency and Advocacy undertaken
Ptr: Wishart, Mrs H Laura . . . . *Oct 1992
Wood, Mr Charles Jeremy. . . . . *Nov 1970

YIEWSLEY, Middlesex

HINE SOLICITORS
18d Fairfield Road Yiewsley Middlesex UB7 8EX
Tel: 01895 443317 *Fax:* 01895 421419 *Dx:* 47660 WEST DRAYTON
Office: Beaconsfield, Bracknell, Cheltenham, Gerrards Cross, Oxford, Princes Risborough, Swindon

YORK

THE AFFORDABLE LAW CO LTD ‡
25 Boroughbridge Road York YO26 5RT
Tel: 01904 788877 *Fax:* 01904 788876
Emergency telephone 01904 632244
E-mail: info@philipcrowe.co.uk
List of partners: P Crowe
Work: E G H J1 K1 N O Q S1 S2 W Z(k,l,q,r)
Emergency Action, Agency, Advocacy and Fixed Fee Interview undertaken
SPr: Crowe, Mr Philip . . . . *§Nov 1975

APPLEYARD LEES
Innovation Centre York Science Park Heslington York YO10 5DG
Tel: 01904 567973 *Fax:* 01904 567975
E-mail: york@appleyardlees.com
Office: Burnley, Chester, Halifax, Harrogate, Huddersfield, Leeds, Liverpool, Manchester, Preston, Sheffield, Stockton-on-Tees

BROOKE WILLIAMS ‡
St Martins House Micklegate York YO1 6LN
Tel: 01904 677888 *Fax:* 01904 677990
E-mail: brookeyork@safemark.co.uk
List of partners: C Grundell, B V G Walton Williams
Office: Bridlington, Hull, Leeds
Work: D1 K1 N
Emergency Action, Agency, Advocacy, Fixed Fee Interview and Legal Aid undertaken
SPr: Walton Williams, Mrs Brooke Valerie Gail LLB(Hons) . *Jan 1992
Ast: Dale, Mrs Brenda LLB; LLM. . . . . Mar 1993

COLLIER LAW ‡
99a Hempland Lane York YO31 1AT
Tel: 01904 427407 *Fax:* 01904 413565
E-mail: michael@collierlaw.co.uk

COOPER & CO ‡
PO Box 759 York YO30 6WR
Tel: 01904 626266 *Fax:* 01904 626216
List of partners: T E Cooper
Work: A2
SPr: Cooper, Mr Trevor E BA(Hons)(Law) . . . . *Nov 1987

CORRIES SOLICITORS ‡
Rowntree Wharf Navigation Road York YO1 9WE
Tel: 0845 241 5566 *Fax:* 01904 527431 *Dx:* 1595 YORK 2
E-mail: advice@corries.co.uk
List of partners: B Corrie, M Dawson, T Murden, G M Saville
Work: N S1 W
Ptr: Corrie, Mr Bruce . . . . Nov 1992
Murden, Mr Tim LLB(Hons) . . . . Oct 2000
Saville, Mrs Gill M LLB . . . . *Nov 1992
Dir: Dawson, Mr Mark LLB(Hons) . . . . *Oct 1995
Asoc: Coulson, Mr John Roderick BA(Hons). . . . . *Nov 1994
Waller, Mr Martin LLB(Hons) . . . . *Nov 1998
Ast: Bonnett, Mr Howard. . . . . *Sep 2002
Collingwood, Mr Dominic . . . . Nov 2002
Desira, Mr Rob . . . . Feb 2003
Farman, Mrs Tracy LLB. . . . . *Oct 1989
Gillies, Mr Matthew LLB. . . . . *Jul 2000
Merrill, Miss Victoria. . . . . Dec 2003
Whiteley, Miss Karen LLB . . . . *Apr 2003

COWLING SWIFT & KITCHIN ‡
8 Blake Street York YO1 8XJ
Tel: 01904 625678 / 625679 *Fax:* 01904 620214 *Dx:* 61550 YORK 1
E-mail: enquiries@csksolicitors.co.uk
List of partners: R W Rusby, A L Ware
Work: A1 E F1 G J1 K1 L N O Q S1 S2 W Z(q)
Agency, Fixed Fee Interview and Legal Aid undertaken
Ptr: Rusby, Mr Richard William BA. . . . . *Dec 1976
Ware, Mr Alan Leslie . . . . *Sep 1988
Ast: Spence, Miss Claire Rachael LLB; LSF; MA Blackstone Law Prize; Simpson Curtis Co Law Prize. . . . . *Oct 1995

CROMBIE WILKINSON ‡
Clifford House 19 Clifford Street York YO1 9RJ
Tel: 01904 624185 *Fax:* 01904 623078 *Dx:* 61501 YORK 1
E-mail: york@crombiewilkinson.co.uk
List of partners: J A Bartram, J N Broadbridge, A J Faulkes, N A Largan, E J Morris, D G Mortor, D C Myles, D Norgate, N R Porter, S Richardson, M R Watson
Office: Malton, Selby
Languages: French, German
Work: A1 A2 A3 B1 C1 C2 C3 D1 D2 E F1 J1 K1 K2 K3 K4 L M1 N O P Q R1 R2 S1 S2 T1 T2 W Z(b,c,d,e,k,l,o,p,r,t,za)
Emergency Action, Agency, Advocacy, Fixed Fee Interview, Legal Aid undertaken, Legal Aid Franchise and Member of Accident Line
Dir: Bartram, Mrs Jennifer Ann LLB(Hons)(Lond) . . . . *Feb 1981
Faulkes, Mr Andrew J LLB . . . . *Dec 1976
Largan, Mr Neil Anthony LLB(Hons) ♦. . . . . *Feb 1996
Morris, Mrs Emma Jane BA. . . . . *Oct 1997
Mortor, Mr Duncan Gerald MA; LPC. . . . . *Oct 1999
Myles, Mr D Christopher. . . . . *Nov 1993
Norgate, Mr Darren LLB. . . . . *Jul 1999
Richardson, Miss Sharon . . . . *Sep 1999
Watson, Mr M Richard BA. . . . . *Mar 1987
Asoc: Greenhalgh, Mrs Julie D BA(Hons) . . . . *§Sep 1988
Mitchell, Mrs Abigail Louise LLB(Hons) . . . . Oct 1995
Poulter, Miss Belinda Jane BA(Hons) . . . . *Jun 2005
Ramsden, Mrs Sally Cathryn LLB . . . . *Nov 1994
Roberts, Mrs Jessica Penelope BSc(Hons)(Psychology); PGDipLaw . . . . Sep 2001
Ast: Marson, Miss Gemma LLB; LPC . . . . Apr 2008
Moore, Miss Faye Louise LLB(Hons) . . . . Feb 2010
Workman, Mr James Robert Alistair LLB(Hons) . . . *Feb 2009

DANIELS & COMPANY ‡
96 Micklegate York YO1 6JX
Tel: 01904 679999

DARWIN MCGROGAN ‡
Second Floor Tower House York YO1 9SB
Tel: 01904 613077 *Fax:* 01904 613066
Emergency telephone 01904 613077
E-mail: contact@darwinmcgrogan.co.uk

DENISON TILL ‡
Stamford House Piccadilly York YO1 9PP
Tel: 01904 611411 *Fax:* 01904 646972 *Dx:* 65206 YORK 6
E-mail: info@denisontill.com
List of partners: C P Barton, J P Cripwell, H J Crook, A M M Duncan, J C Goodrich, D W Grice, B P Harrington, M G B Hepworth, G Hevey, L P M Lennox, C A Lindsay, A P Ridge, S A Robinson, J C Spittle
Languages: French, German, Italian, Spanish
Work: A1 A3 B1 C1 C2 C3 D1 E F1 F2 I J1 J2 K1 K3 K4 L M1 M2 N O P Q R1 R2 S1 S2 T1 T2 U1 U2 V W X Z(b,c,d,e,k,l,m,o,p,x,z)
Fixed Fee Interview undertaken
Ptr: Barton, Mr Christopher P LLB(Leeds) . . . . *Nov 1985
Cripwell, Mr Jonathan P. . . . . Feb 1989
Crook, Miss Hilary Jane BA; DipRSA . . . . *Nov 1994
Duncan, Mr Alistair M M LLB(Leeds) . . . . *Nov 1979
Goodrich, Mr John C MA(Cantab). . . . . *§Jun 1971
Grice, Mr David W BA(Oxon) . . . . *Mar 1979
Harrington, Mr Brian Patrick LLB . . . . *Oct 1994
Hepworth, Mr Mark G B BA(Dunelm) . . . . *Jul 1980
Hevey, Mr Gareth LLB; ACIArb . . . . Nov 1981
Lennox, Mr Lionel P M LLB Registrar of the Diocese and Province of York Notary Public . . . . *Nov 1973
Lindsay, Mr C Andrew LLB . . . . *Jun 1984
Ridge, Mr Anthony P MA(Oxon). . . . . *Jan 1969
Robinson, Miss Sally A BA(Hons). . . . . *Nov 1989
Spittle, Ms Johanne C LLB; ACIArb . . . . *Dec 1986
Asoc: Jones, Mr Gareth E LLB(Hons) . . . . Oct 1993
O'Hara, Ms Helen M BA(Hons); CPE; LPC . . . . . . Aug 1997
Ast: Banerjee, Miss Nina S BA; CPE; LPC. . . . . Nov 1997
Harrison, Ms Lisa . . . . Sep 2002
Plews, Mr Michael . . . . Oct 2002
Taylor Wilson, Mrs Catherine Mary Winifred. . . . . May 1997
Thomson-Smith, Mr Christopher BA. . . . . *Jan 1999
Weston, Ms Alexandra Louise LLB . . . . Nov 1996

DICKINSON DEES
The Chocolate Works Bishopthorpe Road York YO23 1DE
Tel: 0844 984 1500 *Fax:* 0844 984 1501
E-mail: law@dickinson-dees.com
Office: London EC4, Newcastle upon Tyne (2 offices), Stockton-on-Tees
Ptr: Ashworth, Mr Philip LLB. . . . . *Oct 1983
Rogers, Mr Christian Patrick LLB . . . . *Sep 1995
Asoc: Howe, Miss Nicola BA(French & German); CPE; LPC . Sep 1997

DRIVERS ‡
56a Bootham York YO30 7BZ
Tel: 01904 625661 *Fax:* 01904 646259 *Dx:* 61503 YORK
E-mail: info@drivers-solicitors.co.uk
List of partners: G Knowles, S G Thorn
Office: Malton
Work: A1 E F1 J1 K1 L N Q S1 S2 W Z(h,l)
Fixed Fee Interview undertaken
Ptr: Knowles, Mr George BA ♦. . . . . *§Oct 1982
Ast: Barnett, Mr David E LLB . . . . *§Feb 1976
McAfee, Mrs Samantha MA. . . . . *§Sep 2005
Shepherd, Miss Angela LLB. . . . . *§Feb 2003

EBOR LAW LIMTED ‡
7 High Petergate York YO1 7EN
Tel: 01904 650960 *Fax:* 01904 632444 *Dx:* 61508 YORK
E-mail: info@eborlaw.co.uk

PAUL FOSTER & CO ‡
178a York Road Haxby York YO32 3EP
Tel: 01904 765159 *Fax:* 01904 765159
List of partners: P G Foster
Work: S1
SPr: Foster, Mr Paul Godfrey LLB . . . . *Dec 1971

GILLINGS AND WALKER ‡
Rechabite Building 21 Clifford Street York YO1 9RQ
Tel: 01904 655755 *Fax:* 01904 623803
E-mail: mw@gwkyork.demon.co.uk
List of partners: M R H Walker
Work: A1 B1 C1 D1 E F1 G H J1 K1 L M1 N P S1 T1 V W Z(l,n)
Emergency Action, Agency, Advocacy, Fixed Fee Interview, Legal Aid undertaken and Member of Accident Line
Ptr: Walker, Mr Michael R H. . . . . *§Jul 1970

GRAYS ‡
Duncombe Place York YO1 7DY
Tel: 01904 634771 *Fax:* 01904 610711 *Dx:* 61505 YORK
E-mail: enquiries@grayssolicitors.co.uk
List of partners: C C Goodway, J M Knowles, B J Mitchell, L Rickatson, P B Williams
Languages: French, Italian
Work: A1 A2 C1 E F1 J1 K1 K3 K4 L N O Q R1 R2 S1 S2 T1 T2 W X Z(d,h,m,n,p,q,x)
Agency and Advocacy undertaken
Ptr: Goodway, C C BA. . . . . *§Mar 1981
Knowles, Mr John Martin LLB(Manc) . . . . *§Oct 1982
Mitchell, Mr Brian James MA(Cantab). . . . . *§Nov 1993
Rickatson, Mrs Lyn LLB. . . . . *§Apr 1981
Williams, Mr Philip Benjamin MA(Cantab) . . . . . . *Sep 2001
Ast: Blick, Miss Gillian BSc(Hons) . . . . *Oct 2004
Goodway, Mrs Catherine R . . . . *Mar 1980
Grandison, Emma. . . . . Dec 1994

GUEST WALKER & CO ‡
12a The Shambles York YO1 7LZ
Tel: 01904 624903 *Fax:* 01904 611181 *Dx:* 61519 YORK
E-mail: solicitors@guestwalker.co.uk
List of partners: N A S Goodman, J C Guest, J A Walker
Languages: French
Work: A1 C1 D1 D2 E F1 G J1 K1 K3 L N O P Q R2 S1 S2 V W Z(l)
Emergency Action, Agency, Advocacy, Fixed Fee Interview, Legal Aid undertaken and Legal Aid Franchise
Ptr: Goodman, Miss Nicola Anne Sarah LLB(Hons) . . . *Nov 1990
Guest, Mr John C LLB . . . . *§Jan 1969
Walker, Mr John A MA . . . . *Nov 1982
Ast: Bell, Miss Jenny. . . . . *Nov 2001
Riley, Ms Karen LLB(Hons); LPC . . . . *Dec 1995

HAGUE & DIXON ‡
Cumberland House Cumberland Street York YO1 9SR
Tel: 01904 627111 *Fax:* 01904 611378 *Dx:* 61549 YORK
E-mail: chris.barton@hague-dixon.co.uk
List of partners: C D Barton, R C Dixon, A C Morris, D L Taylor
Office: Pickering, York
Work: C1 D1 E J1 K1 K3 L S1 S2 U2 W Z(l)
Emergency Action, Agency and Fixed Fee Interview undertaken
Ptr: Barton, Mr Christopher D BSc. . . . . *§Jan 1979
Taylor, Miss Dawn Louise LLB. . . . . *Jul 1999
Ast: Chaplin, Ms Jane BSc. . . . . *May 2005

HAGUE & DIXON
Bank House 1 The Square Stamford Bridge York YO41 1AG
Tel: 01759 371634 *Fax:* 01759 372910
Dx: 67840 STAMFORD BRIDGE
E-mail: roger.dixon@hague-dixon.co.uk
Office: Pickering, York
Work: A1 E J1 K1 K3 L S1 S2 W Z(l,m)
Emergency Action, Agency and Fixed Fee Interview undertaken
Ptr: Dixon, Mr Roger Charles BA(Dunelm). . . . . *§Mar 1972
Ast: Holloway, Ms Thea A P LLB. . . . . *Feb 2011
McTernan, Mrs Claire Louise LLB . . . . *Sep 2009

HARROWELLS ‡
1 St Saviourgate York YO1 8ZQ
Tel: 01904 558600 *Fax:* 01904 655855 *Dx:* 61506 YORK
List of partners: S R K Black, H Brunton, N Combes, B W Copley, A G Gowar, A C Harris, E J Harrow, R Hugill, W H Kaye, J P Lewis Ogden, J K Millar, H S Morgan, R P Onyett, J A Reynard, J C Scott, R G C Seaton, M P Thorpe, R C Wood
Office: York (2 offices)
Languages: French, German, Russian, Spanish
Work: K1 K3 K4 N S1 T1 W Z(q,r)
Agency, Advocacy, Fixed Fee Interview and Legal Aid Franchise
Ptr: Brunton, Helen . . . . Sep 1999
Copley, Mr Brian William . . . . *Mar 1985
Gowar, Mr Andrew G . . . . Nov 1993
Harrow, Mrs Elspeth J LLB(Hons). . . . . *Dec 1986
Kaye, Mr William H . . . . *Dec 1996
Morgan, Mrs Hudda Sara LLB. . . . . *Nov 1994
Onyett, Mr Robert Paul BA . . . . *Sep 1992
Reynard, Mr John A. . . . . *Sep 1997
Seaton, Mr Robert G C LLB(Lond) . . . . *Nov 1980
Wood, Mr Richard C . . . . *Sep 1997
Ast: Andrews, Lucy . . . . Jan 2007
Birch, Mr Gareth . . . . Jan 2010
Clarke, Mr Nicholas Andrew. . . . . Apr 1994
Garnett, Mr Ciaran . . . . Jan 2010
Griffiths, Rachel Anne. . . . . Dec 2007
Hill, Mr Samuel . . . . Jan 2009
Lloyd, Mr Jonathan . . . . Aug 1991
Louw, Mr Derek Raymond. . . . . Oct 1982
Moore, Dawn . . . . Jul 2010
Rogers, Rowena . . . . Aug 2003
Ryder, Mr Edward. . . . . Sep 2003
White, Nicola . . . . Jul 2007

HARROWELLS
Moorgate House Clifton Moorgate York YO30 4WY
Tel: 01904 690111 *Fax:* 01904 692111 *Dx:* 61464 HAXBY
Office: York (2 offices)
Work: A1 B1 C1 C2 E J1 O Q R2 S2 Z(c,d,e,q,za)
Agency and Fixed Fee Interview undertaken
Ptr: Black, Mr Simon Rupert Kay LLB(Hons). . . . . . . *Dec 1994
Combes, Mr Nathan. . . . . Apr 2002
Harris, Mrs Alison Clare BA(Hons) . . . . *§Apr 1995
Hugill, Mr Richard. . . . . Sep 2001
Lewis Ogden, Mr James Philip BA(Jt Hons) . . . . . *Oct 1987
Scott, Mr James C . . . . *Nov 1980
Thorpe, Mr Martin P LLB . . . . *Nov 1986
Ast: Fielding, Nicola . . . . Jan 2005
Horner, Marie . . . . Oct 2004
Kilvington, Mr Gregory. . . . . Jul 2009
Mitchell, Mrs Abigail Louise LLB(Hons) . . . . Oct 1995
Roberts, Mrs Jessica Penelope BSc(Hons)(Psychology); PGDipLaw . . . . Sep 2001
Con: Black, Mr David C BA(Dunelm) . . . . *Jan 1978

See p112 for the Key to Work Categories & other symbols

HARROWELLS
Westow House Main Street Haxby York YO32 3HS
Tel: 01904 760237 *Fax:* 01904 761555 *Dx:* 61460 HAXBY
Office: York (2 offices)
Work: K1 S1 W
Agency, Advocacy and Fixed Fee Interview undertaken
Ptr: Millar, Mr John Kevin LLB(Hons) . . . . *§Oct 1983

HETHERTONS LLP ‡
Tudor Court Opus Avenue York Business Park York YO26 6RS
Tel: 01904 528200 *Fax:* 01904 791506 *Dx:* 61545 YORK
E-mail: law@hethertons.co.uk
List of partners: S T Crack, D C Hallam, T S J Henry, S F Nellar
Office: Boroughbridge
Work: A1 B1 C1 D1 E F1 J1 J2 K1 K3 L N O Q S1 S2 T1 T2 W Z(c,l,q)
Emergency Action, Agency, Advocacy, Fixed Fee Interview, Legal Aid undertaken and Legal Aid Franchise
Ptr: Crack, Mr Simon T LLB . . . . *Aug 1997
Henry, Mr Thomas St John BA(Hons) . . . . *Jan 2000
Nellar, Mr Simon F BA . . . . *Nov 1983
Asoc: Acton, Miss Caroline BA . . . . Apr 2009
Conyers-Kelly, Mr Toby BA . . . . *Sep 1983
Guest, Ms Natasha LLB. . . . . Mar 2006
Matfin, Mrs Elizabeth Jane BA . . . . Oct 2002
Shaw, Miss Sarah J LLB . . . . *Apr 2009
Stephens, Mrs Barbara Rosemary BA(Hons); LLB(Hons) . . . . *Sep 2002
Stevens, Mr Gareth Robert LLB. . . . . *Apr 2007
Thompson, Miss Nicola LLB. . . . . *Nov 2006
Weatherley-Wright, Mrs Claire. . . . . *Nov 2004
Yeates, Mrs Joanne LLB(Hons) . . . . *Nov 1994

HOWARD & BYRNE SOLICITORS ‡
148 Lawrence Street York YO10 3EB
Tel: 01904 431421 *Fax:* 01904 411664

INGRAMS
10 Great North Way York Business Park York YO26 6RB
Tel: 01904 520600 *Fax:* 01904 520630 *Dx:* 62584 ACOMB YORK
E-mail: enquiries@ingramssolicitors.co.uk
Office: Hull
Languages: Dutch, Gaelic, German, Hindi, Lithuanian, Punjabi, Urdu
Work: A1 E J1 K1 K3 K4 L N Q R1 S1 S2 T2 W Z(c,q,r)
Fixed Fee Interview undertaken
Ptr: Copp, Ms Catherine Louise . . . . *Nov 1993
Stott, Mr Paul LLB(Leics) Assistant Deputy Coroner. . *Oct 1984
Bamforth, Ms Dianna . . . . NSP
Asoc: Copley, Ms Elaine. . . . . Jul 1984
Markland, Mrs Gillian FILEx. . . . . Nov 2003
Smith, Ms Emily. Feb 2006
Ast: Khanna, Ms Tina . . . . Jun 2007
Merchant, Mr David. . . . . Apr 2009
Seavor, Ms Jennifer. . . . . Mar 2008
Selby, Mrs Edel Mary . . . . Jun 2008

BARBARA JACOBS & CO ‡
3 Westfield House Millfield Lane York YO26 6GA
Tel: 01904 786012 *Fax:* 01904 798421 *Dx:* 61500 YORK
E-mail: baj@barbarajacobs.co.uk

MICHAEL KIRBY SOLICITORS ‡
Suite C2 The Raylor Centre James Street York YO10 3DW
Tel: 01904 415932 *Fax:* 01904 427946
E-mail: michaelkirby@btconnect.com
List of partners: M Kirby
Languages: French
Work: E F1 J1 K1 K3 K4 L N P Q S1 S2 W Z(j,l,m,w)
Emergency Action, Agency, Advocacy and Fixed Fee Interview undertaken
SPr: Kirby, Mr Michael LLB(Lond) . . . . *Jul 1977

KITCHING WALKER ‡
8 Bondgate Helmsley York YO62 5BR
Tel: 01493 772107 *Dx:* 63741 KIRKBYMOORSIDE
E-mail: post@kitchingwalker.co.uk

LANGLEYS
Queen's House Micklegate York YO1 6WG
Tel: 01904 610886 *Fax:* 01904 611086 *Dx:* 720620 YORK 21
E-mail: info@langleys.co.uk
Office: Lincoln, Newark
Work: A1 B1 C1 C2 C3 D1 E F1 G H J1 K1 K2 L N O Q R1 R2 S1 S2 V W Z(b,c,h,j,l,m,n,p,r)
Emergency Action, Agency, Advocacy, Fixed Fee Interview, Legal Aid undertaken, Legal Aid Franchise and Member of Accident Line
Ptr: Baylis, Mr Stephen . . . . Nov 1991
Brown, Mrs Helen Gray BA; CPE; LSF . . . . *Nov 1993
Buckton, Mrs Fiona J M BA . . . . *§Oct 1986
Conlon, Mr John BA(Hons); LLM . . . . *Apr 1997
Cross, Mr Tim. . . . . Nov 1988
Day, Mr Mark . . . . *Oct 1995
Edwards, Mr Huw M LLB . . . . *Feb 1990
Fearn, Mr Andrew. . . . . Mar 1976
Foyster, Mr Robin C. . . . . *Dec 1988
Garfitt, Mr David A . . . . *Dec 1991
Hindmarch, Ms Kate . . . . Oct 1995
Horner, Mr Peter J BA(Law). . . . . *Oct 1986
Howitt, Miss Rebecca LLB . . . . *Feb 1992
Jones, Mr Will LLB . . . . *Nov 1994
Kay, Mr Andrew. Nov 1988
Mackle, Mr Roger. . . . . Sep 1996
Ripley, Mr Rob . . . . Oct 1991
Saunders, Mrs Kathryn BA(Hons) . . . . *Nov 1983
Scott, Mr Giles Sandford . . . . *§Jan 1980
Scott, Mr Jeremy BA(Hons); LLM . . . . *Mar 1992
Taylor, Mr Roger BA Notary Public . . . . *§Jun 1975
Thompson, Mr David J LLB . . . . *§Jun 1986
Towler, Mr James LLB. . . . . *Sep 1982
Warner, Emma . . . . Dec 1999
Wood, Mr David LLB . . . . *Sep 1996
Asoc: Brook, Ms Fiona . . . . Jan 2003
Chard, Mr Daniel . . . . Jan 2005
Gray, Ms Samantha. . . . . Jan 2003
Leeson, Miss Elizabeth Hazel. . . . . Jul 1998
McGowan, Ms Alison . . . . Jan 2007
Morris, Miss Elizabeth LLB(Hons). . . . . *Sep 2004
Robinson, Mr Phil. . . . . Jan 2004
Taylor, Ms Kelly. Jan 2008

Ast: Bovington, Ms Victoria . . . . Jan 2007
Grant, Ms Jennifer . . . . Jan 2007
Mounsey, Ms Sara . . . . Jan 2003
Randall, Miss Joanne LLB. . . . . Nov 1993
Sheppard, Ms Kirsten. . . . . Jan 1999

P J LAWRENCE SOLICITOR ‡
7 Aspen Way Slingsby York YO62 4AR
Tel: 01653 627180 *Fax:* 01653 627180

LIEBERMAN ‡
3 Westfield House Millfield Lane Nether Poppleton York YO26 6GA
Tel: 01904 780972 *Fax:* 01904 788495 *Dx:* 61527 YORK
E-mail: neil.lieberman@liebermansolicitor.co.uk
Work: B1 C1 F1 O Q Z(q)

MBA SOLICITORS ‡
14 Clifford Street York YO1 9RD
Tel: 01904 666888
Emergency telephone 07071 666888
E-mail: lh@mbasolicitors.co.uk
List of partners: P Brown, L Hassan, R H Minion, D Morrison, M Thompson
Ptr: Brown, Mr Philip BA(Hons) . . . . Aug 1997
Hassan, Mr Liam . . . . Jan 2005
Minion, Mr Richard H BA . . . . *Nov 1993
Morrison, Mr Damien LLB(Hons) . . . . Sep 1994
Thompson, Mr Mark. . . . . Aug 1998

MAYNARDS SOLICITORS ‡
The Biocentre Innovation Way York Science Park York YO10 5NY
Tel: 01904 435100

MINSTER LAW LIMITED ‡
Alexander House Hospital Fields Road York YO10 4DZ
Tel: 0845 600 3272 *Fax:* 01904 663860 *Dx:* 61596 YORK 2
E-mail: info@minsterlaw.co.uk
Office: Wakefield

MITCHELLS ‡
2 Peckitt Street York YO1 9SF
Tel: 01904 623751 *Fax:* 01904 623155
E-mail: philip@mitchellssolicitors.co.uk
List of partners: P A Chapman, D L Scott
Languages: French, Italian
Work: C1 D1 E J1 J2 K1 L O Q S1 T2 W Z(k,p,q)
Emergency Action, Agency, Advocacy, Fixed Fee Interview and Legal Aid undertaken
Ptr: Chapman, Mr Philip A MA(Oxon) . . . . *Jun 1973
Scott, Mr David Lee LLB(Hons); LLM . . . . *Nov 1993

NAISH ESTATE AGENTS AND SOLICITORS ‡
3 High Petergate York YO1 7EN
Tel: 01904 653564 *Fax:* 01904 640067
E-mail: naish@naishproperty.co.uk

PATTINSON & BREWER
1 Bridge Street York YO1 6WD
Est: 1891
Tel: 01904 680000 *Fax:* 01904 680001 *Dx:* 61565 YORK 1
E-mail: enquiries@pattinsonbrewer.co.uk
Office: Bristol, London WC1
Languages: Welsh
Work: N Q Z(q,r)
Legal Aid undertaken and Member of Accident Line
Ptr: Radcliffe, Ms Jane LLB(Hons)(L'pool) . . . . *Feb 1990
Thompson, Mr Ron . . . . Sep 1998

PHEBY & CO ‡
8a Front Street Acomb York YO24 3BZ
Tel: 01904 789900 *Fax:* 01904 788384 *Dx:* 62586 ACOMB
E-mail: jp@pheby.co.uk
List of partners: J D Pheby
Work: K1 L N S1 W X
Fixed Fee Interview, Legal Aid undertaken and Legal Aid Franchise
Ptr: Pheby, Mr Julian D . . . . *Feb 1989
Ast: Hopwood, Mr Stephen James BA(Hons). . . . . . . *Nov 2003

CHRISTINE PICK SOLICITORS ‡
52a Market Place York YO43 3AL
Tel: 01430 873593 *Fax:* 01430 879210
E-mail: law@cpick.plus.com

PRYERS ‡
Blackthorn House Northminster Business Park Upper Poppleton York YO26 6QW
Tel: 01904 528640 *Fax:* 01904 528646
E-mail: info@pryers-solicitors.co.uk

RG SOLICITORS
14 Clifford Street York YO1 9RD
Tel: 01904 234095 *Fax:* 0844 414 5135 *Dx:* 720630 YORK 21
E-mail: york@rgsolicitors.co.uk
Office: Sidcup

RICHARDSON & CO
1 Peckit Street Clifford's Tower York YO1 9SF
Tel: 01904 642727 *Fax:* 01904 642737
E-mail: mail@richardsonlaw.co.uk
Office: Leeds

ROBERTSONS ‡
75 Walmgate York YO1 9TZ
Tel: 01904 658551 *Fax:* 01904 658556
List of partners: A J P Howard
Work: G H K1 Z(l)
Emergency Action, Agency, Advocacy, Fixed Fee Interview, Legal Aid undertaken and Legal Aid Franchise
Ptr: Howard, Mr A John P. . . . . Oct 1985
Ast: Howard, Mrs Sally A . . . . Dec 1987

ROLLITS LLP
Rowntree Wharf Navigation Road York YO1 9WE
Tel: 01904 625790 *Fax:* 01904 625807 *Dx:* 61534 YORK
E-mail: info@rollits.com
Office: Hull
Languages: French, German
Work: A1 A3 B1 C1 C2 C3 D1 E F1 F2 J1 J2 K1 K2 L M1 M2 N O P Q R1 S1 T1 T2 U2 W Z(b,c,d,e,f,h,j,k,l,o,p,q,s,t)
Agency, Advocacy, Legal Aid undertaken and Member of Accident Line
Ptr: Frogson, Mr Richard LLB(Hons). . . . . Sep 1999
Lane, Mr John Richard LLB; AKC . . . . *Oct 1988

Oliver, Mr Douglas Robert MA(Oxon) . . . . *Oct 1983
Stirk, Mr Richard Ian LLB; LLM . . . . Nov 1999
Asoc: Barr, Mrs Munro BA; CPE; LPC. . . . . Sep 2001
Digwood, Mr Andrew J LLB . . . . Sep 2001
Engleman, Mr Craig Arthur BA Willis Mills Prize . . . . *Oct 1994
Morrison, Mrs Gerry Linda BA(Hons)(History); PGDipLaw . . . . Sep 2004
Myles, Mrs Karen LLB. . . . . Sep 1993
Ast: Brad, Mrs Susan Elizabeth LLB . . . . Sep 2004

SACHEDINAS SOLICITORS ‡
3 Westfield House Millfield Lane York YO26 6GA
Tel: 01904 793195 *Fax:* 01904 782650
E-mail: jes@sachlaw.co.uk

CHRIS SAYER SOLICITORS ‡
164 Fulford Road York YO10 4DA
Tel: 01904 638038 *Fax:* 0845 468 0146
E-mail: info@chrissayer.co.uk

SYKES LEE & BRYDSON ‡
Judges Court Coney Street York YO1 9NE
Tel: 01904 731100 *Fax:* 01904 731101 *Dx:* 61537 YORK
Emergency telephone 07711 396544
E-mail: info@sykeslee.co.uk
List of partners: H M I Bayman, P F K Joslin, S J Partridge
Office: York
Work: A1 B2 C1 D1 E F1 F2 G H J1 K1 K3 K4 L N O Q R1 S1 S2 T2 V W Z(l,p,q)
Emergency Action, Agency, Advocacy, Fixed Fee Interview, Legal Aid undertaken, Legal Aid Franchise and Member of Accident Line
Ptr: Bayman, Mr Harry M I MA(Oxon) . . . . *Nov 1988
Joslin, Mr Peter F K LLB . . . . *Apr 1974
Partridge, Mr Steven J LLB . . . . *Dec 1985
Ast: Clarke, Ms Joanna . . . . *Apr 2006
Dawson, Mrs Helen L BA(Law) . . . . *Jan 1984
Moore, Mrs Antonia A L BA . . . . *Apr 2000
Con: Bloss, Ms Joanna M BA. . . . . *Dec 1987

SYKES LEE & BRYDSON
Bintay House 13 York Road Acomb York YO24 4LW
Tel: 01904 529000 *Fax:* 01904 529001 *Dx:* 62582 ACOMB
E-mail: info@sykeslee.co.uk
Office: York
Languages: French
Work: A1 B1 C1 D1 D2 F1 G H J1 K1 K3 K4 L N O Q R1 S1 T1 T2 V W X Z(k,l,o,p)
Emergency Action, Agency, Advocacy, Fixed Fee Interview, Legal Aid undertaken, Legal Aid Franchise and Member of Accident Line
Ptr: Partridge, Mr Steven J LLB . . . . *Dec 1985
Ast: Cutts, Mr Iain John LLB . . . . *Nov 1993
Con: Bloss, Ms Joanna M BA. . . . . *Dec 1987

MARCUS C TOPHAM ‡
9 School Lane Fulford York YO10 4LU
Tel: 01904 639413 *Fax:* 01904 639413

JONATHAN TOWERS SOLICITOR ‡
West House Nun Monkton York YO26 8ER
Tel: 01423 330351 *Fax:* 01423 330264
E-mail: jonathantowers@btinternet.com
Work: W

WALKERS ‡
31 Bootham York YO30 7BT
Tel: 01904 633220
E-mail: walkerlaw@btconnect.com

WARE & KAY LLP ‡
Sentinel House Peasholme Green York YO1 7PP
Tel: 01904 716000 *Fax:* 01904 716100 *Dx:* 61510 YORK 1
E-mail: law@warekay.co.uk
List of partners: R W Boreham, D J Hyams, P A Kay, D A Liddell, M N Peach
Office: Wetherby
Languages: Mandarin
Work: A1 B1 C1 C2 D1 E F1 J1 J2 K1 K3 K4 L N O P Q R1 R2 S1 S2 T1 T2 U2 W Z(b,c,j,l,o,q,s,t)
Emergency Action, Agency, Advocacy and Fixed Fee Interview undertaken
Ptr: Hyams, Mr David Julian. . . . . *Apr 1997
Kay, Mr Peter A BA . . . . *§Aug 1981
Liddell, Mr David A LLB; Dip PI Lit. . . . . *§Apr 1980
Asoc: Eedle, Miss Penelope Ruth LLB. . . . . *Dec 1984
Kershaw, Mr David Robert BA. . . . . *Feb 1983
Presley, Mrs Clare . . . . Jan 2008
Stevens, Mrs Holly BA(Hons) . . . . *Mar 2003
Ast: Cooper, Mrs Nicola LLB. . . . . Jan 2009
Con: Leach, Mr Jonathan David LLB . . . . *§Apr 1981

YORKLAW LTD (T/A BURN & COMPANY) ‡
Ebor House Millfield Lane Nether Poppleton York YO26 6QY
Tel: 01904 655442 *Fax:* 01904 627107 *Dx:* 61523 YORK 1
E-mail: burnco@qualitysolicitors.com
List of partners: G N Burn, S M Burn, S Knowles, C L Rutter
Office: Easingwold
Work: A3 C1 C2 D1 E F1 J1 K1 K2 K3 K4 Q S1 S2 W
Legal Aid Franchise
Dir: Burn, Mr Graeme N BA(Hons)(Law). . . . . §Sep 1982
Burn, Mr Steven M LLB; ACIArb. . . . . §Jul 1984
Knowles, Mr Stephen LLB(Hons) . . . . Jun 1993
Rutter, Ms Claire L LLB . . . . §Oct 1983
Asoc: Trueman, Mrs Claire Louise. . . . . Apr 2009
Whittaker, Mrs Lindsey Claire BA . . . . May 2007
Ast: Jackson, Mrs Natalie Ann . . . . Aug 2009

YORSOLICITOR ‡
105 The Mount York YO24 1GY
Tel: 01904 449933 *Fax:* 07733 443555
E-mail: emcm@yorsolicitor.co.uk

YSTRAD MYNACH, Caerphilly

CASWELL JONES
Unit 4 Pierhead Building 29 Bedwlywyn Road Ystrad Mynach Caerphilly CF82 7AA
Tel: 01443 816622 *Fax:* 01443 812097 *Dx:* 132153 CAERPHILLY 3
E-mail: ystrad@caswelljones.com
Office: Caerphilly

OWEN & O'SULLIVAN ‡
5 The Square Ystrad Mynach Caerphilly CF82 7DZ
Tel: 01443 862263 *Fax:* 01443 813291
Emergency telephone 07721 454546
E-mail: askp87@dsl.pipex.com
List of partners: T P O'Sullivan, C Owen
Languages: French, Welsh
Work: A1 B1 C1 D1 E F1 G H J1 K1 L N O Q R1 S1 T1 T2 V W Z(c,e,f,j,k,l,p,q,w)
Emergency Action, Agency, Advocacy, Legal Aid undertaken and Legal Aid Franchise
Ptr: O'Sullivan, Mr Timothy P . . . . *Oct 1987
Owen, Miss Catrin LLB . . . . Oct 1987

YSTRADGYNLAIS, Powys

GEORGE & D'AMBRA
41 Heol Eglwys Ystradgynlais Powys SA9 1EY
Tel: 01639 842420 *Fax:* 01639 845691
Emergency telephone 01792 290376
Office: Aberdare, Blackwood, Merthyr Tydfil (2 offices)
Languages: Welsh
Work: D1 G H J1 K1 L M1 N P S1 V Z(l)
Emergency Action, Agency, Advocacy, Fixed Fee Interview, Legal Aid undertaken and Member of Accident Line

GRAEME JOHN SOLICITORS
(in association with Berwyn Davies & A F Brooks)
3a Commercial Street Ystradgynlais Powys SA9 1HD
Tel: 01639 843404 *Fax:* 01639 881227
Emergency telephone 01639 843404
E-mail: info@graemejohn.co.uk
Office: Aberdare (3 offices), Tonypandy
Languages: Welsh
Work: A1 C1 D1 D2 E F1 J1 J2 K1 L N P Q R1 S1 S2 T1 V W Z(g,i,l,p,q,r)
Emergency Action, Agency, Advocacy, Fixed Fee Interview, Legal Aid undertaken and Member of Accident Line

COUNTRY PUBLIC AUTHORITIES, COMMERCIAL ORGANISATIONS ETC, ENGLAND & WALES – BY TOWN

ABERAERON, Ceredigion

CEREDIGION COUNTY COUNCIL
Penmorfa Aberaeron Ceredigion SA46 0PA
Tel: 01545 570881 *Fax:* 01545 572029 *Dx:* 92401 ABERAERON
Sol: Brookes, Mr Geoffrey N Solicitor . . . . *Jan 1975
Dyson, Mr Mark E LLB Solicitor . . . . *Oct 1986
Jones, Miss Claire N LLB Assistant Director of Legal Services . . . . *Oct 1989
Morgan, Miss E M Bronwen LLB(Wales) Director of Corporate & Legal Services . . . . *Jan 1983
Stephens, Mr Rhys BA(Hons); MA Assistant Solicitor . *Jun 1994
Watkin, Mr Richard O LLB(Wales) Chief Executive . . *Nov 1971

CLERK TO JUSTICES OFFICE
21 Alban Square Aberaeron Ceredigion SA46 0DB
Tel: 01545 570886 *Fax:* 01545 570295 *Dx:* 92405 ABERAERON
Sol: Evans, Mrs Caryl Julie Senior Legal Adviser. . . . . . Nov 1993

ABERYSTWYTH, Ceredigion

FARMERS UNION OF WALES
Llys Amaeth Plas Gogerddan Aberystwyth Ceredigion SY23 3BT
Tel: 01970 820820 *Fax:* 01970 820821
E-mail: head.office@fuw.org.uk
Sol: Jones, Mr Barrie W BA(Hons)(Law) Solicitor. . . . . . *Feb 1982

THE NATIONAL LIBRARY OF WALES
Penglais Aberystwyth Ceredigion SY23 3BU
Tel: 01970 632800 *Fax:* 01970 615709
Sol: Mainwaring, Mr Mark William MA(Cantab) Director of Corporate Services . . . . *Feb 1982

ABINGDON, Oxfordshire

CROWN PROSECUTION SERVICE THAMES VALLEY
The Courtyard Lombard Street Abingdon Oxfordshire OX14 5SE
Tel: 01235 551900 *Fax:* 01235 551901 *Dx:* 35859 ABINGDON
Sol: Cranshaw, Ms Rochelle. . . . . Dec 1989
Harrison, Mr Paul J . . . . Oct 1980
Hitchcock, Mrs Carolyn J S LLB. . . . . *Apr 1978
Jonckheer, Ms M Jennifer BA . . . . Sep 1975
Saunders, Ms Shan A M . . . . Oct 1994
Shears, Ms Sarah D . . . . Oct 1985
Stone, Mr Jonathan Richard LLB(Hons). . . . . Jan 1999
White, Mr William J BA . . . . May 1974

VALE OF WHITE HORSE DISTRICT COUNCIL
Abbey House Abingdon Oxfordshire OX14 3JE
Tel: 01235 520202 *Fax:* 01235 547609 *Dx:* 35863 ABINGDON
Sol: Quayle, Mr David M LLB; DipLG Director of Support Services . . . . *Oct 1981

ACCRINGTON, Lancashire

HYNDBURN BOROUGH COUNCIL
Legal and Democratic Services Scaitcliffe House Ormerod Street Lancaster Lancashire BB5 0PF
Tel: 01254 388111 *Fax:* 01254 392597
E-mail: chief@hyndburn.gov.uk
Sol: Bullock, Mr Peter BA . . . . Jul 1997
Ellis, Miss Jane A LLB; DipLG Head of Legal and Democratic Services . . . . Nov 1991
Hedges, Mrs Susan LLB(Hons); Law Society Dip (Local Government Law & Practice) Legal Services Manager . . . . Sep 1998
McMillan, Mr Gordon BA(Hons); LLM; DipLG Solicitor. *Dec 1983

ADDLESTONE, Surrey

RUNNYMEDE BOROUGH COUNCIL
Civic Offices Station Road Addlestone Surrey KT15 2AH
Tel: 01932 838383 *Fax:* 01932 838384 *Dx:* 46350 ADDLESTONE
Sol: Barnes, Mrs Karolina Dorota BCS(Law & Russian) Sweet & Maxwell Law Prize 1997 Assistant Solicitor . . . . *Mar 2002
Bennett, Mr Bruce LLB Assistant Solicitor . . . . *Jun 1990
Gardiner, Mr Andrew BA Head of Law. . . . . *Jan 1982
Keenan, Mrs Sarah J BA(Dunelm) Assistant Solicitor . *Sep 1984
Pearson, Mr Andrew M Director of Administration and Leisure . . . . *Dec 1977
Pugh, Mrs Rachel Helen LLB(Hons) Assistant Solicitor*Aug 2002

ALDERLEY EDGE, Cheshire

EMERSON DEVELOPMENTS (HOLDINGS) LTD
Emerson House Heyes Lane Alderley Edge Cheshire SK9 7LF
Tel: 01625 588420 *Fax:* 01625 588185 *Dx:* 15421 ALDERLEY EDGE
E-mail: anne.weatherby@emerson.co.uk
Sol: Broadhurst, Mr Eric E LLB(Hons) Solicitor. . . . . . *Apr 1975
Burgess, Mr J Paul BA(Hons)(Law) Solicitor. . . . . *Feb 1988
Hedley, Mr David J BSc(Hons) Solicitor . . . . *Oct 1988
Honychurch, Miss Julie V LLB(Hons) Solicitor . . . . *Nov 1983
Priestley, Ms Kathy M LLB(Hons) Solicitor. . . . . . *Apr 1973
Weatherby, Ms Anne C BA(Law) Co Solicitor . . . . . *Jan 1982

ALNWICK, Northumberland

ALNWICK DISTRICT COUNCIL
Allerburn House Denwick Lane Alnwick Northumberland NE66 1YY
Tel: 01665 510505 *Fax:* 01665 605099
E-mail: tfarrell@alnwick.gov.uk
Sol: Farrell, Mr Anthony DMS; MCMI Head of Legal & Democratic Services . . . . *Jan 1979
Masson, Mr Neil J LLB(Hons); DipLG Assistant Solicitor . . . . *Apr 1998

ALTRINCHAM, Greater Manchester

CASTLEMERE PROPERTIES LTD
Alpha House 12 Oxford Road Altrincham Greater Manchester WA14 2EB
Tel: 0161 941 3499 *Fax:* 0161 928 2745
E-mail: cal@castlemereproperties.com
Sol: Lindemann, Mr Clive A LLB(Lond) Director / Group Solicitor . . . . *Jun 1976

AMERSHAM, Buckinghamshire

CHILTERN DISTRICT COUNCIL
Council Offices King George V Road Amersham Buckinghamshire HP6 5AW
Tel: 01494 729000 *Fax:* 01494 732097 *Dx:* 50711 AMERSHAM
E-mail: hpatters@chiltern.gov.uk
Sol: Hall, Mr Peter A Principal Solicitor. . . . . §Jul 1969
Markham, Mrs Susan Dip LG Principal Solicitor . . . *§May 1984
Myles, Ms Paulette LLB(Hons) Planning & Litigation Solicitor . . . . *Feb 2004
Patterson, Mr Robert J H BA(Hons)(Law) Head of Legal Services . . . . *Jan 1991

HUMAN AND LEGAL RESOURCES
Unit 11 Haddenham Business Park Thame Road Aylesbury Buckinghamshire HP17 8LJ
Tel: 0871 222 3880 *Fax:* 0871 222 3881
E-mail: julia@humanandlegal.com
Sol: Bryk, Mr Jonathan Adam LLB(Hons) Legal Adviser . . Sep 2001
Carter, Mrs Julia Margaret BSc; DipLaw Legal Director*Mar 1996

NATIONAL HOUSE BUILDING COUNCIL
NHBC House Davey Avenue Milton Keynes MK5 8FP
Tel: 0870 241 4302 *Dx:* 50712 AMERSHAM
E-mail: ahodder@nhbc.co.uk
Sol: Cannon, Mrs Sara BA(Hons) Senior Solicitor . . . . . *Oct 1988
Hodder, Mr Alistair R BSc; DipLaw Head of Legal . . . *Nov 1994
Pembroke, Mr Roy S LLB Solicitor . . . . *§Apr 1976

AMESBURY, Wiltshire

NAVY ARMY & AIR FORCE INSTITUTES
London Road Amesbury Wiltshire SP4 7EN
Tel: 01980 627000 *Fax:* 01980 627100
Sol: Pink, Mr Raymond H Solicitor. . . . . *Feb 1973

ANDOVER, Hampshire

TEST VALLEY BOROUGH COUNCIL
Legal Service Beech Hurst Weyhill Road Andover Hampshire SP10 3AJ
Tel: 01264 368000 *Fax:* 01264 332625 *Dx:* 123080 ANDOVER 6
Sol: Ankcorn, Mr David R Conveyancing Solicitor . . . . . *Dec 1979
Bacon, Mrs Joanna LLB Assistant Solicitor . . . . . . *Nov 1982
Harrold, Mr Keith H BA Common Law Solicitor . . . . May 1982
Powell, Ms Carole LLB Solicitor. . . . . Sep 1991
Tovey, Mrs Susan Jane Head of Legal Services . . . . *Nov 1976

ASHFORD, Kent

ASHFORD BOROUGH COUNCIL
Civic Centre Tannery Lane Ashford Kent TN23 1PL
Tel: 01233 331111 *Fax:* 01233 330649
Dx: 151140 ASHFORD (KENT) 7
E-mail: terry.mortimer@ashford.gov.uk
Sol: Baker, Mr Jeremy David Ivan MA(Cantab) Principal Solicitor Strategic Development . . . . *Nov 1995
Bassendine, Mr John S Senior Solicitor . . . . *Jul 1971
Mortimer, Mr Terence W LLB Head of Legal & Democratic Services . . . . *Jan 1982

HEADLEY BROTHERS LTD
The Invicta Press Queens Road Ashford Kent TN24 8HH
Tel: 01233 623131 *Fax:* 01233 612345 *Dx:* 30228 ASHFORD (KENT)
E-mail: jon.pitt@headley.co.uk
Sol: Pitt, Mr Jonathan R LLB(Exon) Solicitor . . . . *§Jan 1982

ASHINGTON, Northumberland

WANSBECK DISTRICT COUNCIL
Town Hall Ashington Northumberland NE63 8RX
Tel: 01670 532292 *Fax:* 01670 520136
Sol: Findlay, Mrs Laura LLB(Hons) Assistant Solicitor . . . *Mar 2005
Forster, Mrs Carolyn LLB Solicitor. . . . . *Apr 2000

ASHTON-UNDER-LYNE, Greater Manchester

TAMESIDE MAGISTRATES COURT
Henry Square Ashton-under-Lyne Greater Manchester OL6 7TP
Tel: 0161 330 2023 *Fax:* 0161 343 1498
Sol: Burrows, Miss Ann Judith DML; LSF; CTP Head of Legal Services . . . . Mar 1988

TAMESIDE METROPOLITAN BOROUGH COUNCIL
Council Offices Wellington Road Ashton-under-Lyne Greater Manchester OL6 6DL
Tel: 0161 342 3028 *Fax:* 0161 342 2747
Sol: Davy, Mr Alan K BA; DipLG; Cert Mgmt Assistant Borough Solicitor. . . . . *Nov 1980
Graham, Miss Michelle BA(Hons) Solicitor. . . . . . . *Apr 2005
Hargreaves, Ms Lynn Angela LLB(Hons) Solicitor . . . Jan 2000
Hubbard, Miss Joanna Jane BA(Hons) Solicitor . . . . *Sep 2002
Mynes, Ms Sarah A LLB(Hons) Solicitor. . . . . *Nov 1994
Pickard, Ms Melanie J LLB Senior Solicitor (Social Services) . . . . *Nov 1991
Robertson, Ms Alison Jane LLB Principal Solicitor (Social Services) . . . . *Sep 1998
Stait, Mrs Beverley Gail LLB(Hons) Solicitor. . . . . . *Aug 2001
Stewart, Miss Sandra-Jane BSc(Jt Hons) Borough Solicitor . . . . *Sep 1996
Turner, Mr Paul A LLB Deputy Borough Solicitor. . . . *Feb 1995

ATHERSTONE, Warwickshire

NORTH WARWICKSHIRE BOROUGH COUNCIL
Council House South Street Atherstone Warwickshire CV9 1BD
Tel: 01827 715341 *Fax:* 01827 719225 *Dx:* 23956 ATHERSTONE
Sol: Hutchinson, Mr Jeremy LLB; MBA Chief Executive . . *Apr 1980
Maxey, Mr Steven John BA(Hons) Principal Solicitor. . *Jan 2002
Oliver, Mr Peter J R LLB(Leics) Solicitor to the Council *Apr 1973
Ryan, Ms Annie LLB Assistant Solicitor . . . . Jan 2004

AYLESBURY, Buckinghamshire

AYLESBURY VALE DISTRICT COUNCIL
66 High Street Aylesbury Buckinghamshire HP20 1SD
Tel: 01296 585858 *Fax:* 01296 585640
Sol: Desai, Mr Looqman LLB(Hons) Society of Town Clerks Prize; Law Society's Diploma in Local Government Law Practice 2002 Senior Solicitor . . . . Feb 2000
Fleming, Mrs Sally P BA Senior Solicitor. . . . . *Apr 1981
Matcham, Ms Alison LLB Senior Solicitor . . . . Jan 1980
Sparshott, Mr Steven David LLB Solicitor . . . . Jul 2005
Stubbs, Mrs Katherine A LLB Solicitor. . . . . *Oct 1990
Swift, Ms Joanna E BA Head of Legal Services . . . . *May 1981

BRITISH AMERICAN TOBACCO UK LTD
Oxford Road Aylesbury Buckinghamshire HP21 8SZ
Tel: 01296 335000 *Fax:* 01296 335970
E-mail: gbq97@dial.pipex.com
Sol: Fleetwood, Ms Victoria Anne LLB(Hons) Solicitor . . . Mar 1990
Gilbey, Mrs Teresa H John Mackrell Prize Solicitor. . . *Nov 1983

BUCKINGHAMSHIRE COUNTY COUNCIL
Old County Offices Walton Street Aylesbury Buckinghamshire HP20 1UA
Tel: 01296 383653 *Fax:* 01296 382421 *Dx:* 97401 AYLESBURY 2
E-mail: legal@buckscc.gov.uk
Sol: Ballard, Ms Marianne Martell LLB(Hons) Solicitor . . . *Oct 1985
Britten, Mr Graham LLB(Hons) Solicitor . . . *Jul 2002
Carey, Miss Anna Louise LLB Solicitor . . . *Sep 2005
Davies, Mrs M C Anne BA Head of Legal and Democratic Services . . . *Dec 1973
Forsythe, Ms Linda LLB Solicitor . . . *Jun 1978
Gibson, Mrs Yvonne BA(Hons)(Cantab) Acting Principal Solicitor . . . *Apr 1981
Horley, Mr Neville John BA(Hons); BSc Solicitor. . . *Dec 1993
Johnston, Mr Peter LLB(Hons) Solicitor . . . *Jul 2006
Norman-Thorpe, Miss Hayley Suzanne LLB(Hons) . *§Mar 1999
Oxbury, Ms Charlotte Nicola LLB Solicitor . . . *Oct 1992
Popat, Mr Rajesh Kumar LLB(Hons) Group Solicitor. *Dec 1994
Shepherd, Mrs Glynis J Solicitor. . . . *May 1999
Silk, Mrs Heather S D LLB(Hons) Solicitor. . . . *Nov 1999
Swan, Ms Vanessa Mary BA(Hons); LPC; CPE; BCC Solicitor - Child Care . . . Sep 1999
Valentine, Miss Rebecca Elizabeth LLB Solicitor. . . *Dec 2005
Wengraf, Miss Luisa Maria BA Solicitor . . . Sep 2007

CENTRAL BUCKINGHAMSHIRE MAGISTRATES COURT
Walton Street Aylesbury Buckinghamshire HP21 7QZ
Tel: 01296 554350 *Fax:* 01296 554320
Sol: Mace, Miss Samantha BA(Hons) Acting Deputy Justices' Clerk . . . Apr 1994

BAGSHOT, Surrey

ZINCOX RESOURCES PLC
Knightway House Park Street Bagshot Surrey GU19 5AQ
Tel: 01276 450100 *Fax:* 01276 850281
Sol: Wynter Bee, Mr Peter F TD . . . *Sep 1979

BAKEWELL, Derbyshire

PEAK DISTRICT NATIONAL PARK AUTHORITY
Aldern House Baslow Road Bakewell Derbyshire DE45 1AE
Tel: 01629 816200 *Fax:* 01629 816310
E-mail: aldern@peakdistrict.org
Sol: Pope, Mrs Loren Helen LLB Assistant Solicitor . . . *Nov 1991
Primhak, Mrs Beverley H LLB Head of Law . . . *Apr 1976
Taylor, Mrs Louckia LLB Assistant Solicitor . . . *Mar 1993

BAMBER BRIDGE, Lancashire

ERIC WRIGHT GROUP LTD
Sceptre House Sceptre Way Bamber Bridge Lancashire PR5 6AW
Tel: 01772 698822 *Fax:* 01772 628811
Sol: Carter, Mrs Annabel Mary LLB(Hons) Solicitor. . . *Apr 1980
Collier, Mr Michael E MA(Oxon) Director. . . *Mar 1980
Kumar, Ms Manisha LLB(Hons) Solicitor. . . Sep 1999
Ward, Mr Neil Geoffry LLB(Nott'm) Group Solicitor. . . *Oct 1983

BANBURY, Oxfordshire

CHERWELL DISTRICT COUNCIL
Bodicote House Bodicote Banbury Oxfordshire OX15 4AA
Tel: 01295 252535 *Fax:* 01295 263143 *Dx:* 24224 BANBURY
Sol: Bell, Mr Nigel Thomas Healy BA Assistant Solicitor . . Sep 2003
Christie, Mrs Susan MA(Hons) Assistant Solicitor . . . *Jun 1976
Crouch, Ms Jennifer LLB(Hons); MA Assistant Solicitor Nov 2000
Scarborough, Mr John Henry Law Society - Outstanding Performance in LPC Head of Legal and Democratic Services . . . *Oct 1996
Wilkinson, Ms Pamela Dorothy LLB(Hons) Assistant Solicitor . . . *Jan 1978

THE COPYRIGHTS GROUP LTD
23 West Bar Banbury Oxfordshire OX16 9SA
Tel: 01295 672050 *Fax:* 01295 672060
E-mail: enquiries@copyrights.co.uk
Sol: Halsall, Mr Martin Peter LLB(Hons); LLM; LS Finals Company Solicitor. . . *Dec 1994

BARKING, Essex

LONDON BOROUGH OF BARKING & DAGENHAM
Town Hall Barking Essex IG11 7LU
Tel: 020 8592 4500 / 8252 8233 *Dx:* 8511 BARKING
Sol: Colman, Mr Nigel J LLB Solicitor . . . Oct 1984
Feild, Mr Paul R Solicitor . . . Dec 1991
Hanton, Mr Robert W LLB(Lond) . . . *Dec 1973
Huddie, Mr Patrick J MA . . . *Aug 1971
Letters, Mr Richard J Solicitor. . . Nov 1976
Saleem, Mr Muhammad Solicitor . . . Jul 1993

HSBC INSURANCE (UK) LTD
Academy Place Brook Street Brentwood Essex CM14 5NQ
Tel: 01277 842174 *Fax:* 01277 842401
Sol: Burdett, Miss Lisa Olwen LLB; MA Head of Legal . . . Oct 1985
O'Mahony, Mr Declan FILEx National Law Society Prize Deputy Head of Legal. . . Nov 2005
O'Neill, Miss Vicki Laura LLB(Hons) Assistant Solicitor Nov 2006

BARNSLEY, South Yorkshire

BARNSLEY MAGISTRATES COURT
Court House PO Box 17 Barnsley South Yorkshire S70 2DW
Tel: 01226 320000 *Fax:* 01226 320048 *Dx:* 12279 BARNSLEY
Sol: McGuire, Mrs Jane Mary Solicitor. . . Dec 1991

BARNSLEY METROPOLITAN BOROUGH COUNCIL
Yorkshire House 18 Shambles Street Barnsley South Yorkshire S70 2SW
Tel: 01226 770770 *Fax:* 01226 773099 *Dx:* 12266 BARNSLEY
E-mail: townhall@barnsley.gov.uk
Sol: Cook, Ms Jane LLB(Hons) Solicitor . . . *Nov 1992
Frosdick, Mr Andrew Christopher LLB; DipLG Deputy Borough Secretary . . . *Oct 1984
Kenny, Mr Michael B LLB Borough Secretary . . . *Dec 1968
Kirk, Mr Garry P LLB Assistant Solicitor. . . May 1985
Koniarski, Mr Michal S LLB Assistant Solicitor. . . *Feb 1995
Leadbetter, Miss Jane L LLB Assistant Solicitor . . . *§Feb 1992
McCluskey, Mr Malcolm Winston BA(Econ); LLB Assistant Solicitor. . . *Jan 1991
Parker, Mr Stephen E LLB Principal Solicitor . . . Jun 1977
Roberts, Mrs Debra A BA(Law) Principal Solicitor . . . Oct 1986

GORDON JOPLING (FOOD INGREDIENTS) LTD
Carlton Industrial Estate Shawfield Road Carlton Barnsley South Yorkshire S71 3HS
Tel: 01226 733288 *Fax:* 01226 733113
Sol: Jopling, Ms Caroline P Solicitor . . . *Feb 1984

SOUTH YORKS JOINT SECRETARIAT (FIRE, POLICE, PENSIONS, PASSENGER TRANSPORT)
18 Regent Street Barnsley South Yorkshire S70 2HG
Tel: 01226 772856 *Fax:* 01226 772899
Sol: Cutting, Mr David BA; PGDipLP Assistant Solicitor. . . Nov 1999
Oades, Miss Maureen V LLB Solicitor. . . *Dec 1980

BARNSTAPLE, Devon

NORTH DEVON DISTRICT COUNCIL
Civic Centre North Walk Barnstaple Devon EX31 1EA
Tel: 01271 327711 *Fax:* 01271 388261
E-mail: info@northdevon.gov.uk
Sol: Blatchford, Mr Trevor John BA(Law) Head of Contentious Law . . . Apr 2002
Dasent, Mrs Susan M LLB(Hons) Solicitor. . . Oct 1991
Evans, Ms Beryl BSc(Hons)(Econ) . . . *Jul 1973
Hunter, Mr Damian Mark LLB Assistant Solicitor. . . Nov 2003
McGovern, Miss Tanya BSc(Hons) Solicitor . . . Dec 2005
Smart, Mr Michael J Head of Non Contentious . . . *Feb 1983

BARROW-IN-FURNESS, Cumbria

FURNESS & DISTRICT PETTY SESSIONAL DIVISION
Magistrates' Court Abbey Road Barrow-in-Furness Cumbria LA14 5QX
Tel: 01229 820161 *Fax:* 01229 870287
Dx: 63909 BARROW-IN-FURNESS
Sol: Collinson, Mr David John DML; DMS Legal Adviser . . Jan 1991
Jones, Mr Christopher H Legal Adviser . . . Jun 1992

BARRY, Vale of Glamorgan

VALE OF GLAMORGAN COUNCIL
Civic Offices Holton Road Barry Vale of Glamorgan CF63 4RU
Tel: 01446 700111 *Fax:* 01446 709300 *Dx:* 38553 BARRY
Sol: Evans, Mr Peter H Director of Legal & Regulatory Services . . . *§Feb 1980
Ham, Miss Jocelyn Sarah BA Lawyer . . . Nov 1998
Marles, Miss Deborah LLB(Hons) Head of Legal Services . . . *Mar 1990
Thornton, Miss Frances Irene LLB; LLM Lawyer. . . *Dec 1995
Walsh, Mr Kevin Michael BA(Hons) Solicitor. . . Nov 1985
Winter-Evans, Mrs Jodi Elizabeth LLB(Hons) Lawyer *Sep 2001

BASILDON, Essex

BASILDON DISTRICT COUNCIL
The Basildon Centre St Martin's Square Basildon Essex SS14 1DL
Tel: 01268 533333 *Fax:* 01268 294451 *Dx:* 53008 BASILDON
Sol: Browne, Mrs Lorraine J A S Legal Services Manager . *Jan 1996
Hamilton, Ms Lisa Legal Manager (Litigation) . . . *Sep 2000

FDR LTD
FDR House Christopher Martin Road Basildon Essex SS14 9AA
Tel: 01268 296431 *Fax:* 01268 296429
Sol: Rayman, Miss Rosalind LLB(Hons)(Law) Counsel. . *May 1993
Tutton, Miss Nicola Clare LLB; PGDip Assistant Counsel . . . *Jun 2006
Vantyghem, Mr Jon E MA(Cantab); AIL General Counsel & Company Secretary. . . *Oct 1978
Wharton, Mr Tsim Alan Farrington MA(Oxon); MBA Solicitor . . . *Jan 1999

BASINGSTOKE, Hampshire

THE AUTOMOBILE ASSOCIATION
Group Legal Services Fanum House 9 Basing View Basingstoke Hampshire RG21 4EA
Tel: 01256 491588 *Fax:* 01256 494666
Sol: Appleton, Ms Patricia A Solicitor. . . Jan 1987

BASINGSTOKE & DEANE BOROUGH COUNCIL
Legal Services Civic and Democratic Offices London Road Basingstoke Hampshire RG21 4AH
Tel: 01256 845402 *Fax:* 01256 845200 *Dx:* 3008 BASINGSTOKE
E-mail: chris.guy@basingstoke.gov.uk
Sol: Batcheler, Miss Lisa Joanne LLB(Hons) Lawyer/ Manager . . . *Aug 2002
Dawe, Miss Jennifer Ann LLB(Hons) Solicitor . . . *Aug 2004
Findlay, Mr Fergus A BA(Hons) Solicitor. . . *Sep 2003
Guy, Mr Christopher J LLB(Hons) Head Of Legal and Democratic Services . . . *May 1984
Maxfield, Mrs Caroline M Lawyer/ Manager . . . *May 1978

DE LA RUE PLC
De La Rue House Viables Basingstoke Hampshire RG22 4BS
Tel: 01256 605000
E-mail: louise.fluker@delarue.com
Sol: Cust, Mr Gary BA; MBA Legal Adviser . . . *Jan 1979
Denham, Mr Douglas R W BCom; LLB; DipLP; Solicitor Scotland . . . *Feb 1991
Joyce, Ms Elizabeth M BA(Mod)(Legal Science) Solicitor . . . *Jan 1991

ELI LILLY UK LTD
Lilly House Priestley Road Basingstoke Hampshire RG24 9NL
Tel: 01256 315000
Sol: Pezzack, Ms Susan D LLB Solicitor. . . *Oct 1990

LATTICE PROPERTY HOLDINGS LTD
Aviary Court Wade Road Basingstoke Hampshire RG24 8GZ
Tel: 01256 308803 *Fax:* 01256 308627 *Dx:* 123701 BASINGSTOKE
Sol: Bentzien, Mr Stephen Robert LLB Solicitor and Legal Manager . . . Oct 1981

MOTOROLA PCS
Redwood Crockford Chineham Basingstoke Hampshire RG24 8WQ
Tel: 01256 790790 *Fax:* 01256 817481
Sol: Offer, Mr Scott LLB(Lond) Legal Adviser. . . *Nov 1989

NORTH WEST HAMPSHIRE MAGISTRATES COURT
The Court House London Road Basingstoke Hampshire RG21 4AB
Tel: 01252 366000 *Fax:* 01252 811447 *Dx:* 145110 ALDERSHOT 4
Sol: Black, Mr Jonathan S W LLM; Chartered FCIPD Solicitor Solicitor. . . *Nov 1980

UFB GROUP PLC
Northern Cross Basing View Basingstoke Hampshire RG21 4HL
Tel: 01256 377377 *Fax:* 01256 377300
Sol: Heaton, Mr Graeme Russell BA; LLB Solicitor. . . *Mar 1991

WESSEX HOUSING PARTNERSHIP LTD
Chailey Court 25-27 Winchester Road Basingstoke Hampshire RG21 8UE
Tel: 01256 844506 *Fax:* 01256 350976
E-mail: kha@kha.org.uk
Sol: Bacon-Campbell, Mrs Heather LLB(Hons) Principal Solicitor . . . *May 1981
Hartwell, Mr Julian Edward Michael LLB Solicitor . . Apr 1980
Sandison, Ms Jacqueline Anne Gordon LLB Solicitor . Nov 1990
Zuberi, Mrs Salma Rasheed LLB(Hons) Solicitor. . . *Nov 1995

BATH, Bath & North East Somerset

BATH & WANSDYKE MAGISTRATES COURT
North Parade Road Bath Bath & North East Somerset BA1 5AF
Tel: 01225 463281 *Fax:* 01225 420225
Sol: Stevens, Mr Nicholas J . . . *Jul 1975

HELPHIRE (UK) LTD
Pinesgate Lower Bristol Road Bath Bath & North East Somerset BA2 3DP
Tel: 01225 321000
Sol: Holding, Mr Peter F LLB(B'ham) Solicitor . . . *Oct 1988
Symons, Mr Michael J LLB Solicitor. . . *Dec 1979

WESSEX WATER SERVICES LTD
Claverton Down Road Claverton Down Bath Bath & North East Somerset BA2 7WW
Tel: 01225 526000 *Fax:* 01225 528313
Sol: Johnson, Mrs Susan F Assistant Solicitor . . . *Jan 1989
Phillips, Mr Andrew J LLB Company Secretary & Solicitor . . . *Nov 1985
Rata, Mr Christopher W LLB Solicitor . . . *Apr 1993

BATLEY, West Yorkshire

CATTLES PLC
Kingston House Centre 27 Business Park Woodhead Road Batley West Yorkshire WF17 9TD
Tel: 01924 444466 *Fax:* 01924 442255
Sol: Hallam, Mrs Penny LLB(Hons) Legal Compliance Manager . . . *Jul 2002
Todd, Mr Roland Charles William MA(Oxon)(Modern History) Company Secretary & Legal Counsel . . . *Nov 1986

BEACONSFIELD, Buckinghamshire

DIVORCE LAW INFO
The Pump House Penn Road Beaconsfield Buckinghamshire HP9 2TN
Tel: 01494 681335
E-mail: sheelamac@divorcelaw.info.co.uk
Sol: Mackintosh, Mrs Sheela LLB(Hons) Proprietor. . . *Aug 1991

BEDFORD, Bedfordshire

BEDFORD BOROUGH COUNCIL
Town Hall Bedford Bedfordshire MK40 1SJ
Tel: 01234 267422 *Fax:* 01234 221606 *Dx:* 5600 BEDFORD
Sol: Doorne, Mr David. . . Jan 1979
Fordham, Mr Timothy J BA(Law) Service Manager (Legal Services) . . . *Sep 1985
Gough, Mr Michael LLB Head of Corporate Administration & Monitoring (Solicitor to the Council) . . . *Dec 1978
Knapp, Ms Dee BA . . . Oct 1990
Ledran, Mr Kenneth J Principal Solicitor. . . *§Jun 1994

BEDFORDSHIRE COUNTY COUNCIL
County Hall Cauldwell Street Bedford Bedfordshire MK42 9AP
Tel: 01234 363222 *Fax:* 01234 228619 *Dx:* 117105 BEDFORD 4
Sol: Atkinson, Mr John C BA(Wales) Head of Legal & Member Services . . . *Nov 1976
Begum, Ms Parveen LPC; Combined Studies(2:2) Solicitor . . . Nov 1997
Bennett, Mr Nigel H LLB Managing Solicitor. . . *Oct 1978
Cole, Mr Graham H LLB Solicitor . . . *Jan 1985
Hallam, Miss Lisa LLB(Hons) Solicitor. . . Jan 2000
Mitchell, Miss Patricia M BA(Lond); LLM(Leics) Solicitor . . . Nov 1974
Parmar, Miss Anna-Maria BA(Law) Solicitor. . . *Feb 1988
Wansbrough, Mr Roger D LLB(Leeds) County Solicitor Jan 1971
Wilkinson, Mr Richard C LLB Director of Business Services . . . *Jun 1971

See p112 for the Key to Work Categories & other symbols

NORTH BEDFORDSHIRE MAGISTRATES COURT
The Shire Hall 3 St Pauls Square Bedford Bedfordshire MK40 1SQ
Tel: 01234 319100 *Fax:* 01234 319114 *Dx:* 729420 BEDFORD 10
Sol: Marshall, Ms Jennifer Jane BA(Hons) Courts' Legal Adviser . . . . Sep 1997

BEESTON, Nottinghamshire

BROXTOWE BOROUGH COUNCIL
Council Offices Foster Avenue Beeston Nottinghamshire NG9 1AB
Tel: 0115 917 7777 *Fax:* 0115 917 3131 *Dx:* 11663 BEESTON
E-mail: cbrown@broxbcl.demon.co.uk
Sol: Brown, Mr P D Christopher LLB Director of Legal Administrative Services . . . . *Dec 1974
Cotton, Mrs Jane E LLB Solicitor . . . . *Nov 1984
Langton, Ms Bonita S Solicitor . . . . Dec 1998
Smith, Mr Jeremy Julian MA . . . . Oct 1995
Thomas, Mrs Susan J LLB Solicitor . . . . Feb 1989

PLESSEY NETWORK & OFFICE SYSTEMS
Legal Adviser Beeston Nottinghamshire NG9 1LA
Tel: 0115 943 0300
Sol: Woodhead, Mr Christopher F Solicitor . . . . Oct 1979

BENFLEET, Essex

CASTLE POINT BOROUGH COUNCIL
Council Offices Kiln Road Benfleet Essex SS7 1TF
Tel: 01268 882200 *Fax:* 01268 882453
Dx: 39603 HADLEIGH ESSEX
Sol: Smith, Mr Andrew R MA; BA(Hons); DipLG Director of Legal and Support Services (Monitoring Officer) . . . . Feb 1993
Wilson, Ms Fiona M Solicitor . . . . *Oct 2000

BERKELEY, Gloucestershire

MAGNOX ELECTRIC PLC
Berkeley Centre Berkeley Gloucestershire GL13 9PB
Tel: 01452 652222 / 01453 813484 *Fax:* 01453 813821
Sol: Speirs, Mr John R LLB; MA Solicitor . . . . Jul 1979
Warner-Smith, Ms Elizabeth A Solicitor . . . . Dec 1994

BERWICK-UPON-TWEED, Northumberland

BERWICK-UPON-TWEED BOROUGH COUNCIL
Council Offices Wallace Green Berwick-Upon-Tweed Northumberland TD15 1ED
Tel: 01289 330044 *Fax:* 01289 330540
Dx: 67798 BERWICK-UPON-TWEED
Sol: Cawthorn, Mr Edward O TD LLB Chief Executive . . . . Mar 1973
Henry, Mr William Edward MA; LLB Solicitor . . . . May 1995

BEVERLEY, East Riding of Yorkshire

CLERK TO THE JUSTICES
Beverley Magistrates' Court Champney Road Beverley East Riding of Yorkshire HU17 9EJ
Tel: 01482 861607 *Fax:* 01482 882004
Sol: Shepherd, Mr Ian P Clerk to the Justices . . . . *Jun 1984

EAST RIDING OF YORKSHIRE COUNCIL
Legal Services County Hall Beverley East Riding of Yorkshire HU17 9BA
Tel: 01482 887700 *Fax:* 01482 393109 *Dx:* 28318 BEVERLEY
Sol: Birkinshaw, Ms Jane L LLB Solicitor . . . . Feb 1980
Blake-Barward, Mr Vincent BA(Hons) Solicitor . . . . Jan 2004
Buckley, Mr Mathew Dale BA Solicitor . . . . Jan 1994
Hartley, Miss Alison LLB(Hons) . . . . Nov 1995
Hayden, Mrs Diane LLB(Hons) Solicitor . . . . Dec 2000
Leathley, Ms Sheila BSc Solicitor . . . . Aug 1995
Lockwood, Ms Susan M LLB Solicitor . . . . *Mar 1980
Nicholson, Miss Lisa Jane LLB(Hons) Solicitor . . . . *Sep 1999
Spencer, Mr Tom P BA; MA Head of Litigation & Regulatory Services . . . . *Oct 1996
Wilkinson, Miss Louise R Solicitor . . . . Nov 1994

BEXHILL, East Sussex

ROTHER DISTRICT COUNCIL
Town Hall Bexhill East Sussex TN39 3JX
Tel: 01424 787878 *Fax:* 01424 787879 *Dx:* 8103 BEXHILL-ON-SEA
E-mail: chiefexec@rother.gov.uk
Sol: Edwards, Mr David I MA(Cantab) Legal Services Manager . . . . *Feb 1978
Guiver, Ms Jane Ellen LLB(Hons) Property & Contracts Lawyer . . . . *Dec 2006

BEXLEYHEATH, Kent

LONDON BOROUGH OF BEXLEY
Civic Offices Broadway Bexleyheath Kent DA6 7LB
Tel: 020 8303 7777 *Fax:* 020 8294 6071 *Dx:* 31807 BEXLEYHEATH
Sol: Atkins, Mr Guy LLB(Hons) Senior Solicitor . . . . Aug 1998
Cannon, Ms Sarah L LLB Senior Solicitor . . . . Apr 1996
Gask, Miss Philippa Jane BA Assistant Solicitor . . . . *Oct 2001
Jones, Ms Laura A BA(Hons) Solicitor . . . . Feb 1991
Maughan, Mr Andrew L LLB(Hons); MA(Manc) Assistant Director (Legal Services) . . . . *Oct 1990
Ogunrinde, Ms Rachel LLB; PGDip University of Warwick Award for Most Promising Law Student 1986 Solicitor . . . . *Jan 2001
Putnam, Ms Susan BA(Hons) Solicitor . . . . *Nov 1982
Sparling, Mr Gregory James LLB; BA Solicitor . . . . Jul 2005
West, Mr Brian P BA(Law) Principal Solicitor . . . . *Oct 1982

BEXLEY MAGISTRATES COURT
Norwich Place Bexleyheath Kent DA6 7NB
Tel: 020 8304 5211 *Fax:* 020 8303 6849
Dx: 100150 BEXLEYHEATH 3
Sol: Pilmore-Bedford, Ms Carolyn A Deputy Clerk to the Justices Training Secretary South East London Magistrates' Association . . . . *Feb 1982

WOOLWICH PLC
Watling Street Bexleyheath Kent DA6 7RR
Tel: 020 8298 5000 *Fax:* 01322 555708 *Dx:* 90000 BEXLEYHEATH 2
Sol: Cugley, Mr John Henry Senior Solicitor . . . . *Dec 1981
Small, Ms Jennifer LLB; LLM Solicitor . . . . Jan 1991
Tupman, Mr John E C Leics Law Society Prize Solicitor . . . . *Dec 1977
Webber, Mr Michael F Chief Solicitor . . . . Aug 1981
Wells, Ms Denise LLB Solicitor . . . . *Dec 1992

BIDEFORD, Devon

TORRIDGE DISTRICT COUNCIL
Riverbank House Bideford Devon EX39 2QG
Tel: 01237 428700 *Fax:* 01237 425972 *Dx:* 53606 BIDEFORD
E-mail: ken.miles@torridge.gov.uk
Sol: Miles, Mr Kenneth Douglas FILEx Solicitor . . . . Oct 2004

BINGLEY, West Yorkshire

BRADFORD & BINGLEY PLC
PO Box 2 Main Street Bingley West Yorkshire BD16 2LW
Tel: 01274 555555 *Dx:* 11898 BINGLEY
Sol: Evans, Miss Theo Harriet BA Senior Solicitor . . . . Nov 1998
Fagan, Miss Victoria LLB(Hons); PGDip Senior Commercial Solicitor . . . . Nov 2002
Franks, Mrs Mary B BA(Law) Solicitor . . . . *Oct 1987
Jordan, Mr Paul G Group Solicitor . . . . *May 1987

BIRKENHEAD, Merseyside

HM LAND REGISTRY - BIRKENHEAD
Old Market House 13 Hamilton Street Old Market Birkenhead Merseyside CH41 5FL
Tel: 0151 473 1110 *Fax:* 0151 473 0251 *Dx:* 14300 BIRKENHEAD 3
Sol: Bickley, Mr John Assistant Land Registrar . . . . *Jul 1979
Brough, Mr Patrick J MA(Cantab) Land Registrar . . . . *§Dec 1974
Inge, Miss Vivien J BA(Hons)(Dunelm)(Law) Assistant Land Registrar . . . . *May 1986
Pope, Mr Charles A MA(Oxon) Assistant Land Registrar . . . . *§Apr 1973
Tanner, Mr Keith BA(Dunelm); LLB(Hons) Assistant Land Registrar . . . . Mar 1999

HM LAND REGISTRY - BIRKENHEAD (ROSEBRAE)
Rosebrae Court Woodside Ferry Approach Birkenhead Merseyside CH41 6DU
Tel: 0151 472 6666 *Fax:* 0151 472 6789 *Dx:* 24270 BIRKENHEAD 4
Sol: Booth, Mrs Louise F LLB Assistant Land Registrar . . . . *Aug 1996
Salter, Mrs Nia Pennant BA(Hons)(Dunelm)(Law) Assistant Land Registrar . . . . Oct 1984
Taylor, Mr M LLB Senior Assistant Land Registrar . . . . *Dec 1976
Wright, Mr Nigel K LLB Assistant Land Registrar . . . . *Jun 1978

BIRMINGHAM, West Midlands

ASTON LEGAL CENTRE
UEP 29 Trinity Road Aston Birmingham West Midlands B6 6AJ
Tel: 0121 523 0965 *Fax:* 0121 551 7359
Sol: Campbell, Ms Jane G Solicitor . . . . Nov 1991

BASS TAVERNS LTD
Cape Hill PO Box 27 Birmingham West Midlands B16 0PQ
Tel: 0121 558 1481 *Fax:* 0121 558 2515
Sol: Kennedy, Ms Bronagh BA(Oxon) Solicitor . . . . *Nov 1988

BIRMINGHAM CITY COUNCIL LEGAL & DEMOCRATIC SERVICES
Ingleby House 11-14 Cannon Street Birmingham West Midlands B2 5EN
Tel: 0121 303 2066 *Fax:* 0121 303 1312 *Dx:* 13053 BIRMINGHAM
Sol: Ahmed, Mrs Saadia LLB(Hons) Solicitor . . . . *Jan 2000
Aratoon, Ms Kaluinder Kaur LLB(Hons) Solicitor . . . . Jun 2003
Atkins, Ms Elaine BA(Hons) Solicitor . . . . Sep 1994
Averill, Mrs Rebecca BA(Hons); CPE; LSF Associated Law Societies of Wales Prize Solicitor . . . . *Feb 1996
Barker, Mrs Alison M BA(Law) Senior Solicitor . . . . *Oct 1984
Barker, Mr Robert M LLB Principal Solicitor . . . . *Jun 1979
Bassey, Ranjit LLB(Hons) Senior Solicitor . . . . *Sep 1995
Bhopal, Mr Sanjeev K LLB Solicitor . . . . Jan 2001
Birch, Miss Deirdre Ann BA(Hons) Solicitor . . . . *Apr 1997
Burgerman, Mr Benjamin Gareth LLB(Hons) Solicitor . . . . May 2004
Burgess, Mr Ian Stuart LLB(Hons) Solicitor . . . . *Dec 2001
Burrell, Ms Suzanne Angela LLB(Hons) Solicitor . . . . May 2005
Butler-Hunter, Ms Carmen LLB(Hons) Solicitor . . . . *Dec 1994
Clarke, Ms Sonya BA; CPE; LPC Senior Solicitor . . . . *Sep 1998
Connelly, Mr Robert Thomas LLB(Hons) Senior Solicitor . . . . *Feb 1990
Dhillon, Mrs Surinder Pal Kaur LLB(Hons) Senior Solicitor . . . . Apr 1998
Dodsley, Mrs Claire H LLB Senior Solicitor . . . . *Oct 1988
Evans, Mr Stuart John LLB(Hons) Principal Solicitor . . . . *Jul 1989
Hall, Mr Andrew J LLB Senior Solicitor . . . . *Nov 1986
Harvey, Ms Aneta Cerlena LLB Solicitor . . . . *Sep 1998
Hayre, Mr Jagdeep Singh BA(Hons); LSF Senior Solicitor . . . . *Jun 1993
Homfray, Mrs Elizabeth Hilary LLDip Solicitor . . . . Apr 2007
Kettle, Miss Julia R LLB Senior Solicitor . . . . *Apr 1983
Kiteley, Mrs Helen J LLB(Hons) Solicitor . . . . *Nov 1989
Lampert, Mrs Jill M J BA Solicitor . . . . *Oct 1990
Lea, Mrs Nicola Elizabeth LLB Assistant Solicitor . . . . Jan 1992
Lineker, Miss Jane Caroline LLB(Hons); LSF Senior Solicitor . . . . *Feb 1996
Lloyd, Mr Roger E Principal Solicitor . . . . *§Dec 1971
Lopes, Mrs Amanda Louise Solicitor . . . . Dec 1990
Mahmood, Safda LLB(Hons) Senior Solicitor . . . . *Aug 1996
Marshall, Miss Tracy LLB; DipLG Senior Solicitor . . . . Jan 1992
Miller, Mrs Farida BA; LLB Senior Solicitor . . . . Oct 1992
Morgan, Ms Lisa C LLB Principal Solicitor . . . . Nov 1992
Mortimer, Mr Simon A BA Solicitor . . . . Jan 1985
Murray, Miss Charmaine E LLB Principal Solicitor . . . . Oct 1986
Nicholson, Mr Mark Adrian LLB(Hons) Solicitor . . . . Dec 1993
Norris, Mr Raymond W LLB(Lond) Solicitor . . . . *May 1972
O'Ryan, Mr Jerome I LLB; DipLG Principal Solicitor . . . . May 1991
Pamar, Mr Rajesh LLB(Hons) Solicitor . . . . Dec 2002
Priest, Ms Katharine Sally BA(Hons); DipLG Principal Solicitor . . . . Jul 1995
Quailey, Mrs Myrtle Joy LLB(Hons) Solicitor . . . . Mar 2002
Robson, Ms Jane A BA(Hons) Assistant Director . . . . Nov 1982
Saeed, Ms Fahmeeda Kauser BA(Law) Solicitor . . . . Sep 2001
Shingari, Mr Varun Kumar BA(Hons)(Law with Business); Dip(Business Law) Solicitor . . . . Nov 2000
Sidhu, Tarndip S LLB; LPC Senior Solicitor . . . . Sep 1998
Singh, Mrs Sukhwinder Senior Solicitor . . . . Oct 1994
Sinnott, Miss Clare Louise LLB(Hons); LPC Solicitor . . . . Sep 2002
Tatlow, Mr David V LLM Assistant Director . . . . Jan 1970
Taylor, Mrs Wendy R BA(Law) Principal Solicitor . . . . Nov 1984
Underwood, Mrs Alison Mary LLB(Hons) Senior Solicitor . . . . *Jul 1999
Watts, Mrs Sally Jean LLB(Hons) Solicitor . . . . Aug 1996
Willimott, Mr Paul John BSc(Hons) Solicitor . . . . *May 1992
Wynn, Mr John W LLB(Hons); DipLG Assistant Director *Jul 1978
Yafai, Mrs Faten BA(Law) Solicitor . . . . *Oct 2000
Zulfiqar, Ms Nabila Senior Solicitor . . . . Oct 1993

BIRMINGHAM CITY UNIVERSITY
City North Campus Birmingham West Midlands B42 2SU
Tel: 0121 331 5000 *Fax:* 0121 331 7994
Sol: Arrand, Mrs Margaret Suzanne LLB(Hons) Solicitor . . . . *Apr 1978

BIRMINGHAM SETTLEMENT
Reynolds House Annexe Newbury Road Newtown Birmingham West Midlands B19 2RH
Tel: 0121 250 3000 *Fax:* 0121 250 3050
E-mail: info@bdl.org.uk
Sol: Mullane, Mrs Claire BA(Hons) Debt Adviser . . . . Jan 2000

CADBURY SCHWEPPES PLC (LEGAL DEPT)
Franklin House Bournville Lane Bournville Birmingham West Midlands B30 2NB
Tel: 0121 625 7000
Sol: Chapman, Ms Kay Elizabeth LLB(Hons) Commercial Lawyer . . . . *Oct 1996
Foster, Mr David C LLB Solicitor . . . . *Oct 1988
Hodgin, Mr Mark BA(Hons)(English Lit) CPE- Cavendish Prize (UCE); LPC - Lord Hailsham Prize Litigation Solicitor . . . . Jan 1997
Keating, Mr Michael E LLB Solicitor . . . . *Mar 1973
Perrott, Mr John LLB Solicitor . . . . *Jun 1976
Terry, Mr Marcus R J C LLB Commercial Lawyer . . . . *Oct 1984
Van Den Berg, Miss Angela Maria BA(Hons)(Oxon)(Jurisprudence) Senior Commercial Lawyer . . . . Jan 1996
Wheeler, Mr John Spencer Charles BSc(Chemistry Law); CPE(Business) Senior Intellectual Property CounselOct 2002

CENTRO (WEST MIDLANDS PASSENGER TRANSPORT EXEC)
16 Summer Lane Birmingham West Midlands B19 3SD
Tel: 0121 200 2787 *Fax:* 0121 214 7010 *Dx:* 712530 BIRMINGHAM
Sol: Irving, Mrs Hilary K LLB Head of Legal & Democratic Services . . . . *Sep 1996
Thomas, Miss Frieda LLB Project & Land Solicitor . . . . *Sep 1990

L W COLE (DISTRIBUTORS) LTD
Castle Vale Industrial Estate 20 Maybrook Road Minworth Birmingham West Midlands B76 8BE
Tel: 0121 351 2299 *Fax:* 0121 351 4894
Sol: Skinner, Ms Angela P BSc; LLB Solicitor . . . . Aug 1985

COMMISSION FOR RACIAL EQUALITY
Third Floor Lancaster House Newhall Street Birmingham West Midlands B3 1NA
Tel: 0121 710 3000 *Fax:* 0121 710 3001
Sol: Hughes, Ms Sian E MPhil; LLB Solicitor . . . . *Dec 1991

CROWN PROSECUTION SERVICE WEST MIDLANDS
14th Floor Colmore Gate 2 Colmore Row Birmingham West Midlands B3 2QA
Tel: 0121 262 1300 *Fax:* 0121 262 1500
Dx: 719540 BIRMINGHAM 45
Sol: Blundell, Mr David I LLB(Hons) Chief Crown Prosecutor . . . . *Apr 1972

EEF WEST MIDLANDS ASSOCIATION
St James's House Frederick Road Edgbaston Birmingham West Midlands B15 1JJ
Tel: 0121 456 2222 *Fax:* 0121 454 6745
Sol: Hartley, Mr Ian John LLB Employee Relations Executive . . . . *Aug 1986
Koser, Ms Reyhana BSc(Hons) Employee Relations Executive . . . . *Sep 2003
Linnett, Ms Victoria LLB Employee Relations Executive*Oct 1994
Lloyd, Mr J Anthony Employment Law Director . . . . *Dec 1976
McKessy, Mrs Emma LLB; MA Employee Relations Executive . . . . *Apr 2004
Sheppard, Mr Roger M Employee Relations Executive Dec 1974
Withers, Mr Scott Paul LLB Employee Relations Executive . . . . *Sep 1997
Wyresdale, Miss Judith LLB Area Director . . . . *Mar 1988

ERNST & YOUNG
1 Colmore Square Birmingham West Midlands B4 6HQ
Tel: 0121 535 2000 *Fax:* 0121 535 2001
Sol: Burston, Mr Richard J Solicitor . . . . Mar 1988

HSBC LEGAL DEPARTMENT
8th Floor 12 Calthorpe Road Edgbaston Birmingham West Midlands B15 1QZ
Tel: 0121 455 2740 *Fax:* 0121 455 2770
Dx: 712633 BIRMINGHAM 32
Sol: Devlia, Arun LLB Deputy Head of Legal, Commercial Banking . . . . *Apr 1999
Falconer, Mr Graeme McDonald LLB(Hons) Deputy Head Of Legal, Personal Financial Services . . . . *Feb 1981
Ford, Mr Keith David BA; LLM Head of Legal . . . . *Nov 1991
Hamilton, Mr Duncan James Fraser LLB(Hons)(B'ham) Deputy Head Of Legal, Personal Transational Banking . . . . *Dec 1987
Holyhead, Ms Lisa BA Solicitor . . . . *Nov 1995
Horton, Mrs Deborah Solicitor . . . . *Nov 1994
Hunt, Mr Jamie I LLB Solicitor . . . . *Oct 1990

Hussain, Mr Razia Mohammed BA(Hons) Solicitor. . . *Oct 1995
Kent, Mr Jeremy Peter Brenton LLB; MA Solicitor . . *Jun 1992
Nightingale, Ms Julia BA Solicitor . . . . *Oct 1987
Phillips, Miss Anne C LLB Solicitor . . . . *Nov 1990
Stewart, Mrs Kate LLB(Hons) Solicitor. . . . . *May 2005

IMI PLC
Lakeside Solihull Parkway Birmingham Business Park Birmingham West Midlands B37 7XZ
Tel: 0121 717 3700 *Fax:* 0121 717 3781
Sol: Boulton, Mr Paul A Solicitor . . . . Nov 1994
Bower, Miss J C Assistant Secretary Solicitor . . . . . Mar 2000
O'Shea, Mr John Solicitor . . . . Feb 1987

LEGAL AID AREA OFFICE NO 6 (WEST MIDLAND)
Centre City Podium 5 Hill Street Birmingham West Midlands B5 4UD
Tel: 0121 632 6541 *Dx:* 13041 BIRMINGHAM
Sol: Brydson, Miss Lindsay A LLB Area Manager Notary Public . . . . *§Dec 1973
Lissett, Mr Stephen W MA(Oxon) Solicitor. . . . . . . *Jun 1980

PRICEWATERHOUSECOOPERS LLP
Cornwall Court 19 Cornwall Street Birmingham West Midlands B3 2DT
Tel: 0121 200 3000 *Fax:* 0121 200 2464
Sol: Coleclough, Mr Stephen D LLB(Sheff); ATII Solicitor. *Sep 1986

RESOLUTION PLC
1 Wythall Green Wythall Birmingham West Midlands B47 6WG
Tel: 01564 828888 *Fax:* 01564 828822
Sol: Bird, Mr James C M LLB Head of Legal . . . . *Oct 1991
Sinclair, Ms Catherine LLB Solicitor . . . . Oct 1991

SALTLEY AND NECHELLS LAW CENTRE
2 Alum Rock Road Saltley Birmingham West Midlands B8 1JB
Tel: 0121 328 2307 *Fax:* 0121 327 7486
E-mail: snlc@snlc.co.uk
Sol: Boyle, Mr Julian Martin LLM Senior Solicitor. . . . . . Feb 2001

SEVERN TRENT WATER LTD
2297 Coventry Road Birmingham West Midlands B26 3PU
Tel: 0121 722 4000 *Fax:* 0121 722 4228 *Dx:* 21806 SHELDON
E-mail: professionalservices@severntrent.co.uk
Sol: Ali, Mr Zahid LLB(Hons) Senior Solicitor. . . . . . . *Dec 2001
Barson, Mr Keith LLB(Hons) Principal Solicitor. . . . *Sep 1994
Lake, Ms Tracy Louise Senior Solicitor . . . . *Nov 2001
Mottram, Mr Clive J G BA(Hons) Company Solicitor. *Nov 1984
Pruce, Mr Anthony S BA Legal Services Manager. . *Nov 1985
Scheepers, Mr Michael Andre BA; BProc Senior Solicitor . . . . Jun 2003

ST MODWEN PROPERTIES PLC
Sir Stanley Clark House 7 Ridgeway Quinton Business Park Birmingham West Midlands B32 1AF
Tel: 0121 222 9400 *Fax:* 0121 222 9401
Sol: Glossop, Mr Charles C A MA(Cantab) Chief Executive *Jul 1967

TRW AUTOMOTIVE
College Road Perry Barr Birmingham West Midlands B44 8DU
Tel: 0121 623 4532 *Fax:* 0121 623 4535
Sol: Almond, Mr Paul M BA Assistant General Counsel . *Dec 1979

UNIVERSITY OF BIRMINGHAM
Legal Services Birmingham West Midlands B15 2TT
Tel: 0121 414 3637 *Fax:* 0121 414 3585
E-mail: law@bham.ac.ukl
Sol: Ash, Mr David LLB(Sheff) Solicitor; Deputy Director of Legal Services . . . . *Jan 1980
Dawson, Ms Diana M BSc; CPE; LSF Solicitor . . . . *Oct 1988
Piggott, Mr James T L BA Assistant Solicitor . . . . . Apr 1988
Pike, Ms Carolyn M E LLB(B'ham) Birmingham Law Society Book Prize Solicitor, Director of Legal Services . . *Oct 1985

WEST MIDLANDS POLICE AUTHORITY
Legal Services Department PO Box 52 Lloyd House Birmingham West Midlands B4 6NQ
Tel: 0121 626 5143 *Fax:* 0121 626 5003 *Dx:* 24926 BIRMINGHAM 4
Sol: Campbell, Miss Emma Jane LLB(Hons); LPC Solicitor *Mar 2006
Kilbey, Mr John M LLB(Hons) Force Solicitor . . . . *May 1976
Smith, Miss Lisa-Marie LLB(Hons) Deputy Force Solicitor . . . . *Jan 1999
Woodman, Mr Jason John BSc Solicitor. . . . . *Apr 1997

WEST MIDLANDS PROBATION BOARD
1 Victoria Square Birmingham West Midlands B1 1BD
Tel: 0121 631 3484 ext: 2007 *Fax:* 0121 631 3749
Sol: Steer, Mr Richard A Secretary & Legal Adviser to the Committee . . . . *§Jul 1971

WEST MIDLANDS TRAVEL LTD
1 Sovereign Court 8 Graham Street Birmingham West Midlands B1 3JR
Tel: 0121 254 7200 *Fax:* 0121 254 7277
Sol: Richards, Mr Lewis LLB(Hull) Solicitor. . . . . *Jun 1968
Rolfe, Mr Christopher J LLB(Wales) Solicitor . . . . . *Jun 1969

BISHOP'S STORTFORD, Hertfordshire

EAST HERTFORDSHIRE DISTRICT COUNCIL
Council Offices The Causeway Bishop's Stortford Hertfordshire CM23 2EN
Tel: 01279 655261 *Fax:* 01279 502015
Dx: 50431 BISHOP'S STORTFORD
E-mail: simon.drinkwater@eastherts.gov.uk
Sol: Drinkwater, Mr Simon P LLB(Lond) Assistant Director of Law & Control . . . . Jan 1980

BISHOPS CLEEVE, Gloucestershire

BOVIS HOMES LTD
South West Region Cleeve Hall Cheltenham Road Bishops Cleeve Gloucestershire GL52 8GD
Tel: 01242 662400 *Fax:* 01242 662471
Dx: 137901 BISHOPS CLEEVE 2
Sol: Carnegie, Mr Keith LLB(Hons) Regional Legal Director*Nov 1995
Stokes, Mr Richard Ian LLB(Hons) Deputy Legal Director . . . . *Jul 1995

BLACKBURN, Blackburn

BLACKBURN WITH DARWEN BOROUGH COUNCIL
Town Hall King William Street Blackburn Blackburn BB1 7DY
Tel: 01254 585585 *Fax:* 01254 585289
Sol: Berry, Miss Sylvia Janet FILEx Deputy Head of Legal Services . . . . *Sep 2003
Bremers, Mr John Edward Projects Manager . . . . . *Jun 1976
Comstive, Ms Linda LLB(Hons); DipLG Director of Legal Services . . . . *Oct 1989
Hammond, Mrs Sally Jane BA(Hons) Senior Solicitor (Social Care) . . . . *Jan 2004
Johnson, Miss Paula Jean LLB(Hons) Solicitor (Social Care) . . . . *Aug 1996
Kauser, Miss Rizwana LLB(Hons); LPC Solicitor. . . *May 2007
Khalifa, Mrs Sajeda LLB Senior Solicitor (Litigation) . . *Apr 2005
Saghir, Miss Rabia LLB(Hons); LPC Solicitor . . . . . *Apr 2007

FORK TRUCK HIRE LTD
Unit 8 Watford St Business Park Blackburn Blackburn BB1 7LD
Tel: 01254 691303 *Fax:* 01254 676373
Sol: Sadiq, Mr Mohammed A Solicitor . . . . Oct 1993

BLACKPOOL

BLACKPOOL BOROUGH COUNCIL
Town Hall PO Box 11 Blackpool FY1 1NB
Tel: 01253 477450 *Fax:* 01253 477449
Sol: Baines, Miss Christine A BTech Chief Solicitor. . . . . *Jan 1982
Cartmell, Miss Victoria Louise BA(Hons); PGDip Licensing Solicitor. . . . . Mar 2007
Laher, Mr Asad Hasan Solicitor . . . . *Sep 2002
Lewis, Mr J W Mark LLB(Hons) Head of Legal and Democratic Services . . . . *Dec 1979
Lindsay, Mrs Julie Anne LLB . . . . *Jun 1999
Long, Ms Alison S LLB(Hons) Principal Solicitor Litigation (Social Services & Housing) . . . . *Oct 1991
Mottershead, Mr Paul Derek BA(Hons) Principal Solicitor - Litigation . . . . *Dec 1984
Pickup, Mrs Maureen BA Principal Solicitor (Property & Commercial) . . . . *Apr 1978
White, Mrs A V Carmel LLB(Hons) . . . . *Jun 1984

BLACKPOOL PLEASURE BEACH GROUP
525 Promenade Blackpool FY4 1EZ
Tel: 01253 341033 *Fax:* 01253 401098
Sol: Kilgallon, Mr Nigel LLB Assistant Group Company Secretary . . . . Jul 1987

BLAYDON-ON-TYNE, Tyne & Wear

BLAYDON MAGISTRATES COURT
Larch Road Blaydon-on-Tyne Tyne & Wear NE21 5AJ
Tel: 0191 414 4244 *Fax:* 0191 414 2537
Sol: Livesley, Mr Christopher J BA(Hons) Justices' Clerk for Gateshead & S.Tyneside Justices Clerk. . . . *§Dec 1976

BODMIN, Cornwall

EAST CORNWALL MAGISTRATES COURTS
The Magistrates' Courts PO Box 2 Launceston Road Bodmin Cornwall PL31 1XQ
Tel: 01208 262700 *Fax:* 01208 77198
Sol: Anthony, Mr Huw Legal Adviser . . . . *Sep 1995
Hancocks, Mr Ivan Legal Adviser . . . . *Jan 1992
Hobson, Mr Karl Douglas James LLB(Hons); ACIM; ACiPD Deputy Clerk to the Justices . . . . *Apr 1995
Kinsley, Mr Paul Legal Adviser . . . . *Jan 2001
Williams, Ms Lorna Patricia Legal Adviser. . . . . . *Nov 1994
Wills, Mr Ian BA(Hons) Legal Adviser . . . . *Oct 1996

BOLTON, Greater Manchester

BOLTON MAGISTRATES COURT
The Courts Civic Centre PO Box 24 Bolton Greater Manchester BL1 1QX
Tel: 01204 558200 *Fax:* 01204 364373 *Dx:* 707360 BOLTON 6
Sol: Connolly, Mr Alan James Principal Legal Advisor . . *Dec 1990
Greenwood, Mrs Jayne LLB(Hons) Legal Adviser . . . Mar 2004
Hutchinson, Miss Nicola Commendation LPC Legal Adviser . . . . Dec 2004
Standish, Ms Trudi A Legal Adviser . . . . *Nov 2000
Taberner, Mrs Christine Alice BA(Hons) Senior Legal Adviser . . . . *Jul 1986
Walker, Mr Robert Ernest Selwyn BA; MBA; MCIPD Head of Legal Services Bolton. . . . . *Jun 1979

BOLTON METROPOLITAN BOROUGH COUNCIL
Town Hall Victoria Square Bolton Greater Manchester BL1 1RU
Tel: 01204 333333 *Fax:* 01204 301060
E-mail: boltonmbc.legal@iclweb.com
Sol: Aswat, Miss Amina Ismail LLB(Hons) Solicitor. . . . *Nov 1997
Begum, Miss Rehana BA(Hons); CPE; LPC Solicitor . Sep 1996
Gaskell, Mrs Anne Solicitor . . . . Jun 1991
Gorman, Ms Helen LLB(Hons) Solicitor . . . . *Oct 1990
Lewis, Mrs Hilary LLB Senior Lawyer . . . . *Apr 1980
Mackley, Mr David BA(Hons) Solicitor. . . . . Jul 2001
Morris, Mr Andrew BA(Wales); MA(L'pool) Solicitor . *Nov 1990
Owen, Miss Ceri Iona Evan LLB(Hons) Solicitor. . . . *Oct 1991
Parr, Mr Gary J BA(Oxon); MA . . . . *Nov 1990
Pope, Ms Nikki BA; MPhil Solicitor . . . . Nov 1997
Stone, Mrs Susan Caroline BA(Hons) Solicitor. . . . *Apr 1981
Stoney, Ms Margaret C BA Assistant Head of Legal Services . . . . *Oct 1984
Waudby, Miss Catherine E LLB Solicitor. . . . . . . *Feb 1991
Wilson, Mr Peter Solicitor Assistant Deputy Coroner. . *Jan 1974

BOREHAMWOOD, Hertfordshire

P E S CONSULTING LTD
9 Gables Avenue Borehamwood Hertfordshire WD6 4SP
Sol: Bailey, Miss Sharon J BA Solicitor. . . . . *Oct 1980

PINNACLE INSURANCE PLC
Pinnacle House A1 Barnet Way Borehamwood Hertfordshire WD6 2XX
Tel: 020 8207 9000 *Fax:* 020 8207 2078
E-mail: matthew.lorimer@cardifpinnacle.com
Sol: Brady, Ms Abigail LLB Solicitor . . . . *Nov 1994
Georgeou, Ms Andrea Sophia LLB(Hons); LLM Solicitor . . . . *Sep 2000
Kotecha, Ms Poona Solicitor. . . . . Apr 2007
Lewin, Mr Jonathan Solicitor. . . . . Mar 2007
Livingston, Mrs Sarah Solicitor . . . . Mar 2004
Lorimer, Mr Matthew Justin LLB Head of Legal . . . *Oct 1992
Talisman, Mrs Naomi Solicitor. . . . . *Sep 2000

BOSTON, Lincolnshire

BOSTON BOROUGH COUNCIL
Municipal Buildings West Street Boston Lincolnshire PE21 8QR
Tel: 01205 314200 *Fax:* 01205 364604 *Dx:* 26823 BOSTON
Sol: Newboult-Robertson, Mrs Kim Marie Assistant Solicitor Sep 2003

BOURNEMOUTH

BOURNEMOUTH BOROUGH COUNCIL
Town Hall Borne Avenue Bournemouth BH2 6DY
Tel: 01202 451178 *Fax:* 01202 451001
Dx: 156942 BOURNEMOUTH 3
E-mail: khai.ngnyen@bournemouth.gov.uk
Sol: Cole, Mrs Linda Ann BA Senior Solicitor. . . . . . . *Mar 2002
Coulter, Ms Tanya J LLB(Hons) Principal Solicitor . . *Nov 1996
Ferguson, Mrs Maxine Senior Solicitor. . . . . *Sep 1998
Gollogly, Mr Brendan R BA(Hons) Senior Solicitor. . . . Oct 2004
Nguyen, Mr Khai Licencie en Droit Legal Service Manager . . . . *Mar 1981
O'Sullivan, Miss Elizabeth M LLB Senior Solicitor . . . Sep 2001
Poole, Miss Susan Patricia LLB(Hons) Senior Solicitor*Sep 1993
Postings, Mrs Joy B Juris; LLB Head of Law and Corporate Governance. . . . . Nov 1987
Rafter, Miss Nicolette J LLB(Hons) Senior Solicitor . *Apr 1991
Travers, Ms Susan J LLB(Hons) Principal Solicitor. . *Oct 1991
Turner, Mrs Susan BA(Hons) Senior Solicitor . . . . . *Apr 1994
Whittle, Mr Martin LLB(Exon) Principal Solicitor . . . *§Jul 1973
Williams, Miss Helen E LLB Senior Solicitor. . . . . . *Jun 1979

CROWN PROSECUTION SERVICE DORSET
1st Floor Oxford House Oxford Road Bournemouth BH8 8HA
Tel: 01202 498700 *Fax:* 01202 498701 *Dx:* 7699 BOURNEMOUTH
Sol: Baugh, Mr Julian N Solicitor. . . . . Jun 1989
Branford, Miss Carolyn R BA Solicitor. . . . . Jun 1985
Cordy, Ms Theresa A Solicitor. . . . . Jun 1977
Graham, Mr Ian A Solicitor . . . . Dec 1973
Grier, Mr Clifford Solicitor . . . . Jan 1994
Griffin, Mr Paul Solicitor. . . . . *Jun 1977
Hall, Mr Roger Solicitor . . . . *Jun 1974
Hopkins, Mrs Shirley H LLB Solicitor. . . . . Oct 1979
Kingdon, Mr Jonathan F BA Solicitor . . . . *Oct 1982
Matthews, Mr Patrick L J BSc(Lond) Solicitor . . . . *§Dec 1977
O'Sullivan, Mr Timothy D J Solicitor. . . . . Apr 1988
Oakley, Mr Richard J Solicitor. . . . . Feb 1988
Revell, Mr John W BA Solicitor . . . . *Jan 1973
Tewksbury, Mr Peter R BA(Oxon) Solicitor. . . . . . *Jul 1971
Woodward, Mrs Julia A BA Solicitor. . . . . *§Apr 1981

LLOYDS TSB ASSET FINANCE DIVISION LTD
Vanburgh House Grange Drive Southampton SO30 2AF
Tel: 01489 776880 *Fax:* 01489 776885
Sol: Collins, Ms Rosemary C Solicitor . . . . Mar 1989
Dickins, Mr Guy C BA Solicitor . . . . *May 1988
Hallatt, Mr F David LLB Head of Legal Services. . . *Nov 1970
Kilbee, Mr Michael P Legal Director. . . . . *Jun 1972

MCCARTHY & STONE PLC
Homelife House 26-32 Oxford Road Bournemouth BH8 8EZ
Tel: 01202 292480 *Fax:* 01202 298616 / 508093
Dx: 7665 BOURNEMOUTH
E-mail: trevor.green@mccarthyandstone.co.uk
Sol: Bowman, Mrs Rosemary W Solicitor. . . . . *Dec 1980
Chase, Mrs Beverley M LLB; LLM Solicitor . . . . . *Dec 1979
Green, Mr Trevor L LLB Company Secretary & Head of Legal Services . . . . *Nov 1971
Heath, Mr Julian James Martin LLB Solicitor. . . . . . Oct 1986
Southorn, Mr Andrew Timothy MA(Oxon) Principle Land Solicitor . . . . *Jun 1974

BRACKNELL, Bracknell Forest

AVIS MANAGEMENT SERVICES LTD
Avis House Park Road Bracknell Bracknell Forest RG12 2EW
Tel: 01344 462644 *Fax:* 01344 869194
Sol: Nicholson, Ms Judith A Solicitor. . . . . Apr 1980

BRACKNELL FOREST BOROUGH COUNCIL
Easthampstead House Town Square Bracknell Bracknell Forest RG12 1AQ
Tel: 01344 424642 *Fax:* 01344 352236 *Dx:* 33611 BLACKNELL
Sol: Bhatti, Mrs Inderjit LLB Assistant Solicitor. . . . . . *Aug 1998
Brewster, Ms Helen BA(Hons) Senior Assistant Solicitor . . . . Nov 1992
Bull, Mr Simon John CQSW Assistant Borough Solicitor . . . . May 1992
Heard, Mr Simon George BA(Hons)(Law) Assistant Borough Solicitor. . . . . *Mar 1981
Igbiniyesu, Mr Anthony O BA(Hons) Senior Assistant Solicitor . . . . Apr 1998
Sellick, Mr Simon C BA(Bris) Principal Legal Assistant *Mar 1978
Watts, Mrs Jennifer Anne Senior Solicitor . . . . Nov 1994
Woods, Mrs Jacqueline BA Assistant Solicitor. . . . . Mar 1986

See p112 for the Key to Work Categories & other symbols

CIT GROUP (UK) LTD
Ringside House 79 High Street Bracknell Bracknell Forest RG12 1DZ
Tel: 01344 827200 *Fax:* 01344 383901
Sol: McKee, Mr Mark A Solicitor . . . . Mar 1998

CADENCE DESIGN SYSTEMS LTD
Bagshot Road Bracknell Bracknell Forest RG12 0PH
Tel: 01344 865445 *Fax:* 01344 866510
E-mail: chrisp@cadence.com
Sol: Pahljina, Mr Christopher Joseph LLB; LLM Solicitor . . *Sep 1994

DELL COMPUTER CORPORATION LTD
Milbank House Western Road Bracknell Bracknell Forest RG12 1RW
Tel: 01344 860456
Sol: Norman, Mr D Richard LLM Solicitor . . . . *Jan 1979
Peacock, Ms Belinda LLB(Hull) Solicitor . . . . Nov 1990

HEWLETT-PACKARD LTD
Amen Corner Cain Road Bracknell Bracknell Forest RG12 1HN
Tel: 01344 360000 *Fax:* 01344 362224
Sol: Bains, Mr P Nigel BA Senior Commercial Lawyer . . . *Apr 1979
John, Mr Gareth Luke Sefton LLB(Exon) Legal Counsel UK & Ireland . . . . *Mar 1994
Patterson, Mr John M LLB Senior Commercial Lawyer *Dec 1988

MSAS CARGO INTERNATIONAL LTD
Ocean House The Ring Bracknell Bracknell Forest RG12 1AW
Tel: 01344 52222 *Fax:* 01344 710037
Sol: Wood, Mrs Susan C BA(Law) Solicitor . . . . *Feb 1988

MOWLEM PLC
Foundation House Eastern Road Bracknell Bracknell Forest RG12 2UZ
Tel: 01344 426826 *Fax:* 01344 868621
Sol: Jackson, Mr Bruce LLM; BSc Solicitor . . . . *Jul 1979

NOVELL UK LTD
Novell House 1 Arlington Square Downshire Way Bracknell Bracknell Forest RG12 1WA
Tel: 01344 724000 *Fax:* 01344 724250
E-mail: ncurphey@novell.com
Sol: Maru, Nitin Solicitor . . . . *Jan 1990

BRADFORD, West Yorkshire

BRADFORD LAW CENTRE
31 Manor Row Bradford West Yorkshire BD1 4PX
Tel: 01274 306617
Sol: Manley, Ms Isabel A BA Solicitor . . . . *Jan 1986

BRADFORD MAGISTRATES COURT
PO Box 187 The Tyrls Bradford West Yorkshire BD1 1JL
Tel: 01274 390111 *Fax:* 01274 391731
Sol: Gray, Mr Frank District Legal Director . . . . *Nov 1983

CITY OF BRADFORD METROPOLITAN DISTRICT COUNCIL
City Hall Market Street Bradford West Yorkshire BD1 1HY
Tel: 01274 752236 *Fax:* 01274 730337 *Dx:* 11758 BRADFORD
E-mail: suzan.hemingway@bradford.gov.uk
Sol: Bailey, Ms Linda J MA Senior Solicitor . . . . *Oct 1989
Balsham, Mr Jonathan S LLB; FRSA Senior Solicitor *§Jun 1977
Bell, Ms Sarah Christine BA Senior Solicitor . . . . . Jan 1991
Davies, Mrs Catherine E BSc Deputy Team Solicitor . . *Oct 1989
Dwyer, Mr Paul Team Solicitor . . . . *Jun 1989
Fleming, Mr Stephen Michael FILEx Senior Solicitor . . *Jun 1994
Gleeson, Ms Joanne Solicitor . . . . Jan 1998
Gul, Miss Zahida Saba LLB(Hons); LLM; LPC . . . . *Aug 2004
Hill, Ms Amanda C LLB(Hons) Team Solicitor . . . . *§Oct 1989
Howard, Miss Sandra Louise LLB Deputy Team Leader Jan 1996
King, Ms Patricia E BA Senior Solicitor . . . . *Dec 1990
Lewis-Smith, Mr Dyfrig Wyn LLB(Hons) Senior Solicitor Sep 1996
Moraghan, Ms Marion R LLB Senior Solicitor . . . . . *Oct 1989
Mosley, Mrs Karen E BA Senior Solicitor . . . . *Jan 1985
Ryatt, Mr Harjit BA(Hons)(Law) Dept. Team Leader . . *Dec 1997
Sheldon, Mrs Claire E LLB(Hons) Senior Solicitor . . . Apr 1996
Smith, Ms Mary C BA Senior Solicitor . . . . Nov 1988
Suadwa, Mr Francis BA Team Solicitor . . . . *Dec 1986
Wilson, Ms Rosalind M S MA . . . . *Oct 1982
Winter, Mr Richard J BA(Law); LLB(Hons) Team Solicitor . . . . *Sep 1981

PROVIDENT PERSONAL CREDIT LTD
Colonnade Sunbridge Road Bradford West Yorkshire BD1 2LQ
Tel: 01274 733321 *Fax:* 01274 734397
Sol: Allison, Mr Peter LLB Solicitor . . . . *Jan 1982
Rees, Mr David M LLB Group Legal Adviser . . . . . . *Apr 1977

UNITED COOPERATIVES LTD
Sandbrook Park Sandbrook Way Rochdale Greater Manchester OL11 1RX
Tel: 01706 202020 *Fax:* 01706 202194
E-mail: steven.silver@coop.co.uk
Sol: Everett, Mr Stephen Raymond BA(Hons) Solicitor . . . *Jan 1973
Parry, Mr Stephen BSc Solicitor . . . . Sep 2001
Silver, Mr Steven Russell BA(Dunelm) Head of Legal Services . . . . *Jun 1986

WEST YORKSHIRE FIRE & CIVIL DEFENCE AUTHORITY
Oakroyd Hall Birkenshaw Bradford West Yorkshire BD11 2DY
Tel: 01274 682311 *Fax:* 01274 655892
Sol: Barnes, Mr Michael G BA(Sheff) Solicitor . . . . . . *Oct 1982

YORKSHIRE BUILDING SOCIETY
Group Legal Yorkshire House Yorkshire Drive Bradford West Yorkshire BD5 8LJ *Fax:* 01274 472251 *Dx:* 11762 BRADFORD 1
E-mail: cjfaulkner@ybs.co.uk
Sol: Faulkner, Mr C John BA(Lond) General Counsel . . . *Dec 1977

YORKSHIRE WATER SERVICES LTD
Western House Halifax Road Bradford West Yorkshire BD6 2SZ
Tel: 01274 804159 *Fax:* 01274 804158
Sol: Clyne, Miss Lisa Marie LLB(Hons) Assistant Commercial Solicitor . . . . Aug 2006
Flood, Ms Shona J LLB; MA(Environmental Law) Senior Solicitor . . . . *Nov 1989
Goldthorp, Mr Dominic LLB Solicitor . . . . *Aug 2004
Kaur, Miss Perminder LLB(Hons) Solicitor . . . . Sep 2001
McFarlane, Mr Stuart Douglas LLB Head of Legal Services . . . . Mar 1984

Newton, Mr Andrew LLB(Hons) Solicitor . . . . Nov 2000
Stevens, Mr Matthew David Rhys LLB(Hons) Solicitor . Jun 2000

BRECON, Powys

BRECON BEACONS NATIONAL PARK AUTHORITY
Plas-y-Ffynnon Cambrian Way Brecon Powys LD3 7HP
Tel: 01874 624437 *Fax:* 01874 622574
E-mail: enquiries@breconbeacons.org
Sol: Coughlan, Mrs Lynne LLB Solicitor . . . . Oct 1990

POWYS COUNTY COUNCIL
Neuadd Brycheiniog Cambrian Way Brecon Powys LD3 7HR
Tel: 01874 624141 *Fax:* 01874 612046
Sol: Doylend, Mr Richard O LLB Chief Executive . . . . . Jun 1972
Eagle, Mr Roger J BA(Keele) Deputy Chief Executive . Jul 1975
Meredith, Mr Clarence J LLB; DMA; ACIS Principal Solicitor . . . . *Jul 1990

BRENTFORD, Middlesex

CONSOLIDATED FINANCIAL INSURANCE
Building 11 Chiswick Park Chiswick High Road London W4 5XR
Tel: 020 8380 3000 *Fax:* 020 8380 3065
Sol: Purcell, Miss Sally A LLB . . . . Nov 1995

BRENTWOOD, Essex

BISHOPSCOURT GROUP SERVICES LTD
6th Floor Regent House Hubert Road Brentwood Essex CM14 4JE
Tel: 01277 247304 *Fax:* 01277 247320
Sol: Billing, Mr Michael J ACII; Cert PFS; FCol Group Company Secretary . . . . *Oct 1982

BRENTWOOD BOROUGH COUNCIL
Council Offices Ingrave Road Brentwood Essex CM15 8AY
Tel: 01277 261111 *Fax:* 01277 312743 *Dx:* 5001 BRENTWOOD
Sol: Keane, Mr Brian D P LLB Solicitor . . . . Feb 1980

COUNTRYSIDE PROPERTIES PLC
Countryside House The Drive Brentwood Essex CM13 3AT
Tel: 01277 260000 *Fax:* 01277 690618 *Dx:* 124280 BRENTWOOD 4
Sol: Dowding, Ms Angela B MA(Business Law) Group Chief Solicitor . . . . Oct 1987
Kelly, Ms Louise Assistant Solicitor . . . . Jul 1997
Stephenson, Ms Colleen M Assistant Solicitor . . . . . *Dec 1992

FCE BANK PLC
Jubilee House The Drive Brentwood Essex CM13 3AR
Tel: 01277 692280 / 692281 *Fax:* 01277 233722
Sol: Robinson, Mr David Nicholas LLB(Hons) Legal Adviser Nov 1994

FORD MOTOR COMPANY LTD
Central Office Eagle Way Brentwood Essex CM13 3BW
Tel: 01277 253000 *Fax:* 01277 252676
Sol: Khan, Miss Monazza LLB Director of Legal Affairs . . . *Oct 1988
Page, Mr Clive C LLB(Lond) Company Secretary & Senior Attorney O.G.C. . . . . *Jun 1979
Robinson, Mr David Nicholas LLB(Hons) . . . . Nov 1994

LOVATS
Highway House 171 Kings Road Brentwood Essex CM14 4EJ
Tel: 01277 263081 *Fax:* 01277 260101 *Dx:* 96150 BRENTWOOD 2
E-mail: gareth_e@hway.co.uk
Sol: Hall, Ms Karen J Legal Executive . . . . Jan 1999
Olley, Alyce Solicitor . . . . Sep 1996

BRIDGEND

BRIDGEND COUNTY BOROUGH COUNCIL
Civic Offices Angel Street Bridgend CF31 4WB
Tel: 01656 643643 *Fax:* 01656 657899 *Dx:* 151420 BRIDGEND 6
Sol: Barry, Miss Sharon C LLB Principal Solicitor . . . . . . *Oct 1995
Batten, Mr J Hywel Senior Solicitor . . . . *Sep 1976
Belliss, Miss Charlotte K Dip LG Senior Solicitor . . . . *Oct 1998
Daniel, Mr Stephen W LLB(Wales) Monitoring Officer (Solicitor to the Council) . . . . Jul 1974
Davies, Ms Eileen LLB Senior Solicitor . . . . *May 1986
Godfrey, Mr Richard Julian MA(Oxon) Senior Solicitor . *Jun 1980
Hughes, Mr Robert S LLB(Wolv) Principal Solicitor . . *Mar 1983
Jolley, Mr P Andrew BA; LLB; LLM; MBA Head of Legal Services . . . . Oct 1991

SOUTH WALES POLICE
Police Headquarters Cowbridge Road Bridgend CF31 3SU
Tel: 01656 869476 *Fax:* 01656 302103
Sol: Brennan, Mrs Nia Prys LLB Senior Solicitor . . . . . . *Nov 1995
Hill, Mr R Leighton LLB(Wales) Assistant Director, Legal Services . . . . *§Mar 1986
Madge, Mr David Gareth LLB(Wales) Director of Legal Services . . . . *§Oct 1979
White, Mrs Nicola J LLB(Hons) Assistant Solicitor . . . *Feb 2003

BRIDGWATER, Somerset

SEDGEMOOR DISTRICT COUNCIL
Bridgwater House King Square Bridgwater Somerset TA6 3AR
Tel: 01278 424391 / 435435 *Fax:* 01278 446412
Dx: 80619 BRIDGWATER
Sol: Spencer, Mr Colin . . . . *Dec 1965

BRIGHTON, Brighton & Hove

BRIGHTON HOUSING TRUST
Community Base Queens Road Brighton Brighton & Hove BN1 3XG
Tel: 01273 234737 *Fax:* 01273 234736
Sol: Fanning, Mr Stephen James BA(Hons) Solicitor . . . . *Jun 1993

EAST SUSSEX COUNTY COUNCIL
Law Courts Edward Street Brighton Brighton & Hove BN2 2LG
Tel: 01273 670888 *Fax:* 01273 790260 *Dx:* 97482 LEWES 3
Sol: Carter, Ms Susan M LLB(Hons) Solicitor . . . . *Jul 1979
Goodbody, Miss Samantha Jane Ward MA Legal Adviser . . . . *Nov 1988

2

BRISTOL

ALCAN HOLDINGS UK LTD AND LAWSON MARDON PACKAGING LTD AND BRITISH ALCAN ALUMINIUM PLC
AL House 83 Tower Road North Warmley Bristol BS30 8XP
Tel: 0117 915 3000 *Fax:* 0117 915 3057
E-mail: kate.anthony-wilkinson@alcan.com
Sol: Anthony Wilkinson, Ms Katherine F LLB(Hons) Director of Legal Services & Company Secretary . . . . *Oct 1989

AVON & BRISTOL LAW CENTRE
2 Moon Street Stokes Croft Bristol BS2 8QE
Tel: 0117 924 8662 *Fax:* 0117 924 8020
E-mail: mail@ablc.demon.co.uk
Sol: Garel, Ms Janine Myfanwy LLB; LSF Solicitor . . . . . *Jan 1995
Goodridge, Ms Claire LLB Solicitor . . . . *May 2003
O'Sullivan, Mr Michael John LLB Solicitor . . . . *Jul 1991

BANK OF IRELAND UK FINANCIAL SERVICES
PO Box 27 Temple Quay Bristol BS99 7AX
Tel: 0117 979 2222 *Fax:* 0117 929 1115 *Dx:* 98850 BRISTOL
Sol: Duncan, Chris BCom Solicitor . . . . May 1997
Meyler, Mr Gary BCL Solicitor . . . . *Jan 1991
Williams, Mr Thomas A S LLB Senior Lawyer . . . . . Jan 1998

BRISTOL CITY COUNCIL
Legal Department Council House College Green Bristol BS1 5TR
Tel: 0117 922 2000 *Fax:* 0117 922 2172 *Dx:* 7827
Sol: Allen, Mrs Lara M J LLB Solicitor . . . . Nov 1993
Aziz, Ms Naseem Solicitor . . . . Apr 2001
Bhogal, Mrs Manjit Kaur LLB Solicitor . . . . *Oct 1996
Bond, Ms Frances LLB(Hons); PGDip Lyons Davidson Prize Solicitor . . . . Sep 2000
Brooke-Taylor, Mr John Dury Solicitor . . . . Nov 1972
Burgoyne, Miss Diane E LLB Solicitor . . . . *Nov 1991
Cox, Mr David . . . . Jul 1997
Dawson, Ms Sheelagh E M BA Solicitor . . . . *Feb 1984
Daya, Mrs Shahzia Solicitor . . . . Mar 1993
Denford, Mr Robin Solicitor . . . . May 1996
Dunsdon, Mr Tom C Solicitor . . . . Nov 2003
Etim-Gorst, Miss Teresa Solicitor . . . . Sep 1997
Evans, Mr Andrew . . . . Apr 1991
Freestone, Miss Catherine May LLB Solicitor . . . . . *Sep 1991
Fryer, Ms Catherine A Solicitor . . . . Jan 2006
Gould, Ms Heidi Louise Solicitor . . . . *Oct 1995
Grazier, Ms Elizabeth Solicitor . . . . Mar 2002
Harvey, Ms Lynne J Solicitor . . . . Sep 2005
Hill, Mr David Kevin BSc(Hons)(Econ) Solicitor . . . . *Oct 2001
Horner, Miss Frances M BA Solicitor . . . . *Sep 1986
Johnson, Ms Rachel M Solicitor . . . . Sep 2002
Kendrick, Miss Angela J BA Solicitor . . . . *Mar 1980
Lank, Ms Claudia BA Solicitor . . . . Sep 1990
Leach, Ms Alison S Solicitor . . . . Oct 1991
Lodge, Ms Lisa- Sian Solicitor . . . . Sep 2000
McNamara, Mr Stephen BA Head Of Legal Services . *Oct 1985
Malarby, Mr Peter A LLB(Exon) Solicitor . . . . *Feb 1983
Mansfield, Mrs Joanne M LLB Solicitor . . . . *Mar 1989
Martin, Ms Louise Solicitor . . . . Dec 1988
Moore, Mr Oliver E Solicitor . . . . Oct 1992
Nugent, Ms Anne Solicitor . . . . Feb 2003
Powell, Mrs Pauline S Solicitor . . . . Jan 1995
Reynolds, Mr Edward M MA(Cantab) Solicitor . . . . . Oct 1998
Roberts, Ms Joanna Solicitor . . . . §Jan 1996
Rollason, Ms Nancy LLB Solicitor . . . . Aug 1990
Seneque, Ms Genevieve BSc Solicitor . . . . *Sep 1990
Sharland, Ms Sarah B Solicitor . . . . Nov 1991
Simpson, Ms Dierdre Solicitor . . . . Sep 1998
Stibbs, Miss Nicola LLB Solicitor . . . . *Sep 2002
Wiles, Mr Barrington J LLB(Hons) . . . . *Apr 1974
Wilford, Miss Penny BSc Solicitor . . . . *Nov 1992
Woodward, Ms Helen . . . . Apr 1991

BRISTOL WATER PLC
PO Box 218 Bridgwater Road Bristol BS99 7AU
Tel: 0117 966 5881 *Fax:* 0117 963 3755
E-mail: stephen.robson@bristolwater.co.uk
Sol: Robson, Mr Stephen C R LLB Company Secretary . . May 1995
Scrivens, Mr Stuart Neil LLB Solicitor . . . . Jan 1993

BRITISH AEROSPACE AIRBUS
Legal Department New Filton House Bristol BS99 7AR
Tel: 0117 966 5881 *Fax:* 0117 936 2680
Sol: Jones, Ms Catherine A LLB(Lond) Solicitor . . . . . . *Sep 1988

CAPITA GROUP PLC
Quays Office Park Conference Avenue Portishead Bristol BS20 7LZ
Tel: 01275 840840 *Fax:* 01275 840830
Sol: Parmar, Ms Inderjit S Solicitor . . . . Apr 1992

CROWN PROSECUTION SERVICE AVON & SOMERSET
2nd Floor Froomsgate House Rupert Street Bristol BS1 2QJ
Tel: 0117 930 2800 *Fax:* 0117 930 2810 *Dx:* 78120 BRISTOL
Sol: Carpenter, Mr Stephen C Solicitor . . . . Jun 1981
Diaper, Mr Simon J Solicitor . . . . May 1983
Jones, Mr Christopher T LLB(Lond) . . . . *Dec 1966
Lane, Mrs Alexandra M LLB Solicitor . . . . *Feb 1980
Llewelyn, Mr William W Solicitor . . . . *Dec 1970
Macdonald, Miss Patricia M Solicitor . . . . Nov 1984
May, Mrs Anne C BA(Law) Solicitor . . . . *Feb 1981
Meyer, Miss Lindi G LLB Solicitor . . . . Jul 1988
Philip, Ms Sarah Solicitor . . . . Jun 1989
Pixton, Mr Brian L Solicitor . . . . *Feb 1970
Smith, Mr Peter R C LLB Solicitor . . . . Jan 1982
Vining, Mr Rupert L Solicitor . . . . Feb 1990
Westcott, Ms Rosetta Solicitor . . . . Sep 1994

DAS LEGAL EXPENSES INSURANCE & CO LTD
DAS House Quayside Temple Back Bristol BS1 6NH
Tel: 0117 934 2000 *Fax:* 0117 934 2109
Sol: Howells, Mr David A Deputy Claims Manager . . . . . *Feb 1977

EEF WESTERN
Engineer's House The Promenade Clifton Down Bristol BS8 3NB
Tel: 0117 906 4800 *Fax:* 0117 973 6010
E-mail: mktg@eef-west.org.uk
Sol: Chesterfield, Mr Hugh N E LLB . . . . . *Apr 1981
Menzies, Mr Luke BA(Hons) ER Advisor. . . . Oct 1997

GE CAPITAL SOLUTIONS
2630 The Quadrant Aztec West Bristol BS32 4GQ
Tel: 0870 241 8899 *Fax:* 0870 191 0456
E-mail: janet.gregory@gecapital.com
Sol: Gregory, Ms Janet A LLB(Lond) Solicitor . . . *§Apr 1977

IMPERIAL TOBACCO GROUP PLC
PO Box 244 Upton Road Southville Bristol BS99 7UJ
Tel: 0117 963 6636 *Fax:* 0117 966 7957
Sol: Evans, Mr Roger LLB(Hons); LLM Solicitor(Intellectual Property Counsel. . . . Sep 2000
Haines, Mr Simon CPE; LPC Legal Counsel. . . . Jun 2002
Hamshaw-Thomas, Mr Charles W MA(Cantab) Solicitor . . . . *Dec 1985
Matloubi, Miss Rebekah LLB Lawyer . . . . Sep 2002
Tate, Mr Conrad R LLB Senior Legal Counsel . . . *Sep 1997

LEGAL AID AREA OFFICE NO 4 (SOUTH WESTERN)
Queen's Quay 33-35 Queen Square Bristol BS1 4LU
Tel: 0117 921 4801 *Dx:* 7852 BRISTOL
Sol: Clark, Ms Pauline Susan LLB Solicitor. . . . *Nov 1991
Richards, Mr Robin W V Solicitor . . . . *Oct 1976
Stevens, Mr John R MA(Cantab) Solicitor . . . *May 1984

LLOYDS TSB GROUP PLC
Canons House Canons Way Bristol BS99 7LB
Tel: 0117 905 5500
Sol: Badham, Ms Jayne Solicitor. . . . Jan 2001
Chan, Ms Mei Yen LLB(Bris) Laurence Kingsley Prize for Drafting & Pleading Solicitor. . . . *Oct 1992
Crawford, Ms Lisa Senior Solicitor. . . . Jan 1991
Howells, Mr Phillip Maxwell LLB(Hons) Solicitor . . . *Jun 1993
Wright, Miss Kim L LLB Senior Solicitor . . . *Sep 1989

MERCHANT INVESTORS ASSURANCE CO LTD
St Bartholomew's House Lewins Mead Bristol BS1 2NH
Tel: 0117 926 6366 *Fax:* 0117 975 2144
E-mail: enq@merchant-investors.co.uk
Sol: Edmonds, Mr Martin Westmoreland Solicitor. . . . Jul 1994

ORANGE PCS LTD
St James Court Great Park Road Bradley Stoke Bristol BS32 4QJ
Tel: 0870 376 8888 *Fax:* 01454 618501
Sol: Bellamy, Ms Sonia V LLB(Hons) Senior Legal Counsel May 1994
Doyle, Mrs Amanda LLB(Hons)(Warw) UK Group Counsel . . . . *Oct 1988
Gibson, Ms Lyndall Claire BA(Biochemistry); CPE; LSF; PGDipIPLP Legal Adviser. . . . *Nov 1994
Harrap, Mr Richard John LLB(Hons); PGDipLP Legal Adviser . . . . *Sep 1996
Knight, Ms Kathryn Jane LLB(ELS) Legal Adviser . . *Sep 1999
Nicoll, Miss Susan Margaret MA; LLB(Hons); DipLP Legal Adviser . . . . Dec 1987
Ralston, Mr Michael D Senior Legal Counsel . . . *§Jul 1976
Redford-Crowe, Mr David Charles LLB(Hons) Legal Adviser . . . . Nov 1993
Sandford, Mr Jeremy Wilfrid BA; CPE; LPC Legal Adviser . . . . *Sep 1998
Smith, Mr Richard Lindley BA(Hons) Legal Advisor . . Sep 1996
Speed, Mr Thomas Prescott LLB Legal Adviser . . . *§Oct 1993
Tomlinson, Ms Sarah Ann Catherine BA; CPE; LSF Legal Adviser . . . . *Nov 1995
Tucker, Mr Adam LLB(Hons) Senior Legal Advisor. . . *Oct 1996

RAC MOTORING SERVICES
RAC House Great Park Road Bradley Stoke Bristol BS32 4QN
Tel: 0870 553 3533 *Fax:* 01454 208222
Sol: Bradley, Mr Phillip B LLB . . . . Apr 2000
Butler, Mr Craig LLB . . . . *Nov 1994
Coleman, Mr Neil LLB(Hons) . . . . Oct 1993
Greer, Mr Alastair D. . . . . Aug 2001
Kaur, Mrs Lakhbir LLB(Hons); LLM . . . . Dec 2002
Mitchell, Mr Shaun P LLB(Hons); LSF. . . . Oct 2000

REDROW PLC
Redrow House 79 Macrae Road Ham Green Bristol BS20 0EB
Tel: 01275 813350 *Fax:* 01275 813365
Dx: 33365 WESTBURY-ON-TRYM
E-mail: nick.dell@redrow.co.uk
Sol: Dell, Mr Nicholas John BA(Hons); LLM Legal Director & Company Solicitor. . . . *May 1990

ROLLS-ROYCE PLC
PO Box 3 Filton Bristol BS34 7QE
Tel: 0117 979 7149 *Fax:* 0117 979 7208
Sol: Revelle, Mr Peter Charles Solicitor . . . . *Apr 1968

SOMERFIELD STORES LTD
Somerfield House Whitchurch Lane Bristol BS14 0TJ
Tel: 0117 935 6135 *Fax:* 0117 301 0030
Sol: Bailey, Mr Miles Thomas LLB; BA Property Solicitor. *Sep 2001
Eastwood, Mr David J Employment Solicitor. . . . *Jan 1998
Nightingale, Ms Catherine BA Commercial Solicitor . . Jun 2006

SUSTRANS LTD
2 Cathedral Square College Green Bristol BS1 5DD
Tel: 0117 926 8893 *Fax:* 0117 915 0225
Sol: Otty, Mrs Susan MA(Cantab) Solicitor. . . . *Jul 1965

TILEFLAIR LTD
Highwood Lane Cribbs Causeway Bristol BS34 5TQ
Tel: 0117 959 8877 *Fax:* 0117 959 8801
Sol: Broadhurst, Mrs Lesley R LLB Company Director, Secretary & Solicitor. . . . *Dec 1978

UNITED BRISTOL HEALTHCARE NHS TRUST
Trust Headquarters Marlborough Street Bristol BS1 3NG
Tel: 0117 928 3730
E-mail: peter.harrowing@ubht.nhs.uk
Sol: Harrowing, Mr Peter D Solicitor . . . . Jun 1997

UNIVERSITY OF THE WEST OF ENGLAND, BRISTOL
Faculty of Law Coldharbour Lane Frenchay Bristol BS16 1QY
Tel: 0117 965 6261 *Fax:* 0117 976 3841
E-mail: universityofthewestofbristol@uwe.ac.uk
Sol: Evans, Mr William L H MA University Secretary & Solicitor . . . . *Jan 1969

BROADWAY, Worcestershire

GLOBAL SOLUTIONS LTD
Farncombe House Broadway Worcestershire WR12 7LJ
Tel: 01386 858585
Sol: Gordon, Mr James Christian Douglas LLB Company Solicitor . . . . Oct 1983
Major, Mrs Sandra M LLB(Hons) Group Legal Director & Company Secretary. . . . *Oct 1988

BROMLEY, Kent

BROMLEY MAGISTRATES COURT
The Court House 1 London Road Bromley Kent BR1 1RA
Tel: 0845 601 3600 *Fax:* 020 8437 3506 *Dx:* 119601 BROMLEY 8
Sol: Boateng-Ennin, Mrs Nana Akousa A LLB(Business Law) Legal Adviser . . . . Sep 2005
Morgan, Mrs Valerie A C LLB Deputy Clerk to the Justices . . . . *Oct 1983

NORMAN BUTCHER AND JONES HOLDINGS LTD
NBJ House 2 Southlands Road Bromley Kent BR2 9QP
Sol: Hutchison, Mr Roger A LLB Solicitor. . . . *§Jun 1970

MSB INTERNATIONAL PLC
Hanover Place 8 Ravensbourne Road Bromley Kent BR1 1HP
Tel: 020 8315 9000 *Fax:* 020 8315 9001
E-mail: legal@msb.com
Sol: Marlow, Mr Graham J BA(Hons) Company Solicitor . . *Oct 1996

BROMSGROVE, Worcestershire

BROMSGROVE DISTRICT COUNCIL
Council House Burcot Lane Bromsgrove Worcestershire B60 1AA
Tel: 01527 881288 *Fax:* 01527 881414 *Dx:* 17279 BROMSGROVE
E-mail: daleh@bromsgrove.gov.uk
Sol: Burton, Mr Andrew R LLB Head of Legal Services. . . Oct 1989
Stevens, Ms D Ivy BA Solicitor . . . . Jun 1972

BURNHAM-ON-SEA, Somerset

PETER ROSSITER & CO
9-11 Abingdon Street Burnham-on-Sea Somerset TA8 1PH
Tel: 01278 780143 *Fax:* 01278 793143
E-mail: peter@peterrossiterandco.co.uk
Sol: Rossiter, Mr Peter Stephen Licensed Conveyancer Sole Practioner. . . . Jan 1987

BURNLEY, Lancashire

BURNLEY BOROUGH COUNCIL
Town Hall Manchester Road Burnley Lancashire BB11 1JA
Tel: 01282 425011 *Fax:* 01282 452536
Sol: Talbot, Mr David Andrew LLB Senior Solicitor . . . *Oct 1985
Wilcock, Mr David LLB(Hons) Head of Legal Services. Sep 1996

BURTON-ON-TRENT, Staffordshire

EAST STAFFORDSHIRE BOROUGH COUNCIL
Town Hall Burton-on-Trent Staffordshire DE14 2EB
Tel: 01283 508000 *Fax:* 01283 535412
Dx: 700331 BURTON-ON-TRENT 2
Sol: Duckitt, Mr David Nicholas LLB; DipLG Head of Legal and Democratic Services . . . . *Oct 1988
Passam, Miss Diane L FILEx Principal Solicitor . . *Oct 2001
Wakefield, Mrs Angela Jayne BA(Hons) Solicitor . . . Oct 1992

BURY, Greater Manchester

ALPHAFOOD LTD
Remar House Geoffrey Street Bury Greater Manchester BL9 6DW
Tel: 0161 797 8600 *Fax:* 0161 763 1116
Sol: Fruhman, Mr Henry Lawrence LLB Director . . . . *Dec 1979

BURY MAGISTRATES COURT
The Courthouse Tenters Street Bury Greater Manchester BL9 0HX
Tel: 0161 447 8600 *Fax:* 0161 447 8630 *Dx:* 707370 BURY
Sol: Furber, Mr David W LLB(Hons) Senior Court Clerk . . Aug 1997
Livesey, Mrs Karen Anne DML; LLB(Hons) Senior Court Clerk . . . . Nov 2000
Reid, Miss Christine E DML Senior Court Clerk . . . Mar 1991

BURY METROPOLITAN BOROUGH COUNCIL
Town Hall Knowsley Street Bury Greater Manchester BL9 0SW
Tel: 0161 253 7771 *Fax:* 0161 705 5119
Sol: Batham, Ms Elaine M BA Principal Solicitor . . . . Oct 1989
Fitzmaurice, Ms Christine Solicitor. . . . Oct 1982
Hammond, Miss Jayne M LLB Assistant Solicitor . . . May 1989
Mann, Mr Richard M LLB Assistant Council Solicitor. . Jun 1979
Monaghan, Mr Stanley BA Council Solicitor . . . . Dec 1975
Sou, Ms Julie LLB Solicitor . . . . *§Mar 1992

TETROSYL LTD
Bevis Green Works Walmersley Bury Greater Manchester BL9 6RE
Sol: Mort, Mr Stephen G LLB(Hons) Solicitor. . . . *Dec 1987

BURY ST EDMUNDS, Suffolk

ST EDMUNDSBURY BOROUGH COUNCIL
Borough Offices Angel Hill Bury St Edmunds Suffolk IP33 1XB
Tel: 01284 763233 *Fax:* 01284 757155
Dx: 57223 BURY ST EDMUNDS
E-mail: legal.services@stedsbc.gov.uk
Sol: Bowes, Miss Joy BA(Hons)(Oxon) Head of Legal and Democratic Services . . . . *Oct 1987
Parfitt, Mrs Elizabeth W A BA(Hons) Solicitor . . . *Feb 1985

UNITED STATES AIR FORCE
HQ 3AF/JAI RAF Mildenhall Bury St Edmunds Suffolk IP28 8NF
Tel: 01638 543533 *Fax:* 01638 543026
Sol: Feehan, Mr John David AB; LLB Legal Adviser, International Law. . . . *Jan 1999
James, Lyndon B Solicitor. . . . *Dec 1974

CAERNARFON, Gwynedd

CLERK TO THE JUSTICES
Magistrates' Clerks Office 12 Market Street Caernarfon Gwynedd LL55 1RT
Tel: 01286 675200 / 675288 *Fax:* 01286 678691
Dx: 713562 CAERNARFON 5
Sol: Jones, Mr John Grant LLB(Hons)(Wales) Justices' Clerk; Justices Chief Executive . . . . *Jul 1971
Thomas, Iolo W LLB Clerk to the Justices. . . . *Mar 1977

GWYNEDD COUNCIL
Shirehall Street Caernarfon Gwynedd LL55 1SH
Tel: 01286 672255 *Fax:* 01286 673993 *Dx:* 713561 CAERNARFON 5
Sol: Ap Gareth, Mr Rhun LLB Solicitor. . . . Jan 1998
Edwards, Mrs Ruth Elisabeth LLB(Hons) . . . . Oct 1993
Evans, Mr Iwan Gwilym Devenport LLB(Hons); DipLG Legal Services Manager. . . . Sep 1989
Jones, Mr Dafydd Richard BSc(Wales) Law Soc Dip Local Govt Law Solicitor . . . . *Mar 1987
Jones, Mr Gareth W LLB(L'pool) Senior Manager Legal and Administration. . . . *Jul 1975
Phillips, Ms Dilys A LLB Head of Administration and Public Protection. . . . *Jan 1984
Roberts, Mrs Shan Eurian MA; LLB(Edin) . . . . *Dec 1977

WESTERN DIVISION SERVICE MAGISTRATES COURT
10-12 Market Street Caernarfon Gwynedd LL55 1RT
Tel: 01286 675200 *Fax:* 01286 678691 *Dx:* 713562 CAERNARFON 5
Sol: Jones, Ms Helen BA(Hons) Principal Court Clerk . . Sep 1995
Parry, Mrs Carys Court Clerk . . . . Feb 1997
Parry, Miss Catrin Wynne LLB(Hons) Solicitor. . . . *Jul 1996
Williams, Ms Bethan M LLB Court Clerk . . . . May 1988
Williams, Mrs Manon Deputy Clerk to the Justices . . . May 1985

CAERPHILLY

FIRST NATIONAL BANKS PLC
PO Box No 1 Caerphilly CF8 2YD
Tel: 029 2086 0133
Sol: Bell, Mr John H LLB Senior Solicitor. . . . *Sep 1985
Phillips, Mrs Agnes LLB Solicitor . . . . Feb 1987

CAMBERLEY, Surrey

KINGSMEAD PARKS LTD
Kingsmead House Mytchett Road Camberley Surrey GU16 6AE
Tel: 01252 512324 *Fax:* 01252 541689
Sol: Wheatley, Mr Peter J BSc Solicitor . . . . *Jan 1970

SURREY HEATH BOROUGH COUNCIL
Surrey Heath House Knoll Road Camberley Surrey GU15 3HD
Tel: 01276 707100 *Fax:* 01276 707446 *Dx:* 32722 CAMBERLEY
E-mail: legal.services@surreyheath.gov.uk
Sol: Salmon, Mrs Julia Mary LLB(Hons) Solicitor. . . . *Aug 1990
Wells, Miss Kate Ann Assistant Solicitor. . . . *Jan 2002
Whelan, Mrs Karen Alexandra Director of Support Services . . . . *Jan 1994

CAMBORNE, Cornwall

KERRIER DISTRICT COUNCIL
Council Offices Dolcoath Avenue Camborne Cornwall TR14 8SX
Tel: 01209 614000 *Fax:* 01209 614490
E-mail: ceo@kerrier.gov.uk
Sol: Ball, Mr John R LLB Assistant Solicitor . . . . *§Dec 1977
Dunstan, Ms Elizabeth F Chief Solicitor . . . . *Jan 1974
Hooper, Mr William David LLB Assistant Solicitor . . . Jul 1970
Kitto, Mr Julian BA(Hons) Head of Legal Service and Monitoring Officer . . . . *Oct 1997
Micciche, Mr Angelo James LLB(Hons) Assistant . . *Feb 1999
Pearce, Mr William Mark BA Assistant Solicitor . . . Jan 1999
Stokes, Mr Matthew Assistant Solicitor . . . . Nov 1998

CAMBRIDGE, Cambridgeshire

BAYER CROPSCIENCE LTD
230 Cambridge Science Park Milton Road Cambridge Cambridgeshire CB4 0WB
Tel: 01223 226500 *Fax:* 01223 226561
Sol: Hastings, Mrs Maggie Anne LLB Solicitor . . . . *Oct 1993

BIRDLIFE INTERNATIONAL
Wellbrook Court Girton Road Cambridge Cambridgeshire CB3 0NA
Sol: Miller, Mr Patrick D LLB Solicitor. . . . *Oct 1984

CAMBRIDGE CITY COUNCIL
The Guildhall Market Square Cambridge Cambridgeshire CB2 3QJ
Tel: 01223 457000 *Fax:* 01223 457409 *Dx:* 5854 CAMBRIDGE
E-mail: legal@cambridge.gov.uk
Sol: Calder, Mrs Rachel Elizabeth BSc; PG(Dip) Solicitor. . Oct 2004
Castle, Mr Richard W LLM(Lond); Barrister Solicitor. *§Jun 1971
Connell, Mrs Jane LLB; PGDip Principal Solicitor . . . Jan 1984

See p112 for the Key to Work Categories & other symbols

Patton, Ms Carol V BA Solicitor . . . . Sep 1991
Pugh, Mr Simon Richard LLB Head of Legal Services *May 1981
Rao, Mrs Prerna Ronta BSL; LLB Solicitor. . . . . Jul 2004
Walden, Mrs Claire Louise BA(Hons); CPE; LPC Principal Solicitor. . . . . Apr 1992
Watts, Mrs Victoria Louise LLB(Hons) Solicitor . . . . Sep 1999

CAMBRIDGESHIRE COUNTY COUNCIL
Box no RES 1001 Shire Hall Castle Hill Cambridge Cambridgeshire CB3 0AP
Tel: 01223 717111 *Fax:* 01223 717074 *Dx:* 137872 CAMBRIDGE 9
Sol: Braun, Mr Richard H BA; LLB Solicitor. . . . . *Feb 1990
Edge, Miss Suzanne M LLB Solicitor . . . . Nov 1996
Farr, Mr Timothy John LLB(Hons)(Law with German) Head of Legal Services . . . . *Sep 1997
Fisher, Miss Caroline Solicitor. . . . . Nov 1990
Gudgin, Mrs Hilary Anne BA(Hons) Solicitor. . . . . . *Oct 1985
Newman, Mrs Catherine E LLB(Hons) Assistant Solicitor . . . . *Nov 1995
Rosmarin, Mr David B LLB Local Government Solicitor *Jan 1969
Stafford, Miss Jane Louise LLB(Hons)(with French) Solicitor . . . . *Oct 1994
White, Miss Karen Diane LLB Solicitor. . . . . *Apr 1991

DOMINO PRINTING SCIENCES PLC
Bar Hill Cambridge Cambridgeshire CB3 8TU
Tel: 01954 781888 *Fax:* 01954 782713
E-mail: richard.pryn@domino-printing.co.uk
Sol: Pryn, Mr Richard J LLB Company Secretary. . . . . . Jul 1986

FLYNET LTD
King William House The Causeway Burwell Cambridge Cambridgeshire CB5 0DU
E-mail: douglasl@flynet.co.uk
Sol: Linnette, Mr Douglas James Jubilee Prizeman Solicitor . Jul 1994

THE GENERICS GROUP AG
Harston Mill Harston Cambridge Cambridgeshire CB2 5NH
Tel: 01223 875200 *Fax:* 01223 875201
E-mail: helen.barrett-hague@genericsgroup.com
Sol: Barrett-Hague, Ms Helen Patricia LLB(Hons)(Law) Group Legal Advisor . . . . *Oct 1993
Ward, Miss Claire Louise Solicitor. . . . . *Sep 2002

LEGAL AID AREA OFFICE NO 11 (EASTERN)
Kett House Station Road Cambridge Cambridgeshire CB1 2JT
Tel: 01223 366511 *Fax:* 01223 222608 *Dx:* 5803 CAMBRIDGE
Sol: Mason, Mr Simon N BA(Oxon) Solicitor . . . . *Sep 1983

NAPP PHARMACEUTICAL HOLDINGS LTD
Cambridge Science Park Milton Road Cambridge Cambridgeshire CB4 0GW
Tel: 01223 424444 *Fax:* 01223 424442
Sol: De Jong, Ms Loraine M BSc; Dr Jur Senior Legal Adviser . . . . *Mar 1995
Hodge, Mr Tim LLB(Hons) Legal Advisor . . . . . . *Sep 2001
Lea, Mr Bryan G BA Solicitor . . . . *Nov 1986

SOUTH CAMBRIDGESHIRE DISTRICT COUNCIL
South Cambridgeshire Hall Cambourne Business Park Cambourne Cambridge Cambridgeshire CB23 6EA
Tel: 0845 045 0500 *Fax:* 01954 713150 *Dx:* 729500 CAMBRIDGE 15
E-mail: scdc@scambs.gov.uk
Sol: Dunnett, Miss Catriona C LLB; ZI; LLB(Scottish Law) Principal Solicitor Notary Public. . . . . Apr 1999
Lord, Mr David Allen Dip LG Senior Lawyer . . . . . . *Dec 1992
Virginia, Fu Lawyer . . . . Sep 2003

UNIVERSITY OF CAMBRIDGE
St John's College Cambridge Cambridgeshire CB2 1TP
Tel: 01223 338600 *Fax:* 01223 337720
Sol: Nolan, Mr Richard C BA(Cantab) Solicitor. . . . . . . Nov 1991

CANNOCK, Staffordshire

CANNOCK CHASE DISTRICT COUNCIL
Civic Centre PO BOX 28 Beecroft Road Cannock Staffordshire WS11 1BG
Tel: 01543 462621 *Fax:* 01543 464321
Sol: Barrett, Mr Matthew James LLB(Hons) Legal Services Manager . . . . *Nov 1980
Kenny, Mrs Aurona W BSc(Hons)(Econ) Council Solicitor . . . . *Jun 1976
McGoldrick, Mrs Joyce P LLB(Hons) Principal Solicitor *Oct 1986
Turner, Mr Simon William LLB Senior Solicitor. . . . . *Sep 1996

TAYLOR WIMPEY UK LTD
Chase House Park Plaza Cannock Staffordshire WS12 2DD
Tel: 01543 496766 *Fax:* 01543 496757 *Dx:* 16088 CANNOCK
Sol: Crouch, Mr David J LLB(Hons) Solicitor . . . . *Oct 1990
Cummings, Mrs Diana A Solicitor . . . . *Jan 1994
Howard, Mr Peter Edward LLB Solicitor . . . . *Nov 1973
Oldnall, Mr Terence M J Solicitor . . . . *Dec 1977
Phillips, Mr James LLB(Nott'm) Legal Director. . . . . *Jun 1978

CANTERBURY, Kent

CANTERBURY CITY COUNCIL
Council Offices Military Road Canterbury Kent CT1 1YW
Tel: 01227 862000 *Fax:* 01227 862020 *Dx:* 99713 CANTERBURY 3
E-mail: mark.ellender@canterbury.gov.uk
Sol: Ellender, Mr Mark T Head of Legal & Committee Services . . . . *Jun 1979
Franklin, Ms Janet M LLB Deputy Head of Legal Services . . . . *Dec 1980
Goldsack, Mrs Pauline Solicitor . . . . Dec 1997

KENT COUNTY COUNCIL
Legal Services Canterbury 27 Castle Street Canterbury Kent CT1 2PX
Tel: 01227 767020 *Fax:* 01227 780671
Sol: Chapman, Mr Trevor BA Solicitor . . . . *Feb 1991
O'Connor, Miss Gail Maree BA; LLB Solicitor . . . . . Aug 1995
Preece, Miss Stephanie Nancy LSF; LLB Assistant Solicitor . . . . Jul 1995
Robinson, Mr Philip James MA(Cantab) Solicitor . . . Jan 1980

KENT LAW CLINIC
Eliot College The University Canterbury Kent CT2 7NS
Tel: 01227 823311 *Fax:* 01227 824858
Sol: Carpenter, Ms Catherine M Solicitor. . . . . Mar 1983

CARDIFF

CARDIFF COUNTY COUNCIL
County Hall Atlantic Wharf Cardiff CF10 4UW
Tel: 029 2087 2000 *Fax:* 029 2087 2488 *Dx:* 200753 CARDIFF BAY
Sol: Anderton, Mr Paul N Senior Legal Manager . . . . . *Jan 1975
Ariyadasa, Ms Kumi LLB(Hons) Solicitor. . . . . *Oct 2004
Coles, Mrs Vesna LLB Planning Lawyer. . . . . Feb 1997
Davies, Ms Sheila LLB Legal Manager (Community). . *Jun 1990
Donavan, Mrs Marcia Clare BA(Hons) Solicitor . . . . . Jan 1999
Ellis, Miss Polly LPC Solicitor . . . . *Sep 2001
Ham, Mr Stephen Edwin LPC Solicitor. . . . . Nov 2005
Jones, Mrs Susan LLB Solicitor . . . . *Nov 1991
Marr, Mr David D LLB Legal Manager (Litigation) . . . *Apr 1981
Pursey, Mr Clive R LLB(Wales) Solicitor. . . . . *Nov 1984
Reynolds, Miss Julia Elizabeth BA(Hons) Solicitor. . . *Mar 2002
Roberts, Mr David Mark BSc(Hons) Solicitor. . . . . . Feb 2001
Roberts, Mr Dylan Tomos LLB(Hons) Solicitor. . . . . Sep 2004
Shimell, Mr Geoffrey C LLB Legal Manager (Property & Development). . . . . *Jun 1975
Taylor, Mrs Carys Enidwen BA(Hons); LLB(Hons) Solicitor . . . . *Sep 2000
Weale, Miss Sheila Elizabeth LLB; Dip Local Govt Law Solicitor . . . . *Oct 1988
Weston, Miss Leanne Jay LLB Solicitor . . . . *Jan 2005
Yeoman, Mrs Sian Allison BA(Hons) Solicitor . . . . *Sep 2003

CARDIFF MAGISTRATES COURT
Magistrates' Clerks Office Fitzalan Place Cardiff CF24 0RZ
Tel: 029 2046 3040
Sol: Davies, Miss Leisa Jane LLB(Hons) Legal Adviser. . . May 1995
Edlin, Miss Anne B LLB(Manc) Solicitor . . . . *Jun 1977
Gerrard, Mr Trevor Alun LLB Legal Adviser . . . . . . Jan 2000
Godfrey, Mrs Siobhan Melissa LLB(Hons) Legal AdviserNov 1993
Jones, Miss Sarah Jane LLB(Hons) Legal Adviser. . . . Jul 2001
Morgan, Mr Huw David BA(Hons) Court Legal Adviser.*Nov 1986
Payne, Miss Tracey Joanne LLB Court Legal Adviser . *Sep 1998
Potgieter, Mrs Diana C LLB(Hons) Solicitor . . . . . . *Oct 1983
Waygood, Mr Martyn John LLB(Hons); MBA Clerk to the Justices. . . . . *Apr 1992

ENVIRONMENT AGENCY (WALES)
Cambria House 29 Newport Road Cardiff CF24 0TP
Tel: 0870 850 6506 *Fax:* 029 2046 6417 *Dx:* 121376 CARDIFF 2
E-mail: enquiries@environment-agency.gov.uk
Sol: Cavell, Mr David George Regional Solicitor . . . . . . Sep 1996
Chapman, Mrs Jane BA(Hons) Solicitor . . . . *Oct 2004
Graves, Mr Andrew BSc(Hons) Solicitor. . . . . Nov 1997
Lewis, Miss Natasha LLB Solicitor. . . . . Jun 2004
Simms, Mrs Juliette Angela LLB; DipLP Solicitor. . . *Oct 1997
Thomas, Miss Katherine Mary LLB(Hons) Solicitor. . . Apr 1999
Tunstall, Mr Roger LLB Solicitor. . . . . *Sep 2003
Yakub, Mr Mohammed Ahson LLB . . . . Feb 2001

LEGAL SERVICES COMMISSION WALES OFFICE
Marland House Central Square Cardiff CF1 1PF
Tel: 0845 608 7070
Sol: Jarrett, Mr A Hugh LLB(Wales) Solicitor. . . . . . . *Apr 1978
Mallorie, Miss Sarah E M LLB Solicitor . . . . *Dec 1982
Owen, Mr Jonathan Morgan LLB(Lond) Solicitor. . . . *Nov 1980
Williams, Mrs J Hilary LLB(Wales) Solicitor . . . . . . *Dec 1976

PEACOCK GROUP LTD
Atlantic House Tyndall Street Cardiff CF1 5BE
Tel: 029 2027 0228
Sol: Ellard, Mr Stephen Charles Solicitor. . . . . *Jun 1994
Wigley, Mr Islwyn T LLB Solicitor . . . . *Jun 1968

PRINCIPALITY BUILDING SOCIETY
PO Box 89 Principality Buildings Queen Street Cardiff CF10 1UA
Tel: 029 2038 2000 *Fax:* 029 2037 4567 *Dx:* 144240 CARDIFF 29
Sol: Perry, Ms Jennifer A LLB Head of Legal Services . . . *§Mar 1985
Philip, Ms Tanya A LLB; LLM Assistant Legal Adviser . *Dec 2004
Smith, Mr Stuart Anthony BA(Law) Senior Manager Members Services . . . . Jan 1979
Warman, Mr Haydn LLB Secretary . . . . *Jun 1974

S4C
Parc Ty Glas Cardiff CF4 5DU
Tel: 029 2074 7444 *Fax:* 029 2075 4444
Sol: Griffiths, Ms Sara LLB Head of Legal Affairs. . . . . . *Nov 1987

SPEAKEASY ADVICE CENTRE
2 Arabella Street Roath Cardiff CF24 4TA
Tel: 029 2045 3111 *Fax:* 029 2045 1064
E-mail: s.ac@speakeasyadvice.co.uk
Sol: Palmer, Mr Warren Edward LLB Director . . . . *Nov 2000
Reid, Miss Lynda M LLB(Hons) Solicitor. . . . . *Jun 1990

WELSH DEVELOPMENT AGENCY LEGAL SERVICES
Trafalgar House 5 Fitzalan Place Cardiff CF24 0ED
Tel: 029 2082 8681 *Fax:* 029 2044 2695 *Dx:* 14920 CARDIFF 33
E-mail: julie.batten@wdu.co.uk
Sol: Clarke, Mr Paul LLB(Hons) Solicitor. . . . . Sep 2002
Clarke, Mrs Patricia M BA(Hons) Head Of Legal Services . . . . *Oct 1980
Dasent, Mrs Susan M LLB(Hons) Senior Commercial Lawyer . . . . Oct 1991
Griffiths, Mr Huw Rhoslyn LLB(Hons); DipLP; LLM Commercial Law Commercial Property Solicitor . . . . *Oct 1999
Neal, Mr Nicholas G LLB(Hons) Executive Director Land Development & Legal Services . . . . *Oct 1973
Palmer, Mr Thomas David LLB . . . . *Nov 2004
Rees, Miss Jacquelyn Mary BA Senior Solicitor . . . . *Jun 1992

WELSH HEALTH LEGAL SERVICES
PO Box 150 25-30 Lambourne Crescent Llanishen Cardiff CF14 5BG
Tel: 029 2031 5500 *Fax:* 029 2031 5555 *Dx:* 136736 CARDIFF
Sol: Dawson, Mrs Elizabeth LLB(Wales) Solicitor. . . . . . *Jul 2001
Ferguson, Miss Anne-Louise BA(Hons) Managing Solicitor . . . . *Mar 1981
Griffith, Mrs Rhian LLB Solicitor . . . . *Oct 1984
Harris, Mr Mark LLB; LLM; Cert HSM Solicitor. . . . . *Aug 1996
Hynes, Mr Andrew LLB(Wales) Solicitor. . . . . *Nov 1991
Jackson, Ms Tracey Anne LLB Solicitor . . . . *Oct 1996
Kaged, Mr David LLB Solicitor. . . . . *Sep 2001
Llewellyn, Mrs Vanessa LLB Solicitor . . . . *Aug 1996
Mansel, Mrs Elizabeth C LLB(Hons) Solicitor . . . . . *Oct 1998
Rees, Ms Rhiannon LLB Solicitor . . . . *Aug 1997
Sparkes, Mrs Anne Elizabeth LLB(Wales) Solicitor. . . *Nov 1998
Spencer, Miss Deborah LLB(Hons)(Wales) Solicitor . . *Jan 1990
Stallard, Miss Elizabeth BA(Law) Solicitor . . . . . . *Oct 1984
Symonds, Mrs Lorna Alexis LLB Solicitor . . . . *Oct 1995
Walcot, Ms Alison LLB(Wales) Solicitor . . . . *Nov 1998
Watt, Ms Sarah Jane LLB(Hons) Solicitor . . . . . . *§May 1996
Webber, Ms Fiona LLB(Wales) Solicitor . . . . *Feb 1999
Williams, Miss Eifiona Meleri Solicitor . . . . *Aug 2004

CARLISLE, Cumbria

CARLISLE CITY COUNCIL
Civic Centre Carlisle Cumbria CA3 8QG
Tel: 01228 817000 *Fax:* 01228 817048 *Dx:* 63037 CARLISLE
Sol: Egan, Mr John M LLB(Manc) Director of Legal and Democratic Services . . . . *Apr 1974
Gray, Mrs Rachel Penelope Anne LLB(Hons) Assistant Solicitor . . . . *Sep 2001
Lambert, Mr Mark David LLB(Hons) Head of Legal Services . . . . *Jul 1999
Liddle, Mrs Clare Joanne BA(Hons) Principal Solicitor. . Jul 1997

CROWN PROSECUTION SERVICE CUMBRIA
1st Floor Stocklund House Castle Street Carlisle Cumbria CA3 8SY
Tel: 01228 882900 *Fax:* 01228 882910 *Dx:* 63032 CARLISLE
Sol: Bayly, Mr Peter J LLB Solicitor . . . . *§Jul 1977
Binstead, Mr D Richard BA(Newc) Solicitor . . . . . . Jul 1976
Dwyer, Mr Patrick A BA(Oxon) Solicitor . . . . *Jul 1974
Hansford, Mr David G LLB(Newc) Solicitor . . . . . . Apr 1972
Lovett, Mr Alan R BA(Nott'm) Solicitor. . . . . *§Dec 1979

CUMBRIA COUNTY COUNCIL
Legal Services Unit The Courts English Street Carlisle Cumbria CA3 8LZ
Tel: 01228 607374 / 607351 *Fax:* 01228 607376
Dx: 63023 CARLISLE
Sol: Blamires, Mr Benedict H LLM; MA Assistant Solicitor . *Jun 1991
Brodie, Mr Paul Stewart LLB(Hons) Assistant Solicitor.*Nov 2006
Claydon, Mr Richard H LLB Assistant Head of Legal Services . . . . *Dec 1975
Devlin, Mr Michael B LLB(Lond) Senior Solicitor. . . . Feb 1982
Elliott, Mr Anthony E BA(Hons) Assistant Solicitor. . . Apr 1981
Farnworth, Mr Jonathan BA(Hons)(Law); LLB Assistant Solicitor . . . . *Nov 1997
Hurst, Miss Claire Rebecca LLB Assistant Solicitor . . Apr 2003
Jay, Mr Laurence P BA(Oxon) Principal Solicitor. . . . *Jun 1978
Longworth, Mrs Margaret Anna Assistant Solicitor. . . Nov 1978
Moffat, Ms Helen LLB Assistant Solicitor. . . . . Dec 1989
Robinson, Mrs Sara Anne LLB(Hons) Assistant SolicitorOct 1985
Smith, Mrs Alison J LLB(Newc) Assistant Head of Legal Services(Child Care) . . . . Oct 1982
Turner, Mrs Kate Elizabeth LLB; LLM Assistant SolicitorMay 2003
Walker, Mr Brian Head of Legal Services . . . . . . *§Dec 1974
Wilkinson, Mr Geoffrey M J BA(Law) Assistant Solicitor . . . . *Nov 1982
Willman, Mrs Gillian M BA Assistant Solicitor . . . . . Oct 1982
Wilson, Mr David Martin LLB(Hons) Assistant Solicitor. Jan 1987

CARMARTHEN, Carmarthenshire

CARMARTHENSHIRE COUNTY COUNCIL
County Hall Carmarthen Carmarthenshire SA31 1JP
Tel: 01267 224010 *Fax:* 01267 224652 *Dx:* 51403 CARMARTHEN
E-mail: dlthomas@carmarthenshire.gov.uk
Sol: Edgecombe, Mr Robert John LLB Solicitor. . . . . . *Sep 1994
Evans, Mr Alan Leyton BA(Hons) Assistant Solicitor. . *Mar 2001
Evans, Dorian R Senior Solicitor. . . . . *Jun 1979
Evans, Mrs Hilary E LLB(Wales) Assistant Solicitor . . *Dec 1976
Evans, Mrs Margaret Ann BA(Hons) Assistant Solicitor*Dec 1996
Grafton, Mr Philip Jonathan BA(Hons)(Government) Senior Solicitor. . . . . *Nov 1992
Martin, Mr Joel Sven LLB(Hons) Assistant Solicitor . *May 2002
Murphy, Mr Steven Patrick LLB Assistant Solicitor. . . *Oct 1990
Rees-Jones, Mrs Linda O LLB(Wales) Senior Solicitor. *Oct 1982
Thomas, Mr David Lyn LLB Head of Administration and Law . . . . *Dec 1974
Thomas, Mrs Rebecca Elaine LLB Assistant Solicitor . *Jan 2003

CROWN PROSECUTION SERVICE DYFED POWYS
Heol Penlanffos Tanerdy Carmarthen Carmarthenshire SA31 2EZ
Tel: 01267 242100 *Fax:* 01267 242111 *Dx:* 51411 CARMARTHEN
Sol: Crossley, Ms Susan J Solicitor . . . . Oct 1982
Harvey, Creighton BA Solicitor. . . . . Jul 1980
Jenkins, Mr Iwan Solicitor . . . . Oct 1987
Lindsay, Mr David R Solicitor . . . . Jan 1987
Lloyd, Mr Peter L BA Solicitor . . . . *Oct 1990
Neave, Mr Gerald H Solicitor . . . . *Dec 1975
Rowlands, Mr Simon A LLB Solicitor. . . . . Jun 1975

DYFED POWYS POLICE AUTHORITY
PO Box 99 Llangunnor Carmarthen Carmarthenshire SA31 2PF
Tel: 01267 226440 *Fax:* 01267 226448 *Dx:* 120328 CARMARTHEN 4
E-mail: martin.beckett@dyfed-powys.pnn.police.uk
Sol: Beckett, Mr Martin R LLB(Lond) Force Legal Adviser . *Dec 1975
Reeves, Mr Keith Bevan LLB; LLM Clerk to the Authority . . . . *Jun 1978

CASTLE DONINGTON, Leicestershire

BRITISH MIDLAND AIRWAYS LTD
Donington Hall Castle Donington Leicestershire DE74 2SB
Tel: 01332 854089 *Fax:* 01332 850301
Sol: Havard, Ms Paula M LLB Head Of Legal . . . . *Dec 1986
MacDonald-Preston, Mr Simon LLB; I Eng; AMRAeS Group Legal Advisor. . . . . Jul 2003
Owen, Mr David A LLB(Hons) Group Legal Advisor . . *Oct 2000

CENTRAL NETWORKS
Herald Way Pegasus Business Park East Midlands Airport Castle Donington Leicestershire DE74 2TU
Tel: 0800 096 3080
Sol: Hammond, Ms Stephanie Kay BA(Hons)(Law) Legal Counsel and Company Secretary. . . . . May 1987

CATERHAM, Surrey

CROUDACE LTD
Croudace House Godstone Road Caterham Surrey CR3 6XQ
Tel: 01883 346464 *Fax:* 01883 349927 *Dx:* 36803 CATERHAM
Sol: Boakes, Mr Simon John BA(Hons)(Law & Econ) Assistant Solicitor. . . . . *Jan 1993
Wigner, Mr Stewart E MA(Cantab) Head of Legal Department . . . . *Jun 1975

CHAPEL-EN-LE-FRITH, Derbyshire

HIGH PEAK BOROUGH COUNCIL
Council Offices Hayfield Road Chapel-en-le-Frith Derbyshire SK23 0QJ
Tel: 0845 129 7777 *Fax:* 01663 752055
E-mail: borough-council@highpeak.gov.uk
Sol: Boxall, Mrs Susan Nicoll LLB; DipLP Solicitor . . . . *Sep 2001
de Bruin, Ms Nicola Ann LLB(Hons) Solicitor and Legal Services Business Manager . . . . *Dec 1998
Hopley, Ms Elisa LLB(Hons); DipLPractice Solicitor . . *Jun 2004
Stafford, Mrs Rosemary V LLB(Hons) Head of Legal & Democratic Services . . . . *Oct 1985

CHATHAM, Medway Towns

KENT RELIANCE BUILDING SOCIETY
Reliance House Sun Pier Chatham Medway Towns ME4 4ET
Tel: 01634 848944 *Fax:* 01634 835793 *Dx:* 6710 CHATHAM
Sol: Castling, Mr Stephen H P LLB(L'pool) Solicitor . . . . *Oct 1979

CHEADLE, Greater Manchester

THE AUTOMOBILE ASSOCIATION
Lambert House Stockport Road Cheadle Greater Manchester SK8 2DY
Tel: 0161 485 6188 *Fax:* 0161 488 7260
Sol: Pearson, Mr Philip W BA Manager Legal Services Notary Public . . . . Jun 1978

BOVIS HOMES LTD
Northern Region Eden Point Three Acres Lane Cheadle Hulme Greater Manchester SK9 1BQ
Tel: 0161 488 5000 *Fax:* 0161 488 5088
Sol: Clark, Mrs Jennifer Ellen Legal Director . . . . May 1992
Hopkins, Mr Michael LLB(Hons) Solicitor . . . . Jul 2004

CHEADLE HULME, Greater Manchester

BASF PLC
Earl Road Cheadle Hulme Greater Manchester SK8 6QG
Tel: 0161 488 5634 *Fax:* 0161 485 3234
E-mail: andrew.hartley@basf-plc.co.uk
Sol: Hartley, Mr Andrew LLB Manager Legal Services . . . *May 1981

CHELMSFORD, Essex

ANGLIA RUSKIN UNIVERSITY
Anglia Law School Bishop Hall Lane Chelmsford Essex CM1 1SQ
Tel: 01245 493131 *Fax:* 01245 493134
Sol: Duxbury, Mrs Sarah Elizabeth LLB(Hons); DipLP; PGCE Senior Lecturer, LPC. . . . . *Feb 1998
Menzies, Mr Christopher LLB(Hons) FT LPC Pathway Leader . . . . *Jan 2001
Ramsay, Ms Julia K BA(Hons)(Law) Programme Leader (Professional). . . . . *Oct 1986
Squire, Ms Lindsey Elisabeth LLM Principle Lecturer . Jul 1974

BRITVIC SOFT DRINKS LTD
Britvic House Broomfield Way Chelmsford Essex CM1 1TU
Tel: 01245 261871 *Fax:* 01245 267147
Sol: OM, Miss Gillian LLB Head of Legal. . . . . *Oct 1992

CHELMSFORD BOROUGH COUNCIL
Civic Centre Duke Street Chelmsford Essex CM1 1JE
Tel: 01245 606606 *Fax:* 01245 606245 *Dx:* 123305 CHELMSFORD 7
E-mail: mailbox@chelmsfordbc.gov.uk
Sol: Ashurst, Ms Catherine M LLB Senior Solicitor. . . . . *Aug 1974
Butcher, Mr William LLB; DipLG Solicitor . . . . . . *Nov 1985
De Val, Mrs Susan J I LLB Head of Legal and Business Services . . . . *Jan 1986
Doole, Ms Nicola J BA(Law) Solicitor . . . . *Aug 1998
Dowler, Mr Mervyn L MA(Cantab) Principal Solicitor. . Apr 1981
Neave, Ms Ruth Russet LLB Solicitor . . . . *Aug 1996

CROWN PROSECUTION SERVICE ESSEX
County House 100 New London Road Chelmsford Essex CM2 0RG
Tel: 01245 455800 *Fax:* 01245 455964
Dx: 139160 CHELMSFORD 11
Sol: Barker, Miss Araluen Lisa LLB . . . . *Jun 1989

ESSEX COUNTY COUNCIL
County Hall Market Road Chelmsford Essex CM1 1LX
Tel: 0845 743 0430 *Fax:* 01245 352710
Dx: 123300 CHELMSFORD 7
Sol: Beer, Mr Derek Laurence Leslie BA . . . . *Dec 1978
Campbell, Mrs Michelle Solicitor. . . . . Nov 2003
Davies, Mr Paul Ian Dip LG . . . . *§Dec 1991
Denholm, Mr Paul Michael LLB Senior Solicitor . . . . Oct 2002
Dyton, Mr Christopher John LLB(Hons) Team Manager Sep 1997
Edwards, Mrs Laura LLB(Hons) Solicitor. . . . . *Aug 2003
Gilbert, Mr Giles Egerton LLB Assistant . . . . Apr 2002
Hallam, Mrs Alexandra J LLB(Hons). . . . . *Sep 1983
Hodkinson, Miss Lorene LLB Senior Solicitor . . . . . Apr 2004
Jarlett, Mrs Shirley Elizabeth BA Team Manager. . . . *Oct 1982
Jones, Mr Derek LLB(Hons) Solicitor . . . . Jan 1988
Julian, Ms Amanda LLB(Hons) . . . . *Apr 2000
Lapite, Mrs Ameenat Olasumbo BA; LLB(Hons). . . . Mar 2000
Lapite, Mr Ladi BA(Hons); LLB(Hons). . . . . *Aug 1998
Mascarenhas, Miss Joanne LLB(Hons) Solicitor. . . . *Feb 2003
Mehta, Miss Uma LLB(Hons); Dip Child Care(1994). . Apr 1991
Meikle, Mrs Carolyn LLB(Hons); LPC Com Solicitor . . Mar 2007
Millward, Miss Jacqueline H C LLB; DipLGP Environmental Law Team Manager . . . . *Nov 1987
Owoso-Yianoma, Mrs Nora LLB(Hons) Senior Solicitor Jan 2001
Pavitt, Mr Nicholas BA(Hons); LLM . . . . *Dec 1991
Peachman, Ms Tracey Jean Elizabeth LLB(Hons); LSF*Apr 1993
Rashid, Ms Saima LLB(Hons) Child Care Solicitor. . . Jul 1999
Taylor, Miss Natasha BA(Hons); LLB . . . . Jan 2001
Thomson, Mr Philip M LLB(Hons) . . . . *Jul 1980
Tilsley, Mr John R LLB . . . . Apr 1972
Whaymand, Mrs Carolyn PGDipLaw; FILEX Ernest Ormain Prize Child Care Solicitor . . . . Nov 2001
Woodyard, Mr Stephen R BA(Hons). . . . . *Jan 1985

JUST LAW LTD
Amlin House Parkway Chelmsford Essex CM2 0UR
Tel: 01245 396444 *Fax:* 01245 396644 *Dx:* 146060 CHELMSFORD
E-mail: mfield@justlaw.co.uk
Sol: Field, Mr Mark Ashley BA(Hons) Principal Solicitor . *§Mar 1981
Hope, Mr Jeremy R LLB(Hons); LLM Solicitor . . . . *§Sep 1999
Read, Mr Kevin . . . . *Nov 1998

CHELTENHAM, Gloucestershire

CHELMIX CONCRETE
Church Farm Leckhampton Cheltenham Gloucestershire GL53 0QJ
Tel: 01242 224763 *Fax:* 01242 237727
Sol: Hicks, Mr Jeremy William BA(Exon) Director. . . . . . Jun 1978

CHELSEA BUILDING SOCIETY
Group Legal Services Thirlestaine Road Cheltenham Gloucestershire GL53 7AL*Dx:* 32850 CHELTENHAM 2
Sol: Greenwell, Mrs Gillian M BA . . . . *Dec 1980
Murtagh, Mr Bede LLB Senior Solicitor . . . . Dec 1993

CHELTENHAM BOROUGH COUNCIL
Municipal Offices PO Box 12 Promenade Cheltenham Gloucestershire GL50 1PP
Tel: 01242 262626 *Fax:* 01242 264309 *Dx:* 7406 CHELTENHAM
E-mail: legal@cheltenham.gov.uk
Sol: Baker, Mr Quentin Assistant Director Legal Services & Monitoring Officer. . . . . *Oct 1999
Lewis, Mr Peter M BA Head of Legal Services. . . . . *Jun 1987

ROBERT HITCHINS LTD
The Manor Boddington Cheltenham Gloucestershire GL51 0TJ
Tel: 01242 680694 *Fax:* 01242 680701
Sol: Hitchins, Mr Jeremy C MA(Cantab); LLB(Cantab) Managing Director. . . . . *Apr 1981
Morgan, Mr Michael S LLB Solicitor . . . . *Sep 1992
Perry, Mr Andrew David BA Solicitor. . . . . Dec 2006
Perry, Ms Carolyn M LLB(Lond) Head of Legal Department . . . . *Jun 1983
Redfern, Miss Rachel LLB Solicitor . . . . *Oct 2002

KRAFTS FOODS UK LTD
St Georges House Bayshill Road Cheltenham Gloucestershire GL50 3AE
Tel: 01242 236101 *Fax:* 01242 284103
Sol: Moore, Mr Clive Leslie LLB Chief Legal Counsel & Company Secretary . . . . *§Apr 1985
Rattray, Ms Christine Jane LLB; LLM Senior Legal Counsel . . . . *Sep 1994

LECKHAMPTON DAIRIES LTD
Church Farm Leckhampton Cheltenham Gloucestershire GL53 0QJ
Sol: Hicks, Mr Jeremy William BA(Exon) Director. . . . . . Jun 1978

CHERTSEY, Surrey

THE COMPASS GROUP
Compass House Chertsey Surrey KT16 9BQ
Tel: 01932 573000 *Fax:* 01932 569956
Sol: O'Connor, Mr John M Solicitor. . . . . *Aug 1964

CHESHUNT, Hertfordshire

BROXBOURNE BOROUGH COUNCIL
Bishops College Churchgate Cheshunt Hertfordshire EN8 9XJ
Tel: 01992 785555 *Fax:* 01992 785578
E-mail: legal@broxbourne.gov.uk
Sol: Connell, Mrs Patricia LLB Principal Assistant Solicitor *Nov 1975
Miles, Mr Gavin W LLB; TD Head of Legal Services. . *Oct 1985
Webb, Miss Sian Louise LLB(Hons) Solicitor . . . . . Oct 2005

CHESTER, Cheshire

ALCHEMA LTD
Sutton House Capenhurst Technology Park Capenhurst Chester Cheshire CH1 6EH
Tel: 0151 348 2010 *Fax:* 0151 348 2011
E-mail: mailbox@chemisphere.co.uk
Sol: Lloyd-Watts, Ms Georgina E LLB(Hons) Managing Director/ Company Lawyer . . . . *Oct 1990

BANK OF SCOTLAND
Thistle House City Road Chester Cheshire CH88 3AN
Tel: 01244 690000 *Fax:* 01244 311373 *Dx:* 21641 CHESTER
Sol: Cooper, Mr Graham J LLB(Hons) Solicitor. . . . . . *Nov 1984
Lang, Mrs Colette Michelle LLB Solicitor. . . . . . . *Nov 1991
McClenan, Mr Michael S LLB Deputy Group Solicitor . *Oct 1987
Reynolds, Miss Patricia A LLB Solicitor . . . . *Oct 1987
Wilton, Mr Christopher Scott LLB(Hons) Solicitor . . . *Nov 1992

CHESHIRE COUNTY COUNCIL
Legal Services County Hall Chester Cheshire CH1 1SF
Tel: 01244 602382 *Fax:* 01244 603819 *Dx:* 717531 CHESTER 15
E-mail: keith.moores@cheshire.gov.uk
Sol: Antrobus, Miss Suzanne BA(History) Senior Solicitor Corporate . . . . Nov 1997
Bryan, Mr David James LLB(Hons) Solicitor. . . . . Oct 1994
Budd, Mr Gerard L LLB(Hons)(Exon) Head of Legal Services . . . . *Nov 1983
Cordiner, Mr Michael J M LLB(Hons) Senior Solicitor . *Jan 2000
Ellison, Mrs Alison LLB Senior Solicitor . . . . Jun 1998
Flynn, Mr Michael F BA(Hons); DPA Head of Member Services . . . . *Feb 1983
Gold, Mrs Sally J BA(Hons); LLM Locum Employment Lawyer . . . . Mar 1985
Henshaw, Mrs Janet LLB(Hons) Property Law 1987 Solicitor . . . . Dec 2002
Laing, Mr Andrew Mark LLB(Hons); LPC; RGN Moses Ackah Prize (Liverpool John Moores University) 2000; The Atkinson Prize (Liverpool Law Society) 2002 Senior Legal Executive. Sep 2004
Leadbetter, Mr Andrew LLB(Hons) Group Solicitor. . *Jan 1988
McGinn, Mr Nicholas S LLB(Lond) Group Solicitor (Environment) . . . . *Dec 1978
Mackinnon, Mrs Stephanie Jane LLB; DipLaw Solicitor Jan 2002
Makin, Ms Helen LPC Solicitor (Social Services) . . *Nov 1998
Noble, Mr David P BA(Hons) Solicitor. . . . . *Jan 1999
Riley, Mr Charles Solicitor. . . . . Jun 2001
Rowland, Ms Sarah-Jane LLB(Hons) Solicitor . . . . *Nov 1992
Vaccaro, Ms Helen Mary BA; DipLaw Solicitor (Locum)*Mar 1999

CHESTER & DISTRICT HOUSING TRUST
Centurion House 77 Northgate Street Chester Cheshire CH1 2HQ
Tel: 01244 305475 *Fax:* 01244 305695
E-mail: p.burton@cdht.org
Sol: Burton, Mr Paul D LLB Solicitor . . . . *Sep 1999

CHESTER CITY COUNCIL
The Forum Northgate Street Chester Cheshire CH1 2HS
Tel: 01244 324324 *Fax:* 01244 400128 *Dx:* 722412 CHESTER 17
Sol: Bates, Mr Martin S G BA(Hons) Solicitor . . . . . . *§Oct 1990
Brodie, Mrs Kathryn A LLB Solicitor. . . . . *Oct 1986
Centeleghe, Mr Domenico LLB(Hons) Solicitor . . . . *Jul 1989
Gaukroger, Miss Catherine M LLB Solicitor . . . . . . *Oct 1984
Hubbard, Mr Lee Stephen LLB(Hons) Solicitor. . . . *Jun 2006
Kerry, Mr Charles V LLB(Sheff) Solicitor to the Council*Dec 1981
MacAndrew, Mrs Heloise S BA(Hons); PGDipLaw; LPC Lawyer Contracts & Litigation . . . . *Oct 2004
McIlwaine, Mrs Karen LLB Assistant Solicitor . . . . . *Apr 1994
Richardson, Mr John LLB Solicitor. . . . . Jun 1993
Whiting, Mrs Vanessa LLB(Hons); LLM Solicitor. . . . Sep 2001

THE COLLEGE OF LAW CHESTER
Christleton Hall Christleton Chester Cheshire CH3 7AB
Tel: 0800 289997
Sol: Adams, Mr Trevor M BSc(Belfast); Bagr; PhD; MRSC; C Chem Lecturer. . . . . Dec 1989
Ashton, Ms Deborah Senior Lecturer . . . . Nov 1992
Bamford, Keir A LLB Senior Lecturer . . . . Apr 1993
Beanland, Mr Christopher Senior Lecturer. . . . . . . Nov 1992
Buzzard, Mr Neil Deputy Director . . . . Jan 1998
Chatterton, Ms Tricia Regional Director . . . . *Oct 1989
Collinson, Mr Robert J LLB(Lancs); BCL(Oxon) Senior Lecturer . . . . *Nov 1988
Cross, Mr Ian Deputy Director Academic . . . . Nov 1973
Draycott, Mrs Carol A LLB Senior Lecturer . . . . . . *Oct 1987
Dyne, Ms Anne Lecturer. . . . . Jan 1987
Earlam, Ms Bridget Senior Lecturer . . . . Jul 1998
Evans, Miss Ceri LLB; LLM; Dip Lecturer . . . . Mar 1999
Evans, Ms Susan Senior Lecturer . . . . Nov 1986
Gausden, Mr Peter Deputy Director Vocational . . . . Nov 1973
Gordon, Ms Elizabeth Lecturer . . . . Jan 1998
Grateley, Mrs Jo Senior Lecturer . . . . Jan 1996
Haggett, Mr Richard W LLB Deputy Director (Vocational) . . . . Sep 1999
Heshon, Mr Denis Senior Lecturer. . . . . Oct 1982
Iliff, Mr Mike Senior Lecturer. . . . . Nov 1988
Jenks, Ms Helen LLB Lecturer. . . . . *Nov 1994
Jones, Ms Alyson Senior Lecturer. . . . . Sep 1989
Jones, Mr Richard Principal Lecturer . . . . Jul 1975
Kennedy, Ms Kay L Lecturer. . . . . Jul 1997
Landis, Ms Jacqui Senior Lecturer. . . . . Jan 1992
MacKenzie, Ms Jane E Senior Lecturer . . . . Dec 1988
Morgan, Mr Anthony Senior Lecturer . . . . Nov 1984
Morgan, Ms Gill Senior Lecturer. . . . . Nov 1982
Morgan, Mr Giles A LLB Senior Lecturer. . . . . *Nov 1975
Price, Mr Carl J LLB Lecturer . . . . Sep 1999
Savage, Ms Tracy Lecturer . . . . Nov 1991
Shephard, Ms Catherine Lecturer . . . . Jan 1999
Smith, Ms Heather Senior Lecturer . . . . Nov 1991
Tully, Mrs Vanessa Elizabeth Senior Lecturer . . . . *Dec 1993
Waring, Mr Mike Senior Lecturer . . . . Nov 1980
Wilde, Mr Peter M Senior Lecturer. . . . . Dec 1973
Woods, Miss Deborah BA Senior Lecturer. . . . . . . *Oct 1991

CROWN PROSECUTION SERVICE CHESHIRE
2nd Floor Windsor House Pepper Street Chester Cheshire CH1 1TD
Tel: 01244 408600 *Fax:* 01244 408658 *Dx:* 20019 CHESTER
Sol: Hughes, Mr Barry LLB(Hons) Barrister. . . . . Nov 1983

LEGAL AID AREA OFFICE NO 12 (CHESTER & N WALES)
Pepper House Pepper Row Chester Cheshire CH1 1DW
Tel: 01244 315455 *Dx:* 19981 CHESTER
Sol: Gaskell, Mr Edmund Michael LLB(Hons) Assistant Solicitor . . . . *Dec 1980

MBNA EUROPE BANK LTD
Chester Business Park Chester Cheshire CH4 9FB
Tel: 01244 672002 *Fax:* 01244 672044
Sol: Barodekar, Ms Jacqueline F LLM(Hons) Solicitor . . *Nov 1989
Benavides, Ms Anne-Marie BA(Hons)(Law & Spanish)*Nov 1989
Shamsadeen, Miss Bnar LLB(Hons); LPC Corporate Solicitor . . . . *Apr 2005
Broughton, Ms Lucy Solicitor . . . . *Nov 1995
Budd, Ms Katy LLB(Hons) Solicitor . . . . *Jul 1999
Foreman, Mr Timothy M BA(Hons) Solicitor . . . . . *Jan 1999
Hatton, Mr Wayne LLB(Hons); LPC; Cert In Data Protection Corporate Solicitor . . . . *May 2004
Klein, Mrs Julie A LLB(Hons) Solicitor. . . . . *Oct 1993
Kurthausen, Mr Phillip LLB Solicitor. . . . . *Oct 1998
Pumfrey, Mrs Donna W . . . . *Sep 1976
Worden, Ms Nicola Solicitor. . . . . *Mar 1998

See p112 for the Key to Work Categories & other symbols

CHESTERFIELD, Derbyshire

BOLSOVER DISTRICT COUNCIL
Sherwood Lodge Bolsover Chesterfield Derbyshire S44 6NF
Tel: 01246 240000 *Fax:* 01246 242424
E-mail: enquiries@bolsover.gov.uk
Sol: Dyer, Mr Alfred Geoffrey MA; MBA; MSc Senior Solicitor . . . . *Jan 1974
Fieldsend, Mr James LLB Solicitor. . . . . *Apr 1994
Sternberg, Mrs Sarah E A BA Solr to the Council . . . *Oct 1985

CHESTERFIELD BOROUGH COUNCIL
Town Hall Rose Hill Chesterfield Derbyshire S40 1LP
Tel: 01246 345345 *Fax:* 01246 345270 *Dx:* 12356 CHESTERFIELD
E-mail: keith.ross@chesterfield.gov.uk
Sol: Davies, Ms Barbara Assistant Solicitor. . . . *Mar 1974
Oliver, Mr Stephen LLB Assistant Solicitor. . . . *Apr 1992
Rogers, Mr Gerard P BA Senior Assistant Solicitor . . *Nov 1985
Ross, Mr Keith BA(Dunelm) Head of Legal Scrutiny and Democratic Services . . . . *Feb 1978
Walker, Mrs Amanda M LLB Assistant Solicitor . . . *Dec 1980

CHESTERFIELD LAW CENTRE
44 Park Road Chesterfield Derbyshire S40 1LF
Tel: 01246 550674 / 204570 *Fax:* 01246 551069
E-mail: chesterfieldlawcentre@dial.pipex.com
Sol: Bird, Ms Alice Elizabeth LLB Solicitor . . . . Apr 2005
McIlveen, Mr Tony BA; PGCE Solicitor . . . . Feb 1986

NORTH EAST DERBYSHIRE DISTRICT COUNCIL
Council House Saltergate Chesterfield Derbyshire S40 1LF
Tel: 01246 231111 *Fax:* 01246 217446
Sol: Murphy, Mrs Gylian I BCL; NUI Head of Legal & Democratic Services . . . . *Jan 1991
Smith, Mrs Naomi S BA(Law); LLB(Hons) Principal Solicitor . . . . *Oct 1990

CHICHESTER, West Sussex

CHICHESTER & DISTRICT MAGISTRATES COURTS
6 Market Avenue Chichester West Sussex PO19 1YE
Tel: 01243 817000 *Fax:* 01243 533655
Sol: Bathurst, Mr David J C LLB Divisional Legal Manager / Principal Assistant . . . . *Dec 1990
Brown, Ms Susan DML; LLB(Hons) Solicitor. . . . *Dec 1999
Dack, Mr Christopher Solicitor. . . . *Dec 1990
Evans, Mrs Chloe Louise BA Deputy Divisional Legal Manager . . . . *Aug 1994
Fane De Salis, Mr Mark Timothy BA(Hons) Solicitor. . *Mar 1995
Redstone, Mr David Martin Dip Mag Law; CPE Solicitor . . . . *Dec 1993

CHICHESTER DISTRICT COUNCIL
East Pallant House East Pallant Chichester West Sussex PO19 1TY
Tel: 01243 785166 *Fax:* 01243 776766 *Dx:* 30340 CHICHESTER
E-mail: helpline@chichester.gov.uk
Sol: Golding, Ms Nicola J LARTPI Principal Solicitor . . . *Nov 1989
Kelley, Mr Michael J DMA; DMS. . . . *Jul 1980
Sully, Mr Michael J LLB Principal Solicitor . . . . *Oct 1979

WEST SUSSEX COUNTY COUNCIL
Head of Legal Services County Hall West Street Chichester West Sussex PO19 1RQ
Tel: 01243 777100 *Fax:* 01243 777952 *Dx:* 30330 CHICHESTER
Sol: Boniface, Miss Sally L DipLaw Solicitor . . . . *Nov 1999
Boothroyd, Miss Sara Melanie LLB Solicitor. . . . *Nov 1995
Field, Miss Vanessa Lyndsey BA(Hons) Assistant Solicitor . . . . *May 2002
Gardiner, Mrs Fiona Louise LLB(Hons); LEG DIP Solicitor . . . . *Jan 2001
Gibbs, Miss Rebecca Louise LLB; PGDipLP Assistant Solicitor . . . . *Sep 2003
Henshall, Mr Mark Andrew LLB; BA; PGDipLaw Assistant Solicitor. . . . *Jan 2004
Henshaw, Mrs Diane M F LLB Senior Solicitor. . . . *Oct 1988
Hollingsworth, Ms Rosamund A BA; Dip(Soc Admin) Senior Solicitor. . . . *May 1982
Kendall, Mr Michael P MA(Cantab) County Secretary . *Oct 1975
Kershaw, Mr Anthony J LLB; DipLG Principal Solicitor. *Nov 1985
May, Mrs Hilary A LLB Solicitor . . . . *Jan 1986
Mepham, Miss Susan Louise DipLP Solicitor . . . . *Nov 1995
Moutrey, Mrs Rebecca S CPE; LPC Law Society Prize 2001 Assistant Solicitor. . . . Sep 2002
Payne, Mr Howard LLB Principal Solicitor . . . . Dec 1973
Webber, Miss Ruth LLB(Hons) Solicitor . . . . *Feb 1998
Wilson, Mrs Karen Lesley BA(Hons). . . . *Nov 1995

CHIPPENHAM, Wiltshire

NORTH WILTSHIRE DISTRICT COUNCIL
Monkton Park Chippenham Wiltshire SN15 1ER
Tel: 01249 706111 *Fax:* 01249 462283 *Dx:* 34208 CHIPPENHAM
E-mail: pjeremiah@northwilts.gov.uk
Sol: Jeremiah, Mr Peter Leonard LLB Solicitor/Team Leader (Legal Services) . . . . *Dec 1979
Taylor, Mr Paul Robert John BA(Hons); ACIS Assistant Solicitor . . . . *Sep 1994
Tilley, Mrs Jacqueline J LLB(Bris) Conveyancing Solicitor . . . . *Apr 1977

CHORLEY, Lancashire

CHORLEY BOROUGH COUNCIL
Town Hall Market Street Chorley Lancashire PR7 1DP
Tel: 01257 515151 *Fax:* 01257 515197 *Dx:* 18411 CHORLEY
E-mail: richardtownson.cblegal@virgin.net
Sol: Curtis, Mr Ian K BA(Hons); Cert Mgmnt Deputy Borough Solicitor . . . . Oct 1988
Davies, Mr Jeffrey W MA; LLM(Cantab) Sheffield Edmund Thomas Child & Broderip Prizes/ Scott Scholarship Chief Executive. . . . *Jun 1969
Townson, Mr Richard LLB(Hons) Director of Legal & Personal Services . . . . *Mar 1982

CHORLEY MAGISTRATES' COURT
St Thomas's Square Chorley Lancashire PR7 1DS
Tel: 01257 225000 *Fax:* 01257 261948 *Dx:* 707530 CHORLEY 5
Sol: Dean, Ms Kathleen Ann LLB Legal Adviser . . . . Dec 2002

MAYFAIR TREASURY LTD
Gleadhill House Dawbers Lane Euxton Chorley Lancashire PR7 6EA
Tel: 01257 269400 *Fax:* 01257 269997
Sol: Revitt, Ms Kathryn LLB Solicitor. . . . *Nov 1989

CHRISTCHURCH, Dorset

CHRISTCHURCH BOROUGH COUNCIL
Civic Offices Bridge Street Christchurch Dorset BH23 1AZ
Tel: 01202 495000 *Fax:* 01202 495107
Sol: Fairbairn, Mr David BSc(Hons); MA Head of Legal & Democratic Services . . . . *Oct 1987

CIRENCESTER, Gloucestershire

CIRENCESTER TOWN COUNCIL
Dyer House 3 Dyer Street Cirencester Gloucestershire GL7 2PP
Tel: 01285 655646 *Fax:* 01285 643843
E-mail: clerk@cirencester.gov.uk
Sol: Crook, Mr Andrew Rennie Town Clerk. . . . *Dec 1972

COTSWOLD DISTRICT COUNCIL
Legal Services Section Council Offices Trinity Road Cirencester Gloucestershire GL7 1PX
Tel: 01285 623000 *Fax:* 01285 623916
Dx: 144422 CIRENCESTER 2
Sol: Patel, Mrs Bhavna LLB Solicitor to the Council . . . *May 1989

ST JAMES'S PLACE
St James's Place House Dollar Street Cirencester Gloucestershire GL7 2AQ
Tel: 01285 640302 *Fax:* 01285 653993
Sol: Gladman, Mr Hugh J C LLB(Soton) Solicitor. . . . May 1988
Titterton, Mr Simon Douglas LLB Assistant Solicitor . . . Jul 1998

CLACTON-ON-SEA, Essex

TENDRING DISTRICT COUNCIL
Westleigh House Carnarvon Road Clacton-on-Sea Essex CO15 6QF
Tel: 01255 686567 *Fax:* 01255 686410 *Dx:* 34660 CLACTON
Sol: Geale, Mrs Margaret E LLB(Hons); DMS Principal Solicitor . . . . *§Dec 1974
Gibson-Davies, Mr Michael E Principal Solicitor . . . *Jan 1982
Hawkins, Mr John LLB(Hons) Chief Executive. . . . *Apr 1974
Reeves, Mr William Robert BA(Hons); LLB(Hons) Solicitor . . . . *Mar 1982
Walter-Browne, Miss O Sian J LLB(Hons); DipLG; DipEmp Head of Legal Services . . . . *Feb 1990

CLEETHORPES, North East Lincolnshire

NORTH EAST LINCOLNSHIRE BOROUGH COUNCIL
Civic Offices Knoll Street Cleethorpes North East Lincolnshire DN35 8LN
Tel: 01472 324001 *Fax:* 01472 324131 *Dx:* 83536 GRIMSBY
Sol: Conolly, Mrs Elizabeth M LLB . . . . Jun 1977
Lloyd-Jones, Ms Margaret E LLB(Hons) Senior Solicitor (Community) . . . . *Jul 1980
Murray, Mr John A LLB Assistant Solicitor. . . . Oct 1987
Walsh, Mr Robert BA(Hons) Solicitor . . . . Jun 1996
Walters, Mr Michael J LLB(Soton); DMS. . . . Oct 1978
Ward, Mr Gary Melvyn LLB; LSF Solicitor . . . . *Sep 1994
Wilson, Mr M Richard LLB(Hull); DPA Deputy Director of Law & Administration. . . . Apr 1975

CLITHEROE, Lancashire

RIBBLE VALLEY BOROUGH COUNCIL
Council Offices Church Walk Clitheroe Lancashire BB7 2RA
Tel: 01200 425111 *Fax:* 01200 414488 *Dx:* 15157 CLITHEROE
E-mail: catherine.moore@ribblevalley.gov.uk
Sol: Hill, Ms Mair Joanne LLB(Hons) Solicitor . . . . Sep 1999
Nuttall, Mrs Deborah Louise LLB Solicitor . . . . Mar 2002
Rice, Mrs Diane E LLB Legal Services Manager. . . *Dec 1983

COALVILLE, Leicestershire

ASHBY-DE-LA-ZOUCH PETTY SESSIONAL DIVISION
Clerks Office Vaughan Street Coalville Leicestershire LE67 3DP
Tel: 01530 810661 *Fax:* 01530 813427
Sol: Essat, Mr Altaf Hussein LLB(Hons) Solicitor. . . . *Jun 2002
Marshall, Mrs Rachel Alexandra LLB(Hons) Head of Legal Services . . . . *Feb 1994

NORTH WEST LEICESTERSHIRE DISTRICT COUNCIL
Council Offices Whitwick Road Coalville Leicestershire LE67 3FJ
Tel: 01530 454545 *Fax:* 01530 454506 *Dx:* 23662 COALVILLE
Sol: Kirkham, Mr John R MA(Oxon) Head of Legal Services *Jul 1980

COBHAM, Surrey

CARGILL PLC
Knowle Hill Park Fairmile Lane Cobham Surrey KT11 2PD
Tel: 01932 861000 *Fax:* 01932 861286
Sol: Reynolds, Mr John Christopher MA(Oxon); LLM(Michigan) Cargill Europe, General Counsel . . . . Nov 1975

CODSALL, Staffordshire

SOUTH STAFFORDSHIRE COUNCIL
Council Offices Codsall Staffordshire WV8 1PX
Tel: 01902 696000 *Fax:* 01902 696800 *Dx:* 18036 CODSALL
Sol: Barnfield, Leslie T LLB Chief Executive . . . . *Apr 1972
Hollingworth, Ms Patricia Diane LLB Solicitor . . . . *Jan 1996
Levesley, Mr Rolf BA Strategic Director (Legal) . . . . *Jun 1977

COLCHESTER, Essex

CHILDRENS LEGAL CENTRE
University of Essex Wivenhoe Park Colchester Essex CO4 3SQ
Tel: 01206 872466 / 873828 *Fax:* 01206 874026
E-mail: yvonne@essex.ac.uk
Sol: Frank, Ms Elizabeth LLB Solicitor . . . . May 1993
Popiolek, Mrs Hilary Jane LLB Solicitor . . . . *Sep 1982
Spencer, Miss Yvonne Maria MA Solicitor - Advocate (All Higher Courts) . . . . Apr 2000
Surgenor, Ms Simone LLB(Hons) Solicitor. . . . Mar 2002
Thomas, Mrs Julia BA(Hons) Solicitor. . . . *Dec 1979

COLCHESTER BOROUGH COUNCIL
Legal Services PO Box 884 Town Hall Colchester Essex CO1 1FR
Tel: 01206 282222 *Fax:* 01206 573911
Dx: 729040 COLCHESTER 15
Sol: Lord-Lynch, Mrs Claudia LLB(Hons); DipLaw Planning Solicitor . . . . Apr 2002
Maye, Miss Louise LLB(Hons) Property & Planning Lawyer . . . . Nov 2006

EASTGATE ASSISTANCE LTD
Eastgate House Stephenson Road The Business Park Colchester Essex CO4 4QR
Tel: 0870 523 4500 *Fax:* 0870 523 4508 *Dx:* 3626 COLCHESTER
Sol: Beevers, Mr Paul James LLB(Hons) Solicitor . . . . *Apr 1996
Bulsing, Mrs Belinda Eurwen BA(Hons); MA Solicitor . *Nov 1995
Cornhouse, Mr Martin Jason LLB(Hons) Solicitor . . *Nov 1995
Faulkner, Mr Stuart Mark BA(Hons) Solicitor. . . . Nov 1997
Holland, Mrs Penelope Susan Solicitor . . . . Nov 1996
Islip, Mr Lawrence A G LLB(Hons) Solicitor . . . . *Jul 1978
Jones, Ms Karen Patricia BA(Hons) Solicitor. . . . *Mar 1993
Kilbey, Mr Ian C LLB Solicitor . . . . *Dec 1990
McGlade, Mr Stephen LLB(Hons) Solicitor. . . . *Oct 1994
Millard, Miss Fiona Anne LLB Solicitor. . . . *Oct 1991
Miller, Mrs Vivienne E LLB Solicitor . . . . *Oct 1986
Patel, Ms Nayna BSc; BA Solicitor . . . . *Jun 1992
Pinn, Mr Matthew D LLB(Hons) Solicitor. . . . *Oct 1990
Pirozzolo, Mr L Rocco LLB(Hons) Solicitor. . . . May 1991
Rowles, Ms Ceinwen BA(Hons) Solicitor. . . . *Oct 1991
Salmon, Miss June Frances LLB(Hons); LLM Solicitor. Mar 1993
Scott, Mrs Daphne Ann LLB(Hons) Solicitor . . . . *Apr 1992
Smith, Ms Louise S LLB Solicitor . . . . Oct 1992
Smith, Mr Peter J BA(Oxon) Solicitor . . . . *Jul 1965
Taylor, Miss Rosemary Stewart LLB(Hons) Solicitor . *Oct 1994
Tye, Mr Simon P Solicitor . . . . *Apr 1987
Watkins, Mrs Ruth Carolyn LLB(Hons) Solicitor . . . . *Apr 1992

THE ROYAL LONDON MUTUAL INSURANCE SOCIETY LTD
55 Gracechurch Street London EC3V 0RL
Tel: 020 7506 6500 *Fax:* 020 7506 6682
Sol: Elley, Mrs Emma Mary Louisa LLB; BA In-House Lawyer . . . . Nov 2004
Guy, Ms Susan Cropley BSc(Econ) Group Legal Adviser - Property. . . . *Dec 1978
Harris, Miss Victoria Jane BSc(Hons)(Microbiology) Solicitor . . . . Mar 2003
Johnson, Mr Joseph B LLB(Manc) Assistant Solicitor *May 1981

COLEFORD, Gloucestershire

FOREST OF DEAN DISTRICT COUNCIL
Council Offices High Street Coleford Gloucestershire GL16 8HG
Tel: 01594 810000 *Fax:* 01594 812470
Sol: Harding, Mr Laurence J LLB(Lond); Dip Solicitor. . . . Nov 1974

COLESHILL, Warwickshire

BOVIS HOMES LTD
Central Region 1 Bromwich Court Highway Point Coleshill Warwickshire B46 1JU
Tel: 01675 437000 *Fax:* 01675 437068 *Dx:* 728340 COLESHILL 2
Sol: Bryan, Miss Joanne LLB Solicitor . . . . Aug 2001
Orluta, Mrs Samantha Anne BA(Jt Hons) . . . . Oct 1996

COLWYN BAY, Conwy

NORTH WALES MAGISTRATES COURTS' COMMITTEE
1st Floor Midland Bank Annexe 16 Ebberston Road West Colwyn Bay Conwy LL28 4AP
Tel: 01492 541573 *Fax:* 01492 541661
Sol: Jones, Mr John Grant LLB(Hons)(Wales) . . . . *Jul 1971

CONWY

CONWY COUNTY BOROUGH COUNCIL
Bodlondeb Conwy LL32 8DU
Tel: 01492 576108 *Fax:* 01492 576116 *Dx:* 24628 CONWY
E-mail: iwan.davies@conwy.gov.uk
Sol: Barker, Mr Clifford D LLB(Hons) Chief Executive Non-Practising Solicitor. . . . *Dec 1974
Cooper, Mr Wayne Gary BA(Hons); CPE; LSF. . . . *Jun 1990
Davies, Mr Iwan LLB(Hons); MBA Head of Legal Services . . . . *Dec 1989
Dunn, Mr John Solicitor Notary Public. . . . *Jul 1975
Hughes, Ms Janet M BA(Hons); DipLG Solicitor. . . . *Nov 1991
Jones, Mrs Delyth Eluned FILEx Solicitor . . . . *Sep 1998
Jones, Mrs Janet Wynne LLB(Hons); DipLG. . . . *Jul 1974
Williams, Ms Ceri R Solicitor . . . . *Aug 1998

CORBY, Northamptonshire

CORBY BOROUGH COUNCIL
Grosvenor House George Street Corby Northamptonshire NN17 1QB
Tel: 01536 402551 *Fax:* 01536 464109 *Dx:* 12915 CORBY
Sol: Aley, Mr Simon John MBA; LLB; DipLG Head of Legal and Democratic Services . . . *Nov 1987
Channer, Mr Nigel BA Senior Solicitor. . . . Aug 2002
Granger, Miss Emma M BA(Hons); DipTP; DipLaw; LLB(Hons); MRTPI Legal Services Manager. . . . *Jul 2003
Wale, Miss Sarah Elisabeth LLB(Hons) Solicitor. . . . May 1990

COVENTRY, West Midlands

COVENTRY BUILDING SOCIETY
Oakfield House PO Box 600 Binley Business Park Coventry West Midlands CV3 9YR
Tel: 024 7665 3516 *Fax:* 024 7665 3576 *Dx:* COVENTRY 2
Sol: Rambhai, Mr Nailesh Kantilal MA(Oxon) Secretary& Solicitor . . . *Feb 1999

COVENTRY CITY COUNCIL
First Floor Casselden House Greyfriars Lane Coventry West Midlands CV1 2GX
Tel: 024 7683 4863 *Fax:* 024 7683 2527 *Dx:* 18868 COVENTRY 2
Sol: Bajaj, Ms Angel A Lawyer. . . . Oct 1998
Bodalia, Ms Reema BA(Hons) Senior Solicitor. . . . Aug 1997
Buckley, Mrs Vicki Ann Principal Lawyer (Group Leader) . . . *Dec 1990
Carter, Ms Gillian Margaret BA Principal Lawyer (Group Leader) . . . Oct 1993
Greaves, Miss Dee F M LLB(Hons) Solicitor. . . . Oct 1993
Hinde, Mr Christopher R BA(Dunelm) . . . *Oct 1979
Langley White, Ms Janice Lavina Senior Lawyer. . . . Oct 1993
Lilley, Ms Rosalyn Senior Lawyer . . . Apr 1985
Rice, Miss Kathleen Julia BA(Hons) Head Of Legal Services . . . *Apr 1987
Singh, Ms Kuldip Lawyer . . . Nov 1998
Smith, Mr Mark A BA(Hons) Lawyer. . . . *Nov 1997

THE COVENTRY DISTRICT LAND REGISTRY
Leigh Court Torrington Avenue Tile Hill Coventry West Midlands CV4 9XZ
Tel: 024 7686 0860 *Fax:* 024 7686 0021 *Dx:* 18900 COVENTRY 3

LEX TRANSFLEET LTD
Lex House Westwood Business Park Torwood Close Coventry West Midlands CV4 8HX
Tel: 024 7669 4494 *Fax:* 024 7647 0419
Sol: Calladine, Mr Paul G BA(Law) Solicitor . . . *§Oct 1995

PEUGEOT CITROEN AUTOMOBILES UK LTD
Pinley House PO Box 227 DJUK Coventry West Midlands CV3 1ND
Tel: 024 7688 4258 *Fax:* 024 7688 4001
E-mail: roger.lewis@mpsa.com
Sol: Lewis, Mr Roger MA(Cantab) Director Legal & Company Secretary . . . *Oct 1980

POWERGEN PLC
Legal Department Westwood Business Park Westwood Way Coventry West Midlands CV4 8LG
Tel: 024 7642 4748 / 4000 *Fax:* 024 7645 2248
Sol: Hammond, Miss Stephanie K BA(Law) Solicitor . . . *May 1987
Loweth, Mr James H BSc Solicitor. . . . *Dec 1976
Stark, Ms Fiona S Solicitor . . . *Oct 1986
Thomas, Ms Chantal M Solicitor. . . . Jul 1997

CRAWLEY, West Sussex

AVESCO GROUP PLC
Unit E2 Sussex Manor Business Park Gatwick Road Crawley West Sussex RH10 9NH
Tel: 01293 583400 *Fax:* 01293 583410
E-mail: mail@avesco.co.uk
Sol: Conn, Mr Nicholas S LLB Company Secretary. . . . *Oct 1981

BARBOCK ENERGY LTD
11 The Boulevard Crawley West Sussex RH10 1UX
Tel: 01293 584974 *Fax:* 01293 584951
E-mail: crichards@mitsuibabcock.com
Sol: Richards, Mr Carl LLB Company Solicitor . . . Jan 2002

CRAWLEY BOROUGH COUNCIL
Town Hall The Boulevard Crawley West Sussex RH10 1UZ
Tel: 01293 438000 *Fax:* 01293 511803 *Dx:* 57139 CRAWLEY
Sol: Gatherer, Miss Alison LLB. . . . Nov 1993
Nelson-Wehrmeyer, Mrs Susanne Lin B Juris; LLB; MBA Assistant Borough Secretary (Legal) . . . *Sep 1992

EDF ENERGY NETWORKS LTD
Cross Keys 50-52 The Broadway Crawley West Sussex RH10 1HF
Tel: 01293 656070 *Fax:* 01293 656053 *Dx:* 85700 CRAWLEY
E-mail: christopher.baker@edfenergy.com
Sol: Baiter, Mr Christopher John ACIS Principal Solicitor. . . Jan 1982
Baker, Mr Christopher J Solicitor . . . *Jan 1982

THOMSON TRAINING & SIMULATION LTD
Gatwick Road Crawley West Sussex RH10 2RL
Tel: 01293 562822 *Fax:* 01293 563366
Sol: Willmott, Mr Barry Legal Manager. . . . *Aug 1989

VIRGIN ATLANTIC AIRWAYS LTD
The Office Manor Royal Crawley West Sussex RH10 9NU
Tel: 01293 562345 *Fax:* 01293 747186
Sol: Farrow, Ms Frances E LLB Solicitor. . . . Nov 1989
Harding, Mr Jonathan P S J Solicitor . . . Nov 1994
Weston, J A Solicitor . . . Dec 1992

CREWE, Cheshire

BENTLEY MOTORS LTD
Pym's Lane Crewe Cheshire CW1 3PL
Tel: 01270 255155 *Fax:* 01270 500620
Sol: Armitage, Mr Andrew Thomas LLB Company Secretary & Solicitor. . . . *May 1981

CREWE & NANTWICH BOROUGH COUNCIL
Municipal Buildings Earle Street Crewe Cheshire CW1 2BJ
Tel: 01270 537102 *Fax:* 01270 537759 *Dx:* 725220 CREWE 8
E-mail: riddell.graham@crewe-nantwich.gov.uk
Sol: Allen, Miss Rebecca LLB(Hons) Assistant Solicitor . . *Jan 2002
Goddard, Mrs Rachel Assistant Solicitor. . . . *Jan 1983
Henshall, Mr Christopher J Borough Solicitor . . . *Jan 1981

SOUTH CHESHIRE MAGISTRATES COURT
Law Courts Civic Centre Crewe Cheshire CW1 2DT
Tel: 0870 162 6261 *Fax:* 01270 589357
Sol: Eeles, Miss Julia M Area Director . . . Jan 2000
Walsh, Mr Steven LLB Justices' Clerk. . . . Jul 1978

CROMER, Norfolk

NORTH NORFOLK DISTRICT COUNCIL
Council Offices Holt Road Cromer Norfolk NR27 9EL
Tel: 01263 513811 *Fax:* 01263 516335 *Dx:* 31008 CROMER
Sol: Bull, Mr Graham BA(Oxon) Assistant Chief Executive . *Jun 1977
Pettifer, Mr Martin J LLB; DipLG Head of Legal Services . . . *Nov 1989

CROWBOROUGH, East Sussex

WEALDEN DISTRICT COUNCIL
Council Offices Pine Grove Wealden Crowborough East Sussex TN6 1DH
Tel: 01892 653311 *Fax:* 01892 602223 *Dx:* 36860 CROWBOROUGH
Sol: Abbott, Mr Trevor Principal Solicitor. . . . Dec 2002
Johnson, Mr Geoffrey A LLB(Soton) Principal Solicitor. Jul 1979
Scarpa, Mr Vittorio P M BA; LLB Solicitor to the Council; Law Society Planning Panel . . . *Jun 1979

CROYDON, Surrey

ALLDERS (CROYDON) LTD
2 North End Croydon Surrey CR9 1SB
Tel: 020 8603 7400 *Fax:* 020 8603 7666
E-mail: caroline.chard@allders.com
Sol: Chard, Miss Caroline R LLB(Bris) Solicitor & Company Secretary. . . . *Jun 1974

BOURJOIS LTD
Queens Way Croydon Surrey CR9 4DL
Tel: 020 8688 7131 *Fax:* 020 8688 0012
Sol: Hamilton, Mr Martin LLB(Soton) Legal Director/Company Secretary/Deputy Chairman. . . . *May 1977

ALEXANDER FORBES FINANCIAL SERVICES
Leon House 233 High Street Croydon Surrey CR9 9AF
Tel: 020 8686 0660 *Fax:* 020 8688 6302
Sol: Prince, Ms Karen P BA(Hons); MPhil Company Lawyer Oct 1994

LAND REGISTRY - CROYDON OFFICE
Trafalgar House 1 Bedford Park Croydon Surrey CR0 2AQ
Tel: 020 8388 3288 *Fax:* 020 8781 9110 *Dx:* 2699 CROYDON 3
E-mail: croydon.office@landregistry.gsi.gov.uk
Sol: Allen, Ms Jane Assistant Land Registrar. . . . *Sep 1991
Bailey, Ms Elizabeth Joy LLB Assistant Land Registrar City Councillor. . . . *Oct 1988
Dosaj, Ms Ashu Kumari Assistant Land Registrar . . *Mar 1992
Shaw, Mrs Angela Mary LLB Assistant Land Registrar *Nov 2000

MONDIAL ASSISTANCE (UK) LTD
Mondial House 102 George Street Croydon Surrey CR9 1AJ
Tel: 020 8681 2525 *Fax:* 020 8603 0201
E-mail: legal@mondial-assistance.co.uk
Sol: Deluca, Ms Wendreda Solicitor . . . Nov 1993

NESTLE UK LTD
St George's House Croydon Surrey CR9 1NR
Tel: 020 8667 5260 *Fax:* 020 8667 5775
Sol: Dancey, Miss Helen P Solicitor . . . Nov 1998
Delamere, Miss Rachel C BA(Hons); CPE; LPC Lawyer (Intellectual Property). . . . *Oct 1998
Heath, Miss Natalie BA(German); CPE; LSF Property Lawyer . . . *Nov 1994
Liggett, Mr Matthew Lawyer. . . . Apr 1998
Roffey, Mr Nigel P Manager Group Taxation Department . . . *Apr 1968
Whitehead, Mr Adrian J LLB(Lond) Solicitor. . . . *Nov 1988

CWMBRAN, Torfaen

GWENT CONSTABULARY
Police Headquarters Croesyceiliog Cwmbran Torfaen NP44 2XJ
Dx: 131334 CWMBRAN 2
Sol: Williams, Mr Alan LLB; DipLGP Solicitor. . . . *Jan 1989

DAGENHAM, Essex

LONDON BOROUGH OF BARKING & DAGENHAM
Civic Centre Dagenham Essex RM10 7BN
Tel: 020 8592 4500 *Fax:* 020 8227 3698 *Dx:* 8511 BARKING
Sol: Hanton, Mr Robert W LLB(Lond) Solicitor . . . *Dec 1973
Huddie, Mr Patrick J MA Assistant Head of Legal Services Solicitor. . . . *Aug 1971

DARLINGTON

DARLINGTON BOROUGH COUNCIL
Town Hall Feethams Darlington DL1 5QT
Tel: 01325 388055 *Fax:* 01325 388318 *Dx:* 69280 DARLINGTON 6
Sol: Catterick, Mrs Andrea BA(Hons)(Oxon) Solicitor. . . *Sep 1995
Cookson, Mr Neil A BA; PhD; MIFA. . . . *Nov 1992
Hemus, Mrs Lesley BA Solicitor. . . . *Feb 1988
Morgan, Ms Janine Catharine LLB Solicitor . . . Jan 1999
Parry, Miss Nicola Clare LLB Solicitor . . . *Dec 2003
Whitehead, Ms Catherine Harriet BA(Hons); DipLG(Law) Borough Solicitor . . . Oct 1994
Whitehead, Miss Dawn LLB(Hons); DipLP Solicitor . *Aug 1997

DARTFORD, Kent

DARTFORD BOROUGH COUNCIL
Civic Centre Home Gardens Dartford Kent DA1 1DR
Tel: 01322 343434 *Fax:* 01322 343422 *Dx:* 31908 DARTFORD
E-mail: legal.services@dartford.gov.uk
Sol: Cotton, Miss Sarah LLB(Hons) Assistant Solicitor (Conveyancing). . . . *Sep 1992

PANEL AGENCY LTD
Maple House 5 Over Minnis New Ash Green Longfield Dartford Kent DA3 8JA
Tel: 01474 872578 *Fax:* 01474 872426
E-mail: markwilson@panelagency.com
Sol: Wilson, Mr Mark S LLB(Hons); MSc Director . . . *§May 1992

DEAL, Kent

THE LIFEBOAT
The Strand Walmer Deal Kent CT14 7DY
Tel: 01304 374475
Sol: Carter, Ms Christine A Solicitor . . . Dec 1974

DEESIDE, Flintshire

THE BIG FOOD GROUP PLC
Deeside Industrial Park Second Avenue Deeside Flintshire CH5 2NW
Tel: 01244 830100 *Fax:* 01244 520564
Sol: Burrell, Miss Jayne K LLB; IP Diploma Solicitor . . . Mar 2000
Chilton, Mr Mark LLB Group Solicitor . . . *Oct 1987

DAVID MCLEAN LEGAL SERVICES
Vinters House Deeside Industrial Park Deeside Flintshire CH5 2LA
Tel: 01244 283500 *Fax:* 01244 280747
E-mail: legalservices@davidmcleanhumes.co.uk
Sol: Caplan, Mr Colin P Manager . . . Jun 1979

DENHAM, Buckinghamshire

SOUTH BUCKS DISTRICT COUNCIL
Council Offices Capswood Oxford Road Denham Buckinghamshire UB9 4LH
Tel: 01895 837200 *Fax:* 01895 837277
Dx: 40621 GERRARDS CROSS
E-mail: lynne.reardon@southbucks.gov.uk
Sol: Bharj, Mrs Ranjit BA; PGDipLaw Assistant Solicitor . . *Oct 2004
Dell, Mrs Anna Marie Dip Legal Studies Principal . . . *Oct 1996
Gibson, Mr Timothy Wells BA Senior Assistant Solicitor*Apr 1980
Lakhanpaul, Miss Angela LLM; LLB Legal Assistant. . Dec 2006
Reardon, Miss Lynne LLB Head of Legal Services. . *Dec 1986

DERBY

BALFOUR BEATTY POWER NETWORKS LTD
Raynesway Derby DE21 7BG
Tel: 01332 288537 *Fax:* 01332 674219
Dx: 28744 DERBY RAYNESWAY
Sol: Lee, Mr Andrew Colin ACIArb Company Solicitor . . . *Jul 1979

CROWN PROSECUTION SERVICE DERBYSHIRE
5th Floor St Peters House Gower Street Derby DE1 1SB
Tel: 01332 614000 *Dx:* 725818 DERBY 22
Sol: Gunn, Mr Brian Malcolm OBE LLB Chief Crown Prosecutor . . . *Jun 1975

CROWN PROSECUTION SERVICE DERBYSHIRE
7th Floor St Peter's House Gower Street Derby DE1 1SB
Tel: 01332 614000 *Fax:* 01332 614009 *Dx:* 725818 DERBY 22
Sol: Zimand, Miss Zofia Anna LLB. . . . *Apr 1976

DERBY CITY COUNCIL
Council House Corporation Street Derby DE1 2FS
Tel: 01332 293111 *Fax:* 01332 255834 *Dx:* 723462 DERBY 20
Sol: Barrington, Ms Helen Elizabeth LLB(Hons) Solicitor . . Aug 1997
Constable, Mr Robin M LLB(Hons) Solicitor . . . *Oct 1990
Cooper, Miss Susan Allison FILEx; DipLP Solicitor. . Oct 1996
Dunlop, Ms Lindsay J Solicitor. . . . Nov 1996
Foote, Mr Michael A LLB Director of Corporate Services . . . *Jun 1977
Gill, Miss Rajwant Kaur Solicitor. . . . *Aug 2003
Hogg, Ms Hannah M LLB Solicitor. . . . *Apr 1992
Leslie, Mr Stuart BA(Hons) Chief Legal Officer . . . *Oct 1981
Pollard, Mrs Anna M LLB Solicitor. . . . *Oct 1988
Povey, Mrs Linda LLB Solicitor . . . *Oct 1990
Sheehan, Mrs Anita FILEx; LLB Solicitor . . . *Jan 2000
Teasdale, Mr Stephen W LLB Solicitor. . . . *Aug 1989
Thomas, Mr Andrew P C Principal Solicitor . . . *§Apr 1980

DERBY HOSPITALS NHS FOUNDATION TRUST
Derby City General Hospital Uttoxeter Road Derby DE22 3NE
Tel: 01332 785419 *Fax:* 01332 788671
E-mail: victoria.stewart@derbyhospitals.nhs.uk
Sol: Murray, Mr Stephen BSc(Hons); LLB Solicitor. . . . Nov 1991
Stewart, Mrs Victoria LLB(Hons) Solicitor . . . Aug 1996

ROLLS-ROYCE PLC
PO Box 31 Moor Lane Derby DE24 8BJ
Tel: 01332 242424 *Fax:* 01332 248963
Sol: Holliday, Mr Stuart A LLB Senior Legal Adviser . . . *Jun 1974
Macmillan, Mr Peter T A LLB Senior Legal Adviser . *Nov 1983
Revelle, Mr Peter Charles Senior Legal Adviser. . . *Apr 1968
Saint, Miss Beverley BSc(Hons) Legal Adviser . . . *Oct 1991
Salt, Mr Steven P LLB Senior Legal Adviser. . . . *Jan 1986
Wood, Miss Alison N LLB Legal Adviser. . . . *Nov 1988

SOFTWARE AG UK LTD
Hudson House Hudson Way Pride Park Derby DE24 8HS
Tel: 01332 611000 *Fax:* 01332 611222

 See p112 for the Key to Work Categories & other symbols

E-mail: tim.fox@softwareag.co.uk
Sol: Fox, Mr Timothy N Company Solicitor . . . . *Oct 1991

VOICE: THE UNION FOR EDUCATION PROFESSIONALS
2 St James Court Friar Gate Derby DE1 1BT
Tel: 01332 372337 *Fax:* 01332 290310
E-mail: hq@voicetheunion.org.uk
Sol: Brierley, Mr David J MA Union Solicitor . . . . Feb 1979

DEVIZES, Wiltshire

KENNET DISTRICT COUNCIL
Browfort Bath Road Devizes Wiltshire SN10 2AT
Tel: 01380 724911 *Fax:* 01380 720835 *Dx:* 42909 DEVIZES
E-mail: kentishtowncab@camdencabservice.org.uk
Sol: Boden, Mr Mark J LLB(Hons) Chief Executive. . . . . *Jan 1983
Lee, Miss Janet LLB(Hons) Lawyer . . . . *Apr 1983

DEWSBURY, West Yorkshire

BATLEY & DEWSBURY MAGISTRATES COURT
Court House Grove Street Dewsbury West Yorkshire WF13 1JP
Tel: 01924 468287 *Fax:* 01924 430483
Sol: Carruthers, Ms Linda Legal Team Manager . . . . . . Oct 1995

DIDCOT, Oxfordshire

UNITED KINGDOM ATOMIC ENERGY AUTHORITY
Legal Department Building 521 Harwell Didcot Oxfordshire OX11 0RA
Tel: 01235 436984 *Fax:* 01235 436850
E-mail: david.west@ukaea.org.uk
Sol: Scott, Mr Martin J R LLB(Hons) Commercial Solicitor . *Mar 1995

UNITED KINGDOM NIREX LTD
Curie Avenue Harwell Didcot Oxfordshire OX11 0RH
Tel: 01235 825500 *Fax:* 01235 821902
E-mail: claire.harvey@nirex.co.uk
Sol: Harvey, Mrs Claire BA(Hons) Solicitor. . . . . Jan 1990

DONCASTER, South Yorkshire

DONCASTER MAGISTRATES COURT
The Law Courts College Road PO Box 49 Doncaster South Yorkshire DN1 3HT
Tel: 01302 366711 *Fax:* 01302 347359 *Dx:* 12574 DONCASTER 1
Sol: Broderick, Mrs Margaret Joy LLB(Hons) Senior Legal Advisor . . . . Mar 1977
Cherry, Mr Richard Michael LLB(Hons) Legal Adviser . *Jan 2002
Cornall, Mr David Andrew Principal Legal Adviser . . . Jan 1990
Crowley, Miss Rosemary Anne Senior Legal Adviser . Jan 1993
Frankland, Mrs Helen C BA(Law) Senior Legal Adviser *Jun 1980
Hanby, Mrs Karen Julie Senior Legal Adviser . . . . . Jul 1996
Hazell, Mr Richard John LLB(Hons) District Legal Director . . . . Apr 1979
Kaur, Miss Gurjinder LLB(Hons) Solicitor/Legal Adviser*Dec 2005
Kennedy, Ms Anne Patricia BA(Hons) Legal Advisor. . . Jul 1993
Smith, Miss Sarah Annette LLB(Hons) Legal Advisor . Mar 2005

DONCASTER METROPOLITAN BOROUGH COUNCIL
Copley House Waterdale Doncaster South Yorkshire DN1 3EQ
Tel: 01302 734651 *Fax:* 01302 735614 *Dx:* 12569 DONCASTER
Sol: Bailey, Miss Marie-Clare BSc(Hons)(Politics & Modern History) Senior Legal Officer, Solicitor . . . . *Dec 2003
Dobson, Mrs Nicola J Senior Legal Officer. . . . . . . Nov 2004
Evans, Mr Paul Justin BA Director of Legal & Democratic Services . . . . Nov 1995
Fawcus, Mr Scott LLB(Hons) Senior Legal Officer. . . . Aug 2002
Pointon, Mr Neil LLB(Hons)(Leics) Principal Legal Officer . . . . *Oct 1980
Potts, Mrs Helen LLB Senior Legal Officer. . . . . . *Sep 1998
Thomas, Mr James R BA Principal Legal Officer. . . . *Aug 1991
Wilson, Miss Helen LLB; BA(Hons); LawDip Senior Legal Officer . . . . *Sep 1997
Winnard, Mrs Karen D LLB Senior Legal Officer. . . . *Oct 1988

UK COAL PLC
Harworth Park Blyth Road Harworth Doncaster South Yorkshire DN11 8DB
Tel: 01302 751751 *Fax:* 01302 746554
Sol: West, Mr Andrew D LLB Solicitor . . . . *Nov 1988

DORCHESTER, Dorset

DORSET COUNTY COUNCIL
County Hall Colliton Park Dorchester Dorset DT1 1XJ
Tel: 01305 251000 *Fax:* 01305 224399 *Dx:* 8716 DORCHESTER
E-mail: (name)@dorsetcc.gov.uk
Sol: Beverley, Mrs Lesley Susan BSc(Hons) Solicitor. . . . *Nov 1989
Charlton, Ms Susan P LLB Solicitor Social Services. *May 1989
Goodwin, Miss Catherine J LLB Solicitor . . . . Mar 1989
Hounsell, Mrs Shan Mary Law Society Prize 1991 Solicitor . . . . Dec 1993
Le Helloco, Mrs Lindsay S BA Solicitor . . . . *Dec 1983
Mair, Mr Jonathan LLB; DipLG Head of Legal and Democratic Services . . . . *Oct 1992
Menaldino, Mr Danilo L LLB Principal Solicitor. . . . . . *Apr 1982
Sheppard, Mrs Beverley J LLB Solicitor . . . . *Oct 1984
Taylor, Mrs Elaine M LLB(Hons) Director of Corporate Services . . . . Jan 1981
Workman, Mrs Lisa Jane BA Solicitor . . . . *Oct 1993
Zeiss, Mrs Susan Joan BA; LLB; Admitted Attorney RSA(1984) Principal Solicitor . . . . Nov 2004

ELDRIDGE POPE & CO PLC
Weymouth Avenue Dorchester Dorset DT1 1QT
Tel: 01305 251251 *Fax:* 01305 258300
E-mail: dorchester@eldridge-pope.co.uk
Sol: Pope, Mr Jeremy J R OBE MA(Cantab) Managing Director . . . . *Jul 1969

MAGNA HOUSING GROUP LTD
Hollands House Poundbury Road Dorchester Dorset DT1 1SW
Tel: 01305 216000 *Fax:* 01305 216099 *Dx:* 8729 DORCHESTER
E-mail: hollands@magna.org.uk
Sol: Lakeman, Mr Conrad BA Group Director of Governance . . . . *Nov 1983
Taylor, Mr Michael LLB Solicitor . . . . *Nov 2000

WEST DORSET DISTRICT COUNCIL
Council Offices Stratton House 58/60 High West Street Dorchester Dorset DT1 1UZ
Tel: 01305 251010 *Fax:* 01305 252495 *Dx:* 8724 DORCHESTER
E-mail: a.muir@westdorset-dc.gov.uk
Sol: Mauger, Mrs Susan LLB(Hons); PGDipLP Solicitor . . Mar 2003
Muir, Mr Alan S LLB(Lond); MCMI Legal Services Manager . . . . *§Dec 1976

DORKING, Surrey

FRIENDS PROVIDENT
Legal Department Pixham End Dorking Surrey RH4 1QA
Tel: 01306 654925 *Fax:* 01306 876863 *Dx:* 133753 DORKING 3
E-mail: anne.murray@friendsprovident.co.uk
Sol: Ali-Shah, Mr Iqbal Senior Solicitor. . . . . *Nov 1999
Amerigo, Mr Lee Robert LLB Solicitor . . . . *Sep 1999
Barratt, Mr Michael Senior Solicitor . . . . *§Dec 1980
Devereux, Mr Robert J Senior Solicitor . . . . *Jun 1980
Dunlop, Mrs Jane Senior Commercial Solicitor. . . . . Jan 2002
Ellis, Mrs Belinda Margaret LLB Solicitor . . . . *Oct 2005
Ellis, Mr Gordon Director of Legal Services & Group Secretary . . . . *Apr 1981
Elmore-Jones, Mr Michael R Senior Solicitor . . . . . *Nov 1972
Green, Mr David G LLB Senior Solicitor. . . . . *Jan 1976
Hands, Ms Joanna B A Head of Legal . . . . *Nov 1984
Towndrow, Miss Joanne FILEx Senior Commercial Solicitor . . . . *Nov 1998

MOLE VALLEY DISTRICT COUNCIL
Pippbrook Dorking Surrey RH4 1SJ
Tel: 01306 885001 *Fax:* 01306 876821 *Dx:* 57306 DORKING
E-mail: robert.burn@molevalley.gov.uk
Sol: Burn, Mr Robert J LLB(Hull) Head of Legal Services. *Dec 1977
Harris, Mr Christopher P Principal Solicitor . . . . . . *Oct 1997
Ikram, Mr Raheem LLB Commercial Solicitor . . . . . Sep 2002
Restell, Mrs Gwen Property Solicitor. . . . . *Mar 1971

DOVER, Kent

DOVER DISTRICT COUNCIL
Council Offices White Cliffs Business Park Dover Kent CT16 3PJ
Tel: 01304 821199 *Fax:* 01304 872325 *Dx:* 6312 DOVER
E-mail: legal@dov.gov.uk
Sol: May, Mr Lee D LLB(Hons) Solicitor . . . . *Jun 2001
Prentice, Miss Louise E LLB(Hons) Solicitor. . . . . . *Sep 2006
Rudd, Mr Antony H R BA(Law) Solicitor to the Council.*Mar 1985

DUDLEY, West Midlands

DUDLEY METROPOLITAN BOROUGH COUNCIL
Legal & Property Services 5 Ednam Road Dudley West Midlands DY1 1HL
Tel: 01384 815326 *Fax:* 01384 815325 *Dx:* 12767 DUDLEY
E-mail: legal@vin1.dudley.gov.uk
Sol: Breakwell, Mrs Gail S LLB(Hons) Senior Solicitor . . . *Nov 1989
Edwards, Mr Keith D Principal Solicitor . . . . *Dec 1977
Hadley, Mr David Samuel Solicitor. . . . . *Nov 2001
Hartley, Ms Jane Mary LLB(Hons) Leicester University Labour Law Prize 1993 Senior Solicitor . . . . *Jul 1998
Holder, Mr Timothy John LLB(Hons) Solicitor . . . . *May 2002
Karim, Mr Mohammed Jalil BA(Hons) Solicitor. . . . . *Jan 2001
Kidd, Miss Helen Mary BA(Hons) Solicitor. . . . . . . Jan 2000
Marsh, Mrs Susan M BA(Hons) Senior Solicitor . . . . *Oct 1990
Polychronakis, Mr John LLB Chief Legal & Property Officer . . . . *Apr 1977
Rhodes, Mr Simon James LLB(Hons) Solicitor. . . . . *May 2005
Southerton, Mrs Katrina Ann Solicitor . . . . *Dec 1994
Tart, Mr Philip LLB(Hons) Principal Solicitor . . . . . . Dec 1991
Tuckley, Miss Rebecca BA(Hons) Solicitor. . . . . . . *Feb 2004

DUFFIELD, Derbyshire

DERBYSHIRE BUILDING SOCIETY
Duffield Hall Duffield Derbyshire DE56 1AG
Tel: 01332 841000 *Fax:* 01332 844666
Sol: Ashurst, Mr Graham H MA(Oxon) Stephen Heelis Prize Solicitor . . . . *Jun 1976
Owen, Mr Robert J H LLB Legal Services Manager . . *Oct 1994

DUKINFIELD, Greater Manchester

ROLAND BARDSLEY HOMES LTD
Globe Square Dukinfield Greater Manchester SK16 4RG
Tel: 0161 330 5555 *Fax:* 0161 343 1862
Sol: Signey, Mr Geoffrey Martin LLB Solicitor. . . . . *Jun 1972

DUNSTABLE, Bedfordshire

RENAULT TRUCKS UK LTD
Boscombe Road Dunstable Bedfordshire LU5 4LX
Tel: 01582 471122 *Fax:* 01582 479077
E-mail: nick.jeffery@renault-trucks.com
Sol: Jeffery, Mr John Nicholas BSc Legal Advisor . . . . *May 1994

SOUTH BEDFORDSHIRE DISTRICT COUNCIL
The District Offices High Street North Dunstable Bedfordshire LU6 1LF
Tel: 01582 472222 *Fax:* 0845 849 6116 *Dx:* 57012 DUNSTABLE
E-mail: sbdc@southbedsdc.gov.uk
Sol: Emerton, Mr Andrew R L BA(Law) Solicitor . . . . . . *Dec 1985
Kang, Mr Amerjit Singh BA(Hons) Solicitor . . . . . . *Mar 1988

Ronan, Mr Michael Mare LLB(Hons); DipLG; Cert Mgmt Deputy Legal Services Manager. . . . . *Jan 2000
Sutton, Mr Ernest J A LLB(Lond); MRICS . . . . *Jun 1983

2

DURHAM, Co Durham

CROWN PROSECUTION SERVICE DURHAM
Elvet House Hallgarth Street Durham Co Durham DH1 3AT
Tel: 0191 383 5800 *Fax:* 0191 383 5801 *Dx:* 60227 DURHAM
Sol: Bolam, Mr Philip J LLB(Leics) Solicitor . . . . Nov 1972
Brabban, Mr William Solicitor . . . . Jan 1977
Chadwick, Mr David B BA(Dunelm)(Law) Solicitor. . . Apr 1974
Clark, Ms Alison G LLB Solicitor. . . . . Oct 1991
Corrighan, Mr Jeffrey Solicitor. . . . . Jun 1977
Cowen, Mr Richard LLB Solicitor . . . . Nov 1974
Crook, Mr David F LLB Solicitor. . . . . *Oct 1991
Haigh, Mrs Jennifer A BA Solicitor. . . . . *Apr 1987
Ho, Ms Jade Y LLB(B'ham) Solicitor. . . . . Oct 1990
Kirkup, Ms Lesley A Solicitor . . . . Nov 1982
Lees, Miss Fiona G E LLB(Newc) Solicitor. . . . . . . Jul 1973
Orange, Mr Steven J LLB Solicitor. . . . . *§Jul 1979
Scutt, Mr David J LLB(East Anglia) Solicitor. . . . . . *Oct 1983
Smith, Mr Peter A Solicitor . . . . *§Feb 1975
Taylor, Mr Geoffrey W LLB Solicitor . . . . Apr 1970
Thomas, Mr James S M BA(Law) Solicitor. . . . . . . *Jun 1986
Walker, Mr Michael I Solicitor . . . . Jul 1979
Wilkinson, Mr David Solicitor . . . . Jan 1992
Williamson, Mr Christopher A LLB(Cantab) Solicitor . *§Apr 1980

DURHAM CITY COUNCIL
17 Claypath Durham Co Durham DH1 1RH
Tel: 0191 386 6111 *Fax:* 0191 301 8219 *Dx:* 60239 DURHAM
Sol: Blackie, Mrs Lesley Gillian LLB(Newc) Director of Legal and Administrative Services . . . . *Oct 1971
Greenlay, Mrs Clare L LLB Legal and Democratic Services Manager . . . . Jan 2001

DURHAM COUNTY COUNCIL
Corporate Services County Hall Durham Co Durham DH1 5UL
Tel: 0191 383 3513 *Fax:* 0191 383 4455 *Dx:* 722100 DURHAM 16
E-mail: elizabeth.wilson@durham.gov.uk
Sol: Benjamin, Mrs Charlotte Jane BA; CPE; LPC Solicitor.*Sep 2001
Clayton, Mrs Kelsey LLB Principal Solicitor . . . . . . *Oct 1990
Davies, Mrs Lesley-Anne LLB Acting Director of Corporate Services . . . . *Oct 1976
Ewin, Mr Anthony H BA(Oxon) Assistant Director . . . *Dec 1973
Freeman, Mrs Claudine BA(Hons) Employment Law Paper 1st Prize 1993 Solicitor . . . . *Nov 1995
Harrison, Mrs Amy Louise BA Solicitor . . . . *Sep 2005
Harrison, Mr Martin E LLB Assistant Head of Legal Services . . . . *Feb 1988
Holding, Mrs Patricia BA Solicitor . . . . *Oct 1988
Klein, Ms Andrea Jane LLB Solicitor. . . . . *Dec 1993
Longbottom, Mrs Colette Anne BA Assistant Head of Legal Services . . . . Sep 1985
Lonsdale, Ms Kate Louise BA(Hons) Solicitor . . . . . Sep 2000
Matkin, Mrs Christine LLB; MA Solicitor . . . . *Jan 1987
Smith, Mr Bryan Wade BA(Hons) Assistant Director . *May 1994
Stebbings, Miss Alison LLB Solicitor. . . . . *Aug 1991
Walker, Mrs Linda M LLB Head of Legal Services . . . *Oct 1984

DURHAM DISTRICT LAND REGISTRY
Southfield House Southfield Way Durham Co Durham DH1 5TR
Tel: 0191 301 3500 *Fax:* 0191 301 0020

HM LAND REGISTRY - DURHAM (BOLDON) OFFICE
Boldon House Wheatlands Way Pity Me Durham Co Durham DH1 5GJ
Tel: 0191 301 2345 *Fax:* 0191 301 2300 *Dx:* 60860 DURHAM 6
Sol: Bulmer, Mrs Alaine LLB(Manc) Assistant Land Registrar . . . . *Mar 1979
Campbell, Mr Clifford James George MA(Oxon); Dip Assistant Land Registrar . . . . *Nov 1988
Clough, Ms Frances V LLB(Newc) Assistant Land Registrar . . . . *Nov 1993
Foley, Mrs Margaret A LLB; LLM R T Richardson Assistant Land Registrar . . . . *May 1992
Logan, A J BA(Hons) Assistant Land Registrar . . . . . Jul 1983
Simpson, Miss C Helen LLB Assistant Land Registrar. *Jul 1985
Timothy, Mr Patrick Joseph LLB Land Registrar . . . . *Apr 1970

NORTHUMBRIAN WATER LTD
Legal Affairs Abbey Road Pity Me Durham Co Durham DH1 5FJ
Tel: 0870 608 4820 *Fax:* 0191 301 6712 *Dx:* 717041 DURHAM 15
E-mail: firstname.surname@nwl.co.uk
Sol: Beveridge, Ms D Maria BA Senior Commercial Lawyer *Oct 1987
Gray, Miss Nadine Elsa BA(Cantab) Senior Lawyer . . *Oct 1982
Kelly, Mr Paul Senior Lawyer . . . . *Dec 1991
Parker, Mr Martin LLB Head of Legal Affairs. . . . . . *Oct 1983
Whitworth, Miss Diane Isabella BA; MA Senior Lawyer *Dec 1997

EASTBOURNE, East Sussex

C BREWER & SONS LTD
Albany House Ashford Road Eastbourne East Sussex BN21 3TR
Tel: 01323 411080 *Fax:* 01323 412056
E-mail: solicitor@brewers.co.uk
Sol: Davies-Ratcliff, Ms Katie LLB Company Solicitor. . . . *Jul 1996
Dobbs, Mr Richard A E Company Secretary. . . . . . . *Jul 1978

EASTBOURNE BOROUGH COUNCIL
1 Grove Road Eastbourne East Sussex BN21 4WT
Tel: 01323 410000 *Fax:* 01323 641842 *Dx:* 6921 EASTBOURNE
Sol: Ray, Mr Martin H LLB(B'ham) Assistant Chief Executive Solicitor to Council. . . . . *Apr 1974
Reynard, Mr Mark V LLB(Leics) Principal Solicitor. . . *Nov 1984

EASTLEIGH, Hampshire

EASTLEIGH BOROUGH COUNCIL
Civic Offices Leigh Road Eastleigh Hampshire SO50 9YN
Tel: 023 8068 8068 *Fax:* 023 8062 9277 *Dx:* 122381 EASTLEIGH 2
Sol: Batteson, Miss Wendi LLB(Hons) Assistant Head of Legal and Democratic Services . . . . *Feb 1993
Black, Ms Kirsten Louise LLB Solicitor. . . . . Sep 2005

Joss, Miss Susan BA; PGDipLP Assistant Legal Head Of Legal & Democratic Services . . . . Oct 2003
Ward, Mr Allan R BA(Hons); MBA Head of Legal and Democratic Services . . . . *Sep 1987

NORWICH UNION HEALTHCARE LTD
Chilworth House Hampshire Corporate Park Eastleigh Hampshire SO53 3RY
Tel: 023 8037 2270 ***Fax:*** 023 8037 3282
E-mail: gabrielle.dixey@norwich-union.co.uk
Sol: Brown, Mrs Jessica LLB; LSF Solicitor . . . . *Nov 1995
Dixey, Miss Gabrielle Suzanne LLB; PGDip Head of Legal . . . . *Sep 1993
Wild, Miss Katrina BA(Hons)(Philosophy); CPE; LPC Commercial Solicitor . . . . Aug 2002

EBBW VALE, Blaenau Gwent

BLAENAU GWENT BOROUGH COUNCIL
Municipal Offices Civic Centre Ebbw Vale Blaenau Gwent NP23 6XB
Tel: 01495 350555 ***Fax:*** 01495 355291 ***Dx:*** 43956 EBBW VALE
Sol: Banks, Miss Gillian Patricia BA(Hons)(History) Assistant Solicitor . . . . *Feb 1996
John, Mr Dylan LLB(Wales) Chief Legal Officer / County Solicitor . . . . *May 1983
Jones, Miss Andrea M LLB Solr Personal Services . . *Oct 1990
Phillips, Mr J Hugh LLB Solicitor Environmental Services . . . . *Jun 1977
Richardson, Mrs Lynn Wendy LLB Solicitor Child Care *Jul 1992

EDGWARE, Middlesex

HALEGATE PROPERTIES LTD
120 High Street Edgware Middlesex HA8 7EL
Tel: 020 8951 1616 ***Fax:*** 020 8951 1427 ***Dx:*** 57170 EDGWARE
Sol: Bloch, Leslie M LLB Solicitor . . . . *Jul 1971

REGAL INVESTMENTS LTD
4 Handel Close Edgware Middlesex HA8 9NW
Sol: Prager, Mrs Barbara I Solicitor. . . . . *May 1982

ELLESMERE PORT, Cheshire

ELLESMERE PORT & NESTON BOROUGH COUNCIL
Council Offices 4 Civic Way Ellesmere Port Cheshire CH65 0BE
Tel: 0151 356 6789 ***Fax:*** 0151 355 4305
Sol: Bush, Mrs Joanna M LLB(Hons) Assistant Solicitor . *Sep 1991
Chapman, Mr Christopher LLB(Hons)(Lond) Borough Solicitor . . . . *Nov 1973
Henshaw, Mr Michael William MA; LLB Principal Solicitor . . . . Apr 2002
Odaka, Miss Gertrude Hazel LLB Legal Unit Manager *Nov 1993

ELY, Cambridgeshire

EAST CAMBRIDGESHIRE DISTRICT COUNCIL
The Grange Nutholt Lane Ely Cambridgeshire CB7 4PL
Tel: 01353 665555 ***Fax:*** 01353 665240 ***Dx:*** 41001 ELY
Sol: Barker, Mr David Nigel BA(Hons) Principal Solicitor . . Nov 1990
Camp, Ms Margaret Anne FILEx Senior Legal AssistantOct 1997

EPPING, Essex

EPPING FOREST DISTRICT COUNCIL
Civic Offices High Street Epping Essex CM16 4BZ
Tel: 01992 564000 ***Fax:*** 01992 578018 ***Dx:*** 40409 EPPING
Sol: Agyeman, Miss Marion LLB(Hons) Conveyancing Solicitor . . . . *Dec 2007
Ferreira, Ms Rosaline F. . . . . *May 1998
Mitchell, Ms Alison V A Principal Solicitor . . . . . . *Dec 1975
O'Boyle, Miss Colleen R LLB; Dip Loc Gov Law 1989 Solicitor to the Council / Director of Corporate Support Services . . . . *Dec 1985

EPSOM, Surrey

W S ATKINS CONSULTANTS LTD
Woodcote Grove Ashley Road Epsom Surrey KT18 5BW
Tel: 01372 726140 ***Fax:*** 01372 740055 ***Dx:*** 134680 EPSOM 10
Sol: Higgins, Mr Robert BA(Hons); C Eng Solicitor. . . . *Sep 2000
Percival, Mr Mark BSc(Hons) Solicitor. . . . . *Sep 1999
Randall, Ms Anne E Solicitor . . . . *Nov 1998

EPSOM & EWELL BOROUGH COUNCIL
Town Hall The Parade Epsom Surrey KT18 5BY
Tel: 01372 732000 ***Fax:*** 01372 732149 ***Dx:*** 30713 EPSOM
E-mail: tsmith@epsom-ewell.gov.uk
Sol: Mayhead, Ms Kirsty Elizabeth BA(Hons) Solicitor . . *Sep 2003
Sadka-Surowiak, Danuta M LLB Solicitor . . . . . . *Aug 1980
Smith, Mr Trevor BA(Hons) Chief Solicitor & Estates Services Manager . . . . *Dec 1977

NATIONAL COUNTIES BUILDING SOC
National Counties House Church Street Epsom Surrey KT17 4NL
Tel: 01372 742211 ***Fax:*** 01372 745607 ***Dx:*** 30729 EPSOM
E-mail: info@ncbs.co.uk
Sol: Mendoza, Mrs Kathryn Elizabeth LLB(Hons) Associate Director, Compliance & Legal Services. . . . . *Dec 1983

TOYOTA (GB) PLC
Great Burgh Burgh Heath Epsom Surrey KT18 5UX
Tel: 01737 363633 ***Fax:*** 01737 367700
E-mail: harry.jones@tgb.toyota.co.uk
Sol: Jones, Mr Harry BA(Hons) Company Solicitor Justice of the Peace. . . . . *Dec 1980

ESHER, Surrey

DAIRY CREST GROUP PLC
Dairy Crest House Littleworth Road Claygate Esher Surrey KT10 9PN
Tel: 01372 472285 ***Fax:*** 01372 472283
Sol: Newton, Mr Roger J LLB(Sheff); JP FCIS Company Secretary Justice of the Peace . . . . *Jun 1973
Slettengren, Miss Caroline Louise BSc(Hons); DipLaw In-House Lawyer . . . . May 2000

ELMBRIDGE BOROUGH COUNCIL
Civic Centre High Street Esher Surrey KT10 9SD
Tel: 01372 474198 ***Fax:*** 01372 474972 ***Dx:*** 36302 ESHER
Sol: Briody, Mrs Carmel Annette LLB(Hons) Senior Solicitor Nov 1992
Browne, Mrs Claire Louise BSc(Hons); IICSA(Grad); PGDipLaw Solicitor. . . . . Mar 2006
Davies, Mr Roger N Principal Solicitor. . . . . *Jul 1971
Rutter, Mrs Frances A LLB Borough Solicitor . . . . . *Oct 1990

EXETER, Devon

CROWN PROSECUTION SERVICE DEVON & CORNWALL
Hawkins House Pynes Hill Rydon Lane Exeter Devon EX2 5SS
Tel: 01392 288000 ***Fax:*** 01392 288008 ***Dx:*** 135606 EXETER 16
E-mail: andrew.cresswell@cps.gsi.gov.uk
Sol: Cresswell, Mr Andrew LLB Chief Crown Prosecutor . . *Jan 1977

DEVON COUNTY COUNCIL
County Hall Topsham Road Exeter Devon EX2 4QD
Tel: 01392 382000 ***Fax:*** 01392 382286 ***Dx:*** 8345 EXETER
Sol: Clarey, Mr Simon K C MA(Oxon) Solicitor . . . . *Oct 1987
Gash, Mr Roger MA County Solicitor . . . . *Dec 1975
Hibbs, Miss Ninette C BA(Law) Solicitor. . . . . *Jul 1990
Law, Mr Timothy J Assistant Solicitor . . . . Sep 1996
Poole, Ms Sarah BSc(Hons) Solicitor . . . . Feb 1991
Sweeney, Mr John A BA(Oxon) Assistant County Solicitor . . . . Apr 1981
Thomas, Mr Charles J A MA(Cantab) Solicitor. . . . . *Oct 1984
Vickery, Mrs Maeve BA(Hons)(Philosophy); DipLaw Employment Lawyer . . . . *Jan 2000

ENVIRONMENT AGENCY (SOUTH WEST REGION)
Manley House Kestrel Way Exeter Devon EX2 7LQ
Tel: 0870 850 6506 ***Fax:*** 01392 442112 ***Dx:*** 121350 EXETER 12
Sol: Constable, Mrs Judith BA(Hons) . . . . *Dec 2000
Hayden, Mr Nicholas Timothy LLB Solicitor . . . . . *Sep 2001
Strouts, Mr Edward M BSc Solicitor. . . . . *Jul 1975
Welsh, Ms Ruth Joanne LLB; LLM(Int Law; Sumna Cum Laude) Principal Solicitor . . . . *Apr 1993

EXETER CITY COUNCIL
Civic Centre Paris Street Exeter Devon EX1 1JN
Tel: 01392 277888 ***Fax:*** 01392 265654 ***Dx:*** 8323 EXETER
Sol: Al-Khafaji, Miss Baan LLB Head of Legal Services . . *Jun 1994
Cridland, Mr Graham J Solicitor . . . . *Nov 1996
Farooqi, Ms Sarah Bano BSc Solicitor. . . . . Mar 1998

PENNON GROUP PLC
Peninsula House Rydon Lane Exeter Devon EX2 7HR
Tel: 01392 446677 ***Fax:*** 01392 443939 ***Dx:*** 119850 EXETER 10
E-mail: jnmarshall@pennon-group.co.uk
Sol: Jelley, Mr John Christopher BA; LLM Legal Manager . *Oct 1986
Langmead, Mrs Alison Jayne . . . . Nov 1999
Marle, Miss Kirsten LLB(Hons); LPC Solicitor . . . . . Mar 2005
Podger, Mr Alan J Senior Legal Adviser . . . . Jul 1973
Pugsley, Mr Simon Anthony Pugsley LLB(Hons)(Exon) Senior Legal Adviser Notary Public. . . . . *Sep 1993
Shaw, Mrs Louise D BA. . . . . *Mar 1986
White, Ms Sharon Carol LLB . . . . *Oct 1984
Woodier, Mr Kenneth D Group General Counsel & Company Secretary . . . . *Jul 1985

ROYAL COLLEGE OF NURSING
11/15 Dix's Field Exeter Devon EX1 1QA
Tel: 0845 456 7829 ***Fax:*** 01392 213025
Sol: Grayson, Mr Anthony Robert LLB Regional Solicitor. *Feb 1979
Mazarezo, Miss Geetha BA; DipLaw Assistant Solicitor Dec 2003
Sharma, Mrs Neeta LLB(Hons) Principal Solicitor . . *May 1993

FAREHAM, Hampshire

FAREHAM BOROUGH COUNCIL
Civic Offices Civic Way Fareham Hampshire PO16 7PU
Tel: 01329 236100 ***Fax:*** 01329 824505 ***Dx:*** 40814 FAREHAM
E-mail: legalservices@fareham.gov.uk
Sol: Bailey, Mrs Gina Marie LLM Solicitor to the Council . *Oct 1981
Horsler, Mrs Patricia A LLB Principal Solicitor . . . . *Dec 1976
Rickwood, Mrs Kathryn A BA Principal Solicitor . . . . *Feb 1988

FARNBOROUGH, Hampshire

AON CONSULTING
Briarcliff House Kingsmead Farnborough Hampshire GU14 7TE
Tel: 01252 768000 ***Fax:*** 01252 378582
Sol: Gracey, Miss Caroline Solicitor . . . . *Jun 1992

RUSHMOOR BOROUGH COUNCIL
Council Offices Farnborough Road Farnborough Hampshire GU14 7JU
Tel: 01252 398398 ***Fax:*** 01252 524017
Dx: 122250 FARNBOROUGH 2
E-mail: klimmer@rushmoor.gov.uk
Sol: Bosi, Mrs Kiki BA(Hons) Assistant Solicitor . . . . . *Sep 1981
Limmer, Miss Karen G LLB Solicitor to the Council . *Mar 1987
Lovelock, Mr Michael R BA; LLB; BSc; MSc Principal Solicitor . . . . *Jan 1980
Milton, Mrs Diane M LLB(Lond) Legal Services Manager . . . . *Aug 1980

FARNHAM, Surrey

PARQUE SECURITIES LTD
Friars Way Tilford Farnham Surrey GU10 2AJ
Tel: 01252 781470 ***Fax:*** 01252 781475
E-mail: cjq@quelch.demon.co.uk
Sol: Quelch, Mr Christopher John Director . . . . *Jul 1969

FELTHAM, Middlesex

HOUNSLOW PETTY SESSIONS AREA
Magistrates Court Hanworth Road Feltham Middlesex TW13 5AF
Tel: 020 8917 3400 ***Fax:*** 020 8917 3527 ***Dx:*** 133821 FELTHAM 3
Sol: Lynam, Mrs Jane LLB Bench Legal Manager . . . . . *Mar 1978

FLEET, Hampshire

HART DISTRICT COUNCIL
Harlington Way Fleet Hampshire GU51 4AE
Tel: 01252 622122 ***Fax:*** 01252 626886 ***Dx:*** 32632 FLEET
Sol: Herbert, Mr Charles C BA Solr to the Council . . . . . *Jun 1973

PARAMETRIC TECHNOLOGY (UK) LTD
Innovation House Harvest Crescent Fleet Hampshire GU51 2QR
Tel: 01252 817600 ***Fax:*** 01252 810722
Sol: Dunn, Mr Charles C W BA Solicitor . . . . *Nov 1991
Jones, Miss Louise Catherine LLB(Hons) Associate European Counsel. . . . . *Mar 1993

FLEETWOOD, Lancashire

HALSALL DAVID PLC
Eastham House Copse Road Fleetwood Lancashire FY7 7NY
Tel: 01253 778888 ***Fax:*** 01253 63503
Sol: Halsall, Mr David A LLB Solicitor . . . . Apr 1978

FLINT, Flintshire

REDROW PLC
Redrow House St David's Park Flint Flintshire CH5 3RX
Tel: 01244 520044 ***Fax:*** 01244 520564
Dx: 708570 ST DAVIDS PARK
Sol: Cope, Mr Graham Anthony LLM; LLB(Hons) Head Of Legal . . . . *§Oct 1989
Mason, Mr Iain H R BA Legal Director. . . . . *Sep 1984
Robinson, Mr Neil LLB; ACIB; MSI Assistant Solicitor *Sep 1998
Walker, Mrs Rhiannon E BA(Hons) Company Secretary & Head of Legal. . . . . *Mar 1980

FOLKESTONE, Kent

EUROTUNNEL
UK Terminal PO Box 2000 Folkestone Kent CT18 8XY
Tel: 01303 283900 ***Fax:*** 01303 283901
Sol: Lattin, Mr Paul David BA(Hons); CPE Legal Adviser. . Sep 2002
Morrison, Mr Ken Glencross LLB(Hons) Legal Director*Nov 1992

SHEPWAY DISTRICT COUNCIL
Civic Centre Castle Hill Avenue Folkestone Kent CT20 2QY
Tel: 01303 852248 ***Fax:*** 01303 852293 ***Dx:*** 4912 FOLKESTONE
E-mail: shepway.dc@shepwaydc.gov.uk
Sol: Culligan, Miss Estelle BA . . . . *Jul 2001
Gabell, Mrs Joanna Marie Solicitor to the Council . . *Nov 2001
Wignall, Mr Peter James LLB Director of Democratic Services . . . . *Jul 1983

FOREST ROW, East Sussex

RYDON GROUP LTD
Rydon House Forest Row East Sussex RH18 5DW
Tel: 01342 825151 ***Fax:*** 01342 826770 ***Dx:*** 117778 FOREST ROW
Sol: Ivanec, Ms Aileen A Solicitor . . . . *Jan 1998
Kitchin, Mr John E LLB(Lond) Group Solicitor . . . . . *Apr 1978
Palmer, Miss Anne D LLB Solicitor . . . . *Sep 1980
Shutler, Mr Timothy Martin LLB Solicitor. . . . . Jul 2004

GARSTANG, Lancashire

LANCASHIRE MAGISTRATES COURTS COMMITTEE
PO Box 717 Weind House Parkhill Road Garstang Lancashire PR3 1EY
Tel: 01995 601596 ***Fax:*** 01995 601776
E-mail: debbie.hindley@nmcourts-service.gsi.gov.uk
Sol: Robinson, Mr John BA Director of Legal Services . . *§Jun 1980

GATESHEAD, Tyne & Wear

GATESHEAD LAW CENTRE
1 Walker Terrace Gateshead Tyne & Wear NE8 1EB
Tel: 0191 440 8575 ***Fax:*** 0191 440 8580
Sol: Martin, Mr Gerald Francis LLB(Dunelm) Manager . . *Nov 1982

GATESHEAD MAGISTRATES COURT
Warwick Street Gateshead Tyne & Wear NE8 1DT
Tel: 0191 477 5821 ***Fax:*** 0191 478 7825 ***Dx:*** 67783 GATESHEAD 3
Sol: Johnston, Mrs Elizabeth A LLB(Nott'm) Justices' Clerks Assistant . . . . *Nov 1980
Livesley, Mr Christopher J BA(Hons) . . . . *§Dec 1976
Logan, Mr Peter A BA(Lond) Justices' Clerks Assistant*Jan 1983

GATESHEAD METROPOLITAN BOROUGH COUNCIL
Civic Centre Regent Street Gateshead Tyne & Wear NE8 1HH
Tel: 0191 433 3000 ***Fax:*** 0191 433 2103 ***Dx:*** 60308 GATESHEAD
Sol: Barker, Mr Michael Alexander BA(Hons) Head of Commercial and Development. . . . . *Jul 1995
Best, Mr Ian LLB(Hons) Solicitor. . . . . *Jan 1998
Briton, Mr Timothy LLB(Hons) Solicitor . . . . Sep 2001
Clark, Mr John S LLB(Hons) Solicitor . . . . *Mar 1979
Cook, Ms Janice Social Services Health & Education . Dec 1992
Gamble, Ms Suzanne Gayle Solicitor . . . . Sep 2000
Goodfellow, Mr Philip J LLB Solicitor (Development). *Dec 1990
Hill, Mrs Deborah A LLB Head of Litigation . . . . . *Dec 1983

See p112 for the Key to Work Categories & other symbols

Kelly, Mr Roger M LLB Chief Executive Deputy Clerk & Solicitor to Northumbria Police Authority . . . . *Dec 1978
Kesteven, Ms Maureen A BA Strategic Director Legal & Corporate Services . . . . *Dec 1988
Nayak, Mr Pramod Solicitor . . . . Apr 2003
Stokoe, Mrs Nichola Jane BA(Hons) Principal Legal Assistant . . . . Oct 1991
Willmott, Mrs Stella Ann BA Litigation Manager . . . . Nov 1994
Wirz, Mr Nicholas LLM; BA(Hons) Sunderland Prize for Best Law Student Solicitor . . . . Aug 1999
Wise, Miss Deborah Louise Solicitor . . . . Nov 2002
Witehead, Mrs Joanne Christina LLB Solicitor . . . . . Aug 1997

GERRARDS CROSS, Buckinghamshire

UNIQ PLC
1 Chalfont Park Gerrards Cross Buckinghamshire SL9 0UN
Tel: 01753 276186 *Fax:* 01753 276051
Sol: McDonald, Mr Andrew John LLB Group Counsel . . . *Aug 1998

GLOUCESTER, Gloucestershire

CHELTENHAM & GLOUCESTER PLC
Chief Office Barnett Way Gloucester Gloucestershire GL4 3RL
Tel: 01452 372372 *Fax:* 01452 375570 *Dx:* 55251 GLOUCESTER 2
E-mail: cglegal@cglegal.demon.co.uk
Sol: Cocks, Miss Rachel LLB Solicitor . . . . Sep 2002
Crawford, Mrs Lisa H G LLB(Hons) Senior Lawyer . . . *Oct 1989
Fullen, Ms Anne D LLB(Hons); Cert PLS Commercial Lawyer . . . . *Jan 1993
Hale, Mr Nicholas Paul LLB(Hons) Mortgage Lawyer . *Sep 1996
Pike, Ms E Anne BA(Hons)(Law) Senior Lawyer . . . . Sep 1987
Riossi, Mr Noel C LLB(Hons) Commercial Solicitor . . *Feb 1987
Smyth, Mr Christopher Head of Legal Services . . . . *Oct 1980
Wyatt, Ms Sharon C LLB(Hons) Solicitor . . . . *Oct 1987

GLOUCESTER CITY COUNCIL
North Warehouse The Docks Gloucester Gloucestershire GL1 2EP
Tel: 01452 522232 *Fax:* 01452 396140 *Dx:* 7516 GLOUCESTER
Sol: Isaac, Mr Stephen Keith BA(Hons) Solicitor . . . . . . *May 1998
Spencer, Mr Gary Norman LLB; CPA Head of Legal Services . . . . *Apr 1982
Thomas, Mr Stephen J L LLB Senior Solicitor . . . . *May 1985
Woodward, Miss Helen Jane LLB Law Clerk . . . . . . *Apr 2006

GLOUCESTER LAW CENTRE
75-81 Eastgate Street Gloucester Gloucestershire GL1 1PN
Tel: 01452 423492 *Fax:* 01452 387594
E-mail: admin@gloucesterlawcentre.co.uk
Sol: Puddicombe, Mr Andrew BA Solicitor . . . . *Jun 1993
Whitworth, Ms Anne BA Solicitor . . . . *Jun 1983

GLOUCESTERSHIRE COUNTY COUNCIL - LEGAL & DEMOCRATIC SERVICES
Quayside House Quay Street Gloucester Gloucestershire GL1 2TZ
Tel: 01452 425203 *Fax:* 01452 426790
Dx: 133275 GLOUCESTER 11
E-mail: nrsec@gloucestershire.gov.uk
Sol: Evans, Mr Timothy Team Manager Commercial . . . . Oct 1990
Felgate, Mr William BA Lawyer . . . . Sep 2000
Forrest, Miss Kelly Ann LLB(Hons) Team Manager, Childrens Services . . . . Feb 1997
Gadsden, Miss Jane C MA Lawyer . . . . *Nov 1991
Haygarth, Miss Althea Vanessa Lawyer (Property) . . . Mar 2005
Knowlman, Mrs Ruth M LLB Lawyer . . . . *Oct 1982
Maitland, Ms Lee LLB Lawyer Advocate . . . . Aug 2006
Parkinson, Miss Gillian Mary Team Manager (Environmental Services) . . . . Dec 1993
Powell, Mr William M LLB Lawyer . . . . Oct 1977
Rees, Mr David J Solicitor: Environment Directorate (Secondment) . . . . *Dec 1989
Roberts, Mr Nigel James MA(Cantab) Director of Law and Administration . . . . *§Jan 1982
Timbrell, Mr Alan C Team Manager, Adult Services . . *May 1973
Wood, Ms Samantha Alicia PGDip; FILEX Acting Assistant Director of Law & Administration . . . . *Sep 1997
Woodward, Mrs Moira Jane LLB(Hons) Lawyer . . . . Mar 2002
Wray, Mrs Christine Anne Lynne MA(Oxon) Assistant Director of Law & Administration Notary Public . . . . *§Apr 1979

GLOUCESTERSHIRE MAGISTRATES' COURTS
PO Box 9051 Gloucester Gloucestershire GL1 2XG
Tel: 01452 420100 *Fax:* 01452 833551 / 833555
Dx: 9866 GLOUCESTER 5
Sol: Benbow, Ms Cheryl Senior Legal Adviser . . . . Oct 1994

LAND REGISTRY - GLOUCESTER OFFICE
Twyver House Bruton Way Gloucester Gloucestershire GL1 1DQ
Tel: 01452 511111 *Fax:* 01452 510050 *Dx:* 7599 GLOUCESTER 3
Sol: Barton, Mrs J LLB(Hons) Assistant Land Registrar . . . Apr 1981
Brothers, Ms Katharine LLB(Hons) Assistant Land Registrar . . . . *Nov 1986
Brough, Mr Patrick J MA(Cantab) Assistant Land Registrar . . . . *§Dec 1974
Curtis, Mr Andrew Assistant Land Registrar . . . . . . Oct 1995
Jenkins, Mrs Julie E LLB Land Registrar . . . . *Dec 1986
Lewis, Mr Timothy H O LLB Senior Assistant Land Registrar . . . . *Jul 1975
Powell, Mrs P J LLB Assistant Land Registrar . . . . . Jun 1978
Taverner, S G Senior Assistant Land Registrar Notary Public . . . . *Jan 1973
Whiteside, Mr James Dean LLB Assistant Land Registrar . . . . *Sep 1997

LINCOLN FINANCIAL GROUP
Barnet Way Barnwood Gloucester Gloucestershire GL4 3RZ
Tel: 0845 678 8888 *Fax:* 01452 634300
Sol: Dawbarn, Mr Mark L LLB Company Secretary & Legal Director . . . . *Jan 1965
Fuller, Miss Stephanie M Senior Legal Adviser . . . . . *Feb 1993
Wilson, Mr Malcolm G W MA(Oxon) Senior Legal Adviser . . . . *Apr 1982

TRANSCO
Glevum House Bristol Road Gloucester Gloucestershire GL2 5YA
Tel: 01452 307307
Sol: Ritchie, Mr Andrew J A MA(Oxon) Regional Solicitor . *Jun 1972

GODALMING, Surrey

WAVERLEY BOROUGH COUNCIL
Council Offices The Burys Godalming Surrey GU7 1HR
Tel: 01483 523333 *Fax:* 01483 523267 *Dx:* 58303 GODALMING 1
Sol: Austin, Mrs Lyndsay S J LLB Head of Legal & Estates Services . . . . *Mar 1986
Bainbridge, Mr Daniel J K LLB Assistant Solicitor . . *Aug 2005
Renaudon, Miss Laura Elizabeth BSc(Hons)(Econ); PGDipLaw; PGDipLP Assistant Solicitor . . . . *Jul 2003
Sims, Mr Jeremy J LLM; MPhil Senior Solicitor . . . . *§Jul 1973
Smith, Mr Trevor BA(Hons) Solicitor . . . . *Dec 1977

GOSFORTH, Tyne & Wear

HOME GROUP LTD
2 Gosforth Park Way Salters Lane Newcastle upon Tyne Tyne & Wear NE12 8ET
Tel: 0845 155 1234 *Fax:* 0845 155 0394 *Dx:* 60365 GOSFORTH
Sol: Dent, Mr Laurence BA(Hons) Administration Director, Company Secretary . . . . *Jun 1978

NORTHERN ROCK PLC
Northern Rock House Gosforth Tyne & Wear NE3 4PL
Tel: 0191 285 7191 *Fax:* 0191 279 4747 *Dx:* 60352 GOSFORTH
Sol: Ashcroft, Mr Peter D BSc(Hons) Assistant Director . . *Sep 2000
Dhirani, Ms Sharandeep LLB(Hons) Solicitor . . . . . *Sep 1998
Fitzpatrick, Mr Jasan LLB(Hons) Head of Legal . . . . *Sep 1999
Greener, Mr Colin T LLB Solicitor . . . . *Mar 2000
Huntingdon, Mrs Julie Suzanne Solicitor . . . . *Dec 2003
Soulsby, Mr Andrew William LLB(Hons) Solicitor . . . *Mar 1997
Taylor, Mr Colin LLB(Sheff) Group Company Secretary . . . . *§Dec 1981
Williams, Mr Gwilym C LLB(Wales) Assistant Director Regional Chair of C&I . . . . *Oct 1977

GOSPORT, Hampshire

GOSPORT BOROUGH COUNCIL
Town Hall Gosport Hampshire PO12 1EB
Tel: 023 9258 4242 *Fax:* 023 9254 5587 *Dx:* 136568 GOSPORT 2
Sol: Bishop, Mr Roy Property Lawyer . . . . *Dec 1991
Edwards, Miss Linda J LLB(Hons) Borough Solicitor . *Oct 1989
Paterson, Mr James Squires LLB(Hons) Litigation Lawyer . . . . Mar 2003

GRANTHAM, Lincolnshire

SOUTH KESTEVEN DISTRICT COUNCIL
Council Offices St Peter's Hill Grantham Lincolnshire NG31 6PZ
Tel: 01476 406080 *Fax:* 01476 406000 *Dx:* 27024 GRANTHAM
Sol: Lansdowne, Miss Rachel BA; DipLP Solicitor . . . . Mar 2006
Youles, Mrs Caroline L BA(Hons) Legal Services Manager . . . . *Apr 1987

SOUTH LINCOLNSHIRE MAGISTRATES COURTS
Justices Clerks Office Harlaxton Road Grantham Lincolnshire NG31 6SB
Tel: 01476 563438 *Fax:* 01476 567200 *Dx:* 711100 GRANTHAM 4
Sol: Brett, Mrs Corinne Solicitor . . . . *Nov 1996
Handley, Mrs Jennifer Ann Solicitor . . . . *Dec 1995

GRAVESEND, Kent

GRAVESHAM BOROUGH COUNCIL
Civic Centre Windmill Street Gravesend Kent DA12 1AU
Tel: 01474 564422 *Fax:* 01474 337453 *Dx:* 6804 GRAVESEND
Sol: Goodman, Mr Martin Timothy LLB(Hons) Corporate Lawyer . . . . *Mar 1999
Hayley, Mr Michael J BA Head of Legal Services . . . *Oct 1985

GRAYS, Thurrock

THURROCK BOROUGH COUNCIL
Civic Offices New Road Grays Thurrock RM17 6SL
Tel: 01375 390000 *Fax:* 01375 652782 *Dx:* 141040 GRAYS 3
E-mail: legal@thurrock.gov.uk
Sol: Bhandal, Ms Baljit R Assistant Solicitor . . . . *Apr 1992
Blades, Ms Monica Y Head of Legal & Democratic Services . . . . *Apr 1989
Edge, Mr Philip L MA(Cantab) Senior Assistant Solicitor . . . . *Jun 1989
Lawson, Mr David M G BA(Hons)(Law); Former Barrister Senior Litigation Solicitor Co-ordinator Legal Action Group Jun 1991

GREAT YARMOUTH, Norfolk

GREAT YARMOUTH BOROUGH COUNCIL
Town Hall Great Yarmouth Norfolk NR30 2QF
Tel: 01493 856100 *Fax:* 01493 846332
Dx: 41121 GREAT YARMOUTH
Sol: Skinner, Mr Christopher F LLB; DipLG Head of Legal Services . . . . *Mar 1983
Swan, Ms Nicola Jane Solicitor & Deputy Monitoring Officer . . . . *Dec 2002

GREAT YARMOUTH MAGISTRATES COURT
Magistrates Court House North Quay Great Yarmouth Norfolk NR30 1PW
Tel: 01493 849800 *Fax:* 01493 852169
Dx: 139400 GREAT YARMOUTH 3
E-mail: greatyarmouth.court@hmcourts-service.gsi.gov.uk
Sol: Ratcliffe, Mr David Justices' Clerk . . . . *Feb 1989

GRIMSBY, North East Lincolnshire

GRIMSBY MAGISTRATES COURT
Victoria Street Grimsby North East Lincolnshire DN31 1PD
Tel: 01472 320444 *Fax:* 01472 320441 *Dx:* 707680 GRIMSBY 5
Sol: Houlden, Mr Philip C DML; CMS; DMS . . . . *Oct 1986

NORTH EAST LINCOLNSHIRE BOROUGH COUNCIL
Municipal Offices Town Hall Square Grimsby North East Lincolnshire DN31 1HU
Tel: 01472 313131 *Fax:* 01472 324022 *Dx:* 13536 GRIMSBY 1
Sol: Conolly, Mrs Elizabeth M LLB Principal Solicitor . . . . Jun 1977
Walters, Mr Michael J LLB(Soton); DMS Borough Solicitor & Head of Legal Services . . . . Oct 1978

GUILDFORD, Surrey

ALLIANZ INSURANCE PLC
57 Ladymead Guildford Surrey GU1 1DB
Tel: 01483 552730 *Fax:* 01483 532904
Sol: Bola, Ms Adenike LLB(Hons) Solicitor Manager . . . . Dec 1995
Kiddle Morris, Mr Christopher J LLB Company Secretary . . . . Aug 1976
Marchington, Ms Sandra M LLB Solicitor . . . . *Oct 1987
Newson, Mr Barry R BSocSc(Hons) Solicitor . . . . . *Mar 1990

AVENTIS PHARMA LIMITED T/A SANOFI-AVENTIS
One Onslow Street Guildford Surrey GU1 4YS
Tel: 01483 505515 *Fax:* 01483 554835
E-mail: helen.roberts@sanofi-aventis.com
Sol: Roberts, Ms Helen A R LLB; Maitrise; AKC Head of Legal Services . . . . *Apr 1993

THE COLLEGE OF LAW GUILDFORD
Braboeuf Manor Portsmouth Road St Catherines Guildford Surrey GU3 1HA
Tel: 01483 460200 *Fax:* 01483 460305 *Dx:* 47 GUILDFORD
E-mail: info@lawcol.co.uk
Sol: Atkins, Mrs Rebecca Senior Lecturer . . . . *Oct 1991
Bartlett, Ms Sue Senior Lecturer . . . . *Dec 1993
Bramley, Mrs Sheila Lucy LLB Deputy Director (Staffing) . . . . Jan 1975
Burton, Ms Imogen BA Branch Director . . . . Apr 1992
Cartledge, Ms Andrea Senior Lecturer . . . . Aug 1987
Cheesman, Ms Jill Senior Lecturer . . . . Jan 1974
Cousal, Ms Helen Senior Lecturer . . . . *Nov 1989
Davies, Ms Lorraine Deputy Director Vocational StudiesAug 1979
Dickson, Ms Vicky Senior Lecturer . . . . Oct 1994
George, Miss Lindsey Senior Lecturer . . . . Mar 1987
Hancock, Mr Nick Senior Lecturer . . . . *Sep 1986
Hansel, Ms Elizabeth Sue Senior Lecturer . . . . Apr 1992
Holtam, Mr John F Associate Professor . . . . *Oct 1982
Hutchings, Mrs Alice Elizabeth LLB(Hons)(European French Law) Senior Lecturer . . . . Jan 1989
Kimbell, Mrs Harriet MBE LLB; LLM Associate Professor . . . . *Jan 1978
Longshaw, Mrs Alexis Associate Professor . . . . . . *Nov 1982
McWhirter, Ms Paula Senior Lecturer . . . . *Mar 1980
Mardell, Ms Julie Senior Lecturer . . . . Nov 1989
Newdick, Ms Lyn Senior Lecturer . . . . Nov 1983
Paltridge, Mr Stuart R LLB(Wales) Senior Lecturer . . *Apr 1971
Partridge, Ms Annabel Senior Lecturer . . . . Jul 1993
Petley, Mr Michael Solicitor . . . . *Jan 1975
Pooley, Mrs Sarah Louise BA; MLitt Senior Lecturer . . *Sep 1995
Revenico, Ms Hellen Elaine BA Stokes Memorial 1978; Cliffords Inn 1979 Lecturer . . . . Nov 1981
Rodell, Mrs Anne Lesley MA; CPE; LSF Lecturer . . . . Dec 1987
Rutter, Ms Ruth Senior Lecturer . . . . Dec 1992
Serfozo, Mrs Kate Senior Lecturer . . . . *Dec 1990
Talbot, Mrs Rachel L LLB(Newc) Lecturer . . . . May 1996
Theobold, Ms Jo Senior Lecturer . . . . *Apr 1990
Tucker, Mr William M BSc(Hons) Lecturer . . . . *Sep 1997
van der Klugt, Ms Diana E BA Senior Lecturer . . . . . *Jun 1976
Warmingham, Mr Gareth John . . . . *Oct 1994
Watson, Mrs Helen Ann BSc(Hons); PGCE Senior Lecturer . . . . Oct 1994
Whitters, Miss Bernadette M BA(Law); LLM Associate Professor . . . . *Jan 1980
Wiener, Mrs Cassandra Anna Mary Lecturer . . . . . . Jan 1997

GUILDFORD BOROUGH COUNCIL
Millmead House Millmead Guildford Surrey GU2 4BB
Tel: 01483 505050 *Fax:* 01483 444996 *Dx:* 2472 GUILDFORD
Sol: Brewer, Mrs Glynis M BA(Bris) Principal Solicitor . . *Dec 1977
Fisher, Mrs Judith BA; LLM Solicitor . . . . *Dec 1980
Giles, Mr Michael M V LLB(B'ham) Solicitor . . . . . . *Jul 1973
Hodgson, Mrs Alison M LLB(Hons) Legal Assistant . . *Feb 1985
Lingard, Mr Richard G LLB(Soton) Head of Legal & Property Services . . . . *Jul 1980
Roberts, Mr Leslie W BA; Cert Ed; MSc Senior Solicitor . . . . *Aug 1987
Stanfield, Mr Adrian T LLB(Hons) Senior Solicitor . . . *Mar 2001
Sutherland, Miss Helen B Director . . . . *Feb 1974

PHILIPS ELECTRONICS UK LTD
The Philips Centre Guildford Business Park Guildford Surrey GU2 8XH
Tel: 01483 298623 *Fax:* 01483 298861
Sol: Morris, Mr Michael G MBA; FCIS Company Secretary *§Jan 1971

HADLEIGH, Suffolk

BABERGH DISTRICT COUNCIL
Council Offices Corks Lane Hadleigh Suffolk IP7 6SJ
Tel: 01473 822801 *Fax:* 01473 825742 *Dx:* 85055 BABERGH
Sol: Saward, Ms Kathryn Solicitor To The Council . . . . . *Oct 2001
Smith, Ms Karen A LLB(Leics) Assistant Solicitor . . . *Sep 1985
Whatling, Ms Caroline Assistant Solicitor . . . . *Apr 2003

HALE, Greater Manchester

BRITANNIA HOTELS LTD
Halecroft Hale Road Hale Greater Manchester WA15 8RE
Tel: 0161 904 8686 *Fax:* 0161 904 5301
Sol: Ashton, Ms Susan M LLB Group Solicitor . . . . *Dec 1976

HALIFAX, West Yorkshire

CALDERDALE MAGISTRATES COURT
PO Box 32 Harrison Road Halifax West Yorkshire HX1 2AN
Tel: 01422 360695 *Fax:* 01422 347874
Sol: Airy, Mr Gordon Michael District Legal Director . . . . Aug 1998

CALDERDALE METROPOLITAN BC CORPORATE SERVICES DIRECTORATE
Westgate House Westgate Halifax West Yorkshire HX1 1PS
Tel: 01422 357257 *Fax:* 01422 393073
E-mail: ian.hughes@calderdale.gov.uk
Sol: Astbury, Mr Mark BA; Dip(Applied Soc Studies); CQSW Senior Solicitor. . . . *Nov 1993
Dalziel, Ms Caroline LLB Pettitt Bursary 1980; Maxwell Law Prize 1981; Sir Henry Barber Law Scholarship 1982 Commercial Solicitor . . . *Nov 1985
Field, Mr Jason Darrel BA; LLM Senior Solicitor. . . *Feb 2003
Foulke, Mr Robert James BA Solicitor Employment . . Jul 1998
Helliwell, Mrs Katherine LLB Principal Solicitor. . . . *§Jul 1990
Houshmand, Mrs Jeannine Lynn BA(Hons) Senior Solicitor . . . *Nov 1994
Hughes, Mr Ian Rees LLB(Hons) Legal Services Manager . . . *Nov 1990
Livesey, Ms Bernadette M LLB Chief Law and Administration Officer . . . *Mar 1984
McGrath, Mr Paul Assistant Solicitor. . . . *Aug 1995
Mahlanglu, Mr Nhlanhla LLB(Hons); MSc; MA Solicitor (Commercial) . . . Dec 2006
Middleton, Mrs Catherine Lynne LLB Safeguarding Solicitor . . . Mar 2004
Parkinson, Ms Catherine A LLB Group Director . . . *Nov 1987
Reynolds, Mr James Barry LLB(Hons) Senior Solicitor *Sep 2000
Riaz, Miss Razia LLB(Hons) Assistant Solicitor . . . *Sep 2005
Slomski, Mr Peter LLB(Hons) . . . *May 1998

HBOS PLC
Trinity Road Halifax West Yorkshire HX1 2RG
Tel: 0870 600 5000 *Fax:* 01422 333453 *Dx:* 11896 HALIFAX
Sol: Benison, Ms Meiner A LLB Solicitor. . . . Oct 1991
Camidge, Mrs Teresa Mary LLB Solicitor . . . Nov 1990
Carnall, Mr Matthew LLB; Licence En Droit Corporate Solicitor . . . Sep 2003
Ezekiel, Mr Marcus BA(Hons) Head of Legal - HBOS Retail . . . Nov 1988
Floyd, Mr Kevin G MA Solicitor . . . *Oct 1986
Gaunt, Mrs Angela M LLB Solicitor . . . *Nov 1985
Greenwood, Mr James Daniel MA; GDL Lending Lawyer . . . Dec 2006
Greenwood, Mr Scott LLB Solicitor . . . *Aug 1999
Hanson, Ms Ruth LLB Solicitor . . . Feb 1989
Hinchliffe, Miss Rachel Adele LLB Solicitor . . . Jul 2005
Houghton, Mr David M LLB Solicitor. . . . *Oct 1982
Hulbert, Mr Graham BA Solicitor. . . . Mar 1988
Kirkaldy, Mr Ian R LLB Solicitor . . . *Oct 1986
Kirsch, Ms Susan G LLB Solicitor . . . Nov 1987
Mitcheson, Mrs Caroline L MA Solicitor . . . *Feb 1991
Moore, Mr Stephen D LLB Employment Lawyer. . . . Nov 1998
O'Hara, Ms Lucy Catherine LLB; DipLP Senior SolicitorNov 2000
Swift, Mr Mark LLB(Hons) Lending & Banking Lawyer. Oct 2001
Wilby, Miss Neola LLB Banking Lawyer . . . Sep 2007
Woodhead, Mr John G LLB Solicitor. . . . *Nov 1992

HALSTEAD, Essex

BOLT BUILDING SUPPLIES LTD
Bluebridge Industrial Estate Colchester Road Halstead Essex CO9 2EX
Tel: 01787 477261 *Fax:* 01787 475680
Sol: Burrett, Mr Terence L LLB Company Solicitor . . . Jul 1975

HARLOW, Essex

HARLOW DISTRICT COUNCIL
The Civic Centre The Water Gardens College Square Harlow Essex CM20 1WG
Tel: 01279 446611 *Fax:* 01279 446767 *Dx:* 40550 HARLOW
Sol: Harrow, Mr Peter Solicitor. . . . May 1993
Ireland, Ms Mary E Solicitor. . . . *Feb 1966
Robinson, Mr Mark A LLB(Hons) Solicitor . . . Mar 1989
Willcox, Mr Owen LLB Solicitor . . . *Mar 1982

HARROGATE, North Yorkshire

HARROGATE BOROUGH COUNCIL
Council Offices Crescent Gardens Harrogate North Yorkshire HG1 2SG
Tel: 01423 500600 *Fax:* 01423 556010 *Dx:* 11962 HARROGATE
E-mail: steve.prosser@harrogate.gov.uk
Sol: Ashton, Ms Lynne V Solicitor . . . Oct 1994
Cooper, Mrs Gillian L LLB Principal Solicitor. . . . *Apr 1984
Firbank, Miss Corinne LLB(Hons) Solicitor. . . . Nov 1996
Power, Mr Robert F BA Principal Solicitor . . . Jul 1981
Prosser, Mr Stephen J BA Chief Solicitor . . . *Jul 1981

HARROW, Middlesex

BOVIS CONSTRUCTION LTD
Bovis House 142 Northolt Road Harrow Middlesex HA2 0EE
Tel: 020 8422 3488
Sol: Tipple, Mr Paul J LLB Solicitor. . . . *Jul 1971

GE MONEY HOME FINANCE LIMITED
53-61 College Road Harrow Middlesex HA1 1FB
Tel: 020 8861 1313 *Fax:* 020 8861 2731 *Dx:* 4250 HARROW
Sol: Xavier-Phillips, Mrs Agnes LLB Head of Legal. . . . *Feb 1987

HM LAND REGISTRY - HARROW SUB OFFICE
Lyon House Lyon Road Harrow Middlesex HA1 2EU
Tel: 020 8235 1181 *Fax:* 020 8862 0176 *Dx:* 4299 HARROW 4
E-mail: harrow.office@landregistry.gsi.gov.uk
Sol: Acharya, Ms Sushma Assistant Land Registrar . . . *Apr 1988
Basu-Owen, Mrs B Rumku Assistant Land Registrar. *Apr 1999
Ebrahimi, Miss Jane Yvette Assistant Land Registrar *Nov 1999
Maroo, Mr Ajay LLB(Hons) Assistant Land Registrar. *Sep 1999
Mobbs, Mr James Kenneth BA(Hons) Assistant Land Registrar . . . *Sep 2000
Reich, Mr Lawrence James BA(Hons); DipLaw Assistant Land Registrar . . . *Jul 2001
Tate, Mr Colin Land Registrar . . . *Dec 1972

HARTLEPOOL

HARTLEPOOL BOROUGH COUNCIL
Civic Centre Victoria Road Hartlepool TS24 8AY
Tel: 01429 266522 *Fax:* 01429 523481 *Dx:* 60669 HARTLEPOOL
Sol: Carman, Mrs Alyson Elizabeth LLB Solicitor. . . . Mar 2002
Devlin, Mr Peter John BSc; LLB; LLM:DMS Legal Services Manager . . . *Sep 1987
Macnab, Mr Anthony H LLB Solicitor . . . *Nov 1988

HASTINGS, East Sussex

HASTINGS BOROUGH COUNCIL
Town Hall Queens Road Hastings East Sussex TN34 1QR
Tel: 01424 781066 *Fax:* 01424 781743 *Dx:* 7055 HASTINGS
Sol: Butters, Mrs Jayne LLB(Lond) Borough Solicitor. . . . Aug 1977
Cameron, Mrs Kirsty Reddin LLB; Dip Local Gov Principal Solicitor. . . . Jan 2000

HATFIELD, Hertfordshire

THREE VALLEYS WATER PLC
PO Box 48 Bishops Rise Hatfield Hertfordshire AL10 9HL
Tel: 01707 268111 *Fax:* 01707 277198
Sol: Monod, Mr Tim J W LLB Head of Legal Services . . . Oct 1997
Pilsworth, Mr Ian L LLB(Newc) Assistant Solicitor . . . *Jul 1977

HAVANT, Hampshire

HAVANT BOROUGH COUNCIL
Civic Offices Civic Centre Road Havant Hampshire PO9 2AX
Tel: 023 9247 4174 *Fax:* 023 9248 0263 *Dx:* 50005 HAVANT
Sol: Griffith, Mr Paul D J BA Principal Solicitor. . . . *Nov 1987
Newbury, Miss Hannah Crystal Senior Solicitor . . . *Jan 1983

HAVERFORDWEST, Pembrokeshire

PEMBROKESHIRE COUNTY COUNCIL
County Hall Haverfordwest Pembrokeshire SA61 1TP
Tel: 01437 764551 *Fax:* 01437 776476
Dx: 98295 HAVERFORDWEST
Sol: Annett, Ms Susan Peta LLB Solicitor . . . Nov 1995
Davies, Mrs Jill Frances FILEx Solicitor . . . Jan 1998
Forrest, Mrs Sara F A LLB Principal Solicitor(child care) . . . *Apr 1980
Harding, Mr Laurence J LLB(Lond); Dip Monitoring Officer . . . Nov 1974
Harries, Mr Jeffrey Albert LLB(Hons) Solicitor . . . *Mar 1993
Kent, Mr Michael Anthony Solicitor . . . *§Dec 1980
Martin, Miss Sally Ann LLB(Hons) Solicitor . . . *Sep 2001
Miller, Mr Huw John LLB(Leics) Head of Legal & Committee Services . . . *Jul 1983
Parry-Jones, Mr D Bryn MA(Oxon) Chief Executive . *Mar 1980

HAYWARDS HEATH, West Sussex

MID SUSSEX DISTRICT COUNCIL
Oaklands Oaklands Road Haywards Heath West Sussex RH16 1SS
Tel: 01444 458166 *Fax:* 01444 450027
Dx: 300320 HAYWARDS HEATH 1
Sol: Clark, Mr Thomas Julian BSc; BA(Exon)(Law) Solicitor to the Council . . . *Feb 1986
Currall, Franca LLB(Hons) Assistant Solicitor . . . Apr 2007
McGough, Mrs Clare Margaret BA Solicitor . . . Sep 2001

MID SUSSEX MAGISTRATES COURT
Bolnore Road Haywards Heath West Sussex RH16 4BA
Tel: 01444 417611 *Fax:* 01444 472639
Sol: McNally, Ms Karin M Divisional Legal Manager . . . *Apr 1988

NATIONAL ASSOCIATION OF HEAD TEACHERS
1 Heath Square Boltro Road Haywards Heath West Sussex RH16 1BL
Tel: 01444 472472 *Fax:* 01444 472473
E-mail: info@naht.org.uk
Sol: Hart, Sir David M OBE FRSA Herbert Ruse Prize General Secretary & Solicitor . . . *Jun 1963
Poole, Mr Ian W BA Assistant Solicitor . . . *May 1982
Thomas, Mr Simon R BA . . . *Nov 1990

SUSSEX (NORTHERN) AREA PSA CRAWLEY, HORSHAM & MID SUSSEX COURT HOUSES
Divisional Legal Manager Bolnore Road Haywards Heath West Sussex RH16 4BA
Tel: 01444 417611 *Fax:* 01444 472639
Dx: 135596 HAYWARDS HEATH 6
Sol: McNally, Ms Karin M . . . *Apr 1988

HEMEL HEMPSTEAD, Hertfordshire

DACORUM BOROUGH COUNCIL
Civic Centre Marlowes Dacorum Borough Hemel Hempstead Hertfordshire HP1 1HH
Tel: 01442 228000 *Fax:* 01442 228746
Dx: 8804 HEMEL HEMPSTEAD
Sol: Baker, Mr Steven C BA(Hons) Solicitor to the Council . *Jul 1988
Brookes, Mr Mark Robin LLB(Hons) Planning Solicitor (Team Manager). . . . Apr 2002
Pope, Ms Noele P M MA(Oxon) Legal Services Manager . . . *Oct 1990

HENGOED, Caerphilly

CAERPHILLY COUNTY BOROUGH COUNCIL
Tredomen House Tredomen Park Ystrad Mynach Hengoed Caerphilly CF82 7WF
Tel: 01443 815588 *Fax:* 01443 863154 *Dx:* 145140 CAERPHILLY 5
E-mail: perkid@caerphilly.gov.uk
Sol: Ead, Mrs Susan LLB; DipLaw Solicitor. . . . *Mar 2003
Gladwyn, Mrs Bethan Anne LLB Solicitor . . . *Sep 2003
Gordon, Mr Geoffrey R T LLB Senior Assistant Solicitor . . . *Dec 1976
Nicholas, Mr Lyndsey Sandbrook LLB(Wales) Senior Solicitor . . . *Aug 1975
Owen, Mrs Rachel Angela FILEx Senior Solicitor . . . *Oct 1997
Perkins, Mr Daniel LLB Head of Legal Services & Monitoring Officer . . . *Oct 1990
Richards, Mr David Gareth LLB; DipLG Principal Solicitor . . . *Jan 1986
Rogers, Mr John C LLB Principal Solicitor. . . . *Mar 1980
Williams, Mrs Gail Williams PGDipLaw Principal Solicitor/ Deputy Monitoring Officer. . . . Jan 2004

HEREFORD, Herefordshire

HEREFORD MAGISTRATES COURT
Bath Street Hereford Herefordshire HR1 2HE
Tel: 01562 514000 *Fax:* 01562 514111
Sol: Burton, Mr Richard Jonathan BA(Hons) Area Legal Manager . . . *May 1993
Willmott, Mr Stephen John Deputy Area Legal ManagerSep 2002

HEREFORDSHIRE COUNCIL
Legal Services Brockington 35 Hafod Road Hereford Herefordshire HR1 1SH
Tel: 01432 260000 *Fax:* 01432 260206 *Dx:* 135296 HEREFORD 3
Sol: Coughtrie, Mrs Kate Janice LLB(Hons) Solicitor. . . . Apr 1999
Franklin, Mrs Andrea BSc(Hons)(Econ) Property Lawyer . . . Dec 1990
Howarth, Mr John MSc Principal Lawyer. . . . Dec 1976
O'Keefe, Mr Kevin John LLB(Hons) Legal Practice Manager . . . *Oct 1988

COUNTY OF HEREFORDSHIRE DISTRICT COUNCIL
Brockington 35 Hafod Road Hereford Herefordshire HR1 1SH
Tel: 01432 260266 *Fax:* 01432 260206 *Dx:* 135296 HEREFORD
E-mail: kokeefe@herefordshire.gov.uk
Sol: Coughtrie, Ms Kate J LLB(Hons) Senior Solicitor . . . May 1999
Crilly, Mr Peter F P LLB Principal Lawyer . . . Oct 1990
Franklin, Mrs Andrea BSc(Hons) Property Lawyer. . . . Jan 1990
Hardy, Mr Geoffrey BA(Hons) Principal Lawyer . . . *Aug 1992
Howarth, Mr John MSc Solicitor. . . . Dec 1976
McLaughlin, Mr Alan J LLB Head of Legal & Democratic Services . . . *Dec 1992
O'Keefe, Mr Kevin John LLB(Hons) Legal Practice Manager . . . *Oct 1988
Pringle, Mr Neil M BA(Dunelm) Chief Executive . . . *Nov 1973
Rhead, Mr Adrian J LLM; LLB Assistant Solicitor . . . *Jan 1986
Robinson, Mr Mark Andrew LLB(Hons) Assistant Solicitor . . . *Mar 1989

PRECISION CASTPARTS CORP
Holmer Road Hereford Herefordshire HR4 9SL
Tel: 01432 382200 *Fax:* 01432 264030
Sol: Edelstyn, Mr Paul LLB European Legal Counsel. . . *Nov 1993

HERTFORD, Hertfordshire

HERTFORDSHIRE COUNTY COUNCIL
County Hall Pegs Lane Hertford Hertfordshire SG13 8DQ
Tel: 01992 555555 *Fax:* 01992 555541 *Dx:* 145781 HERTFORD 4
Sol: Andrade, Mr Luis Manuel Carvahlo BA(Hons) Senior Solicitor . . . Apr 1998
Ashby, Mr Brian John BSc(Econ) Retired Jun 98 Head of Property Law Notary Public. . . . *Dec 1974
Atkins, Miss Stephanie J M MA(Hons) Solicitor . . . *Oct 1995
Briscoe, Mrs Janet LLM Solicitor . . . Oct 1994
Collins, Mrs Meera LLB(Hons). . . . *Aug 1996
Cunningham, Mrs Christine Solicitor. . . . Mar 1996
Davis, Miss Deborah BA(Hons) Solicitor. . . . Jul 1997
Donner, Miss Lillian BA(Econ & Law) Solicitor Notary Public . . . *Nov 2006
Fryett- Kerr, Mrs Victoria LLB(Hons). . . . Sep 1999
Gurney, Miss Laura LLB(Hons) Solicitor. . . . Sep 2006
Jones, Ms Rachael LLB Solicitor . . . Sep 1989
Kaiser, Miss Stephanie Catherine LLB(Hons) . . . Nov 1999
Kaye, Miss Ilisa Simone LPC; FILEX Solicitor. . . . Nov 1996
Kemp, Mr Peter Colin LLB. . . . Feb 2004
Laycock, Mr Andrew L MA(Cantab) County Secretary . Jun 1978
Lewis, Mrs Tessa LLB. . . . Nov 2003
McCreery, Ms Nasreen Jane BA(Hons) Solicitor. . . . Jan 2005
Murray, Mrs Linda Margaret FILEx Senior Conveyancing Assistant . . . Sep 1974
Ogbonnaya, Mr Damian BA(Hons); LLB(Hons) Solicitor Jul 2002
Pettitt, Mrs Kathryn LLB(Hons) Assistant County Secretary (Corporate Law). . . . *Apr 1984
Rajaratnam, Miss Mrinalini Solicitor . . . *Dec 1992
Simon, Mrs Dorothy Mary LLB(Hons) Assistant County Secretary . . . Jan 1983
Sonola, Ms Adedla O MA; DipLG; LLB(Hons); BL Solicitor . . . Aug 1999
Stammers, Ms Stephanie BA(Hons). . . . Oct 1981
Stapleton, Ms Adelle Priscilla FILEx Legal Executive . Sep 2000
Thornton, Ms Julie LLB(Hons) Solicitor. . . . Jun 1999
White, Mrs Danielle BA(Hons); CPE Assistant. . . . Dec 2002
Wing, Mrs Rosalind LLB; LPC; DipTrans(IOL) Solicitor. Apr 2005

RIALTO HOMES PLC
Bayfordbury Lower Hatfield Road Hertford Hertfordshire SG13 8EE
Tel: 01992 823589 *Fax:* 01992 823503
Sol: Reid, Mr Stephen J P BA(Dunelm) Group Solicitor. . . *Jun 1981

See p112 for the Key to Work Categories & other symbols

HEXHAM, Northumberland

TYNEDALE DISTRICT COUNCIL
Council Offices Hexham House Hexham Northumberland NE46 3NH
Tel: 01434 652200 *Fax:* 01434 652421 *Dx:* 63216 HEXHAM
Sol: Bracken, Mr Peter John BSc Solicitor . . . . Feb 2007
Pointer, Mr Garry C BA Solicitor. . . . . *Oct 1985
Sinnamon, Miss Mary Elizabeth LLB(Hons) Solicitor. . .Jul 2002

HIGH WYCOMBE, Buckinghamshire

WYCOMBE & BEACONSFIELD MAGISTRATES COURT
Easton Street High Wycombe Buckinghamshire HP11 1LR
Tel: 01494 651035 *Fax:* 01494 651030
Dx: 97883 HIGH WYCOMBE 3
E-mail: wycombe.magistrates@hmcourts-service.gsi.gov.uk
Sol: Dennis, Mrs Angela Maria Michela LLB(Hons) Senior Legal Adviser . . . . *Feb 1997
Forbes, Miss Daffodil Kayleen Senior Legal Advisor. . *Jan 1995
Walton, Mrs Susan Pamela DMS Deputy Justices' Clerk . . . . *Dec 1991
Warner, Mrs Margaret Valerie Louise LLB(Hons) Senior Legal Adviser . . . . *Dec 1989

WYCOMBE DISTRICT COUNCIL
Council Offices Queen Victoria Road High Wycombe Buckinghamshire HP11 1BB
Tel: 01494 461002 *Fax:* 01494 421235 *Dx:* 4411 HIGH WYCOMBE
Sol: Dongray, Mr David M BA District Solicitor . . . . *Apr 1977
Herries-Smith, Mrs Catherine Juliet BA; MA; LLB Principal Solicitor. . . . . *Dec 1989
Khanna, Mrs Kiran LLB(Hons) Solicitor . . . . *Mar 1991
Nawaz, Mrs Ifathara LLB(Hons) Principal Solicitor. . . *Nov 1991
Ruddock, Mr David R BA Corporate Solicitor . . . . . *Jan 1982
Wilson, Ms Sarah Louise BA(Hons); DMS Principal Solicitor . . . . *Nov 1998

HILLINGDON, Middlesex

HILLINGDON LAW CENTRE
12 Harold Avenue Hillingdon Middlesex UB3 4QW
Tel: 020 8561 9400 *Fax:* 020 8756 0837
E-mail: hillingdon@lawyersonline.co.uk
Sol: Kaur, Ms Narinder LLB Supervising Solicitor. . . . . . Aug 1994

HINCKLEY, Leicestershire

HINCKLEY AND RUGBY BUILDING SOCIETY
Upper Bond Street Hinckley Leicestershire LE10 1DG
Tel: 01455 894026 *Fax:* 01455 618506 *Dx:* 716435 HINCKLEY
Sol: Howard, Ms Julia Neale LLB Solicitor and Secretary. . *Apr 1984

HINCKLEY MAGISTRATES COURT
Upper Bond Street Hinckley Leicestershire LE10 1NZ
Sol: Essat, Mr Altaf Hussein LLB(Hons) Solicitor. . . . . . *Jun 2002
Marshall, Mrs Rachel Alexandra LLB(Hons) Head of Legal Services . . . . *Feb 1994

WOLTERS KLUWER (UK) LTD
Croner House Wheatfield Way Hinckley Leicestershire LE10 1YG
Tel: 01455 897361 *Fax:* 01455 895412
Sol: Anderson, Mr Peter David ACIS Solicitor . . . . *Oct 1980
Bali, Ms Rekha LLB(Hons) Solicitor . . . . *Aug 2002

HODDESDON, Hertfordshire

MERCK SHARP & DOHME LTD
Hertford Road Hoddesdon Hertfordshire EN11 9BU
Tel: 01992 452509 *Fax:* 01992 470189
Sol: Parker, Ms Jane R MA Legal Adviser . . . . *Jul 1987

HOOK, Hampshire

E E F SOUTH
Station Road Hook Hampshire RG27 9TL
Tel: 01256 763969 *Fax:* 01256 768530
E-mail: info@eef-south.org.uk
Sol: Balogun, A Solicitor . . . . *May 1992
Cole, Ms Penelope Anne LLB Solicitor. . . . . Jan 1990
Hobbs, Miss Fiona Solicitor . . . . Jan 2002
Khalil, Mr Omar BA(Hons) Solicitor . . . . Oct 1995
Pender, Mr Simon Joseph BA Head of Legal & Employment Affairs. . . . . *Nov 1989

HORSHAM, West Sussex

HORSHAM DISTRICT COUNCIL
Creditors Section Park House North Street Horsham West Sussex RH12 1RL
Tel: 01403 215100 *Fax:* 01403 215487 *Dx:* 57609 HORSHAM 6
E-mail: legaladmin@horsham.gov.uk
Sol: Creswick, Miss Elizabeth S BA; LLB Principal Solicitor.*Sep 1987
Davison, Mr Ian R MA(Oxon) Council Secretary And Solicitor . . . . *Oct 1981
Healy, Mrs Amardip K LLB(Hons) Principal Solicitor . . *Jul 1990
Herbert, Ms S Sandra A Corporate Solicitor . . . . . . *Dec 1992
Rae, Mrs Fiona Assistant Solicitor. . . . . *Sep 2001

RSPCA
Wilberforce Way Southwater Horsham West Sussex RH13 9RS
Tel: 0870 010 1181 *Fax:* 0870 753 0048 *Dx:* 57628 HORSHAM 6
E-mail: legal_sevices@rspca.org.uk
Sol: Cush, Mr John William LLB(Hons); LLM Commercial Lawyer Notary Public . . . . *May 2000
Foreman, Miss Sasha Charity & Commercial Lawyer . *Sep 2001
Gale, Mr Christopher R LLB(Hons) Head of Legal Services . . . . *Dec 1975
Gibbs, Mrs Amanda Catherine LLB; MBA(Legal Practice) Commercial Lawyer. . . . . *Aug 1996
Goodfellow, Mr Raymond Neil LLM; LLB Chief Legal Adviser . . . . *Oct 1992
Watson-Cook, Miss Estelle Lisa LLB(Hons) . . . . . . *Nov 1995

HOUNSLOW, Middlesex

HERTZ EUROPE LTD
11 Vine Street Uxbridge Hounslow Middlesex UB8 1QE
Tel: 01895 553500 *Fax:* 01895 553728
Sol: Davies, Mr Bryn BBusSc; LLB Counsel . . . . Sep 2003
Finch, Mr John R MA Senior Counsel . . . . *Dec 1974

HOUNSLOW LAW CENTRE LTD
51 Lampton Road Hounslow Middlesex TW3 1JG
Tel: 020 8570 9505 *Fax:* 020 8572 0730
Sol: Lartey, Ms Veronica Solicitor . . . . *Oct 2003

HOVE, Brighton & Hove

BRIGHTON & HOVE COUNCIL - LEGAL SERVICES
PO Box 2500 Kings House Grand Avenue Hove Brighton & Hove BN3 2SR
Tel: 01273 290000 *Fax:* 01273 291073 *Dx:* 59286 HOVE
Sol: Bailey, Mr Alex Mason LLB Principal Solicitor . . . . . *Oct 1987
Bruce, Mr Robert W Principal Solicitor. . . . . *Dec 1981
Culbert, Miss Elizabeth Clare Senior Lawyer. . . . . . *Nov 1995
Ghebre-Ghiorghis, Mr Mesfin LLB Senior Lawyer . . . *Oct 1989
Heys, Mr John A LLB(Soton) Principal Solicitor . . . . *Jun 1976
Hughes, Ms Angharad BA(Hons); LLM Lawyer . . . . May 1991
MacKenzie, Ms Annaliisa K BA Senior Lawyer. . . . . *Jul 1982
Martin, Mrs Lynne J BA(Hons) Lawyer. . . . . *Dec 1981
Nicol, Ms Joanne Lawyer . . . . *Apr 1999
Sidell, Ms Rebecca L BA; MA Lawyer . . . . Oct 1995
Vernon-Hunt, Mr Jonathan M BA Principal Solicitor . . *Oct 1986
Woodley, Ms Elizabeth J Senior Lawyer. . . . . *Jul 1985
Woodward, Mrs Hilary K BA(Hons) Senior Commercial Lawyer . . . . Dec 1989

HUDDERSFIELD, West Yorkshire

KIRKLEES METROPOLITAN BOROUGH COUNCIL
2nd Floor Civic Centre 3 Huddersfield West Yorkshire HD1 2TG
Tel: 01484 221421 *Fax:* 01484 221423 *Dx:* 710090 HUDDERSFIELD
E-mail: legal.lawlib@kirklees.gov.uk
Sol: Anwar, Miss Shanaz LLB Senior Legal Officer. . . . . *Sep 1999
Arshad, Ms Yasmin LLB(Hons); LPC Senior Legal Officer . . . . *Dec 1997
Barnes, Mr Mark Nicholas LLB(Hons); LLM Robson Rhodes Insolvency Law Prize 1998 Senior Legal Officer. . *Aug 2001
Betteridge, Miss Susan L LLB(Hons) Head of Legal Services . . . . *Oct 1991
Bird, Ms Joanna Mildred BA(Hons) Senior Legal Officer . . . . *Nov 1997
Chapman, Mr John Henry BA(Hons) Senior Legal Officer . . . . *Sep 1991
Cheesman, Mrs Catherine Ann LLB(Hons) Senior Legal Officer . . . . *Oct 2001
Fairlie, Mrs Clare Marie LLB(Hons) Senior Legal Officer . . . . *Oct 1996
Field, Mr Jason Darrel BA; LLM Senior Legal Officer . *Feb 2003
Hannen, Miss Patricia LLB(Hons) Senior Legal Officer.*Dec 1995
Kingham-Slater, Ms Josephine M LLB Senior Legal Officer . . . . *Sep 1991
Larrad, Mr Karl A BA(Hons); LLM Principal Legal Officer . . . . *Feb 1991
Lorenzelli, Mr Clifford Joseph BA Senior Legal Officer. *Mar 1996
Lukoczki, Mr Charles Alexander PGDipLaw(CPE); PGDipLP Senior Legal Officer. . . . . *Mar 2006
Micolson, Mr MA LLM Senior Legal Officer . . . . . . Dec 1993
Miller, Miss Margaret LLB(Hons) Principal Legal Officer*Oct 1994
Nawaz, Miss Yasmin Bi LLB(Hons) Assistant Legal Officer . . . . *Apr 2004
Park, Ms Kirstine S LLB. . . . . *Mar 1995
Pearson, Mr Dermot James BA(Hons)(Econ) Senior Legal Officer . . . . *Jan 1990
Power, Mr W Russell Senior Legal Officer. . . . . . . *Jan 1976
Redfern, Ms Vanessa LLB Principal Legal Officer . . . *Dec 1995
Sheikh, Miss Syka LLB(Hons); LPC Conveyancing 2001) Litigation (2001) Senior Legal Officer . . . . *Oct 2004
Snadden, Mrs Gillian Ann Solicitor. . . . . *Mar 2005
Sorby, Mr Mathew BA(Hons)(English) . . . . *Mar 2007
Wilberforce, Mrs Jessica Caroline Louise BSc(Hons); PGDip Law; PGDipLP Senior Legal Officer. . . . . *Jun 2002
Wilkes, Miss Deborah Jane BA(Hons) Senior Legal Officer . . . . *Aug 1996

HULL, Kingston upon Hull

HM LAND REGISTRY - HULL
Earle House Colonial Street Hull Kingston upon Hull HU2 8JN
Tel: 01482 223244 *Fax:* 01482 224278 *Dx:* 26700 HULL 4
Sol: Andrew, Mr Johnson LLB Assistant Land Registrar . . Nov 1984
Cavill, Mr Darren BA; LLB Assistant Land Registrar . . *Sep 1995
Coveney, S LLB Land Registrar. . . . . *Dec 1975
Duxbury, Mr Paul LLB Assistant Land Registrar. . . . Oct 1991
Edon, Mr John A LLB(Lond) Assistant Land Registrar . *Dec 1978
Hargreave, Mrs Alison M MA(Cantab) Assistant Land Registrar . . . . Jun 1979
Littlefair, Mrs S Assistant Land Registrar. . . . . Jul 1976
Watt, Mrs A Assistant Land Registrar . . . . Nov 1980

KINGSTON UPON HULL CITY COUNCIL
The Guildhall Alfred Gelder Street Hull Kingston upon Hull HU1 2AA
Tel: 01482 300300 *Fax:* 01482 615062 *Dx:* 11394 HULL
Sol: Belfield, Mrs Sonia Kate LLB(Hons); MA Solicitor . . . Jan 2004
Chester, Mr Nathan Louis LLB Solicitor . . . . *Sep 1995
Dearing, Mr Peter Solicitor . . . . *May 1986
Dennett, Ms Alison Solicitor. . . . . §Oct 1995
Duxbury, Mrs Anne F LLB Solicitor . . . . *Oct 1991
Gateshill, Ms Josephine Carole BA(Hons) Solicitor . . . *Nov 1981
Harrison, Ms Sarah Frances MA; Jurisprudence Coombes Exhibition, Somerville College 1998 Solicitor. . . . Sep 2001
Jepson, Mr John Seymour LLB Solicitor. . . . . *Dec 1974
Johnson, Mr Andrew P LLB Solicitor. . . . . Nov 1984
Owst, Miss Adrienne Rosemary BA(Hons) Solicitor . . *Jun 1993
Ross-Appleby, Mrs Anne Maria LLB(Hons) Solicitor . . Jan 1993
Taylor, Mr Jonathan R LLB; MA(Econ) Solicitor . . . . *Oct 1987
Taylor, Mrs Margaret J LLB; MA Town Clerk. . . . . . *Apr 1973
Turner, Mr Stephen David LLB Solicitor . . . . *Dec 1986

NORTHERN FOODS PLC
2180 Century Way Thorpe Park Leeds West Yorkshire LS15 8ZB
Tel: 0113 390 0110 *Fax:* 0113 390 0211
Sol: McLean, Miss Georgina LLB Solicitor . . . . *Sep 2000
Simpson, Mr Alexander Daniel Keeler Commercial Lawyer . . . . *Sep 2002
Sore, Miss Justine Millicent Charlotte LLB(Hons); LPC Senior Employment Lawyer . . . . *Sep 2000
Williams, Mrs Carol BA Solicitor, Head of Legal & Company Secretary . . . . *May 1985

HUNTINGDON, Cambridgeshire

AWG PLC
Anglian House Ambury Road Huntingdon Cambridgeshire PE29 3NZ
Tel: 01480 323140 *Fax:* 01480 323288
Sol: Firth, Mr Patrick G LLB Company Secretary and Group Legal Counsel. *Jul 1980
Sudbury, Mr Roger G BA(Cantab) Commercial Solicitor . . . . *Sep 1990

CAMBRIDGE CONSTABULARY
Police Headquarters Hinchingbrooke Park Huntingdon Cambridgeshire PE29 6NP
Tel: 01480 456111 *Fax:* 01480 422362
Sol: Grogan, Mr Ciaran Assistant Solicitor . . . . Dec 2001

HUNTINGDONSHIRE DISTRICT COUNCIL
Pathfinder House St Mary's Street Huntingdon Cambridgeshire PE29 3TN
Tel: 01480 388388 *Fax:* 01480 388099
Dx: 140316 HUNTINGDON SC
Sol: Meadowcroft, Mr Colin LLB Head of Legal & Estates *May 1979
Monks, Mr David LLB; AKC; LLM(Lond); FCIS; MBIM Chief Executive . . . . *Oct 1976
Smalley, Wayland A BA(Oxon) Solicitor . . . . *Jan 1982
Stevens, Miss Vicki BA(Hons) Solicitor . . . . Nov 1997

HUYTON, Merseyside

KNOWSLEY METROPOLITAN BOROUGH COUNCIL
PO Box 21 Municipal Buildings Archway Road Huyton Merseyside L36 9YU
Tel: 0151 443 3593 *Fax:* 0151 443 3550 *Dx:* 713891 HUYTON 3
Sol: Chan, Miss Lyana Grace LLB(Hons) Assistant. . . . . *Jul 2006
Dearing, Mr Michael George LLB(Hons) Senior Solicitor . . . . *Apr 1996
Fagan, Mr Nigel K LLB(Hons) Senior Solicitor. . . . . *Oct 1989
Ferguson, Mrs Angela Bernice Assistant Solicitor . . . *Sep 2002
Gora, Miss Barbara Wieslawa LLB(Hons) Assistant Solicitor . . . . *Jun 2005
Heath, Miss Beryl LLB(Hons) Borough Solicitor and Secretary . . . . *Oct 1982
Johnson, Mr Alan James Assistant Solicitor . . . . . . *Nov 1994
Maher, Ms Judith R LLB(Hons) Senior Solicitor . . . . *Dec 1993
Meredith, Miss Victoria LLB(Hons) Senior Solicitor. . . *Jun 2001
Miller, Mrs Johanna Elizabeth LLB Director . . . . . . Sep 1992
Murphy, Mr Peter J BA(Hons); MA Deputy Head of Legal Services . . . . *May 1982
Nicholson, Mrs Julia M LLB(Hons) Senior Solicitor. . . *Oct 1985
Pask, Miss Susan J LLB(Hons) Assistant Solicitor. . . . *Nov 1989
Pritchard, Mr Kevin W LLB Principal Solicitor . . . . . *Oct 1987

ILFORD, Essex

REDBRIDGE MAGISTRATES COURT
850 Cranbrook Road Barkingside Ilford Essex IG6 1HW
Tel: 0845 601 3600 *Fax:* 020 8550 2101 *Dx:* 99327 BARKINGSIDE
Sol: Knowles, Mrs Elaine DML; CPE Senior Legal Advisor . Jul 1994
Morgan-McGovern, Mrs Sandra LLB(Hons) Legal Advisor . . . . Sep 2004
Rose, Mrs Ilanit Louise LLB Legal Advisor. . . . . Jan 2004
Tang, Miss Josephine LLB(Hons) Senior Legal Advisor . Jul 2001
Trup, Mr Daniel BA(Politics with History); LLM(International Law); CPE; LPC Senior Legal Advisor. . . . . . . Mar 2000

ILKESTON, Derbyshire

EREWASH BOROUGH COUNCIL
Town Hall Ilkeston Derbyshire DE7 5RP
Tel: 0115 907 2244 *Fax:* 0115 907 1121 *Dx:* 10318 ILKESTON
Sol: Fearn, Mrs Bridget LLB Solicitor. . . . . *Jul 2001
Minnighan, Ms Mary Elaine BA(Hons) Deputy Director Legal and Democratic Services and Monitoring Officer. . . . . . *Nov 1993
Morris, Mr Brendan M LLB Legal Services Manager. . *§Apr 1981

IPSWICH, Suffolk

CROWN PROSECUTION SERVICE SUFFOLK
St Vincent House 1 Cutler Street Ipswich Suffolk IP1 1UL
Tel: 01473 282100 *Fax:* 01473 282101 *Dx:* 3266 IPSWICH
Sol: Yule, Mr Christopher John Solicitor . . . . *Jan 1969

IPSWICH BOROUGH COUNCIL
Grafton House 15-17 Russell Road Ipswich Suffolk IP1 2DE
Tel: 01473 432000 *Fax:* 01473 432326 *Dx:* 3225 IPSWICH
E-mail: legal@ipswich.gov.uk
Sol: Airey, Miss Claudine Theresa PGDipLaw; FILEX Solicitor . . . . *Nov 2004
Barritt-Hayes, Mrs Claire Ba(hons) Legal Services Manager . . . . Nov 2003
Hunt, Mr Timothy James Finbarr MA Solicitor . . . . . Apr 1976
Ramsden, Mr Clive R H Solicitor . . . . *Jun 1974
Seeley, Mr Ian B(Law) Principal Solicitor. . . . . Sep 1996
Turner, Mr Paul A LLB Coporate Legal Advisor / Monitoring Officer . . . . *Feb 1995

MID SUFFOLK DISTRICT COUNCIL
Council Offices 131 High Street Needham Market Ipswich Suffolk IP6 8DL
Tel: 01449 720711 *Fax:* 01499 721946
E-mail: legal@midsuffolk.gov.uk
Sol: Reed, Mr Jonathan Corporate Legal Advisor . . . . . *Dec 1989
Rickard, Mr Ian F LLB(Lond) District Monitoring Officer *Apr 1976

SUFFOLK COUNTY COUNCIL
Endeavour House 8 Russell Road Ipswich Suffolk IP1 2BX
Tel: 01473 583000
E-mail: customerservice@csduk.com
Sol: Alexander, Miss Jennifer C LLB Solicitor. . . . . . . *Jan 1995
Brennan, Ms Anna S LLB Solicitor. . . . . Oct 1993
Girling, Sarah . . . . Jan 2009
Inniss, Mr Nigel M BA(Hons); DipLaw; Politics. . . . *Sep 1998
Jenkins, Mr Giles C BA Solicitor. . . . . Nov 1990
Jenkins, Miss Justine Elizabeth LLB(Hons) Solicitor . . Sep 1998
Leonard, Ms Marie Georgina LLB(Hons). . . . . Sep 1996
Maher, Alexandra . . . . Jan 2008
Molander, Ms Lisa Ann BA; MA Solicitor. . . . . Oct 1996
Taylor, Victoria . . . . Sep 2007
White, Mr David I LLB; MA Assistant County Solicitor . *Oct 1985

ISLEWORTH, Middlesex

GILLETTE MANAGEMENT INC
Great West Road Isleworth Middlesex TW7 5NP
Tel: 020 8560 1234 *Fax:* 020 8568 4082
Sol: Mee, Mr Peter G V LLB(Cantab) Deputy General Counsel . . . . Nov 1977
Reynolds, Mr John Jeffrey MA(Oxon) Director (London Legal Dep't). . . . . Jul 1991

MOWLEM PLC
White Lion Court Swan Street Isleworth Middlesex TW7 6RN
Tel: 020 8568 9111 *Fax:* 020 8560 5981
Sol: Haynes, Mr Gavin MA(Oxon) Solicitor. . . . . Jan 1996
Kearney, Mr Anthony T LLB Solicitor . . . . *Dec 1984
Starkey, Mr Paul Michael MSc(Construction Law & Arbitration) In-House Counsel. . . . . Jan 1993
Woodward, Mr Keith MA(Cantab) Company Secretary & Chief Legal Officer . . . . *Oct 1979

IVER, Buckinghamshire

CUMMINS ENGINE COMPANY LTD
Unit 1b Uniongate Ridgeway Trading Estate Iver Buckinghamshire SL0 9HX
Tel: 020 8700 6920 *Fax:* 020 8949 5604

KENDAL, Cumbria

CUMBRIA COUNTY COUNCIL
Legal Services Unit County Offices Kendal Cumbria LA9 4RQ
Tel: 01539 773123 *Fax:* 01539 773124
Sol: Haughin, Ms Emma J LLB Assistant Solicitor . . . . . Apr 1999
Shiels, Mrs Patricia BA(Hons) Senior Solicitor. . . . . May 1987
Smith, Ms Katherine M Assistant Solicitor . . . . Sep 1996
Sowerby, Mrs Helen Jane BA Assistant Solicitor. . . . Jan 1999

LAKE DISTRICT NATIONAL PARK AUTHORITY
Murley Moss Oxenholme Road Kendal Cumbria LA9 7RL
Tel: 01539 724555 *Fax:* 01539 740822
E-mail: hq@lake-district.gov.uk
Sol: Sheerin, Mr James BA Head of Legal Services . . . . Oct 1988
Wood, Miss Julie Susan LLB(Hons) Legal Adviser. . *Nov 1995

SOUTH LAKELAND DISTRICT COUNCIL
South Lakeland House Lowther Street Kendal Cumbria LA9 4UQ
Tel: 01539 733333 *Fax:* 01539 740300 *Dx:* 63428 KENDAL
Sol: Fenwick, Mrs Sandra LLB(Hons); MSc; DipLG Senior Solicitor . . . . Aug 1998
Neal, Mr Matthew P LLB(Hons) Principal Solicitor . . *Mar 1995
Storr, Miss Debbie T LLB(Hons) Executive Director (Central Services) . . . . *Nov 1995

SOUTH LAKELAND MAGISTRATES' COURT
Burneside Road PO Box 35 Kendal Cumbria LA9 4TJ
Tel: 01539 720478 *Fax:* 01539 740502 *Dx:* 707870 KENDAL 4
Sol: Evans, Mr Simon N LLB; DMS; MIPD . . . . *Nov 1982

KETTERING, Northamptonshire

KETTERING BOROUGH COUNCIL
Municipal Offices Bowling Green Road Kettering Northamptonshire NN15 7QX
Tel: 01536 410333 *Fax:* 01536 410795 *Dx:* 12816 KETTERING
E-mail: jonathaneatough@kettering.gov.uk
Sol: Chadwick, Mr James LLB(Hons) Community Protection Solicitor . . . . Jun 2006
Eatough, Mr Jonathan Marcus LLB; DipLG Head of Democratic & Legal Services . . . . *Jan 1993
Hollands, Mr Geoffrey C Senior Community Protection Solicitor . . . . *Dec 1982
Stewart, Mr Brian Lewis BA(Oxon) Legal Services Manager . . . . *Jun 1977

KEYNSHAM, Bath & North East Somerset

BATH & NORTH EAST SOMERSET COUNCIL
The Guildhall High Street Bath Bath & North East Somerset BA1 5AW
Tel: 01225 394041 *Fax:* 01225 394043
Sol: Brookes, Miss Amanda K BA Senior Assistant Solicitor *Jan 1980
Hitchman, Mr Vernon F BA City Solicitor. . . . . Jun 1980
Hosking, Miss Dawn B D LLB(Hons) Senior Legal Adviser . . . . *Oct 1992
Ind, Ms Linda BA(Hons) Senior Child Care Lawyer . . Aug 1991
Jones, Miss Rebecca E LLB Solicitor . . . . *Feb 1983
Malarby, Mr Peter A LLB(Exon) Solicitor. . . . . . . *Feb 1983
Reed, Mr Andrew B BA(Law) Assistant Solicitor. . . . *Jul 1984

KIDDERMINSTER, Worcestershire

BROMSGROVE & REDDITCH MAGISTRATES COURT
Kidderminster Magistrates Court Comberton Place Kidderminster Worcestershire DY10 1QQ
Tel: 01562 514000
Sol: Coughlan, Mr Christopher Joseph LL Dip; DML Senior Legal Advisor . . . . Nov 2002
Greenway, Mr Kevin Philip MBA; Diploma in Magisterial Law Deputy Area Legal Manager - North Worcestershire Magistrates' Courts . . . . Jun 1993
Hines, Mr Phillip Neil DMS Area Legal Manager. . . . Dec 1991
Mckenna, Morgan Lewis LLB; CTP Legal Adviser . . . Jun 1996
Tuckley, Ms Patricia A CPE; Dip Magisterial Law; Certificate in Training Legal Adviser. . . . . Jan 1988

KING'S LYNN, Norfolk

BOROUGH COUNCIL OF KING'S LYNN AND WEST NORFOLK
King's Court Chapel Street King's Lynn Norfolk PE30 1EX
Tel: 01553 616270 *Fax:* 01553 616728 *Dx:* 57825 KING'S LYNN
E-mail: richard.mann@west-norfolk.gov.uk
Sol: Campion, Ms Teresa LLB(Hons) Solicitor . . . . . . *Nov 1996
Hunt, Mr Ian J BSc; FGS Senior Solicitor . . . . Sep 2004

KINGSTON UPON THAMES, Surrey

ROYAL BOROUGH OF KINGSTON UPON THAMES
Guildhall High Street Kingston upon Thames Surrey KT1 1EU
Tel: 020 8546 2121 *Fax:* 020 8547 5127
Dx: 31515 KINGSTON UPON THAMES
Sol: Bishop, Mr Nicholas A BA(Law) Head of Legal Services . . . . *Feb 1988
Conlon, Mr Charles A BA; LLB; DipTP; MRTPI Principal Solicitor . . . . *Jul 1979
Fellows, Mr David LLB Deputy Head of Legal Services *Dec 1990
Girdlestone, Miss Victoria Margaret BA(Hons) Assistant Solicitor . . . . Oct 1996
Guy-Spratt, Mr Alan M LLB Principal Solicitor . . . . . *Jun 1977
Mazerelo, Miss Geetha BA; DipLaw Assistant Solicitor Dec 2003
Newnham, Mr John S BA(Business Law) Assistant Director . . . . *Jun 1979
Sharma, Mrs Neeta LLB(Hons) Principal Solicitor . . *May 1993

SURREY COUNTY COUNCIL
County hall Penrhyn Road Kingston upon Thames Surrey KT1 2DN
Tel: 020 8541 9088 *Fax:* 020 8541 9115
Dx: 31509 KINGSTON UPON THAMES
Sol: Al-Nakeeb, Miss Rena LLB(Hons) Solicitor . . . . . May 2005
Baker, Mrs Sarah Elizabeth BA; LLM . . . . *Nov 1980
Bryant, Ms Yolanda Elizabeth . . . . *Nov 2004
Charlton, Mrs Ann E LLB . . . . *Nov 1981
Deards, Mr Thomas James LLB; LLM. . . . . Mar 2002
Desai, Mr Fatima Bibi LLB(Hons); LPC; DipLG . . . . Jul 2003
El-Shatoury, Ms Nancy LLB. . . . . Sep 1993
Fox, Mrs Naz LLB. . . . . Feb 1988
Freemantle, Mrs Jan LLB . . . . Oct 1992
Gardner, Mr Peter A BA. . . . . *Oct 1980
Hickman, Mrs Rachel Frances LLB(Hons) Senior Solicitor . . . . *May 1998
McLoughlin, Ms Carmel B LLB . . . . *Oct 1989
Mortimer, Mrs Joanna H C BA. . . . . *Jun 1978
Newbold, Miss Geraldine S LLB(Hons) . . . . *Sep 1999
Polley, Ms Janet LLB(Hons). . . . . *Sep 1998
Rackham, Mrs Diane Elizabeth LLB; LPC Solicitor. . *Mar 2003
Stott, Ms Catherine LLB. . . . . *Nov 1994
Wells, Mr Allan J W LLB(Hons) . . . . *Jan 1985

KIRKBY-IN-ASHFIELD, Nottinghamshire

ASHFIELD DISTRICT COUNCIL
Council Offices Urban Road Kirkby-in-Ashfield Nottinghamshire NG17 8DA
Tel: 01623 450000 *Fax:* 01623 457585
Sol: Akhtar, Ms Farzana LLB Senior Solicitor. . . . . . . *Apr 2002
Dennis, Mrs Ruth L LLB(Hons) Solicitor . . . . *Jan 1999
Rogers, Miss Nicola Cerisa LLB(Hons); PGDip Assistant Solicitor. . . . . *Feb 2004

KNUTSFORD, Cheshire

AMEC PLC
Booths Park Chelford Road Knutsford Cheshire WA16 8QZ
Tel: 01565 683123 *Fax:* 01565 683149
E-mail: frazer.carolis@amec.com
Sol: Davin, Ms Julie LLB(Hons) Senior Legal Adviser. . . *Sep 1996
Don Carolis, Mr Frazer Anthony Senior Legal Adviser Notary Public. . . . . *Jan 1973
Smith, Mr Kevin LLB(Hons); MCIArb; FCIOB . . . . . Feb 1993
Stoker, Mrs Theresa Ann LLB(Hons) Legal Adviser . . Jun 2004
Thomas, Mr Anthony Mark BA(Hons); LLM Legal Adviser . . . . *Sep 2005

LANCASTER, Lancashire

LANCASTER CITY COUNCIL
Town Hall Dalton Square Lancaster Lancashire LA1 1PJ
Tel: 01524 582000 *Fax:* 01524 582030 *Dx:* 63531 LANCASTER
Sol: Gorst, Mr Luke David BSc(Hons); PGDip Assistant Solicitor . . . . Sep 2005
Humphreys, Mr Alan Robert Legal Services Manager *Nov 1997
Parkinson, Mrs Angela Mary LLB(Hons) Senior Solicitor . . . . Feb 1988
Taylor, Mrs Sarah BA(Oxon); DipLG Head of Legal & Human Resources . . . . *Oct 1983
Walmsley, Mr Rephael BA; PGDip Assistant Solicitor . *Apr 2007

LEAMINGTON SPA, Warwickshire

WARWICK DISTRICT COUNCIL
Riverside House Milverton Hill Leamington Spa Warwickshire CV32 5HZ
Tel: 01926 450000 *Fax:* 01926 456611
Dx: 29123 LEAMINGTON SPA
Sol: Flanagan, Ms Clare BCL Solicitor . . . . *Dec 1999
Herbert, Mrs Karen Anne LLB(Hons) Solicitor . . . . Oct 2005

LEATHERHEAD, Surrey

ESSO PETROLEUM COMPANY LTD
Law Department ExxonMobil House Ermyn Way Leatherhead Surrey KT22 8UX
Tel: 01372 222000 *Fax:* 01372 222622
Sol: Milne, Ms Natalie LLB Counsel . . . . *Sep 1995
Peake, Mr Roger H LLB Senior Counsel. . . . . . . *Dec 1983
Sharma, Bhavna LLB Solicitor. . . . . Nov 1993

KELLOGG BROWN & ROOT (UK) LTD
Hill Park Court Springfield Drive Leatherhead Surrey KT22 7NL
Tel: 01372 865000 *Fax:* 01372 866951
Sol: Cranston, Miss Helen BA; PGDL Solicitor . . . . . . Aug 2006
Ferguson, Mr Paul E C LLB(Hons) Solicitor . . . . . *Oct 1987
Horner, Mr Michael Barry LLB Solicitor . . . . *Jan 1968
Lyon, Mr David BA Solicitor . . . . *Oct 1992
Nelhams, Mr Martin LLB Solicitor . . . . *Dec 1986
Owen, Miss Susan M LLB Solicitor . . . . *Oct 1983
Taylor, Cailean M M LLB(Glasgow); Admitted Solicitor Scotland 1973 Solicitor. . . . . *May 1985

LEEDS, West Yorkshire

ENVIRONMENT AGENCY (NORTH EAST REGION)
Rivers House 21 Park Square South Leeds West Yorkshire LS1 2QG
Tel: 0870 850 6506 *Fax:* 0113 231 2483
Sol: Bloxwich, Miss Rebecca BA Solicitor . . . . Jan 2002
Bolt, Ms Carol Principal Solicitor. . . . . *Jan 1986
Flannery, Miss Maura Josephine LLB Solicitor. . . . . *Jul 1979
Fogg, Ms Jillian Elaine BA(Hons) Principal Solicitor . *Aug 1987
Howard, Mr Raymond James BA Principal Solicitor . . *Oct 1994
Leach, Mrs Caroline LLB Principal Solicitor . . . . . *Apr 1999
Reid, Mr Benjamin LLB(Hons); LLM Solicitor . . . . . Jan 2004
Ruane, Ms Catherine Bridget Regional Solicitor. . . . . Sep 1995

HAREHILLS & CHAPELTOWN LAW CENTRE
263 Roundhay Road Leeds West Yorkshire LS8 4HS
Tel: 0113 249 1100
Sol: Karavadra, Ms Rita M Solicitor . . . . Oct 1993

LEEDS CITY COUNCIL
Civic Hall Calverley Street Leeds West Yorkshire LS1 1UR
Tel: 0113 224 3513 *Fax:* 0113 395 0475 *Dx:* 715295 LEEDS 33
Sol: Ahmed, Ms Shanaz Principal Legal Officer . . . . . May 2003
Allen, Ms Caroline LLB Head of Development and Regulatory Unit. . . . . Oct 1993
Backhouse, Mr George Dean LLB Solicitor . . . . . . Apr 2000
Benson, Ms Helen MA(Hons) Principal Legal Officer Member of West Yorkshire Probation Board. . . . . Nov 1994
Blackmore, Ms Karen Claire Solicitor . . . . May 1997
Boorman, Mr Stephen BA(Hons); CPE; DipLP Solicitor *Oct 1996
Briggs, Mrs Sheila M Principal Legal Officer. . . . . . May 1980
Byrne, Miss Maureen Ann BA Solicitor . . . . *Dec 1992
Collins, Miss Clare A LLB Solicitor. . . . . *Nov 1990
Davenport, Ms Elizabeth M Solicitor. . . . . Nov 1993
Des Forges, Mr Richard John . . . . Oct 1995
Eaton, Mr Andrew LLB Solicitor . . . . *Oct 1988
Edge, Lyndsay Solicitor . . . . Apr 2005
Feltham, Ms Katherine Jane CPE; LPC . . . . Aug 1996
Gaborak, Miss Ruth LLB Solicitor . . . . §Feb 1987
Gaskell, Miss Caroline Louise LLB Principal Legal Officer . . . . *Nov 1992
Gillen, Mr Gerard A BA(Hons) Solicitor . . . . *Jan 1999
Gledhill, Mrs Alex B A LLB(Hons) . . . . Oct 1992
Hameed, Mr Habib Rehman LLB(Hons) Solicitor. . . . Apr 2002
Hargreaves, Ms Joanne LLB Solicitor . . . . *Sep 2000
Hoare, Mrs Patricia LLB Principal Legal Officer . . . . Feb 1993
Hosking, Mr Andrew L Principal Legal Officer . . . . . Jul 1979
Jackson, Miss Theresa N BA(Law) Chief Legal Officer. Oct 1986
Kean, Mr Grahame Jonathan BA Deputy Monitoring Officer . . . . Jun 1981
Kelly, Mr Patrick LLB Section Head Property & Finance Section . . . . Jun 1998
Koshar, Mrs Safeena Solicitor. . . . . Nov 2000
Leonard, Miss Dagmar M A LLB Solicitor . . . . *Jan 1982
Lodder, Ms Janet BA Principal Legal Officer. . . . . . Dec 1987
Macey, Mr Derrick Victor Solicitor . . . . Oct 1996
McGuinness, Mr Terence LLB(Hons) Solicitor . . . . . *Jul 1978
Machin, Mr Andrew Solicitor. . . . . *Nov 1998
Mahmood, Mr Raja Umar . . . . *Jul 2004
Marshall, Mrs Gillian Section Head Housing Litigation . Feb 1996
Marshall, Mrs Helen M LLB Principal Legal Officer. . . . Oct 1978
Moran, Ms Marianne Solicitor . . . . Nov 1998
Murphy, Ms Nicola BA Solicitor . . . . Nov 1993
O'Shea, Miss Mary C LLB Section Head Employment, Education & General. . . . . Oct 1984
Oldroyd, Ms Anne E BA. . . . . *Oct 1984
Oxtoby, Miss Debra E M LLB; LLM; Law Society's Diploma Principal Legal Officer. . . . . *Oct 1986
Perry, Miss Helen L BA(Hons)(Law) Solicitor . . . . . Jan 2001
Pollard, Miss Anne-Marie LLB(Hons) Solicitor . . . . . Apr 2003
Roberts, Ms Rebbecca Dorra Solicitor. . . . . *Sep 1999
Sadler, Mrs Katherine N LLB Solicitor . . . . Oct 1996
Spafford, Mr Ian LLB(Hons); LLM Head of Community Services and Litigation . . . . *Jul 1976
Stringer, Miss Jacqueline V . . . . Apr 2000
Turnbull, Mr Mark J BA(Law) Head of Property Finance & Technology Unit. . . . . *Oct 1985
Turnock, Mr Stuart A BSc(Econ) Senior Assistant Chief Legal Officer . . . . §Jun 1976
Wade, Mr Robertson James. . . . . *Dec 1979
Weir, Ms Karen LLB(Hons)(Reading); Dip Local Government Principal Legal Officer. . . . . *Jan 1991

See p112 for the Key to Work Categories & other symbols

LEEDS METROPOLITAN UNIVERSITY
Leeds Law School Cloth Hall Court Quebec Street Leeds West Yorkshire LS1 2HA
Tel: 0113 812 9028 *Fax:* 0113 812 6092
E-mail: lawadmin@leedsmet.ac.uk
Sol: Creasey, Mr D Julian S BA(Oxon) Solicitor . . . . . *§Dec 1978
Sommerlad, Dr Hilary A K BA(Cantab); PGCE; DPhil Solicitor . . . . *Feb 1989
Tighe, Ms Maria E LLB Solicitor. . . . . *Jun 1975
Walker, Ms Bridget E M BA(Dunelm) Solicitor . . . . *Feb 1986

LEGAL SERVICES COMMISSION NO 9 (NORTH EASTERN)
Harcourt House Chancellor Court 21 The Calls Leeds West Yorkshire LS2 7EH
Tel: 0113 390 7300 *Dx:* 12068 LEEDS
Sol: Gaskell, Mr Mark A LLB(Newc) Solicitor. . . . . *Jan 1983
Heys, Miss Lorraine F P R BA Solicitor . . . . *Nov 1983
Lewis, Ms Justina BA; LLB Senior Legal Adviser . . . Oct 1996
Lloyd, Ms Rhiannon Astrid BSc Senior Legal Advisor . Oct 1994

ROYAL COLLEGE OF NURSING
Raven House 81 Clarendon Road Leeds West Yorkshire LS2 9PJ
Tel: 0113 244 3648
Sol: Catterall, Mrs Lucy Maria BSc(Hons) Solicitor . . . . *Sep 1993
Gardiner, Mr David N BA Solicitor. . . . . *Oct 1984
Hotchin, Mrs Susan Lynn BA(History); CPE; LSF Regional Solicitor. . . . . *Jan 1987
Houghton, Miss Lavinia Mary BA Solicitor. . . . . *Apr 1993

THISTLE HOTELS PLC
2 The Calls Leeds West Yorkshire LS2 7JU
Tel: 0113 243 9111 *Fax:* 0113 244 0238
Sol: Baxandall, Mrs Catherine Elizabeth MA(Oxon) Board Member of Yorkshire Youth & Music . . . . *Feb 1986

WEST YORKSHIRE PASSENGER TRANSPORT EXECUTIVE
Wellington House 40-50 Wellington Street Leeds West Yorkshire LS1 2DE
Tel: 0113 251 7436 *Fax:* 0113 251 7389
Sol: Daji, Mr Javid Ahmed LLB(Hons) Solicitor. . . . . *May 1999
Morrison, Mr Michael Edward Dip LG Secretary & Solicitor . . . . *Dec 1984
O'Connell, Mrs Alison M LLB(Hons) Solicitor . . . . *Aug 1982

YORKSHIRE ELECTRICITY GROUP PLC
Wetherby Road Scarcroft Leeds West Yorkshire LS14 3HS
Tel: 0113 289 2123 *Fax:* 0113 289 5611
Sol: Bean, Mr Richard T MBA Solicitor. . . . . *Dec 1981
Deebank, Ms Judith M LLB(Nott'm) Solicitor. . . . . *Oct 1988
Dickinson, Mr Roger LLB Group Secretary & Solicitor . *Jan 1976
Forrest, Chantal B LLB Solicitor. . . . . Jan 1989
Over, Mr John L BA Solicitor . . . . . *Jun 1977

LEEK, Staffordshire

AMOS DEVELOPMENTS LTD
Legal Office Barnfield Bradnop Leek Staffordshire ST13 7NN
Tel: 01588 266664 *Fax:* 01538 266828
Sol: Johnson, Mr William David LLB(Hons) Solicitor . . . . *Oct 1970

BRITANNIA BUILDING SOCIETY
Britannia House Cheadle Road Leek Staffordshire ST13 5RG
Tel: 01538 399399 *Fax:* 01538 399261 *Dx:* 16351 LEEK
Sol: Williams, Mr Stephen LLB(Lond) Chief Solicitor . . . . *Jun 1976

STAFFORDSHIRE MOORLANDS DISTRICT COUNCIL
Moorlands House Stockwell Street Leek Staffordshire ST13 6HQ
Tel: 01538 483483 *Fax:* 01538 387813 *Dx:* 16361 LEEK
Sol: Sherratt, Mrs Glynis Anne BA(Hons)(Law) Solicitor . . . *Jul 1977
Trillo, Mr Julian Mark LLB(Hons) Corporate Director & Monitoring Officer . . . . . *Jun 1993

LEICESTER

HM LAND REGISTRY - LEICESTER
Westbridge Place Leicester LE3 5DR
Tel: 0116 265 4000 / 4001 *Fax:* 0116 265 4008
Dx: 11900 LEICESTER 5
Sol: Brown, Mrs Frances M LLB Assistant Land Registrar .*Nov 1981
Goodfellow, Mrs Jackie LLB District Land Registrar . . *Apr 1981
Moore, Miss Elizabeth Anne BA(Hons) Assistant Land Registrar . . . . *Sep 1997
Oukellou, Miss Nadia BSc(Hons); CPE; LPC Solicitor / Assistant Land Registrar. . . . . *Sep 2003
Owen, Mrs Lesley A LLB Assistant Land Registrar . . *Oct 1982
Parker, Mr John V MA Assistant Land Registrar. . . . *Oct 1986

LETCHWORTH, Hertfordshire

NORTH HERTFORDSHIRE DISTRICT COUNCIL
Council Offices Gernon Road Letchworth Hertfordshire SG6 3JF
Tel: 01462 474000 *Fax:* 01462 474227 *Dx:* 31317 LETCHWORTH
Sol: White, Mrs Katherine Marie LLB Senior Lawyer . . . . Jul 2004

LEWES, East Sussex

EAST SUSSEX COUNTY COUNCIL
County Hall St Anne's Crescent Lewes East Sussex BN7 1SG
Tel: 01273 481000 *Fax:* 01273 473321 *Dx:* 97482 LEWES 3
Sol: Addison, Miss Yolanda K LLB(Hons) Litigation Lawyer. Jul 2005
Baker, Mr Philip James LLB(Hons) Solicitor . . . . . *Sep 1997
Boocock, Miss Verity Hanna Marie BSc(Hons); PGDipLaw Solicitor. . . . . *Sep 2001
Doran-Robinson, Miss Rachel Anne. . . . . May 1994
Grout, Mr Richard J LLB Senior Solicitor. . . . . *Sep 1987
Hauge, Mrs Joanna Caroline BA; DipLP. . . . . Feb 1998
Molloy, Mr Kevin J LLB Solicitor. . . . . *Sep 1997
Nelson, Mrs Ann Hilary LLB(Bris) Senior Solicitor . . *May 1976
Nicol, Mr Gregory Kenneth FILEx . . . . . Jan 2004
Ogden, Mr S Andrew LLB Director of Law. . . . . *Nov 1980
Reid, Mrs Angela K G Head of Legal Services. . . . *Jun 1971
Ruddock-West, Mr Jonathan BSc(Econ Pol) Assistant Director of Law. . . . . Aug 1982
Simmonds, Ms Johanne BSc(Hons); PGDipLaw Solicitor . . . . *Jun 2007
Tillman, Mrs Cathryn Maura BA(Hons) . . . . *Nov 1999
Wells, Mr Michael LLB Solicitor-Property & Contracts . *Nov 1986

LEYBURN, North Yorkshire

YORKSHIRE DALES NATIONAL PARK AUTHORITY
Yoredale Bainbridge Leyburn North Yorkshire DL8 3EL
Tel: 0870 166 6333 / 01969 652323 *Fax:* 01969 652399
E-mail: legal.services@yorkshiredales.org.uk
Sol: Bevan, Miss Clare Teresa BA(Hons) Senior Legal Officer . . . . *Oct 1995
Daly, Mr Richard Thomas MA(Oxon) . . . . *Nov 1982

LINCOLN, Lincolnshire

CITY OF LINCOLN COUNCIL
City Hall Beaumont Fee Lincoln Lincolnshire LN1 1DD
Tel: 01522 881188 *Fax:* 01522 521736
E-mail: legal@lincoln.gov.uk
Sol: Dawson, Mr Philip Solicitor . . . . . Jan 1984
Godison, Mrs Tamsin Margaret Solicitor. . . . . Oct 2001
Sinclair, Miss Rachel LLB(Hons) Solicitor . . . . *Jul 2004
Wheater, Mrs Carolyn Jane Legal Services Manager . *Jun 1994

LINCOLNSHIRE COUNTY COUNCIL RESOURCES - LEGAL SERVICES
County Offices Newland Lincoln Lincolnshire LN1 1YP
Tel: 01522 552222 *Fax:* 01522 552138 *Dx:* 701680 LINCOLN 5
Sol: Anwar, Mr Faisal LLB(Hons) Solicitor . . . . *Jun 1993
Burke, Mrs Sally Louise BA(Hons)(Law) Solicitor . . . *Feb 1986
Coleman, Mr David R BA Solicitor. . . . . *Nov 1990
Corby, Ms Nicola J LLB Solicitor. . . . . *Jul 1990
Crouch, Mrs Ruth A LLB(Hons); LSF Solicitor. . . . *Oct 1988
Drabble, Mr Richard A BA(Legal Studies) Solicitor. . *Dec 1980
Earle, Mrs Anne LLB Solicitor . . . . . Apr 2004
Granger, Miss Ruth Ellen LLB; LSF Solicitor. . . . *Jan 1999
Hanley, Mr Jeremy Clive LLB Solicitor. . . . . Mar 1988
Kerfoot, Mrs Helen Jane LLB(Hons) Solicitor . . . . *Nov 1993
Key, Miss Jane LLB(Hons) Natwest Prize For Law; Dean's Prize For Law Solicitor . . . . . Sep 2004
Middleton, Mr John Leigh BA(Hons). . . . . *Sep 1999
Reeve, Ms Elisabeth S J LLB(Hons) Solicitor . . . . *Feb 1989
Simpson, Mrs Claire R LLB Solicitor. . . . . *Dec 1997
Van der Feijst, Mrs Caroline G BA(Law) Solicitor . . . *Nov 1988
Walker, Mr Alan P LLB(Hons) Solicitor. . . . . *Jun 1974

LISKEARD, Cornwall

CARADON DISTRICT COUNCIL
Luxstowe House Liskeard Cornwall PL14 3DZ
Tel: 01579 341000 *Fax:* 01579 341220
Sol: Diggens, Mrs Marguerite V LLB(Hons)(Lond) Legal Member Services Manager. . . . . *Nov 1975
Keat, Mr Kingsley Robert LLB(Hons) Principle Lawyer (Litigation) . . . . *Aug 2001
Martin, Mrs Elizabeth Anne LLB(Hons) Solicitor . . . . *Aug 1995

LITTLEHAMPTON, West Sussex

ARUN DISTRICT COUNCIL
The Arun Civic Centre Maltravers Road Littlehampton West Sussex BN17 5LF
Tel: 01903 716133 *Fax:* 01903 730442 *Dx:* 57406 LITTLEHAMPTON
Sol: Johnson, Mr William A LLB . . . . . *Oct 1989
Jones, Delwyn LLB(Hons) Planning Solicitor. . . . . *Oct 1988

LIVERPOOL, Merseyside

CHARITY COMMISSION
20 Kings Parade Queens Dock Liverpool Merseyside L3 4DQ
Tel: 0151 703 1500 *Fax:* 0151 703 1557
Sol: Somerfield, Mr Peter W MA(Cantab); LLM Solicitor . *§Dec 1972

CROWN PROSECUTION SERVICE MERSEYSIDE
7th Floor Royal Liver Building Pier Head Liverpool Merseyside L3 1HN
Tel: 0151 239 6400 *Fax:* 0151 239 6410 *Dx:* 700596 LIVERPOOL 4
Sol: Holt, Mr John BA(Hons) Chief Crown Prosecutor . . . Oct 1978

ISLINGTON POTTERY & HOUSEWARES CO
Unit 8 & 9 Spitfire Avenue Speke Hall Road Liverpool Merseyside L24 9GQ
Tel: 0151 486 1888 *Fax:* 0151 486 1467
Sol: Endfield, Mr Anthony E LLB(Manc) Legal Adviser . . . *Jun 1978

LEGAL SERVICES COMMISSION REGIONAL OFFICE (MERSEYSIDE)
Cavern Court 8 Matthew Street Liverpool Merseyside L2 6RE
Tel: 0151 242 5200 *Fax:* 0151 242 5394 *Dx:* 14208 LIVERPOOL
E-mail: liverpool@legalservices.co.uk
Sol: Binks, Mr John Stephen LLB(Hons) Contract Manager. *Jan 1985
Gaskell, Mr Edmund Michael LLB(Hons) Solicitor . . . *Dec 1980

LIME PICTURES LIMITED
Campus Manor Childwall Abbey Road Liverpool Merseyside L16 0JP
Tel: 0151 722 9122 *Fax:* 0151 722 1969
E-mail: jbibby@limepictures.com
Sol: Bibby, Mrs Joanne M L LLB(Hons) Director of Legal & Business Affairs. . . . . *Dec 1986

THE LITTLEWOODS ORGANISATION PLC
100 Old Hall Street Liverpool Merseyside L70 1AB
Tel: 0151 235 3055 *Fax:* 0151 235 3151
Sol: Duggan, Mrs Fiona E R LLB Solicitor . . . . . Oct 1979
Hogarth, Mr Mark J B LLB Commercial Law Company Secretary . . . . *Nov 1979
Newall, Mr Alan LLB; Dip Wel Law Solicitor . . . . . *Oct 1978

LIVERPOOL 8 LAW CENTRE
34-36 Princes Road Toxteth Liverpool Merseyside L8 1TH
Tel: 0151 709 7222 *Fax:* 0151 708 8178
Sol: Simm, Mr Peter BA Solicitor. . . . . *Feb 1986

THE MERSEY DOCKS & HARBOUR CO
Maritime Centre Port of Liverpool Liverpool Merseyside L21 1LA
Tel: 0151 949 6000 *Fax:* 0151 949 6338
E-mail: sue.mcnicholl@merseydocks.co.uk
Sol: Bowley, Mr William J LLB(Bris) Group Director of Legal Services . . . . *May 1973
Chadwick, Mr Geoffrey M LLB Commercial Lawyer . . *Dec 1981
Hrynkiewicz, Z H BA Assistant Solicitor . . . . *Dec 1976
Marrison, Ms Caroline Ruth BA Solicitor. . . . . *Sep 2000

MERSEYSIDE POLICE
Police HQ PO Box 59 Canning Place Liverpool Merseyside L69 1JD
Tel: 0151 777 8080 *Fax:* 0151 777 8086
Sol: Clarke, Mr James LLB; MSc; PGCert Solicitor. . . . . Oct 1992
Leslie, Ms Maria LLB(Hons) Assistant Force Solicitor . Jun 2002
Mercer, Mrs Helen M LLB(L'pool) Force Solicitor. . . . Dec 1974
Vernon, Mr Peter LLB Deputy Force Solicitor . . . . . May 1990

ROYAL LIVER ASSURANCE LTD
Royal Liver Building Pier Head Liverpool Merseyside L3 1HT
Tel: 0151 236 1451 *Fax:* 0151 600 4349 *Dx:* 700595 LIVERPOOL 4
Sol: Gannon, Ms Cecilia M LLB(Hons) Head of Legal Department . . . . *Mar 1988
Kirrane, Mr Michael J P BA(Hons); Admitted in Ireland 1994 Assistant Solicitor. . . . . Jun 1997

UNISYS INSURANCE SERVICES LIMITED
101 Old Hall Street Liverpool Merseyside L3 9BD
Tel: 0151 328 2918 *Fax:* 0151 328 2976
Sol: Kent, Mr Patrick Dominic LLB(Hons) Solicitor (Agent Finance Litigation Unit) . . . . . *Nov 1993
Robinson, Mr Anthony Canice LLB(Hons) Solicitor / Legal Manager . . . . . *Jan 1980

VAUXHALL COMMUNITY LAW CENTRE
Vauxhall Multi Services Centre Silvester Street Liverpool Merseyside L5 8SE
Tel: 0151 482 2001 *Fax:* 0151 482 2057
Sol: Taylor, Mr David M Solicitor. . . . . Apr 1988

LLANDRINDOD WELLS, Powys

POWYS COUNTY COUNCIL
County Hall Spa Road East Llandrindod Wells Powys LD1 5LG
Tel: 01597 826000 *Fax:* 01597 826220
Sol: Edwards, Mr Colin BA(Hons)(Law) Solicitor . . . . . *Nov 1982
Foxley, Mrs Jayne Melanie BA(Hons); DipLG Solicitor. Jan 1994
Harris, Miss Elizabeth Kate LLB(Hons) Assistant Solicitor (Corporate) . . . . . Oct 2003
Kealey, Miss Janet Elizabeth ILEX; LPC Employee - In-house . . . . . Oct 2001
McVey, Miss Kirsten Craig LLB; PGDip (Practise at the Bar) Solicitor. . . . . Oct 2005
Meredith, Mr Clarence John LLB; DipLG; FCIS Head of Legal Scrutiny & Democratic Services. . . . . Jul 1990
Pinney, Mr Robert Clive LLB Solicitor . . . . . *Feb 1986
Tamboo, Miss Saira Osman LLB(Hons) Solicitor. . . . Nov 2005
Vaughan, Mr William Nigel P LLB(Hons) Solicitor Notary Public . . . . . Jan 1982

LLANDUDNO, Conwy

CLERK TO THE JUSTICES
The Courthouse Conwy Road Llandudno Conwy LL30 1GA
Tel: 01492 871333 *Fax:* 01492 872321 *Dx:* 11365 LLANDUDNO
Sol: Mahy, Mr Julian H Deputy Clerk to the Justices . . . . May 1981

LLANGEFNI, Anglesey

CYNGOR SIR YNYS MON (ISLE OF ANGLESEY COUNTY COUNCIL)
Council Offices Llangefni Anglesey LL77 7TW
Tel: 01248 750057 *Fax:* 01248 752132 *Dx:* 701771 LLANGEFNI
Sol: Ball, Miss Lynn LLB Director (Legal & Committee Services) . . . . . Apr 1992
Burnell, Mr Robert N BA; LLB Assistant Solicitor. . . . *Oct 1991
Gardner, Mr James L LLB County Solicitor . . . . . *Apr 1971
Hughes, Mr Owain Rhys LLB(Wales); DipLG Solicitor . *Oct 1986
Jones, Mr R Meirion LLB(L'pool) Solicitor For The Monitoring Officer . . . . . *Jul 1975
Lewis, Caren LLB Solicitor . . . . . Apr 1979
Roberts, Mr John Gwynedd LLB(Hons) Senior Solicitor *Jan 1981

LONG STRATTON, Norfolk

SOUTH NORFOLK DISTRICT COUNCIL
South Norfolk House Swan Lane Long Stratton Norfolk NR15 2XE
Tel: 01508 533633 *Fax:* 01508 533675
Dx: 130080 LONG STRATTON 2
E-mail: legal@s-norfolk.gov.uk
Sol: Eddison, Mrs Tamsin Principal Solicitor . . . . . Oct 2001
Phillips, Mrs Carolyn M LLB(Wales) Solicitor. . . . . *Jul 1977
Shortman, Mr Stuart Lockwood LLB(Bris) Solicitor to the Council Part-time Tribunal Judge . . . . . *§Apr 1979

LOUGHBOROUGH, Leicestershire

3M HEALTH CARE LTD
3M House 1 Morley Street Loughborough Leicestershire LE11 1EP
Tel: 01509 611611 *Fax:* 01509 237288
Sol: Brown, Mr Ian R BA Legal Adviser . . . . . *Sep 1990
Vann Jones, Mr Alfred D G Legal Adviser . . . . . . Sep 1999

CHARNWOOD BOROUGH COUNCIL
Southfields Loughborough Leicestershire LE11 2TX
Tel: 01509 263151 *Fax:* 01509 211703
Dx: 19628 LOUGHBOROUGH
Sol: Handford, Mrs Elizabeth LLB Solicitor . . . . *Dec 2000
Holland, Miss Anne E BA Assistant Solicitor. . . . . . *Jul 1984
Taylor, Mrs Christine E F LLB(Hons) Manager of Legal Services . . . . *Oct 1986

LOUTH, Lincolnshire

LOUTH TOWN COUNCIL
The Town Hall Eastgate Louth Lincolnshire LN11 9NL
Tel: 01507 617305 *Fax:* 01507 617305
E-mail: clerk@louthtowncouncil.gov.uk
Sol: Weir, Mr Frederick P DMA Town Clerk. . . . . *Jul 1979

LOWESTOFT, Suffolk

CLERK TO THE JUSTICES
Court House Old Nelson Street Lowestoft Suffolk NR32 1HJ
Tel: 01502 501060 *Fax:* 01502 513875 *Dx:* 41219 LOWESTOFT
Sol: Whomes, Mr Ivan Solicitor. . . . . Jan 1978

WAVENEY DISTRICT COUNCIL
Town Hall High Street Lowestoft Suffolk NR32 1HS
Tel: 01502 562111 *Fax:* 01502 589327 *Dx:* 41220 LOWESTOFT
Sol: Cox, Mr Peter R LLB Solicitor. . . . . *Nov 1986

LUDLOW, Shropshire

SOUTH SHROPSHIRE DISTRICT COUNCIL
The Shirehall Abbey Foregate Shrewsbury Shropshire SY2 6ND
Tel: 0345 678 9000
Sol: Ditton, Mr Simon Matthew BSc(Hons)(Law) Principal Solicitor . . . . *Nov 1989

LUTON, Luton

LUTON BOROUGH COUNCIL
Town Hall George Street Luton Luton LU1 2BQ
Tel: 01582 546000 *Fax:* 01582 546994 *Dx:* 5926 LUTON
Sol: Cormack, Mrs Mary Patricia LLB Principal Solicitor (Litigation) . . . . Dec 1984
Hill, Mrs Jennie K LLB(Lond) Solicitor . . . . *Mar 1976
Hussain, Mrs Farida Iasmin BSc(Hons) Solicitor. . . *Aug 2003
McDonald, Ms Alison LLB(Hons) Principal Solicitor . . Oct 1988
Mercer, Mrs Vivienne M LLB Principal Solicitor . . . *Apr 1975
Murphy, Miss Maria BA(Hons); Dip(Social Work); MA; PGDipLaw; PGDipLP Solicitor. . . . . *Jul 2003
Newman, Mr John R Solicitor . . . . *Sep 1977
Secker, Mr John F LLB(Sheff) Solicitor . . . . *May 1976
Sowah, Ms Vicky LLB; LLM Solicitor. . . . . Nov 2000
Stevens, Mr Richard J BA Borough Secretary. . . . . *§Oct 1979
Tobin, Mr Clive Henry Employee - In House Local Government . . . . Dec 2006
Tynan, Ms Nicole LLB(Hons) Solicitor . . . . Nov 1992
Vale, Mrs Brenda Christine Interim Principal Solicitor (Property & Planning) . . . . Jan 1998
Watson, Mr David John Solicitor. . . . . *Oct 2003

SOUTH BEDFORDSHIRE MAGISTRATES COURTS
Stuart Street Luton Luton LU1 5BL
Tel: 01582 524200 *Fax:* 01582 524252 *Dx:* 151660 LUTON 16
Sol: Wesson, Mr Andrew M Clerk to the Justices/Head of Legal Services - Bedfordshire . . . . *Feb 1976

VAUXHALL MOTORS LTD
Griffin House Osborne Road Luton Luton LU1 3YT
Tel: 01582 721122 *Fax:* 01582 427400
Sol: Benjamin, Mr Keith J LLB General Counsel . . . . . . *Apr 1982
Galvin, Mrs Lesley LLB(Nott'm) Assistant General Counsel . . . . *Nov 1985

LYNDHURST, Hampshire

NEW FOREST DISTRICT COUNCIL
Appletree Court Lyndhurst Hampshire SO43 7PA
Tel: 023 8028 5000 *Fax:* 023 8028 5543 *Dx:* 123010 LYNDHURST 2
Sol: Appleton, Mr Michael C LLB Solicitor . . . . *May 1981
Heaselden, Mrs Nathalie Burnett LLB(Hons) Solicitor *Mar 1999
O'Rourke, Grainne LLB(Hons) Head of Legal & Democratic Services . . . . *Oct 1993

LYTHAM, Lancashire

FYLDE BOROUGH COUNCIL
Town Hall Lytham Lancashire FY8 1LW
Tel: 01253 658658 *Fax:* 01253 713113
Sol: Curtis, Mr Ian K BA(Hons); Cert Mgmnt Unit Business Manager (Legal & Democratic Services) . . . . Oct 1988

LAND REGISTRY - LYTHAM OFFICE
Birkenhead House East Beach Lytham Lancashire FY8 5AB
Tel: 01253 849849 / 840012 *Fax:* 01253 840000
Dx: 14500 LYTHAM ST ANNES 3
Sol: Abbott, Miss Alison L LLB(Hons) Assistant Land Registrar . . . . *Nov 1996
Aldworth, Mr William LLB(Manc) Assistant Land Registrar . . . . *§Oct 1974
Hodgson, Ms Susan M BA Assistant Land Registrar. *Dec 1977
Withnell, Mr Marcus H BA; LLB Assistant Land Registrar . . . . *Nov 1991

MACCLESFIELD, Cheshire

ASTRAZENECA
Alderley House Alderley Park Macclesfield Cheshire SK10 4TF
Tel: 01625 582828 *Fax:* 01625 585618
Sol: Flitcroft, Miss Joanne LLM; MA(Cantab); LSF Senior Counsel . . . . Jan 1997
Gorecki, Mr Andrew Zenon BA(Hons)(Lond) Senior Counsel . . . . *Feb 1984
Hayward, Mr Andrew G BA(Oxon) Senior Counsel . . Nov 1991
McGillivray, Ms Shiona LLB(Hons); DipLP Senior Counsel . . . . Sep 1988
McIlveen, Mr William BA Senior Counsel . . . . *Oct 1989
Sherville-Payne, Mr Robert LLB; LLM Senior Counsel *Mar 1997

CIBA SPECIALTY CHEMICALS PLC
Charter Way Macclesfield Cheshire SK10 2NX
Tel: 01625 421933 *Fax:* 01625 615632
E-mail: ian.stewart@cibasc.com
Sol: Stewart, Mr Ian E F MA(Oxon) Company Secretary & Solicitor . . . . *Aug 1971
Wilkinson, Ms Rachel Anne BA(Law); ATT Solicitor . *Nov 1990

CHESHIRE EAST COUNCIL
Westfields Middlewich Road Sandbach Cheshire CW11 1HZ
Tel: 0300 123 5500
Sol: Horton, Mrs Vivienne Jean LLB(Hons) Chief Executive Apr 1981
Mault, Miss Nicola LLB(Hons) Planning Solicitor. . . . Sep 2000
Riordan, Miss Katharine LLB(Hons) Licensing Solicitor Jan 2004

MAIDENHEAD, Windsor & Maidenhead

COMMONWEALTH WAR GRAVES COMMISSION
2 Marlow Road Maidenhead Windsor & Maidenhead SL6 7DX
Tel: 01628 507137 *Fax:* 01628 507134
E-mail: legal@cwgc.org
Sol: Reddie, Mr Graham C Legal Adviser & Solicitor . . . *Dec 1975
Stedman, Miss Gillian S LLM Deputy Legal Adviser . . Oct 1978

COSTAIN ENGINEERING & CONSTRUCTION LTD
Costain House Nicholsons Walk Maidenhead Windsor & Maidenhead SL6 1LN
Tel: 01628 842444 *Fax:* 01628 842554
E-mail: tracey.wood@costain.com
Sol: Love, Mr Stephen BA(Hons)(Law) Legal Adviser. . . *Oct 1979
Starkey, Mr Paul Solicitor . . . . *Dec 1995
Wood, Miss Tracey Alison LLB Head Of Legal. . . . *Sep 1994

THE RANK GROUP PLC
Statesman House Stafferton Way Maidenhead Windsor & Maidenhead SL6 1AY
Tel: 01628 504000 *Fax:* 01628 504393
Sol: Cotton, Mr Andrew R LLB Licensing Solicitor . . . . *Sep 1984
Dumbleton, Mr John LLB Director of Legal Services. . *Jun 1972
Grant, Mr Thomas R BA Legal Adviser . . . . *Sep 2001
Howells, Mrs Rebecca LLB Legal Adviser . . . . . . *Sep 2001
Sabberton-Coe, Mr Richard LLB Senior Legal Adviser *Feb 1997

WINDSOR & MAIDENHEAD BOROUGH COUNCIL
Town Hall St Ives Road Maidenhead Windsor & Maidenhead SL6 1RF
Tel: 01628 798888 *Fax:* 01628 796408 *Dx:* 6422 MAIDENHEAD
Sol: Allen, Miss Tracy Ann LPC Solicitor. . . . . Nov 2002
Bowry, Ms Lorna Senior Solicitors Team Leader. . . . *Jul 1997
Felton, Ms Linda Planning Lawyer. . . . . Jan 2006
Hills, Miss Diana M MA(Cantab) Borough Secretary. *Sep 1980
Lunn, Mr David C OBE LLB(Bris) Chief Executive . . . *Apr 1970
McKinnon, Ms Amanda Sheona LLB(Hons) Contracts Lawyer . . . . Aug 1998
Pringle, Mrs Jayne Marie LLB(Hons) Senior Solicitor . *Oct 1990
Westhead, Miss Victoria LLM; BSc(Hons); PGDL Solicitor . . . . Nov 1974

WYETH
Huntercombe Lane South Taplow Maidenhead Windsor & Maidenhead SL6 0PH
Tel: 01628 604377 *Fax:* 01628 414869
Sol: Holgate, Mr Benjamin James Michael LLB(Hons) Legal Director . . . . *Sep 1992
Millard, Dr Rosemary A BSc(Hons); PhD Senior Legal Adviser . . . . Sep 1995
Varcoe-Cocks, Mr Michael D MA(Cantab) Senior Legal Advisor . . . . *Jan 1973

MAIDSTONE, Kent

KENT COUNTY COUNCIL
Legal & Democratic Services County Hall Sessions House Maidstone Kent ME14 1XQ
Tel: 01622 694320 *Fax:* 01622 694383 *Dx:* 123693 MAIDSTONE 6
E-mail: geoff.wild@kent.gov.uk
Sol: Barber, Ms Carolyn Solicitor (Social Services Group – Canterbury) . . . . Jan 1996
Chapman, Mr Trevor Senior Solicitor (Social Services Group-Canterbury). . . . . Feb 1991
Choudhury, Abdus Barrister Legal Advisor (Litigation) . Nov 1996
Clark, Mr Ian G MA(Cantab) Principal Solicitor. . . . *Jun 1972
Frankham, Mrs Frances M LLB Senior Solicitor . . . . *Jul 1985
Harrison, Mr Edward J Senior Solicitor . . . . *Oct 1980
Hoque, Ms Michelle Barrister . . . . Jul 2004
Ismail, Mrs Nasim. . . . . Nov 1988
Khroud, Miss Amandeep LLB; LLM . . . . Sep 2004
McCutcheon, Mrs Elizabeth Jane Gylby. . . . . Oct 1993
MacKenzie-Ingle, Ms Lucinda LLB(Hons) . . . . . . *Dec 1997
Maher, Ms Carmel LLB Solicitor (Social Services Group Cantrebury). . . . . Jan 1978
Mulholland, Mr Peter A LLB; MBA; MIL Principal Solicitor . . . . *Oct 1977
O'Connor, Miss Gail Maree BA; LLB Solicitor (Social Services Group- Canterbury) . . . . Aug 1995
Radford, Mr Mark BA Solicitor. . . . . *Sep 1991
Robinson, Ms Penelope Barrister Legal Adviser (Social Services Group) . . . . Jan 1986
Rummins, Mr Mark Stanley Senior Solicitor . . . . . . Dec 1980
Walsh, Mr Peter R BA(Kent); LLM(Lond) Senior Solicitor . . . . *Aug 1984
Wild, Mr Geoffrey D LLB; DipLG County Secretary . *Dec 1986

MAIDSTONE BOROUGH COUNCIL
Maidstone House King Street Maidstone Kent ME15 6JQ
Tel: 01622 602000 *Fax:* 01622 692246 *Dx:* 4819 MAIDSTONE
Sol: Bolas, Mrs Jayne E BA Senior Solicitor . . . . *Oct 1988
Fisher, Mr Stephen P BA Head of Corporate Law & Monitoring Officer . . . . *Dec 1980
Trueman, Mr Ian K BA Senior Solicitor . . . . *May 1981

STA INTERNATIONAL LTD T/A STA GRAYDON
Colman House King Street Maidstone Kent ME14 1DN
Tel: 01622 600900 *Fax:* 01622 600396
E-mail: admin@staonline.com
Sol: Yau, Mrs F Milhana LLB(Hons); LSF Solicitor . . . . *Sep 1992

MALDON, Essex

MALDON DISTRICT COUNCIL
Council Offices Princes Road Maldon Essex CM9 5DL
Tel: 01621 854477 *Fax:* 01621 852575
E-mail: simon.quelch@maldon.gov.uk
Sol: Quelch, Mr Simon J LLB Solicitor to the Council. . . *Sep 1983

MALTON, North Yorkshire

RYEDALE DISTRICT COUNCIL
Ryedale House Malton North Yorkshire YO17 0HH
Tel: 01653 600666 *Fax:* 01653 696801 *Dx:* 723621 MALTON 2
E-mail: name@ryedale.gov.uk
Sol: Brown, Mrs Fiona Bridget BA(Hons); LLB(Hons) Assistant Solicitor. *Nov 1999
Winship, Mr K Anthony LLB; DipLG; Dip PEL Council Solicitor . . . . *May 1990

MALVERN, Worcestershire

MALVERN HILLS DISTRICT COUNCIL
Council House Avenue Road Malvern Worcestershire WR14 3AF
Tel: 01684 862151 *Fax:* 01684 862473 *Dx:* 17608 MALVERN
Sol: Brain, Mrs Marjorie Anne MA(Cantab) Senior Solicitor. *Oct 1998
Jonsberg, Ms Lin Legal Services Manager. . . . . . *Nov 1994
Lester, Mrs Cheryl Caroline LLB Solicitor . . . . *Apr 2003
Snape, Mr Nigel E BA Sheffield Prize 1984 Head of Legal & Governance. . . . . *Dec 1986

MANCHESTER, Greater Manchester

CO-OPERATIVE INSURANCE SOCIETY LTD
CIS Building Miller Street Manchester Greater Manchester M60 0AL
Tel: 0161 832 8686 *Fax:* 0161 903 5957
Dx: 700001 MANCHESTER 6
Sol: Beattie, Ms Victoria LLB(Hons) Solicitor. . . . . Nov 1999
Conyers, Miss Joanne LLB; LSF Head of Employment*Nov 1992
Hopley, Miss Prudence Katie LLB(Hons) Head of Litigation . . . . *Jan 1990
Hurd, Mrs Joanna Elaine LLB; MSc Solicitor. . . . . Oct 1996
Jones, Ms Amanda Solicitor. . . . . Oct 2001
Kerns, Mr Peter William Director of Legal Services . *May 1979
Machin, Mr Robert James BA(Hons); DipLaw; DipLP Commercial Solicitor . . . . Oct 2004
McKeating, Miss Colette LLB(Hons). . . . . *May 1990
Manfield-Cooke, Mrs Christine E BA(Hons) . . . . . *Oct 1982
Parsons, Mr Christopher Jonathan MA Head of Insurance Contract & Commercial . . . . *Oct 1990
Poulton, Miss Susan M BA(Law) . . . . *Jun 1984
Prescott, Mrs Karen E BA(Hons)(Law) Sweet & Maxwell Law Prize . . . . *Nov 1995
Reynolds, Ms Olga M LLB(Hons) . . . . *Mar 1985
Severs, Mr David J A LLB Assistant Solicitor Magistrate . . . . *Mar 1976
Taylor, Mr Paul Prys LLB(Hons); LPC Commercial Solicitor . . . . Sep 2001
Wells, Mr Samuel J LLB(Hons) . . . . *Feb 1986

CO-OPERATIVE WHOLESALE SOCIETY LTD
PO Box 53 New Century House Manchester Greater Manchester M60 4ES
Tel: 0161 834 1212 *Fax:* 0161 834 3147
Sol: Eyre, Mr Nicholas A MA. . . . . *Oct 1983

COOPERATIVE BANK PLC
PO Box 101 1 Balloon Street Manchester Greater Manchester M60 4EP
Tel: 0161 832 3456 *Fax:* 0161 903 5956
Dx: 700003 MANCHESTER 6
Sol: James, Mrs Sally-Ann BA(Hons); LSF Head of Bank Commercial. *Nov 1986
Kerns, Mr Peter William Director of Legal Services . *May 1979
Moulden, Ms Valerie J Contract Solicitor. . . . . Mar 2001

EQUALITY & HUMAN RIGHTS COMMISSION
Arndale House Arndale Centre Manchester Greater Manchester M4 3AQ
Tel: 0161 829 8100 *Fax:* 01925 884000
Sol: Davies, Miss Chantal M LPC Principal Legal Officer. . Sep 1998
Hewitt, Ms Wendy LLB(Hons) Principal Legal Officer . Oct 1994
Hockney, Miss Clare J BA(Hons) Principal Legal Solicitor . . . . *Dec 1995
Lakin, Mr James A MA(Cantab) Legal Adviser. . . . *Dec 1974
Slater, Ms Hilary Jane MA(Hons)(Cantab) Principal Legal Officer . . . . *Dec 1988

FEDERAL-MOGUL CORPORATION
Manchester International Office Style Road Trafford Park Manchester Greater Manchester M22 5TN
Tel: 0161 955 5200 *Fax:* 0161 955 5203
Sol: Turner, Mr Jeremy D LLB Solicitor. . . . . *Dec 1989

G U S HOME SHOPPING LTD
Universal House Devonshire Street Manchester Greater Manchester M60 6EL
Tel: 0161 277 4708 *Fax:* 0161 277 4952
Sol: Harland, Mr Philip F LLB Associate Director Legal Affairs . . . . *§Mar 1981

See p112 for the Key to Work Categories & other symbols

GREATER MANCHESTER CPS
8th Floor Sunlight House PO Box 237 Manchester Greater Manchester M60 3PS
Tel: 0161 827 4700 *Fax:* 0161 827 4932
Dx: 710288 MANCHESTER 3
Sol: Holt, Mr John BA(Hons). . . . . Oct 1978

GREATER MANCHESTER PASSENGER TRANSPORT EXECUTIVE
2 Piccadilly Place Manchester Greater Manchester M1 3BG
Tel: 0161 242 6000 *Fax:* 0161 228 3291
E-mail: publicity@gmpte.gov.uk
Sol: Tristram, Mr Timothy H LLB; MCIT Director (Monitoring & Corporate Services). . . . . *Nov 1973

INFOGRAMES UNITED KINGDOM LTD
9th Floor Landmark House Hammersmith Bridge Road London W6 9EJ
Tel: 020 8222 9700 *Fax:* 020 8222 9858
Sol: Cooper, Mrs Sally MA(Cantab); RTMA; MITMA FRSA. *Nov 1979
Peel, Mr Tim LLB Solicitor. . . . . Apr 1998

KELLOGG MANAGEMENT SERVICES (EUROPE) LTD
The Kellogg Building Talbot Road Manchester Greater Manchester M16 0PU
Tel: 0161 869 2000 *Fax:* 0161 869 2713
Sol: Ainley, Mr Jonathan Nigel BA(Dunelm) Director Legal Affairs Europe . . . . . *Feb 1986
Goodman, Mr Benjamin Gordon LLB; LPC Legal Adviser UK & ROI. . . . . *Oct 2000

LEGAL AID AREA OFFICE NO 7 (NORTH WESTERN)
Lee House 90 Great Bridgewater Street Manchester Greater Manchester M1 5JW
Tel: 0845 602 1400 *Dx:* 14343 MANCHESTER 2
Sol: Barnshaw, Mr Frank S BA(Dunelm) Solicitor. . . . . *Feb 1969
Bartram, Mr Robert LLB Solicitor . . . . . *Oct 1980
Thompson, Mr Geoffrey J LLB(Lond) Group Manager . *Dec 1968

THE MANCHESTER AIRPORT GROUP PLC
Manchester Airport Manchester Greater Manchester M90 1QX
Tel: 0871 271 0711 *Fax:* 0161 489 2257
Sol: Connor, Mr Frank PGDipLaw Group Legal Services Manager . . . . . Dec 2003
Purdy, Mr Geoffrey ILEX; HNC(Public Administration) Group Legal Services Manager. . . . . May 1999
Robertson, Mrs Sonita Ann Group Legal Advisor(Property) . . . . . Oct 2000
Terry, Miss Emma Louise Corporate Counsel - Head of Group Legal . . . . . Oct 1995

MANCHESTER CITY COUNCIL
Town Hall Albert Square Manchester Greater Manchester M60 2LA
Tel: 0161 234 5000 *Fax:* 0161 234 3207
Dx: 714441 MANCHESTER 2
Sol: Ackers, Ms June BA Principal Solicitor . . . . . *Apr 1987
Baker, Ms Teresa A Principal Solicitor. . . . . Apr 1976
Bosiaki, Ms Angela . . . . . Sep 1996
Carlton, Ms Erica . . . . . Dec 1994
Curtis, Ms Louise Francis LLB Solicitor . . . . . *Oct 1993
Dearing, Mr Michael. . . . . Apr 1996
Evans, Mr Jonathan K. . . . . Mar 1991
Gardner, Mr Desmond Robert BSc(Hons) . . . . . Nov 1995
Howells, Mrs Elizabeth LLB . . . . . Oct 1988
Karkera, Ms Poornima LLB . . . . . Dec 1985
Lund, Mr John R Assistant City Solicitor. . . . . Oct 1977
McCarrigle, Ms Colette C . . . . . Oct 1990
Miller, Ms Helen BA(Hons) Solicitor . . . . . Nov 1996
Orrell, Mrs Susan A LLB City Solicitor. . . . . *Apr 1972
Pearson, Mr David A . . . . . Oct 1993
Ransley, Mrs Olivia T P C BA(York) Principal Solicitor . *Oct 1985
Skipworth, Mr Timothy Lee MA(Oxon); DipLG Law Soc Local Government Group Trust Fund Prize 1992 Principal Solicitor . . . . . *Jul 1990
Smith, Ms Katherine M Solicitor. . . . . Sep 1996
Suringar, Ms Moira BA; MA Acting Assistant City Solicitor . . . . . *Apr 1979
Tierney, Ms Celia BA . . . . . Sep 1993
Treacy, Ms Elizabeth J LLB Principal Solicitor . . . . . *Jul 1984

CITY OF MANCHESTER MAGISTRATES' COURTS
Crown Square Manchester Greater Manchester M60 1PR
Tel: 0161 832 7272 *Fax:* 0161 832 5421
Sol: Todd, Mrs Jacqueline LLB; LLM Head of Legal ServicesFeb 1991

NCC GROUP
Manchester Technology Centre Oxford Road Manchester Greater Manchester M1 7ED
Tel: 0161 209 5200 *Fax:* 0161 209 5100
E-mail: felicity.brandwood@nccglobal.com
Sol: Brandwood, Mrs Felicity M BA(Hons)(Dunelm) Solicitor/ Company Secretary. . . . . *Sep 1982
Conlon, Miss Eileen Solicitor . . . . . *Oct 2001
Hill, Mrs Gillian Elizabeth Senior Solicitor . . . . . Sep 1995

ODEON & UCI CINEMAS
Lee House 90 Great Bridgewater Street Manchester Greater Manchester M1 5JW
Tel: 0161 455 4000 *Fax:* 0161 455 4076
Sol: Barr, Miss Samantha BA Legal Counsel. . . . . Sep 1997
Jagannath, Vidya BA; LLM Legal Counsel - UK & Ireland . . . . . Oct 1993

PEEL MANAGEMENT LIMITED
Peel Dome The Trafford Centre Manchester Greater Manchester M17 8PL
Tel: 0161 629 8200 *Fax:* 0161 629 8332
Sol: Hayes, Mr Neil Hanson LLB(Manc) Solicitor. . . . . *Oct 1991
Hosker, Mr Peter J LLB . . . . . *Apr 1981
Phillpotts, Miss Beverley A LLB . . . . . *Mar 1984
Straughton, Mrs Catherine L Solr . . . . . *Sep 1998

SOUTH MANCHESTER LAW CENTRE
584 Stockport Road Longsight Manchester Greater Manchester M13 0RQ
Tel: 0161 225 5111 *Fax:* 0161 225 0210
Sol: Ismail, Ms Sajida LLB; MA Solicitor . . . . . Aug 1992
Leung, Mr Koleman LLB(Hons) Caseworker. . . . . *Jan 1993

WYTHENSHAWE LAW CENTRE
260 Brownley Road Wythenshawe Manchester Greater Manchester M22 5EB
Tel: 0161 498 0905 *Fax:* 0161 498 0906
Sol: Graham, Mr John David BA(Oxon) Solicitor . . . . . Nov 1978
Hodges, Mrs Gillian LLB(Hons) Solicitor. . . . . Jul 1999

MANSFIELD, Nottinghamshire

MANSFIELD DISTRICT COUNCIL
Civic Centre Chesterfield Road South Mansfield Nottinghamshire NG19 7BH
Tel: 01623 463463 *Fax:* 01623 463900
E-mail: jburton@mansfield.gov.uk
Sol: Burton, Mr John Richard BA(Lond) Solicitor to the Council & Monitoring Officer. . . . . *Dec 1980
Neely, Mr Richard G D MA; LLB Assistant Solicitor . . *Mar 1981

MANSFIELD MAGISTRATES COURT
HM Courts' Service The Court House Rosemary Street Mansfield Nottinghamshire NG19 6EE
Tel: 01623 451500 *Fax:* 01623 451648 *Dx:* 179560 MANSFIELD 9
Sol: Hope, Mr Stuart William LLB Deputy Clerk to the Justices . . . . . Jan 1992
Rodgerson, Ms Ann LLB Senior Legal Adviser. . . . . Jan 1999

MARCH, Cambridgeshire

FENLAND DISTRICT COUNCIL
Fenland Hall County Road March Cambridgeshire PE15 8NQ
Tel: 01354 654321 *Fax:* 01354 606914 *Dx:* 30955 MARCH
Sol: Kang, Mr Amerjit Singh BA(Hons) Head of Legal Services . . . . . *Mar 1988
Murillo, Miss Antonia BA(Hons); MSc; DipLG Solicitor . *Nov 1991

MIDDLE LEVEL COMMISSIONERS
Middle Level Offices Dartford Road March Cambridgeshire PE15 8AF
Tel: 01354 653232 *Fax:* 01354 659619
E-mail: admin@middlelevel.gov.uk
Sol: Smith, Mr Iain A D BA(Law) Clerk & Chief Executive to the Commissioners Clerk to Internal Drainage Boards *§Jan 1981

MARGATE, Kent

THANET DISTRICT COUNCIL
Council Offices Cecil Street Thanet Margate Kent CT9 1XZ
Tel: 01843 577000 *Fax:* 01843 577536 *Dx:* 30555 MARGATE
Sol: Borley, Mr Peter W LLB Head of Member and Democratic Services/Monitoring Officer . . . . . *Dec 1980
Davies, Mr Alun J Assistant Solicitor. . . . . *§Feb 1979
Mapplebeck, Mr Barrie H LLB Senior Solicitor. . . . . *May 1987
Reilly, Mr Peter Joseph BA Assistant Solicitor . . . . . *Oct 1995

MARKET DRAYTON, Shropshire

DANBANK DEVELOPMENT LTD
Estate Office Old Spring Hall Market Drayton Shropshire TF9 2PE
Tel: 01630 658282 *Dx:* 26936 MARKET DRAYTON
Sol: Ward, Ms Christine M Solicitor. . . . . Jan 1966

MARKET HARBOROUGH, Leicestershire

HARBOROUGH DISTRICT COUNCIL
Council Offices Adam & Eve Street Market Harborough Leicestershire LE16 7AG
Tel: 01858 821341 *Fax:* 01858 821336
Dx: 27317 MARKET HARBOROUGH
Sol: Lander, Mr Hugh William LLB(Lond) Conveyancing Solicitor . . . . . *§Dec 1973
Roberts, Mrs Susan BA(Hons) Assistant Solicitor . . . May 2003

JS LAW
37 The Point Market Harborough Leicestershire LE16 7QU
Tel: 0870 380 4000 *Fax:* 0870 755 3270
Sol: Smith, Mr Jeremy . . . . . Jan 1989

MATLOCK, Derbyshire

DERBYSHIRE COUNTY COUNCIL
County Hall Smedley Street Matlock Derbyshire DE4 3AG
Tel: 01629 580000 *Fax:* 01629 538326
E-mail: john.mcelvaney@derbyshire.gov.uk
Sol: Amey, Mrs Natalie LLB Solicitor. . . . . Jun 2004
Blackburn, Mr David Solicitor . . . . . Feb 2006
Bloor, Miss Jeanette LLB Senior Solicitor . . . . . Jan 2001
Boyle, Miss Sarah Solicitor . . . . . May 2007
Brent, Mr Stephen LLB Senior Solicitor . . . . . Feb 1991
Brewin, Mrs Lisa Solicitor . . . . . Oct 2000
Carter, Mr Kevin Solicitor . . . . . Sep 2001
Collins, Mrs Jacqueline W BA(Dunelm) Assistant Director of Legal Services . . . . . *Oct 1985
Cruise, Mr Robert Solicitor . . . . . Oct 2008
Edwards, Mrs Lisa Solicitor . . . . . Apr 2003
Fairman, Mrs Mary Solicitor. . . . . Jan 1990
Gembali, Mrs Madhuri Solicitor . . . . . Aug 1996
Lakin, Miss Jane Elizabeth LLB(Hons) Principal Solicitor . . . . . *Nov 1994
McElvaney, Mr John LLB Director of Legal Services. . *Oct 1981
Nanner, Mr Billy LLB(Hons) Solicitor. . . . . *Mar 1992
Needham, Miss Hayley Solicitor. . . . . Dec 2008
Olney, Miss Linzi Solicitor . . . . . Nov 2007
Peat, Mr Paul G DipLP Principal Solicitor . . . . . *Nov 1996
Riley, Mrs Karen D BA; LLB Assistant Director of Legal Services . . . . . *Oct 1988
Roberts, Ms Rebecca Jane Senior Solicitor . . . . . Nov 1996
Roberts, Miss Sinead Solicitor. . . . . Jul 2006
Scully, Miss Paula Solicitor . . . . . Oct 1994
Sharma, Miss Monica Solicitor. . . . . Jul 1999
Taylor, Louisa Senior Solicitor. . . . . Nov 1991
Tingle, Mrs Elizabeth Clare LLB(Hons); Dip Gov Senior Solicitor . . . . . Sep 1983
Waterhouse, Ms Leanne Solicitor . . . . . Apr 1995
Wild, Miss Elizabeth Jane LLB Solicitor . . . . . Dec 2000

DERBYSHIRE DALES DISTRICT COUNCIL
Town Hall Bank Road Matlock Derbyshire DE4 3NN
Tel: 01629 761100 *Fax:* 01629 761307
Sol: Cooper, Mr Reginald S J BA(Hons) . . . . . *Aug 1989

MELKSHAM, Wiltshire

AVON RUBBER PLC
Hampton Park West Semington Road Melksham Wiltshire SN12 6NB
Tel: 01225 896800 *Fax:* 01225 896898
E-mail: peter.fairbairn@avon-rubber.com
Sol: Fairbairn, Mr Peter J BA(Hons) Company Secretary. . *Jun 1976
Ingrey-Counter, Mr Miles LLB(Hons) Assistant Group Legal Advisor . . . . . *Sep 2000

MELTON MOWBRAY, Leicestershire

MELTON BOROUGH COUNCIL
Council Offices Nottingham Road Melton Mowbray Leicestershire LE13 0UL
Tel: 01664 502502 *Fax:* 01664 410283 *Dx:* 722422 MELTON 6
E-mail: reception@melton.gov.uk
Sol: Hudson, Mrs Deborah Stacey BA(Hons); DipLG; CMS Head of Legal Services, Monitoring Officer. . . . . Jan 1979
Nanner, Mr Billy LLB(Hons) Principal Solicitor . . . . . *Mar 1992

MERTHYR TYDFIL

DWR CYMRU CYF
Pentwyn Road Nelson Merthyr Tydfil CF46 6LY
Tel: 01443 425627 *Fax:* 01443 425756
E-mail: peter.t.jones@dwrcymru.com
Sol: Jones, Mr Thomas Peter LLB Legal Business Manager*Oct 1978
Thorpe, Mrs Christine Solicitor. . . . . Jan 2000

MERTHYR TYDFIL COUNTY BOROUGH COUNCIL
Civic Centre Castle Street Merthyr Tydfil CF47 8AN
Tel: 01685 725000 *Fax:* 01685 725060
E-mail: pauline.dorricott@merthyr.gov.uk
Sol: Ballinger, Mr Peter Assistant Solicitor . . . . . *Dec 1991
Bow, Mrs Rebecka Louisa LPC Solicitor. . . . . Nov 2003
Chapman, Mr Gareth Wayne LLM; DBA; DipLG; FCIM Deputy Chief Executive and Director of Customer Corporate Services . . . . . *Dec 1988
Donnelly, Miss Frances Linda LLB(Hons); LPC Solicitor . . . . . *Dec 2006
Jones, Mr Simon David BSc(Hons)(Combined Sciences); LSF Solicitor. . . . . *Jan 1995
Kennedy, Miss Carys M LLB(Hons) Solicitor. . . . . *Sep 1988
Morgan, Mr Geraint LLB(Hons) Assistant Solicitor. . *Nov 2002

MERTHYR TYDFIL MAGISTRATES COURT
Law Courts Glebeland Place Merthyr Tydfil CF47 8BU
Tel: 01685 721731 *Fax:* 01685 723919
Sol: Burge, Ms Kerrie LLB(Wales) Solicitor. . . . . *Sep 1990

MIDDLESBROUGH

MIDDLESBROUGH COUNCIL
Town Hall PO Box 99A Middlesbrough TS1 2QQ
Tel: 01642 245432 *Fax:* 01642 729888
Dx: 60532 MIDDLESBROUGH
Sol: Caveney, Mr Michael LLM; LLB Solicitor. . . . . Nov 2005
Chisholm, Mrs Marguerite Principal Solicitor (Property & Regeneration). . . . . Jan 1998
Cunningham, Mrs Catherine Louise Northumbrian Water Property Solutions Prize 2003 Solicitor . . . . . Dec 2003
Dewar-Finch, Ms Sue BA Senior Solicitor . . . . . Nov 1994
Hill, Ms Maria Ann LLB(Hons) Solicitor . . . . . Feb 1996
Long, Mr Richard G Director of Legal & Democratic Services . . . . . *Dec 1980
Metcalfe, Ms Katharine Elizabeth BA; LLB Solicitor . . Sep 2001
Roberts, Mr Bryn BSc; LLM Solicitor. . . . . *Oct 1998
Robson, Mr Graham L LLB Principal Solicitor . . . . . *Jun 1977
Thompson, Ms Jeanette Louise BA(Hons) Principal Solicitor . . . . . Sep 1995
Vickers, Mr Stephen G Solicitor . . . . . *Jan 1972
Wright, Mr Noel E LLB Senior Solicitor . . . . . *Nov 1981

REDCAR AND CLEVELAND BOROUGH COUNCIL
Town Hall Fabian Road South Bank Redcar Redcar & Cleveland TS6 9AR
Tel: 01642 466201 *Fax:* 01642 444578 *Dx:* 60041 NORMANBY
Sol: Dooris, Mrs Rachel LLB(Hons); DipLG; GradICSA Head of Legal Services . . . . . *Jan 1997
Frankland, Mr Richard J LLB(L'pool) Assistant Chief Executive (Legal & Democratic Services) . . . . . *Jul 1979
Graham, Mrs Caroline E LLB Senior Solicitor (Community Safety) . . . . . *Oct 1999
Newton, Mr Steven K CPE; LPC Law Society Prize for Outstanding Performance on LPC Senior Legal Officer . . . . . Nov 2006
Tompkinson, Mr Gerard F LLB(L'pool) Senior Solicitor. . *Dec 1986
Wilson, Mr Keith LLB Procurement Lawyer . . . . . *Nov 1981
Wilson, Miss Lesley LLB(Hons); MBA Senior Solicitor (Litigation & General) . . . . . *Apr 1993
Youngs, Mrs Joanne LPC Solicitor. . . . . Nov 2005

MIDDLETON, Greater Manchester

BRITISH VITA PLC
Oldham Road Middleton Greater Manchester M24 2DB
Tel: 0161 643 1133 *Fax:* 0161 655 3957
Sol: Parry, Mrs Catherine Jane LLB Solicitor. . . . . *Sep 1994
Stirzaker, Mr Mark R BA(Kent) Company Secretary & Solicitor . . . . . *Jun 1980

MILDENHALL, Suffolk

FOREST HEATH DISTRICT COUNCIL
District Offices College Heath Road Mildenhall Suffolk IP28 7EY
Tel: 01638 719000 *Fax:* 01638 716493
E-mail: info@forest-heath.gov.uk
Sol: Burnip, Mr David W BA Chief Executive . . . . *Dec 1975
Heard, Mr Peter BA(Hons) Solicitor . . . . *Oct 1983

MILTON KEYNES

DAIMLER CHRYSLER UK LTD
Tongwell Milton Keynes MK15 8BA
Tel: 01908 245000 *Fax:* 01908 245086
Sol: Evans, Ms Chrissi R LLB General Counsel . . . . . . *Jan 1990
Palmer, Mrs Jill Frances BSocSc General Manager Customer Services . . . . Sep 1994

ENGLISH PARTNERSHIPS
Central Business Exchange 414-428 Midsummer Boulevard Milton Keynes MK9 2EA
Tel: 01908 692692 *Fax:* 01908 353771 *Dx:* 31410 MILTON KEYNES
Sol: Roberts, Ms Judith M P BA(Essex) Head of Legal Services . . . . Aug 1978

INSTITUTE OF CHARTERED ACCOUNTANTS IN ENGLAND & WALES
Level 1 Metropolitan House 321 Avebury Boulevard Milton Keynes MK9 2FZ
Tel: 01908 248100 *Fax:* 01908 248088 *Dx:* 31427 MILTON KEYNES
E-mail: generalenquiries@icaew.com
Sol: Jowett, Mr Benjamin LLB(Hons) Senior Legal Adviser *Feb 1991
Peto, Miss Lisa Maria DML; LPC; PSC Legal Adviser . *Oct 1994
Williams, Ms Ann BA(Hons); LLB Deputy Head of Legal Services Dept. . . . . *Nov 1992

MILTON KEYNES COUNCIL
Saxon Court 502 Avebury Boulevard Milton Keynes MK9 3HS
Tel: 01908 691691 *Fax:* 01908 252600 *Dx:* 31406 MILTON KEYNES
Sol: Ali, Mr Iftakhar Principal Lawyer. . . . . *Feb 1997
Oxbury, Ms Charlotte N LLB. . . . . *Oct 1992
Wright, Ms D Christa MA; B Phil Group Solicitor. . . . *Jan 1989

MOBIL OIL COMPANY LTD
Mobil House 500-600 Witan Gate Milton Keynes MK9 1ES
Tel: 01908 853000 *Fax:* 01908 853966
Dx: 84764 MILTON KEYNES 3
Sol: Nash, Mr Stephen R LLB(Manc) Solicitor . . . . . . *Mar 1977
Stephen, Mr Kenneth G LLB Solicitor . . . . *Sep 1989

MOLINS PLC
11 Tanners Drive Blakelands Milton Keynes MK14 5LU
Tel: 01908 219000 *Fax:* 01908 216499
Sol: Cannon, Mrs Sara BA(Hons) Director of Legal Affairs & Company Secretary. . . . . *Oct 1988

TAYLOR WIMPEY UK LIMITED LEGAL SERVICES
Second Floor Beech House 551 Avebury Boulevard Milton Keynes MK9 3DR
Tel: 01908 209030 *Fax:* 01908 209035
Dx: 31426 MILTON KEYNES 1
Sol: Campbell, Mr Michael Robert BA(Hons) Solicitor . . . *Jan 1988
Carr, Mr Peter A LLB(Wales); Sol Sup Ct of NSW Aust (Sept 1982) Legal Director . . . . *Sep 1980
Dore, Mr Michael J LLB Solicitor. . . . . *Dec 1973
Griffiths, Miss Catherine J LLB(L'pool) Solicitor . . . *Dec 1978
Rayner, Miss Alison W BA Solicitor . . . . *Oct 1983

MOLD, Flintshire

FLINTSHIRE COUNTY COUNCIL
County Hall Mold Flintshire CH7 6NR
Tel: 01352 702411 *Fax:* 01352 700289 *Dx:* 708590 MOLD 4
E-mail: legal@flintshire.gov.uk
Sol: Davies, Mr Barry C LLB Solicitor to the Council . . . . May 1975
Davies, Mr David M LLB Solicitor to the Council. . . *Dec 1982
Evans, Mr Peter J LLB(Wales) Assistant Director . . . Jan 1979
Fletcher, Mrs Mary Caroline MA Solicitor . . . . Oct 1989
Gaskell, Mr John Damian LLB; PGDip Solicitor . . . . . Dec 2003
Hanrahan, Ms Margaret E BSc; LLM Solicitor . . . . . Dec 1978
Humphreys, Mr Robert M BA(Hons) Solicitor . . . . . . Feb 1989
Jones, Miss Anwen BA(Hons)(Law) Corporate Solicitor*Jun 1984
Jones, Ms Sian LLB(Hons) Solicitor. . . . . Nov 1994
Pedreschi, Miss Louise LLB(Hons) Solicitor . . . . . *Dec 1995
Tomlinson, Ms Bryony Jane BA; PGDL Solicitor. . . . Aug 2002
Vernon, Miss Bethan Jane Morris LLB(Hons) Solicitor *Dec 1994
Williams, Mr Richard G LLB Solicitor . . . . Oct 1990

MORPETH, Northumberland

CASTLE MORPETH BOROUGH COUNCIL
Council Offices Longhirst Hall Longhirst Morpeth Northumberland NE61 3LR
Tel: 01670 535000 *Fax:* 01670 794764
Sol: Lancaster, Ms Helen LLB Solicitor. . . . . *Jan 1995

NORTHUMBERLAND COUNTY COUNCIL
County Hall Morpeth Northumberland NE61 2EF
Tel: 01670 533000 *Fax:* 01670 533238
Sol: Bailey, Mrs Barbara A BA(Hons)(Law) Assistant Solicitor . . . . *Jun 1982
Elcoate, Mrs Heather Lindsey BA(Hons) Solicitor . . . Jan 1986
Hussain, Ms Saeeda Gohar LSF Assistant Solicitor . . *Jul 1994
Iley, Mrs Marilyn Ruth BA(Law) Maxwell Law Prize Principal Solicitor (Childcare) . . . . *Apr 1981
James, Mr John P G LLB(Hons); LLM Assistant Solicitor . . . . Oct 1991
Mellish, Mr Mark W BA(Hons) Assistant Solicitor . . . Jan 1990
Middleton, Ms Alison BA(Hons); LLB Solicitor . . . . . Nov 2004
Moore, Mrs Susan M LLB(Hons) Assistant Solicitor . . Sep 1997
Murray, Miss Carmel LLB(Hons) Solicitor . . . . Sep 2003
Rickitt, Mr Stephen E LLB; DPA Principal Solicitor (Environment, Regeneration & Procurement). . . . . *Nov 1981
Stewart, Miss Melissa Fay BA(Hons) Solicitor. . . . . *Apr 2001

Tilson, Mr Peter BA Assistant Solicitor. . . . . *§Feb 1981
Watts, Mr Peter LLB Legal and Administrative Services Manager . . . . *Jun 1981

NEATH, Neath Port Talbot

NEATH PORT TALBOT MAGISTRATES' COURT
Magistrates' Clerks Office Fairfield Way Neath Neath Port Talbot SA11 1RF
Tel: 01639 765900 *Fax:* 01639 765954
Sol: Hehir, Mr James Pascal F BA; MBA Solicitor . . . . *Feb 1984

NELSON, Lancashire

PENDLE BOROUGH COUNCIL
Town Hall Market Street Nelson Lancashire BB9 7LG
Tel: 01282 661661 *Fax:* 01282 661630 *Dx:* 14669 NELSON
E-mail: legal@pendle.gov.uk
Sol: Culshaw, Mr Howard P BA Assistant Solicitor . . . . *Nov 1991
Frost, Mr Peter J LLB Senior Solicitor . . . . *May 1986
Mousdale, Mr Philip LLB(Lond) Executive Director (Community Engagement) . . . . *May 1979
Townson, Mr Richard LLB(Hons) Legal Services Manager . . . . *Mar 1982

NEWARK, Nottinghamshire

ABLEHOMES LTD
4 Castlegate Newark Nottinghamshire NG24 1AX
Tel: 01636 611662 *Fax:* 01636 611680
Sol: Horner, Mrs Diana M LLB Company Director . . . . *May 1980

NEWARK & SHERWOOD DISTRICT COUNCIL
Kelham Hall Kelham Newark Nottinghamshire NG23 5QX
Tel: 01636 650000 *Fax:* 01636 655239
Sol: Cole, Mrs Kirstin H LLB Assistant Chief Executive. . . *Apr 1981
Lawrence, Mr Richard M LLB; DipLG Principal Solicitor . . . . *Dec 1980
Roberts, Miss Elizabeth Megan LLB; LPC Assistant Solicitor . . . . Dec 2006
White, Mrs Karen LLB(Hons) Head of Legal & Democratic Services . . . . *Aug 1993

NEWBURY, West Berkshire

WEST BERKSHIRE COUNCIL
Council Offices Market Street Newbury West Berkshire RG14 5LD
Tel: 01635 42400 *Fax:* 01635 519431 *Dx:* 30825 NEWBURY
Sol: Armour, Miss Sharon Louise BSc(Hons)(Biochemistry); PgDL Solicitor. Jun 2003
Clarke, Miss Sarah BA(Hons)(Law) Environment Team Leader . . . . Oct 2001
Coles, Miss Alison BA(Hons) Solicitor . . . . *Aug 2005
Foster, Mrs Sarah A BA(Hons) Legal Services Manager . . . . *Mar 1988
Gread, Miss Joanne LLB; LLM Solicitor . . . . Jul 2005
Hogan, Ms Leigh Jean LLB(Hons) Corporate Team Leader . . . . *Sep 2000
Holling, Mr David LLB; LARTPI Head of Legal & Electoral Services . . . . *Jan 1981
McFarlane, Miss Catriona Calder BSc(Hons); LLM(UCL) Solicitor. Sep 2004
Mistry, Mrs Seema LLB(Hons); LPD Solicitor . . . . . Nov 2005
Pike, Mr Geoffrey BA(Keele); LLM(Soton) Solicitor Chairman Social Security & Disability Appeals Tribunal; MAT . . . . *§Jun 1974
Sheikh, Mr Shiraz Amjad LLB(Hons) Solicitor - Projects & Education. *Dec 2005
Thomas, Miss Annette C LLB(Wales) Principal Solicitor . . . . *Dec 1986

NEWCASTLE UNDER LYME, Staffordshire

NEWCASTLE UNDER LYME BOROUGH COUNCIL
Civic Offices Merrial Street Newcastle Under Lyme Staffordshire ST5 2AG
Tel: 01782 717717 *Fax:* 01782 742215
Dx: 20959 NEWCASTLE UNDER LYME
Sol: Clisby, Mr Paul W BA(Hons) Legal Services Manager *Aug 1991
Hall, Miss Lisa FILEx Assistant Solicitor. . . . . . . *Nov 2001
Washington, Mr Paul R FILEx; FSELP; M Inst PSA Principal Solicitor. *Dec 1992

NEWCASTLE UPON TYNE, Tyne & Wear

ENVIRONMENT AGENCY (NORTH EAST REGION)
Tyneside House Newcastle Business Park Skinnerburn Road Newcastle upon Tyne Tyne & Wear NE4 7AR
Tel: 0191 203 4000 *Fax:* 0191 203 4004
Sol: Silvester, Mrs Lynda Kathleen Anne Principal Solicitor. *Jul 1977

NEWCASTLE BUILDING SOCIETY
Portland House New Bridge Street Newcastle upon Tyne Tyne & Wear NE1 8AL
Tel: 0191 244 2000 *Fax:* 0191 244 2008
Dx: 61010 NEWCASTLE UNDER LYME
Sol: Petrie, Mr Charles A LLB Legal Services Manager. . *Sep 1993
Todd, Mr Leslie LLB Chief Solicitor & Secretary . . . . *Apr 1981
Williams, Ms Jane W BSc Assistant Solicitor Legal Services Group. *Feb 1987

NEWCASTLE UPON TYNE CITY COUNCIL
Civic Centre Barras Bridge Newcastle upon Tyne Tyne & Wear NE99 2BN
Tel: 0191 232 8520 *Fax:* 0191 277 7127 *Dx:* 62552 JESMOND
Sol: Aplin, Mrs Carol Solicitor . . . . Sep 1988
Bagshaw, Mrs Joanne LLB(Hons) Solicitor . . . . . . *Jan 1997
Bulman, Miss Melanie LLB(Hons) Assistant Solicitor. *Sep 2000
Burns, Miss Alison Jane Solicitor . . . . Nov 1991
Dagg, Mr Stephen Martin Solicitor. . . . . Oct 2002
Daly, Ms Patricia Elizabeth BA; PGCE; LLB Solicitor. . *Oct 1995
Dixon, Mr Andrew John Solicitor. . . . . Mar 2005
Dixon, Ms Rachel Solicitor. . . . . Aug 2002
Dodds, Mrs Valerie A LLB(L'pool) Head of Legal Services . . . . *Dec 1974
Fagan, Miss Gerardine Mary LLB Solicitor. . . . . . *Mar 1989
Franks, Ms Zoe Solicitor. . . . . Apr 2002
Headley, Ms Catherine Yvonne Solicitor. . . . . Aug 2001
Kane, Ms Joyce MA; LLB Senior Solicitor . . . . *Jan 1974
McChlery, Mrs Yvonne BA; LLB Solicitor. . . . . *Oct 1993
McManus, Ms Sonya Solicitor. . . . . Aug 2003
Mowat, Ms Denise Mary O'Brien Solicitor . . . . May 1994
Muffitt, Mrs Annette Rosemary BA(Hons) Solicitor. . . *Nov 1990
Murphy, Ms Karina Louise Solicitor . . . . Sep 2005
Ord, Ms Helen Margaret Solicitor . . . . Nov 1999
Ovens, Mr Stuart R BA(Sussex) Assistant Head of Legal Services . . . . *Dec 1977
Pearson, Mrs Susan Solicitor . . . . Dec 1991
Renney, Mrs Claire Solicitor. . . . . *Jan 2006
Robson, Mrs Carol A LLB Solicitor. . . . . *Nov 1989
Sacco, Miss J L Nicola BA(Newc) Solicitor. . . . . . *Feb 1988
Softly, Mr John R LLB Assistant Head of Legal Services (Major Projects) . . . . *Nov 1994
Sunter, Mr Tom Gordon LLB(Hons); LLM Senior SolicitorJul 2001
Turnbull, Ms Sharon Theresa BA(Hons) Solicitor . . . *Oct 1991
Turner, Mr Christopher John Alex . . . . Dec 2004
Walker, Ms Kerry A BA Solicitor. . . . . *Oct 1993
Wardle, Mr John Allan Senior Solicitor. . . . . Mar 1987
Wilson, Miss Helen P BA(Durham) Solicitor . . . . . . *Oct 1989

NORTHUMBRIA PROBATION BOARD
Lifton House Eslington Road Jesmond Newcastle upon Tyne Tyne & Wear NE2 4SP
Tel: 0191 240 7351 *Fax:* 0191 240 2749
E-mail: chris.mackie@northumbria.probation.gsi.gov.uk
Sol: Mackie, Mr Christopher E BA(Law); DipLG Secretary & Solicitor . . . . *Oct 1982

TYNE & WEAR PASSENGER TRANSPORT EXECUTIVE
Nexus House St James Boulevard Newcastle upon Tyne Tyne & Wear NE1 4AX
Tel: 0191 203 3333 *Fax:* 0191 203 3180
E-mail: colin.whittle@nexus.org.uk
Sol: Rhodes, Ms Alison LLB(Bris) Solicitor. . . . . *Nov 1991
Tindall, Mrs Sarah Ann LLB(Hons) Solicitor . . . . . *Sep 1998
Whittle, Mr Colin BA(Law) Head of Legal Services. . *May 1989

NEWPORT, Isle of Wight

ISLE OF WIGHT COUNCIL
3rd Floor County Hall High Street Newport Isle of Wight PO30 1UD
Tel: 01983 823207 *Fax:* 01983 823699 *Dx:* 56361 NEWPORT (IOW)
Sol: Drake, Mr Matthew Raymond LLB Solicitor . . . . . *Sep 2000
Fiore, Miss Davina LLB Director of Legal & Democratic Services & Monitoring Officer. . . . . Oct 1988
Gaudion, Miss Laura Jane LLB(Hons) Assistant Solicitor . . . . *Jan 2004
Hill, Miss Kate Nicole LLB; Higher Rights Employment & Litigation Solicitor. . . . . Jun 2006
Humphray, Miss Martine Rachel HND; BA(Hons); PGDL; LPC Solicitor. *Sep 2007
Miles, Mrs Helen Elizabeth Dip LG Legal Team Leader*Dec 1992
West, Ms April L BA(Hons) Assistant Democratic Services Manager . . . . *Oct 1997

NEWPORT

NEWPORT CITY COUNCIL
Civic Centre Newport NP20 4UR
Tel: 01633 656656 *Fax:* 01633 244721
Dx: 33238 NEWPORT (GWENT) 1
Sol: Ashurst, Mr James G BA Head of Law & Standards . . Dec 1977
Boughey, Mrs Lucy Jane LLB; LPC Assistant Solicitor Secretary to Solicitors in Local Government South & Mid Wales Branch . . . . *Sep 2000
Cadenhead, Mr Simon David BA(Hons)(Modern History) Assistant Solicitor. . . . . Jun 1994
Evans, Ms Joanne LLB Solicitor. . . . . Oct 1991
Evans, Mr Jonathan Charles MEng . . . . Jun 1998
Fletcher, Mrs Alex LLB(Hons) Assistant Solicitor. . . . *Jul 1998
Holcombe, Ms Juliet LLB Senior Solicitor . . . . *Nov 1985
Hughes, Miss Sheila M MA(Cantab) Senior Solicitor. . *Oct 1985
Jayne, Ms Joanne LLM Senior Solicitor . . . . Sep 1990
Lewis, Ms Alison BA Assistant Solicitor . . . . Nov 1992
Price, Mr Gareth D LLB Levi Owen Prize; Morgan Owen Prize; Maxwell Law Prize Chief Legal Officer. . . . . . . *Oct 1983
Stafford, Mrs Gemma Louise Davies LPC . . . . *Sep 2002
Sturley, Ms Lynn Marie LLB . . . . *Sep 1990

NEWTON ABBOT, Devon

TEIGNBRIDGE DISTRICT COUNCIL
Forde House Newton Abbot Devon TQ12 4XX
Tel: 01626 361101 *Fax:* 01626 215169
Dx: 121075 NEWTON ABBOT 5
Sol: Aggett, Mrs Susan C Solicitor to the Council. . . . . *Dec 1987
Barnes, Mr Simon N LLB Strategic Manager. . . . . . *Jun 1977
Davies, Ms Katherine L Assistant Solicitor. . . . . . . *Oct 2007
Moors, Mr Duncan Principal Secretary. . . . . *Nov 2000

NORTH SHIELDS, Tyne & Wear

NORTH TYNESIDE COUNCIL
Quadrant The Silverlink North Cobalt Business Park Newcastle upon Tyne Tyne & Wear NE27 0BY
Tel: 0191 643 5000 *Fax:* 0191 643 2430
Sol: Atkinson, Mrs Zoe BA(Hons) Solicitor . . . . Jul 2004
Ballantyne, Mr Stephen George LLB(Hons) Assistant Solicitor . . . . *Jul 2002
Clifford, Mrs Jenifer Margaret Foster LLB(Hons) Solicitor . . . . *Mar 1985
Coombs, Miss Helen M LLB Senior Assistant Solicitor *Sep 1989

See p112 for the Key to Work Categories & other symbols

Geary, Ms Vivienne M BA; LLM Manager Legal Service . . . *Jan 1986
Humphries, Miss Carol Ann LLB Assistant Solicitor . . *Nov 1994
Innes, Ms Wendy S MA(Hons) Senior Assistant Solicitor . . . *Oct 1993
Lucas, Mrs Maria Elizabeth LLB(Hons); MA Head of Legal & Democratic Services & Monitoring Officer . . . . *Jun 1990
Ng, Ms Kit Fong Irene LLB; LLM Senior Assistant Solicitor . . . *Nov 1989
Turnbull, Mrs Caroline LLB Assistant Solicitor . . . . May 2003
Wafer, Mrs Lynsey . . . *Aug 2004
Watson, Miss Louise LLB; DipLP Assistant Solicitor . . Nov 2000

NORTHALLERTON, North Yorkshire

BROADACRES HOUSING ASSOCIATION
Broadacres House Mountview Standard Way Northallerton North Yorkshire DL6 2YD
Tel: 01609 767900 *Fax:* 01609 777017
Sol: Burton, Mr Mark LLB(Hull) Solicitor . . . *Jun 1981

E WOOD HOLDINGS PLC
Unit 1 Mile House Business Park Darlington Road Northallerton North Yorkshire DL6 2NW
Tel: 01609 788716 *Fax:* 01609 761040
E-mail: rickmackness@talk21.com
Sol: Mackness, Mr Donald Richard LLB Group Solicitor . *May 1971

HAMBLETON DISTRICT COUNCIL
Civic Centre Stone Cross Northallerton North Yorkshire DL6 2UU
Tel: 01609 779977 *Fax:* 01609 767228
Dx: 61650 NORTHALLERTON
Sol: Richards, Mr J Martyn BA(Law) Head of Legal Services . . . Nov 1985

NORTH YORKSHIRE COUNTY COUNCIL
County Hall Racecourse Lane Northallerton North Yorkshire DL7 8AD
Tel: 01609 780780 *Fax:* 01609 780447
Dx: 69140 NORTHALLERTON 3
E-mail: legal.services@northyorks.gov.uk
Sol: Beighton, Mrs Moira P LLB(Hons) Corporate Solicitor (Professional Support) . . . Feb 1996
Boddy, Mrs Alison M BA(Hons) Principal Solicitor . . *Jan 1981
Branley, Ms Claire Elizabeth BA(Hons); CPE(Law); DipLP . . . *Sep 1997
Eddon, Mr George H LLB(Leeds) Social Services Law Manager . . . *Oct 1988
Galloway, Ms Karen Solicitor . . . *Jun 1999
Gatrell, Miss Catriona LLB(Hons) Principal Lawyer . . Feb 1996
Lindup, Mr Richard P Solicitor. . . . *Jun 1989
McKeon, Mr Callum LLB(Hons) Senior Solicitor/Corporate Governance. . . . Dec 1995
Meredith, Miss Emma Louise BA(Hons) Child Care Lawyer . . . Mar 2004
Nelson, Mr Gary James LLB(Hons) Solicitor. . . . Oct 2000
Pegg, Mrs Caroline Anne Solicitor. . . . *Jan 1986
Somers, Mrs Hazel J BA(Hons) Solicitor. . . . *Nov 1995
Woods, Mr Gilbert M MA(Oxon). . . . *Jun 1974

NORTHAMPTON, Northamptonshire

CROWN PROSECUTION SERVICE NORTHAMPTONSHIRE
Beaumont House Cliftonville Northampton Northamptonshire NN1 5BE
Tel: 01604 823600 *Fax:* 01604 823651 *Dx:* 18512 NORTHAMPTON
Sol: Bradfield, Miss Hilary J Branch Crown Prosecutor. . *May 1976

GO CONVEYANCING
4 Albion Place Northampton Northamptonshire NN1 1UD
Tel: 01604 636868 *Fax:* 01604 603454 *Dx:* 12450 NORTHAMPTON
E-mail: info@goconveyancing.co.uk
Sol: Kennaird-Banner, Mrs Suzanne LLB Solicitor . . . . *Jul 2000

NORTHAMPTON BOROUGH COUNCIL
The Guildhall St Giles Square Northampton Northamptonshire NN1 1DE
Tel: 01604 837837 *Fax:* 01604 838554
Dx: 703139 NORTHAMPTON 6
E-mail: solicitors@northampton.gov.uk
Sol: Amas, Mrs Linda V LLB(Nott'm) Chief Solicitor . . . *Jun 1969
Boyd, Mrs Theresa E LLB Solicitor . . . *Nov 1992
Fernandes, Mr Francis J LLB(Hons); LLM; MBA; LARTPI Solicitor to the Council . . . *Nov 1992
Liburd, Miss Julie Michelle LLB(Hons) Solicitor . . . *Feb 2002
Newham, Mr Peter A LLB(Leeds) Borough Solicitor . *May 1967

NORTHAMPTONSHIRE COUNTY COUNCIL
County Hall George Row Northampton Northamptonshire NN1 1DN
Tel: 01604 236236 *Fax:* 01604 237167 *Dx:* 12481 NORTHAMPTON
Sol: Bates, Ms Claire Alicia Solicitor . . . *Jan 1992
Duncan, Mr Peter D H LLB(Sheff) Senior Solicitor. . *§Dec 1974
George, Mrs Debra C LLB Solicitor . . . *Mar 1990
Holden, Ms Louise Anne Solicitor . . . *Nov 1991
Price-Jones, Mr Justin Henry CPE; LPC Senior Solicitor . . . Sep 1998
Simpson, Miss Deana Louise BA(Hons). . . . *Aug 1990
Smith, Mr Victor H P LLB(Soton) Acting Head of Legal Services . . . Dec 1978
Titterton, Mrs Julie BA Solicitor . . . *Oct 1986
Trott, Ms Elizabeth J LLB Solicitor. . . . *Oct 1990

NORTHAMPTONSHIRE MAGISTRATES COURTS
Regents Pavilion Summerhouse Road Moulton Park Northampton Northamptonshire NN3 6AS
Tel: 01604 497000 *Fax:* 01536 497010
Sol: Armstrong, Miss Judith Lorraine LPC Bench Legal Adviser . . . Nov 1996
Brathwaite, Mrs Karen Emma Jane LLB(Hons) Court Clerk . . . *Jun 1992
Clarke, Mr Neil M OBE Clerk to the Justices Northamptonshire . . . *Dec 1979
Drage, Mr Andrew William DML; LPC; PSC Court Clerk . . . *Nov 1996
Hartgroves, Mr Robert DML; LLB(Hons); DMS Bench Legal Adviser . . . *Nov 1996

Johnson, Miss Joanna Lindsay Catherine LLB(Hons) Simmons & Simmons Commercial Law Prize; NFU Mutual Insurance Law Prize Court Clerk. . . . *Sep 1997
Munday, Mr Simon G LLB(Hons); DML; DMS Court Clerk . . . *May 1996
Ray, Mr Andrew DML; LSF Bench Legal Adviser . . *Mar 1994
Vincent, Mrs Susan Gail LLB(Hons) Bench Legal Adviser . . . *Aug 1996

PERSIMMON PLC
3 Waterside Way Bedford Road Northampton Northamptonshire NN4 7XD
Tel: 01604 884600 *Fax:* 01604 884677
Dx: 711060 NORTHAMPTON 28
Sol: Balderstone, Mr Christopher J L BA(Hons)(Oxon) Regional Solicitor. . . . *Oct 1988
McGuiness, Mr Shaun David LLB(Hons) Company Solicitor . . . Nov 1992

THOMSONS
The Suite Unit D Caswell Road Northampton Northamptonshire NN4 7PW
Tel: 020 8913 5364 *Fax:* 020 8913 5181
Sol: Thomson, Mr Hamish N M Solicitor . . . Jun 1974

NORWICH, Norfolk

NORFOLK COUNTY COUNCIL - LEGAL SERVICES
County Hall Martineau Lane Norwich Norfolk NR1 2DH
Tel: Minicom: 0844 800 8011 *Fax:* 01603 222899
Dx: 135926 NORWICH 13
E-mail: information@norfolk.gov.uk
Sol: Anthony, Mrs Fiona E LLM Solicitor . . . Oct 1991
Bell, Mr Steven Christian BA(Hons) Solicitor. . . . Jan 2006
Black, Mrs Emma LLB(Hons) Solicitor. . . . *Jan 1997
Brown, Mr Christopher J LLB Solicitor. . . . *Oct 1984
Carter, Mrs Kathleen Anne BA(Hons); LLB Solicitor Child Protection. . . . Oct 1992
Cary, Ms Pamela J BA Assistant Head of Law. . . . *Jan 1984
Clark, Ms Sharon BA(Law) Senior Solicitor . . . Oct 1988
Core, Mr George V MSc; LLB; BA Solicitor . . . Mar 2000
Crosskill, Mr James LLB(Hons) Senior Solicitor . . . Apr 2001
Croxen, Miss Fiona LLB Charlotte Ashby Memorial Prize 1985 Senior Solicitor . . . Sep 1989
Ferguson, Mr Hugh LLB(Hons); DipLP Solicitor . . . Jul 2006
Garwood, Mr Michael LLB(Hons) Cambridge & District Law Society Prize For Best Overall Performance In Legal Practice Course 2005 Solicitor . . . Nov 2005
Gibb, Miss Sarah LLB Solicitor . . . Sep 2006
Gibbs, Mrs Julia Kathleen BA(Hons) Solicitor . . . Aug 1996
Jenkinson, Ms Sarah C Solicitor. . . . *Oct 1995
Jolley, Ms Imogen H MA Solicitor . . . Sep 1996
Joyce, Mr Michael LLB(Hons) Solicitor. . . . Mar 1990
McNeill, Ms Victoria Anne MA Head Of Law & Monitoring Officer Executive Director of NHS Trust; Pension Fund Trustee . . . Apr 1987
Norman, Miss Sarah LLB(Hons) Solicitor . . . Nov 1992
Russell, Miss Lorna LLB(Hons) Solicitor. . . . *Mar 1994
Smy, Miss Sarah Ruth LLB(Hons) Solicitor . . . *Nov 1990
Storie, Mr David C P MA; LLB; ACIB Solicitor . . . *§Jul 1990
Turna, Miss Darjinder BSc; LLM; Dip Solicitor . . . Sep 2003

NORWICH CITY COUNCIL
City Hall St Peter's Street Norwich Norfolk NR2 1NH
Tel: 01603 212212 *Fax:* 01603 213020 *Dx:* 5278 NORWICH
Sol: Brims, Mr Nigel B BA(Oxon) Senior Solicitor. . . . *Sep 1980
Johnson, Mr David P LLB Solicitor to the Council . . . *Jan 1983
Lowens, Mr David A BA; DipLG Solicitor. . . . *Feb 1989

NORWICH UNION INSURANCE GROUP
PO Box 89 Surrey Street Norwich Norfolk NR1 3NS
Tel: 01603 622200 *Fax:* 01603 681307 *Dx:* 84903 NORWICH 3
Sol: Alcorn, Mrs Helen Solicitor . . . Mar 2000
Barlow, Mr George R . . . *Oct 1995
Calderbank, Ms Jane BA Mortgage Finance Solicitor . *Oct 1987
Clark, Ms Lyndsey K Solicitor. . . . Sep 1999
Clayden, Mr Dominic J BA(English) Head of Claims Legal . . . *Feb 1994
Colley, Ms Tania Solicitor . . . Dec 2004
Crosbie, Miss Rachel Marie LLB Solicitor . . . Dec 2001
Dawson, Ms Salena LLB(Hons) Solicitor. . . . Nov 2002
Donegan, Ms Louise BA(Hons); CPE Solicitor. . . . Sep 1997
Dyer, Mrs Lydia R M Solicitor . . . Jun 2002
Eastham, Ms Jocelyn J LLB Mortgage Finance Solicitor . . . *§Mar 1985
Eaton, Mr Angus G BSc(Hons) Director of Group Legal*Oct 1995
Eleanor, Mr Nicholas J R TD BA(Hons) Solicitor. . . . *§Jul 1984
Fish, Mr David R BA Senior Life & Pensions Adviser . Dec 1978
Gammer, Ms Fay C BA; M Inst TMA . . . *Oct 1981
Gibb, Miss Gillian Solicitor. . . . Apr 2005
Gidney, Mr Stephen J LLB; LLM Commercial Solicitor. *Oct 1991
Grand, Mr Howard Solicitor . . . Sep 2000
Gray, Mr Alistair David Solicitor . . . Sep 2000
Greaves, Mr Paul Nicholas Solicitor. . . . Nov 2005
Hardy, Mrs Valerie Patricia . . . *Sep 2002
Harris, Ms Donna C LLB Director of Legal Services (Property) . . . *Oct 1983
Hartford, Mr Robert R Solicitor . . . Sep 2005
Henderson, Mr James Gordon BA Property Solicitor. . Sep 2002
Holkham, Miss Anna M BA(Nott'm) Life & Pensions Solicitor . . . *Mar 1984
Hopkins, Mr D Mark MA(Cantab) . . . *§Jan 1982
Howlett, Mr Paul L Mortgage Finance Solicitor. . . . *§Apr 1981
Jackson-Nichols, Ms Amanda LLB; LLM Senior Commercial Solicitor. . . . Oct 1991
Janday, Ms Sonia Property Solicitor. . . . Sep 2004
Jones, Mr Graham BA(Hons); MBA Chief Solicitor. . . *Jun 1977
Kay, Mr Andrew Lawrence Thomas Solicitor. . . . Nov 2003
Lingwood, Mr William E LLB Senior Litigation Solicitor.*Nov 1988
McAnlis, Ms Rosemary Solicitor. . . . May 2003
Madaan, Mr Ashish Solicitor. . . . Sep 2001
Marshall, Ms Clair Louise . . . *Dec 1991
Maskell, Ms Anne C LLB Solicitor . . . Jun 1975
Matthews, Mr Andrew N LLB Senior Litigation Solicitor *Feb 1982
Milnthorpe, Mr Gavin Solicitor . . . Sep 2006
Morgan, Mr Simon Gareth Solicitor . . . Jun 1994
Orr, Ms Suzanne L Solicitor. . . . Dec 1999
Page, Miss Fiona J BA . . . *§Oct 1982
Patel, Mukta Solicitor . . . May 2006
Robson, Ms Catherine Solicitor . . . Oct 1999
Rogers, Ms Alexandra N J Solicitor . . . Nov 2005

Roy, Mr Stephen Russell BA Mortgage Finance Solicitor . . . *Sep 1994
Sims, Miss Rachel Elizabeth Property Solicitor . . . . Jan 2007
Spicker, Mr Richard H BA Head of Company Commercial Legal . . . *Dec 1980
Swallow, Mr Mark S J LLB(B'ham) Property Solicitor. . *Oct 1989
Sweet-Escott, Mrs Ellen R Solicitor . . . Sep 1999
Taylor, Mrs Clare Solicitor. . . . Oct 2001
Thompson, Mrs Stephanie Joanne . . . *Sep 2002
Tootell, Ms Emma L BA Solicitor. . . . Apr 1999
Turner, Mr Timothy Robert BA(Hons); MA Solicitor. . *Nov 1993
Vickers, Mr Timothy R LLB Securities Solicitor. . . . *Nov 1993
Ware, Mrs Alexandra M BA(Law) Mortgage Finance Solicitor . . . *§Jun 1977
Will, Mr Dominic P J Solicitor . . . Sep 2000
Willis, Mr Kevin Richard BA(Hons) Life & Pensions Solicitor . . . *Sep 1997
Wilman, Mrs Jennifer Jane Director of UFE Legal . . . Oct 1987
Woodhouse, Ms Andrea L Mortgage Finance Solicitor. *Oct 1997
Woodrow, Mr Richard David. . . . *Sep 2002
Woollett, Mrs Jane Emily BA(Cantab)(Law) . . . *Sep 2000
Woollett, Mr Martyn Charles LLB Solicitor . . . Sep 2000
yacoubou, Miss Caroline Jane FILEx Solicitor. . . . Nov 2006

NOTTINGHAM

ALLIANCE BOOTS PLC
1 Thane Road West Nottingham NG90 1BS
Tel: 0115 950 6111 *Fax:* 0115 949 3634 *Dx:* 712061 BEESTON 2
Sol: Charlton, Mr David F . . . *Jul 1976
Foster, Mr David C G General Counsel, Retail Division*Nov 1984
Horner, Mr Ben Solicitor. . . . *Sep 2001
Hulme, Mr Andrew J Solicitor . . . *Oct 1995
James, Ms Afanwen Solicitor . . . *Oct 1986
Lee, Mr Kerry Head of Group, Intellectual Property . *Oct 1995
Rayner, Miss Heather E A Solicitor . . . *Nov 1991
Straw, Miss Helen Margaret LLB . . . *Oct 1983

GEDLING BOROUGH COUNCIL
Civic Centre Arnot Hill Park Arnold Nottingham NG5 6LU
Tel: 0115 901 3901 *Fax:* 0115 901 3920
E-mail: legal&admin@gedling.gov.uk
Sol: Barrington, Ms Helen Elizabeth LLB(Hons) Senior Solicitor . . . Aug 1997
Blasdale, Miss Diane V BA(Nott'm) Solicitor. . . . *Aug 1982
Sale, Mrs Susan M LLB; DipLG Head of Legal & Democratic Services . . . *Oct 1977
Sugden, Mrs Lynette LLB Solicitor. . . . *Nov 1995
Whyley, Mrs Francesca Lucy LLB(Hons) Solicitor . . . Jun 2004

HM LAND REGISTRY - NOTTINGHAM (EAST)
Robins Wood Road Nottingham NG8 3RQ
Tel: 0115 906 5353 *Fax:* 0115 936 0036
Dx: 716126 NOTTINGHAM 26

HM LAND REGISTRY - NOTTINGHAM (WEST)
Chalfont Drive Nottingham NG8 3RN
Tel: 0115 935 1166 *Fax:* 0115 935 0038 *Dx:* 10298 NOTTINGHAM 3

LEGAL SERVICES COMMISSION
Fothergill House 16 King Street Nottingham NG1 2AS
Tel: 0115 908 4200 *Fax:* 0115 908 4397 *Dx:* 10035 NOTTINGHAM
Sol: Dix, Mr Stephen C LLB Solicitor. . . . *Jan 1979
Stone, Mr Edward B Solicitor . . . *Nov 1970
Storey, Miss Linda BJuris Regional Director. . . . *Nov 1976

NOTTINGHAM CITY COUNCIL (CITY SEC DEPT)
The Guildhall Burton Street Nottingham NG1 4BT
Tel: 0115 915 5555 *Fax:* 0115 915 4004
Dx: 719182 NOTTINGHAM 34
E-mail: lette.baker@nottinghamcity.gov.uk
Sol: Barrett, Mrs Ann E LLB Senior Solicitor . . . *Oct 1989
Bernard-Carlin, Mr John F Senior Solicitor. . . . *Oct 1992
Bestwick, Miss Tamazin Elizabeth Ann LLB(Hons) Assistant Solicitor. . . . Sep 2003
Bianchina, Ms Clare BA(Hons) Solicitor . . . Oct 1995
Bibby, Miss Sarah Jane LLB Senior Solicitor. . . . Aug 1993
Brown, Ms Paulette Kay Marie Solicitor . . . Sep 1999
Grant, Miss Natalie Jean LLB; LPC Solicitor. . . . Sep 2003
Heffron, Ms Jacqueline Kay BA Solicitor. . . . *§Jul 1994
Hussain, Ms Misbah LLB Solicitor. . . . Jan 2000
Irwin, Ms Judith Ann LLB(Hons) Solicitor . . . Oct 1986
Jansari, Mr Asit D LLB(Hons) Solicitor. . . . *Mar 2002
Kane, Ms Roseann LLB(Hons) Solicitor Notary Public . *Apr 1989
Knowles, Miss Claire Jane BA(Law & German) Solicitor Apr 2000
Ludford-Thomas, Mr Jonathan F BA(Hons) Senior Solicitor . . . Sep 1998
Matthews, Mrs Diane J BSc(Hons); AKL Solicitor . . . Jun 1998
Matthews, Ms Naomi Rose LLB Solicitor . . . Jul 1997
Molyneux, Ms Sarah E LLB Legal Services Manager . *Jan 1988
O'Connell, Mr C Glen LLB; LLM Director of Legal Services and Projects. . . . Mar 1984
Okafor, Miss Agatha BA(Hons); LLM Solicitor . . . . Nov 2001
Oliver, Ms Christine Solicitor. . . . Apr 2005
Pickstone, Mr John E LLB; LLM Senior Solicitor. . . . Dec 1974
Rudman, Miss Sarah Solicitor. . . . Sep 2003
Russell, Mr Ian Martin Robert Solicitor. . . . Nov 1998
Stirling, Ms Jacqueline Jamima BA(Hons)(Law & Society) Solicitor. . . . *Aug 2001
Thomson, Mrs Kathryn S LLB(Hons) Solicitor . . . *Nov 1982
Townroe, Mr Malcolm Robinson Legal Services Manager . . . *Nov 1994
Walker, Ms Alison Lorna PGDipLaw; LPC Solicitor. . . Jan 2002
Waters, Miss Victoria Nicola Solicitor . . . Nov 1976

NOTTINGHAM LAW CENTRE
119 Radford Road Hyson Green Nottingham NG7 5DU
Tel: 0115 978 7813 *Fax:* 0115 979 2969
E-mail: nottlawcentre@btconnect.com
Sol: Denton, Ms Sally Catherine LLB Senior Solicitor. . . *Nov 1994
Downey, Ms Anne Caroline LLB Solicitor . . . May 1999

NOTTINGHAM MAGISTRATES COURT
Carrington Street Nottingham NG2 1EE
Tel: 0115 955 8111 *Fax:* 0115 955 8139
Dx: 719030 NOTTINGHAM 32
Sol: Anwar, Mrs Iram LLB(Hons)(Law). . . . *Oct 1996
Lewis, Mr Marcus Wesley LLB(Hons); MA Senior Legal Adviser . . . May 2000
Lord, Mr Trevor LLB(Hons) . . . Mar 1994

Rodgerson, Ms Ann LLB(Hons) Senior Legal Adviser . Dec 1999
Young, Miss Gillian BA Blackstone Prize 1993. . . . . Aug 1996

NUNEATON, Warwickshire

NUNEATON AND BEDWORTH BOROUGH COUNCIL
Town Hall Coton Road Nuneaton Warwickshire CV11 5AA
Tel: 024 7637 6376 *Fax:* 024 7637 6238 *Dx:* 16458 NUNEATON
E-mail: philip.richardson@nuneaton-bedworthbc.gov.uk
Sol: Neale, Mr Mark BA(Hons)(Law) Senior Legal Officer . Jun 2005
Shaddock, Mrs Kameljit Kaur BA(Hons) Legal Officer . Jan 1997
White, Miss Wendy LLB(Hons); DipLG Senior Legal Officer . . . *Apr 1995
Whitney, Mrs Elaine Kathleen LLM; DipLG Senior Legal Officer . . . Dec 1991

OAKHAM, Rutland

RUTLAND COUNTY COUNCIL
Catmose Oakham Rutland LE15 6HP
Tel: 01572 722577 *Fax:* 01572 758307 *Dx:* 28340 OAKHAM
E-mail: legal@rutland.gov.uk
Sol: Joseph, Mr Nigel LLB(Hons); FILEX Assistant Solicitor Jul 2001
Lea, Mrs Ruth BA(Hons); MBA; PGDipLaw Assistant Solicitor . . . *Feb 2006
Pook, Mr Geoffrey A LLB Head of Legal Services . . . *Oct 1976

OLDBURY, West Midlands

SANDWELL METROPOLITAN BOROUGH COUNCIL
Sandwell Council House Freeth Street Oldbury West Midlands B69 3DE
Tel: 0121 569 2200 *Fax:* 0121 569 3210 *Dx:* 710070 SANDWELL
Sol: Broxton, Mrs Michelle LLB Group Manager . . . . . *Feb 1986
Campbell, Mr David Ian LLB(Hons) Senior Solicitor . . Feb 1999
Cartwright, Mr John Leonard LLB(Hons) Assistant Solicitor . . . *May 1996
Cork, Mrs Karen Elizabeth FILEx Senior Solicitor . . *Oct 1994
Cork, Mr Stephen J LLB Head of Legal Services . . . *Jun 1974
Deller, Mrs Inderjit K LLB(Hons) Group Manager . . . *Nov 1985
Egginton, Miss Jayne Mary LLB(Hons) Senior Solicitor*Dec 1994
Kingham, Mr Lee LLB Assistant Solicitor . . . . §Jun 1990
Oliver, Miss Charmain June LLB(Hons) Senior Solicitor Jan 1999
Reid, Miss Bernadette Assistant Solicitor . . . . . . *Aug 1999
Sharma, Mrs Neeraj BA(Hons) . . . . *Mar 1987
Summers, Mr Frederick N BSc(Wales)(Econ) Chief Executive . . . *Oct 1978
Tour, Mr Surjit LLB(Hons) Solicitor. . . . . Mar 1999
Wright, Mr Stewart LLB(Hons); MBA Group Manager; Solicitor . . . Jun 1989

WARLEY MAGISTRATES COURT
Law Courts Oldbury Ringway Oldbury West Midlands B69 4JN
Tel: 0121 511 2222 *Fax:* 0121 544 8492 *Dx:* 708330 OLDBURY 3
E-mail: sandwellmagistrates@btinternet.com
Sol: Griffin, Mr John E DML; DMS; MPD Justices' Clerk . *Sep 1985

OLDHAM, Greater Manchester

OLDHAM LAW CENTRE
1st Floor Archway House Bridge Street Oldham Greater Manchester OL1 1ED
Tel: 0161 627 0925 *Fax:* 0161 620 3411
E-mail: legal@oldhamlawcentre.org
Sol: Jabin, Mrs Talat LPC Solicitor. . . . . *Dec 2001
Jewell, Mr Peter LLB Solicitor. . . . . *Nov 1995
Johnson, Mr Paul LLB(Lond) Solicitor. . . . . *Jun 1983

OLDHAM METROPOLITAN BOROUGH COUNCIL
Civic Centre PO Box 33 West Street Oldham Greater Manchester OL1 1UL
Tel: 0161 911 3000 *Fax:* 0161 911 4826 *Dx:* 710000 OLDHAM
Sol: Entwistle, Mr Paul A LLB Group Solicitor (Policy/Contracts) . . . *Mar 1990
Harwood, Mrs Angela Bernadette BA(Hons)(Law) Solicitor to the Council . . . . . Feb 1988
Jones, Mr Lewis BA(Hons); LLM; LPC. . . . . *Aug 1996
Oliver, Mr Peter James BSc(Hons) Solicitor. . . . . . *Nov 1993
Rushton, Ms Sophie BA Solicitor . . . . *Nov 1993

ORMSKIRK, Lancashire

WEST LANCASHIRE DISTRICT COUNCIL
Council Offices 52 Derby Street Ormskirk Lancashire L39 2DF
Tel: 01695 577177 *Fax:* 01695 585082
E-mail: gill.rowe@westlancdc.gov.uk
Sol: Broderick, Mr Terence P Legal Services Manager . . *May 1996
Gardner, Mr Lee Raymond BA(Hons) Principal SolicitorAug 2004
Hynes, Mr Michael LLB Assistant Solicitor. . . . . . *Jan 2002
Jones, Mr Matthew Edward Principal Solicitor. . . . *Sep 1999
Rowe, Mrs Gillian L LLB Council Secretary & Solicitor. *Oct 1983
Sparrow, Mrs Tina LLB Assistant Solicitor. . . . . . *Jul 2002
Williams, Mrs Judith Christine BA(Hons) Assistant Solicitor . . . *May 2001

OSWESTRY, Shropshire

OSWESTRY BOROUGH COUNCIL
Council Offices Castle View Oswestry Shropshire SY11 1JR
Tel: 01691 671111 *Fax:* 01691 677348 *Dx:* 26610 OSWESTRY
E-mail: postroom@oswestry-bc.gov.uk
Sol: Hull, Mr Kevin Malcolm LLB(Hons) Solicitor . . . . . . May 1998

OXFORD, Oxfordshire

HARTWELL PLC
Faringdon Road Cumnor Oxford Oxfordshire OX2 9RE
Tel: 01865 866000
Sol: Holt, Miss Georgina Suzanne LLB Solicitor . . . . . . Oct 2001

OXFORD CITY COUNCIL
Town Hall Blueboar Street Oxford Oxfordshire OX1 1BX
Tel: 01865 249811 *Fax:* 01865 252694
Sol: Brown, Ms Susan Valerie Solicitor. . . . . *Dec 1992
Chirnside, Mrs Kathleen Elizabeth LLB; Dip Soc Admin(Oxon) Solicitor. . . . . *Nov 1970
Fennell, Ms Victoria LLB(Hons) Solicitor. . . . . Nov 2003
Griffiths, Ms Emma Louise LLB(Hons) Solicitor . . . . Sep 1997
King, Mr Jeremy P BSc Solicitor. . . . . *May 2002
Liddar, Mrs Helen Alexandra Solicitor . . . . Oct 1991
Pownall, Mr James LLB Solicitor . . . . *Oct 1979
Smith, Mr Daniel M BA(Hons) Solicitor . . . . *Sep 1997
Thomas, Mr Clive L LLB(Wales) Solicitor . . . . . . *Jan 1974
Thomas, Mr Jeremy John LLB(Hons) . . . . *Jan 1997

OXFORDSHIRE COUNTY COUNCIL
County Hall New Road Oxford Oxfordshire OX1 1ND
Tel: 01865 792422 *Fax:* 01865 815447 *Dx:* 4310 OXFORD
Sol: Buckley, Mrs Bronwen M LLB Solicitor. . . . . *Oct 1980
Chamberlain, Mrs Fionnuala BA Principal Solicitor. . *Aug 1991
Clark, Mr Peter G BA(Wales) Head of Legal & Democratic Services & County Solicitor. . . . . *Dec 1985
Cloake, Mrs Joanna LLB Solicitor . . . . *Mar 2005
Goodlad, Mr Richard Darrius LLB; LLM; PGDipLP Assistant Solicitor. . . . . *Mar 2003
Graham, Mr Nicholas LLB(Hons) Principal Solicitor . *Sep 1996
Jerram, Miss Claire Elizabeth MA(Cantab) Assistant Solicitor . . . *Oct 1995
McCallum, Mrs Patricia A BA(Hons) Assistant Solicitor*Sep 1997
Olavesen, Mrs Nicole Marie BA(Oxon) Assistant Solicitor . . . *Nov 1995
Phizackerley, Miss Katherine Alexandra BA Assistant Solicitor . . . *Sep 2001
Quartly, Mrs Janet BA(Hons)(History); CPE; LPC Solicitor . . . *Oct 2002
Sims, Miss Hayley LLB(Hons) Assistant Solicitor . . *Feb 2006
Taplin, Ms Julia BA(Hons) Principal Solicitor. . . . . *Dec 1980
Wade, Mrs Elizabeth P LLB Assistant Solicitor. . . . *Jul 1977
Waite, Mrs Josephine Mary BA; PGDipLaw; PGCertLP Assistant Solicitor. . . . . *Sep 2002
Watts, Mrs Carol A BA Principal Solicitor . . . . . . *Apr 1979

OXTED, Surrey

TANDRIDGE DISTRICT COUNCIL
Council Offices Station Road East Oxted Surrey RH8 0BT
Tel: 01883 722000 *Fax:* 01883 732954 *Dx:* 39359 OXTED
E-mail: legal@tandridgegov.uk
Sol: Hadida, Mrs Susan LLB(Hons); PGCE; DipLG Senior Lawyer . . . *May 1991
Hitchcock, Mr James C E MA(Cantab) Principal Solicitor . . . *Nov 1986
Komosa, Mr Andrew K Assistant Solicitor . . . . . . *May 1999
Moore, Mr Clive R BA(Hons)(Law); DMS Assistant Chief Executive (Legal) . . . . *Sep 1987

PENRITH, Cumbria

EDEN DISTRICT COUNCIL
Town Hall Penrith Cumbria CA11 7QF
Tel: 01768 817817 *Fax:* 01768 890470
Sol: Foote, Mr Paul G BA(Hons) Director of Corporate and Legal Services . . . . *Dec 1980
Young, Mr Simon David LLB(Hons) Legal Services Manager . . . *Jun 2000

PENTRE, Rhondda Cynon Taff

RHONDDA CYNON TAFF COUNTY BOROUGH COUNCIL
Municipal Offices Llewellyn Street Pentre Rhondda Cynon Taff CF41 7BT
Tel: 01443 424300 *Fax:* 01443 423229 *Dx:* 115542 PENTRE
E-mail: anthony.mullins@rhondda-cynon-taff.gov.uk
Sol: Clements, Miss M Julie Solicitor. . . . . *May 1988
Davies, Mr John D C LLB(Wales); Dip Local Govt Law & Practice Solicitor . . . . *Dec 1982
Enticott, Mrs Isabel Clare LLB(Hons) Solicitor . . . . *Mar 1999
Humphreys, Mr Simon Anthony Senior Legal Assistant . . . *May 2000
Jones, Mrs Meira Ellen Rees BA(Hons)(Law) Principal Solicitor . . . *Oct 1987
McCarthy, Mrs Paula Louise BSc(Econ) LPC Outstanding Performance 2002/03. . . . . Oct 2003
Nicholls, Mr Paul Jeremy BA(Hons) Solicitor. . . . . *Dec 1993
Richards, Mr Marcus H BSc(Hons)(Econ) Solicitor. . *§Jul 1998
Smith, Mrs Rachel Alexandra Louise BA(Hons); BSc *Sep 1999
Williams, Mr Gethin LLB(Hons) Head of Legal Services *Jul 1974

PERSHORE, Worcestershire

WYCHAVON DISTRICT COUNCIL
The Civic Centre Queen Elizabeth Drive Pershore Worcestershire WR10 1PT
Tel: 01386 565000 *Fax:* 01386 561089 *Dx:* 25934 PERSHORE
Sol: Marshall, Mr Ian G LLB(Leics) Head of Legal & Support Services . . . . *Oct 1977
Patel, Mrs Meesha LLB Solicitor. . . . . *Aug 2004
Roberts, Mrs Carol LLB(Hons) Principal Solicitor . . *Nov 1995
Taylor, Mr Paul Jonathan BA(Hons); MA. . . . . *Jul 2004

PETERBOROUGH

ENVIRONMENT AGENCY (ANGLIAN REGION)
Kingfisher House Goldhay Way Orton Goldhay Peterborough PE2 5ZR
Tel: 01733 371811 *Fax:* 01733 231840
Dx: 701640 ORTON GOLDHAY
Sol: Brosnan, Miss Anne M LLB(Hons); MSc Principal Solicitor . . . *Mar 1984
Bywater, Mr Kevin LLB Solicitor. . . . . Aug 1998
Leader, Mr Steve J B Solicitor. . . . . Jul 1999
McDonald, Dr Anne-Lise PhD. . . . . Mar 2003
Tordoff, Mrs Miriam A LLB Senior Legal Assistant. . . Sep 2002
Shone, Miss Della LLB; MA(Hons) Regional Legal Services Manager . . . . Oct 1984
Sillitto, Miss Helen Elizabeth LLB; LLM . . . . Sep 2004
Ward, Miss Sarah LLB(Hons) Principal Solicitor . . . . *Oct 1990

NORWICH AND PETERBOROUGH BUILDING SOCIETY
Lynch Wood Peterborough PE2 6WZ
Tel: 01733 372372 *Fax:* 01733 372080 *Dx:* 29181 LYNCH WOOD
Sol: Bird, Miss Susan A LLB(Hons) Commercial Solicitor. . *Oct 1989

PETERBOROUGH CITY COUNCIL
Town Hall Bridge Street Peterborough PE1 1HG
Tel: 01733 747474 *Fax:* 01733 452524
Dx: 12310 PETERBOROUGH
Sol: Abbott, Mrs Michelle FILEx Lawyer . . . . Jul 2002
Beasley, Mrs Gillian R LLB Chief Executive . . . . . *Mar 1985
Blyth, Mr J Melvyn LLB Senior Solicitor - Planning, Environment and Property . . . . *Apr 1987
Denness, Miss Carrie LLB(Hons) Principal Solicitor . *Aug 2003
Evans, Mr Philip BA(Hons) Principal Solicitor . . . . . Jul 2001
Lewis, Mrs Elaine Valerie Pirie LLM; LLB; BL(Hons) Lawyer . . . *Mar 1992
Patel, Manu C LLB Solicitor. . . . . *May 1992
Snedden, Mr Benjamin N LLB; BA Legal Advisor . . . . Nov 2005
Welton, Mrs Margaret FILEx Senior Lawyer (Commercial & Contracts) . . . . Jan 1993

PETERBOROUGH MAGISTRATES COURT
Bridge Street Peterborough PE1 1ED
Tel: 01223 314311 *Fax:* 01733 313749
Dx: 702304 PETERBOROUGH 8
Sol: Brown, Mrs Rebecca Jayne LLB(Hons) Principal Legal Adviser . . . Sep 1994
Duley, Ms Susan Elizabeth BA(Hons) Legal Adviser. . Mar 2002
Owens, Mrs Eleanor Jayne BA(Hons); LLB(Hons); MA(Cantab) Legal Project Manager . . . . Jan 1997
Przedborski, Mr Andrew Alexander LLB(Hons) Legal Project Manager . . . . Dec 1994

SHARMAN & COMPANY LTD
Newark Road Eastern Industry Peterborough PE1 5TD
Tel: 01733 555300 *Fax:* 01733 555400
Sol: Sharman, Mr Patrick G MA(Cantab) Solr & Chairman of Company. . . . . *Jan 1965

PETERSFIELD, Hampshire

EAST HAMPSHIRE DISTRICT COUNCIL
Penns Place Petersfield Hampshire GU31 4EX
Tel: 01730 266551 *Fax:* 01730 233935 *Dx:* 100403 PETERSFIELD
E-mail: michael_lawther@easthants.gov.uk
Sol: Jones, Mr William David Stephen LLB; MA Solicitor (Property) . . . *Nov 1988
Leach, Mr Nicholas Ian BA; LLB(Hons); PGDipLP Judges Prize for Performance in Commercial Law Principal Solicitor . . . *Mar 2000
Williams, Mrs Diana Meredith BA Principal Solicitor . *Nov 1987

PLYMOUTH

HM LAND REGISTRY - PLYMOUTH
Plumer House Tailyour Road Crownhill Plymouth PL6 5HY
Tel: 01752 636000 / 636123 *Fax:* 01752 636161
Dx: 8299 PLYMOUTH 4
Sol: Bedford, Mrs Carol A BA Assistant Land Registrar. . . *Jun 1976
Berry, A G BA(Oxon) Assistant Land Registrar . . . *Jun 1979
Hattersley, Mrs R J Assistant Land Registrar . . . . *Dec 1987
Nightingale, Mr P Assistant Land Registrar . . . . . *Dec 1988
Pain, A J Land Registrar . . . . *Dec 1973
Parham, H G MA(Oxon) Senior Assistant Land Registrar . . . *Apr 1974
Smart, Mrs C F Assistant Land Registrar . . . . . . *Apr 1985
Turner, Mrs R Assistant Land Registrar . . . . *Mar 1991

HALLIBURTON
Devon Port Royal Dockyards Plymouth PL1 4SG
Sol: Farrow, Mr Timothy J BSc(Hons)(Econ) Senior Counsel . . . *Jan 1983

PLYMOUTH CITY COUNCIL
Floor 3 Civic Centre Plymouth PL1 2AA
Tel: 01752 668000 *Fax:* 01752 306082 *Dx:* 8278 PLYMOUTH 2
Sol: Evans, Ms Beryl BSc(Hons)(Econ) Solicitor . . . . . . *Jul 1973
Evans, Miss Delyth Jenkins LLB(Wales); Dip (Local Government Law & Practice) Solicitor . . . . *Jun 1979
Gilbert, Mr Malcolm S LLB(Hons) Head of Legal Practice . . . *Sep 1991
Osborne, Mrs Sarah Ann PGDipLP Lawyer . . . . . *§Nov 1997
Pinwell, Mr Gareth David Solicitor. . . . . *Jan 1992
Wentworth, Mr Stewart MA(Oxon) Principal Lawyer . . Nov 1990

PLYMOUTH JUSTICES' CLERK
Magistrates Court St Andrew Street Plymouth PL1 2DP
Tel: 01752 206200 *Fax:* 01752 206194
Sol: Campbell, Mr Roy Alec LLB; BSc Legal Adviser. . . . Mar 1996
Smith, Mr Timothy A M BA(Dunelm)(Law) Justices' Clerk Clerk to the East Cornwall Justices . . . . *Mar 1980
Stonebanks, Ms Susan Solicitor. . . . . *Jan 1991

PONTEFRACT, West Yorkshire

PONTEFRACT MAGISTRATES COURT
Court House Front Street Pontefract West Yorkshire WF8 1BW
Tel: 01977 691600 *Fax:* 01977 691610
Sol: Cooksey, Mr John Peter. . . . . Mar 1992
Rigg, Mrs Carla Tracey . . . . Jul 1993
Smith, Mrs Rosamund LLB . . . . Dec 2000

PONTEFRACT PETTY SESSIONAL DIVISION
Magistrates Court Front Street Pontefract West Yorkshire WF8 1BW
Tel: 01977 723600 *Fax:* 01977 723610
Sol: Goodman, Mr Raymond District Legal Director . . . *Dec 1994

See p112 for the Key to Work Categories & other symbols

PONTELAND, Northumberland

NORTHUMBRIA POLICE
Northumbria Police HQ North Road Ponteland Northumberland NE20 0BL
Tel: 01661 872555 *Fax:* 01661 868038
Sol: Aubrey, Ms Denise E LLB Force Solicitor . . . . *Oct 1987

PONTYPOOL, Torfaen

TORFAEN BOROUGH COUNCIL
Civic Centre Pontypool Torfaen NP4 6YB
Tel: 01495 766373 *Fax:* 01495 766399 *Dx:* 44257 PONTYPOOL
E-mail: joan.harvey@torfaen.gov.uk
Sol: Harries, Delyth N LLB Principal Solicitor. . . . . Dec 1993
Jones, Miss Amanda LLB(Hons); LPC Solicitor . . . . Feb 2000
Raynor, Kurt N A LLB. . . . . *Apr 1974
Willis, Mrs Lynda BA Principal Solicitor . . . . *Jul 1980

POOLE

BOROUGH OF POOLE
Legal and Democratic Services Room 159 Civic Centre Poole BH15 2RU
Tel: 01202 262808 *Fax:* 01202 262818 *Dx:* 123820 POOLE 7
E-mail: dhamerton@poole.gov.uk
Sol: Ashley, Mrs Diana J A BA. . . . . *Nov 1984
Housego, Ms Shirley-Ellen Elizabeth LLB; ACMA . . . Sep 2002
Martin, Mr Timothy M LLB(Hons) . . . . *Feb 1988
Mondon, Mrs Sara J . . . . *Jan 1999
Thorne, Miss Katrina J BSc(Hons); DipLS. . . . . . . *Jan 1999
Woodroffe, Mr Peter W H BA(Hons). . . . . *Dec 1978

POOLE MAGISTRATES COURT
Law Courts Park Road Poole BH15 2RJ
Tel: 01202 745309 *Fax:* 01202 711996 *Dx:* 123822 POOLE 7
Sol: Barcham, Miss Gaye B Principal Legal Adviser . . . . Dec 1987

PORT TALBOT, Neath Port Talbot

NEATH PORT TALBOT COUNTY BOROUGH COUNCIL
Civic Centre Port Talbot Neath Port Talbot SA11 3QZ
Tel: 01639 763333 *Fax:* 01639 763370 *Dx:* 135226 PORT TALBOT 2
Sol: Anthony, Ms Joanne LLB; DipLP Solicitor . . . . Nov 1994
Davies, Mr Iwan G H LLB(Wales) Senior Solicitor . . . Apr 1988
Davies, Mr Stephen Keith LLB(Hons) Senior Lawyer. . Aug 1993
John, Mrs Carole A LLB(Wales) Head of Legal Services . . . . Dec 1974
Jones, Mrs Sharon Rebecca LLB; MA Lawyer/Solicitor Apr 2000
Michael, Mr David LLB(Wales) Assistant Director (Legal Services) . . . . *Dec 1983
Rees, Mr David A P LLB Senior Solicitor . . . . Mar 1983
Roderick, Mr Aled W MSc Property Solicitor. . . . . . Jan 1989
Watkins, Mr Paul Solicitor. . . . . May 1999

PORTISHEAD, North Somerset

AVON & SOMERSET CONSTABULARY
PO Box 37 Valley Road Portishead North Somerset BS20 8QJ
Tel: 01275 816270 *Fax:* 01275 814522
E-mail: sue.dauncey@avonandsomerset.police.uk
Sol: Adieze, Mr Okechukwu LLB(Hons) Assistant Solicitor . Apr 2004
Dauncey, Ms Susan A LLB Solicitor to Chief Constable Nov 1980
Hagley, Ms Juliet Karen BA(Hons)(Law & English) Senior Lawyer . . . . *Feb 1987
Johnson, Mr Daniel BA; CPE; LPC Lawyer . . . . . . Aug 2005
Molnar, Ms Lilian BA(Hons)(Law) Senior Lawyer. . . *Feb 1985
Parsons, Mrs Melanie LLB Lawyer . . . . .Jul 2006

PORTSMOUTH

PORTSMOUTH CITY COUNCIL
Civic Offices Guildhall Square Portsmouth PO1 2PX
Tel: 023 9283 4034 *Fax:* 023 9283 4076 *Dx:* 2244 PORTSMOUTH
Sol: Barratt, Mrs Susan Solicitor. . . . . *Oct 1993
Blair, Mrs Tracy Ann LLB(Hons); DipLP Solicitor. . . . Jan 2004
Clark, Mr Ian J BA Solicitor . . . . *Oct 1989
Cox, Mrs Mary J Head of Legal Services . . . . *Mar 1990
Kerr, Mr Stephen P BA(Lond); LLM Solicitor. . . . . . *Dec 1975
Lawther, Mr Michael Terence BA City Solicitor. . . . . *Dec 1986
Patrick, Mr Neil R LLB(Hons) Solicitor. . . . . *Apr 1993
Price, Miss Judith H LLB Solicitor . . . . *Oct 1993
Spencer, Ms Lesley LPC Solicitor . . . . *Nov 1996

PORTSMOUTH MAGISTRATES COURT
The Law Courts Winston Churchill Avenue Portsmouth PO1 2DQ
Tel: 023 9281 9421
Sol: Marshall, Mrs Carolyn D LLB Solicitor. . . . . Oct 1988
Morgan, Mr James Simon LLB(Ashcroft) Solicitor . . . Oct 1992
Oakford, Mrs Julia BA; DMS Deputy Clerk to the Justices . . . . Sep 1983
Redstone, Ms Gillian DML Solicitor . . . . Dec 1992
Titcombe, Ms Andrea D Solicitor. . . . . Jan 1991
Tricker, Ms Kim L DML Senior Legal Adviser . . . . . *Feb 1990

POULTON-LE-FYLDE, Lancashire

WYRE BOROUGH COUNCIL
Wyre Civic Centre Breck Road Poulton-le-Fylde Lancashire FY6 7PU
Tel: 01253 891000 *Fax:* 01253 899000
Sol: Grimshaw, Miss Mary B LLB(Hons) Senior Solicitor . . *Oct 1990
Matthew, Miss Wendy BA(Hons); PGDipLaw Assistant Solicitor . . . . Apr 2004
O'Connor, Miss Elizabeth A LLB(Hons) Legal Services Manager . . . . *Feb 1985

PRESTON, Lancashire

LANCASHIRE COUNTY COUNCIL
PO Box 78 County Hall Preston Lancashire PR1 8XJ
Tel: 01772 254868 *Fax:* 01772 533612
Sol: Anderson, Miss Jill K LLB Solicitor. . . . . *Oct 1985
Baxter, Miss Jillian BA(Hons)(Law) Assistant Solicitor . *Jan 1993
Blackburn, Miss Ruth Margaret LLB(Hons) Solicitor . . *Nov 1994
Blinkho, Mr Ian Graeme LLB(Hons); PGDip Principal Solicitor . . . . *Feb 1990
Bradshaw, Miss Diane BA Solicitor . . . . *Oct 2004
Brewer, Miss Lynn LLB; MSc; LG Dip Solicitor. . . . . Mar 2002
Buksmann, Ms Judy LLB Principal Solicitor:Child Protection . . . . *Jan 1990
Croall, Mr David E LLB(Hons) Senior Solicitor. . . . . *Jul 1980
Cullen, Miss Beverley BA(Business Studies) Assistant Group Head (Community Services). . . . . *Oct 1994
Dalton, Miss Louisa Jane LLB(Hons); PGDip Solicitor . *Sep 2005
Fisher, Mr Ian M BA(Hons) Head of Legal Services . . *Dec 1986
Green, Miss Rachel Elizabeth LLB(Hons) . . . . . . *May 2003
Hayes, Mrs Kerian Elizabeth LLB(Hons). . . . . *Jul 2004
Isbister, Mr Leslie J BA(Law) Solicitor . . . . *Apr 1985
Johnson, Mrs Julia LLB; MA Solicitor . . . . *Feb 2003
Johnson, Ms Valerie May BSc(Hons); CPE; LPC Solicitor . . . . *Feb 2003
Martin, Mrs Judith A LLB Childcare Solicitor. . . . . . *Oct 1991
Moon, Miss Rosemary LLB(Hons)(Law) Assistant Solicitor . . . . *Apr 1996
Murray, Mr Ian P BA(Law). . . . . *Mar 1983
Naderi, Mrs Dawn LLB(Hons); DipLG; PGDip EdLaw Assistant Group Head (Child Protection) . . . . *Oct 1988
Sales, Miss Laura LLB Assistant Unit Manager . . . . *Nov 1986
Sandford, Mr Paul David LLB Solicitor. . . . . Oct 2002
Smallwood, Mrs Elizabeth A LLB Senior Principal Solicitor . . . . *Jun 1970
Taylforth, Mrs Rebecca BA(Hons) Solicitors . . . . . . *Mar 1998
Taylor, Mr Philip J Senior Solicitor. . . . . *Jul 1974
Turner, Mrs P Jane LLB Senior Solicitor. . . . . *Oct 1984
Vickery, Mrs Samantha Jane LLB(Hons) Solicitor . . . *Aug 2002
Williams-White, Mr Christian Jon Dominic BA(Hons) Solicitor . . . . Oct 2001
Young, Mr Ian BA(Hons) Assistant Head of Legal Services . . . . *Oct 1987

LAND REGISTRY - LANCASHIRE OFFICE
Wrea Brook Court Lytham Road Warton Preston Lancashire PR4 1TE
Tel: 01772 836700 *Fax:* 01772 836970 *Dx:* 721560 LYTHAM 6
Sol: Barr, Mrs A L Assistant Land Registrar . . . . Nov 1989
Cook, Mrs Stephanie J Assistant Land Registrar. . . . Oct 1996
Morrell, Mr Terry Assistant Land Registrar. . . . . . . Oct 1996
Morrison, Miss Laura Elizabeth LLB Assistant Land Registar . . . . Feb 2002
Wallwork, Mrs Lorraine Land Registrar . . . . Feb 1977

PRESTON BOROUGH COUNCIL
Town Hall Preston Lancashire PR1 2RL
Tel: 01772 906101 *Fax:* 01772 906323
Sol: Bremers, Mr John Edward Assistant Director (Corporate Projects) . . . . *Jun 1976
Elwood, Mrs Caroline J LLB(Manc); Dip Loc Govmt Law Director of Corporate Services. . . . . *Nov 1982
Haley, Mr David MA(Cantab) Group Solicitor (Criminal & Regulation) . . . . *§Aug 1979
Harrison, Mrs Shirley A LLB(Hull) Assistant Director (Legal & Administration) . . . . *Apr 1980
Heath, Miss Beryl LLB Head of Legal Services . . . . *Oct 1982
Smith, Miss Lisa-Marie LLB(Hons) Solicitor . . . . . . *Jan 1999

SOUTH RIBBLE BOROUGH COUNCIL
Civic Centre West Paddock Preston Lancashire PR25 1DH
Tel: 01772 421491 *Fax:* 01772 625283
E-mail: legal@southribble.gov.uk
Sol: Gray, Mrs Karen LLB(Hons) Principal Solicitor. . . . . *Sep 1998
Rich, Mr Anthony John Edmund TD TD; MA; LLB; DipLG; FCMI Head of Legal and Democratic Services Deputy District Judge. . . . . *§Apr 1981
Safdar, Ms Tasneem LLB(Hons) Solicitor . . . . *May 2003
Wheelan, Mr David BA(Hons) Legal Practice Manager. *Jan 1987

RAWTENSTALL, Lancashire

ROSSENDALE BOROUGH COUNCIL
Town Hall Rawtenstall Lancashire BB4 7LZ
Tel: 01706 217777 *Fax:* 01706 873577
E-mail: rossendalebc@compuserve.com
Sol: Lester, Mr Richard W LLB Assistant Solicitor . . . . . *Apr 1973

READING

BANK OF IRELAND HOME MORTGAGES LTD
Plaza West Bridge Street Reading RG1 2LZ
Tel: 01734 393393 *Fax:* 01734 587040 *Dx:* 4029 READING
Sol: Forsyth, Mrs Jill LLB(Hons) Company Solicitor. . . . . Apr 1981

CITI FINANCIAL EUROPE PLC
Citigroup Centre Canada Square London E14 5LB
E-mail: john.nightingale@citi.com
Sol: Foster, Miss Alexandra LLB(Hons) Solicitor . . . . . . *Mar 1985
Hall, Mr Michael J LLB(Lond) Solicitor. . . . . *Nov 1972
Nightingale, Mr John Alan BA(CNAA) Solicitor. . . . . Sep 1983
Travis, Mr David Roy BA(Hons)(Law & French); DipLP Solicitor . . . . *Sep 2001
Waxler, Ms Raquel LLB(Hons) Solicitor . . . . *Nov 1990

ENVIRONMENT AGENCY (THAMES REGION)
Kings Meadow House Kings Meadow Road Reading RG1 8DQ
Tel: 0870 850 6506 *Fax:* 0118 950 0388 *Dx:* 121325 READING
Sol: Allen, Miss Suzanne Lesley LLB(Hons); LSF Solicitor (In-house Litigation). *Jan 1991
Carty, Mr Peter C LLM Principal Solicitor . . . . Jul 1989
Graydon, Mr Jeremy Robert Martin LLB(Hons) Principal Solicitor . . . . Nov 1987
Hayhurst, Ms Penelope Siobhan Principal Solicitor . . Feb 2001
Plytas, Mr Anthony J LLB; DMA Regional Solicitor. . . *Mar 1981
Kochanek, Mr Barry Francis LSF . . . . *Jan 1971

GIBB LTD
Gibb House London Road Reading RG6 1BL
Tel: 0118 963 5000 *Fax:* 0118 949 1054
E-mail: mnorris@gibb.co.uk
Sol: Norris, Mr Michael T MA(Cantab) Solr, Commercial Director . . . . *Nov 1983

LEGAL SERVICES COMMISSION
Dukesbridge House 23 Duke Street Reading RG1 4SA
Tel: 0118 955 8600
Sol: Ederley Harris, Mrs Adrienne A LLB Solicitor . . . . . Aug 1980
Keith, Miss Helen LLB Senior Solicitor. . . . . *Oct 1986
Pinks, Miss Anne E LLB Area Manager . . . . *Oct 1975
Rosenak, Ms Anita O H E BA Solicitor. . . . . *Oct 1986

READING BOROUGH COUNCIL
Civic Offices Civic Centre Reading RG1 7AE
Tel: 0118 939 0900 *Fax:* 0118 939 0767
Dx: 40124 READING (CASTLE STREET)
Sol: Atkinson, Mr Andrew Charles LLB(Hons)(Dunelm) Principal Solicitor. . . . . *May 1995
Batty, Mrs Elizabeth J BSc(Hons) Solicitor. . . . . . . *Dec 2003
Binitie, Mrs Jite LLB; LPC Solicitor . . . . *Oct 2004
Bradbeer, Miss Shirley J BA(Hons) Senior Solicitor . . *Feb 1983
Brooks, Mr Christopher J BSc Solicitor . . . . *Nov 1986
Castle, Miss Sarah Jane BA; DipLaw Solicitor Kent Women Solicitors . . . . *Aug 1994
Gibson, Mrs Eleanor B J MA(Hons) Solicitor. . . . . . *Nov 1991
Gillard, Mrs Alexandra Jane BA(Hons); MBA . . . . . Apr 1988
Lacey, Miss Katherine A BA Solicitor . . . . *Nov 1989
Leslie, Mr Simon C BA(Hons); MBA Maxwell Law Prize 1978 Solicitor. . . . . Apr 1983
Obradovic, Mrs Susan E LLB(Lond) Solicitor . . . . . *§Jul 1978
Sharma, Miss Sanowar LLB(Hons) Solicitor . . . . . . May 1992
Sillett, Mr Andrew E W Solicitor . . . . *Jun 1976
Smith, Mrs Umera BA(Hons) Solicitor Local Authority. Dec 2000
Thomas, Mrs Karen E LLB Solicitor . . . . *Dec 1979
Thomlinson, Mrs Alara Ruth BA(Hons) Housing LawyerSep 1994
Wingrove, Mrs Ruth Mary Solicitor. . . . . Oct 2000
Wolfle, Mr Christopher J BA(Hons) Solicitor . . . . . . May 1996

T B I FINANCIAL SERVICES LTD
1st Floor The Robert Cort Building Elgar Road South Reading RG2 0DL
Tel: 0118 931 3800 *Fax:* 0118 975 2296
Sol: Birch, Miss Louise BA; LPC Assistant Solicitor. . . . *Apr 2008
Jones, Mr David Frank Donaldson LLB Company Secretary & Legal Director. *Jul 1980

THAMES WATER UTILITIES LIMITED
Clearwater Court Vastern Road Reading RG1 8DB
Tel: 0118 373 8000 *Fax:* 0118 373 8500
Sol: Adshead, Mrs Anna Michelle . . . . Oct 1998
Beeson, Mr Peter G Solicitor . . . . *Dec 1989
Bhogal, Mrs Tirpat Kaur LLB(Hons) Solicitor. . . . . . Sep 2000
Byrne, Mr Simon H B Juris; LLB Legal Services Manager . . . . *Aug 1992
Chapman, Mr Colin LLB Solicitor Water Operations . . Apr 1979
De Viell, Miss Marie L LLB Litigation Solicitor . . . . *Nov 1991
Goldfinch, Ms Marjorie BA. . . . . Sep 2005
Mendham, Mr Stephen Russell BA(Hons) . . . . Oct 1983
Smith, Mrs Sarah J BA(Hons) Solicitor . . . . Jan 2000
Turner, Mr Matthew A LLB Solicitor . . . . *Oct 1999

REDCAR, Redcar & Cleveland

ICI CHEMICALS & POLYMERS LTD
Wilton Centre Redcar Redcar & Cleveland TS10 4RF
Tel: 01642 435629 *Fax:* 01642 435622
E-mail: john_kay@ici.com
Sol: Goodfellow, Dr John Alexander PhD; BSc(Hons) Litigation Manager . . . . Aug 1999

REDDITCH, Worcestershire

GKN PLC (LEGAL DEPT)
PO Box 55 Ipsley House Ipsley Church Lane Redditch Worcestershire B98 0TL
Tel: 01527 517715 *Fax:* 01527 533470
Sol: Brostoff, Mr Martin A LLB(Manc) Senior Legal Adviser. *Oct 1994
Hughes, Mr David Andrew LLB; LPC Senior Legal Adviser . . . . *Sep 1998
Radford, Mr David N G LLB Deputy Head of Legal Department . . . . *Oct 1987
Thomson, Mr Gary A BSc(Hons); CPE; LPC; Dip IP Law & Practice CPHYS; MInstP Senior Legal Adviser - IP *Oct 1997

REDDITCH BOROUGH COUNCIL
Town Hall Walter Stranz Square Redditch Worcestershire B98 8AH
Tel: 01527 64252 *Fax:* 01527 65216 *Dx:* 19106 REDDITCH
Sol: Flanagan, Ms Clare BCL Legal Services Manager. . . *Dec 1999
Hussain, Mr Amar BA(Hons) Solicitor . . . . Feb 2005
Mullins, Ms Susan Jane Elizabeth LLB(with French) Head of Legal Demographic & Property Services . . . . . . *Nov 1995
Teepe, Mr Andreas BA Senior Solicitor . . . . Sep 1993

REIGATE, Surrey

REIGATE & BANSTEAD BOROUGH COUNCIL
Town Hall Reigate Surrey RH2 0SH
Tel: 01737 276000 *Fax:* 01737 276070 *Dx:* 54102 REIGATE 2
Sol: Coronel, Ms Debra Ann BA(Law) Head of Legal & Property Services . . . . *Feb 1987
Ogden, Mrs Yvonne S LLB Solicitor. . . . . *Apr 1980

RICHMOND, North Yorkshire

RICHMONDSHIRE DISTRICT COUNCIL
Swale House Frenchgate Richmond North Yorkshire DL10 4JE
Tel: 01748 829100 *Fax:* 01748 825071
Dx: 65047 RICHMOND NORTH YORKS
Sol: McKeon, Mr Callum LLB(Hons) Head of Legal ServicesDec 1995

RICHMOND UPON THAMES, Surrey

BELRON INTERNATIONAL LTD
Milton Park Stroude Road Egham Surrey TW20 9EL
Tel: 01784 476800 *Fax:* 01784 472900
Sol: Bass, Mr Robert LLB(Leeds) Assistant General Counsel . . . *Oct 1983
Lane, Ms Jennifer A Legal Adviser . . . *Jan 1984

FAIR TRIALS ABROAD TRUST
Bench House Ham Street Richmond upon Thames Surrey TW10 7HR
Tel: 020 8332 2800 *Fax:* 020 8332 2800
Sol: Jakobi, Mr Stephen R BA(Cantab). . . . *Jun 1969

RICHMOND UPON THAMES MAGISTRATES COURT
The Court House Parkshot Richmond upon Thames Surrey TW9 2RF
Tel: 020 8948 2101 *Fax:* 020 8332 2628 *Dx:* 100257 RICHMOND 2
Sol: Akinyanju, Babatunde LLB Principal Legal Adviser. . . Jun 1995
Lowdell, Mr David K BA Clerk to the Justices . . . Jan 1967

RICKMANSWORTH, Hertfordshire

CADBURY SCHWEPPES EUROPE, MIDDLE EAST & AFRICA
Commercial Centre Hertford Place Denham Way Rickmansworth Hertfordshire WD3 9XB
Tel: 01923 483483
E-mail: ghada.yazbeck@csplc.com
Sol: Yazbeck, Mrs Ghada LLM(Washington) Region Counsel . . . Mar 1993

SKANSKA UK PLC
Maple Cross House Denham Way Maple Cross Rickmansworth Hertfordshire WD3 9SW
Tel: 01923 776666 *Fax:* 01923 423864
Sol: Chapman, Mr Adrian J BSc(Hons) Solicitor . . . *Oct 1992
Collingwood, Mr Martin B BA(Law); ACIArb Legal Advisor . . . *Jul 1981
Cornwell, Mr Nigel R BA(Bris) Solicitor . . . *§May 1982
Galloway, Mr Mark L BA Solicitor . . . *May 1981
Westbury, Mr Richard J M BA; LLB(Alberta); MSc; LLM Legal Advisor . . . *Aug 1987

THREE RIVERS DISTRICT COUNCIL
Three Rivers House Northway Rickmansworth Hertfordshire WD3 1RL
Tel: 01923 776611 *Fax:* 01923 727213
Dx: 38271 RICKMANSWORTH
Sol: Jeal, Ms Jacqueline A Solicitor . . . May 1974
Morgan, Mrs Anne E LLB(Wales) Solr to the Council *Sep 1983

RIPLEY, Derbyshire

AMBER VALLEY BOROUGH COUNCIL
Town Hall Market Place Ripley Derbyshire DE5 3XE
Tel: 01773 570222 *Fax:* 01773 841616
E-mail: enquiry@ambervalley.gov.uk
Sol: Benski, Mr Paul M LLB Principal Solicitor . . . *Jun 1986
Carney, Mr Peter M Chief Executive. . . . *Jul 1984

ROCHDALE, Greater Manchester

ROCHDALE METROPOLITAN BOROUGH COUNCIL
PO Box 15 Town Hall The Esplanade Rochdale Greater Manchester OL16 1AB
Tel: 01706 647474 *Fax:* 01706 864755 *Dx:* 22831 ROCHDALE
E-mail: catherine.witham@rochdale.gov.uk
Sol: Barker, Ms Heather D LLB Solicitor . . . *Jun 1980
Burley, Mr Keith LLB Solicitor . . . *Nov 1975
Butterfield, Mrs Ann Katherine BA(Hons) Solicitor (Social Services) . . . *Feb 1987
Coyne, Ms Lynn E Solicitor . . . *Aug 1993
Cunningham, Ms Elizabeth LLB Solicitor. . . . Jan 1980
Dargan-Cole, Mrs Anne Michelle BSocSc Solicitor. . *Nov 1992
Earl, Mr Timothy James LLB(Hons) Senior Solicitor . *Nov 1998
McCondach, Mr Ian BSc(Hons) Meritorious Performance (Law Society) 1998. . . . *Dec 1998
Moss, Ms Jennifer BA; MA; DipLG Senior Social Services Solicitor. . . . *May 1990
Mukhtar, Mrs Rifat BA(Hons); PGDip Legal Assistant *Nov 2007
Shah, Miss Asimah LLB Solicitor . . . *Jan 2004
Taylor, Ms Anne Assistant Borough Solicitor. . . . *Feb 1989
Witham, Ms Catherine LLB(Hons); LLM(Harv) Lancaster Morcambe & District Law Prize 1992 Borough Solicitor . . . Sep 2002

ROCHDALE MIDDLETON & HEYWOOD MAGISTRATES COURT
Court House Town Meadows Rochdale Greater Manchester OL16 1AR
Tel: 01706 514800 *Fax:* 01706 514850
Sol: Wood, Mr Frederick BA Head of Legal Services Head of Legal Services . . . *Jan 1984

ROCHFORD, Essex

ROCHFORD DISTRICT COUNCIL
Council Offices 3-19 South Street Rochford Essex SS4 1BW
Tel: 01702 546366 *Fax:* 01702 545737 *Dx:* 39751 ROCHFORD
E-mail: legal.services@rochford.gov.uk
Sol: Honey, Mr Richard J BA Corporate Director (Law,Planning & Administration) . . . *§Jun 1980
Khan, Mr Nicholas LLB(Hons) Solicitor . . . *Apr 2004
Law, Miss Angela Sau-chun LLB(Hons) Solicitor. . . *Jun 2004

ROMFORD, Essex

HAVERING MAGISTRATES' COURT
Court House 19 Main Road Romford Essex RM1 3BH
Tel: 0845 601 3600 *Fax:* 01708 794270 *Dx:* 131527 ROMFORD 8
Sol: Came, Mr Richard Harold Senior Legal Adviser . . . *Nov 2001
Nunn, Mrs Natasha Jane LLB Legal Adviser. . . . Jan 1997
Shirlaw, Mrs Sara B Senior Legal Adviser . . . *Feb 1990

ROTHERHAM, South Yorkshire

ROTHERHAM MAGISTRATES COURT
District Legal Director The Statutes Rotherham South Yorkshire S60 1YW
Tel: 01709 839339 *Fax:* 01709 370082 *Dx:* 12619 ROTHERHAM
Sol: Banks, Ms Joanne M LLB(Hons); CMS Legal Services Manager . . . Dec 1987
Bowler, Mr Neil LLB Solicitor . . . Mar 1996
Cooper, Ms Alison LLB(Hons) Solicitor . . . Feb 1998
Kaye, Mrs Karen Mary Solicitor . . . *Jul 1992
O'Dowd, Mr Christopher Gerard MBA; LLB(Hons) District Legal Director. . . . Dec 1990
Parker-Gray, Mrs Kimberley Frances LLM; LLB Court Clerk . . . *May 1993

ROTHERHAM METROPOLITAN BOROUGH COUNCIL
Civic Building Walker Place Rotherham South Yorkshire S65 1UF
Tel: 01709 382121 *Fax:* 01709 823598
Sol: Concannon, Mr Neil Paul LPC; PSC Solicitor . . . Oct 2001
Doyle, Lesley Anne Solicitor. . . . Nov 1994
Fisher, Mrs Anne LLB(Hons); DLP Solicitor . . . *Oct 1996
Fletcher, Mr Stuart John LLB(Hons) Head of Litigation *Nov 1995
Gledhill, Mr Ian R MA(Cantab) Principal Office (Legal) *Mar 1985
Hobson, Ms Ruth BA; MSc; CPE; LPC Solicitor. . . . Jul 2002
Jeffries, Miss Frances Alyx BA(Hons) Solicitor. . . *Sep 1985
Johnson, Miss Madeleine PGD Solicitor. . . . *Dec 1988
MacDonald, Mr Kenneth Ewan BA; LLB Solicitor . . *Mar 1991
Marjoram, Miss Rebecca Jane LLB Solicitor. . . . *May 2006
Masheder, Mr Iain George BA(Hons)(Law) Solicitor . . *Jun 1977
Mumford, Mr Timothy C MA(Oxon) Director of Legal Services . . . *Aug 1973
Reilly, Ms Mary Katherine LLB(Hons); LPC Solicitor . . Aug 2004
Steele, Linton H LLB(Manch) Solicitor. . . . *Mar 1980
Waller, Mr Richard LLB Solicitor. . . . *Feb 1991

RUGBY, Warwickshire

RUGBY BOROUGH COUNCIL
Town Hall Evreux Way Rugby Warwickshire CV21 2LB
Tel: 01788 533533 *Fax:* 01788 533409 *Dx:* 11681 RUGBY
E-mail: marie.filcek@rugby.gov.uk
Sol: Bradford, Ms Carol A LLB Head of Legal & Administration . . . *Oct 1983
Gabbitas, Mr Andrew A LLB Director of Corporate Services . . . *Jul 1979
Tyrrell, Mrs Deborah G LLB Solicitor. . . . *Oct 1987

RUNCORN, Cheshire

HALTON MAGISTRATES COURT
The Law Courts Halton Lea Runcorn Cheshire WA7 2HA
Tel: 01928 716130 *Fax:* 01928 790150 *Dx:* 17793 WARRINGTON 1
Sol: Swift, Mr Donald C LLB(B'ham) Justices' Clerk . . . *Jul 1970

RUTHIN, Denbighshire

DENBIGHSHIRE COUNTY COUNCIL
County Hall Wynnstay Road Ruthin Denbighshire LL15 1YN
Tel: 01824 706000 *Fax:* 01824 706293 *Dx:* 21839 RUTHIN
E-mail: dcc-legal@denbighshire.gov.uk
Sol: Brookes, Miss Amanda Jane LLB(Hons) Project Manager . . . *Sep 1996
Carter, Mr David M Legal Officer . . . Jan 1983
Cordiner, Mrs Susan A LLB Solicitor. . . . *Apr 1989
Griffiths, Miss Jane Elizabeth BA Solicitor. . . . Jan 2007
Grisdale, Miss Nia LLB Solicitor. . . . *Sep 2002
Hearle, Mr Ian K BA County Clerk. . . . *Jul 1980
Kennedy, Miss Jane R LLB(Hons)(Lond) DipLG; LARTPI Legal Services Manager. . . . *Nov 1976
Kyte, Ms Vanessa Elizabeth Solicitor . . . Feb 2003
Morgan-Platt, Mrs Catharine Anne Louise LLB(Hons) *May 1996
Roberts, Miss Heidi BA Solicitor. . . . *Sep 2002
Wright, Mrs Alison LLB(Hons) Solicitor . . . *Jan 2001

SAFFRON WALDEN, Essex

UTTLESFORD DISTRICT COUNCIL
Council Offices London Road Uttlesford Saffron Walden Essex CB11 4ER
Tel: 01799 510510 *Fax:* 01799 516550
Dx: 200307 SAFFRON WALDEN
E-mail: legal@uttlesford.gov.uk
Sol: Nicholson, Mrs Catherine LLB(Hons); PGDip . . . Nov 2003
Oliva, Ms C M LLB; LG dip . . . Nov 1996
Perry, Mr Michael John LLB(Hons) Head of Legal Services . . . *Oct 1975

SALFORD, Greater Manchester

HM REVENUE & CUSTOMS
Solicitor's Office Ralli Quays (West) 3 Stanley Street Salford Greater Manchester M60 9LB
Tel: 0870 785 8545 *Fax:* 0870 785 8528 *Dx:* 742371 SALFORD 20
Sol: Boddy, Mr John Nicholas BA(Hons) Lawyer. . . . *Dec 1992
Bolton, Mr Gary Stewart LLB(Hons) Lawyer. . . . *Jan 1991
Foster, Mrs Eve BSc(Hons); PGDipLaw Lawyer. . . . Oct 2000
Morris, Miss Millie Caroline LLB(Hons) Senior Lawyer *Nov 1992
Mortcock, Miss Jacqueline Anne Solicitor . . . Sep 2006
Nightingale, Mrs Maksuda Bibi LLB(Hons) Lawyer. . . Aug 1998
Seehra, Mrs Amrita BA(Hons); MA; PGDipLaw Solicitor . . . Nov 2002
Shaw, Mr Richard William Henry LLB Senior Lawyer. . *Oct 1988
Stewart, Mrs Emma BA(Jt Hons)(Law with German) Lawyer . . . *Jul 2002
Taylor, Miss Paula M LLB(Hons) Senior Lawyer . . . *Oct 1993
Tepper, Mrs Jane MA(Oxon); PGD(European Law) Lawyer . . . *Jan 1979
Whelan, Miss Kathryn A LLB Senior Lawyer. . . . *Jan 1989

CITY OF SALFORD MAGISTRATES COURT
Town Hall Bexley Square Salford Greater Manchester M3 6DJ
Tel: 0161 834 9457 *Fax:* 0161 839 1806 *Dx:* 708270 SALFORD
Sol: McNeill, Mr Terence Joseph MIPD Solicitor Clerk to the Justices . . . *Jan 1987

SALISBURY, Wiltshire

SALISBURY MAGISTRATES COURT
43-55 Milford Street Salisbury Wiltshire SP1 2BP
Tel: 01722 333225 *Fax:* 01722 413395 *Dx:* 58022 SALISBURY
Sol: Wilcock, Mr Graham P DML Solicitor . . . *Sep 1986

SANDBACH, Cheshire

CONGLETON BOROUGH COUNCIL
Westfields Middlewich Road Sandbach Cheshire CW11 1HZ
Tel: 01270 763231 *Fax:* 01270 769323 *Dx:* 15658 SANDBACH
Sol: Byrom, Ms Sheela Jane LLB(Hons) Principal Solicitor *Nov 1992
Dillon, Ms Sheila H LLB(Manc) Principal Solicitor . . Feb 1987
Ingram, Mrs Margaret J BSc; MBA Law & Administration . . . *Oct 1980

SCARBOROUGH, North Yorkshire

SCARBOROUGH BOROUGH COUNCIL
Town Hall St Nicholas Street Scarborough North Yorkshire YO11 2HG
Tel: 01723 232348 *Fax:* 01723 501665
Dx: 719232 SCARBOROUGH 5
E-mail: philip.newell@scarborough.gov.uk
Sol: Bell, Mr Michael F LLB Planning & Litigation Solicitor *Mar 1984
Davison, Mr Richard LLB(Hons) Assistant Solicitor . *May 2002
Dixon, Mrs Lisa BA(Hons) Property & Contracts Solicitor . . . *Sep 1996
Newell, Mr Philip S LLB Head of Legal Services. . . *Dec 1974
Trebble, Mr John M LLB Chief Executive . . . *Mar 1973

SCUNTHORPE, North Lincolnshire

NORTH LINCOLNSHIRE COUNCIL
Pittwood House Ashby Road Scunthorpe North Lincolnshire DN16 1AB
Tel: 01724 296296 *Fax:* 01724 296219 *Dx:* 14717 SCUNTHORPE
Sol: Batt, Mr Simon John Linden LLB(Hons) Principal Solicitor . . . *Dec 1993
Bell, Mr William Stuart FILEx Solicitor. . . . Dec 1994
Burrell, Mrs Lucy Adele LLB Solicitor . . . May 2005
Coleman, Mrs Paula BA. . . . Feb 2002
Garbutt, Mr Michael LLB(Nott'm) Solicitor . . . *Dec 1975
Hogg, Mr Jonathan G LLB Solicitor . . . Sep 1981
Monaghan, Miss Sarah BA(Hons) Solicitor . . . *Nov 2001
Philips, Mr David John Principal Solicitor . . . Nov 1998
Taylor, Mrs Angela BA(Hons) Solicitor. . . . Sep 2005
Wilcockson, Mrs Valerie LLB; DipLG Solicitor . . . Jun 1979
Wood, Mr Michael LLB; DMS Solicitor. . . . *May 1971

SELBY, North Yorkshire

SELBY DISTRICT COUNCIL
Civic Centre Portholme Road Selby North Yorkshire YO8 0SB
Tel: 01757 705101 *Fax:* 01757 292229 *Dx:* 27408 SELBY
Sol: Burns, Mr Peter John Senior Solicitor . . . *May 1982
Crosby, Mrs Anneliese BA Assistant Solicitor . . . *Jan 2000

SEVENOAKS, Kent

SEVENOAKS DISTRICT COUNCIL
Council Offices Argyle Road Sevenoaks Kent TN13 1HQ
Tel: 01732 227000 *Fax:* 01732 227176 *Dx:* 30006 SEVENOAKS
Sol: Leach, Mr John W LLB(Lond) Principal Solicitor. . . *Dec 1972
Nuttall, Mrs Christine Jennifer LLB(Hons) Guild of Graduates Prize (Birmingham University) 1983 Head of Legal and Committee Services and Monitoring Officer . . . *Mar 1987
Stanfield, Mr Adrian T LLB(Hons) Legal Services Manager . . . *Mar 2001

SHEFFIELD, South Yorkshire

HENRY BOOT PLC
Banner Cross Hall Sheffield South Yorkshire S11 9PD
Tel: 0114 255 5444 *Fax:* 0114 258 7670
Sol: Foster, Mrs Eleanor S S LLB(Hons); MCIArb Group Solicitor . . . *Jan 1988

CLERK TO SHEFFIELD JUSTICES
Magistrates Court Castle Street Sheffield South Yorkshire S3 8LU
Tel: 0114 276 0760 *Fax:* 0114 272 0129 *Dx:* 10599 SHEFFIELD
Sol: Atkinson, Mr John M G Dip Mag Law; CPE; PGDipLP Senior Legal Adviser. . . . Dec 1995
Blagdon, Miss Sarah LLB(Hons) Senior Legal Adviser. Apr 1995
Dhar, Mrs Vrinda Senior Legal Adviser . . . Jan 1999
Fisher, Miss Elizabeth LLB District Legal Director . . *Dec 1980
Foster, Ms Sally LLB Legal Adviser . . . May 2005
Gabbitas, Mrs Emma Louise LLB(Hons)(Law) Legal Advisor . . . Apr 2004
Greco, Miss Maria Assunta Teresa LLB(Hons) Senior legal Adviser. . . . *Oct 1994
Head, Mr Gregory John LLB(Hons) Legal Adviser. . *Nov 2005
Lockwood, Mrs Margaret A LLB(Hons) Principal Legal Adviser . . . *Nov 1997
Ndungu, Miss Esther Wanjiru LLB Legal Adviser. . . *Jun 2004

 See p112 for the Key to Work Categories & other symbols

Spruce, Mr Tim A J LLB(Hons); MBA Legal Team Manager . . . *Feb 1994
Syed, Ms Sa-i-qah LLB Law Society Prize 2001 Legal Adviser . . . Nov 2005

SHEFFIELD CITY COUNCIL
Town Hall Surrey Street Sheffield South Yorkshire S1 2HH
Tel: 0114 273 4019 *Fax:* 0114 273 5003 *Dx:* 10580 SHEFFIELD
Sol: Bashforth, Mrs Elizabeth M BA(Law) Assistant Head of Deputy . . . *Feb 1983
Bashir, Mrs Salma LLB(Hons) Solicitor . . . Jun 1998
Broadhurst, Ms Deborah LLB(Hons) Solicitor . . . *Oct 1997
Chisholm, Mr Patrick Hugh LLB Senior Solicitor . . . Oct 2002
Chisolm, Ms Ruth Alison LLB Solicitor (Litigation) . . . *Dec 1994
Eaton, Ms Deborah J BA(Hons) Principal Solicitor . . . *Jun 1990
Eccleston, Mr Steve BSc Senior Solicitor . . . *Nov 1991
Essam, Ms Cathryn BA Senior Solicitor . . . Jun 1988
Kempka, Mrs Patricia M LLB Senior Solicitor . . . Oct 1993
Sellar, Mr David Alexander Hendry LLB Solicitor . . . Dec 1995
Toogood, Mr Andrew A J LLB Principal Solicitor . . . *Dec 1975
Twaite, Mr Douglas LLB(Hons)(B'ham); ALCM Senior Solicitor . . . Apr 1977
Twomey, Mr Brendan Finbar BA(Hons); LSF Assistant Solicitor . . . *Feb 1994
Ward, Mr Julian G LLB Principal Solicitor . . . *Apr 1972
Woodhead, Mrs Frances BA(Law) Head of Legal Services . . . Jan 1985
Wormald, Mr Stephen Solicitor . . . Aug 2000
Wynter, Miss Nadine LLB(Hons) Assistant Solicitor . . . Dec 2003

SHEFFIELD LAW CENTRE
Waverley House 10 Joiner Street Sheffield South Yorkshire S3 8GW
Tel: 0114 273 1501
E-mail: post@slc.org.uk
Sol: Nelson, Ms Hilary Solicitor . . . Apr 1988
Petrie, Ms Jane E BA; MA; MA Senior Solicitor . . . *Nov 1984

SOUTH YORKSHIRE PASSENGER TRANSPORT EXECUTIVE
11 Broad Street West Sheffield South Yorkshire S1 2BQ
Tel: 0114 276 7575 *Fax:* 0114 275 9908
Sol: Davenport, Mr Stephen C Legal Services Manager . . . *Feb 1998
Elliott, Miss Jacqueline PGDipLaw; LPC Solicitor . . . Oct 2007
Gandy, Ms Lorraine LLB(Hons) Principal Solicitor & Secretary to the Executive . . . *Oct 1992

TUFFNELLS PARCELS EXPRESS LTD
Shepcote House Shepcote Lane Sheffield South Yorkshire S9 1UW
Tel: 0114 256 1111 *Fax:* 0114 256 0459
Sol: Gregory, Mr Paul H LLB Managing Director . . . *Jun 1977

SHEFFORD, Bedfordshire

MID BEDFORDSHIRE DISTRICT COUNCIL
Priory House Monks Walk Chicksands Shefford Bedfordshire SG17 5TQ
Tel: 0845 230 4040 *Dx:* 153440 SHEFFORD
Sol: Lyons, Miss Susan E BA Managing Solicitor . . . *Feb 1988
Morris, Mrs Barbara H Director of Corporate & Democratic Services . . . *Jan 1991
Woolsey, Mr Mark LLB(Hons); PGDipLP Solicitor . . . *Oct 2006

SHEPTON MALLET, Somerset

MENDIP DISTRICT COUNCIL
Council Offices Cannards Grave Road Shepton Mallet Somerset BA4 5BT
Tel: 01749 343399 *Fax:* 01749 341422
Dx: 43001 SHEPTON MALLET
E-mail: i'ansona@mendip.gov.uk
Sol: I'Anson, Mr Adrian F Solicitor . . . *Jul 1974

SHOREHAM-BY-SEA, West Sussex

ADUR DISTRICT COUNCIL
Civic Centre Ham Road Shoreham-by-Sea West Sussex BN43 6PR
Tel: 01273 263300 *Fax:* 01273 263075
Dx: 59765 SHOREHAM-BY-SEA
E-mail: jeremy.cook@adur.gov.uk
Sol: Ashton, Mr Robert Joseph Michael LLB Assistant Solicitor . . . Dec 1974
Cook, Mr Jeremery O LLB(Hons) Head of Legal and Democratic Services . . . Jul 1982
Sale, Mrs Susan C BA(Hons); CPE; LPC Assistant Solicitor . . . *Nov 1999

SHREWSBURY, Shropshire

SECURITY INVESTMENTS (INDUSTRIAL) LTD
Benbow Business Park Harlescott Lane Shrewsbury Shropshire SY1 3EQ
Tel: 01743 454455 *Fax:* 01743 454457
Sol: Yaxley, Mr Christopher W LLB; FCA; ATII Solicitor . . . *Feb 1974

SHREWSBURY AND ATCHAM BOROUGH COUNCIL
The Guildhall Frankwell Quay Shrewsbury Shropshire SY3 8HQ
Tel: 01743 281000 *Fax:* 01743 281040
E-mail: legal@shrewsbury-atcham.gov.uk
Sol: Gordon, Mr Christopher Dip LG Senior Solicitor . . . *Jun 1972
Hosker, Mr John MA; DipLG Assistant Solicitor . . . *Mar 1989
White, Mr Graham John LLB Assistant Solicitor . . . *May 2002

SIDMOUTH, Devon

EAST DEVON DISTRICT COUNCIL
Station Road Knowle Sidmouth Devon EX10 8HL
Tel: 01395 516551 *Fax:* 01395 517507 *Dx:* 48705 SIDMOUTH
Sol: Pocock, Ms Rachel Laura LLB(Lond); MBA Head of Legal and Member Services . . . *Aug 1981
Salter, Mr Giles Edward BA(Hons) Assistant . . . *Oct 2005

Seddon, Mr Andrew Harvey BA; ACIS Senior Solicitor . *Oct 1982
Williams, Mr Mark R LLB(Hons); MBA; DipLG Chief Executive (Non-practising Solicitor) . . . *Oct 1985

SILSDEN, West Yorkshire

LILY DRIVER INVESTMENTS
Crossfield Skipton Road Silsden West Yorkshire BD20 9AA
Tel: 01535 653959 *Fax:* 01535 657605
E-mail: tjrwilson@clara.co.uk
Sol: Wilson, Mr Timothy John Ratcliffe MSc; FRSA Partner Notary Public . . . Nov 1971

SITTINGBOURNE, Kent

SWALE BOROUGH COUNCIL
Swale House East Street Sittingbourne Kent ME10 3HT
Tel: 01795 417324 *Fax:* 01795 417327
Dx: 59900 SITTINGBOURNE 2
E-mail: legal@swale.gov.uk
Sol: Hawkins, Mr Michael R LLB Senior Solicitor . . . *Jun 1974
Milne, Mr William D TD LLB; LARTPI Borough Solicitor *Jul 1981
Price, Ms Donna Mary LLB Assistant Solicitor . . . *Jan 2005
Wallen, Miss Catherine Senior Assistant Solicitor . . . §Sep 1999

SKIPTON, North Yorkshire

CRAVEN DISTRICT COUNCIL
Council Offices Granville Street Skipton North Yorkshire BD23 1PS
Tel: 01756 700600 *Fax:* 01756 706257
Sol: Moppett, Ms Annette Jane . . . *Oct 2005
Townson, Mr Richard LLB(Hons) Head of Legal Services . . . *Mar 1982
Turnbull, Mr Michael F MA(Oxon) Solicitor . . . *Sep 1979

SKIPTON BUILDING SOCIETY
Principal Office The Bailey Skipton North Yorkshire BD23 1DN
Tel: 01756 705000 *Fax:* 01756 705769 *Dx:* 21757 SKIPTON
E-mail: thealy@skipton.co.uk
Sol: Davidson, Mrs Gillian M LLB(B'ham) Company Solicitor of Homeloan Management Limited . . . *Oct 1989
Dawson, Mr John W LLB Secretary & General Manager & Solicitor . . . *Dec 1972
Healy, Mr Timothy G LLB(Leeds) Head of Legal Services . . . *Jun 1981
Overy, Miss Kirstie Jane LLB Solicitor . . . *Oct 1993
Rogan, Mrs Ingrid C LLB Solicitor . . . *Oct 1981
Swinden, Mr Michael B LLB(Warw) Solicitor . . . *Oct 1985

SLOUGH

LEE COOPER GROUP LTD
Lee Cooper House 17 Bath Road Slough SL1 3UF
Tel: 01753 771908 *Fax:* 01753 779295
E-mail: dfarrington@leecooper.com
Sol: Farrington, Mr David J BA(Oxon) Company Secretary . *Oct 1977

RECKITT BENCKISER PLC
103-105 Bath Road Slough SL1 3UH
Tel: 01753 217800
E-mail: christopher.roberts@reckittbenckiser.com
Sol: Roberts, Mr Christopher C B MA; LLB; MBA SVP Legal; General Counsel . . . Apr 1992

SLOUGH BOROUGH COUNCIL
Town Hall Bath Road Slough SL1 3UQ
Tel: 01753 552288 *Fax:* 01753 875183 *Dx:* 42270 SLOUGH WEST
Sol: Bell, Mrs Jill LLB(Hons); DipLG Assistant Director & Procurement Services . . . *Jun 1982
Channa, Mrs Kuldip K BA(Hons); DipLG Solicitor (Litigation) . . . *Oct 1997
Chaudry, Mr Assaf Rashid BA(Hons) Contracts Solicitor . . . *Dec 1990
Crawford, Miss Elaine Fiona BSc(Hons); DipLaw Solicitor (Contracts) . . . *Nov 2004
Quayle, Mr Steven M LLB; DipLG; Legal Associate RTPI Legal Services Chief Officer & Society of Town Clerks (Dip LG) . . . *Sep 1981

SOLIHULL, West Midlands

ENVIRONMENT AGENCY (MIDLANDS REGION)
Sapphire East 550 Streetsbrook Road Solihull West Midlands B91 1QT
Tel: 0121 711 2324 *Fax:* 0121 711 5824 *Dx:* 702280 SOLIHULL 3
E-mail: shirley.flannery@environment-agency.gov.uk
Sol: Andrews, Mrs Claire Deisha LLB Solicitor . . . *Feb 1997
Gill, Mrs Kalbir LLB(Hons) Solicitor . . . *Jan 2000
Hicken, Mrs Jessica BA(Hons) Principal Solicitor . . . Sep 1990
Hulse, Mrs Elizabeth V LLB Principal Solicitor . . . *Mar 1996
Lodhi, Ms Sheila LLB; LPC Solicitor . . . *§Sep 1996
Middleton-Cassini, Mrs Kiranjeet Kaur BA(Hons)(Law with English) Solicitor . . . *Jul 2004
Rees, Mr David BSc(Econ) Principal Solicitor . . . *Jun 1994
Robson, Ms Jill Diane FILEx; LPC; CPE Solicitor . . . Dec 1998
Taylor, Mr Jonathan Richard LLB; MA(Econ) Regional Solicitor . . . Oct 1987

GOODRICH CONTROL SYSTEMS
Stratford Road Solihull West Midlands B90 4LA
Tel: 0121 451 5711 *Fax:* 0121 451 5875
E-mail: robert.fulton@goodrich.com
Sol: Fulton, Mr Robert Andrew LLB(Sheff) Chief European Counsel . . . *Apr 1980

NATIONAL GRID PLC
National Grid Park Warwick Technology Park Gallows Hill Warwick Warwickshire CV34 6DA
Tel: 01926 653000 *Fax:* 01926 654378
Sol: Ajaz, Mr Mohammed LLB Solicitor . . . Dec 1999
Allison, Ms Rosemary E M . . . Oct 1993
Bach, Mr Damian John LLB(Hons) Solicitor . . . Sep 2000
Bidwell, Mrs Janet Elizabeth BA Solicitor . . . Jan 1991
Clayton, Mrs Karen Ann LLB(Hons) Solicitor . . . Sep 1999

Cooke, Mrs Charlotte Louise BA(Hons) Senior Solicitor *Apr 2001
Danagher, Mr Dermot Kevin John BA(Hons) Senior Commercial Solicitor . . . Dec 1984
Davidson, Mr Adam BA Solicitor . . . *Mar 2001
Dennehy, Ms Angela Mary BA(Hons)(English & Law); Cert ED Director of Legal Services & Company Secretary . Oct 1981
Freeman, Mr Russell John Selwyn BA(Hons)(Econ & Social History); CPD; LPC Senior Property Lawyer . . . Sep 1999
Gillespie, Mrs Karen LLB Solicitor . . . Oct 1992
Green, Mr Andrew Q S LLB(Hons) Legal Adviser . . . *Dec 1973
Hawthorne, Ms Diana Louise MSc(Law); PGDipLP; MCIWEM Legal & Contracts Officer . . . Sep 2003
Henchley, Mr Malcolm V BA(Hons)(Law & Politics) Solicitor . . . Sep 1996
Higgins, Ms Susan LLB(Hons) . . . Apr 1997
Hill, Mrs Harriet Valentine BA; MA(Cantab) Senior Legal Advisor . . . Jun 1993
Hutchinson, Mrs Joanna BA; LLM Solicitor . . . Jan 1997
Kay, Ms Alison Barbara LLB UK General Counsel and Company Secretary . . . Jan 1989
Leedham, Mr Ian P LLM Senior Counsel . . . *Sep 1995
McAlister, Mr Lewis John Woodburn BA(Hons) Group Deputy General Counsel . . . Jan 1992
Munsey, Mr Jonathan Ross LLB Senior Counsel . . . *Oct 1995
Noble, Mr Mark David LLB(Hons) Corporate Counsel . Sep 1994
Quinn, Miss Angela M LLB . . . *Dec 1984
Rayner, Mrs Valerie LLB(Hons) Head of Property Legal . . . *Sep 1989
Riley, Mr Richard MSc; BSc Solicitor . . . Apr 1999
Tyrer, Mr Andrew Philip LLB(Hons) General Counsel . *Nov 1991
Walsh, Mr Damien Michael LLB Solicitor . . . Oct 1995
Williams, Mr David James Gwynne LLB Solicitor . . . Jan 1988
Wynn-Evans, Mr James Richard MA(Oxon); BCL Solicitor . . . Sep 1997

THE PARAGON GROUP OF COMPANIES PLC
St Catherines Court Herbert Road Solihull West Midlands B91 3QE
Tel: 0121 711 3333 *Fax:* 0121 711 1330 *Dx:* 14031 SOLIHULL 2
Sol: Shelton, Mr Richard Dominic LLB John Fridmann Prize Head of Legal Services / Group Solicitor . . . *Oct 1985
Virdee, Mrs Gurminder K BA Solicitor . . . *Oct 1985

SOLIHULL MAGISTRATES COURT
The Courthouse Homer Road Solihull West Midlands B91 3RD
Tel: 0121 705 8101 *Fax:* 0121 711 2045 *Dx:* 708350 SOLIHULL 14
Sol: Blick, Miss Pamela Susan LLB; MBA Senior Legal Adviser . . . *Oct 1979
Chonan, Miss Mita LLB(Hons) Legal Advisor . . . *Sep 2005
Debnath, Mr Tapan LLB; LPC Legal Adviser . . . *Jun 2003
Fedeski, Ms Susan LLB(Hons) Solicitor . . . *Aug 1997
James, Mrs Linda Grace LLB(Hons) Solicitor . . . *Oct 1999
McCourt, Mrs Fiona Jane LLB; ACIPD; MCMI Legal Team Manager . . . *Dec 1991
O'Meara, Ms Clare M LLB Solicitor . . . *Jan 1991
Tumber, Ms Tara LLB(Hons); LPC Legal Advisor . . . *Oct 2003

SOLIHULL METROPOLITAN BOROUGH COUNCIL
The Council House PO Box 18 Solihull West Midlands B91 3QS
Tel: 0121 704 6000 *Fax:* 0121 704 6008
E-mail: legal@solihull.gov.uk
Sol: Blamire-Brown, Mr Michael P LLB Assistant Chief Executive & Solicitor to Council . . . *Mar 1972
Davies, Mrs Debra J LLB Senior Solicitor . . . *Oct 1987
Ewens, Mr Robert A BA(Hons)(Law) Solicitor . . . *Dec 1980
Frost, Miss Alison Jane LLB(Hons) Assistant Solicitor . *Oct 1996
Gill, Santokh LLB; PGDipLP Assistant Solicitor . . . *May 1998
Ohdedar, Miss Donna LLB Principal Solicitor . . . *Apr 1998
Willis, Mrs Sheelagh Francesca Christine BA(Law) Solicitor . . . Dec 1979

SOUTH SHIELDS, Tyne & Wear

PORT OF TYNE AUTHORITY
Maritime House Tyne Dock South Shields Tyne & Wear NE34 9PT
Tel: 0191 455 2671 *Fax:* 0191 455 4687
Sol: Denton-Hawkes, Ms Melissa M LLB Director Corporate Services . . . *§Dec 1980

SOUTH TYNESIDE MAGISTRATES COURT
Millbank Secretan Way South Shields Tyne & Wear NE33 1RG
Tel: 0191 455 8800 *Fax:* 0191 427 4499
Sol: Arnold, Miss Suzy L BA(Hons)(Government & Public Policy); CPE; LPC Legal Adviser . . . *Dec 1999
Barker, Mrs Carol A Principal Assistant . . . *Aug 1996
Clarke, Mr Paul E MA(Hons) Senior Court Clerk . . . *Feb 1997
Livesley, Mr Christopher J BA(Hons) Justices Clerk . *§Dec 1976
O'Hare, Mr Simon J A LLB; DipLP Deputy Clerk to the Justices . . . *Nov 1997
Suotton, Mrs Lisa A BA(English Lit); CPE; LPC Legal Advisor . . . *May 2002

SOUTH TYNESIDE METROPOLITAN BOROUGH COUNCIL
Town Hall and Civic Offices Westoe Road South Shields Tyne & Wear NE33 2RL
Tel: 0191 427 1717 *Fax:* 0191 455 0208
Dx: 60850 SOUTH SHIELDS 4
Sol: Breen, Mr Eamonn BA Principal Solicitor . . . *§Dec 1989
Broome, Mr Benjamin Gilbert Solicitor . . . Mar 2002
Brown, Mrs Elizabeth BA(Law) Senior Solicitor . . . *§Feb 1986
Clements, Mr Mark Principal Solicitor . . . *§Mar 1987
Dexter, Miss Michelle Suzanne LLB(Hons) Principal Solicitor . . . *§Apr 2000
George, Mrs Paula Denise LLB Solicitor . . . *§Oct 1991
Gorton, Mrs Claire Alexandra Solicitor . . . Feb 2001
Gribble, Ms Judith Eileen LLB(Hons) Senior Solicitor *§Nov 1993
Harding, Mr Michael G Legal Manager . . . *§Apr 1992
Hayton, Miss Gill Solicitor . . . *§Oct 2005
Johnson, Ms Nicole Principal Solicitor . . . *§Feb 2005
Leach, Ms Jennifer Solicitor . . . Feb 2006
Leahy, Mr Denis A BA(Hons) Principal Solicitor . . . *Mar 1986
McCann, Mr Paul Solicitor . . . Aug 2006
McLean, Mrs Denise Helen Solicitor . . . Sep 1997
Poulter, Mrs Jane LLB(Hons) Solicitor . . . *§May 2004
Prior, Mrs Julie Legal Consultant . . . *§Mar 2002
Rumney, Mr John L Solicitor . . . Oct 1996
Russell, Mr Alan LLB(Lond) Principal Solicitor . . . *§Jan 1976
Scott, Mr Brian Thomas LLB(Brunel); DipLG; Dip Mgmt(Open) Head of Corporate Governance . . . *§Oct 1984
Thompson, Mr Martin Dryden BA(Cantab) Solicitor . *§Apr 1977
Tindle, Ms Aimee Joanna . . . *§Nov 2004

Tramnor, Mr David Solicitor . . . . Nov 2006
Winter, Mr Craig Solicitor . . . . Aug 2000

SOUTHALL, Middlesex

SOUTHALL RIGHTS LTD
54 High Street Southall Middlesex UB1 3DB
Tel: 020 8571 4920 *Fax:* 020 8571 9584
Sol: Khamisa, Ms Nazma BA(Hons) Solicitor. . . . . . . *May 2001
Shingadia, Dakshesh Nathalal BA(Hons) Principal Solicitor . . . . *May 1999

SOUTHAMPTON

SKANDIA LIFE ASSURANCE CO LTD
Skandia House Portland Terrace Southampton SO14 7EJ
Tel: 023 8033 4411 *Fax:* 023 8022 0464
Sol: Eardley, Mr Duncan John Lane LLB Legal Manager . *Nov 1991
Griffin, Mr Christopher Richard BSc Solicitor. . . . . Sep 2001
Harris, Mrs Angela BA(Hons) Legal Manager . . . . *Mar 1993
Phillips, Mr Roger Q MA(Cantab) Head of Legal. . . . *Oct 1985

SOUTHAMPTON CITY COUNCIL
Civic Centre Southampton SO14 7LY
Tel: 023 8022 3855 *Fax:* 023 8083 2308
Sol: Attrill, Mr Ben LLB(Hons); LLM(Ec) Solicitor . . . . . Aug 2003
Barber, Mr Paul J LLB. . . . . *Apr 1981
Beal, Mrs Sarah Elizabeth BA. . . . . Mar 1972
Collison, Mr Simon Brian BA Senior Procurement Solicitor . . . . *Nov 1996
Elton, Ms Claire Bridget LLB(Hons) . . . . §Jan 1989
Felton, Mr Roger . . . . May 2000
Forrest, Mr Andrew LLB. . . . . *Aug 1990
Granger, Mrs Karen A BA Solicitor . . . . *Jul 1987
Greaves, Mrs Ann L. . . . . *Jan 1988
Hull, Miss Lynn Karen. . . . . Apr 2005
Kigonya, Mrs Mary . . . . *Jul 1998
Otudeko, Mrs Fehintola M BA; LLB . . . . *Dec 1994
Ray, Ian. May 2010
Wilson, Mrs Catherine Sarah BA; CPE; PGDLP Senior Procurement Solicitor. . . . . Sep 1999

SOUTHEND-ON-SEA

SOUTHEND-ON-SEA BOROUGH COUNCIL
Civic Centre Victoria Avenue Southend-on-Sea Southend-on-Sea SS2 6ER
Tel: 01702 215000 *Fax:* 01702 215110 *Dx:* 2812 SOUTHEND
Sol: Baker, Mr James H Principal Solicitor . . . . *Mar 1987
Buchan, Ms Edwina J LLB Assistant Solicitor . . . . . Jun 1976
Elek, Ms Jill K BA Principal Solicitors . . . . *Feb 1984
Fyson, Miss Lorraine M LLB(Business Law); LPC; HND(Business Finance) Assistant Solicitor . . . . Dec 2002
Henry, Ms Siobhan LPC Assistant Solicitor . . . . . . Sep 2001
Spencer, Mrs Jean Elizabeth MA Assistant Solicitor . . Dec 1992
Williams, Mr John K BA Deputy Town Clerk & Monitoring Officer . . . . *Feb 1983

SOUTHPORT, Merseyside

SEFTON METROPOLITAN BOROUGH COUNCIL
Town Hall Lord Street Southport Merseyside PR8 1DA
Tel: 01704 533133 *Fax:* 01704 533133
E-mail: legal.department@sefton.gov.uk
Sol: Brown, Miss Gillian P Solicitor. . . . . *Dec 1992
Cowley, Mr Peter N LLB Principal Solicitor. . . . . . *Jan 1981
Currie, Miss Julie S LLB Solicitor . . . . *Sep 1990
Elwood, Mrs Caroline J LLB(Manc); Dip Loc Govmt Law Legal Director. . . . . *Nov 1982
Hyde, Miss Christina J LLB Solicitor. . . . . *Oct 1989
McCullough, Mr David MBA Principal Solicitor. . . . *Feb 1994
Mackey, Mr David BA(Law) Assistant Legal Director. . *Feb 1982
Orr, Mrs Lisa BA(Hons) Solicitor. . . . . Nov 1995
Peplow, Ms Anne E BA(Hons) Principal Solicitor. . . *Feb 1988
Steele, Mr Trevor Moncur Assistant Solicitor. . . . . *Nov 2003
Stevens, Ms Rachel Elizabeth BA(Law) . . . . May 2003

SPENNYMOOR, Co Durham

SEDGEFIELD BOROUGH COUNCIL
Council Offices Green Lane Spennymoor Co Durham DL16 6JQ
Tel: 01388 816166 *Fax:* 01388 817251
E-mail: dahall@sedgefield.gov.uk
Sol: Hall, Mr Dennis A LLB; LLM; Legal Associate RTPI Solicitor to the Council . . . . *Oct 1981
Rackstraw, Mr David I BSc; DipLG Principal Solicitor . *Apr 1981
Traynor, Mr Andrew Dip LG Assistant Solicitor. . . . *Aug 1999

ST ALBANS, Hertfordshire

FABER MAUNSELL LTD
Marlborough House Upper Marlborough Road St Albans Hertfordshire AL1 3UT
Tel: 020 8784 5784 / 8639 3579 *Fax:* 020 8784 5700
Sol: Corbett, Mr Kevin BSc; MICE; MIStructE Group Legal Director . . . . *Oct 1995

MURCO PETROLEUM LTD
4 Beaconfield Road St Albans Hertfordshire AL1 3RH
Tel: 01727 892494 *Fax:* 01727 945853
E-mail: murco-uk@murphyoilcorp.com
Sol: Haylock, Ms Patricia E LLB(Hons) Company Secretary*Oct 1992

ST ALBANS DISTRICT COUNCIL
Civic Centre St Peters Street St Albans Hertfordshire AL1 3JE
Tel: 01727 866100 *Fax:* 01727 819255 *Dx:* 6178 ST ALBANS 1
E-mail: legal@stalbans.gov.uk
Sol: Fyson, Miss Lorraine M LLB(Business Law); LPC; HND(Business Finance) Assistant Solicitor . . . . Dec 2002

Lovelady, Mr Michael LLB Head of Legal & Democratic Services . . . . *Aug 1977
Turner, Charles S LLB Principal Solicitor. . . . . . . *Oct 1986

ST AUSTELL, Cornwall

RESTORMEL BOROUGH COUNCIL
Council Offices 39 Penwinnick Road St Austell Cornwall PL25 5DR
Tel: 01726 223612 *Fax:* 01726 223613 *Dx:* 144560 ST AUSTELL 3
E-mail: legalenquires@restormel.gov.uk
Sol: Blanning, Mr John P BA Assistant Solicitor . . . . . *Feb 1988
Clemens, Mr Adrian St J LLB Assistant Solicitor. . . *Dec 1980

ST HELENS, Merseyside

PILKINGTON PLC
Prescot Road St Helens Merseyside WA10 3TT
Tel: 01744 28882 *Fax:* 01744 57597
Sol: Bayley, Mr Christopher R LLB(Manc) Legal Adviser . . Oct 1979
Halligan, Miss Julie P LLB(L'pool) Solicitor. . . . . . *Oct 1987
McKenna, Mr John Solicitor . . . . *Dec 1970
McKillop, Mr Ian J LLB Solicitor . . . . *Mar 1979

ST HELENS BOROUGH COUNCIL
Town Hall Victoria Square St Helens Merseyside WA10 1HP
Tel: 01744 456000 *Fax:* 01744 456208 *Dx:* 19484 ST HELENS
E-mail: peterblackburn@sthelens.gov.uk
Sol: Aspinwall, Miss Sharon LLB Solicitor . . . . Nov 2000
Bakewell, Mrs Janet K LLB(Hons) Senior Solicitor. . . *Jul 1999
Blackburn, Mr Peter LLB Assistant Chief Executive (Legal & Admin Services) . . . . *Oct 1983
Ellement, Mrs Nina Gudgeon LLB(Hons) Solicitor . . *Mar 2003
Fisher, Mr Mark Edward BA(Hons) Principal Solicitor *Feb 1988
Ireland, Mr John T BA(L'pool) Solicitor. . . . . *Jan 1977
Quirk, Mrs Annette E BA(Hons) Solicitor. . . . . . . *Dec 1986
Ramsumair, Miss Laura Marie LLB(Hons) . . . . Oct 2004
Sanderson, Mrs Angela M BA Principal Solicitor. . . . *Mar 1985
Whalebone, Ms Jillian Lynn BA; LLB; GDLP; QLTT Solicitor St Helens Council/Solicitor of Supreme Court England & Wales/NSW, Australia. . . . . Apr 2006

ST IVES, Cambridgeshire

ASPHALTIC ROOFING SUPPLIES LTD
Harding Way St Ives Cambridgeshire PE17 4YJ
Tel: 01480 466777 *Fax:* 01480 300269
Sol: Ahmad, Mr Imran LLB Group Solicitor. . . . . *Aug 1992

STAFFORD, Staffordshire

CENTRAL & SOUTH WEST STAFFORDSHIRE MAGISTRATES COURT
The Court House South Walls Stafford Staffordshire ST16 3DW
Tel: 01785 223144 *Fax:* 01785 258508 *Dx:* 14575 STAFFORD 1
Sol: Jones, Mrs Margaret Joan Senior Legal Adviser. . . . Dec 1991
Priestley, Mrs Vicky LLB Legal Adviser . . . . Nov 1999
Tilley, Mrs Louise Wendy LLB Senior Legal Adviser . . Jan 1993

STAFFORD BOROUGH COUNCIL
Civic Centre Riverside Stafford Staffordshire ST16 3AQ
Tel: 01785 619000 *Fax:* 01785 619119 *Dx:* 723320 STAFFORD 7
Sol: Curran, Mr Ian K BA(Hons) Legal Services Manager. *Nov 2001
Simcox-Parry, Ms Elizabeth LLB Senior Solicitor. . . . *Jul 1998
Turner, Mr Simon William LLB Solicitor . . . . Sep 1996
Welch, Mr Alistair R LLB Head of Law & Administration . . . . *Jan 1979

STAFFORDSHIRE COUNTY COUNCIL
County Buildings 16 Martin Street Stafford Staffordshire ST16 2LG
Tel: 01785 223121 *Fax:* 01785 278355 *Dx:* 712320 STAFFORD 5
Sol: Ackroyd, Mr Richard D C LLB(Hons); FILEX Senior Solicitor . . . . *Jul 1994
Baptist, Miss Kirsty Solicitor. . . . . *May 2002
Brammer, Mr David Anthony BA Senior Solicitor. . . . *Oct 1989
Davis, Mr Colin C LLB Senior Solicitor. . . . . *Apr 1975
Delrio Walker, Ms Lisa Mary Emma LLB Senior Solicitor . . . . *Mar 1991
Evans, Mrs Carol Assistant Director. . . . . *Mar 1984
Evans, Mrs Jean LLB Assistant Clerk (Personal Services) . . . . *Oct 1990
Gannon, Mr Anthony Christopher FILEx Senior Solicitor . . . . *May 1993
Gilani, Ms Farah D Senior Solicitor . . . . *Feb 1993
Goodwin, Mrs Elaine LLB(Hons) Senior Solicitor. . . *Sep 1995
Hodges, Mr John Anthony BA Maxwell Law Prize Senior Solicitor. *Nov 1982
Hollis, Mr Simon John Solicitor . . . . *Oct 1990
Johnston, Mr Lindsay Alexander LLB(Hons); LLM Sweet & Maxwell Law Prize 1993/4 Solicitor . . . . *Oct 2002
Knopp-McCabe, Mrs Jacqueline Lesley Senior Solicitor*Oct 1994
Nation, Ms Valerie D Solicitor . . . . *§Mar 1961
Owen, Mrs Geraldine F BA(Hons) Senior Solicitor. . . . *Oct 1990
Parsons, Ms Bridget LLB Senior Solicitor . . . . *Apr 1998
Rowe, Ms Michelle Solicitor. . . . . *Sep 2003
Rowland, Miss Anne LLB Senior Solicitor . . . . *Mar 1990
Sawford, Ms Frances A LLB Solicitor . . . . *Oct 1986
Sharma, Ms Neelam Solicitor . . . . *Sep 1999
Vickery, Mrs Samantha Jane LLB(Hons) Solicitor . . . *Aug 2002
Wallis, Mr Alan R LLB(Exon) Deputy Clerk (Environmental Services) . . . . *Oct 1970
Wood, Mrs Mandy Solicitor . . . . *Aug 2004

STAINES, Middlesex

SPELTHORNE BOROUGH COUNCIL
Council Offices Knowle Green Staines Middlesex TW18 1XB
Tel: 01784 451499 *Fax:* 01784 463356 *Dx:* 98044 STAINES 2
Sol: Davey, Mrs Ann K LLB Assistant Chief Executive . . *Apr 1971
Hunt, Mr Christopher D LLB Solicitor . . . . *Nov 2000
Monk, Mrs Victoria Louise BA(Hons) Principal Solicitor Sep 2002
Whelan, Mrs Karen Alexandra Head of Legal Services *Jan 1994

STANMORE, Middlesex

CHEVAL PROPERTY FINANCE PLC
Meridian House 69-71 Clarendon Road Watford Hertfordshire WD17 1DS
Tel: 020 8385 3920 *Fax:* 020 8385 3921 *Dx:* 51505 WATFORD 2
Sol: Margolis, Mr Alan S LLB Legal & Compliance Manager*Apr 1991

STEVENAGE, Hertfordshire

STEVENAGE BOROUGH COUNCIL
Daneshill House Danestrete Stevenage Hertfordshire SG1 1HN
Tel: 01438 242242 *Fax:* 01438 242197 *Dx:* 6022 STEVENAGE
Sol: Froggatt, Mr Paul H BA Borough Solicitor . . . . . . *Mar 1982
Sobti, Prabhjit Singh BSc; LLB; LLM; DipLG Solicitor . Apr 1995
Vale, Mr Robert W LLB(Soton); Dip Loc Gov Law 1992 Principal Solicitor. . . . . *Jun 1981

STOCKPORT, Greater Manchester

MAN B&W DIESEL LTD
Bramhall Moor Lane Hazel Grove Stockport Greater Manchester SK7 5AQ
Tel: 0161 419 3125 *Fax:* 0161 419 3151
Sol: Durose, Miss Ann Louise LLB General Counsel & Company Secretary. . . . . *Jan 1991

STOCKPORT METROPOLITAN BOROUGH COUNCIL
Mount Tabor Mottram Street Stockport Greater Manchester SK1 3PA
Tel: 0161 480 4949 *Fax:* 0161 477 9835 *Dx:* 22605 STOCKPORT 2
Sol: Buckley, Mr Steven LLB Child Care Solicitor. . . . . . Dec 2001
Carter, Mrs Susan T LLB(Hons) Solicitor . . . . *Jun 1995
Dodds, Mrs Michelle LLB . . . . Oct 2000
Halsall, Mr Michael BSc Head of Legal Services. . . . Oct 1977
Humphries, Mr Barry S LLB(B'ham) Manager Contract & Competition. *Jul 1977
Martin, Ms Davinia BA(Hons) Childcare Solicitor. . . . Mar 1991
Morton, Mrs Joy LLB(Hons) Planning & Highways Solicitors . . . . Mar 2002
Nickson, Ms Deborah Solicitor. . . . . Nov 1993
Parkinson, Mr Paul LLB; DML Senior Planning & Highways Solicitor. . . . . Nov 1983
Puzio, Miss Iolanda LLB Solicitor . . . . Mar 1999
Soren, Mr Hamza LLB Litigation Solicitor . . . . Jan 2004

STOCKTON-ON-TEES

AKER KVAERNER ENGINEERING SERVICES LTD
Phoenix House 3 Surtees Way Surtees Business Park Stockton-on-Tees TS18 3HR
Tel: 01642 334142 *Fax:* 01642 334001
Sol: Fernie, Mr John William David MA(Oxon) Commercial Director & Company Secretary. . . . . *Dec 1976

STOCKTON-ON-TEES BOROUGH COUNCIL
Municipal Buildings Church Road Stockton-on-Tees TS18 1LD
Tel: 01642 393939 *Fax:* 01642 527062
Dx: 60611 STOCKTON-ON-TEES
Sol: Bond, Mr David E LLB(Sheff) Director of Law & Democracy . . . . *Dec 1981
Butcher, Miss Julie R Assistant Solicitor. . . . . . . *Sep 1997
Douglas, Ms Jill BA Principal Solicitor . . . . *Nov 1990
Garlick, Mr George BA Chief Executive . . . . *Dec 1985
Garrett, Mrs Elaine-Christie BA(Hons); LPC Assistant Solicitor . . . . *Aug 1996
Grant, Mrs Julie D LLB Head of Legal Services . . . . *Apr 1989
Hart, Miss Karen LLB(Hons) Assistant Solicitor . . . . *Jun 1996
McKenzie, Miss Roisin LLB(Hons) Assistant Solicitor . May 2005
McNamee, Miss April Violet Solicitor & Barrister (Non-Practising) . . . . Nov 2004
Morton, Mr Gerard LLB Principal Solicitor . . . . Jan 2002
Nertney, Mr Jonathan M Assistant Solicitor . . . . . . *Apr 1999
Pearson, Mrs Sheila M BA Principal Solicitor . . . . *Mar 1980

STOKE-ON-TRENT

HM CORONERS CHAMBERS
547 Hartshill Road Hartshill Stoke-on-Trent ST4 6HF
Tel: 01782 234777 *Fax:* 01782 234783
E-mail: ian.stewartsmith@stoke.gov.uk
Sol: Smith, Mr Ian Stewart LLB H M Coroner H M Coroner*§Mar 1977

JUSTICES CLERKS OFFICE
Baker Street Fenton Stoke-on-Trent ST4 3BX
Tel: 01782 845353 *Fax:* 01782 744782 *Dx:* 700402 FENTON
Sol: Benson, Mr Michael P BA Solicitor . . . . *Dec 1981

MICHELIN TYRE PLC
Campbell Road Stoke-on-Trent ST4 4EY
Tel: 01782 402266 *Fax:* 01782 402268
Sol: Booth, Ms Jane Lesley BA(Hons) Johnson Baker Ellis Prize Head of Legal. . . . . *§Sep 1992
Duddy, Ms Gill BA(Hons) . . . . Dec 1989

STOKE-ON-TRENT CITY COUNCIL
PO Box 636 Civic Centre Glebe Street Stoke-on-Trent ST4 1RN
Tel: 01782 234567 *Fax:* 01782 232377
Dx: 21058 STOKE-ON-TRENT
Sol: Clarke, Mr Gerrard L Principal Solicitor . . . . Oct 1994
Cumberbatch, Mr Matthew BA(Hons); DipLP Solicitor . Nov 1997
Hackney, Mr Paul A LLB(Hons) Assistant Director Legal Services . . . . *Dec 1978
Herward, Miss Susan M LLB Solicitor . . . . Oct 1997
Lovatt, Miss Clare Ann LLB(Hons) Solicitor . . . . . . *Dec 1994
Mann, Mr Roger G BSc(Hons); LLB(Hons) Solicitor . . Jul 2000
Richards, Mrs Ruth Solicitor. . . . . *Jul 1998
Savage, Mrs Julie BA(Law) Solicitor. . . . . Sep 1997
Whitehouse, Ms Carmaine A LLB Solicitor. . . . . . . Feb 1994
Winstanley, Mr Jonathan M LLB(Newc) Director of Law & Administration. . . . . *Jun 1974

See p112 for the Key to Work Categories & other symbols

JOSIAH WEDGWOOD & SONS LTD
Barlaston Stoke-on-Trent ST12 9ES
Tel: 01782 282394 *Fax:* 01782 204501
Sol: Downie, Mr Mark L LLB Assistant Company Secretary. *Jun 1985

STOURPORT-ON-SEVERN, Worcestershire

WYRE FOREST DISTRICT COUNCIL
Civic Centre New Street Stourport-on-Severn Worcestershire DY13 8UJ
Tel: 01562 820505 *Fax:* 01299 879688
E-mail: caroline.caygill@wyreforestdc.gov.uk
Sol: Alexander, Ms Jane LLB Property Solicitor . . . . . . Sep 1990
Caygill, Ms Caroline S LLB(Hons) Head of Legal Services . . . . *Nov 1987
Cummings, Mrs Nicola Claire Litigation Solicitor. . . . Sep 2000
Delin, Mr Walter LLB Chief Executive . . . . *Dec 1974

STRATFORD-UPON-AVON, Warwickshire

STRATFORD-ON-AVON DISTRICT COUNCIL
Elizabeth House Church Street Stratford-upon-Avon Warwickshire CV37 6HX
Tel: 01789 267575 *Fax:* 01789 260207
Dx: 700737 STRATFORD-UPON-AVON 2
E-mail: (name)@stratford-dc.gov.uk
Sol: Cruden, Mr Peter A LLB; DipLG; MBA Legal Services Manager . . . . *Nov 1988
Johnson, Mr Brian Director of Legal & Administrative Services . . . . *Jan 1980
McRavey-Williams, Ms Pauline BA Solicitor . . . . . . *Mar 1982
Page, Mrs Amanda C LLB; LLM Solicitor . . . . *Dec 1993
Sweeting, Mr David F Solicitor. . . . . *Aug 1975

STRETFORD, Greater Manchester

TRAFFORD METROPOLITAN BOROUGH COUNCIL
Trafford Town Hall Talbot Road Stretford Greater Manchester M32 0TH
Tel: 0161 912 1212 *Fax:* 0161 912 4294
Sol: Cooper, Mr Graham J LLB; Dip SW Solicitor. . . . . . *§Jun 1972
Dawson, Miss Helen Elizabeth LLB(Hons). . . . . . . Jan 1991
Done, Mrs Lesley A LLB Solicitor . . . . *Nov 1985
Dunn, Mrs Beverley E BA Solicitor . . . . *May 1987
Ferry, Ms Margaret A LLB Solicitor . . . . Nov 1987
Glinka, Miss Dominique Francesca LLB(Hons) Solicitor *Jul 2006
Kefford, Mrs Marie C LLB(Leics) Solicitor . . . . Jul 1989
Le Fevre, Ms Jane L LLB(Hons) Principal Solicitor. . . *Apr 1980
Rosa, Mrs Madeleine J L BA Solicitor . . . . *Feb 1991
Wilkes, Mrs Jean Linda LLB Solicitor . . . . *Aug 1980
Williamson, Ms Patricia BA Solicitor. . . . . *Nov 1984

STROUD, Gloucestershire

STROUD AND SWINDON BUILDING SOCIETY
Rowcroft Stroud Gloucestershire GL5 3BG
Tel: 01453 757011 *Fax:* 01453 752307 *Dx:* 122260 STROUD 3
Sol: Davies, Miss Tara Jane Blanche MA(Oxon) Group Solicitor . . . . *Sep 1998
Harrison, Mrs Melanie Frances BA(Hons) Solicitor. . . *Apr 1999
Steedman, Mrs Joanne LLB Solicitor . . . . *Oct 1989

STROUD DISTRICT COUNCIL
Ebley Mill Westward Road Stroud Gloucestershire GL5 4UB
Tel: 01453 766321 *Fax:* 01453 754935
Sol: Jones, Mrs Lisa Marie DipLP; ILEX . . . . *Nov 1996
Lowe, Ms Larissa BA; BEd; MSc; PGDL Principal Solicitor . . . . *Jan 2000
Maslen, Mr Richard Edward Alan Principal Solicitor . *Feb 1986
Pollock, Mr Thomas James BSc Assistant Solicitor . . *Nov 2004
Spencer, Mr Colin Head of Legal Services. . . . . . *Dec 1965

SUNBURY-ON-THAMES, Middlesex

ADT FKE & SECURITY PLC
Security House The Summit Hanworth on Thames Sunbury-on-Thames Middlesex TW16 5DB
Tel: 01932 743333 *Fax:* 01932 743155
Sol: McKisack, Ms Louise Solicitor. . . . . *Nov 1993

BP CHEMICALS LTD
Building 200 Chertsey Road Sunbury-on-Thames Middlesex TW16 7LN
Tel: 01932 738320 *Fax:* 01932 774215
E-mail: saundecp@bp.com
Sol: Saunders, Mr Colin P BA(Cantab) General Counsel. . *Jul 1975

SUNDERLAND, Tyne & Wear

ARRIVA PLC
Admiral Way Doxford International Business Park Sunderland Tyne & Wear SR3 3XP
Tel: 0191 520 4000 *Fax:* 0191 520 4001 *Dx:* 68754 SUNDERLAND
Sol: Applegarth, Mr D Christopher J Group Solicitor . . . . *Feb 1983

CITY OF SUNDERLAND
City Solicitor Civic Centre Sunderland Tyne & Wear SR2 7DN
Tel: 0191 520 5555 *Dx:* 60729 SUNDERLAND
E-mail: city.solicitor@sunderland.gov.uk
Sol: Barry, Mr Martin John LLB Solicitor . . . . Jan 1997
Bennett, Ms Lynne BSc Senior Solicitor . . . . *Nov 1987
Bonar, Ms Joanna C LLB Solicitor. . . . . Oct 1991
Brown, Ms Sarah Moya LLB(Hons) Solicitor. . . . . . Oct 1995
Burke, Mrs Helen . . . . Jun 2004
Collinson, Miss Julienne LLB Senior Solicitor . . . . . *Dec 1995
Forster, Mr Steven Barry LLB . . . . Sep 2001
Hedley, Miss Jane E LLB Senior Solicitor . . . . *Feb 1987
Hood, Ms Rhiannon S C BA(Hons) Principal Lawyer. . Apr 1991
Marshall, Mrs Marion E BA(Law) Solicitor . . . . *Oct 1978
Rowson, Mr Jonathon Mark LLB . . . . Jan 2001
Thompson, Mr David J B Solicitor. . . . . Feb 1999
Waugh, Ms Elaine LLB Assistant City Solicitor. . . . . *Dec 1990
Wotherspoon, Mr James LLB Solicitor. . . . . Nov 1992

SUNDERLAND MAGISTRATES COURT
Gillbridge Avenue Sunderland Tyne & Wear SR1 3AP
Tel: 0191 514 1621 *Fax:* 0191 565 8564 *Dx:* 67757 SUNDERLAND
Sol: Brown, Ms Elaine LLB; LPC Solicitor . . . . Nov 1996
Turner, Ms Vivienne Jayne LLB Solicitor. . . . . *Mar 1994

SURBITON, Surrey

NUFFIELD HOSPITALS
Nuffield House 1-4 The Crescent Surbiton Surrey KT6 4BN
Tel: 020 8390 1200 *Fax:* 020 8399 6726
Sol: Holben, Mr David G BA; LLM Company Secretary & Solicitor . . . . *§Jun 1986
Vincent, Mrs Kathryn LLB(Hons) CCH Publications Prize 1990; Lace Mawer Prize 1990 Assistant Company Solicitor . . . . *Nov 1993

SUTTON, Surrey

FIRST ASSIST
Marshall's Court Marshall's Road Sutton Surrey SM1 4DU
Tel: 020 8652 1313 *Fax:* 020 8661 7604
Sol: Blackmore, Mr Peter H LLB(Exon) Solicitor . . . . . *§Mar 1970
Davey, Mr Martin P K LLB Legal Adviser . . . . *Jul 1975
Haddock, Mr John K BA(Law); Dip(Pet Law) Senior Legal Adviser . . . . *Dec 1981
Showell, Mr Stuart V MA(Cantab) Group Solicitor . . . Jun 1975

SWADLINCOTE, Derbyshire

SOUTH DERBYSHIRE DISTRICT COUNCIL
Civic Offices Civic Way Swadlincote Derbyshire DE11 0AH
Tel: 01283 221000 *Fax:* 01283 228734 *Dx:* 23912 SWADLINCOTE
Sol: Green, Mrs Judith LLB Senior Legal Officer . . . . . *May 1981
McCaskie, Ms Andrea Gail LLB(Hons) Head of Legal & Democratic Services . . . . *Oct 1995
Tsoi, Miss Jeanette Yin Ying LLB(Hons); Post Graduate Certificate (Legal Practice) Principal Legal Officer . *Nov 2002

SWANSEA

CITY & COUNTY OF SWANSEA
Legal Services County Hall Oystermouth Road Swansea SA1 3SN
Tel: 01792 636000 *Fax:* 01792 636340 *Dx:* 82807 SWANSEA 2
Sol: Arran, Mr Patrick LLB Senior Solicitor . . . . *Nov 1999
Battersby, Ms Christine Mary LLB Assistant Solicitor. . Jul 1975
Daycock, Mr David Martyn LLB(Wales); PGCE Solicitor to the Council . . . . *Aug 1992
Esney, Mr Richard David LLB(Hons) Assistant Solicitor Sep 2002
Harries, Miss Shiela Margaret BA Assistant Solicitor. . Jun 2003
Heys, Mrs Sharon Margarot BSc(Econ); PGDipLaw; LPC Solicitor. . . . Sep 2004
Hooper, Miss Janet L LLB(Wales) Education Social Services & Housing Directorate Lawyer. . . . *Oct 1983
Humphries, Ms Sian L BA(Hons) Senior Solicitor . . . *Feb 1998
Isaac, Mrs Mary Carolyn LLB(Hons) Assistant Solicitor Mar 2004
Jeremiah, Mr Adrian John LLB(Hons); ACIArb Solicitor - Litigation . . . . Oct 2000
Jones, Miss Stephanie LLB(Hons) Senior Lawyer . . . Jun 2003
Richards, Ms Sandra LLB(Hons) Senior Solicitor - Housing . . . . *Sep 1998
Townsley, Ms Janine Andrea LLB(Hons) Senior Solicitor . . . . *Apr 2000

DISTRICT LAND REGISTRY
Ty Bryn Glas High Street Swansea SA1 1PW
Tel: 01792 458877 *Fax:* 01792 473236 *Dx:* 33700 SWANSEA 2

SWANSEA MAGISTRATES COURT
Grove Place Swansea SA1 5DB
Tel: 01792 655171 *Fax:* 01792 651066
Sol: Pritchard, Mr Jonathan LLB(Hons) Legal Advisor . . . Nov 1993

SWINDON

ARVAL PHH LTD
PHH Centre Windmill Hill Whitehill Way Swindon SN5 6PE
Tel: 01793 884671 *Fax:* 01793 886056
Sol: Ahl, Ms Jo LLB; LSF Senior Lawyer. . . . . *Dec 1993
Brand, Mr Julian Alastair BA(Hons) Head of Legal Services . . . . *Jul 1996
Elly, Mr Mark Nicholas Charles BA; DipLaw Company Lawyer . . . . *Sep 1998

CENDANT RELOCATION
Frankland Road Blaygrove Swindon SN5 8RS
Tel: 01793 756000 *Fax:* 01793 756033
Sol: Lowe, Ms Frances Louisa Atkinson MBA Head of Legal Services . . . . Nov 1993

NATIONAL POWER PLC
Windmill Hill Business Park Whitehall Way Swindon SN5 6PB
Tel: 01793 877777 *Fax:* 01793 892851
Sol: Wheeler, Mr Stuart J K LLB(Bris) Solicitor. . . . . . . Apr 1975

SWINDON BOROUGH COUNCIL
Civic Offices Euclid Street Swindon SN1 2JH
Tel: 01793 463000 *Fax:* 01793 490420 *Dx:* 133055 SWINDON 16
Sol: Cox, Mrs Christine D LLB(Wales) Solicitor. . . . . . . *Oct 1986
Ferguson, Mr Andrew C LLB(Leeds) Head of Litigation & Personal Services. . . . *Oct 1983
Garrett, Mrs Judith BA(Hons) Solicitor. . . . . *Jun 1981
Maples, Mr Francis H MA Solicitor. . . . . *Jan 1979
Preet-Ryatt, Miss Jyoti Solicitor . . . . Jan 1983
Taylor, Mr Stephen P MA(Oxon) Director of Law and Democratic Services . . . . *Dec 1980
Wirth, Mr H Phillip LLB Senior Solicitor . . . . *Apr 1991

SWINTON, Greater Manchester

SALFORD CITY COUNCIL
Civic Centre Chorley Road Swinton Greater Manchester M27 5DA
Tel: 0161 794 4711 *Fax:* 0161 794 6595 *Dx:* 712100 SWINTON 2
E-mail: anthony.rich@salford.gov.uk
Sol: Ashton, Ms Lorraine BA Principal Solicitor/Team Leader . . . . *Apr 1995
Bailey, Miss Margaret Anne Law Society Council Member for Trainees 2001-03 Solicitor. . . . Apr 2002
Black, Mr Moshe LLB(Hons) Solicitor . . . . Aug 1994
Ebizie, Mrs Chidilim Principal Legal Assistant . . . . . *Sep 2000
Edwards, Miss Melinda BA(Hons)(Cantab); MA(Cantab) Solicitor . . . . Jan 2003
Hatton, Mr Anthony Peter BA(Hons) Principal Solicitor / Team Leader . . . . *Feb 1997
Heyes, Mr J Philip LLB(Manc) Solicitor . . . . *Jun 1968
Hooper, Ms Kendal Elizabeth LLB(Hons) Solicitor . . *Sep 1996
Jackson, Mrs Vivien R LLB Senior Solicitor . . . . . . *Apr 1983
Jones, Mrs Nicola Mary BA(Hons); CPE; LSF Solicitor. Oct 1994
O'Reilly, Miss Michelle LLB Solicitor. . . . . May 2005
Roberts, Mr James Huw MA(Cantab) Solicitor. . . . . . Aug 2000
Roxborough, Mrs Sian Eira Evan LLB(Hons) Principal Solicitor/ Team Leader . . . . *Apr 1994
Scott, Mr Paul Michael Solicitor . . . . *Dec 1998
Sheard, Mr Ian Dip LG Assistant Director (Legal) . . . *Dec 1989
Smith, Miss Nicola J LLB Solicitor. . . . . *Oct 1987
Towey, Mr Gerald P LLB Solicitor . . . . Jan 1986
Waldman, Mrs Bonita Maureen MA; BA; CQSW; DipLawJul 1997

TADWORTH, Surrey

LEGAL & GENERAL GROUP PLC
Legal & General House St Monicas Kingswood Tadworth Surrey KT20 6EU
Tel: 01737 370370 *Fax:* 01737 362977
Sol: Timms, Mr Geoffrey J BA(Hons). . . . . Jun 1990

TAMWORTH, Staffordshire

TAMWORTH BOROUGH COUNCIL
Municipal Offices Marmion House Lichfield Street Tamworth Staffordshire B79 7BZ
Tel: 01827 709258 *Fax:* 01827 709271
E-mail: jane-hackett@tamworth.gov.uk
Sol: Hackett, Mrs Jane Marie Solicitor to the Council Notary Public . . . . Jul 2007

TAUNTON, Somerset

SOMERSET COUNTY COUNCIL
County Hall Taunton Somerset TA1 4DY
Tel: 0845 345 9166 *Fax:* 01823 355060 *Dx:* 122470 TAUNTON 7
Sol: Abbott, Mr Mark J BA Assistant Solicitor. . . . . . . *Dec 1986
Blackmore, Miss Jacqueline LLB(Hons) Solicitor. . . . *Jan 1995
Boon, Mr Michael J Assistant Solicitor. . . . . Jun 1975
Carter, Ms Susan M LLB(Hons) Principal Solicitor . . . Jul 1979
Clarke, Miss Honor C LLB Principal Solicitor. . . . . *Sep 1983
Connon, Miss Heather P N LLB Assistant Solicitor. . . *Nov 1990
Corry, Mr David D LLB(Hons) County Solicitor. . . . . . *Nov 1972
Hogg, Mr Richard C BA(Hons) Assistant Solicitor . . . *Dec 1979
Mein, Ms Nicola BA(Hons) Assistant Solicitor . . . . . *Jul 2001

TAUNTON DEANE BOROUGH COUNCIL
The Deane House Belvedere Road Taunton Somerset TA1 1HE
Tel: 01823 356356 *Fax:* 01823 356329
Sol: Casey, Miss Angela Maria LLB(Hons) Planning & Litigation Solicitor. . . . *Jul 2003
Jackson, Mrs Judith M BSc Senior Solicitor . . . . . . *Dec 1976
Taylor, Ms Alison LLB Enforcement Solicitor. . . . . . Sep 1992
Taylor, Mr R Ian Chief Solicitor . . . . *Jun 1972
Thornberry, Mr Jeremy J BA(Cantab) Solr to the Council . . . . *Jul 1971

TAVISTOCK, Devon

WEST DEVON BOROUGH COUNCIL
Council Offices Kilworthy Park Drake Road Tavistock Devon PL19 0BZ
Tel: 01822 615911 *Fax:* 01822 614840 *Dx:* 82405 TAVISTOCK
Sol: Bowen, Mrs Catherine Jane BA(Hons) Borough Solicitor . . . . *Sep 1989
Incoll, Mr David J LLB; DMA; FCIS Solicitor. . . . . . *Jun 1980

TELFORD, Shropshire

BOROUGH OF TELFORD & WREKIN
Civic Offices PO Box 215 Telford Shropshire TF3 4LF
Tel: 01952 380000 *Fax:* 01952 383253 *Dx:* 712120 TELFORD 5
E-mail: carol.radforth@telford.gov.uk
Sol: Bates, Mrs Susan Jill LLB(Hons); DipLP Solicitor . . . *Feb 1997
Berkeley, Mrs Yvette MA Senior Solicitor . . . . *Apr 1999
Branson, Mr Marcus BA(Hons) Senior Solicitor . . . *May 1989
Cumberbatch, Mr Matthew Joseph BA(Hons) Group Solicitor . . . . *Nov 1997
Darbhanga, Mrs Shindy LLB(Hons) Senior Solicitor . . *Oct 1988
Fisher, Ms Kirsty L LLB(Hons) Group Solicitor. . . . . *Feb 1992
Fowkes, Mrs Lorraine Lesley LLB(Hons) Solicitor . . . *Apr 2002
Fownes, Miss Emma Louise BSc(Hons); CPE Solicitor Oct 2005
Griffin, Miss Eileen LLB Senior Solicitor . . . . *Mar 1989
Kertland-Peake, Mrs Grace BA(Hons); LL Dip; LPC Solicitor-Litigation & Environment . . . . Aug 2007
Odell, Mrs Georgina LLB Group Solicitor . . . . *Mar 1993
Ross, Mr Ian P LLB Senior Solicitor . . . . *Nov 1987
Street, Mrs Tina LLB Solicitor . . . . Jan 1989
Swann, Mr Wayne Charles LLB(Hons) Solicitor . . . *Jul 1980
Woliter, Mr Roger C Internal Head of Legal Services . *Feb 1983

LAND REGISTRY - TELFORD OFFICE
Parkside Court Hall Park Way Telford Shropshire TF3 4LR
Tel: 01952 290355 *Fax:* 01952 290356 *Dx:* 28100 TELFORD 2

NATIONAL WESTMINSTER BANK PLC
Kendal Court Ironmasters Way Telford Shropshire TF3 4DT
Tel: 01952 206000 *Fax:* 01952 206666
Sol: Green, Miss Julie Solicitor. . . . . . *Nov 1992

TELFORD MAGISTRATES COURT
Justices Clerks Office Telford Square Malinsgate Telford Shropshire TF3 4HX
Tel: 01952 204500 *Fax:* 01952 204554
Sol: Bickerdike, Mrs Anita Y LLB(Hons) Area Legal Manager . . . . . . *Dec 1987
Corbally, Miss Sian Louise LLB Legal Advisor . . . . . Jan 2006
Derbyshire, Miss Sarah Louise LLB(Hons); PSC Senior Legal Advisor . . . . . Jul 2000
Hindley, Miss Katherine Lucie LLB Legal Advisor . . *Sep 2001
Lees, Mrs Joanne BA(Hons) Deputy Area Legal Manager . . . . . *Jan 1996
McLellan, Ms Christine Ann LLB(Hons) Senior Legal Advisor . . . . . *Oct 1999
Nickless, Miss Kerry LLB(Hons); LPC Senior Legal Advisor . . . . . *Oct 1998

TEWKESBURY, Gloucestershire

TEWKESBURY BOROUGH COUNCIL
Council Offices PO Box 7 Gloucester Road Tewkesbury Gloucestershire GL20 5TT
Tel: 01684 272012 *Fax:* 01684 272040 *Dx:* 11406 TEWKESBURY
E-mail: shirin.wotherspoon@tewkesbury.gov.uk
Sol: Aylett, Mr Martin J Assistant Solicitor . . . . . *Dec 1991
Freckleton, Ms Sara J Solr to the Council . . . . . *Dec 1986
Gemmell, Mrs Rosemarie E B LLB; DipLG Conveyancer . . . . . *Jan 1983
Wotherspoon, Mrs Shirin LLB Senior Solicitor . . . . *Feb 1987

THORNBURY, South Gloucestershire

SOUTH GLOUCESTERSHIRE COUNCIL
The Council Offices Castle Street Thornbury South Gloucestershire BS35 1HF
Tel: 01454 868686 *Fax:* 01454 865979 *Dx:* 48357 THORNBURY
E-mail: mailbox@southglos.gov.uk
Sol: Anderson, Ms Catherine S LLB(Hons) Solicitor . . . *Nov 1992
Andrews, Mr Eric J LLB Solicitor. . . . . *Oct 1981
Gill, Miss Juliet Louise BA(Hons) Solicitor . . . . . Apr 2004
Griffiths, Mr Andrew D BA(Hons) Solicitor . . . . . *May 1989
Hewitt, Mr Michael LLB(Hons) Solicitor . . . . . *Aug 1991
Johnson, Mr Christopher Brian LLB; MA Solicitor . . . Oct 1973
Leamon, Mrs Dawn LLB(Hons) Solicitor. . . . . Jun 2003
McCarthy, Ms Elaine BSc; MSc; FILEx Law Society - LPC 1st Solicitor . . . . . *Aug 2006
McCormack, Mr John Charles LLB(Hons); DCA Head of Legal & Democratic Services . . . . . *May 1998
Marks, Miss Donna Cherie BA(Hons) Solicitor. . . . . Jun 2003
Prosser, Mrs Hilary Anne BSc; MPhil Solicitor . . . . . *Nov 1989
Sinclair, Mrs Gill LLB(Hons); DipLG . . . . . *Feb 1991
Sweetman, Ms Maria BA(Hons) Assistant Solicitor. . *Nov 1996
Vaughan, Mr John Gareth LLB Solicitor . . . . . *Oct 1978
Whitefoot, Miss Patricia May Solicitor . . . . . Nov 2005

THORNTON HEATH, Surrey

BALFOUR BEATTY CIVIL ENGINEERING LTD
7 Mayday Road Thornton Heath Surrey CR7 7XA
Tel: 020 8684 6922 *Fax:* 020 8710 5158
Sol: Tierney, Mr Declan LLB Company Solicitor . . . . . *Sep 1992

THRAPSTON, Northamptonshire

EAST NORTHAMPTONSHIRE DISTRICT COUNCIL
East Northamptonshire House Cedar Drive Thrapston Northamptonshire NN14 4LZ
Tel: 01832 742000 *Fax:* 01832 734839 *Dx:* 701611 THRAPSTON
Sol: Pritchard, Mr Neil Derek LLB . . . . . *Apr 1993
Rothwell, Miss Lynne BA(Hons) Solicitor . . . . . Mar 2003

TIVERTON, Devon

MID DEVON DISTRICT COUNCIL
Phoenix House Phoenix Lane Tiverton Devon EX16 6PP
Tel: 01884 255255 *Fax:* 01884 234318 *Dx:* 49011 TIVERTON
Sol: Cooper, Mrs Nicola . . . . . *Nov 2006
Johnson, Mr Simon BSc Principal Solicitor. . . . . *Jun 1994
Langdon, Mr Philip LLB(Hons) Assistant Solicitor . . . *Jun 1988
Shadbolt, Mrs Jan E LLB(Wales) Director of Corporate Services . . . . . *§Nov 1983

TORQUAY, Torbay

ALLENS
16a Fore Street St Marychurch Torquay Torbay TQ1 4NA
Tel: 01803 324500 *Fax:* 01803 316790
Sol: Keen, Mr Antony Paul Clow LLB Consultant. . . . . *§Sep 1972

SOUTH DEVON MAGISTRATES' COURTS
1st Floor Justices' Clerk's Office Riviera House Torquay Torbay TQ2 7TT
Tel: 01803 612211 *Fax:* 01803 618618
Sol: Roveri, Mr Alessandro Carlo Legal Adviser . . . . . Sep 1995
Spink, Ms Rhianedd LLB(Hons) Legal Adviser. . . . . Mar 2001

TORBAY COUNCIL
Town Hall Castle Circus Torquay Torbay TQ1 3DR
Tel: 01803 201201 *Fax:* 01803 207492 *Dx:* 59006 TORQUAY
E-mail: philip.taylor@torbay.gov.uk
Sol: Ammar, Ms Claire Frances BA Solicitor . . . . . *Oct 1992
Bond, Mrs Anne-Marie LLB(Hons) Solicitor . . . . *Sep 2001
Bond, Miss Janine LLB Solicitor. . . . . *Aug 1997
Butler, Mr Anthony Solicitor . . . . . Oct 1984
Delaney, Miss Ailsa Mary LLB Senior Solicitor. . . . . *Jan 1995
Goodwin, Mrs Samantha Karen BA(Hons) Senior Legal Officer . . . . . *Dec 2000
Harries, Miss Jessica Solicitor. . . . . Sep 2007
Lee, Ms Lorna Senior Solicitor. . . . . *Jun 1998
Prashar, Sanjay BSc(Hons) Solicitor (Head of Legal) . *Jan 1996
Pryor, Mr Stephen R Dip LG Solicitor . . . . . *§Jan 1980
Shute, Mr Jeremy David Senior Solicitor. . . . . *Nov 1986
Wills, Miss Jayne Helen PGDipLP Solicitor . . . . . *Nov 2003

TOTNES, Devon

SOUTH HAMS DISTRICT COUNCIL
Follaton House Plymouth Road Totnes Devon TQ9 5NE
Tel: 01803 861234 *Fax:* 01803 861477 *Dx:* 300050 TOTNES 2
E-mail: legal@southhams.gov.uk
Sol: Ditton, Mr Simon Matthew BSc(Hons)(Law) Solicitor. *Nov 1989
Fowlds, Mrs R LLB(Hons) Principal Solicitor. . . . . *Nov 1998
Williams, Mr Kevin N MA(Hons)(Oxon) Head of Corporate Services . . . . . *Jul 1977

TOWCESTER, Northamptonshire

SOUTH NORTHAMPTONSHIRE COUNCIL
Council Offices Springfields Towcester Northamptonshire NN12 6AE
Tel: 01327 322322 *Fax:* 01327 322114 *Dx:* 16938 TOWCESTER
Sol: Hargan, Mrs Sarah Kay BA(Hons); LLB Solicitor. . . . Apr 1995
Lane, Mr Kevin Paul MA(Cantab) Birmingham Law Society Bronze Medal Head of Corporate Support. . . . *Oct 1983
Nathasingh, Mrs Chetna LLB(Hons) Principal Legal Officer . . . . . Mar 1993

TROWBRIDGE, Wiltshire

WEST WILTSHIRE DISTRICT COUNCIL
Bradley Road Trowbridge Wiltshire BA14 0RD
Tel: 01225 770396 *Fax:* 01225 761053 *Dx:* 116891 TROWBRIDGE 3
Sol: Best, Mr Simon J LLB(Hons) Principal Lawyer. . . . *Jan 1990
Woodcock, Mr Peter LLB(Lond) Head of Democratic Services . . . . . *Dec 1975

WILTSHIRE COUNTY COUNCIL
County Hall Bythesea Road Trowbridge Wiltshire BA14 8JN
Tel: 01225 713000 *Fax:* 01225 713095 / 713998
Dx: 43102 TROWBRIDGE
Sol: Gerrard, Mr Stephen G BSc(Hons) Solicitor to the County Council . . . . . *Mar 1983
Gibbons, Mr Ian R LLB(Bris) Assistant Solicitor to the County Council . . . . . *Oct 1984
Mills, Ms Barbara BA(Lond) Principal Solicitor. . . . *Feb 1991
Tasker, Ms Mary E LLB(Auckland) Principal Solicitor. . Oct 1987

TRURO, Cornwall

CARRICK DISTRICT COUNCIL
Carrick House Pydar Street Truro Cornwall TR1 1EB
Tel: 01872 224400 *Fax:* 01872 242104 *Dx:* 81232 TRURO
Sol: Andrews, Mr Mark J BA. . . . . *May 2002
Curnow, Mrs Naomi Akua LLB(Hons) Solicitor. . . . . *Jul 2005
Kitto, Mr Julian BA(Hons) Head of Legal, Democratic and Property Services. . . . . *Oct 1997
Newton, Mrs A Gail M BA Strategic Director - Internal Services . . . . . *Apr 1981
Winskill, Mr John P LLB; FCIS Chief Executive . . . . *Jan 1978

CORNWALL COUNTY COUNCIL
County Hall Treyew Road Truro Cornwall TR1 3AY
Tel: 01872 322197 *Fax:* 01872 323833 *Dx:* 122620 TRURO 4
Sol: Brown, Ms Jane BA(Hons) Senior Solicitor . . . . . Dec 1993
Hosking, Mrs Justine Lucy LLB Deputy Head of Team *Feb 1992
Jackson, Ms Karen J BA; CPE Head of Children & Adults Legal Team . . . . . *Mar 1989
John, Mrs Paula BA(Hons) Senior Solicitor . . . . . *Oct 1995
Kennaway, Mr Ian M LLB(Warw) County Solicitor . . *Nov 1976
Linehan, Dr Catherine M BSc; PhD Head of Company, Commercial & Employment Team. . . . . *§Jun 1991
Lingard, Ms Miranda Solicitor . . . . . Nov 1993
LLoyd-King, Miss Rebecca Corporate Lawyer. . . . . Oct 2003
Lynes, Mr Stephen LLB Senior Solicitor. . . . . Mar 1996
Main, Miss Deborah Jeannette BA(Hons) Assistant Solicitor . . . . . May 2004
Randall, Mrs Elizabeth LLB Head of Highways, Planning & Property Legal Team . . . . . *Jun 1980
Rutherford, Mrs Virginia LLB Senior Solicitor . . . . . *Jun 1977
Stolworthy, Mrs Deborah Jayne LLB(Hons)(Law) Senior Solicitor . . . . . Nov 1991
Tregidga, Mr Philip R Senior Solicitor . . . . . *Feb 1976
Williams, Mr Richard A LLB Head of Legal Services. *May 1987

G J HENDRA LTD
6 & 7 Lemon Street Truro Cornwall TR1 2LQ
Tel: 01872 277212
Sol: Rowe, Mr R Anthony LLB Company Secretary. . . . . §Jul 1967

PETTY SESSIONAL DIVISIONS OF EAST PENWITH, FALMOUTH AND KERRIER ISLES
W Cornwall Magistrates Courts PO Box 60 Truro Cornwall TR1 3HQ
Tel: 01872 274075 / 277375 *Fax:* 01872 276227
Sol: Farmer, Mr Paul R LLB(Lond) Solicitor . . . . . Nov 1971
Hart, Mr Derek R Principal Assistant . . . . . Feb 1988

TUNBRIDGE WELLS, Kent

SURVEYORS INDEMNITY MANAGEMENT SERVICES
SPA House 18 Upper Grosvenor Road Tunbridge Wells Kent TN1 2EP
Tel: 01892 528333 *Fax:* 01892 614637
E-mail: si@pmurrells.freeserve.co.uk
Sol: Murrells, Mr Paul Graham Principal . . . . . *§Nov 1972

TUNBRIDGE WELLS BOROUGH COUNCIL
Town Hall Tunbridge Wells Kent TN1 1RS
Tel: 01892 526121 *Fax:* 01892 554027
Dx: 3929 TUNBRIDGE WELLS
E-mail: alan.turner@tunbridgewells.gov.uk
Sol: Bond, Miss Suzanne BA(Hons) Principal Solicitor . . . *Jul 1993
Creed, Miss Bronwyn LLB(Hons); ACIS Principal Solicitor . . . . . *Aug 1991
Jardine, Ms Katherine Fiona BA(Hons); PGDL; LPC Assistant Solicitor. . . . . *Sep 2005

UTTOXETER, Staffordshire

J C BAMFORD EXCAVATORS LTD
Rocester Uttoxeter Staffordshire ST14 5JP
Tel: 01889 590312 *Fax:* 01889 594049
E-mail: michael.hargreaves@jcb.com
Sol: Hargreaves, Mr Michael BA(Hons) Group Legal Director . . . . . *Apr 1981
Leadbeater, Mr Edward T D LLB Group Commercial Director . . . . . *Oct 1968
Teanby, Miss Joanne LLB Group Solicitor . . . . . Oct 1992

UXBRIDGE, Middlesex

AIB GROUP (UK) PLC (LEGAL AND SECURITIES DEPT)
Bankcentre-Britain Belmont Road Uxbridge Middlesex UB8 1SA
Tel: 01895 272222 *Fax:* 01895 619315 *Dx:* 45104 UXBRIDGE
Sol: Bellis, Mrs Brenda M Solicitor. . . . . Mar 1985
Peck, Ms Tiana Jennifer LLB Head of Legal Services & Company Secretary. . . . . Oct 1988

COCA-COLA ENTERPRISES LTD
Charter Place Uxbridge Middlesex UB8 1EZ
Tel: 01895 231313 *Fax:* 01895 239092
Sol: Blake, Ms Amber E LLB Senior Legal Counsel . . . *Sep 2000
Goodkind, Ms Louise LLB; LPC Legal Counsel . . . . *Oct 2002
Hebbron, Mrs Melanie Grace LLB Senior Legal Counsel . . . . . Jan 1998
Meadows, Mr Paul D LLB(Hons) Legal Director & Company Secretary . . . . . *Jun 1990
Saunders, Mr Carl R LLB(Hons) Legal Manager. . . . *Feb 1997
Sehgal, Mr Sunil LLB(Hons) Legal Counsel . . . . . *Dec 1998
Van Reesh, Mr Paul LLB; LLM Legal Counsel. . . . . Jul 2005

GENERAL MILLS UK
Harman House George Street Uxbridge Middlesex UB8 1QQ
Tel: 01895 201133 *Fax:* 01895 201101
Sol: Gardner, Mr Roger John MA(Cantab) Legal Director, Europe . . . . . *Apr 1976

UNISYS EUROPEAN SERVICES LTD
Bakers Court Bakers Road Uxbridge Middlesex UB8 1RG
Tel: 01895 862108 *Fax:* 01895 862010
E-mail: pavel.klimov@unisys.com
Sol: Klimov, Dr Pavel PhD General Counsel, EMEA . . . . Jan 2001

WADEBRIDGE, Cornwall

NORTH CORNWALL DISTRICT COUNCIL
Council Offices Higher Trenant Road Wadebridge Cornwall PL27 6TW
Tel: 01208 893259 *Fax:* 01208 893255
Sol: Lloyd-Jones, Miss Sally A LLB Head of Legal Services *Jan 1979

WAKEFIELD, West Yorkshire

WAKEFIELD COURT HOUSE
Cliff Parade Wakefield West Yorkshire WF1 2TW
Tel: 01924 303461 *Fax:* 01924 303465
E-mail: sally.jones@hmcourts-service.gsi.gov.uk
Sol: Caven, Mrs Jane Lucy Legal Adviser . . . . . *Dec 1993
Goodman, Mr Raymond District Legal Director . . . *Dec 1994
Jones, Mrs Sally Anne Legal Manager. . . . . *Nov 1991
Lister, Mrs Joanne Claire LLB Legal Adviser. . . . *Sep 2001
Speight, Mrs Jayne Elaine LLB Legal Advisor . . . . *Feb 1999

WAKEFIELD MAGISTRATES COURT
The Court House Clifford Parade Wakefield West Yorkshire WF1 2TW
Tel: 01924 303746 *Fax:* 01924 303465 *Dx:* 708370 WAKEFIELD
Sol: Daley, Mr Bernard Mark BA(Hons); PGDL Blackstone Publishing Prize 2001; Law Society National Prize 2003 Legal Adviser . . . . . *Oct 2005

WAKEFIELD METROPOLITAN DISTRICT COUNCIL
County Hall Bond Street Wakefield West Yorkshire WF1 2QW
Tel: 01924 306090 *Fax:* 01924 305243
Sol: Ahmed, Mrs Robina Kauser LLB(Hons); PGDipLP Senior Legal Officer . . . . . Jul 2003
Brooking, Mr Christopher BA(Hons)(Law) Principal Solicitor . . . . . *Sep 1984
Crosse, Mr John P LLB Solicitor. . . . . *Nov 1989
Gleave, Miss Catherine Elizabeth BA(Hons); PGDL Senior Legal Officer . . . . . *Oct 2002
Lall, Mrs Paramjit Kaur LLB(Hons) Senior Legal Officer (Child Care Solicitor). . . . . Sep 1996
Lees, Mr John Charles LLB Senior Legal Officer. . . . Jun 1975
Mumford, Miss Sarah Gillian BA Principal Commercial Lawyer . . . . . Jun 1981
Musto, Miss Lia M A LLB Professor John Finan Memorial Prize for Academic Excellence 1998 Senior Legal Officer*Jun 2002
Newton, Mr Denis LLB; DPA Senior Legal Officer . . *Mar 1975
Ogden, Mrs Mary E LLB Assistant Head of Legal & Democratic Services . . . . . *May 1986
Oki, Ms Doris Erebi LLB Solicitor . . . . . Dec 1995
Pepperell, Mrs Jacqueline A LLB(Hons) Head of Legal & Democratic Services . . . . . *Dec 1977
Powell, Mr Philip BA(Hons) Senior Legal Officer. . . . Aug 2000
Senior, Mr Robert M W Senior Legal Officer. . . . . *Feb 1980

WEST YORKSHIRE PROBATION BOARD
Cliff Hill House Sandy Walk Wakefield West Yorkshire WF1 2DJ
Tel: 01924 885300 *Fax:* 01924 885395
Sol: Thorpe, Mr Nigel J LLB Secretary to the Probation Board . . . . . *Jul 1978

See p112 for the Key to Work Categories & other symbols

WALLASEY, Merseyside

WIRRAL BOROUGH COUNCIL
Town Hall Brighton Street Wallasey Merseyside CH44 8ED
Tel: 0151 638 7070 *Fax:* 0151 691 8468 *Dx:* 708630 SEACOMBE
E-mail: legal@wirral.gov.uk
Sol: Abraham, Mr David K LLB(Wales) Solicitor . . . . . . *Jan 1989
Cassidy, Ms Victoria C Solicitor . . . . Nov 2003
Eyitene, Mr Gregory O Solicitor . . . . Jan 2003
Goacher, Mr Simon C LLB(Hons) . . . . Apr 1996
Green, Ms Angela M BA Treasurer Association of Women Solicitors . . . . *Jan 1990
Hughes, Mr Colin J B BA(Oxon) Winter Williams Law Prize Assistant Borough Solicitor . . . . *Jun 1974
Jones, Mr Royston LLB Assistant Borough Solicitor . . . Jul 1975
Reaney, Mr Mark E LLB Assistant Borough Solicitor. . *Oct 1984
Richards, Ms Suzanne Solicitor . . . . Jan 2006
Shaw, Ms Lucy V LLB Solicitor . . . . Dec 1991

WALLINGFORD, Oxfordshire

SOUTH OXFORDSHIRE DISTRICT COUNCIL
Benson Lane Crowmarsh Gifford Wallingford Oxfordshire OX10 8QS
Tel: 01491 823345 *Fax:* 01491 823658
Dx: 144121 WALLINGFORD 2
E-mail: legal.services@southoxon.gov.uk
Sol: Price, Mr Ian T BA(Hons)(Law) Senior Solicitor . . . . *Jan 1985
Reed, Mrs Margaret G LLB Head of Legal and Democratic Services . . . . *Feb 1984

WALLINGTON, Surrey

SUTTON MAGISTRATES' COURT
The Court House Shotfield Wallington Surrey SM6 0JA
Tel: 020 8770 5950 *Fax:* 020 8770 5977 *Dx:* 59957 WALLINGTON
Sol: Kingaby, Mrs Emma Jayne Court Clerk . . . . Dec 1995
Sunderland, Mr John C LLB Clerk to the Justices . . . *Jan 1975

WALSALL, West Midlands

WALSALL METROPOLITAN BOROUGH COUNCIL
Legal Services Civic Centre Darwall Street Walsall West Midlands WS1 1TP
Tel: 01922 650000 *Fax:* 01922 646142 *Dx:* 12149 WALSALL
E-mail: coxt@walsall.gov.uk
Sol: Abel, Mr David Solicitor . . . . *Sep 2002
Bennett-Matthews, Mrs Sharon LLB(Hons) Solicitor . . *Jul 2002
Campbell, Miss Natasha J LLB Solicitor . . . . *Jun 2000
Cartwright, Mr John L LLB(Hons) Solicitor . . . . . . *May 1996
Cox, Mr Tony M LLB Head of Law . . . . *Jan 1992
Dean, Ms Heather M BA(Hons) Solicitor . . . . *Oct 1992
Gill, Mr Bhupinder S Assistant Director for Legal and Democratic Services . . . . *Mar 1994
Levesley, Mrs Lynn LLB(Hons) Solicitor . . . . *Oct 1989
Orcott, Mr Mark Solicitor . . . . *Aug 2004
Patouchas, Mr Dominic LLB(Hons) Solicitor . . . . . . Dec 1994
Portman, Mr Stuart Head of Law . . . . *Dec 1999
Ross, Ms Gillian LLB Solicitor . . . . *Mar 1984
Samuda, Miss Fiona BA(Hons)(Law) Solicitor . . . . . *Jun 2003
Giles, Miss Tracy M LLB(Hons) Service and Case Manager . . . . *Sep 2001
Winter, Mrs Helen Service & Case Manager. . . . . . *Oct 1988

WANTAGE, Oxfordshire

CROWN PACKAGING UK PLC
Downsview Road Wantage Oxfordshire OX12 9BP
Tel: 01235 402611 *Fax:* 01235 402578
Sol: Davidson, Mr John LLB Vice President / European General Counsel. . . . . *Jun 1976

WILLIAMS GRAND PRIX ENGINEERING LTD
Grove Wantage Oxfordshire OX12 0DQ
Tel: 01235 777700 *Fax:* 01235 764705
Sol: Moffat, Ms Jane BA(Hons); LLB; LLM General Counsel Mar 2005

WARLEY, West Midlands

LLOYDS CHEMISTS PLC LEGAL SERVICES
Langley House 5 Summit Crescent Warley West Midlands B66 1DA
Tel: 0121 553 6633 *Fax:* 0121 525 4462
Sol: Craddock, Mr Roger LLB Divisional Solicitor. . . . . *§Mar 1979

WARRINGTON, Warrington

BRITISH NUCLEAR FUELS PLC
1100 Daresbury Park Daresbury Warrington WA4 4GB
Tel: 01925 832000 *Fax:* 01925 654539
Sol: Quint, Ms Susan M Group Legal Director . . . . *Dec 1992

BURTONWOOD BREWERY PLC
Bold Lane Burtonwood Warrington WA5 4PJ
Tel: 01902 711811 *Fax:* 01902 329169
Sol: D'Arcy, Miss Lynne LLB Managing Director . . . . . *May 1982
Lawson, Mrs Carole M BA(Law) Company Solicitor . *May 1985

THE ENVIRONMENT AGENCY (NORTH WEST REGION [HQ])
PO Box 12 Richard Fairclough House Knutsford Road Warrington WA4 1HG
Tel: 01925 653999 *Fax:* 01925 574736 *Dx:* 709290 WARRINGTON 5
E-mail: nick.webb@environment.agency.gov.uk
Sol: Bowen, Ms Liz BA(Hons); MSc Principal Solicitor . . . *Mar 1992
Bradley, Mr David R LLB(Hons) Solicitor. . . . . *Feb 1999
Healey, Mr Damien P BA Principal Solicitor . . . . . . *Jul 1976
Shaw, Ms Suzanne BSc(Hons); MSc; LLM Law Society Prize for Outstanding Achievement 2003 Solicitor. . . . . . *Dec 2004
Shaw, Mrs Tracey E LLB(Sheff); DipLG Principal Solicitor . . . . *Oct 1988
Swensson, Mr Martin LLB(Hons); LPC Timpron Martin Prize; Birch Cullimore Prize Solicitor. . . . . *Sep 2000
Warn, Mr Timothy John LLB Principal Solicitor. . . . . *Jun 1973
Watson, Mrs Nicola Jane LLB(Hons); LLM Principal Solicitor . . . . *Mar 1998
Webb, Mr Nicholas Anthony MA; LLM(Environmental Law) Regional Solicitor NW Group Chairman of UKELA.*Dec 1991

THE NATIONAL TRUST
Heelis Kemble Drive Swindon SN2 2NA
Tel: 01793 817400
Sol: Ainsley, Ms Louise Property Lawyer. . . . . Jan 2004
Ashworth, Mrs Sarah LLB Senior Property Lawyer. . . Nov 1990
Butler, Mr Timothy J MA Solicitor . . . . *Nov 1984
Carlisle, Mr Samuel Commercial Lawyer. . . . . Mar 2006
Coleman, Miss Sally M Solicitor. . . . . *May 1996
Coulthard, Mr Robert Hood LLB Property Solicitor. . . *Oct 1968
Dearlove, Mr Jonathan Robert LLB(Hons) Property Lawyer . . . . Sep 2001
Gleave, Mr Patrick LLB Property Lawyer . . . . Sep 2003
Greenhaf, Ms Sarah Louise Property Lawyer . . . . . Sep 1999
Harman-Bishop, Mr Adrian Piers Property Lawyer. . . . May 1978
McCormack, Mr Patrick James BSc Property Lawyer . *Oct 1991
Nicholson, Mr Timothy Charles BA(Hons); CPE Senior Property Lawyer . . . . *Oct 1989
Richardson, Mr Roger John LLB(Hons)(Exon) Agricultural Lawyer . . . . *Apr 1979
Thompson, Mr David Mark LLB(Hons) Morgan Bruce Prize for Land Law; First Year in Land Law; Best Mature Student Property Lawyer. Apr 1997
Watts, Ms Hilary Louise Senior Property Lawyer. . . . Sep 2002

PERSIMMON PLC
Legal Department Persimmon House Stonecross Park Yew Tree Way Warrington WA3 3JD
Tel: 01942 277277 *Fax:* 01942 277234
Dx: 728300 LEIGH (GOLBORNE)
Sol: Bowen, Mr Peter L Company Solicitor. . . . . Jan 1978

SELLAFIELD LTD
Hinton House Risley Warrington WA3 6AS
Sol: Carr, Mr Andrew Michael LLB Solicitor. . . . . Oct 1997

UNITED UTILITIES
Haweswater House Lingley Mere Business Park Great Sankey Warrington WA5 3LP
Tel: 01925 237000 *Fax:* 01925 237066
Sol: Bogle, Mrs Louise LLB(Hons) Solicitor. . . . . Feb 1990
Fisher, Mr William D LLB(Manc) Assistant Solicitor . *§Apr 1978
Hall, Mrs Emma L C BSc(Hons); CPE; LPC Commercial Solicitor . . . . Sep 1998
Hosker, Mr David P LLB. . . . . Jun 1973
Prytherch, Mr John D . . . . *§Dec 1974
Thomson, Ms Claire BA(Hons) Employee . . . . Apr 2003
Wood, Mr David James BA(Hons) Litigation Solicitor . Jan 1995

VOLEX GROUP PLC
Dornoch House Kelvin Close Birchwood Science Park Warrington WA3 7JX
Tel: 01925 830101 *Fax:* 01925 830141
E-mail: wendy.tate@volex.com
Sol: Tate, Miss Wendy PGDip LS; CPE Company Secretary . . . . *Nov 2002

WARRINGTON BOROUGH COUNCIL
Town Hall Sankey Street Warrington WA1 1UH
Tel: 01925 444400 *Fax:* 01925 413449 *Dx:* 17760 WARRINGTON
Sol: Holmes, Mr John E LLB(Warw) Principal Solicitor . . . Jan 1987
Mason, Mr Ian G BA(Hons) Head of Legal, Licensing & Land Charges . . . . Dec 1990
Spiers, Mrs Karin J LLB(L'pool) Principal Solicitor . . . *Jan 1979

WARWICK, Warwickshire

CONOCOPHILLIPS LTD
Conoco Phillips Centre 2 Kingmaker Court Warwick Technology Park Warwick Warwickshire CV34 6DB
Tel: 01926 404000 *Fax:* 01926 404797
Sol: Swallow, Mr Richard Philipson Barber LSF Company Secretary . . . . *Dec 1969

NATIONAL GRID
NGT House Warwick Technology Park Gallows Hill Warwick Warwickshire CV34 6DD
Tel: 01926 653000 *Fax:* 01926 655630
Sol: Gillespie, Mrs Karen LLB . . . . Oct 1992

VFS FINANCIAL SERVICES (UK) LTD
Wedgnock Lane Warwick Warwickshire CV34 5YA
Tel: 01926 498888 *Fax:* 01926 410278
Sol: Lane, Mrs Julia M MA(Cantab) Company Solicitor and Company Secretary . . . . *Dec 1977

WARWICKSHIRE COUNTY COUNCIL
Shire Hall Warwick Warwickshire CV34 4RR
Tel: 01926 410410 *Fax:* 01926 412946 *Dx:* 723362 WARWICK 5
Sol: Arben, Mrs Lisa Helen LLB(Hons) Solicitor . . . . . . Sep 1996
Arrowsmith, Mrs Donna Lisa LLB(Hons) Solicitor . . . *Apr 2004
Belcher, Mrs Ann M MA(Cantab) Solicitor . . . . Oct 1985
Carter, Mr David G MA; LLB Strategic Director of Performance & Development . . . . *Dec 1979
Duxbury, Mrs Sarah Elizabeth LLB(Hons); DipLP; PGCE Corporate Legal Services Manager . . . . *Feb 1998
Endall, Mr Peter A J LLB(Hons); PhD; DipLG Senior Solicitor . . . . *Oct 1993
Evans, Miss Ruth Louise BSc(Hons) . . . . Jan 2004
Fairweather, Mr Paul Sebastian LLB(Hons); DipLP Solicitor . . . . *Sep 2001
Gould, Ms Victoria J LLB(Hons) Young People Legal Services Manager . . . . Dec 1990
Grasby, Mrs Katharine Emma BA(Hons)(Law) Solicitor Sep 1997
Hallworth, Miss Alison F MA(Cantab) Senior Solicitor . *Oct 1986
Lawrence, Miss Amanda Michelle MA(Hons)(Oxon) Solicitor . . . . Sep 1997
Marriott, Mr Ian Leslie LLB Community & Environment Legal Services Manager. . . . . Nov 1984
Needham, Mrs A Greta LLB(Hons)(Wales) Head of Law & Governance. . . . . *Apr 1974
Newman, Miss Julie BA(Hons) Senior Solicitor . . . . Jan 1999
Nolte- Conlon, Mrs Natasha Marie BA; JD Solicitor . . *Aug 2003
Pollard, Miss Helen J BA Solicitor. . . . . *Jan 1984
Pugh, Miss Anna BA; PGDip Solicitor . . . . Oct 2001
Reynolds, Mr David Charles BA(Hons) Solicitor . . . . *Sep 2004
Tucker, Mrs Rosslyn Anne LLB(Hons) Solicitor . . . . Feb 1992
Williams, Ms Rebecca J LLB(Hons); LPC Solicitor. . . *Sep 1998

2

WATFORD, Hertfordshire

BRITISH WATERWAYS BOARD
64 Clarendon Road Watford Hertfordshire WD17 1DA
Tel: 01923 226422 *Fax:* 01923 201378
Sol: Barton, Mrs Anna Maria BSc(Hons) Solicitor. . . . . *Sep 2003
Deards, Mr Thomas James LLB; LLM Solicitor . . . . Mar 2002
Fendrich, Mr Paul Benedict MA(Cantab) Solicitor . . *§Nov 1994
Johnson, Mr Nigel I BSc(Econ) Legal Director. . . . *Sep 1980
O'Shea, Miss Greta Assumpta solicitor . . . . *Aug 2005
Smith, Ms Julie BSc(Hons); MSc Solicitor . . . . . . *Sep 2002

RHODIA UK LTD
Oak House Reeds Crescent Watford Hertfordshire WD24 4QP
Tel: 01923 485758 *Fax:* 01923 485928
E-mail: jane.palmer@eu.rhodia.com
Sol: Palmer, Ms Jane BA General Counsel. . . . . Dec 1990

TAYLOR WOODROW CONSTRUCTION LEGAL DEPARTMENT
41 Clarendon Road Watford Hertfordshire WD17 1TR
Tel: 01923 478442 *Fax:* 01923 478806
E-mail: simon.williams@uk.taylorwoodrow.com
Sol: Foster, Mr Simon David LLB Solicitor . . . . *Oct 1995
Parker, Mr Christopher BSc Solicitor. . . . . *Nov 1994
Williams, Mr William S G LLB(Soton) Solicitor. . . . *Nov 1978

WATFORD BOROUGH COUNCIL
Town Hall Watford Hertfordshire WD17 3EX
Tel: 01923 226400 *Fax:* 01923 278366 *Dx:* 4514 WATFORD
Sol: Chen, Mrs Carol J BA Head of Legal & Democratic Services . . . . *Oct 1984
McKenzie, Mr Jason Richard LLB; DipLP Solicitor. . *Sep 1999
Njoku, Mrs Chinedu T LLB; BL Solicitor . . . . *Mar 1998
Willis, Ms Angela LLB(Hons) Legal Services Manager.*Nov 1990

WEALDSTONE, Middlesex

HARROW MAGISTRATES COURT (CLERKS OFFICE)
Court House Rosslyn Crescent Wealdstone Middlesex HA1 2JY
Tel: 020 8427 5146 *Dx:* 30451 HARROW 3
Sol: Cropper, Mr Gordon G LLB Clerk to the Justices . . . *Dec 1974

WELLINGBOROUGH, Northamptonshire

WELLINGBOROUGH BOROUGH COUNCIL
Council Offices Swanspool Wellingborough Northamptonshire NN8 1BP
Tel: 01933 229777 *Fax:* 01933 441380
Dx: 12865 WELLINGBOROUGH
E-mail: chiefexecutive@wellingborough.gov.uk
Sol: Stewart, Mr Brian Lewis BA(Oxon) Legal Services Manager . . . . *Jun 1977

WELSHPOOL, Powys

POWYS COUNTY COUNCIL
Neuadd Maldwyn Severn Road Welshpool Powys SY21 7AS
Tel: 01938 552828 *Fax:* 01938 555010
Sol: Edwards, Mr Colin BA(Hons)(Law) Solicitor . . . . . . *Nov 1982

WELWYN GARDEN CITY, Hertfordshire

ROCHE PRODUCTS LTD
6 Falcon Way Shire Park Welwyn Garden City Hertfordshire AL7 1TW
Tel: 01707 366000 *Fax:* 01707 366817
Sol: Bijmolen-Reed, Ms Andrea J LLB Solicitor. . . . . . *Sep 1996
Daniel, Mr Richard D BA Director Legal Affairs & Company Secretary . . . . *Jul 1981
Harris, Miss Kelly Anne BSc(Hons) Solicitor. . . . . . Jan 1997
Reich, Mr Oren LLB Solicitor . . . . *Apr 2004

WELWYN HATFIELD DISTRICT COUNCIL
Council Offices The Campus Welwyn Garden City Hertfordshire AL8 6AE
Tel: 01707 357000 *Fax:* 01707 357373
Dx: 30075 WELWYN GARDEN CITY
Sol: Choudhry, Mr Muhammad Shahbaz Khah BA(Hons)(Law); DipLG Legal Services Manager . . . . *Nov 1982
Davies, Mrs Melinda J LLB Deputy Chief Executive . . *Sep 1979

WEM, Shropshire

NORTH SHROPSHIRE DISTRICT COUNCIL
Edinburgh House New Street North Shropshire Wem Shropshire SY4 5DB
Tel: 01939 232771 *Fax:* 01939 238404 *Dx:* 27386 WEM
E-mail: legal@northshropshiredc.gov.uk
Sol: Sanders, Mrs Jean H LLB Chief Solicitor . . . . *Dec 1983

WEST BRIDGFORD, Nottinghamshire

NOTTINGHAMSHIRE COUNTY COUNCIL LEGAL SERVICES DIVISION
Centenary House 1 Wilford Lane West Bridgford Nottinghamshire NG2 7QZ
Tel: 0115 977 3478 *Fax:* 0115 977 3815 *Dx:* 723420 NOTTINGHAM
Sol: Baker, Mr Steven H LLB(Sheff) Solicitor. . . . . *Feb 1978
Bashir, Ms Nussrat LLB(Hons) Solicitor . . . . Oct 2004
Bearman, Mrs Susan Louise BA Solicitor . . . . *Jul 2004

Birkett, Mrs Nathalie Annara LLB; LPC Solicitor . . . . Apr 2005
Carter, Mrs Bernadette Clare LLB(Newc); LSF(Hons) R T Richardson Prize 1985 Solicitor . . . . *Oct 1987
Dickinson, Mrs Heather Fay LLB Solicitor . . . . . . *Jan 1994
Dunbar, Mrs Linda J BA Solicitor . . . . *Sep 1985
England, Mr Paul A BA(Cantab) Solicitor . . . . . . *Sep 1978
Finlay, Mr Andrew S LLB Solicitor . . . . §Dec 1987
Francis, Mrs Jayne M LLB; PGDip Ed Law Solicitor . . *Oct 1987
Haywood, Mrs Catherine Elizabeth LLB Solicitor. . . . Dec 2002
Hunter, Miss Emma Kirstie BA(Hons); LPC Solicitor. . . Jan 2006
Kasbia, Karamjit Singh Solicitor . . . . Jul 1999
Khatoon, Miss Uzma LLB; LPC Solicitor. . . . . . . *Sep 2005
McCarthy, Ms Linda Joy LLB Solicitor . . . . Aug 2001
Richeux, Mrs Sorriya BA(Hons)(Law) Solicitor. . . . . May 2002
Robinson, Mrs Ishkan LLB(Hons); DipLP; A Inst A M Solicitor . . . . Nov 1995
Shepherd, Miss June LLB Solicitor . . . . *Oct 1986
Slosarska, Miss Krystyna M BA Solicitor. . . . . Oct 1985
Sumby, Mrs Katharine Mary BA(Hons) Solicitor . . . *Feb 1982
Wakerley, Ms Sarah Elizabeth LLB Solicitor . . . . . *Nov 1991
Whittingham, Mrs Marcia O BA(Hons); CPE; DipLaw Solicitor . . . . Aug 1999

RUSHCLIFFE BOROUGH COUNCIL
Civic Centre Pavilion Road Trent Bridge West Bridgford Nottinghamshire NG2 5FE
Tel: 0115 981 9911 *Fax:* 0115 945 5882
Dx: 719907 WEST BRIDGFORD
E-mail: info@rushcliffe.gov.uk
Sol: Anderson, Mr Peter Lewis BA Senior Legal Assistant . Nov 1996
Cox, Mr Paul Jonathan LLB; DipLG Borough Solicitor *Feb 1984
Norman, Mr Ian A FILEx Legal Services Manager . . *May 1990

WEST BROMWICH, West Midlands

WEST BROMWICH MAGISTRATES COURT
Lombard Street West West Bromwich West Midlands B70 8ED
Tel: 0121 533 3333 *Fax:* 0121 533 1312
Dx: 14627 WEST BROMWICH
Sol: Bergum, Mr Gerald S Clerk to the Justices . . . . . . Dec 1961

WEST MALLING, Kent

TONBRIDGE & MALLING BOROUGH COUNCIL
Gibson Building Gibson Drive Kings Hill West Malling Kent ME19 4LZ
Tel: 01732 876030 *Fax:* 01732 842170 *Dx:* 92865 WEST MALLING
E-mail: legal.services@tmbc.gov.uk
Sol: Francis, Ms Lynn LLB(Hons) Solicitor . . . . *Oct 1992
Henderson, Mr Ian K LLB(Hons) Solicitor . . . . . . *Nov 1986
Robinson, Mr Duncan H BA(Dunelm) Chief Solicitor. . *Jul 1978

WESTON-SUPER-MARE, North Somerset

NORTH SOMERSET DISTRICT COUNCIL
Town Hall Walliscote Grove Road Weston-super-Mare North Somerset BS23 1UJ
Tel: 01934 888888 *Fax:* 01934 634884
Dx: 8411 WESTON-SUPER-MARE
E-mail: legal@n-somerset.gov.uk
Sol: Blake, Mrs Katy Vivian LLB(Hons). . . . . Nov 1984
Brain, Mr Nicholas P LLB Legal Services Manager . . *Oct 1987
Buck, Mrs Susan M BA(Hons); LPC Solicitor . . . . . Oct 1996
Fear, Miss Natalie Dianne LLB(Hons) Senior Legal Adviser Mental Health Panel . . . . *Jul 1996
Nicholson, Mr Malcolm L LLB Solr to the Council . . *Nov 1983
Rich, Miss Ann Assistant Solicitor. . . . . *Dec 1992
Robertson, Miss Fiona A PGDip; LPC Solicitor . . . *Mar 1996
Sherman, Miss Lorraine DipLaw; DipLP Senior Legal Adviser Secretary to Clevedon and District Ladies Circle. *Sep 1998
Wood, Mrs Patricia Jeanette BEd(Hons) Senior Legal Adviser . . . . *Aug 1996

WEYBRIDGE, Surrey

GALLAHER LTD
Members Hill Brooklands Road Weybridge Surrey KT13 0QU
Tel: 01932 859777 *Fax:* 01932 372570
Sol: Bennett, Mrs Stephanie Ann Senior Legal Counsel . . *Oct 1998
Bingham, Mr Andrew LLB Senior Legal Counsel (Litigation & Regulatory Affairs) . . . . Sep 1999
Hope, Miss Emily LLB Solicitor . . . . Mar 2005
Jenkins, Ms Helen Anne Legal Counsel . . . . *Sep 1997
Keevil, Mr Thomas S LLB; FCIA Company Secretary and General Counsel . . . . *Oct 1986
Krangle, Mr Max Alfred LLB Legal Counsel . . . . . . *Sep 2000
Lee, Ms Maria Lawyer at Austria Tabak . . . . Aug 2005
Miller, Mr Robin Paul LLB(Hons) Senior Legal Counsel *Oct 1996
Money, Mr Andrew Legal Counsel. . . . . Nov 2002
Walker, Mr Edward Grosvenor Solicitor . . . . Jan 2001
Wise, Ms Suzanne E LLB Group Head of Legal . . . *Nov 1986
Zagel, Mrs Danielle LLB(Hons); BA Assistant Legal Counsel . . . . Jul 2003

PROCTER & GAMBLE UK (LEGAL DEPT)
The Heights Brooklands Weybridge Surrey KT13 0XP
Tel: 01932 896000 *Fax:* 01932 896749
Sol: Ellison, Ms Rowena LLB Counsel . . . . *May 1995
Keen, Ms Sarah J BA(Hons) Senior Counsel . . . . *Nov 1992
McCarthy, Mr Andrew Charles BA(Dunelm) General Counsel . . . . *Dec 1976

WEYMOUTH, Dorset

WEYMOUTH & PORTLAND BOROUGH COUNCIL
Council Offices North Quay Weymouth Dorset DT4 8TA
Tel: 01305 838000 *Fax:* 01305 838289
Sol: Altree, Mrs Lara BA(Hons) Legal Services Manager. . *Jan 1997
Earnshaw, Mrs Melanie Jayne BA(Hons) Legal & Democratic Services Unit Manager . . . . *Sep 1995
Mustoe, Mr John K BA(Hons)(Lond) Solicitor . . . . *Dec 1976

WHITEHAVEN, Cumbria

COPELAND BOROUGH COUNCIL
The Copeland Centre Catherine Street Whitehaven Cumbria CA28 7SJ
Tel: 01946 852585 *Fax:* 01946 598311 *Dx:* 62904 WHITEHAVEN
E-mail: legalsection@copelandbc.gov.uk
Sol: Boyce, Mr Clinton A LLB(Leeds) Legal Services Manager . . . . *Sep 1986
Jepson, Mr Martin LLM Head of Legal and Democratic Services . . . . *Jun 1980

WIDNES, Cheshire

HALTON BOROUGH COUNCIL
Municipal Building Kingsway Widnes Cheshire WA8 7QF
Tel: 0151 424 2061 *Fax:* 0151 471 7301 *Dx:* 24302 WIDNES 1
E-mail: hdl@halton.gov.uk
Sol: Baker, Ms Lesley . . . . May 2002
Barnett, Mr Robert James Charles LLB(Hons); DipLG Local Government Prize 1978 Group Solicitor Policy & Regeration . . . . *Jun 1978
Capper, Miss Lisa Victoria LLB Solicitor . . . . Jul 2005
Gill, Miss Irene Ruth Edwina BA(Hons) Group Solicitor*Mar 1981
Pearce, Mrs Janette Elizabeth LLB(Hons); LLM . . . . Nov 1968
Scott, Miss Mary F E LLB Council Solicitor . . . . . . *Apr 1974
Tradewell, Mr John K LLB; MBA Council Solicitor . . *Apr 1987
Tully, Mr John LLB(Lond); LLM(B'ham); DipLG Council Solicitor . . . . *Jun 1977

WIGAN, Greater Manchester

WIGAN BOROUGH COUNCIL
Town Hall Library Street Wigan Greater Manchester WN1 1YN
Tel: 01942 244991 *Fax:* 01942 827093 *Dx:* 702075 WIGAN 2
Sol: Anderson, Ms G Patricia LLB(Hons) Solicitor . . . . . Jan 1998
Beressi, Ms Roisin M LLB(Hons) Senior Solicitor . . . Nov 1989
Brown, Mrs Christine Jane LLB(Hons) Solicitor . . . . Mar 1987
Crittenden, Mr Michael I K LLB Principal Conveyancer. Mar 1974
Curran, Mrs Kathryn Ann BA Solicitor . . . . Sep 2002
Davies, Mrs Janet E LLB; DipLG Senior Solicitor . . . *Nov 1990
Hassett, Mr Peter LLB Senior Solicitor. . . . . *Sep 1989
Henderson, Miss Alison LLB Solicitor . . . . Jun 2005
Hillman, Mrs Shirley LLB Principal Solicitor (Planning). *Jul 1976
Irvine, Mr Robert LLB(Hons); DipLP Solicitor . . . . . Jul 2006
Knowles, Miss Gillian BA(Hons). . . . . *Jan 1997
Lawson, Mr Kevin P BA(Law) Service Director Borough Solicitor . . . . Mar 1980
Lawton, Mrs Rosalind LLB Assistant Director . . . . . *Jul 1977
McKenzie, Mrs Margaret G MA(Oxon) Principal Solicitor . . . . *Jan 1985
McNally, Ms Joyce BA(Hons); MSc Solicitor. . . . . *Dec 1994
Milson, Miss Caroline LLB Solicitor . . . . May 2007
Robert, Mr Derek A LLB Principal Solicitor (Social Services) . . . . Mar 1986
Robinson, Ms Joanna K BA(Hons) Senior Solicitor . . *Apr 1991
Rowlands, Mr John F BA Principal Solicitor . . . . . *Dec 1980
Taylor, Mrs Susan LLB(Hons) Housing Solicitor . . . . Oct 2004
Ward, Mr Simon David LLB Solicitor. . . . . *Feb 1992
Whitworth, Mr Brendan J LLB(Hons) Solicitor . . . . . Jul 2000

WIGSTON, Leicestershire

OADBY & WIGSTON BOROUGH COUNCIL
Council Offices Station Road Wigston Leicestershire LE18 2DR
Tel: 0116 288 8961 *Fax:* 0116 288 7828
E-mail: legal@oadby.wigston.gov.uk
Sol: Court, Mrs Anne Elizabeth LLB(Hons) Head of Legal & Licensing . . . . *Aug 2003

WILLITON, Somerset

WEST SOMERSET DISTRICT COUNCIL
Council Offices 20 Fore Street Williton Somerset TA4 4QA
Tel: 01643 703704 *Fax:* 01984 633022 *Dx:* 117701 WILLITON
E-mail: westsomersetdc@westsomerset.gov.uk
Sol: Howes, Mr Timothy D LLB(Exon) Chief Executive . . *Nov 1986

WILMSLOW, Cheshire

INFORMATION COMMISIONER
Wycliffe House Water Lane Wilmslow Cheshire SK9 5AF
Tel: 01625 545700 *Fax:* 01625 524510 *Dx:* 20819 WILMSLOW
E-mail: mail@ico.gsi.gov.uk
Sol: Dennehy, Ms Lucienne F Solicitor. . . . . *Nov 1994
Dersley, Miss Geraldine Karen BA(Hons) Principal Solicitor . . . . *Mar 1995
Devitt, Ms Catherine Lucy LLB Solicitor . . . . *Oct 1988
Parr, Ms Julia BA(Hons) Solicitor . . . . *May 1990
Rudgard, Mrs Sian E BA(Hons) Solicitor. . . . . . . *Nov 1985
Taylor, Mr Philip James LLB Solicitor . . . . *Apr 1999
Thorogood, Mr Mark Solicitor . . . . *Jan 2003
Tyler, Mr Nicholas Maurice BA(Hons) Legal Director. *Nov 1990
Witkowski, Mrs Janet Christine LLB(Hons) Maxwell Law Prize Principal Solicitor . . . . *Oct 1990

WIMBORNE, Dorset

COBHAM PLC
Brook Road Wimborne Dorset BH21 2BJ
Tel: 01202 857552 *Fax:* 01202 840523
E-mail: popej@cobham.com
Sol: Pope, Mr John M LLB; FCIS Solicitor & Company Secretary . . . . *Jul 1979

EAST DORSET DISTRICT COUNCIL
Furzehill Wimborne Dorset BH21 4HN
Tel: 01202 886201 *Fax:* 01202 841390 *Dx:* 140871 WIMBORNE 2
E-mail: kmallett@eastdorset.gov.uk
Sol: Course, Mr Gary A Assistant Solicitor . . . . *Nov 1988
Mallett, Mr Keith G LLB Head of Legal Services. . . *Aug 1980

TEACHERS' BUILDING SOCIETY
Allenview House Hanham Road Wimborne Dorset BH21 1AG
Tel: 01202 843503 *Fax:* 01202 841694 *Dx:* 45315 WIMBORNE
E-mail: karen.flaherty@teachersbs.co.uk
Sol: Flaherty, Ms Karen Ann BA(Hons) Solicitor & SecretaryMay 1997

WINCHESTER, Hampshire

HAMPSHIRE COUNTY COUNCIL
The Castle Winchester Hampshire SO23 8UJ
Tel: 01962 841841 *Fax:* 01962 840215 *Dx:* 2510 WINCHESTER
Sol: Brayshaw, Mrs Angela M LLB Senior Solicitor. . . . *Jun 1974
Buckett, Mrs Christine BA Litigation Manager . . . . *Mar 1999
Clark, Mrs Amanda Hilarie BA(Hons)(Oxon). . . . . *Nov 1989
Cronan, Mrs Geraldine D BA Senior Solicitor . . . . *Mar 1979
Ellam, Miss Elizabeth BSc(Hons) Senior Solicitor . . *Dec 1990
Everatt, Mrs Karen LLB Senior Solicitor . . . . Jan 2001
Feltham, Mr Alan Senior Legal Officer. . . . . *Jul 1978
Gardner, Mr Kevin R LLB Head of Legal Practice . . *Mar 1987
Keitley, Mrs Julia LLB Senior Legal Assistant . . . . . Aug 1988
McCutcheon, Mrs Jacqueline A LLB Solicitor . . . . *Oct 1990
Pattison, Mr Jeffrey A LLB(Lond) Head of Legal & Corporate Services . . . . *Mar 1976
Penny, Mr Jeremy Justin BA . . . . Sep 1997
Phillipson, Ms Katharine Ruth Solicitor. . . . . *Oct 1994
Robertson, Mr Peter C B LLB(Lond) Chief Executive . Oct 1975
Seaton-Fry, Ms Maria LLB Sweet & Maxwell Law Prize 1997 . . . . Jan 2003
Thomas, Mrs Caroline Elizabeth LLB; LLM Legal Assistant . . . . Jan 1987
Ward, Miss Suzanne LLB; DipLaw. . . . . Sep 2004
Woodhouse, Mrs Kathleen Emily BA(English & Drama); CPE; LSF(Guildford) Solicitor . . . . Jan 1996
Wootten, Miss Nicola Louise BA(Hons) Childcare Solicitor Local Authority . . . . Feb 1997

IBM UNITED KINGDOM LTD
Hursley Park Winchester Hampshire SO21 2JN
Tel: 01962 815000 *Fax:* 020 7202 5935
Sol: Ford, Mr Anthony D E MA; LLB(Cantab) Senior Counsel . . . . *Jan 1979

WINCHESTER CITY COUNCIL
City Offices Colebrook Street Winchester Hampshire SO23 9LJ
Tel: 01962 840222 *Fax:* 01962 848555 *Dx:* 120400 WINCHESTER 5
E-mail: css@winchester.gov.uk
Sol: Bone, Mr Howard N LLB Head of Legal Services . . . *Oct 1987
Fallon, Mrs Emily Jane BA(Hons) Licensing & Property Solicitor . . . . Oct 2003
Scott, Mrs Elizabeth Maria LLB Property & Contracts Solicitor . . . . *Oct 1983
Sutherland, Miss Fiona BA(Law) Planning & Information Solicitor . . . . Oct 1986
Tetstall, Ms Cynthia R LLB(Hons) Licensing & Property Solicitor . . . . Nov 1984
Whetnall, Mr Stephen LLB(Manc) Corporate Director (Governance). . . . . *Apr 1981

WINDLESHAM, Surrey

THE BOC GROUP PLC
The Priestly Centre 10 Priestly Road Surrey Research Park Guildford Surrey GU2 7XY
Tel: 01483 579857
Sol: Brackfield, Mr Andrew C MA(Cantab) Senior Counsel, Corporate . . . . §Dec 1980
Deeming, Mr Nicholas MBA Group Legal Director & Company Secretary . . . . *Oct 1979
Ford, Mr Thomas P L BSocSc; MBA Associate Counsel . . . . *Apr 1996
Hastings, Mrs Tara LLB; BEc Corporate Counsel . . . Dec 2001
Langton, Mr Timothy LLB(Hons)(Law) General Counsel-Global Compliance. . . . . Mar 1998
O'Neill, Mr Francis General Counsel - Legal Operations Jul 1981
Patterson, Mr Ben LLB Senior Counsel . . . . *Oct 1988
Rowlands, Ms Melanie Jane MA(Law) General Counsel . . . . *Sep 1992
Williams, Mr Roger Q BSc(Hons); MIOSH Regional General Counsel. . . . . *Jan 1979

WINDSOR, Windsor & Maidenhead

HFC LEGAL DEPARTMENT
North Street Winkfield Windsor Windsor & Maidenhead SL4 4TD
Tel: 01344 892435 *Fax:* 01344 892423
Sol: Rivers, Mr C John LLB(L'pool) Solicitor & Company Secretary . . . . *Jan 1984

WINSFORD, Cheshire

VALE ROYAL BOROUGH COUNCIL
Wyvern House The Drumber Winsford Cheshire CW7 1AH
Tel: 01606 862862 *Fax:* 01606 867665 *Dx:* 722040
Sol: Bramhall, Mrs Judith BA(Hons)(Law) Senior Solicitor . May 1996
Crane, Miss Fiona M BA(Law); DipLG; MBA Head of Legal & Democratic Services . . . . *Oct 1983
Ingram, Mrs Margaret J BSc; MBA Principal Solicitor . *Oct 1980
McCormack, Mrs Lynda Jayne LLB(Hons). . . . . . . Apr 2005
Maddocks, Ms Rachel BA; CPE; LSF Senior Solicitor . Nov 1992
Newton, Mrs Christine Rebecca LLB Legal Officer. . . Nov 1995

WITHAM, Essex

PERSIMMON PLC
10 Collingwood Road Witham Essex CM8 2EA
Tel: 01376 518811 *Fax:* 01376 514926 *Dx:* 33421 WITHAM
Sol: Dempster, Miss A Jayne LLB(Hons) Company Solicitor . . . . *May 1989

See p112 for the Key to Work Categories & other symbols

WITNEY, Oxfordshire

WEST OXFORDSHIRE DISTRICT COUNCIL
Council Offices Woodgreen Witney Oxfordshire OX28 1NB
Tel: 01993 861581 *Fax:* 01993 861450
E-mail: legal@westoxon.gov.uk
Sol: Baggley, Mr James David John Solicitor. . . . . *Jan 2005
Redzikowska, Ms Caroline LLB; DipLG Head of Legal Services Monitoring Officer. . . . . *Oct 1990

WOKING, Surrey

NORTH WEST SURREY MAGISTRATES COURT
The Court House Station Approach Woking Surrey GU22 7YL
Tel: 01483 714950 *Fax:* 01483 712500
Sol: Dunford, Mr Martin T Head of Legal Services . . . . . *Feb 1980

WOKING BOROUGH COUNCIL
Civic Offices Gloucester Square Woking Surrey GU21 6YL
Tel: 01483 755855 *Fax:* 01483 768746 *Dx:* 2931 WOKING
E-mail: wokbc@woking.gov.uk
Sol: Bryant, Mr Peter N Principal Solicitor . . . . *Nov 1983
Harrison, Mr Alan LLB Borough Secretary & Solicitor to the Council . . . . *May 1985

WOKINGHAM

WOKINGHAM DISTRICT COUNCIL
PO Box 152 Civic Offices Shute End Wokingham RG40 1WJ
Tel: 0118 974 6000 *Fax:* 0118 974 6542 *Dx:* 33506 WOKINGHAM
Sol: Ghose, Mr Azhar M LLB(Hons) . . . . *Oct 1994
Green, Mr Christopher J LLB; LARTPI Principal Solicitor . . . . *Feb 1983
Isaacs, Mrs Laurel Julietta LLB Solicitor. . . . . *Jul 2002
Lawley, Mr Colin J LLB Principal Solicitor . . . . *Jan 1979
Nelson-Wehrmeyer, Mrs Susanne Lin B Juris; LLB; MBA Corporate Head of Legal, Democratic Services . . *Sep 2002
Severin, Mrs Mary E Solicitor . . . . Jan 1998

WOLVERHAMPTON, West Midlands

CARILLION PLC
Birch Street Wolverhampton West Midlands WV1 4HY
Tel: 01902 422431 *Fax:* 01902 316165
Sol: Anderson, Mr David LLB(Hons) Legal Director. . . . . *Oct 1985
Annison, Ms Rebecca Mary BA(Hons); LPC Solicitor . *Sep 2005
Ashwell, Mr Matthew LLB(Hons) Solicitor . . . . *Sep 2004
Buck, Mr Christopher MA Solicitor. . . . . *Sep 2003
Charlson, Mrs Jennifer Senior Solicitor . . . . *Sep 1998
Chesworth, Miss Keeley Jane LLB(Hons) Principal Solicitor . . . . *Sep 2000
Evans, Mrs Katherine Elizabeth BSc; GDLS/CPE Solicitor . . . . Sep 2003
Humphreys, Mr Kim A BA(Law) Legal Director. . . . . *Oct 1987
Kitchingman, Ms Fleur LLB(Hons); LawDip . . . . . . Dec 2000
Mackreth, Miss Jane LLB(Hons) Solicitor . . . . *Jun 2000
Mutter, Mr Jeremy LLB Legal Director. . . . . *Oct 1995
Pratt, Ms Elaine LLB . . . . Sep 2000
Ragunathan, Miss Theeba LLB Solicitor. . . . . *Nov 2000
Savage, Ms Isabelle LLB(Hons) Solicitor . . . . *Jun 2001
Shepley, Ms Alison M LLB(Hons); MBA Legal Director.*Nov 1987
Sylvester, Ms Sharmila LLB(Hons) Solicitor . . . . . . *Mar 2003
Tapp, Mr Richard F LLB; LLM; MBA; FCIS; MCIArb; FRSA Company Secretary & Director of Legal Services . *Apr 1984
Trowbridge, Mrs Karyn Lisa LLB(Hons); LLM . . . . . Oct 1991
Wan, Ms Lynn BA(Hons); CPE; MSc; Dip(Local Govt Law); MBA Principal Solicitor . . . . *Apr 1998

TARMAC LTD
Millfields Road Ettingshall Wolverhampton West Midlands WV4 6JP
Tel: 01902 353522 *Fax:* 01902 382699
Sol: Bradshaw, Mr John R Group Commercial Solicitor-Aggregate Products . . . . *Jun 1981
Hannon, Ms Debra Jane Assistant Group Property Solicitor . . . . *Sep 2005
Stirk, Mr James R MA(Cantab) George Long Prize; Squire Scholar Company Secretary and Group Solicitor . *Nov 1984
Walley, Mr Kevin Stanley LLB(Hons) Commercial and Corporate Solicitor-Building Products . . . . *Oct 1994
Whitehouse, Mrs Beverley E LLB(B'ham) Group Property Solicitor. . . . . *Oct 1987

WOLVERHAMPTON CITY COUNCIL
Civic Centre St Peters Square Wolverhampton West Midlands WV1 1RG
Tel: 01902 556556 *Fax:* 01902 554970
Sol: Bennett, Mrs Louise J BA(Hons); CPE; LPC Principal Solicitor . . . . Sep 1998
Bryan, Mr John Fitzgerald Solicitor . . . . Sep 2005
Christie, Ms Tracy Joanna Principal Solicitor. . . . . . *Nov 1998
Daniels, Miss Lucinda Joan LLB Principal Solicitor. . . *Mar 1997
Davis, Ms Fiona J BA; MBA Principal Solicitor. . . . . *Feb 1988
Hardwick, Mrs Sarah LLB; LLM Solicitor (Environmental Services Local Authority) . . . . Feb 1999
Hill, Ms Amanda Jane LLB Assistant . . . . Feb 1991
Hopkins, Miss Jane E BA(Hons) Solicitor . . . . *Jul 1980
Kembrey, Ms Susan BA(Hons); MSc Solicitor . . . . . . *Jan 1986
Marshall, Mr Robert Solicitor . . . . Nov 2002
Noor, Ms Jasbir Kaur LLB; LLDip Shakespeare Prize for Obligations II Solicitor. . . . . *Dec 2004
Webb, Mr Michael J Principal Solicitor. . . . . *Jul 1980

WOODBRIDGE, Suffolk

THE NOTARIES SOCIETY
PO Box 226 Melton Woodbridge Suffolk IP12 1WX
Tel: 01394 380436 *Fax:* 01394 383772 *Dx:* 41412 WOODBRIDGE
E-mail: secretary@thenotariessociety.org.uk
Sol: Vaughan, Mr Christopher James Notary Public Former President Notary Public . . . . *Dec 1973

SUFFOLK COASTAL DISTRICT COUNCIL
Council Offices Melton Hill Woodbridge Suffolk IP12 1AU
Tel: 01394 383789 *Fax:* 01394 385100 *Dx:* 41400 WOODBRIDGE
E-mail: customerservices@suffolkcoastal.gov.uk
Sol: De Prez, Mr Ian S BA(Hons)(Bris); DipLG Senior Solicitor . . . . *§Nov 1989
Slater, Mrs Hilary LLB(Hons)(Nott'm) Head of Legal & Democratic Services . . . . *Mar 1987
Tomiak, Mrs Shelagh Joy BA(Hons); MA(Lond); PGCE; Solicitor Assistant Solicitor. . . . . *Nov 2001

WOODFORD GREEN, Essex

MULALLEY
Teresa Gavin House Woodford Avenue Woodford Green Essex IG8 8FA
Tel: 020 8551 9999 *Fax:* 020 8551 1363
Sol: Taylor, Mr Timothy Adam LLB Sole Company Solicitor. *Jul 1994

WORCESTER, Worcestershire

WORCESTER CITY COUNCIL
Guildhall High Street Worcester Worcestershire WR1 2EY
Tel: 01905 723471 *Fax:* 01905 722028 *Dx:* 716287 WORCESTER
Sol: Golding, Miss Patricia Veronica BA Solicitor. . . . . . *Nov 2001
Porter, Miss Doreen LLB Legal & Democratic Services Manager . . . . *Dec 1980
Rushton, Mrs Wendy Barbara BA Senior Solicitor . . . *Sep 1993

WORCESTERSHIRE COUNTY COUNCIL
County Hall Spetchley Road Worcester Worcestershire WR5 2NP
Tel: 01905 766335 *Fax:* 01905 766677 *Dx:* 29941 WORCESTER 2
E-mail: legalservices@worcestershire.gov.uk
Sol: Dunham, Mrs Ellen M LLB(Hons) Solicitor. . . . . . . *Feb 1987
Elliott, Mr David A LLB; DipLG Principal Solicitor . . . *Oct 1985
Hitchman, Mrs Catherine Grace LLB(Hons) . . . . . . *Jan 2002
Hobbs, Mr John Edward BSc(Hons); LLM; MRICS Director of Environmental Services. . . . . Aug 1995
Jones, Mr Lewis BA(Hons); LLM Principal Solicitor . . Aug 1996
Mallinson, Mr Simon P BA(Hons); DipLG Head of Legal and Democratic Services . . . . *Oct 1985
Moore, Mr Alan C BA(Hons) Principal Solicitor. . . . . *Oct 1977
Perons, Ms Katherine J LLB(Hons) Solicitor. . . . . . *Nov 1989
Stockton, Mrs Christine M Solicitor . . . . *Sep 1986
Terrell, Mrs Filomena LLB(Hons); DipLG Solicitor . . . *Dec 1994
Williamson, Miss Heather BA(Hons) Solicitor . . . . . Nov 1999
Wilson, Ms Deborah LLB(Hons) Solicitor . . . . *Jun 1998

WORKINGTON, Cumbria

WEST CUMBRIA MAGISTRATES COURTS
Hall Park Ramsay Brow Workington Cumbria CA14 4AS
Tel: 01900 62244 *Fax:* 01900 68644 *Dx:* 68690 WORKINGTON
Sol: Allcard, Miss Joanne L LLB Solicitor. . . . . May 1996
Armstrong, Mr Christopher J BA Clerk to the Justices . *Dec 1975
Heron, Mrs Lesley BA; LLB Court Clerk . . . . Oct 1996
Jepson, Mr Timothy BA Deputy Clerk to the Justices . . Jul 1984
Mattok, Mr John D LLB Court Clerk . . . . Oct 1984

WORKSOP, Nottinghamshire

BASSETLAW DISTRICT COUNCIL
Queens Buildings Potter Street Worksop Nottinghamshire S80 2AH
Tel: 01909 533533 *Fax:* 01909 501246 *Dx:* 723180 WORKSOP 3
E-mail: legal@bassetlaw.gov.uk
Sol: Dawson, Mr Richard Andrew LLB(Sheff) Assistant Solicitor . . . . *Jun 1977
Walsham, Miss Yvonne LLB Principal Solicitor. . . . . *Jun 1976
Yates, Mr David LLB Assistant Solicitor . . . . *Apr 1974

WORKSOP MAGISTRATES COURT
The Court House 30 Potter Street Worksop Nottinghamshire S80 2AJ
Tel: 01909 486111 *Fax:* 01909 473521
Sol: Foster, Ms Sandra Bed; DML; CPE; LPC Senior Legal Adviser . . . . Oct 1996
Smith, Mrs Karen LLB Senior Legal Adviser. . . . . . Aug 1993

WORTHING, West Sussex

ENVIRONMENT AGENCY (SOUTHERN)
Guildbourne House Chatsworth Road Worthing West Sussex BN11 1LD
Tel: 01903 820692 *Fax:* 01903 821832 *Dx:* 3713 WORTHING
Sol: Davies, Mr Martin J LLB(Wales); MA Regional Legal Manager . . . . *Feb 1983
Ferguson, Mr Angus N E BA(Hons); DMS. . . . . . . *Feb 1983
Pollard, Miss Judith L BA(Kent) Regional Solicitor. . . . Nov 1984
Starks, Mr Gordon Charles LLB Solicitor. . . . . Jan 1995

JUSTICES' CLERK'S OFFICE
PO BOX 199 Worthing West Sussex BN11 1JE
Tel: 01903 210981 *Fax:* 01903 820746
Sol: Dean, Miss Carin BA(Hons) Legal Adviser. . . . . . . *Jan 1994
Meech, Mr James Robert LLB(Hons) Legal Adviser . . Oct 2004

SOUTHERN WATER SERVICES LTD
Southern House Yeoman Road Worthing West Sussex BN13 3NX
Tel: 01903 264444 *Fax:* 01903 262185
E-mail: legal@southernwater.co.uk
Sol: Alexander, Mr Stephen J LLB Group Solicitor . . . . . Jul 1973
Hall, Mr Kevin G LLB Company Secretary. . . . . Jul 1980
Harrington, Ms Jennifer A LLB Group Solicitor. . . . . *Oct 1989
Statton, Mrs Joanne FILEx Assistant Solicitor . . . . . Nov 2005

WORTHING BOROUGH COUNCIL
Town Hall Chapel Road Worthing West Sussex BN11 1HA
Tel: 01903 239999 *Fax:* 01903 214384 *Dx:* 142960 WORTHING 10
Sol: Watson, Ms Julie BA(Hons) Corporate Lawyer. . . . . Jan 1992

WORTHING MAGISTRATES COURT
PO Box 199 Christchurch Road Worthing West Sussex BN11 1JE
Tel: 01903 210981 *Fax:* 01903 820746 *Dx:* 98233 WORTHING 4
Sol: Dean, Miss Carin BA(Hons) Legal Adviser. . . . . . . *Jan 1994

WREXHAM

WREXHAM COUNTY BOROUGH COUNCIL
Guildhall Wrexham LL11 1AY
Tel: 01978 292000 *Fax:* 01978 292207 *Dx:* 26672 WREXHAM
Sol: Barry, Miss Helen Caroline LLB(Hons) Senior Solicitor. Jan 1994
Coxon, Mr Trevor LLB(B'ham) Chief Legal & Democratic Services Officer. . . . . *Aug 1981
Davies, Miss Louise LLB(Hons) Solicitor. . . . . Jul 1997
Edwards, Mrs Sarah L LLB Senior Solicitor . . . . . . Sep 1994
Jones, Miss Glenda LLB(Hons) Principal Solicitor . . . *Mar 1979
Jones, Miss Lisa LLB(Hons) Solicitor . . . . Oct 1996
Pennington, Mrs Deborah S Law Society Prize for Outstanding Achievement on LPC 1998 Solicitor. . . . . *Sep 2000
Roberts, Mrs Linda J LLB Senior Solicitor . . . . *Oct 1992
Rowlands, Mr T Aled LLB(Hons) Solicitor . . . . *Sep 1996
Williams, Miss Ffion BA(Hons) Solicitor . . . . Sep 1996
Wyn Thomas, Ms Sioned LLB(Hons)(Law with French) Senior Solicitor. . . . . Jan 1988

YEOVIL, Somerset

AGUSTAWESTLAND LEGAL DEPT - YEOVIL
Westland Works Lysander Road Yeovil Somerset BA20 2YB
Tel: 01935 702240 *Fax:* 01935 703864
Sol: Cranidge, Mr Neil A LLB(Hons) Legal Counsel . . . . *Dec 1993
Elliott, Mr Martin G MA(Cantab) Legal Counsel . . . *§Oct 1978
Lee, Mr William D LLB(Hons) General Counsel . . . . *Dec 1967
Speake, Mr Wayne R LLB(Hons) Legal Counsel. . . . *Oct 1988

SOUTH SOMERSET DISTRICT COUNCIL
The Council Offices Brympton Way Yeovil Somerset BA20 2DS
Tel: 01935 462462 *Fax:* 01935 462666
E-mail: ian.clarke@southsomerset.gov.uk
Sol: Clarke, Mr Ian David LLB(Hons) Solicitor to the Council *Jul 1987
Legg, Mr Robin Andrew Shane BSc Assistant Solicitor *Mar 1980
Watson, Mrs Angela BA(Hons) Assistant Solicitor . . . *Oct 2005

YORK

THE COLLEGE OF LAW YORK
Bishopthorpe Road York YO23 2GA
Tel: 0800 289997
Sol: Biles, Mr Gerard LLB Maxwell Law Prize 1988 Senior Lecturer . . . . *Nov 1991
Carmichael, Ms Feona Principal Lecturer . . . . Nov 1988
Dearden, Ms Rebecca MA(Cantab) Lecturer. . . . . . *Oct 1995
Green, Ms Deborah L LLB; ACIA Senior Lecturer . . . *Nov 1987
Greene, Mr James Lecturer. . . . . Sep 1998
Holland, Miss Gayle E LLB(Hons) Lecturer . . . . . . *Sep 1997
Hubble, Mr Patrick L Lecturer . . . . *Nov 1995
Laws, Mrs Wendy LLB(Leeds) Lecturer . . . . *Jan 1986
Lill, Mr Jeffrey BA Principal Lecturer. . . . . *Oct 1990
McNaull, Mhairis Senior Lecturer . . . . Mar 1991
Maddock, Mr Malcolm Deputy Director Vocational . . . Jan 1977
Olley, Mr Nick Director of Internal Affairs . . . . . . May 1984
Seager, Ms Amanda Senior Lecturer . . . . Oct 1988
Toczek, Mr Laurence R LLB Senior Lecturer. . . . . . *Oct 1985

NORWICH UNION LIFE
2 Rougier Street York YO90 1UU
Tel: 01904 452210 *Fax:* 01904 452856
Sol: Donegan, Ms Louise BA(Hons); CPE Senior Solicitor . Sep 1997
Eleanor, Mr Nicholas J R TD BA(Hons) Legal Risks Manager . . . . *§Jul 1984
Fish, Mr David R BA Head of Legal . . . . Dec 1978
Gordon, Ms Joy Helen LLB; DipLP Solicitor . . . . . . Jul 1990
Hough, Miss Gillian Solicitor. . . . . Sep 2004
Kay, Mr Andrew L T BA(Hons) Solicitor . . . . Sep 2003
McAnlis, Mrs Rosie LLB Solicitor . . . . Jan 2000
Madaan, Mr Ashish Solicitor. . . . . Sep 2001
Morgan, Mr Simon LLB(Law & French Law) Solicitor. . Sep 1993
Robson, Mrs Kate European Legal Studies Lancaster University 1996 Solicitor . . . . Oct 1999
Street, Miss Louise Marie BA Employee. . . . . Sep 2006
Tootell, Ms Emma L BA Solicitor. . . . . Apr 1999
Willis, Mr Kevin Richard BA(Hons) Solicitor - Product Lawyer . . . . *Sep 1997
Wilman, Ms Jennifer Jane BSc Director Of Legal Services . . . . *Sep 1987
Yacoubou, Miss Caroline Jane FILEx Assistant SolicitorNov 2006
Young, Miss Louise LLB Solicitor . . . . Sep 2003

PERSIMMON HOMES LEGAL DEPARTMENT
Persimmon House Fulford York YO19 4FE
Tel: 01904 642199 *Fax:* 01904 652097 *Dx:* 711680 FULFORD
E-mail: garethhale@persimmonhomes.com
Sol: Baird, Mr James A LLB Company Solicitor. . . . . . . *Jul 1977
Francis, Mr Gerald Neil Legal Director. . . . . *Jun 1980
Hale, Mr Gareth K E BA Regional Solicitor . . . . . . *Jun 1980

SHEPHERD CONSTRUCTION LTD
Frederick House Fulford Road York YO10 4EA
Tel: 01904 660400 *Fax:* 01904 660577
E-mail: philipbrown@shepherd-construction.co.uk
Sol: Brown, Mr Philip LLB(Hons); BA Legal Director . . . . *Jun 1978

CITY OF YORK COUNCIL
The Guildhall York YO1 8QS
Tel: 01904 551045 *Fax:* 01904 551047 *Dx:* 61583 YORK 1
E-mail: suzan.hemingway@york.gov.uk
Sol: Blackburn, Mr Mark S D LLB Solicitor . . . . *Feb 1990
Blythe, Mr Martin LLB Solicitor . . . . *Jan 1979
Hemingway, Ms Suzan Claire Solicitor. . . . . Oct 1988
Lewis, Mr Steven Christopher BA(Hons) Solicitor . . . May 1987
McCusker, Mr Glen Solicitor. . . . . Mar 1986
Perara, Mrs Melanie Solicitor . . . . Nov 1992

YORK MAGISTRATES
Clifford Street York YO1 9RE
Tel: 01757 293500 *Fax:* 01757 293501
Sol: Simpson, Glyndwr Deputy Clerk to the Justices Deputy Clerk to the Justice . . . . *§Oct 1982

SECTION 3

SOLICITORS

CONTENTS

ENGLAND & WALES FIRMS – A-Z

Key to symbols

‡= Principal office

1

174 Law
‡Birkenhead *p134* 0151 647 7372

1st Solicitors
‡Stafford *p392*. 01785 213234

3

3 Spires Solicitors Limited
‡Birmingham *p135*. 0121 333 1296

A

@ Cornwall Law
‡Truro *p414* . . . . .01872 222688 / 222712

A2 Accident Solicitors
‡Rochdale *p365* 01706 343322

AA & Co Solicitors
‡London SE18 *p3* 020 8317 3333

AA Law (Lancashire) Ltd
‡Blackburn *p145*. 0845 644 0786

AA Law Solicitors
‡Skegness *p380*. 01754 896970 / 07733 228081 / 07900 913830

AB Law
‡Harrow *p241* 020 8426 5613

ABM Solicitors
‡Hayes *p245* 020 8848 8600

ABS Solicitors
‡Hastings *p243* 0845 083 0003

AB Solicitors
‡Wembley *p426* 020 8900 2099

ABT Law LLP
‡Bury *p170* 0161 764 6476

ABV Solicitors
‡Hayes *p245* 0844 587 9996

ACT Solicitors
‡Norwich *p333*. 01603 610611

A City Law Firm LLP
‡London EC2 *p3*. 020 7426 0382

ADB Law
‡St Albans *p389*. 01727 842586

ADF Law LLP
‡Manchester *p300*. 0844 826 3670

ADH Law
‡London N15 *p3*. 020 3240 1010

ADL Solicitors
‡Halifax *p238* 01422 339994

AEW Litigation
‡Sutton Coldfield *p403*. 0121 354 8640

AFL Solicitors
‡Bournemouth *p151* 01202 729999

AGH Solicitors
‡Bolton *p148* 01204 364433

AGR Solicitors
‡Mansfield *p311* 01623 460444
Shirebrook *p378* 01623 748522

AHM Law
‡Surbiton *p402* 020 8339 9195

A HALSALL & CO
‡Birkenhead *p134* 0151 647 6323
Wirral *p435*. 0151 678 9090
Wirral *p435*. 0151 648 7111

AI Law Limited
‡Bolton *p148* 01204 454344

AJA Solicitors
‡London N17 *p3*. 020 8888 2142

AJR Solicitors
‡Kingswinford *p268* 0875 500 1201
‡Woking *p436* . . . 01932 342107 / 07979 241761

AKD Solicitors
‡Telford *p409* 01952 260777

AKL Solicitors
‡Luton *p294*. 01582 454365

AKP Solicitors Ltd
‡London E6 *p3* 020 8472 4462

AK Solicitors
‡London E1 *p3* 020 7377 9366

AKZ Solicitors
‡Birmingham *p135*. 0121 326 0500

A Kay Pietron & Paluch
‡Ealing W3 *p3*. 020 8992 9997

ALB Law
‡Southport *p388*. 01704 500771

ALD Legal Limited
‡Harrow *p241* 020 8869 0422

ALMT Legal
‡London EC3 *p3*. 020 7645 9190

AMA Law
‡Cardiff *p177* 029 2048 1313

AMC Law
‡Northampton *p331* 01604 611980 / 01908 767014

AMD Solicitors
‡Bristol *p160*. 0117 962 1460
Bristol *p160*. 0117 973 8205
Bristol *p160*. 0117 923 5562
Bristol *p160*. 0117 974 4100

AM Law Limited
‡Nottingham *p335*. 0115 960 3673

AM Legal Consultants Co Ltd
‡London NW2 *p3*

AMR Solicitors
‡Hounslow *p253*. 020 8622 3783

AMS Solicitors
‡Preston *p356*. 01772 653333

AMV Law
‡Barnet *p123* 020 8245 0039

AMZ Law
‡London W2 *p3* 020 7724 7888

ANB Law
‡Peterborough *p346*. 01733 565900

ANP Solicitors
‡Benfleet *p131*. 01702 556688

APC Solicitors
‡Birmingham *p135*. 0121 242 3000

APD Solicitors
‡London W1 *p3* 020 7287 7880

APP Law
‡Frodsham *p227*. 01928 788537

The A P Partnership Ltd
‡Peterborough *p346*. 01733 891081

APT Solicitors
‡Croydon *p204* 020 8689 7292

AQSA Law Chambers
‡London E7 *p3* 020 8552 5833

ARC Solicitors
‡Birmingham *p135*. 0121 449 1188

AR Legal Solicitors
‡London W4 *p3* 020 8747 9090

AR Solicitors
‡Manchester *p300*. 0161 955 4206

ASB Aspire
‡Maidstone *p298* 0845 063 6465

ASB Law
‡Crawley *p202*. 01293 603600
Maidstone *p298*. 01622 656500

ASK Solicitors
‡Rossendale *p367*. 01706 217774

AS Law
‡Liverpool *p285* 0151 707 1212

A S Solicitors
‡Walsall *p419* 01922 682822

AST Hampsons
‡Rochdale *p365* 01706 522311
Manchester *p300* 0161 681 1169

AST Hampsons (incorporating Warhurst and co)
‡Bury *p170* 0161 764 3317

ATE Solicitors
‡London E16 *p3*. 020 7476 8739

AT@Law LLP
‡Cheltenham *p187*. 0800 019 5933

AWB Charlesworth LLP
‡Keighley *p263* 01535 613678
Skipton *p381* 01756 793333

AWB Partnership LLP
‡Guildford *p235* 01483 302345

AW Law
‡Esher *p219*. 01372 469100

AYB Law Solicitors
‡Preston *p356*. 01772 250605

A'Court & Co
‡Windsor *p434*. 01753 857146

A-Z Law Solicitors
‡Wandsworth SW12 *p3* 020 8355 0830

AZrights Solicitors
‡Islington N1 *p3* 020 7700 1414

AZ Solicitors
‡Ilford *p259* 020 8553 1049

Aaron & Partners LLP Solicitors
‡Chester *p190*. 01244 405555
Manchester *p300*. 0161 935 8334

Aarons
‡Bradford *p153* 01274 668722

Aaronson & Co
‡London W8 *p3* 020 7376 9124

Aaskells Solicitors & Advocates
‡London N14 *p3*. 020 8920 2400

Abacus Solicitors
‡Manchester *p300*. 0161 833 0044
Warrington *p421* 01925 210999

Abbey Court Solicitors
‡Clitheroe *p196* 01254 824963

Abbey Gate Limited
‡Coventry *p199* 024 7666 1511

Abbey Law
‡Almondsbury *p115* 01454 202102

Abbey Law Solicitors
‡Burton-on-Trent *p170*. 01283 539718

Abbey Solicitors
‡Manchester *p300*. 0161 835 9933

Abbeycroft Solicitors
‡Manchester *p300*. 0161 235 5367

Abbiss Cadres LLP
‡London EC4 *p3*. 020 3051 5711

Abbot Beresford
‡London WC1 *p3* 020 7405 5529

Abbott & Co
‡Walkden *p419* 0161 799 8003

Abbott Bailey Solicitors
‡Middlesbrough *p314* 01642 246617

Abbott Cresswell LLP
‡London SW14 *p3*. 020 8876 4478

Abbott Fahlbusch
‡London NW1 *p3* 020 7284 6970

Abbott Forbes Solicitors
‡Oxford *p342* 01865 794855

Abbott Law LLP
‡London W11 *p3*. 020 7616 8442

Abbott Lloyd Howorth
‡Maidenhead *p298* 01628 798800

Simon Abbott
‡London SE1 *p3*. 020 3283 4230

Abbotts Solicitors
‡Glossop *p230*. 01457 858483
‡Worcester *p439* 01905 339181

Abboushi Associates
‡London N3 *p3* 020 8343 4045

Abdullah Solicitors
‡Ilford *p259* 020 8554 6595

Abel-Brown Solicitors
‡Uppingham *p417*. 01572 822945

Abels
‡Southampton *p385* 023 8022 0317

Abensons
‡Liverpool *p285* 0151 733 3111

Abiloye & Co
‡London E12 *p3*. 020 8478 5678

Able Bishop Ltd
‡Bury St Edmunds *p171*. 01359 245141

Able Solicitors
‡London NW9 *p3* 020 8358 3580

Ablett & Stebbing
‡London W1 *p3* 020 7935 7720

Ablitts
‡Bromley SE26 *p3*. 020 8776 8783

Abney Garsden McDonald
‡Cheadle *p185* 0161 482 8822

Abraham & Co Solicitors
‡Mold *p318* 01352 755595
‡Wrexham *p442*. 01978 291600

D Abraham & Co
‡London W1 *p3* 020 7989 0501

Glen Abraham & Co
‡Cardiff *p177* 029 2037 7226

S Abraham Solicitors
‡Surbiton *p402* 020 8390 0044

Abrahams Dresden
‡London EC1 *p3*. 020 7251 3663

Abrahams Solicitors
‡Halifax *p238* 01422 381333

Abrahamson & Associates
‡London NW11 *p3*. 020 8458 1100

Abrams Collyer
‡Lymington *p296* 01590 677888

Absolute Law Ltd
‡London E8 *p3* 020 7812 9222

Absolute Legal
‡Surbiton *p402* 020 8390 5222

Absolutely Legal
‡Richmond upon Thames SW14 *p3* 020 8487 1000

Access Employment Law Limited
‡Lytham *p296* . . . 0845 121 2789 / 01253 731199

Access Law
‡Southampton *p385* 023 8087 8600

Accident Advice Solicitors
‡Northwich *p333*. 0844 846 0499

Accident Solicitors Direct
‡Sheffield *p375* 0800 163 622

Acer Solicitors
‡Kenilworth *p264* 01926 866644

Acharyas
‡Leicester *p278* 0116 251 7520

Achillea & Co
‡Waltham Forest E4 *p3* 020 8529 8555

Achom & Partners
‡London N4 *p3* 020 7281 7222

Joseph Ackerman
‡London NW4 *p3* 020 8457 6700
London NW4 *p4*

Ackers
‡Maidenhead *p298* 01628 622300

Ackers & Company Solicitors
‡Manchester *p300*. 0161 442 2656

Ackers Clayton Reeve
‡Twyford *p416*. 0118 982 8800

Acklam Bond Noor
‡Accrington *p114* 01254 872272
Blackburn *p145*. 01254 56068
Dewsbury *p210*. 01924 465786

Ackland & Co
‡Cardiff *p177* 029 2064 1461

Acorn Solicitors
‡Taunton *p408*. 01823 273010

Act Family Law
‡Plymouth *p349* 01752 226224

Act Legal
‡Brighton *p159* 01273 565656

Act (Norfolk) LLP
‡Thetford *p410* 01842 765577

Active Legal
‡Sutton Coldfield p403 . . . 0121 355 4700

David Acton & Co
‡Solihull p382 . . . 01564 730028

Actons
‡Nottingham p335 . . . 0115 910 0200

Acumen Business Law
‡Hove p254 . . . 0845 867 8978
Burgess Hill p168 . . . 01444 810070

Adam Law
‡Sheffield p375 . . . 0114 256 0111

Adam Solicitors
‡Manchester p300 . . . 0161 795 6119

Adams
‡Newcastle upon Tyne p323 . . . 0191 261 0361

Adams & Co
‡Birmingham p135 . . . 0121 523 3491

Adams & Remers
‡Lewes p283 . . . 01273 480616
London SW1 p4 . . . 020 7024 3600

Ashley Adams Conveyancing
‡Leicester p278 . . . 0845 234 0241

Adams Burrows
‡Bristol p160 . . . 0117 970 2246

Adams Delmar
‡Hampton p238 . . . 020 8941 2097

G Adams & Co Solicitors
‡Hornchurch p252 . . . 0844 800 0816

Adams Harrison
‡Saffron Walden p370 . . . 01799 523441
Haverhill p244 . . . 01440 705731 / 702485
Sawston p372 . . . 01223 832939

Adams Hetherington
‡Cramlington p201 . . . 01670 714622 / 714635
Ashington p119 . . . 01670 850520

Margaret Adams Law
‡Grimsby p234 . . . 01472 358999
Malton p300 . . . 01944 711011
Scarborough p372 . . . 01723 372237

Mark Adams LLB
‡London W1 p4 . . . 020 7494 4441 / 07976 478562

Adams Moore Family Law
‡Milton Keynes p316 . . . 01908 201200
Bedford p129 . . . 01234 330900
Bletchley p147 . . . 01908 640150
Corby p199 . . . 01536 201600
Daventry p207 . . . 01327 300771
Luton p295 . . . 01582 481555
Northampton p331 . . . 01604 633000

Adams Solicitors
‡London E1 p4 . . . 020 7790 2000
London W1 p4 . . . 020 7182 4500
London SW6 p4 . . . 020 7471 1744

Adamsons Law
‡Bolton p148 . . . 0808 129 3786 / 01204 362835

Adan & Co
‡Maidstone p298 . . . 01622 600488

Adcocks Solicitors Ltd
‡Lichfield p284 . . . 0845 470 8081
West Bromwich p427 . . . 0845 470 8181

Addie & Co
‡London WC2 p4 . . . 020 7395 3740

Addies
‡Fleetwood p226 . . . 01253 772128

Addison Aaron (Birmingham) Limited
‡Birmingham p135 . . . 0121 262 3773

Addison Law
‡Emsworth p218 . . . 01243 372306

Addison Legal
‡Stockport p395 . . . 0161 660 9232

ADDISON O'HARE
‡Walsall p419 . . . 01922 725515

Addison Oliver Moore
‡Watford p423 . . . 07930 968578 / 01268 833020
Northampton p331 01604 622331 / 07930 968578

Addleshaw Goddard
‡London EC1 p4 . . . 020 7606 8855
Leeds p271 . . . 0113 209 2000
Manchester p300 . . . 0161 934 6000

Addlestone Keane Solicitors
‡Leeds p271 . . . 0113 244 6700

Adel & Haque
‡Leeds p271 . . . 0844 871 1482

Adel Jibs Solicitors
‡Enfield p218 . . . 020 3417 3859

Aden & Co
‡Southall p384 . . . 020 8574 0114

Adesemowo & Co
‡London SE10 p4 . . . 020 8692 9700

Adie O'Reilly LLP
‡Lincoln p284 . . . 01522 577088

Adilsons
‡London NW2 p4 . . . 020 8452 3793

Adlams LLP
‡St Neots p392 . . . 01480 474061
Huntingdon p258 . . . 01480 458885

Adlex Solicitors
‡London NW3 p4 . . . 020 7317 8404

Adrian & Co
‡London NW5 p4 . . . 020 7485 8450 / 7267 1240

ADVANCE LEGAL
‡Burton-on-Trent p170 . . . 01283 544492

Advisa Solicitors
‡London W1 p4 . . . 0845 388 9623

Advocates Solicitors
‡Ilford p259 . . . 020 8553 5656

Advocacy Direct
‡Carnforth p183 . . . 01524 824606

Aegis Law Ltd
‡Wirral p435 . . . 0845 270 2093

Aegis Legal
‡Altrincham p116 . . . 0161 927 3800

Aequitas Law LLP
‡London W1 p4 . . . 020 7495 2776

Aequitas Legal
‡Manchester p301 . . . 0161 358 0800

Affinity Law LLP
‡Leicester p278 . . . 0116 262 7292

M C Affleck & Co
‡Ringwood p364 . . . 01425 478502

The Affordable Law Co Ltd
‡York p444 . . . 01904 788877

Afrifa & Partners
‡London SW9 p4 . . . 020 7820 9177

Agape Solicitors
‡Edgware p217 . . . 020 8952 9694

D J Ahern Solicitors
‡Chorley p194 . . . 01257 268944

Ahmad & Williams Solicitors
‡Birmingham p135 . . . 0121 328 4282
Birmingham p135 . . . 0121 558 6881

Ahmads Solicitors
‡London SW15 p4 . . . 020 8788 1234

Ahmed & Co
‡Camden NW1 p4 . . . 020 7383 2243

Ahmed Solicitors
‡Birmingham p135 . . . 0121 507 1030

J E Aidin
‡Pulborough p358 . . . 01798 872531

Aim Legal Ltd
‡Manchester p301 . . . 0161 832 1770

Aiston Solicitors
‡Croydon p204 . . . 020 8681 0123

Aitchison & Co
‡London WC2 p4 . . . 020 7240 0020

Aitken Associates
‡Islington N1 p4 . . . 020 7700 6006

Aitken Law
‡Tunbridge Wells p414
. . . 01892 750049 / 07771 674379

Akal Solicitors
‡Ilford p259 . . . 020 8477 0280

Isaac Akande & Co Solicitors
‡Dagenham p206 . . . 020 8593 2992

David Ake & Co
‡Leeds p271 . . . 0113 244 8808

Akermans
‡Worthing p441 . . . 01903 820413
Storrington p399 . . . 01903 745353

Akhigbe & Akhigbe Solicitors (A & A Solicitors)
‡Grays p233 . . . 01375 384386

Akin & Law LLP
‡London EC1 p4 . . . 020 7878 2800

Akin Gump Strauss Hauer & Feld
‡London E1 p4 . . . 020 7012 9600

Akodu & Co Solicitors
‡London SW8 p4 . . . 020 7587 1111

Akther & Darby
‡Walsall p419 . . . 01922 634175

Nasreen Al-Gafoor & Co Solicitors
‡Leeds p271 . . . 0113 230 0083

Alaga & Co
‡London SW16 p4 . . . 020 8764 7073

ALAN TURNER & CO
‡Bath p127 . . . 01225 336260

Alanross Solicitors
‡Harrow p241 . . . 01923 848200

Alban Gould Baker & Co
‡Islington N7 p4 . . . 020 7607 5085

Albany Reed Solicitors
‡Ruislip p368 . . . 020 8429 7497

Albany Solicitors
‡Cardiff p177 . . . 029 2047 2728

Alberto Perez Cedillo Spanish Lawyers And Solicitors
‡London WC2 p4 . . . 020 3077 0000

Albin & Co
‡Reading p359 . . . 0118 957 4018

Albinson Napier & Co
‡Warrington p421 . . . 01925 634681

Albion Gee & Co
‡London W4 p4 . . . 020 8742 7600

E J C Album
‡London E14 p4 . . . 020 7971 5667

Alcock & Smalley
‡Macclesfield p297 . . . 01625 431530

Alderman Partners
‡Manchester p301 . . . 0161 448 8451

Alderson Dodds
‡Blyth p147 . . . 01670 352293

Alderson Legal
‡Manchester p301 . . . 0161 242 6859

Alderwicks Solicitors Limited
‡Bath p127 . . . 01225 731400

Aldridge Brownlee Solicitors LLP
‡Bournemouth p151 . . . 01202 294411
Bournemouth p151 . . . 01202 527008
Bournemouth p151 . . . 01202 526343
Christchurch p194 . . . 01425 282150

Ross Aldridge LLP
‡Cheltenham p187 . . . 01242 707400

Alen-Buckley & Co
‡Wandsworth SW17 p4 . . . 020 8767 8336

Aletta Shaw Solicitors
‡Bexleyheath p132 . . . 020 8301 4884

Alexander & Co
‡Derby p208 . . . 01332 600005
Derby p208 . . . 01332 600011

Alexander & Partners
‡Brent NW10 p5 . . . 020 8965 7121

Alexander JLO
‡London E1 p5 . . . 020 7791 3600
‡London E4 p5 . . . 020 8527 3401
‡London E14 p5 . . . 020 7531 8820
London E14 p5 . . . 020 7537 7000

Alexander Johnson
‡London E2 p5 . . . 020 7739 1563

Alexander Lawyers LLP
‡Chelmsford p186 . . . 01245 216050
London W1 p5 . . . 01245 216050

Alexander Marks LLP
‡Westminster W1 p5 . . . 020 7317 1166

Michael Alexander & Co
‡Manchester p301 . . . 0845 839 2011

Alexander Paul
‡Tiverton p412 . . . 01884 252361

Alexander Solicitors
‡Harrow p241 . . . 020 8426 9060
‡London EC4 p5 . . . 020 3384 1000
Luton p295 . . . 01582 727888

Alexanders Solicitors Limited
‡Wetherby p429 . . . 01937 543350

Alexandrian Solutions LLP
‡Birmingham p135 . . . 0121 663 0024

Alexandrou & Co
‡Barnet p123 . . . 020 8447 1503

Alexen Avocats
‡London WC2 p5 . . . 020 7497 8034

Alexiou Fisher Philipps
‡London W1 p5 . . . 020 7409 1222

Alexus Associates Solicitors
‡Ilford p259 . . . 020 8911 9300

Alfano & Co
‡Loughton p294 . . . 020 8414 9271

Alfred James & Co
‡Croydon p204 . . . 020 8681 4627

Alfred Truman
‡Bicester p132 . . . 01869 252761
Buckingham p167 . . . 01280 822217

Ali & Co Solicitor
Bradford p153 . . . 01274 391197

Ali & Co Solicitors
‡Huddersfield p255 . . . 01484 517887

S Ali & Company Solicitors
‡London EC1 p5 . . . 020 7608 2005
Haringey N8 p5 . . . 020 8340 5544

Alison Legal Practice
‡Aberystwyth p114 . . . 01970 610908

Alistairs
‡Bristol p160 . . . 0117 961 3952

Alkan & Co Solicitors
‡Redbridge p362 . . . 020 8554 9201

Alker & Ball
‡Wigan p432 . . . 01942 246241

Alkers Solicitors
‡Poulton-le-Fylde p355 . . . 01253 892237

All About Rights Law Practice
‡Dartford p206 . . . 01322 424570

Allan Garrick
‡Lancaster p269 . . . 01524 62985

Allan Janes LLP
‡High Wycombe p249 . . . 01494 521301

Allan Jay Paine & Co
‡Enfield N13 p5 . . . 020 8886 1404

Allan Rutherford
‡Norwich p333 . . . 01603 621722

Allansons LLP
‡Bolton p148 . . . 0161 220 8484

Allen & Overy LLP
‡London E1 p5 . . . 020 3088 0000
London E14 p6 . . . 020 3088 0000

Allen Barfields
‡Croydon p204 . . . 020 8680 2050
West Wickham p428 . . . 020 8654 2706

Allen Hoole Solicitors
‡Bristol p160 . . . 0117 942 0901
Cheltenham p187 . . . 01242 522201

Allens
‡Bungay p168 . . . 01986 893928
‡Portsmouth p354 . . . 023 9282 2411
Halesworth p237 . . . 01986 875246

Allerton Kaye
‡Bradford p153 . . . 01274 370066
‡Bradford p153 . . . 01274 379840

Alletsons
‡Burnham-on-Sea p169 . . . 01278 780151

Alletsons Ltd
‡Bridgwater p157 . . . 01278 456621

Alliance Solicitors
‡Harrow p241 . . . 020 8206 3530
‡Kenton p264 . . . 020 8204 3000

Allied Law Chambers
‡London N7 p6 . . . 020 7281 4924

Allied Solicitors
‡Manchester p301 . . . 0161 660 1505

Allington Hughes
‡Wrexham p442 . . . 01978 291000
Chester p190 . . . 01244 312166

Allison & Reilly Solicitors
‡Manchester p301 0844 805 4735 / 0161 643 5923

Allison Solicitors
‡Chelmsford p186 . . . 01245 218244

Charles Allotey
‡Thornton Heath p411 . . . 020 8664 8155

Allsopp & Co
‡Solihull p382 . . . 0121 705 9020
Solihull p382 . . . 0121 704 4282

Allweis & Co
‡Salford p370 . . . 0161 792 1020

Allwyn Sanger Solicitors
‡Windsor p434 . . . 0845 217 1377

J P Almond & Co
Wirral p435 . . . 0151 632 2336

Almy & Thomas
‡Torquay p412 . . . 01803 299131

Chris Alnutt
‡Wickford p431 . . . 01268 561541

Alpha Lexis Law Firm
‡Elstree p218 . . . 0845 194 7340 / 01923 731150

Alpha Solicitors
‡Rochdale p365 . . . 01706 646111

Alsters Kelley
‡Leamington Spa p270 . . . 0844 561 0100
Coventry p199 . . . 0844 561 0100
Nuneaton p339 . . . 0844 561 0100

Alston Ashby
‡Chatham p184 . . . 01634 845051
Chatham p184 . . . 01634 842017

Altaf Solicitors
‡Bradford p153 . . . 01274 400405

David Alterman & Co
‡London NW11 p6 . . . 020 8209 1234

Altermans
‡London N3 p6 . . . 020 8346 1777

Alternative Family Law
‡London SE1 p6 . . . 020 7407 4007

Altmore Business Law
‡Oakham p339 . . . 0845 094 9000

Alton & Co Solicitors
‡Accrington p114 . . . 01254 385104

Alun Thomas & John
‡Aberystwyth p114 . . . 01970 615900

Alwena Jones & Jones
‡Blaenau Ffestiniog p147 . . . 01766 831882
Tywyn p416 . . . 01654 711499

Amakhala Limited
‡North Shields p330 . . . 0191 293 1500

Amal Solicitors
‡Huddersfield p255 . . . 01484 431999

Aman Solicitors Advocates (London) Ltd
‡Wembley p426 . . . 020 8782 3776

Aman Solicitors Advocates Ltd
Birmingham p135 . . . 0121 328 4455

Amber Solicitors LLP
‡Hull p256 . . . 01482 216799

Alan Ambridge Solicitor
‡London SW16 p6 . . . 020 8835 8287

Ambrose
‡Durham p214 . . . 0191 386 7260

Ambrose Appelbe
‡London WC2 p6 . . . 020 7242 7000

Ameer Meredith
‡Cambridge p174 . . . 01223 577077

Amelans
‡Manchester p301 . . . 0161 434 4545

Amer Sargent & Co
‡London SW18 p6 . . . 0845 612 1006

Ames Kent
‡Frome p227 . . . 01373 462017

Amicus Solicitors & Advocates
‡Minehead p317 . . . 01643 701888

Amicus Solicitors And Advocates
‡Bridgwater *p157* 01278 664060
‡Taunton *p408* 01823 353111

J M Amin & Co
‡Wembley *p426* 020 8903 3766

Amm Solicitors Ltd (Faith King Solicitors)
‡Bolton *p148* 01204 369123

Amory Glass & Co
‡Wembley *p426* 020 8904 8236

Amosu Robinshaw Solicitors
‡Croydon *p204* 020 8688 2573

Amphlett Chatterton
‡Leamington Spa *p270* 01926 311427

Amphlett Lissimore
‡Croydon SE19 *p6* 020 8771 5254

Amphletts
‡Colwyn Bay *p198* 01492 532296

Amwells
‡London N5 *p6* 0845 130 9792

Amy & Co
‡London EC3 *p6* 020 7539 3535

Ana Kanellos Furlong Solicitor
‡London SW8 *p6* 020 7627 8131

Anami Law Iincorporating Kirkwoods
‡Bushey *p171* 020 8950 1155

Anaysse-Jacobs Solicitors
‡London SE18 *p6* 020 8316 5000

Dipak Ancharya & Co Solicitors
‡Leicester *p278* 0116 266 0627

Andells Solicitors
‡Watford *p423* 01923 682328

Anderson & Co Solicitors
‡Birkenhead *p134* 0151 647 1500

Anderson & Company
‡Shillingford *p378* 01865 858878

Anderson Castle & Co Limited
‡London WC2 *p6* 020 7831 4445

Anderson Fidler
‡Enfield *p218* 020 8804 6596

Jackie Anderson
‡Farnham *p224* 01252 332132 / 07752 329079

Anderson Longmore & Higham
‡Petworth *p348* 01798 342391
Billingshurst *p133* 01403 782710
Chichester *p192* 01243 787899
Storrington *p399* 01903 745666

Michael Anderson & Co
Whickham *p430* 0191 488 1221

Anderson Middleton
‡Liverpool *p285* 0151 236 5599

Anderson Partnership
‡Chesterfield *p191* 01246 220737

R W Anderson & Co
‡Westminster W1 *p6* 020 7323 4520

Anderson Reeves Solicitors
‡Birmingham *p135* 0800 014 1529

Anderson Ross Solicitors
‡Harrow *p241* 020 3170 6030

Andersons
‡Croydon *p204* 020 8680 3131
‡Eye *p223* 01379 873510

Andersons Solicitors
‡Harrogate *p239* 01423 527852
‡Nottingham *p335* 0115 947 0641

Andrew & Andrew Solicitors
‡Portsmouth *p354* 023 9266 1381

Andrew & Co LLP
‡Lincoln *p284* 01522 512123
Newark *p322* 01636 673743

Andrew Macbeth Cash & Co
Wirksworth *p435* 01629 822553

S C Andrew LLP
‡London EC4 *p6* 020 7183 1701

Andrews & Monroe Solicitors
‡Croydon *p204* 020 8686 5862 / 07521 844993

Andrews Angel Solicitors
‡Durham *p214* 0191 370 9890
‡Ilford *p259* 020 8911 9289

George Anthony Andrews Solicitors
‡London W3 *p6* 020 8746 0550

J Andrews
‡Harrow *p241* 020 8422 9814

Andrews McQueen
‡Bournemouth *p151* 01202 290628

Mark Andrews
‡Leighton Buzzard *p282* 01525 371616

Mark Andrews & Co
‡Bristol *p160* 0117 983 8880

Andrews Martin
‡Swindon *p406* 01793 641707

Maurice Andrews
‡Birmingham *p135* 0121 554 4900

Andrews Solicitors
‡Bridgend *p157* 0870 112 7330

Andrews Stanton & Ringrose
‡Bourne *p151* 01778 422626

Thomas Andrews & Partners
‡Wrexham *p442* 01978 291506
Bala *p121* 01678 520893

AndrewsLaw Solicitor
‡Bridgnorth *p157* 01746 769700

Angel & Co
‡Coventry *p200* 024 7625 2211
‡Westminster W1 *p6* 020 7495 0555

Angel Law
‡Islington N1 *p6* 020 7837 7877

Angel Wilkins
‡Wantage *p421* 01235 775100

Angell & Co
‡Bath *p127* 01225 484244

Jonathan Angell & Co
‡London EC4 *p6* 020 7947 3366

Angels Solicitors
‡Chester *p190* 0151 480 6636

Anglo Law Solicitors
‡Grays *p233* 01708 862786

Anglo-Spanish Law
‡Hathersage *p244* 01433 631508

Anjorin & Co
‡Orpington *p341* 01689 891192

Ankamah Gunn Ltd
‡London W1 *p6* 020 7355 5109

J F K Annear
‡Ilfracombe *p261* 01271 882239

Anning Law
‡Worcester *p439* 01905 641934

Charles Annon & Co
‡London W6 *p6* 020 7603 5539

Anooma & Hegoda
‡London N8 *p6* 020 8348 7772

Ansah Solicitors
‡Lambeth SE27 *p6* 020 8761 5271

Ansari Solicitors
‡Manchester *p301* 0161 225 2277

Anselm Eldergill
‡Twickenham *p416* 07971 198742

Ansons LLP
‡Lichfield *p284* 01543 263456
Cannock *p176* 01543 466660

Antares Legal LLP
‡Harrow *p241* 020 8621 5313

Antell & Co
‡London SW13 *p6* 020 8563 0793

Anthony & Jarvie
‡Bridgend *p157* 01656 652737

Bruce Anthony Solicitors
‡Belper *p130* 01773 857999

Anthony Chambers Limited
‡New Malden *p321* 020 8942 2499

ANTHONY GOLD
‡London SE1 *p6* 020 7940 4000
London SW16 *p6* 020 7940 4000
London SE17 *p6* 020 7940 4000

ANTHONY HOLDEN CROFTS & CO
‡Brentford *p156* 020 8568 7768
Ealing W13 *p6* 020 8840 7878

Anthony Jeremy & May
‡Cardiff *p177* 029 2034 0313

Anthony Solicitors
‡Enfield N21 *p6* 020 8360 4333

Antinghams Solicitors
‡Maidenhead *p298* 01628 825395

George A Antoniades
‡London N4 *p6* 020 8800 4146

Antons
‡London N8 *p6* 020 8888 6211

Antrobus Solicitors
‡Wilmslow *p433* 07919 561266

Michael Anvoner & Co
‡Barnet *p123* 020 8449 0003

Apex Law LLP
‡Bexleyheath *p132* 020 8306 1455
‡Dartford *p207* 01322 277732
Bexleyheath *p132* 01322 333201

Apex Solicitors
‡London SE15 *p6* 020 7635 6160

Apfel Carter
‡Lytham *p296* 01253 725265 / 712216

Aplin Stockton Fairfax
‡Banbury *p122* 01295 251234

Appleby
‡London EC3 *p7* 020 7283 6061

Appleby & Co
‡Scarborough *p372* 01723 351994 / 07891 511152

APPLEBY HOPE & MATTHEWS
‡Middlesbrough *p314* 01642 440444
Stockton-on-Tees *p396* 01642 617000

APPLEBY SHAW
‡Windsor *p434* 01753 860606

Applebys
‡Bradford *p153* 01274 728838

Applebys Solicitors
‡Huddersfield *p255* 01484 550944

Applebys Wills & Probate Solicitors
‡Failsworth *p223* 0161 669 4365 / 07900 246677

Appleton Massey
‡Bromley *p166* 0845 812 1002

Appleyard Lees
‡Leeds *p271* 0113 246 5353
Burnley *p169* 01282 412506
Chester *p190* 01244 321124
Halifax *p238* 01422 330110
Harrogate *p240* 01423 538448
Huddersfield *p255* 01484 483000
Liverpool *p286* 0151 331 5016
Manchester *p301* 0161 835 9655
Preston *p356* 01772 884642
Sheffield *p375* 0114 270 0611
Stockton-on-Tees *p396* 0191 301 7191
York *p444* 01904 567973

Mark Appleyard Limited
‡Doncaster *p211* 01302 640210

Aquila Law
‡Teignmouth *p409* 01626 870280 / 07799 773567

Daniel Aramide Solicitors
‡Rainham *p359* 01708 525961 / 07973 907417

Arani & Co
‡Southall *p384* 020 8893 5000

Aravindans
‡Newham E6 *p7* 020 8503 5034

Arbis LLP
‡London E1 *p7* 020 7481 2188

Arc Property Solicitors LLP
‡Harrogate *p240* 0800 612 9097
London W1 *p7* 0800 612 9097

Archer & Archer
‡Ely *p218* 01353 662203

Archer & Wilcock
‡Great Yarmouth *p234* 01493 369700

Archer Fields Solicitors
‡Ilford *p259* 020 8518 5600

Archer Rusby LLP
‡Rickmansworth *p364* 01923 432696

Archers Law LLP
‡Stockton-on-Tees *p396* 01642 636500

Archers Solicitors
‡Chelmsford *p186* 01245 216888

Archon Solicitors
‡London EC4 *p7* 020 7397 9650

Arden Solicitors (Immigration Specialist)
‡London W5 *p7* 020 8997 8885

Arena Legal Solicitors
‡Leeds *p271* 0800 599 9450

Grant Argent & Co
‡Brent NW2 *p7* 020 8452 7651

H T Argent & Son
‡Saxmundham *p372* 01728 602323
Aldeburgh *p115* 01728 452133

E G Arghyrakis & Co
‡London EC4 *p7* 020 7353 2302

Argyles
‡Tamworth *p407* 01827 56276

Arion Law
‡London EC2 *p7* 020 3178 3944

Ark Solicitors
‡Birmingham *p135* 0121 753 7130

ARKrights Solicitors
‡Watford *p423* 01923 233477

Arlington Crown Solicitors
‡London N13 *p7* 020 8882 1166

Arlington Solicitors
‡Brighton *p159* 01273 696962
‡London SE17 *p7* 020 7703 4002

Arlingtons Sharmas Solicitors
‡London SW1 *p7* 020 7299 8999

Armitage & Co
‡Exeter *p220* 01392 251364 / 214786

Armitage & Guest
‡Wakefield *p418* 01924 371877

Armitage Sykes LLP
‡Huddersfield *p255* 01484 538121
Brighouse *p158* 01484 714431
Huddersfield *p255* 01484 344140

Armstrong & Co
‡London SE23 *p7* 020 8699 3477

Armstrong Foulkes
‡Middlesbrough *p314* 01642 231110

Gerald Armstrong & Co
‡Sunderland *p401* 0191 514 0966

Armstrong James LLP
‡Reading *p359* 0800 169 2210

Armstrong Law LLP
‡London E1 *p7* 020 8556 7090

Armstrong Luty Solicitors
‡Skipton *p381* 01756 799977

Armstrongs
‡London SW19 *p7* 020 8543 6800

Arndale Solicitors
‡Leeds *p271* 0113 243 1280

Arnheim & Co
‡Bromley *p166* 020 8295 4818

Arnison & Co Solicitors Limited
‡Penrith *p346* 01768 862007

Arnold & Co
‡Oldbury *p340* 0121 552 2382

Arnold & Porter LLP
‡London EC2 *p7* 020 7786 6100

Arnold Brierley & Robinson
‡Oldham *p340* 0161 678 1122

Arnold Davies Vincent Evans
‡Lampeter *p269* 01570 422233
Tregaron *p413* 01974 298816

Arnold Deacon Greene & Co
‡Sleaford *p381* 01529 414414

Arnold Fooks Chadwick LLP
‡London W1 *p7* 020 7499 3007

G A Arnold
‡Macclesfield *p297* 01625 615424

Arnold George & Co
‡Ilford *p259* 020 8554 5484

Arnold Greenwood
‡Kendal *p264* 01539 720049
Milnthorpe *p316* 01539 562424

K A Arnold & Co
‡London N1 *p7* 020 7354 4926

Arnold Lambert Solicitors
‡Reading *p359* 0118 918 7610

Arnold Thomson Limited
‡Towcester *p413* 01327 350266

Arnolds
‡Swansea *p404* 01792 418094
Morriston *p319* 01792 533049

Arnotts
‡Witney *p436* 0844 372 1333

Arona Sarwar LLP
‡London E17 *p7* 020 8520 5170

Arora Ashton Patel
‡Ilford *p259* 020 8554 6263

Arora Bailey
‡Cheam *p185* 020 8661 0000

Arora Lodhi Heath
‡London W3 *p7* 020 8993 9995
London NW5 *p7* 020 7267 3281

Arora Solicitors
‡London E7 *p7* 020 8472 6869

Arscotts
‡Hove *p254* 01273 735289

Javid Arshad & Co
‡Bradford *p153* 01274 493153

Arthur & Co
‡Pinner *p348* 020 8866 8282

Anna Arthur Associates
‡Woking *p436* 01483 222499

Arthur Smiths
‡Wigan *p432* 01942 242815

Aruan Consuting Limited
‡London SW7 *p7* 020 7225 2696

Ascot & Chase
‡Bromley *p166* 020 8313 9009
Bromley *p166* 020 8462 3344

Ascot Lawyers
‡Bracknell *p153* 01344 783890

Ascroft Rae
‡Leyland *p283* 01772 434488

Ascroft Whiteside
‡Blackpool *p146* 01253 766866

Asghar & Co
‡Southall *p384* 020 8843 0010
Slough *p381* 01753 535577

Ash Clifford
‡Bridgwater *p157* 01278 451327

Ash Norton Solicitors
‡London W5 *p7* 020 8991 3330 / 8991 3331

Ash Solicitors
‡Hexham *p249* 01434 609829
‡Hounslow *p253* 020 8570 8588

Ashbournes Solicitors
‡Harrow *p241* 020 8863 6966

Ashburns Solicitors
‡Barking *p123* 020 8591 5297

Christine Ashby Solicitors
‡Ottery St Mary *p342* 01404 814303

Ashby Cohen Solicitors Limited
London EC4 *p7* 020 3201 0062

Ashby Cohen Solicitors Ltd
‡London W1 *p7* 020 7408 1338

Ashby Family Law Practice
‡Derby *p208* 01332 293293

Asher & Tomar
‡Southall *p384* 020 8867 7737

Asher Broomfield
‡Romsey *p366* 01794 501033 / 07799 551820

Asher Prior Bates
‡Colchester *p197* 01206 573089

Ashfields
‡Cheadle *p185* 0161 495 2960

Ashfords LLP
‡Exeter *p220* 01392 337000
Bristol *p160* 0117 321 8000
London W1 *p7* 020 3581 8970

Plymouth *p349* . . . 01752 521500
Taunton *p408* . . . 01823 232300
Tiverton *p412* . . . 01884 203000

Alan Ashley & Co
‡London EC4 *p7* . . . 020 7822 7482

Clive Ashman
‡Pontyclun *p352* . . . 01443 231177

Ashmans Solicitors
‡Dewsbury *p210* . . . 01924 501717

Ashmoles Solicitors
‡Norwich *p333* . . . 01603 629749

Ashoka & Co
‡Woburn Sands *p436* . . . 01908 288120

Barry Ashton
‡Llangollen *p292* . . . 01978 861140

Ashton Bell
‡Leeds *p271* . . . 0113 243 8688

Ashton Bond Gigg
‡Nottingham *p335* . . . 0115 947 6651

Ashton KCJ
‡Ipswich *p262* . . . 01473 232425
Bury St Edmunds *p171* . . . 01284 762331
Bury St Edmunds *p171* . . . 01284 761233
Cambridge *p174* . . . 01223 363111
Felixstowe *p225* . . . 01394 277188
Norwich *p333* . . . 01603 703070
Thetford *p410* . . . 01842 752401

Malcolm Ashton
‡Falmouth *p223* . . . 01326 313100

Ashton Page Solicitors
‡Hounslow *p253* . . . 020 8622 3671

Ashurst LLP
‡London EC2 *p7* . . . 020 7638 1111

Ashwood Solicitors Ltd
‡Manchester *p301* . . . 0161 248 4444

Colin Ashworth & Co
Oldham *p340* . . . 01706 845002

David A Ashworth
‡Bewdley *p131* . . . 01299 861056

George S Ashworth
‡Nantwich *p320* . . . 01270 623723

Ashworth Law LLP
‡Harrogate *p240* . . . 01423 534500

Ashworths Solicitors
‡London SW19 *p8* . . . 0845 370 1000

Askbeg Solicitors
‡London SE8 *p8* . . . 020 8320 2272

Askew Bunting Solicitors LLP
‡Middlesbrough *p314* . . . 01642 252555
Guisborough *p237* . . . 01287 635151

Askews
‡Redcar *p362* . . . 01642 475252
Middlesbrough *p314* . . . 01642 475252
Stockton-on-Tees *p396* . . . 01642 475252

Aslan Charles Kousetta LLP
‡London W1 *p8* . . . 020 3326 2280

Asons Solicitors Limited
‡Bolton *p148* . . . 01204 520720

Aspect Law
‡Walsall *p419* . . . 0871 288 3212

Aspell & Co Ltd
‡Leamington Spa *p270* . . . 01926 337613

Aspen Court Solicitors Limited
‡Birmingham *p135* . . . 0845 094 4912

Aspinall & Co
‡Bolton *p148* . . . 01204 388200

Aspinall Wright
‡Glossop *p230* . . . 01457 854645

Aspley Law Limited
‡Billericay *p133* . . . 07939 039850

The Associate Law Firm
‡Newcastle upon Tyne *p323* . . . 0191 280 4110

Astbury and Company
‡Cheltenham *p187* . . . 01242 604303

Astburys
‡Lewes *p283* . . . 01273 405900

Peter Astill & Co
‡Birstall *p143* . . . 0116 221 4885

Astills
‡Leicester *p278* . . . 0116 249 4450

Astle Paterson Ltd
‡Burton-on-Trent *p170* . . . 01283 531366

Aston Bond LLP
‡Slough *p381* . . . 01753 486777
Reading *p359* . . . 01889 596031

Aston Brooke Solicitors
‡Harrow *p241* . . . 020 8901 7901

Aston Carter Solicitors
‡Birmingham *p135* . . . 0121 684 3009
Hounslow *p253* . . . 020 8538 0287 / 0288

Aston Clark
‡London W3 *p8* . . . 020 8752 1122

Astons
‡Northampton *p331* . . . 01327 706700 / 706705

Astwood Law
‡Redditch *p362* . . . 01527 892200

Asuelime Solicitors
‡Manchester *p301* . . . 0161 224 7596

Atanda Solicitors
‡London SE1 *p8* . . . 020 7231 3060

Atha & Co
‡Middlesbrough *p314* . . . 01642 222575

Atha Strong & Co
‡Redcar *p362* . . . 01642 482421

Atherton Godfrey
‡Doncaster *p211* . . . 01302 320621

Athi Law LLP
‡West Bromwich *p427* . . . 0121 553 5555
Sheffield *p375* . . . 0114 255 8001

Athuraliyage Solicitors
‡London E1 *p8* . . . 020 7377 0144

C M Atif & Co
‡Wandsworth SW17 *p8* . . . 020 8767 4913

Atkins & Co
‡Esher *p220* . . . 01372 477188

Atkins Bassett
‡Hinckley *p250* . . . 01455 632685

Atkins Hope Solicitors
‡Croydon *p204* . . . 020 8680 5018

Atkins Law Solicitors
‡Exeter *p220* . . . 01392 671657

Atkins Thomson
Bury St Edmunds *p171* . . . 01284 767766

Atkinson & Co
‡Newport *p328* . . . 01633 251118

Atkinson & Firth
‡Shipley *p378* . . . 01274 584305

Atkinson Cave & Stuart
‡Blackpool *p146* . . . 01253 293151

G A Atkinson
‡Nottingham *p335* . . . 0115 969 3650

Atkinson McCall
‡Harrogate *p240* . . . 01423 501531

Atkinson Ritson
‡Carlisle *p181* . . . 01228 525221
Wigton *p432* . . . 01697 343241

Atkinson Spence
‡Birmingham *p135* . . . 0121 507 9930

Atkinsonhodgson LLP
‡Manchester *p301* . . . 0870 300 8790
Nantwich *p320*

Atlantic Solicitors
Milton Keynes *p316* . . . 01908 255560 / 255826

Atlee Chung & Company
‡London W1 *p8* . . . 020 7287 9988

Atter Mackenzie & Co
‡Evesham *p220* . . . 01386 425300

Atteys
‡Doncaster *p211* . . . 01302 340400
Barnsley *p124* . . . 01226 212345
Retford *p363* . . . 01777 713355
Sheffield *p375* . . . 0114 276 6767
Wath-upon-Dearne *p424* . . . 01709 872106

Atti & Co
‡London SE14 *p8* . . . 020 7639 3636

Atticus Legal LLP
‡Manchester *p301* . . . 0161 957 8888

Atticus Solicitors
‡Newcastle under Lyme *p323* . . . 01782 629840

Attiyah Lone
‡London W6 *p8* . . . 020 8735 9999

Attwaters
‡Loughton *p294* . . . 020 8508 2111
Harlow *p239* . . . 01279 638888

Attwells Solicitors
‡Ipswich *p262* . . . 01473 746000
London NW8 *p8* . . . 020 7722 9898

Attwood & Co
‡Grays *p233* . . . 01375 378122 / 378123

Attwood Solicitors
‡Stoke-on-Trent *p397* . . . 01782 608420 / 0800 145 5105

W M Attwood & Son
‡Cradley Heath *p201* . . . 01384 566523 / 566128

Janet Auckland Solicitor
‡Exeter *p220* . . . 01392 210152

Audleys Solicitors
‡Luton *p295* . . . 01582 482999

Audu & Co
‡Islington N1 *p8* . . . 020 7278 9340

Aughton Ainsworth
‡Salford *p370* . . . 0161 877 8555

David Auld & Co
‡Morpeth *p319* . . . 01670 505844
Bedlington *p130* . . . 01670 826870

Auleys Solicitors
‡Peterborough *p346* . . . 01354 650375

Aurangzeb Khan Solicitors
‡Bradford *p153* . . . 01274 548549

Austen Whetham & Guest
‡Bridport *p158* . . . 01308 422236

Austin & Berns Solicitors
‡Harrow *p241* . . . 020 8429 5937

Austin & Carnley
‡Leighton Buzzard *p282* . . . 01525 372140

Edward Austin
‡Shrewsbury *p379* . . . 01743 236222

Austin Edwards Solicitors
‡Pinner *p348* . . . 020 8429 0741

Austin Kemp Solicitors
‡Huddersfield *p255* . . . 01484 483033

Austin Law Solicitors LLP
‡London W2 *p8* . . . 020 7723 5171

Austin Ray
‡Milton Keynes *p316* . . . 01908 769648

AUSTIN RYDER & CO
‡Enfield N9 *p8* . . . 020 8804 5111
Cheshunt *p189* . . . 01992 624804
London NW1 *p8* . . . 020 7833 0882

AUSTINS LLP
‡Luton *p295* . . . 01582 456222

Austins Penny & Thorne
Berkhamsted *p131* . . . 01442 872141

Austins Solicitors
‡London W4 *p8* . . . 0800 377 7716

The Austreng Partnership
‡Salisbury *p371*

Avalon Solicitors
‡Warrington *p421* . . . 01925 232111

Avadis & Co
‡London NW5 *p8* . . . 020 7267 4240

Averta Employment Lawyers
‡Birmingham *p135* . . . 0870 421 1952

Averton Wallace & Co
‡Wembley *p426* . . . 020 8902 9440

Avery Emerson Solicitors
‡Ilford *p259* . . . 020 8215 0884

Avery Knights Solicitors Limited
‡Willenhall *p432* . . . 0121 609 7240
Willenhall *p432* . . . 0845 458 6293

Avery Naylor
‡Swansea *p404* . . . 01792 463276

Philip Avery & Co
‡Llanelli *p292* . . . 01554 746295
Ammanford *p117* . . . 01269 596655

Michael Aves Planning Consultant
‡Sudbury *p401* . . . 01787 237911

Avetoom & Company
‡Kingston upon Thames *p267* . . . 020 8547 0690

Awan Solicitors
‡Kenley *p264* . . . 020 8781 1838
Croydon *p204* . . . 020 8781 1838

Awdry Bailey & Douglas
‡Devizes *p210* . . . 01380 722311
Calne *p173* . . . 01249 815110
Marlborough *p313* . . . 01672 518620
Wootton Bassett *p439* . . . 01793 853200

Awklaw
‡Tunbridge Wells *p414* . . . 01892 533999

Awtani Immigration Solicitors
‡London W1 *p9* . . . 020 7868 2222

Axiom Solicitors
‡Bradford *p153* . . . 01274 664471

Axiom Stone
‡Edgware *p217* . . . 020 8951 6989

Ayman Solicitors
‡Manchester *p301* . . . 0161 225 8333

Ayres Waters
‡Stockport *p395* . . . 0161 480 5229

Azam & Co Solicitors
‡London EC3 *p9* . . . 020 7709 0707

Azar Freedman & Co
‡London N1 *p9* . . . 020 7704 7500

Azhar & Co
‡Slough *p381* . . . 01753 779637

Aziz Solicitors Limited
‡Birmingham *p135* . . . 0121 683 6938

Azzopardi & Co
‡London WC2 *p9* . . . 020 7353 6060

B

B&C Solicitors - The Law Shop
‡Scarborough *p372* . . . 01723 379777

BAS Solicitors
‡Bracknell *p153* . . . 01344 862111

BA Solicitors
‡Birmingham *p135* . . . 0121 773 4200

BBL Solicitors LLP
‡Guildford *p235* . . . 01483 838154

BBT Law
‡Wakefield *p418* . . . 0845 833 3351

BCC Solicitors
‡Brackley *p153* . . . 01280 702238
Witney *p436* . . . 01993 770778

BCL BURTON COPELAND
‡London WC2 *p9* . . . 020 7430 2277

BDH Solicitors
‡Birkenhead *p134* . . . 0151 666 0300
‡Ellesmere Port *p217* . . . 0151 355 7171

BE Legal
‡Brighton *p159* . . . 01273 704525
‡Burton-on-Trent *p170* . . . 01283 517717

BHB Law Limited
‡Coventry *p200* . . . 024 7655 5191

BHP Law
‡Durham *p214* . . . 0191 384 0840
Darlington *p206* . . . 01325 466794
Halifax *p238* . . . 01422 250650
Newcastle upon Tyne *p323* . . . 0191 221 0898
Newton Aycliffe *p330* . . . 01325 312534
North Shields *p330* . . . 0191 257 2213
Stockton-on-Tees *p396* . . . 01642 672770

BHR Law
Exeter *p220* . . . 01392 496100

BHW Commercial Solicitors
‡Leicester *p278* . . . 0116 289 6229

B J & Co Solicitors
‡Liverpool *p286* . . . 0151 227 7777

BJ Law Solicitors Limited
‡Cardiff *p177* . . . 029 2046 1006

BKRW Limited
‡Folkestone *p226* . . . 01303 255369
Dover *p212* . . . 01304 219282
Ramsgate *p359* . . . 01843 852953

BKS Solicitors
‡London SE20 *p9* . . . 020 8776 9388

BK Solicitors
‡Birmingham *p135* . . . 0121 440 1881

BLB Solicitors
‡Trowbridge *p413* . . . 01225 755656
Bath *p127* . . . 01225 462871
Bradford-on-Avon *p155* . . . 01225 866541
Swindon *p406* . . . 01793 615011

B Legal Limited
‡Marlow *p313* . . . 01628 496687

BMD Law
‡Liverpool *p286* . . . 0151 222 5777
‡Middlewich *p315* . . . 0800 6123 579

BMG Solicitors
‡Birmingham *p135* . . . 0121 358 8855

BMV Solicitors
‡Birmingham *p135* . . . 0121 248 1980

B P Collins LLP
‡Gerrards Cross *p229* . . . 01753 889995

BPE Homemove LLP
‡Cheltenham *p187* . . . 01242 708800

BPE Solicitors LLP
‡Cheltenham *p187* . . . 01242 224433
London WC1 *p9* . . . 020 7387 1437

BPL Solicitors Ltd
‡Dorchester *p212* . . . 01305 214200
Yeovil *p443* . . . 0845 345 3131

BRM Solicitors
‡Chesterfield *p191* . . . 01246 555111

BSB Solicitors
‡London NW1 *p9* . . . 020 7837 3456

BSB Solicitors Limited
‡Wolverhampton *p437* . . . 01902 810114

BSG Solicitors LLP
‡London N3 *p9* . . . 020 8343 4411
Bushey *p171* . . . 020 8955 7690

BTLaw Solicitors
‡Hatfield *p244* . . . 01707 258154

BTMK Solicitors LLP
‡Southend-on-Sea *p387* . . . 01702 339222
Southend-on-Sea *p387* . . . 01702 339222

BTW Solicitors
‡Wirral *p435* . . . 0151 677 3333

BWF Solicitors
‡London E8 *p9* . . . 020 7241 7180

BWS
‡Brighton *p159* . . . 0700 067 9000

BWTLaw LLP
‡Epsom *p219* . . . 01372 725655
Sutton *p402* . . . 020 8643 5311

Babylaw Solicitors
‡Syston *p407* . . . 0844 561 1161

William Bache
‡Salisbury *p371* . . . 01722 713370

William Bache Solicitors Limited
London EC1 *p9* . . . 020 7831 1311

Baches
‡West Bromwich *p427* . . . 0121 553 3286 / 553 7076

Backhouse Jones Ltd
‡Clitheroe *p196* . . . 01254 828300

Backhouse Solicitors
‡Chelmsford *p186* . . . 01245 216626

Peter Badham & Co
‡London W14 *p9* . . . 020 7603 9798

Badhams Law (A Trading Name of Parabis Law LLP)
‡Croydon *p204* . . . 0844 245 4000

Baehrs
‡Bournemouth *p151* . . . 01202 292075

Ursula Bagnall Divorce & Family Law Solicitors
‡Cowes *p201* . . . 01983 247221

Brian Bailes
‡Newcastle under Lyme *p323* . . . 01782 626214

Bailey & Bailey
‡Middlesbrough *p315* . . . 01642 240991

Bailey & Cogger
‡Tonbridge *p412* . . . 01732 353305

Bailey & Haigh
‡Selby *p373* . . . 01757 705191
Goole *p231* . . . 01405 780200

Bailey & Tofield
‡Broadway *p166*. 01386 854851

Bailey Morgan & Co
‡Skegness *p380*. . . . . .01754 768383 / 763007

Bailey Nicholson Grayson
‡Woodford Green *p439* 020 8418 2900
Ware *p421* 0844 939 6889

Scott Bailey
‡Lymington *p296* 01590 676933

Bailey Smailes
‡Huddersfield *p255* 01484 435543
Holmfirth *p251* 01484 686000

Bailey Wain & Curzon
‡Stoke-on-Trent *p397* 01782 847934

William Bailey
‡Southwark SE22 *p9* 020 8693 9615

Bailey Wright & Co
‡Birmingham *p135*. 0845 475 1996

Baileys
‡Brackley *p153* 01280 701166
‡Cheadle *p185* 0161 488 4688
‡Cheltenham *p187*. 01242 514477

Bailhache Shaw Marsden
‡Taunton *p408*. 01823 351122

Baily Gibson
‡Beaconsfield *p128* 01494 672661
High Wycombe *p249* 01494 442661

David L Bain
‡Bourne End *p151*. 07974 257555

Baines Bagguley Solicitors
‡Morecambe *p318*. 01524 413294

Baines Wilson LLP
‡Carlisle *p181* 01228 552600

Bains & Co Solicitors
‡Tipton *p412*. 0121 520 9990

Bains Cohen LLP
‡Barking *p123*. 020 8252 7373
London N3 *p9* 020 8252 7373
London EC3 *p9*. 020 8252 7373
London N8 *p9* 020 8252 7373

Bains Solicitors
‡Wellingborough *p424*. 01933 440000

James E Baird
‡Sunderland *p401* 0191 514 5888

A Bajwa & Co
‡London E1 *p9* 020 7423 0006

Farooq Bajwa & Co
‡London W1 *p9* 020 3174 0332

Bake & Co Solicitors
‡Birmingham *p135*. 0121 616 5025

Baker & Co
‡Godalming *p231* 01428 687717

Baker & Duke
‡Ilminster *p261* 01460 52293

Baker & McKenzie
‡London EC4 *p9*. 020 7919 1000

Baker Botts LLP
‡London EC2 *p9*. 020 7726 3636

D R Baker Solicitor
‡Bury St Edmunds *p171*. 01284 764600

Baker Ellis Solicitors
‡Manchester *p301*. 0161 225 2525

Baker Gray & Co
‡Blaydon-on-Tyne *p147* 0191 414 4869
Newcastle upon Tyne *p323*. . . . 0191 222 0203

Helen Baker Solicitor
‡Rochester *p366* 01634 255265

Baker Macdonald
‡Sevenoaks *p374* 01732 457978

Michael Baker Solicitors Limited
‡Farnborough *p224* 01252 744600
Redhill *p362* 01252 744600

Michael Bakers Solicitors Limited
Aldershot *p115* 01252 744600

Baker Sanford LLP
‡London WC2 *p9* 020 7061 6448

Bakers
‡Mitcham *p318* 020 8648 0363

Bakers Solicitors
‡Glossop *p230*. 01457 859123

Bakewells
‡Derby *p208*. 01332 348791

Bal Dhaliwal Solicitors
‡Peterborough *p346*. 01733 552000

Bala & Co
‡London E6 *p9* 020 8548 8808

Baldwin & Co
‡London SE16 *p9* 020 7237 3035

Baldwin & Robinson Law LLP
‡Oxted *p344*. 01883 708155

Baldwin Townsend & Co
‡Cwmbran *p206*. 01633 866007

Baldwin Wyatt Solicitors
‡Burnley *p169* 01282 429999

Balfour Law
‡Peterborough *p346*. 01733 324444

Balham Law Partnership
‡London SW12 *p9*

Balinda & Co
‡London E7 *p9* 020 8221 4541

E M Ball & Co
‡Watford *p423*. 01923 213456

Joanne Ball Solicitors
‡Liverpool *p286* 0151 724 6645

Ballam
‡Birkenhead *p134* 0151 647 8977

Ballantyne Grant LLP
‡Chester *p190*. 01244 394230

Ballantyne Taylor Solicitors
‡London SW4 *p9*

Balsara & Co
‡London EC1 *p9*. 020 7797 6300

Bambridges Solicitors Limited
‡Boston *p151* 01205 310510

E J Bamforth Solicitors
‡Chester *p190*. 01244 357209

Bana Vaid & Associates
‡Uxbridge *p417* 01895 272481
Hayes *p245*. 020 8813 6262

The Banahan Tennant Partnership Limited
‡Dudley *p213* 01384 253288

Bance Commercial Law
‡Redhill *p362* 01737 226034

Band Hatton LLP
‡Coventry *p200* 024 7663 2121

M H Banharally & Co
‡London E13 *p9*. 020 8471 7572

Bank Solicitors
‡Redditch *p362* 0845 604 6504

Banks Carrington & Co
‡Blackpool *p146*. . . . .01253 622269 / 315223

David Banks Solicitors
‡Newcastle upon Tyne *p323*. . . . 0191 266 4776

Banks Kelly
‡London EC2 *p9*. 020 7248 4231

M I Banks
‡Stretford *p400* 0161 864 1961

Sandra Banks Solicitor
‡Lewes *p283* 01273 470434

Bankside Commercial Solicitors
‡Southwark SE1 *p9* 020 7654 0200

Bankside Law Ltd
‡London SE1 *p9*. 0844 745 4000

Bankside Property Limited
‡Southwark SE1 *p9* 020 7654 7500

John L Banky Solicitors
‡Reading *p359* 0118 930 4630

Banner Jones
‡Chesterfield *p191*. 01246 560560
Chesterfield *p191*. 01246 827516
Chesterfield *p192*. 01246 861250
Chesterfield *p191*. 01246 209773
Dronfield *p213* 01246 414438
Sheffield *p375* 0114 275 5266

Bannister & Co
‡Yeovil *p443*. 01935 433133

Bannister Bates Property Lawyers
‡Morecambe *p318*. 01524 416300

Bannister Preston
‡Sale *p370* 0161 973 2434
Irlam *p263* 0161 775 0444

Bannons
‡Liverpool *p286* 0151 227 1818

Bansal & Co
‡Southall *p384*. 020 3118 2063

Barber & Co
‡Glossop *p230*. 0845 803 0991
‡Preston *p356*. 01772 203520

Barber-Lomax
‡Bedford *p129*. 01234 721108

Robert Barber & Sons
‡Nottingham *p335*. 0115 878 9000
Eastwood *p216*. 01773 787878
Hucknall *p255* 0115 955 2299

Barber Titleys
‡Harrogate *p240*. 01423 502211

Barber Young Burton & Rind
‡Westminster SW1 *p9*. 020 3376 6706

Barcan Woodward
‡Bristol *p160*. 0117 963 5237
Bristol *p161*. 0117 925 8080
Bristol *p161*. 0117 923 2141

Sarah Barclay & Co
‡Blackpool *p146*. 01253 356051

Barclay Taylor
‡London EC4 *p9*. 0845 054 4069

Max Barford & Co
‡Tunbridge Wells *p414*. 01892 539379

Bargate Murray
‡London EC2 *p9*. 020 7729 7778

Michael Barham & Co
‡Cambridge *p174* 01223 415797

J E Baring & Co
‡London EC1 *p9*. 020 7242 8966

Stan Baring Solicitor
‡Godalming *p231* 01483 860986

Barings Solicitors
‡Manchester *p301*. 0161 200 9960

Bark & Co
‡London EC4 *p9*. 020 7353 1990

A F Barker & Co
‡Berkhamsted *p131* 01442 863336

Barker & Co
‡Hull *p256*. 01482 219966

Barker Austin
‡London E1 *p9* 020 7377 1933

Barker Booth & Eastwood
‡Blackpool *p146*. 01253 362500

Barker Evans Private Client Law
‡Nottingham *p335*. 0800 978 8582

Barker Gillette
‡London W1 *p9* 020 7636 0555

Barker Gooch & Swailes
‡Enfield *p218* 020 8366 3161
London N21 *p9*. . . . .020 8886 5928 / 8886 5734

Barker Gotelee Solicitors
‡Ipswich *p262*. 01473 611211

Barker Son & Isherwood LLP
‡Andover *p118*. 01264 353411
Andover *p118*. 01264 791156
Overton *p342*. 01256 770211
Whitchurch *p430* 01256 896262

Barkers
‡Bolton *p148* 01204 370011

John Barkers
‡Grimsby *p234* 01472 358686
Cleethorpes *p195*. 01472 695218
Louth *p294*. 01507 604773
Mablethorpe *p297* 01507 477673

T S Barkes & Son
‡Moreton-in-Marsh *p319*. 01608 650332

Barlin
‡Reigate *p363*. 01737 231340

Barlow Lyde & Gilbert LLP
‡London EC3 *p10* 020 7876 5000
Manchester *p301*. 0161 829 6400
Oxford *p342* 01865 336600

BARLOW ROBBINS LLP
‡Guildford *p235* 01483 562901
Godalming *p231* 01483 417121
Guildford *p235* 01483 543200
Woking *p436* 01483 748500

BARLOW ROWLAND
‡Accrington *p114* 01254 300400

Barlows
‡Leicester *p278* 0116 251 8295
Market Harborough *p312*. 01858 410040

Barnard & Co
Filton *p226* 0117 969 2773

Barnard & Tomlin
Luton *p295*. 01582 453366

Barnes & Partners
‡London N18 *p10* 020 8884 2277
Cheshunt *p189* 01992 626366
Enfield *p218* 020 8366 3333
Hackney N16 *p10*. 020 7241 5577
Haringey N15 *p10* 020 8801 0085
Haringey N8 *p10* 020 8340 6697
Harlow *p239* 01279 418601
London E4 *p10*. 020 8524 9222
Pinner *p348* 020 8866 5566
Ware *p421* 01920 460823

Barnes & Taylor
‡Southend-on-Sea *p387* 01702 347300

Arthur Barnes & Co
‡London EC1 *p10* 020 7278 3046

Barnes Coleman & Co
‡Benfleet *p131*. 01702 558211

F Barnes & Son
‡Romford *p366* 01708 745183
Romford *p366* 01708 743727

Barnes Gillett
‡Brentwood *p156* 01277 226491

Barnes Harrild & Dyer
‡Croydon *p204* 020 8681 5128

James E Barnes
‡Ealing W13 *p10* 020 8810 7100

Kervin Barnes Limited
‡London SW14 *p10* 020 7887 6296

Barnes Marsland
‡Margate *p312*. 01843 221466
Broadstairs *p166* 01843 861595

Barnes Richards Rutter
‡Chepstow *p189*. 01291 628898

Barnes Sarney & Game
‡Rayleigh *p359* . . . . .01268 773881 / 774785

Barnet Family Law
‡Barnet *p123* 020 8440 2229

Barnet Solicitors
‡London E8 *p10*. 020 7249 2668

Barnett Alexander Conway Ingram
‡London N3 *p10*. 020 8349 7680

James S Barnett
‡Hungerford *p258* 01488 658461

Marcus Barnett
‡London SW1 *p10*. 020 7235 9215

Norman H Barnett & Co
‡London E6 *p11* 020 8471 2112

Barnetts
‡Southport *p388*. 0870 787 3600

Barney & Company Solicitors
‡Somerton *p383*. . 01458 270296 / 07766 095865

David Barney & Co
‡Stevenage *p394* 01438 314281

Baron Grey
‡Twickenham *p416* 020 8891 4311

Paul R Baron
‡Carshalton *p183* 020 8401 2251

Robin Baron Commercial Lawyers
‡Camden NW5 *p11* 020 7485 4477

Brian Barr Solicitors
‡Manchester *p301*. 0161 720 6700

Barr Ellison LLP
‡Cambridge *p174* 01223 417200
Cambridge *p174* 01223 411315

Barratt Goff & Tomlinson
‡Nottingham *p335*. 0115 931 5171

Barrco Limited
‡Tadworth *p407* 01737 833850

Barrea LLP
‡High Wycombe *p249* 01494 537699

Barrett & Associates
‡Marlow *p313* 01628 476283

Barrett & Co Solicitors LLP
‡Reading *p359* 0118 958 9711
Didcot *p210*. 01235 851220

Barrett & Thomson
‡Slough *p381* 01753 437416

Barrett Nelligan Solicitors
‡Fleetwood *p226* 01253 771664
Blackpool *p146*. 01253 292848

Barretts
‡London WC1 *p11*. 020 7248 0551

Barricella Hughes Marchant
‡Ipswich *p262*. 01473 226225

Barriga McDonald Solicitors
‡Conwy *p199* 01978 358157

Barrington & Sons
‡Burnham-on-Sea *p169* 01278 782371

Barrington Charles Edwards & Co
‡London SE20 *p11* . .020 8659 7228 / 8659 7227
London SE25 *p11*. . .020 8656 8318 / 8656 8319

Barrington Scholfield
‡Bridgwater *p157* . . . . .01278 422858 / 422873

Barringtons Solicitors
‡Farnham *p224* 01252 741751

Barrow & Cook
‡St Helens *p391*. 01744 23271

Kenneth M Barrow & Co
‡Seaham *p373* 0191 513 0333

M R Barrow
‡Poole *p352*. 01202 737745

Barry & Blott
‡Bristol *p161*. . . . . . 0117 962 9161 / 962 9171

Barry & Co
‡Pevensey Bay *p348* . . .01323 766370 / 768382

David J Barry
‡Ross-on-Wye *p367*. 01989 564209

Lesley P Barry
‡Windsor *p434*. 01753 860061

Barrys
‡London WC2 *p11*. 020 7645 8270

Bart-Williams & Co
‡Ilford *p259* 020 8551 4747

Bartlett Gooding & Weelen
‡Shepton Mallet *p378* 01749 343091
Castle Cary *p183*. 01963 350888
Cheddar *p186* 01934 745400
Glastonbury *p229*. 01458 832510

J W Bartlett & Co
‡Teddington *p408* 020 8943 9831

Bartletts
‡Haringey N8 *p11* . . .020 8340 2202 / 8340 2203

Bartletts Solicitors
‡Liverpool *p286* 0151 227 3391
Chester *p190*. 01244 313301
Chester *p190*. 01244 313301
Liverpool *p286* 0151 228 7730
Liverpool *p286* 0151 521 7333

Anthony Barton
‡Islington N1 *p11* 020 7700 7348

Atha Barton & Co
‡Guisborough *p237* 01287 633242

David Barton Solicitor Advocate
‡Maidstone *p298* 01622 695587

Barton Legal
‡Leeds *p271*. 0113 202 9550

Barton Solicitors
‡Barton-upon-Humber *p126* 01652 618376

William Barton
‡Sutton *p402* 020 8642 4858

Bartons
‡Kingsbridge *p267*. 01548 855655
Bristol *p161*. 0117 925 6000
Plymouth *p349* 01752 675740
Salcombe *p370*. 01548 843005

Skelton-in-Cleveland p381 . . . . 01287 651521
Totnes p413 . . . . 01803 864705

Bartram & Co
‡Ealing W13 p11. . . . . 020 8840 0444

Barwells
‡Eastbourne p215 . . . . 01323 411505
Newhaven p327 . . . . 01273 514213
Peacehaven p345 . . . . 01273 582271
Seaford p373. . . . . 01323 899331

Barwise & Co
‡St Helens p391. . . . . 0151 292 7800

Baser & Co
‡Batley p128 . . . . 01924 452950

Graham Bash & Co
‡Hackney E5 p11 . . . . 020 8985 8892

Robert L Bashforth & Co
‡Chesterfield p192. . . . . 01246 200204

S S Basi & Co
‡Ilford p259 . . . . 020 8518 1236

Baskin Ross & Co
‡London NW11 p11 . . . . 020 8458 5688

Bassets
‡Rochester p366 . . . . 01634 400161
Gillingham p229 . . . . 01634 575464

AP Bassett Solicitors
‡Lostwithiel p293 . . . . 01208 871485
Bodmin p148 . . . . 01208 871485

Bassi Solicitors
‡Birmingham p135. . . . . 0121 554 0868

Doreen Neale Bastable Solicitor
‡Birmingham p135. . . . . 0121 744 3611

Bastian Lloyd Morris Solicitor Advocates
‡Milton Keynes p316. . . . . 01908 546580

Bastows Divorce Solicitors
‡Southampton p385 . . . . 023 8045 5366

Batchelor Myddelton
‡Potters Bar p355 . . . . 01707 647088

Batchelor Sharp
‡Bristol p161. . . . . 01454 319100
Kingswood p268 . . . . 0117 967 1772
Knowle p269 . . . . 0117 977 0717

BATCHELORS SOLICITORS
‡Bromley p166. . . . . 020 8768 7000
London WC1 p11 . . . . 020 7269 9027

Janie Batchford Solicitors
‡London EC1 p11 . . . . 020 7060 3089

Christopher Bate
‡Bangor p122 . . . . 01248 372395

Bate Edmonds Snape
‡Coventry p200 . . . . 024 7622 0707

Richard T Bate & Co
‡Tetbury p410. . . . . 01666 503722

Alastair Bateman & Co
‡Bradford p153 . . . . 01274 739973

Batemans
‡Hemel Hempstead p246 . . . . . 01442 834344

Bates & Mountain
‡Grimsby p235 . . . . 01472 357291
Caistor p172 . . . . 01472 851224

Bates Brunel Solicitors
Hook p252 . . . . 01256 709900
Leigh-on-Sea p282 . . . . 01702 472222

Bates NVH
‡London WC2 p11. . . . . 020 7936 2930
Fleet p226 . . . . 01252 629292
Hook p252 . . . . 01256 760074
Hook p252 . . . . 01252 844443

Nicholas Bates
‡Basingstoke p126 . . . . 01256 331278

Bates Wells & Braithwaite
‡Ipswich p262. . . . . 01473 219282

Bates Wells & Braithwaite London LLP
‡London EC4 p11 . . . . 020 7551 7777

Bath Law
Bath p127 . . . . 01225 401200

Bathurst Brown Downie & Airey LLP
‡Twickenham p416 . . . . 020 8892 1537

H Batra & Co
‡London SW1 p11. . . . . 0845 017 5588

Batt Broadbent
‡Salisbury p371 . . . . 01722 411141

Battens
‡Yeovil p443. . . . . 01935 846000
Dorchester p212 . . . . 01305 250560
Sherborne p378 . . . . 01935 814811
Weymouth p430 . . . . 01305 774666

Battrick Clark Solicitors Ltd
‡Bristol p161. . . . . 0117 973 1391

Gordon A Battrick & Co
‡Bridgend p157 . . . . 01656 768111

Marcus Baum
‡Southend-on-Sea p387. . . . . . 01702 346677

Bavisi Legal Limited
‡Northwood p333 . 01923 835870 / 07811 439999

Bawtrees LLP
‡Witham p435. . . . . 01376 513491

Baxendale Vanzie
‡Halifax p238

Baxter & Co
‡Bournemouth p151 . . . . 01202 530249

Baxter Brown McArthur
‡London SW11 p11 . . . . 020 7924 8130

Baxter Caulfield
‡Huddersfield p255 . . . . 01484 519519

Deborah Baxter & Co
‡Reading p360 . . . . 0118 958 6855

Baxter Webbe Solicitors
‡Hatfield p244 . . . . 01707 259354

Baxters
‡Hull p256. . . . . 01482 224011
Tamworth p407. . . . . 01827 899059

Bay Advocates Criminal Defence Lawyers
‡Torquay p412. . . . . 01803 408290

Bayer Solicitors
‡Maidenhead p298 . . . . 01628 770392

Bayham Solicitors
Sevenoaks p374 . . . . 01732 882546

Bayham Solicitors LLP
‡Tunbridge Wells p414. . . . . . . 01892 891999

John Bayles & Co
‡Birtley p144. . . . . 0191 410 2142
Durham p214. . . . . 0191 386 1161

Bayley Law Ltd (BYL)
‡Salford p370 . . . . 0870 837 3300

Allan L Bayliss
‡Conwy p199 . . . . 01978 761595

Baynards
‡Bexleyheath p132 . . . . 020 8304 5113

T G Baynes
‡Bexleyheath p132 . . . . 020 8301 7777
Dartford p207. . . . . 01322 295555
Orpington p341. . . . . .01689 886000 / 886042

John Bays & Co
‡Haringey N22 p11 . . . . 020 8881 3609

Bazeer & Co
‡London SW19 p11 . . . . 020 8543 6600

Bazeley Barnes & Bazeley
‡Bideford p132 . . . . 01237 473122

Martin Beach (House Owners Conveyancers Ltd)
‡London NW2 p11. . . . . 020 8452 6622

Beachrofts
‡London SE18 p11 . . . . 020 8301 8183

Beachwood Solicitors
‡Leeds p271. . . . . . . 0113 359 3067 / 200 8770

Beacon Law Practice
‡Ilfracombe p261 . . . . 01271 867056

Beacon Solicitors Limited
‡Ilford p259 . . . . 020 8553 1893

Beadle Pitt & Gottschalk
‡Canterbury p176 . . . . 01227 464481

David Beadnall
‡Middlesbrough p315 . . . . 01642 311635

Beale and Company Solicitors LLP
‡London WC2 p11. . . . . 020 7240 3474
Bristol p161. . . . . 0117 915 4021

Nigel W Beaman
‡Cannock p176 . . . . 01543 574474

Bearders
‡Halifax p238 . . . . . . .01422 365215 / 343427
Brighouse p158. . . . . 01484 710571

Beardsells
‡Cheadle p185 . . . . 0161 477 2288

Deborah Bearham & Co
‡Tadworth p407 . . . . 01737 812707

Bearing Sachs Solicitors LLP
‡London E15 p11 . . . . 020 8555 4552

Beashel Solicitors
‡Warminster p421 . . . . 01985 220680

Beasley Johnson Loyns
‡Walsall p419 . . . . 01922 644433

Mark Beattie
‡London W4 p11. . . . . 020 8742 7319

Beaty & Co
‡Wigton p432 . . . . 01697 342121

Beauchamps
‡Westminster W1 p11 . . . . 020 7724 7724

Beaufort Law
‡Chipping Sodbury p193. . . . . . 01225 339329

Beaumonde Law Practice
‡Pinner p348 . . . . 020 8868 1614

Beaumont Legal
‡Wakefield p418. . . . . 0845 122 8100

Beaumonts
‡Hereford p247 . . . . 01432 352345
Bromyard p167. . . . . 01885 488442

The Beavis Partnership
‡Chelmsford p186 . . . . 01245 264748
Witham p435. . . . . 01376 500255

Oliver Bebb
‡Horsham p253 . . . . 0845 603 2808

S M Beck Solicitors
‡London SW1 p11. . . . . 020 7730 8401

Beck Solicitors
‡Harrogate p240. . . . . 01423 528808

Beckerley Hall Solicitors
‡Cardiff p177 . . . . 029 2075 5777

Beckett & Co
‡Preston p356. . . . . 01772 315200

Beckett Bemrose Hagen
‡Wirral p435. . . . . 0151 326 2340
Wallasey p419 . . . . 0151 630 1206

Beckett Solicitors
‡Croydon p204 . . . . 020 8405 0750
‡Gillingham p229 . . . . 01634 263774

Bedford Family Law
‡Bedford p129. . . . . 01234 363211

Bedfords
‡Somerton p383. . . . . 01458 888153

Bedfords Solicitors
‡Luton p295. . . . . 01582 519736

Bedwell Watts & Co
‡Scarborough p372 . . . .01723 373356 / 363553

David W Beech
‡Westminster W1 p11 . . . . 020 7493 4932

Beech Jones de Lloyd
‡Cardiff p177 . . . . 029 2062 3247
Liverpool p286 . . . . 0151 236 2924

Beecham Fisher Ridley
‡Southend-on-Sea p387. . . . . . 01702 348384

Beecham Peacock
‡Newcastle upon Tyne p323. . . . 0191 232 3048

Beechmast Consultancy Limited
‡Marlborough p313 . . . . 01672 810399

Beechwood Solicitors
‡Eynsham p223 . . . . 01865 883344

Beecroft Maxwell
‡Canvey Island p177 . . . . 01268 511999

Beeley & Co Solicitors
‡Cheadle p185 . . . 0800 195 2537 / 0161 492 5970
Brighton p159. . . . . 01273 748464

Beemans Solicitors
‡Harrow p241 . . . . 020 8901 7565

Raymond Beer & Co
‡Chatham p184 . . . . 01634 814911

Beers LLP
‡Kingsbridge p267. . . . . 01548 857000
Plymouth p349 . . . . 01752 246000

Beesley & Co
‡Manchester p301. . . . . 0161 445 3678

Beesons
‡Milton Keynes p316. . . . . 01908 271171

Beeston Shenton
‡Newcastle under Lyme p323 . . . 01782 662424
Knutsford p269 . . . . 01565 754444
Sandbach p371. . . . . 01270 750057

Beetenson & Gibbon
‡Grimsby p235 . . . . 01472 240251
Louth p294 . . . . 01507 600610

Beeton Edwards
‡Southampton p385 . . . . 023 8038 2850

Beevers Solicitors
‡Ashton-under-Lyne p119 . . . . . 0161 339 9697

Roy Thomas Begley & Co
‡Swansea p404 . . . . . .01792 643797 / 643798

Begum & Co
‡London SW18 p11 . . . . 020 8877 0242

John A Behn Twyford & Co
‡Liverpool p286 . . . . 0151 236 0367

Behr & Co
‡Brynmawr p167. . . . . 01495 310581

Norman Beigel & Co
‡London NW11 p11 . . . . 020 8455 8183

Beightons
‡Derby p208. . . . . 01332 346430

Belcher Frost
‡Emsworth p218. . . . . 01243 377231

Bell & Buxton
‡Sheffield p375 . . . . 0114 249 5969

Bell & Co
‡Cheam p185 . . . . 020 8642 6099
‡Liverpool p286 . . . . 0151 928 8686
Cheam p185 . . . . 020 8642 6099
Sutton p402 . . . . 020 8661 8611

C C Bell & Son
‡Bedford p129. . . . . 01234 363251

Harold Bell & Co
‡Ewell p220 . . . . 020 8393 0231

Joseph N Bell
‡Lewes p283 . . . . 01273 897377

Bell Lamb & Joynson
‡Liverpool p286 . . . . 0844 412 4348
Liverpool p286 . . . . 0844 412 4348
Runcorn p369 . . . . 0844 412 4348
Warrington p421 . . . . 0844 412 4348
Weaverham p424. . . . . 0844 412 4348

Bell Lax Litigation
‡Sutton Coldfield p403. . . . . . . 0121 355 0011

Bell Park Kerridge
‡Carlisle p181 . . . . 01228 888999
‡Cockermouth p197 . . . . 01900 820800

R Bell & Son
‡Hartlepool p242. . . . . 01429 273165

Bell Wright & Co
‡Gainsborough p228. . . . . 01427 611722

David Bellchamber & Co
‡Cobham p196 . . . . 01932 702233

John Bellis & Co
‡Penmaenmawr p346 . . . . 01492 622377
Conwy p199 . . . . 01248 680527

Juliet Bellis & Co
‡Uckfield p416. . . . . 01825 750811

Bellis Kennan Gribble & Co
‡Southport p388. . . . . 01704 532217

Robin Bellis
‡Swanage p404 . . . . 01929 425722

Bells
‡Romsey p366. . . . . 01794 513328

Bells Solicitors
‡Farnham p224 . . . . 01252 733733

Belmont & Lowe
‡London EC1 p11 . . . . 020 7608 4600

Belmores
‡Norwich p334. . . . . 01603 499999

Belshaw & Curtin
‡London SE5 p11 . . . . 020 7708 3311

Belshaws Solicitors Limited
‡Stockport p395 . . . . 0161 477 5377

Belvederes
‡London WC2 p12. . .020 7404 5262 / 7405 0046

Bemrose & Ling
‡Derby p208. . . . . 01332 347300

Ben Hoare Bell & Co
‡Sunderland p401 . . . . 0191 565 3112
Newcastle upon Tyne p323. . . . 0191 275 2626
Sunderland p401 . . . . 0191 516 0466
Sunderland p401 . . . . 0191 565 3112

Bendall & Sons
‡Newmarket p327. . . . . 01638 661116
Mildenhall p316. . . . . 01638 712243

Bendall Roberts
‡Ely p218 . . . . 01353 663581

David Bendell & Co
‡Hinckley p250 . . . . 01455 619322

Bendles
‡Carlisle p181 . . . . 01228 522215

Benedek Joels Solicitors
‡London NW11 p12 . . . . 020 8458 0005

Benhams
‡Thame p410 . . . . 020 7581 5636

Harold Benjamin
‡Harrow p241 . . . . 020 8422 5678

Benn Cameron Solicitors
‡London SW17 p12 . . . . 020 8672 8306

Bennett & Co
‡Liverpool p286 . . . . 0151 733 2372

Bennett & Co Solicitors
‡Maidstone p298 . . . . 01622 682808

Bennett & Ryan Solicitors
‡Isleworth p263 . . . . 020 8568 2800

Ann C Bennett
‡London SW3 p12. . . . . 020 7352 7494

Bennett Griffin
‡Worthing p441 . . . . 01903 229925
Ferring p225 . . . . 01903 229999
Rustington p369 . . . . 01903 777690

James B Bennett & Co
‡Crawley p202. . . . . 01293 544044

Bennett Oakley & Partners
‡Burgess Hill p168. . . . . 01444 235232

Bennett Richmond
‡Lanchester p270 . . . . 01207 521843
Consett p199 . . . . 01207 504141

Simon Bennett
‡Marlow p313 . . . . 01628 478088

Bennett Smith Partnership
‡Caernarfon p172 . . . . 01248 679000

Bennett Welch & Co
‡London SE19 p12 . . . . 020 8670 6141

Bennetts
‡Macclesfield p297 . . . . 01625 424666

Bennetts Law Practice Ltd
‡Clacton-on-Sea p195. . . . . . . 01255 254400

Bennetts Legal
‡Shrewsbury p379. . . . . 0844 472 2378

Bennetts Solicitors Attorneys & Notaries
‡Wrington p443 . . . . 01934 862786

Benson & Co
‡Hastings p243 . . . . 01424 433601

J Benson Solicitors
‡London NW6 p12. . . . . 020 7316 1884

James Benson & Co
‡Liverpool p286 . . . . 0151 236 8755

Benson Mazure LLP
‡Westminster W1 p12 . . . . 020 7486 8091

Benson Watkins
‡Swansea p404 . . . . 01792 704320
Swansea p404 . . . . 01792 464564

Benson Watkins & Co Limited
‡Cardiff p177 . . . . . 029 2038 2486

Bentley & Co
‡Pudsey p358 . . . . . 0113 236 0550

Bentley Solicitors
‡Crewe p203 . . . . . 01270 509800

Bentleys
‡Waltham Forest E17 p12 . . . . . 020 8521 8751

Bentleys Solicitors
‡Leeds p271. . . . . 0113 274 0100

Bentleys Stokes & Lowless
‡London E1 p12. . . . . 020 7782 0990

Benussi & Co
‡Birmingham p135. . . . . 0121 248 4001

Beor Wilson Lloyd
‡Swansea p405 . . . . . 01792 655178

Berg Legal
‡Manchester p301. . . . . 0161 833 9211

Paul Berg & Taylor
‡Harpenden p239 . . . . . 01582 760161

Simon Bergin
‡Stockport p395. . . . . 0161 432 9945

The Berkeley Group PLC
‡Cobham p196 . . . . . 01932 868555

Berkeley Law Limted
‡London W1 p12 . . . . . 020 7399 0930

Berkeley Solicitors
‡Droylsden p213. . . . . 0161 371 0011

Berkeleys Solicitors
‡Croydon p204 . . . . . 020 8760 5064

Berkleys
‡High Wycombe p249 . . . . . 0870 446 0704

Berkson Globe Partnership
‡Liverpool p286 . . . . . 0151 236 1234

Berkson Wallace Solicitors
‡Wallasey p419 . . . . . 0151 691 6900
Ellesmere Port p217 . . . . . 0151 355 4412

Daniel Berman & Co
‡London NW5 p12. . . . . 020 7428 7798

Bermans LLP
‡Liverpool p286 . . . . . 0151 224 0500
Manchester p301. . . . . 0161 827 4600

Bernard Chill & Axtell
‡Southampton p385. . . . . 023 8022 8821
Eastleigh p216 . . . . . 023 8061 3197

Daniel Bernstein & Co
‡London NW3 p12. . . . . 020 7435 8921

Howard Bernstein Solicitors
‡Glossop p230. . . . . 01457 863999

Berri's
‡Greenford p234. . . . . 020 8537 3377

Berry & Berry
‡Tunbridge Wells p414. . . . . 01892 526344
‡Walkden p419 . . . . . 0161 790 1411
Eccles p216 . . . . . 0161 789 7414
Maidstone p299. . . . . 01622 690777
Manchester p301. . . . . 0161 796 7920
Manchester p301. . . . . 0161 703 7300
Tonbridge p412. . . . . 01732 355911

Berry & Walton Solicitors
‡King's Lynn p266. . . . . 01553 764398
King's Lynn p266. . . . . 01485 571366

H L F Berry & Co
Failsworth p223. . . . . 0161 681 4005

Berry Redmond & Robinson
‡Weston-super-Mare p429. . . . . 01934 513963
Weston-super-Mare p429. . . . . 01934 619000
Winscombe p434. . . . . 01934 842811

Berry Smith LLP
‡Cardiff p177 . . . . . 029 2034 5511
Bridgend p157 . . . . . 01656 645525
Bristol p161. . . . . 0845 602 5846
London WC2 p12. . . . . 0845 603 8337

Berrymans Lace Mawer
‡London EC2 p12 . . . . . 020 7638 2811
Birmingham p135. . . . . 0121 643 8777
Bristol p161. . . . . 0117 975 8649
Cardiff p177 . . . . . 029 2044 7667
Leeds p271. . . . . 0113 236 2002
Liverpool p286 . . . . . 0151 236 2002
Manchester p301. . . . . 0161 236 2002
Southampton p385 . . . . . 023 8023 6464
Stockton-on-Tees p396 . . . . . 01642 661630

Berrys
‡Tilehurst p411 . . . . . 0118 942 2333

Berrys Solicitors
‡Blackpool p146. . . . . 01253 620022

Berwicks
‡Bradford p153 . . . . . 01274 498784

Berwin Leighton Paisner LLP
‡London EC4 p12 . . . . . 020 7760 1000

Berwins Solicitors Limited
‡Harrogate p240. . . . . 01423 509000

Beshoffs Solicitors
‡Aylesbury p120. . . . . 01296 621180

Best & Soames Limited
‡London EC1 p12 . . . . . 020 7014 3525

Melanie Best Employment Lawyer
‡Baldock p121. . . . . 01223 597832

Richard Best & Co
‡Rugby p368 . . . . . 01788 571135

Best Solicitors LLP
‡St Albans p389. . . . . 01727 884688

Best Solicitors
‡Sheffield p375 . . . . . 0114 281 3636

Beswicks
‡Stoke-on-Trent p397 . . . . . 01782 205000
Hanley p239 . . . . . 01782 205000

Betesh Partnership
‡Manchester p301. . . . . 0161 834 2623
Hale p237 . . . . . 0161 926 1430
Manchester p301. . . . . 0161 740 4918

Simon Bethel Solicitors
‡London SE13 p12 . . . . . 020 8297 7933

Betteridges
‡Hertford p248. . . . . 01992 505406

Betts & Co Solicitors Ltd
‡Ashford p119. . . . . 01304 213172

Julia T Betts
‡Nottingham p336. . . . . 01623 499080

Kim Betts & Co
‡Loughton p294. . . . . 020 8508 5505

Beulah Solicitors
‡London SE28 p12 . . . . . 020 8331 0305

Bevan Brittan LLP
‡Bristol p161. . . . . 0870 194 1000
Birmingham p135. . . . . 0870 194 1000
London EC4 p12 . . . . . 0870 194 1000

Bevan Burrows Solicitors
‡Dorking p212. . . . . 01306 876960

Bevan Jones
‡Llanarth p291. . . . . 01545 580746

Bevan Kidwell
‡London EC1 p12 . . . . . 020 7843 1820

Bevan-Evans & Capehorn Solicitors
‡Cheltenham p187. . . . . 01242 234564

Bevans
‡Bristol p161. . . . . 0117 923 7249
London WC2 p12. . . . . 020 7353 9995

Beverley Davies Guthrie
‡Cardiff p177 . . . . . 029 2037 3582

Malcolm G Beverley Solicitors
‡Chorley p194. . . . . 01257 231462

Bevirs
‡Swindon p406 . . . . . 01793 532363
Calne p173. . . . . 01249 814536
Wootton Bassett p439 . . . . . 01793 848900

Bevis Rowntree
‡Midhurst p315 . . . . . 01730 812201

Beviss & Beckingsale
‡Axminster p120. . . . . 01297 630700
Chard p184. . . . . 01460 269700
Honiton p252. . . . . 01404 548050
Seaton p373 . . . . . 01297 626950

Beynon & Co
‡Birmingham p135. . . . . 0121 444 0099

Beynons
‡Orpington p341. . . . . 01689 861008

Beynons Nicholls
‡London EC4 p12 . . . . . 020 7353 5860

Bhailok Fielding
‡Preston p356. . . . . 01772 202191

Bhakar Tomlinson
‡Wellington p425 . . . . . 01952 270555

Bhatia Best
‡Nottingham p336 . . . . . 0115 950 3231
Derby p208. . . . . 01332 203000
Mansfield p311 . . . . . 01623 427944

Bhatt Murphy
‡Hackney N1 p12 . . . . . 020 7729 1115

Bhavsar Patel Solicitors
‡Leicester p279 . . . . . 0116 254 9477

Bhogal Partners
‡Hounslow p253. . . . . 020 8572 9867

Bibi Gadwah Solicitors
‡London E14 p12 . . . . . 020 7377 6102

Bickley Wheatley & Co
‡Birmingham p135. . . . . 0121 377 6266

Biddle Mason & Co - Notary Public
‡Warwick p422 . . . . . 01926 484264

Biddulphs
‡Rainham p359 . . . . . 01634 363535

Biggs & Co
‡Wokingham p437. . . . . 0118 989 4511

David Bigmore & Co
‡Wrexham p442. . . . . 01978 855058

Bignalls
‡Westminster W1 p12 . . . . . 020 7637 3071

Bikelawyer, Motorcycle Accident Solicitors
‡Llantwit Major p292. . . . . 01446 794199

Bilbeisi & Co Solicitors
‡Barnet N20 p12. . . . . 020 8446 7262

Bilbeisi Solicitors
‡Barnet p123 . . . . . 020 8275 3355

David Billingham & Partners
‡Cheltenham p187. . . . . 01242 676224
Tewkesbury p410. . . . . 01684 276469

Billson & Sharp
‡Leicester p279 . . . . . 0116 255 9911
Leicester p279 . . . . . 0116 270 2260

Billy Hughes & Co Solicitors
‡Leeds p271. . . . . 0845 680 0863

Bilmes LLP
‡London WC2 p12. . . . . 020 7490 9656
Brighton p159. . . . . 01273 380202

Bilson Henaku Solicitors
‡London SE23 p12 . . . . . 020 8291 1043

Bilton Hammond LLP
‡Mansfield p311 . . . . . 01623 675800
Chesterfield p192. . . . . 01246 232418

Binas Solicitors
‡Manchester p301. . . . . 0161 257 0060

Bindman & Co
‡Whickham p430 . . . . . 0191 488 4950

Bindmans LLP
‡London WC1 p12. . . . . 020 7833 4433

Bingham & Co
‡Leicester p279 . . . . . 0116 253 0091

Bingham McCutchen (London) LLP
‡London EC2 p12 . . . . . 020 7661 5300

Robert Bingham Solicitors
‡Liverpool p286 . . . . . 0151 630 7171

Helen Binks Solicitor
‡Mirfield p318 . . . . . 01924 497720

Binnion Lindsay-Veal LLP
‡Stourport-on-Severn p399 . . . . . 01299 827860
Worcester p439. . . . . 01905 747809

Birch & Co
‡Gosforth p231 . . . . . 0191 284 5030 / 284 6040

Birch Reynardson & Co
‡Thame p410 . . . . . 01844 281184

Birchall Blackburn LLP
‡Preston p356. . . . . 01772 561663
Chester p190. . . . . 0844 980 2430
Chorley p194 . . . . . 01257 279011
Formby p227 . . . . . 01704 832222
Leyland p283. . . . . 01772 433775
Manchester p301. . . . . 0161 236 0662
Morecambe p319. . . . . 01524 833838
Preston p356. . . . . 01772 744744
Southport p388. . . . . 01704 232323

Birchall Ryan Solicitors
‡Congleton p198. . . . . 01260 297070
Crewe p203 . . . . . .01270 211115

Bircham Dyson Bell
‡Westminster SW1 p13 . . . . . 020 7227 7000

Birchfield
Stoke-on-Trent p397 . . . . . 01782 216888

Birchfields
‡Manchester p301. . . . . 0161 835 9865

Birchley Titmus Commercial Solicitors
‡London W1 p13 . . . . . 020 7408 9427

A J Bird & Co
‡London SW1 p13. . . . . 020 7808 7908

Bird & Bird LLP
‡London EC4 p13 . . . . . 020 7415 6000

BIRD & CO
‡Grantham p232. . . . . 01476 591711
Newark p322 . . . . . 01636 650880

BIRD & DANIELS
‡Shipley p378 . . . . . 01274 580999

Bird & Lovibond
‡Uxbridge p417 . . . . . 01895 256151
Greenford p234. . . . . 020 8578 6936
Ruislip p368 . . . . . 01895 636037

Ernest Bird & Sons
‡Westminster W2 p13 . . . . . 020 7262 3814

Bird Wilford & Sale
‡Loughborough p293 . . . . . 01509 232611

Birds Solicitors
‡Wandsworth SW18 p13. . . . . 020 8874 7433

Birdsall & Snowball
‡Scarborough p372 . . . . . 01723 351351
Filey p226 . . . . . 01723 515151

Birdy & Co
‡Wembley p426 . . . . . 020 8900 9112

Biriyok Show Solicitors
‡London SE16 p13 . . . . . 020 7237 4646

John Birkby & Co
‡Oldham p340. . . . . 0161 626 5686

Birkett Long LLP
‡Colchester p197 . . . . . 01206 217300
Chelmsford p186 . . . . . 01245 453800

Birketts LLP
‡Ipswich p262. . . . . 01473 232300
Cambridge p174 . . . . . 01223 326600
Norwich p334. . . . . 01603 232300

Birketts LLP (Wollastons LLP)
Chelmsford p186 . . . . . 01245 211211

Birnberg Peirce & Partners
‡Camden NW1 p13 . . . . . 020 7911 0166

Birol & Co Solicitors
‡London N16 p13 . . . . . 020 7923 4065

Jean Birtwell Solicitor
‡Bury p170 . . . . . 01204 866533

Biscoes
‡Portsmouth p354. . . . . 023 9266 0261
Gosport p232. . . . . 023 9251 2030
Petersfield p348 . . . . . 01730 264799
Portchester p353 . . . . . 023 9237 0634

Waterlooville p423 . . . . . 023 9225 1257
Wickham p431 . . . . . 01329 833249

Bishop & Co
‡New Mills p321. . . . . 01663 746730
Marple p313 . . . . . 0161 427 1441 / 427 5543

Bishop & Light
‡Brighton p159 . . . . . 01273 626288
‡Eastbourne p215. . . . . 01323 434822
‡Hove p254 . . . . . 01273 732733

BISHOP & SEWELL LLP
‡London WC1 p13. . . . . 020 7631 4141

Bishop Akers & Co
‡Swanley p404 . . . . . 01322 660617
Swanley p404 . . . . . 01322 666766

David Bishop & Co
‡Liverpool p286 . . . . . 01704 878421

Bishop Lloyd & Jackson
‡Ealing W5 p13 . . . . . 020 8832 1162

Bishop McBride Olden
‡Cardiff p177 . . . . . 029 2049 0111

Bissmire Fudge & Co
‡Haverfordwest p244 . . . . . 01437 764723
Pembroke Dock p345. . . . . 01646 685501

Bittermann & Wood
‡North Shields p330. . 0191 257 3211 / 259 6806

Bivonas Limited Solicitors
‡London EC3 p13 . . . . . 020 7337 2600

Black & Co
‡Earl Shilton p214. . . . . 01455 844005

Black Graf & Co
‡London NW3 p13. . . . . 020 7586 1141

John Black Solicitors
‡Northwich p333. . . . . 01606 330044
‡Sale p370 . . . . . 0161 972 5999

Black Norman
‡Crosby p203 . . . . . 0151 931 2777

Stephen Black Solicitors
‡Altrincham p116 . . . . . 0161 924 2230

Black Stone Solicitors
‡London SW19 p13

Blackbourn Andrews Limited
‡Shrewsbury p379. . . . . 01743 233255

Blackburn & Co
‡Dorchester p212 . . . . . 01305 858050
‡Fleetwood p226 . . . . . 01253 872238
Thornton Cleveleys p411 . . . . . 01253 853101

Blackfords LLP
‡Croydon p204 . . . . . 020 8686 6232
Cardiff p177 . . . . . 029 2044 4070
London EC4 p13 . . . . . 020 8686 6232
Woking p436 . . . . . 01483 723331

Blackhams Solicitors
‡Birmingham p135. . . . . 0121 233 6900

Blackhurst Budd LLP
‡Blackpool p146. . . . . 01253 629300
Blackpool p146. . . . . 01253 629300
Blackpool p146. . . . . 01253 629300

Blackhurst Swainson Goodier LLP
‡Lancaster p269. . . . . 01524 32471
Preston p356. . . . . 01772 253841

Blackledge & Co
‡Lytham p296 . . . . . 01253 730070

Charles Blacklock & Co
‡Monmouth p318 . . . . . 01600 714444

Blacklocks
‡Brentwood p156 . . . . . 01277 725057

Lionel Blackman
‡Epsom p219 . . . . . 01372 728941

Patrick Blackmore
‡Menai Bridge p314 . . . . .01248 715987 / 714987

Blacks
‡Leeds p271. . . . . 0113 207 0000
Leeds p271. . . . . 0113 207 0000

Blackstone Law Solicitors & Advocates LLP
‡Leeds p271. . . . . 0113 247 3949

Blackstones Solicitors
‡Northwood p333 . . . . . 01923 828244

C A W Blackwell
‡Royston p368. . . . . 01763 243803

Blackwell Sanders Peper Martin LLP
‡London EC1 p13 . . . . . 020 7788 5073

Blackwell-West
‡Ferndown p225. . . . . 01202 892300

Blackwells Solicitors
‡Keighley p263 . . . . . 01535 600005

BlackWhite Solicitors
‡London E15 p13 . . . . . 020 8522 4150

Blain Boland & Co
Willaston p432 . . . . . 0151 327 1301

Blain Boland & Thomas Ltd
‡Ellesmere Port p217 . . . . . 0151 355 2645

Blair Allison & Co
‡Birmingham p135. . . . . 0121 233 2904

Blake Cassels & Graydon LLP
‡London EC4 p13 . . . . . 020 7429 3550

Charlotte Blake
‡London NW5 p13. . . . . 020 7485 4010

Blake Lapthorn
‡Portsmouth p354 . . . . . 023 9222 1122

Chandlers Ford p184 . . . . 023 8090 8090
London EC1 p13 . . . . 020 7405 2000
Oxford p342 . . . . 01865 248607

Blake-Turner & Co
‡London EC3 p14 . . . . 020 7480 6655

Blakeley Solicitors
‡Bradford p153 . . . . 01274 831141

Blakemores
‡Birmingham p135. . . . . 0121 234 7200
Leamington Spa p270 . . . . . . 01926 457300

William Blakeney
‡Westminster WC2 p14 . . . . . 020 7717 8510

Blaker Son & Young
‡Lewes p283 . . . . 01273 480234

Blakestons
‡Driffield p213. . . . . 01377 253476

Blakewater Solicitors Ltd
‡Blackburn p145. . . . . 01254 261515

Blanchards Bailey LLP
‡Blandford Forum p147 . . . . . 01258 459361
Dorchester p212 . . . . 01305 251222
Shaftesbury p374. . . . . 01747 440447
Stalbridge p393. . . . . 01963 363593

Bland & Co Solicitors
‡Luton p295. . . . . 01582 730544

Blandfords
‡London W1 p14 . . . . 020 7935 7373

Blandy & Blandy
‡Reading p360 . . . . 0118 951 6800

Michael Blandy Solicitors
‡Hastings p243 . . . . 01424 712545

Blaser Mills
‡High Wycombe p249. . . . . . . 01494 450171
Amersham p117 . . . . 01494 728021
Aylesbury p120. . . . . 01296 434416
Chesham p189. . . . . 01494 782291
Harrow p241 . . . . 020 8427 6262
Rickmansworth p364 . . . . 01923 776211
Staines p393. . . . . 01784 462511

Blatchfords
‡Harrow p241 . . . . 020 8422 1181

Blavo & Co Solicitors
‡London WC1 p14. . . . . 020 7025 2020
Guildford p235 . . . . 01483 243456
London EC2 p14 . . . . 020 7729 9286
London N3 p14. . . . . 020 8349 8020
St Albans p389. . . . . 01727 732800
Uxbridge p417 . . . . 01895 204848

Blavo & Co Solictors
Enfield p218 . . . . 020 8363 8296

Andrea Bleackley & Co
‡Southport p388. . . . . 01704 500297

Bleasdale & Co
‡Whitehaven p431. . . . . 01946 692165

Blick & Co
‡London E1 p14. . . . . 020 7247 9696

Helen Bligh Employment Law Services
‡Sevenoaks p374 . . . . 01732 458302

Blight Broad & Skinnard
‡Callington p173. . . . . 01579 382213

Blight Skinnard
‡Saltash p371. . . . . 01752 842141

Block Associates Limited
‡Romford p366 . . . . 01708 723399

BLOCKS
‡Ipswich p262. . . . . 01473 230033
Felixstowe p225 . . . . 01394 283241

BLOKH SOLICITORS
‡London W1 p14 . . . . 020 7034 7055

Leonard Blomstrand
‡London SE20 p14 . . . . 020 8776 7707

Julian Bloom & Co
‡Bushey p171 . . . . 020 8950 3001

BGR Bloomer
‡Chester p190. . . 01244 852040 / 0800 180 4169

Blores
‡Henley-on-Thames p247 . . . . . 01491 579265

Blount Hemmings
‡Kingswinford p268 . . . . 01384 400565
Kingswinford p268 . . . . 01384 400565

Bloxhams
‡Leicester p279 . . . . 0116 222 3302

Blue Sky Law
‡Cheadle p185 . . . . 0161 246 6077

Blue Sky Law Limited
‡Manchester p301. . . . . 0161 618 1032

Bluestone & Co
‡London E7 p14. . . . . 020 8470 2266

Bluetts Solicitors
‡Ealing W5 p14 . . . . 0800 157 7574

Andrew C Blundy Solicitors
‡Greenwich SE10 p14. . . . . . 020 8293 3633

Ann Blyth-Cook & Co
‡Southend-on-Sea p387. . . . . . 01702 462999

Blythe Liggins
‡Leamington Spa p270 . . . . . . 01926 831231

Bobbetts Mackan
‡Bristol p161. . . . . 0117 929 9001

Andrew Boddy Solicitors
‡Kettering p265 . . . . 01536 714900

Kevin Bodley
‡Holsworthy p251 . . . . 01409 221460

Bodnar & Co
‡Leeds p271. . . . . 0113 294 4944

Richard Body & Co
‡St Leonards-on-Sea p392 . . . . 01424 201301

Bokhari & Co
‡London W2 p14 . . . . 020 7724 7010

Bolitho Way
‡Portsmouth p354. . . . . 023 9282 0747
Ryde p369 . . . . 01983 817060

Bollin Legal Associates LTD
‡Birmingham p135. . . . . 0121 200 8400
‡Macclesfield p297 . . . . 01625 667150

Bolt Burdon
‡Islington N1 p14 . . . . 020 7288 4700

David Bolton & Associates
‡Cobham p196 . . . . 01932 868074

Bolton-Jones & Co
‡Liverpool p286 . . . . 0151 733 2241

Kevin Bolton Solicitor
‡Manchester p301. . . . . 0161 834 6776

Boltons Solicitors
‡Bolton p148 . . . . 01204 704090

J Bon Solicitors
‡London E6 p14. . . . . 020 8471 8822

Bonallack & Bishop
‡Salisbury p371 . . . . 01722 422300
Amesbury p117. . . . . 01980 622992
Andover p118. . . . . 01264 364433
Verwood p418 . . . . 01202 834450

Bond & Co Solicitors
‡South Croydon p383 . . . . . . 020 8405 0596

A J Bond & Co
‡Bromley p166. . . . . 020 8464 2229

Bond Adams LLP
‡Leicester p279 . . . . 0116 285 8080

Bond Joseph
‡Canterbury p176 . . . . 01227 453545

P R M Bond & Co
‡London WC1 p14. . . . . 020 7242 0058

Bond Pearce LLP
‡Plymouth p349 . . . . 0845 415 0000
Bristol p161. . . . . 0845 415 0000
London EC3 p14 . . . . 0845 415 0000
Southampton p385 . . . . 0845 415 0000

Bond Solicitors
‡London E14 p14 . . . . 020 7513 1113

Bone & Payne LLP
‡Llandudno p291 . . . . 01492 876354
‡Old Colwyn p340. . . . . 01492 515371
Colwyn Bay p198. . . . . 01492 532385

Mark Bone Solicitors
‡Liverpool p286 . . . . 0151 427 6380

Bonell & Co
‡Stratford-upon-Avon p400 . . . . 01789 299115

Bonelli Erede Pappalardo LLP
‡London EC4 p14 . . . . 020 7776 3488

Peter Bonner & Co
‡Lewisham SE13 p14 . . . . . . 020 8297 1727

Bonnetts Solicitors LLP
‡Hounslow p253. . . . . 020 8570 5286
Whitton p431 . . . . 020 8898 2022

Bonningtons Solicitors
‡Harrow p241 . . . . 020 8908 6363

Harry Boodhoo & Co
‡Withington p436 . . . . 0161 445 0588

Boodle Hatfield
‡Westminster W1 p14. . . . . . . 020 7629 7411
Oxford p343 . . . . 01865 790744

Robert A Booker
‡Alton p116 . . . . 01420 83570

Bookers & Bolton
‡Alton p116 . . . . 01420 82881 / 88903

Boote Edgar Esterkin
‡Manchester p301. . . . . 0161 832 7888

C W Booth
Peterlee p347. . . . . 0191 586 7682

C W Booth & Co
‡Bishop Auckland p144 . . . . . . 01388 606660

Booth Ince & Knowles
Denton p208 . . . . 0161 336 7011
Hyde p259 . . . . 0161 368 2134

S Booth & Co
‡Islington N1 p14 . . . . 020 7226 3366

Boothroyds
‡London SE6 p14 . . . . 020 8690 4848

Boots Starke Goacher
‡Crawley p202. . . . . 01293 539789

Geoffrey Borg & Co
‡Ramsgate p359 . . . . 01843 591378

Borg Knight Employment Solicitors
‡Chatham p184 . .01634 757001 / 020 7099 8135
Rochester p366. .01634 757001 / 020 7099 8135

Borlase & Company
‡Helston p246. . . . . 01326 574988

Borneo Hughes Martell LLP
‡Northampton p331 . . . . 01604 624822

Boscos
‡Leeds p271. . . . . 0113 209 1510

D S Bosher & Co
‡Hove p254 . . . . 01273 721913
Peacehaven p345 . . . . 01273 585771

Bosley & Co
‡Brighton p159 . . . . 01273 608181

K Boswell Solicitors
‡Washington p423. . . . . 0191 417 6471

Boswells
‡Windsor p434. . . . . 01753 620888

Bosworths
‡East Molesey p215 . . . . 020 8941 3151

Bott & Company
‡Wilmslow p433 . . . . 01625 415800

Bottrill & Co
‡Pinner p348 . . . . 020 8429 1010

Bottrills Solicitors
‡Barnet p123 . . . . 020 8440 8188 / 8441 1125

Bouchard & Associates
‡London SW6 p14. . . . . 020 7736 1823

Bouchers with Allansons LLP
Manchester p301 . . . . 0161 220 8484

Boulter & Co
Waltham Cross p420 . . . . . . 01992 787811

Boulter & Company
‡London N8 p14. . . . . 020 8340 0222

Arthur Boulton Solicitors
Stoke-on-Trent p397 . . . . . . 01782 813315

Harish C Bouri
‡Newcastle upon Tyne p323. . . . 0191 281 4860

Bourne Jaffa
‡Birmingham p135. . . 0121 443 3486 / 444 8440

Bourne Jaffa & Co
‡Birmingham p135. . . . . 0121 451 3338
‡Birmingham p136. . . . . 0121 451 1661

Bousfield Gaskin McGoin
‡Redcar p362 . . . . 01642 495717

Henry Boustred & Sons
‡London N6 p14. . . . . 020 8348 5223

Bowcock & Pursaill
‡Leek p278 . . . . 01538 399199
Hanley p239 . . . . 01782 200000

Bowcock Cuerden LLP
‡Nantwich p320 . . . . 01270 611106

Bowden Jones Solicitors
‡Cardiff p177 . . . . 029 2048 4550

Bowen Muscatt
‡London W1 p14 . . . . 020 7908 3800

Bowens
‡Hitchin p251 . . . . 01462 441443

Bower & Bailey
‡Oxford p343 . . . . 01865 311133
Banbury p122. . . . . 01295 265566
Swindon p406 . . . . 01793 610466
Witney p436 . . . . 01993 705095

Christine E Bower
‡Twickenham p416 . . . . 020 8898 1615

Bower Conlon
‡Tonbridge p412. . . . . 01732 850318

Bower Cotton Khaitan
‡London EC4 p15 . . . . 020 7353 1313

Bower Harris
‡Manchester p301. . . . . 0161 832 9404

John Bower
‡London NW11 p15 . . . . 020 8455 8366

Bowermans
‡Port Talbot p353 . . . . 01639 891892

Bowers
‡London NW2 p15. . . . . 020 8455 9881

Bowers & Jessup
‡Folkestone p227 . . . . 01303 850678

Eric Bowes & Co
‡Solihull p382 . . . . 0121 744 3691

James Bowie Caton & Co
‡Ferndown p225. . . . . .01202 875646 / 877225

Sabina Bowler-Reed
‡Bristol p161. . . . . 01275 373111

Bowles & Co
‡Epsom p219 . . . . 01372 725241

Bowling & Co
‡London E15 p15 . . . . 020 8221 8000

Bruce Bowling & Co
‡Doncaster p211. . . . . 01302 320607
Doncaster p211

Bowman & Co
‡Newquay p329 . . . . 01637 875065
‡Poole p352. . . . . 01202 716171

Bowman & Drew Limited
‡Sevenoaks p374 . . . . 0845 221 1322

Bowser Ollard & Bentley
‡Wisbech p435 . . . . 01945 583194
March p312. . . . . 01354 652606

Boyce & Co Solicitors
‡Taunton p408. . . . . 01823 210670

Boyce Hatton
‡Torquay p412. . . . . 01803 403403

Boyd Carter
‡Braintree p155 . . . . 01376 555000

Matthew Boyer Solicitors
‡Chagford p184 . . . . 01647 432222

Boyes Sutton & Perry
‡Barnet p123 . . . . 020 8449 9155

Boyes Turner
‡Reading p360 . . . . 0118 959 7711

G Boyle
‡Aylesbury p120. . . . . 01296 630090

John Boyle & Co
‡Redruth p362. . . . . 01209 213507
Truro p414 . . . . 01872 272356

Boys & Maughan
‡Margate p312. . . . . 01843 234000
Birchington p134 . . . . 01843 842356
Broadstairs p166 . . . . 01843 868861
Ramsgate p359. . . . . 01843 595990

Brabners Chaffe Street
‡Liverpool p286 . . . . 0151 600 3000
Manchester p301. . . . . 0161 836 8800
Preston p356 . . . . 01772 823921

Bracewell & Giuliani LLP
‡London EC4 p15 . . . . 020 3159 4220

Bracher Rawlins LLP
‡London WC1 p15. . . . . 020 7404 9400

Brachers
‡Maidstone p299 . . . . 01622 690691

Bradberrys
‡Hayes p245 . . . . 020 8813 6962

BRADBURY ROBERTS & RABY
‡Scunthorpe p373. . . . . 01724 854000

Bradbury Steed
‡Littlehampton p285 . . . . 01903 717048

Braddon & Snow
‡Hoddesdon p251 . . . . 01992 464552

Bradford & Co
‡Nailsea p320 . . . . . . .01275 856302 / 856303
Bristol p161. . . . . 0117 963 5261

Bradin Trubshaw & Kirwan Solicitors LLP
‡Lichfield p284. . . . . 01543 421840

Aboudi Bradley & Co
‡Macclesfield p297 . . . . 01625 428749

Bradley & Jefferies Solicitors Limited
‡Derby p208. . . . . 01332 221722

Andrew Bradley
‡Basingstoke p126 . . . . 01256 478119

Helen M Bradley
‡Stockbridge p395. . . . . 01264 860200

J Patrick F Bradley
‡London W4 p15 . . . . 020 7024 3624

Bradley Saul Solicitors
‡Chipping Norton p193 . . . . . . 01608 648020

Bradleys
‡Dover p212. . . . . 01304 204080

Bradly Trimmer
‡Alton p116 . . . . 01420 88024

Bradshaw Hollingsworth Solicitors
‡Leicester p279 . . . . 0116 204 2500

Bradshaws Hamer Park & Haworth
‡Lytham p296 . . . . . . .01253 724251 / 728451
Blackpool p146. . . . . 01253 621531

Bradwell & Co Solicitors Limited
‡Leeds p271. . . . . 0113 242 1000

Brady Eastwood Pierce & Stewart
‡Lewisham SE8 p15. . . . . . . 020 8692 8181
Dartford p207. . . . . 020 8692 8181

Mark Brady Law LLP
‡London W1 p15 . . . . 020 7099 5936

Brady Solicitors
‡Nottingham p336. . . . . 0115 985 3450

Braidwood Law Practice Solicitors
‡Croydon p204 . . . . 020 8726 7926

Braikenridge & Edwards
‡Barnet p123 . . . . . 020 8449 1171 / 8441 7862

Brain Chase Coles
‡Basingstoke p126 . . . . 01256 354481

Brain Sinnott & Co
‡Kingswood p268 . . . . 0117 960 6880
Bristol p161. . . . . 0117 965 1030

Brains
‡St Austell p391 . . . . 01726 68111
Truro p414 . . . . 01872 276363

Bramhall Solicitors
‡Bramhall p155 . . . . 0161 439 9777

Bramhalls
‡Chester p190. . . . 01244 888002 / 07843 472356
‡Neston p321 . . . . 0151 336 7616

Bramsdon & Childs
‡Southsea p388. . . . . 023 9282 1251

Bramwell Browne Odedra
‡Chesham p189. . . . . 01494 782244

Brand & Co
‡Cheam p185 . . . . 020 8641 2771

Andrew C N Brand
‡Swindon p406 . . . . 01285 810328

C M Brand
‡Heswall p249. . . . . 0151 342 3081

Kenneth Brand & Co
‡London NW4 p15. . . . . 020 8202 6751

Brand Mellon LLP
‡Gloucester *p230* 01452 524088
Cheltenham *p187* 01242 227266

Robert Brand & Co
‡Westminster W1 *p15* 020 7935 2408

Henri Brandman & Co
‡London W1 *p15* 020 7224 0616

Brandsworth
‡London N5 *p15* 07919 575020

Branton Bridge
‡Salford *p370* 0161 834 2888

Brar & Co
‡Newcastle upon Tyne *p323* 0191 276 6880

Brasiers Law
‡Birmingham *p136* 0845 130 8455

Braund & Fedrick
Sidcup *p380* 020 8300 6515

Bray & Bray
‡Leicester *p279* 0116 254 8871
Hinckley *p250* 01455 639900
Market Harborough *p312* 01858 467181

Bray & Dilks
‡Truro *p414* 01872 271717
Falmouth *p223* 01326 212021

Bray & Krais Solicitors
‡London SW6 *p15* 020 7384 3050

Richard Bray & Co
‡London WC2 *p15* 020 7497 3561

Frank Brazell & Partners
‡London N1 *p15* 020 7689 8989

Ian F Brazier Solicitors
‡Dorchester *p212* 01308 898682

Breakthrough Family Law Solutions
‡Chesham *p189* 01494 776696

Breakwells
‡Birmingham *p136* 0121 222 2606

Jayne Brearley & Co Solicitors
‡Todmorden *p412* . . . . 01706 812926 / 817755

John S Brearley
‡High Wycombe *p249* 01494 512775

Peter Brearley & Co
‡Leeds *p272* 0113 259 1761

Brearleys
‡Brighouse *p158* 01484 714400

Brearleys Solicitors
‡Batley *p128* 01924 473065
Birstall *p144* 01924 443900
Cleckheaton *p195* 01274 864002

Brecher
‡London W1 *p15* 020 7563 1000

Breedy Handerson LLP
‡London W1 *p15* 020 7268 2260

Breedy Henderson LLP
‡London NW3 *p15* . 020 7419 4135 / 07841 094160

Breens Solicitors
‡Southport *p388* 01704 532890
Liverpool *p286* 0151 928 6544

Breese-Gwyndaf
‡Porthmadog *p353* . . . . 01766 512253 / 514227
Barmouth *p123* 01341 280317
Harlech *p239* 01766 780334

Breeze & Wyles Solicitors LLP
‡Hertford *p248* 01992 558411
Bishop's Stortford *p144* 01279 715333
Cheshunt *p189* 01992 642333
Enfield *p218* 020 8366 6411

Brennans Solicitors
‡Wallsend *p419* 0191 262 5133

M M E Brenninkmeyer
‡London W1 *p15* 020 7917 1897

Bretherton Law
‡St Albans *p389* 01727 869293

Brethertons LLP
‡Rugby *p368* 01788 579579
Banbury *p122* 01295 270999
Rugby *p368* 01788 551611
Rugby *p368* 01788 579579

Alastair J Brett
‡London SW6 *p15* 020 7736 0071

R M Brett & Co
‡Cardiff *p177* 029 2023 0440

Brett Wilson LLP
‡London EC1 *p15* 020 7183 8950

Bretts Solicitors
‡Chelmsford *p186* 01245 401233

Brevitts
‡Birmingham *p136* 0121 472 4131

Brewer Harding & Rowe
‡Barnstaple *p125* 01271 342271
Barnstaple *p125* 01271 342271
Bideford *p132* 01237 472666
Braunton *p156* 01271 812033
Ilfracombe *p261* 01271 863495

Breydons Solicitors
‡Great Yarmouth *p234* 01493 331057

Brian Ruff Angus & Jewers
‡Wickford *p431* 01268 761126

Brice & Co
‡Bristol *p161* 0117 973 7484
‡Bures *p168* 01787 227199
‡Colchester *p197* 01206 710168

Brice Droogleever & Co
‡Kensington & Chelsea SW3 *p15*
. . . . 020 7730 9925 / 7730 7231

Bridge Burke Solicitors
‡Kingston upon Thames *p267* . . . 020 8972 8018

Bridge McFarland
‡Grimsby *p235* 01472 311711
Grimsby *p235* 01472 311711
Grimsby *p235* 01472 311711
Hull *p256* 01482 320620
Lincoln *p284* 01522 518888
Mablethorpe *p297* 01507 478285
Market Rasen *p312* 01673 843723
Skegness *p380* 01754 762266

Bridge McFarland Haddon Owen
Louth *p294* 01507 605883

Bridge Sanderson Munro
‡Doncaster *p211* 01302 321621
Thorne *p411* 01405 814136
Wath-upon-Dearne *p424* 01709 873321

Bridgehouse Partners
‡Bicester *p132* 01869 243457

Bridgehouse Partners LLP
‡Birmingham *p136* 0121 314 0000
‡London W1 *p15* 020 7851 7160
Birmingham *p136* 0121 233 0919

Bridgeman Kettle
‡Bletchley *p147* 01908 376321

Derrick Bridges & Co
‡Barnet *p123* 020 8449 7326

ELLIOTT BRIDGMAN
‡Telford *p409* 01952 684544

Graham Bridgman & Co
‡Reading *p360* 0118 933 1818

Bridle Hathaway
‡Enderby *p218* 0116 239 4014

Jonathan Brierly
‡Penarth *p345* 029 2071 2230

Briffa
‡Islington N1 *p15* 020 7288 6003

David Briggs & Co
‡London SW3 *p15* 020 7823 9040

Briggs Sayer & Co
‡Belper *p130* 01773 825246
Ripley *p364* 01773 744011

Brighouse Wolff
‡Ormskirk *p341* 01695 573202
Maghull *p298* 0151 520 2717
Skelmersdale *p381* 01695 722577
Skelmersdale *p381* 01695 717000

Brighouses
‡Southport *p388* . . . . . 01704 534101 / 500151

Bright & Sons
‡Maldon *p299* 01621 852323
Witham *p435* 01376 512338

Keith B Bright
‡Sutton Coldfield *p403* 0121 351 6296

Bright (South West) LLP
‡Plymouth *p349* 01752 388884

Brightlaw Limited
‡Worthing *p441* 0345 652 2201

Brightley Commercial
‡Newquay *p329* 01872 519087

Brightstone Law LLP
‡Elstree *p218* 020 8731 3080

Brightway Solicitors
‡London SE18 *p15* 020 8309 8808

Brigid Turner & Co Ltd
‡Daventry *p207* 01327 263950

Brignalls Balderston Warren
‡Stevenage *p394* 01438 359311
Baldock *p121* 01462 490100
Biggleswade *p133* 01767 313813
Knebworth *p269* 01438 812374
Letchworth *p283* 01462 482248

Brimble & Co
‡Halifax *p238* 01422 322121

Brindles Solicitors
‡Tonbridge *p412* 01732 852688

BRINDLEY TWIST TAFFT & JAMES
‡Coventry *p200* 024 7653 1532
Birmingham *p136* 0121 214 8989

Stephen D Brine Solicitors
‡Liverpool *p286* 0151 734 5000

Brinley Morris Rees & Jones
‡Llanelli *p292* 01554 774241

David Brinning
‡Cardiff *p177* 029 2039 7364

Brion & Co
‡London WC1 *p15* 020 7831 5556

Bristows
‡London EC4 *p15* 020 7400 8000

Britannia Law Practice
‡Birmingham *p136* 0121 356 3030

John Britten Law Limited
‡Nottingham *p336* 0115 910 0200

Britton & Co
‡Weston-super-Mare *p429* 01934 522000

Oliver Britton
‡Potters Bar *p355* 01707 660375

Brittons
‡Bourne End *p151* 01628 533350
Beaconsfield *p128* 01494 730722

C M Broadbent
‡Macclesfield *p297* 01625 500038

Broadbents
‡Alfreton *p115* 01773 832511
Chesterfield *p192* 01246 540955
Derby *p208* 01332 369090
Heanor *p246* 01773 769891
Mansfield *p311* 01623 412870
Sutton-in-Ashfield *p404* 01623 441123

Broadbridge Grimes & Solicitors
‡London SW19 *p16* 020 8545 1480

Broadgate Legal
‡London EC2 *p16* 020 7856 2406

Broadway Solicitors
‡Oldham *p340* 0161 669 6179

Broadway Solictors
‡Wandsworth SW17 *p16* 020 8767 7718

Brockbank Curwen Cain & Hall
‡Whitehaven *p431* 01946 692194
Cockermouth *p197* 01900 827222
Maryport *p313* 01900 813488
Workington *p440* 01900 603563

Brockington Carroll
‡Godalming *p231* 01252 703770

Brocklesby & Co
‡London SW19 *p16* 020 8540 9966

Brockmans
‡Stockbridge *p395* 01264 810910

Brodie & Company Limited
‡Manchester *p302* 0161 829 3900

Brodie Smith & Mahoney
‡Cardiff *p177* . . . . 029 2022 1848 / 2022 7680

Bromets Jackson Heath
‡Tadcaster *p407* 01937 832371

John Bromfield & Company Ltd
‡Nuneaton *p339* 024 7638 2343

Bromiley Holcroft & Co
‡Southport *p388* 0870 236 0000

Bromleys Solicitors LLP
‡Ashton-under-Lyne *p120* 0161 330 6821
Manchester *p302* 0161 932 1572

Bromptons
‡London W8 *p16* 020 7937 0005

Brook Martin & Co
‡Westminster W1 *p16* 020 7935 8520

Brook Oliver
New Milton *p321* 01425 616809

W Brook & Co
‡Goldthorpe *p231* 01709 898697

Brooke North LLP
‡Leeds *p272* 0113 283 2100
London W1 *p16* 0870 120 8336

Brooke Williams
‡York *p444* 01904 677888
Bridlington *p158* 01262 409409
Hull *p256* 01482 610886
Leeds *p272* 0113 246 8400

Brooke-Taylors
‡Buxton *p172* 01298 22741

ROGER BROOKER & CO
‡Chelmsford *p186* 01245 351924

Brookes & Co
‡Chichester *p192* 01243 780333
‡London EC3 *p16* 020 7621 0067

Brooklyn Solicitors
‡Harrow *p241* 020 8861 4004

Brookman
‡London WC1 *p16* 020 7430 8470

Brooks
‡Shipston-on-Stour *p378* 01608 664406

Brooks & Co
‡Fetcham *p226* 01372 362042
London WC1 *p16* 020 7887 1437

A F Brooks & Co
‡Stoke-on-Trent *p397* 01782 415007

A H Brooks & Co
‡Leek *p278* 01538 383201
Cheadle *p185* 01538 754253

Brooks & Partners
‡Camberley *p173* 01276 681217

Jane Brooks Law
‡Hull *p256* 01482 893366

Lawrence Brooks
‡Cranbrook *p202* 01580 715175

Roger Brooks & Co
‡Leek *p278* 01538 385656

Brooks Solicitors
‡Chesterfield *p192* 01246 220552
‡Shipley *p378* 01274 596724

Brooks Suleman Solicitors LLP
‡Birmingham *p136* 0121 384 5768

Brookson Legal Services
‡Warrington *p421* . 0845 058 1500 / 01925 235704

BrookStreet des Roches LLP
‡Abingdon *p114* 01235 836600

Broome Palmer Solicitors
‡London SW19 *p16* 020 8944 0343

Broomhall & Co
‡Birmingham *p136* 0121 633 4868

Broomhead & Saul
‡Taunton *p408* 01823 288121
Ilminster *p261* 01460 57056

Bross Bennett
‡London N6 *p16* 020 8340 0444

N C Brothers & Co
‡Reading *p360* 0118 958 9966

P H Brothwell
‡Folkestone *p227* 01303 253368

Broudie Jackson Canter
Liverpool *p286* 0151 227 1429

Brough Hall & Co
‡Skegness *p380* 01754 768641

Michael Brough and Cohen
‡Beaconsfield *p128* 01494 680420

Browell Smith & Co
‡Newcastle upon Tyne *p323* 0871 474 3030
Ashington *p119* 0871 474 3030
Cramlington *p201* 0871 474 3030
Newcastle upon Tyne *p323* 0871 474 3030
Newcastle upon Tyne *p323* 0871 474 3030
Stockton-on-Tees *p396* 0871 474 3030
Stoke-on-Trent *p397* 0871 474 3030
Sunderland *p401* 0871 474 3030

Brown & Co
‡Basildon *p126* 01268 243610
‡Chalfont St Giles *p184* 01494 874175

Brown & Company
‡Market Harborough *p312* 01858 434204

Brown & Corbishley
‡Newcastle under Lyme *p323* . . . 01782 717888
Sandbach *p371* 01270 768033

Brown & Emery
‡Watford *p423* 01923 225255

Brown & Murray
Millom *p316* 01229 772562

Brown & Vautier
‡Frome *p227* 01373 465222

A R Brown & Co
‡Worthing *p441* 01903 237118

Anne Brown Solicitors
‡London N21 *p16* 020 8364 2121

Brown Barron
‡Barrow-in-Furness *p125* 01229 828814

BROWN BEER NIXON MALLON
‡Redcar *p362* 01642 490202
Middlesbrough *p315* 01642 254182

Charles Brown Solicitors
‡Sutton *p402* 020 8722 8868

Colin Brown & Kidson
‡Whitby *p430* 01947 603391

Dennis Brown Solicitors
‡Colchester *p197* 01206 505060

Gordon Brown Associates
‡Chester-le-Street *p191* 0191 388 1778
Newcastle upon Tyne *p324* 0191 388 1778

Brown Holliday & Clements
‡North Shields *p330* 0191 257 0431

J E Brown & Co
‡Keighley *p263* 01535 653311

J R Brown & Co
‡Clevedon *p195* 01275 879292

Laurence Brown Solicitor
‡London W2 *p16* 020 7792 9727

Michael A Brown & Co
‡Rhyl *p363* 01745 332722

Peter Brown & Co Solicitors LLP
‡Barnet *p124* 020 8447 3277

Philip Brown & Co
‡London W1 *p16* . . . 020 7935 7235 / 7935 7270

Richard Brown & Co
‡Peterborough *p346* 0870 850 3062

Brown Rudnick Berlack Israels LLP
‡London W1 *p16* 020 7851 6000

Thomas Lindsey Brown & Co
‡Southend-on-Sea *p387* 01702 466266

Brown Turner Ross
‡Liverpool *p287* 0151 236 2233
‡Southport *p388* 01704 542002

W J H Brown
‡Richmond upon Thames *p364* . . 020 8332 1566

William H Brown
‡Harwich *p243* 01255 503125

Yvonne Brown & Co
‡London N10 *p16* . . . . . 020 8444 7254 / 8171

Brown-Hovelt Veale Nelson
‡Grayshott *p233* 01428 607433

Henry Browne Solicitors
‡Birmingham *p136* 0121 765 3332

Browne Jacobson LLP
‡Nottingham *p336* 0115 976 6000
Birmingham *p136* 0121 237 3900
London EC3 *p16* 020 7539 4900

Paul Browne
‡Oakham *p339* 01572 757565

Peter Browne
‡Bristol *p161* 0117 944 1966

Browner Milne-Davidson
‡Tavistock *p408* 01822 617666

Browning & Co
‡Looe *p293* 01503 262119 / 262129

Browns
‡Burnham *p168* 01628 660440
‡Marlow *p313* 01628 476988
Amersham *p117* 01494 723535
Aylesbury *p120* 01296 338633
Beaconsfield *p128* 01494 677771 / 677021
Bourne End *p151* 01628 531800
High Wycombe *p249* 01494 716171
High Wycombe *p249* 01494 452211
Maidenhead *p298* 01628 672767
Princes Risborough *p358* 01844 344123
Thame *p410* 01844 260800

Browns Solicitors
‡Bromley *p166* 020 7831 8111

Browns Solicitors Limited
‡Bradford *p153* 01274 778000

Fiona Bruce & Co LLP
‡Warrington *p421* 01925 263273

Bruce McGregor & Co Solicitors
‡Teddington *p408* 020 8977 4435

Bruffell Williams Solicitors
‡Guildford *p235* 01483 511108

Brumell & Sample
‡Morpeth *p319* 01670 512336

Brunswick Law
‡Westerham *p428* 01959 561515 / 563163

Brunswicks LLP
‡Birkenhead *p134* 0870 766 8400

Brunton & Co
‡Aberystwyth *p114* 01970 612567 / 617931
Machynlleth *p298* 01654 703110 / 703121

Brutton & Co
‡Fareham *p223* 01329 236171

BRYAN & ARMSTRONG
‡Mansfield *p311* 01623 626039
Mansfield *p311* 01623 624505

BRYAN & CO SOLICITORS
‡Middlesbrough *p315* 01642 322928

Bryan & Mercer
‡St Albans *p389* 01727 861414

Andrew Bryce & Co
‡Cambridge *p174* 01223 437011

David Bryson Solicitor
‡Newcastle upon Tyne *p324* 0191 209 3461

Paul Bryson Solicitor
‡Hyde *p259* 01457 763340

Buchanan & Llewellyn
‡Ferndown *p225* 01202 873355
Westbourne *p428* 01202 752525

Buchanans Solicitors
‡High Wycombe *p250* 01628 810707

David Buck & Co
‡Brighton *p159* 01273 621745

Buckles Solicitors LLP
‡Peterborough *p346* 01733 888888
Stamford *p393* 01780 484570

Charles Buckley
‡Altrincham *p116* 0161 928 2439

Bucks Solicitors
‡Aylesbury *p120* 01296 331600
‡High Wycombe *p250* 01494 530303

Bude Nathan Iwanier
‡London NW11 *p16* 020 8458 5656

Bude Storz
‡Hackney N16 *p16* 020 8800 2800

Vincent Buffoni & Co
‡Islington N1 *p16* 020 7251 8484

Buglear Bate & Co
‡Woking *p436* 01483 715527 / 724246

Bukhari & Co Solicitors Limited
‡Nelson *p320* 01282 611234

BULCRAIGS
‡Wandsworth SW18 *p16*
020 8870 2207 / 8877 0531

Bulfin & Co Employment Law Solicitors
‡Pinner *p348* 020 8866 0044

Bull & Bull
‡Canterbury *p176* 01227 714860
Faversham *p225* 01795 534553
Herne Bay *p248* 01227 742660

Bull & Co
‡Andover *p118* 01264 352495

Paul Bullen & Co
‡Doncaster *p211* 01302 819000

Buller Jeffries
‡Birmingham *p136* 0121 212 2620
Coventry *p200* 024 7622 8734

Bullivant & Partners
‡London EC4 *p16* 020 7332 8250

Bunce-Linsell
‡Wembley *p426* 020 8904 2229

Bunce Solicitors
‡Ruislip *p368* 020 8582 0150

The Bundle Business Ltd
‡Kendal *p264* 01539 729441

David Bunn & Co
‡Birmingham *p136* 0121 476 8481
Birmingham *p136* 0121 441 3322
Birmingham *p136* 0121 459 9714

A Bunning Solicitor
‡Broseley *p167* 01952 883688

Bunting & Riley
‡Buxton *p172* 01298 767495

Burch Phillips & Co
‡West Drayton *p427* 01895 442141

Burchell Williams Limited
‡Brighton *p159* 01273 606555

David Burcher & Co
‡London NW2 *p16* 020 8452 4127

Burd Ward Solicitors
‡Wallasey *p419* 0151 639 8273

Stephen Burdon Solicitors
‡Nottingham *p336* 0115 950 0054

Harriet Burge Solicitors
‡Stowmarket *p399* 01449 710308

Burges Salmon
‡Bristol *p161* 0117 939 2000

Carole Burgher
‡Birmingham *p136* 0121 449 2002

Burgoyne & Co
‡Walsall *p420* 01922 616916

Burke & Co
Bristol *p161* 0117 931 4499

Burketts Solicitors
‡Southend-on-Sea *p387*
01702 462 323 / 07957 241939

Burkill Govier
‡Farnham *p224* 01252 717171

Burley & Geach
‡Petersfield *p348* 01730 262401
Grayshott *p233* 01428 605355
Haslemere *p243* 01428 656011
Liphook *p285* 01428 722334

F E Burlingham Johnson
‡Hove *p254* 01273 748555

Ian Burlingham Solicitor
‡Basingstoke *p126*

Robin Burman & Co
‡Manchester *p302* 0161 860 7123

Burn & Co
‡Wheathampstead *p430* 01438 833446

Andrew Burn Solicitors
‡Stourbridge *p399* 01384 826361

Simon Burn Solicitors
‡Birmingham *p136* 0121 371 0301
‡Cheltenham *p187* 01242 228444

Burnand Brazier Tisdall
‡Hove *p254* 01273 734022
Worthing *p441* 01903 502155
Worthing *p441* 01903 235002

Burnett Barker
‡Bury St Edmunds *p171* 01284 701131

Burnetts
‡Carlisle *p181* 01228 552222
Carlisle *p182* 01228 552222
Newcastle upon Tyne *p324* 0191 300 1833
Whitehaven *p431* 01946 550250

Burney Legal Solicitors
‡Woodford *p439* 020 8551 2211

Derek A Burnham
‡Leicester *p279* 01664 424517

Burningham & Brown
‡Bath *p127* 01225 320090

Burnley-Jones Bate & Co
‡London SW19 *p16* 020 8542 8101

Burr Sugden
‡Keighley *p263* 01535 605407

Burrell Jenkins
‡Cannock *p176* 01543 505040

Burroughs
‡Maidstone *p299* 01622 676976 / 676982

BURROWS
‡Harrow *p241* 020 8904 7725 / 8904 4150

Burrows Bussin
‡Manchester *p302* 0161 833 1411

Burstalls
‡Hull *p256* 01482 621800

Don Burstow Solicitor
‡Horsham *p253* 01403 891660

Burstow Law Solicitors
‡Horley *p252* 01342 844215

Burt Brill & Cardens
‡Brighton *p159* 01273 604123
‡East Grinstead *p215* 01342 306288
‡Worthing *p441* 01903 235196

Burt Staples & Maner LLP
‡London EC4 *p16* 020 7353 4722

Burton & Burton Solicitors LLP
‡Nottingham *p336* 0845 094 2500
Nottingham *p336*

Burton & Co LLP
‡Lincoln *p284* 01522 523215
Sleaford *p381* 01529 306008 / 306009

Burton & Dyson
‡Gainsborough *p228* 01427 610761

Burton Burton & Ho LLP
‡Leeds *p272* 0113 297 8787

C R Burton & Co
‡London SE20 *p16* 020 8778 4455 / 8659 5775

Burton Copeland LLP
‡Manchester *p302* 0161 827 9500
Sale *p370* 0161 905 8530

John Burton Solicitors
‡Stone *p398* 01785 814818

Julie Burton
‡Bangor *p122* 01248 364750

Burton Stancliffe & Co
‡Thatcham *p410* 01635 867967

Burton Woolf & Turk
‡London EC1 *p16* 020 7831 6478

BURTONS
‡Pembury *p345* 01892 824577

Burtonwoods
‡London WC1 *p16* 020 7636 2448

BURY & WALKERS LLP
‡Barnsley *p124* 01226 733533
Leeds *p272* 0113 244 4227
Wombwell *p438* 01226 753433

BUSBYS SOLICITORS
‡Bude *p168* 01288 359000

Kenneth Bush
‡King's Lynn *p266* 01553 692737
King's Lynn *p266* 01553 692233

Business Lawyers Limited
‡High Wycombe *p250* 0845 130 6608

Business Property Law LLP
‡Manchester *p302* 0161 209 3760

Buss Murton LLP
‡Tunbridge Wells *p415* 01892 510222
Cranbrook *p202* 01580 712215
Dartford *p207* 01322 220235

Martin Busst & Co
‡Bangor *p122* 01248 355564

Butcher & Barlow LLP
‡Bury *p170* 0161 764 4062
Bramhall *p155* 0161 439 8228
Bury *p170* 0161 764 5141
Frodsham *p227* 01928 733871
Leigh *p281* 01942 674144
Northwich *p333* 01606 47523
Prestwich *p357* 0161 773 2969
Runcorn *p369* 01928 572268
Runcorn *p369* 01928 576056
Sandbach *p372* 01270 762521
Tyldesley *p416* 01942 883669

Butcher Andrews
‡Fakenham *p223* 01328 863131
Holt *p251* 01263 712023

Butcher Burns LLP
‡London WC1 *p16* 020 7713 7100

Butcher Mcphee Solicitors
‡Blackpool *p146* 01253 892888

Alan Buthee & Co
‡Northampton *p331* 01604 622301

Butler & Co
‡Oakham *p340* 01572 737740
‡Taunton *p408* 01823 323665

Butler & Kandler
‡Ilkley *p261* 01943 816207

Caroline Butler
‡Midhurst *p316* 01730 816782

Clive Butler
‡London SW6 *p16* 020 7731 2281

Butler Hall & Co
‡Birmingham *p136* 0121 456 3171

Malcolm Butler & Co
‡Maidstone *p299* 01622 749596
Walsall *p420* 01922 704048

Ronald Butler
‡Camborne *p173* 01209 716620

Thomas Butler & Son
‡Broughton-in-Furness *p167* 01229 716336
Millom *p316* 01229 772553

Butt Solicitors
‡Luton *p295* 01582 413471

Butters David Grey & Co
‡Hastings *p243* 01424 424949 / 715171

J G Butterworth
‡Mold *p318* 07984 167453

Butterworths
‡Bolton *p148* 01204 678334
‡Carlisle *p182* 01228 593939
‡Carlisle *p182* 01228 516400
Penrith *p346* 01768 868989

James Button & Co
‡Matlock *p313* 01629 735566

Button Legal LLP
‡Coventry *p200* 024 7652 5457

Buxleys Services Limited
‡Royston *p368* 01763 838471

Richard Buxton
‡Cambridge *p174* 01223 328933

Buxton Ryan & Co Solicitors
‡Harlow *p239* 01279 420288

Martin Byne
‡Bristol *p161* 0117 973 1019

Bynes
‡Torquay *p412* 01803 295692

Byrne & Co
‡Southport *p388* 01704 545912

Byrne & Partners
‡London EC4 *p16* 020 7842 1616

Byrne Frodsham & Co
‡Widnes *p431* 0151 424 5601

John Byrne & Co
‡Cambridge *p174* 01223 370063

M M Byrne Solicitor
‡Nuneaton *p339* 01455 292124

The Byrne Practice
‡Doncaster *p211* 01302 711211

Byron Fearn
‡Dunstable *p214* 01582 605822

Byrt & Co Solicitors
‡London WC2 *p16* 020 7745 7337

Bywaters Topham Phillips LLP
‡Harrogate *p240* 01423 879556

C

C&C Family Law
‡Plymouth *p349* 01752 222211

C&G Solicitors
‡Deeside *p208* 01244 821255

C&P Solicitors
‡Chorley *p194* 0845 601 2101

C&S Solicitors
‡Kidderminster *p265* 0845 272 0066
Bewdley *p131* 01562 752199

CAG Solicitors
‡Chobham *p193* 01276 488082

CA Law
‡Doncaster *p211* 01302 347755

C A Legal
London SW1 *p16*

CAS Law Limited
‡London SW17 *p17* 07786 272579

CB4law
‡Cambridge *p174* 01223 316666

CB Law Solicitors
‡Leicester *p279* 0116 254 5566

CB Legal
‡Camden WC1 *p17* 020 7323 9192

CBY Solicitors
‡Exeter *p220* 01404 822452

CCW Law Solicitors Limited
‡Ammanford *p117* 01269 851905

CCW Solicitors
‡Spalding *p389* 01775 718669

CE Law
‡Prescot *p355* 0151 670 0456

CFB Partnership
‡London E11 *p17* 020 8532 9911

CFK Legal
‡Liverpool *p287* 0151 708 6222

CGM
‡Southampton *p385* 023 8063 2733

CIPIT Solicitors
‡London NW3 *p17* 020 8457 7457

CJ Associates
‡London W1 *p17*

CJH Solicitors
‡Derby *p208* 01332 362509

CKFT
‡London NW3 *p17* 020 7431 7262

CKM Solicitors
‡Durham *p214* 0191 384 9080
Consett *p199* 01207 509020

C K Solicitors
‡London E11 *p17* 020 8536 9911
Ilford *p259* 020 3285 8988

CK Solicitors
‡Chichester *p192* 01243 603393

CLB Lawyers (Caswell Lane Bowater Solicitors)
‡Dudley *p213* 01384 451731
Dudley *p213* 01384 451731

CL Law
‡Hounslow *p253* 020 8577 1222

CL Management Solutions Limited
‡Brackley *p153* 01280 702605

CLS Services
‡London E14 *p17*

CMG Law
‡Bolton *p148* 01204 467400

CMHT Solicitors
‡Walsall *p420* 01922 646400
Brownhills *p167* 01543 372347
Walsall *p420* 01922 743525

CMS Cameron McKenna LLP
‡London EC1 *p17* 020 7367 3000
Bristol *p162* 0117 930 0200
London EC3 *p17* 020 7367 3000

C M Solicitors
‡Middlesbrough *p315* 01642 242996

CM Solicitors
‡Manchester *p302* 0845 094 4544

C NICHOLLS
‡Bodmin *p148* 01208 76969

CRM Law LLP
‡Sutton *p402* 020 8661 1177

CRS Solicitors Limited
‡Altrincham *p116* 0161 980 8500

C-Rey Conveyancing
‡Shaftesbury *p374* 01747 812263

CSL Associates
‡Slough *p381* 01753 245546

CS Law
‡Harrow *p241* 020 8901 4089

CVC Solicitors
‡Penzance *p346* 01736 362313
Hayle *p245* 01736 752246
St Ives *p392* 01736 795456

CVS Solicitors
‡London W1 *p17* 020 7493 2903

CW Law Solicitors Limited
‡Bristol *p162* 0845 604 7298

John F S Cabot
‡London SW6 *p17* 020 7384 9583

Cadge & Gilbert
‡Bungay *p168* 01986 893134
Loddon *p292* . . . . . . .01508 520361 / 520362

Cadmans Law & Property
‡Cleckheaton *p195* 01274 874231

Cadwalader Wickersham & Taft
‡London WC2 *p17* 020 7170 8700

Cahill De Fonseka Solicitors
‡London SW19 *p17* 020 7998 3488

Cahill Gordon & Reindel
‡London EC2 *p17* 020 7920 9800

Cains Advocates Limited
‡London EC2 *p17* 020 7367 0030

Caj Solicitors
‡Winchester *p433* 01962 877100

Caladashins
‡Ealing W13 *p17* 020 8832 9000

James Calderbank
‡Cullompton *p205* 01823 680697

Caldicott Gallimore
‡Leominster *p282* 01568 614168
Hereford *p247* 01432 261200

Cale Solicitors
‡London SE10 *p17* 020 8694 2269

Calibre Solicitors Limited
‡Manchester *p302* 0870 458 4418

Caliskan Carter Solicitors
‡London EC1 *p17* 020 7239 8291

Callaghan & Co
‡Westminster W1 *p17* 020 7486 8173

Callaghans
‡Farnham *p224* 01252 723477

Robert Callen Solicitors
‡Pinner *p348* 020 8966 9777

Callistes
‡Lambeth SW2 *p17* 020 7501 8388
London EC4 *p17* 020 7936 9033
London W1 *p17* 020 3402 2139

Calow & Co
‡Reigate *p363* 01737 248480

Calthorpe Solicitors
‡Birmingham *p136* 0121 452 4955

Calthrops
‡Spalding *p389* 01775 724381
Holbeach *p251* 01406 422621

John B Calver & Co
‡Westminster W2 *p17* 020 7221 9181

Calvert Smith & Sutcliffe
‡Richmond upon Thames *p364* . . 020 8940 0017

Calvert Solicitors
‡Southwark SE1 *p17* 020 7234 0707

Stanley M Calvert
‡North Shields *p330* 0191 258 1528

Calyon
‡London EC2 *p18* 020 7214 5000

Camacom Law Solicitors Ltd
‡Ickenham *p259* 01895 678314

Cambridge Family Law Practice LLP
‡Cambridge *p174* 01223 443333

Cameron Deacon LLP
‡London EC3 *p18* 020 7621 2214

Cameron Jones Hussell & Howe
‡Port Talbot *p353* 01639 885261

Cameron Solicitors
‡Berkhamsted *p131* 01442 870303
‡Leighton Buzzard *p282* 01525 300370

Cameron Taylor
‡London SE1 *p18*

Camerons Jones
‡Harrow *p241* 020 8423 6666

Camerons Solicitors LLP
‡London W1 *p18* 020 7866 6010

Camidge & Co
‡Leeds *p272* 0113 245 7859

Camilla Baldwin
‡London W9 *p18* 020 7286 5189

Andrew Campbell & Co
‡Hemel Hempstead *p246* 01442 355215

Campbell Chambers
‡London EC1 *p18* 020 7691 8777

Campbell Commercial Law
‡London EC4 *p18* 020 7489 7771

Campbell Courtney & Cooney
‡Camberley *p173* 01276 25100

Fiona Campbell
‡Kensington & Chelsea W11 *p18* . 020 7243 1982

Campbell Hooper & Co LLP
‡Sunningdale *p402* 01344 622141

Campbell Law Solicitors
‡Milton Keynes *p316* 0845 226 8118

Lisa Campbell Solicitor
‡Birmingham *p136* 07779 099870

Robert Campbell & Company
‡Braunton *p156* 0870 241 2139

Robert Campbell
‡Huddersfield *p255* 01484 843323

Sarah Campbell Solicitors
‡Warwick *p422* 01926 691110

Campbell Solicitors
‡Birmingham *p136* 0121 270 6343

Campbell Systems Ltd
‡Manchester *p302* . 07770 123082 / 0161 495 2880

Campbell-Taylor Solicitors
‡Hackney N16 *p18* 0845 567 2457
London W10 *p18* 0845 567 2457

Campion & Co
‡Nottingham *p336* 0115 947 6373

Camps Solicitors
‡Birkenhead *p134* 0151 201 8080

Canal Legal
‡Ripon *p365* 01765 606666

Candey LLP
‡London WC2 *p18* 020 3370 8888

Henry Cane & Son
‡Brighton *p159* 01273 604091

Canning & Co
‡Warrington *p421* 01925 630012

Cannings Connolly
‡London EC1 *p18* 020 7329 9000

Cantelli & Co
‡Bicester *p132* 01869 324899

Canter Levin & Berg
‡Liverpool *p287* 0151 239 1000
Kirkby *p268* 0151 546 4562
St Helens *p391* 01744 634141

Cantor Law Solicitors
‡Manchester *p302* 0161 273 7600

Canty & Co
‡Birmingham *p136* 0121 688 5000

Cape Hill Solicitors
‡Birmingham *p136* 0121 532 3018

Capital Law LLP
‡Cardiff *p177* 0333 240 0489
London EC1 *p18* 0333 240 0489

Capital Legal Solicitors
‡Uxbridge *p417* 01895 876534

Capital Solicitors LLP
‡London E1 *p18* 020 7377 0847

Gary Caplan Solicitors
‡Leeds *p272* 0113 216 3118

Caplans
‡Harrow *p241* 020 8864 0111

Elizabeth Caple
‡Bristol *p162* 0117 907 5699

Irving Caplin & Co
‡Wandsworth SW18 *p18* 020 8874 7633

Amanda Capon Solicitors
‡Southampton *p385* 01489 574778

Capper & Jones
‡Mold *p318* 01352 752020

Capron & Helliwell
‡Stalham *p393* 01692 581231
Wroxham *p443* 01603 783818

T A Capron & Co
‡Grays *p233* 01375 378331

Capstick-Dale & Partners
‡Romford *p366* 01708 722466

Capsticks Solicitors LLP
‡London SW19 *p18* 020 8780 2211
Birmingham *p136* 0121 230 1500

Cardinal Solicitors
‡London NW6 *p18* 020 7691 4501

Graham Cardona
‡Milton Keynes *p316* 01908 225672

Careless & Kemp
‡Ventnor *p418* 01983 852626
Sandown *p372* 01983 400456

The Carers's Legal Centre
‡Christchurch *p194* 07740 432159 / 01425 674844

Carey Law
‡Alton *p116*

Carey Olsen
‡London EC2 *p18* 020 7796 3911

Caris Robson LLP
‡Prudhoe *p358* 01661 836851
Newcastle upon Tyne *p324* . . . 0191 264 6664

Michael J Carless Solicitor
‡Wolverhampton *p437* 01902 897743

Carlsons
‡London N20 *p18* . . .020 8445 3331 / 8445 5752

Carlton Cabral Solicitor
‡Reigate *p363* 01737 222717

Carlton Place Law
‡Southampton *p385* 023 8048 0007

Carltons Solicitors
‡Birmingham *p136* 0121 766 7447

Carlyon & Son
‡Truro *p414* 01872 278641

Carmichael & Heathfield
‡Newcastle upon Tyne *p324* . . . 0191 230 3010

Graeme Carmichael
‡Ipswich *p262* 01473 252159

Carney Solicitors Ltd
‡Hanley *p239* 01782 272999
Leek *p278* 01538 381444

Terence Carney
‡Hebburn *p246* . . . . 0191 483 5422 / 483 8771
South Shields *p383* 0191 456 3201

Carngie Brown Limited
‡London SW6 *p18* 020 8906 6731

Caro Taylor Solicitors
‡Poole *p352* 01202 678444

Carpenter & Co
‡Wallington *p419* 020 8669 5145

Carpenters
‡Birkenhead *p134* 0870 780 1870
‡Birkenhead *p134* 0844 249 0844

Carpenters Rose
‡London NW7 *p18* 020 8906 0088

Alan Carr Solicitors
‡Cirencester *p195* 01285 710358

Carr & Co
‡Banbury *p122* . . . . . .01295 275168 / 261744
‡Blyth *p147* 01670 351251
‡Huddersfield *p255* 01484 467860
‡St Albans *p389* 01727 866155
Gosforth *p231* 0191 284 0363
Morpeth *p319* 01670 515182

Carr & Kaye Solicitors
‡London NW3 *p18* 0333 900 0770
Welwyn Garden City *p425* 0845 241 5136

Carr Hepburn Solicitors Ltd
‡Hemel Hempstead *p246* 01442 241466

Carr Hewitt & Co
‡Heywood *p249* 01706 624240

S A Carr & Co
‡Hackney E8 *p18* 020 8986 5438

Carrick Read (Leeds) Solicitors LLP
‡Leeds *p272* 0113 246 7878

Carrick Read Solicitors LLP
‡Hull *p256* 01482 211160

Carrington & Associates
‡London EC4 *p18* 020 7822 1855

Carringtons Solicitors
‡Nottingham *p336* 0115 958 3472

Carritt & Co LLP
‡London W1 *p18* 020 7323 2765

Anthony Carroll & Co
‡Lincoln *p284* 01522 544017

Michael Carroll & Co
‡London N17 *p18* 020 8365 9900

Carrs Solicitors Limited
‡Bolton *p148* 01204 496898

Cars Solicitors
‡Lichfield *p284* 01543 303450

Carson & Co (Solicitors) Limited
‡London SE3 *p18* 0845 455 0055

Carter & Carter Solicitors
‡Disley *p210* 01663 761890

Carter & Carter Solicitors Ltd
‡Matlock *p313* 01663 735031

Carter and Company
‡London SE1 *p18* 020 8295 2984

Anthony C Carter
‡Plymouth *p349* 01752 255000

Barbara Carter
‡Birmingham *p136* 0121 441 3238

Carter Bells LLP
‡Kingston upon Thames *p267* . . . 020 8939 4000

Carter Devile
‡Ilford *p259* 020 8590 1066
Buckhurst Hill *p167* 020 8506 0636

Carter Fox Solicitors
‡Bradford *p153* 01274 665775

George Carter
‡London EC4 *p18* 020 7440 8800

Carter Law
‡Manchester *p302* 0844 414 0667

Carter Lemon Camerons
‡London EC1 *p18* 020 7406 1000

Carter Moore Solicitors
‡Manchester *p302* 0845 873 7333
London EC4 *p18* 0845 873 7333
Manchester *p302* 0845 873 7333

Carter Perry Bailey LLP
‡London EC3 *p18* 020 7863 6600

Carter Read & Dove
‡Swindon *p406* 01793 617617

Ross Carter
‡Brockenhurst *p166* 01590 624422

Carter Slater & Co
‡Northampton *p331* 01604 717505

Carter Vincent Jones Davis
‡Bangor *p122* 01248 362551

CARTER-RUCK
‡London EC4 *p18* 020 7353 5005

Carters
‡London W1 *p19* 020 7763 7130
‡Peterborough *p347* 0845 075 4101
‡Pontefract *p351* 01977 703224

Cartier & Co
‡London WC2 *p19* 020 7405 7777

Cartmell Shepherd
‡Carlisle *p182* 01228 516666
Brampton *p156* 01697 72378
Carlisle *p182* 01228 514077
Haltwhistle *p238* 01434 320362
Penrith *p346* 01768 862326

Cartridges
‡Exeter *p220* 01392 256854

Cartwright Adams Solicitors Limited
‡London W1 *p19* 020 7408 9270

Cartwright & Co
‡Kirkham *p268* . . . . . .01772 683116 / 687010

Cartwright Clark Solicitors
‡Milton Keynes *p316* 01908 325600

Cartwright Cunningham Haselgrove & Co
‡Waltham Forest E17 *p19* 020 8520 1021
Woodford Green *p439* 020 8506 5200

G Cartwright & Co
‡Chatteris *p185* 01354 692607

Cartwright King
‡Nottingham *p336* 0115 958 7444
Birmingham *p136* 0121 270 1988
Derby *p208* 01332 346111
Gateshead *p228* 0191 487 6775
Leicester *p279* 0116 253 9222
Sheffield *p375* 0114 321 1000

Carver Jones
‡Hereford *p247* 01432 274301

Carvers (Part of the Wilkes Partnership LLP)
Birmingham *p136* 0121 784 8484

Carvill & Johnson LLP
‡Birmingham *p136* 0121 476 9000

Jeremy Case Solicitor
‡Oswestry *p342* 01691 656563

Casey Legal
‡Peterborough *p347* 01733 233301

Caseys
‡Highbridge *p250* 01278 794495

Caseys Solicitors
‡Bingley *p133* 01274 560105
‡Bingley *p133* 01274 510656

Castle Law
‡Cowbridge *p201* 07772 368086

The Castle Partnership
‡Guildford *p235* 01483 300905
Woking *p436* 01483 730062

Castle Sanderson
‡Leeds *p272* 0113 232 1919

Castles
‡Hurstpierpoint *p258* . . .01273 836007 / 837107

Alison Castrey Limited
‡Bristol *p162* 0117 962 2356

Caswell Jones
‡Caerphilly *p172* 029 2086 4888
Ystrad Mynach *p445* 01443 816622

Catchpole Law
‡Salisbury *p371* . . 01725 552788 / 07920 585944

Penny Catchpole Solicitors
‡Winchester *p433* 01962 866522

Cater Leydon Millard Limited
‡Abingdon *p114* 01235 821115

Cathcarts
‡Ickenham *p259* . . . . .01895 631942 / 675631

Catteralls
‡Wakefield *p418* 01924 291122

Caulker & Co
‡London N17 *p19* 020 8801 9020

Caulker & Ozkutan
‡London E8 *p19* 020 7241 0759

Caunters
‡Liskeard *p285* . . . . .01579 343165 / 343484

Hugh A Cauthery
‡Wisbech *p435* 01945 464692

Bryan Cave
‡London EC2 *p19* 020 7207 1100

J P Cave & Co
‡Thame *p410* 01844 216208

Cavell Solicitors LLP
‡London E1 *p19* 020 7426 5520

Cavendish Law
‡London W1 *p19* 020 7495 2188
‡London EC2 *p19* 020 7147 9974

Caversham Solicitors Ltd
‡Reading *p360* 0118 947 8638

Cawthron Kelbrick Lane & Co
‡Harrogate *p240* 01423 561661

Caylaw
‡Kingston upon Thames *p267* 020 8547 4422

Cayton & Co
‡London EC3 *p19* 020 7264 2242

Cedars & Co
‡Greenwich SE9 *p19* 020 8331 6161

Central Law Practice
‡London WC1 *p19* 020 3051 2187

Certus Solicitors
‡Bradford *p153* 01274 722199

Chabra Cass & Co
‡Brent NW2 *p19* 020 8450 9833 / 8452 2200

Chadbourne & Parke
‡London EC4 *p19* 020 7337 8000

Chadwick Lawrence
‡Huddersfield *p255* 01484 519999
Halifax *p238* 01422 330601
Morley *p319* 0113 252 3452
Wakefield *p418* 01924 379078

Lee Chadwick & Co
‡Witney *p436* 01993 703272

Chadwicks Solicitors
‡Leyland *p283* 01772 424080

Chadwyck-Healey & Co
‡London EC4 *p19* 020 7353 6900

Chafes
‡Stockport *p395* 0161 477 1525
Alderley Edge *p115* 01625 585404
New Mills *p321* 01663 743344
Wilmslow *p433* 01625 531676

Challenor & Son
‡Abingdon *p114* 01235 520013

Challenor Gardiner
‡Oxford *p343* 01865 721451

Challinors
‡West Bromwich *p427* 0121 553 3211
Birmingham *p136* 0121 212 9393
Halesowen *p237* 0121 550 0481
Nottingham *p336* 0115 871 4510
Wolverhampton *p437* 01902 428121

Chamba & Co
‡Wolverhampton *p437* 01902 454749

Chamberlain Martin Solicitors
‡Bognor Regis *p148* 01243 825211
Littlehampton *p285* 01903 713814 / 716548

Chamberlain Thomas & Co
‡Wirral *p435* 0151 633 2800

Chamberlains
‡Bishop's Waltham *p144* 01489 896141

CHAMBERLINS
‡Hitchin *p251* 01462 623456
‡Great Yarmouth *p234* 01493 857621
Beccles *p129* 01502 713131
Caister-on-Sea *p172* 01493 720019
Great Yarmouth *p234* 01493 600113
Lowestoft *p294* 01502 573241

Chambers & Co
‡Chester *p190* 01244 403411
‡Norwich *p334* 01603 616155

Chambers & Hind (Stapleford)
‡Nottingham *p336* 0115 949 1141

Chambers Fletcher LLP
‡Northwich *p333* 01606 780400

Chambers Rutland & Crauford
‡London N12 *p19* 020 8446 2777

Chambers Solicitors
‡Bradford *p153* 01274 301450
Slough *p381* 01753 522204

J R Champkin
‡Evesham *p220* 01386 871287

James Chan & Co
‡London EC4 *p19* 0844 848 9988

Chan Neill Solicitors
‡London EC1 *p19* 020 7253 7781

Chance Hunter Solicitors
‡Manchester *p302* 0161 877 1200

Chance Hunter Solicitors LLP
‡Salford *p370* 0845 478 6354

Chancellor Solicitors
‡Birmingham *p136* 0121 446 4408

Chancellors Lea Brewer
‡Bexleyheath *p132* 020 8303 0077

Chancery CS Solicitors
‡London SW9 *p19* 020 7737 6379

The Chancery Partnership Solicitors
‡London EC4 *p19* 020 7822 8840

Chancery Solicitors
‡London SE1 *p19* 020 7754 5455

Chandarana & Co
‡Ilford *p259* 020 8503 4500

Chandler Harris LLP
‡Manchester *p302* 0161 834 2200

Chandler Ray
‡Buckingham *p167* 01280 814040
Buckingham *p167* 01280 821572 / 825555
Winslow *p435* 01296 712204 / 712729

Chands & Co
‡Pinner *p348* 020 8933 8332

changing-homes.com
‡Waterlooville *p423* 023 9224 6699

Chanter Ferguson
‡Bideford *p132* 01237 478751
Barnstaple *p125* 01271 342268

Chapel Court Solicitors
‡London SE1 *p19* 020 7378 8726

Chaplin & Co
‡Stanmore *p394* 020 8954 8202

Chapman Dhillon Solicitors
‡Leeds *p272* 0113 240 1041

Susan Chapman
‡Nailsea *p320* 01275 401996

Chapmans Solicitors
‡Bramhall *p155* 0161 440 7702
‡Sutton *p402* 020 8337 3801

B A Chappell & Co
‡Chelmsford *p186* 01245 251650

Chappell Pascoe
‡Crowborough *p204* 01892 664348

Chapple & Co
‡March *p312* 01354 652550

Adrian Chard & Co
‡Basingstoke *p126* 01256 363944

Charles & Co
‡Birmingham *p136* 0121 236 1985

Charles Coleman LLP
‡Windsor *p434* 01753 861115

Graham Charles & Co
‡Tunbridge Wells *p415* 01892 511766

J M Charles & Co
‡Ickenham *p259* 01895 634402

Charles Lucas & Marshall
‡Newbury *p322* 01635 521212
Hungerford *p258* 01488 682506
Swindon *p406* 01793 511055
Wantage *p421* 01235 771234

Oliver Charles
‡Leicester *p279* 0116 243 1166

Charles Russell LLP
‡London EC4 *p19* 020 7203 5000
Cambridge *p174* 01223 465465
Cheltenham *p187* 01242 221122
Guildford *p235* 01483 252525
Oxford *p343* 0845 359 0090

Charlesworth Nicholl & Co
‡Crediton *p203* 01363 774706

Charlson Simmons
‡Malvern *p300* 01684 891385

Bill Charlton Solicitors
‡Gosport *p232* 023 9250 3366

Charltons Solicitors
‡Biddulph *p132* 01782 522111

CHARSLEY HARRISON LLP
‡Windsor *p434* 01753 851591
Slough *p381* 01753 517600

CHARTER HOUSE CONVEYANCING
‡Southampton *p385* 023 8022 8714

Chartwell & Sadlers
‡London SE15 *p19* 020 7635 5255

Chase Solicitors
‡London E18 *p19* 020 8989 9956

Chaselaw Solicitors
‡Oxford *p343* 01865 314800

Chatsworth Legal
‡Oakham *p340* 01572 759777

Chattertons Solicitors
‡Boston *p151* 01205 351114
Boston *p151* 01205 310025
Grantham *p232* 01476 591550
Horncastle *p252* 01507 522456
Lincoln *p284* 01522 814600
Newark *p322* 01636 673731
Sleaford *p381* 01529 411500
Spalding *p389* 01775 768774
Stamford *p393* 01780 764145

D L Chaudhri & Co
‡Manchester *p302* 0161 224 6728

Chaudhury Solicitors
‡Bradford *p153* 01274 732999

Chauncy & Co
‡London EC3 *p19* 020 7929 0330

Chawner Grey & Co
‡Weston-super-Mare *p429* 01934 417768 / 623541

Cheal Associates Ltd
‡Ferndown *p225* 0845 508 9370

Chebsey & Co
‡Beaconsfield *p128* 01494 670440
Burnham *p168* 01628 660077
Windsor *p434* 01753 833737

Cheesman & Co
‡Liverpool *p287* 0151 258 1212

Cheethams
‡Penkridge *p345* 01785 714761

Francis H Chenery
‡Diss *p210* 01379 644055

Chenery Maher & Co
‡Clitheroe *p196* 01200 422264

Chennells
‡Westcliff-on-Sea *p428* 01702 349971 / 352195

Chequers Solicitors Ltd
‡Hayes *p245* 020 8606 1000

Cherith Solicitors LLP
‡London E9 *p19* 020 8986 2882

Chesham & Co
‡Barnet NW9 *p20* 020 8205 3656

Chester & Co
‡Bournemouth *p151* 01202 395395

H N E Chesterfield
‡Bristol *p162* 0117 968 8148

Chestnutts
‡Ainsdale *p114* 01704 572221

Chesworths
‡Stoke-on-Trent *p397* 01782 599992
Stoke-on-Trent *p397* 01782 599993

Chetna & Co Solicitors
‡Cardiff *p177* 029 2049 4322

Chetty & Patel
‡Leicester *p279* 0116 254 6222

P Chevalier & Co
‡Surbiton *p402* 020 3393 8217

Cheyney Goulding
‡Guildford *p236* 01483 567676

Chhokar & Co
‡Southall *p384* 020 8574 2488

Chichester Family Law Practice
‡Chichester *p192* 01243 787335

Chilcotts
‡Tavistock *p408* 01822 612535 / 614242

Child & Child
‡London SW1 *p20* 020 7235 8000
‡London SW1 *p20* 020 7235 1288

The Child Law Partnership
‡Guildford *p236* 01483 543790
Basingstoke *p126* 01256 630080

Childlaw
‡Epping *p219* 01992 570300

Children & Families Law Firm
‡London SW9 *p20* 020 7582 6002

The Childrens Legal Practice Ltd
‡Fareham *p223* 01329 823322

Childrens Workforce and Development Council
‡Leeds *p272* 0113 244 6311

Chiltern Legal Solicitors
‡Marlow *p313* 01628 472119

Chiltern Solicitors
‡Luton *p295* 01582 439795

Chinnery & Co Solicitors
‡Manchester *p302* 0161 233 7010

John S Chinnery Solicitor
‡Norwich *p334* 01603 742141

Chinyoka & Co
‡Leeds *p272* 0113 276 8800 / 276 8801

Chipatiso & Co Solicitors
‡London E12 *p20* 020 8514 9870

G & I Chisholm
‡Bodmin *p148* 01208 74242

Chisholms
‡Wadebridge *p418* 01208 812470 / 814205

Chiu & Benson
‡London SW1 *p20* 020 7930 1133

Chivers Easton Brown
‡Surbiton *p402* 020 8390 0081
Surbiton *p402* 020 8390 6155

Chivers Solicitors
‡Bingley *p133* 01274 561666
Durham *p214* 0191 383 2222

Chivers Walsh Smith and Irvine & Co
‡Bradford *p153* 01274 740077

Cho & Co
‡Watford *p423* 01923 650377

Chopra & Gill Solicitors
‡Wolverhampton *p437* 01902 621277

Zaman Choudhury & Co
‡London N15 *p20* 020 8881 4511

Chowdhury & Co
‡London E1 *p20* 020 7790 6991

Chris Solicitors
‡Greenwich SE18 *p20* 020 8855 0903

Christchurch Solicitors
‡Barking *p123* 020 8591 5934

Alexander Christian
‡Harrow *p241* 020 8863 7800

Gary Christianson
‡Stafford *p392* 01902 763971 / 07733 895565

Christie Solicitors
‡Louth *p294* 01507 617716

Christofi Wells & Co
‡London E11 *p20* 020 8539 3123

Christos Wybrew Kenneth Shaw & Co
‡Enfield *p218* 020 8366 1345 / 8367 0840

C P Christou LLP
‡London N12 *p20* 020 8446 6777

Chronnell Hibbert
‡Stockport *p395* 0161 494 6085
Hyde *p259* 0161 368 3434

Chua's Solicitors
‡London EC4 *p20* 020 7242 6789

Chubb & Co
‡Matlock *p313* 01629 581252

Chubb Bulleid
‡Wells *p425* 01749 836100
Somerton *p383* 01749 836100
Street *p400* 01749 836100

Chubblaw Limited
‡Matlock *p313* 01629 581700

Chung & Platt
‡Manchester *p302* 0161 228 6777

Church & Co
‡London SW1 *p20* 020 7828 4194

Church Lane Solicitors Limited
‡London E11 *p20* 020 8539 2022

Roy Kenneth Church
‡Gorseinon *p231* 01792 371420

Churchers
‡Fareham *p223* 01329 822333
Gosport *p232* 023 9260 3400
Lee-on-the-Solent *p271* 023 9255 1500
Portsmouth *p354* 023 9221 0170
Portsmouth *p354* 023 9286 2424
Ryde *p369* 01983 614541

Churchgate Legal LLP
‡Cardiff *p177* 0800 533 5795

Churchills Solicitors
‡London NW4 *p20* 020 8457 2981

Churchward & Co
‡London EC3 *p20* 020 7816 5442

Ciampa Solicitors
‡Bedford *p129* 01234 341525

City Law Chambers
‡Luton *p295* 01582 418308

City Law Financial LLP
‡London EC2 *p20* 020 7367 0100

City Law Limited
‡Milton Keynes *p316* 01908 369333

City Law Solicitors
‡Cardiff *p177* 029 2045 5797
‡Wembley *p426* 020 7663 8030

City Lawyers
‡St Albans *p390* 01727 739774

City Legal
‡Newport *p328* 01633 259844

City Net Law
‡London EC3 *p20* 020 7863 6635

Citygate Solicitors
‡London E1 *p20* 020 7375 2930

Claim Time Limited
‡Birmingham *p136* 0845 051 8080

Claira Collinson Legal
‡Northumberland *p333*
01661 844185 / 07985 015408

Clapham & Co
‡London SW8 *p20* 020 7622 9747

Clapham & Collinge
Sheringham *p378* 01263 823398

Guy Clapham & Co
‡London W1 *p20* 020 7935 1095

Clapham Law Chambers
‡London SW4 *p20* 020 7207 1913

Roger A Clapham
‡Mirfield *p318* 01924 521178

Antony Clapp
‡Maidstone *p299* 01622 815940

Geoffrey Clapp
‡Carlisle *p182* 01228 810228

Claremont Crawt
‡Brighton *p159* 01273 727906

Claremont Richards
‡London EC4 *p20* 020 7353 3030

Clarion Solicitors LLP
‡Leeds *p272* 0113 246 0622

Clark & Weeks
‡Plymouth *p349* 01752 345311
Ivybridge *p263* 01752 698869

Anthony Clark & Co
‡Lincoln *p284* 01522 512321

Barry Clark Solicitor
‡Bradford *p153* 01274 544844

CLARK BROOKES
‡West Bromwich *p427* 0121 553 2576

Chris Clark
Cannock *p176* 01543 573004

Chris Clark Solicitors & Estate Agents
‡Stafford *p392* 01785 241842 / 241944

David Clark & Co
‡London NW3 *p20* 020 7433 1562

Clark Holt
‡Swindon p406 . . . . 01793 617444
Neil Clark
‡Northampton p331 . . . . 01604 583684
R A W Clark & Co
‡Morpeth p319 . . . . 01670 512391
Clark Ricketts LLP
‡London WC2 p20 . . . . 020 7240 6767
Robin F Clark & Co
‡Gravesend p232 . . . . 01474 334444
Susan Clark Solicitor
‡Haywards Heath p245 . . . . . . 01444 454530
Clark Willis
‡Darlington p206 . . . . .01325 281111
Catterick Garrison p183 . . . . . . 01748 830000
Darlington p206 . . . . .01325 281111
Clarke & Hartland Solicitors
‡Cardiff p177 . . . . 029 2048 3181
Penarth p345 . . . . 029 2071 1181
Clarke Kiernan
‡Tonbridge p412 . . . . 01732 360999
Tonbridge p412 . . . . 01892 537999
Clarke Mairs
‡Newcastle upon Tyne p324 . . . . 0845 111 0795
The Clarke Partnership
‡Stockport p395 . . . . 0161 474 6600
Peter Clarke Solicitors
‡Totton p413 . . . . 023 8066 6636
Raymond Clarke & Co Solicitors
‡Hounslow p253 . . . . 020 3250 0000
Clarke Willmott
‡Birmingham p136 0845 209 1000 / 0117 305 6000
Bristol p162 . . 0845 209 1000 / 0117 305 6000
London EC4 p20 0845 209 1000 / 0117 305 6000
Manchester p302 0845 209 1000 / 0117 305 6000
Southampton p385
. . . . 0845 209 1000 / 0117 305 6000
Taunton p408 . . 0845 209 1000 / 0117 305 6000
Clarkes
‡Telford p409 . . . . 01952 291666
Newport p329 . . . . 01952 281060
Shrewsbury p379 . . . . 01743 231531
Telford p409 . . . . 01952 618787
Wellington p425 . . . . 01952 223548
ClarksLegal LLP
‡Reading p360 . . . . 0118 958 5321
Cardiff p177 . . . . 029 2055 7500
London WC2 p20 . . . . 020 7539 8000
Swansea p405 . . . . 0118 958 5321
Clarkson Hirst
‡Lancaster p269 . . . . 01524 39760
Barrow-in-Furness p125 . . . . . 01229 820600
Kendal p264 . . . . 01539 736916
Clarkson Wright & Jakes Ltd
‡Orpington p341 . . . . 01689 887887
Claude Hornby & Cox
‡London EC4 p20 . . . . 020 7332 8269
Claudine Meyrand
‡London SW7 p20 . . . . 020 7589 6468
Clausen Miller LLP
‡London EC3 p20 . . . . 020 7645 7970
ClaydenLaw
‡Oxford p343 . . . . 01865 339640
Clayton
‡Staines p393 . . . . 01784 227590
Clayton Mott
‡Nottingham p336 . . . . 0115 941 7422
Clayton Mott & Lawton
Sutton-in-Ashfield p404 . . . . . . 01623 556601
Claytons
‡St Albans p390 . . . . 01727 865765
Clear Law Ltd
‡Manchester p302 . . . . 0870 850 8652
Clearwater Conveyancing Limited
‡Plymouth p349 . . . . 0870 700 0230
Cleary Gottlieb Steen & Hamilton
‡London EC2 p20 . . . . 020 7614 2200
Cleaver Thompson Ltd
‡Alfreton p115 . . . . 01773 832193
Clay Cross p195 . . . . 01246 865048
Clegg Manuel
‡Islington EC1 p20 . . . . 020 7847 5600
‡London EC1 p20
Cleggs
‡Nottingham p336 . . . . 0115 977 5877
Clematis Law
‡Crawley p202 . . . 01293 45 647 / 07595 469023
Clement Hughes & Co
‡Prestatyn p356 . . . . 01745 852121
Tim Clement-Jones
‡London SW4 p20 . . . . 020 7622 4205
Clements and Co
‡Cardiff p177 . . . . 029 2036 1771
C L Clemo & Co
‡London SW20 p20 . . . . 020 8944 1017
Pamela Clemo & Co
‡Kingston upon Thames p267 . . . 020 8949 8791
F J Cleveland
‡London WC2 p20 . . . . 020 7405 5875
Cleveland Solicitors
‡London E1 p20 . . . . 020 7377 8866

Cleverdons
‡Enfield p218 . . . . 020 8367 5375
Clifford Chance
‡London E14 p20 . . . . 020 7006 1000
Clifford Cowling & Co
‡Farnham p224 . . . . 01252 725726
Clifford Harris & Co
‡London W1 p21 . . . . 020 7486 0031
Clifford Holmes Solicitors
‡Cheltenham p188 . . . . 01242 529933
Clifford Howard & Co
‡Okehampton p340 . . . . 01837 861455
Clifford Johnston & Co
‡Manchester p302 . . . . 0161 975 1900
Manchester p302 . . . . 0161 249 2700
Clifford Joseph
‡Maidenhead p298 . . . . 01628 823331
Clifford Poole & Co
‡Salford p370 . . . . 0161 736 0160
Clifford Smith & Buchanan
‡Burnley p169 . . . . 01282 452611
Colne p198 . . . . 01282 860606
Nelson p320 . . . . 01282 693182
Cliffords
‡Alderley Edge p115 . . . . 01625 582257
Douglas Clift & Co
‡Lancaster p269 . . . . 01524 32437
Clifton Ingram LLP
‡Wokingham p437 . . . . 0118 978 0099
Reading p360 . . . . 0118 957 3425
Clifton Owen Solicitors
‡Maidenhead p298 . . . . 01628 783891
Clinch Solicitors
‡Ashton-under-Lyne p120 . . . . . 0161 441 0390
Clinton Davis Pallis
‡London N8 p21 . . . . 020 8880 5000
Clintons
‡London WC2 p21 . . . . 020 7379 6080
Clodes Solicitors
‡Barry p126 . . . . 01446 720777
Cardiff p177 . . . 029 2076 5050 / 01446 720777
Cloney & Co
‡Lytham p296 . . . . 01253 712116
Clore & Co
‡London WC1 p21 . . . . 020 8922 0563
Close Thornton
‡Darlington p206 . . . . 01325 466461
Clough & Willis
‡Bury p170 . . . . 0161 764 5266
Peter Clough & Co
‡Sheerness p375 . . . . 01795 669299
Clovis Khuja Solicitors
‡Oxford p343 . . . . 01865 200150
Cluley & Co
‡Winsford p434 . . . . 01606 553719
Clutton Cox Solicitors
‡Chipping Sodbury p193 . . . . . 01454 312125
Clyde & Co
‡Guildford p236 . . . . .020 7876 5000
Clyde & Co LLP
‡London EC3 p21 . . . . 020 7623 1244
London EC3 p21 . . . . 020 7623 1244
Clyde Chappell & Botham
‡Stoke-on-Trent p397 . . . . 01782 599577
Co-operative Group Legal Services
‡Manchester p302 . . . . 0161 827 5296
Martin Coakley
‡Haslemere p243 . . . . 01428 648888
Coaster Legal
‡Bath p127 . . . . 01225 421543
Coates Allbutt Edmondson & Taylor
‡Tankerton p407 . . . . . .01227 272617 / 262813
Eric Coates
‡London SE1 p21 . . . . 020 7720 3278
Garth Coates Solicitors
‡London W1 p21 . . . . 020 7993 6299
Coates Solicitors
‡Sheffield p375 . . . . 0114 251 1111
Caroline Coats Solicitors
‡Southampton p385 . . . . 023 8089 0919
Cobains
‡Blackpool p146 . . . . 01253 290092
Cobbetts LLP
‡Manchester p302 . . . . 0845 404 2404
Birmingham p136 . . . . 0845 404 2404
Leeds p272 . . . . 0845 404 2404
London WC1 p21 . . . . 0845 404 2404
Cobham Solicitors
‡London W8 p21
Cobleys LLP
‡Liverpool p287 . . . . 0151 242 9000
Cochranes Law Firm Limited
‡Billingham p133 . . . . 01642 366800
Cockburns Solicitors
‡Guildford p236 . . . . 01483 452848
Cockertons
‡Bakewell p121 . . . . 01629 812613
Peter J Cockle
‡Chelmsford p186 . 01245 225534 / 020 7015 1850

Cocks Lloyd
‡Nuneaton p339 . . . . 024 7664 1642
Cockshott Peck Lewis
‡Southport p388 . . . . 01704 534034
Ainsdale p114 . . . . 01704 574144
Southport p388 . . . . 01704 211649
John Codling
‡Princes Risborough p358 . . . . . 01494 488720
Coffers
‡Amersham p117 . . . . 01494 727323
Graham Coffey & Co
‡Manchester p302 . . . . 0161 200 2440
Coffey Graham LLP
‡London W1 p21 . . . . 020 3145 1170
Coffin Mew & Clover
‡Fareham p223 . . . . 01329 825617
Gosport p232 . . . . 023 9252 3111
Portsmouth p354 . . . . 023 9238 8021
Southampton p385 . . . . 023 8033 4661
Cogent Law
‡Leeds p272 . . . . 0844 245 4452
Croydon p204 . . . . 0844 245 4452
Cohen Cramer Solicitors
‡Leeds p272 . . . . 0800 542 9408
Danielle Cohen Solicitors
‡London NW1 p21 . . . . 020 7267 4133
David Cohen & Co
‡London NW4 p21 . . . . 020 8202 8937
Cohen Filippini
‡Altrincham p116 . . . . 0161 929 9993
Julian Cohen
‡London N20 p21 . . . . 020 3016 3935
Liz Cohen Solicitor
‡London N10 p21 . . . . 020 8444 4003
Colborne Coulman & Lawrence
‡Newport p328 . . . . . .01633 264194 / 264196
Coldham Shield & Mace
‡London E4 p21 . . . . 020 8524 6323
Cole & Co
‡Norwich p334 . . . . 01603 617018
Cole & Yousaf
‡Rotherham p367 . 01709 367944 / 07982 884240
Cole Associates
‡London W1 p21 . . . . 020 7958 9370
Cole Bentley & Co
‡Great Yarmouth p234 . . . . 01493 330660
Colebournes Solicitors and Advocates
‡Blackpool p146 . . . . 01253 293195
Coleman & Betts
‡Kingston upon Thames p267 . . . 020 8549 4402
Charles Coleman & Co
‡Reading p360 . . . . 0118 958 1578
Colemans
‡Chelmsford p186 . . . . 01245 264494
‡Haywards Heath p245 . . . . . . 01444 459555
Colemans - CTTS
‡Manchester p302 . . . . 0161 876 2500
Barnet p124 . . . . 020 8441 1213
Kingston upon Thames p267 . . . 020 8296 9966
Colemans Solicitors LLP
‡Maidenhead p298 . . . . 01628 631051
Coles Miller Solicitors LLP
‡Poole p352 . . . . 01202 673011
Bournemouth p151 . . . . 01202 511512
Bournemouth p151 . . . . 01202 293226
Broadstone p166 . . . . 01202 694891
Roy Coles & Co
‡Bristol p162 . . . . 0117 925 6257
Coles Solicitors
‡Northallerton p331 . . . . 01609 780717
Colette Stroud Solicitors
‡Ponteland p351 . . . . 01661 820444
COLEY & TILLEY
‡Birmingham p136 . . . . 0121 643 5531
A J Colfer Solicitors
‡Fleet p226 . . . . 01252 623565
Collard & Co
‡Highworth p250 . . . . 01793 765327
Collards Solicitors
‡Sheffield p375 . . . . 0114 273 8149
Bryan Colley & Co
‡Stourport-on-Severn p399 . . . . 01299 871066
Christine Collier Solicitor
‡Plymouth p349 . . . . 01752 666972
Collier Law
‡York p444 . . . . 01904 427407
Collier Littler
‡Altrincham p116 . . . . 0161 980 6046
Anthony Collins Solicitors LLP
‡Birmingham p137 . . . . 0121 200 3242
Collins Benson Goldhill LLP
‡Westminster W1 p21 . . . . 020 7436 5151
David Collins Solicitors
‡Leeds p272 . . . . 0113 289 2530
Collins Dryland & Thorowgood LLP
‡Henley-on-Thames p247 . . . . . 01491 572323
Tilehurst p411 . . . . 0118 942 2448
E M Collins & Co
‡Pinner p348 . . . . 020 8866 1820

John Collins & Partners LLP
‡Swansea p405 . . . . 01792 773773
Collins Long
‡Southwark SE1 p21 . . . . 020 7401 9800
Simone Collins & Co
‡Stanmore p394
Collins Solicitors
‡Watford p423 . . . . 01923 223324
Collis & Co
‡Wandsworth SW17 p22 . . . . . 020 8767 3332
John Collis Solicitors
‡London EC2 p22 . . . . 020 7539 6690
Eve Collmans
‡Yateley p443 . . . . 01252 404456
Collyer Bristow LLP
‡London WC1 p22 . . . . 020 7242 7363
COLMAN COYLE LLP
‡Islington N1 p22 . . . . 020 7354 3000
George Mitchell Colman & Co
‡Birmingham p137 . . . . 0121 427 7700
C E P Colombotti
‡London W1 p22 . . . . 020 7569 1054
Coltman Warner Cranston LLP
‡Coventry p200 . . . . 024 7662 7262
Colvin & Partners
‡London W2 p22 . . . . 020 7402 4222
Comercrawley
‡Diss p210 . . . . 01379 644311
Bernie Comiskey
‡Cheshunt p189 . . . . 01992 632606
Commercial & Legal Group (CLG)
‡Birmingham p137 . . . . 0121 326 6611
The Commercial Law Practice
‡Weymouth p430 . . . . 01305 779545
‡Wimborne p433 . . . . 01202 843976
Commercial Legal Solutions
‡Cardiff p177 . . . . 029 2089 2211
K J Commons & Co
‡Workington p440 . . . . 01900 604698
Carlisle p182 . . . . 01228 822666
Whitehaven p431 . . . . 01946 66699
Community Law Clinic Solicitors Ltd
‡London NW10 p22
The Community Law Partnership
‡Birmingham p137 . . . . 0121 685 8595
The Compensation Clinic
‡Ashford p119 . . . . 01233 645678
The Compensation Lawyers
‡Stanmore p394
Compensation Solicitors Online
‡Edgware p217 . . . . 0845 345 7144
Complete Law LLP
‡Southampton p385 . . . . 01489 885788
Reading p360 . . . . 0118 969 5514
Comptons
‡Camden NW1 p22 . . . . 020 7485 0888
Concept Law Solicitors
‡Nelson p321 . . . . 01282 700200
Confreys
‡Cardiff p177 . . . . 029 2045 8080
Conifer & Pines Solicitors
‡Ilford p259 . . . . 020 8709 2077
Coninghams Solicitors
‡London SW1 p22 . . . . 020 8296 1957
Michael B Conn
‡London NW11 p22 . . . . 020 8455 1111
Connell Associates
‡Liverpool p287 . . . . 0151 236 2011
The Connexion Partnership
‡Manchester p302 . . . . 0870 160 1160
Birmingham p137 . . . . 0121 633 6606
Connolley & Company
‡Wolverhampton p437 . . . . 01902 326000
Richard Connor Solicitors
‡Ramsgate p359 . . . . 01227 749777
K J Conroy Solicitors
‡Birmingham p137 . . . . 0121 212 1575
Conroys Solicitors
‡Truro p414 . . . . 01872 272457
Consilium Legal
‡Birmingham p137 . . . . 0845 241 5656
Constantine & Summers
‡Camberley p173 . . . . 01276 23211
Constantinou Solicitors
‡Long Eaton p293 . . . . 0115 849 8000
Contego Intellectual Property
‡London WC2 p22 . . . . 020 7849 3430
Convey UK Solicitors Limited
‡Newport p328 . . . . 01633 261223
Conveyancing Direct Ltd
‡St Leonards-on-Sea p392 . . . . 0845 788 8666
Conveyancing Expert Limited
‡Manchester p302 . . . . 0844 412 5857
Conway & Co
‡Harrow p241 . . . . 020 8863 0535
‡Henley-on-Thames p247 . . . . . 01491 411122
Greenford p234 . . . . 020 8575 2191
Henley-on-Thames p247 . . . . . 01491 411122

Conway & Conway
‡Westcliff-on-Sea *p428* 01702 710373

Conybeare Solicitors
‡London W1 *p22* 0870 753 0925

Conyers Dill & Pearman
‡London EC2 *p22* 020 7374 2444

Coodes
‡St Austell *p391* 01726 874700
Holsworthy *p251* 01409 253425
Launceston *p270* 01566 770000
Liskeard *p285* 01579 347600
Newquay *p329* 01637 878111
Penzance *p346* 01736 362294
Truro *p414* 01872 246200

Cook & Partners
‡Croydon *p204* 020 8655 4466

Cook & Talbot
‡Southport *p388* 01704 535216

Charles Cook and Company Limited
‡Portishead *p354* 01275 390432

Mark Cook Solicitors
‡Sunderland *p401* 0191 567 7244

Richard Cook Solicitors
‡London NW7 *p22* 020 8371 3490

Robert Cook & Co Solicitors
‡Fleet *p226* 01252 812957

Cook Taylor
‡Greenwich SE18 *p22* 020 8854 1166

Cook Taylor Woodhouse
‡London SE9 *p22* 020 8859 0936
Dartford *p207* 01322 223223

Chris Cooke and Co
Sheffield *p375* 0114 282 3433

Cooke Painter Limited
‡Bristol *p162* 01275 835569
Bristol *p162* 01275 400037
Bristol *p162* 0117 971 4074
Bristol *p162* 0117 971 6765
Knowle *p269* 0117 977 7403

Cooke Young & Keidan LLP
‡London EC4 *p22* 020 7148 7800

Cooks
‡Newcastle under Lyme *p323* . . . 01782 611090

Coole & Haddock
‡Worthing *p441* 01903 213511
Horsham *p253* 01403 210200

Coomber Rich
‡Basingstoke *p126* 01256 812202

Sharon Coomber
‡Colchester *p197* 01206 769342

Neil Coombes Solicitor Ltd
‡Huddersfield *p255* 01484 303585

Anthony Coombs
‡Manchester *p302* 0161 445 3789

Cooper & Co
‡York *p444* 01904 626266

B D H Cooper Ltd
‡Haywards Heath *p245* 01444 831127

David Cooper & Co
‡London EC4 *p22* 020 7583 8338

Cooper Ford
‡Altrincham *p116* 0161 929 2414

J Cooper
‡London E1 *p22* 020 7790 0441

Jonathan P Cooper
‡Guildford *p236* 07956 551898

Cooper Kenyon Burrows
‡Manchester *p302* 0161 834 7374

Cooper Lingard
‡Leigh-on-Sea *p282* 01702 715411

Cooper Nimmo
‡Blackpool *p146* 01253 626793

Paul Cooper & Co
‡Leicester *p279* 0116 255 4477

Cooper Rollason Solicitors
‡Telford *p409* 01952 204242

Sheila Cooper LLB
‡London NW6 *p22* 020 7372 0510

Cooper Son & Caldecott
‡Henley-on-Thames *p247* 01491 574203

Cooper Sons Hartley & Williams
‡Buxton *p172* 01298 77511
Chapel-en-le-Frith *p184* 01298 812138

Cooper Stott
‡Durham *p214* 0191 384 7210

Thomas Cooper
‡London EC3 *p22* 020 7481 8851

Cooper Whiteman
‡London WC1 *p22* 020 7831 5222

CooperBurnett
‡Tunbridge Wells *p415* 01892 515022

R T Coopers Solicitors
‡London E1 *p22* 020 7488 9947

Coopers Solicitors
‡Worthing *p441* 01903 872130

Cope & Co Solicitors Limited
‡Manchester *p302* 0161 214 7950
Liverpool *p287* 0151 600 5262

Copeman Markham Solicitors
‡Hull *p256* 01482 212979

Copes Solicitors
Kings Nympton *p267* 01769 581581

Copitch
‡Haringey N10 *p22* 020 8883 9831

John Copland & Son
‡Sheerness *p375* 01795 664431

Copley Davies
‡St Albans *p390* 01727 764978

Copleys
‡St Ives *p391* 01480 464515
Huntingdon *p258* 01480 456191

Rosamund Coppen & Company
‡Bath *p127* 0330 440 1802

Copper Stone Solicitors
‡London E1 *p22* 020 7173 6175

Corbain Solicitors
‡London N17 *p22* 020 8801 3737

Corbett & Co International Construction Lawyers Ltd
‡Teddington *p409* 020 8614 6200

Helen E F Corbett
‡Guildford *p236* 01483 450777

Tania Corbett
‡Pinner *p348* 020 8868 6100

Corbetts Solicitors
‡Ware *p421* 01920 872929

Corbin & Hassan
‡London E1 *p22* 020 7247 6518

Donna L Corbin
‡Petersfield *p348* 01730 261288

Corcorans
‡Worthing *p441* 01903 824428

Cordell & Co
‡Dorking *p212* 01306 743003

Bernard Cordell
‡London NW3 *p22* 020 8209 3752

John B Cordingley & Co
‡Bradford *p153* 01274 736646

Cordner Lewis
‡Cardiff *p177* 029 2047 5640

Corfield Solicitors
‡Bristol *p162* 0117 968 8890
‡Budleigh Salterton *p168* 01395 567102

Corford International LLP
‡London E4 *p22* 020 8527 6217

Janet M Corke
‡Liverpool *p287* 0151 726 0443

Corker Binning Solicitors
‡London WC2 *p22* 020 7353 6000

Cormact Cawley & Co
‡London E1 *p22* 020 7702 2654

Cornelian Lawyers And Mediators
‡London EC4 *p22* 0845 009 1377

Cornell & Co
‡Leominster *p282* 01568 612288

Cornerstoneking
‡London SE14 *p22* 020 7635 6033

Cornerstones
‡London E17 *p22* 020 8520 6330

Cornfield Law
‡Eastbourne *p215* 01323 412512

Cornish Forfar & Allen
‡Liverpool *p287* 0151 227 1831
Wirral *p435* 0151 630 4343

Cornwall Defence Solicitors
‡St Austell *p391* 01726 892842
Truro *p414* 01872 561201

Teresa M Cornwell
‡Oxted *p344* . . . . 01883 712721 / 722594

Cornwells
‡Bradford *p153* 01274 675631

Corper Solicitors
‡London E15 *p22* 020 8555 6006

Corporate Legal
‡Ryde *p369* 0845 458 9448

Corporateblue
‡Bolton *p148* 01204 399966

Corren Troen
‡London SW1 *p22* 020 7798 9344

Corries Solicitors
‡York *p444* 0845 241 5566

Cost Advocates Limited
‡London EC3 *p23* 0870 402 7871

Costley & Partners Solicitors
‡Caerphilly *p172* . . . 029 2086 4666 / 2088 5705

Cotisens Solicitors
‡Barking *p123* 020 8594 8683

Cotswold Conveyancing Centre
‡Gloucester *p230* 01452 545678

Cotterhill Hitchman LLP
‡Sutton Coldfield *p403* 0121 323 1860

Cottrill Stone Lawless
‡Manchester *p302* 0161 835 3681

Couchmans LLP
‡London WC1 *p23* 020 7611 9660

Coulsdon Solicitors (Tremont Midwest Solicitors)
‡Coulsdon *p199* 020 8660 0810

Coulson Read Lewis Solicitors
‡Hereford *p247* 01432 357005

Countrywide Conveyancing Direct
Lichfield *p284* 01543 302223

Countrywide PLC
‡Witham *p435* 01376 533700

Countrywide Property Lawyers
‡Manchester *p302* 0870 380 9000
‡Northampton *p331* 01604 795208
Cardiff *p177* 029 2044 2100

Coupe Bradbury
‡Lytham *p296* 01253 736670
Kirkham *p268* 01772 683000

Coupland Cavendish Solicitors
‡Oldham *p340* 0161 652 5689

Hilary A Courtneidge
‡Hertford *p248* 01992 589120

Courtyard Solicitors LLP
‡London SW19 *p23* 020 8946 9466

Alexander Cousins Criminal Defence Solicitors
‡Leeds *p272* 0113 394 4175

Cousins Business Law
‡Birmingham *p137* 0121 778 3212

Cousins Tyrer
‡Leeds *p272* 0113 247 0400

Covent Garden Family Law
‡Camden WC2 *p23* 020 7257 6130

Covington & Burling LLP
‡London WC2 *p23* 020 7067 2000

David Cowan
‡Dorking *p212* 01306 886622

Coward and Sahdev Solicitors
‡London WC1 *p23* 020 7745 7220

Cowells Solicitors
‡Westerham *p429* 01959 563420

Leonie Cowen & Associates
‡London NW6 *p23* 020 7604 5870

Philip Cowen
‡Altrincham *p116* 0161 928 1720

Cowen Ross Solicitors
‡London N1 *p23* 020 7241 1140

Ian Cowie
‡Guisborough *p237* 01287 636401

Cowle Smart
‡Cheltenham *p188* . . . . 01242 222744 / 570700

Cowles
‡Croydon SW16 *p23* 020 8679 1811

Cowley Di Giorgio & Co
‡Bedford *p129* 01234 218171

Cowling Swift & Kitchin
‡York *p444* . . . . 01904 625678 / 625679

Cowlings
‡Mexborough *p314* 01709 587538
Doncaster *p211* 01302 723366

Cowlishaw & Mountford
‡Uttoxeter *p417* 01889 565211

Eric Cowsill Solicitor
‡Ivybridge *p263* 01752 205202

Cox & Hodgetts
‡Evesham *p220* 01386 442513

Anthony F Cox
‡Guildford *p236* 01483 562422

Cox Burley Solicitors
‡Liskeard *p285* 01579 340020

CHRISTOPHER COX SOLICITORS
‡Northampton *p331* 01604 882287

Cox Cooper Limited
‡Birmingham *p137* 0121 777 0015

Cox Roderick LLP
‡London SW4 *p23* 020 7819 4262

Coxons
‡West Bridgford *p427* 0115 981 2000

Coyle White Devine
‡Amersham *p117* 0845 094 5945
London WC2 *p23* 0845 094 5945

Coyne Learmonth
‡Liverpool *p287* 0845 602 0870

Cozen O'Connor LLP
‡London EC3 *p23* 020 7864 2000

Cozens-Hardy LLP
‡Norwich *p334* 01603 625231

Cozens Moxon & Harts
‡Teddington *p409* . . . 020 8977 8486 / 8977 4424
Hampton *p238* 020 8979 4333

Crabtree Chadwick
‡Pudsey *p358* 0113 290 9499

Cracknells
‡Guildford *p236* 01483 535558

Craddock Hodgson & Wildin
‡Gainsborough *p228* 01427 615221

Craffrey & Company
‡Birmingham *p137* . . . 0121 326 6977 / 706 7907

Alexander Craig Solicitors
‡Cambridge *p174* 01223 348910

Melanie Craig Solicitors
‡Leeds *p272* 0113 244 4081

Craigen Wilders & Sorrell
‡London N8 *p23* 020 8888 2255

Crallans
‡Bath *p127* 01225 326417

Cramer Pelmont
‡London W1 *p23* 020 7016 3016
London N8 *p23* 020 8340 0091

Cramp & Co
‡Eastbourne *p215* 01323 720581

Dudley Cramp & Co
‡Sittingbourne *p380* 01795 420024

Crampton Pym & Lewis
‡Oswestry *p342* 01691 653301

Crane & Staples
‡Welwyn Garden City *p425* 01707 329333

Crane & Walton
‡Coalville *p196* 01530 834466
Ashby-de-la-Zouch *p118* 01530 414111
Leicester *p279* 0116 255 1901

Cranes
‡Barry *p126* 01446 720444

Crangle Edwards
‡Stretford *p400* . 0161 865 2993 / 865 7816 / 865 5875
Cheadle *p185* 0161 428 2331

Cravath Swaine & Moore LLP
‡London EC2 *p23* 020 7453 1000

Crawford
‡London WC2 *p23* 020 7872 5495

Crawford Solicitors
‡London EC1 *p23* 020 7831 3343
‡London W1 *p23* 0845 000 9500

T H R Crawley
‡London W4 *p23* 020 8994 8643

Martin Cray & Co
‡Brighton *p159* 01273 673226

Cray Valley Solicitors Limited
‡Orpington *p341* 020 8302 4968

David Crayford
‡Reading *p360* 0118 931 1447

Creagh Brown & Co Solicitors
‡Esher *p220* 020 8224 0610

Creans Solicitors
‡Felixstowe *p225* 01394 273481

Cree Godfrey & Wood
‡London N2 *p23* 020 8883 9414

Creed Lane Law Group
‡Cambridge *p174* 01223 327771
‡London EC4 *p23* 020 7248 6817

Creighton & Partners
‡London WC1 *p23* 020 7976 2233
Staines *p393* 01784 426710

Crellins Carter Solicitors
‡Weybridge *p429* 01932 858833

Crescent Law
‡Morden *p318* 020 8640 2300

Cresco Legal Solicitors
‡London NW1 *p23* 020 3356 4938
Oxford *p343* 01865 339360

Cresswell & Co
‡London W4 *p23* 020 8742 0070

Graham Crewe
‡Knutsford *p269* 07545 964984

Crichtons Solicitors
‡Nottingham *p336* 0845 331 2464

Crick & Freeman
‡Maldon *p299* 01621 852606

Crick & Mardling
‡Stone *p398* . . . . 01785 812650 / 812434

Crickhollow Solicitors
‡Stanmore *p394* 020 8907 3535

Criminal Defence Associates
‡Boston *p151* 01205 364777

Criminal Defence Milton Keynes Solicitors
‡Milton Keynes *p316* 01908 379225

Criminal Defence Solicitors
‡Westminster WC2 *p23* 020 7353 7000

Criminal Law Solicitors
‡Pontefract *p351* 01977 707999
Selby *p374* 01757 241199

Crimson Phoenix Solicitors
‡Barking *p123* 020 8591 6500

Cripps Harries Hall LLP
‡Tunbridge Wells *p415* 01892 515121
London WC2 *p23* 020 7930 7879

Crisp & Co Solicitors
‡Guildford *p236* 01483 570810
Kingston upon Thames *p267* 020 8546 7969
London E14 *p23* 0844 800 6863

Critchley Hall Solicitors
‡Leyburn *p283* 01969 625526

Crockett & Co
‡Leeds *p272* 0113 226 0111

Mark Croft Solicitor
‡Derby *p208* 01332 671133

Shirley Croft Solicitors
‡Chelmsford *p186* 01245 380019

Croftons
‡Manchester *p302* 0161 214 6180

Crofts
‡Kettering p265 . . . 01536 518742

Crombie Wilkinson
‡York p444 . . . 01904 624185
Malton p300 . . . 01653 600070
Selby p374 . . . 01757 708957

Crompton Halliwell
‡Bury p170 . . . 0161 797 9222

Agnes Crompton-Roberts Solicitor
‡Solihull p382 . . . 0121 707 2309

Cromwells Law Limited
‡London W1 p23 . . . 020 7887 6474

Charles Crookes & Jones
‡Caerphilly p172 . . . 029 2086 0628

Charles Crookes Limited
‡Cardiff p178 . . . 029 2049 1271

Charles Crookes with George Tudor & de Winton
Brecon p156 . . . 01874 625151

Crookeslaw Solicitors
‡Cranbrook p202 . . . 01580 754884

Crosby & Moore Solicitors
‡Hove p254 . . . 01273 863295

Simon Crosfield & Co
‡Ripon p365 . . . 01765 692277

David Cross & Co
‡Thornbury p411 . . . 01454 419696

Cross Ram & Co
‡Halesworth p237 . . . 01986 873636
Framlingham p227 . . . 01728 724111

Cross Solicitors
‡Connah's Quay p199 . . . 01244 822101

Stanley H Cross & Co
‡Chorley p194 . . . 01257 272222

Stefan Cross Solicitors
‡Newcastle upon Tyne p324 . . . 0191 226 6686

Derek Crossan
‡Helmsley p246 . . . 01439 770070

Crosse & Crosse
‡Exeter p220 . . . 01392 258451

Crosse Wyatt & Co
‡Devonport p210 . . . 01769 580059

Crosse Wyatt Verney & Ayre
‡South Molton p383 . . . 01769 572157

Crosslands Employment Law Plus
‡Didcot p210 . . . 01235 838606

Crossmans
‡Radstock p358 . . . 01761 431688

Crossmans MTA
‡Cambridge p174 . . . 01223 451442
London EC4 p23
Manchester p302 . . . 01223 451442

Crossmans Solicitors Limited
‡Thornbury p411 . . . 01454 412278 / 412004

Crowdy & Rose
‡Faringdon p224 . . . 01367 240285
Lechlade p271 . . . 01367 252644

Crowe Humble Wesencraft
‡Newcastle upon Tyne p324 . . . 0191 287 2221

Crowell & Moring
‡London EC4 p23 . . . 020 7413 0011

Crowley & Co
‡Cardiff p178 . . . 029 2045 8895

PAUL CROWLEY & CO
‡Liverpool p287 . . . 0151 264 7363
Liverpool p287 . . . 0151 264 7363
Liverpool p287 . . . 0151 286 4515

Crown and Mehria Solicitors
‡Aylesbury p120 . . . 01296 392403

Crown Law Solicitors
‡Colchester p197 . . . 01206 273499

Crowther Solicitors
‡London EC1 p23 . . . 020 7785 6944 / 6945

A S Croxson
‡London SW14 p23 . . . 020 8998 3097

A S Croxson Solicitors
‡London W5 p23

Ian Cruickshank & Co
‡Jarrow p263 . . . 0191 428 0900

Cruickshanks Solicitors
‡London W1 p23 . . . 020 7487 4468

Michael Crumley Solicitor
‡Plymouth p349 . . . 01752 264474

Richard Crumly
‡Thatcham p410 . . . 01635 866166

Crumplins
‡Camden NW1 p23 . . . 020 7483 0282

Crumpsall Solicitors
‡Manchester p302 . . . 0161 492 0300

Crutes
‡Newcastle upon Tyne p324 . . . 0191 233 9700
Carlisle p182 . . . 01228 525195
Stockton-on-Tees p396 . . . 01642 623400

Crystal Partners Solicitors
‡London N8 p23 . . . 0845 500 0240

Cubism Limited
‡London WC2 p23 . . . 020 7831 0101

Philip H Cuerden Solicitors
‡Preston p356 . . . 01772 203303

Cuff And Gough LLP
‡Banstead p122 . . . 01737 851827

Cullen Hammond
‡Sunderland p401 . . . 0191 501 8062

Michael Cullen & Partners
‡Billericay p133 . . . 01277 623132

Cullimore Dutton
‡Chester p190 . . . 01244 356789

Cumberland Ellis Peirs
‡London WC1 p23 . . . 020 7242 0422

Cumbria Employment Solicitors
‡Penrith p346 . . . 01768 484938

Cumming & Riley
‡Grays p233 . . . 01375 383691

Cumming Hodgkinson Dickinson
‡Bolton p148 . . . 01204 523108 / 528396

Cummings
‡London SW11 p24 . . . 020 7585 1406

Amanda Cunliffe Solicitors Ltd
‡Macclesfield p297 . . . 01625 667166

N Cunliffe-Lister
‡Driffield p213 . . . 01377 236006

Cunningham Blake
‡London SE3 p24 . . . 020 8463 0071
Lewisham SE13 p24 . . . 020 8463 9800

John Cunningham & Associates
‡Ormskirk p341 . . . 01695 581007

Martin Cunningham Solicitors
‡Stockport p395 . . . 0161 456 5857

Cunninghams
‡Manchester p302 . . . 0161 833 1600

Cunningtons
‡Braintree p155 . . . 01376 326868
Braintree p155 . . . 01376 326868
Croydon p205 . . . 020 8688 8446
Ilford p259 . . . 020 8553 0002
Solihull p382 . . . 0121 705 6868
Wickford p431 . . . 01268 732268

Currey & Co
‡Westminster SW1 p24 . . . 020 7802 2700

Stella Currie
‡London EC2 p24 . . . 020 7638 9979

Daniel Curry & Co
‡Croydon p205 . . . 020 8680 2188

Curry Popeck
‡London W1 p24 . . . 020 7224 6633
Kenton p264 . . . 020 8907 2000 / 8907 8896

Curtis
‡Plymouth p349 . . . 01752 204444

Alan Curtis Solicitors
‡Monmouth p318 . . . 01600 772288

David Curtis & Co
‡Leicester p279 . . . 0116 270 2402

Curtis Davis Garrard
‡Uxbridge p417 . . . 020 8734 2800

Kenneth Curtis & Co
‡Birmingham p137 . . . 0121 356 1161
Redditch p362 . . . 01527 61967

Curtis Law Solicitors
‡Blackburn p145 . . . 01254 297130

Curtis Mallet-Prevost Colt & Mosle LLP
‡London EC2 p24 . . . 020 7710 9800

Curtis Parkinson
‡Nottingham p336 . . . 0115 931 7000
Nottingham p336 . . . 0800 056 6042

Curtis Turner & Drukker Ltd
‡London EC4 p24 . . . 020 7353 1770

Curwens
‡Enfield p218 . . . 020 8363 4444
Cheshunt p189 . . . 01992 631461
Hoddesdon p251 . . . 01992 463727
Waltham Abbey p420 . . . 01992 712549

Patrick J Cusack & Co
‡Harrow p241 . . . 020 8863 3414

Cuthbert & Co
‡Peterborough p347 . . . 01733 564655

Susan Cuthbertson & Co
‡Ilkley p261 . . . 01943 602811

Cuthbertsons
‡Blyth p148 . . . 01670 352121
Ashington p119 . . . 01670 813524

Cutler Buttery Solicitors
‡Halesowen p237 . . . 0121 550 0010

Cuttle & Co
‡Manchester p302 . . . 0161 835 2050

Cuttle & Co Solicitors
Oldham p340 . . . 0161 678 7443

Cyfraith JRL Law
‡Llanrwst p292 . . . 01492 641222

Cygnet Family Law
‡Cleveland p196 . . . 01642 777680

Cyril Morris Arkwright
‡Bolton p148 . . . 01204 535261

D

DAC Beachcroft
‡London EC4 p24 . . . 020 7242 1011
Birmingham p137 . . . 0121 698 5200
Bristol p162 . . . 0117 918 2000
Leeds p272 . . . 0113 251 4700
London EC4 p24 . . . 020 7936 2222
London EC3 p24 . . . 020 7208 6800
London EC3 p24 . . . 020 7936 2222
London EC3 p24 . . . 020 7894 6960
Manchester p303 . . . 0161 934 3000
Manchester p303 . . . 0161 839 8396
Newcastle upon Tyne p324 . . . 0191 404 4000
Newport p328 . . . 0844 980 0400
Winchester p433 . . . 01962 705500

Law Offices of Paul D'Ambrogio
‡Chester p190 . . . 0870 442 2654

Oliver D'Sa Solicitors
‡Leicester p279 . . . 0116 275 5549

D & A Solicitors
‡Birmingham p137 0121 523 3601 / 0845 803 5961

DASH Solicitors
‡Southall p384 . . . 07813 506291

DBL Talbots LLP
‡Stourbridge p399 . . . 01384 445850
Codsall p197 . . . 01902 843427
Dudley p213 . . . 01384 459551
Dudley p213 . . . 01384 252471
Kidderminster p265 . . . 01562 749910
Wolverhampton p437 . . . 01902 427561

DB Law
‡Camborne p173 . . . 01209 712428
Falmouth p223 . . . 01326 211609
Penzance p346 . . . 01736 364261
St Ives p392 . . . 01736 793883

DBP Law Solicitors
‡London NW9 p24 . . . 020 8200 2356

DBS Law Ltd
‡Birmingham p137 . . . 0844 277 0800

DC Employment Solicitors
‡Southampton p385 . . . 0844 800 7072

DDE Law
‡Prescot p355 . . . 0151 493 9993

D E T Child
‡London SW19 p24 . . . 020 8540 3087

DFA Law LLP
‡Northampton p331 . . . 01604 609560
Northampton p331 . . . 01604 609560

DF Legal LLP
‡Tewkesbury p410 . . . 01684 850750
Ledbury p271 . . . 01531 633222

DF Solicitors
‡London SE9 p24 . . . 020 3223 1061

dgb Solicitors
‡Chatham p184 . . . 01634 304000
‡Wirral p435 . . . 0151 342 2211

DG Law
‡London SW11 p24 . . . 0845 634 6253

D Goldsmith & Co
‡Marlborough p313 . . . 01672 512168

DH Law Solicitors LLP
‡London W7 p24 . . . 020 8840 8008
Hayes p245 . . . 020 8840 8008
London SW1 p24 . . . 020 8840 8008

DHP Trustee Campany
‡Norwich p334

DJK Solicitors
‡Waltham Abbey p420 . . . 01992 718880

DJ Solicitors
‡Northwood p333 . . . 01923 828668

DKLL Solicitors
‡Coulsdon p199 . . . 020 8668 0419

DKLM Solicitors
‡London EC1 p24 . . . 020 7549 7888

DLA Piper UK LLP
‡London EC2 p24 . . . 0870 011 1111
Birmingham p137 . . . 0870 011 1111
Leeds p272 . . . 0870 011 1111
Liverpool p287 . . . 0870 011 1111
Manchester p303 . . . 0870 011 1111
Sheffield p375 . . . 0870 011 1111

DLC Solicitors Limited
‡Darwen p207 . . . 01254 761234

DL Legal LLP
‡London WC1 p25 . . . 0845 456 9800

DMB Law
‡Sevenoaks p374 . . . 01732 228800

DMH Stallard LLP
‡Brighton p159 . . . 01273 329833
Crawley p202 . . . 01293 605000
London EC4 p25 . . . 020 7822 1500

The D M Partnership
‡Birmingham p137 . . . 0121 200 0930

DP Law Ltd t/a David Prosser & Co
‡Bridgend p157 . . . 01656 645921

DPNA Solicitors
‡London SE4 p25 . . . 020 8177 7199

DRG Solicitors LLP
‡Manchester p303 . . . 0870 060 6075

DRM Conveyancing
‡Clitheroe p196 . . . 01200 428102

DR Solicitors
‡Guildford p236 . . . 01483 511555

DSM Legal Solicitors
‡Warrington p421 . . . 0845 009 0863

DTM Legal LLP
‡Chester p190 . . . 01244 354800

DWF
‡Liverpool p287 . . . 0151 907 3000
Leeds p272 . . . 0113 261 6000
London EC4 p25 . . . 020 7645 9500
Manchester p303 . . . 0161 603 5000
Newcastle upon Tyne p324 . . . 0191 350 6173
Preston p356 . . . 01772 556677

DWFM Beckman
‡Westminster W1 p25 . . . 020 7872 0023

DW Law
‡Hatfield p244 . . . 01707 261177

DW Solicitors
‡Northampton p331 . . . 01604 624222

DWT Legal Ltd
‡Kidderminster p265 . . . 0844 770 3799

Graham Dack & Company
March p312 . . . 01354 661700

Graham Dack & Company (inc Battersby James)
‡Chatteris p185 . . . 01354 695885

Shazad H Dad Solicitors
‡Bradford p153 . . . 01274 731000

Gordon Dadds
‡London W1 p25 . . . 020 7493 6151

Adrian Dagger
‡Crawley p202 . . . 01293 403399

Dakers
‡Brighton p159 . . . 01273 571685

Dakers Marriott Solicitors
‡Strood p400 . . . 01634 813300

Dale & Co Solicitors Lincoln
‡Lincoln p284 . . . 01522 513399

Dale And Dale
‡Chipping Norton p193 . . . 0845 603 1573

Dale & Newbery LLP
‡Staines p393 . . . 01784 464491

Stephanie Dale & Co
‡Hove p254 . . . 01273 748333

Dale-Lace & Co
‡Beaconsfield p129 . . . 01494 675269

Dale-Stevens LLP
‡London EC4 p25 . . . 020 7929 2247 / 7929 3897
Felixstowe p225 . . . 020 7929 2247

Dalgarno Solicitors
‡Warrington p421 . . . 0870 444 1501

Dallas & Co
‡Reading p360 . . . 0118 976 7500

Dallow & Dallow
‡Wolverhampton p437 . . . 01902 420208

Dalton & Hague
‡Sedbergh p373 . . . 01539 620365

Dalton Barrett Solicitors
‡London E14 p25 . . . 020 7537 7904

Dalton Holmes Gray
‡London W1 p25 . . . 020 7025 7878

Martin C Dalton
‡Horsham p253 . . . 01403 266642

Daltons
‡Eastbourne p215 . . . 01323 720040
‡Stamford p393 . . . 01780 762526
Oakham p340 . . . 01572 722002 / 724343

Daltons Solicitors
‡Petersfield p348 . . . 01730 262816

James Daly Legal Consultancy
‡Andover p118 . . . 07870 592467 / 0870 420 5451

Simon Daly Solicitors
‡Stockton-on-Tees p396 . . . 01642 604074

Danby & Co
‡Cottingham p199 . . . 01536 771110
‡Northampton p331 . . . 01604 604573

Daniel & Edwards
‡Ramsgate p359 . . . 01843 594651

Daniel and Harris
‡Camden NW6 p25 . . . 020 7625 0202

Daniel & Partners
‡Barking p123

Leona Daniel
‡Hassocks p243 . . . 01273 845024

Daniels & Company
‡York p444 . . . 01904 679999

George Daniels Associates
‡Wembley p426 . . . 020 8728 8726

Adrian Dann & Company
‡Southend-on-Sea p387 . . . 01702 348802

Danobeitia & Forster
‡London NW5 p25 . . . 020 8876 4733 / 7267 2286

Dar & Co
‡Manchester p303 . . . 0161 225 3777

Darby & Darby
‡Torquay p412 . . . 01803 313656

M J Darby & Co
‡Halesowen p237 . . . 0121 421 7933

Darbys Solicitors LLP
‡Oxford p343 . . . 01865 811700

W H Darbyshire & Son
‡Blackpool p146 . . . 01253 346646
Lytham p296 . . . 01253 736134

Adam Darcy
‡London NW9 *p25*

Dare Emmanuel Solicitors
‡London E1 *p25* 020 7392 9566

Joseph Darios Solicitors
‡Southampton *p385* 023 8023 7575

Marie Dark Solicitors
‡Chepstow *p189* 01291 621638

Darling & Stephensons
‡Darlington *p206* 01325 489000
Barnard Castle *p123* 01325 489000

Darlington Hardcastles
‡Rickmansworth *p364* 01923 774272

Darlingtons
‡Edgware *p217* . . . .020 8952 0033 / 8951 6666

Paul Darnborough Solicitors
‡Manchester *p303* 0161 881 9479

Tony Dart Solicitors & Advocate
‡Barnstaple *p125* 01271 341742

Darwin Bowie Ltd
‡Narberth *p320* 01834 860436

Darwin Gray
‡Cardiff *p178* 029 2082 9100
Newport *p328* 01633 415440

Darwin McGrogan
‡York *p444* 01904 613077

Dass Solicitors
‡Birmingham *p137* 0121 248 4000
London SW1 *p25* 020 7802 5040

Dassaur Solicitors
‡Birmingham *p137* 0121 702 2758

Dave & Co Solicitors
‡Rayleigh *p359* 01268 773211

Davenport & Scott
‡Ambleside *p117* 01539 431919

Jeremy Davenport
‡Hockley *p251* 01702 205163

Davenport Law Limited
‡Ilkley *p261* 01943 608226

Davenport Lyons
‡London W1 *p25* 020 7468 2600

Davey Franklin Jones
‡Cirencester *p195* 01285 654875
Gloucester *p230* 01452 508800

David & Snape
‡Bridgend *p157* 01656 661115
Porthcawl *p353* . . . . . .01656 782070 / 785038

Aubrey David
‡Westminster W1 *p25* 020 7224 4410

DAVID CONWAY & CO
‡London W1 *p26* 020 7258 3000

David James & Company
‡Aberystwyth *p114* 01970 615789

Paul David Consulting Limited
‡London NW4 *p26* 07715 420980

Davidson & Co
‡Edgware *p217* 020 8951 5656

Davidson Broadbent & Co
‡Harrogate *p240* 01423 561229

Christopher Davidson Solicitors LLP
‡Cheltenham *p188* 01242 581481

Davidson Flynn Duke Solicitors
‡Birkenhead *p134* 0151 513 3333

A Daphne Davidson-Kelly
‡Liphook *p285* 01428 727978

Davidson Large LLP
‡Harrogate *p240* 01423 727272
Billingham *p133* 01740 665050

Davidson Merali & Co
‡London W8 *p26* 020 7937 2525

Davidson Morris Solicitors
‡London W1 *p26* 0845 413 7000

Paul Davidson Taylor
‡Horsham *p253* 01403 262333

Roberta Davidson
‡Surbiton *p402* 020 8399 6704

Sheldon Davidson Solicitors
‡Whitefield *p430* 0161 796 5445

Davidson Smith & Co
‡Bedford *p130* 01234 351971

W A G Davidson & Co
‡London W3 *p26* 020 8992 4884

A M Davies
‡Harrogate *p240* 01423 772860

Davies & Co
‡Bromley *p166* 020 8460 6668

Davies & Co Solicitors Cyfreithwyr
‡Caernarfon *p172* . 01286 675715 / 07754 715113

Davies & Company
‡Stockport *p395* 0161 355 5500

Davies & Davies Associates Limited
‡London EC2 *p26* 0800 840 4025
Banbury *p122* 0800 840 4025

Davies & Gribbin Solicitors
‡Ormskirk *p341* 01695 573433

Davies & Jones Solicitors
‡Cardiff *p178* 029 2046 5296

Davies & Partners
‡Gloucester *p230* 01452 612345
Almondsbury *p115* 01454 619619
Birmingham *p137* 0121 616 4450

Anthony M Davies Solicitors
‡Hereford *p247* 01432 349004

Davies Battersby Ltd
‡London EC3 *p26* 020 7621 1090

Davies Bays & Co t/a Windsor & Co
Haringey N17 *p26* 020 8808 3237

Davies Bell & Reed
‡Newcastle upon Tyne *p324* 0191 232 8058

Davies Blunden & Evans
‡Farnborough *p224* 01252 541633
Yateley *p443* 01252 872617

D E Davies & Co
‡Epsom *p219* 020 8368 0048

David H N Davies
‡Salisbury *p371* 01722 322272

David L R Davies & Co
‡Ammanford *p117* . . . . .01269 593463 / 592119

Edward T Davies Sons & Tiltman
‡Pontyclun *p352* 01443 225446

George Davies Solicitors LLP
‡Manchester *p303* 0161 236 8992

Davies Gore Lomax
‡Leeds *p273* 0113 242 2797

Helen Davies Solicitors
‡Batley *p128* 07855 965381

Hywel Davies & Co
‡Bala *p121* 01678 520307

Davies Ingram & Harvey
‡Swansea *p405* 01792 653764

J M Lynn Davies
‡Denbigh *p208* 01745 817564

Jeremy Davies & Co
‡London SW7 *p26* 020 7589 4999

Davies Johnson & Co (Shipping & Commercial Solicitors)
‡Plymouth *p349* 01752 226020

Lawrence Davies & Co
‡Hammersmith & Fulham SW6 *p26* 020 7381 1171

Davies Morgante Law Limited
‡London SW19 *p26* 020 8944 7700

Davies Murray-White & Co
‡Stratford-upon-Avon *p400* 01789 295544

Neil Davies & Partners LLP
‡Birmingham *p137* 0121 200 7040

Davies Parsons Allchurch
‡Llanelli *p292* 01554 749144
Swansea *p405* 01792 461146

Davies Partnership
‡Helston *p246* 01326 573767
St Agnes *p389* 01872 553131

Davies Prichard & Weatherill
‡Cardiff *p178* 029 2037 7471

R George Davies & Co
‡Abergavenny *p113* 01873 852535

Rhidian Davies & Co Solicitors
‡Cardiff *p178* 029 2056 2913

Richard Stephen Davies
‡Mold *p318* 01352 754468

Ruth Davies LLB Solicitor
‡Bridgend *p157* 01656 860644

Davies Solicitors
‡Cambridge *p174* 01223 842211
Cambridge *p174* 01223 696444

Davies Sully Wilkins
‡Caerphilly *p172* 029 2088 7828

Tudor H Davies
‡St Asaph *p390* 01745 583806

W Davies
‡Woking *p436* 01483 744900

Davis & Co
‡Amersham *p117* 01494 787587
‡Ilford *p259* 020 8551 4228
‡Leicester *p279* 0116 285 4774
‡London EC3 *p26* 020 7621 1091

Davis & Co (Solicitors) Limited
‡London WC1 *p26* 020 8123 6373

Davis Blank Furniss
‡Manchester *p303* 0161 832 3304
Glossop *p230* 01457 860606

Davis Davidson
‡Beverley *p131* 01482 881278

Davis Gregory Ltd
‡Cheltenham *p188* 01242 235202

Ian Davis
‡London N14 *p26* 020 8886 1830

Leigh Davis
‡London W1 *p26* 020 7631 0302

Nigel Davis Solicitors
‡Belper *p131* 01335 372889

Davis Priest & Co
‡Redditch *p362* 01527 69231

Ralph Davis
‡Islington EC1 *p26* 020 7253 7200

Davis Simmonds Donaghey
‡Gillingham *p229* 01634 852700
Herne Bay *p248* 01227 361690
Sittingbourne *p380* 01795 599931

Davis Solicitors
‡London SW6 *p26* 020 7930 6996

Davis Wood
‡Bristol *p162* 0117 965 3504

Davis-Law Associates
‡Chalfont St Peter *p184* 01753 888776

Davisons
‡Birmingham *p137* 0121 685 1234
Birmingham *p137* 0121 685 1255
Birmingham *p137* 0121 685 1248
Sutton Coldfield *p403* 0121 323 2525

Davitt & Co
‡London NW2 *p26* 020 7566 8244

Davitt Jones Bould
‡Taunton *p408* 01823 279279

Dawar & Co
‡Ilford *p259* 020 8550 4741

William Dawes & Co
‡Rye *p370* 01797 223177

Dawson & Burgess with Bell Dallman & Co
‡Doncaster *p211* 01302 349463
Doncaster *p211* 01302 834744
Doncaster *p211*

Dawson Cornwell
‡London WC1 *p26* 020 7242 2556

Graham Dawson & Co
‡Bexley *p132* 01322 558811

Dawson Hart
‡Uckfield *p416* 01825 762281

J F Dawson
‡Beaconsfield *p129* 01494 670566

Dawson Lloyd & Co
‡Reading *p360* 0118 966 9238

Dawson Mason & Carr
‡Guildford *p236* 01483 576169
Farnham *p225* 01252 725771

Dawson Solicitors
‡Wolverhampton *p437* 01902 759944

Daybells LLP
‡London E15 *p26* 020 8555 4321

Abigail Daykin & Co
‡Farnham *p225* . . . 01252 719155 / 07774 259331

Nicholas Daykin Solicitors
‡Attleborough *p120* 01953 453774

Daysparkes
‡London WC1 *p26* 020 7242 8018

Charles De Alwis
‡Chadwell Heath *p183* 020 8597 5717

De Brauw Blackstones Westbroek
‡London EC4 *p26* 020 7337 3510

De Coninck Solicitors
‡Stoke-on-Trent *p397* 01270 883484

De Cruz Solicitors
‡London W1 *p26* 020 7493 4265

Stanley De Leon
‡Potters Bar *p355* 01707 657277

De Maid Solicitors & Advocates
‡Cardiff *p178* 029 2023 5575

David De Mallet Morgan
‡Polegate *p351* 01323 871100

De Marco Hunter
‡Coventry *p200* 024 7621 4440

De Mello Kamath & Co
‡Wembley *p426* 020 8902 5284

Maureen De Pietro
‡Bristol *p162* 0117 962 8772

Edward De Silva & Co
‡Southall *p384* 020 8571 2299

De Soyza & Fernando
‡London SE21 *p26* 020 8670 9918

Ines De Vecchi
‡London SW12 *p26* 020 8675 0152

Gordon de Vere
St Albans *p390* 01727 758126

De Vita Norris Solicitors
‡Barton-upon-Humber *p126* 01652 661960

Deakin & Co
‡Warrington *p421* 01942 738580

Dean & Co
‡Stourbridge *p399* 01384 352525
Dudley *p213* 01384 352525

Gordon Dean Solicitors
‡Norwich *p334* 01603 767671
Great Yarmouth *p234*

John M Dean & Co
‡Denton *p208* 0161 337 9665

Roger Dean & Co
‡Biggin Hill *p133* 01959 542872

Dean Solicitors
‡Rochdale *p365* 01706 661400

Dean Wilson Laing
‡Brighton *p159* 01273 327241

Malcolm Dear Whitfield Evans LLP
‡Kenton *p265* 020 8907 4366

James M R Debenham
‡Dorchester *p212* 0845 230 0644

Debenhams Ottaway
‡St Albans *p390* 01727 837161
Radlett *p358* 01923 857171

Debevoise & Plimpton
‡London EC2 *p26* 020 7786 9000

Debidins
‡Ealing W13 *p26* . . .020 8567 1381 / 8567 6343

Debridge Solicitors
‡Hackney E5 *p26* 020 8986 2581

Deccan Prime Solicitors
‡Harrow *p241* 020 3008 6769

Dechert
‡London EC4 *p26* 020 7184 7000

Decimus Fearon
‡London SW1 *p26* 020 7823 0450

Dedicated Accident Solicitors
‡Derby *p208* 01332 869286

Dee & Griffin
‡Gloucester *p230* 01452 617288
Gloucester *p230* 01452 724343

T A Deegan
‡Whitton *p431* 020 8755 2574

Deen Solicitors
‡Luton *p295* 01582 484900

Deen Wahid
‡Oldham *p340* 0161 241 7676

Deibel & Allen
‡Portslade-by-Sea *p354* 01273 430999

Deighton Guedalla
‡London EC1 *p26* 020 7713 9434

Del & Co Solicitors
‡London N17 *p26* 020 8880 9393

Claudio Del Giudice
‡London EC2 *p26* 020 7613 2788

John Delaney & Co
‡Leeds *p273* 0113 246 8151

Dellapina & Co Solicitors
‡Knutsford *p269* 01565 634100

Delta Legal
‡Stockport *p395* 0870 350 5101

Claire Delves
‡Northampton *p331* 01327 831050

Michael Demidecki
‡London W9 *p26* 020 7266 3607

Dempster Binning LLP
‡Chandlers Ford *p184* 023 8062 1790

Denby & Co
‡Barrow-in-Furness *p125* 01229 822366
Ulverston *p416* 01229 582283

Samantha Denham Solicitors
‡Hastings *p243* . . . . . .01424 718822 / 719111

Denhams
‡Guildford *p236* 01483 456450

Denison Till
‡York *p444* 01904 611411

Denleys
‡Taunton *p408* 01643 707998

Denning Solicitors
‡London E7 *p26* 020 8519 2999

Dennings LLP
‡Tipton *p412* 0121 520 3599

Dennis Morris Solicitor
‡Tonbridge *p412* 01622 833048

Dennison Greer Solicitors
‡Manchester *p303* 0845 807 7788

Denniss Matthews
‡London SE20 *p27* . .020 8778 7301 / 8778 7631

Dent Abrams Solicitors
‡London W6 *p27* 0845 833 2318
Southampton *p385* 0845 833 2318

The Dental Law Partnership
‡Nantwich *p320* 01270 613320

The Dental Law Partnership Solicitors
‡Borehamwood *p150* 020 8387 1587

Chris Denton
‡Burley-in-Wharfedale *p168* 01943 607828

Denton Solicitors
‡London E18 *p27* 020 8989 7477

Dervan Solicitors
‡Liverpool *p287* 0151 225 0150

Derwent Law Solicitors
‡Derby *p208* 01332 416655

K J Desbottes & Co
‡Caterham *p183* 01883 343460

Desor & Co
‡Hayes *p245* 020 8569 0708

J P A Devane Solicitor
‡Woking *p436* 01483 472760

Devas Keogh James
‡Peterborough *p347* 01733 340666

Devassey Legal
‡Nottingham *p336* 0115 852 4710
London W1 *p27* 020 7182 4226

Devereaux Solicitors
‡London WC2 *p27* 020 7242 7766

Devereux & Co
‡Bristol *p162* 0117 959 3344
Bristol *p162* 0117 938 0222

Devers & Co Solicitors
‡Leeds *p273* . . . 01977 783363

Devine & Co
‡Ellesmere Port *p217* . . . 0151 356 2009

Laura Devine Solicitors
‡London EC2 *p27* . . . 020 7710 0700

Devine Law
‡Hull *p256* . . . 01482 212077

Devine Okeeffe Solicitors
‡Leamington Spa *p270* . . . 01926 888947

Devonalds
‡Pontypridd *p352* . . . 01443 404700
Cardiff *p178* . . . 01443 755189
Pontypridd *p352* . . . 01443 404331
Talbot Green *p407* . . . 01443 223888
Tonypandy *p412* . . . 01443 434343

Devonshires
‡London EC2 *p27* . . . 020 7628 7576

Dewar Hogan
‡London EC4 *p27* . . . 020 7634 9550

Dewes LLP
‡Tamworth *p407* . . . 01827 58391

Dewey & LeBoeuf
‡London EC3 *p27* . . . 020 7459 5000

Dewey Ballantine
‡London EC2 *p27* . . . 020 7456 6000

Anthony J Dewhurst
‡Chorley *p194* . . . 01257 480715

Dews Witcomb
‡Leicester *p279* . . . 0116 233 4499

Dexter Henry & Co
‡London SW16 *p27* . . . 020 8769 5550

Dexter Montague LLP
‡Reading *p360* . . . 0118 939 3999

Deygoo & Co Solicitors
‡Thornton Heath *p411* . . . 020 8664 9224

Dhanju Mclean & Anwar Solicitors
‡Iver *p263* . . . 01753 651743

Dhillon & Co
‡London E13 *p27* . . . 020 8471 7884
Southend-on-Sea *p387* . . . 01702 393022

Dhillons
‡Ilford *p260* . . . 020 8262 6565

Diamond Solicitors Limited
‡London E1 *p27* . . . 020 7247 0707

Diamonds
‡Buckhurst Hill *p167* . . . 020 8559 0778

Dias Solicitors
‡London WC2 *p27* . . . 020 7866 8110
London W1 *p27* . . . 020 7031 1117

Hector Diaz & Co
‡London WC1 *p27* . . . 020 7404 9349

Dibbens
‡Wimborne *p433* . . . 01202 882456

Dickens & Co
‡Crowthorne *p204* . . . 01344 772901 / 776151

Dickenson Martin
‡Warrington *p421* . . . 01925 574748

Dickins Hopgood Chidley LLP
‡Hungerford *p258* . . . 01488 683555

Dickins Shiebert
‡Potters Bar *p355* . . . 01707 851100

Dickinson & Co
‡Stamford *p393* . . . 01780 752581

Dickinson Dees
‡Newcastle upon Tyne *p324* . . . 0191 279 9000
London EC4 *p27* . . . 0844 984 1500
Newcastle upon Tyne *p324* . . . 0844 984 1500
Stockton-on-Tees *p397* . . . 0844 984 1500
York *p444* . . . 0844 984 1500

Dickinson Manser
‡Poole *p352* . . . 01202 673071
Broadstone *p166* . . . 01202 692308 / 694490

Dickinson Parker Hill
‡Ormskirk *p341* . . . 01695 574201

Dickinson Solicitors Limited
‡London SW8 *p27* . . . 020 7820 1669

Dickinson Wood
‡Doncaster *p211* . . . 01302 329504

Dickinsons
‡Blackpool *p146* . . . 01253 781010
Blackpool *p146* . . . 01253 795577

Dickson Haslam
‡Kirkham *p268* . . . 01772 685109
Lytham *p296* . . . 01253 730111
Preston *p356* . . . 01772 883100

Dickson Minto WS
‡London EC2 *p27* . . . 020 7628 4455

Dicksons Solicitors Ltd
‡Stoke-on-Trent *p397* . . . 01782 262424
Cheadle *p185* . . . 01782 262424
Stoke-on-Trent *p397* . . . 01782 262424

Didlaw
‡Liphook *p285* . . . 01428 724685

Didsbury Family Law
‡Manchester *p303* . . . 0161 434 0600

Digwa Cousins
‡Leeds *p273* . . . 0113 249 6661

Dilworth Lamb & Co
‡Orpington *p341* . . . 01689 821119

Dilwyns
‡Llandrindod Wells *p291* . . . 01597 822707

Din Solicitors
‡Halifax *p238* . . . 01422 320485

Dinning Consultancy
‡Didcot *p210* . . . 07900 215065

Disken & Co
‡Dewsbury *p210* . . . 01924 464101

The Dispute Resolution Practice
‡Guildford *p236* . . . 01483 205325

Rosemary Ditchman
‡Dereham *p209* . . . 01362 683530

Divine Legal Practise
‡Wembley *p426* . . . 020 8970 2198

Divorce & Family Law Practice
‡Birmingham *p137* . . . 0121 200 0890

The Divorce Practice
‡Westbury-on-Trym *p428*

Divorce Solicitors Online
‡London EC1 *p27* . . . 020 7870 6263

Dixon & Templeton
‡Fordingbridge *p227* . . . 01425 652194
Ringwood *p364* . . . 01425 476231

Dixon Coles & Gill
‡Wakefield *p418* . . . 01924 373467
Wakefield *p418* . . . 01924 263166 / 263899

Dixon Coles & Goddard
‡Leicester *p279* . . . 0116 236 4708

Dixon Law Limited
‡Leeds *p273* . . . 0113 204 2470

Dixon Lewis Solicitors
‡Wellington *p425* . . . 01952 245700
Craven Arms *p202* . . . 01588 672399

Dixon Phillips Ltd
‡Cambridge *p174* . . . 01223 352007

Dixon Rigby Keogh
‡Sandbach *p372* . . . 01270 766550
Middlewich *p315* . . . 01606 835736
Northwich *p333* . . . 01606 48111
Winsford *p434* . . . 01606 557211

Dixon Stewart
‡New Milton *p321* . . . 01425 621515

Dixon Stewart Solicitors
Highcliffe *p250* . . . 01425 279222

Dixon Thomasson Partnership
‡Oldham *p340* . . . 01706 843230
‡Rochdale *p365* . . . 01706 525253

Dixon Ward
‡Richmond upon Thames *p364* . . . 020 8940 4051
Ham *p238* . . . 020 8546 0225 / 8549 2615

Do I Have A Case? (Tom Street & Co)
‡Frome *p228* . . . 0800 014 8727

Doberman Deen
Newcastle upon Tyne *p324* . . . 0191 281 7468

Stephen Doberman Solicitor
‡Newcastle upon Tyne *p324* . . . 0191 281 0333

David Doble
‡London WC1 *p27* . . . 020 7831 1516

Dobson & Sleeman
‡Middlesbrough *p315* . . . 01642 231707

Julian Dobson Solicitors
‡Brighton *p159* . . . 01273 766355

Dobsons
‡Orpington *p341* . . . 01689 886300

Dobsons Solicitors
‡Altrincham *p116* . . . 01694 17775

Vincent Docherty & Co
‡Camden NW1 *p27* . . . 020 7723 1284

Dockland Solicitors LLP
‡London E14 *p27* . . . 020 7531 2990

Guy Dodd Solicitors
‡Chester *p190* . . . 01244 315577

DODD LEWIS SOLICITORS
‡London SE3 *p27* . . . 020 8852 1255

Dodds & Partners
‡Leicester *p279* . . . 0116 253 8585

Malcolm Dodds & Co
‡Carlisle *p182* . . . 01228 529444

Paul Dodds Solicitors
‡Wallsend *p419* . . . 0191 263 6200

The Doffman Isaacs Partnership
‡London NW8 *p27* . . . 020 7722 0999

Dogra & Co
‡Southall *p384* . . . 020 8571 7741

Dollman & Pritchard
‡Caterham *p183* . . . 01883 347823

Dolmans
‡Cardiff *p178* . . . 029 2034 5531

Dolphine Solicitors
‡London SE5 *p27* . . . 020 7358 6160

Dominic & Co Solicitors Ltd
‡Liverpool *p287* . . . 0151 722 5540

Don Solicitors
‡Wembley *p426* . . . 020 8782 1130

Donald Race & Newton
Burnley *p169* . . . 01282 433241

Donaldson Dunstall
‡Bexhill *p131* . . . 01424 216329

Donaldson West
‡Crowborough *p204* . . . 01892 662233

John Donkin & Co
‡Gateshead *p228* . . . 0191 495 2896 / 477 1781
Washington *p423* . . . 0191 416 9444

Donnelly & Elliott Limited
‡Gosport *p232* . . . 023 9250 5500

Donnelly McArdle Adamson
‡Sunderland *p401* . . . 0191 510 9911
Darlington *p206* . . . 01325 482299
Hartlepool *p243* . . . 01429 274732
Peterlee *p347* . . . 0191 586 3581
Stockton-on-Tees *p397* . . . 01642 345151
Sunderland *p401* . . . 0191 510 3020

Donns
‡Manchester *p303* . . . 0161 834 3311

Donovan Newton Limited
‡Nottingham *p336* . . . 0115 985 6600

Dootsons LLP
‡Leigh *p282* . . . 01942 673431
Atherton *p120* . . . 01942 882172
Culcheth *p205* . . . 01925 765212

Dorade Law
‡Dartmouth *p207* . . . 01803 835187

Doran & Co
‡Coulsdon *p199* . . . 020 8660 6947

Dorcas Funmi & Co
‡Erith *p219* . . . 01322 335005

Dorians
‡Derby *p208* . . . 01332 680580

Dorling Cottrell
‡Benfleet *p131* . . . 01268 795530
Basildon *p126* . . . 01268 796000

Benjamin H Dorman
‡Ascot *p118* . . . 01344 622276

Dorman Joseph Wachtel
‡London E1 *p27* . . . 020 7680 6300

Dorsey & Whitney
‡London EC2 *p27* . . . 020 7588 0800

Dotcom Solicitors
‡London N17 *p27* . . . 020 8880 9000

Double & Megson
‡Market Deeping *p312* . . . 01778 341494
Bourne *p151* . . . 01778 423376

Theodore Dougan Solicitors
‡London SE1 *p27* . . . 020 7463 2111

Adam Douglas & Son
‡Alnwick *p115* . . . 01665 602363
Amble *p117* . . . 01665 710744
Berwick-upon-Tweed *p131* . . . 01289 306479

Charles Douglas Solicitors
‡London W1 *p27* . . . 020 7866 6190

Douglas-Jones Mercer
‡Swansea *p405* . . . 01792 650000

Douglas Solicitors
‡Redhill *p362* . . . 01737 780295

Douglass Simon
‡Brentford *p156* . . . 020 8560 3888
London SW5 *p27* . . . 020 7373 4429

Doves Solicitors
‡London SE1 *p27* . . . 020 7232 5100

Peter Dovey and Co
‡London W11 *p27* . . . 020 7616 8424

Downes & Siddall
‡Lincoln *p284* . . . 01522 543343

Downey & Co
‡Bradford *p153* . . . 01274 883515

DOWNIE & GADBAN
‡Alton *p116* . . . 01420 82879

Downs
‡Dorking *p212* . . . 01306 880110
‡Godalming *p231* . . . 01483 861848

G E Downs
‡South Shields *p383* . . . 0191 427 4745

C H Downton
‡Doncaster *p211* . . . 01302 360060

David Downton & Co
‡Milton Keynes *p316* . . . 01908 563030

Dowse & Co
‡Hackney E8 *p27* . . . 020 7254 6205

Dowse Baxter
‡London SW19 *p27* . . . 020 8946 9110

Dowson Billington
‡Preston *p356* . . . 01772 556807

Amanda Doyle Law Services
‡Bristol *p162* . . . 07973 201327

Andrew Doyle & Co Solicitors
‡Preston *p356* . . . 01772 561611

Doyle Clayton Solicitors Limited
‡London EC2 *p27* . . . 020 7329 9090
London E14 *p27* . . . 020 7038 8051
Reading *p360* . . . 0118 959 6839

Rona Doyle & Co
‡Ashford *p119* . . . 01233 812244

Dozie & Co
‡Haringey N15 *p27* . . . 020 8808 2244

Draper & Co
‡Farnham *p225* . . . 01252 727374

Draper & Co Solicitors
‡Aldershot *p115* . . . 01252 318151

Draycott Browne Solicitors
‡Manchester *p303* . . . 0161 228 2244
Sale *p370* . . . 0161 972 0999

Drayson Law Limited
‡Solihull *p382* . . . 0845 643 9800

Drew Jones Solicitors
‡Coventry *p200* . . . 024 7655 5511

Brian Drewitt
‡Stockport *p395* . . . 0845 260 0855

Driscoll Young Solicitors
‡Newport *p328* . . . 01633 266999

Driver Belcher Solicitors
‡Bishop's Waltham *p144* . . . 01489 892101 / 892102
Southampton *p385* . . . 01489 785737

Drivers
‡York *p444* . . . 01904 625661
Malton *p300* . . . 01653 600075

Driving Defences LLP
‡Bury *p170* . . . 0844 335 0767
‡London W1 *p27* . . . 020 7903 5144

Druces LLP
‡London EC2 *p27* . . . 020 7638 9271

Druitts
‡Bournemouth *p151* . . . 01202 551863

Drummond Walker Solicitors
‡Luton *p295* . . . 0872 111 4336

Drummonds
‡Chester *p190* . . . 01244 408300

Gwendoline Drury
‡Cottingham *p199* . . . 01482 840201

Drydens
‡Bradford *p153* . . . 01274 378000

DRYSDALES
‡Southend-on-Sea *p387* . . . 01702 423400

David Du Pre & Co
‡London WC1 *p28* . . . 020 7430 1950

A Dua & Co
‡Greenford *p234* . . . 0845 430 4086

Duane Morris
‡London EC1 *p28* . . . 020 7786 2100

Duchennes
‡Bedford *p130* . . . 01234 356678

Musa Dudhia & Co
‡London W1 *p28* . . . 020 7499 5353

Jacqueline Duff
‡Morpeth *p319* . . . 01669 621987

Scott Duff & Co
‡Penrith *p346* . . . 01768 865551
Carlisle *p182* . . . 01228 531054
Keswick *p265* . . . 01768 774321

Duffield Harrison LLP
‡Hoddesdon *p251* . . . 01992 442911
Hertford *p248* . . . 01992 587065

Duffield Stunt
‡Chelmsford *p186* . . . 01245 262351

Duffy Fowler Gabbi Solicitors
‡Hebden Bridge *p246* . . . 01422 844110

Dugdale Solicitors
‡Gillingham *p229* . . . 01634 580606

Valentine Duggins
‡Wallasey *p419* . . . 0151 638 4844

Gerald Duke Solicitor
‡Dorchester *p212* . . . 01305 340100

Dundas & Duce
‡Maidstone *p299* . . . 01622 681867

Dundas & Wilson CS LLP
‡London WC2 *p28* . . . 020 7240 2401

Dunham Guest & Lyons
‡Cannock *p176* . . . 01543 462121

Dunn & Baker
‡Exeter *p221* . . . 01392 285000
Cullompton *p205* . . . 01884 33818

Dunn & Co
‡Kingston upon Thames *p267* . . . 020 8541 1332

Peter Dunn & Co
‡Sunderland *p401* . . . 0191 568 9000

Dunn Simpson & Co
‡Bridgwater *p158* . . . 01278 424272

Dunne Gray
‡Altrincham *p116* . . . 0161 928 8877

Dunning & Co
‡London SE5 *p28* . . . 020 7733 6217

Dunning Anderson
‡Carterton *p183* . . . 01993 840200

Thomas Dunton Solicitors
‡Orpington *p342* . . . 01689 822554

David Dunwoody & Co
‡Newbury *p322* . . . 01635 354333

Uma Duraisingam
‡Waltham Forest E17 *p28* . . . 020 8521 1314

The Dures Partnership LLP
‡Liverpool *p287* . . . 0151 242 5111

David Durn & Co
‡Ruislip *p368* . . . 01895 612400

Dutton Gregory
‡Winchester *p433* . . . 01962 844333
Bournemouth *p151* . . . 01202 315005
Southampton *p385* . . . 023 8022 1344

Dutton Law Limited
‡Newcastle under Lyme p323 . . .01782 565900 / 07754 588302

Duval Vassiliades Solicitors
‡London EC3 p28 . . . . 020 7623 8580

Duxburys Solicitors
‡Tunbridge Wells p415. . . . . . . 01892 538762

Sarah Dwight Solicitor
‡Birmingham p137. . . . . 0121 702 2100

Dwyers
‡Ashton-under-Lyne p120 . . . . . 0161 308 3928

Dyakowski Gafford
‡Chipping Norton p193 . . . . . . 01608 643051

Dylan Conrad Kreolle
‡London NW4 p28. . . . . 020 8359 1123

DYNE DREWETT SOLICITORS LTD
Wincanton p433 . . . . 01963 32374
‡Sherborne p378 . . . . 01935 813691
Shepton Mallet p378 . . . . 01749 342323

Dyne Solicitors Limited
‡Chester p190. . . . . 01829 773100

Keith Dyson & Co
‡Manchester p304. . . . . 0161 832 9933

Dzimitrowicz York
‡Croydon p205 . . . . 020 8667 0340

E

E&K Solicitors & Estate Agents
‡Manchester p304. . . . . 0161 256 3915

EAD Solicitors LLP
‡Liverpool p287 . . . . 0151 291 2500
Huddersfield p255 . . . . 01484 437448
Liverpool p287 . . . . 0151 734 4339

E A Law
‡Barnet p124 . . . . 020 8805 5307

E&A Law
‡London W1 p28 . . . . 020 3178 7918

E & J Law LLP
‡Thornton Heath p411 . . . . 020 8684 5515

EB Legal Solicitors
‡Wilmslow p433 . . . . 01625 544753

EBR Attridge LLP
‡London N17 p28 . . . . 020 8808 0774
London SW11 p28 . . . . 020 7228 7050
London SE16 p28 . . . . 020 7231 5166
London WC1 p28. . . . . 020 7842 8600
London NW10 p28 . . . . 020 8961 5146

E-Business Legal
‡London N1 p28. . . . . 020 7704 0253

EEI Solicitors
‡Liverpool p287 . . . . 0151 707 8004

E G Law
‡London W8 p28 . . . . 020 7937 5594

EG Legal
‡Ripley p364. . . . . 01773 749955

ELC Solicitors
‡Ealing W5 p28 . . . . 020 8566 4045

EL Murphy & Co
‡Croydon p205 . . . . 020 8680 2638

ELS International Lawyers LLP
‡London WC2 p28. . . . . 020 7212 9000

ELS Solicitors
‡Ilford p260 . . . . 020 8262 5010

EMB Solicitors
‡Maidstone p299 . . . . 01634 313002

EMD Law LLP
‡St Leonards-on-Sea p392. . . . . 01424 420261

EMW
‡Milton Keynes p316. . . . . 0845 070 6000
London WC2 p28. . . . . 0845 070 6000

ENT Law
‡Southampton p385 . . . . 01329 834100

EOS Law
‡London WC2 p28. . . . . 020 3402 2800

ES Law
‡Herne Bay p248 . . . . 01227 283388

EWA Davis Solicitors & Notary Public
‡Torquay p412. . . . . 01803 607662

Eager & Co
‡Skegness p380. . . . . 01754 766688

Eagle Solicitors
‡London SE11 p28 . . . . 020 7840 0671

Eagles Solicitors
‡London SW19 p28 . . . . 020 8543 3938

Earl & Crocker
‡Liskeard p285 . . . . 01579 345304
Looe p293 . . . . 01503 265884

Earle & Waller
‡London N13 p28 . . . . 020 8888 7866

EarthRights Solicitors
‡Bishop's Stortford p144. . . . . . 01279 874172

Eason Law
‡Billingham p133 . . . . 01642 371371

Geraldine East Solicitor
‡London NW3 p28. . . . . 020 7794 9884

Christine Easter Solicitors
‡Brentwood p156 . . . . 01277 821506

Easthams Solicitors Limited
‡Blackpool p146. . . . . 0800 032 1432

Eastleys
‡Paignton p345 . . . . 01803 559257
Brixham p166. . . . . 01803 853266
Totnes p413 . . . . 01803 864888

Eastleys Defence Service
‡Plymouth p349 . . . . 01752 500281

Eastwoods Solicitors
‡London EC4 p28 . . . . 020 3137 4800

Eaton & Few
‡St Ives p391 . . . . 01480 301558

Eaton-Evans & Morris
‡Haverfordwest p244 . . . . 01437 763383

Eaton Ryan & Taylor
‡Birmingham p138. . . . . 0121 236 1999

Eaton Smith LLP
‡Huddersfield p255 . . . . 01484 821300

Eatons
‡Bradford p153 . . . . 0845 660 0660
Leeds p273. . . . . 0845 660 0660
Otley p342 . . . . 0845 660 0660

Eaves
‡Milford Haven p316. . . . . 01646 695785

David Ebert & Co
‡Southampton p385 . . . . 023 8047 7625

Ebor Law Limted
‡Leeds p273. . . . . 0113 237 2740
‡York p444 . . . . 01904 650960

Ebury House Solicitors
‡London W1 p28 . . . . 020 7355 7050

Eccles Heddon
‡Ripon p365. . . . . 01765 601717
Bedale p129 . . . . 01677 422422
Thirsk p411. . . . . 01845 522324

Eckford Rands
‡Northampton p331 . . . . 01604 621001

Eddowes Perry Adams Roberts & Co
‡Birmingham p138. . . . . 0121 373 7395

Eddowes Perry & Osbourne
‡Sutton Coldfield p403. . . . . . . 0121 686 9444
Sutton Coldfield p403. . . . . . . 0121 686 9666
Sutton Coldfield p403. . . . . . . 0121 686 9444

Eddowes Waldron
‡Derby p208. . . . . 01332 348484

David Ede Solicitors
‡London SE18 p28 . . . . 020 8316 4758

Edell Jones & Lessers
‡London E6 p28. . . . . 020 8548 5700

Eden & Co
‡Manchester p304. . . . . 0161 237 1116

Eden Solicitors
‡Hayes p245 . . . . 020 8848 7999

Edenfield Solicitors
‡Oldham p340. . . . . 0161 345 7574

Edgar Cule & Evans
‡Pentre p346 . . . . 01443 434179

Edgerley Harris Solicitors
‡Winchester p433 . . . . 01962 779861

Edison Law
‡Richmond upon Thames p364 . . 020 8406 0084

Edmondson Hall
‡Newmarket p327 . . . . 01638 560556

G E Edmondson-Jones
‡Easingwold p215. . . . . 01347 821615

Edmondsons
‡St Albans p390. . . . . 01727 866497

Edmunds & Co
‡Gainsborough p228. . . . . 01427 679817
‡Sutton Coldfield p403. . . . . . . 0121 350 0987
Walsall p420 . . . . 0845 260 5050

Sarah Edmunds Legal
‡Lewes p283 . . . . 01273 407970

S J Edney
‡Swindon p406 . . . . 0800 421234

Edridges & Drummonds
‡South Croydon p383 . . . . 020 8651 1218

C K Edrupt
‡Bradford p154 . . . . 01274 731111

Edward Oliver & Bellis
‡Ilford p260 . . . . 020 8500 4168
‡Ilford p260 . . . . 020 8553 1214

ALAN EDWARDS & CO
‡Kensington & Chelsea W8 p28 . . 020 7221 7644

Edwards & Grant Solicitors
‡Leicester p279 . . . . 0116 255 2110

Edwards Angell Palmer & Dodge
‡London EC2 p28 . . . . 020 7583 4055

Edwards Clegg
‡Beeston p130. . . . . 0115 922 4537

Edwards Davies Solicitors
‡Bromley p166. . . . . 020 8437 0900

Edwards Duthie
‡Ilford p260 . . . . 020 8514 9000
London E13 p29 . . . . 020 8514 9000
London E6 p29 . . . . 020 8514 9000

E Edwards Son & Noice
‡Billericay p133 . . . . 01277 658551

Leigh Edwards & Co
‡Kidlington p266. . . . . 01865 378243

Martin Edwards
‡Shifnal p378 . . . . 01952 462118

Nigel Edwards & Co
‡Maidstone p299 . . . . 01622 690575

Peter Edwards Law
‡Wirral p435. . . . . 0151 632 6699

R L Edwards & Partners
‡Bridgend p157 . . . . 01656 656861
Maesteg p298 . . . . 01656 733297
Porthcawl p353. . . . . 01656 784151
Treorchy p413 . . . . 01443 775000

Roger Edwards & Co
‡Tredegar p413 . . . . 01495 722865

Edwards Solicitors
‡Melton Mowbray p314 . . . . . . 01664 566606

T S Edwards & Son
‡Newport p328 . . . . 01633 257166
Hengoed p247 . . . . 01443 814161

Edwards Vaziraney
‡Beckenham p129. . . . . 020 8249 6536

Edwin Coe LLP
‡London WC2 p29. . . . . 020 7691 4000

Joe Egan Solicitors
‡Bolton p149 . . . . 01204 386214
Bolton p149. . . . . 01204 368060

Thomas Eggar LLP
‡Chichester p192 . . . . 01243 786111
Crawley p202. . . . . 01293 742700
London EC4 p29 . . . . 020 7842 0000
Newbury p322 . . . . 01635 571000
Southampton p385 . . . . 023 8083 1100
Worthing p441 . . . . 01903 234411

Egmont Solicitors & Notary Public
‡London W1 p29 . . . . 020 7494 3885

Egorov Puginsky Afanasiev & Partners LLP
‡London EC4 p29 . . . . 020 7822 7060

A A Ehrenzweig & Co
‡London N12 p29 . . . . 020 7584 1516

Mark Eisenthal & Co
‡London WC2 p29. . . . . 020 7379 3475

Elborne Mitchell LLP
‡London EC3 p29 . . . . 020 7320 9000

Elder Rahimi Limited
‡London E1 p29. . . . . 020 7377 6600
Folkestone p227 . . . . 07920 747475

Eldridges
‡Newport p328 . . . . 01983 524741
Freshwater p227 . . . . 01983 752492
Ryde p369 . . . . 01983 562241

Element Law Limited
‡Nottingham p337 .0115 984 5220 / 020 3239 4711

Elgee Pinks Solicitors
‡Westerham p429. . . . . 01959 568100
Reigate p363. . . . . 01737 247554

Elias & Co
‡Borehamwood p150 . . . . 020 8387 1333

Elin & Associates
‡Basingstoke p126 . . . . 01256 358864

Elite Solicitors Limited
‡Bristol p162 . . . . 0117 952 5777

Ellen Court Partnership Solicitors
‡Preston p356. . . . . 01772 882888

Ellicotts
‡London N20 p29 . . .020 8445 5257 / 8445 2880

Ellicotts & Co Solicitors
‡Sevenoaks p374 . . . . 01959 522442

Elliot Mather LLP
‡Chesterfield p192. . . . . 01246 231288
Chesterfield p192. . . . . 01246 231288
Mansfield p311 . . . . 01623 655666
Matlock p313. . . . . 01629 584885

Elliots Bond & Banbury
‡Ealing W5 p29 . . . . 020 8567 0176

Elliott & Allen
‡Sedgley p373. . . . . 01902 677204

Elliott & Co
‡Birmingham p138. . . . . 0121 236 9690
‡Wolverhampton p437. . . . . . . 01902 894020

Elliott & Williams
‡London N8 p29. . . . . 020 7566 8244

Martin Elliott & Co
‡Colchester p197 . . . . 01206 767112

P L Elliott & Co
‡High Wycombe p250. . . . . . . 01494 817599

Simon Elliott Solicitor
‡Bournemouth p151 . . . . 01202 767200

Elliotts Solicitors
‡Southampton p385 . . . . 023 8063 1540

Ellis & Co
‡Chester p190. . . . . 01244 319388

B K Ellis & Co
‡Borehamwood p150 . . . . 020 8386 8686

Ellis Davies & Co
‡Caernarfon p172 . . . . 01286 672437

Ellis Jones
‡Bournemouth p151 . . . . 01202 525333
Poole p352. . . . . 01202 709898

Ringwood p364. . . . . 01425 484848
Swanage p404 . . . . 01929 422233

Ellis Lakin & Co
‡Pickering p348 . . . . 01751 472121

Mark Ellis & Co
‡Hornchurch p252. . . . .01708 471808 / 471587

Richard Ellis & Co
Leeds p273. . . . . 0113 228 4000

Ellis Taylor Law LLP
‡London WC2 p29. . . . . 020 7405 0206

W A Ellis
‡London SW3 p29

Ellis-Fermor & Negus
‡Ripley p364 . . . . 01773 744744
Beeston p130. . . . . 0115 922 1591
Belper p131 . . . . 01773 821665
Long Eaton p293 . . . . 0115 972 5222

Ellison & Co
‡Cardiff p178 . . . . 029 2038 2508

Ellison & Thomas
‡Stretford p400 . . . . 0161 865 3827

Ellisons
‡Colchester p197 . . . . 01206 764477
Clacton-on-Sea p195 . . . . 01255 421248
Frinton-on-Sea p227 . . . . 01255 851000
Harwich p243. . . . . 01255 502428

Ellum LLP
‡London E1 p29. . . . . 020 7481 0977

Elm Solicitors
‡Newbury p322 . . 01635 248336 / 0118 907 1954

Elmhirst Parker LLP
‡Barnsley p124 . . . . 01226 282238
Leeds p273. . . . . 01977 682219
Selby p374. . . . . 01757 703602
Selby p374. . . . . 01757 703895

Els & Cole Solicitors
‡Rayleigh p359 . . . . 01268 747006

Elsbys Solicitors
‡Hailsham p237 . . 01323 440030 / 0800 011 2797

M J Elsdon
‡North Walsham p331. . . . . . . 01692 403562
Barnstaple p125 . . . . 01271 817661

Else Solicitors LLP
‡Burton-on-Trent p170. . . . . . . 01283 526200
Birmingham p138. . . . . 0121 212 6560

Elsey & Hodson
‡Peterborough p347. . . . . 01733 314064

Elston Germain Davidson
‡London SE1 p29 . . . . 020 3195 7272

Elthorn Solicitors
‡London W5 p29 . . . . 020 8579 3838

Elton & Co
‡Camden NW1 p29 . . . . 020 7267 7373

Eltringham & Co
‡Newcastle upon Tyne p324. . . . 0191 266 5878

Elvin & Co
‡Loughborough p293 . . . . 01509 852454

Elwyn Jones & Co
‡Bangor p122 . . . . 01248 370224

Ely Law Practice
‡Cardiff p178 . . . . 029 2038 7738

Embertons
‡Enfield p218 . . . . 020 8364 4249

Emerald Law Solicitors
‡Liverpool p287 . . . . 0800 804 8158

Emerald Solicitors
‡Chatham p184 . . . . 01634 407500

Emeritus Legal
‡Cardiff p178 . . . . 029 2056 7836

Emerly Halil And Brown Solicitors
‡London E8 p29. . . . .020 7241 4433 / 8519 5500

Emery Hogg
‡Tonypandy p412 . . . . 01443 433317

Emery Johnson Partnership
‡Leicester p279 . . . . 0116 255 4855

C T Emezie Solicitors
‡Ilford p260 . . . . 020 3489 9113

Emin Read Solicitors
‡Battle p128. . . . . 01424 775967
‡London SE24 p29 . . . . 020 7733 9898
‡London SE3 p29 . . . . 020 8218 1773

H Emir & Co
‡London N16 p29 . . . . 020 8806 8480

Emmerson Brown & Brown
‡Deal p207 . . . . 01304 362146
Dover p212. . . . . 01304 211766
Sandwich p372. . . . . 01304 612444

Emmerson Law Limited
‡Reading p360 . . . . 0118 900 0980

Emmerson Solicitors
Gosforth p231 . . . . 0191 284 6989

Emmersons Solicitors
‡Sunderland p401. . . . . 0191 567 6667

Hal Emmett & Co
‡Maghull p298. . . . . 0151 531 7666

Emmetts Solicitors
‡Preston p356. . . . . 01772 785213

Emmott & Co
‡Leeds p273. . . . . 0113 251 5008

Emmott Snell & Co
‡Bedford p130 . . . 01234 360140

Steven J Emmott
‡Bradford p154 . . . 01274 309791

Employee Solicitors
‡London SE5 p29 . . . 0870 730 8880

Employment Integration
‡Leamington Spa p270 . . . 01926 612679

The Employment Law Consultancy
‡Beaconsfield p129 . . . 01494 673123

Employment Law Diversity & Discrimination Service-Elizabeth Carney
‡Leicester p279 . . 07900 212188 / 0116 212 1099

Employment Law Plus
‡Abingdon p114 . . . 01235 861919

The Employment Law Practice
‡Reading p360 . . . 0118 375 9288

Employment Law Solicitors Direct
‡Bingley p133 . . . 01274 786056

Employment Relations
‡Canterbury p176 . . . 01303 840001

Employment Solicitors London Limited
‡London EC2 p29 . . . 020 7426 0382

Emporiko Dikaio Legal Services
‡Swindon p406 . . . 01793 701864

Emporium Solicitors
‡Bargoed p123 . . . 01443 878800

Emrys Jones & Co
‡Welshpool p425 . . . 01938 552510
Bishops Castle p144 . . . 01588 638793

Emsleys
‡Leeds p273 . . . 0113 232 0037
‡Leeds p273 . . . 01977 680088
‡Rothwell p368 . . . 0113 201 4900
Castleford p183 . . . 01977 550115
Crossgates p204 . . . 0113 260 3115
Garforth p228 . . . 0113 286 8746
Leeds p273 . . . 0113 232 1030
Rothwell p368 . . . 0113 282 4939

The Endeavour Partnership LLP
‡Stockton-on-Tees p397 . . . 01642 610300

Endlars
‡Manchester p304 . . . 0161 795 4333

Energy Transact LLP
‡Alton p116 . . . 020 7096 0116

Enever Freeman & Co
‡Ruislip p368 . . . 01895 634031
Ruislip p369 . . . 01895 676385 / 676386

Max Engel & Co LLP
‡Northampton p331 . . . 01604 887450

England & Co
‡Great Yarmouth p234 . . 01493 844308 / 844309
Great Yarmouth p234 . . 01493 740795 / 748174
Great Yarmouth p234 . . . 01493 604990

England John Solicitors
‡Shrewsbury p379 . . . 01743 233700

England Kerr Hands & Co
‡Birmingham p138 . . . 0121 427 9898

England Palmer
‡Islington EC1 p29 . . . 020 7278 2800
Guildford p236 . . . 01483 459161

England Stickland & Neale
‡Birmingham p138 . . . 0121 377 7773

Engleharts
‡Hove p254 . . . 01273 204411

The English Cogger Partnership
‡Winchester p433 . . . 01962 858800

Ennon & Co Solicitors
‡London N4 p29 . . . 020 7281 2123

Enoch Evans LLP
‡Walsall p420 . . . 01922 720333

Entrust Pension Recovery Limited
‡Manchester p304 . . . 0870 365 8000

Environmental Law Consultancy
‡Manchester p304 . . . 0845 860 0595

Epitome Law
‡Cambridge p174 . . . 01223 303162

Equal Justice Ltd
‡London WC1 p29 . . . 020 7405 5292

Equilaw Ltd
‡Gloucester p230 . . . 01452 657999

Equitable Solicitors
‡London SE11 p29 . . . 020 7820 8236

Equitas Law Limited
‡Leicester p279 . . . 0116 275 5054

Equitas Solicitors Limited
‡Preston p356 . . . 01772 655196

Equity Solicitors
‡Birmingham p138 . . . 0121 554 7470

Ergo Law Limited
‡Cardiff p178 . . . 0845 300 6441

Eric Robinson Solicitors
‡Southampton p385 . . . 023 8042 5000
Chandlers Ford p184 . . . 023 8025 4676
Hythe p259 . . . 023 8084 4304
Southampton p386 . . . 023 8022 6891
Southampton p385 . . . 01489 788922
Southampton p385 . . . 023 8042 5000

The Eric Whitehead Partnership
‡Cheadle p185 . . . 01538 755761

Erica Peat & Diable
‡London E8 p29 . . . 020 8533 7999

Ernest & Co Solicitors
‡London N16 p29 . . . 020 7254 2244

Ernest & Company
‡London N15 p29 . . . 020 8880 2222

Richard Erridge & Co
‡Wotton-under-Edge p442 . . . 01454 418615

Ersan & Co Solicitors Limited
‡London N8 p29 . . . 020 8342 7070

Harvey Escott & Co
‡Burnham-on-Crouch p169 01621 784838 / 784839

John L Escott
‡Southend-on-Sea p387 . . . 01702 433110

Eshagian & Co
‡London NW1 p29 . . . 020 7388 5599

Eskinazi & Co
‡London N12 p29 . . . 020 8445 7707

J Esner & Co
‡Bolton p149 . . . 01204 522562

Espilon Solicitors
‡Ormskirk p341 . . . 01704 894945

Espley & Co
‡Liverpool p288 . . . 01704 830200

Ess Ess Bilan Solicitors
‡Kenton p265 . . . 0844 800 1747

Essential Employment Law Services Limited
‡Bridport p158 . . . 01308 459459

Essential Rights
‡Sheffield p375 . . . 0114 255 4526

Essex Solicitors
‡Ilford p260 . . . 020 8554 7123

Estate and Corporate Solicitors
‡Dartford p207 . . . 01322 292101

Charles Ete & Co
‡London SE5 p29 . . . 020 7820 9818

Eternal Alliances
‡London SE13 p30 . . . 0845 271 2828

Eton Law
‡Luton p295 . . . 01582 726900

Ettinger & Vickers
‡Ellesmere Port p217 . . . 0151 339 1640

European Business Lawyers Limited
‡London WC2 p30 . . . 0807 395 2180

Evans & Co
‡Cardiff p178 . . . 029 2048 0054
‡Gillingham p229 . . . 020 7232 1325
‡Spennymoor p389 . . . 01388 815317
Ferryhill p226 . . . 01740 657444

Evans & Davies
‡Aberaeron p113 . . . 01545 570335

Evans & Ellis
‡Chepstow p189 . . . 01291 622814

Evans & Greaves
‡Caerphilly p172 . . . 029 2086 6001

Evans and Jones Solicitors LLP
‡Cardiff p178 . . . 029 2002 0909

Evans + Webb
‡Malvern p300 . . . 01684 562526

Evans Bissett Solicitors
‡London NW5 p30 . . . 020 7428 6090

Evans Cook Solicitors
‡Wellingborough p424 . . . 01933 278259

Evans Derry Binnion
Warwick p422 . . . 01675 464400

Evans Derry Rennie & Co
‡Birmingham p138 . . . 0121 770 1721

Evans Dodd LLP
‡London W1 p30 . . . 020 7491 4729

Graham Evans & Partners
‡Swansea p405 . . . 01792 655822

Evans Harvey Law
‡Plymouth p349 . . . 01752 785715

James A Evans & Co Solicitors
‡Newcastle under Lyme p323 . . . 01782 714007

Keith Evans & Company
‡Newport p328 . . . 01633 257721
Abergavenny p113 . . . 01873 852239
Cwmbran p206 . . . 01633 860900

Evans London Solicitors
‡London W1 p30 . . . 020 8144 8001

Evans Main Solicitors
‡Sevenoaks p374 . . . 01732 464848

Marion Evans
‡Bewdley p131 . . . 01299 402741

Martin Evans Solicitor
‡Bristol p162 . . . 0117 975 4460

Mary Evans & Co
‡Carmarthen p182 . . . 01267 233881

N K Evans & Co
‡Greenwich SE10 p30 . . . 020 8853 1414

Evans Powell & Co
‡Llanelli p292 . . . 01554 772632

Evans Quartermaine Solicitors
‡Caerphilly p172 . . . 01685 840404

Shirley M Evans
‡Grange-over-Sands p232 . . . 01539 535208

T R Evans Hughes & Co
‡Holyhead p251 . . . 01407 762204
Amlwch p117 . . . 01407 830400

Evans Wallace Solicitors
‡London W1 p30 . . . 0845 838 2984

J E Evans-Jackson & Co
‡London EC1 p30 . . . 020 7608 3098

Evans-Roberts
‡Machynlleth p298 . . . 01654 702335 / 702336

Eveling Legal & Advisory Ltd
‡Exeter p221 . . . 01392 479002

Everatt's
‡Harrow p241 . . . 020 8424 0088

Everett Tomlin Lloyd & Pratt
‡Newport p328 . . . 01633 251801
Pontypool p352 . . . 01495 763333

Evergreen Solicitors
‡London EC2 p30 . . . 020 7448 5151

Eversfield & Co
‡London WC2 p30 . . . 020 7836 5547

Eversheds LLP
‡London EC2 p30 . . . 0845 497 9797
Birmingham p138 . . . 0845 497 9797
Cambridge p174 . . . 0845 497 9797
Cardiff p178 . . . 0845 497 9797
Ipswich p262 . . . 0845 497 9797
Leeds p273 . . . 0845 497 9797
Manchester p304 . . . 0845 497 9797
Newcastle upon Tyne p324 . . . 0845 497 9797
Nottingham p337 . . . 0845 497 9797

Eversley & Co
‡Islington N1 p30 . . . 020 7607 0001

Everyman Legal Ltd
‡Witney p436 . . . 0845 868 0960

Everys
‡Honiton p252 . . . 01404 41221
Budleigh Salterton p168 . . . 01395 442223
Exeter p221 . . . 01392 477983
Exmouth p222 . . . 01395 264384
Honiton p252 . . . 01404 43431
Ottery St Mary p342 . . . 01404 813446
Seaton p373 . . . 01297 21105
Sidmouth p380 . . . 01395 577983
Taunton p408 . . . 01823 337636

Ewan & Co Solicitors
‡Ilford p260 . . . 020 8514 5687

Peter J Ewart & Co Solicitors
‡Fairford p223 . . . 01285 713715

Ewart Price
‡Welwyn Garden City p425 . . . 01707 332383

Ewart Price & Primhak
London NW3 p30 . . . 020 7267 7344

Ewings & Co
‡London SE20 p30 . . . 020 8778 1126

Excalibur Solicitors
‡Solihull p382 . . . 01564 774480

Excel Law
‡Ilford p260 . . . 020 8500 6476

Excel Legal
‡Bury p170 . . . 0161 764 1035

Excel Solicitors
‡London SE28 p30 . . . 020 8854 1201

Excello Law Limited
‡Reading p360 . . . 0845 257 9449

Exlex Solicitors
‡Birmingham p138 . . . 0121 331 4155

Express Solicitors
‡Manchester p304 . . . 0800 158 5274

Eyre & Co
‡Birmingham p138 . . . 0121 784 4722

David Eyres
Sheffield p375 . . . 0114 249 3222

F

F&L Legal LLP
‡London WC2 p30 . . . 020 7404 4140

FA Law
‡Oldham p340 . . . 0161 665 0070

FBC Manby Bowdler LLP
‡Wolverhampton p437 . . . 01902 578000
Bridgnorth p157 . . . 01746 761436
Shrewsbury p379 . . . 01743 241551
Telford p409 . . . 01952 292129
Willenhall p432 . . . 01902 366566

F B Jevons Riley & Pope
‡Edenbridge p216 . . . 01732 864411

FDC Law
‡Frome p228 . . . 01373 465051
Frome p228 . . . 01373 463311
Keynsham p265 . . . 0117 916 1088
Radstock p358 . . . 01761 417575

FLK Solicitors
‡London E10 p30 . . . 020 8558 9699

FS Conveyancing
‡Borehamwood p150 . . . 020 8387 4143

FS Law Solicitors & Advocates
‡Gravesend p232 . . . 01474 533338

FST Solicitors Limited
‡Cliftonville p196 . . . 01843 234160

FSU Law Limited
‡Barnet p124 . . . 0700 397 3240

FWD Law Associates
‡Newport p328 . . . 01633 660440

Faber & Co
‡Birmingham p138 . . . 0121 236 5751

Fabmelia Manuel
‡London SE1 p30 . . . 020 7378 9593

Face to Face
‡Norwich p334 . . . 01603 625100

Fadiga & Co Solicitors
‡Wandsworth SW17 p30 . . . 020 8672 8779
London E7 p30 . . . 020 8470 5656

Faegre & Benson LLP
‡London EC4 p30 . . . 020 7450 4500

Fahm & Co
‡Blackwood p147 . . . 01495 224973

Fahri Jacob
‡London N8 p30 . . . 020 8347 4070
Hatfield p244 . . . 07908 144464

Edward Fail Bradshaw & Waterson
‡London E1 p30 . . . 020 7790 4032
London EC3 p30 . . . 020 7264 2016

Barrie Fairbairn Solicitors
‡Leicester p279 . . . 0116 244 8272

Fairbairn Smith & Co
‡London N17 p30 . . . 020 8808 4901

Fairbrother & Darlow
‡Bracknell p153 . . . 01344 420808

Fairchild Dobbs
‡Gerrards Cross p229 . . . 01753 883127

Fairchild Greig
‡London W3 p30 . . . 020 8993 6886

Fairfax Solicitors Limited
‡Leeds p273 . . . 0113 823 3443

J M Fairhall
‡Poole p352 . . . 01202 735962

Fairlaw Solicitors
‡London N16 p30 . . . 0845 459 0271

Fairweather & Co Solicitors
‡Canterbury p176 . . . 01227 784337

Fairweather Stephenson & Co
‡Felixstowe p225 . . . 01394 277941
‡Leiston p282 . . . 01728 832832
Aldeburgh p115 . . . 01728 454595

Fairweather Whillis & Toghill Solicitors
‡High Wycombe p250 . . . 01494 445545

Falcon Legal
‡Bromley p166 . . . 020 8290 6787

Paul Fallon & Co
‡Watford p423 . . . 01923 226795

R M Falvey & Co
‡London SW3 p30 . . . 020 7100 3414

Family Affairs
‡Swindon p406 . . . 0333 240 1040

Family Law Associates LLP
‡Haringey N8 p30 . . . 020 8342 7760

Family Law Consultancy
‡Norwich p334 . . . 01603 664000

Family Law Consultants
‡Cheltenham p188 . . . 01242 222201

Family Law In Cornwall
‡St Austell p391 . . . 0845 604 2985

Family Law in Partnership LLP
‡London WC2 p30 . . . 020 7420 5000

The Family Law Partnership LLP
‡Leatherhead p271 . . . 01372 700890

The Family Law Practice
‡London E1 p30 . . . 020 7791 0432

Family Law Solicitors
‡Leicester p279 . . . 0116 239 5544

Family Law Solutions
‡Slough p381 . . . 0845 603 2237

Family Legal
‡Middlewich p315 . . . 01606 841273

Family Matters Solicitors
‡Torquay p412 . . . 01803 328577

The Family Solicitor
‡Weston-super-Mare p429
. . . 01934 625551 / 07837 797427

Mike Fanning Solicitors
‡Keswick p265 . . . 01768 775454

Fanshaw Porter & Hazlehurst
‡Birkenhead p134 . . . 0151 647 4051

Stuart Fantham
‡Aylesbury p121 . . . 01296 620300
Milton Keynes p316 . . . 01908 250001

Mr M Faquir
‡Wolverhampton p438 . . . 01902 424887

Faradays Law Limited
‡London SE10 p30 . . . 020 8432 9473

Faradays Solicitors Ltd
‡London N7 p30 . . . 020 7281 1001

Farani Taylor
‡London WC1 p30 . . . 020 7242 1666

Rebecca L Faret Solicitors
‡Flitwick p226 . . . . 01525 712112
Farley Dwek LLP
‡Manchester p304. . . . . 0161 272 5222
Farleys Solicitors LLP
‡Blackburn p145. . . . . 01254 367855
Accrington p114 . . . . 01254 367853
Blackburn p145. . . . . 01254 367856
Blackburn p145. . . . . 01254 367854
Burnley p169 . . . . 01282 798664
Manchester p304 . . . . 0161 660 4254
Kealy Farmar & Co
‡Henley-on-Thames p247 . . . . 01491 410393
Farmar Miller Rabin Gordon
‡Edgware p217 . . . . 020 8381 3339
G M Farmer
‡Skegness p380. . . . . 01754 763767
Farnfield & Nicholls
‡Gillingham p229 . . . . 01747 825432
Shaftesbury p374. . . . . 01747 854244
Sturminster Newton p401. . . . . 01258 474270
Warminster p421 . . . . 01985 214661
Farnsworth Morgan Bakhat
‡Blackburn p145. . . . . 01254 274700
Farnworth Rose
‡Nelson p321 . . . . 01282 695400
Farnworth Shaw
‡Colne p198. . . . . 01282 865885
Colne p198. . . . . 01282 864081
Nelson p321 . . . . 01282 699996
Deborah Farquhar-Snaith Family Law Solicitor
‡London SE3 p30 . . . . 020 8858 6562
John Farr-Davies & Co
‡Carmarthen p182. . . . . 01267 231818
Farrah and Co Solicitors
‡Brentford p156 . . . . 020 8582 5762
Farrell & Hobbs
‡Manchester p304. . . . . 0161 445 1000
Farrell Martin Nee
‡London SW11 p30 . . . . 020 7819 2320
Farrell Matthews & Weir
‡London W6 p30 . . . . 020 8746 3771
London W6 p31. . . . . 020 8741 1482
Farrells Solicitors
‡Bristol p162. . . . . 0117 944 4664
Farrer & Co LLP
‡London WC2 p31. . . . . 020 3375 7000
Farrer & Co Trust Corporation Limited
‡London WC2 p31. . . . . 020 7242 2022
Farringdons
‡London WC1 p31. . . . . 020 7242 0949
Farrington & Co
‡Reading p360 . . . . 0118 947 8914
Farrow Solicitors
‡Stoke-on-Trent p397 . . . . . . 01782 341121
Fashanu & Co
‡Grays p233. . . . . 01375 385588
Fasken Martineau LLP
‡London W1 p31 . . . . 020 7917 8500
Fasttrac Solicitors
‡Crewkerne p203 . . . . 01460 279288
Favell Smith & Lawson
Hathersage p244 . . . . 01433 650718
Favell Smith & Lawson Solicitors
‡Sheffield p375 . . . . 0114 272 4381
FAWCETT & PATTNI
‡Walsall p420 . . . . 01922 640424
Birmingham p138. . . . . 0121 200 1013
Gillian Fazan & Co
‡Kingsbridge p267. . . . . 01548 856663
Graham Fear & Co
‡Enfield p218 . . . . 020 8363 3331
Jeremy Fear & Co
‡London N11 p31 . . . . 020 8361 7915
Fearnley & Co
‡Ealing W5 p31 . . . . 020 8579 9898
‡Macclesfield p297 . . . . 01625 427303
Fearon & Co
‡Guildford p236 . . . . 01483 540840
Feeny & Co
‡Bristol p162 . . . . 0117 923 9477
Feld McKay & Donner Solicitors
‡Rochdale p365. . . . . 01706 645656
Fell Kilvington & Co
‡Kirkby Stephen p268 . . . . . . 01768 371495
Fellowes Solicitors
‡London E17 p31 . . . . 020 8520 7392
R Felstead Solicitors
‡London SW15 p31 . . . . 020 8789 3856
Felton & Co
‡Stanmore p394. . . . . 01923 839599
Feltons
‡London E14 p31 . . . . 0870 751 5600
Fenchurch Law LLP
‡London EC2 p31 . . . . 020 7337 6116
Fendom Dawson & Partners
‡High Wycombe p250 . . . . . . 01494 450361
Fendom Dawson & Towner
Marlow p313 . . . . 01628 477808
Andrew J Fenny & Co
‡Cramlington p201. . . . . 01670 737393
Fentimans
‡Knowle p269 . . . . 01564 779459
Fentons
‡Failsworth p223 . . . . 0161 682 7101
Manchester p304 . . . . 0161 786 8320
Fentons Solicitors LLP
‡London WC2 p31 020 7580 0143 / 0845 026 4749
‡Manchester p304. . . . . 0161 238 6400
Fenwick Elliott
‡London WC2 p31. . . . . 020 7421 1986
Ferdinand Kelly
‡Sutton Coldfield p403. . . . . . 01827 893526
Ferguson Bricknell
‡Oxford p343 . . . . 01865 241814
Oxford p343 . . . . 01865 767567
Craig Ferguson & Co LLP
‡Leicester p279 . . . . 0116 270 5088
Helen Margaret Ferguson
‡Newcastle upon Tyne p324. . . . 0191 284 8844
Joan Ferguson & Co
‡Manchester p304. . . . . 0161 795 5866
Ferguson Solicitors
‡London EC4 p31 . . . . 020 7822 2999
Fernandes Vaz
‡Edgware p217 . . . . 020 8381 3932
Fernando & Co
‡Wandsworth SW17 p31. . . . . 020 8767 4611
Indira Fernando
‡Southall p384. . . . . 020 8575 6544
Fernando Scornik Gerstein Solicitors
‡London WC1 p31. . . . . 020 7404 8400
Ferns
‡London SW4 p31. . . . . 020 7498 9537
Brian Ferris
‡Tunbridge Wells p415. . . . . . 01892 518609
Fidex Law
‡London NW9 p31. . . . . 020 8457 3258
Fidler & Pepper
‡Sutton-in-Ashfield p404. . . . . .01623 451111
Kirkby-in-Ashfield p268 . . . . .01623 451111
Mansfield p311 . . . . .01623 451111
Stephen Fidler & Co
‡London EC1 p31 . . . . 020 7353 8999
A J Field & Co
‡Sheerness p375 . . . . 01795 580600
Marlow p313 . . . . 01628 488055
Sittingbourne p380 . . . . 01795 436363
Field & Co
‡London EC3 p31 . . . . 020 7329 8615
Field Cunningham & Co
‡Manchester p304. . . . . 0161 834 4734
Field Fisher Waterhouse LLP
‡London EC3 p31 . . . . 020 7861 4000
Field Martin
‡Sevenoaks p374 . . . . 01732 463934
Field Overell
‡Leamington Spa p270 . . . . . . 01926 422101
Coventry p200 . . . . 024 7622 9582
Field Seymour Parkes
‡Reading p360 . . . . 0118 951 6200
Alison Fielden & Co
‡Cirencester p195. . . . . 01285 653261
Fielden Law LLP
‡Clitheroe p196 . . . . 01254 828410
Fieldhouse & Co LLP
‡Redhill p362 . . . . 01737 277668
Fieldings
‡Seaford p373. . . . . 01323 492493
Fieldings Porter
‡Bolton p149 . . . . 01204 540900
Westhoughton p429 . . . . 01942 814089
Figueiredo & Bowman
‡Hackney EC2 p32 . . . . 020 7739 5599
Filatov Goldberg Musatov LLP
‡London W1 p32 . . . . 020 3178 5769
Linda Filby Solicitor
‡Seaford p373. . . . . 01273 695321
M H Files & Co
‡Surbiton p402 . . . . 020 8398 3646
Filor Employment Lawyers
‡Crediton p203 . . 01647 231475 / 07891 055856
Financial Markets Law International
‡St Albans p390. . . . . 01727 845897
Finch Legal Solicitors
‡Crowborough p204. . . . . 01892 610046
Mark Findlow & Co
‡Macclesfield p297 . . . . 01625 617306
Finers Stephens Innocent LLP
‡London W1 p32 . . . . 020 7323 4000
Finlay Solicitors
‡Worthing p441 . . . . 07976 371743
Finn Gledhill
‡Halifax p238 . . . . 01422 330000
Hebden Bridge p246 . . . . . . 01422 842451
Paul Finn Solicitors
‡Bude p168 . . . . 01288 356256
Kim Finnis Solicitor
‡Guildford p236 . . . . 01483 539100
The Firm Solicitors LLP
‡Birmingham p138. . . . . 0121 709 6506
Redditch p362 . . . . 0121 709 6506
Solihull p382 . . . . 0121 709 6506
Firmlegal Solicitors
‡Shrewsbury p379. . . . . 01743 273777
First Beacon Legal Services
Cardiff p178 . . . . 029 2023 7777
First Conveyancing
‡London SE23 p32 . . . . 020 8291 5427
First Conveyancing.co.uk
‡Penarth p345. . . . . 029 2070 2449
First Defence
‡Bedford p130. . . . . 01234 263263
Northampton p331 . . . . 01604 745470
Wellingborough p424 . . . . . . 01933 442666
A D Firth & Co
‡Macclesfield p297 . . . . 01625 261840
Firth Lindsay
‡Sheffield p375 . . . . 0114 276 0586
Fischer & Co
‡Barnet N12 p32. . .020 8346 7036 / 8922 0689
Fish & Co
‡Wolverhampton p438. . . . . . . 01902 826464
Fish and Fish Solicitors
‡Crewe p203 . . . . 0844 736 1887
Fishburns
‡London EC3 p32 . . . . 020 7280 8888
Ashley Fisher & Co
‡Blackpool p146. . . . . 01253 751585
Fisher Cowe Solicitors
‡Norwich p334. . . . . 01603 878383
D Fisher & Co
‡Borough Green p150 . . . . . . 01732 884299
Fisher Jones Greenwood LLP
‡Colchester p197 . . . . 01206 578282
Chelmsford p186 . . . . 01245 890110
Clacton-on-Sea p195 . . . . . . 01255 323103
Colchester p197 . . . . 01206 835300
Fisher Law
‡Borehamwood p150 . . . . 020 8387 4057
Fisher Levine & Co
‡London N2 p32
Fisher Meredith
‡Lambeth SE11 p32. . . . . . . 020 7091 2700
Richmond upon Thames p364 . . 020 8334 7927
Michael J Fisher & Co
‡Carlisle p182. . . . . 01228 592686
Oliver Fisher
‡London W11 p32 . . . . 020 3219 0145
Fisher Sands
‡Hornchurch p252. . . . . 01708 474019
Fisher Scoggins Waters LLP
‡London EC4 p32 . . . . 020 7489 2035
Fishers
‡Ashby-de-la-Zouch p118 . . . . 01530 412167
‡London EC2 p32 . . . . 020 7613 8111
Swadlincote p404. . . . . 01283 217193
Fishman & Co Solicitors
‡London W1 p32 . . . . 020 7935 3500
David Fishwick
‡London W11 p32 . . . . 020 7792 8811
Fison & Co
‡Ipswich p262. . . . . 01473 280900
Fitchett & Co Solicitors
‡Guildford p236 . . . . 01483 243587
Howard Fitton
‡Lymm p296. . . . . 01925 757565
Fitz Solicitors
‡Slough p382 . . . . 01753 592000
Fitzgerald-Harts
‡Boroughbridge p150 . . . . . . 01423 322312
Fitzgrahams
‡St Leonards-on-Sea p392. . . . 01424 446666
Fitzhugh Gates
‡Brighton p159 . . . . 01273 686811
Shoreham-by-Sea p378. . . . . . 01273 461381
Fitzpatrick & Co
‡London SE14 p32 . . . . 020 8691 5112
Andrew Fitzpatrick
‡Manchester p304. . . . . 0161 248 9799
Flack & Co
‡Wandsworth SW18 p32. . . . . 020 8875 1888
Flackwoods Solicitors
‡Horsham p253 . . . . 01403 738777
Fladgate LLP
‡London WC2 p32. . . . . 020 3036 7000
Flanagans Solicitors
‡Eynsham p223 . . . . 01865 430040
Thomas Flavell & Sons
‡Hinckley p250 . . . . 01455 610747
Earl Shilton p214 . . . . 01455 842297
Market Bosworth p312 . . . . . . 01455 290203
Fleet Solicitors LLP
‡Bristol p162. . . . . 0845 603 3273
Cheltenham p188
Brendan Fleming
‡Birmingham p138. . . . . 0121 683 5000
Fletcher & Co Solicitors
‡Knutsford p269 . . . . 01565 755411
Altrincham p116 . . . . 0161 926 8026
Fletcher Dervish
‡Haringey N8 p33 . . . . 020 8800 4615
J P Fletcher & Co
‡London W1 p33 . . . . 020 7494 4700
R M Fletcher & Co
‡Redcar p362 . . . . 01642 490400
Ronald Fletcher & Co
‡London W9 p33 . . . . 020 7624 0041
Fletchers
‡Southport p388. . . . . 01704 546919
‡Winsford p434 . . . . . .01606 556322 / 556324
Preston p356. . . . . 0871 971 1621
P A Fleury
‡London EC2 p33 . . . . 020 7374 4434
P A Fleury & Co
‡London EC4 p33 . . . . 020 7329 3405
Flexpro Services Limited
‡Huntingdon p258. . . . . 020 7060 2205
Flint Bishop Solicitors
‡Derby p208. . . . . 01332 340211
Ashbourne p118 . . . . 01335 342208
Nottingham p337 . . . . 0115 964 4450
Claire Flood Solicitors
‡Brentwood p156 . . . . 01277 202869
Keith Flower & Co
‡Pinner p348 . . . . 020 8868 1277
Terence Flynn & Co
‡Coulsdon p199 . . . . 020 8660 8061
Rowena Foat Solicitors
‡Ormskirk p341
Fodens
‡Much Wenlock p320 . . . . . . 01952 726111
Anthony Foley
‡Accrington p114 . . . . 01254 391223
Foley Harrison
‡Gateshead p228 . . . . 0191 477 6333
Neil Foley & Co
‡Pontypridd p352 . . . . 01443 406085
Follett Stock LLP
‡Truro p414 . . . . 01872 241700
Exeter p221 . . . . 01392 449370
Fonseca & Partners
‡Abergavenny p113 . . . . 01873 857114
‡Ebbw Vale p216 . . . . 01495 303124
Foort Tayler
‡Great Dunmow p233 . . . . 01371 875200
Foot Anstey
‡Plymouth p349 . . . . 01752 675000
Exeter p221 . . . . 01392 411221
Taunton p408. . . . . 01823 625600
Truro p414 . . . . 01872 243300
Footner & Ewing
‡Southampton p386 . . . . 023 8033 2991
Romsey p366. . . . . 01794 512345
Southampton p386 . . . . 023 8044 8266
Totton p413. . . . . 023 8086 3493
Forbes
‡Blackburn p145. . . . . 01254 54374
Accrington p114 . . . . 01254 872111
Accrington p114 . . . . 01254 872111
Blackburn p145. . . . . 01254 662831
Blackburn p145. . . . . 01254 580000
Chorley p194. . . . . 01257 260600
Leeds p273. . . . . 0113 244 6688
Manchester p304 . . . . 0161 918 0000
Preston p356. . . . . 01772 220022
Forbes Anderson Free
‡London W1 p33 . . . . 020 7291 3500
Forbes Hall LLP
‡Woodford Green p439 . . . . . . 020 8498 0080
London EC2 p33 . . . . 020 7729 9111
Forbes Maclean
‡Leigh-on-Sea p282. . . . . . . 01702 472747
Ford & Warren
‡Leeds p273. . . . . 0113 243 6601
Andrew M Ford
‡Ashby-de-la-Zouch p118 . . . . 01530 561734
Andrew M Ford Solicitors
‡Leicester p279 . . . . 0845 075 4059
Ford Banks Irwin
‡Manchester p304. . . . . 0161 866 8999
John Ford Solicitors
‡London N4 p33. . . . . 020 8800 6464
Ford Legal Solicitors
‡Bolton p149 . . . . 01204 374825
‡Bolton p149 . . . . 01204 656393
Lindsay Ford Solicitors Ltd
‡Caerphilly p172. . . . . 029 2088 2441
Ford Simey LLP
‡Exeter p221 . . . . 01392 274126
Exmouth p222 . . 01395 272241 / 0800 169 3741
Honiton p252. . . 01404 540020 / 0800 169 3741
Sidmouth p380 . . 01395 577061 / 0800 169 3741
Fordlittle
‡Sittingbourne p380 . . . . 01795 436111

Foreman & Co
‡Bushey *p172* . . . 07956 513563
‡Doncaster *p211* . . . 01427 891892

Foreman Laws
‡Hitchin *p251* . . . 01462 458711

Roy Foreman & Co
‡Grimsby *p235* . . . 01472 355262

Foremans LLP
‡Baldock *p121* . . . 01462 499077
‡Chester *p190* . . . 01244 625500

Forest Edge Legal Practice
‡Verwood *p418* . . . 01202 376787

Forest Solicitors
‡London SE13 *p33* . . . 020 8534 1025

Foresters Solicitors
‡London E17 *p33* . . . 020 8521 5999

Forman Welch & Bellamys
‡Twickenham *p416* . . 020 8892 8907 / 8892 7733

Frank Forney & Partners LLP
‡Haringey N22 *p33* . . 020 8889 1971 / 8888 5481

J A Forrest & Co
‡Westminster SW1 *p33* . . . 020 7233 9140

Forrester & Forrester
‡Chippenham *p193* . . . 01249 444300
Malmesbury *p300* . . . 01666 822671

Geoffrey Forrester & Co
‡Jarrow *p263* . . . 0191 420 0820
South Shields *p383* . . . 0191 456 2255

Forresters
‡Barrow-in-Furness *p125* . . . 01229 820297

Forshaws Davies Ridgway LLP
‡Warrington *p422* . . . 01925 230000
Frodsham *p227* . . . 01928 739300
Warrington *p422* . . . 01925 230000
Warrington *p422* . . . 01925 230000
Warrington *p422* . . . 01925 604713

Forster & Wheeler
‡Birmingham *p138* . . . 0121 421 4888

Forster Dean Ltd
‡Liverpool *p288* . . . 0151 203 4300
Birkenhead *p134* . . . 0151 203 1281
Bootle *p150* . . . 0151 933 0062
Chorley *p194* . . . 01257 262960
Crewe *p203* . . . 01270 254064
Eccles *p216* . . . 0161 707 4000
Ellesmere Port *p217* . . . 0151 356 7484
Huyton *p258* . . . 0151 203 2144
Leigh *p282* . . . 01942 604404
Liverpool *p288* . . . 0151 259 1717
Liverpool *p288* . . . 0151 228 5522
Liverpool *p288* . . . 0151 264 8822
Liverpool *p288* . . . 0151 524 2443
Oldham *p340* . . . 0161 669 4940
Preston *p357* . . . 01772 284643
Rochdale *p365* . . . 01706 390400
Runcorn *p369* . . . 01928 590999
St Helens *p391* . . . 01744 755577
Stockport *p395* . . . 0161 870 3585
Warrington *p422* . . . 01925 575566
Widnes *p431* . . . 0151 495 3270
Widnes *p431* . . . 0151 422 0982
Wigan *p432* . . . 01942 366365

Forsters LLP
‡Westminster W1 *p33* . . . 020 7863 8333

Forsyth Simpson
‡London W1 *p33* . . . 020 7612 7615

Fort & Co
‡Slough *p382* . . . 01753 691224

Forte Law
‡Barry *p126* . . . 01446 713599

Fortescue Graham & Lloyd
‡Leatherhead *p271* . . . 01372 374895
Great Bookham *p233* . . . 01372 456221

Forth & Co
‡Yarm *p443* . . . 01642 784000

Fortress Law
‡Bromley *p166* . . . 020 8466 8998

Fortune Law
‡London W1 *p33* . . . 020 7440 2540

Forum Law Limited
‡Solihull *p382* . . . 0844 335 8456

Foskett Marr Gadsby & Head
‡Epping *p219* . . . 01992 578642
Loughton *p294* . . . 020 8502 3991

Fosse Law
‡Leicester *p279* . . . 0116 262 0290
Loughborough *p293* . . . 01509 231000
Melton Mowbray *p314* . . . 01664 500022

Foster & Foster
‡Enfield *p218* . . . 0844 568 6877

Foster & Partners
‡Bristol *p162* . . . 0117 961 5300
Bristol *p162* . . . 0117 922 0229

David J Foster & Co
‡Tamworth *p407* . . . 01827 58333 / 58334

Foster Harrington
‡Camberley *p173* . . . 01276 692233

Paul Foster & Co
‡York *p444* . . . 01904 765159

Foster Wells
‡Aldershot *p115* . . . 01252 343567

FosterLaw Solicitors
‡Skipton *p381* . . . 01756 700110

Fosters
‡Norwich *p334* . . . 01603 620508
Bungay *p168* . . . 01986 895251
Lowestoft *p294* . . . 01502 573307
Wymondham *p443* . . . 01953 607724

Fosters Law Limited
‡Canterbury *p176*
‡Herne Bay *p248* . . . 01227 283634
Broadstairs *p166* . . . 01843 340200

Fosters Solicitors
‡Neston *p321* . . . 0151 342 9828

Fountain Solicitors Limited
‡Walsall *p420* . . . 01922 645429

Fowler de Pledge
‡Cambridge *p174* . . . 01223 311291

Peter J Fowler
‡Wimborne *p433* . . . 01202 849242

Scott Fowler
‡Northampton *p331* . . . 01604 750506

John Fowlers LLP Solicitors
‡Colchester *p197* . . . 01206 576151
Brightlingsea *p159* . . . 01206 302694

Fox
‡London EC3 *p33* . . . 020 7618 2400

Fox Hartley
‡Bristol *p162* . . . 0117 917 7210
London EC3 *p33* . . . 0117 917 7210

Fox Whitfield
‡Manchester *p304* . . . 0161 283 1276

Fox Williams
‡London EC2 *p33* . . . 020 7628 2000

Joseph Foxler & Co
‡Bury *p170* . . . 0161 797 4126

Malcolm C Foy & Co
‡Doncaster *p211* . . . 01302 340005
Rotherham *p367* . . . 01709 836866

Foyen & Co
‡London EC1 *p33* . . . 020 7490 6336

Foys Solicitors
‡Doncaster *p211* . . . 01302 327136
Rotherham *p367* . . . 01709 375561
Sheffield *p375* . . . 0114 246 7609
Sheffield *p375* . . . 0114 251 1702
Worksop *p441* . . . 01909 473560

Fragomen LLP
‡London WC1 *p33* . . . 020 3077 5000

Margaret M Frame & Co
‡Ilford *p260* . . . 020 8518 6767

Frame Smith & Co
‡Aldershot *p115* . . . 01252 330330
‡Guildford *p236* . . . 01483 599377
‡Horley *p252* . . . 01293 785885

Alyson France & Co
‡Wirral *p435* . . . 0151 348 4400

Francis Alexander Solicitors
‡Stockport *p395* . . . 0161 432 3633

Francis & Buck
‡Cardiff *p178* . . . 029 2034 4995

Francis & Co
‡Chepstow *p189* . . . 01291 622237
‡Cranleigh *p202* . . . 01483 267222

Francis & How
‡Chesham *p189* . . . 01494 782541

Ann Francis & Co Solicitors
‡London SW2 *p33* . . . 020 7326 7266

Daniel Francis Solicitors
‡Maidstone *p299* . . . 01622 669460

Francis Law LLP
‡Lydney *p296* . . . 01594 842242

Francis-Trowe Solicitors
‡Talbot Green *p407* . . . 01443 231555

Francis Wilks & Jones LLP
‡London EC1 *p34* . . . 020 7841 0390

Frank & Co
‡London W1 *p34* . . . 020 7224 3837

Franklands Solicitors
‡London NW5 *p34* . . . 020 7485 0300

Franklin & Co
‡Bakewell *p121* . . . 01629 814461

Franklins
‡Abingdon *p114* . . . 01235 553222
‡Dunstable *p214* . . . 01582 699111
‡Leighton Buzzard *p282* . . . 01525 376611

Franklins LLP
‡Northampton *p332* . . . 01604 828282
Milton Keynes *p317* . . . 01908 660966

Franks & Co
‡London EC4 *p34* . . . 020 7242 8008

Leslie Franks Solicitors
‡London NW5 *p34* . . . 020 7428 7787

Franks Solicitors
‡Hackney E8 *p34* . . . 020 8533 4477

Fraser Brown
‡Nottingham *p337* . . . 0115 988 8777
Bingham *p133* . . . 01949 830812
Nottingham *p337* . . . 0115 933 5311

Charles Fraser & Co
‡Bury St Edmunds *p171* . . . 01284 750111

Fraser Dawbarns
‡Wisbech *p435* . . . 01945 461456
Downham Market *p213* . . . 01366 383171
King's Lynn *p266* . . . 01553 666600
March *p312* . . . 01354 602880

Fraser-Macnamara Limited
‡Halesowen *p237* . . . 0121 550 7308

Fraser Wise & Co
‡Grantham *p232* . . . 01476 566646 / 561870

Frazer Bradshaw
‡Bromley *p166* . . . 020 8466 5588

Frearsons
‡Skegness *p380* . . . 01754 897600

Ian C Free
‡West Kirby *p428* . . . 0151 625 0000

Doreen Freear Solicitor
‡Macclesfield *p297* . . . 01625 611711

Freeclaim Solicitors
Manchester *p304* . . . 0161 437 9999

Freed & Co
‡Cardiff *p178* . . . 029 2022 2685

Freedman Green Dhokia
‡Camden NW8 *p34* . . . 020 7625 6003
Camden NW8 *p34* . . . 020 7625 6003
Camden NW8 *p34* . . . 020 7624 2981

Freedman Sharman & Co
‡Borehamwood *p150* . . . 020 8953 9111

Freedmans
‡London W4 *p34* . . . 020 8987 9155

Freedmans Law
‡London W1 *p34* . . . 020 3170 7155

Freeman & Co
‡Manchester *p304* . . . 0161 236 7007

Freeman & Co Solicitors
‡Wetherby *p429* . . . 01937 583111

Freeman & Partners
‡Westminster NW1 *p34* . . . 020 7724 5855

Freeman Box
‡London W1 *p34* . . . 020 7486 9041

Freeman Harris
‡London SE1 *p34* . . . 020 7231 7150

Freeman Johnson
‡Darlington *p206* . . . 01325 466221
Durham *p214* . . . 0191 386 4843 / 386 9619
Northallerton *p331* . . . 01609 772160
Spennymoor *p389* . . . 01388 814389

Freeman Keep On Driving Ltd
‡Manchester *p304* . . . 0161 233 2130

Richard Freeman & Co
‡Kensington & Chelsea SW3 *p34* . 020 7351 5151

Freemans
‡Newcastle upon Tyne *p324* . . . 0191 222 1030

Freemans Solicitors
‡Bath *p127* . . . 01225 330733
‡London W1 *p34* . . . 020 7935 3522

Freemans Solicitors and Notaries
‡Liverpool *p288* . . . 0151 227 3435

Freer & Archer
‡Leicester *p279* . . . 0116 241 3199

Freers
‡Middlesbrough *p315* . . . 01642 244666

Freeth Cartwright LLP
‡Nottingham *p337* . . . 0115 936 9369
Birmingham *p138* . . . 0845 634 2575
Derby *p208* . . . 01332 361000
Leicester *p279* . . . 0116 248 1100
Manchester *p304* . . . 0845 634 2540

French & Co
‡Nottingham *p337* . . . 0115 955 1111

French & Co Solicitors Ltd
‡Sutton Coldfield *p403* . . . 0121 362 7330

Charles French & Co
‡Truro *p414* . . . 01872 263813

French Law Matters
‡Bournemouth *p152* . . . 01202 355480

The French Law Practice
‡London NW3 *p34* . . . 07971 616893

P K P French
‡Harrow *p241* . . . 020 8861 8832

Freshfields Bruckhaus Deringer LLP
‡London EC4 *p34* . . . 020 7936 4000

Frettens Solicitors
‡Christchurch *p194* . . . 01202 491777
New Milton *p321* . . . 01425 610100

Shirley Fretwell
‡Ilkeston *p261* . . . 0115 932 3623

Fridays Property Lawyers
‡London WC1 *p34* . . . 0845 644 0337

Fried Frank Harris Shriver & Jacobson LLP
‡London EC1 *p34* . . . 020 7972 9600

Friend & Co
‡Walton-on-Thames *p420* . . . 01932 242962

Jack Friend & Co
‡Wembley *p426* . . . 020 8904 4281

Michael Friend
‡Esher *p220* . . . 01372 468098

Friis & Radstone
‡Stevenage *p394* . . . 01438 741001

Julia Frimond Solicitors
‡Guildford *p236* . . . 01483 452224

FRISBY & CO
‡Stafford *p392* . . . 01785 244114
London EC4 *p34* . . . 020 7936 6399
Stafford *p392*

R G Frisby & Small
‡Leicester *p279* . . . 0116 233 5522
Leicester *p279* . . . 01455 282832

Frisby Solicitors Limited
‡Cannock *p176*

Fritchley Goldsmith
‡Barnsley *p124* . . . 01226 215600

Frodshams
‡St Helens *p391* . . . 01744 626600

C From & Co
‡London W4 *p34* . . . 020 8995 6153

Froriep Renggli
‡London EC4 *p34* . . . 020 7236 6000

R J Frost & Co
‡London SW13 *p34* . . . 020 8563 1453

Fruhman Davies Livingstones
‡Manchester *p304* . . . 0161 833 0578

J Howard Fry Solicitor
‡London SW19 *p34* . . . 020 8543 7700

Fugler & Co
‡Maidenhead *p298* . . . 01628 670935

Fuglers
‡London W1 *p34* . . . 020 7323 6450

Fujioka Company Limited
‡London EC2 *p34* . . . 020 7614 5806

Fulbright & Jaworski LLP
‡London EC4 *p34* . . . 020 7832 3600

Fulchers
‡Woking *p436* . . . 01483 885522

Fulchers of Farnborough
‡Farnborough *p224* . . . 01252 522475

Fulcrum Law LLP
‡London W2 *p34* . . . 020 7043 7534

FullagarBrooks
‡Swindon *p406* . . . 01793 777007

John Fuller & Partners Limited
‡Hemel Hempstead *p246* . . . 01422 233856

Fullers
‡Rugby *p368* . . . 01788 542288

Fullers Family Law Practice LLP
‡Bedford *p130* . . . 01234 343134

Fulton Robertson
‡Amersham *p117* . . . 01494 722326

Funnell & Perring
‡Hastings *p243* . . . 01424 426287

M D Furber & Co
‡Poole *p352* . . . 0870 766 1831

Furley Page LLP
‡Canterbury *p176* . . . 01227 763939
Chatham *p185* . . . 01634 828277
London EC3 *p34* . . . 020 7816 3642
Whitstable *p431* . . . 01227 274241

Furness Evans
Manchester *p304*

W M Furness & Son
Irlam *p263* . . . 0161 775 9962 / 775 6765

Furnivals Solicitors
‡Haywards Heath *p245* . . . 01444 473082

Fursdon Knapper
‡Plymouth *p349* . . . 01752 309090
Cambridge *p174* . . . 020 8123 3872

Furse Sanders & Co
‡South Molton *p383* . . . 01769 572251

Charles Fussell & Co
‡London WC2 *p34* . . . 020 7520 9323

FUSSELL WRIGHT
‡Bristol *p162* . . . 0117 927 9117
Bristol *p162* . . . 0117 971 3535

FUTTER CHAPMAN SOLICITORS
‡Peterborough *p347* . . . 0870 162 4499

Fynmores
‡Bexhill *p132* . . . 01424 732333

G

GB Law
‡Brentwood *p156* . . . 0800 321 3328

GB Solicitors Ltd
‡Fareham *p224* . . . 01329 282817

GCA Solicitors (Giffen Couch & Archer)
‡Luton *p295* . . . 01582 410041

GCL Solicitors
‡Guildford *p236* . . . 01483 577091

GC Law
‡Hereford *p248* . . . 01432 275397

GCS Property Solicitors
‡Stafford *p392* . . . 01785 604820

GH Cornish LLP
‡Ilford *p260* . . . 020 8090 0800
London EC4 *p34* . . . 020 8090 0800

G H Law
‡Croydon *p205* . . . 020 8680 5095

GHP Legal
‡Wrexham *p442* 01978 291456
Llangollen *p292* 01978 860313
Oswestry *p342* 01691 659194

GHW Solicitors
‡Bury *p170* 01204 882373

GKR Law Solicitors
‡Chester *p190* 0151 549 4120

GK Solicitors
‡Liverpool *p288* 0151 220 2838

GLP Solicitors
‡Manchester *p304* 0161 834 6721
Bury *p170* 0161 764 1818
Manchester *p304* 0161 795 5531
Manchester *p304* 0161 793 0901
Manchester *p304* 0161 703 8677
Middleton *p315* 0161 653 6295
Prestwich *p357* 0161 773 8626

GLRS Phoenix LLP
‡Stroud *p400* 01453 763433
Dursley *p214* 01453 547221
Stonehouse *p398* 01453 825151
Stroud *p400* 01453 757381

GMG
‡London E13 *p34* 020 7511 3771

GMH Solicitors
‡Guildford *p236* 07545 571569

GPB Solicitors LLP
‡Stratford-upon-Avon *p400* 01789 261131

GPT Solicitors
‡Wembley *p426* . . . .020 8904 6495 / 8904 6598

GQ Employment Law
‡London EC2 *p34* 020 3375 0330
Reading *p361* 020 3375 0331

GQS Limited
‡Birmingham *p138* 0121 733 7070

GR Solicitors
‡Manchester *p304* 0161 793 6565

GSC Solicitors
‡London EC1 *p34* 020 7822 2222

GSD Law Ltd
‡Leeds *p273* 0113 388 4897

GSE Legals
‡Gateshead *p228* . 0191 215 5008 / 07711 047335

GS Solicitors
‡Hinckley *p250* 01455 618763

GT Law Solicitors
‡Braintree *p155* 01245 360148
‡Liverpool *p288* 0844 414 9771

GT Stewart Solicitors
‡London SE1 *p34* 020 7089 0600
‡London SE1 *p34* 020 7394 7488

GWS Solicitors
‡Warrington *p422* 0330 123 9011

Gabb & Co
‡Abergavenny *p113* 01873 852432
Crickhowell *p203* 01873 810629

J H Gabb & Co Solicitors
‡Cheltenham *p188* 07970 011693

Gabbitas Robins
‡Marlow *p313* 01628 472600

Gabbs LLP
‡Hereford *p248* 01432 353481
Hay-on-Wye *p245* 01497 820312
Leominster *p282* 01568 616333

Gabriel Basil Solicitors
‡London N17 *p34* 020 8801 0289

Gabriels Solicitors
‡Formby *p227* 01704 831554

Gadsby Wicks
‡Chelmsford *p186* 01245 494929

Angela Gaff
‡London E1 *p34* 020 7265 8710

Martin Gaffney Legal Services
‡Rothwell *p368* 0113 282 7988

Galbraith Branley
‡London N12 *p34* 020 8446 8474

Donald Galbraith & Co
‡London N12 *p34* 020 8492 2700

Gales
‡Bournemouth *p152* . . . .01202 512227 / 512446

David Gall LLB Solicitor
‡Hawes *p245* 01969 667171

Robert Gallacher Soliticors
‡Consett *p199* 01207 581143

Gallant Macmillan LLP
‡London W1 *p34* 020 7758 4720

Stephen Gallico Solicitors
‡Haywards Heath *p245* 01444 411333

D W Gallifant
‡West Mersea *p428* 01206 383050

J D Gallimore
‡Leominster *p283* 01568 616345

Galloway Hughes Solicitors
‡Esher *p220* . . .01372 237070 / 020 8398 8188

Natalie Gamble Associates
‡Salisbury *p371* 0844 357 1602

Gamlins
‡Abergele *p113* 01745 357333
‡Denbigh *p208* 01745 812422
‡Llandudno *p291* 01492 860420
‡Ruthin *p369* 01824 702102
Bangor *p122* 01248 672414
Colwyn Bay *p198* 01492 532275
Colwyn Bay *p198* 01492 547156
Conwy *p199* 01492 593201
Holywell *p252* 01352 714822
Rhyl *p363* 01745 343500

Gammon Bell & Co
‡Eastleigh *p216* 023 8068 4900

Gammon Piercy & Gaiger
‡Eastleigh *p216* 023 8065 8200
Southampton *p386* 023 8065 8180

Gamon Arden & Co
‡Liverpool *p288* 0151 709 2222

Gandecha & Pau
‡Barnet NW9 *p34* 020 8905 0900

Ganderton Solicitors
‡Birmingham *p138* 0121 708 1944

Gandhi & Co Solicitors
‡Harrow *p241* 020 8909 0800

David S Gandy
‡Hale *p237* 0161 980 2334

Gangar & Co
‡West Bromwich *p427* 0121 553 4166

Gani & Co
‡Lambeth SW9 *p35* 020 7733 8169

I R Gannicott
‡Bourton-on-the-Water *p153* . . . 01451 820265

Gannons Limited
‡Camden WC1 *p35* 020 7438 1060

Ganpate
‡London NW4 *p35* 020 8202 5092

Gans & Co Solicitors LLP
‡London SE15 *p35* 020 7469 7010
London SE8 *p35* 020 8691 4464
London SE8 *p35* 020 7820 8222

Gants Hill Solicitors
‡London E11 *p35* 0845 359 0058

Garbetts
‡Taunton *p408* 01984 667506

Garcha & Co
‡London E1 *p35* 020 7375 1888

Gard & Co
‡Plymouth *p349* 01752 668246

Garden House Solicitors
‡Hertford *p248* 01992 422128

Gardiner & Co
‡London NW6 *p35* 020 7435 0810

Gardiners Solicitors
London W14 *p35* 020 7603 7245

Gardner Austin
‡Westminster SW1 *p35* 020 7831 2600

Gardner Champion
‡Rugeley *p368* . . . . . . .01889 576121 / 582116

Gardner Croft LLP
‡Canterbury *p176* 01227 813400

Gardner Dallimore
‡Hereford *p248* 01432 263535

Gardner Iliff & Dowding
‡Cannock *p176* 01543 466941

Gardner Leader LLP
‡Newbury *p322* 01635 508080
Thatcham *p410* 01635 508080

Gardner Thorpe
Haslemere *p243* 01428 661151

F S Garford
‡London NW6 *p35* 020 7604 4554

D H Garland
‡Coulsdon *p199* 020 8660 7049

Garlands Solicitors
‡Chorley *p194* 01257 474477

G C Garlick
‡Aylesbury *p121* 01296 651481

Garner & Hancock Solicitors LLP
‡Isleworth *p263* 020 8232 9560

GARNER CANNING
‡Tamworth *p407* 01827 314004
Atherstone *p120* 01827 713543
Birmingham *p138* 0121 749 5577

Garner Canning Vickery
Sutton Coldfield *p403* 0121 323 2646

Garner Hutchings
‡Westminster SW1 *p35* 020 7932 2400

Garners Solicitors
‡Stamford *p393* 01780 751196

Garnett Williams Powell
‡Rhyl *p363* 01745 334658

J Garrard & Allen
‡Olney *p341* 01234 711215

Garrards
‡Shrewsbury *p379* 01743 341140

Garrett Long Solicitors
‡Leicester *p279* 0116 236 4875

Garricks Solicitors
‡Blackburn *p145* 01254 268790

Garrods Solicitors
‡Chelmsford *p186* 01245 492494

Garside & Hoy
‡Wealdstone *p424* 020 8427 5656

Garson & Co
‡Pinner *p348* 020 8429 4111

Garstangs
‡Bolton *p149* 01204 531118
London WC2 *p35* 020 7427 5678

E Michael Garston
‡London W14 *p35* 020 7603 2903

Garton & Co
‡Leeds *p273* 0113 231 0766

Gartsides
‡Newport *p328* 01633 213411
Abergavenny *p113* 01873 857555
Ebbw Vale *p216* 01495 302109

Garvins Solicitors
‡Manchester *p304* 0161 495 2880

Gaskell & Walker
‡Bridgend *p157* 01656 653122
Cowbridge *p201* 01446 772212

Gateley LLP
‡Birmingham *p138* 0121 234 0000
Leicester *p279* 0116 285 9000
London EC4 *p35* 020 7653 1600
Manchester *p304* 0161 836 7700
Nottingham *p337* 0115 983 8200

Gates & Moloney
‡Lancing *p270* 01903 766046

Gates and Partners
‡London EC3 *p35* 020 7220 5950

Peter G Gates
‡Horsham *p253* 01403 753636

Gattas Denfield Solicitors
‡London NW9 *p35* 020 8204 7181
Harrow *p241* 020 8204 9290

John Gaunt & Partners
‡Sheffield *p375* 0114 266 8664

Gavin Edmondson Solicitors
‡Northwich *p333* 01606 43762

Gavins Solicitors
‡London N6 *p35* 020 8374 4459

Gawor & Co
‡London E1 *p35* 020 7481 8888

Roger Gay & Co
‡Somerton *p383* 01458 273137

Gaynham King & Mellor
‡Penrith *p346* 01768 864651
Appleby *p118* 01768 351422

Gaynor-Smith Owen & Co
‡Malvern *p300* 01684 560771

Kevin Geaney
‡Kidlington *p266* 01865 379498

Gedye & Sons (Solicitors) Ltd
‡Grange-over-Sands *p232* 01539 532313

Gee & Edwards
‡Swansea *p405* . . . . .01792 465806 / 464937

Craig Gee
‡Manchester *p304* 0161 666 9999

Nicholas Gee
‡Sutton Coldfield *p403* 0121 353 3543

Gelbergs LLP
‡Islington N1 *p35* 020 7226 0570

Geldards LLP
‡Cardiff *p178* 029 2023 8239
Derby *p208* 01332 331631
Nottingham *p337* 0115 983 3650

Gellhorns
‡Bordon *p150* 01420 205032

Gelson Haylor
‡Southwark SE1 *p35* 020 7928 0675

Diane Genders Solicitors
‡Lincoln *p284* 01522 516500
Nottingham *p337* 0115 852 4750

Genesis Legal Services Limited
‡Bournemouth *p152* 01202 552255

Genga & Co
‡Wembley *p426* 020 8795 5020

Geoff Taylor Solicitor
‡Cambridge *p174* 01954 211761

Geoffrey Morris & Ashton
‡Wrexham *p442* 01978 291322
Mold *p318* 01352 754711

George & Co
‡Bury St Edmunds *p171* 01449 737582

George & D'Ambra
Merthyr Tydfil *p314* 01685 371153
Ystradgynlais *p446* 01639 842420

George Davies & Evans Limited
‡Cardigan *p181* 01239 612308

George H Coles & Co
‡Hove *p254* 01273 205101

GEORGE IDE LLP
‡Chichester *p192* 01243 786668
Bognor Regis *p148* 01243 829231
Chichester *p192* 01243 786668
Chichester *p192*

Michael George & Company
‡Dewsbury *p210* 01924 488884

P George & Co
‡Haringey N8 *p35* 020 8341 9080

William George & Son
‡Porthmadog *p354* . . . .01766 512011 / 512474

Kay Georgiou
‡London EC1 *p35* 020 7831 3685

Roulla Georgiou
‡Barnet N14 *p35* 020 8368 0220

Gepp & Sons
‡Chelmsford *p186* 01245 493939
Colchester *p197* 01206 369889

Gershon & Goldstein
‡Edgware *p217* 020 8952 5272

Reena Ghai Solicitors
‡Hounslow *p253* 020 8759 9959

Gherson & Co
‡London W1 *p35* 020 7724 4488

Ghuman Solicitors
‡Salford *p370* 0161 278 2562

Giambrone Law
‡London EC1 *p35* 020 7183 9482

Gianni Origoni & Partners
‡London EC2 *p35* 020 7397 1700

Gibbens Solicitors
‡Stockton-on-Tees *p397* 01642 702481

Deborah Gibbins & Co
‡Billericay *p133* 01268 270866

Duncan Gibbins Solicitors
‡Prescot *p355* 0151 949 5757

Ann Gibbon & Co
‡Twickenham *p416* 020 8891 2707

Gibbons Solicitors
‡Ipswich *p262* 01473 822488

Jeremy Gibbs & Co
‡Amersham *p117* 01494 724671

Gibson & Co
‡Hexham *p249* 01434 602131
Newcastle upon Tyne *p324* 0191 273 3817

Gibson Dunn & Crutcher LLP
‡London EC4 *p35* 020 7071 4000

Gibson Young
‡London SW11 *p35* . .020 7228 2211 / 7228 2213

Timothy J Gibsons
‡Alresford *p116* 01962 736926

Gichard & Co
‡Rotherham *p367* 01709 365531

Peter Giddens & Co
‡Cambridge *p174* 01954 250089

Gide Loyrette Nouel LLP
‡London EC2 *p35* 020 7382 5500

Giffen Couch & Archer
‡Leighton Buzzard *p282* 01525 372681
‡Stony Stratford *p399* 01908 563911

Gilbert Davies & Partners
‡Welshpool *p425* 01938 552727

Mark Gilbert Morse
‡Newcastle upon Tyne *p325* 0191 261 0096

Gilbert Stephens
‡Exeter *p221* 01392 424242
Ottery St Mary *p342* 01404 812228
Sidmouth *p380* 01395 512443

Gilbert Turner Coomber
‡Waltham Forest E17 *p35* 020 8520 5886

Gilchrist Solicitors
‡London W1 *p35* 020 7667 6868

Gildener Brett
‡Penzance *p346* 01736 332533

Gilead Balms
‡Barking *p123* 020 8594 4788

Gilead Balms Solicitors
‡Dagenham *p206* 020 8595 2211

C J Giles & Co
‡Wokingham *p437* 0118 978 1017

Giles Dixon
‡Richmond upon Thames *p364* . . 020 8241 1059

Giles Hunter Partnership
‡Chester-le-Street *p191* 0191 388 7041
‡Consett *p199* 01207 590285

Paul Giles
‡Nottingham *p337* 0115 933 3275

Gill Akaster
‡Plymouth *p349* 01752 203500

Gill & Co
‡Ilford *p260* 020 8554 8774

Gill Bowness
‡Nottingham *p337* 01509 674355

Gill Jennings & Every
‡London EC2 *p35* 020 7377 1377

M K Gill Solicitors
‡Gravesend *p232* 01474 353399
‡Hounslow *p253* 020 8572 4509

Gill Steel Law Practice
‡Winchester *p433* 01962 776442

Gill Turner Tucker
‡Maidstone *p299* 01622 759051

Gillan & Co
‡West Wickham *p428* 020 8777 4600

Gillanders
‡Cheltenham *p188* 01242 583434

Gillespies
‡Walsall *p420* 01922 627474

Gillhams Solicitors LLP
‡London EC4 *p35* 020 7353 2732
London NW10 *p35* 020 8965 4266

David Gillies Solicitor
‡Cranbrook *p202* 01580 715523

Gillies Solicitors LLP
‡Brighton *p159* 01273 206050

Gillings and Walker
‡York *p444* 01904 655755

Gillman-Smith Lee Solicitors
‡Twickenham *p416* 020 8744 0909

Gilroy Steel
‡Brackley *p153* 01280 709426
Buckingham *p168* 01280 815538
Northampton *p332* 01604 620890

Ginn & Co
‡Cambridge *p174* 01223 358275

Girasol Services
‡Hove *p254* 01273 701679

Girlings
‡Canterbury *p177* 01227 768374
Ashford *p119* 01233 664711
Ashford *p119* 01233 647377
Herne Bay *p248* 01227 367355
Margate *p312* 01843 220274

Girlings Personal Injury Claims Limited
‡Canterbury *p177* 01227 768374

Gisby Harrison
‡Cheshunt *p189* 01707 878300

David Gist Solicitors
‡Bristol *p162* 0117 927 9111

Gittins McDonald
‡Wrexham *p442* 01978 291662

Glade Law Limited
‡London EC2 *p35* 020 7156 5199

Gladstone Solicitors
‡Newark *p322* 01636 640641
Derby *p209* 01332 203403
Nottingham *p337* 0115 955 5050
Nottingham *p337* 0115 978 1666

Gladstones
‡Crowborough *p204* 01892 610260

Ruth Gladwin Solicitor
‡London N16 *p35* 020 7241 1685

Glaisyers
‡Birmingham *p138* 0121 233 2971
‡Tamworth *p407* 01827 61011

Glaisyers Solicitors LLP
‡Manchester *p304* 0161 832 4666
Manchester *p304* 0161 224 3311

GlamorganLaw
‡Cardiff *p178* 029 2022 5472
Cowbridge *p201* 01446 771742
Pontypridd *p352* 01443 408455

Glandfield & Cruddas
‡Uttoxeter *p417* 01889 565657

Glansfields
‡Mansfield *p311* 01623 627827

Glanville Robinson
‡Plymouth *p349* . . 01752 500281 / 07530 625206

Glanvilles
‡Fareham *p224* 01329 282841
Havant *p244* 023 9249 2300
Newport *p328* 01983 527878

Glass Law
‡London NW1 *p35* 0870 066 1953

Glassbrooks Limited
‡Lytham *p297* 0800 316 6484

Nigel Glassey Solicitor
‡Stockport *p395* 0161 443 1395

Glazer Delmar
‡London SE22 *p35* 020 8299 0021

Gledhill Solicitors
‡Brighton *p159* 01273 719083

Glinert Davis
‡Westminster W1 *p36* 020 7724 4442

Global Lawyer LLP
‡London NW8 *p36*

Global Solicitors
‡Stockport *p395* 0161 427 0553

Globe Wareing Cropper
‡Liverpool *p288* 0151 486 8833

Glovers Solicitors LLP
‡London W1 *p36* 020 7935 8882

Glynnes
‡Ealing *p214* 020 8997 1437

Glynns Solicitors
‡Bristol *p162* 01761 490883

Goad & Butcher
‡Settle *p374* 01729 823500

Leo Goatley & Co
‡Gloucester *p230* 01452 548293

Godloves
‡Leeds *p273* 0113 225 8811
Leeds *p273* 0113 286 8822
Leeds *p273* 0113 225 8864
Leeds *p273* 0113 225 8874

Godwins
‡Winchester *p433* 01962 841484
Aberystwyth *p114* 01970 624244

Goffeys
‡Southport *p388* 01704 531755

Mathew Gold & Company
‡London N3 *p36* 020 8343 3678

Mel Goldberg Law
‡London W1 *p36* 020 7355 0310

Goldbergs
‡Plymouth *p349* 01752 660023

Beverley Golden
‡Southampton *p386* 023 8086 7137

Golden Leaver LLP
‡London SW1 *p36* 020 3159 5160

Golden Solicitors
‡London NW1 *p36* 020 7424 7898

Goldens
‡Pinner *p348* 020 8429 8282

Goldfields Solicitors
‡London SE18 *p36* 020 8316 0511

Goldkorn Mathias Gentle Page LLP
‡London WC1 *p36* 020 7631 1811

Goldkorn Solicitors
‡London SE5 *p36* 020 7703 1144

Goldman Bailey Solicitors
‡London NW1 *p36* 020 3326 2585

Goldman Law
‡Richmond upon Thames *p364* . . 020 8332 2310

Goldman Marc Limited
‡High Wycombe *p250* 01494 478930

Goldring & Co
‡Rainham *p359* 01634 260012

Goldsmith Williams
‡Liverpool *p288* 0845 373 3737

Goldspring Jones Solicitors Limited
‡Ashford *p119* 01843 227631

J J Goldstein & Co
‡London NW4 *p36* 020 8202 1899

Goldstein Legal
‡Windsor *p434* 01753 865165

Richard S Goldstein
‡London W1 *p36* 020 7499 8200

Sally Goldstone Family Law
‡Swansea *p405* 01792 456139

Sandra Goldstone
‡Twickenham *p416* 020 8287 3635

Goldstones
‡Swansea *p405* 01792 643021

Goldsworth Solicitors
‡London SE15 *p36* 020 7358 8150
‡London N18 *p36* 020 8887 1350

Goldwaters
‡Newcastle upon Tyne *p324* 0191 232 2653

Gomer Williams & Co
‡Llanelli *p292* 01554 755101

Clive Gomes Solicitors
‡Wembley *p426* 020 8904 2614

Gomez Acebo & Pombo
‡London EC4 *p36* 020 7329 5407

Good & Co Solicitors LLP
‡Bradford *p154* 0845 388 8901

Goodall Barnett James
‡St Leonards-on-Sea *p392* 01424 444475
Horley *p252* 01293 414448

Goodge Law
‡London W1 *p36* 020 7636 9222

Goodgers
‡London WC2 *p36* 020 7520 9012

GOODHAND AND FORSYTH QUALITYSOLICITORS
‡Redhill *p362* 01737 773533

Jacqueline Goodlad
‡Cockermouth *p197* 01900 825524

David Goodman
‡London NW10 *p36* . .020 8969 0646 / 8969 0966

David Goodman & Co
‡Westminster W1 *p36* 020 7323 3369

Goodman Derrick LLP
‡London EC4 *p36* 020 7404 0606

Goodman GDP Solicitors LLP
‡Liverpool *p288* 0151 707 0090

Goodman Harvey LLP
‡Manchester *p305* 0161 819 6622

Goodman King
‡Tavistock *p408* 01822 615510

N J Goodman & Co
‡Altrincham *p116* 0161 928 0990

Goodman Ray
‡Hackney EC1 *p36* 020 7608 1227
London EC2 *p36* 020 7608 1227

S B Goodman
‡Brentwood *p156* 01277 262703

Goodmans
‡Waterloo *p423* 0151 257 6000

Goodsells
‡London SW4 *p36* 020 7622 2221

Rodney Goodson
‡Norwich *p334* 01603 632832

Goodswens
‡Redcar *p362* 01642 482424

Goodwin & Co
‡London SW16 *p36* 020 8677 9554

C Z Goodwin
‡Amersham *p117* 01494 724446

Goodwin Cowley
‡Lowestoft *p294* 01502 532700

Jonathan Goodwin Solicitor Advocate
‡Chester *p190* 01244 853120

Mark Goodwin & Co
‡Wilmslow *p433* 01625 526495

Goodwin Stevens Solicitors
‡Halifax *p238* 01422 300101

Goodwins Family Law Solicitors
‡Harrow *p241* 020 8423 3525

GoodyBurrett LLP
‡Colchester *p197* 01206 577676

Goodyear & Co
‡Blyth *p148* 01670 362379

Caroline Goorney Soliicitor
‡Gosforth *p231* 0191 285 9411

Gopal Gupta Solicitors
‡London NW10 *p36* 020 8838 0008

Gordon & Co
‡London W1 *p36* 020 7486 9150

Gordon & Penney
‡Weston-super-Mare *p429* 01934 414161

Gordon Lutton
‡Hereford *p248* 01432 355345

R Gordon Roberts Laurie & Co
‡Llangefni *p292* . . . . . .01248 722215 / 723312
Beaumaris *p129* . . . . .01248 810210 / 810532

Stuart Gordon Solicitor & Advocate
‡Leeds *p273* 0113 244 4999

Gordons
‡London WC1 *p36* 020 7421 9421
Guildford *p236* 01483 451900

Gordons LLP
‡Bradford *p154* 01274 202202
Leeds *p273* 0113 227 0100

Gordons Solicitors LLP
‡Marlow *p313* 01628 487487
Maidenhead *p298* 0870 777 1122

Gore Legal
‡Ealing W5 *p36* 020 8810 1652

Antony Gorley & Co
‡Newbury *p322* 01635 551321

Gorman Hamilton
‡Newcastle upon Tyne *p324* 0191 232 1123
Ipswich *p262* 01473 408073
Leeds *p274* 0113 386 2600

Gorrara Haden Solicitors
‡Birmingham *p138* 0121 452 8787

Gorvins
‡Stockport *p395* 0161 930 5151

Goshen Solicitors
‡Birmingham *p138* 0121 686 3170

Gosschalks
‡Hull *p256* 01482 324252

Gotelee
‡Ipswich *p262* 01473 211121
Hadleigh *p237* 01473 822102

Gotleys Solicitors
‡Frome *p228* 01373 454546

Gough & Co Solicitors
‡London E11 *p36* 020 8926 3080

Gough Clinton & Broom
‡Welling *p424* 020 8301 9000

Gough Davies
‡Bargoed *p123* 01443 839393

H F T Gough & Co
‡Whitehaven *p431* 01946 692461

R S Gough & Co
‡Wolverhampton *p438* 01902 420200

Gough-Thomas & Scott
‡Ellesmere *p217* 01691 622413
Oswestry *p342* 01691 655600

Goughs
‡Calne *p173* 01249 812086
Chippenham *p193* 01249 444499
Corsham *p199* 01249 712193
Devizes *p210* 01380 726913
Melksham *p314* 01225 703036
Trowbridge *p414* 01225 762683

Gould & Swayne
‡Street *p400* 01458 442433
Burnham-on-Sea *p169* 01278 783272
Glastonbury *p229* 01458 833700
Wells *p425* 01749 675535

J S L Goulden
‡London NW3 *p36* 020 7435 8887

Graham Gover Solicitor
‡Exeter *p221* 01392 423090

R Govier Solicitors
‡Cannock *p176* 01543 469919

Dominic Goward & Co
‡Faversham *p225* 01795 529025

Gowens LLP
‡Croydon *p205* 020 8680 2200

Marjorie E Gowlett
‡Huntingdon *p258* 01487 822229

Gowlings
‡Preston *p357* 01772 251287

Gowlings (UK) LLP
‡London EC3 *p36* 020 3004 3500

Gowmans
‡Paignton *p345* 01803 546100

Grace & Co
‡London W1 *p36* 020 7935 7938
‡Warrington *p422* 01925 242488

Grace-Springs Solicitors
‡Barking *p123* 020 8591 5290

Stuart Grace Associates
‡Eastbourne *p215* 01323 433000

Graceland Solicitors
‡London SE13 *p36*
‡London SE18 *p36* 020 8836 9350

Graff & Redfern
‡Richmond upon Thames *p364* . 020 8940 0860 / 8948 2815

Graham & Rosen
‡Hull *p257* 01482 323123

Graham Clayton Solicitors
‡Chester-le-Street *p191* 0191 389 0999
Bolton *p149* 01204 521434
Cardiff *p178* 029 2049 1818
Doncaster *p211* 01302 342448
Ilford *p260* 020 8554 5525
Stafford *p392* 01785 244129

William Graham Law Limited
‡Cardiff *p178* 029 2089 5100

Grahame Stowe Bateson
‡Leeds *p274* 0113 246 8163
Harrogate *p240* 01423 562121
Leeds *p274* 0113 255 8666
Leeds *p274* 0113 274 4611
Leeds *p274* 0113 276 0044

Grainger Appleyard
‡Doncaster *p211* 01302 327257

Gramdan Solicitors
‡Birmingham *p138* 0121 786 1196
‡London W3 *p36* 020 8749 7282

Granary Chambers
‡Bexhill *p132* 01424 733008

Grange & Castle
‡London SE1 *p36* 020 7967 7070

Andre Grant & Co
‡Haringey N15 *p36* 020 8800 8802

Grant Saw Solicitors LLP
‡Greenwich SE10 *p36* 020 8858 6971

Grants Solicitors
‡Croydon *p205* 020 8288 8899
‡Fleet *p226* 01252 622288

Granville-West
‡Pontypool *p352* 01495 751111
Caldicot *p172* 01291 423999

Granville-West Chivers & Morgan
Abertillery *p113* 01495 217070
Blackwood *p147* 01495 223161
Newport *p328* 01495 243268
Risca *p365* 01633 612353

Gray & Co
‡Manchester *p305* 0161 237 3360

David Gray Solicitors
‡Newcastle upon Tyne *p324* 0191 232 9547

Gordon Gray
‡Selsdon *p374* 020 8657 3444

Gray Hooper Holt LLP
‡Redhill *p362* 01737 761004

Leonard Gray
‡Chelmsford *p186* 01245 504904

Walter Gray & Co
‡Ryde *p369* 01983 563765
Cowes *p201* . . . . . . .01983 281188 / 296010

Grays
‡York *p444* 01904 634771

Grayson Willis Bennett
‡Sheffield *p375* 0114 290 9500
Rotherham *p367* 01709 720287

Graysons
‡Sheffield *p375* 0114 272 9184
Chesterfield *p192* 01246 229393

Graystons
‡Wirral *p435* 0151 645 0055

Grazing Hill Law Partners
‡London N1 *p37* 020 7354 1444

Great Western Solicitors
‡Swindon *p406* 01793 436007

Greater London Solicitors
‡Croydon *p205* 020 8684 7044

Greathead & Whitelock
‡Pembroke *p345* 01646 682101

Greaves Brewster LLP
‡Cheddar *p186* 01934 745880

Christopher J Greaves
‡Rothwell *p368* 0113 282 7988

The Grech Gooden Partnership LLP
‡Cardiff *p178* 029 2022 2255
Cardiff *p178* 029 2045 0600

Green & Co
‡Maidstone *p299* 01622 676769

Barry Green
‡Brierley Hill *p158* 01384 566332

C M Green & Co
‡Aldershot *p115* 01252 326501

Christopher Green McCarrahers
Southampton *p386* 023 8084 2765

GEORGE GREEN LLP
‡Cradley Heath *p201* 01384 410410

Ian Green Consulting
‡London NW3 *p37* 07860 539360

Green Immigration Consultancy
‡Crewe *p203* 01270 811617

Matthew John Green
‡Horsham *p253* 01403 210200

Roger Green & Co
‡Billericay *p133* 01277 659441

Green Williamson Solicitors
‡Wakefield *p418* 01924 291400
Leeds *p274* 0113 394 4120

GREEN WRIGHT CHALTON ANNIS
‡Worthing *p441* 01903 234064
Rustington *p369* 01903 774131
Arundel *p118* 01903 881122
Lancing *p270* 01903 752918
Steyning *p395* 01903 814190
Worthing *p441* 01903 700220

GREENBERG TRAURIG MAHER LLP
‡London EC3 *p37* 020 3349 8700

Greene & Greene
‡Bury St Edmunds *p171* 01284 762211

Peter Greene & Co
‡Crawley *p202* 07546 231812

Greenfield Whiston
‡Kettering *p265* 01536 410880

Greenfields
‡Chichester *p192* 01243 773654

Greenfields Solicitors
‡London N9 *p37* 020 8884 1166

Adam F Greenhalgh & Co
‡Bolton *p149* 0845 074 3491

Peter D Greenhalgh
‡Glossop *p230* 01457 861319

Greenhalghs Solicitors
‡Skelmersdale *p381* 0333 200 5200

Greenhead Solicitors
‡Huddersfield *p255* 01484 546022

Greenhouse Stirton & Co
‡London EC1 *p37* 020 7490 3456

GREENLAND HOUCHEN POMEROY
‡Norwich *p334* 01603 660744
Attleborough *p120* 01953 453143
Watton *p424* 01953 882864
Long Stratton *p293* 01508 530033
Wymondham *p443* 01953 606351

GREENLAND SOLICITORS
‡Camden NW1 *p37* 020 7428 0777

Greens
‡Ludlow *p294* 01584 873918

A S Greenstreet Solicitor
‡Chelmsford *p186* 01245 603505

Colina Greenway
‡Cambridge *p174* 01223 451072

Greenways
‡Newquay *p329* . . . . . 01637 872361 / 872251

Greenwood & Co
‡London EC1 *p37* 020 7831 8386

Greenwoods
‡Knaresborough *p268* 01423 862975
‡London EC3 *p37* 020 7220 7818
Bristol *p162* 0117 910 0200
Fareham *p224* 01489 882900
London WC1 *p37* 020 7323 4632
Manchester *p305* 0161 245 6520
Milton Keynes *p317* 01908 298200

Greenwoods Solicitors LLP
‡Peterborough *p347* 01733 887700

Louise Greer
‡Maidenhead *p298* 01628 781693

Gregg Latchams LLP
‡Bristol *p162* 0117 906 9400

Gregorian Emerson Family Law Solicitors
‡London SW6 *p37* 01483 898076

Gregory Abrams Davidson LLP
‡Liverpool *p288* 0151 236 5000
Liverpool *p288* 0151 733 3353
Liverpool *p288* 0151 494 0777
London NW11 *p37* . . 020 8209 0166 / 8458 9322

Charles Gregory Associates
‡London E11 *p37* 020 8988 1118

GREGORY ROWCLIFFE MILNERS
‡London WC1 *p37* 020 7242 0631

Gregorys Solicitors
Stockport *p395* 0161 456 8125

Gregsons
‡Liverpool *p288* 0151 703 2550
‡London SW19 *p37* 020 8946 1173
‡Nottingham *p337* 0115 941 1999
Liverpool *p288* . . . . 0151 924 6444 / 236 6120

Gregsons Solicitors
‡Holywell *p252* 01352 871978

Maureen P Grenville
‡Duffield *p214* 01332 841789

David G Grey Solicitor
‡Preston *p357* 01995 600190

Grid Law Limited
‡Bournemouth *p152* 01202 961342

Grier Olubi Solicitors
‡London EC2 *p37* 020 7256 7770

Grierson Shaw & Co
‡Durham *p214* 0191 386 2434

Grieves Solicitors
‡Huddersfield *p255* 01484 300192

Griffin Law
‡Cranbrook *p202* 01580 236120

Neil Griffin & Co
‡Honiton *p252* 01404 42609

Gareth Griffith & Company
‡Caernarfon *p172* 01286 676869

Griffith Smith Conway
‡Hove *p254* 01273 821577

Griffith Smith Farrington Webb
‡Brighton *p159* 01273 324041
Hassocks *p243* 01273 843405
Henfield *p247* 01273 492045

Griffiths & Hughes Parry
‡Holywell *p252* . . . . . 01352 711815 / 711945

Griffiths Ings Ltd
‡Barry *p126* 01446 725180
Cardiff *p178* 029 2034 0178

M J R Griffiths
‡Falmouth *p223* . . 07768 644006 / 01326 218711

Richard Griffiths & Co
‡Salisbury *p371* 01722 329966
Chippenham *p193* 01249 446300

Griffiths Robertson
‡Reading *p361* 0118 958 5049

Shirley Griffiths
‡Hythe *p259* 01303 266689

Stephanie F Griffiths
‡Kingston upon Thames *p267* . . . 020 8546 5986

Grigsby Eddleston & Co
‡Stevenage *p394* 01438 742525

Grimshaws Solicitors Limited
‡Clevedon *p196* 01275 875216

Grindall & Hanna Solicitors
‡Southwark SE22 *p37* 020 8299 3801

Grindeys LLP
‡Stoke-on-Trent *p397* 01782 846441
Stoke-on-Trent *p397* 01782 846441
Stoke-on-Trent *p398* 01782 846441
Stone *p398* 01785 810780

Grindrod & Co
‡Wellington *p425* 01952 243064

Grindrods
‡Newton-le-Willows *p330* 01925 221321

Paul Gromett & Co
‡London W1 *p37* 020 7631 2066

Gromyko Amedu Solicitors
‡London SW2 *p37* 020 8678 8996

Groom Wilkes & Wright LLP
‡Hitchin *p251* 01462 714300

Gross & Co
‡Bury St Edmunds *p171* 01284 763333

Gross & Curjel
‡Woodbridge *p438* 01394 383436

Grosscurth & Co
‡Moreton *p319* 0151 678 8212

Andrew Grove & Co
‡Cambridge *p174* 01223 367133

Martin L Grove
‡Saltburn-by-the-Sea *p371* 01287 650675
Middlesbrough *p315* 01642 456615

Grove Solicitors
‡London N5 *p37* 020 7226 2226

Grove Tompkins Bosworth
‡Birmingham *p138* . . . 0121 236 9341 / 236 8091

Groves & Co
‡London NW5 *p37*

Martin Groves Solicitors
‡Leamington Spa *p270* 01926 629007

Grower Freeman
‡London NW1 *p37* 020 7723 3040

M C Grumbridge
‡London W4 *p37* 020 8994 0929

Grundy & Co
‡Chipping Sodbury *p193* 01386 849290

Wesley Gryk
‡Lambeth SE1 *p37* 020 7401 6887

Grylls & Paige
‡Redruth *p363* . . . . . 01209 215261 / 215357

Gudgeons Prentice
‡Stowmarket *p399* 01449 613101

Gudsons Solicitors
‡London N3 *p37* 020 8371 8389

Guellec-Digby & Co
‡Northampton *p332* 01604 878961

Alida Guest
‡London W11 *p37* 020 7727 6273

Guest & Co
‡Cuckfield *p205* 01444 413731

Guest Pritchard & Co
Old Colwyn *p340* 01492 515371

Guest Walker & Co
‡York *p444* 01904 624903

Guildhall Solicitors
‡Coventry *p200* 024 7622 5556

Guile Nicholas
‡London N12 *p37* 020 8492 2290
Kingston upon Thames *p267* . . . 020 8549 4282

GUILLAUMES SOLICITORS
‡Weybridge *p430* 01932 840111
Weybridge *p430* 01932 840111

Guise Solicitors
‡London E1 *p37* 020 7264 0350

Thomas Guise
‡Worcester *p439* 01905 723131
Studley *p401* 01527 852600

A K Gulati & Co
‡Sutton *p402* 020 8770 7979

Gulay Mehmet
‡London WC1 *p37* 020 7400 1565

Gulbenkian Andonian Solicitors
‡London WC1 *p37* 020 7269 9590

Gull Thompson
‡Nottingham *p337* 0115 966 5599

Gullands
‡Maidstone *p299* 01622 678341

Gulsen & Co Solicitors
‡London N18 *p37* 020 8803 4196

Gumersalls
‡Epsom *p219* 01372 721122

Gummer & Singh
‡Hounslow *p253* 020 8572 6905

Guney Clark & Ryan
‡London N16 *p37* 020 7275 7788

Gurney-Champion & Co
‡Portsmouth *p354* 023 9282 1100
Newport *p328* 01983 522665

Gurney Harden Solicitors Limited
‡Ashford *p119* 01233 624488

Gurneys
‡Framlingham *p227* 01728 621372

Howard Gurpiner
‡London N17 *p37* 020 8885 3337

Gurusinghe & Co
‡Wembley *p426* 020 8903 5349

Guthrie Jones & Jones
‡Bala *p121* 01678 520428
Denbigh *p208* 01745 814817
Dolgellau *p211* 01341 422604

Guy Williams Layton
‡Liverpool *p288* 0151 236 7171
Wirral *p435* . . . . . 0151 342 1831 / 342 6144

George H Guyer
‡Burnley *p169* 01282 773438

The Gwyn George Partnership
‡Aberdare *p113* . . . . . 01685 874629 / 871133
Blackwood *p147* 01495 222214
Merthyr Tydfil *p314* 01685 377035

H

H2O Law LLP
‡London EC4 *p37* 020 7405 4700

H&G Properties
‡Chippenham *p193* 01249 656144

H&M Solicitors Ltd
‡Slough *p382* 01753 524128

H&R Hughes Solicitors LLP
‡Heathfield *p246* 01435 890101

H & S Legal
‡Colchester *p197* . 01206 500181 / 020 7096 9060

H & V Solicitors
‡Peterborough *p347* 01733 743743

H&V Solicitors
‡West Bromwich *p427* 0121 525 2555

HCB Solicitors
‡Redditch *p362* 01527 62688
Alcester *p115* 01789 765522
Lichfield *p284* 01543 414426
Solihull *p382* 0121 705 2255
Stratford-upon-Avon *p400* 01789 270452
Walsall *p420* 01922 720000

HCLS LLP
‡London W1 *p37* 020 7499 4779

HC Solicitors LLP
‡Peterborough *p347* 01733 882800
Oundle *p342* 01832 273506

HGF Law
‡Leeds *p274* 0113 233 0148
London WC2 *p37* 020 7440 8900

HJD Solicitors
‡Cottingham *p199* 01482 310870

HJ Legal
‡Kingston upon Thames *p267* . . . 020 8408 5299
‡New Malden *p321* 020 8241 8784

H J Walker Sibia
‡Birkenhead *p134* 0151 649 0950

HKB Wiltshires
‡Great Yarmouth *p234* 01493 855676
Lowestoft *p294* 01502 582338

HKH Kenwright & Cox Solicitors
‡Ilford *p260* 020 8553 9600

HKK Law
‡Isleworth *p263* 020 7060 1127

HK Lawyers Limited
‡Birmingham *p138* 0121 515 0006

H K Solicitors
‡Morden *p318* 020 8646 7485

HL Interactive
‡Manchester *p305* 0845 365 3869

HL Law
‡Cheadle *p185* 0161 428 1000

HL Legal & Collections
‡Redditch *p362* 01527 586500

hlw Keeble Hawson LLP
‡Sheffield *p375* 0114 272 2061
Doncaster *p211* 01302 366831
Leeds *p274* 0113 244 3121
Sheffield *p376* 0114 276 5555

HMA Law Solicitors
‡Birmingham *p138* 0121 200 1400

HMG Law LLP
‡Oxford *p343* 01865 244661
Bicester *p132* 01869 252244

HM Law
‡Wokingham *p437* 0118 977 1718

HPA Solicitors
‡Accrington *p114* 01254 238310
‡Blackburn *p145* 01254 274786

HRJ Law LLP
‡Hitchin *p251* 01462 628888
Welwyn Garden City *p425* 01707 887700

HRO Grant Dawe LLP
‡London W6 *p37* 020 7386 2240

HRS Family Law Solicitors
‡Dudley *p213* 01384 458835

HR Solicitor
‡Nottingham *p337* 0115 946 2949

HR Solicitors
‡Bolton *p149* 01204 402000

HSBS Law Limited
‡Slough *p382* 01753 475400

HSCO Solicitors
‡St Albans *p390* 01727 738538

HSK Solicitors
Bolton *p149* 01204 526465

HSK Solicitors LLP
‡Manchester *p305* 0161 795 4818

HS Law Solicitors & Notaries
‡Greenford *p234* 020 8578 5688

HSR Law (Hayes, Son & Richmond)
‡Gainsborough *p228* 01427 613831
Doncaster *p211* 01302 347800
Epworth *p219* 01427 872206

HSR Solicitors
‡London E1 *p37* 020 7791 1111

HS Solicitors Limited
‡Birmingham *p138* 0121 477 3377

HT Legal Limited t/a Harrison Townend & Ormeshers
‡Hyde *p259* 0161 368 1559
Glossop *p230* 01457 868825

HWP Limited
‡Hull *p257* 01482 629295

HW Solicitors
‡Huddersfield *p255* 01484 518356

Maurice Hackenbroch & Co
‡Edgware *p217* 020 8958 4000

Hacking Ashton LLP
‡Newcastle under Lyme *p323* 01782 715555

Hackman Solicitors
‡Wembley *p426* 020 8902 6282

Hadaway & Hadaway
‡North Shields *p330* 0191 257 0382

Haddock & Co Solicitors
‡Horsham *p253* 01403 865330

Haddock & Company
‡Halifax *p238* 01422 366010

Hadfield & Co
‡Welling *p424* 020 8301 0808

Hadfields Butt & Bowyer
‡Farnham *p225* 01252 716101

Hadgkiss Hughes & Beale
‡Birmingham *p138* 0121 449 5050
Birmingham *p139* 0121 778 2161
Birmingham *p139* 0121 707 8484

Hadley Law Associates LLP
‡Barnet *p124* 020 8441 1856

Hafezis Solicitors
‡London E1 *p37* 020 7377 0600

Hafiz & Haque Solicitors
‡London E2 *p37* 020 7729 1911

Haftke Limited
‡West Malling *p428* 020 7193 5371

Robert Hagger & Co
‡Tunbridge Wells *p415* 01892 515795

Hague & Dixon
‡York *p444* 01904 627111
Pickering *p348* 01751 475222
York *p444* 01759 371634

HAGUE LAMBERT
‡Knutsford *p269* 01565 652411
Macclesfield *p297* 01625 616480
Manchester *p305* 0161 834 6066
Urmston *p417* 0161 747 7321

HAIDER KENNEDY LEGAL SERVICES LTD
‡London SE25 *p37* 020 8771 2323

Haider Solicitors
‡Halifax *p238* 01422 321632

Alexander Haigh & Co
‡Brentwood *p156* 01277 216320

Haighs Solicitors
‡Mirfield *p318* 01924 489197

Hains & Lewis Ltd
‡Haverfordwest *p244* 0845 408 0125
Carmarthen *p182* 0845 408 0125
Narberth *p320* 0845 408 0125

Hal-Solicitors
‡Uxbridge *p417* 01895 270907 / 270908
Uxbridge *p417* 01895 251700

Halborg & Co Solicitors
‡Hinckley *p250* 01455 233323

Halborg & Co (Solicitors)
‡Leicester *p280* 0116 255 1010

Haldanes
‡Stevenage *p394* 01438 312525
London W1 *p37* 020 7437 5629

Hale & Hopkins
‡Swindon *p406* 01793 522277

G V Hale & Co
‡Barnsley *p124* 01226 785100
‡Doncaster *p211* 01302 360606

Hale Solicitors
‡Stockport *p395* 0161 439 0999

Halebury Ventures Limited
‡London W1 *p38* 020 7127 2500

Lindsay Halewood-Dodd
‡Lancaster *p269* 01524 846024

Alan Hall
‡Gateshead *p228* 0191 477 7224

Hall & Co
‡London SE5 *p38*
‡Warrington *p422* 01925 245858

Hall Ennion & Young
‡Ely *p218* 01353 662918
Ely *p218* 01353 860453

Frederic Hall
‡Folkestone *p227* 01303 851185
Dover *p213* 01304 202411

Keith Hall Juviler & Co
‡Greenford *p234* 020 8578 3133 / 8578 5373

Michael Hall
‡Letchworth *p283* 01462 674767

R C Hall Solicitors
‡London N17 *p38* 020 8801 2345

Hall Reynolds
‡Bidford-on-Avon *p133* 01789 772955

Hall Smith Whittingham LLP
‡Nantwich *p320* 01270 610300
Crewe *p203* 01270 212000

Susan Hall & Co
‡Hitchin *p251* 01462 433800

Hall Ward & Fox
‡Weston-super-Mare *p429* 01934 626656 / 626657

Hallam-Peel & Co
‡London WC2 *p38* 020 3006 1661

Hallam Solicitors
‡Leeds *p274* 0113 228 5306

Hallens Solicitors
‡Hounslow *p253* 020 8622 3729

Hallett & Co
‡Ashford *p119* 01233 625711
Ashford *p119* 01233 504700
New Romney *p322* 01797 362824

Hallett Employment Law Services
‡Lutterworth *p296* 01455 208886

Graham Halliday & Co
‡London N12 *p38* 020 8445 4071

Halliday Reeves Law Firm
‡Gateshead *p228* 0191 477 7728 / 0844 811 2147

Halliday Reeves
‡Gateshead *p228* 0191 477 7728
Doncaster *p211* 01302 560969

Hallinan Blackburn Gittings & Nott
‡Westminster SW1 *p38* 020 7233 3999

John J Halliwell & Co
‡Silsden *p380* 01535 653094

Lesley Halliwell Solicitors
‡Darwen *p207* 01254 773800

Hallmark Solicitors
‡Hull *p257* 01482 616616 / 0845 680 8251

HallmarkHulme
‡Worcester *p439* 01905 726600

Hallows Associates
‡Mold *p318* 01352 752773 / 758603 / 0800 525696

Halpins
‡London SW1 *p38* 020 3286 6041

Michael W Halsall
‡Newton-le-Willows *p330* 01942 727000

John Halson Solicitors
‡Liverpool *p288* 0151 708 8123
‡Liverpool *p288* 0151 524 4540

Lawrence Hamblin
‡Henley-on-Thames *p247* 01491 411884
Reading *p361* 0118 951 6180 / 951 6190

Hameed & Co
‡London NW10 *p38* 020 8830 1335

Hamer Childs
‡Worcester *p439* 01905 724565

Hamers
‡Rossendale *p367* 01706 222260

Hamers Solicitors
‡Hull *p257* 01482 326666

Hamilton & Co Advokatbyra
‡London W8 *p38* 020 7795 4775

Hamilton Davies
‡Stevenage *p394* 01438 315898

Hamilton Downing Quinn
‡London WC1 *p38* 020 7831 8939

Hamilton Gerard Solicitors
‡Greenwich SE10 *p38* 020 8692 1492

Hamilton Pratt
‡Warwick *p422* 01926 838900

Susanne M E Hamilton & Co
‡Cardiff *p178* 01443 842347

Hamiltons
‡Leeds *p274* 0113 244 6455

HAMLINS LLP
‡London W1 *p38* 020 7355 6000

Hammill Burton Lloyd
‡Kew *p265* 020 8392 6392

Hammon Oakley
‡Coventry *p200* 024 7644 8585

Hammond Bale
‡London W1 *p38* 020 7499 7624

Philip J Hammond & Sons
‡Leicester *p280* 0116 251 7171

Hamnett Osborne Tisshaw
‡Haywards Heath *p245* 01444 443030

Hampshire Law
‡Andover *p118* 01264 326344

Hampson Hughes (HH Law Ltd)
‡Liverpool *p288* 0333 240 1234

Paul Hampton
‡London SW1 *p38* 020 7932 2450

Hamptons Solicitors
‡London WC2 *p38* 020 7395 6050

Hamstead Law Practice
‡Birmingham *p139* 0121 357 6500
‡Birmingham *p139* 0121 357 6500 / 012 1357 6500

Hamways Walker Owens
‡Edenbridge *p216* 01732 866666

J Arnold Hancock & Co
‡Stretford *p400* 0161 865 2267

Hancock Quins
‡Watford *p423* 01923 650850

R Hancock & Son
‡Callington *p173* 01579 383101

Hancocks
‡Banbury *p122* 01295 253211

Hancocks Solicitors Ltd
‡Nottingham *p337* 0844 474 3377

Nicholas Hancox Solicitors
‡Norwich *p334* 01603 821012

Hand Morgan & Owen
‡Stafford *p393* 01785 211411
Rugeley *p368* 01889 583871

Handley Brown LLP
‡Preston *p357* 01772 652255

Handley Law Limited
‡Liverpool *p288* 0845 676 9228

Edward Hands & Lewis
‡Loughborough *p293* 01509 216161

Hands Law
‡Clifton *p196* 0117 905 9262

Lee Handy & Co
‡Birmingham *p139* 0121 377 6773

Hanif Solicitors
‡Birmingham *p139* 0121 771 3399

Hannafords
‡Salisbury *p371* 01725 514632

Hannah & Mould
‡London SW1 *p38* 020 7384 9527

Hannays Solicitors and Advocates
‡South Shields *p383* 0191 456 7893 / 455 5361

Hanne & Co
‡London SW11 *p38* 020 7228 0017

Hannells Solicitors Derby
‡Derby *p209* 01332 705505

Hanney Dawkins & Jones
‡Pinner *p348* 020 8866 2144

Hannides Hewstone & Co
‡Southampton *p386* 023 8078 6770

Hanover Solicitors
‡London SW3 *p38* 0870 383 1974

HANRATTY & CO
‡Newtown *p330* 01686 626239

Hansards Solicitors
‡Bradford *p154* 01274 403797

Hansel Henson LLP
‡London W1 *p38* 020 7307 5145

Hansell Drew & Co
‡Dartmouth *p207* 01803 834555

Hansell Wilkes & Co
‡Dartmouth *p207* 01803 833993

Hansells
‡Norwich *p334* 01603 615731
Aylsham *p121* 01263 734313
Cromer *p203* 01263 512003
North Walsham *p331* 01692 404351
Norwich *p334*
Sheringham *p378* 01263 822176

Hansen Palomares
‡Lambeth SE11 *p38* 020 7640 4600

Hanson & Co
‡Oldham *p340* 0161 626 6116

Hanson Woods Solicitors
‡Ilford *p260* 020 8590 9220

Hanson Young and Co Ltd
‡Harrow *p241* 020 8861 8374

Hanwell Chambers
‡London W7 *p38* 020 8840 8555

Haq Hamilton Hughes
‡London E10 *p38* 020 8503 7228

Haq Solicitors
‡Huddersfield *p256* 01484 533759

Haque & Hausmann Solicitors and Commissioner For Oaths
Newcastle upon Tyne *p325* 0191 272 5197

Harazi
‡London SW2 *p38* 020 7733 4099 / 4165

Harbans Singh
‡Birmingham *p139* 0121 551 4496
Oldbury *p340* 0121 544 9100

Harbord & Co
‡Epsom *p219* 01372 720077

Harbottle & Lewis LLP
‡London W1 *p38* 020 7667 5000

Harcus Sinclair
‡London WC2 *p38* 020 7242 9700

Hard Hat Legal Limited
‡Ilkley *p261* 07545 347600

Paul Harden & Co
‡London W5 *p39* 0800 756 1436

Juliet Hardick Solicitors
‡Bath *p127* 01225 311177

Charles Harding & Co
‡Wembley *p426* 020 8795 0990

Harding Evans LLP
‡Newport *p328* 01633 244233

Harding Swinburne Jackson & Co
‡Sunderland *p401* 0191 565 8194

Hardington Hogg Solicitors
‡Alnwick *p115* 01665 605566
Morpeth *p319* 01670 515955

Hardman & Watson
‡Broadstairs *p166* 01843 863479

Hardman & Whittles
‡Heywood *p249* 01706 369027

Hardman Wood
‡Blackburn *p145* 01254 295540

Hardmans
‡Deal *p207* 01304 373377

A C S Hards & Co
‡New Malden *p321* 020 8942 2258

Gaby Hardwicke
‡Bexhill *p132* 01424 730945
Bexhill *p132* 01424 842206
Eastbourne *p215* 01323 435900
Hastings *p243* 01424 438011

Hardy McBride & Co
‡Bromley *p166* 020 8460 1999

Hardy Miles Titterton
‡Ripley *p364* 01773 747000
Alfreton *p115* 01773 580280
Duffield *p214* 01332 841115

Paul F Harfitt & Co
‡Wem *p426* 01939 232775

Hargreaves
‡Barking *p123* 020 8594 2473

Hargreaves & Co
‡Manchester *p305* 0161 445 6461

Hargreaves Gilman
‡Manchester *p305* 0161 443 1711

Hargreaves Mounteney Solicitors
‡Stockport *p395* 0161 440 9901

Ralph Haring Solicitors
‡St Albans *p390* 01727 843576 / 07831 110528

Haris Ali & Co Solicitors
‡Hounslow *p253* 020 8570 8400

Harkin Lloyd Solicitors
‡Liverpool *p288* 0151 255 0740

Harman & Harman
‡London SW2 *p39* 01227 452977

Harmans
‡Mansfield *p311* 01623 629224

J K Harmshaw
‡Chippenham *p193* 01225 891786

Harnett & Co
‡Bristol *p163* 0117 965 5366

Harney & Wells
‡Brighton *p159* 01273 684666

Harney Westwood & Riegels
‡London EC4 *p39* 020 7842 6080

Harold G Walker
‡Bournemouth *p152* 01202 203200
Broadstone *p166* 01202 692448 / 695361
Christchurch *p194* 01202 482202
Verwood *p418* 01202 823308
Wimborne *p433* 01202 881454

Alistair Harper & Co
‡Haywards Heath *p245* 01444 457890

Harper & Odell
‡Islington EC1 *p39* 020 7490 0500

Harper Law
‡Romsey *p366* 01794 322364

Harpers
‡Camden WC1 *p39* 020 7405 8888

Nicola Harries Solicitor
‡Chipping Ongar *p193* 01277 362332

Will Harrington & Co
‡Sutton Coldfield *p403* 0121 321 1999

Harringtons
‡Brighton *p159* 01273 606069

Alan Harris
‡Plymouth *p350* 01752 223655

Harris & Co
‡Crawley *p202* 01293 537551
‡London N3 *p39* 020 3330 7289
‡Southsea *p388* 023 9278 5757
London W1 *p39*

Harris & Green Solicitors
‡Leeds *p274* 0113 276 8866

Harris & Harris
Frome *p228* 01373 463366
Wells *p425* 01749 674747

Anthony Harris & Co
‡New Milton *p321* 01425 638288

Brian Harris & Co
‡London W1 *p39* 020 7935 5541

Harris Cartier LLP
‡Slough *p382* 01753 810710
London WC2 *p39* 020 7405 7100

Christopher Harris & Co
‡Sheerness *p375* 01795 661521
Sittingbourne *p380* 01795 437268

Harris Cuffaro & Nichols
‡Harlow *p239* 01279 444456

D Harris & Co International
‡London W1 *p39* 020 7600 5600

Harris da Silva
‡Islington EC1 *p39* 020 7713 0700

David W Harris & Co
‡Pontypridd *p352* 01443 486666
Bridgend *p157* 01656 862424
Talbot Green *p407* 01443 223265

E A Harris & Co Ltd
‡Shotton *p378* 01244 822555
Buckley *p168* 01244 541505

Edward Harris Solicitors
‡Swansea *p405* 01792 772505

Harris Fowler
‡Taunton *p408* 01823 251515

Gabriel Harris
‡Barnet N3 *p39* 020 8343 1355

Harris Hagan
‡London EC1 *p39* 020 7002 7636

J C Harris
‡Pontefract *p351* 01977 795450

Leslie Harris Solicitors & Advocates
‡Lytham *p297* 01253 724974

Harris Paley Schone Ltd
‡Brighton *p159* 01273 600009

Richard Harris Solicitors
‡Torpoint *p412* 01752 822224

T R Harris Arnold & Co
‡Gorseinon *p231* 01792 892166 / 891331

Harris Temperley
‡London W6 *p39* 020 8233 2989

Harris Waters Solicitors
‡Ilford *p260* 020 8478 0888

Harris Williams Solicitors
‡Kenilworth *p264* 01926 852000

Harris-Barrington & Co Solicitor
‡London SE8 *p39* 020 8469 3880

Alan Harrison & Co
‡Wembley *p426* 020 8900 0262

Harrison & Associates
‡Newcastle upon Tyne *p325* 0191 281 6221

Harrison Bundey
Leeds *p274* 0113 200 7400

Chris Harrison Law
‡Truro *p414* 01872 241408

Harrison Clark LLP
‡Worcester *p439* 01905 612001
Cheltenham *p188* 01242 269198
Hereford *p248* 01432 267928
Ross-on-Wye *p367* 01989 562377
Worcester *p439* 01905 612001

Harrison Drury & Co
‡Preston *p357* 01772 258321

Harrison Grant
‡London NW5 *p39* 020 7267 6727

J M Harrison
‡Bampton *p122* 01993 852222

John F Harrison
‡Ashby-de-la-Zouch *p118* 01530 563655

Karena Harrison Solicitors
‡New Milton *p321* 01425 627187

Kristina Harrison
Salford *p370* 0161 832 7766

Harrison Li Solicitors LLP
‡Camberley *p173* 01276 27700

M J Harrison
‡Scarborough *p372* 01723 865578

Harrison Morgan
‡London E8 *p39*

Harrisons
‡Reading *p361* 0118 959 8974
Reading *p361* 0118 944 8898

David Harrisons Solicitors
‡Waltham Forest E11 *p39* 020 8522 4907

Harrisons Gardener
‡Rickmansworth *p364* 01923 776877

HARRISONS SOLICITORS LLP
‡Welshpool *p425* 01938 552545

Harrisons Solicitors
‡London EC4 *p39* 020 3008 8245
‡Manchester *p305* 0161 819 2511

Harrisons Solicitors LLP
Newtown *p330* 01686 625134

Harrop White Vallance & Dawson
‡Mansfield *p311* 01623 629221

Harrops
‡Oxted *p344* 01883 712940

Harrow Law Partnership
‡Wealdstone *p424* 020 8863 7888

Harrow Law Practice
‡Harrow *p241* 020 8909 0202

Harrow Solicitors & Advocates
‡Wealdstone *p424* 020 8863 0788

Harrowell & Atkins
‡Berkhamsted *p131* 01442 865671

Harrowells
‡York *p444* 01904 558600
York *p445* 01904 760237
York *p444* 01904 690111

Hart Brown Solicitors
‡Guildford *p236* 0800 068 8177
Cobham *p196* 0800 068 8177
Cranleigh *p202* 0800 068 8177
Godalming *p231* 0800 068 8177
London SW19 *p39* 0800 068 8177
Woking *p437* 0800 068 8177

Charles Hart Solicitors
‡Cheddar *p186* 01934 742315

J H Hart & Co
‡London E6 *p39* 020 8472 2652

Hart Jackson & Sons
‡Ulverston *p416* 01229 583291

Hart Jackson Hall Smith
‡Newcastle upon Tyne *p325* 0191 261 5181

Hart Reade
‡Eastbourne *p215* 01323 727321
Hailsham *p237* 01323 841481
Polegate *p351* 01323 487051

Edward Harte LLP
‡Brighton *p159* 01273 662750

Harter & Loveless
‡Islington N1 *p39* 020 7688 2900

David Harter
‡London N1 *p39* 020 7607 1163

Harters
‡London N1 *p39* 020 7607 5768

Harthills
‡Rotherham *p367* 01709 377399

Hartlaw LLP
‡Wetherby *p429* 01937 547000

Hartley & Worstenholme
‡Castleford *p183* 01977 732222
Pontefract *p351* 01977 732222

Hartley Thomas & Wright
‡Rochdale *p365* 01706 644118

Hartnell Chanot & Partners Family Law Specialists
‡Exeter *p221* 01392 421777

Hartnell Solicitors
‡Truro *p414* 01872 520630

Hartnells
‡London SE5 *p39* 020 7703 9222

Hartwig Notary Chambers
‡Croydon *p205* 020 8681 2893
London SW1 *p39* 020 7235 1504
London W1 *p39* 020 7470 7131

Harvey Camford LLP
‡London EC2 *p39* 0844 879 4137

Harvey Copping & Harrison
‡Wickford *p431* . . . . . 01268 733381 / 763211
Chelmsford *p186* 01245 322956

Harvey Ingram Borneos
Bedford *p130* 01234 353221
Milton Keynes *p317* 01908 696002
Newport Pagnell *p329* 01908 613545

Harvey Ingram LLP
‡Leicester *p280* 0116 254 5454
Birmingham *p139* 0121 214 1200

Keith Harvey & Co
‡Market Harborough *p312* 01858 464327

Harvey Roberts
‡Stockport *p395* 0161 443 2828

Sally Harvey
‡Newtown *p330* 01686 621033

Harvey Son & Filby
‡Ipswich *p262* 01473 712962
Birmingham *p139* 0121 632 6092
London WC2 *p39* 020 3159 4235

Harveys
‡Deeside *p208* 01244 836667
‡Liss *p285* 01730 895000
‡Luton *p295* 01582 458567

Harveys Solicitors
Flint *p226* 01352 734003

Harwood & Co
‡Worcester *p440* 01905 420855

C W Harwood & Co
‡Leeds *p274* 0113 245 7027

Hasan Solicitors
‡Birmingham *p139* 0121 778 4003

Haseltine Lake & Co
‡Leeds *p274* 0113 233 9400
London WC1 *p39* 020 7611 7900

Haskell & Co Solicitors
‡Ashford *p119* 01233 664020

Haslam & Payne
‡London SW1 *p39* 020 7828 8725

Haslaw & Co LLP
‡London E12 *p39* 020 8514 5551

Haswell & Cornberg
‡Newcastle upon Tyne *p325* 0191 276 5300

Hatch Brenner
‡Norwich *p334* 01603 660811

Hatch Legal
‡Leeds *p274* 0113 234 6328

Hatchers Solicitors LLP
‡Shrewsbury *p379* 01743 248545
Shrewsbury *p379* 01743 467641
Whitchurch *p430* 01948 663361

David C Hatfield & Co
‡Jarrow *p263* . . . . . 0191 489 7639 / 489 9450

Hathaways
‡Gateshead *p228* 0191 477 2288
Gateshead *p228* 0191 482 8700

Hatrick & Co
‡London SE3 *p39* 020 8293 7070

Hatten Wyatt
‡Gravesend *p232* 01474 351199
Gravesend *p233* 01474 351199

Hattens Solicitors
‡Grays *p233* . . . . 01375 374851 / 373516

Hattersleys
‡Mexborough *p314* 01709 582434

Hatton
‡Daventry *p207* 01327 301201

Hatton Law
‡Chatham *p185* 01634 686822

Hattons Solicitors
‡St Helens *p391* 01744 744400
Widnes *p431* 0151 495 2228

Hausfeld & Co LLP
‡London EC4 *p39* 020 7665 5000

C H Hausmann & Co
‡London W1 *p39* 020 7436 6333

Havillands
‡Romford *p366* 01708 766559

Haw & Co
‡London SE5 *p39*

A V Hawkins & Co
‡Harrow *p241* . . . . . 020 8422 2364 / 8422 2466

Hawkins Hatton LLP
‡Dudley *p213* 01384 216840

Hawkins Ross Limited
‡Stockton-on-Tees *p397* . 01642 613647 / 678888

Hawkins Solicitors
‡King's Lynn *p266* 01553 691661
‡Milton Keynes *p317* 01908 262680
King's Lynn *p266* 01485 501586

Hawkridge & Co
‡Gillingham *p229* 01634 854381

George Hawks Solicitor
‡Somerton *p383* 01963 240409

R J Hawksley & Co
‡Camberley *p173* 01252 890400

Hawkswell Kilvington LLP
‡Wakefield *p418* 01924 258719

Hawley & Rodgers
‡Loughborough *p293* 01509 230333
Bingham *p133* 01949 836879
Nottingham *p337* 0115 955 9000

Haworth & Gallagher
‡Birkenhead *p134* 0151 647 8624
Wallasey *p419* . . . . 0151 638 5457 / 638 6088

Haworth & Nuttall
‡Blackburn *p145* 01254 272640
Accrington *p114* 01254 236221
Great Harwood *p234* 01254 884253

Haworth Brotherton
‡Thornton Cleveleys *p411* 01253 852356

George Haworth Chappell & Whitworth
‡Bury *p170* 01706 824811

Haworth Holt Bell Limited
‡Altrincham *p116* 0161 928 7136

Hay & Kilner
‡Newcastle upon Tyne *p325* 0191 232 8345
Wallsend *p419* 0191 262 8231

Hayat & Co
‡Enfield *p218* 020 8360 4485

Phillip M Haycock
‡Birmingham *p139* 0121 788 1234

Hayes & Storr
‡Fakenham *p223* 01328 863231
Holt *p251* 01263 712835
King's Lynn *p266* 01553 778900
Sheringham *p378* 01263 825959
Wells-next-the-Sea *p425* 01328 710210

Hayes Clifford & Co
‡Tilehurst *p411* 0118 941 8416

Edward Hayes LLP
‡Chichester *p192* 01243 781431
Bognor Regis *p148* 01243 822655
Chichester *p192* 01243 672124
Havant *p244* 023 9247 9872
Littlehampton *p285* 01903 759024
London EC4 *p39* 020 7353 0011
London EC2 *p39* 020 7353 0011
Worthing *p441* 01903 215999

Hayes Law LLP
‡Eastleigh *p216* 023 8061 2890
London W6 *p39* 020 3159 4248

Haygarth Jones
‡St Helens *p391*

Hayman Solicitors
‡Guildford *p236* 01483 600900

Haynes & Co
‡London W4 *p39* 020 8987 6076

Haynes Orme
‡London EC4 *p39* 020 7356 0990

Hayre & Co
‡Bradford *p154* 01274 744405

Hayre Georgiou & Hayre Limited
‡Tipton *p412* 0121 557 7766

Hays & Company Solicitors
‡Cambridge *p174* 0800 011 6489

Stanley Hays
‡Heckmondwike *p246* 01924 403809

Hayton Winkley
‡Kendal *p264* 01539 720136
Windermere *p434* 01539 446585

Hayward Baker
‡Fareham *p224* 0800 107 7321

Derek J Hayward & Co
‡Chatham *p185* 01634 815651

Haywards
‡Stowmarket *p399* 01449 613631

Hazell & Co
‡Sawbridgeworth *p372* 01279 726604

Hazelwoods
‡London EC4 *p39* 020 7936 4844

Hazlemere
High Wycombe *p250*

The Head Partnership
‡Reading *p361* 0118 975 6622
Henley-on-Thames *p247* 01491 570900

Headd Solicitors
‡London N17 *p39* 020 7566 8244

Headleys
‡Lutterworth *p296* 01455 554466
Hinckley *p250* 01455 637815

Susan Heads & Company
‡Chislehurst *p193* 020 8467 5544

Heald Nickinson
‡Camberley *p173* 01276 680000

Heald Solicitors
‡Milton Keynes *p317* 01908 662277

Healds
‡Wigan *p432* 01942 241511

A G Heale Ltd
‡Cardiff *p178* 029 2056 2566
‡Cardiff *p178* . . . 029 2062 3121 / 07802 442624

Healey Colbon
‡Luton *p295* 01582 405500

Healey Kenyon McAteer Solicitors
‡Liverpool *p288* 0151 261 9857
Prescot *p356* 0151 261 9857

Healy Connor Mulcahy
‡Rochdale *p365* 01706 718188

Healys LLP
‡London EC4 *p39* 020 7822 4000
Brighton *p159* 01273 685888

Heaney Watson
‡Liverpool *p288* 0151 293 2936
Liverpool *p288* 0151 282 5555
Liverpool *p288* 0151 256 7777
Manchester *p305* 0800 567 7597 / 0161 359 3347

William J Heard
‡London EC4 *p40* 020 7329 7370

Hearne & Co
‡Bearwood *p129* 0121 420 3636

Heartlands Solicitors
‡Birmingham *p139* 0121 327 0255

Heath & Blenkinsop
‡Warwick *p422* 01926 492407

Heath Buckeridge
‡Maidenhead *p298* 01628 671636

Heath Sons & Broome
‡Manchester *p305* 0161 681 1933
Failsworth *p223* 0161 682 8535

William Heath & Co
‡Westminster W2 *p40* 020 7402 3151
London SW11 *p40* 020 7350 1068

Heather Mains & Co
‡London NW7 *p40* 020 8906 6660

Heather Thomas Consulting
‡London EC2 *p40* 020 7588 0686

Heatons LLP
‡Manchester *p305* 0161 835 8010

Heaven & Co
‡Solihull *p382* 01564 770598

Heaven & Company
‡Birmingham *p139* 0121 444 0456

Hebbar & Co
‡Northolt *p333* 020 8423 8234

Heckford Norton
‡Stevenage *p395* 01438 312211
Letchworth *p283* 01462 682244
Saffron Walden *p370* 01799 522636

Hedges
‡Wallingford *p419* 01491 839839
Didcot *p210* 01235 811888

Hedley Solicitors
‡Blyth *p148* 01670 361055

Hedley Visick & Co
‡Eastleigh *p216* 023 8061 1133

Hedleys
‡Nottingham *p337* 0115 947 3506

Hedleys & Co
‡Sunderland *p401* 0191 567 0101
‡Sunderland *p401* 0191 548 2323

Hedleys Solicitors LLP
‡East Horsley *p215* 01483 284567
Croydon *p205* 020 8667 0677
Leatherhead *p271* 01483 284667

Heelis Solicitors
‡Appleby *p118* 01768 351591

Heer Manak
‡Coventry *p200* 024 7666 4000
Coventry *p200* 024 7666 4000

Hegarty LLP
‡Peterborough *p347* 01733 346333
Stamford *p393* 01780 752066

Helder Roberts & Co
Chagford *p184* 01647 433161

Hellawell & Co
‡Newbiggin-by-the-Sea *p322* 01670 817223

Hellewell Pasley & Brewer
‡Batley *p128* 01924 472596
Dewsbury *p210* 01924 455515

Raymond Hemingray
‡Peterborough *p347* 01733 262523

R W Hemmings & Co
‡Leicester *p280* 0116 255 8500
‡Taunton *p408* 01823 325090

Law Offices of Richard Hemmings Solicitor
‡Ipswich *p262* 01473 833844

Hempsons
‡Westminster WC2 *p40* 020 7839 0278
Harrogate *p240* 01423 522331
Manchester *p305* 0161 228 0011
Newcastle upon Tyne *p325* 0191 230 0669

Hemsleys
‡Chester p190. . . . . 01244 382400

Henchleys
‡Littlehampton p285 . . . . 01903 726477
Worthing p441 . . . . 01903 877657

Charles Henley
‡Market Harborough p312 . . . . . 01536 771811

Henley Law
‡Liverpool p288 . . . . 0151 726 0976

Henleys
‡Basingstoke p126 . . . . 01256 840084

Henmans LLP
‡Oxford p343 . . . . 01865 781000

Hennah & Co
‡Etchingham p220. . . . . 01580 819171

Henneberry & Co
‡London NW6 p40. . . . . 020 8830 1907

Hennessy & Hammudi
‡Reading p361 . . . . 0118 939 3559

Hennings Solicitors
‡Brighton p159 . . . . 01273 505800

Henriques Griffiths
‡Bristol p163. . . . . 0117 909 4000
Bristol p163. . . . . 0117 965 9444
Bristol p163. . . . . 0117 973 2950
Winterbourne p435 . . . . 01454 854000

Henry & Company
‡Swindon p406 . . . . 01793 832000

Henry Hughes & Hughes
‡London SW16 p40 . . . . 020 8765 2700

Ian Henry & Co Solicitors
‡Willenhall p432. . . . . 01902 366615

Henrys Solicitors Ltd
‡Glossop p230. . . . . 01457 864143
‡Stockport p395 . . . . 0161 477 8558
Poynton p355. . . . . 01625 630880
Stockport p395 . . . . 01663 742222

Rosemary E Hensby
‡Worthing p441 . . . . 01903 244953

Henscott Solicitors
‡London E17 p40 . . . . 0870 880 0007

Henshaw Pratt Solicitors
‡Wakefield p418. . . . . 01924 882405

Henshaw Solicitors
‡Newport Pagnell p329 . . . . . . 01908 211202

Hentys LLP
‡Waterlooville p423 . . . . 023 9224 6710

M R Hepburn
‡Sutton Coldfield p403. . . . . . . 0121 378 0440

Hepburns
‡London SE22 p40 . . . . 020 8299 3376
‡Oxted p344. . . . . 01883 723712

Heppenstalls
‡New Milton p321 . . . . 01425 610078
Lymington p296. . . . . 01590 689500
Lyndhurst p296. . . . . 023 8028 2885

Heptonstalls LLP
‡Goole p231. . . . . 01405 765661
Howden p255. . . . . 01430 430209
Pontefract p351. . . . . 01977 602804
Pontefract p351. . . . . 01977 602804
Scunthorpe p373 . . . . 01724 289959

Herald Solicitors
‡High Wycombe p250 . . . . 0845 250 1778

Herbert & Cholmeley
‡Banbury p122 . . . . 01295 263556

Herbert Reeves & Co
‡London EC2 p40 . . . . 020 7739 6660

Herbert Smith LLP
‡London EC2 p40 . . . . 020 7374 8000

Herbertlewis Solicitors
‡Borehamwood p150 . . . . 020 8731 4560

Herefords Solicitors Limited
‡London W2 p41 . . . . 020 7221 3180

Hereward & Foster
‡London E16 p41 . . . . 020 7476 6600

Heringtons
‡Battle p128. . . . . 01424 772401
Eastbourne p215 . . . . 01323 411020
Hastings p243 . . . . 01424 434192
Rye p370. . . . . 01797 222955

Heritage Solicitors
‡Birmingham p139. . . . . 07791 805116

Hermans Solicitors
‡Macclesfield p297 . . . . 01625 611224

Hermeling
‡Bromley p166. . . . . 020 8295 1573

Hermer & Evans
‡Cardiff p178 . . . .029 2038 7766 / 2022 4009

Richard Herne & Co Solicitors
‡Staple Hill p394. . . . . 0117 957 4508

Catherine Herries-Smith Solicitor
‡High Wycombe p250. . . . . 01494 880705

Herrington & Carmichael LLP
‡Camberley p173 . . . . 01276 686222
Wokingham p437. . . . . 0118 977 4045

Hersi & Co Solicitors
‡London NW7 p41. . . . . 020 8906 7795

Herzog & Associates
‡Liverpool p288 . . . . 0844 499 5717

Heseltine Bray & Welsh
‡Barnsley p124 . . . . 01226 210777

Heseltons Solicitors
‡Harrow p241 . . . . 020 8864 6171

Hesling Henriques
‡Maidstone p299 . . . . 01622 678877

Heslop & Platt
‡Leeds p274. . . . . 0113 393 1930

Heston Law Chambers
‡Hounslow p254. . . . . 020 8577 4545

The Hetherington Partnership
‡Wirral p435. . . . . 0151 632 3411

Hetheringtons Solicitors Limited
‡Romford p366 . . . . 01708 341500

Hethertons LLP
‡York p445 . . . . 01904 528200
Boroughbridge p150 . . . . 01423 322940

Hetts
‡Scunthorpe p373. . . . . 01724 843287
Scunthorpe p373. . . . . 01724 270290

Hetts Johnson Whiting
‡Brigg p158 . . . . 01652 655101

G M Hewett Solicitor
‡London E16 p41 . . . . 020 7476 2544

Martyn Hewett Solicitor
‡Shepherdswell p377 . . . . 01304 831888

Hewetts
‡Reading p361 . . . . 0118 957 5337

Hewison & Nixon
‡Pontefract p351 . . . . 01977 700705

Hewisons
Featherstone p225

Hewitson & Harker Limited
‡Kirkby Stephen p268 . . . . 01768 371534

Hewitsons
‡Cambridge p174 . . . . 01223 461155
Milton Keynes p317. . . . . 01908 247010
Northampton p332 . . . . 01604 233233
Saffron Walden p370. . . . . . . 01799 522471

Hewitt Burrough & Co
‡Dartford p207. . . . . 01322 273833

Hewitts
‡Bishop Auckland p144 . . . . . . 01388 604691
Crook p203. . . . . 01388 762466
Darlington p206. . . . . 01325 468573
Newton Aycliffe p330 . . . . 01325 316170
Stockton-on-Tees p397 . . . . . . 01642 673701

Nicholas Hewlitt Family Law Practice
‡Launceston p270. . . . . 01566 777774

Hextalls
‡London EC2 p41 . . . . 020 7382 0700

Hextalls Limited
‡London E1 p41. . . . . 020 7488 1224

Heydons
‡Potters Bar p355 . . . . 01707 879646

Heyes Samuel
‡Ryde p369 . . . . 01983 615615

Heylin Legal Limited
‡Manchester p305. . . . . 0161 205 2073
‡Oldham p340. . . . . 0161 626 4561

Heyman & Co
‡Leigh p282 . . . . 01942 604135

Hiace Solicitors
‡Croydon p205 . . . . 020 8686 3777

Hibbert Lucas Butter
Ellesmere p217. . . . . 01691 622408
Whitchurch p430 . . . . 01948 662231

Hibberts LLP
‡Nantwich p320 . . . . 01270 624225
Crewe p203 . . . . 01270 215117
Tarporley p408 . . . . 01829 733338

Hickman & Rose
‡London N15 p41 . . . . 020 7700 2211

Kathryn Hickmott
‡London W4 p41 . . . . 020 8995 6194

Hierons
‡London SW1 p41. . . . . 020 3328 4510

Tom Higgin Children and Family Solicitor
‡Norwich p334. . . . . 01508 558752

Higgins & Co
‡Birkenhead p134 . . . . 0151 653 5222

Catherine Higgins Law Firm
‡Liverpool p288 . . . . 0151 236 8840

Thomas Higgins & Co
‡Wallasey p419 . . . . 0151 630 8006

David J Higginson
‡Altrincham p116 . . . . 0161 980 3321

Higgs & Sons
‡Brierley Hill p158 . . . . 0845 111 5050
Kingswinford p268 . . . . 01384 342100

Andrew M Higgs & Co
‡Haslemere p243 . . . . 07771 725541

Highcross Law LLP
‡Leicester p280 . . . . 0116 262 0001

Highfields Law Practice
‡Cambridge p174 . . . . 01954 210363

Highgate Hill Solicitors
‡London N19 p41 . . . . 020 8804 9412

Hilcrest Solicitors LLP
‡Ilford p260 . . . . 020 8911 9169

Hileys
‡Thirsk p411. . . . . 01845 522278
Easingwold p215 . . . . 01347 821234

Hill & Co
‡Aldershot p115 . . . . 01252 319441
‡Altrincham p116 . . . . 0161 928 3201

Andrew Hill
‡Batley p128. . . . . 01924 423353

C J Hill Solicitor
‡Buntingford p168 . . . . 07973 781670

Charles Hill & Co Solicitors
‡London SE5 p41 . . . . 020 7525 6630

Charles Hill Hubbard
‡Chichester p192 . . . . 01243 781000

Hill Dehghan Solicitors
‡Scarborough p372 . . . . 01723 360500

Hill Dickinson LLP
‡Liverpool p288 . . . . 0151 600 8000
‡Liverpool p289 . . . . 0151 236 5400
Chester p190. . . . . 01244 896600
London EC3 p41 . . . . 020 7283 9033
Manchester p305. . . . . 0161 817 7200
Sheffield p376 . . . . 0114 229 7907

Geoffrey Hill & Co
‡Hinckley p250 . . . . 01455 637715

Graham Hill Solicitors
‡Kettering p265 . . . 01536 726381 / 07941 504346

Hill Hofstetter LLP
‡Solihull p382 . . . . 0121 210 6000

Janette Hill & Co Solicitors
‡Hay-on-Wye p245 . . . . 01497 821000

Hill Johnson
‡Surbiton p402 . . . . 020 8390 0185

Joseph Hill & Co
‡London N15 p41 . . . . 020 8880 3535

Michael Hill Partnership
‡Leicester p280 . . . . 0116 254 1609

HilliersHRW Solicitors
‡Kempston p264. . . . . 01234 858000
Stevenage p395 . . . . 01438 346000

Hillis Solicitors
‡Manchester p305. . . . . 0161 248 0500

The Hillman Partnership
‡Swindon p406 . . . . 01793 642100

Hills (Oldham)
‡Oldham p340. . . . . 0161 652 3231

Paul Hills & Co
‡Chichester p193 . . . . 01243 671782

Hills Solicitors Limited
‡Bolton p149 . . . . 01204 388300
Altrincham p116 . . . . 0161 928 0961

Hillyer McKeown LLP
‡Chester p190. . . . . 01244 318131
Bebington p129. . . . . 0151 645 4255
Wrexham p442 . . . . 01978 229346

Hilmi + Partners LLP
‡London W1 p41 . . . . 020 7659 0340

Hilton Law
‡Manchester p305. . . . . 0161 932 1739

Hilton Legal
‡Oldham p340. . . 01457 830126 / 07771 725530

Hilton Norbury
‡Wigan p432 . . . . 01942 241424

Himayah Solicitors
‡Birmingham p139. . . . . 0121 356 5007

Hinchliffes
‡Malvern p300. . . . . 01684 580900

Hinckley Birch & Brown
‡Lichfield p284. . . . . 01543 262491

B G Hindle
‡Haywards Heath p246 . . . . . . 01444 443636

Hindle Campbell
‡North Shields p330. . . . . 0191 296 1777

Hindley & Co
‡London N5 p41. . . . . 020 7609 1161

Hindley Parsons Kapoor
‡London N2 p41. . . . . 020 8883 0313

Hindocha & Co
‡Wembley p426 . . . . 020 8903 1120

Hine & Co
‡Exeter p221 . . . . 01392 832937

Hine Downing Solicitors
‡Falmouth p223. . . . . 01326 316655

Hine Solicitors
‡Beaconsfield p129 . . . . 01494 685588
Bracknell p153 . . . . 01344 667300
Cheltenham p188. . . . . 01242 256686
Gerrards Cross p229 . . . . 01753 482400
Oxford p343 . . . . 01865 339660
Princes Risborough p358. . . . . 01844 274556
Swindon p406 . . . . 01793 698027
Yiewsley p444 . . . . 01895 443317

Hines & Co
‡Watford p423. . . . . 01923 431714

Hipkin & Co
‡Whitley Bay p431. . . . . 0191 253 3509

S Hirsch & Co
‡London N3 p41. . . . . 020 8371 3284

Dominic Hirst LLB
‡Harrogate p240. . . . . 01423 701527

Hitchman & Co
‡Dartford p207. . . . . 01322 556648

C Hoare & Co
‡London EC4 p41 . . . . 020 7353 4522

Mark Hoare
‡Chepstow p189. . . . . 01291 630356

J R Hobbs & Co
‡Slough p382 . . . . 01753 524466

Hoben Johnson
‡Rushden p369 . . . . 01933 411375
Wellingborough p424 . . . . 01933 277666

Hobsons
‡Warrington p422 . . . . 01942 725111

HOCKFIELD & CO
‡Lambeth SE11 p41. . . . . 020 7582 8784

Antony Hodari & Co
‡Manchester p305. . . . . 0161 832 4781

Hodders
‡London NW10 p41 . . . . 020 8965 9862
‡London NW10 p41 . . . . 020 8965 9878
High Wycombe p250 . . . . 01494 511345
London SW11 p41 . . . . 020 7720 1647
London NW10 p41 . . . . 020 8838 1537
Wembley p426 . . . . 020 8902 9604

David Hodes & Co
‡Bristol p163. . . . . 0117 905 8705

Alan Hodge Solicitors
‡Bristol p163. . . . . 01454 888098

Hodge Halsall
‡Southport p388. . . . . 01704 531991
Ainsdale p115 . . . . 01704 577171

John Hodge Solicitors
‡Weston-super-Mare p429. . . . . 01934 623511
Bristol p163. . . . . 0117 929 2281
Clevedon p196 . . . . 01275 874213
Wedmore p424. . . . . .01934 713030 / 712431
Weston-super-Mare p429. . . . . 01934 425999
Yatton p443. . . . . 01934 833208

HODGE JONES & ALLEN LLP
‡London NW1 p41. . . . . 020 7874 8300

Stuart Hodge Corporate Lawyers
‡Birmingham p139. . . . . 0121 214 2490

Hodgkinsons Solicitors
‡Skegness p380. . . . . 01754 897150

Hodgson & Angus
‡Stanhope p394. . . . . 01388 528517

Hodgson Coulthard & Co
‡Houghton Le Spring p253. . . . . 0191 584 3333

Julia Hodgson Solicitors
‡Eastleigh p216 . . . . 023 8065 1100

Hodgsons & Mortimer
‡Darlington p206. . . . . 01325 250111 / 355956
Richmond p363. . . . . 01748 850950

Hodkin & Co
‡East Grinstead p215 . . . . 01342 325765

Hoffman-Bokaei Solicitors
‡London NW3 p42. . . . . 020 7433 2380
London NW7 p42. . . . . 020 3114 2117

Hoffman Male & Co
‡Swindon p406 . . . . 01793 538198

Hogan & Hartson
‡London EC4 p42 . . . . 020 7367 0200

Hogan Brown
‡Liverpool p289 . . . . 0151 243 7500

Hogan Lisle
‡Westminster W1 p42 . . . . 020 7224 3300

Hogan Lovells International LLP
‡London EC1 p42 . . . . 020 7296 2000

Hoganco
‡Sutton p402 . . . . 020 8642 9999

Hogans
‡Prescot p356. . . . . 0151 430 7529

Irene Hogarth Criminal Defence
‡Newton Abbot p329. . . . . 01626 337373

Charles Hoile
‡Newbury p322 . . . . 01635 45595

Holden & Co
‡Hastings p243 . . . . 01424 722422
Ashford p119 . . . . 01233 663000
Maidstone p299. . . . . 01622 757665

Holden Haie
‡London E3 p42. . . . . 020 8983 4130

John Holden
‡Keighley p263 . . . . 01535 667826

Nigel Holden & Co
Blackburn p145. . . . . 01254 682424
Nelson p321 . . . . 01254 682424

Holden Son & Ullock
‡Thornton Cleveleys p411 .01253 852613 / 862606

Holdens
‡Lancaster p269. . . . . 01524 32484
Kendal p264 . . . . 01539 720629

Holding Parsons
‡London EC4 p42 . . . . 020 7430 9474

Hole & Pugsley
‡Tiverton p412. . . . . 01884 252827

Andrew Holland Law
‡Keighley p263 . . . . 01535 658274

Barry K Holland
‡Birkenhead *p134* 0151 666 2181

W Elaine Holland
‡Bolton *p149* 01204 849253

Holley & Steer
‡Burnham-on-Sea *p169* 01278 788991

Hollies Solicitors And Advocates Limited
‡Bromsgrove *p167*. 01527 831800
Stourbridge *p399* 01384 402211

Hollingworth Bissell
‡London EC4 *p42* 020 7653 1994

Hollis & Co
‡Sutton-in-Ashfield *p404*. 01623 443344

Linda Holloway & Co
‡St Albans *p390*. 01727 841651

Holls Solicitors
‡Beckenham *p129*. 020 8658 9767

Holman Copeland
‡Lewisham SE13 *p42* . 020 8852 1162 / 8852 2632

Holman Fenwick Willan
‡London EC3 *p42* 020 7264 8000

Holme Roberts & Owen
‡London EC3 *p42* 020 7015 0520

Holmes & Hills LLP
‡Braintree *p155* 01376 320456
Halstead *p238* 01787 475312

Antony A Holmes
‡Broadway *p166*. 01386 858107

David Holmes & Co
‡Great Yarmouth *p234*. 01493 658291

Holmes Dean & Co
‡Arundel *p118* 01903 884949

Laurence Holmes Solicitors
‡Congresbury *p198* 01934 838445

Holroyd & Co
‡Huddersfield *p256* 01484 645464
Huddersfield *p256* 01484 645464

Holt & Longworth
‡Burnley *p169*. 01282 414740
‡Rossendale *p367*. . . . .01706 213251 / 229131

Brett Holt Solicitors
‡Worcester Park *p440*. 020 8337 0174
Epsom *p219* 020 8393 0102
Surbiton *p402*. 020 8399 1195

Simon A Holt & Co
‡Preston *p357*. 01772 250871

Holts Solicitors
‡Ipswich *p262* 01473 217272

Honley Law Practice
‡Holmfirth *p251* 01484 667853

Honniball & Co
‡Thame *p410* 01844 261484

Anthony Hood Family Law Solicitor
‡Bishop Auckland *p144* 01388 609886

Hood Vores & Allwood
‡Dereham *p209* 01362 692424
Aylsham *p121* 01263 732123

William Hood & Co
‡Macclesfield *p297* 01625 611819

Hook & Partners
‡Canvey Island *p177* 01268 692255

Philip Hook
‡Norwich *p334*. 01603 250050

Hoole & Co
‡Bristol *p163*. 0117 969 1436
Bristol *p163*. 0117 942 8871

Hooper Holt & Co
‡Redhill *p362* 01737 761111

John Hooper & Co
‡Nottingham *p337*. 0115 941 5566

Hope & Co
‡Charlbury *p184*. 01494 483182

Hopkin Murray Beskine
‡London N4 *p42*. 020 7272 1234

Hopkins
‡Mansfield *p311* 01623 468468
Mansfield *p311* 01623 460460
Nottingham *p337* 0115 910 5555

Hopkins & Co
‡London SW1 *p42*. . .020 7808 7744 / 7233 8686

Hopkins Law LLP
‡Cardiff *p178* 029 2039 5888
Cardiff *p178* 029 2073 3000
Cowbridge *p201* 01446 774151

Wendy Hopkins Family Law Practice LLP
‡Cardiff *p178* 029 2034 2233

Hopley Pierce & Bird
‡Wrexham *p443*. 01978 315100

Andrew Hopper QC
‡Pontyclun *p352*. 01443 237788

Horace Wright Solicitors
‡Wembley *p426* 020 8908 1804

Peter Horada
‡London NW2 *p43*. 020 8450 0737

Horn & Co
‡London EC3 *p43* 020 7816 5960

Hornby & Levy
‡London SW9 *p43*. 020 7737 0909

Hornby Baker Jones & Wood
‡Newport *p328* 01633 262848
Chipping Sodbury *p193*

Horne & Company
‡Macclesfield *p297* 01625 820920

HORNE ENGALL & FREEMAN LLP
‡Egham *p217* 01784 432292

Hornsby De Gray Solicitors LLP
‡Brecon *p156* 07791 747091
Twickenham *p416* 07808 585586

Horrocks & Co
‡Leeds *p274*. 0113 230 7944

Horsey Lightly
‡Newbury *p322* 01635 580858
Westminster SW1 *p43* 020 7222 8844

Horsey Lightly Fynn
‡Bournemouth *p152*. 01202 551991

Horsman Solicitors Ltd
‡Lewes *p283* 01273 474743

Richard Horth
‡Brackley *p153* 01280 703773

Horton & Moss
‡Ilkeston *p261*. . . . . 0115 932 1431 / 930 8208

Thomas Horton LLP
‡Birmingham *p139*. 0121 445 7373
‡Bromsgrove *p167*. 01527 871641

Horwich Cohen Coghlan
‡Manchester *p305*. 0161 830 4600
London EC4 *p43* 020 7332 2230

Horwich Farrelly
‡Manchester *p305*. 0161 834 3585

Horwood & James LLP
‡Aylesbury *p121*. 01296 487361

Hoshi & Co Solicitors
‡London N19 *p43* 020 7485 5180

Hossacks
‡Kettering *p265* 01536 518638

Hotchkiss Warburton
‡Crediton *p203* 01363 774752

C J Hough & Co Ltd
‡Crawley *p202*. . . . . . .01293 734592 / 734596

Hough Halton & Soal
‡Carlisle *p182* 01228 524379

Houghton Pigot & Co
‡Wigan *p432* . . . . . . .01942 241288 / 824424
Ashton-in-Makerfield *p119* 01942 270757

Houghtons Solicitors Ltd
‡Eastcote *p216* 020 8429 7451

Houldsworths
‡Clitheroe *p196* 01254 825757
Clitheroe *p196* 01200 422152

John Hoult & Co
‡Scunthorpe *p373*. 01724 281312

Houlton Carr
‡Bridlington *p158* 01262 677979

Houseman Benner
‡Haywards Heath *p246* 01444 414081

Houseman Solicitors
‡Aylesbury *p121*. 01296 682791

Housemans
‡Newcastle upon Tyne *p325*. . . . 0191 232 1307
London EC3 *p43* 020 3170 6000

Housing & Property Law Partnership
‡Islington EC1 *p43*. 020 7553 9000

Housing Law Services
‡Battle *p128*. 01424 774738

Houthoff Burma
‡London EC2 *p43* 020 7422 5050

Howard & Byrne Solicitors
‡York *p445* 01904 431421

Howard & Co
‡Barnsley *p124* 01226 215215
Barnsley *p124* 01226 211888

Howard & Company
‡Westminster W1 *p43* 020 7486 6610

Howard & Over
‡Plymouth *p350* 01752 556606
Ivybridge *p263* 01752 690123
Plymouth *p350* 01752 405774

Fiona M Howard
‡London NW1 *p43*. 020 7482 2705

Frank Howard
‡Warrington *p422* 01925 653481

The Howard Partnership Limited
Aylesbury *p121*. 01296 770372

Philip & Robert Howard
‡Castleford *p183* 01977 551320
Barnsley *p124* 01226 780840

Howard Pollok & Webb
‡Norwich *p334*. 01603 660051

Richard Howard & Co LLP
‡London WC2 *p43*. 020 7831 4511

Robert Howard
‡Plymouth *p350* 01752 251851

Howard Schneider Spiro Steele
‡Barnet *p124* 020 8216 2020

Howard Solicitors
‡Manchester *p305*. 0800 876 6749

HOWARD STONE
‡London EC1 *p43* 020 7490 5900

Howards
‡London NW6 *p43*. 020 7328 1947

Howarth & Co
‡Wetherby *p429*. 01937 584020

Howarth Goodman
‡Manchester *p305*. 0161 832 5068

Howarth Scott
‡Bexleyheath *p132* 020 8303 4658

Susan Howarth & Co
‡Northwich *p333*. 01606 48777

Howe & Co
‡Ealing W5 *p43* 020 8840 4688

Howe & Spender
‡Port Talbot *p353* 01639 881571
Neath *p320*. 01639 881571

John Howe & Co
‡Pudsey *p358* 0113 236 3936

Nick Howe Solicitors
‡London EC1 *p43* 020 7397 8430

The Howe Practice
‡Stockport *p395* 0161 480 2629

Robert Howe
‡Bristol *p163*. 01225 873480

Howell & Co
‡Birmingham *p139*. 0121 778 5031
‡London E7 *p43*. 020 8221 4536

Howell Hylton
‡Camborne *p173* 01209 613014

Howell Jones & Co
‡Llanrwst *p292* 01492 640277
Abergele *p113* . . . . . .01745 826282 / 825845

Howell-Jones LLP
‡Kingston upon Thames *p267* . . . 020 8549 5186
Cheam *p186* 020 8642 8142
Leatherhead *p271* 01372 860650
London SW20 *p43* 020 8947 7991
London WC2 *p43*. 020 7183 0919
Walton-on-Thames *p420* 01932 234500

Howells
‡Cardiff *p178* 029 2040 4020
Caerphilly *p172*. 029 2086 7111
Newport *p328*. 01633 227960
Swansea *p405* 01792 410016
Talbot Green *p407* 01443 230411

Howells LLP
‡Hull *p257*. 01482 317420
‡Leicester *p280* 0845 456 0074
‡Sheffield *p376* 0114 249 6666
Barnsley *p124* 01226 805190
Rotherham *p367* 01709 364000

T Vincent Howells & Co
‡Harrow *p241* 020 8863 6655

Howells Williams
‡Shrewsbury *p379*. 01743 241429
Telford *p409* 01952 582631

David Howes Solicitors
‡Horley *p252* 01293 822280

Howes Percival LLP
‡Northampton *p332* 01604 230400
Leicester *p280* 0116 247 3500
London WC2 *p43*. 020 3040 0200
Manchester *p306*. 0161 259 0400
Milton Keynes *p317*. 01908 672682
Norwich *p334*. 01603 762103

Howlett Clarke Crowther Wood
‡Brighton *p159* . . . . . . .01273 327272 / 326341

Howlett Clarke Solicitors
Hove *p254* 01273 419728

Howman & Co
‡Ruislip *p369* 01895 621777

Hoxtons Solicitors
‡Islington EC1 *p43*. 020 7729 9229

Christopher Hoyle & Co
‡Kendal *p264* 01539 822078

Hubball & Co
‡Sutton Coldfield *p403*. 0121 323 4822

K W Hubbard & Co
‡Gloucester *p230* 01452 414406

Hubbard Pegman & Witney
‡London W6 *p43* 020 8735 9770

Nicholas Huber & Co
‡Tiverton *p412*. 01884 255515

Hudgell & Partners
‡Greenwich SE18 *p43*. 020 8854 1331

Neil Hudgell Solicitors
‡Hull *p257*. 01482 787771
Hull *p257*. 01482 787771

Hudson And Associates Solicitors-Advocates Ltd
‡Kirkby Lonsdale *p268*. 0800 019 9768

Hudson & Co
‡London WC1 *p43*. . .020 7405 4812 / 7831 3282

Hudson & Taylor
‡Rochdale *p365* 01706 644525

Hudson Brown
‡London W1 *p43* 020 7518 0370

Hudson Mcconaghugh Solicitors
‡London E18 *p43* 020 8530 2005

Hudson Webb
‡Plympton *p351* 01752 290447

Hudsons
‡London SE11 *p43* 020 7793 8740

Hudsons Hart & Borrows
‡Richmond *p363*. 01748 824333

Geoffrey Hueting & Co
‡Bath *p127* 01225 465828

Huggins & Lewis Foskett
‡Redbridge E18 *p43*. 020 8989 3000

Hugh Cartwright & Amin
‡London WC1 *p43*. 020 7632 4200

Hugh James
‡Cardiff *p179* 029 2022 4871
London E14 *p43* 020 7038 8301

Hugh Jones & Co
‡London N3 *p43*. 020 8346 2236

A L Hughes & Co
‡London SW16 *p43* 020 8769 7100

Hughes & Company
‡Tring *p413* 01442 891717

Hughes & Dorman
‡London EC4 *p43* 020 3402 2325

Hughes Carlisle Law
‡Warrington *p422* 0845 519 2699

Carys Hughes
‡Llangefni *p292* 01248 750941

D R Hughes
‡Wootton Bassett *p439* 01793 840077

Edward Hughes
‡Colwyn Bay *p198*. 01492 535640
‡Rhyl *p363* . . . . .01745 343661 / 344551

Elizabeth A Hughes
‡Wantage *p421* 01235 868438

Hughes Enterprise Law Practice
‡Bristol *p163*. 0117 959 6424

Hughes Fowler Carruthers
‡London WC2 *p43*. 020 7421 8383

Gareth Hughes & Co
‡Salford *p370* 0161 832 3562

Hughes Griffiths Partnership
‡Swansea *p405* 01792 458275

Gwynne Hughes
‡Aberaeron *p113* 01545 570861
New Quay *p321* 01545 560525

J A Hughes
‡Barry *p126* 01446 411000
Cardiff *p179* 029 2061 9700
Penarth *p345*. 029 2070 2449

J Charles Hughes & Co
‡Dolgellau *p211* 01341 422464
Harlech *p239*. 01766 780818

J W Hughes & Co
‡Conwy *p199* 01492 596596
Llandudno *p291* 01492 874774

Hughes Jenkins Solicitors
‡Aberdare *p113* 01685 886611

John Hughes & Co
‡Liverpool *p289* 01704 832244

Hughes Paddison
‡Cheltenham *p188*. 01242 574244

The Hughes Parry Partnership
‡Holywell *p252* 01352 712422

Hughes Solicitors
‡Romford *p366* 020 7566 8244

Hughes Walker
‡Bury *p170* 0870 744 5952

Hughes Way
‡Havant *p244* 023 9245 9020

Hughes Willson Solicitors
‡London W1 *p43* 020 7631 0131

Hughes-Narborough & Thomas
‡Greenwich SE18 *p43*. 020 8854 1291

Hughmans
‡London EC4 *p44* 020 7246 6560

Hujan & Co Solicitors
‡Birmingham *p139*. 0121 766 7345

Huka & Co
‡London NW6 *p44*. 020 7624 9341

Carla Hull Solicitors Limited
‡Solihull *p382* 0845 466 4333

M C Hullah & Co
‡Nailsea *p320*. 01275 855561

Hullock & Co Solicitors
‡Ipswich *p262* 01473 286686

Huma Law Associates
‡Luton *p295*. 01582 731330

Human Law
‡London N21 *p44* 0844 800 3249
‡Ware *p421* 01920 462202

Humble Munson LLP
‡Peterborough *p347*. 01733 254815

Humd Solicitors
‡Manchester *p306*. 0161 225 5598

Nigel J Humes & Co
‡Chester-le-Street *p191* 0191 388 8737

Humfrys & Symonds
‡Hereford p248 . . . . . .01432 359261 / 276276
‡Leominster p283 . . . . 01568 613612

Ann L Humphrey
‡London SE1 p44 . . . . 020 7378 9370

Humphrey Roberts & Bott
‡Aberystwyth p114. . . . . 01970 617618

Humphreys & Co
‡Bristol p163. . . . . 0117 929 2662

V L Humphreys & Co
‡Guildford p236 . . . . 01483 574342

Humphries Kirk
‡Wareham p421. . . . . 01929 552141
Bournemouth p152. . . . . .01202 421111
Dorchester p212 . . . . 01305 251007
Poole p352. . . . . 01202 715815
Poole p352. . . . . 01202 725400
Swanage p404 . . . . 01929 423301

Mark Humphries Legal
‡London EC4 p44 . . . . 020 3440 5490

Humphrys & Co
‡Rhyl p363 . . . . 01745 343158
Colwyn Bay p198. . . . . 01492 532255
Wrexham p443. . . . . 01978 313399

Hunt & Hunt
‡Romford p366 . . . . 01708 764433

Hunt & Lisners
‡Northampton p332 . . . . 01604 846705
London NW4 p44. . . . . 020 8202 3746

Hunt & Morgan
‡Cardiff p179 . . . . 029 2034 1234

Hunt & Wrigley
‡Northallerton p331 . . . . 01609 772502

David C Hunt
‡London SE7 p44 . . . . 020 8856 6350

Karen Hunte & Co Solicitors
‡London N11 p44 . . . . 020 8361 6277

Norman Hunter
‡Cliftonville p196. . . . . 07766 313613

P M Hunter & Co
‡London SE24 p44 . . . . 020 7737 7725

Hunter Peddell Property Law
‡Esher p220. . . . . 01372 477900

HUNTERS
‡London WC2 p44. . . . . 020 7412 0050
Towcester p413. . . . . 01327 830895
‡London WC2 p44. . . . . 020 7412 0050
‡Westcliff-on-Sea p428 . . . . . . 01702 353093

HUNTLEY LEGAL
‡London W4 p44 . . . . 0844 873 2831

Hunton & Garget
‡Richmond p364. . . . . 01748 850400

Hunton & Williams
‡London EC3 p44 . . . . 020 7220 5700

Hunts
‡Cheltenham p188. . . . . 01242 525777

Hurleys
‡Bournemouth p152 . . . . 01202 436100

Hurlow & Partners
‡Cardiff p179 . . . . 029 2039 6087

Andrew Hurrell Solicitors
‡Benfleet p131. . . . . 01702 558286
Thorpe Bay p411 . . . . .01702 582211 / 582030

Dorothy A Hurrell
‡London W8 p44 . . . . 020 7938 5355

C J Hurrion
‡Sevenoaks p374 . . . . 01732 833997

A C B Hurst & Co
‡Henley-on-Thames p247 . . . . . 01491 572699

E B Hurst
‡Worthing p442 . . . . 01903 246818

Keith M Hurst
‡Widnes p431 . . . . 0151 420 0900

Robert A Hurst
‡London NW11 p44 . . . . 020 8209 1733

Husband Forwood Morgan
‡Liverpool p289 . . . . 0151 236 9626

Husband Saye
‡Cardiff p179 . . . . 029 2034 5217

Mohammed Hussain Solicitors
‡Keighley p263 . . . . 01535 692999

Rozita Hussain Solicitors
‡Withington p436 . . . . 0161 448 8222

Hussain Solicitors Limited
‡Birmingham p139. . . . . 0121 766 7474

R James Hutcheon Solicitors
‡Prescot p356 . . . . 0151 431 0548

Hutcheson Forrest
‡Bath p127 . . . . 01225 312311

Michael Hutchings
‡Warminster p421 . . . . 07768 105777

Hutchins & Co
‡Hackney E5 p44 . . . . 020 8986 3911

Hutchinson
‡Beaconsfield p129 . . . . 01494 680775

Hutchinson & Buchanan
‡Ripon p365. . . . . 01765 602156

Chris Hutchinson & Co
‡Hull p257. . . . . 01482 326404

Hutchinson Mainprice
‡Westminster SW1 p44 . . . . . . 020 7259 0121

Nick Hutchinson & Co
‡Cheltenham p188. . . . . 01242 261515

Hutchinson Thomas
‡Neath p320. . . . . 01639 645061

Hutchinsons Employment Solicitors
‡Nottingham p337. . . . . 0115 959 9700

Hutchinsons Solicitors Limited
‡Marlborough p313 . . . . 01672 838216

Hutharts Law Firm
‡Gateshead p228 . . . . 0191 490 0031

Hutsby Mees
‡Stafford p393. . . . . 01785 259211

Hutton's
‡Cardiff p179 . . . . 029 2037 8621

Hyam Lehrer
‡London W1 p44 . . . . 020 7499 0104

Henry Hyams
‡Leeds p274. . . . . 0113 243 2288

Hyde Law
‡London W1 p44 . . . . 020 7022 0058

Howard Hyman & Co
‡London N12 p44 . . . . 020 8446 5511

Scott Hyman & Co
‡Oldham p340. . . . . 0161 628 7018

I

IA Solicitors
‡London NW4 p44. . . . . 020 8201 7728

IBA Solicitors
‡Dewsbury p210. . . . . 01924 455000

IBB Solicitors
‡Uxbridge p417 . . . . 0845 638 1381
Chesham p189 . . . . 0845 638 1381

ICS Solicitors
‡Croydon p205 . . . . 020 8664 4670

ID Law
‡Redditch p362 . . . . 01527 596010

IEC Solicitors
‡London NW10 p44 . . . . 020 8830 2784

IEI Solicitors
‡Edgware p217 . . . . 020 8952 7047
Birmingham p139. . . . . 0121 554 6445
Norwich p334. . . . . 01603 283621

IE Law
‡Slough p382 . . . . 01753 554040

ILS Solicitors
‡Durham p214. . . . . 0191 378 2030

IMR Solicitors
‡Liverpool p289 . . . . 0151 521 0055

IPS Law LLP
‡Manchester p306. . . . . 0161 830 4710

I S Law
‡Chorley p194. . . . . 01257 754854

I Will Solicitors Ltd
‡Birmingham p139. . . . . 0121 683 6940

Iacopi Palmer Solicitors LLP
‡Gloucester p230 . . . . 01452 416452

Ian N Gunby & Co
‡Milnthorpe p316 . . . . 01539 562044

Ibbotson Brady
‡Leeds p274. . . . . 0113 366 3022

Ideal Solicitors
‡London E12 p44 . . . . 020 8552 8624

Idicullla Solicitors
‡Southampton p386 . . . . 023 8063 0905

Idris & Co
‡Leicester p280 . . . . 0116 249 0100

iFocus
‡East Grinstead p215 . . . . 020 7566 8244

Ifrahim & Co Solicitors
‡Ilford p260 . . . . 020 8911 9222

Anthony Igbiniyesu
‡Crowthorne p204. . . . . 01344 779579

Ignatiou-Fakhouri & Co Solicitors
‡London E2 p44. . . . . 020 7739 8454

Igor & Co
‡Hammersmith & Fulham SW6 p44 020 7384 7580

Jorge Iguacel Spanish Lawyers
‡Southend-on-Sea p387. . . . . . 01702 333341

Ikie Solicitors LLP
‡London SE13 p44 . . . . 020 8463 0808

iLaw Legal Services Ltd
‡London EC4 p44 . . . . 020 7489 2059

Ilett & Clark Solicitors
‡Worksop p441 . . . . 01909 500544

Imlaw
‡Saltburn-by-the-Sea p371. . . . . 0870 720 3477

Immanuel & Co
‡London EC4 p44 . . . . 020 7213 9901

Imperium Law LLP
‡Cannock p176 . . . . 01543 437203
‡Macclesfield p297 . . . . 01625 619062
‡Nuneaton p339. . . . . 024 7634 5060

Inal & Co
‡Islington N1 p44 . . . . 020 7354 5272

Inayat Solicitors
‡Harrow p241 . . . . 020 3178 2450

Incasso LLP
‡Leeds p274. . . . . 0845 404 1999

Ince & Co Services Ltd
‡London E1 p44. . . . . 020 7481 0010

Independent Pension Trustee Limited
‡London EC3 p45 . . . . 020 7247 6555

Indus Solicitors
‡Luton p295. . . . . 01582 431441

Inesons
‡Cleckheaton p195 . . . . 01274 872202

Infields
‡Kingston upon Thames p267 . . 020 8977 7633 / 8977 1149

The Information Law Practice
‡Evesham p220. . . . . 01386 793632

Inghams
‡Blackpool p146. . . . . 01253 626642
Blackpool p146 . . . . 01253 353308
Fleetwood p226. . . . . 01253 873481
Knott-End-on-Sea p269. . . . . . 01253 810547
Poulton-le-Fylde p355. . . . . . . 01253 890545
Thornton Cleveleys p411 . . . . . 01253 824111

Darryl Ingram & Co
‡London NW4 p45. . . . . 020 8202 0843

Ingram Winter Green
‡Camden WC1 p45 . . . . 020 7845 7400

Ingrams
‡Hull p257. . . . . 01482 358850
York p445 . . . . 01904 520600

Injury Specialists Solicitors Limited
‡Uxbridge p417 . . . . 01895 207150

Paul Inman & Co
‡Doncaster p211. . . . . 01302 349395

William Innes
‡London SW4 p45. . . . . 020 7622 4893

Innstep (Nominees) Limited
‡London EC1 p45 . . . . 020 7490 4000

Insaaf Solicitors
‡Derby p209. . . . . 01332 595020

Insley & Partners
‡Bournemouth p152 . . . . 01202 510167
Ferndown p225. . . . . 01202 876117

Inspire Law
‡Banbury p122 . . . . 01295 298211

Integrum Law
‡Birkenhead p134 . . . . 0151 649 1626

International Family Law Chambers
‡London WC2 p45. . . . . 020 7583 5040

The International Family Law Group
‡London WC2 p45. . . . . 020 3178 5668

The International Property Law Centre
London E1 p45 . . . . 0844 578 4000

The International Property Law Centre LLP
‡London E1 p45. . . . . 020 7173 6180

Inyama & Co
‡London NW5 p45. . . . . 020 7482 8863

Ireland Abrahams
‡Harrow p241 . . . . 020 8864 5557

John Ireland & Co
‡London W11 p45 . . . . 020 7792 1666

T R Ireland
‡Sidcup p380 . . . . 020 8300 6487

Iris Law Firm
‡Gateshead p228 . . . . 0191 477 0055

Irvine & Partners
‡London EC1 p45 . . . . 020 3176 0300

Mariel Irvine
‡London EC1 p45 . . . . 020 7606 0517

Irvine Thanvi Natas
‡London E15 p45 . . . . 020 8522 7707

Irving & Co
‡Camden NW1 p45 . . . . 020 7428 9600
Brighton p159. . . . . 01273 665460

Irving M Shapiro
‡Manchester p306. . . . . 0161 798 8832

Irvings
‡Harrow p241 . . . . 020 8427 6600
‡Liverpool p289 . . . . 0800 954 0243
Liverpool p289 . . . . 0800 954 0243

Irvings Solicitors
Derby p209. . . . . 01332 346036

Irwin Mitchell LLP
‡Sheffield p376 . . . . 0870 150 0100
Birmingham p139. . . . . 0870 150 0100
Bristol p163. . . . . 0870 150 0100
Leeds p274. . . . . 0870 150 0100
London EC1 p45 . . . . 0870 150 0100
Manchester p306 . . . . 0870 150 0100
Newcastle upon Tyne p325 . . . . 0870 150 0100

Isaac & Co
‡Oxford p343 . . . . 01865 516449

Andrew Isaacs
‡Doncaster p212 . . . . 01302 349480

David Isaacs
‡Henley-on-Thames p247 . . . . . 01491 577130
Sutton p402 . . . . 020 8770 1901

The Isaacs Practice
‡Bournemouth p152 . . . . 01202 299999

Aubrey Isaacson Solicitors
‡Prestwich p357. . . . . 0161 959 5000
Bury p170 . . . . 0161 959 5050
Prestwich p357. . . . . 0161 772 4000
Whitefield p430. . . . . 0161 959 6000

Isadore Goldman Solicitors
‡London EC4 p45 . . . . 020 7353 1000

Isherwood & Hose
‡Heywood p249 . . . . . .01706 360032 / 368741
Rochdale p365 . . . . . .01706 359090 / 522225

Isis Legal
‡Melton Mowbray p314 . .01664 560707 / 560708

Isis Legal Limited
‡Kettering p265 . . . . . . .01536 485398 / 485888

The Islamic Wills Company Ltd
‡London SE28 p45 . . . . 0845 813 2323

Ismail & Co
‡Enfield p218 . . . . 020 8804 1065

Ismail & Ghani
‡Bradford p154 . . . . 01274 737546

Ison Harrison
‡Leeds p274. . . . . 0113 284 5000
Garforth p228. . . . . 0113 286 1455
Guiseley p237 . . . . 01943 889080
Ilkley p261 . . . . 01943 889100
Leeds p274. . . . . 0113 232 6530

Israel Strange & Conlon
‡Islington EC1 p45. . . . . 020 7833 8453

Issat & Co Solicitors
‡London SE1 p45 . . . . 020 7939 9900

John Itsagwede & Co
‡London SE15 p45 . . . . 020 7732 8750

Iverson Stanley Holmes Commercial Solicitors
‡Banbury p122 . . . . 01295 688923

Ives & Co
‡Nottingham p337. . . . . 0115 937 2408

Ives-Keeler & Co
‡Norwich p334. . . . . 01603 219298

Iwan Davies & Co
‡Pontypridd p352 . . . . 01443 485566

Iyama Solicitors
‡Southwark SE1 p45 . . . . 020 7357 0709

Izod Evans
‡London SE1 p45 . . . . 020 7015 1850

J

JBL Law
‡Leeds p274. . . . . 0113 200 2000

JB Law
‡Macclesfield p297 . . . . 01625 443190

JBR Law
‡Newark p322. . . . . 01636 642842

JBS Solicitors
‡Beckenham p129. . . . . 0845 643 5050

JCP Law
‡Wimborne p433 . . . . 01202 813658

JCS Solicitors
‡St Albans p390. . . . . 01438 820946

J D Law LLP
‡London EC4 p45 . . . . 020 7438 0990

JDS Solicitors
‡London E15 p45 . . . . 020 8221 0233

JD Solicitors
‡Willenhall p432. . . . . 01902 632123

JEH
‡London EC4 p45 . . . . 020 7583 8853

JF Law Solicitors
‡London SE5 p45 . . . . 020 7277 0444

JFS Law Limited
‡Cramlington p201. . . . . 0191 237 1216

JGE Solicitors
‡London N17 p45 . . . . 020 8885 6477

JGQC Solicitors
‡Lincoln p284 . . . . 01522 595441

JG Solicitors
‡Manchester p306. . . . . 0845 009 0975

JGT
‡Burnley p169 . . . . 01282 426722

JH Law Limited
‡Rugby p368 . . . . 0845 638 4440

JJ Solicitors
‡Oundle p342 . . . . 01832 238088

JL Law
‡Stoke-on-Trent p398 . . . . 01782 328171

JLS Solicitors
‡Farnham p225 . . . . 01252 726741

JL Solicitors
‡Luton p295. . . .01582 488688 / 020 8816 8106

JMA HR & Legal Ltd
‡Farnham p225 . . . . 01252 821792

The JMC Practice
‡Poole p353. . . . . 01202 757435

JMD Law Limited
‡Cardiff p179 . . . . 029 2045 6780

JMP Solicitors
‡Grantham *p232* . . . 01476 568100
Warrington *p422* . . . 0845 680 1895

JMS Solicitors
‡Cheadle *p185* . . . 0161 486 3390
‡Manchester *p306* . . . 0161 772 7927

JMW Solicitors
‡Manchester *p306* . . . 0845 872 6666

JNP Legal
‡Merthyr Tydfil *p314* . . . 01685 350421
Nelson *p320* . . . 01443 450561

JP Mitchell
‡Hampton *p238* . . . 020 3151 2711

JPS Law Solicitors
‡Westminster W1 *p45* . . . 020 7935 9955

JSK Law
‡Pinner *p349* . . . 020 8426 1750

JS Law
‡Hayes *p245* . . . 020 8817 1004

JSP Solicitors
‡Lincoln *p284* . . . 01522 537353
‡Skegness *p380* . . . 01754 762252 / 01522 537353

JST Lawyers
‡Liverpool *p289* . . . 0151 282 2828

JVA Law
‡London W11 *p45* . . . 020 3220 0070

JW Law
‡Wimborne *p433* . . . 01202 690658

JWP Solicitors
‡Wakefield *p418* . . . 01924 387171
Leeds *p274* . . . 0113 346 6030

Jac Law
‡Calne *p173* . . . 01249 760717

Jackamans
‡Ipswich *p262* . . . 01473 255591
Diss *p210* . . . 01379 643555
Felixstowe *p225* . . . 01394 279636
Harleston *p239* . . . 01379 854455

Richard Jacklin & Co
‡Southport *p388* . . . 01704 500024
Liverpool *p289* . . . 0151 243 1313

Jacklyn Dawson
‡Newport *p328* . . . 01633 262952
Monmouth *p318* . . . 01600 716660

Jackman Woods
‡Winchcombe *p433* . . . 01242 602378

Jackson & Co
‡Lutterworth *p296* . . . 01455 556321
Birstall *p143* . . . 0116 267 6263

Andrew Jackson
‡Hull *p257* . . . 01482 325242

Andrew Jackson & Co
‡Liverpool *p289* . . . 0151 487 8426
Liverpool *p289* . . . 0151 709 5816 / 488 1000

Angela Jackson
‡London N1 *p45* . . . 020 7609 5615

Arthur Jackson & Co
‡Rotherham *p367* . . . 01709 363876
Rotherham *p367* . . . 01709 547284

Jackson Barrett & Gass
‡Wilmslow *p433* . . . 01625 523988

Jackson Brierley Hudson Stoney
‡Rochdale *p365* . . . 01706 644187 / 649214

James Jackson Solicitor
‡London N10 *p45* . . . 020 8245 2365

Julia Jackson Solicitors
‡Marlow *p313* . . . 01628 440582

Jackson Parton
‡London E1 *p45* . . . 020 7702 0085

Jackson Quinn
Newark *p322* . . . 01636 610175
Worksop *p441* . . . 01909 480066

Simon Jackson Solicitors
‡Oswestry *p342* . . . 01691 791439

Jackson West
‡Stratford-upon-Avon *p400* . . . 01789 204020

Jacksons
‡Fordingbridge *p227* . . . 01425 652110
‡Wirral *p435* . . . 0151 632 3386

Jacksons Law
‡Newcastle upon Tyne *p325* . . . 0191 580 0183

Jacksons Solicitors
‡London W1 *p45* . . . 020 3058 0512

Jacobs Allen Hammond
‡London W1 *p45* . . . 020 7299 9800

Jacobs & Reeves
‡Poole *p353* . . . 01202 674425
Poole *p353* . . . 01202 731849
Wimborne *p433* . . . 01202 880382

Anthony Jacobs & Co
‡Cardiff *p179* . . . 029 2048 3509

Barbara Jacobs & Co
‡York *p445* . . . 01904 786012

D H K Jacobs & Co
‡London E12 *p45* . . . 020 8514 7466

Jacobs Forbes Solicitors
‡London N17 *p45* . . . 020 8880 4154

Gary Jacobs & Co
‡London E18 *p45* . . . 020 8536 4050

Jacobs Solicitors
‡Ellesmere Port *p217* . . . 0151 355 8481
‡London E6 *p46* . . . 020 8821 9222
Shotton *p379* . . . 01244 816211

Stanley Jacobs
‡Barnet N3 *p46* . . . 020 8349 4241

Jacobsen & Co
‡London SW6 *p46* . . . 020 7736 6277

Jacobsens
‡London EC2 *p46* . . . 020 7608 2568

Paul R Jacobson & Co
‡Leeds *p274* . . . 0113 269 3925

Jade Law Solicitors
‡Enfield *p219* . . . 020 8363 7000

Jaffe Porter Crossick
‡London NW6 *p46* . . . 020 7625 4424

Jakes & Co
‡New Ollerton *p321* . . . 01623 860581

Alun James & Co
‡Uxbridge *p417* . . . 01895 811511

James & Co
‡Brighton *p159* . . . 01273 665470

Ashley James Solicitors
‡Birmingham *p139* . . . 0845 643 1234

Bernard James
‡Bishop Auckland *p144* . . . 01388 458868

Charles James & Co
‡London W1 *p46* . . . 020 7969 2740

Colin D James
Guildford *p236* . . . 01483 303456

D R James & Son
‡Pontardawe *p351* . . . 01792 862334

Gwyn James Solicitors
‡Coleford *p198* . . . 01594 833042
Cinderford *p195* . . . 01594 822277

Huw James Solicitor
‡Swansea *p405* . . . 01792 643476 / 411600

Julian James
‡London NW5 *p46*. 020 7448 5200 / 07801 140980

James Legal Solicitors
‡Hull *p257* . . . 01482 488000
Leeds *p275* . . . 0113 390 6021

Margaret James
‡Westminster SW1 *p46* . . . 020 7834 3447

Richard James
‡Newcastle Emlyn *p322* . . . 01239 710455

James Solicitors
‡London SE18 *p46* . . . 020 8555 9545

James Ware Baxter Schoenfeld LLP
‡London WC1 *p46* . . . 020 7269 9025

Jameson & Hill
‡Hertford *p248* . . . 01992 554881
Ware *p421* . . . 01920 460531

Jamieson & Co
‡Newcastle upon Tyne *p325* . . . 0191 281 0063

Jamieson Fitzpatrick Solicitors
‡Keighley *p263* . . . 01535 600657

Janes
‡London SW1 *p46* . . . 020 7930 5100

Janis-Zaheer
‡Watford *p423* . . . 01923 448138

Jansons Solicitors
‡Birmingham *p139* . . . 0121 773 4142

Anne Jarvis & Co
‡Harrogate *p240* . . . 01423 858582

J B Jarvis
‡Mansfield *p311* . . . 01623 404360
‡Mansfield *p311* . . . 01623 747400

Jasper & Vincent
‡Southampton *p386* . . . 01489 885788

Jaswal Johnston Boyle
‡London W1 *p46* . . . 020 7317 1540

Andrew Jay & Co
Lincoln *p284* . . . 01522 539111

Andrew Jay & Co (Philip Hanby Limited)
‡Gainsborough *p228* . . . 01427 612412

Anthony Jayes LLP
‡London W1 *p46* . . . 020 7291 9110

Jayne McKenzie Smith
‡Barnstaple *p125* . . . 01271 329020

David Jeacock
‡Wootton Bassett *p439* . . . 01793 854111

Jeary & Lewis
‡Chippenham *p193* . . . 01249 444484
Swindon *p406* . . . 01793 435577

Jeff Lloyd
‡Barry *p126* . . . 01446 741919

Jefferies Essex LLP
‡Westcliff-on-Sea *p428* . . . 01702 332311

Jefferies LLP
‡Altrincham *p116* . . . 0800 342 3191

Julian Jefferson
‡Plymouth *p350* . . . 01752 250850

M E Jeffery
‡Northampton *p332* . . . 01604 643241

Jeffrey Doctors & Marchant
‡Watford *p423* . . . 01923 231250

Jeffrey Green Russell
‡London W1 *p46* . . . 020 7339 7000

Sian Jeffrey
‡Oxford *p343* . . . 01865 920550

Jeffreys & Powell
‡Brecon *p156* . . . 01874 622106
Builth Wells *p168* . . . 01982 553224

Jeffreys Solicitors
‡Swansea *p405* . . . 01792 886899 / 07966 220535

Jein Solicitors
‡London SE13 *p46* . . . 020 8852 5214

Trevor Jenkin Solicitor
‡Reading *p361* . . . 07798 686706

H Jenkins & Hughes
‡Holyhead *p251* . . . 01407 762301

Jenkins Law
‡London SW18 *p46* . . . 020 8879 0656

Michael Jenkins
‡Gravesend *p233* . . . 01474 822787

Richard Jenkins
‡London SW3 *p46* . . . 01794 388596

Jenners Conveyancing
‡Newquay *p329* . . . 01637 850611

Jennings
‡Llanelli *p292* . . . 01554 772331

Jennings IP & Media Solicitors
‡Sevenoaks *p374* . . . 01732 762340

Jennings Legal Services
‡Carlisle *p182* . . . 0870 777 7100

Jennings Perks & Co
‡Walsall *p420* . . . 01922 459000

R D Y Jennings & Co
‡Malton *p300* . . . 01653 691515

Walter Jennings & Sons
‡London NW5 *p46* . . . 020 7485 8626

Jens Hills Solicitors LLP
‡London EC1 *p46* . . . 020 7490 8160

Jepsen & Co
‡Leatherhead *p271* . . . 01483 281720

Jepson & Co
‡Scarborough *p372* . . . 01723 859249
Scarborough *p372* . . . 01723 341340

Jerman Simpson Pearson & Samuels
‡Southend-on-Sea *p387* . . . 01702 610071
Basildon *p126* . . . 01268 820111

Jeromes
‡Newport *p328* . . . 01983 522664
Sandown *p372* . . . 01983 402026
Shanklin *p374* . . . 01983 862643

Jestyn Jeffreys
‡Neath *p320* . . . 01639 635641

Anthony Jewell & Co
‡Pontypridd *p352* . . . 01443 493357

Jewels Solicitors
‡Stafford *p393* . . . 01785 602030
Cannock *p176* . . . 01543 577505

Jeya & Co
‡Newham E12 *p46* . . . 020 8552 1999

Jirehouse Capital
‡London WC1 *p46* . . . 020 8906 6662

Jiva Solicitors
‡London W1 *p46* . . . 020 7290 0400

Jo & Co Solicitors
‡London EC2 *p46* . . . 020 7778 0715

Jobling & Knape
‡Lancaster *p269* . . . 01524 598300
Great Eccleston *p233* . . . 01995 670083
Morecambe *p319* . . . 01524 416960

Jobling Gowler
‡Macclesfield *p297* . . . 01625 614250

Joelson Wilson LLP
‡Westminster W1 *p46* . . . 020 7580 5721

Johal & Co
‡Harrow *p241* . . . 020 8422 1221

Johal Laker Solicitors
‡Chesham *p189* . . . 01494 771743

Johar & Co
‡Leicester *p280* . . . 0116 254 3345

Johl & Walters Solicitors
‡Leicester *p280* . . . 0116 255 7806

John & Co
‡London SW9 *p46* . . . 020 7737 4141

Graeme John Solicitors
‡Aberdare *p113* . . . 01685 878563
Aberdare *p113* . . . 01685 872491
Aberdare *p113* . . . 01685 873565
Tonypandy *p412* . . . 01443 423797
Ystradgynlais *p446* . . . 01639 843404

John Hamilton Leyshon Solicitors
‡Porth *p353* . . . 01443 680000
Pontypridd *p352* . . . 01443 403666

The John Hughes Law Practice
‡Birmingham *p139* . . . 0845 130 2855

Paul John
‡London E15 *p46* . . . 020 8215 1205

The John W Davies Partnership
‡Newport *p329* . . . 01633 841773

Johns & Saggar
‡London WC1 *p46* . . . 020 3490 1475

Johns Gilbert & Frankton
‡Rugby *p368* . . . 01788 576384

V J G Johns & Son
‡Fishguard *p226* . . . 01348 873671

Johnson & Clarence
‡Midhurst *p316* . . . 01730 812244

Johnson & Co
‡London W9 *p46* . . . 020 7266 9977

Johnson & Gaunt
‡Banbury *p122* . . . 01295 256271 / 271200

Andrew M Johnson
‡Canterbury *p177* . . . 01227 811713 / 811714

Brett Johnson
‡Brockenhurst *p166* . . . 01590 612731

Johnson Crilly Solicitors LLP
‡London SW19 *p46* . . . 020 8544 1412
‡Upminster *p416* . . . 01708 228069

F E Johnson & Co
‡Uxbridge *p417* . . . 01895 821818

Gary Johnson & Co
‡Middlesbrough *p315* . . . 01642 222834

Tim Johnson-Law
‡London EC4 *p46* . . . 020 7036 9120

Johnson McCabe
‡Brighton *p159* . . . 01273 822500

Malcolm Johnson & Co
‡Surbiton *p402* . . . 020 8399 5272

Marianne Johnson Family Law Practice
‡Skegness *p380* . . . 01754 812812

Pamela K Johnson Solicitor
‡Poulton-le-Fylde *p355* . . . 01253 812400

THE JOHNSON PARTNERSHIP
‡Nottingham *p337* . . . 0115 941 9141
Derby *p209* . . . 01332 370473
Mansfield *p311* . . . 01623 427575
Chesterfield *p192* . . . 01246 520930

RICHARD JOHNSON & PARTNERS
‡Hawes *p245* . . . 01969 667000
Leyburn *p283* . . . 01969 625577

Mark Johnson-Watts
‡Oxford *p343* . . . 01865 302800

Johnson Yates Limited
‡Manchester *p306* . . . 0161 835 9977

Johnsons Solicitors LLP
‡Reading *p361* . . . 0118 922 7220

Hilary Johnston
‡Beaconsfield *p129* . . . 01494 678230

Glynis A Johnstone
‡Oxted *p344* . . . 01883 716894

Jolliffe & Co
‡Chester *p190* . . . 01244 310022

Jonas Roy Bloom
‡Birmingham *p139* . . . 0121 212 4111

The Jonathan Morrissey Practice
‡Bournemouth *p152* . . . 01202 310999

Jones & Co
‡Retford *p363* . . . 01777 703827
Bawtry *p128* . . . 01302 710555

Jones & Duffin Solicitors LLP
‡Leicester *p280* . . . 0116 222 1555

Anthony Jones
‡Lancaster *p269* . . . 01524 221200

Barrie Y Jones & Co
‡Llantwit Major *p292* . . . 01446 793835 / 794542
Bridgend *p157* . . . 01656 657929

C J Jones Solicitors
‡London EC1 *p46* . . . 020 7253 7419

Claire Jones & Associates
‡Wakefield *p418* . . . 01924 290029

Jones Clarke Limited
‡St Albans *p390* . . . 01727 845101

Colin Jones
‡Barry *p126* . . . 01446 420043

Cyril Jones & Co
‡Wrexham *p443* . . . 01978 367830
Shotton *p379* . . . 01244 812109
Wrexham *p443* . . . 01978 263131

David Jones & Co
‡Llandudno *p291* . . . 01492 874336

David L Jones
‡Croydon *p205* . . . 020 8656 1915

David Morgan Jones
‡Colchester *p197* . . . 01206 766749

David Warren Jones
‡Birmingham *p139* . . . 0121 414 1949

Jones Day
‡London EC4 *p46* . . . 020 7039 5959

Diane Jones
‡Faringdon *p224* . . . 01367 240624

F Arthur Jones & Co
‡Exmouth *p222* . . . 01395 265668

Jones Fitzpatrick Solicitors
‡Manchester *p306* . . . 0161 225 2070

G Lloyd Jones & Co
‡Prestatyn *p356* . . . 01745 888666

Gary Jones Solicitors
‡Ammanford *p117* . . . 01269 597978

Geraint Jones & Co
‡Newtown p330 . . . . 01686 627935
Llandrindod Wells p291 . . . . . . 01597 822244

Gerald Jones & Co
‡Thetford p410 . . . . . . 01842 754466 / 754467

Glyn Jones & Co
‡Doncaster p212 . . . . 01302 340430

Gordon Jones & Co
‡Birmingham p139 . . . . 0121 453 8151

Jones Gough LLP Solicitors
‡Stockport p395 . . . . 0845 373 2585

Gwilym Jones & Davies with Bryant & Co
‡Mountain Ash p319 . . . . 01443 472206

HEK Jones Solicitors
‡Cardiff p179 . . . . 029 2044 0070

J R Jones
‡Birmingham p139 . . . . 0121 777 7864
‡London W5 p47 . . . . 020 8566 2595

Jeremy Jones
‡Crawley p202 . . . . 01342 713148

John Jones & Co
‡Pontefract p351 . . . . 01977 615522

Joseph A Jones & Co
‡Lancaster p269 . . . . 01524 63371

Kenneth Jones
‡Kidsgrove p266 . . . . 01782 771113

Jones Knowles Warburton
‡Stockport p395 . . . . 0161 474 1992

Jones Law Partnership
‡Marple p313 . . . . 0161 426 0030

M P Jones & Co
‡Plymouth p350 . . . . 01752 269007

Maria Jones
‡Bromley p166 . . . . 020 8290 5103

Mark Jones & Partners
‡Liverpool p289 . . . . 0151 286 9594
Birkenhead p134 . . . . 0151 647 9594

Michael A Jones & Co
‡Elmswell p218 . . . . 01359 242941

Michael Leighton Jones
‡Bargoed p123 . . . . 01443 830228
‡Hengoed p247 . . . . 01443 816400

Jones Myers LLP
‡Leeds p275 . . . . 0113 246 0055

Jones Nickolds
‡Beckenham p129 . . . . 020 3405 2300

Norman Jones - Personal Injury Specialists
‡Birkenhead p134 . . . . 0151 647 7001

P Lloyd Jones & Co
‡Mold p318 . . . . 01352 758533 / 758534
Buckley p168 . . . . . . 01244 547119 / 547110

The Jones Partnership
‡Mold p318 . . . . 01352 753388

Jones Robertson
‡Widnes p431 . . . . 0151 423 3661
Northwich p333 . . . . 01606 331188
Runcorn p369 . . . . 01928 711119

T G Jones & Associates
‡Swansea p405 . . . . 01792 469717

T Llewellyn Jones
‡Neath p320 . . . . 01639 643635
Swansea p405 . . . . 01639 842235

Terry Jones Solicitors & Advocates
‡Shrewsbury p379 . . . . 01743 285888
Newport p329 . . . . 01952 810307
Telford p409 . . . . 01952 297979

Thos R Jones & Son
‡Liverpool p289 . . . . 0151 928 0715

W T Jones
‡London WC1 p47 . . 020 7405 4631 / 7242 7767

Wynne D A Jones
‡Cardiff p179 . . . . 029 2056 9496

Jonro Solicitors
‡Milton Keynes p317 . . . . 07734 318890

Derek M Jordan
‡Settle p374 . . . . . . 01729 823589 / 823514
Bentham p131 . . . . 01524 261254

Janet L Jordan Solicitors
‡Cardiff p179 . . . . 029 2081 0439

Jordans
‡Dewsbury p210 . . . . 01924 457171
‡Rowley Regis p368 . . . . 0121 559 2922
Castleford p183 . . . . 01977 518778
Wakefield p418 . . . . 01924 387110

Joseph & Co Solicitors
‡Bradford p154 . . . . 01274 526940
‡London SW2 p47 . . . . 020 8671 1149

Joseph & White
‡Wembley p426 . . . . 020 8795 2020

Hugh Joseph Solicitors
‡Stockport p395 . . . . 0161 975 0600

Josephs Solicitors LLP
‡Blackburn p145 . . . . 01254 677099

Josiah Hincks
‡Leicester p280 . . . . 0116 255 1811
Blaby p145 . . . . 0116 264 3430
Coalville p196 . . . . 01530 835041

Josiah Lake Gardiner LLP
‡London EC1 p47 . . . . 020 7713 7011

Josiah-Lake Solicitors
‡London W1 p47 . . . . 020 7439 2900

Joves Solicitors
‡London SE13 p47 . . . . 020 8852 4544

Joy & Co
‡London E12 p47 . . . . 020 8514 8188

Joyce Legal
‡Birmingham p139 . . . . 0121 262 1800

W R Joyce Solicitors LLP
‡Cannock p176

Joyya Law Associates
‡Manchester p306 . . . . 0161 795 5566

Judge & Partners
‡Manchester p306 . . . . 0161 819 5300

Judge & Priestley
‡Bromley p166 . . . . 020 8290 0333

Judge Sykes Frixou
‡London WC2 p47 . . . . 020 7379 5114

Judkins Solicitors
‡Hertford p248 . . . . 01992 500456

Julius & Co Solicitors
‡London E11 p47 . . . . 020 8989 2929

Julius Ceasar Solicitors
‡London SE1 p47 . . . . 020 7708 8888

Juma Law Practice
‡Harrow p241 . . . . 020 8861 1199

Jump & Co Solicitors
‡Chichester p193 . . . . 01243 778508

Jung & Co
‡Southall p384 . . . . 020 8813 8996

Virginia Juras & Co
‡Bromley p166 . . . . 020 8402 9403

Jusmount & Co
‡Birmingham p139 . . . . 0121 773 8911

JusProwess Solicitors & Advocates
‡Hounslow p254 . . . . 020 8814 0208

Just Costs Solicitors
‡Manchester p306 . . . . 0161 435 6069
Chesterfield p192 . . . . 01246 267961
Leeds p275 . . . . 0113 366 3193
London WC2 p47 . . . . 020 7758 2155
Manchester p306 . . . . 0161 618 1095

Just Employment
‡Guildford p236 . . . . 01483 303636
Brighton p159 . . . . 01483 303636
Reading p361 . . . . 0118 963 9328

Just Immigration Solicitors
‡Guildford p236 . . . . 01483 243566

Just Law Solicitors
‡Prestwich p358 . . . . 0161 798 6611

Robert M Justice Tax & Trust Consultant
‡Reigate p363 . . . . 01737 222700

Jasvir Jutla & Co
‡Leicester p280 . . . . 0116 254 0809

K

K4 Law
‡Leicester p280 . . . . 0116 216 0510

K&L Gates LLP
‡London EC4 p47 . . . . 020 7648 9000

K&S @ Law Solicitors
‡London SE18 p47 . . . . 020 8331 0505

KBL Solicitors
‡Bolton p149 . . . . 01204 527777

KBS Solicitors
‡Bradford p154 . . . . 01274 725655

KC Law Chambers Solicitors
‡London E8 p47 . . . . 020 7254 3353

KCP Law
‡Hounslow p254 . . . . 020 8572 1212

KD Law Limited
‡London EC2 p47 . . . . 020 7947 4027

KD Solicitors
‡Gateshead p228 . . . . 0191 469 3322

K E Conveyancing
‡Brixham p166 . . . . 01803 882024

KG Solicitors Limited
‡Blackburn p145 . . . . 01245 685695

K H F Solicitors
‡Manchester p306 . . . . 0161 654 6300
‡Manchester p306 . . . . 0161 205 3909

KHF Solicitors Limited
‡Salford p370 . . . . 0161 832 6677

KJD
‡Stoke-on-Trent p398 . . . . 01782 202020

KK & Co Solicitors
‡Newcastle upon Tyne p325 . . . . 0191 273 5733

KKS Solicitors
‡Croydon p205 . . . . 020 8239 8585

KK Solicitors
‡London N12 p47 . . . . 020 8446 3240

KL Property Lawyers
‡West Malling p428 . . . . 01732 873041

KLS Law
‡Warrington p422 . . . . 01925 428198
London EC1 p47 . . . . 020 7553 7923

K Law Solicitors
‡Ascot p118 . . . . 01344 620344

KMA Solicitors
‡Ipswich p262 . . . . 01473 760046

KM Tamlin
‡Liverpool p289 . . . . 0151 428 2088

KPM Solicitors
‡London WC2 p47 . . . . 020 7404 1995

KSFLP
‡Taunton p408 . . . . 01823 256494

KSG Solicitors
‡Manchester p306 . . . . 01942 896426

KSH Law Firm
‡Newcastle upon Tyne p325 . . . . 0191 232 5232

KSL Solicitors
‡Harrow p241 . . . . 020 8206 2666

KS Law
‡Hounslow p254 . . . . 020 8569 6637

KSP Solicitors
‡Hatfield p244 . . . . 01707 264277

KSRI Solicitors
‡Borehamwood p150 . 020 8357 6871 / 8213 3073

KTP Solicitors
‡Bridgend p157 . . . . 01656 869002
Bridgend p157 . . . . 01656 655755
Pontypridd p352 . . . . 01443 485141
Porth p353 . . . . 01443 687222

KW Law
‡Warwick p422 . . . . 01926 498981

Kabir Ahmed & Co Solicitors
‡Bradford p154 . . . . 01274 739939

Kagan & Co
‡London SE4 p47 . . . . 020 8694 9969

Kagan Moss & Co
‡Teddington p409 . . . . 020 8977 6633

Kaihiva & Co
‡Ilford p260 . . . . 020 8553 0303

Jane Kaim-Caudle & Co
‡Watford p423 . . . . 01923 219061

Kaim Todner Ltd
‡London EC4 p47 . . . . 020 7353 6660
Ashford p119 . . . . 01233 662002
Islington N1 p47 . . . . 020 7700 0070
London SE17 p47 . . . . 020 7701 4747

Kaj & Co
‡London N7 p47 . . . . 020 7700 7826

Kalam Solicitors
‡London E1 p47 . . . . 020 7247 4884

Kalber Struckley & Co
‡London W1 p47 . . . . 020 7734 1102

Kale & Co
‡Bournemouth p152 . . . . 01202 552375
‡Wolverhampton p438 . . . . 01902 772500

Kalee Lau & Co
‡Penarth p345 . . . . 029 2071 1400

Chris Kallis Solicitors
‡Plymouth p350 . . . . 01752 225060

Kalra & Co
‡Waltham Forest E10 p48 . . . . . 020 8539 0123

Kaltons
‡London N1 p48 . . . . 020 7278 1817

Kamal Solicitors
‡Ilford p260 . . . . 020 8553 7733

Kamberley Solicitors
‡London N14 p48 . . . . 020 8886 9718

Kamrans Solicitors
‡Leeds p275 . . . . 0113 245 5000

Kanaga Solicitors
‡London SW19 p48 . . . . 020 8544 1100

Richard Kanani & Co
‡Hampton p238 . . . . 020 8941 8363

Peter Kandler & Co
‡London W10 p48 . . . . 020 8960 9222

H S Kang & Co
‡Barking p123 . . . . 020 8594 5465
Southall p384 . . . . 020 8571 7258

Kangs Solicitors
‡Birmingham p139 . . . . 0121 449 9888
Birmingham p139 . . . . 0121 784 3015
London EC4 p48 . . . . 020 7936 6396
Manchester p306 . . . . 0161 618 1098

Kapadia Solicitors
‡Bolton p149 . . . . 01204 655614

Kapadia Stuart Solicitors
‡London N1 p48 . . . . 0871 575 0522

Kapasi & Co Solicitors
‡Oldbury p340 . . . . 0121 544 8289

Kapoor & Co
‡Hounslow p254 . . . . 020 8538 2778

Stuart Karatas Solicitors
‡London E8 p48 . . . . 020 7923 8600
‡London N9 p48 . . . . 020 8887 1360

Karim & Co
‡Leeds p275 . . . . 0113 249 1662

Sajjad Karim Solicitors
‡Manchester p306 . . . . 0161 860 7572

Karis Spyris LLP
‡Enfield p219 . . . . 020 8443 7000

P Karma & Co
‡London NW6 p48 . . . . 020 7624 8814

Karslakes Solicitors Limited
‡Guildford p236 . . . . 01483 454242

Kash Tutter & Co
‡Derby p209 . . . . 01332 272727

Kaslers Solicitors LLP
‡West Malling p428 . . . . 0845 270 2511
London E14 p48 . . . . 020 7712 1751

Kataria Solicitors
‡Birmingham p139 . . . . 0121 554 5404

KattenMuchinRosenmanCornish LLP
‡London EC2 p48 . . . . 020 7776 7620

Kaufmanlegal
‡Manchester p306 . . . . 0161 205 3955

Kauldhar & Co
‡Birmingham p139 . . . . 0121 358 6868

Kaura & Co
‡London N12 p48 . . . . 020 8445 4069

Kavanagh & Co
‡Eckington p216 . . . . 01246 432349

Kaye & Co
‡Pinner p349 . . . . 020 8428 0010

D C Kaye & Co
‡Great Missenden p234 . 01494 864650 / 862226
Wendover p427 . . . . 01296 620443

Laurence Kaye Solicitors
‡Radlett p358 . . . . 01923 352117

Leon Kaye Solicitors
‡London SW11 p48 . . . . 020 7228 2020

Kayes Solicitors
‡Pudsey p358 . . . . 0113 290 0380
Portishead p354 . . . . 01275 399933

Keane & Co
‡Aldeburgh p115 . . . . 01728 453595

Keaney Whitehead Partnership LLP (KWP)
‡Liverpool p289 . . . . 0151 255 1790

Yvonne Kearney
‡Witney p436 . . . . 01993 776018

Kearneys
‡Oakham p340 . . . . 01572 823605

Kearns & Co
‡Swansea p405 . . . . 01792 463111

Alistair Keeble
‡Clacton-on-Sea p195 . . . . 01255 818900

Keelers
‡Kenilworth p264 . . . . 01926 853555

Keelys LLP
‡Lichfield p284 . . . . 01543 420000
London EC2 p48 . . . . 020 7422 8686

Andrew Keen & Co
‡London E18 p48 . . . . 020 8989 3123

Andrew Keenan & Co
‡London SE20 p48 . . . . 020 8659 0332

Keene & Kelly
‡Mold p318 . . . . 01352 753882

Keene Marsland
‡Tunbridge Wells p415 . . . . 01892 526442

Keepers Legal LLP
‡Gillingham p229 . . . . 0845 609 9069

Keeping & Co
‡Alton p116 . . . . 01420 85221

Keer-Keer & Co
‡Hemel Hempstead p246 . 01442 216755 / 216756

The Keith Jones Partnership
‡Birkenhead p134 . . . . 0151 650 6830

Lindsay J Keith Solicitor
‡Hassocks p243 . . . . 01273 832444

Kelcey & Hall
‡Bristol p163 . . . . 0117 927 9604

Kellock & Johnson
‡Totnes p413 . . . . 01803 862414
Newton Abbot p329 . . . . 01626 335454

Kellocks
‡Preston p357 . . . . 01772 828382

Kelly & Co
‡Leeds p275 . . . . 0113 244 2113

Kelly & Co Solicitors
‡Leicester p280 . . . . 0116 200 1998

Michael Kelly & Co
‡Hanham p238 . . . . 0117 967 6559

Noel Kelly Solicitor
‡Coventry p200 . . . . 024 7671 5720

Shirley Kelly Solicitors
‡Manchester p306 . . . . 0161 248 5999

Kellys
‡Brighton p160 . . . . 01273 674898

Kellys Solicitors
‡Robertsbridge p365 . . . . 01424 838151

Kelsall & Company
‡Chester p190 . . . . 01244 320610

David Keltie Associates
‡London EC4 p48 . . . . 020 7329 8888

Kemi Law Chambers
‡London NW10 p48 . . . . 020 8965 6000

J A Kemp & Co
‡London WC1 *p48* 020 7405 3292

Kemp Little LLP
‡London EC2 *p48* 020 7600 8080

Richard P Kemp BA Solicitor
‡Martock *p313* 01935 822572

Kempner & Partners
‡Leeds *p275* 0113 393 1921

Kemps Solicitors
‡Oldham *p340* 0161 633 0555
Hyde *p259* 0161 366 8181

Caroline Kemsley-Pein
‡Market Harborough *p312* 01858 525639

Ken'D Solicitors
‡London NW2 *p48* 020 8438 6666

Timothy Kench & Co
‡Great Missenden *p234* 01494 864153

Kendall & Davies
‡Bourton-on-the-Water *p153* 01451 820277
Burford *p168* 01993 822025
Moreton-in-Marsh *p319* 01608 650312
Stow-on-the-Wold *p399* 01451 830295

Kennards Wells
‡London E11 *p48* 020 8539 8338
Epping *p219* 01992 570505
Redbridge *p362* 020 8550 5103

Howard Kennedy LLP
‡London W1 *p48* 020 7636 1616

J E Kennedy & Co
‡Harrow *p241* 020 8864 3056

John Kennedy & Co
Westminster SW1 *p49* 020 7222 0441

Kennedys
‡London EC3 *p49* 020 7667 9667
Birmingham *p139* 0121 214 8000
Cambridge *p174* 01223 533060
Chelmsford *p186* 0845 838 4800
Maidstone *p299* 01622 625625
Manchester *p306* 0161 829 2599
Sheffield *p376* 0114 253 2000
Taunton *p408* 01823 692600

Kenneth Elliott & Rowe
‡Romford *p366* 01708 757575

Duncan Kenney
‡Worcester *p440* 01905 25221

Kenny Solicitors
‡Arundel *p118* 01903 331021
‡Chichester *p193* 01243 887880

Kensington Law Chambers
‡London W14 *p49* 020 7739 1032

Kensington Solicitors
‡London SW15 *p49* 020 8488 5798
‡London WC1 *p49* 07931 820928

Kent & Co Solicitors
‡Norwich *p334* 01493 751351

John Kent Solicitor and Licensing Consultant
‡Nottingham *p338* 0115 993 4285

Kent Solicitors
‡London N9 *p49* 020 8805 9735

Kenwright & Lynch
‡Wandsworth SW17 *p49* 020 8767 1211

Kenwright Walker Wyllie
‡East Molesey *p215* 020 8979 1131

Kenyon Son & Craddock
‡Doncaster *p212* 01405 813108
Goole *p231* 01405 720850

A Patrick Keogh
‡London N10 *p49* 020 8883 4412

Keogh Caisley
‡Tunbridge Wells *p415* 01892 548411

Keoghs and Nicholls, Lindsell & Harris
‡Altrincham *p116* 0161 928 9321

Keoghs LLP
‡Bolton *p149* 01204 677000
Coventry *p200* 024 7665 8200

Kepier Law
‡Durham *p214* 0191 374 1402

Keppe & Partners Solicitors
‡Twickenham *p416* 020 8891 4488

Keppe Rofer
‡Brecon *p156* 01874 624627

Kerman & Co LLP
‡London WC2 *p49* 020 7539 7272

Kerry Hilton Wilson Solicitor
‡Andover *p118* 01264 738788

Kerseys
‡Ipswich *p262* 01473 213311

Kerwoods
‡Redditch *p362* 01527 584444

Kevill Kirkham & Grayson
‡Chorley *p194* . . . . . . .01257 263676 / 269212

Kevills
‡Chorley *p194* 01257 265711

Kevin Brown Solicitor
‡Poole *p353* . . . . 01202 620907 / 07977 191059

Kew Law LLP
‡Braintree *p155* 01376 550073
‡Colchester *p197* 01206 564546

‡Maldon *p299* 01621 843056
‡Witham *p436* 01376 500049

Key2Law LLP
‡Ewell *p220* 020 8393 0941
London WC1 *p49* 020 7404 2121

Christopher Key & Co
‡Boscastle *p150* 01840 250200

Keypoint Law LLP
‡Doncaster *p212* 01302 329655

Keys Solicitors
‡Sevenoaks *p374* 01732 823110

Keystone Law
‡London SW6 *p49* 020 7152 6550

Khakhar & Co
‡Ilford *p260* 020 8478 9881

Khalaf & Co
‡Lowestoft *p294* 0845 601 9193

Iqbal Khalil & Co
‡Peterborough *p347* 01733 552772

A Zeb Khan Solicitors
‡Birmingham *p139* 0121 327 5999

Khan & Co
‡Smethwick *p382* 0121 565 4292
‡Wolverhampton *p438* 01902 424477

Khan & Partners
‡London E12 *p49* 020 8470 6969

Azam Khan & Co Solicitors
‡London SW16 *p49* 020 8769 3320

Christian Khan Solicitors
‡London WC1 *p49* 020 7631 9500

Imran Khan & Partners
‡London WC1 *p49* 020 7404 3004

The Khan Partnership LLP
‡London WC1 *p49* 020 7612 2530

Khan Solicitors
‡Bradford *p154* 01274 301999
‡Manchester *p306* 0161 256 2100
‡Reading *p361* 0118 958 3615

Khans
‡Ilford *p260* 020 8553 5995

Khatry Solicitors
‡London W1 *p49* 020 7016 8860

Khattak Solicitors
‡London W7 *p49* 020 8579 7976
‡Whitefield *p430* 0161 796 5800

Kher Solicitors
‡Leeds *p275* 01422 836622

Khindria & Co
‡London WC1 *p49* 020 7430 0556

Khirri Solicitors
‡West Bromwich *p427* 0121 500 4020

T A Khoo Solicitors
‡Birmingham *p139* 0121 666 7088 / 0560 156 7863

A K Khullar & Co
‡Hounslow *p254* 020 8569 4488

Kidd & Co
‡Maidenhead *p298* 01628 762762

Kidd & Spoor
‡Whitley Bay *p431* 0191 297 0011
Newcastle upon Tyne *p325* 0191 273 9217

Kidd Rapinet
‡London WC2 *p49* 020 7205 2115
Aylesbury *p121* 0845 017 9616
Farnham *p225* 0845 017 9609
High Wycombe *p250* 0845 017 9607
Maidenhead *p298* 0845 017 9608
Reading *p361* 0845 017 8750
Slough *p382* 0845 017 9638

Kidd Spoor Taylor
‡North Shields *p330* 0191 257 3101

Kidson Bray & Lawson
‡Hindhead *p251* 01428 605222
London SE11 *p49* 020 7582 0111

Kidwells
‡Hereford *p248* 01432 278179

Kieran & Co
‡Worcester *p440* 01905 28635

KieranClarkeGreen
‡Chesterfield *p192* 01246 211006
Chesterfield *p192* . . . . .01246 230359 / 234937
Staveley *p394* 01246 280099

Kiers & Co
‡London WC1 *p49* 020 7729 9497

Andrew J Kilby
‡Gravesend *p233* 01474 355758

Kilic Has & Onay LLP
‡London N16 *p49* 020 7254 7111

Kilpatrick & Co
‡Burnham *p168* 07834 258605

Kilroys
‡Birmingham *p139* 0121 270 1002

Kimbells LLP
‡Milton Keynes *p317* 01908 668555

Kimberly Wayne & Diamond Solicitors
‡London SE2 *p49* 020 8310 0738
London SE18 *p49* 020 8317 0896

Kinas Solicitors
‡London N1 *p49* 020 7249 0907

King & Co
‡Altrincham *p116* 0161 924 2274
‡Cambridge *p175* . . . . .01223 365432 / 566038
Cambridge *p175* 01954 251818

King & Spalding International LLP
‡London EC2 *p49* 020 7551 7500

Anthony King & Co
‡Basildon *p126* 01268 240400

King Davies & Partners
‡Maesteg *p298* 01656 732911

James King
‡Ryde *p369* 01983 564134

King Lawes Legal
‡St Neots *p392* 01480 860299

King Partners Solicitors
‡London N16 *p49* 020 8802 9592
‡Milton Keynes *p317* 01908 643122

King Prior Macdonald Bridge
‡Gravesend *p233* 01474 325678
Rochester *p366* 01634 272720

Rodney King & Partners
‡Bristol *p163* 0117 926 5201

King Solicitors
‡Northampton *p332* 01604 491939
‡Southall *p384* 020 8571 2239

King Street Solicitors
‡Wakefield *p418* 01924 332395

Sylvia King
‡Brighton *p160* 01273 573837

Kingfields Solicitors
‡London W1 *p49* 0845 459 0007

Kings Solicitors
‡Harrow *p241* 020 8901 7585
‡Ivybridge *p263* 01752 895252
‡Minehead *p317* 01643 709600

Kings Solicitors Practice
‡Huddersfield *p256* 01484 602218

Kingscourt Solicitors
‡London SW6 *p49* 020 8690 5999

Kingsfords
‡Ashford *p119* 01233 624545
Ashford *p119* 01233 665544

Peter Kingshill & Co
‡Worthing *p442* 01903 218210

Kingsley Brookes
‡Huddersfield *p256* 01484 302800

Kingsley David Solicitors Limited
‡Milton Keynes *p317* 01908 325555

Kingsley Knight
‡Harrow *p242* 020 8931 3441

Kingsley Napley
‡London EC1 *p50* 020 7814 1200

Kingsley Rose Solicitors
‡Rhyl *p363* 01745 355535

Kingsley Smith Solicitors LLP
‡Chatham *p185* 01634 811118

Andrew Kingston & Co
‡Hull *p257* 01482 216217

Kingstons Solicitors
‡London SW19 *p50* 020 8540 0468
‡Newcastle upon Tyne *p325* . . . 0191 226 0333

Kingswell Berney
‡Gosport *p232* 023 9258 2211

Kingswell Watts
‡Dewsbury *p210* 01924 461236

Kingswood Legal Limited
‡Birmingham *p140* 0121 772 7779

Kinread Solicitors
‡Ripon *p365* 01765 607200

Kinsey & Co Solicitors
‡Baildon *p121* 01274 589900

Kinsey-Jones Solicitors
‡Cardiff *p179* 0560 126 7303

Kirby & Co
‡London SW19 *p50* 020 8545 7171

Davina Kirby Solicitor
‡Chesham *p189* 01494 764646

J F Kirby
‡Pershore *p346* 01386 751760

Michael Kirby Solicitors
‡York *p445* 01904 415932

Kirby Sheppard
‡Kingswood *p268* 0845 840 0045
Bristol *p163* 0845 840 0045
Thornbury *p411* 0845 840 0045

Kirbys
‡Harrogate *p240* 01423 542000

Kirbys Solicitors
‡Newcastle upon Tyne *p325* 01661 867010

Charles Kirit & Co
‡London E15 *p50* 020 8221 0827

Kirk & Partners
‡London SE9 *p50* 020 8850 2484

Kirkham Edwards Solicitors
‡Warrington *p422* 01925 414614

John Kirkhope & Co
‡Weston-super-Mare *p429* 01934 644647

Kirkland & Ellis International LLP
‡London EC3 *p50* 020 7469 2000

Kirkland & Lane
‡Southwell *p389* . . . . . .01636 813128 / 812180

Kirklands
‡Romsey *p366* 01794 513466
Totton *p413* 023 8066 3313

Kirkup Lascelles & Creed
Peterlee *p347* 0191 586 8646

Kirkwoods
‡Stanmore *p394* 020 8954 8555

M C Kirton & Co
‡London W4 *p50* 020 8987 8880

Kirwans
‡Birkenhead *p134* 0151 608 9078
Liverpool *p289* 0151 229 5600
Moreton *p319* 0151 677 3433

Kitching Kneale & Co
‡Great Ayton *p233* 01642 723713

Kitching Walker
‡Kirkbymoorside *p268* 01751 431237
‡York *p445* 01493 772107

Kite Griffin
‡Bracknell *p153* 01344 425637

Kiteleys Solicitors Limited
‡Bournemouth *p152* 01202 299992
Southampton *p386* 023 8090 9091

Kitson & Trotman
‡Beaminster *p129* 01308 862313
Bridport *p158* 01308 427436
Lyme Regis *p296* 01297 442580

Kitsons LLP
‡Torquay *p413* 01803 202020
Exeter *p221* 01392 455555
Newton Abbot *p329* 01626 203366
Plymouth *p350* 01752 603040

Jack Klar Solicitors
‡Halesowen *p237* 0121 561 5958

Klein Solicitors
‡London W1 *p50* 020 7958 9080

Klien & Co
‡Salford *p370* 0161 708 0815

Klimt & Co
‡Westminster W1 *p50* 020 7486 4432

Kloosmans
‡Southend-on-Sea *p387* 01702 600090

Richard J Knaggs & Co
‡Redcar *p362* 01642 487011

Knapman & Co
‡Paignton *p345* 01803 522700

Jane Kneil & Co
‡Umberleigh *p416* 01769 560557

Belinda Knight Solicitor
‡Reading *p361* 0118 900 1712

Knight Mcgoldrick Solicitors
‡Chester *p190* 01244 349710

Knight Polson
Fareham *p224* 01329 339455
Winchester *p434* 01962 706243

Knight Polson Solicitors
‡Eastleigh *p216* 023 8064 4822

Richard Knight & Co
‡Syston *p407* 0116 260 0021

Knight-Webb Solicitors
‡London SE24 *p50* 020 7207 6195

Knights
‡London W9 *p50* 020 8964 1212
‡Tunbridge Wells *p415* 01892 537311

Knights Solicitors LLP
‡Newcastle under Lyme *p323* . . . 01782 619225
Alderley Edge *p115* 01625 586686
Cheltenham *p188* 01242 524654

Knipe Woodhouse-Smith
‡Chalfont St Peter *p184* . .01753 887877 / 889149

Knocker & Foskett
‡Sevenoaks *p374* 01732 459931

R E Knodt Solicitor
‡Benfleet *p131* 01268 566465

Knowles & Co Solicitors
‡Hyde *p259* 0161 366 8200

Knowles Benning
‡Luton *p295* 01582 798000
Dunstable *p214* 01582 667711
Shefford *p377* 01462 814824

Jennifer Knowles Solicitors
‡Carnforth *p183* 01524 241417

Knowles Solicitors
‡Liverpool *p289* 0870 753 0850
‡London WC2 *p50* 0870 753 0852

Knox Insolvency
‡Llandudno *p291* 0845 387 0105

Brian Koffman & Co
‡Manchester *p306* 0161 832 3852

Luke Kore Solicitors
‡London SE17 *p50* 020 7277 3880

Kostick Hanan Herskovic LLP
‡London N16 *p50* 020 8800 8866

Kothala & Co
‡Wembley *p426* 020 8902 4932

Leslie Kovacs
‡London EC1 *p50* 020 7251 8529

Kramer & Co
‡London N3 *p50* 020 8346 8070

Stephen Krebs & Co
‡Oldham *p340* 0161 652 0507

Krells
‡Withington *p436* 0161 445 8649

Kremers Solicitors Limited
‡Gosport *p232* 0845 021 2222

D M Krempel
‡Buntingford *p168* 01763 288569

Kris Sen Solicitors
‡London SW16 *p50* 020 8769 7125

Krish Ratna
‡Southall *p384* 020 8574 6303

Krish Solicitors
‡Southall *p384* 020 8893 6661

Kromann Reumert
‡London EC2 *p50* 020 7920 3030

Kruzins
‡Cardiff *p179* 029 2039 0101

Kuddus Solicitors
‡London E1 *p50* 020 7247 5476

Kuddus Solicitors (UK) Ltd
‡London E8 *p50* 020 7241 0560

Kuit Steinart Levy
‡Manchester *p306* 0161 832 3434

N S Kumar
‡Ilford *p260* 020 8554 3393

Kumari-Banga Solicitors
‡Wolverhampton *p438* 01902 423651

Kundert & Co
‡Coventry *p200* 024 7622 7741
Coventry *p200* 024 7668 4928

Robert Kyle & Co
‡Marlow *p313* 01628 475751

Adonis Kyriakides & Co
‡Westminster W2 *p50* 020 7229 3800

Kyriakides & Braier
‡London W1 *p50* 020 7637 3289

L

LB & Co Solicitors
‡London E1 *p50* 020 7655 4941

LDJ Solicitors
‡Nuneaton *p339* 024 7674 5000
Hinckley *p250* 01455 637030

LD Law
‡Harlow *p239* 01279 441266
Norwich *p334*

LE Law Solicitors
‡Loughton *p294* 020 8508 4691

LGFL LLP
‡Yateley *p443* 01252 877327

LG Lawyers
‡London SE1 *p50* 020 7379 0000

LGP Solicitors
‡Marlow *p313* 01628 404620

Lh Legal Limited
‡London NW11 *p51* 020 8458 4415

L J Law
‡Cwmbran *p206* 01633 626977

LK Baltica Solicitors
‡London W1 *p51* 020 7935 2960

LKNY Law
‡London W6 *p51* . 07931 516912 / 020 8735 6500

LKS Employment Law
‡Manchester *p306* 0161 434 6446

LK Solicitors
‡Orpington *p342* 01689 878141

LLC Law
‡London W14 *p51* 020 7471 0371

LL Law LLP
‡London E14 *p51* 020 7987 7198

LM Solicitors
‡Rugby *p368* 01788 550016

LPS Solicitors Limited
‡Bradford *p154* 01274 392007

L R P Solicitors
‡Harrow *p242* 020 8581 1292

LR Solicitors
‡Wakefield *p418* 01924 257896

LSG Solicitors
‡London W1 *p51* 020 7851 0100

LT Law
‡London W1 *p51* 020 7025 8332

LXL Limited
‡Richmond upon Thames *p364* . . 020 8439 8810

Labrums
‡St Albans *p390* 01727 858807

Simon Lacey Law Associates
‡Weymouth *p430* 01305 777711

Laceys
‡Bournemouth *p152* 01202 557256
Bournemouth *p152* 01202 755980
Poole *p353* 01202 743286

David Lacide & Co
‡Skelmersdale *p381* 01695 722444

Ladas & Parry
‡London EC4 *p51* 020 7242 5566

B D Laddie
‡Westminster SW1 *p51* 020 7963 8585

Laderman & Co
‡Redbridge E18 *p51* 020 8530 7319

Ladermans
‡London NW4 *p51* 020 8203 6136

Lages & Co
‡Wadhurst *p418* 01892 784419

David Lago & Co Solicitors and Mediators
‡Crewe *p203* 01270 504850

Lahiff & Co
‡Greenwich SE18 *p51* 020 8855 5656

Laing & Co
‡London N6 *p51* 020 8341 1147

Lake Jackson
‡London E1 *p51* 020 7490 3356
Norwich *p334* 01603 715519

Lake Legal LLP
‡Leeds *p275* 0845 190 0001

Lakhani & Co
‡Brent NW9 *p51* 020 8204 7100

Sushma Lal
‡Oldham *p340* 0161 627 2479

Lam & Meerabux Solicitors
‡Croydon *p205* 020 8253 0099

Lamb & Co
‡Wirral *p435* 0808 252 8001

Lamb & Holmes
‡Kettering *p265* 01536 513195
Corby *p199* 01536 745168

Lamb & Kavanagh
‡Camden NW1 *p51* 020 7209 2481

Lamb & Smart
‡New Milton *p321* 01425 613434

Lamb Brooks LLP
‡Basingstoke *p126* 01256 844888

Stephen J Lamb
‡Southwark SE24 *p51* 020 7738 6838

Lambe Corner
‡Hereford *p248* 01432 355301

Lambert Pugh
‡Norwich *p334* 01603 462796

Lambert Taylor & Gregory
‡Gateshead *p228* 0191 477 0616

Lamberts
‡Sevenoaks *p374* 01732 460565
Paddock Wood *p344* 01892 833456

Lampier & Co
‡London EC4 *p51* 020 7694 8666

Lampkin & Co
‡Deeside *p208* 01244 525725

Lamport Bassitt
‡Southampton *p386* 023 8083 7777
Reading *p361* 0845 077 6600

Lancaster Parr
‡Shepton Mallet *p378*
. . . . 01749 850276 / 07976 710623

Lancasters
‡Bridlington *p158* 01262 602401
‡Epsom *p219* 01372 724931
‡London W4 *p51* 020 8742 1314

Bruce Lance & Co
‡High Wycombe *p250* 01494 450494
Poole *p353* 01202 679379

Land Law LLP
‡Altrincham *p116* 0161 928 8383

Landau & Cohen
‡Elstree *p218* 0845 331 2477

H Landau & Co
‡Edgware *p217* 020 8959 6991

Landau Zeffertt Weir
‡London SE1 *p51* 020 7357 9494

Landmark Solicitors LLP
‡Leeds *p275* 0113 244 0591

Landons
‡Brentwood *p156* 01277 210021

Elizabeth Landy
‡Hove *p255* 01273 415264

Lane & Co
‡Cheltenham *p188* . . . . 01242 524785 / 222421
‡Walsall *p420* 01922 721259

Lane Graham Solicitors
‡London E14 *p51* 020 7712 1715

J S Lane & Co
‡Bushey *p172* 020 8950 1782

Kevin Lane & Co
‡Port Talbot *p353* 01639 893700

Lane-Smith & Shindler LLP
‡Manchester *p306* 0845 658 4848

Jon Lang
‡London EC3 *p51* 020 7868 1685

Dale Langley & Co
‡London EC3 *p51* 020 7464 8433
London E14 *p51* 020 7464 8433

Huw Langley
‡Weston-super-Mare *p429* 07718 354074

Langley Wellington
‡Gloucester *p230* 01452 521286
Churchdown *p195* 01452 856846

Langleys
‡Lincoln *p284* 01522 888555
Newark *p322* 01636 706508
York *p445* 01904 610886

Sharon Langridge Employment Lawyers
‡Newcastle upon Tyne *p325* 0191 222 1221

Lansbury Worthington
‡London W6 *p51* 020 8563 9797

Lansdale & Holdsworth
‡Bolton *p149* 01204 491111

Lansdowne & Co
‡Leeds *p275* 0113 243 9270

Lansdowne Solicitors
‡London N5 *p51* 020 7226 7825

Lanyon Bowdler LLP
‡Shrewsbury *p379* 01743 280280
Hereford *p248* 01432 378379
Ludlow *p294* 01584 872333
Oswestry *p342* 01691 652241
Oswestry *p342*
Telford *p409* 01952 291222
Wellington *p425* 01952 244721

Larby Williams with Gwyn & Gwyn
‡Cowbridge *p201* 01446 775535

Larcomes LLP
‡Portsmouth *p354* 023 9266 1531
Waterlooville *p423* 023 9224 6666

Large & Gibson
‡Southsea *p388* 023 9229 6296

Largo Law
‡Wakefield *p418* 01924 886555

Larken & Co
‡Newark *p322* 01636 703333

Larkin & James
‡West Byfleet *p427* 01932 355433

Samuel L Larye & Co
‡Brentford *p156* 020 8568 7022

Last Cawthra Feather LLP
‡Bradford *p154* 01274 848800
Baildon *p121* 01274 583106
Ilkley *p261* 01943 601020
Leeds *p275* 0113 244 0876
Shipley *p378* 01274 585459

Latham & Co
‡Melton Mowbray *p314* 01664 563012
Loughborough *p293* 01509 238822

Latham & Watkins LLP
‡London EC2 *p51* 020 7710 1000

John Latham & Co
‡Swindon *p406* 01793 430133

Lathar Solicitors
‡Birmingham *p140* 0121 454 2625

Latif Adams Solicitors
‡Southall *p384* 020 8574 2255

Latif Solicitors
‡Newcastle upon Tyne *p325* 0191 230 0646

LATIMER HINKS
‡Darlington *p206* 01325 341500

Latimer Lee LLP
‡Prestwich *p358* 0161 798 9000
Bolton *p149* 0161 798 9000
Bury *p171* 0871 128 9000
Heywood *p249* 01706 628008

Latitude Law
‡Manchester *p306* 0161 234 6800

Lattey & Dawe
‡London EC2 *p51* 020 7623 2345

Laurel & Co
‡London SE9 *p51* 020 8331 6655

L G Laurella
‡Ealing W5 *p51* 020 8840 5761

Laven Legal Services Limited
‡London SW7 *p51* 020 7594 4973

Lavery Haynes
‡London NW3 *p51* 020 7435 7441

Lavin Copitch
‡Manchester *p306* 0161 223 5484
Altrincham *p116* 0161 941 6462

Law Abroad
‡Hemel Hempstead *p247* 0800 298 4298

Law & Lawyers
‡London E12 *p51* . 07793 452184 / 020 8586 5657

Law Brand
‡Stevenage *p395* 01438 367373
Hitchin *p251* 01462 457167

Law Connect
‡Birmingham *p140* 0845 833 6690

The Law Department
‡London NW10 *p51* 020 7898 0585

Law Express
‡Bristol *p163* 01275 378700

Law Firm Ltd
‡London W1 *p51* 020 7907 1460

Law Hurst & Taylor
‡Westcliff-on-Sea *p428* 01702 337864

Law:Matix
‡Macclesfield *p297* 01625 828877

The Law Office of Richard Stephens
‡London WC2 *p51* 020 7470 8767

Law Partners Solicitors Ltd
‡London EC1 *p51* 0870 600 9444

The Law Partnership
‡Coventry *p200* 024 7668 7211
‡Harrow *p242* 020 8416 7004

The Law Practice
‡Canterbury *p177* 01227 733595
‡Llanelli *p292* 0800 612 9318

The Law Practice (UK) Limited
‡Birmingham *p140* 0121 778 2371

Law Works Leagal Services Limited
‡London SW1 *p51* 020 7233 7566

Lawana & Co Solicitors
‡London SE13 *p51* 020 8461 0700

Lawbridge Solicitors
‡Sidcup *p380* 020 8308 3610

Lawbyweb Solicitors
‡Chichester *p193* 01243 773072

Lawcomm Solicitors
‡Fareham *p224* 01489 864100

Lawdit Solicitors
‡Sandown *p372* 01983 402294
‡Southampton *p386* 023 8023 5979

Lawford Davies Denoon
‡London EC1 *p51* 020 8616 1887

Lawmen Solicitors
‡Hayes *p245* 020 8561 6090

Lawmobility
‡Worthing *p442* 01903 500896

Lawrance & Holder
‡Potters Bar *p355* 01707 645317

Lawrence & Associates
‡London SE5 *p52* 020 7326 3941

Lawrence & Co
‡London W9 *p52* 020 7266 4333

H Lawrence & Co
‡London N6 *p52* . . . 020 7482 2613 / 7482 4212

Lawrence Hamblin
‡Beaconsfield *p129* 01494 683610

Lawrence Hamblin QualitySolicitors
‡High Wycombe *p250* 01494 838780

J C Lawrence & Co
‡Daventry *p207* 07837 287747

Lawrence Law
‡London SW15 *p52* 020 8788 0055

P J Lawrence Solicitor
‡York *p445* 01653 627180

Patrick Lawrence
‡Gravesend *p233* 01474 356441

Lawrence-Reynolds Solicitors
‡Birmingham *p140*. 0121 784 5321 / 07983 377712

Lawrences
‡Wellingborough *p424* 01933 442324

Lawrenson Solicitors
‡Broadstone *p166* 01202 657058

David Laws Solicitor
‡Norwich *p334* . . . 01603 871126 / 07933 149810

Lawsmiths
‡Sale *p370* 0161 972 7700

Lawsolve LLP
‡Cambridge *p175* 01223 412333

Lawson & Co
‡Ingatestone *p261* 01277 354515

Lawson & Thompson
‡Ashington *p119* 01670 813588
Bedlington *p130* 01670 530700
Blyth *p148* 01670 361959

Lawson Anthony Solicitors
‡Marlow *p313* 01628 472330

Lawson Coppock & Hart
‡Manchester *p306* 0161 832 5944

David V Lawson Solicitors
‡Ilford *p260* 020 8554 8848

Lawson George
‡London N14 *p52* 020 8920 3131

Lawson Lewis & Co
‡Eastbourne *p215* 01323 720142
Peacehaven *p345* 01273 582680

Lawson Taylor LLP
‡Burnley *p169* 01282 477588

Lawson Turner & Gilbert
‡London SE16 *p52* 020 7394 1311
Dover *p213* 01304 226338

Lawson West Solicitors Limited
‡Leicester *p280* 0116 212 1000
Market Harborough *p312* 01858 445480
Wigston *p432* 0116 212 1080

Lawson-Cruttenden & Co
‡London WC1 *p52* 020 7405 0833

Lawsons Solicitors
‡Wakefield *p418* 01324 202000

Owen Lawton
‡Plymouth *p350* 01752 201169

Lawtons Solicitors
‡Bedford p130 . . . . 01525 717500
‡Luton p295 . . . . 01582 410111

Lawtons Solicitors Limited
‡Bedford p130 . . . . 01234 356235

Lawvue Solicitors
‡Isleworth p263 . . . . 020 8568 6607

Lawyer In a Hard Hat Limited
‡Basingstoke p127 . . . . 01256 889840

Lawyers 4 IT
‡Coventry p200 . . . . 07747 806651

Lax & Co LLP
‡London EC3 p52 . . . . 020 7623 9432

Karen Layland Solicitors
‡Solihull p382 . . . . 0800 328 8841

Layton & Co
‡Haverfordwest p244 . . . . 01437 766671

Layton-Law.com
‡Blackpool p146 . . . . 01253 399311

Robert Layton & Co
‡London W3 p52 . . . . 020 8993 5208

Laytons
‡London EC4 p52 . . . . 020 7842 8000
Guildford p236 . . . . 01483 407000
Manchester p306 . . . . 0161 834 2100

Layzell Solicitors Limited
‡Brockenhurst p166 . . . . 01590 623770
‡Dorchester p212 . . . . 01305 264657

Layzells
‡London N10 p52 . . . . 020 8444 0202

J S Lazar
‡London E12 p52 . . . . 020 8553 5301

Lea & Co
‡Stockport p396 . . . . 0161 480 6691

Anthony Lea & Co
‡Sutton Coldfield p403 . . . . 0121 382 5550

Leach Rawlence & Hart
‡Croydon p205 . . . . 020 8680 5850

Leadbeater & Kay
‡Stoke-on-Trent p398 . . . . 01782 201933

Leader Van Bosch Solicitors
‡Ashford p119 . . . . 01233 622321

Brian Leah Employment Law Solicitor
‡Penrith p346 . . . . 01769 88640

Anita Leaker Solicitor
‡Carlisle p182 . . . . 01228 521383

Lean & Co
‡Fleet p226 . . . . 01252 816757

Karina Leapman & Co
‡London NW6 p52 . . . . 020 7794 7741

Learmond Criqui Sokel
‡London NW3 p52 . . . . 020 7431 0707

Leathems Solicitors
‡Whaley Bridge p430 . . . . 01663 733431

Leathes Prior
‡Norwich p334 . . . . 01603 610911

Geoffrey Leaver Solicitors LLP
‡Milton Keynes p317 . . . . 01908 692769

Lebreton Towell Solicitor
‡Tarporley p408 . . . . 01829 751459

Michael A Leckey
‡Lytham p297 . . . . 01253 726100

Lecote Solicitors
‡London W1 p52 . . . . 07870 164686

Alfred Ledger & Sons
‡Rochdale p365 . . . . 01706 645910

Ledgisters
‡London W6 p52 . . . . 020 8746 1122

Lee & Company
‡Camberley p173 . . . . 01276 20911

Lee & Kan
‡London W1 p52 . . . . 020 7287 8888

Lee & Priestley LLP
‡Leeds p275 . . . . 0845 129 2300

Lee & Tallamy Solicitors
‡Ely p218 . . . . 01353 722723

Lee & Thompson
‡London W1 p52 . . . . 020 7935 4665

Andrew Lee & Co
‡Maidstone p299 . . . . 01622 750101

Lee Associates
Wandsworth SW17 p52 . . . . 020 8682 9797

Lee Bolton Monier-Williams
‡Westminster SW1 p52 . . . . 020 7222 5381

Christine Lee & Co (Solicitors) Ltd
‡Birmingham p140 . . . . 0121 666 6228
London W1 p52 . . . . 020 7287 6233

F A Lee & Co Criminal Defence Solicitors
‡Wembley p426 . . . . 020 8904 0700

G H Lee & Co
‡Leyland p283 . . . . 01772 424383

Jacqueline Lee Solicitor
‡Haywards Heath p246 . . . . 01444 473372

Laurence Lee & Co
‡Liverpool p289 . . . . 0151 259 1211 / 259 2824

Marcus Lee & Co
‡Gerrards Cross p229 . . . . 01753 887991

Martin Lee & Co
‡Mansfield p312 . . . . 01623 651886

Stewart Lee
‡London N3 p52 . . . . 020 8346 2769

Lee-Barber Goodrich & Co
‡Torquay p413 . . . . 01803 295535

Leech & Co
‡Manchester p306 . . . . 0161 279 0279
Bath p127 . . . . 01225 354673

Leeds Day
‡St Neots p392 . . . . 01480 474661
Huntingdon p258 . . . . 01480 454301
St Ives p392 . . . . 01480 464600

Leelanes Solicitors LLP
‡London EC3 p52 . . . . 020 7220 9410

David Lees & Co
‡Knowle p269 . . . . 0117 972 1261

Lees Solicitors LLP
‡Birkenhead p134 . . . . 0151 647 9381
Heswall p249 . . . . 0151 342 6273
West Kirby p428 . . . . 0151 625 9364

Lefevre & Co
‡Orpington p342 . . . . 01689 856835 / 856836

Legal Advice Direct Solicitors
‡Witney p436 . . . . 01993 700434

Legal Alliances Worldwide Ltd
‡Kidderminster p265 . . . . 01562 756830

Legal City
‡London N3 p52 . . . . 020 8922 3282

Legal Domain Limited
‡Nottingham p338 . . . . 01949 843125

Legal Eagles
‡Ilford p260 . . . . 0870 999 2911

Legal Escrow & Arbitration Services Limited
‡Leamington Spa p270 . . . . 0870 164 2264

Legal Hobbit
‡London EC2 p52 . . . . 020 7194 8400

Legal Management Solutions
‡Chester p190 . . . . 0871 871 0286

Legal Move
‡Bradford p154 . . . . 0870 600 4818

Legal Moves (Braddon & Snow Limited)
‡Hertford p248 . . . . 01992 536503

The Legal Partners Limited
‡Richmond upon Thames p364 . . . . 020 8334 8049

The Legal Practice Solicitors
‡Wembley p426 . . . . 020 8903 7017

Legal Risk
‡Liverpool p289 . . . . 0845 330 6791

Legal Services For Business
‡Farnham p225 . . . . 01252 850853

Legal Services For Children
‡Hengoed p247 . . . . 01443 866296

Legal Solutions Partnership
‡Luton p295 . . . . 01582 417208

Legal Swan Solicitors
‡Birmingham p140 . . . . 0121 551 7866

Legal Team Limited
‡Aylesbury p121 . . . . 01296 336077

Legality Solicitors
‡Manchester p306 . . . . 0161 212 1718

Legitimus Solicitors
‡London EC3 p52 . . . . 020 3402 6009

Lei Dat & Baig Solicitors
‡Liverpool p289 . . . . 0151 258 1868
‡Liverpool p289 . . . . 0151 708 8787

Leigh Bailey Solicitors
‡Preston p357 . . . . 01772 744719

LEIGH DAY & CO
‡London EC1 p52 . . . . 020 7650 1200

David Leigh-Hunt
‡Leamington Spa p270 . . . . 01926 427400

Leigh Turton Dixon
‡Middlesbrough p315 . . . . 01642 241101
Stockton-on-Tees p397 . . . . 01642 345230

Leigh White
‡Crowborough p204 . . . . 01892 655808

Leigh Young Solicitors
‡Stroud p400 . . . . 01453 762114

Wayne Leighton
‡Edgware p217 . . . . 020 8951 2988

J B Leitch & Co
‡Liverpool p289 . . . . 0151 708 2250

Leland Swaby Clarke & Norris
‡Romford p366 . . . . 01708 762227

David Lemco & Co
‡London N13 p53 . . . . 020 8882 1074

Lemon & Co
‡Swindon p406 . . . . 01793 527141

Lennons
‡Chesham p189 . . . . 01494 773377
Amersham p117 . . . . 01494 433177

Lennox Bywater
‡London NW7 p53 . . . . 020 8906 1206

Tom Lenon Solicitor
‡Sherborne p378 . . . . 07981 500357

Monica Lentin & Co
‡Cambridge p175 . . . . 01223 314452

Leo Abse & Cohen
‡Cardiff p179 . . . . 029 2038 3252 / 2034 5421
Newport p329 . . . . 01633 224417
Swansea p405 . . . . 01792 762030

Leonard & Co
‡Southampton p386 . . . . 023 8023 4433
Southampton p386 . . . . 023 8023 3242

Anthony Leonard Associates
‡Croydon p205 . . . . 020 8288 3548
Croydon p205 . . . . 020 8654 7757

Leonard Crane Solicitors
‡Hook p252 . . . . 0118 932 6105

Leonard Lowy & Co
‡London NW1 p53 . . . . 020 7788 4333

Edward Leonards Solicitors
‡London SE17 p53 . . . . 020 7252 7676

Law Offices of Joan Leopold
‡London NW1 p53 . . . . 020 7485 5540

Lesley Leporati
‡Beckenham p129 . . . . 020 8639 3515

Leport & Co
‡Banbury p122 . . . . 01295 257328 / 268181

Leslie & Co
‡Hounslow p254 . . . . 020 8577 5491 / 8572 7252

Leslieowen
‡London SW20 p53 . . . . 07711 047549

Lester Aldridge LLP
‡Bournemouth p152 . . . . 01202 786161
Bournemouth p152 . . . . 01202 597700
London WC2 p53 . . . . 0844 967 0785
Southampton p386 . . . . 023 8082 0400

Lester Dominic Solicitors
‡London N3 p53 . . . . 020 8371 7400

Lester Maddrell
‡Cheltenham p188 . . . . 01242 222147

Lester Morrill
‡Leeds p275 . . . . 0113 245 8549

Letchers
‡Ringwood p364 . . . . 01425 471424

The Letting Group
‡South Shields p384 . . . . 0191 497 5333
Darlington p206 . . . . 01325 460330

Letts & Co
‡Canterbury p177 . . . . 01227 471555

Leung & Co
‡Bristol p163 . . . . 0117 920 9230

Levales Solicitors LLP
‡Aldershot p115 . . . . 01252 334915

Levenes Employment
‡London WC1 p53 . . . . 020 7148 7850

Levenes Solicitors
‡Haringey N22 p53 . . . . 020 8881 7777 / 8881 6764
Birmingham p140 . . . . 0121 212 0000

Levetts
‡London SE8 p53 . . . . 020 7237 7771

Levi Solicitors LLP
‡Leeds p275 . . . . 0113 244 9931
‡London EC2 p53 . . . . 020 7763 6407
Bradford p154 . . . . 01274 709709

Keith Levin & Co
‡Huyton p258 . . . . 0151 480 5777

Marshall F Levine & Associates
‡London NW3 p53 . . . . 020 7586 7149

Levine Mellins Klarfeld
‡Stanmore p394 . . . . 020 8954 7474

Levison Meltzer Pigott
‡London EC4 p53 . . . . 020 7556 2400

Leviten Thompson & Co
‡Sheffield p376 . . . . 0114 276 9321

Levman Solicitors
‡Denham p208 . . . . 0845 603 8362

Levy & Co Solicitors LLP
‡Witham p436 . . . . 01376 511819
Braintree p155 . . . . 01376 511819

Jane Levy Solicitors
‡London NW1 p53 . . . . 020 7788 4288

P S Levy & Co
‡London W1 p53 . . . . 020 7486 7717

Lewes Smith
‡Lewes p283 . . . . 01273 483455

Michael Lewin Solicitors
‡Leeds p275 . . . . 0113 393 0231

Lewington Law For Business
‡Milton Keynes p317 . . . . 01908 232226

Lewis & Co
‡London NW4 p53 . . . . 020 8202 4343
‡Oldham p340 . . . . 0161 626 4444

Lewis & Dick
‡Epsom p219 . . . . 020 8393 0055
Crawley p202 . . . . 01293 526031

Lewis & Lines
‡Abertillery p113 . . . . 01495 212286

Brian Lewis & Co
‡London EC4 p53 . . . . 020 7583 9900

C T Lewis & Co
‡Leeds p275 . . . . 0113 245 9726

Cheryl Lewis & Co
‡Birkenhead p134 . . . . 0151 652 1451

Lewis Cutner & Co
‡London NW3 p53 . . . . 020 7433 2552

David Lewis & Co
‡Hemsworth p247 . . . . 01977 614064

Duncan Lewis & Co
‡Hackney E8 p53 . . . . 020 7923 4020
Harrow p242 . . . . 020 7923 4020
London W12 p53 . . . . 020 7923 4020
London SE14 p53 . . . . 020 7923 4020
London SW17 p53 . . . . 020 7923 4020
Romford p366 . . . . 020 7923 4020

Lewis Francis Blackburn Bray
‡Sheffield p376 . . . . 0114 272 9721

G Lewis and Co Solicitors
‡Luton p295 . . . . 01582 486429

G B Lewis
‡Bath p127 . . . . 01373 831004

G Huw Lewis
‡Neath p320 . . . . 01639 637181

Lewis Goldsmith Solicitors
‡Pinner p349 . . . . 020 8866 5989

Lewis Green & Co Solicitors
‡London W1 p53 . . . . 0845 094 8044

Lewis Hymanson Small Solicitors LLP
‡Manchester p306 . . . . 0161 827 1800

Jon Lewis & Co Solicitors
‡Newport p329 . . . . 01633 256601

Lewis Lewis & Company Ltd
‡St Clears p391 . . . . 01994 231044
Carmarthen p182 . . . . 01267 231666
Tenby p410 . . . . 01834 844844

Lewis Nedas & Co
‡Camden NW1 p53 . . . . 020 7387 2032

Lewis Onions Solicitors
‡Birmingham p140 . . . . 0121 200 7240

Lewis Rodgers Solicitors
‡Winsford p434 . . . . 01606 861858
Macclesfield p297 . . . . 01625 429114

Lewis Sidhu Solicitors
‡London W5 p53 . . . . 020 8832 7321

Lewis Silkin LLP
‡London EC4 p53 . . . . 020 7074 8000
Oxford p343 . . . . 01865 263070

Lewis Terrance Rose Solicitors
‡London N14 p54 . . . . 020 8920 9970

Lewis Wheeler Solicitor
‡Grayshott p233 . . . . 01483 600099

Lewis Whittle
‡Caerphilly p172 . . . . 029 2088 1378

Lex Law
‡London EC4 p54 . . . . 020 7183 0529

Lexica Law
‡London W1 p54 . . . . 020 7158 0031
Canterbury p177 . . . . 01227 764141

Lexicon Insurance Services
‡London SE1 p54 . . . . 020 7981 9888

Lexis Law Solicitors
‡London SW19 p54

Lexus Law
‡Nottingham p338 . . . . 0800 032 1007

Li & Co Solicitor
‡Kensington & Chelsea W10 p54 . . . . 020 8964 8525

Lia Solicitors
‡Birmingham p140 . . . . 0121 444 0020

Liberty & Co Solicitors
‡London SE18 p54 . . . . 020 8331 0660

Licensing Legal
‡Manchester p306 . . . . 0161 237 9961

Lichfield Reynolds
‡Stoke-on-Trent p398 . . . . 01782 313212
Stoke-on-Trent p398 . . . . 01782 289122
Stoke-on-Trent p398 . . . . 01782 595599

Stephen Lickrish & Associates Limited
‡Manchester p306 . . . . 0161 237 1913

Liddell and Company
‡Romford p366 . . . . 01708 775999
Benfleet p131 . . . . 01268 565769
Billericay p133 . . . . 01277 636426

Liddys Property Solicitors
Wakefield p418

Liddys Solicitors
‡Wakefield p418 . . . . 01924 780753

E C Lidster & Co
‡Grimsby p235 . . . . 01472 348417

Lieberman
‡York p445 . . . . 01904 780972

Liefman Rose & Co
‡Manchester p306 . . . . 0161 740 7878

Lightfoot O'Brien Westcott
‡Woodbridge p438 . . . . 01394 386336
London W1 p54 . . . . 01394 386336

Lightfoots LLP
‡Thame p410 . . . . 01844 212305

Lighthouse Solicitors
‡Harrow p242 . . . . 020 3170 7588 / 3170 7589

Jane Liles Solicitors
‡Harrow p242 . . . . 020 8248 0301

William H Lill & Co
‡Altrincham p116 . . . . 0161 928 8111
Lymm p296. . . . . . . .01925 753170 / 755668

Lillywhite Williams & Co
‡Dagenham p206 . . . . 020 8593 7471

Lim & Partners
‡Croydon p205 . . . . 020 8649 9988

J Lim Legal Limited
‡Surbiton p402 . . . . 020 8149 6341

C S Lima & Co
‡London W1 p54 . . . . 020 7935 1881

Limbach Banham
‡Royston p368. . . . . 01763 242257

Kate Limbert Solicitors
‡Lingfield p285 . . . . 01342 837765

LIN & CO SOLICITORS
‡Birmingham p140. . . . . 0121 244 2300
Sutton Coldfield p403. . . . . . . 0121 244 2300

Lincoln Harford Solicitors LLP
‡Wembley p426 . . . . 020 8903 1750

Lincoln-Lewis & Co
‡Birmingham p140. . . . . 0121 454 7011

Lincoln's Chambers Solicitors
‡London E1 p54. . . . . 020 7375 0062

Lincoln Solicitors
‡Manchester p306. . . . . 0161 442 2552

Lincolns Law Solicitors
‡Peterborough p347. . . . . 01733 897700

Lincolns Solicitors
‡London E13 p54 . . . . 020 8471 6328
‡Northwood p333 . . . . 01923 820909

Linder Myers Solicitors
‡Manchester p306. . . . . 0844 984 6000
Manchester p307. . . . . 0844 984 6400
Shrewsbury p379. . . . . 0844 984 6002
Swinton p407. . . . . 0161 794 5957

Lindley Clough
Pudsey p358 . . . . 0113 257 0523

Lindleys
‡Bristol p163. . . . . 0117 926 2408
Clevedon p196 . . . . 01275 877277

Lindops
‡Southend-on-Sea p387. . . . . . 01702 431791

Lindsay & Jockelson
‡London SE17 p54 . . . . 020 7701 9898

Frances Lindsay & Co
‡Maidenhead p298 . . . . 01628 643667

Lindsay Sait & Turner
‡Woking p437. . . . . 01483 604033

Gillian Linford Solicitor
‡Poole p353. . . . . 01202 254090

Lings Solicitors
‡Worthing p442 . . . . 01903 700303

Link2Law
‡London EC2 p54 . . . . 020 8448 5091
London W1 p54. . . . . 020 7989 5091

Linked Law
‡Norwich p334. . . 01362 688946 / 07833 332055

Linklaters LLP
‡London EC2 p54 . . . . 020 7456 2000

Links Legal
‡Ilford p260 . . . . 020 8551 0999

Linkside Solicitors
‡London NW7 p54. . . . . 020 8371 8445

Guy Linley-Adams
‡Hereford p248 . . . . 01432 379093

Linn & Associates Solicitors
‡Clacton-on-Sea p195. . . . . . . 01255 224660
Gillingham p229 . . . . 01634 577154
Harwich p243. . . . . 01255 240880

Linnitts Solicitors
‡Newton Abbot p329. . . . . 01626 333380

Linskills Solicitors
‡Liverpool p289 . . . . 0151 236 2224

Paul Linton & Co
‡Watford p423. . . . . 01923 230478

Liss Gulhane Innes & Co
‡Romford p366 . . . . 01708 764440
Ilford p260 . . . . 020 8501 0777

Listen (Law) Limited
‡Gerrards Cross p229 . . . . 01753 883531

Lister Brady
‡Worcester p440 . . . . 01905 20010

The Lister Croft Partnership
‡Wakefield p418. . . . . 0871 220 1333
Pudsey p358 . . . . 0113 257 0526

Lita Gale
‡London W8 p54 . . . . 020 7404 2899

S G Litchfield
‡London NW8 p54. . . . . 020 7624 2103

Jane Litherland Solicitor
‡Hathersage p244 . . . . 01433 659990

Lithman & Co
‡Westminster W1 p55 . . . . 020 7935 2212

Little & Co
‡Winchester p434 . . . . 01962 774222

Guy Littler
‡Kensington & Chelsea W14 p55 . 020 7373 3700

Littons
‡London W1 p55 . . . . 020 7495 0518

Livingstone & Co
‡Manchester p307. . . . . 0161 833 0578

Howard Livingstone Solicitor
‡London N2 p55. . . . . 020 8365 2962

Livingstons
‡Ulverston p416 . . . . 01229 585555
Barrow-in-Furness p125 . . . . . 01229 828300
Dalton-in-Furness p206. . . . . . 01229 462126

Liz Solicitors
‡Enfield p219 . . . . 020 8370 4980

Robert Lizar
‡Manchester p307. . . . . 0161 226 2319
Manchester p307. . . . . 0161 860 7797
Manchester p307. . . . . 0161 227 7777

T O L Llewellin & Co
‡Haverfordwest p244 . . . . 01437 767140

Llewellyn Jones & Co
‡Mold p318 . . . . 01352 755305
Ruthin p369 . . . . 01824 704495

Lloyd & Associates
‡London SW7 p55. . . . . 020 7589 9599

Lloyd & Rowe
‡Cardiff p179 . . . . 029 2045 8999

Lloyd Brennand
‡Brentford p156 . . . . 020 8569 9020

Lloyd Green Solicitors
‡Chelmsford p187. . . . . 01245 294600

Lloyd Jones & Co
‡Westcliff-on-Sea p428 . . . . . . 01702 710338

Joseph Lloyd
‡St Asaph p391 . . . . 01745 583648

M V Lloyd
‡Fareham p224 . . . . 023 9228 0944
Portsmouth p355 . . . . 023 9238 6757

Lloyd Platt & Co
‡London N3 p55. . . . . 020 8343 2998

Lloyd Rehman & Co
‡London EC4 p55 . . . . 020 7778 7550

LloydLaw LLP
‡London SE1 p55 . . . . 020 7403 5050

Lloyds & Cooper
‡Leominster p283 . . . . 01568 613236

Lloyds PR Solicitors
‡London NW10 p55 . . . . 020 8963 1050
Watford p423. . . . . 01923 201717

Lloyds Solicitors
Oldham p340. . . . . 0161 652 9996

Llys Cennen Solicitors
‡Ammanford p117. . . . 01269 592658 / 592790

Loble Solicitors
‡London SE1 p55 . . . . 020 7939 9100

Loch Associates
‡London EC1 p55 . . . . 020 3301 5357
Tunbridge Wells p415. . . . . . . 01892 773970

Lock & Marlborough
‡London W3 p55 . . . . 020 8993 7231

Peter Lock & Company Solicitors
‡South Croydon p383 . . . . 020 8688 2208

Robert Locke
‡Fareham p224 . . . . 01329 822722

Lockett Loveday McMahon
‡Manchester p307. . . . . 0161 237 3627

Lockharts Solicitors
‡London WC1 p55. . . . . 020 7383 7111

Lockings
‡Hull p257. . . . . 0845 075 4197
Beverley p131 . . . . 01482 300500
Hull p257. . . . . 01482 300280

Lockyers
‡Bishop's Stortford p144. . . . . . 01279 505970

Lodders Solicitors LLP
‡Stratford-upon-Avon p400 . . . . 01789 293259
Cirencester p195 . . . . 01285 659535
Henley-in-Arden p247. . . . . . . 01564 792261

Sam Lodh
‡Sheffield p376 . . . . 0114 243 5395

Lofthouse & Co
‡Castleford p183 . . . . 01977 603347

Logos UK Limited
‡London EC2 p55 . . . . 020 7920 3020

Lomax Geddes & Co
‡Manchester p307. . . . . 0161 834 4722

Lomax Lloyd-Jones & Co
‡Southwark SE1 p55 . . . . 020 7703 6461

London Law Firm
‡London E10 p55 . . . . 020 8539 9869

London Legal Solicitors
‡Southall p384. . . . . 020 8571 6889

London Solicitors LLP
‡London N17 p55 . . . . 020 8808 1285

Judith M Long
‡Southwark SE1 p55 . . . . 020 7403 3337

Roger Long & Co
‡Croydon p205 . . . . 020 8668 5071

Longden Walker & Renney
‡Sunderland p401. . . . . 0191 567 7024

Longe & Co
‡Norwich p335. . . . . 01603 660027

Longespe & Co
‡Llanrwst p292 . . . . 01492 642363

Longfords
‡Oldham p340. . . . . 0161 665 4400

Longlands Solicitors
‡Warrington p422 . . . . 01925 634277

Longmores
‡Hertford p248. . . . . 01992 300333

Longs Solicitors
‡Tonbridge p412. . . . . 01732 360895

Longstaff & Midgley
‡Scarborough p372 . . . . 01723 351751

Lonsdale & Mayall Solicitors
‡Swanley p404 . . . . 01322 660880

LOOSEMORES
‡Cardiff p179 . . . . 029 2022 4433

Lopian Wagner
‡Manchester p307. . . . . 0161 834 2324

Lord Bissell & Brook
‡London EC3 p55 . . . . 020 7327 4534

E D C Lord & Co
‡Hayes p245 . . . . 020 8848 9988
Ealing W13 p55. . . . . 020 8579 9292
Potters Bar p355 . . . . 01707 659499

Lords
‡Wakefield p418. . . . . 01924 380830

Lords Legal Services Limited
‡Clitheroe p196 . . . . 01200 440977

Lords Solicitors LLP
‡Ilford p260 . . . . 020 8518 2226

Lorimer & Co
‡London SW1 p55. . . . . 020 7592 7660

Lorimers
‡Buckingham p168 . . . .01280 812132 / 813405

Lorrells LLP
‡London EC1 p55 . . . . 020 7681 8888

Losanaa & Co Solicitors
‡London E6 p55. . . . . 020 8503 4409

Anthony Louca Solicitors
‡Westminster NW1 p55 . . . . . . 020 7723 9889

Loudouns
‡London EC4 p55 . . . . 020 3178 4136

Loughran & Co International Lawyers
‡London W1 p55 . . . . 020 7355 2051

Loughridge Bowler
‡Coventry p200 . . . . 024 7663 1632

A Louis & Co Immigration Law Practice
‡London SE18 p55

Lound Mulrenan & Jefferies Solicitors
‡Southwark SE1 p55 . . . . 020 7793 4012

Lovatt & Co
‡London E1 p55. . . . . 020 7247 9336

Clive Lovatt Solicitor
‡London SW15 p55 . . . . 020 8788 9716

James Love & Co Solicitors Limited
‡Harrogate p240. . . . . 0845 621 8000

Loveday & Keighley
‡Matlock p313. . . . . . . 01629 583142 / 56660

Lovegrove & Eliot
‡Windsor p434. . . . . 01753 851133

Lovejoy Solicitors Limited
‡Bingham p133 . . . . 01949 876105

Lovell Chohan & Co
‡Hounslow p254. . . . . 020 8814 7599

Lovell Son & Pitfield
‡Camden WC1 p55 . . . . 020 7242 7883

Michael A Loveridge
‡Clitheroe p196 . . . . 01200 442600

Lovetts PLC
‡Guildford p236 . . . . 01483 457500

Seth Lovis & Co
‡London WC2 p55. . . . . 020 7240 7020

Lovsey Marsh
‡Birmingham p140. . . . . 0121 212 0255

Alan Lowe & Co
‡Amersham p117 . . . . 01494 787598

Lowe & Co
‡Bedford p130. . . . . 01234 764731

Gordon Lowe & Co
‡Bristol p163. . . . . 01454 326833

Lowe Legal Services
‡Blandford Forum p147 . . . . . . 01258 881142

Nicholas Lowe
‡Beaconsfield p129 . . . . 01494 680480

Lowes
‡Rainham p359 . . . . .01634 371111

Lowick McKay
‡Cheadle p185 . . . . 0161 491 5588

Lowrie & Co
‡Cobham p196 . . . . 01932 865818

Lowthian Gray Family Law
‡Newcastle upon Tyne p325. . . . 0191 281 0082

Leonard Lowy
‡London W4 p55 . . . . 020 8956 2785

Loxford Solicitors
‡London E6 p55. . . . . 020 8548 1155

Loxley Legal Services LLP
‡Wotton-under-Edge p442. . . . . 01453 700620

Loynton & Co
‡Birmingham p140. . . . 0121 327 0118 / 327 0652

Lu Oliphant Solicitors
‡Edgware p217 . . . . 020 8238 2822

A G Lucas & Co
‡Cardiff p179 . . . . 029 2026 3628

Lucas & Wyllys
‡Great Yarmouth p234. . . . . . . 01493 855555
Great Yarmouth p234. . . . . . . 01493 663124
Great Yarmouth p234. . . . . . . 01493 855555
Lowestoft p294 . . . . 01502 500123

Lucas Law Limited
‡London E8 p55. . . . . 020 7812 9067

Lucas Law Solicitors
‡Penarth p345. . . . . 029 2070 8963

Lucas McMullan Jacobs
‡Loughton p294 . . . . 020 8418 3222

Paul Lucas & Co
‡Aylesbury p121. . . . . 01296 484022

Ludlow Lane Solicitors
‡Coulsdon p199 . . . . 01737 550967

Richard Ludlow & Co
‡Stratford-upon-Avon p400 . . . . 01789 552872
Solihull p382 . . . . 01789 552872

Luff Brook Carter Solicitors
‡Ferndown p225. . . . . 01202 871311

Lumb & Macgill
‡Bradford p154 . . . . 01274 730666

Lumsdons Solicitors LLP
‡Stourport-on-Severn p399 . . . . 01299 827766
Worcester p440. . . . . 01905 730670

Lundstrams Solicitors
‡Newcastle upon Tyne p325. . . . 01782 660050

Lundys
‡Driffield p213. . . . . 01377 252831

Lunn Groves
‡Stourbridge p399. . . . . 01384 397355

Lawrence Lupin
‡Wembley p426 . . . . 020 8733 7200

Lupton Fawcett
‡Leeds p275. . . . . 0113 280 2000
Sheffield p376 . . . . 0114 276 6607

Lupton Reddish
‡Rugby p368 . . . . . . .01788 542241 / 565163

Luqmani Thompson & Partners
‡London N22 p55 . . . . 020 8365 7800

Geoffrey Lurie
‡Newcastle upon Tyne p325. . . . 0191 232 1800

A J Lutley
‡Ashtead p119. . . . . 01372 279066

Luton Family Law
‡Luton p295. . . . . 01582 522385

Luttons Dunford
‡Gloucester p230 . . . . 01452 529751

Lycett Conveyancing Solicitors
‡Hailsham p237 . . . . 01323 449552

Chris Lynam
‡Sunningdale p402 01344 628863 / 07860 590456

Lynch Hall & Hornby
‡Harrow p242 . . . . 020 8864 0722

Lyndales Solicitors
‡London WC1 p55. . . . . 020 7391 1000

Michael Lynn & Co
‡London SW7 p55. . . . . 020 7225 3681

Nigel Lynn Associates
‡London EC4 p55

Peter Lynn & Partners
‡Swansea p405 . . . . 01792 450010
Morriston p319 . . . . 01792 310731
Penarth p345. . . . . 029 2071 3620
Swansea p405 . . . . 01792 863633

Lyons Davidson
‡Bristol p163. . . . . 0117 904 6000
Cardiff p179 . . . . 029 2030 3710
Leeds p275. . . . . 0113 368 6161
New Malden p321 . . . . 020 8336 6900
Plymouth p350 . . . . 01752 300530
Solihull p382 . . . . 0121 683 8310

Lyons Rounsfell
‡Westbury-on-Trym p428 . . . . . 0117 950 6506
Bristol p163. . . . . 0117 967 5252

Lyons Solicitor
‡Herne Bay p248 . 01227 360801 / 07906 759286

Lyons Solicitors
‡Slough p382 . . . . 01628 661999

Lyons Wilson
‡Manchester p307. . . . . 0161 830 7777

Trevor Lyttleton MBE
‡Westminster W1 p55 . . . . 020 7402 4810

M

M&A Solicitors LLP
‡Cardiff p179 . . . . 029 2048 2288

3

M & D Law LLP
‡Aylesbury p121. . . . . 01296 436703

M & K Solicitors
‡Luton p295. . . . . 01582 732503

M&M Solicitors
‡Leicester p280 . . . . 0116 285 2300
Loughborough p293 . . . . . . 01509 214262

M&N Solicitors
‡Birmingham p140. . . . . 0121 356 1999

M&S Legal
‡Northwich p333. . . . . 01606 330202

M&S Solicitors Limited
‡Coalville p196 . . . . 01530 266000

M23LAW Solicitors (Hedley-Saunders & Co)
‡Crawley p202. . . . . 0844 264 0999

MA Law (Solicitors) LLP
‡London W2 p55 . . . . 020 7723 1311

MA Solicitors
‡Luton p295. . . . . 01582 431110

MBA Solicitors
‡York p445 . . . . 01904 666888

MB Law Limited
‡Hounslow p254. . . . . 020 8863 3666

MB Solicitors Ltd trading as MB Law
‡Leeds p275. . . . . 0113 242 4444

MC Law
‡Petersfield p348 . . . . 01730 261979

MD Solicitors
‡Stroud p400 . . . . 01453 752015

M D T Law
‡Corby p199. . . . . 01536 400038

MFG Solicitors
‡Cleobury Mortimer p195 . . . . 01299 270210
‡Kidderminster p265. . . . . . . 01562 820181
Bromsgrove p167. . . . . 01527 831691
Halesowen p237 . . . . 0121 550 0777
Oswestry p342 . . . . 01691 684817
Telford p409 . . . . 01952 641651
Worcester p440. . . . . 01905 610410

MHHP Law LLP
‡Barnet p124 . . . . 020 8275 5556

Mhlaw
‡London EC2 p55 . . . . 020 7628 7757

M H Law Solicitors
‡Southall p384. . . 020 7096 5056 / 07504 599737

M H Legal
‡Mansfield p312. . . . . 01623 620384

MHM Solicitors
‡Leicester p280 . . . . 0845 234 0230

MH Solicitors
‡Willenhall p433. . . . . 01902 605083

M H Solicitors Limited
‡London SE25 p55 020 8656 7845 / 07092 807422

MJC Solicitors
‡Bolton p149 . . . . 01204 491915

M J Legal
‡Egham p217 . . . . 01784 433780

MJP Justice Limited
‡Liverpool p289 . . . . 0151 243 6700

MJP Law
‡Bournemouth p152. . . . . . . 01202 582582
‡Verwood p418 . . . . 01202 823666
‡Wimborne p433 . . . . 01202 842929

MKB Solicitors LLP
‡Barnsley p124 . . . . 01226 210000

MK Law
‡London SE6 p55
‡London SE8 p55. . . . . 020 8692 2694

MK Legal Solicitors
‡Milton Keynes p317. . . . . . . 01908 577680

MKM Solicitors
‡London E7 p55. . . . . 020 8548 9490

MKS Solicitors
‡Southampton p386. . . . . . . 023 8039 6952

ML Law Ltd
‡Eastleigh p216 . . . . 023 8060 0661
Chandlers Ford p184 . . . . . . 023 8026 9570

MLM Cartwright
‡Cardiff p179 . . . . 029 2046 2562

MLS Solicitors LLP
‡Stockport p396. . . . . 0161 968 7037

The MLT Partnership
‡Ruislip p369 . . . . 01895 676251

M Law
‡London W1 p55 . . . . 020 7927 6240
London W1 p55. . . . . 020 7927 6240

MMS Law
‡London EC2 p55 . . . . 020 7749 4199

MMS Solicitors
‡Hull p257. . . . . 01482 499199
‡Withernsea p436. . . . . 01964 612318
Hornsea p253 . . . . 01964 537700

MM Solicitors
‡Wokingham p437. . . . . 0118 989 3788

MNS Law
‡Wembley p426. . . . . 020 8902 0083

MNS Solicitors & Company
‡Westcliff-on-Sea p428 . . . . . 01702 352971

MPG Solicitors
‡Carlisle p182. . . . . 01228 625700

MPH Solicitors
‡Manchester p307. . . . . 0161 832 7722
Bury St Edmunds p171. . . . . 01284 811870

MPM Legal LLP
‡Reading p361 . . . . 0118 900 1880

MPR Solicitors LLP
‡Hounslow p254. . . . . 020 8607 4660

MRH Solicitors
‡Bolton p149 . . . . 01204 535333

M R Law
‡Harlow p239 . . . . 01279 430166

MRN Leeds
‡Leeds p275. . . . . 0113 247 1549

M R Solicitors
‡London E4 p55. . . . . 020 8518 1956

MSB Solicitors LLP
‡Liverpool p289 . . . . 0151 281 9040
Liverpool p289 . . . . 0151 281 9040
Liverpool p289 . . . . 0151 281 9040

MS Law LLP
‡Manchester p307. . . . . 0161 772 4500

MS-Legal Solicitors
‡London WC2 p56. . . . . 020 7726 7380

MSP Legal Services LLP
‡Hartlepool p243. . . . . 01429 232204

MTC Law Limited
‡London W1 p56 . . . . 020 7486 7708

MTG Solicitors
‡Hayes p245 . . . . 020 8569 3131
Hayes p245. . . . . 020 8754 5577

MWA Solicitors
‡Guildford p236 . . . . 01483 506100

MWG Solicitors
‡Manchester p307. . . . . 0161 835 2446

MWP Solicitors
‡Basildon p126 . . . . 01268 527131

MWRLaw Ltd
‡Preston p357. . . . . 01772 254201

MWT Solicitors
‡Liverpool p289 . . . . 0151 282 2615

Geraldine McAleese & Co
‡London W4 p56 . . . . 020 8987 8381

McAlinneys Solicitors
‡Wakefield p419. . . . . 01924 377017

Macalister White
‡Ramsgate p359 . . . . 01843 572789

Mcallister Olivarius
‡London W6 p56 . . . . 020 7386 1047

McAras Solicitors LLP
‡Leeds p275. . . . . 0113 243 4333

Macartan & Co
‡London SE10 p56 . . . . 020 8269 0057

Macaskill's
‡Buckley p168. . . . . 01244 544477

Macauley & Co
‡Hungerford p258 . . . . 01488 682348

Macauley Smith & Co
‡London SE8 p56 . . . . 020 8692 4088

McBride & Co Solicitors
‡Altrincham p116 . . . . 0161 929 0229

McBride Wilson & Co
‡London WC2 p56. . . . . 020 7242 1300

D K Macbryde & Co
‡Prestatyn p356. . . . . 01745 856404

Jacqueline McCabe Limited
‡Stafford p393. . . . . 01785 212521

McCarthy & White
‡Thornbury p411. . . . . 01454 413696

McCarthy Bennett Holland
‡Wigan p432 . . . . 01942 206060

David McCarthy
‡London W1 p56 . . . . 020 7569 1500

John McCarthy & Co
‡Newcastle upon Tyne p325. . . . 0191 276 9500

McCarthy Stewart & Booty Solicitors
‡Bury St Edmunds p171. . . . . 01284 748927
Stowmarket p400. . . . . 01449 612343

Mccarthy Tetrault
‡London EC4 p56 . . . . 020 7489 5700

McCartneys
‡Feltham p225. . . . . 020 8751 6051

Hilary McCauley Solicitors Limited
‡Cheadle Hulme p185. . . . . . 0161 485 6723

Mccauley-Slowe Solicitors
‡London SW16 p56 . . . . 020 8696 7253

McCloy Legal
‡Bradford-on-Avon p155. . . . . 01225 866563

McClure Naismith
‡London EC4 p56 . . . . 020 7623 9155

McConnell Law
‡Richmond upon Thames p364 . 020 8255 9500 / 07726 794821

Andrew McCooey & Co
‡Sittingbourne p380 . . . . . . 01795 470686

John McCormack Solicitor & Advocate
‡Stourbridge p399 . . . . 0560 343 7516

McCormacks
‡Birmingham p140. . . . . 0121 200 2777
‡London E1 p56. . . . . 020 7791 2000
Basildon p126 . . . . 01268 525999
London E15 p56 . . . . 020 7791 2000
London EC1 p56 . . . . 020 7791 2000

Neil McCormick
‡Frome p228 . . . . 01373 455700

McCormicks
‡Harrogate p240. . . . . 01423 530630

McCorry Connolly Solicitors
‡Romford p366 . . . . 01708 727269

Edward McCourt & Co
‡Watford p423. . . . . . .01923 448401 / 448402

David McCrum Ltd
‡Glastonbury p230. . . . . 01458 851530

McDaniel & Co
‡Newcastle upon Tyne p325. . . . 0191 281 4000

McDermott French
‡Newton Abbot p329. . . . . . . 01626 200177

Joe Mcdermott Solicitors
‡Basingstoke p127 . . . . 07720 723072

McDermott Will & Emery UK LLP
‡London EC2 p56 . . . . 020 7577 6900

McDonagh Solicitors
‡Birkenhead p134 . . . . 0151 650 2150

McDonald & Co
‡Westminster SW1 p56 . . . . . 020 7834 2679

MacDonald Chapman
‡London WC1 p56. . . . . 020 7404 9005

Mcdonald Cohen
‡Beaconsfield p129 . . . . 01494 677421

Iain Macdonald Solicitors
‡St Helens p391. . . . . 01744 612549

MacDonald Law
‡Northampton p332 . . . . 01933 664827

MacDonald Oates LLP
‡Petersfield p348 . . . . 01730 268211
Midhurst p316 . . . . 01730 816711

Roberta McDonald
‡Birmingham p140. . . . . 0121 449 6821

John A McDonnell
‡Norwich p335. . . . . 01508 570387

Avril McDowell
‡Twickenham p416 . . . . 020 8891 1566

David McEldowney
‡Havant p244 . . . . 023 9245 1007

Mcevedys
‡London W2 p56 . . . . 020 7243 6122

McEwen Parkinson
‡Westminster W1 p56 . . . . . . 020 7487 4361

Macey & Co
‡Greenwich SE3 p56 . . . . . . 020 8853 2710

McFaddens LLP
‡London EC2 p56 . . . . 020 7588 9080
Birmingham p140. . . . . 0121 452 5040

Macfarlaine
‡Oldham p340. . . . . 0161 624 2149

B J Macfarlane & Co
‡London EC3 p56 . . . . 020 7190 2988

Cordelia Mcfarlane Solicitor
‡Sherborne p378 . . . . 01935 817875

Gary Mcfarlane
‡Bristol p163. . . . . 0117 941 4844

McFarlane Watts & Company Solicitors
‡Watlington p424 . . . . 0700 077 7529

Macfarlanes
‡London EC4 p56 . . . . 020 7831 9222

McGanns Law
‡Northampton p332 . . . . 0845 071 4393

McGlennons
‡Merton SW19 p56 . . . . 020 8946 6015

McGlinchey & Co
‡Cheam p186 . . . . 020 8330 7979

Elaine McGloin
‡East Grinstead p215 . . . . . . 01342 328000

McGrath & Co
‡Birmingham p140. . . . . 0121 643 4121

McGrath Immigration Solicitors Partnership
Birmingham p140. . . . . 0121 643 4124

J McGrath
‡Sutton Coldfield p403. . . . . . 0121 355 4749

McGrath Litigation Partnership
Birmingham p140. . . . . 0121 643 4828

McGregor Wilshire Limited
‡Buckingham p168 . . . . 01280 815301

McGregors
‡Tamworth p407. . . . . 01827 313999

McGrigors LLP
‡London EC4 p56 . . . . 020 7054 2500
Manchester p307. . . . . 0161 935 8337

Malcolm McGuinness
‡Altrincham p116 . . . . 0161 928 7134

McGuireWoods London LLP
‡London EC4 p57. . . . . 020 7632 1600

John T P Mcguirk
‡London SW10 p57 . . . . 020 7376 8175

McHale & Co
‡Altrincham p116 . . . . 0161 928 3848

Machins Solicitors LLP
‡Luton p295. . . . . 01582 514000

McHugh Solicitors
‡Newcastle under Lyme p323 . . . 01782 628888

McIlhatton & de Brús
‡London SE20 p57 . . . . 020 8676 7896

McillMurrays Solicitors
‡Leeds p275. . . . . 0113 322 7903
St Albans p390. . . . . 01727 221655

Tina MacInnes
‡Swanage p404 . . . . 01929 427227

Mackarness & Lunt
‡Petersfield p348 . . . . 01730 265111

Mackay & Co
‡Birmingham p140. . . . . 0121 454 1814
‡Faversham p225 . . . . 01795 536061

McKay Law
‡Leeds p275. . . . . .0845 23 5571

McKays Solicitors
‡Liverpool p289 . . . . 0151 702 4858

McKeag & Co
‡Gosforth p231 . . . . 0191 213 1010

Austin McKee
‡London SW19 p57 . . . . 020 8946 6265

B J McKenna & Co Solicitors
‡Stockport p396. . . . . 0161 432 5757

Erna McKenna Donelly
‡Weybridge p430 . . . . 01932 844651

McKenna Donnelly & Co
‡Westminster SW1 p57 . . . . . 020 7821 9927

McKennas Solicitors
‡Liverpool p289 . . . . 07853 372037

Brian Mackenow & Co
‡Sunderland p401 . . . . 0191 565 6262

Mackenzie & Co
‡Hounslow p254. . . . . 020 8569 6289

McKenzie Bell Solicitors
‡Sunderland p401 . . . . 0191 567 4857
Washington p423. . . . . 0191 416 2605

McKenzie Brackman
‡London WC1 p57. . . . . 020 7580 8111

Mackenzie Dillon
‡Broadstairs p166 . . . . 01843 604222

Gavin McKenzie
‡Shrewsbury p379. . . . . 01743 235957

John Mackenzie
‡Henley-on-Thames p247 . . . . 01491 411022

Mackenzie Johnson Solicitors
‡Sandy p372 . . . . 01767 641209

Mackenzie Jones
‡Chester p190. . . . . 01244 355523
‡St Asaph p391 . . . . 01745 536030
Prestatyn p356 . . . . 01745 852110

McKenzie Law Limited
‡Telford p409 . . . . 01952 288390

McKenzie Richards
‡Mayfield p314 . . . . 01435 872025

McKenzies
‡London N9 p57. . . . . 020 8350 4114
Hertford p248. . . . . 01992 503344

McKeowns Solicitors Ltd
‡St Albans p390. . . . . 0800 032 8328
Milton Keynes p317. . . . . . . 0800 032 8328

Mackesys
‡London SE14 p57 . . . . 020 7639 0888

Harvey McKibbin Solicitors
‡Sutton Coldfield p403. . . . . . 0121 240 9115

Maura McKibbin: Collaborative Solicitor
‡Altrincham p117 . . . . 0161 928 5974

Glynis M Mackie
‡Gosforth p232 . . . . 0191 236 5308

Karen Mackie Solicitor
‡Farnham p225 . . . . 01252 713013

McKinleys
‡Nottingham p338 . . . . 0115 951 8010

McKinnells
‡Lincoln p284 . . . . 01522 541181

Mackintosh & Co
‡Richmond upon Thames p364 . 020 8332 2864

Mackintosh Duncan
‡Southwark SE1 p57 . . . . . . 020 7357 6464

Mackrell & Thomas
‡Liverpool p289 . . . . 0151 480 3666

Brian Mackrell & Co Ltd
‡Hove p255 . . . . 01273 823456

Mackrell Turner Garrett
‡London WC2 p57. . . . . 020 7240 0521
Addlestone p114 . . . . 01932 342181
Woking p437 . . . . 01483 476022
Woking p437 . . . . 01483 755609

Macks Solicitors
‡Middlesbrough p315 . . . . . . 01642 252828
Redcar p362 . . . . 01642 252828

Maclachlan
‡Sherborne p378 . . . . 01935 817736
Gillingham p229 . . . . 01747 822103

Ian McLachlan
‡Redditch p362 . . . . 01527 63883

MacLaren Britton
‡Nottingham p338 . . . . 0115 941 1469

Robert McLaren Planning & Property Solicitors
‡Petersfield p348 . . . . 01730 818202

Robert McLaren Solicitor
‡Horsham p253 . . . . 01403 823440

Maclaren Warner
‡Stapleford p394 . . . . 0115 939 5252
Beeston p130. . . . . 0115 943 6696
Eastwood p216. . . . . 01773 713846
Ilkeston p261 . . . . 0115 930 4994

McLarty & Co
‡London E17 p57

MacLaverty Cooper Atkins
‡Kingston upon Thames p267 . . . 020 8549 9994

Maclay & Co
‡London SE1 p57 . . . . 020 7701 8827

Maclay Murray & Spens LLP
London EC2 p57 . . . . 020 7002 8500

McLee & Co Solicitors
‡London W1 p57 . . . . 020 7569 3103

MacLeish Littlestone Cowan
‡Redbridge E11 p57. . . . . 020 8514 3000
Barking p123 . . . . 020 8514 3000
Ilford p260 . . . . 020 8514 3000
Sawbridgeworth p372. . . . . . . 01279 722453

McLellans
‡Hertford p249. . . . . 01992 532000

Barry Macloskey Solicitors
‡Wrexham p443. . . . . 01978 852485

McLoughlin & Company LLP
‡Shrewsbury p379. . . . . 01743 272272
London WC2 p57. . . . . 020 7183 6025

Patrick Mcloughlin & Co
‡Huyton p258 . . . . 0151 482 1236

J F McMahon
‡Northampton p332 . . . . 01604 494340

McManus Seddon
‡Bradford p154 . . . . 01274 741841

Hamish M McMillan
‡London EC4 p57 . . . . 020 7430 1789

MacMillan Ltd
‡London N1 p57

Penny Macmillan Employment Law Solicitors Limited
‡Sutton Coldfield p403. . . . . . . 0121 311 2758

McMillan Williams
‡Coulsdon p199 . . . . 020 8668 4131
Carshalton p183 . . . . 020 8432 2041
Croydon p205 . . . . 01689 848311
Mitcham p318 . . . . 020 8648 4044
South Croydon p383 . . . . 020 8253 7600
Thornton Heath p411 . . . . 020 8653 8844
Wallington p419 . . . . 020 8669 4962

McMillan Williams Solicitors
‡Bexleyheath p132 . . . . 020 8303 0168
‡Brighton p160 . . . . 01273 254004

Macmillans
‡Wadebridge p418. . . . . 01208 812415

McMillen Hamilton McCarthy
‡London E3 p57. . . . . 020 8980 6060

Peter M Mcmurtrie Solicitor And Notary Public
‡Gloucester p230 . . . . 01452 840373

Macnab Clarke
‡Abingdon p114. . . . . 01235 555700

McNair & Co
‡Hammersmith & Fulham SW6 p57 020 7371 7896

Macnamara King Solicitors
‡Warwick p422 . . . . 01926 499889
Coventry p200

McNamara Ryan
‡Weybridge p430 . . . . 01932 846041

Lisa Marie McNulty
‡Blackburn p145. . . . . 01254 248209

McPhersons
‡Ealing W13 p57 . . . . 020 8840 9017
‡Stockbridge p395. . . . . 01794 389002

Elizabeth McQuay
‡Oxford p343 . . . . 01869 351229

MacQuillan & Co
‡Ebbw Vale p216 . . . . 01495 304382
Tredegar p413 . . . . 01495 725031

MacRae & Co LLP
‡Southwark SE1 p57 . . . . 020 7378 7716

Macrory Ward
‡Barnet p124 . . . . 020 8440 3258

Macs Law
‡London W6 p57 . . . . 020 8748 8431

McTaggart Solicitors
‡Cardiff p179 . . . . 029 2023 4090

McTernans
‡Woodbridge p439. . . . . 01728 627929

Alison McVay
‡Taunton p408. . . . . 01823 401118

McWalter & Co
‡Cheltenham p188. . . . . 01242 676106

David Madams Solicitor
‡Market Harborough p312. . . . . 01536 771077

Maddersons
‡Broxbourne p167. . . . . 01992 444421

Maddison-Ward & Co
‡Leighton Buzzard p282. . . . . . 01525 873274

Maddocks Clarke
‡Altrincham p117 . . . . 0844 805 5170

Madge Lloyd & Gibson
‡Gloucester p230 . . . . 01452 520224
Newent p327. . . . . 01531 820088

Madley Hughes & Co Solicitors
‡Bury St Edmunds p171. . . . . . 01284 810612

Maffey & Brentnall
‡Watford p423. . . . . 01923 234607

Steven Dean Magac & Co
‡Barnet p124 . . . . 020 8441 3399

Conor Magill
‡Newbury p322 . . . . 01635 255217

Magna Law
‡Bristol p163. . . . . 01275 332000

Thomas Magnay & Co
‡Gateshead p229 . . . . 0191 477 3333
Whickham p430 . . . 0191 488 7459 / 488 7766

Magne & Co Solicitors
‡Surbiton p402 . . . . 020 8399 3939

Magrath LLP
‡London W1 p57 . . . . 020 7495 3003

Heidi Maguire Associates
‡Salford p370 . . . . 0161 828 3030

James Maguire & Co
‡Wilmslow p433 . . 01625 529456 / 07739 247630

Maguires Solicitors
‡Manchester p307. . . . . 0161 835 9872

Magwells
‡Islington EC1 p57. . . . . 020 7833 2244

Mahany & Co Solicitors LLP
‡Horley p252 . . . . 01293 772888

Maher & Co
‡Maidenhead p298 . . . . 01628 675239

Mahesen & Co
‡Wandsworth SW17 p57. . . . . . 020 8682 2846

JAE Mahmood Solicitor
‡Farnborough p224 . . . . 01252 517459

Mahmood Mirza Solicitors
‡Sheffield p376 . . . . 0114 256 1490

Mary Mahon Solicitors
‡Hebden Bridge p246 . . . . 01422 844997

Maidments
Birmingham p140. . . . . 0870 403 4000
Bolton p149. . . . . 0870 403 4000
Sale p370 . . . . 0870 403 4000
Salford p370 . . . . 0870 403 4000

Charles S Maidstone
‡Reading p361 . . . . 0118 959 4545

H H Mainprice
‡Westminster SW1 p57 . . . . . . 020 7730 8705

Maisto E Associati
‡London EC2 p57. . . . . 020 7374 0299

Maitland
‡London WC1 p58. . . . . 020 3077 1234

Maitland Hudson & Co LLP
‡London EC4 p58 . . . . 020 7832 0460

Maitland Walker
‡Minehead p318. . . . . 01643 707777
Cheltenham p188. . . . . 01242 285855

Majella O'Neill Solicitors
‡Solihull p382 . . . . 01564 739298

Major & Co
‡Guildford p236 . . . . 01483 455771

Major Family Law
‡Ponteland p351. . . . . 01661 824582

Makanda & Co
‡London N19 p58 . . . . 020 7272 8844

Makanda Bart
‡London N15 p58 . . . . 020 8802 0034

Makin Dixon Solicitors
‡Bradford p154 . . . . 01274 747747
Halifax p238 . . . . 01422 363184
Harrogate p240. . . . . 01423 500035
Keighley p263 . . . . 01535 605040
Skipton p381 . . . . 01756 797284
Todmorden p412 . . . . 01706 839787

E Rex Makin & Co
‡Liverpool p289 . . . . 0151 709 4491

M A Makinde Solicitor
‡Harrow p242 . . . . 020 8099 1780

Makka Solicitors Ltd
‡London SW17 p58 . . . . 020 8767 9090

Makwana Solicitors
‡London NW10 p58 . . . . 020 8451 1999

Malcolm & Co Solicitors
‡London E2 p58. . . . . 020 7613 4300

Malcolm Wilson & Cobby
‡Worthing p442 . . . . 01903 237581
Lancing p270. . . . . 01903 765991
Worthing p442 . . . . 01903 244973

Male & Wagland
‡Potters Bar p355 . . . . 01707 657171
Barnet p124 . . . . 020 8449 9669

Malekin Law
‡Cardiff p180 . . . . 029 2023 1222

Amjad Malik Solicitors
‡Rochdale p365. . . . . 01706 346111

Malik & Malik Solicitors
‡Brent NW10 p58 . . . . 020 8830 3050

Malik & Michael
‡London NW10 p58 . . . . 020 7724 2223
‡London E1 p58. . . . . 020 7247 8458

Malik Legal Solicitor Limited
‡Manchester p307. . . . . 0161 795 6217

Malik Solicitors
‡Bradford p154 . . . . 01274 727773

Malits Solicitors
‡Ellesmere Port p217
. . . . 07966 203386 / 0151 356 9046

Mallesons Stephen Jaques
‡London EC2 p58 . . . . 020 7778 7170

Malletts Solicitors
‡King's Lynn p266. . . . . 01553 777744
‡Milton Keynes p317. . . . . 01908 226138
London WC1 p58. . . . . 020 7061 3760

Mallia & Co
‡Cardiff p180 . . . . 029 2022 0044

Malloy & Barry
‡Cardiff p180 . . . . 029 2034 3434

Maltas & Co
‡Barnsley p125 . . . . 01226 781596

Manches LLP
‡London WC2 p58. . . . . 020 7404 4433
Oxford p343 . . . . 01865 722106
Reading p361. . . . . 0118 982 2640

Manchesters
‡South Croydon p383 . . . . 020 8651 3118

Mandel Corporate
‡London SW6 p58. . . . . 020 7386 6651

Mandel Katz & Brosnan LLP
‡London EC4 p58 . . . . 020 7653 5678

Mander Cruickshank Solicitors LLP
‡Coalville p196 . . . . 01530 510666
Hinckley p250 . . . . 01455 614208

Mander Hadley & Co
‡Coventry p200 . . . . 024 7663 1212

Stuart J Mander & Co
‡Walsall p420 . . . . 01922 642018

Mandla Bhomra & Co
‡Birmingham p140. . . . . 0121 523 3384

Mandy Peters Solicitors
‡London SE12 p58 . . . . 020 8297 4000

Vivien Manfield
‡Winchester p434 . . . . 01962 853930

Mang & Co
‡London N17 p58 . . . . 020 8808 5898

Mangala & Kalum Solicitors
‡London E7 p58. . . . . 020 8519 0261

Manis
‡Thornton Heath p411 . . . . 020 8239 7111

Manley Turnbull
‡Cheltenham p188. . . . . 01451 851882

Alan Mann & Co
‡St Albans p390. . . . . .01727 833281 / 846012

Mann & Co
‡Tipton p412. . . . . 0121 555 7000

Mann & Company
‡Kettering p265 . . . . 01536 520025

Mann Jenkins
‡Moretonhampstead p319 . . . . . 01647 440000

Neil E Mann
‡Prestwich p358
. . . . 0161 832 8806 / 720 8199 / 773 1775
Kendal p264 . . . . 01539 729772

Robert Mann
‡Oswestry p342. . . . . 01691 671926

Manners Pimblett Solicitors
‡Poynton p355. . . . . 01625 850888

Manogaran & Co
‡Waltham Forest E17 p58 . . . . . 020 8521 5757

Manor Law Family Solicitors
‡Hertford p249. . . . . 01992 306616

Mansfield Fellowes Solicitors
‡Cardiff p180 . . . . 029 2050 4101

Thomas Mansfield LLP
‡Croydon p205 . . . . 0845 601 7756
Birmingham p140. . . . . 0845 601 7756
London E1 p58. . . . . 0845 601 7756
Manchester p307. . . . . 0845 601 7756

Dean Manson Solicitors
‡London SW17 p58 . . . . 020 8767 5000

Mansouri & Son
‡Croydon p205 . . . . 020 8401 7352

John Mant Solicitors
‡Wantage p421 . . . . 01235 762900

Mantilla And Stonerwood Solicitors
‡Birmingham p140. . . . . 0121 236 7959

Mantins Solicitors & Notaries
‡Southwold p389 . . . . 01502 724750

Manuel Martin & Associates
‡London W1 p58 . . . . 020 7631 5161

Manuel Swaden
‡London NW6 p58. . . . . 020 7431 4999

Maples Solicitors LLP
‡Spalding p389 . . . . 01775 722261

Maples Teesdale LLP
‡London EC2 p58. . . . . 020 7600 3800

Maples Teesdale
‡London WC2 p58. . . . . 020 7831 6501

Maplestones
‡Ickenham p259. . . . . 01895 632255

Mapletoft & Co
‡London SW15 p58 . . . . 020 8785 2414

March Solicitors
‡Newbury p322 . . . . 0845 204 2020

Marchant Harries & Co
‡Aberdare p113 . . . . 01685 885500
Aberdare p113 . . . . 01685 813655
Mountain Ash p319. . . . . 01443 476444

Marchants Solicitors
‡Mansfield p312. . . . . 01623 655111
Kirkby-in-Ashfield p268 . . . . . 01623 688400

Marches Law
‡Tenbury Wells p409. . . . . 01584 819535
Hereford p248 . . . . 01432 355366

K M Mardell & Co
‡Aylesbury p121. . . . . 01296 468575

Margary & Miller
‡Felixstowe p225 . . . . 01394 273333
Southwold p389 . . . . 01502 723308
Woodbridge p439. . . . . 01394 382777
Woodbridge p439. . . . . 01394 388605

Margetts & Ritchie
‡Birmingham p140. . . . . 0121 236 5517

Jennifer C Margrave
‡Guildford p236 . . . . 01483 562722

Margraves
‡Llandrindod Wells p291. . . . . . 01597 825565

Marine Law Solicitors
‡Newcastle upon Tyne p325. . . . 0191 261 1567

Saul Marine & Co
‡London NW7 p58. . . . . 020 8959 3611

Stella Maris Solicitors LLP
‡London W1 p58 . . . . 0800 098 8388

Mark & Co
‡London W14 p58 . . .020 7603 3710 / 7602 6942
‡London N13 p58 . . . . 020 8920 9999

Markand & Co
‡London E7 p58. . . . . 020 8470 1422

Andrew Markham & Co
‡Carmarthen p182. . . . .01267 221550 / 236199
‡Llanelli p292 . . . . 01269 842888

Marks & Clerk Solicitors LLP
‡Cambridge p175 . . . . 01223 345539

Marks & Clerk
‡London WC2 p58. . . . . 020 7420 0250
Birmingham p140. . . . . 0121 643 5881
Cheltenham p188. . . . . 01242 524520
Leeds p275. . . . . 0113 389 5600
Leicester p280
Liverpool p289 . . . . 0151 243 5400
Manchester p307. . . . . 0161 233 5800
Oxford p344 . . . . 01865 397900

Marks and Marks Solicitors
‡Harrow p242 . . . . 020 8426 8000

Marks Miller & Co
‡Billericay p133 . . . . 01277 633991

O M Marks & Co
‡Barnet N3 p58 . . . . 020 8371 6689

Veronique Marot & Co
‡Leeds p275. . . . . 0113 258 2021

Jeremy Marozzi
‡London SW19 p58 . . . . 020 8544 2800

Marrache & Co
‡London W1 p58 . . . . 020 7569 1000

Marriott Davies Yapp
‡Sutton p402 . . . . 020 8643 9794

Marriott Harrison
‡London WC1 p59. . . . . 020 7209 2000

Laurence Marron Solicitors
‡London EC3 p59 . . . . 020 8382 3770

Marrons
‡Leicester p280 . . . . 0116 289 2200
‡Newcastle upon Tyne p325. . . . 0191 281 1304

Marsden & Co
‡Winchester p434 . . . . 01962 841550

Marsden Duncan
‡Cliftonville p196. . . . . 01843 295741
Birchington p134 . . . . .01843 295743 / 841161
Ramsgate p359. . . . . 01843 584500

MARSDEN RAWSTHORN LLP
‡Preston p357. . . . . 01772 799600
Chorley p194 . . . . 01257 279511

MARSDENS SOLICITORS
‡Nelson p321 . . . . 01282 611899

A B Marsh Solicitors
‡Burnley p169 . . . . 0800 169 4849
‡Salford p371 . . . . 0161 839 2626

Marsh & Co
‡Lancaster p269. . . . . 01524 68102

Marsh & Partners Solicitors
‡Enfield p219 . . . . 020 8805 1184

Marsh Brown & Co
‡Lewisham SE13 *p59* 020 8852 0052
Dean Marsh & Co
‡Brighton *p160* 01273 823770
Peter W Marsh & Co
‡Melton Mowbray *p314* 01664 566471
William Marsh Solicitor
‡Penarth *p345*. 029 2051 5818
Marshall & Mason Solicitors
‡London E15 *p59* 020 8555 3999
Marshall Glover Limited
‡Dursley *p214*. . . 0844 801 1422 / 07917 356064
‡Lancaster *p269*. 0844 801 1422
‡Newcastle upon Tyne *p325*. . . . 0191 519 7460
Marshall Haines
‡Letchworth *p283* 01462 680955
Marshall Hall & Levy
‡South Shields *p384*. 0191 455 3181
Marshall Hatchick
‡Woodbridge *p439*. 01394 388411
London W1 *p59*. 020 7935 3272
Stephen Marshall
‡Purley *p358* 020 8660 4141
Marshalls
‡Godalming *p231* 01483 416101
‡Plymouth *p350*. 01752 254555
Woking *p437* 01483 730531
Marsons Solicitors LLP
‡Bromley *p166*. 020 8313 1300
MarstonHarbottle
‡Hexham *p249* 01434 602486
Martin Adams & McColl
‡Northampton *p332* 01604 634123
Martin & Co
‡Manchester *p307*. 0161 228 6195
Martin & Strain
‡Pwllheli *p358* 01758 612042
Carl Martin Solicitors
‡Ilford *p260* . . . . 020 8554 7764 / 07851 376156
I Anthony D Martin
‡Chorley *p194*. 01257 451383
John P Martin & Co
‡Scarborough *p372* 01723 500922
Paul Martin & Co
‡Romford *p366* 01708 380210
Martin Searle
‡Brighton *p160* 01273 609911
Croydon *p205* 020 8256 4490
Martin Tolhurst Partnership LLP
‡Gravesend *p233* 01474 325531
Ashford *p119* 01233 505555
Longfield *p293* 01474 706168
MARTIN-KAYE LLP
‡Telford *p409* 01952 272222
Martin-Simms Solicitors
‡London E7 *p59*. 020 8552 7042
Martine Alan
‡London W1 *p59* 020 3089 4086
Martins
‡Eccles *p216* 0161 707 3660
Brockenhurst *p166* 01590 623252
Cheadle *p185*. 0161 428 3102
Martyn Amey & Co
‡Bromsgrove *p167*. 01527 576060
MARTYN PROWEL
‡Cardiff *p180* 029 2047 0909
MartynsRose Solicitors
‡Hounslow *p254*. 020 8538 1397
London E8 *p59*
Marziano Khatry Mak Solicitors
‡London E6 *p59*
B C Mascarenhas
‡Haringey N22 *p59* 020 8889 6246
Masefield Solicitors LLP
‡Ledbury *p271*. 01531 632377
Maskell Edwards & Associates
‡Uxbridge *p417* 01895 272226
Maskery & Co
‡Consett *p199*. 01207 588300
Mason & Beer
‡East Grinstead *p215* 01342 311255
Mason & Co
‡Altrincham *p117* 0161 941 5757
Mason & Co Solicitors
‡Hull *p257*. 01482 310170
Mason Baggott & Garton
‡Scunthorpe *p373*. 01724 868611
Brigg *p158* 01652 654111
Epworth *p219*. 01427 872661
Mason Bullock Solicitors
‡Northampton *p332* 01604 601575
Mason Hayes
‡Manchester *p307*. 0161 266 1129
London WC2 *p59*. 020 7717 8493
Helen Mason & Co Solicitors
‡Burton-on-Trent *p170*. 01629 815175
Mason Palmer
‡Barnsley *p125* 01226 709100
Perry Mason Solicitors
‡Torquay *p413*. 01803 299000

James Mason Tucker
‡Newton Abbot *p329*. 01626 204060
Mason-Apps Smallmans & Co
‡Maidenhead *p298* . . . .01628 636148 / 636149
Mason-Watts & Co
‡Newcastle Emlyn *p322* 01239 711521
Massers
‡Nottingham *p338* 0115 851 1666
West Bridgford *p427* 0115 851 1666
Masseys LLP
‡London EC4 *p59* 020 7634 9595
Massucco Buttress
‡Cambridge *p175* 01223 463183
Masters Legal Services Limited
‡London SW1 *p59*. 020 7198 8024
Mastrovito & Associates
‡London WC1 *p59*. 020 7025 2375
Match Solicitors
‡London EC4 *p59* 020 7353 6881
Mather & Co
‡Colchester *p197* 01206 322763
Matheson Ormsby Prentice
‡London EC3 *p59* 020 7618 6750
Christopher Mathew Solicitors
‡Wembley *p426* . . . . . .020 8782 1142 / 1146
Caroline Mathews Solicitors
‡Dartford *p207*. 01322 552275
Eryl Mathias
‡Llanwrda *p292* 01588 650664
Mathys & Squire
‡London EC1 *p59* 020 7830 0000
Matini Montecristo
‡London W1 *p59* 0845 299 7866
Matrix Legal
‡Kingston upon Thames *p267* . . . 020 8481 3727
Matrix Solicitors
‡Derby *p209*. 01332 363454
‡Wirral *p435*. 0151 677 3999
Matthew & Matthew Limited
‡Southbourne *p387* 01202 431943
Matthew Arnold & Baldwin LLP
‡Watford *p423*. 01923 202020
London EC4 *p59* 020 7936 4600
Milton Keynes *p317*. 01908 687880
A S Matthews & Co
‡Manchester *p307*. 0161 747 2262
John Matthews Solicitor
‡Brighton *p160* 01273 928714
Matthews Lewis & Co
‡Chester *p191*. 01244 327750
Mark Matthews & Co
‡Tamworth *p407*. 01827 65765
Rachael Matthews Solicitors
‡Chesham *p189*. 01494 758573
T A Matthews
‡Hereford *p248* 01432 352121
Leominster *p283* 01568 615905
W H Matthews & Co
‡Islington EC1 *p59*. 020 7251 4942
Kingston upon Thames *p267* . . . 020 8549 0264
Staines *p393* 01784 453154
Sutton *p402* 020 8642 6677
Matwala Vyas LLP
‡Ilford *p260* 020 8597 5097
Maunsell Bower
‡Wandsworth SE1 *p59*. 020 7378 9592
Judith Maurice Solicitors
‡London N17 *p59* 020 8808 8018
Maurice Nadeem & Atif
‡London W1 *p59* 020 7723 3424
Maurice Turnor Gardner LLP
‡London EC2 *p59*. 020 7012 8610
Maus Solicitors
‡London SE6 *p59* 020 8695 0000
Maven Solicitors
‡Leeds *p275*. 0113 366 3221
Mawdsleys
‡Southport *p388*. 01704 537676
MAX BITEL GREENE LLP
‡Islington N1 *p59* 020 7354 2767
Max Gold Law
‡Hull *p257*. 01482 224900
Max Owen Solicitors
‡Bridport *p158*. 01308 485680
Richard Max & Co Solicitors
‡London WC2 *p59*. 020 7240 2400
Maxine Cox Solicitors
‡Hitchin *p251* 01438 833875
Maxwell Alves
‡London WC1 *p59*. 020 7632 6950
Maxwell Alves Solicitors
‡London WC1 *p59*. 020 7269 6470
Maxwell Gillott (MG Law Ltd)
‡Lancaster *p270*. 0844 858 3900
Maxwell Hodge Solicitors
‡Liverpool *p289* 0151 526 9321
Formby *p227* 01704 872156
Heswall *p249*. 0151 342 6447
Huyton *p258* 0151 489 6161

Kirkby *p268*. 0151 548 7370
Liverpool *p289* 0151 227 4545
Maghull *p298*. 0151 526 7131
West Kirby *p428* 0151 625 9154
Maxwell Winward LLP
‡London EC4 *p59* 020 7651 0000
May & Co
‡Barnet NW9 *p59* 020 8200 6116
John May Law
‡London W8 *p59* 020 7792 2900
May May & Merrimans
‡London WC1 *p59*. 020 7405 8932
May Morris & Co
‡London SE23 *p59* 020 8699 1000
Maya & Co Solicitors
‡Coventry *p200* 024 7670 0417
Maya Solicitors
‡Oldham *p340*. 0161 284 6907
Gerard Maye Legal Limited
‡Brighton *p160* 01273 560444
Brighton *p160*. 01273 560426
Littlehampton *p285* 01903 734341
Mayer Brown International LLP
‡London EC2 *p59* 020 3130 3000
London EC3 *p60* 020 3130 3000
Mayfair Solicitors
‡London W1 *p60* 020 7493 0740
Mayflower Solicitors
‡Birmingham *p140*. 0845 233 0003
Mayland Porter
‡Woodbridge *p439*. 01394 615795
Andrew Maynard & Co
‡Bath *p127* 01225 461146
Maynards Solicitors
‡York *p445* 01904 435100
Mayo Wynne Baxter LLP
‡Brighton *p160* 01273 775533
East Grinstead *p215* 01342 310600
Eastbourne *p215* 01323 730543
Lewes *p283* 01273 477071
Seaford *p373*. 01323 891412
Mays Brown
‡London E1 *p60*. 020 7264 0600
Maysons Solicitors LLP
‡Burnley *p169*. 01282 416069
Meaby & Co
‡London SE5 *p60* 020 7703 5034
Meaby & Co Trading as Hart Scales & Hodges
‡Dorking *p212*. 01306 884432
Meaby & Co (Trading as Leo and Stockton)
‡Kingston upon Thames *p267* . . . 020 8546 9074
Meaby & Co (Trading as Setfords)
Guildford *p237* 01483 408780
James Mead
‡Brighton *p160* 01273 677420
Meade & Co
‡London N14 *p60* 020 8886 3643
Meade-King
‡Bristol *p163*. 0117 926 4121
Meade Law Solicitors
‡Bolton *p149* 01204 365398
Meadows & Moran
‡Romford *p366* 01708 753400
Meadows Fraser LLP
‡Weybridge *p430* 01932 852057
Mears Hobbs & Durrant
‡Lowestoft *p294*. 01502 583621
Beccles *p129*. 01502 715818
Great Yarmouth *p234*. 01493 665413
Robert Meaton & Co
‡Manchester *p307*. 0845 634 9955
Media Law Consultancy Limited
‡London NW5 *p60*. 020 7482 3011
Mediation Now Ltd
‡Portsmouth *p355*. 023 9262 6897
Emsworth *p218*. 01243 377426
Fareham *p224* 01329 232114
Petersfield *p348* 01730 266605
Petersfield *p348* 01730 266605
Medlicott & Benson
‡London SW1 *p60*. 020 7839 2818
Medlicott Snows
‡Bishops Castle *p145* 01588 638425
Knighton *p269* 01547 528332
Medyckyj & Co
‡Haringey N2 *p60* 020 8442 0000
Louise Mee Limited
‡Leicester *p280* 0116 289 2200
Meer & Co
‡London NW11 *p60* 020 8458 4554
Bill Meeson
‡Preston *p357*. 01772 796597
Meesons
‡Ringwood *p364*. 01425 472315
Fordingbridge *p227*. 01425 655251
Lakshman Meewella
‡London SW7 *p60*. 020 7370 6595

F W Meggitt & Co
‡Sheffield *p376* 0114 272 7955
Megsons LLP
‡Oldham *p340*. 0161 633 6131
Bradford *p154* 01274 738444
Meikles
‡Ferryhill *p226*. 01740 652811
Barnard Castle *p123* 01833 690505
Bishop Auckland *p144* 01388 451122
Spennymoor *p389* 01388 814336
Stockton-on-Tees *p397* 01740 620255
Melani & Company Solicitors
‡London NW9 *p60*. 020 8201 5976
Melanie Lazarus & Co
‡Bridgend *p157* 01656 750888
Joseph Melchior & Co
‡London NW6 *p60*. 020 7435 7738
Meldrum Young Solicitors
‡St Albans *p390*. 01727 840333
Hertford *p249*. 01992 535866
Watford *p423* 01923 231598
Melia & Mumford
‡Camberley *p173* 01252 836554
Melkerts Solicitors Limited
‡Lutterworth *p296* 01788 860088
Mellersh & Co
‡Islington EC1 *p60*. 020 7251 2361
Mellor & Jackson
‡Oldham *p340*. 0161 624 7081
Royton *p368* 0161 624 0387
Mellor Hargreaves Solicitors
‡Oldham *p341*. 0800 811 844
Kenneth W Mellor
‡Rochester *p366* 01634 724951
Melrose Solicitors
‡London N17 *p60* 020 8801 8919
Memery Crystal
‡London WC2 *p60*. 020 7242 5905
Mendell Solicitors
‡Manchester *p307*. 0844 800 2427
Mendips Solicitors
‡Luton *p295*. . . . 01582 720000 / 07981 000664
Menneer Shuttleworth
‡Bexhill *p132* 01424 730630
St Leonards-on-Sea *p392*. 01424 720044
Mensons & Associates
‡London SE9 *p60* . . . . . 020 3145 3918 / 3917
The Mental Health Practice
‡Bournemouth *p152*01202 269023 / 07961 053639
Jan Mentha Solicitors
‡Cambridge *p175* 01223 502090
Menzies Law
‡Bristol *p163*. 0845 113 0150
S Merali Solicitor Advocate
‡Westminster W1 *p60* 020 7724 0508
Mercers
‡Henley-on-Thames *p247* 01491 572138
Henley-on-Thames *p247* 01491 572138
Merchant Legal LLP
‡London EC4 *p60* 020 7332 2251
New Malden *p321* 020 8949 5116
Simon Merchant Property Solicitor
‡St Neots *p392* 01480 860808
Mercian Law Limited
‡Tamworth *p407*. 0844 736 1980
Mercury Legal LLP
‡Chester *p191*. 0800 612 7703
Mercy Messenger
‡Birmingham *p140*. 0121 770 1221
Daventry *p207* 01327 301745
Hilary Meredith Solicitors
‡Wilmslow *p433*. 01625 539922
Meridian Private Client LLP
‡Solihull *p382* 0121 711 4800
Merrett & Co
‡Bristol *p163*. 01275 331228
Merrick Solicitors
‡Manchester *p307*. 0161 838 5410
Merricks Formerly Merrick Kelleher
‡Wadebridge *p418*. . . . .01208 812068 / 813104
Merrils Ede Solicitors
‡Cardiff *p180* 029 2037 1131
Penarth *p345*. 029 2037 1131
The Merriman Partnership
‡Marlborough *p313* 01672 512244
Merriman Waine & Co
Pewsey *p348*. 01672 563666
Merriman White
‡London EC4 *p60* 020 7421 1900
Merritt & Co
‡Yarm *p443* 01642 885555
Merrony Wall
‡Twickenham *p416* 020 8898 4700
Merry & Co
‡Ryde *p369* 01983 811722
Meryl Evans Cyfreithwraig/Solicitor
‡Penarth *p345*. 029 2019 5871
Messenger & Co
‡Henley-on-Thames *p247* 01491 576272

3

Lindsay Messenger Solicitors
‡Cambridge *p175* 01223 508860

Metcalfe Copeman & Pettefar
‡Wisbech *p435* 01945 464331
King's Lynn *p266* 01553 778102
Peterborough *p347* 01733 865880
Thetford *p410* 01842 756100

Metcalfe Harveys
‡Bordon *p150* 01420 479962

Metcalfe Johnston McCormick
‡Eccles *p216* 0161 789 3481 / 788 9021

Metcalfes
‡Bristol *p164* 0117 929 0451

Metis Law LLP
‡Leeds *p275* 0113 242 4099

Charles Mia Limited
‡London SW1 *p60* 020 7529 5848

Mian & Co
‡Birmingham *p140* 0121 684 8000

Michael & Company
‡Merton SW20 *p60* 020 8944 0877

Michael Conn Goldsobel
‡London W1 *p60* 020 7580 8902

Michael Gerard Mcfall
‡London SW11 *p60* 07801 413302

Michael Henderson & Co
‡Washington *p423* 0191 415 1158

Michaels & Co
‡Woodford Green *p439* 020 8245 1138

Micheal Seifert
‡London W1 *p60* 020 3206 2700

Michelmores LLP
‡Exeter *p221* 01392 688688
London W1 *p60* 020 7659 7660
Sidmouth *p380* 01395 512515

Middlesex Law Chambers
‡Southall *p384* 020 8843 1172

Middleton & Upsall LLP
‡Warminster *p421* 01985 214444

Chris Middleton Solicitor
‡Rotherham *p367* 01709 365020

Middleton Dummer
‡Oldbury *p340* 0121 544 4788

Middleweeks Solicitors
‡Manchester *p307* 0161 839 7255

Midwinters
‡Cheltenham *p188* 01242 514674

Milbank Tweed Hadley & McCloy
‡London EC2 *p60* 020 7615 3000

Milburns
‡Cockermouth *p197* 01900 898010

Milburns Solicitors
‡Workington *p440* 01900 67363
Maryport *p313* 01900 813541
Whitehaven *p431* 01946 694818

Mildwaters Consulting LLP
‡Rugby *p368* 07867 970971 / 01788 560824

Miles & Cash
‡Heanor *p246* 01773 530000
Ripley *p365* 01773 742222

Miles & Partners
‡London E1 *p60* 020 7426 0400

Miles Hutchinson & Lithgow
‡Middlesbrough *p315* 01642 242698
Saltburn-by-the-Sea *p371* 01287 623049 / 622056

Miles-Pierce Solicitors
‡Birmingham *p140* 0800 987 5305

Miles Planning Solicitors
‡Kenilworth *p264* 01608 661111

Chris Mileson
‡Gravesend *p233* 01474 816517

Milford & Dormor
‡Axminster *p120* 01297 32206 / 32207
‡Cullompton *p206* 01823 680846
Chard *p184* 01460 65335 / 61000
Ilminster *p261* 01460 55445
Seaton *p373* 01297 20528

Millan Solicitors
‡Bradford *p154* 01274 660111

Elizabeth M Millar
‡London N6 *p60* 020 8348 3228

Millar Kingsley
‡Surbiton *p402* 020 8390 8727

Neil Millar & Co Solicitors
‡Manchester *p307* 0161 870 0177

Millbank Edge LLP
‡Manchester *p307* 0161 725 7920

Millbank Solicitors
‡London EC1 *p60* 020 7100 1313

Miller & Co Solicitors
‡Haywards Heath *p246* 01444 443366

C M Miller Solicitors
‡Barnet *p124* 020 8449 6151

Caroline Miller & Co
‡Dorking *p212* 01306 627160

Miller Clayton
‡Stanmore *p394* 020 8954 5280

Clifford Miller
‡Beckenham *p129* 020 8663 0044

Daniel Miller
‡Bromley *p167* 020 8460 3247

Miller Evans & Co
‡London E14 *p60* 020 7987 2515

Miller Gardner
‡Manchester *p307* 0161 877 4777

Geoffrey Miller Solicitors
‡Manchester *p307* 0161 274 5580

J S Miller Solicitors
‡Manchester *p307* 0161 274 5588

Miller Law Practice
‡Haringey N8 *p60* 020 8340 2953

Miller Lyons Solicitors
‡Glastonbury *p230* 01458 833660
‡Wells *p425* 01749 674150

Miller Parris
‡Worthing *p442* 01903 205771

Peter J Miller
‡Wandsworth SW17 *p60* 0870 321 7561

Miller Rosenfalck
‡London EC1 *p61* 020 7553 9930

Miller Sands
‡Cambridge *p175* 01223 202345

Stuart Miller & Co
‡Haringey N22 *p61* 020 8888 5225

T R S Miller Solicitors
Hythe *p259* 01303 266861

Tracey Miller Family Law
‡Liverpool *p290* 0151 515 3036

Millerchip Peachey
‡Coventry *p200* 024 7624 3615

Andrew Millet Solicitor
‡London NW3 *p61* 020 7691 4327

Millgate Woodbridge
‡Ampthill *p118* 01525 864820

Millgates Solicitors
‡Leighton Buzzard *p282* 01525 869616

Peter Millican & Co
‡Ashington *p119* 01670 528450

Millichaps
‡Reading *p361* 0118 959 9631 / 07866 704035

Millichips
‡West Bromwich *p427* 0121 500 6363
Solihull *p382* 0121 624 4000

Millington Wallace & Co
‡London N14 *p61* 020 8882 1051

Mills & Bann
‡Newbury *p322* 01635 521545 / 32000

Mills & Co
‡Ashton-in-Makerfield *p119* 01942 719655
‡London W2 *p61* 020 7313 5777
‡Newcastle upon Tyne *p325* 0191 233 2222

Mills & Reeve
‡Cambridge *p175* 01223 364422
Birmingham *p140* 0121 454 4000
Leeds *p275* 0844 561 0011
London EC3 *p61* 020 7648 9220
Manchester *p307* 0844 561 0011
Norwich *p335* 01603 660155

Mills Chody LLP
‡Kenton *p265* 020 8909 0400
Hatch End *p244* 020 8428 2272

Mills Curry
‡Eastcote *p216* 020 8868 8841

David M D Mills
‡Shipston-on-Stour *p378* 0870 753 7700

George Mills
‡Washington *p423* 0191 416 2182

Jeffrey Mills
‡St Neots *p392* 01480 475871 / 219699
Sawtry *p372* 01487 832404
St Ives *p392* 01480 495616 / 494810 / 465757

Miln Macleod Solicitors
‡Exeter *p221* 01392 686920

Milne & Lyall
‡Bridport *p158* 01308 422362

Geoffrey Milne
‡Wellington *p425* 01952 223300 / 223381
Wolverhampton *p438* 01902 373000

Milne Moser
‡Kendal *p264* 01539 729786 / 725582
Milnthorpe *p316* 01539 562263

Milner Elledge
‡Dagenham *p206* 020 8984 0940

Henry Milner & Co
‡London EC1 *p61* 020 7831 9944

Thomas Milner & Co
‡Ely *p218* 01353 860005

Milners Solicitors
‡Leeds *p275* 0113 245 0852
Barnsley *p125* 01226 391173
Pontefract *p351* 01977 644864
Wakefield *p419* 01924 386711

Milton Francis & Hughes Solicitors
‡Oswestry *p342* 01691 654662

Paul Anthony Milton Solicitors
‡Maidenhead *p298* 01628 670497

Milwyn Jenkins
‡Newtown *p330* 01686 626218

Milwyn Jenkins & Jenkins Limited
‡Llanidloes *p292* 01686 412166

Minahan Hirst & Co
‡Cheadle Hulme *p185* 0161 485 8131

Minaides Robson
‡London EC4 *p61* 020 7831 7761

Minards Pavlou
‡Liverpool *p290* 0151 476 2000

Mincoffs Solicitors LLP
‡Newcastle upon Tyne *p325* 0191 281 6151

Minogue & Co
‡London W3 *p61* 020 8752 0540

Minster Law Limited
‡York *p445* 0845 600 3272
Wakefield *p419* 0845 600 3272

Minter Ellison
‡London EC2 *p61* 020 7448 4800

Mintons
‡Leeds *p275* 0113 245 7575

Mintz Levin Cohn Ferris Glovsky & Popeo LLP
‡London EC2 *p61* 020 7726 4000

Mir & Co Solicitors
‡Bradford *p154* 0845 652 0720

Miramar Legal
‡London E2 *p61* 020 3328 1600

A A Mirsons Solicitors Limited
‡London EC4 *p61* 020 7822 2699
Leeds *p275* 0845 050 5678
London SE7 *p61* 020 8856 5500

Mirza & Co
‡Waltham Forest E17 *p61* 020 8520 4416

Mishcon de Reya
‡London WC1 *p61* 020 7440 7000

A V A Mitchell & Co
‡Woodford Green *p439* 020 8504 7766

Alistair Mitchell
‡Bridgnorth *p157* 01746 761545

Mitchell & Co
‡Woodbridge *p439* 01394 386421

Christopher B Mitchell
‡London SW1 *p61* 020 7930 4944

David Rubie Mitchell & Co
‡Sutton *p403* 020 8641 0575

Mitchell Dodds & Co
‡Whitley Bay *p431* 0191 252 2396 / 252 9557

Ian Mitchell Solicitors
‡London SE23 *p61* 020 8291 9767

J P Mitchell
‡London W4 *p61* 020 8994 4565

P M Mitchell
‡London E9 *p61* 020 8986 6934

The Mitchell Plampin Partnership
‡Maldon *p299* 01621 852566

Mitchell Simmonds Solicitors
‡London SE10 *p61* 020 8469 1441

Mitchell Solicitors
‡Harpenden *p239* 01582 414002

Mitchell Wilde
‡Nottingham *p338* 0115 964 8236

Mitchells
‡York *p445* 01904 623751

Mitchells Solicitors
‡Northenden *p333* 0161 945 2299

Barbara Mitchels Solicitor
‡Exmouth *p223* 0870 405 1957

Mitchiners
‡London SE24 *p61* 020 8637 9165

Mitre Consultancy
‡Stone *p398* 01889 505678

A E Mizler & Co Solicitors
‡Pinner *p349* 020 8420 1175

Nikki Modie & Co
‡Croydon *p205* 0870 700 0160

Modsons Solicitors
‡London SE16 *p61* 020 7237 4466

Modus Legal
‡Chester *p191* 01244 372584

Moeran Oughtred & Co
‡Bushey *p172* 020 8421 7175
‡Watford *p423* 01923 256263

Moerans
‡Edgware *p217* 020 8952 0242
Radlett *p358*

Mogers
‡Bath *p127* 01225 750000

Moghadassi & Associates
‡London W1 *p61* 020 7667 6555

Duncan Moghal
‡Newport *p329* 01633 211600
Cardiff *p180* 029 2064 4999

Mohabirs
‡London SW4 *p61* 020 7720 5742 / 7622 5495

John Mohamed & Co
‡Bedworth *p130* 024 7649 1964

Mohammed & Co Solicitors
‡Preston *p357* 01772 888700

B H Mohammed
‡Birmingham *p140* 0121 772 4464

Mohindra Maini Solicitors LLP
‡Manchester *p307* 0161 236 9833

Molesworths Bright Clegg
‡Rochdale *p365* 01706 356666

J B Moloney & Co
‡Leicester *p280* 0116 230 1950

M E Moloney & Company
‡London NW10 *p61* 020 8090 0449
‡London NW2 *p61* 020 7328 9521

Mondair Solicitors
‡Peterborough *p347* 01733 244459

Monioro Less & Co
‡London SE23 *p61* 020 8291 7657

Monk & Turner Solicitors LLP
‡London E1 *p61* 020 7790 3772

Jane Monks Solicitors
‡Manchester *p308* 0161 839 0092

Monro Fisher Wasbrough LLP
‡London WC1 *p61* 020 7404 7001

Mary Monson Solicitors Limited
‡London EC4 *p61* 0161 794 0088

Mary Monson Solicitors Ltd
‡Swinton *p407* 0161 794 0088 / 0808 155 4870

Montague Harris
‡Bristol *p164* 01454 322722 / 313362

Montague Lambert & Co
‡Ealing W5 *p61* 020 8997 2288

Montague Solicitors
‡London N1 *p61* 020 7226 8238

Carole Montano
‡Esher *p220* 01372 465128

Montlake & Co
‡Banstead *p122* 01737 352211

H Montlake & Co
‡Ilford *p260* 020 8532 4800

Moody & Woolley
‡Derby *p209* 01332 344221

P W Moody
‡Barnet *p124* 020 8440 1443

Philip Moody & Co
‡Kew *p265* 020 8948 6388

Moon & Co
‡Ashford *p119* 01233 714055

Moon Beever Solicitors
‡Braintree *p155* 0844 736 9775

Mooneerams Limited
‡Cardiff *p180* 029 2048 3615

Mooney Everett Solicitors
‡Ormskirk *p341* 01695 574111

Moorcroft Wilson Solicitors
‡London NW3 *p61* 020 7794 1771

Moorcrofts LLP
‡Marlow *p313* 01628 470000

Moore & Tibbits
‡Warwick *p422* 01926 491181

Moore Blatch Solicitors
‡Lymington *p296* 01590 625800
Richmond upon Thames *p364* 020 8744 0766
Southampton *p386* 023 8071 8000
Southampton *p386* 023 8071 8000
Wickham *p431* 01489 884100

Moore Brown & Dixon LLP
‡Tewkesbury *p410* 01684 292341
Upton-upon-Severn *p417* 01684 592675

Caroline Moore Law
‡Sheffield *p376* 0114 360 0035

Jane Moore Solicitors
‡Tonbridge *p412* 01732 835555

Nicholas Moore Specialist Employment Lawyers
‡Wellington *p425* 01823 421556

Sheila Moore
‡Durham *p214* 0191 386 5621

Moore Solicitors
‡Wednesbury *p424* 0121 531 0442

Stephen Moore & Co
‡Rugby *p368* 01788 535127
Northampton *p332* 01604 601000

Trevor F Moore & Co
‡Leicester *p280* 01530 261719

Moorehouse Solicitors
‡London N15 *p61* 020 8808 9212

Henry Moorhead & Co
‡Hythe *p259* 01303 262525

Moorhead James LLP
‡London EC4 *p61* 020 7831 8888

Moosa-Duke
‡Leicester *p280* 0800 952 0010

Moran & Co
‡Tamworth *p407* 01827 54631

Nina Moran-Watson
‡Clacton-on-Sea *p195* 0845 241 5633

I A Morcowitz
‡Hove *p255* 01273 251769
‡St Albans *p390* 01727 840570

Mordens Solicitors
‡Morden *p318*

Mordi & Co Solicitors
‡London N7 *p61* 020 7619 9666

More Fisher Brown
‡London EC4 *p61* . . . 020 7330 8000

Moreb Limited
‡Llandeilo *p291* . . . 01558 822215

Morecrofts Solicitors LLP
‡Liverpool *p290* . . . 0151 236 8871
Birkenhead *p134* . . . 0151 666 2210
Crosby *p203* . . . 0151 924 9234
Liverpool *p290* . . . 0151 428 1911

Moreland & Co Solicitors
‡Haringey N22 *p61* . . . 020 8881 8833

Morgan & Co
‡Basingstoke *p127* . . . 01256 329888
‡Stourbridge *p399* . . . 01384 440069
‡Swindon *p406* . . . 01793 512982

Morgan & Lamplugh
‡Hastings *p243* . . . 01424 721821

Morgan & Morgan
‡London W1 *p61* . . . 020 7493 1978

Morgan & Richardson
‡Cardigan *p181* . . . 01239 612302

Morgan Brown & Cahill Solicitors
‡Manchester *p308* . . . 0161 740 7468
London WC2 *p61* . . . 0845 303 7416
Salford *p371* . . . 0161 834 6662

Morgan Clarke Solicitors
‡Cirencester *p195* . . . 01285 650066

Morgan Cole
‡Cardiff *p180* . . . 029 2038 5385
Bristol *p164* . . . 0117 916 7220
Oxford *p344* . . . 01865 262600
Reading *p361* . . . 0118 955 3000
Reading *p361* . . . 0118 982 2500
Swansea *p405* . . . 01792 634634

Morgan Denton Jones LLP
‡Cardiff *p180* . . . 029 2053 7740

Douglas Morgan Solicitors
‡Harrow *p242* . . . 020 8863 3655

Godfrey Morgan
‡Norwich *p335* . . . 01603 595700

Morgan Hall Solicitors
‡Ilford *p260* . . . 020 8514 4448

James Morgan Solicitors
‡Cardiff *p180* . . . 029 2038 2111 / 2022 1600

John Morgan & Partners
‡Mountain Ash *p319* . . . 01443 473708

John Morgan Solicitors
‡Birmingham *p140* . . . 0121 233 1852

Morgan Jones & Pett
‡Norwich *p335* . . . 01603 877000

L Morgan & Co
‡Brent NW10 *p61* . . . 020 8965 2850

Morgan Laroche
‡Swansea *p405* . . . 01792 776756

Morgan Lewis & Bockius
‡London EC4 *p61* . . . 020 3201 5000

Morgan Mark Solicitors
‡Ilford *p260* . . . 020 8553 0255

Morgan Reed Solicitors
‡London W2 *p61* . . . 020 7402 9000

Richard C Morgan
‡London NW6 *p61* . . . 020 8459 0646

Morgan Rose Solicitors
‡London WC2 *p62* . . . 020 7242 2520

Morgan Russell LLP
‡Esher *p220* . . . 01372 461411

Stephen Morgan & Co
‡Exeter *p221* . . . 01392 215121

Morgan Walker
‡London WC2 *p62* . . . 020 7831 8333

Morgans
‡Abergavenny *p113* . . . 01873 859993
‡Cardiff *p180* . . . 029 2072 9888
‡Swansea *p405* . . . 01792 512403
Cardiff *p180* . . . 029 2059 5155
Milford Haven *p316* . . . 01646 697039
Swansea *p405* . . . 01792 479150

Morgans Solicitors
‡Harrow *p242* . . . 020 7912 9390
‡London EC3 *p62* . . . 020 7481 1003

Morley Brown & Co
‡Boston *p151* . . . 01205 364986

C P Morley
‡Manchester *p308* . . . 0161 865 1771

John Morley & Co
‡Rainham *p359* . . . 01634 375444
Chatham *p185* . . . 01634 668516

Morlings
‡Maidstone *p299* . . . 01622 673081

Mornements Solicitors
‡Yeovil *p443* . . . 01935 863333

Moroneys
‡Attleborough *p120* . . . 01953 455806
Wymondham *p443* . . . 01953 607042

Morris & Bates
‡Aberystwyth *p114* . . . 01970 625566
Knighton *p269* . . . 01547 520130
Llandrindod Wells *p291* . . . 01597 829055

Morris & Co Solicitors
‡Chelmsford *p187* . . . 01245 345999

Anthony Morris Solicitors
‡Crawley *p202* . . . 01293 519619

Beverley Morris & Co
‡Lewisham SE3 *p62* . . . 020 8852 4433
London EC4 *p62* . . . 020 8852 4433
London SE13 *p62* . . . 020 8852 4433

Duncan Morris Solicitors Limited
‡Marlborough *p313* . . . 01672 515193

Morris Goddard & Ward Solicitors
‡Devizes *p210* . . . 0845 680 2425

Ieuan Morris & Co
Llandovery *p291* . . . 01550 720300 / 720780

John Morris Solicitors
‡Cardiff *p180* . . . 029 2066 7788

Mark Morris Solicitors
‡London EC2 *p62* . . . 020 7274 8155

N C Morris & Co
‡London SW7 *p62* . . . 020 7584 8764
Salisbury *p371* . . . 01722 415215

Nicholas Morris
‡London W11 *p62* . . . 020 7792 0890

Morris Orman Hearle
‡Cheltenham *p188* . . . 01242 257188

Morris Read & Co
‡Wolverhampton *p438* . . . 01902 420973 / 710004

Morris Scott & Co
‡Christchurch *p194* . . . 01425 278866

Morris Southerland
‡Canterbury *p177* . . . 01227 830462

Tamsin Morris
‡Nottingham *p338* . . . 0115 962 1649

Morrish Solicitors LLP
‡Leeds *p276* . . . 0113 245 0733
Bradford *p154* . . . 01274 745328
Yeadon *p443* . . . 0113 250 7792

Morrison & Foerster (UK) LLP
‡London EC2 *p62* . . . 020 7920 4000

Morrison & Masters Limited
‡Swindon *p406* . . . 01793 526601

M A Morrison
‡Shrewsbury *p379* . . . 01743 874986

Morrison Spowart
‡London SE6 *p62* . . . 020 8698 9200

MORRISONS SOLICITORS LLP
‡Redhill *p362* . . . 01737 854500
Camberley *p173* . . . 01276 686005
London SW19 *p62* . . . 020 8971 1020
Woking *p437* . . . 01483 726146

JOHN MORSE SOLICITORS
‡Swansea *p405* . . . 01792 648111

Mortimer Clarke Solicitors Limited
‡Steyning *p395* . . . 0845 370 9280

Mortimers
‡Bridgnorth *p157* . . . 01746 761000
Hereford *p248* . . . 01432 355572
Ludlow *p294* . . . 01584 871000

Morton Fraser LLP
‡London EC1 *p62* . . . 020 7397 8621

Morton Law Associates
‡Yeovil *p443* . . . 01935 310500

Morton Price
‡Sheffield *p376* . . . 0114 266 4141

Morton Pugh Welch
‡London EC2 *p62* . . . 020 7374 4141

Morton Solicitors
‡Dunstable *p214* . . . 01582 501240

Mortons
‡Stockport *p396* . . . 0161 477 1121
‡Sunderland *p401* . . . 0191 514 4323

Moseley Chapman & Skemp
‡Sutton Coldfield *p404* . . . 0121 355 4537

Moseley George
‡Cardigan *p181* . . . 01239 623960

R J Moseley LLP
‡Monmouth *p318* . . . 07785 518923

Moseleys
‡Lichfield *p284* . . . 01543 414100

Moss & Co
‡Hackney E5 *p62* . . . 020 8986 8336

Moss & Co Solicitors
‡Gerrards Cross *p229* . . . 01753 895428

Moss & Coleman
‡Hornchurch *p252* . . . 01708 446781

Moss & Haselhurst
Winsford *p435* . . . 01606 592159

Moss & Poulson
‡Shrewsbury *p379* . . . 01743 350571

Moss Beachley Mullem & Coleman
‡Westminster W1 *p62* . 020 7402 1401 / 7723 5783

Moss Fallon LLP
‡Marlborough *p313* . . . 01672 542120

Moss Solicitors LLP
‡Loughborough *p293* . . . 01509 217770
Coalville *p196* . . . 01530 815747

Mosse Solicitors
‡Portchester *p353* . . . 0800 011 6462

Mosshaselhurst
‡Northwich *p333* . . . 01606 74301

Mossop & Bowser
‡Holbeach *p251* . . . 01406 422651
Long Sutton *p293* . . . 01406 363212

Francis Mostyn & Co
‡Slough *p382* . . . 01753 545322

Motley & Hope
‡Biggleswade *p133* . . . 01767 600600

Motor Industry Legal Services
‡London SW5 *p62* . . . 020 7244 6790
Exeter *p222* . . . 020 7244 6790

Motoring Law Defence
Bath *p128* . . . 0808 178 3288

Motoring Lawyers Online
‡Nottingham *p338* . 01623 726242 / 07799 383239

Motoringlawyers.com
‡Altrincham *p117* . . . 0161 233 0900

Mountain Partnership
‡Lewisham SE14 *p62* . . . 020 7732 3737

Move With Us
‡St Ives *p392* . . . 01480 356058 / 0800 074 0242

Mowbray City Advocates
Bath *p128* . . . 01225 400666

Mowbray Woodwards Solicitors
‡Bath *p128* . . . 01225 485700

Mowll & Mowll
‡Dover *p213* . . . 01304 873344

Moxon & Barker
‡Pontefract *p351* . . . 01977 602999

Moxons
‡Pontefract *p351* . . . 01977 703215

E J Moyle
‡Littlehampton *p285* . . . 01903 725143
Rustington *p369* . . . 01903 784447

Mr Laws Solicitors
‡Wandsworth SW17 *p62*
. . . 020 8767 9717 / 8672 3447

Muckle LLP
‡Newcastle upon Tyne *p325* . . . 0191 211 7777

Mugford & Co
‡Fareham *p224* . . . 01329 844555

Elizabeth Muirhead Solicitors
‡London WC2 *p62* . . . 020 7936 4445

Mulberry's Employment Law Solicitors
Brighton *p160* . . . 01273 573850

Mulberrys Employment Law Solicitors
‡London SW1 *p62* . . . 020 7808 7180

Mulcahy Smith
‡Gateshead *p229* . . . 0191 490 1000

Mulcare Jenkins
‡Haywards Heath *p246* . . . 01444 459954

Mulderrigs Solicitors Ltd
‡Rawtenstall *p359* . . . 01706 222852
Oldham *p341* . . . 0161 665 0123

Mullaney & Co
‡Eastbourne *p215* . . . 01323 431292

Stephen Mullarkey Solicitors
‡Holywell *p252* . . . 01352 710657
Flint *p226* . . . 01352 733770

Mullenders
‡Woking *p437* . . . 01483 771733

Helen M Mullins
‡Burntwood *p170* . . . 01543 674295

Mullis & Peake
‡Romford *p366* . . . 01708 784000
Chadwell Heath *p184* . . . 020 8599 2417

Maria D Mulroe Solicitor
‡Camberley *p173* . . . 01252 521556

Mulrooney Craghill Limited
‡Brighton *p160* . . . 01273 692020

Mundays LLP
‡Cobham *p196* . . . 01932 590500

Mundy's
‡Hereford *p248* . . . 01432 265630

Trevor Munn
‡Walton-on-Thames *p420* . . . 01932 269153

Munro Solicitors
‡London E7 *p62* . . . 020 8503 1718
Woodford *p439* . . . 020 8503 1718

Murdochs
‡Waltham Forest E11 *p62* . . . 020 8530 7291

Murphy & Co
‡Watford *p423* . . . 01923 288043

D J Murphy Solicitors
‡Cardiff *p180* . . . 029 2022 1300

M J Murphy
‡Pinner *p349* . . . 020 8866 8929

Simon J Murphy
‡Liverpool *p290* . . . 0151 559 9748

Stuart Q Murphy
‡West Byfleet *p427* . . . 01932 355755

Murray Armstrong Solicitors
‡London W1 *p62* . . . 020 7887 6040

Murray Bayliss
‡Coventry *p200* . . . 024 7663 2950

Murray Bray
‡Beeston *p130* . . . 0115 925 6300

C M Murray
‡London E14 *p62* . . . 020 7718 0090

Murray Cairns & Co
‡Wellington *p425* . . . 01952 261650

Murray Hay Solicitors
‡London SW15 *p62* . . . 020 8780 1225

Murray Hills Solicitors
‡Bridlington *p158* . . . 01262 672249

James Murray Solicitors
‡Bootle *p150* . . . 0151 933 3333
Liverpool *p290* . . . 0151 207 9910

Lynn Murray & Co
‡Cranleigh *p202* . . . 0844 815 0373

Martin Murray & Associates
‡West Drayton *p427* . . . 01895 431332
Reading *p361* . . . 0118 950 8577
Slough *p382* . . . 01753 551313

Murray Roach Solicitors
‡Nailsea *p320* . . . 01275 858266 / 852705

Robin Murray & Co
‡Chatham *p185* . . . 01634 832332

Stephen Murray & Co
‡Perivale *p346* . . . 020 8997 9669

Murrays
‡Bodmin *p148* . . . 01208 72863

Murrays Partnership
‡Southwark SE1 *p62* . . . 020 7701 8653

Murrays Solicitors
‡Bradford *p154* . . . 01274 304448

Murrell Ashworth LLP
‡Truro *p414* . . . 01872 226990

Murrell Associates LLP
‡Newquay *p329* . . . 01872 511270

Warren Murton
‡London WC1 *p62* . . . 020 7404 5511

Leonard B G Muscat
‡Gosforth *p232* . . . 0191 285 8510

Muscatt Walker Hayim
‡London W1 *p62* . . . 020 7486 5131

Mushtaq & Co
‡Birmingham *p140* . . . 0121 622 1786

Mustafa Solicitors
‡Levenshulme *p283* . . . 0161 248 0400

Mustoe Shorter
‡Weymouth *p430* . . . 01305 752700
Dorchester *p212* . . . 01305 250900

Mybrief Solicitors
‡Chatham *p185* . . . 01634 544544

MYER WOLFF
‡Hull *p257* . . . 01482 223693

Myers & Co
‡Stoke-on-Trent *p398* . . . 01782 577000

Myers Fletcher & Gordon
‡London W6 *p62* . . . 020 7610 4433

Jeffrey Myers & Co
‡Leeds *p276* . . . 0113 242 2455

Myers Lister Price
‡Altrincham *p117* . . . 0161 926 9969

Myers Solicitors
‡Worthing *p442* . . . 01903 211088

Andrew Myerson & Co
‡Worthing *p442* . . . 01903 700961

Myles Reback & Co
‡Edgware *p217* . . . 020 8958 8525

Mylles & Co
‡Sunninghill *p402* . . . 01344 623388

Joseph Mynah
‡London N17 *p62* . . . 020 8365 9940

Joseph Mynah & Co Solicitors
‡London EC1 *p62* . . . 020 7430 9696

Myton Law Limited
‡Hull *p257* . . . 01482 382080

N

NA Commercial
‡Doncaster *p212* . . . 01302 341300

N B Law
‡Lincoln *p284* . . . 01526 344858

NBM Eason
Ashby-de-la-Zouch *p118* . . . 01530 560545

NBM Massucco Shelbourne
Cambridge *p175* . . . 01223 211992

NC Law Ltd
‡Milton Keynes *p317* . . . 01908 520295

NCTM LLP
‡London EC3 *p62* . . . 020 7375 9900

NFLA LTD
‡Nottingham *p338* . . . 0115 945 4555
Wellingborough *p424* . . . 01933 222700
Chesterfield *p192* . . . 01246 471900
Rotherham *p367* . . . 01709 373000
Sheffield *p376* . . . 0114 213 3888

NGA
‡Burnley *p169* . . . 01282 457295
Burnley *p169* . . . 01282 450144
Colne *p198* . . . 01282 862000

NK Legal Solicitors Limited
‡Manchester *p308* . . . 0161 249 3994

N Legal
‡Sutton Coldfield p404. . . . . . . 0121 355 8885

NP Lawyers
‡Blackburn p145. . . . . 01254 671100

NP Solicitors
‡Hounslow p254. . . . . 020 8577 7799

NUT SOLICITORS
‡London WC1 p62. . . . . 020 7380 4734

NWL Solicitors
‡London NW6 p63. . . . . 020 7435 9624

NW Law Solicitors
‡Manchester p308. . . . . 0161 772 9922

Nabarro LLP
‡London WC1 p63. . . . . 020 7524 6000
Sheffield p376 . . . . 0114 279 4000

Nadat Solicitors
‡Dewsbury p210. . . . . 01924 505071

Nadim Associates Solicitors Limited
‡Birkenhead p134 . . . . 0151 651 2040
Liverpool p290 . . . . 0151 549 2522

Nag & Co Solicitors
‡London SW9 p63. . . . . 020 7737 1211

Nahlis Christou
‡London WC1 p63. . . . . 020 7278 6888

Dylan Nair Solicitors
‡Preston p357. . . . . 01772 254779

Nairnsey Fisher & Lewis
‡Benfleet p131. . . . . 01268 566655

Naish Estate Agents And Solicitors
‡York p445 . . . . 01904 653564

Nalders Quality Solicitors
‡Truro p414 . . . . 01872 241414
Camborne p173 . . . . 01209 714278
Falmouth p223 . . . . 01326 313441
Helston p246 . . . . 01326 574001
Newquay p329 . . . . 01637 871414
Penzance p346. . . . . 01736 364014
St Austell p391 . . . . 01726 879333
Truro p414 . . . . 01872 241414

Nandy & Co
‡Newham E7 p63 . . . . 020 8536 1800

Nantes
‡Bridport p158. . . . . 01308 422313
Dorchester p212 . . . . 01305 250100
Weymouth p430 . . . . 01305 771000

Napthens LLP
‡Preston p357. . . . . 01772 888444
Blackburn p145. . . . . 01254 667733
Blackpool p146. . . . . 01253 622305
Chorley p194. . . . . 0845 260 2111

Nash & Co Solicitors LLP
‡Plymouth p350. . . . . 01752 664444

J G Nash
‡Stroud p400 . . . . 01453 833652

John Nash & Co Solicitors
‡Wallington p419 . . . . 020 8647 1148

Nasim & Co Solicitors
‡London E7 p63. . . . . 020 8552 8612

Nasir & Co Law Firm
‡London WC2 p63. . . . . 020 7405 3818

Nat Jen Soyege Solicitors
‡London E17 p63 . . . . 020 8509 8543

NatAdo Solicitors
‡London SE8 p63 . . . . 020 8691 9700

Nathan Aaron Solicitors
‡London SE6 p63 . 020 8695 0135 / 07940 356453

Nathan & Co
‡London SW19 p63 . . . . 020 8542 1805

Nathan (KP) & Co
‡Ilford p260 . . . . 020 8551 1661

Nathan Suresh & Amirthan
‡Wembley p426. . . . . 020 8574 1058

V J Nathan Solicitors
‡New Malden p321 . . . . 020 8336 2226

Nathaniel & Co
‡Hackney E8 p63 . . . . 020 7923 0500

Nathene & Co
‡London NW3 p63. . . . . 020 7431 5020

National Lawyer Services- Assault Claims UK
‡Liverpool p290 . . . . 0800 731 8344

Nationwide Probate Solicitors
‡Sheffield p376 . . . . 0114 256 4774

Nationwide Solicitors
‡Ilford p260 . . . . 020 8983 8944

Nauntons Solicitors
‡Sunderland p401 . . . . 0191 521 3047
Peterlee p348. . . . . 0191 527 4050

Nautadutilh
‡London EC2 p63. . . . . 020 7786 9100

Neale Turk
‡Fleet p226 . . . . 01252 811070
Basingstoke p127. . . . . 01256 473013

Neale Turk Rochfort
‡Farnborough p224 . . . . 01252 515155
Camberley p173 . . . . 01276 20551

Neasham Lloyd
‡Bicester p132. . . . . 01869 252161

Ned Nwoko
‡Ealing W5 p63 . . . . 020 8997 6733

Needham Poulier & Partners
‡London N17 p63 . . . . 020 8808 6622

Needhams
‡Bradford p154 . . . . 01274 371088
Bridport p158. . . . . 01308 440034

Needhams Solicitors
‡Leeds p276. . . . . 0800 731 0105

The Needle Partnership
‡Leeds p276. . . . . 0113 237 4008

Alexander Neil
‡London N7 p63. . . . . 020 7609 8000

John A Neil
‡Bristol p164. . . . . 0117 344 5003

Neil McQueen Duncan & Egner
‡Newcastle upon Tyne p326. . . 0191 232 7469

Neil Myerson LLP
‡Altrincham p117 . . . . 0161 941 4000
Altrincham p117 . . . . 0161 941 4000

Neil Ross Sutcliffe & Co
‡Manchester p308. . . . . 0161 838 5454

Neil William Biggs
‡London NW3 p63. . . . . 020 7794 4659

Neirizi Swan Solicitors
‡Richmond upon Thames p364 . . 020 8255 1013

William Nelhams
‡London NW2 p63. . . . . 020 8458 8044

Nellen
‡Westminster W1 p63 . . . . 020 7499 8122

Nelson Guest & Partners
‡Sidcup p380 . . . . .020 8309 5010 / 8309 0558
New Romney p322 . . . . 07870 497468
Sidcup p380 . . . . 020 8309 5010

Nelson Nichols
‡Portsmouth p355 . . . . 023 9265 0623

Nelsons
‡London SE1 p63 . . . . 020 7403 4000
‡Nottingham p338 . . . . 0115 958 6262
‡Tenterden p410. . . . . 01580 767100
Derby p209. . . . . 01332 372372
Leicester p280 . . . . 0116 222 6666

Nesbit Law Group LLP
‡Bury p171 . . . . 0161 763 0050
Leeds p276. . . . . 0113 380 1631
Liverpool p290 . . . . 0845 463 2836
Wembley p426 . . . . 020 8901 9820

Net Employment Solicitors
‡Ashford p119 . . . . 020 8906 6804

Nether Edge Law
‡Sheffield p376 . . . . 0114 268 7638

Neumans LLP
‡London EC4 p63 . . . . 020 7429 3900

Neves
‡Luton p295. . . . . 01582 725311
Northampton p332 . . . . 01604 814500

Neves and Dyer Solicitors
‡Hitchin p251 . . . . 01462 420978

Neves Scott
‡Dartford p207. . . . . 01322 277732

Neves Solicitors
Harpenden p239 . . . . 01582 715234
Milton Keynes p317. . . . . 01908 304560

Henry Nevill & Co
‡Burnham-on-Sea p169 . . . . . . 01278 793936

John Neville & Co
‡London SW9 p63. . . . . 020 3372 4071

Neville-Jones & Co
‡Wareham p421. . . . . 01929 552471
Swanage p404 . . . . . .01929 422666 / 423761

New Hampton Law
‡Birmingham p141. . . . . 0121 551 9777

New Media Law LLP
‡London W1 p63 . . . . 020 7734 9777

Ian Newbery & Co
‡Poole p353. . . . . 01202 669986

Newbold & Co
‡Cwmbran p206. . . . . 01633 874715

Gary Newbury
‡Porthcawl p353. . . . . 01656 773590

Newbys
‡Stockton-on-Tees p397. .01642 673733 / 676666
Guisborough p237 . . . .01287 632208 / 632209
Middlesbrough p315 . . .01642 247717 / 247967

Newells
‡Halifax p238 . . . . 01422 250250

Robert Newey & Co
‡London SE1 p63 . . . . 020 7407 9434

NewLaw Solicitors
‡Cardiff p180 . . . . 0870 756 6870
‡Cardiff p180 . . . . 0845 521 0945

Newman & Bond
‡Barnsley p125 . . . . 01226 213434

Newman Law
‡Barnet N3 p63 . . . . 020 8349 2655

Patrick Newman & Co
‡Lewes p283 . . . . 01273 479991

Newmans
‡London W1 p63 . . . . 020 3170 7045

Newmans Solicitors
‡Horley p252 . . . . 01293 771521

Newshams Limited
‡London WC2 p63. . . . . 020 7470 8820

Newsome Vaughan LLP
‡Coventry p200 . . . . 024 7663 3433

NEWSTEAD & WALKER
‡Otley p342 . . . . 01943 461414

Alfred Newton & Co
‡Stockport p396 . . . . 0161 480 6551 / 480 1245
Stockport p396 . . . . 0161 430 8831
Wilmslow p433 . . . . 01625 523647

Charles Newton & Co
‡Eastwood p216. . . . . 01773 535535
Ilkeston p261 . . . . 0115 930 5070

Newton Law Practice
‡Birmingham p141. . . . . 0121 357 0100

Newtons
‡Camden NW3 p63 . .020 7794 9696 / 7435 5351

Nexus Solicitors
‡Manchester p308. . . . . 0161 819 4900
Knutsford p269 . . . . 01565 632152

Nicholas & Co
‡Birmingham p141. . . . . 0121 444 3822
‡London W1 p63 . . . . 020 7323 4450

Nicholas & Partners
‡Manchester p308. . . . . 0161 202 4999

Nicholas Hancock Solicitor
‡Hassocks p243. . . . . 01273 841815

Nicholas Solicitors
‡Wembley p426 . . . . 07869 259049

Nicholls & Co Limited
‡Birmingham p141. . . . . 0845 194 9570

Nicholls & Co
‡Harrogate p240. . . . . 01423 530103

Nicholls & Sainsbury
‡Saltash p371 . . . . 01752 846116

Nicholls Brimble & Co
‡Smethwick p382 . . . . 0121 429 8016

Nicholls Christie & Crocker
‡Uxbridge p417 . . . . 01895 256216
Harrow p242 . . . . 020 8863 6366

Nicholls Henstock & Stevenson
‡Altrincham p117 . . . . 0161 980 6099

Nicholls Lindsell & Harris and Ingham & Wainwright
‡Poynton p355. . . . . 01625 876411

Nicholls Locke
‡Altrincham p117 . . . . 0161 904 9595

Mark Nicholls
‡Kettering p265 . . . . 01536 502843

Nichols & Nichols Solicitors
‡Oxted p344. . . . . 01883 734751

Nichols Marcy Dawson
‡Walton-on-Thames p420 . . . . . 01932 219500

Nicholson & Morgan
‡Ponteland p351. . . . . .01661 871012 / 823381

Nicholson Davis Solicitors
‡West Bridgford p427
. . . . 0333 577 0977 / 0115 933 8636

Iain Nicholson & Co
‡Ponteland p351. . . . . 01661 823863

Nicholson Martin Legge & Miller
‡Houghton Le Spring p253. . . . . 0191 584 2841
Stanley p394 . . . . 01207 232277

Nicholson Portnell
‡Hexham p249 . . . . 01434 603656

Nicholsons
‡Chorley p194. . . . . 01772 601700

Nicholsons Solicitors LLP
‡Lowestoft p294. . . . . 01502 532300

Nicol Denvir & Purnell
‡Cardiff p180 . . . . 029 2079 6311

Nicolaou Solicitors
‡Hertford p249. . . . . 01707 877707

Nicole Little
‡Bristol p164. . . . . 07909 966231

Nicos & Co
‡Haringey N22 p63 . . . . 020 8888 1166

Alan Niekirk Solicitor
‡Brampton p156. . . . . 01697 72833

Nigel Broadhead Mynard
‡Chelmsford p187 . . . . 01245 269909

Nigel Davis Solicitors
‡Burton-in-Kendal p170 . . . . . . 01524 784260

NIGHTINGALES SOLICITORS LIMITED
‡Stockport p396 . . . . 01663 764038

Nikolich & Carter
‡Manchester p308. . . . . 0161 831 7044

Nile Arnall Solicitors
‡Bristol p164. . . . . 0117 909 8898

Niman & Co
‡Haringey N15 p63 . . . . 020 8809 4923

Nixon Peabody International LLP
‡London EC4 p63 . . . . 020 7653 9760

Noble
‡Shefford p377 . . . . 01462 814055
Luton p295 . . . . 01582 749490
Welwyn Garden City p425 . . . . 01707 326241

Noble Harbour Solicitors
‡Milford Haven p316. . . . . 01646 663991
Pembroke Dock p345. . . . . . . 01646 681559

Noble Solicitors
‡Luton p295 . . . . 01582 454083

NOCKOLDS
‡Bishop's Stortford p144. . . . . . 01279 755777

Nomos Legal Services Limited
‡Ascot p118 . . . . 07894 253120

Rodney W Noon & Co Solicitors
‡Harrogate p240. . . . . 01423 564555

Noorani Law
‡London W1 p63 . . . . 020 7486 1131

Noori Rashid & Co Solicitors
‡Southall p384. . . . . 020 8893 6787

Norcliffe & Co
‡Huddersfield p256 . . . . 01484 514907

Norcross Lees & Riches
‡Oldham p341. . . . . 0161 624 6034

Noronha Advogados
‡London SW3 p64. . . . . 020 7581 5040

NORRIE WAITE & SLATER
‡Sheffield p377 . . . . 0114 276 6166
Rotherham p367 . . . . 01709 523983
Sheffield p377 . . . . 0114 248 4890
Sheffield p377 . . . . 0114 276 5015

Norris & Miles
‡Tenbury Wells p409. . . . . 01584 810575

North Ainley Halliwell
‡Oldham p341. . . . . 0161 624 5614

North Solicitors
‡Blackpool p147. . . . . 01253 200300

North Star Tax
‡Tadcaster p407. . . . . 01937 830065

North West Employment Law
‡Chorley p194. . . . . 01257 231458

North Yorkshire Law
‡Scarborough p372 . . . . 01723 360001
Helmsley p246 . . . . 01439 770207
Whitby p430 . . . . 01947 602131

Mike Northern Legal
‡Gravesend p233 . . . . 01474 329961

Northone Solicitors LLP
‡Leeds p276. . . . . 0845 863 0832

Northrop McNaughtan Deller
‡London W9 p64 . . . . 020 7289 7300

Northwood Law Practice
‡Northwood p333 . . . . 01923 826208

Northwood Reid
‡Oxford p344 . . . . 01865 811101

Norton & Co
‡Denton p208 . . . . 0161 223 5411
‡Prescot p356. . . . . 0151 426 7001
Hyde p259 . . . . 0161 366 8333

Paul Norton & Co
‡Luton p295. . . . . 01582 494970

Norton Peskett
‡Great Yarmouth p234. . . . . . . 01493 652204
‡Lowestoft p294. . . . . 01502 533000
Beccles p129. . . . . 01502 718700
Great Yarmouth p234. . . . . . . 01493 849200
Halesworth p238 . . . . 01986 872513

Norton Rose LLP
‡London SE1 p64 . . . . 020 7283 6000

Martin Nossel & Co
‡Basildon p126 . . . . 01268 289555

Notable Services LLP
‡London W1 p64 . . . . 020 7034 5204

Nottage & Co
‡London NW1 p64

Novalex Solicitors
‡Milton Keynes p317. . . . . 01908 440020

Now Legal
‡Fareham p224 . . . . 0845 678 0150

Nowell Meller Solicitors Limited
‡Stafford p393. . . . . 01785 252377
Stoke-on-Trent p398

Nualaw Limited
‡Southam p385 . . . . 01926 888953

Number One Legal Ltd
‡Doncaster p212 . . . . 01302 760457
High Wycombe p250 . . . . 01628 528555

A R Nunn
‡Bridgnorth p157 . . . . 01746 768400

Nunn Rickard Solicitors Adovocates
‡Exeter p222 . . . . 01392 200888

T N Nunns
‡Bexleyheath p132 . . . . 020 8304 2538

Nur & Co Solicitors
‡Bradford p154 . . . . 01274 656465

Nuttall Hogg
‡Stockport p396. . . . . 0161 480 0901

Nutter & Richards Solicitors
‡Caldicot p172. . . . . 01291 420361

Nyland & Beattie
‡Widnes p432. . . . . 0151 424 5656

B M Nyman & Co
‡Haringey N2 p64 . . . . 020 8365 3060

O

Gordon O'Brien
‡Huyton *p258* 0151 489 4899

O'Brien Lewis & James
Cardiff *p180* 029 2061 1471

Stefanie O'Bryen Solicitor
‡Watlington *p424* 01491 614700

O'Callaghan & Co
‡London WC1 *p64* 020 7831 3455

B S O'Connor & Co
‡Romford *p366* 01708 700042

Bryan O'Connor & Co
‡Southwark SE1 *p64* 020 7407 2643

John O'Connor Solicitors
‡Derby *p209* 01332 345533
Nottingham *p338* 0115 958 6848

Sean O'Connor
‡Tonbridge *p412* 01732 365378

O'Connors LLP
‡Liverpool *p290* 0151 906 1000

O'Donnells
‡Preston *p357* 01772 881000

O'Garra's
‡Leeds *p276* 0113 247 1477

O'Gorman & Co
‡Warwick *p422* 01926 409900

Thomas O'Gorman Solicitors
‡Sutton Coldfield *p403* 0121 321 2820

O'Hara Solicitors
‡Waterlooville *p423* 023 9225 9822

Theresa O'Hare Solicitor
‡Wimborne *p433* 01202 840153

O'Keeffe & Co
‡Woking *p437* 01483 740734

O'Keeffe Solicitors
‡Brent NW6 *p64* 020 7644 8800

O'Mahoney & Company
‡Birmingham *p141* 0121 355 5571

O'Malley Solicitors
‡Cambridge *p175* 01954 202075

O'Melveny & Myers LLP
‡London EC4 *p64* 020 7088 0000

J O'Neill & Co
‡Southport *p388* 0800 234 6173

James O'Neill
‡Morden *p318* 020 8648 1631

John O'Neill & Co
‡Gosforth *p232* 0191 246 4000

Karen O'Neill & Co
‡Newton Abbot *p329* 01626 366399

O'Neill Morgan Solicitors Limited
‡Stockport *p396* 0161 429 8383

O'Neill Patient
‡Stockport *p396* 0161 483 8555

O'Neill Solicitors
‡Newcastle upon Tyne *p326* 0191 232 9008

O'Reilly's Solicitors Limited
‡Salford *p371* 0161 819 5999

O'Riordan & Co
‡Chorley *p194* 01257 262837

O'Rourke Reid & Co
‡Leeds *p276* 0113 245 7811

Cliona O'Tuama
‡London EC4 *p64* 020 7489 2015

OBW Perera
‡Colchester *p197* 01206 541111

OCL Solicitors Limited
‡Derby *p209* 01332 753572

OGR Stock Denton
‡London N3 *p64* 020 8349 0321

OJN Solicitors
‡Enfield *p219* 020 3232 2135

OMW Solicitors
‡Burton-on-Trent *p170* 01283 563401 / 530333

OP Law
‡Loughton *p294* 020 8418 8380

ORJ Solicitors LLP
‡Stafford *p393* 01785 223440

ORR Litchfield LLP
‡London WC2 *p64* 020 7395 2180

Oak Solicitors Limited
‡London SW1 *p64* 020 7960 6043

Oak Tree Solicitors
‡Sheffield *p377* 01909 547103

Jane Oakes
‡Cambridge *p175* 01223 253733

The Oakes Partnership
‡Macclesfield *p297* 01625 422944

Oakland & Co
‡London NW8 *p64* 020 7722 7257

The Oakley Shee Partnership
‡London SE1 *p64* 020 7089 9066

Vincent Oakley Solicitor
‡Wolverhampton *p438* 01902 743333

Oakleys Solicitors
‡London SW10 *p64* 020 7351 1399

Oaks Solicitors
‡Huddersfield *p256* 01484 542754
‡London NW6 *p64* 020 7644 0203
‡Wembley *p426* 020 8970 2159

Oates Hanson
‡Huddersfield *p256* 01484 300609

Obadiah Rose Solicitors
‡London SE4 *p64* 020 8691 0222

Obaseki Solicitors
‡London E2 *p64* 020 7739 7549

Oberman Law
‡Camden WC1 *p64* 020 7242 6154

David A Obrart
‡London WC2 *p64* 020 7379 4441

Occasio Legal
‡Manchester *p308* 0161 831 9961

Ocean Property Lawyer
‡Bristol *p164* 0117 916 6600

Michael Oerton
‡Barnstaple *p125* 01271 378686

Beverley Ogden & Co
‡Lewes *p283* 01273 474159

Ogden Lyles & Fox
‡Eccles *p216* 0161 789 2793
Irlam *p263* 0161 775 3744

Ogier
‡London EC2 *p64* 020 7160 5000

Ogilvy Renault
‡London EC3 *p64* 020 7444 1910

Oglethorpe & Broatch
Keswick *p265* 01768 772125

OGLETHORPE STURTON & GILLIBRAND
‡Lancaster *p270* 01524 846846
Kirkby Lonsdale *p268* 01524 271388

JONATHAN OGLEY & ASSOCIATES - SPANISH PROPERTY LAWYERS
‡Exeter *p222* 01392 462282

Anthony Ogunfeibo & Co
‡London SE5 *p64* 020 7501 9898

Okafor & Co Solicitors
‡Barking *p123* 020 8594 7266

Okell & Stewart
‡Ross-on-Wye *p367* 01989 762009

Ola Leslie Solicitors
‡London WC2 *p64* 020 7183 0084

Oldham Marsh Page Flavell
‡Melton Mowbray *p314* 01664 563162

Oldhams Solicitors & Advocates
‡Baldock *p121* 01462 895444

A Oldschool & Co
‡London N1 *p64* 020 7359 8345

Olephant Solicitors
‡London WC2 *p64* 020 7486 9627

Olisakwe Vincent Onuegbu
‡London EC1 *p64* 020 7613 1166

Oliver & Co
‡Chester *p191* 01244 312306

Edward Oliver & Co
‡Cheshunt *p189* 01992 633491

Oliver Legal
‡Ipswich *p262* 01473 359222

Olliers
‡Manchester *p308* 0161 834 1515

Olswang LLP
‡London WC1 *p64* 020 7067 3000
Reading *p361* 020 7067 3000

M Olubi Solicitors
‡Lambeth SW9 *p64* 020 7737 3400 / 07956 394567

Margaret Olusegun
‡London SE2 *p64* 01322 431807 / 07882 194223

On Demand Lawyers
‡London SE13 *p65* 0800 234 3529

On Demand Lawyers Ltd
‡Lincoln *p284* 01522 806386

On Legal
‡Halifax *p238* 01274 608353

One Source Full Services
‡Beckenham *p129* 020 8432 4077

Onhand Counsel Limited
‡St Albans *p390* 01727 867289

Onions & Davies
‡Market Drayton *p312* 01630 652405

John Onions
‡Stratford-upon-Avon *p400* 01789 269899

Onside Law
‡London SW6 *p65* 020 7384 6920

Onyems & Partners
‡Waltham Forest E17 *p65* 020 8520 2500

Openshaws
‡Bideford *p132* 01237 478900

Michael Oppler & Co
‡London SW14 *p65* 020 8878 4195 / 8878 4180

Optima Legal Services Limited
Newcastle upon Tyne *p326* 0844 571 6700

Optima Legal Services Ltd
‡Bradford *p154* 0871 880 8080

Optimum Law Solicitors
‡Bootle *p150* 0845 649 8101

Optimus Law Group
‡London SW1 *p65* 020 3178 7958

Oracle Solicitors
‡London W1 *p65* 0870 752 1388

Orbis Solicitors
‡Ramsbottom *p359* 01706 283610

Orchid Law
‡Ashford *p119* 01233 822250

Origin Limited
‡London NW5 *p65* 020 7424 1950

Orion Solicitors LLP
‡Hounslow *p254* 020 8577 7130

Orme & Slade Ltd
‡Ledbury *p271* 01531 632226

Ormerods
‡Croydon *p205* 020 8686 5000
London SW19 *p65* 020 8686 5000
Reigate *p363* 020 8686 5000

Ormrods Solicitors & Advocates
‡Thornton Cleveleys *p411* 01253 850777

Orrick Herrington & Sutcliffe LLP
‡London EC2 *p65* 020 7862 4600

Ortolan Legal Limited
‡Warrington *p422* 01925 830895
London W1 *p65* 020 7903 5074

Osborn Abas Hunt
‡Manchester *p308* 0161 200 8450

Osborne & Co
‡Birmingham *p141* 0121 200 1074

Osborne Clarke
‡Bristol *p164* 0117 917 3000
London EC2 *p65* 020 7105 7000
Reading *p361* 0118 925 2000

Osborne Morris & Morgan
‡Leighton Buzzard *p282* 01525 378177
Milton Keynes *p317* 01908 373282

R J Osborne & Co
‡Corby *p199* 01536 204111
Northampton *p332* 01604 636279
Wellingborough *p424* 01933 273400

Osbornes
‡Camden NW1 *p65* 020 7485 8811

Osborns
‡Colwyn Bay *p198* 01492 532056 / 532820

Osibanjo Ete & Co
‡London SE5 *p65* 020 7708 0077

Osler Donegan Taylor
‡Brighton *p160* 01273 710712
Hassocks *p243* 01273 831574

Oslers Solicitors
‡Cambridge *p175* 01223 352558
Stowmarket *p400* 01449 774670

Osman Ward & Sons
‡Hove *p255* 01273 778787 / 778788

Osmans Solicitors
‡Hounslow *p254* 020 8538 7666

Osmond & Osmond
‡London EC4 *p65* 020 7583 3434

Otten Penna Ltd
‡Northenden *p333* 0161 945 1431
Manchester *p308* 0161 248 3660

Peter Otto & Co Solicitors
‡London SE15 *p65* 020 7252 8278

Oury Clark
‡London WC1 *p65* 020 7607 4300

S R Outram & Co
‡Boston *p151* 01205 365342

Howard Outred & Co
‡Dartford *p207* 01322 224881

Ouvry Creed Solicitors
‡Tetbury *p410* 01666 504005

Ouvry Goodman & Co
‡Sutton *p403* 020 8642 7571

Over Taylor Biggs
‡Exeter *p222* 01392 823811

Overburys & Raymond Thompson
‡Norwich *p335* 01603 610481
Diss *p211* 01379 641221

Owen & Co
‡London NW10 *p65* 020 8459 4836 / 8459 7263
‡Redhill *p362* 01737 760036

Owen & O'Sullivan
‡Ystrad Mynach *p446* 01443 862263

Owen & Osullivan
‡Cardiff *p180* 029 2044 4082

Glyn Owen & Co
‡Colwyn Bay *p198* 01492 532649
Abergele *p113* 01745 833411

Gwyneth O Owen Solicitor
‡Hereford *p248* 01544 318738

I J Owen & Co
‡Oldham *p341* 0161 633 9999

Mark D Owen Solicitors
‡Chippenham *p193* 0161 827 8525

Owen Nash & Co
‡Walsall *p420* 01922 746746

Nigel Owen & Co
‡Chislehurst *p193* 020 8295 1989

Rosie Owen Solicitor
‡Walsall *p420* 01922 712440

Owen White
‡Slough *p382* 01753 876800

Owen White & Catlin
‡Feltham *p225* 020 8890 2836
Addlestone *p114* 01932 845020
Ashford *p119* 01784 254188
Hounslow *p254* 020 8570 5471
London W4 *p65* 020 8987 1400
London W6 *p65* 020 8741 7171
Shepperton *p377* 01932 220451

The Owen-Kenny Partnership
‡Chichester *p193* 01243 532777
Bognor Regis *p148* 01243 864865
Chichester *p193* 01243 532790

John Owens Solicitor
‡St Asaph *p391* 01745 582333

Owens Solicitors
‡Luton *p295* 01582 451210

Owens Stevens Solicitors
‡London E5 *p65* 020 8966 7555

Owoyele Dada & Co
‡London SE5 *p65* 020 7703 4145

Oxford Employment Law Solicitors
‡Oxford *p344* 01865 487136
High Wycombe *p250*

Oxford Law Group
‡Oxford *p344* 01865 297300

Oxley & Coward Solicitors LLP
‡Rotherham *p367* 01709 510999

Oxley & Walsh
‡Weston-super-Mare *p429* 01934 517500

Ozon Solicitors
‡Manchester *p308* 0161 832 0050

Ozoran Turkan & Co
‡London N16 *p65* 020 7354 0802

P

PAIL Solicitors
‡London W1 *p65* 020 7305 7491

P B & W SOLICITORS LLP T/A POOLEY BENDALL & WATSON
‡Ely *p218* 01353 666075
Ely *p218* 01638 780170

P B BRADLEY
‡Stockton-on-Tees *p397* 01642 672220

PB Law
‡Southwick *p389* 01273 592624

PB Legal Limited
‡Crawley *p202* 01293 553000

PBW Solicitors
‡Plymouth *p350* 01752 222206

PCB Lawyers LLP
‡London W1 *p65* 020 7486 2566

PCB Litigation LLP
‡London EC1 *p65* 020 7831 2691

PCB Solicitors LLP
‡Shrewsbury *p379* 01743 248148
Church Stretton *p194* 01694 723818
Knighton *p269* 01547 520254
Ludlow *p294* 01584 878456
Telford *p409* 01952 403000

PCJ Solicitors (LLD)
‡Liverpool *p290* 0151 236 6400

PCM Solicitors LLP
‡London EC4 *p65* 020 7959 2422

PDJ Law
‡Great Dunmow *p233* 01371 871600

P G Solicitors
‡London SW12 *p65* 020 8675 2175

P Ganz & Co
‡Sittingbourne *p380* 01795 830009

PI+ Solicitors
‡Church Stretton *p194* 01694 722134

PJE Solicitors
‡Pontypridd *p352* 01443 408647 / 07970 269478

PJH Law
‡Stamford *p393* 0870 350 5805

P J Legal
‡Spalding *p389* 01406 420023

PJW Legal
‡Liverpool *p290* 0151 427 0274

PJW Solicitors
‡Swansea *p405* 01792 897654

PMN Law
‡Worsley *p441* 0161 799 0768

PPG Criminal Law Ltd
‡Farnborough *p224* 01252 362626

PSR Solicitors
‡Shotton *p379* 0800 321 3239 / 07737 137358

PWC Solicitors
‡Ilford *p260* 020 8478 8791

PWP Solicitors
‡Chelmsford *p187* 01277 841104

PWT Advice Limited
‡Dorking *p212* 0845 833 9025

Pabla & Pabla Solicitors
‡Manchester *p308* 0161 234 2650

Pace Legal Services Limited
‡Bingley *p133* 01274 566886

Valerie Pack Solicitor
‡Henley-in-Arden *p247* 01564 792806

Padva Haslam-Jones & Partners
‡London EC4 *p65* 020 7353 5555

A H Page
‡Ilford *p260* 020 8554 1985

Page & Co
‡Altrincham *p117* 07977 023944

Page Gulliford & Gregory Limited
‡Southampton *p386* 023 8022 5821

M S Page
‡Brighton *p160*

Page Nelson
‡Lincoln *p285* 01522 531741

Painsmith
‡Alton *p116* 01420 565310

Painters
‡Kidderminster *p266* 01562 822295
Kidderminster *p266* 01562 822295
Stourport-on-Severn *p399* 01299 822033

Paisleys
‡Workington *p440* 01900 602235

Kumari Palany & Co
‡London WC2 *p65* 020 7849 3420

Palis Solicitors
‡London NW6 *p65* 020 7604 3572

Palka Downton Solicitors
‡Ringwood *p364* 01425 479997

Colin Palmer & Co
‡Lowestoft *p294* 01502 589277

Palmer Hodgson & Heyes
‡Thornton Cleveleys *p411* 01253 824216
Fleetwood *p226* 01253 778231

J P Palmer Solicitor
‡Leominster *p283* 01568 616253

Palmer Ray
‡Bristol *p164* 0117 944 4678

Palmers
‡Basildon *p126* 01268 240000
‡Bedford *p130* 01234 211161
Grays *p233* 01375 484444
South Woodham Ferrers *p384* 01245 322111

Palmers Criminal Defence Solicitors
‡Deal *p207* 01304 380572

PALMERS SOLICITORS
‡Kingston upon Thames *p267* 020 8549 7444

Panesar & Co
‡Grays *p233* 01375 383283

Pannone LLP
‡Manchester *p308* 0161 909 3000
Altrincham *p117* 0161 926 1960

Parabis Law LLP
‡Folkestone *p227*
‡Halifax *p238* 0844 984 4900

Paragon Law
‡Nottingham *p338* 0115 964 4123
London SW1 *p65* 020 7494 3781

Paragon Law Ltd
‡Leeds *p276* 0113 391 7670

Parcton Law Chambers Solicitors
‡Scunthorpe *p373* 01724 847711

Pardoes
‡Bridgwater *p158* 01278 457891
Taunton *p408* 01823 446200
Yeovil *p444* 01935 382680

Parfitt Cresswell
‡London SW6 *p65* 020 7381 8311
London SE12 *p65* 020 8297 9392

Parfitt Law
‡London SW12 *p65*

Paris & Co
‡Stratford-upon-Avon *p400* 01789 298177

Paris Smith LLP
‡Southampton *p386* 023 8048 2482

Judith Parish Solicitor
‡Weybridge *p430* 01932 842022

Parisi Tax LLP
‡Sutton Coldfield *p403* 07747 100141 / 07958 233827

J Keith Park & Co
‡St Helens *p391* 01744 636000

Park Law
‡Camberley *p173* 01276 804788

Park Legal Services
‡Westcliff-on-Sea *p428* 01702 346641

Park Woodfine Heald Mellows LLP
‡Bedford *p130* 01234 400000
Northampton *p332* 01604 233200
Rushden *p369* 01933 397000

Parker & Co
‡London EC2 *p65* 020 7614 4030
‡London EC2 *p65* 020 7614 3577

Parker Arrenberg
‡London SE6 *p65* 020 8695 2330

Parker Bird Gardner
‡Huddersfield *p256* 01484 825200

Parker Bird Whiteley
‡Huddersfield *p256* 01484 423300

Parker Bullen
‡Salisbury *p371* 01722 412000
Andover *p118* 01264 400500

Parker Grego Cullen & Ball
‡Birmingham *p141* 0121 200 3031

Parker Rhodes Hickmotts
‡Rotherham *p367* 01709 511100
Rotherham *p367* 01709 365116

Parker Thomas
‡London WC2 *p65* 020 7242 5462

Parkers
‡Stockport *p396* 0161 477 9451

Parkes Browne
‡Andover *p118* 01264 333336

Elaine Parkes Solicitors
‡Rye *p370* 01424 883183

Parkes Wilshire Johnson
‡Barnet *p124* 020 8441 1556
Barnet *p124* 020 8364 9955

Parkhouse & Co
‡Bristol *p164* 0117 962 9978

Dale Parkinson & Co
‡Aldeburgh *p115* 01728 453338

Parkinson Wright LLP
‡Worcester *p440* 01905 726789
Droitwich *p213* 01905 775533
Evesham *p220* 01386 761176

Parlby Calder Solicitors
‡Plymouth *p350* 01752 600833

Parlett Kent
‡London EC1 *p66* 020 7430 0712
Exeter *p222* 01392 494455

Parmar & Co Solicitors
‡Preston *p357* 0845 094 4646

Parmars
‡Leicester *p280* 0116 255 5155
Loughborough *p293* 01509 261823

Parnalls Solicitors Limited
‡Launceston *p270* 01566 772375

Parr & Company
‡Leicester *p280* 0116 284 8031

Parrish Solicitors
‡Olney *p341* 01234 711701

Parrott & Coales LLP
‡Aylesbury *p121* 01296 318500

Parry & Co
‡Prescot *p356* 0870 380 4424

Parry Carver
‡Wellington *p425* 01952 641291
Telford *p409* 01952 504757

Parry Davies Clwyd-Jones & Lloyd
‡Llangefni *p292* 01248 723106
Amlwch *p117* 01407 831777 / 830665
Benllech *p131* 01248 852782
Caernarfon *p172* 01286 673381
Pwllheli *p358* 01758 703000 / 701155

Parry Law
‡Whitstable *p431* 01227 276276
Herne Bay *p248* 01227 361131

Michael J Parry
‡Criccieth *p203* 01766 523114

N S Parry Solicitor
‡Halesowen *p237* 0121 550 0194

W Parry & Co
‡Swansea *p405* 01792 470037

Parry Welch Lacey
‡Liverpool *p290* 0151 480 4061

J M Parsons & Co
‡Llanelli *p292* 01554 779940

O H Parsons & Partners
‡London WC2 *p66* 020 7379 7277
Mansfield *p312* 01623 274000

Partners & Co
‡London E11 *p66* 020 8988 9500

Partners Employment Lawyers
‡London EC2 *p66* 0844 800 9239
Epping *p219* 0844 800 9239

Partridge Allen & Co
‡Walsall *p420* 01922 452860

Partridge & Wilson
‡Bury St Edmunds *p171* 01284 762281

Pascalides & Co
‡London WC1 *p66* 020 7837 0049

Passmore Lewis & Jacobs
‡Barry *p126* 01446 721000

Patani & Co
‡Harrow *p242* 020 8909 0449

Patchell Davies (Trading Name of PD Law Ltd)
‡Blackwood *p147* 01495 227128

Patel & Bhatoa
‡Bradford *p154* 01274 669023

Patel & Co
‡Daventry *p207* 01327 311213

Patel & Joachim LLP
‡Ilford *p260* 020 8477 1399

Geeta Patel & Company
‡London N11 *p66* 020 8365 7377

J C Patel
‡Wembley *p426* 020 8903 3519

M M Patel & Co
‡London NW8 *p66* 020 7722 7673

Musa A Patel & Co
‡Dewsbury *p210* 01924 437800
Bradford *p154* 01274 747777

Patersons
‡Lancaster *p270* 01524 843336

Patersons Solicitors
‡Bolton *p149* 01204 308889

Paton & Carpenter
‡Llanelli *p292* 01554 774760 / 751680

Paton Walsh Laundy
‡London SW19 *p66* 020 8946 2229

Patricia Bhutta & Ruth Caro LLP
‡Cheltenham *p188* 01451 832386
Botley *p151* 01865 863128

Patricks Solicitors
‡Newham E12 *p66* 020 8548 8844

Anthony Patten Solicitors
‡Jarrow *p263* 0191 423 3638

Patterson Glenton & Stracey
‡South Shields *p384* 0800 011 6487
Newcastle upon Tyne *p326* 0191 232 8628
South Shields *p384* 0800 011 6487

Patterson Law
‡Newton Abbot *p329* 01626 359800

Margaret Patterson
‡Altrincham *p117* 0161 941 4862

Patterson Sebastian & Co
‡Harrow *p242* 020 3178 5867

Patterson Wolf & Co
‡Ryton *p370* 0191 488 7777

Pattersons Solicitors
‡Halifax *p238* 01422 353555

Pattichi Hill & Croques
‡Ilford *p260* 020 8911 8233

Pattinson & Brewer
‡London WC1 *p66* 020 7400 5100
Bristol *p164* 0117 917 1100
York *p445* 01904 680000

Pattmans
‡Bromsgrove *p167* 01527 872947

Patton Moreno & Asvat
‡London W1 *p66* 020 7491 9200

Patwa Solicitors
‡Bearwood *p129* 0121 429 8666

Paul Ashley Henry
‡Moreton-in-Marsh *p319* 01608 651621

Christian Paul Solicitors
‡Wallington *p419*

Paul G Murrells
‡Tunbridge Wells *p415* 01892 528333

Paul Gubbay Solicitors
‡London W2 *p66* 020 7262 7821

Paul Hastings Janofsky & Walker LLP
‡London E1 *p66* 020 7710 2000

Paul Paveley
‡Southampton *p386* 023 8029 2123

The Paul Rooney Partnership
‡Liverpool *p290* 0151 227 2851

Payne & Gamage
‡Newark *p322* 01636 640649

Payne & Payne
‡Hull *p257* 01482 326446
Hull *p257* 01482 326446

Payne Hicks Beach
‡London WC2 *p66* 020 7465 4300

Margaret Payne
‡Carlisle *p182* 01228 521383

Payne Marsh Stillwell
‡Southampton *p386* 023 8022 3957

Payne Skillington
‡Coventry *p200* 024 7663 3044

Paynes
‡Bedworth *p130* 024 7631 9820

Paynes Solicitors
‡Deal *p207* 01304 372441

M J Payton & Co
‡Malvern *p300* 01684 563318

Payton's Solicitors
‡London EC4 *p66* 020 7405 1999

Peace Farnell Limited
‡London SW19 *p66* 020 3086 8990

Peace Revitt
‡Barnsley *p125* 01226 341111 / 210077
Rotherham *p367* 01709 898454

Peach Grey & Co
‡Southampton *p386* 023 8033 4695

Peachey & Co
‡London WC2 *p66* 020 7316 5200

Peacock & Co
‡London SW19 *p66* 020 8944 5290

Bernard Pearce & Co
‡Enfield *p219* 020 8804 5271

Ian Pearce And Co Solicitors
‡Poole *p353* 01202 681699

James Pearce & Co
‡Birmingham *p141* 0121 784 1886
Birmingham *p141* 0121 360 1300
Birmingham *p141* 0121 382 6622
Sutton Coldfield *p404* 0121 351 5575

R E Pearce & Co
‡Wallington *p419* 020 8652 3574

Pearce West Solicitors
‡Oxford *p344* 01865 812020
Reading *p361* 0118 925 6218

Pearcelegal LLP
‡Solihull *p383* 0844 412 7899

Pearl & Co
‡London NW4 *p66* 020 8202 6202
London N15 *p66* 020 8808 4898
Stanmore *p394* 020 8958 4889

Pearl Baker
‡Rayleigh *p359* 01268 745568

Pearless de Rougemont & Co
‡East Grinstead *p215* 01342 323687

J Pearlman
‡London NW11 *p66* 020 8458 9266

Richard Pearlman & Co
London N1 *p66* 020 7490 7224

Richard Pearlman LLP
‡London EC2 *p66* 020 7739 6100

Pearlmans Solicitors LLP
‡London NW4 *p66* 020 8201 6311

Pearman Smith
‡Walsall *p420* 01922 624164

Pearne & Co
‡Cheltenham *p188* 01242 530622

Pearson & Pearson
‡Kirkby Lonsdale *p268* 01524 271222
Ingleton *p262* 01524 241368
Kendal *p264* 01539 729555
Windermere *p434* 01539 447825

Pearson Caulfield
‡Newcastle upon Tyne *p326* 0191 261 8878

Pearson Fielding Polson
‡Liverpool *p290* 0151 236 3636

Pearson Hinchliffe
‡Oldham *p341* 0161 785 3500

Pearson Lowe
‡Westminster W1 *p66* 020 7224 0888

Pearson Maddin Solicitors
‡New Malden *p321* 020 8949 9500

Pearson Rowe
‡Birmingham *p141* 0121 236 7388

Pearson Solicitors
‡Wisbech *p435* 01945 467053

Pearsons
‡Gillingham *p229* 01634 280150

Pearsons & Ward
‡Malton *p300* 01653 692247

Pearsons Solicitors
‡London SE8 *p66* 020 8694 6498

Graham Peart
‡Manchester *p308* 0161 434 9040

Peasegoods
‡Manchester *p308* 0161 205 2772

Malcolm Peet & Co
‡Wigan *p432* 01257 427867
Atherton *p120* 01942 876115

Pegden & Co
‡London N21 *p66* 020 8360 4715

Peiris Solicitors
‡London N22 *p66* 020 8888 3616

S C Pelentrides & Co
‡London N17 *p66* 020 8365 1688

Pellmans
‡Eynsham *p223* 01865 884400

Pellys Solicitors
‡Cambridge *p175* 01223 654220

Pellys Solicitors Limited
‡Saffron Walden *p370* 01799 514420

Anne M C Pember
‡Northampton *p332* 01604 624732

Pemberton Greenish LLP
‡London SW3 *p66* 020 7591 3333

Pemberton Reid
‡Harrogate *p240* 01423 87308

Pembrokes Solicitors
‡London EC2 *p66* 0800 689 9163

M Pender
‡Woking *p437* 01932 352653

Pendrigh Makin
‡Reigate *p363* 01737 221518
Sevenoaks *p374* 01732 463030

Penfold & McPherson
‡Winchester *p434* 01962 840310

Pengelly & Rylands
‡Tenterden *p410* 01580 762248 / 763008

Pengillys LLP
‡Weymouth *p430* 01305 768888
Dorchester *p212* 01305 768888

The Penhale Practice
‡Morecambe *p319* 01524 401010

Peniel Solicitors
‡Romford *p366* 020 8590 2247

Penman Johnson
‡Watford *p424* . . . . . .01923 225212 / 239566

Penmans
‡Coventry *p200* 024 7622 6575
‡Stanford-le-Hope *p394* 01375 677777
Corringham *p199* 01375 673968
Kenilworth *p264* 01926 858222
Wellesbourne *p424* 01789 470022

Penn Faraday Solicitors
‡Manchester *p308* 0161 832 7550

Penn Sassoli
‡Royston *p368* . . . . . .01763 245234 / 245957

Pennine Kennedy Solicitors
Manchester *p308* 0161 881 3133

Pennine Law
‡Barnsley *p125* 01226 369600
Sheffield *p377* 01226 763551

Pennine Solicitors
‡Rochdale *p365* 01706 671434

Penningtons
‡London EC2 *p66* 020 7457 3000
Basingstoke *p127* 01256 407100
Godalming *p231* 01483 791800

Pension & Investment Partners LLP
‡Leeds *p276* 0113 202 9529

Pension Partners
‡Worcester *p440* 0845 050 6222

Pepi & Co
‡London N14 *p67* 020 8886 0500

Pepperells
‡Scunthorpe *p373* 01724 871999
Hull *p257* 01482 326511

Percival Rose & Co
‡Hythe *p259* 01303 884964

Percy Holt & Nowers
‡Croydon *p205* 020 8688 3603

Percy Hughes & Roberts
‡Birkenhead *p134* 0151 666 9090

Percy Short & Cuthbert
‡Islington N7 *p67* 020 7700 0265

Perera & Co
‡London E7 *p67* 020 8503 0030

Perrins Solicitors LLP
‡Harpenden *p239* 01582 466140

Perry Clements Solicitors
‡Waltham Cross *p420* 01992 655930

PERRY HAY & CO
‡Richmond upon Thames *p364*
. . . . .020 8940 8115 / 8332 7532

Ian Persaud
‡Ipswich *p262* 01473 281103

Personal Injury Practice Ltd
‡Northwich *p333* 01606 350000

Pert & Malim
‡Grantham *p232* 01476 561631

Peter Bloxham
‡London WC2 *p67* 020 7240 0708

Peter Burrows & Co
‡Bristol *p164* 0117 963 6366

Peter Peter & Wright
‡Holsworthy *p251* 01409 253262
Bideford *p133* 01237 472233
Bude *p168* 01288 352101
Okehampton *p340* 01837 52379

Nick Peterken Solicitor
‡Bradford *p154* 01274 733322

Peters & Co
‡Harlow *p239* 01279 453331
Chelmsford *p187* 01279 453331
Dunstable *p214* 01279 453331

Peters & Peters
‡London EC4 *p67* 020 7629 7991

James Peters & Co
‡Sheffield *p377* 0114 278 8900

PETERS LANGSFORD DAVIES
‡Launceston *p270* 01566 772451

Petersfields LLP
‡Cambridge *p175* 01223 451010

Peterson Solicitors
‡Southport *p388* 01704 504350

Petersons
‡Newport *p329* 01633 255151

Petherbridge Bassra Solicitors
‡Bradford *p154* 01274 724114

P M Petherbridge & Co
‡Halesowen *p237* 0121 550 0271

Sue Petritz
‡Horsham *p253* 01403 790218

Petrou & Co
‡London N14 *p67* 020 8920 5800

Petrou Law Partnership
‡London N4 *p67* 020 8802 9393

David Pett & Co
‡Birmingham *p141* 0845 223 8822

Peyto Law
‡Fleet *p226* 01252 617119

Pheby & Co
‡York *p445* 01904 789900

Phil Solicitors
‡London N13 *p67* 020 8888 6199

Philcox Gray & Co
‡London SE15 *p67* 020 7703 2285

Julian Philip & Co
‡Shepperton *p377* 01932 254354

Philipp & Co
‡London N2 *p67* 020 7566 8244

Philippou & Co
‡London N13 *p67* 020 8882 4222

Phillips
‡Freshwater *p227* 01983 755050
‡Mansfield *p312* 01623 658556

Phillips & Co
‡Ludlow *p294* 01584 873156
‡Salisbury *p371* 01722 321666

Phillips & Leigh
‡London EC4 *p67* 020 7822 8888

Phillips & Phillips
‡Harrow *p242* . . . . .020 8422 4435 / 8422 8155

David Phillips & Partners
‡Bootle *p150* 0151 922 5525
Birmingham *p141* 0844 842 5525
Bootle *p150* 0151 933 5525
Chadwell Heath *p184* 020 8597 5557
Leicester *p281* 0116 298 5525
Liverpool *p290* 0151 236 3331
London W1 *p67* 020 7486 5525
London SE18 *p67* 020 8597 5557
London E1 *p67* 020 7709 3061
Manchester *p308* 0161 860 7354
Nelson *p321* 01282 877244
Wealdstone *p424* 020 8861 3800

Fiona Phillips
‡London NW7 *p67* 020 8959 9097

Phillips Green & Murphy
‡Swansea *p405* 01792 468684

Nicola Phillips Solicitors
‡Horsham *p253* . .01403 258965 / 0845 040 5901

Phillips Osbourne
‡Slough *p382* 01628 663344

Samuel Phillips Law Firm
‡Newcastle upon Tyne *p326* . . . 0191 232 8451

Phillips Solicitors
‡Basingstoke *p127* 01256 460830

Phoenix Law Partnership
‡London SW19 *p67* 020 8543 9290

Phoenix Solicitors
‡Leicester *p281* 0116 254 2863

Phoenix Solicitors & Advocates Limited
‡Torquay *p413* 01803 219220

Phoros Trustees (UK) Limited
‡London EC2 *p67* 020 3178 4320

Photiades
‡St Albans *p390* 01727 833134
Harpenden *p239* 01582 766261

Christine Pick Solicitors
‡York *p445* 01430 873593

Pickering & Butters
‡Stafford *p393* 01785 603060
Rugeley *p368* 01889 803080

Duncan A Pickering
‡Bourne *p151* 01778 421757

Janet Pickering
‡Much Birch *p320* 01981 541264

John Pickering & Partners LLP
‡Halifax *p238* 0808 144 0959
Liverpool *p290* 0808 144 0958
Manchester *p308* 0808 144 0957

Pickerings LLP
‡Tamworth *p407* 01827 317070

Peter William Pickles
‡Carlisle *p182* 01697 472223

Roger Pickles & Co
‡Blackburn *p145* 01254 51000

Pickup & Scott
‡Aylesbury *p121* 01296 397794

Pickworths
‡Hemel Hempstead *p247* 01442 261731

Pictons Solicitors LLP
‡Luton *p295* 01582 870870
Hemel Hempstead *p247* 01442 242441
Milton Keynes *p317* 01908 663511

Emyr Pierce & Co
‡Cardiff *p180* 029 2061 6002

Pierce Glynn
‡Southwark SE1 *p67* 020 7407 0007
Bristol *p164* 0117 317 8133

Piercy & Co
‡London SE21 *p67*

Myria Pieri & Co Solicitors
‡London SE24 *p67* 020 7274 8488

Pierre Thomas & Partners
‡London W6 *p67* 020 7602 0305

Francis Piesse
‡London W6 *p67* 020 8748 0010

Richard Pietrowski & Co
‡Guildford *p237* 01483 505398

Pigotts
‡Dover *p213* . . . . . . .01304 210614 / 212206

Pilgrim & Webster
‡Hinckley *p250* 01455 634851

Pilkingtons Solicitors
‡Liverpool *p290* 01704 876624

Pillai & Jones
‡London E15 *p67* 020 8555 3675

Alister Pilling
‡Camborne *p173* 01209 613800

Edward Pilling & Co
‡Oxford *p344* 01865 741122

Pillsbury Winthrop Shaw Pittman LLP
‡London EC2 *p67* 020 7847 9500

Malcolm Pimlott Property Solicitor
‡Hyde *p259* 0161 367 1044

Pinders
‡Derby *p209* 01332 364751

Pinders Solicitors
‡Hatfield *p244* 01707 871514

Pindoria Solicitors
‡London EC2 *p67*
Stanmore *p394* 020 8951 6959

Pinhorn Burnet
‡Hammersmith & Fulham SW6 *p67* 020 7385 6688

Pini Franco LLP
‡London EC1 *p67* 020 7566 3140

Pinidiya Solicitors
‡Southall *p384* 020 8571 3535

Pinkerton Leeke & Co
‡Cheltenham *p188* 01242 237477

Pinkney Grunwells Lawyers LLP
‡Scarborough *p372* 01723 352125
Bridlington *p158* 01262 673445
Filey *p226* 01723 890634
Whitby *p430* 01947 601122

Pinnacle Solicitors
‡Wembley *p426* 020 8970 2132

Pinney Talfourd LLP
‡Upminster *p416* 01708 229444
Brentwood *p156* 01277 268700
Hornchurch *p252* 01708 511000

Pinniger Finch & Co
‡Westbury *p428* 01373 823791

Christopher Pinnion & Co
‡Southend-on-Sea *p387* 01702 338218

Pinsent Masons LLP
‡London EC2 *p67* 020 7418 7000
Birmingham *p141* 0121 200 1050
Bristol *p164* 0117 924 5678
Leeds *p276* 0113 244 5000
Manchester *p308* 0161 234 8234

Pinto Potts LLP
‡Aldershot *p115* 0800 316 4434
Fleet *p226* 01252 361200

Michael W Pipe
‡Paignton *p345* . . . . . .01803 559746 / 529797

Piper Smith Watton LLP
‡London SW1 *p68* 020 7222 9900

H Pipes & Co
‡Melbourne *p314* 01332 862113

Pires Law Firm
‡Carshalton *p183* 020 8648 1671

Pirie Palmann
‡Peterborough *p347* 01733 427799

Alfred Pirotta
‡Waltham Forest E11 *p68* 020 8281 1771

Pitman & Co
‡Bedford *p130* 01234 831333

Pitman Blackstock White
‡Lydney *p296* 01594 842475
Gloucester *p230* 01452 381818

Pitmans LLP
‡Reading *p361* 0118 958 0224
London EC2 *p68* 020 7634 4620

Pitmans SK Sport & Entertainment LLP
‡London EC2 *p68* 020 7634 4620

Pitt & Cooksey
‡Bridgnorth *p157* . . . . .01746 763101 / 763642

Pittalis & Co
‡London N12 *p68* 020 8446 9555

C Pittordou & Co
‡Potters Bar *p355* 01707 663760

PJ Thorniley Solicitors
‡Chester *p191* 01244 394225

Place Blair & Hatch
‡Northallerton *p331* 01609 780101

Placidi & Co
‡Southampton *p386* 01489 579804

Plainlaw LLP
‡Oxford *p344* 01865 240202

Plane Legal LLP
‡Ryde *p369* 07774 847052

The Planning Law Practice
‡Bishop's Stortford *p144* 01279 652505

Damian J Plant & Co
‡Kenilworth *p264* . . . .01926 847741 / 854677

M A Plant
‡Southminster *p388* . . . .01621 773185 / 772794

Charles Platel Solicitors
‡Wokingham *p437* 0118 978 4866

Platinum Partnership Solicitors
‡Bradford *p154* 0845 490 5000

Platt & Fishwick
‡Wigan *p432* 01942 243281
Wigan *p432* 01257 402430

Platt Halpern
‡Oldham *p341* 0161 626 4955
Manchester *p308* 0161 224 2555
Manchester *p309* 0161 834 3114

David Playford & Co
‡Portishead *p354* 01275 840111

Pleass Thomson & Co
‡Clacton-on-Sea *p195* 01255 221133
Colchester *p198* 01206 307454

Plexus Law (A Trading Name of Parabis Law LLP)
Colchester *p198* 0844 245 4950
Evesham *p220* 01386 769160
Leeds *p276* 0844 245 4100
London EC3 *p68* 0844 245 4000
London EC2 *p68* 020 7763 6103
Manchester *p309* 0844 245 4100
Manchester *p309* 0161 214 7933

Plowden-Wardlaw Solicitors
‡London SE23 *p68* 020 7958 1676

Pluck Andrew & Co
‡Hyde *p259* 0161 368 6311
Ashton-under-Lyne *p120* 0161 330 2875

Pococks Solicitors of Whitstable
‡Whitstable *p431* 01227 770222

Ann Pointer
‡Tavistock *p408* 01822 614882

Pollard Bower Solicitors
‡Burnley *p169* 01282 457624

T G Pollard & Co
‡Wells *p425* 01749 674722

Pollecoff Solicitors Ltd
‡London EC2 *p68* 020 7608 2568

Pollok Webb & Gall
‡Great Yarmouth *p234* 01493 853725

Morag Polmear Commercial Lawyer
‡Newcastle upon Tyne *p326* . . . 0191 281 8050

Polpitiya & Co
‡Southall *p384* 020 8813 9282

Lee Pomerance
‡London NW4 *p68* 020 8201 6299

Pond Marsh
‡Blackpool *p147* 01253 620466

Poole & Co
‡Crewkerne *p203* 01460 279100
Ilminster *p261* 01460 52293
London WC1 *p68* 020 7269 9023

Poole Alcock
‡Sandbach *p372* 01270 762325
Alsager *p116* 01270 876550
Chester *p191* 01244 408130
Congleton *p198* 01260 275337
Crewe *p203* 01270 256665
Crewe *p203* 01270 502880
Nantwich *p320* 01270 625478
Northwich *p333* 01606 350445
Warrington *p422* 01925 573447

Poole Townsend
‡Barrow-in-Furness *p125* 01229 811811
Dalton-in-Furness *p206* 01229 467565
Grange-over-Sands *p232* 01539 533316
Kendal *p264* 01539 734455
Ulverston *p416* 01229 588111

Pooley Dale & Co
‡Swindon *p406* 01793 488848

Pope & Co
‡Cromer *p203* 01263 513355
‡Sittingbourne *p380* 01795 474004

J & S P Pope
‡Exeter *p222* 01392 274006

Mike Pope Solicitor
‡Workington *p441* 01900 608363

Poppleston Allen
‡Nottingham *p338* 0115 953 8500
London WC2 *p68* 020 7936 5869

Port & Co
‡Leeds *p276* 0113 242 1212

Porter & Co
‡Sutton *p403* 020 8643 5111

Angela Porter Solicitors
‡Kidlington *p266* 01865 841414

Porter Associates
‡Prescot *p356* 0151 430 9160

David Porter & Co
‡Hull *p257* 01482 325863

Porter Dodson
‡Yeovil *p444* 01935 424581
Dorchester *p212* 01305 262525
Sherborne *p378* 01935 813101
Taunton *p408* 01823 625800
Wellington *p425* 01823 666622

Porters Solicitors
‡Huyton *p259* 0151 489 9427

Portland Legal Services
‡Portland *p354* 01305 866162
Portmans Solicitors
‡Esher *p220*. 01372 464488
Portner & Jaskel LLP
‡London W1 *p68* 020 7616 5300
Portrait Solicitors
‡London WC2 *p69*. 020 7092 6990
Portway Solicitors
‡London E13 *p69* 020 7476 5500
Postlethwaite & Co
‡London WC2 *p69*. 020 7470 8805
Pothecary Witham Weld
‡Westminster SW1 *p69* 020 7821 8211
Potter & Co
‡Matlock *p313*. 01629 582308
Eric Potter Clarkson
‡Nottingham *p338*. 0115 955 2211
Potter Jones & Co
‡St Helens *p391*. 01744 730376
Potter Owtram & Peck
‡Haslemere *p243* 01428 642321
Potter Rees (Serious Injury) Solicitors
‡Manchester *p309*. 0161 237 5888
Potter Shelley & Co
‡Huntingdon *p258* 01480 459531
Stanley J Potts
‡Sunderland *p401* 0191 510 3880
A J Powell & Co
‡Tunbridge Wells *p415*. . . 01892 548784 / 07919 336790
Powell & Co
‡London SE18 *p69* 020 8854 9131
‡Sutton Coldfield *p404*. 0121 355 1001
Powell & Young
‡Pocklington *p351*. 01759 302113
Powell Davies Solicitors
‡Aberystwyth *p114*. 01970 636599
Powell Eddison Freeman & Wilks
‡Harrogate *p240*. 01423 564551
Powell Forster
‡Lambeth SW2 *p69* 020 7737 8111
Powell Gilbert LLP
‡London EC4 *p69* 020 3040 8000
J H Powell & Co
‡Derby *p209*. 01332 372211
S J Powell & Co
‡Congleton *p198*. 01206 292592
Powell Spencer & Partners
‡London NW6 *p69*. 020 7604 5600
‡London W5 *p69* 020 8231 0956
Powells
‡Walton-on-the-Naze *p421*. . . . 01255 675698
‡Weston-super-Mare *p429*. . . . 01934 623501
Power Scott Solicitors
‡Stanley *p394* 01207 230125
Powis & Co
‡Clacton-on-Sea *p195* 01255 233400
Powleys
‡Lowestoft *p294* 01502 581121
John Poyser Solicitors
‡Manchester *p309*. 0161 860 7354
Littleborough *p285* 01706 375968
Pragash & McKenzie
‡Wandsworth SW17 *p69*. 020 8682 2332
Pragesh & McKenzie Solicitors
‡Thornton Heath *p411* 020 8689 0089
PraKtice Legal
‡Rotherham *p367* 01709 790403
Prasad Solicitors
‡Dewsbury *p210*. 01924 464949
Pratchetts Solicitors
‡Peterborough *p347*. 0870 350 8609
Precision Law
‡Sudbury *p401* 01787 211778
Preiskel & Co LLP
‡London EC4 *p69* 020 7583 2120
Premier Law
‡Welwyn Garden City *p425* 01707 830030
Premier Legal Limited
‡Nottingham *p338*. 0845 070 0505
Premier Property Lawyers Ltd
‡Enderby *p218* 0845 234 0217
Premier Solicitors
‡Bedford *p130*. 01234 358080
Prescotts
‡Kidderminster *p266*. 01562 829982
Prester Coleman & Co
‡Northampton *p332* 01604 633133
Prestige Law Solicitors LLP
‡Bolton *p149* 01204 385555
A J Preston Solicitors
‡Newton-le-Willows *p330* 01925 273150
Preston And Company
‡London W1 *p69* 020 7486 8666
Preston Goldburn
‡Falmouth *p223* 01326 318900

Preston Mellor Harrison
‡Chislehurst *p193* 020 8468 7025
Miles Preston & Co
‡London EC4 *p69* 020 7583 0583
Preston Redman
‡Bournemouth *p152*. 01202 292424
Preston-Rouse & Co
‡Camden WC1 *p69* 020 7269 9020
Prestons
‡Poulton-le-Fylde *p355* 01253 882426
Prestons & Kerlys
‡Brentwood *p156* 01277 211755
Prettys
‡Ipswich *p262*. 01473 232121
Chelmsford *p187* 01245 295295
Preuveneers & Co
‡Mitcham *p318* 020 8646 4885
Price & Co Solicitors
‡Bristol *p164*. 0117 949 4144
Price & Kelway
‡Milford Haven *p316*. 01646 695311
Price & Slater
‡Altrincham *p117* 0161 615 5554
Price & Son
‡Haverfordwest *p244* 01437 765331
David Price Solicitors & Advocates
‡London EC4 *p69* 020 7353 9999
Price Law
‡Liverpool *p290* 0151 222 0115
Price Mears & Co
‡Rochdale *p365* 01706 653331
Price Mistry
‡Birmingham *p141*. 0121 200 1577
Neil Price Law
‡Worcester *p440* 01905 422911
PricewaterhouseCoopers Legal LLP
‡London SE1 *p69* 020 7212 1616
Pricketts
‡Stockport *p396* 0161 429 8000
Buxton *p172* 01298 22874
L V Priestley & Son
‡Church Stretton *p195*. 01694 722254
Prime & Co
‡Rugby *p368* 01788 576289
Prime Law
‡Cardiff *p180* 0845 519 0266
PRINCE EVANS
‡Ealing W5 *p69* 020 8567 3477
Prince McCulloch Solicitors
‡Chesterfield *p192*. 0845 331 2723
Principle Law Limited
‡Cardiff *p180* 029 2047 0800
Prior Cumberlidge & Pugh with Jeffery Parr & Co
‡Birmingham *p141*. 0121 707 9211
Prior Law
‡London SE27 *p69* 020 8761 2302
Pritchard & Co
‡Bangor *p122* 01248 370017
Pritchard Edwards & Co
‡Carmarthen *p182*. 01267 234022
Pritchard Englefield
‡London EC2 *p69* 020 7972 9720
Pritchard Jones Evans Lane
‡Caernarfon *p172* 01286 673387
Pritchard Joyce & Hinds
‡Beckenham *p129*. 020 8658 3922
Theo Pritchett
‡Henley-in-Arden *p247* 01564 742215
Pritchetts
‡Westbury-on-Trym *p428* . 0117 307 0266 / 07722 714650
Pro-Leagle
‡Croydon *p205* 020 8680 0088
The Probate Firm
‡Hexham *p249* 01434 600024
Probert & Gray
‡Neath *p320*. 01639 643501
Procol & Candor Solicitors
‡Ealing W3 *p69* 020 8993 4646
Proctor Moore Solicitors
‡London N21 *p69* 020 8364 3111
Proddow Mackay
‡Sheffield *p377* 0114 249 3311
Maidenhead *p298*. 01628 776847
Proffitt & Mann
‡Lowestoft *p294* 01502 538582
Progression Solicitors
‡Ulverston *p416* 01229 580956
ProLegal Limited
‡London EC3 *p69* 020 7743 6700
Prolegis Solicitors LLP
‡Bradford *p154* . . . 07967 109388 / 01274 718690
Properts
‡Chepstow *p189*. 01291 627268
Caldicot *p172*. 01633 882282
Property Law Partners
‡Woking *p437* 01483 768629

Property Lawyers Direct Limited
‡Leicester *p281* 0116 270 3000
Property Legal Solicitors
‡Hale *p237* 0161 941 7449
‡London N14 *p69* 020 8360 7259
Propertyfast Conveyancing Solicitors
Leeds *p276*. 0113 287 2000
Proskauer Rose
‡London W1 *p69* 020 7016 3600
Prospect Law
‡Derby *p209*. 01332 818785
Prospect Solicitors
‡London W4 *p69* 020 8899 6063
Protopapas
‡London W1 *p69* 020 7636 2100
Prowse Thomas
‡Brixham *p166*. 01803 882210
Prusinski Solicitors
‡Loughborough *p293* 01509 233622
Pryers
‡York *p445* 01904 528640
Pryor Jordan Solicitors
‡Nottingham *p338*. 0844 824 3117
Public Interest Lawyers
‡Birmingham *p141*. 0121 515 5069
Public Law Solicitors
‡Birmingham *p141*. 0121 256 0326
Anthony Pugh
‡Barry *p126* 01446 751493
Donald Pugh Solicitor
‡London E4 *p69*. 020 8524 6700
Pulham & Co
‡Saxmundham *p372*. 01728 602084
Nigel S Pullen
‡Perranporth *p346*. 01872 571046
Truro *p414* . . . . .01872 274404 / 276456
Pulvers
‡Watford *p424*. 01923 240666
Pumfrey & Lythaby
‡Orpington *p342*. 01689 833657
Punatar & Co Solicitors
‡London N19 *p69* 020 7272 3330
London E1 *p69*. 020 7173 6111
Punch Robson
‡Middlesbrough *p315* 01642 230700
Middlesbrough *p315* 01642 298830
Stockton-on-Tees *p397* 01642 754050
PURCELL PARKER
‡Birmingham *p141*. 0121 236 9781
Purcell Solicitors
‡Milton Keynes *p317*. 01908 693000
Michael Purden Solicitor
‡Newcastle upon Tyne *p326*. . . . 0191 232 1006
Frank Purdy
‡Westminster W1 *p69* 020 7408 6190
Purdys
‡Reepham *p363*. 01603 870606
Pure Corporate Solicitors
‡Prestatyn *p356* 01745 888061
Pure Employment Law
‡Chichester *p193* 01243 836840
Pure Law LLP
‡Brentwood *p156* 01277 897300
The Purkiss Partnership
‡Farnham *p225* 01252 344311
Puxon Murray LLP
‡London EC3 *p69* 020 7464 4390
James Pyke & Co
‡London SE24 *p70* 020 7733 0081
Pyms
‡Belper *p131* 01773 822307
Pysdens Solicitors
‡London EC3 *p70*. 020 7702 4442

Q

Q & A Solicitors
‡Manchester *p309*. 0161 955 4440
Qamar Solicitors
‡Dewsbury *p210*. 01924 488199
Qayoum & Co Solicitors
‡Bradford *p154* 01274 225098
Quality Solicitors Burroughs Day
‡Bristol *p164*. 0117 929 0333
Portishead *p354* 01275 843213
Quality Solicitors Chapman & Chubb
‡Alfreton *p115*. 01773 540480
Alfreton *p115* 01773 540480
Quality Solicitors Clarke & Son
‡Basingstoke *p127* 01256 320555
Quality Solicitors Copley Clark
‡Sutton *p403* 020 8643 7221
Banstead *p122* 01737 362131
Quality Solicitors HPJV
‡Newport *p329* 01633 242526
Quality Solicitors Mewies
‡Skipton *p381* 01756 799000

QualitySolicitors C Turner
‡Blackburn *p145*. 01254 688400
QualitySolicitors D'Angibau
‡Boscombe *p151* 01202 393506
Poole *p353*. 01202 708634
Poole *p353*. 01202 672598
QualitySolicitors Gruber Garratt
‡Oldham *p341*. 0161 665 3502
Ashton-under-Lyne *p120* 0161 344 2244
Radcliffe *p358* 0161 724 0203
Stalybridge *p393* 0161 303 2328
Worsley *p441*. 0161 794 7479
QualitySolicitors Hill & Abbott
‡Chelmsford *p187* 01245 258892
QualitySolicitors Jackson & Canter
‡Liverpool *p290* 0151 282 1700
QualitySolicitors Jordans
‡Doncaster *p212* 01302 365374
Sheffield *p377* 01909 773627
QualitySolicitors Palmers
‡Fetcham *p226* 01372 454791
Quanticks
‡Reigate *p363*. 01737 233555
Quantrills
‡Ipswich *p263*. 01473 688100
Quantum Law LLP
‡Newcastle upon Tyne *p326*. . . . 0845 226 9008
Quantum Solicitors
‡Worcester *p440* 01905 673311
Quantus Law Solicitors
‡Nottingham *p338*. 0115 960 6565
Quarters Solicitors
‡Bury *p171* 01706 829553
Quastel Midgen LLP
‡London W1 *p70* 020 7908 2525
Quay Legal
‡Bristol *p164*. 0117 344 5108
Quee & Mayanja Solicitors Ltd
‡London NW10 *p70* 020 8438 4547
Queens Solicitors
‡Leicester *p281* 0116 274 7927
D J Quelch
‡Horsham *p253* 01403 865096
Quentin Solt LLP
‡Hatton *p244* 01926 808080
Quercus Law
‡London EC4 *p70*. 020 7936 9816
Quinn & Co
‡Chorley *p194*. 01257 241818
‡Exeter *p222* . . . . 07951 450282 / 01392 248858
Quinn Emanuel Urquhart & Sullivan LLP
‡London EC4 *p70*. 020 7653 2000
Quinn Mantion
‡London E14 *p70* 020 7512 2600
Quinn Melville
‡Liverpool *p290* 0151 236 3340
Quist Solicitors
‡London EC2 *p70* 020 7596 2813

R

R&H Law
‡Croydon *p205* 0800 046 1472
RBM Davies & Partners LLP
‡Neston *p321* 0151 336 6611
RBM Solicitors
‡Coventry *p201* 024 7652 0999
RB Partnership Solicitors
‡Barnet *p124* 020 8275 3877
RCN Legal Services Limited
‡Waterlooville *p423* 023 9236 0914
RFB Associate Limited
‡Milton Keynes *p317*. 01908 410844
RG Law
‡London N11 *p70* 020 8368 5155
RG Legal Solicitors
‡Cardiff *p180* 029 2049 0047
RG Solicitors
‡Sidcup *p380* 020 8269 9900
York *p445* 01904 234095
RHF Solicitors
‡Manchester *p309*. 0161 839 9009
RH Law LLP
‡Manchester *p309*. 0161 286 1111
RH Solicitors
‡Leeds *p276*. 0113 203 1363
RHW Solicitors LLP
‡Guildford *p237* 01483 302000
RJM Solicitors
‡Merthyr Tydfil *p314*. 01685 373721
RJR Solicitors
‡Ryde *p369* 01983 562201
Freshwater *p227* 01983 752115
Newport *p328*. 01983 526924
R J Solicitors Ltd
‡Cleethorpes *p195*. 01472 699599

RKS Solicitors
‡Dewsbury *p210*. 01924 439106

RLS Solicitors
‡London WC2 *p70*. 020 7812 6607

RM Legal Solicitors
‡Southampton *p386* 023 8092 6060

RMPI Solicitors
‡London W1 *p70* 020 7318 4444

R O C K Solicitors
‡London SW12 *p70* 020 8673 5819

RPM Legal
‡Kettering *p265* 01536 722266
Huntingdon *p258* 01480 396396
Stratford-upon-Avon *p400*. 01789 295656

RPN Solicitors
‡Edgware *p217* . . 020 8621 4380 / 07870 567245

R R & Co London Maritime & Energy Solicitors
‡London EC3 *p70* 020 7816 5496

RSE Solicitors
Purley *p358*

RTL Solicitors
‡Cardiff *p180* 029 2023 4030
Bridgend *p157* 01656 665850

RT Law
‡Birmingham *p141*. 0121 459 1414

RVH Solicitors
‡London NW7 *p70*. 020 8371 6656

RW Law
‡Horsham *p253* 01306 700021

RWPS LLP
‡Poole *p353*. 01202 466669
Poole *p353*. 01202 707897

RWP Solicitors
‡Pangbourne *p345*. 0118 984 2266

Penny Raby & Co
‡Pershore *p346* 01386 555114

Donald Race & Newton
‡Burnley *p169*. 01282 433241
Colne *p198*. 01282 864500

Radcliffes Le Brasseur
‡Westminster SW1 *p70* 020 7222 7040
Cardiff *p180* 029 2034 3035
Leeds *p276*. 0113 234 1220

Gillian Radford & Co
‡Westminster W10 *p70* 020 8960 4366

Radia & Co
‡Harrow *p242* 020 8424 2261

Rae & Co Solicitors
‡Southwark SE1 *p70* 020 7407 6256

Rae Nemazee LLP
‡London W4 *p70* 020 8996 1722

Raffles Haig Solicitors
‡London EC1 *p70* 020 7107 2343

Rafina Solicitors
‡Wembley *p426* 020 8908 6742

Rafiq & Co
‡Leeds *p276*. 0113 240 7556

Raghib Ahsan Solicitors
‡Birmingham *p141*. 0121 551 1846 / 07941 284617

Rahman & Co
‡London N15 *p70* 020 8809 4643

Rahman Ravelli Solicitors
‡Halifax *p238* 01422 346666

Rai Legal
‡West Bromwich *p427*
. . . . 0121 580 0511 / 07976 926156

Rai Solicitor
‡Slough *p382* 01753 576800

Railton
‡Brighton *p160* 01273 738285

R Toby Raimes
‡Newcastle upon Tyne *p326*. . . . 0191 230 8086

Rain Gaskell Solicitors
‡Manchester *p309*. 0161 257 2933

Rainer Hughes
‡Brentwood *p156* 01227 226644
Brentwood *p156* 01277 226644

Rait & Co
‡Hayes *p245* 020 8842 0101

Raj & Pillai
‡Hounslow *p254*. 020 8572 7245

Raja & Co
‡London SW17 *p70* 020 8543 4974
‡Wandsworth SW17 *p70*. 020 8772 4900

Chris Raja
‡Edgware *p217* 020 8952 1990

Rajput Solicitors
‡Birmingham *p141*. 0121 777 0300

Rakkani Solicitors
‡Leicester *p281* 0116 299 2999

Raleys
‡Barnsley *p125* 01226 211111

Ralley Solicitors
‡Newport Pagnell *p329* 01908 211234

Ralli Solicitors
‡Manchester *p309*. 0870 998 9000

Ralph & Co
‡Newquay *p329* 01637 872218
Wadebridge *p418*. 01208 812277

Ramsbottom & Co Solicitors Limited
‡Hayling Island *p245*. 023 9246 5931

Ramsdens Solicitors
‡Huddersfield *p256* 01484 821500
Dewsbury *p210*. 01924 455391
Elland *p217*. 01422 372478
Halifax *p238* 01422 330700
Holmfirth *p251* 01484 690040
Huddersfield *p256* 01484 558066
Huddersfield *p256* 01484 844116
Mirfield *p318* 01924 499251

Ramsey Robinson Solicitors
‡Hexham *p249* 01434 610442

Randell Lloyd & Martin
‡Llanelli *p292* 01554 772149

Randle Thomas LLP
‡Helston *p246*. 01326 572951

Ranga & Co
‡London NW10 *p70*. 020 8451 4518

Ranson Houghton
‡Andover *p118*. 01264 351533
Basingstoke *p127*. 01256 816759
Salisbury *p371* 01722 328871

Ransons
‡Walton-on-Thames *p421* 01932 269448

Joseph Raphael Solicitors
‡Huddersfield *p256* 01484 530003

Rapid Response Solicitors
‡Hull *p257*. 01482 345800
‡Hull *p257*. 01482 475762

Rashid & Co Solicitors
‡Birmingham *p141*. 0121 356 0078

Rasiah & Co
‡London SW19 *p70* 020 8543 4040

Isabelle E Rastall
‡Chelmsford *p187* 01245 349966

Ratcliffe & Bibby
‡Carnforth *p183* 01524 734884
Lancaster *p270*. 01524 39039
Morecambe *p319*. 01524 410424

Ratcliffe Duce & Gammer LLP
‡Reading *p361* 0118 957 4291
Wokingham *p437*. 0118 978 3681

Ratcliffe Solicitors
‡Rugby *p368* 01788 833151

Ratcliffes Solicitors
‡Sittingbourne *p380* 01795 477505

Ratip Solicitors
‡London SW16 *p70* 020 8677 0625

Ratna & Co
‡London E6 *p70*. 020 8470 8818

Ratnakumar & Co
‡Ilford *p260* 020 8551 1411

Rausa Mumford
‡Cardiff *p180* 029 2034 4341

Ravals Legal Service
‡Ilford *p260* 020 8590 3407

K Ravi Solicitors
‡Pinner *p349* 020 8866 7800

Ravi Sethi Solicitors
‡Hounslow *p254*. 020 8570 7450

Ravi Solicitors
‡Harrow *p242* 020 8426 1178

Ravian Solicitors
‡Birmingham *p141*. 0121 322 4922

Charmini Ravindran & Co
‡Sutton *p403* 020 8770 7874

Raw & Co
‡Beckenham *p129*. 020 8658 2965

Rawal & Co
‡London N12 *p70* 020 8445 0303

Rawlings Giles
‡London SW11 *p71* 020 7223 2765

Rawlins Davy PLC
‡Bournemouth *p152*. 01202 558844

Rawlison Butler LLP
‡Crawley *p202*. 01293 527744
Horsham *p253* 01403 252492
London W1 *p71*. 020 7887 4548

Raworths LLP
‡Harrogate *p240*. 01423 566666

Rawstorne Heran Solicitors
‡Stratford-upon-Avon *p400* 01789 267646

Ray Borley & Dunkley
‡Stony Stratford *p399* 01908 563232

Ray Nixon Brown
‡Leighton Buzzard *p282*. 01525 372247

Rayat & Co Solicitors
‡Slough *p382* 01753 736815

Rayden Solicitors
‡St Albans *p390*. 020 7112 1453

AL Rayment
‡Chelmsford *p187* 01245 466624

Raymond & Co
‡Islington N1 *p71* 020 7359 0422

Colin Rayner & Co
‡Bolton *p149* 01204 591145

Rayners
‡Chippenham *p193* 01249 650394

The Re-Mortgage Solicitors
‡Leeds *p276*. 0845 053 1160

Read & Co
‡Twickenham *p416* 020 8892 8063

Read Cooper
‡Thame *p410* 01844 260038
Princes Risborough *p358*. 01844 345788

Read Dunn Connell
‡Bradford *p154* 01274 723858
Ilkley *p261* 01943 601173

Francis Read
‡London W1 *p71* 020 7499 4055

Read Law Associates
‡Macclesfield *p297* 01625 429131

Read Roper & Read
‡Manchester *p309*. 0161 832 6905

G & M B Reade
‡Leiston *p282* 01728 833495

T G Readman
‡Plymouth *p350* 01752 880238

Keith Ready & Co
‡Barton-upon-Humber *p126* 01652 632215

Real Estate Law Limited
‡Worthing *p442* 01903 263721

M Reale Solicitors Ltd
‡London SE1 *p71* 020 7921 0525

Michael Reason & Partners LLP
‡London EC4 *p71* 020 7489 2048

Rebecca Emmett Employment Law Consultancy
‡London EC1 *p71* 020 3008 4327

Rebian Solicitors
‡Leeds *p276*. . . . . . 0113 251 2251 / 250 6373

Rebuck Law
‡London WC1 *p71*. 020 7440 4744

Recompense Solicitors Ltd
‡Totnes *p413* 0800 037 5817

Recovery Assist LLP
‡Bury *p171* 0161 762 4949

Reculver Solicitors
‡London EC1 *p71* 020 7324 6271

Red Kite Law
‡Pembroke *p345* 01646 683222
Carmarthen *p183*. 01267 239000
Carmarthen *p183*. 01994 240305
Haverfordwest *p244* 01437 763332
Milford Haven *p316*. 01646 698008
Pembroke Dock *p345*. 01646 681529
Tenby *p410*. 01834 842122

Red Law Solicitors LLP
‡Oldbury *p340*. 0121 010 8727

Redd
‡London EC1 *p71* 020 7776 4760

Reddie & Grose
‡Cambridge *p175* 01223 360350

M Selvi Reddy
‡Caterham *p183*. 01883 340578

Redfearns
‡Heckmondwike *p246* . . 01924 403745 / 404601

Redfern & Co
‡Birmingham *p141*. 0121 236 1801

Redferns
‡Harrow *p242* 020 8424 7070
‡Weymouth *p430* . . . . . 01305 781401 / 782704
Portland *p354*. 01305 823636

Mark Redler & Co
‡Stafford *p393*. 01785 256445

Redmans Solicitors
‡Richmond upon Thames *p364* . . 020 3397 3603

Redmonds Solicitors
‡Oldham *p341*. 01457 879500

R E Redrup & Company
‡Eastcote *p216* 020 8866 4097

The Reece-Jones Partnership
‡Sevenoaks *p374* 01732 457575

Michael J Reed Ltd
‡Carmarthen *p183*. 01267 281675

RICHARD REED
‡Sunderland *p402*. 0191 567 0465

Reed Ryder & Meikle
‡North Shields *p331*. 0191 257 3222

S M Reed & Co
‡Hove *p255* 01273 727351

Reed Smith LLP
London EC2 *p71* 020 3116 3000

Reeds Family Law Solicitors
‡Wakefield *p419*. 01924 201001

Reeds Solicitors
‡Oxford *p344* 01865 260230

Reemans Solicitors
‡Hounslow *p254*. 020 8622 3638

Alun Rees Solicitor
‡Cardiff *p180* 029 2056 3732

Clive Rees Solicitor
‡Swansea *p405* 01792 474201

David Edward Rees & Co
‡Treorchy *p413* 01443 776361

Rees Davies & Partners
‡Swansea *p405* 01792 645962

Rees Myers Solicitors
‡London E7 *p71* 020 8534 4311

Rees Page
‡Wolverhampton *p438*. 01902 577777
Bilston *p133* 01902 577776

Scott Rees & Co
‡Skelmersdale *p381*. 01695 722222

Rees Wood Terry
‡Cardiff *p180* 029 2040 8800

Rees-Roberts Solicitors
‡Liverpool *p290* 0151 255 1300

Reeves & Co
‡Maidstone *p299* 01622 692220

Reeves & Co Solicitors Limited
‡Ashford *p119*. 01233 665054

Reeves Fisher & Sams
‡Brentwood *p156* 01277 202500

Regal Law Solicitors
‡Ilford *p260* 020 8553 4420

Regal Solicitors
‡Prestwich *p358*. 0161 773 3183

Regency Solicitors
‡London NW6 *p71*. 020 7625 5666

Regent Associates Solicitors
‡Northolt *p333*. 020 8841 1100

Regents & Co Solicitors
‡London SW12 *p71*

Regents Solicitors
‡Manchester *p309*. 0161 265 6975

Regnum Solicitors
‡London N1 *p71*. 020 7923 3855

Regulatory Legal Solicitors
‡Stourbridge *p399* 01384 426400

Rehmans Solicitors Ltd
‡Bedford *p130*. 01234 350244

Reid & Co Solicitors
‡Birmingham *p141*. 0121 450 4240

Christine Reid Solicitor
‡Oxford *p344* 01865 864195

Reid Sinclair & Co
‡London SE15 *p71* 020 7358 1110

Reilly & Co Solicitors
‡Birmingham *p141*. 0121 744 4090

Law Offices of Suzanne M Reisman
‡London SW1 *p71*. . . 020 7324 6244 / 7898 9338

Reiss Solicitors
‡Bradford *p154* 01274 395858

Reliance Law
‡London W1 *p71* 020 7436 8733

Remar & Co
‡London SE5 *p71* 020 7252 6722

Joachim G Remde Solicitors
‡London WC2 *p71*. 020 7812 6620

Renaissance
‡London E17 *p71* 020 8521 1100

Renata & Co
‡Birmingham *p141*. 0121 777 7333

Renders
‡Cardiff *p180* 029 2054 4900

Renney & Co Solicitors
‡Bath *p128* 01225 326435

Renshaw Derrick & Co
‡Bournemouth *p152*. 01202 552777

Renshaw Gilchrist & Co
‡Fleetwood *p226* 01253 873569

Renshaws
‡Kendal *p264* 01539 740666

Reorient Legal
‡London EC3 *p71* 020 7645 8255

Res Ipsa Solicitors
‡Birmingham *p141*. 0121 643 0044

Residential Property Lawyers LTD
‡Cirencester *p195*. 01285 651515

Resolute Solicitors
‡Harrogate *p240*. 01423 526444

Rest Harrow & Co Solicitors
‡London SW19 *p71* 020 8544 2752

Reston's Solicitors Limited
‡Warrington *p422* 0870 755 8998

Reward Litigation Ltd
‡Birmingham *p141*. 0845 366 9336

Rexton Law LLP
‡St Albans *p390*. 020 8819 5899

Reynards Solicitors
‡Stockport *p396*. . . . 0161 217 7000 / 217 7002

Reynolds & Hawkes
‡Milton Keynes *p317*. 01908 366521

Reynolds Colman Bradley LLP
‡London EC3 *p71* 020 7220 4700

D H Reynolds
‡Dorchester *p212* 01305 269740

Reynolds Dawson
‡London WC2 *p71*. 020 7839 2373 / 07659 130481

Deborah Reynolds
‡Pentre *p346* 01443 440888

Reynolds Johns Partnership
‡Bishop's Stortford *p144* 01279 508626

Julie Reynolds Solicitors
‡Tunbridge Wells *p415* 01892 673418

Reynolds Macdonald
‡London EC1 *p71* 020 7490 3336

Malcolm Reynolds & Associates
‡Chepstow *p189* 01291 628217

Margaret Reynolds Solicitor
‡Grays *p233* 01375 390239

Mark Reynolds Solicitors LLP
‡Liverpool *p290* 0151 525 7222

Michael P Reynolds Solicitor
‡Leigh-on-Sea *p282* 01702 473548

Reynolds Parry-Jones
‡High Wycombe *p250* 01494 525941

Pauline Reynolds and Co
‡Kirkby *p268* 0151 546 4583

Reynolds Porter Chamberlain LLP
‡London E1 *p71* 020 3060 6000
Bristol *p164* 020 3060 6000

Riaz Khan & Co
‡Barnsley *p125* 01226 283006

Riaz Solicitors
‡Bradford *p154* 01274 662154

Rice-Jones & Smiths
‡London EC1 *p72* 020 7831 2506

Rich & Baily
‡Haringey N8 *p72* 020 8340 2481

Rich & Carr Freer Bouskell
‡Leicester *p281* 0116 253 8021
Blaby *p145* 0116 242 6039
Lutterworth *p296* 0116 242 6048
Oadby *p339* 0116 242 6021
Syston *p407* 0116 242 6036

Richard Filleul Solicitor
‡Wimborne *p433* 01202 849484

Richard George & Jenkins
‡Newtown *p330* 01686 626210

Richard Nelson Business Defence Solicitors
‡Nottingham *p338* 0115 986 3636
Bristol *p164* 0117 942 5678
Cardiff *p180* 029 2064 7513
Manchester *p309* 0161 880 0040
Solihull *p383* 0121 707 7666

Richards & Lewis
‡Ebbw Vale *p216* 01495 350018

Richards & Morgan LLP
‡Bournemouth *p152* 01202 424234

David B Richards
‡Barnsley *p125* 01266 281929

J G Richards
‡Larkfield *p270* 01732 870377

Richards Kibbe & Orbe
‡London EC2 *p72* 020 7033 3150

Martin B Richards
‡London NW7 *p72* 020 8906 1841

R Miles Richards & Co
‡Pontypridd *p352* 01443 202237

Roger Richards
‡Paignton *p345* 01803 845191
Brixham *p166* 01803 854123

Scott Richards
‡Teignmouth *p409* 01626 772441

Richards Solicitors
‡Edgware *p217* 020 8731 5929

Richards Thomas Solicitors
‡Brecon *p156* 01874 623371
‡Cardiff *p180* 01443 757738

Richardson & Co
‡Leeds *p276* 0113 243 1714
York *p445* 01904 642727

Richardson & Davies
‡Coventry *p201* 024 7622 2001

Richardson Law Solicitors
‡Manchester *p309* 0161 266 1114

Richardson Mail Solicitors
‡Sale *p370* 0161 968 3400

Richardson Smith & Co
‡Chesham *p189* 01494 772773

Richardson Solicitors
‡Worthing *p442* 01903 831000

Richardsons Solicitors
‡Hemel Hempstead *p247* 01442 500500

Peter Richbell & Co Solicitors
‡Chelmsford *p187* 01245 355300

Richmond & Barnes
‡London EC1 *p72* 020 7195 2266

Richmond & Co
‡Horsforth *p253* 0113 259 1188

Richmond Anderson Goudie
‡Chester-le-Street *p191* 0191 388 7884

Richmonds
‡Newcastle upon Tyne *p326* 0191 232 2155
Newcastle upon Tyne *p326* 0191 270 1711

Rickards & Cleaver
‡Alfreton *p115* 01773 832204

Rickerbys LLP
‡Cheltenham *p188* 01242 224422

Rider Support Services
‡London SW15 *p72* 020 8246 4900

Ridley & Co
‡Westminster SW1 *p72* 020 7828 7656

Ridley & Hall
‡Huddersfield *p256* 01484 538421

Ridley's
‡Witney *p436* 01993 776341

Ridouts
‡London W1 *p72* 020 7317 0340

Ries Solicitors
‡London WC2 *p72* 020 3397 0499

Garth Rigby & Co
‡Ashton-in-Makerfield *p119* 01942 717378

Rigby Golding
Sunbury-on-Thames *p401* 01932 765741

Lee Rigby Partnership
‡Leyland *p283* 01772 421748

Rigg & Co
‡Bristol *p164* 0117 377 7473

Riley & Co
‡London N5 *p72* 07785 231190

Graham M Riley & Co
‡Southport *p388* 01704 532229

Riley Hayes & Co
‡Wolverhampton *p438* 01902 773666
Bilston *p133* 01902 353300

Jeffrey H Riley Consultant Solicitor
‡Warrington *p422* 01925 740862

Riley Langdon
‡Durham *p214* 0191 378 7620

A V Rillo & Co
‡Enfield *p219* 0800 093 7623

Stephen Rimmer LLP
‡Eastbourne *p216* 01323 644222

Frederick Rine Solicitors
‡Barnet *p124* 020 8440 9833

The Ringrose Law Group
Lincoln *p285* 01522 561020

Rippon Patel & French
‡Westminster W1 *p72* 020 7323 0404

Risbygate Solicitors
‡Bury St Edmunds *p171* 01284 756822

Risdon Hosegood
‡Williton *p433* 01984 632277
Dulverton *p214* 01398 322100
Minehead *p318* . . . . . .01643 703123 / 700008
Taunton *p408* 01823 251571
Wiveliscombe *p436* 01984 623203

Riseam Sharples
‡London WC2 *p72* 020 7836 9555

Rishi & Co Solicitors
‡Hounslow *p254* 020 8570 6862

Rita Sen Solicitors
‡Bognor Regis *p148* 01243 263658
Bognor Regis *p148* 01243 263658

Rix & Kay Solicitors LLP
‡Uckfield *p416* 01825 700177
Hove *p255* 01273 329797
London W1 *p72* 020 7871 1012
Seaford *p373* 0845 165 8178
Sevenoaks *p374* 01732 440855

Rix Mclaren
‡Scunthorpe *p373* 01724 872038

Rixons Solicitors
‡Folkestone *p227* 01303 850090

RJ Solicitors
‡Bradford *p154* 01274 900563

Roach Pittis
‡Newport *p328* 01983 524431

Philip Roache
‡Pembroke Dock *p345* 01646 682603

Helen Robbins Solicitors
‡Waltham Forest E11 *p72* 020 8558 0038

The Robert Davies Partnership
‡Newport *p329* 01633 413500

Robert Lunn & Lowth
‡Stratford-upon-Avon *p400* 01789 292238

Alan Roberts & Co
‡Chester *p191* 01244 562754

Roberts & Robyns
‡Pwllheli *p358* 01758 612362

Roberts & Smith
‡Nelson *p321* 01282 619000

Benjamin Roberts Solicitors
‡Halifax *p238* 01422 356633

Roberts Buckley
‡Manchester *p309* 0161 835 1234

C Roberts
‡Harrow *p242* 020 8864 9929

D P Roberts Hughes & Denye
‡Birkenhead *p134* 0151 647 6000
Ellesmere Port *p217* 0151 355 6699

David Roberts & Co
‡New Brighton *p321* 0151 639 9595

Roberts Jackson Solicitors
‡Wilmslow *p433* 01625 522215

Jane E Roberts
‡Northampton *p332* 01604 494431

Jeremy Roberts & Co
‡Peterborough *p347* . . . .01733 343943 / 342172

Roberts McCracken
‡Brent NW10 *p72* 0870 420 5658

Roberts Moore Nicholas Jones
‡Birkenhead *p134* 0151 647 0000

Paul Roberts
‡London EC3 *p72* 020 7264 0500

Peter Roberts Solicitor
‡Alrewas *p116* 01283 790045

Roberts Rose Partnership
‡Leicester *p281* 0116 251 5120

Roberts Solicitors
‡Macclesfield *p297* 01625 431111

Stephen Roberts & Co
‡Tilbury *p411* 01375 841841

Anthony Robertshaw Solicitors
‡Halifax *p238* 01422 246002

John Robertson
‡Widnes *p432* 0151 423 6500

Robertson Rivers
‡East Molesey *p215* 020 8979 6077

Robertsons
‡Cardiff *p180* 029 2023 7777
‡York *p445* 01904 658551
Barry *p126* 01446 745660

Robin Moran LLB (Hons)
‡Pontypridd *p352* 01443 406801

Robinson & Co
‡London EC1 *p72* 020 7405 5180

Robinson & Kinrade
‡Sutton *p403* 020 8770 2020

Robinson & Murphy
‡Newcastle upon Tyne *p326* 0191 230 5023

Robinson Allfree
‡Ramsgate *p359* 01843 592361
Broadstairs *p166* 01843 865261
Cliftonville *p196* 01843 228635

C M Robinson
‡Deal *p207* 01304 363236

John Robinson & Co
‡Hull *p258* 01482 324818

Robinson Le Grice
‡St Ives *p392* 01736 797973

Mark Robinson Transactional Intellectual Property Services
‡London W13 *p72* 07881 951308

Michael Robinson
‡London SW7 *p72* 020 7584 5038

Paul Robinson Solicitors
‡Westcliff-on-Sea *p428* 01702 338338

R P Robinson
‡Leicester *p281* 0116 262 1462

Robinson Ravani & Co
‡London E7 *p72* 020 8548 9402

Robinson's Solicitors
‡Poulton-le-Fylde *p355* 01253 882522

Vivienne Robinson
‡London E11 *p72* 020 8279 8899

Robinsons
‡Derby *p209* 01332 291431
‡Liverpool *p290* 0151 227 2555
‡Shoeburyness *p378* 01702 298282
Ilkeston *p261* 0115 932 4101

Robinsons Solicitors
‡Hull *p258* 01482 212401

Robotham & Co
‡Derby *p209* 01332 346018

Robson & Co
‡Hythe *p259* . . . . .01303 264581 / 267413

Robson Palmer
‡South Shields *p384* 0191 455 4561

Robyns Owen
‡Pwllheli *p358* 01758 613177

Robyns Owen & Son
Porthmadog *p354* 01766 514747

Roche & Co
‡London EC4 *p72* 020 7831 2209

John Roche
‡Pembroke Dock *p345* 01646 622626

Rochford & Co
‡Southampton *p386* 023 8045 8268

Rochman Landau LLP
‡London W1 *p72* 020 7544 2424

Rock Solicitors
‡London N22 *p73* 020 8888 1555

Roderick Ramage
‡Stafford *p393* . . . 01785 223030 / 07785 707111

Rodericks
‡Llanelli *p292* 01554 773424

Rodgers & Burton
‡London SW13 *p73* 020 8939 6300

Rodman Pearce Solicitors
‡Luton *p295* 01582 424234

Frank Roe Solicitors
‡St Helens *p391* 01744 24218

Tony Roe Solicitors
‡Reading *p361* 0118 930 2360

Roebucks
‡Blackburn *p145* 01254 274000
Accrington *p114* 01254 306560
Blackburn *p145* 01254 503070

Roelens Solicitors Wimbledon
‡London SW19 *p73* 020 8554 8002

Angela Rogan
‡Kendal *p264* 01539 724140

Roger James Clements & Partners
‡Newport *p329* 01633 257844
Newport *p329* . . . . . . .01633 263316 / 663316
Risca *p365* 01633 614166

Rogers & Co
‡Buckhurst Hill *p167* 020 8498 9910
‡Wolverhampton *p438* 01902 310312

Rogers & Co Criminal Law Solicitors
‡Kidderminster *p266* 01562 861864

Rogers & Co Solicitors
‡Leeds *p276* 0113 246 9984
‡London EC1 *p73* 020 7060 1189

Rogers & Norton
‡Norwich *p335* 01603 666001
Norwich *p335* 01603 268910

Rogerson Galvin
‡Ashton-under-Lyne *p120* . . 0161 344 2027 / 335 9005

Rogols Solicitors
‡Birmingham *p141* 0121 329 2087

Rohan & Co
‡Haywards Heath *p246* 01444 450901

Rokeby Johnson Baars
‡London W1 *p73* 020 7499 4990

The Roland Partnership
‡Chester *p191* 01244 659404

Roland Robinsons & Fentons LLP
‡Blackpool *p147* 01253 621432
Lytham *p297* 01253 734253

Roli Solicitors
‡Westminster SW1 *p73* 020 7224 9777

Rollasons
‡Daventry *p207* 01327 301771
‡Leamington Spa *p270* 01926 883431

Rollingsons
‡London EC1 *p73* 020 7611 4848

Rollits LLP
‡Hull *p258* 01482 323239
York *p445* 01904 625790

Will Rolt Solicitors
‡Bath *p128* 01225 426390

Romain Coleman & Co
‡Waltham Forest E17 *p73* 020 8520 3322

Romano Ferrari Stroud
‡Aberdare *p113* 01685 883143

Ronald Fletcher Baker LLP
‡London EC1 *p73* 020 7613 1402
London W1 *p73* 020 7467 5757

Ronaldsons
‡London WC1 *p73* 020 7580 6075
‡Norwich *p335* 01603 618883

Ronik Solicitors
‡London SE18 *p73* 020 8317 6778

Rooks Rider
‡London EC1 *p73* 020 7689 7000

Rooney & Co
‡Wirral *p435* 0151 632 4175

Richard Rooney & Co
‡Merton SW19 *p73* 020 8947 8024

Rooper & Whately
‡London W1 *p73* 020 7399 0824

Rootes & Alliott
‡Folkestone *p227* 01303 851100

Ropemakers Solicitors
‡London E6 *p73* 020 8586 8500

Ropes & Gray International LLP
‡London EC4 *p73* 020 3122 1100

Rose & Dunn
‡Runcorn *p369* 01928 572030

Rose & Rose Solicitors
‡Kingston upon Thames *p267* . . . 020 8974 7490

Anthony Rose & Co
‡Rendcomb *p363* 01242 870040

Christopher Rose & Co
‡Penryn *p346* . . . . . . .01326 372461 / 374430

Ian Rose & Firth
‡Whitley Bay *p431* 0191 252 0113

Jonathan S Rose
‡Barnet *p124* 020 8447 4870

Rose Law
‡Bilston *p133* 01902 495049

Robin Rose
‡Northampton *p332* 01604 760168

Rose Samuel Odele & Partners
‡London SE26 *p73* 020 8676 3449

Roseblade & Co
‡Burntwood *p170* 01543 898591

John H Rosen & Co
‡Westminster W1 *p73* 020 7262 2471

Lynne V Rosen
‡Loughton *p294* . . . 020 8508 0804
R A Rosen & Co
‡London W1 *p73* . . . 020 7629 6566
Rosenberg & Co
‡Barnet NW2 *p73* . . . 020 7431 8832
Rosenblatt
‡London EC4 *p73* . . . 020 7955 0880
Rosetta Thomas Solicitors
‡Southport *p388* . . . 01704 543344 / 07883 302770
Roshanian Payman International Solicitors
‡London W1 *p73* . . . 020 7499 2712
Roskell Davies & Co
‡Birmingham *p141* . . . 0121 354 1515 / 355 1011
Rosleys
‡Nottingham *p338* . . . 0115 958 0584
Rosling King
‡London EC4 *p73* . . . 020 7353 2353
Ross & Co
‡London WC2 *p73* . . . 020 7831 1099
Ross & Craig
‡Westminster W1 *p73* . . . 020 7262 3077
Ross & Son
‡Horley *p252* . . . 01293 782425
Charles Ross Solicitors
‡Barnet *p124* . . . 020 8216 2300
Ross Coates
‡Ipswich *p263* . . . 01473 695400
Ipswich *p263* . . . 01473 222303
Ipswich *p263* . . . 01473 621800
Ross Green & Crowe
‡Dartford *p207* . . . 01322 225353
John Ross
‡London NW11 *p73* . . . 020 8458 1924
Laurence Ross & Associates
‡Radlett *p358* . . . 01923 850099
Martin Ross Solicitor
‡Hove *p255* . . . 01273 559128
Michael Ross & Co
‡London NW8 *p73* . . . 020 7286 0002
Paul Ross & Company
‡Manchester *p309* . . . 0161 832 0706
Philip Ross & Co
‡London W1 *p73* . . . 020 7636 6969
Bushey *p172* . . . 020 8090 9191
Samuel Ross Solicitors
‡London SE5 *p74* . . . 020 7701 4664
Ross Solicitors Ltd
‡Swindon *p406* . . . 01793 512960
Ross Williams
‡Hitchin *p251* . . . 01462 636666
Ross-Brown & Birtwistle
‡Rochdale *p365*
S D Rosser & Co
‡London NW10 *p74* . . . 020 8451 3848
Rossides Caine
‡London N13 *p74* . . . 020 8882 9292
RossLegal LLP
‡Salford *p371* . . . 0161 720 7200 / 0845 612 0222
Rosthorns Solicitors
‡Accrington *p114* . . . 01254 398213
J Rostron
‡Southport *p388* . . . 01704 551414
Rothera Dowson
‡Nottingham *p338* . . . 0115 910 0600
Beeston *p130* . . . 0115 916 5200
Nottingham *p338* . . . 0115 952 0900
Nottingham *p338* . . . 0115 916 5200
West Bridgford *p427* . . . 0115 914 0077
Rotherham & Co
‡Coventry *p201* . . . 024 7622 7331
Rotherys
‡Cleckheaton *p195* . . . 01274 876785
Rothwell & Evans
‡Swinton *p407* . . . 0161 794 1830
Sale *p370* . . . 0161 969 7341
Rouse Legal (Formerly Willoughby & Partners)
‡London E14 *p74* . . . 020 7536 4100
Routh Clarke Solicitors
‡Leighton Buzzard *p282* . . . 01296 662770 / 01525 373322
Routledge Quill & Co
‡Wormley *p441* . . . 01428 682589
Row & Scott
‡Newcastle upon Tyne *p326* . . . 0191 273 9929
Consett *p199* . . . 01207 591810
Morpeth *p319* . . . 01665 713544
Rowberry Morris
‡Reading *p361* . . . 0118 958 5611
Richmond upon Thames *p364* . . . 020 8334 4860
Staines *p393* . . . 01784 457655
Tadley *p407* . . . 0118 981 2992
Rowberrys
‡Crowthorne *p204* . . . 01344 775311
Rowbis Solicitors
‡Gloucester *p230* . . . 01452 301903
David Rowe & Co
‡Bideford *p133* . . . 01237 425525
Rowe Radcliffe
‡South Croydon *p383* . . . 020 8680 2070
Scott Rowe
‡Axminster *p120* . . . 01297 32345
Chard *p184* . . . 01460 63336
Lyme Regis *p296* . . . 01297 443777
Rowe Sparkes Partnership
‡Havant *p244* . . . 023 9248 6886
Southampton *p386* . . . 023 8021 3890
Southsea *p389* . . . 023 9248 6886
Rowel Genn Solicitors
‡London W1 *p74* . . . 020 7182 4097
Jonathan Rowell & Co
‡London NW5 *p74* . . . 020 7482 2663
Rowland Tildesley & Harris
‡Willenhall *p433* . . . 01902 366571
Rowlands & Co
‡Abergavenny *p113* . . . 01873 850983
Rowley Dickinson
‡Manchester *p309* . . . 0161 834 4215
Leicester *p281*
R H Rowley
‡Coventry *p201* . . . 024 7630 1996
Rowlinsons
‡Frodsham *p227* . . . 01928 735333
Rowntree & Berry
‡Fleetwood *p226* . . . 01253 872581
Poulton-le-Fylde *p355* . . . 01253 893599
Roxburgh Milkins
‡Bristol *p164* . . . 0845 241 9500
Adrianne Roy
‡Enfield *p219* . . . 020 8292 9101
Royce & Co
‡London SW6 *p74* . . . 020 7736 9103
Royce Marshall & Co
‡Retford *p363* . . . 07765 404753
Royds LLP
‡London EC4 *p74* . . . 020 7583 2222
Morden *p318* . . . 020 8542 1067
Roys
‡Carlisle *p182* . . . 01228 526385
Roythornes LLP
‡Spalding *p389* . . . 01775 842500
Newmarket *p327* . . . 01638 561320
Nottingham *p338* . . . 0115 948 4555
Peterborough *p347* . . . 01733 558585
Rubicon Law
‡London WC2 *p74* . . . 020 7438 2888
Rubin Lewis O'Brien
‡Cwmbran *p206* . . . 01633 867000
Cardiff *p180* . . . 029 2077 9988
Rubinstein Phillips LLP
‡London WC2 *p74* . . . 020 7925 2244
Rubric Lois King & Co
‡Birmingham *p141* . . . 0121 453 5133 / 453 3301
Rudd Jepson
‡Bromley *p167* . . . 020 8313 0555
Paul Rudd
‡Grimsby *p235* . . . 01472 350881
Rudds
‡Westcliff-on-Sea *p428* . . . 01702 347853
Rayleigh *p359* . . . 01268 778152
Rudge & Co
‡Birmingham *p141* . . . 0121 200 1775
Rudlings & Wakelam
‡Thetford *p410* . . . 01842 754151
Brandon *p156* . . . 01842 810300
Bury St Edmunds *p171* . . . 01284 755771
Long Melford *p293* . . . 01787 464778
Rudzki and Jones
‡Derby *p209* . . . 0845 519 2999
Andrew Rugg
‡Taunton *p408* . . . 01823 326822
Rundlewalker
‡Exeter *p222* . . . 01392 209209
Runhams
‡Bradford *p154* . . . 01274 532233
Runnett and Co
‡Carmarthen *p183* . . . 01994 438068
Rupert Bear Murray Davies
‡Nottingham *p338* . . . 0115 924 3333
Rupert Bedford Solicitor
‡Glastonbury *p230* . . . 01458 850120
Rushton Hinchy Solicitors
‡St Helens *p391* . . . 0845 054 0564
Rushworth & Glyn Owen
‡Rhyl *p363* . . . 01745 343843
Russell & Co
‡Malvern *p300* . . . 01684 892000
Russell & Co Solicitors and Estate Agents
‡Crawley *p202* . . . 01293 561965 / 0845 300 2809
Russell & Russell
‡Bolton *p149* . . . 01204 399299
‡Chester *p191* . . . 01244 405700
Atherton *p120* . . . 01942 884469
Bolton *p150* . . . 01204 699432
Bolton *p150* . . . 01204 707926
Bolton *p150* . . . 01204 375700
Bury *p171* . . . 0161 762 2888
Middleton *p315* . . . 0161 653 6200
C J Russell MA(Cantab)
‡London W2 *p74* . . . 020 7243 2455
Howard Russell & Co
‡London W4 *p74* . . . 020 8747 0731
Russell Jones & Walker
‡London WC2 *p74* . . . 020 7657 1555
Birmingham *p141* . . . 0121 233 8300
Bristol *p164* . . . 0117 374 2222
Cardiff *p180* . . . 029 2026 2800
Manchester *p309* . . . 0161 383 3500
Newcastle upon Tyne *p326* . . . 0191 323 3000
Sheffield *p377* . . . 0114 276 6868
Wakefield *p419* . . . 01924 234300
P Russell & Co
‡London W6 *p74* . . . 020 8233 2943
R E O Russell
‡Marlborough *p313* . . . 01672 564352
Tim Russell
‡London W6 *p74* . . . 020 8741 4403
Russell Wise
‡London E1 *p74*
Russell Wise Solicitors
‡London N22 *p74* . . . 020 8889 8300
Russell Worth
‡Plympton *p351* . . . 01752 334100
RUSSELL-COOKE LLP
‡London SW15 *p74* . . . 020 8789 9111
Kingston upon Thames *p267* . . . 020 8546 6111
London WC1 *p74* . . . 020 7405 6566
RUSSELLS
‡London W1 *p75* . . . 020 7439 8692
‡London E4 *p75* . . . 020 8529 5933
Rust & Co
‡Accrington *p114* . . . 01254 390015
Rustem Guardian Solicitors
‡London EC4 *p75* . . . 020 7936 8000
Rustons & Lloyd
‡Newmarket *p327* . . . 01638 661221
Rutherford Solicitors
‡Portsmouth *p355* . . . 023 9273 5700
Rutherfords
‡Tamworth *p407* . . . 01827 311411
Birmingham *p141* . . . 0121 749 4488
Tamworth *p407* . . . 01827 310410
Rutter & Rutter
‡Wincanton *p433* . . . 01963 32224
Mere *p314* . . . 01747 860295
Rutters
‡Shaftesbury *p374* . . . 01747 852377
Gillingham *p229* . . . 01747 822005
Christopher J L Ryan
‡Bishop's Stortford *p144* . . . 01279 815970
John Ryan Solicitor
‡Halifax *p238* . . . 01422 207684
P T Ryan & Co
‡King's Lynn *p266* . . . 01553 761741
Ryan Property Law LLP
‡Pudsey *p358* . . . 0113 236 2334
Ryan Solicitors
‡Manchester *p309* . . . 0161 238 8668
Rylands Law
‡Hathersage *p244* . . . 01433 650878
Rylatt Chubb
‡London EC4 *p75* . . . 020 3170 8978
Rymer Media Law
‡London N10 *p75* . . . 07767 887972

S

S & V Solicitors
‡Slough *p382* . . . 01753 722130 / 07767 637582
SA Law
‡St Albans *p390* . . . 01727 798000
SA Law Chambers
‡Ilford *p260* . . . 020 8554 0012
SAS Daniels LLP
‡Stockport *p396* . . . 0161 475 7676
Bramhall *p155* . . . 0161 475 7680
Chester *p191* . . . 01244 305900
Congleton *p198* . . . 01260 282300
Macclesfield *p297* . . . 01625 442100
SAS Solicitors
‡Ilford *p261* . . . 020 8220 2900
SB Law
‡Hounslow *p254* . . . 020 8570 4041
SBM Solicitors
‡Hounslow *p254* . . . 020 8577 2474
SB Solicitors
‡London E1 *p75* . . . 020 7539 1900
SBW Lawyers
‡St Helens *p391* . . . 01744 762070
S C Law
‡London SE22 *p75* . . . 020 8693 0900
SC Law
‡Harrow *p242* . . . 020 8864 4913
SC Legal Services Ltd
‡Dover *p213* . . . 01304 210514
SDK Law
‡Burgess Hill *p168* . . . 01444 240393
SD Solicitors
‡London E1 *p75* . . . 020 7702 7966
SEB Solicitors
‡London E2 *p75* . . . 020 7729 9042
S E Law
‡Northwich *p333* . . . 01606 333533
SEN Legal Limited
‡Bury St Edmunds *p171* . . . 01284 723952
SFN Solicitors
‡Burnley *p169* . . . 01282 421284
‡Clitheroe *p196* . . . 01200 426811
SFS Legal Ltd
‡Leicester *p281* . . . 0845 257 6470
SGH Martineau LLP
‡Birmingham *p142* . . . 0870 763 2000
London EC3 *p75* . . . 020 7264 4444
SGM Solicitors
‡Stockport *p396* . . . 0161 947 4990
SH Family Law
‡Bristol *p164* . . . 0117 960 1437
SHK Solicitors
‡Barrow-upon-Humber *p126* . . . 01469 531388 / 07793 204890
SIS Law
‡Menai Bridge *p314* . . . 01248 800900
SJ Berwin LLP
‡London EC4 *p75* . . . 020 7111 2222
SJ LAW
‡London E17 *p75* . . . 020 8520 6600
S J Legal Limited
‡Stockport *p396* . . . 0845 658 0142
SJP Solicitors
‡Hunstanton *p258* . . . 01485 532662
SJS Solicitors
‡Wandsworth SW12 *p75* . . . 020 8675 4436
SJ Solicitors
‡Ilford *p261* . . . 020 8548 3700
SKG Solicitors
‡Milton Keynes *p317* . . . 01908 528745
SK Legal Solicitors
‡Peterborough *p347* . . . 01733 565295
SLA Solicitors
‡London SE5 *p75* . . . 020 7703 1070
SL & Co
‡Knowle *p269* . . . 01564 777250
SLP Solicitors
‡Stanmore *p394* . . . 020 8420 7950
SMi Group Ltd
‡London SE1 *p75* . . . 020 7827 6725
SMK Solicitors
‡Stoke-on-Trent *p398* . . . 01782 213666
SM Solicitors
‡Chester *p191* . . . 01244 314722
SMWLaw
‡London SW1 *p75* . . . 020 7060 0766
SN Law
‡Newcastle upon Tyne *p326* . . . 0191 230 8119
SNR Denton
‡London EC4 *p75* . . . 020 7242 1212
Milton Keynes *p317* . . . 01908 690260
SP Law
‡Northampton *p332* . . . 01604 638905
SRB Legal LLP
‡Newport *p329* . . . 01633 817033
SSB Solicitors
‡London SW6 *p75* . . . 020 7348 7630
ST Entertainment Law
‡London NW5 *p75* . . . 020 7504 5859
ST Law Solicitors
‡Ilford *p261* . . . 020 8478 5599
SV Law
‡London W5 *p75* . . . 020 8567 8989
SVS Solicitors
‡Gerrards Cross *p229* . . . 01753 889123
SW19 Lawyers
‡London SW19 *p76* . . . 020 8947 7997
SWL Dispute Resolution
‡High Wycombe *p250* . . . 01494 616007
S W Solicitor Ltd
‡Barton-upon-Humber *p126* 01652 639051 / 07811 102086
SZ Law Ltd
‡London W1 *p76* . . . 020 3056 4761
S Z Solicitors
‡Southall *p384* . . . 020 8574 1794
Deborah A Sabalot Regulatory Consulting
‡St Albans *p390* . . . 01727 859434
Sabeers Solicitors
‡London W12 *p76* . . . 020 8740 7007
Sabi & Associates
‡London W1 *p76* . . . 020 7414 0069
Sacaloffs Solicitors
‡London WC1 *p76* . . . 020 3178 6124
Sach Solicitors
‡London E1 *p76* . . . 020 7680 1133

Sachedinas Solicitors
‡York *p445* 01904 793195

Sacker & Partners LLP
‡London EC2 *p76* 020 7329 6699

David Sacker & Co
‡London NW3 *p76* 020 7433 1437

Sackvilles
‡Hornchurch *p252* 01708 446704
Rainham *p359* 01708 552804

Safaaz Solicitors
‡Birmingham *p142* 0121 772 7428

David R Saffrin
‡Stanmore *p394* 020 8954 3090

Saffron Solicitors
‡Birmingham *p142* 0121 698 8558

Sagelaw
‡Brighton *p160* 01273 387246

Saggars Solicitors
‡Ealing W13 *p76* 020 8579 5755

Sahni & Co
‡Smethwick *p382* 0121 558 5222

Sahota Solicitors
‡London WC2 *p76* 0845 630 2095

R Saifuddin
‡Bromley *p167* 020 8466 1266

Sainsburys
‡Denton *p208* 0161 336 7027

Saints Solicitors
‡Birmingham *p142* 0121 523 7865

Sakhi Solicitors
‡Leicester *p281* 0116 253 6236

Sal & Co
‡London N18 *p76* 020 8807 5888

Salam & Co
‡Chester *p191* 01244 344577 / 07738 719265

Salans
‡London EC4 *p76* 020 7429 6000
Bromley *p167* 020 8460 2237

Salehs LLP
‡Manchester *p309* 0161 434 9991

Salena Dawson & Co
‡Thetford *p411* 01953 883535

Salhan & Company
‡Birmingham *p142* 0121 605 6000
Bilston *p133* 01902 407207

Salinger Solicitors & Notary Public
‡Kensington & Chelsea W8 *p76* 020 7937 8524

Salmons
‡Newcastle under Lyme *p323* 01782 621266
Stoke-on-Trent *p398* 01782 639827

Salmonworks Limited
‡Witham *p436* 07748 962350

Michael Salt
‡Rochdale *p365* 01706 646655

Salt Veeder
‡Bury *p171* 0161 797 5650

Salter Rees & Kelly
‡Swansea *p405* 01792 470707
Ammanford *p118* 01269 592023

Chris Saltrese Solicitors
‡Southport *p388* 01704 535512

Salusburys Harding & Barnett
‡Leicester *p281* 0116 262 9033 / 262 6052
Leicester *p281* 0116 262 6052
Market Harborough *p312* 01455 282757

Sam & Co
‡London N15 *p76* 020 8808 0020

Sam Solicitors
‡Sutton *p403* 020 8770 7143

Samars Solicitors
‡Hounslow *p254* 020 8570 4716

Samble Burton & Worth
‡Burton-on-Trent *p170* 01283 565731

Sampson & Co
‡Redditch *p362* 01527 66221

Sampson Coward LLP
‡Salisbury *p371* 01722 410664

David Sampson & Co
‡London N2 *p76* 020 8458 0345

Samuel & Co
‡London NW5 *p76* 020 7267 4240

Samuel & Co Solicitors
‡Barking *p123* 020 8594 5000

Alan Samuels & Co
‡London N3 *p76* 0845 900 0116

Samuels & Co Solicitors
‡London EC2 *p76* 020 7073 2860
Leeds *p276* 0113 394 4117

Lawrence C Samuels LLB Solicitor
‡Northwood *p333* 01923 824708

Samuels Solicitors
‡Barnstaple *p125* 01271 343457

Samy & Co
‡Harrow *p242* 020 8861 2424

Thomas Sanchez Solicitors
‡Croydon *p205* 020 3372 5387

Anthony Sandall and Co
‡Reading *p361* 0118 958 5505

Sanders & Co
‡Rainham *p359* 0844 353 3553
‡Stourbridge *p399* 01384 375437 / 378991
Harold Wood *p239* 0844 353 3553

Austin Sanders Law Firm Limited
‡Darlington *p206* 01325 360360

Sanders Brickwood
‡Cirencester *p195* 01285 654601

Sanders Witherspoon LLP
‡Brentwood *p156* 01277 221010
Brentwood *p156* 01277 221010

Christine Sanderson
‡Gosforth *p232* 0191 285 9633

Sanderson McCreath & Edney
‡Berwick-upon-Tweed *p131* 01289 306724

Sandersons
‡Hull *p258* 01482 324662
Beverley *p131* 01482 324662

Sandhill Solicitors
‡Manchester *p309* 0161 249 2280

Sandhu & Shah
‡London E7 *p76* 020 8552 4100

Sandom Robinson
‡South Croydon *p383* 020 8651 7020

Sukhy Sanghera
‡Gerrards Cross *p229* 01753 885006

R R Sanghvi & Co
‡Harrow *p242* 020 8515 0490

Sansbury Douglas
‡Bristol *p164* 0117 926 5341
Bristol *p164* 0117 955 2663
Knowle *p269* 0117 963 5044

Santers Solicitors
‡Barking *p123* 020 8594 7542

Saracens
‡London W1 *p76* 020 7631 0770

Saracens Solicitors LLP
‡London W1 *p76* 020 7725 7115

Sarangi Coyle Solicitors
‡Lytham *p297* 01253 735919

Sarfo Solicitors
‡Cambridge *p175* 01223 305551

Peter R Sargent
‡Grimsby *p235* 01472 887670

Sarginsons Law LLP
‡Coventry *p201* 024 7655 3181

Sasto & Klinger
‡London W1 *p76* 020 7631 4714

S Satha & Co
‡Newham E12 *p76* 020 8471 9484

J V Saujani & Co
‡Harrow *p242* 020 8861 2606

Helen and Ian Saul Solicitors
‡Bognor Regis *p148* 01243 268996 / 07929 132111

RAYMOND SAUL & CO
‡London E1 *p76* 020 7480 5840

Thomas Saul & Co
‡Whitefield *p430* 0161 773 2833

Saulet & Co
‡Southsea *p389* 023 9281 9442

Saunders & Co
‡Richmond upon Thames *p364* 020 8332 2995

Saunders Bearman LLP
‡London W1 *p76* 020 7224 2618

Saunders Goodin Riddleston Solicitors
‡Ipswich *p263* 01473 225600

Saunders Law Partnership LLP
‡London WC2 *p76* 020 7632 4300

Mark Saunders & Co
‡Gorseinon *p231* 01792 892692

Saunders Roberts
‡Evesham *p220* 01386 442558

WGR Saunders & Son
‡London SE25 *p76* 020 8653 4482

Savage Crangle
‡Skipton *p381* 01756 794611
Otley *p342* 01943 465050

R A Savage & Co
‡Welwyn Garden City *p425* 01707 373037
London NW3 *p76* 020 7431 7711

Savages
‡Corbridge *p199* 01434 632505

Savas & Savage Solicitors Limited
‡Ellesmere Port *p218* 0151 357 2375

Savery & Pennington
‡Cardiff *p181* 029 2045 7222

Savill & Co
‡Windlesham *p434* 01276 451292

Norman Saville & Co
‡London N10 *p76* 020 8883 9711

Savilles
‡Cheadle *p185* 0161 491 8540

Saviours Solicitors
‡London SE18 *p77* 020 8855 1855

Savjani & Co
‡London NW10 *p77* 020 8961 3352

Sawarn & Co Ltd Solicitors
‡Derby *p209* 07984 431319

Chris Sayer Solicitors
‡York *p445* 01904 638038

Sayer Moore & Co
‡London W3 *p77* 020 8993 7571

Sayers
Harrow *p242* 020 8861 4191

Scaiff LLP
‡Worcester *p440* 01905 727700

Scanlan & Co
‡London EC4 *p77* 020 7353 5215

Scanlans
‡Sunderland *p402* 0191 565 2565

Scannell Evans
‡Stanford-le-Hope *p394* 01375 642240

Scannells Hunt
‡Brentwood *p156* 01277 223242

D R Sceats Solicitor
‡Surbiton *p402* 020 8399 5457

Schillings
‡London WC1 *p77* 020 7034 9000

Schneider Page
‡London E1 *p77* 020 7480 5477
Guildford *p237* 01483 535997

Schofield & Associates
‡Solihull *p383* 01564 739103

Schofield Sweeney
‡Bradford *p154* 01274 306000
Leeds *p276* 0113 220 6270

Schofields Solicitors
‡Barnstaple *p125* 01271 882790

Kaye Scholer LLP
‡London EC1 *p77* 020 7014 0550

J P Scholes
‡Bamford *p121* 01433 651625

Peter Scholl & Co
‡London WC1 *p77* 020 7025 2292

Robert Schon Tax Planning
‡London N6 *p77* 020 7267 5010

Schroder Reid Solicitors
‡Ascot *p118* 0845 643 6413 / 01344 295309

Schubert Murphy
‡London N21 *p77* 020 8360 2599

Schulte Roth & Zabel
‡London W1 *p77* 020 7081 8000

Schultze & Braun LLP
‡London EC2 *p77* 020 7156 5029

Sciolti & Co
‡Brigg *p158* 01652 655845

Scott Dixon Reilly Wilkes
Witney *p436* 01295 201210

Scott Dixon Reilly Wilkes Solicitors
‡Kidlington *p266* 01865 594104

Scott Doyle Molyneux Solicitors
‡Ormskirk *p341* 01695 573555

J Scott & Co Solicitors
‡Maidenhead *p298* 01628 777233

Scott-Moncrieff Harbour & Sinclair
‡London NW5 *p77* 020 7485 5588

Scott Son & Chitty
‡Ashtead *p119* 01372 276211

Scotts Holt & Sellars
‡Bromsgrove *p167* 01527 872711

Scotts Wright
‡Leyburn *p283* 01966 22227
Catterick Garrison *p183* 01748 832431
Hawes *p245* 01969 667215

David Scourfield
‡Middlesbrough *p315* 01642 874999

Scrase Employment Solicitors
‡Bristol *p165* 0117 985 1026

Scrivenger Seabrook
‡St Neots *p392* 01480 214900

Scudamores
‡Woodford Green *p439* 0844 880 2323

Scully & Sowerbutts
Brentford *p156* 020 8758 9333

Scully & Sowerbutts Solicitors
‡London N3 *p77* 020 8346 2804
Twickenham *p416* 020 8892 2463

Dermot Scully Solicitors
‡Hove *p255*

P R Scully & Co Solicitors
‡St Helens *p391* 01744 755800

Scutt Beaumont Solicitors Ltd
‡Leicester *p281* 0116 254 4200
Ashby-de-la-Zouch *p118* 01530 563999
Corby *p199* 01536 744847

Ian R Scutt
‡Chesterfield *p192* 01246 203952

Seabourne Lawleys
‡Northwood *p333* 01923 820639

Seakens Solicitors
‡Virginia Water *p418* 01344 843666

Searle & Burge (with Harding Evans)
‡Newport *p329* 01633 267107

Geoffrey Searle Planning Solicitors
‡Billericay *p133* 01277 633014

Sears & Co
‡Andover *p118* 01264 336951

SEARS TOOTH
‡London W1 *p77* 020 7499 5599

Seatons Solicitors
‡Corby *p199* 01536 276300
Kettering *p265* 01536 311690
Kettering *p265* 01536 762773

Indra Sebastian Solicitors
‡Harrow *p242* 020 8427 3303

Sebastians
‡London EC4 *p77* 020 7583 2105

Secretan Troyanov
‡London WC1 *p77* 020 7404 1199

Anthony Seddon & Co
‡London EC4 *p77* 020 7842 0800

Seddon Thomson
‡Manchester *p309* 0161 720 8000

Seddons
‡Westminster W1 *p77* 020 7725 8000

Richard Sedgley & Co
‡Bournemouth *p152* 01202 556222

Alicia R F Sedgwick Solicitors
‡Leigh-on-Sea *p282* 01702 476269

David Sedgwick Solicitors
‡Bridgend *p157* 01656 767766

Sedgwick Detert Moran & Arnold
‡London EC3 *p77* 020 7929 1829

Sedgwick Kelly LLP
‡Watford *p424* 01923 228311

Sedgwick Phelan & Partners
‡Middleton *p315* 0161 653 5299

Robert C Seeckts
‡Tunbridge Wells *p415* 01892 537615

Nigel Seed Solicitor
‡Bognor Regis *p148* 01243 855195

Elizabeth Seeley
‡Ealing W5 *p77* 020 8840 2788

A Seelhoff Solicitors
‡London W6 *p77* 020 3178 4337

Segens Blount Petre
‡Westminster EC4 *p77* 020 7332 2222

Sehdeva Law
‡Birmingham *p142* 0121 343 1316

Sehgal & Co
‡Birmingham *p142* 0121 772 2226

Seifert & Co
‡Cobham *p196* 01932 866788

Michael Seifert
‡London W1 *p77* 020 7734 3263

Selby & Co
‡Highworth *p250* 01793 762327

Brian Selby
‡Leeds *p276* 0113 269 5102

Seldon Ward & Nuttall
‡Bideford *p133* 01237 479121

John D Sellars & Co
‡Sutton *p403* 020 8661 7014

Selva & Co
‡London NW6 *p77* 020 7328 3330

Selvarajah & Co
‡Barnet NW9 *p77* 020 8204 7884

Selwyn & Co
‡London N15 *p77* 020 8881 2272

Semple Fraser LLP
‡Manchester *p309* 0161 907 3771

Senior Calveley & Hardy
‡Lytham *p297* 01253 733333
Kirkham *p268* 01772 671177
Poulton-le-Fylde *p355* 01253 882883

Philip Senior & Co
‡Retford *p363* 01777 869545

Brian L Senter
‡Stourbridge *p399* 01384 375649

Sentinels Solicitors Ltd
‡Manchester *p309* 0161 998 2862

Sephton Lee Wilkinson Solicitors
‡Preston *p357* 01772 884144 / 07789 886 525

Sergeant & Collins
‡Scunthorpe *p373* 01724 864215

Serious Law LLP - The Serious Law Practice
‡Bolton *p150* 0800 616 681

SERJEANT & SON
‡Ramsey *p359* 01487 812325

Sethi & Co
‡Sunbury-on-Thames *p401* 01932 772121

The Sethi Partnership Solicitors
‡Eastcote *p216* 020 8866 6464

Severn Law Solicitors
‡Chepstow *p189* 01291 630451

Martin Sewell Family Law Solicitor & Advocate
‡Gravesend *p233* 01474 323251

Sewell Mullings Logie LLP
‡Cirencester *p195* 01285 650000

Seymours
‡Coventry *p201* 024 7655 3961
‡London EC4 *p77* 020 7236 4322

Seymours + Solicitors
‡Brighton *p160* 01273 628808
Horsham *p253* 01403 839261

Shacklocks
‡Mansfield *p312* 01623 626141
Belper *p131* 01773 822333
Derby *p209* 01332 559281
Ripley *p365* 01773 743513

R A Shadbolt
‡London W1 *p77* 01737 844184

Shaddai & Company (Solicitors & Advocates) Limited
‡London N17 *p77* 020 3417 6552

Elizabeth Shaer Solicitor
‡Westcliff-on-Sea *p428* 01702 348710

Shah & Sons Solicitors
‡Manchester *p309* 0161 224 8444

Atul Shah
‡Wealdstone *p424* 020 8861 5000

Howard Shah Solicitors
‡Shrewsbury *p379* 0800 092 5523

Shah Law Chambers
‡Wembley *p426* 020 8900 9529

Syed Shaheen Solicitors
‡London E1 *p77* 020 7247 2470

Shahid Rahman
‡London E1 *p77* 020 7480 9090

Shahin & Co
‡Potters Bar *p355* 01707 658722

Shahzads Solicitors
‡London E13 *p77* 0845 466 2299

Shahzads Solicitors & Estate Agents
‡London E17 *p77* 020 8503 7979

Shaidy & Co
‡Westminster W2 *p77* 020 7229 6703

Shakespeares
‡Birmingham *p142* 0121 237 3000
Leicester *p281* 0116 318 3711
Moreton-in-Marsh *p319* 0845 630 8833
Nottingham *p339* 0115 945 3700
Shipston-on-Stour *p378* 0845 630 8833
Stratford-upon-Avon *p400* 0845 630 8833

Shallcross & Co
‡St Albans *p390* 01727 847804

Shammah Nicholls LLP
‡Manchester *p309* 0161 832 9272

Shan & Co
‡Harrow *p242* 020 8864 7070

Shanahan Wormald Davis Solicitors & Advocates
‡Cardiff *p181* 029 2019 0184

Shanaz & Partners Solicitors
‡London E1 *p77* 020 7375 2898

Shanklys Solicitors Ltd
‡Manchester *p309* 0161 773 5222

Shanley Wright Judge Property Lawyers
‡Rochdale *p365* 01706 861188

Shanthi & Co
‡London N4 *p77* 020 7561 9494

J M Shaoul
‡Altrincham *p117* 0161 819 1133

Shapland & Co
‡Camden NW1 *p77* 020 7383 7030

Shariff & Co
‡Kenton *p265* 020 8907 1817

Shariful Solicitors
‡London SW19 *p77* 020 8542 4284

Sharma & Co Solicitors
‡London E6 *p77* 020 8552 5022

L Sharma & Co Solicitors
‡London E13 *p77* 020 8471 6676
Ilford *p261* 020 8478 0064

N Sharma & Co Solicitors
‡Hounslow *p254* 020 8569 5600

Sharma Solicitors
‡London WC1 *p77* 0845 430 0145

Sharman & Son
‡Liverpool *p290* 0151 932 0333

Sharman Law
‡Bedford *p130* 01234 303030
Ampthill *p118* 01525 750750

Sharp & Partners
‡Nottingham *p339* 0115 959 0055
Long Eaton *p293* 0115 973 4111
Nottingham *p339* 0115 920 0020
Nottingham *p339* 0115 965 4881

Sharp & Rimmer
‡St Mawes *p392* 01326 270291

Christine Sharp & Co
‡Heywood *p249* 01706 623513

Sharp Family Law
‡Bath *p128* 01225 448955
Bristol *p165* 01225 448955

Sharpe & Co
‡Harrow *p242* 020 8422 4555
‡Harrow *p242* 020 8423 7323
Ashford *p119* 01784 247376

Sharpe & Perl
‡Dartford *p207* 01474 872576 / 873359

Sharpe Pritchard
‡London WC1 *p77* 020 7405 4600

Sharpes
‡London E4 *p77* 020 8527 2388

Sharpfields & Co
‡Barking *p123* 020 8594 0010

Sharples & Co
‡Bristol *p165* 0117 942 8214

Sharratts Family Law Limited
‡Wolverhampton *p438* 01902 759500

Sharratts (London) LLP
‡Westerham *p429* 01959 568000

Amanda Shaw Solicitors
‡Horsham *p253* 01403 710742

Shaw & Ashton
‡Pontefract *p351* 01977 703232

Shaw & Co
‡Newcastle upon Tyne *p326* 0800 019 1248
Doncaster *p212* 0800 019 1248
Telford *p409* 0800 019 1248

Barry Shaw
‡London SE9 *p78* 020 8850 7976

Shaw Davenport & Wardle
‡Blackpool *p147* 01253 622281

Shaw Gillis
‡Morley *p319* 0113 252 0331

Shaw Graham Kersh
‡London W1 *p78* 020 7734 9700

Shaw Lloyd & Co
‡London EC4 *p78* 020 7353 9936

Shaw Marsden
‡Taunton *p408* 01823 330944

T I Shawdon & Co
‡Leatherhead *p271* 01372 200037

Shean Solicitors Ltd
‡Altrincham *p117* 07711 130677 / 0161 929 1922

Shearer & Co Solicitors
‡Chippenham *p193* 01249 657744

Shearman & Sterling LLP
‡London EC2 *p78* 020 7655 5000

Shearman Bowen & Co Solicitors
‡London EC1 *p78*

Sheehans Solicitors
‡Neath *p320* 01639 630844
Port Talbot *p353* 01639 883237

Sheehy-Smith
‡Derby *p209* 01332 755409

Sheikh & Co
‡London N4 *p78* 020 7263 5588
‡London N3 *p78* 020 8343 0693

Sheirs Solicitors
‡Bradford *p155* 01274 499922

Shelbournes Solicitors
‡Cambridge *p175* 01954 208064

Shelley & Co
‡Cambridge *p175* 01223 359441
‡Maidstone *p299* 01622 663060

Sheltons
‡Hucknall *p255* 0115 955 3444
Nottingham *p339* 0115 955 3444
Nottingham *p339* 0115 955 3444

Shentons
‡Winchester *p434* 01962 844544

Shepherd & Co
‡Towcester *p413* 01327 350185

SHEPHERD + WEDDERBURN LLP
‡London EC4 *p78* 020 7429 4900

Clive Shepherd & Co
‡Walsall *p420* 01922 647797

Shepherd Evans Solicitors
‡Macclesfield *p297* 01625 503909

Shepherd Harris & Co
‡Enfield *p219* 020 8363 8341
Waltham Cross *p420*

M A Shepherd & Co
‡London N3 *p78* 020 8343 2346

Martin Shepherd & Co
‡Enfield *p219* 020 8367 3230
‡London N12 *p78* 020 8446 4301
London N9 *p78* 020 8373 8373

Shepherd Reynolds Solicitors
‡Sale *p370* 0161 969 6415

Shepherds Solicitors
‡Barnsley *p125* 0800 073 2221

Crispian Shepley
‡Walton-on-Thames *p421* 01923 221122

Sheppards Solicitors Ltd
‡Stafford *p393* 01785 257155

T J Shepperson
‡Norwich *p335* 01603 763096

Sheppersons
‡Horley *p252* 01293 772424
Reigate *p363* 01737 244987

Shergill & Co
‡Hounslow *p254* 020 8570 2323

Sheridan & Co
‡Kingston upon Thames *p267* 020 8541 1181

Sheridan & Stretton
‡London W6 *p78* 020 8748 7340

Sheridan Bowles Solicitors
‡Great Yarmouth *p234* 01493 859848

D R Sheridan & Co
‡Bushey *p172* 020 8950 6768

Sheridan Gold LLP
‡Reigate *p363* 01737 735088

Sheridans
‡London WC1 *p78* 020 7079 0100

Sherrards
‡Haywards Heath *p246* 01444 473344
‡St Albans *p390* 01727 832830
London W1 *p78* 020 7478 9010
West Drayton *p427* 020 8757 5670

Sherrs
‡London WC1 *p78* 020 7862 5859

Sherwins Limited
‡Braintree *p155* 0845 890 9210

Sherwood Dunham
‡Wellingborough *p424* 01933 276147

Sherwood-Smith Tilley & Co
‡Houghton Le Spring *p253* 0191 584 3186

Sherwood Solicitors
‡Brighton *p160* 01273 608221

Sherwood Wheatley
‡Kingston upon Thames *p267* 020 8546 0144

David Shine & Kharbanda
‡Southall *p384* 020 8571 6001 / 8571 6002

Gordon Shine & Co
‡London NW10 *p78* 020 8969 7033

Shipley Solicitors Limited
‡Liverpool *p290* 0151 705 3440

Shipton Hallewell & Co
‡Chesterfield *p192* 01246 232140

Shire Solicitors
‡Bradford *p155* 01274 727373

Shires Defence Solicitors
‡Leicester *p281* 0116 262 6367

John Shirley & Co
‡Burnham-on-Sea *p169* 01278 780202

Shirtcliffe & Reston Solicitors
‡Thirsk *p411* 01845 526222

Shoarns Solicitors Christopher Sheehan LLB
‡Blandford Forum *p147* 01258 880214

Shook Hardy & Bacon LLP
‡London EC4 *p78* 020 7332 4500

Shoosmiths
‡Northampton *p332*
0370 086 3000 / 01604 543000
Basingstoke *p127* 0370 086 6200 / 01256 696200
Birmingham *p142* 0370 086 4000 / 0121 335 4440
Fareham *p224* 0370 086 6800 / 01489 616800
London WC2 *p78* 020 3178 7168
Manchester *p309* 0370 086 5600 / 01604 543000
Milton Keynes *p317*
0370 086 8300 / 01908 488300
Nottingham *p339* 0370 086 5000 / 0115 906 5000
Reading *p361* 0370 086 8800 / 0118 965 8765

Shores Anchor Solicitors
‡London NW6 *p78* 020 7372 1966

Short Richardson & Forth LLP
‡Newcastle upon Tyne *p326* 0191 232 0283

W J Short & Co
‡Oxford *p344* 01865 724102

Shortlands Solicitors
‡London W6 *p78* 020 8822 3330

Shouriefears
‡Bracknell *p153* 01344 302136

Stuart V Showell & Co
‡Sutton *p403* 020 8661 7605

Shranks
‡London WC1 *p78* 020 7831 6677

SHULMANS
‡Leeds *p276* 0113 245 2833

Shupak & Co Solicitors
‡London EC3 *p78* 020 7236 4400

Shuttari Paul & Co
‡Southall *p384* 020 8574 7151

Sibley & Co
‡London WC2 *p78* 020 7395 9790

Siddiqui & Co
‡Harrow *p242* 020 8423 2400

Sidhu & Co
‡Birmingham *p142* 07831 293903

Sidley Austin Brown & Wood
‡London EC2 *p78* 020 7360 3600

Leonard Sieve & Co
‡Liverpool *p290* 0151 291 7700

Sigma Law Solicitors
‡Bradford *p155* 01274 391100 / 0844 879 3447

Sigma Solicitors
‡Accrington *p114* 01254 391222

Douglas Silas Solicitors
‡London N3 *p78* 0870 743 3377

Jeanette Silburn
‡Alresford *p116* 01962 773777

Adrian Silk Solicitor
‡London W9 *p78* 020 7266 5070

Silk Solicitors
‡Blackburn *p146* 01254 266616

Silks
‡Oldbury *p340* 0121 511 2233
Netherton *p321* 01384 236101
Smethwick *p382* 0121 558 1147

SILLS & BETTERIDGE LLP
‡Lincoln *p285* 01522 542211
Boston *p151* 01205 364615
Coningsby *p199* 01526 344444
Gainsborough *p228* 01427 616816
Skegness *p381* 01754 610101
Sleaford *p381* 01529 302800
Spalding *p389* 01775 714874
Spilsby *p389* 01790 752277

SILVER FITZGERALD
‡Cambridge *p175* 01223 562001

Richard Silver
‡Manchester *p309* 0161 834 9494

Silver Shemmings LLP
‡London SW1 *p78* 0845 345 1244
Cardiff *p181* 029 2047 4570
Epping *p219* 0845 345 1244

Silverbeck Rymer
‡Chelmsford *p187* 0845 050 8001
‡Liverpool *p290* 0151 236 9594

Silvercoin & Co
‡London W1 *p78* 020 7409 7474

Silverdale Solicitors
‡Manchester *p309* 0161 740 0333

Frances J Silverman
‡Billingshurst *p133* 01403 783696

Silverman Livermore
‡Runcorn *p369* 01928 714121

Silverman Sherliker LLP
‡London EC2 *p78* 020 7749 2700

Silvermiths
‡Southport *p388* 01704 542490

Silversmiths
‡Bootle *p150* 0151 922 6066

Silvesters Solicitors
‡Dudley *p213* 01384 240880

Simcocks
London WC2 *p79* 020 3043 4243

Simkins
‡Baldock *p121* 01462 892221

Michael Simkins LLP
‡London WC1 *p79* 020 7874 5600

Simman Solicitors
‡Croydon *p205* 020 8686 1085

Simmonds Grant
‡Oakham *p340* 01572 756866

Simmonds Hurford
‡Swansea *p405* 01792 462729 / 641070

Simmonds Solicitors
‡Poole *p353* 01202 666417

Simmons & Co
‡Tonbridge *p412* 01622 831823

Simmons & Simmons
‡London EC2 *p79* 020 7628 2020

Charles Simmons
‡Ilford *p261* 020 8514 0000

Simmons Gleek Solicitors
‡London W1 *p79* 020 7580 9090

Robert Simmons Legal Services Limited
‡Frimley *p227* 01252 267980

Roger Simmons & Co
‡Harrow *p242* 020 8909 9298

Simmons Stein
‡Stanmore *p394* 020 8954 8080

T K Simmons
‡Ashford *p119* 01233 740664

Simo & Co
‡Harrow *p242* 020 8866 6333

Simon Adams Solicitors
‡Manchester *p309* 0161 773 2222

Simon & Co
‡Southall *p384* 020 8571 3883

J A Simon & Co
‡Liverpool *p290* 0151 256 6669

Jeremy Simon & Co
‡Watford *p424* 01923 219292

Paul L Simon
‡Westminster W1 *p79* 020 7486 0541

Robert Simon & Co
‡Shoreham-by-Sea *p378* 01273 452333

Robin Simon LLP
‡London EC3 *p79* 0333 010 0000
Birmingham *p142* 0333 010 0000
Leeds *p276* 0333 010 0000
Manchester *p309* 0333 010 0000

Ross Simon & Co Solicitors
‡London SW9 *p79* 020 7738 7953

Thomas Simon
‡Cardiff *p181* 029 2055 7200

Alan Simons & Co
‡Penarth *p345* 029 2070 3991

Simons Levine & Co
‡Barnet N12 *p79* 020 8446 4273

Simons Muirhead & Burton
‡London W1 *p79* 020 7734 4499
Simons Rodkin Litigation Solicitors
‡London N12 *p79* 020 8446 6223
Simplex Law
‡London SE1 *p80* 0844 736 5653
Simply Law
‡Watford *p424* 01923 426600
Simply Legal Solicitors
‡London E12 *p80* 020 8514 7734
Alan Simpson & Co
‡Rayleigh *p359* 01268 745406
Simpson Duxbury
‡Bradford *p155* 01274 734166
Simpson Heald Pearson
‡Wigan *p432* 01942 495999
Ian Simpson & Co
‡Oldham *p341* 0161 622 4939
Simpson Millar LLP
‡Leeds *p276* 0844 858 3200
Birmingham *p142* 0844 858 3500
Bristol *p165* 0844 858 3600
Cardiff *p181* 0844 858 3700
Gateshead *p229* 0844 858 3000
London EC1 *p80* 0844 858 3400
London SW19 *p80* 0844 858 3800
Manchester *p309* 0844 858 3300
Simpson Sissons & Brooke
‡Sheffield *p377* 0114 241 3970
Simpson Thacher & Bartlett LLP
‡London EC2 *p80* 020 7275 6500
Simpsons Solicitors
‡Cheadle Hulme *p185* 0161 485 6030
Sims Cook & Teague
‡Thornbury *p411* 01454 414342
Bristol *p165* 0117 927 2141
Ali Sinclair Solutions
‡London E6 *p80* 020 8552 6001
Sinclair Solicitors
‡Liverpool *p290* 0151 236 5377
Sinclairs
‡Birmingham *p142* 0121 708 2144
‡London NW4 *p80* . . . 020 8202 8222 / 8202 2042
‡Penarth *p345* 029 2070 6444
Cardiff *p181* 029 2038 8398
Janet Sinden & Co
‡Hastings *p243* 01424 425285
Laurence Singer Solicitor
‡Amersham *p117* 01494 431400
BS Singh & Co
‡Bristol *p165* 0117 935 4500
G Singh
‡Ealing W5 *p80* 020 8567 2661
Singh Karran & Co
‡Hounslow *p254* 020 8570 5776
Robin Singh & Co Solicitors
‡Birmingham *p142* 0121 515 1500
Singhania & Co Ltd
‡London SW1 *p80* 020 7799 1688
Singleton Saunders Flood Solicitors
‡Dover *p213* 01304 240080
Singleton Winn McDermott Solicitors
‡Newcastle upon Tyne *p326* 0191 265 8817
Singletons
‡Pinner *p349* 020 8866 1934
Singletons Austin Ryder
‡Enfield *p219* 020 8363 0101
Enfield *p219* 020 8364 0500
Sinnertons
‡Banstead *p123* 01737 212000
Sintons LLP
‡Newcastle upon Tyne *p326* 0191 226 7878
G S Sira
‡Lichfield *p284* . . . . 01543 254382 / 254383
Sirius Business Law Ltd
‡Wells *p425* 0844 209 8500
Sitters & Co
‡Plymouth *p350* 01752 220464
Sittons Solicitors
‡Horsham *p253* 01403 267377
K Siva & Co
‡Wembley *p426* 020 8904 2577
Sk Nagra Solicitors
‡Gravesend *p233* 01474 333270
Skadden Arps Slate Meagher & Flom (UK) LLP
‡London E14 *p80* 020 7519 7000
Skanthabalan Solicitors
‡London E15 *p80* 020 8555 2710
Skellern & Co
‡Wakefield *p419* 01924 298780
The Skemp Partnership
‡Manchester *p310* 0800 040 7566 / 0161 238 5400
Carol Sketchley Solicitor
‡Coventry *p201* 01676 530514
David W Skinner Solicitor
‡Cambridge *p175* 01954 201075
J M Skinner & Co
‡Birkenhead *p135* 0151 666 1122

R W Skinner & Son
‡Burton-on-Trent *p170* 01283 561694
Julie Skitt Solicitor
‡Plymouth *p350* 01752 793572
Slade & Fletcher Solicitors
‡London SE5 *p80* 020 7733 6506
J R Slade
‡Maldon *p300* 01621 828397
Slade Legal
‡Abingdon *p114* 01235 521920
Didcot *p210* 01235 511211
Wallingford *p419* 01491 839346
Richard Slade & Company
‡London WC1 *p80* 020 7160 0900
Slater Bradley & Co
‡Wandsworth SW15 *p80* 020 8788 1008
Slater Heelis Collier Littler
‡Sale *p370* 0161 969 3131
Sale *p370* 0161 969 3131
Slater Rhodes Solicitors
‡Yeovil *p444* 01935 848595
Slaughter and May
‡London EC1 *p80* 020 7600 1200
Barry Slavin & Co
‡London W1 *p80* 020 7612 9010
Slee Blackwell
‡Barnstaple *p125* 01271 372128
Bideford *p133* 01237 425225
Braunton *p156* 01271 812019
Exeter *p222* 01392 423000
South Molton *p383* 01769 573771
Sleep & Co
‡Tavistock *p408* 01822 618850
Sleigh & Son
Droylsden *p213* 0161 370 2198
Sleigh Son & Booth
‡Droylsden *p213* 0161 370 9524
Sloan & Co
‡London W1 *p80* 020 7917 2865
Peter A C Sloan
‡Reading *p361* 0118 930 5030
Sloan Plumb Wood
‡Peterborough *p347* 01733 302410
Martyn Slocombe & Co
‡Malvern *p300* 01684 574001
Slotine Legal
‡London SW1 *p80* 020 8528 1049
Slough Solicitors
‡Slough *p382* . . . 01753 535422 / 0800 051 7624
C C Smale Solicitors
‡Bacup *p121* 01706 873737
David Small
‡Hungerford *p258* . 01488 684287 / 07713 094759
Martin Smalley & Co
‡Nottingham *p339* 0115 955 6555
Roger David Smallman
‡Coventry *p201* 01676 535283
Keith Smart & Co
‡Cwmbran *p206* 01633 872031
Smart Law Solicitors LLP
‡Ely *p218* 01353 720903
Cambridge *p175* 01223 451057
Philip Smart & Associates
‡Cheltenham *p188* 01242 529333
Alan Smeath & Co
‡Woburn Sands *p436* . . 01908 584307 / 584331
Henry Smee & Co
‡London N20 *p80* 020 8446 3131
Smith & Copsey
‡Wallsend *p419* 0191 262 4428
Newcastle upon Tyne *p326*
Smith & Graham
Peterlee *p348* 0191 517 3393
Smith & Tetley
‡Ashton-under-Lyne *p120* 0161 330 2865
Smith & Wells
‡Coventry *p201* 024 7655 3040
Andrew Smith
‡Weybridge *p430* 07852 132420
Ashley Smith & Co
‡Lewisham SE13 *p80* 020 8463 0099
Smith Bates
‡Lyndhurst *p296* 023 8028 3414
Belinda Smith & Co Solicitors
‡Peterborough *p347* 01733 267414
Smith Braithwaite
‡London W1 *p80* 020 7437 4244
Smith Brown & Sprawson
‡Dunstable *p214* 01582 601233
Luton *p295* 01582 876900
Smith Chamberlain
‡Wellingborough *p425* 01933 224971
Derek Smith & Co
‡Bolton *p150* 01204 389089
Bury *p171* 01706 829750
E Smith & Co
‡Kington *p268* 01544 231010
Eric H Smith
‡Burnley *p169* 01282 432141

F W Smith, Riches & Co
‡London SW1 *p80* 020 7930 0833
Smith Gadd & Co
‡Horsham *p253* 01403 271222
Geoffrey T Smith & Co
‡Wolverhampton *p438* 01902 426961
Glenn Smith & Co
‡Peterborough *p347* 01778 343272
Graham Smith Property Lawyers
‡Watford *p424* 01923 227212
Helen Smith Solicitor
‡Cheltenham *p188* 07766 412615
Ian Smith & Co Solicitors
‡Doncaster *p212* 01427 892884
J H Smith
‡Carlisle *p182* 01228 521383
Smith Jones Solicitors
Kenilworth *p264* 01926 859933
K J Smith Solicitors
‡Henley-on-Thames *p247* 01491 630000
Smith Law Partnership
‡Braintree *p155* 01376 321311
Smith Llewelyn Partnership
‡Swansea *p405* 01792 464444
Martin Smith & Co
‡Borehamwood *p150* 020 8953 0636
Martin T Smith
‡Leighton Buzzard *p282* 01525 374183
Mary Smith Solicitor
‡Lowestoft *p294* 01502 511977
Smith May Solicitors
‡Cambridge *p175* 01223 415372
Michael Smith & Co
‡Ipswich *p263* 01473 226231
The Smith Partnership
‡Derby *p209* 01332 225300
‡Derby *p209* 01332 225225
Burton-on-Trent *p170* 01283 536471
Burton-on-Trent *p170* 01283 548282
Leicester *p281* 0116 247 2000
Leicester *p281* 0116 255 6292
Stoke-on-Trent *p398* 01782 324454
Swadlincote *p404* 01283 226444
Patrick Smith & Co
‡Wantage *p421* 01235 772212
Smith-Rahman Associates
‡London N10 *p80* 020 7566 8244
Robert Smith & Co
‡Stroud *p401* 01453 757435
Smith Roddam
‡Bishop Auckland *p144* 01388 603073
Crook *p203* 01388 762564
Shildon *p378* 01388 772661
Rosemary Smith & Co
‡Crowthorne *p204* 01344 777441
Roy Smith & Co
‡Christchurch *p194* . . . . 01202 473413 / 473414
Smith Solicitor LLP
‡Halifax *p238* 01422 383380
Smith Sutcliffe
‡Burnley *p169* 01282 426251
Padiham *p344* 01282 778434
T C Smith
‡Berwick-upon-Tweed *p131* 01289 307409
W F Smith LLP
‡Watton *p424* 01953 880800
Dereham *p209* 01362 852900
Swaffham *p404* 01760 336083
Smithfield Partners Limited
‡London EC4 *p80* 0845 539 1000
SmithJones Solicitors Ltd
‡Burnley *p169* 01282 855400
Smiths Law LLP
‡London WC2 *p80* 020 7395 8631
Maurice Smiths
‡Castleford *p183* 01977 557171
Pontefract *p351* 01977 794395
Smiths Solicitors
‡Barnstaple *p125* 01271 314888
Smithson Hinds Morris
‡Leeds *p276* 0113 245 0456
Smithsons
‡Manchester *p310* 0844 888 0551
Smyth Barkham
‡London WC2 *p80* 020 7632 9550
John Smythe & Co
‡Kingston upon Thames *p267* . . . 020 8546 1390
Snipelaw
‡Blackpool *p147* 01253 844444
Snow Hill Legal
‡London EC1 *p80* 020 7334 9191
Snowball Worthy Lowe
‡Sunderland *p402* 0191 565 3221
Sohal & Co
‡Greenford *p234* 020 8575 2424
Sohan Rabheru Services Limited
‡Stockport *p396* 0845 241 1299
Jerzy Sokol Solicitor
‡London W1 *p80* 020 8123 9513

Solicitor Direct
‡Leyland *p283* 01772 424999
Solicitorhelp
‡Wirral *p435* 0151 522 3410
Solicitors Active
‡Leeds *p277* 0113 248 9805
The Solicitors Chambers
‡Pontefract *p351* 01977 599999
Solicitors Direct
‡Bradford *p155* 01274 776000
Solicitors First LLP
‡Wandsworth SW17 *p80* 0870 770 7016
London SW17 *p80* 020 8673 0116
Solicitors Property Shop Keighley
‡Keighley *p264* 01535 608844
Solicitors Title
‡Exeter *p222* 01392 207900
Solomon Law
‡Peterborough *p347* 01733 312424
Solomon Levy
‡Luton *p295* . . . . 01582 425817 / 414948
M J Solomon & Partners
‡London E1 *p80* 020 7377 2778
‡London N8 *p80* 020 8888 4446
The Solomon Partnership Solicitors LLP
‡Blackburn *p146* 01254 667358
Manchester *p310* 0161 225 2555
Solomon Sinclair Law Firm
‡London N14 *p80* 020 8882 5091
Solomon Taylor & Shaw
‡London NW3 *p80* 020 7431 1912
Solomons Legal
‡Solihull *p383* 01564 711101
Solomons Solicitors
‡Bournemouth *p152* 01202 802807
‡Ilford *p261* 020 8514 7414
Solutions Legal Solicitors
‡Stansted Mountfitchet *p394* 020 8166 0700
Soma & Co Solicitors
‡Harrow *p242* 020 8423 0203
Somers & Blake
‡London W7 *p80* 020 8567 7025
Somerton & Fletcher
‡Cambridge *p175* 01223 566596
Somerville & Savage
‡Torquay *p413* 01803 312700
Torquay *p413* 01803 324500
Sona Solicitors
‡Leicester *p281* 0116 268 2300
Soni & Kaur
‡Brentford *p156* 020 8568 6464
Sonn Macmillan
‡London E1 *p80* 020 7377 8889
Sony Sadaf Haroon Solicitors
‡St Albans *p390* 01727 568353
Soods Solicitors
‡Ilford *p261* 020 8597 0000
Sookias & Sookias
‡London W1 *p80* 020 7465 8000
Soper & Co
‡Malvern *p300* 01684 568495
Sorrells Solicitors
‡Chipping Ongar *p193* 01277 365532
Michael Soul & Associates
‡London WC2 *p80* 020 7353 3358
Soulsby Williamson
‡Ruislip *p369* 01895 636999
Sound Advice LLP
‡London WC2 *p80* 020 7420 4300
Catherine Sousa Solicitors
‡Southampton *p386* 023 8071 3060
South England Solicitors
‡Kenton *p265* 0800 848 8991
South West Family Law
‡Radstock *p358* 01761 233289
South West Law Limited
‡Bristol *p165* 0117 314 6400
Southampton Row Solicitors Limited
‡London WC1 *p81* 020 3178 4463
Southbank Solicitors
‡London SW9 *p81*
Southbridge Solicitors
‡London SE1 *p81* 020 7928 5488
Southcombe & Hayley
‡Westminster W1 *p81* 020 7935 6631
Southcote Scott
‡London W1 *p81* 020 7034 7035
Southern Stewart & Walker
‡South Shields *p384* 0191 427 0770
South Shields *p384* 0191 456 7788
Southerns
‡Burnley *p169* 01282 422711
Burnley *p169* 01282 438446
Colne *p198* 01282 863113
Nelson *p321* 01282 603663
Southfields Solicitors
‡Wandsworth SW18 *p81* 020 8877 3421

Southgate & Co
‡London N15 *p81* 020 8809 0010

Southwell Mott
‡Lichfield *p284*. . . . . . .01543 252102 / 251484

J D Southworth
‡Bourne End *p151*. 01628 522407

Sovereign Solicitors
‡Bury *p171* 0161 280 0582
‡Shipley *p378* 01274 809696

John Sowerby Limited
‡Bridport *p158*. 01308 424090

SpainWilliams LLP
‡West Malling *p428* 01732 523590

David Spalding Solicitors
‡Wrexham *p443*. 01978 851688

C A Sparkes Solicitors
‡Wirral *p435*. 0151 625 3777

Sparling Benham & Brough
‡Colchester *p198* 01206 733733
‡Manningtree *p311* 01206 392201
Frinton-on-Sea *p227* 01255 679222

Sparrow & Trieu Solicitors
‡London W1 *p81* 020 7287 6608

Speakman & Co
‡Crewe *p203* 01270 214237

Spearing Waite LLP
‡Leicester *p281* 0116 262 4225

Spearpoint Franks Solicitors Ltd
‡Brighton *p160* 01273 748749

Frank E L Spears
‡Burton-on-Trent *p170*. 01283 511474

The Specter Partnership
‡Birkenhead *p135* 0151 647 3000
London EC1 *p81* 020 7251 9900
Warrington *p422* 01925 428360

Dr Linda S Spedding
‡London SW6 *p81*. 020 7610 2025

SPEECHLY BIRCHAM LLP
‡London EC4 *p81* 020 7427 6400

Speeding Solicitor / MAJ Law Solicitors
‡Widnes *p432* . . . 0151 422 8020 / 07810 804464

Spence & Horne
‡Hackney E8 *p81* 020 8985 2277

Irena Spence
‡Cambridge *p175* 01223 713300
Cambridge *p175* 01223 713300

Spencer & Fisch
Leeds *p277*. 0113 264 7603

Spencer Davies
‡Grassington *p232*. 01756 753015

Spencer Ewin Mulvihill
‡Harrogate *p240*. 01423 509826

Spencer Howard
‡Worthing *p442* 01903 538869

Ian Spencer & Co
‡Newbury *p322* 01635 528424

Spencer Shaw
‡Birmingham *p142*. 0121 698 8507

Spencer Skuse
‡Cardiff *p181* 029 2034 3993

Spencers Lawyers Limited
‡Winchester *p434* 01962 850171

Spenser Underhill Newmark LLP
‡London WC1 *p81*. 020 7269 9026

J D Spicer & Co
‡London NW6 *p81*. 020 7625 5590
Birmingham *p142*. 0121 222 4213
London EC4 *p81* 020 7651 0850

Spicketts Battrick Law Practice
‡Pontypridd *p352* 01443 407221
Cardiff *p181* 029 2046 1480
Cardiff *p181* 029 2046 7150

Spiegel & Utrera Ltd
‡London NW1 *p81*. 020 7284 3700

Geoffrey Spiller Solicitors
‡Eastbourne *p216*. 01323 419566

G Spilsbury & Co
‡Mountain Ash *p319*. 01443 473213

Spiropoulos Lawal Solicitors
‡London SE4 *p81* 020 8469 0669

C J Spoor & Co
‡Rushden *p369* 01933 419499

Louis Spragg & Co
‡Dudley *p213* . . . . . . .01384 211621 / 211622

Sprake & Kingsley
‡Bungay *p168*. 01986 892721
Beccles *p129*. 01502 713214

Spratt Endicott
‡Banbury *p122* 01295 204000
Banbury *p122*. 01295 204000
Banbury *p122*. 01295 204000

H Michael Spring
‡Port Talbot *p353* 01639 897075

Spring Law
‡London WC2 *p81*. 020 7930 4158

Sproull Solicitors LLP
‡Camelford *p176* 01840 212315
Bodmin *p148* 01208 72328
Port Isaac *p353*. 01840 212315

Spurlings Solicitors
‡Christchurch *p194* 01202 473321

Squire Sanders (UK) LLP
‡Leeds *p277*. 0113 284 7000
Birmingham *p142*. 0121 222 3000
London EC2 *p81* 020 7655 1000
Manchester *p310*. 0161 830 5000

Sri Kanth & Co
‡Wembley *p426* 020 8795 0648

Sriharans
‡Southall *p384*. 020 8843 9974

Louis Ssekkono Solicitors
‡London WC2 *p82*. 020 7839 1772

St Albans Solicitors
‡St Albans *p390*. 01727 884658

St Helens Law Limited
‡St Helens *p391*. 01744 454433

Terence St J Millett
‡London SW7 *p82*. 020 7581 7500

St Luce & Co
‡London SE15 *p82* 020 7635 9131

St Stephens Consultancy Services Limited
‡Brough *p167* 01430 441383

St Valchikwe Solicitors
‡Ilford *p261* 020 8597 7118

Adrian Stables
‡Somerton *p383*. 0845 873 6180

Stables & Co
‡Halesowen *p237* 0121 585 3820
Kidderminster *p266*
Stourbridge *p399* 01384 390581

Richard Stace Employment Law Services
‡Ipswich *p263* 0844 800 8505

Stachiw Bashir Green
‡Bradford *p155* 01274 404010
Bradford *p155* 01274 404010

Stafford Eales
‡Wotton-under-Edge *p442*. 0117 370 0500

Stafford Young Jones
‡London EC4 *p82* 020 7623 9490

Stainforth Solicitors
‡Ilford *p261* 020 8510 1683

Stala Erimos Charalambous & Co
‡London N14 *p82* 020 8886 5970

James Stallard & Co
‡London WC2 *p82*. 020 7430 1861

Stallard March & Edwards
‡Worcester *p440* 01905 723561
Worcester *p440*. 01905 613404
Worcester *p440*. 01905 613404

Stamp Jackson and Procter
‡Hull *p258*. 01482 324591

Stamps Family Solicitors
‡Hull *p258*. 01482 323495

Standish Associates
‡Bristol *p165*. 0117 924 9204

Standley & Co
‡Knowle *p269* 01564 776287

Stanford & Lambert
‡Newcastle upon Tyne *p327*. . . . 0191 232 6226

Stanger Stacey & Mason
‡Witney *p436* 01993 776491

Stanley & Co
‡Wembley *p427* 020 8903 7864

Stanley Smith Hill & Co
‡Carshalton *p183* 020 8669 0044
Banstead *p123* 01737 358001

Stanley Tee LLP
‡Cambridge *p175* 01223 311141
Saffron Walden *p370* 01799 527299

Charles Stansfield
‡Wilmslow *p433*. 01625 539695

Laura Stansfield & Co
‡Wilmslow *p433*. 01625 529409

Stanton & Doran
‡Upminster *p417* 01708 641781

Stanton-Dunne & Co
‡Chelmsford *p187* 01245 460303

Stantons
‡Gravesend *p233* 01474 579940

Stapleton & Son
‡Stamford *p393* 01780 751226

Stapleton Gardner & Co
‡Morley *p319* 0113 253 8111

Linda Stapleton & Co
Gloucester *p230* 01452 423870

Stapletons Solicitors
‡London N13 *p82* 020 8886 6876

Stapley & Co
‡Loughton *p294* 020 8502 1934
Woodford Green *p439*

Starbuck & Mack
‡Fareham *p224* 01329 285341

Starke & Co Family Law
‡Haywards Heath *p246* 01444 416116

Starkie & Gregory
‡Long Eaton *p293* 0115 849 9000

Starr & Partners LLP
‡London EC4 *p82* 020 7199 1450

Statham Gill Davies
‡London W1 *p82* 020 7317 3210

Status Legal
‡Croydon *p205* 020 8649 9204

Hugh Staunton
‡Grantham *p232*. 01476 861972

Steadman Jones & Bell
‡Ammanford *p118* 01269 592306

Steadmans
‡Tunbridge Wells *p415*. 01892 511102

R W Stebbings
‡Plymouth *p350* 01752 202287

Steed & Steed LLP
‡Sudbury *p401* 01787 373387
Braintree *p155* 01376 552828

Steel & Clunis
‡Birmingham *p142*. 0121 523 9191

Steel & Co
‡Wetherby *p429*. 01937 845539
Knaresborough *p268* 01423 869977

Steel & Hitchcock
‡Carmarthen *p183*. 01267 236781

Steel & Shamash
‡Lambeth SE1 *p82* 020 7803 3999

L A Steel
‡Barnsley *p125* 01226 770909

Steele & Son
‡Clitheroe *p196* 01200 444321
‡Colne *p198*. 01282 868000
Barnoldswick *p124* 01282 813385

STEELE FORD & NEWTON
‡Nelson *p321* 01282 692531

R T Steele & Spencer
‡Chester *p191*. . . . . . .01244 318016 / 314531

Steele Raymond
‡Bournemouth *p152* 01202 294566

Steeles
‡Norwich *p335*. 0870 609 0200
Diss *p211*. 01379 652141
London EC2 *p82* 020 7421 1720

Steels
‡Warrington *p422* 01925 632676
Warrington *p422* 01925 261354

Steen & Co Employment Solicitors
‡Oxford *p344* 01865 784101

Lynne Steen Commercial Solicitor
‡Chorley *p194*. 01257 452044

Steene & Co
‡Elstree *p218* 020 8953 7707

Steer and Co
‡Bristol *p165*. 0117 230 9700

Richard Steer & Co
‡Teddington *p409* 020 8977 8621

Steinbergs
‡Liverpool *p290* 0151 521 4491

Steinfeld Law LLP
‡London W1 *p82* 020 7725 1313

Stembridge Solicitors
‡Hexham *p249* 01434 618696

Stenfield Solicitors
‡Harrow *p242* 020 8422 2179

Stennett & Stennett
‡London N14 *p82* 020 8920 3190

J P Stent Solicitor
‡Ilkeston *p261*. 0115 930 6099

Stephen & Associates Limited
‡London SW1 *p82*. 020 7930 2500

Stephen Gisby & Co
‡Bristol *p165*. 0117 915 4562

Stephens & Scown
‡Exeter *p222* 01392 210700
St Austell *p391* 01726 74433
Truro *p414* 01872 265100

Stephens & Son LLP
‡Chatham *p185* 01634 811444

Jonathan Stephens & Co
‡Usk *p417*. 01291 673344

Lawrence Stephens
‡London EC1 *p82* 020 7935 1211

Louise Stephens & Co
‡Risca *p365* . . . . .01633 614005 / 601144

Stephens McDonald & Robson
‡Newcastle upon Tyne *p327*. . . . 0191 232 0675

Stephens Wheeler Cooke & Sons
‡Luton *p295*. 01582 720175

Stephenson Harwood
‡London EC2 *p82* 020 7329 4422

John Stephenson & Co
‡St Albans *p390*. 01727 847983

Stephenson Reynell
‡Windermere *p434* 01539 488622

Stephensons
‡Brierley Hill *p158* 01384 79731
Wombourne *p438*. 01902 894187

Stephensons Solicitors LLP
‡Leigh *p282*. 01942 777777
Bolton *p150*. 01942 777777
Bolton *p150*. 01942 777777
Leigh *p282*. 01942 777777
Manchester *p310*. 0161 832 8844
St Helens *p391*. 01942 777777
Wigan *p432*. 01942 777777
Wigan *p432*. 01942 777777

Stepien Lake
‡London W1 *p83* 020 7467 3030

Steptoe & Johnson
‡London EC2 *p83* 020 7367 8000

Sterling Law
‡Loughborough *p293* 01509 263790

Sterling Solicitors
‡Birmingham *p142*. 0121 772 0777

Elliott Stern Solicitors
‡London N17 *p83* 020 8801 0444

Vivien Stern Solicitor
‡Camden NW6 *p83* 020 7328 5532

Lawrence Sternberg & Co
‡Barnet *p124* 020 8440 5550

Sternberg Reed
‡Barking *p123*. 020 8591 3366
Grays *p233*. 01375 486500
London NW1 *p83*. 020 7485 5558
Romford *p366* 01708 766155

Sterratt & Co
‡Barnoldswick *p124* 01282 813731
Skipton *p381* 01756 795069

Steven Young & Co
‡Gloucester *p230* 01452 332882
Cheltenham *p188*. 01242 257269

Stevens
‡Haverhill *p244* 01440 762511
‡Stoke-on-Trent *p398* 01782 343353
Saffron Walden *p370* 01799 526849
Stafford *p393*. 01785 250908
Stoke-on-Trent *p398* 01782 813200
Wolverhampton *p438* 01902 772776

Stevens & Bolton
‡Guildford *p237* 01483 302264

J A Stevens & Co
‡Epsom *p219* 01372 745288

Stevens Lucas
‡Chirk *p193* 01691 777949
Oswestry *p342* 01691 670999

Paul Stevens & Co
‡Bristol *p165*. 0117 942 9308

Stevens Son & Pope
‡Burgess Hill *p168*. 01444 246377

Wade Stevens & Co
‡Orpington *p342*. 01689 831122

stevensdrake
‡Crawley *p202*. 01293 596900

Chris Stevenson
‡Doncaster *p212* 01302 341243

Stevensons Solicitors
‡Dereham *p209* 01362 860300

Peter Steward & Co
‡Great Yarmouth *p234*. 01493 332277

G T Stewart Solicitors
‡London SE22 *p83* 020 8299 6000

Stewarts Law LLP
‡London EC4 *p83* 020 7822 8000
Leeds *p277*. 0113 222 0022

Stewarts Legal
‡Cardiff *p181* 0845 621 6217

Michael J Stibbard & Co
‡Norwich *p335*. 01603 619845

Stibbe
‡London EC2 *p83* 020 7466 6300

E John Stiff
‡Cheadle *p185* 0161 491 0461

Stilemans
‡London N14 *p83* 020 8882 1047

Stilwell & Harby
‡Dover *p213*. 01304 206850

Frank Stimpson & Son
‡London SE23 *p83* 020 8699 7644

David Stinson & Co
‡Rochester *p366* 01622 711300

Stirling & Co
‡Bristol *p165*. 0117 931 4435

Stirling Law Commercial Law Firm
‡Manchester *p310*. 0161 241 5510

Stitt & Co
‡London EC4 *p83* 020 7832 0840

Harold Stock & Co
‡Ashton-under-Lyne *p120* .01457 835597 / 835034
‡Ashton-under-Lyne *p120* 01457 836152
Ashton-under-Lyne *p120* 01457 838136
Failsworth *p223*. 0161 682 2400

Stock Moran Swalwell
‡Wigan *p432* 01942 771771

Stockdale & Reid Ltd
‡North Shields *p331* 0191 257 1341
Monkseaton *p318*. 0191 251 9494

Stockdale Solicitors
‡Lancaster *p270*. 01524 753026

Stocker & Co
‡Thame *p410* 01844 216995

Stockinger
‡London EC4 *p83* 020 7833 0448

Stockler Brunton
‡London EC4 *p83* 020 7404 6661

Stockslegal Ltd
‡Manchester *p310* 0800 988 9055

Anthony Stockton
‡Coventry *p201* 01676 535790
Bishop's Stortford *p144* 01279 464530

Stoddart & Company
‡Salisbury *p371* 01722 417111

Stoffel & Co
‡Beckenham *p129* 020 8650 8157

The Stokes Partnership
‡Crewkerne *p203* 01460 279279

Stokes Solicitors
‡Portsmouth *p355* 023 9266 1541
Portsmouth *p355* 023 9282 8131

Stokesley Family Law
‡Middlesbrough *p315* 01642 714071

Stokoe Partnership
‡Waltham Forest E11 *p83* 020 8558 8884
London WC2 *p83* 020 3427 5710
Manchester *p310* 0161 237 5755

Stone & Stone
‡Morden *p318* 020 8540 2202

Stone Joseph Solicitors
‡London SW10 *p83* 020 7854 9098

Stone King LLP
‡Bath *p128* 01225 337599
Cambridge *p176* 01223 451070
London EC1 *p83* 020 7796 1007

Stone Milward Rapers
‡Chichester *p193* 01243 780211
Chichester *p193* 01243 602832

STONE ROWE BREWER LLP
‡Twickenham *p416* 020 8891 6141

Stonehage Law Limited
‡London W1 *p83* 020 7087 0000

Stones
‡London W1 *p83* 020 7935 4848

Stones Solicitors LLP
‡Exeter *p222* 01392 666777
Okehampton *p340* 01837 650200

Andrew Storch
‡Reading *p361* 0118 958 4407

Storey & Co
‡Stokesley *p398* 01642 712132

Stork & Coles
‡London WC1 *p84* 020 7404 6021

Storrar Cowdry
‡Chester *p191* 01244 400567
Chester *p191* 01244 400567

Story & Robison
‡Norwich *p335* 01603 626355
‡Norwich *p335* 01953 851125

Stowe Family Law LLP
‡Altrincham *p117* 0161 926 1410
‡Harrogate *p241* 01423 532600

Stowe Simon
‡Hednesford *p246* 01543 877131

A M Strachan & Co
‡Hackney N1 *p84* 020 7729 0003

Fiona Strachan
‡Saffron Walden *p370* 01799 541331

Stradbrokes Solicitors
‡Leeds *p277* 0113 279 0722

Strafford Law Limited
‡London EC2 *p84* 020 7628 7975

Strain Keville
‡Westminster W1 *p84* 020 7323 5000

Strand Solicitors
‡London WC2 *p84* 020 3393 3009
London W4 *p84* 020 3393 3009

Strasons
‡London SW16 *p84* 020 8677 7534

Stratem Law
‡London W4 *p84* 07816 440692

Stratford Solicitors
‡Macclesfield *p297* 01625 820275
Poynton *p355* 01625 878204

Straw & Pearce
‡Loughborough *p293* 01509 268931

Streathers Clapham LLP
London SW4 *p84* 020 7622 7257

Streathers Highgate LLP
London N6 *p84* 020 3074 1900

Streathers Solicitors LLP
‡London W1 *p84* 020 7034 4200

Street & Company Solicitors
‡Bridgnorth *p157* 0845 544 0499

David Street & Company
‡Crawley *p202* 01293 616191

John Street Solicitors
‡London WC1 *p84* 020 7623 8822

Streeter Marshall
‡Croydon *p205* 020 8680 2638
Purley *p358* 020 8660 6455
Warlingham *p421* 01883 622433

Strick & Bellingham
‡Swansea *p405* 01792 641201

Stringer Smith & Levett
‡London NW3 *p84* 020 7435 0436

Stringfellow & Co
‡London W14 *p84* 020 7371 4040

Stripes Solicitors
‡Manchester *p310* 0161 832 5000

The Stroud Stitson Partnership
‡Plymouth *p350* 01752 660066

Strube & Co
‡London SE26 *p84* 020 8659 3020

Stuart Hurrion & Green
‡Bexleyheath *p132* 020 8298 1595

Stuart Malcolm LLP
‡Oxford *p344* 01865 601240

Stuart Smith & Burnett
‡Bridlington *p158* 01262 678128

Stuarts
Gerrards Cross *p229* 01753 892244

Stuckey Carr & Co
‡Storrington *p399* 01903 743201
Pulborough *p358* 01798 875358

Studio Legale International Lombardo
‡Kingston upon Thames *p267* 020 3274 0016

Stunt Palmer & Robinson
‡London E2 *p84* 020 7739 6927

William Sturges & Co
‡Westminster SW1 *p84* 020 7873 1000

D E Sturgess
‡Romsey *p367* 01794 830791

Sturgess Perring Solicitors
‡Leeds *p277* 07980 552942

Sturtivant & Co
‡London W1 *p84* 020 7486 9524

P M Suchak & Co
‡Leicester *p281* 0116 299 0007
Harrow *p242* 020 8422 7707

Sugare & Co
‡Leeds *p277* 0113 244 6978

Sugiyama & Co
‡Farnham *p225* 01252 820500

Sullivan Consulting
‡London W14 *p84* 020 7603 1893

Sullivan & Cromwell
‡London EC4 *p84* 020 7959 8900

Sullivans Solicitors LLP
‡Enfield *p219* 020 8363 3888

Sultan Lloyd
‡Birmingham *p142* 0121 248 2850

Sumal Creasey
‡Leicester *p281* 0116 275 5400

Sumal Creasey Solicitors
‡Leicester *p281* 0116 274 3800

Summers
‡London W1 *p84* 020 7224 2024

Summers Nigh Law LLP
‡Northampton *p332* 01604 771136

Summit Law LLP
‡London W1 *p84* 020 7467 3980

Sumner & Main
‡Worthing *p442* 01903 239420

Sumner & Tabor
‡Berkhamsted *p131* 01442 862797 / 872311

Sundip Murria Solicitors Limited
‡Willenhall *p433* 0844 567 4999

Sunley Solicitors
‡Whitstable *p431* 01227 274455

Sunrise Solicitors Limited
‡London SW19 *p84* 020 8543 0999

SurbitonLaw LLP
‡Surbiton *p402* 020 8399 8900

Suriya & Co
‡Hounslow *p254* 020 8569 6352
‡London SW17 *p84* 020 8682 1131
‡London E1 *p84* 020 7247 0444

Surjj Legal Limited
‡Stanmore *p394* 020 3278 8849

Surrey Solicitors
‡Croydon *p205* 020 8666 0330

Sussex Defence Solicitors
‡Worthing *p442* 01903 261127

Sussex Law Solicitors
‡Brighton *p160* 01273 561312

Sutcliffes
‡Rawtenstall *p359* 01706 215107

Sutovic & Hartigan
‡London W3 *p84* 020 8993 5544

Andrew Sutton Law
‡Northampton *p332* 07816 308265

Clive Sutton Solicitor
‡Lymington *p296* 01590 672595

Sutton-Mattocks & Co LLP
‡London SW13 *p84* 020 8876 8811
London W4 *p84* 020 8994 7344

Nicholas Sutton Solicitors
‡Bewdley *p131* 01299 405626

Suttons
‡London W1 *p84* 020 7935 5279

SVArmstrong
‡Leeds *p277* 01904 520150

Svedberg Law
‡London SW1 *p84* 020 7368 7000

Svetlova LLP
‡London SW1 *p84* 020 7117 6444

Swabey & Co
‡London SW6 *p84* 020 7731 7777

Swaby Clarke & Norris
‡Barking *p123* 020 8507 1882

Swain & Co
‡London SE8 *p84* 0800 021 3272 / 020 8692 9100
‡Southampton *p386* 023 8063 1111
Havant *p244* 023 9248 3322

Swain & Co Solicitors
‡Liverpool *p290* 0808 168 0550 / 0151 255 2286

John Swales
‡Ashford *p119* 01233 732590

Swan Turton
‡London WC2 *p84* 020 7520 9555

Swanboroughs LLP
‡Uckfield *p416* 01825 733334

David K Swann
‡Rochdale *p365* 01706 366557

Swanns
‡King's Lynn *p266* 01553 811747

Swatton Taylor Dutton
‡Tring *p413* 01442 825566

Swayne Johnson Solicitors
‡Denbigh *p208* 01745 812835
Llandudno *p291* 01492 876271
Ruthin *p369* 01824 703833
St Asaph *p391* 01745 582535

Sweeney Miller
‡Sunderland *p402* 0191 568 2050

Sweetman Burke & Sinker
‡Ealing W13 *p84* 020 8840 2572

Sweetmans Solicitors
‡Whitchurch *p430* 0800 141 2620 / 01829 770903

Swift Property Lawyers
‡Welwyn Garden City *p426*

Swinburne & Jackson LLP
‡Gateshead *p229* 0191 477 2531 / 477 3222
Chester-le-Street *p191* 0191 388 7221
Hexham *p249* 01434 607035
Ryton *p370* 0191 413 3468 / 413 2630
Washington *p423* 0191 416 0004

L L Swinburne
‡Gosforth *p232* 0191 285 7544

Swinburne Maddison
‡Durham *p214* 0191 384 2441 / 384 7455

Swinburne Snowball & Jackson
‡Consett *p199* 01207 502532

John Swindell and Co Solicitors
‡Blackburn *p146* 01254 52400

Swinnerton Moore Solicitors
‡London EC4 *p84* 020 7236 7111

Switalski's
‡Wakefield *p419* 01924 882000
Bradford *p155* 01274 720314
Dewsbury *p210* 01924 869940
Halifax *p238* 01422 284350
Huddersfield *p256* 01484 821650
Leeds *p277* 0113 223 1400

Sydney Mitchell
‡Birmingham *p142* 0121 698 2200 / 0808 166 8827
‡Flitwick *p226* 01525 175520
Birmingham *p142* 0121 722 2969 / 0808 166 5638
Solihull *p383* 0121 746 3300

Syeds Solicitors
‡Birmingham *p142* 0121 622 5800
Manchester *p310* 0161 795 2111

Sykes Anderson LLP
‡London EC2 *p85* 020 3178 3770

David Sykes Solicitor
‡Lancaster *p270* 01524 845849

Sykes Lee & Brydson
‡York *p445* 01904 731100
York *p445* 01904 529000

Sylvester Amiel Lewin & Horne LLP
‡London N12 *p85* 020 8446 4000

Sylvester Mackett
‡Trowbridge *p414* 01225 755621
Warminster *p421* 01985 217464 / 217114

P B Sylvester & Co
‡Wandsworth SW16 *p85* 020 8769 6767

SYMES BAINS BROOMER
‡Scunthorpe *p373* 01724 281616
Epworth *p219* 01427 872479
Goole *p231* 01405 763853
Grimsby *p235* 01472 360991
Howden *p255* 01430 430230

Symes Robinson & Lee
‡Crediton *p203* 01363 775566
Budleigh Salterton *p168* 01395 445581
Exeter *p222* 01392 270867

Symons & Gay
‡Romford *p366* 01708 744211

Synergy Employment Law Solicitors
‡London N1 *p85* 020 7851 4411

Systech Solicitors
‡London SE1 *p85* 020 7234 3520
Leeds *p277* 0113 388 8080
Liverpool *p290* 0151 707 1019
Manchester *p310* 0161 219 8008

T

TBI Solicitors
‡Hartlepool *p243* 0800 052 6824 / 01429 264101
Barnard Castle *p123* 01833 638326
Billingham *p133* 01740 646000

TJL Solicitors
‡Manchester *p310* 0800 634 0280

TJM Law
‡Beckenham *p129* 020 8662 6090

TKD Solicitors
‡Hammersmith & Fulham W6 *p85* 020 8741 8050

TLS
‡Derby *p209* 01332 372182

TLT Solicitors
‡Bristol *p165* 0117 917 7777
London EC2 *p85* 020 3465 4000

TLW Solicitors
‡North Shields *p331* 0800 169 5925

TMB Associates Solicitors
‡Grays *p233* 01375 378809

TM Fortis Solicitor
‡Manchester *p310* 0161 220 6040

TMJ Law Solicitors
‡Northampton *p332* 01604 608111

TMJ Legal Services LLP
‡Hartlepool *p243* 01429 235616
Durham *p214* 0191 383 0111
Peterlee *p348* 0191 586 5711
Wingate *p434* 01429 838225

TMP Solicitors LLP
‡London E14 *p85* 020 7712 1732

TMS Legal Cost Consultants
‡Lyndhurst *p296* 023 8081 6630

TM Solicitors
‡North Ferriby *p330* 01482 638645

TPC Solicitors
‡Manchester *p310* 0161 832 8867

TPP Law Limited
‡London SE1 *p85* 020 7620 0888

TQ Solicitors
‡Leigh *p282* 01942 671166
Northwich *p333* 01942 671166

TRG Law
‡Woking *p437* 01483 730303

TRP Solicitors
‡Birmingham *p142* 0121 616 4700

T S Law Limited
‡Chatham *p185* 01634 311876

TSP Legal
‡Reading *p361* 0118 907 6341

TTS Solicitors
‡London E17 *p85* 020 8521 4686

TV Edwards LLP
‡London E1 *p85* 020 7790 7000
Cambridge *p176* 020 7790 7000
London EC4 *p85* 020 7790 7000
London SE8 *p85* 020 7790 7000
London N15 *p85* 020 7790 7000
London SW11 *p85* 020 7790 7000
London E15 *p85* 020 3141 1000
London E1 *p85* 020 7790 7000
London E1 *p85* 020 7790 7000

TWG Ltd
‡Sawbridgeworth *p372* 01279 600003

TWM Solicitors LLP
‡Guildford *p237* 01483 752700
Cranleigh *p202* 01483 273515
Epsom *p219* 01372 729555
Leatherhead *p271* 01372 374148
London SW19 *p85* 020 8946 6454
Reigate *p363* 01737 221212

TW Solicitors
‡London SE7 *p85* 020 8293 8933

David Tagg & Co
‡London SW6 *p85* 020 7736 0999
London SW6 *p85* 020 7610 6676

M Taher & Co Solicitors
‡London EC3 *p85* 020 7929 7600

Tahir Solicitors
‡Manchester *p310* 0161 740 2333

Tahmina & Co
‡Grays *p233* 01375 384200

Tait Farrier Graham
‡Gateshead *p229* 0191 490 0108
Berwick-upon-Tweed *p131* 01289 309851
Newcastle upon Tyne *p327* 0191 272 3713

Taj Solicitors
‡Cardiff *p181* 029 2023 5332
London E14 *p85* 020 7537 3002

Takk & Company Limited
‡Maidstone *p299* 01622 661333

Talat Naveed Solicitors
‡Hounslow p254 . . . . 020 8577 6666

Talbot & Co
‡Burton-on-Trent p170 . . . . 01283 564716

Talbot Walker LLP
‡Andover p118 . . . . 01264 363354
Basingstoke p127 . . . . 01256 332404

Talbots Legal Advice Centre
Stourbridge p399 . . . . .01384 445850 / 447777

Tallar LLP
‡Birmingham p142 . . . . 0845 555 1501

Tallents Solicitors
‡Newark p322 . . . . 01636 671881
Mansfield p312 . . . . 01623 666700
Southwell p389 . . . . 01636 813411

Aileen Tallintire Solicitors
‡South Shields p384 . . . . 0191 454 1101

Tanburghs
‡London W12 p85 . . . . 020 8749 8902

Tanburghs O'Brien Lahaise
‡Camden NW6 p85 . . . . 020 7372 6614

Tanda Migliorini & Associates LLP
‡London WC1 p85 . . . . 020 3170 7687

T R Taner & Co
‡Haringey N8 p85 . . . . 020 8348 1267

Tang Bentley & Jackson
‡Fareham p224 . . . . 01329 220401

David Tang & Co
‡London W1 p85 . . . . 020 7439 4675

Tann & Tann Solicitors
‡Wembley p427 . . . . 020 8902 6810
Harrow p242 . . . . 020 8909 3688

Tanna & Co
‡Leicester p281 . . . . 0116 268 2500

Tannas Solicitors
‡Leicester p281 . . . . 0116 258 1560

Tanner & Taylor LLP
‡Aldershot p115 . . . . 01252 316565
Ascot p118 . . . . 01344 876633
Farnborough p224 . . . . 01252 549555
Farnham p225 . . . . 01252 733770

Tanners
‡Cirencester p195 . . . . 01285 659061

A P Tansey
‡Hatfield p244 . . . . 01302 843859

R F Tansey
‡Thame p410 . . . . 01844 218000

Tarbox Robinson & Partners
‡Northwood p333 . . . . 01923 836595

Tarkel Solicitors
‡Bradford p155 . . 01274 918481 / 0800 988 4471

Tarran & Co
‡Manchester p310 . . . . 0161 834 3689

Robert Tarren Solicitors
‡Bristol p165 . . . . 0845 121 4716

Tassells
‡Faversham p225 . . . . 01795 533337

Ann J Tate & Co
‡East Grinstead p215 . . . . 01342 811278

Tates Solicitors
‡Leeds p277 . . . . 0113 242 2290

Brian H Taub & Co
‡London N6 p85 . . . . 020 8340 4471

Taveners
‡Oxford p344 . . . . .0844 879 319

Tavistock Law Limited
‡London EC4 p85 . . . . 0845 260 6034

Alan Taylor & Co
‡London EC1 p85 . . . . 020 7251 3222

Taylor & Emmet LLP
‡Sheffield p377 . . . . 0114 218 4000
Dronfield p213 . . . . 0114 218 4000
Sheffield p377 . . . . 0114 218 4000

Andrew J Taylor
‡Cheadle p185 . . . . 0161 428 1875

Angela Taylor Criminal Solicitors
‡Manchester p310 . . . . 0161 256 2233

Taylor Bracewell
‡Doncaster p212 . . . . 01302 341414

Taylor Bridge LLP
‡London SE1 p86 . . . . 020 7407 2463

David Taylor Solicitors
‡Liverpool p290 . . . . 0151 227 2557

Taylor Fawcett
‡Harrogate p241 . . . . 01423 538111

Taylor Goodchild Solicitors
‡Middlesbrough p315 . . . . 01642 430000
Middlesbrough p315 . . . . 01642 430000

Taylor Haldane Barlex LLP
‡Chelmsford p187 . . . . 0845 293 7688
Benfleet p131 . . . . 01702 339168
Braintree p155 . . . . 0845 293 7688
Ipswich p263 . . . . 0845 293 7688
Southend-on-Sea p387 . . . . 01702 339168

Taylor Hampton Solicitors LLP
‡London WC2 p86 . . . . 020 7427 5970

Judith Taylor LLB
‡Winscombe p434 . . . . 01934 843353

Julian Taylor Solicitors
‡Oxford p344 . . . . 01869 351833

Taylor Legal
‡Crewe p203 . . . . 01270 500844

Taylor Lewis
‡Cardigan p131 . . . . 01239 621999

Mark Taylor & Co
‡London SW10 p86 . . . . 020 7349 7373

Michael Taylor & Associates
‡Bromley p167 . . . . 020 8437 0707
Manchester p310 . . . . 0161 255 2700
Urmston p417 . . . . 0161 746 7776

Paul Taylor Solicitors
‡Exeter p222 . . . .0870 850 8045 / 07810 836696
‡Plymouth p350 . . . . 01392 811728

Taylor Phillips
‡Hayes p245 . . . . 020 8561 7367

Rex Taylor & Meadows
‡West Kirby p428 . . . . 0151 625 6414

Roland Taylor & Co
‡Braintree p155 . . . . 01376 330099

Taylor Rose Law
‡Peterborough p347 . . . . 01733 865600

Sharon Taylor Associates
‡Poole p353 . . . . 01202 759769

Simon Taylor Solicitor
‡Worthing p442 . . . . 01903 261580

Taylor Street Solicitors LLP
‡Aldershot p115 . . . . 01252 400999

Taylor Vaughan Solicitors
‡Bury p171 . . . . 0161 763 1066

Taylor Vinters
‡Cambridge p176 . . . . 01223 423444

Taylor Walton LLP
‡Luton p295 . . . . 01582 731161
Harpenden p239 . . . . 01582 765111
St Albans p390 . . . . 01727 845245

Taylor Wessing
‡London EC4 p86 . . . . 020 7300 7000
Cambridge p176 . . . . 01223 446400

Taylor Wood Solicitors
‡Grays p233 . . . . 01375 480053 / 01375 651543

Taylors
‡Blackburn p146 . . . . 0844 800 0263
‡Redditch p362 . . . . 01527 544221
Manchester p310 . . . . 0844 800 0263

Taylors Legal
‡Ilford p261 . . . . 020 8501 4959

Taylors Solicitors
‡Boroughbridge p150 . . . . 01423 325566
‡Braunton p156 . . . . 01271 812811
Ilfracombe p261 . . . . 01271 864134

Tayntons LLP Solicitors
‡Gloucester p230 . . . . 01452 522047

Teacher Stern LLP
‡London WC1 p86 . . . . 020 7242 3191

David Teague
‡Plymouth p350 . . . . 01752 600950

Technology Commercial And Outsourcing Law Limited
‡Bath p128 . . . . 07545 642724

Technology Law Alliance
‡London WC2 p86 . . . . 0845 351 9090
Birmingham p143 . . . . 0845 351 9090

Tedstone George & Tedstone
‡Penkridge p345 . . . . 01785 712243

Stanley Tee
‡Bishop's Stortford p144 . . . . . 01279 755200
Braintree p155 . . . . 01376 552277
Great Dunmow p233 . . . . 01371 872166

Alison Teece Solicitor
‡Preston p357 . . . . 01772 877238

J Tehrani Solicitors
‡London W1 p86 . . . . 020 7409 7878
‡Taunton p408 . . . . 0845 257 4007

Teifi Law Limited
‡Llandysul p292 . . . . 01559 362744

Mark Telfer
‡Marlborough p313 . . . . 01672 520517

Temperley Taylor LLP
‡Middleton p315 . . . . 0161 643 2411
Heywood p249 . . . . 01706 623511

Templars Solicitors
‡Slough p382 . . . . 01753 550476

Temple & Co Commercial Solicitors
‡Daventry p207 . . . . 0845 241 4045

Temple Bright LLP
‡Bristol p165 . . . . 0117 920 0056

Temple Heelis LLP
‡Kendal p264 . . . . 01539 723757
Windermere p434 . . . . 01539 442455

Temple Law Solicitors
‡Cardiff p181 . . . . 029 2083 8970

G J Templeman Solicitors
‡Ealing W7 p86 . . . . 020 8566 1200

Templetons Solicitors
‡Harrow p242 . . . . 020 8861 8310

Tennakoons
‡Edgware p217 . . . . 020 8442 8484

Tennant & Knight
‡Brighton p160 . . . . 01273 202050

Tennents
‡London W1 p86 . . . . 020 7935 0640

Terrells LLP
‡Peterborough p347 . . . . 01733 896789
Huntingdon p258 . . . . 01480 454987
Stamford p394 . . . . 01780 481129

Terrie Pridie & Co Solicitors
‡Monkseaton p318 . . . . 0191 289 4770

Terry & Co
‡Ingatestone p261 . . . . 01277 354518

Terry Ballard and Co
‡Eastbourne p216 . . . . 01323 413413

Florence Terry Solicitor & Mediator
‡London WC2 p86 . . . . 020 7936 4664

Kaye Tesler & Co Inc Michael D Kaye & Co
‡London N15 p86 . . . . 020 8809 6756

Tessa Hennessy Solicitor
‡Oxford p344 . . . . 01865 723727
‡Oxford p344 . . . . 01865 723727 / 07773 991643

Tetlow Powell
‡London E14 p86

Geoffrey Tew & Co
‡Leicester p281 . . . . 0116 255 6200

Gerald V Tew
‡London SW15 p86 . . . . 020 8788 1628

Thackray Williams
‡Bromley p167 . . . . 020 8290 0440
Beckenham p129 . . . . 020 8663 0503
West Wickham p428 . . . . 020 8777 6698

Christina Thain & Co
‡Hunstanton p258 . . . . 01485 525458

D B Thakerar & Co
‡Edgware p217 . . . . 020 8951 3113

Thakker & Co
‡Harrow p242 . . . . 020 8424 0571

Thakrar & Co
‡Harrow p242 . . . . 020 8427 3480
‡Southall p385 . . . . .020 8571 5851 / 8843 1599

VP Thakrar & Co
‡Stanmore p394 . . . . 020 8905 0021

Thaliwal Bridge Solicitors
‡Leicester p281 . . . . 0116 274 5252

Joseph Thaliyan Solicitors
‡London E6 p86 . . . . 020 8586 2222

Thames Chambers Solicitors
‡London E1 p86 . . . . 020 7375 1500

Thatcher & Hallam
‡Midsomer Norton p316 . . . . . . 01761 414646

Francis Thatcher & Co
‡Leigh-on-Sea p282 . . . . 01702 471000

Thea Limited
‡London WC2 p86 . . . . 020 7277 8649

Theaker Loadsman & Reynolds
‡Hove p255 . . . . 01273 229500

Theva & Co
‡London SW19 p86 . . . . 020 8542 6667

Thirus
‡London SW19 p87 . . . . 020 8542 3358

Thomas & Co
‡Birmingham p143 . . . . 0121 444 0030
‡Bridgnorth p157 . . . . 01746 762929

Thomas & Edge
‡Derby p209 . . . . 01332 346681

Thomas & Meighen
‡Newcastle upon Tyne p327 . . . . 0191 214 0355

Thomas & Thomas Solicitors
‡Maesteg p298 . . . . 01656 733265

Thomas Andrew & Daodu Solicitors
‡Westminster W1 p87 . . . . 020 7224 9522

Thomas Boyd Whyte
‡Bexleyheath p132 . . . . 020 8303 7755

Thomas Capital Property Lawyers
‡Gloucester p230 . . . . 01452 657950
Gloucester p230 . . . . 01452 857033
London W1 p87 . . . . 020 7101 0300

Thomas Chaytor
‡Marlow p313 . . . . 01628 477889

Clare Thomas & Co
‡Newport p329 . . . . 01952 820050

DL Thomas Solicitors
‡Crawley p202 . . . 01342 715215 / 07988 699140

David & Roy Thomas & Co
‡Pontardulais p351 . . . . 01792 882410

David Thomas Solicitors
‡London W1 p87 . . . . 020 7724 8605

Dean Thomas & Co
‡Worksop p441 . . . . 01909 500511
Chesterfield p192 . . . . 01246 810050
Retford p363 . . . . 01777 703100

Eleri Thomas & Co Ltd
‡Newcastle Emlyn p323 . . . . . . 01239 710942

Emyr Thomas & Son
‡Caernarfon p172 . . . . .01286 672307 / 672308

H E Thomas & Co
‡Greenwich SE18 p87 . . . . 020 8854 3036

Philip Thomas & Co Solicitors
‡Bridgend p157 . . . . 01656 658123

Rose Thomas & Co
‡Lampeter p269 . . . . 01570 423300

Sian Thomas & Daughter Solicitors
‡Bridgend p157 . . . . 01656 645439

Thomas Simpson Solicitors Ltd
‡Winchester p434 . . . . 01962 820228

Thomas Solicitors
‡Long Eaton p293 . . . . 0115 946 1061
Loughborough p293 . . . . 01509 611061

Stephen Thomas Law
‡West Malling p428 01732 321114 / 07774 612651

Steve Thomas & Co
‡Haverfordwest p244 . . . . 01437 890500

Sydney G Thomas & Co
‡Builth Wells p168 . . . . 01982 553289

Thompson & Co
‡Sunderland p402 . . . . 0191 565 6290
‡Wandsworth SW17 p87 . . . . . . 020 8767 5005

Thompson & Cooke LLP
‡Stalybridge p393 . . . . 0161 338 2614
Stalybridge p393 . . . . 0161 338 2614

Thompson & Jackson
‡Plymouth p350 . . . . . .01752 665037 / 221171

Thompson & Lilley
‡London W1 p87 . . . . 020 7499 3633

Thompson Allen LLP
‡Brighton p160 . . . . 01273 608003

Andrew Thompson & Co
‡Leeds p277 . . . . 0113 383 5314

C J Thompson
‡Newcastle upon Tyne p327 . . . . 0191 226 8998

Guy Thompson & Co
‡London EC2 p87 . . . . 020 7074 0110
‡London SE24 p87 . . . . 020 7274 6874

Henry Thompson & Sons
‡Grantham p232 . . . . 01476 563226
Bingham p133 . . . . 01949 836800

Janet R Thompson
‡Peterborough p347 . . . . 01733 347247

Keith R Thompson & Co
‡Immingham p261 . . . . 01469 510510

Keith S Thompson Solicitor
‡Amble p117 . . . . 01665 713723

Thompson Leatherdale
‡Reading p361 . . . . 0118 959 1773

Mark Thompson Law
‡Exeter p222 . . . . 01392 314086

Mark Thompson Solicitor
‡Bury St Edmunds p171 . . . . . . 01842 766353

Thompson Smith & Puxon
‡Colchester p198 . . . . 01206 574431
Clacton-on-Sea p195 . . . . 01255 221919

Thompsons (formerly Robin/Brian Thompson & Partners)
‡London WC1 p87 . . . . 020 7290 0000
Birmingham p143 . . . . 0121 262 1200
Bristol p165 . . . . 0117 304 2400
Cardiff p181 . . . . 029 2044 5300
Chelmsford p187 . . . . 01245 228800
Dagenham p206 . . . . 020 8596 7700
Derby p209 . . . . 01332 224680
Harrow p242 . . . . 020 8872 8600
Leeds p277 . . . . 0113 205 6300
Liverpool p290 . . . . 0151 224 1600
London SW19 p87 . . . . 020 8947 4163
Manchester p310 . . . . 0161 819 3500
Middlesbrough p315 . . . . 01642 554162
Newcastle upon Tyne p327 . . . . 0191 269 0400
Nottingham p339 . . . . 0115 989 7200
Plymouth p350 . . . . 01752 675810
Sheffield p377 . . . . 0114 270 3300
South Shields p384 . . . . 0191 497 4440
Southampton p387 . . . . 023 8021 2040
Stoke-on-Trent p398 . . . . 01782 406200
Swansea p406 . . . . 01792 484920
Wolverhampton p438 . . . . 01902 771551

Thomson & Bancks LLP
‡Tewkesbury p410 . . . . 01684 299633
Pershore p346 . . . . 01386 562000

Peter Thomson
‡Lambeth SW9 p87 . . . . 020 7733 6196

Thomson Snell & Passmore
‡Tunbridge Wells p415 . . . . 01892 510000
Dartford p207 . . . . 01322 623700

THOMSON WEBB & CORFIELD
‡Cambridge p176 . . . . 01223 578070
Cambridge p176 . . . . 01223 518317
Cambridge p176 . . . . 01223 578068

Thomson Wilson Pattinson
‡Kendal p264 . . . . 01539 721945
Windermere p434 . . . . 01539 442233

Thorburn & Co
‡Henley-on-Thames p247 . . . . . 01491 577625

Thoree & Co Solicitors
‡London SW9 p87 . . . . 020 7924 9668

Thorn Drury & Searles
‡Ramsgate p359 . . . . 01843 593381

Richard Thorn & Co
‡Brighton p160 . . . . 01273 625600

Thorne & Co Solicitors
‡Dorchester p212 . . . . 01305 251166

Andrew Thorne & Co
‡Shaw *p374* 01706 290488
Shaw *p374* 01706 841775

Thorne Legal Consulting
‡Farnham *p225* 01252 708105

Lindsay Thorne Solicitors
‡Llanelli *p292* 01554 773146

Thorne Segar
‡Minehead *p318* 01643 703234

Thorneloe & Co
‡Maidstone *p299* 01622 859416

Thornes
‡Wolverhampton *p438* 01902 313311

Thorneycroft Solicitors
‡Crewe *p203* 01477 536999

Thorneycroft Solicitors Ltd
‡Macclesfield *p297* 01625 503444

Thornhills
‡Manchester *p310* 0161 228 3003

Thornleys Limited
‡Plymouth *p350* 01752 406977

Thornton & Co
‡Hammersmith & Fulham W12 *p87* 020 8743 3000
‡Lytham *p297* 01253 782808

Lynn Thornton
‡Crewe *p203* 01270 567987

Thornton Solicitors
Telford *p409* 0845 438 7795

Thorntons Solicitors
‡Shrewsbury *p379* 01743 341770

Thorp Parker LLP
‡Stokesley *p398* 01642 711354

Thorpe & Co
‡Scarborough *p372* 01723 364321
Filey *p226* 01723 515555
Malton *p300* 01653 694899
Whitby *p430* 01947 603465

The Thrasher Walker Partnership
‡Stockport *p396* 0161 442 6240

Three Clear Solutions Limited
‡London NW2 *p87* 020 8438 0624

Three Counties Law
‡Bewdley *p131* 07789 436481

Thrings LLP
‡London SW1 *p87* 020 7766 5600
Bath *p128* 01225 340000
Bristol *p165* 0117 930 9500
Swindon *p406* 01793 410800

Barbara Thubron
‡Durham *p214* 0191 383 0600

Peter Thubron & Co
‡Sunderland *p402* 0191 510 1221

Max Thum
‡Basingstoke *p127* 01256 862161

Thurloe & Lyndhurst LLP
‡London WC2 *p87* 0333 123 2255
London SW7 *p87*

Thurnhills
‡Preston *p357* 01772 251762
Garstang *p228* 01995 603142

Thursfields
‡Kidderminster *p266* 01562 820575
Kidderminster *p266* 01562 820575
Stourport-on-Severn *p399* 01299 827517
Worcester *p440* 01905 730450

Thurstan Hoskin Solicitors
‡Redruth *p363* 01209 213646

Tibb & Co
‡Barnet NW9 *p87* 020 8905 0486

A S Tibber & Co Solicitors
‡Stanmore *p394* 020 8954 4705

Tibbits Fisher
‡Birmingham *p143* 0121 707 3900

Sean C Tickell
‡London N6 *p87* 020 8341 1000

Tickle Hall Cross
‡St Helens *p391* 0800 854379
Prescot *p356* 0800 854379

Karen Tickner
‡London NW11 *p87* 07900 698899

Nicola J Tiernan Solicitors
‡Bramhall *p156* 0161 439 5286

Tierney & Co
‡Dinnington *p210* 01909 550730
Rotherham *p367* 01709 709000

Tilbrook's
‡Chipping Ongar *p193* 01277 896000

Tilbury Goddard
‡Thornton Heath *p411* 020 8684 5581

Tilley & Co
‡St Albans *p390* 01727 840467

John Tillotson
‡Stockton-on-Tees *p397* 01642 676000

Tilly Bailey & Irvine LLP
Stockton-on-Tees *p397* 01642 673797

Joseph Tily Solicitors
‡London E2 *p87* 020 7101 0232

Tim Marks
‡Cheddar *p186* 01934 744133

Time Solicitors
‡London E11 *p87* 020 8558 4455

Timms
‡Ashby-de-la-Zouch *p119* 01530 564498
‡Derby *p209* 01332 364436
Burton-on-Trent *p170* . . . 01283 561531 / 544417

M R Timms & Co Limited
‡Dudley *p213* 01384 458848

Timms Solicitors
Swadlincote *p404* 01283 214231

Tinklin Springall
‡Bromley *p167* 020 8402 6222
Beckenham *p129* 020 8402 7222

Tinn Criddle & Co
‡Alford *p115* 01507 462882
Spilsby *p389* 01790 756810
Sutton-on-Sea *p404* 01507 443043

Tinsdills
‡Hanley *p239* 01782 262031
Leek *p278* 01538 399332
Newcastle under Lyme *p323* . . . 01782 612311
Sandbach *p372* 01270 761111

Roberta Tish Solicitors
‡Wandsworth SW11 *p87* 020 7223 6966

Andrew Tobias & Co
‡London W1 *p87* 020 7935 8399

Tobins Solicitors
‡Manchester *p310* 0161 884 0950

L Anne Todd Solicitor
‡London N3 *p87* 020 8343 1088

P A Todd & Co
‡Leicester *p281* 0116 273 3091

Todmans SRE
‡Rayleigh *p359* 01268 774073

Tolcher & Co Marine Solicitors
‡Portsmouth *p355* 023 9273 7008

Tolhurst Fisher LLP
‡Southend-on-Sea *p387* 01702 352511
Chelmsford *p187* 01245 495111

Toller Beattie LLP
‡Barnstaple *p125* 01271 341000

Tollers LLP
‡Northampton *p332* 01604 258558
Corby *p199* 01536 276727
Kettering *p265* 01536 520111
Milton Keynes *p317* 01908 396230

Julia Tolson Family Solicitor
‡Stourbridge *p399* 01384 346467

Tomleys
‡Newtown *p330* 01686 626641

Tomlinson & Dickinson
Sudbury *p401* . . . . . . 01787 375189 / 376820

Peter F Tomlinson & Co
‡Bath *p128* 01225 484232

Chris Toms Solicitor
‡Wigton *p432* 01697 352931

Lisa Tonge Solicitors
‡Worsley *p441* 0161 241 6118

Tonkin & Co
‡Leeds *p277* 0113 269 2058

Tonner Johns Ratti
‡Swansea *p406* 01792 643296

Marcus C Topham
‡York *p445* 01904 639413

Tosswill & Co
‡Lambeth SW2 *p87* 020 8674 9494

Total Law
‡Manchester *p310* 0161 238 4990

Touchstone Legal Service
‡St Albans *p390* 07787 283749

Toussaint & Co
‡Wembley *p427* 020 8903 6111

Toussaints
‡Birmingham *p143* 0121 523 5050

Tovell & Co
‡London W4 *p87*

Towcester Family Law Practice
‡Towcester *p413* 01327 358321

Tower Law
‡Liverpool *p290* . . 0844 745 2035 / 07850 030100

Towerbridge Tax Practice
‡London EC4 *p87* 020 7407 9899

Towerhouse Consulting LLP
‡London W1 *p87* 0870 800 5300

Jonathan Towers Solicitor
‡York *p445* 01423 330351

Towler Brown
‡Frome *p228* 01373 452955

Town & Country Lawyers
‡Cheltenham *p188* 01242 587900

Towns Needham & Co
‡Manchester *p310* 0161 832 3721

Townsend Family Law
‡Waltham Abbey *p420* 01992 892214

Townsend Harrison Ltd
‡Malton *p300* 01653 693259

Townsend Solicitors
‡Poole *p353* . . . 0800 876 6870 / 01202 540200

Townshends LLP
‡Coleshill *p198* 01675 467333
Birmingham *p143* 0121 214 1540
Coventry *p201* 024 7644 8606

Tozers
‡Exeter *p222* 01392 207020
Newton Abbot *p329* 01626 207020
Plymouth *p350* 01752 206460
Teignmouth *p409* 01626 772376

Tracey Barlow Furniss & Co
‡Worksop *p441* 01909 472355
Retford *p363* 01777 707677

Matthew Trackman & Co
‡London NW8 *p87* 020 7355 4441

Trading Terms Limited
‡London SW19 *p87* 020 8946 2355

Trafficlawyers4u Limited
‡Ashton-under-Lyne *p120* 0800 032 5930

Traill & Co Brennand & Wilson
‡Blandford Forum *p147* 01258 452555

Trant & Richards
‡Carmarthen *p183* 01267 236426

Tranter Cleere & Co
‡Manchester *p310* 0161 428 1569

Tranters
‡Manchester *p310* 0161 998 9999
Stockport *p396* 0161 480 9999

Travers Smith LLP
‡London EC1 *p87* 020 7295 3000

Keith Traves
‡Newport *p328* 01983 525988

Travlaw LLP
‡Leeds *p277* 0113 258 0033

Traymans
‡Hackney N16 *p88* 020 7249 9980

Treanors
‡Sunderland *p402* 0191 565 7395

Treasures
‡Gloucester *p230* 01452 525351

Treasury Solicitors
‡London SW1 *p88*

Trelfa & Co
‡Hampton *p238* 020 8941 1249

Ronnie Tremlett & Co
‡Brighton *p160* 01273 696132

Tremletts
‡Hove *p255* 01903 214279

Alison Trent & Co
‡London EC4 *p88* 020 7583 3350

TrentSide Legal
‡Gainsborough *p228* 01427 616977

Trethowans LLP
‡Salisbury *p371* 01722 412512
Southampton *p387* 023 8032 1000

Trevor Clarke (The Pension Lawyer)
‡Stourbridge *p399* 01384 396339

Trevor Griffiths & Humphries
‡Blackwood *p147* 01495 225236

Trevor Thomas Scott & Jenkins
‡Swansea *p406* 01792 843821

Trident Legal Limited
‡Ilford *p261* 020 8478 5476

Trinity Advocates
‡Exeter *p222* 01392 927111

Trinity International LLP
‡London EC4 *p88* 020 7653 9700

Trinity Law Partnership
‡Birmingham *p143* 0121 212 3141

Trinity Law Solicitors
‡Huddersfield *p256* 01484 300196

Trinity Legal Solicitors
‡Bedford *p130* 01234 826890

Trinity Solicitors
‡London E15 *p88* 020 8555 3030
Chelmsford *p187* 0870 850 1153

Trinity Solicitors LLP
‡London NW1 *p88* 020 7428 0880

Carol A Triplett Solicitor
‡Birmingham *p143* 0121 682 8247

Triune Solicitors
‡Enfield *p219* 020 8804 5410

Trivedy Solicitors
‡Wembley *p427* 020 8904 5615

Trobridges
‡Plymouth *p350* 01752 664022
Torpoint *p412* 01752 812787

Trott & Gentry
‡London N1 *p88* 020 3119 3150

Troutman Sanders LLP
‡London EC2 *p88* 020 7038 6650

Trowers & Hamlins
‡London EC3 *p88* 020 7423 8000
Exeter *p222* 01392 217466
Manchester *p310* 0161 211 0000

Truelegal Solicitors
‡Exeter *p222* 01392 879414

Truman-Moore
‡Verwood *p418* 01202 824677
Christchurch *p194* 01425 673994

Trust Solicitors Limited
‡Bishop's Stortford *p144* 01279 655232

Trustee Solutions Limited
‡London EC2 *p88* 020 7667 0216

Amie Tsang & Co
‡Manchester *p310* 0161 236 8821

James Tsang & Co
‡London W1 *p88* 020 7287 0451

Tubbs & Co
‡Scarborough *p373* 01723 352666

Sue Tuck & Co
‡Kensington & Chelsea SW7 *p88* 020 7385 7733

Adam Tucker & Co
‡Bristol *p165* 020 7193 6341

Tucker Turner Kingsley Wood & Co
‡London WC1 *p88* 020 7242 3303
London WC1 *p88* 020 7242 3303

Tuckers
‡Manchester *p310* 0161 233 4321
Birmingham *p143* 0121 236 4324
London W1 *p88* 020 7388 8333
London SE5 *p88* 020 7703 2324

Tudor Williams & Co
‡Wrexham *p443* 01978 362006

Tudur Owen Roberts Glynne & Co
‡Caernarfon *p172* . . . . 01286 672207 / 672851
Bangor *p122* . . . . . . 01248 362315 / 355826
Bangor *p122* 01248 600171
Blaenau Ffestiniog *p147* 01766 830206
Holyhead *p251* 01407 762374
Menai Bridge *p314* 01248 712624

Tulloch & Co
‡London W1 *p89* 020 7318 1180

Tummings Solicitors
‡Sidcup *p380* 020 8850 4465

Tunnard & Co
‡Ripon *p365* 01765 605629

Turbervilles
‡Uxbridge *p417* 01895 201700
‡Uxbridge *p417* 01895 201700
Chorleywood *p194* . . . 01923 284112 / 285869
Uxbridge *p417* 01895 231311

Turnbull Garrard
‡Shrewsbury *p379* . . . . 01743 350851 / 351332

Turnbull Rutherford Solicitors
‡London SW19 *p89* 020 8545 6600

A L Turner & Co
‡London NW7 *p89* 020 8906 8084

Turner & Co Solicitors
‡London W1 *p89* 020 7038 3701

Turner & Wall
‡Keighley *p264* 01535 607831

Andrew Turner Solicitors
‡Hull *p258* 01482 606151

Turner Atkinson & Ward
‡Worksop *p441* 01909 473489
Mansfield *p312* 01623 823450

Turner Bayley Thompson Warmington
‡Dudley *p213* . . . . . . 01384 253331 / 253771

Turner Cary Partnership Solicitors
‡West Bromwich *p427*
. . . . 0121 553 3017 / 07900 216284

Turner Coulston
‡Northampton *p333* 01604 622101
Kettering *p265* 01536 523434

Hamish Turner
‡Torquay *p413* 01803 213806

Turner March LLP Solicitors
‡Rossendale *p367* 01706 854167

Turner Parkinson
‡Manchester *p310* 0161 833 1212

Turner Pearson
‡Preston *p357* 01772 562222
‡Preston *p357* 01772 751775
Garstang *p228* 01995 604536

Turner Solicitors
‡Bridgend *p157* 01656 768500

Turners
‡Cross Hills *p204* 01535 634149

Turners Solicitors LLP
‡Bournemouth *p153* 01202 291291

Turpin & Miller
‡Oxford *p344* 01865 770111

Tustain Jones & Co
‡Nuneaton *p339* 024 7664 1222
Bedworth *p130* 024 7664 3222

Twell & Co
‡Newport *p328* 01983 539999

P A Twist & Co
‡Poole *p353* 01202 709050

Twomlows
‡Caldicot *p172* 01291 422753
Chepstow *p189* 01291 623323
Monmouth *p318* 01600 716200

Twyfords Property Law Firm
‡Alnwick *p115* 01665 576040

Ty Arian
‡Swansea *p406* 01792 484200

Tyler Law
‡Amesbury p117. . . . . 0870 403 0200
‡Canvey Island p177 . . . . . 01268 630850
W A Tyler & Co
‡Birstall p144 . . . . . 0116 267 6900
Tylers Solicitors
‡Radcliffe p358 . . . . . 0161 723 1183
Tynan Solicitors
‡Stevenage p395 . . . . . 01438 356333
Tyndallwoods
‡Birmingham p143. . . . . 0121 624 1111
Birmingham p143. . . . . 0121 693 2222
Tyrer Law
‡Crewe p203 . . . . . 01270 842424
Tyrer Roxburgh & Co
‡Haringey N22 p89 . . . . . 020 8889 3319
Tzanev & Co Lawyers
‡Esher p220. . . . . 020 8224 2779

U

UK Immigration & Property Solicitors Ltd
‡London W2 p89 . . . . . 0845 463 1561
UK Migration Lawyers Ltd
‡Birmingham p143. . . . . 0121 702 1407
UK Traffic Law
‡Hemel Hempstead p247 . . . . . 01442 209200
Ullah Law Associates
‡London NW10 p89 . . . . . 020 8830 4800
Ultimate Law Limited
‡Altrincham p117 . . . . . 0161 710 2030
Umbrella Legal Solicitors
‡Bradford p155 . . . . . 01274 737001
Underhill Langley & Wright
‡Wolverhampton p438. . . . . 01902 423431
Bridgnorth p157. . . . . 01746 764171
Wolverhampton p438. . . . . 01902 782606
Underwood & Co
‡Totton p413. . . . . 023 8087 1479 / 8086 0827
H A Underwood Solicitors
‡Sheerness p375 . . . . . 01795 663555
J G Underwood
‡London SW1 p89. . . . . 020 7730 4019
Underwood Solicitors LLP
‡Westminster W1 p89 . . . . . 020 7526 6000
Underwood Vinecombe LLP
‡Derby p209. . . . . 01332 836666
Ungoed-Thomas & King Limited
‡Carmarthen p183. . . . . 01267 237441
United Solicitors
‡Manchester p310. . . . . 0161 225 8181
Universa Law Ltd
‡London WC1 p89
Universal Solicitors
‡London E1 p89. . . . . 020 7377 5511
Unsworth & Wood
‡Wigan p432 . . . . . 01942 242400
Unsworth Rose
‡Camden NW1 p89 . . . . . 020 7483 4411
Uppal Taylor
‡Nottingham p339. . . . . 0115 982 0770
Uprights Solicitors
‡Leek p278 . . . . . 01538 388809
Upstream Law
‡Twickenham p416 . . . . . 020 8894 9528
Uria & Menendez
‡London EC4 p89 . . . . . 020 7645 0280
Urrutia & Co
‡Barry p126 . . . . . 0800 013 2315
Usiskin & Co
‡Oxford p344 . . . . . 01865 322160
Usmani King Solicitors
‡Leighton Buzzard p282. . . . . 01525 377911

V

VHS Fletchers Solicitors
‡Nottingham p339. . . . . 0115 959 9550
Ilkeston p261. . . . . 0115 944 1233
VKM Solicitors
‡Wolverhampton p438. . . . . 01902 311155
VLS Solicitors
‡London N17 p89 . . . . . 020 8808 7999
VMD Solicitors
‡Ilford p261 . . . . . 020 8514 8703
VMS Solicitors LLP
‡London EC4 p89. . . . . 020 7936 1999
VS Law Solicitors
‡Hayes p245 . . . . . 020 8817 1027
Vachaviolos Solicitors
‡Maldon p300 . . . . . 01621 855516
Vadher & Company Solicitors
‡Leicester p281 . . . . . 0116 261 9122
Jay Vadher & Co
‡London E15 p89 . . . . . 020 8519 3000
Vahib & Co
‡London N4 p89. . . . . 020 8348 0055
Vale Solicitors
‡Barry p126 . . . . . 01446 733191
Llantwit Major p292. . . . . 01446 795456
Valens Solicitors
‡London WC2 p89. . . . . 020 7745 7320
Vallelys
‡Letchworth p283 . . . . . 01462 483800
Van Arkadie
‡Harrow p242 . . . . . 020 8938 4687
Van Baaren & Wright
‡Richmond upon Thames p364 . . 020 8940 2525
Van Doorne
‡London EC4 p89 . . . . . 020 7648 0400
Van Eaton Solicitors
‡London SW16 p89 . . . . . 020 8769 6739
Van Straten Solicitors
‡London W10 p89. . . . . 020 8588 9660
Marina C Van't Goor
‡Milford Haven p316. . . . . 01646 697700
Vance Harris
‡Crowborough p204 . . . . . 01892 653434
London E14 p89 . . . . . 020 7538 5232
Vanderpump & Sykes
‡Enfield p219 . . . . . 020 8367 3999
Vanguards LLP
‡London E12 p89 . . . . . 020 8586 2426
Jay Vara & Co
‡London SW16 p89 . . . . . 020 8679 1292
Vardag Solicitors Ltd
‡London WC2 p89. . . . . 020 7404 9290
A D Varley & Co
‡Blackburn p146. . . . . 01254 582777
Preston p357. . . . . 01772 556777
Varley Hibbs LLP
‡Coventry p201 . . . . . 024 7663 1000
Vasuki Solicitors
‡London E12 p89 . . . . . 020 8470 6655
Vaughan & Co
‡Leeds p277. . . . . 0113 261 1044
Vaughan & Davies
‡Kington p268 . . . . . 01544 230325
Presteigne p356 . . . . . 01544 267731
H Vaughan Vaughan & Co
‡Builth Wells p168. . . . . 01982 552331 / 553571
Rhayader p363. . . . . 01982 552331
Rhys Vaughan
‡Manchester p311 . . . . . 0161 224 1439
Veale Wasbrough Vizards
‡Bristol p165. . . . . 0117 925 2020
London EC4 p89 . . . . . 020 7405 1234
Vectis Law Solicitors
‡Newport p328 . . . . . 01983 533006
Vector
‡Altrincham p117 . . . . . 0161 929 3579
Ved & Co
‡London NW10 p89 . . . . . 020 8459 8686
Paul Veitch Solicitor
‡Holt p251. . . . . 01263 741751
Veitch Penny
‡Exeter p222 . . . . . 01392 278381
Crediton p203 . . . . . 01363 772244
Veja & Co Solicitors
‡Hayes p245 . . . . . 020 8581 1502
Leicester p281 . . . . . 0116 255 5557
Veja and Co Solicitors
Southall p385. . . . . 020 8574 2626
Velocity Legal
‡Leeds p277. . . . . 0113 237 9940
Venner Shipley & Co
‡London EC1 p89 . . . . . 020 7600 4212
Venters Solicitors
‡London SE5 p89 . . . . . 020 7277 0110
Reigate p363. . . . . 01737 229610
Verdant Solicitors
‡Edgware p217 . . . . . 020 8905 3199
Verisona Solicitors
‡Waterlooville p423 . . . . . 023 9226 5251
Havant p244 . . . . . 023 9249 2472
Portsmouth p355 . . . . . 023 9238 0112
Veritas Solicitors LLP
‡Blackburn p146. . . . . 01254 504999
Verma & Co
‡Wembley p427 . . . . . 020 8903 0309
Verma & Sharma Law Associates
‡Hayes p245 . . . . . 020 8817 1052
Versus Law Solicitors
‡Manchester p311. . . . . 0845 555 0606
Vertex Law
‡West Malling p428 . . . . . 01732 224000
Veseys Solicitors
‡Birmingham p143. . . . . 0121 523 1123
Vickers & Co
‡Ealing W13 p89 . . . 020 8579 2559 / 8840 3999
Vickers Chisman & Wishlade
‡Stockton-on-Tees p397. . . . . 01642 615439
Victor Clifford Solicitors
‡Croydon p205 . . . . . 07947 446310
Victor Henry
‡Birmingham p143. . . 0121 236 3473 / 232 4666
Victor Lissack Roscoe & Coleman
‡London W1 p89 . . . . . 020 7487 2505
Victor Welsh Solicitor & Notary
‡Liverpool p290. . 0151 724 1855 / 07855 544259
Victory At Law Solicitors
‡London SE10 p89 . . . . . 020 8853 8335
Victory Legal Costs Solicitors
‡Fareham p224 . . . . . 0844 980 1690
Victory Solicitors
‡London SW16 p89 . . . . . 020 8769 6838
Videss Ltd
‡Bradford p155 . . . . . 01274 851577
Vihps Legal
‡Frimley p227 . . . . . 0845 450 8445
Vijay & Co
‡Hayes p245 . . . . . 020 8573 5578
Vijayapalans
‡Hounslow p254. . . . . 020 8755 3239
Viking Law
‡Crawley p203. . . . . 01293 886807
P R Vince Solicitors
‡Forest Row p227. . . . . 01342 822112
Vincent & Co
‡Wigan p432 . . . . . 01942 241421
Wigan p432. . . . . 01257 425121
Benjamin Vincent Solicitors
‡London E11 p89 . . . . . 020 8532 2266
Vincent French & Browne
‡London WC1 p89. . . . . 020 7831 4994
Vincent Laverys
‡Preston p357. . . . . 01772 555176
Vincent Solicitora
‡Southall p385. . . . . 020 8574 0666
Vincent Sykes & Higham LLP
‡Thrapston p411. . . . . 01832 732161
Vincents
Poulton-le-Fylde p355. . . . . 01253 810643
Vincents Solicitors
‡Fleetwood p226 . . . . . 01253 773377
‡Garstang p228 . . . . . 01995 606442
Vine Orchards
‡Exmouth p223 . . . . . 01395 273035 / 264646
Vines Legal Limited
‡Matlock p313. . . . . 01629 761680
Vingoe Lloyd
‡Helston p246. . . . . 01326 555800
Vingoe Lloyd Solicitors
Hayle p245. . . . . 01736 754075
St Ives p392 . . . . . 01736 797335
Vinson & Elkins LLP
‡London EC2 p89 . . . . . 020 7065 6000
Virgo Solicitors
‡London N17 p89 . . . . . 020 8885 3999
Virtual Lawyers Limited
‡London SW15 p89 . . . . . 0330 100 0320
Virtuoso Legal
‡Leeds p277. . . . . 0844 800 8871
Joan Vis Solicitors
‡London N17 p89 . . . . . 020 8808 8969
Vivash Hunt
‡Worcester Park p440. . . . . 020 8330 1961
Vivienne Robinson
‡Ely p218 . . . . . 01353 722020
Vizards Livesey Cameron Walker
‡London EC1 p89 . . . . . 020 7490 5861
David Vlahos Solicitors
‡London SW1 p89. . . . . 020 7590 3175
Volks Hedleys
‡Kensington & Chelsea SW7 p89 . 020 7584 6733
Simon J Vollans & Co
‡Cardiff p181 . . . . . 01633 680478
Vroobel Kaye
‡Harrow p242 . . . . . 020 8427 5006
Vyman Solicitors
‡Gravesend p233 . . . . . 01474 537270
Harrow p242 . . . . . 020 8427 9080
Maidstone p299. . . . . 01634 887282

W

W&J Solicitors
‡Harrow p242 . . . . . 020 8863 8700
WB Legal LLP
‡Christchurch p194 . . . . . 0870 402 0555
WBW Solicitors
‡Newton Abbot p329. . . . . 01626 202404
Bovey Tracey p153. . . . . 01626 833263
Exeter p222 . . . . . 01392 202404
Torquay p413. . . . . 0870 701 4321
WE Solicitors LLP
‡Manchester p311 0870 165 9413 / 0161 684 3722
W Evans George & Sons
Newcastle Emlyn p323 . . . . . 01239 710228
WGS Solicitors
‡Westminster W2 p90 . . . . . 020 7723 1656
WH Law LLP
‡Dudley p213 . . . . . 01384 216920
WK Solicitors
‡Birmingham p143. 0121 440 7664 / 07841 290176
WSM Solicitors LLP
‡London SW19 p90 . . . . . 020 8879 4300
WT Law LLP
‡London EC3 p90. . . . . 020 7680 8620
WTS Legal
‡London NW6 p90. . . . . 020 7435 4588
WACE MORGAN
‡Shrewsbury p379. . . . . 01743 280100
Shrewsbury p380. . . . . 01743 280100
Shrewsbury p380. . . . . 01743 266866
Wachtel Fox & Co
Rickmansworth p364 . . . . . 01923 775651
Waddington & Son
‡Burnley p169. . . . . 01282 426666
Padiham p344 . . . . . 01282 778813
Waddington Webber
‡Keighley p264 . . . . . 01535 662644 / 662647
Wade & Davies
‡Great Dunmow p233 . . . . . 01371 872816
Wadesons Solicitors
‡London SW6 p90. . . . . 020 7384 3333
S V Wadsworth & Co
‡Solihull p383 . . . . . 0121 745 8550
Wafer-Phillips
‡Liverpool p290 . . . . . 0151 256 7898
Wagner & Co
‡London N20 p90 . . . . . 020 8361 5588
Wai Leung Solicitors
‡Maidstone p299 . . . . . 01622 772416
Wains
‡Macclesfield p297 . . . . . 01625 429511
Congleton p198. . . . . 01260 279414
Wainwright & Cummins
‡Lambeth SW9 p90 . . . . . 020 7737 9330
Lambeth SW2 p90 . . . . . 020 7326 7460
Lynn M Wainwright
‡Willenhall p433 . . . . . 01902 609842
G A Waite Solicitor
‡Crowborough p204 . . . . . 01892 652800
Matthew Waite & Co
‡Tring p413 . . . . . 01442 890111
Waitt & Co Solicitors
‡Canterbury p177 . . . . . 01227 470600
Folkestone p227 . . . . . 01303 211999
Wake Smith & Tofields
‡Sheffield p377 . . . . . 0114 266 6660
Sheffield p377 . . . . . 0114 266 6660
Wakeel Partnership
‡Newcastle upon Tyne p327. . . 0191 275 3777
Scott Walby LLP
‡Bournemouth p153 . . . . . 01202 311112
Waldegraves
‡London W5 p90 . . . . . 020 8166 0881
Waldron & Schofield
‡Heywood p249 . . . . . 01706 624029
Waldrons
‡Brierley Hill p158 . . . . . 01384 811811
Dudley p213 . . . . . 01384 811811
Kingswinford p268 . . . . . 01384 811811
Tipton p412. . . . . 01384 811811
Walsall p420 . . . . . 01384 811811
Worcester p440. . . . . 01384 811811
Walker & Co
‡Rotherham p367 . . . . . 01709 817112
‡Walsall p420 . . . . . 01922 639080
Walker & Co Solicitors
‡London SE1 p90 . . . . . 020 7939 7757
Walker & Walker
‡Sevenoaks p374 . . . . . 01732 450699
Adam Walker & Co
‡Ilkley p261 . . . . . 07904 979879
Clive Walker
‡Leeds p277. . . . . 0113 268 4660
Dale R Walker Solicitor
‡Sevenoaks p374 . . . . . 020 8466 0967
Walker Foster
‡Skipton p381 . . . . . 01756 700200
Barnoldswick p124 . . . . . 01282 812340
Silsden p380 . . . . . 01535 653408
Walker Foster with Kennedy Thompson
Ilkley p261 . . . . . 01943 609969
Grenville J Walker
‡Blandford Forum p147 . . . . . 01258 459911
Bournemouth p153 . . . . . 01202 752594
Portland p354. . . . . 01305 862211
Weymouth p430 . . . . . 01305 759090
J A Walker Solicitor
‡Leicester p281 . . . . . 0116 270 1233
Walker Lahive
‡Plymouth p350 . . . . . 01752 551722
Walker Morris
‡Leeds p277. . . . . 0113 283 2500
Percy Walker & Co
‡Hastings p243 . . . . . 01424 721234

Walker Prestons
‡Blackburn *p146*. 01254 772265

H J Walker Sibia
‡Liverpool *p291* 0151 227 2600

Walker Smith Way
‡Chester *p191*. 0844 346 3100
Ashton-under-Lyne *p120* 0844 346 3100
Birmingham *p143*. 0844 346 3100
Liverpool *p291* 0844 346 3100
London SW11 *p90* 0844 346 3100
Wrexham *p443*. 0844 346 3100

Walker Tomaszewski Solicitors
‡Camden NW1 *p90* 020 7722 7740

Walker Wallis Solicitors
‡Cambridge *p176* 01223 393805

Walkers
‡Hounslow *p254*. 020 8572 2691
‡London EC3 *p90* 020 7220 4999
‡Rossendale *p367*. 01706 213565
‡York *p445* 01904 633220
Burnley *p169* 01282 411138

The Walkers Partnership
‡Royston *p368*. . . . . . .01763 241121 / 248896
Royston *p368*. 01763 248896

Walkers Solicitors
‡Brighton *p160* 01273 564939
‡Cranbrook *p202* 01580 713649
Brighton *p160*. 01273 309193

WALL JAMES CHAPPELL
‡Stourbridge *p399*. 01384 371622

H D Wallace-Jones
‡Blandford Forum *p147* 01929 471236

Wallace McNally
‡Coventry *p201* 024 7622 0300

Wallace Robinson & Morgan
‡Solihull *p383* 0121 705 7571
Solihull *p383* 01564 779393

Waller & Hart
‡Camborne *p173* . . . . .01209 714064 / 719871

John Waller & Co
‡Burton-on-Trent *p170*. 01283 505950

Moira L Waller
‡Burton-on-Trent *p170*. 01283 821365

Waller Needham & Green
‡Peterborough *p347*. 01733 311422
Peterborough *p347* 01733 262182

Waller Pollins
‡Edgware *p217* 020 8238 5858

Wallers
‡Newcastle upon Tyne *p327*. . . . 0191 261 2281

Karen Wallis Law LLP
‡Frome *p228* 01373 473240

Wallis Prance
‡Basingstoke *p127* 01256 464311

Wallis Solicitors
‡Gloucester *p231* 01452 720827

J K Walmsley
‡Edgware *p217* 020 8952 0211

Keith Walmsley
‡Carshalton *p183* 020 8669 3643

Walsh & Company
‡Truro *p414* 01872 870923

Frances J Walsh
‡Stroud *p401* 01453 755092

Walter Wilson Richmond
‡Harrow *p242* 020 8427 8484

Walters & Barbary
‡Camborne *p173* 01209 712454

Walters & Co
‡Dudley *p213* 01902 661400

Walters & Plaskitt
‡Stoke-on-Trent *p398* 01782 819611
‡Stoke-on-Trent *p398* 01782 845807
Stoke-on-Trent *p398* 01782 830038
Stoke-on-Trent *p398* 01782 844500

Walters & Williams
‡Carmarthen *p183*. 01267 236686

A M Walters & Co
‡Ilford *p261* 020 8551 5894

Anthony Walters & Co
‡Bishop Auckland *p144* 01388 662222

Walton & Co
‡Leeds *p278*. 0113 245 8100

Walton Mills & Co
‡Southampton *p387*. 023 8047 7221

WALTONS & MORSE LLP
‡London EC3 *p90* 020 7623 4255

Wanham Longhurst & Co
‡Bury St Edmunds *p171*. 01284 735808

Wannop Fox Staffurth & Bray
‡Chichester *p193* 01243 778844
Bognor Regis *p148* 01243 864001
Havant *p244* 01243 778844
Littlehampton *p285* 01903 721112
Worthing *p442* 01903 228200
Worthing *p442* 01903 228200
Worthing *p442* 01903 201120

Wansbroughs
‡Devizes *p210*. 01380 733300
Melksham *p314*. 01225 703222

Wanstalls Solicitors
‡Durham *p214*. . . . . . 0191 375 6676 / 375 6658

Waran & Co
‡London SW4 *p90*. 020 7498 3328

Waran Solicitors
‡Richmond upon Thames *p364* . . 020 7993 8403

Warcup Skene
‡Alnwick *p115* 01665 606100

Ward & Rider Limited
‡Coventry *p201* 024 7655 5400

Ward Benger
‡London WC1 *p90*. 020 7242 2900

Ward Bolton
‡London W1 *p90* 020 7060 1285

Ward Gethin
‡King's Lynn *p266* 01553 660033
Swaffham *p404*. 01760 721992

Ward Hadaway
‡Leeds *p278*. 0113 205 6600
‡Newcastle upon Tyne *p327*. . . . 0191 204 4000

Ward Legal Ltd
‡Burnley *p169* 01282 775788

Michael Ward
‡Sheffield *p377* 0114 233 6198

Ward Scott LLP
‡Hull *p258*. 01482 489870
Beverley *p131* 01482 887667

Wards Solicitors
‡Bristol *p165*. 0117 929 2811
Bristol *p165*. 01454 204880
Clevedon *p196* 01275 850470
Nailsea *p320* 01275 858515
Portishead *p354* 01275 850460
Staple Hill *p394*. 0117 943 4800
Weston-super-Mare *p429*. 01934 413535
Weston-super-Mare *p429*. 01934 428811
Yate *p443* 01454 316789

Wards Solicitors (Family Law Enquiries)
Weston-super-Mare *p429*. 01934 428800

Ware & Kay LLP
‡York *p445* 01904 716000
Wetherby *p429* 01937 583210

Waring & Co
‡Barnet *p124* 0870 444 2782
Bolton *p150*. 01204 550160

Waring Associates LLP
‡Rotherham *p367* . 01709 365286 / 07976 957125

The Waring Partnership LLP
‡Hythe *p259*. 023 8084 9381

Warings Solicitors
‡Blackpool *p147*. 01253 293106

Warnapala & Co Ltd
‡Southall *p385*. 020 8571 1823

Steven Warne Solicitor
‡Scunthorpe *p373* 01724 279449

Warner & Richardson
‡Winchester *p434* 01962 868366

Warner Associates
‡London NW1 *p90*. 020 7788 4111

Warner Goodman LLP
‡Fareham *p224* 01329 288121
Portsmouth *p355* 023 9275 3575
Southampton *p387* 023 8063 9311

T M Warner & Co
‡Kidlington *p266*. 01865 379311

Warners Solicitors
‡Tonbridge *p412*. 01732 770660
Sevenoaks *p374* 01732 747900

Linda S Warren
‡Northwood *p333* 01923 821213

Rodney Warren & Co
‡Eastbourne *p216* 01323 430430

Warrens Boyes & Archer
‡Huntingdon *p258* 01480 411331

James Warry & Co
‡Coleford *p198* 01594 833184

Warsi Solicitors
‡Brentford *p156* . . . . . . 020 8261 4637 / 4639

Wartnabys
‡Market Harborough *p312*. 01858 463322

Warwick & Barker
‡Rustington *p369* 01903 775051

Warwick Solicitors
‡Birmingham *p143*. 0121 778 1188 / 07956 822250

Wason & Co
‡Potters Bar *p355* 01707 664888

Rosalind Watchorn
‡Sheffield *p377* 0114 229 0160

Waterfields Solicitors
‡London E3 *p90* 020 8981 4460

The Waterfront Partnership Solicitors
‡London SE1 *p90* 020 7234 0200

J P Waterhouse & Co
‡Banbury *p122* 01295 267555

Watermans
‡London N13 *p90* 020 8888 2820

Waters & Co
‡Birmingham *p143*. 01675 463855

Sean Waters
‡Bournemouth *p153* 01202 767200

Waterson Hicks
‡London EC3 *p90* 020 7929 6060

Wates Solicitors
‡Barking *p123* 020 8214 1010

Watkin & Co
‡Sutton Coldfield *p404*. 0121 321 2200

Kathleen Watkin
‡Plymouth *p350* 01752 666715

Watkins & Gunn
‡Pontypool *p352*. 01495 762244
Newport *p329*. 01633 262122

David Watkins
‡Pontypridd *p352* 01443 409401

Gail Watkins & Co
‡Birmingham *p143*. 0121 427 9583

Maria Watkins (Legal Service) Limited
‡Harpenden *p239* 07702 817433

Watkins Solicitors
‡Bristol *p165*. 0117 939 0350

Watkins Stewart & Ross
‡Ipswich *p263* 01473 226266

Ms Denise Watling
‡Southport *p388* 01704 500055

Watmores
‡London WC2 *p90*. 020 7430 1512

Alasdair Watson & Co
‡Newcastle upon Tyne *p327*. . . . 0191 488 4521

Watson & Brown
‡South Shields *p384*. 0191 455 0251

Watson Brady Ltd
‡Liss *p285*. 01730 827033

Watson Burton LLP
‡Newcastle upon Tyne *p327*. . . . 0845 901 2100
Leeds *p278*. 0845 901 2100
London EC3 *p90* 0845 901 2100

Watson Farley & Williams
‡London EC2 *p90* 020 7814 8000

Watson Law Solicitors
‡Milton Keynes *p317*. 01908 311366

Watson Marshal
‡London W4 *p90* 020 8987 0100

Watson Nevill
‡Maidstone *p299* 01622 661177

Paul J Watson
‡Middlesbrough *p315* 01642 293427

The Watson Ramsbottom Partnership
‡Blackburn *p146*. 01254 672222
Darwen *p207*. 01254 701111
Great Harwood *p234* . . .01254 884422 / 883020

Watson Solicitors
‡Warrington *p422* 01925 571212

Watson Woodhouse
‡Middlesbrough *p315* 01642 247656
Darlington *p206*. 01642 670634
Stockton-on-Tees *p397* 01642 247656

Watsons
‡Leeds *p278*. 0845 053 1150

Watsons Solicitors
‡Llandudno *p291* 01492 860006

Brian Watters Solicitors
‡Helston *p246* 01326 565975

A M R Watts
‡High Wycombe *p250* 01494 481576

Watts & Leeding
‡London SE9 *p90* 020 8850 6366

Duncan Watts LLP
‡Warwick *p422* 01926 493485

G M Watts
‡South Croydon *p383* 020 8657 0391

Waugh & Co
‡Haywards Heath *p246* 01444 451666

Waugh & Musgrave
‡Cockermouth *p197* 01900 823127

Waugh Moody & Mulcahy
‡Newcastle upon Tyne *p327*. . . . 0191 232 8107
Blaydon-on-Tyne *p147* 0191 414 2967

V G Waugh
‡Peterlee *p348* 0191 527 2727

Waughs
‡East Grinstead *p215* 01342 323545

Wayman & Long
‡Sudbury *p401* 01787 277375

John S Wayman
‡Godalming *p231* 01483 429822

Weatherhead & Butcher
‡Bingley *p143* 01274 562322

Weaver Rose Solicitors
‡London W5 *p90* 020 8579 6060

Webb & Co Property Solicitors
‡Camberley *p173* 01276 26994

Andrew Webb
‡Bristol *p165*. 0117 953 8408

D J Webb & Co
‡London E1 *p90*. 020 7480 5999

David Webb & Co
‡Westcliff-on-Sea *p428* 01702 392939
Westcliff-on-Sea *p428*

Dennis J Webb
‡Worthing *p442* 01903 236006

Gareth Webb & Co Solicitors
‡Yeovil *p444*. 01935 428885

Kathy Webb & Co
‡Guisborough *p237* 01287 633331

Anne Webber & Co
‡Cambridge *p176* 01223 370073

Webbers Solicitors
‡Ruislip *p369* 0845 604 5988

Webster Dixon LLP
‡London EC1 *p90* 020 7353 8300

Webster O'Brien LLP
‡Stockport *p396* 0161 283 3750

Richard Webster & Co
‡Eastleigh *p216* 023 8061 4583

Websters
‡Loughborough *p293* 01509 415116

Wedlake Bell LLP
‡London WC1 *p91*. 020 7395 3000

Susan Weeden & Company
‡Keighley *p264* 01535 658488

Weerakoon Solicitors
‡Hounslow *p254*. 020 8814 1883

Stephen Weighell & Co
‡Swindon *p406* 01793 600724

Weightmans LLP
‡Liverpool *p291* 0151 227 2601
Birmingham *p143*. 0121 632 6100
Dartford *p207*. 020 7822 1900
Knutsford *p269* 01565 634234
Leicester *p281* 0116 253 9747
London EC4 *p91* 020 7822 1900
Manchester *p311* 0161 233 7330
Manchester *p311* 0161 233 7330

Weil Gotshal & Manges
‡London EC4 *p91* 020 7903 1000

Austin Weinberg
‡London N2 *p91*. 020 8815 0720

Weir & Co Solicitors
‡Skipton *p381* 01756 701300

Paul Weiss
‡London EC2 *p91* 020 7367 1600

Welbeck Anin Solicitors
‡London SE5 *p91* 020 7733 3838

Welbeck Law LLP
‡London W1 *p91* 020 7467 3999

Welburn & Co
‡Southampton *p387* 023 8023 0500

Welch & Co
‡Cardigan *p181* 01239 614070
Cardigan *p181*

Michael Welch & Co
‡London WC1 *p91*. 020 7831 4668

John Welch & Stammers
‡Witney *p436* 01993 703941

Weld & Beavan
‡Enfield *p219* 020 8363 1281

Nigel Weller & Co
‡Lewes *p283* 01273 487123

Wellers Law Group LLP
‡Bromley *p167*. 020 8464 4242
London WC1 *p91*. 020 7242 7265

Wells Burcombe LLP
‡West Drayton *p427*. 01895 449288
St Albans *p390*. 01727 840900

Wells Connor & Co
‡Horsforth *p253* 0113 239 0088

The Wells Law Partnership
‡Bolton *p150* 01204 709959

Wells Legal Solicitors
‡Hockley *p251*. 01702 203646

Welton Harrison
‡Hessle *p249* 01482 627711

Wembley Law Solicitor
‡Wembley *p427* 020 8902 0202

Douglas Wemyss Solicitors
‡Leicester *p281* 0116 299 9199

Wendy Holmes Solicitors
‡Shoreham-by-Sea *p378* 01273 455015

Werenowski Solicitors
‡Colchester *p198* 01206 367907

Wessex Solicitors Chambers Ltd
‡Portsmouth *p355*. 023 9238 1114

Julie West Solicitor
‡Leatherhead *p271* 01372 383273

West London Law Solicitors
‡Ealing W7 *p91* 020 8434 3508

Simon West
‡Bath *p128* 01225 482001

Trevor West Property Lawyer
‡Crowborough *p204* 01892 853135

Westfield Solicitors
‡Bromley *p167*. 020 8228 1260

Westgarths
‡Sunderland *p402* 0191 565 5000

Westmans Law
‡London NW10 *p91* 020 8912 2470

Westminsters Solicitors
‡Preston *p357* 01772 833560

John Weston & Co
‡Felixstowe *p225* 01394 282527

Westwood Solicitors
‡Manchester *p311* 0161 832 6178

Whale Rock Legal Limited
‡London EC2 *p91* 020 7726 5080

Ian Whalley
‡Blackburn *p146*. 01254 676472 / 07896 241032

Wharton & Wharton
‡Westminster W1 *p91* 020 7038 3577

Whatley & Co
‡Barnet NW9 *p91* 020 8205 1411 / 8205 8931

Whatley Lane
‡Newmarket *p327* 01638 561133
Bury St Edmunds *p171* 01284 330251

Whatley Recordon
‡Malvern *p300* 01684 892939

Whatley Weston & Fox
‡Worcester *p440* 01905 731731

Alan Wheatley
‡Worthing *p442* 01903 216116

J B Wheatley & Co
‡London SE8 *p91* 020 8479 8000

Wheeler Galvin & Wheeler
‡Harrow *p242* 020 8868 7344

Michael Wheeler
‡Daventry *p207* 01327 844299

Paul Wheeler Solicitor
‡Newport *p328* 01983 533938

Wheelers
‡Aldershot *p115* 01252 316316

Francina Whelan & Co
‡Wetherby *p429* 01937 534022

Whelan Worner Limited
‡London W1 *p91* 020 7409 1872

Andrew Wheldon Solicitors
‡Hemel Hempstead *p247* 01442 242999

Wheltons
‡Guildford *p237* 01483 537633

Whetham & Green
‡Burgess Hill *p168* 01444 233403

Whetter Duckworth Fowler
‡Oxford *p344* 01865 872206
Kidlington *p266* 01865 842100

Whimsters Solicitors
‡London SE3 *p91* 020 8269 2444

Alistair J Whipps
‡Southend-on-Sea *p388* 01702 616516

Whiskers
‡Harlow *p239* 01279 439439
Bishop's Stortford *p144* 01279 501550
Epping *p219* 01992 561111
Woodford *p439* 020 8505 4777

Whitaker Firth
‡Bradford *p155* 01274 381900

John Whitcroft
‡Bristol *p165* 0117 922 7740

Alvin H White
‡Ely *p218* 01353 688228

White & Black Legal LLP
‡Chipping Norton *p193* 0800 035 2656

White & Case LLP
‡London EC2 *p91* 020 7532 1000

White & Co
‡Harrow *p242* 020 8933 6192
‡Lincoln *p285* 01522 548400
‡London NW1 *p91* 020 7258 0206
‡Southend-on-Sea *p388* 01702 340340
Gloucester *p231* 01452 413222

The White Dalton Partnership
‡Leighton Buzzard *p282* 0800 783 6191

Geoff White Solicitors
‡Horley *p252* 01293 776916

Graham White & Co
‡Bushey *p172* 020 8950 5304

V E White & Co
‡Strood *p400* 01634 739195
Rainham *p359* 01634 376555

Whitecross Solicitors
‡Islington EC1 *p91* 020 7251 5533

Whitefields Solicitors
‡London E10 *p91* 020 3208 0980

Whiteford Crocker
‡Plymouth *p350* 01752 550711
Ivybridge *p263* 01752 698488
Plympton *p351* 01752 335994
Saltash *p371* 01752 843134

Whitehead & Low
‡Blyth *p148* 01670 541531

Whitehead Monckton
‡Maidstone *p299* 01622 698000
Tenterden *p410* 01580 765722

Whitehead Vizard
‡Salisbury *p371* 01722 412141

Whitehead Woodward & Co
‡Wrexham *p443* 01978 855478

Whiteheads
‡Newcastle under Lyme *p323* 01782 615278

Whiteheads Solicitors Limited
‡Chorley *p194* 01257 266008

Anne Whitehorn
‡Enfield *p219* 020 8360 1882

Whitehorns
‡Edgware *p217* 020 8440 9900

Whitehorse Solicitors
‡London SE18 *p91* 020 8317 1293

Caroline Whiteley
‡London EC2 *p91* 020 7638 4219

Whitelock & Storr
‡London WC1 *p91* 020 7405 3913

Whitemans
‡Gloucester *p231* 01452 411601

Whitemans Solicitors
‡Cheltenham *p189* 01242 529514

Whiterose Blackmans Solicitors LLP
‡Leeds *p278* 0113 216 5507

Whiteside & Knowles Ltd
‡Morecambe *p319* 01524 416315

Whitestone Solicitors
‡Rochdale *p366* 01706 661591

Whitfield & Co Solicitors
‡Tunbridge Wells *p415* 01892 529500

Whitfields
‡Formby *p227* 01704 878501

Kathryn Whitford Solicitor
‡Truro *p414* 01872 275300

Whiting & Mason
‡New Mills *p321* 01663 742432 / 747958
Marple *p313* 0161 427 1040

Whiting & Purches
‡Solihull *p383* 0121 605 5050

Charles Whiting
‡Chelmsford *p187* 01245 496911

John Whiting & Co
‡Launceston *p270* 01566 777677

Hugh Whitlock
‡Milford-on-Sea *p316* 01590 644777

Whitman Breed
‡Luton *p296* 01582 635077

Whitstons
‡London SE3 *p91* 020 8853 5226

Whittingdales
‡London WC2 *p91* 020 7831 5591

Whittinghams
‡Bridgend *p157* 01656 653485
Porthcawl *p353* 01656 788823

John Whittle Robinson
‡Preston *p357* 01772 203000

Whittuck Taylor & Caines
‡Keynsham *p265* 0117 986 3504

Whitworth & Green
‡Blackpool *p147* 01253 772912

Whitworth & Green Solicitors
‡Manchester *p311* 0161 832 3547

Wholley Goodings LLP
‡Morpeth *p319* 01670 519714
Bedlington *p130* 01670 824080

Whyte & Co
‡Gillingham *p229* 01634 852377

Wick & Co Solicitors
‡Pinner *p349* 020 8429 2950

Widdows Mason
‡Leigh *p282* 01942 673311
Warrington *p422* 01925 632267
Westhoughton *p429* 01942 816515
Wigan *p432* 01942 244294

Widdows Pilling & Co
‡Walkden *p419* 0161 790 1825

Wiggin LLP
‡Cheltenham *p189* 01242 224114
London W1 *p91* 020 7612 9612

Wiggin Osborne Fullerlove
‡Cheltenham *p189* 01242 710200
London SW1 *p91* 020 7290 2456

Guy Wigmore Solicitor
‡Southport *p388* 01704 222277

Douglas Wignall & Co
‡London WC2 *p91* 020 7583 1362

Wikborg Rein
‡London EC2 *p91* 020 7367 0300

R K Wilcock
‡Manchester *p311* 0161 602 3395

Sally Wilcock & Co Solicitors
‡Solihull *p383* 0121 270 6289

Wilde & Co
‡Neston *p321* 0151 353 1899

Wilde Law
‡Truro *p414* 01872 321070

Wildings
‡Birmingham *p143* 0121 786 2555

Max Wiley & Co
‡Holt *p251* 01263 711771

Wilford Smith Solicitors
‡Rotherham *p367* 01709 828044

Wilfred Light & Reid
‡Southampton *p387* 023 8077 7817

The Wilkes Partnership LLP
‡Birmingham *p143* 0121 233 4333

Anthony D Wilkin
‡Trowbridge *p414* 01225 765526

Wilkin Chapman Epton Blades
Lincoln *p285* 01522 512345

Wilkin Chapman Goolden
Grimsby *p235* 0870 460 2586

Wilkin Chapman Grange Solicitors
Alford *p115* 01507 466767
Grimsby *p235* 01472 262626
Horncastle *p252* 01507 527521
Louth *p294* 01507 606161
Mablethorpe *p297* 01507 479824
Market Rasen *p313* 01673 841300

Wilkin Chapman LLP
‡Grimsby *p235* 01472 262626
Beverley *p131* 01482 398398
Sutton-on-Sea *p404* 01507 440400

Wilkins
‡Aylesbury *p121* 01296 424681

Wilkins & Co
‡Dagenham *p206*

Wilkins & Thompson
‡Uttoxeter *p417* 01889 562875

Wilkins Beaumont Suckling
‡London EC3 *p91* 020 7264 2226

Wilkinson & Butler
‡St Neots *p392* 01480 219229

Jane V Wilkinson
‡Blandford Forum *p147* 01258 817719

Matthew Wilkinson Solicitors Ltd
‡Middlesbrough *p315* 01642 218888

R A Wilkinson & Co
‡Birkenhead *p135* 0151 647 6259

Wilkinson Woodward
‡Halifax *p238* 01422 339600
Huddersfield *p256* 01484 483800

Wilkinsons
‡London E11 *p91* 020 8532 9270

Paul Wilks & Co
‡Ryde *p369* 01983 614657

Wilks Price Hounslow
‡Ryde *p369* 01983 566241

Will Harrington
Tamworth *p407* 0844 846 1999

Willans & Co Limited
‡St Albans *p390* 01727 840549

Willans LLP
‡Cheltenham *p189* 01242 514000

Simon Willans & Co
‡Royston *p368* 01763 242454

Willcox Lewis LLP
‡Norwich *p335* 01508 480100

Willem Louw Solicitor-Advocate
‡Doncaster *p212* 01302 562590

Willett & Co
‡Bury St Edmunds *p171* 01284 701323

Willetts Marsden
‡Warrington *p422* 01925 230020

William Hinshelwood
‡Ipswich *p263* 01473 785359

A Williams & Co
‡London W1 *p91* 020 3287 3519 / 3516

Williams & Airey
‡Carlisle *p182* 01228 829530

Williams & Co Solicitors
‡Cleckheaton *p195* 01274 851608

Williams & Co
‡Ampthill *p118* 01525 405566
‡Bridgnorth *p157* 01746 762157 / 765603
‡Edgware *p217* 020 8952 8882
‡Luton *p296* 01582 723322

Andrew Williams Solicitors
‡Leeds *p278* 0113 244 1911

Angela Williams
‡Oxted *p344* 01883 714618

Williams Beales & Co
‡Hay-on-Wye *p245* 01497 820302

Eirian J Williams a'i Gwmni
‡Llandysul *p292* 01559 363244

Gareth Williams Solicitors
‡Birkenhead *p135* 0845 490 0700

Geoffrey Williams & Christopher Green
‡Cardiff *p181* 029 2034 3377

Williams Gorman LLP
‡Haringey N8 *p91*

Hugh Williams Son & Co
‡Llandeilo *p291* 01558 823417
Llandovery *p291* 01550 721500

Jane Williams Employment Law Solicitors
‡Chelmsford *p187*. 01245 251007 / 07740 409054

L G Williams & Prichard
‡Cardiff *p181* 029 2022 9716

Williams MacDougall & Campbell
‡Worthing *p442* 01903 214186

Mair Williams Solicitors
‡Aberystwyth *p114* 01970 615529

Martin J Williams & Co
‡Wandsworth SW18 *p92* 020 8875 9833

Paul L Williams Solicitors
‡Newport *p329* 01633 213555

Peter Williams & Co
‡Swansea *p406* 01792 465597

Williams Powell
‡London WC1 *p92* 020 7242 7005

R N Williams & Co Limited
‡Wolverhampton *p438* 01902 429051

R R Williams & Son
‡Sutton Coldfield *p404* 0121 354 7870

RTP Williams Limited
‡Haverfordwest *p244* 01437 762321

Richard Williams
‡London W11 *p92* 020 7221 1188

Robert G Williams & Co Solicitors
‡Croydon *p205* 020 8681 3121

Robin Williams
‡Tunbridge Wells *p415* 01892 863057

Rose Williams & Partners
‡Wolverhampton *p438* 01902 710822

Williams Solicitors
‡Colchester *p198* 01206 584320 / 298877

Williams Thompson
‡Christchurch *p194* 01202 484242

W J Williams & Davies
‡Cardigan *p181* 01239 612262

Walter Williams
‡Fishguard *p226* 01348 873223

Williams Woolley
‡Petworth *p348* 01798 342581
Haslemere *p243*

Williamson & Barnes
‡Deal *p207* 01304 373154

Williamson & Soden
‡Solihull *p383* 0121 733 8000
Birmingham *p143* 0121 333 4848

Williamson Edwards
‡Rickmansworth *p364* 01923 718601

Williamson Hill
‡Middlesbrough *p315* 01642 217961

John Williamson Solicitor
‡Wandsworth SW17 *p92* 020 8673 7508

Malcolm A H M Williamson
‡Farnham *p225* 0845 230 1022

Paul S Williamson
‡Berkhamsted *p131* 01442 862475

Williamsons
‡Hull *p258* 01482 323697
‡Whitley Bay *p431* 0191 252 7711
Driffield *p213* 01377 252022
Hexham *p249* 01434 602643 / 606308

Williamsons Solicitors
‡Crewkerne *p203* 01460 200450

Kathryn Williets Solicitor
‡Halesowen *p237* 0121 501 2731

Williscroft & Co
‡Bradford *p155* 01274 305380

Willkie Farr & Gallagher LLP
‡London EC2 *p92* 020 7696 5454

Wills & Probate Countrywide
‡Tavistock *p408* 01626 334455

Wills Chandler
‡Basingstoke *p127* 01256 322911

Wills Chandler Beach
‡Fleet *p226* 01252 613351
Hook *p252* 01256 764646 / 764647

George Wills Solicitors
‡London SW9 *p92* 020 7095 9001

Wills Link Associates Limited
‡Ruislip *p369* 01895 636573

Willson Hawley & Co
‡Nuneaton *p339* 024 7638 7821

WilmerHale
‡London EC2 *p92* 020 7645 2400
London W1 *p92* 020 7872 1000
Oxford *p344* 01235 823000

Wilmot & Co Solicitors LLP
‡Cirencester *p195* 01285 650551

Wilmot Thompson
‡Bristol *p165* 0117 927 6583

Wilson & Berry
‡Bracknell *p153* 01344 420555

Wilson & Bird
‡Aylesbury *p121* 01296 436766

Wilson & Co
‡Chelmsford *p187* 01245 202602
‡London N17 *p92* 020 8808 7535

Wilson & Co Solicitors
‡Hartlepool *p243* 01429 869523
‡Middlesbrough *p315* 01642 222292

Alan Wilson Solicitors
‡Newcastle upon Tyne *p327* 0191 273 2555

3

Ashley Wilson
‡London SW1 *p92* 020 7802 4802

Wilson Barca LLP
‡London W1 *p92* 020 7272 2072
London N19 *p92* 020 7272 2072

Wilson Browne
‡Kettering *p265* 01536 410041
Higham Ferrers *p250* 01933 410000
Leicester *p281* 0116 251 7181
Northampton *p333* 01604 876697
Wellingborough *p425* 01933 279000

Wilson Browne Commerical Law
Kettering *p265* 01536 410014

Wilson Bullough Walton & Knowles
‡Newton-le-Willows *p330* .01925 224569 / 224560

C Wilson Solicitors
‡Chorley *p194* 01257 451333

Wilson Cowie & Dillon
‡Liverpool *p291* 0151 706 7000

Wilson Davies & Co
‡Harlow *p239* 01279 426486

Wilson Devonald Ltd
‡Swansea *p406* 01792 484566

Wilson Finlay
‡London SW13 *p92*

G M Wilson
‡Wakefield *p419* 01924 291111
Barnsley *p125* 01226 794140

Gareth Wilson
‡Monmouth *p318* 01600 772500

Giles Wilson
‡Leigh-on-Sea *p282* 01702 477106
Rochford *p366* 01702 477106

Wilson Gunn Patent and Trade Mark Attorneys
‡Manchester *p311* 0161 827 9400

J M Wilson Solicitors
‡Birmingham *p143* 0121 356 4556

N R Wilson
‡Kenilworth *p264* 01926 857631

P E Wilson & Co
‡London SE27 *p92* 020 8761 3555

Richard Wilson Solicitors Ltd
‡Goring *p231* 01491 879100

Robert Wilson Solicitors
‡Okehampton *p340* 01837 55880

Wilson Wakefield Solicitors
‡Hayling Island *p245* 023 9246 4475

Wilsons
‡Leeds *p278* 0113 264 3444
Bradford *p155* 01274 693600
Bradford *p155* 01274 616400
Horsforth *p253* 0113 258 6888
Pudsey *p358* 0113 236 2333

Wilsons Solicitors
‡Barking *p123* . . 020 8185 6005 / 07985 207267
‡Oxford *p344* 01865 874497

Wilsons Solicitors LLP
‡Salisbury *p371* 01722 412412
London WC2 *p92* 020 7998 0420

Wimal & Co
‡Thornton Heath *p411* 020 8689 7503

Wimbledon Solicitors
‡London SW19 *p92* 020 8543 3302
London SW17 *p92* 020 8767 0800

S Winayak
‡Leatherhead *p271* 020 8941 6022

Winch & Winch
‡Chatham *p185* 01634 830111

Winchester Legal
‡Winchester *p434* 01962 841041

Winchesters Solicitors Limited
‡Birmingham *p143* 0800 634 4679

Winckworth Sherwood LLP
‡London SE1 *p92* 020 7593 5000
Oxford *p344* 01865 297200

Windeatts
‡Totnes *p413* 01803 862233
Kingsbridge *p267* 01548 852727

Winder Taylor Fallows
‡Bolton *p150* . . . . . . .01204 389908 / 522888
Bolton *p150* 01204 697467
Bolton *p150* 01204 498970

Ellen Yee-Man Windsor
‡Coventry *p201* 024 7641 4984

Wingate Wong Solicitors
‡London W2 *p92* 020 7723 1228

Winn Solicitors Limited
‡Newcastle upon Tyne *p327* 0191 276 1000

Penelope J Winnard
‡Holywell *p252* 01352 780229

Winston & Strawn LLP
‡London EC2 *p92* 020 7011 8700

Winston Solicitors LLP
‡Leeds *p278* 0113 320 5000

E J Winter & Son
‡Reading *p361* 0118 957 4424

Paul Winter & Co
‡London EC4 *p92* 020 7936 2433

Winter Scott
‡London EC2 *p92* 020 7367 8989

Winterbotham Smith Penley LLP
‡Stroud *p401* 01453 847200
Dursley *p214* 01453 541940
Nailsworth *p320* 01453 832566

Winters
‡St Ives *p392* 01480 377377

Winters & Co
‡Ware *p421* 01920 466696

Wintle & Co
‡Bognor Regis *p148* 01243 863021
Bognor Regis *p148* 01243 586611
Selsey *p374* 01243 605947

Winton & Winton
‡Newbury *p322* 01635 814418

Winton Raynes & Co
‡Swindon *p406* 01793 522688

Winwards
‡Milton Keynes *p317* 01908 502559

K J Wiper
‡Darlington *p206* 01325 242645

Wirral Family Law & Mediation
‡Bromborough *p166* 0151 343 3150

Wisdom Law
‡Hove *p255* 01273 272861

Wise Geary
‡Banbury *p122* 01295 278500

Wiseman Lee LLP
‡Newham E6 *p92* 020 8215 1000
Redbridge E11 *p92* 020 8215 1000
Waltham Forest E17 *p92* 020 8215 1000

Paul Wiseman Investigations
‡Oswestry *p342* 01691 655732

Wismayers
‡Great Bookham *p233* 01372 451114

Withers & Rogers
‡London SE1 *p92* 020 7663 3500
Birmingham *p143* 0121 245 3900
Bristol *p165* 0117 925 3030
Leamington Spa *p270* 01926 336111

Graham Withers & Co
‡Market Drayton *p312* 01630 657222
Shrewsbury *p380* 01743 236345

Withers LLP
‡London EC4 *p92* 020 7597 6000

Kevin Withey Solicitor
‡Bristol *p165* 01225 874569

Withy King Solicitors
‡Bath *p128* 01225 425731
Abingdon *p114* 01235 555345
Bath *p128* 01225 425731
Marlborough *p313* 01672 514781
Oxford *p344* 01865 792300
Swindon *p407* 01793 536526
Thame *p410* 01844 261966
Trowbridge *p414* 01225 777464

Witts Moloney Solicitors
‡Hemel Hempstead *p247* 0845 127 1333

Wixted & Co Ltd
‡London SW18 *p93*

Matthew Wokenson
‡London SE15 *p93*

Wolfe McClancy & Co
‡London SW7 *p93* 020 7581 8033

Wolfe Myers & Co
‡London W1 *p93* 020 7580 7426
London NW4 *p93* 020 8202 8546

Wolferstans
‡Plymouth *p351* 01752 663295
Plymouth *p351* 01752 401515

Wolfson & Co
‡Manchester *p311* 0161 873 8999

Leslie Wolfson & Co
‡London W1 *p93*

Wollen Michelmore Solicitors
‡Torquay *p413* 01803 213251
Dartmouth *p207* 01803 213251
Newton Abbot *p330* 01626 332266
Paignton *p345* 01803 521692

Wolsey Probate
‡Ipswich *p263* 01473 230000

Wolton & Co
‡Deal *p207* 01304 389789

Elizabeth Wong & Company
‡London WC2 *p93* 020 7766 5228

Nadine Wong & Co
‡London W2 *p93* 020 7243 8888

Wontner & Sons
‡London WC2 *p93* 020 7936 2414

Clive G Wood & Co
‡Stockport *p396* 0161 480 1000

The Wood Glaister Partnership
‡Solihull *p383* 0121 705 8151

Jeremy Wood & Co
‡Yeovil *p444* 01935 426047

John G Wood
‡London W1 *p93* 020 7580 2277

John G K Wood
‡Westminster W1 *p93* 020 7439 1122

Lawrence Wood
‡Wroxham *p443* 01603 783711

Rupert Wood & Son
‡Ashton-under-Lyne *p120* 0161 330 9121

Wood's Solicitors
‡Disley *p210* 01663 765511

Wood Sherwood & Co
‡Pocklington *p351* 01759 302791

Stephen Wood
‡Norwich *p335* 01603 766539

Woodcock & Thompson
‡Northampton *p333* 01604 758855
Daventry *p207* 01327 312121

Anne Woodcock & Co
‡St Albans *p390* 01727 861212

Woodcocks
‡Haslingden *p243* 01706 213356
Bacup *p121* 01706 874487
Bury *p171* 0161 761 4611
Ramsbottom *p359* 01706 824011
Rawtenstall *p359* . . . . .01706 225621 / 215018

Woodfines LLP
‡Bedford *p130* 01234 270600
Bletchley *p147* 01908 366333
Cambridge *p176* 01223 411421
Milton Keynes *p317* 01908 202150
Sandy *p372* 01767 680251

Woodford Robinson
‡Northampton *p333* 01604 624926

Woodford Stauffer
‡Farnborough *p224* 01252 375376

Woodford Wise Solicitors
‡Ilford *p261* 020 8550 2506

Woodfords Solicitors LLP
‡London SW6 *p93* 020 7731 0750

Woodgate & Co
‡Southsea *p389* 023 9283 5790

Woodgrange Solicitors
‡London E7 *p93* 020 8534 2400

Woodhead & Hoole
‡Chesterfield *p192* . . . .01246 233149 / 209001

Woodhouse & Company
‡Wolverhampton *p438* 01902 773616
Sutton Coldfield *p404* 0121 355 5601
Walsall *p420* 01922 612523

Woodhouse Daughtrey Solicitor
‡Gerrards Cross *p229* 01753 883309

The Woodland Davies Partnership LLP
‡Hay-on-Wye *p245* 01497 820406
Brecon *p156* 01874 624422
Hereford *p248* 01432 353727
Kington *p268* 01544 230841
Talgarth *p407* 01874 711744

Daniel Woodman and Co Ltd
‡Bristol *p165* 0117 902 8003

Richard A Woodman
‡Harpenden *p239* 01582 768222

Woodroffes
‡Westminster SW1 *p93* 020 7730 0001

Aidan Woods & Co
‡Bristol *p165* 0117 952 2006

Woods Solicitors
‡Chester *p191* 01244 340560
‡Pontefract *p351*

Woodthorpe Medical Law
‡Nottingham *p339* 0115 966 1345

Woodwards
‡Biggleswade *p133* 01767 601111

Woolacott & Co
‡Lancing *p270* . . . . . . .01903 763011 / 764334

Michael G Wooldridge
‡Birmingham *p143* 0121 706 2259

Woolf Simmonds
‡Westminster W1 *p93* 020 7262 1266

Woollastons
‡Sutton Coldfield *p404* 0121 355 5516
‡Sutton Coldfield *p404* 0121 308 4030

Woollcombe Yonge
‡Plymouth *p351* 01752 660384

Woolley & Co
‡Bridgnorth *p157* 01746 765311
‡Warwick *p423* 01789 267377

Woolley Beardsleys & Bosworth
‡Loughborough *p293* 01509 212266

Woolley Bevis Diplock
‡Brighton *p160* 01273 323231
Hove *p255* 01273 722532

J C Woolley
‡Holbeach *p251* 01406 423777

Woolliscrofts
‡Hanley *p239* 01782 204000
Alsager *p116* 01270 875915
Newcastle under Lyme *p323* 01782 662545
Stoke-on-Trent *p398* 01782 577246

Woolsey Morris & Kennedy
‡Sidcup *p380* 020 8300 9321

Woolwich Lander & Savage
‡Liverpool *p291* 0151 733 5807

Sarah Wootton Solicitors
‡Coulsdon *p199* 01737 553812

The Worcester Family Law Practice
‡Worcester *p440* 01905 730900

Worger Howcroft
‡Bingley *p133* 01274 511246

Working Law Solicitors
‡Cromer *p203* 01263 576607

Wornham & Co Solicitors
‡Birmingham *p143* 0121 236 7999

Woralls Solicitors
‡Preston *p357* 01772 612494

Worsdell & Vintner
‡Ickenham *p259* 01895 672631
Harefield *p239* 01895 824713

Worthingtons
‡Folkestone *p227* 01303 850206

David Paxton Worthy
‡Sunderland *p402* 0191 522 7977

Wortley Byers
‡Brentwood *p156* 01277 268368

Wortley Redmayne Kershaw
‡Chelmsford *p187* 01245 491122

Wosskow Brown
‡Sheffield *p377* 0114 256 1560

WOWLAW Solicitors
‡Tunbridge Wells *p415* 01892 511066

Wragg Mark-Bell Solicitors
‡Carlisle *p182* 01228 711728
Carlisle *p182* 01228 510077

Wragge & Co LLP
‡Birmingham *p143* 0121 233 1000
London EC1 *p93* 0870 903 1000

Wray & Co
‡Bishop's Stortford *p144* 01279 505964

Nicholas Wray Solicitor
‡Haverhill *p244* 01440 704467

Wren Martin
‡Stockton-on-Tees *p397* 01642 603609

Wright & Co
‡Harpenden *p239* 01582 767686
‡London SW3 *p93* 020 7584 7557
‡Pontefract *p351* 01977 878130

Wright & Lord
‡Morecambe *p319* 01524 402050
Morecambe *p319* 01524 402050

Wright & McMillan Bennett
‡Telford *p409* 01952 291100

Wright & Morton
‡Sunderland *p402* 0191 567 4289

Wright & Wright
‡Guildford *p237* 01483 531264

Christopher Wright & Co
‡Twickenham *p416* 020 8607 9666

Desmond Wright & Co
‡Hayes *p245* 020 8561 4888

Wright Hassall LLP
‡Leamington Spa *p270* 01926 886688

J Wright
‡Lytham *p297* 01253 727875

WRIGHT SON & PEPPER LLP
‡Camden WC1 *p93* 020 7242 5473

William Wright & Son
‡Dudley *p213* 01384 255344

Wrightway Solicitors
‡London SE13 *p93* 020 8297 0044

Wrigley Claydon
‡Oldham *p341* 0161 624 6811
Todmorden *p412* 01706 815712

Wrigleys Solicitors LLP
‡Leeds *p278* 0113 244 6100
Sheffield *p377* 0114 267 5588

The Write Will Service
‡Leigh-on-Sea *p282* 01702 713155

J C Wroe & Co
‡Reading *p362* 0118 959 1496

Robert Wrynne Solicitors
‡Bournemouth *p153* 01202 422622

www.elawyers.co.uk
‡Liverpool *p291* 0151 489 9900

Alexandra Wyatt Divorce And Family Law Solicitor
‡London WC2 *p93* 020 7936 4446

Wycombe Hurd & Co
‡London WC2 *p93* 020 7925 0313

Michael Wydra & Co
‡Westminster W1 *p93* 020 7437 3640

Wykeham & Co
‡Chippenham *p193* 01249 721010

Wykeham Hurford Sheppard & Son LLP
‡Battle *p128* 01424 775088
Chislehurst *p193* . . .020 8297 0393 / 8467 8307
Tenterden *p410* 01580 762251

Wykes O'Donnell Williams
Ilkeston *p261* 0115 932 8776

David Wyld & Co
‡London EC4 *p93* 020 7583 7920

Wylie Kay
‡Blackpool *p147* 01253 296297

Ieuan Wyn Jones
‡Llangefni *p292* 01248 722261

Denis Wynn & Co
‡Chipping Norton *p193* 01608 643036

Y

YHM Solicitors
‡Leeds *p278*. 0113 240 8781

YVA Solicitors
‡London N12 *p93* 020 8445 9898

Yaffe Jackson Ostrin
‡Liverpool *p291* 0151 236 5555
Liverpool *p291* 0151 259 2666

Yanakas Votsis Achillea
‡London N12 *p93*

Shirley May Yard
‡Sidmouth *p380*. 01395 577199

Yarwood & Stubley
‡Blyth *p148* 01670 361211

Yarwood Stimpson & Co
‡Whitley Bay *p431*. 0191 297 0123

Yasmin and Shaid Solicitors
‡Leeds *p278*. 0113 271 3939

Yates & Co
‡Nottingham *p339*. 0115 947 4486
Nottingham *p339*

Yates Ardern
‡Ashton-under-Lyne *p120* 0161 330 3332
‡Glossop *p230*. 01457 857863
Oldham *p341*. 0161 287 3331

Yates Barnes
‡Chorley *p194*. 01257 267014

P H Yeung
‡London W1 *p93* 020 7287 1882

David Yip & Co Solicitors
‡Manchester *p311*. 0161 236 1880

R I Yonge Solicitors
‡Haslemere *p243* 01428 644219

P C D York & Co
‡London W6 *p93* 020 8741 4512

Yorklaw Ltd (t/a Burn & Company)
‡York *p445* 01904 655442
Easingwold *p215*. 01347 822188

Yorkshire Law Solicitors
‡Brough *p167* 01430 422422

YorSolicitor
‡York *p445* 01904 449933

Young & Co
‡Bedford *p130*. . . . . . .01234 346411 / 344211
‡Stoke-on-Trent *p398* 01782 339200

Young & Lee
‡Birmingham *p143*. 0121 633 3233

Young Coles & Langdon
‡Hastings *p244* 01424 437878
Bexhill *p132* 01424 210013

D Young & Co
‡Southampton *p387*. 023 8071 9500
London EC1 *p93* 020 7269 8550

Gordon Young Solicitors Ltd
‡Luton *p296*. 01582 405577
Welwyn Garden City *p426* 01582 405577

Grenville Young Solicitor
‡Portsmouth *p355*. 023 9237 2192

Hugh Young
‡Nottingham *p339*. 0115 988 6050

Julian Young & Co
‡London W1 *p93* 020 7724 8414

Mark Young & Co
‡Ipswich *p263*. 01473 226630

S D Young
‡St Neots *p392* 01480 470411

Simon Young
‡Crediton *p203* . . 01363 774248 / 07815 291487

Young Swistak Solicitors
‡Melton Mowbray *p314* 01664 501801

Youngs
‡Cardiff *p181* 029 2076 3211

Youngs Criminal Defence Services Limited
‡Sheffield *p377* 0114 249 5444

S A Younis Solicitors
‡Bradford *p155* 01274 579900

Your Lawyers Limited
‡Chesterfield *p192*. 0871 310 0144

Sarah Youren Planning Solicitors Limited
‡London N1 *p93*. 0845 481 8136

Yu & Co Solicitors
‡Manchester *p311*. 0161 638 0960

Yugin & Partners
‡Stanmore *p394*. 020 8954 2410

Yungs Solicitors
‡Cardiff *p181* 029 20 62 8019

Yvonne Mcgarry Solicitor
‡Petersfield *p348* 01730 265118

Z

ZMS Solicitor
‡Leicester *p281* 0116 247 0790

ZSA Law
‡Hillingdon *p250*. 01923 834300

A Zacharia & Co Solicitors
‡Sheffield *p377* 0114 261 9203

Zacharia & Co
‡Oldham *p341*. 0161 620 8888

Zahra & Co
‡London E1 *p93*. 020 7375 1231

Zaidi Solicitors
‡Luton *p296*. 01582 431333

Zaiwalla & Co
‡London WC2 *p93*. 020 7312 1000

Zak Solicitors
‡Birmingham *p143*. 0121 554 8244

A E P Zaleski
‡London SW18 *p93* 020 8875 1791

Zaman Solicitors
‡London E1 *p93*. 020 7702 7555

Zatman & Co
‡Manchester *p311*. 0161 832 2500

Zelin & Zelin
‡London W2 *p94* 020 7262 1405
London W1 *p94*. 020 7287 1777

Peter Zelnik & Co
‡Biggin Hill *p133*. 01959 570730

Zermansky & Partners
‡Leeds *p278*. 0113 245 9766

Zhonglun W&D LLP
‡London EC4 *p94* 020 7623 8889

Ziadies
‡London SW9 *p94*. 020 7737 0934

Zimmers
‡London NW11 *p94* 0870 770 0171
‡London NW1 *p94*. 020 7284 6970

Zorro Law
‡London N20 *p94* 0845 000 0219

Zuriel Solicitors
‡London SE11 *p94* 020 7582 5543

Zyda Law
‡Nantwich *p320* 01270 620660

SECTION 4

SOLICITORS

CONTENTS

Firms Specialisations

Accounting Standards
Admiralty
Adoption
Agricultural Law, Holdings & Property
Air Law
Animals, Farming, Forestry
Arbitration & Mediation
Banking Law
Bankruptcy & Insolvency
Building Law, Building Contracts
Charity Law
Child Care & Wardship
Clinical Negligence
Commercial & Company Law
Commercial Conveyancing
Commercial Property
Communications & Telecommunications
Competition Law
Computer Law
Consumer Law – Agreements, Credit, Licensing, Sale of Goods
Consumer Protection – Advertising, Trade Descriptions, Trading Standards, Product Liability
Copyright, Patents, Trade Marks & Intellectual Property
Crime – General
Crime – Juvenile
Data Protection
Divorce & Matrimonial
Ecclesiastical Law
Education Law
Elderly
Employment Law
Entertainment, Artists & Performers
Environmental Liability
European Community Law
Family Law
Family Mediation
Fraud
Health & Safety at Work
Housing Association Law
Housing, Landlord & Tenant
Human Rights & Civil Liberties
Immigration & Nationality
Insurance Law
International Law
Internet & e-commerce
Islamic Law
Libel, Slander & Defamation
Liquor, Betting & Gaming Licensing
Litigation, Accidents, Injury, Criminal Injury Compensation, Personal Injury
Litigation, Commercial
Litigation, General
Local Government
Mental Health
Mergers & Acquisitions
Mines, Minerals, Oil & Gas
Pensions, Investments & Financial Services
Planning, Compulsory Purchase, Lands Tribunal
Printing & Publishing
Professional Negligence
Property – Finance, Development
Race & Sex Discrimination
Rating Law
Regulated by the FSA for Investment Business
Residential Conveyancing
Road Haulage Licensing
Sports Law
Taxation – Business
Taxation – Personal
Welfare Benefits
Wills, Trusts & Probate

FIRMS SPECIALISATION INDEX

ACCOUNTING STANDARDS

DAC Beachcroft
p24 London EC4 020 7242 1011

ADMIRALTY

E G Arghyrakis & Co
p7 London EC4 020 7353 2302
Blick & Co
p14 London 020 7247 9696
Brookes & Co
p16 London EC3 020 7621 0067
Thomas Cooper
p22 London EC3 020 7481 8851
Davies Battersby Ltd
p26 London EC3 020 7621 1090
Davies Johnson & Co (Shipping & Commercial Solicitors)
p349 Plymouth 01752 226020
Elborne Mitchell LLP
p29 London EC3 020 7320 9000
Holman Fenwick Willan
p42 London EC3 020 7264 8000
Jackson Parton
p45 London 020 7702 0085
Price & Kelway
p316 Milford Haven 01646 695311
Reed Smith LLP
p71 London EC2 020 3116 3000
Swinnerton Moore Solicitors
p84 London EC4 020 7236 7111
Waltons & Morse LLP
p90 London EC3 020 7623 4255
Waterson Hicks
p90 London EC3 020 7929 6060
Winter Scott
p92 London EC2 020 7367 8989

ADOPTION

Abensons
p285 Liverpool 0151 733 3111
Deborah Baxter & Co
p360 Reading 0118 958 6855
Sabina Bowler-Reed
p161 Bristol 01275 373111
Graeme Carmichael
p262 Ipswich 01473 252159
Barbara Carter
p136 Birmingham 0121 441 3238
Children & Families Law Firm
p20 London SW9 020 7582 6002
Covent Garden Family Law
p23 Camden 020 7257 6130
Crosse & Crosse
p220 Exeter 01392 258451
Cygnet Family Law
p196 Cleveland 01642 777680
Davies Gore Lomax
p273 Leeds 0113 242 2797
Family Law in Partnership LLP
p30 London WC2 020 7420 5000
Gardner Croft LLP
p176 Canterbury 01227 813400
Gaynham King & Mellor
p118 Appleby 01768 351422
p346 Penrith 01768 864651
Peter Giddens & Co
p174 Cambridge 01954 250089
Gill & Co
p260 Ilford 020 8554 8774
Goodman Ray
p36 Hackney 020 7608 1227
Maureen P Grenville
p214 Duffield 01332 841789
A K Gulati & Co
p402 Sutton 020 8770 7979
Hartnell Chanot & Partners Family Law Specialists
p221 Exeter 01392 421777
Hawley & Rodgers
p337 Nottingham 0115 955 9000
Hodders
p250 High Wycombe 01494 511345
Wendy Hopkins Family Law Practice LLP
p178 Cardiff 029 2034 2233
Frank Howard
p422 Warrington 01925 653481
Hunters
p44 London WC2 020 7412 0050
IBB Solicitors
p417 Uxbridge 0845 638 1381
Jones Myers LLP
p275 Leeds 0113 246 0055
Kingsfords
p119 Ashford 01233 624545
Lloyd Platt & Co
p55 London N3 020 8343 2998
McAras Solicitors LLP
p275 Leeds 0113 243 4333
Roberta McDonald
p140 Birmingham 0121 449 6821
NFLA Ltd
p192 Chesterfield 01246 471900
p338 Nottingham 0115 945 4555
p367 Rotherham 01709 373000
p376 Sheffield 0114 213 3888
Samuel Phillips Law Firm
p326 Newcastle upon Tyne 0191 232 8451
Alister Pilling
p173 Camborne 01209 613800
Jane E Roberts
p332 Northampton 01604 494431
Rupert Bear Murray Davies
p338 Nottingham 0115 924 3333
Russell-Cooke LLP
p267 Kingston upon Thames 020 8546 6111
R A Savage & Co
p425 Welwyn Garden City 01707 373037
Stantons
p233 Gravesend 01474 579940
John Swales
p119 Ashford 01233 732590
Thompson Smith & Puxon
p198 Colchester 01206 574431
Kathy Webb & Co
p237 Guisborough 01287 633331
Whiskers
p239 Harlow 01279 439439
Woollcombe Yonge
p351 Plymouth 01752 660384
The Worcester Family Law Practice
p440 Worcester 01905 730900

AGRICULTURAL LAW, HOLDINGS & PROPERTY

Alfred Truman
p167 Buckingham 01280 822217
Arnison & Co Solicitors Limited
p346 Penrith 01768 862007
Arnold Davies Vincent Evans
p413 Tregaron 01974 298816
Arnold Thomson Limited
p413 Towcester 01327 350266
Askew Bunting Solicitors LLP
p314 Middlesbrough 01642 252555
Awdry Bailey & Douglas
p173 Calne 01249 815110
p210 Devizes 01380 722311
Barber Titleys
p240 Harrogate 01423 502211
Barker Gotelee Solicitors
p262 Ipswich 01473 611211
Birdsall & Snowball
p226 Filey 01723 515151
Bond Pearce LLP
p161 Bristol 0845 415 0000
p14 London EC3 0845 415 0000
p349 Plymouth 0845 415 0000
p385 Southampton 0845 415 0000
Boodle Hatfield
p14 London W1 020 7629 7411
p343 Oxford 01865 790744
Bowcock & Pursaill
p278 Leek 01538 399199
Bruce Bowling & Co
p211 Doncaster 01302 320607
Brachers
p299 Maidstone 01622 690691
Brethertons LLP
p368 Rugby 01788 579579
Bridge McFarland
p235 Grimsby 01472 311711
p297 Mablethorpe 01507 478285
p312 Market Rasen 01673 843723
Bridge McFarland Haddon Owen
p294 Louth 01507 605883
Browne Jacobson LLP
p336 Nottingham 0115 976 6000
Burstalls
p256 Hull 01482 621800
Chamberlains
p144 Bishop's Waltham 01489 896141
Chandler Ray
p167 Buckingham 01280 814040
Chattertons Solicitors
p252 Horncastle 01507 522456
Clarion Solicitors LLP
p272 Leeds 0113 246 0622
Cockertons
p121 Bakewell 01629 812613
Coodes
p251 Holsworthy 01409 253425
p285 Liskeard 01579 347600
Cullimore Dutton
p190 Chester 01244 356789
Graham Dack & Company (inc Battersby James)
p185 Chatteris 01354 695885
Daltons
p340 Oakham 01572 722002 / 724343
Davis Davidson
p131 Beverley 01482 881278
Nigel Davis Solicitors
p131 Belper 01335 372889
William Dawes & Co
p370 Rye 01797 223177
Denison Till
p444 York 01904 611411
Drivers
p300 Malton 01653 600075
Ellis Lakin & Co
p348 Pickering 01751 472121
Eric Robinson Solicitors
p386 Southampton 023 8022 6891
FBC Manby Bowdler LLP
p157 Bridgnorth 01746 761436
p379 Shrewsbury 01743 241551
Farnfield & Nicholls
p374 Shaftesbury 01747 854244
Fitzgerald-Harts
p150 Boroughbridge 01423 322312
Thomas Flavell & Sons
p312 Market Bosworth 01455 290203
Ford Simey LLP
p221 Exeter 01392 274126
Fraser Brown
p133 Bingham 01949 830812
Fraser Dawbarns
p213 Downham Market 01366 383171
p266 King's Lynn 01553 666600
p435 Wisbech 01945 461456
Goad & Butcher
p374 Settle 01729 823500
Grainger Appleyard
p211 Doncaster 01302 327257
Leonard Gray
p186 Chelmsford 01245 504904
Grays
p444 York 01904 634771
Greenland Houchen Pomeroy
p120 Attleborough 01953 453143
p334 Norwich 01603 660744
HMG Law LLP
p132 Bicester 01869 252244
p343 Oxford 01865 244661
HSR Law (Hayes, Son & Richmond)
p211 Doncaster 01302 347800
p219 Epworth 01427 872206
p228 Gainsborough 01427 613831
Hall Ward & Fox
p429 Weston-super-Mare 01934 626656 / 626657
Hallett & Co
p119 Ashford 01233 625711
Hand Morgan & Owen
p393 Stafford 01785 211411
Hansells
p121 Aylsham 01263 734313
Harrisons Solicitors LLP
p425 Welshpool 01938 552545
Hayes & Storr
p223 Fakenham 01328 863231
Heald Solicitors
p317 Milton Keynes 01908 662277
Heptonstalls LLP
p255 Howden 01430 430209
Hibberts LLP
p203 Crewe 01270 215117
Higgs & Sons
p158 Brierley Hill 0845 111 5050
John Hodge Solicitors
p163 Bristol 0117 929 2281
Hodgson & Angus
p394 Stanhope 01388 528517
Hole & Pugsley
p412 Tiverton 01884 252827
Hood Vores & Allwood
p209 Dereham 01362 692424
Horwood & James LLP
p121 Aylesbury 01296 487361
Jeffreys & Powell
p156 Brecon 01874 622106
Keane & Co
p115 Aldeburgh 01728 453595
Kellock & Johnson
p413 Totnes 01803 862414
Knights Solicitors LLP
p115 Alderley Edge 01625 586686
p188 Cheltenham 01242 524654
p323 Newcastle under Lyme 01782 619225
LG Lawyers
p50 London SE1 020 7379 0000
Lambe Corner
p248 Hereford 01432 355301
Lanyon Bowdler LLP
p342 Oswestry 01691 652241
Larby Williams with Gwyn & Gwyn
p201 Cowbridge 01446 775535
Latimer Hinks
p206 Darlington 01325 341500
Lee Bolton Monier-Williams
p52 London W1 020 7222 5381
Lodders Solicitors LLP
p400 Stratford-upon-Avon 01789 293259
Longstaff & Midgley
p372 Scarborough 01723 351751

Lundys
p213 . . . . Driffield 01377 252831
MFG Solicitors
p440 . . . . Worcester 01905 610410
McPhersons
p395 . . . . Stockbridge 01794 389002
Margary & Miller
p389 . . . . Southwold 01502 723308
May May & Merrimans
p59 . . . . . . London WC1 020 7405 8932
Moxon & Barker
p351 . . . . Pontefract 01977 602999
Napthens LLP
p357 . . . . Preston 01772 888444
Neves
p295 . . . . Luton 01582 725311
Neves Solicitors
p239 . . . . Harpenden 01582 715234
Nicholson Portnell
p249 . . . . Hexham 01434 603656
Oxley & Coward Solicitors LLP
p367 . . . . Rotherham 01709 510999
PCB Solicitors LLP
p269 . . . . Knighton 01547 520254
p379 . . . . Shrewsbury 01743 248148
Pearsons & Ward
p300 . . . . Malton 01653 692247
Pellmans
p223 . . . . Eynsham 01865 884400
Pemberton Greenish LLP
p66 . . . . London SW3 020 7591 3333
Peter Peter & Wright
p251 . . . . Holsworthy 01409 253262
p340 . . . . Okehampton 01837 52379
Poole Alcock
p198 . . . . Congleton 01260 275337
Porter Dodson
p212 . . . . Dorchester 01305 262525
Prettys
p262 . . . . Ipswich 01473 232121
Raworths LLP
p240 . . . . Harrogate 01423 566666
Rickerbys LLP
p188 . . . . Cheltenham 01242 224422
Risdon Hosegood
p436 . . . . Wiveliscombe 01984 623203
Robinson Le Grice
p392 . . . . St Ives 01736 797973
Roythornes LLP
p327 . . . . Newmarket 01638 561320
p389 . . . . Spalding 01775 842500
Serjeant & Son
p359 . . . . Ramsey 01487 812325
Shakespeares
p319 . . . . Moreton-in-Marsh 0845 630 8833
p378 . . . . Shipston-on-Stour 0845 630 8833
p400 . . . . Stratford-upon-Avon 0845 630 8833
Sharman Law
p118 . . . . Ampthill 01525 750750
Sills & Betteridge LLP
p389 . . . . Spilsby 01790 752277
T C Smith
p131 . . . Berwick-upon-Tweed 01289 307409
Spearing Waite LLP
p281 . . . . Leicester 0116 262 4225
Sprake & Kingsley
p129 . . . . Beccles 01502 713214
Squire Sanders (UK) LLP
p142 . . . . . . Birmingham 0121 222 3000
William Sturges & Co
p84 . . . . London W1 020 7873 1000
TBI Solicitors
p123 . . . . . . Barnard Castle 01833 638326
Stanley Tee
p144 . . . . Bishop's Stortford 01279 755200
Thrings LLP
p128 . . . . Bath 01225 340000
p87 . . . . London SW1 020 7766 5600
p406 . . . . Swindon 01793 410800
Tinn Criddle & Co
p115 . . . . Alford 01507 462882
p389 . . . . Spilsby 01790 756810
Trethowans LLP
p371 . . . . Salisbury 01722 412512
Vincent Sykes & Higham LLP
p411 . . . . Thrapston 01832 732161
Walker Smith Way
p191 . . . . Chester 0844 346 3100
Wansbroughs
p210 . . . . Devizes 01380 733300
p314 . . . . Melksham 01225 703222
Warners Solicitors
p374 . . . . Sevenoaks 01732 747900
p412 . . . . Tonbridge 01732 770660
Wilkin Chapman Epton Blades
p285 . . . . Lincoln 01522 512345
Wilkin Chapman Grange Solicitors
p235 . . . . Grimsby 01472 262626
Eirian J Williams a'i Gwmni
p292 . . . . Llandysul 01559 363244
Windeatts
p267 . . . . Kingsbridge 01548 852727
Withers LLP
p92 . . . . London EC4 020 7597 6000
Withy King Solicitors
p407 . . . . Swindon 01793 536526
Wright Hassall LLP
p270 . . . . . Leamington Spa 01926 886688
Wrigleys Solicitors LLP
p278 . . . . Leeds 0113 244 6100

AIR LAW

Clark Ricketts LLP
p20 . . . . London WC2 020 7240 6767
MPH Solicitors
p307 . . . . Manchester 0161 832 7722

ANIMALS, FARMING, FORESTRY

Burstalls
p256 . . . . Hull 01482 621800
Cooper & Co
p444 . . . . York 01904 626266
Nigel Davis Solicitors
p131 . . . . Belper 01335 372889
Fulton Robertson
p117 . . . . Amersham 01494 722326
Harper Law
p366 . . . . Romsey 01794 322364
Holdens
p264 . . . . Kendal 01539 720629
Knights
p415 . . . . . Tunbridge Wells 01892 537311
Robinson Le Grice
p392 . . . . St Ives 01736 797973
Nigel Weller & Co
p283 . . . . Lewes 01273 487123
Jane V Wilkinson
p147 . . . . . Blandford Forum 01258 817719

ARBITRATION & MEDIATION

AMD Solicitors
p160 . . . . Bristol 0117 962 1460
Alexander Paul
p412 . . . . Tiverton 01884 252361
E G Arghyrakis & Co
p7 . . . . London EC4 020 7353 2302
Bermans LLP
p286 . . . . Liverpool 0151 224 0500
Bevans
p161 . . . . Bristol 0117 923 7249
p12 . . . . London WC2 020 7353 9995
Bond Pearce LLP
p161 . . . . Bristol 0845 415 0000
p14 . . . . London EC3 0845 415 0000
p349 . . . . Plymouth 0845 415 0000
p385 . . . . Southampton 0845 415 0000
Browne Jacobson LLP
p336 . . . . Nottingham 0115 976 6000
Christopher Cox Solicitors
p331 . . . . Northampton 01604 882287
Clarion Solicitors LLP
p272 . . . . Leeds 0113 246 0622
Thomas Cooper
p22 . . . . London EC3 020 7481 8851
Corbett & Co International Construction Lawyers Ltd
p409 . . . . Teddington 020 8614 6200
Crowell & Moring
p23 . . . . London EC4 020 7413 0011
Curtis Davis Garrard
p417 . . . . Uxbridge 020 8734 2800
DAC Beachcroft
p24 . . . . London EC4 020 7242 1011
Davidson Large LLP
p240 . . . . Harrogate 01423 727272
Davies Johnson & Co (Shipping & Commercial Solicitors)
p349 . . . . Plymouth 01752 226020
Nigel Davis Solicitors
p131 . . . . Belper 01335 372889
Thomas Dunton Solicitors
p342 . . . . Orpington 01689 822554
Family Law in Partnership LLP
p30 . . . . London WC2 020 7420 5000
Fenwick Elliott
p31 . . . . London WC2 020 7421 1986
Ford Simey LLP
p221 . . . . Exeter 01392 274126
Freedmans
p34 . . . . London W4 020 8987 9155
George Ide LLP
p192 . . . . Chichester 01243 786668
Greenhouse Stirton & Co
p37 . . . . London EC1 020 7490 3456
HMG Law LLP
p132 . . . . Bicester 01869 252244
p343 . . . . Oxford 01865 244661
Heald Solicitors
p317 . . . . Milton Keynes 01908 662277
A G Heale Ltd
p178 . . . . Cardiff 029 2056 2566
LG Lawyers
p50 . . . . London SE1 020 7379 0000
Lee Bolton Monier-Williams
p52 . . . . London W1 020 7222 5381
Maxwell Winward LLP
p59 . . . . London EC4 020 7651 0000
Medyckyj & Co
p60 . . . . Haringey 020 8442 0000
Morgan Walker
p62 . . . . London WC2 020 7831 8333
Morton Pugh Welch
p62 . . . . London EC2 020 7374 4141
Pinsent Masons LLP
p141 . . . . Birmingham 0121 200 1050
p67 . . . . London EC2 020 7418 7000
Placidi & Co
p386 . . . . Southampton 01489 579804
Rawlings Giles
p71 . . . . London SW11 020 7223 2765
Raworths LLP
p240 . . . . Harrogate 01423 566666
Rouse Legal (Formerly Willoughby & Partners)
p74 . . . . London E14 020 7536 4100
Skadden Arps Slate Meagher & Flom (UK) LLP
p80 . . . . London E14 020 7519 7000
Solomon Taylor & Shaw
p80 . . . . London NW3 020 7431 1912
Stewarts Law LLP
p277 . . . . Leeds 0113 222 0022
p83 . . . . London EC4 020 7822 8000
William Sturges & Co
p84 . . . . London W1 020 7873 1000
Temple & Co Commercial Solicitors
p207 . . . . Daventry 0845 241 4045
Tudor Williams & Co
p443 . . . . Wrexham 01978 362006
Walker Morris
p277 . . . . Leeds 0113 283 2500
Waltons & Morse LLP
p90 . . . . London EC3 020 7623 4255
Wedlake Bell LLP
p91 . . . . London WC1 020 7395 3000
WilmerHale
p92 . . . . London EC2 020 7645 2400
p344 . . . . Oxford 01235 823000
Winter Scott
p92 . . . . London EC2 020 7367 8989
Withy King Solicitors
p407 . . . . Swindon 01793 536526

BANKING LAW

Addleshaw Goddard
p4 . . . . London EC1 020 7606 8855
Ashurst LLP
p7 . . . . London EC2 020 7638 1111
CMS Cameron McKenna LLP
p17 . . . . London 020 7367 3000
Thomas Cooper
p22 . . . . London EC3 020 7481 8851
Minter Ellison
p61 . . . . London EC2 020 7448 4800
Morgan Lewis & Bockius
p61 . . . . London EC4 020 3201 5000
Morgan Walker
p62 . . . . London WC2 020 7831 8333
Mornements Solicitors
p443 . . . . Yeovil 01935 863333
Nautadutilh
p63 . . . . London EC2 020 7786 9100
Oglethorpe Sturton & Gillibrand
p270 . . . . Lancaster 01524 846846
SGH Martineau LLP
p142 . . . . Birmingham 0870 763 2000
SNR Denton
p75 . . . . London EC4 020 7242 1212
Sidley Austin Brown & Wood
p78 . . . . London EC2 020 7360 3600

BANKRUPTCY & INSOLVENCY

Addlestone Keane Solicitors
p271 . . . . Leeds 0113 244 6700
Andersons Solicitors
p335 . . . . Nottingham 0115 947 0641
Arnold Fooks Chadwick LLP
p7 . . . . London W1 020 7499 3007
K A Arnold & Co
p7 . . . . London N1 020 7354 4926
Awdry Bailey & Douglas
p173 . . . . Calne 01249 815110
p210 . . . . Devizes 01380 722311
Bannister Bates Property Lawyers
p318 . . . . Morecambe 01524 416300
J E Baring & Co
p9 . . . . London EC1 020 7242 8966
Baxter Caulfield
p255 . . . . Huddersfield 01484 519519
Joseph N Bell
p283 . . . . Lewes 01273 897377
Bell Lax Litigation
p403 . . . . . Sutton Coldfield 0121 355 0011
Bevan Brittan LLP
p161 . . . . Bristol 0870 194 1000
Birchall Blackburn LLP
p194 . . . . Chorley 01257 279011
p301 . . . . Manchester 0161 236 0662
p356 . . . . Preston 01772 561663
Black Norman
p203 . . . . Crosby 0151 931 2777
Blythe Liggins
p270 . . . . . Leamington Spa 01926 831231
Bond Pearce LLP
p161 . . . . Bristol 0845 415 0000
p14 . . . . London EC3 0845 415 0000
p349 . . . . Plymouth 0845 415 0000
p385 . . . . Southampton 0845 415 0000
Boyes Turner
p360 . . . . Reading 0118 959 7711
Bridge McFarland
p235 . . . . Grimsby 01472 311711
p297 . . . . Mablethorpe 01507 478285
p312 . . . . . . Market Rasen 01673 843723
Graham Bridgman & Co
p360 . . . . Reading 0118 933 1818
Brooke North LLP
p272 . . . . Leeds 0113 283 2100
N C Brothers & Co
p360 . . . . Reading 0118 958 9966
Browne Jacobson LLP
p16 . . . . London EC3 020 7539 4900
p336 . . . . Nottingham 0115 976 6000
CMS Cameron McKenna LLP
p162 . . . . Bristol 0117 930 0200
Carrick Read Solicitors LLP
p256 . . . . Hull 01482 211160
Child & Child
p20 . . . . London SW1 020 7235 8000
Clarion Solicitors LLP
p272 . . . . Leeds 0113 246 0622
Robin F Clark & Co
p232 . . . . Gravesend 01474 334444
Cooper Stott
p214 . . . . Durham 0191 384 7210
CooperBurnett
p415 . . . . . Tunbridge Wells 01892 515022
DAC Beachcroft
p24 . . . . London EC4 020 7242 1011
p303 . . . . Manchester 0161 934 3000
Dass Solicitors
p137 . . . . Birmingham 0121 248 4000
Julian Dobson Solicitors
p159 . . . . Brighton 01273 766355
Dodd Lewis Solicitors
p27 . . . . London SE3 020 8852 1255
Max Engel & Co LLP
p331 . . . . Northampton 01604 887450
Eric Robinson Solicitors
p386 . . . . Southampton 023 8022 6891
Field Fisher Waterhouse LLP
p31 . . . . London EC3 020 7861 4000
Foot Anstey
p221 . . . . Exeter 01392 411221
Ford Simey LLP
p221 . . . . Exeter 01392 274126
Gartsides
p328 . . . . Newport 01633 213411
Gateley LLP
p138 . . . . Birmingham 0121 234 0000
Mark Gilbert Morse
p325 . . Newcastle upon Tyne 0191 261 0096
hlw Keeble Hawson LLP
p376 . . . . Sheffield 0114 276 5555
HMG Law LLP
p132 . . . . Bicester 01869 252244
p343 . . . . Oxford 01865 244661
Harris Cartier LLP
p39 . . . . London WC2 020 7405 7100
p382 . . . . Slough 01753 810710
Higgs & Sons
p158 . . . . Brierley Hill 0845 111 5050
Hills Solicitors Limited
p116 . . . . Altrincham 0161 928 0961
Hillyer McKeown LLP
p190 . . . . Chester 01244 318131
Huggins & Lewis Foskett
p43 . . . . Redbridge 020 8989 3000
Hunt & Morgan
p179 . . . . Cardiff 029 2034 1234
Ince & Co Services Ltd
p44 . . . . London E1 020 7481 0010
Insley & Partners
p152 . . . . Bournemouth 01202 510167
Isadore Goldman Solicitors
p45 . . . . London EC4 020 7353 1000
Jacobs & Reeves
p353 . . . . Poole 01202 731849
Jaffe Porter Crossick
p46 . . . . London NW6 020 7625 4424

See p542 for the Firms Specialisations

LG Lawyers
p50 London SE1 020 7379 0000
J B Leitch & Co
p289 Liverpool 0151 708 2250
Letchers
p364 Ringwood 01425 471424
Lewis Cutner & Co
p53 London NW3 020 7433 2552
Lupton Fawcett
p275 Leeds 0113 280 2000
McLoughlin & Company LLP
p379 Shrewsbury 01743 272272
Matthew Arnold & Baldwin LLP
p423 Watford 01923 202020
Max Bitel Greene LLP
p59 Islington 020 7354 2767
Meade-King
p163 Bristol 0117 926 4121
Michelmores LLP
p60 London W1 020 7659 7660
Mincoffs Solicitors LLP
p325 Newcastle upon Tyne 0191 281 6151
Moorhead James LLP
p61 London EC4 020 7831 8888
Nicholas Morris
p62 London W11 020 7792 0890
Mundays LLP
p196 Cobham 01932 590500
D J Murphy Solicitors
p180 Cardiff 029 2022 1300
Nautadutilh
p63 London EC2 020 7786 9100
Nicholsons Solicitors LLP
p294 Lowestoft 01502 532300
Niman & Co
p63 Haringey 020 8809 4923
Parkinson Wright LLP
p440 Worcester 01905 726789
W Parry & Co
p405 Swansea 01792 470037
Pinsent Masons LLP
p141 Birmingham 0121 200 1050
p276 Leeds 0113 244 5000
p308 Manchester 0161 234 8234
Pittalis & Co
p68 London N12 020 8446 9555
Rickerbys LLP
p188 Cheltenham 01242 224422
Richard Rooney & Co
p73 Merton 020 8947 8024
Ross Coates
p263 Ipswich 01473 621800
SA Law
p390 St Albans 01727 798000
SGH Martineau LLP
p75 London EC3 020 7264 4444
Sharpe Pritchard
p77 London WC1 020 7405 4600
Spearing Waite LLP
p281 Leicester 0116 262 4225
Squire Sanders (UK) LLP
p142 Birmingham 0121 222 3000
p277 Leeds 0113 284 7000
William Sturges & Co
p84 London W1 020 7873 1000
Underwood Solicitors LLP
p89 London W1 020 7526 6000
Walker Morris
p277 Leeds 0113 283 2500
Wedlake Bell LLP
p91 London WC1 020 7395 3000
Weightmans LLP
p311 Manchester 0161 233 7330
Withers LLP
p92 London EC4 020 7597 6000
Withy King Solicitors
p407 Swindon 01793 536526
Wosskow Brown
p377 Sheffield 0114 256 1560

BUILDING LAW, BUILDING CONTRACTS

Alexander Paul
p412 Tiverton 01884 252361
Breeze & Wyles Solicitors LLP
p248 Hertford 01992 558411
Corbett & Co International Construction Lawyers Ltd
p409 Teddington 020 8614 6200
Eric Cowsill Solicitor
p263 Ivybridge 01752 205202
Ellis Taylor Law LLP
p29 London WC2 020 7405 0206
Fenwick Elliott
p31 London WC2 020 7421 1986
Freedmans
p34 London W4 020 8987 9155
Immanuel & Co
p44 London EC4 020 7213 9901
Neil McCormick
p228 Frome 01373 455700
McLoughlin & Company LLP
p379 Shrewsbury 01743 272272
Maples Teesdale LLP
p58 London EC2 020 7600 3800
Maxwell Winward LLP
p59 London EC4 020 7651 0000
Morton Pugh Welch
p62 London EC2 020 7374 4141
Nalders Quality Solicitors
p246 Helston 01326 574001
Perrins Solicitors LLP
p239 Harpenden 01582 466140
Pinsent Masons LLP
p164 Bristol 0117 924 5678
p308 Manchester 0161 234 8234
J H Powell & Co
p209 Derby 01332 372211
SGH Martineau LLP
p75 London EC3 020 7264 4444
Silver Shemmings LLP
p78 London SW1 0845 345 1244

CHARITY LAW

Peter Badham & Co
p9 London W14 020 7603 9798
Bates Wells & Braithwaite London LLP
p11 London EC4 020 7551 7777
Bazeley Barnes & Bazeley
p132 Bideford 01237 473122
Bircham Dyson Bell
p13 London W1 020 7227 7000
Birdy & Co
p426 Wembley 020 8900 9112
Robin Burman & Co
p302 Manchester 0161 860 7123
Claytons
p390 St Albans 01727 865765
Leonie Cowen & Associates
p23 London NW6 020 7604 5870
Craigen Wilders & Sorrell
p23 London N8 020 8888 2255
Charles Crookes with George Tudor & de Winton
p156 Brecon 01874 625151
Daltons
p340 Oakham 01572 722002 / 724343
J F Dawson
p129 Beaconsfield 01494 670566
Ellis-Fermor & Negus
p293 Long Eaton 0115 972 5222
England & Co
p234 Great Yarmouth 01493 604990
p234 Great Yarmouth 01493 740795 / 748174
p234 Great Yarmouth 01493 844308 / 844309
Farrer & Co LLP
p31 London WC2 020 3375 7000
Grays
p444 York 01904 634771
Griffith Smith Farrington Webb
p159 Brighton 01273 324041
Harvey Son & Filby
p262 Ipswich 01473 712962
Heath & Blenkinsop
p422 Warwick 01926 492407
Heppenstalls
p296 Lyndhurst 023 8028 2885
Hunters
p44 London WC2 020 7412 0050
JW Law
p433 Wimborne 01202 690658
Johns & Saggar
p46 London WC1 020 3490 1475
Lewis & Dick
p219 Epsom 020 8393 0055
A J Lutley
p119 Ashtead 01372 279066
MacDonald Oates LLP
p316 Midhurst 01730 816711
McEwen Parkinson
p56 London W1 020 7487 4361
Glynis M Mackie
p232 Gosforth 0191 236 5308
Marriott Davies Yapp
p402 Sutton 020 8643 9794
Mitchell Dodds & Co
p431 Whitley Bay 0191 252 2396 / 252 9557
Cliona O'Tuama
p64 London EC4 020 7489 2015
Penman Johnson
p424 Watford 01923 225212 / 239566
Portrait Solicitors
p69 London WC2 020 7092 6990
J H Powell & Co
p209 Derby 01332 372211
Ramsdens Solicitors
p256 Huddersfield 01484 821500
Robinsons
p261 Ilkeston 0115 932 4101
Roebucks
p145 Blackburn 01254 503070
Russell-Cooke LLP
p74 London SW15 020 8789 9111
p74 London WC1 020 7405 6566
Rutters
p374 Shaftesbury 01747 852377
Senior Calveley & Hardy
p297 Lytham 01253 733333
Stone King LLP
p128 Bath 01225 337599
p176 Cambridge 01223 451070
p83 London EC1 020 7796 1007
Talbot & Co
p170 Burton-on-Trent 01283 564716
Tozers
p409 Teignmouth 01626 772376
Waller Pollins
p217 Edgware 020 8238 5858
Max Wiley & Co
p251 Holt 01263 711771
Winckworth Sherwood LLP
p344 Oxford 01865 297200
Wrigleys Solicitors LLP
p278 Leeds 0113 244 6100
p377 Sheffield 0114 267 5588
Young Coles & Langdon
p244 Hastings 01424 437878

CHILD CARE & WARDSHIP

@ Cornwall Law
p414 Truro 01872 222688 / 222712
Abensons
p285 Liverpool 0151 733 3111
Aitchison & Co
p4 London WC2 020 7240 0020
Aitken Associates
p4 Islington 020 7700 6006
Albin & Co
p359 Reading 0118 957 4018
Alexander & Partners
p5 Brent 020 8965 7121
Alletsons Ltd
p157 Bridgwater 01278 456621
Alun Thomas & John
p114 Aberystwyth 01970 615900
Amphletts
p198 Colwyn Bay 01492 532296
Andersons Solicitors
p335 Nottingham 0115 947 0641
Anthony Gold
p6 London SE1 020 7940 4000
Arani & Co
p384 Southall 020 8893 5000
Ashby Family Law Practice
p208 Derby 01332 293293
Askew Bunting Solicitors LLP
p314 Middlesbrough 01642 252555
Aston Clark
p8 London W3 020 8752 1122
Atherton Godfrey
p211 Doncaster 01302 320621
Atkinson & Co
p328 Newport 01633 251118
Atkinson & Firth
p378 Shipley 01274 584305
Atkinson McCall
p240 Harrogate 01423 501531
Atkinson Ritson
p181 Carlisle 01228 525221
Atlee Chung & Company
p8 London W1 020 7287 9988
Attwaters
p294 Loughton 020 8508 2111
Attwood & Co
p233 Grays 01375 378122 / 378123
David Auld & Co
p130 Bedlington 01670 826870
Avadis & Co
p8 London NW5 020 7267 4240
Avery Naylor
p404 Swansea 01792 463276
Bailey Wright & Co
p135 Birmingham 0845 475 1996
Baker Gray & Co
p323 Newcastle upon Tyne 0191 222 0203
Banner Jones
p213 Dronfield 01246 414438
Barker Booth & Eastwood
p146 Blackpool 01253 362500
Barkers
p148 Bolton 01204 370011
Bassets
p366 Rochester 01634 400161
Deborah Baxter & Co
p360 Reading 0118 958 6855
Bazeley Barnes & Bazeley
p132 Bideford 01237 473122
Beecham Peacock
p323 Newcastle upon Tyne 0191 232 3048
Beevers Solicitors
p119 Ashton-under-Lyne 0161 339 9697
Behr & Co
p167 Brynmawr 01495 310581
Bendles
p181 Carlisle 01228 522215
Simon Bennett
p313 Marlow 01628 478088
Richard Best & Co
p368 Rugby 01788 571135
David Billingham & Partners
p187 Cheltenham 01242 676224
Birchall Blackburn LLP
p356 Preston 01772 561663
Biscoes
p354 Portsmouth 023 9266 0261
Blackhurst Budd LLP
p146 Blackpool 01253 629300
Bobbetts Mackan
p161 Bristol 0117 929 9001
Borneo Hughes Martell LLP
p331 Northampton 01604 624822
Bottrill & Co
p348 Pinner 020 8429 1010
Sabina Bowler-Reed
p161 Bristol 01275 373111
John Boyle & Co
p362 Redruth 01209 213507
Bradbury Roberts & Raby
p373 Scunthorpe 01724 854000
Bradleys
p212 Dover 01304 204080
Brain Chase Coles
p126 Basingstoke 01256 354481
Bramwell Browne Odedra
p189 Chesham 01494 782244
Brearleys Solicitors
p128 Batley 01924 473065
Bretherton Law
p389 St Albans 01727 869293
Brown Beer Nixon Mallon
p362 Redcar 01642 490202
Bryan & Armstrong
p311 Mansfield 01623 624505
Burstalls
p256 Hull 01482 621800
Kenneth Bush
p266 King's Lynn 01553 692737
Bynes
p412 Torquay 01803 295692
CB4law
p174 Cambridge 01223 316666
CLB Lawyers (Caswell Lane Bowater Solicitors)
p213 Dudley 01384 451731
CMHT Solicitors
p167 Brownhills 01543 372347
p420 Walsall 01922 646400
p420 Walsall 01922 743525
Cameron Jones Hussell & Howe
p353 Port Talbot 01639 885261
Graeme Carmichael
p262 Ipswich 01473 252159
S A Carr & Co
p18 Hackney 020 8986 5438
Barbara Carter
p136 Birmingham 0121 441 3238
Cartridges
p220 Exeter 01392 256854
Castles
p258 Hurstpierpoint 01273 836007 / 837107
Chafes
p395 Stockport 0161 477 1525
Chamberlins
p234 Great Yarmouth 01493 857621
Charsley Harrison LLP
p434 Windsor 01753 851591
Children & Families Law Firm
p20 London SW9 020 7582 6002
Churchers
p354 Portsmouth 023 9221 0170
Douglas Clift & Co
p269 Lancaster 01524 32437
Close Thornton
p206 Darlington 01325 466461
Anthony Collins Solicitors LLP
p137 Birmingham 0121 200 3242
Conveyancing Direct Ltd
p392 St Leonards-on-Sea 0845 788 8666
Coodes
p270 Launceston 01566 770000
p414 Truro 01872 246200
Cook Taylor
p22 Greenwich 020 8854 1166
Copitch
p22 Haringey 020 8883 9831
John Copland & Son
p375 Sheerness 01795 664431
Covent Garden Family Law
p23 Camden 020 7257 6130
Crockett & Co
p272 Leeds 0113 226 0111
Crombie Wilkinson
p444 York 01904 624185

Crosse & Crosse
p220 Exeter 01392 258451

Crosse Wyatt Verney & Ayre
p383 South Molton 01769 572157

Paul Crowley & Co
p287 Liverpool 0151 264 7363

Cumming & Riley
p233 Grays 01375 383691

Cygnet Family Law
p196 Cleveland 01642 777680

DLC Solicitors Limited
p207 Darwen 01254 761234

Davies & Co
p166 Bromley 020 8460 6668

Davies Gore Lomax
p273 Leeds 0113 242 2797

Lawrence Davies & Co
p26 Hammersmith & Fulham 020 7381 1171

Dawson Cornwell
p26 London WC1 020 7242 2556

John Delaney & Co
p273 Leeds 0113 246 8151

Claire Delves
p331 Northampton 01327 831050

Desor & Co
p245 Hayes 020 8569 0708

Dickinson Manser
p352 Poole 01202 673071

Dodd Lewis Solicitors
p27 London SE3 020 8852 1255

Dootsons LLP
p282 Leigh 01942 673431

David Du Pre & Co
p28 London WC1 020 7430 1950

Scott Duff & Co
p182 Carlisle 01228 531054

Dunning & Co
p28 London SE5 020 7733 6217

Earl & Crocker
p285 Liskeard 01579 345304

Eaton-Evans & Morris
p244 Haverfordwest 01437 763383

Edwards Duthie
p29 London E13 020 8514 9000

R L Edwards & Partners
p157 Bridgend 01656 656861

Ellis-Fermor & Negus
p130 Beeston 0115 922 1591

Elsey & Hodson
p347 Peterborough 01733 314064

England & Co
p234 Great Yarmouth 01493 844308 / 844309

Fairbrother & Darlow
p153 Bracknell 01344 420808

Family Law in Partnership LLP
p30 London WC2 020 7420 5000

Favell Smith & Lawson Solicitors
p375 Sheffield 0114 272 4381

Fawcett & Pattni
p420 Walsall 01922 640424

Joan Ferguson & Co
p304 Manchester 0161 795 5866

Finn Gledhill
p238 Halifax 01422 330000

Fish & Co
p438 Wolverhampton 01902 826464

Fletcher Dervish
p33 Haringey 020 8800 4615

Foot Anstey
p408 Taunton 01823 625600

Foster & Partners
p162 Bristol 0117 922 0229
p162 Bristol 0117 961 5300

Joseph Foxler & Co
p170 Bury 0161 797 4126

Franklins
p214 Dunstable 01582 699111

Fulchers
p436 Woking 01483 885522

Gardner Croft LLP
p176 Canterbury 01227 813400

Gartsides
p328 Newport 01633 213411

Gaynham King & Mellor
p118 Appleby 01768 351422
p346 Penrith 01768 864651

Gaynor-Smith Owen & Co
p300 Malvern 01684 560771

Craig Gee
p304 Manchester 0161 666 9999

Geoffrey Morris & Ashton
p318 Mold 01352 754711

George Ide LLP
p192 Chichester 01243 786668

Reena Ghai Solicitors
p253 Hounslow 020 8759 9959

Deborah Gibbins & Co
p133 Billericay 01268 270866

Peter Giddens & Co
p174 Cambridge 01954 250089

Gill & Co
p260 Ilford 020 8554 8774

Glansfields
p311 Mansfield 01623 627827

Beverley Golden
p386 Southampton 023 8086 7137

Goodman Ray
p36 Hackney 020 7608 1227

Goodwin Cowley
p294 Lowestoft 01502 532700

Gordon & Penney
p429 Weston-super-Mare 01934 414161

Gowmans
p345 Paignton 01803 546100

Grahame Stowe Bateson
p240 Harrogate 01423 562121

Granville-West
p352 Pontypool 01495 751111

Leonard Gray
p186 Chelmsford 01245 504904

Graysons
p375 Sheffield 0114 272 9184

Green Williamson Solicitors
p418 Wakefield 01924 291400

Gregorys Solicitors
p395 Stockport 0161 456 8125

Maureen P Grenville
p214 Duffield 01332 841789

Grylls & Paige
p363 Redruth 01209 215261 / 215357

HKB Wiltshires
p234 Great Yarmouth 01493 855676

Hains & Lewis Ltd
p244 Haverfordwest 0845 408 0125

Hall Smith Whittingham LLP
p203 Crewe 01270 212000

Hallett & Co
p119 Ashford 01233 625711

Hamnett Osborne Tisshaw
p245 Haywards Heath 01444 443030

Hancocks
p122 Banbury 01295 253211

Hanne & Co
p38 London SW11 020 7228 0017

Harman & Harman
p39 London SW2 01227 452977

Harrison Bundey
p274 Leeds 0113 200 7400

Edward Harte LLP
p159 Brighton 01273 662750

Harthills
p367 Rotherham 01709 377399

Hartnell Chanot & Partners Family Law Specialists
p221 Exeter 01392 421777

Hathaways
p228 Gateshead 0191 477 2288

Hawley & Rodgers
p293 Loughborough 01509 230333
p337 Nottingham 0115 955 9000

Haworth & Nuttall
p114 Accrington 01254 236221

Hay & Kilner
p419 Wallsend 0191 262 8231

Heaney Watson
p288 Liverpool 0151 256 7777
p288 Liverpool 0151 282 5555
p288 Liverpool 0151 293 2936
p305 Manchester 0800 567 7597 / 0161 359 3347

Heppenstalls
p296 Lymington 01590 689500

Heyes Samuel
p369 Ryde 01983 615615

Hodders
p250 High Wycombe 01494 511345

John Hodge Solicitors
p163 Bristol 0117 929 2281

Hodgsons & Mortimer
p206 Darlington 01325 250111 / 355956

Hogans
p356 Prescot 0151 430 7529

Holdens
p264 Kendal 01539 720629

Hopkin Murray Beskine
p42 London N4 020 7272 1234

Wendy Hopkins Family Law Practice LLP
p178 Cardiff 029 2034 2233

Howard & Co
p124 Barnsley 01226 211888

Frank Howard
p422 Warrington 01925 653481

Susan Howarth & Co
p333 Northwich 01606 48777

Howells
p178 Cardiff 029 2040 4020
p405 Swansea 01792 410016

Howells LLP
p376 Sheffield 0114 249 6666

Hughes Fowler Carruthers
p43 London WC2 020 7421 8383

Humphrys & Co
p363 Rhyl 01745 343158

Hunters
p44 London WC2 020 7412 0050

IBB Solicitors
p417 Uxbridge 0845 638 1381

JNP Legal
p314 Merthyr Tydfil 01685 350421

Jacobs & Reeves
p353 Poole 01202 731849

Anne Jarvis & Co
p240 Harrogate 01423 858582

Andrew Jay & Co
p284 Lincoln 01522 539111

Jefferies Essex LLP
p428 Westcliff-on-Sea 01702 332311

Jeffreys & Powell
p156 Brecon 01874 622106

Jestyn Jeffreys
p320 Neath 01639 635641

Jewels Solicitors
p393 Stafford 01785 602030

Jones Myers LLP
p275 Leeds 0113 246 0055

T Llewellyn Jones
p405 Swansea 01639 842235

Jane Kaim-Caudle & Co
p423 Watford 01923 219061

Keene & Kelly
p318 Mold 01352 753882

Kelcey & Hall
p163 Bristol 0117 927 9604

Keoghs and Nicholls, Lindsell & Harris
p116 Altrincham 0161 928 9321

Christian Khan Solicitors
p49 London WC1 020 7631 9500

Kirby & Co
p50 London SW19 020 8545 7171

Kirby Sheppard
p268 Kingswood 0845 840 0045

Knowles Benning
p295 Luton 01582 798000

Kundert & Co
p200 Coventry 024 7668 4928

LD Law
p239 Harlow 01279 441266

Lamb & Kavanagh
p51 Camden 020 7209 2481

Leonard & Co
p386 Southampton 023 8023 3242
p386 Southampton 023 8023 4433

Keith Levin & Co
p258 Huyton 0151 480 5777

Leviten Thompson & Co
p376 Sheffield 0114 276 9321

Lichfield Reynolds
p398 Stoke-on-Trent 01782 313212

Linskills Solicitors
p289 Liverpool 0151 236 2224

Robert Lizar
p307 Manchester 0161 226 2319

Lloyd Platt & Co
p55 London N3 020 8343 2998

Llys Cennen Solicitors
p117 Ammanford 01269 592658 / 592790

Lock & Marlborough
p55 London W3 020 8993 7231

Roger Long & Co
p205 Croydon 020 8668 5071

Lumb & Macgill
p154 Bradford 01274 730666

Lyons Wilson
p307 Manchester 0161 830 7777

MWP Solicitors
p126 Basildon 01268 527131

McAras Solicitors LLP
p275 Leeds 0113 243 4333

Roberta McDonald
p140 Birmingham 0121 449 6821

McKinnells
p284 Lincoln 01522 541181

McManus Seddon
p154 Bradford 01274 741841

McMillan Williams Solicitors
p132 Bexleyheath 020 8303 0168

Madge Lloyd & Gibson
p230 Gloucester 01452 520224
p327 Newent 01531 820088

Martyn Prowel
p180 Cardiff 029 2047 0909

May May & Merrimans
p59 London WC1 020 7405 8932

Merry & Co
p369 Ryde 01983 811722

Mills Chody LLP
p265 Kenton 020 8909 0400

Mortons
p401 Sunderland 0191 514 4323

Motley & Hope
p133 Biggleswade 01767 600600

E J Moyle
p285 Littlehampton 01903 725143

Murrays
p148 Bodmin 01208 72863

Murrays Partnership
p62 Southwark 020 7701 8653

Myer Wolff
p257 Hull 01482 223693

NFLA Ltd
p192 Chesterfield 01246 471900
p338 Nottingham 0115 945 4555
p367 Rotherham 01709 373000
p376 Sheffield 0114 213 3888

Nalders Quality Solicitors
p223 Falmouth 01326 313441

Nicholls Christie & Crocker
p417 Uxbridge 01895 256216

Northwood Law Practice
p333 Northwood 01923 826208

Norton & Co
p259 Hyde 0161 366 8333

Norton Peskett
p294 Lowestoft 01502 533000

Nowell Meller Solicitors Limited
p393 Stafford 01785 252377

Nyland & Beattie
p432 Widnes 0151 424 5656

Oldhams Solicitors & Advocates
p121 Baldock 01462 895444

Overburys & Raymond Thompson
p335 Norwich 01603 610481

Oxford Law Group
p344 Oxford 01865 297300

Oxley & Coward Solicitors LLP
p367 Rotherham 01709 510999

Parkinson Wright LLP
p220 Evesham 01386 761176

Patterson Glenton & Stracey
p384 South Shields 0800 011 6487

Pearson Caulfield
p326 Newcastle upon Tyne 0191 261 8878

The Penhale Practice
p319 Morecambe 01524 401010

Penman Johnson
p424 Watford 01923 225212 / 239566

Percy Short & Cuthbert
p67 Islington 020 7700 0265

Sue Petritz
p253 Horsham 01403 790218

Philcox Gray & Co
p67 London SE15 020 7703 2285

Phillips & Co
p371 Salisbury 01722 321666

Samuel Phillips Law Firm
p326 Newcastle upon Tyne 0191 232 8451

Alister Pilling
p173 Camborne 01209 613800

Platt Halpern
p309 Manchester 0161 834 3114
p341 Oldham 0161 626 4955

Pluck Andrew & Co
p259 Hyde 0161 368 6311

Pond Marsh
p147 Blackpool 01253 620466

Porter Dodson
p444 Yeovil 01935 424581

Prester Coleman & Co
p332 Northampton 01604 633133

Punch Robson
p315 Middlesbrough 01642 230700

Gillian Radford & Co
p70 London W1 020 8960 4366

Ralph & Co
p329 Newquay 01637 872218

Ranson Houghton
p118 Andover 01264 351533

Ratcliffe Duce & Gammer LLP
p437 Wokingham 0118 978 3681

Red Kite Law
p183 Carmarthen 01267 239000

Redfearns
p246 Heckmondwike 01924 403745 / 404601

Richard Reed
p402 Sunderland 0191 567 0465

Richmond Anderson Goudie
p191 Chester-le-Street 0191 388 7884

Rickards & Cleaver
p115 Alfreton 01773 832204

Riley Hayes & Co
p438 Wolverhampton 01902 773666

Jane E Roberts
p332 Northampton 01604 494431

R P Robinson
p281 Leicester 0116 262 1462

Rollingsons
p73 London EC1 020 7611 4848

Rooks Rider
p73 London EC1 020 7689 7000

Rootes & Alliott
p227 Folkestone 01303 851100

Rudlings & Wakelam
p171 Bury St Edmunds 01284 755771
p410 Thetford 01842 754151

Runhams
p154 Bradford 01274 532233

Rupert Bear Murray Davies
p338 Nottingham 0115 924 3333

See p542 for the Firms Specialisations

Russell-Cooke LLP
p267 Kingston upon Thames 020 8546 6111

R A Savage & Co
p425 Welwyn Garden City 01707 373037

Seddon Thomson
p309 Manchester 0161 720 8000

Martin Sewell Family Law Solicitor & Advocate
p233 Gravesend 01474 323251

Sheehans Solicitors
p320 Neath 01639 630844

Sills & Betteridge LLP
p389 Spalding 01775 714874

Silver Fitzgerald
p175 Cambridge 01223 562001

Simpson Duxbury
p155 Bradford 01274 734166

Laurence Singer Solicitor
p117 Amersham 01494 431400

Sitters & Co
p350 Plymouth 01752 220464

The Skemp Partnership
p310
Manchester 0800 040 7566 / 0161 238 5400

Martin Smalley & Co
p339 Nottingham 0115 955 6555

Smith Brown & Sprawson
p295 Luton 01582 876900

The Smith Partnership
p398 Stoke-on-Trent 01782 324454

Southern Stewart & Walker
p384 South Shields 0191 427 0770

Sparling Benham & Brough
p227 Frinton-on-Sea 01255 679222

Spencer Skuse
p181 Cardiff 029 2034 3993

Spicketts Battrick Law Practice
p181 Cardiff 029 2046 1480
p352 Pontypridd 01443 407221

St Luce & Co
p82 London SE15 020 7635 9131

Stanley Tee LLP
p175 Cambridge 01223 311141

Stantons
p233 Gravesend 01474 579940

Linda Stapleton & Co
p230 Gloucester 01452 423870

Steel & Shamash
p82 Lambeth 020 7803 3999

Stevens
p244 Haverhill 01440 762511

Straw & Pearce
p293 Loughborough 01509 268931

Sugare & Co
p277 Leeds 0113 244 6978

John Swales
p119 Ashford 01233 732590

Swinburne & Jackson LLP
p229 Gateshead 0191 477 2531 / 477 3222

Switalski's
p419 Wakefield 01924 882000

R F Tansey
p410 Thame 01844 218000

Michael Taylor & Associates
p417 Urmston 0161 746 7776

Sharon Taylor Associates
p353 Poole 01202 759769

Thompson & Cooke LLP
p393 Stalybridge 0161 338 2614

Thompson Smith & Puxon
p198 Colchester 01206 574431

Thorpe & Co
p372 Scarborough 01723 364321

Tudur Owen Roberts Glynne & Co
p122 Bangor 01248 362315 / 355826
p251 Holyhead 01407 762374

Turbervilles
p417 Uxbridge 01895 231311

Vallelys
p283 Letchworth 01462 483800

Venters Solicitors
p89 London SE5 020 7277 0110
p363 Reigate 01737 229610

WBW Solicitors
p413 Torquay 0870 701 4321

Walters & Barbary
p173 Camborne 01209 712454

Warner Goodman LLP
p387 Southampton 023 8063 9311

Watson Solicitors
p422 Warrington 01925 571212

Kathy Webb & Co
p237 Guisborough 01287 633331

Welch & Co
p181 Cardigan 01239 614070

J B Wheatley & Co
p91 London SE8 020 8479 8000

Whiskers
p239 Harlow 01279 439439

Wholley Goodings LLP
p130 Bedlington 01670 824080

Williams MacDougall & Campbell
p442 Worthing 01903 214186

Williscroft & Co
p155 Bradford 01274 305380

Wills Chandler
p127 Basingstoke 01256 322911

Wilson Browne
p281 Leicester 0116 251 7181
p425 Wellingborough 01933 279000

Winterbotham Smith Penley LLP
p401 Stroud 01453 847200

Wiseman Lee LLP
p92 Waltham Forest 020 8215 1000

Wolferstans
p351 Plymouth 01752 401515

Wollen Michelmore Solicitors
p345 Paignton 01803 521692
p413 Torquay 01803 213251

Woodcocks
p121 Bacup 01706 874487
p171 Bury 0161 761 4611

Woodford Stauffer
p224 Farnborough 01252 375376

Woollcombe Yonge
p351 Plymouth 01752 660384

The Worcester Family Law Practice
p440 Worcester 01905 730900

William Wright & Son
p213 Dudley 01384 255344

Yates & Co
p339 Nottingham 0115 947 4486

Zermansky & Partners
p278 Leeds 0113 245 9766

CLINICAL NEGLIGENCE

Advance Legal
p170 Burton-on-Trent 01283 544492

Ameer Meredith
p174 Cambridge 01223 577077

Anthony Gold
p6 London SW16 020 7940 4000

Armstrong Foulkes
p314 Middlesbrough 01642 231110

Attwaters
p294 Loughton 020 8508 2111

Sarah Barclay & Co
p146 Blackpool 01253 356051

Barratt Goff & Tomlinson
p335 Nottingham 0115 931 5171

Bentley Solicitors
p203 Crewe 01270 509800

Bonallack & Bishop
p371 Salisbury 01722 422300

Bridge McFarland
p284 Lincoln 01522 518888

Bridge McFarland Haddon Owen
p294 Louth 01507 605883

Brindley Twist Tafft & James
p200 Coventry 024 7653 1532

Cadmans Law & Property
p195 Cleckheaton 01274 874231

Challinors
p136 Birmingham 0121 212 9393

Clark Willis
p206 Darlington 01325 281111

Collins Solicitors
p423 Watford 01923 223324

K J Commons & Co
p182 Carlisle 01228 822666
p431 Whitehaven 01946 66699
p440 Workington 01900 604698

Dale & Newbery LLP
p393 Staines 01784 464491

Davies & Partners
p115 Almondsbury 01454 619619
p137 Birmingham 0121 616 4450
p230 Gloucester 01452 612345

Dedicated Accident Solicitors
p208 Derby 01332 869286

Dicksons Solicitors Ltd
p397 Stoke-on-Trent 01782 262424

Donns
p303 Manchester 0161 834 3311

Dunn & Baker
p221 Exeter 01392 285000

Eastwoods Solicitors
p28 London EC4 020 3137 4800

S J Edney
p406 Swindon 0800 421234

Rebecca L Faret Solicitors
p226 Flitwick 01525 712112

Freemans
p324 Newcastle upon Tyne 0191 222 1030

GHP Legal
p342 Oswestry 01691 659194

Gadsby Wicks
p186 Chelmsford 01245 494929

Girlings Personal Injury Claims Limited
p177 Canterbury 01227 768374

David Gist Solicitors
p162 Bristol 0117 927 9111

Glynns Solicitors
p162 Bristol 01761 490883

Antony Gorley & Co
p322 Newbury 01635 551321

Graystons
p435 Wirral 0151 645 0055

Grieves Solicitors
p255 Huddersfield 01484 300192

Grindeys LLP
p397 Stoke-on-Trent 01782 846441

hlw Keeble Hawson LLP
p274 Leeds 0113 244 3121
p375 Sheffield 0114 272 2061

HRJ Law LLP
p251 Hitchin 01462 628888
p425 Welwyn Garden City 01707 887700

Harman & Harman
p39 London SW2 01227 452977

Harrowells
p444 York 01904 558600

Hempsons
p305 Manchester 0161 228 0011

Heptonstalls LLP
p231 Goole 01405 765661
p351 Pontefract 01977 602804
p351 Pontefract 01977 602804
p373 Scunthorpe 01724 289959

Hodge Jones & Allen LLP
p41 London NW1 020 7874 8300

Simon A Holt & Co
p357 Preston 01772 250871

Irwin Mitchell LLP
p139 Birmingham 0870 150 0100
p376 Sheffield 0870 150 0100

Ison Harrison
p274 Leeds 0113 284 5000

Jacobs & Reeves
p353 Poole 01202 674425
p433 Wimborne 01202 880382

Jobling Gowler
p297 Macclesfield 01625 614250

Keppe & Partners Solicitors
p416 Twickenham 020 8891 4488

Lanyon Bowdler LLP
p379 Shrewsbury 01743 280280

Lee & Priestley LLP
p275 Leeds 0845 129 2300

Lees Solicitors LLP
p134 Birkenhead 0151 647 9381

Leigh Day & Co
p52 London EC1 020 7650 1200

Lester Morrill
p275 Leeds 0113 245 8549

Linder Myers Solicitors
p306 Manchester 0844 984 6000

MPH Solicitors
p307 Manchester 0161 832 7722

McMillan Williams
p199 Coulsdon 020 8668 4131
p205 Croydon 01689 848311
p411 Thornton Heath 020 8653 8844

Maxwell Gillott (MG Law Ltd)
p270 Lancaster 0844 858 3900

Maxwell Hodge Solicitors
p268 Kirkby 0151 548 7370

Mayo Wynne Baxter LLP
p160 Brighton 01273 775533

Millan Solicitors
p154 Bradford 01274 660111

Morgan Jones & Pett
p335 Norwich 01603 877000

Morgans
p180 Cardiff 029 2072 9888

Pannone LLP
p308 Manchester 0161 909 3000

Parlett Kent
p222 Exeter 01392 494455
p66 London EC1 020 7430 0712

Preston Goldburn
p223 Falmouth 01326 318900

Raleys
p125 Barnsley 01226 211111

The Roland Partnership
p191 Chester 01244 659404

Rowbis Solicitors
p230 Gloucester 01452 301903

Russell Jones & Walker
p309 Manchester 0161 383 3500
p419 Wakefield 01924 234300

Russell-Cooke LLP
p74 London SW15 020 8789 9111

Scrivenger Seabrook
p392 St Neots 01480 214900

Sheridan & Co
p267 Kingston upon Thames 020 8541 1181

Shoosmiths
p127
Basingstoke 0370 086 6200 / 01256 696200

Smith Llewelyn Partnership
p405 Swansea 01792 464444

Stamp Jackson and Procter
p258 Hull 01482 324591

Stephensons Solicitors LLP
p432 Wigan 01942 777777

Sternberg Reed
p123 Barking 020 8591 3366

Peter Steward & Co
p234 Great Yarmouth 01493 332277

Swain & Co
p244 Havant 023 9248 3322
p386 Southampton 023 8063 1111

Thompsons (formerly Robin/Brian Thompson & Partners)
p165 Bristol 0117 304 2400
p181 Cardiff 029 2044 5300
p398 Stoke-on-Trent 01782 406200

Tozers
p222 Exeter 01392 207020

Trethowans LLP
p371 Salisbury 01722 412512

S V Wadsworth & Co
p383 Solihull 0121 745 8550

Walker Smith Way
p443 Wrexham 0844 346 3100

Wiseman Lee LLP
p92 Newham 020 8215 1000

Withy King Solicitors
p128 Bath 01225 425731

4

COMMERCIAL & COMPANY LAW

Aaron & Partners LLP Solicitors
p190 Chester 01244 405555

Abensons
p285 Liverpool 0151 733 3111

Able Bishop Ltd
p171 Bury St Edmunds 01359 245141

Ablitts
p3 Bromley 020 8776 8783

Acklam Bond Noor
p114 Accrington 01254 872272

Addies
p226 Fleetwood 01253 772128

Addlestone Keane Solicitors
p271 Leeds 0113 244 6700

Alexander Lawyers LLP
p186 Chelmsford 01245 216050

Allan Janes LLP
p249 High Wycombe 01494 521301

Allen Hoole Solicitors
p160 Bristol 0117 942 0901

Alsters Kelley
p270 Leamington Spa 0844 561 0100

Anderson & Company
p378 Shillingford 01865 858878

Andrew & Co LLP
p322 Newark 01636 673743

Angel & Co
p6 London W1 020 7495 0555

Anthony Gold
p6 London SE1 020 7940 4000

Apfel Carter
p296 Lytham 01253 725265 / 712216

Armitage Sykes LLP
p255 Huddersfield 01484 538121

Arnold Fooks Chadwick LLP
p7 London W1 020 7499 3007

Arscotts
p254 Hove 01273 735289

Ashfords LLP
p160 Bristol 0117 321 8000
p220 Exeter 01392 337000
p7 London W1 020 3581 8970
p408 Taunton 01823 232300

Askew Bunting Solicitors LLP
p314 Middlesbrough 01642 252555

Astle Paterson Ltd
p170 Burton-on-Trent 01283 531366

Atherton Godfrey
p211 Doncaster 01302 320621

Atkins Bassett
p250 Hinckley 01455 632685

Atkinson Ritson
p181 Carlisle 01228 525221

Awdry Bailey & Douglas
p173 Calne 01249 815110
p210 Devizes 01380 722311

BLB Solicitors
p413 Trowbridge 01225 755656

B P Collins LLP
p229 Gerrards Cross 01753 889995

BWTLaw LLP
p219 Epsom 01372 725655

Baily Gibson
p249 High Wycombe 01494 442661

Baines Wilson LLP
p181 Carlisle 01228 552600

Bakewells
p208 Derby 01332 348791

Banner Jones
p191 Chesterfield 01246 560560

Bannister Bates Property Lawyers
p318 Morecambe 01524 416300

Barker Gillette
p9 London W1 020 7636 0555

Barker Gotelee Solicitors
p262 Ipswich 01473 611211

Barlow Robbins LLP
p235 . . . Guildford 01483 562901
p436 . . . Woking 01483 748500

Barrett & Co Solicitors LLP
p359 . . . Reading 0118 958 9711

Batchelor Myddelton
p355 . . . Potters Bar 01707 647088

Batchelors Solicitors
p166 . . . Bromley 020 8768 7000

Baxter Caulfield
p255 . . . Huddersfield 01484 519519

T G Baynes
p132 . . . Bexleyheath 020 8301 7777

Beale and Company Solicitors LLP
p11 . . . London WC2 020 7240 3474

Bell & Buxton
p375 . . . Sheffield 0114 249 5969

Bell & Co
p402 . . . Sutton 020 8661 8611

Harold Benjamin
p241 . . . Harrow 020 8422 5678

Bennett Griffin
p225 . . . Ferring 01903 229999
p441 . . . Worthing 01903 229925

Paul Berg & Taylor
p239 . . . Harpenden 01582 760161

Bermans LLP
p301 . . . Manchester 0161 827 4600

Berry Smith LLP
p157 . . . Bridgend 01656 645525
p177 . . . Cardiff 029 2034 5511

Berwin Leighton Paisner LLP
p12 . . . London EC4 020 7760 1000

Berwins Solicitors Limited
p240 . . . Harrogate 01423 509000

Betesh Partnership
p301 . . . Manchester 0161 834 2623

Bevan Brittan LLP
p161 . . . Bristol 0870 194 1000
p12 . . . London EC4 0870 194 1000

Bevan Kidwell
p12 . . . London EC1 020 7843 1820

Bhakar Tomlinson
p425 . . . Wellington 01952 270555

Bignalls
p12 . . . London W1 020 7637 3071

Birchall Blackburn LLP
p356 . . . Preston 01772 561663

Bircham Dyson Bell
p13 . . . London W1 020 7227 7000

Birkett Long LLP
p186 . . . Chelmsford 01245 453800
p197 . . . Colchester 01206 217300

Birketts LLP
p262 . . . Ipswich 01473 232300

Biscoes
p348 . . . Petersfield 01730 264799
p354 . . . Portsmouth 023 9266 0261

Black Norman
p203 . . . Crosby 0151 931 2777

Blackhams Solicitors
p135 . . . Birmingham 0121 233 6900

Blake Lapthorn
p184 . . . Chandlers Ford 023 8090 8090
p342 . . . Oxford 01865 248607
p354 . . . Portsmouth 023 9222 1122

Blandy & Blandy
p360 . . . Reading 0118 951 6800

Blocks
p225 . . . Felixstowe 01394 283241
p262 . . . Ipswich 01473 230033

Julian Bloom & Co
p171 . . . Bushey 020 8950 3001

Blythe Liggins
p270 . . . Leamington Spa 01926 831231

Boodle Hatfield
p14 . . . London W1 020 7629 7411
p343 . . . Oxford 01865 790744

Bower & Bailey
p122 . . . Banbury 01295 265566

Boyce Hatton
p412 . . . Torquay 01803 403403

Boyes Turner
p360 . . . Reading 0118 959 7711

Brabners Chaffe Street
p286 . . . Liverpool 0151 600 3000
p301 . . . Manchester 0161 836 8800

Bracher Rawlins LLP
p15 . . . London WC1 020 7404 9400

Brachers
p299 . . . Maidstone 01622 690691

Bray & Bray
p279 . . . Leicester 0116 254 8871

Breeze & Wyles Solicitors LLP
p248 . . . Hertford 01992 558411

Brethertons LLP
p122 . . . Banbury 01295 270999
p368 . . . Rugby 01788 579579

Bridge McFarland
p235 . . . Grimsby 01472 311711
p297 . . . Mablethorpe 01507 478285
p312 . . . Market Rasen 01673 843723

Brignalls Balderston Warren
p269 . . . Knebworth 01438 812374

Brindley Twist Tafft & James
p200 . . . Coventry 024 7653 1532

Bristows
p15 . . . London EC4 020 7400 8000

Brittons
p128 . . . Beaconsfield 01494 730722

Brockmans
p395 . . . Stockbridge 01264 810910

Brook Oliver
p321 . . . New Milton 01425 616809

Brooke North LLP
p272 . . . Leeds 0113 283 2100

Brooks & Partners
p173 . . . Camberley 01276 681217

BrookStreet des Roches LLP
p114 . . . Abingdon 01235 836600

Broomhall & Co
p136 . . . Birmingham 0121 633 4868

Browne Jacobson LLP
p16 . . . London EC3 020 7539 4900

Bryan & Armstrong
p311 . . . Mansfield 01623 626039

Buckles Solicitors LLP
p346 . . . Peterborough 01733 888888

Burkill Govier
p224 . . . Farnham 01252 717171

Robin Burman & Co
p302 . . . Manchester 0161 860 7123

Burr Sugden
p263 . . . Keighley 01535 605407

Kenneth Bush
p266 . . . King's Lynn 01553 692233

Buss Murton LLP
p202 . . . Cranbrook 01580 712215
p415 . . . Tunbridge Wells 01892 510222

Butcher & Barlow LLP
p369 . . . Runcorn 01928 572268

CKFT
p17 . . . London NW3 020 7431 7262

CMS Cameron McKenna LLP
p162 . . . Bristol 0117 930 0200
p17 . . . London 020 7367 3000

CVS Solicitors
p17 . . . London W1 020 7493 2903

Christopher Cox Solicitors
p331 . . . Northampton 01604 882287

Camerons Jones
p241 . . . Harrow 020 8423 6666

Cannings Connolly
p18 . . . London EC1 020 7329 9000

Capsticks Solicitors LLP
p18 . . . London SW19 020 8780 2211

Carrington & Associates
p18 . . . London EC4 020 7822 1855

Carter Bells LLP
p267 . Kingston upon Thames 020 8939 4000

Castles
p258 . Hurstpierpoint 01273 836007 / 837107

Cathcarts
p259 . . . Ickenham 01895 631942 / 675631

James Chan & Co
p19 . . . London EC4 0844 848 9988

Chandler Harris LLP
p302 . . . Manchester 0161 834 2200

Chaplin & Co
p394 . . . Stanmore 020 8954 8202

Charles Russell LLP
p187 . . . Cheltenham 01242 221122
p235 . . . Guildford 01483 252525
p19 . . . London EC4 020 7203 5000
p343 . . . Oxford 0845 359 0090

Charsley Harrison LLP
p434 . . . Windsor 01753 851591

Chattertons Solicitors
p151 . . . Boston 01205 351114
p284 . . . Lincoln 01522 814600

Francis H Chenery
p210 . . . Diss 01379 644055

Claremont Richards
p20 . . . London EC4 020 7353 3030

Clark Holt
p406 . . . Swindon 01793 617444

Clarke Willmott
p162 . Bristol 0845 209 1000 / 0117 305 6000
p408 Taunton 0845 209 1000 / 0117 305 6000

ClarksLegal LLP
p177 . . . Cardiff 029 2055 7500
p20 . . . London WC2 020 7539 8000
p360 . . . Reading 0118 958 5321
p405 . . . Swansea 0118 958 5321

Clarkson Wright & Jakes Ltd
p341 . . . Orpington 01689 887887

Clifton Ingram LLP
p437 . . . Wokingham 0118 978 0099

Cloney & Co
p296 . . . Lytham 01253 712116

Clough & Willis
p170 . . . Bury 0161 764 5266

Clyde & Co LLP
p21 . . . London EC3 020 7623 1244

Cobbetts LLP
p302 . . . Manchester 0845 404 2404

Coffin Mew & Clover
p385 . . . Southampton 023 8033 4661

Colborne Coulman & Lawrence
p328 . . . Newport 01633 264194 / 264196

Colemans
p245 . . . Haywards Heath 01444 459555

Colemans Solicitors LLP
p298 . . . Maidenhead 01628 631051

Anthony Collins Solicitors LLP
p137 . . . Birmingham 0121 200 3242

Collins Benson Goldhill LLP
p21 . . . London W1 020 7436 5151

Collyer Bristow LLP
p22 . . . London WC1 020 7242 7363

Conway & Co
p247 . . . Henley-on-Thames 01491 411122

CooperBurnett
p415 . . . Tunbridge Wells 01892 515022

Cornfield Law
p215 . . . Eastbourne 01323 412512

Cottrill Stone Lawless
p302 . . . Manchester 0161 835 3681

Cox Cooper Limited
p137 . . . Birmingham 0121 777 0015

Dudley Cramp & Co
p380 . . . Sittingbourne 01795 420024

Crane & Staples
p425 . . . Welwyn Garden City 01707 329333

Cripps Harries Hall LLP
p415 . . . Tunbridge Wells 01892 515121

David Cross & Co
p411 . . . Thornbury 01454 419696

Crowell & Moring
p23 . . . London EC4 020 7413 0011

Cruickshanks Solicitors
p23 . . . London W1 020 7487 4468

Crutes
p182 . . . Carlisle 01228 525195
p324 . . Newcastle upon Tyne 0191 233 9700
p396 . . . Stockton-on-Tees 01642 623400

Cumberland Ellis Peirs
p23 . . . London WC1 020 7242 0422

Curry Popeck
p24 . . . London W1 020 7224 6633

Curwens
p218 . . . Enfield 020 8363 4444
p420 . . . Waltham Abbey 01992 712549

DAC Beachcroft
p303 . . . Manchester 0161 934 3000
p328 . . . Newport 0844 980 0400

DBL Talbots LLP
p437 . . . Wolverhampton 01902 427561

DFA Law LLP
p331 . . . Northampton 01604 609560

DMB Law
p374 . . . Sevenoaks 01732 228800

DWF
p287 . . . Liverpool 0151 907 3000
p303 . . . Manchester 0161 603 5000

DWT Legal Ltd
p265 . . . Kidderminster 0844 770 3799

Dakers Marriott Solicitors
p400 . . . Strood 01634 813300

Simon Daly Solicitors
p396 . . . Stockton-on-Tees 01642 604074

Darling & Stephensons
p123 . . . Barnard Castle 01325 489000
p206 . . . Darlington 01325 489000

Darlingtons
p217 . . Edgware 020 8952 0033 / 8951 6666

Davenport Lyons
p25 . . . London W1 020 7468 2600

Aubrey David
p25 . . . London W1 020 7224 4410

David Conway & Co
p26 . . . London W1 020 7258 3000

Christopher Davidson Solicitors LLP
p188 . . . Cheltenham 01242 581481

Davidson Large LLP
p240 . . . Harrogate 01423 727272

Paul Davidson Taylor
p253 . . . Horsham 01403 262333

George Davies Solicitors LLP
p303 . . . Manchester 0161 236 8992

W Davies
p436 . . . Woking 01483 744900

Davis Blank Furniss
p303 . . . Manchester 0161 832 3304

J F Dawson
p129 . . . Beaconsfield 01494 670566

Dean Wilson Laing
p159 . . . Brighton 01273 327241

Denison Till
p444 . . . York 01904 611411

Dickens & Co
p204 . . Crowthorne 01344 772901 / 776151

Dickinson Manser
p352 . . . Poole 01202 673071

Dodd Lewis Solicitors
p27 . . . London SE3 020 8852 1255

Dolmans
p178 . . . Cardiff 029 2034 5531

Dootsons LLP
p282 . . . Leigh 01942 673431

Dowse Baxter
p27 . . . London SW19 020 8946 9110

Brian Drewitt
p395 . . . Stockport 0845 260 0855

Duane Morris
p28 . . . London EC1 020 7786 2100

Duchennes
p130 . . . Bedford 01234 356678

Duffield Harrison LLP
p251 . . . Hoddesdon 01992 442911

Dyne Drewett Solicitors Ltd
p378 . . . Shepton Mallet 01749 342323

ELC Solicitors
p28 . . . Ealing 020 8566 4045

EMW
p316 . . . Milton Keynes 0845 070 6000

Eaton Smith LLP
p255 . . . Huddersfield 01484 821300

Edwin Coe LLP
p29 . . . London WC2 020 7691 4000

Thomas Eggar LLP
p192 . . . Chichester 01243 786111
p202 . . . Crawley 01293 742700
p29 . . . London EC4 020 7842 0000
p441 . . . Worthing 01903 234411

Elborne Mitchell LLP
p29 . . . London EC3 020 7320 9000

Ellis-Fermor & Negus
p130 . . . Beeston 0115 922 1591

Enoch Evans LLP
p420 . . . Walsall 01922 720333

Evans Dodd LLP
p30 . . . London W1 020 7491 4729

Everett Tomlin Lloyd & Pratt
p352 . . . Pontypool 01495 763333

FBC Manby Bowdler LLP
p379 . . . Shrewsbury 01743 241551
p437 . . . Wolverhampton 01902 578000

FDC Law
p228 . . . Frome 01373 463311

Farleys Solicitors LLP
p145 . . . Blackburn 01254 367855

Fasken Martineau LLP
p31 . . . London W1 020 7917 8500

Fentimans
p269 . . . Knowle 01564 779459

Field Fisher Waterhouse LLP
p31 . . . London EC3 020 7861 4000

Field Seymour Parkes
p360 . . . Reading 0118 951 6200

Fieldings Porter
p149 . . . Bolton 01204 540900

Finers Stephens Innocent LLP
p32 . . . London W1 020 7323 4000

D Fisher & Co
p150 . . . Borough Green 01732 884299

Fisher Jones Greenwood LLP
p186 . . . Chelmsford 01245 890110

Fishers
p118 . . . Ashby-de-la-Zouch 01530 412167

Fladgate LLP
p32 . . . London WC2 020 3036 7000

Thomas Flavell & Sons
p250 . . . Hinckley 01455 610747

Follett Stock LLP
p414 . . . Truro 01872 241700

Foot Anstey
p221 . . . Exeter 01392 411221

Forbes
p145 . . . Blackburn 01254 54374

Forbes Hall LLP
p439 . . . Woodford Green 020 8498 0080

Foreman Laws
p251 . . . Hitchin 01462 458711

Forshaws Davies Ridgway LLP
p422 . . . Warrington 01925 230000

Forth & Co
p443 . . . Yarm 01642 784000

Foskett Marr Gadsby & Head
p219 . . . Epping 01992 578642

Peter J Fowler
p433 . . . Wimborne 01202 849242

Scott Fowler
p331 . . . Northampton 01604 750506

Fox Williams
p33 . . . London EC2 020 7628 2000

Francis Law LLP
p296 . . . Lydney 01594 842242

Franks & Co
p34 . . . London EC4 020 7242 8008

Fraser Brown
p337 . . . Nottingham 0115 933 5311

Fraser Dawbarns
p435 . . . Wisbech 01945 461456

Richard Freeman & Co
p34 . . Kensington & Chelsea 020 7351 5151

Freeth Cartwright LLP
p279 . . . Leicester 0116 248 1100

Fruhman Davies Livingstones
p304 . . . Manchester 0161 833 0578

Fuglers
p34 . . . London W1 020 7323 6450

FullagarBrooks
p406 Swindon 01793 777007

GHP Legal
p442 Wrexham 01978 291456

GLP Solicitors
p304 Manchester 0161 834 6721

GPB Solicitors LLP
p400 Stratford-upon-Avon 01789 261131

GPT Solicitors
p426 Wembley 020 8904 6495 / 8904 6598

Gannons Limited
p35 Camden 020 7438 1060

Gardner Croft LLP
p176 Canterbury 01227 813400

Garner Hutchings
p35 London W1 020 7932 2400

Gartsides
p113 Abergavenny 01873 857555
p328 Newport 01633 213411

Gateley LLP
p138 Birmingham 0121 234 0000

Geldards LLP
p178 Cardiff 029 2023 8239
p337 Nottingham 0115 983 3650

George & Co
p171 Bury St Edmunds 01449 737582

Mark Gilbert Morse
p325 Newcastle upon Tyne 0191 261 0096

Gill Turner Tucker
p299 Maidstone 01622 759051

Gillespies
p420 Walsall 01922 627474

Gisby Harrison
p189 Cheshunt 01707 878300

Goldring & Co
p359 Rainham 01634 260012

David Goodman & Co
p36 London W1 020 7323 3369

Gordons
p36 London WC1 020 7421 9421

Gordons LLP
p273 Leeds 0113 227 0100

Gorvins
p395 Stockport 0161 930 5151

Gosschalks
p256 Hull 01482 324252

Gotelee
p262 Ipswich 01473 211121

Goughs
p199 Corsham 01249 712193

Grant Saw Solicitors LLP
p36 Greenwich 020 8858 6971

George Green LLP
p201 Cradley Heath 01384 410410

Greene & Greene
p171 Bury St Edmunds 01284 762211

Greenwoods Solicitors LLP
p347 Peterborough 01733 887700

Gregory Abrams Davidson LLP
*p37*London NW11 020 8209 0166 / 8458 9322

Gregory Rowcliffe Milners
p37 London WC1 020 7242 0631

Griffith Smith Farrington Webb
p159 Brighton 01273 324041

Grindeys LLP
p397 Stoke-on-Trent 01782 846441

Guest & Co
p205 Cuckfield 01444 413731

Gullands
p299 Maidstone 01622 678341

Guy Williams Layton
p288 Liverpool 0151 236 7171

HCB Solicitors
p284 Lichfield 01543 414426
p420 Walsall 01922 720000

HC Solicitors LLP
p347 Peterborough 01733 882800

HKB Wiltshires
p234 Great Yarmouth 01493 855676

hlw Keeble Hawson LLP
p274 Leeds 0113 244 3121
p375 Sheffield 0114 272 2061

HM Law
p437 Wokingham 0118 977 1718

HSR Law (Hayes, Son & Richmond)
p211 Doncaster 01302 347800
p228 Gainsborough 01427 613831

Hacking Ashton LLP
p323 Newcastle under Lyme 01782 715555

Hadfield & Co
p424 Welling 020 8301 0808

Hague & Dixon
p444 York 01904 627111

Hague Lambert
p305 Manchester 0161 834 6066

Hall Reynolds
p133 Bidford-on-Avon 01789 772955

Hall Smith Whittingham LLP
p320 Nantwich 01270 610300

Hall Ward & Fox
p429
Weston-super-Mare 01934 626656 / 626657

Hamilton Davies
p394 Stevenage 01438 315898

Hamilton Pratt
p422 Warwick 01926 838900

Hamlins LLP
p38 London W1 020 7355 6000

Hammond Bale
p38 London W1 020 7499 7624

Harbottle & Lewis LLP
p38 London W1 020 7667 5000

Harding Evans LLP
p328 Newport 01633 244233

Gaby Hardwicke
p243 Hastings 01424 438011

Harris & Harris
p228 Frome 01373 463366

Brian Harris & Co
p39 London W1 020 7935 5541

Harris Cartier LLP
p39 London WC2 020 7405 7100
p382 Slough 01753 810710

Harrison Clark LLP
p439 Worcester 01905 612001

Harrisons Solicitors LLP
p425 Welshpool 01938 552545

Harrowells
p444 York 01904 690111

Hart Brown Solicitors
p236 Guildford 0800 068 8177

Hart Jackson Hall Smith
p325 Newcastle upon Tyne 0191 261 5181

Hartlaw LLP
p429 Wetherby 01937 547000

Harvey Ingram Borneos
p130 Bedford 01234 353221
p317 Milton Keynes 01908 696002

Hatchers Solicitors LLP
p379 Shrewsbury 01743 248545

C H Hausmann & Co
p39 London W1 020 7436 6333

Haworth & Nuttall
p145 Blackburn 01254 272640

Haworth Holt Bell Limited
p116 Altrincham 0161 928 7136

Hayes & Storr
p223 Fakenham 01328 863231

Edward Hayes LLP
p192 Chichester 01243 672124

Heald Solicitors
p317 Milton Keynes 01908 662277

Heath Buckeridge
p298 Maidenhead 01628 671636

Hegarty LLP
p347 Peterborough 01733 346333

R W Hemmings & Co
p408 Taunton 01823 325090

Hempsons
p240 Harrogate 01423 522331

Henmans LLP
p343 Oxford 01865 781000

Hewetts
p361 Reading 0118 957 5337

Higgs & Sons
p158 Brierley Hill 0845 111 5050

Hill Dickinson LLP
p190 Chester 01244 896600
p288 Liverpool 0151 600 8000
p41 London EC3 020 7283 9033
p305 Manchester 0161 817 7200

Hillyer McKeown LLP
p129 Bebington 0151 645 4255
p190 Chester 01244 318131

Hindle Campbell
p330 North Shields 0191 296 1777

Hipkin & Co
p431 Whitley Bay 0191 253 3509

John Hodge Solicitors
p163 Bristol 0117 929 2281

Holdens
p264 Kendal 01539 720629

Holroyd & Co
p256 Huddersfield 01484 645464

Hopkins
p311 Mansfield 01623 468468

Frank Howard
p422 Warrington 01925 653481

Richard Howard & Co LLP
p43 London WC2 020 7831 4511

Howell-Jones LLP
p267 Kingston upon Thames 020 8549 5186

Hudson & Co
p43. London WC1 020 7405 4812 / 7831 3282

Huggins & Lewis Foskett
p43 Redbridge 020 8989 3000

Hugh James
p179 Cardiff 029 2022 4871

A L Hughes & Co
p43 London SW16 020 8769 7100

Humphries Kirk
p212 Dorchester 01305 251007
p352 Poole 01202 725400

Hunt & Morgan
p179 Cardiff 029 2034 1234

Ilett & Clark Solicitors
p441 Worksop 01909 500544

Ince & Co Services Ltd
p44 London E1 020 7481 0010

Ingram Winter Green
p45 Camden 020 7845 7400

Insley & Partners
p152 Bournemouth 01202 510167

Irvings
p289 Liverpool 0800 954 0243

Irwin Mitchell LLP
p139 Birmingham 0870 150 0100
p274 Leeds 0870 150 0100
p376 Sheffield 0870 150 0100

Isadore Goldman Solicitors
p45 London EC4 020 7353 1000

JW Law
p433 Wimborne 01202 690658

Jacobs & Reeves
p353 Poole 01202 731849
p433 Wimborne 01202 880382

Jacobsen & Co
p46 London SW6 020 7736 6277

Jaffe Porter Crossick
p46 London NW6 020 7625 4424

David Jeacock
p439 Wootton Bassett 01793 854111

Jefferies Essex LLP
p428 Westcliff-on-Sea 01702 332311

Jobling & Knape
p269 Lancaster 01524 598300
p319 Morecambe 01524 416960

Jolliffe & Co
p190 Chester 01244 310022

Jones Day
p46 London EC4 020 7039 5959

Judge & Priestley
p166 Bromley 020 8290 0333

Judge Sykes Frixou
p47 London WC2 020 7379 5114

KSH Law Firm
p325 Newcastle upon Tyne 0191 232 5232

Keelers
p264 Kenilworth 01926 853555

Keelys LLP
p284 Lichfield 01543 420000

Kemp Little LLP
p48 London EC2 020 7600 8080

Howard Kennedy LLP
p48 London W1 020 7636 1616

Keogh Caisley
p415 Tunbridge Wells 01892 548411

Keoghs LLP
p149 Bolton 01204 677000

Kerman & Co LLP
p49 London WC2 020 7539 7272

Kidson Bray & Lawson
p49 London SE11 020 7582 0111

Kilroys
p139 Birmingham 0121 270 1002

Kimbells LLP
p317 Milton Keynes 01908 668555

Kingsley Napley
p50 London EC1 020 7814 1200

Kirby Sheppard
p163 Bristol 0845 840 0045

Kirklands
p366 Romsey 01794 513466
p413 Totton 023 8066 3313

Kirwans
p134 Birkenhead 0151 608 9078

Kyriakides & Braier
p50 London W1 020 7637 3289

Laderman & Co
p51 Redbridge 020 8530 7319

Ladermans
p51 London NW4 020 8203 6136

Lambe Corner
p248 Hereford 01432 355301

Lamport Bassitt
p361 Reading 0845 077 6600
p386 Southampton 023 8083 7777

Langleys
p284 Lincoln 01522 888555

Lanyon Bowdler LLP
p342 Oswestry 01691 652241

Last Cawthra Feather LLP
p154 Bradford 01274 848800

Latimer Hinks
p206 Darlington 01325 341500

Lawson Coppock & Hart
p306 Manchester 0161 832 5944

Laytons
p236 Guildford 01483 407000
p52 London EC4 020 7842 8000
p306 Manchester 0161 834 2100

Lee & Thompson
p52 London W1 020 7935 4665

Lee Bolton Monier-Williams
p52 London W1 020 7222 5381

Leeds Day
p258 Huntingdon 01480 454301
p392 St Ives 01480 464600
p392 St Neots 01480 474661

Lennons
p189 Chesham 01494 773377

Lennox Bywater
p53 London NW7 020 8906 1206

Lester Aldridge LLP
p53 London WC2 0844 967 0785

Lewis & Co
p53 London NW4 020 8202 4343

Lock & Marlborough
p55 London W3 020 8993 7231

Longs Solicitors
p412 Tonbridge 01732 360895

Loosemores
p179 Cardiff 029 2022 4433

Lupton Fawcett
p275 Leeds 0113 280 2000

Peter Lynn & Partners
p319 Morriston 01792 310731

Lyons Davidson
p321 New Malden 020 8336 6900

Lyons Wilson
p307 Manchester 0161 830 7777

MFG Solicitors
p409 Telford 01952 641651

MLM Cartwright
p179 Cardiff 029 2046 2562

M Law
p55 London W1 020 7927 6240

MSP Legal Services LLP
p243 Hartlepool 01429 232204

MacDonald Oates LLP
p316 Midhurst 01730 816711

McEwen Parkinson
p56 London W1 020 7487 4361

McGrigors LLP
p56 London EC4 020 7054 2500

Machins Solicitors LLP
p295 Luton 01582 514000

Brian Mackenow & Co
p401 Sunderland 0191 565 6262

Mackrell Turner Garrett
p57 London WC2 020 7240 0521
p437 Woking 01483 755609

Maclay Murray & Spens LLP
p57 London EC2 020 7002 8500

MacRae & Co LLP
p57 Southwark 020 7378 7716

Maitland Walker
p318 Minehead 01643 707777

Manches LLP
p343 Oxford 01865 722106

Maples Solicitors LLP
p389 Spalding 01775 722261

O M Marks & Co
p58 Barnet 020 8371 6689

Veronique Marot & Co
p275 Leeds 0113 258 2021

Marriott Davies Yapp
p402 Sutton 020 8643 9794

Marriott Harrison
p59 London WC1 020 7209 2000

Marsden Rawsthorn LLP
p194 Chorley 01257 279511
p357 Preston 01772 799600

Marshall Hall & Levy
p384 South Shields 0191 455 3181

Martin-Kaye LLP
p409 Telford 01952 272222

Matthew Arnold & Baldwin LLP
p423 Watford 01923 202020

Maunsell Bower
p59 Wandsworth 020 7378 9592

Max Gold Law
p257 Hull 01482 224900

Maxwell Hodge Solicitors
p289 Liverpool 0151 526 9321

May May & Merrimans
p59 London WC1 020 7405 8932

Mayo Wynne Baxter LLP
p283 Lewes 01273 477071

Memery Crystal
p60 London WC2 020 7242 5905

Menneer Shuttleworth
p392 St Leonards-on-Sea 01424 720044

Merritt & Co
p443 Yarm 01642 885555

Metcalfe Copeman & Pettefar
p410 Thetford 01842 756100
p435 Wisbech 01945 464331

Metcalfe Johnston McCormick
p216 Eccles 0161 789 3481 / 788 9021

Metcalfes
p164 Bristol 0117 929 0451

Michael Conn Goldsobel
p60 London W1 020 7580 8902

Michelmores LLP
p221 Exeter 01392 688688

Neil Millar & Co Solicitors
p307 Manchester 0161 870 0177

C M Miller Solicitors
p124 Barnet 020 8449 6151

Mills Chody LLP
p265 Kenton 020 8909 0400

4

Mincoffs Solicitors LLP
p325 . . Newcastle upon Tyne 0191 281 6151
Minter Ellison
p61. . . . . . . London EC2 020 7448 4800
Mogers
p127 . . . . .Bath 01225 750000
Molesworths Bright Clegg
p365 . . . . Rochdale 01706 356666
H Montlake & Co
p260 . . . . Ilford 020 8532 4800
Moorcrofts LLP
p313 . . . . Marlow 01628 470000
Moore Blatch Solicitors
p386 . . . . Southampton 023 8071 8000
Moorhead James LLP
p61. . . . . . . London EC4 020 7831 8888
Morgan Cole
p180 . . . . Cardiff 029 2038 5385
p405 . . . . Swansea 01792 634634
Morgan Walker
p62. . . . . . . London WC2 020 7831 8333
Nicholas Morris
p62. . . . . London W11 020 7792 0890
Morrisons Solicitors LLP
p362 . . . . .Redhill 01737 854500
John Morse Solicitors
p405 . . . . Swansea 01792 648111
Morton Price
p376 . . . . Sheffield 0114 266 4141
Morton Solicitors
p214 . . . . Dunstable 01582 501240
Moss Solicitors LLP
p293 . . . . . . Loughborough 01509 217770
Muckle LLP
p325 . . Newcastle upon Tyne 0191 211 7777
Mundays LLP
p196 . . . . .Cobham 01932 590500
D J Murphy Solicitors
p180 . . . . Cardiff 029 2022 1300
Warren Murton
p62. . . . . London WC1 020 7404 5511
Myers Fletcher & Gordon
p62. . . . . London W6 020 7610 4433
Nabarro LLP
p376 . . . . Sheffield 0114 279 4000
Napthens LLP
p145 . . . . Blackburn 01254 667733
p357 . . . . Preston 01772 888444
Nautadutilh
p63. . . . . . . London EC2 020 7786 9100
Neale Turk
p127 . . . . . . Basingstoke 01256 473013
Ned Nwoko
p63. . . . . Ealing 020 8997 6733
Neil Myerson LLP
p117 . . . . Altrincham 0161 941 4000
Nellen
p63. . . . . . . London W1 020 7499 8122
Nelsons
p338 . . . . Nottingham 0115 958 6262
Ian Newbery & Co
p353 . . . . Poole 01202 669986
Newsome Vaughan LLP
p200 . . . . Coventry 024 7663 3433
Nicholsons Solicitors LLP
p294 . . . . Lowestoft 01502 532300
Nightingales Solicitors Limited
p396 . . . . Stockport 01663 764038
North Ainley Halliwell
p341 . . . . .Oldham 0161 624 5614
Norton Peskett
p294 . . . . Lowestoft 01502 533000
O'Neill Patient
p396 . . . . Stockport 0161 483 8555
ORJ Solicitors LLP
p393 . . . . Stafford 01785 223440
Oglethorpe Sturton & Gillibrand
p270 . . . . Lancaster 01524 846846
Openshaws
p132 . . . . Bideford 01237 478900
Ormerods
p205 . . . . Croydon 020 8686 5000
Osborne Clarke
p164 . . . . .Bristol 0117 917 3000
p65. . . . . London EC2 020 7105 7000
p361 . . . . Reading 0118 925 2000
Osmond & Osmond
p65. . . . . London EC4 020 7583 3434
Oury Clark
p65. . . . . London WC1 020 7607 4300
Ouvry Goodman & Co
p403 . . . . Sutton 020 8642 7571
Overburys & Raymond Thompson
p335 . . . . Norwich 01603 610481
Oxley & Coward Solicitors LLP
p367 . . . . Rotherham 01709 510999
P B & W Solicitors LLP t/a Pooley Bendall & Watson
p218 . . . . Ely 01353 666075
Palmers
p126 . . . . .Basildon 01268 240000
p233 . . . . Grays 01375 484444
p384 . South Woodham Ferrers 01245 322111

Parfitt Cresswell
p65. . . . . London SW6 020 7381 8311
Paris Smith LLP
p386 . . . . . . Southampton 023 8048 2482
Parker Bullen
p118 . . . . Andover 01264 400500
Parkes Wilshire Johnson
p124 . . . . Barnet 020 8441 1556
Parkinson Wright LLP
p440 . . . . .Worcester 01905 726789
Parry Law
p248 . . . . .Herne Bay 01227 361131
p431 . . . . Whitstable 01227 276276
Payne Hicks Beach
p66. . . . . . . London WC2 020 7465 4300
Pemberton Greenish LLP
p66. . . . . . . London SW3 020 7591 3333
M Pender
p437 . . . . Woking 01932 352653
Penningtons
p127 . . . . Basingstoke 01256 407100
p231 . . . . Godalming 01483 791800
p66. . . . . London EC2 020 7457 3000
Perry Hay & Co
p364
. . . Richmond upon Thames 020 8940 8115 / 8332 7532
Phillips Solicitors
p127 . . . . Basingstoke 01256 460830
Pickering & Butters
p393 . . . . Stafford 01785 603060
Pickerings LLP
p407 . . . . Tamworth 01827 317070
Pictons Solicitors LLP
p247 . . . .Hemel Hempstead 01442 242441
p295 . . . . Luton 01582 870870
p317 . . . . Milton Keynes 01908 663511
Pini Franco LLP
p67. . . . . London EC1 020 7566 3140
Pinsent Masons LLP
p276 . . . . .Leeds 0113 244 5000
p67. . . . . London EC2 020 7418 7000
Piper Smith Watton LLP
p68. . . . . London SW1 020 7222 9900
Pitmans LLP
p361 . . . . Reading 0118 958 0224
Pittalis & Co
p68. . . . . London N12 020 8446 9555
Charles Platel Solicitors
p437 . . . . .Wokingham 0118 978 4866
Poole Alcock
p372 . . . . Sandbach 01270 762325
Preiskel & Co LLP
p69. . . . . London EC4 020 7583 2120
Preston-Rouse & Co
p69. . . . . Camden 020 7269 9020
Pricketts
p172 . . . . Buxton 01298 22874
Pritchard Englefield
p69. . . . . London EC2 020 7972 9720
Quality Solicitors Clarke & Son
p127 . . . . Basingstoke 01256 320555
Quality Solicitors Copley Clark
p122 . . . . Banstead 01737 362131
QualitySolicitors Hill & Abbott
p187 . . . . Chelmsford 01245 258892
RJR Solicitors
p328 . . . . Newport 01983 526924
RMPI Solicitors
p70. . . . . London W1 020 7318 4444
Donald Race & Newton
p169 . . . . Burnley 01282 433241
Radcliffes Le Brasseur
p70. . . . . London W1 020 7222 7040
Ralli Solicitors
p309 . . . . Manchester 0870 998 9000
Ramsdens Solicitors
p318 . . . . Mirfield 01924 499251
Ransons
p421 . . . Walton-on-Thames 01932 269448
Rawlings Giles
p71. . . . . .London SW11 020 7223 2765
Rawlins Davy PLC
p152 . . . . Bournemouth 01202 558844
Rawlison Butler LLP
p202 . . . . Crawley 01293 527744
Raworths LLP
p240 . . . . Harrogate 01423 566666
Redferns
p430 . . . Weymouth 01305 781401 / 782704
Reed Smith LLP
p71. . . . . London EC2 020 3116 3000
Reston's Solicitors Limited
p422 . . . . Warrington 0870 755 8998
Reynolds Parry-Jones
p250 . . . . High Wycombe 01494 525941
Rich & Carr Freer Bouskell
p281 . . . . Leicester 0116 253 8021
Richardson & Davies
p201. . . . . Coventry 024 7622 2001
Rickerbys LLP
p188 . . . . Cheltenham 01242 224422

Stephen Rimmer LLP
p216 . . . . Eastbourne 01323 644222
Roach Pittis
p328 . . . . .Newport 01983 524431
The Robert Davies Partnership
p329 . . . . .Newport 01633 413500
Roberts Buckley
p309 . . . . .Manchester 0161 835 1234
Robinsons
p261 . . . . Ilkeston 0115 932 4101
Rollingsons
p73. . . . . London EC1 020 7611 4848
Ronald Fletcher Baker LLP
p73. . . . . London EC1 020 7613 1402
Rooks Rider
p73. . . . . London EC1 020 7689 7000
Richard Rooney & Co
p73. . . . . Merton 020 8947 8024
Rosenblatt
p73. . . . . London EC4 020 7955 0880
Ross & Craig
p73. . . . . London W1 020 7262 3077
Roys
p182 . . . . Carlisle 01228 526385
Rudlings & Wakelam
p171 . . . . Bury St Edmunds 01284 755771
Russell-Cooke LLP
p74. . . . . . . .London SW15 020 8789 9111
Russells
p75. . . . . London W1 020 7439 8692
SA Law
p390 . . . . St Albans 01727 798000
SAS Daniels LLP
p396 . . . . Stockport 0161 475 7676
SJ Berwin LLP
p75. . . . . London EC4 020 7111 2222
SNR Denton
p75. . . . . London EC4 020 7242 1212
p317 . . . . Milton Keynes 01908 690260
Salehs LLP
p309 . . . . .Manchester 0161 434 9991
Saunders Law Partnership LLP
p76. . . . . . . London WC2 020 7632 4300
Scaiff LLP
p440 . . . . Worcester 01905 727700
J P Scholes
p121 . . . . Bamford 01433 651625
Seddons
p77. . . . . London W1 020 7725 8000
Brian L Senter
p399 . . . . Stourbridge 01384 375649
Shakespeares
p142 . . . . . . .Birmingham 0121 237 3000
p400 . . . Stratford-upon-Avon 0845 630 8833
Shammah Nicholls LLP
p309 . . . . .Manchester 0161 832 9272
Shoosmiths
p224 Fareham 0370 086 6800 / 01489 616800
p332
. Northampton 0370 086 3000 / 01604 543000
p361 Reading 0370 086 8000 / 0118 965 8765
Short Richardson & Forth LLP
p326 . . Newcastle upon Tyne 0191 232 0283
Shulmans
p276 . . . . .Leeds 0113 245 2833
Sidhu & Co
p142 . . . . Birmingham 07831 293903
Silverman Sherliker LLP
p78. . . . . London EC2 020 7749 2700
Simpson Duxbury
p155 . . . . .Bradford 01274 734166
Ian Simpson & Co
p341 . . . . .Oldham 0161 622 4939
Sims Cook & Teague
p165 . . . . .Bristol 0117 927 2141
Singletons
p349 . . . . Pinner 020 8866 1934
Sintons LLP
p326 . . Newcastle upon Tyne 0191 226 7878
Slater Heelis Collier Littler
p370 . . . . Sale 0161 969 3131
Slee Blackwell
p125 . . . . .Barnstaple 01271 372128
Martyn Slocombe & Co
p300 . . . . Malvern 01684 574001
The Smith Partnership
p209 . . . . Derby 01332 225225
Snowball Worthy Lowe
p402 . . . . Sunderland 0191 565 3221
Solicitors Direct
p155 . . . . .Bradford 01274 776000
Solomon Taylor & Shaw
p80. . . . . London NW3 020 7431 1912
Spearing Waite LLP
p281 . . . . Leicester 0116 262 4225
Spratt Endicott
p122 . . . . .Banbury 01295 204000
Squire Sanders (UK) LLP
p142 . . . . .Birmingham 0121 222 3000
p277 . . . . .Leeds 0113 284 7000
Stafford Young Jones
p82. . . . . London EC4 020 7623 9490

James Stallard & Co
p82. . . . . London WC2 020 7430 1861
Stallard March & Edwards
p440 . . . . Worcester 01905 613404
Hugh Staunton
p232 . . . . Grantham 01476 861972
Steele Raymond
p152 . . . . Bournemouth 01202 294566
Steeles
p335 . . . . .Norwich 0870 609 0200
Stephens & Scown
p222 . . . . .Exeter 01392 210700
p391 . . . . St Austell 01726 74433
Lawrence Stephens
p82. . . . . London EC1 020 7935 1211
Stephensons Solicitors LLP
p282 . . . . Leigh 01942 777777
p432 . . . . Wigan 01942 777777
Steptoe & Johnson
p83. . . . . London EC2 020 7367 8000
Wade Stevens & Co
p342 . . . . Orpington 01689 831122
stevensdrake
p202 . . . . Crawley 01293 596900
Harold Stock & Co
p120 . . . Ashton-under-Lyne 01457 838136
Stones Solicitors LLP
p222 . . . . .Exeter 01392 666777
Stork & Coles
p84. . . . . London WC1 020 7404 6021
Storrar Cowdry
p191 . . . . Chester 01244 400567
Svedberg Law
p84. . . . . London SW1 020 7368 7000
Sydney Mitchell
p142
. Birmingham 0121 698 2200 / 0808 166 8827
Sylvester Mackett
p414 . . . . Trowbridge 01225 755621
TBI Solicitors
p243
. . Hartlepool 0800 052 6824 / 01429 264101
Talbot Walker LLP
p118 . . . . Andover 01264 363354
Tanner & Taylor LLP
p115 . . . . Aldershot 01252 316565
Taylor Walton LLP
p295 . . . . Luton 01582 731161
Taylors
p146 . . . . .Blackburn 0844 800 0263
p310 . . . . .Manchester 0844 800 0263
Temple & Co Commercial Solicitors
p207 . . . . Daventry 0845 241 4045
Thompson Smith & Puxon
p198 . . . . .Colchester 01206 574431
Thompsons (formerly Robin/Brian Thompson & Partners)
p87. . . . . London SW19 020 8947 4163
Thomson Webb & Corfield
p176 . . . . Cambridge 01223 578070
Andrew Thorne & Co
p374 . . . . Shaw 01706 290488
Thorp Parker LLP
p398 . . . . Stokesley 01642 711354
Thrings LLP
p165 . . . . .Bristol 0117 930 9500
p406 . . . . .Swindon 01793 410800
Thursfields
p266 . . . . Kidderminster 01562 820575
p440 . . . . Worcester 01905 730450
Tinn Criddle & Co
p389 . . . . Spilsby 01790 756810
Tinsdills
p372 . . . . Sandbach 01270 761111
Tolhurst Fisher LLP
p187 . . . . Chelmsford 01245 495111
p387 . . . . Southend-on-Sea 01702 352511
Toller Beattie LLP
p125 . . . . .Barnstaple 01271 341000
Trethowans LLP
p387 . . . . Southampton 023 8032 1000
Turbervilles
p417 . . . . .Uxbridge 01895 231311
Turner Coulston
p333 . . . . Northampton 01604 622101
Turner Parkinson
p310 . . . . .Manchester 0161 833 1212
Vance Harris
p89. . . . . London E14 020 7538 5232
P R Vince Solicitors
p227 . . . . Forest Row 01342 822112
Waldrons
p158 . . . . Brierley Hill 01384 811811
Wallace Robinson & Morgan
p383 . . . . Solihull 0121 705 7571
Walsh & Company
p414 . . . . Truro 01872 870923
Ward Hadaway
p327 . . Newcastle upon Tyne 0191 204 4000
Ware & Kay LLP
p445 . . . . York 01904 716000
Warner Goodman LLP
p387 . . . . Southampton 023 8063 9311

See p542 for the Firms Specialisations

Warners Solicitors
p374 Sevenoaks 01732 747900
p412 Tonbridge 01732 770660
Watson Burton LLP
p327 Newcastle upon Tyne 0845 901 2100
Wedlake Bell LLP
p91 London WC1 020 7395 3000
Weightmans LLP
p207 Dartford 020 7822 1900
p311 Manchester 0161 233 7330
Wellers Law Group LLP
p167 Bromley 020 8464 4242
p91 London WC1 020 7242 7265
Wheelers
p115 Aldershot 01252 316316
Whiskers
p239 Harlow 01279 439439
Whitehead Monckton
p299 Maidstone 01622 698000
Whittingdales
p91 London WC2 020 7831 5591
Wilde & Co
p321 Neston 0151 353 1899
The Wilkes Partnership LLP
p143 Birmingham 0121 233 4333
Wilkin Chapman Epton Blades
p285 Lincoln 01522 512345
Wilkin Chapman LLP
p235 Grimsby 01472 262626
Wilkinson & Butler
p392 St Neots 01480 219229
Willans LLP
p189 Cheltenham 01242 514000
Willett & Co
p171 Bury St Edmunds 01284 701323
Williamson & Soden
p143 Birmingham 0121 333 4848
Malcolm A H M Williamson
p225 Farnham 0845 230 1022
Wilsons Solicitors LLP
p371 Salisbury 01722 412412
Winder Taylor Fallows
p150 Bolton 01204 389908 / 522888
Winterbotham Smith Penley LLP
p401 Stroud 01453 847200
Wise Geary
p122 Banbury 01295 278500
Withers LLP
p92 London EC4 020 7597 6000
Withy King Solicitors
p128 Bath 01225 425731
Wolferstans
p351 Plymouth 01752 663295
Wollen Michelmore Solicitors
p413 Torquay 01803 213251
Woodcocks
p243 Haslingden 01706 213356
Woodford Stauffer
p224 Farnborough 01252 375376
Woodroffes
p93 London W1 020 7730 0001
Woolf Simmonds
p93 London W1 020 7262 1266
Woollastons
p404 Sutton Coldfield 0121 355 5516
Woolley & Co
p423 Warwick 01789 267377
Woolsey Morris & Kennedy
p380 Sidcup 020 8300 9321
Wosskow Brown
p377 Sheffield 0114 256 1560
Wright Son & Pepper LLP
p93 Camden 020 7242 5473
Wrigley Claydon
p341 Oldham 0161 624 6811
p412 Todmorden 01706 815712
Wycombe Hurd & Co
p93 London WC2 020 7925 0313
Yugin & Partners
p394 Stanmore 020 8954 2410
Zermansky & Partners
p278 Leeds 0113 245 9766
Zimmers
p94 London NW11 0870 770 0171

COMMERCIAL CONVEYANCING

Ablitts
p3 Bromley 020 8776 8783
Acklam Bond Noor
p145 Blackburn 01254 56068
Alan Turner & Co
p127 Bath 01225 336260
Aldridge Brownlee Solicitors LLP
p151 Bournemouth 01202 526343
Alen-Buckley & Co
p4 Wandsworth 020 8767 8336
Alexander Marks LLP
p5 London W1 020 7317 1166
Amphlett Chatterton
p270 Leamington Spa 01926 311427
Anami Law Incorporating Kirkwoods
p171 Bushey 020 8950 1155
Michael Anderson & Co
p430 Whickham 0191 488 1221
R W Anderson & Co
p6 London W1 020 7323 4520
Andrew & Co LLP
p284 Lincoln 01522 512123
p322 Newark 01636 673743
Anthony Gold
p6 London SW16 020 7940 4000
Anthony Holden Crofts & Co
p156 Brentford 020 8568 7768
p6 Ealing 020 8840 7878
Appleby Shaw
p434 Windsor 01753 860606
Grant Argent & Co
p7 Brent 020 8452 7651
Argyles
p407 Tamworth 01827 56276
Armitage Sykes LLP
p255 Huddersfield 01484 538121
Arnold & Co
p340 Oldbury 0121 552 2382
Arnold Deacon Greene & Co
p381 Sleaford 01529 414414
Arscotts
p254 Hove 01273 735289
Malcolm Ashton
p223 Falmouth 01326 313100
Austin Ryder & Co
p8 Enfield 020 8804 5111
Bailey & Bailey
p315 Middlesbrough 01642 240991
Bailey & Cogger
p412 Tonbridge 01732 353305
Bailey Morgan & Co
p380 Skegness 01754 768383 / 763007
Banks Carrington & Co
p146 Blackpool 01253 622269 / 315223
Banner Jones
p375 Sheffield 0114 275 5266
Barker Gooch & Swailes
p9 London N21 020 8886 5928 / 8886 5734
Barlows
p278 Leicester 0116 251 8295
Barnes & Partners
p10 Haringey 020 8801 0085
Barnes Richards Rutter
p189 Chepstow 01291 628898
Bathurst Brown Downie & Airey LLP
p416 Twickenham 020 8892 1537
T G Baynes
p207 Dartford 01322 295555
John Bays & Co
p11 Haringey 020 8881 3609
Beesons
p316 Milton Keynes 01908 271171
Bells Solicitors
p224 Farnham 01252 733733
Harold Benjamin
p241 Harrow 020 8422 5678
Berkson Wallace Solicitors
p217 Ellesmere Port 0151 355 4412
p419 Wallasey 0151 691 6900
Berry Redmond & Robinson
p429 Weston-super-Mare 01934 513963
Bevis Rowntree
p315 Midhurst 01730 812201
Bignalls
p12 London W1 020 7637 3071
Bilton Hammond LLP
p311 Mansfield 01623 675800
Bishop & Co
p313 Marple 0161 427 1441 / 427 5543
Blackhurst Swainson Goodier LLP
p356 Preston 01772 253841
Blake Lapthorn
p342 Oxford 01865 248607
Bonnetts Solicitors LLP
p431 Whitton 020 8898 2022
Bookers & Bolton
p116 Alton 01420 82881 / 88903
Borneo Hughes Martell LLP
p331 Northampton 01604 624822
Bower & Bailey
p406 Swindon 01793 610466
Bowers
p15 London NW2 020 8455 9881
R M Brett & Co
p177 Cardiff 029 2023 0440
Brian Ruff Angus & Jewers
p431 Wickford 01268 761126
C M Broadbent
p297 Macclesfield 01625 500038
Brockmans
p395 Stockbridge 01264 810910
Brown & Co
p126 Basildon 01268 243610
Peter Brown & Co Solicitors LLP
p124 Barnet 020 8447 3277
Philip Brown & Co
p16 London W1 020 7935 7235 / 7935 7270
Brown-Hovelt Veale Nelson
p233 Grayshott 01428 607433
Brutton & Co
p223 Fareham 01329 236171
Bryan & Armstrong
p311 Mansfield 01623 626039
Burch Phillips & Co
p427 West Drayton 01895 442141
Burley & Geach
p233 Grayshott 01428 605355
Robin Burman & Co
p302 Manchester 0161 860 7123
Burr Sugden
p263 Keighley 01535 605407
Burrows
p241 Harrow 020 8904 7725 / 8904 4150
Burtonwoods
p16 London WC1 020 7636 2448
Butcher & Barlow LLP
p155 Bramhall 0161 439 8228
Thomas Butler & Son
p167 Broughton-in-Furness 01229 716336
p316 Millom 01229 772553
Callaghan & Co
p17 London W1 020 7486 8173
Calvert Solicitors
p17 Southwark 020 7234 0707
Henry Cane & Son
p159 Brighton 01273 604091
Irving Caplin & Co
p18 Wandsworth 020 8874 7633
Carlsons
p18 London N20 020 8445 3331 / 8445 5752
Carter Bells LLP
p267 Kingston upon Thames 020 8939 4000
Cedars & Co
p19 Greenwich 020 8331 6161
Lee Chadwick & Co
p436 Witney 01993 703272
Chafes
p433 Wilmslow 01625 531676
Chamberlins
p172 Caister-on-Sea 01493 720019
Chattertons Solicitors
p151 Boston 01205 351114
p322 Newark 01636 673731
Francis H Chenery
p210 Diss 01379 644055
Chequers Solicitors Ltd
p245 Hayes 020 8606 1000
Chestnutts
p114 Ainsdale 01704 572221
Chesworths
p397 Stoke-on-Trent 01782 599992
p397 Stoke-on-Trent 01782 599993
Chhokar & Co
p384 Southall 020 8574 2488
Chisholms
p418 Wadebridge 01208 812470 / 814205
Chung & Platt
p302 Manchester 0161 228 6777
Churchers
p223 Fareham 01329 822333
p232 Gosport 023 9260 3400
Claremont Richards
p20 London EC4 020 7353 3030
Clifford Smith & Buchanan
p198 Colne 01282 860606
p320 Nelson 01282 693182
Clifton Ingram LLP
p437 Wokingham 0118 978 0099
Cloney & Co
p296 Lytham 01253 712116
Colemans - CTTS
p124 Barnet 020 8441 1213
Collins Dryland & Thorowgood LLP
p411 Tilehurst 0118 942 2448
Collis & Co
p22 Wandsworth 020 8767 3332
George Mitchell Colman & Co
p137 Birmingham 0121 427 7700
Comptons
p22 Camden 020 7485 0888
Coodes
p270 Launceston 01566 770000
p391 St Austell 01726 874700
Cook & Talbot
p388 Southport 01704 535216
Cooke Painter Limited
p162 Bristol 01275 835569
Corbin & Hassan
p22 London 020 7247 6518
Cornwells
p153 Bradford 01274 675631
Courtyard Solicitors LLP
p23 London SW19 020 8946 9466
Cozens-Hardy LLP
p334 Norwich 01603 625231
Crabtree Chadwick
p358 Pudsey 0113 290 9499
Cramer Pelmont
p23 London N8 020 8340 0091
Cross Ram & Co
p237 Halesworth 01986 873636
Cruickshanks Solicitors
p23 London W1 020 7487 4468
Curwens
p218 Enfield 020 8363 4444
DB Law
p173 Camborne 01209 712428
DFA Law LLP
p331 Northampton 01604 609560
DJK Solicitors
p420 Waltham Abbey 01992 718880
Dale-Lace & Co
p129 Beaconsfield 01494 675269
Marie Dark Solicitors
p189 Chepstow 01291 621638
Darlington Hardcastles
p364 Rickmansworth 01923 774272
Aubrey David
p25 London W1 020 7224 4410
David Conway & Co
p26 London W1 020 7258 3000
Davies Prichard & Weatherill
p178 Cardiff 029 2037 7471
Davis & Co
p259 Ilford 020 8551 4228
Davis-Law Associates
p184 Chalfont St Peter 01753 888776
Davitt Jones Bould
p408 Taunton 01823 279279
Stanley De Leon
p355 Potters Bar 01707 657277
Dickins Hopgood Chidley LLP
p258 Hungerford 01488 683555
Dickinson Wood
p211 Doncaster 01302 329504
Dickson Haslam
p268 Kirkham 01772 685109
p356 Preston 01772 883100
Dixon Coles & Goddard
p279 Leicester 0116 236 4708
Dodd Lewis Solicitors
p27 London SE3 020 8852 1255
Donaldson Dunstall
p131 Bexhill 01424 216329
Donaldson West
p204 Crowborough 01892 662233
Downey & Co
p153 Bradford 01274 883515
Downs
p231 Godalming 01483 861848
Brian Drewitt
p395 Stockport 0845 260 0855
Drivers
p300 Malton 01653 600075
Scott Duff & Co
p265 Keswick 01768 774321
Dutton Gregory
p385 Southampton 023 8022 1344
Dyne Drewett Solicitors Ltd
p378 Shepton Mallet 01749 342323
p433 Wincanton 01963 32374
Eastleys
p166 Brixham 01803 853266
Eaves
p316 Milford Haven 01646 695785
Eckford Rands
p331 Northampton 01604 621001
Alan Edwards & Co
p28 Kensington & Chelsea 020 7221 7644
Edwards Duthie
p260 Ilford 020 8514 9000
Martin Edwards
p378 Shifnal 01952 462118
Nigel Edwards & Co
p299 Maidstone 01622 690575
B K Ellis & Co
p150 Borehamwood 020 8386 8686
Ellis-Fermor & Negus
p364 Ripley 01773 744744
Elmhirst Parker LLP
p124 Barnsley 01226 282238
p273 Leeds 01977 682219
Emrys Jones & Co
p425 Welshpool 01938 552510
Enever Freeman & Co
p368 Ruislip 01895 634031
p369 Ruislip 01895 676385 / 676386
Shirley M Evans
p232 Grange-over-Sands 01539 535208
Everett Tomlin Lloyd & Pratt
p352 Pontypool 01495 763333
F B Jevons Riley & Pope
p216 Edenbridge 01732 864411
Farnworth Shaw
p198 Colne 01282 864081
John Farr-Davies & Co
p182 Carmarthen 01267 231818
Fendom Dawson & Partners
p250 High Wycombe 01494 450361
Fischer & Co
p32 Barnet 020 8346 7036 / 8922 0689

D Fisher & Co
p150 Borough Green 01732 884299
Fisher Jones Greenwood LLP
p186 Chelmsford 01245 890110
Fishman & Co Solicitors
p32 London W1 020 7935 3500
Fitzgerald-Harts
p150 Boroughbridge 01423 322312
Foot Anstey
p408 Taunton 01823 625600
Footner & Ewing
p366 Romsey 01794 512345
Ford Banks Irwin
p304 Manchester 0161 866 8999
Forman Welch & Bellamys
p416 Twickenham 020 8892 8907 / 8892 7733
Forth & Co
p443 Yarm 01642 784000
Foskett Marr Gadsby & Head
p294 Loughton 020 8502 3991
Foster Harrington
p173 Camberley 01276 692233
Peter J Fowler
p433 Wimborne 01202 849242
Franklins LLP
p332 Northampton 01604 828282
Freedman Green Dhokia
p34 Camden 020 7625 6003
Freeman Johnson
p214 Durham 0191 386 4843 / 386 9619
Richard Freeman & Co
p34 Kensington & Chelsea 020 7351 5151
Friis & Radstone
p394 Stevenage 01438 741001
Frodshams
p391 St Helens 01744 626600
Fuglers
p34 London W1 020 7323 6450
Fulchers of Farnborough
p224 Farnborough 01252 522475
Furse Sanders & Co
p383 South Molton 01769 572251
Fussell Wright
p162 Bristol 0117 927 9117
D W Gallifant
p428 West Mersea 01206 383050
Gamlins
p363 Rhyl 01745 343500
Garner Hutchings
p35 London W1 020 7932 2400
Gattas Denfield Solicitors
p35 London NW9 020 8204 7181
Gavins Solicitors
p35 London N6 020 8374 4459
Gedye & Sons (Solicitors) Ltd
p232 Grange-over-Sands 01539 532313
Geoffrey Morris & Ashton
p318 Mold 01352 754711
p442 Wrexham 01978 291322
Jeremy Gibbs & Co
p117 Amersham 01494 724671
Girlings
p119 Ashford 01233 664711
Goodhand and Forsyth QualitySolicitors
p362 Redhill 01737 773533
R Gordon Roberts Laurie & Co
p129 Beaumaris 01248 810210 / 810532
Gordons
p36 London WC1 020 7421 9421
H F T Gough & Co
p431 Whitehaven 01946 692461
Green Wright Chalton Annis
p118 Arundel 01903 881122
p369 Rustington 01903 774131
p441 Worthing 01903 700220
Greenland Houchen Pomeroy
p443 Wymondham 01953 606351
Greens
p294 Ludlow 01584 873918
Greenways
p329 Newquay 01637 872361 / 872251
Gregg Latchams LLP
p162 Bristol 0117 906 9400
Grigsby Eddleston & Co
p394 Stevenage 01438 742525
Gross & Curjel
p438 Woodbridge 01394 383436
HSK Solicitors
p149 Bolton 01204 526465
HSR Law (Hayes, Son & Richmond)
p228 Gainsborough 01427 613831
Hadgkiss Hughes & Beale
p139 Birmingham 0121 707 8484
p139 Birmingham 0121 778 2161
Hague & Dixon
p444 York 01759 371634
Hague Lambert
p269 Knutsford 01565 652411
Hanratty & Co
p330 Newtown 01686 626239
Hargreaves & Co
p305 Manchester 0161 445 6461
Harold G Walker
p194 Christchurch 01202 482202
Chris Harrison Law
p414 Truro 01872 241408
Harvey Copping & Harrison
p431 Wickford 01268 733381 / 763211
Harvey Son & Filby
p262 Ipswich 01473 712962
Hatchers Solicitors LLP
p379 Shrewsbury 01743 248545
Heath Buckeridge
p298 Maidenhead 01628 671636
Heckford Norton
p283 Letchworth 01462 682244
Hedleys & Co
p401 Sunderland 0191 567 0101
Hellewell Pasley & Brewer
p128 Batley 01924 472596
Henleys
p126 Basingstoke 01256 840084
Henriques Griffiths
p163 Bristol 0117 965 9444
M R Hepburn
p403 Sutton Coldfield 0121 378 0440
Hepburns
p344 Oxted 01883 723712
Heppenstalls
p296 Lyndhurst 023 8028 2885
Herbert & Cholmeley
p122 Banbury 01295 263556
Heringtons
p128 Battle 01424 772401
p243 Hastings 01424 434192
Hetts Johnson Whiting
p158 Brigg 01652 655101
Hileys
p215 Easingwold 01347 821234
Geoffrey Hill & Co
p250 Hinckley 01455 637715
Paul Hills & Co
p193 Chichester 01243 671782
Hodders
p41 London NW10 020 8965 9862
Holden Son & Ullock
p411
Thornton Cleveleys 01253 852613 / 862606
Horsey Lightly
p322 Newbury 01635 580858
Horsey Lightly Fynn
p152 Bournemouth 01202 551991
Hotchkiss Warburton
p203 Crediton 01363 774752
Houseman Benner
p246 Haywards Heath 01444 414081
Howard & Company
p43 London W1 020 7486 6610
Fiona M Howard
p43 London NW1 020 7482 2705
Howard Stone
p43 London EC1 020 7490 5900
Howarth & Co
p429 Wetherby 01937 584020
The Howe Practice
p395 Stockport 0161 480 2629
Geoffrey Hueting & Co
p127 Bath 01225 465828
Hugh Cartwright & Amin
p43 London WC1 020 7632 4200
Humfrys & Symonds
p248 Hereford 01432 359261 / 276276
V L Humphreys & Co
p236 Guildford 01483 574342
Humphries Kirk
p152 Bournemouth 01202 421111
p404 Swanage 01929 423301
Hunters
p44 London WC2 020 7412 0050
Hutcheson Forrest
p127 Bath 01225 312311
Insley & Partners
p225 Ferndown 01202 876117
Irvings
p241 Harrow 020 8427 6600
Isherwood & Hose
p365 Rochdale 01706 359090 / 522225
Ives & Co
p337 Nottingham 0115 937 2408
Jackson & Co
p143 Birstall 0116 267 6263
Jackson Brierley Hudson Stoney
p365 Rochdale 01706 644187 / 649214
Jacksons
p435 Wirral 0151 632 3386
Jacobs & Reeves
p353 Poole 01202 674425
Stanley Jacobs
p46 Barnet 020 8349 4241
Jameson & Hill
p421 Ware 01920 460531
Walter Jennings & Sons
p46 London NW5 020 7485 8626
Jeromes
p328 Newport 01983 522664
Jeya & Co
p46 Newham 020 8552 1999
Jones & Co
p363 Retford 01777 703827
W T Jones
p47 London WC1 020 7405 4631 / 7242 7767
Jordans
p418 Wakefield 01924 387110
K&L Gates LLP
p47 London EC4 020 7648 9000
Kaura & Co
p48 London N12 020 8445 4069
Leon Kaye Solicitors
p48 London SW11 020 7228 2020
Kellock & Johnson
p329 Newton Abbot 01626 335454
Kelly & Co
p275 Leeds 0113 244 2113
Richard P Kemp BA Solicitor
p313 Martock 01935 822572
Kendall & Davies
p168 Burford 01993 822025
p319 Moreton-in-Marsh 01608 650312
p399 Stow-on-the-Wold 01451 830295
Kennards Wells
p219 Epping 01992 570505
Kenneth Elliott & Rowe
p366 Romford 01708 757575
Kenwright Walker Wyllie
p215 East Molesey 020 8979 1131
Keogh Caisley
p415 Tunbridge Wells 01892 548411
Khan & Co
p438 Wolverhampton 01902 424477
Kidd Rapinet
p121 Aylesbury 0845 017 9616
p49 London WC2 020 7205 2115
p361 Reading 0845 017 8750
King Solicitors
p384 Southall 020 8571 2239
Kloosmans
p387 Southend-on-Sea 01702 600090
Krish Ratna
p384 Southall 020 8574 6303
Robert Kyle & Co
p313 Marlow 01628 475751
B D Laddie
p51 London W1 020 7963 8585
Lancasters
p219 Epsom 01372 724931
p51 London W4 020 8742 1314
Land Law LLP
p116 Altrincham 0161 928 8383
Langley Wellington
p195 Churchdown 01452 856846
Lattey & Dawe
p51 London EC2 020 7623 2345
Lavery Haynes
p51 London NW3 020 7435 7441
H Lawrence & Co
p52 London N6 020 7482 2613 / 7482 4212
Lawson Turner & Gilbert
p213 Dover 01304 226338
Leach Rawlence & Hart
p205 Croydon 020 8680 5850
Leech & Co
p306 Manchester 0161 279 0279
The Legal Practice Solicitors
p426 Wembley 020 8903 7017
Wayne Leighton
p217 Edgware 020 8951 2988
P S Levy & Co
p53 London W1 020 7486 7717
Lewis & Co
p53 London NW4 020 8202 4343
Lewis & Dick
p202 Crawley 01293 526031
Lewis Francis Blackburn Bray
p376 Sheffield 0114 272 9721
Lin & Co Solicitors
p140 Birmingham 0121 244 2300
p403 Sutton Coldfield 0121 244 2300
Lithman & Co
p55 London W1 020 7935 2212
Livingstone & Co
p307 Manchester 0161 833 0578
Livingstons
p416 Ulverston 01229 585555
M V Lloyd
p224 Fareham 023 9228 0944
p355 Portsmouth 023 9238 6757
Lorrells LLP
p55 London EC1 020 7681 8888
Lu Oliphant Solicitors
p217 Edgware 020 8238 2822
Richard Ludlow & Co
p400 Stratford-upon-Avon 01789 552872
Geoffrey Lurie
p325 Newcastle upon Tyne 0191 232 1800
Elaine McGloin
p215 East Grinstead 01342 328000
Brian Mackenow & Co
p401 Sunderland 0191 565 6262
McKenzie Bell Solicitors
p401 Sunderland 0191 567 4857
Mackrell Turner Garrett
p437 Woking 01483 476022
McNair & Co
p57 Hammersmith & Fulham 020 7371 7896
McPhersons
p57 Ealing 020 8840 9017
MacRae & Co LLP
p57 Southwark 020 7378 7716
Macrory Ward
p124 Barnet 020 8440 3258
Maddocks Clarke
p117 Altrincham 0844 805 5170
Thomas Magnay & Co
p430 Whickham 0191 488 7459 / 488 7766
Maher & Co
p298 Maidenhead 01628 675239
Manuel Swaden
p58 London NW6 020 7431 4999
Saul Marine & Co
p58 London NW7 020 8959 3611
Veronique Marot & Co
p275 Leeds 0113 258 2021
Marsden Duncan
p134 Birchington 01843 295743 / 841161
p196 Cliftonville 01843 295741
Marshall Hall & Levy
p384 South Shields 0191 455 3181
Martin Tolhurst Partnership LLP
p233 Gravesend 01474 325531
Martin-Kaye LLP
p409 Telford 01952 272222
Mason Baggott & Garton
p158 Brigg 01652 654111
p219 Epworth 01427 872661
Matthew & Matthew Limited
p387 Southbourne 01202 431943
T A Matthews
p248 Hereford 01432 352121
F W Meggitt & Co
p376 Sheffield 0114 272 7955
Merriman Waine & Co
p348 Pewsey 01672 563666
Metcalfe Copeman & Pettefar
p347 Peterborough 01733 865880
Miller Evans & Co
p60 London 020 7987 2515
Miller Lyons Solicitors
p230 Glastonbury 01458 833660
Peter J Miller
p60 Wandsworth 0870 321 7561
Mills & Co
p119 Ashton-in-Makerfield 01942 719655
Mills Chody LLP
p244 Hatch End 020 8428 2272
George Mills
p423 Washington 0191 416 2182
Geoffrey Milne
p438 Wolverhampton 01902 373000
Minaides Robson
p61 London EC4 020 7831 7761
J B Moloney & Co
p280 Leicester 0116 230 1950
Montlake & Co
p122 Banstead 01737 352211
Morris & Bates
p114 Aberystwyth 01970 625566
Morrish Solicitors LLP
p443 Yeadon 0113 250 7792
E J Moyle
p369 Rustington 01903 784447
Warren Murton
p62 London WC1 020 7404 5511
Leonard B G Muscat
p232 Gosforth 0191 285 8510
Mylles & Co
p402 Sunninghill 01344 623388
N Legal
p404 Sutton Coldfield 0121 355 8885
Nahlis Christou
p63 London WC1 020 7278 6888
Nelsons
p410 Tenterden 01580 767100
Neves Solicitors
p239 Harpenden 01582 715234
Neville-Jones & Co
p404 Swanage 01929 422666 / 423761
Newstead & Walker
p342 Otley 01943 461414
Newtons
p63 Camden 020 7794 9696 / 7435 5351
Nicholls Christie & Crocker
p242 Harrow 020 8863 6366
Nightingales Solicitors Limited
p396 Stockport 01663 764038
Norris & Miles
p409 Tenbury Wells 01584 810575
Oberman Law
p64 Camden 020 7242 6154
Oglethorpe & Broatch
p265 Keswick 01768 772125

See p542 for the Firms Specialisations

Owen White & Catlin
p225 Feltham 020 8890 2836
P B & W Solicitors LLP t/a Pooley Bendall & Watson
p218 Ely 01353 666075
p218 Ely 01638 780170
Parfitt Cresswell
p65 London SW6 020 7381 8311
Parker Bird Gardner
p256 Huddersfield 01484 825200
Parmars
p293 Loughborough 01509 261823
J C Patel
p426 Wembley 020 8903 3519
Paton Walsh Laundy
p66 London SW19 020 8946 2229
Patricks Solicitors
p66 Newham 020 8548 8844
Patwa Solicitors
p129 Bearwood 0121 429 8666
M J Payton & Co
p300 Malvern 01684 563318
Pearl & Co
p394 Stanmore 020 8958 4889
Pearson Lowe
p66 London W1 020 7224 0888
Pearson Maddin Solicitors
p321 New Malden 020 8949 9500
Penmans
p394 Stanford-le-Hope 01375 677777
Perrins Solicitors LLP
p239 Harpenden 01582 466140
Perry Hay & Co
p364
Richmond upon Thames 020 8940 8115 / 8332 7532
Peter Peter & Wright
p168 Bude 01288 352101
Petersons
p329 Newport 01633 255151
Pickworths
p247 Hemel Hempstead 01442 261731
Pigotts
p213 Dover 01304 210614 / 212206
Pinkerton Leeke & Co
p188 Cheltenham 01242 237477
Platt & Fishwick
p432 Wigan 01942 243281
Portner & Jaskel LLP
p68 London W1 020 7616 5300
Pricketts
p396 Stockport 0161 429 8000
Purdys
p363 Reepham 01603 870606
Quality Solicitors Burroughs Day
p354 Portishead 01275 843213
Quality Solicitors Clarke & Son
p127 Basingstoke 01256 320555
QualitySolicitors D'Angibau
p353 Poole 01202 672598
RJR Solicitors
p227 Freshwater 01983 752115
Ralph & Co
p418 Wadebridge 01208 812277
Ramsdens Solicitors
p217 Elland 01422 372478
Ratna & Co
p70 London E6 020 8470 8818
Rawlins Davy PLC
p152 Bournemouth 01202 558844
Read Cooper
p410 Thame 01844 260038
Red Kite Law
p244 Haverfordwest 01437 763332
p316 Milford Haven 01646 698008
p345 Pembroke 01646 683222
Redfern & Co
p141 Birmingham 0121 236 1801
Redferns
p242 Harrow 020 8424 7070
Richard Reed
p402 Sunderland 0191 567 0465
Rees Wood Terry
p180 Cardiff 029 2040 8800
R Miles Richards & Co
p352 Pontypridd 01443 202237
Riseam Sharples
p72 London WC2 020 7836 9555
Rix & Kay Solicitors LLP
p416 Uckfield 01825 700177
Roberts Buckley
p309 Manchester 0161 835 1234
Peter Roberts Solicitor
p116 Alrewas 01283 790045
Robinson Allfree
p166 Broadstairs 01843 865261
Robson Palmer
p384 South Shields 0191 455 4561
Rochman Landau LLP
p72 London W1 020 7544 2424
Romain Coleman & Co
p73 Waltham Forest 020 8520 3322
Rowland Tildesley & Harris
p433 Willenhall 01902 366571
Royds LLP
p74 London EC4 020 7583 2222
Rudd Jepson
p167 Bromley 020 8313 0555
Andrew Rugg
p408 Taunton 01823 326822
Russell-Cooke LLP
p74 London WC1 020 7405 6566
Rutters
p229 Gillingham 01747 822005
Sackvilles
p359 Rainham 01708 552804
Sal & Co
p76 London N18 020 8807 5888
Peter R Sargent
p235 Grimsby 01472 887670
Saunders Bearman LLP
p76 London W1 020 7224 2618
Savjani & Co
p77 London NW10 020 8961 3352
Seakens Solicitors
p418 Virginia Water 01344 843666
Segens Blount Petre
p77 London W1 020 7332 2222
Seifert & Co
p196 Cobham 01932 866788
Brian L Senter
p399 Stourbridge 01384 375649
Sethi & Co
p401 Sunbury-on-Thames 01932 772121
Shammah Nicholls LLP
p309 Manchester 0161 832 9272
Sharples & Co
p165 Bristol 0117 942 8214
Sheikh & Co
p78 London N4 020 7263 5588
Gordon Shine & Co
p78 London NW10 020 8969 7033
Shirtcliffe & Reston Solicitors
p411 Thirsk 01845 526222
Shoarns Solicitors Christopher Sheehan LLB
p147 Blandford Forum 01258 880214
Shranks
p78 London WC1 020 7831 6677
Sills & Betteridge LLP
p389 Spilsby 01790 752277
Simon & Co
p384 Southall 020 8571 3883
Jeremy Simon & Co
p424 Watford 01923 219292
Singleton Saunders Flood Solicitors
p213 Dover 01304 240080
Skanthabalan Solicitors
p80 London E15 020 8555 2710
Slade Legal
p114 Abingdon 01235 521920
Sleigh & Son
p213 Droylsden 0161 370 2198
Sleigh Son & Booth
p213 Droylsden 0161 370 9524
E Smith & Co
p268 Kington 01544 231010
Martin T Smith
p282 Leighton Buzzard 01525 374183
Mary Smith Solicitor
p294 Lowestoft 01502 511977
Smith Sutcliffe
p344 Padiham 01282 778434
Solicitors Active
p277 Leeds 0113 248 9805
Solicitors Title
p222 Exeter 01392 207900
Soma & Co Solicitors
p242 Harrow 020 8423 0203
Somerton & Fletcher
p175 Cambridge 01223 566596
Michael Soul & Associates
p80 London WC2 020 7353 3358
Sprake & Kingsley
p129 Beccles 01502 713214
Stapley & Co
p294 Loughton 020 8502 1934
Starkie & Gregory
p293 Long Eaton 0115 849 9000
Hugh Staunton
p232 Grantham 01476 861972
Steel & Co
p268 Knaresborough 01423 869977
Steele & Son
p124 Barnoldswick 01282 813385
p196 Clitheroe 01200 444321
Steels
p422 Warrington 01925 632676
Richard Steer & Co
p409 Teddington 020 8977 8621
Lawrence Stephens
p82 London EC1 020 7935 1211
Stephensons Solicitors LLP
p432 Wigan 01942 777777
Stepien Lake
p83 London W1 020 7467 3030
Stilwell & Harby
p213 Dover 01304 206850
Frank Stimpson & Son
p83 London SE23 020 8699 7644
Harold Stock & Co
p120 Ashton-under-Lyne 01457 838136
Stocker & Co
p410 Thame 01844 216995
Stork & Coles
p84 London WC1 020 7404 6021
Stunt Palmer & Robinson
p84 London E2 020 7739 6927
Sutton-Mattocks & Co LLP
p84 London W4 020 8994 7344
Swaby Clarke & Norris
p123 Barking 020 8507 1882
TMJ Legal Services LLP
p214 Durham 0191 383 0111
David Tagg & Co
p85 London SW6 020 7610 6676
T R Taner & Co
p85 Haringey 020 8348 1267
Tann & Tann Solicitors
p427 Wembley 020 8902 6810
Taylors
p146 Blackburn 0844 800 0263
p310 Manchester 0844 800 0263
Taylors Solicitors
p156 Braunton 01271 812811
Temple Heelis LLP
p264 Kendal 01539 723757
Emyr Thomas & Son
p172 Caernarfon 01286 672307 / 672308
Thompson Allen LLP
p160 Brighton 01273 608003
Thomson & Bancks LLP
p346 Pershore 01386 562000
Thurloe & Lyndhurst LLP
p87 London WC2 0333 123 2255
Thurstan Hoskin Solicitors
p363 Redruth 01209 213646
Tierney & Co
p367 Rotherham 01709 709000
Tinn Criddle & Co
p115 Alford 01507 462882
Tolhurst Fisher LLP
p187 Chelmsford 01245 495111
p387 Southend-on-Sea 01702 352511
Peter F Tomlinson & Co
p128 Bath 01225 484232
Tozers
p329 Newton Abbot 01626 207020
p409 Teignmouth 01626 772376
Treasures
p230 Gloucester 01452 525351
Tyndallwoods
p143 Birmingham 0121 693 2222
Unsworth Rose
p89 Camden 020 7483 4411
Vance Harris
p89 London E14 020 7538 5232
Vaughan & Davies
p268 Kington 01544 230325
H Vaughan Vaughan & Co
p168 Builth Wells 01982 552331 / 553571
p363 Rhayader 01982 552331
WBW Solicitors
p153 Bovey Tracey 01626 833263
Matthew Waite & Co
p413 Tring 01442 890111
Walker & Walker
p374 Sevenoaks 01732 450699
H J Walker Sibia
p291 Liverpool 0151 227 2600
Wallace Robinson & Morgan
p383 Solihull 01564 779393
Waller Pollins
p217 Edgware 020 8238 5858
Walter Wilson Richmond
p242 Harrow 020 8427 8484
Waran & Co
p90 London SW4 020 7498 3328
Ward Gethin
p404 Swaffham 01760 721992
Warings Solicitors
p147 Blackpool 01253 293106
Linda S Warren
p333 Northwood 01923 821213
Waugh & Co
p246 Haywards Heath 01444 451666
David Webb & Co
p428 Westcliff-on-Sea 01702 392939
Dennis J Webb
p442 Worthing 01903 236006
Webster Dixon LLP
p90 London EC1 020 7353 8300
Wellers Law Group LLP
p91 London WC1 020 7242 7265
Whetter Duckworth Fowler
p344 Oxford 01865 872206
Whiteside & Knowles Ltd
p319 Morecambe 01524 416315
Max Wiley & Co
p251 Holt 01263 711771
Wilks Price Hounslow
p369 Ryde 01983 566241
Willans LLP
p189 Cheltenham 01242 514000
Williams Thompson
p194 Christchurch 01202 484242
Williams Woolley
p348 Petworth 01798 342581
Wilmot Thompson
p165 Bristol 0117 927 6583
Wilson Barca LLP
p92 London W1 020 7272 2072
S Winayak
p271 Leatherhead 020 8941 6022
Winch & Winch
p185 Chatham 01634 830111
Wright & Co
p239 Harpenden 01582 767686
Yorkshire Law Solicitors
p167 Brough 01430 422422
Young & Co
p130 Bedford 01234 346411 / 344211
Young Coles & Langdon
p132 Bexhill 01424 210013
Yugin & Partners
p394 Stanmore 020 8954 2410
A E P Zaleski
p93 London SW18 020 8875 1791

COMMERCIAL PROPERTY

Aaron & Partners LLP Solicitors
p190 Chester 01244 405555
Able Bishop Ltd
p171 Bury St Edmunds 01359 245141
Abrahamson & Associates
p3 London NW11 020 8458 1100
Acklam Bond Noor
p145 Blackburn 01254 56068
David Acton & Co
p382 Solihull 01564 730028
Adcocks Solicitors Ltd
p284 Lichfield 0845 470 8081
Aiston Solicitors
p204 Croydon 020 8681 0123
Aldridge Brownlee Solicitors LLP
p151 Bournemouth 01202 526343
Alen-Buckley & Co
p4 Wandsworth 020 8767 8336
Alexander Lawyers LLP
p186 Chelmsford 01245 216050
Alfred James & Co
p204 Croydon 020 8681 4627
Alliance Solicitors
p264 Kenton 020 8204 3000
Anthony Gold
p6 London SE1 020 7940 4000
p6 London SW16 020 7940 4000
Apfel Carter
p296 Lytham 01253 725265 / 712216
Aplin Stockton Fairfax
p122 Banbury 01295 251234
Grant Argent & Co
p7 Brent 020 8452 7651
Argyles
p407 Tamworth 01827 56276
Armitage & Co
p220 Exeter 01392 251364 / 214786
Arnison & Co Solicitors Limited
p346 Penrith 01768 862007
Arnold & Co
p340 Oldbury 0121 552 2382
Arnold Davies Vincent Evans
p413 Tregaron 01974 298816
Arnold George & Co
p259 Ilford 020 8554 5484
K A Arnold & Co
p7 London N1 020 7354 4926
Arnold Thomson Limited
p413 Towcester 01327 350266
Ashfords LLP
p160 Bristol 0117 321 8000
p220 Exeter 01392 337000
p7 London W1 020 3581 8970
p349 Plymouth 01752 521500
p408 Taunton 01823 232300
Alan Ashley & Co
p7 London EC4 020 7822 7482
Malcolm Ashton
p223 Falmouth 01326 313100
Atherton Godfrey
p211 Doncaster 01302 320621
Atkins Bassett
p250 Hinckley 01455 632685
Atteys
p375 Sheffield 0114 276 6767

B P Collins LLP
p229 Gerrards Cross 01753 889995
BPE Solicitors LLP
p187 Cheltenham 01242 224433
Baileys
p187 Cheltenham 01242 514477
Baily Gibson
p249 High Wycombe 01494 442661
Baines Wilson LLP
p181 Carlisle 01228 552600
Band Hatton LLP
p200 Coventry 024 7663 2121
Barber Titleys
p240 Harrogate 01423 502211
Barker Booth & Eastwood
p146 Blackpool 01253 362500
Barker Gillette
p9 London W1 020 7636 0555
Barlow Robbins LLP
p235 Guildford 01483 562901
p436 Woking 01483 748500
Barnes & Partners
p10 London N18 020 8884 2277
Barr Ellison LLP
p174 Cambridge 01223 417200
Barrett & Co Solicitors LLP
p210 Didcot 01235 851220
Bartletts
p11 Haringey 020 8340 2202 / 8340 2203
Batchelor Myddelton
p355 Potters Bar 01707 647088
Batchelors Solicitors
p166 Bromley 020 8768 7000
Bell Lamb & Joynson
p286 Liverpool 0844 412 4348
Belshaw & Curtin
p11 London SE5 020 7708 3311
Belvederes
p12 London WC2 020 7404 5262 / 7405 0046
Harold Benjamin
p241 Harrow 020 8422 5678
Bennett & Co
p286 Liverpool 0151 733 2372
Benson & Co
p243 Hastings 01424 433601
Benson Mazure LLP
p12 London W1 020 7486 8091
Paul Berg & Taylor
p239 Harpenden 01582 760161
Simon Bergin
p395 Stockport 0161 432 9945
Berry Smith LLP
p157 Bridgend 01656 645525
p177 Cardiff 029 2034 5511
Berwin Leighton Paisner LLP
p12 London EC4 020 7760 1000
Berwins Solicitors Limited
p240 Harrogate 01423 509000
Betesh Partnership
p301 Manchester 0161 834 2623
Bevan Brittan LLP
p135 Birmingham 0870 194 1000
p12 London EC4 0870 194 1000
Bevan Kidwell
p12 London EC1 020 7843 1820
Beviss & Beckingsale
p120 Axminster 01297 630700
p184 Chard 01460 269700
p373 Seaton 01297 626950
Birchall Blackburn LLP
p301 Manchester 0161 236 0662
Biscoes
p348 Petersfield 01730 264799
p354 Portsmouth 023 9266 0261
Bivonas Limited Solicitors
p13 London EC3 020 7337 2600
Black Graf & Co
p13 London NW3 020 7586 1141
Blackhams Solicitors
p135 Birmingham 0121 233 6900
Blake Lapthorn
p184 Chandlers Ford 023 8090 8090
p354 Portsmouth 023 9222 1122
Blandy & Blandy
p360 Reading 0118 951 6800
Blick & Co
p14 London 020 7247 9696
Julian Bloom & Co
p171 Bushey 020 8950 3001
Blythe Liggins
p270 Leamington Spa 01926 831231
Bottrills Solicitors
p123 Barnet 020 8440 8188 / 8441 1125
Bourne Jaffa
p135 Birmingham 0121 443 3486 / 444 8440
Bowcock & Pursaill
p278 Leek 01538 399199
Bowling & Co
p15 London E15 020 8221 8000
Bowser Ollard & Bentley
p435 Wisbech 01945 583194
Boyes Turner
p360 Reading 0118 959 7711
Boys & Maughan
p359 Ramsgate 01843 595990
Brabners Chaffe Street
p301 Manchester 0161 836 8800
Brachers
p299 Maidstone 01622 690691
Bradbury Roberts & Raby
p373 Scunthorpe 01724 854000
Andrew C N Brand
p406 Swindon 01285 810328
Kenneth Brand & Co
p15 London NW4 020 8202 6751
Brecher
p15 London W1 020 7563 1000
Brewer Harding & Rowe
p125 Barnstaple 01271 342271
Brian Ruff Angus & Jewers
p431 Wickford 01268 761126
David Briggs & Co
p15 London SW3 020 7823 9040
Brignalls Balderston Warren
p121 Baldock 01462 490100
p133 Biggleswade 01767 313813
p269 Knebworth 01438 812374
p283 Letchworth 01462 482248
p394 Stevenage 01438 359311
C M Broadbent
p297 Macclesfield 01625 500038
Brook Oliver
p321 New Milton 01425 616809
Roger Brooker & Co
p186 Chelmsford 01245 351924
Brooks & Partners
p173 Camberley 01276 681217
BrookStreet des Roches LLP
p114 Abingdon 01235 836600
Brown & Company
p312 Market Harborough 01858 434204
Peter Brown & Co Solicitors LLP
p124 Barnet 020 8447 3277
Brown Turner Ross
p287 Liverpool 0151 236 2233
Browne Jacobson LLP
p16 London EC3 020 7539 4900
Bryan & Armstrong
p311 Mansfield 01623 626039
Bulcraigs
p16 Wandsworth 020 8870 2207 / 8877 0531
Bull & Co
p118 Andover 01264 352495
Buller Jeffries
p136 Birmingham 0121 212 2620
Burkill Govier
p224 Farnham 01252 717171
CB Legal
p17 Camden 020 7323 9192
CGM
p385 Southampton 023 8063 2733
CLB Lawyers (Caswell Lane Bowater Solicitors)
p213 Dudley 01384 451731
CVS Solicitors
p17 London W1 020 7493 2903
Callaghans
p224 Farnham 01252 723477
Calvert Solicitors
p17 Southwark 020 7234 0707
Cannings Connolly
p18 London EC1 020 7329 9000
Canty & Co
p136 Birmingham 0121 688 5000
Capsticks Solicitors LLP
p18 London SW19 020 8780 2211
Carlyon & Son
p414 Truro 01872 278641
Carter Lemon Camerons
p18 London EC1 020 7406 1000
Cartwright Cunningham Haselgrove & Co
p19 Waltham Forest 020 8520 1021
Castle Sanderson
p272 Leeds 0113 232 1919
Castles
p258 Hurstpierpoint 01273 836007 / 837107
Chamberlains
p144 Bishop's Waltham 01489 896141
Chambers Fletcher LLP
p333 Northwich 01606 780400
Chancellors Lea Brewer
p132 Bexleyheath 020 8303 0077
Charles Russell LLP
p187 Cheltenham 01242 221122
p235 Guildford 01483 252525
Charsley Harrison LLP
p381 Slough 01753 517600
p434 Windsor 01753 851591
Chattertons Solicitors
p232 Grantham 01476 591550
p252 Horncastle 01507 522456
p381 Sleaford 01529 411500
p389 Spalding 01775 768774
Child & Child
p20 London SW1 020 7235 8000
Chubb Bulleid
p400 Street 01749 836100
Claremont Richards
p20 London EC4 020 7353 3030
Anthony Clark & Co
p284 Lincoln 01522 512321
Clark Holt
p406 Swindon 01793 617444
Clarke Willmott
p162 Bristol 0845 209 1000 / 0117 305 6000
p408 Taunton 0845 209 1000 / 0117 305 6000
ClarksLegal LLP
p177 Cardiff 029 2055 7500
p20 London WC2 020 7539 8000
p360 Reading 0118 958 5321
p405 Swansea 0118 958 5321
Clintons
p21 London WC2 020 7379 6080
Cobbetts LLP
p302 Manchester 0845 404 2404
Cocks Lloyd
p339 Nuneaton 024 7664 1642
Coffin Mew & Clover
p223 Fareham 01329 825617
Cohen Filippini
p116 Altrincham 0161 929 9993
Colemans - CTTS
p302 Manchester 0161 876 2500
Colemans Solicitors LLP
p298 Maidenhead 01628 631051
Coles Miller Solicitors LLP
p352 Poole 01202 673011
Coley & Tilley
p136 Birmingham 0121 643 5531
Anthony Collins Solicitors LLP
p137 Birmingham 0121 200 3242
Collins Benson Goldhill LLP
p21 London W1 020 7436 5151
Collyer Bristow LLP
p22 London WC1 020 7242 7363
Comptons
p22 Camden 020 7485 0888
Conway & Co
p247 Henley-on-Thames 01491 411122
Coodes
p414 Truro 01872 246200
Cooke Painter Limited
p162 Bristol 01275 400037
Cottrill Stone Lawless
p302 Manchester 0161 835 3681
Cracknells
p236 Guildford 01483 535558
Croftons
p302 Manchester 0161 214 6180
David Cross & Co
p411 Thornbury 01454 419696
Crosse & Crosse
p220 Exeter 01392 258451
Paul Crowley & Co
p287 Liverpool 0151 264 7363
Crutes
p182 Carlisle 01228 525195
p324 Newcastle upon Tyne 0191 233 9700
p396 Stockton-on-Tees 01642 623400
Cullimore Dutton
p190 Chester 01244 356789
Cumberland Ellis Peirs
p23 London WC1 020 7242 0422
Curry Popeck
p264 Kenton 020 8907 2000 / 8907 8896
p24 London W1 020 7224 6633
DAC Beachcroft
p328 Newport 0844 980 0400
DBL Talbots LLP
p213 Dudley 01384 459551
DFA Law LLP
p331 Northampton 01604 609560
dgb Solicitors
p184 Chatham 01634 304000
DW Solicitors
p331 Northampton 01604 624222
Graham Dack & Company (inc Battersby James)
p185 Chatteris 01354 695885
Dale & Newbery LLP
p393 Staines 01784 464491
Daltons Solicitors
p348 Petersfield 01730 262816
Darlingtons
p217 Edgware 020 8952 0033 / 8951 6666
Darwin Gray
p178 Cardiff 029 2082 9100
Jeremy Davenport
p251 Hockley 01702 205163
David & Snape
p157 Bridgend 01656 661115
Aubrey David
p25 London W1 020 7224 4410
David Conway & Co
p26 London W1 020 7258 3000
Christopher Davidson Solicitors LLP
p188 Cheltenham 01242 581481
Davidson Large LLP
p240 Harrogate 01423 727272
Paul Davidson Taylor
p253 Horsham 01403 262333
Davies & Partners
p115 Almondsbury 01454 619619
p137 Birmingham 0121 616 4450
p230 Gloucester 01452 612345
David H N Davies
p371 Salisbury 01722 322272
Davis Blank Furniss
p303 Manchester 0161 832 3304
Davitt Jones Bould
p408 Taunton 01823 279279
Dawson Mason & Carr
p236 Guildford 01483 576169
Roger Dean & Co
p133 Biggin Hill 01959 542872
Dean Wilson Laing
p159 Brighton 01273 327241
Denison Till
p444 York 01904 611411
Denniss Matthews
p27 London SE20 020 8778 7301 / 8778 7631
Dexter Montague LLP
p360 Reading 0118 939 3999
Dickinson Manser
p352 Poole 01202 673071
Dodd Lewis Solicitors
p27 London SE3 020 8852 1255
Donnelly & Elliott Limited
p232 Gosport 023 9250 5500
Dootsons LLP
p205 Culcheth 01925 765212
Downie & Gadban
p116 Alton 01420 82879
Downs
p212 Dorking 01306 880110
p231 Godalming 01483 861848
Dowse Baxter
p27 London SW19 020 8946 9110
Drysdales
p387 Southend-on-Sea 01702 423400
Valentine Duggins
p419 Wallasey 0151 638 4844
Dundas & Duce
p299 Maidstone 01622 681867
Dunn & Co
p267 Kingston upon Thames 020 8541 1332
Dyne Solicitors Limited
p190 Chester 01829 773100
EMW
p316 Milton Keynes 0845 070 6000
Eaton Smith LLP
p255 Huddersfield 01484 821300
Thomas Eggar LLP
p192 Chichester 01243 786111
p202 Crawley 01293 742700
p29 London EC4 020 7842 0000
p441 Worthing 01903 234411
Ellis-Fermor & Negus
p130 Beeston 0115 922 1591
Elvin & Co
p293 Loughborough 01509 852454
Hal Emmett & Co
p298 Maghull 0151 531 7666
Max Engel & Co LLP
p331 Northampton 01604 887450
Engleharts
p254 Hove 01273 204411
Enoch Evans LLP
p420 Walsall 01922 720333
Evans & Davies
p113 Aberaeron 01545 570335
Everatt's
p241 Harrow 020 8424 0088
FBC Manby Bowdler LLP
p409 Telford 01952 292129
p432 Willenhall 01902 366566
p437 Wolverhampton 01902 578000
Fairchild Dobbs
p229 Gerrards Cross 01753 883127
Farleys Solicitors LLP
p145 Blackburn 01254 367855
Fasken Martineau LLP
p31 London W1 020 7917 8500
Feeny & Co
p162 Bristol 0117 923 9477
Field Seymour Parkes
p360 Reading 0118 951 6200
Finers Stephens Innocent LLP
p32 London W1 020 7323 4000
Finn Gledhill
p238 Halifax 01422 330000
Firth Lindsay
p375 Sheffield 0114 276 0586
Fishers
p118 Ashby-de-la-Zouch 01530 412167
Fladgate LLP
p32 London WC2 020 3036 7000
Flint Bishop Solicitors
p208 Derby 01332 340211

See p542 for the Firms Specialisations

Foot Anstey
p349 . . . Plymouth 01752 675000
Forbes Hall LLP
p439 . . . Woodford Green 020 8498 0080
Ford & Warren
p273 . . . Leeds 0113 243 6601
Ford Banks Irwin
p304 . . . Manchester 0161 866 8999
Foreman Laws
p251 . . . Hitchin 01462 458711
Forshaws Davies Ridgway LLP
p422 . . . Warrington 01925 230000
Forsters LLP
p33 . . . London W1 020 7863 8333
Foskett Marr Gadsby & Head
p219 . . . Epping 01992 578642
Peter J Fowler
p433 . . . Wimborne 01202 849242
Scott Fowler
p331 . . . Northampton 01604 750506
Francis & Co
p189 . . . Chepstow 01291 622237
Francis Law LLP
p296 . . . Lydney 01594 842242
Franklin & Co
p121 . . . Bakewell 01629 814461
Franklins LLP
p317 . . . Milton Keynes 01908 660966
Fraser Brown
p133 . . . Bingham 01949 830812
p337 . . . Nottingham 0115 988 8777
Fraser Dawbarns
p213 . . . Downham Market 01366 383171
p266 . . . King's Lynn 01553 666600
p435 . . . Wisbech 01945 461456
Freeman Johnson
p214 . . . Durham 0191 386 4843 / 386 9619
Freeth Cartwright LLP
p279 . . . Leicester 0116 248 1100
Fruhman Davies Livingstones
p304 . . . Manchester 0161 833 0578
GCA Solicitors (Giffen Couch & Archer)
p295 . . . Luton 01582 410041
GLRS Phoenix LLP
p400 . . . Stroud 01453 757381
GPT Solicitors
p426 . . . Wembley 020 8904 6495 / 8904 6598
GSC Solicitors
p34 . . . London EC1 020 7822 2222
Gabbs LLP
p248 . . . Hereford 01432 353481
Ganpate
p35 . . . London NW4 020 8202 5092
Gardner Austin
p35 . . . London W1 020 7831 2600
Garner Canning
p120 . . . Atherstone 01827 713543
p138 . . . Birmingham 0121 749 5577
p407 . . . Tamworth 01827 314004
Garner Canning Vickery
p403 . . . Sutton Coldfield 0121 323 2646
Garner Hutchings
p35 . . . London W1 020 7932 2400
Gartsides
p113 . . . Abergavenny 01873 857555
Geldards LLP
p178 . . . Cardiff 029 2023 8239
p337 . . . Nottingham 0115 983 3650
Girlings
p248 . . . Herne Bay 01227 367355
Gisby Harrison
p189 . . . Cheshunt 01707 878300
Glaisyers Solicitors LLP
p304 . . . Manchester 0161 832 4666
Glazer Delmar
p35 . . . London SE22 020 8299 0021
Goldwaters
p324 . . . Newcastle upon Tyne 0191 232 2653
Rodney Goodson
p334 . . . Norwich 01603 632832
GoodyBurrett LLP
p197 . . . Colchester 01206 577676
Gordons
p236 . . . Guildford 01483 451900
Gordons LLP
p154 . . . Bradford 01274 202202
p273 . . . Leeds 0113 227 0100
Gosschalks
p256 . . . Hull 01482 324252
Goughs
p173 . . . Calne 01249 812086
p193 . . . Chippenham 01249 444499
p199 . . . Corsham 01249 712193
p210 . . . Devizes 01380 726913
p314 . . . Melksham 01225 703036
p414 . . . Trowbridge 01225 762683
Grace & Co
p36 . . . London W1 020 7935 7938
George Green LLP
p201 . . . Cradley Heath 01384 410410
Greenland Houchen Pomeroy
p293 . . . Long Stratton 01508 530033
p334 . . . Norwich 01603 660744
p443 . . . Wymondham 01953 606351
Griffith Smith Conway
p254 . . . Hove 01273 821577
Griffith Smith Farrington Webb
p159 . . . Brighton 01273 324041
Grigsby Eddleston & Co
p394 . . . Stevenage 01438 742525
Guest & Co
p205 . . . Cuckfield 01444 413731
Gullands
p299 . . . Maidstone 01622 678341
Gurney-Champion & Co
p354 . . . Portsmouth 023 9282 1100
Guy Williams Layton
p288 . . . Liverpool 0151 236 7171
HC Solicitors LLP
p342 . . . Oundle 01832 273506
HKB Wiltshires
p294 . . . Lowestoft 01502 582338
hlw Keeble Hawson LLP
p376 . . . Sheffield 0114 276 5555
HM Law
p437 . . . Wokingham 0118 977 1718
HSR Law (Hayes, Son & Richmond)
p211 . . . Doncaster 01302 347800
Hacking Ashton LLP
p323 . . . Newcastle under Lyme 01782 715555
Hague Lambert
p297 . . . Macclesfield 01625 616480
p305 . . . Manchester 0161 834 6066
p417 . . . Urmston 0161 747 7321
Hall Reynolds
p133 . . . Bidford-on-Avon 01789 772955
Hall Ward & Fox
p429
. Weston-super-Mare 01934 626656 / 626657
HallmarkHulme
p439 . . . Worcester 01905 726600
Lawrence Hamblin
p247 . . . Henley-on-Thames 01491 411884
Hamilton Downing Quinn
p38 . . . London WC1 020 7831 8939
Hamlins LLP
p38 . . . London W1 020 7355 6000
Hammond Bale
p38 . . . London W1 020 7499 7624
Hamways Walker Owens
p216 . . . Edenbridge 01732 866666
Hanney Dawkins & Jones
p348 . . . Pinner 020 8866 2144
Hanover Solicitors
p38 . . . London SW3 0870 383 1974
Juliet Hardick Solicitors
p127 . . . Bath 01225 311177
Gaby Hardwicke
p243 . . . Hastings 01424 438011
Harold G Walker
p166 . . . Broadstone 01202 692448 / 695361
p194 . . . Christchurch 01202 482202
Harper & Odell
p39 . . . Islington 020 7490 0500
Hart Brown Solicitors
p236 . . . Guildford 0800 068 8177
Hart Jackson Hall Smith
p325 . . . Newcastle upon Tyne 0191 261 5181
Harter & Loveless
p39 . . . Islington 020 7688 2900
Hartlaw LLP
p429 . . . Wetherby 01937 547000
Harvey Ingram Borneos
p130 . . . Bedford 01234 353221
p317 . . . Milton Keynes 01908 696002
Sally Harvey
p330 . . . Newtown 01686 621033
C W Harwood & Co
p274 . . . Leeds 0113 245 7027
Hatchers Solicitors LLP
p379 . . . Shrewsbury 01743 248545
A V Hawkins & Co
p241 . . . Harrow 020 8422 2364 / 8422 2466
Hawley & Rodgers
p293 . . . Loughborough 01509 230333
p337 . . . Nottingham 0115 955 9000
Healys LLP
p159 . . . Brighton 01273 685888
Hegarty LLP
p347 . . . Peterborough 01733 346333
R W Hemmings & Co
p408 . . . Taunton 01823 325090
Hempsons
p240 . . . Harrogate 01423 522331
p40 . . . London W1 020 7839 0278
p305 . . . Manchester 0161 228 0011
Herrington & Carmichael LLP
p173 . . . Camberley 01276 686222
p437 . . . Wokingham 0118 977 4045
Heyman & Co
p282 . . . Leigh 01942 604135
Hill Dickinson LLP
p190 . . . Chester 01244 896600
p288 . . . Liverpool 0151 600 8000
p41 . . . London EC3 020 7283 9033
p305 . . . Manchester 0161 817 7200
HilliersHRW Solicitors
p395 . . . Stevenage 01438 346000
Hine Downing Solicitors
p223 . . . Falmouth 01326 316655
Hogan Lisle
p42 . . . London W1 020 7224 3300
Hole & Pugsley
p412 . . . Tiverton 01884 252827
Philip Hook
p334 . . . Norwich 01603 250050
Hopkins
p337 . . . Nottingham 0115 910 5555
Housing & Property Law Partnership
p43 . . . Islington 020 7553 9000
Howard Schneider Spiro Steele
p124 . . . Barnet 020 8216 2020
Susan Howarth & Co
p333 . . . Northwich 01606 48777
Hudson & Co
p43 London WC1 020 7405 4812 / 7831 3282
Hugh Cartwright & Amin
p43 . . . London WC1 020 7632 4200
Hugh James
p179 . . . Cardiff 029 2022 4871
A L Hughes & Co
p43 . . . London SW16 020 8769 7100
J A Hughes
p345 . . . Penarth 029 2070 2449
Humphries Kirk
p352 . . . Poole 01202 725400
p421 . . . Wareham 01929 552141
Andrew Hurrell Solicitors
p131 . . . Benfleet 01702 558286
A C B Hurst & Co
p247 . . . Henley-on-Thames 01491 572699
E B Hurst
p442 . . . Worthing 01903 246818
Hutcheson Forrest
p127 . . . Bath 01225 312311
Nick Hutchinson & Co
p188 . . . Cheltenham 01242 261515
Ingram Winter Green
p45 . . . Camden 020 7845 7400
Irvings
p241 . . . Harrow 020 8427 6600
Irwin Mitchell LLP
p274 . . . Leeds 0870 150 0100
Ismail & Ghani
p154 . . . Bradford 01274 737546
Israel Strange & Conlon
p45 . . . Islington 020 7833 8453
JW Law
p433 . . . Wimborne 01202 690658
Jaffe Porter Crossick
p46 . . . London NW6 020 7625 4424
Jennings Perks & Co
p420 . . . Walsall 01922 459000
Jeromes
p372 . . . Sandown 01983 402026
Jobling & Knape
p233 . . . Great Eccleston 01995 670083
p269 . . . Lancaster 01524 598300
p319 . . . Morecambe 01524 416960
The John W Davies Partnership
p329 . . . Newport 01633 841773
Jones & Co
p128 . . . Bawtry 01302 710555
W T Jones
p47 London WC1 020 7405 4631 / 7242 7767
Judge Sykes Frixou
p47 . . . London WC2 020 7379 5114
K&L Gates LLP
p47 . . . London EC4 020 7648 9000
KBL Solicitors
p149 . . . Bolton 01204 527777
KJD
p398 . . . Stoke-on-Trent 01782 202020
Kagan Moss & Co
p409 . . . Teddington 020 8977 6633
Keelers
p264 . . . Kenilworth 01926 853555
Keene Marsland
p415 . . . Tunbridge Wells 01892 526442
Kelly & Co
p275 . . . Leeds 0113 244 2113
Howard Kennedy LLP
p48 . . . London W1 020 7636 1616
Kevill Kirkham & Grayson
p194 . . . Chorley 01257 263676 / 269212
Kidd Rapinet
p121 . . . Aylesbury 0845 017 9616
p49 . . . London WC2 020 7205 2115
p361 . . . Reading 0845 017 8750
Kidson Bray & Lawson
p49 . . . London SE11 020 7582 0111
Kimbells LLP
p317 . . . Milton Keynes 01908 668555
King Prior Macdonald Bridge
p233 . . . Gravesend 01474 325678
King Solicitors
p384 . . . Southall 020 8571 2239
Kingsfords
p119 . . . Ashford 01233 624545
Kingsley Smith Solicitors LLP
p185 . . . Chatham 01634 811118
Kirwans
p134 . . . Birkenhead 0151 608 9078
Kitsons LLP
p413 . . . Torquay 01803 202020
Knights Solicitors LLP
p115 . . . Alderley Edge 01625 586686
p188 . . . Cheltenham 01242 524654
p323 . . . Newcastle under Lyme 01782 619225
Kundert & Co
p200 . . . Coventry 024 7622 7741
Kyriakides & Braier
p50 . . . London W1 020 7637 3289
LDJ Solicitors
p339 . . . Nuneaton 024 7674 5000
Laceys
p152 . . . Bournemouth 01202 557256
Lamb & Holmes
p199 . . . Corby 01536 745168
p265 . . . Kettering 01536 513195
Lamb Brooks LLP
p126 . . . Basingstoke 01256 844888
Lambe Corner
p248 . . . Hereford 01432 355301
Lamberts
p374 . . . Sevenoaks 01732 460565
Land Law LLP
p116 . . . Altrincham 0161 928 8383
Larcomes LLP
p354 . . . Portsmouth 023 9266 1531
Large & Gibson
p388 . . . Southsea 023 9229 6296
Last Cawthra Feather LLP
p378 . . . Shipley 01274 585459
Lattey & Dawe
p51 . . . London EC2 020 7623 2345
Lawrance & Holder
p355 . . . Potters Bar 01707 645317
Lawson Coppock & Hart
p306 . . . Manchester 0161 832 5944
Laytons
p236 . . . Guildford 01483 407000
p306 . . . Manchester 0161 834 2100
Lean & Co
p226 . . . Fleet 01252 816757
Lee & Priestley LLP
p275 . . . Leeds 0845 129 2300
Leech & Co
p306 . . . Manchester 0161 279 0279
Leeds Day
p258 . . . Huntingdon 01480 454301
p392 . . . St Ives 01480 464600
p392 . . . St Neots 01480 474661
Lees Solicitors LLP
p134 . . . Birkenhead 0151 647 9381
Wayne Leighton
p217 . . . Edgware 020 8951 2988
Lester Aldridge LLP
p53 . . . London WC2 0844 967 0785
Letchers
p364 . . . Ringwood 01425 471424
Leung & Co
p163 . . . Bristol 0117 920 9230
Levine Mellins Klarfeld
p394 . . . Stanmore 020 8954 7474
P S Levy & Co
p53 . . . London W1 020 7486 7717
Lewis Silkin LLP
p53 . . . London EC4 020 7074 8000
Lithman & Co
p55 . . . London W1 020 7935 2212
Livingstone & Co
p307 . . . Manchester 0161 833 0578
Lloyd Jones & Co
p428 . . . Westcliff-on-Sea 01702 710338
Lodders Solicitors LLP
p400 . . . Stratford-upon-Avon 01789 293259
Judith M Long
p55 . . . Southwark 020 7403 3337
Longs Solicitors
p412 . . . Tonbridge 01732 360895
Loosemores
p179 . . . Cardiff 029 2022 4433
E D C Lord & Co
p245 . . . Hayes 020 8848 9988
MFG Solicitors
p440 . . . Worcester 01905 610410
MLM Cartwright
p179 . . . Cardiff 029 2046 2562
MSB Solicitors LLP
p289 . . . Liverpool 0151 281 9040
MSP Legal Services LLP
p243 . . . Hartlepool 01429 232204
Hilary McCauley Solicitors Limited
p185 . . . Cheadle Hulme 0161 485 6723
MacDonald Oates LLP
p348 . . . Petersfield 01730 268211
McEwen Parkinson
p56 . . . London W1 020 7487 4361
Mackenzie Jones
p391 . . . St Asaph 01745 536030
Mackrell Turner Garrett
p57 . . . London WC2 020 7240 0521

See p542 for the Firms Specialisations

Stevens Lucas
p193 .... Chirk 01691 777949
stevensdrake
p202 .... Crawley 01293 596900
Harold Stock & Co
p120
..Ashton-under-Lyne 01457 835597 / 835034
p120 ... Ashton-under-Lyne 01457 838136
Stockdale & Reid Ltd
p318 .... Monkseaton 0191 251 9494
Stockler Brunton
p83 ..... London EC4 020 7404 6661
Stokes Solicitors
p355 .... Portsmouth 023 9282 8131
Straw & Pearce
p293 .... Loughborough 01509 268931
David Street & Company
p202 .... Crawley 01293 616191
Sumner & Main
p442 .... Worthing 01903 239420
Sutton-Mattocks & Co LLP
p84 .... London SW13 020 8876 8811
Swinburne & Jackson LLP
p423 .... Washington 0191 416 0004
Swinnerton Moore Solicitors
p84 .... London EC4 020 7236 7111
Sydney Mitchell
p142
. Birmingham 0121 698 2200 / 0808 166 8827
p383 .... Solihull 0121 746 3300
Sylvester Mackett
p414 .... Trowbridge 01225 755621
TBI Solicitors
p123 ..... Barnard Castle 01833 638326
TWM Solicitors LLP
p219 .... Epsom 01372 729555
p271 .... Leatherhead 01372 374148
p85 ...... London SW19 020 8946 6454
p363 .... Reigate 01737 221212
Tanner & Taylor LLP
p115 .... Aldershot 01252 316565
Tanners
p195 .... Cirencester 01285 659061
A P Tansey
p244 .... Hatfield 01302 843859
Taylor & Emmet LLP
p377 .... Sheffield 0114 218 4000
Taylor Walton LLP
p295 .... Luton 01582 731161
David & Roy Thomas & Co
p351 .... Pontardulais 01792 882410
Thompson Allen LLP
p160 .... Brighton 01273 608003
Thompsons (formerly Robin/Brian Thompson & Partners)
p87 ...... London SW19 020 8947 4163
Thomson & Bancks LLP
p346 .... Pershore 01386 562000
Thorn Drury & Searles
p359 .... Ramsgate 01843 593381
Thornton & Co
p87. Hammersmith & Fulham 020 8743 3000
Thorp Parker LLP
p398 .... Stokesley 01642 711354
Thrings LLP
p165 .... Bristol 0117 930 9500
p87 ...... London SW1 020 7766 5600
p406 .... Swindon 01793 410800
Thurloe & Lyndhurst LLP
p87 ...... London WC2 0333 123 2255
Tinsdills
p372 .... Sandbach 01270 761111
Tolhurst Fisher LLP
p187 .... Chelmsford 01245 495111
p387 .... Southend-on-Sea 01702 352511
Tollers LLP
p265 .... Kettering 01536 520111
Peter F Tomlinson & Co
p128 .... Bath 01225 484232
Alison Trent & Co
p88 .... London EC4 020 7583 3350
Trethowans LLP
p387 .... Southampton 023 8032 1000
Trowers & Hamlins
p222 .... Exeter 01392 217466
James Tsang & Co
p88 .... London W1 020 7287 0451
Turner Parkinson
p310 .... Manchester 0161 833 1212
Turners Solicitors LLP
p153 .... Bournemouth 01202 291291
Underwood Solicitors LLP
p89 .... London W1 020 7526 6000
Unsworth Rose
p89 .... Camden 020 7483 4411
Vance Harris
p204 .... Crowborough 01892 653434
Veale Wasbrough Vizards
p165 .... Bristol 0117 925 2020
Veitch Penny
p203 .... Crediton 01363 772244
Verisona Solicitors
p423 ...... Waterlooville 023 9226 5251
Verma & Co
p427 .... Wembley 020 8903 0309
Vyman Solicitors
p233 .... Gravesend 01474 537270
p242 .... Harrow 020 8427 9080
Walker Foster
p124 ...... Barnoldswick 01282 812340
p380 .... Silsden 01535 653408
Walker Foster with Kennedy Thompson
p261 .... Ilkley 01943 609969
Percy Walker & Co
p243 .... Hastings 01424 721234
Walker Smith Way
p191 .... Chester 0844 346 3100
Walsh & Company
p414 .... Truro 01872 870923
Wanham Longhurst & Co
p171 .... Bury St Edmunds 01284 735808
Wansbroughs
p210 .... Devizes 01380 733300
p314 .... Melksham 01225 703222
Ward Hadaway
p327 .. Newcastle upon Tyne 0191 204 4000
Warner Goodman LLP
p355 .... Portsmouth 023 9275 3575
Warners Solicitors
p374 .... Sevenoaks 01732 747900
p412 .... Tonbridge 01732 770660
Kathleen Watkin
p350 .... Plymouth 01752 666715
Watson Nevill
p299 .... Maidstone 01622 661177
Weatherhead & Butcher
p133 .... Bingley 01274 562322
Dennis J Webb
p442 .... Worthing 01903 236006
Weightmans LLP
p207 .... Dartford 020 7822 1900
p269 .... Knutsford 01565 634234
Whatley & Co
p91 .... Barnet 020 8205 1411 / 8205 8931
Whitehead Monckton
p410 .... Tenterden 01580 765722
Hugh Whitlock
p316 ...... Milford-on-Sea 01590 644777
Wilde & Co
p321 .... Neston 0151 353 1899
The Wilkes Partnership LLP
p143 .... Birmingham 0121 233 4333
Wilkin Chapman Epton Blades
p285 .... Lincoln 01522 512345
Wilkin Chapman Grange Solicitors
p235 .... Grimsby 01472 262626
Wilkin Chapman LLP
p235 .... Grimsby 01472 262626
Willans LLP
p189 .... Cheltenham 01242 514000
L G Williams & Prichard
p181 .... Cardiff 029 2022 9716
Wills & Probate Countrywide
p408 .... Tavistock 01626 334455
Winterbotham Smith Penley LLP
p320 .... Nailsworth 01453 832566
Wise Geary
p122 .... Banbury 01295 278500
Wiseman Lee LLP
p92 .... Redbridge 020 8215 1000
Lawrence Wood
p443 .... Wroxham 01603 783711
Wood's Solicitors
p210 .... Disley 01663 765511
Woodfines LLP
p372 .... Sandy 01767 680251
Woodford Stauffer
p224 .... Farnborough 01252 375376
Richard A Woodman
p239 .... Harpenden 01582 768222
Woodroffes
p93 .... London W1 020 7730 0001
Woolacott & Co
p270 .... Lancing 01903 763011 / 764334
Woolf Simmonds
p93 .... London W1 020 7262 1266
Woollastons
p404 .... Sutton Coldfield 0121 355 5516
Woollcombe Yonge
p351 .... Plymouth 01752 660384
Wosskow Brown
p377 .... Sheffield 0114 256 1560
Wragg Mark-Bell Solicitors
p182 .... Carlisle 01228 711728
Wright & Co
p239 .... Harpenden 01582 767686
Wright & Wright
p237 .... Guildford 01483 531264
Wykeham & Co
p193 .... Chippenham 01249 721010
P H Yeung
p93 .... London W1 020 7287 1882
Yorklaw Ltd (t/a Burn & Company)
p445 .... York 01904 655442
Zermansky & Partners
p278 .... Leeds 0113 245 9766

COMMUNICATIONS & TELECOMMUNICATIONS

Bird & Bird LLP
p13 .... London EC4 020 7415 6000
Morrison & Foerster (UK) LLP
p62 .... London EC2 020 7920 4000
Osborne Clarke
p164 .... Bristol 0117 917 3000
p65 .... London EC2 020 7105 7000
p361 .... Reading 0118 925 2000
Payne & Payne
p257 .... Hull 01482 326446
Preiskel & Co LLP
p69 .... London EC4 020 7583 2120
Vivienne Robinson
p72 .... London E11 020 8279 8899
Steptoe & Johnson
p83 .... London EC2 020 7367 8000
Taylor Wessing
p86 .... London EC4 020 7300 7000

COMPETITION LAW

Ferdinand Kelly
p403 .... Sutton Coldfield 01827 893526
Gregory Rowcliffe Milners
p37 .... London WC1 020 7242 0631
Henmans LLP
p343 .... Oxford 01865 781000
Michael Hutchings
p421 .... Warminster 07768 105777
Kemp Little LLP
p48 .... London EC2 020 7600 8080
Laytons
p52 .... London EC4 020 7842 8000
Maitland Walker
p318 .... Minehead 01643 707777
Clifford Miller
p129 .... Beckenham 020 8663 0044
Vivienne Robinson
p72 .... London E11 020 8279 8899
SJ Berwin LLP
p75 .... London EC4 020 7111 2222
J P Scholes
p121 .... Bamford 01433 651625
Singletons
p349 .... Pinner 020 8866 1934
Stewarts Law LLP
p277 .... Leeds 0113 222 0022
p83 .... London EC4 020 7822 8000

COMPUTER LAW

Anderson & Company
p378 .... Shillingford 01865 858878
BCL Burton Copeland
p9 .... London WC2 020 7430 2277
Bird & Bird LLP
p13 .... London EC4 020 7415 6000
Bristows
p15 .... London EC4 020 7400 8000
CIPIT Solicitors
p17 .... London NW3 020 8457 7457
Faegre & Benson LLP
p30 .... London EC4 020 7450 4500
Goodman King
p408 .... Tavistock 01822 615510
Hardy McBride & Co
p166 .... Bromley 020 8460 1999
Herrington & Carmichael LLP
p437 .... Wokingham 0118 977 4045
Laceys
p152 ...... Bournemouth 01202 557256
McGrigors LLP
p56 .... London EC4 020 7054 2500
Radcliffes Le Brasseur
p70 .... London W1 020 7222 7040
Richard Nelson Business Defence Solicitors
p164 .... Bristol 0117 942 5678
p338 .... Nottingham 0115 986 3636
Sharpe Pritchard
p77 .... London WC1 020 7405 4600
Sheridans
p78 .... London WC1 020 7079 0100
Clive Walker
p277 .... Leeds 0113 268 4660

CONSUMER LAW - AGREEMENTS, CREDIT, LICENSING, SALE OF GOODS

Bell Lax Litigation
p403 .... Sutton Coldfield 0121 355 0011
Bermans LLP
p301 .... Manchester 0161 827 4600
Brightstone Law LLP
p218 .... Elstree 020 8731 3080
Carters
p351 .... Pontefract 01977 703224
ClarksLegal LLP
p360 .... Reading 0118 958 5321
Clintons
p21 .... London WC2 020 7379 6080
Edward Harte LLP
p159 .... Brighton 01273 662750
Haslam & Payne
p39 .... London SW1 020 7828 8725
Richard P Kemp BA Solicitor
p313 .... Martock 01935 822572
Northwood Law Practice
p333 .... Northwood 01923 826208
Pitman Blackstock White
p296 .... Lydney 01594 842475
Reston's Solicitors Limited
p422 .... Warrington 0870 755 8998
Richard Rooney & Co
p73 .... Merton 020 8947 8024
TWM Solicitors LLP
p363 .... Reigate 01737 221212
Taylor Lewis
p181 .... Cardigan 01239 621999
Weightmans LLP
p281 .... Leicester 0116 253 9747
Willetts Marsden
p422 .... Warrington 01925 230020

CONSUMER PROTECTION - ADVERTISING, TRADE DESCRIPTIONS, TRADING STANDARDS, PRODUCT LIABILITY

Bell Lax Litigation
p403 .... Sutton Coldfield 0121 355 0011
Heer Manak
p200 .... Coventry 024 7666 4000
Whiting & Purches
p383 .... Solihull 0121 605 5050

COPYRIGHT, PATENTS, TRADE MARKS & INTELLECTUAL PROPERTY

Anderson & Company
p378 .... Shillingford 01865 858878
Birketts LLP
p262 .... Ipswich 01473 232300
Bonallack & Bishop
p371 .... Salisbury 01722 422300
Briffa
p15 .... Islington 020 7288 6003
Bristows
p15 .... London EC4 020 7400 8000
CIPIT Solicitors
p17 .... London NW3 020 8457 7457
Carter-Ruck
p18 .... London EC4 020 7353 5005
Chua's Solicitors
p20 .... London EC4 020 7242 6789
Davenport Lyons
p25 .... London W1 020 7468 2600
EMW
p316 ..... Milton Keynes 0845 070 6000
Faegre & Benson LLP
p30 .... London EC4 020 7450 4500
Fasken Martineau LLP
p31 .... London W1 020 7917 8500
GSC Solicitors
p34 .... London EC1 020 7822 2222
Gordons
p36 .... London WC1 020 7421 9421
Gray & Co
p305 .... Manchester 0161 237 3360
HGF Law
p37 .... London WC2 020 7440 8900
Hamilton Pratt
p422 .... Warwick 01926 838900
Healys LLP
p159 .... Brighton 01273 685888
Humphreys & Co
p163 .... Bristol 0117 929 2662
Robert A Hurst
p44 .... London NW11 020 8209 1733
King Prior Macdonald Bridge
p366 .... Rochester 01634 272720
Kirwans
p319 .... Moreton 0151 677 3433
Trevor Lyttleton MBE
p55 .... London W1 020 7402 4810
McNair & Co
p57. Hammersmith & Fulham 020 7371 7896
Manches LLP
p343 .... Oxford 01865 722106

Marriott Harrison
p59 . . . . London WC1 020 7209 2000
Martin-Kaye LLP
p409 . . . . .Telford 01952 272222
Medyckyj & Co
p60. . . . . Haringey 020 8442 0000
Clifford Miller
p129 . . . . . . .Beckenham 020 8663 0044
Nicolaou Solicitors
p249 . . . . Hertford 01707 877707
B M Nyman & Co
p64. . . . . Haringey 020 8365 3060
Parker Bullen
p371 . . . . Salisbury 01722 412000
J H Powell & Co
p209 . . . . Derby 01332 372211
Rochman Landau LLP
p72. . . . . London W1 020 7544 2424
Rohan & Co
p246 . . . . .Haywards Heath 01444 450901
Rouse Legal (Formerly Willoughby & Partners)
p74. . . . . . . London E14 020 7536 4100
P Russell & Co
p74. . . . . London W6 020 8233 2943
Shook Hardy & Bacon LLP
p78. . . . . London EC4 020 7332 4500
Shoosmiths
p332
. Northampton 0370 086 3000 / 01604 543000
Michael Simkins LLP
p79. . . . . . . London WC1 020 7874 5600
Taylors
p310 . . . . .Manchester 0844 800 0263
Vincent Sykes & Higham LLP
p411 . . . . Thrapston 01832 732161
Wragge & Co LLP
p93. . . . . London EC1 0870 903 1000
Wright Hassall LLP
p270 . . . . .Leamington Spa 01926 886688

CRIME - GENERAL

@ Cornwall Law
p414 . . . . . .Truro 01872 222688 / 222712
AGH Solicitors
p148 . . . . Bolton 01204 364433
Able Bishop Ltd
p171 . . . . Bury St Edmunds 01359 245141
Ahmed & Co
p4 . . . . Camden 020 7383 2243
Albin & Co
p359 . . . . Reading 0118 957 4018
Alderson Dodds
p147 . . . . Blyth 01670 352293
Aldridge Brownlee Solicitors LLP
p151 . . . . Bournemouth 01202 294411
Alexander & Partners
p5 . . . . Brent 020 8965 7121
Michael Alexander & Co
p301 . . . . . . Manchester 0845 839 2011
Allan Rutherford
p333 . . . . Norwich 01603 621722
Allen Hoole Solicitors
p160 . . . . .Bristol 0117 942 0901
Allens
p237 . . . . Halesworth 01986 875246
Alletsons Ltd
p157 . . . . .Bridgwater 01278 456621
Alsters Kelley
p339 . . . . Nuneaton 0844 561 0100
Andersons Solicitors
p239 . . . . Harrogate 01423 527852
Anglo-Spanish Law
p244 . . . . Hathersage 01433 631508
Appleby Hope & Matthews
p314 . . . . . .Middlesbrough 01642 440444
p396 . . . . Stockton-on-Tees 01642 617000
Appleby Shaw
p434 . . . . Windsor 01753 860606
Arani & Co
p384 . . . . .Southall 020 8893 5000
Armitage Sykes LLP
p255 . . . . .Huddersfield 01484 344140
Arora Lodhi Heath
p7 . . . . .London W3 020 8993 9995
Ash Clifford
p157 . . . . .Bridgwater 01278 451327
Aston Clark
p8 . . . . London W3 020 8752 1122
Atkins Hope Solicitors
p204 . . . . Croydon 020 8680 5018
Atkins Law Solicitors
p220 . . . . Exeter 01392 671657
Atkinson Cave & Stuart
p146 . . . . Blackpool 01253 293151
Atlee Chung & Company
p8 . . . . London W1 020 7287 9988
Audu & Co
p8 . . . . Islington 020 7278 9340
David Auld & Co
p130 . . . . .Bedlington 01670 826870
p319 . . . . Morpeth 01670 505844
Austin Ryder & Co
p189 . . . . Cheshunt 01992 624804
Avery Naylor
p404 . . . . Swansea 01792 463276
B&C Solicitors - The Law Shop
p372 . . . . Scarborough 01723 379777
BCL Burton Copeland
p9 . . . . .London WC2 020 7430 2277
BTMK Solicitors LLP
p387 . . . . Southend-on-Sea 01702 339222
BWTLaw LLP
p219 . . . . Epsom 01372 725655
Bailey & Haigh
p373 . . . . Selby 01757 705191
Baker Gray & Co
p323 . . Newcastle upon Tyne 0191 222 0203
Bankside Law Ltd
p9 . . . . London SE1 0844 745 4000
Bannister & Co
p443 . . . . Yeovil 01935 433133
Bark & Co
p9 . . . . London EC4 020 7353 1990
Barker & Co
p256 . . . . Hull 01482 219966
Barker Booth & Eastwood
p146 . . . . Blackpool 01253 362500
John Barkers
p297 . . . . .Mablethorpe 01507 477673
Barnes Harrild & Dyer
p204 . . . . Croydon 020 8681 5128
Marcus Barnett
p10. . . . . London SW1 020 7235 9215
Norman H Barnett & Co
p11. . . . . London E6 020 8471 2112
Paul R Baron
p183 . . . . Carshalton 020 8401 2251
Barricella Hughes Marchant
p262 . . . . Ipswich 01473 226225
Lesley P Barry
p434 . . . . .Windsor 01753 860061
Bartlett Gooding & Weelen
p378 . . . . . Shepton Mallet 01749 343091
Atha Barton & Co
p237 . . . . Guisborough 01287 633242
S S Basi & Co
p259 . . . . Ilford 020 8518 1236
Nicholas Bates
p126 . . . . Basingstoke 01256 331278
Bazeer & Co
p11. . . . . London SW19 020 8543 6600
Beecham Peacock
p323 . . Newcastle upon Tyne 0191 232 3048
Beevers Solicitors
p119 . . Ashton-under-Lyne 0161 339 9697
Belmores
p334 . . . . Norwich 01603 499999
Ben Hoare Bell & Co
p323 . . Newcastle upon Tyne 0191 275 2626
Bennett Griffin
p369 . . . . .Rustington 01903 777690
Bennett Richmond
p270 . . . . Lanchester 01207 521843
Daniel Berman & Co
p12. . . . . London NW5 020 7428 7798
Bernard Chill & Axtell
p385 . . . . . . Southampton 023 8022 8821
Berry & Berry
p299 . . . . Maidstone 01622 690777
p412 . . . . Tonbridge 01732 355911
Berry Redmond & Robinson
p429 . . . Weston-super-Mare 01934 513963
Richard Best & Co
p368 . . . . Rugby 01788 571135
Beswicks
p239 . . . . Hanley 01782 205000
Bhatia Best
p336 . . . . Nottingham 0115 950 3231
David Billingham & Partners
p187 . . . . Cheltenham 01242 676224
Bilton Hammond LLP
p192 . . . . Chesterfield 01246 232418
p311 . . . . Mansfield 01623 675800
Bindmans LLP
p12. . . . . . . London WC1 020 7833 4433
Bird & Co
p232 . . . . Grantham 01476 591711
p322 . . . . Newark 01636 650880
Birnberg Peirce & Partners
p13. . . . . Camden 020 7911 0166
Bishop & Co
p321 . . . . New Mills 01663 746730
Bishop McBride Olden
p177 . . . . Cardiff 029 2049 0111
Blackburn & Co
p226 . . . . Fleetwood 01253 872238
Blackhurst Budd LLP
p146 . . . . Blackpool 01253 629300
Blaser Mills
p120 . . . . Aylesbury 01296 434416
p249 . . . . High Wycombe 01494 450171
Ann Blyth-Cook & Co
p387 . . . . . Southend-on-Sea 01702 462999
Bobbetts Mackan
p161 . . . . .Bristol 0117 929 9001
Bone & Payne LLP
p198 . . . . Colwyn Bay 01492 532385
p291 . . . . Llandudno 01492 876354
C W Booth & Co
p144 . . . . . .Bishop Auckland 01388 606660
D S Bosher & Co
p254 . . . . Hove 01273 721913
Bowser Ollard & Bentley
p312 . . . . March 01354 652606
p435 . . . . .Wisbech 01945 583194
John Boyle & Co
p362 . . . . Redruth 01209 213507
Bradleys
p212 . . . . Dover 01304 204080
Bramwell Browne Odedra
p189 . . . . Chesham 01494 782244
Brand Mellon LLP
p230 . . . . Gloucester 01452 524088
Bray & Bray
p250 . . . . Hinckley 01455 639900
p279 . . . . Leicester 0116 254 8871
Brearleys Solicitors
p128 . . . . Batley 01924 473065
Brewer Harding & Rowe
p125 . . . . .Barnstaple 01271 342271
p261 . . . . .Ilfracombe 01271 863495
Brice & Co
p168 . . . . Bures 01787 227199
Bridge McFarland
p284 . . . . Lincoln 01522 518888
Brignalls Balderston Warren
p394 . . . . .Stevenage 01438 359311
Brinley Morris Rees & Jones
p292 . . . . Llanelli 01554 774241
Brook Oliver
p321 . . . . New Milton 01425 616809
Brooke-Taylors
p172 . . . . Buxton 01298 22741
Broomhead & Saul
p261 . . . . Ilminster 01460 57056
Broudie Jackson Canter
p286 . . . . Liverpool 0151 227 1429
Brown & Corbishley
p323 . Newcastle under Lyme 01782 717888
Brown & Emery
p423 . . . . Watford 01923 225255
Brown Beer Nixon Mallon
p362 . . . . Redcar 01642 490202
Brown Turner Ross
p388 . . . . Southport 01704 542002
Bryan & Armstrong
p311 . . . . Mansfield 01623 624505
David Buck & Co
p159 . . . . Brighton 01273 621745
Burchell Williams Limited
p159 . . . . Brighton 01273 606555
Stephen Burdon Solicitors
p336 . . . . Nottingham 0115 950 0054
Burnett Barker
p171 . . . . . Bury St Edmunds 01284 701131
Burroughs
p299 . . . . Maidstone 01622 676976 / 676982
Burton & Co LLP
p381 . . . . Sleaford 01529 306008 / 306009
C R Burton & Co
p16 London SE20 020 8778 4455 / 8659 5775
Burton Copeland LLP
p302 . . . . .Manchester 0161 827 9500
p370 . . . . Sale 0161 905 8530
CMHT Solicitors
p420 . . . . Walsall 01922 646400
p420 . . . . Walsall 01922 743525
C Nicholls
p148 . . . . Bodmin 01208 76969
CVC Solicitors
p245 . . . . Hayle 01736 752246
p392 . . . . St Ives 01736 795456
James Calderbank
p205 . . . . Cullompton 01823 680697
Caldicott Gallimore
p282 . . . . Leominster 01568 614168
Canter Levin & Berg
p287 . . . . Liverpool 0151 239 1000
Terence Carney
p246 . . .Hebburn 0191 483 5422 / 483 8771
Carr & Co
p255 . . . . . . .Huddersfield 01484 467860
Carter Slater & Co
p331 . . . . Northampton 01604 717505
Carters
p351 . . . . Pontefract 01977 703224
Cartwright King
p336 . . . . Nottingham 0115 958 7444
Carvill & Johnson LLP
p136 . . . . .Birmingham 0121 476 9000
J P Cave & Co
p410 . . . . Thame 01844 216208
Chabra Cass & Co
p19. . . . . . .Brent 020 8450 9833 / 8452 2200
Chadwyck-Healey & Co
p19. . . . . London EC4 020 7353 6900
Chafes
p395 . . . . Stockport 0161 477 1525
Challinors
p427 . . . . . West Bromwich 0121 553 3211
Chapple & Co
p312 . . . . March 01354 652550
Chebsey & Co
p128 . . . . Beaconsfield 01494 670440
Chronnell Hibbert
p259 . . . . Hyde 0161 368 3434
Churchers
p354 . . . . Portsmouth 023 9286 2424
Clark Brookes
p427 . . . . . West Bromwich 0121 553 2576
Chris Clark
p176 . . . . Cannock 01543 573004
David Clark & Co
p20. . . . . London NW3 020 7433 1562
Clark Willis
p183 . . . . . .Catterick Garrison 01748 830000
Clarke & Hartland Solicitors
p177 . . . . Cardiff 029 2048 3181
Peter Clarke Solicitors
p413 . . . . .Totton 023 8066 6636
Clarkes
p409 . . . . .Telford 01952 291666
p425 . . . . .Wellington 01952 223548
Clarkson Hirst
p264 . . . . Kendal 01539 736916
Claude Hornby & Cox
p20. . . . . London EC4 020 7332 8269
Coffers
p117 . . . . Amersham 01494 727323
Coffin Mew & Clover
p354 . . . . Portsmouth 023 9238 8021
Colebournes Solicitors and Advocates
p146 . . . . Blackpool 01253 293195
K J Commons & Co
p182 . . . . Carlisle 01228 822666
p431 . . . . .Whitehaven 01946 66699
p440 . . . . Workington 01900 604698
Coodes
p329 . . . . Newquay 01637 878111
Cook Taylor
p22. . . . . Greenwich 020 8854 1166
Sharon Coomber
p197 . . . . .Colchester 01206 769342
Cooper & Co
p444 . . . . York 01904 626266
Sheila Cooper LLB
p22. . . . . London NW6 020 7372 0510
John Copland & Son
p375 . . . . .Sheerness 01795 664431
Corcorans
p441 . . . . Worthing 01903 824428
Crangle Edwards
p185 . . . . Cheadle 0161 428 2331
Criminal Defence Solicitors
p23. . . . . London W1 020 7353 7000
Crombie Wilkinson
p374 . . . . Selby 01757 708957
Crompton Halliwell
p170 . . . . Bury 0161 797 9222
Crosse Wyatt Verney & Ayre
p383 . . . . South Molton 01769 572157
Crowley & Co
p178 . . . . Cardiff 029 2045 8895
Cumming & Riley
p233 . . . . Grays 01375 383691
Cunninghams
p302 . . . . .Manchester 0161 833 1600
Cuthbertsons
p119 . . . . Ashington 01670 813524
p148 . . . . Blyth 01670 352121
Cuttle & Co
p302 . . . . .Manchester 0161 835 2050
Cuttle & Co Solicitors
p340 . . . . .Oldham 0161 678 7443
DB Law
p173 . . . . .Camborne 01209 712428
p346 . . . . Penzance 01736 364261
Daniel & Edwards
p359 . . . . Ramsgate 01843 594651
David James & Company
p114 . . . . Aberystwyth 01970 615789
Lawrence Davies & Co
p26. .Hammersmith & Fulham 020 7381 1171
Davies Parsons Allchurch
p292 . . . . Llanelli 01554 749144
Davis-Law Associates
p184 . . . . . . Chalfont St Peter 01753 888776
Nicholas Daykin Solicitors
p120 . . . . .Attleborough 01953 453774
De Maid Solicitors & Advocates
p178 . . . . Cardiff 029 2023 5575
John Delaney & Co
p273 . . . . .Leeds 0113 246 8151
Denby & Co
p125 . . . . . .Barrow-in-Furness 01229 822366
Denhams
p236 . . . . Guildford 01483 456450

See p542 for the Firms Specialisations

4

Devas Keogh James
p347 . . . . . . Peterborough 01733 340666
Dobsons
p341 . . . . Orpington 01689 886300
Dollman & Pritchard
p183 . . . . Caterham 01883 347823
Downes & Siddall
p284 . . . . Lincoln 01522 543343
Draycott Browne Solicitors
p303 . . . . . . .Manchester 0161 228 2244
Dunn & Baker
p221 . . . . Exeter 01392 285000
EBR Attridge LLP
p28. . . . . . .London SE16 020 7231 5166
p28. . . . . . .London SW11 020 7228 7050
Eager & Co
p380 . . . . Skegness 01754 766688
Eddowes Perry & Osbourne
p403 . . . . .Sutton Coldfield 0121 686 9444
p403 . . . . .Sutton Coldfield 0121 686 9666
Edwards Duthie
p29. . . . . . . London E13 020 8514 9000
R L Edwards & Partners
p157 . . . . Bridgend 01656 656861
p413 . . . . .Treorchy 01443 775000
Joe Egan Solicitors
p149 . . . . Bolton 01204 368060
Elliot Mather LLP
p192 . . . . Chesterfield 01246 231288
p311 . . . . Mansfield 01623 655666
Elsey & Hodson
p347 . . . . . . Peterborough 01733 314064
Elwyn Jones & Co
p122 . . . . Bangor 01248 370224
Harvey Escott & Co
p169
. Burnham-on-Crouch 01621 784838 / 784839
Evans & Co
p226 . . . . Ferryhill 01740 657444
Evans & Davies
p113 . . . . .Aberaeron 01545 570335
Everett Tomlin Lloyd & Pratt
p352 . . . . Pontypool 01495 763333
Edward Fail Bradshaw & Waterson
p30. . . . . London 020 7264 2016
p30. . . . . London 020 7790 4032
Fairbrother & Darlow
p153 . . . . Bracknell 01344 420808
Fairweather Stephenson & Co
p225 . . . . .Felixstowe 01394 277941
Favell Smith & Lawson Solicitors
p375 . . . . Sheffield 0114 272 4381
Brian Ferris
p415 . . . . . Tunbridge Wells 01892 518609
Fieldings Porter
p149 . . . . Bolton 01204 540900
Firth Lindsay
p375 . . . . Sheffield 0114 276 0586
Andrew Fitzpatrick
p304 . . . . .Manchester 0161 248 9799
Fletcher Dervish
p33. . . . . Haringey 020 8800 4615
Foot Anstey
p408 . . . . Taunton 01823 625600
Forbes
p145 . . . . Blackburn 01254 580000
p356 . . . . Preston 01772 220022
Ford Simey LLP
p222 Exmouth 01395 272241 / 0800 169 3741
Roy Foreman & Co
p235 . . . . Grimsby 01472 355262
Forresters
p125 . . . .Barrow-in-Furness 01229 820297
John Fowlers LLP Solicitors
p197 . . . . .Colchester 01206 576151
Joseph Foxler & Co
p170 . . . . Bury 0161 797 4126
Foys Solicitors
p211 . . . . Doncaster 01302 327136
Franklins
p214 . . . . Dunstable 01582 699111
Franklins LLP
p332 . . . . . . Northampton 01604 828282
Fraser Dawbarns
p213 . . . . Downham Market 01366 383171
p266 . . . . King's Lynn 01553 666600
Frisby & Co
p392 . . . . Stafford 01785 244114
Fritchley Goldsmith
p124 . . . . .Barnsley 01226 215600
GC Law
p248 . . . . .Hereford 01432 275397
GHP Legal
p342 . . . . Oswestry 01691 659194
GLP Solicitors
p315 . . . . Middleton 0161 653 6295
Gangar & Co
p427 . . . . . West Bromwich 0121 553 4166
Gani & Co
p35. . . . . Lambeth 020 7733 8169
Garcha & Co
p35. . . . . London 020 7375 1888

Gardner Dallimore
p248 . . . . .Hereford 01432 263535
Gartsides
p113 . . . . Abergavenny 01873 857555
p216 . . . . .Ebbw Vale 01495 302109
Gaskell & Walker
p157 . . . . Bridgend 01656 653122
Gaynor-Smith Owen & Co
p300 . . . . Malvern 01684 560771
Craig Gee
p304 . . . . .Manchester 0161 666 9999
Gepp & Sons
p197 . . . . .Colchester 01206 369889
Reena Ghai Solicitors
p253 . . . . .Hounslow 020 8759 9959
Gildener Brett
p346 . . . . Penzance 01736 332533
Gittins McDonald
p442 . . . . Wrexham 01978 291662
Glaisyers
p138 . . . . . . .Birmingham 0121 233 2971
Glandfield & Cruddas
p417 . . . . Uttoxeter 01889 565657
Glansfields
p311 . . . . Mansfield 01623 627827
Goldstones
p405 . . . . Swansea 01792 643021
Gomer Williams & Co
p292 . . . . Llanelli 01554 755101
Clive Gomes Solicitors
p426 . . . . Wembley 020 8904 2614
Goodall Barnett James
p252 . . . . .Horley 01293 414448
p392 . . . St Leonards-on-Sea 01424 444475
Goodhand and Forsyth QualitySolicitors
p362 . . . . .Redhill 01737 773533
Gordon & Penney
p429 . . . Weston-super-Mare 01934 414161
R Gordon Roberts Laurie & Co
p292 . . . .Llangefni 01248 722215 / 723312
Grahame Stowe Bateson
p240 . . . . Harrogate 01423 562121
p274 . . . . .Leeds 0113 246 8163
p274 . . . . .Leeds 0113 255 8666
p274 . . . . .Leeds 0113 274 4611
David Gray Solicitors
p324 . . Newcastle upon Tyne 0191 232 9547
Grayson Willis Bennett
p375 . . . . Sheffield 0114 290 9500
Green & Co
p299 . . . . Maidstone 01622 676769
Christopher Green McCarrahers
p386 . . . . Southampton 023 8084 2765
Green Williamson Solicitors
p418 . . . . Wakefield 01924 291400
Greenfield Whiston
p265 . . . . Kettering 01536 410880
Gregsons
p337 . . . . Nottingham 0115 941 1999
Gareth Griffith & Company
p172 . . . . Caernarfon 01286 676869
Grindrods
p330 . . . .Newton-le-Willows 01925 221321
Gullands
p299 . . . . Maidstone 01622 678341
H2O Law LLP
p37. . . . . London EC4 020 7405 4700
Haddock & Company
p238 . . . . Halifax 01422 366010
Hains & Lewis Ltd
p320 . . . . Narberth 0845 408 0125
Haldanes
p37. . . . . London W1 020 7437 5629
Hallinan Blackburn Gittings & Nott
p38. . . . . London W1 020 7233 3999
John J Halliwell & Co
p380 . . . . Silsden 01535 653094
Hamer Childs
p439 . . . . Worcester 01905 724565
Hammon Oakley
p200 . . . . Coventry 024 7644 8585
Hamnett Osborne Tisshaw
p245 . . . . . .Haywards Heath 01444 443030
Hannays Solicitors and Advocates
p383 South Shields 0191 456 7893 / 455 5361
Hanne & Co
p38. . . . . . . .London SW11 020 7228 0017
Hanratty & Co
p330 . . . . Newtown 01686 626239
Hansell Drew & Co
p207 . . . . .Dartmouth 01803 834555
Harbans Singh
p139 . . . . .Birmingham 0121 551 4496
Hardy McBride & Co
p166 . . . . Bromley 020 8460 1999
Hargreaves Gilman
p305 . . . . .Manchester 0161 443 1711
Alistair Harper & Co
p245 . . . . .Haywards Heath 01444 457890
Harrison Bundey
p274 . . . . .Leeds 0113 200 7400
Harrison Clark LLP
p367 . . . . Ross-on-Wye 01989 562377

John F Harrison
p118 . . . Ashby-de-la-Zouch 01530 563655
Harrop White Vallance & Dawson
p311 . . . . Mansfield 01623 629221
Harthills
p367 . . . . Rotherham 01709 377399
Hasan Solicitors
p139 . . . . .Birmingham 0121 778 4003
Hathaways
p228 . . . . Gateshead 0191 477 2288
Hay & Kilner
p419 . . . . Wallsend 0191 262 8231
Stanley Hays
p246 . . . . . Heckmondwike 01924 403809
Headleys
p250 . . . . .Hinckley 01455 637815
Heath Sons & Broome
p305 . . . . .Manchester 0161 681 1933
Heckford Norton
p283 . . . . Letchworth 01462 682244
Hemsleys
p190 . . . . Chester 01244 382400
Heseltine Bray & Welsh
p124 . . . . .Barnsley 01226 210777
Hethertons LLP
p445 . . . . York 01904 528200
Hewitt Burrough & Co
p207 . . . . Dartford 01322 273833
Hewitts
p397 . . . . Stockton-on-Tees 01642 673701
Heyman & Co
p282 . . . . Leigh 01942 604135
Hickman & Rose
p41. . . . . .London N15 020 7700 2211
Hillis Solicitors
p305 . . . . .Manchester 0161 248 0500
Hills (Oldham)
p340 . . . . Oldham 0161 652 3231
Hindle Campbell
p330 . . . . North Shields 0191 296 1777
Hodge Jones & Allen LLP
p41. . . . . London NW1 020 7874 8300
Hodgson Coulthard & Co
p253 . . . . .Houghton Le Spring 0191 584 3333
Hogan Brown
p289 . . . . Liverpool 0151 243 7500
Charles Hoile
p322 . . . . Newbury 01635 45595
Holden & Co
p243 . . . . .Hastings 01424 722422
John Holden
p263 . . . . .Keighley 01535 667826
Holdens
p269 . . . . .Lancaster 01524 32484
Hoole & Co
p163 . . . . .Bristol 0117 942 8871
p163 . . . . .Bristol 0117 969 1436
Hornby Baker Jones & Wood
p328 . . . . .Newport 01633 262848
Howard & Co
p124 . . . . .Barnsley 01226 215215
Howells LLP
p367 . . . . Rotherham 01709 364000
J A Hughes
p126 . . . . Barry 01446 411000
J W Hughes & Co
p199 . . . . Conwy 01492 596596
Humphrys & Co
p363 . . . . .Rhyl 01745 343158
Hurlow & Partners
p179 . . . . Cardiff 029 2039 6087
Henry Hyams
p274 . . . . .Leeds 0113 243 2288
Inghams
p146 . . . . Blackpool 01253 626642
p226 . . . . Fleetwood 01253 873481
Isherwood & Hose
p249 . . . . Heywood 01706 360032 / 368741
JNP Legal
p314 . . . . . . Merthyr Tydfil 01685 350421
Gary Jacobs & Co
p45. . . . . London E18 020 8536 4050
Jameson & Hill
p248 . . . . Hertford 01992 554881
Janes
p46. . . . . . . London SW1 020 7930 5100
Jasper & Vincent
p386 . . . . Southampton 01489 885788
Andrew Jay & Co
p284 . . . . .Lincoln 01522 539111
Andrew Jay & Co (Philip Hanby Limited)
p228 . . . . Gainsborough 01427 612412
Julian Jefferson
p350 . . . . Plymouth 01752 250850
Michael Jenkins
p233 . . . . Gravesend 01474 822787
Jennings Perks & Co
p420 . . . . Walsall 01922 459000
Johar & Co
p280 . . . . Leicester 0116 254 3345
The John W Davies Partnership
p329 . . . . .Newport 01633 841773

The Johnson Partnership
p209 . . . . Derby 01332 370473
p311 . . . . Mansfield 01623 427575
p337 . . . . Nottingham 0115 941 9141
Jonas Roy Bloom
p139 . . . . .Birmingham 0121 212 4111
The Jonathan Morrissey Practice
p152 . . . . Bournemouth 01202 310999
Geraint Jones & Co
p330 . . . . Newtown 01686 627935
Mark Jones & Partners
p289 . . . . Liverpool 0151 286 9594
P Lloyd Jones & Co
p318 . . . . . . Mold 01352 758533 / 758534
Jones Robertson
p369 . . . . Runcorn 01928 711119
T Llewellyn Jones
p405 . . . . Swansea 01639 842235
Terry Jones Solicitors & Advocates
p379 . . . . Shrewsbury 01743 285888
Jordans
p210 . . . . Dewsbury 01924 457171
Kaim Todner Ltd
p119 . . . . Ashford 01233 662002
p47. . . . . Islington 020 7700 0070
p47. . . . . London EC4 020 7353 6660
p47. . . . . . . London SE17 020 7701 4747
Kangs Solicitors
p139 . . . . .Birmingham 0121 449 9888
Kaufmanlegal
p306 . . . . .Manchester 0161 205 3955
Andrew Keenan & Co
p48. . . . . . . London SE20 020 8659 0332
Kelcey & Hall
p163 . . . . .Bristol 0117 927 9604
Keppe Rofer
p156 . . . . Brecon 01874 624627
Christian Khan Solicitors
p49. . . . . London WC1 020 7631 9500
Kidd & Spoor
p431 . . . . .Whitley Bay 0191 297 0011
KieranClarkeGreen
p192 . . . . Chesterfield 01246 211006
Anthony King & Co
p126 . . . . .Basildon 01268 240400
Rodney King & Partners
p163 . . . . .Bristol 0117 926 5201
Kingsley Brookes
p256 . . . . .Huddersfield 01484 302800
Kirby Sheppard
p268 . . . . Kingswood 0845 840 0045
Kirwans
p134 . . . . Birkenhead 0151 608 9078
Knowles Benning
p295 . . . . Luton 01582 798000
Simon Lacey Law Associates
p430 . . . . .Weymouth 01305 777711
Lambert Taylor & Gregory
p228 . . . . Gateshead 0191 477 0616
Lansbury Worthington
p51. . . . . London W6 020 8563 9797
Lanyon Bowdler LLP
p409 . . . . .Telford 01952 291222
Large & Gibson
p388 . . . . Southsea 023 9229 6296
Larken & Co
p322 . . . . Newark 01636 703333
Samuel L Larye & Co
p156 . . . . Brentford 020 8568 7022
Law Partners Solicitors Ltd
p51. . . . . London EC1 0870 600 9444
Lawson & Thompson
p119 . . . . Ashington 01670 813588
p130 . . . . .Bedlington 01670 530700
Owen Lawton
p350 . . . . Plymouth 01752 201169
Layton & Co
p244 . . . . . . .Haverfordwest 01437 766671
Leadbeater & Kay
p398 . . . . Stoke-on-Trent 01782 201933
Ledgisters
p52. . . . . London W6 020 8746 1122
Monica Lentin & Co
p175 . . . . Cambridge 01223 314452
Leonard & Co
p386 . . . . . . Southampton 023 8023 3242
p386 . . . . . . Southampton 023 8023 4433
Leslie & Co
p254 . Hounslow 020 8577 5491 / 8572 7252
Lester Morrill
p275 . . . . .Leeds 0113 245 8549
Letchers
p364 . . . . Ringwood 01425 471424
Levenes Solicitors
p53. . . .Haringey 020 8881 7777 / 8881 6764
Keith Levin & Co
p258 . . . . Huyton 0151 480 5777
Leviten Thompson & Co
p376 . . . . Sheffield 0114 276 9321
G Huw Lewis
p320 . . . . Neath 01639 637181

Lichfield Reynolds
p398 Stoke-on-Trent 01782 289122
p398 Stoke-on-Trent 01782 313212
E C Lidster & Co
p235 Grimsby 01472 348417
Linn & Associates Solicitors
p243 Harwich 01255 240880
Linskills Solicitors
p289 Liverpool 0151 236 2224
Robert Lizar
p307 Manchester 0161 226 2319
Lloyd Brennand
p156 Brentford 020 8569 9020
Lloyd Rehman & Co
p55 London EC4 020 7778 7550
Llys Cennen Solicitors
p117 Ammanford 01269 592658 / 592790
Robert Locke
p224 Fareham 01329 822722
Roger Long & Co
p205 Croydon 020 8668 5071
Lound Mulrenan & Jefferies Solicitors
p55 Southwark 020 7793 4012
Lucas & Wyllys
p234 Great Yarmouth 01493 663124
p234 Great Yarmouth 01493 855555
Lumb & Macgill
p154 Bradford 01274 730666
M23LAW Solicitors (Hedley-Saunders & Co)
p202 Crawley 0844 264 0999
MFG Solicitors
p409 Telford 01952 641651
MSB Solicitors LLP
p289 Liverpool 0151 281 9040
McCarthy Stewart & Booty Solicitors
p400 Stowmarket 01449 612343
McCormicks
p240 Harrogate 01423 530630
McDonald & Co
p56 London W1 020 7834 2679
Malcolm McGuinness
p116 Altrincham 0161 928 7134
McKeag & Co
p231 Gosforth 0191 213 1010
McKenzie Bell Solicitors
p401 Sunderland 0191 567 4857
Gavin McKenzie
p379 Shrewsbury 01743 235957
McKinnells
p284 Lincoln 01522 541181
Mackrell & Thomas
p289 Liverpool 0151 480 3666
MacLaverty Cooper Atkins
p267 Kingston upon Thames 020 8549 9994
McManus Seddon
p154 Bradford 01274 741841
McMillen Hamilton McCarthy
p57 London E3 020 8980 6060
McPhersons
p395 Stockbridge 01794 389002
Malletts Solicitors
p266 King's Lynn 01553 777744
Mander Hadley & Co
p200 Coventry 024 7663 1212
Mansouri & Son
p205 Croydon 020 8401 7352
Maples Solicitors LLP
p389 Spalding 01775 722261
Andrew Markham & Co
p182 Carmarthen 01267 221550 / 236199
Martin & Strain
p358 Pwllheli 01758 612042
Mayo Wynne Baxter LLP
p215 Eastbourne 01323 730543
Meikles
p397 Stockton-on-Tees 01740 620255
Meldrum Young Solicitors
p390 St Albans 01727 840333
Merry & Co
p369 Ryde 01983 811722
Mian & Co
p140 Birmingham 0121 684 8000
Middleweeks Solicitors
p307 Manchester 0161 839 7255
Miles Hutchinson & Lithgow
p371
Saltburn-by-the-Sea 01287 623049 / 622056
Millichips
p427 West Bromwich 0121 500 6363
Geoffrey Milne
p425 Wellington 01952 223300 / 223381
Alistair Mitchell
p157 Bridgnorth 01746 761545
Mohabirs
p61 London SW4 020 7720 5742 / 7622 5495
Moore & Tibbits
p422 Warwick 01926 491181
Morecrofts Solicitors LLP
p134 Birkenhead 0151 666 2210
John Morgan Solicitors
p140 Birmingham 0121 233 1852

Mulcahy Smith
p229 Gateshead 0191 490 1000
James Murray Solicitors
p150 Bootle 0151 933 3333
p290 Liverpool 0151 207 9910
Martin Murray & Associates
p361 Reading 0118 950 8577
p382 Slough 01753 551313
p427 West Drayton 01895 431332
Murrays Partnership
p62 Southwark 020 7701 8653
Myer Wolff
p257 Hull 01482 223693
Ned Nwoko
p63 Ealing 020 8997 6733
Needham Poulier & Partners
p63 London N17 020 8808 6622
Needhams
p154 Bradford 01274 371088
Nicholls Christie & Crocker
p417 Uxbridge 01895 256216
Mark Nicholls
p265 Kettering 01536 502843
Nicol Denvir & Purnell
p180 Cardiff 029 2079 6311
Noble
p377 Shefford 01462 814055
Norcross Lees & Riches
p341 Oldham 0161 624 6034
Norrie Waite & Slater
p377 Sheffield 0114 248 4890
p377 Sheffield 0114 276 6166
Gordon O'Brien
p258 Huyton 0151 489 4899
O'Garra's
p276 Leeds 0113 247 1477
O'Keeffe Solicitors
p64 Brent 020 7644 8800
O'Neill Solicitors
p326 Newcastle upon Tyne 0191 232 9008
Oliver & Co
p191 Chester 01244 312306
Olliers
p308 Manchester 0161 834 1515
R J Osborne & Co
p199 Corby 01536 204111
Oslers Solicitors
p400 Stowmarket 01449 774670
Owen White & Catlin
p225 Feltham 020 8890 2836
PCB Solicitors LLP
p269 Knighton 01547 520254
p379 Shrewsbury 01743 248148
Page Nelson
p285 Lincoln 01522 531741
Painters
p399 Stourport-on-Severn 01299 822033
Paisleys
p440 Workington 01900 602235
Musa A Patel & Co
p210 Dewsbury 01924 437800
Margaret Payne
p182 Carlisle 01228 521383
Peach Grey & Co
p386 Southampton 023 8033 4695
Pearson Caulfield
p326 Newcastle upon Tyne 0191 261 8878
Pearson Fielding Polson
p290 Liverpool 0151 236 3636
The Penhale Practice
p319 Morecambe 01524 401010
Penmans
p264 Kenilworth 01926 858222
Pepperells
p373 Scunthorpe 01724 871999
Percy Short & Cuthbert
p67 Islington 020 7700 0265
Petherbridge Bassra Solicitors
p154 Bradford 01274 724114
Phillips
p312 Mansfield 01623 658556
Samuel Phillips Law Firm
p326 Newcastle upon Tyne 0191 232 8451
Pickup & Scott
p121 Aylesbury 01296 397794
Pinniger Finch & Co
p428 Westbury 01373 823791
Michael W Pipe
p345 Paignton 01803 559746 / 529797
Place Blair & Hatch
p331 Northallerton 01609 780101
Platt Halpern
p308 Manchester 0161 224 2555
p309 Manchester 0161 834 3114
p341 Oldham 0161 626 4955
Pluck Andrew & Co
p259 Hyde 0161 368 6311
Pond Marsh
p147 Blackpool 01253 620466
Poole Alcock
p203 Crewe 01270 256665
p333 Northwich 01606 350445

Poole Townsend
p125 Barrow-in-Furness 01229 811811
Powleys
p294 Lowestoft 01502 581121
Pragesh & McKenzie Solicitors
p411 Thornton Heath 020 8689 0089
Price & Kelway
p316 Milford Haven 01646 695311
Purcell Parker
p141 Birmingham 0121 236 9781
Quality Solicitors Mewies
p381 Skipton 01756 799000
QualitySolicitors C Turner
p145 Blackburn 01254 688400
QualitySolicitors Gruber Garratt
p341 Oldham 0161 665 3502
QualitySolicitors Jordans
p212 Doncaster 01302 365374
Donald Race & Newton
p169 Burnley 01282 433241
Rainer Hughes
p156 Brentwood 01227 226644
Rawstorne Heran Solicitors
p400 Stratford-upon-Avon 01789 267646
Red Kite Law
p183 Carmarthen 01267 239000
p345 Pembroke Dock 01646 681529
Redfearns
p246 Heckmondwike 01924 403745 / 404601
Michael J Reed Ltd
p183 Carmarthen 01267 281675
Rees Page
p133 Bilston 01902 577776
Richardson Smith & Co
p189 Chesham 01494 772773
Richmond Anderson Goudie
p191 Chester-le-Street 0191 388 7884
Lee Rigby Partnership
p283 Leyland 01772 421748
Riley Hayes & Co
p438 Wolverhampton 01902 773666
Stephen Rimmer LLP
p216 Eastbourne 01323 644222
Roach Pittis
p328 Newport 01983 524431
Roberts Moore Nicholas Jones
p134 Birkenhead 0151 647 0000
Paul Robinson Solicitors
p428 Westcliff-on-Sea 01702 338338
R P Robinson
p281 Leicester 0116 262 1462
Roger James Clements & Partners
p329 Newport 01633 263316 / 663316
Robin Rose
p332 Northampton 01604 760168
Ross Solicitors Ltd
p406 Swindon 01793 512960
Rowbis Solicitors
p230 Gloucester 01452 301903
Rowland Tildesley & Harris
p433 Willenhall 01902 366571
Rundlewalker
p222 Exeter 01392 209209
Russell Jones & Walker
p141 Birmingham 0121 233 8300
p164 Bristol 0117 374 2222
p180 Cardiff 029 2026 2800
p74 London WC2 020 7657 1555
p309 Manchester 0161 383 3500
p326 Newcastle upon Tyne 0191 323 3000
p377 Sheffield 0114 276 6868
p419 Wakefield 01924 234300
Russell-Cooke LLP
p267 Kingston upon Thames 020 8546 6111
Michael Salt
p365 Rochdale 01706 646655
Sanders & Co
p399 Stourbridge 01384 375437 / 378991
Sanders Witherspoon LLP
p156 Brentwood 01277 221010
Sansbury Douglas
p164 Bristol 0117 926 5341
Sarginsons Law LLP
p201 Coventry 024 7655 3181
S Satha & Co
p76 Newham 020 8471 9484
Scanlans
p402 Sunderland 0191 565 2565
Scotts Wright
p283 Leyburn 01966 22227
Seatons Solicitors
p199 Corby 01536 276300
Sehgal & Co
p142 Birmingham 0121 772 2226
Sergeant & Collins
p373 Scunthorpe 01724 864215
Sharman Law
p130 Bedford 01234 303030
Shaw Graham Kersh
p78 London W1 020 7734 9700
Shelley & Co
p175 Cambridge 01223 359441

Clive Shepherd & Co
p420 Walsall 01922 647797
Shepherd Harris & Co
p219 Enfield 020 8363 8341
Gordon Shine & Co
p78 London NW10 020 8969 7033
Siddiqui & Co
p242 Harrow 020 8423 2400
Silks
p321 Netherton 01384 236101
p382 Smethwick 0121 558 1147
Sills & Betteridge LLP
p151 Boston 01205 364615
p381 Skegness 01754 610101
p389 Spalding 01775 714874
Richard Silver
p309 Manchester 0161 834 9494
Singleton Winn McDermott Solicitors
p326 Newcastle upon Tyne 0191 265 8817
Smith & Copsey
p419 Wallsend 0191 262 4428
Ashley Smith & Co
p80 Lewisham 020 8463 0099
Smith Bates
p296 Lyndhurst 023 8028 3414
Smith Brown & Sprawson
p295 Luton 01582 876900
J H Smith
p182 Carlisle 01228 521383
The Smith Partnership
p170 Burton-on-Trent 01283 536471
p281 Leicester 0116 247 2000
p398 Stoke-on-Trent 01782 324454
p404 Swadlincote 01283 226444
Solomon Levy
p295 Luton 01582 425817 / 414948
Sonn Macmillan
p80 London 020 7377 8889
Southern Stewart & Walker
p384 South Shields 0191 456 7788
Southerns
p169 Burnley 01282 438446
p198 Colne 01282 863113
p321 Nelson 01282 603663
Spencer & Fisch
p277 Leeds 0113 264 7603
H Michael Spring
p353 Port Talbot 01639 897075
St Luce & Co
p82 London SE15 020 7635 9131
Steadman Jones & Bell
p118 Ammanford 01269 592306
R W Stebbings
p350 Plymouth 01752 202287
Steele & Son
p198 Colne 01282 868000
Steele Ford & Newton
p321 Nelson 01282 692531
Lawrence Stephens
p82 London EC1 020 7935 1211
Stephensons Solicitors LLP
p282 Leigh 01942 777777
Sternberg Reed
p366 Romford 01708 766155
Steven Young & Co
p188 Cheltenham 01242 257269
p230 Gloucester 01452 332882
Stevens
p370 Saffron Walden 01799 526849
p393 Stafford 01785 250908
p398 Stoke-on-Trent 01782 343353
Chris Stevenson
p212 Doncaster 01302 341243
Stokoe Partnership
p83 Waltham Forest 020 8558 8884
Andrew Storch
p361 Reading 0118 958 4407
Straw & Pearce
p293 Loughborough 01509 268931
David Street & Company
p202 Crawley 01293 616191
Sugare & Co
p277 Leeds 0113 244 6978
Switalski's
p419 Wakefield 01924 882000
Sykes Lee & Brydson
p445 York 01904 529000
p445 York 01904 731100
Symes Bains Broomer
p373 Scunthorpe 01724 281616
Talbot Walker LLP
p118 Andover 01264 363354
p127 Basingstoke 01256 332404
Talbots Legal Advice Centre
p399 Stourbridge 01384 445850 / 447777
Tanburghs O'Brien Lahaise
p85 Camden 020 7372 6614
Tang Bentley & Jackson
p224 Fareham 01329 220401
Tanner & Taylor LLP
p115 Aldershot 01252 316565
Taylor Lewis
p181 Cardigan 01239 621999

See p542 for the Firms Specialisations

Sharon Taylor Associates
p353 Poole 01202 759769

Thompson & Co
p87 Wandsworth 020 8767 5005

Thompsons (formerly Robin/Brian Thompson & Partners)
p277 Leeds 0113 205 6300
p377 Sheffield 0114 270 3300

Thomson Webb & Corfield
p176 Cambridge 01223 578068

Thornes
p438 Wolverhampton 01902 313311

Peter Thubron & Co
p402 Sunderland 0191 510 1221

Thursfields
p440 Worcester 01905 730450

Tosswill & Co
p87 Lambeth 020 8674 9494

Tracey Barlow Furniss & Co
p363 Retford 01777 707677

Ronnie Tremlett & Co
p160 Brighton 01273 696132

Trobridges
p350 Plymouth 01752 664022
p412 Torpoint 01752 812787

Tudor Williams & Co
p443 Wrexham 01978 362006

Tudur Owen Roberts Glynne & Co
p122 Bangor 01248 362315 / 355826
p122 Bangor 01248 600171
p147 Blaenau Ffestiniog 01766 830206
p172 Caernarfon 01286 672207 / 672851
p251 Holyhead 01407 762374
p314 Menai Bridge 01248 712624

VHS Fletchers Solicitors
p339 Nottingham 0115 959 9550

Jay Vadher & Co
p89 London E15 020 8519 3000

Rhys Vaughan
p311 Manchester 0161 224 1439

Veja and Co Solicitors
p385 Southall 020 8574 2626

Veseys Solicitors
p143 Birmingham 0121 523 1123

Vickers & Co
p89 Ealing 020 8579 2559 / 8840 3999

Vickers Chisman & Wishlade
p397 Stockton-on-Tees 01642 615439

Victor Lissack Roscoe & Coleman
p89 London W1 020 7487 2505

Vyman Solicitors
p233 Gravesend 01474 537270

WBW Solicitors
p413 Torquay 0870 701 4321

Waddington Webber
p264 Keighley 01535 662644 / 662647

Wains
p297 Macclesfield 01625 429511

Waitt & Co Solicitors
p177 Canterbury 01227 470600

Clive Walker
p277 Leeds 0113 268 4660

Walker Lahive
p350 Plymouth 01752 551722

Walkers
p367 Rossendale 01706 213565

Walter Wilson Richmond
p242 Harrow 020 8427 8484

Wannop Fox Staffurth & Bray
p148 Bognor Regis 01243 864001
p442 Worthing 01903 201120

Wansbroughs
p210 Devizes 01380 733300
p314 Melksham 01225 703222

Warner Goodman LLP
p355 Portsmouth 023 9275 3575

Rodney Warren & Co
p216 Eastbourne 01323 430430

Watkins & Gunn
p352 Pontypool 01495 762244

Alasdair Watson & Co
p327 Newcastle upon Tyne 0191 488 4521

Paul J Watson
p315 Middlesbrough 01642 293427

V G Waugh
p348 Peterlee 0191 527 2727

Weightmans LLP
p207 Dartford 020 7822 1900

Welch & Co
p181 Cardigan 01239 614070

Nigel Weller & Co
p283 Lewes 01273 487123

Wessex Solicitors Chambers Ltd
p355 Portsmouth 023 9238 1114

Simon West
p128 Bath 01225 482001

Whatley Recordon
p300 Malvern 01684 892939

J B Wheatley & Co
p91 London SE8 020 8479 8000

Whitelock & Storr
p91 London WC1 020 7405 3913

Whitfields
p227 Formby 01704 878501

Whiting & Purches
p383 Solihull 0121 605 5050

Whittinghams
p157 Bridgend 01656 653485

Widdows Mason
p282 Leigh 01942 673311
p422 Warrington 01925 632267
p432 Wigan 01942 244294

Wilkinson & Butler
p392 St Neots 01480 219229

Wilkinson Woodward
p238 Halifax 01422 339600

Williams & Co
p217 Edgware 020 8952 8882
p296 Luton 01582 723322

Williams MacDougall & Campbell
p442 Worthing 01903 214186

Williamson & Soden
p143 Birmingham 0121 333 4848
p383 Solihull 0121 733 8000

Wills Chandler
p127 Basingstoke 01256 322911

Wilson & Bird
p121 Aylesbury 01296 436766

Wilson & Co
p92 London N17 020 8808 7535

Windeatts
p413 Totnes 01803 862233

Wiseman Lee LLP
p92 Newham 020 8215 1000
p92 Waltham Forest 020 8215 1000

Woodcocks
p121 Bacup 01706 874487
p171 Bury 0161 761 4611
p359 Rawtenstall 01706 225621 / 215018

Woodfines LLP
p147 Bletchley 01908 366333

Woodford Robinson
p333 Northampton 01604 624926

Aidan Woods & Co
p165 Bristol 0117 952 2006

Michael G Wooldridge
p143 Birmingham 0121 706 2259

Wragg Mark-Bell Solicitors
p182 Carlisle 01228 711728

Nicholas Wray Solicitor
p244 Haverhill 01440 704467

Wright & McMillan Bennett
p409 Telford 01952 291100

Wright & Morton
p402 Sunderland 0191 567 4289

Desmond Wright & Co
p245 Hayes 020 8561 4888

William Wright & Son
p213 Dudley 01384 255344

Yarwood Stimpson & Co
p431 Whitley Bay 0191 297 0123

Yates Ardern
p120 Ashton-under-Lyne 0161 330 3332

P H Yeung
p93 London W1 020 7287 1882

P C D York & Co
p93 London W6 020 8741 4512

Gordon Young Solicitors Ltd
p296 Luton 01582 405577

Julian Young & Co
p93 London W1 020 7724 8414

Youngs Criminal Defence Services Limited
p377 Sheffield 0114 249 5444

CRIME - JUVENILE

Alexander & Partners
p5 Brent 020 8965 7121

Arora Lodhi Heath
p7 London W3 020 8993 9995

BCL Burton Copeland
p9 London WC2 020 7430 2277

Bannister & Co
p443 Yeovil 01935 433133

Barker & Co
p256 Hull 01482 219966

Norman H Barnett & Co
p11 London E6 020 8471 2112

Paul R Baron
p183 Carshalton 020 8401 2251

Barricella Hughes Marchant
p262 Ipswich 01473 226225

Nicholas Bates
p126 Basingstoke 01256 331278

Beecham Peacock
p323 Newcastle upon Tyne 0191 232 3048

Belmores
p334 Norwich 01603 499999

Ben Hoare Bell & Co
p323 Newcastle upon Tyne 0191 275 2626

Daniel Berman & Co
p12 London NW5 020 7428 7798

David Billingham & Partners
p187 Cheltenham 01242 676224

Bishop McBride Olden
p177 Cardiff 029 2049 0111

Blackhurst Budd LLP
p146 Blackpool 01253 629300

Bleasdale & Co
p431 Whitehaven 01946 692165

Ann Blyth-Cook & Co
p387 Southend-on-Sea 01702 462999

C W Booth & Co
p144 Bishop Auckland 01388 606660

Brice & Co
p168 Bures 01787 227199

Broudie Jackson Canter
p286 Liverpool 0151 227 1429

Brown Beer Nixon Mallon
p362 Redcar 01642 490202

David Buck & Co
p159 Brighton 01273 621745

Burchell Williams Limited
p159 Brighton 01273 606555

Stephen Burdon Solicitors
p336 Nottingham 0115 950 0054

Burton & Co LLP
p381 Sleaford 01529 306008 / 306009

Burton Copeland LLP
p302 Manchester 0161 827 9500
p370 Sale 0161 905 8530

James Calderbank
p205 Cullompton 01823 680697

Caldicott Gallimore
p282 Leominster 01568 614168

Carr & Co
p255 Huddersfield 01484 467860

Carter Slater & Co
p331 Northampton 01604 717505

Carters
p351 Pontefract 01977 703224

Cartwright King
p336 Nottingham 0115 958 7444

Chabra Cass & Co
p19 Brent 020 8450 9833 / 8452 2200

Chadwyck-Healey & Co
p19 London EC4 020 7353 6900

Chafes
p395 Stockport 0161 477 1525

Chapple & Co
p312 March 01354 652550

Churchers
p271 Lee-on-the-Solent 023 9255 1500
p354 Portsmouth 023 9286 2424

Clark Brookes
p427 West Bromwich 0121 553 2576

Claude Hornby & Cox
p20 London EC4 020 7332 8269

Coffers
p117 Amersham 01494 727323

Sheila Cooper LLB
p22 London NW6 020 7372 0510

John Copland & Son
p375 Sheerness 01795 664431

Corcorans
p441 Worthing 01903 824428

Criminal Defence Solicitors
p23 London W1 020 7353 7000

Cunninghams
p302 Manchester 0161 833 1600

Cuttle & Co
p302 Manchester 0161 835 2050

De Maid Solicitors & Advocates
p178 Cardiff 029 2023 5575

John Delaney & Co
p273 Leeds 0113 246 8151

Devas Keogh James
p347 Peterborough 01733 340666

Dobsons
p341 Orpington 01689 886300

Draycott Browne Solicitors
p303 Manchester 0161 228 2244

Eager & Co
p380 Skegness 01754 766688

Eddowes Perry & Osbourne
p403 Sutton Coldfield 0121 686 9444

Joe Egan Solicitors
p149 Bolton 01204 368060

Edward Fail Bradshaw & Waterson
p30 London 020 7264 2016
p30 London 020 7790 4032

Brian Ferris
p415 Tunbridge Wells 01892 518609

Andrew Fitzpatrick
p304 Manchester 0161 248 9799

Fletcher Dervish
p33 Haringey 020 8800 4615

Forbes
p145 Blackburn 01254 580000

Roy Foreman & Co
p235 Grimsby 01472 355262

Fritchley Goldsmith
p124 Barnsley 01226 215600

GC Law
p248 Hereford 01432 275397

Gani & Co
p35 Lambeth 020 7733 8169

Garcha & Co
p35 London 020 7375 1888

Gardner Dallimore
p248 Hereford 01432 263535

Gartsides
p216 Ebbw Vale 01495 302109

Gepp & Sons
p197 Colchester 01206 369889

Clive Gomes Solicitors
p426 Wembley 020 8904 2614

Goodall Barnett James
p252 Horley 01293 414448
p392 St Leonards-on-Sea 01424 444475

Goodhand and Forsyth QualitySolicitors
p362 Redhill 01737 773533

Grayson Willis Bennett
p375 Sheffield 0114 290 9500

Green & Co
p299 Maidstone 01622 676769

Hallinan Blackburn Gittings & Nott
p38 London W1 020 7233 3999

Hamer Childs
p439 Worcester 01905 724565

Hansell Drew & Co
p207 Dartmouth 01803 834555

Hardy McBride & Co
p166 Bromley 020 8460 1999

Alistair Harper & Co
p245 Haywards Heath 01444 457890

John F Harrison
p118 Ashby-de-la-Zouch 01530 563655

Hasan Solicitors
p139 Birmingham 0121 778 4003

Heath Sons & Broome
p305 Manchester 0161 681 1933

Hemsleys
p190 Chester 01244 382400

M R Hepburn
p403 Sutton Coldfield 0121 378 0440

Hickman & Rose
p41 London N15 020 7700 2211

Hogan Brown
p289 Liverpool 0151 243 7500

John Holden
p263 Keighley 01535 667826

Howells LLP
p376 Sheffield 0114 249 6666

Humphrys & Co
p363 Rhyl 01745 343158

JNP Legal
p314 Merthyr Tydfil 01685 350421

Janes
p46 London SW1 020 7930 5100

Julian Jefferson
p350 Plymouth 01752 250850

Michael Jenkins
p233 Gravesend 01474 822787

The Johnson Partnership
p209 Derby 01332 370473
p311 Mansfield 01623 427575
p337 Nottingham 0115 941 9141

Jonas Roy Bloom
p139 Birmingham 0121 212 4111

The Jonathan Morrissey Practice
p152 Bournemouth 01202 310999

Kangs Solicitors
p139 Birmingham 0121 449 9888

Kaufmanlegal
p306 Manchester 0161 205 3955

Andrew Keenan & Co
p48 London SE20 020 8659 0332

Rodney King & Partners
p163 Bristol 0117 926 5201

Kingsley Brookes
p256 Huddersfield 01484 302800

Lansbury Worthington
p51 London W6 020 8563 9797

Large & Gibson
p388 Southsea 023 9229 6296

Samuel L Larye & Co
p156 Brentford 020 8568 7022

Lawson & Thompson
p130 Bedlington 01670 530700

Owen Lawton
p350 Plymouth 01752 201169

Ledgisters
p52 London W6 020 8746 1122

Monica Lentin & Co
p175 Cambridge 01223 314452

Leonard & Co
p386 Southampton 023 8023 3242

Leviten Thompson & Co
p376 Sheffield 0114 276 9321

G Huw Lewis
p320 Neath 01639 637181

E C Lidster & Co
p235 Grimsby 01472 348417

Linn & Associates Solicitors
p243 Harwich 01255 240880

Linskills Solicitors
p289 Liverpool 0151 236 2224

Lloyd Brennand
p156 Brentford 020 8569 9020

Lound Mulrenan & Jefferies Solicitors
p55 . . . Southwark 020 7793 4012

Lumb & Macgill
p154 . . . Bradford 01274 730666

M23LAW Solicitors (Hedley-Saunders & Co)
p202 . . . Crawley 0844 264 0999

McCarthy Stewart & Booty Solicitors
p400 . . . Stowmarket 01449 612343

Malcolm McGuinness
p116 . . . Altrincham 0161 928 7134

Gavin McKenzie
p379 . . . Shrewsbury 01743 235957

Mackrell & Thomas
p289 . . . Liverpool 0151 480 3666

MacLaverty Cooper Atkins
p267 . Kingston upon Thames 020 8549 9994

Meldrum Young Solicitors
p390 . . . St Albans 01727 840333

Merry & Co
p369 . . . Ryde 01983 811722

Mian & Co
p140 . . . Birmingham 0121 684 8000

Middleweeks Solicitors
p307 . . . Manchester 0161 839 7255

John Morgan Solicitors
p140 . . . Birmingham 0121 233 1852

Morgans
p180 . . . Cardiff 029 2072 9888

Martin Murray & Associates
p361 . . . Reading 0118 950 8577
p382 . . . Slough 01753 551313
p427 . . . West Drayton 01895 431332

Murrays Partnership
p62 . . . Southwark 020 7701 8653

Needham Poulier & Partners
p63 . . . London N17 020 8808 6622

Mark Nicholls
p265 . . . Kettering 01536 502843

Noble
p377 . . . Shefford 01462 814055

O'Garra's
p276 . . . Leeds 0113 247 1477

O'Keeffe Solicitors
p64 . . . Brent 020 7644 8800

Olliers
p308 . . . Manchester 0161 834 1515

R J Osborne & Co
p199 . . . Corby 01536 204111

Oslers Solicitors
p400 . . . Stowmarket 01449 774670

Musa A Patel & Co
p210 . . . Dewsbury 01924 437800

Margaret Payne
p182 . . . Carlisle 01228 521383

Peach Grey & Co
p386 . . . Southampton 023 8033 4695

Pearson Fielding Polson
p290 . . . Liverpool 0151 236 3636

Petherbridge Bassra Solicitors
p154 . . . Bradford 01274 724114

Phillips
p312 . . . Mansfield 01623 658556

Purcell Parker
p141 . . . Birmingham 0121 236 9781

Quality Solicitors Mewies
p381 . . . Skipton 01756 799000

Red Kite Law
p345 . . . Pembroke Dock 01646 681529

Redfearns
p246 . Heckmondwike 01924 403745 / 404601

Michael J Reed Ltd
p183 . . . Carmarthen 01267 281675

Riley Hayes & Co
p438 . . . Wolverhampton 01902 773666

Robin Rose
p332 . . . Northampton 01604 760168

Ross Solicitors Ltd
p406 . . . Swindon 01793 512960

Russell Jones & Walker
p74 . . . London WC2 020 7657 1555
p377 . . . Sheffield 0114 276 6868

Michael Salt
p365 . . . Rochdale 01706 646655

Sanders & Co
p399 . . . Stourbridge 01384 375437 / 378991

Sansbury Douglas
p164 . . . Bristol 0117 926 5341

Scanlans
p402 . . . Sunderland 0191 565 2565

Scotts Wright
p283 . . . Leyburn 01966 22227

Shaw Graham Kersh
p78 . . . London W1 020 7734 9700

Shelley & Co
p175 . . . Cambridge 01223 359441

Siddiqui & Co
p242 . . . Harrow 020 8423 2400

Silks
p382 . . . Smethwick 0121 558 1147

Richard Silver
p309 . . . Manchester 0161 834 9494

Singleton Winn McDermott Solicitors
p326 . . Newcastle upon Tyne 0191 265 8817

Smith & Copsey
p419 . . . Wallsend 0191 262 4428

Ashley Smith & Co
p80 . . . Lewisham 020 8463 0099

Smith Brown & Sprawson
p295 . . . Luton 01582 876900

J H Smith
p182 . . . Carlisle 01228 521383

The Smith Partnership
p281 . . . Leicester 0116 247 2000

Sonn Macmillan
p80 . . . London 020 7377 8889

Southern Stewart & Walker
p384 . . . South Shields 0191 456 7788

H Michael Spring
p353 . . . Port Talbot 01639 897075

R W Stebbings
p350 . . . Plymouth 01752 202287

Steele Ford & Newton
p321 . . . Nelson 01282 692531

Sternberg Reed
p366 . . . Romford 01708 766155

Steven Young & Co
p188 . . . Cheltenham 01242 257269
p230 . . . Gloucester 01452 332882

Stevens
p393 . . . Stafford 01785 250908
p398 . . . Stoke-on-Trent 01782 343353

Stokoe Partnership
p83 . . . Waltham Forest 020 8558 8884

Andrew Storch
p361 . . . Reading 0118 958 4407

David Street & Company
p202 . . . Crawley 01293 616191

Sugare & Co
p277 . . . Leeds 0113 244 6978

Switalski's
p419 . . . Wakefield 01924 882000

Tang Bentley & Jackson
p224 . . . Fareham 01329 220401

Taylor Lewis
p181 . . . Cardigan 01239 621999

Peter Thubron & Co
p402 . . . Sunderland 0191 510 1221

Tosswill & Co
p87 . . . Lambeth 020 8674 9494

Ronnie Tremlett & Co
p160 . . . Brighton 01273 696132

VHS Fletchers Solicitors
p339 . . . Nottingham 0115 959 9550

Rhys Vaughan
p311 . . . Manchester 0161 224 1439

Veseys Solicitors
p143 . . . Birmingham 0121 523 1123

Vickers Chisman & Wishlade
p397 . . . Stockton-on-Tees 01642 615439

Victor Lissack Roscoe & Coleman
p89 . . . London W1 020 7487 2505

Waitt & Co Solicitors
p177 . . . Canterbury 01227 470600

Walker Lahive
p350 . . . Plymouth 01752 551722

Wannop Fox Staffurth & Bray
p442 . . . Worthing 01903 201120

Warner Goodman LLP
p355 . . . Portsmouth 023 9275 3575

Paul J Watson
p315 . . . Middlesbrough 01642 293427

V G Waugh
p348 . . . Peterlee 0191 527 2727

Nigel Weller & Co
p283 . . . Lewes 01273 487123

Wessex Solicitors Chambers Ltd
p355 . . . Portsmouth 023 9238 1114

Whitelock & Storr
p91 . . . London WC1 020 7405 3913

Williamson & Soden
p383 . . . Solihull 0121 733 8000

Wilson & Bird
p121 . . . Aylesbury 01296 436766

Woodfines LLP
p147 . . . Bletchley 01908 366333

Woodford Robinson
p333 . . . Northampton 01604 624926

Aidan Woods & Co
p165 . . . Bristol 0117 952 2006

Michael G Wooldridge
p143 . . . Birmingham 0121 706 2259

Nicholas Wray Solicitor
p244 . . . Haverhill 01440 704467

Desmond Wright & Co
p245 . . . Hayes 020 8561 4888

Yates Ardern
p120 . . . Ashton-under-Lyne 0161 330 3332

P C D York & Co
p93 . . . London W6 020 8741 4512

Gordon Young Solicitors Ltd
p296 . . . Luton 01582 405577

Julian Young & Co
p93 . . . London W1 020 7724 8414

Youngs Criminal Defence Services Limited
p377 . . . Sheffield 0114 249 5444

DATA PROTECTION

BCL Burton Copeland
p9 . . . London WC2 020 7430 2277

Rouse Legal (Formerly Willoughby & Partners)
p74 . . . London E14 020 7536 4100

Elizabeth Seeley
p77 . . . Ealing 020 8840 2788

DIVORCE & MATRIMONIAL

A'Court & Co
p434 . . . Windsor 01753 857146

AR Legal Solicitors
p3 . . . London W4 020 8747 9090

AWB Charlesworth LLP
p263 . . . Keighley 01535 613678

Act Family Law
p349 . . . Plymouth 01752 226224

The Affordable Law Co Ltd
p444 . . . York 01904 788877

Aiston Solicitors
p204 . . . Croydon 020 8681 0123

Akermans
p399 . . . Storrington 01903 745353

Alexander Marks LLP
p5 . . . London W1 020 7317 1166

Alfred James & Co
p204 . . . Croydon 020 8681 4627

Alker & Ball
p432 . . . Wigan 01942 246241

Ambrose Appelbe
p6 . . . London WC2 020 7242 7000

Anderson Longmore & Higham
p133 . . . Billingshurst 01403 782710
p348 . . . Petworth 01798 342391
p399 . . . Storrington 01903 745666

Anthony Gold
p6 . . . London SE17 020 7940 4000
p6 . . . London SW16 020 7940 4000

Aplin Stockton Fairfax
p122 . . . Banbury 01295 251234

Appleby Shaw
p434 . . . Windsor 01753 860606

Arnold Greenwood
p264 . . . Kendal 01539 720049

Aspinall & Co
p148 . . . Bolton 01204 388200

Astle Paterson Ltd
p170 . . . Burton-on-Trent 01283 531366

Austin Ryder & Co
p189 . . . Cheshunt 01992 624804
p8 . . . London NW1 020 7833 0882

BBL Solicitors LLP
p235 . . . Guildford 01483 838154

BWF Solicitors
p9 . . . London E8 020 7241 7180

Baehrs
p151 . . . Bournemouth 01202 292075

Bailey Wain & Curzon
p397 . . . Stoke-on-Trent 01782 847934

Bambridges Solicitors Limited
p151 . . . Boston 01205 310510

John Barkers
p195 . . . Cleethorpes 01472 695218
p234 . . . Grimsby 01472 358686
p294 . . . Louth 01507 604773
p297 . . . Mablethorpe 01507 477673

Barlows
p278 . . . Leicester 0116 251 8295

Barr Ellison LLP
p174 . . . Cambridge 01223 417200

T G Baynes
p341 . . . Orpington 01689 886000 / 886042

Behr & Co
p167 . . . Brynmawr 01495 310581

Bell & Co
p402 . . . Sutton 020 8661 8611

David Bellchamber & Co
p196 . . . Cobham 01932 702233

Bells
p366 . . . Romsey 01794 513328

Simon Bennett
p313 . . . Marlow 01628 478088

Bernard Chill & Axtell
p385 . . . Southampton 023 8022 8821

Beswicks
p239 . . . Hanley 01782 205000

Bhatia Best
p336 . . . Nottingham 0115 950 3231

Bilton Hammond LLP
p192 . . . Chesterfield 01246 232418

Blackhurst Swainson Goodier LLP
p356 . . . Preston 01772 253841

Blakemores
p270 . . . Leamington Spa 01926 457300

Blight Broad & Skinnard
p173 . . . Callington 01579 382213

Booth Ince & Knowles
p208 . . . Denton 0161 336 7011

Borlase & Company
p246 . . . Helston 01326 574988

Bottrill & Co
p348 . . . Pinner 020 8429 1010

Bower & Bailey
p122 . . . Banbury 01295 265566
p436 . . . Witney 01993 705095

Bretherton Law
p389 . . . St Albans 01727 869293

Brethertons LLP
p368 . . . Rugby 01788 579579

Brignalls Balderston Warren
p283 . . . Letchworth 01462 482248

Roger Brooker & Co
p186 . . . Chelmsford 01245 351924

Broomhead & Saul
p261 . . . Ilminster 01460 57056
p408 . . . Taunton 01823 288121

Brown Beer Nixon Mallon
p362 . . . Redcar 01642 490202

Bryan & Armstrong
p311 . . . Mansfield 01623 624505

Buchanan & Llewellyn
p428 . . . Westbourne 01202 752525

Buckles Solicitors LLP
p346 . . . Peterborough 01733 888888
p393 . . . Stamford 01780 484570

Burrows
p241 . . . Harrow 020 8904 7725 / 8904 4150

Butcher Andrews
p223 . . . Fakenham 01328 863131
p251 . . . Holt 01263 712023

Butler & Kandler
p261 . . . Ilkley 01943 816207

CMHT Solicitors
p167 . . . Brownhills 01543 372347

Cadmans Law & Property
p195 . . . Cleckheaton 01274 874231

Callaghans
p224 . . . Farnham 01252 723477

Carr & Co
p147 . . . Blyth 01670 351251
p231 . . . Gosforth 0191 284 0363
p319 . . . Morpeth 01670 515182

Carver Jones
p247 . . . Hereford 01432 274301

Chamberlins
p251 . . . Hitchin 01462 623456

Chilcotts
p408 . . . Tavistock 01822 612535 / 614242

Chisholms
p418 . . Wadebridge 01208 812470 / 814205

Anthony Clark & Co
p284 . . . Lincoln 01522 512321

Clark Willis
p183 . . . Catterick Garrison 01748 830000

Cleaver Thompson Ltd
p115 . . . Alfreton 01773 832193
p195 . . . Clay Cross 01246 865048

Clifford Smith & Buchanan
p169 . . . Burnley 01282 452611

Clifton Ingram LLP
p360 . . . Reading 0118 957 3425

Clough & Willis
p170 . . . Bury 0161 764 5266

Charles Coleman & Co
p360 . . . Reading 0118 958 1578

E M Collins & Co
p348 . . . Pinner 020 8866 1820

Cooper Whiteman
p22 . . . London WC1 020 7831 5222

CooperBurnett
p415 . . . Tunbridge Wells 01892 515022

Courtyard Solicitors LLP
p23 . . . London SW19 020 8946 9466

Crane & Staples
p425 . . . Welwyn Garden City 01707 329333

Creagh Brown & Co Solicitors
p220 . . . Esher 020 8224 0610

Crockett & Co
p272 . . . Leeds 0113 226 0111

Cuttle & Co Solicitors
p340 . . . Oldham 0161 678 7443

dgb Solicitors
p184 . . . Chatham 01634 304000

Martin C Dalton
p253 . . . Horsham 01403 266642

David James & Company
p114 . . . Aberystwyth 01970 615789

Edward De Silva & Co
p384 . . . Southall 020 8571 2299

Debidins
p26 . . . Ealing 020 8567 1381 / 8567 6343

Desor & Co
p245 . . . Hayes 020 8569 0708

Devereux & Co
p162 . . . Bristol 0117 938 0222

See p542 for the Firms Specialisations

Dixon Rigby Keogh
p434 Winsford 01606 557211

Dodd Lewis Solicitors
p27. London SE3 020 8852 1255

Paul Dodds Solicitors
p419 Wallsend 0191 263 6200

Scott Duff & Co
p182 Carlisle 01228 531054

Duffield Stunt
p186 Chelmsford 01245 262351

Dunham Guest & Lyons
p176 Cannock 01543 462121

Dutton Gregory
p385 Southampton 023 8022 1344

Elliots Bond & Banbury
p29. Ealing 020 8567 0176

Ellisons
p227 Frinton-on-Sea 01255 851000

Emrys Jones & Co
p425 Welshpool 01938 552510

Evans & Ellis
p189 Chepstow 01291 622814

Rebecca L Faret Solicitors
p226 Flitwick 01525 712112

Farnworth Shaw
p321 Nelson 01282 699996

Fieldings Porter
p149 Bolton 01204 540900
p429 Westhoughton 01942 814089

Forshaws Davies Ridgway LLP
p227 Frodsham 01928 739300
p422 Warrington 01925 604713

Foster & Partners
p162 Bristol 0117 922 0229

Freedman Green Dhokia
p34. Camden 020 7624 2981

Julia Frimond Solicitors
p236 Guildford 01483 452224

Fulchers of Farnborough
p224 Farnborough 01252 522475

GHP Legal
p342 Oswestry 01691 659194

Gales
p152 Bournemouth 01202 512227 / 512446

Gamlins
p363 Rhyl 01745 343500

Deborah Gibbins & Co
p133 Billericay 01268 270866

Gill Akaster
p349 Plymouth 01752 203500

Gillespies
p420 Walsall 01922 627474

Girlings
p119 Ashford 01233 647377
p248 Herne Bay 01227 367355
p312 Margate 01843 220274

Gittins McDonald
p442 Wrexham 01978 291662

Glaisyers
p407 Tamworth 01827 61011

Goodhand and Forsyth QualitySolicitors
p362 Redhill 01737 773533

GoodyBurrett LLP
p197 Colchester 01206 577676

Graysons
p375 Sheffield 0114 272 9184

Greenways
p329 Newquay 01637 872361 / 872251

Gregorys Solicitors
p395 Stockport 0161 456 8125

Andrew Grove & Co
p174 Cambridge 01223 367133

Guillaumes Solicitors
p430 Weybridge 01932 840111

Gurneys
p227 Framlingham 01728 621372

HCB Solicitors
p284 Lichfield 01543 414426

Hadfield & Co
p424 Welling 020 8301 0808

Hadfields Butt & Bowyer
p225 Farnham 01252 716101

Hague Lambert
p269 Knutsford 01565 652411
p297 Macclesfield 01625 616480

Hains & Lewis Ltd
p320 Narberth 0845 408 0125

Hall Smith Whittingham LLP
p203 Crewe 01270 212000
p320 Nantwich 01270 610300

Hand Morgan & Owen
p368 Rugeley 01889 583871

Hanratty & Co
p330 Newtown 01686 626239

Hansells
p331 North Walsham 01692 404351
p378 Sheringham 01263 822176

Harold G Walker
p152 Bournemouth 01202 203200

Stanley Hays
p246 Heckmondwike 01924 403809

Heaney Watson
p288 Liverpool 0151 256 7777
p288 Liverpool 0151 282 5555
p288 Liverpool 0151 293 2936
p305
Manchester 0800 567 7597 / 0161 359 3347

Hedleys & Co
p401 Sunderland 0191 567 0101

Henneberry & Co
p40. London NW6 020 8830 1907

Hethertons LLP
p445 York 01904 528200

Hilton Norbury
p432 Wigan 01942 241424

Hine Downing Solicitors
p223 Falmouth 01326 316655

Mark Hoare
p189 Chepstow 01291 630356

Hodge Jones & Allen LLP
p41. London NW1 020 7874 8300

Hodgsons & Mortimer
p206 Darlington 01325 250111 / 355956

David Holmes & Co
p234 Great Yarmouth 01493 658291

Holroyd & Co
p256 Huddersfield 01484 645464

Hopkin Murray Beskine
p42. London N4 020 7272 1234

Hopkins
p311 Mansfield 01623 460460
p337 Nottingham 0115 910 5555

Horne Engall & Freeman LLP
p217 Egham 01784 432292

Howells LLP
p367 Rotherham 01709 364000

Hughes Fowler Carruthers
p43. London WC2 020 7421 8383

J A Hughes
p179 Cardiff 029 2061 9700

Humphries Kirk
p152 Bournemouth 01202 421111
p212 Dorchester 01305 251007
p352 Poole 01202 715815

Hurlow & Partners
p179 Cardiff 029 2039 6087

Husband Forwood Morgan
p289 Liverpool 0151 236 9626

Hutchinson & Buchanan
p365 Ripon 01765 602156

IBB Solicitors
p189 Chesham 0845 638 1381

Ilett & Clark Solicitors
p441 Worksop 01909 500544

The International Family Law Group
p45. London WC2 020 3178 5668

The Isaacs Practice
p152 Bournemouth 01202 299999

Bernard James
p144 Bishop Auckland 01388 458868

Anne Jarvis & Co
p240 Harrogate 01423 858582

Andrew Jay & Co
p284 Lincoln 01522 539111

Johns Gilbert & Frankton
p368 Rugby 01788 576384

Gordon Jones & Co
p139 Birmingham 0121 453 8151

Jordans
p183 Castleford 01977 518778

Kendall & Davies
p153 Bourton-on-the-Water 01451 820277

Keoghs and Nicholls, Lindsell & Harris
p116 Altrincham 0161 928 9321

Keppe & Partners Solicitors
p416 Twickenham 020 8891 4488

KieranClarkeGreen
p192 Chesterfield 01246 211006
p394 Staveley 01246 280099

Anthony King & Co
p126 Basildon 01268 240400

Kirk & Partners
p50. London SE9 020 8850 2484

Kundert & Co
p200 Coventry 024 7622 7741
p200 Coventry 024 7668 4928

Simon Lacey Law Associates
p430 Weymouth 01305 777711

Laderman & Co
p51. Redbridge 020 8530 7319

Lakhani & Co
p51. Brent 020 8204 7100

Lawson West Solicitors Limited
p312 Market Harborough 01858 445480
p432 Wigston 0116 212 1080

Lawson-Cruttenden & Co
p52. London WC1 020 7405 0833

Lebreton Towell Solicitor
p408 Tarporley 01829 751459

Lees Solicitors LLP
p249 Heswall 0151 342 6273
p428 West Kirby 0151 625 9364

Leonard & Co
p386 Southampton 023 8023 4433

Levison Meltzer Pigott
p53. London EC4 020 7556 2400

Lewis Cutner & Co
p53. London NW3 020 7433 2552

Lin & Co Solicitors
p403 Sutton Coldfield 0121 244 2300

Lita Gale
p54. London W8 020 7404 2899

Lorimers
p168 Buckingham 01280 812132 / 813405

Lumsdons Solicitors LLP
p399 Stourport-on-Severn 01299 827766

MWP Solicitors
p126 Basildon 01268 527131

MacLaren Britton
p338 Nottingham 0115 941 1469

Madge Lloyd & Gibson
p230 Gloucester 01452 520224
p327 Newent 01531 820088

Thomas Magnay & Co
p229 Gateshead 0191 477 3333

Malletts Solicitors
p266 King's Lynn 01553 777744

Mansouri & Son
p205 Croydon 020 8401 7352

Marsden Duncan
p196 Cliftonville 01843 295741

Marsden Rawsthorn LLP
p194 Chorley 01257 279511

Marsh & Co
p269 Lancaster 01524 68102

Martin Adams & McColl
p332 Northampton 01604 634123

Martin Tolhurst Partnership LLP
p233 Gravesend 01474 325531
p293 Longfield 01474 706168

Martin-Kaye LLP
p409 Telford 01952 272222

Masefield Solicitors LLP
p271 Ledbury 01531 632377

James Mason Tucker
p329 Newton Abbot 01626 204060

Mason-Apps Smallmans & Co
p298 Maidenhead 01628 636148 / 636149

Matthews Lewis & Co
p191 Chester 01244 327750

Maxwell Hodge Solicitors
p298 Maghull 0151 526 7131

Mayo Wynne Baxter LLP
p215 East Grinstead 01342 310600

Medlicott Snows
p145 Bishops Castle 01588 638425
p269 Knighton 01547 528332

Mercy Messenger
p140 Birmingham 0121 770 1221

Merrony Wall
p416 Twickenham 020 8898 4700

Milwyn Jenkins
p330 Newtown 01686 626218

Elizabeth Muirhead Solicitors
p62. London WC2 020 7936 4445

Myer Wolff
p257 Hull 01482 223693

Nicholls Christie & Crocker
p417 Uxbridge 01895 256216

Nightingales Solicitors Limited
p396 Stockport 01663 764038

Norton & Co
p356 Prescot 0151 426 7001

O'Neill Morgan Solicitors Limited
p396 Stockport 0161 429 8383

Ouvry Creed Solicitors
p410 Tetbury 01666 504005

Overburys & Raymond Thompson
p211 Diss 01379 641221

P B & W Solicitors LLP t/a Pooley Bendall & Watson
p218 Ely 01353 666075

Parker Bird Gardner
p256 Huddersfield 01484 825200

Parry Carver
p409 Telford 01952 504757
p425 Wellington 01952 641291

Payne Marsh Stillwell
p386 Southampton 023 8022 3957

Pellmans
p223 Eynsham 01865 884400

Pendrigh Makin
p374 Sevenoaks 01732 463030

Penmans
p199 Corringham 01375 673968

Perry Hay & Co
p364
Richmond upon Thames 020 8940 8115 / 8332 7532

Peter Peter & Wright
p133 Bideford 01237 472233
p340 Okehampton 01837 52379

Sue Petritz
p253 Horsham 01403 790218

Phillips & Co
p371 Salisbury 01722 321666

Poole Alcock
p116 Alsager 01270 876550
p198 Congleton 01260 275337
p203 Crewe 01270 256665
p320 Nantwich 01270 625478
p333 Northwich 01606 350445
p372 Sandbach 01270 762325

Powell & Young
p351 Pocklington 01759 302113

Powleys
p294 Lowestoft 01502 581121

Punch Robson
p315 Middlesbrough 01642 230700
p315 Middlesbrough 01642 298830
p397 Stockton-on-Tees 01642 754050

Pyms
p131 Belper 01773 822307

Quality Solicitors Chapman & Chubb
p115 Alfreton 01773 540480

QualitySolicitors Jackson & Canter
p290 Liverpool 0151 282 1700

Rafina Solicitors
p426 Wembley 020 8908 6742

Rainer Hughes
p156 Brentwood 01227 226644

Richard Reed
p402 Sunderland 0191 567 0465

Rich & Carr Freer Bouskell
p145 Blaby 0116 242 6039
p296 Lutterworth 0116 242 6048
p407 Syston 0116 242 6036

Richardson & Davies
p201 Coventry 024 7622 2001

Rix & Kay Solicitors LLP
p416 Uckfield 01825 700177

Robson & Co
p259 Hythe 01303 264581 / 267413

Ronaldsons
p335 Norwich 01603 618883

Ross Coates
p263 Ipswich 01473 222303

Laurence Ross & Associates
p358 Radlett 01923 850099

Rotherham & Co
p201 Coventry 024 7622 7331

Russell & Co Solicitors and Estate Agents
p202 Crawley 01293 561965 / 0845 300 2809

Sackvilles
p252 Hornchurch 01708 446704

Schillings
p77. London WC1 020 7034 9000

Sears Tooth
p77. London W1 020 7499 5599

Segens Blount Petre
p77. London W1 020 7332 2222

Christine Sharp & Co
p249 Heywood 01706 623513

Shepherd Harris & Co
p219 Enfield 020 8363 8341

Sills & Betteridge LLP
p228 Gainsborough 01427 616816
p381 Skegness 01754 610101
p389 Spalding 01775 714874

Simons Levine & Co
p79. Barnet 020 8446 4273

Singleton Saunders Flood Solicitors
p213 Dover 01304 240080

Slade Legal
p114 Abingdon 01235 521920

Smith Chamberlain
p425 Wellingborough 01933 224971

Smith Gadd & Co
p253 Horsham 01403 271222

Solicitor Direct
p283 Leyland 01772 424999

Spicketts Battrick Law Practice
p181 Cardiff 029 2046 1480

Sproull Solicitors LLP
p148 Bodmin 01208 72328
p176 Camelford 01840 212315
p353 Port Isaac 01840 212315

Linda Stapleton & Co
p230 Gloucester 01452 423870

Wade Stevens & Co
p342 Orpington 01689 831122

Stone Milward Rapers
p193 Chichester 01243 602832

Stone Rowe Brewer LLP
p416 Twickenham 020 8891 6141

Swinburne Snowball & Jackson
p199 Consett 01207 502532

Symes Bains Broomer
p373 Scunthorpe 01724 281616

R F Tansey
p410 Thame 01844 218000

Thompson & Jackson
p350 Plymouth 01752 665037 / 221171

Peter Thomson
p87. Lambeth 020 7733 6196

Thomson Webb & Corfield
p176 Cambridge 01223 578068

Thorneycroft Solicitors Ltd
p297 Macclesfield 01625 503444

Thrings LLP
p87. London SW1 020 7766 5600

4

Thursfields
p266 . . . . . . Kidderminster 01562 820575
p399 . . . Stourport-on-Severn 01299 827517
Trelfa & Co
p238 . . . . Hampton 020 8941 1249
Tudur Owen Roberts Glynne & Co
p251 . . . . Holyhead 01407 762374
Turners
p204 . . . . Cross Hills 01535 634149
Turners Solicitors LLP
p153 . . . . . . Bournemouth 01202 291291
Vincent & Co
p432 . . . . Wigan 01257 425121
WBW Solicitors
p222 . . . . Exeter 01392 202404
p329 . . . . . . Newton Abbot 01626 202404
Wains
p198 . . . . Congleton 01260 279414
p297 . . . . Macclesfield 01625 429511
Matthew Waite & Co
p413 . . . . Tring 01442 890111
Wall James Chappell
p399 . . . . Stourbridge 01384 371622
Rodney Warren & Co
p216 . . . . Eastbourne 01323 430430
Duncan Watts LLP
p422 . . . . Warwick 01926 493485
Whitfields
p227 . . . . Formby 01704 878501
Wholley Goodings LLP
p130 . . . . Bedlington 01670 824080
Wilkin Chapman Grange Solicitors
p252 . . . . Horncastle 01507 527521
Wilkinson Woodward
p238 . . . . Halifax 01422 339600
Wilks Price Hounslow
p369 . . . . Ryde 01983 566241
Willett & Co
p171 . . . . Bury St Edmunds 01284 701323
Williams & Co
p296 . . . . Luton 01582 723322
RTP Williams Limited
p244 . . . . Haverfordwest 01437 762321
Wills Chandler Beach
p226 . . . . Fleet 01252 613351
Wolferstans
p351 . . . . Plymouth 01752 401515
Nadine Wong & Co
p93 . . . . London W2 020 7243 8888
Woolley & Co
p423 . . . . Warwick 01789 267377
Wylie Kay
p147 . . . . Blackpool 01253 296297
Yorklaw Ltd (t/a Burn & Company)
p215 . . . . Easingwold 01347 822188
p445 . . . . York 01904 655442
Peter Zelnik & Co
p133 . . . . Biggin Hill 01959 570730

ECCLESIASTICAL LAW

Blain Boland & Co
p432 . . . . Willaston 0151 327 1301
Blain Boland & Thomas Ltd
p217 . . . . . . Ellesmere Port 0151 355 2645
Chattertons Solicitors
p284 . . . . Lincoln 01522 814600
Claytons
p390 . . . . St Albans 01727 865765
Dixon Coles & Gill
p418 . . . . Wakefield 01924 263166 / 263899
Ellis-Fermor & Negus
p293 . . . . Long Eaton 0115 972 5222
Raymond Hemingray
p347 . . . . Peterborough 01733 262523
Roebucks
p145 . . . . Blackburn 01254 274000
p145 . . . . Blackburn 01254 503070
Stone King LLP
p128 . . . . Bath 01225 337599
J G Underwood
p89 . . . . London SW1 020 7730 4019
Winckworth Sherwood LLP
p92 . . . . London SE1 020 7593 5000
p344 . . . . Oxford 01865 297200

EDUCATION LAW

AMD Solicitors
p160 . . . . Bristol 0117 923 5562
p160 . . . . Bristol 0117 962 1460
Ashfords LLP
p160 . . . . Bristol 0117 321 8000
Bailey Wright & Co
p135 . . . . Birmingham 0845 475 1996
Children & Families Law Firm
p20 . . . . London SW9 020 7582 6002
DMH Stallard LLP
p159 . . . . Brighton 01273 329833
p202 . . . . Crawley 01293 605000
Farrer & Co LLP
p31 . . . . London WC2 020 3375 7000
John Ford Solicitors
p33 . . . . London N4 020 8800 6464
John Hoult & Co
p373 . . . . Scunthorpe 01724 281312
Maxwell Gillott (MG Law Ltd)
p270 . . . . Lancaster 0844 858 3900
Maxwell Hodge Solicitors
p268 . . . . Kirkby 0151 548 7370
Morecrofts Solicitors LLP
p290 . . . . Liverpool 0151 236 8871
NUT Solicitors
p62 . . . . London WC1 020 7380 4734
Ormerods
p205 . . . . Croydon 020 8686 5000
Pardoes
p158 . . . . Bridgwater 01278 457891
Pearcelegal LLP
p383 . . . . Solihull 0844 412 7899
Pheby & Co
p445 . . . . York 01904 789900
SGH Martineau LLP
p142 . . . . Birmingham 0870 763 2000
Thomas Saul & Co
p430 . . . . Whitefield 0161 773 2833
Smith Sutcliffe
p344 . . . . Padiham 01282 778434
Stone King LLP
p128 . . . . Bath 01225 337599
p176 . . . . Cambridge 01223 451070
p83 . . . . London EC1 020 7796 1007
Swain & Co
p386 . . . . Southampton 023 8063 1111
Veale Wasbrough Vizards
p165 . . . . Bristol 0117 925 2020

ELDERLY

Act Legal
p159 . . . . Brighton 01273 565656
Aldridge Brownlee Solicitors LLP
p151 . . . . Bournemouth 01202 527008
Andrews Martin
p406 . . . . Swindon 01793 641707
Anthony Gold
p6 . . . . London SE17 020 7940 4000
p6 . . . . London SW16 020 7940 4000
Anthony Holden Crofts & Co
p6 . . . . Ealing 020 8840 7878
Ascroft Whiteside
p146 . . . . Blackpool 01253 766866
Bearders
p238 . . . . . Halifax 01422 365215 / 343427
R Bell & Son
p242 . . . . Hartlepool 01429 273165
Berry & Berry
p414 . . . . Tunbridge Wells 01892 526344
Julia T Betts
p336 . . . . Nottingham 01623 499080
Booth Ince & Knowles
p208 . . . . Denton 0161 336 7011
Brains
p391 . . . . St Austell 01726 68111
Bryan & Armstrong
p311 . . . . Mansfield 01623 626039
Burtons
p345 . . . . Pembury 01892 824577
Butler & Kandler
p261 . . . . Ilkley 01943 816207
Cameron Jones Hussell & Howe
p353 . . . . Port Talbot 01639 885261
Campbell-Taylor Solicitors
p18 . . . . Hackney 0845 567 2457
Carpenter & Co
p419 . . . . Wallington 020 8669 5145
Ross Carter
p166 . . . . Brockenhurst 01590 624422
Cowles
p23 . . . . Croydon 020 8679 1811
Coxons
p427 . . . . West Bridgford 0115 981 2000
Daniel Curry & Co
p205 . . . . Croydon 020 8680 2188
Dale & Newbery LLP
p393 . . . . Staines 01784 464491
Davies Partnership
p389 . . . . St Agnes 01872 553131
Dean & Co
p213 . . . . Dudley 01384 352525
p399 . . . . Stourbridge 01384 352525
Dodd Lewis Solicitors
p27 . . . . London SE3 020 8852 1255
FDC Law
p228 . . . . Frome 01373 465051
Goodhand and Forsyth QualitySolicitors
p362 . . . . Redhill 01737 773533
Greenhouse Stirton & Co
p37 . . . . London EC1 020 7490 3456
Griffith Smith Farrington Webb
p243 . . . . Hassocks 01273 843405
p247 . . . . Henfield 01273 492045
Hall Smith Whittingham LLP
p203 . . . . Crewe 01270 212000
p320 . . . . Nantwich 01270 610300
Hand Morgan & Owen
p393 . . . . Stafford 01785 211411
Edward Hands & Lewis
p293 . . . . Loughborough 01509 216161
Harnett & Co
p163 . . . . Bristol 0117 965 5366
Hayes & Storr
p251 . . . . Holt 01263 712835
Heppenstalls
p296 . . . . Lymington 01590 689500
Heringtons
p243 . . . . Hastings 01424 434192
Higgs & Sons
p268 . . . . Kingswinford 01384 342100
Hunters
p44 . . . . London WC2 020 7412 0050
Ison Harrison
p228 . . . . Garforth 0113 286 1455
Richard Jacklin & Co
p289 . . . . Liverpool 0151 243 1313
p388 . . . . Southport 01704 500024
Gwyn James Solicitors
p195 . . . . Cinderford 01594 822277
Jobling & Knape
p233 . . . . Great Eccleston 01995 670083
p319 . . . . Morecambe 01524 416960
Kagan Moss & Co
p409 . . . . Teddington 020 8977 6633
Kellock & Johnson
p329 . . . . Newton Abbot 01626 335454
p413 . . . . Totnes 01803 862414
LD Law
p239 . . . . Harlow 01279 441266
Lanyon Bowdler LLP
p425 . . . . Wellington 01952 244721
Jennifer C Margrave
p236 . . . . Guildford 01483 562722
Martin Adams & McColl
p332 . . . . Northampton 01604 634123
Menneer Shuttleworth
p132 . . . . Bexhill 01424 730630
Miller Sands
p175 . . . . Cambridge 01223 202345
Myer Wolff
p257 . . . . Hull 01482 223693
Osman Ward & Sons
p255 . . . . Hove 01273 778787 / 778788
Parker Bullen
p118 . . . . Andover 01264 400500
Pricketts
p396 . . . . Stockport 0161 429 8000
Richard Reed
p402 . . . . Sunderland 0191 567 0465
Rowlinsons
p227 . . . . Frodsham 01928 735333
Sackvilles
p359 . . . . Rainham 01708 552804
Sharples & Co
p165 . . . . Bristol 0117 942 8214
Swinburne Snowball & Jackson
p199 . . . . Consett 01207 502532
Rosalind Watchorn
p377 . . . . Sheffield 0114 229 0160
Wayman & Long
p401 . . . . Sudbury 01787 277375
Denis Wynn & Co
p193 . . . . Chipping Norton 01608 643036
Young Coles & Langdon
p132 . . . . Bexhill 01424 210013

EMPLOYMENT LAW

AB Law
p241 . . . . Harrow 020 8426 5613
The A P Partnership Ltd
p346 . . . . Peterborough 01733 891081
Aaron & Partners LLP Solicitors
p190 . . . . Chester 01244 405555
Abrahamson & Associates
p3 . . . . London NW11 020 8458 1100
Advance Legal
p170 . . . . Burton-on-Trent 01283 544492
Albinson Napier & Co
p421 . . . . Warrington 01925 634681
Aldridge Brownlee Solicitors LLP
p151 . . . . Bournemouth 01202 294411
Alfred James & Co
p204 . . . . Croydon 020 8681 4627
Alfred Truman
p132 . . . . Bicester 01869 252761
Allan Janes LLP
p249 . . . . High Wycombe 01494 521301
Allington Hughes
p442 . . . . Wrexham 01978 291000
Anthony Gold
p6 . . . . London SW16 020 7940 4000
Aplin Stockton Fairfax
p122 . . . . Banbury 01295 251234
Archon Solicitors
p7 . . . . London EC4 020 7397 9650
Anna Arthur Associates
p436 . . . . Woking 01483 222499
Ashfords LLP
p349 . . . . Plymouth 01752 521500
Atkins Law Solicitors
p220 . . . . Exeter 01392 671657
B P Collins LLP
p229 . . . . Gerrards Cross 01753 889995
Backhouse Jones Ltd
p196 . . . . Clitheroe 01254 828300
Baehrs
p151 . . . . Bournemouth 01202 292075
Bailey Wright & Co
p135 . . . . Birmingham 0845 475 1996
Baines Wilson LLP
p181 . . . . Carlisle 01228 552600
Bambridges Solicitors Limited
p151 . . . . Boston 01205 310510
Banner Jones
p191 . . . . Chesterfield 01246 560560
Bark & Co
p9 . . . . London EC4 020 7353 1990
Barlow Robbins LLP
p235 . . . . Guildford 01483 562901
p436 . . . . Woking 01483 748500
Barnes Harrild & Dyer
p204 . . . . Croydon 020 8681 5128
Barnes Richards Rutter
p189 . . . . Chepstow 01291 628898
Paul R Baron
p183 . . . . Carshalton 020 8401 2251
Batchelor Myddelton
p355 . . . . Potters Bar 01707 647088
Batchelors Solicitors
p166 . . . . Bromley 020 8768 7000
Richard T Bate & Co
p410 . . . . Tetbury 01666 503722
Bates Wells & Braithwaite London LLP
p11 . . . . London EC4 020 7551 7777
Bathurst Brown Downie & Airey LLP
p416 . . . . Twickenham 020 8892 1537
Beale and Company Solicitors LLP
p11 . . . . London WC2 020 7240 3474
Beers LLP
p267 . . . . Kingsbridge 01548 857000
p349 . . . . Plymouth 01752 246000
Beevers Solicitors
p119 . . . . . Ashton-under-Lyne 0161 339 9697
David Bellchamber & Co
p196 . . . . Cobham 01932 702233
Berkeley Solicitors
p213 . . . . Droylsden 0161 371 0011
Richard Best & Co
p368 . . . . Rugby 01788 571135
Bevan Brittan LLP
p135 . . . . Birmingham 0870 194 1000
Bevans
p161 . . . . Bristol 0117 923 7249
p12 . . . . London WC2 020 7353 9995
Bignalls
p12 . . . . London W1 020 7637 3071
Bindmans LLP
p12 . . . . London WC1 020 7833 4433
Bird & Bird LLP
p13 . . . . London EC4 020 7415 6000
Birkett Long LLP
p186 . . . . Chelmsford 01245 453800
Blandy & Blandy
p360 . . . . Reading 0118 951 6800
Bone & Payne LLP
p198 . . . . Colwyn Bay 01492 532385
p291 . . . . Llandudno 01492 876354
Bowcock Cuerden LLP
p320 . . . . Nantwich 01270 611106
Brabners Chaffe Street
p286 . . . . Liverpool 0151 600 3000
Bracher Rawlins LLP
p15 . . . . London WC1 020 7404 9400
Bradbury Roberts & Raby
p373 . . . . Scunthorpe 01724 854000
Brand Mellon LLP
p230 . . . . Gloucester 01452 524088
Brignalls Balderston Warren
p394 . . . . Stevenage 01438 359311
Brindley Twist Tafft & James
p200 . . . . Coventry 024 7653 1532
John Bromfield & Company Ltd
p339 . . . . Nuneaton 024 7638 2343
BrookStreet des Roches LLP
p114 . . . . Abingdon 01235 836600
Bulfin & Co Employment Law Solicitors
p348 . . . . Pinner 020 8866 0044
Burroughs
p299 . . . . Maidstone 01622 676976 / 676982
Burt Brill & Cardens
p159 . . . . Brighton 01273 604123
Burton Woolf & Turk
p16 . . . . London EC1 020 7831 6478
Bury & Walkers LLP
p272 . . . . Leeds 0113 244 4227
Buss Murton LLP
p207 . . . . Dartford 01322 220235
Butcher Andrews
p223 . . . . Fakenham 01328 863131

See p542 for the Firms Specialisations

CB Legal
p17 . . . Camden 020 7323 9192

Camerons Jones
p241 . . . Harrow 020 8423 6666

Camps Solicitors
p134 . . . Birkenhead 0151 201 8080

Carpenter & Co
p419 . . . Wallington 020 8669 5145

Carrington & Associates
p18 . . . London EC4 020 7822 1855

Carter-Ruck
p18 . . . London EC4 020 7353 5005

Cartwright Cunningham Haselgrove & Co
p19 . . . Waltham Forest 020 8520 1021

Chadwick Lawrence
p319 . . . Morley 0113 252 3452

Chanter Ferguson
p125 . . . Barnstaple 01271 342268

Chaplin & Co
p394 . . . Stanmore 020 8954 8202

Charles Russell LLP
p343 . . . Oxford 0845 359 0090

Chattertons Solicitors
p151 . . . Boston 01205 310025
p322 . . . Newark 01636 673731

Cheethams
p345 . . . Penkridge 01785 714761

H N E Chesterfield
p162 . . . Bristol 0117 968 8148

Child & Child
p20 . . . London SW1 020 7235 8000

Robin F Clark & Co
p232 . . . Gravesend 01474 334444

Clark Willis
p206 . . . Darlington 01325 281111

ClarksLegal LLP
p177 . . . Cardiff 029 2055 7500
p20 . . . London WC2 020 7539 8000
p405 . . . Swansea 0118 958 5321

Clarkson Wright & Jakes Ltd
p341 . . . Orpington 01689 887887

Clifton Ingram LLP
p360 . . . Reading 0118 957 3425

Martin Coakley
p243 . . . Haslemere 01428 648888

Cobbetts LLP
p302 . . . Manchester 0845 404 2404

Colemans
p245 . . . Haywards Heath 01444 459555

Colemans - CTTS
p302 . . . Manchester 0161 876 2500

Coley & Tilley
p136 . . . Birmingham 0121 643 5531

Collins Benson Goldhill LLP
p21 . . . London W1 020 7436 5151

Collyer Bristow LLP
p22 . . . London WC1 020 7242 7363

Connolley & Company
p437 . . . Wolverhampton 01902 326000

Conway & Co
p247 . . . Henley-on-Thames 01491 411122

Cox Cooper Limited
p137 . . . Birmingham 0121 777 0015

Coyne Learmonth
p287 . . . Liverpool 0845 602 0870

Cozens-Hardy LLP
p334 . . . Norwich 01603 625231

Dudley Cramp & Co
p380 . . . Sittingbourne 01795 420024

Crutes
p324 . . Newcastle upon Tyne 0191 233 9700

Cumberland Ellis Peirs
p23 . . . London WC1 020 7242 0422

Curtis
p349 . . . Plymouth 01752 204444

Curwens
p420 . . . Waltham Abbey 01992 712549

DAC Beachcroft
p328 . . . Newport 0844 980 0400

DSM Legal Solicitors
p421 . . . Warrington 0845 009 0863

DWF
p287 . . . Liverpool 0151 907 3000
p303 . . . Manchester 0161 603 5000

DW Solicitors
p331 . . . Northampton 01604 624222

Darbys Solicitors LLP
p343 . . . Oxford 01865 811700

Darwin Gray
p178 . . . Cardiff 029 2082 9100

Davis Blank Furniss
p303 . . . Manchester 0161 832 3304

J F Dawson
p129 . . . Beaconsfield 01494 670566

Dean Wilson Laing
p159 . . . Brighton 01273 327241

Debidins
p26 . . . Ealing 020 8567 1381 / 8567 6343

Dickins Hopgood Chidley LLP
p258 . . . Hungerford 01488 683555

Dodd Lewis Solicitors
p27 . . . London SE3 020 8852 1255

Downie & Gadban
p116 . . . Alton 01420 82879

David Downton & Co
p316 . . . Milton Keynes 01908 563030

Dowse & Co
p27 . . . Hackney 020 7254 6205

Doyle Clayton Solicitors Limited
p27 . . . London EC2 020 7329 9090
p360 . . . Reading 0118 959 6839

Druitts
p151 . . . Bournemouth 01202 551863

Duane Morris
p28 . . . London EC1 020 7786 2100

Thomas Dunton Solicitors
p342 . . . Orpington 01689 822554

EMW
p316 . . . Milton Keynes 0845 070 6000

Eastleys
p345 . . . Paignton 01803 559257

Eaton Ryan & Taylor
p138 . . . Birmingham 0121 236 1999

Edwards Angell Palmer & Dodge
p28 . . . London EC2 020 7583 4055

Edwards Duthie
p29 . . . London E6 020 8514 9000

Elton & Co
p29 . . . Camden 020 7267 7373

England & Co
p234 . . . Great Yarmouth 01493 604990
p234 Great Yarmouth 01493 740795 / 748174

Evans & Davies
p113 . . . Aberaeron 01545 570335

FBC Manby Bowdler LLP
p437 . . . Wolverhampton 01902 578000

Farnworth Shaw
p198 . . . Colne 01282 865885

Fentimans
p269 . . . Knowle 01564 779459

Ferguson Solicitors
p31 . . . London EC4 020 7822 2999

Finn Gledhill
p238 . . . Halifax 01422 330000

Fishman & Co Solicitors
p32 . . . London W1 020 7935 3500

Follett Stock LLP
p221 . . . Exeter 01392 449370
p414 . . . Truro 01872 241700

Foot Anstey
p349 . . . Plymouth 01752 675000

Forbes Hall LLP
p33 . . . London EC2 020 7729 9111

Ford & Warren
p273 . . . Leeds 0113 243 6601

Foster Harrington
p173 . . . Camberley 01276 692233

Fox Williams
p33 . . . London EC2 020 7628 2000

Franklins LLP
p317 . . . Milton Keynes 01908 660966

Franks & Co
p34 . . . London EC4 020 7242 8008

Freedman Green Dhokia
p34 . . . Camden 020 7625 6003

Frettens Solicitors
p194 . . . Christchurch 01202 491777

Fruhman Davies Livingstones
p304 . . . Manchester 0161 833 0578

FullagarBrooks
p406 . . . Swindon 01793 777007

GHP Legal
p442 . . . Wrexham 01978 291456

GLP Solicitors
p304 . . . Manchester 0161 834 6721

GPB Solicitors LLP
p400 . . . Stratford-upon-Avon 01789 261131

Gabbs LLP
p248 . . . Hereford 01432 353481

Gales
p152 . Bournemouth 01202 512227 / 512446

Gannons Limited
p35 . . . Camden 020 7438 1060

Garden House Solicitors
p248 . . . Hertford 01992 422128

Garrods Solicitors
p186 . . . Chelmsford 01245 492494

Gelbergs LLP
p35 . . . Islington 020 7226 0570

George & Co
p171 . . . Bury St Edmunds 01449 737582

George Ide LLP
p192 . . . Chichester 01243 786668

Gill Akaster
p349 . . . Plymouth 01752 203500

Gill Turner Tucker
p299 . . . Maidstone 01622 759051

Girlings
p119 . . . Ashford 01233 664711

Glaisyers Solicitors LLP
p304 . . . Manchester 0161 832 4666

Glynnes
p214 . . . Ealing 020 8997 1437

Goodhand and Forsyth QualitySolicitors
p362 . . . Redhill 01737 773533

GoodyBurrett LLP
p197 . . . Colchester 01206 577676

Gordons LLP
p154 . . . Bradford 01274 202202

Gorvins
p395 . . . Stockport 0161 930 5151

Goughs
p173 . . . Calne 01249 812086

Grays
p444 . . . York 01904 634771

Greenwoods Solicitors LLP
p347 . . . Peterborough 01733 887700

Griffith Smith Conway
p254 . . . Hove 01273 821577

Gross & Co
p171 . . . Bury St Edmunds 01284 763333

H2O Law LLP
p37 . . . London EC4 020 7405 4700

HKB Wiltshires
p234 . . . Great Yarmouth 01493 855676

HRJ Law LLP
p251 . . . Hitchin 01462 628888

Hague Lambert
p305 . . . Manchester 0161 834 6066

Hallett & Co
p119 . . . Ashford 01233 625711

Hamilton Davies
p394 . . . Stevenage 01438 315898

Hamilton Downing Quinn
p38 . . . London WC1 020 7831 8939

Hancocks
p122 . . . Banbury 01295 253211

Hanne & Co
p38 . . . London SW11 020 7228 0017

Charles Harding & Co
p426 . . . Wembley 020 8795 0990

Harding Evans LLP
p328 . . . Newport 01633 244233

Harman & Harman
p39 . . . London SW2 01227 452977

Harold G Walker
p152 . . . Bournemouth 01202 203200

Harper Law
p366 . . . Romsey 01794 322364

Harris & Harris
p228 . . . Frome 01373 463366

Brian Harris & Co
p39 . . . London W1 020 7935 5541

Harrowells
p444 . . . York 01904 690111

Hart Brown Solicitors
p236 . . . Guildford 0800 068 8177

Edward Harte LLP
p159 . . . Brighton 01273 662750

Haslam & Payne
p39 . . . London SW1 020 7828 8725

Hawley & Rodgers
p293 . . . Loughborough 01509 230333

Haworth & Nuttall
p114 . . . Accrington 01254 236221

Haworth Holt Bell Limited
p116 . . . Altrincham 0161 928 7136

Healds
p432 . . . Wigan 01942 241511

Healys LLP
p159 . . . Brighton 01273 685888

Heckford Norton
p395 . . . Stevenage 01438 312211

Hegarty LLP
p347 . . . Peterborough 01733 346333

Hellewell Pasley & Brewer
p128 . . . Batley 01924 472596

Hempsons
p240 . . . Harrogate 01423 522331
p40 . . . London W1 020 7839 0278
p305 . . . Manchester 0161 228 0011

Hewetts
p361 . . . Reading 0118 957 5337

Hill Hofstetter LLP
p382 . . . Solihull 0121 210 6000

Hodgsons & Mortimer
p363 . . . Richmond 01748 850950

Hogan Lisle
p42 . . . London W1 020 7224 3300

Simon A Holt & Co
p357 . . . Preston 01772 250871

Horwood & James LLP
p121 . . . Aylesbury 01296 487361

Hossacks
p265 . . . Kettering 01536 518638

Hough Halton & Soal
p182 . . . Carlisle 01228 524379

Howard & Company
p43 . . . London W1 020 7486 6610

Howell-Jones LLP
p267 . Kingston upon Thames 020 8549 5186

Hughes Paddison
p188 . . . Cheltenham 01242 574244

Humphries Kirk
p352 . . . Poole 01202 725400

Hunters
p44 . . . London WC2 020 7412 0050

Immanuel & Co
p44 . . . London EC4 020 7213 9901

Irwin Mitchell LLP
p274 . . . Leeds 0870 150 0100
p45 . . . London EC1 0870 150 0100

The Isaacs Practice
p152 . . . Bournemouth 01202 299999

JSP Solicitors
p380 Skegness 01754 762252 / 01522 537353

Arthur Jackson & Co
p367 . . . Rotherham 01709 363876

Johns & Saggar
p46 . . . London WC1 020 3490 1475

P Lloyd Jones & Co
p318 . . . Mold 01352 758533 / 758534

Jordans
p418 . . . Wakefield 01924 387110

Josiah Hincks
p196 . . . Coalville 01530 835041
p280 . . . Leicester 0116 255 1811

Just Employment
p236 . . . Guildford 01483 303636

KBL Solicitors
p149 . . . Bolton 01204 527777

KJD
p398 . . . Stoke-on-Trent 01782 202020

KSH Law Firm
p325 . . Newcastle upon Tyne 0191 232 5232

D C Kaye & Co
p234
. . . Great Missenden 01494 864650 / 862226

Leon Kaye Solicitors
p48 . . . London SW11 020 7228 2020

Keelys LLP
p284 . . . Lichfield 01543 420000

Kennards Wells
p219 . . . Epping 01992 570505

Keoghs LLP
p149 . . . Bolton 01204 677000

Kerman & Co LLP
p49 . . . London WC2 020 7539 7272

Kirbys
p240 . . . Harrogate 01423 542000

Kirk & Partners
p50 . . . London SE9 020 8850 2484

Knights
p415 . . . Tunbridge Wells 01892 537311

Knocker & Foskett
p374 . . . Sevenoaks 01732 459931

LDJ Solicitors
p339 . . . Nuneaton 024 7674 5000

Labrums
p390 . . . St Albans 01727 858807

B D Laddie
p51 . . . London W1 020 7963 8585

Lakhani & Co
p51 . . . Brent 020 8204 7100

Lancasters
p219 . . . Epsom 01372 724931

H Landau & Co
p217 . . . Edgware 020 8959 6991

Lane & Co
p420 . . . Walsall 01922 721259

Langleys
p284 . . . Lincoln 01522 888555

Lanyon Bowdler LLP
p379 . . . Shrewsbury 01743 280280

Last Cawthra Feather LLP
p378 . . . Shipley 01274 585459

Lawson West Solicitors Limited
p280 . . . Leicester 0116 212 1000

Laytons
p306 . . . Manchester 0161 834 2100

Leeds Day
p392 . . . St Ives 01480 464600

Lester Aldridge LLP
p53 . . . London WC2 0844 967 0785

Lewis Silkin LLP
p53 . . . London EC4 020 7074 8000
p343 . . . Oxford 01865 263070

Lexica Law
p177 . . . Canterbury 01227 764141

Lloyd Green Solicitors
p187 . . . Chelmsford 01245 294600

Judith M Long
p55 . . . Southwark 020 7403 3337

Longs Solicitors
p412 . . . Tonbridge 01732 360895

Loosemores
p179 . . . Cardiff 029 2022 4433

Peter Lynn & Partners
p319 . . . Morriston 01792 310731

Lyons Davidson
p321 . . . New Malden 020 8336 6900

MB Solicitors Ltd trading as MB Law
p275 . . . Leeds 0113 242 4444

MLM Cartwright
p179 . . . Cardiff 029 2046 2562

M Law
p55 . . . London W1 020 7927 6240

Machins Solicitors LLP
p295 . . . Luton 01582 514000

4

Brian Mackenow & Co
p401 . . . Sunderland 0191 565 6262
McKenzie Bell Solicitors
p401 . . . Sunderland 0191 567 4857
McKeowns Solicitors Ltd
p390 . . . St Albans 0800 032 8328
MacLaren Britton
p338 . . . Nottingham 0115 941 1469
Maclay Murray & Spens LLP
p57 . . . London EC2 020 7002 8500
McLellans
p249 . . . Hertford 01992 532000
Magrath LLP
p57 . . . London W1 020 7495 3003
Manuel Swaden
p58 . . . London NW6 020 7431 4999
Saul Marine & Co
p58 . . . London NW7 020 8959 3611
Veronique Marot & Co
p275 . . . Leeds 0113 258 2021
Marriott Davies Yapp
p402 . . . Sutton 020 8643 9794
Marsh Brown & Co
p59 . . . Lewisham 020 8852 0052
Martin-Kaye LLP
p409 . . . Telford 01952 272222
Max Gold Law
p257 . . . Hull 01482 224900
Mayo Wynne Baxter LLP
p215 . . . East Grinstead 01342 310600
Merrony Wall
p416 . . . Twickenham 020 8898 4700
Metcalfe Copeman & Pettefar
p435 . . . Wisbech 01945 464331
Neil Millar & Co Solicitors
p307 . . . Manchester 0161 870 0177
Miller Law Practice
p60 . . . Haringey 020 8340 2953
Mitchells
p445 . . . York 01904 623751
A E Mizler & Co Solicitors
p349 . . . Pinner 020 8420 1175
Moorhead James LLP
p61 . . . London EC4 020 7831 8888
Moroneys
p120 . . . Attleborough 01953 455806
p443 . . . Wymondham 01953 607042
Morrish Solicitors LLP
p276 . . . Leeds 0113 245 0733
Morrisons Solicitors LLP
p362 . . . Redhill 01737 854500
Morton Pugh Welch
p62 . . . London EC2 020 7374 4141
Motley & Hope
p133 . . . Biggleswade 01767 600600
Mowbray Woodwards Solicitors
p128 . . . Bath 01225 485700
Muckle LLP
p325 . . . Newcastle upon Tyne 0191 211 7777
Mullis & Peake
p366 . . . Romford 01708 784000
Warren Murton
p62 . . . London WC1 020 7404 5511
Myer Wolff
p257 . . . Hull 01482 223693
NUT Solicitors
p62 . . . London WC1 020 7380 4734
Neale Turk
p226 . . . Fleet 01252 811070
Newbys
p237 . . . Guisborough 01287 632208 / 632209
Newmans Solicitors
p252 . . . Horley 01293 771521
Nightingales Solicitors Limited
p396 . . . Stockport 01663 764038
Nockolds
p144 . . . Bishop's Stortford 01279 755777
Stefanie O'Bryen Solicitor
p424 . . . Watlington 01491 614700
Osler Donegan Taylor
p160 . . . Brighton 01273 710712
Over Taylor Biggs
p222 . . . Exeter 01392 823811
Owen White & Catlin
p225 . . . Feltham 020 8890 2836
Oxford Employment Law Solicitors
p344 . . . Oxford 01865 487136
Pardoes
p158 . . . Bridgwater 01278 457891
Parkinson Wright LLP
p213 . . . Droitwich 01905 775533
Partridge & Wilson
p171 . . . Bury St Edmunds 01284 762281
Patterson Glenton & Stracey
p326 . . . Newcastle upon Tyne 0191 232 8628
Pattinson & Brewer
p66 . . . London WC1 020 7400 5100
p445 . . . York 01904 680000
Payne Marsh Stillwell
p386 . . . Southampton 023 8022 3957
M J Payton & Co
p300 . . . Malvern 01684 563318
Pellmans
p223 . . . Eynsham 01865 884400
Pendrigh Makin
p363 . . . Reigate 01737 221518
Penman Johnson
p424 . . . Watford 01923 225212 / 239566
Percy Hughes & Roberts
p134 . . . Birkenhead 0151 666 9090
Peters & Co
p239 . . . Harlow 01279 453331
Peters Langsford Davies
p270 . . . Launceston 01566 772451
Pickering & Butters
p393 . . . Stafford 01785 603060
Pickworths
p247 . . . Hemel Hempstead 01442 261731
Pictons Solicitors LLP
p247 . . . Hemel Hempstead 01442 242441
p295 . . . Luton 01582 870870
p317 . . . Milton Keynes 01908 663511
Pitman Blackstock White
p296 . . . Lydney 01594 842475
Charles Platel Solicitors
p437 . . . Wokingham 0118 978 4866
Plexus Law (A Trading Name of Parabis Law LLP)
p220 . . . Evesham 01386 769160
p68 . . . London EC3 0844 245 4000
Poole & Co
p203 . . . Crewkerne 01460 279100
Pritchard Englefield
p69 . . . London EC2 020 7972 9720
Quality Solicitors Burroughs Day
p164 . . . Bristol 0117 929 0333
Quality Solicitors Copley Clark
p122 . . . Banstead 01737 362131
QualitySolicitors D'Angibau
p151 . . . Boscombe 01202 393506
Donald Race & Newton
p169 . . . Burnley 01282 433241
Rainer Hughes
p156 . . . Brentwood 01277 226644
Raleys
p125 . . . Barnsley 01226 211111
Ramsdens Solicitors
p256 . . . Huddersfield 01484 821500
Ransons
p421 . . . Walton-on-Thames 01932 269448
Richard Reed
p402 . . . Sunderland 0191 567 0465
Reynolds Johns Partnership
p144 . . . Bishop's Stortford 01279 508626
Rix & Kay Solicitors LLP
p255 . . . Hove 01273 329797
Alan Roberts & Co
p191 . . . Chester 01244 562754
Jeremy Roberts & Co
p347 . . . Peterborough 01733 343943 / 342172
Laurence Ross & Associates
p358 . . . Radlett 01923 850099
Rubin Lewis O'Brien
p206 . . . Cwmbran 01633 867000
Rudlings & Wakelam
p410 . . . Thetford 01842 754151
Russell Jones & Walker
p141 . . . Birmingham 0121 233 8300
p164 . . . Bristol 0117 374 2222
p180 . . . Cardiff 029 2026 2800
p326 . . . Newcastle upon Tyne 0191 323 3000
Russell-Cooke LLP
p74 . . . London SW15 020 8789 9111
SAS Daniels LLP
p396 . . . Stockport 0161 475 7676
Sampson Coward LLP
p371 . . . Salisbury 01722 410664
Sedgwick Kelly LLP
p424 . . . Watford 01923 228311
Sedgwick Phelan & Partners
p315 . . . Middleton 0161 653 5299
Elizabeth Seeley
p77 . . . Ealing 020 8840 2788
Seifert & Co
p196 . . . Cobham 01932 866788
Serjeant & Son
p359 . . . Ramsey 01487 812325
Shacklocks
p312 . . . Mansfield 01623 626141
Shakespeares
p319 . . . Moreton-in-Marsh 0845 630 8833
p339 . . . Nottingham 0115 945 3700
Sharman Law
p130 . . . Bedford 01234 303030
Sharpe Pritchard
p77 . . . London WC1 020 7405 4600
Sharpes
p77 . . . London E4 020 8527 2388
M A Shepherd & Co
p78 . . . London N3 020 8343 2346
Crispian Shepley
p421 . . . Walton-on-Thames 01923 221122
T J Shepperson
p335 . . . Norwich 01603 763096
Sheridan & Stretton
p78 . . . London W6 020 8748 7340
Shoosmiths
p361 Reading 0370 086 8800 / 0118 965 8765
Short Richardson & Forth LLP
p326 . . . Newcastle upon Tyne 0191 232 0283
Shulmans
p276 . . . Leeds 0113 245 2833
Sills & Betteridge LLP
p285 . . . Lincoln 01522 542211
Silver Fitzgerald
p175 . . . Cambridge 01223 562001
Silverman Sherliker LLP
p78 . . . London EC2 020 7749 2700
Simpson Millar LLP
p276 . . . Leeds 0844 858 3200
p80 . . . London EC1 0844 858 3400
Slade Legal
p114 . . . Abingdon 01235 521920
Slater Heelis Collier Littler
p370 . . . Sale 0161 969 3131
Slee Blackwell
p125 . . . Barnstaple 01271 372128
Solomon Taylor & Shaw
p80 . . . London NW3 020 7431 1912
Southerns
p169 . . . Burnley 01282 422711
Stafford Young Jones
p82 . . . London EC4 020 7623 9490
James Stallard & Co
p82 . . . London WC2 020 7430 1861
Steeles
p335 . . . Norwich 0870 609 0200
Sternberg Reed
p123 . . . Barking 020 8591 3366
Suttons
p84 . . . London W1 020 7935 5279
Sylvester Mackett
p414 . . . Trowbridge 01225 755621
TPC Solicitors
p310 . . . Manchester 0161 832 8867
TWM Solicitors LLP
p237 . . . Guildford 01483 752700
Tann & Tann Solicitors
p427 . . . Wembley 020 8902 6810
Taylor Walton LLP
p295 . . . Luton 01582 731161
Thompsons (formerly Robin/Brian Thompson & Partners)
p165 . . . Bristol 0117 304 2400
p181 . . . Cardiff 029 2044 5300
p187 . . . Chelmsford 01245 228800
p277 . . . Leeds 0113 205 6300
p87 . . . London SW19 020 8947 4163
p87 . . . London WC1 020 7290 0000
p310 . . . Manchester 0161 819 3500
p377 . . . Sheffield 0114 270 3300
p398 . . . Stoke-on-Trent 01782 406200
Thrings LLP
p128 . . . Bath 01225 340000
p165 . . . Bristol 0117 930 9500
Thursfields
p266 . . . Kidderminster 01562 820575
Tierney & Co
p210 . . . Dinnington 01909 550730
Tinsdills
p372 . . . Sandbach 01270 761111
Toller Beattie LLP
p125 . . . Barnstaple 01271 341000
Tozers
p222 . . . Exeter 01392 207020
Alison Trent & Co
p88 . . . London EC4 020 7583 3350
Tudor Williams & Co
p443 . . . Wrexham 01978 362006
Tudur Owen Roberts Glynne & Co
p172 . . . Caernarfon 01286 672207 / 672851
Turbervilles
p417 . . . Uxbridge 01895 231311
Veale Wasbrough Vizards
p165 . . . Bristol 0117 925 2020
Veitch Penny
p222 . . . Exeter 01392 278381
S V Wadsworth & Co
p383 . . . Solihull 0121 745 8550
Waldrons
p158 . . . Brierley Hill 01384 811811
H J Walker Sibia
p291 . . . Liverpool 0151 227 2600
Walker Smith Way
p120 . . . Ashton-under-Lyne 0844 346 3100
Ward & Rider Limited
p201 . . . Coventry 024 7655 5400
Warners Solicitors
p374 . . . Sevenoaks 01732 747900
p412 . . . Tonbridge 01732 770660
Webster Dixon LLP
p90 . . . London EC1 020 7353 8300
Wellers Law Group LLP
p167 . . . Bromley 020 8464 4242
p91 . . . London WC1 020 7242 7265
Alan Wheatley
p442 . . . Worthing 01903 216116
Wheelers
p115 . . . Aldershot 01252 316316
Whetter Duckworth Fowler
p344 . . . Oxford 01865 872206
V E White & Co
p400 . . . Strood 01634 739195
Whitehead Woodward & Co
p443 . . . Wrexham 01978 855478
Wilkin Chapman Grange Solicitors
p235 . . . Grimsby 01472 262626
Wilkin Chapman LLP
p235 . . . Grimsby 01472 262626
Willans & Co Limited
p390 . . . St Albans 01727 840549
Wills Chandler Beach
p226 . . . Fleet 01252 613351
p252 . . . Hook 01256 764646 / 764647
Wilsons Solicitors LLP
p371 . . . Salisbury 01722 412412
Winston Solicitors LLP
p278 . . . Leeds 0113 320 5000
Woodcocks
p243 . . . Haslingden 01706 213356
Woolf Simmonds
p93 . . . London W1 020 7262 1266
Wragge & Co LLP
p93 . . . London EC1 0870 903 1000
Wrigleys Solicitors LLP
p278 . . . Leeds 0113 244 6100

ENTERTAINMENT, ARTISTS & PERFORMERS

Addleshaw Goddard
p4 . . . London EC1 020 7606 8855
Angel & Co
p6 . . . London W1 020 7495 0555
Biscoes
p431 . . . Wickham 01329 833249
Henri Brandman & Co
p15 . . . London W1 020 7224 0616
Collins Long
p21 . . . Southwark 020 7401 9800
Freedmans
p34 . . . London W4 020 8987 9155
FullagarBrooks
p406 . . . Swindon 01793 777007
Goldkorn Mathias Gentle Page LLP
p36 . . . London WC1 020 7631 1811
Gray & Co
p305 . . . Manchester 0161 237 3360
Hanover Solicitors
p38 . . . London SW3 0870 383 1974
Harbottle & Lewis LLP
p38 . . . London W1 020 7667 5000
Richard Howard & Co LLP
p43 . . . London WC2 020 7831 4511
Jacobsen & Co
p46 . . . London SW6 020 7736 6277
King Prior Macdonald Bridge
p366 . . . Rochester 01634 272720
Lee & Thompson
p52 . . . London W1 020 7935 4665
Trevor Lyttleton MBE
p55 . . . London W1 020 7402 4810
McCloy Legal
p155 . . . Bradford-on-Avon 01225 866563
Magrath LLP
p57 . . . London W1 020 7495 3003
Clifford Miller
p129 . . . Beckenham 020 8663 0044
Nicolaou Solicitors
p249 . . . Hertford 01707 877707
Rohan & Co
p246 . . . Haywards Heath 01444 450901
P Russell & Co
p74 . . . London W6 020 8233 2943
Russells
p75 . . . London W1 020 7439 8692
SA Law
p390 . . . St Albans 01727 798000
Sheridans
p78 . . . London WC1 020 7079 0100
Michael Simkins LLP
p79 . . . London WC1 020 7874 5600
WGS Solicitors
p90 . . . London W1 020 7723 1656

ENVIRONMENTAL LIABILITY

Adams
p323 . . . Newcastle upon Tyne 0191 261 0361
Alan Ashley & Co
p7 . . . London EC4 020 7822 7482
Biggs & Co
p437 . . . Wokingham 0118 989 4511
John S Brearley
p249 . . . High Wycombe 01494 512775

See p542 for the Firms Specialisations

Richard Buxton
p174 Cambridge 01223 328933
Dyne Solicitors Limited
p190 Chester 01829 773100
Espilon Solicitors
p341 Ormskirk 01704 894945
Gross & Co
p171 Bury St Edmunds 01284 763333
Merrett & Co
p163 Bristol 01275 331228
Silver Shemmings LLP
p78 London SW1 0845 345 1244
Dr Linda S Spedding
p81 London SW6 020 7610 2025
Malcolm A H M Williamson
p225 Farnham 0845 230 1022

EUROPEAN COMMUNITY LAW

Richard Buxton
p174 Cambridge 01223 328933
Ferdinand Kelly
p403 Sutton Coldfield 01827 893526
Alida Guest
p37 London W11 020 7727 6273
Irwin Mitchell LLP
p45 London EC1 0870 150 0100
Lennox Bywater
p53 London NW7 020 8906 1206
Vivienne Robinson
p72 London E11 020 8279 8899
J P Scholes
p121 Bamford 01433 651625
Dr Linda S Spedding
p81 London SW6 020 7610 2025
Temple & Co Commercial Solicitors
p207 Daventry 0845 241 4045

FAMILY LAW

@ Cornwall Law
p414 Truro 01872 222688 / 222712
174 Law
p134 Birkenhead 0151 647 7372
A'Court & Co
p434 Windsor 01753 857146
AGR Solicitors
p378 Shirebrook 01623 748522
AKP Solicitors Ltd
p3 London E6 020 8472 4462
AMD Solicitors
p160 Bristol 0117 923 5562
AST Hampsons (incorporating Warhurst and co)
p170 Bury 0161 764 3317
Abbott Cresswell LLP
p3 London SW14 020 8876 4478
S Abraham Solicitors
p402 Surbiton 020 8390 0044
Acklam Bond Noor
p114 Accrington 01254 872272
Act Family Law
p349 Plymouth 01752 226224
Adams Delmar
p238 Hampton 020 8941 2097
Addies
p226 Fleetwood 01253 772128
Addison O'Hare
p419 Walsall 01922 725515
Adlams LLP
p258 Huntingdon 01480 458885
p392 St Neots 01480 474061
Aitchison & Co
p4 London WC2 020 7240 0020
Aitken Associates
p4 Islington 020 7700 6006
Akermans
p441 Worthing 01903 820413
Alban Gould Baker & Co
p4 Islington 020 7607 5085
Albin & Co
p359 Reading 0118 957 4018
Alderson Dodds
p147 Blyth 01670 352293
Aldridge Brownlee Solicitors LLP
p151 Bournemouth 01202 294411
Michael Alexander & Co
p301 Manchester 0845 839 2011
Alfred Truman
p132 Bicester 01869 252761
Allan Jay Paine & Co
p5 Enfield 020 8886 1404
Allan Rutherford
p333 Norwich 01603 621722
Allens
p237 Halesworth 01986 875246
p354 Portsmouth 023 9282 2411
Allington Hughes
p442 Wrexham 01978 291000
Alsters Kelley
p199 Coventry 0844 561 0100
p270 Leamington Spa 0844 561 0100
p339 Nuneaton 0844 561 0100
Alun Thomas & John
p114 Aberystwyth 01970 615900
Alwena Jones & Jones
p147 Blaenau Ffestiniog 01766 831882
p416 Tywyn 01654 711499
J M Amin & Co
p426 Wembley 020 8903 3766
Amphlett Chatterton
p270 Leamington Spa 01926 311427
Amphletts
p198 Colwyn Bay 01492 532296
Anderson Partnership
p191 Chesterfield 01246 220737
Andrew & Andrew Solicitors
p354 Portsmouth 023 9266 1381
Andrew & Co LLP
p284 Lincoln 01522 512123
p322 Newark 01636 673743
Anthony Gold
p6 London SE17 020 7940 4000
p6 London SW16 020 7940 4000
Antons
p6 London N8 020 8888 6211
Apfel Carter
p296 Lytham 01253 725265 / 712216
Aplin Stockton Fairfax
p122 Banbury 01295 251234
Appleby Hope & Matthews
p314 Middlesbrough 01642 440444
p396 Stockton-on-Tees 01642 617000
Appleby Shaw
p434 Windsor 01753 860606
Arani & Co
p384 Southall 020 8893 5000
Armitage & Guest
p418 Wakefield 01924 371877
Armitage Sykes LLP
p255 Huddersfield 01484 344140
Anna Arthur Associates
p436 Woking 01483 222499
Ashby Family Law Practice
p208 Derby 01332 293293
Ashfords LLP
p412 Tiverton 01884 203000
Astills
p278 Leicester 0116 249 4450
Astle Paterson Ltd
p170 Burton-on-Trent 01283 531366
Atkins Hope Solicitors
p204 Croydon 020 8680 5018
Atkinson & Co
p328 Newport 01633 251118
Atkinson & Firth
p378 Shipley 01274 584305
Atkinson Cave & Stuart
p146 Blackpool 01253 293151
Atkinson McCall
p240 Harrogate 01423 501531
Attwood & Co
p233 Grays 01375 378122 / 378123
Audu & Co
p8 Islington 020 7278 9340
David Auld & Co
p130 Bedlington 01670 826870
p319 Morpeth 01670 505844
Austin Ryder & Co
p189 Cheshunt 01992 624804
p8 Enfield 020 8804 5111
p8 London NW1 020 7833 0882
Avery Emerson Solicitors
p259 Ilford 020 8215 0884
Avery Naylor
p404 Swansea 01792 463276
B&C Solicitors - The Law Shop
p372 Scarborough 01723 379777
BLB Solicitors
p413 Trowbridge 01225 755656
BTMK Solicitors LLP
p387 Southend-on-Sea 01702 339222
BWTLaw LLP
p219 Epsom 01372 725655
Ursula Bagnall Divorce & Family Law Solicitors
p201 Cowes 01983 247221
Bailey & Bailey
p315 Middlesbrough 01642 240991
Bailey & Cogger
p412 Tonbridge 01732 353305
Bailey & Haigh
p373 Selby 01757 705191
Baileys
p187 Cheltenham 01242 514477
Baines Bagguley Solicitors
p318 Morecambe 01524 413294
Baker Gray & Co
p323 Newcastle upon Tyne 0191 222 0203
Baker Macdonald
p374 Sevenoaks 01732 457978
Bakewells
p208 Derby 01332 348791
Baldwin Townsend & Co
p206 Cwmbran 01633 866007
Band Hatton LLP
p200 Coventry 024 7663 2121
Banks Kelly
p9 London EC2 020 7248 4231
John L Banky Solicitors
p359 Reading 0118 930 4630
Banner Jones
p192 Chesterfield 01246 861250
p213 Dronfield 01246 414438
Robert Barber & Sons
p335 Nottingham 0115 878 9000
Barber Titleys
p240 Harrogate 01423 502211
Barcan Woodward
p161 Bristol 0117 923 2141
Max Barford & Co
p414 Tunbridge Wells 01892 539379
Barker Son & Isherwood LLP
p118 Andover 01264 353411
p118 Andover 01264 791156
p342 Overton 01256 770211
p430 Whitchurch 01256 896262
Barkers
p148 Bolton 01204 370011
John Barkers
p195 Cleethorpes 01472 695218
p294 Louth 01507 604773
Barlow Robbins LLP
p231 Godalming 01483 417121
p235 Guildford 01483 543200
p436 Woking 01483 748500
Barlows
p312 Market Harborough 01858 410040
Barnes & Partners
p239 Harlow 01279 418601
p10 London N18 020 8884 2277
Barnes Coleman & Co
p131 Benfleet 01702 558211
Barnes Harrild & Dyer
p204 Croydon 020 8681 5128
Barnes Richards Rutter
p189 Chepstow 01291 628898
Marcus Barnett
p10 London SW1 020 7235 9215
Norman H Barnett & Co
p11 London E6 020 8471 2112
Barrett & Co Solicitors LLP
p210 Didcot 01235 851220
Barrett & Thomson
p381 Slough 01753 437416
David J Barry
p367 Ross-on-Wye 01989 564209
Bartlett Gooding & Weelen
p229 Glastonbury 01458 832510
p378 Shepton Mallet 01749 343091
Bartletts
p11 Haringey 020 8340 2202 / 8340 2203
Atha Barton & Co
p237 Guisborough 01287 633242
Barwells
p373 Seaford 01323 899331
Bassets
p229 Gillingham 01634 575464
p366 Rochester 01634 400161
Batchelors Solicitors
p166 Bromley 020 8768 7000
Richard T Bate & Co
p410 Tetbury 01666 503722
Battens
p212 Dorchester 01305 250560
p378 Sherborne 01935 814811
Deborah Baxter & Co
p360 Reading 0118 958 6855
Baxters
p407 Tamworth 01827 899059
T G Baynes
p207 Dartford 01322 295555
Bazeley Barnes & Bazeley
p132 Bideford 01237 473122
Nigel W Beaman
p176 Cannock 01543 574474
Bearders
p238 Halifax 01422 365215 / 343427
Beaumonts
p247 Hereford 01432 352345
Bell & Buxton
p375 Sheffield 0114 249 5969
Bell Lamb & Joynson
p286 Liverpool 0844 412 4348
R Bell & Son
p242 Hartlepool 01429 273165
Bell Wright & Co
p228 Gainsborough 01427 611722
Bemrose & Ling
p208 Derby 01332 347300
Ben Hoare Bell & Co
p323 Newcastle upon Tyne 0191 275 2626
Bendall & Sons
p327 Newmarket 01638 661116
Bendles
p181 Carlisle 01228 522215
Simon Bennett
p313 Marlow 01628 478088
Benussi & Co
p135 Birmingham 0121 248 4001
Berkeley Solicitors
p213 Droylsden 0161 371 0011
Bernard Chill & Axtell
p216 Eastleigh 023 8061 3197
Berry & Berry
p299 Maidstone 01622 690777
p412 Tonbridge 01732 355911
p414 Tunbridge Wells 01892 526344
Berry Redmond & Robinson
p429 Weston-super-Mare 01934 513963
Berry Smith LLP
p157 Bridgend 01656 645525
Beswicks
p239 Hanley 01782 205000
Betteridges
p248 Hertford 01992 505406
Beviss & Beckingsale
p252 Honiton 01404 548050
Bilton Hammond LLP
p311 Mansfield 01623 675800
Bindman & Co
p430 Whickham 0191 488 4950
Birchall Blackburn LLP
p194 Chorley 01257 279011
Bird & Co
p232 Grantham 01476 591711
p322 Newark 01636 650880
Bird & Lovibond
p417 Uxbridge 01895 256151
Birdy & Co
p426 Wembley 020 8900 9112
John Birkby & Co
p340 Oldham 0161 626 5686
Birkett Long LLP
p197 Colchester 01206 217300
Biscoes
p423 Waterlooville 023 9225 1257
p431 Wickham 01329 833249
Bishop & Co
p321 New Mills 01663 746730
Bishop & Sewell LLP
p13 London WC1 020 7631 4141
Blakemores
p135 Birmingham 0121 234 7200
p270 Leamington Spa 01926 457300
Blakestons
p213 Driffield 01377 253476
Blanchards Bailey LLP
p147 Blandford Forum 01258 459361
p212 Dorchester 01305 251222
p374 Shaftesbury 01747 440447
Blaser Mills
p120 Aylesbury 01296 434416
p241 Harrow 020 8427 6262
p364 Rickmansworth 01923 776211
Bleasdale & Co
p431 Whitehaven 01946 692165
Blick & Co
p14 London 020 7247 9696
Blight Skinnard
p371 Saltash 01752 842141
Blocks
p225 Felixstowe 01394 283241
p262 Ipswich 01473 230033
Bolton-Jones & Co
p286 Liverpool 0151 733 2241
Bonallack & Bishop
p117 Amesbury 01980 622992
p118 Andover 01264 364433
p371 Salisbury 01722 422300
A J Bond & Co
p166 Bromley 020 8464 2229
Bone & Payne LLP
p198 Colwyn Bay 01492 532385
p291 Llandudno 01492 876354
Bottrill & Co
p348 Pinner 020 8429 1010
Eric Bowes & Co
p382 Solihull 0121 744 3691
Sabina Bowler-Reed
p161 Bristol 01275 373111
Bowser Ollard & Bentley
p312 March 01354 652606
Boyce Hatton
p412 Torquay 01803 403403
Boyes Sutton & Perry
p123 Barnet 020 8449 9155
John Boyle & Co
p362 Redruth 01209 213507
Boys & Maughan
p359 Ramsgate 01843 595990
Bradbury Roberts & Raby
p373 Scunthorpe 01724 854000
Brain Chase Coles
p126 Basingstoke 01256 354481
Brains
p391 St Austell 01726 68111
Bramsdon & Childs
p388 Southsea 023 9282 1251

4

Bramwell Browne Odedra
p189 Chesham 01494 782244
Brand Mellon LLP
p230 Gloucester 01452 524088
Bray & Bray
p250 Hinckley 01455 639900
p312 Market Harborough 01858 467181
Breens Solicitors
p286 Liverpool 0151 928 6544
Brethertons LLP
p368 Rugby 01788 579579
Brewer Harding & Rowe
p125 Barnstaple 01271 342271
p132 Bideford 01237 472666
p261 Ilfracombe 01271 863495
Elliott Bridgman
p409 Telford 01952 684544
Brignalls Balderston Warren
p133 Biggleswade 01767 313813
p283 Letchworth 01462 482248
Brinley Morris Rees & Jones
p292 Llanelli 01554 774241
Brockbank Curwen Cain & Hall
p431 Whitehaven 01946 692194
John Bromfield & Company Ltd
p339 Nuneaton 024 7638 2343
Brooke-Taylors
p172 Buxton 01298 22741
Brooks
p378 Shipston-on-Stour 01608 664406
A H Brooks & Co
p278 Leek 01538 383201
Broomhall & Co
p136 Birmingham 0121 633 4868
Broomhead & Saul
p261 Ilminster 01460 57056
p408 Taunton 01823 288121
Bross Bennett
p16 London N6 020 8340 0444
Brown & Corbishley
p323 Newcastle under Lyme 01782 717888
Brown Barron
p125 Barrow-in-Furness 01229 828814
Brown Beer Nixon Mallon
p362 Redcar 01642 490202
Fiona Bruce & Co LLP
p421 Warrington 01925 263273
Brutton & Co
p223 Fareham 01329 236171
Buckles Solicitors LLP
p346 Peterborough 01733 888888
p393 Stamford 01780 484570
Buglear Bate & Co
p436 Woking 01483 715527 / 724246
Bull & Bull
p176 Canterbury 01227 714860
p248 Herne Bay 01227 742660
Burch Phillips & Co
p427 West Drayton 01895 442141
Burn & Co
p430 Wheathampstead 01438 833446
Burnand Brazier Tisdall
p254 Hove 01273 734022
p441 Worthing 01903 235002
Burnett Barker
p171 Bury St Edmunds 01284 701131
Burningham & Brown
p127 Bath 01225 320090
Burroughs
p299 Maidstone 01622 676976 / 676982
Burt Brill & Cardens
p159 Brighton 01273 604123
Burton & Co LLP
p381 Sleaford 01529 306008 / 306009
C R Burton & Co
p16 London SE20 020 8778 4455 / 8659 5775
Burton Woolf & Turk
p16 London EC1 020 7831 6478
Burtonwoods
p16 London WC1 020 7636 2448
Bury & Walkers LLP
p438 Wombwell 01226 753433
Buss Murton LLP
p202 Cranbrook 01580 712215
p207 Dartford 01322 220235
p415 Tunbridge Wells 01892 510222
Butcher & Barlow LLP
p170 Bury 0161 764 5141
p369 Runcorn 01928 572268
CB4law
p174 Cambridge 01223 316666
CMHT Solicitors
p420 Walsall 01922 646400
p420 Walsall 01922 743525
C Nicholls
p148 Bodmin 01208 76969
CVC Solicitors
p245 Hayle 01736 752246
p346 Penzance 01736 362313
p392 St Ives 01736 795456
Caldicott Gallimore
p282 Leominster 01568 614168
Cameron Jones Hussell & Howe
p353 Port Talbot 01639 885261

Camerons Jones
p241 Harrow 020 8423 6666
Canter Levin & Berg
p287 Liverpool 0151 239 1000
Caplans
p241 Harrow 020 8864 0111
Graeme Carmichael
p262 Ipswich 01473 252159
Terence Carney
p246 Hebburn 0191 483 5422 / 483 8771
S A Carr & Co
p18 Hackney 020 8986 5438
Barbara Carter
p136 Birmingham 0121 441 3238
Carvill & Johnson LLP
p136 Birmingham 0121 476 9000
Caswell Jones
p172 Caerphilly 029 2086 4888
Caunters
p285 Liskeard 01579 343165 / 343484
Caversham Solicitors Ltd
p360 Reading 0118 947 8638
Chadwick Lawrence
p319 Morley 0113 252 3452
Chafes
p433 Wilmslow 01625 531676
Challenor Gardiner
p343 Oxford 01865 721451
Challinors
p136 Birmingham 0121 212 9393
p427 West Bromwich 0121 553 3211
Chamberlain Martin Solicitors
p148 Bognor Regis 01243 825211
Chamberlins
p234 Great Yarmouth 01493 600113
p234 Great Yarmouth 01493 857621
Chambers Rutland & Crauford
p19 London N12 020 8446 2777
Chancellors Lea Brewer
p132 Bexleyheath 020 8303 0077
Chanter Ferguson
p125 Barnstaple 01271 342268
Chapple & Co
p312 March 01354 652550
Charles Coleman LLP
p434 Windsor 01753 861115
Charlesworth Nicholl & Co
p203 Crediton 01363 774706
Chattertons Solicitors
p151 Boston 01205 310025
p381 Sleaford 01529 411500
Chebsey & Co
p128 Beaconsfield 01494 670440
Cheesman & Co
p287 Liverpool 0151 258 1212
Chenery Maher & Co
p196 Clitheroe 01200 422264
Chestnutts
p114 Ainsdale 01704 572221
Chesworths
p397 Stoke-on-Trent 01782 599992
Chetty & Patel
p279 Leicester 0116 254 6222
Chronnell Hibbert
p259 Hyde 0161 368 3434
Chubb Bulleid
p400 Street 01749 836100
p425 Wells 01749 836100
Churchers
p271 Lee-on-the-Solent 023 9255 1500
p354 Portsmouth 023 9286 2424
Clark & Weeks
p349 Plymouth 01752 345311
David Clark & Co
p20 London NW3 020 7433 1562
Robin F Clark & Co
p232 Gravesend 01474 334444
Clark Willis
p183 Catterick Garrison 01748 830000
Clarke & Hartland Solicitors
p177 Cardiff 029 2048 3181
Peter Clarke Solicitors
p413 Totton 023 8066 6636
Clarkson Hirst
p264 Kendal 01539 736916
Clarkson Wright & Jakes Ltd
p341 Orpington 01689 887887
Clayton Mott
p336 Nottingham 0115 941 7422
Clayton Mott & Lawton
p404 Sutton-in-Ashfield 01623 556601
Clement Hughes & Co
p356 Prestatyn 01745 852121
Cleverdons
p218 Enfield 020 8367 5375
Clifford Poole & Co
p370 Salford 0161 736 0160
Douglas Clift & Co
p269 Lancaster 01524 32437
Clifton Ingram LLP
p360 Reading 0118 957 3425
Cluley & Co
p434 Winsford 01606 553719

Clyde Chappell & Botham
p397 Stoke-on-Trent 01782 599577
Cocks Lloyd
p339 Nuneaton 024 7664 1642
Coffin Mew & Clover
p232 Gosport 023 9252 3111
p354 Portsmouth 023 9238 8021
p385 Southampton 023 8033 4661
Cohen Filippini
p116 Altrincham 0161 929 9993
Colborne Coulman & Lawrence
p328 Newport 01633 264194 / 264196
Charles Coleman & Co
p360 Reading 0118 958 1578
Colemans Solicitors LLP
p298 Maidenhead 01628 631051
Coles Miller Solicitors LLP
p151 Bournemouth 01202 511512
p166 Broadstone 01202 694891
Collins Dryland & Thorowgood LLP
p411 Tilehurst 0118 942 2448
E M Collins & Co
p348 Pinner 020 8866 1820
Collins Solicitors
p423 Watford 01923 223324
K J Commons & Co
p182 Carlisle 01228 822666
p431 Whitehaven 01946 66699
p440 Workington 01900 604698
Connolley & Company
p437 Wolverhampton 01902 326000
Conveyancing Direct Ltd
p392 St Leonards-on-Sea 0845 788 8666
Coodes
p285 Liskeard 01579 347600
p329 Newquay 01637 878111
p414 Truro 01872 246200
Cook Taylor Woodhouse
p22 London SE9 020 8859 0936
Cooks
p323 Newcastle under Lyme 01782 611090
Cooper Sons Hartley & Williams
p172 Buxton 01298 77511
p184 Chapel-en-le-Frith 01298 812138
Copitch
p22 Haringey 020 8883 9831
Cornwells
p153 Bradford 01274 675631
Covent Garden Family Law
p23 Camden 020 7257 6130
Cowlishaw & Mountford
p417 Uttoxeter 01889 565211
Cozens Moxon & Harts
p409 Teddington 020 8977 8486 / 8977 4424
Cozens-Hardy LLP
p334 Norwich 01603 625231
Crangle Edwards
p185 Cheadle 0161 428 2331
Creagh Brown & Co Solicitors
p220 Esher 020 8224 0610
Crockett & Co
p272 Leeds 0113 226 0111
Crombie Wilkinson
p444 York 01904 624185
Crompton Halliwell
p170 Bury 0161 797 9222
Crossmans MTA
p174 Cambridge 01223 451442
Paul Crowley & Co
p287 Liverpool 0151 264 7363
Cumming Hodgkinson Dickinson
p148 Bolton 01204 523108 / 528396
Daniel Curry & Co
p205 Croydon 020 8680 2188
Cuthbertsons
p119 Ashington 01670 813524
p148 Blyth 01670 352121
Cuttle & Co Solicitors
p340 Oldham 0161 678 7443
Cygnet Family Law
p196 Cleveland 01642 777680
DBL Talbots LLP
p197 Codsall 01902 843427
p213 Dudley 01384 252471
p437 Wolverhampton 01902 427561
DB Law
p173 Camborne 01209 712428
p346 Penzance 01736 364261
DMB Law
p374 Sevenoaks 01732 228800
DP Law Ltd t/a David Prosser & Co
p157 Bridgend 01656 645921
DWT Legal Ltd
p265 Kidderminster 0844 770 3799
Graham Dack & Company (inc Battersby James)
p185 Chatteris 01354 695885
Dakers
p159 Brighton 01273 571685
Dakers Marriott Solicitors
p400 Strood 01634 813300
Dale & Newbery LLP
p393 Staines 01784 464491

Daltons
p215 Eastbourne 01323 720040
Daltons Solicitors
p348 Petersfield 01730 262816
Daniel & Edwards
p359 Ramsgate 01843 594651
W H Darbyshire & Son
p146 Blackpool 01253 346646
Darling & Stephensons
p206 Darlington 01325 489000
David & Snape
p157 Bridgend 01656 661115
Davies & Co
p166 Bromley 020 8460 6668
Davies Bell & Reed
p324 Newcastle upon Tyne 0191 232 8058
Davies Blunden & Evans
p224 Farnborough 01252 541633
Davies Gore Lomax
p273 Leeds 0113 242 2797
Lawrence Davies & Co
p26 Hammersmith & Fulham 020 7381 1171
Davies Parsons Allchurch
p292 Llanelli 01554 749144
Davis & Co
p259 Ilford 020 8551 4228
Davis Priest & Co
p362 Redditch 01527 69231
Davisons
p137 Birmingham 0121 685 1234
William Dawes & Co
p370 Rye 01797 223177
Dawson & Burgess with Bell Dallman & Co
p211 Doncaster 01302 834744
Dawson Cornwell
p26 London WC1 020 7242 2556
Nicholas Daykin Solicitors
p120 Attleborough 01953 453774
Stanley De Leon
p355 Potters Bar 01707 657277
Edward De Silva & Co
p384 Southall 020 8571 2299
Denby & Co
p125 Barrow-in-Furness 01229 822366
Denhams
p236 Guildford 01483 456450
Desor & Co
p245 Hayes 020 8569 0708
Devereux & Co
p162 Bristol 0117 938 0222
p162 Bristol 0117 959 3344
Dexter Montague LLP
p360 Reading 0118 939 3999
Dickinson Wood
p211 Doncaster 01302 329504
Dickson Haslam
p268 Kirkham 01772 685109
Dicksons Solicitors Ltd
p397 Stoke-on-Trent 01782 262424
p397 Stoke-on-Trent 01782 262424
Divorce & Family Law Practice
p137 Birmingham 0121 200 0890
Dixon Coles & Gill
p418 Wakefield 01924 373467
Dixon Rigby Keogh
p315 Middlewich 01606 835736
p333 Northwich 01606 48111
Dixon Stewart
p321 New Milton 01425 621515
Dodd Lewis Solicitors
p27 London SE3 020 8852 1255
Paul Dodds Solicitors
p419 Wallsend 0191 263 6200
Donaldson Dunstall
p131 Bexhill 01424 216329
Dootsons LLP
p205 Culcheth 01925 765212
Adam Douglas & Son
p131 Berwick-upon-Tweed 01289 306479
Douglas-Jones Mercer
p405 Swansea 01792 650000
Downes & Siddall
p284 Lincoln 01522 543343
Downie & Gadban
p116 Alton 01420 82879
Dowse & Co
p27 Hackney 020 7254 6205
Draper & Co
p225 Farnham 01252 727374
Driver Belcher Solicitors
p385 Southampton 01489 785737
David Du Pre & Co
p28 London WC1 020 7430 1950
Scott Duff & Co
p346 Penrith 01768 865551
Duffield Harrison LLP
p251 Hoddesdon 01992 442911
Dunn & Baker
p221 Exeter 01392 285000
Dunning & Co
p28 London SE5 020 7733 6217

See p542 for the Firms Specialisations

Thomas Dunton Solicitors
p342 . . . . Orpington 01689 822554
Dyne Drewett Solicitors Ltd
p378 . . . . . Shepton Mallet 01749 342323
EBR Attridge LLP
p28. . . . . . . London SE16 020 7231 5166
ELC Solicitors
p28. . . . . Ealing 020 8566 4045
Eastleys
p345 . . . . Paignton 01803 559257
p413 . . . . Totnes 01803 864888
Eaton-Evans & Morris
p244 . . . . . . Haverfordwest 01437 763383
Eccles Heddon
p365 . . . . Ripon 01765 601717
Eddowes Perry & Osbourne
p403 . . . . Sutton Coldfield 0121 686 9444
p403 . . . . Sutton Coldfield 0121 686 9666
Edmondson Hall
p327 . . . . Newmarket 01638 560556
Edwards Duthie
p260 . . . . Ilford 020 8514 9000
p29. . . . . . . London E13 020 8514 9000
p29. . . . . London E6 020 8514 9000
Nigel Edwards & Co
p299 . . . . Maidstone 01622 690575
R L Edwards & Partners
p413 . . . . Treorchy 01443 775000
Elliot Mather LLP
p192 . . . . Chesterfield 01246 231288
p311 . . . . Mansfield 01623 655666
Ellis & Co
p190 . . . . Chester 01244 319388
Ellis Jones
p151 . . . . . Bournemouth 01202 525333
p364 . . . . Ringwood 01425 484848
Ellisons
p195 . . . . . Clacton-on-Sea 01255 421248
p243 . . . . Harwich 01255 502428
Elmhirst Parker LLP
p124 . . . . Barnsley 01226 282238
p374 . . . . Selby 01757 703895
Elsey & Hodson
p347 . . . . . . Peterborough 01733 314064
Elton & Co
p29. . . . . Camden 020 7267 7373
Eltringham & Co
p324 . . Newcastle upon Tyne 0191 266 5878
Elwyn Jones & Co
p122 . . . . Bangor 01248 370224
Emmerson Brown & Brown
p207 . . . . Deal 01304 362146
Emsleys
p204 . . . . Crossgates 0113 260 3115
Max Engel & Co LLP
p331 . . . . . . Northampton 01604 887450
England & Co
p234 . . . . . Great Yarmouth 01493 604990
p234 Great Yarmouth 01493 740795 / 748174
p234 Great Yarmouth 01493 844308 / 844309
Eric Robinson Solicitors
p184 . . . . . Chandlers Ford 023 8025 4676
p259 . . . . Hythe 023 8084 4304
Harvey Escott & Co
p169
. Burnham-on-Crouch 01621 784838 / 784839
Evans & Ellis
p189 . . . . Chepstow 01291 622814
Mary Evans & Co
p182 . . . . Carmarthen 01267 233881
FBC Manby Bowdler LLP
p157 . . . . Bridgnorth 01746 761436
p409 . . . . Telford 01952 292129
p432 . . . . Willenhall 01902 366566
FDC Law
p228 . . . . Frome 01373 463311
p358 . . . . Radstock 01761 417575
Fairbrother & Darlow
p153 . . . . Bracknell 01344 420808
Fairweather Stephenson & Co
p225 . . . . Felixstowe 01394 277941
Farleys Solicitors LLP
p169 . . . . Burnley 01282 798664
Farnfield & Nicholls
p229 . . . . Gillingham 01747 825432
p421 . . . . Warminster 01985 214661
Farrells Solicitors
p162 . . . . Bristol 0117 944 4664
Favell Smith & Lawson Solicitors
p375 . . . . Sheffield 0114 272 4381
Andrew J Fenny & Co
p201 . . . . Cramlington 01670 737393
Fentimans
p269 . . . . Knowle 01564 779459
Joan Ferguson & Co
p304 . . . . Manchester 0161 795 5866
Finn Gledhill
p246 . . . . . . Hebden Bridge 01422 842451
Paul Finn Solicitors
p168 . . . . Bude 01288 356256
Firth Lindsay
p375 . . . . Sheffield 0114 276 0586
Fish & Co
p438 . . . . . Wolverhampton 01902 826464
Fishers
p404 . . . . Swadlincote 01283 217193
Thomas Flavell & Sons
p214 . . . . Earl Shilton 01455 842297
Ronald Fletcher & Co
p33. . . . . London W9 020 7624 0041
Fletchers
p388 . . . . Southport 01704 546919
Flint Bishop Solicitors
p208 . . . . Derby 01332 340211
Follett Stock LLP
p221 . . . . Exeter 01392 449370
Forbes
p145 . . . . Blackburn 01254 580000
p356 . . . . Preston 01772 220022
Andrew M Ford Solicitors
p279 . . . . Leicester 0845 075 4059
Lindsay Ford Solicitors Ltd
p172 . . . . Caerphilly 029 2088 2441
Ford Simey LLP
p222 Exmouth 01395 272241 / 0800 169 3741
Forresters
p125 . . . . . . Barrow-in-Furness 01229 820297
Forshaws Davies Ridgway LLP
p227 . . . . Frodsham 01928 739300
Foster & Partners
p162 . . . . Bristol 0117 961 5300
David J Foster & Co
p407 . . . . Tamworth 01827 58333 / 58334
Fountain Solicitors Limited
p420 . . . . Walsall 01922 645429
John Fowlers LLP Solicitors
p197 . . . . Colchester 01206 576151
Joseph Foxler & Co
p170 . . . . Bury 0161 797 4126
Foys Solicitors
p211 . . . . Doncaster 01302 327136
p367 . . . . Rotherham 01709 375561
Francis & Co
p189 . . . . Chepstow 01291 622237
Franklins
p214 . . . . Dunstable 01582 699111
Franklins LLP
p317 . . . . . . Milton Keynes 01908 660966
Franks & Co
p34. . . . . London EC4 020 7242 8008
Fraser Brown
p133 . . . . Bingham 01949 830812
p337 . . . . Nottingham 0115 988 8777
Frearsons
p380 . . . . Skegness 01754 897600
Doreen Freear Solicitor
p297 . . . . Macclesfield 01625 611711
Freedman Green Dhokia
p34. . . . . Camden 020 7624 2981
Freer & Archer
p279 . . . . Leicester 0116 241 3199
French & Co
p337 . . . . Nottingham 0115 955 1111
French & Co Solicitors Ltd
p403 . . . . Sutton Coldfield 0121 362 7330
Julia Frimond Solicitors
p236 . . . . Guildford 01483 452224
Fuglers
p34. . . . . London W1 020 7323 6450
Fulchers
p436 . . . . Woking 01483 885522
Funnell & Perring
p243 . . . . Hastings 01424 426287
GC Law
p248 . . . . Hereford 01432 275397
GLP Solicitors
p315 . . . . Middleton 0161 653 6295
p357 . . . . Prestwich 0161 773 8626
GLRS Phoenix LLP
p400 . . . . Stroud 01453 757381
GPB Solicitors LLP
p400 . . . Stratford-upon-Avon 01789 261131
Gales
p152 . Bournemouth 01202 512227 / 512446
Gangar & Co
p427 . . . . West Bromwich 0121 553 4166
Garner Canning
p120 . . . . Atherstone 01827 713543
p138 . . . . Birmingham 0121 749 5577
p407 . . . . Tamworth 01827 314004
Garner Canning Vickery
p403 . . . . Sutton Coldfield 0121 323 2646
Garrods Solicitors
p186 . . . . Chelmsford 01245 492494
Gartsides
p216 . . . . Ebbw Vale 01495 302109
Gaskell & Walker
p157 . . . . Bridgend 01656 653122
Gates & Moloney
p270 . . . . Lancing 01903 766046
Gaynham King & Mellor
p118 . . . . Appleby 01768 351422
p346 . . . . Penrith 01768 864651
Craig Gee
p304 . . . . Manchester 0161 666 9999
Geoffrey Morris & Ashton
p442 . . . . Wrexham 01978 291322
Reena Ghai Solicitors
p253 . . . . Hounslow 020 8759 9959
Deborah Gibbins & Co
p133 . . . . Billericay 01268 270866
Gichard & Co
p367 . . . . Rotherham 01709 365531
Giffen Couch & Archer
p399 . . . . Stony Stratford 01908 563911
Gilbert Stephens
p342 . . . . . . Ottery St Mary 01404 812228
Gill & Co
p260 . . . . Ilford 020 8554 8774
Gill Turner Tucker
p299 . . . . Maidstone 01622 759051
Ginn & Co
p174 . . . . Cambridge 01223 358275
Gittins McDonald
p442 . . . . Wrexham 01978 291662
Glaisyers
p138 . . . . Birmingham 0121 233 2971
p407 . . . . Tamworth 01827 61011
Glaisyers Solicitors LLP
p304 . . . . Manchester 0161 832 4666
Glandfield & Cruddas
p417 . . . . Uttoxeter 01889 565657
Glansfields
p311 . . . . Mansfield 01623 627827
Goad & Butcher
p374 . . . . Settle 01729 823500
Godwins
p114 . . . . Aberystwyth 01970 624244
Goldstones
p405 . . . . Swansea 01792 643021
Goldwaters
p324 . . Newcastle upon Tyne 0191 232 2653
Gomer Williams & Co
p292 . . . . Llanelli 01554 755101
Goodhand and Forsyth QualitySolicitors
p362 . . . . Redhill 01737 773533
Goodman King
p408 . . . . Tavistock 01822 615510
Goodman Ray
p36. . . . . Hackney 020 7608 1227
Goodwin Cowley
p294 . . . . Lowestoft 01502 532700
Goodwins Family Law Solicitors
p241 . . . . Harrow 020 8423 3525
Gordon & Penney
p429 . . . Weston-super-Mare 01934 414161
R Gordon Roberts Laurie & Co
p292 . . . . Llangefni 01248 722215 / 723312
Gorvins
p395 . . . . Stockport 0161 930 5151
H F T Gough & Co
p431 . . . . Whitehaven 01946 692461
Goughs
p193 . . . . Chippenham 01249 444499
p199 . . . . Corsham 01249 712193
p210 . . . . Devizes 01380 726913
p314 . . . . Melksham 01225 703036
p414 . . . . Trowbridge 01225 762683
Gould & Swayne
p169 . . . . Burnham-on-Sea 01278 783272
Gowlings
p357 . . . . Preston 01772 251287
Gowmans
p345 . . . . Paignton 01803 546100
Grahame Stowe Bateson
p274 . . . . Leeds 0113 255 8666
p274 . . . . Leeds 0113 274 4611
p274 . . . . Leeds 0113 276 0044
Grainger Appleyard
p211 . . . . Doncaster 01302 327257
Granville-West
p352 . . . . Pontypool 01495 751111
Granville-West Chivers & Morgan
p113 . . . . Abertillery 01495 217070
David Gray Solicitors
p324 . . Newcastle upon Tyne 0191 232 9547
Graysons
p375 . . . . Sheffield 0114 272 9184
Christopher Green McCarrahers
p386 . . . . . . Southampton 023 8084 2765
Green Wright Chalton Annis
p441 . . . . Worthing 01903 234064
Greenfield Whiston
p265 . . . . Kettering 01536 410880
Greenland Houchen Pomeroy
p120 . . . . Attleborough 01953 453143
p334 . . . . Norwich 01603 660744
p424 . . . . Watton 01953 882864
Gregg Latchams LLP
p162 . . . . Bristol 0117 906 9400
Gregory Abrams Davidson LLP
p288 . . . . Liverpool 0151 236 5000
p288 . . . . Liverpool 0151 494 0777
p288 . . . . Liverpool 0151 733 3353
Gregorys Solicitors
p395 . . . . Stockport 0161 456 8125
Gregsons
p337 . . . . Nottingham 0115 941 1999
Gareth Griffith & Company
p172 . . . . Caernarfon 01286 676869
Griffith Smith Conway
p254 . . . . Hove 01273 821577
Shirley Griffiths
p259 . . . . Hythe 01303 266689
Stephanie F Griffiths
p267 . Kingston upon Thames 020 8546 5986
Grylls & Paige
p363 . . . . . Redruth 01209 215261 / 215357
A K Gulati & Co
p402 . . . . Sutton 020 8770 7979
Gulbenkian Andonian Solicitors
p37. . . . . London WC1 020 7269 9590
Gumersalls
p219 . . . . Epsom 01372 721122
Gurney-Champion & Co
p354 . . . . Portsmouth 023 9282 1100
Gurneys
p227 . . . . Framlingham 01728 621372
Guthrie Jones & Jones
p211 . . . . Dolgellau 01341 422604
HCB Solicitors
p362 . . . . Redditch 01527 62688
HC Solicitors LLP
p347 . . . . . . Peterborough 01733 882800
HKB Wiltshires
p294 . . . . Lowestoft 01502 582338
HKH Kenwright & Cox Solicitors
p260 . . . . Ilford 020 8553 9600
HRJ Law LLP
p251 . . . . Hitchin 01462 628888
Hague & Dixon
p348 . . . . Pickering 01751 475222
p444 . . . . York 01904 627111
Hague Lambert
p269 . . . . Knutsford 01565 652411
p297 . . . . Macclesfield 01625 616480
p417 . . . . Urmston 0161 747 7321
Hains & Lewis Ltd
p244 . . . . . Haverfordwest 0845 408 0125
Frederic Hall
p227 . . . . Folkestone 01303 851185
HallmarkHulme
p439 . . . . Worcester 01905 726600
Hameed & Co
p38. . . . . . . London NW10 020 8830 1335
Hammon Oakley
p200 . . . . Coventry 024 7644 8585
Hamways Walker Owens
p216 . . . . Edenbridge 01732 866666
Hancocks
p122 . . . . Banbury 01295 253211
Edward Hands & Lewis
p293 . . . . Loughborough 01509 216161
Hannays Solicitors and Advocates
p383 South Shields 0191 456 7893 / 455 5361
Hannides Hewstone & Co
p386 . . . . Southampton 023 8078 6770
Harcus Sinclair
p38. . . . . . . London WC2 020 7242 9700
Charles Harding & Co
p426 . . . . Wembley 020 8795 0990
Hardman & Watson
p166 . . . . Broadstairs 01843 863479
Hardman Wood
p145 . . . . Blackburn 01254 295540
Harper & Odell
p39. . . . . Islington 020 7490 0500
Harris & Harris
p228 . . . . Frome 01373 463366
T R Harris Arnold & Co
p231 . . . Gorseinon 01792 892166 / 891331
Harrison Bundey
p274 . . . . Leeds 0113 200 7400
Harrison Clark LLP
p367 . . . . Ross-on-Wye 01989 562377
p439 . . . . Worcester 01905 612001
Harrop White Vallance & Dawson
p311 . . . . Mansfield 01623 629221
Harrowells
p444 . . . . York 01904 558600
p445 . . . . York 01904 760237
Hart Brown Solicitors
p231 . . . . Godalming 0800 068 8177
Hart Reade
p215 . . . . Eastbourne 01323 727321
p237 . . . . Hailsham 01323 841481
Harthills
p367 . . . . Rotherham 01709 377399
Hartley & Worstenholme
p183 . . . . Castleford 01977 732222
p351 . . . . Pontefract 01977 732222
Hartnell Chanot & Partners Family Law Specialists
p221 . . . . Exeter 01392 421777
Harvey Copping & Harrison
p186 . . . . Chelmsford 01245 322956
p431 . . . . Wickford 01268 733381 / 763211
Hatchers Solicitors LLP
p379 . . . . Shrewsbury 01743 467641
Hathaways
p228 . . . . Gateshead 0191 477 2288
Hatton
p207 . . . . Daventry 01327 301201

Hawkins Ross Limited
p397 Stockton-on-Tees 01642 613647 / 678888
R J Hawksley & Co
p173 Camberley 01252 890400
Haworth & Nuttall
p145 Blackburn 01254 272640
Haworth Brotherton
p411 Thornton Cleveleys 01253 852356
Hay & Kilner
p419 Wallsend 0191 262 8231
Hayat & Co
p218 Enfield 020 8360 4485
Hayes Clifford & Co
p411 Tilehurst 0118 941 8416
Haywards
p399 Stowmarket 01449 613631
Heaney Watson
p288 Liverpool 0151 256 7777
p288 Liverpool 0151 282 5555
p288 Liverpool 0151 293 2936
p305 Manchester 0800 567 7597 / 0161 359 3347
Heath Sons & Broome
p305 Manchester 0161 681 1933
Heckford Norton
p370 Saffron Walden 01799 522636
Heer Manak
p200 Coventry 024 7666 4000
Hegarty LLP
p393 Stamford 01780 752066
Hellewell Pasley & Brewer
p128 Batley 01924 472596
p210 Dewsbury 01924 455515
Henchleys
p285 Littlehampton 01903 726477
Henriques Griffiths
p163 Bristol 0117 909 4000
p435 Winterbourne 01454 854000
Heppenstalls
p296 Lymington 01590 689500
p321 New Milton 01425 610078
Heringtons
p243 Hastings 01424 434192
p370 Rye 01797 222955
Heseltine Bray & Welsh
p124 Barnsley 01226 210777
Hewetts
p361 Reading 0118 957 5337
Hewitt Burrough & Co
p207 Dartford 01322 273833
Hewitts
p203 Crook 01388 762466
p397 Stockton-on-Tees 01642 673701
Heyes Samuel
p369 Ryde 01983 615615
Heyman & Co
p282 Leigh 01942 604135
Joseph Hill & Co
p41 London N15 020 8880 3535
HilliersHRW Solicitors
p395 Stevenage 01438 346000
Hillis Solicitors
p305 Manchester 0161 248 0500
Hills (Oldham)
p340 Oldham 0161 652 3231
Hills Solicitors Limited
p116 Altrincham 0161 928 0961
Hillyer McKeown LLP
p129 Bebington 0151 645 4255
Hine Downing Solicitors
p223 Falmouth 01326 316655
Hipkin & Co
p431 Whitley Bay 0191 253 3509
Hodders
p250 High Wycombe 01494 511345
John Hodge Solicitors
p429 Weston-super-Mare 01934 623511
Hodge Jones & Allen LLP
p41 London NW1 020 7874 8300
Hodgson Coulthard & Co
p253 Houghton Le Spring 0191 584 3333
Hodgsons & Mortimer
p363 Richmond 01748 850950
Hogans
p356 Prescot 0151 430 7529
Holden & Co
p243 Hastings 01424 722422
Holdens
p269 Lancaster 01524 32484
Holmes & Hills LLP
p155 Braintree 01376 320456
p238 Halstead 01787 475312
David Holmes & Co
p234 Great Yarmouth 01493 658291
Laurence Holmes Solicitors
p198 Congresbury 01934 838445
Holt & Longworth
p367 Rossendale 01706 213251 / 229131
Hood Vores & Allwood
p209 Dereham 01362 692424
Hoole & Co
p163 Bristol 0117 942 8871
p163 Bristol 0117 969 1436

Hopkin Murray Beskine
p42 London N4 020 7272 1234
Wendy Hopkins Family Law Practice LLP
p178 Cardiff 029 2034 2233
Horsey Lightly
p43 London W1 020 7222 8844
p322 Newbury 01635 580858
Horwood & James LLP
p121 Aylesbury 01296 487361
John Hoult & Co
p373 Scunthorpe 01724 281312
Howard & Co
p124 Barnsley 01226 211888
p124 Barnsley 01226 215215
Howard & Over
p263 Ivybridge 01752 690123
p350 Plymouth 01752 556606
Howard Stone
p43 London EC1 020 7490 5900
Howarth & Co
p429 Wetherby 01937 584020
Susan Howarth & Co
p333 Northwich 01606 48777
Howell & Co
p139 Birmingham 0121 778 5031
Howell-Jones LLP
p267 Kingston upon Thames 020 8549 5186
p420 Walton-on-Thames 01932 234500
Howells
p405 Swansea 01792 410016
Howells LLP
p367 Rotherham 01709 364000
p376 Sheffield 0114 249 6666
Howlett Clarke Solicitors
p254 Hove 01273 419728
Hughes & Company
p413 Tring 01442 891717
Hughes Fowler Carruthers
p43 London WC2 020 7421 8383
J W Hughes & Co
p199 Conwy 01492 596596
p291 Llandudno 01492 874774
Hughes Paddison
p188 Cheltenham 01242 574244
Hughes-Narborough & Thomas
p43 Greenwich 020 8854 1291
Humfrys & Symonds
p248 Hereford 01432 359261 / 276276
Humphries Kirk
p421 Wareham 01929 552141
Hunt & Hunt
p366 Romford 01708 764433
Hunters
p44 London WC2 020 7412 0050
Hurlow & Partners
p179 Cardiff 029 2039 6087
Hutsby Mees
p393 Stafford 01785 259211
Henry Hyams
p274 Leeds 0113 243 2288
Howard Hyman & Co
p44 London N12 020 8446 5511
Ian N Gunby & Co
p316 Milnthorpe 01539 562044
Inghams
p146 Blackpool 01253 626642
p226 Fleetwood 01253 873481
p411 Thornton Cleveleys 01253 824111
Ingrams
p257 Hull 01482 358850
p445 York 01904 520600
International Family Law Chambers
p45 London WC2 020 7583 5040
The International Family Law Group
p45 London WC2 020 3178 5668
Irvings Solicitors
p209 Derby 01332 346036
Isherwood & Hose
p249 Heywood 01706 360032 / 368741
Ison Harrison
p274 Leeds 0113 232 6530
JSP Solicitors
p380Skegness 01754 762252 / 01522 537353
Jackamans
p239 Harleston 01379 854455
Arthur Jackson & Co
p367 Rotherham 01709 363876
Gary Jacobs & Co
p45 London E18 020 8536 4050
Bernard James
p144 Bishop Auckland 01388 458868
Gwyn James Solicitors
p195 Cinderford 01594 822277
Jameson & Hill
p421 Ware 01920 460531
Anne Jarvis & Co
p240 Harrogate 01423 858582
Jasper & Vincent
p386 Southampton 01489 885788
Andrew Jay & Co (Philip Hanby Limited)
p228 Gainsborough 01427 612412

Jennings Perks & Co
p420 Walsall 01922 459000
Jeromes
p374 Shanklin 01983 862643
Jestyn Jeffreys
p320 Neath 01639 635641
Jewels Solicitors
p393 Stafford 01785 602030
Johnson & Clarence
p316 Midhurst 01730 812244
Jolliffe & Co
p190 Chester 01244 310022
Jones & Co
p128 Bawtry 01302 710555
p363 Retford 01777 703827
Geraint Jones & Co
p330 Newtown 01686 627935
Jones Myers LLP
p275 Leeds 0113 246 0055
P Lloyd Jones & Co
p318 Mold 01352 758533 / 758534
Jones Robertson
p369 Runcorn 01928 711119
Terry Jones Solicitors & Advocates
p379 Shrewsbury 01743 285888
Jordans
p368 Rowley Regis 0121 559 2922
Josiah Hincks
p196 Coalville 01530 835041
p280 Leicester 0116 255 1811
Kaim Todner Ltd
p119 Ashford 01233 662002
p47 Islington 020 7700 0070
p47 London EC4 020 7353 6660
p47 London SE17 020 7701 4747
Jane Kaim-Caudle & Co
p423 Watford 01923 219061
D C Kaye & Co
p234 Great Missenden 01494 864650 / 862226
Alistair Keeble
p195 Clacton-on-Sea 01255 818900
Keelys LLP
p284 Lichfield 01543 420000
Keene & Kelly
p318 Mold 01352 753882
Keene Marsland
p415 Tunbridge Wells 01892 526442
Keer-Keer & Co
p246 Hemel Hempstead 01442 216755 / 216756
Richard P Kemp BA Solicitor
p313 Martock 01935 822572
Keoghs and Nicholls, Lindsell & Harris
p116 Altrincham 0161 928 9321
Keppe Rofer
p156 Brecon 01874 624627
Kerseys
p262 Ipswich 01473 213311
Kevills
p194 Chorley 01257 265711
Kidd & Spoor
p431 Whitley Bay 0191 297 0011
King Davies & Partners
p298 Maesteg 01656 732911
Rodney King & Partners
p163 Bristol 0117 926 5201
Kingsfords
p119 Ashford 01233 624545
Kirby & Co
p50 London SW19 020 8545 7171
Kirbys
p240 Harrogate 01423 542000
Kirklands
p366 Romsey 01794 513466
Knipe Woodhouse-Smith
p184 Chalfont St Peter 01753 887877 / 889149
LDJ Solicitors
p339 Nuneaton 024 7674 5000
Simon Lacey Law Associates
p430 Weymouth 01305 777711
B D Laddie
p51 London W1 020 7963 8585
Lamport Bassitt
p361 Reading 0845 077 6600
p386 Southampton 023 8083 7777
Lancasters
p51 London W4 020 8742 1314
Bruce Lance & Co
p250 High Wycombe 01494 450494
J S Lane & Co
p172 Bushey 020 8950 1782
Langley Wellington
p230 Gloucester 01452 521286
Lanyon Bowdler LLP
p409 Telford 01952 291222
p425 Wellington 01952 244721
Larken & Co
p322 Newark 01636 703333
Last Cawthra Feather LLP
p378 Shipley 01274 585459
The Law Partnership
p242 Harrow 020 8416 7004

H Lawrence & Co
p52 London N6 020 7482 2613 / 7482 4212
Lawson & Thompson
p119 Ashington 01670 813588
p130 Bedlington 01670 530700
Lawson West Solicitors Limited
p312 Market Harborough 01858 445480
p432 Wigston 0116 212 1080
Lawson-Cruttenden & Co
p52 London WC1 020 7405 0833
Owen Lawton
p350 Plymouth 01752 201169
Layton & Co
p244 Haverfordwest 01437 766671
Leadbeater & Kay
p398 Stoke-on-Trent 01782 201933
Lebreton Towell Solicitor
p408 Tarporley 01829 751459
Lennons
p117 Amersham 01494 433177
p189 Chesham 01494 773377
Lester Morrill
p275 Leeds 0113 245 8549
Levenes Solicitors
p53 Haringey 020 8881 7777 / 8881 6764
Levison Meltzer Pigott
p53 London EC4 020 7556 2400
Lichfield Reynolds
p398 Stoke-on-Trent 01782 289122
p398 Stoke-on-Trent 01782 313212
Lin & Co Solicitors
p140 Birmingham 0121 244 2300
Linder Myers Solicitors
p306 Manchester 0844 984 6000
Lloyd Brennand
p156 Brentford 020 8569 9020
Lloyd Jones & Co
p428 Westcliff-on-Sea 01702 710338
Lloyd Platt & Co
p55 London N3 020 8343 2998
Llys Cennen Solicitors
p117 Ammanford 01269 592658 / 592790
Roger Long & Co
p205 Croydon 020 8668 5071
Lopian Wagner
p307 Manchester 0161 834 2324
Lowrie & Co
p196 Cobham 01932 865818
Loynton & Co
p140 Birmingham 0121 327 0118 / 327 0652
Lucas & Wyllys
p234 Great Yarmouth 01493 663124
p234 Great Yarmouth 01493 855555
Lumsdons Solicitors LLP
p440 Worcester 01905 730670
MB Solicitors Ltd trading as MB Law
p275 Leeds 0113 242 4444
MFG Solicitors
p409 Telford 01952 641651
p440 Worcester 01905 610410
MMS Solicitors
p436 Withernsea 01964 612318
McAras Solicitors LLP
p275 Leeds 0113 243 4333
D K Macbryde & Co
p356 Prestatyn 01745 856404
McCarthy & White
p411 Thornbury 01454 413696
McCarthy Stewart & Booty Solicitors
p400 Stowmarket 01449 612343
McCormicks
p240 Harrogate 01423 530630
McDonald & Co
p56 London W1 020 7834 2679
MacDonald Oates LLP
p316 Midhurst 01730 816711
p348 Petersfield 01730 268211
Roberta McDonald
p140 Birmingham 0121 449 6821
McKeag & Co
p231 Gosforth 0191 213 1010
McKinnells
p284 Lincoln 01522 541181
Barry Macloskey Solicitors
p443 Wrexham 01978 852485
McMillan Williams Solicitors
p132 Bexleyheath 020 8303 0168
Macmillans
p418 Wadebridge 01208 812415
McMillen Hamilton McCarthy
p57 London E3 020 8980 6060
McPhersons
p395 Stockbridge 01794 389002
Elizabeth McQuay
p343 Oxford 01869 351229
Macrory Ward
p124 Barnet 020 8440 3258
Madge Lloyd & Gibson
p230 Gloucester 01452 520224
p327 Newent 01531 820088
Maffey & Brentnall
p423 Watford 01923 234607

See p542 for the Firms Specialisations

4

See p542 for the Firms Specialisations

Waddington Webber
p264 . . . Keighley 01535 662644 / 662647
Wade & Davies
p233 . . . Great Dunmow 01371 872816
Wainwright & Cummins
p90 . . . Lambeth 020 7326 7460
Walker & Walker
p374 . . . Sevenoaks 01732 450699
Walkers
p367 . . . Rossendale 01706 213565
Wall James Chappell
p399 . . . Stourbridge 01384 371622
Wallace Robinson & Morgan
p383 . . . Solihull 01564 779393
Walter Wilson Richmond
p242 . . . Harrow 020 8427 8484
Walters & Barbary
p173 . . . Camborne 01209 712454
A M Walters & Co
p261 . . . Ilford 020 8551 5894
Wannop Fox Staffurth & Bray
p193 . . . Chichester 01243 778844
p442 . . . Worthing 01903 228200
Ward & Rider Limited
p201 . . . Coventry 024 7655 5400
Wards Solicitors
p394 . . . Staple Hill 0117 943 4800
Ware & Kay LLP
p429 . . . Wetherby 01937 583210
p445 . . . York 01904 716000
Warings Solicitors
p147 . . . Blackpool 01253 293106
Warners Solicitors
p374 . . . Sevenoaks 01732 747900
p412 . . . Tonbridge 01732 770660
Rodney Warren & Co
p216 . . . Eastbourne 01323 430430
Watkins & Gunn
p352 . . . Pontypool 01495 762244
Alasdair Watson & Co
p327 . . . Newcastle upon Tyne 0191 488 4521
Watson Nevill
p299 . . . Maidstone 01622 661177
Paul J Watson
p315 . . . Middlesbrough 01642 293427
Watson Solicitors
p422 . . . Warrington 01925 571212
Duncan Watts LLP
p422 . . . Warwick 01926 493485
V G Waugh
p348 . . . Peterlee 0191 527 2727
Kathy Webb & Co
p237 . . . Guisborough 01287 633331
Susan Weeden & Company
p264 . . . Keighley 01535 658488
Weightmans LLP
p269 . . . Knutsford 01565 634234
Welch & Co
p181 . . . Cardigan 01239 614070
Wellers Law Group LLP
p167 . . . Bromley 020 8464 4242
J B Wheatley & Co
p91 . . . London SE8 020 8479 8000
Whetter Duckworth Fowler
p266 . . . Kidlington 01865 842100
V E White & Co
p400 . . . Strood 01634 739195
Whitehead Monckton
p299 . . . Maidstone 01622 698000
Whiteside & Knowles Ltd
p319 . . . Morecambe 01524 416315
Whitfields
p227 . . . Formby 01704 878501
Whiting & Mason
p321 . . . New Mills 01663 742432 / 747958
John Whiting & Co
p270 . . . Launceston 01566 777677
Whittinghams
p157 . . . Bridgend 01656 653485
Wholley Goodings LLP
p130 . . . Bedlington 01670 824080
Widdows Mason
p429 . . . Westhoughton 01942 816515
p432 . . . Wigan 01942 244294
Widdows Pilling & Co
p419 . . . Walkden 0161 790 1825
Wilkin Chapman Grange Solicitors
p294 . . . Louth 01507 606161
Wilkins & Thompson
p417 . . . Uttoxeter 01889 562875
Wilkinson & Butler
p392 . . . St Neots 01480 219229
Willans & Co Limited
p390 . . . St Albans 01727 840549
Williams & Co
p217 . . . Edgware 020 8952 8882
Williams Beales & Co
p245 . . . Hay-on-Wye 01497 820302
Williams MacDougall & Campbell
p442 . . . Worthing 01903 214186
R N Williams & Co Limited
p438 . . . Wolverhampton 01902 429051
Williams Thompson
p194 . . . Christchurch 01202 484242
Williamson & Barnes
p207 . . . Deal 01304 373154
Williamson & Soden
p143 . . . Birmingham 0121 333 4848
Williamson Hill
p315 . . . Middlesbrough 01642 217961
Williamsons
p258 . . . Hull 01482 323697
p431 . . . Whitley Bay 0191 252 7711
Williscroft & Co
p155 . . . Bradford 01274 305380
Wills Chandler Beach
p252 . . . Hook 01256 764646 / 764647
Willson Hawley & Co
p339 . . . Nuneaton 024 7638 7821
Wilson & Co
p92 . . . London N17 020 8808 7535
Wilson Browne
p281 . . . Leicester 0116 251 7181
p425 . . . Wellingborough 01933 279000
Wilsons
p358 . . . Pudsey 0113 236 2333
Wilsons Solicitors LLP
p371 . . . Salisbury 01722 412412
Winder Taylor Fallows
p150 . . . Bolton 01204 389908 / 522888
p150 . . . Bolton 01204 697467
Winston Solicitors LLP
p278 . . . Leeds 0113 320 5000
Winterbotham Smith Penley LLP
p320 . . . Nailsworth 01453 832566
Winton Raynes & Co
p406 . . . Swindon 01793 522688
Wiseman Lee LLP
p92 . . . Newham 020 8215 1000
p92 . . . Waltham Forest 020 8215 1000
Wolferstans
p351 . . . Plymouth 01752 401515
p351 . . . Plymouth 01752 663295
Wollen Michelmore Solicitors
p330 . . . Newton Abbot 01626 332266
p413 . . . Torquay 01803 213251
Clive G Wood & Co
p396 . . . Stockport 0161 480 1000
Rupert Wood & Son
p120 . . . Ashton-under-Lyne 0161 330 9121
Woodcock & Thompson
p333 . . . Northampton 01604 758855
Woodcocks
p121 . . . Bacup 01706 874487
p171 . . . Bury 0161 761 4611
p243 . . . Haslingden 01706 213356
p359 . . . Rawtenstall 01706 225621 / 215018
Woodfines LLP
p317 . . . Milton Keynes 01908 202150
Woodford Robinson
p333 . . . Northampton 01604 624926
Woolacott & Co
p270 . . . Lancing 01903 763011 / 764334
Woolley Beardsleys & Bosworth
p293 . . . Loughborough 01509 212266
Woolliscrofts
p239 . . . Hanley 01782 204000
p398 . . . Stoke-on-Trent 01782 577246
The Worcester Family Law Practice
p440 . . . Worcester 01905 730900
Worger Howcroft
p133 . . . Bingley 01274 511246
Wright & Co
p351 . . . Pontefract 01977 878130
Wright & McMillan Bennett
p409 . . . Telford 01952 291100
Wright & Morton
p402 . . . Sunderland 0191 567 4289
Wright Son & Pepper LLP
p93 . . . Camden 020 7242 5473
Wrigley Claydon
p341 . . . Oldham 0161 624 6811
p412 . . . Todmorden 01706 815712
Yarwood Stimpson & Co
p431 . . . Whitley Bay 0191 297 0123
Yates & Co
p339 . . . Nottingham 0115 947 4486
P C D York & Co
p93 . . . London W6 020 8741 4512
Young & Co
p398 . . . Stoke-on-Trent 01782 339200
S D Young
p392 . . . St Neots 01480 470411
Ziadies
p94 . . . London SW9 020 7737 0934

FAMILY MEDIATION

AMD Solicitors
p160 . . . Bristol 0117 962 1460
Aitchison & Co
p4 . . . London WC2 020 7240 0020
Aitken Associates
p4 . . . Islington 020 7700 6006
Alun Thomas & John
p114 . . . Aberystwyth 01970 615900
Anthony Gold
p6 . . . London SW16 020 7940 4000
Robert Barber & Sons
p335 . . . Nottingham 0115 878 9000
Birchall Blackburn LLP
p194 . . . Chorley 01257 279011
Brain Chase Coles
p126 . . . Basingstoke 01256 354481
Bromleys Solicitors LLP
p120 . . . Ashton-under-Lyne 0161 330 6821
Bross Bennett
p16 . . . London N6 020 8340 0444
Brown Beer Nixon Mallon
p362 . . . Redcar 01642 490202
CB4law
p174 . . . Cambridge 01223 316666
Caswell Jones
p172 . . . Caerphilly 029 2086 4888
Chamberlins
p129 . . . Beccles 01502 713131
Chenery Maher & Co
p196 . . . Clitheroe 01200 422264
Clifford Johnston & Co
p302 . . . Manchester 0161 249 2700
Craigen Wilders & Sorrell
p23 . . . London N8 020 8888 2255
Crane & Staples
p425 . . . Welwyn Garden City 01707 329333
Curtis Parkinson
p336 . . . Nottingham 0115 931 7000
Dawson Cornwell
p26 . . . London WC1 020 7242 2556
Divorce & Family Law Practice
p137 . . . Birmingham 0121 200 0890
David Du Pre & Co
p28 . . . London WC1 020 7430 1950
Eastleys
p345 . . . Paignton 01803 559257
Elmhirst Parker LLP
p374 . . . Selby 01757 703895
Joan Ferguson & Co
p304 . . . Manchester 0161 795 5866
GCA Solicitors (Giffen Couch & Archer)
p295 . . . Luton 01582 410041
Hardman Wood
p145 . . . Blackburn 01254 295540
Hellewell Pasley & Brewer
p210 . . . Dewsbury 01924 455515
Richard Howard & Co LLP
p43 . . . London WC2 020 7831 4511
Jackson Brierley Hudson Stoney
p365 . . . Rochdale 01706 644187 / 649214
Keppe & Partners Solicitors
p416 . . . Twickenham 020 8891 4488
Landons
p156 . . . Brentwood 01277 210021
Lawson West Solicitors Limited
p432 . . . Wigston 0116 212 1080
Levison Meltzer Pigott
p53 . . . London EC4 020 7556 2400
Lewis & Dick
p202 . . . Crawley 01293 526031
McMillen Hamilton McCarthy
p57 . . . London E3 020 8980 6060
Elizabeth McQuay
p343 . . . Oxford 01869 351229
Mercy Messenger
p140 . . . Birmingham 0121 770 1221
Monro Fisher Wasbrough LLP
p61 . . . London WC1 020 7404 7001
John Morgan & Partners
p319 . . . Mountain Ash 01443 473708
Elizabeth Muirhead Solicitors
p62 . . . London WC2 020 7936 4445
Myer Wolff
p257 . . . Hull 01482 223693
Nowell Meller Solicitors Limited
p393 . . . Stafford 01785 252377
P B & W Solicitors LLP t/a Pooley Bendall & Watson
p218 . . . Ely 01353 666075
Paris Smith LLP
p386 . . . Southampton 023 8048 2482
Pumfrey & Lythaby
p342 . . . Orpington 01689 833657
Rochman Landau LLP
p72 . . . London W1 020 7544 2424
Rudlings & Wakelam
p171 . . . Bury St Edmunds 01284 755771
Russell-Cooke LLP
p267 . . . Kingston upon Thames 020 8546 6111
SAS Daniels LLP
p155 . . . Bramhall 0161 475 7680
Sethi & Co
p401 . . . Sunbury-on-Thames 01932 772121
Storey & Co
p398 . . . Stokesley 01642 712132
Thorpe & Co
p372 . . . Scarborough 01723 364321
Venters Solicitors
p89 . . . London SE5 020 7277 0110
p363 . . . Reigate 01737 229610
Veseys Solicitors
p143 . . . Birmingham 0121 523 1123
Warners Solicitors
p374 . . . Sevenoaks 01732 747900
Duncan Watts LLP
p422 . . . Warwick 01926 493485

FRAUD

Andersons Solicitors
p239 . . . Harrogate 01423 527852
p335 . . . Nottingham 0115 947 0641
Arora Lodhi Heath
p7 . . . London W3 020 8993 9995
BCL Burton Copeland
p9 . . . London WC2 020 7430 2277
Bankside Law Ltd
p9 . . . London SE1 0844 745 4000
Bannister Bates Property Lawyers
p318 . . . Morecambe 01524 416300
Bark & Co
p9 . . . London EC4 020 7353 1990
Barker Gillette
p9 . . . London W1 020 7636 0555
Daniel Berman & Co
p12 . . . London NW5 020 7428 7798
Bevan Brittan LLP
p161 . . . Bristol 0870 194 1000
Bivonas Limited Solicitors
p13 . . . London EC3 020 7337 2600
Bobbetts Mackan
p161 . . . Bristol 0117 929 9001
Stephen Burdon Solicitors
p336 . . . Nottingham 0115 950 0054
Burton Copeland LLP
p302 . . . Manchester 0161 827 9500
p370 . . . Sale 0161 905 8530
Byrne & Partners
p16 . . . London EC4 020 7842 1616
Capsticks Solicitors LLP
p18 . . . London SW19 020 8780 2211
Chabra Cass & Co
p19 . . . Brent 020 8450 9833 / 8452 2200
Chadwyck-Healey & Co
p19 . . . London EC4 020 7353 6900
Clark Brookes
p427 . . . West Bromwich 0121 553 2576
Clarke & Hartland Solicitors
p177 . . . Cardiff 029 2048 3181
Claude Hornby & Cox
p20 . . . London EC4 020 7332 8269
Criminal Defence Solicitors
p23 . . . London W1 020 7353 7000
Crowell & Moring
p23 . . . London EC4 020 7413 0011
Davis-Law Associates
p184 . . . Chalfont St Peter 01753 888776
De Maid Solicitors & Advocates
p178 . . . Cardiff 029 2023 5575
Dobsons
p341 . . . Orpington 01689 886300
Dowse Baxter
p27 . . . London SW19 020 8946 9110
Draycott Browne Solicitors
p303 . . . Manchester 0161 228 2244
EBR Attridge LLP
p28 . . . London SW11 020 7228 7050
Eric Robinson Solicitors
p386 . . . Southampton 023 8022 6891
Edward Fail Bradshaw & Waterson
p30 . . . London 020 7790 4032
Fritchley Goldsmith
p124 . . . Barnsley 01226 215600
Gani & Co
p35 . . . Lambeth 020 7733 8169
Garcha & Co
p35 . . . London 020 7375 1888
Gaynor-Smith Owen & Co
p300 . . . Malvern 01684 560771
HKH Kenwright & Cox Solicitors
p260 . . . Ilford 020 8553 9600
Hallinan Blackburn Gittings & Nott
p38 . . . London W1 020 7233 3999
Hamer Childs
p439 . . . Worcester 01905 724565
Hamnett Osborne Tisshaw
p245 . . . Haywards Heath 01444 443030
Harbans Singh
p139 . . . Birmingham 0121 551 4496
Brian Harris & Co
p39 . . . London W1 020 7935 5541
Hatton
p207 . . . Daventry 01327 301201
Edward Hayes LLP
p192 . . . Chichester 01243 672124
p192 . . . Chichester 01243 781431
p441 . . . Worthing 01903 215999
Hemsleys
p190 . . . Chester 01244 382400

4

Hickman & Rose
p41 London N15 020 7700 2211
Hill Dickinson LLP
p190 Chester 01244 896600
p288 Liverpool 0151 600 8000
p41 London EC3 020 7283 9033
p305 Manchester 0161 817 7200
Hodge Jones & Allen LLP
p41 London NW1 020 7874 8300
Hogan Brown
p289 Liverpool 0151 243 7500
Howell & Co
p139 Birmingham 0121 778 5031
Huggins & Lewis Foskett
p43 Redbridge 020 8989 3000
IBB Solicitors
p417 Uxbridge 0845 638 1381
Ince & Co Services Ltd
p44 London E1 020 7481 0010
Janes
p46 London SW1 020 7930 5100
The Johnson Partnership
p209 Derby 01332 370473
p311 Mansfield 01623 427575
p337 Nottingham 0115 941 9141
Jonas Roy Bloom
p139 Birmingham 0121 212 4111
The Jonathan Morrissey Practice
p152 Bournemouth 01202 310999
Mark Jones & Partners
p289 Liverpool 0151 286 9594
Kangs Solicitors
p139 Birmingham 0121 449 9888
Andrew Keenan & Co
p48 London SE20 020 8659 0332
Kelcey & Hall
p163 Bristol 0117 927 9604
Christian Khan Solicitors
p49 London WC1 020 7631 9500
Kingsley Brookes
p256 Huddersfield 01484 302800
Kingsley Napley
p50 London EC1 020 7814 1200
Law Partners Solicitors Ltd
p51 London EC1 0870 600 9444
MSB Solicitors LLP
p289 Liverpool 0151 281 9040
Mackrell Turner Garrett
p57 London WC2 020 7240 0521
Malletts Solicitors
p58 London WC1 020 7061 3760
Martyn Prowel
p180 Cardiff 029 2047 0909
Middleweeks Solicitors
p307 Manchester 0161 839 7255
Martin Murray & Associates
p361 Reading 0118 950 8577
O'Keeffe Solicitors
p64 Brent 020 7644 8800
Olliers
p308 Manchester 0161 834 1515
PCB Litigation LLP
p65 London EC1 020 7831 2691
Pearson Fielding Polson
p290 Liverpool 0151 236 3636
Pinsent Masons LLP
p141 Birmingham 0121 200 1050
p276 Leeds 0113 244 5000
Richard Nelson Business Defence Solicitors
p164 Bristol 0117 942 5678
p338 Nottingham 0115 986 3636
Roche & Co
p72 London EC4 020 7831 2209
Russell-Cooke LLP
p74 London SW15 020 8789 9111
Sansbury Douglas
p164 Bristol 0117 926 5341
Saunders Law Partnership LLP
p76 London WC2 020 7632 4300
Shaw Graham Kersh
p78 London W1 020 7734 9700
Shook Hardy & Bacon LLP
p78 London EC4 020 7332 4500
Richard Silver
p309 Manchester 0161 834 9494
Sternberg Reed
p366 Romford 01708 766155
Stewarts Law LLP
p277 Leeds 0113 222 0022
p83 London EC4 020 7822 8000
Talbot Walker LLP
p127 Basingstoke 01256 332404
Tang Bentley & Jackson
p224 Fareham 01329 220401
Peter Thubron & Co
p402 Sunderland 0191 510 1221
Victor Lissack Roscoe & Coleman
p89 London W1 020 7487 2505
Walker Morris
p277 Leeds 0113 283 2500
Whitelock & Storr
p91 London WC1 020 7405 3913
Woodroffes
p93 London W1 020 7730 0001
Aidan Woods & Co
p165 Bristol 0117 952 2006
Yates Ardern
p120 Ashton-under-Lyne 0161 330 3332

HEALTH & SAFETY AT WORK

The A P Partnership Ltd
p346 Peterborough 01733 891081
BCL Burton Copeland
p9 London WC2 020 7430 2277
Barratt Goff & Tomlinson
p335 Nottingham 0115 931 5171
Bevan Brittan LLP
p135 Birmingham 0870 194 1000
Andrew Bryce & Co
p174 Cambridge 01223 437011
Bulfin & Co Employment Law Solicitors
p348 Pinner 020 8866 0044
Buller Jeffries
p200 Coventry 024 7622 8734
Castle Sanderson
p272 Leeds 0113 232 1919
Dyne Solicitors Limited
p190 Chester 01829 773100
Elvin & Co
p293 Loughborough 01509 852454
Espilon Solicitors
p341 Ormskirk 01704 894945
Fawcett & Pattni
p420 Walsall 01922 640424
Michael Friend
p220 Esher 01372 468098
Grahame Stowe Bateson
p240 Harrogate 01423 562121
Grieves Solicitors
p255 Huddersfield 01484 300192
HRJ Law LLP
p425 Welwyn Garden City 01707 887700
Haslam & Payne
p39 London SW1 020 7828 8725
Ibbotson Brady
p274 Leeds 0113 366 3022
Just Employment
p236 Guildford 01483 303636
Pinsent Masons LLP
p164 Bristol 0117 924 5678
Richard Nelson Business Defence Solicitors
p164 Bristol 0117 942 5678
p338 Nottingham 0115 986 3636
Michael Salt
p365 Rochdale 01706 646655
Shacklocks
p312 Mansfield 01623 626141
Thompsons (formerly Robin/Brian Thompson & Partners)
p310 Manchester 0161 819 3500
Watmores
p90 London WC2 020 7430 1512
Whiting & Purches
p383 Solihull 0121 605 5050

HOUSING ASSOCIATION LAW

174 Law
p134 Birkenhead 0151 647 7372
A Halsall & Co
p435 Wirral 0151 678 9090
Batchelors Solicitors
p166 Bromley 020 8768 7000
Chamberlain Martin Solicitors
p148 Bognor Regis 01243 825211
Croftons
p302 Manchester 0161 214 6180
DMH Stallard LLP
p159 Brighton 01273 329833
p202 Crawley 01293 605000
Devonshires
p27 London EC2 020 7628 7576
Greenland Houchen Pomeroy
p334 Norwich 01603 660744
HM Law
p437 Wokingham 0118 977 1718
Hockfield & Co
p41 Lambeth 020 7582 8784
Housing & Property Law Partnership
p43 Islington 020 7553 9000
Lexica Law
p177 Canterbury 01227 764141
Marsons Solicitors LLP
p166 Bromley 020 8313 1300
Mornements Solicitors
p443 Yeovil 01935 863333
Nalders Quality Solicitors
p246 Helston 01326 574001
Norrie Waite & Slater
p377 Sheffield 0114 248 4890
Owen White
p382 Slough 01753 876800
Perrins Solicitors LLP
p239 Harpenden 01582 466140
Prince Evans
p69 Ealing 020 8567 3477
Sedgwick Phelan & Partners
p315 Middleton 0161 653 5299
Trowers & Hamlins
p222 Exeter 01392 217466
Winckworth Sherwood LLP
p92 London SE1 020 7593 5000
Wright Hassall LLP
p270 Leamington Spa 01926 886688

HOUSING, LANDLORD & TENANT

AKP Solicitors Ltd
p3 London E6 020 8472 4462
Adcocks Solicitors Ltd
p284 Lichfield 0845 470 8081
Adrian & Co
p4 London NW5 020 7485 8450 / 7267 1240
Alcock & Smalley
p297 Macclesfield 01625 431530
Allan Rutherford
p333 Norwich 01603 621722
Alletsons Ltd
p157 Bridgwater 01278 456621
Anthony Gold
p6 London SW16 020 7940 4000
Atkinson Cave & Stuart
p146 Blackpool 01253 293151
Atlee Chung & Company
p8 London W1 020 7287 9988
Bakers
p318 Mitcham 020 8648 0363
Barnes & Partners
p10 Haringey 020 8801 0085
Marcus Barnett
p10 London SW1 020 7235 9215
Barrett & Thomson
p381 Slough 01753 437416
Bassets
p229 Gillingham 01634 575464
p366 Rochester 01634 400161
Bazeer & Co
p11 London SW19 020 8543 6600
Beesley & Co
p301 Manchester 0161 445 3678
Belshaw & Curtin
p11 London SE5 020 7708 3311
Bishop & Sewell LLP
p13 London WC1 020 7631 4141
Booth Ince & Knowles
p208 Denton 0161 336 7011
Eric Bowes & Co
p382 Solihull 0121 744 3691
Bradleys
p212 Dover 01304 204080
Brethertons LLP
p368 Rugby 01788 551611
David Briggs & Co
p15 London SW3 020 7823 9040
Brignalls Balderston Warren
p121 Baldock 01462 490100
Bryan & Armstrong
p311 Mansfield 01623 626039
Burton Woolf & Turk
p16 London EC1 020 7831 6478
Bury & Walkers LLP
p272 Leeds 0113 244 4227
Butcher & Barlow LLP
p155 Bramhall 0161 439 8228
Butcher Burns LLP
p16 London WC1 020 7713 7100
CVC Solicitors
p245 Hayle 01736 752246
p392 St Ives 01736 795456
S A Carr & Co
p18 Hackney 020 8986 5438
Chambers Rutland & Crauford
p19 London N12 020 8446 2777
Cheesman & Co
p287 Liverpool 0151 258 1212
P Chevalier & Co
p402 Surbiton 020 3393 8217
C P Christou LLP
p20 London N12 020 8446 6777
Clifford Johnston & Co
p302 Manchester 0161 249 2700
Clinton Davis Pallis
p21 London N8 020 8880 5000
Coffin Mew & Clover
p223 Fareham 01329 825617
Conway & Co
p247 Henley-on-Thames 01491 411122
Cramer Pelmont
p23 London N8 020 8340 0091
Cunningtons
p155 Braintree 01376 326868
Daniel Curry & Co
p205 Croydon 020 8680 2188
Jeremy Davies & Co
p26 London SW7 020 7589 4999
Devonshires
p27 London EC2 020 7628 7576
Dewar Hogan
p27 London EC4 020 7634 9550
Dodd Lewis Solicitors
p27 London SE3 020 8852 1255
Dowse & Co
p27 Hackney 020 7254 6205
EBR Attridge LLP
p28 London SW11 020 7228 7050
Alan Edwards & Co
p28 Kensington & Chelsea 020 7221 7644
Edwards Duthie
p29 London E6 020 8514 9000
R L Edwards & Partners
p413 Treorchy 01443 775000
Emsleys
p204 Crossgates 0113 260 3115
Fishers
p404 Swadlincote 01283 217193
Ronald Fletcher & Co
p33 London W9 020 7624 0041
Fursdon Knapper
p349 Plymouth 01752 309090
GCA Solicitors (Giffen Couch & Archer)
p295 Luton 01582 410041
Gales
p152 Bournemouth 01202 512227 / 512446
Gattas Denfield Solicitors
p35 London NW9 020 8204 7181
Gomer Williams & Co
p292 Llanelli 01554 755101
Rodney Goodson
p334 Norwich 01603 632832
Greenland Houchen Pomeroy
p443 Wymondham 01953 606351
Gregory Abrams Davidson LLP
p288 Liverpool 0151 236 5000
p288 Liverpool 0151 494 0777
Guest & Co
p205 Cuckfield 01444 413731
Hansen Palomares
p38 Lambeth 020 7640 4600
Harter & Loveless
p39 Islington 020 7688 2900
William Heath & Co
p40 London W1 020 7402 3151
Paul Hills & Co
p193 Chichester 01243 671782
Hockfield & Co
p41 Lambeth 020 7582 8784
Antony Hodari & Co
p305 Manchester 0161 832 4781
Hodders
p41 London NW10 020 8838 1537
Hodgkinsons Solicitors
p380 Skegness 01754 897150
Holden & Co
p243 Hastings 01424 722422
Antony A Holmes
p166 Broadway 01386 858107
Hopkins
p311 Mansfield 01623 460460
Housing & Property Law Partnership
p43 Islington 020 7553 9000
Howard Schneider Spiro Steele
p124 Barnet 020 8216 2020
J A Hughes
p345 Penarth 029 2070 2449
J W Hughes & Co
p291 Llandudno 01492 874774
Hunt & Lisners
p332 Northampton 01604 846705
Henry Hyams
p274 Leeds 0113 243 2288
Israel Strange & Conlon
p45 Islington 020 7833 8453
Graeme John Solicitors
p446 Ystradgynlais 01639 843404
Terry Jones Solicitors & Advocates
p379 Shrewsbury 01743 285888
Kent & Co Solicitors
p334 Norwich 01493 751351
The Law Partnership
p242 Harrow 020 8416 7004
Wayne Leighton
p217 Edgware 020 8951 2988
J B Leitch & Co
p289 Liverpool 0151 708 2250
Linder Myers Solicitors
p379 Shrewsbury 0844 984 6002
Loynton & Co
p140 Birmingham 0121 327 0118 / 327 0652
Mackrell Turner Garrett
p437 Woking 01483 755609
Malcolm Wilson & Cobby
p442 Worthing 01903 237581

See p542 for the Firms Specialisations

Saul Marine & Co
p58 . . . London NW7 020 8959 3611
O M Marks & Co
p58 . . . Barnet 020 8371 6689
Martin-Kaye LLP
p409 . . . Telford 01952 272222
Meesons
p227 . . . Fordingbridge 01425 655251
N C Morris & Co
p62 . . . London SW7 020 7584 8764
Nandy & Co
p63 . . . Newham 020 8536 1800
Norrie Waite & Slater
p377 . . . Sheffield 0114 276 6166
The Oakley Shee Partnership
p64 . . . London SE1 020 7089 9066
Osler Donegan Taylor
p160 . . . Brighton 01273 710712
Paton Walsh Laundy
p66 . . . London SW19 020 8946 2229
Peasegoods
p308 . . . Manchester 0161 205 2772
Peters & Co
p239 . . . Harlow 01279 453331
Pheby & Co
p445 . . . York 01904 789900
Poole Alcock
p116 . . . Alsager 01270 876550
David Porter & Co
p257 . . . Hull 01482 325863
Powell Forster
p69 . . . Lambeth 020 7737 8111
Powleys
p294 . . . Lowestoft 01502 581121
Gillian Radford & Co
p70 . . . London W1 020 8960 4366
Richard Reed
p402 . . . Sunderland 0191 567 0465
Roskell Davies & Co
p141 . Birmingham 0121 354 1515 / 355 1011
Ross & Craig
p73 . . . London W1 020 7262 3077
Ross & Son
p252 . . . Horley 01293 782425
R H Rowley
p201 . . . Coventry 024 7630 1996
Russell-Cooke LLP
p74 . . . London WC1 020 7405 6566
SNR Denton
p317 . . . Milton Keynes 01908 690260
Sandom Robinson
p383 . . . South Croydon 020 8651 7020
Atul Shah
p424 . . . Wealdstone 020 8861 5000
T J Shepperson
p335 . . . Norwich 01603 763096
Shirtcliffe & Reston Solicitors
p411 . . . Thirsk 01845 526222
Simmonds Solicitors
p353 . . . Poole 01202 666417
Soma & Co Solicitors
p242 . . . Harrow 020 8423 0203
Spence & Horne
p81 . . . Hackney 020 8985 2277
Terence St J Millett
p82 . . . London SW7 020 7581 7500
Stones Solicitors LLP
p222 . . . Exeter 01392 666777
Swain & Co
p244 . . . Havant 023 9248 3322
Tanburghs O'Brien Lahaise
p85 . . . Camden 020 7372 6614
Thompson Allen LLP
p160 . . . Brighton 01273 608003
Thompson & Cooke LLP
p393 . . . Stalybridge 0161 338 2614
Peter Thomson
p87 . . . Lambeth 020 7733 6196
Towers & Hamlins
p222 . . . Exeter 01392 217466
James Tsang & Co
p88 . . . London W1 020 7287 0451
Tyndallwoods
p143 . . . Birmingham 0121 624 1111
Vickers & Co
p89 . . . Ealing 020 8579 2559 / 8840 3999
Waring & Co
p124 . . . Barnet 0870 444 2782
Watson Marshal
p90 . . . London W4 020 8987 0100
Whitehead Woodward & Co
p443 . . . Wrexham 01978 855478
Willans & Co Limited
p390 . . . St Albans 01727 840549
Williams & Co
p217 . . . Edgware 020 8952 8882
Winckworth Sherwood LLP
p344 . . . Oxford 01865 297200
Wismayers
p233 . . . Great Bookham 01372 451114
Young Coles & Langdon
p244 . . . Hastings 01424 437878
S D Young
p392 . . . St Neots 01480 470411
A E P Zaleski
p93 . . . London SW18 020 8875 1791

HUMAN RIGHTS & CIVIL LIBERTIES

Advance Legal
p170 . . . Burton-on-Trent 01283 544492
Anthony Gold
p6 . . . London SW16 020 7940 4000
Bindmans LLP
p12 . . . London WC1 020 7833 4433
Birnberg Peirce & Partners
p13 . . . Camden 020 7911 0166
Broudie Jackson Canter
p286 . . . Liverpool 0151 227 1429
Campbell-Taylor Solicitors
p18 . . . Hackney 0845 567 2457
Carter-Ruck
p18 . . . London EC4 020 7353 5005
Chadwick Lawrence
p418 . . . Wakefield 01924 379078
Coninghams Solicitors
p22 . . . London SW1 020 8296 1957
Fisher Meredith
p32 . . . Lambeth 020 7091 2700
Andrew Fitzpatrick
p304 . . . Manchester 0161 248 9799
French & Co
p337 . . . Nottingham 0115 955 1111
Gregsons
p337 . . . Nottingham 0115 941 1999
Wesley Gryk
p37 . . . Lambeth 020 7401 6887
Alida Guest
p37 . . . London W11 020 7727 6273
Hameed & Co
p38 . . . London NW10 020 8830 1335
Harbans Singh
p139 . . . Birmingham 0121 551 4496
Harris & Co
p39 . . . London N3 020 3330 7289
Hayat & Co
p218 . . . Enfield 020 8360 4485
Hossacks
p265 . . . Kettering 01536 518638
Irwin Mitchell LLP
p376 . . . Sheffield 0870 150 0100
Leigh Day & Co
p52 . . . London EC1 020 7650 1200
Leslie & Co
p254 . Hounslow 020 8577 5491 / 8572 7252
MSB Solicitors LLP
p289 . . . Liverpool 0151 281 9040
Ormerods
p205 . . . Croydon 020 8686 5000
Oury Clark
p65 . . . London WC1 020 7607 4300
Patwa Solicitors
p129 . . . Bearwood 0121 429 8666
Clive Walker
p277 . . . Leeds 0113 268 4660

IMMIGRATION & NATIONALITY

AGH Solicitors
p148 . . . Bolton 01204 364433
AR Legal Solicitors
p3 . . . London W4 020 8747 9090
Aaronson & Co
p3 . . . London W8 020 7376 9124
Adrian & Co
p4 . London NW5 020 7485 8450 / 7267 1240
Ahmed & Co
p4 . . . Camden 020 7383 2243
Alfred Truman
p132 . . . Bicester 01869 252761
R W Anderson & Co
p6 . . . London W1 020 7323 4520
Antons
p6 . . . London N8 020 8888 6211
Appleby Shaw
p434 . . . Windsor 01753 860606
Aravindans
p7 . . . Newham 020 8503 5034
Atkins Law Solicitors
p220 . . . Exeter 01392 671657
Aurangzeb Khan Solicitors
p153 . . . Bradford 01274 548549
BWF Solicitors
p9 . . . London E8 020 7241 7180
Bartram & Co
p11 . . . Ealing 020 8840 0444
Bazeer & Co
p11 . . . London SW19 020 8543 6600
Birnberg Peirce & Partners
p13 . . . Camden 020 7911 0166
Bishop McBride Olden
p177 . . . Cardiff 029 2049 0111
N C Brothers & Co
p360 . . . Reading 0118 958 9966
Cedars & Co
p19 . . . Greenwich 020 8331 6161
Chetty & Patel
p279 . . . Leicester 0116 254 6222
Chhokar & Co
p384 . . . Southall 020 8574 2488
Chung & Platt
p302 . . . Manchester 0161 228 6777
Corbin & Hassan
p22 . . . London 020 7247 6518
Crowley & Co
p178 . . . Cardiff 029 2045 8895
DBL Talbots LLP
p399 . . . Stourbridge 01384 445850
Edward De Silva & Co
p384 . . . Southall 020 8571 2299
Doyle Clayton Solicitors Limited
p27 . . . London EC2 020 7329 9090
p360 . . . Reading 0118 959 6839
B K Ellis & Co
p150 . . . Borehamwood 020 8386 8686
Ellis Taylor Law LLP
p29 . . . London WC2 020 7405 0206
Fahm & Co
p147 . . . Blackwood 01495 224973
Foot Anstey
p349 . . . Plymouth 01752 675000
Fountain Solicitors Limited
p420 . . . Walsall 01922 645429
Fursdon Knapper
p349 . . . Plymouth 01752 309090
Ganpate
p35 . . . London NW4 020 8202 5092
David Gray Solicitors
p324 . . Newcastle upon Tyne 0191 232 9547
Shirley Griffiths
p259 . . . Hythe 01303 266689
Gross & Co
p171 . . Bury St Edmunds 01284 763333
Wesley Gryk
p37 . . . Lambeth 020 7401 6887
Alida Guest
p37 . . . London W11 020 7727 6273
Gulbenkian Andonian Solicitors
p37 . . . London WC1 020 7269 9590
HKH Kenwright & Cox Solicitors
p260 . . . Ilford 020 8553 9600
HSK Solicitors
p149 . . . Bolton 01204 526465
Hameed & Co
p38 . . . London NW10 020 8830 1335
Charles Harding & Co
p426 . . . Wembley 020 8795 0990
Harris & Co
p39 . . . London N3 020 3330 7289
Hasan Solicitors
p139 . . . Birmingham 0121 778 4003
Hayat & Co
p218 . . . Enfield 020 8360 4485
Heer Manak
p200 . . . Coventry 024 7666 4000
Henneberry & Co
p40 . . . London NW6 020 8830 1907
Joseph Hill & Co
p41 . . . London N15 020 8880 3535
Hogan Lisle
p42 . . . London W1 020 7224 3300
Hoole & Co
p163 . . . Bristol 0117 942 8871
p163 . . . Bristol 0117 969 1436
Ismail & Ghani
p154 . . . Bradford 01274 737546
Jeya & Co
p46 . . . Newham 020 8552 1999
Virginia Juras & Co
p166 . . . Bromley 020 8402 9403
Jasvir Jutla & Co
p280 . . . Leicester 0116 254 0809
Khan & Co
p438 . . . Wolverhampton 01902 424477
Knights Solicitors LLP
p115 . . . Alderley Edge 01625 586686
p188 . . . Cheltenham 01242 524654
p323 . Newcastle under Lyme 01782 619225
Krish Ratna
p384 . . . Southall 020 8574 6303
Lawson Turner & Gilbert
p213 . . . Dover 01304 226338
Leslie & Co
p254 . Hounslow 020 8577 5491 / 8572 7252
Leung & Co
p163 . . . Bristol 0117 920 9230
Lin & Co Solicitors
p140 . . . Birmingham 0121 244 2300
p403 . . . Sutton Coldfield 0121 244 2300
Lu Oliphant Solicitors
p217 . . . Edgware 020 8238 2822
Magne & Co Solicitors
p402 . . . Surbiton 020 8399 3939
Mansouri & Son
p205 . . . Croydon 020 8401 7352
Millan Solicitors
p154 . . . Bradford 01274 660111
Moeran Oughtred & Co
p423 . . . Watford 01923 256263
Mohammed & Co Solicitors
p357 . . . Preston 01772 888700
Muscatt Walker Hayim
p62 . . . London W1 020 7486 5131
Nandy & Co
p63 . . . Newham 020 8536 1800
Ned Nwoko
p63 . . . Ealing 020 8997 6733
Niman & Co
p63 . . . Haringey 020 8809 4923
Oldhams Solicitors & Advocates
p121 . . . Baldock 01462 895444
Patel & Bhatoa
p154 . . . Bradford 01274 669023
Geeta Patel & Company
p66 . . . London N11 020 8365 7377
J C Patel
p426 . . . Wembley 020 8903 3519
Patricks Solicitors
p66 . . . Newham 020 8548 8844
S C Pelentrides & Co
p66 . . . London N17 020 8365 1688
Philcox Gray & Co
p67 . . . London SE15 020 7703 2285
Pickup & Scott
p121 . . . Aylesbury 01296 397794
Prospect Solicitors
p69 . . . London W4 020 8899 6063
Rafina Solicitors
p426 . . . Wembley 020 8908 6742
Ratna & Co
p70 . . . London E6 020 8470 8818
Runhams
p154 . . . Bradford 01274 532233
S Satha & Co
p76 . . . Newham 020 8471 9484
Sheikh & Co
p78 . . . London N4 020 7263 5588
Singhania & Co Ltd
p80 . . . London SW1 020 7799 1688
Solicitors Active
p277 . . . Leeds 0113 248 9805
Sookias & Sookias
p80 . . . London W1 020 7465 8000
Sparrow & Trieu Solicitors
p81 . . . London W1 020 7287 6608
Spence & Horne
p81 . . . Hackney 020 8985 2277
Stanley & Co
p427 . . . Wembley 020 8903 7864
TKD Solicitors
p85 . Hammersmith & Fulham 020 8741 8050
Talbots Legal Advice Centre
p399 . . Stourbridge 01384 445850 / 447777
T R Taner & Co
p85 . . . Haringey 020 8348 1267
David Tang & Co
p85 . . . London W1 020 7439 4675
Tann & Tann Solicitors
p427 . . . Wembley 020 8902 6810
Thompson & Co
p87 . . . Wandsworth 020 8767 5005
Trinity Solicitors LLP
p88 . . . London NW1 020 7428 0880
Tyndallwoods
p143 . . . Birmingham 0121 624 1111
Veja and Co Solicitors
p385 . . . Southall 020 8574 2626
Verma & Co
p427 . . . Wembley 020 8903 0309
Wilson & Co
p92 . . . London N17 020 8808 7535
Nadine Wong & Co
p93 . . . London W2 020 7243 8888
Wragg Mark-Bell Solicitors
p182 . . . Carlisle 01228 711728
Youngs Criminal Defence Services Limited
p377 . . . Sheffield 0114 249 5444
Zaiwalla & Co
p93 . . . London WC2 020 7312 1000
Ziadies
p94 . . . London SW9 020 7737 0934

INSURANCE LAW

Barlow Lyde & Gilbert LLP
p10 . . . London EC3 020 7876 5000
Berrymans Lace Mawer
p135 . . . Birmingham 0121 643 8777
p271 . . . Leeds 0113 236 2002
p286 . . . Liverpool 0151 236 2002
p12 . . . London EC2 020 7638 2811
p385 . . . Southampton 023 8023 6464
Brookes & Co
p16 . . . London EC3 020 7621 0067

INTERNATIONAL LAW

INTERNET & E-COMMERCE

ISLAMIC LAW

LIBEL SLANDER & DEFAMATION

LIQUOR, BETTING & GAMING LICENSING

LITIGATION, ACCIDENTS, INJURY, CRIMINAL INJURY COMPENSATION, PERSONAL INJURY

See p542 for the Firms Specialisations

John Barkers
p234 Grimsby 01472 358686
Barlow Robbins LLP
p235 Guildford 01483 562901
Barnes & Partners
p239 Harlow 01279 418601
p10. London N18 020 8884 2277
Barr Ellison LLP
p174 Cambridge 01223 411315
Barratt Goff & Tomlinson
p335 Nottingham 0115 931 5171
Barrett & Thomson
p381 Slough 01753 437416
Barry & Co
p348 Pevensey Bay 01323 766370 / 768382
Bartlett Gooding & Weelen
p229 Glastonbury 01458 832510
p378 Shepton Mallet 01749 343091
Battens
p443 Yeovil 01935 846000
T G Baynes
p132 Bexleyheath 020 8301 7777
Beasley Johnson Loyns
p419 Walsall 01922 644433
Beaty & Co
p432 Wigton 01697 342121
Beaumonts
p247 Hereford 01432 352345
Beers LLP
p349 Plymouth 01752 246000
Beesley & Co
p301 Manchester 0161 445 3678
Bell Lamb & Joynson
p286 Liverpool 0844 412 4348
Belshaw & Curtin
p11. London SE5 020 7708 3311
Bemrose & Ling
p208 Derby 01332 347300
Bendall & Sons
p327 Newmarket 01638 661116
Bennett Griffin
p225 Ferring 01903 229999
p441 Worthing 01903 229925
Berkson Wallace Solicitors
p217 Ellesmere Port 0151 355 4412
p419 Wallasey 0151 691 6900
Bernard Chill & Axtell
p216 Eastleigh 023 8061 3197
p385 Southampton 023 8022 8821
Berrymans Lace Mawer
p135 Birmingham 0121 643 8777
p271 Leeds 0113 236 2002
p286 Liverpool 0151 236 2002
p12. London EC2 020 7638 2811
p301 Manchester 0161 236 2002
p385 Southampton 023 8023 6464
Berrys Solicitors
p146 Blackpool 01253 620022
Betesh Partnership
p301 Manchester 0161 834 2623
Malcolm G Beverley Solicitors
p194 Chorley 01257 231462
Bindman & Co
p430 Whickham 0191 488 4950
Birchall Blackburn LLP
p301 Manchester 0161 236 0662
Bird & Co
p232 Grantham 01476 591711
Bird & Lovibond
p234 Greenford 020 8578 6936
p417 Uxbridge 01895 256151
Birdy & Co
p426 Wembley 020 8900 9112
John Birkby & Co
p340 Oldham 0161 626 5686
Birketts LLP
p262 Ipswich 01473 232300
Biscoes
p431 Wickham 01329 833249
Bissmire Fudge & Co
p244 Haverfordwest 01437 764723
p345 Pembroke Dock 01646 685501
Blackburn & Co
p226 Fleetwood 01253 872238
Blackhurst Swainson Goodier LLP
p356 Preston 01772 253841
Patrick Blackmore
p314 Menai Bridge 01248 715987 / 714987
Blackwell-West
p225 Ferndown 01202 892300
Blake Lapthorn
p354 Portsmouth 023 9222 1122
Blakemores
p135 Birmingham 0121 234 7200
Blaser Mills
p241 Harrow 020 8427 6262
p249 High Wycombe 01494 450171
p364 Rickmansworth 01923 776211
Borneo Hughes Martell LLP
p331 Northampton 01604 624822
D S Bosher & Co
p254 Hove 01273 721913
Bower & Bailey
p343 Oxford 01865 311133
p406 Swindon 01793 610466
Bowser Ollard & Bentley
p435 Wisbech 01945 583194
Boyce Hatton
p412 Torquay 01803 403403
Boys & Maughan
p359 Ramsgate 01843 595990
Bradbury Roberts & Raby
p373 Scunthorpe 01724 854000
Bramsdon & Childs
p388 Southsea 023 9282 1251
Kenneth Brand & Co
p15. London NW4 020 8202 6751
Bray & Bray
p279 Leicester 0116 254 8871
Brearleys Solicitors
p128 Batley 01924 473065
Brethertons LLP
p122 Banbury 01295 270999
p368 Rugby 01788 579579
Brian Ruff Angus & Jewers
p431 Wickford 01268 761126
Bridge McFarland
p284 Lincoln 01522 518888
Brightstone Law LLP
p218 Elstree 020 8731 3080
Brockbank Curwen Cain & Hall
p431 Whitehaven 01946 692194
p440 Workington 01900 603563
Brooke-Taylors
p172 Buxton 01298 22741
Brooks
p378 Shipston-on-Stour 01608 664406
A H Brooks & Co
p278 Leek 01538 383201
Broomhead & Saul
p261 Ilminster 01460 57056
p408 Taunton 01823 288121
Brown Barron
p125 Barrow-in-Furness 01229 828814
Brown Turner Ross
p287 Liverpool 0151 236 2233
p388 Southport 01704 542002
Fiona Bruce & Co LLP
p421 Warrington 01925 263273
Bryan & Armstrong
p311 Mansfield 01623 626039
Buckles Solicitors LLP
p346 Peterborough 01733 888888
Bull & Bull
p176 Canterbury 01227 714860
p248 Herne Bay 01227 742660
Buller Jeffries
p136 Birmingham 0121 212 2620
p200 Coventry 024 7622 8734
Burr Sugden
p263 Keighley 01535 605407
Burton Burton & Ho LLP
p272 Leeds 0113 297 8787
Kenneth Bush
p266 King's Lynn 01553 692737
Buss Murton LLP
p207 Dartford 01322 220235
Butcher & Barlow LLP
p170 Bury 0161 764 5141
Bynes
p412 Torquay 01803 295692
CGM
p385 Southampton 023 8063 2733
C Nicholls
p148 Bodmin 01208 76969
John F S Cabot
p17. London SW6 020 7384 9583
Cadmans Law & Property
p195 Cleckheaton 01274 874231
Campbell Courtney & Cooney
p173 Camberley 01276 25100
Camps Solicitors
p134 Birkenhead 0151 201 8080
Canter Levin & Berg
p287 Liverpool 0151 239 1000
Carr & Co
p147 Blyth 01670 351251
p231 Gosforth 0191 284 0363
p319 Morpeth 01670 515182
Cartridges
p220 Exeter 01392 256854
Chadwick Lawrence
p319 Morley 0113 252 3452
p418 Wakefield 01924 379078
Chandler Harris LLP
p302 Manchester 0161 834 2200
Chattertons Solicitors
p151 Boston 01205 310025
Chebsey & Co
p128 Beaconsfield 01494 670440
Chestnutts
p114 Ainsdale 01704 572221
Chesworths
p397 Stoke-on-Trent 01782 599992
C P Christou LLP
p20. London N12 020 8446 6777
Churchers
p354 Portsmouth 023 9221 0170
The Clarke Partnership
p395 Stockport 0161 474 6600
Clarkes
p425 Wellington 01952 223548
Clarkson Hirst
p264 Kendal 01539 736916
Cleaver Thompson Ltd
p115 Alfreton 01773 832193
Douglas Clift & Co
p269 Lancaster 01524 32437
Clifton Ingram LLP
p437 Wokingham 0118 978 0099
Close Thornton
p206 Darlington 01325 466461
Clough & Willis
p170 Bury 0161 764 5266
Cockertons
p121 Bakewell 01629 812613
Coffin Mew & Clover
p223 Fareham 01329 825617
Colebournes Solicitors and Advocates
p146 Blackpool 01253 293195
Colemans
p245 Haywards Heath 01444 459555
Colemans - CTTS
p302 Manchester 0161 876 2500
Coles Miller Solicitors LLP
p352 Poole 01202 673011
Coley & Tilley
p136 Birmingham 0121 643 5531
Collins Solicitors
p423 Watford 01923 223324
Connolley & Company
p437 Wolverhampton 01902 326000
Coodes
p285 Liskeard 01579 347600
Cooks
p323 Newcastle under Lyme 01782 611090
Sharon Coomber
p197 Colchester 01206 769342
Cooper Sons Hartley & Williams
p184 Chapel-en-le-Frith 01298 812138
Cooper Stott
p214 Durham 0191 384 7210
Cooper Whiteman
p22. London WC1 020 7831 5222
Cornfield Law
p215 Eastbourne 01323 412512
Corries Solicitors
p444 York 0845 241 5566
Coupe Bradbury
p296 Lytham 01253 736670
Coyne Learmonth
p287 Liverpool 0845 602 0870
Cozens-Hardy LLP
p334 Norwich 01603 625231
Croftons
p302 Manchester 0161 214 6180
Crombie Wilkinson
p374 Selby 01757 708957
Crompton Halliwell
p170 Bury 0161 797 9222
Crumplins
p23. Camden 020 7483 0282
Cuttle & Co
p302 Manchester 0161 835 2050
DLC Solicitors Limited
p207 Darwen 01254 761234
DP Law Ltd t/a David Prosser & Co
p157 Bridgend 01656 645921
DSM Legal Solicitors
p421 Warrington 0845 009 0863
Dakers
p159 Brighton 01273 571685
Dale & Newbery LLP
p393 Staines 01784 464491
Martin C Dalton
p253 Horsham 01403 266642
Darbys Solicitors LLP
p343 Oxford 01865 811700
W H Darbyshire & Son
p146 Blackpool 01253 346646
Davey Franklin Jones
p195 Cirencester 01285 654875
p230 Gloucester 01452 508800
David James & Company
p114 Aberystwyth 01970 615789
Sheldon Davidson Solicitors
p430 Whitefield 0161 796 5445
Davies Bays & Co t/a Windsor & Co
p26. Haringey 020 8808 3237
Davies Parsons Allchurch
p292 Llanelli 01554 749144
Davis Blank Furniss
p230 Glossop 01457 860606
Davis Priest & Co
p362 Redditch 01527 69231
Graham Dawson & Co
p132 Bexley 01322 558811
Dedicated Accident Solicitors
p208 Derby 01332 869286
Denhams
p236 Guildford 01483 456450
Dexter Montague LLP
p360 Reading 0118 939 3999
Dixon Rigby Keogh
p315 Middlewich 01606 835736
p434 Winsford 01606 557211
Donnelly & Elliott Limited
p232 Gosport 023 9250 5500
Donns
p303 Manchester 0161 834 3311
Douglas-Jones Mercer
p405 Swansea 01792 650000
Downes & Siddall
p284 Lincoln 01522 543343
Downs
p212 Dorking 01306 880110
Druitts
p151 Bournemouth 01202 551863
Drummonds
p190 Chester 01244 408300
Drysdales
p387 Southend-on-Sea 01702 423400
Duchennes
p130 Bedford 01234 356678
Scott Duff & Co
p182 Carlisle 01228 531054
p265 Keswick 01768 774321
p346 Penrith 01768 865551
Duffield Harrison LLP
p251 Hoddesdon 01992 442911
Dunning & Co
p28. London SE5 020 7733 6217
EBR Attridge LLP
p28. London SE16 020 7231 5166
Earl & Crocker
p285 Liskeard 01579 345304
Eastwoods Solicitors
p28. London EC4 020 3137 4800
Eaton & Few
p391 St Ives 01480 301558
Eaton Ryan & Taylor
p138 Birmingham 0121 236 1999
Eddowes Perry & Osbourne
p403 Sutton Coldfield 0121 686 9444
S J Edney
p406 Swindon 0800 421234
Edwards Duthie
p260 Ilford 020 8514 9000
R L Edwards & Partners
p157 Bridgend 01656 656861
Joe Egan Solicitors
p149 Bolton 01204 368060
Thomas Eggar LLP
p192 Chichester 01243 786111
p202 Crawley 01293 742700
p29. London EC4 020 7842 0000
p441 Worthing 01903 234411
Eldridges
p328 Newport 01983 524741
Ellis Jones
p151 Bournemouth 01202 525333
Elton & Co
p29. Camden 020 7267 7373
Emsleys
p204 Crossgates 0113 260 3115
FBC Manby Bowdler LLP
p432 Willenhall 01902 366566
FDC Law
p228 Frome 01373 465051
Fairchild Greig
p30. London W3 020 8993 6886
Fairweather Stephenson & Co
p282 Leiston 01728 832832
Farleys Solicitors LLP
p145 Blackburn 01254 367855
p169 Burnley 01282 798664
Farnworth Shaw
p198 Colne 01282 865885
p321 Nelson 01282 699996
Fentons
p223 Failsworth 0161 682 7101
p304 Manchester 0161 786 8320
Ferguson Bricknell
p343 Oxford 01865 241814
Field Overell
p200 Coventry 024 7622 9582
Paul Finn Solicitors
p168 Bude 01288 356256
Flanagans Solicitors
p223 Eynsham 01865 430040
Ronald Fletcher & Co
p33. London W9 020 7624 0041
Fletchers
p388 Southport 01704 546919
Flint Bishop Solicitors
p208 Derby 01332 340211
Forbes
p145 Blackburn 01254 662831
p356 Preston 01772 220022
Andrew M Ford Solicitors
p279 Leicester 0845 075 4059
Ford Banks Irwin
p304 Manchester 0161 866 8999

Ford Simey LLP
p222 Exmouth 01395 272241 / 0800 169 3741
Forshaws Davies Ridgway LLP
p227 . . . . Frodsham 01928 739300
Fountain Solicitors Limited
p420 . . . . Walsall 01922 645429
Foys Solicitors
p211 . . . . Doncaster 01302 327136
Francis Law LLP
p296 . . . . Lydney 01594 842242
Freemans
p324 . . Newcastle upon Tyne 0191 222 1030
Freer & Archer
p279 . . . . Leicester 0116 241 3199
Michael Friend
p220 . . . . Esher 01372 468098
Fulchers
p436 . . . . Woking 01483 885522
GHP Legal
p442 . . . . Wrexham 01978 291456
GLP Solicitors
p304 . . . . Manchester 0161 834 6721
p357 . . . . Prestwich 0161 773 8626
GPT Solicitors
p426 . .Wembley 020 8904 6495 / 8904 6598
Gadsby Wicks
p186 . . . . Chelmsford 01245 494929
Gamlins
p363 . . . . Rhyl 01745 343500
Gangar & Co
p427 . . . . . West Bromwich 0121 553 4166
Garden House Solicitors
p248 . . . . Hertford 01992 422128
Gardner Iliff & Dowding
p176 . . . . Cannock 01543 466941
Gichard & Co
p367 . . . . Rotherham 01709 365531
Gilbert Stephens
p342 . . . . . .Ottery St Mary 01404 812228
Gildener Brett
p346 . . . . Penzance 01736 332533
Girlings Personal Injury Claims Limited
p177 . . . . Canterbury 01227 768374
David Gist Solicitors
p162 . . . . Bristol 0117 927 9111
Glaisyers
p138 . . . . Birmingham 0121 233 2971
Glynns Solicitors
p162 . . . . Bristol 01761 490883
Godwins
p114 . . . . Aberystwyth 01970 624244
Goldens
p348 . . . . Pinner 020 8429 8282
Goldsmith Williams
p288 . . . . Liverpool 0845 373 3737
Goldstones
p405 . . . . Swansea 01792 643021
Goldwaters
p324 . . Newcastle upon Tyne 0191 232 2653
Goodhand and Forsyth QualitySolicitors
p362 . . . . .Redhill 01737 773533
R Gordon Roberts Laurie & Co
p292 . . . . .Llangefni 01248 722215 / 723312
Gordons LLP
p154 . . . . Bradford 01274 202202
p273 . . . . Leeds 0113 227 0100
Antony Gorley & Co
p322 . . . . Newbury 01635 551321
Goughs
p193 . . . . Chippenham 01249 444499
Gowmans
p345 . . . . Paignton 01803 546100
Grahame Stowe Bateson
p274 . . . . Leeds 0113 246 8163
Grainger Appleyard
p211 . . . . Doncaster 01302 327257
Granville-West Chivers & Morgan
p113 . . . . Abertillery 01495 217070
Leonard Gray
p186 . . . . Chelmsford 01245 504904
Graystons
p435 . . . . Wirral 0151 645 0055
Green Williamson Solicitors
p418 . . . . Wakefield 01924 291400
Greenfield Whiston
p265 . . . . Kettering 01536 410880
Greenwoods
p37. . . . . London EC3 020 7220 7818
Gregory Abrams Davidson LLP
p288 . . . . Liverpool 0151 236 5000
p288 . . . . Liverpool 0151 494 0777
p288 . . . . Liverpool 0151 733 3353
Grieves Solicitors
p255 . . . . .Huddersfield 01484 300192
Gareth Griffith & Company
p172 . . . . Caernarfon 01286 676869
Grindeys LLP
p397 . . . . . Stoke-on-Trent 01782 846441
p397 . . . . . Stoke-on-Trent 01782 846441
Grindrods
p330 . . . .Newton-le-Willows 01925 221321
Andrew Grove & Co
p174 . . . . Cambridge 01223 367133

H2O Law LLP
p37. . . . . London EC4 020 7405 4700
HCB Solicitors
p362 . . . . Redditch 01527 62688
hlw Keeble Hawson LLP
p211 . . . . Doncaster 01302 366831
HSK Solicitors
p149 . . . . Bolton 01204 526465
HT Legal Limited t/a Harrison Townend & Ormeshers
p259 . . . . Hyde 0161 368 1559
Haddock & Company
p238 . . . . Halifax 01422 366010
Hague Lambert
p269 . . . . Knutsford 01565 652411
Hall Reynolds
p133 . . . . . .Bidford-on-Avon 01789 772955
Lawrence Hamblin
p247 . . . Henley-on-Thames 01491 411884
Hammon Oakley
p200 . . . . Coventry 024 7644 8585
Hansells
p121 . . . . .Aylsham 01263 734313
p331 . . . . . . North Walsham 01692 404351
p378 . . . . Sheringham 01263 822176
Hansen Palomares
p38. . . . . Lambeth 020 7640 4600
Harold G Walker
p152 . . . . Bournemouth 01202 203200
Harper & Odell
p39. . . . . Islington 020 7490 0500
Chris Harrison Law
p414 . . . . Truro 01872 241408
Harrowells
p444 . . . . York 01904 558600
Hartlaw LLP
p429 . . . . Wetherby 01937 547000
Hartley & Worstenholme
p183 . . . . Castleford 01977 732222
p351 . . . . Pontefract 01977 732222
Haworth & Nuttall
p114 . . . . Accrington 01254 236221
p145 . . . . Blackburn 01254 272640
Hayes & Storr
p223 . . . . Fakenham 01328 863231
Headleys
p250 . . . . Hinckley 01455 637815
Healds
p432 . . . . Wigan 01942 241511
William Heath & Co
p40. . . . . London W1 020 7402 3151
Hellewell Pasley & Brewer
p210 . . . . Dewsbury 01924 455515
Henchleys
p285 . . . . Littlehampton 01903 726477
Heptonstalls LLP
p231 . . . . Goole 01405 765661
p351 . . . . Pontefract 01977 602804
p351 . . . . Pontefract 01977 602804
p373 . . . . Scunthorpe 01724 289959
Hewitts
p203 . . . . Crook 01388 762466
p397 . . . . Stockton-on-Tees 01642 673701
Hextalls
p41. . . . . London EC2 020 7382 0700
Heyes Samuel
p369 . . . . Ryde 01983 615615
Hillis Solicitors
p305 . . . . Manchester 0161 248 0500
Hillyer McKeown LLP
p190 . . . . Chester 01244 318131
Hindle Campbell
p330 . . . . North Shields 0191 296 1777
Hipkin & Co
p431 . . . . Whitley Bay 0191 253 3509
Hockfield & Co
p41. . . . . Lambeth 020 7582 8784
Antony Hodari & Co
p305 . . . . Manchester 0161 832 4781
John Hodge Solicitors
p429 . . . Weston-super-Mare 01934 623511
Hodge Jones & Allen LLP
p41. . . . . London NW1 020 7874 8300
Hodgkinsons Solicitors
p380 . . . . Skegness 01754 897150
Hodgson Coulthard & Co
p253 . . . .Houghton Le Spring 0191 584 3333
Charles Hoile
p322 . . . . Newbury 01635 45595
Laurence Holmes Solicitors
p198 . . . . Congresbury 01934 838445
Holt & Longworth
p367 . . Rossendale 01706 213251 / 229131
Simon A Holt & Co
p357 . . . . Preston 01772 250871
Hopkins
p311 . . . . Mansfield 01623 460460
p311 . . . . Mansfield 01623 468468
Hornby Baker Jones & Wood
p328 . . . . Newport 01633 262848
Hough Halton & Soal
p182 . . . . Carlisle 01228 524379

Robert Howard
p350 . . . . Plymouth 01752 251851
Howell-Jones LLP
p420 . . . Walton-on-Thames 01932 234500
Neil Hudgell Solicitors
p257 . . . . Hull 01482 787771
Hughes & Company
p413 . . . . Tring 01442 891717
J W Hughes & Co
p199 . . . . Conwy 01492 596596
p291 . . . . Llandudno 01492 874774
Hunton & Garget
p364 . . . . Richmond 01748 850400
Hutchinson & Buchanan
p365 . . . . Ripon 01765 602156
Howard Hyman & Co
p44. . . . . .London N12 020 8446 5511
Ibbotson Brady
p274 . . . . .Leeds 0113 366 3022
Immanuel & Co
p44. . . . . London EC4 020 7213 9901
Inghams
p146 . . . . Blackpool 01253 626642
p226 . . . . Fleetwood 01253 873481
Ingrams
p257 . . . . Hull 01482 358850
p445 . . . . York 01904 520600
Irvings
p289 . . . . Liverpool 0800 954 0243
Aubrey Isaacson Solicitors
p357 . . . . Prestwich 0161 959 5000
Ison Harrison
p274 . . . . Leeds 0113 232 6530
p274 . . . . Leeds 0113 284 5000
JSP Solicitors
p380Skegness 01754 762252 / 01522 537353
Jacklyn Dawson
p328 . . . . Newport 01633 262952
Jameson & Hill
p248 . . . . Hertford 01992 554881
Jasper & Vincent
p386 . . . . Southampton 01489 885788
Andrew Jay & Co (Philip Hanby Limited)
p228 . . . . Gainsborough 01427 612412
Jewels Solicitors
p393 . . . . Stafford 01785 602030
Jobling Gowler
p297 . . . . Macclesfield 01625 614250
Johar & Co
p280 . . . . Leicester 0116 254 3345
Gary Johnson & Co
p315 . . . . Middlesbrough 01642 222834
Cyril Jones & Co
p443 . . . . Wrexham 01978 263131
Jones Law Partnership
p313 . . . . Marple 0161 426 0030
Mark Jones & Partners
p289 . . . . Liverpool 0151 286 9594
T Llewellyn Jones
p405 . . . . Swansea 01639 842235
Jordans
p183 . . . . Castleford 01977 518778
p210 . . . . Dewsbury 01924 457171
p368 . . . . Rowley Regis 0121 559 2922
Judge & Priestley
p166 . . . . Bromley 020 8290 0333
KSH Law Firm
p325 . . Newcastle upon Tyne 0191 232 5232
D C Kaye & Co
p234
. . .Great Missenden 01494 864650 / 862226
Keer-Keer & Co
p246
. . Hemel Hempstead 01442 216755 / 216756
Kenneth Elliott & Rowe
p366 . . . . Romford 01708 757575
Keoghs LLP
p149 . . . . Bolton 01204 677000
p200 . . . . Coventry 024 7665 8200
Kevills
p194 . . . . Chorley 01257 265711
Christopher Key & Co
p150 . . . . Boscastle 01840 250200
Keypoint Law LLP
p212 . . . . Doncaster 01302 329655
Anthony King & Co
p126 . . . . Basildon 01268 240400
King Davies & Partners
p298 . . . . Maesteg 01656 732911
Kingswell Watts
p210 . . . . Dewsbury 01924 461236
Kirby Sheppard
p268 . . . . Kingswood 0845 840 0045
p411 . . . . Thornbury 0845 840 0045
Knipe Woodhouse-Smith
p184
. . .Chalfont St Peter 01753 887877 / 889149
Labrums
p390 . . . . St Albans 01727 858807
Lamb & Holmes
p199 . . . . Corby 01536 745168
p265 . . . . Kettering 01536 513195

Lamport Bassitt
p361 . . . . Reading 0845 077 6600
p386 . . . . . . Southampton 023 8083 7777
Bruce Lance & Co
p250 . . . . High Wycombe 01494 450494
H Landau & Co
p217 . . . . Edgware 020 8959 6991
Lane & Co
p420 . . . . Walsall 01922 721259
J S Lane & Co
p172 . . . . Bushey 020 8950 1782
Langley Wellington
p230 . . . . Gloucester 01452 521286
Langleys
p445 . . . . York 01904 610886
Lansbury Worthington
p51. . . . . London W6 020 8563 9797
Lanyon Bowdler LLP
p342 . . . . Oswestry 01691 652241
Last Cawthra Feather LLP
p154 . . . . Bradford 01274 848800
Law Partners Solicitors Ltd
p51. . . . . London EC1 0870 600 9444
H Lawrence & Co
p52. . London N6 020 7482 2613 / 7482 4212
Lawson West Solicitors Limited
p280 . . . . Leicester 0116 212 1000
Leech & Co
p306 . . . . Manchester 0161 279 0279
Leigh Day & Co
p52. . . . . London EC1 020 7650 1200
Levenes Solicitors
p53. . . Haringey 020 8881 7777 / 8881 6764
Lewis Cutner & Co
p53. . . . . . . London NW3 020 7433 2552
Lichfield Reynolds
p398 . . . . Stoke-on-Trent 01782 289122
Liddell and Company
p366 . . . . Romford 01708 775999
Linder Myers Solicitors
p306 . . . . Manchester 0844 984 6000
p379 . . . . Shrewsbury 0844 984 6002
The Lister Croft Partnership
p358 . . . . Pudsey 0113 257 0526
Livingstons
p416 . . . . Ulverston 01229 585555
Robert Lizar
p307 . . . . Manchester 0161 226 2319
Lloyd Green Solicitors
p187 . . . . Chelmsford 01245 294600
Lock & Marlborough
p55. . . . . London W3 020 8993 7231
Longden Walker & Renney
p401 . . . . Sunderland 0191 567 7024
Loosemores
p179 . . . . Cardiff 029 2022 4433
E D C Lord & Co
p245 . . . . Hayes 020 8848 9988
Lorrells LLP
p55. . . . . London EC1 020 7681 8888
Lucas & Wyllys
p234 . . . . . Great Yarmouth 01493 855555
Geoffrey Lurie
p325 . . Newcastle upon Tyne 0191 232 1800
Peter Lynn & Partners
p319 . . . . Morriston 01792 310731
Lyons Davidson
p321 . . . . New Malden 020 8336 6900
MB Solicitors Ltd trading as MB Law
p275 . . . . Leeds 0113 242 4444
MPH Solicitors
p307 . . . . Manchester 0161 832 7722
MSP Legal Services LLP
p243 . . . . Hartlepool 01429 232204
MWP Solicitors
p126 . . . . Basildon 01268 527131
MacDonald Oates LLP
p348 . . . . Petersfield 01730 268211
Mackenzie Jones
p391 . . . . St Asaph 01745 536030
McKeowns Solicitors Ltd
p390 . . . . St Albans 0800 032 8328
Mackrell & Thomas
p289 . . . . Liverpool 0151 480 3666
MacLeish Littlestone Cowan
p57. . . . . Redbridge 020 8514 3000
McMillan Williams
p199 . . . . Coulsdon 020 8668 4131
p205 . . . . Croydon 01689 848311
p411 . . . . Thornton Heath 020 8653 8844
Maddocks Clarke
p117 . . . . Altrincham 0844 805 5170
Manis
p411 . . . . . . Thornton Heath 020 8239 7111
Alan Mann & Co
p390 . . . St Albans 01727 833281 / 846012
Mann & Company
p265 . . . . Kettering 01536 520025
Margary & Miller
p225 . . . . Felixstowe 01394 273333
p439 . . . . Woodbridge 01394 382777
Marsh Brown & Co
p59. . . . . Lewisham 020 8852 0052

See p542 for the Firms Specialisations

Marsons Solicitors LLP
p166 . . . . Bromley 020 8313 1300
Martin & Strain
p358 . . . . Pwllheli 01758 612042
Martin-Kaye LLP
p409 . . . . .Telford 01952 272222
Massers
p338 . . . . Nottingham 0115 851 1666
p427 . . . . . West Bridgford 0115 851 1666
T A Matthews
p248 . . . . Hereford 01432 352121
Maxwell Hodge Solicitors
p268 . . . . Kirkby 0151 548 7370
p289 . . . . Liverpool 0151 526 9321
p428 . . . . West Kirby 0151 625 9154
Mayo Wynne Baxter LLP
p160 . . . . .Brighton 01273 775533
p215 . . . . East Grinstead 01342 310600
p215 . . . . Eastbourne 01323 730543
p283 . . . . .Lewes 01273 477071
Meikles
p144 . . . . .Bishop Auckland 01388 451122
Mellor & Jackson
p340 . . . . .Oldham 0161 624 7081
Metcalfe Copeman & Pettefar
p266 . . . . King's Lynn 01553 778102
p347 . . . . . . Peterborough 01733 865880
p435 . . . . .Wisbech 01945 464331
Metcalfes
p164 . . . . .Bristol 0117 929 0451
Mian & Co
p140 . . . . .Birmingham 0121 684 8000
Middleton Dummer
p340 . . . . .Oldbury 0121 544 4788
Milburns Solicitors
p431 . . . . Whitehaven 01946 694818
p440 . . . . Workington 01900 67363
Millan Solicitors
p154 . . . . Bradford 01274 660111
Neil Millar & Co Solicitors
p307 . . . . Manchester 0161 870 0177
Millichips
p427 . . . . . West Bromwich 0121 500 6363
George Mills
p423 . . . . Washington 0191 416 2182
Milne Moser
p264 . . . . .Kendal 01539 729786 / 725582
Milwyn Jenkins & Jenkins Limited
p292 . . . . Llanidloes 01686 412166
The Mitchell Plampin Partnership
p299 . . . . Maldon 01621 852566
Moeran Oughtred & Co
p423 . . . . Watford 01923 256263
Molesworths Bright Clegg
p365 . . . . Rochdale 01706 356666
Moore Blatch Solicitors
p386 . . . . . . Southampton 023 8071 8000
Moore Brown & Dixon LLP
p410 . . . . Tewkesbury 01684 292341
p417 . . . Upton-upon-Severn 01684 592675
Moran & Co
p407 . . . . .Tamworth 01827 54631
Morecrofts Solicitors LLP
p134 . . . . Birkenhead 0151 666 2210
Morgan Jones & Pett
p335 . . . . Norwich 01603 877000
Morley Brown & Co
p151 . . . . Boston 01205 364986
Morris & Bates
p291 . . . . Llandrindod Wells 01597 829055
Morrish Solicitors LLP
p276 . . . . .Leeds 0113 245 0733
Mortons
p401 . . . . Sunderland 0191 514 4323
Moss & Haselhurst
p435 . . . . Winsford 01606 592159
Moss Solicitors LLP
p293 . . . . . . .Loughborough 01509 217770
Moxons
p351 . . . . Pontefract 01977 703215
E J Moyle
p285 . . . . Littlehampton 01903 725143
Mugford & Co
p224 . . . . Fareham 01329 844555
James Murray Solicitors
p150 . . . . Bootle 0151 933 3333
p290 . . . . Liverpool 0151 207 9910
Murray Roach Solicitors
p320 . . . . . Nailsea 01275 858266 / 852705
Myer Wolff
p257 . . . . Hull 01482 223693
NUT Solicitors
p62. . . . . London WC1 020 7380 4734
Nalders Quality Solicitors
p173 . . . . .Camborne 01209 714278
Napthens LLP
p145 . . . . Blackburn 01254 667733
Nash & Co Solicitors LLP
p350 . . . . Plymouth 01752 664444
Neale Turk
p226 . . . . .Fleet 01252 811070
Needhams
p154 . . . . .Bradford 01274 371088

Neil McQueen Duncan & Egner
p326 . . Newcastle upon Tyne 0191 232 7469
Neville-Jones & Co
p421 . . . . Wareham 01929 552471
Newbys
p237 . . Guisborough 01287 632208 / 632209
Alfred Newton & Co
p396 . . . . .Stockport 0161 430 8831
p396 . . Stockport 0161 480 6551 / 480 1245
p433 . . . . Wilmslow 01625 523647
Nicol Denvir & Purnell
p180 . . . . Cardiff 029 2079 6311
Nightingales Solicitors Limited
p396 . . . . Stockport 01663 764038
Norcliffe & Co
p256 . . . . .Huddersfield 01484 514907
Norcross Lees & Riches
p341 . . . . .Oldham 0161 624 6034
North Ainley Halliwell
p341 . . . . .Oldham 0161 624 5614
Norton & Co
p259 . . . . Hyde 0161 366 8333
p356 . . . . Prescot 0151 426 7001
Nyland & Beattie
p432 . . . . Widnes 0151 424 5656
OGR Stock Denton
p64. . . . . London N3 020 8349 0321
ORJ Solicitors LLP
p393 . . . . Stafford 01785 223440
Gordon O'Brien
p258 . . . . Huyton 0151 489 4899
O'Donnells
p357 . . . . Preston 01772 881000
O'Neill Morgan Solicitors Limited
p396 . . . . Stockport 0161 429 8383
Oliver & Co
p191 . . . . Chester 01244 312306
Onions & Davies
p312 . . . . . Market Drayton 01630 652405
Osbornes
p65. . . . . Camden 020 7485 8811
Osler Donegan Taylor
p160 . . . . .Brighton 01273 710712
Over Taylor Biggs
p222 . . . . Exeter 01392 823811
Painters
p266 . . . . Kidderminster 01562 822295
p399 . . . Stourport-on-Severn 01299 822033
Paisleys
p440 . . . . Workington 01900 602235
Palmers Criminal Defence Solicitors
p207 . . . . Deal 01304 380572
Pardoes
p158 . . . . .Bridgwater 01278 457891
Paris & Co
p400 . . . Stratford-upon-Avon 01789 298177
Parlett Kent
p222 . . . . .Exeter 01392 494455
p66. . . . . . . London EC1 020 7430 0712
Parry Carver
p425 . . . . Wellington 01952 641291
Patel & Bhatoa
p154 . . . . .Bradford 01274 669023
Patterson Glenton & Stracey
p326 . . Newcastle upon Tyne 0191 232 8628
p384 . . . . . South Shields 0800 011 6487
Pattinson & Brewer
p164 . . . . .Bristol 0117 917 1100
p66. . . . . . . London WC1 020 7400 5100
p445 . . . . York 01904 680000
Payne & Payne
p257 . . . . Hull 01482 326446
Pearcelegal LLP
p383 . . . . Solihull 0844 412 7899
Pearson Caulfield
p326 . . Newcastle upon Tyne 0191 261 8878
Peasegoods
p308 . . . . Manchester 0161 205 2772
Pepperells
p373 . . . . Scunthorpe 01724 871999
Petrou Law Partnership
p67. . . . . London N4 020 8802 9393
Pheby & Co
p445 . . . . York 01904 789900
Pickworths
p247 . . . . Hemel Hempstead 01442 261731
Damian J Plant & Co
p264 . . . . Kenilworth 01926 847741 / 854677
Platt & Fishwick
p432 . . . . Wigan 01942 243281
Platt Halpern
p308 . . . . .Manchester 0161 224 2555
Plexus Law (A Trading Name of Parabis Law LLP)
p220 . . . . Evesham 01386 769160
p68. . . . . London EC3 0844 245 4000
Poole Alcock
p320 . . . . Nantwich 01270 625478
Porter Associates
p356 . . . . Prescot 0151 430 9160
David Porter & Co
p257 . . . . Hull 01482 325863

Porter Dodson
p212 . . . . Dorchester 01305 262525
p444 . . . . Yeovil 01935 424581
Portmans Solicitors
p220 . . . . Esher 01372 464488
Portner & Jaskel LLP
p68. . . . . London W1 020 7616 5300
Powell Forster
p69. . . . . Lambeth 020 7737 8111
Prettys
p262 . . . . Ipswich 01473 232121
Price Mears & Co
p365 . . . . Rochdale 01706 653331
Prusinski Solicitors
p293 . . . . . . Loughborough 01509 233622
Quality Solicitors Burroughs Day
p164 . . . . .Bristol 0117 929 0333
Quality Solicitors Chapman & Chubb
p115 . . . . Alfreton 01773 540480
Quality Solicitors Copley Clark
p403 . . . . Sutton 020 8643 7221
QualitySolicitors C Turner
p145 . . . . Blackburn 01254 688400
QualitySolicitors Gruber Garratt
p341 . . . . .Oldham 0161 665 3502
p358 . . . . Radcliffe 0161 724 0203
QualitySolicitors Hill & Abbott
p187 . . . . Chelmsford 01245 258892
Quinn Mantion
p70. . . . . London E14 020 7512 2600
RJR Solicitors
p328 . . . . Newport 01983 526924
Raleys
p125 . . . . Barnsley 01226 211111
Ralli Solicitors
p309 . . . . .Manchester 0870 998 9000
Ratcliffe & Bibby
p183 . . . . Carnforth 01524 734884
p270 . . . . .Lancaster 01524 39039
Rawlison Butler LLP
p253 . . . . Horsham 01403 252492
Red Kite Law
p244 . . . . . . Haverfordwest 01437 763332
p316 . . . . Milford Haven 01646 698008
Redferns
p242 . . . . Harrow 020 8424 7070
Richard Reed
p402 . . . . Sunderland 0191 567 0465
Scott Rees & Co
p381 . . . . Skelmersdale 01695 722222
Reynolds Parry-Jones
p250 . . . . . . High Wycombe 01494 525941
Rice-Jones & Smiths
p72. . . . . London EC1 020 7831 2506
Richards & Morgan LLP
p152 . . . . Bournemouth 01202 424234
Richardson & Co
p276 . . . . .Leeds 0113 243 1714
Peter Richbell & Co Solicitors
p187 . . . . Chelmsford 01245 355300
Roach Pittis
p328 . . . . Newport 01983 524431
Alan Roberts & Co
p191 . . . . Chester 01244 562754
Roberts & Smith
p321 . . . . Nelson 01282 619000
Roberts Moore Nicholas Jones
p134 . . . . Birkenhead 0151 647 0000
Robyns Owen
p358 . . . . Pwllheli 01758 613177
Rogers & Norton
p335 . . . . Norwich 01603 666001
The Roland Partnership
p191 . . . . Chester 01244 659404
Romain Coleman & Co
p73. . . . . . Waltham Forest 020 8520 3322
Rothwell & Evans
p407 . . . . Swinton 0161 794 1830
Rowberry Morris
p361 . . . . Reading 0118 958 5611
Rowley Dickinson
p309 . . . . Manchester 0161 834 4215
Paul Rudd
p235 . . . . Grimsby 01472 350881
Rundlewalker
p222 . . . . Exeter 01392 209209
Runhams
p154 . . . . Bradford 01274 532233
Russell & Co Solicitors and Estate Agents
p202 Crawley 01293 561965 / 0845 300 2809
Russell & Russell
p315 . . . . Middleton 0161 653 6200
Russell Jones & Walker
p141 . . . . Birmingham 0121 233 8300
p164 . . . . Bristol 0117 374 2222
p180 . . . . Cardiff 029 2026 2800
p74. . . . . London WC2 020 7657 1555
p309 . . . . Manchester 0161 383 3500
p326 . . Newcastle upon Tyne 0191 323 3000
p377 . . . . Sheffield 0114 276 6868
p419 . . . . Wakefield 01924 234300
Rutters
p374 . . . . Shaftesbury 01747 852377

SAS Daniels LLP
p198 . . . . Congleton 01260 282300
SLP Solicitors
p394 . . . . Stanmore 020 8420 7950
Salmons
p398 . . . . . Stoke-on-Trent 01782 639827
Salt Veeder
p171 . . . . Bury 0161 797 5650
Salusburys Harding & Barnett
p281 . . . . Leicester 0116 262 6052
Samuels Solicitors
p125 . . . . .Barnstaple 01271 343457
Sanders Brickwood
p195 . . . . Cirencester 01285 654601
Raymond Saul & Co
p76. . . . . London E1 020 7480 5840
Thomas Saul & Co
p430 . . . . Whitefield 0161 773 2833
Sayers
p242 . . . . Harrow 020 8861 4191
Scaiff LLP
p440 . . . . Worcester 01905 727700
Scotts Wright
p183 . . . . Catterick Garrison 01748 832431
Scrivenger Seabrook
p392 . . . . .St Neots 01480 214900
Seabourne Lawleys
p333 . . . . Northwood 01923 820639
Seatons Solicitors
p199 . . . . Corby 01536 276300
Seddon Thomson
p309 . . . . Manchester 0161 720 8000
Sehgal & Co
p142 . . . . .Birmingham 0121 772 2226
Serjeant & Son
p359 . . . . Ramsey 01487 812325
Shakespeares
p142 . . . . .Birmingham 0121 237 3000
Clive Shepherd & Co
p420 . . . . Walsall 01922 647797
Sheridan & Co
p267 . Kingston upon Thames 020 8541 1181
D R Sheridan & Co
p172 . . . . Bushey 020 8950 6768
Shoosmiths
p127
. Basingstoke 0370 086 6200 / 01256 696200
p224 Fareham 0370 086 6800 / 01489 616800
Sidhu & Co
p142 . . . . Birmingham 07831 293903
Silks
p321 . . . . Netherton 01384 236101
Sills & Betteridge LLP
p228 . . . . . . Gainsborough 01427 616816
p285 . . . . Lincoln 01522 542211
p381 . . . . Sleaford 01529 302800
Simons Levine & Co
p79. . . . . Barnet 020 8446 4273
Simons Rodkin Litigation Solicitors
p79. . . . . London N12 020 8446 6223
Simpson Millar LLP
p276 . . . . .Leeds 0844 858 3200
p80. . . . . London EC1 0844 858 3400
Sintons LLP
p326 . . Newcastle upon Tyne 0191 226 7878
The Skemp Partnership
p310
. Manchester 0800 040 7566 / 0161 238 5400
Slade Legal
p210 . . . . Didcot 01235 511211
Slater Heelis Collier Littler
p370 . . . . Sale 0161 969 3131
Slee Blackwell
p125 . . . . .Barnstaple 01271 372128
p133 . . . . .Bideford 01237 425225
Smith Jones Solicitors
p264 . . . . .Kenilworth 01926 859933
Smith Llewelyn Partnership
p405 . . . . Swansea 01792 464444
The Smith Partnership
p170 . . . . . Burton-on-Trent 01283 536471
p404 . . . . Swadlincote 01283 226444
T C Smith
p131 . . Berwick-upon-Tweed 01289 307409
SmithJones Solicitors Ltd
p169 . . . . Burnley 01282 855400
Solicitors Direct
p155 . . . . Bradford 01274 776000
Solomon Levy
p295 . . . . . . Luton 01582 425817 / 414948
Southern Stewart & Walker
p384 . . . . . . South Shields 0191 427 0770
Southerns
p169 . . . . Burnley 01282 422711
Sparling Benham & Brough
p198 . . . . .Colchester 01206 733733
p227 . . . . . Frinton-on-Sea 01255 679222
Spicketts Battrick Law Practice
p181 . . . . Cardiff 029 2046 1480
p352 . . . . .Pontypridd 01443 407221
Sproull Solicitors LLP
p148 . . . . Bodmin 01208 72328
p176 . . . . Camelford 01840 212315
p353 . . . . Port Isaac 01840 212315

Adrian Stables
p383 Somerton 0845 873 6180
Stables & Co
p237 Halesowen 0121 585 3820
Stanley Smith Hill & Co
p123 Banstead 01737 358001
Stanley Tee LLP
p175 Cambridge 01223 311141
Steele Ford & Newton
p321 Nelson 01282 692531
Steeles
p335 Norwich 0870 609 0200
Stephens & Scown
p414 Truro 01872 265100
Stephens & Son LLP
p185 Chatham 01634 811444
John Stephenson & Co
p390 St Albans 01727 847983
Stephenson Reynell
p434 Windermere 01539 488622
Stephensons Solicitors LLP
p282 Leigh 01942 777777
p282 Leigh 01942 777777
Sternberg Reed
p123 Barking 020 8591 3366
Sterratt & Co
p124 Barnoldswick 01282 813731
Stevens Lucas
p342 Oswestry 01691 670999
Peter Steward & Co
p234 Great Yarmouth 01493 332277
Harold Stock & Co
p120
Ashton-under-Lyne 01457 835597 / 835034
Stokes Solicitors
p355 Portsmouth 023 9282 8131
Stones Solicitors LLP
p340 Okehampton 01837 650200
Streeter Marshall
p205 Croydon 020 8680 2638
Swain & Co
p386 Southampton 023 8063 1111
Sydney Mitchell
p142
Birmingham 0121 698 2200 / 0808 166 8827
Symes Robinson & Lee
p203 Crediton 01363 775566
TBI Solicitors
p243
Hartlepool 0800 052 6824 / 01429 264101
TMJ Legal Services LLP
p214 Durham 0191 383 0111
p243 Hartlepool 01429 235616
TPC Solicitors
p310 Manchester 0161 832 8867
Talbot Walker LLP
p118 Andover 01264 363354
Taylor Bracewell
p212 Doncaster 01302 341414
Taylor Legal
p203 Crewe 01270 500844
Michael Taylor & Associates
p417 Urmston 0161 746 7776
Stanley Tee
p144 Bishop's Stortford 01279 755200
Temple Heelis LLP
p264 Kendal 01539 723757
Tennant & Knight
p160 Brighton 01273 202050
Thomas & Co
p143 Birmingham 0121 444 0030
Dean Thomas & Co
p441 Worksop 01909 500511
Henry Thompson & Sons
p232 Grantham 01476 563226
Thompsons (formerly Robin/Brian Thompson & Partners)
p165 Bristol 0117 304 2400
p181 Cardiff 029 2044 5300
p187 Chelmsford 01245 228800
p277 Leeds 0113 205 6300
p290 Liverpool 0151 224 1600
p87 London WC1 020 7290 0000
p310 Manchester 0161 819 3500
p327 Newcastle upon Tyne 0191 269 0400
p339 Nottingham 0115 989 7200
p377 Sheffield 0114 270 3300
p398 Stoke-on-Trent 01782 406200
Andrew Thorne & Co
p374 Shaw 01706 290488
Thorneycroft Solicitors Ltd
p297 Macclesfield 01625 503444
Thurnhills
p357 Preston 01772 251762
Tickle Hall Cross
p356 Prescot 0800 854379
Tierney & Co
p367 Rotherham 01709 709000
Tilbrook's
p193 Chipping Ongar 01277 896000
Timms
p170 Burton-on-Trent 01283 561531 / 544417
p209 Derby 01332 364436
Timms Solicitors
p404 Swadlincote 01283 214231
Tinsdills
p239 Hanley 01782 262031
Tollers LLP
p265 Kettering 01536 520111
Tracey Barlow Furniss & Co
p363 Retford 01777 707677
Sue Tuck & Co
p88 Kensington & Chelsea 020 7385 7733
Turner Coulston
p333 Northampton 01604 622101
Turner Pearson
p228 Garstang 01995 604536
Jay Vadher & Co
p89 London E15 020 8519 3000
A D Varley & Co
p146 Blackburn 01254 582777
p357 Preston 01772 556777
Veitch Penny
p222 Exeter 01392 278381
WBW Solicitors
p222 Exeter 01392 202404
p329 Newton Abbot 01626 202404
Wace Morgan
p379 Shrewsbury 01743 280100
Waddington Webber
p264 Keighley 01535 662644 / 662647
Waldrons
p158 Brierley Hill 01384 811811
Walker Smith Way
p120 Ashton-under-Lyne 0844 346 3100
p191 Chester 0844 346 3100
p443 Wrexham 0844 346 3100
Walkers
p367 Rossendale 01706 213565
Wannop Fox Staffurth & Bray
p148 Bognor Regis 01243 864001
Waran & Co
p90 London SW4 020 7498 3328
Ward & Rider Limited
p201 Coventry 024 7655 5400
Ward Gethin
p266 King's Lynn 01553 660033
Wards Solicitors
p394 Staple Hill 0117 943 4800
Ware & Kay LLP
p429 Wetherby 01937 583210
Waring & Co
p124 Barnet 0870 444 2782
Steven Warne Solicitor
p373 Scunthorpe 01724 279449
Watmores
p90 London WC2 020 7430 1512
Watson Burton LLP
p327 Newcastle upon Tyne 0845 901 2100
Weightmans LLP
p269 Knutsford 01565 634234
p281 Leicester 0116 253 9747
Whatley Recordon
p300 Malvern 01684 892939
John Whitcroft
p165 Bristol 0117 922 7740
V E White & Co
p400 Strood 01634 739195
Whiteside & Knowles Ltd
p319 Morecambe 01524 416315
Whittinghams
p157 Bridgend 01656 653485
Widdows Mason
p282 Leigh 01942 673311
p422 Warrington 01925 632267
p429 Westhoughton 01942 816515
p432 Wigan 01942 244294
Widdows Pilling & Co
p419 Walkden 0161 790 1825
Guy Wigmore Solicitor
p388 Southport 01704 222277
Wilkin Chapman Grange Solicitors
p252 Horncastle 01507 527521
p294 Louth 01507 606161
Matthew Wilkinson Solicitors Ltd
p315 Middlesbrough 01642 218888
R N Williams & Co Limited
p438 Wolverhampton 01902 429051
Williamson & Barnes
p207 Deal 01304 373154
Williamson & Soden
p383 Solihull 0121 733 8000
Williamson Hill
p315 Middlesbrough 01642 217961
Williamsons
p258 Hull 01482 323697
Willson Hawley & Co
p339 Nuneaton 024 7638 7821
Wilson Barca LLP
p92 London W1 020 7272 2072
Wilson Browne
p281 Leicester 0116 251 7181
p425 Wellingborough 01933 279000
Wilson Bullough Walton & Knowles
p330
Newton-le-Willows 01925 224569 / 224560
Winder Taylor Fallows
p150 Bolton 01204 389908 / 522888
Winston Solicitors LLP
p278 Leeds 0113 320 5000
Wolferstans
p351 Plymouth 01752 663295
Rupert Wood & Son
p120 Ashton-under-Lyne 0161 330 9121
Woodfines LLP
p130 Bedford 01234 270600
p147 Bletchley 01908 366333
p176 Cambridge 01223 411421
Woodhouse & Company
p438 Wolverhampton 01902 773616
Woolliscrofts
p239 Hanley 01782 204000
Woolsey Morris & Kennedy
p380 Sidcup 020 8300 9321
Wright & Co
p351 Pontefract 01977 878130
Wright & Lord
p319 Morecambe 01524 402050
Wright & McMillan Bennett
p409 Telford 01952 291100
Young & Co
p398 Stoke-on-Trent 01782 339200
S D Young
p392 St Neots 01480 470411
Ziadies
p94 London SW9 020 7737 0934

LITIGATION, COMMERCIAL

AB Law
p241 Harrow 020 8426 5613
Abrahamson & Associates
p3 London NW11 020 8458 1100
Aiston Solicitors
p204 Croydon 020 8681 0123
Alexander Paul
p412 Tiverton 01884 252361
E G Arghyrakis & Co
p7 London EC4 020 7353 2302
Ashfords LLP
p220 Exeter 01392 337000
p349 Plymouth 01752 521500
Ashurst LLP
p7 London EC2 020 7638 1111
Avery Emerson Solicitors
p259 Ilford 020 8215 0884
BCL Burton Copeland
p9 London WC2 020 7430 2277
BPE Solicitors LLP
p187 Cheltenham 01242 224433
J E Baring & Co
p9 London EC1 020 7242 8966
Barlow Lyde & Gilbert LLP
p10 London EC3 020 7876 5000
Batchelors Solicitors
p166 Bromley 020 8768 7000
Beale and Company Solicitors LLP
p11 London WC2 020 7240 3474
Nigel W Beaman
p176 Cannock 01543 574474
Behr & Co
p167 Brynmawr 01495 310581
Belvederes
p12 London WC2 020 7404 5262 / 7405 0046
Benson Mazure LLP
p12 London W1 020 7486 8091
Berkson Wallace Solicitors
p217 Ellesmere Port 0151 355 4412
p419 Wallasey 0151 691 6900
Bermans LLP
p286 Liverpool 0151 224 0500
p301 Manchester 0161 827 4600
Berry Smith LLP
p177 Cardiff 029 2034 5511
Berrymans Lace Mawer
p271 Leeds 0113 236 2002
p301 Manchester 0161 236 2002
Bhakar Tomlinson
p425 Wellington 01952 270555
Birkett Long LLP
p186 Chelmsford 01245 453800
p197 Colchester 01206 217300
Bivonas Limited Solicitors
p13 London EC3 020 7337 2600
Blake Lapthorn
p184 Chandlers Ford 023 8090 8090
Bookers & Bolton
p116 Alton 01420 82881 / 88903
Bowcock Cuerden LLP
p320 Nantwich 01270 611106
Brabners Chaffe Street
p286 Liverpool 0151 600 3000
p301 Manchester 0161 836 8800
Graham Bridgman & Co
p360 Reading 0118 933 1818
Briffa
p15 Islington 020 7288 6003
Brookes & Co
p16 London EC3 020 7621 0067
Brooks
p378 Shipston-on-Stour 01608 664406
Brooks & Co
p226 Fetcham 01372 362042
N C Brothers & Co
p360 Reading 0118 958 9966
Bryan & Armstrong
p311 Mansfield 01623 626039
Buckles Solicitors LLP
p346 Peterborough 01733 888888
Bury & Walkers LLP
p272 Leeds 0113 244 4227
Byrne & Partners
p16 London EC4 020 7842 1616
CKFT
p17 London NW3 020 7431 7262
John F S Cabot
p17 London SW6 020 7384 9583
Christopher Cox Solicitors
p331 Northampton 01604 882287
Cannings Connolly
p18 London EC1 020 7329 9000
Caplans
p241 Harrow 020 8864 0111
Carlsons
p18 London N20 020 8445 3331 / 8445 5752
Carrington & Associates
p18 London EC4 020 7822 1855
Carter Lemon Camerons
p18 London EC1 020 7406 1000
Carter-Ruck
p18 London EC4 020 7353 5005
Cartwright Cunningham Haselgrove & Co
p19 Waltham Forest 020 8520 1021
Castle Sanderson
p272 Leeds 0113 232 1919
Chafes
p433 Wilmslow 01625 531676
Challinors
p427 West Bromwich 0121 553 3211
James Chan & Co
p19 London EC4 0844 848 9988
Chandler Harris LLP
p302 Manchester 0161 834 2200
Charles Russell LLP
p19 London EC4 020 7203 5000
Chattertons Solicitors
p381 Sleaford 01529 411500
P Chevalier & Co
p402 Surbiton 020 3393 8217
Chua's Solicitors
p20 London EC4 020 7242 6789
Clarke Willmott
p408 Taunton 0845 209 1000 / 0117 305 6000
Clarkes
p409 Telford 01952 291666
Clausen Miller LLP
p20 London EC3 020 7645 7970
Clintons
p21 London WC2 020 7379 6080
Clyde & Co LLP
p21 London EC3 020 7623 1244
Coffin Mew & Clover
p385 Southampton 023 8033 4661
Collins Long
p21 Southwark 020 7401 9800
Coninghams Solicitors
p22 London SW1 020 8296 1957
Conway & Co
p247 Henley-on-Thames 01491 411122
Cooper Stott
p214 Durham 0191 384 7210
Corbett & Co International Construction Lawyers Ltd
p409 Teddington 020 8614 6200
Cox Cooper Limited
p137 Birmingham 0121 777 0015
Cozens-Hardy LLP
p334 Norwich 01603 625231
Crombie Wilkinson
p444 York 01904 624185
Crutes
p182 Carlisle 01228 525195
p396 Stockton-on-Tees 01642 623400
Curwens
p218 Enfield 020 8363 4444
p420 Waltham Abbey 01992 712549
Dale & Newbery LLP
p393 Staines 01784 464491
Simon Daly Solicitors
p396 Stockton-on-Tees 01642 604074
Dass Solicitors
p137 Birmingham 0121 248 4000
Christopher Davidson Solicitors LLP
p188 Cheltenham 01242 581481
Paul Davidson Taylor
p253 Horsham 01403 262333
Davies Johnson & Co (Shipping & Commercial Solicitors)
p349 Plymouth 01752 226020

See p542 for the Firms Specialisations

4

stevensdrake
p202 Crawley 01293 596900

Harold Stock & Co
p120 Ashton-under-Lyne 01457 835597 / 835034

Stockdale & Reid Ltd
p318 Monkseaton 0191 251 9494

Stockler Brunton
p83 London EC4 020 7404 6661

Streeter Marshall
p205 Croydon 020 8680 2638

Suttons
p84 London W1 020 7935 5279

Tanners
p195 Cirencester 01285 659061

Taylors
p146 Blackburn 0844 800 0263

Tilbrook's
p193 Chipping Ongar 01277 896000

Tinsdills
p239 Hanley 01782 262031

Alison Trent & Co
p88 London EC4 020 7583 3350

Sue Tuck & Co
p88 Kensington & Chelsea 020 7385 7733

Turner Coulston
p333 Northampton 01604 622101

Turners Solicitors LLP
p153 Bournemouth 01202 291291

Underwood Solicitors LLP
p89 London W1 020 7526 6000

Vyman Solicitors
p242 Harrow 020 8427 9080

Walker Foster
p381 Skipton 01756 700200

Ward Hadaway
p327 Newcastle upon Tyne 0191 204 4000

Waters & Co
p143 Birmingham 01675 463855

Waterson Hicks
p90 London EC3 020 7929 6060

Watson Burton LLP
p327 Newcastle upon Tyne 0845 901 2100

Webster Dixon LLP
p90 London EC1 020 7353 8300

Whittingdales
p91 London WC2 020 7831 5591

Wilde & Co
p321 Neston 0151 353 1899

The Wilkes Partnership LLP
p143 Birmingham 0121 233 4333

WilmerHale
p92 London EC2 020 7645 2400
p344 Oxford 01235 823000

Wise Geary
p122 Banbury 01295 278500

Wiseman Lee LLP
p92 Redbridge 020 8215 1000

Wismayers
p233 Great Bookham 01372 451114

Woodfines LLP
p130 Bedford 01234 270600
p176 Cambridge 01223 411421
p317 Milton Keynes 01908 202150

Zaiwalla & Co
p93 London WC2 020 7312 1000

Zimmers
p94 London NW11 0870 770 0171

LITIGATION, GENERAL

AB Law
p241 Harrow 020 8426 5613

AR Legal Solicitors
p3 London W4 020 8747 9090

AWB Charlesworth LLP
p263 Keighley 01535 613678

Aaronson & Co
p3 London W8 020 7376 9124

S Abraham Solicitors
p402 Surbiton 020 8390 0044

Albinson Napier & Co
p421 Warrington 01925 634681

Alderson Dodds
p147 Blyth 01670 352293

Alexander Lawyers LLP
p186 Chelmsford 01245 216050

Alexander Marks LLP
p5 London W1 020 7317 1166

Allan Janes LLP
p249 High Wycombe 01494 521301

J P Almond & Co
p435 Wirral 0151 632 2336

Ameer Meredith
p174 Cambridge 01223 577077

J M Amin & Co
p426 Wembley 020 8903 3766

Angel & Co
p6 London W1 020 7495 0555

Anthony Gold
p6 London SW16 020 7940 4000

Aplin Stockton Fairfax
p122 Banbury 01295 251234

Appleby Shaw
p434 Windsor 01753 860606

Archer & Archer
p218 Ely 01353 662203

Arnold Greenwood
p316 Milnthorpe 01539 562424

Ascroft Whiteside
p146 Blackpool 01253 766866

David Auld & Co
p319 Morpeth 01670 505844

Aurangzeb Khan Solicitors
p153 Bradford 01274 548549

BBL Solicitors LLP
p235 Guildford 01483 838154

Baehrs
p151 Bournemouth 01202 292075

Banks Kelly
p9 London EC2 020 7248 4231

J E Baring & Co
p9 London EC1 020 7242 8966

Stan Baring Solicitor
p231 Godalming 01483 860986

Barlow Lyde & Gilbert LLP
p10 London EC3 020 7876 5000

Barlow Robbins LLP
p235 Guildford 01483 562901

Barnes & Partners
p239 Harlow 01279 418601

Barr Ellison LLP
p174 Cambridge 01223 411315
p174 Cambridge 01223 417200

Barrett & Co Solicitors LLP
p359 Reading 0118 958 9711

David J Barry
p367 Ross-on-Wye 01989 564209

Barwells
p215 Eastbourne 01323 411505

S S Basi & Co
p259 Ilford 020 8518 1236

Batchelors Solicitors
p166 Bromley 020 8768 7000

Richard T Bate & Co
p410 Tetbury 01666 503722

Bathurst Brown Downie & Airey LLP
p416 Twickenham 020 8892 1537

Nigel W Beaman
p176 Cannock 01543 574474

Beasley Johnson Loyns
p419 Walsall 01922 644433

Beesley & Co
p301 Manchester 0161 445 3678

Joseph N Bell
p283 Lewes 01273 897377

Belvederes
p12 London WC2 020 7404 5262 / 7405 0046

Bendles
p181 Carlisle 01228 522215

Berkeley Solicitors
p213 Droylsden 0161 371 0011

Bermans LLP
p286 Liverpool 0151 224 0500

Berry & Berry
p299 Maidstone 01622 690777
p414 Tunbridge Wells 01892 526344

Berwins Solicitors Limited
p240 Harrogate 01423 509000

Betteridges
p248 Hertford 01992 505406

Bevans
p161 Bristol 0117 923 7249
p12 London WC2 020 7353 9995

Malcolm G Beverley Solicitors
p194 Chorley 01257 231462

Biscoes
p423 Waterlooville 023 9225 1257

Black Graf & Co
p13 London NW3 020 7586 1141

Blake Lapthorn
p342 Oxford 01865 248607

A J Bond & Co
p166 Bromley 020 8464 2229

Bowser Ollard & Bentley
p312 March 01354 652606

Bracher Rawlins LLP
p15 London WC1 020 7404 9400

Breeze & Wyles Solicitors LLP
p248 Hertford 01992 558411

Brewer Harding & Rowe
p132 Bideford 01237 472666

Brinley Morris Rees & Jones
p292 Llanelli 01554 774241

Brittons
p128 Beaconsfield 01494 730722

Bromleys Solicitors LLP
p120 Ashton-under-Lyne 0161 330 6821

Brooks & Co
p226 Fetcham 01372 362042

Broomhead & Saul
p261 Ilminster 01460 57056
p408 Taunton 01823 288121

Brutton & Co
p223 Fareham 01329 236171

Bryan & Armstrong
p311 Mansfield 01623 626039

Buglear Bate & Co
p436 Woking 01483 715527 / 724246

Burnand Brazier Tisdall
p254 Hove 01273 734022

Burnett Barker
p171 Bury St Edmunds 01284 701131

Burton & Co LLP
p284 Lincoln 01522 523215

C R Burton & Co
p16 London SE20 020 8778 4455 / 8659 5775

Butcher Burns LLP
p16 London WC1 020 7713 7100

John F S Cabot
p17 London SW6 020 7384 9583

Callaghans
p224 Farnham 01252 723477

Canty & Co
p136 Birmingham 0121 688 5000

Carter Bells LLP
p267 Kingston upon Thames 020 8939 4000

Carvill & Johnson LLP
p136 Birmingham 0121 476 9000

Challinors
p136 Birmingham 0121 212 9393

Chaplin & Co
p394 Stanmore 020 8954 8202

Charles Russell LLP
p235 Guildford 01483 252525

Chattertons Solicitors
p232 Grantham 01476 591550
p284 Lincoln 01522 814600

Chilcotts
p408 Tavistock 01822 612535 / 614242

Chua's Solicitors
p20 London EC4 020 7242 6789

Churchers
p223 Fareham 01329 822333
p354 Portsmouth 023 9221 0170

Clarke Willmott
p162 Bristol 0845 209 1000 / 0117 305 6000

Clinton Davis Pallis
p21 London N8 020 8880 5000

Colemans - CTTS
p124 Barnet 020 8441 1213

Collins Long
p21 Southwark 020 7401 9800

Comptons
p22 Camden 020 7485 0888

Cooper Son & Caldecott
p247 Henley-on-Thames 01491 574203

Cowlishaw & Mountford
p417 Uttoxeter 01889 565211

Dudley Cramp & Co
p380 Sittingbourne 01795 420024

Crumplins
p23 Camden 020 7483 0282

N Cunliffe-Lister
p213 Driffield 01377 236006

Curry Popeck
p24 London W1 020 7224 6633

Cuthbertsons
p148 Blyth 01670 352121

DBL Talbots LLP
p265 Kidderminster 01562 749910

DB Law
p346 Penzance 01736 364261

DSM Legal Solicitors
p421 Warrington 0845 009 0863

Simon Daly Solicitors
p396 Stockton-on-Tees 01642 604074

Darling & Stephensons
p206 Darlington 01325 489000

Darlingtons
p217 Edgware 020 8952 0033 / 8951 6666

Darwin Gray
p178 Cardiff 029 2082 9100

Davies Bays & Co t/a Windsor & Co
p26 Haringey 020 8808 3237

Hywel Davies & Co
p121 Bala 01678 520307

Jeremy Davies & Co
p26 London SW7 020 7589 4999

W Davies
p436 Woking 01483 744900

Davis Blank Furniss
p230 Glossop 01457 860606

Davis Davidson
p131 Beverley 01482 881278

Debidins
p26 Ealing 020 8567 1381 / 8567 6343

Denniss Matthews
p27 London SE20 020 8778 7301 / 8778 7631

Dickins Hopgood Chidley LLP
p258 Hungerford 01488 683555

Dodd Lewis Solicitors
p27 London SE3 020 8852 1255

Downie & Gadban
p116 Alton 01420 82879

David Downton & Co
p316 Milton Keynes 01908 563030

Driver Belcher Solicitors
p385 Southampton 01489 785737

Drummonds
p190 Chester 01244 408300

Peter Dunn & Co
p401 Sunderland 0191 568 9000

ELC Solicitors
p28 Ealing 020 8566 4045

EMW
p316 Milton Keynes 0845 070 6000

Eaton Smith LLP
p255 Huddersfield 01484 821300

Elliots Bond & Banbury
p29 Ealing 020 8567 0176

Ellis Jones
p151 Bournemouth 01202 525333

Fahm & Co
p147 Blackwood 01495 224973

Fairbairn Smith & Co
p30 London N17 020 8808 4901

Ferguson Solicitors
p31 London EC4 020 7822 2999

Fidler & Pepper
p404 Sutton-in-Ashfield 01623 451111

Field Overell
p200 Coventry 024 7622 9582

Finers Stephens Innocent LLP
p32 London W1 020 7323 4000

Fisher Meredith
p32 Lambeth 020 7091 2700

Fleet Solicitors LLP
p162 Bristol 0845 603 3273

Fletchers
p388 Southport 01704 546919

Follett Stock LLP
p221 Exeter 01392 449370
p414 Truro 01872 241700

Forbes
p145 Blackburn 01254 662831

Forbes Hall LLP
p33 London EC2 020 7729 9111
p439 Woodford Green 020 8498 0080

Lindsay Ford Solicitors Ltd
p172 Caerphilly 029 2088 2441

J A Forrest & Co
p33 London W1 020 7233 9140

Foys Solicitors
p367 Rotherham 01709 375561

Freer & Archer
p279 Leicester 0116 241 3199

French & Co
p337 Nottingham 0115 955 1111

Frettens Solicitors
p194 Christchurch 01202 491777

Frisby & Co
p392 Stafford 01785 244114

Fursdon Knapper
p349 Plymouth 01752 309090

Furse Sanders & Co
p383 South Molton 01769 572251

GLRS Phoenix LLP
p400 Stroud 01453 763433

Gadsby Wicks
p186 Chelmsford 01245 494929

Gales
p152 Bournemouth 01202 512227 / 512446

Garden House Solicitors
p248 Hertford 01992 422128

Gardner Austin
p35 London W1 020 7831 2600

J Garrard & Allen
p341 Olney 01234 711215

Gelbergs LLP
p35 Islington 020 7226 0570

Gillanders
p188 Cheltenham 01242 583434

Girlings
p119 Ashford 01233 664711

Godwins
p433 Winchester 01962 841484

Goldkorn Mathias Gentle Page LLP
p36 London WC1 020 7631 1811

Goodhand and Forsyth QualitySolicitors
p362 Redhill 01737 773533

David Goodman & Co
p36 London W1 020 7323 3369

Goughs
p210 Devizes 01380 726913

Grant Saw Solicitors LLP
p36 Greenwich 020 8858 6971

Greene & Greene
p171 Bury St Edmunds 01284 762211

Greens
p294 Ludlow 01584 873918

Greenwoods
p37 London EC3 020 7220 7818

Gregory Abrams Davidson LLP
p37 London NW11 020 8209 0166 / 8458 9322

Shirley Griffiths
p259 Hythe 01303 266689

Guillaumes Solicitors
p430 Weybridge 01932 840111

See p542 for the Firms Specialisations

Gurney-Champion & Co
p354 . . . . . . Portsmouth 023 9282 1100
Guthrie Jones & Jones
p121 . . . . Bala 01678 520428
HCB Solicitors
p420 . . . . Walsall 01922 720000
HGF Law
p37. . . . . . . London WC2 020 7440 8900
Hague Lambert
p269 . . . . Knutsford 01565 652411
p417 . . . . Urmston 0161 747 7321
Haldanes
p37. . . . . London W1 020 7437 5629
Hamilton Pratt
p422 . . . . Warwick 01926 838900
Hansell Wilkes & Co
p207 . . . . Dartmouth 01803 833993
Harcus Sinclair
p38. . . . . . . London WC2 020 7242 9700
Harper Law
p366 . . . . Romsey 01794 322364
Harrison Clark LLP
p439 . . . . Worcester 01905 612001
Harrisons Solicitors
p305 . . . . Manchester 0161 819 2511
C W Harwood & Co
p274 . . . . Leeds 0113 245 7027
R J Hawksley & Co
p173 . . . . Camberley 01252 890400
Edward Hayes LLP
p192 . . . . Chichester 01243 672124
p192 . . . . Chichester 01243 781431
p441 . . . . Worthing 01903 215999
Hayton Winkley
p264 . . . . Kendal 01539 720136
Headleys
p250 . . . . Hinckley 01455 637815
Heath Buckeridge
p298 . . . . Maidenhead 01628 671636
Hedleys & Co
p401 . . . . Sunderland 0191 567 0101
Hempsons
p40. . . . . London W1 020 7839 0278
Henneberry & Co
p40. . . . . . . London NW6 020 8830 1907
Henriques Griffiths
p163 . . . . Bristol 0117 909 4000
Heringtons
p370 . . . . Rye 01797 222955
Herrington & Carmichael LLP
p437 . . . . Wokingham 0118 977 4045
Hextalls
p41. . . . . . . London EC2 020 7382 0700
Hibberts LLP
p203 . . . . Crewe 01270 215117
Hills Solicitors Limited
p116 . . . . Altrincham 0161 928 0961
Mark Hoare
p189 . . . . Chepstow 01291 630356
Hodders
p41. . . . . . London NW10 020 8838 1537
p41. . . . . . London SW11 020 7720 1647
Hook & Partners
p177 . . . . . . Canvey Island 01268 692255
Hopkins
p337 . . . . Nottingham 0115 910 5555
Robert Howard
p350 . . . . Plymouth 01752 251851
Howard Stone
p43. . . . . . . London EC1 020 7490 5900
Howell Jones & Co
p113 . . . . Abergele 01745 826282 / 825845
Howells
p178 . . . . Cardiff 029 2040 4020
Hubball & Co
p403 . . . . . Sutton Coldfield 0121 323 4822
Humphries Kirk
p352 . . . . Poole 01202 715815
Hunt & Lisners
p332 . . . . Northampton 01604 846705
Hunters
p44. . . . . . . London WC2 020 7412 0050
Ibbotson Brady
p274 . . . . Leeds 0113 366 3022
Aubrey Isaacson Solicitors
p357 . . . . Prestwich 0161 959 5000
JPS Law Solicitors
p45. . . . . London W1 020 7935 9955
Jackamans
p239 . . . . Harleston 01379 854455
Jeromes
p328 . . . . Newport 01983 522664
Johar & Co
p280 . . . . Leicester 0116 254 3345
The John W Davies Partnership
p329 . . . . Newport 01633 841773
Johns & Saggar
p46. . . . . . . London WC1 020 3490 1475
Jolliffe & Co
p190 . . . . Chester 01244 310022
Josiah Hincks
p196 . . . . Coalville 01530 835041
p280 . . . . Leicester 0116 255 1811

Judge & Priestley
p166 . . . . Bromley 020 8290 0333
Judge Sykes Frixou
p47. . . . . London WC2 020 7379 5114
Kaufmanlegal
p306 . . . . Manchester 0161 205 3955
Andrew Keen & Co
p48. . . . . London E18 020 8989 3123
Keene Marsland
p415 . . . . . . Tunbridge Wells 01892 526442
Keer-Keer & Co
p246
. . Hemel Hempstead 01442 216755 / 216756
Richard P Kemp BA Solicitor
p313 . . . . Martock 01935 822572
Keoghs LLP
p200 . . . . Coventry 024 7665 8200
Kilroys
p139 . . . . Birmingham 0121 270 1002
Kingsfords
p119 . . . . Ashford 01233 665544
Kirby & Co
p50. . . . . . . London SW19 020 8545 7171
Kitsons LLP
p413 . . . . Torquay 01803 202020
Labrums
p390 . . . . St Albans 01727 858807
Laceys
p353 . . . . Poole 01202 743286
Lamb Brooks LLP
p126 . . . . Basingstoke 01256 844888
Lanyon Bowdler LLP
p409 . . . . Telford 01952 291222
Larcomes LLP
p354 . . . . Portsmouth 023 9266 1531
The Law Partnership
p242 . . . . Harrow 020 8416 7004
Lawson & Thompson
p119 . . . . Ashington 01670 813588
Layton & Co
p244 . . . . Haverfordwest 01437 766671
Leeds Day
p258 . . . . Huntingdon 01480 454301
p392 . . . . St Neots 01480 474661
Lloyds & Cooper
p283 . . . . Leominster 01568 613236
Robert Locke
p224 . . . . Fareham 01329 822722
Longstaff & Midgley
p372 . . . . Scarborough 01723 351751
Loveday & Keighley
p313 . . . . . . Matlock 01629 583142 / 56660
Lovell Son & Pitfield
p55. . . . . Camden 020 7242 7883
Lowrie & Co
p196 . . . . Cobham 01932 865818
McBride Wilson & Co
p56. . . . . . . London WC2 020 7242 1300
Neil McCormick
p228 . . . . Frome 01373 455700
McKeag & Co
p231 . . . . Gosforth 0191 213 1010
Mackrell Turner Garrett
p437 . . . . Woking 01483 755609
MacLeish Littlestone Cowan
p57. . . . . Redbridge 020 8514 3000
McManus Seddon
p154 . . . . Bradford 01274 741841
Hamish M McMillan
p57. . . . . . . London EC4 020 7430 1789
Magrath LLP
p57. . . . . London W1 020 7495 3003
Malletts Solicitors
p58. . . . . . . London WC1 020 7061 3760
Martin-Kaye LLP
p409 . . . . Telford 01952 272222
Massers
p338 . . . . Nottingham 0115 851 1666
p427 . . . . . . West Bridgford 0115 851 1666
Maunsell Bower
p59. . . . . Wandsworth 020 7378 9592
Maxwell Hodge Solicitors
p227 . . . . Formby 01704 872156
p298 . . . . Maghull 0151 526 7131
Meesons
p364 . . . . Ringwood 01425 472315
Midwinters
p188 . . . . Cheltenham 01242 514674
Miller Sands
p175 . . . . Cambridge 01223 202345
Minaides Robson
p61. . . . . . . London EC4 020 7831 7761
Moran & Co
p407 . . . . Tamworth 01827 54631
Morecrofts Solicitors LLP
p203 . . . . Crosby 0151 924 9234
John Morgan & Partners
p319 . . . . Mountain Ash 01443 473708
Morrisons Solicitors LLP
p62. . . . . . . London SW19 020 8971 1020
Morton Solicitors
p214 . . . . Dunstable 01582 501240

Mugford & Co
p224 . . . . Fareham 01329 844555
Mulcare Jenkins
p246 . . . . . Haywards Heath 01444 459954
D J Murphy Solicitors
p180 . . . . Cardiff 029 2022 1300
Murray Roach Solicitors
p320 . . . . . Nailsea 01275 858266 / 852705
Nalders Quality Solicitors
p329 . . . . Newquay 01637 871414
Napthens LLP
p146 . . . . Blackpool 01253 622305
Ian Newbery & Co
p353 . . . . Poole 01202 669986
Newstead & Walker
p342 . . . . Otley 01943 461414
Norris & Miles
p409 . . . . Tenbury Wells 01584 810575
John O'Neill & Co
p232 . . . . Gosforth 0191 246 4000
O'Neill Solicitors
p326 . . Newcastle upon Tyne 0191 232 9008
Oberman Law
p64. . . . . Camden 020 7242 6154
Osmond & Osmond
p65. . . . . . . London EC4 020 7583 3434
Ouvry Creed Solicitors
p410 . . . . Tetbury 01666 504005
Ouvry Goodman & Co
p403 . . . . Sutton 020 8642 7571
Nigel Owen & Co
p193 . . . . Chislehurst 020 8295 1989
Page Gulliford & Gregory Limited
p386 . . . . Southampton 023 8022 5821
Palmers Solicitors
p267 . Kingston upon Thames 020 8549 7444
Parker Bullen
p371 . . . . Salisbury 01722 412000
Parkes Wilshire Johnson
p124 . . . . Barnet 020 8441 1556
Parmars
p293 . . . . . . Loughborough 01509 261823
W Parry & Co
p405 . . . . Swansea 01792 470037
Partridge & Wilson
p171 . . . . . Bury St Edmunds 01284 762281
Patwa Solicitors
p129 . . . . Bearwood 0121 429 8666
Bernard Pearce & Co
p219 . . . . Enfield 020 8804 5271
Peter Peter & Wright
p168 . . . . Bude 01288 352101
Peters Langsford Davies
p270 . . . . Launceston 01566 772451
Petersons
p329 . . . . Newport 01633 255151
Powell Eddison Freeman & Wilks
p240 . . . . Harrogate 01423 564551
Price & Kelway
p316 . . . . Milford Haven 01646 695311
Pritchard Englefield
p69. . . . . London EC2 020 7972 9720
Pritchard Joyce & Hinds
p129 . . . . Beckenham 020 8658 3922
Protopapas
p69. . . . . London W1 020 7636 2100
Quality Solicitors Mewies
p381 . . . . Skipton 01756 799000
QualitySolicitors D'Angibau
p151 . . . . Boscombe 01202 393506
Queens Solicitors
p281 . . . . Leicester 0116 274 7927
Rainer Hughes
p156 . . . . Brentwood 01227 226644
Ramsdens Solicitors
p238 . . . . Halifax 01422 330700
Randle Thomas LLP
p246 . . . . Helston 01326 572951
Read Dunn Connell
p154 . . . . Bradford 01274 723858
Redferns
p430 . . . Weymouth 01305 781401 / 782704
Richard Reed
p402 . . . . Sunderland 0191 567 0465
Scott Rees & Co
p381 . . . . Skelmersdale 01695 722222
Rich & Carr Freer Bouskell
p281 . . . . Leicester 0116 253 8021
Risdon Hosegood
p408 . . . . Taunton 01823 251571
p436 . . . . Wiveliscombe 01984 623203
Rix & Kay Solicitors LLP
p255 . . . . Hove 01273 329797
Alan Roberts & Co
p191 . . . . Chester 01244 562754
Jeremy Roberts & Co
p347 . Peterborough 01733 343943 / 342172
Roberts McCracken
p72. . . . . Brent 0870 420 5658
Paul Robinson Solicitors
p428 . . . . . Westcliff-on-Sea 01702 338338
Rodgers & Burton
p73. . . . . . . London SW13 020 8939 6300

Rollasons
p207 . . . . Daventry 01327 301771
Rothwell & Evans
p407 . . . . Swinton 0161 794 1830
Rowberry Morris
p393 . . . . Staines 01784 457655
Royce Marshall & Co
p363 . . . . Retford 07765 404753
Roythornes LLP
p338 . . . . Nottingham 0115 948 4555
Rubin Lewis O'Brien
p206 . . . . Cwmbran 01633 867000
Russell & Russell
p315 . . . . Middleton 0161 653 6200
Russell-Cooke LLP
p74. . . . . . . London SW15 020 8789 9111
SLP Solicitors
p394 . . . . Stanmore 020 8420 7950
Samuels Solicitors
p125 . . . . Barnstaple 01271 343457
Sanders Witherspoon LLP
p156 . . . . Brentwood 01277 221010
D R Sceats Solicitor
p402 . . . . Surbiton 020 8399 5457
Brian L Senter
p399 . . . . Stourbridge 01384 375649
Atul Shah
p424 . . . . Wealdstone 020 8861 5000
Sharpes
p77. . . . . London E4 020 8527 2388
Sheehans Solicitors
p353 . . . . Port Talbot 01639 883237
Sherwood Wheatley
p267 . Kingston upon Thames 020 8546 0144
Sidhu & Co
p142 . . . . Birmingham 07831 293903
Silverman Sherliker LLP
p78. . . . . London EC2 020 7749 2700
Silvesters Solicitors
p213 . . . . Dudley 01384 240880
Simmons Stein
p394 . . . . Stanmore 020 8954 8080
Simon & Co
p384 . . . . Southall 020 8571 3883
Simpson Millar LLP
p80. . . . . London EC1 0844 858 3400
Sinclairs
p80. London NW4 020 8202 8222 / 8202 2042
Slater Heelis Collier Littler
p370 . . . . Sale 0161 969 3131
Martyn Slocombe & Co
p300 . . . . Malvern 01684 574001
Smith Bates
p296 . . . . Lyndhurst 023 8028 3414
Smith Jones Solicitors
p264 . . . . Kenilworth 01926 859933
Smith Law Partnership
p155 . . . . Braintree 01376 321311
SmithJones Solicitors Ltd
p169 . . . . Burnley 01282 855400
Sookias & Sookias
p80. . . . . London W1 020 7465 8000
Stanley & Co
p427 . . . . Wembley 020 8903 7864
Steeles
p211 . . . . Diss 01379 652141
Stephens & Scown
p391 . . . . St Austell 01726 74433
p414 . . . . Truro 01872 265100
Peter Steward & Co
p234 . . . . . Great Yarmouth 01493 332277
Stone & Stone
p318 . . . . Morden 020 8540 2202
Stone Rowe Brewer LLP
p416 . . . . Twickenham 020 8891 6141
Sykes Lee & Brydson
p445 . . . . York 01904 529000
p445 . . . . York 01904 731100
TMJ Legal Services LLP
p434 . . . . Wingate 01429 838225
Talbot & Co
p170 . . . . Burton-on-Trent 01283 564716
Tassells
p225 . . . . Faversham 01795 533337
Terrells LLP
p347 . . . . Peterborough 01733 896789
Thomson Webb & Corfield
p176 . . . . Cambridge 01223 578070
Tierney & Co
p210 . . . . Dinnington 01909 550730
Tilbrook's
p193 . . . . . Chipping Ongar 01277 896000
Tinsdills
p239 . . . . Hanley 01782 262031
Trinity Solicitors LLP
p88. . . . . London NW1 020 7428 0880
Trobridges
p350 . . . . Plymouth 01752 664022
p412 . . . . Torpoint 01752 812787
Sue Tuck & Co
p88. . . Kensington & Chelsea 020 7385 7733
Turnbull Garrard
p379 . . Shrewsbury 01743 350851 / 351332

Jay Vadher & Co
p89 . . . London E15 020 8519 3000
Van Baaren & Wright
p364 Richmond upon Thames 020 8940 2525
Vyman Solicitors
p233 . . . Gravesend 01474 537270
Walsh & Company
p414 . . . Truro 01872 870923
A M Walters & Co
p261 . . . Ilford 020 8551 5894
Walters & Barbary
p173 . . . Camborne 01209 712454
Warners Solicitors
p374 . . . Sevenoaks 01732 747900
p412 . . . Tonbridge 01732 770660
Wartnabys
p312 . . . Market Harborough 01858 463322
Watmores
p90 . . . London WC2 020 7430 1512
David Webb & Co
p428 . . . Westcliff-on-Sea 01702 392939
Weightmans LLP
p281 . . . Leicester 0116 253 9747
Simon West
p128 . . . Bath 01225 482001
Alan Wheatley
p442 . . . Worthing 01903 216116
Whetter Duckworth Fowler
p266 . . . Kidlington 01865 842100
Whittingdales
p91 . . . London WC2 020 7831 5591
Matthew Wilkinson Solicitors Ltd
p315 . . . Middlesbrough 01642 218888
L G Williams & Prichard
p181 . . . Cardiff 029 2022 9716
Wills Chandler
p127 . . . Basingstoke 01256 322911
Wilmot & Co Solicitors LLP
p195 . . . Cirencester 01285 650551
Wilson & Bird
p121 . . . Aylesbury 01296 436766
Wilsons
p358 . . . Pudsey 0113 236 2333
Wismayers
p233 . . . Great Bookham 01372 451114
Wollen Michelmore Solicitors
p330 . . . Newton Abbot 01626 332266
Woodfines LLP
p130 . . . Bedford 01234 270600
p176 . . . Cambridge 01223 411421
p372 . . . Sandy 01767 680251
Worger Howcroft
p133 . . . Bingley 01274 511246
Wragge & Co LLP
p93 . . . London EC1 0870 903 1000
Wylie Kay
p147 . . . Blackpool 01253 296297
P H Yeung
p93 . . . London W1 020 7287 1882
Peter Zelnik & Co
p133 . . . Biggin Hill 01959 570730

LOCAL GOVERNMENT

Adams
p323 . . . Newcastle upon Tyne 0191 261 0361
Berrymans Lace Mawer
p135 . . . Birmingham 0121 643 8777
p286 . . . Liverpool 0151 236 2002
p385 . . . Southampton 023 8023 6464
James Button & Co
p313 . . . Matlock 01629 735566
Leonie Cowen & Associates
p23 . . . London NW6 020 7604 5870
DMH Stallard LLP
p159 . . . Brighton 01273 329833
p202 . . . Crawley 01293 605000
Langleys
p284 . . . Lincoln 01522 888555
Merrett & Co
p163 . . . Bristol 01275 331228
Geoffrey Searle Planning Solicitors
p133 . . . Billericay 01277 633014

MENTAL HEALTH

Atteys
p363 . . . Retford 01777 713355
Banner Jones
p192 . . . Chesterfield 01246 861250
Elliott Bridgman
p409 . . . Telford 01952 684544
Julie Burton
p122 . . . Bangor 01248 364750
CMHT Solicitors
p167 . . . Brownhills 01543 372347
Campbell-Taylor Solicitors
p18 . . . Hackney 0845 567 2457
Cartwright King
p336 . . . Nottingham 0115 958 7444
Chronnell Hibbert
p259 . . . Hyde 0161 368 3434
Clark Willis
p206 . . . Darlington 01325 281111
Clifford Johnston & Co
p302 . . . Manchester 0161 249 2700
Confreys
p177 . . . Cardiff 029 2045 8080
Sharon Coomber
p197 . . . Colchester 01206 769342
DLC Solicitors Limited
p207 . . . Darwen 01254 761234
Elwyn Jones & Co
p122 . . . Bangor 01248 370224
Fish & Co
p438 . . . Wolverhampton 01902 826464
Grahame Stowe Bateson
p274 . . . Leeds 0113 246 8163
Maureen P Grenville
p214 . . . Duffield 01332 841789
John F Harrison
p118 . . . Ashby-de-la-Zouch 01530 563655
Hills (Oldham)
p340 . . . Oldham 0161 652 3231
Hogans
p356 . . . Prescot 0151 430 7529
Irvings Solicitors
p209 . . . Derby 01332 346036
Kaim Todner Ltd
p119 . . . Ashford 01233 662002
p47 . . . Islington 020 7700 0070
p47 . . . London EC4 020 7353 6660
p47 . . . London SE17 020 7701 4747
Keppe Rofer
p156 . . . Brecon 01874 624627
KieranClarkeGreen
p394 . . . Staveley 01246 280099
Knapman & Co
p345 . . . Paignton 01803 522700
McCarthy & White
p411 . . . Thornbury 01454 413696
Tina MacInnes
p404 . . . Swanage 01929 427227
Andrew Markham & Co
p182 . . . Carmarthen 01267 221550 / 236199
Meikles
p397 . . . Stockton-on-Tees 01740 620255
Murrays
p148 . . . Bodmin 01208 72863
Myer Wolff
p257 . . . Hull 01482 223693
Needham Poulier & Partners
p63 . . . London N17 020 8808 6622
O'Donnells
p357 . . . Preston 01772 881000
R J Osborne & Co
p199 . . . Corby 01536 204111
Oxford Law Group
p344 . . . Oxford 01865 297300
Margaret Payne
p182 . . . Carlisle 01228 521383
Pickup & Scott
p121 . . . Aylesbury 01296 397794
Prester Coleman & Co
p332 . . . Northampton 01604 633133
Punch Robson
p315 . . . Middlesbrough 01642 230700
p315 . . . Middlesbrough 01642 298830
Red Kite Law
p410 . . . Tenby 01834 842122
Roebucks
p145 . . . Blackburn 01254 274000
Sedgwick Phelan & Partners
p315 . . . Middleton 0161 653 5299
Sills & Betteridge LLP
p151 . . . Boston 01205 364615
Southerns
p169 . . . Burnley 01282 438446
Steel & Shamash
p82 . . . Lambeth 020 7803 3999
Wessex Solicitors Chambers Ltd
p355 . . . Portsmouth 023 9238 1114
Williscroft & Co
p155 . . . Bradford 01274 305380

MERGERS & ACQUISITIONS

Addleshaw Goddard
p4 . . . London EC1 020 7606 8855
Addlestone Keane Solicitors
p271 . . . Leeds 0113 244 6700
Arnold Fooks Chadwick LLP
p7 . . . London W1 020 7499 3007
Ashurst LLP
p7 . . . London EC2 020 7638 1111
BPE Solicitors LLP
p187 . . . Cheltenham 01242 224433
Baxter Caulfield
p255 . . . Huddersfield 01484 519519
Bennett Griffin
p441 . . . Worthing 01903 229925
Bevan Brittan LLP
p12 . . . London EC4 0870 194 1000
Black Norman
p203 . . . Crosby 0151 931 2777
Blackhams Solicitors
p135 . . . Birmingham 0121 233 6900
Boodle Hatfield
p14 . . . London W1 020 7629 7411
p343 . . . Oxford 01865 790744
Brooke North LLP
p272 . . . Leeds 0113 283 2100
CVS Solicitors
p17 . . . London W1 020 7493 2903
James Chan & Co
p19 . . . London EC4 0844 848 9988
Charles Russell LLP
p343 . . . Oxford 0845 359 0090
Clark Holt
p406 . . . Swindon 01793 617444
Cottrill Stone Lawless
p302 . . . Manchester 0161 835 3681
Curtis
p349 . . . Plymouth 01752 204444
DAC Beachcroft
p303 . . . Manchester 0161 934 3000
Davies Battersby Ltd
p26 . . . London EC3 020 7621 1090
Dootsons LLP
p282 . . . Leigh 01942 673431
EMW
p316 . . . Milton Keynes 0845 070 6000
Evans Dodd LLP
p30 . . . London W1 020 7491 4729
Faegre & Benson LLP
p30 . . . London EC4 020 7450 4500
Field Fisher Waterhouse LLP
p31 . . . London EC3 020 7861 4000
Fisher Jones Greenwood LLP
p186 . . . Chelmsford 01245 890110
Forshaws Davies Ridgway LLP
p422 . . . Warrington 01925 230000
Fox Williams
p33 . . . London EC2 020 7628 2000
Gannons Limited
p35 . . . Camden 020 7438 1060
Gateley LLP
p138 . . . Birmingham 0121 234 0000
Geldards LLP
p337 . . . Nottingham 0115 983 3650
Gregory Rowcliffe Milners
p37 . . . London WC1 020 7242 0631
Grindeys LLP
p398 . . . Stone 01785 810780
hlw Keeble Hawson LLP
p376 . . . Sheffield 0114 276 5555
Hamlins LLP
p38 . . . London W1 020 7355 6000
Harris Cartier LLP
p39 . . . London WC2 020 7405 7100
p382 . . . Slough 01753 810710
Harrisons Solicitors LLP
p425 . . . Welshpool 01938 552545
Hart Jackson Hall Smith
p325 . . . Newcastle upon Tyne 0191 261 5181
Harvey Ingram Borneos
p130 . . . Bedford 01234 353221
p317 . . . Milton Keynes 01908 696002
Henmans LLP
p343 . . . Oxford 01865 781000
Jefferies Essex LLP
p428 . . . Westcliff-on-Sea 01702 332311
Kemp Little LLP
p48 . . . London EC2 020 7600 8080
Kerman & Co LLP
p49 . . . London WC2 020 7539 7272
Kingsley Napley
p50 . . . London EC1 020 7814 1200
Lawson Coppock & Hart
p306 . . . Manchester 0161 832 5944
Laytons
p236 . . . Guildford 01483 407000
p52 . . . London EC4 020 7842 8000
Lee & Priestley LLP
p275 . . . Leeds 0845 129 2300
Lupton Fawcett
p275 . . . Leeds 0113 280 2000
Lyons Wilson
p307 . . . Manchester 0161 830 7777
McGrigors LLP
p56 . . . London EC4 020 7054 2500
Alan Mann & Co
p390 . . . St Albans 01727 833281 / 846012
Matthew Arnold & Baldwin LLP
p423 . . . Watford 01923 202020
Max Bitel Greene LLP
p59 . . . Islington 020 7354 2767
Merritt & Co
p443 . . . Yarm 01642 885555
Mincoffs Solicitors LLP
p325 . . . Newcastle upon Tyne 0191 281 6151
H Montlake & Co
p260 . . . Ilford 020 8532 4800
Moorcrofts LLP
p313 . . . Marlow 01628 470000
Morgan Lewis & Bockius
p61 . . . London EC4 020 3201 5000
Morrison & Foerster (UK) LLP
p62 . . . London EC2 020 7920 4000
Moss Solicitors LLP
p293 . . . Loughborough 01509 217770
Mowll & Mowll
p213 . . . Dover 01304 873344
Mullis & Peake
p366 . . . Romford 01708 784000
Mundays LLP
p196 . . . Cobham 01932 590500
Nabarro LLP
p63 . . . London WC1 020 7524 6000
Nellen
p63 . . . London W1 020 7499 8122
Oglethorpe Sturton & Gillibrand
p270 . . . Lancaster 01524 846846
Openshaws
p132 . . . Bideford 01237 478900
P B & W Solicitors LLP t/a Pooley Bendall & Watson
p218 . . . Ely 01353 666075
Parkinson Wright LLP
p440 . . . Worcester 01905 726789
Pinsent Masons LLP
p67 . . . London EC2 020 7418 7000
Preston-Rouse & Co
p69 . . . Camden 020 7269 9020
RMPI Solicitors
p70 . . . London W1 020 7318 4444
Rollingsons
p73 . . . London EC1 020 7611 4848
Rooks Rider
p73 . . . London EC1 020 7689 7000
SJ Berwin LLP
p75 . . . London EC4 020 7111 2222
Seddons
p77 . . . London W1 020 7725 8000
Sidley Austin Brown & Wood
p78 . . . London EC2 020 7360 3600
Sims Cook & Teague
p165 . . . Bristol 0117 927 2141
Skadden Arps Slate Meagher & Flom (UK) LLP
p80 . . . London E14 020 7519 7000
Martyn Slocombe & Co
p300 . . . Malvern 01684 574001
Spratt Endicott
p122 . . . Banbury 01295 204000
Stamp Jackson and Procter
p258 . . . Hull 01482 324591
Swinburne & Jackson LLP
p423 . . . Washington 0191 416 0004
Taylor Wessing
p86 . . . London EC4 020 7300 7000
Turner Parkinson
p310 . . . Manchester 0161 833 1212
Vyman Solicitors
p242 . . . Harrow 020 8427 9080
Warner Goodman LLP
p387 . . . Southampton 023 8063 9311
Weightmans LLP
p311 . . . Manchester 0161 233 7330
Wheelers
p115 . . . Aldershot 01252 316316
WilmerHale
p92 . . . London EC2 020 7645 2400
p344 . . . Oxford 01235 823000
Woollastons
p404 . . . Sutton Coldfield 0121 355 5516
Zaiwalla & Co
p93 . . . London WC2 020 7312 1000

MINES, MINERALS, OIL & GAS

Bentley Solicitors
p203 . . . Crewe 01270 509800
Andrew Bryce & Co
p174 . . . Cambridge 01223 437011

PENSIONS, INVESTMENTS & FINANCIAL SERVICES

Bells Solicitors
p224 . . . Farnham 01252 733733
Eric Cowsill Solicitor
p263 . . . Ivybridge 01752 205202
Girlings
p177 . . . Canterbury 01227 768374
Matthew John Green
p253 . . . Horsham 01403 210200
Sacker & Partners LLP
p76 . . . London EC2 020 7329 6699
M A Shepherd & Co
p78 . . . London N3 020 8343 2346

See p542 for the Firms Specialisations

Wiggin Osborne Fullerlove
p189 . . . . Cheltenham 01242 710200
Wrigleys Solicitors LLP
p278 . . . . Leeds 0113 244 6100

PLANNING, COMPULSORY PURCHASE, LANDS TRIBUNAL

Adams
p323 . . Newcastle upon Tyne 0191 261 0361
Armitage & Co
p220 . . . . . Exeter 01392 251364 / 214786
Alan Ashley & Co
p7 . . . . London EC4 020 7822 7482
C M Brand
p249 . . . . Heswall 0151 342 3081
John S Brearley
p249 . . . . . High Wycombe 01494 512775
C M Broadbent
p297 . . . . Macclesfield 01625 500038
Richard Buxton
p174 . . . . Cambridge 01223 328933
Carter Lemon Camerons
p18. . . . . London EC1 020 7406 1000
Dakers Marriott Solicitors
p400 . . . . Strood 01634 813300
Davitt Jones Bould
p408 . . . . Taunton 01823 279279
Downs
p231 . . . . Godalming 01483 861848
Ellis-Fermor & Negus
p364 . . . . Ripley 01773 744744
Elvin & Co
p293 . . . . . . Loughborough 01509 852454
Espilon Solicitors
p341 . . . . Ormskirk 01704 894945
FBC Manby Bowdler LLP
p409 . . . . Telford 01952 292129
Fahm & Co
p147 . . . . Blackwood 01495 224973
Horsey Lightly
p43. . . . . London W1 020 7222 8844
p322 . . . . Newbury 01635 580858
Horsey Lightly Fynn
p152 . . . . Bournemouth 01202 551991
Hossacks
p265 . . . . Kettering 01536 518638
A L Hughes & Co
p43. . . . . . . London SW16 020 8769 7100
Humphreys & Co
p163 . . . . Bristol 0117 929 2662
Jameson & Hill
p248 . . . . Hertford 01992 554881
Kingsley Smith Solicitors LLP
p185 . . . . Chatham 01634 811118
Knights
p415 . . . . . Tunbridge Wells 01892 537311
Lages & Co
p418 . . . . Wadhurst 01892 784419
Merrett & Co
p163 . . . . Bristol 01275 331228
Nalders Quality Solicitors
p246 . . . . Helston 01326 574001
Osborne Clarke
p65. . . . . . . London EC2 020 7105 7000
Osborns
p198 . . Colwyn Bay 01492 532056 / 532820
Ramsdens Solicitors
p256 . . . . Huddersfield 01484 821500
Peter Roberts Solicitor
p116 . . . . Alrewas 01283 790045
Russell-Cooke LLP
p74. . . . . . . London WC1 020 7405 6566
Geoffrey Searle Planning Solicitors
p133 . . . . Billericay 01277 633014
Stafford Eales
p442 . . . Wotton-under-Edge 0117 370 0500
Thurloe & Lyndhurst LLP
p87. . . . . . . London WC2 0333 123 2255
Wall James Chappell
p399 . . . . Stourbridge 01384 371622
Malcolm A H M Williamson
p225 . . . . Farnham 0845 230 1022

PRINTING & PUBLISHING

CIPIT Solicitors
p17. . . . . . . London NW3 020 8457 7457
Manches LLP
p58. . . . . . . London WC2 020 7404 4433

PROFESSIONAL NEGLIGENCE

Anthony Gold
p6 . . . . . . London SW16 020 7940 4000
Bankside Law Ltd
p9 . . . . London SE1 0844 745 4000
Bentley Solicitors
p203 . . . . Crewe 01270 509800
Berrymans Lace Mawer
p12. . . . . London EC2 020 7638 2811
p301 . . . . Manchester 0161 236 2002
Bhakar Tomlinson
p425 . . . . Wellington 01952 270555
Campbell Courtney & Cooney
p173 . . . . Camberley 01276 25100
Carter-Ruck
p18. . . . . London EC4 020 7353 5005
Clausen Miller LLP
p20. . . . . . . London EC3 020 7645 7970
Cooper Whiteman
p22. . . . . . . London WC1 020 7831 5222
Dewar Hogan
p27. . . . . . . London EC4 020 7634 9550
Dodd Lewis Solicitors
p27. . . . . . . London SE3 020 8852 1255
Fairchild Greig
p30. . . . . London W3 020 8993 6886
Fleet Solicitors LLP
p162 . . . . Bristol 0845 603 3273
p188 . . . . Cheltenham
Glynns Solicitors
p162 . . . . Bristol 01761 490883
Goldkorn Mathias Gentle Page LLP
p36. . . . . . . London WC1 020 7631 1811
Graystons
p435 . . . . Wirral 0151 645 0055
Hansen Palomares
p38. . . . . Lambeth 020 7640 4600
Hockfield & Co
p41. . . . . Lambeth 020 7582 8784
Hodge Jones & Allen LLP
p41. . . . . London NW1 020 7874 8300
Loveday & Keighley
p313 . . . . . Matlock 01629 583142 / 56660
MSB Solicitors LLP
p289 . . . . Liverpool 0151 281 9040
Neil McCormick
p228 . . . . Frome 01373 455700
Owen White
p382 . . . . Slough 01753 876800
PCB Litigation LLP
p65. . . . . . . London EC1 020 7831 2691
Parlett Kent
p222 . . . . Exeter 01392 494455
p66. . . . . London EC1 020 7430 0712
Reynolds Porter Chamberlain LLP
p71. . . . . London E1 020 3060 6000
Rosling King
p73. . . . . . . London EC4 020 7353 2353
Russell-Cooke LLP
p74. . . . . . . London SW15 020 8789 9111
Stockler Brunton
p83. . . . . London EC4 020 7404 6661
David Tagg & Co
p85. . . . . . . London SW6 020 7736 0999
Thornleys Limited
p350 . . . . Plymouth 01752 406977
Simon West
p128 . . . . Bath 01225 482001
Matthew Wilkinson Solicitors Ltd
p315 . . . . . . Middlesbrough 01642 218888

PROPERTY - FINANCE, DEVELOPMENT

Batchelors Solicitors
p166 . . . . Bromley 020 8768 7000
Brecher
p15. . . . . London W1 020 7563 1000
Burkill Govier
p224 . . . . Farnham 01252 717171
CKFT
p17. . . . . . . London NW3 020 7431 7262
Charsley Harrison LLP
p381 . . . . Slough 01753 517600
Davies & Partners
p115 . . . . . . Almondsbury 01454 619619
p137 . . . . Birmingham 0121 616 4450
p230 . . . . Gloucester 01452 612345
Devonshires
p27. . . . . London EC2 020 7628 7576
Dodd Lewis Solicitors
p27. . . . . . . London SE3 020 8852 1255
Evans Dodd LLP
p30. . . . . London W1 020 7491 4729
Foreman Laws
p251 . . . . Hitchin 01462 458711
J Garrard & Allen
p341 . . . . Olney 01234 711215
Hill Hofstetter LLP
p382 . . . . Solihull 0121 210 6000
Horsey Lightly
p43. . . . . London W1 020 7222 8844
Cyril Jones & Co
p443 . . . . Wrexham 01978 263131
Keelers
p264 . . . . Kenilworth 01926 853555
Kerseys
p262 . . . . Ipswich 01473 213311
Lennons
p189 . . . . Chesham 01494 773377
Lita Gale
p54. . . . . London W8 020 7404 2899
Maples Teesdale LLP
p58. . . . . London EC2 020 7600 3800
Peter J Miller
p60. . . . . Wandsworth 0870 321 7561
Morton Price
p376 . . . . Sheffield 0114 266 4141
Muckle LLP
p325 . . Newcastle upon Tyne 0191 211 7777
N Legal
p404 . . . . Sutton Coldfield 0121 355 8885
Osborne Clarke
p164 . . . . Bristol 0117 917 3000
p361 . . . . Reading 0118 925 2000
Plexus Law (A Trading Name of Parabis Law LLP)
p276 . . . . Leeds 0844 245 4100
Price Mears & Co
p365 . . . . Rochdale 01706 653331
QualitySolicitors Jackson & Canter
p290 . . . . Liverpool 0151 282 1700
Ronald Fletcher Baker LLP
p73. . . . . London EC1 020 7613 1402
Rosenblatt
p73. . . . . London EC4 020 7955 0880
Rosling King
p73. . . . . London EC4 020 7353 2353
Roythornes LLP
p327 . . . . Newmarket 01638 561320
p389 . . . . Spalding 01775 842500
Saunders Bearman LLP
p76. . . . . London W1 020 7224 2618
Sharratts (London) LLP
p429 . . . . Westerham 01959 568000
Stafford Eales
p442 . . . Wotton-under-Edge 0117 370 0500
Stones Solicitors LLP
p222 . . . . Exeter 01392 666777
Walker & Walker
p374 . . . . Sevenoaks 01732 450699

RACE & SEX DISCRIMINATION

Bulfin & Co Employment Law Solicitors
p348 . . . . Pinner 020 8866 0044
H N E Chesterfield
p162 . . . . Bristol 0117 968 8148
Dodd Lewis Solicitors
p27. . . . . London SE3 020 8852 1255
Dolmans
p178 . . . . Cardiff 029 2034 5531
Doyle Clayton Solicitors Limited
p27. . . . . London EC2 020 7329 9090
p360 . . . . Reading 0118 959 6839
Fisher Meredith
p32. . . . . Lambeth 020 7091 2700
Just Employment
p236 . . . . Guildford 01483 303636
A E Mizler & Co Solicitors
p349 . . . . Pinner 020 8420 1175
Oxford Employment Law Solicitors
p344 . . . . Oxford 01865 487136
Pattinson & Brewer
p66. . . . . London WC1 020 7400 5100
p445 . . . . York 01904 680000
Elizabeth Seeley
p77. . . . . Ealing 020 8840 2788
TPC Solicitors
p310 . . . . Manchester 0161 832 8867
Thompsons (formerly Robin/Brian Thompson & Partners)
p187 . . . . Chelmsford 01245 228800
p87. . . . . London WC1 020 7290 0000

RATING LAW

hlw Keeble Hawson LLP
p274 . . . . Leeds 0113 244 3121
p375 . . . . Sheffield 0114 272 2061

REGULATED BY THE FSA FOR INVESTMENT BUSINESS

Engleharts
p254 . . . . Hove 01273 204411
HT Legal Limited t/a Harrison Townend & Ormeshers
p259 . . . . Hyde 0161 368 1559
Harwood & Co
p440 . . . . Worcester 01905 420855
William Heath & Co
p40. . . . . London W1 020 7402 3151
Herbert Reeves & Co
p40. . . . . London EC2 020 7739 6660
Heydons
p355 . . . . Potters Bar 01707 879646
Hunters
p44. . . . . . . London WC2 020 7412 0050
Miles Preston & Co
p69. . . . . London EC4 020 7583 0583
Russell-Cooke LLP
p74. . . . . . . London SW15 020 8789 9111
Yarwood & Stubley
p148 . . . . Blyth 01670 361211

RESIDENTIAL CONVEYANCING

174 Law
p134 . . . . Birkenhead 0151 647 7372
ABS Solicitors
p243 . . . . Hastings 0845 083 0003
AGR Solicitors
p378 . . . . Shirebrook 01623 748522
A Halsall & Co
p134 . . . . Birkenhead 0151 647 6323
A Kay Pietron & Paluch
p3 . . . . Ealing 020 8992 9997
AMD Solicitors
p160 . . . . Bristol 0117 973 8205
AST Hampsons (incorporating Warhurst and co)
p170 . . . . Bury 0161 764 3317
Abbott Cresswell LLP
p3 . . . . London SW14 020 8876 4478
S Abraham Solicitors
p402 . . . . Surbiton 020 8390 0044
Acklam Bond Noor
p145 . . . . Blackburn 01254 56068
Act Legal
p159 . . . . Brighton 01273 565656
David Acton & Co
p382 . . . . Solihull 01564 730028
Adams Delmar
p238 . . . . Hampton 020 8941 2097
Adlams LLP
p258 . . . . Huntingdon 01480 458885
p392 . . . . St Neots 01480 474061
Adrian & Co
p4 . London NW5 020 7485 8450 / 7267 1240
Advance Legal
p170 . . . . Burton-on-Trent 01283 544492
The Affordable Law Co Ltd
p444 . . . . York 01904 788877
Akermans
p399 . . . . Storrington 01903 745353
p441 . . . . Worthing 01903 820413
Alan Turner & Co
p127 . . . . Bath 01225 336260
Alban Gould Baker & Co
p4 . . . . Islington 020 7607 5085
Alcock & Smalley
p297 . . . . Macclesfield 01625 431530
Aldridge Brownlee Solicitors LLP
p151 . . . . Bournemouth 01202 526343
p194 . . . . Christchurch 01425 282150
Alfred Truman
p167 . . . . Buckingham 01280 822217
Alker & Ball
p432 . . . . Wigan 01942 246241
Allan Jay Paine & Co
p5 . . . . Enfield 020 8886 1404
Allen Hoole Solicitors
p160 . . . . Bristol 0117 942 0901
Allens
p237 . . . . Halesworth 01986 875246
p354 . . . . Portsmouth 023 9282 2411
J P Almond & Co
p435 . . . . Wirral 0151 632 2336
Alsters Kelley
p199 . . . . Coventry 0844 561 0100
Alwena Jones & Jones
p147 . . . . Blaenau Ffestiniog 01766 831882
p416 . . . . Tywyn 01654 711499
Ambrose Appelbe
p6 . . . . London WC2 020 7242 7000
Amphlett Chatterton
p270 . . . . . Leamington Spa 01926 311427
Amphletts
p198 . . . . Colwyn Bay 01492 532296
Anami Law Iincorporating Kirkwoods
p171 . . . . Bushey 020 8950 1155
Anderson Longmore & Higham
p133 . . . . Billingshurst 01403 782710
p348 . . . . Petworth 01798 342391
p399 . . . . Storrington 01903 745666
Michael Anderson & Co
p430 . . . . Whickham 0191 488 1221
Andersons Solicitors
p239 . . . . Harrogate 01423 527852
Andrew & Andrew Solicitors
p354 . . . . Portsmouth 023 9266 1381
Andrews Martin
p406 . . . . Swindon 01793 641707

See p542 for the Firms Specialisations

Calvert Solicitors
p17 Southwark 020 7234 0707
Campbell Courtney & Cooney
p173 Camberley 01276 25100
Camps Solicitors
p134 Birkenhead 0151 201 8080
Henry Cane & Son
p159 Brighton 01273 604091
Caplans
p241 Harrow 020 8864 0111
Irving Caplin & Co
p18 Wandsworth 020 8874 7633
Carlsons
p18 London N20 020 8445 3331 / 8445 5752
Carlyon & Son
p414 Truro 01872 278641
Carr & Co
p147 Blyth 01670 351251
p231 Gosforth 0191 284 0363
p255 Huddersfield 01484 467860
p319 Morpeth 01670 515182
Carver Jones
p247 Hereford 01432 274301
Caswell Jones
p172 Caerphilly 029 2086 4888
Cathcarts
p259 Ickenham 01895 631942 / 675631
Caunters
p285 Liskeard 01579 343165 / 343484
J P Cave & Co
p410 Thame 01844 216208
Caversham Solicitors Ltd
p360 Reading 0118 947 8638
Cedars & Co
p19 Greenwich 020 8331 6161
Chadwick Lawrence
p418 Wakefield 01924 379078
Lee Chadwick & Co
p436 Witney 01993 703272
Challenor Gardiner
p343 Oxford 01865 721451
Chamberlains
p144 Bishop's Waltham 01489 896141
Chamberlins
p129 Beccles 01502 713131
p172 Caister-on-Sea 01493 720019
p234 Great Yarmouth 01493 600113
p234 Great Yarmouth 01493 857621
p251 Hitchin 01462 623456
Chambers Fletcher LLP
p333 Northwich 01606 780400
Chandler Ray
p167 Buckingham 01280 814040
Chanter Ferguson
p125 Barnstaple 01271 342268
Susan Chapman
p320 Nailsea 01275 401996
Charles Coleman LLP
p434 Windsor 01753 861115
Charlesworth Nicholl & Co
p203 Crediton 01363 774706
Charsley Harrison LLP
p381 Slough 01753 517600
Chattertons Solicitors
p252 Horncastle 01507 522456
p389 Spalding 01775 768774
Chawner Grey & Co
p429
Weston-super-Mare 01934 417768 / 623541
Cheethams
p345 Penkridge 01785 714761
Francis H Chenery
p210 Diss 01379 644055
Chequers Solicitors Ltd
p245 Hayes 020 8606 1000
Cheswortths
p397 Stoke-on-Trent 01782 599993
Chhokar & Co
p384 Southall 020 8574 2488
Chilcotts
p408 Tavistock 01822 612535 / 614242
Chisholms
p418 Wadebridge 01208 812470 / 814205
Chubb Bulleid
p400 Street 01749 836100
p425 Wells 01749 836100
Chung & Platt
p302 Manchester 0161 228 6777
Churchers
p232 Gosport 023 9260 3400
p271 Lee-on-the-Solent 023 9255 1500
Clark & Weeks
p263 Ivybridge 01752 698869
p349 Plymouth 01752 345311
Anthony Clark & Co
p284 Lincoln 01522 512321
Chris Clark
p176 Cannock 01543 573004
David Clark & Co
p20 London NW3 020 7433 1562
Clarkes
p425 Wellington 01952 223548
Clayton Mott
p336 Nottingham 0115 941 7422
Clayton Mott & Lawton
p404 Sutton-in-Ashfield 01623 556601
Claytons
p390 St Albans 01727 865765
Cleaver Thompson Ltd
p195 Clay Cross 01246 865048
Clement Hughes & Co
p356 Prestatyn 01745 852121
Cleverdons
p218 Enfield 020 8367 5375
Clifford Poole & Co
p370 Salford 0161 736 0160
Clifford Smith & Buchanan
p169 Burnley 01282 452611
p198 Colne 01282 860606
p320 Nelson 01282 693182
Clinton Davis Pallis
p21 London N8 020 8880 5000
Close Thornton
p206 Darlington 01325 466461
Cluley & Co
p434 Winsford 01606 553719
Clyde Chappell & Botham
p397 Stoke-on-Trent 01782 599577
Martin Coakley
p243 Haslemere 01428 648888
Coffin Mew & Clover
p232 Gosport 023 9252 3111
p354 Portsmouth 023 9238 8021
Cohen Filippini
p116 Altrincham 0161 929 9993
Colemans - CTTS
p124 Barnet 020 8441 1213
Coles Miller Solicitors LLP
p151 Bournemouth 01202 511512
p166 Broadstone 01202 694891
p352 Poole 01202 673011
Collins Dryland & Thorowgood LLP
p411 Tilehurst 0118 942 2448
Collis & Co
p22 Wandsworth 020 8767 3332
George Mitchell Colman & Co
p137 Birmingham 0121 427 7700
Conway & Co
p247 Henley-on-Thames 01491 411122
Coodes
p251 Holsworthy 01409 253425
p270 Launceston 01566 770000
p329 Newquay 01637 878111
p391 St Austell 01726 874700
Cook & Talbot
p388 Southport 01704 535216
Cook Taylor
p22 Greenwich 020 8854 1166
Cook Taylor Woodhouse
p22 London SE9 020 8859 0936
Cooke Painter Limited
p162 Bristol 01275 400037
p162 Bristol 01275 835569
Cooks
p323 Newcastle under Lyme 01782 611090
Cooper Son & Caldecott
p247 Henley-on-Thames 01491 574203
Cooper Sons Hartley & Williams
p172 Buxton 01298 77511
p184 Chapel-en-le-Frith 01298 812138
Copitch
p22 Haringey 020 8883 9831
Corbin & Hassan
p22 London 020 7247 6518
Corries Solicitors
p444 York 0845 241 5566
Hilary A Courtneidge
p248 Hertford 01992 589120
Cowles
p23 Croydon 020 8679 1811
Cowlishaw & Mountford
p417 Uttoxeter 01889 565211
Coxons
p427 West Bridgford 0115 981 2000
Cozens Moxon & Harts
p409 Teddington 020 8977 8486 / 8977 4424
Crabtree Chadwick
p358 Pudsey 0113 290 9499
Cracknells
p236 Guildford 01483 535558
Craigen Wilders & Sorrell
p23 London N8 020 8888 2255
Cramer Pelmont
p23 London N8 020 8340 0091
Crangle Edwards
p185 Cheadle 0161 428 2331
Crombie Wilkinson
p374 Selby 01757 708957
Charles Crookes with George Tudor & de Winton
p156 Brecon 01874 625151
David Cross & Co
p411 Thornbury 01454 419696
Cross Ram & Co
p237 Halesworth 01986 873636
Crossmans MTA
p174 Cambridge 01223 451442
Crowley & Co
p178 Cardiff 029 2045 8895
Cruickshanks Solicitors
p23 London W1 020 7487 4468
Crumplins
p23 Camden 020 7483 0282
Cumming Hodgkinson Dickinson
p148 Bolton 01204 523108 / 528396
N Cunliffe-Lister
p213 Driffield 01377 236006
Cunningtons
p155 Braintree 01376 326868
Curry Popeck
p264 Kenton 020 8907 2000 / 8907 8896
Curtis
p349 Plymouth 01752 204444
Curtis Parkinson
p336 Nottingham 0115 931 7000
Cuthbertsons
p119 Ashington 01670 813524
DBL Talbots LLP
p197 Codsall 01902 843427
p213 Dudley 01384 252471
p213 Dudley 01384 459551
p265 Kidderminster 01562 749910
p399 Stourbridge 01384 445850
p437 Wolverhampton 01902 427561
DJK Solicitors
p420 Waltham Abbey 01992 718880
DMB Law
p374 Sevenoaks 01732 228800
DP Law Ltd t/a David Prosser & Co
p157 Bridgend 01656 645921
Dale & Newbery LLP
p393 Staines 01784 464491
Dale-Lace & Co
p129 Beaconsfield 01494 675269
Martin C Dalton
p253 Horsham 01403 266642
Daltons
p215 Eastbourne 01323 720040
Daniel & Edwards
p359 Ramsgate 01843 594651
W H Darbyshire & Son
p146 Blackpool 01253 346646
Marie Dark Solicitors
p189 Chepstow 01291 621638
Darling & Stephensons
p123 Barnard Castle 01325 489000
Darlington Hardcastles
p364 Rickmansworth 01923 774272
Jeremy Davenport
p251 Hockley 01702 205163
Davey Franklin Jones
p195 Cirencester 01285 654875
p230 Gloucester 01452 508800
David & Snape
p157 Bridgend 01656 661115
Sheldon Davidson Solicitors
p430 Whitefield 0161 796 5445
Davies Bell & Reed
p324 Newcastle upon Tyne 0191 232 8058
Davies Blunden & Evans
p224 Farnborough 01252 541633
David H N Davies
p371 Salisbury 01722 322272
Hywel Davies & Co
p121 Bala 01678 520307
Jeremy Davies & Co
p26 London SW7 020 7589 4999
Davies Partnership
p389 St Agnes 01872 553131
Davies Prichard & Weatherill
p178 Cardiff 029 2037 7471
Davis & Co
p259 Ilford 020 8551 4228
Davis Blank Furniss
p230 Glossop 01457 860606
Davis Davidson
p131 Beverley 01482 881278
Davis Priest & Co
p362 Redditch 01527 69231
Davisons
p137 Birmingham 0121 685 1234
Dawson & Burgess with Bell Dallman & Co
p211 Doncaster 01302 834744
Graham Dawson & Co
p132 Bexley 01322 558811
Dawson Mason & Carr
p236 Guildford 01483 576169
Stanley De Leon
p355 Potters Bar 01707 657277
Dean & Co
p213 Dudley 01384 352525
p399 Stourbridge 01384 352525
Roger Dean & Co
p133 Biggin Hill 01959 542872
Samantha Denham Solicitors
p243 Hastings 01424 718822 / 719111
Denniss Matthews
p27 London SE20 020 8778 7301 / 8778 7631
Chris Denton
p168 Burley-in-Wharfedale 01943 607828
Devereux & Co
p162 Bristol 0117 959 3344
Dibbens
p433 Wimborne 01202 882456
Dickens & Co
p204 Crowthorne 01344 772901 / 776151
Dickinson Wood
p211 Doncaster 01302 329504
Dickson Haslam
p268 Kirkham 01772 685109
p356 Preston 01772 883100
Dicksons Solicitors Ltd
p397 Stoke-on-Trent 01782 262424
Dixon Coles & Gill
p418 Wakefield 01924 263166 / 263899
p418 Wakefield 01924 373467
Dixon Coles & Goddard
p279 Leicester 0116 236 4708
Dixon Rigby Keogh
p315 Middlewich 01606 835736
p333 Northwich 01606 48111
p434 Winsford 01606 557211
Dixon Stewart
p321 New Milton 01425 621515
Dodd Lewis Solicitors
p27 London SE3 020 8852 1255
Paul Dodds Solicitors
p419 Wallsend 0191 263 6200
Dollman & Pritchard
p183 Caterham 01883 347823
Donaldson Dunstall
p131 Bexhill 01424 216329
Donaldson West
p204 Crowborough 01892 662233
Adam Douglas & Son
p131 Berwick-upon-Tweed 01289 306479
Downey & Co
p153 Bradford 01274 883515
Downie & Gadban
p116 Alton 01420 82879
Draper & Co
p225 Farnham 01252 727374
Driver Belcher Solicitors
p385 Southampton 01489 785737
Drivers
p300 Malton 01653 600075
Drummonds
p190 Chester 01244 408300
Scott Duff & Co
p265 Keswick 01768 774321
p346 Penrith 01768 865551
Duffield Stunt
p186 Chelmsford 01245 262351
Valentine Duggins
p419 Wallasey 0151 638 4844
Dundas & Duce
p299 Maidstone 01622 681867
Dunham Guest & Lyons
p176 Cannock 01543 462121
Dunn & Co
p267 Kingston upon Thames 020 8541 1332
Peter Dunn & Co
p401 Sunderland 0191 568 9000
Sarah Dwight Solicitor
p137 Birmingham 0121 702 2100
Dyne Drewett Solicitors Ltd
p433 Wincanton 01963 32374
Eastleys
p166 Brixham 01803 853266
p413 Totnes 01803 864888
Eaves
p316 Milford Haven 01646 695785
Eccles Heddon
p365 Ripon 01765 601717
Eckford Rands
p331 Northampton 01604 621001
Eddowes Perry & Osbourne
p403 Sutton Coldfield 0121 686 9444
p403 Sutton Coldfield 0121 686 9666
Edmondson Hall
p327 Newmarket 01638 560556
Alan Edwards & Co
p28 Kensington & Chelsea 020 7221 7644
Martin Edwards
p378 Shifnal 01952 462118
Nigel Edwards & Co
p299 Maidstone 01622 690575
Eldridges
p328 Newport 01983 524741
Elliot Mather LLP
p311 Mansfield 01623 655666
Ellis & Co
p190 Chester 01244 319388
B K Ellis & Co
p150 Borehamwood 020 8386 8686
Ellis Jones
p352 Poole 01202 709898
p364 Ringwood 01425 484848
p404 Swanage 01929 422233
Ellis Lakin & Co
p348 Pickering 01751 472121

See p542 for the Firms Specialisations

Hayes & Storr
p251 . . . Holt 01263 712835
p425 . . . Wells-next-the-Sea 01328 710210
Hayes Clifford & Co
p411 . . . Tilehurst 0118 941 8416
Stanley Hays
p246 . . . Heckmondwike 01924 403809
Hayton Winkley
p264 . . . Kendal 01539 720136
Haywards
p399 . . . Stowmarket 01449 613631
Heath & Blenkinsop
p422 . . . Warwick 01926 492407
Heckford Norton
p370 . . . Saffron Walden 01799 522636
p395 . . . Stevenage 01438 312211
Hegarty LLP
p393 . . . Stamford 01780 752066
R W Hemmings & Co
p408 . . . Taunton 01823 325090
Henchleys
p285 . . . Littlehampton 01903 726477
Henleys
p126 . . . Basingstoke 01256 840084
Henriques Griffiths
p163 . . . Bristol 0117 965 9444
p435 . . . Winterbourne 01454 854000
M R Hepburn
p403 . . . Sutton Coldfield 0121 378 0440
Hepburns
p344 . . . Oxted 01883 723712
Heppenstalls
p321 . . . New Milton 01425 610078
Heptonstalls LLP
p255 . . . Howden 01430 430209
Herbert & Cholmeley
p122 . . . Banbury 01295 263556
Heringtons
p128 . . . Battle 01424 772401
Heseltine Bray & Welsh
p124 . . . Barnsley 01226 210777
Hethertons LLP
p445 . . . York 01904 528200
Hetts Johnson Whiting
p158 . . . Brigg 01652 655101
Hewitt Burrough & Co
p207 . . . Dartford 01322 273833
Hewitts
p203 . . . Crook 01388 762466
Hibberts LLP
p203 . . . Crewe 01270 215117
Higgs & Sons
p268 . . . Kingswinford 01384 342100
Hileys
p215 . . . Easingwold 01347 821234
Joseph Hill & Co
p41 . . . London N15 020 8880 3535
Hilton Norbury
p432 . . . Wigan 01942 241424
Mark Hoare
p189 . . . Chepstow 01291 630356
Antony Hodari & Co
p305 . . . Manchester 0161 832 4781
Hodders
p41 . . . London NW10 020 8965 9862
p41 . . . London SW11 020 7720 1647
John Hodge Solicitors
p429 . . . Weston-super-Mare 01934 623511
Hodgson & Angus
p394 . . . Stanhope 01388 528517
Hodgsons & Mortimer
p363 . . . Richmond 01748 850950
Charles Hoile
p322 . . . Newbury 01635 45595
Holden Son & Ullock
p411
. Thornton Cleveleys 01253 852613 / 862606
Linda Holloway & Co
p390 . . . St Albans 01727 841651
Holmes & Hills LLP
p155 . . . Braintree 01376 320456
p238 . . . Halstead 01787 475312
Antony A Holmes
p166 . . . Broadway 01386 858107
David Holmes & Co
p234 . . . Great Yarmouth 01493 658291
Holt & Longworth
p367 . . . Rossendale 01706 213251 / 229131
Philip Hook
p334 . . . Norwich 01603 250050
Hopkins
p311 . . . Mansfield 01623 468468
Hornby Baker Jones & Wood
p328 . . . Newport 01633 262848
Horne Engall & Freeman LLP
p217 . . . Egham 01784 432292
Hotchkiss Warburton
p203 . . . Crediton 01363 774752
John Hoult & Co
p373 . . . Scunthorpe 01724 281312
Houseman Benner
p246 . . . Haywards Heath 01444 414081

Howard & Co
p124 . . . Barnsley 01226 211888
p124 . . . Barnsley 01226 215215
Howard & Over
p263 . . . Ivybridge 01752 690123
p350 . . . Plymouth 01752 556606
Fiona M Howard
p43 . . . London NW1 020 7482 2705
Howard Schneider Spiro Steele
p124 . . . Barnet 020 8216 2020
Howarth & Co
p429 . . . Wetherby 01937 584020
The Howe Practice
p395 . . . Stockport 0161 480 2629
Howell Jones & Co
p113 . . . Abergele 01745 826282 / 825845
Howells
p178 . . . Cardiff 029 2040 4020
p405 . . . Swansea 01792 410016
Howlett Clarke Solicitors
p254 . . . Hove 01273 419728
Neil Hudgell Solicitors
p257 . . . Hull 01482 787771
Geoffrey Hueting & Co
p127 . . . Bath 01225 465828
Hughes & Company
p413 . . . Tring 01442 891717
J A Hughes
p126 . . . Barry 01446 411000
p179 . . . Cardiff 029 2061 9700
p345 . . . Penarth 029 2070 2449
Hughes Paddison
p188 . . . Cheltenham 01242 574244
Hughes-Narborough & Thomas
p43 . . . Greenwich 020 8854 1291
Nigel J Humes & Co
p191 . . . Chester-le-Street 0191 388 8737
Humfrys & Symonds
p248 . . . Hereford 01432 359261 / 276276
V L Humphreys & Co
p236 . . . Guildford 01483 574342
Humphries Kirk
p152 . . . Bournemouth 01202 421111
p212 . . . Dorchester 01305 251007
p352 . . . Poole 01202 715815
p421 . . . Wareham 01929 552141
Hunt & Hunt
p366 . . . Romford 01708 764433
Hunt & Lisners
p332 . . . Northampton 01604 846705
Hunters
p44 . . . London WC2 020 7412 0050
p413 . . . Towcester 01327 830895
Hunton & Garget
p364 . . . Richmond 01748 850400
Andrew Hurrell Solicitors
p131 . . . Benfleet 01702 558286
A C B Hurst & Co
p247 . . . Henley-on-Thames 01491 572699
E B Hurst
p442 . . . Worthing 01903 246818
Husband Forwood Morgan
p289 . . . Liverpool 0151 236 9626
Hutcheson Forrest
p127 . . . Bath 01225 312311
Nick Hutchinson & Co
p188 . . . Cheltenham 01242 261515
Hutsby Mees
p393 . . . Stafford 01785 259211
IBB Solicitors
p189 . . . Chesham 0845 638 1381
Ian N Gunby & Co
p316 . . . Milnthorpe 01539 562044
Inghams
p411 . . . Thornton Cleveleys 01253 824111
Ingrams
p257 . . . Hull 01482 358850
p445 . . . York 01904 520600
Insley & Partners
p225 . . . Ferndown 01202 876117
Isherwood & Hose
p249 . . . Heywood 01706 360032 / 368741
p365 . . . Rochdale 01706 359090 / 522225
Ismail & Ghani
p154 . . . Bradford 01274 737546
Ison Harrison
p228 . . . Garforth 0113 286 1455
p274 . . . Leeds 0113 232 6530
p274 . . . Leeds 0113 284 5000
Ives & Co
p337 . . . Nottingham 0115 937 2408
JPS Law Solicitors
p45 . . . London W1 020 7935 9955
Jackamans
p239 . . . Harleston 01379 854455
Jacklyn Dawson
p328 . . . Newport 01633 262952
Jackson & Co
p143 . . . Birstall 0116 267 6263
Arthur Jackson & Co
p367 . . . Rotherham 01709 363876
Jacksons
p435 . . . Wirral 0151 632 3386

Jacobs & Reeves
p353 . . . Poole 01202 674425
p433 . . . Wimborne 01202 880382
Stanley Jacobs
p46 . . . Barnet 020 8349 4241
Jacobsen & Co
p46 . . . London SW6 020 7736 6277
Gwyn James Solicitors
p195 . . . Cinderford 01594 822277
Walter Jennings & Sons
p46 . . . London NW5 020 7485 8626
Jepsen & Co
p271 . . . Leatherhead 01483 281720
Jeromes
p372 . . . Sandown 01983 402026
p374 . . . Shanklin 01983 862643
Jeya & Co
p46 . . . Newham 020 8552 1999
Jobling & Knape
p233 . . . Great Eccleston 01995 670083
Graeme John Solicitors
p446 . . . Ystradgynlais 01639 843404
Johns Gilbert & Frankton
p368 . . . Rugby 01788 576384
Johnson & Clarence
p316 . . . Midhurst 01730 812244
Gary Johnson & Co
p315 . . . Middlesbrough 01642 222834
Pamela K Johnson Solicitor
p355 . . . Poulton-le-Fylde 01253 812400
Cyril Jones & Co
p443 . . . Wrexham 01978 263131
Gordon Jones & Co
p139 . . . Birmingham 0121 453 8151
Jones Law Partnership
p313 . . . Marple 0161 426 0030
Jones Robertson
p369 . . . Runcorn 01928 711119
W T Jones
p47. London WC1 020 7405 4631 / 7242 7767
Jordans
p368 . . . Rowley Regis 0121 559 2922
Virginia Juras & Co
p166 . . . Bromley 020 8402 9403
Kagan Moss & Co
p409 . . . Teddington 020 8977 6633
Jane Kaim-Caudle & Co
p423 . . . Watford 01923 219061
Kaura & Co
p48 . . . London N12 020 8445 4069
Keane & Co
p115 . . . Aldeburgh 01728 453595
Alistair Keeble
p195 . . . Clacton-on-Sea 01255 818900
Andrew Keen & Co
p48 . . . London E18 020 8989 3123
Keene & Kelly
p318 . . . Mold 01352 753882
Kelly & Co
p275 . . . Leeds 0113 244 2113
Richard P Kemp BA Solicitor
p313 . . . Martock 01935 822572
Kendall & Davies
p153 . . Bourton-on-the-Water 01451 820277
p168 . . . Burford 01993 822025
p319 . . . Moreton-in-Marsh 01608 650312
p399 . . . Stow-on-the-Wold 01451 830295
Kent & Co Solicitors
p334 . . . Norwich 01493 751351
Kenwright Walker Wyllie
p215 . . . East Molesey 020 8979 1131
Keogh Caisley
p415 . . . Tunbridge Wells 01892 548411
Kevill Kirkham & Grayson
p194 . . . Chorley 01257 263676 / 269212
Kevills
p194 . . . Chorley 01257 265711
Christopher Key & Co
p150 . . . Boscastle 01840 250200
Khan & Co
p438 . . . Wolverhampton 01902 424477
Kidd & Spoor
p431 . . . Whitley Bay 0191 297 0011
Kidd Rapinet
p121 . . . Aylesbury 0845 017 9616
p49 . . . London WC2 020 7205 2115
p361 . . . Reading 0845 017 8750
Kidson Bray & Lawson
p251 . . . Hindhead 01428 605222
p49 . . . London SE11 020 7582 0111
KieranClarkeGreen
p394 . . . Staveley 01246 280099
King Davies & Partners
p298 . . . Maesteg 01656 732911
King Prior Macdonald Bridge
p233 . . . Gravesend 01474 325678
Kingsfords
p119 . . . Ashford 01233 665544
Kingswell Watts
p210 . . . Dewsbury 01924 461236
Kirby Sheppard
p163 . . . Bristol 0845 840 0045
p411 . . . Thornbury 0845 840 0045

Kirk & Partners
p50 . . . London SE9 020 8850 2484
Kirklands
p366 . . . Romsey 01794 513466
p413 . . . Totton 023 8066 3313
Kloosmans
p387 . . . Southend-on-Sea 01702 600090
Knapman & Co
p345 . . . Paignton 01803 522700
Knocker & Foskett
p374 . . . Sevenoaks 01732 459931
Krish Ratna
p384 . . . Southall 020 8574 6303
Kundert & Co
p200 . . . Coventry 024 7622 7741
p200 . . . Coventry 024 7668 4928
Robert Kyle & Co
p313 . . . Marlow 01628 475751
Laceys
p353 . . . Poole 01202 743286
Ladermans
p51 . . . London NW4 020 8203 6136
Lages & Co
p418 . . . Wadhurst 01892 784419
Lamb & Holmes
p199 . . . Corby 01536 745168
p265 . . . Kettering 01536 513195
Lambert Taylor & Gregory
p228 . . . Gateshead 0191 477 0616
Lamberts
p374 . . . Sevenoaks 01732 460565
Lancasters
p219 . . . Epsom 01372 724931
Bruce Lance & Co
p250 . . . High Wycombe 01494 450494
Landons
p156 . . . Brentwood 01277 210021
J S Lane & Co
p172 . . . Bushey 020 8950 1782
Langley Wellington
p195 . . . Churchdown 01452 856846
Langleys
p445 . . . York 01904 610886
Larby Williams with Gwyn & Gwyn
p201 . . . Cowbridge 01446 775535
Larcomes LLP
p354 . . . Portsmouth 023 9266 1531
Lattey & Dawe
p51 . . . London EC2 020 7623 2345
Lavery Haynes
p51 . . . London NW3 020 7435 7441
Lawrance & Holder
p355 . . . Potters Bar 01707 645317
Lawson Turner & Gilbert
p213 . . . Dover 01304 226338
Lawson West Solicitors Limited
p280 . . . Leicester 0116 212 1000
Leach Rawlence & Hart
p205 . . . Croydon 020 8680 5850
Leadbeater & Kay
p398 . . . Stoke-on-Trent 01782 201933
Lean & Co
p226 . . . Fleet 01252 816757
Lees Solicitors LLP
p249 . . . Heswall 0151 342 6273
p428 . . . West Kirby 0151 625 9364
The Legal Practice Solicitors
p426 . . . Wembley 020 8903 7017
Lennons
p117 . . . Amersham 01494 433177
P S Levy & Co
p53 . . . London W1 020 7486 7717
Lewis & Co
p53 . . . London NW4 020 8202 4343
Lewis & Dick
p202 . . . Crawley 01293 526031
p219 . . . Epsom 020 8393 0055
Lewis Francis Blackburn Bray
p376 . . . Sheffield 0114 272 9721
Lexica Law
p177 . . . Canterbury 01227 764141
E C Lidster & Co
p235 . . . Grimsby 01472 348417
Lincoln-Lewis & Co
p140 . . . Birmingham 0121 454 7011
The Lister Croft Partnership
p358 . . . Pudsey 0113 257 0526
Livingstone & Co
p307 . . . Manchester 0161 833 0578
M V Lloyd
p224 . . . Fareham 023 9228 0944
p355 . . . Portsmouth 023 9238 6757
Lloyds & Cooper
p283 . . . Leominster 01568 613236
Longden Walker & Renney
p401 . . . Sunderland 0191 567 7024
Lopian Wagner
p307 . . . Manchester 0161 834 2324
E D C Lord & Co
p245 . . . Hayes 020 8848 9988
Lorimers
p168 . . Buckingham 01280 812132 / 813405

See p542 for the Firms Specialisations

See p542 for the Firms Specialisations

Woodhouse & Company
p438 Wolverhampton 01902 773616
Richard A Woodman
p239 Harpenden 01582 768222
Woolacott & Co
p270 Lancing 01903 763011 / 764334
Michael G Wooldridge
p143 Birmingham 0121 706 2259
Woolley Beardsleys & Bosworth
p293 Loughborough 01509 212266
Woolliscrofts
p239 Hanley 01782 204000
p398 Stoke-on-Trent 01782 577246
Wright & Co
p239 Harpenden 01582 767686
p351 Pontefract 01977 878130
Wright & Lord
p319 Morecambe 01524 402050
Wright & Morton
p402 Sunderland 0191 567 4289
Wright & Wright
p237 Guildford 01483 531264
Wrigley Claydon
p341 Oldham 0161 624 6811
p412 Todmorden 01706 815712
Wykeham & Co
p193 Chippenham 01249 721010
Denis Wynn & Co
p193 Chipping Norton 01608 643036
Yarwood Stimpson & Co
p431 Whitley Bay 0191 297 0123
Yates & Co
p339 Nottingham 0115 947 4486
Yorklaw Ltd (t/a Burn & Company)
p215 Easingwold 01347 822188
Yorkshire Law Solicitors
p167 Brough 01430 422422
Young & Co
p130 Bedford 01234 346411 / 344211
p398 Stoke-on-Trent 01782 339200
Yugin & Partners
p394 Stanmore 020 8954 2410
A E P Zaleski
p93 London SW18 020 8875 1791
Peter Zelnik & Co
p133 Biggin Hill 01959 570730

ROAD HAULAGE LICENSING

Backhouse Jones Ltd
p196 Clitheroe 01254 828300
Barker Gotelee Solicitors
p262 Ipswich 01473 611211
Grindeys LLP
p398 Stone 01785 810780
Robert Locke
p224 Fareham 01329 822722
Ouvry Creed Solicitors
p410 Tetbury 01666 504005
Red Kite Law
p410 Tenby 01834 842122
Stephensons Solicitors LLP
p282 Leigh 01942 777777
Treasures
p230 Gloucester 01452 525351
Waugh & Musgrave
p197 Cockermouth 01900 823127
Woodfines LLP
p317 Milton Keynes 01908 202150

SPORTS LAW

Bates Wells & Braithwaite London LLP
p11 London EC4 020 7551 7777
Beswicks
p397 Stoke-on-Trent 01782 205000
Henri Brandman & Co
p15 London W1 020 7224 0616
George Davies Solicitors LLP
p303 Manchester 0161 236 8992
Dolmans
p178 Cardiff 029 2034 5531
Eastwoods Solicitors
p28 London EC4 020 3137 4800
Edmondson Hall
p327 Newmarket 01638 560556
Gray & Co
p305 Manchester 0161 237 3360
Harbottle & Lewis LLP
p38 London W1 020 7667 5000
David Jeacock
p439 Wootton Bassett 01793 854111
Lennox Bywater
p53 London NW7 020 8906 1206
MSB Solicitors LLP
p289 Liverpool 0151 281 9040
McCloy Legal
p155 Bradford-on-Avon 01225 866563
Paris & Co
p400 Stratford-upon-Avon 01789 298177
Ransons
p421 Walton-on-Thames 01932 269448
Russell-Cooke LLP
p74 London SW15 020 8789 9111
p74 London WC1 020 7405 6566
Sandersons
p258 Hull 01482 324662
Michael Simkins LLP
p79 London WC1 020 7874 5600
Terrells LLP
p347 Peterborough 01733 896789
Waring & Co
p124 Barnet 0870 444 2782

TAXATION - BUSINESS

Bywaters Topham Phillips LLP
p240 Harrogate 01423 879556
Dass Solicitors
p137 Birmingham 0121 248 4000
Heydons
p355 Potters Bar 01707 879646
Stephen J Lamb
p51 Southwark 020 7738 6838
Margraves
p291 Llandrindod Wells 01597 825565
Robert Newey & Co
p63 London SE1 020 7407 9434
QualitySolicitors D'Angibau
p353 Poole 01202 708634
Ramsdens Solicitors
p318 Mirfield 01924 499251
Richard Reed
p402 Sunderland 0191 567 0465
Sandersons
p258 Hull 01482 324662
Sidley Austin Brown & Wood
p78 London EC2 020 7360 3600
Skadden Arps Slate Meagher & Flom (UK) LLP
p80 London E14 020 7519 7000
Sykes Anderson LLP
p85 London EC2 020 3178 3770
Willcox Lewis LLP
p335 Norwich 01508 480100
Wycombe Hurd & Co
p93 London WC2 020 7925 0313

TAXATION - PERSONAL

H T Argent & Son
p372 Saxmundham 01728 602323
Bircham Dyson Bell
p13 London W1 020 7227 7000
Bowcock & Pursaill
p278 Leek 01538 399199
Bowcock Cuerden LLP
p320 Nantwich 01270 611106
Bray & Bray
p312 Market Harborough 01858 467181
Brumell & Sample
p319 Morpeth 01670 512336
Burley & Geach
p285 Liphook 01428 722334
Bywaters Topham Phillips LLP
p240 Harrogate 01423 879556
Ross Carter
p166 Brockenhurst 01590 624422
Chawner Grey & Co
p429
Weston-super-Mare 01934 417768 / 623541
Coupe Bradbury
p296 Lytham 01253 736670
Cozens-Hardy LLP
p334 Norwich 01603 625231
Ellis Jones
p352 Poole 01202 709898
Fishers
p118 Ashby-de-la-Zouch 01530 412167
Franklin & Co
p121 Bakewell 01629 814461
Gabbs LLP
p248 Hereford 01432 353481
Goldring & Co
p359 Rainham 01634 260012
Hague Lambert
p269 Knutsford 01565 652411
Hart Brown Solicitors
p196 Cobham 0800 068 8177
p202 Cranleigh 0800 068 8177
p231 Godalming 0800 068 8177
Hart Reade
p351 Polegate 01323 487051
Hayes & Storr
p425 Wells-next-the-Sea 01328 710210
Heydons
p355 Potters Bar 01707 879646
Linda Holloway & Co
p390 St Albans 01727 841651
Hunters
p44 London WC2 020 7412 0050
p413 Towcester 01327 830895
IBB Solicitors
p189 Chesham 0845 638 1381
Richard Jacklin & Co
p289 Liverpool 0151 243 1313
p388 Southport 01704 500024
Jacklyn Dawson
p328 Newport 01633 262952
Kidson Bray & Lawson
p251 Hindhead 01428 605222
Stephen J Lamb
p51 Southwark 020 7738 6838
Lodders Solicitors LLP
p400 Stratford-upon-Avon 01789 293259
Loughridge Bowler
p200 Coventry 024 7663 1632
Mackintosh & Co
p364 Richmond upon Thames 020 8332 2864
Manchesters
p383 South Croydon 020 8651 3118
Margraves
p291 Llandrindod Wells 01597 825565
Merricks Formerly Merrick Kelleher
p418 Wadebridge 01208 812068 / 813104
Mills Curry
p216 Eastcote 020 8868 8841
Robert Newey & Co
p63 London SE1 020 7407 9434
Iain Nicholson & Co
p351 Ponteland 01661 823863
Cliona O'Tuama
p64 London EC4 020 7489 2015
Richard Reed
p402 Sunderland 0191 567 0465
SGH Martineau LLP
p142 Birmingham 0870 763 2000
Senior Calveley & Hardy
p268 Kirkham 01772 671177
Slade Legal
p419 Wallingford 01491 839346
Sookias & Sookias
p80 London W1 020 7465 8000
Speechly Bircham LLP
p81 London EC4 020 7427 6400
Sykes Anderson LLP
p85 London EC2 020 3178 3770
Wiggin Osborne Fullerlove
p189 Cheltenham 01242 710200
Willcox Lewis LLP
p335 Norwich 01508 480100
Wrigleys Solicitors LLP
p278 Leeds 0113 244 6100
Wycombe Hurd & Co
p93 London WC2 020 7925 0313

WELFARE BENEFITS

AMD Solicitors
p160 Bristol 0117 923 5562
Ahmed & Co
p4 Camden 020 7383 2243
Chetty & Patel
p279 Leicester 0116 254 6222
Conveyancing Direct Ltd
p392 St Leonards-on-Sea 0845 788 8666
Morgan & Co
p399 Stourbridge 01384 440069
Niman & Co
p63 Haringey 020 8809 4923
Rees Page
p133 Bilston 01902 577776
Salmons
p398 Stoke-on-Trent 01782 639827
Sehgal & Co
p142 Birmingham 0121 772 2226
Verisona Solicitors
p423 Waterlooville 023 9226 5251

WILLS, TRUSTS & PROBATE

AGR Solicitors
p378 Shirebrook 01623 748522
A Halsall & Co
p134 Birkenhead 0151 647 6323
p435 Wirral 0151 678 9090
A Kay Pietron & Paluch
p3 Ealing 020 8992 9997
AMD Solicitors
p160 Bristol 0117 973 8205
AST Hampsons (incorporating Warhurst and co)
p170 Bury 0161 764 3317
AWB Charlesworth LLP
p263 Keighley 01535 613678
Aaronson & Co
p3 London W8 020 7376 9124
Abbott Cresswell LLP
p3 London SW14 020 8876 4478
Ablitts
p3 Bromley 020 8776 8783
Act Legal
p159 Brighton 01273 565656
David Acton & Co
p382 Solihull 01564 730028
Adams Delmar
p238 Hampton 020 8941 2097
Adcocks Solicitors Ltd
p284 Lichfield 0845 470 8081
Addison O'Hare
p419 Walsall 01922 725515
Adlams LLP
p258 Huntingdon 01480 458885
p392 St Neots 01480 474061
The Affordable Law Co Ltd
p444 York 01904 788877
Akermans
p399 Storrington 01903 745353
p441 Worthing 01903 820413
Alan Turner & Co
p127 Bath 01225 336260
Alban Gould Baker & Co
p4 Islington 020 7607 5085
Alcock & Smalley
p297 Macclesfield 01625 431530
Aldridge Brownlee Solicitors LLP
p151 Bournemouth 01202 527008
p194 Christchurch 01425 282150
Alen-Buckley & Co
p4 Wandsworth 020 8767 8336
Alfred Truman
p167 Buckingham 01280 822217
Alker & Ball
p432 Wigan 01942 246241
Allan Jay Paine & Co
p5 Enfield 020 8886 1404
Allington Hughes
p442 Wrexham 01978 291000
J P Almond & Co
p435 Wirral 0151 632 2336
Alsters Kelley
p199 Coventry 0844 561 0100
p270 Leamington Spa 0844 561 0100
p339 Nuneaton 0844 561 0100
Alwena Jones & Jones
p147 Blaenau Ffestiniog 01766 831882
p416 Tywyn 01654 711499
Ambrose Appelbe
p6 London WC2 020 7242 7000
J M Amin & Co
p426 Wembley 020 8903 3766
Anami Law Iincorporating Kirkwoods
p171 Bushey 020 8950 1155
Anderson Longmore & Higham
p133 Billingshurst 01403 782710
p348 Petworth 01798 342391
p399 Storrington 01903 745666
Michael Anderson & Co
p430 Whickham 0191 488 1221
Anderson Partnership
p191 Chesterfield 01246 220737
R W Anderson & Co
p6 London W1 020 7323 4520
Andrews Martin
p406 Swindon 01793 641707
Angel & Co
p200 Coventry 024 7625 2211
Anglo-Spanish Law
p244 Hathersage 01433 631508
Anthony Gold
p6 London SW16 020 7940 4000
Anthony Holden Crofts & Co
p156 Brentford 020 8568 7768
Michael Anvoner & Co
p123 Barnet 020 8449 0003
Aplin Stockton Fairfax
p122 Banbury 01295 251234
Archer & Archer
p218 Ely 01353 662203
H T Argent & Son
p372 Saxmundham 01728 602323
Armitage & Guest
p418 Wakefield 01924 371877
Arnison & Co Solicitors Limited
p346 Penrith 01768 862007
Arnold Deacon Greene & Co
p381 Sleaford 01529 414414
Arnold Greenwood
p264 Kendal 01539 720049
p316 Milnthorpe 01539 562424
Anna Arthur Associates
p436 Woking 01483 222499
Ascroft Whiteside
p146 Blackpool 01253 766866
Ashfords LLP
p7 London W1 020 3581 8970
p412 Tiverton 01884 203000
Aspinall & Co
p148 Bolton 01204 388200
Astills
p278 Leicester 0116 249 4450

See p542 for the Firms Specialisations

Cooper Son & Caldecott
p247 . . . Henley-on-Thames 01491 574203
Cooper Sons Hartley & Williams
p172 . . . Buxton 01298 77511
Cornfield Law
p215 . . . Eastbourne 01323 412512
Cornwells
p153 . . . Bradford 01274 675631
Corries Solicitors
p444 . . . York 0845 241 5566
Coupe Bradbury
p296 . . . Lytham 01253 736670
Hilary A Courtneidge
p248 . . . Hertford 01992 589120
Courtyard Solicitors LLP
p23. . . . London SW19 020 8946 9466
Cowles
p23. . . . Croydon 020 8679 1811
Eric Cowsill Solicitor
p263 . . . Ivybridge 01752 205202
Coxons
p427 . . . West Bridgford 0115 981 2000
Coyne Learmonth
p287 . . . Liverpool 0845 602 0870
Cozens Moxon & Harts
p409 . Teddington 020 8977 8486 / 8977 4424
Cozens-Hardy LLP
p334 . . . Norwich 01603 625231
Crabtree Chadwick
p358 . . . Pudsey 0113 290 9499
Cracknells
p236 . . . Guildford 01483 535558
Creagh Brown & Co Solicitors
p220 . . . Esher 020 8224 0610
Cripps Harries Hall LLP
p415 . . . Tunbridge Wells 01892 515121
Charles Crookes with George Tudor & de Winton
p156 . . . Brecon 01874 625151
Cross Ram & Co
p237 . . . Halesworth 01986 873636
Crosse Wyatt Verney & Ayre
p383 . . . South Molton 01769 572157
Crossmans MTA
p174 . . . Cambridge 01223 451442
Cullimore Dutton
p190 . . . Chester 01244 356789
Cumming & Riley
p233 . . . Grays 01375 383691
Cumming Hodgkinson Dickinson
p148 . . . Bolton 01204 523108 / 528396
N Cunliffe-Lister
p213 . . . Driffield 01377 236006
Cunningtons
p155 . . . Braintree 01376 326868
Curry Popeck
p264 . . . Kenton 020 8907 2000 / 8907 8896
Curtis Parkinson
p336 . . . Nottingham 0115 931 7000
DBL Talbots LLP
p197 . . . Codsall 01902 843427
p213 . . . Dudley 01384 252471
p213 . . . Dudley 01384 459551
p265 . . . Kidderminster 01562 749910
p399 . . . Stourbridge 01384 445850
dgb Solicitors
p184 . . . Chatham 01634 304000
DJK Solicitors
p420 . . . Waltham Abbey 01992 718880
DW Solicitors
p331 . . . Northampton 01604 624222
DWT Legal Ltd
p265 . . . Kidderminster 0844 770 3799
Dale & Newbery LLP
p393 . . . Staines 01784 464491
Daltons
p215 . . . Eastbourne 01323 720040
Daltons Solicitors
p348 . . . Petersfield 01730 262816
Darbys Solicitors LLP
p343 . . . Oxford 01865 811700
Marie Dark Solicitors
p189 . . . Chepstow 01291 621638
Darling & Stephensons
p123 . . . Barnard Castle 01325 489000
Darlington Hardcastles
p364 . . . Rickmansworth 01923 774272
Jeremy Davenport
p251 . . . Hockley 01702 205163
Davey Franklin Jones
p195 . . . Cirencester 01285 654875
p230 . . . Gloucester 01452 508800
Sheldon Davidson Solicitors
p430 . . . Whitefield 0161 796 5445
Davies Bell & Reed
p324 . Newcastle upon Tyne 0191 232 8058
Davies Blunden & Evans
p224 . . . Farnborough 01252 541633
David H N Davies
p371 . . . Salisbury 01722 322272
George Davies Solicitors LLP
p303 . . . Manchester 0161 236 8992

Hywel Davies & Co
p121 . . . Bala 01678 520307
Davies Partnership
p389 . . . St Agnes 01872 553131
Davies Prichard & Weatherill
p178 . . . Cardiff 029 2037 7471
W Davies
p436 . . . Woking 01483 744900
Davisons
p137 . . . Birmingham 0121 685 1234
William Dawes & Co
p370 . . . Rye 01797 223177
Dawson & Burgess with Bell Dallman & Co
p211 . . . Doncaster 01302 834744
Graham Dawson & Co
p132 . . . Bexley 01322 558811
Nicholas Daykin Solicitors
p120 . . . Attleborough 01953 453774
Dean & Co
p213 . . . Dudley 01384 352525
p399 . . . Stourbridge 01384 352525
Roger Dean & Co
p133 . . . Biggin Hill 01959 542872
Denby & Co
p125 . . . Barrow-in-Furness 01229 822366
Samantha Denham Solicitors
p243 . . . Hastings 01424 718822 / 719111
Chris Denton
p168 . . Burley-in-Wharfedale 01943 607828
Devereux & Co
p162 . . . Bristol 0117 938 0222
p162 . . . Bristol 0117 959 3344
Dibbens
p433 . . . Wimborne 01202 882456
Dickens & Co
p204 . . Crowthorne 01344 772901 / 776151
Dicksons Solicitors Ltd
p397 . . . Stoke-on-Trent 01782 262424
p397 . . . Stoke-on-Trent 01782 262424
Dixon Coles & Gill
p418 . . . Wakefield 01924 263166 / 263899
p418 . . . Wakefield 01924 373467
Dixon Coles & Goddard
p279 . . . Leicester 0116 236 4708
Dixon Rigby Keogh
p333 . . . Northwich 01606 48111
Dixon Stewart
p321 . . . New Milton 01425 621515
Dodd Lewis Solicitors
p27. . . . London SE3 020 8852 1255
Dollman & Pritchard
p183 . . . Caterham 01883 347823
Donaldson West
p204 . . . Crowborough 01892 662233
Donnelly & Elliott Limited
p232 . . . Gosport 023 9250 5500
Dootsons LLP
p205 . . . Culcheth 01925 765212
Adam Douglas & Son
p131 . . Berwick-upon-Tweed 01289 306479
Downey & Co
p153 . . . Bradford 01274 883515
Downie & Gadban
p116 . . . Alton 01420 82879
Downs
p212 . . . Dorking 01306 880110
Draper & Co
p225 . . . Farnham 01252 727374
Druitts
p151 . . . Bournemouth 01202 551863
Duffield Stunt
p186 . . . Chelmsford 01245 262351
Valentine Duggins
p419 . . . Wallasey 0151 638 4844
Dunham Guest & Lyons
p176 . . . Cannock 01543 462121
Dunn & Co
p267 . Kingston upon Thames 020 8541 1332
Peter Dunn & Co
p401 . . . Sunderland 0191 568 9000
Dutton Gregory
p385 . . . Southampton 023 8022 1344
Sarah Dwight Solicitor
p137 . . . Birmingham 0121 702 2100
Dyne Drewett Solicitors Ltd
p433 . . . Wincanton 01963 32374
EMW
p316 . . . Milton Keynes 0845 070 6000
Earl & Crocker
p285 . . . Liskeard 01579 345304
Eastleys
p166 . . . Brixham 01803 853266
p413 . . . Totnes 01803 864888
Eaton & Few
p391 . . . St Ives 01480 301558
Eaton-Evans & Morris
p244 . . . Haverfordwest 01437 763383
Eccles Heddon
p365 . . . Ripon 01765 601717

Eckford Rands
p331 . . . Northampton 01604 621001
Eddowes Perry & Osbourne
p403 . . . Sutton Coldfield 0121 686 9444
Martin Edwards
p378 . . . Shifnal 01952 462118
Edwin Coe LLP
p29. . . . London WC2 020 7691 4000
Eldridges
p328 . . . Newport 01983 524741
Elliots Bond & Banbury
p29. . . . Ealing 020 8567 0176
Ellis & Co
p190 . . . Chester 01244 319388
Ellis Jones
p352 . . . Poole 01202 709898
p364 . . . Ringwood 01425 484848
p404 . . . Swanage 01929 422233
Ellis Lakin & Co
p348 . . . Pickering 01751 472121
Ellisons
p195 . . . Clacton-on-Sea 01255 421248
p227 . . . Frinton-on-Sea 01255 851000
p243 . . . Harwich 01255 502428
Elmhirst Parker LLP
p273 . . . Leeds 01977 682219
p374 . . . Selby 01757 703895
Eltringham & Co
p324 . . Newcastle upon Tyne 0191 266 5878
Emmerson Brown & Brown
p207 . . . Deal 01304 362146
Hal Emmett & Co
p298 . . . Maghull 0151 531 7666
Enever Freeman & Co
p368 . . . Ruislip 01895 634031
p369 . . . Ruislip 01895 676385 / 676386
Eric Robinson Solicitors
p184 . . . Chandlers Ford 023 8025 4676
p259 . . . Hythe 023 8084 4304
Evans & Co
p226 . . . Ferryhill 01740 657444
Evans & Ellis
p189 . . . Chepstow 01291 622814
Mary Evans & Co
p182 . . . Carmarthen 01267 233881
Shirley M Evans
p232 . . Grange-over-Sands 01539 535208
Everatt's
p241 . . . Harrow 020 8424 0088
FBC Manby Bowdler LLP
p157 . . . Bridgnorth 01746 761436
p379 . . . Shrewsbury 01743 241551
F B Jevons Riley & Pope
p216 . . . Edenbridge 01732 864411
FDC Law
p228 . . . Frome 01373 465051
p358 . . . Radstock 01761 417575
Fairbairn Smith & Co
p30. . . . London N17 020 8808 4901
Fairchild Dobbs
p229 . . . Gerrards Cross 01753 883127
Fairchild Greig
p30. . . . London W3 020 8993 6886
Fairweather Stephenson & Co
p282 . . . Leiston 01728 832832
Rebecca L Faret Solicitors
p226 . . . Flitwick 01525 712112
Farnfield & Nicholls
p229 . . . Gillingham 01747 825432
p374 . . . Shaftesbury 01747 854244
p421 . . . Warminster 01985 214661
Farnworth Shaw
p198 . . . Colne 01282 864081
John Farr-Davies & Co
p182 . . . Carmarthen 01267 231818
Farrells Solicitors
p162 . . . Bristol 0117 944 4664
Farrer & Co LLP
p31. . . . London WC2 020 3375 7000
Feeny & Co
p162 . . . Bristol 0117 923 9477
Fendom Dawson & Partners
p250 . . . High Wycombe 01494 450361
Andrew J Fenny & Co
p201 . . . Cramlington 01670 737393
Fentons
p223 . . . Failsworth 0161 682 7101
Ferguson Bricknell
p343 . . . Oxford 01865 241814
Fidler & Pepper
p404 . . . Sutton-in-Ashfield 01623 451111
Field Overell
p200 . . . Coventry 024 7622 9582
Fieldings Porter
p429 . . . Westhoughton 01942 814089
Finn Gledhill
p246 . . . Hebden Bridge 01422 842451
Fischer & Co
p32. . . Barnet 020 8346 7036 / 8922 0689
D Fisher & Co
p150 . . . Borough Green 01732 884299
Fitzgerald-Harts
p150 . . . Boroughbridge 01423 322312

Thomas Flavell & Sons
p214 . . . Earl Shilton 01455 842297
p250 . . . Hinckley 01455 610747
p312 . . . Market Bosworth 01455 290203
Foot Anstey
p221 . . . Exeter 01392 411221
Footner & Ewing
p366 . . . Romsey 01794 512345
Forbes
p145 . . . Blackburn 01254 54374
Forbes Hall LLP
p33. . . . London EC2 020 7729 9111
Forman Welch & Bellamys
p416 Twickenham 020 8892 8907 / 8892 7733
J A Forrest & Co
p33. . . . London W1 020 7233 9140
Forresters
p125 . . . Barrow-in-Furness 01229 820297
Forshaws Davies Ridgway LLP
p422 . . . Warrington 01925 604713
Forsters LLP
p33. . . . London W1 020 7863 8333
Foskett Marr Gadsby & Head
p219 . . . Epping 01992 578642
p294 . . . Loughton 020 8502 3991
David J Foster & Co
p407 . . . Tamworth 01827 58333 / 58334
Francis & Co
p189 . . . Chepstow 01291 622237
p202 . . . Cranleigh 01483 267222
Franklin & Co
p121 . . . Bakewell 01629 814461
Franklins LLP
p332 . . . Northampton 01604 828282
Fraser Brown
p337 . . . Nottingham 0115 933 5311
Frearsons
p380 . . . Skegness 01754 897600
Freedman Green Dhokia
p34. . . . Camden 020 7624 2981
French & Co Solicitors Ltd
p403 . . . Sutton Coldfield 0121 362 7330
Frettens Solicitors
p194 . . . Christchurch 01202 491777
Shirley Fretwell
p261 . . . Ilkeston 0115 932 3623
Friis & Radstone
p394 . . . Stevenage 01438 741001
Julia Frimond Solicitors
p236 . . . Guildford 01483 452224
Frodshams
p391 . . . St Helens 01744 626600
Fulton Robertson
p117 . . . Amersham 01494 722326
Funnell & Perring
p243 . . . Hastings 01424 426287
Fussell Wright
p162 . . . Bristol 0117 927 9117
p162 . . . Bristol 0117 971 3535
GB Solicitors Ltd
p224 . . . Fareham 01329 282817
GLP Solicitors
p357 . . . Prestwich 0161 773 8626
GLRS Phoenix LLP
p400 . . . Stroud 01453 763433
Gales
p152 . Bournemouth 01202 512227 / 512446
D W Gallifant
p428 . . . West Mersea 01206 383050
Gardner Iliff & Dowding
p176 . . . Cannock 01543 466941
J Garrard & Allen
p341 . . . Olney 01234 711215
Gates & Moloney
p270 . . . Lancing 01903 766046
Gavins Solicitors
p35. . . . London N6 020 8374 4459
Gedye & Sons (Solicitors) Ltd
p232 . . . Grange-over-Sands 01539 532313
Gelbergs LLP
p35. . . . Islington 020 7226 0570
Jeremy Gibbs & Co
p117 . . . Amersham 01494 724671
Gibson & Co
p324 . Newcastle upon Tyne 0191 273 3817
Giffen Couch & Archer
p399 . . . Stony Stratford 01908 563911
Gill Akaster
p349 . . . Plymouth 01752 203500
Gillanders
p188 . . . Cheltenham 01242 583434
Ginn & Co
p174 . . . Cambridge 01223 358275
Girlings
p119 . . . Ashford 01233 647377
p177 . . . Canterbury 01227 768374
p312 . . . Margate 01843 220274
Glazer Delmar
p35. . . . London SE22 020 8299 0021
Goad & Butcher
p374 . . . Settle 01729 823500
Godwins
p433 . . . Winchester 01962 841484

See p542 for the Firms Specialisations

Kitsons LLP
p413 Torquay 01803 202020
Kloosmans
p387 Southend-on-Sea 01702 600090
Knapman & Co
p345 Paignton 01803 522700
Knipe Woodhouse-Smith
p184
Chalfont St Peter 01753 887877 / 889149
Knowles Benning
p295 Luton 01582 798000
Robert Kyle & Co
p313 Marlow 01628 475751
LD Law
p239 Harlow 01279 441266
Laceys
p353 Poole 01202 743286
Laderman & Co
p51 Redbridge 020 8530 7319
Ladermans
p51 London NW4 020 8203 6136
Lages & Co
p418 Wadhurst 01892 784419
Lamb Brooks LLP
p126 Basingstoke 01256 844888
Lambert Taylor & Gregory
p228 Gateshead 0191 477 0616
Lancasters
p219 Epsom 01372 724931
p51 London W4 020 8742 1314
H Landau & Co
p217 Edgware 020 8959 6991
Landons
p156 Brentwood 01277 210021
Langley Wellington
p195 Churchdown 01452 856846
p230 Gloucester 01452 521286
Lanyon Bowdler LLP
p425 Wellington 01952 244721
Larby Williams with Gwyn & Gwyn
p201 Cowbridge 01446 775535
Larken & Co
p322 Newark 01636 703333
Last Cawthra Feather LLP
p154 Bradford 01274 848800
Latimer Hinks
p206 Darlington 01325 341500
Lavery Haynes
p51 London NW3 020 7435 7441
Lawrance & Holder
p355 Potters Bar 01707 645317
Lawson West Solicitors Limited
p312 Market Harborough 01858 445480
Leach Rawlence & Hart
p205 Croydon 020 8680 5850
Lebreton Towell Solicitor
p408 Tarporley 01829 751459
Lees Solicitors LLP
p249 Heswall 0151 342 6273
p428 West Kirby 0151 625 9364
The Legal Practice Solicitors
p426 Wembley 020 8903 7017
Lennons
p117 Amersham 01494 433177
Levine Mellins Klarfeld
p394 Stanmore 020 8954 7474
Lewis & Dick
p219 Epsom 020 8393 0055
Lewis Francis Blackburn Bray
p376 Sheffield 0114 272 9721
Lincoln-Lewis & Co
p140 Birmingham 0121 454 7011
Linder Myers Solicitors
p379 Shrewsbury 0844 984 6002
The Lister Croft Partnership
p358 Pudsey 0113 257 0526
Livingstons
p416 Ulverston 01229 585555
Lloyd Jones & Co
p428 Westcliff-on-Sea 01702 710338
M V Lloyd
p224 Fareham 023 9228 0944
p355 Portsmouth 023 9238 6757
Lloyds & Cooper
p283 Leominster 01568 613236
Longden Walker & Renney
p401 Sunderland 0191 567 7024
Longstaff & Midgley
p372 Scarborough 01723 351751
Loosemores
p179 Cardiff 029 2022 4433
Lorimers
p168 Buckingham 01280 812132 / 813405
Loughridge Bowler
p200 Coventry 024 7663 1632
Lovell Son & Pitfield
p55 Camden 020 7242 7883
Lu Oliphant Solicitors
p217 Edgware 020 8238 2822
Richard Ludlow & Co
p400 Stratford-upon-Avon 01789 552872
Lumsdons Solicitors LLP
p399 Stourport-on-Severn 01299 827766
p440 Worcester 01905 730670
Lundys
p213 Driffield 01377 252831
Trevor Lyttleton MBE
p55 London W1 020 7402 4810
MMS Solicitors
p436 Withernsea 01964 612318
D K Macbryde & Co
p356 Prestatyn 01745 856404
Hilary McCauley Solicitors Limited
p185 Cheadle Hulme 0161 485 6723
McGlennons
p56 Merton 020 8946 6015
Elaine McGloin
p215 East Grinstead 01342 328000
Glynis M Mackie
p232 Gosforth 0191 236 5308
Mackintosh & Co
p364 Richmond upon Thames 020 8332 2864
Mackrell Turner Garrett
p437 Woking 01483 476022
Barry Macloskey Solicitors
p443 Wrexham 01978 852485
Hamish M McMillan
p57 London EC4 020 7430 1789
Macmillans
p418 Wadebridge 01208 812415
McPhersons
p57 Ealing 020 8840 9017
Macrory Ward
p124 Barnet 020 8440 3258
Maffey & Brentnall
p423 Watford 01923 234607
Thomas Magnay & Co
p430 Whickham 0191 488 7459 / 488 7766
Maher & Co
p298 Maidenhead 01628 675239
Manchesters
p383 South Croydon 020 8651 3118
Mander Hadley & Co
p200 Coventry 024 7663 1212
Alan Mann & Co
p390 St Albans 01727 833281 / 846012
Mann & Company
p265 Kettering 01536 520025
John Mant Solicitors
p421 Wantage 01235 762900
Manuel Swaden
p58 London NW6 020 7431 4999
Margary & Miller
p225 Felixstowe 01394 273333
p389 Southwold 01502 723308
p439 Woodbridge 01394 382777
Margraves
p291 Llandrindod Wells 01597 825565
Marsden Duncan
p134 Birchington 01843 295743 / 841161
Marsh & Co
p269 Lancaster 01524 68102
MarstonHarbottle
p249 Hexham 01434 602486
John P Martin & Co
p372 Scarborough 01723 500922
Martin Tolhurst Partnership LLP
p293 Longfield 01474 706168
Martin-Kaye LLP
p409 Telford 01952 272222
Masefield Solicitors LLP
p271 Ledbury 01531 632377
Mason Baggott & Garton
p373 Scunthorpe 01724 868611
James Mason Tucker
p329 Newton Abbot 01626 204060
Mason-Apps Smallmans & Co
p298 Maidenhead 01628 636148 / 636149
Matthew & Matthew Limited
p387 Southbourne 01202 431943
A S Matthews & Co
p307 Manchester 0161 747 2262
Matthews Lewis & Co
p191 Chester 01244 327750
W H Matthews & Co
p402 Sutton 020 8642 6677
Maxwell Hodge Solicitors
p227 Formby 01704 872156
p428 West Kirby 0151 625 9154
Mayo Wynne Baxter LLP
p160 Brighton 01273 775533
p215 Eastbourne 01323 730543
p373 Seaford 01323 891412
Medlicott Snows
p145 Bishops Castle 01588 638425
p269 Knighton 01547 528332
Meesons
p364 Ringwood 01425 472315
Megsons LLP
p154 Bradford 01274 738444
Meikles
p123 Barnard Castle 01833 690505
Mellor & Jackson
p340 Oldham 0161 624 7081
Menneer Shuttleworth
p132 Bexhill 01424 730630
Merrils Ede Solicitors
p345 Penarth 029 2037 1131
Merriman Waine & Co
p348 Pewsey 01672 563666
Metcalfe Copeman & Pettefar
p266 King's Lynn 01553 778102
Metcalfe Johnston McCormick
p216 Eccles 0161 789 3481 / 788 9021
Michelmores LLP
p380 Sidmouth 01395 512515
Middleton Dummer
p340 Oldbury 0121 544 4788
Midwinters
p188 Cheltenham 01242 514674
Milburns Solicitors
p431 Whitehaven 01946 694818
p440 Workington 01900 67363
Miller Evans & Co
p60 London 020 7987 2515
Miller Lyons Solicitors
p230 Glastonbury 01458 833660
Miller Parris
p442 Worthing 01903 205771
T R S Miller Solicitors
p259 Hythe 01303 266861
Mills & Co
p119 Ashton-in-Makerfield 01942 719655
Mills Chody LLP
p244 Hatch End 020 8428 2272
Mills Curry
p216 Eastcote 020 8868 8841
Geoffrey Milne
p425 Wellington 01952 223300 / 223381
p438 Wolverhampton 01902 373000
Milton Francis & Hughes Solicitors
p342 Oswestry 01691 654662
Milwyn Jenkins
p330 Newtown 01686 626218
Milwyn Jenkins & Jenkins Limited
p292 Llanidloes 01686 412166
Mitchell Dodds & Co
p431 Whitley Bay 0191 252 2396 / 252 9557
The Mitchell Plampin Partnership
p299 Maldon 01621 852566
Mohabirs
p61 London SW4 020 7720 5742 / 7622 5495
J B Moloney & Co
p280 Leicester 0116 230 1950
Monro Fisher Wasbrough LLP
p61 London WC1 020 7404 7001
Montlake & Co
p122 Banstead 01737 352211
Moody & Woolley
p209 Derby 01332 344221
Moore Brown & Dixon LLP
p410 Tewkesbury 01684 292341
Moreb Limited
p291 Llandeilo 01558 822215
Morecrofts Solicitors LLP
p290 Liverpool 0151 428 1911
Morgan & Co
p127 Basingstoke 01256 329888
Morgans
p113 Abergavenny 01873 859993
Moroneys
p120 Attleborough 01953 455806
p443 Wymondham 01953 607042
Morris & Bates
p269 Knighton 01547 520130
p291 Llandrindod Wells 01597 829055
Morrish Solicitors LLP
p443 Yeadon 0113 250 7792
Morrisons Solicitors LLP
p173 Camberley 01276 686005
p437 Woking 01483 726146
John Morse Solicitors
p405 Swansea 01792 648111
Mowbray Woodwards Solicitors
p128 Bath 01225 485700
Moxons
p351 Pontefract 01977 703215
E J Moyle
p369 Rustington 01903 784447
Mulcare Jenkins
p246 Haywards Heath 01444 459954
Stuart Q Murphy
p427 West Byfleet 01932 355755
Stephen Murray & Co
p346 Perivale 020 8997 9669
Myer Wolff
p257 Hull 01482 223693
Mylles & Co
p402 Sunninghill 01344 623388
Nahlis Christou
p63 London WC1 020 7278 6888
Nash & Co Solicitors LLP
p350 Plymouth 01752 664444
Neil McQueen Duncan & Egner
p326 Newcastle upon Tyne 0191 232 7469
Nelsons
p338 Nottingham 0115 958 6262
Neves
p295 Luton 01582 725311
Neville-Jones & Co
p404 Swanage 01929 422666 / 423761
p421 Wareham 01929 552471
Newbys
p237 Guisborough 01287 632208 / 632209
Alfred Newton & Co
p396 Stockport 0161 430 8831
p396 Stockport 0161 480 6551 / 480 1245
p433 Wilmslow 01625 523647
Newtons
p63 Camden 020 7794 9696 / 7435 5351
Nicholls Brimble & Co
p382 Smethwick 0121 429 8016
Nicholls Christie & Crocker
p242 Harrow 020 8863 6366
Nicholls Lindsell & Harris and Ingham & Wainwright
p355 Poynton 01625 876411
Iain Nicholson & Co
p351 Ponteland 01661 823863
Nightingales Solicitors Limited
p396 Stockport 01663 764038
O'Brien Lewis & James
p180 Cardiff 029 2061 1471
John O'Connor Solicitors
p209 Derby 01332 345533
Sean O'Connor
p412 Tonbridge 01732 365378
John O'Neill & Co
p232 Gosforth 0191 246 4000
O'Neill Morgan Solicitors Limited
p396 Stockport 0161 429 8383
O'Neill Patient
p396 Stockport 0161 483 8555
Cliona O'Tuama
p64 London EC4 020 7489 2015
Oates Hanson
p256 Huddersfield 01484 300609
Oberman Law
p64 Camden 020 7242 6154
Beverley Ogden & Co
p283 Lewes 01273 474159
Oglethorpe & Broatch
p265 Keswick 01768 772125
Oglethorpe Sturton & Gillibrand
p268 Kirkby Lonsdale 01524 271388
Onions & Davies
p312 Market Drayton 01630 652405
Osborns
p198 Colwyn Bay 01492 532056 / 532820
Osman Ward & Sons
p255 Hove 01273 778787 / 778788
Overburys & Raymond Thompson
p211 Diss 01379 641221
Owen & Co
p362 Redhill 01737 760036
Gwyneth O Owen Solicitor
p248 Hereford 01544 318738
P B & W Solicitors LLP t/a Pooley Bendall & Watson
p218 Ely 01353 666075
PBW Solicitors
p350 Plymouth 01752 222206
PCB Solicitors LLP
p269 Knighton 01547 520254
p379 Shrewsbury 01743 248148
Page Gulliford & Gregory Limited
p386 Southampton 023 8022 5821
Colin Palmer & Co
p294 Lowestoft 01502 589277
Palmers
p126 Basildon 01268 240000
p384 South Woodham Ferrers 01245 322111
Palmers Solicitors
p267 Kingston upon Thames 020 8549 7444
Parfitt Cresswell
p65 London SW6 020 7381 8311
Judith Parish Solicitor
p430 Weybridge 01932 842022
Parker Rhodes Hickmotts
p367 Rotherham 01709 365116
Parkes Wilshire Johnson
p124 Barnet 020 8441 1556
Parry Carver
p409 Telford 01952 504757
Parry Law
p248 Herne Bay 01227 361131
p431 Whitstable 01227 276276
Patterson Glenton & Stracey
p326 Newcastle upon Tyne 0191 232 8628
Bernard Pearce & Co
p219 Enfield 020 8804 5271
Pearcelegal LLP
p383 Solihull 0844 412 7899
Pearl & Co
p394 Stanmore 020 8958 4889
Pearlmans Solicitors LLP
p66 London NW4 020 8201 6311
Pearson Maddin Solicitors
p321 New Malden 020 8949 9500

Pearsons & Ward
p300 . . . . .Malton 01653 692247
Peasegoods
p308 . . . . .Manchester 0161 205 2772
Pendrigh Makin
p363 . . . . Reigate 01737 221518
p374 . . . . Sevenoaks 01732 463030
Penmans
p199 . . . . Corringham 01375 673968
p264 . . . . .Kenilworth 01926 858222
p394 . . . . Stanford-le-Hope 01375 677777
Penningtons
p127 . . . . .Basingstoke 01256 407100
p231 . . . . Godalming 01483 791800
p66. . . . . London EC2 020 7457 3000
Perry Hay & Co
p364
. . .Richmond upon Thames 020 8940 8115 / 8332 7532
Peter Peter & Wright
p133 . . . . .Bideford 01237 472233
p251 . . . . Holsworthy 01409 253262
Peters Langsford Davies
p270 . . . . Launceston 01566 772451
Christine Pick Solicitors
p445 . . . . .York 01430 873593
Pickerings LLP
p407 . . . . Tamworth 01827 317070
Peter William Pickles
p182 . . . . Carlisle 01697 472223
Richard Pietrowski & Co
p237 . . . . Guildford 01483 505398
Pilgrim & Webster
p250 . . . . .Hinckley 01455 634851
Pini Franco LLP
p67. . . . . London EC1 020 7566 3140
Pinkerton Leeke & Co
p188 . . . . Cheltenham 01242 237477
Pinniger Finch & Co
p428 . . . . Westbury 01373 823791
C Pittordou & Co
p355 . . . . Potters Bar 01707 663760
Pleass Thomson & Co
p195 . . . . . Clacton-on-Sea 01255 221133
Poole & Co
p203 . . . . Crewkerne 01460 279100
Poole Townsend
p125 . . . . Barrow-in-Furness 01229 811811
Pope & Co
p203 . . . . Cromer 01263 513355
Porter Dodson
p212 . . . . Dorchester 01305 262525
p444 . . . . Yeovil 01935 424581
Portrait Solicitors
p69. . . . . London WC2 020 7092 6990
Potter & Co
p313 . . . . Matlock 01629 582308
Powell & Co
p404 . . . . . .Sutton Coldfield 0121 355 1001
Powell & Young
p351 . . . . Pocklington 01759 302113
Powis & Co
p195 . . . . . Clacton-on-Sea 01255 233400
Preston Goldburn
p223 . . . . Falmouth 01326 318900
Price Mears & Co
p365 . . . . Rochdale 01706 653331
Pricketts
p172 . . . . Buxton 01298 22874
p396 . . . . .Stockport 0161 429 8000
Theo Pritchett
p247 . . . . . Henley-in-Arden 01564 742215
Anthony Pugh
p126 . . . . Barry 01446 751493
Pulham & Co
p372 . . . . Saxmundham 01728 602084
Punch Robson
p397 . . . . Stockton-on-Tees 01642 754050
Purdys
p363 . . . . Reepham 01603 870606
Pyms
p131 . . . . .Belper 01773 822307
Quality Solicitors Burroughs Day
p354 . . . . .Portishead 01275 843213
Quality Solicitors Chapman & Chubb
p115 . . . . Alfreton 01773 540480
Quality Solicitors Clarke & Son
p127 . . . . .Basingstoke 01256 320555
Quality Solicitors Copley Clark
p403 . . . . Sutton 020 8643 7221
QualitySolicitors D'Angibau
p353 . . . . Poole 01202 672598
p353 . . . . Poole 01202 708634
QualitySolicitors Hill & Abbott
p187 . . . . Chelmsford 01245 258892
QualitySolicitors Jackson & Canter
p290 . . . . Liverpool 0151 282 1700
QualitySolicitors Palmers
p226 . . . . .Fetcham 01372 454791
RJR Solicitors
p227 . . . . Freshwater 01983 752115
Rainer Hughes
p156 . . . . .Brentwood 01277 226644
Ralph & Co
p418 . . . . Wadebridge 01208 812277
Ramsdens Solicitors
p217 . . . . Elland 01422 372478
p238 . . . . Halifax 01422 330700
p318 . . . . Mirfield 01924 499251
Randle Thomas LLP
p246 . . . . Helston 01326 572951
Ranson Houghton
p118 . . . . Andover 01264 351533
Ratcliffe Duce & Gammer LLP
p361 . . . . Reading 0118 957 4291
p437 . . . . .Wokingham 0118 978 3681
Rawlison Butler LLP
p253 . . . . Horsham 01403 252492
Read Dunn Connell
p154 . . . . .Bradford 01274 723858
Read Law Associates
p297 . . . . .Macclesfield 01625 429131
Red Kite Law
p345 . . . . Pembroke 01646 683222
Redfern & Co
p141 . . . . .Birmingham 0121 236 1801
Redferns
p430 . . . . . Weymouth 01305 781401 / 782704
Richard Reed
p402 . . . . Sunderland 0191 567 0465
Rees Wood Terry
p180 . . . . Cardiff 029 2040 8800
Reynolds Johns Partnership
p144 . . . . . Bishop's Stortford 01279 508626
Rich & Carr Freer Bouskell
p145 . . . . Blaby 0116 242 6039
p281 . . . . Leicester 0116 253 8021
p296 . . . . Lutterworth 0116 242 6048
p407 . . . . Syston 0116 242 6036
Richards & Morgan LLP
p152 . . . . Bournemouth 01202 424234
R Miles Richards & Co
p352 . . . . .Pontypridd 01443 202237
Scott Richards
p409 . . . . Teignmouth 01626 772441
Richardson & Co
p276 . . . . .Leeds 0113 243 1714
Rix & Kay Solicitors LLP
p373 . . . . .Seaford 0845 165 8178
p416 . . . . Uckfield 01825 700177
Roberts & Smith
p321 . . . . Nelson 01282 619000
Peter Roberts Solicitor
p116 . . . . Alrewas 01283 790045
Robertson Rivers
p215 . . . . East Molesey 020 8979 6077
Robinson Allfree
p166 . . . . Broadstairs 01843 865261
p359 . . . . Ramsgate 01843 592361
Robinson Le Grice
p392 . . . . St Ives 01736 797973
Robotham & Co
p209 . . . . Derby 01332 346018
Robson & Co
p259 . . . . . . Hythe 01303 264581 / 267413
Robson Palmer
p384 . . . . . . .South Shields 0191 455 4561
Robyns Owen
p358 . . . . Pwllheli 01758 613177
Roger James Clements & Partners
p329 . . . . . Newport 01633 263316 / 663316
Christopher Rose & Co
p346 . . . . .Penryn 01326 372461 / 374430
Roskell Davies & Co
p141 . Birmingham 0121 354 1515 / 355 1011
Ross & Son
p252 . . . . Horley 01293 782425
Ross Coates
p263 . . . . Ipswich 01473 222303
p263 . . . . Ipswich 01473 621800
Rothera Dowson
p130 . . . . .Beeston 0115 916 5200
p338 . . . . Nottingham 0115 910 0600
p338 . . . . Nottingham 0115 916 5200
p338 . . . . Nottingham 0115 952 0900
p427 . . . . . . West Bridgford 0115 914 0077
Rowe Radcliffe
p383 . . . . . South Croydon 020 8680 2070
Scott Rowe
p296 . . . . Lyme Regis 01297 443777
Rowland Tildesley & Harris
p433 . . . . Willenhall 01902 366571
Rowley Dickinson
p309 . . . . .Manchester 0161 834 4215
Rowlinsons
p227 . . . . Frodsham 01928 735333
Royce & Co
p74. . . . . London SW6 020 7736 9103
Royce Marshall & Co
p363 . . . . Retford 07765 404753
Royds LLP
p318 . . . . Morden 020 8542 1067
Roys
p182 . . . . Carlisle 01228 526385
Roythornes LLP
p327 . . . . Newmarket 01638 561320
p347 . . . . Peterborough 01733 558585
Rudd Jepson
p167 . . . . Bromley 020 8313 0555
Paul Rudd
p235 . . . . Grimsby 01472 350881
Andrew Rugg
p408 . . . . Taunton 01823 326822
Russell-Cooke LLP
p267 . Kingston upon Thames 020 8546 6111
p74. . . . . . . .London SW15 020 8789 9111
p74. . . . . London WC1 020 7405 6566
Rutters
p374 . . . . Shaftesbury 01747 852377
SAS Daniels LLP
p155 . . . . Bramhall 0161 475 7680
p198 . . . . Congleton 01260 282300
Sackvilles
p252 . . . . Hornchurch 01708 446704
p359 . . . . Rainham 01708 552804
Salmons
p323 . Newcastle under Lyme 01782 621266
Samble Burton & Worth
p170 . . . . Burton-on-Trent 01283 565731
Sanders Brickwood
p195 . . . . Cirencester 01285 654601
Peter R Sargent
p235 . . . . .Grimsby 01472 887670
Sarginsons Law LLP
p201 . . . . Coventry 024 7655 3181
Saunders & Co
p364 Richmond upon Thames 020 8332 2995
Scotts Wright
p183 . . . . Catterick Garrison 01748 832431
Seakens Solicitors
p418 . . . . Virginia Water 01344 843666
Senior Calveley & Hardy
p268 . . . . Kirkham 01772 671177
p297 . . . . Lytham 01253 733333
Serjeant & Son
p359 . . . . .Ramsey 01487 812325
The Sethi Partnership Solicitors
p216 . . . . Eastcote 020 8866 6464
Shakespeares
p339 . . . . Nottingham 0115 945 3700
Sheridan & Co
p267 . Kingston upon Thames 020 8541 1181
D R Sheridan & Co
p172 . . . . Bushey 020 8950 6768
Sherwood Solicitors
p160 . . . . Brighton 01273 608221
Shoarns Solicitors Christopher Sheehan LLB
p147 . . . . .Blandford Forum 01258 880214
Sills & Betteridge LLP
p228 . . . . Gainsborough 01427 616816
p381 . . . . .Sleaford 01529 302800
Silvesters Solicitors
p213 . . . . Dudley 01384 240880
Simmonds Hurford
p405 . . . .Swansea 01792 462729 / 641070
J A Simon & Co
p290 . . . . Liverpool 0151 256 6669
Robert Simon & Co
p378 . . . . Shoreham-by-Sea 01273 452333
Alan Simons & Co
p345 . . . . .Penarth 029 2070 3991
Sinclairs
p80. London NW4 020 8202 8222 / 8202 2042
Singhania & Co Ltd
p80. . . . . London SW1 020 7799 1688
Singleton Saunders Flood Solicitors
p213 . . . . Dover 01304 240080
Singletons Austin Ryder
p219 . . . . Enfield 020 8363 0101
Sintons LLP
p326 . . Newcastle upon Tyne 0191 226 7878
Skanthabalan Solicitors
p80. . . . . London E15 020 8555 2710
Slade Legal
p210 . . . . Didcot 01235 511211
p419 . . . . Wallingford 01491 839346
Slee Blackwell
p133 . . . . Bideford 01237 425225
Sleigh & Son
p213 . . . . .Droylsden 0161 370 2198
Sleigh Son & Booth
p213 . . . . .Droylsden 0161 370 9524
Smith & Tetley
p120 . . . Ashton-under-Lyne 0161 330 2865
E Smith & Co
p268 . . . . Kington 01544 231010
Smith Gadd & Co
p253 . . . . Horsham 01403 271222
Smith Law Partnership
p155 . . . . Braintree 01376 321311
Martin Smith & Co
p150 . . . . Borehamwood 020 8953 0636
Martin T Smith
p282 . . . . Leighton Buzzard 01525 374183
Rosemary Smith & Co
p204 . . . . Crowthorne 01344 777441
Solicitors Title
p222 . . . . .Exeter 01392 207900
Somerton & Fletcher
p175 . . . . Cambridge 01223 566596
Somerville & Savage
p413 . . . . Torquay 01803 324500
Southerns
p198 . . . . Colne 01282 863113
p321 . . . . Nelson 01282 603663
Sparling Benham & Brough
p198 . . . . .Colchester 01206 733733
p227 . . . . . Frinton-on-Sea 01255 679222
Speakman & Co
p203 . . . . .Crewe 01270 214237
Ian Spencer & Co
p322 . . . . Newbury 01635 528424
Spencer Skuse
p181 . . . . Cardiff 029 2034 3993
Sprake & Kingsley
p129 . . . . Beccles 01502 713214
Adrian Stables
p383 . . . . .Somerton 0845 873 6180
Stables & Co
p237 . . . . Halesowen 0121 585 3820
Stallard March & Edwards
p440 . . . . .Worcester 01905 613404
Standley & Co
p269 . . . . Knowle 01564 776287
Stapley & Co
p294 . . . . Loughton 020 8502 1934
Starkie & Gregory
p293 . . . . Long Eaton 0115 849 9000
Hugh Staunton
p232 . . . . Grantham 01476 861972
Steadman Jones & Bell
p118 . . . . Ammanford 01269 592306
Steed & Steed LLP
p401 . . . . .Sudbury 01787 373387
Steel & Co
p268 . . . . . Knaresborough 01423 869977
Steele & Son
p124 . . . . . . Barnoldswick 01282 813385
p196 . . . . Clitheroe 01200 444321
Steeles
p211 . . . . .Diss 01379 652141
Stephens & Son LLP
p185 . . . . Chatham 01634 811444
Jonathan Stephens & Co
p417 . . . . Usk 01291 673344
Stephenson Reynell
p434 . . . . Windermere 01539 488622
Sterratt & Co
p124 . . . . Barnoldswick 01282 813731
Stevens Lucas
p193 . . . . Chirk 01691 777949
Stilwell & Harby
p213 . . . . Dover 01304 206850
Frank Stimpson & Son
p83. . . . . .London SE23 020 8699 7644
Stirling & Co
p165 . . . . .Bristol 0117 931 4435
Stocker & Co
p410 . . . . Thame 01844 216995
Stoffel & Co
p129 . . . . .Beckenham 020 8650 8157
Stone & Stone
p318 . . . . Morden 020 8540 2202
Stone King LLP
p83. . . . . London EC1 020 7796 1007
Stone Milward Rapers
p193 . . . . .Chichester 01243 602832
Storrar Cowdry
p191 . . . . Chester 01244 400567
Stuart Smith & Burnett
p158 . . . . .Bridlington 01262 678128
Sumner & Main
p442 . . . . Worthing 01903 239420
Sutton-Mattocks & Co LLP
p84. . . . . . . .London SW13 020 8876 8811
p84. . . . . London W4 020 8994 7344
Svedberg Law
p84. . . . . London SW1 020 7368 7000
Swaby Clarke & Norris
p123 . . . . Barking 020 8507 1882
Swayne Johnson Solicitors
p369 . . . . Ruthin 01824 703833
L L Swinburne
p232 . . . . Gosforth 0191 285 7544
Swinburne Snowball & Jackson
p199 . . . . Consett 01207 502532
John Swindell and Co Solicitors
p146 . . . . .Blackburn 01254 52400
Sydney Mitchell
p142
. Birmingham 0121 722 2969 / 0808 166 5638
Sykes Anderson LLP
p85. . . . . London EC2 020 3178 3770
Symes Bains Broomer
p231 . . . . Goole 01405 763853
Symes Robinson & Lee
p203 . . . . .Crediton 01363 775566
TBI Solicitors
p123 . . . . . Barnard Castle 01833 638326
p243
. . Hartlepool 0800 052 6824 / 01429 264101

See p542 for the Firms Specialisations

TMJ Legal Services LLP
p214 . . . Durham 0191 383 0111
p434 . . . Wingate 01429 838225

TWM Solicitors LLP
p202 . . . Cranleigh 01483 273515
p219 . . . Epsom 01372 729555
p237 . . . Guildford 01483 752700
p271 . . . Leatherhead 01372 374148
p85 . . . London SW19 020 8946 6454
p363 . . . Reigate 01737 221212

David Tagg & Co
p85 . . . London SW6 020 7736 0999

Talbot & Co
p170 . . . Burton-on-Trent 01283 564716

Tanner & Taylor LLP
p225 . . . Farnham 01252 733770

Tanners
p195 . . . Cirencester 01285 659061

A P Tansey
p244 . . . Hatfield 01302 843859

Tassells
p225 . . . Faversham 01795 533337

Taylor & Emmet LLP
p377 . . . Sheffield 0114 218 4000

Taylor Bracewell
p212 . . . Doncaster 01302 341414

Taylor Legal
p203 . . . Crewe 01270 500844

Taylor Walton LLP
p239 . . . Harpenden 01582 765111
p390 . . . St Albans 01727 845245

Taylors Solicitors
p156 . . . Braunton 01271 812811

Stanley Tee
p144 . . . Bishop's Stortford 01279 755200
p155 . . . Braintree 01376 552277

Terrells LLP
p347 . . . Peterborough 01733 896789

David & Roy Thomas & Co
p351 . . . Pontardulais 01792 882410

Dean Thomas & Co
p363 . . . Retford 01777 703100

Emyr Thomas & Son
p172 . . . Caernarfon 01286 672307 / 672308

Thompson & Jackson
p350 . . . Plymouth 01752 665037 / 221171

Thomson & Bancks LLP
p346 . . . Pershore 01386 562000

Peter Thomson
p87 . . . Lambeth 020 7733 6196

Thomson Webb & Corfield
p176 . . . Cambridge 01223 518317
p176 . . . Cambridge 01223 578068

Thomson Wilson Pattinson
p264 . . . Kendal 01539 721945

Thorn Drury & Searles
p359 . . . Ramsgate 01843 593381

Andrew Thorne & Co
p374 . . . Shaw 01706 290488
p374 . . . Shaw 01706 841775

Thorne Segar
p318 . . . Minehead 01643 703234

Thorneycroft Solicitors Ltd
p297 . . . Macclesfield 01625 503444

Thornleys Limited
p350 . . . Plymouth 01752 406977

Thornton & Co
p87 . . . Hammersmith & Fulham 020 8743 3000

Thorp Parker LLP
p398 . . . Stokesley 01642 711354

Thurnhills
p357 . . . Preston 01772 251762

Thursfields
p399 . . . Stourport-on-Severn 01299 827517

Thurstan Hoskin Solicitors
p363 . . . Redruth 01209 213646

Tibbits Fisher
p143 . . . Birmingham 0121 707 3900

Tickle Hall Cross
p356 . . . Prescot 0800 854379

Tierney & Co
p210 . . . Dinnington 01909 550730
p367 . . . Rotherham 01709 709000

Timms
p209 . . . Derby 01332 364436

Tinn Criddle & Co
p115 . . . Alford 01507 462882
p389 . . . Spilsby 01790 756810

Tozers
p329 . . . Newton Abbot 01626 207020
p409 . . . Teignmouth 01626 772376

Trethowans LLP
p371 . . . Salisbury 01722 412512

Tudur Owen Roberts Glynne & Co
p122 . . . Bangor 01248 600171
p147 . . . Blaenau Ffestiniog 01766 830206
p314 . . . Menai Bridge 01248 712624

Tunnard & Co
p365 . . . Ripon 01765 605629

Turners
p204 . . . Cross Hills 01535 634149

Tustain Jones & Co
p130 . . . Bedworth 024 7664 3222
p339 . . . Nuneaton 024 7664 1222

Tyndallwoods
p143 . . . Birmingham 0121 693 2222

Underhill Langley & Wright
p157 . . . Bridgnorth 01746 764171
p438 . . . Wolverhampton 01902 423431

J G Underwood
p89 . . . London SW1 020 7730 4019

Ungoed-Thomas & King Limited
p183 . . . Carmarthen 01267 237441

Vallelys
p283 . . . Letchworth 01462 483800

Vance Harris
p204 . . . Crowborough 01892 653434

A D Varley & Co
p146 . . . Blackburn 01254 582777

Vaughan & Davies
p268 . . . Kington 01544 230325

H Vaughan Vaughan & Co
p168 . . . Builth Wells 01982 552331 / 553571
p363 . . . Rhayader 01982 552331

Veitch Penny
p203 . . . Crediton 01363 772244

P R Vince Solicitors
p227 . . . Forest Row 01342 822112

Vincent & Co
p432 . . . Wigan 01257 425121

Vincent Sykes & Higham LLP
p411 . . . Thrapston 01832 732161

Vingoe Lloyd Solicitors
p245 . . . Hayle 01736 754075

WBW Solicitors
p153 . . . Bovey Tracey 01626 833263
p222 . . . Exeter 01392 202404
p413 . . . Torquay 0870 701 4321

W Evans George & Sons
p323 . . . Newcastle Emlyn 01239 710228

Wace Morgan
p379 . . . Shrewsbury 01743 280100

Wade & Davies
p233 . . . Great Dunmow 01371 872816

Wains
p198 . . . Congleton 01260 279414

Wainwright & Cummins
p90 . . . Lambeth 020 7326 7460

Walker Foster
p124 . . . Barnoldswick 01282 812340
p380 . . . Silsden 01535 653408
p381 . . . Skipton 01756 700200

Walker Foster with Kennedy Thompson
p261 . . . Ilkley 01943 609969

Percy Walker & Co
p243 . . . Hastings 01424 721234

Walker Smith Way
p443 . . . Wrexham 0844 346 3100

Wallace Robinson & Morgan
p383 . . . Solihull 0121 705 7571

Wanham Longhurst & Co
p171 . . . Bury St Edmunds 01284 735808

Wannop Fox Staffurth & Bray
p148 . . . Bognor Regis 01243 864001
p193 . . . Chichester 01243 778844
p442 . . . Worthing 01903 228200

Ward Gethin
p266 . . . King's Lynn 01553 660033
p404 . . . Swaffham 01760 721992

Ware & Kay LLP
p445 . . . York 01904 716000

Steven Warne Solicitor
p373 . . . Scunthorpe 01724 279449

Warners Solicitors
p374 . . . Sevenoaks 01732 747900
p412 . . . Tonbridge 01732 770660

Linda S Warren
p333 . . . Northwood 01923 821213

Wartnabys
p312 . . . Market Harborough 01858 463322

Rosalind Watchorn
p377 . . . Sheffield 0114 229 0160

Waters & Co
p143 . . . Birmingham 01675 463855

Kathleen Watkin
p350 . . . Plymouth 01752 666715

Watson Marshal
p90 . . . London W4 020 8987 0100

Waugh & Co
p246 . . . Haywards Heath 01444 451666

Waugh & Musgrave
p197 . . . Cockermouth 01900 823127

Wayman & Long
p401 . . . Sudbury 01787 277375

Weatherhead & Butcher
p133 . . . Bingley 01274 562322

Susan Weeden & Company
p264 . . . Keighley 01535 658488

Whatley & Co
p91 . . . Barnet 020 8205 1411 / 8205 8931

Whatley Recordon
p300 . . . Malvern 01684 892939

Whetter Duckworth Fowler
p266 . . . Kidlington 01865 842100
p344 . . . Oxford 01865 872206

Whitehead Monckton
p299 . . . Maidstone 01622 698000
p410 . . . Tenterden 01580 765722

Whiting & Mason
p321 . . . New Mills 01663 742432 / 747958

John Whiting & Co
p270 . . . Launceston 01566 777677

Hugh Whitlock
p316 . . . Milford-on-Sea 01590 644777

Wiggin Osborne Fullerlove
p189 . . . Cheltenham 01242 710200

Guy Wigmore Solicitor
p388 . . . Southport 01704 222277

Max Wiley & Co
p251 . . . Holt 01263 711771

Wilkins & Thompson
p417 . . . Uttoxeter 01889 562875

Jane V Wilkinson
p147 . . . Blandford Forum 01258 817719

Willcox Lewis LLP
p335 . . . Norwich 01508 480100

Willett & Co
p171 . . . Bury St Edmunds 01284 701323

Willetts Marsden
p422 . . . Warrington 01925 230020

Williams & Co
p296 . . . Luton 01582 723322

Williams Beales & Co
p245 . . . Hay-on-Wye 01497 820302

Eirian J Williams a'i Gwmni
p292 . . . Llandysul 01559 363244

RTP Williams Limited
p244 . . . Haverfordwest 01437 762321

Williams Thompson
p194 . . . Christchurch 01202 484242

Williams Woolley
p348 . . . Petworth 01798 342581

Williamsons
p431 . . . Whitley Bay 0191 252 7711

Wills & Probate Countrywide
p408 . . . Tavistock 01626 334455

Wills Chandler Beach
p226 . . . Fleet 01252 613351

Wilmot & Co Solicitors LLP
p195 . . . Cirencester 01285 650551

Wilmot Thompson
p165 . . . Bristol 0117 927 6583

Wilson Bullough Walton & Knowles
p330
. . Newton-le-Willows 01925 224569 / 224560

Winch & Winch
p185 . . . Chatham 01634 830111

Windeatts
p267 . . . Kingsbridge 01548 852727
p413 . . . Totnes 01803 862233

Winder Taylor Fallows
p150 . . . Bolton 01204 697467

Winterbotham Smith Penley LLP
p320 . . . Nailsworth 01453 832566
p401 . . . Stroud 01453 847200

Winton Raynes & Co
p406 . . . Swindon 01793 522688

Wiseman Lee LLP
p92 . . . Redbridge 020 8215 1000

Withy King Solicitors
p128 . . . Bath 01225 425731

Wollen Michelmore Solicitors
p345 . . . Paignton 01803 521692

Clive G Wood & Co
p396 . . . Stockport 0161 480 1000

Lawrence Wood
p443 . . . Wroxham 01603 783711

Rupert Wood & Son
p120 . . . Ashton-under-Lyne 0161 330 9121

Wood's Solicitors
p210 . . . Disley 01663 765511

Woodcock & Thompson
p333 . . . Northampton 01604 758855

Woodfines LLP
p372 . . . Sandy 01767 680251

Woodhouse & Company
p438 . . . Wolverhampton 01902 773616

Richard A Woodman
p239 . . . Harpenden 01582 768222

Woolley Beardsleys & Bosworth
p293 . . . Loughborough 01509 212266

Woolliscrofts
p398 . . . Stoke-on-Trent 01782 577246

Woolsey Morris & Kennedy
p380 . . . Sidcup 020 8300 9321

Worger Howcroft
p133 . . . Bingley 01274 511246

Wright & Lord
p319 . . . Morecambe 01524 402050

Wright & Wright
p237 . . . Guildford 01483 531264

Wright Son & Pepper LLP
p93 . . . Camden 020 7242 5473

Wrigleys Solicitors LLP
p278 . . . Leeds 0113 244 6100
p377 . . . Sheffield 0114 267 5588

Wykeham & Co
p193 . . . Chippenham 01249 721010

Wylie Kay
p147 . . . Blackpool 01253 296297

Denis Wynn & Co
p193 . . . Chipping Norton 01608 643036

Yorklaw Ltd (t/a Burn & Company)
p215 . . . Easingwold 01347 822188
p445 . . . York 01904 655442

Yorkshire Law Solicitors
p167 . . . Brough 01430 422422

Young & Co
p130 . . . Bedford 01234 346411 / 344211

Young Coles & Langdon
p132 . . . Bexhill 01424 210013
p244 . . . Hastings 01424 437878

SECTION 5

SOLICITORS

CONTENTS

PUBLICLY FUNDED LEGAL SERVICES – COMMUNITY LEGAL SERVICE

5

Work Categories

Actions Against the Police
Clinical Negligence
Community Care
Consumer & General Contract
Debt
Education
Employment
Family
Housing
Immigration / Nationality
Mental Health
Personal Injury
Welfare Benefits

ACTIONS AGAINST THE POLICE

Abney Garsden McDonald *p185* 0161 482 8822
Anderson Ross Solicitors *p241* 020 3170 6030
Arani & Co *p384* 020 8893 5000
Ballam *p134* 0151 647 8977
Bawtrees LLP *p435* 01376 513491
Beesley & Co *p301* 0161 445 3678
Belshaws Solicitors Limited *p395* 0161 477 5377
Ben Hoare Bell & Co *p401* 0191 565 3112
Ben Hoare Bell & Co *p323* 0191 275 2626
Bennett Richmond *p270* 01207 521843
Best Solicitors *p375* 0114 281 3636
Bhatt Murphy *p12* 020 7729 1115
Bindmans LLP *p12* 020 7833 4433
Birchall Blackburn LLP *p301* 0161 236 0662
Birnberg Peirce & Partners *p13* 020 7911 0166
Bishop McBride Olden *p177* 029 2049 0111
Blackfords LLP *p204* 020 8686 6232
Bobbetts Mackan *p161* 0117 929 9001
Brearleys Solicitors *p144* 01924 443900
Broudie Jackson Canter *p286* 0151 227 1429
Caldicott Gallimore *p282* 01568 614168
Chadwick Lawrence *p319* 0113 252 3452
Chadwick Lawrence *p238* 01422 330601
Chadwick Lawrence *p255* 01484 519999
Clarion Solicitors LLP *p272* 0113 246 0622
Clarke Kiernan *p412* 01732 360999
Clifford Johnston & Co *p302* 0161 249 2700
Clifford Johnston & Co *p302* 0161 975 1900
Douglas Clift & Co *p269* 01524 32437
Clinton Davis Pallis *p21* 020 8880 5000
Coles Miller Solicitors LLP *p352* 01202 673011
Coninghams Solicitors *p22* 020 8296 1957
DB Law *p346* 01736 364261
DB Law *p223* 01326 211609
DB Law *p392* 01736 793883
Edwards Duthie *p260* 020 8514 9000
Edwards Duthie *p29* 020 8514 9000
Edwards Duthie *p29* 020 8514 9000
R L Edwards & Partners *p157* 01656 656861
Ennon & Co Solicitors *p29* 020 7281 2123
Farleys Solicitors LLP *p145* 01254 367855
Farleys Solicitors LLP *p145* 01254 367856
Fisher Meredith *p32* 020 7091 2700
Fletcher Dervish *p33* 020 8800 4615
Fraser Wise & Co *p232* 01476 566646 / 561870
GC Law *p248* 01432 275397
Craig Gee *p304* 0161 666 9999
GEORGE IDE LLP *p192* 01243 786668
Goldkorn Mathias Gentle Page LLP *p36* 020 7631 1811
David Gray Solicitors *p324* 0191 232 9547
Gregsons *p337* 0115 941 1999
Harding Evans LLP *p328* 01633 244233
Christopher Harris & Co *p375* 01795 661521
Harrison Bundey *p274* 0113 200 7400
Hatten Wyatt *p232* 01474 351199
Hickman & Rose *p41* 020 7700 2211
HODGE JONES & ALLEN LLP *p41* 020 7874 8300
Hoole & Co *p163* 0117 942 8871
Howells LLP *p367* 01709 364000
Howells LLP *p376* 0114 249 6666
J W Hughes & Co *p199* 01492 596596
Henry Hyams *p274* 0113 243 2288
Ison Harrison *p228* 0113 286 1455
Ison Harrison *p274* 0113 232 6530
Ison Harrison *p274* 0113 284 5000
Jepson & Co *p372* 01723 859249
Jobling Gowler *p297* 01625 614250
Terry Jones Solicitors & Advocates *p379* 01743 285888
Terry Jones Solicitors & Advocates *p409* 01952 297979
Jordans *p210* 01924 457171
Jordans *p183* 01977 518778
Jordans *p418* 01924 387110
Kaim Todner Ltd *p47* 020 7701 4747
Kaim Todner Ltd *p47* 020 7353 6660
Kaim Todner Ltd *p47* 020 7700 0070
Kaim Todner Ltd *p119* 01233 662002
Kerseys *p262* 01473 213311
Christian Khan Solicitors *p49* 020 7631 9500
Khan Solicitors *p154* 01274 301999
Lansbury Worthington *p51* 020 8563 9797
Lawson & Thompson *p130* 01670 530700
Lester Morrill *p275* 0113 245 8549
Letchers *p364* 01425 471424
Leviten Thompson & Co *p376* 0114 276 9321
Robert Lizar *p307* 0161 226 2319
Robert Lizar *p307* 0161 860 7797
E Rex Makin & Co *p289* 0151 709 4491
Mallia & Co *p180* 029 2022 0044
Marshall Hall & Levy *p384* 0191 455 3181
Milne & Lyall *p158* 01308 422362
Morgans *p180* 029 2072 9888
Moss & Co *p62* 020 8986 8336
James Murray Solicitors *p150* 0151 933 3333
James Murray Solicitors *p290* 0151 207 9910
Nelsons *p338* 0115 958 6262
Norrie Waite & Slater *p367* 01709 523983
Norrie Waite & Slater *p377* 0114 276 5015
David Phillips & Partners *p150* 0151 922 5525
Pluck Andrew & Co *p120* 0161 330 2875
QualitySolicitors Jackson & Canter *p290* 0151 282 1700
Rawal & Co *p70* 020 8445 0303
Red Kite Law *p183* 01267 239000
Samars Solicitors *p254* 020 8570 4716
Saulet & Co *p389* 023 9281 9442
Saunders Law Partnership LLP *p76* 020 7632 4300
SILLS & BETTERIDGE LLP *p381* 01529 302800
SILLS & BETTERIDGE LLP *p285* 01522 542211
SILLS & BETTERIDGE LLP *p151* 01205 364615
SILLS & BETTERIDGE LLP *p199* 01526 344444
Solomon Levy *p295* 01582 425817 / 414948
Stephensons Solicitors LLP *p282* 01942 777777
G T Stewart Solicitors *p83* 020 8299 6000
Tait Farrier Graham *p229* 0191 490 0108
Tranters *p310* 0161 998 9999
Tyndallwoods *p143* 0121 624 1111
Wilkin Chapman Epton Blades *p285* 01522 512345
Wilsons Solicitors *p344* 01865 874497
Worthingtons *p227* 01303 850206

CLINICAL NEGLIGENCE

Alsters Kelley *p339* 0844 561 0100
Alsters Kelley *p199* 0844 561 0100
Alsters Kelley *p270* 0844 561 0100
Ameer Meredith *p174* 01223 577077
ANTHONY GOLD *p6* 020 7940 4000
ANTHONY GOLD *p6* 020 7940 4000
ANTHONY GOLD *p6* 020 7940 4000
Archers Law LLP *p396* 01642 636500
Armstrong Foulkes *p314* 01642 231110
Ashton KCJ *p174* 01223 363111
Ashton KCJ *p171* 01284 761233
Ashton KCJ *p333* 01603 703070
Atherton Godfrey *p211* 01302 320621
Attwaters *p294* 020 8508 2111
Attwaters *p239* 01279 638888
Barcan Woodward *p160* 0117 963 5237
Barcan Woodward *p161* 0117 925 8080
Barcan Woodward *p161* 0117 923 2141
Sarah Barclay & Co *p146* 01253 356051
Brian Barr Solicitors *p301* 0161 720 6700
Barratt Goff & Tomlinson *p335* 0115 931 5171
Ben Hoare Bell & Co *p401* 0191 565 3112
Ben Hoare Bell & Co *p323* 0191 275 2626
Bindmans LLP *p12* 020 7833 4433
Blake Lapthorn *p342* 01865 248607
Bonallack & Bishop *p117* 01980 622992
Bonallack & Bishop *p118* 01264 364433
Bonallack & Bishop *p371* 01722 422300
Bridge McFarland *p235* 01472 311711
Bridge McFarland *p284* 01522 518888
Bridge McFarland Haddon Owen *p294* 01507 605883
BRINDLEY TWIST TAFFT & JAMES *p200* 024 7653 1532
Burnetts *p181* 01228 552222
Burnetts *p182* 01228 552222
Butcher & Barlow LLP *p170* 0161 764 4062
Butcher & Barlow LLP *p333* 01606 47523
Chadwick Lawrence *p319* 0113 252 3452
Chadwick Lawrence *p238* 01422 330601
Chadwick Lawrence *p255* 01484 519999
Clarke Willmott *p162* 0845 209 1000 / 0117 305 6000
Clarke Willmott *p408* 0845 209 1000 / 0117 305 6000
Clarkson Wright & Jakes Ltd *p341* 01689 887887
Coffin Mew & Clover *p385* 023 8033 4661
Coffin Mew & Clover *p354* 023 9238 8021
Coffin Mew & Clover *p232* 023 9252 3111
Coffin Mew & Clover *p223* 01329 825617
Colemans - CTTS *p302* 0161 876 2500
Anthony Collins Solicitors LLP *p137* 0121 200 3242
John Collins & Partners LLP *p405* 01792 773773
K J Commons & Co *p440* 01900 604698
K J Commons & Co *p431* 01946 66699
K J Commons & Co *p182* 01228 822666
Dale & Newbery LLP *p393* 01784 464491
Darbys Solicitors LLP *p343* 01865 811700
David & Snape *p353* 01656 782070 / 785038
Davies & Partners *p230* 01452 612345
Dicksons Solicitors Ltd *p397* 01782 262424
Dicksons Solicitors Ltd *p397* 01782 262424
Donns *p303* 0161 834 3311
S J Edney *p406* 0800 421234
Edwards Duthie *p260* 020 8514 9000
Edwards Duthie *p29* 020 8514 9000
Edwards Duthie *p29* 020 8514 9000
Fairweather & Co Solicitors *p176* 01227 784337
Fletchers *p388* 01704 546919
Freemans *p324* 0191 222 1030
Gadsby Wicks *p186* 01245 494929
Gardner Leader LLP *p322* 01635 508080
Garside & Hoy *p424* 020 8427 5656
GEORGE IDE LLP *p192* 01243 786668
Graysons *p375* 0114 272 9184
Graystons *p435* 0151 645 0055
hlw Keeble Hawson LLP *p211* 01302 366831
hlw Keeble Hawson LLP *p375* 0114 272 2061
hlw Keeble Hawson LLP *p274* 0113 244 3121
HRJ Law LLP *p251* 01462 628888
HRJ Law LLP *p425* 01707 887700
Lawrence Hamblin *p247* 01491 411884
Lawrence Hamblin *p361* 0118 951 6180 / 951 6190
Hansells *p331* 01692 404351
Hansells *p121* 01263 734313
Hansells *p378* 01263 822176
Harding Evans LLP *p328* 01633 244233
Harman & Harman *p39* 01227 452977
Harris Cartier LLP *p382* 01753 810710
Harrison Bundey *p274* 0113 200 7400
Harrowells *p445* 01904 760237
Harrowells *p444* 01904 558600
Harrowells *p444* 01904 690111
Hart Brown Solicitors *p202* 0800 068 8177

Hart Brown Solicitors *p231* . . . 0800 068 8177
Hart Brown Solicitors *p236* . . . 0800 068 8177
Hart Brown Solicitors *p196* . . . 0800 068 8177
Harvey Ingram LLP *p280* . . . 0116 254 5454
Hay & Kilner *p325* . . . 0191 232 8345
Henmans LLP *p343* . . . 01865 781000
Heptonstalls LLP *p255* . . . 01430 430209
Heptonstalls LLP *p231* . . . 01405 765661
Heptonstalls LLP *p373* . . . 01724 289959
Hewitsons *p332* . . . 01604 233233
Hewitsons *p370* . . . 01799 522471
Hewitsons *p174* . . . 01223 461155
HODGE JONES & ALLEN LLP *p41* . . . 020 7874 8300
Howells LLP *p367* . . . 01709 364000
Howells LLP *p376* . . . 0114 249 6666
Ison Harrison *p228* . . . 0113 286 1455
Ison Harrison *p274* . . . 0113 232 6530
Ison Harrison *p274* . . . 0113 284 5000
Jobling Gowler *p297* . . . 01625 614250
Christian Khan Solicitors *p49* . . . 020 7631 9500
Lanyon Bowdler LLP *p379* . . . 01743 280280
Lanyon Bowdler LLP *p409* . . . 01952 291222
Lanyon Bowdler LLP *p425* . . . 01952 244721
Latimer Lee LLP *p358* . . . 0161 798 9000
Lee & Priestley LLP *p275* . . . 0845 129 2300
Lees Solicitors LLP *p428* . . . 0151 625 9364
Lees Solicitors LLP *p249* . . . 0151 342 6273
Lees Solicitors LLP *p134* . . . 0151 647 9381
LEIGH DAY & CO *p52* . . . 020 7650 1200
Lester Morrill *p275* . . . 0113 245 8549
Longden Walker & Renney *p401* . . . 0191 567 7024
Charles Lucas & Marshall *p322* . . . 01635 521212
MMS Solicitors *p436* . . . 01964 612318
MPH Solicitors *p307* . . . 0161 832 7722
McMillan Williams *p199* . . . 020 8668 4131
McMillan Williams *p419* . . . 020 8669 4962
McMillan Williams *p205* . . . 01689 848311
McMillan Williams *p411* . . . 020 8653 8844
McMillan Williams *p383* . . . 020 8253 7600
MARTYN PROWEL *p180* . . . 029 2047 0909
Maxwell Gillott (MG Law Ltd) *p270* . . . 0844 858 3900
Maxwell Hodge Solicitors *p268* . . . 0151 548 7370
Maxwell Hodge Solicitors *p298* . . . 0151 526 7131
Mayo Wynne Baxter LLP *p160* . . . 01273 775533
Hilary Meredith Solicitors *p433* . . . 01625 539922
Metcalfes *p164* . . . 0117 929 0451
Michelmores LLP *p221* . . . 01392 688688
Milburns Solicitors *p440* . . . 01900 67363
Milburns Solicitors *p313* . . . 01900 813541
Mincoffs Solicitors LLP *p325* . . . 0191 281 6151
Mintons *p275* . . . 0113 245 7575
Morgan Jones & Pett *p335* . . . 01603 877000
Nelsons *p338* . . . 0115 958 6262
Osborne Morris & Morgan *p282* . . . 01525 378177
Over Taylor Biggs *p222* . . . 01392 823811
Pannone LLP *p308* . . . 0161 909 3000
Pardoes *p158* . . . 01278 457891
Pardoes *p408* . . . 01823 446200
Park Woodfine Heald Mellows LLP *p130* . 01234 400000
Parker Rhodes Hickmotts *p367* . . . 01709 511100
Parlett Kent *p66* . . . 020 7430 0712
Parlett Kent *p222* . . . 01392 494455
Pattinson & Brewer *p66* . . . 020 7400 5100
Pattinson & Brewer *p445* . . . 01904 680000
Pearson Hinchliffe *p341* . . . 0161 785 3500
Samuel Phillips Law Firm *p326* . . . 0191 232 8451
John Pickering & Partners LLP *p238* . . . 0808 144 0959
Poole Alcock *p320* . . . 01270 625478
Potter Rees (Serious Injury) Solicitors *p309* . . . 0161 237 5888
Preston Goldburn *p223* . . . 01326 318900
Pritchard Englefield *p69* . . . 020 7972 9720
Raleys *p125* . . . 01226 211111
Ranson Houghton *p118* . . . 01264 351533
Robinson Allfree *p359* . . . 01843 592361
Robinson Allfree *p166* . . . 01843 865261
The Roland Partnership *p191* . . . 01244 659404
RUSSELL-COOKE LLP *p74* . . . 020 8789 9111
Russell Jones & Walker *p180* . . . 029 2026 2800
Scrivenger Seabrook *p392* . . . 01480 214900
Sheridan & Co *p267* . . . 020 8541 1181
Simpson Millar LLP *p276* . . . 0844 858 3200
Smith Llewelyn Partnership *p405* . . . 01792 464444
Stamp Jackson and Procter *p258* . . . 01482 324591
Stanley Tee LLP *p175* . . . 01223 311141
Stephensons Solicitors LLP *p282* . . . 01942 777777
Sternberg Reed *p123* . . . 020 8591 3366
Stewarts Law LLP *p83* . . . 020 7822 8000
Stewarts Law LLP *p277* . . . 0113 222 0022
Swain & Co *p386* . . . 023 8063 1111
Swain & Co *p244* . . . 023 9248 3322
TBI Solicitors *p243* . . . 0800 052 6824 / 01429 264101
TPC Solicitors *p310* . . . 0161 832 8867
Talbot Walker LLP *p118* . . . 01264 363354
Talbot Walker LLP *p127* . . . 01256 332404
Taylor & Emmet LLP *p377* . . . 0114 218 4000
Teacher Stern LLP *p86* . . . 020 7242 3191
Thompson Smith & Puxon *p198* . . . 01206 574431
Thomson Snell & Passmore *p415* . . . 01892 510000
Tilly Bailey & Irvine LLP *p397* . . . 01642 673797
Tozers *p329* . . . 01626 207020
Tozers *p222* . . . 01392 207020
Trethowans LLP *p371* . . . 01722 412512
Trethowans LLP *p387* . . . 023 8032 1000
WBW Solicitors *p329* . . . 01626 202404
WBW Solicitors *p153* . . . 01626 833263
WBW Solicitors *p413* . . . 0870 701 4321
WBW Solicitors *p222* . . . 01392 202404
Walker Smith Way *p443* . . . 0844 346 3100
Walker Smith Way *p191* . . . 0844 346 3100
Walker Smith Way *p120* . . . 0844 346 3100
Weightmans LLP *p311* . . . 0161 233 7330
Williamsons *p258* . . . 01482 323697
Wilson Browne *p425* . . . 01933 279000
Wiseman Lee LLP *p92* . . . 020 8215 1000
Wiseman Lee LLP *p92* . . . 020 8215 1000
Withy King Solicitors *p128* . . . 01225 425731

COMMUNITY CARE

Adlams LLP *p392* . . . 01480 474061
Ben Hoare Bell & Co *p401* . . . 0191 565 3112
Ben Hoare Bell & Co *p323* . . . 0191 275 2626
Best Solicitors *p375* . . . 0114 281 3636
Broudie Jackson Canter *p286* . . . 0151 227 1429
Burton & Co LLP *p284* . . . 01522 523215
Julie Burton *p122* . . . 01248 364750
Campbell Law Solicitors *p316* . . . 0845 226 8118
Campbell-Taylor Solicitors *p18* . . . 0845 567 2457
Clark Willis *p206* . . . 01325 281111
Clark Willis *p183* . . . 01748 830000
The Community Law Partnership *p137* . . . 0121 685 8595
Edwards Duthie *p260* . . . 020 8514 9000
Edwards Duthie *p29* . . . 020 8514 9000
Edwards Duthie *p29* . . . 020 8514 9000
Peter Edwards Law *p435* . . . 0151 632 6699
Fisher Meredith *p32* . . . 020 7091 2700
John Ford Solicitors *p33* . . . 020 8800 6464
Glaisyers Solicitors LLP *p304* . . . 0161 832 4666
Glaisyers Solicitors LLP *p304* . . . 0161 224 3311
Hansen Palomares *p38* . . . 020 7640 4600
Hiace Solicitors *p205* . . . 020 8686 3777
Hickman & Rose *p41* . . . 020 7700 2211
Holls Solicitors *p129* . . . 020 8658 9767
Hossacks *p265* . . . 01536 518638
Howells LLP *p367* . . . 01709 364000
Howells LLP *p376* . . . 0114 249 6666
Gwyn James Solicitors *p195* . . . 01594 822277
Gwyn James Solicitors *p198* . . . 01594 833042
Keoghs and Nicholls, Lindsell & Harris *p116* . . . 0161 928 9321
Duncan Lewis & Co *p53* . . . 020 7923 4020
Llewellyn Jones & Co *p369* . . . 01824 704495
Mackintosh Duncan *p57* . . . 020 7357 6464
Marshall Hall & Levy *p384* . . . 0191 455 3181
Maxwell Gillott (MG Law Ltd) *p270* . . . 0844 858 3900
Milne & Lyall *p158* . . . 01308 422362
Morgans *p180* . . . 029 2072 9888
Morrison Spowart *p62* . . . 020 8698 9200
Payne & Gamage *p322* . . . 01636 640649
QualitySolicitors Jackson & Canter *p290* . 0151 282 1700
Ridley & Hall *p256* . . . 01484 538421
Samars Solicitors *p254* . . . 020 8570 4716
Saulet & Co *p389* . . . 023 9281 9442
TBI Solicitors *p243* . . . 0800 052 6824 / 01429 264101
TV Edwards LLP *p85* . . . 020 7790 7000
TV Edwards LLP *p85* . . . 020 7790 7000
Tyrer Roxburgh & Co *p89* . . . 020 8889 3319
WBW Solicitors *p329* . . . 01626 202404
WBW Solicitors *p153* . . . 01626 833263
WBW Solicitors *p222* . . . 01392 202404
Wilkin Chapman Epton Blades *p285* . . . 01522 512345
Wilsons Solicitors *p344* . . . 01865 874497
Worthingtons *p227* . . . 01303 850206
Zermansky & Partners *p278* . . . 0113 245 9766

CONSUMER & GENERAL CONTRACT

Abels *p385* . . . 023 8022 0317
Adlams LLP *p392* . . . 01480 474061
Allington Hughes *p442* . . . 01978 291000
Anderson Partnership *p191* . . . 01246 220737
Arscotts *p254* . . . 01273 735289
Ashfords LLP *p412* . . . 01884 203000
Ashfords LLP *p408* . . . 01823 232300
Ashton KCJ *p171* . . . 01284 762331
Ashton KCJ *p262* . . . 01473 232425
Aston Clark *p8* . . . 020 8752 1122
Atteys *p211* . . . 01302 340400
Attwood & Co *p233* . . . 01375 378122 / 378123
BLB Solicitors *p413* . . . 01225 755656
BLB Solicitors *p406* . . . 01793 615011
Ursula Bagnall Divorce & Family Law Solicitors *p201* . . . 01983 247221
Banks Kelly *p9* . . . 020 7248 4231
Banner Jones *p191* . . . 01246 209773
Max Barford & Co *p414* . . . 01892 539379
Barker Booth & Eastwood *p146* . . . 01253 362500
John Barkers *p294* . . . 01507 604773
Bates N V H *p11* . . . 020 7936 2930
Bawtrees LLP *p435* . . . 01376 513491
Ben Hoare Bell & Co *p401* . . . 0191 565 3112
Ben Hoare Bell & Co *p323* . . . 0191 275 2626
Ben Hoare Bell & Co *p401* . . . 0191 516 0466
Bennett Richmond *p270* . . . 01207 521843
Bernard Chill & Axtell *p385* . . . 023 8022 8821
Best Solicitors *p375* . . . 0114 281 3636
Birchall Blackburn LLP *p356* . . . 01772 561663
Biscoes *p348* . . . 01730 264799
Biscoes *p354* . . . 023 9266 0261
Biscoes *p423* . . . 023 9225 1257
Biscoes *p431* . . . 01329 833249
Biscoes *p232* . . . 023 9251 2030
Biscoes *p353* . . . 023 9237 0634
Blackhurst Budd LLP *p146* . . . 01253 629300
Bolitho Way *p354* . . . 023 9282 0747
Boyce Hatton *p412* . . . 01803 403403
John Boyle & Co *p414* . . . 01872 272356
Brearleys Solicitors *p128* . . . 01924 473065
Brearleys Solicitors *p144* . . . 01924 443900
Brennans Solicitors *p419* . . . 0191 262 5133
Brighouse Wolff *p341* . . . 01695 573202
Brighouse Wolff *p381* . . . 01695 722577
Brighouses *p388* . . . 01704 534101 / 500151
Brooks *p378* . . . 01608 664406
Broomhead & Saul *p408* . . . 01823 288121
Broomhead & Saul *p261* . . . 01460 57056
Burges Salmon *p161* . . . 0117 939 2000
Burley & Geach *p243* . . . 01428 656011
Burley & Geach *p233* . . . 01428 605355
Burley & Geach *p285* . . . 01428 722334
Burton & Burton Solicitors LLP *p336* . . . 0845 094 2500
Burton & Co LLP *p284* . . . 01522 523215
Burton & Co LLP *p381* . . . 01529 306008 / 306009
BURY & WALKERS LLP *p124* . . . 01226 733533
Kenneth Bush *p266* . . . 01553 692233
Kenneth Bush *p266* . . . 01553 692737
CMHT Solicitors *p420* . . . 01922 646400
CVC Solicitors *p346* . . . 01736 362313
Campbell Courtney & Cooney *p173* . . . 01276 25100
Carmichael & Heathfield *p324* . . . 0191 230 3010
Cartwright Cunningham Haselgrove & Co *p19* . . . 020 8520 1021
Chadwick Lawrence *p418* . . . 01924 379078
Chadwick Lawrence *p319* . . . 0113 252 3452
Chadwick Lawrence *p238* . . . 01422 330601
Chadwick Lawrence *p255* . . . 01484 519999
Chafes *p395* . . . 0161 477 1525
Challinors *p136* . . . 0121 212 9393
Chambers Solicitors *p381* . . . 01753 522204
Chanter Ferguson *p132* . . . 01237 478751
Chattertons Solicitors *p252* . . . 01507 522456
Chattertons Solicitors *p284* . . . 01522 814600
G & I Chisholm *p148* . . . 01208 74242
Churchers *p271* . . . 023 9255 1500
Churchers *p232* . . . 023 9260 3400
Churchers *p223* . . . 01329 822333
Churchers *p354* . . . 023 9221 0170
Clark Willis *p183* . . . 01748 830000
Coffin Mew & Clover *p385* . . . 023 8033 4661
Coffin Mew & Clover *p354* . . . 023 9238 8021
Coffin Mew & Clover *p232* . . . 023 9252 3111
Coffin Mew & Clover *p223* . . . 01329 825617
Coles Miller Solicitors LLP *p352* . . . 01202 673011
Coles Miller Solicitors LLP *p151* . . . 01202 511512
Collins Solicitors *p423* . . . 01923 223324
Coodes *p285* . . . 01579 347600
Cooper Lingard *p282* . . . 01702 715411
Cooper Sons Hartley & Williams *p184* . . . 01298 812138
Cornfield Law *p215* . . . 01323 412512
DBL Talbots LLP *p197* . . . 01902 843427
Darling & Stephensons *p206* . . . 01325 489000
Davies Sully Wilkins *p172* . . . 029 2088 7828
Daybells LLP *p26* . . . 020 8555 4321
Desor & Co *p245* . . . 020 8569 0708
Dixon Stewart *p321* . . . 01425 621515
Douglas-Jones Mercer *p405* . . . 01792 650000
Scott Duff & Co *p182* . . . 01228 531054
Eaton Smith LLP *p255* . . . 01484 821300
Eatons *p153* . . . 0845 660 0660
Edwards Duthie *p260* . . . 020 8514 9000
Edwards Duthie *p29* . . . 020 8514 9000
Edwards Duthie *p29* . . . 020 8514 9000
R L Edwards & Partners *p157* . . . 01656 656861
Thomas Eggar LLP *p441* . . . 01903 234411
Thomas Eggar LLP *p202* . . . 01293 742700
Thomas Eggar LLP *p192* . . . 01243 786111
Elliot Mather LLP *p192* . . . 01246 231288
Ellis-Fermor & Negus *p364* . . . 01773 744744

See p603 for the Community Legal Service Work Categories

Ellis-Fermor & Negus p130 0115 922 1591
Ellis-Fermor & Negus p293 0115 972 5222
Eric Robinson Solicitors p184 023 8025 4676
Eric Robinson Solicitors p385 023 8042 5000
Farnfield & Nicholls p374 01747 854244
A J Field & Co p375 01795 580600
Finn Gledhill p238 01422 330000
Fisher Jones Greenwood LLP p186 01245 890110
Fisher Jones Greenwood LLP p197 01206 578282
Fletcher Dervish p33 020 8800 4615
Forbes p145 01254 54374
Forbes p114 01254 872111
Forbes p356 01772 220022
Ford Simey LLP p221 01392 274126
Ford Simey LLP p380 01395 577061 / 0800 169 3741
Ford Simey LLP p222 01395 272241 / 0800 169 3741
Forshaws Davies Ridgway LLP p227 01928 739300
Fosters p334 01603 620508
Fosters p168 01986 895251
Foys Solicitors p375 0114 246 7609
Fraser Dawbarns p435 01945 461456
Fraser Dawbarns p266 01553 666600
Fraser Dawbarns p213 01366 383171
GLP Solicitors p304 0161 834 6721
GLP Solicitors p357 0161 773 8626
GLP Solicitors p304 0161 793 0901
Gabb & Co p203 01873 810629
Gardner Leader LLP p410 01635 508080
Gartsides p113 01873 857555
George H Coles & Co p254 01273 205101
Gilbert Turner Coomber p35 020 8520 5886
Glaisyers p138 0121 233 2971
Glanvilles p328 01983 527878
Godloves p273 0113 225 8864
Godloves p273 0113 225 8874
Goldbergs p349 01752 660023
Goldstones p405 01792 643021
HC Solicitors LLP p347 01733 882800
Hadaway & Hadaway p330 0191 257 0382
Haider Kennedy Legal Services Ltd p37 020 8771 2323
HallmarkHulme p439 01905 726600
Hansells p203 01263 512003
Harding Evans LLP p328 01633 244233
Harding Swinburne Jackson & Co p401 0191 565 8194
Harpers p39 020 7405 8888
Christopher Harris & Co p375 01795 661521
Christopher Harris & Co p380 01795 437268
David W Harris & Co p352 01443 486666
Harvey Ingram Borneos p130 01234 353221
Harvey Ingram Borneos p317 01908 696002
Heer Manak p200 024 7666 4000
Henriques Griffiths p163 0117 909 4000
Henriques Griffiths p435 01454 854000
Herrington & Carmichael LLP p437 0118 977 4045
Herrington & Carmichael LLP p173 01276 686222
Hetts p373 01724 843287
Hetts p373 01724 270290
Hewetts p361 0118 957 5337
Hewitts p330 01325 316170
Hewitts p206 01325 468573
Hood Vores & Allwood p209 01362 692424
Howells LLP p367 01709 364000
Howells LLP p376 0114 249 6666
Humphrys & Co p363 01745 343158
Ismail & Co p218 020 8804 1065
JMD Law Limited p179 029 2045 6780
JMW Solicitors p306 0845 872 6666
Jackamans p262 01473 255591
Jackamans p210 01379 643555
Jackamans p225 01394 279636
Jefferies Essex LLP p428 01702 332311
Jepson & Co p372 01723 859249
Jobling & Knape p319 01524 416960
Johar & Co p280 0116 254 3345
Geraint Jones & Co p330 01686 627935
Geraint Jones & Co p291 01597 822244
Kennards Wells p48 020 8539 8338
Kerseys p262 01473 213311
Kidd Rapinet p382 0845 017 9638
Kidd Rapinet p298 0845 017 9608
Kirby Sheppard p411 0845 840 0045
Kirby Sheppard p268 0845 840 0045
Kitsons LLP p413 01803 202020
Kitsons LLP p329 01626 203366
Kitsons LLP p221 01392 455555
Kitsons LLP p350 01752 603040
Knowles Benning p295 01582 798000
LD Law p239 01279 441266
Laceys p353 01202 743286
Lancasters p158 01262 602401
Langleys p445 01904 610886
Larken & Co p322 01636 703333
Law Hurst & Taylor p428 01702 337864
The Law Partnership p242 020 8416 7004
Lawson & Thompson p130 01670 530700
Leathes Prior p334 01603 610911
Leigh Turton Dixon p315 01642 241101
Letchers p364 01425 471424
Levi Solicitors LLP p275 0113 244 9931
Linder Myers Solicitors p307 0844 984 6400
Linder Myers Solicitors p306 0844 984 6000
Gordon Lowe & Co p163 01454 326833
Peter Lynn & Partners p405 01792 450010
Peter Lynn & Partners p319 01792 310731
MFG Solicitors p265 01562 820181
MFG Solicitors p167 01527 831691
MWRLaw Ltd p357 01772 254201
McKenzie Bell Solicitors p401 0191 567 4857
Marchant Harries & Co p113 01685 885500
Marchant Harries & Co p319 01443 476444
Marchants Solicitors p312 01623 655111
Marshall Hall & Levy p384 0191 455 3181
Mayo Wynne Baxter LLP p215 01323 730543
Mayo Wynne Baxter LLP p160 01273 775533
Mayo Wynne Baxter LLP p283 01273 477071
Michelmores LLP p221 01392 688688
Miller Gardner p307 0161 877 4777
Mills Chody LLP p265 020 8909 0400
Mincoffs Solicitors LLP p325 0191 281 6151
Moseleys p284 01543 414100
Moss Beachley Mullem & Coleman p62 020 7402 1401 / 7723 5783
Mustoe Shorter p430 01305 752700
Nalders Quality Solicitors p414 01872 241414
Nalders Quality Solicitors p223 01326 313441
Nalders Quality Solicitors p246 01326 574001
Nalders Quality Solicitors p173 01209 714278
Nalders Quality Solicitors p329 01637 871414
Nalders Quality Solicitors p346 01736 364014
Alfred Newton & Co p433 01625 523647
Alfred Newton & Co p396 0161 480 6551 / 480 1245
Alfred Newton & Co p396 0161 430 8831
NIGHTINGALES SOLICITORS LIMITED p396 01663 764038
NORRIE WAITE & SLATER p377 0114 276 6166
North Yorkshire Law p372 01723 360001
OGR Stock Denton p64 020 8349 0321
Ouvry Goodman & Co p403 020 8642 7571
Painters p399 01299 822033
Park Woodfine Heald Mellows LLP p130 01234 400000
Patchell Davies (Trading Name of PD Law Ltd) p147 01495 227128
Payne & Gamage p322 01636 640649
Pengillys LLP p430 01305 768888
Pengillys LLP p212 01305 768888
Penmans p394 01375 677777
Peter Peter & Wright p340 01837 52379
PETERS LANGSFORD DAVIES p270 01566 772451
Philippou & Co p67 020 8882 4222
Pictons Solicitors LLP p317 01908 663511
Pinkney Grunwells Lawyers LLP p158 01262 673445
Porter Dodson p425 01823 666622
Porter Dodson p408 01823 625800
Powells p429 01934 623501
Preston Goldburn p223 01326 318900
Pritchard Edwards & Co p182 01267 234022
QualitySolicitors Gruber Garratt p358 0161 724 0203
RJR Solicitors p227 01983 752115
RJR Solicitors p369 01983 562201
RJR Solicitors p328 01983 526924
Ralph & Co p329 01637 872218
Ramsdens Solicitors p210 01924 455391
Rawal & Co p70 020 8445 0303
Red Kite Law p410 01834 842122
Red Kite Law p183 01267 239000
Red Kite Law p345 01646 683222
Red Kite Law p244 01437 763332
Red Kite Law p345 01646 681529
Red Kite Law p316 01646 698008
Stephen Rimmer LLP p216 01323 644222
Rippon Patel & French p72 020 7323 0404
Roach Pittis p328 01983 524431
Robinson Allfree p359 01843 592361
Robinson Allfree p166 01843 865261
Paul Robinson Solicitors p428 01702 338338
Rowberry Morris p361 0118 958 5611
Royds LLP p74 020 7583 2222
Rudlings & Wakelam p410 01842 754151
Rudlings & Wakelam p171 01284 755771
Russell Jones & Walker p74 020 7657 1555
SJP Solicitors p258 01485 532662
Samars Solicitors p254 020 8570 4716
Sanders Witherspoon LLP p156 01277 221010
Santers Solicitors p123 020 8594 7542
Saulet & Co p389 023 9281 9442
Sharman Law p130 01234 303030
Shentons p434 01962 844544
Shepherd Harris & Co p219 020 8363 8341
Slee Blackwell p125 01271 372128
Slee Blackwell p222 01392 423000
Smith Llewelyn Partnership p405 01792 464444
The Smith Partnership p170 01283 536471
The Smith Partnership p404 01283 226444
Smith Solicitor LLP p238 01422 383380
Solomon Levy p295 01582 425817 / 414948
Steele Raymond p152 01202 294566
Stephens & Scown p222 01392 210700
Stephens & Scown p391 01726 74433
Stephens & Scown p414 01872 265100
Stephensons Solicitors LLP p282 01942 777777
Stephensons Solicitors LLP p432 01942 777777
Stephensons Solicitors LLP p282 01942 777777
Stokes Solicitors p355 023 9282 8131
Stone King LLP p128 01225 337599
Stones Solicitors LLP p222 01392 666777
Stunt Palmer & Robinson p84 020 7739 6927
Swain & Co p386 023 8063 1111
Swain & Co p244 023 9248 3322
Swinburne & Jackson LLP p229 0191 477 2531 / 477 3222
Swinburne & Jackson LLP p191 0191 388 7221
TBI Solicitors p243 0800 052 6824 / 01429 264101
TLT Solicitors p165 0117 917 7777
David Tagg & Co p85 020 7736 0999
Tanner & Taylor LLP p115 01252 316565
Taylor Lewis p181 01239 621999
Taylor Vinters p176 01223 423444
Temple Heelis LLP p264 01539 723757
Terrells LLP p347 01733 896789
Dean Thomas & Co p192 01246 810050
Thorpe & Co p430 01947 603465
Thorpe & Co p226 01723 515555
Tilley & Co p390 01727 840467
Timms p170 01283 561531 / 544417
Timms p209 01332 364436
Timms Solicitors p404 01283 214231
Tozers p329 01626 207020
Tozers p409 01626 772376
Tozers p222 01392 207020
Alison Trent & Co p88 020 7583 3350
Trobridges p412 01752 812787
Trobridges p350 01752 664022
Tyndallwoods p143 0121 624 1111
WBW Solicitors p329 01626 202404
WBW Solicitors p153 01626 833263
WBW Solicitors p413 0870 701 4321
WBW Solicitors p222 01392 202404
Walker & Co p367 01709 817112
Waller Needham & Green p347 01733 262182
Waller Needham & Green p347 01733 311422
Walters & Barbary p173 01209 712454
Wansbroughs p314 01225 703222
Wards Solicitors p165 0117 929 2811
Wards Solicitors p429 01934 413535
Wards Solicitors p394 0117 943 4800
Wards Solicitors p429 01934 428811
Wards Solicitors p165 01454 204880
Watson Burton LLP p327 0845 901 2100
Watson Woodhouse p397 01642 247656
Whetter Duckworth Fowler p266 01865 842100
Whiskers p219 01992 561111
Whiskers p239 01279 439439
Kathryn Whitford Solicitor p414 01872 275300
Wilkin Chapman Epton Blades p285 01522 512345
Willett & Co p171 01284 701323
Williams & Co p217 020 8952 8882
R N Williams & Co Limited p438 01902 429051
Wilson Browne p333 01604 876697
Wilson Browne p265 01536 410041
Wilsons Solicitors p344 01865 874497
Winters & Co p421 01920 466696
Wintle & Co p148 01243 863021
Wolferstans p351 01752 663295
Wollen Michelmore Solicitors p413 01803 213251
Woodfines LLP p372 01767 680251
Woodfines LLP p147 01908 366333
Woodfines LLP p317 01908 202150
Woodfines LLP p176 01223 411421
Worger Howcroft p133 01274 511246
Worthingtons p227 01303 850206

DEBT

Acklam Bond Noor p145 01254 56068
Adlams LLP p392 01480 474061
Alderson Dodds p147 01670 352293
Allan Rutherford p333 01603 621722
Allen Hoole Solicitors p160 0117 942 0901
Allington Hughes p442 01978 291000
J M Amin & Co p426 020 8903 3766
Arscotts p254 01273 735289
Ashfords LLP p412 01884 203000
Ashfords LLP p408 01823 232300
Ashton KCJ p171 01284 762331
Ashton KCJ p262 01473 232425
Askews p362 01642 475252
Askews p396 01642 475252
Aston Clark p8 020 8752 1122
Atkinson Cave & Stuart p146 01253 293151
Atteys p211 01302 340400
Attwood & Co p233 01375 378122 / 378123

E J Bamforth Solicitors *p190* 01244 357209
Banks Kelly *p9* 020 7248 4231
Banner Jones *p191* 01246 560560
Banner Jones *p213* 01246 414438
Banner Jones *p191* 01246 827516
Banner Jones *p192* 01246 861250
Banner Jones *p191* 01246 209773
Max Barford & Co *p414* 01892 539379
Barker Booth & Eastwood *p146* 01253 362500
John Barkers *p195* 01472 695218
John Barkers *p294* 01507 604773
John Barkers *p234* 01472 358686
John Barkers *p297* 01507 477673
Barnes Coleman & Co *p131* 01702 558211
Bates N V H *p11* 020 7936 2930
Bawtrees LLP *p435* 01376 513491
Beesley & Co *p301* 0161 445 3678
Beetenson & Gibbon *p235* 01472 240251
Ben Hoare Bell & Co *p401* 0191 565 3112
Ben Hoare Bell & Co *p323* 0191 275 2626
Ben Hoare Bell & Co *p401* 0191 516 0466
Bernard Chill & Axtell *p385* 023 8022 8821
Best Solicitors *p375* 0114 281 3636
Birchall Blackburn LLP *p356* 01772 561663
Blackhurst Budd LLP *p146* 01253 629300
Bolitho Way *p354* 023 9282 0747
D S Bosher & Co *p254* 01273 721913
Boyce Hatton *p412* 01803 403403
Brearleys Solicitors *p128* 01924 473065
Brearleys Solicitors *p144* 01924 443900
Brennans Solicitors *p419* 0191 262 5133
Brighouses *p388* . . . . 01704 534101 / 500151
Brooks *p378* 01608 664406
Burges Salmon *p161* 0117 939 2000
Burley & Geach *p233* 01428 605355
Burton & Co LLP *p284* 01522 523215
Burton & Co LLP *p381* . . . . 01529 306008 / 306009
Kenneth Bush *p266* 01553 692737
Butcher & Barlow LLP *p170* 0161 764 5141
CMHT Solicitors *p167* 01543 372347
CMHT Solicitors *p420* 01922 646400
CVC Solicitors *p346* 01736 362313
Cartwright Cunningham Haselgrove & Co *p19* 020 8520 1021
Caswell Jones *p172* 029 2086 4888
Chadwick Lawrence *p418* 01924 379078
Chadwick Lawrence *p238* 01422 330601
Chambers Solicitors *p381* 01753 522204
Chanter Ferguson *p132* 01237 478751
Chattertons Solicitors *p284* 01522 814600
Churchers *p271* 023 9255 1500
Churchers *p232* 023 9260 3400
Churchers *p223* 01329 822333
Churchers *p354* 023 9221 0170
Clark Willis *p206* 01325 281111
Clark Willis *p183* 01748 830000
Clarke Kiernan *p412* 01732 360999
Clarkson Hirst *p269* 01524 39760
Coles Miller Solicitors LLP *p352* 01202 673011
Cooper Lingard *p282* 01702 715411
Cooper Sons Hartley & Williams *p184* 01298 812138
Cornfield Law *p215* 01323 412512
Richard Crumly *p410* 01635 866166
Daniel Curry & Co *p205* 020 8680 2188
Darling & Stephensons *p206* 01325 489000
Dickinson Manser *p352* 01202 673071
Dickinsons *p146* 01253 781010
Dixon Stewart *p321* 01425 621515
Paul Dodds Solicitors *p419* 0191 263 6200
Scott Duff & Co *p182* 01228 531054
Peter Dunn & Co *p401* 0191 568 9000
Thomas Dunton Solicitors *p342* 01689 822554
Edwards Duthie *p260* 020 8514 9000
Edwards Duthie *p29* 020 8514 9000
Edwards Duthie *p29* 020 8514 9000
R L Edwards & Partners *p157* 01656 656861
Elliot Mather LLP *p192* 01246 231288
Ellis-Fermor & Negus *p364* 01773 744744
Ellis-Fermor & Negus *p130* 0115 922 1591
Ellis-Fermor & Negus *p293* 0115 972 5222
Eric Robinson Solicitors *p184* 023 8025 4676
Eric Robinson Solicitors *p385* 023 8042 5000
Evans & Greaves *p172* 029 2086 6001
Fahri Jacob *p30* 020 8347 4070
A J Field & Co *p375* 01795 580600
Paul Finn Solicitors *p168* 01288 356256
Fisher Jones Greenwood LLP *p186* 01245 890110
Fletcher Dervish *p33* 020 8800 4615
Fonseca & Partners *p216* 01495 303124
Forbes *p114* 01254 872111
Ford Simey LLP *p221* 01392 274126
Ford Simey LLP *p380* . . . . 01395 577061 / 0800 169 3741
Ford Simey LLP *p222* . . . . 01395 272241 / 0800 169 3741
Fosters *p334* 01603 620508
Fosters *p168* 01986 895251
Fraser Dawbarns *p435* 01945 461456
Fraser Dawbarns *p266* 01553 666600

French & Co *p337* 0115 955 1111
GLP Solicitors *p315* 0161 653 6295
GLP Solicitors *p357* 0161 773 8626
GLP Solicitors *p304* 0161 793 0901
Gartsides *p328* 01633 213411
Glaisyers *p138* 0121 233 2971
Glaisyers Solicitors LLP *p304* 0161 832 4666
Glaisyers Solicitors LLP *p304* 0161 224 3311
Glanvilles *p328* 01983 527878
Godloves *p273* 0113 225 8864
Godloves *p273* 0113 225 8874
Goldbergs *p349* 01752 660023
Goldkorn Mathias Gentle Page LLP *p36* . . 020 7631 1811
Goldstones *p405* 01792 643021
Gordons LLP *p273* 0113 227 0100
Grants Solicitors *p205* 020 8288 8899
HC Solicitors LLP *p347* 01733 882800
HKH Kenwright & Cox Solicitors *p260* . . 020 8553 9600
Hadaway & Hadaway *p330* 0191 257 0382
Hains & Lewis Ltd *p244* 0845 408 0125
HallmarkHulme *p439* 01905 726600
Hannays Solicitors and Advocates *p383* . . . . 0191 456 7893 / 455 5361
Harding Evans LLP *p328* 01633 244233
Harding Swinburne Jackson & Co *p401* . . 0191 565 8194
Christopher Harris & Co *p375* 01795 661521
Christopher Harris & Co *p380* 01795 437268
David W Harris & Co *p352* 01443 486666
Harrison Clark LLP *p439* 01905 612001
Harrison Clark LLP *p439* 01905 612001
Harrison Clark LLP *p188* 01242 269198
Harrow Solicitors & Advocates *p424* 020 8863 0788
Harvey Ingram Borneos *p130* 01234 353221
Havillands *p366* 01708 766559
Hawley & Rodgers *p337* 0115 955 9000
Hay & Kilner *p419* 0191 262 8231
Heckford Norton *p283* 01462 682244
Henriques Griffiths *p163* 0117 909 4000
Hereward & Foster *p41* 020 7476 6600
Herrington & Carmichael LLP *p437* 0118 977 4045
Herrington & Carmichael LLP *p173* 01276 686222
Hetts *p373* 01724 270290
Hewetts *p361* 0118 957 5337
Hewitts *p330* 01325 316170
Hewitts *p144* 01388 604691
Hewitts *p206* 01325 468573
Hewitts *p203* 01388 762466
Holls Solicitors *p129* 020 8658 9767
Hood Vores & Allwood *p209* 01362 692424
Howells LLP *p367* 01709 364000
Howells LLP *p376* 0114 249 6666
J A Hughes *p345* 029 2070 2449
J A Hughes *p126* 01446 411000
J W Hughes & Co *p199* 01492 596596
Humphrys & Co *p363* 01745 343158
Humphrys & Co *p443* 01978 313399
Ismail & Co *p218* 020 8804 1065
JMW Solicitors *p306* 0845 872 6666
Jackamans *p225* 01394 279636
Jackamans *p239* 01379 854455
Jennings *p292* 01554 772331
Jepson & Co *p372* 01723 859249
Johar & Co *p280* 0116 254 3345
Kerseys *p262* 01473 213311
Khan Solicitors *p154* 01274 301999
Kidd Rapinet *p382* 0845 017 9638
Kidd Rapinet *p298* 0845 017 9608
Kirby Sheppard *p411* 0845 840 0045
Kirby Sheppard *p268* 0845 840 0045
Laceys *p353* 01202 743286
Lancasters *p158* 01262 602401
Langleys *p445* 01904 610886
Larken & Co *p322* 01636 703333
Law Hurst & Taylor *p428* 01702 337864
The Law Partnership *p242* 020 8416 7004
Leathes Prior *p334* 01603 610911
Leigh Turton Dixon *p315* 01642 241101
Letchers *p364* 01425 471424
Levi Solicitors LLP *p275* 0113 244 9931
Lewis & Lines *p113* 01495 212286
Linder Myers Solicitors *p307* 0844 984 6400
Linder Myers Solicitors *p306* 0844 984 6000
The Lister Croft Partnership *p358* 0113 257 0526
MFG Solicitors *p265* 01562 820181
MFG Solicitors *p167* 01527 831691
MWP Solicitors *p126* 01268 527131
MWRLaw Ltd *p357* 01772 254201
McCormicks *p240* 01423 530630
Marchant Harries & Co *p113* 01685 885500
Marchant Harries & Co *p319* 01443 476444
Marchants Solicitors *p312* 01623 655111
Marshall Hall & Levy *p384* 0191 455 3181
Mason Baggott & Garton *p219* 01427 872661
Matthew Arnold & Baldwin LLP *p423* . . 01923 202020
Mayo Wynne Baxter LLP *p215* 01323 730543
Mayo Wynne Baxter LLP *p160* 01273 775533
Mayo Wynne Baxter LLP *p283* 01273 477071

Michelmores LLP *p221* 01392 688688
Miller Gardner *p307* 0161 877 4777
Mincoffs Solicitors LLP *p325* 0191 281 6151
Molesworths Bright Clegg *p365* 01706 356666
Morgans *p180* 029 2072 9888
Moss Beachley Mullem & Coleman *p62* . . . . 020 7402 1401 / 7723 5783
Mustoe Shorter *p430* 01305 752700
Nalders Quality Solicitors *p414* 01872 241414
Nalders Quality Solicitors *p223* 01326 313441
Nalders Quality Solicitors *p246* 01326 574001
Nalders Quality Solicitors *p173* 01209 714278
Nalders Quality Solicitors *p329* 01637 871414
Nalders Quality Solicitors *p346* 01736 364014
Nandy & Co *p63* 020 8536 1800
Alfred Newton & Co *p433* 01625 523647
Alfred Newton & Co *p396* . . . 0161 480 6551 / 480 1245
Alfred Newton & Co *p396* 0161 430 8831
NORRIE WAITE & SLATER *p377* 0114 276 6166
North Yorkshire Law *p372* 01723 360001
Norton Peskett *p294* 01502 533000
Painters *p399* 01299 822033
Park Woodfine Heald Mellows LLP *p130* . 01234 400000
Parker Rhodes Hickmotts *p367* 01709 511100
Passmore Lewis & Jacobs *p126* 01446 721000
Patchell Davies (Trading Name of PD Law Ltd) *p147* 01495 227128
Payne & Gamage *p322* 01636 640649
Bernard Pearce & Co *p219* 020 8804 5271
Pengillys LLP *p430* 01305 768888
Pengillys LLP *p212* 01305 768888
Penmans *p394* 01375 677777
Peters & Peters *p67* 020 7629 7991
Pictons Solicitors LLP *p295* 01582 870870
Pictons Solicitors LLP *p317* 01908 663511
Pictons Solicitors LLP *p247* 01442 242441
Powells *p429* 01934 623501
Preston Goldburn *p223* 01326 318900
QualitySolicitors Gruber Garratt *p358* . . . 0161 724 0203
Ralph & Co *p329* 01637 872218
Rawal & Co *p70* 020 8445 0303
Red Kite Law *p410* 01834 842122
Red Kite Law *p345* 01646 683222
Red Kite Law *p244* 01437 763332
Red Kite Law *p345* 01646 681529
Red Kite Law *p316* 01646 698008
Stephen Rimmer LLP *p216* 01323 644222
Rippon Patel & French *p72* 020 7323 0404
Roach Pittis *p328* 01983 524431
Robinson Allfree *p359* 01843 592361
Paul Robinson Solicitors *p428* 01702 338338
Roland Robinsons & Fentons LLP *p147* . 01253 621432
Will Rolt Solicitors *p128* 01225 426390
Rootes & Alliott *p227* 01303 851100
Rowberry Morris *p361* 0118 958 5611
Rudlings & Wakelam *p410* 01842 754151
SJP Solicitors *p258* 01485 532662
Samars Solicitors *p254* 020 8570 4716
Sandersons *p131* 01482 324662
Santers Solicitors *p123* 020 8594 7542
Saulet & Co *p389* 023 9281 9442
Selvarajah & Co *p77* 020 8204 7884
Shentons *p434* 01962 844544
Clive Shepherd & Co *p420* 01922 647797
Silks *p340* 0121 511 2233
Slee Blackwell *p222* 01392 423000
Smith Llewelyn Partnership *p405* 01792 464444
The Smith Partnership *p170* 01283 536471
The Smith Partnership *p404* 01283 226444
Smith Solicitor LLP *p238* 01422 383380
Maurice Smiths *p351* 01977 794395
Solomon Levy *p295* . . . . 01582 425817 / 414948
Spicketts Battrick Law Practice *p352* . . . 01443 407221
Stachiw Bashir Green *p155* 01274 404010
Stachiw Bashir Green *p155* 01274 404010
Standley & Co *p269* 01564 776287
STEELE FORD & NEWTON *p321* 01282 692531
Steele Raymond *p152* 01202 294566
Stephens & Scown *p222* 01392 210700
Stephens & Scown *p391* 01726 74433
Stephens & Scown *p414* 01872 265100
Stephensons Solicitors LLP *p282* 01942 777777
Stephensons Solicitors LLP *p391* 01942 777777
Stephensons Solicitors LLP *p432* 01942 777777
Stephensons Solicitors LLP *p282* 01942 777777
Stone King LLP *p128* 01225 337599
Stones Solicitors LLP *p340* 01837 650200
Stones Solicitors LLP *p222* 01392 666777
Swain & Co *p386* 023 8063 1111
Swain & Co *p244* 023 9248 3322
Swinburne & Jackson LLP *p229* 0191 477 2531 / 477 3222
SYMES BAINS BROOMER *p373* 01724 281616
Symes Bains Broomer *p235* 01472 360991
TBI Solicitors *p243* . . . . . 0800 052 6824 / 01429 264101
TLT Solicitors *p165* 0117 917 7777
TMJ Legal Services LLP *p434* 01429 838225
TMJ Legal Services LLP *p243* 01429 235616

See p603 for the Community Legal Service Work Categories

TMJ Legal Services LLP *p348* . . . 0191 586 5711
TMJ Legal Services LLP *p214* . . . 0191 383 0111
Tanner & Taylor LLP *p115* . . . 01252 316565
Taylor Lewis *p181* . . . 01239 621999
Temple Heelis LLP *p264* . . . 01539 723757
Terrells LLP *p347* . . . 01733 896789
Thackray Williams *p167* . . . 020 8290 0440
Thorpe & Co *p430* . . . 01947 603465
Thorpe & Co *p226* . . . 01723 515555
Tilley & Co *p390* . . . 01727 840467
Tilly Bailey & Irvine LLP *p397* . . . 01642 673797
Timms *p170* . . . 01283 561531 / 544417
Timms *p209* . . . 01332 364436
Timms Solicitors *p404* . . . 01283 214231
Toller Beattie LLP *p125* . . . 01271 341000
Tozers *p350* . . . 01752 206460
Alison Trent & Co *p88* . . . 020 7583 3350
Trobridges *p412* . . . 01752 812787
Trobridges *p350* . . . 01752 664022
Marina C Van't Goor *p316* . . . 01646 697700
WBW Solicitors *p329* . . . 01626 202404
WBW Solicitors *p153* . . . 01626 833263
WBW Solicitors *p413* . . . 0870 701 4321
WBW Solicitors *p222* . . . 01392 202404
Walker & Co *p367* . . . 01709 817112
Waller Needham & Green *p347* . . . 01733 262182
Walters & Barbary *p173* . . . 01209 712454
Wansbroughs *p314* . . . 01225 703222
Wards Solicitors *p165* . . . 0117 929 2811
Wards Solicitors *p429* . . . 01934 413535
Wards Solicitors *p394* . . . 0117 943 4800
Wards Solicitors *p429* . . . 01934 428811
Whetter Duckworth Fowler *p266* . . . 01865 842100
Kathryn Whitford Solicitor *p414* . . . 01872 275300
Wilkin Chapman Epton Blades *p285* . . . 01522 512345
Willett & Co *p171* . . . 01284 701323
Williams & Co *p217* . . . 020 8952 8882
Wilson Browne *p333* . . . 01604 876697
Wilson Browne *p265* . . . 01536 410041
Wilsons Solicitors *p344* . . . 01865 874497
Wintle & Co *p148* . . . 01243 863021
Wolferstans *p351* . . . 01752 663295
Wollen Michelmore Solicitors *p413* . . . 01803 213251
Woodcocks *p359* . . . 01706 225621 / 215018
Woodcocks *p121* . . . 01706 874487
Worger Howcroft *p133* . . . 01274 511246

EDUCATION

Adlams LLP *p392* . . . 01480 474061
Ashton KCJ *p174* . . . 01223 363111
Ashton KCJ *p171* . . . 01284 761233
Ashton KCJ *p333* . . . 01603 703070
Bailey Wright & Co *p135* . . . 0845 475 1996
Max Barford & Co *p414* . . . 01892 539379
Ben Hoare Bell & Co *p401* . . . 0191 565 3112
Ben Hoare Bell & Co *p323* . . . 0191 275 2626
Burges Salmon *p161* . . . 0117 939 2000
Julie Burton *p122* . . . 01248 364750
Davies Gore Lomax *p273* . . . 0113 242 2797
Edwards Duthie *p260* . . . 020 8514 9000
Edwards Duthie *p29* . . . 020 8514 9000
Edwards Duthie *p29* . . . 020 8514 9000
Fisher Meredith *p32* . . . 020 7091 2700
John Ford Solicitors *p33* . . . 020 8800 6464
French & Co *p337* . . . 0115 955 1111
Gregory Abrams Davidson LLP *p288* . . . 0151 236 5000
Gregory Abrams Davidson LLP *p288* . . . 0151 733 3353
Gregory Abrams Davidson LLP *p288* . . . 0151 494 0777
Christopher Harris & Co *p375* . . . 01795 661521
Christopher Harris & Co *p380* . . . 01795 437268
Langley Wellington *p230* . . . 01452 521286
Levenes Solicitors *p53* . . . 020 8881 7777 / 8881 6764
Marshall Hall & Levy *p384* . . . 0191 455 3181
Maxwell Gillott (MG Law Ltd) *p270* . . . 0844 858 3900
Michelmores LLP *p221* . . . 01392 688688
Morecrofts Solicitors LLP *p290* . . . 0151 236 8871
Samuel Phillips Law Firm *p326* . . . 0191 232 8451
Rawal & Co *p70* . . . 020 8445 0303
Ridley & Hall *p256* . . . 01484 538421
Russell Jones & Walker *p180* . . . 029 2026 2800
Samars Solicitors *p254* . . . 020 8570 4716
Saulet & Co *p389* . . . 023 9281 9442
The Sethi Partnership Solicitors *p216* . . . 020 8866 6464
Sinclairs *p345* . . . 029 2070 6444
Solomon Levy *p295* . . . 01582 425817 / 414948
Swain & Co *p386* . . . 023 8063 1111
Swain & Co *p244* . . . 023 9248 3322
Swinburne & Jackson LLP *p229* 0191 477 2531 / 477 3222
Teacher Stern LLP *p86* . . . 020 7242 3191
WBW Solicitors *p329* . . . 01626 202404
WBW Solicitors *p153* . . . 01626 833263
Wilkin Chapman Epton Blades *p285* . . . 01522 512345
Williscroft & Co *p155* . . . 01274 305380
Wilsons Solicitors *p344* . . . 01865 874497
Worthingtons *p227* . . . 01303 850206

EMPLOYMENT

ASB Law *p298* . . . 01622 656500
Acklam Bond Noor *p145* . . . 01254 56068
Adlams LLP *p392* . . . 01480 474061
Alderson Dodds *p147* . . . 01670 352293
Allington Hughes *p190* . . . 01244 312166
Allington Hughes *p442* . . . 01978 291000
J M Amin & Co *p426* . . . 020 8903 3766
Archer & Archer *p218* . . . 01353 662203
Ashfords LLP *p412* . . . 01884 203000
Ashfords LLP *p408* . . . 01823 232300
Ashton KCJ *p171* . . . 01284 762331
Ashton KCJ *p262* . . . 01473 232425
Aston Clark *p8* . . . 020 8752 1122
Atteys *p211* . . . 01302 340400
Attwaters *p294* . . . 020 8508 2111
Attwaters *p239* . . . 01279 638888
Attwood & Co *p233* . . . 01375 378122 / 378123
BLB Solicitors *p413* . . . 01225 755656
BLB Solicitors *p406* . . . 01793 615011
Bailey Wright & Co *p135* . . . 0845 475 1996
Ballam *p134* . . . 0151 647 8977
Banks Kelly *p9* . . . 020 7248 4231
Max Barford & Co *p414* . . . 01892 539379
Barker Booth & Eastwood *p146* . . . 01253 362500
Barnes Coleman & Co *p131* . . . 01702 558211
Bates N V H *p11* . . . 020 7936 2930
Bawtrees LLP *p435* . . . 01376 513491
Beecham Peacock *p323* . . . 0191 232 3048
Beetenson & Gibbon *p235* . . . 01472 240251
Ben Hoare Bell & Co *p401* . . . 0191 516 0466
Bennett Richmond *p270* . . . 01207 521843
Bernard Chill & Axtell *p385* . . . 023 8022 8821
Best Solicitors *p375* . . . 0114 281 3636
Bindmans LLP *p12* . . . 020 7833 4433
Birchall Blackburn LLP *p356* . . . 01772 561663
Blackhurst Budd LLP *p146* . . . 01253 629300
Bobbetts Mackan *p161* . . . 0117 929 9001
D S Bosher & Co *p254* . . . 01273 721913
Boyce Hatton *p412* . . . 01803 403403
BRADBURY ROBERTS & RABY *p373* . . . 01724 854000
Brearleys Solicitors *p128* . . . 01924 473065
Brennans Solicitors *p419* . . . 0191 262 5133
Bridge McFarland *p235* . . . 01472 311711
Bridge McFarland *p284* . . . 01522 518888
Bridge Sanderson Munro *p411* . . . 01405 814136
Brighouses *p388* . . . 01704 534101 / 500151
Brooks *p378* . . . 01608 664406
Gordon Brown Associates *p191* . . . 0191 388 1778
BRYAN & ARMSTRONG *p311* . . . 01623 626039
BRYAN & ARMSTRONG *p311* . . . 01623 624505
Burges Salmon *p161* . . . 0117 939 2000
Burley & Geach *p233* . . . 01428 605355
Burton & Co LLP *p284* . . . 01522 523215
Burton & Co LLP *p381* . . . 01529 306008 / 306009
Kenneth Bush *p266* . . . 01553 692737
Butcher & Barlow LLP *p170* . . . 0161 764 5141
CVC Solicitors *p346* . . . 01736 362313
Cartwright Cunningham Haselgrove & Co *p19* . . . 020 8520 1021
Chadwick Lawrence *p319* . . . 0113 252 3452
Chadwick Lawrence *p238* . . . 01422 330601
Chadwick Lawrence *p255* . . . 01484 519999
Chattertons Solicitors *p252* . . . 01507 522456
Clark Willis *p206* . . . 01325 281111
Clark Willis *p183* . . . 01748 830000
Clarke Kiernan *p412* . . . 01732 360999
Clarkson Hirst *p269* . . . 01524 39760
Coffin Mew & Clover *p385* . . . 023 8033 4661
Coffin Mew & Clover *p354* . . . 023 9238 8021
Coffin Mew & Clover *p232* . . . 023 9252 3111
Coffin Mew & Clover *p223* . . . 01329 825617
Coles Miller Solicitors LLP *p352* . . . 01202 673011
Coles Miller Solicitors LLP *p151* . . . 01202 511512
Cooper Lingard *p282* . . . 01702 715411
Cooper Sons Hartley & Williams *p184* . . . 01298 812138
Cornfield Law *p215* . . . 01323 412512
Richard Crumly *p410* . . . 01635 866166
DB Law *p392* . . . 01736 793883
DFA Law LLP *p331* . . . 01604 609560
DFA Law LLP *p331* . . . 01604 609560
Darling & Stephensons *p206* . . . 01325 489000
De Soyza & Fernando *p26* . . . 020 8670 9918
Dickinson Manser *p352* . . . 01202 673071
Dickinsons *p146* . . . 01253 781010
Dixon Stewart *p321* . . . 01425 621515
Dowse & Co *p27* . . . 020 7254 6205
Scott Duff & Co *p182* . . . 01228 531054
Peter Dunn & Co *p401* . . . 0191 568 9000
Thomas Dunton Solicitors *p342* . . . 01689 822554
Eaton Smith LLP *p255* . . . 01484 821300
Eatons *p153* . . . 0845 660 0660
Edwards Duthie *p260* . . . 020 8514 9000
Edwards Duthie *p29* . . . 020 8514 9000
Edwards Duthie *p29* . . . 020 8514 9000
Elliot Mather LLP *p192* . . . 01246 231288
Ellis-Fermor & Negus *p364* . . . 01773 744744
Ellis-Fermor & Negus *p130* . . . 0115 922 1591
Eric Robinson Solicitors *p385* . . . 023 8042 5000
Everys *p380* . . . 01395 577983
Fairweather & Co Solicitors *p176* . . . 01227 784337
A J Field & Co *p375* . . . 01795 580600
Finn Gledhill *p238* . . . 01422 330000
Paul Finn Solicitors *p168* . . . 01288 356256
Fisher Jones Greenwood LLP *p186* . . . 01245 890110
Fisher Jones Greenwood LLP *p197* . . . 01206 578282
Fisher Meredith *p32* . . . 020 7091 2700
Fletcher Dervish *p33* . . . 020 8800 4615
Flint Bishop Solicitors *p208* . . . 01332 340211
Forbes *p114* . . . 01254 872111
Forbes *p356* . . . 01772 220022
Forbes *p145* . . . 01254 580000
Ford Simey LLP *p221* . . . 01392 274126
Ford Simey LLP *p380* . . . 01395 577061 / 0800 169 3741
Ford Simey LLP *p222* . . . 01395 272241 / 0800 169 3741
Fosters *p168* . . . 01986 895251
Malcolm C Foy & Co *p211* . . . 01302 340005
Malcolm C Foy & Co *p367* . . . 01709 836866
Foys Solicitors *p211* . . . 01302 327136
Foys Solicitors *p441* . . . 01909 473560
Foys Solicitors *p367* . . . 01709 375561
Foys Solicitors *p375* . . . 0114 251 1702
Fraser Dawbarns *p435* . . . 01945 461456
Fraser Dawbarns *p266* . . . 01553 666600
Fraser Dawbarns *p213* . . . 01366 383171
Freer & Archer *p279* . . . 0116 241 3199
GLP Solicitors *p304* . . . 0161 834 6721
GLP Solicitors *p357* . . . 0161 773 8626
Gamlins *p363* . . . 01745 343500
Gardner Leader LLP *p410* . . . 01635 508080
Garner & Hancock Solicitors LLP *p263* . . . 020 8232 9560
Gartsides *p328* . . . 01633 213411
GEORGE IDE LLP *p192* . . . 01243 786668
George Ide LLP *p148* . . . 01243 829231
Glanvilles *p328* . . . 01983 527878
Goldbergs *p349* . . . 01752 660023
Goldstones *p405* . . . 01792 643021
Gordons LLP *p273* . . . 0113 227 0100
Goughs *p210* . . . 01380 726913
Grainger Appleyard *p211* . . . 01302 327257
GREENLAND HOUCHEN POMEROY *p334* . . . 01603 660744
Gregsons *p37* . . . 020 8946 1173
HC Solicitors LLP *p347* . . . 01733 882800
Hadaway & Hadaway *p330* . . . 0191 257 0382
Hallens Solicitors *p253* . . . 020 8622 3729
Hamilton Downing Quinn *p38* . . . 020 7831 8939
Hansells *p203* . . . 01263 512003
Harding Swinburne Jackson & Co *p401* . . . 0191 565 8194
Harman & Harman *p39* . . . 01227 452977
Harpers *p39* . . . 020 7405 8888
Christopher Harris & Co *p375* . . . 01795 661521
Christopher Harris & Co *p380* . . . 01795 437268
Harrison Clark LLP *p439* . . . 01905 612001
Harrison Clark LLP *p439* . . . 01905 612001
Harrison Clark LLP *p188* . . . 01242 269198
Harvey Ingram Borneos *p130* . . . 01234 353221
Hawley & Rodgers *p293* . . . 01509 230333
Hay & Kilner *p325* . . . 0191 232 8345
Heer Manak *p200* . . . 024 7666 4000
Henriques Griffiths *p163* . . . 0117 909 4000
Herrington & Carmichael LLP *p437* . . . 0118 977 4045
Herrington & Carmichael LLP *p173* . . . 01276 686222
Hetts *p373* . . . 01724 843287
Hetts *p373* . . . 01724 270290
Hewetts *p361* . . . 0118 957 5337
Hewitts *p330* . . . 01325 316170
Hewitts *p144* . . . 01388 604691
Hewitts *p206* . . . 01325 468573
Hewitts *p203* . . . 01388 762466
Holden & Co *p243* . . . 01424 722422
Hood Vores & Allwood *p209* . . . 01362 692424
Howells LLP *p367* . . . 01709 364000
Howells LLP *p376* . . . 0114 249 6666
J W Hughes & Co *p199* . . . 01492 596596
Irwin Mitchell LLP *p274* . . . 0870 150 0100
Jepson & Co *p372* . . . 01723 859249
Christian Khan Solicitors *p49* . . . 020 7631 9500
Kidd Rapinet *p382* . . . 0845 017 9638
Kidd Rapinet *p298* . . . 0845 017 9608
Kirby Sheppard *p411* . . . 0845 840 0045
Kirby Sheppard *p268* . . . 0845 840 0045
Kitsons LLP *p221* . . . 01392 455555
Knowles Benning *p295* . . . 01582 798000
Lancasters *p158* . . . 01262 602401
Langleys *p445* . . . 01904 610886
Last Cawthra Feather LLP *p121* . . . 01274 583106
Lawson & Thompson *p130* . . . 01670 530700
Leathes Prior *p334* . . . 01603 610911
Leonard & Co *p386* . . . 023 8023 3242
Leonard & Co *p386* . . . 023 8023 4433
Letchers *p364* . . . 01425 471424
Levi Solicitors LLP *p275* . . . 0113 244 9931

Linder Myers Solicitors p307 . . . 0844 984 6400
Linder Myers Solicitors p306 . . . 0844 984 6000
The Lister Croft Partnership p358 . . . 0113 257 0526
Livingstons p416 . . . 01229 585555
MFG Solicitors p265 . . . 01562 820181
MWP Solicitors p126. . . . 01268 527131
MWRLaw Ltd p357 . . . 01772 254201
McKenzie Bell Solicitors p401 . . . 0191 567 4857
Mackintosh Duncan p57 . . . 020 7357 6464
MacLaren Britton p338 . . . 0115 941 1469
Marchant Harries & Co p113. . . . 01685 885500
Marchants Solicitors p312. . . . 01623 655111
Marshall Hall & Levy p384 . . . 0191 455 3181
Mason Baggott & Garton p219 . . . 01427 872661
Matthew Arnold & Baldwin LLP p423 . . 01923 202020
Mayo Wynne Baxter LLP p215. . . . 01323 730543
Mayo Wynne Baxter LLP p160. . . . 01273 775533
Mayo Wynne Baxter LLP p283. . . . 01273 477071
Michelmores LLP p221 . . . 01392 688688
Milne & Lyall p158 . . . 01308 422362
Morgans p180. . . . 029 2072 9888
Moss Beachley Mullem & Coleman p62. . . . 020 7402 1401 / 7723 5783
Motley & Hope p133 . . . 01767 600600
Mustoe Shorter p430. . . . 01305 752700
Myers Lister Price p117 . . . 0161 926 9969
Nalders Quality Solicitors p414. . . . 01872 241414
Nalders Quality Solicitors p223. . . . 01326 313441
Nalders Quality Solicitors p173. . . . 01209 714278
Nalders Quality Solicitors p329. . . . 01637 871414
Nalders Quality Solicitors p346. . . . 01736 364014
Nelsons p338 . . . 0115 958 6262
Alfred Newton & Co p433 . . . 01625 523647
Alfred Newton & Co p396 . . . 0161 480 6551 / 480 1245
Alfred Newton & Co p396 . . . 0161 430 8831
NIGHTINGALES SOLICITORS LIMITED p396 . . . 01663 764038
NORRIE WAITE & SLATER p377 . . . 0114 276 6166
North Yorkshire Law p372 . . . 01723 360001
Ouvry Goodman & Co p403 . . . 020 8642 7571
Palmers p126 . . . 01268 240000
Pardoes p158 . . . 01278 457891
Pardoes p408 . . . 01823 446200
Park Woodfine Heald Mellows LLP p130 . 01234 400000
Parker Rhodes Hickmotts p367. . . . 01709 511100
Parnalls Solicitors Limited p270 . . . 01566 772375
Patchell Davies (Trading Name of PD Law Ltd) p147 . . . 01495 227128
Payne & Gamage p322 . . . 01636 640649
Pearson Hinchliffe p341. . . . 0161 785 3500
Pearson Maddin Solicitors p321 . . . 020 8949 9500
Pengillys LLP p430. . . . 01305 768888
Pengillys LLP p212. . . . 01305 768888
Penmans p394 . . . 01375 677777
Peters & Peters p67 . . . 020 7629 7991
Philippou & Co p67 . . . 020 8882 4222
Samuel Phillips Law Firm p326. . . . 0191 232 8451
Pictons Solicitors LLP p317. . . . 01908 663511
Pictons Solicitors LLP p247. . . . 01442 242441
Pollecoff Solicitors Ltd p68 . . . 020 7608 2568
Porter Dodson p408 . . . 01823 625800
Powells p429 . . . 01934 623501
QualitySolicitors Gruber Garratt p358 . . . 0161 724 0203
Quinn Melville p290. . . . 0151 236 3340
Ralph & Co p329. . . . 01637 872218
Red Kite Law p410. . . . 01834 842122
Red Kite Law p345. . . . 01646 683222
Red Kite Law p244. . . . 01437 763332
Red Kite Law p345. . . . 01646 681529
Red Kite Law p316. . . . 01646 698008
Richmond Anderson Goudie p191 . . . 0191 388 7884
Roach Pittis p328. . . . 01983 524431
Robinson Allfree p166. . . . 01843 865261
Paul Robinson Solicitors p428 . . . 01702 338338
Robinsons p209. . . . 01332 291431
Roebucks p145 . . . 01254 274000
Rootes & Alliott p227 . . . 01303 851100
Royds LLP p74. . . . 020 7583 2222
Rudlings & Wakelam p410. . . . 01842 754151
Rudlings & Wakelam p171 . . . 01284 755771
Russell Jones & Walker p74 . . . 020 7657 1555
SA Law p390. . . . 01727 798000
SJP Solicitors p258. . . . 01485 532662
Samars Solicitors p254. . . . 020 8570 4716
Santers Solicitors p123. . . . 020 8594 7542
Saulet & Co p389 . . . 023 9281 9442
The Sethi Partnership Solicitors p216 . . . 020 8866 6464
Sharman Law p130. . . . 01234 303030
Sharp & Partners p339 . . . 0115 959 0055
Shentons p434 . . . 01962 844544
Silks p340. . . . 0121 511 2233
Silverbeck Rymer p290 . . . 0151 236 9594
Silverman Sherliker LLP p78. . . . 020 7749 2700
Slee Blackwell p125 . . . 01271 372128
The Smith Partnership p170 . . . 01283 536471
The Smith Partnership p404 . . . 01283 226444
Smith Roddam p144 . . . 01388 603073
Smith Solicitor LLP p238 . . . 01422 383380
W F Smith LLP p209. . . . 01362 852900
Solomon Levy p295 . . . 01582 425817 / 414948
Stachiw Bashir Green p155 . . . 01274 404010
Standley & Co p269 . . . 01564 776287
Steele Raymond p152 . . . 01202 294566
Stephens & Scown p222. . . . 01392 210700
Stephens & Scown p391. . . . 01726 74433
Stephens & Scown p414. . . . 01872 265100
Stephensons Solicitors LLP p282 . . . 01942 777777
Stephensons Solicitors LLP p391 . . . 01942 777777
Stephensons Solicitors LLP p432 . . . 01942 777777
Stokes Solicitors p355 . . . 023 9282 8131
Stone King LLP p128 . . . 01225 337599
Stones Solicitors LLP p340 . . . 01837 650200
Swain & Co p244. . . . 023 9248 3322
Swinburne & Jackson LLP p229 0191 477 2531 / 477 3222
TBI Solicitors p243. . . . 0800 052 6824 / 01429 264101
TBI Solicitors p123. . . . 01833 638326
Tanner & Taylor LLP p115. . . . 01252 316565
Temple Heelis LLP p264 . . . 01539 723757
Terrells LLP p347 . . . 01733 896789
Thackray Williams p167. . . . 020 8290 0440
Thompsons (formerly Robin/Brian Thompson & Partners) p181 . . . 029 2044 5300
Thompsons (formerly Robin/Brian Thompson & Partners) p165 . . . 0117 304 2400
Thorpe & Co p430. . . . 01947 603465
Thorpe & Co p226. . . . 01723 515555
Tilley & Co p390. . . . 01727 840467
Timms p170. . . . 01283 561531 / 544417
Timms p209. . . . 01332 364436
Timms Solicitors p404 . . . 01283 214231
Tozers p329. . . . 01626 207020
Tozers p409. . . . 01626 772376
Tozers p222. . . . 01392 207020
Tozers p350. . . . 01752 206460
Alison Trent & Co p88 . . . 020 7583 3350
Trobridges p412 . . . 01752 812787
Trobridges p350 . . . 01752 664022
Tyndallwoods p143 . . . 0121 624 1111
WBW Solicitors p329 . . . 01626 202404
WBW Solicitors p153 . . . 01626 833263
WBW Solicitors p413 . . . 0870 701 4321
WBW Solicitors p222 . . . 01392 202404
Walker & Co p367. . . . 01709 817112
Waller Needham & Green p347 . . . 01733 262182
Waller Needham & Green p347 . . . 01733 311422
Walters & Barbary p173. . . . 01209 712454
Wards Solicitors p165 . . . 0117 929 2811
Wards Solicitors p429 . . . 01934 413535
Wards Solicitors p394 . . . 0117 943 4800
Wards Solicitors p429 . . . 01934 428811
Wards Solicitors p443 . . . 01454 316789
Warner Goodman LLP p387 . . . 023 8063 9311
Watson Woodhouse p397 . . . 01642 247656
Webster Dixon LLP p90. . . . 020 7353 8300
Whiskers p239 . . . 01279 439439
Wilkin Chapman Epton Blades p285. . . . 01522 512345
Willett & Co p171 . . . 01284 701323
Williams & Co p217 . . . 020 8952 8882
Wilson Browne p333. . . . 01604 876697
Wilson Browne p281. . . . 0116 251 7181
Wilson Browne p425. . . . 01933 279000
Wilson Browne p265. . . . 01536 410041
Wilsons Solicitors p344 . . . 01865 874497
Wolferstans p351. . . . 01752 663295
Wollen Michelmore Solicitors p413 . . . 01803 213251
Woodfines LLP p130. . . . 01234 270600
Worger Howcroft p133 . . . 01274 511246
Worthingtons p227. . . . 01303 850206

FAMILY

174 Law p134. . . . 0151 647 7372
@ Cornwall Law p414 . . . 01872 222688 / 222712
A-Z Law Solicitors p3 . . . 020 8355 0830
AGR Solicitors p311 . . . 01623 460444
AGR Solicitors p378 . . . 01623 748522
AKP Solicitors Ltd p3 . . . 020 8472 4462
AMD Solicitors p160. . . . 0117 962 1460
ASB Law p298 . . . 01622 656500
AS Law p285 . . . 0151 707 1212
AWB Charlesworth LLP p381 . . . 01756 793333
Aaronson & Co p3. . . . 020 7376 9124
Abbott & Co p419 . . . 0161 799 8003
Abels p385 . . . 023 8022 0317
Abensons p285 . . . 0151 733 3111
Abney Garsden McDonald p185 . . . 0161 482 8822
Abrams Collyer p296. . . . 01590 677888
Acklam Bond Noor p145 . . . 01254 56068
Adams Harrison p370 . . . 01799 523441
Adams Harrison p244 . . . 01440 705731 / 702485
Addies p226. . . . 01253 772128
ADDISON O'HARE p419. . . . 01922 725515
Adlams LLP p258 . . . 01480 458885
Adlams LLP p392 . . . 01480 474061
Aitken Associates p4. . . . 020 7700 6006
Alban Gould Baker & Co p4 . . . 020 7607 5085
Albin & Co p359 . . . 0118 957 4018
Alderson Dodds p147 . . . 01670 352293
Aldridge Brownlee Solicitors LLP p151 . . . 01202 294411
Aletta Shaw Solicitors p132 . . . 020 8301 4884
Alexander & Partners p5 . . . 020 8965 7121
Michael Alexander & Co p301 . . . 0845 839 2011
Allan Rutherford p333. . . . 01603 621722
Allansons LLP p148 . . . 0161 220 8484
Alletsons Ltd p157 . . . 01278 456621
Allington Hughes p190 . . . 01244 312166
Allington Hughes p442 . . . 01978 291000
Alsters Kelley p339. . . . 0844 561 0100
Alsters Kelley p199. . . . 0844 561 0100
Alsters Kelley p270. . . . 0844 561 0100
Ambrose Appelbe p6 . . . 020 7242 7000
J M Amin & Co p426 . . . 020 8903 3766
Amphlett Lissimore p6 . . . 020 8771 5254
Amphletts p198. . . . 01492 532296
Anderson Partnership p191 . . . 01246 220737
Andersons Solicitors p335 . . . 0115 947 0641
Andrew & Andrew Solicitors p354. . . . 023 9266 1381
Andrew Macbeth Cash & Co p435. . . . 01629 822553
Andrews McQueen p151 . . . 01202 290628
Maurice Andrews p135 . . . 0121 554 4900
Thomas Andrews & Partners p442. . . . 01978 291506
Angel & Co p200. . . . 024 7625 2211
Angell & Co p127 . . . 01225 484244
Ansons LLP p284. . . . 01543 263456
APPLEBY HOPE & MATTHEWS p314 . 01642 440444
Appleby Hope & Matthews p396. . . . 01642 617000
Arani & Co p384 . . . 020 8893 5000
Archer & Archer p218. . . . 01353 662203
Archers Law LLP p396 . . . 01642 636500
Armitage Sykes LLP p255. . . . 01484 538121
Armitage Sykes LLP p158. . . . 01484 714431
Armitage Sykes LLP p255. . . . 01484 344140
Gerald Armstrong & Co p401. . . . 0191 514 0966
Arnison & Co Solicitors Limited p346 . . . 01768 862007
Arnold Greenwood p264 . . . 01539 720049
Arora Ashton Patel p259 . . . 020 8554 6263
Arscotts p254 . . . 01273 735289
Arthur & Co p348 . . . 020 8866 8282
Arthur Smiths p432 . . . 01942 242815
Ash Clifford p157. . . . 01278 451327
Ashfords LLP p412. . . . 01884 203000
Ashfords LLP p220. . . . 01392 337000
Ashfords LLP p408. . . . 01823 232300
Ashton KCJ p171. . . . 01284 762331
Ashton KCJ p262. . . . 01473 232425
Ashton KCJ p225. . . . 01394 277188
Ashton KCJ p174. . . . 01223 363111
Ashton KCJ p171. . . . 01284 761233
Ashton KCJ p333. . . . 01603 703070
Askew Bunting Solicitors LLP p237 . . . 01287 635151
Askew Bunting Solicitors LLP p314 . . . 01642 252555
Askews p362 . . . 01642 475252
Askews p396 . . . 01642 475252
Aspinall & Co p148 . . . 01204 388200
Aspinall Wright p230 . . . 01457 854645
Aston Clark p8 . . . 020 8752 1122
Atherton Godfrey p211 . . . 01302 320621
Atkins Hope Solicitors p204. . . . 020 8680 5018
Atkinson & Co p328. . . . 01633 251118
Atkinson & Firth p378. . . . 01274 584305
Atkinson Cave & Stuart p146 . . . 01253 293151
Atkinson McCall p240. . . . 01423 501531
Atkinson Ritson p181 . . . 01228 525221
Atkinson Ritson p432 . . . 01697 343241
Atter Mackenzie & Co p220 . . . 01386 425300
Atteys p211 . . . 01302 340400
Atteys p124 . . . 01226 212345
Atteys p424 . . . 01709 872106
Atteys p363 . . . 01777 713355
Attwaters p294 . . . 020 8508 2111
Attwaters p239 . . . 01279 638888
Attwood & Co p233 . . . 01375 378122 / 378123
David Auld & Co p130 . . . 01670 826870
David Auld & Co p319 . . . 01670 505844
AUSTIN RYDER & CO p189 . . . 01992 624804
AUSTIN RYDER & CO p8. . . . 020 8804 5111
Avadis & Co p8 . . . 020 7267 4240
Avery Naylor p404. . . . 01792 463276
Awdry Bailey & Douglas p210 . . . 01380 722311
Awdry Bailey & Douglas p173 . . . 01249 815110
Awdry Bailey & Douglas p439 . . . 01793 853200
Ayres Waters p395 . . . 0161 480 5229
B&C Solicitors - The Law Shop p372 . . . 01723 379777
BHP Law p214 . . . 0191 384 0840
BHP Law p330 . . . 01325 312534
BHP Law p206 . . . 01325 466794
BHP Law p323 . . . 0191 221 0898
BHP Law p238 . . . 01422 250650
BHP Law p330 . . . 0191 257 2213
BHP Law p396 . . . 01642 672770

See p603 for the Community Legal Service Work Categories

BLB Solicitors *p413* . . . 01225 755656
BLB Solicitors *p406* . . . 01793 615011
BTMK Solicitors LLP *p387* . . . 01702 339222
Baches *p427* . . . 0121 553 3286 / 553 7076
Ursula Bagnall Divorce & Family Law Solicitors *p201* . . . 01983 247221
Bailey & Cogger *p412* . . . 01732 353305
Bailey & Haigh *p373* . . . 01757 705191
Bailey Wright & Co *p135* . . . 0845 475 1996
Baily Gibson *p128* . . . 01494 672661
Baily Gibson *p249* . . . 01494 442661
Baker & Duke *p261* . . . 01460 52293
Baker Gray & Co *p147* . . . 0191 414 4869
Baker Gray & Co *p323* . . . 0191 222 0203
Bakewells *p208* . . . 01332 348791
Band Hatton LLP *p200* . . . 024 7663 2121
Banks Kelly *p9* . . . 020 7248 4231
John L Banky Solicitors *p359* . . . 0118 930 4630
Banner Jones *p213* . . . 01246 414438
Banner Jones *p191* . . . 01246 827516
Banner Jones *p192* . . . 01246 861250
Banner Jones *p191* . . . 01246 209773
Bannister Preston *p263* . . . 0161 775 0444
Bannister Preston *p370* . . . 0161 973 2434
Barcan Woodward *p160* . . . 0117 963 5237
Barcan Woodward *p161* . . . 0117 925 8080
Barcan Woodward *p161* . . . 0117 923 2141
Max Barford & Co *p414* . . . 01892 539379
Barker Booth & Eastwood *p146* . . . 01253 362500
Barkers *p148* . . . 01204 370011
John Barkers *p195* . . . 01472 695218
John Barkers *p294* . . . 01507 604773
John Barkers *p234* . . . 01472 358686
John Barkers *p297* . . . 01507 477673
Barnes & Partners *p10* . . . 020 8884 2277
Barnes & Partners *p239* . . . 01279 418601
Barnes & Partners *p421* . . . 01920 460823
Barnes Coleman & Co *p131* . . . 01702 558211
F Barnes & Son *p366* . . . 01708 745183
Barnes Harrild & Dyer *p204* . . . 020 8681 5128
Norman H Barnett & Co *p11* . . . 020 8471 2112
Barrea LLP *p249* . . . 01494 537699
Barrett & Thomson *p381* . . . 01753 437416
Barrington Charles Edwards & Co *p11* . . . 020 8656 8318 / 8656 8319
Barrow & Cook *p391* . . . 01744 23271
Bartlett Gooding & Weelen *p183* . . . 01963 350888
Bartlett Gooding & Weelen *p378* . . . 01749 343091
Bartlett Gooding & Weelen *p229* . . . 01458 832510
Atha Barton & Co *p237* . . . 01287 633242
Bartons *p413* . . . 01803 864705
Barwells *p373* . . . 01323 899331
Bassets *p229* . . . 01634 575464
Bassets *p366* . . . 01634 400161
Bates & Mountain *p235* . . . 01472 357291
Bates N V H *p11* . . . 020 7936 2930
Battens *p212* . . . 01305 250560
Battens *p443* . . . 01935 846000
Battens *p430* . . . 01305 774666
Bawtrees LLP *p435* . . . 01376 513491
Deborah Baxter & Co *p360* . . . 0118 958 6855
Baxters *p256* . . . 01482 224011
Baxters *p407* . . . 01827 899059
Bazeley Barnes & Bazeley *p132* . . . 01237 473122
Beashel Solicitors *p421* . . . 01985 220680
Beaumonts *p247* . . . 01432 352345
The Beavis Partnership *p186* . . . 01245 264748
The Beavis Partnership *p435* . . . 01376 500255
Bedwell Watts & Co *p372* . . . 01723 373356 / 363553
Beecham Peacock *p323* . . . 0191 232 3048
Beecroft Maxwell *p177* . . . 01268 511999
Beetenson & Gibbon *p235* . . . 01472 240251
Beevers Solicitors *p119* . . . 0161 339 9697
Roy Thomas Begley & Co *p404* . . . 01792 643797 / 643798
Behr & Co *p167* . . . 01495 310581
Bell Lamb & Joynson *p369* . . . 0844 412 4348
Bell Lamb & Joynson *p286* . . . 0844 412 4348
R Bell & Son *p242* . . . 01429 273165
John Bellis & Co *p346* . . . 01492 622377
John Bellis & Co *p199* . . . 01248 680527
Bemrose & Ling *p208* . . . 01332 347300
Ben Hoare Bell & Co *p401* . . . 0191 565 3112
Ben Hoare Bell & Co *p323* . . . 0191 275 2626
Ben Hoare Bell & Co *p401* . . . 0191 516 0466
Bendall & Sons *p316* . . . 01638 712243
Bendall & Sons *p327* . . . 01638 661116
Bendles *p181* . . . 01228 522215
Harold Benjamin *p241* . . . 020 8422 5678
Bennett Griffin *p441* . . . 01903 229925
Bennett Griffin *p225* . . . 01903 229999
Bennett Griffin *p369* . . . 01903 777690
Bennett Richmond *p270* . . . 01207 521843
Benson Watkins *p404* . . . 01792 704320
Berkeley Solicitors *p213* . . . 0161 371 0011
Berkson Globe Partnership *p286* . . . 0151 236 1234
Bernard Chill & Axtell *p216* . . . 023 8061 3197
Bernard Chill & Axtell *p385* . . . 023 8022 8821
Berry & Berry *p414* . . . 01892 526344
Berry & Berry *p412* . . . 01732 355911
Berry & Berry *p299* . . . 01622 690777
Berry & Berry *p301* . . . 0161 703 7300
Berry Redmond & Robinson *p434* . . . 01934 842811
Berry Redmond & Robinson *p429* . . . 01934 619000
Berry Redmond & Robinson *p429* . . . 01934 513963
Berry Smith LLP *p157* . . . 01656 645525
Berwins Solicitors Limited *p240* . . . 01423 509000
Best Solicitors *p375* . . . 0114 281 3636
Beswicks *p239* . . . 01782 205000
Bevirs *p406* . . . 01793 532363
Bevirs *p173* . . . 01249 814536
Beviss & Beckingsale *p373* . . . 01297 626950
Bhatia Best *p336* . . . 0115 950 3231
Bibi Gadwah Solicitors *p12* . . . 020 7377 6102
Bickley Wheatley & Co *p135* . . . 0121 377 6266
David Billingham & Partners *p187* . . . 01242 676224
Billson & Sharp *p279* . . . 0116 255 9911
Bilton Hammond LLP *p311* . . . 01623 675800
Bilton Hammond LLP *p192* . . . 01246 232418
Bindman & Co *p430* . . . 0191 488 4950
Bindmans LLP *p12* . . . 020 7833 4433
Birchall Blackburn LLP *p356* . . . 01772 561663
Birchall Blackburn LLP *p194* . . . 01257 279011
BIRD & CO *p232* . . . 01476 591711
BIRD & CO *p322* . . . 01636 650880
Bird & Daniels *p378* . . . 01274 580999
Birkett Long LLP *p197* . . . 01206 217300
Birkett Long LLP *p186* . . . 01245 453800
Biscoes *p348* . . . 01730 264799
Biscoes *p354* . . . 023 9266 0261
Biscoes *p423* . . . 023 9225 1257
Biscoes *p431* . . . 01329 833249
Biscoes *p232* . . . 023 9251 2030
Biscoes *p353* . . . 023 9237 0634
Bishop & Co *p321* . . . 01663 746730
Black Norman *p203* . . . 0151 931 2777
Blackfords LLP *p204* . . . 020 8686 6232
Blackhurst Budd LLP *p146* . . . 01253 629300
Blackhurst Swainson Goodier LLP *p356* . . . 01772 253841
Blackhurst Swainson Goodier LLP *p269* . . . 01524 32471
Blair Allison & Co *p135* . . . 0121 233 2904
Blake Lapthorn *p354* . . . 023 9222 1122
Blakemores *p270* . . . 01926 457300
Blakemores *p135* . . . 0121 234 7200
Blaker Son & Young *p283* . . . 01273 480234
Blakestons *p213* . . . 01377 253476
Blanchards Bailey LLP *p147* . . . 01258 459361
Blandy & Blandy *p360* . . . 0118 951 6800
Blaser Mills *p364* . . . 01923 776211
Blaser Mills *p241* . . . 020 8427 6262
Blaser Mills *p249* . . . 01494 450171
Blaser Mills *p120* . . . 01296 434416
Bleasdale & Co *p431* . . . 01946 692165
Blight Skinnard *p371* . . . 01752 842141
BLOCKS *p225* . . . 01394 283241
Blythe Liggins *p270* . . . 01926 831231
Bobbetts Mackan *p161* . . . 0117 929 9001
Bolitho Way *p354* . . . 023 9282 0747
Bolt Burdon *p14* . . . 020 7288 4700
A J Bond & Co *p166* . . . 020 8464 2229
Bond Joseph *p176* . . . 01227 453545
Bone & Payne LLP *p291* . . . 01492 876354
Bone & Payne LLP *p198* . . . 01492 532385
Peter Bonner & Co *p14* . . . 020 8297 1727
Harry Boodhoo & Co *p436* . . . 0161 445 0588
C W Booth & Co *p144* . . . 01388 606660
Borneo Hughes Martell LLP *p331* . . . 01604 624822
D S Bosher & Co *p254* . . . 01273 721913
Bosley & Co *p159* . . . 01273 608181
Arthur Boulton Solicitors *p397* . . . 01782 813315
Eric Bowes & Co *p382* . . . 0121 744 3691
Sabina Bowler-Reed *p161* . . . 01275 373111
Bowling & Co *p15* . . . 020 8221 8000
Bowser Ollard & Bentley *p435* . . . 01945 583194
Bowser Ollard & Bentley *p312* . . . 01354 652606
Boyce Hatton *p412* . . . 01803 403403
Boyes Turner *p360* . . . 0118 959 7711
John Boyle & Co *p362* . . . 01209 213507
John Boyle & Co *p414* . . . 01872 272356
Boys & Maughan *p312* . . . 01843 234000
Boys & Maughan *p166* . . . 01843 868861
Boys & Maughan *p359* . . . 01843 595990
Brachers *p299* . . . 01622 690691
BRADBURY ROBERTS & RABY *p373* . . . 01724 854000
Brain Chase Coles *p126* . . . 01256 354481
Brain Sinnott & Co *p268* . . . 0117 960 6880
Brain Sinnott & Co *p161* . . . 0117 965 1030
Brains *p391* . . . 01726 68111
Brains *p414* . . . 01872 276363
Bramsdon & Childs *p388* . . . 023 9282 1251
Bramwell Browne Odedra *p189* . . . 01494 782244
Brand & Co *p185* . . . 020 8641 2771
Brar & Co *p323* . . . 0191 276 6880
Bray & Bray *p279* . . . 0116 254 8871
Bray & Bray *p312* . . . 01858 467181
Bray & Bray *p250* . . . 01455 639900
Brearleys Solicitors *p128* . . . 01924 473065
Brearleys Solicitors *p144* . . . 01924 443900
Breese-Gwyndaf *p353* . . . 01766 512253 / 514227
Breese-Gwyndaf *p239* . . . 01766 780334
Breeze & Wyles Solicitors LLP *p248* . . . 01992 558411
Breeze & Wyles Solicitors LLP *p144* . . . 01279 715333
Brennans Solicitors *p419* . . . 0191 262 5133
Brethertons LLP *p368* . . . 01788 579579
Brethertons LLP *p122* . . . 01295 270999
Brewer Harding & Rowe *p125* . . . 01271 342271
Brewer Harding & Rowe *p261* . . . 01271 863495
Brewer Harding & Rowe *p132* . . . 01237 472666
Bridge McFarland *p235* . . . 01472 311711
Bridge McFarland *p284* . . . 01522 518888
Bridge McFarland Haddon Owen *p294* . . . 01507 605883
Bridge Sanderson Munro *p411* . . . 01405 814136
Bridge Sanderson Munro *p211* . . . 01302 321621
Bridge Sanderson Munro *p424* . . . 01709 873321
Derrick Bridges & Co *p123* . . . 020 8449 7326
ELLIOTT BRIDGMAN *p409* . . . 01952 684544
Brighouse Wolff *p298* . . . 0151 520 2717
Brighouse Wolff *p341* . . . 01695 573202
Brighouse Wolff *p381* . . . 01695 722577
Brighouses *p388* . . . 01704 534101 / 500151
Bright & Sons *p299* . . . 01621 852323
Bright & Sons *p435* . . . 01376 512338
Brightstone Law LLP *p218* . . . 020 8731 3080
Brignalls Balderston Warren *p283* . . . 01462 482248
Brignalls Balderston Warren *p394* . . . 01438 359311
Broadbents *p404* . . . 01623 441123
Broadway Solicitors *p16* . . . 020 8767 7718
Brockbank Curwen Cain & Hall *p431* . . . 01946 692194
Brockbank Curwen Cain & Hall *p313* . . . 01900 813488
Brockbank Curwen Cain & Hall *p197* . . . 01900 827222
Brockbank Curwen Cain & Hall *p440* . . . 01900 603563
John Bromfield & Company Ltd *p339* . . . 024 7638 2343
Bromleys Solicitors LLP *p120* . . . 0161 330 6821
Brook Oliver *p321* . . . 01425 616809
Brooke-Taylors *p172* . . . 01298 22741
Brookes & Co *p192* . . . 01243 780333
Brooks *p378* . . . 01608 664406
Broomhead & Saul *p408* . . . 01823 288121
Broomhead & Saul *p261* . . . 01460 57056
Broudie Jackson Canter *p286* . . . 0151 227 1429
Brown & Corbishley *p323* . . . 01782 717888
Brown & Corbishley *p371* . . . 01270 768033
Brown & Murray *p316* . . . 01229 772562
Brown & Vautier *p227* . . . 01373 465222
BROWN BEER NIXON MALLON *p362* . . . 01642 490202
Gordon Brown Associates *p191* . . . 0191 388 1778
Brown Turner Ross *p388* . . . 01704 542002
Fiona Bruce & Co LLP *p421* . . . 01925 263273
Brutton & Co *p223* . . . 01329 236171
BRYAN & ARMSTRONG *p311* . . . 01623 626039
BRYAN & ARMSTRONG *p311* . . . 01623 624505
Bull & Bull *p248* . . . 01227 742660
Burges Salmon *p161* . . . 0117 939 2000
Burley & Geach *p243* . . . 01428 656011
Burley & Geach *p233* . . . 01428 605355
Burley & Geach *p285* . . . 01428 722334
Burnett Barker *p171* . . . 01284 701131
Burnetts *p181* . . . 01228 552222
Burrell Jenkins *p176* . . . 01543 505040
Burstalls *p256* . . . 01482 621800
Burton & Burton Solicitors LLP *p336* . . . 0845 094 2500
Burton & Co LLP *p284* . . . 01522 523215
Burton & Co LLP *p381* . . . 01529 306008 / 306009
Burton & Dyson *p228* . . . 01427 610761
C R Burton & Co *p16* . . . 020 8778 4455 / 8659 5775
BURY & WALKERS LLP *p124* . . . 01226 733533
BURY & WALKERS LLP *p438* . . . 01226 753433
Busbys Solicitors *p168* . . . 01288 359000
Kenneth Bush *p266* . . . 01553 692233
Kenneth Bush *p266* . . . 01553 692737
Buss Murton LLP *p207* . . . 01322 220235
Butcher & Barlow LLP *p170* . . . 0161 764 4062
Butcher & Barlow LLP *p357* . . . 0161 773 2969
Butcher & Barlow LLP *p369* . . . 01928 572268
Butcher & Barlow LLP *p416* . . . 01942 883669
Butcher & Barlow LLP *p170* . . . 0161 764 5141
Butcher & Barlow LLP *p333* . . . 01606 47523
Butcher & Barlow LLP *p281* . . . 01942 674144
Butcher & Barlow LLP *p369* . . . 01928 576056
Butterworths *p182* . . . 01228 593939
Button Legal LLP *p200* . . . 024 7652 5457
Bynes *p412* . . . 01803 295692
Byrne Frodsham & Co *p431* . . . 0151 424 5601
CB4law *p174* . . . 01223 316666
CMHT Solicitors *p420* . . . 01922 743525
CMHT Solicitors *p167* . . . 01543 372347
CMHT Solicitors *p420* . . . 01922 646400
CVC Solicitors *p245* . . . 01736 752246
CVC Solicitors *p346* . . . 01736 362313
Cadmans Law & Property *p195* . . . 01274 874231
Caldicott Gallimore *p282* . . . 01568 614168
Cameron Jones Hussell & Howe *p353* . . . 01639 885261

5

Camerons Jones p241 020 8423 6666
Campbell Chambers p18 020 7691 8777
Campbell Courtney & Cooney p173 01276 25100
Campbell Hooper & Co LLP p402 01344 622141
Canning & Co p421 01925 630012
Canter Levin & Berg p287 0151 239 1000
Caplans p241 020 8864 0111
Careless & Kemp p418 01983 852626
Careless & Kemp p372 01983 400456
Caris Robson LLP p358 01661 836851
Caris Robson LLP p324 0191 264 6664
Carmichael & Heathfield p324 0191 230 3010
Graeme Carmichael p262 01473 252159
Terence Carney p246 0191 483 5422 / 483 8771
Carr & Co p147 01670 351251
Carr & Co p231 0191 284 0363
Carr & Co p319 01670 515182
Carr Hepburn Solicitors Ltd p246 01442 241466
S A Carr & Co p18 020 8986 5438
Barbara Carter p136 0121 441 3238
Carters p351 01977 703224
Cartridges p220 01392 256854
Cartwright Cunningham Haselgrove & Co p19 020 8520 1021
Carvers (Part of the Wilkes Partnership LLP) p136 0121 784 8484
Carvill & Johnson LLP p136 0121 476 9000
Caseys p250 01278 794495
Caswell Jones p172 029 2086 4888
Catteralls p418 01924 291122
Chadwick Lawrence p418 01924 379078
Chadwick Lawrence p319 0113 252 3452
Chadwick Lawrence p238 01422 330601
Chadwick Lawrence p255 01484 519999
Chafes p433 01625 531676
Chafes p395 0161 477 1525
Chafes p321 01663 743344
Challenor Gardiner p343 01865 721451
Challinors p427 0121 553 3211
Challinors p136 0121 212 9393
Chamberlain Martin Solicitors p148 01243 825211
Chamberlins p234 01493 857621
Chambers & Hind (Stapleford) p336 0115 949 1141
Chambers Fletcher LLP p333 01606 780400
Chambers Rutland & Crauford p19 020 8446 2777
Chambers Solicitors p381 01753 522204
Chanter Ferguson p125 01271 342268
Chanter Ferguson p132 01237 478751
Chapmans Solicitors p402 020 8337 3801
Chappell Pascoe p204 01892 664348
Chapple & Co p312 01354 652550
Charlesworth Nicholl & Co p203 01363 774706
Charltons Solicitors p132 01782 522111
Chattertons Solicitors p252 01507 522456
Chattertons Solicitors p381 01529 411500
Chattertons Solicitors p232 01476 591550
Chattertons Solicitors p389 01775 768774
Chattertons Solicitors p151 01205 310025
Chattertons Solicitors p284 01522 814600
Chebsey & Co p128 01494 670440
Chilcotts p408 01822 612535 / 614242
Children & Families Law Firm p20 020 7582 6002
Chivers Easton Brown p402 020 8390 0081
Chivers Walsh Smith and Irvine & Co p153 01274 740077
Chronnell Hibbert p259 0161 368 3434
Chubb Bulleid p425 01749 836100
Churchers p271 023 9255 1500
Churchers p232 023 9260 3400
Churchers p223 01329 822333
Churchers p354 023 9221 0170
Clarion Solicitors LLP p272 0113 246 0622
Anthony Clark & Co p284 01522 512321
CLARK BROOKES p427 0121 553 2576
David Clark & Co p20 020 7433 1562
Clark Willis p206 01325 281111
Clark Willis p183 01748 830000
Clarke & Hartland Solicitors p177 029 2048 3181
Clarke & Hartland Solicitors p345 029 2071 1181
Clarke Kiernan p412 01732 360999
Peter Clarke Solicitors p413 023 8066 6636
Clarke Willmott p162 0845 209 1000 / 0117 305 6000
Clarke Willmott p408 0845 209 1000 / 0117 305 6000
Clarkes p379 01743 231531
Clarkes p425 01952 223548
Clarkes p409 01952 291666
Clarkson Hirst p269 01524 39760
Clayton Mott p336 0115 941 7422
Cleaver Thompson Ltd p115 01773 832193
Clifford Johnston & Co p302 0161 249 2700
Clifford Johnston & Co p302 0161 975 1900
Clifford Poole & Co p370 0161 736 0160
Douglas Clift & Co p269 01524 32437
Clifton Ingram LLP p437 0118 978 0099
Close Thornton p206 01325 466461
Clough & Willis p170 0161 764 5266
Cluley & Co p434 01606 553719
Cobains p146 01253 290092
Cobleys LLP p287 0151 242 9000
Cocks Lloyd p339 024 7664 1642
Coffin Mew & Clover p385 023 8033 4661
Coffin Mew & Clover p354 023 9238 8021
Coffin Mew & Clover p232 023 9252 3111
Coffin Mew & Clover p223 01329 825617
Colebournes Solicitors and Advocates p146 01253 293195
Coles Miller Solicitors LLP p352 01202 673011
Coles Miller Solicitors LLP p166 01202 694891
Coles Miller Solicitors LLP p151 01202 511512
COLEY & TILLEY p136 0121 643 5531
Collard & Co p250 01793 765327
Anthony Collins Solicitors LLP p137 0121 200 3242
Collins Solicitors p423 01923 223324
K J Commons & Co p440 01900 604698
K J Commons & Co p431 01946 66699
Constantine & Summers p173 01276 23211
Conveyancing Direct Ltd p392 0845 788 8666
Conway & Co p241 020 8863 0535
Conway & Co p234 020 8575 2191
Coodes p391 01726 874700
Coodes p414 01872 246200
Coodes p270 01566 770000
Coodes p329 01637 878111
Coodes p285 01579 347600
Coodes p346 01736 362294
Cook Taylor p22 020 8854 1166
Coole & Haddock p441 01903 213511
Cooper Lingard p282 01702 715411
Cooper Nimmo p146 01253 626793
Cooper Sons Hartley & Williams p184 01298 812138
Copitch p22 020 8883 9831
John Copland & Son p375 01795 664431
Copleys p258 01480 456191
Cornfield Law p215 01323 412512
Coupe Bradbury p296 01253 736670
Covent Garden Family Law p23 020 7257 6130
David Cowan p212 01306 886622
Cowlishaw & Mountford p417 01889 565211
Cozens-Hardy LLP p334 01603 625231
Craigen Wilders & Sorrell p23 020 8888 2255
Cramp & Co p215 01323 720581
Crampton Pym & Lewis p342 01691 653301
Crane & Staples p425 01707 329333
Crane & Walton p196 01530 834466
Crangle Edwards p400 0161 865 2993 / 865 7816 / 865 5875
Crangle Edwards p185 0161 428 2331
Martin Cray & Co p159 01273 673226
Creighton & Partners p23 020 7976 2233
Crisp & Co Solicitors p236 01483 570810
Crockett & Co p272 0113 226 0111
Crombie Wilkinson p444 01904 624185
Crombie Wilkinson p300 01653 600070
Crombie Wilkinson p374 01757 708957
Charles Crookes & Jones p172 029 2086 0628
Cross Solicitors p199 01244 822101
Stanley H Cross & Co p194 01257 272222
Crosse & Crosse p220 01392 258451
Crosse Wyatt Verney & Ayre p383 01769 572157
Crossmans p358 01761 431688
Crossmans MTA p174 01223 451442
PAUL CROWLEY & CO p287 0151 264 7363
Paul Crowley & Co p287 0151 264 7363
Ian Cruickshank & Co p263 0191 428 0900
Richard Crumly p410 01635 866166
Michael Cullen & Partners p133 01277 623132
Cumming Hodgkinson Dickinson p148 01204 523108 / 528396
Daniel Curry & Co p205 020 8680 2188
Kenneth Curtis & Co p137 0121 356 1161
Curtis Parkinson p336 0800 056 6042
Curtis Parkinson p336 0115 931 7000
Cuttle & Co p302 0161 835 2050
Cuttle & Co Solicitors p340 0161 678 7443
Cyfraith JRL Law p292 01492 641222
Cygnet Family Law p196 01642 777680
Cyril Morris Arkwright p148 01204 535261
DBL Talbots LLP p265 01562 749910
DBL Talbots LLP p213 01384 252471
DBL Talbots LLP p197 01902 843427
DBL Talbots LLP p437 01902 427561
DBL Talbots LLP p399 01384 445850
DB Law p346 01736 364261
DB Law p173 01209 712428
DB Law p223 01326 211609
DFA Law LLP p331 01604 609560
DFA Law LLP p331 01604 609560
DLC Solicitors Limited p207 01254 761234
DP Law Ltd t/a David Prosser & Co p157 01656 645921
Daltons p215 01323 720040
Daniel & Edwards p359 01843 594651
Daniel and Harris p25 020 7625 0202
Leona Daniel p243 01273 845024
Darbys Solicitors LLP p343 01865 811700
W H Darbyshire & Son p146 01253 346646
Darling & Stephensons p206 01325 489000
David & Snape p157 01656 661115
David & Snape p353 01656 782070 / 785038
Davidson Smith & Co p130 01234 351971
Davies & Co p166 020 8460 6668
Davies & Partners p230 01452 612345
Davies & Partners p115 01454 619619
Davies Blunden & Evans p224 01252 541633
George Davies Solicitors LLP p303 0161 236 8992
Davies Gore Lomax p273 0113 242 2797
Hywel Davies & Co p121 01678 520307
Lawrence Davies & Co p26 020 7381 1171
Davies Parsons Allchurch p292 01554 749144
R George Davies & Co p113 01873 852535
Davies Sully Wilkins p172 029 2088 7828
Davis Priest & Co p362 01527 69231
Davis Wood p162 0117 965 3504
Davisons p137 0121 685 1255
Davisons p137 0121 685 1248
Davisons p137 0121 685 1234
Dawson & Burgess with Bell Dallman & Co p211 01302 834744
Dawson Cornwell p26 020 7242 2556
Nicholas Daykin Solicitors p120 01953 453774
De Soyza & Fernando p26 020 8670 9918
Debenhams Ottaway p390 01727 837161
John Delaney & Co p273 0113 246 8151
Denby & Co p416 01229 582283
Denby & Co p125 01229 822366
Denniss Matthews p27 020 8778 7301 / 8778 7631
Desor & Co p245 020 8569 0708
Devonalds p352 01443 404331
Devonalds p412 01443 434343
Dibbens p433 01202 882456
Dickinson Manser p352 01202 673071
Dickinsons p146 01253 781010
Dicksons Solicitors Ltd p397 01782 262424
Dicksons Solicitors Ltd p397 01782 262424
Dixon Lewis Solicitors p425 01952 245700
Dixon Stewart p321 01425 621515
Dixon Stewart Solicitors p250 01425 279222
Dobson & Sleeman p315 01642 231707
Dodds & Partners p279 0116 253 8585
Paul Dodds Solicitors p419 0191 263 6200
Dollman & Pritchard p183 01883 347823
John Donkin & Co p228 0191 495 2896 / 477 1781
Donnelly & Elliott Limited p232 023 9250 5500
Donnelly McArdle Adamson p243 01429 274732
Dootsons LLP p282 01942 673431
Dootsons LLP p205 01925 765212
Douglas-Jones Mercer p405 01792 650000
Douglass Simon p156 020 8560 3888
Downes & Siddall p284 01522 543343
Dowse & Co p27 020 7254 6205
Dowson Billington p356 01772 556807
Driver Belcher Solicitors p144 01489 892101 / 892102
Scott Duff & Co p182 01228 531054
Scott Duff & Co p346 01768 865551
Scott Duff & Co p265 01768 774321
Duffield Harrison LLP p251 01992 442911
Dunn & Baker p221 01392 285000
Peter Dunn & Co p401 0191 568 9000
Dunning & Co p28 020 7733 6217
Thomas Dunton Solicitors p342 01689 822554
Dutton Gregory p385 023 8022 1344
Dwyers p120 0161 308 3928
Dyne Drewett Solicitors Ltd p378 01935 813691
Dyne Drewett Solicitors Ltd p378 01749 342323
Earl & Crocker p285 01579 345304
Eastleys p413 01803 864888
Eastleys p345 01803 559257
Eastleys p166 01803 853266
Eaton & Few p391 01480 301558
Eaton-Evans & Morris p244 01437 763383
Eaton Smith LLP p255 01484 821300
Eatons p153 0845 660 0660
Eddowes Waldron p208 01332 348484
Edell Jones & Lessers p28 020 8548 5700
Edwards Duthie p260 020 8514 9000
Edwards Duthie p29 020 8514 9000
Edwards Duthie p29 020 8514 9000
E Edwards Son & Noice p133 01277 658551
R L Edwards & Partners p157 01656 656861
R L Edwards & Partners p413 01443 775000
Joe Egan Solicitors p149 01204 368060
Thomas Eggar LLP p441 01903 234411
Thomas Eggar LLP p202 01293 742700
Thomas Eggar LLP p192 01243 786111
Elliot Mather LLP p192 01246 231288
Elliott & Allen p373 01902 677204
Ellis-Fermor & Negus p364 01773 744744
Ellis-Fermor & Negus p130 0115 922 1591
Ellis-Fermor & Negus p293 0115 972 5222
Ellis Lakin & Co p348 01751 472121
Ellisons p197 01206 764477
Ellisons p243 01255 502428
Elsey & Hodson p347 01733 314064
Elwyn Jones & Co p122 01248 370224

See p603 for the Community Legal Service Work Categories

Emery Johnson Partnership p279 0116 255 4855
Emmerson Brown & Brown p212 01304 211766
Emsleys p368 0113 282 4939
England & Co p234 01493 844308 / 844309
England & Co p234 01493 740795 / 748174
England & Co p234 01493 604990
England Stickland & Neale p138 0121 377 7773
Eric Robinson Solicitors p184 023 8025 4676
Eric Robinson Solicitors p386 023 8022 6891
Eric Robinson Solicitors p259 023 8084 4304
Eric Robinson Solicitors p385 01489 788922
Eric Robinson Solicitors p385 023 8042 5000
The Eric Whitehead Partnership p185 01538 755761
Charles Ete & Co p29 020 7820 9818
Evans & Greaves p172 029 2086 6001
Evans Main Solicitors p374 01732 464848
Mary Evans & Co p182 01267 233881
Evans-Roberts p298 01654 702335 / 702336
Everett Tomlin Lloyd & Pratt p352 01495 763333
Eversheds LLP p174 0845 497 9797
Everys p380 01395 577983
Everys p342 01404 813446
Everys p252 01404 41221
Everys p222 01395 264384
Everys p373 01297 21105
Everys p221 01392 477983
Ewings & Co p30 020 8778 1126
FDC Law p228 01373 463311
FDC Law p228 01373 465051
FDC Law p358 01761 417575
Fahri Jacob p30 020 8347 4070
Fairbairn Smith & Co p30 020 8808 4901
Fairbrother & Darlow p153 01344 420808
Fairweather Stephenson & Co p282 01728 832832
Faradays Solicitors Ltd p30 020 7281 1001
Farleys Solicitors LLP p114 01254 367853
Farleys Solicitors LLP p145 01254 367855
Farleys Solicitors LLP p169 01282 798664
Farleys Solicitors LLP p145 01254 367856
Farnfield & Nicholls p421 01985 214661
Farnfield & Nicholls p374 01747 854244
Farnworth Shaw p321 01282 699996
Farnworth Shaw p198 01282 864081
Farrell Matthews & Weir p31 020 8741 1482
Farrell Matthews & Weir p30 020 8746 3771
Favell Smith & Lawson Solicitors p375 0114 272 4381
FAWCETT & PATTNI p420 01922 640424
Feld McKay & Donner Solicitors p365 01706 645656
Fentimans p269 01564 779459
Joan Ferguson & Co p304 0161 795 5866
Fernando & Co p31 020 8767 4611
A J Field & Co p375 01795 580600
A J Field & Co p380 01795 436363
Field Overell p270 01926 422101
Alison Fielden & Co p195 01285 653261
Fieldings Porter p149 01204 540900
Finn Gledhill p238 01422 330000
Paul Finn Solicitors p168 01288 356256
Fish & Co p438 01902 826464
Ashley Fisher & Co p146 01253 751585
Fisher Jones Greenwood LLP p186 01245 890110
Fisher Jones Greenwood LLP p197 01206 578282
Fisher Meredith p32 020 7091 2700
Fishers p404 01283 217193
Fitzhugh Gates p159 01273 686811
Fitzhugh Gates p378 01273 461381
Brendan Fleming p138 0121 683 5000
Fletcher Dervish p33 020 8800 4615
Ronald Fletcher & Co p33 020 7624 0041
Fletchers p388 01704 546919
Flint Bishop Solicitors p208 01332 340211
Foley Harrison p228 0191 477 6333
Fonseca & Partners p113 01873 857114
Fonseca & Partners p216 01495 303124
Foot Anstey p221 01392 411221
Foot Anstey p349 01752 675000
Foot Anstey p408 01823 625600
Forbes p114 01254 872111
Forbes p356 01772 220022
Forbes p145 01254 580000
Forbes p194 01257 260600
Lindsay Ford Solicitors Ltd p172 029 2088 2441
Ford Simey LLP p221 01392 274126
Ford Simey LLP p380 01395 577061 / 0800 169 3741
Ford Simey LLP p222 01395 272241 / 0800 169 3741
Forrester & Forrester p300 01666 822671
Forrester & Forrester p193 01249 444300
Geoffrey Forrester & Co p263 0191 420 0820
Forresters p125 01229 820297
Forshaws Davies Ridgway LLP p422 01925 230000
Forshaws Davies Ridgway LLP p422 01925 230000
Forshaws Davies Ridgway LLP p227 01928 739300
Forshaws Davies Ridgway LLP p422 01925 230000
Forshaws Davies Ridgway LLP p422 01925 604713
Forster Dean Ltd p431 0151 495 3270
Forster Dean Ltd p369 01928 590999
Forster Dean Ltd p431 0151 422 0982
Foster & Partners p162 0117 961 5300
Foster & Partners p162 0117 922 0229
David J Foster & Co p407 01827 58333 / 58334
Fosters p334 01603 620508
Fosters p168 01986 895251
John Fowlers LLP Solicitors p197 01206 576151
John Fowlers LLP Solicitors p159 01206 302694
Joseph Foxler & Co p170 0161 797 4126
Malcolm C Foy & Co p211 01302 340005
Malcolm C Foy & Co p367 01709 836866
Foys Solicitors p211 01302 327136
Foys Solicitors p441 01909 473560
Foys Solicitors p375 0114 246 7609
Foys Solicitors p367 01709 375561
Foys Solicitors p375 0114 251 1702
Francis Law LLP p296 01594 842242
Franklins p214 01582 699111
Franklins LLP p332 01604 828282
Fraser Brown p133 01949 830812
Fraser Dawbarns p435 01945 461456
Fraser Dawbarns p266 01553 666600
Fraser Dawbarns p213 01366 383171
Frearsons p380 01754 897600
Freeman Johnson p389 01388 814389
Freeman Johnson p206 01325 466221
Freeman Johnson p214 0191 386 4843 / 386 9619
Freer & Archer p279 0116 241 3199
French & Co p337 0115 955 1111
Frettens Solicitors p194 01202 491777
R G Frisby & Small p279 0116 233 5522
R G Frisby & Small p279 01455 282832
Fulchers p436 01483 885522
Fullers Family Law Practice LLP p130 01234 343134
Funnell & Perring p243 01424 426287
Fynmores p132 01424 732333
GCA Solicitors (Giffen Couch & Archer) p295 01582 410041
GHP Legal p342 01691 659194
GHP Legal p442 01978 291456
GLP Solicitors p315 0161 653 6295
GLP Solicitors p304 0161 834 6721
GLP Solicitors p357 0161 773 8626
GLP Solicitors p304 0161 795 5531
GLP Solicitors p304 0161 793 0901
GLRS Phoenix LLP p214 01453 547221
GLRS Phoenix LLP p400 01453 757381
Gabriels Solicitors p227 01704 831554
Galbraith Branley p34 020 8446 8474
Donald Galbraith & Co p34 020 8492 2700
Gamlins p199 01492 593201
Gamlins p363 01745 343500
Gangar & Co p427 0121 553 4166
Gardner Champion p368 01889 576121 / 582116
Gardner Leader LLP p410 01635 508080
Gardner Leader LLP p322 01635 508080
Garner & Hancock Solicitors LLP p263 020 8232 9560
GARNER CANNING p407 01827 314004
Garner Canning p138 0121 749 5577
Garner Canning p120 01827 713543
Garnett Williams Powell p363 01745 334658
Garrods Solicitors p186 01245 492494
Garside & Hoy p424 020 8427 5656
Gartsides p328 01633 213411
Gartsides p113 01873 857555
Gaskell & Walker p157 01656 653122
Gates & Moloney p270 01903 766046
Gaynham King & Mellor p118 01768 351422
Gaynham King & Mellor p346 01768 864651
Gaynor-Smith Owen & Co p300 01684 560771
Gee & Edwards p405 01792 465806 / 464937
Craig Gee p304 0161 666 9999
Geoffrey Morris & Ashton p442 01978 291322
Geoffrey Morris & Ashton p318 01352 754711
George Davies & Evans Limited p181 01239 612308
George H Coles & Co p254 01273 205101
GEORGE IDE LLP p192 01243 786668
George Ide LLP p148 01243 829231
Reena Ghai Solicitors p253 020 8759 9959
Deborah Gibbins & Co p133 01268 270866
Gichard & Co p367 01709 365531
Giffen Couch & Archer p282 01525 372681
Gilbert Stephens p221 01392 424242
Gilbert Turner Coomber p35 020 8520 5886
C J Giles & Co p437 0118 978 1017
Gill & Co p260 020 8554 8774
Gill Akaster p349 01752 203500
Gill Turner Tucker p299 01622 759051
Ginn & Co p174 01223 358275
Girlings p177 01227 768374
Girlings p248 01227 367355
Girlings p312 01843 220274
Gittins McDonald p442 01978 291662
Glaisyers p138 0121 233 2971
Glaisyers Solicitors LLP p304 0161 832 4666
Glaisyers Solicitors LLP p304 0161 224 3311
Glansfields p311 01623 627827
Glanvilles p244 023 9249 2300
Glanvilles p328 01983 527878
Godloves p273 0113 225 8811
Godloves p273 0113 286 8822
Godloves p273 0113 225 8864
Godloves p273 0113 225 8874
Godwins p114 01970 624244
Goldbergs p349 01752 660023
Goldstones p405 01792 643021
Goodman Ray p36 020 7608 1227
Goodwin Cowley p294 01502 532700
GoodyBurrett LLP p197 01206 577676
Gordon & Penney p429 01934 414161
R Gordon Roberts Laurie & Co p292 01248 722215 / 723312
Gordons LLP p154 01274 202202
Gorvins p395 0161 930 5151
Gosschalks p256 01482 324252
H F T Gough & Co p431 01946 692461
Goughs p210 01380 726913
Goughs p314 01225 703036
Goughs p199 01249 712193
Gowmans p345 01803 546100
Graham & Rosen p257 01482 323123
Grahame Stowe Bateson p274 0113 246 8163
Grahame Stowe Bateson p274 0113 274 4611
Grainger Appleyard p211 01302 327257
Grants Solicitors p205 020 8288 8899
Granville-West p352 01495 751111
Granville-West Chivers & Morgan p365 01633 612353
Granville-West Chivers & Morgan p328 01495 243268
David Gray Solicitors p324 0191 232 9547
Gray Hooper Holt LLP p362 01737 761004
Leonard Gray p186 01245 504904
Graysons p375 0114 272 9184
Greathead & Whitelock p345 01646 682101
Christopher Green McCarrahers p386 023 8084 2765
Green Williamson Solicitors p418 01924 291400
Greenfield Whiston p265 01536 410880
Adam F Greenhalgh & Co p149 0845 074 3491
GREENLAND HOUCHEN POMEROY p424 01953 882864
GREENLAND HOUCHEN POMEROY p334 01603 660744
GREENLAND HOUCHEN POMEROY p120 01953 453143
Gregory Abrams Davidson LLP p288 0151 236 5000
Gregory Abrams Davidson LLP p288 0151 733 3353
Gregory Abrams Davidson LLP p288 0151 494 0777
Gregorys Solicitors p395 0161 456 8125
Neil Griffin & Co p252 01404 42609
Gareth Griffith & Company p172 01286 676869
Griffith Smith Farrington Webb p243 01273 843405
Griffith Smith Farrington Webb p159 01273 324041
Griffith Smith Farrington Webb p247 01273 492045
Griffiths & Hughes Parry p252 01352 711815 / 711945
Richard Griffiths & Co p371 01722 329966
Grylls & Paige p363 01209 215261 / 215357
Guest Walker & Co p444 01904 624903
GUILLAUMES SOLICITORS p430 01932 840111
A K Gulati & Co p402 020 8770 7979
Gullands p299 01622 678341
The Gwyn George Partnership p113 01685 874629 / 871133
The Gwyn George Partnership p314 01685 377035
HCB Solicitors p362 01527 62688
HC Solicitors LLP p347 01733 882800
HKH Kenwright & Cox Solicitors p260 020 8553 9600
hlw Keeble Hawson LLP p211 01302 366831
hlw Keeble Hawson LLP p375 0114 272 2061
HSR Law (Hayes, Son & Richmond) p228 01427 613831
HSR Law (Hayes, Son & Richmond) p211 01302 347800
Hadaway & Hadaway p330 0191 257 0382
Hadgkiss Hughes & Beale p138 0121 449 5050
Hadgkiss Hughes & Beale p139 0121 707 8484
Haider Kennedy Legal Services Ltd p37 020 8771 2323
Hains & Lewis Ltd p320 0845 408 0125
Hains & Lewis Ltd p244 0845 408 0125
Hall Ennion & Young p218 01353 662918
Frederic Hall p227 01303 851185
Frederic Hall p213 01304 202411
Hall Smith Whittingham LLP p203 01270 212000
Hall Smith Whittingham LLP p320 01270 610300
Hallam-Peel & Co p38 020 3006 1661
Hallett & Co p119 01233 625711
HallmarkHulme p439 01905 726600
Hallows Associates p318 01352 752773 / 758603 / 0800 525696
Hameed & Co p38 020 8830 1335
Hamers Solicitors p257 01482 326666
Hamilton Downing Quinn p38 020 7831 8939
Hammon Oakley p200 024 7644 8585
Hamnett Osborne Tisshaw p245 01444 443030
Hancock Quins p423 01923 650850
Hancocks p122 01295 253211
Edward Hands & Lewis p293 01509 216161
Hannays Solicitors and Advocates p383 0191 456 7893 / 455 5361
Hanne & Co p38 020 7228 0017

5

Hanney Dawkins & Jones *p348* 020 8866 2144
Hannides Hewstone & Co *p386* 023 8078 6770
HANRATTY & CO *p330* 01686 626239
Hansell Wilkes & Co *p207* 01803 833993
Hansells *p203* 01263 512003
Hansells *p334* 01603 615731
Hansells *p331* 01692 404351
Hansells *p121* 01263 734313
Hansells *p378* 01263 822176
Harbans Singh *p139* 0121 551 4496
Harding Evans LLP *p328* 01633 244233
Harding Swinburne Jackson & Co *p401* 0191 565 8194
Hardman & Watson *p166* 01843 863479
Hardman Wood *p145* 01254 295540
Hardmans *p207* 01304 373377
Gaby Hardwicke *p243* 01424 438011
Gaby Hardwicke *p132* 01424 842206
Gaby Hardwicke *p132* 01424 730945
Gaby Hardwicke *p215* 01323 435900
Hardy Miles Titterton *p364* 01773 747000
Harman & Harman *p39* 01227 452977
Harney & Wells *p159* 01273 684666
Will Harrington & Co *p403* 0121 321 1999
Harris & Harris *p228* 01373 463366
Christopher Harris & Co *p375* 01795 661521
Christopher Harris & Co *p380* 01795 437268
David W Harris & Co *p352* 01443 486666
E A Harris & Co Ltd *p168* 01244 541505
Leslie Harris Solicitors & Advocates *p297* 01253 724974
T R Harris Arnold & Co *p231* 01792 892166 / 891331
Harris Temperley *p39* 020 8233 2989
Harrison Bundey *p274* 0113 200 7400
Harrison Clark LLP *p367* 01989 562377
Harrison Clark LLP *p439* 01905 612001
Harrison Clark LLP *p439* 01905 612001
Harrison Clark LLP *p188* 01242 269198
HARRISONS SOLICITORS LLP *p425* 01938 552545
Harrop White Vallance & Dawson *p311* 01623 629221
Harrow Solicitors & Advocates *p424* 020 8863 0788
Hart Brown Solicitors *p437* 0800 068 8177
Charles Hart Solicitors *p186* 01934 742315
Hart Jackson & Sons *p416* 01229 583291
Hart Jackson Hall Smith *p325* 0191 261 5181
Edward Harte LLP *p159* 01273 662750
Harthills *p367* 01709 377399
Hartlaw LLP *p429* 01937 547000
Hartley & Worstenholme *p351* 01977 732222
Hartley & Worstenholme *p183* 01977 732222
Hartley Thomas & Wright *p365* 01706 644118
Hartnell Chanot & Partners Family Law Specialists *p221* 01392 421777
Harvey Ingram Borneos *p130* 01234 353221
Harvey Ingram Borneos *p317* 01908 696002
Hatchers Solicitors LLP *p379* 01743 248545
Hathaways *p228* 0191 477 2288
Hatten Wyatt *p232* 01474 351199
Hawley & Rodgers *p337* 0115 955 9000
Hawley & Rodgers *p293* 01509 230333
Haworth & Nuttall *p145* 01254 272640
Haworth & Nuttall *p114* 01254 236221
Hay & Kilner *p419* 0191 262 8231
Hay & Kilner *p325* 0191 232 8345
Phillip M Haycock *p139* 0121 788 1234
Hayes & Storr *p223* 01328 863231
Hayes & Storr *p378* 01263 825959
Edward Hayes LLP *p192* 01243 781431
Edward Hayes LLP *p148* 01243 822655
Edward Hayes LLP *p192* 01243 672124
Edward Hayes LLP *p285* 01903 759024
Edward Hayes LLP *p244* 023 9247 9872
Stanley Hays *p246* 01924 403809
Haywards *p399* 01449 613631
The Head Partnership *p361* 0118 975 6622
Heald Nickinson *p173* 01276 680000
Healds *p432* 01942 241511
Heaney Watson *p288* 0151 282 5555
Heaney Watson *p288* 0151 256 7777
Heaney Watson *p288* 0151 293 2936
Heaney Watson *p305* 0800 567 7597 / 0161 359 3347
Heath Sons & Broome *p305* 0161 681 1933
Heath Sons & Broome *p223* 0161 682 8535
Heckford Norton *p370* 01799 522636
Heckford Norton *p283* 01462 682244
Hedges *p210* 01235 811888
Hedleys *p337* 0115 947 3506
Hegarty LLP *p347* 01733 346333
Hegarty LLP *p393* 01780 752066
Hellewell Pasley & Brewer *p128* 01924 472596
Hellewell Pasley & Brewer *p210* 01924 455515
Henriques Griffiths *p163* 0117 909 4000
Henriques Griffiths *p435* 01454 854000
Heppenstalls *p321* 01425 610078
Heptonstalls LLP *p255* 01430 430209
Heptonstalls LLP *p231* 01405 765661
Hereward & Foster *p41* 020 7476 6600
Heringtons *p370* 01797 222955
Heringtons *p243* 01424 434192
Heringtons *p215* 01323 411020
Herrington & Carmichael LLP *p437* 0118 977 4045
Herrington & Carmichael LLP *p173* 01276 686222
Heseltine Bray & Welsh *p124* 01226 210777
Hethertons LLP *p445* 01904 528200
Hetts *p373* 01724 843287
Hetts *p373* 01724 270290
Hewetts *p361* 0118 957 5337
Hewison & Nixon *p351* 01977 700705
Hewitts *p397* 01642 673701
Hewitts *p330* 01325 316170
Hewitts *p144* 01388 604691
Hewitts *p206* 01325 468573
Hewitts *p203* 01388 762466
Heyes Samuel *p369* 01983 615615
Heyman & Co *p282* 01942 604135
Hibberts LLP *p203* 01270 215117
Hibberts LLP *p320* 01270 624225
Charles Hill Hubbard *p192* 01243 781000
Hill Dickinson LLP *p288* 0151 600 8000
Hill Dickinson LLP *p190* 01244 896600
Hill Dickinson LLP *p41* 020 7283 9033
Hill Dickinson LLP *p305* 0161 817 7200
Michael Hill Partnership *p280* 0116 254 1609
HilliersHRW Solicitors *p395* 01438 346000
HilliersHRW Solicitors *p264* 01234 858000
Hills (Oldham) *p340* 0161 652 3231
Hills Solicitors Limited *p116* 0161 928 0961
Hillyer McKeown LLP *p129* 0151 645 4255
Hillyer McKeown LLP *p190* 01244 318131
Hilton Norbury *p432* 01942 241424
Hindle Campbell *p330* 0191 296 1777
Hine Downing Solicitors *p223* 01326 316655
Hoben Johnson *p369* 01933 411375
Hodders *p41* 020 8965 9862
Hodders *p250* 01494 511345
Hodders *p41* 020 8838 1537
Hodge Halsall *p388* 01704 531991
HODGE JONES & ALLEN LLP *p41* 020 7874 8300
Hodgson Coulthard & Co *p253* 0191 584 3333
Hodgsons & Mortimer *p363* 01748 850950
Hodgsons & Mortimer *p206* 01325 250111 / 355956
Charles Hoile *p322* 01635 45595
Holden & Co *p243* 01424 722422
Holdens *p269* 01524 32484
Holls Solicitors *p129* 020 8658 9767
Holman Copeland *p42* 020 8852 1162 / 8852 2632
Holt & Longworth *p367* 01706 213251 / 229131
Hood Vores & Allwood *p209* 01362 692424
Hoole & Co *p163* 0117 969 1436
Hoole & Co *p163* 0117 942 8871
Hooper Holt & Co *p362* 01737 761111
Hopkin Murray Beskine *p42* 020 7272 1234
Hopkins *p311* 01623 468468
Hopkins *p311* 01623 460460
Wendy Hopkins Family Law Practice LLP *p178* 029 2034 2233
Hopley Pierce & Bird *p443* 01978 315100
Hornby & Levy *p43* 020 7737 0909
Hornby Baker Jones & Wood *p328* 01633 262848
Thomas Horton LLP *p167* 01527 871641
Horwich Cohen Coghlan *p305* 0161 830 4600
Hough Halton & Soal *p182* 01228 524379
Houldsworths *p196* 01254 825757
Howard & Co *p124* 01226 215215
Howard & Co *p124* 01226 211888
Howard & Over *p350* 01752 556606
Howard & Over *p263* 01752 690123
Frank Howard *p422* 01925 653481
Philip & Robert Howard *p183* 01977 551320
Howarth Scott *p132* 020 8303 4658
Susan Howarth & Co *p333* 01606 48777
Howe & Spender *p353* 01639 881571
Howe & Spender *p320* 01639 881571
Howell & Co *p139* 0121 778 5031
Howell Jones & Co *p113* 01745 826282 / 825845
Howell Jones & Co *p292* 01492 640277
Howells *p178* 029 2040 4020
Howells *p172* 029 2086 7111
Howells *p405* 01792 410016
Howells *p407* 01443 230411
Howells *p328* 01633 227960
Howells LLP *p367* 01709 364000
Howells LLP *p376* 0114 249 6666
Howlett Clarke Crowther Wood *p159* 01273 327272 / 326341
Howlett Clarke Solicitors *p254* 01273 419728
Hudgell & Partners *p43* 020 8854 1331
Huggins & Lewis Foskett *p43* 020 8989 3000
Hugh Cartwright & Amin *p43* 020 7632 4200
Hugh James *p179* 029 2022 4871
Edward Hughes *p363* 01745 343661 / 344551
Gwynne Hughes *p113* 01545 570861
J A Hughes *p345* 029 2070 2449
J A Hughes *p126* 01446 411000
J W Hughes & Co *p199* 01492 596596
J W Hughes & Co *p291* 01492 874774
Humfrys & Symonds *p248* 01432 359261 / 276276
Humphries Kirk *p421* 01929 552141
Humphries Kirk *p212* 01305 251007
Humphries Kirk *p404* 01929 423301
Humphries Kirk *p352* 01202 715815
Humphries Kirk *p152* 01202 421111
Humphrys & Co *p363* 01745 343158
Humphrys & Co *p443* 01978 313399
Hunt & Hunt *p366* 01708 764433
Hurleys *p152* 01202 436100
Hurlow & Partners *p179* 029 2039 6087
Rozita Hussain Solicitors *p436* 0161 448 8222
Hutchins & Co *p44* 020 8986 3911
Hutchinson Thomas *p320* 01639 645061
Hutsby Mees *p393* 01785 259211
Hutton's *p179* 029 2037 8621
Henry Hyams *p274* 0113 243 2288
Howard Hyman & Co *p44* 020 8446 5511
IBB Solicitors *p417* 0845 638 1381
IBB Solicitors *p189* 0845 638 1381
Inesons *p195* 01274 872202
Inghams *p411* 01253 824111
Inghams *p226* 01253 873481
Inghams *p146* 01253 626642
Darryl Ingram & Co *p45* 020 8202 0843
Irvings Solicitors *p209* 01332 346036
Irwin Mitchell LLP *p376* 0870 150 0100
Irwin Mitchell LLP *p274* 0870 150 0100
Isherwood & Hose *p249* 01706 360032 / 368741
Ison Harrison *p228* 0113 286 1455
Ison Harrison *p274* 0113 232 6530
Ison Harrison *p274* 0113 284 5000
JMW Solicitors *p306* 0845 872 6666
JNP Legal *p314* 01685 350421
JNP Legal *p320* 01443 450561
Jackamans *p262* 01473 255591
Jackamans *p210* 01379 643555
Jackamans *p225* 01394 279636
Jackamans *p239* 01379 854455
Andrew Jackson *p257* 01482 325242
Andrew Jackson & Co *p289* 0151 709 5816 / 488 1000
Jackson West *p400* 01789 204020
Jacobs & Reeves *p353* 01202 674425
Jacobs & Reeves *p433* 01202 880382
Jacobs & Reeves *p353* 01202 731849
Gary Jacobs & Co *p45* 020 8536 4050
Jacobs Solicitors *p217* 0151 355 8481
Gwyn James Solicitors *p195* 01594 822277
Gwyn James Solicitors *p198* 01594 833042
Andrew Jay & Co (Philip Hanby Limited) *p228* 01427 612412
Jeary & Lewis *p193* 01249 444484
Jefferies Essex LLP *p428* 01702 332311
Jennings *p292* 01554 772331
Jepson & Co *p372* 01723 859249
Jeromes *p328* 01983 522664
Jestyn Jeffreys *p320* 01639 635641
Anthony Jewell & Co *p352* 01443 493357
Jewels Solicitors *p393* 01785 602030
Jobling & Knape *p319* 01524 416960
Jobling & Knape *p269* 01524 598300
Johar & Co *p280* 0116 254 3345
Graeme John Solicitors *p113* 01685 872491
V J G Johns & Son *p226* 01348 873671
Johnson & Gaunt *p122* 01295 256271 / 271200
Jones & Co *p363* 01777 703827
Jones & Duffin Solicitors LLP *p280* 0116 222 1555
Claire Jones & Associates *p418* 01924 290029
Cyril Jones & Co *p443* 01978 263131
Cyril Jones & Co *p379* 01244 812109
Geraint Jones & Co *p330* 01686 627935
Geraint Jones & Co *p291* 01597 822244
Gwilym Jones & Davies with Bryant & Co *p319* 01443 472206
Michael Leighton Jones *p123* 01443 830228
Jones Myers LLP *p275* 0113 246 0055
Jones Robertson *p369* 01928 711119
Terry Jones Solicitors & Advocates *p329* 01952 810307
Terry Jones Solicitors & Advocates *p379* 01743 285888
Terry Jones Solicitors & Advocates *p409* 01952 297979
Thos R Jones & Son *p289* 0151 928 0715
Jordans *p210* 01924 457171
Jordans *p368* 0121 559 2922
Jordans *p183* 01977 518778
Jordans *p418* 01924 387110
Josiah Hincks *p280* 0116 255 1811
Jung & Co *p384* 020 8813 8996
Jane Kaim-Caudle & Co *p423* 01923 219061
Kaim Todner Ltd *p47* 020 7701 4747
Kaim Todner Ltd *p47* 020 7353 6660
Kaim Todner Ltd *p47* 020 7700 0070
Kaim Todner Ltd *p119* 01233 662002
Kale & Co *p438* 01902 772500
Peter Kandler & Co *p48* 020 8960 9222
Keene & Kelly *p318* 01352 753882
Kelcey & Hall *p163* 0117 927 9604
Kennards Wells *p48* 020 8539 8338

See p603 for the Community Legal Service Work Categories

Kenwright Walker Wyllie p215 020 8979 1131
Kenyon Son & Craddock p212 01405 813108
Kenyon Son & Craddock p231 01405 720850
Keoghs and Nicholls, Lindsell & Harris p116 0161 928 9321
Keppe Rofer p156 01874 624627
Kerseys p262 01473 213311
Kerwoods p362 01527 584444
Khan Solicitors p154 01274 301999
Kidd & Spoor p431 0191 297 0011
Kidd & Spoor p325 0191 273 9217
Kidd Rapinet p382 0845 017 9638
Kidd Rapinet p298 0845 017 9608
Kidd Rapinet p121 0845 017 9616
KieranClarkeGreen p192 01246 211006
KieranClarkeGreen p394 01246 280099
Anthony King & Co p126 01268 240400
King Davies & Partners p298 01656 732911
Rodney King & Partners p163 0117 926 5201
Kingsfords p119 01233 665544
Kingsfords p119 01233 624545
Kingswell Berney p232 023 9258 2211
Kirby & Co p50 020 8545 7171
Kirby Sheppard p411 0845 840 0045
Kirby Sheppard p268 0845 840 0045
Kirkup Lascelles & Creed p347 0191 586 8646
Kirwans p134 0151 608 9078
Kirwans p319 0151 677 3433
Kirwans p289 0151 229 5600
Kitching Walker p268 01751 431237
Kitsons LLP p413 01803 202020
Kitsons LLP p329 01626 203366
Kitsons LLP p221 01392 455555
Kitsons LLP p350 01752 603040
Richard J Knaggs & Co p362 01642 487011
Knowles Benning p295 01582 798000
Kundert & Co p200 024 7668 4928
LDJ Solicitors p339 024 7674 5000
LD Law p239 01279 441266
Simon Lacey Law Associates p430 01305 777711
Laceys p353 01202 743286
Laceys p152 01202 557256
Lamb & Holmes p265 01536 513195
Lamb & Holmes p199 01536 745168
Lancasters p158 01262 602401
Bruce Lance & Co p250 01494 450494
Bruce Lance & Co p353 01202 679379
Landons p156 01277 210021
Kevin Lane & Co p353 01639 893700
Langley Wellington p230 01452 521286
Langleys p445 01904 610886
Lanyon Bowdler LLP p379 01743 280280
Lanyon Bowdler LLP p342 01691 652241
Lanyon Bowdler LLP p409 01952 291222
Lanyon Bowdler LLP p425 01952 244721
Larcomes LLP p354 023 9266 1531
Larcomes LLP p423 023 9224 6666
Large & Gibson p388 023 9229 6296
Larken & Co p322 01636 703333
Last Cawthra Feather LLP p378 01274 585459
Last Cawthra Feather LLP p261 01943 601020
Last Cawthra Feather LLP p154 01274 848800
Last Cawthra Feather LLP p121 01274 583106
Latham & Co p293 01509 238822
Latimer Lee LLP p358 0161 798 9000
Lavin Copitch p306 0161 223 5484
Law Hurst & Taylor p428 01702 337864
The Law Partnership p242 020 8416 7004
Lawrence & Co p52 020 7266 4333
Lawrence Law p52 020 8788 0055
Patrick Lawrence p233 01474 356441
Lawson & Thompson p130 01670 530700
Lawson Lewis & Co p215 01323 720142
Lawson Lewis & Co p345 01273 582680
Owen Lawton p350 01752 201169
Layton & Co p244 01437 766671
Karina Leapman & Co p52 020 7794 7741
Leathes Prior p334 01603 610911
Lee & Company p173 01276 20911
Lees Solicitors LLP p428 0151 625 9364
Lees Solicitors LLP p249 0151 342 6273
Lees Solicitors LLP p134 0151 647 9381
Leigh Turton Dixon p315 01642 241101
Leo Abse & Cohen p179 029 2038 3252 / 2034 5421
Leonard & Co p386 023 8023 3242
Leonard & Co p386 023 8023 4433
Lester Morrill p275 0113 245 8549
Letchers p364 01425 471424
Levenes Solicitors p140 0121 212 0000
Levi Solicitors LLP p275 0113 244 9931
Levine Mellins Klarfeld p394 020 8954 7474
Leviten Thompson & Co p376 0114 276 9321
Lewis & Lines p113 01495 212286
Cheryl Lewis & Co p134 0151 652 1451
Duncan Lewis & Co p53 020 7923 4020
Duncan Lewis & Co p53 020 7923 4020
Lewis Nedas & Co p53 020 7387 2032
Lichfield Reynolds p398 01782 289122
Lichfield Reynolds p398 01782 313212
Linder Myers Solicitors p307 0844 984 6400
Linder Myers Solicitors p306 0844 984 6000
Linskills Solicitors p289 0151 236 2224
The Lister Croft Partnership p358 0113 257 0526
Livingstons p206 01229 462126
Livingstons p416 01229 585555
Robert Lizar p307 0161 226 2319
Robert Lizar p307 0161 860 7797
Llewellyn Jones & Co p369 01824 704495
Lloyd & Associates p55 020 7589 9599
Lloyd Brennand p156 020 8569 9020
Llys Cennen Solicitors p117 01269 592658 / 592790
Lock & Marlborough p55 020 8993 7231
Lockings p257 01482 300280
Lomax Geddes & Co p307 0161 834 4722
Roger Long & Co p205 020 8668 5071
Anthony Louca Solicitors p55 020 7723 9889
Lovegrove & Eliot p434 01753 851133
Lovsey Marsh p140 0121 212 0255
Gordon Lowe & Co p163 01454 326833
Lucas & Wyllys p294 01502 500123
Lucas & Wyllys p234 01493 855555
Lucas & Wyllys p234 01493 663124
Charles Lucas & Marshall p322 01635 521212
Lumsdons Solicitors LLP p399 01299 827766
Lumsdons Solicitors LLP p440 01905 730670
Lawrence Lupin p426 020 8733 7200
Peter Lynn & Partners p405 01792 450010
Peter Lynn & Partners p319 01792 310731
Lyons Rounsfell p428 0117 950 6506
MFG Solicitors p265 01562 820181
MFG Solicitors p167 01527 831691
MFG Solicitors p409 01952 641651
MFG Solicitors p440 01905 610410
MSB Solicitors LLP p289 0151 281 9040
MWP Solicitors p126 01268 527131
MWRLaw Ltd p357 01772 254201
McAras Solicitors LLP p275 0113 243 4333
D K Macbryde & Co p356 01745 856404
McCarthy Stewart & Booty Solicitors p400 01449 612343
McCormacks p56 020 7791 2000
McCormicks p240 01423 530630
Roberta McDonald p140 0121 449 6821
Machins Solicitors LLP p295 01582 514000
B J McKenna & Co Solicitors p396 0161 432 5757
McKenzie Bell Solicitors p401 0191 567 4857
McKenzies p57 020 8350 4114
McKinnells p284 01522 541181
MacLaren Britton p338 0115 941 1469
MacLeish Littlestone Cowan p260 020 8514 3000
MacLeish Littlestone Cowan p57 020 8514 3000
McManus Seddon p154 01274 741841
McMillan Williams p199 020 8668 4131
McMillan Williams p419 020 8669 4962
McMillan Williams p205 01689 848311
McMillan Williams p411 020 8653 8844
McMillan Williams p383 020 8253 7600
McMillan Williams Solicitors p132 020 8303 0168
McMillen Hamilton McCarthy p57 020 8980 6060
Madge Lloyd & Gibson p327 01531 820088
Madge Lloyd & Gibson p230 01452 520224
Thomas Magnay & Co p229 0191 477 3333
Mahany & Co Solicitors LLP p252 01293 772888
Maidments p149 0870 403 4000
Maidments p370 0870 403 4000
Maidments p370 0870 403 4000
Makanda Bart p58 020 8802 0034
E Rex Makin & Co p289 0151 709 4491
Malletts Solicitors p58 020 7061 3760
Mallia & Co p180 029 2022 0044
Malloy & Barry p180 029 2034 3434
Mander Cruickshank Solicitors LLP p196 01530 510666
Mander Hadley & Co p200 024 7663 1212
Stuart J Mander & Co p420 01922 642018
Maples Solicitors LLP p389 01775 722261
Marchant Harries & Co p113 01685 885500
Marchant Harries & Co p319 01443 476444
Marchants Solicitors p312 01623 655111
Andrew Markham & Co p182 01267 221550 / 236199
MARSDEN RAWSTHORN LLP p194 01257 279511
MARSDEN RAWSTHORN LLP p357 01772 799600
A B Marsh Solicitors p371 0161 839 2626
Marshall Hall & Levy p384 0191 455 3181
Marshalls p350 01752 254555
MarstonHarbottle p249 01434 602486
Martin & Strain p358 01758 612042
MARTIN-KAYE LLP p409 01952 272222
Martins p216 0161 707 3660
MARTYN PROWEL p180 029 2047 0909
Mason & Beer p215 01342 311255
Mason-Apps Smallmans & Co p298 01628 636148 / 636149
Mason Baggott & Garton p158 01652 654111
Mason Baggott & Garton p373 01724 868611
Mason Baggott & Garton p219 01427 872661
Massers p338 0115 851 1666
Massers p427 0115 851 1666
Matthew Arnold & Baldwin LLP p423 01923 202020
T A Matthews p248 01432 352121
Matwala Vyas LLP p260 020 8597 5097
Mawdsleys p388 01704 537676
Max Gold Law p257 01482 224900
Maxwell Hodge Solicitors p249 0151 342 6447
Maxwell Hodge Solicitors p298 0151 526 7131
Maxwell Hodge Solicitors p428 0151 625 9154
Maxwell Hodge Solicitors p258 0151 489 6161
Mayo Wynne Baxter LLP p215 01323 730543
Mayo Wynne Baxter LLP p160 01273 775533
Mayo Wynne Baxter LLP p283 01273 477071
Mayo Wynne Baxter LLP p373 01323 891412
Mayo Wynne Baxter LLP p215 01342 310600
Mears Hobbs & Durrant p294 01502 583621
Medlicott Snows p145 01588 638425
Medlicott Snows p269 01547 528332
Meesons p364 01425 472315
Meikles p123 01833 690505
Meikles p397 01740 620255
Meikles p389 01388 814336
Meikles p226 01740 652811
Meikles p144 01388 451122
Merricks Formerly Merrick Kelleher p418 01208 812068 / 813104
Merry & Co p369 01983 811722
Metcalfe Copeman & Pettefar p435 01945 464331
Metcalfe Copeman & Pettefar p410 01842 756100
Metcalfe Copeman & Pettefar p266 01553 778102
Metcalfe Copeman & Pettefar p347 01733 865880
Metcalfe Johnston McCormick p216 0161 789 3481 / 788 9021
Michelmores LLP p221 01392 688688
Milburns Solicitors p440 01900 67363
Milburns Solicitors p313 01900 813541
Miles & Cash p365 01773 742222
Miles & Partners p60 020 7426 0400
Miles Hutchinson & Lithgow p315 01642 242698
Miles Hutchinson & Lithgow p371 01287 623049 / 622056
Miller Law Practice p60 020 8340 2953
Miller Parris p442 01903 205771
Millichips p382 0121 624 4000
Millichips p427 0121 500 6363
Mills & Reeve p335 01603 660155
Mills & Reeve p175 01223 364422
Mills Chody LLP p265 020 8909 0400
Mills Chody LLP p244 020 8428 2272
George Mills p423 0191 416 2182
Milne & Lyall p158 01308 422362
Milner Elledge p206 020 8984 0940
Minahan Hirst & Co p185 0161 485 8131
Mincoffs Solicitors LLP p325 0191 281 6151
Mitchells p445 01904 623751
Mogers p127 01225 750000
Mohammed & Co Solicitors p357 01772 888700
Molesworths Bright Clegg p365 01706 356666
Moore Blatch Solicitors p296 01590 625800
Moreb Limited p291 01558 822215
Morecrofts Solicitors LLP p290 0151 236 8871
Morecrofts Solicitors LLP p203 0151 924 9234
Morecrofts Solicitors LLP p290 0151 428 1911
Morecrofts Solicitors LLP p134 0151 666 2210
Morgan & Lamplugh p243 01424 721821
Morgan & Richardson p181 01239 612302
Morgans p180 029 2072 9888
Morley Brown & Co p151 01205 364986
John Morley & Co p359 01634 375444
Morlings p299 01622 673081
Morris & Bates p114 01970 625566
Morris & Bates p291 01597 829055
Morrison & Masters Limited p406 01793 526601
Morrison Spowart p62 020 8698 9200
Mortimers p157 01746 761000
Mortons p401 0191 514 4323
Moseley George p181 01239 623960
Moseleys p284 01543 414100
Moss & Haselhurst p435 01606 592159
Moss Beachley Mullem & Coleman p62 020 7402 1401 / 7723 5783
Mosshaselhurst p333 01606 74301
Motley & Hope p133 01767 600600
Mowbray Woodwards Solicitors p128 01225 485700
Moxons p351 01977 703215
E J Moyle p369 01903 784447
E J Moyle p285 01903 725143
Mulcahy Smith p229 0191 490 1000
Stephen Mullarkey Solicitors p226 01352 733770
Stephen Mullarkey Solicitors p252 01352 710657
Mullis & Peake p366 01708 784000
James Murray Solicitors p150 0151 933 3333
James Murray Solicitors p290 0151 207 9910
Martin Murray & Associates p382 01753 551313
Martin Murray & Associates p427 01895 431332
Martin Murray & Associates p361 0118 950 8577
Murrays p148 01208 72863

Mushtaq & Co *p140* . . . 0121 622 1786
Mustoe Shorter *p430* . . . 01305 752700
MYER WOLFF *p257* . . . 01482 223693
Myers Lister Price *p117* . . . 0161 926 9969
NBM Massucco Shelbourne *p175* . . . 01223 211992
NFLA LTD *p338* . . . 0115 945 4555
NGA *p198* . . . 01282 862000
Nalders Quality Solicitors *p414* . . . 01872 241414
Nalders Quality Solicitors *p223* . . . 01326 313441
Nalders Quality Solicitors *p246* . . . 01326 574001
Nalders Quality Solicitors *p173* . . . 01209 714278
Nalders Quality Solicitors *p329* . . . 01637 871414
Nalders Quality Solicitors *p346* . . . 01736 364014
Nandy & Co *p63* . . . 020 8536 1800
Napthens LLP *p146* . . . 01253 622305
Nash & Co Solicitors LLP *p350* . . . 01752 664444
Neasham Lloyd *p132* . . . 01869 252161
Nelsons *p338* . . . 0115 958 6262
Newbold & Co *p206* . . . 01633 874715
Newbys *p237* . . . 01287 632208 / 632209
Newbys *p315* . . . 01642 247717 / 247967
Newman & Bond *p125* . . . 01226 213434
Alfred Newton & Co *p433* . . . 01625 523647
Alfred Newton & Co *p396* . . . 0161 480 6551 / 480 1245
Alfred Newton & Co *p396* . . . 0161 430 8831
Nicholas & Partners *p308* . . . 0161 202 4999
Nicholls Christie & Crocker *p417* . . . 01895 256216
Nicholls Henstock & Stevenson *p117* . . . 0161 980 6099
Nicholls Lindsell & Harris and Ingham & Wainwright *p355* . . . 01625 876411
Nicholson Martin Legge & Miller *p394* . . . 01207 232277
Nicholson Martin Legge & Miller *p253* . . . 0191 584 2841
Nicholson Portnell *p249* . . . 01434 603656
Nicol Denvir & Purnell *p180* . . . 029 2079 6311
NIGHTINGALES SOLICITORS LIMITED *p396* . . . 01663 764038
Norcross Lees & Riches *p341* . . . 0161 624 6034
NORRIE WAITE & SLATER *p377* . . . 0114 276 6166
Norrie Waite & Slater *p377* . . . 0114 248 4890
Norrie Waite & Slater *p367* . . . 01709 523983
Norris & Miles *p409* . . . 01584 810575
North Ainley Halliwell *p341* . . . 0161 624 5614
North Yorkshire Law *p372* . . . 01723 360001
Northwood Law Practice *p333* . . . 01923 826208
Norton & Co *p259* . . . 0161 366 8333
Norton Peskett *p129* . . . 01502 718700
Norton Peskett *p294* . . . 01502 533000
Norton Peskett *p238* . . . 01986 872513
Martin Nossel & Co *p126* . . . 01268 289555
Nowell Meller Solicitors Limited *p393* . . . 01785 252377
Nyland & Beattie *p432* . . . 0151 424 5656
O'Garra's *p276* . . . 0113 247 1477
O'Neill Solicitors *p326* . . . 0191 232 9008
O'Riordan & Co *p194* . . . 01257 262837
OGR Stock Denton *p64* . . . 020 8349 0321
OMW Solicitors *p170* . . . 01283 563401 / 530333
Michael Oerton *p125* . . . 01271 378686
Ogden Lyles & Fox *p216* . . . 0161 789 2793
OGLETHORPE STURTON & GILLIBRAND *p268* . . . 01524 271388
Oldham Marsh Page Flavell *p314* . . . 01664 563162
Oldhams Solicitors & Advocates *p121* . . . 01462 895444
Oliver & Co *p191* . . . 01244 312306
Ormerods *p205* . . . 020 8686 5000
Osbornes *p65* . . . 020 7485 8811
Otten Penna Ltd *p333* . . . 0161 945 1431
Otten Penna Ltd *p308* . . . 0161 248 3660
Ouvry Goodman & Co *p403* . . . 020 8642 7571
Overburys & Raymond Thompson *p335* . . . 01603 610481
Owen & O'Sullivan *p446* . . . 01443 862263
The Owen-Kenny Partnership *p193* . . . 01243 532777
Owen White & Catlin *p225* . . . 020 8890 2836
Owen White & Catlin *p254* . . . 020 8570 5471
Oxford Law Group *p344* . . . 01865 297300
Oxley & Coward Solicitors LLP *p367* . . . 01709 510999
P B & W SOLICITORS LLP T/A POOLEY BENDALL & WATSON *p218* . . . 01353 666075
P B & W SOLICITORS LLP T/A POOLEY BENDALL & WATSON *p218* . . . 01638 780170
PB Law *p389* . . . 01273 592624
PCB Solicitors LLP *p379* . . . 01743 248148
PCB Solicitors LLP *p194* . . . 01694 723818
PCB Solicitors LLP *p294* . . . 01584 878456
Page Nelson *p285* . . . 01522 531741
Painters *p266* . . . 01562 822295
Painters *p399* . . . 01299 822033
Palmer Hodgson & Heyes *p226* . . . 01253 778231
Palmer Hodgson & Heyes *p411* . . . 01253 824216
Palmers *p126* . . . 01268 240000
Pardoes *p158* . . . 01278 457891
Pardoes *p408* . . . 01823 446200
J Keith Park & Co *p391* . . . 01744 636000
Park Woodfine Heald Mellows LLP *p130* . . . 01234 400000
Parker Bird Gardner *p256* . . . 01484 825200
Parker Rhodes Hickmotts *p367* . . . 01709 365116
Parker Rhodes Hickmotts *p367* . . . 01709 511100
Elaine Parkes Solicitors *p370* . . . 01424 883183

Parkinson Wright LLP *p440* . . . 01905 726789
Parkinson Wright LLP *p220* . . . 01386 761176
Parkinson Wright LLP *p213* . . . 01905 775533
Parnalls Solicitors Limited *p270* . . . 01566 772375
Parrott & Coales LLP *p121* . . . 01296 318500
Parry Carver *p425* . . . 01952 641291
Parry Davies Clwyd-Jones & Lloyd *p292* . . . 01248 723106
Parry Davies Clwyd-Jones & Lloyd *p117* . . . 01407 831777 / 830665
Parry Davies Clwyd-Jones & Lloyd *p358* . . . 01758 703000 / 701155
Parry Davies Clwyd-Jones & Lloyd *p172* . . . 01286 673381
Parry Law *p248* . . . 01227 361131
Partridge & Wilson *p171* . . . 01284 762281
Passmore Lewis & Jacobs *p126* . . . 01446 721000
Patchell Davies (Trading Name of PD Law Ltd) *p147* . . . 01495 227128
Musa A Patel & Co *p210* . . . 01924 437800
Musa A Patel & Co *p154* . . . 01274 747777
Patterson Glenton & Stracey *p384* . . . 0800 011 6487
Payne & Gamage *p322* . . . 01636 640649
Payne & Payne *p257* . . . 01482 326446
M J Payton & Co *p300* . . . 01684 563318
Peace Revitt *p125* . . . 01226 341111 / 210077
Peace Revitt *p367* . . . 01709 898454
Bernard Pearce & Co *p219* . . . 020 8804 5271
James Pearce & Co *p141* . . . 0121 784 1886
Pearson Hinchliffe *p341* . . . 0161 785 3500
Pearsons *p229* . . . 01634 280150
Pengillys LLP *p430* . . . 01305 768888
Pengillys LLP *p212* . . . 01305 768888
Penman Johnson *p424* . . . 01923 225212 / 239566
Penmans *p394* . . . 01375 677777
Penmans *p199* . . . 01375 673968
Penmans *p424* . . . 01789 470022
Pennine Solicitors *p365* . . . 01706 671434
Penningtons *p231* . . . 01483 791800
Penningtons *p66* . . . 020 7457 3000
Pepperells *p373* . . . 01724 871999
Pepperells *p257* . . . 01482 326511
Percy Hughes & Roberts *p134* . . . 0151 666 9090
Percy Short & Cuthbert *p67* . . . 020 7700 0265
PETERS LANGSFORD DAVIES *p270* . . . 01566 772451
Pheby & Co *p445* . . . 01904 789900
Philippou & Co *p67* . . . 020 8882 4222
Phillips *p312* . . . 01623 658556
Phillips & Co *p371* . . . 01722 321666
David Phillips & Partners *p150* . . . 0151 922 5525
Samuel Phillips Law Firm *p326* . . . 0191 232 8451
Pickerings LLP *p407* . . . 01827 317070
Pictons Solicitors LLP *p295* . . . 01582 870870
Pictons Solicitors LLP *p317* . . . 01908 663511
Pictons Solicitors LLP *p247* . . . 01442 242441
Pinkney Grunwells Lawyers LLP *p158* . . . 01262 673445
Pinkney Grunwells Lawyers LLP *p372* . . . 01723 352125
Pinniger Finch & Co *p428* . . . 01373 823791
Pinto Potts LLP *p115* . . . 0800 316 4434
Place Blair & Hatch *p331* . . . 01609 780101
M A Plant *p388* . . . 01621 773185 / 772794
Platt & Fishwick *p432* . . . 01942 243281
Platt Halpern *p308* . . . 0161 224 2555
Platt Halpern *p341* . . . 0161 626 4955
David Playford & Co *p354* . . . 01275 840111
Pleass Thomson & Co *p195* . . . 01255 221133
Pluck Andrew & Co *p120* . . . 0161 330 2875
Pluck Andrew & Co *p259* . . . 0161 368 6311
Pollard Bower Solicitors *p169* . . . 01282 457624
T G Pollard & Co *p425* . . . 01749 674722
Pollecoff Solicitors Ltd *p68* . . . 020 7608 2568
Pond Marsh *p147* . . . 01253 620466
Poole & Co *p203* . . . 01460 279100
Poole Alcock *p203* . . . 01270 256665
Poole Alcock *p320* . . . 01270 625478
Poole Townsend *p416* . . . 01229 588111
Poole Townsend *p264* . . . 01539 734455
Pope & Co *p380* . . . 01795 474004
J & S P Pope *p222* . . . 01392 274006
Porter Associates *p356* . . . 0151 430 9160
Porter Dodson *p425* . . . 01823 666622
Porter Dodson *p408* . . . 01823 625800
Porter Dodson *p212* . . . 01305 262525
Porter Dodson *p444* . . . 01935 424581
Powell Spencer & Partners *p69* . . . 020 7604 5600
Powells *p429* . . . 01934 623501
Power Scott Solicitors *p394* . . . 01207 230125
Powis & Co *p195* . . . 01255 233400
Powleys *p294* . . . 01502 581121
Prester Coleman & Co *p332* . . . 01604 633133
Preston Goldburn *p223* . . . 01326 318900
Preston Redman *p152* . . . 01202 292424
Pritchard Edwards & Co *p182* . . . 01267 234022
Pumfrey & Lythaby *p342* . . . 01689 833657
Punch Robson *p315* . . . 01642 230700
Punch Robson *p315* . . . 01642 298830
Punch Robson *p397* . . . 01642 754050
QualitySolicitors C Turner *p145* . . . 01254 688400
QualitySolicitors D'Angibau *p151* . . . 01202 393506

QualitySolicitors Gruber Garratt *p120* . . . 0161 344 2244
QualitySolicitors Gruber Garratt *p341* . . . 0161 665 3502
QualitySolicitors Gruber Garratt *p358* . . . 0161 724 0203
QualitySolicitors Gruber Garratt *p393* . . . 0161 303 2328
QualitySolicitors Hill & Abbott *p187* . . . 01245 258892
QualitySolicitors Jackson & Canter *p290* . . . 0151 282 1700
QualitySolicitors Jordans *p212* . . . 01302 365374
RJR Solicitors *p227* . . . 01983 752115
RJR Solicitors *p369* . . . 01983 562201
RJR Solicitors *p328* . . . 01983 526924
Donald Race & Newton *p169* . . . 01282 433241
Donald Race & Newton *p198* . . . 01282 864500
Gillian Radford & Co *p70* . . . 020 8960 4366
Ralph & Co *p329* . . . 01637 872218
Ramsdens Solicitors *p238* . . . 01422 330700
Ramsdens Solicitors *p251* . . . 01484 690040
Ramsdens Solicitors *p256* . . . 01484 821500
Ramsdens Solicitors *p210* . . . 01924 455391
Ranson Houghton *p118* . . . 01264 351533
Ranson Houghton *p127* . . . 01256 816759
Ratcliffe & Bibby *p319* . . . 01524 410424
Ratcliffe & Bibby *p270* . . . 01524 39039
Ratcliffe Duce & Gammer LLP *p361* . . . 0118 957 4291
Ratcliffe Duce & Gammer LLP *p437* . . . 0118 978 3681
Charmini Ravindran & Co *p403* . . . 020 8770 7874
Rawal & Co *p70* . . . 020 8445 0303
Rawstorne Heran Solicitors *p400* . . . 01789 267646
Ray Borley & Dunkley *p399* . . . 01908 563232
Ray Nixon Brown *p282* . . . 01525 372247
Colin Rayner & Co *p149* . . . 01204 591145
Read Dunn Connell *p154* . . . 01274 723858
Keith Ready & Co *p126* . . . 01652 632215
Red Kite Law *p410* . . . 01834 842122
Red Kite Law *p183* . . . 01267 239000
Red Kite Law *p345* . . . 01646 683222
Red Kite Law *p244* . . . 01437 763332
Red Kite Law *p345* . . . 01646 681529
Red Kite Law *p316* . . . 01646 698008
Redfearns *p246* . . . 01924 403745 / 404601
Redferns *p354* . . . 01305 823636
RICHARD REED *p402* . . . 0191 567 0465
Rees Page *p133* . . . 01902 577776
Rees Page *p438* . . . 01902 577777
Reynolds Parry-Jones *p250* . . . 01494 525941
Richard George & Jenkins *p330* . . . 01686 626210
Richards & Lewis *p216* . . . 01495 350018
Roger Richards *p345* . . . 01803 845191
Scott Richards *p409* . . . 01626 772441
Richardson Smith & Co *p189* . . . 01494 772773
Richmond Anderson Goudie *p191* . . . 0191 388 7884
Richmonds *p326* . . . 0191 232 2155
Rickards & Cleaver *p115* . . . 01773 832204
Ridley & Hall *p256* . . . 01484 538421
Garth Rigby & Co *p119* . . . 01942 717378
Lee Rigby Partnership *p283* . . . 01772 421748
Riley Hayes & Co *p438* . . . 01902 773666
Stephen Rimmer LLP *p216* . . . 01323 644222
Risdon Hosegood *p433* . . . 01984 632277
Risdon Hosegood *p408* . . . 01823 251571
Risdon Hosegood *p318* . . . 01643 703123 / 700008
Roach Pittis *p328* . . . 01983 524431
Helen Robbins Solicitors *p72* . . . 020 8558 0038
Robert Lunn & Lowth *p400* . . . 01789 292238
D P Roberts Hughes & Denye *p134* . . . 0151 647 6000
Jane E Roberts *p332* . . . 01604 494431
Roberts Moore Nicholas Jones *p134* . . . 0151 647 0000
Robertsons *p180* . . . 029 2023 7777
Robinson Allfree *p359* . . . 01843 592361
Robinson Allfree *p166* . . . 01843 865261
Paul Robinson Solicitors *p428* . . . 01702 338338
R P Robinson *p281* . . . 0116 262 1462
Robinsons *p261* . . . 0115 932 4101
Robinsons *p209* . . . 01332 291431
Robson & Co *p259* . . . 01303 264581 / 267413
Rodgers & Burton *p73* . . . 020 8939 6300
Frank Roe Solicitors *p391* . . . 01744 24218
Roebucks *p145* . . . 01254 274000
Rogerson Galvin *p120* . . . 0161 344 2027 / 335 9005
Roland Robinsons & Fentons LLP *p147* . . . 01253 621432
Rollasons *p207* . . . 01327 301771
Ronald Fletcher Baker LLP *p73* . . . 020 7613 1402
Ronaldsons *p335* . . . 01603 618883
Rootes & Alliott *p227* . . . 01303 851100
Rosleys *p338* . . . 0115 958 0584
Rothera Dowson *p130* . . . 0115 916 5200
Rothera Dowson *p338* . . . 0115 910 0600
Rothera Dowson *p427* . . . 0115 914 0077
Rothera Dowson *p338* . . . 0115 952 0900
Rothera Dowson *p338* . . . 0115 916 5200
Rotherham & Co *p201* . . . 024 7622 7331
Rothwell & Evans *p407* . . . 0161 794 1830
Rowberry Morris *p407* . . . 0118 981 2992
Rowberry Morris *p361* . . . 0118 958 5611
Rowbis Solicitors *p230* . . . 01452 301903
Rowland Tildesley & Harris *p433* . . . 01902 366571
Rowntree & Berry *p226* . . . 01253 872581
Rowntree & Berry *p355* . . . 01253 893599

See p603 for the Community Legal Service Work Categories

Royce Marshall & Co *p363* 07765 404753
Rubin Lewis O'Brien *p206* 01633 867000
Rubin Lewis O'Brien *p180* 029 2077 9988
Rudlings & Wakelam *p410* 01842 754151
Rudlings & Wakelam *p156* 01842 810300
Rudlings & Wakelam *p171* 01284 755771
Rundlewalker *p222* 01392 209209
Russell & Co *p300* 01684 892000
Russell & Russell *p149* 01204 399299
Russell & Russell *p150* 01204 699432
Russell & Russell *p150* 01204 707926
Russell & Russell *p171* 0161 762 2888
Russell & Russell *p120* 01942 884469
Russell & Russell *p191* 01244 405700
Russell Jones & Walker *p74* 020 7657 1555
RUSSELL-COOKE LLP *p74* 020 8789 9111
RUSSELL-COOKE LLP *p267* 020 8546 6111
Rustons & Lloyd *p327* 01638 661221
Rutherfords *p407* 01827 311411
SA Law *p390* 01727 798000
SAS Daniels LLP *p297* 01625 442100
SAS Daniels LLP *p198* 01260 282300
SFN Solicitors *p169* 01282 421284
SJP Solicitors *p258* 01485 532662
Sackvilles *p359* 01708 552804
Sainsburys *p208* 0161 336 7027
Salmons *p398* 01782 639827
Salmons *p323* 01782 621266
Salt Veeder *p171* 0161 797 5650
Samuels Solicitors *p125* 01271 343457
Sanders & Co *p399* 01384 375437 / 378991
Sanders Witherspoon LLP *p156* 01277 221010
Sandersons *p131* 01482 324662
Santers Solicitors *p123* 020 8594 7542
Saulet & Co *p389* 023 9281 9442
Saunders Goodin Riddleston Solicitors *p263* 01473 225600
R A Savage & Co *p425* 01707 373037
Scaiff LLP *p440* 01905 727700
Scott-Moncrieff Harbour & Sinclair *p77* 020 7485 5588
Scotts Wright *p283* 01966 22227
Scotts Wright *p183* 01748 832431
Scutt Beaumont Solicitors Ltd *p281* 0116 254 4200
Seatons Solicitors *p199* 01536 276300
Seddon Thomson *p309* 0161 720 8000
John D Sellars & Co *p403* 020 8661 7014
Sergeant & Collins *p373* 01724 864215
SERJEANT & SON *p359* 01487 812325
The Sethi Partnership Solicitors *p216* 020 8866 6464
Martin Sewell Family Law Solicitor & Advocate *p233* 01474 323251
Seymours *p201* 024 7655 3961
Shakespeares *p339* 0115 945 3700
Shanaz & Partners Solicitors *p77* 020 7375 2898
Sharman Law *p130* 01234 303030
Sharp & Partners *p339* 0115 959 0055
Sheikh & Co *p78* 020 8343 0693
Sheltons *p255* 0115 955 3444
Sheltons *p339* 0115 955 3444
Sheltons *p339* 0115 955 3444
Shentons *p434* 01962 844544
Clive Shepherd & Co *p420* 01922 647797
Shepherd Harris & Co *p219* 020 8363 8341
Martin Shepherd & Co *p219* 020 8367 3230
Sheppersons *p252* 01293 772424
Sheppersons *p363* 01737 244987
Sherwood Wheatley *p267* 020 8546 0144
Shipton Hallewell & Co *p192* 01246 232140
Shirtcliffe & Reston Solicitors *p411* 01845 526222
SILLS & BETTERIDGE LLP *p381* 01529 302800
SILLS & BETTERIDGE LLP *p285* 01522 542211
SILLS & BETTERIDGE LLP *p381* 01754 610101
SILLS & BETTERIDGE LLP *p151* 01205 364615
SILLS & BETTERIDGE LLP *p199* 01526 344444
Silver Fitzgerald *p175* 01223 562001
Silverman Livermore *p369* 01928 714121
Simmonds Solicitors *p353* 01202 666417
Alan Simpson & Co *p359* 01268 745406
Simpson Duxbury *p155* 01274 734166
Simpson Millar LLP *p276* 0844 858 3200
Sinclairs *p345* 029 2070 6444
Laurence Singer Solicitor *p117* 01494 431400
Singleton Winn McDermott Solicitors *p326* 0191 265 8817
Singletons Austin Ryder *p219* 020 8363 0101
Sitters & Co *p350* 01752 220464
Slater Bradley & Co *p80* 020 8788 1008
Slee Blackwell *p125* 01271 372128
Slee Blackwell *p222* 01392 423000
Slee Blackwell *p133* 01237 425225
Martin Smalley & Co *p339* 0115 955 6555
Smith & Copsey *p419* 0191 262 4428
Smith & Tetley *p120* 0161 330 2865
Smith Brown & Sprawson *p295* 01582 876900
Smith Chamberlain *p425* 01933 224971
Geoffrey T Smith & Co *p438* 01902 426961
Smith Llewelyn Partnership *p405* 01792 464444
The Smith Partnership *p170* 01283 536471
The Smith Partnership *p170* 01283 548282
The Smith Partnership *p404* 01283 226444
The Smith Partnership *p398* 01782 324454
Smith Roddam *p144* 01388 603073
Rosemary Smith & Co *p204* 01344 777441
Smith Solicitor LLP *p238* 01422 383380
Smith Sutcliffe *p344* 01282 778434
Smith Sutcliffe *p169* 01282 426251
T C Smith *p131* 01289 307409
W F Smith LLP *p424* 01953 880800
W F Smith LLP *p209* 01362 852900
SmithJones Solicitors Ltd *p169* 01282 855400
Maurice Smiths *p183* 01977 557171
Maurice Smiths *p351* 01977 794395
Solomon Levy *p295* 01582 425817 / 414948
Southern Stewart & Walker *p384* 0191 456 7788
Southern Stewart & Walker *p384* 0191 427 0770
Southerns *p169* 01282 422711
Southerns *p321* 01282 603663
Southerns *p198* 01282 863113
Southerns *p169* 01282 438446
Sparling Benham & Brough *p198* 01206 733733
Spence & Horne *p81* 020 8985 2277
Irena Spence *p175* 01223 713300
Spencer Skuse *p181* 029 2034 3993
J D Spicer & Co *p81* 020 7625 5590
Spicketts Battrick Law Practice *p352* 01443 407221
Spicketts Battrick Law Practice *p181* 029 2046 1480
St Luce & Co *p82* 020 7635 9131
Stachiw Bashir Green *p155* 01274 404010
Stachiw Bashir Green *p155* 01274 404010
Standley & Co *p269* 01564 776287
Linda Stapleton & Co *p230* 01452 423870
Steed & Steed LLP *p401* 01787 373387
Steed & Steed LLP *p155* 01376 552828
Steel & Shamash *p82* 020 7803 3999
Steele & Son *p124* 01282 813385
Steele & Son *p198* 01282 868000
STEELE FORD & NEWTON *p321* 01282 692531
Steele Raymond *p152* 01202 294566
Steinbergs *p290* 0151 521 4491
Stephens & Scown *p222* 01392 210700
Stephens & Scown *p391* 01726 74433
Stephens & Scown *p414* 01872 265100
Stephens McDonald & Robson *p327* 0191 232 0675
Stephensons Solicitors LLP *p282* 01942 777777
Stephensons Solicitors LLP *p391* 01942 777777
Stephensons Solicitors LLP *p432* 01942 777777
Stephensons Solicitors LLP *p282* 01942 777777
Sternberg Reed *p123* 020 8591 3366
Stevens *p244* 01440 762511
Stevens *p370* 01799 526849
Stevens Son & Pope *p168* 01444 246377
Chris Stevenson *p212* 01302 341243
G T Stewart Solicitors *p83* 020 8299 6000
Stilwell & Harby *p213* 01304 206850
Stokes Solicitors *p355* 023 9282 8131
Stokes Solicitors *p355* 023 9266 1541
Stone King LLP *p128* 01225 337599
Stone Milward Rapers *p193* 01243 780211
STONE ROWE BREWER LLP *p416* 020 8891 6141
Stones Solicitors LLP *p340* 01837 650200
Stones Solicitors LLP *p222* 01392 666777
Straw & Pearce *p293* 01509 268931
John Street Solicitors *p84* 020 7623 8822
Streeter Marshall *p205* 020 8680 2638
Stuart Smith & Burnett *p158* 01262 678128
Stunt Palmer & Robinson *p84* 020 7739 6927
William Sturges & Co *p84* 020 7873 1000
Sumner & Tabor *p131* 01442 862797 / 872311
Swain & Co *p386* 023 8063 1111
Swain & Co *p244* 023 9248 3322
John Swales *p119* 01233 732590
Swayne Johnson Solicitors *p391* 01745 582535
Swayne Johnson Solicitors *p208* 01745 812835
Sweetman Burke & Sinker *p84* 020 8840 2572
Swinburne & Jackson LLP *p229* 0191 477 2531 / 477 3222
Swinburne & Jackson LLP *p423* 0191 416 0004
Swinburne & Jackson LLP *p370* 0191 413 3468 / 413 2630
Swinburne & Jackson LLP *p191* 0191 388 7221
Swinburne Maddison *p214* 0191 384 2441 / 384 7455
Swinburne Snowball & Jackson *p199* 01207 502532
Sydney Mitchell *p383* 0121 746 3300
Sydney Mitchell *p142* 0121 698 2200 / 0808 166 8827
Sydney Mitchell *p142* 0121 722 2969 / 0808 166 5638
Sykes Lee & Brydson *p445* 01904 731100
Sykes Lee & Brydson *p445* 01904 529000
Sylvester Mackett *p414* 01225 755621
SYMES BAINS BROOMER *p373* 01724 281616
Symes Bains Broomer *p235* 01472 360991
Symes Bains Broomer *p231* 01405 763853
Symons & Gay *p366* 01708 744211
TBI Solicitors *p243* 0800 052 6824 / 01429 264101
TBI Solicitors *p123* 01833 638326
T G Baynes *p207* 01322 295555
T G Baynes *p132* 020 8301 7777
TLT Solicitors *p165* 0117 917 7777
TMJ Legal Services LLP *p434* 01429 838225
TMJ Legal Services LLP *p243* 01429 235616
TMJ Legal Services LLP *p348* 0191 586 5711
TMJ Legal Services LLP *p214* 0191 383 0111
TV Edwards LLP *p85* 020 7790 7000
TV Edwards LLP *p85* 020 7790 7000
TV Edwards LLP *p85* 020 7790 7000
TWM Solicitors LLP *p85* 020 8946 6454
David Tagg & Co *p85* 020 7736 0999
Tait Farrier Graham *p229* 0191 490 0108
Tait Farrier Graham *p327* 0191 272 3713
Talbots Legal Advice Centre *p399* 01384 445850 / 447777
Tallents Solicitors *p322* 01636 671881
Tallents Solicitors *p312* 01623 666700
Tanburghs *p85* 020 8749 8902
Tanner & Taylor LLP *p225* 01252 733770
Tanner & Taylor LLP *p224* 01252 549555
Tanner & Taylor LLP *p115* 01252 316565
R F Tansey *p410* 01844 218000
Tarbox Robinson & Partners *p333* 01923 836595
Taylor & Emmet LLP *p377* 0114 218 4000
Taylor Fawcett *p241* 01423 538111
Taylor Lewis *p181* 01239 621999
Michael Taylor & Associates *p417* 0161 746 7776
Taylor Vinters *p176* 01223 423444
Taylor Walton LLP *p239* 01582 765111
Taylor Walton LLP *p295* 01582 731161
Taylor Walton LLP *p390* 01727 845245
Tayntons LLP Solicitors *p230* 01452 522047
Stanley Tee *p155* 01376 552277
Stanley Tee *p144* 01279 755200
Temperley Taylor LLP *p315* 0161 643 2411
Temple Heelis LLP *p264* 01539 723757
Tennant & Knight *p160* 01273 202050
Terrells LLP *p347* 01733 896789
Terrells LLP *p258* 01480 454987
Terrells LLP *p394* 01780 481129
Thackray Williams *p167* 020 8290 0440
Thakker & Co *p242* 020 8424 0571
Thatcher & Hallam *p316* 01761 414646
Thomas Boyd Whyte *p132* 020 8303 7755
Dean Thomas & Co *p363* 01777 703100
Dean Thomas & Co *p441* 01909 500511
Dean Thomas & Co *p192* 01246 810050
H E Thomas & Co *p87* 020 8854 3036
Rose Thomas & Co *p269* 01570 423300
Thompson Smith & Puxon *p195* 01255 221919
Thompson Smith & Puxon *p198* 01206 574431
Thomson & Bancks LLP *p410* 01684 299633
Thomson Webb & Corfield *p176* 01223 578068
Thomson Wilson Pattinson *p264* 01539 721945
Thomson Wilson Pattinson *p434* 01539 442233
Thornes *p438* 01902 313311
Thornleys Limited *p350* 01752 406977
Thorpe & Co *p430* 01947 603465
Thorpe & Co *p372* 01723 364321
Thorpe & Co *p300* 01653 694899
Thorpe & Co *p226* 01723 515555
The Thrasher Walker Partnership *p396* 0161 442 6240
Thrings LLP *p128* 01225 340000
Thrings LLP *p406* 01793 410800
Thursfields *p440* 01905 730450
Thursfields *p399* 01299 827517
Thursfields *p266* 01562 820575
Thurstan Hoskin Solicitors *p363* 01209 213646
Tibbits Fisher *p143* 0121 707 3900
Tickle Hall Cross *p356* 0800 854379
Tickle Hall Cross *p391* 0800 854379
Tilley & Co *p390* 01727 840467
Tilly Bailey & Irvine LLP *p397* 01642 673797
Timms *p170* 01283 561531 / 544417
Timms *p209* 01332 364436
Timms Solicitors *p404* 01283 214231
Tinsdills *p278* 01538 399332
Toller Beattie LLP *p125* 01271 341000
Tollers LLP *p265* 01536 520111
Tomleys *p330* 01686 626641
Tonner Johns Ratti *p406* 01792 643296
Tozers *p329* 01626 207020
Tozers *p409* 01626 772376
Tozers *p222* 01392 207020
Tozers *p350* 01752 206460
Tracey Barlow Furniss & Co *p441* 01909 472355
Tracey Barlow Furniss & Co *p363* 01777 707677
Traymans *p88* 020 7249 9980
Treasures *p230* 01452 525351
Trobridges *p412* 01752 812787
Trobridges *p350* 01752 664022
Tudur Owen Roberts Glynne & Co *p122* 01248 362315 / 355826
Tudur Owen Roberts Glynne & Co *p172* 01286 672207 / 672851
Tudur Owen Roberts Glynne & Co *p147* 01766 830206
Tunnard & Co *p365* 01765 605629
Turbervilles *p417* 01895 201700
Turbervilles *p417* 01895 201700
Turnbull Garrard *p379* 01743 350851 / 351332

Turner & Wall *p264* 01535 607831
Turner Pearson *p357* 01772 562222
Tustain Jones & Co *p339* 024 7664 1222
Tustain Jones & Co *p130* 024 7664 3222
Tyndallwoods *p143* 0121 624 1111
Tyrer Roxburgh & Co *p89* 020 8889 3319
VHS Fletchers Solicitors *p339* 0115 959 9550
Vallelys *p283* 01462 483800
Van Baaren & Wright *p364* 020 8940 2525
Marina C Van't Goor *p316* 01646 697700
Varley Hibbs LLP *p201* 024 7663 1000
Rhys Vaughan *p311* 0161 224 1439
Veale Wasbrough Vizards *p165* 0117 925 2020
Veja and Co Solicitors *p385* 020 8574 2626
Venters Solicitors *p89* 020 7277 0110
Venters Solicitors *p363* 01737 229610
Vickers & Co *p89* 020 8579 2559 / 8840 3999
Vickers Chisman & Wishlade *p397* 01642 615439
Vincent Laverys *p357* 01772 555176
Vingoe Lloyd Solicitors *p245* 01736 754075
WBW Solicitors *p329* 01626 202404
WBW Solicitors *p153* 01626 833263
WBW Solicitors *p413* 0870 701 4321
WBW Solicitors *p222* 01392 202404
W Evans George & Sons *p323* 01239 710228
WACE MORGAN *p379* 01743 280100
Waddington & Son *p344* 01282 778813
Waddington & Son *p169* 01282 426666
Waddington Webber *p264* 01535 662644 / 662647
Wains *p297* 01625 429511
Wains *p198* 01260 279414
Wainwright & Cummins *p90* 020 7326 7460
Wake Smith & Tofields *p377* 0114 266 6660
Wake Smith & Tofields *p377* 0114 266 6660
Waldron & Schofield *p249* 01706 624029
Waldrons *p268* 01384 811811
Walker & Co *p420* 01922 639080
Walker & Co *p367* 01709 817112
Grenville J Walker *p147* 01258 459911
Grenville J Walker *p430* 01305 759090
Walkers *p367* 01706 213565
The Walkers Partnership *p368* 01763 241121 / 248896
The Walkers Partnership *p368* 01763 248896
Waller Needham & Green *p347* 01733 262182
Waller Needham & Green *p347* 01733 311422
Walter Wilson Richmond *p242* 020 8427 8484
Walters & Barbary *p173* 01209 712454
Wannop Fox Staffurth & Bray *p442* 01903 228200
Wannop Fox Staffurth & Bray *p193* 01243 778844
Wansbroughs *p314* 01225 703222
Wansbroughs *p210* 01380 733300
Ward Hadaway *p327* 0191 204 4000
Wards Solicitors *p165* 0117 929 2811
Wards Solicitors *p429* 01934 413535
Wards Solicitors *p394* 0117 943 4800
Wards Solicitors *p429* 01934 428811
Wards Solicitors *p165* 01454 204880
Wards Solicitors *p443* 01454 316789
Warings Solicitors *p147* 01253 293106
Warner Goodman LLP *p387* 023 8063 9311
Warner Goodman LLP *p224* 01329 288121
Warner Goodman LLP *p355* 023 9275 3575
Rodney Warren & Co *p216* 01323 430430
Wartnabys *p312* 01858 463322
Watkins & Gunn *p352* 01495 762244
Alasdair Watson & Co *p327* 0191 488 4521
Watson Burton LLP *p327* 0845 901 2100
Paul J Watson *p315* 01642 293427
The Watson Ramsbottom Partnership *p234* 01254 884422 / 883020
The Watson Ramsbottom Partnership *p146* 01254 672222
Watson Solicitors *p422* 01925 571212
Watson Woodhouse *p397* 01642 247656
V G Waugh *p348* 0191 527 2727
Kathy Webb & Co *p237* 01287 633331
Weightmans LLP *p269* 01565 634234
Weightmans LLP *p311* 0161 233 7330
Welch & Co *p181* 01239 614070
The Wells Law Partnership *p150* 01204 709959
Whatley Recordon *p300* 01684 892939
J B Wheatley & Co *p91* 020 8479 8000
Wheelers *p115* 01252 316316
Wheltons *p237* 01483 537633
Whetter Duckworth Fowler *p266* 01865 842100
Whetter Duckworth Fowler *p344* 01865 872206
Whiskers *p219* 01992 561111
Whiskers *p239* 01279 439439
Whiteford Crocker *p371* 01752 843134
Whiteford Crocker *p351* 01752 335994
Whiteford Crocker *p350* 01752 550711
Whiteford Crocker *p263* 01752 698488
Whiting & Mason *p313* 0161 427 1040
Wholley Goodings LLP *p319* 01670 519714
Wholley Goodings LLP *p130* 01670 824080
Widdows Mason *p432* 01942 244294
Widdows Mason *p282* 01942 673311
The Wilkes Partnership LLP *p143* 0121 233 4333
Wilkin Chapman Epton Blades *p285* 01522 512345
Wilkin Chapman Grange Solicitors *p294* 01507 606161
Wilkin Chapman Grange Solicitors *p252* 01507 527521
Wilkin Chapman LLP *p235* 01472 262626
Wilkins *p121* 01296 424681
Wilkinson & Butler *p392* 01480 219229
Wilkinson Woodward *p238* 01422 339600
Wilks Price Hounslow *p369* 01983 566241
Willett & Co *p171* 01284 701323
Williams & Co *p217* 020 8952 8882
Williams MacDougall & Campbell *p442* 01903 214186
Peter Williams & Co *p406* 01792 465597
R N Williams & Co Limited *p438* 01902 429051
Williamson & Barnes *p207* 01304 373154
Williamsons *p213* 01377 252022
Williamsons *p258* 01482 323697
Williscroft & Co *p155* 01274 305380
Wilson & Berry *p153* 01344 420555
Wilson & Bird *p121* 01296 436766
Wilson & Co *p92* 020 8808 7535
Wilson & Co Solicitors *p315* 01642 222292
Wilson Barca LLP *p92* 020 7272 2072
Wilson Browne *p333* 01604 876697
Wilson Browne *p281* 0116 251 7181
Wilson Browne *p425* 01933 279000
Wilson Browne *p265* 01536 410041
Wilson Browne *p250* 01933 410000
Giles Wilson *p282* 01702 477106
Wilsons Solicitors *p344* 01865 874497
Winterbotham Smith Penley LLP *p214* 01453 541940
Winterbotham Smith Penley LLP *p320* 01453 832566
Winterbotham Smith Penley LLP *p401* 01453 847200
Winters & Co *p421* 01920 466696
Wintle & Co *p148* 01243 863021
Wiseman Lee LLP *p92* 020 8215 1000
Wiseman Lee LLP *p92* 020 8215 1000
Graham Withers & Co *p380* 01743 236345
Withy King Solicitors *p128* 01225 425731
Withy King Solicitors *p410* 01844 261966
Withy King Solicitors *p414* 01225 777464
Withy King Solicitors *p128* 01225 425731
Withy King Solicitors *p407* 01793 536526
Withy King Solicitors *p313* 01672 514781
Wolferstans *p351* 01752 663295
Wolferstans *p351* 01752 401515
Wollen Michelmore Solicitors *p413* 01803 213251
Clive G Wood & Co *p396* 0161 480 1000
Rupert Wood & Son *p120* 0161 330 9121
Woodcocks *p359* 01706 824011
Woodcocks *p171* 0161 761 4611
Woodcocks *p359* 01706 225621 / 215018
Woodcocks *p121* 01706 874487
Woodfines LLP *p372* 01767 680251
Woodfines LLP *p130* 01234 270600
Woodfines LLP *p147* 01908 366333
Woodfines LLP *p317* 01908 202150
Woodfines LLP *p176* 01223 411421
Woodford Robinson *p333* 01604 624926
Woollcombe Yonge *p351* 01752 660384
Woolley Bevis Diplock *p160* 01273 323231
Woolliscrofts *p398* 01782 577246
The Worcester Family Law Practice *p440* 01905 730900
Worger Howcroft *p133* 01274 511246
Worthingtons *p227* 01303 850206
Wortley Redmayne Kershaw *p187* 01245 491122
Wright & McMillan Bennett *p409* 01952 291100
William Wright & Son *p213* 01384 255344
Wrigley Claydon *p341* 0161 624 6811
Wrigley Claydon *p412* 01706 815712
Wykes O'Donnell Williams *p261* 0115 932 8776
Yarwood & Stubley *p148* 01670 361211
Yarwood Stimpson & Co *p431* 0191 297 0123
Yates & Co *p339* 0115 947 4486
Young & Co *p398* 01782 339200
Young & Lee *p143* 0121 633 3233
Youngs *p181* 029 2076 3211
Zelin & Zelin *p94* 020 7262 1405
Zermansky & Partners *p278* 0113 245 9766
Ziadies *p94* 020 7737 0934

HOUSING

A-Z Law Solicitors *p3* 020 8355 0830
AGR Solicitors *p311* 01623 460444
AGR Solicitors *p378* 01623 748522
AKP Solicitors Ltd *p3* 020 8472 4462
Aaronson & Co *p3* 020 7376 9124
Abels *p385* 023 8022 0317
Adlams LLP *p392* 01480 474061
Ahmed & Co *p4* 020 7383 2243
Alderson Dodds *p147* 01670 352293
Allen Hoole Solicitors *p160* 0117 942 0901
Alletsons Ltd *p157* 01278 456621
Allington Hughes *p442* 01978 291000
Andrew & Andrew Solicitors *p354* 023 9266 1381
ANTHONY GOLD *p6* 020 7940 4000
ANTHONY GOLD *p6* 020 7940 4000
ANTHONY GOLD *p6* 020 7940 4000
Archer & Archer *p218* 01353 662203
Arscotts *p254* 01273 735289
Ashfords LLP *p412* 01884 203000
Ashfords LLP *p408* 01823 232300
Ashton KCJ *p171* 01284 762331
Ashton KCJ *p262* 01473 232425
Askews *p362* 01642 475252
Askews *p396* 01642 475252
Aston Clark *p8* 020 8752 1122
Atkinson Cave & Stuart *p146* 01253 293151
Atteys *p211* 01302 340400
BLB Solicitors *p406* 01793 615011
BTMK Solicitors LLP *p387* 01702 339222
E J Bamforth Solicitors *p190* 01244 357209
Banner Jones *p191* 01246 560560
Banner Jones *p213* 01246 414438
Banner Jones *p191* 01246 827516
Banner Jones *p192* 01246 861250
Banner Jones *p191* 01246 209773
Max Barford & Co *p414* 01892 539379
Barker Booth & Eastwood *p146* 01253 362500
John Barkers *p195* 01472 695218
John Barkers *p294* 01507 604773
John Barkers *p234* 01472 358686
John Barkers *p297* 01507 477673
Norman H Barnett & Co *p11* 020 8471 2112
Barrett & Thomson *p381* 01753 437416
Bates N V H *p11* 020 7936 2930
Bawtrees LLP *p435* 01376 513491
Beetenson & Gibbon *p235* 01472 240251
Beevers Solicitors *p119* 0161 339 9697
Ben Hoare Bell & Co *p401* 0191 565 3112
Ben Hoare Bell & Co *p323* 0191 275 2626
Ben Hoare Bell & Co *p401* 0191 516 0466
Bernard Chill & Axtell *p385* 023 8022 8821
Richard Best & Co *p368* 01788 571135
Best Solicitors *p375* 0114 281 3636
Bhatia Best *p336* 0115 950 3231
Bindmans LLP *p12* 020 7833 4433
Birchall Blackburn LLP *p356* 01772 561663
Biscoes *p348* 01730 264799
Biscoes *p354* 023 9266 0261
Biscoes *p423* 023 9225 1257
Biscoes *p431* 01329 833249
Biscoes *p232* 023 9251 2030
Biscoes *p353* 023 9237 0634
Blackhurst Budd LLP *p146* 01253 629300
Bolitho Way *p354* 023 9282 0747
Harry Boodhoo & Co *p436* 0161 445 0588
Eric Bowes & Co *p382* 0121 744 3691
Boyce Hatton *p412* 01803 403403
John Boyle & Co *p362* 01209 213507
Brain Chase Coles *p126* 01256 354481
Brain Sinnott & Co *p268* 0117 960 6880
Brain Sinnott & Co *p161* 0117 965 1030
Bramwell Browne Odedra *p189* 01494 782244
Brennans Solicitors *p419* 0191 262 5133
Brighouses *p388* 01704 534101 / 500151
Brooks *p378* 01608 664406
Broomhead & Saul *p408* 01823 288121
Broudie Jackson Canter *p286* 0151 227 1429
Burges Salmon *p161* 0117 939 2000
Burton & Co LLP *p284* 01522 523215
Burton & Co LLP *p381* 01529 306008 / 306009
Butcher & Barlow LLP *p170* 0161 764 5141
CMHT Solicitors *p420* 01922 743525
CMHT Solicitors *p167* 01543 372347
CMHT Solicitors *p420* 01922 646400
CVC Solicitors *p346* 01736 362313
Carmichael & Heathfield *p324* 0191 230 3010
S A Carr & Co *p18* 020 8986 5438
Cartridges *p220* 01392 256854
Cartwright Cunningham Haselgrove & Co *p19* 020 8520 1021
Caswell Jones *p172* 029 2086 4888
Challinors *p136* 0121 212 9393
Chambers Rutland & Crauford *p19* 020 8446 2777
Chambers Solicitors *p381* 01753 522204
Chanter Ferguson *p132* 01237 478751
Charltons Solicitors *p132* 01782 522111
Chattertons Solicitors *p252* 01507 522456
Chattertons Solicitors *p151* 01205 310025
Chattertons Solicitors *p284* 01522 814600
Churchers *p271* 023 9255 1500
Churchers *p232* 023 9260 3400
Churchers *p223* 01329 822333
Churchers *p354* 023 9221 0170
Clark Willis *p206* 01325 281111
Clark Willis *p183* 01748 830000
Clarke Kiernan *p412* 01732 360999
Clarkson Hirst *p269* 01524 39760
Clifford Johnston & Co *p302* 0161 249 2700
Clifford Johnston & Co *p302* 0161 975 1900
Clinton Davis Pallis *p21* 020 8880 5000
Coffin Mew & Clover *p385* 023 8033 4661

See p603 for the Community Legal Service Work Categories

Firm	Page	Telephone
Coffin Mew & Clover	*p354*	023 9238 8021
Coffin Mew & Clover	*p232*	023 9252 3111
Coffin Mew & Clover	*p223*	01329 825617
Coles Miller Solicitors LLP	*p352*	01202 673011
Anthony Collins Solicitors LLP	*p137*	0121 200 3242
Collins Solicitors	*p423*	01923 223324
The Community Law Partnership	*p137*	0121 685 8595
Coodes	*p285*	01579 347600
Coodes	*p346*	01736 362294
Cooper Lingard	*p282*	01702 715411
Cooper Sons Hartley & Williams	*p184*	01298 812138
Cornfield Law	*p215*	01323 412512
Crombie Wilkinson	*p444*	01904 624185
Crombie Wilkinson	*p300*	01653 600070
Richard Crumly	*p410*	01635 866166
Daniel Curry & Co	*p205*	020 8680 2188
Darling & Stephensons	*p206*	01325 489000
Davies Gore Lomax	*p273*	0113 242 2797
Davies Sully Wilkins	*p172*	029 2088 7828
Daybells LLP	*p26*	020 8555 4321
De Soyza & Fernando	*p26*	020 8670 9918
Desor & Co	*p245*	020 8569 0708
Dickinson Manser	*p352*	01202 673071
Dickinsons	*p146*	01253 781010
Dixon Stewart	*p321*	01425 621515
Dixon Stewart Solicitors	*p250*	01425 279222
Paul Dodds Solicitors	*p419*	0191 263 6200
Dowse & Co	*p27*	020 7254 6205
Scott Duff & Co	*p182*	01228 531054
Scott Duff & Co	*p346*	01768 865551
Thomas Dunton Solicitors	*p342*	01689 822554
Eaton Smith LLP	*p255*	01484 821300
ALAN EDWARDS & CO	*p28*	020 7221 7644
Edwards Duthie	*p260*	020 8514 9000
Edwards Duthie	*p29*	020 8514 9000
Edwards Duthie	*p29*	020 8514 9000
R L Edwards & Partners	*p157*	01656 656861
Elliot Mather LLP	*p192*	01246 231288
Fahri Jacob	*p30*	020 8347 4070
A J Field & Co	*p375*	01795 580600
Fieldings Porter	*p149*	01204 540900
Paul Finn Solicitors	*p168*	01288 356256
Fisher Jones Greenwood LLP	*p186*	01245 890110
Fisher Jones Greenwood LLP	*p197*	01206 578282
Fisher Meredith	*p32*	020 7091 2700
Fletcher Dervish	*p33*	020 8800 4615
Ronald Fletcher & Co	*p33*	020 7624 0041
Fletchers	*p388*	01704 546919
Forbes	*p114*	01254 872111
Forbes	*p356*	01772 220022
Forbes	*p145*	01254 580000
Forbes	*p194*	01257 260600
Ford Simey LLP	*p221*	01392 274126
Ford Simey LLP	*p380*	01395 577061 / 0800 169 3741
Ford Simey LLP	*p222*	01395 272241 / 0800 169 3741
Fosters	*p334*	01603 620508
Fosters	*p168*	01986 895251
French & Co	*p337*	0115 955 1111
GCA Solicitors (Giffen Couch & Archer)	*p295*	01582 410041
GLP Solicitors	*p315*	0161 653 6295
GLP Solicitors	*p304*	0161 834 6721
GLP Solicitors	*p357*	0161 773 8626
GLP Solicitors	*p304*	0161 795 5531
GLP Solicitors	*p304*	0161 793 0901
Donald Galbraith & Co	*p34*	020 8492 2700
Gartsides	*p328*	01633 213411
Gartsides	*p113*	01873 857555
Craig Gee	*p304*	0161 666 9999
George H Coles & Co	*p254*	01273 205101
GEORGE IDE LLP	*p192*	01243 786668
Gilbert Turner Coomber	*p35*	020 8520 5886
Glaisyers	*p138*	0121 233 2971
Glaisyers Solicitors LLP	*p304*	0161 832 4666
Glaisyers Solicitors LLP	*p304*	0161 224 3311
Glanvilles	*p328*	01983 527878
Godloves	*p273*	0113 225 8811
Godloves	*p273*	0113 286 8822
Godloves	*p273*	0113 225 8864
Goldbergs	*p349*	01752 660023
Goldkorn Mathias Gentle Page LLP	*p36*	020 7631 1811
Goldstones	*p405*	01792 643021
Grainger Appleyard	*p211*	01302 327257
David Gray Solicitors	*p324*	0191 232 9547
GREENLAND HOUCHEN POMEROY	*p334*	01603 660744
GREENLAND HOUCHEN POMEROY	*p120*	01953 453143
Gregory Abrams Davidson LLP	*p288*	0151 236 5000
Gregorys Solicitors	*p395*	0161 456 8125
Gregsons	*p37*	020 8946 1173
Gregsons	*p337*	0115 941 1999
The Gwyn George Partnership	*p113*	01685 874629 / 871133
HC Solicitors LLP	*p347*	01733 882800
HKH Kenwright & Cox Solicitors	*p260*	020 8553 9600
Hadaway & Hadaway	*p330*	0191 257 0382
Hallam-Peel & Co	*p38*	020 3006 1661
HallmarkHulme	*p439*	01905 726600
Hameed & Co	*p38*	020 8830 1335
Hanne & Co	*p38*	020 7228 0017
Hansen Palomares	*p38*	020 7640 4600
Harding Evans LLP	*p328*	01633 244233
Harding Swinburne Jackson & Co	*p401*	0191 565 8194
Harpers	*p39*	020 7405 8888
Christopher Harris & Co	*p375*	01795 661521
Christopher Harris & Co	*p380*	01795 437268
David W Harris & Co	*p352*	01443 486666
Harrow Solicitors & Advocates	*p424*	020 8863 0788
Edward Harte LLP	*p159*	01273 662750
Harter & Loveless	*p39*	020 7688 2900
Harvey Ingram Borneos	*p130*	01234 353221
Harvey Ingram Borneos	*p317*	01908 696002
Havillands	*p366*	01708 766559
Hawley & Rodgers	*p337*	0115 955 9000
Hawley & Rodgers	*p293*	01509 230333
Heckford Norton	*p283*	01462 682244
Henriques Griffiths	*p163*	0117 909 4000
Heptonstalls LLP	*p231*	01405 765661
Hereward & Foster	*p41*	020 7476 6600
Herrington & Carmichael LLP	*p437*	0118 977 4045
Herrington & Carmichael LLP	*p173*	01276 686222
Hetts	*p373*	01724 843287
Hetts	*p373*	01724 270290
Hewetts	*p361*	0118 957 5337
Hewitts	*p330*	01325 316170
Hewitts	*p144*	01388 604691
Hewitts	*p206*	01325 468573
Hewitts	*p203*	01388 762466
HODGE JONES & ALLEN LLP	*p41*	020 7874 8300
Holden & Co	*p243*	01424 722422
Holls Solicitors	*p129*	020 8658 9767
Hood Vores & Allwood	*p209*	01362 692424
Hopkin Murray Beskine	*p42*	020 7272 1234
Hopkins	*p311*	01623 468468
Hopkins	*p311*	01623 460460
Howarth Scott	*p132*	020 8303 4658
Howells LLP	*p367*	01709 364000
Howells LLP	*p376*	0114 249 6666
Hudgell & Partners	*p43*	020 8854 1331
J W Hughes & Co	*p199*	01492 596596
Humphrys & Co	*p363*	01745 343158
Hunt & Hunt	*p366*	01708 764433
Hutchins & Co	*p44*	020 8986 3911
Hutton's	*p179*	029 2037 8621
Henry Hyams	*p274*	0113 243 2288
Darryl Ingram & Co	*p45*	020 8202 0843
Ismail & Co	*p218*	020 8804 1065
Iyama Solicitors	*p45*	020 7357 0709
JMW Solicitors	*p306*	0845 872 6666
Gwyn James Solicitors	*p198*	01594 833042
T Llewellyn Jones	*p320*	01639 643635
Terry Jones Solicitors & Advocates	*p379*	01743 285888
Terry Jones Solicitors & Advocates	*p409*	01952 297979
Peter Kandler & Co	*p48*	020 8960 9222
Kennards Wells	*p48*	020 8539 8338
Keoghs and Nicholls, Lindsell & Harris	*p116*	0161 928 9321
Keppe Rofer	*p156*	01874 624627
Kerseys	*p262*	01473 213311
Kidd Rapinet	*p298*	0845 017 9608
Anthony King & Co	*p126*	01268 240400
Kirby Sheppard	*p411*	0845 840 0045
Kirby Sheppard	*p268*	0845 840 0045
Kitsons LLP	*p221*	01392 455555
Laceys	*p353*	01202 743286
Lancasters	*p158*	01262 602401
Langleys	*p445*	01904 610886
Law Hurst & Taylor	*p428*	01702 337864
Lawrence & Co	*p52*	020 7266 4333
Lawson & Thompson	*p130*	01670 530700
Karina Leapman & Co	*p52*	020 7794 7741
Leathes Prior	*p334*	01603 610911
Leonard & Co	*p386*	023 8023 3242
Leonard & Co	*p386*	023 8023 4433
Letchers	*p364*	01425 471424
Lewis & Lines	*p113*	01495 212286
Duncan Lewis & Co	*p53*	020 7923 4020
Duncan Lewis & Co	*p53*	020 7923 4020
Lewis Nedas & Co	*p53*	020 7387 2032
Lichfield Reynolds	*p398*	01782 289122
Lichfield Reynolds	*p398*	01782 313212
Linder Myers Solicitors	*p307*	0844 984 6400
Linder Myers Solicitors	*p306*	0844 984 6000
Robert Lizar	*p307*	0161 226 2319
Robert Lizar	*p307*	0161 860 7797
Llewellyn Jones & Co	*p369*	01824 704495
Anthony Louca Solicitors	*p55*	020 7723 9889
Gordon Lowe & Co	*p163*	01454 326833
MFG Solicitors	*p265*	01562 820181
MWP Solicitors	*p126*	01268 527131
McGrath & Co	*p140*	0121 643 4121
McKenzie Bell Solicitors	*p401*	0191 567 4857
Marchant Harries & Co	*p113*	01685 885500
Marchants Solicitors	*p312*	01623 655111
Saul Marine & Co	*p58*	020 8959 3611
Marshall Hall & Levy	*p384*	0191 455 3181
Mason Baggott & Garton	*p219*	01427 872661
Matthew Arnold & Baldwin LLP	*p423*	01923 202020
Mayo Wynne Baxter LLP	*p215*	01323 730543
Mayo Wynne Baxter LLP	*p160*	01273 775533
Mayo Wynne Baxter LLP	*p283*	01273 477071
Michelmores LLP	*p221*	01392 688688
Miles & Partners	*p60*	020 7426 0400
George Mills	*p423*	0191 416 2182
Milne & Lyall	*p158*	01308 422362
Molesworths Bright Clegg	*p365*	01706 356666
Morecrofts Solicitors LLP	*p134*	0151 666 2210
Morgans	*p180*	029 2072 9888
Morrison Spowart	*p62*	020 8698 9200
Moss & Co	*p62*	020 8986 8336
Moss Beachley Mullem & Coleman	*p62*	020 7402 1401 / 7723 5783
Mountain Partnership	*p62*	020 7732 3737
E J Moyle	*p369*	01903 784447
E J Moyle	*p285*	01903 725143
James Murray Solicitors	*p150*	0151 933 3333
James Murray Solicitors	*p290*	0151 207 9910
Mustoe Shorter	*p430*	01305 752700
Myers Lister Price	*p117*	0161 926 9969
Nalders Quality Solicitors	*p414*	01872 241414
Nalders Quality Solicitors	*p223*	01326 313441
Nalders Quality Solicitors	*p173*	01209 714278
Nalders Quality Solicitors	*p329*	01637 871414
Nalders Quality Solicitors	*p346*	01736 364014
Nandy & Co	*p63*	020 8536 1800
Alfred Newton & Co	*p396*	0161 480 6551 / 480 1245
NORRIE WAITE & SLATER	*p377*	0114 276 6166
Norrie Waite & Slater	*p377*	0114 248 4890
Norrie Waite & Slater	*p367*	01709 523983
North Yorkshire Law	*p372*	01723 360001
Northwood Law Practice	*p333*	01923 826208
Norton Peskett	*p294*	01502 533000
Ormerods	*p205*	020 8686 5000
Osbornes	*p65*	020 7485 8811
Ouvry Goodman & Co	*p403*	020 8642 7571
J Keith Park & Co	*p391*	01744 636000
Park Woodfine Heald Mellows LLP	*p130*	01234 400000
Parker Rhodes Hickmotts	*p367*	01709 511100
Patchell Davies (Trading Name of PD Law Ltd)	*p147*	01495 227128
Payne & Gamage	*p322*	01636 640649
Payne & Payne	*p257*	01482 326446
Pearson Hinchliffe	*p341*	0161 785 3500
Peasegoods	*p308*	0161 205 2772
Pengillys LLP	*p430*	01305 768888
Pengillys LLP	*p212*	01305 768888
Percy Short & Cuthbert	*p67*	020 7700 0265
Pheby & Co	*p445*	01904 789900
Philippou & Co	*p67*	020 8882 4222
David Phillips & Partners	*p150*	0151 922 5525
Pickup & Scott	*p121*	01296 397794
Pictons Solicitors LLP	*p295*	01582 870870
Pictons Solicitors LLP	*p317*	01908 663511
Pictons Solicitors LLP	*p247*	01442 242441
Platt Halpern	*p308*	0161 224 2555
Pollecoff Solicitors Ltd	*p68*	020 7608 2568
Polpitiya & Co	*p384*	020 8813 9282
Powells	*p429*	01934 623501
Preston Goldburn	*p223*	01326 318900
QualitySolicitors Gruber Garratt	*p358*	0161 724 0203
QualitySolicitors Jackson & Canter	*p290*	0151 282 1700
Gillian Radford & Co	*p70*	020 8960 4366
Ralph & Co	*p329*	01637 872218
Rawal & Co	*p70*	020 8445 0303
Red Kite Law	*p410*	01834 842122
Red Kite Law	*p183*	01267 239000
Red Kite Law	*p345*	01646 683222
Red Kite Law	*p244*	01437 763332
Red Kite Law	*p345*	01646 681529
Red Kite Law	*p316*	01646 698008
Stephen Rimmer LLP	*p216*	01323 644222
Rippon Patel & French	*p72*	020 7323 0404
Roach Pittis	*p328*	01983 524431
Helen Robbins Solicitors	*p72*	020 8558 0038
Robinson Allfree	*p359*	01843 592361
Roland Robinsons & Fentons LLP	*p147*	01253 621432
Will Rolt Solicitors	*p128*	01225 426390
Rootes & Alliott	*p227*	01303 851100
Rowberry Morris	*p361*	0118 958 5611
Rudlings & Wakelam	*p410*	01842 754151
SJP Solicitors	*p258*	01485 532662
Samars Solicitors	*p254*	020 8570 4716
Samy & Co	*p242*	020 8861 2424
Sanders Witherspoon LLP	*p156*	01277 221010
Santers Solicitors	*p123*	020 8594 7542
Saulet & Co	*p389*	023 9281 9442
Selvarajah & Co	*p77*	020 8204 7884
The Sethi Partnership Solicitors	*p216*	020 8866 6464
Sheikh & Co	*p78*	020 8343 0693
Shentons	*p434*	01962 844544

Clive Shepherd & Co p420 01922 647797
Silks p340 0121 511 2263
Slee Blackwell p125 01271 372128
Slee Blackwell p222 01392 423000
Geoffrey T Smith & Co p438 01902 426961
The Smith Partnership p170 01283 536471
The Smith Partnership p404 01283 226444
Smith Solicitor LLP p238 01422 383380
Solomon Levy p295 01582 425817 / 414948
Spence & Horne p81 020 8985 2277
Spicketts Battrick Law Practice p352 01443 407221
Stachiw Bashir Green p155 01274 404010
Stachiw Bashir Green p155 01274 404010
Steel & Shamash p82 020 7803 3999
Steele Raymond p152 01202 294566
Stephens & Scown p222 01392 210700
Stephens & Scown p391 01726 74433
Stephens & Scown p414 01872 265100
Stephens McDonald & Robson p327 0191 232 0675
Stephensons Solicitors LLP p282 01942 777777
Stephensons Solicitors LLP p391 01942 777777
Stephensons Solicitors LLP p432 01942 777777
Stephensons Solicitors LLP p282 01942 777777
Sternberg Reed p123 020 8591 3366
G T Stewart Solicitors p83 020 8299 6000
Stone King LLP p128 01225 337599
Stones Solicitors LLP p340 01837 650200
Stones Solicitors LLP p222 01392 666777
A M Strachan & Co p84 020 7729 0003
Straw & Pearce p293 01509 268931
Streeter Marshall p205 020 8680 2638
Stunt Palmer & Robinson p84 020 7739 6927
Swain & Co p386 023 8063 1111
Swain & Co p244 023 9248 3322
Sweetman Burke & Sinker p84 020 8840 2572
Swinburne & Jackson LLP p229 0191 477 2531 / 477 3222
TBI Solicitors p243 0800 052 6824 / 01429 264101
TMJ Legal Services LLP p434 01429 838225
TMJ Legal Services LLP p243 01429 235616
TMJ Legal Services LLP p348 0191 586 5711
TMJ Legal Services LLP p214 0191 383 0111
TV Edwards LLP p85 020 7790 7000
TV Edwards LLP p85 020 7790 7000
David Tagg & Co p85 020 7736 0999
Tanburghs O'Brien Lahaise p85 020 7372 6614
Taylor & Emmet LLP p377 0114 218 4000
Temple Heelis LLP p264 01539 723757
Thackray Williams p167 020 8290 0440
H E Thomas & Co p87 020 8854 3036
Thorpe & Co p430 01947 603465
Thorpe & Co p372 01723 364321
Thorpe & Co p226 01723 515555
Tilley & Co p390 01727 840467
Tilly Bailey & Irvine LLP p397 01642 673797
Timms p170 01283 561531 / 544417
Timms p209 01332 364436
Timms Solicitors p404 01283 214231
Tozers p350 01752 206460
Traymans p88 020 7249 9980
Alison Trent & Co p88 020 7583 3350
Trobridges p412 01752 812787
Trobridges p350 01752 664022
Tyndallwoods p143 0121 624 1111
Tyrer Roxburgh & Co p89 020 8889 3319
Marina C Van't Goor p316 01646 697700
Vickers & Co p89 020 8579 2559 / 8840 3999
WBW Solicitors p329 01626 202404
WBW Solicitors p153 01626 833263
WBW Solicitors p413 0870 701 4321
WBW Solicitors p222 01392 202404
Wainwright & Cummins p90 020 7737 9330
Wainwright & Cummins p90 020 7326 7460
Walker & Co p367 01709 817112
Waller Needham & Green p347 01733 262182
Walters & Barbary p173 01209 712454
Wansbroughs p314 01225 703222
Wards Solicitors p165 0117 929 2811
Wards Solicitors p429 01934 413535
Wards Solicitors p394 0117 943 4800
Wards Solicitors p429 01934 428811
Warnapala & Co Ltd p385 020 8571 1823
Watson Woodhouse p397 01642 247656
Whetter Duckworth Fowler p266 01865 842100
Wilkin Chapman Epton Blades p285 01522 512345
Willett & Co p171 01284 701323
Williams & Co p217 020 8952 8882
Williscroft & Co p155 01274 305380
Wilson & Co Solicitors p315 01642 222292
Wilson Barca LLP p92 020 7272 2072
Wilson Browne p333 01604 876697
Wilsons Solicitors p344 01865 874497
Wintle & Co p148 01243 863021
Wolferstans p351 01752 663295
Wollen Michelmore Solicitors p413 01803 213251
Woodcocks p171 0161 761 4611
Woodcocks p121 01706 874487
Woodfines LLP p130 01234 270600
Worger Howcroft p133 01274 511246
Zelin & Zelin p94 020 7262 1405
Zermansky & Partners p278 0113 245 9766
Ziadies p94 020 7737 0934

IMMIGRATION / NATIONALITY

A-Z Law Solicitors p3 020 8355 0830
AS Law p285 0151 707 1212
Aaronson & Co p3 020 7376 9124
Abiloye & Co p3 020 8478 5678
Afrifa & Partners p4 020 7820 9177
Ahmed & Co p4 020 7383 2243
J M Amin & Co p426 020 8903 3766
Maurice Andrews p135 0121 554 4900
Ashton KCJ p262 01473 232425
Ashton KCJ p225 01394 277188
Aston Clark p8 020 8752 1122
Barrea LLP p249 01494 537699
Bartram & Co p11 020 8840 0444
S S Basi & Co p259 020 8518 1236
Bates N V H p11 020 7936 2930
Beecham Peacock p323 0191 232 3048
Ben Hoare Bell & Co p401 0191 565 3112
Ben Hoare Bell & Co p323 0191 275 2626
Ben Hoare Bell & Co p401 0191 565 3112
Bindmans LLP p12 020 7833 4433
Birchall Blackburn LLP p356 01772 561663
Birchall Blackburn LLP p301 0161 236 0662
Birnberg Peirce & Partners p13 020 7911 0166
Biscoes p354 023 9266 0261
Blakemores p135 0121 234 7200
Brain Sinnott & Co p161 0117 965 1030
Brar & Co p323 0191 276 6880
Broudie Jackson Canter p286 0151 227 1429
Campbell Chambers p18 020 7691 8777
Chinyoka & Co p272 0113 276 8800 / 276 8801
Clifford Johnston & Co p302 0161 249 2700
Clifford Johnston & Co p302 0161 975 1900
Corbin & Hassan p22 020 7247 6518
Crowley & Co p178 029 2045 8895
DBL Talbots LLP p213 01384 252471
DBL Talbots LLP p399 01384 445850
DLC Solicitors Limited p207 01254 761234
Davies Blunden & Evans p224 01252 541633
Daybells LLP p26 020 8555 4321
Dhillon & Co p27 020 8471 7884
Dicksons Solicitors Ltd p397 01782 262424
Dicksons Solicitors Ltd p397 01782 262424
Dodds & Partners p279 0116 253 8585
Donnelly McArdle Adamson p243 01429 274732
Edwards Duthie p29 020 8514 9000
Edwards Duthie p29 020 8514 9000
Eric Robinson Solicitors p385 023 8042 5000
Fadiga & Co Solicitors p30 020 8672 8779
Figueiredo & Bowman p32 020 7739 5599
Fisher Jones Greenwood LLP p197 01206 578282
Fisher Meredith p32 020 7091 2700
Fletcher Dervish p33 020 8800 4615
Fosters p168 01986 895251
Fountain Solicitors Limited p420 01922 645429
Freer & Archer p279 0116 241 3199
French & Co p337 0115 955 1111
Gangar & Co p427 0121 553 4166
Gartsides p328 01633 213411
Genga & Co p426 020 8795 5020
Godloves p273 0113 225 8864
Grants Solicitors p205 020 8288 8899
David Gray Solicitors p324 0191 232 9547
Wesley Gryk p37 020 7401 6887
Hameed & Co p38 020 8830 1335
Harbans Singh p139 0121 551 4496
Harrison Bundey p274 0113 200 7400
Harrow Solicitors & Advocates p424 020 8863 0788
Harvey Ingram Borneos p130 01234 353221
Hasan Solicitors p139 0121 778 4003
Havillands p366 01708 766559
Hayat & Co p218 020 8360 4485
Heer Manak p200 024 7666 4000
Hereward & Foster p41 020 7476 6600
Hetts p373 01724 843287
Hiace Solicitors p205 020 8686 3777
Hoole & Co p163 0117 969 1436
Hoole & Co p163 0117 942 8871
Howe & Co p43 020 8840 4688
Howells LLP p367 01709 364000
Howells LLP p376 0114 249 6666
Rozita Hussain Solicitors p436 0161 448 8222
Henry Hyams p274 0113 243 2288
Irving & Co p45 020 7428 9600
Ison Harrison p228 0113 286 1455
Ison Harrison p274 0113 232 6530
Ison Harrison p274 0113 284 5000
Iyama Solicitors p45 020 7357 0709
Johar & Co p280 0116 254 3345
Kaim Todner Ltd p119 01233 662002
H S Kang & Co p123 020 8594 5465
King Solicitors p384 020 8571 2239
Lancasters p158 01262 602401
Latimer Lee LLP p358 0161 798 9000
Lawrence & Co p52 020 7266 4333
Lawson Turner & Gilbert p213 01304 226338
Leathes Prior p334 01603 610911
Leigh Turton Dixon p315 01642 241101
Leonard & Co p386 023 8023 3242
Leonard & Co p386 023 8023 4433
Leslie & Co p254 020 8577 5491 / 8572 7252
Duncan Lewis & Co p53 020 7923 4020
Duncan Lewis & Co p53 020 7923 4020
Linder Myers Solicitors p306 0844 984 6000
Robert Lizar p307 0161 226 2319
Robert Lizar p307 0161 860 7797
Lloyd & Associates p55 020 7589 9599
Longfords p340 0161 665 4400
Anthony Louca Solicitors p55 020 7723 9889
Lawrence Lupin p426 020 8733 7200
MKS Solicitors p386 023 8039 6952
McKenzie Bell Solicitors p401 0191 567 4857
Makanda & Co p58 020 7272 8844
Makanda Bart p58 020 8802 0034
Malik & Michael p58 020 7247 8458
Mangala & Kalum Solicitors p58 020 8519 0261
Mayo Wynne Baxter LLP p215 01323 730543
Miles Hutchinson & Lithgow p315 01642 242698
Miles Hutchinson & Lithgow p371 01287 623049 / 622056
Mirza & Co p61 020 8520 4416
Mohammed & Co Solicitors p357 01772 888700
Molesworths Bright Clegg p365 01706 356666
Moss Beachley Mullem & Coleman p62 020 7402 1401 / 7723 5783
Mountain Partnership p62 020 7732 3737
Nandy & Co p63 020 8536 1800
O'Keeffe Solicitors p64 020 7644 8800
Ormerods p205 020 8686 5000
Parker Rhodes Hickmotts p367 01709 511100
Musa A Patel & Co p210 01924 437800
Musa A Patel & Co p154 01274 747777
Patricks Solicitors p66 020 8548 8844
Payne & Gamage p322 01636 640649
James Pearce & Co p141 0121 784 1886
S C Pelentrides & Co p66 020 8365 1688
Pengillys LLP p430 01305 768888
Penningtons p231 01483 791800
Penningtons p66 020 7457 3000
Perera & Co p67 020 8503 0030
Phillips & Co p371 01722 321666
Pickup & Scott p121 01296 397794
Polpitiya & Co p384 020 8813 9282
Powell Spencer & Partners p69 020 7604 5600
QualitySolicitors Jackson & Canter p290 0151 282 1700
Raja & Co p70 020 8772 4900
Ratna & Co p70 020 8470 8818
The Ringrose Law Group - Paul Cooper p151 01205 311511
The Ringrose Law Group - Richard Harwood p285 01522 814700
Rogerson Galvin p120 0161 344 2027 / 335 9005
SFN Solicitors p169 01282 421284
Samars Solicitors p254 020 8570 4716
Scott-Moncrieff Harbour & Sinclair p77 020 7485 5588
Scudamores p439 0844 880 2323
Sehgal & Co p142 0121 772 2226
Selvarajah & Co p77 020 8204 7884
The Sethi Partnership Solicitors p216 020 8866 6464
Sheikh & Co p78 020 7263 5588
Sheikh & Co p78 020 8343 0693
Simply Legal Solicitors p80 020 8514 7734
Geoffrey T Smith & Co p438 01902 426961
Soods Solicitors p261 020 8597 0000
Southerns p321 01282 603663
Southerns p169 01282 438446
Spence & Horne p81 020 8985 2277
J D Spicer & Co p81 020 7625 5590
Sri Kanth & Co p426 020 8795 0648
Sriharans p384 020 8843 9974
Stanley & Co p427 020 8903 7864
Stephens & Scown p222 01392 210700
Stephens & Scown p391 01726 74433
Stephens & Scown p414 01872 265100
Sutovic & Hartigan p84 020 8993 5544
Thompson & Co p87 020 8767 5005
Trinity Solicitors LLP p88 020 7428 0880
Tuckers p88 020 7388 8333
Tyndallwoods p143 0121 624 1111
Tyrer Roxburgh & Co p89 020 8889 3319
Veja and Co Solicitors p385 020 8574 2626
Walter Wilson Richmond p242 020 8427 8484
Warnapala & Co Ltd p385 020 8571 1823
The Watson Ramsbottom Partnership p146 01254 672222
Wilson & Co p92 020 8808 7535
J M Wilson Solicitors p143 0121 356 4556
Woodfines LLP p130 01234 270600

See p603 for the Community Legal Service Work Categories

ZMS Solicitor p281 . . . 0116 247 0790
Zelin & Zelin p94 . . . 020 7262 1405
Ziadies p94 . . . 020 7737 0934

MENTAL HEALTH

AMD Solicitors p160 . . . 0117 923 5562
David Ake & Co p271 . . . 0113 244 8808
Allen Hoole Solicitors p160 . . . 0117 942 0901
Antell & Co p6 . . . 020 8563 0793
APPLEBY HOPE & MATTHEWS p314 . . . 01642 440444
Ashton KCJ p171 . . . 01284 762331
Ashton KCJ p262 . . . 01473 232425
Ashton KCJ p225 . . . 01394 277188
David Auld & Co p319 . . . 01670 505844
Barnes Coleman & Co p131 . . . 01702 558211
Norman H Barnett & Co p11 . . . 020 8471 2112
Alastair Bateman & Co p153 . . . 01274 739973
Beetenson & Gibbon p235 . . . 01472 240251
Ben Hoare Bell & Co p401 . . . 0191 565 3112
Ben Hoare Bell & Co p323 . . . 0191 275 2626
Ben Hoare Bell & Co p401 . . . 0191 565 3112
Richard Best & Co p368 . . . 01788 571135
Best Solicitors p375 . . . 0114 281 3636
Bindmans LLP p12 . . . 020 7833 4433
Birchall Blackburn LLP p356 . . . 01772 561663
Bridge McFarland p284 . . . 01522 518888
ELLIOTT BRIDGMAN p409 . . . 01952 684544
Broudie Jackson Canter p286 . . . 0151 227 1429
Burton & Dyson p228 . . . 01427 610761
Julie Burton p122 . . . 01248 364750
CGM p385 . . . 023 8063 2733
CMHT Solicitors p167 . . . 01543 372347
CMHT Solicitors p420 . . . 01922 646400
CVC Solicitors p346 . . . 01736 362313
Campbell Law Solicitors p316 . . . 0845 226 8118
Campbell-Taylor Solicitors p18 . . . 0845 567 2457
Cartwright King p336 . . . 0115 958 7444
Cartwright King p279 . . . 0116 253 9222
Clark Willis p206 . . . 01325 281111
Clark Willis p183 . . . 01748 830000
Clifford Johnston & Co p302 . . . 0161 249 2700
Clifford Johnston & Co p302 . . . 0161 975 1900
Coffin Mew & Clover p385 . . . 023 8033 4661
Coffin Mew & Clover p354 . . . 023 9238 8021
Coffin Mew & Clover p232 . . . 023 9252 3111
Coffin Mew & Clover p223 . . . 01329 825617
Coles Miller Solicitors LLP p352 . . . 01202 673011
Coles Miller Solicitors LLP p151 . . . 01202 511512
Anthony Collins Solicitors LLP p137 . . . 0121 200 3242
Sharon Coomber p197 . . . 01206 769342
Curwens p218 . . . 020 8363 4444
DLC Solicitors Limited p207 . . . 01254 761234
Dale & Co Solicitors Lincoln p284 . . . 01522 513399
Darbys Solicitors LLP p343 . . . 01865 811700
Dozie & Co p27 . . . 020 8808 2244
David Ede Solicitors p28 . . . 020 8316 4758
Edwards Duthie p260 . . . 020 8514 9000
Edwards Duthie p29 . . . 020 8514 9000
Edwards Duthie p29 . . . 020 8514 9000
Peter Edwards Law p435 . . . 0151 632 6699
R L Edwards & Partners p157 . . . 01656 656861
Elwyn Jones & Co p122 . . . 01248 370224
Fairweather & Co Solicitors p176 . . . 01227 784337
Fieldings Porter p149 . . . 01204 540900
Fish & Co p438 . . . 01902 826464
Fisher Meredith p32 . . . 020 7091 2700
Fosters p334 . . . 01603 620508
John Fowlers LLP Solicitors p197 . . . 01206 576151
John Fowlers LLP Solicitors p159 . . . 01206 302694
Malcolm C Foy & Co p211 . . . 01302 340005
Malcolm C Foy & Co p367 . . . 01709 836866
GHP Legal p442 . . . 01978 291456
GEORGE IDE LLP p192 . . . 01243 786668
Gilbert Stephens p221 . . . 01392 424242
Godloves p273 . . . 0113 225 8811
Gowmans p345 . . . 01803 546100
Grahame Stowe Bateson p274 . . . 0113 246 8163
David Gray Solicitors p324 . . . 0191 232 9547
HC Solicitors LLP p347 . . . 01733 882800
Hadaway & Hadaway p330 . . . 0191 257 0382
Harman & Harman p39 . . . 01227 452977
John F Harrison p118 . . . 01530 563655
Hart Brown Solicitors p437 . . . 0800 068 8177
Harthills p367 . . . 01709 377399
Hay & Kilner p419 . . . 0191 262 8231
Heer Manak p200 . . . 024 7666 4000
Heringtons p243 . . . 01424 434192
Heringtons p215 . . . 01323 411020
Hewitts p330 . . . 01325 316170
Hewitts p144 . . . 01388 604691
Hewitts p206 . . . 01325 468573
Hewitts p203 . . . 01388 762466
Hickman & Rose p41 . . . 020 7700 2211
Hills (Oldham) p340 . . . 0161 652 3231
Holdens p269 . . . 01524 32484
Hornby & Levy p43 . . . 020 7737 0909
Howard & Over p350 . . . 01752 556606
Howells LLP p367 . . . 01709 364000
Howells LLP p376 . . . 0114 249 6666
Henry Hyams p274 . . . 0113 243 2288
Irvings Solicitors p209 . . . 01332 346036
Ison Harrison p228 . . . 0113 286 1455
Ison Harrison p274 . . . 0113 232 6530
Jefferies Essex LLP p428 . . . 01702 332311
Jobling & Knape p319 . . . 01524 416960
Terry Jones Solicitors & Advocates p379 . . . 01743 285888
Terry Jones Solicitors & Advocates p409 . . . 01952 297979
Kaim Todner Ltd p47 . . . 020 7701 4747
Kaim Todner Ltd p47 . . . 020 7353 6660
Kaim Todner Ltd p47 . . . 020 7700 0070
KieranClarkeGreen p192 . . . 01246 211006
KieranClarkeGreen p394 . . . 01246 280099
Larken & Co p322 . . . 01636 703333
Robert Lizar p307 . . . 0161 226 2319
Robert Lizar p307 . . . 0161 860 7797
Llewellyn Jones & Co p369 . . . 01824 704495
MFG Solicitors p409 . . . 01952 641651
McCarthy & White p411 . . . 01454 413696
Tina MacInnes p404 . . . 01929 427227
Mackintosh Duncan p57 . . . 020 7357 6464
Mallia & Co p180 . . . 029 2022 0044
Andrew Markham & Co p182 . . . 01267 221550 / 236199
Mayo Wynne Baxter LLP p215 . . . 01323 730543
Meikles p397 . . . 01740 620255
Meikles p389 . . . 01388 814336
Meikles p226 . . . 01740 652811
Miles & Partners p60 . . . 020 7426 0400
Stuart Miller & Co p61 . . . 020 8888 5225
Morgans p180 . . . 029 2072 9888
Moss Solicitors LLP p293 . . . 01509 217770
Mowbray Woodwards Solicitors p128 . . . 01225 485700
Murrays p148 . . . 01208 72863
Needham Poulier & Partners p63 . . . 020 8808 6622
Alfred Newton & Co p396 . . . 0161 480 6551 / 480 1245
Noble p377 . . . 01462 814055
Nowell Meller Solicitors Limited p393 . . . 01785 252377
O'Donnells p357 . . . 01772 881000
Ormerods p205 . . . 020 8686 5000
Otten Penna Ltd p333 . . . 0161 945 1431
Otten Penna Ltd p308 . . . 0161 248 3660
Oxford Law Group p344 . . . 01865 297300
Pardoes p158 . . . 01278 457891
Pardoes p408 . . . 01823 446200
J Keith Park & Co p391 . . . 01744 636000
Partridge & Wilson p171 . . . 01284 762281
Margaret Payne p182 . . . 01228 521383
Peters & Co p239 . . . 01279 453331
Phillips & Co p371 . . . 01722 321666
Pickup & Scott p121 . . . 01296 397794
Prester Coleman & Co p332 . . . 01604 633133
Pritchard Edwards & Co p182 . . . 01267 234022
Punch Robson p315 . . . 01642 230700
Punch Robson p315 . . . 01642 298830
Punch Robson p397 . . . 01642 754050
QualitySolicitors Gruber Garratt p120 . . . 0161 344 2244
QualitySolicitors Gruber Garratt p341 . . . 0161 665 3502
QualitySolicitors Gruber Garratt p358 . . . 0161 724 0203
QualitySolicitors Gruber Garratt p393 . . . 0161 303 2328
QualitySolicitors Jackson & Canter p290 . . . 0151 282 1700
Quinn Melville p290 . . . 0151 236 3340
Rausa Mumford p180 . . . 029 2034 4341
Rawstorne Heran Solicitors p400 . . . 01789 267646
Red Kite Law p345 . . . 01646 683222
Red Kite Law p244 . . . 01437 763332
Red Kite Law p345 . . . 01646 681529
Red Kite Law p316 . . . 01646 698008
Richmond Anderson Goudie p191 . . . 0191 388 7884
The Ringrose Law Group - Nerina Farmer p381 . . . 01529 301300
The Ringrose Law Group - Paul Cooper p151 . . . 01205 311511
The Ringrose Law Group - Richard Harwood p285 . . . 01522 814700
Roberts Moore Nicholas Jones p134 . . . 0151 647 0000
Roebucks p145 . . . 01254 274000
Rudlings & Wakelam p410 . . . 01842 754151
Rudlings & Wakelam p156 . . . 01842 810300
Rudlings & Wakelam p171 . . . 01284 755771
SFN Solicitors p169 . . . 01282 421284
Samars Solicitors p254 . . . 020 8570 4716
Sanders Witherspoon LLP p156 . . . 01277 221010
Scott-Moncrieff Harbour & Sinclair p77 . . . 020 7485 5588
SILLS & BETTERIDGE LLP p381 . . . 01529 302800
SILLS & BETTERIDGE LLP p285 . . . 01522 542211
SILLS & BETTERIDGE LLP p151 . . . 01205 364615
SILLS & BETTERIDGE LLP p199 . . . 01526 344444
The Smith Partnership p170 . . . 01283 548282
Southerns p169 . . . 01282 422711
Southerns p169 . . . 01282 438446
Steel & Shamash p82 . . . 020 7803 3999
Sternberg Reed p123 . . . 020 8591 3366
Stone Milward Rapers p193 . . . 01243 780211
Swain & Co p386 . . . 023 8063 1111
Swain & Co p244 . . . 023 9248 3322
TBI Solicitors p243 . . . 0800 052 6824 / 01429 264101
TBI Solicitors p123 . . . 01833 638326
TV Edwards LLP p85 . . . 020 7790 7000
TV Edwards LLP p85 . . . 020 7790 7000
Thorpe & Co p372 . . . 01723 364321
Thursfields p440 . . . 01905 730450
Thursfields p266 . . . 01562 820575
Tickle Hall Cross p356 . . . 0800 854379
Timms p170 . . . 01283 561531 / 544417
Timms p209 . . . 01332 364436
Timms Solicitors p404 . . . 01283 214231
Victor Lissack Roscoe & Coleman p89 . . . 020 7487 2505
WBW Solicitors p153 . . . 01626 833263
WBW Solicitors p413 . . . 0870 701 4321
WBW Solicitors p222 . . . 01392 202404
The Walkers Partnership p368 . . . 01763 241121 / 248896
The Walkers Partnership p368 . . . 01763 248896
Andrew Webb p165 . . . 0117 953 8408
Whiskers p239 . . . 01279 439439
Wilson Browne p281 . . . 0116 251 7181
Wilson Browne p425 . . . 01933 279000
Giles Wilson p282 . . . 01702 477106
Withy King Solicitors p128 . . . 01225 425731
Withy King Solicitors p414 . . . 01225 777464
Withy King Solicitors p128 . . . 01225 425731
Withy King Solicitors p407 . . . 01793 536526
Withy King Solicitors p313 . . . 01672 514781
Wolton & Co p207 . . . 01304 389789
Woodfines LLP p130 . . . 01234 270600
Young & Co p398 . . . 01782 339200

PERSONAL INJURY

ASB Law p298 . . . 01622 656500
Abels p385 . . . 023 8022 0317
Abney Garsden McDonald p185 . . . 0161 482 8822
Alderson Dodds p147 . . . 01670 352293
Alexander & Partners p5 . . . 020 8965 7121
Allansons LLP p148 . . . 0161 220 8484
Allen Hoole Solicitors p160 . . . 0117 942 0901
Allington Hughes p190 . . . 01244 312166
Allington Hughes p442 . . . 01978 291000
Ameer Meredith p174 . . . 01223 577077
J M Amin & Co p426 . . . 020 8903 3766
Andrew & Andrew Solicitors p354 . . . 023 9266 1381
Maurice Andrews p135 . . . 0121 554 4900
Thomas Andrews & Partners p442 . . . 01978 291506
Archer & Archer p218 . . . 01353 662203
Archers Law LLP p396 . . . 01642 636500
Arscotts p254 . . . 01273 735289
Ash Clifford p157 . . . 01278 451327
Ashfords LLP p412 . . . 01884 203000
Ashfords LLP p220 . . . 01392 337000
Ashfords LLP p408 . . . 01823 232300
Ashton KCJ p171 . . . 01284 762331
Ashton KCJ p262 . . . 01473 232425
Ashton KCJ p225 . . . 01394 277188
Ashton KCJ p174 . . . 01223 363111
Ashton KCJ p171 . . . 01284 761233
Ashton KCJ p333 . . . 01603 703070
Askew Bunting Solicitors LLP p237 . . . 01287 635151
Askews p362 . . . 01642 475252
Aston Clark p8 . . . 020 8752 1122
Atkins Hope Solicitors p204 . . . 020 8680 5018
Atkinson & Co p328 . . . 01633 251118
Atteys p211 . . . 01302 340400
Atteys p124 . . . 01226 212345
Atteys p363 . . . 01777 713355
Attwaters p294 . . . 020 8508 2111
Attwaters p239 . . . 01279 638888
Attwood & Co p233 . . . 01375 378122 / 378123
Avadis & Co p8 . . . 020 7267 4240
BLB Solicitors p413 . . . 01225 755656
BLB Solicitors p406 . . . 01793 615011
BRM Solicitors p191 . . . 01246 555111
Bakewells p208 . . . 01332 348791
Band Hatton LLP p200 . . . 024 7663 2121
Banks Kelly p9 . . . 020 7248 4231
Banner Jones p191 . . . 01246 560560
Banner Jones p213 . . . 01246 414438
Banner Jones p191 . . . 01246 827516
Banner Jones p192 . . . 01246 861250
Banner Jones p191 . . . 01246 209773
Barcan Woodward p160 . . . 0117 963 5237
Barcan Woodward p161 . . . 0117 925 8080
Barcan Woodward p161 . . . 0117 923 2141
Max Barford & Co p414 . . . 01892 539379
Barker Booth & Eastwood p146 . . . 01253 362500
John Barkers p294 . . . 01507 604773
Barnes & Taylor p387 . . . 01702 347300
Barnes Coleman & Co p131 . . . 01702 558211
Barr Ellison LLP p174 . . . 01223 417200
Barr Ellison LLP p174 . . . 01223 411315
Barratt Goff & Tomlinson p335 . . . 0115 931 5171

Bates N V H *p11* 020 7936 2930
Battens *p212* 01305 250560
Battens *p443* 01935 846000
Battens *p430* 01305 774666
Bawtrees LLP *p435* 01376 513491
Beetenson & Gibbon *p235* 01472 240251
Beevers Solicitors *p119* 0161 339 9697
Bell Lamb & Joynson *p286* 0844 412 4348
Belshaws Solicitors Limited *p395* 0161 477 5377
Ben Hoare Bell & Co *p401* 0191 565 3112
Ben Hoare Bell & Co *p323* 0191 275 2626
Ben Hoare Bell & Co *p401* 0191 516 0466
Bennett Griffin *p441* 01903 229925
Bennett Griffin *p225* 01903 229999
Bennett Griffin *p369* 01903 777690
Bennett Richmond *p270* 01207 521843
Berkeley Solicitors *p213* 0161 371 0011
Berkson Wallace Solicitors *p419* 0151 691 6900
Berkson Wallace Solicitors *p217* 0151 355 4412
Bernard Chill & Axtell *p385* 023 8022 8821
Berry Redmond & Robinson *p429* 01934 619000
Berry Redmond & Robinson *p429* 01934 513963
Best Solicitors *p375* 0114 281 3636
Beswicks *p239* 01782 205000
Beviss & Beckingsale *p373* 01297 626950
Bindmans LLP *p12* 020 7833 4433
Birchall Blackburn LLP *p356* 01772 561663
Bird & Daniels *p378* 01274 580999
Biscoes *p348* 01730 264799
Biscoes *p354* 023 9266 0261
Biscoes *p423* 023 9225 1257
Biscoes *p431* 01329 833249
Biscoes *p232* 023 9251 2030
Biscoes *p353* 023 9237 0634
Blackhurst Budd LLP *p146* 01253 629300
Blake Lapthorn *p184* 023 8090 8090
Blake Lapthorn *p354* 023 9222 1122
Blandy & Blandy *p360* 0118 951 6800
Blaser Mills *p120* 01296 434416
Bobbetts Mackan *p161* 0117 929 9001
Bolitho Way *p354* 023 9282 0747
D S Bosher & Co *p254* 01273 721913
Boyce Hatton *p412* 01803 403403
Boyes Turner *p360* 0118 959 7711
Boys & Maughan *p312* 01843 234000
Brearleys Solicitors *p128* 01924 473065
Brearleys Solicitors *p144* 01924 443900
Brennans Solicitors *p419* 0191 262 5133
Bridge McFarland *p235* 01472 311711
Bridge McFarland *p284* 01522 518888
Bridge McFarland Haddon Owen *p294* 01507 605883
Bridge Sanderson Munro *p411* 01405 814136
Bridge Sanderson Munro *p211* 01302 321621
Bridge Sanderson Munro *p424* 01709 873321
Derrick Bridges & Co *p123* 020 8449 7326
Brighouses *p388* 01704 534101 / 500151
Brightstone Law LLP *p218* 020 8731 3080
Brooke-Taylors *p172* 01298 22741
Brown & Vautier *p227* 01373 465222
Brown Turner Ross *p388* 01704 542002
Bull & Bull *p248* 01227 742660
Burley & Geach *p243* 01428 656011
Burley & Geach *p233* 01428 605355
Burley & Geach *p285* 01428 722334
Burton & Burton Solicitors LLP *p336* 0845 094 2500
Burton & Co LLP *p284* 01522 523215
Burton & Co LLP *p381* 01529 306008 / 306009
BURY & WALKERS LLP *p124* 01226 733533
Kenneth Bush *p266* 01553 692233
Kenneth Bush *p266* 01553 692737
Butcher & Barlow LLP *p170* 0161 764 5141
Byrne Frodsham & Co *p431* 0151 424 5601
CMHT Solicitors *p420* 01922 743525
CMHT Solicitors *p167* 01543 372347
CMHT Solicitors *p420* 01922 646400
Cadmans Law & Property *p195* 01274 874231
Campbell Courtney & Cooney *p173* 01276 25100
Caplans *p241* 020 8864 0111
Carr & Co *p147* 01670 351251
Carr & Co *p231* 0191 284 0363
Carr & Co *p319* 01670 515182
Cartridges *p220* 01392 256854
Cartwright Cunningham Haselgrove & Co *p19* 020 8520 1021
Chadwick Lawrence *p418* 01924 379078
Chadwick Lawrence *p319* 0113 252 3452
Chadwick Lawrence *p238* 01422 330601
Chadwick Lawrence *p255* 01484 519999
Chafes *p433* 01625 531676
Challinors *p427* 0121 553 3211
Challinors *p136* 0121 212 9393
Chambers Fletcher LLP *p333* 01606 780400
Chanter Ferguson *p132* 01237 478751
Charltons Solicitors *p132* 01782 522111
Chattertons Solicitors *p389* 01775 768774
Chattertons Solicitors *p284* 01522 814600
Churchers *p271* 023 9255 1500
Churchers *p232* 023 9260 3400
Clarion Solicitors LLP *p272* 0113 246 0622
Clarkes *p379* 01743 231531
Clarkes *p425* 01952 223548
Clarkes *p409* 01952 291666
Clarkson Hirst *p269* 01524 39760
Clifford Johnston & Co *p302* 0161 249 2700
Clifford Johnston & Co *p302* 0161 975 1900
Clifford Poole & Co *p370* 0161 736 0160
Douglas Clift & Co *p269* 01524 32437
Coffin Mew & Clover *p385* 023 8033 4661
Coffin Mew & Clover *p354* 023 9238 8021
Coffin Mew & Clover *p232* 023 9252 3111
Coffin Mew & Clover *p223* 01329 825617
Colebournes Solicitors and Advocates *p146* 01253 293195
Coles Miller Solicitors LLP *p352* 01202 673011
Coles Miller Solicitors LLP *p151* 01202 511512
Anthony Collins Solicitors LLP *p137* 0121 200 3242
Collins Solicitors *p423* 01923 223324
K J Commons & Co *p440* 01900 604698
K J Commons & Co *p182* 01228 822666
Cooper Lingard *p282* 01702 715411
Cooper Sons Hartley & Williams *p184* 01298 812138
Copleys *p258* 01480 456191
Cornfield Law *p215* 01323 412512
Cowlishaw & Mountford *p417* 01889 565211
Cozens-Hardy LLP *p334* 01603 625231
Martin Cray & Co *p159* 01273 673226
Charles Crookes & Jones *p172* 029 2086 0628
Cross Solicitors *p199* 01244 822101
Cuttle & Co *p302* 0161 835 2050
DBL Talbots LLP *p197* 01902 843427
DBL Talbots LLP *p437* 01902 427561
DFA Law LLP *p331* 01604 609560
DFA Law LLP *p331* 01604 609560
DP Law Ltd t/a David Prosser & Co *p157* 01656 645921
Darbys Solicitors LLP *p343* 01865 811700
W H Darbyshire & Son *p146* 01253 346646
Darling & Stephensons *p206* 01325 489000
David & Snape *p353* 01656 782070 / 785038
Davies & Partners *p230* 01452 612345
Davies & Partners *p115* 01454 619619
Davies Parsons Allchurch *p292* 01554 749144
Davies Sully Wilkins *p172* 029 2088 7828
Davis Wood *p162* 0117 965 3504
Daybells LLP *p26* 020 8555 4321
Denby & Co *p416* 01229 582283
Desor & Co *p245* 020 8569 0708
Devonalds *p412* 01443 434343
Dibbens *p433* 01202 882456
Dickinson Manser *p352* 01202 673071
Dickinsons *p146* 01253 781010
Dicksons Solicitors Ltd *p397* 01782 262424
Dicksons Solicitors Ltd *p397* 01782 262424
Dixon Stewart *p321* 01425 621515
Dixon Stewart Solicitors *p250* 01425 279222
Dodds & Partners *p279* 0116 253 8585
Donnelly McArdle Adamson *p206* 01325 482299
Donns *p303* 0161 834 3311
Dorians *p208* 01332 680580
Douglas-Jones Mercer *p405* 01792 650000
Dowse & Co *p27* 020 7254 6205
Draycott Browne Solicitors *p303* 0161 228 2244
Driver Belcher Solicitors *p144* 01489 892101 / 892102
Scott Duff & Co *p182* 01228 531054
Scott Duff & Co *p346* 01768 865551
Peter Dunn & Co *p401* 0191 568 9000
Dunning & Co *p28* 020 7733 6217
Thomas Dunton Solicitors *p342* 01689 822554
Dutton Gregory *p385* 023 8022 1344
Eaton & Few *p391* 01480 301558
Eaton Smith LLP *p255* 01484 821300
Eddowes Waldron *p208* 01332 348484
Edwards Duthie *p260* 020 8514 9000
Edwards Duthie *p29* 020 8514 9000
Edwards Duthie *p29* 020 8514 9000
R L Edwards & Partners *p157* 01656 656861
R L Edwards & Partners *p413* 01443 775000
Thomas Eggar LLP *p441* 01903 234411
Thomas Eggar LLP *p202* 01293 742700
Thomas Eggar LLP *p192* 01243 786111
Elliot Mather LLP *p192* 01246 231288
Ellis-Fermor & Negus *p364* 01773 744744
Ellis-Fermor & Negus *p130* 0115 922 1591
Eric Robinson Solicitors *p184* 023 8025 4676
Eric Robinson Solicitors *p385* 023 8042 5000
The Eric Whitehead Partnership *p185* 01538 755761
Everett Tomlin Lloyd & Pratt *p352* 01495 763333
Eversheds LLP *p174* 0845 497 9797
Everys *p380* 01395 577983
Everys *p342* 01404 813446
Everys *p252* 01404 41221
Everys *p222* 01395 264384
Everys *p373* 01297 21105
Everys *p221* 01392 477983
Fairweather Stephenson & Co *p282* 01728 832832
Farnfield & Nicholls *p374* 01747 854244
Fernando & Co *p31* 020 8767 4611
A J Field & Co *p375* 01795 580600
Field Overell *p270* 01926 422101
Finn Gledhill *p238* 01422 330000
Paul Finn Solicitors *p168* 01288 356256
Fisher Jones Greenwood LLP *p186* 01245 890110
Fisher Jones Greenwood LLP *p197* 01206 578282
Fitzhugh Gates *p159* 01273 686811
Fitzhugh Gates *p378* 01273 461381
Fletcher Dervish *p33* 020 8800 4615
Fletchers *p388* 01704 546919
Flint Bishop Solicitors *p208* 01332 340211
Fonseca & Partners *p216* 01495 303124
Foot Anstey *p408* 01823 625600
Forbes *p145* 01254 54374
Forbes *p114* 01254 872111
Forbes *p356* 01772 220022
John Ford Solicitors *p33* 020 8800 6464
Ford Simey LLP *p221* 01392 274126
Ford Simey LLP *p380* 01395 577061 / 0800 169 3741
Ford Simey LLP *p222* 01395 272241 / 0800 169 3741
Forshaws Davies Ridgway LLP *p227* 01928 739300
Forster Dean Ltd *p431* 0151 495 3270
Forster Dean Ltd *p369* 01928 590999
Foster & Partners *p162* 0117 961 5300
Foster & Partners *p162* 0117 922 0229
Fosters *p334* 01603 620508
Fosters *p168* 01986 895251
John Fowlers LLP Solicitors *p197* 01206 576151
Malcolm C Foy & Co *p211* 01302 340005
Malcolm C Foy & Co *p367* 01709 836866
Franklins LLP *p332* 01604 828282
Fraser Dawbarns *p435* 01945 461456
Fraser Dawbarns *p266* 01553 666600
Fraser Dawbarns *p213* 01366 383171
Freeman Johnson *p206* 01325 466221
Freeman Johnson *p214* 0191 386 4843 / 386 9619
Freemans *p324* 0191 222 1030
Freer & Archer *p279* 0116 241 3199
Freeth Cartwright LLP *p279* 0116 248 1100
Michael Friend *p220* 01372 468098
GH Cornish LLP *p260* 020 8090 0800
GLP Solicitors *p315* 0161 653 6295
GLP Solicitors *p304* 0161 834 6721
GLP Solicitors *p357* 0161 773 8626
GLP Solicitors *p304* 0161 793 0901
Gabb & Co *p203* 01873 810629
Gadsby Wicks *p186* 01245 494929
Gangar & Co *p427* 0121 553 4166
Gardner Leader LLP *p410* 01635 508080
Gardner Leader LLP *p322* 01635 508080
Garner & Hancock Solicitors LLP *p263* 020 8232 9560
Gartsides *p328* 01633 213411
Gaynor-Smith Owen & Co *p300* 01684 560771
Geldards LLP *p178* 029 2023 8239
George H Coles & Co *p254* 01273 205101
GEORGE IDE LLP *p192* 01243 786668
Gilbert Turner Coomber *p35* 020 8520 5886
David Gist Solicitors *p162* 0117 927 9111
Gittins McDonald *p442* 01978 291662
Glaisyers *p138* 0121 233 2971
Glanvilles *p244* 023 9249 2300
Glanvilles *p328* 01983 527878
Godloves *p273* 0113 225 8864
Godloves *p273* 0113 225 8874
Goldstones *p405* 01792 643021
Gordons LLP *p273* 0113 227 0100
Gosschalks *p256* 01482 324252
H F T Gough & Co *p431* 01946 692461
Goughs *p210* 01380 726913
Graham & Rosen *p257* 01482 323123
Grants Solicitors *p205* 020 8288 8899
David Gray Solicitors *p324* 0191 232 9547
Graysons *p375* 0114 272 9184
Graystons *p435* 0151 645 0055
Adam F Greenhalgh & Co *p149* 0845 074 3491
Gregory Abrams Davidson LLP *p288* 0151 236 5000
Griffiths & Hughes Parry *p252* 01352 711815 / 711945
The Gwyn George Partnership *p113* 01685 874629 / 871133
The Gwyn George Partnership *p314* 01685 377035
HC Solicitors LLP *p347* 01733 882800
hlw Keeble Hawson LLP *p375* 0114 272 2061
Hadaway & Hadaway *p330* 0191 257 0382
Hadgkiss Hughes & Beale *p138* 0121 449 5050
Frederic Hall *p227* 01303 851185
Frederic Hall *p213* 01304 202411
Hallam-Peel & Co *p38* 020 3006 1661
HallmarkHulme *p439* 01905 726600
Hamers Solicitors *p257* 01482 326666
Hansells *p203* 01263 512003
Hansells *p334* 01603 615731
Hansells *p331* 01692 404351
Hansells *p121* 01263 734313
Hansells *p378* 01263 822176
Harding Evans LLP *p328* 01633 244233
Harding Swinburne Jackson & Co *p401* 0191 565 8194

See p603 for the Community Legal Service Work Categories

Hardmans *p207* 01304 373377
Harman & Harman *p39* 01227 452977
Harris Cartier LLP *p382* 01753 810710
Christopher Harris & Co *p375* 01795 661521
Christopher Harris & Co *p380* 01795 437268
David W Harris & Co *p352* 01443 486666
Leslie Harris Solicitors & Advocates *p297* 01253 724974
Harrison Clark LLP *p439* 01905 612001
Harrison Clark LLP *p439* 01905 612001
Harrison Clark LLP *p188* 01242 269198
HARRISONS SOLICITORS LLP *p425* 01938 552545
Hart Brown Solicitors *p202* 0800 068 8177
Hart Brown Solicitors *p437* 0800 068 8177
Hart Brown Solicitors *p231* 0800 068 8177
Hart Brown Solicitors *p236* 0800 068 8177
Hart Brown Solicitors *p196* 0800 068 8177
Charles Hart Solicitors *p186* 01934 742315
Edward Harte LLP *p159* 01273 662750
Harvey Ingram Borneos *p130* 01234 353221
Harvey Ingram Borneos *p317* 01908 696002
Harvey Ingram LLP *p280* 0116 254 5454
Hatchers Solicitors LLP *p379* 01743 248545
Hathaways *p228* 0191 477 2288
Hatten Wyatt *p232* 01474 351199
Hawley & Rodgers *p337* 0115 955 9000
Hawley & Rodgers *p293* 01509 230333
Hay & Kilner *p325* 0191 232 8345
Hayes & Storr *p378* 01263 825959
Edward Hayes LLP *p192* 01243 781431
Edward Hayes LLP *p148* 01243 822655
Edward Hayes LLP *p192* 01243 672124
Edward Hayes LLP *p285* 01903 759024
Edward Hayes LLP *p244* 023 9247 9872
Heckford Norton *p283* 01462 682244
Heer Manak *p200* 024 7666 4000
Hellewell Pasley & Brewer *p128* 01924 472596
Hellewell Pasley & Brewer *p210* 01924 455515
Henriques Griffiths *p163* 0117 909 4000
Henriques Griffiths *p435* 01454 854000
Henrys Solicitors Ltd *p395* 01663 742222
Henrys Solicitors Ltd *p355* 01625 630880
Heptonstalls LLP *p231* 01405 765661
Hereward & Foster *p41* 020 7476 6600
Herrington & Carmichael LLP *p437* 0118 977 4045
Herrington & Carmichael LLP *p173* 01276 686222
Hetts *p373* 01724 843287
Hetts *p373* 01724 270290
Hewetts *p361* 0118 957 5337
Hewitts *p330* 01325 316170
Hewitts *p144* 01388 604691
Hewitts *p206* 01325 468573
Hewitts *p203* 01388 762466
Heyes Samuel *p369* 01983 615615
Hickman & Rose *p41* 020 7700 2211
Michael Hill Partnership *p280* 0116 254 1609
HilliersHRW Solicitors *p264* 01234 858000
Hoben Johnson *p369* 01933 411375
HODGE JONES & ALLEN LLP *p41* 020 7874 8300
Hodgson Coulthard & Co *p253* 0191 584 3333
Holden & Co *p243* 01424 722422
Holdens *p269* 01524 32484
Hood Vores & Allwood *p209* 01362 692424
Hopkins *p311* 01623 468468
Hopkins *p311* 01623 460460
Hornby Baker Jones & Wood *p328* 01633 262848
Thomas Horton LLP *p167* 01527 871641
Howe & Co *p43* 020 8840 4688
Howells *p178* 029 2040 4020
Howells *p172* 029 2086 7111
Howells *p405* 01792 410016
Howells *p407* 01443 230411
Howells *p328* 01633 227960
Howells LLP *p367* 01709 364000
Howells LLP *p376* 0114 249 6666
Hugh James *p179* 029 2022 4871
J W Hughes & Co *p199* 01492 596596
J W Hughes & Co *p291* 01492 874774
Humphrys & Co *p363* 01745 343158
Hunt & Hunt *p366* 01708 764433
Hutchins & Co *p44* 020 8986 3911
Hutchinson Thomas *p320* 01639 645061
Hutton's *p179* 029 2037 8621
Henry Hyams *p274* 0113 243 2288
Inghams *p411* 01253 824111
Inghams *p226* 01253 873481
Darryl Ingram & Co *p45* 020 8202 0843
Irwin Mitchell LLP *p376* 0870 150 0100
Irwin Mitchell LLP *p274* 0870 150 0100
Ison Harrison *p228* 0113 286 1455
Ison Harrison *p274* 0113 232 6530
Ison Harrison *p274* 0113 284 5000
JMD Law Limited *p179* 029 2045 6780
JMW Solicitors *p306* 0845 872 6666
JNP Legal *p314* 01685 350421
JNP Legal *p320* 01443 450561
Jackamans *p225* 01394 279636
Andrew Jackson *p257* 01482 325242
Jacobs & Reeves *p353* 01202 674425
Jefferies Essex LLP *p428* 01702 332311
Jewels Solicitors *p393* 01785 602030
Jobling Gowler *p297* 01625 614250
Johar & Co *p280* 0116 254 3345
Johnson & Gaunt *p122* 01295 256271 / 271200
T Llewellyn Jones *p320* 01639 643635
Jordans *p210* 01924 457171
Jordans *p183* 01977 518778
Jordans *p418* 01924 387110
Josiah Hincks *p280* 0116 255 1811
Judge & Priestley *p166* 020 8290 0333
Keene & Kelly *p318* 01352 753882
Kelcey & Hall *p163* 0117 927 9604
Kennards Wells *p48* 020 8539 8338
Keppe Rofer *p156* 01874 624627
Kerseys *p262* 01473 213311
Kerwoods *p362* 01527 584444
Kidd Rapinet *p382* 0845 017 9638
Kidd Rapinet *p298* 0845 017 9608
Kidd Rapinet *p121* 0845 017 9616
KieranClarkeGreen *p394* 01246 280099
Kingsfords *p119* 01233 665544
Kingsfords *p119* 01233 624545
Kingswell Berney *p232* 023 9258 2211
Kirby Sheppard *p411* 0845 840 0045
Kirby Sheppard *p268* 0845 840 0045
Kitsons LLP *p413* 01803 202020
Kitsons LLP *p329* 01626 203366
Kitsons LLP *p221* 01392 455555
Kitsons LLP *p350* 01752 603040
Knowles Benning *p295* 01582 798000
LDJ Solicitors *p339* 024 7674 5000
LD Law *p239* 01279 441266
Laceys *p353* 01202 743286
Laceys *p152* 01202 557256
Lancasters *p158* 01262 602401
Bruce Lance & Co *p250* 01494 450494
Langleys *p445* 01904 610886
Lansbury Worthington *p51* 020 8563 9797
Lanyon Bowdler LLP *p379* 01743 280280
Lanyon Bowdler LLP *p342* 01691 652241
Lanyon Bowdler LLP *p409* 01952 291222
Lanyon Bowdler LLP *p425* 01952 244721
Larcomes LLP *p354* 023 9266 1531
Larcomes LLP *p423* 023 9224 6666
Last Cawthra Feather LLP *p121* 01274 583106
Law Hurst & Taylor *p428* 01702 337864
Lawrence & Co *p52* 020 7266 4333
Lawrence Law *p52* 020 8788 0055
Layton & Co *p244* 01437 766671
Leathes Prior *p334* 01603 610911
Lee & Priestley LLP *p275* 0845 129 2300
Lees Solicitors LLP *p428* 0151 625 9364
Lees Solicitors LLP *p249* 0151 342 6273
Lees Solicitors LLP *p134* 0151 647 9381
LEIGH DAY & CO *p52* 020 7650 1200
Leigh Turton Dixon *p315* 01642 241101
Leport & Co *p122* 01295 257328 / 268181
Lester Morrill *p275* 0113 245 8549
Letchers *p364* 01425 471424
Levi Solicitors LLP *p275* 0113 244 9931
Lewis & Lines *p113* 01495 212286
Lichfield Reynolds *p398* 01782 313212
Linder Myers Solicitors *p307* 0844 984 6400
Linder Myers Solicitors *p306* 0844 984 6000
Linskills Solicitors *p289* 0151 236 2224
The Lister Croft Partnership *p358* 0113 257 0526
Longden Walker & Renney *p401* 0191 567 7024
Lorimers *p168* 01280 812132 / 813405
Lucas & Wyllys *p294* 01502 500123
Lucas & Wyllys *p234* 01493 855555
Lucas & Wyllys *p234* 01493 663124
Charles Lucas & Marshall *p322* 01635 521212
MFG Solicitors *p265* 01562 820181
MFG Solicitors *p167* 01527 831691
MSB Solicitors LLP *p289* 0151 281 9040
MWP Solicitors *p126* 01268 527131
MWRLaw Ltd *p357* 01772 254201
McCormicks *p240* 01423 530630
McKenzie Bell Solicitors *p401* 0191 567 4857
McKinnells *p284* 01522 541181
McMillan Williams *p199* 020 8668 4131
McMillan Williams *p419* 020 8669 4962
McMillan Williams *p205* 01689 848311
McMillan Williams *p411* 020 8653 8844
McMillan Williams *p383* 020 8253 7600
Marchant Harries & Co *p113* 01685 885500
Marchant Harries & Co *p319* 01443 476444
Marchants Solicitors *p312* 01623 655111
MARTIN-KAYE LLP *p409* 01952 272222
MARTYN PROWEL *p180* 029 2047 0909
Mason Baggott & Garton *p219* 01427 872661
Matthew Arnold & Baldwin LLP *p423* 01923 202020
T A Matthews *p248* 01432 352121
Maxwell Gillott (MG Law Ltd) *p270* 0844 858 3900
Mayo Wynne Baxter LLP *p215* 01323 730543
Mayo Wynne Baxter LLP *p160* 01273 775533
Mayo Wynne Baxter LLP *p283* 01273 477071
Mayo Wynne Baxter LLP *p373* 01323 891412
Meesons *p364* 01425 472315
Hilary Meredith Solicitors *p433* 01625 539922
Metcalfe Copeman & Pettefar *p435* 01945 464331
Metcalfe Copeman & Pettefar *p410* 01842 756100
Metcalfe Copeman & Pettefar *p266* 01553 778102
Metcalfe Copeman & Pettefar *p347* 01733 865880
Metcalfes *p164* 0117 929 0451
Michelmores LLP *p221* 01392 688688
Milburns Solicitors *p440* 01900 67363
Miller Gardner *p307* 0161 877 4777
Millichips *p382* 0121 624 4000
Millichips *p427* 0121 500 6363
Mills Chody LLP *p265* 020 8909 0400
Mincoffs Solicitors LLP *p325* 0191 281 6151
Mintons *p275* 0113 245 7575
Morecrofts Solicitors LLP *p290* 0151 236 8871
Morgan Jones & Pett *p335* 01603 877000
Morgans *p180* 029 2072 9888
Morris Scott & Co *p194* 01425 278866
Moseleys *p284* 01543 414100
Moss & Haselhurst *p435* 01606 592159
Moss Beachley Mullem & Coleman *p62* 020 7402 1401 / 7723 5783
E J Moyle *p285* 01903 725143
Stephen Mullarkey Solicitors *p226* 01352 733770
Mustoe Shorter *p430* 01305 752700
Myers Lister Price *p117* 0161 926 9969
Nalders Quality Solicitors *p414* 01872 241414
Nalders Quality Solicitors *p223* 01326 313441
Nalders Quality Solicitors *p173* 01209 714278
Nalders Quality Solicitors *p329* 01637 871414
Nelsons *p338* 0115 958 6262
Newbys *p315* 01642 247717 / 247967
Alfred Newton & Co *p433* 01625 523647
Alfred Newton & Co *p396* 0161 480 6551 / 480 1245
Alfred Newton & Co *p396* 0161 430 8831
NIGHTINGALES SOLICITORS LIMITED *p396* 01663 764038
NORRIE WAITE & SLATER *p377* 0114 276 6166
North Ainley Halliwell *p341* 0161 624 5614
North Yorkshire Law *p372* 01723 360001
Norton Peskett *p129* 01502 718700
Norton Peskett *p294* 01502 533000
OGR Stock Denton *p64* 020 8349 0321
Michael Oerton *p125* 01271 378686
Ogden Lyles & Fox *p216* 0161 789 2793
OGLETHORPE STURTON & GILLIBRAND *p268* 01524 271388
Oldhams Solicitors & Advocates *p121* 01462 895444
Overburys & Raymond Thompson *p335* 01603 610481
Owen White & Catlin *p225* 020 8890 2836
Painters *p266* 01562 822295
Painters *p399* 01299 822033
Pannone LLP *p308* 0161 909 3000
Pardoes *p158* 01278 457891
Pardoes *p408* 01823 446200
Park Woodfine Heald Mellows LLP *p130* 01234 400000
Parker Rhodes Hickmotts *p367* 01709 511100
Parkinson Wright LLP *p440* 01905 726789
Parlett Kent *p66* 020 7430 0712
Parlett Kent *p222* 01392 494455
Parnalls Solicitors Limited *p270* 01566 772375
Partridge & Wilson *p171* 01284 762281
Passmore Lewis & Jacobs *p126* 01446 721000
Patchell Davies (Trading Name of PD Law Ltd) *p147* 01495 227128
Pattinson & Brewer *p445* 01904 680000
Payne & Gamage *p322* 01636 640649
Bernard Pearce & Co *p219* 020 8804 5271
Pearson Hinchliffe *p341* 0161 785 3500
Pengillys LLP *p430* 01305 768888
Penmans *p394* 01375 677777
Penningtons *p231* 01483 791800
David Phillips & Partners *p150* 0151 922 5525
Samuel Phillips Law Firm *p326* 0191 232 8451
Pickering & Butters *p368* 01889 803080
John Pickering & Partners LLP *p238* 0808 144 0959
Pictons Solicitors LLP *p295* 01582 870870
Pictons Solicitors LLP *p317* 01908 663511
Pictons Solicitors LLP *p247* 01442 242441
Pinkney Grunwells Lawyers LLP *p158* 01262 673445
Platt Halpern *p308* 0161 224 2555
Pluck Andrew & Co *p120* 0161 330 2875
Pluck Andrew & Co *p259* 0161 368 6311
Poole Alcock *p320* 01270 625478
Poole & Co *p203* 01460 279100
Porter Dodson *p425* 01823 666622
Porter Dodson *p408* 01823 625800
Porter Dodson *p444* 01935 424581
Potter Rees (Serious Injury) Solicitors *p309* 0161 237 5888
Powell Spencer & Partners *p69* 020 7604 5600
Powells *p429* 01934 623501
Pritchard Englefield *p69* 020 7972 9720

QualitySolicitors Gruber Garratt *p358* . . . 0161 724 0203
QualitySolicitors Gruber Garratt *p393* . . . 0161 303 2328
RJR Solicitors *p227* . . . 01983 752115
RJR Solicitors *p369* . . . 01983 562201
RJR Solicitors *p328* . . . 01983 526924
Donald Race & Newton *p169* . . . 01282 433241
Donald Race & Newton *p198* . . . 01282 864500
Raleys *p125* . . . 01226 211111
Ramsdens Solicitors *p251* . . . 01484 690040
Ramsdens Solicitors *p256* . . . 01484 821500
Ramsdens Solicitors *p210* . . . 01924 455391
Red Kite Law *p410* . . . 01834 842122
Red Kite Law *p183* . . . 01267 239000
Red Kite Law *p345* . . . 01646 683222
Red Kite Law *p244* . . . 01437 763332
Red Kite Law *p345* . . . 01646 681529
Red Kite Law *p316* . . . 01646 698008
Reynolds Parry-Jones *p250* . . . 01494 525941
Richmond Anderson Goudie *p191* . . . 0191 388 7884
Ridley & Hall *p256* . . . 01484 538421
Lee Rigby Partnership *p283* . . . 01772 421748
Stephen Rimmer LLP *p216* . . . 01323 644222
Risdon Hosegood *p433* . . . 01984 632277
Risdon Hosegood *p318* . . . 01643 703123 / 700008
Roach Pittis *p328* . . . 01983 524431
D P Roberts Hughes & Denye *p134* . . . 0151 647 6000
Robinson Allfree *p359* . . . 01843 592361
Robinson Allfree *p166* . . . 01843 865261
Paul Robinson Solicitors *p428* . . . 01702 338338
Robinsons *p209* . . . 01332 291431
Roland Robinsons & Fentons LLP *p147* . . . 01253 621432
Rowberry Morris *p361* . . . 0118 958 5611
Rowbis Solicitors *p230* . . . 01452 301903
Rowntree & Berry *p226* . . . 01253 872581
Rowntree & Berry *p355* . . . 01253 893599
Royds LLP *p74* . . . 020 7583 2222
Rudlings & Wakelam *p410* . . . 01842 754151
Rudlings & Wakelam *p171* . . . 01284 755771
Russell & Russell *p171* . . . 0161 762 2888
RUSSELL-COOKE LLP *p74* . . . 020 8789 9111
Russell Jones & Walker *p164* . . . 0117 374 2222
Russell Jones & Walker *p74* . . . 020 7657 1555
Russell Jones & Walker *p419* . . . 01924 234300
Russell Jones & Walker *p141* . . . 0121 233 8300
Russell Jones & Walker *p309* . . . 0161 383 3500
Russell Jones & Walker *p377* . . . 0114 276 6868
Russell Jones & Walker *p326* . . . 0191 323 3000
Russell Jones & Walker *p180* . . . 029 2026 2800
Rutherfords *p407* . . . 01827 311411
SA Law *p390* . . . 01727 798000
SAS Daniels LLP *p297* . . . 01625 442100
SJP Solicitors *p258* . . . 01485 532662
Sainsburys *p208* . . . 0161 336 7027
Salmons *p398* . . . 01782 639827
Salmons *p323* . . . 01782 621266
Sanders Witherspoon LLP *p156* . . . 01277 221010
Saulet & Co *p389* . . . 023 9281 9442
Seddon Thomson *p309* . . . 0161 720 8000
John D Sellars & Co *p403* . . . 020 8661 7014
The Sethi Partnership Solicitors *p216* . . . 020 8866 6464
Shakespeares *p339* . . . 0115 945 3700
Sharman Law *p130* . . . 01234 303030
Sharp & Partners *p339* . . . 0115 959 0055
Sheltons *p255* . . . 0115 955 3444
Sheltons *p339* . . . 0115 955 3444
Sheltons *p339* . . . 0115 955 3444
Shentons *p434* . . . 01962 844544
Shepherd Harris & Co *p219* . . . 020 8363 8341
Sheridan & Co *p267* . . . 020 8541 1181
Silks *p340* . . . 0121 511 2233
Silks *p321* . . . 01384 236101
SILLS & BETTERIDGE LLP *p381* . . . 01529 302800
SILLS & BETTERIDGE LLP *p285* . . . 01522 542211
SILLS & BETTERIDGE LLP *p151* . . . 01205 364615
Slee Blackwell *p125* . . . 01271 372128
Slee Blackwell *p222* . . . 01392 423000
Smith Llewelyn Partnership *p405* . . . 01792 464444
The Smith Partnership *p170* . . . 01283 536471
The Smith Partnership *p404* . . . 01283 226444
The Smith Partnership *p398* . . . 01782 324454
Smith Solicitor LLP *p238* . . . 01422 383380
W F Smith LLP *p209* . . . 01362 852900
Solomon Levy *p295* . . . 01582 425817 / 414948
Southern Stewart & Walker *p384* . . . 0191 427 0770
Southerns *p169* . . . 01282 422711
Irena Spence *p175* . . . 01223 713300
Spencer Skuse *p181* . . . 029 2034 3993
Standley & Co *p269* . . . 01564 776287
Steel & Shamash *p82* . . . 020 7803 3999
Steele Raymond *p152* . . . 01202 294566
Stephens & Scown *p222* . . . 01392 210700
Stephens & Scown *p391* . . . 01726 74433
Stephens & Scown *p414* . . . 01872 265100
Stephens McDonald & Robson *p327* . . . 0191 232 0675
Stephensons Solicitors LLP *p282* . . . 01942 777777
Stephensons Solicitors LLP *p391* . . . 01942 777777
Stephensons Solicitors LLP *p432* . . . 01942 777777
Stephensons Solicitors LLP *p282* . . . 01942 777777
Stewarts Law LLP *p83* . . . 020 7822 8000
Harold Stock & Co *p120* . . . 01457 838136
Stokes Solicitors *p355* . . . 023 9282 8131
Stone King LLP *p128* . . . 01225 337599
STONE ROWE BREWER LLP *p416* . . . 020 8891 6141
Stones Solicitors LLP *p340* . . . 01837 650200
Stones Solicitors LLP *p222* . . . 01392 666777
Swain & Co *p386* . . . 023 8063 1111
Swain & Co *p244* . . . 023 9248 3322
Swinburne & Jackson LLP *p423* . . . 0191 416 0004
Swinburne & Jackson LLP *p191* . . . 0191 388 7221
Swinburne Maddison *p214* . . . 0191 384 2441 / 384 7455
TBI Solicitors *p243* . . . 0800 052 6824 / 01429 264101
TV Edwards LLP *p85* . . . 020 7790 7000
TV Edwards LLP *p85* . . . 020 7790 7000
Tait Farrier Graham *p327* . . . 0191 272 3713
Talbot Walker LLP *p118* . . . 01264 363354
Talbot Walker LLP *p127* . . . 01256 332404
Tallents Solicitors *p322* . . . 01636 671881
Tallents Solicitors *p312* . . . 01623 666700
Tanner & Taylor LLP *p115* . . . 01252 316565
Tarbox Robinson & Partners *p333* . . . 01923 836595
Taylor & Emmet LLP *p377* . . . 0114 218 4000
Taylor Lewis *p181* . . . 01239 621999
Michael Taylor & Associates *p417* . . . 0161 746 7776
Taylor Vinters *p176* . . . 01223 423444
Taylor Walton LLP *p239* . . . 01582 765111
Taylor Walton LLP *p295* . . . 01582 731161
Taylor Walton LLP *p390* . . . 01727 845245
Temperley Taylor LLP *p315* . . . 0161 643 2411
Temple Heelis LLP *p264* . . . 01539 723757
Tennant & Knight *p160* . . . 01273 202050
Terrells LLP *p347* . . . 01733 896789
Thackray Williams *p167* . . . 020 8290 0440
Thompson & Co *p402* . . . 0191 565 6290
Thompson Smith & Puxon *p198* . . . 01206 574431
Thompsons (formerly Robin/Brian Thompson & Partners) *p181* . . . 029 2044 5300
Thompsons (formerly Robin/Brian Thompson & Partners) *p377* . . . 0114 270 3300
Thompsons (formerly Robin/Brian Thompson & Partners) *p277* . . . 0113 205 6300
Thompsons (formerly Robin/Brian Thompson & Partners) *p165* . . . 0117 304 2400
Thomson Snell & Passmore *p415* . . . 01892 510000
Richard Thorn & Co *p160* . . . 01273 625600
Thorpe & Co *p430* . . . 01947 603465
Thorpe & Co *p226* . . . 01723 515555
Thrings LLP *p128* . . . 01225 340000
Thrings LLP *p406* . . . 01793 410800
Tilley & Co *p390* . . . 01727 840467
Tilly Bailey & Irvine LLP *p397* . . . 01642 673797
Timms *p170* . . . 01283 561531 / 544417
Toller Beattie LLP *p125* . . . 01271 341000
Tozers *p329* . . . 01626 207020
Tozers *p409* . . . 01626 772376
Tozers *p222* . . . 01392 207020
Tozers *p350* . . . 01752 206460
Tracey Barlow Furniss & Co *p441* . . . 01909 472355
Tracey Barlow Furniss & Co *p363* . . . 01777 707677
Tranters *p310* . . . 0161 998 9999
Treasures *p230* . . . 01452 525351
Alison Trent & Co *p88* . . . 020 7583 3350
Trobridges *p412* . . . 01752 812787
Trobridges *p350* . . . 01752 664022
Turnbull Garrard *p379* . . . 01743 350851 / 351332
Turner & Wall *p264* . . . 01535 607831
Turner Pearson *p357* . . . 01772 562222
Veale Wasbrough Vizards *p165* . . . 0117 925 2020
WBW Solicitors *p329* . . . 01626 202404
WBW Solicitors *p153* . . . 01626 833263
WBW Solicitors *p413* . . . 0870 701 4321
WBW Solicitors *p222* . . . 01392 202404
Waddington & Son *p169* . . . 01282 426666
Waldron & Schofield *p249* . . . 01706 624029
Waldrons *p268* . . . 01384 811811
Walker & Co *p367* . . . 01709 817112
The Walkers Partnership *p368* . . . 01763 241121 / 248896
The Walkers Partnership *p368* . . . 01763 248896
Waller Needham & Green *p347* . . . 01733 311422
Walters & Barbary *p173* . . . 01209 712454
Wansbroughs *p314* . . . 01225 703222
Ward Hadaway *p327* . . . 0191 204 4000
Wards Solicitors *p165* . . . 0117 929 2811
Wards Solicitors *p429* . . . 01934 413535
Wards Solicitors *p394* . . . 0117 943 4800
Wards Solicitors *p429* . . . 01934 428811
Wards Solicitors *p165* . . . 01454 204880
Wards Solicitors *p443* . . . 01454 316789
Waring & Co *p124* . . . 0870 444 2782
Warner Goodman LLP *p387* . . . 023 8063 9311
Warner Goodman LLP *p224* . . . 01329 288121
Watkins & Gunn *p352* . . . 01495 762244
Watson Burton LLP *p327* . . . 0845 901 2100
The Watson Ramsbottom Partnership *p234* . . . 01254 884422 / 883020
Watson Woodhouse *p397* . . . 01642 247656
V G Waugh *p348* . . . 0191 527 2727
Whetter Duckworth Fowler *p266* . . . 01865 842100
Whiskers *p219* . . . 01992 561111
Whiskers *p239* . . . 01279 439439
Whitemans *p231* . . . 01452 411601
Wilkin Chapman Epton Blades *p285* . . . 01522 512345
Wilkins *p121* . . . 01296 424681
Willett & Co *p171* . . . 01284 701323
Peter Williams & Co *p406* . . . 01792 465597
Williamsons *p258* . . . 01482 323697
Wilson Barca LLP *p92* . . . 020 7272 2072
Wilson Browne *p333* . . . 01604 876697
Wilson Browne *p281* . . . 0116 251 7181
Wilson Browne *p425* . . . 01933 279000
Wilson Browne *p265* . . . 01536 410041
Winterbotham Smith Penley LLP *p214* . . . 01453 541940
Winterbotham Smith Penley LLP *p401* . . . 01453 847200
Winters & Co *p421* . . . 01920 466696
Wintle & Co *p148* . . . 01243 863021
Wiseman Lee LLP *p92* . . . 020 8215 1000
Withy King Solicitors *p128* . . . 01225 425731
Withy King Solicitors *p410* . . . 01844 261966
Wolferstans *p351* . . . 01752 663295
Wollen Michelmore Solicitors *p413* . . . 01803 213251
Woodfines LLP *p372* . . . 01767 680251
Woodfines LLP *p130* . . . 01234 270600
Woodfines LLP *p147* . . . 01908 366333
Woodfines LLP *p317* . . . 01908 202150
Woodfines LLP *p176* . . . 01223 411421
Woodford Robinson *p333* . . . 01604 624926
Woolley Bevis Diplock *p160* . . . 01273 323231

WELFARE BENEFITS

Aaronson & Co *p3* . . . 020 7376 9124
Adams Harrison *p370* . . . 01799 523441
Adams Harrison *p244* . . . 01440 705731 / 702485
Adlams LLP *p392* . . . 01480 474061
Ahmed & Co *p4* . . . 020 7383 2243
Alderson Dodds *p147* . . . 01670 352293
Allan Rutherford *p333* . . . 01603 621722
Allington Hughes *p442* . . . 01978 291000
Maurice Andrews *p135* . . . 0121 554 4900
Arscotts *p254* . . . 01273 735289
Ashfords LLP *p412* . . . 01884 203000
Aston Clark *p8* . . . 020 8752 1122
Attwood & Co *p233* . . . 01375 378122 / 378123
E J Bamforth Solicitors *p190* . . . 01244 357209
Max Barford & Co *p414* . . . 01892 539379
Bawtrees LLP *p435* . . . 01376 513491
Beecham Peacock *p323* . . . 0191 232 3048
Bell Lamb & Joynson *p286* . . . 0844 412 4348
Ben Hoare Bell & Co *p401* . . . 0191 565 3112
Ben Hoare Bell & Co *p323* . . . 0191 275 2626
Ben Hoare Bell & Co *p401* . . . 0191 516 0466
Best Solicitors *p375* . . . 0114 281 3636
Beviss & Beckingsale *p373* . . . 01297 626950
Blackhurst Budd LLP *p146* . . . 01253 629300
Brennans Solicitors *p419* . . . 0191 262 5133
Bridge McFarland *p284* . . . 01522 518888
Brighouses *p388* . . . 01704 534101 / 500151
Brooks *p378* . . . 01608 664406
Broudie Jackson Canter *p286* . . . 0151 227 1429
Burton & Co LLP *p284* . . . 01522 523215
Burton & Co LLP *p381* . . . 01529 306008 / 306009
Butcher & Barlow LLP *p170* . . . 0161 764 5141
CMHT Solicitors *p420* . . . 01922 646400
CVC Solicitors *p346* . . . 01736 362313
Carmichael & Heathfield *p324* . . . 0191 230 3010
Caswell Jones *p172* . . . 029 2086 4888
Clark Willis *p206* . . . 01325 281111
Clark Willis *p183* . . . 01748 830000
Clarkson Hirst *p269* . . . 01524 39760
Coffin Mew & Clover *p354* . . . 023 9238 8021
The Community Law Partnership *p137* . . . 0121 685 8595
Cooper Lingard *p282* . . . 01702 715411
Cooper Sons Hartley & Williams *p184* . . . 01298 812138
Copleys *p258* . . . 01480 456191
Richard Crumly *p410* . . . 01635 866166
Cunninghams *p302* . . . 0161 833 1600
Cuttle & Co *p302* . . . 0161 835 2050
Darling & Stephensons *p206* . . . 01325 489000
Davies Gore Lomax *p273* . . . 0113 242 2797
Dixon Stewart *p321* . . . 01425 621515
Dixon Stewart Solicitors *p250* . . . 01425 279222
Paul Dodds Solicitors *p419* . . . 0191 263 6200
Peter Dunn & Co *p401* . . . 0191 568 9000
Edwards Duthie *p260* . . . 020 8514 9000
Edwards Duthie *p29* . . . 020 8514 9000
Edwards Duthie *p29* . . . 020 8514 9000
R L Edwards & Partners *p157* . . . 01656 656861
Elliot Mather LLP *p192* . . . 01246 231288
Eric Robinson Solicitors *p385* . . . 023 8042 5000
Farleys Solicitors LLP *p114* . . . 01254 367853
A J Field & Co *p375* . . . 01795 580600

See p603 for the Community Legal Service Work Categories

- **Fisher Jones Greenwood LLP** *p186* . . . 01245 890110
- **Fisher Jones Greenwood LLP** *p197* . . . 01206 578282
- **Fisher Meredith** *p32* . . . 020 7091 2700
- **Fletcher Dervish** *p33* . . . 020 8800 4615
- **Fonseca & Partners** *p216* . . . 01495 303124
- **Forbes** *p114* . . . 01254 872111
- **Forbes** *p356* . . . 01772 220022
- **Forbes** *p145* . . . 01254 580000
- **Forbes** *p194* . . . 01257 260600
- **Ford Simey LLP** *p380* . . . 01395 577061 / 0800 169 3741
- **Ford Simey LLP** *p222* . . . 01395 272241 / 0800 169 3741
- **Fosters** *p168* . . . 01986 895251
- **Foys Solicitors** *p211* . . . 01302 327136
- **Foys Solicitors** *p441* . . . 01909 473560
- **Foys Solicitors** *p375* . . . 0114 246 7609
- **Foys Solicitors** *p367* . . . 01709 375561
- **Foys Solicitors** *p375* . . . 0114 251 1702
- **Fraser Dawbarns** *p435* . . . 01945 461456
- **Fraser Dawbarns** *p266* . . . 01553 666600
- **Fraser Dawbarns** *p213* . . . 01366 383171
- **Freer & Archer** *p279* . . . 0116 241 3199
- **French & Co** *p337* . . . 0115 955 1111
- **GLP Solicitors** *p315* . . . 0161 653 6295
- **GLP Solicitors** *p304* . . . 0161 834 6721
- **GLP Solicitors** *p357* . . . 0161 773 8626
- **GLP Solicitors** *p304* . . . 0161 793 0901
- **Gangar & Co** *p427* . . . 0121 553 4166
- **Gartsides** *p113* . . . 01873 857555
- **David Gist Solicitors** *p162* . . . 0117 927 9111
- **Glaisyers** *p138* . . . 0121 233 2971
- **Glaisyers Solicitors LLP** *p304* . . . 0161 832 4666
- **Glaisyers Solicitors LLP** *p304* . . . 0161 224 3311
- **Glanvilles** *p328* . . . 01983 527878
- **Goldstones** *p405* . . . 01792 643021
- **Grants Solicitors** *p205* . . . 020 8288 8899
- **Gregory Abrams Davidson LLP** *p288* . . . 0151 236 5000
- **Gregory Abrams Davidson LLP** *p288* . . . 0151 733 3353
- **Gregory Abrams Davidson LLP** *p288* . . . 0151 494 0777
- **hlw Keeble Hawson LLP** *p211* . . . 01302 366831
- **HSR Law (Hayes, Son & Richmond)** *p228* 01427 613831
- **Hadaway & Hadaway** *p330* . . . 0191 257 0382
- **Hannays Solicitors and Advocates** *p383* . . . 0191 456 7893 / 455 5361
- **Hansen Palomares** *p38* . . . 020 7640 4600
- **Harding Evans LLP** *p328* . . . 01633 244233
- **Harding Swinburne Jackson & Co** *p401* . . . 0191 565 8194
- **Christopher Harris & Co** *p375* . . . 01795 661521
- **Christopher Harris & Co** *p380* . . . 01795 437268
- **David W Harris & Co** *p352* . . . 01443 486666
- **Harrow Solicitors & Advocates** *p424* . . . 020 8863 0788
- **Harvey Ingram LLP** *p280* . . . 0116 254 5454
- **Hawley & Rodgers** *p337* . . . 0115 955 9000
- **Heckford Norton** *p283* . . . 01462 682244
- **Henrys Solicitors Ltd** *p395* . . . 01663 742222
- **Henrys Solicitors Ltd** *p355* . . . 01625 630880
- **Heptonstalls LLP** *p231* . . . 01405 765661
- **Hereward & Foster** *p41* . . . 020 7476 6600
- **Hewetts** *p361* . . . 0118 957 5337
- **Hewitts** *p330* . . . 01325 316170
- **Hewitts** *p144* . . . 01388 604691
- **Hewitts** *p206* . . . 01325 468573
- **Hewitts** *p203* . . . 01388 762466
- **HODGE JONES & ALLEN LLP** *p41* . . . 020 7874 8300
- **Holden & Co** *p243* . . . 01424 722422
- **Hood Vores & Allwood** *p209* . . . 01362 692424
- **Hopkins** *p311* . . . 01623 468468
- **Hopkins** *p311* . . . 01623 460460
- **Howells LLP** *p367* . . . 01709 364000
- **Howells LLP** *p376* . . . 0114 249 6666
- **JNP Legal** *p320* . . . 01443 450561
- **Graeme John Solicitors** *p113* . . . 01685 872491
- **Keppe Rofer** *p156* . . . 01874 624627
- **King Solicitors** *p384* . . . 020 8571 2239
- **Kirby Sheppard** *p411* . . . 0845 840 0045
- **Kirby Sheppard** *p268* . . . 0845 840 0045
- **Lancasters** *p158* . . . 01262 602401
- **Langleys** *p445* . . . 01904 610886
- **Lanyon Bowdler LLP** *p342* . . . 01691 652241
- **Larken & Co** *p322* . . . 01636 703333
- **Last Cawthra Feather LLP** *p121* . . . 01274 583106
- **Latimer Lee LLP** *p358* . . . 0161 798 9000
- **Lawrence & Co** *p52* . . . 020 7266 4333
- **Lawson & Thompson** *p130* . . . 01670 530700
- **Leigh Turton Dixon** *p315* . . . 01642 241101
- **Letchers** *p364* . . . 01425 471424
- **Duncan Lewis & Co** *p53* . . . 020 7923 4020
- **Linder Myers Solicitors** *p307* . . . 0844 984 6400
- **Linder Myers Solicitors** *p306* . . . 0844 984 6000
- **Linskills Solicitors** *p289* . . . 0151 236 2224
- **Lloyd & Rowe** *p179* . . . 029 2045 8999
- **McKenzie Bell Solicitors** *p401* . . . 0191 567 4857
- **Marchants Solicitors** *p312* . . . 01623 655111
- **Marshall Hall & Levy** *p384* . . . 0191 455 3181
- **Mason Baggott & Garton** *p219* . . . 01427 872661
- **Mayo Wynne Baxter LLP** *p215* . . . 01323 730543
- **Mirza & Co** *p61* . . . 020 8520 4416
- **Morgans** *p180* . . . 029 2072 9888
- **Moss Beachley Mullem & Coleman** *p62* . . . 020 7402 1401 / 7723 5783
- **Mustoe Shorter** *p430* . . . 01305 752700
- **Nalders Quality Solicitors** *p223* . . . 01326 313441
- **Alfred Newton & Co** *p396* . . . 0161 480 6551 / 480 1245
- **Norton Peskett** *p294* . . . 01502 533000
- **Martin Nossel & Co** *p126* . . . 01268 289555
- **Oldham Marsh Page Flavell** *p314* . . . 01664 563162
- **J Keith Park & Co** *p391* . . . 01744 636000
- **Park Woodfine Heald Mellows LLP** *p130* . 01234 400000
- **Parker Rhodes Hickmotts** *p367* . . . 01709 511100
- **Patchell Davies (Trading Name of PD Law Ltd)** *p147* . . . 01495 227128
- **Payne & Gamage** *p322* . . . 01636 640649
- **Penningtons** *p66* . . . 020 7457 3000
- **Samuel Phillips Law Firm** *p326* . . . 0191 232 8451
- **Potter Rees (Serious Injury) Solicitors** *p309* . . . 0161 237 5888
- **Powell Spencer & Partners** *p69* . . . 020 7604 5600
- **QualitySolicitors Gruber Garratt** *p358* . . . 0161 724 0203
- **QualitySolicitors Jackson & Canter** *p290* . 0151 282 1700
- **Raja & Co** *p70* . . . 020 8772 4900
- **Ralph & Co** *p329* . . . 01637 872218
- **Rawal & Co** *p70* . . . 020 8445 0303
- **Red Kite Law** *p345* . . . 01646 683222
- **Red Kite Law** *p244* . . . 01437 763332
- **Red Kite Law** *p345* . . . 01646 681529
- **Red Kite Law** *p316* . . . 01646 698008
- **Stephen Rimmer LLP** *p216* . . . 01323 644222
- **Helen Robbins Solicitors** *p72* . . . 020 8558 0038
- **Paul Robinson Solicitors** *p428* . . . 01702 338338
- **Robinsons** *p209* . . . 01332 291431
- **Roland Robinsons & Fentons LLP** *p147* . . 01253 621432
- **Will Rolt Solicitors** *p128* . . . 01225 426390
- **SJP Solicitors** *p258* . . . 01485 532662
- **Samars Solicitors** *p254* . . . 020 8570 4716
- **Samy & Co** *p242* . . . 020 8861 2424
- **Saulet & Co** *p389* . . . 023 9281 9442
- **Sehgal & Co** *p142* . . . 0121 772 2226
- **Selvarajah & Co** *p77* . . . 020 8204 7884
- **Sheikh & Co** *p78* . . . 020 8343 0693
- **Clive Shepherd & Co** *p420* . . . 01922 647797
- **Singleton Winn McDermott Solicitors** *p326* . . . 0191 265 8817
- **Slee Blackwell** *p125* . . . 01271 372128
- **Slee Blackwell** *p222* . . . 01392 423000
- **Geoffrey T Smith & Co** *p438* . . . 01902 426961
- **The Smith Partnership** *p170* . . . 01283 536471
- **The Smith Partnership** *p404* . . . 01283 226444
- **Smith Solicitor LLP** *p238* . . . 01422 383380
- **Southerns** *p169* . . . 01282 422711
- **Southerns** *p321* . . . 01282 603663
- **Southerns** *p169* . . . 01282 438446
- **Sriharans** *p384* . . . 020 8843 9974
- **Stachiw Bashir Green** *p155* . . . 01274 404010
- **Steed & Steed LLP** *p155* . . . 01376 552828
- **Stephensons Solicitors LLP** *p282* . . . 01942 777777
- **Stephensons Solicitors LLP** *p391* . . . 01942 777777
- **Stephensons Solicitors LLP** *p432* . . . 01942 777777
- **Stephensons Solicitors LLP** *p282* . . . 01942 777777
- **Stones Solicitors LLP** *p340* . . . 01837 650200
- **Swain & Co** *p386* . . . 023 8063 1111
- **Swain & Co** *p244* . . . 023 9248 3322
- **Swinburne & Jackson LLP** *p229* 0191 477 2531 / 477 3222
- **TBI Solicitors** *p243* . . . 0800 052 6824 / 01429 264101
- **TV Edwards LLP** *p85* . . . 020 7790 7000
- **TV Edwards LLP** *p85* . . . 020 7790 7000
- **Talbots Legal Advice Centre** *p399* .01384 445850 / 447777
- **Tanner & Taylor LLP** *p225* . . . 01252 733770
- **Taylor Street Solicitors LLP** *p115* . . . 01252 400999
- **H E Thomas & Co** *p87* . . . 020 8854 3036
- **Thorpe & Co** *p430* . . . 01947 603465
- **Thorpe & Co** *p226* . . . 01723 515555
- **Tilley & Co** *p390* . . . 01727 840467
- **Tilly Bailey & Irvine LLP** *p397* . . . 01642 673797
- **Timms** *p170* . . . 01283 561531 / 544417
- **Tozers** *p329* . . . 01626 207020
- **Tozers** *p409* . . . 01626 772376
- **Tozers** *p350* . . . 01752 206460
- **Trobridges** *p412* . . . 01752 812787
- **Trobridges** *p350* . . . 01752 664022
- **Tuckers** *p310* . . . 0161 233 4321
- **Tyrer Roxburgh & Co** *p89* . . . 020 8889 3319
- **Marina C Van't Goor** *p316* . . . 01646 697700
- **WBW Solicitors** *p329* . . . 01626 202404
- **WBW Solicitors** *p153* . . . 01626 833263
- **WBW Solicitors** *p413* . . . 0870 701 4321
- **WBW Solicitors** *p222* . . . 01392 202404
- **Waddington Webber** *p264* . . . 01535 662644 / 662647
- **Walker & Co** *p367* . . . 01709 817112
- **Waller Needham & Green** *p347* . . . 01733 262182
- **Walters & Barbary** *p173* . . . 01209 712454
- **Warnapala & Co Ltd** *p385* . . . 020 8571 1823
- **D J Webb & Co** *p90* . . . 020 7480 5999
- **Wheelers** *p115* . . . 01252 316316
- **Wilkin Chapman Epton Blades** *p285* . . . 01522 512345
- **Willett & Co** *p171* . . . 01284 701323
- **Williams & Co** *p217* . . . 020 8952 8882
- **Williscroft & Co** *p155* . . . 01274 305380
- **Wilson Browne** *p250* . . . 01933 410000
- **J M Wilson Solicitors** *p143* . . . 0121 356 4556
- **Wilsons Solicitors** *p344* . . . 01865 874497
- **Withy King Solicitors** *p128* . . . 01225 425731
- **Withy King Solicitors** *p414* . . . 01225 777464
- **Withy King Solicitors** *p128* . . . 01225 425731
- **Withy King Solicitors** *p407* . . . 01793 536526
- **Withy King Solicitors** *p313* . . . 01672 514781
- **Wolferstans** *p351* . . . 01752 663295
- **Worthingtons** *p227* . . . 01303 850206
- **ZMS Solicitor** *p281* . . . 0116 247 0790
- **Ziadies** *p94* . . . 020 7737 0934

PUBLICLY FUNDED LEGAL SERVICES – CRIMINAL DEFENCE SERVICES

@ Cornwall Law *p414* 01872 222688 / 222712
A-Z Law Solicitors *p3* 020 8355 0830
AS Law *p285* 0151 707 1212
Abbey Solicitors *p300* 0161 835 9933
Abels *p385* 023 8022 0317
Abiloye & Co *p3* 020 8478 5678
Adams Harrison *p370* 01799 523441
Adams Harrison *p244* 01440 705731 / 702485
Ahmed & Co *p4* 020 7383 2243
Ahmed Solicitors *p135* 0121 507 1030
David Ake & Co *p271* 0113 244 8808
Albin & Co *p359* 0118 957 4018
Alderson Dodds *p147* 01670 352293
Aldridge Brownlee Solicitors LLP *p151* 01202 294411
Alexander & Partners *p5* 020 8965 7121
Michael Alexander & Co *p301* 0845 839 2011
Allan Rutherford *p333* 01603 621722
Allansons LLP *p148* 0161 220 8484
Allen Hoole Solicitors *p160* 0117 942 0901
Alletsons Ltd *p157* 01278 456621
Allington Hughes *p190* 01244 312166
Allington Hughes *p442* 01978 291000
Almy & Thomas *p412* 01803 299131
Alsters Kelley *p339* 0844 561 0100
Alsters Kelley *p199* 0844 561 0100
Alsters Kelley *p270* 0844 561 0100
Amphlett Lissimore *p6* 020 8771 5254
Andersons Solicitors *p239* 01423 527852
Andrews McQueen *p151* 01202 290628
Maurice Andrews *p135* 0121 554 4900
Thomas Andrews & Partners *p442* 01978 291506
Ansah Solicitors *p6* 020 8761 5271
Ansons LLP *p284* 01543 263456
APPLEBY HOPE & MATTHEWS *p314* 01642 440444
Appleby Hope & Matthews *p396* 01642 617000
Arani & Co *p384* 020 8893 5000
Archer & Archer *p218* 01353 662203
Argyles *p407* 01827 56276
Gerald Armstrong & Co *p401* 0191 514 0966
Arnison & Co Solicitors Limited *p346* 01768 862007
G A Arnold *p297* 01625 615424
Arora Lodhi Heath *p7* 020 8993 9995
Arora Lodhi Heath *p7* 020 7267 3281
Ash Clifford *p157* 01278 451327
Ashfords LLP *p412* 01884 203000
Ashfords LLP *p220* 01392 337000
Ashton KCJ *p171* 01284 762331
Ashton KCJ *p262* 01473 232425
Ashton KCJ *p225* 01394 277188
Aston Clark *p8* 020 8752 1122
Atkins Hope Solicitors *p204* 020 8680 5018
Atkins Law Solicitors *p220* 01392 671657
Atkinson & Co *p328* 01633 251118
Atkinson Cave & Stuart *p146* 01253 293151
Atlee Chung & Company *p8* 020 7287 9988
Atter Mackenzie & Co *p220* 01386 425300
Atteys *p211* 01302 340400
Atteys *p124* 01226 212345
Atteys *p424* 01709 872106
Audu & Co *p8* 020 7278 9340
David Auld & Co *p130* 01670 826870
David Auld & Co *p319* 01670 505844
Austin & Carnley *p282* 01525 372140
Avery Naylor *p404* 01792 463276
B&C Solicitors - The Law Shop *p372* 01723 379777
BHP Law *p214* 0191 384 0840
BHP Law *p330* 01325 312534
BHP Law *p206* 01325 466794
BHP Law *p323* 0191 221 0898
BHP Law *p238* 01422 250650
BHP Law *p330* 0191 257 2213
BHP Law *p396* 01642 672770
BLB Solicitors *p406* 01793 615011
BTMK Solicitors LLP *p387* 01702 339222
BTMK Solicitors LLP *p387* 01702 339222
Baches *p427* 0121 553 3286 / 553 7076
Bailey Nicholson Grayson *p439* 020 8418 2900
Baily Gibson *p249* 01494 442661
Bains Cohen LLP *p123* 020 8252 7373
Bains Solicitors *p424* 01933 440000
Baker Gray & Co *p147* 0191 414 4869
Baker Gray & Co *p323* 0191 222 0203
Ballam *p134* 0151 647 8977
E J Bamforth Solicitors *p190* 01244 357209
Bankside Commercial Solicitors *p9* 020 7654 0200
Bankside Law Ltd *p9* 0844 745 4000
Banner Jones *p191* 01246 560560
Banner Jones *p213* 01246 414438
Banner Jones *p191* 01246 827516
Banner Jones *p192* 01246 861250
Banner Jones *p191* 01246 209773
Bannister & Co *p443* 01935 433133
Bannister Preston *p370* 0161 973 2434
Bark & Co *p9* 020 7353 1990
Barker & Co *p256* 01482 219966
John Barkers *p195* 01472 695218
John Barkers *p294* 01507 604773
John Barkers *p234* 01472 358686
John Barkers *p297* 01507 477673
Barnes Coleman & Co *p131* 01702 558211
Barnes Harrild & Dyer *p204* 020 8681 5128
Norman H Barnett & Co *p11* 020 8471 2112
Barricella Hughes Marchant *p262* 01473 226225
Kenneth M Barrow & Co *p373* 0191 513 0333
Bartlett Gooding & Weelen *p183* 01963 350888
Bartlett Gooding & Weelen *p378* 01749 343091
Bartlett Gooding & Weelen *p229* 01458 832510
S S Basi & Co *p259* 020 8518 1236
Bassets *p229* 01634 575464
Bassets *p366* 01634 400161
Alastair Bateman & Co *p153* 01274 739973
Bates & Mountain *p235* 01472 357291
Bates N V H *p11* 020 7936 2930
Nicholas Bates *p126* 01256 331278
Baxter Brown McArthur *p11* 020 7924 8130
Bay Advocates Criminal Defence Lawyers *p412* 01803 408290
Bazeley Barnes & Bazeley *p132* 01237 473122
Beecham Peacock *p323* 0191 232 3048
Beetenson & Gibbon *p235* 01472 240251
Beevers Solicitors *p119* 0161 339 9697
Bell Lamb & Joynson *p369* 0844 412 4348
Bell Lamb & Joynson *p286* 0844 412 4348
John Bellis & Co *p346* 01492 622377
John Bellis & Co *p199* 01248 680527
Belmores *p334* 01603 499999
Belshaws Solicitors Limited *p395* 0161 477 5377
Ben Hoare Bell & Co *p401* 0191 565 3112
Ben Hoare Bell & Co *p323* 0191 275 2626
Ben Hoare Bell & Co *p401* 0191 516 0466
Bennett Richmond *p270* 01207 521843
James Benson & Co *p286* 0151 236 8755
Benson Watkins *p404* 01792 704320
Berkson Globe Partnership *p286* 0151 236 1234
Daniel Berman & Co *p12* 020 7428 7798
Bernard Chill & Axtell *p385* 023 8022 8821
Berry & Berry *p414* 01892 526344
Berry & Berry *p412* 01732 355911
Berry & Berry *p299* 01622 690777
Berry & Berry *p301* 0161 703 7300
Berry Redmond & Robinson *p434* 01934 842811
Berry Redmond & Robinson *p429* 01934 619000
Richard Best & Co *p368* 01788 571135
Best Solicitors *p375* 0114 281 3636
Beswicks *p239* 01782 205000
Betts & Co Solicitors Ltd *p119* 01304 213172
Beynon & Co *p135* 0121 444 0099
Bhatia Best *p336* 0115 950 3231
Bhatt Murphy *p12* 020 7729 1115
David Billingham & Partners *p187* 01242 676224
Bilton Hammond LLP *p311* 01623 675800
Bilton Hammond LLP *p192* 01246 232418
Bindmans LLP *p12* 020 7833 4433
Birchall Blackburn LLP *p356* 01772 561663
Birchall Blackburn LLP *p194* 01257 279011
BIRD & CO *p232* 01476 591711
BIRD & CO *p322* 01636 650880
Bird & Daniels *p378* 01274 580999
Birds Solicitors *p13* 020 8874 7433
Birnberg Peirce & Partners *p13* 020 7911 0166
Biscoes *p354* 023 9266 0261
Bishop & Co *p321* 01663 746730
Bishop & Light *p159* 01273 626288
Bishop McBride Olden *p177* 029 2049 0111
Bivonas Limited Solicitors *p13* 020 7337 2600
Black & Co *p214* 01455 844005
Blackburn & Co *p226* 01253 872238
Blackfords LLP *p204* 020 8686 6232
Blackhurst Budd LLP *p146* 01253 629300
Lionel Blackman *p219* 01372 728941
Blackwells Solicitors *p263* 01535 600005
Blake Lapthorn *p354* 023 9222 1122
Blaser Mills *p249* 01494 450171
Blaser Mills *p120* 01296 434416
Bleasdale & Co *p431* 01946 692165
Ann Blyth-Cook & Co *p387* 01702 462999
Bobbetts Mackan *p161* 0117 929 9001
Richard Body & Co *p392* 01424 201301
Bolitho Way *p354* 023 9282 0747
Bonallack & Bishop *p117* 01980 622992
Bonallack & Bishop *p371* 01722 422300
Bond Joseph *p176* 01227 453545
Bone & Payne LLP *p291* 01492 876354
Peter Bonner & Co *p14* 020 8297 1727
Harry Boodhoo & Co *p436* 0161 445 0588
C W Booth & Co *p144* 01388 606660
Bosley & Co *p159* 01273 608181
John Boyle & Co *p362* 01209 213507
Boys & Maughan *p166* 01843 868861
Brady Eastwood Pierce & Stewart *p15* 020 8692 8181
Brain Sinnott & Co *p268* 0117 960 6880
Brain Sinnott & Co *p161* 0117 965 1030
Bramsdon & Childs *p388* 023 9282 1251
Bramwell Browne Odedra *p189* 01494 782244
Bray & Bray *p279* 0116 254 8871
Bray & Bray *p250* 01455 639900
Brearleys Solicitors *p128* 01924 473065
Breese-Gwyndaf *p353* 01766 512253 / 514227
Brennans Solicitors *p419* 0191 262 5133
Brewer Harding & Rowe *p125* 01271 342271
Brewer Harding & Rowe *p261* 01271 863495
Brewer Harding & Rowe *p132* 01237 472666
Brice & Co *p168* 01787 227199
Bridge McFarland *p235* 01472 311711
Bridge McFarland Haddon Owen *p294* 01507 605883
Bridge Sanderson Munro *p411* 01405 814136
Jonathan Brierly *p345* 029 2071 2230
Brighouse Wolff *p341* 01695 573202
Brighouse Wolff *p381* 01695 722577
Keith B Bright *p403* 0121 351 6296
Brignalls Balderston Warren *p394* 01438 359311
Broadbents *p404* 01623 441123
Brockbank Curwen Cain & Hall *p431* 01946 692194
Brockbank Curwen Cain & Hall *p440* 01900 603563
Brook Oliver *p321* 01425 616809
Brooke-Taylors *p172* 01298 22741
Brookes & Co *p192* 01243 780333
Broomhead & Saul *p408* 01823 288121
Broomhead & Saul *p261* 01460 57056
Broudie Jackson Canter *p286* 0151 227 1429
Brown & Corbishley *p323* 01782 717888
Brown & Corbishley *p371* 01270 768033
Brown & Emery *p423* 01923 225255
Brown & Murray *p316* 01229 772562
BROWN BEER NIXON MALLON *p362* 01642 490202
Dennis Brown Solicitors *p197* 01206 505060
Gordon Brown Associates *p191* 0191 388 1778
Richard Brown & Co *p346* 0870 850 3062
Brown Turner Ross *p388* 01704 542002
BRYAN & ARMSTRONG *p311* 01623 626039
BRYAN & ARMSTRONG *p311* 01623 624505
David Buck & Co *p159* 01273 621745
Bullivant & Partners *p16* 020 7332 8250
Bunting & Riley *p172* 01298 767495
Burchell Williams Limited *p159* 01273 606555
Stephen Burdon Solicitors *p336* 0115 950 0054
Burley & Geach *p233* 01428 605355

Burley & Geach *p285* 01428 722334
Burnett Barker *p171* 01284 701131
Burnley-Jones Bate & Co *p16* 020 8542 8101
Burrell Jenkins *p176* 01543 505040
Burroughs *p299* 01622 676976 / 676982
Burton & Co LLP *p284* 01522 523215
Burton & Co LLP *p381* 01529 306008 / 306009
C R Burton & Co *p16* 020 8778 4455 / 8659 5775
Burton Copeland LLP *p302* 0161 827 9500
Burton Copeland LLP *p370* 0161 905 8530
BURY & WALKERS LLP *p124* 01226 733533
BURY & WALKERS LLP *p438* 01226 753433
Kenneth Bush *p266* 01553 692233
Kenneth Bush *p266* 01553 692737
Buxton Ryan & Co Solicitors *p239* 01279 420288
Bynes *p412* 01803 295692
Byrne & Partners *p16* 020 7842 1616
Byrne Frodsham & Co *p431* 0151 424 5601
CGM *p385* 023 8063 2733
CMHT Solicitors *p420* 01922 743525
CMHT Solicitors *p167* 01543 372347
CMHT Solicitors *p420* 01922 646400
C NICHOLLS *p148* 01208 76969
James Calderbank *p205* 01823 680697
Caldicott Gallimore *p282* 01568 614168
Callistes *p17* 020 7501 8388
Cameron Jones Hussell & Howe *p353* 01639 885261
Campbell Chambers *p18* 020 7691 8777
Canter Levin & Berg *p287* 0151 239 1000
Caplans *p241* 020 8864 0111
Carmichael & Heathfield *p324* 0191 230 3010
Carney Solicitors Ltd *p239* 01782 272999
Terence Carney *p246* 0191 483 5422 / 483 8771
Carr & Co *p255* 01484 467860
Carter Slater & Co *p331* 01604 717505
Cartwright Cunningham Haselgrove & Co *p19* 020 8520 1021
Cartwright King *p336* 0115 958 7444
Cartwright King *p279* 0116 253 9222
Caseys *p250* 01278 794495
The Castle Partnership *p235* 01483 300905
Chabra Cass & Co *p19* 020 8450 9833 / 8452 2200
Chadwick Lawrence *p418* 01924 379078
Chadwick Lawrence *p319* 0113 252 3452
Chadwick Lawrence *p238* 01422 330601
Chadwick Lawrence *p255* 01484 519999
Chadwyck-Healey & Co *p19* 020 7353 6900
Chafes *p395* 0161 477 1525
Challinors *p427* 0121 553 3211
Challinors *p136* 0121 212 9393
Chanter Ferguson *p132* 01237 478751
Chapple & Co *p312* 01354 652550
Chattertons Solicitors *p252* 01507 522456
Chattertons Solicitors *p151* 01205 310025
Chattertons Solicitors *p284* 01522 814600
Chebsey & Co *p128* 01494 670440
Chebsey & Co *p168* 01628 660077
Children & Families Law Firm *p20* 020 7582 6002
Chivers Walsh Smith and Irvine & Co *p153* 01274 740077
Churchers *p271* 023 9255 1500
Churchers *p223* 01329 822333
Churchers *p354* 023 9221 0170
Churchers *p354* 023 9286 2424
Clarion Solicitors LLP *p272* 0113 246 0622
Anthony Clark & Co *p284* 01522 512321
CLARK BROOKES *p427* 0121 553 2576
Chris Clark *p176* 01543 573004
Chris Clark Solicitors & Estate Agents *p392* 01785 241842 / 241944
David Clark & Co *p20* 020 7433 1562
Clark Willis *p206* 01325 281111
Clark Willis *p183* 01748 830000
Clarke & Hartland Solicitors *p345* 029 2071 1181
Clarke Kiernan *p412* 01732 360999
Peter Clarke Solicitors *p413* 023 8066 6636
Clarkes *p379* 01743 231531
Clarkes *p425* 01952 223548
Clarkes *p409* 01952 291666
Clarkson Hirst *p269* 01524 39760
Claude Hornby & Cox *p20* 020 7332 8269
Clifford Johnston & Co *p302* 0161 249 2700
Clifford Johnston & Co *p302* 0161 975 1900
Clinton Davis Pallis *p21* 020 8880 5000
Cobains *p146* 01253 290092
Cobleys LLP *p287* 0151 242 9000
Cocks Lloyd *p339* 024 7664 1642
Coffin Mew & Clover *p385* 023 8033 4661
Coffin Mew & Clover *p354* 023 9238 8021
Coffin Mew & Clover *p232* 023 9252 3111
Coffin Mew & Clover *p223* 01329 825617
Cole Bentley & Co *p234* 01493 330660
Colebournes Solicitors and Advocates *p146* 01253 293195
Coles Miller Solicitors LLP *p352* 01202 673011
Coles Miller Solicitors LLP *p151* 01202 511512
Collins Dryland & Thorowgood LLP *p411* 0118 942 2448
K J Commons & Co *p440* 01900 604698
K J Commons & Co *p431* 01946 66699
K J Commons & Co *p182* 01228 822666
Coninghams Solicitors *p22* 020 8296 1957
Coodes *p391* 01726 874700
Coodes *p414* 01872 246200
Coodes *p329* 01637 878111
Cook Taylor *p22* 020 8854 1166
Chris Cooke and Co *p375* 0114 282 3433
Coole & Haddock *p253* 01403 210200
Cooper Kenyon Burrows *p302* 0161 834 7374
Copeman Markham Solicitors *p256* 01482 212979
John Copland & Son *p375* 01795 664431
Copleys *p258* 01480 456191
Corker Binning Solicitors *p22* 020 7353 6000
Cornell & Co *p282* 01568 612288
Cousins Tyrer *p272* 0113 247 0400
David Cowan *p212* 01306 886622
Cramp & Co *p215* 01323 720581
Martin Cray & Co *p159* 01273 673226
Criminal Defence Solicitors *p23* 020 7353 7000
Charles Crookes & Jones *p172* 029 2086 0628
Simon Crosfield & Co *p365* 01765 692277
Cross Solicitors *p199* 01244 822101
Stanley H Cross & Co *p194* 01257 272222
Crosse Wyatt Verney & Ayre *p383* 01769 572157
Crossmans *p358* 01761 431688
Crowe Humble Wesencraft *p324* 0191 287 2221
Crowley & Co *p178* 029 2045 8895
PAUL CROWLEY & CO *p287* 0151 264 7363
Paul Crowley & Co *p287* 0151 264 7363
Ian Cruickshank & Co *p263* 0191 428 0900
Cunninghams *p302* 0161 833 1600
Kenneth Curtis & Co *p137* 0121 356 1161
Patrick J Cusack & Co *p241* 020 8863 3414
Cuttle & Co *p302* 0161 835 2050
Cuttle & Co Solicitors *p340* 0161 678 7443
Cyril Morris Arkwright *p148* 01204 535261
DBL Talbots LLP *p265* 01562 749910
DBL Talbots LLP *p213* 01384 252471
DBL Talbots LLP *p437* 01902 427561
DBL Talbots LLP *p399* 01384 445850
DB Law *p346* 01736 364261
DB Law *p173* 01209 712428
DB Law *p223* 01326 211609
DB Law *p392* 01736 793883
DLC Solicitors Limited *p207* 01254 761234
Dale & Co Solicitors Lincoln *p284* 01522 513399
Stephanie Dale & Co *p254* 01273 748333
Darbys Solicitors LLP *p343* 01865 811700
W H Darbyshire & Son *p146* 01253 346646
Dass Solicitors *p137* 0121 248 4000
David & Snape *p157* 01656 661115
David & Snape *p353* 01656 782070 / 785038
David James & Company *p114* 01970 615789
Davies & Jones Solicitors *p178* 029 2046 5296
Davies Blunden & Evans *p443* 01252 872617
Davies Blunden & Evans *p224* 01252 541633
Hywel Davies & Co *p121* 01678 520307
Lawrence Davies & Co *p26* 020 7381 1171
Davies Parsons Allchurch *p292* 01554 749144
R George Davies & Co *p113* 01873 852535
De Maid Solicitors & Advocates *p178* 029 2023 5575
De Soyza & Fernando *p26* 020 8670 9918
Debridge Solicitors *p26* 020 8986 2581
Dechert *p26* 020 7184 7000
John Delaney & Co *p273* 0113 246 8151
Denby & Co *p416* 01229 582283
Denby & Co *p125* 01229 822366
Denhams *p236* 01483 456450
Devas Keogh James *p347* 01733 340666
Devonalds *p412* 01443 434343
Dhanju Mclean & Anwar Solicitors *p263* 01753 651743
Dhillon & Co *p27* 020 8471 7884
Dixon Stewart *p321* 01425 621515
Dixon Stewart Solicitors *p250* 01425 279222
Dobson & Sleeman *p315* 01642 231707
Dobsons *p341* 01689 886300
Dodds & Partners *p279* 0116 253 8585
Dollman & Pritchard *p183* 01883 347823
John Donkin & Co *p228* 0191 495 2896 / 477 1781
John Donkin & Co *p423* 0191 416 9444
Donnelly McArdle Adamson *p243* 01429 274732
Dorians *p208* 01332 680580
Douglas-Jones Mercer *p405* 01792 650000
Dozie & Co *p27* 020 8808 2244
Draycott Browne Solicitors *p303* 0161 228 2244
Scott Duff & Co *p182* 01228 531054
Scott Duff & Co *p346* 01768 865551
Duffield Harrison LLP *p251* 01992 442911
Dunn & Baker *p221* 01392 285000
Peter Dunn & Co *p401* 0191 568 9000
Dunning & Co *p28* 020 7733 6217
Dyne Drewett Solicitors Ltd *p378* 01935 813691
Eager & Co *p380* 01754 766688
Eastleys *p413* 01803 864888
Eastleys *p345* 01803 559257
Eastleys *p166* 01803 853266
Eaton-Evans & Morris *p244* 01437 763383
Eaton Smith LLP *p255* 01484 821300
Eatons *p153* 0845 660 0660
Eddowes Perry & Osbourne *p403* 0121 686 9444
Eddowes Perry & Osbourne *p403* 0121 686 9666
Eddowes Perry & Osbourne *p403* 0121 686 9444
Eddowes Waldron *p208* 01332 348484
Edwards Duthie *p260* 020 8514 9000
Edwards Duthie *p29* 020 8514 9000
Edwards Duthie *p29* 020 8514 9000
R L Edwards & Partners *p157* 01656 656861
R L Edwards & Partners *p413* 01443 775000
Roger Edwards & Co *p413* 01495 722865
Joe Egan Solicitors *p149* 01204 368060
Elin & Associates *p126* 01256 358864
Elliot Mather LLP *p192* 01246 231288
ELLIOTT BRIDGMAN *p409* 01952 684544
Ellis Davies & Co *p172* 01286 672437
Ellis-Fermor & Negus *p364* 01773 744744
Ellis-Fermor & Negus *p293* 0115 972 5222
Elmhirst Parker LLP *p374* 01757 703895
Elwyn Jones & Co *p122* 01248 370224
Emery Johnson Partnership *p279* 0116 255 4855
England Stickland & Neale *p138* 0121 377 7773
Ennon & Co Solicitors *p29* 020 7281 2123
Enoch Evans LLP *p420* 01922 720333
Eric Robinson Solicitors *p184* 023 8025 4676
Eric Robinson Solicitors *p386* 023 8022 6891
Eric Robinson Solicitors *p259* 023 8084 4304
Eric Robinson Solicitors *p385* 023 8042 5000
The Eric Whitehead Partnership *p185* 01538 755761
Charles Ete & Co *p29* 020 7820 9818
Evans & Greaves *p172* 029 2086 6001
Evans Main Solicitors *p374* 01732 464848
Evans-Roberts *p298* 01654 702335 / 702336
Everett Tomlin Lloyd & Pratt *p352* 01495 763333
Everys *p380* 01395 577983
Everys *p222* 01395 264384
Everys *p373* 01297 21105
Ewings & Co *p30* 020 8778 1126
David Eyres *p375* 0114 249 3222
Faber & Co *p138* 0121 236 5751
Edward Fail Bradshaw & Waterson *p30* 020 7790 4032
Edward Fail Bradshaw & Waterson *p30* 020 7264 2016
Fairbrother & Darlow *p153* 01344 420808
Faradays Solicitors Ltd *p30* 020 7281 1001
Farleys Solicitors LLP *p114* 01254 367853
Farleys Solicitors LLP *p145* 01254 367855
Farleys Solicitors LLP *p169* 01282 798664
Farleys Solicitors LLP *p145* 01254 367856
Farnfield & Nicholls *p374* 01747 854244
Farnworth Shaw *p321* 01282 699996
Farnworth Shaw *p198* 01282 864081
Farrell & Hobbs *p304* 0161 445 1000
Farrell Matthews & Weir *p31* 020 8741 1482
Farrell Matthews & Weir *p30* 020 8746 3771
Favell Smith & Lawson Solicitors *p375* 0114 272 4381
Brian Ferris *p415* 01892 518609
Field Overell *p270* 01926 422101
Fieldings Porter *p149* 01204 540900
Linda Filby Solicitor *p373* 01273 695321
Finn Gledhill *p238* 01422 330000
Ashley Fisher & Co *p146* 01253 751585
Fisher Jones Greenwood LLP *p186* 01245 890110
Fisher Jones Greenwood LLP *p197* 01206 578282
Fisher Meredith *p32* 020 7091 2700
Andrew Fitzpatrick *p304* 0161 248 9799
Brendan Fleming *p138* 0121 683 5000
Fletcher Dervish *p33* 020 8800 4615
Foley Harrison *p228* 0191 477 6333
Neil Foley & Co *p352* 01443 406085
Fonseca & Partners *p216* 01495 303124
Foot Anstey *p221* 01392 411221

See p603 for the Community Legal Service Work Categories

Foot Anstey p349 . . . 01752 675000
Foot Anstey p408 . . . 01823 625600
Forbes p114 . . . 01254 872111
Forbes p356 . . . 01772 220022
Forbes p145 . . . 01254 580000
Forbes p194 . . . 01257 260600
Ford Simey LLP p221 . . . 01392 274126
Ford Simey LLP p380 . . . 01395 577061 / 0800 169 3741
Ford Simey LLP p222 . . . 01395 272241 / 0800 169 3741
Roy Foreman & Co p235 . . . 01472 355262
Geoffrey Forrester & Co p263 . . . 0191 420 0820
Forresters p125 . . . 01229 820297
Forshaws Davies Ridgway LLP p422 . . . 01925 230000
Forshaws Davies Ridgway LLP p227 . . . 01928 739300
Forshaws Davies Ridgway LLP p422 . . . 01925 604713
Fosters p334 . . . 01603 620508
Fosters p168 . . . 01986 895251
John Fowlers LLP Solicitors p197 . . . 01206 576151
John Fowlers LLP Solicitors p159 . . . 01206 302694
Joseph Foxler & Co p170 . . . 0161 797 4126
Foys Solicitors p211 . . . 01302 327136
Foys Solicitors p441 . . . 01909 473560
Foys Solicitors p375 . . . 0114 251 1702
Franklins LLP p332 . . . 01604 828282
Fraser Dawbarns p435 . . . 01945 461456
Fraser Dawbarns p266 . . . 01553 666600
Fraser Dawbarns p213 . . . 01366 383171
Fraser Wise & Co p232 . . . 01476 566646 / 561870
Freeman Johnson p389 . . . 01388 814389
Freeman Johnson p206 . . . 01325 466221
Freeman Johnson p214 . . . 0191 386 4843 / 386 9619
FRISBY & CO p392 . . . 01785 244114
Fritchley Goldsmith p124 . . . 01226 215600
Fulchers of Farnborough p224 . . . 01252 522475
Funnell & Perring p243 . . . 01424 426287
GC Law p248 . . . 01432 275397
GHP Legal p342 . . . 01691 659194
GHP Legal p442 . . . 01978 291456
GLP Solicitors p315 . . . 0161 653 6295
GLP Solicitors p304 . . . 0161 834 6721
GLP Solicitors p304 . . . 0161 793 0901
Gabriels Solicitors p227 . . . 01704 831554
Galbraith Branley p34 . . . 020 8446 8474
Gamlins p363 . . . 01745 343500
Gammon Bell & Co p216 . . . 023 8068 4900
Gangar & Co p427 . . . 0121 553 4166
Gani & Co p35 . . . 020 7733 8169
Garcha & Co p35 . . . 020 7375 1888
Gardiners Solicitors p35 . . . 020 7603 7245
Gardner Dallimore p248 . . . 01432 263535
Gardner Leader LLP p322 . . . 01635 508080
Garstangs p35 . . . 020 7427 5678
Gartsides p328 . . . 01633 213411
Gartsides p113 . . . 01873 857555
Gaskell & Walker p157 . . . 01656 653122
Gattas Denfield Solicitors p35 . . . 020 8204 7181
Gaynor-Smith Owen & Co p300 . . . 01684 560771
Craig Gee p304 . . . 0161 666 9999
Genga & Co p426 . . . 020 8795 5020
Geoffrey Morris & Ashton p442 . . . 01978 291322
George Davies & Evans Limited p181 . . . 01239 612308
George H Coles & Co p254 . . . 01273 205101
George Ide LLP p148 . . . 01243 829231
Gepp & Sons p186 . . . 01245 493939
Gepp & Sons p197 . . . 01206 369889
Reena Ghai Solicitors p253 . . . 020 8759 9959
Gilbert Stephens p221 . . . 01392 424242
Gill & Co p260 . . . 020 8554 8774
Gittins McDonald p442 . . . 01978 291662
Glaisyers p138 . . . 0121 233 2971
Glansfields p311 . . . 01623 627827
Glanvilles p328 . . . 01983 527878
Godloves p273 . . . 0113 225 8864
Goldstones p405 . . . 01792 643021
Gomer Williams & Co p292 . . . 01554 755101
Clive Gomes Solicitors p426 . . . 020 8904 2614
Goodall Barnett James p392 . . . 01424 444475
Goodall Barnett James p252 . . . 01293 414448
GOODHAND AND FORSYTH QUALITYSOLICITORS p362 . . . 01737 773533
GoodyBurrett LLP p197 . . . 01206 577676
Gordon & Penney p429 . . . 01934 414161
R Gordon Roberts Laurie & Co p292 . . . 01248 722215 / 723312
Gosschalks p256 . . . 01482 324252
H F T Gough & Co p431 . . . 01946 692461
Goughs p314 . . . 01225 703036
Gowmans p345 . . . 01803 546100
Grahame Stowe Bateson p274 . . . 0113 246 8163

Grainger Appleyard p211 . . . 01302 327257
David Gray Solicitors p324 . . . 0191 232 9547
Gray Hooper Holt LLP p362 . . . 01737 761004
Grayson Willis Bennett p375 . . . 0114 290 9500
Greathead & Whitelock p345 . . . 01646 682101
The Grech Gooden Partnership LLP p178 029 2022 2255
Green & Co p299 . . . 01622 676769
Christopher Green McCarrahers p386 . . . 023 8084 2765
Green Williamson Solicitors p418 . . . 01924 291400
Adam F Greenhalgh & Co p149 . . . 0845 074 3491
Gregory Abrams Davidson LLP p288 . . . 0151 236 5000
Gregory Abrams Davidson LLP p288 . . . 0151 733 3353
Gregsons p37 . . . 020 8946 1173
Gregsons p337 . . . 0115 941 1999
Grierson Shaw & Co p214 . . . 0191 386 2434
Richard Griffiths & Co p371 . . . 01722 329966
Gullands p299 . . . 01622 678341
The Gwyn George Partnership p113 . . . 01685 874629 / 871133
The Gwyn George Partnership p314 . . . 01685 377035
HC Solicitors LLP p347 . . . 01733 882800
HKH Kenwright & Cox Solicitors p260 . . 020 8553 9600
hlw Keeble Hawson LLP p211 . . . 01302 366831
HSR Law (Hayes, Son & Richmond) p228 01427 613831
HSR Law (Hayes, Son & Richmond) p211 01302 347800
HSR Solicitors p37 . . . 020 7791 1111
Hadaway & Hadaway p330 . . . 0191 257 0382
Haddock & Company p238 . . . 01422 366010
Hadgkiss Hughes & Beale p138 . . . 0121 449 5050
Hadgkiss Hughes & Beale p139 . . . 0121 707 8484
Hains & Lewis Ltd p320 . . . 0845 408 0125
Hains & Lewis Ltd p244 . . . 0845 408 0125
Hall Ennion & Young p218 . . . 01353 662918
Frederic Hall p213 . . . 01304 202411
Halliday Reeves p228 . . . 0191 477 7728
Hallinan Blackburn Gittings & Nott p38 020 7233 3999
Hameed & Co p38 . . . 020 8830 1335
Hamer Childs p439 . . . 01905 724565
Hammon Oakley p200 . . . 024 7644 8585
Hamnett Osborne Tisshaw p245 . . . 01444 443030
Hannays Solicitors and Advocates p383 . . . 0191 456 7893 / 455 5361
Hanne & Co p38 . . . 020 7228 0017
HANRATTY & CO p330 . . . 01686 626239
Hansell Drew & Co p207 . . . 01803 834555
Harbans Singh p139 . . . 0121 551 4496
Harding Evans LLP p328 . . . 01633 244233
Harding Swinburne Jackson & Co p401 . . 0191 565 8194
Hardmans p207 . . . 01304 373377
Hardy McBride & Co p166 . . . 020 8460 1999
Hardy Miles Titterton p364 . . . 01773 747000
Hargreaves Gilman p305 . . . 0161 443 1711
Alistair Harper & Co p245 . . . 01444 457890
Will Harrington & Co p403 . . . 0121 321 1999
Harringtons p159 . . . 01273 606069
Alan Harris p350 . . . 01752 223655
Christopher Harris & Co p375 . . . 01795 661521
Christopher Harris & Co p380 . . . 01795 437268
David W Harris & Co p352 . . . 01443 486666
Harris Paley Schone Ltd p159 . . . 01273 600009
Harrison Bundey p274 . . . 0113 200 7400
Harrison Clark LLP p367 . . . 01989 562377
HARRISONS SOLICITORS LLP p425 . . 01938 552545
Harrop White Vallance & Dawson p311 . . 01623 629221
Harrow Law Partnership p424 . . . 020 8863 7888
Harrow Solicitors & Advocates p424 . . . 020 8863 0788
Charles Hart Solicitors p186 . . . 01934 742315
Hart Jackson & Sons p416 . . . 01229 583291
Harthills p367 . . . 01709 377399
Hartley Thomas & Wright p365 . . . 01706 644118
Hartnells p39 . . . 020 7703 9222
Harvey Ingram Borneos p130 . . . 01234 353221
Harvey Ingram Borneos p317 . . . 01908 696002
Hasan Solicitors p139 . . . 0121 778 4003
Haswell & Cornberg p325 . . . 0191 276 5300
Hatchers Solicitors LLP p379 . . . 01743 248545
Hathaways p228 . . . 0191 477 2288
Hatten Wyatt p232 . . . 01474 351199
Hawley & Rodgers p293 . . . 01509 230333
Haworth & Gallagher p419 . . . 0151 638 5457 / 638 6088
Hay & Kilner p419 . . . 0191 262 8231
Hay & Kilner p325 . . . 0191 232 8345
Phillip M Haycock p139 . . . 0121 788 1234
Edward Hayes LLP p192 . . . 01243 781431
Edward Hayes LLP p148 . . . 01243 822655
Edward Hayes LLP p192 . . . 01243 672124
Edward Hayes LLP p441 . . . 01903 215999
Edward Hayes LLP p39 . . . 020 7353 0011
Edward Hayes LLP p285 . . . 01903 759024

Edward Hayes LLP p244 . . . 023 9247 9872
Stanley Hays p246 . . . 01924 403809
Hayton Winkley p264 . . . 01539 720136
Derek J Hayward & Co p185 . . . 01634 815651
Heath Sons & Broome p305 . . . 0161 681 1933
Heath Sons & Broome p223 . . . 0161 682 8535
Heckford Norton p370 . . . 01799 522636
Heckford Norton p283 . . . 01462 682244
Heckford Norton p395 . . . 01438 312211
Heer Manak p200 . . . 024 7666 4000
Hegarty LLP p347 . . . 01733 346333
Hegarty LLP p393 . . . 01780 752066
Hempsons p40 . . . 020 7839 0278
Hempsons p305 . . . 0161 228 0011
Henrys Solicitors Ltd p395 . . . 01663 742222
Henrys Solicitors Ltd p355 . . . 01625 630880
Henscott Solicitors p40 . . . 0870 880 0007
Heptonstalls LLP p231 . . . 01405 765661
Hereward & Foster p41 . . . 020 7476 6600
Heringtons p215 . . . 01323 411020
Herrington & Carmichael LLP p437 . . . 0118 977 4045
Herrington & Carmichael LLP p173 . . . 01276 686222
Heseltine Bray & Welsh p124 . . . 01226 210777
Hetts p373 . . . 01724 843287
Hetts p373 . . . 01724 270290
Martyn Hewett Solicitor p377 . . . 01304 831888
Hewison & Nixon p351 . . . 01977 700705
Hewitt Burrough & Co p207 . . . 01322 273833
Hewitts p330 . . . 01325 316170
Hewitts p144 . . . 01388 604691
Hewitts p206 . . . 01325 468573
Hewitts p203 . . . 01388 762466
Heyman & Co p282 . . . 01942 604135
Hiace Solicitors p205 . . . 020 8686 3777
Hibberts LLP p203 . . . 01270 215117
Hibberts LLP p320 . . . 01270 624225
Hickman & Rose p41 . . . 020 7700 2211
Hill Dickinson LLP p288 . . . 0151 600 8000
Hill Dickinson LLP p190 . . . 01244 896600
Hill Dickinson LLP p41 . . . 020 7283 9033
Michael Hill Partnership p280 . . . 0116 254 1609
HilliersHRW Solicitors p395 . . . 01438 346000
HilliersHRW Solicitors p264 . . . 01234 858000
The Hillman Partnership p406 . . . 01793 642100
Hills (Oldham) p340 . . . 0161 652 3231
Hindle Campbell p330 . . . 0191 296 1777
Hine Solicitors p229 . . . 01753 482400
HODGE JONES & ALLEN LLP p41 . . . 020 7874 8300
Hodgson Coulthard & Co p253 . . . 0191 584 3333
Hogan Brown p289 . . . 0151 243 7500
Irene Hogarth Criminal Defence p329 . . . 01626 337373
Charles Hoile p322 . . . 01635 45595
Holden & Co p243 . . . 01424 722422
John Holden p263 . . . 01535 667826
Holdens p269 . . . 01524 32484
Holdens p264 . . . 01539 720629
Holt & Longworth p367 . . . 01706 213251 / 229131
Hooper Holt & Co p362 . . . 01737 761111
Hornby Baker Jones & Wood p328 . . . 01633 262848
Horsman Solicitors Ltd p283 . . . 01273 474743
Thomas Horton LLP p167 . . . 01527 871641
Howard & Co p124 . . . 01226 215215
Frank Howard p422 . . . 01925 653481
Philip & Robert Howard p183 . . . 01977 551320
Howe & Spender p353 . . . 01639 881571
Howe & Spender p320 . . . 01639 881571
Howell & Co p139 . . . 0121 778 5031
Howell Jones & Co p113 . . . 01745 826282 / 825845
Howell Jones & Co p292 . . . 01492 640277
Howells LLP p367 . . . 01709 364000
Howells LLP p376 . . . 0114 249 6666
Edward Hughes p363 . . . 01745 343661 / 344551
Gareth Hughes & Co p370 . . . 0161 832 3562
J A Hughes p345 . . . 029 2070 2449
J A Hughes p126 . . . 01446 411000
J Charles Hughes & Co p211 . . . 01341 422464
J W Hughes & Co p199 . . . 01492 596596
Hughmans p44 . . . 020 7246 6560
Humphrys & Co p363 . . . 01745 343158
Humphrys & Co p443 . . . 01978 313399
Hunt & Hunt p366 . . . 01708 764433
Hurleys p152 . . . 01202 436100
Hurlow & Partners p179 . . . 029 2039 6087
Hutchinson Thomas p320 . . . 01639 645061
Henry Hyams p274 . . . 0113 243 2288
IBB Solicitors p417 . . . 0845 638 1381
IBB Solicitors p189 . . . 0845 638 1381
Inesons p195 . . . 01274 872202
Inghams p226 . . . 01253 873481

Inghams *p146* 01253 626642
Darryl Ingram & Co *p45* 020 8202 0843
Paul Inman & Co *p211* 01302 349395
Irvings Solicitors *p209* 01332 346036
Irwin Mitchell LLP *p376* 0870 150 0100
Irwin Mitchell LLP *p274* 0870 150 0100
Isherwood & Hose *p249* 01706 360032 / 368741
Ison Harrison *p228* 0113 286 1455
Ison Harrison *p274* 0113 232 6530
Ison Harrison *p274* 0113 284 5000
Iyama Solicitors *p45* 020 7357 0709
JMW Solicitors *p306* 0845 872 6666
JNP Legal *p314* 01685 350421
Jackamans *p225* 01394 279636
Jacobs & Reeves *p353* 01202 674425
Jacobs & Reeves *p433* 01202 880382
Jacobs & Reeves *p353* 01202 731849
Jacobs Solicitors *p217* 0151 355 8481
Jameson & Hill *p248* 01992 554881
Jamieson & Co *p325* 0191 281 0063
Janes *p46* 020 7930 5100
Jasper & Vincent *p386* 01489 885788
Andrew Jay & Co (Philip Hanby Limited) *p228* 01427 612412
Jeary & Lewis *p193* 01249 444484
Jefferies Essex LLP *p428* 01702 332311
Julian Jefferson *p350* 01752 250850
Jennings *p292* 01554 772331
Jepson & Co *p372* 01723 859249
Jestyn Jeffreys *p320* 01639 635641
Anthony Jewell & Co *p352* 01443 493357
Jobling & Knape *p269* 01524 598300
Johns & Saggar *p46* 020 3490 1475
Johnson & Gaunt *p122* 01295 256271 / 271200
THE JOHNSON PARTNERSHIP *p337* 0115 941 9141
THE JOHNSON PARTNERSHIP *p209* 01332 370473
THE JOHNSON PARTNERSHIP *p311* 01623 427575
The Johnson Partnership *p192* 01246 520930
Jonas Roy Bloom *p139* 0121 212 4111
The Jonathan Morrissey Practice *p152* 01202 310999
Jones & Co *p363* 01777 703827
Cyril Jones & Co *p379* 01244 812109
Geraint Jones & Co *p330* 01686 627935
Geraint Jones & Co *p291* 01597 822244
Gwilym Jones & Davies with Bryant & Co *p319* 01443 472206
Jones Knowles Warburton *p395* 0161 474 1992
Mark Jones & Partners *p289* 0151 286 9594
Jones Robertson *p369* 01928 711119
Terry Jones Solicitors & Advocates *p379* 01743 285888
Terry Jones Solicitors & Advocates *p409* 01952 297979
Thos R Jones & Son *p289* 0151 928 0715
Jordans *p210* 01924 457171
Jordans *p183* 01977 518778
Jordans *p418* 01924 387110
Jung & Co *p384* 020 8813 8996
KCP Law *p254* 020 8572 1212
Kaim Todner Ltd *p47* 020 7701 4747
Kaim Todner Ltd *p47* 020 7353 6660
Kaim Todner Ltd *p47* 020 7700 0070
Kaim Todner Ltd *p119* 01233 662002
Kalber Struckley & Co *p47* 020 7734 1102
Peter Kandler & Co *p48* 020 8960 9222
Kangs Solicitors *p139* 0121 449 9888
Kaufmanlegal *p306* 0161 205 3955
Kavanagh & Co *p216* 01246 432349
Andrew Keenan & Co *p48* 020 8659 0332
Kelcey & Hall *p163* 0117 927 9604
Kemps Solicitors *p340* 0161 633 0555
Kennards Wells *p48* 020 8539 8338
Kenyon Son & Craddock *p212* 01405 813108
Kenyon Son & Craddock *p231* 01405 720850
Keppe & Partners Solicitors *p416* 020 8891 4488
Keppe Rofer *p156* 01874 624627
Christian Khan Solicitors *p49* 020 7631 9500
Khan Solicitors *p154* 01274 301999
Khattak Solicitors *p430* 0161 796 5800
Kidd & Spoor *p431* 0191 297 0011
Kidd & Spoor *p325* 0191 273 9217
Kidd Rapinet *p382* 0845 017 9638
KieranClarkeGreen *p192* 01246 211006
KieranClarkeGreen *p394* 01246 280099
Anthony King & Co *p126* 01268 240400
King Davies & Partners *p298* 01656 732911
Rodney King & Partners *p163* 0117 926 5201
Kingsley Brookes *p256* 01484 302800
Kirby Sheppard *p411* 0845 840 0045
Kirby Sheppard *p268* 0845 840 0045
Kirwans *p134* 0151 608 9078
Kirwans *p319* 0151 677 3433
Kirwans *p289* 0151 229 5600
Kitsons LLP *p413* 01803 202020
Kitsons LLP *p329* 01626 203366
Kitsons LLP *p350* 01752 603040
Knowles Benning *p295* 01582 798000
Brian Koffman & Co *p306* 0161 832 3852
Kundert & Co *p200* 024 7668 4928
LDJ Solicitors *p339* 024 7674 5000
Simon Lacey Law Associates *p430* 01305 777711
Lahiff & Co *p51* 020 8855 5656
Lambert Taylor & Gregory *p228* 0191 477 0616
Lancasters *p158* 01262 602401
Langleys *p445* 01904 610886
Lansbury Worthington *p51* 020 8563 9797
Lanyon Bowdler LLP *p379* 01743 280280
Lanyon Bowdler LLP *p342* 01691 652241
Lanyon Bowdler LLP *p409* 01952 291222
Lanyon Bowdler LLP *p425* 01952 244721
Large & Gibson *p388* 023 9229 6296
Larken & Co *p322* 01636 703333
Samuel L Larye & Co *p156* 020 8568 7022
Last Cawthra Feather LLP *p121* 01274 583106
John Latham & Co *p406* 01793 430133
Law Hurst & Taylor *p428* 01702 337864
Lawrence & Co *p52* 020 7266 4333
Lawrence Law *p52* 020 8788 0055
Lawrences *p424* 01933 442324
Lawson & Thompson *p130* 01670 530700
Owen Lawton *p350* 01752 201169
Layton & Co *p244* 01437 766671
Leathes Prior *p334* 01603 610911
Ledgisters *p52* 020 8746 1122
Laurence Lee & Co *p289* 0151 259 1211 / 259 2824
Leigh Turton Dixon *p315* 01642 241101
Leo Abse & Cohen *p179* 029 2038 3252 / 2034 5421
Leonard & Co *p386* 023 8023 3242
Leonard & Co *p386* 023 8023 4433
Leport & Co *p122* 01295 257328 / 268181
Lester Morrill *p275* 0113 245 8549
Letchers *p364* 01425 471424
Levenes Solicitors *p53* 020 8881 7777 / 8881 6764
Levenes Solicitors *p140* 0121 212 0000
Leviten Thompson & Co *p376* 0114 276 9321
Lewis & Lines *p113* 01495 212286
Duncan Lewis & Co *p53* 020 7923 4020
G Huw Lewis *p320* 01639 637181
Lewis Nedas & Co *p53* 020 7387 2032
Lichfield Reynolds *p398* 01782 289122
Lichfield Reynolds *p398* 01782 313212
E C Lidster & Co *p235* 01472 348417
Linder Myers Solicitors *p307* 0844 984 6400
Linder Myers Solicitors *p306* 0844 984 6000
Linn & Associates Solicitors *p243* 01255 240880
Linskills Solicitors *p289* 0151 236 2224
Livingstons *p206* 01229 462126
Robert Lizar *p307* 0161 226 2319
Robert Lizar *p307* 0161 860 7797
Lloyd & Rowe *p179* 029 2045 8999
Lloyd Brennand *p156* 020 8569 9020
Lloyd Rehman & Co *p55* 020 7778 7550
Llys Cennen Solicitors *p117* 01269 592658 / 592790
Lomax Geddes & Co *p307* 0161 834 4722
Roger Long & Co *p205* 020 8668 5071
Longfords *p340* 0161 665 4400
Lords *p418* 01924 380830
Lound Mulrenan & Jefferies Solicitors *p55* 020 7793 4012
Lumb & Macgill *p154* 01274 730666
M23LAW Solicitors (Hedley-Saunders & Co) *p202* 0844 264 0999
M&M Solicitors *p280* 0116 285 2300
MFG Solicitors *p265* 01562 820181
MFG Solicitors *p409* 01952 641651
MSB Solicitors LLP *p289* 0151 281 9040
MWRLaw Ltd *p357* 01772 254201
McCarthy Stewart & Booty Solicitors *p400* 01449 612343
McCormacks *p56* 020 7791 2000
McCormacks *p56* 020 7791 2000
McCormacks *p140* 0121 200 2777
McCormacks *p126* 01268 525999
McCormicks *p240* 01423 530630
McDermott French *p329* 01626 200177
McGrath & Co *p140* 0121 643 4121
Malcolm McGuinness *p116* 0161 928 7134
McKenzie Bell Solicitors *p401* 0191 567 4857
Gavin McKenzie *p379* 01743 235957
McKenzies *p57* 020 8350 4114
McKinnells *p284* 01522 541181
Mackrell & Thomas *p289* 0151 480 3666
MacLaren Britton *p338* 0115 941 1469
McManus Seddon *p154* 01274 741841
McMillan Williams *p199* 020 8668 4131
McMillan Williams *p419* 020 8669 4962
McMillan Williams *p205* 01689 848311
McMillan Williams *p411* 020 8653 8844
McMillan Williams *p383* 020 8253 7600
McMillan Williams Solicitors *p132* 020 8303 0168
McMillen Hamilton McCarthy *p57* 020 8980 6060
Maidments *p149* 0870 403 4000
Maidments *p370* 0870 403 4000
Maidments *p370* 0870 403 4000
Makanda Bart *p58* 020 8802 0034
E Rex Makin & Co *p289* 0151 709 4491
Malik & Malik Solicitors *p58* 020 8830 3050
Malletts Solicitors *p266* 01553 777744
Malletts Solicitors *p58* 020 7061 3760
Mallia & Co *p180* 029 2022 0044
Malloy & Barry *p180* 029 2034 3434
Mander Cruickshank Solicitors LLP *p196* 01530 510666
Mander Hadley & Co *p200* 024 7663 1212
Stuart J Mander & Co *p420* 01922 642018
Mansouri & Son *p205* 020 8401 7352
Maples Solicitors LLP *p389* 01775 722261
Marchant Harries & Co *p113* 01685 885500
Marchant Harries & Co *p319* 01443 476444
Marchants Solicitors *p312* 01623 655111
Andrew Markham & Co *p182* 01267 221550 / 236199
MARSDEN RAWSTHORN LLP *p194* 01257 279511
MARSDEN RAWSTHORN LLP *p357* 01772 799600
A B Marsh Solicitors *p371* 0161 839 2626
Martin & Strain *p358* 01758 612042
MARTYN PROWEL *p180* 029 2047 0909
Matwala Vyas LLP *p260* 020 8597 5097
Max Gold Law *p257* 01482 224900
Mayo Wynne Baxter LLP *p215* 01323 730543
Mayo Wynne Baxter LLP *p283* 01273 477071
Meikles *p123* 01833 690505
Meikles *p397* 01740 620255
Meikles *p389* 01388 814336
Meikles *p226* 01740 652811
Meikles *p144* 01388 451122
Meldrum Young Solicitors *p390* 01727 840333
Mellor & Jackson *p368* 0161 624 0387
Merry & Co *p369* 01983 811722
Metcalfe Copeman & Pettefar *p435* 01945 464331
Metcalfe Copeman & Pettefar *p410* 01842 756100
Metcalfe Copeman & Pettefar *p266* 01553 778102
Metcalfe Copeman & Pettefar *p347* 01733 865880
Metcalfe Johnston McCormick *p216* 0161 789 3481 / 788 9021
Mian & Co *p140* 0121 684 8000
Middleweeks Solicitors *p307* 0161 839 7255
Miles & Cash *p365* 01773 742222
Miles Hutchinson & Lithgow *p315* 01642 242698
Miles Hutchinson & Lithgow *p371* 01287 623049 / 622056
Miller Gardner *p307* 0161 877 4777
Stuart Miller & Co *p61* 020 8888 5225
Millerchip Peachey *p200* 024 7624 3615
Milne & Lyall *p158* 01308 422362
Milne Moser *p264* 01539 729786 / 725582
Mirza & Co *p61* 020 8520 4416
David Rubie Mitchell & Co *p403* 020 8641 0575
Mohabirs *p61* 020 7720 5742 / 7622 5495
Mohammed & Co Solicitors *p357* 01772 888700
B H Mohammed *p140* 0121 772 4464
Molesworths Bright Clegg *p365* 01706 356666
Mary Monson Solicitors Ltd *p407* 0161 794 0088 / 0808 155 4870
Morecrofts Solicitors LLP *p203* 0151 924 9234
Morecrofts Solicitors LLP *p134* 0151 666 2210
Morgan & Richardson *p181* 01239 612302
John Morgan Solicitors *p140* 0121 233 1852
Morgans *p180* 029 2072 9888
John Morley & Co *p359* 01634 375444
Morlings *p299* 01622 673081
Morris Scott & Co *p194* 01425 278866
Morrish Solicitors LLP *p276* 0113 245 0733
Morrison Spowart *p62* 020 8698 9200
Mortons *p396* 0161 477 1121
Moss & Co *p62* 020 8986 8336
Moss & Haselhurst *p435* 01606 592159
Moss Beachley Mullem & Coleman *p62* 020 7402 1401 / 7723 5783
Moss Solicitors LLP *p293* 01509 217770
Mosshaselhurst *p333* 01606 74301
Mountain Partnership *p62* 020 7732 3737
Mowbray Woodwards Solicitors *p128* 01225 485700
Mr Laws Solicitors *p62* 020 8767 9717 / 8672 3447

See p603 for the Community Legal Service Work Categories

Mulcahy Smith *p229* 0191 490 1000
Stephen Mullarkey Solicitors *p226* 01352 733770
Stephen Mullarkey Solicitors *p252* 01352 710657
Mullenders *p437* 01483 771733
Murdochs *p62* 020 8530 7291
James Murray Solicitors *p150* 0151 933 3333
James Murray Solicitors *p290* 0151 207 9910
Martin Murray & Associates *p382* 01753 551313
Martin Murray & Associates *p427* 01895 431332
Martin Murray & Associates *p361* 0118 950 8577
Robin Murray & Co *p185* 01634 832332
Murrays Partnership *p62* 020 7701 8653
Mushtaq & Co *p140* 0121 622 1786
Mustoe Shorter *p430* 01305 752700
MYER WOLFF *p257* 01482 223693
NGA *p198* 01282 862000
Needham Poulier & Partners *p63* 020 8808 6622
Nelson Guest & Partners *p380* 020 8309 5010 / 8309 0558
Nelsons *p338* 0115 958 6262
Alfred Newton & Co *p433* 01625 523647
Alfred Newton & Co *p396* 0161 430 8831
Nicholas & Partners *p308* 0161 202 4999
Nicholls Christie & Crocker *p417* 01895 256216
Mark Nicholls *p265* 01536 502843
Nile Arnall Solicitors *p164* 0117 909 8898
Noble *p377* 01462 814055
Norcross Lees & Riches *p341* 0161 624 6034
NORRIE WAITE & SLATER *p377* 0114 276 6166
Norrie Waite & Slater *p377* 0114 248 4890
Norrie Waite & Slater *p367* 01709 523983
Norrie Waite & Slater *p377* 0114 276 5015
North Yorkshire Law *p372* 01723 360001
Norton & Co *p259* 0161 366 8333
Norton Peskett *p129* 01502 718700
Norton Peskett *p294* 01502 533000
Norton Peskett *p238* 01986 872513
Nyland & Beattie *p432* 0151 424 5656
O'Garra's *p276* 0113 247 1477
O'Gorman & Co *p422* 01926 409900
O'Keeffe Solicitors *p64* 020 7644 8800
O'Neill Solicitors *p326* 0191 232 9008
OMW Solicitors *p170* 01283 563401 / 530333
Michael Oerton *p125* 01271 378686
Ogden Lyles & Fox *p216* 0161 789 2793
Oldham Marsh Page Flavell *p314* 01664 563162
Oldhams Solicitors & Advocates *p121* 01462 895444
Oliver & Co *p191* 01244 312306
M Olubi Solicitors *p64* 020 7737 3400 / 07956 394567
John Onions *p400* 01789 269899
Ormerods *p205* 020 8686 5000
R J Osborne & Co *p199* 01536 204111
Oslers Solicitors *p400* 01449 774670
Owen & O'Sullivan *p446* 01443 862263
Owen Nash & Co *p420* 01922 746746
Owen White & Catlin *p225* 020 8890 2836
Owen White & Catlin *p119* 01784 254188
Owen White & Catlin *p254* 020 8570 5471
Oxley & Coward Solicitors LLP *p367* 01709 510999
PCB Solicitors LLP *p379* 01743 248148
PCB Solicitors LLP *p194* 01694 723818
PCB Solicitors LLP *p294* 01584 878456
PPG Criminal Law Ltd *p224* 01252 362626
Page Nelson *p285* 01522 531741
Painters *p266* 01562 822295
Painters *p399* 01299 822033
Painters *p266* 01562 822295
Paisleys *p440* 01900 602235
Palmer Hodgson & Heyes *p226* 01253 778231
Palmer Hodgson & Heyes *p411* 01253 824216
Palmers *p126* 01268 240000
Palmers Criminal Defence Solicitors *p207* 01304 380572
Pannone LLP *p308* 0161 909 3000
Pardoes *p158* 01278 457891
Pardoes *p408* 01823 446200
J Keith Park & Co *p391* 01744 636000
Park Woodfine Heald Mellows LLP *p130* 01234 400000
Parker Grego Cullen & Ball *p141* 0121 200 3031
Parkinson Wright LLP *p220* 01386 761176
Parlby Calder Solicitors *p350* 01752 600833
Parry Davies Clwyd-Jones & Lloyd *p292* 01248 723106
Parry Davies Clwyd-Jones & Lloyd *p117* 01407 831777 / 830665
Parry Davies Clwyd-Jones & Lloyd *p172* 01286 673381
Partridge & Wilson *p171* 01284 762281
Patchell Davies (Trading Name of PD Law Ltd) *p147* 01495 227128
Musa A Patel & Co *p210* 01924 437800
Musa A Patel & Co *p154* 01274 747777
Payne & Gamage *p322* 01636 640649

Payne & Payne *p257* 01482 326446
Margaret Payne *p182* 01228 521383
Payton's Solicitors *p66* 020 7405 1999
Peace Revitt *p125* 01226 341111 / 210077
Peace Revitt *p367* 01709 898454
Peach Grey & Co *p386* 023 8033 4695
Pearson Fielding Polson *p290* 0151 236 3636
Pearson Hinchliffe *p341* 0161 785 3500
Penmans *p264* 01926 858222
Penmans *p424* 01789 470022
Pepperells *p373* 01724 871999
Pepperells *p257* 01482 326511
Percy Short & Cuthbert *p67* 020 7700 0265
Peters & Peters *p67* 020 7629 7991
Petherbridge Bassra Solicitors *p154* 01274 724114
Phillips *p312* 01623 658556
Phillips & Co *p371* 01722 321666
David Phillips & Partners *p150* 0151 922 5525
David Phillips & Partners *p290* 0151 236 3331
David Phillips & Partners *p67* 020 7486 5525
David Phillips & Partners *p308* 0161 860 7354
Samuel Phillips Law Firm *p326* 0191 232 8451
Pickup & Scott *p121* 01296 397794
Pictons Solicitors LLP *p295* 01582 870870
Pictons Solicitors LLP *p317* 01908 663511
Pictons Solicitors LLP *p247* 01442 242441
Pinkney Grunwells Lawyers LLP *p158* 01262 673445
Pinniger Finch & Co *p428* 01373 823791
Platt Halpern *p308* 0161 224 2555
Platt Halpern *p341* 0161 626 4955
David Playford & Co *p354* 01275 840111
Pluck Andrew & Co *p120* 0161 330 2875
Pluck Andrew & Co *p259* 0161 368 6311
Pollecoff Solicitors Ltd *p68* 020 7608 2568
Polpitiya & Co *p384* 020 8813 9282
Pond Marsh *p147* 01253 620466
Poole Alcock *p203* 01270 256665
Poole Alcock *p333* 01606 350445
Poole Townsend *p416* 01229 588111
Poole Townsend *p264* 01539 734455
Angela Porter Solicitors *p266* 01865 841414
Porter Dodson *p425* 01823 666622
Porter Dodson *p408* 01823 625800
Porter Dodson *p444* 01935 424581
Powell Spencer & Partners *p69* 020 7604 5600
Powells *p429* 01934 623501
Power Scott Solicitors *p394* 01207 230125
Powleys *p294* 01502 581121
John Poyser Solicitors *p309* 0161 860 7354
Preston Redman *p152* 01202 292424
PURCELL PARKER *p141* 0121 236 9781
Quality Solicitors Mewies *p381* 01756 799000
QualitySolicitors C Turner *p145* 01254 688400
QualitySolicitors D'Angibau *p151* 01202 393506
QualitySolicitors Gruber Garratt *p120* 0161 344 2244
QualitySolicitors Gruber Garratt *p341* 0161 665 3502
QualitySolicitors Gruber Garratt *p358* 0161 724 0203
QualitySolicitors Gruber Garratt *p393* 0161 303 2328
QualitySolicitors Jackson & Canter *p290* 0151 282 1700
QualitySolicitors Jordans *p212* 01302 365374
Quinn Melville *p290* 0151 236 3340
RJR Solicitors *p227* 01983 752115
RJR Solicitors *p369* 01983 562201
RJR Solicitors *p328* 01983 526924
Donald Race & Newton *p169* 01282 433241
Donald Race & Newton *p198* 01282 864500
Rafiq & Co *p276* 0113 240 7556
Raja & Co *p70* 020 8772 4900
Ralph & Co *p329* 01637 872218
Ramsdens Solicitors *p251* 01484 690040
Ranson Houghton *p118* 01264 351533
Ranson Houghton *p127* 01256 816759
Rausa Mumford *p180* 029 2034 4341
Rawal & Co *p70* 020 8445 0303
Rawstorne Heran Solicitors *p400* 01789 267646
Red Kite Law *p410* 01834 842122
Red Kite Law *p345* 01646 683222
Red Kite Law *p244* 01437 763332
Red Kite Law *p345* 01646 681529
Red Kite Law *p316* 01646 698008
Redfearns *p246* 01924 403745 / 404601
Michael J Reed Ltd *p183* 01267 281675
Richard George & Jenkins *p330* 01686 626210
Richard Nelson Business Defence Solicitors *p338* 0115 986 3636
Richard Nelson Business Defence Solicitors *p383* 0121 707 7666
Richards & Lewis *p216* 01495 350018
Roger Richards *p345* 01803 845191

Richardson Smith & Co *p189* 01494 772773
Richmond Anderson Goudie *p191* 0191 388 7884
Richmonds *p326* 0191 232 2155
Rickards & Cleaver *p115* 01773 832204
Garth Rigby & Co *p119* 01942 717378
Lee Rigby Partnership *p283* 01772 421748
Riley Hayes & Co *p438* 01902 773666
Stephen Rimmer LLP *p216* 01323 644222
Risdon Hosegood *p433* 01984 632277
Risdon Hosegood *p318* 01643 703123 / 700008
Rix Mclaren *p373* 01724 872038
Roach Pittis *p328* 01983 524431
D P Roberts Hughes & Denye *p134* 0151 647 6000
Jeremy Roberts & Co *p347* 01733 343943 / 342172
Roberts Moore Nicholas Jones *p134* 0151 647 0000
John Robertson *p432* 0151 423 6500
Robertsons *p180* 029 2023 7777
Robertsons *p445* 01904 658551
John Robinson & Co *p258* 01482 324818
Paul Robinson Solicitors *p428* 01702 338338
R P Robinson *p281* 0116 262 1462
Roche & Co *p72* 020 7831 2209
Frank Roe Solicitors *p391* 01744 24218
Roebucks *p145* 01254 274000
Rogers & Co *p438* 01902 310312
Rogerson Galvin *p120* 0161 344 2027 / 335 9005
Roland Robinsons & Fentons LLP *p147* 01253 621432
Ronald Fletcher Baker LLP *p73* 020 7613 1402
Rose & Dunn *p369* 01928 572030
Paul Ross & Company *p309* 0161 832 0706
Ross Solicitors Ltd *p406* 01793 512960
Rotherham & Co *p201* 024 7622 7331
Rowbis Solicitors *p230* 01452 301903
Rowland Tildesley & Harris *p433* 01902 366571
Rubin Lewis O'Brien *p206* 01633 867000
Rudlings & Wakelam *p156* 01842 810300
Rudlings & Wakelam *p171* 01284 755771
Rundlewalker *p222* 01392 209209
Russell & Co *p300* 01684 892000
Russell & Russell *p149* 01204 399299
Russell & Russell *p191* 01244 405700
Russell Jones & Walker *p164* 0117 374 2222
Russell Jones & Walker *p74* 020 7657 1555
Russell Jones & Walker *p419* 01924 234300
Russell Jones & Walker *p141* 0121 233 8300
Russell Jones & Walker *p309* 0161 383 3500
Russell Jones & Walker *p377* 0114 276 6868
Russell Jones & Walker *p326* 0191 323 3000
Russell Jones & Walker *p180* 029 2026 2800
SA Law *p390* 01727 798000
SFN Solicitors *p169* 01282 421284
SJP Solicitors *p258* 01485 532662
SJS Solicitors *p75* 020 8675 4436
Salhan & Company *p142* 0121 605 6000
Michael Salt *p365* 01706 646655
Samy & Co *p242* 020 8861 2424
Sanders & Co *p399* 01384 375437 / 378991
Sanders Witherspoon LLP *p156* 01277 221010
Sansbury Douglas *p164* 0117 955 2663
Sansbury Douglas *p164* 0117 926 5341
Sansbury Douglas *p269* 0117 963 5044
Santers Solicitors *p123* 020 8594 7542
Sarginsons Law LLP *p201* 024 7655 3181
S Satha & Co *p76* 020 8471 9484
Saulet & Co *p389* 023 9281 9442
Saunders Goodin Riddleston Solicitors *p263* 01473 225600
Saunders Law Partnership LLP *p76* 020 7632 4300
Scanlans *p402* 0191 565 2565
Scott-Moncrieff Harbour & Sinclair *p77* 020 7485 5588
Scott Son & Chitty *p119* 01372 276211
Scotts Wright *p283* 01966 22227
Scotts Wright *p183* 01748 832431
Scudamores *p439* 0844 880 2323
Scutt Beaumont Solicitors Ltd *p281* 0116 254 4200
Seatons Solicitors *p199* 01536 276300
Seddon Thomson *p309* 0161 720 8000
Sehgal & Co *p142* 0121 772 2226
John D Sellars & Co *p403* 020 8661 7014
Sergeant & Collins *p373* 01724 864215
The Sethi Partnership Solicitors *p216* 020 8866 6464
Shapland & Co *p77* 020 7383 7030
Sharman Law *p130* 01234 303030
Sharp & Partners *p339* 0115 959 0055
Shaw Graham Kersh *p78* 020 7734 9700
Shelley & Co *p175* 01223 359441
Shentons *p434* 01962 844544
Clive Shepherd & Co *p420* 01922 647797
Shepherd Evans Solicitors *p297* 01625 503909
Shepherd Harris & Co *p219* 020 8363 8341

Sheridan Bowles Solicitors *p234* 01493 859848
Sherwood Dunham *p424* 01933 276147
Sherwood Wheatley *p267* 020 8546 0144
Gordon Shine & Co *p78* 020 8969 7033
Shipton Hallewell & Co *p192* 01246 232140
Shirtcliffe & Reston Solicitors *p411* 01845 526222
Siddiqui & Co *p242* 020 8423 2400
Silks *p382* 0121 558 1147
Silks *p340* 0121 511 2233
Silks *p321* 01384 236101
SILLS & BETTERIDGE LLP *p381* 01529 302800
SILLS & BETTERIDGE LLP *p285* 01522 542211
SILLS & BETTERIDGE LLP *p381* 01754 610101
SILLS & BETTERIDGE LLP *p151* 01205 364615
SILLS & BETTERIDGE LLP *p199* 01526 344444
Richard Silver *p309* 0161 834 9494
Silversmiths *p150* 0151 922 6066
Simons Muirhead & Burton *p79* 020 7734 4499
Sinclairs *p345* 029 2070 6444
Singleton Winn McDermott Solicitors *p326* 0191 265 8817
R W Skinner & Son *p170* 01283 561694
Slee Blackwell *p125* 01271 372128
Martin Smalley & Co *p339* 0115 955 6555
Smith & Copsey *p419* 0191 262 4428
Ashley Smith & Co *p80* 020 8463 0099
Smith Brown & Sprawson *p295* 01582 876900
Geoffrey T Smith & Co *p438* 01902 426961
J H Smith *p182* 01228 521383
The Smith Partnership *p170* 01283 536471
The Smith Partnership *p404* 01283 226444
The Smith Partnership *p398* 01782 324454
Smith Roddam *p144* 01388 603073
T C Smith *p131* 01289 307409
W F Smith LLP *p424* 01953 880800
W F Smith LLP *p209* 01362 852900
Maurice Smiths *p183* 01977 557171
Smithson Hinds Morris *p276* 0113 245 0456
Solomon Levy *p295* 01582 425817 / 414948
Sonn Macmillan *p80* 020 7377 8889
Soods Solicitors *p261* 020 8597 0000
Southerns *p321* 01282 603663
Southerns *p198* 01282 863113
Southerns *p169* 01282 438446
J D Spicer & Co *p81* 020 7625 5590
G Spilsbury & Co *p319* 01443 473213
Louis Spragg & Co *p213* 01384 211621 / 211622
H Michael Spring *p353* 01639 897075
St Luce & Co *p82* 020 7635 9131
Stables & Co *p237* 0121 585 3820
Standley & Co *p269* 01564 776287
Stanford & Lambert *p327* 0191 232 6226
R W Stebbings *p350* 01752 202287
Steed & Steed LLP *p401* 01787 373387
Steed & Steed LLP *p155* 01376 552828
Steele & Son *p124* 01282 813385
Steele & Son *p196* 01200 444321
Steele & Son *p198* 01282 868000
STEELE FORD & NEWTON *p321* 01282 692531
Steeles *p335* 0870 609 0200
Stephens & Scown *p222* 01392 210700
Stephens & Scown *p391* 01726 74433
Stephens & Scown *p414* 01872 265100
Stephens McDonald & Robson *p327* 0191 232 0675
Stephensons Solicitors LLP *p282* 01942 777777
Stephensons Solicitors LLP *p391* 01942 777777
Stephensons Solicitors LLP *p432* 01942 777777
Stephensons Solicitors LLP *p282* 01942 777777
Sternberg Reed *p123* 020 8591 3366
Sternberg Reed *p366* 01708 766155
Stevens *p244* 01440 762511
Stevens *p370* 01799 526849
Stevens *p398* 01782 343353
Stevens *p398* 01782 813200
Stevens *p393* 01785 250908
Stevens *p438* 01902 772776
Paul Stevens & Co *p165* 0117 942 9308
Chris Stevenson *p212* 01302 341243
G T Stewart Solicitors *p83* 020 8299 6000
Stock Moran Swalwell *p432* 01942 771771
Stokes Solicitors *p355* 023 9282 8131
Stokoe Partnership *p83* 020 8558 8884
Stone King LLP *p128* 01225 337599
Stone Milward Rapers *p193* 01243 780211
Andrew Storch *p361* 0118 958 4407
A M Strachan & Co *p84* 020 7729 0003
Straw & Pearce *p293* 01509 268931
David Street & Company *p202* 01293 616191
Swain & Co *p386* 023 8063 1111
Swain & Co *p244* 023 9248 3322
Sweetman Burke & Sinker *p84* 020 8840 2572
Swinburne & Jackson LLP *p229* 0191 477 2531 / 477 3222
Swinburne & Jackson LLP *p423* 0191 416 0004
Swinburne & Jackson LLP *p370* 0191 413 3468 / 413 2630
Swinburne & Jackson LLP *p191* 0191 388 7221
Swinburne Maddison *p214* 0191 384 2441 / 384 7455
Swinburne Snowball & Jackson *p199* 01207 502532
Sykes Lee & Brydson *p445* 01904 731100
Sykes Lee & Brydson *p445* 01904 529000
Symes Bains Broomer *p235* 01472 360991
TBI Solicitors *p243* 0800 052 6824 / 01429 264101
TMJ Legal Services LLP *p243* 01429 235616
TV Edwards LLP *p85* 020 7790 7000
TV Edwards LLP *p85* 020 7790 7000
TWM Solicitors LLP *p85* 020 8946 6454
Tait Farrier Graham *p229* 0191 490 0108
Tait Farrier Graham *p327* 0191 272 3713
Talbot Walker LLP *p118* 01264 363354
Talbot Walker LLP *p127* 01256 332404
Talbots Legal Advice Centre *p399* 01384 445850 / 447777
Tallents Solicitors *p322* 01636 671881
Tallents Solicitors *p312* 01623 666700
Tanburghs *p85* 020 8749 8902
Tanburghs O'Brien Lahaise *p85* 020 7372 6614
Tang Bentley & Jackson *p224* 01329 220401
Tanner & Taylor LLP *p225* 01252 733770
Tanner & Taylor LLP *p224* 01252 549555
Tanner & Taylor LLP *p115* 01252 316565
Tates Solicitors *p277* 0113 242 2290
Taylor Lewis *p181* 01239 621999
Sharon Taylor Associates *p353* 01202 759769
Taylor Street Solicitors LLP *p115* 01252 400999
Taylor Vinters *p176* 01223 423444
David Teague *p350* 01752 600950
Stanley Tee *p144* 01279 755200
Temple Heelis LLP *p264* 01539 723757
Thomas Boyd Whyte *p132* 020 8303 7755
Dean Thomas & Co *p441* 01909 500511
H E Thomas & Co *p87* 020 8854 3036
Rose Thomas & Co *p269* 01570 423300
Andrew Thompson & Co *p277* 0113 383 5314
Keith R Thompson & Co *p261* 01469 510510
Thompsons (formerly Robin/Brian Thompson & Partners) *p377* 0114 270 3300
Thompsons (formerly Robin/Brian Thompson & Partners) *p277* 0113 205 6300
THOMSON WEBB & CORFIELD *p176* 01223 578070
Thomson Webb & Corfield *p176* 01223 578068
Thomson Wilson Pattinson *p264* 01539 721945
Thomson Wilson Pattinson *p434* 01539 442233
Richard Thorn & Co *p160* 01273 625600
Thornes *p438* 01902 313311
Thorpe & Co *p430* 01947 603465
Thorpe & Co *p372* 01723 364321
Thorpe & Co *p300* 01653 694899
Thorpe & Co *p226* 01723 515555
Peter Thubron & Co *p402* 0191 510 1221
Thursfields *p440* 01905 730450
Thursfields *p266* 01562 820575
Tilley & Co *p390* 01727 840467
Timms *p170* 01283 561531 / 544417
Timms *p209* 01332 364436
Timms Solicitors *p404* 01283 214231
Toller Beattie LLP *p125* 01271 341000
Tosswill & Co *p87* 020 8674 9494
Toussaint & Co *p427* 020 8903 6111
Toussaints *p143* 0121 523 5050
Townshends LLP *p198* 01675 467333
Tracey Barlow Furniss & Co *p441* 01909 472355
Tracey Barlow Furniss & Co *p363* 01777 707677
Tranters *p310* 0161 998 9999
Traymans *p88* 020 7249 9980
Ronnie Tremlett & Co *p160* 01273 696132
Trinity Solicitors LLP *p88* 020 7428 0880
Trobridges *p412* 01752 812787
Trobridges *p350* 01752 664022
Tuckers *p310* 0161 233 4321
Tuckers *p88* 020 7388 8333
Tudur Owen Roberts Glynne & Co *p122* 01248 362315 / 355826
Tudur Owen Roberts Glynne & Co *p172* 01286 672207 / 672851
Tudur Owen Roberts Glynne & Co *p147* 01766 830206
Tyndallwoods *p143* 0121 624 1111
VHS Fletchers Solicitors *p339* 0115 959 9550
Marina C Van't Goor *p316* 01646 697700
Rhys Vaughan *p311* 0161 224 1439
Veja & Co Solicitors *p245* 020 8581 1502
Veja and Co Solicitors *p385* 020 8574 2626
Veseys Solicitors *p143* 0121 523 1123
Vickers & Co *p89* 020 8579 2559 / 8840 3999
Vickers Chisman & Wishlade *p397* 01642 615439
Victor Lissack Roscoe & Coleman *p89* 020 7487 2505
Vincent Laverys *p357* 01772 555176
Vyman Solicitors *p242* 020 8427 9080
WBW Solicitors *p329* 01626 202404
WBW Solicitors *p153* 01626 833263
WBW Solicitors *p413* 0870 701 4321
WBW Solicitors *p222* 01392 202404
W Evans George & Sons *p323* 01239 710228
Waddington & Son *p344* 01282 778813
Waddington & Son *p169* 01282 426666
Waddington Webber *p264* 01535 662644 / 662647
Wains *p297* 01625 429511
Wainwright & Cummins *p90* 020 7737 9330
Wainwright & Cummins *p90* 020 7326 7460
Waitt & Co Solicitors *p177* 01227 470600
Waldron & Schofield *p249* 01706 624029
Waldrons *p268* 01384 811811
Waldrons *p213* 01384 811811
Walker & Co *p420* 01922 639080
Walker & Co *p367* 01709 817112
Grenville J Walker *p147* 01258 459911
Grenville J Walker *p430* 01305 759090
Walker Lahive *p350* 01752 551722
Walker Smith Way *p443* 0844 346 3100
Walker Smith Way *p191* 0844 346 3100
Walkers *p367* 01706 213565
Walkers *p169* 01282 411138
The Walkers Partnership *p368* 01763 241121 / 248896
The Walkers Partnership *p368* 01763 248896
Wallace McNally *p201* 024 7622 0300
Waller Needham & Green *p347* 01733 311422
Walter Wilson Richmond *p242* 020 8427 8484
Walters & Barbary *p173* 01209 712454
Wannop Fox Staffurth & Bray *p148* 01243 864001
Wannop Fox Staffurth & Bray *p193* 01243 778844
Wannop Fox Staffurth & Bray *p442* 01903 201120
Wansbroughs *p314* 01225 703222
Wansbroughs *p210* 01380 733300
Warings Solicitors *p147* 01253 293106
Warner Goodman LLP *p355* 023 9275 3575
Rodney Warren & Co *p216* 01323 430430
Watkins & Gunn *p352* 01495 762244
Watkins Stewart & Ross *p263* 01473 226266
Alasdair Watson & Co *p327* 0191 488 4521
Paul J Watson *p315* 01642 293427
The Watson Ramsbottom Partnership *p207* 01254 701111
Watson Solicitors *p422* 01925 571212
Watson Woodhouse *p397* 01642 247656
V G Waugh *p348* 0191 527 2727
Andrew Webb *p165* 0117 953 8408
Welch & Co *p181* 01239 614070
Nigel Weller & Co *p283* 01273 487123
Wessex Solicitors Chambers Ltd *p355* 023 9238 1114
Simon West *p128* 01225 482001
Whatley Recordon *p300* 01684 892939
J B Wheatley & Co *p91* 020 8479 8000
Whetter Duckworth Fowler *p266* 01865 842100
Whiskers *p219* 01992 561111
Whiskers *p239* 01279 439439
Whitelock & Storr *p91* 020 7405 3913
Whiting & Purches *p383* 0121 605 5050
Wholley Goodings LLP *p319* 01670 519714
Widdows Mason *p432* 01942 244294
Widdows Mason *p282* 01942 673311
Widdows Mason *p422* 01925 632267
Wilford Smith Solicitors *p367* 01709 828044
Wilkin Chapman Epton Blades *p285* 01522 512345
Wilkin Chapman Grange Solicitors *p294* 01507 606161
Wilkin Chapman Grange Solicitors *p252* 01507 527521
Wilkinson & Butler *p392* 01480 219229
Wilkinson Woodward *p238* 01422 339600
Wilks Price Hounslow *p369* 01983 566241
Willett & Co *p171* 01284 701323
Williams & Co *p296* 01582 723322
Williams & Co *p217* 020 8952 8882
Williams MacDougall & Campbell *p442* 01903 214186
R N Williams & Co Limited *p438* 01902 429051
Williamson & Soden *p143* 0121 333 4848
Williamson & Soden *p383* 0121 733 8000
Williamsons *p258* 01482 323697
Wilson & Berry *p153* 01344 420555
Wilson & Bird *p121* 01296 436766
Wilson & Co *p92* 020 8808 7535
Wilson & Co Solicitors *p315* 01642 222292
Wilson Devonald Ltd *p406* 01792 484566

See p603 for the Community Legal Service Work Categories

J M Wilson Solicitors *p143* 0121 356 4556
Wilsons Solicitors *p344* 01865 874497
Windeatts *p413* 01803 862233
Winterbotham Smith Penley LLP *p320* . . 01453 832566
Winterbotham Smith Penley LLP *p401* . . 01453 847200
Wiseman Lee LLP *p92*. 020 8215 1000
Wiseman Lee LLP *p92*. 020 8215 1000
Withy King Solicitors *p128* 01225 425731
Withy King Solicitors *p414* 01225 777464
Withy King Solicitors *p128* 01225 425731
Withy King Solicitors *p407* 01793 536526
Withy King Solicitors *p313* 01672 514781
Anne Woodcock & Co *p390* 01727 861212
Woodcocks *p171* 0161 761 4611
Woodcocks *p359* . . . . .01706 225621 / 215018
Woodcocks *p121* 01706 874487
Woodfines LLP *p130*. 01234 270600
Woodford Robinson *p333* 01604 624926
Aidan Woods & Co *p165* 0117 952 2006
Michael G Wooldridge *p143*. 0121 706 2259
Woollcombe Yonge *p351* 01752 660384
Wragg Mark-Bell Solicitors *p182* 01228 711728
Nicholas Wray Solicitor *p244*. 01440 704467
Wright & McMillan Bennett *p409* 01952 291100
Wright & Morton *p402* 0191 567 4289
Desmond Wright & Co *p245* 020 8561 4888
Wykes O'Donnell Williams *p261*. 0115 932 8776
Yarwood & Stubley *p148* 01670 361211
Yarwood Stimpson & Co *p431* 0191 297 0123
Yates Ardern *p120* 0161 330 3332
P H Yeung *p93*. 020 7287 1882
Young & Co *p398* 01782 339200
Gordon Young Solicitors Ltd *p296* 01582 405577
Julian Young & Co *p93* 020 7724 8414
Young Swistak Solicitors *p314* 01664 501801
Youngs *p181* 029 2076 3211
Youngs Criminal Defence Services Limited *p377* 0114 249 5444
ZMS Solicitor *p281*. 0116 247 0790

5

SECTION 6

SOLICITORS

CONTENTS

Work Categories for Solicitors Firms

A1 Agricultural Law, Holdings & Property
A2 Animals, Farming, Forestry
A3 Arbitration & Mediation
B1 Bankruptcy
B2 Fraud
B3 Accounting Standards
C1 Commercial & Company Law
C2 Mergers & Acquisitions
C3 Competition Law
D1 Child Care & Wardship
D2 Adoption
E Commercial Property
F1 Consumer Law – Agreements, Credit, Licensing, Sale of Goods
F2 Consumer Protection – Advertising, Trade Descriptions, Trading Standards, Product Liability
G Crime – General
H Crime – Juvenile
I Computer Law
J1 Employment Law
J2 Health & Safety at Work
K1 Family Law
K2 Family Mediation
K3 Divorce & Matrimonial
K4 Elderly
L Housing, Landlord & Tenant
M1 European Community Law
M2 International Law
M3 Air Law
M4 Islamic Law
N Litigation, Accidents, Injury, Criminal Injury Compensation, Personal Injury
O Litigation, Commercial
P Environmental Liability
Q Litigation, General
R1 Planning, Compulsory Purchase, Lands Tribunal
R2 Property – Finance, Development
S1 Residential Conveyancing
S2 Commercial Conveyancing
T1 Taxation – Business
T2 Taxation – Personal
U1 Communications & Telecommunications
U2 Internet & e-commerce
V Welfare Benefits
W Wills, Trusts & Probate
X Education Law
Za Admiralty
Zb Banking Law
Zc Building Law, Building Contracts
Zd Charity Law
Ze Copyright, Patents, Trade Marks & Intellectual Property
Zf Entertainment, Artists & Performers
Zg Human Rights & Civil Liberties
Zh Housing Association Law
Zi Immigration & Nationality
Zj Insurance Law
Zk Libel, Slander & Defamation
Zl Liquor, Betting & Gaming Licensing
Zm Mental Health
Zn Mines, Minerals, Oil & Gas
Zo Pensions, Investments & Financial Services
Zp Race & Sex Descrimination
Zq Professional Negligence
Zr Clinical Negligence
Zs Rating Law
Zt Road Haulage Licensing
Zu Local Government
Zv Regulated by the FSA for Investment Business
Zw Sports Law
Zx Ecclesiastical Law
Zy Food & Drugs
Zz Printing & Publishing
Zza Data Protection

INDIVIDUAL SOLICITORS, ENGLAND & WALES – A-Z

A

A'Court, Mrs L A (A'Court & Co) *K1 K2 N S1 D1 Zr K3 W*
Windsor *p434* 01753 857146

A'Court, P M (A'Court & Co) *K1 N W S1 S2 J1 L Q Zr R2*
Windsor *p434* 01753 857146

Aaron, J (Aaron & Partners LLP Solicitors) *C1 C2 E O Zv*
Chester *p190* 01244 405555

Aaron, Miss R D (Squire Sanders (UK) LLP) *O*
Leeds *p277* 0113 284 7000

Aaron, Ms R E (Squire Sanders (UK) LLP)
London EC2 *p81* 020 7655 1000

Aaron, S (Simons Rodkin Litigation Solicitors) *N O G D1 J1 B1 C1 F1 M1 I Zj Zk Zp Zw*
London N12 *p79* 020 8446 6223

Aarons, D (Black Graf & Co) *E C1 S2 J1*
London NW3 *p13* 020 7586 1141

Aaronson, F J (Aaronson & Co) *G H M1 K1 L F1 P D1 J1 W Zi Zl*
London W8 *p3* 020 7376 9124

Aaronson, Ms L F (Aaronson & Co) *Zi K1 J1 R1*
London W8 *p3* 020 7376 9124

Abas, Ms M N (Irwin Mitchell LLP) *B2 J2 P Ze*
Sheffield *p376* 0870 150 0100

Abbas, S (Megsons LLP)
Oldham *p340* 0161 633 6131

Abbate, Miss F V (Squire Sanders (UK) LLP) *O Q Zj*
London EC2 *p81* 020 7655 1000

Abbate, R (Withers LLP) *C2 C1*
London EC4 *p92* 020 7597 6000

Abbess, Miss L M (Hempsons) *E*
Westminster *p40* 020 7839 0278

Abbey, R M (Russell Jones & Walker)
London WC2 *p74* 020 7657 1555

Abbi, S (Higgs & Sons) *N O J1*
Brierley Hill *p158* 0845 111 5050

Abbott, Miss A L (Land Registry - Lytham Office) *S1 S2 W Zi*
Lytham *p464* . . . . .01253 849849 / 840012

Abbott, Ms C (Gotelee) *E S2 R2 A1*
Ipswich *p262* 01473 211121

Abbott, C D K (Kennedys) *O N J1 K1 B1 J2*
Manchester *p306* 0161 829 2599

Abbott, D M (Barlow Lyde & Gilbert LLP)
London EC3 *p10* 020 7247 2277

Abbott, D W (Olliers) *G H B2*
Manchester *p308* 0161 834 1515

Abbott, F R (William Heath & Co) *S1 E L C1 T1*
London SW11 *p40* 020 7350 1068

Abbott, Mrs G M (Clifford Chance)
London E14 *p20* 020 7006 1000

Abbott, H (Norton & Co) *K1 M1 S1 D1 P F1 G H W E*
Hyde *p259* 0161 366 8333

Abbott, J A G (Mander Cruickshank Solicitors LLP) *C1 E G H K1 S1 D1 J1 O Q Zl Zv*
Coalville *p196* 01530 510666

Abbott, J C (Silverman Sherliker LLP) *B1 C1 Q O N J1 Zk Ze Zc A3*
London EC2 *p78* 020 7749 2700

Abbott, J R (Hart Brown Solicitors) *W*
Cobham *p196* 0800 068 8177

Abbott, J S A (Stephenson Harwood) *O Q*
London EC2 *p82* 020 7329 4422

Abbott, K (Peter D Greenhalgh)
Glossop *p230* 01457 861319

Abbott, Mrs L M (Abbott Lloyd Howorth) *B1 Zl C1 S2 E*
Maidenhead *p298* 01628 798800

Abbott, Ms M (Bird & Bird LLP)
London EC4 *p13* 020 7415 6000

Abbott, M (Blaser Mills) *G H*
Aylesbury *p120* 01296 434416

Abbott, Mrs M (Peterborough City Council)
Peterborough *p468* 01733 747474

Abbott, M J (Somerset County Council) *Q K1*
Taunton *p473* 0845 345 9166

Abbott, N (Mills & Reeve) *J1*
Norwich *p335* 01603 660155

Abbott, N R D (Blake Lapthorn) *E P L*
Portsmouth *p354* 023 9222 1122

Abbott, Miss S (Thompson Allen LLP) *O Q L E*
Brighton *p160* 01273 608003

Abbott, S M (Freeth Cartwright LLP) *E*
Leicester *p279* 0116 248 1100
Nottingham *p337* 0115 936 9369

Abbott, T (Wealden District Council)
Crowborough *p456* 01892 653311

Abbott, Ms T D (Emsleys) *K1 K3 D1*
Crossgates *p204* 0113 260 3115

Abbotts, Mrs A (Young & Co) *S1*
Stoke-on-Trent *p398* 01782 339200

Abboushi, Miss R (Abboushi Associates) *Q S1 O N B1 W Ze E J1 Zk Zr*
London N3 *p3* 020 8343 4045

Abdi, M S (Hasan Solicitors) *G H*
Birmingham *p139* 0121 778 4003

Abdulla, M (DWT Legal Ltd) *J1*
Kidderminster *p265* 0844 770 3799

Abedin, Miss S S (Prestons & Kerlys) *W S1*
Brentwood *p156* 01277 211755

Abel, Mrs C R H (Hayes & Storr) *W K4*
Sheringham *p378* 01263 825959

Abel, D (Walsall Metropolitan Borough Council)
Walsall *p475* 01922 650000

Abel, M L (Fruhman Davies Livingstones) *B1 E L N O Q T1 T2 S1 W Zd*
Manchester *p304* 0161 833 0578

Abell, N Q (Wright Hassall LLP) *E R2 S2*
Leamington Spa *p270* 01926 886688

Abell, P M (Field Fisher Waterhouse LLP)
London EC3 *p31* 020 7861 4000

Abenson, E S (Abensons) *C1 E F1 G J1 L N P R1*
Liverpool *p285* 0151 733 3111

Aberdein, P (Bartletts Solicitors) *N Q*
Liverpool *p286* 0151 228 7730

Abernethy, A J (Reed Executive PLC)
London WC2 *p108* 020 7421 1640

Abernethy, Miss D (Nicholson Martin Legge & Miller) *W K1 D1 K3 K4 K2*
Houghton Le Spring *p253* . . 0191 584 2841

Abesamis, Miss M N (Reed Smith LLP)
London EC2 *p71* 020 3116 3000

Abey, M (Dawson Hart) *K1 K2 D1*
Uckfield *p416* 01825 762281

Abeyewardene, Mrs D (Ziadies) *S1 W Zi*
London SW9 *p94* 020 7737 0934

Abeygunasekera, Ms N (Pritchard Englefield)
London EC2 *p69* 020 7972 9720

Abiloye, A O (Abiloye & Co)
London E12 *p3* 020 8478 5678

Ablett, G T (BHP Law) *D1 G H J1 K1 M1 N P W Zl Zm*
Newton Aycliffe *p330* 01325 312534

Ablett, J R (Laurence Lee & Co)
Liverpool *p289* . . . 0151 259 1211 / 259 2824

Ablitt, R H (Ablitts) *S2 C1 E W Q K4*
Bromley *p3* 020 8776 8783

Aboobaker, S (SA Law Chambers) *N*
Ilford *p260* 020 8554 0012

Abraham, B T (Colemans)
Haywards Heath *p245* 01444 459555

Abraham, C (Last Cawthra Feather LLP) *O*
Leeds *p275* 0113 244 0876

Abraham, D K (Wirral Borough Council) *D1 K1*
Wallasey *p475* 0151 638 7070

Abraham, H C (Brachers) *R1 P*
Maidstone *p299* 01622 690691

Abraham, J (Sternberg Reed) *J1 Zl*
Barking *p123* 020 8591 3366

Abraham, J F (Dawson Cornwell) *K1 K3 Zx*
London WC1 *p26* 020 7242 2556

Abraham, Mrs S (S Abraham Solicitors) *J1 K1 L N O Q S1 W Zq*
Surbiton *p402* 020 8390 0044

Abraham, W (Squire Sanders (UK) LLP)
London EC2 *p81* 020 7655 1000

Abrahamian, Ms P (Radcliffes Le Brasseur)
Westminster *p70* 020 7222 7040

Abrahams, Miss C (Bolt Burdon) *N*
Islington *p14* 020 7288 4700

Abrahams, D M (Philip Ross & Co) *S2 E R2 S1*
London W1 *p73* 020 7636 6969

Abrahams, G (Forsters LLP) *W T2*
Westminster *p33* 020 7863 8333

Abrahams, Mrs J (Lloyd Platt & Co) *K1*
London N3 *p55* 020 8343 2998

Abrahams, Ms P A (Lewis Nedas & Co) *L Zh*
Camden *p53* 020 7387 2032

Abrahams, R G (Salans) *B1 C1 F1 J1 L N P S1 W Zb*
London EC4 *p76* 020 7429 6000

Abrahams, R M (Abrahams Dresden) *C1 C2 C3 E I J1 S1 W Ze Zk*
London EC1 *p3* 020 7251 3663

Abrahams, S (Freeman Box)
London W1 *p34* 020 7486 9041

Abrahams, S (Maxwell Winward LLP) *C1 C2 Ze Zb U2*
London EC4 *p59* 020 7651 0000

Abrahamson, B S (Abrahamson & Associates) *C1 E I J1 L N O Q*
London NW11 *p3* 020 8458 1100

Abrahamson, D E (AS Law) *M1 G D1 N P V F1 H J1 Zg Zi Zp*
Liverpool *p285* 0151 707 1212
London NW11 *p3* 020 8458 1100

Abrahamson, E (Broudie Jackson Canter) *D1 Zg*
Liverpool *p286* 0151 227 1429

Abram, J A (Brecher) *S2 E S1 O Q*
London W1 *p15* 020 7563 1000

Abrams, C (SJ Berwin LLP)
London EC4 *p75* 020 7111 2222

Abrams, G (Gregory Abrams Davidson LLP) *N Q*
Liverpool *p288* 0151 236 5000
Liverpool *p288* 0151 494 0777

Abrams, G M (EAD Solicitors LLP) *C1 E L S1*
Liverpool *p287* 0151 291 2500

Abrey, Ms J (Withers LLP) *W*
London EC4 *p92* 020 7597 6000

Abrey, Miss L R (Norman Saville & Co) *S1*
London N10 *p76* 020 8883 9711

Abrol, M (The Wilkes Partnership LLP) *F1 L O Q R1*
Birmingham *p143* 0121 233 4333

Abu Bakar, M S (Gepp & Sons) *S1 S2 Zl L Zi*
Chelmsford *p186* 01245 493939
Colchester *p197* 01206 369889

Abu-Deeb, M (Reynolds Porter Chamberlain LLP)
London E1 *p71* 020 3060 6000

Abubaker, A (Kingswell Watts)
Dewsbury *p210* 01924 461236

Acharya, Ms S (HM Land Registry - Harrow Sub Office) *E L S1*
Harrow *p460* 020 8235 1181

Acheson, Miss E S (Kennedys) *N Zj*
London EC3 *p49* 020 7667 9667

Acheson, G J (Farrer & Co LLP)
London WC2 *p31* 020 3375 7000

Achillea, S (YVA Solicitors) *K1 N Q L F1 G Zl Zi*
London N12 *p93* 020 8445 9898

Achillies, D S (J Keith Park & Co) *G H*
St Helens *p391* 01744 636000

Ackerman, J (Joseph Ackerman)
London NW4 *p3* 020 8457 6700

Ackerman, W (Bond Pearce LLP)
Southampton *p385* 0845 415 0000

Ackermann, N (Hewitsons) *O N F1 Ze*
Cambridge *p174* 01223 461155

Ackers, Ms J (Manchester City Council)
Manchester *p465* 0161 234 5000

Acklam, D I (Acklam Bond Noor) *E S1 W C1 L Zv*
Blackburn *p145* 01254 56068
Accrington *p114* 01254 872272

Ackland, M (MLM Cartwright) *U1 E S2 Zc R2*
Cardiff *p179* 029 2046 2562

Ackland, M J (Fasken Martineau LLP) *E L S1*
London W1 *p31* 020 7917 8500

Ackland, S R (Ackland & Co)
Cardiff *p177* 029 2064 1461

Ackroyd, Mrs A M (Preston Redman) *S1 L R1 E W*
Bournemouth *p152* 01202 292424

Ackroyd, R D C (Staffordshire County Council)
Stafford *p472* 01785 223121

Acock, R J (Lyons Davidson) *C1 T1*
Bristol *p163* 0117 904 6000

Acomb, N (Stevens & Bolton) *W*
Guildford *p237* 01483 302264

Acomb, Miss V E (Wrigleys Solicitors LLP) *Zo W*
Leeds *p278* 0113 244 6100

Acres, Mrs S (Hegarty LLP) *G H*
Peterborough *p347* 01733 346333

Acres, S J (Stanley De Leon) *E S1 W Q S2 K1 C1 O Zl*
Potters Bar *p355* 01707 657277

Acres, Miss V A (Jobling Gowler) *Zr*
Macclesfield *p297* 01625 614250

Acton, A (Stone King LLP) *W S1 E C1 L T1 T2*
Bath *p128* 01225 337599

Acton, Miss C (Berwins Solicitors Limited) *J1*
Harrogate *p240* 01423 509000
York *p445* 01904 528200

Acton, D E (David Acton & Co) *S1 L E W C1 R1 Zc*
Solihull *p382* 01564 730028

Acton, H J (Trowers & Hamlins) *L E S1 Q W Zh Zc*
Exeter *p222* 01392 217466

Acton, J (Trowers & Hamlins)
London EC3 *p88* 020 7423 8000

Acworth, S H A (Downie & Gadban) *A1 D1 E J1 K1 L N O M1 P Zm S1 W*
Alton *p116* 01420 82879

Adabadze, S (Marsons Solicitors LLP) *L*
Bromley *p166* 020 8313 1300

Adair, C W (Goldkorn Mathias Gentle Page LLP) *C1 S2 E S1*
London WC1 *p36* 020 7631 1811

Adam, Ms A A (Gregsons) *O Q Zq*
London SW19 *p37* 020 8946 1173

Adam, Mrs A A (AXA UK PLC)
London E22 *p103* 020 7920 5900

Adam, G H (Wright Son & Pepper LLP) *G O Q Zq*
Camden *p93* 020 7242 5473

Adam, P J (Teacher Stern LLP) *E R1 S1 Zc R2 S2*
London WC1 *p86* 020 7242 3191

Adam, R C (Ashton KCJ) *B1 F1 J1 L O Q*
Bury St Edmunds *p171* . . . 01284 762331

Adam, R T (LG Lawyers) *S2 E*
London SE1 *p50* 020 7379 0000

Adam, S (Reynolds Porter Chamberlain LLP)
London E1 *p71* 020 3060 6000

Adams, A C (SGH Martineau LLP) *B1 F1 M1 N P Zf*
Birmingham *p142* 0870 763 2000

Adams, Mrs A L (Nelsons) *S1 R1*
Nottingham *p338* 0115 958 6262

Adams, A S H (Forresters) *S1 S2 L W T1 T2 R1 C1 A1 E J1 Zj*
Barrow-in-Furness *p125* . . . 01229 820297

Adams, C H (Andrew Kingston & Co) *J1 O Q*
Hull *p257* 01482 216217

Adams, C J (Bishop Akers & Co)
Swanley *p404* 01322 660617

Adams, C M (Nelsons) *N P L*
Nottingham *p338* 0115 958 6262

Adams, D (Streeter Marshall) *N*
Croydon *p205* 020 8680 2638

Adams, D (Joseph Darios Solicitors) *N V*
Southampton *p385* 023 8023 7575

Adams, D M (Irwin Mitchell LLP) *G H B2*
Sheffield *p376* 0870 150 0100

Adams, D P (SJ Berwin LLP) *T1*
London EC4 *p75* 020 7111 2222

Adams, E (The Dental Law Partnership)
Nantwich *p320* 01270 613320

Adams, Mrs E F (Plexus Law (A Trading Name of Parabis Law LLP)) *N*
Evesham *p220* 01386 769160

Adams, Ms E J (DAC Beachcroft)
London EC4 *p24* 020 7242 1011

Adams, E J R (Woolliscrofts) *N Q*
Hanley *p239* 01782 204000

Adams, G A (Pardoes) *B1 F1 L O Q G H Zb Zc Zl*
Bridgwater *p158* 01278 457891

Adams, G A R (Government Legal Service)
London BS1 *p106* 0845 300 0793

Adams, G J W (Green Wright Chalton Annis) *S1 K1 W*
Worthing *p441* 01903 234064
Worthing *p441* 01903 700220

Adams, G R J (Randle Thomas LLP) *Q L E A1 S2 Zq*
Helston *p246* 01326 572951

Adams, Mrs G W (Myer Wolff) *K1 D1 D2*
Hull *p257* 01482 223693

Adams, G W (Hugh James) *S2 C1 R1 P Zl J1 A3 L*
Cardiff *p179* . . . 029 2022 4871

Adams, J A D (Adams Delmar) *E G K1 L S1 W M1 N P*
Hampton *p238* . . . 020 8941 2097

Adams, J A J (Fladgate LLP) *E*
London WC2 *p32* . . . 020 3036 7000

Adams, J R (Morrison & Foerster (UK) LLP) *O Q*
London EC2 *p62* . . . 020 7920 4000

Adams, Miss K L (Drysdales) *Q N S1 J1 L B1 F1*
Southend-on-Sea *p387* . . . 01702 423400

Adams, L (Hughmans) *G H*
London EC4 *p44* . . . 020 7246 6560

Adams, Ms L (DBL Talbots LLP) *J1*
Stourbridge *p399* . . . 01384 445850

Adams, Miss M (TV Edwards LLP) *K1*
London EC3 *p85* . . . 020 7790 7000

Adams, M S (Wilkin Chapman LLP) *S1 E S2*
Beverley *p131* . . . 01482 398398

Adams, N (Goodman Derrick LLP)
London EC4 *p36* . . . 020 7404 0606

Adams, N K (Edwards Angell Palmer & Dodge) *J1 J2 Zp Zi*
London EC2 *p28* . . . 020 7583 4055

Adams, Ms N L (Jonas Roy Bloom) *G H*
Birmingham *p139* . . . 0121 212 4111
Solihull *p383* . . . 0121 733 8000

Adams, Ms P (Olswang LLP) *C1 I C2 Ze*
London WC1 *p64* . . . 020 7067 3000

Adams, Mrs R (Hayton Winkley) *K1*
Kendal *p264* . . . 01539 720136

Adams, R (Jones Day) *E*
London EC4 *p46* . . . 020 7039 5959

Adams, R (MB Solicitors Ltd trading as MB Law) *N Q F1 C1 O Zj Zq A3*
Leeds *p275* . . . 0113 242 4444

Adams, R (Watson Burton LLP) *B1 Q N S1*
Newcastle upon Tyne *p327* . 0845 901 2100

Adams, R A (Crosse & Crosse) *W*
Exeter *p220* . . . 01392 258451

Adams, R D (Adams Hetherington) *S1 E K1 W T1 C1 N G D1 Q Zl*
Cramlington *p201* . .01670 714622 / 714635

Adams, Miss S (Kingsley Napley) *Zi*
London EC1 *p50* . . . 020 7814 1200

Adams, S (Rouse Legal (Formerly Willoughby & Partners)) *Ze*
London E14 *p74* . . . 020 7536 4100

Adams, Mrs S (Kelcey & Hall) *S1 W*
Bristol *p163* . . . 0117 927 9604

Adams, S A (Clifton Ingram LLP) *Q W T2 Zq*
Wokingham *p437* . . . 0118 978 0099

Adams, Miss S L (Aldridge Brownlee Solicitors LLP) *E S2 L R2 S1*
Bournemouth *p151* . . . 01202 526343

Adams, Mrs S M (Williscroft & Co) *K1 D1 D2 K3*
Bradford *p155* . . . 01274 305380

Adams, T (Reorient Legal) *C1 C2 Ze*
London EC3 *p71* . . . 020 7645 8255

Adams, T C J (Barlow Robbins LLP) *T2 W*
Guildford *p235* . . . 01483 543200

Adams, T D S (Adams Burrows) *S1 W*
Bristol *p160* . . . 0117 970 2246

Adams, T M (The College of Law Chester)
Chester *p454* . . . 0800 289997

Adams, V (TWM Solicitors LLP) *K4 T2 V W*
Cranleigh *p202* . . . 01483 273515

Adams, V W (Adams) *L P R1 Zu*
Newcastle upon Tyne *p323* . 0191 261 0361

Adams, W W (Adams & Co)
Birmingham *p135* . . . 0121 523 3491

Adams, Miss Z (Last Cawthra Feather LLP) *Zc F1 Q N S1 W*
Bradford *p154* . . . 01274 848800

Adamson, Ms A L E (Mills & Reeve) *J1 X*
Cambridge *p175* . . . 01223 364422

Adamson, D P (Buller Jeffries) *F1 F2 J2 Zr N O Q Zj Zc Zq*
Birmingham *p136* . . . 0121 212 2620

Adamson, G (Donnelly McArdle Adamson) *G H K1 M1 S1 D1 F1 P N*
Hartlepool *p243* . . . 01429 274732

Adamson, I R (Bircham Dyson Bell) *C1 J1 Zd Zp*
Westminster *p13* . . . 020 7227 7000

Adamson, N T (Raworths LLP) *S1 S2 W*
Harrogate *p240* . . . 01423 566666

Adamson, R K (Max Engel & Co LLP) *K1 D1 J1 Q Zl*
Northampton *p331* . . . 01604 887450

Adamson, Miss T (BPE Solicitors LLP) *A3 Zc O Q*
Cheltenham *p187* . . . 01242 224433

Adcock, Miss E V (Rothera Dowson) *K1 K3*
West Bridgford *p427* . . . 0115 914 0077

Adcock, H (The Wilkes Partnership LLP) *E*
Birmingham *p143* . . . 0121 233 4333

Adcock, M H (Adcocks Solicitors Ltd) *C1 E S1 W L S2 R1*
Lichfield *p284* . . . 0845 470 8081

Addae, T (The Johnson Partnership) *G H B2*
Nottingham *p337* . . . 0115 941 9141

Addae-Anderson, Mrs B (Ziadies) *L Zi*
London SW9 *p94* . . . 020 7737 0934

Addai, Ms R (Judge & Priestley) *B1 O*
Bromley *p166* . . . 020 8290 0333

Addinell, T J (Steeles) *T1 W T2 Zd*
Diss *p211* . . . 01379 652141
Norwich *p335* . . . 0870 609 0200

Addington, R G (Hartley Thomas & Wright) *S1 W L E T1 S2 T2*
Rochdale *p365* . . . 01706 644118

Addington-Smith, N (Allen Barfields) *E S1 C1 W*
Croydon *p204* . . . 020 8680 2050

Addis, P F (Furley Page LLP) *S1 W R1 E C1 A1*
Whitstable *p431* . . . 01227 274241

Addis, W R (Clarkson Wright & Jakes Ltd) *J1*
Orpington *p341* . . . 01689 887887

Addis-Jones, T (Stephenson Harwood) *O A3 C1 Za Zc Zj*
London EC2 *p82* . . . 020 7329 4422

Addison, E S (Austin Ray) *K1 K3 O Q Zq N F1 L Zl*
Milton Keynes *p316* . . . 01908 769648

Addison, G P L (Insinger de Beaufort (Insinger English Trust))
London EC2 *p107* . . . 020 7608 0888

Addison, Mrs J M (Ray Borley & Dunkley) *S1 V W T1 T2*
Stony Stratford *p399* . . . 01908 563232

Addison, Mrs K A (Barker Gotelee Solicitors) *E S2 R2 S1*
Ipswich *p262* . . . 01473 611211

Addison, P R (Powells) *B1 C1 F1 L O Q Zj Zk N Zg*
Weston-super-Mare *p429* . . 01934 623501

Addison, Mrs S A (Howell-Jones LLP) *S1 W S2*
Cheam *p186* . . . 020 8642 8142

Addison, Miss Y K (East Sussex County Council)
Lewes *p463* . . . 01273 481000

Addison Smith, Ms K (Crowell & Moring) *Zj*
London EC4 *p23* . . . 020 7413 0011

Addlestone, B D (Addlestone Keane Solicitors) *N M1 P J1*
Leeds *p271* . . . 0113 244 6700

Addlestone, Ms K (Turbervilles) *S1 S2*
Uxbridge *p417* . . . 01895 201700
Uxbridge *p417* . . . 01895 201700

Addlestone, R K (C W Harwood & Co) *O N K1 Q J1 F1 Ze Zq Zk*
Leeds *p274* . . . 0113 245 7027

Addrison, M K (HilliersHRW Solicitors) *E C1 L W B1*
Stevenage *p395* . . . 01438 346000

Addy, Ms Y (Muscatt Walker Hayim) *B1 F1 J1 L N O Q S1*
London W1 *p62* . . . 020 7486 5131

Addyman, N J S (Cogent Law) *N*
Croydon *p204* . . . 0844 245 4452

Adebiyi, J D A (Skadden Arps Slate Meagher & Flom (UK) LLP) *C2*
London E14 *p80* . . . 020 7519 7000

Adedapo, A (Capsticks Solicitors LLP) *Zr*
London SW19 *p18* . . . 020 8780 2211

Adefuve, Miss O (Stanley De Leon) *E S2 C1 L O Q N A1 R1 R2 S1*
Potters Bar *p355* . . . 01707 657277

Adejobi, O A (Grier Olubi Solicitors) *M1 Za*
London EC2 *p37* . . . 020 7256 7770

Adekanmi, Mrs A (Ziadies) *J1 Zi X*
London SW9 *p94* . . . 020 7737 0934

Adeniran, O (Havillands)
Romford *p366* . . . 01708 766559

Adeogun, Ms K O (Association of Teachers and Lecturers)
London WC2 *p103* . . . 020 7930 6441

Adeola, Mrs O A (Hodgsons & Mortimer) *K3 K1 D1*
Darlington *p206* . . .01325 250111 / 355956

Adere, C (Davies Parsons Allchurch) *A1 S2*
Llanelli *p292* . . . 01554 749144

Adey, R C (Shakespeares) *E S2 R2*
Birmingham *p142* . . . 0121 237 3000

Adieze, O (Avon & Somerset Constabulary)
Portishead *p469* . . . 01275 816270

Adjepong, K (Serious Fraud Office)
London WC1 *p109* . . . 020 7239 7272

Adkin, M G (Mackrell Turner Garrett)
Addlestone *p114* . . . 01932 342181

Adkin, T J (Winterbotham Smith Penley LLP) *K1 D1 Q K2 V*
Nailsworth *p320* . . . 01453 832566

Adkinson, R F (Crane & Walton) *A1 B1 C1 D1 E L S1 T1 V*
Leicester *p279* . . . 0116 255 1901

Adlam, Miss S (Metcalfe Copeman & Pettefar) *N O Q K1*
Peterborough *p347* . . . 01733 865880

Adlard, Ms H E (Charles Russell LLP) *R1*
Cheltenham *p187* . . . 01242 221122

Adlem, Miss S (Talbot Walker LLP) *N Zr J1*
Andover *p118* . . . 01264 363354

Adleman, N (Harbottle & Lewis LLP) *C1 Zf Zv*
London W1 *p38* . . . 020 7667 5000

Adler, Miss C (TWM Solicitors LLP) *K1 K2 D1*
Epsom *p219* . . . 01372 729555

Adler, Ms D G (Hereward & Foster) *E H K1 I L V D1 J1 Zi Zm Zh Zr*
London E16 *p41* . . . 020 7476 6600

Adler, J C (Barretts) *E J1 L S1*
London WC1 *p11* . . . 020 7248 0551

Adler, M (Aubrey David) *E J1 L S1 S2*
Westminster *p25* . . . 020 7224 4410

Adler-Jensen, Ms T (Simmons & Simmons) *Ze*
London EC2 *p79* . . . 020 7628 2020

Adlington, J P N (Trowers & Hamlins) *L E Zh*
London EC3 *p88* . . . 020 7423 8000

Adoki, A (Burnley-Jones Bate & Co) *S1 H G*
London SW19 *p16* . . . 020 8542 8101

Adourian, Miss Y R (Gill Turner Tucker) *W T2*
Maidstone *p299* . . . 01622 759051

Adshead, Mrs A M (Thames Water Utilities Limited)
Reading *p469* . . . 0118 373 8000

Afrifa-Yamoah, K (Afrifa & Partners)
London SW9 *p4* . . . 020 7820 9177

Aftab, F (CKFT)
London NW3 *p17* . . . 020 7431 7262

Afzal, M (Aequitas Law LLP) *Q F1 Zi N J1*
London W1 *p4* . . . 020 7495 2776

Afzal, M (Ford Banks Irwin) *E B1 O Q C1 S1 Zi Zl Zm Zd Ze*
Manchester *p304* . . . 0161 866 8999

Agamian, Miss E J (Brabners Chaffe Street) *W*
Manchester *p301* . . . 0161 836 8800

Aganwal, Ms S (ALMT Legal)
London EC3 *p3* . . . 020 7645 9190

Agar, C A N (Forshaws Davies Ridgway LLP) *A1 B1 C1 E F1 G L M1 R1*
Warrington *p422* . . . 01925 230000

Agar, N S D (CMS Cameron McKenna LLP) *B1 O Zb*
Bristol *p162* . . . 0117 930 0200

Agasee, Ms S (Paul Robinson Solicitors) *K1*
Westcliff-on-Sea *p428* . . . 01702 338338

Ager, D G (Battens) *S2 E*
Yeovil *p443* . . . 01935 846000
Exeter *p221* . . . 01392 688688

Ager, Mrs H L (Crutes) *N O Q*
Newcastle upon Tyne *p324* . 0191 233 9700

Ager, R S (Wollen Michelmore Solicitors)
Newton Abbot *p330* . . . 01626 332266

Aggarwal, K K (Thomson Snell & Passmore) *B1 F1 O Zl B2*
Dartford *p207* . . . 01322 623700

Aggarwal, N (Finers Stephens Innocent LLP) *E*
London W1 *p32* . . . 020 7323 4000

Aggett, Mrs S (Calvert Smith & Sutcliffe) *S1*
Richmond upon Thames *p364*020 8940 0017

Aggett, Mrs S C (Teignbridge District Council)
Newton Abbot *p466* . . . 01626 361101

Agius, Ms R (Hugh James)
Cardiff *p179* . . . 029 2022 4871

Aglionby, Mrs L F (Trowers & Hamlins) *N Q J1 K1*
London EC3 *p88* . . . 020 7423 8000

Agnew, C (Stones Solicitors LLP) *K4 K1 T2 W*
Exeter *p222* . . . 01392 666777

Agnew, D (Blake Lapthorn) *L O Q*
Chandlers Ford *p184* . . . 023 8090 8090

Agnew, Ms D (Moore Blatch Solicitors) *C1 I Zza U2 Ze F1*
Southampton *p386* . . . 023 8071 8000

Agnew, R (Croftons) *E S2 R2 S1*
Manchester *p302* . . . 0161 214 6180

Agnew, Ms Y E (Leo Abse & Cohen) *N Zr*
Cardiff *p179* . . .029 2038 3252 / 2034 5421

Agnihotri, Ms R (Hallett & Co) *Q N J1*
Ashford *p119* . . . 01233 625711

Agrawal, A (Batchelors Solicitors) *Q J1 O Zq*
Bromley *p166* . . . 020 8768 7000

Agyeman, Miss M (Epping Forest District Council)
Epping *p458* . . . 01992 564000

Agyemang, A (Bhogal Partners)
Hounslow *p253* . . . 020 8572 9867

Ahark, Mrs P (Willson Hawley & Co)
Nuneaton *p339* . . . 024 7638 7821

Ahern, J (DLA Piper UK LLP)
London EC2 *p24* . . . 0870 011 1111

Ahl, Ms J (ARVAL PHH Ltd)
Swindon *p473* . . . 01793 884671

Ahlborn, C (Linklaters LLP)
London EC2 *p54* . . . 020 7456 2000

Ahluwalia, J S (Singh Karran & Co) *E N Q B1 C1 K3 K1 O Zq W*
Hounslow *p254* . . . 020 8570 5776

Ahluwalia, M (Walker Morris) *N*
Leeds *p277* . . . 0113 283 2500

Ahluwalia, S (Avery Emerson Solicitors)
Ilford *p259* . . . 020 8215 0884

Ahmad, A (Christian Khan Solicitors)
London WC1 *p49* . . . 020 7631 9500

Ahmad, F (The College of Law)
London WC1 *p105* . . . 0800 289997

Ahmad, H (Max Gold Law) *Q O N F1 Zq K1*
Hull *p257* . . . 01482 224900

Ahmad, I (Asphaltic Roofing Supplies Ltd)
St Ives *p472* . . . 01480 466777

Ahmad, K R (Cuttle & Co Solicitors) *K3 K1 L Q N*
Oldham *p340* . . . 0161 678 7443

Ahmad, Miss M (Johar & Co) *K1 Zi Q F1 V N J1*
Leicester *p280* . . . 0116 254 3345

Ahmad, Miss N (Healys LLP) *S1 S2*
Brighton *p159* . . . 01273 685888

Ahmad, R (Anthony Gold)
London SE1 *p6* . . . 020 7940 4000

Ahmed, Miss A (Armitage Sykes LLP) *O Q N*
Huddersfield *p255* . . . 01484 538121

Ahmed, Mrs A (Williams & Co Solicitors) *W S1 K4*
Cleckheaton *p195* . . . 01274 851608

Ahmed, A (Philip Ross & Co) *O Q N C1*
London W1 *p73* . . . 020 7636 6969

Ahmed, A (Ahmed Solicitors) *G H*
Birmingham *p135* . . . 0121 507 1030

Ahmed, F M (Daybells LLP) *Zi S1 S2 E*
London E15 *p26* . . . 020 8555 4321

Ahmed, I (Ahmed & Co) *G H*
Camden *p4* . . . 020 7383 2243

Ahmed, Ms I (AGH Solicitors) *G N Zi*
Bolton *p148* . . . 01204 364433

Ahmed, K (Himayah Solicitors) *Zi O Q Zu S2 S1 L*
Birmingham *p139* . . . 0121 356 5007

Ahmed, Ms L S (Addleshaw Goddard)
London EC1 *p4* . . . 020 7606 8855
London SE1 *p50* . . . 020 7379 0000

Ahmed, M H (Evans Dodd LLP) *C1 E J1*
London W1 *p30* . . . 020 7491 4729

Ahmed, N (Roberts & Smith) *S1 S2 Q N*
Nelson *p321* . . . 01282 619000

Ahmed, N (Thomas Andrew & Daodu Solicitors) *G L*
Westminster *p87* . . . 020 7224 9522

Ahmed, Ms N (Scott Rees & Co) *N Q*
Skelmersdale *p381* . . . 01695 722222

Ahmed, N A (Howells LLP) *Zi*
Sheffield *p376* . . . 0114 249 6666

Ahmed, Mrs P (Harrison Bundey) *K1 K3*
Leeds *p274* . . . 0113 200 7400

Ahmed, P (Charles Russell LLP) *S1 R2*
London EC4 *p19* . . . 020 7203 5000

Ahmed, R (Blake Lapthorn) *O F1*
Oxford *p342* . . . 01865 248607

Ahmed, Ms R (Powells) *Zb B1 F1 L Zj U2 O Q Zq*
Weston-super-Mare *p429* . . 01934 623501

Ahmed, Mrs R K (Wakefield Metropolitan District Council)
Wakefield *p474* . . . 01924 306090

Ahmed, Mrs S (Birmingham City Council Legal & Democratic Services)
Birmingham *p449* . . . 0121 303 2066

Ahmed, S (Hill Dickinson LLP)
Manchester *p305* . . . 0161 817 7200

Ahmed, Miss S (Joint Council for the Welfare of Immigrants)
London EC1 *p107* . . . 020 7251 8708

Ahmed, S (Tuckers) *N*
Manchester *p310* . . . 0161 233 4321

Ahmed, S (Edwards Duthie) *G H*
London E13 *p29* . . . 020 8514 9000

Ahmed, S (MFG Solicitors) *G H*
Telford *p409* . . . 01952 641651

Ahmed, Ms S (Leeds City Council)
Leeds *p462* . . . 0113 224 3513

Ahmed, Ms S (Shanaz & Partners Solicitors)
London EC3 *p77* . . . 020 7375 2898

Ahmed, Ms S (Rothera Dowson) *L S1*
Nottingham *p338* . . . 0115 916 5200

Ahmed, Mrs S H (Marsden Rawsthorn LLP) *K1 D1 D2 K3*
Preston *p357* . . . 01772 799600

Ahmed, Z (Martin Murray & Associates) *G H B2*
Reading *p361* . . . 0118 950 8577

Ahmed, Ms Z (Shoosmiths) *N*
Basingstoke *p127* . . 0370 086 6200 / 01256 696200

Ahsan, M (Martin-Kaye LLP) *N L*
Telford *p409* . . . 01952 272222

Aidin, Ms J E (J E Aidin)
Pulborough *p358* . . . 01798 872531

Aikman, B W (FBC Manby Bowdler LLP) *A3 B1 O Q*
Wolverhampton *p437* . . . 01902 578000

Ainge, P G (Lumb & Macgill) *G H K1 D1*
Bradford *p154* . . . 01274 730666

Ainley, Miss C A (Meade-King) *S1 S2 E*
Bristol *p163* . . . 0117 926 4121

Ainley, J N (Kellogg Management Services (Europe) Ltd)
Manchester *p465* . . . 0161 869 2000

Ainscoe, R M (Wrigleys Solicitors LLP) *Zo W*
Leeds *p278* . . . 0113 244 6100

Ainscough, G (Crane & Staples) *W S1*
Welwyn Garden City *p425* . . 01707 329333

Ainsley, Ms A J (Mincoffs Solicitors LLP) *N Zr*
Newcastle upon Tyne *p325* . 0191 281 6151

Ainsley, Ms L (The National Trust)
Swindon *p475* . . . 01793 817400

Ainslie, D G (Stone King LLP)
Bath *p128* . . . 01225 337599

Ainsworth, Miss A E (hlw Keeble Hawson LLP) *S1 E S2*
Leeds *p274* . . . 0113 244 3121

Ainsworth, C (Kimbells LLP) *E S2*
Milton Keynes *p317* . . . 01908 668555

Ainsworth, Mrs K E (Sumner & Tabor) *K1 J1 Q O N L D1 B1*
Berkhamsted *p131* . .01442 862797 / 872311

Ainsworth, Ms L (Thornleys Limited) *W*
Plymouth *p350* . . . 01752 406977

Ainsworth, Miss L M (Hogan Lovells International LLP)
London EC1 *p42* . . . 020 7296 2000

Ainsworth, R A (Andersons)
Croydon *p204* . . . 020 8680 3131

Ainsworth, R L (Marsden Rawsthorn LLP) *S1 S2 W*
Preston *p357* . . . 01772 799600

Ainsworth, S R (Napthens LLP) *S1*
Preston *p357* . . . 01772 888444

Air, Miss P M (Nicholson Portnell) *W K4 T2*
Hexham *p249* . . . 01434 603656

Airey, Ms A (Bathurst Brown Downie & Airey LLP) *N Zr Q B1 L O*
Twickenham *p416* . . . 020 8892 1537

Airey, Miss C T (Ipswich Borough Council)
Ipswich *p461* . . . 01473 432000

Airnes, Miss T (Fletchers) *N*
Southport *p388* . . . 01704 546919

Airy, G M (Calderdale Magistrates Court)
Halifax *p460* . . . 01422 360695

Aisbett, A (Pinsent Masons LLP)
Birmingham *p141* . . . 0121 200 1050

Aiston, N A (Aiston Solicitors) *C1 D1 Q O S1 E J1 I B1 L Zd Zc Ze Zf Zv*
Croydon *p204* . . . 020 8681 0123

Aitchison, P W (Aitchison & Co) *D1 K1 D2 Q*
London WC2 *p4* . . . 020 7240 0020

See p634 for the Key to Work Categories

Aitken, Ms C J (Brighouse Wolff) Maghull *p298* 0151 520 2717

Aitken, Mrs F (Mortons) *S1 Q W J1 F1 N S2 K4 L* Sunderland *p401*. 0191 514 4323

Aitken, Miss H L (Pinkerton Leeke & Co) *S1 S2 W* Cheltenham *p188* 01242 237477

Aitken, J M (Fraser Dawbarns) *C1 E A1 T1 W Zc Zv* Wisbech *p435* 01945 461456

Aitken, Miss P (Sintons LLP) *C1 C2 S2 Ze E L F1 U2* Newcastle upon Tyne *p326* . 0191 226 7878

Aitken, S J (Stanley Tee) *N Q* Bishop's Stortford *p144* . . . 01279 755200

Aitkenhead, R M (Insley & Partners) *S1 E C1 W L S2 T2 C2 Zl K4* Ferndown *p225* 01202 876117

Aizlewood, Miss J M (Darbys Solicitors LLP) *K1 D1 K3 Zm* Oxford *p343* 01865 811700

Aizlewood, M (Mills & Reeve) *Zj* Norwich *p335* 01603 660155

Ajai-Ajagbe, Ms E (The College of Law) *S1* London WC1 *p105*. 0800 289997

Ajaz, M (National Grid PLC) Warwick *p471* 01926 653000

Ajimal, Ms O K (Squire Sanders (UK) LLP) London EC2 *p81*. 020 7655 1000

Akaraonye, Miss C (DWF) *N Zr* Liverpool *p287*. 0151 907 3000

Akbar, Miss G (London Borough of Greenwich Legal Services) London SE18 *p106* 020 8921 5123

Ake, D J (David Ake & Co) *G H V D1* Leeds *p271* 0113 244 8808

Akehurst, M J (Gordon Jones & Co) *K3 K1 N J1 Q O F1 L Zg J2* Birmingham *p139* 0121 453 8151

Akerman, J (Olswang LLP) *E S1* London WC1 *p64* 020 7067 3000

Akeroyd, T A (Elborne Mitchell LLP) *N M1 O Zc Zj* London EC3 *p29*. 020 7320 9000

Akhtar, Ms F (Ashfield District Council) Kirkby-in-Ashfield *p462*. . . . 01623 450000

Akhtar, N (Tavistock Law Limited) *C2 C1 E S1* London EC4 *p85*. 0845 260 6034

Akhtar, Mrs N (Scott Rees & Co) *S1* Skelmersdale *p381* 01695 722222

Akhtar, Ms P (Queens Solicitors) *O Q N B1 Zc S2 E F1 K1 L Zi Zg Zk Zq S1* Leicester *p281*. 0116 274 7927

Akhtar, P (Allen & Overy LLP) London E1 *p5* 020 3088 0000

Akhtar, Miss S (Haworth & Nuttall) *C1 S2 E* Blackburn *p145* 01254 272640

Akhtar, Mrs Y (Symes Bains Broomer) *D1 K1 V K3* Scunthorpe *p373*. 01724 281616

Akins, Ms E (Russell-Cooke LLP) *G H B2* Kingston upon Thames *p267*. 020 8546 6111

Akinwale, Mrs J (Philcox Gray & Co) *Zi Zg V L* London SE15 *p67* 020 7703 2285

Akinyanju, B (Richmond upon Thames Magistrates Court) Richmond upon Thames *p470*020 8948 2101

Akitt, I A (Walker Morris) *B1 Zb* Leeds *p277* 0113 283 2500

Akram, Ms G (Ahmed & Co) *G H* Camden *p4* 020 7383 2243

Akram, M (Hacking Ashton LLP) *C1 C2 E U2 Ze* Newcastle under Lyme *p323*. 01782 715555

Akram, Ms N (Blaser Mills) *W T2* Chesham *p189* 01494 782291

Akram, Ms S (Young & Lee) *K1 D1 D2 G Ze Zw* Birmingham *p143* 0121 633 3233

Akram, S (Berry Smith LLP) *C1 C2 C3 B1 Ze Zf* Cardiff *p177* 029 2034 5511

Akroyd, N (John O'Connor Solicitors) *S1 W R1 F1 C1* Derby *p209* 01332 345533

Aksa, Miss Y N (SFN Solicitors) *M4 Zg Zi* Burnley *p169* 01282 421284

Al Jarrah, Ms F (Lansbury Worthington) *G H B2* London W6 *p51* 020 8563 9797

Al Rawi, Z (AR Legal Solicitors) *S2 E G J1 L Q N Zp S1* London W4 *p3*. 020 8747 9090

Al-Gafoor, Ms N (Nasreen Al-Gafoor & Co Solicitors) *W J1* Leeds *p271* 0113 230 0083

Al-Hassan, H (Miles & Partners) London EC3 *p60*. 020 7426 0400

Al-Khafaji, Miss B (Exeter City Council) Exeter *p458* 01392 277888

Al-Nakeeb, Miss R (Surrey County Council) Kingston upon Thames *p462*. 020 8541 9088

Al-Nuaimi, O (Osborne Clarke) *R2* Bristol *p164* 0117 917 3000

Al-Sabbagh, Ms S (Parlett Kent) *Zr* London EC1 *p66*. 020 7430 0712

Al-Wakeel, Mrs D (Brown & Emery) *S1 W K4* Watford *p423* 01923 225255

Alabaster, W (Oglethorpe Sturton & Gillibrand) Lancaster *p270* 01524 846846

Alabi, A (Advocates Solicitors) *N G Zi L V Q S1 S2 K1 W* Ilford *p259*. 020 8553 5656

Alagarajah, S (Alaga & Co) London SW16 *p4* 020 8764 7073

Alahakoon, J (Aldridge Brownlee Solicitors LLP) *S2 S1 R2 L* Bournemouth *p151*. 01202 526343

Alais, S M (Wright Son & Pepper LLP) *C1 E S1 Ze Zf* Camden *p93*. 020 7242 5473

Alam, A (Longfords) *G H S1 E S2* Oldham *p340* 0161 665 4400

Alam, A M (Solicitors Active) *Zi S2 S1* Leeds *p277* 0113 248 9805

Alam, F (Martin Murray & Associates) *G H B2* Slough *p382*. 01753 551313

Alam, Ms S (Huggins & Lewis Foskett) *K1 D1 N Q L V K2* Redbridge *p43*. 020 8989 3000

Alavi, S (Jefferies Essex LLP) *G H* Westcliff-on-Sea *p428* 01702 332311

Albagli, Miss D M (Herbert Smith LLP) *C1 M2 Zb* London EC2 *p40*. 020 7374 8000

Albayaty, Miss A (Penningtons) *E* London EC2 *p66*. 020 7457 3000

Alberstat, P (Osborne Clarke) *Zf* London EC2 *p65*. 020 7105 7000

Albertini, Miss L (Field Fisher Waterhouse LLP) London EC3 *p31*. 020 7861 4000

Albery, P J (Bartons) *S1 S2 E C2 C1* Bristol *p161* 0117 925 6000

Albin, C (Albin & Co) Reading *p359* 0118 957 4018

Albini, Dr S M (Pickerings LLP) *S2 E R1 R2* Tamworth *p407* 01827 317070

Albino, F (Barlow Lyde & Gilbert LLP) *O Q Zj* London EC3 *p10*. 020 7247 2277

Albinson, A J S (Albinson Napier & Co) *S1 W C1 E S2* Warrington *p421* 01925 634681

Albon, C (Wannop Fox Staffurth & Bray) Worthing *p442*. 01903 201120

Albuery, B (Blake Lapthorn) *G H J2* Chandlers Ford *p184* 023 8090 8090

Album, E J C (E J C Album) *C2 O Zb S1 E A3 J1 M2* London E14 *p4* 020 7971 5667

Alcendor, Ms N (Lansbury Worthington) *G H B2* London W6 *p51* 020 8563 9797

Alcock, D (Anthony Collins Solicitors LLP) *Zh Zu* Birmingham *p137* 0121 200 3242

Alcock, G K (Lichfield Reynolds) *M1 P K1 G F1 J1 L H N S1* Stoke-on-Trent *p398*. 01782 595599

Alcock, J H (Davis Blank Furniss) *B1 C1 N E I M1 O J1 Q T1 Zb Zc Zd Zj Zk* Manchester *p303* 0161 832 3304

Alcock, J M (Brindley Twist Tafft & James) *J1* Coventry *p200*. 024 7653 1532

Alcock, Ms L A (Alcock & Smalley) Macclesfield *p297* 01625 431530

Alcock, R E (Chattertons Solicitors) *L S1 S2 E* Sleaford *p381* 01529 411500

Alcorn, Mrs H (Norwich Union Insurance Group) Norwich *p467* 01603 622200

Alcorn, Ms H M (Aviva PLC) *J1* London EC3 *p103* . . 020 7283 7500 / 01603 687905

Aldeiri, M (Arora Lodhi Heath) London W3 *p7*. 020 8993 9995

Alden, Miss C L (Pannone LLP) *C1 C3* Manchester *p308* 0161 909 3000

Alden, M A (Ashfords LLP) *W T2* Exeter *p220* 01392 337000

Alder, C (Blake Lapthorn) *Q* Oxford *p342* 01865 248607

Alder, C B (Blake Lapthorn) *O* Chandlers Ford *p184* 023 8090 8090

Alder, E (Bird & Bird LLP) *I* London EC4 *p13*. 020 7415 6000

Alder, Ms H (Graysons) Sheffield *p375* . . . . 0114 272 9184 Sheffield *p376* 0114 213 3888

Alder, R (Trowers & Hamlins) *J1 O Zg Zp* London EC3 *p88*. 020 7423 8000

Aldersey, D R (Insley & Partners) *S1 W T1* Bournemouth *p152*. 01202 510167

Aldersley, J A (Butcher & Barlow LLP) *N Q O W* Leigh *p281*. 01942 674144

Alderson, C J (Hempsons) *N Zr* Manchester *p305* 0161 228 0011

Alderson, Ms D (Russell-Cooke LLP) London SW15 *p74*. 020 8789 9111

Alderson, E J (Malcolm Wilson & Cobby) *C1 S1 W E K1 L T2* Worthing *p442*. 01903 244973

Alderson, I B (Brabners Chaffe Street) *L Zh O Q Zq A3 J1* Liverpool *p286*. 0151 600 3000

Alderson, R C (Underhill Langley & Wright) *S1 W L E* Wolverhampton *p438* 01902 423431

Alderton, J C (Squire Sanders (UK) LLP) *B1 Zb* Leeds *p277* 0113 284 7000

Alderton, Miss J M (Penman Johnson) *B1 Q N O J1 K1 Zp* Watford *p424* . . . .01923 225212 / 239566

Alderwick, Ms S M (Dexter Montague LLP) *K1 D1* Reading *p360* 0118 939 3999

Aldous, R (Penningtons) Basingstoke *p127* 01256 407100

Aldred, A (Squire Sanders (UK) LLP) Leeds *p277* 0113 284 7000

Aldred, A D (Addleshaw Goddard) *C3 M1 C1 M2 Zg A3* London EC1 *p4* 020 7606 8855

Aldred, Mrs H (Hewitsons) *J1 Zp Zi* Cambridge *p174*. 01223 461155

Aldred, Ms J E (Wiseman Lee LLP) *N Q Zq Zr* Newham *p92* 020 8215 1000

Aldred, P D (CMS Cameron McKenna LLP) *B1 O Zb Zk* London EC3 *p17*. 020 7367 3000

Aldred, S W (Campbell Hooper & Co LLP) *E S1 S2* Sunningdale *p402* 01344 622141

Aldrich, M (Browne Jacobson LLP) *O L Q F1* Nottingham *p336*. 0115 976 6000

Aldrich, Ms P (Fox Williams) *E* London EC2 *p33*. 020 7628 2000

Aldridge, Ms C (Archon Solicitors) London EC4 *p7* 020 7397 9650

Aldridge, Ms C (Bird & Bird LLP) *J1* London EC4 *p13*. 020 7415 6000

Aldridge, Mrs C A (Burges Salmon) Bristol *p161* 0117 939 2000

Aldridge, C J (Penmans) *S1 K1 E D1 L P W J1 H V Zi* Kenilworth *p264* 01926 858222

Aldridge, Mrs J M (Blaser Mills) *S2 S1 W E* Chesham *p189* 01494 782291

Aldridge, P K (Cocks Lloyd) *A1 B1 C1 E F1 L M1 N P* Nuneaton *p339* 024 7664 1642

Aldridge, R P (Ross Aldridge LLP) *N* Cheltenham *p187* 01242 707400

Aldworth, W (Land Registry - Lytham Office) Lytham *p464*. . . . .01253 849849 / 840012

Alegre Climent, J (Thomas Cooper) *M2 Za Zj* London EC3 *p22*. 020 7481 8851

Alen-Buckley, Miss O M D P (Alen-Buckley & Co) *E K1 W S1 L F1 C1 J1 Q* Wandsworth *p4* 020 8767 8336

Alessandrini, Miss S (O'Keeffe Solicitors) *G* Brent *p64* 020 7644 8800

Alesworth, Ms J A K (HMG Law LLP) *T1 T2 W K4 Zo* Oxford *p343* 01865 244661

Aletta, Ms P (Aletta Shaw Solicitors) *K3 D2 K1 Q S1 W D1* Bexleyheath *p132* 020 8301 4884

Alexander, Miss A (Irwin Mitchell LLP) *Zr* Manchester *p306* 0870 150 0100

Alexander, A T (Stevens & Bolton) *C1 B1 T1 J1 F1 Ze Zo Zb* Guildford *p237*. 01483 302264

Alexander, C (King & Spalding International LLP) London EC2 *p49*. 020 7551 7500

Alexander, C A (Tanners) *E C1 S1 L A1* Cirencester *p195*. 01285 659061

Alexander, D A L (Alexander & Co) *S1 E C1 L W R1 A1 T1 Zc* Derby *p208* . . . . 01332 600005 Derby *p208* 01332 600011

Alexander, Ms J (Wyre Forest District Council) Stourport-on-Severn *p473* . . . 01562 820505

Alexander, Miss J C (Suffolk County Council) Ipswich *p462*. 01473 583000

Alexander, Mrs L B (Memery Crystal) *K1 K2 K3* London WC2 *p60* 020 7242 5905

Alexander, L S (Barlow Lyde & Gilbert LLP) London EC3 *p10*. 020 7247 2277

Alexander, M (Marsden Rawsthorn LLP) *C1 S2 E C3 C2 R2* Preston *p357* 01772 799600

Alexander, M (Alexander Lawyers LLP) *E L A1 R1 S1 W* Chelmsford *p186*. 01245 216050

Alexander, M A (Simmons & Simmons) *O Zj* London EC2 *p79*. 020 7628 2020

Alexander, M P (Michael Alexander & Co) *G H K1 L N Q B2 W* Manchester *p301* 0845 839 2011

Alexander, N B R (Whitemans) Gloucester *p231*. 01452 411601

Alexander, Miss N E L (Dolmans) *N Q L* Cardiff *p178* 029 2034 5531

Alexander, P J (Austen Whetham & Guest) *K1 K2* Bridport *p158* 01308 422236

Alexander, R M (Lewis Silkin LLP) *C1 C2* London EC4 *p53*. 020 7074 8000

Alexander, Ms R S (Olswang LLP) *Q Zk* London WC1 *p64* 020 7067 3000

Alexander, S (Clarke Kiernan) *N* Tonbridge *p412* 01732 360999

Alexander, Ms S (Forsters LLP) *K1* Westminster *p33*. 020 7863 8333

Alexander, Mrs S (Clark Willis) *W K4* Darlington *p206* . . . . .01325 281111 Bristol *p163* 0117 904 6000

Alexander, S A (Spicketts Battrick Law Practice) *K1 K3 D1 D2* Cardiff *p181*. 029 2046 1480

Alexander, S J (Southern Water Services Ltd) Worthing *p477*. 01903 264444

Alexander, S P (Brachers) *Zr Zm* Maidstone *p299* 01622 690691

Alexander, Ms S W (Russell & Russell) *K1 D1 K3* Chester *p191* 01244 405700

Alexander, U H B (Furley Page LLP) *A1 S1* Canterbury *p176*. 01227 763939

Alexandre, S R (Dutton Gregory) *B1 J1 O Q Zb Zp* Southampton *p385*. 023 8022 1344

Alexandrou, A E (Alexandrou & Co) *C1 E L B1 O Q S1 H K1 N Zl Zv* Barnet *p123* 020 8447 1503

Alexian, Ms K (Manches LLP) *K1* London WC2 *p58* 020 7404 4433

Alexiou, D A (Alexiou Fisher Philipps) *K1 D1 K2 K3* London W1 *p5*. 020 7409 1222

Alexopoulos, I (DLA Piper UK LLP) London EC2 *p24*. 0870 011 1111

Aley, S J (Corby Borough Council) Corby *p456* 01536 402551

Alfandary, P R (Reed Smith LLP) *J1 C1 Zi* London EC2 *p71*. 020 3116 3000

Alfille, C M (Segens Blount Petre) Westminster *p77*. 020 7332 2222

Alfille, N M (Memery Crystal) *C1 C2* London WC2 *p60* 020 7242 5905

Algar, Ms C (Collyer Bristow LLP) *Ze F2 U2 Zk Zf Zz O Q* London WC1 *p22* 020 7242 7363

Alhadeff, G N (Watmores) *E* London WC2 *p90* 020 7430 1512

Ali, A (Bermans LLP) *J1 Zi* Liverpool *p286*. 0151 224 0500

Ali, A (Crowell & Moring) *A3* London EC4 *p23*. 020 7413 0011

Ali, A (HSK Solicitors) *Zi N Q O Zj S1 W F1 K1 J2 L Zh B1 Zl Zza* Bolton *p149* . . . . 01204 526465 Manchester *p305* 0161 795 4818

Ali, A (Tuckers) *N* Manchester *p310* 0161 233 4321

Ali, B (Armitage Sykes LLP) *E* Huddersfield *p255* 01484 538121

Ali, F (LG Lawyers) London SE1 *p50*. 020 7379 0000

Ali, H (Kaim Todner Ltd) *G H* London EC4 *p47*. 020 7353 6660

Ali, I (Milton Keynes Council) *L S1 R1* Milton Keynes *p466* 01908 691691

Ali, I (LG Lawyers) London SE1 *p50*. 020 7379 0000

Ali, I (The Johnson Partnership) *G H* Nottingham *p337*. 0115 941 9141

Ali, J (King & Spalding International LLP) London EC2 *p49*. 020 7551 7500

Ali, Mrs J (John Poyser Solicitors) *N* Manchester *p309* 0161 860 7354

Ali, J A (Spearing Waite LLP) *Zb C2 C1* Leicester *p281*. 0116 262 4225

Ali, K (Godloves) *F1 O Q L* Leeds *p273* 0113 225 8811

Ali, K F R (Gary Jacobs & Co) London E18 *p45*. 020 8536 4050

Ali, Miss L (Needham Poulier & Partners) *G H Zm* London N17 *p63*. 020 8808 6622

Ali, M (Ali & Co Solicitor) Bradford *p153* 01274 391197

Ali, M (Martin Murray & Associates) *G H B2* West Drayton *p427* 01895 431332

Ali, M (Himayah Solicitors) *E S1 Q* Birmingham *p139* 0121 356 5007

Ali, N (Hodge Jones & Allen LLP) *Zr* London NW1 *p41* 020 7874 8300

Ali, R (Arc Property Solicitors LLP) *S1 S2 E* Harrogate *p240* 0800 612 9097

Ali, R (Ropemakers Solicitors) London E6 *p73* 020 8586 8500

Ali, Ms S (Taylor Walton LLP) *J1* Luton *p295* 01582 731161

Ali, Mrs S (Russell & Russell) *N* Bolton *p150* 01204 375700

Ali, Ms S (Gillian Radford & Co) *L K3 K1 D1* Westminster *p70*. 020 8960 4366

Ali, Miss S (Aaron & Partners LLP Solicitors) *B1 O* Chester *p190* 01244 405555

Ali, S (Ali & Co Solicitor) *N* Bradford *p153* 01274 391197

Ali, S (S Ali & Company Solicitors) *E G J1 K1 L M1 P S1 W Zi Zl Zp* Haringey *p5* 020 8340 5544

Ali, S (J A Kemp & Co) London WC1 *p48* 020 7405 3292

Ali, T (Colman Coyle LLP) *E* Islington *p22*. 020 7354 3000

Ali, T S (Sehgal & Co) *Q G N F1* Birmingham *p142* 0121 772 2226

Ali, Y (Scott Rees & Co) *N Q* Skelmersdale *p381* 01695 722222

Ali, Z (Severn Trent Water Ltd) Birmingham *p450* 0121 722 4000

Ali, Miss Z (Sheridans) *E S1 W S2 Zi* London WC1 *p78* 020 7079 0100

Ali-Shah, I (Friends Provident) Dorking *p457* 01306 654925

Alis, S P (Jacobs Solicitors) *G H M1 N Q L S1 W F1* Shotton *p379* 01244 816211

Alison, Mrs D (Davitt Jones Bould) *R1* Taunton *p408* 01823 279279

Alison, P G (Smith Gadd & Co) *K1 D1* Horsham *p253*. 01403 271222

Alker, R L (Alker & Ball) *W K4* Wigan *p432* 01942 246241

Alladin, Mrs S B (Henry Thompson & Sons) *K1 K3* Grantham *p232* 01476 563226

Allamand, P M (Hart Brown Solicitors) *E L R1 S1 Zc R2* Guildford *p236*. 0800 068 8177

Allan, Miss C L (Child & Child) London SW1 *p20* . . . . . . 020 7235 8000 Islington *p43*. 020 7553 9000

Allan, D R (Marrons) *N* Newcastle upon Tyne *p325* . 0191 281 1304

6

Allan, Ms J H (Thompsons (formerly Robin/Brian Thompson & Partners)) *N*
Newcastle upon Tyne *p327* . 0191 269 0400
Allan, Ms J J (Field Fisher Waterhouse LLP)
London EC3 *p31*. 020 7861 4000
Allan, Miss K L (Berry & Berry) *D1 K1 K3*
Tonbridge *p412* 01732 355911
Allan, L (Plexus Law (A Trading Name of Parabis Law LLP))
Leeds *p276* 0844 245 4100
Allan, M (Pinsent Masons LLP)
London EC2 *p67*. 020 7418 7000
Allan, N F (Segens Blount Petre) *J1 K1 L O Q Ze Zf B1 Zk*
Westminster *p77*. 020 7332 2222
Allan, R J (Civil Aviation Authority)
London WC2 *p105*. 020 7453 6162
Allan, W (Linklaters LLP)
London EC2 *p54*. 020 7456 2000
Allanson, R (Canter Levin & Berg)
Liverpool *p287*. 0151 239 1000
Allanson, R B (Allansons LLP) *N G D1 H F1 K1 O Q C1*
Bolton *p148* 0161 220 8484
Allanson, Ms S V (Russell Jones & Walker) *N*
London WC2 *p74* 020 7657 1555
Allbeson, R (Marrons) *N*
Newcastle upon Tyne *p325* . 0191 281 1304
Allcard, Miss J L (West Cumbria Magistrates Courts)
Workington *p477*. 01900 62244
Allchin, J (Challinors) *G H*
West Bromwich *p427* 0121 553 3211
Allchurch, Ms E (The Owen-Kenny Partnership)
Chichester *p193* 01243 532777
Allchurch, J S (Davies Parsons Allchurch) *N K1 G H*
Llanelli *p292*. 01554 749144
Allcoat, Ms R (Holman Fenwick Willan)
London EC3 *p42*. 020 7264 8000
Allcock, J P M (Bristows) *C1 M1 Ze I*
London EC4 *p15*. 020 7400 8000
Alldis, S P (Woolley Bevis Diplock) *E S2*
Brighton *p160* 01273 323231
Alldred, A J (Hughes & Company) *S2 E N S1*
Tring *p413*. 01442 891717
Allear, D (Evans Dodd LLP) *S2 E S1 R2*
London W1 *p30* 020 7491 4729
Allely, Miss J M (William Wright & Son) *K1 D2 D1*
Dudley *p213*. 01384 255344
Allen, Mrs A (Harding Evans LLP) *D1 K1*
Newport *p328* 01633 244233
Allen, A C (Hill Dickinson LLP) *O Za Zw*
London EC3 *p41*. 020 7283 9033
Allen, Mrs A J (Stone King LLP) *W T2*
Bath *p128* 01225 337599
Allen, A J (NGA)
Burnley *p169* 01282 457295
Allen, Mrs A J P (Squire Sanders (UK) LLP)
Birmingham *p142* 0121 222 3000
Allen, B (Aldridge Brownlee Solicitors LLP) *G*
Bournemouth *p151*. 01202 294411
Allen, Miss B A R (Ashurst LLP)
London EC2 *p7* 020 7638 1111
Allen, Ms C (Leeds City Council)
Leeds *p462* 0113 224 3513
Allen, C (Latham & Watkins LLP)
London EC2 *p51*. 020 7710 1000
Allen, C (Rushton Hinchy Solicitors) *Zr Q N*
St Helens *p391* 0845 054 0564
Allen, Miss C J (Edwards Angell Palmer & Dodge) *S1*
London EC2 *p28*. 020 7583 4055
Allen, C J (Pluck Andrew & Co)
Hyde *p259*. 0161 368 6311
Allen, C J G (Jacobs Allen Hammond) *S2 S1 W R2 Zc E*
London W1 *p45* 020 7299 9800
Allen, D (DLA Piper UK LLP)
London EC2 *p24*. 0870 011 1111
Allen, Ms D (Ison Harrison) *E Q S1*
Leeds *p274* 0113 284 5000
Allen, Mrs D A (Fraser Dawbarns) *K1 D1 S1*
King's Lynn *p266* 01553 666600
Allen, Miss D L (Mills & Reeve) *A1*
Norwich *p335* 01603 660155
Allen, D M (Mayer Brown International LLP)
London EC2 *p59*. 020 3130 3000
Allen, E (Prince Evans)
Ealing *p69*. 020 8567 3477
Allen, Mrs E A (Stephens & Scown) *K1*
Exeter *p222* 01392 210700
Allen, Mrs F M (Shakespeares) *T2 W Zd*
Stratford-upon-Avon *p400* . . 0845 630 8833
Allen, G (Tinn Criddle & Co) *A1 E J1 T1 T2 W*
Alford *p115* 01507 462882
Sutton-on-Sea *p404* 01507 443043
Allen, Ms J (Land Registry - Croydon Office)
Croydon *p456* 020 8388 3288
Allen, Miss J (The Wilkes Partnership LLP) *J1 O*
Birmingham *p143* 0121 233 4333
Allen, Miss J (Kirby Sheppard) *K4 K1 W*
Kingswood *p268*. 0845 840 0045
Allen, J A (Taylor Vinters) *C1 C2 Zb B1*
Cambridge *p176*. 01223 423444
Allen, J D (Rothera Dowson) *W T2 Zd*
Nottingham *p338*. 0115 910 0600
Allen, Ms J E (Gateley LLP) *A3 B1 O Q Zq*
Manchester *p304* 0161 836 7700
Allen, Miss J L (Hughes Paddison) *K3 K1*
Cheltenham *p188* 01242 574244
Allen, J M (Walters & Plaskitt) *G H K1 D1 J1*
Stoke-on-Trent *p398*. 01782 819611
Allen, J R (Poppleston Allen) *Zl*
Nottingham *p338*. 0115 953 8500
Allen, Miss J R (Milne Moser) *C1 S2 E S1 W N J1*
Kendal *p264*. . . . .01539 729786 / 725582
Allen, K (Clarion Solicitors LLP) *G H*
Leeds *p272* 0113 246 0622
Allen, Miss K C (Dawson Cornwell) *K1 K3 D1*
London WC1 *p26* 020 7242 2556
Allen, Ms K E (Glazer Delmar) *Zh L*
London SE22 *p35* 020 8299 0021
Allen, Ms K L (Irwin Mitchell LLP) *N Zr*
Birmingham *p139* 0870 150 0100
Allen, Mrs L M J (Bristol City Council)
Bristol *p451* 0117 922 2000
Allen, M (Thompson Allen LLP) *S2 E L R2 C1*
Brighton *p160* 01273 608003
Allen, Ms M E J (Stephen Gallico Solicitors) *T2 W K4*
Haywards Heath *p245* 01444 411333
Allen, Ms M L (Gotelee) *J1*
Ipswich *p262*. 01473 211121
Allen, N P (Squire Sanders (UK) LLP)
London EC2 *p81*. 020 7655 1000
Allen, P (Barlow Lyde & Gilbert LLP) *C2 C1*
London EC3 *p10*. 020 7247 2277
Allen, P (Morgan Cole)
Oxford *p344* 01865 262600
Allen, P (Willans LLP) *W T2*
Cheltenham *p189* 01242 514000
Allen, P C (Birkett Long LLP) *O Q Zc*
Chelmsford *p186*. 01245 453800
Allen, P C (Deibel & Allen) *S1 W E C1 L K1 S2 R2 T1 Zw*
Portslade-by-Sea *p354*. . . . 01273 430999
Allen, Ms P J (Ashurst LLP) *T1*
London EC2 *p7* 020 7638 1111
Allen, P J H (Hodge Jones & Allen LLP) *N Zr G H K1 D1 K2 Zh L Zm S1 S2 Zg W*
London NW1 *p41* 020 7874 8300
Allen, Miss R (Crewe & Nantwich Borough Council)
Crewe *p456* 01270 537102
Allen, R (Liddell and Company) *N*
Romford *p366* 01708 775999
Allen, R (Lockings)
Hull *p257* 0845 075 4197
Allen, R A (Partridge Allen & Co) *S1 K1 Q W O N L G J1 D1 Zl Zd Zk Zv Zo*
Walsall *p420*. 01922 452860
Allen, R C (Atteys)
Doncaster *p211* 01302 340400
Allen, R C B (Allens) *S1 K1 W G J1 F1 Zl*
Bungay *p168* 01986 893928
Halesworth *p237*. 01986 875246
Allen, Ms S (Reed Smith LLP) *J1*
London EC2 *p71*. 020 3116 3000
Allen, S (Gill Akaster) *O Q F1*
Plymouth *p349*. 01752 203500
Allen, S C (Paris Smith LLP) *S2 E R2*
Southampton *p386*. 023 8048 2482
Allen, Mrs S E (Singletons Austin Ryder) *K1 K3*
Enfield *p219*. 020 8363 0101
Allen, S J (Brindley Twist Tafft & James) *W V*
Coventry *p200*. 024 7653 1532
Allen, S J N (Russell Jones & Walker)
Sheffield *p377* 0114 276 6868
Allen, Miss S L (Environment Agency (Thames Region)) *Q P*
Reading *p469* 0870 850 6506
Allen, Mrs S M (Dixon Coles & Gill) *S1 W K3 K1 T2 K4 S2 L B1 E*
Wakefield *p418* . . .01924 263166 / 263899
Wakefield *p418* 01924 373467
Allen, S P (Thompsons (formerly Robin/Brian Thompson & Partners)) *N*
Plymouth *p350*. 01752 675810
Allen, S R (Battens) *W*
Yeovil *p443* 01935 846000
Allen, S W (Elliott & Allen) *K1 G J1 F1 Q Zl*
Sedgley *p373* 01902 677204
Allen, T (Squire Sanders (UK) LLP)
Birmingham *p142* 0121 222 3000
Allen, Miss T A (Windsor & Maidenhead Borough Council)
Maidenhead *p464* 01628 798888
Allen, Ms T D (Bindmans LLP)
London WC1 *p12* 020 7833 4433
Allen, T D (Allen Hoole Solicitors) *F1 G H K1 D1 L Zi Zl*
Bristol *p160* 0117 942 0901
Allen, T J (DWF) *N Q*
Liverpool *p287*. 0151 907 3000
Skelmersdale *p381* 01695 722222
Allen, W (Booth Ince & Knowles) *W Zm N Q K4*
Hyde *p259*. 0161 368 2134
Allen-Jones, C J (George Green LLP) *K3 K1*
Cradley Heath *p201* 01384 410410
Leamington Spa *p270*. 01926 886688
Alleyne, B R (Segens Blount Petre)
Westminster *p77*. 020 7332 2222
Allford, P M (Reed Smith LLP)
London EC2 *p71*. 020 3116 3000
Allfree, T J (Wedlake Bell LLP) *E S2*
London WC1 *p91* 020 7395 3000
Allgood, Ms M H (Salter Rees & Kelly)
Swansea *p405*. 01792 470707
Alli-Balogun, O (BKS Solicitors) *S1*
London SE20 *p9*. 020 8776 9388
Allin, J M (Lester Aldridge LLP) *N G H*
Bournemouth *p152*. 01202 786161
Allingham, E F (Sims Cook & Teague) *C1 D1 E F1 J1 K1 L M1 N R1 Zl*
Bristol *p165* 0117 927 2141
Allingham, M G (RTP Williams Limited) *K1 K2 D1 K3*
Haverfordwest *p244* 01437 762321
Allison, D F (SGH Martineau LLP) *C1 C2 C3*
Birmingham *p142* 0870 763 2000
Allison, D N (Family Law in Partnership LLP) *K1 K2*
London WC2 *p30* 020 7420 5000
Allison, J (Napthens LLP) *C1*
Preston *p357* 01772 888444
Allison, J (Williams Gorman LLP)
Haringey *p91* . . . .
Allison, J R (Addleshaw Goddard) *C1 C2*
London EC1 *p4* 020 7606 8855
Allison, Miss M (Wrigleys Solicitors LLP) *Zo W J1*
Sheffield *p377* 0114 267 5588
Allison, P (Provident Personal Credit Ltd)
Bradford *p451* 01274 733321
Allison, Ms R E M (National Grid PLC)
Warwick *p471* 01926 653000
Allison, R J (Harding Evans LLP) *S1*
Newport *p328* 01633 244233
Allison, W H (DAC Beachcroft) *O Zj Zk Zq*
London EC4 *p24*. 020 7936 2222
Allman, D (MacLaverty Cooper Atkins)
Kingston upon Thames *p267*. 020 8549 9994
Allman, Ms V A (British Medical Association) *J1 N P Zq*
London WC1 *p104*. 020 7387 4499
Allnutt, C A R (Blake Lapthorn) *E L*
Chandlers Ford *p184* 023 8090 8090
Allotey, C (Charles Allotey)
Thornton Heath *p411*. 020 8664 8155
Allott, Ms J M (Lords) *G H*
Wakefield *p418* 01924 380830
Allred, Miss K A (Darbys Solicitors LLP) *W*
Oxford *p343*. 01865 811700
Allsager, W J F (Alfred Newton & Co) *S1 W K1 G H Q N P K3 J1 L S2 D2 Zm*
Stockport *p396*. . 0161 480 6551 / 480 1245
Allsop, Ms J M A (Wolferstans) *B1 C1*
Plymouth *p351*. 01752 663295
Allsop, Ms S (Levenes Solicitors) *N*
Haringey *p53* . .020 8881 7777 / 8881 6764
Allsop, T K E (Mills & Reeve) *E R2 S2 L R1 S1*
Cambridge *p175*. 01223 364422
Allsopp, E T M (Allsopp & Co) *S1 E L W C1 T1 R1 A1 Zc Zj Zi*
Solihull *p382*. 0121 704 4282
Solihull *p382*. 0121 705 9020
Allsopp, I M (Reynolds Porter Chamberlain LLP)
London E1 *p71* 020 3060 6000
Allsup, Miss C C (The Royal Borough of Kensington & Chelsea)
London W8 *p109* 020 7361 2741
Allsup, R N (DWF) *O Zc A3*
Manchester *p303* 0161 603 5000
Allward, A S (Dollman & Pritchard) *W S1 S2 T2*
Caterham *p183* 01883 347823
Allweis, J A H (Allweis & Co) *B1 J1 K1 L*
Salford *p370*. 0161 792 1020
Allweis, M H P (Dwyers) *B1 N O Q Zq*
Ashton-under-Lyne *p120*. . . 0161 308 3928
Allwood, R J (HSR Law (Hayes, Son & Richmond)) *Q N O W S1 K4*
Doncaster *p211* 01302 347800
Gainsborough *p228* 01427 613831
Alma, Ms E G (Coodes) *K1 D1 D2*
St Austell *p391* 01726 874700
Almaz, N (Saunders Law Partnership LLP) *G H*
London WC2 *p76* 020 7632 4300
Almeida, Ms C (Morgans) *J1*
Cardiff *p180* 029 2072 9888
Almond, A J (A Halsall & Co) *S1 W T1 L E C1*
Birkenhead *p134*. 0151 647 6323
Wirral *p435* 0151 632 2336
Almond, C H S (Beaumonts) *N O Q S2*
Hereford *p247* 01432 352345
Almond, Ms H (Adam Douglas & Son) *D1 K1 L W K3 K4 S1*
Berwick-upon-Tweed *p131*. . 01289 306479
Almond, Miss J (IBB Solicitors) *T2 W Zm*
Chesham *p189* 0845 638 1381
Almond, Mrs K L A (Osborne Clarke) *R2*
London EC2 *p65*. 020 7105 7000
Almond, Mrs L E (Blaser Mills) *K1*
Staines *p393*. 01784 462511
Almond, P M (TRW Automotive)
Birmingham *p450* 0121 623 4532
Almond, R J (Victor Lissack Roscoe & Coleman) *B2 G H S1 S2 W Zm*
London W1 *p89* 020 7487 2505
Almy, P A (Hunters) *C1 E J1 F1 Zd Zv*
London WC2 *p44* 020 7412 0050
Alom, R (Adams Solicitors)
London E1 *p4* 020 7790 2000
Alonzi, A G (Browne Jacobson LLP) *O Zq*
Nottingham *p336*. 0115 976 6000
Alonzi, T (Neil Foley & Co) *F1 G M1 S1 W D1 J1 L E Zl Zt Zo*
Pontypridd *p352*. 01443 406085
Alp, D (Parry Law) *E L R1 S1*
Whitstable *p431*. 01227 276276
Alston, I G (Alston Ashby) *S1 L E W C1 V R1 B1 J1 T1 Zc Ze Zl*
Chatham *p184*. 01634 845051
Alston, Mrs I S (Greene & Greene) *T2 W*
Bury St Edmunds *p171* . . . 01284 762211
Altan, Mrs H S (Birchall Blackburn LLP) *N Zr*
Manchester *p301* 0161 236 0662
Alter, Mrs A (The Mitchell Plampin Partnership) *S1*
Maldon *p299*. 01621 852566
Alter, S (Rochman Landau LLP) *S2 E S1*
London W1 *p72* 020 7544 2424
Alterman, Ms L (Financial Services Authority)
London E14 *p106* 020 7066 1000
Althen, R (Angel Trains Ltd)
London SW1 *p103*. 020 7592 0500
Altman, A J (Williscroft & Co) *K1 K3*
Bradford *p155* 01274 305380
Altman, P R (Thompsons (formerly Robin/Brian Thompson & Partners))
Harrow *p242*. 020 8872 8600
Altmann, Ms G (Pritchard Englefield) *C1 C2 Zp*
London EC2 *p69*. 020 7972 9720
Alton Honeywell, K M S (Arnold Thomson Limited) *T2 W O T1 A1 Zd*
Towcester *p413* 01327 350266
Alton, C S (Elmhirst Parker LLP) *K1 N D1 F2*
Barnsley *p124* 01226 282238
Alton, J (Simmons Stein) *W*
Stanmore *p394* 020 8954 8080
Alton, Ms N (Bircham Dyson Bell)
Westminster *p13*. 020 7227 7000
Alton, P J (Gateley LLP) *C1 E B1 F1 Zb*
Birmingham *p138* 0121 234 0000
Altree, Mrs L (Weymouth & Portland Borough Council)
Weymouth *p476* 01305 838000
Alty, G (Pinsent Masons LLP) *Zl*
Manchester *p308* 0161 234 8234
Alty, G T (John Welch & Stammers) *S1 S2 Zl*
Witney *p436*. 01993 703941
Alun-Jones, N J (Peachey & Co)
London WC2 *p66* 020 7316 5200
Alvarez, J (Machins Solicitors LLP) *C1 E I Ze C2*
Luton *p295* 01582 514000
Alvernhe, P (Mitsubishi Securities International PLC)
London EC2 *p108*. 020 7577 2804
Alvey, J (Shacklocks) *C2 X Zd*
Mansfield *p312* 01623 626141
Amadi, E (Wainwright & Cummins) *A3 B1 D1 F1 Ze J1 Zh L O Q N Zn T1 T2*
Lambeth *p90*. 020 7737 9330
Amador-Bedford, Miss J (Reed Smith LLP) *K1 K3 D1*
London EC2 *p71*. 020 3116 3000
Aman, Ms S (Brightstone Law LLP) *K1 S1 W*
Elstree *p218*. 020 8731 3080
Amandini, P F G (Howard Kennedy LLP) *E R1*
London W1 *p48* 020 7636 1616
Amaning, K (Corbin & Hassan) *Zi*
London EC3 *p22*. 020 7247 6518
Amartey, Miss H (McMillan Williams) *G*
Wallington *p419* 020 8669 4962
Amas, Mrs L V (Northampton Borough Council)
Northampton *p467*. 01604 837837
Amaso, Ms N (London Borough of Greenwich Legal Services)
London SE18 *p106* 020 8921 5123
Ambler, Ms J (Bennetts) *E L S1 W K1 N Q*
Macclesfield *p297* 01625 424666
Amboaje, Ms R V (OGR Stock Denton) *K1 K3*
London N3 *p64* 020 8349 0321
Ambridge, A (David Rubie Mitchell & Co) *G H Zl*
Sutton *p403* 020 8641 0575
Ambridge, G (Edward Hayes LLP) *G H B2*
London EC4 *p39*. 020 7353 0011
Ambrose, A L (Norton Peskett) *S1*
Great Yarmouth *p234* 01493 849200
Lowestoft *p294* 01502 533000
Ambrose, Miss K (Taylor Vinters)
Cambridge *p176*. 01223 423444
Ambrose, R I (Howe & Spender) *G H*
Neath *p320* 01639 881571
Port Talbot *p353*. 01639 881571
Ambrose, Mrs S A (Barlow Robbins LLP) *S1 S2 E*
Godalming *p231*. 01483 417121
Ambrose, S G G (Macmillans) *W*
Wadebridge *p418* 01208 812415
Ameen, R (Wiseman Lee LLP) *C1 O Q L X*
Redbridge *p92*. 020 8215 1000
Ameer, Miss Y S (Ameer Meredith) *N Zr Q*
Cambridge *p174*. 01223 577077
Amer, S N (Coutts & Co)
London WC2 *p105*. 020 7753 1403
Amerigo, L R (Friends Provident)
Dorking *p457* 01306 654925
Amey, Mrs N (Derbyshire County Council) *D1 K1*
Matlock *p465* 01629 580000
Amies, D (Ramsdens Solicitors) *C1 E S2*
Huddersfield *p256* 01484 821500
Amin, A S (Hugh Cartwright & Amin) *Q E O S2 S1 Zv B1 L N R2 Zq F1 A3*
London WC1 *p43* 020 7632 4200
Amin, Miss B (Howard Kennedy LLP) *R2 E*
London W1 *p48* 020 7636 1616
Amin, Miss F (Woolley Bevis Diplock)
Brighton *p160* 01273 323231
Amin, H M (Charles Lucas & Marshall) *S2 E R2 C2*
Newbury *p322*. 01635 521212
Amin, I (Amal Solicitors) *N Q Zi*
Huddersfield *p255* 01484 431999
Amin, J M (J M Amin & Co) *B1 C1 J1 K1 L N O Q S1 V W Zb Zj*
Wembley *p426*. 020 8903 3766
Amin, Mrs K (Kingswell Watts) *N S2 E S1 Zi*
Dewsbury *p210* 01924 461236
Amin, S (Alexiou Fisher Philipps) *K1*
London W1 *p5*. 020 7409 1222

See p634 for the Key to Work Categories

Amin, S (Bosley & Co) G H D1
Brighton p159 01273 608181

Amin, Y (Irwin Mitchell LLP) G H L Zi
Sheffield p376 0870 150 0100

Amison, M R (Trowers & Hamlins) C1 Zc
London EC3 p88 020 7423 8000

Amiss, Ms J (Bury & Walkers LLP) K1 D1 D2 V
Barnsley p124 01226 733533

Amjad, M (Dexter Montague LLP) Zi Zg
Reading p360 0118 939 3999

Amlani, B (SGH Martineau LLP)
Birmingham p142 0870 763 2000

Amlot, T M (Harbottle & Lewis LLP)
London W1 p38 020 7667 5000

Ammar, Ms C F (Torbay Council) Q N J1 L F1 K1
Torquay p474 01803 201201

Amoo-Gottfried, Mrs H (Ansah Solicitors) G H B2 S1 W S2 E
Lambeth p6 020 8761 5271

Amor, Dr N R (Gross & Co) C1 J1 E Ze
Bury St Edmunds p171 01284 763333

Amos, Mrs C (Stevens) G H
Wolverhampton p438 01902 772776

Amos, P W (Stockdale & Reid Ltd) E S1 W O C1
Monkseaton p318 0191 251 9494

Amos, R G (David Barney & Co) G H K1 D1 F1 V L M1
Stevenage p394 01438 314281

Amphlett, Ms J E (Addleshaw Goddard) J1
London EC1 p4 020 7606 8855

Amphlett, M L (Browne Jacobson LLP) N
Birmingham p136 0121 237 3900

Amsden, M (Addleshaw Goddard)
Manchester p300 0161 934 6000

Amzallag, D (K&L Gates LLP)
London EC4 p47 020 7648 9000

Anand, Ms H (Colman Coyle LLP) E
Islington p22 020 7354 3000

Anand, P (Punatar & Co Solicitors) G K1
London N19 p69 020 7272 3330

Anand, Ms S (Alan Edwards & Co) S2 E S1
Kensington & Chelsea p28 020 7221 7644

Anandanadarajah, R (Raj & Pillai) S2 E K3 Zi K1 S1 L Zg Zl V W F1 Ze D1 O
Hounslow p254 020 8572 7245

Anastasiades, M (Rich & Carr Freer Bouskell) N J1 Q O F1 Zr
Leicester p281 0116 253 8021

Anatogu, Mrs H C (Shell International Ltd)
London SE1 p109 020 7934 1234

Anaysse-Jacobs, Mrs N (Anaysse-Jacobs Solicitors) S1 K3 Zi W S2
London SE18 p6 020 8316 5000

Andela, Miss S (Glovers Solicitors LLP) J1
London W1 p36 020 7935 8882

Anderberg, Ms K (Dechert)
London EC4 p26 020 7184 7000

Anders, K (Walker Morris) L O Q Zl
Leeds p277 0113 283 2500

Andersen, W J (Blake Lapthorn) C3 I Ze V
London EC1 p13 020 7405 2000

Anderson, Ms A (Reynolds Porter Chamberlain LLP)
London E1 p71 020 3060 6000

Anderson, C (Royds LLP) C1 C2 F1 M1 M2 U2 Zza
London EC4 p74 020 7583 2222

Anderson, C J (Andersons) S1 E C1 J1 A1 B1 W R1 K1 G Zh Zi Zl
Croydon p204 020 8680 3131

Anderson, Miss C M (Kaim Todner Ltd) G H B2
London EC4 p47 020 7353 6660

Anderson, C R A (Farrer & Co LLP)
London WC2 p31 020 3375 7000

Anderson, Ms C S (South Gloucestershire Council)
Thornbury p474 01454 868686

Anderson, D (Carillion PLC)
Wolverhampton p477 01902 422431

Anderson, D (McGrigors LLP)
London EC4 p56 020 7054 2500

Anderson, D (Sykes Anderson LLP) C1 W T1 T2 C2
London EC2 p85 020 3178 3770

Anderson, D M (Humphries Kirk) S1 E S2
Bournemouth p152 01202 421111

Anderson, D P (Last Cawthra Feather LLP) E L S1 A1 Zc
Bradford p154 01274 848800

Anderson, Miss D S (Irwin Mitchell LLP) N
Leeds p274 0870 150 0100

Anderson, Miss E L (Blake Lapthorn) C1 T1
Portsmouth p354 023 9222 1122

Anderson, Mrs E M (Harvey Ingram LLP) B1 F1 L O Q
Leicester p280 0116 254 5454

Anderson, Ms F J (ConocoPhillips (UK) Ltd) O Q Zj
London W1 p105 020 7408 6000

Anderson, Ms F L (Sternberg Reed) G H B2
Barking p123 020 8591 3366
Romford p366 01708 766155

Anderson, Miss G (Irwin Mitchell LLP) N Zr
Leeds p274 0870 150 0100

Anderson, G (Addleshaw Goddard)
Manchester p300 0161 934 6000

Anderson, Ms G C (Blight Broad & Skinnard) K1 Q N W S1 G J1 F1 Zl K2
Callington p173 01579 382213

Anderson, Ms G P (Wigan Borough Council)
Wigan p476 01942 244991

Anderson, J (Clifford Chance) T1
London E14 p20 020 7006 1000

Anderson, J (Doyle Clayton Solicitors Limited) J1 Zp
Reading p360 0118 959 6839

Anderson, J (Skadden Arps Slate Meagher & Flom (UK) LLP) T1
London E14 p80 020 7519 7000

Anderson, J F R (Jeffreys & Powell) A1 S1 R1 Q L
Brecon p156 01874 622106

Anderson, Miss J K (Lancashire County Council)
Preston p469 01772 254868

Anderson, Miss J L (Brighouse Wolff) W S1
Ormskirk p341 01695 573202

Anderson, Mrs J M (Cozens-Hardy LLP) K1 D1
Norwich p334 01603 625231

Anderson, J N (Anderson Partnership) N O Q F1 C1 G J1 Zq
Chesterfield p191 01246 220737

Anderson, Ms J P (Mayer Brown International LLP) C1 Zc Zb
London EC2 p59 020 3130 3000

Anderson, J R D (Nelsons) G H Zl
Nottingham p338 0115 958 6262

Anderson, J R D (Poppleston Allen) Zl
Nottingham p338 0115 953 8500

Anderson, J W (Richmond Anderson Goudie) C1 E S1 W Zl
Chester-le-Street p191 0191 388 7884

Anderson, Ms K (Edward Fail Bradshaw & Waterson) G H B2
London EC3 p30 020 7790 4032
London EC3 p30 020 7264 2016

Anderson, Ms K (Anthony Gold) N Zr
London SE1 p6 020 7940 4000

Anderson, K (Watson Burton LLP)
Newcastle upon Tyne p327 0845 901 2100

Anderson, Miss K (J M Skinner & Co) N W
Birkenhead p135 0151 666 1122

Anderson, Miss L J (Bristows) C3 I C1 Ze
London EC4 p15 020 7400 8000

Anderson, Ms L R (England & Co) S2 E P R1 W
Great Yarmouth p23401493 844308 / 844309

Anderson, Ms M (Clarke Willmott)
Birmingham p136 0845 209 1000 / 0117 305 6000

Anderson, M E (Beale and Company Solicitors LLP) Zj Zq Zo O
London WC2 p11 020 7240 3474

Anderson, M G (Watkins Stewart & Ross) O Q B1
Ipswich p263 01473 226266

Anderson, M S (Anderson & Company) C1 C3 I J1 M1 M2 Ze Zv
Shillingford p378 01865 858878

Anderson, Mrs M T (Brethertons LLP) E S2 C1 C2
Rugby p368 01788 579579
Rugby p368 01788 579579
London EC2 p71 020 3116 3000

Anderson, Miss N (Fellowes Solicitors) G H
London E17 p31 020 8520 7392

Anderson, P D (Wolters Kluwer (UK) Ltd) C1 F1 E L O N J1 T1 T2 C2 Zc Zj Zp
Hinckley p461 01455 897361

Anderson, P J (Jolliffe & Co) Q K1 N J1 F1 B1 L Zl Zd Zq
Chester p190 01244 310022

Anderson, P L (Rushcliffe Borough Council)
West Bridgford p476 0115 981 9911

Anderson, P T (Morgan Cole) N Zj
Bristol p164 0117 916 7220

Anderson, P W (SJ Berwin LLP)
London EC4 p75 020 7111 2222

Anderson, R E (Read Dunn Connell) N J1 F1 L Zl B1 Q
Bradford p154 01274 723858

Anderson, R J (Hogan Lovells International LLP)
London EC1 p42 020 7296 2000

Anderson, R W (R W Anderson & Co)
Westminster p6 020 7323 4520

Anderson, S (Osborne Clarke) Zb
London EC2 p65 020 7105 7000

Anderson, Mrs S L (Tassells) K1 K3 D1 J1 J2 Zp K2
Faversham p225 01795 533337

Anderson, S M (Donald Race & Newton) S1 W E S2 C1
Burnley p169 01282 433241

Anderson, S P (Walker Morris) Q
Leeds p277 0113 283 2500

Anderson, T (Grant Argent & Co) S1 S2 Q E Zl L W
Brent p7 020 8452 7651

Anderson, Ms T D (Barlow Lyde & Gilbert LLP) Zj
London EC3 p10 020 7247 2277

Anderson, T R B (Reynolds Porter Chamberlain LLP) C1 I U2 Zf
London E1 p71 020 3060 6000

Anderson, Ms V (Edwards Angell Palmer & Dodge)
London EC2 p28 020 7583 4055

Anderson, W W (Owen White) O C1
Slough p382 01753 876800

Anderton, Mrs C (Bristows) O Ze
London EC4 p15 020 7400 8000

Anderton, Ms J (Bates Wells & Braithwaite London LLP) O Q A3 Zd
London EC4 p11 020 7551 7777

Anderton, N (Ratcliffe & Bibby) N K1 Q L J1 F1 B1
Morecambe p319 01524 410424

Anderton, P N (Cardiff County Council)
Cardiff p453 029 2087 2000

Anderton, P S (The Penhale Practice) S1 S2
Morecambe p319 01524 401010

Anderton, R A (Elliot Mather LLP) D1 F1 G H K1 M1 Zl
Mansfield p311 01623 655666

Andonian, B (Gulbenkian Andonian Solicitors) Zi Zg K1
London WC1 p37 020 7269 9590

Andrade, C (Phoenix Solicitors) Zr F1 J1 K1 Zl Q N
Leicester p281 0116 254 2863

Andrade, L M C (Hertfordshire County Council)
Hertford p460 01992 555555

Andrea, P (Wills Group Ltd)
London EC3 p110 020 7488 8111

Andreas, C (Andros Maritime Ltd)
London WC1 p103 020 7831 4388

Andrew, C (Allen & Overy LLP)
London E1 p5 020 3088 0000

Andrew, Ms C M (Network Rail)
London NW1 p108 020 7557 8000
London EC2 p28 020 7583 4055

Andrew, J (HM Land Registry - Hull)
Hull p461 01482 223244

Andrew, M A (Mundays LLP) Zb C1 C2
Cobham p196 01932 590500

Andrew, Mrs P (The Worcester Family Law Practice) K1 K2 K3
Worcester p440 01905 730900

Andrew, Mrs S J (Pluck Andrew & Co) D1 F1 G H K1
Hyde p259 0161 368 6311

Andrewartha, Miss A E (Michael Leighton Jones) D2 K1 L N Q W V
Bargoed p123 01443 830228

Andrewes, R N (Norman Saville & Co) S1 W C1 E R1 T2 Zv
London N10 p76 020 8883 9711

Andrews, A (Steed & Steed LLP) G H
Braintree p155 01376 552828

Andrews, A T C (Reed Smith LLP) Za
London EC2 p71 020 3116 3000

Andrews, Miss C (Gough-Thomas & Scott) N S1 J1 Q O
Ellesmere p217 01691 622413

Andrews, Ms C (Barlow Robbins LLP) S1
Woking p436 01483 748500

Andrews, Ms C C (Keith Hall Juviler & Co) D1 F1 G H K1 L M1 P
Greenford p234 020 8578 3133 / 8578 5373

Andrews, Mrs C D (Environment Agency (Midlands Region))
Solihull p471 0121 711 2324

Andrews, C J (John Fowlers LLP Solicitors) W K4 Zm S1 G
Colchester p197 01206 576151

Andrews, C P (Coodes) G H K1 D1 N F1
Liskeard p285 01579 347600

Andrews, D J (Linder Myers Solicitors) N
Manchester p307 0844 984 6400

Andrews, E J (South Gloucestershire Council)
Thornbury p474 01454 868686

Andrews, Ms G M (Bird & Bird LLP) U1 U2 I C1 M2
London EC4 p13 020 7415 6000

Andrews, H (Shakespeares) E S1 L S2 W A1
Stratford-upon-Avon p400 0845 630 8833

Andrews, Mrs H L (Allen & Overy LLP)
London E1 p5 020 3088 0000

Andrews, Mrs H M (Clifton Ingram LLP) S1
Wokingham p437 0118 978 0099

Andrews, I M G (Linklaters LLP)
London EC2 p54 020 7456 2000

Andrews, Ms J (Quality Solicitors Burroughs Day) J1
Bristol p164 0117 929 0333

Andrews, Mrs J (Wannop Fox Staffurth & Bray) Q J1 L
Bognor Regis p148 01243 864001

Andrews, Ms J (Bates Wells & Braithwaite London LLP) J1 J2 Zd
London EC4 p11 020 7551 7777

Andrews, J I (Steele Raymond) Q N K1 W M3
Bournemouth p152 01202 294566

Andrews, J M (Stone Rowe Brewer LLP) O Q B1 J1 Zc
Twickenham p416 020 8891 6141

Andrews, Mrs K (Wollen Michelmore Solicitors) K4 W
Newton Abbot p330 01626 332266

Andrews, Miss K J (Nabarro LLP)
Sheffield p376 0114 279 4000

Andrews, Mrs K L (Dutton Gregory) K1 D1 K3
Southampton p385 023 8022 1344

Andrews, Miss K M (Carter Read & Dove) S1 W
Swindon p406 01793 617617

Andrews, Miss K M J (Royal Mail Group)
London EC4 p109 020 7250 2468

Andrews, L (Harrowells)
York p444 01904 558600

Andrews, M (Mark Andrews) S1 W
Leighton Buzzard p282 01525 371616

Andrews, M (Mark Andrews & Co) D1 F1 G H L M1 P W Zv
Bristol p160 0117 983 8880

Andrews, M (Hogan Lovells International LLP)
London EC1 p42 020 7296 2000

Andrews, M (Kennedys) Zj
London EC3 p49 020 7667 9667

Andrews, M B (SNR Denton) B1 Zb
London EC4 p75 020 7242 1212

Andrews, M J (Carrick District Council) E S2 R2 C1 C2 A1 F1 S1 L
Truro p474 01872 224400

Andrews, M J (Barlow Robbins LLP) J1
Woking p436 01483 748500
Uckfield p416 01825 750811

Andrews, Mrs M M C (Hartley & Worstenholme) W T1 T2
Castleford p183 01977 732222

Andrews, N A (Laytons)
London EC4 p52 020 7842 8000
Cobham p196 01932 590500

Andrews, N A R (Coles Miller Solicitors LLP) O Q B1 C1 L J1 F1 Zc Ze Zp
Poole p352 01202 673011

Andrews, Ms N K D (Taylor Wessing) I Ze
London EC4 p86 020 7300 7000

Andrews, O R (Oglethorpe Sturton & Gillibrand) C1 E
Lancaster p270 01524 846846

Andrews, P (Thompsons (formerly Robin/Brian Thompson & Partners)) N G
Plymouth p350 01752 675810

Andrews, P (Thomas Andrews & Partners) S1 L E W C1 R1 B1 F1 G H Zc Zh
Wrexham p442 01978 291506

Andrews, P (Shoosmiths)
Nottingham p339 0370 086 5000 / 0115 906 5000

Andrews, P F H G (Steel & Clunis)
Birmingham p142 0121 523 9191

Andrews, Miss P G (Forsters LLP)
Westminster p33 020 7863 8333

Andrews, P I (Daniel Curry & Co) S1 S2 L K1 Q W J1 F1 O N Zl Zq K4
Croydon p205 020 8680 2188

Andrews, Ms R (Robert Lizar) G H
Manchester p307 0161 226 2319

Andrews, R F (Aletta Shaw Solicitors) K3 J1 G K1 K2 Q W J2
Bexleyheath p132 020 8301 4884

Andrews, Ms S (Pinsent Masons LLP) Zo
London EC2 p67 020 7418 7000

Andrews, S D (Marrons) R1 R2 Zu
Leicester p280 0116 289 2200

Andrews, S M (Bell Lax Litigation) N Zr J2
Sutton Coldfield p403 0121 355 0011

Andrews, Miss S V (B P Collins LLP) K1 D1 V
Gerrards Cross p229 01753 889995

Andrews, T J (Waldrons) C1 E Q S1 N O W J1
Walsall p420 01384 811811

Andrews, T J R (Burley & Geach) S1 S2 E A1 W Zm L
Grayshott p233 01428 605355

Andrews, Ms V (Forshaws Davies Ridgway LLP)
Frodsham p227 01928 739300

Androsov, N (Clarkson Wright & Jakes Ltd) C1
Orpington p341 01689 887887
Tunbridge Wells p415 01892 510000

Ang, B (Pinsent Masons LLP)
London EC2 p67 020 7418 7000

Angel, N P (Angel & Co) Zf Ze Q O S1 S2
Westminster p6 020 7495 0555

Angel, N R (Charles Lucas & Marshall) S1
Wantage p421 01235 771234

Angel, P (Andrews Angel Solicitors)
Ilford p259 020 8911 9289

Angel, P G (Manches LLP) C1 C2 Zj
Oxford p343 01865 722106

Angell, C (Ince & Co Services Ltd)
London E1 p44 020 7481 0010

Angell, Ms P (Hogan Lovells International LLP)
London EC1 p42 020 7296 2000

Angell, Miss S J (Angell & Co) D1 K1 L V
Bath p127 01225 484244

Angle, S (Trowers & Hamlins)
London EC3 p88 020 7423 8000

Angulo, Ms M E (Jones Day) C1
London EC4 p46 020 7039 5959

Angus, A S (Brian Ruff Angus & Jewers) D1 D2 K1 W M1 P S1
Wickford p431 01268 761126

Angus, Ms K (FBC Manby Bowdler LLP) Q
Wolverhampton p437 01902 578000

Angus, L (Hogan Lovells International LLP)
London EC1 p42 020 7296 2000

Angus, S (Shoosmiths)
Northampton p332 0370 086 3000 / 01604 543000

Angwin, Mrs K L (Bower & Bailey) S1 S2 E L W Zi R2
Oxford p343 01865 311133
Oxford p343 01865 767567

Ankcorn, D R (Test Valley Borough Council)
Andover p447 01264 368000

Anker, Mrs K L (Silver Fitzgerald) K1 K3
Cambridge p175 01223 562001

Annan, W J (Clifton Ingram LLP) C1 C2 C3 E S2 Ze
Wokingham p437 0118 978 0099

Annand, Prof R E (Humphreys & Co)
Bristol p163 0117 929 2662

Annen, M J (Richard Sedgley & Co) S1 S2 W C1 E J1 K1 N Q R1 Zd Zc
Bournemouth p152 01202 556222

Annett, R A (Lupton Fawcett) C1
Leeds p275 0113 280 2000

Annett, Ms S P (Pembrokeshire County Council)
Haverfordwest p460 01437 764551

Annett, T (Irwin Mitchell LLP) Zr
Manchester p306 0870 150 0100

Annette, A D (Herrington & Carmichael LLP) E S1 S2
Camberley p173 01276 686222

Annetts, I A (Allen & Overy LLP)
London E1 p5 020 3088 0000

Annetts, J (Finers Stephens Innocent LLP) *Zd K4 T2 W*
London W1 *p32* 020 7323 4000

Anning, Miss P (Wolferstans) *Zb E Zu S1 W S2 O*
Plymouth *p351*. 01752 663295

Annison, Ms R M (Carillion PLC)
Wolverhampton *p477* 01902 422431

Anniss, Ms C (Veale Wasbrough Vizards) *J1 Zp*
Bristol *p165* 0117 925 2020

Anns, Ms C (Gardner Leader LLP) *S1 W*
Newbury *p322*. 01635 508080

Anodu, O (Bankside Law Ltd) *B2 G Zq*
London SE1 *p9* 0844 745 4000

Ansah-Twum, Miss W N A (Cambridge House Legal Centre)
London SE5 *p104* . . 020 7703 3051 / 7701 9499

Ansary, Miss N (Clarkson Wright & Jakes Ltd) *Zl O Q*
Orpington *p341* 01689 887887

Ansell, Ms J L (Morgan Cole) *S1 T2 W*
Oxford *p344*. 01865 262600

Ansell, Miss S L (Edward Harte LLP) *K1 K2 D1*
Brighton *p159* 01273 662750

Ansell, Mrs V J (CooperBurnett) *C1 E C2*
Tunbridge Wells *p415* 01892 515022

Anson, Miss A (Donns) *N*
Manchester *p303* 0161 834 3311

Anson, P M (DLA Piper UK LLP) *N O Zj*
Sheffield *p375*. 0870 011 1111

Anson, Mrs S E (Squire Sanders (UK) LLP)
Leeds *p277* 0113 284 7000

Anstee, D R (Kenwright Walker Wyllie) *K1 D1 F1 O Q L*
East Molesey *p215* 020 8979 1131

Anstey, H M (HC Solicitors LLP) *A1 K1 K4 T1 T2 W Zd*
Peterborough *p347* 01733 882800

Anstey, Ms N G (Squire Sanders (UK) LLP) *Q*
London EC2 *p81*. 020 7655 1000

Anstice, Ms R (EDF Energy plc)
London SW1 *p106*. 020 7242 9050

Anstis, Ms C (Debenhams Ottaway) *E*
St Albans *p390* 01727 837161

Anstis, L J E (Boyes Turner) *C1 J1*
Reading *p360* 0118 959 7711

Antell, Ms S (Antell & Co)
London SW13 *p6* 020 8563 0793

Antenen, Mrs C (Amphlett Lissimore) *G H*
Croydon *p6* 020 8771 5254

Anthony Wilkinson, Ms K F (Alcan Holdings UK Ltd and Lawson Mardon Packaging Ltd and British Alcan Aluminium PLC)
Bristol *p451* 0117 915 3000

Anthony, B P (Bruce Anthony Solicitors) *K1 D1 V L W*
Belper *p130* 01773 857999

Anthony, Miss B S (Mills & Reeve) *B1 O C1*
Cambridge *p175*. 01223 364422

Anthony, C R (Greathead & Whitelock)
Pembroke *p345* 01646 682101

Anthony, Mrs F E (Norfolk County Council - Legal Services)
Norwich *p467* . . . Minicom: 0844 800 8011

Anthony, H (East Cornwall Magistrates Courts)
Bodmin *p450* 01208 262700

Anthony, Ms J (Neath Port Talbot County Borough Council) *K1 K2 V*
Port Talbot *p469*. 01639 763333

Anthony, P A E (Thomson Wilson Pattinson) *S1 W E G L Zl H R2*
Kendal *p264*. 01539 721945

Anthony, Mrs R C (SNR Denton) *B1 O Zb*
London EC4 *p75*. 020 7242 1212

Anticoni, Ms S T (Charles Russell LLP) *K1 Q O Zi D1*
London EC4 *p19*. 020 7203 5000

Antill, Ms J (Department for Business, Enterprise and Regulatory Reform)
London SW1 *p105*. 020 7215 0105

Antingham, M A (Osborne Clarke) *C1 I Ze*
Reading *p361* 0118 925 2000

Antolin, Ms S (Wainwright & Cummins) *G H*
Lambeth *p90*. 020 7737 9330

Antoni, Miss M (Bolt Burdon) *N*
Islington *p14*. 020 7288 4700

Antoniades, G A (George A Antoniades) *E F1 K1 N S1 S2 W*
London N4 *p6* 020 8800 4146

Antoniades, N (Shelter Legal Services) *L*
London EC1 *p109* 020 7505 2000

Antoniades, R M (Lee & Thompson)
London W1 *p52* 020 7935 4665

Antonini, Miss L (Universal Music) *O J1 W E Zf Zp*
London W14 *p110*. 020 8910 5000

Antoniou, J M (Blake Lapthorn)
Oxford *p342*. 01865 248607

Antoniou, P (Thackray Williams) *K1*
Beckenham *p129* 020 8663 0503

Antoniw, M (Thompsons (formerly Robin/Brian Thompson & Partners)) *N J1*
Plymouth *p350*. 01752 675810

Anton-Smith, M A J (BPE Solicitors LLP) *E*
Cheltenham *p187* 01242 224433
Cheltenham *p188* 01242 524654

Antram, Ms S E (Kennedys) *N J2 F2*
London EC3 *p49*. 020 7667 9667

Antrobus, Miss S (Cheshire County Council) *K1*
Chester *p454* 01244 602382

Anvoner, M S (Michael Anvoner & Co) *W*
Barnet *p123* 020 8449 0003

Anwar, F (Lincolnshire County Council Resources - Legal Services) *N*
Lincoln *p463*. 01522 552222

Anwar, Mrs I (Nottingham Magistrates Court)
Nottingham *p467*. 0115 955 8111

Anwar, P (Hill Dickinson LLP) *Ze J1 Zk*
Manchester *p305* 0161 817 7200

Anwar, Ms S (Laderman & Co) *Q O K1 W J1 L S1*
Redbridge *p51*. 020 8530 7319

Anwar, Miss S (Kirklees Metropolitan Borough Council)
Huddersfield *p461* 01484 221421

Anwar, S (Southerns) *G H N S1*
Burnley *p169* 01282 422711

Anyamene, R (Jones Day) *O E*
London EC4 *p46*. 020 7039 5959

Anyiam, H (Hiace Solicitors)
Croydon *p205* 020 8686 3777

Anysz, Miss L K (McCormicks) *J1*
Harrogate *p240* 01423 530630

Ap Dafydd, L G (Geraint Jones & Co) *N Q K1 G H J1 Zq*
Newtown *p330*. 01686 627935

Ap Gareth, R (Gwynedd Council)
Caernarfon *p452*. 01286 672255

Apfel, B (Wylie Kay) *S2 Q Zq A3 C1 E*
Blackpool *p147* 01253 296297

Apley, R B G (Richard Wilson Solicitors Ltd) *J1 K1 K2 L O Q N*
Goring *p231* 01491 879100

Aplin, Mrs C (Newcastle Upon Tyne City Council)
Newcastle upon Tyne *p466* . 0191 232 8520

Appalakondiah, V (Duncan Lewis & Co) *K1*
Hackney *p53*. 020 7923 4020

Appelbe, F (Ambrose Appelbe) *A1 S1 T1 W Zd Zo*
London WC2 *p6* 020 7242 7000

Appelboam-Meadows, Mrs A M (Penningtons) *N Zr*
Basingstoke *p127* 01256 407100

Appell, Ms B F (C P Christou LLP) *N L Q K1 W B1 Zl Zc J1 Zq K3*
London N12 *p20*. 020 8446 6777

Appiah, C (Charles Annon & Co)
London W6 *p6*. 020 7603 5539

Appleby, D (John Boyle & Co) *K1 D1*
Redruth *p362* 01209 213507

Appleby, D (Thurstan Hoskin Solicitors) *K3 K1 D1 V*
Redruth *p363* 01209 213646

Appleby, J P (Leonard Gray)
Chelmsford *p186*. 01245 504904

Appleby, Mrs K E (CGM) *S1 W*
Southampton *p385*. 023 8063 2733

Appleby, L J (The Ringrose Law Group - Nerina Farmer) *N*
Sleaford *p381* 01529 301300
Lincoln *p285*. 01522 814700

Appleby, M R J (Housemans) *J2 Q N*
London EC3 *p43*. 020 3170 6000

Applegarth, D C J (Arriva PLC)
Sunderland *p473*. 0191 520 4000

Applegarth, Miss J (Watson Burton LLP) *J1 Q*
Newcastle upon Tyne *p327* . 0845 901 2100

Applegate, Mrs C (Stewarts Law LLP) *Zr N*
London EC4 *p83*. 020 7822 8000

Applegate, C J U (Buckles Solicitors LLP) *W*
Peterborough *p346* 01733 888888

Appleman, S H (Eversley & Co) *E S1 C1 T1 K1 F1 B1 Zh Zb Zk*
Islington *p30*. 020 7607 0001

Appleton, D (Lewis Silkin LLP) *J1 Q O Zo*
London EC4 *p53*. 020 7074 8000

Appleton, J (Galbraith Branley) *G H B2*
London N12 *p34*. 020 8446 8474

Appleton, J (Arthur Smiths) *W S1*
Wigan *p432* 01942 242815

Appleton, J M (Breeze & Wyles Solicitors LLP) *S1 W L*
Enfield *p218*. 020 8366 6411

Appleton, K E (Bristows) *Ze O Q I B1 Zl*
London EC4 *p15*. 020 7400 8000

Appleton, M C (New Forest District Council)
Lyndhurst *p464* 023 8028 5000

Appleton, M J (Boyes Turner) *E L*
Reading *p360* 0118 959 7711

Appleton, Mrs N (Lewis Silkin LLP) *E C1 S2*
London EC4 *p53*. 020 7074 8000

Appleton, Ms P A (The Automobile Association)
Basingstoke *p448* 01256 491588

Appleton, P J (HC Solicitors LLP) *W T2*
Oundle *p342*. 01832 273506

Appleton, S (Last Cawthra Feather LLP) *W*
Shipley *p378*. 01274 585459

Appleton, Ms S (Butcher & Barlow LLP) *S1*
Leigh *p281*. 01942 674144

Appleyard, C J (Mackrell Turner Garrett) *K1 S1 W E M1 N*
Woking *p437*. 01483 476022

Appleyard, Mrs E J (EMW) *C1 Ze I U2 C3 M1*
Milton Keynes *p316* 0845 070 6000

Apps, Miss K M (Tozers) *N*
Exeter *p222* 01392 207020

April, Mrs M V (Memery Crystal) *O J1*
London WC2 *p60* 020 7242 5905

Apthorp, Miss S E (Sears Tooth) *K1*
London W1 *p77* 020 7499 5599

Apthorpe, Ms F M K (Robinsons) *D1 F1 K1 O Q V*
Derby *p209* 01332 291431

Arab, Miss S (Hammon Oakley) *K1 K3 D2 D1*
Coventry *p200*. 024 7644 8585

Araf, Ms F (Squire Sanders (UK) LLP)
London EC2 *p81*. 020 7655 1000

Aram, Miss H C (Humphries Kirk) *Q*
Poole *p352* 01202 725400

Arani, Ms M (Arani & Co) *K1 H G D2 Zi Q*
Southall *p384* 020 8893 5000

Aratoon, Ms K K (Birmingham City Council Legal & Democratic Services)
Birmingham *p449* 0121 303 2066

Aravindan, Mrs R (Aravindans)
Newham *p7* 020 8503 5034
Ilford *p260*. 020 8553 9600

Aravindan, S (Aravindans)
Newham *p7* 020 8503 5034

Arawwawala, Ms S R (Ziadies) *Zi*
London SW9 *p94* 020 7737 0934

Arazi, J E (Barlow Lyde & Gilbert LLP) *Zj*
London EC3 *p10*. 020 7247 2277

Arben, Mrs L H (Warwickshire County Council)
Warwick *p475* 01926 410410

Arboneaux, Mrs D M (Bryan Cave) *T2 W Zd M2*
London EC2 *p19*. 020 7207 1100

Archer, A (Freer & Archer) *F1 G H J1 K1 L S1 V W*
Leicester *p279*. 0116 241 3199

Archer, Miss C (Michelmores LLP) *R2 C3 Zu*
Exeter *p221* 01392 688688

Archer, Miss C (Penningtons)
London EC2 *p66*. 020 7457 3000

Archer, D B (Pitmans LLP) *B1 O Q J1 Zj*
Reading *p361* 0118 958 0224

Archer, G F (Warrens Boyes & Archer) *E S1 A1 C1*
Huntingdon *p258*. 01480 411331

Archer, G J (Bury & Walkers LLP) *S1 Q N J1 L*
Leeds *p272* 0113 244 4227

Archer, I H (Hanney Dawkins & Jones) *E L S1 C1 G N F1 J1 O Q*
Pinner *p348* 020 8866 2144

Archer, Ms K (DAC Beachcroft) *Zj N*
Birmingham *p137* 0121 698 5200

Archer, Mrs L A (Wilkin Chapman LLP) *W T2*
Beverley *p131* 01482 398398

Archer, M A (Gurney-Champion & Co) *S2 C1 E F1 J1 S1 O Q N*
Portsmouth *p354*. 023 9282 1100

Archer, M J (Beale and Company Solicitors LLP) *C1 J1 B1 T1 Zc Zb C2 I Ze U1*
London WC2 *p11* 020 7240 3474

Archer, Q D R (Hogan Lovells International LLP)
London EC1 *p42*. 020 7296 2000

Archer, Ms R M (Debridge Solicitors)
Hackney *p26*. 020 8986 2581

Archer, Ms R M (Pollecoff Solicitors Ltd)
London EC2 *p68*. 020 7608 2568

Archer, Mrs S R (Shakespeares) *Zh L O Q*
Stratford-upon-Avon *p400* . 0845 630 8833

Archer, T J (Reed Smith LLP) *N*
London EC2 *p71*. 020 3116 3000

Archer, Ms V (Thakker & Co) *W S1 S2*
Harrow *p242*. 020 8424 0571

Archibald, Ms B E H (Mills & Reeve) *R2*
Cambridge *p175*. 01223 364422

Archibald, G (Hill Dickinson LLP) *E S1*
Liverpool *p288*. 0151 600 8000

Archibald, Mrs H J (Barlow Robbins LLP) *E S1 S2*
Woking *p436*. 01483 748500

Archibald, S (Blake Lapthorn) *C1*
Chandlers Ford *p184* 023 8090 8090

Arden, Ms E (The College of Law)
London WC1 *p105*. 0800 289997

Arden, Mrs G (Gamon Arden & Co) *W*
Liverpool *p288*. 0151 709 2222

Arden, Ms K J (Remar & Co)
London SE5 *p71*. 020 7252 6722

Arden, M R (Symes Robinson & Lee) *D2 D1 G H K3 K1*
Crediton *p203* 01363 775566

Arden, R H (Gamon Arden & Co) *S1 W Zd*
Liverpool *p288*. 0151 709 2222

Arditti, E P (Ince & Co Services Ltd)
London E1 *p44* 020 7481 0010

Ardren, Mrs C T (Raworths LLP) *K1 D1*
Harrogate *p240* 01423 566666

Arends, G (Ashurst LLP)
London EC2 *p7* 020 7638 1111

Arestis, S (Silverman Sherliker LLP) *B1 O Q C1 J1*
London EC2 *p78*. 020 7749 2700

Argent, D T (Lamb Brooks LLP) *O J1 Q*
Basingstoke *p126* 01256 844888

Argent, G M (Grant Argent & Co) *C1 E F1 S1 S2 L O N R1 P W Zk Zl Zb*
Brent *p7*. 020 8452 7651

Arghyrakis, E G (E G Arghyrakis & Co)
London EC4 *p7* 020 7353 2302
London EC2 *p71*. 020 3116 3000

Argles, R V (C Nicholls) *K1 K2*
Bodmin *p148* 01208 76969

Argyle, Miss N J (Emsleys) *N*
Leeds *p273* 0113 232 1030

Argyle, Miss V L (Atteys) *D1 K1 V W*
Barnsley *p124* 01226 212345
Sheffield *p376* 0870 150 0100

Argyrou, F A (Anthony Louca Solicitors) *G H K1 L N O Q S1 Zi*
Westminster *p55*. 020 7723 9889

Argyrou, Miss S (Gisby Harrison) *S1*
Cheshunt *p189* 01707 878300

Aries, J D (Treasury Solicitors Department)
London WC2 *p110*. 020 7210 3000

Arif, A (Alletsons Ltd) *G H*
Bridgwater *p157* 01278 456621

Arif, A (ClarksLegal LLP) *C1 C2 C3 Zb*
Reading *p360* 0118 958 5321

Ariyadasa, Ms K (Cardiff County Council)
Cardiff *p453* 029 2087 2000

Ark, S (Fentons)
Manchester *p304* 0161 786 8320

Arkell, Ms H (Boodle Hatfield) *E R2*
Westminster *p14*. 020 7629 7411

Arkell, S (EMW) *C1 C2*
Milton Keynes *p316* 0845 070 6000

Arkwright, D P (Cyril Morris Arkwright)
Bolton *p148* 01204 535261

Arkwright, Mrs L L (Cyril Morris Arkwright) *W K4 T2*
Bolton *p148* 01204 535261

Arkwright, T J C (Cyril Morris Arkwright) *C1 S2 E C2 L*
Bolton *p148* 01204 535261

Armer, Ms C (Berwins Solicitors Limited) *E R1 S1 C1*
Harrogate *p240* 01423 509000

Armitage, A T (Bentley Motors Ltd) *C1 C3 F1 M2*
Crewe *p456* 01270 255155

Armitage, Mrs C (Newstead & Walker) *W T2 V K4*
Otley *p342*. 01943 461414

Armitage, Ms C (Trowers & Hamlins)
London EC3 *p88*. 020 7423 8000

Armitage, Mrs C D (ASB Law) *M3 Zb C2*
Crawley *p202* 01293 603600

Armitage, D W K (Squire Sanders (UK) LLP)
Leeds *p277* 0113 284 7000

Armitage, Miss K (Baily Gibson) *K1*
High Wycombe *p249*. 01494 442661
Oxford *p344*. 01865 297300

Armitage, N M (Lupton Fawcett) *O L Q Zb B1 E R2*
Leeds *p275* 0113 280 2000

Armitage, P J (Andrew & Co LLP) *J1 J2 O Q F1 F2 Zq*
Newark *p322* 01636 673743
Newark *p322* 01636 703333

Armitage, R A (Simmons & Simmons)
London EC2 *p79*. 020 7628 2020

Armitage, R M (Field Overell) *W E J1 S1 S2*
Leamington Spa *p270* 01926 422101

Armitage, Mrs S E (Farrells Solicitors) *O Q*
Bristol *p162* 0117 944 4664

Armitage, S M (Armitage & Co) *K1 E R1 S1 W C1 N Zl*
Exeter *p220* . . . . .01392 251364 / 214786

Armour, Miss S L (West Berkshire Council)
Newbury *p466*. 01635 42400

Armsden, Ms C M (Teacher Stern LLP) *C1*
London WC1 *p86* 020 7242 3191

Armstrong, A S (Armstrong Luty Solicitors) *Zr*
Skipton *p381*. 01756 799977

Armstrong, C J (West Cumbria Magistrates Courts)
Workington *p477*. 01900 62244

Armstrong, D C (Hughes Paddison) *C1 S2 E S1*
Cheltenham *p188* 01242 574244

Armstrong, Ms D F (Cartmell Shepherd) *S1 W A1 T1 L E*
Haltwhistle *p238* 01434 320362

Armstrong, D R (Rawlison Butler LLP) *L S1 S2 A1*
Crawley *p202* 01293 527744
Horsham *p253*. 01403 252492

Armstrong, E (Cuthbertsons) *S1 W*
Ashington *p119* 01670 813524

Armstrong, Mrs E F (Latimer Hinks) *K4 S1 W*
Darlington *p206* 01325 341500

Armstrong, G K K (Gerald Armstrong & Co) *D1 F1 G H K1 N S1*
Sunderland *p401*. 0191 514 0966

Armstrong, H (Armstrong Foulkes) *Zr*
Middlesbrough *p314* 01642 231110

Armstrong, Mrs H (Anderson Longmore & Higham) *S1 S2 E*
Petworth *p348* 01798 342391

Armstrong, Ms J (Infields) *K3 K1 L O Q J1*
Kingston upon Thames *p267* 020 8977 7633 / 8977 1149

Armstrong, Ms J (The Ringrose Law Group - David Thornley) *Q N G H*
Grantham *p232* 01476 590200

Armstrong, Ms J A (Dowse & Co) *K1 D1 K3*
Hackney *p27*. 020 7254 6205
London NW6 *p81* 020 7625 5590

Armstrong, J J (Muckle LLP) *E S2 R2 S1*
Newcastle upon Tyne *p325* . 0191 211 7777

Armstrong, Miss J L (Northamptonshire Magistrates Courts)
Northampton *p467* 01604 497000
Bedford *p130* 01234 343134

Armstrong, J P (Duane Morris) *U2 M2 Zza Ze C1 U1 Zf Q Zw*
London EC1 *p28*. 020 7786 2100

Armstrong, J S (CMS Cameron McKenna LLP) *C1 I M1 C3 M2 F1 Ze Zf Zw*
London EC3 *p17*. 020 7367 3000

Armstrong, Mrs L (London Fire & Emergency Planning Authority)
London SE1 *p107* 020 8555 1200

Armstrong, M (Eccles Heddon) *W K4 A1 S1 E T1 T2 S2*
Ripon *p365* 01765 601717
Thirsk *p411* 01845 522324

Armstrong, Miss M (Kirwans) *N*
Liverpool *p289*. 0151 229 5600

Armstrong, N (Charles Russell LLP) *Zk Zf Zza Ze Q*
London EC4 *p19*. 020 7203 5000

See p634 for the Key to Work Categories

Armstrong, N D (Goodman Derrick LLP) *K1 Zk*
London EC4 *p36* 020 7404 0606

Armstrong, Dr N J B (Irwin Mitchell LLP) *V X Zg Zq*
Sheffield *p376* 0870 150 0100

Armstrong, Ms R (Reynolds Porter Chamberlain LLP)
London E1 *p71* 020 3060 6000

Armstrong, R (Wheelers) *N Q*
Aldershot *p115* 01252 316316

Armstrong, Miss R (Gateley LLP) *J1 M1 J2 Zp*
Birmingham *p138* 0121 234 0000

Armstrong, R H (AWB Charlesworth LLP) *K4 W*
Keighley *p263* 01535 613678

Armstrong, R I (Platt & Fishwick) *A1 E C1 T1 S1 W L R1 Zn S2*
Wigan *p432* 01942 243281

Armstrong, S (Trowers & Hamlins)
London EC3 *p88* 020 7423 8000

Armstrong, S A (Hill Dickinson LLP) *O Za A3 M3*
London EC3 *p41* 020 7283 9033

Armstrong-Fox, Mrs J C (Collyer Bristow LLP) *E R1 S1 L*
London WC1 *p22* 020 7242 7363

Armstrong-Langley, Mrs M A (Robert Barber & Sons) *S1 S2*
Nottingham *p335* 0115 878 9000

Arnall, G (Nile Arnall Solicitors) *G H*
Bristol *p164* 0117 909 8898

Arnall, R M (Glaisyers Solicitors LLP) *C1 E L S1 W*
Manchester *p304* 0161 832 4666

Arnaoutis, Mrs N A (Nathene & Co) *K1 D1 S1 M1 W N P Zi*
London NW3 *p63* 020 7431 5020

Arneaud, S J (MacDonald Oates LLP) *Q O L J1*
Petersfield *p348* 01730 268211

Arneill, J I (Rawlison Butler LLP)
Crawley *p202* 01293 527744

Arnett, B W (Roach Pittis) *G H V*
Newport *p328* 01983 524431

Arnett, P W (Warner Goodman LLP) *K1 K2 K3 D1 D2*
Portsmouth *p355* 023 9275 3575

Arnheim, T (Allen & Overy LLP)
London E1 *p5* 020 3088 0000

Arnison, R W H (DLA Piper UK LLP) *E S2 C1 Ze*
Manchester *p303* 0870 011 1111

Arnold, A J (Steele Raymond) *C1 E B1 C2 F1 F2 I L U1 S2 Zc Ze*
Bournemouth *p152* 01202 294566

Arnold, A J (Ouvry Creed Solicitors) *E*
Tetbury *p410* 01666 504005

Arnold, Miss C (Rutters) *K1 S1 Q D1 K3*
Shaftesbury *p374* 01747 852377

Arnold, D (Ashurst LLP)
London EC2 *p7* 020 7638 1111

Arnold, Miss E (David Ede Solicitors)
London SE18 *p28* 020 8316 4758

Arnold, Ms E J (Foot Anstey) *D1 K1 Q Zl Ze*
Plymouth *p349* 01752 675000

Arnold, G A (G A Arnold) *G H*
Macclesfield *p297* 01625 615424

Arnold, Mrs H J (Benussi & Co) *K1 K2 K3*
Birmingham *p135* 0121 248 4001

Arnold, Mrs J (DMB Law) *K1 C1*
Sevenoaks *p374* 01732 228800

Arnold, J (Withers LLP) *T2 W*
London EC4 *p92* 020 7597 6000

Arnold, J F C (Cullimore Dutton) *N L Zl O Q J1 B1 Zg*
Chester *p190* 01244 356789

Arnold, K A (K A Arnold & Co) *B1 C1 K1 J1 L O Q Zc Ze Zk M2 Zq*
London N1 *p7* 020 7354 4926

Arnold, M (Wedlake Bell LLP) *O B1 Q*
London WC1 *p91* 020 7395 3000

Arnold, M D (Arnold & Co) *E S1 W S2 Zl*
Oldbury *p340* 0121 552 2382

Arnold, N (Fisher Meredith) *D2 D1 K1 Zg*
Lambeth *p32* 020 7091 2700

Arnold, N J (Blake Lapthorn)
London EC1 *p13* 020 7405 2000

Arnold, R G (Crane & Walton) *C1 S2 G J1 S1*
Ashby-de-la-Zouch *p118* 01530 414111
Coalville *p196* 01530 834466

Arnold, R M (Wilson Browne) *S1 E C1 K1 W A1 M1 N P*
Northampton *p333* 01604 876697

Arnold, Mrs S (Girls' Day School Trust)
London SW1 *p106* 020 7393 6666

Arnold, S (Osborne Clarke) *O*
Bristol *p164* 0117 917 3000

Arnold, S E (Montague Lambert & Co) *B1 C1 E J1 K1 L R1 S1 T1 W Zi Zk Zp*
Ealing *p61* 020 8997 2288

Arnold, Miss S L (South Tyneside Magistrates Court)
South Shields *p471* 0191 455 8800

Arnold, S W (Ford Simey LLP) *B1 D1 F1 G H J1 K1 M1 P Zm*
Exeter *p221* 01392 274126

Arnot, I J N (Dyne Drewett Solicitors Ltd) *E A1 S1 C1 W T1 L J1 R1 F1*
Sherborne *p378* 01935 813691

Arnot, R (Watson Burton LLP) *J2 Zl Q N*
Newcastle upon Tyne *p327* 0845 901 2100

Arnott, D G (Tinklin Springall) *W E S1 T2*
Beckenham *p129* 020 8402 7222

Arnott, I (Druces LLP) *E S2 R2*
London EC2 *p27* 020 7638 9271

Arnott, J D (Arnotts)
Witney *p436* 0844 372 1333

Arnott, Mrs P S (Burstalls) *K1 K2 D1*
Hull *p256* 01482 621800

Arnsby, M (G T Stewart Solicitors) *G H B2 J2*
London SE22 *p83* 020 8299 6000

Arnstein, P M (Forman Welch & Bellamys) *S1 S2 E L W*
Twickenham *p416* 020 8892 8907 / 8892 7733

Aronsohn, S S (Law Firm Ltd) *E I R1 S1 C1 Zs*
London W1 *p51* 020 7907 1460

Arora, Ms A (Davey Franklin Jones) *K1 K3*
Gloucester *p230* 01452 508800

Arora, Ms A (Arora Bailey) *F1 J1 L Q S1*
Cheam *p185* 020 8661 0000

Arora, Ms N (Arora Ashton Patel)
Ilford *p259* 020 8554 6263

Arora, N (Department for Business, Enterprise and Regulatory Reform)
London SW1 *p105* 020 7215 0105

Arora, R S (Arora Lodhi Heath)
London W3 *p7* 020 8993 9995

Arora, S (Lloyd Brennand) *S1 E W C1 L Q N K1 O*
Brentford *p156* 020 8569 9020

Arora, Ms V (DLA Piper UK LLP)
London EC2 *p24* 0870 011 1111

Arran, Mrs H M (Lamb Brooks LLP) *K1 K2 D1*
Basingstoke *p126* 01256 844888

Arran, P (City & County of Swansea) *B1 F1 J1 O Q N*
Swansea *p473* 01792 636000

Arrand, C W (DLA Piper UK LLP) *Q O Zj*
Birmingham *p137* 0870 011 1111

Arrand, Mrs M S (Birmingham City University) *E W S2 S1 C1 Zd*
Birmingham *p449* 0121 331 5000

Arrenberg, Ms K F (Parker Arrenberg) *Q O J1 Zc E W*
London SE6 *p65* 020 8695 2330

Arridge, C E (Parkinson Wright LLP) *F1 J1 L N O Q*
Worcester *p440* 01905 726789

Arron, N P (Poppleston Allen) *Zl*
Nottingham *p338* 0115 953 8500

Arrowsmith, Mrs D L (Warwickshire County Council)
Warwick *p475* 01926 410410

Arrowsmith-Brown, M R (Mills & Reeve) *W T1 A1 Zd*
Norwich *p335* 01603 660155

Arscott, J P (Stephenson Harwood)
London EC2 *p82* 020 7329 4422

Arscott, K J (Arscotts) *K1 D1 P N M1 C1 W L*
Hove *p254* 01273 735289

Arscott, P J (Arscotts) *S1 L W*
Hove *p254* 01273 735289

Arshad, Ms Y (Kirklees Metropolitan Borough Council)
Huddersfield *p461* 01484 221421

Arstall, Ms S L (The Wood Glaister Partnership) *E L R1 S1 T1*
Solihull *p383* 0121 705 8151

Artaius, Mrs S S (Winterbotham Smith Penley LLP) *W K4*
Nailsworth *p320* 01453 832566

Arter, J J M (Charles Crookes Limited) *O Q C1 Zq Ze Zc C2*
Cardiff *p178* 029 2049 1271

Arthur, A (Fisher Meredith) *Zg*
Lambeth *p32* 020 7091 2700

Arthur, Mrs A M (Anna Arthur Associates) *S1 W T2 D1 K2 S2 K3*
Woking *p436* 01483 222499

Arthur, Miss E E (Tozers) *Zr*
Exeter *p222* 01392 207020

Arthur, G D (Harvey Ingram LLP) *A1 E S1 L Zh*
Leicester *p280* 0116 254 5454

Arthur, H G (Macfarlanes) *Zo*
London EC4 *p56* 020 7831 9222

Arthur, N J (Kelcey & Hall) *G*
Bristol *p163* 0117 927 9604

Arthur, N J (Slee Blackwell) *E C1 C2 R1*
Barnstaple *p125* 01271 372128
Braunton *p156* 01271 812019

Arthur, N L (Ellis Jones) *Zr N Q Zq J2*
Bournemouth *p151* 01202 525333

Arthur, R (Thompsons (formerly Robin/Brian Thompson & Partners)) *J1 Zg*
Bristol *p165* 0117 304 2400

Arthur, R (Bird & Co) *G H*
Grantham *p232* 01476 591711

Arthur, R L (Australia and New Zealand Banking Group Ltd)
London E14 *p103* 020 3229 2121

Arthur, Ms S (Boodle Hatfield)
Westminster *p14* 020 7629 7411

Arthur, W H (D R James & Son) *N Q K1 J1 S1*
Pontardawe *p351* 01792 862334

Arthurs, Mrs C (Manches LLP) *O*
London WC2 *p58* 020 7404 4433

Artley, C W (David Durn & Co) *Q O B1 C1*
Ruislip *p368* 01895 612400

Arullendran, Ms P (Beecham Peacock) *J1 V*
Newcastle upon Tyne *p323* 0191 232 3048

Arunachalam, Miss A (Chadwyck-Healey & Co) *G*
London EC4 *p19* 020 7353 6900
London NW1 *p41* 020 7874 8300

Arundel, D J (Clarion Solicitors LLP) *B1 O Zb*
Leeds *p272* 0113 246 0622
Harrogate *p240* 01423 530630

Arundel, M J (B P Collins LLP) *E S1*
Gerrards Cross *p229* 01753 889995

Arundel, Miss S (Bywaters Topham Phillips LLP) *S1 S2 W T1 T2*
Harrogate *p240* 01423 879556

Arunothayam, M (Nathan & Co)
London SW19 *p63* 020 8542 1805

Arya, D (ZSA Law)
Hillingdon *p250* 01923 834300

Arya, Miss S (ZSA Law)
Hillingdon *p250* 01923 834300

Asbery, Mrs A (Harvey Ingram Borneos)
Milton Keynes *p317* 01908 696002

Asbrey, C D (Hugh James) *A3 O Zq Zc*
Cardiff *p179* 029 2022 4871

Asbury, C W (Byrne Frodsham & Co) *C1 E J1 K1 L S1 W*
Widnes *p431* 0151 424 5601

Asghar, A (Martin Murray & Associates) *G H B2*
Slough *p382* 01753 551313

Asghar, J (Sharpe & Co) *S1 S2 E*
Ashford *p119* 01784 247376

Asghar, K (Rashid & Co Solicitors) *Zi N*
Birmingham *p141* 0121 356 0078

Asghar, M (Asghar & Co) *G K1 N Q W Zl*
Southall *p384* 020 8843 0010

Ash, D (University of Birmingham)
Birmingham *p450* 0121 414 3637

Ash, N (Treasury Solicitors Department)
London WC2 *p110* 020 7210 3000

Ash, S (Barwells) *W K4*
Seaford *p373* 01323 899331

Ash, Mrs S (Murray Hay Solicitors)
London SW15 *p62* 020 8780 1225

Ashall, Ms P A (Linklaters LLP)
London EC2 *p54* 020 7456 2000

Ashall, R (Addlestone Keane Solicitors) *C1 B1 J1 T1*
Leeds *p271* 0113 244 6700

Asharaf, M J (Beers LLP) *F1 J1 K1 N O Q V Zi Zm Zp*
Plymouth *p349* 01752 246000

Ashbridge, J M C (Clark Holt) *Zb C1 C2 R2*
Swindon *p406* 01793 617444

Ashby, B J (Hertfordshire County Council) *C1 E L N O Q R1 S1 C2 A1*
Hertford *p460* 01992 555555

Ashby, Ms C (Christine Ashby Solicitors)
Ottery St Mary *p342* 01404 814303

Ashby, C J A (Alston Ashby) *S1 W K1 T1 E P G C1*
Chatham *p184* 01634 842017

Ashby, D A (Rodgers & Burton)
London SW13 *p73* 020 8939 6300

Ashby, Ms E J (LG Lawyers)
London SE1 *p50* 020 7379 0000

Ashby, G (Whatley Recordon) *K4 T2 V W*
Malvern *p300* 01684 892939

Ashby, J P (Fiona Bruce & Co LLP) *E Zd*
Warrington *p421* 01925 263273

Ashby, K M (Sheridans) *O Zj Q Zf Ze*
London WC1 *p78* 020 7079 0100

Ashby, N J R (Martin Murray & Associates) *G H*
West Drayton *p427* 01895 431332

Ashby, Ms R S (Pritchard Englefield) *N*
London EC2 *p69* 020 7972 9720

Ashby, T (AXA UK PLC)
London E22 *p103* 020 7920 5900

Ashcroft, Mrs A (Mortons) *S1 S2*
Sunderland *p401* 0191 514 4323

Ashcroft, Miss A L (Browne Jacobson LLP) *C1 C2*
Nottingham *p336* 0115 976 6000

Ashcroft, D G (John A Behn Twyford & Co) *G H F1 K1 S1 L J1 W M1*
Liverpool *p286* 0151 236 0367

Ashcroft, Miss L C E (Roebucks) *K1 D1 K3*
Blackburn *p145* 01254 274000

Ashcroft, P D (Northern Rock PLC)
Gosforth *p459* 0191 285 7191

Ashelford, M (Lee & Thompson) *Zf*
London W1 *p52* 020 7935 4665

Ashenhurst, Ms D J (Olswang LLP) *Q Zk*
London WC1 *p64* 020 7067 3000

Asher, A H (Allen & Overy LLP)
London E1 *p5* 020 3088 0000

Asher, C A (S D Rosser & Co) *Q L K1 S2 S1 Zl O W E*
London NW10 *p74* 020 8451 3848

Asher, Miss J (Russell-Cooke LLP) *O C1*
London SW15 *p74* 020 8789 9111

Asher, Miss L (Fendom Dawson & Partners) *S2 K3 K4 Zl Q S1 W*
High Wycombe *p250* 01494 450361

Ashford, Miss A (Blaser Mills) *G*
High Wycombe *p249* 01494 450171

Ashford, C I (DLA Piper UK LLP) *B1*
Leeds *p272* 0870 011 1111

Ashford, C R (Treasury Solicitors Department)
London WC2 *p110* 020 7210 3000

Ashford, M J (TV Edwards LLP) *G H*
London EC3 *p85* 020 7790 7000

Ashford, Miss N (Lawson Lewis & Co) *S1*
Eastbourne *p215* 01323 720142

Ashford, N G M (Gepp & Sons) *C1*
Chelmsford *p186* 01245 493939
Colchester *p197* 01206 369889

Ashford, P R (Cripps Harries Hall LLP) *O Q Zq*
Tunbridge Wells *p415* 01892 515121

Ashford, Mrs S L (Charles Russell LLP) *W T2 Zd*
Guildford *p235* 01483 252525

Ashford, Mrs T (Rowbis Solicitors) *Q O N L J1 B1*
Gloucester *p230* 01452 301903

Ashley Taylor, A M (Hill Dickinson LLP) *Zo A3*
Manchester *p305* 0161 817 7200

Ashley, A J (Alan Ashley & Co) *E P R1 R2 S2 L C1 C2 O Q Zc Zq Zu A1*
London EC4 *p7* 020 7822 7482

Ashley, C (Jackson Brierley Hudson Stoney) *K4 W*
Rochdale *p365* 01706 644187 / 649214

Ashley, Mrs D J A (Borough of Poole)
Poole *p469* 01202 262808

Ashley, Mrs J A (Gardner Champion) *S1 L W*
Rugeley *p368* 01889 576121 / 582116

Ashley, Miss M E (Payne & Payne) *E S1 C1 L T1 R1 B1 A1 W Zs Zc Zd*
Hull *p257* 01482 326446

Ashley, P A G (Gardner Champion) *D1 K1 K3 K2*
Rugeley *p368* 01889 576121 / 582116

Ashley, R (Kaim Todner Ltd) *G H B2*
Ashford *p119* 01233 662002

Ashley, S (Lewis Silkin LLP) *C1 C2*
London EC4 *p53* 020 7074 8000

Ashley-Brown, M A (Canary Wharf Group PLC)
London E14 *p104* 020 7418 2367

Ashman, Ms A (Bryan Cave) *C1 C2*
London EC2 *p19* 020 7207 1100

Ashman, A S J F (Sintons LLP) *N Q O*
Newcastle upon Tyne *p326* 0191 226 7878

Ashman, C (Clive Ashman)
Pontyclun *p352* 01443 231177

Ashman, G (Ashurst LLP)
London EC2 *p7* 020 7638 1111

Ashman, K S (Hogan Lovells International LLP)
London EC1 *p42* 020 7296 2000

Ashman, L H (Baxters) *S1 S2 W*
Tamworth *p407* 01827 899059
Tamworth *p407* 01827 58333 / 58334

Ashmore, C R J (Greenwoods) *N Q L F1*
London EC3 *p37* 020 7220 7818

Ashmore, R (Reynolds Porter Chamberlain LLP)
London E1 *p71* 020 3060 6000

Ashoka, S S (Ashoka & Co) *E*
Woburn Sands *p436* 01908 288120

Ashplant, D J (Lester Aldridge LLP) *C1 Ze M1*
Bournemouth *p152* 01202 786161

Ashplant, Ms E (Taylor Wessing)
London EC4 *p86* 020 7300 7000

Ashtiany, Ms S (Morgan Cole) *J1 Ze Zp*
Oxford *p344* 01865 262600

Ashton, B (Barry Ashton) *D1 F1 G H M1 P V*
Llangollen *p292* 01978 861140

Ashton, D (Shaw & Ashton) *S1 G K1 M1 H P D1 C1 W F1 Zm Zd*
Pontefract *p351* 01977 703232

Ashton, Ms D (The College of Law Chester)
Chester *p454* 0800 289997

Ashton, Ms H T (Irwin Mitchell LLP) *N*
Sheffield *p376* 0870 150 0100

Ashton, H W (Peachey & Co)
London WC2 *p66* 020 7316 5200

Ashton, J M (Sandersons) *B2 G H*
Hull *p258* 01482 324662

Ashton, J T (Turner Coulston) *A1 C1 E L R1 S1*
Northampton *p333* 01604 622101

Ashton, K (Olswang LLP)
London WC1 *p64* 020 7067 3000

Ashton, Miss K A (DWF) *N*
Liverpool *p287* 0151 907 3000

Ashton, Ms L (Salford City Council)
Swinton *p473* 0161 794 4711

Ashton, Ms L V (Harrogate Borough Council)
Harrogate *p460* 01423 500600

Ashton, M (Arora Ashton Patel)
Ilford *p259* 020 8554 6263

Ashton, M A (Malcolm Ashton) *C1 E S1 T1 W Zd S2*
Falmouth *p223* 01326 313100

Ashton, M K (Arscotts) *S2 E C1 Zb Zc S1*
Hove *p254* 01273 735289

Ashton, N J (Woodfines LLP) *W T2*
Bedford *p130* 01234 270600

Ashton, P W (Bridge McFarland) *K1 Zv*
Grimsby *p235* 01472 311711

Ashton, R (Moss & Poulson) *S1 W T2 Zm*
Shrewsbury *p379* 01743 350571

Ashton, R C (Middleton Dummer)
Oldbury *p340* 0121 544 4788

Ashton, R J (Butcher & Barlow LLP) *S1 S2 C1 W J1 Q*
Frodsham *p227* 01928 733871

Ashton, R J M (Adur District Council)
Shoreham-by-Sea *p471* 01273 263300

Ashton, S E (O'Neill Patient) *O N J1 F1 P Zq*
Stockport *p396* 0161 483 8555

Ashton, Ms S M (Britannia Hotels Ltd) *J1 F1 N P Zp*
Hale *p459* 0161 904 8686

Ashton, W (Bramsdon & Childs) *G H Zl*
Southsea *p388* 023 9282 1251

Ashurst, Ms C M (Chelmsford Borough Council)
Chelmsford *p454* 01245 606606

Ashurst, G H (Derbyshire Building Society)
Duffield *p457* 01332 841000

Ashurst, J G (Newport City Council)
Newport *p466* 01633 656656

Ashwell, M (Carillion PLC)
Wolverhampton *p477* 01902 422431

Ashworth, C (Hogan Lovells International LLP)
London EC1 *p42* 020 7296 2000

Ashworth, D A (David A Ashworth) *C1 D1 E G H J1 K1 M1 N*
Bewdley *p131* 01299 861056

6

Ashworth, Mrs F M (Wortley Redmayne Kershaw) *W*
Chelmsford *p187*. 01245 491122

Ashworth, H (Challinors) *N*
West Bromwich *p427* 0121 553 3211
Stafford *p392* 01785 244114

Ashworth, M J (Shell International Ltd)
London SE1 *p109* 020 7934 1234

Ashworth, N J (Thompson & Cooke LLP) *S1 W L E F1 A1 C1 K1 N Zc Zj Zk*
Stalybridge *p393*. 0161 338 2614

Ashworth, P (Dickinson Dees) *C1 T1 W B1 Zo Ze*
York *p444* 0844 984 1500

Ashworth, R C M (Pannone LLP) *E R1 R2 S2*
Manchester *p308* 0161 909 3000

Ashworth, R D (Holmes & Hills LLP) *W*
Braintree *p155*. 01376 320456
Chelmsford *p187*. 01245 491122

Ashworth, Mrs S (The National Trust)
Swindon *p475* 01793 817400

Ashworth, Miss S C (Maxwell Winward LLP) *E S2 L R2*
London EC4 *p59*. 020 7651 0000

Ashworth, S J (SNR Denton) *R1*
London EC4 *p75*. 020 7242 1212

Askew, D F (Askews) *S1 E W*
Redcar *p362*. 01642 475252

Askew, M (Clarke Willmott) *B1*
Bristol *p162* 0845 209 1000 / 0117 305 6000

Askew, P (Askews) *N W E*
Redcar *p362*. 01642 475252

Askew, S H (Askews) *N Zj*
Redcar *p362*. 01642 475252

Askham, A J (Bond Pearce LLP) *J1 O*
Southampton *p385*. 0845 415 0000

Askins, J (Harding Swinburne Jackson & Co) *L Q N*
Sunderland *p401*. 0191 565 8194

Askins, Mrs J K S (Appleby Hope & Matthews) *D1 K1 Zm V*
Middlesbrough *p314* 01642 440444

Askins, Mrs K (Berry Smith LLP) *E*
Cardiff *p177* 029 2034 5511

Askins, S M (Ince & Co Services Ltd) *O Q Za Zj*
London E1 *p44* 020 7481 0010

Askwith, Miss A S L (Taylor Wessing)
London EC4 *p86*. 020 7300 7000

Aslam, Miss F (Crowley & Co) *G Zi S1*
Cardiff *p178* 029 2045 8895

Aslam, Ms N (Glazer Delmar) *L Zh*
London SE22 *p35* 020 8299 0021

Aslam, T (Foys Solicitors) *S2 E S1 W*
Sheffield *p375* 0114 251 1702

Aslan, Ms S A (Howard Kennedy LLP) *Q Zf Zk*
London W1 *p48* 020 7636 1616

Aslanian, A (RMPI Solicitors) *C1 C2 O Q F1 W*
London W1 *p70* 020 7318 4444

Asmar, Ms M C (Herbert Smith LLP) *C1*
London EC2 *p40*. 020 7374 8000

Aspden, Miss J (Hartwig Notary Chambers) *N P M1 K1 J1 C1 B1 L D1 F1 Zb Ze Zi*
Croydon *p205* 020 8681 2893

Aspin, M G (Cartmell Shepherd) *J1 J2 F1*
Carlisle *p182*. 01228 516666

Aspinall, J (Bromiley Holcroft & Co)
Southport *p388* 0870 236 0000

Aspinall, J E (Hall Ennion & Young) *G H K1 S1 W B1 O Zl*
Ely *p218*. 01353 662918

Aspinall, P M (Aspinall Wright) *N S1 W E C1 C3 S2 F1 F2 J1 O Q C2*
Glossop *p230* 01457 854645

Aspinall, Mrs P W (Blake Lapthorn) *E*
Chandlers Ford *p184* 023 8090 8090

Aspinwall, Miss S (St Helens Borough Council)
St Helens *p472* 01744 456000

Aspley, N E (Marchants Solicitors) *D1 G H K1 N Q*
Mansfield *p312* 01623 655111

Asquez, J (Gordons LLP)
Leeds *p273* 0113 227 0100

Asquith, Mrs J (Jordans) *D1 K1 D2*
Dewsbury *p210* 01924 457171

Asquith, M (DWF) *N G M3 F1 Zw*
Manchester *p303* 0161 603 5000

Asscher, M A (Johnson & Clarence) *B1 E F1 J1 N O K1 Q S1 W Zc Ze Zl*
Midhurst *p316* 01730 812244

Asser, C (Ashurst LLP)
London EC2 *p7* 020 7638 1111

Asserson, T R D (Bird & Bird LLP) *O Q Zb A3*
London EC4 *p13*. 020 7415 6000

Assi, G (Bryan Cave) *C1 C2 U2 U1*
London EC2 *p19*. 020 7207 1100

Assim, G D (Shoosmiths) *O Ze Zw F2*
Milton Keynes *p317* . 0370 086 8300 / 01908 488300
Northampton *p332*. . 0370 086 3000 / 01604 543000

Astbury, D (DWF) *A3 B1 O Zq*
Manchester *p303* 0161 603 5000

Astbury, M (Calderdale Metropolitan BC Corporate Services Directorate) *G H K1 V F1 L Q*
Halifax *p460*. 01422 357257

Astbury, Miss S J (Thursfields) *C1*
Kidderminster *p266* 01562 820575

Astbury-Crimes, M (HCB Solicitors) *T2 W*
Walsall *p420*. 01922 720000

Astill, C P (Peter Astill & Co) *B1 K4 Zl Q S1 P M1 N E L F1 J1 W*
Birstall *p143* 0116 221 4885

Astill, S P (Harvey Ingram LLP) *C1*
Leicester *p280*. 0116 254 5454

Astle, E M (Astle Paterson Ltd) *K1 W Zk Zl K3*
Burton-on-Trent *p170* 01283 531366

Astle, J A (Darbys Solicitors LLP) *G H R1 Zl Zy*
Oxford *p343* 01865 811700

Astleford, P D (Dechert)
London EC4 *p26*. 020 7184 7000

Astles, P J G (Kidd Rapinet) *C2 E S2 I Ze*
Slough *p382*. 0845 017 9638

Astley, A (Gullands) *T2 W*
Maidstone *p299* 01622 678341

Astley, Ms C (Blandy & Blandy) *E R1*
Reading *p360* 0118 951 6800

Astley, R (Symes Bains Broomer) *E S1*
Scunthorpe *p373*. 01724 281616

Astley, S (Colemans - CTTS) *N*
Manchester *p302* 0161 876 2500

Aston, Mrs A (Larken & Co) *K1 V*
Newark *p322* 01636 703333

Aston, Mrs I (MFG Solicitors) *K1 K3*
Bromsgrove *p167* 01527 831691
Wolverhampton *p438* 01902 773666

Aston, Ms J A (Brewer Harding & Rowe) *K1 D1 D2 K3*
Barnstaple *p125* 01271 342271

Aston, Mrs S (Lamb Brooks LLP) *S1*
Basingstoke *p126* 01256 844888
Southampton *p386*. 023 8022 3957

Astruc, Ms C (SNR Denton) *Zb*
London EC4 *p75*. 020 7242 1212

Astwood, Miss M (Grahame Stowe Bateson) *E J1 K1 Zm R1 S1 W*
Harrogate *p240* 01423 562121

Aswat, Miss A I (Bolton Metropolitan Borough Council) *N D1 V J1 K1 L S1 Q F1 W Zi Zp Zv Zq Zr*
Bolton *p450* 01204 333333

Atack, Mrs S A (Moseleys) *K1 Q N*
Lichfield *p284* 01543 414100

Atcherley, R A (Paris Smith LLP) *C1 C2 Zb*
Southampton *p386*. 023 8048 2482

Atchison, A S (Vickers & Co) *S1 E W L C1 K1*
Ealing *p89*. . . .020 8579 2559 / 8840 3999

Atchison, G (Harbottle & Lewis LLP) *C1 Zv*
London W1 *p38* 020 7667 5000

Atha, C A S (Atha & Co)
Middlesbrough *p314* 01642 222575

Atha, T (Atha & Co) *Zl*
Middlesbrough *p314* 01642 222575

Atherton, Mrs K (Browne Jacobson LLP) *Zq Zj Zr*
Nottingham *p336*. 0115 976 6000

Atherton, Miss L M (EEF)
London SW1 *p106*. 020 7222 7777

Atherton, Mrs M (Berry Smith LLP) *K1*
Bridgend *p157*. 01656 645525

Atherton, S (Peter Lynn & Partners) *B1 F1 F2 J1 O Q Zq N J2 L Zl Zr Zp Zw*
Morriston *p319*. 01792 310731

Atherton, Miss S L (Squire Sanders (UK) LLP) *Zj*
London EC2 *p81*. 020 7655 1000

Athey, M V (Bayham Solicitors LLP) *C1 B1*
Tunbridge Wells *p414* 01892 891999

Athey, S (Hadaway & Hadaway) *G*
North Shields *p330* 0191 257 0382

Athi, H K (Athi Law LLP) *Zi Zv E L M1 N O Q R1 S1 W Zc Ze Zl*
Sheffield *p375* 0114 255 8001
West Bromwich *p427* 0121 553 5555

Athuraliyage, S (Athuraliyage Solicitors)
London EC3 *p8* 020 7377 0144

Atif, M C (Maurice Nadeem & Atif) *G S1 M1 L K1 H D1 P W*
London W1 *p59* 020 7723 3424

Atkin, E (Wilkin Chapman LLP) *E*
Grimsby *p235* 01472 262626

Atkin, P D (Shaw Davenport & Wardle) *S1 E W L N S2 Zl*
Blackpool *p147* 01253 622281

Atkin, P S R (Jaffe Porter Crossick)
London NW6 *p46* 020 7625 4424

Atkin, R (Ward Hadaway) *R1*
Newcastle upon Tyne *p327* . 0191 204 4000

Atkins, C (Shearman & Sterling LLP) *Zb*
London EC2 *p78*. 020 7655 5000

Atkins, Miss C L (Maples Teesdale LLP) *Zc*
London EC2 *p58*. 020 7600 3800

Atkins, Ms D (Brignalls Balderston Warren) *K1 D1 D2 K3*
Letchworth *p283*. 01462 482248

Atkins, Ms E (Birmingham City Council Legal & Democratic Services)
Birmingham *p449* 0121 303 2066

Atkins, G (London Borough of Bexley)
Bexleyheath *p449* 020 8303 7777

Atkins, G G (Bevan Brittan LLP) *E S2 L R2 S1*
London EC4 *p12*. 0870 194 1000
London WC2 *p58* 020 7404 4433

Atkins, Miss J A (Atkins & Co) *K1 K3 S1*
Esher *p220* 01372 477188

Atkins, J M (Louise Stephens & Co) *N Q O L G F1 K1 W J1 B1 Zl Zq*
Risca *p365* . . . . .01633 614005 / 601144

Atkins, Mrs M C (Davey Franklin Jones) *S1 L E*
Cirencester *p195*. 01285 654875

Atkins, M D (Harrowell & Atkins) *C1 E S1 W*
Berkhamsted *p131*. 01442 865671

Atkins, M M C (Birketts LLP) *B1 A3 I Ze O*
Ipswich *p262*. 01473 232300

Atkins, Mrs N J (The Child Law Partnership) *D1*
Guildford *p236*. 01483 543790
Farnborough *p224* 01252 549555

Atkins, N M (Hogan Lovells International LLP)
London EC1 *p42*. 020 7296 2000

Atkins, Ms R (Schillings) *Q O J1 Zk Zf Zv U2 Ze Zg Zw Zq U1*
London WC1 *p77* 020 7034 9000

Atkins, Mrs R (The College of Law Guildford)
Guildford *p459*. 01483 460200

Atkins, Ms R (Forsters LLP) *E*
Westminster *p33*. 020 7863 8333

Atkins, R J (Taylor Walton LLP)
St Albans *p390* 01727 845245

Atkins, Ms S A (London Underground Ltd)
London SW1 *p107*. 020 7918 3126

Atkins, Mrs S E (Colemans - CTTS) *S1 W T1 T2*
Kingston upon Thames *p267*. 020 8296 9966

Atkins, S J (Knowles Benning)
Shefford *p377* 01462 814824

Atkins, Miss S J M (Hertfordshire County Council) *D1*
Hertford *p460* 01992 555555

Atkins, Miss T (Berry Smith LLP)
Cardiff *p177* 029 2034 5511

Atkins, T R (Stephens & Scown) *S2 S1*
St Austell *p391* 01726 74433

Atkinson, A (Simmons & Simmons)
London EC2 *p79*. 020 7628 2020

Atkinson, A C (Reading Borough Council)
Reading *p469* 0118 939 0900

Atkinson, A N (The Wood Glaister Partnership) *S1 C1 W E L A1 R1 Zm*
Solihull *p383*. 0121 705 8151

Atkinson, Ms B E (Atkinson & Co) *K1 D1 J1 L N*
Newport *p328* 01633 251118

Atkinson, Miss C (Weightmans LLP) *K1 D1 D2 M1 P*
Liverpool *p291*. 0151 227 2601

Atkinson, C J (Philip Ross & Co) *J1 Q U1 O N*
London W1 *p73* 020 7636 6969

Atkinson, C M (Lamb & Holmes) *C1 S2 E C2*
Kettering *p265*. 01536 513195

Atkinson, E C (Wainwright & Cummins)
Lambeth *p90*. 020 7326 7460

Atkinson, Mrs E L (Milburns Solicitors) *K1 D1 K3 Q*
Whitehaven *p431* 01946 694818
Workington *p440*. 01900 67363

Atkinson, E P (Burton Copeland LLP) *G H*
Sale *p370* 0161 905 8530

Atkinson, G A (G A Atkinson) *S1*
Nottingham *p335*. 0115 969 3650

Atkinson, G R (Wortley Redmayne Kershaw) *S1 E L A1 R1*
Chelmsford *p187*. 01245 491122

Atkinson, Mrs H (Bruce Lance & Co)
High Wycombe *p250*. 01494 450494

Atkinson, Mrs H C (Schofield Sweeney) *S1 E A1 L R1*
Bradford *p154* 01274 306000

Atkinson, Miss H F (Forsters LLP) *W T2*
Westminster *p33*. 020 7863 8333

Atkinson, Mrs H M (Atkinson & Firth) *S2 E S1*
Shipley *p378*. 01274 584305
Dewsbury *p210* 01924 457171

Atkinson, J (K&L Gates LLP)
London EC4 *p47*. 020 7648 9000

Atkinson, J (Lupton Fawcett) *B1*
Leeds *p275* 0113 280 2000

Atkinson, J (Stephenson Harwood)
London EC2 *p82*. 020 7329 4422

Atkinson, Miss J (The Ringrose Law Group - Paul Cooper) *S1 S2*
Boston *p151*. 01205 311511

Atkinson, J (Ashurst LLP)
London EC2 *p7* 020 7638 1111

Atkinson, J C (Bedfordshire County Council)
Bedford *p448* 01234 363222

Atkinson, J J (John Howe & Co) *K1 S1 W*
Pudsey *p358*. 0113 236 3936

Atkinson, Miss J L (Irwin Mitchell LLP) *O B1 Zb*
Sheffield *p376* 0870 150 0100

Atkinson, J L (McKinnells) *G H*
Lincoln *p284*. 01522 541181

Atkinson, J M G (Clerk to Sheffield Justices)
Sheffield *p470* 0114 276 0760

Atkinson, J W (Nelsons) *K1*
Nottingham *p338*. 0115 958 6262

Atkinson, M (CMS Cameron McKenna LLP)
London EC3 *p17*. 020 7367 3000

Atkinson, M E (Beaumont Legal) *A1 C1 E K1 L*
Wakefield *p418* 0845 122 8100

Atkinson, P D (Over Taylor Biggs) *N C1 O Q F1 B1 Zt*
Exeter *p222* 01392 823811

Atkinson, P G (KJD) *C1 C3 O Ze Zf*
Stoke-on-Trent *p398*. 01782 202020

Atkinson, P H D (Reynolds Porter Chamberlain LLP) *M1 M2 N O P Q Zc Zj*
London E1 *p71* 020 3060 6000

Atkinson, P R (Pinsent Masons LLP) *R1 Zl Zn Zt*
Leeds *p276* 0113 244 5000

Atkinson, R (Milburns Solicitors) *K1 N D1 Q Zl*
Workington *p440*. 01900 67363

Atkinson, R J F (Robin Murray & Co) *G H*
Chatham *p185*. 01634 832332

Atkinson, S (Gregg Latchams LLP)
Bristol *p162* 0117 906 9400

Atkinson, S (Solomon Taylor & Shaw) *E S1 L S2*
London NW3 *p80* 020 7431 1912

Atkinson, S J (Currey & Co) *W Zd T2*
Westminster *p24*. 020 7802 2700

Atkinson, Miss V A (Richard Pearlman LLP) *A1 E L R1 S1 W Zv*
London EC2 *p66*. 020 7739 6100

Atkinson, Miss V S (Hilton Norbury) *K1 K3 D1 D2 W*
Wigan *p432* 01942 241424

Atkinson, Mrs Z (North Tyneside Council)
Newcastle upon Tyne *p466* . 0191 643 5000

Atlee, J D (Atlee Chung & Company)
London W1 *p8*. 020 7287 9988

Atter, R J (Atter Mackenzie & Co) *G Q A1 I O D1 K1 S1 E R1 Zg Zk H K3 Zc*
Evesham *p220*. 01386 425300

Atterbury, Ms L A (Harvey Ingram LLP) *W*
Leicester *p280*. 0116 254 5454
Leicester *p281*. 0116 262 4225

Atterton, C H (Freeman Johnson) *S1 W C1 L A1 E F1 R1 K1 P Zj*
Durham *p214* . . 0191 386 4843 / 386 9619

Attewell, P (Curtis Parkinson) *A2 S2 K3 J1 K1 K2 L Q N Zq S1 W*
Nottingham *p336*. 0115 931 7000

Attey, J (Wrigleys Solicitors LLP) *E S2 S1 L A1*
Leeds *p278* 0113 244 6100

Attfield, D V (Olswang LLP) *O Q M2 Ze Zf*
London WC1 *p64* 020 7067 3000

Attfield, Ms S (Chattertons Solicitors) *J1*
Lincoln *p284*. 01522 814600

Attle, G (Mills & Reeve) *O X*
Cambridge *p175*. 01223 364422

Attlee, C H (Bryan Cave) *C2 C1 R2 T1 M2 T2 M1 B3 I J1 Zb Ze Zj Zo Zv*
London EC2 *p19*. 020 7207 1100

Attree, S J (Lawson Coppock & Hart) *C1 C2 R2 C3 I Ze J1 Zb F1 F2 Zza M1 M2 U2*
Manchester *p306* 0161 832 5944

Attride, Ms C (Williamson & Soden) *W*
Solihull *p383*. 0121 733 8000

Attridge, D W (EBR Attridge LLP) *D1 G H K1 L N W O Q*
London N17 *p28*. 020 8808 0774
London SW11 *p28* 020 7228 7050

Attrill, B (Southampton City Council)
Southampton *p472*. 023 8022 3855

Attrill, L (Ashurst LLP)
London EC2 *p7* 020 7638 1111

Attrup, Mrs L (Debenhams Ottaway) *B1 Zr J1 Q N*
St Albans *p390* 01727 837161

Attwell, Miss K E (Pannone LLP) *J1 Zp*
Manchester *p308* 0161 909 3000

Attwell, N (Attwells Solicitors) *B1 C1 S2 E L R2 C2 S1*
Ipswich *p262*. 01473 746000

Attwood, A P B (Thompsons (formerly Robin/ Brian Thompson & Partners)) *N Zq*
Stoke-on-Trent *p398*. 01782 406200

Attwood, A W (W M Attwood & Son) *Zv R1 S1 T1 A1 T2 E W*
Cradley Heath *p201* .01384 566523 / 566128

Attwood, Miss B (Berry Smith LLP) *J1*
Cardiff *p177* 029 2034 5511

Attwood, C (Attwood & Co) *O N B1 J1 C1 Q T1 Zb Zc Zj*
Grays *p233* . . . . .01375 378122 / 378123

Attwood, D G (Bellis Kennan Gribble & Co) *E F1 J1 L M1 O Q R1 S1 W Zv Zi Zq*
Southport *p388* 01704 532217

Attwood, P G (DWF) *C1 C2 Zy C3 F1 I F2 Ze P J1 M1 J2 U2 T1*
Liverpool *p287*. 0151 907 3000

Atwal, B (The Smith Partnership) *N Q*
Derby *p209* 01332 225225

Atwal, Miss H K (Mills & Reeve) *R2*
Cambridge *p175*. 01223 364422

Atwal, Mrs M (ClarksLegal LLP) *J1 J2 N Q*
Reading *p360* 0118 958 5321

Atwell, M J (Trowers & Hamlins) *W T2 T1 C2 Zo*
London EC3 *p88*. 020 7423 8000

Aubin-Parvu, Ms N L (LG Lawyers)
London SE1 *p50*. 020 7379 0000

Aubrey, Ms D E (Northumbria Police) *C1 G H K1 M1*
Ponteland *p469* 01661 872555

Aubrey, M J (Mills & Reeve) *A1*
Cambridge *p175*. 01223 364422

Aucott, Mrs K (George Davies Solicitors LLP) *K3 K1*
Manchester *p303* 0161 236 8992

Audsley, Mrs K L (Hutchinson & Buchanan) *K1 K3 L S1*
Ripon *p365* 01765 602156

Audu, M (Audu & Co) *G K1 S1 Zi K3*
Islington *p8* 020 7278 9340

Augu, Miss L S (Sweeney Miller) *L O Q N*
Sunderland *p402*. 0191 568 2050

Auld, B C (Brethertons LLP) *C1 J1 M1 J2*
Banbury *p122* 01295 270999
Rugby *p368* 01788 579579
Rugby *p368* 01788 551611

Auld, D R (Gorman Hamilton) *N Q*
Newcastle upon Tyne *p324* . 0191 232 1123

Auld, M D E (David Auld & Co) *S1 E W G H A1 C1 F1 Zl Zm*
Bedlington *p130* 01670 826870
Morpeth *p319* 01670 505844

Auld, Mrs V L (David Auld & Co)
Bedlington *p130* 01670 826870
Morpeth *p319* 01670 505844

Aulton, Mrs A J (Irwin Mitchell LLP) *C1 C3 I M1 O Ze Zf Zw Zy Zz*
Leeds *p274* 0870 150 0100

Aumayer, D (Edward Oliver & Co) *S1 G H P M1 W J1 L F1 C1*
Cheshunt *p189* 01992 633491

Aung, T S (British American Tobacco)
London WC2 *p104*. 020 7845 1000

See p634 for the Key to Work Categories

Ausden, A M (Lodders Solicitors LLP) *B1 C1 C2*
Stratford-upon-Avon *p400* . . 01789 293259
Austen, Ms M D (Willans LLP) *C1 C2 J1 Zd Ze*
Cheltenham *p189* 01242 514000
Austen-Jones, J D (Healys LLP) *N J2 Zr*
Brighton *p159* 01273 685888
Austin, Ms A (The Stokes Partnership) *E Zl*
Crewkerne *p203* 01460 279279
Austin, D K (Laytons) *E L O R1 R2*
Guildford *p236* 01483 407000
Austin, D T (Reed Smith LLP)
London EC2 *p71* 020 3116 3000
Austin, E (Edward Austin)
Shrewsbury *p379* 01743 236222
Austin, E (Napthens LLP) *W*
Chorley *p194* 0845 260 2111
Austin, G (Crowell & Moring) *B2 G J2*
London EC4 *p23* 020 7413 0011
Austin, G W (Barker Austin) *B1 C1 F1 G J1 M1 N P S1 W Zj Zk Zp*
London EC3 *p9* 020 7377 1933
Austin, J (Boys & Maughan) *F1 G H L N Zl A3*
Margate *p312* 01843 234000
Austin, Miss J E (Hempsons) *N Zr*
Westminster *p40* 020 7839 0278
Austin, J S (Gordons) *E S2 S1*
Guildford *p236* 01483 451900
Austin, J S J (Birketts LLP) *C1 Ze*
Ipswich *p262* 01473 232300
Austin, K (Barlow Lyde & Gilbert LLP)
London EC3 *p10* 020 7247 2277
Austin, Ms L (Levy & Co Solicitors LLP) *G H*
Witham *p436* 01376 511819
Austin, Mrs L S J (Waverley Borough Council)
Godalming *p459* 01483 523333
Austin, Mrs L V (Davies & Partners) *Zr*
Almondsbury *p115* 01454 619619
Austin, Ms M (Ashurst LLP)
London EC2 *p7* 020 7638 1111
Austin, M D (Taylor Wessing)
London EC4 *p86* 020 7300 7000
Austin, N (Gordon Dean Solicitors)
Norwich *p334* 01603 767671
Austin, R A (Seddons) *O M2 B1 Zb Zj A3 Za Zn*
Westminster *p77* 020 7725 8000
Austin, R J P (Higgs & Sons) *S1 K1 M1 E C1 F1 J1 W*
Brierley Hill *p158* 0845 111 5050
Austin, Ms S J (Donald Race & Newton) *W Q K1 T2*
Burnley *p169* 01282 433241
Austin, T J (Andrew Macbeth Cash & Co) *A1 E F1 G K1 L N Q S1 V W Zn Zv*
Wirksworth *p435* 01629 822553
Austin, Miss T M A (Gardner Austin) *S1 S2 E C1 W Zl*
Westminster *p35* 020 7831 2600
Austin-Lea, Mrs E (Bartletts Solicitors) *Q N*
Chester *p190* 01244 313301
Austwick, M P (DAC Beachcroft) *E B1 R1 P Zb Zc*
Bristol *p162* 0117 918 2000
Auton, Miss J E (Brown Beer Nixon Mallon) *K3 K1*
Redcar *p362* 01642 490202
Auton, R M (Walker Morris) *Zu*
Leeds *p277* 0113 283 2500
Auty, Ms A J (Ramsdens Solicitors) *K1 D2 D1 K2 K3*
Huddersfield *p256* 01484 821500
Avadis, L (Avadis & Co) *K1 N*
London NW5 *p8* 020 7267 4240
Aveling, N E H (Glazer Delmar) *S1 S2*
London SE22 *p35* 020 8299 0021
Avent, I M (Penman Johnson) *G H N Q O B1 J1 F1 L Zl Zt*
Watford *p424* . . . . 01923 225212 / 239566
Averill, Mrs R (Birmingham City Council Legal & Democratic Services) *Q N O J1 B1 Ze*
Birmingham *p449* 0121 303 2066
Avern, M I (Harrowell & Atkins) *E F1 G H J1 K1 L M1 S1 P Zl*
Berkhamsted *p131* 01442 865671
Avery, Ms B M (Pritchard Englefield) *J1*
London EC2 *p69* 020 7972 9720
Avery, C H (Pitmans LLP)
Reading *p361* 0118 958 0224
Avery, K (Kennedys) *Q*
London EC3 *p49* 020 7667 9667
Avery, M D (Hoole & Co) *S1*
Bristol *p163* 0117 969 1436
Avery, M L (Waugh Moody & Mulcahy) *S1 W S2 E Zl K4*
Newcastle upon Tyne *p327* . 0191 232 8107
Avery, N B (Ashurst LLP)
London EC2 *p7* 020 7638 1111
Aves, M O (Warners Solicitors) *K1 Q*
Sevenoaks *p374* 01732 747900
Avila, S C (Birkett Long LLP) *C1 C3 F1 I Ze*
Chelmsford *p186* 01245 453800
Avis, P R (MJP Law) *N Q*
Bournemouth *p152* 01202 582582
Avon, Mrs M S M (London Underground Ltd)
London SW1 *p107* 020 7918 3126
Avraam, Mrs M D (Grace & Co) *C1 J2 N S1*
Warrington *p422* 01925 242488
Awad, P F (Kerseys) *W K4*
Ipswich *p262* 01473 213311
Awan, M A (Awan Solicitors)
Croydon *p204* 020 8781 1838
Awan, M A (Awan Solicitors) *G N Q K1 L J1 Zp Zi F1 K3 O*
Kenley *p264* 020 8781 1838
Awan, Miss Y (Clarkson Wright & Jakes Ltd) *J1*
Orpington *p341* 01689 887887
Awdry, G A (Awdry Bailey & Douglas) *S1 A1 C1 E P L W T1 R1 J1 Zh Zd*
Calne *p173* 01249 815110
Devizes *p210* 01380 722311
Wootton Bassett *p439* 01793 853200
Awtani, S (Landau Zeffertt Weir) *Zi W*
London SE1 *p51* 020 7357 9494
Awty, G (Henmans LLP) *E A1 A2*
Oxford *p343* 01865 781000
Awty, S (Terry Jones Solicitors & Advocates) *C1 E J1*
Shrewsbury *p379* 01743 285888
Axe, B T (Barber Titleys) *R1 P Zu*
Harrogate *p240* 01423 502211
Axe, M W (Rawlison Butler LLP) *O*
Crawley *p202* 01293 527744
Axe, Ms R (Ince & Co Services Ltd)
London E1 *p44* 020 7481 0010
Axon, P (Jacobs Solicitors) *N*
Ellesmere Port *p217* 0151 355 8481
Axten, A R (Foot Anstey) *O Zb*
Plymouth *p349* 01752 675000
Axton, Mrs C (The Clarke Partnership) *N*
Stockport *p395* 0161 474 6600
Ayers, D H (Bird & Bird LLP) *C1 U1*
London EC4 *p13* 020 7415 6000
Ayers, M A (J A Kemp & Co)
London WC1 *p48* 020 7405 3292
Aykroyd, Mrs V L (Irwin Mitchell LLP)
London EC1 *p45* 0870 150 0100
Aylett, M J (Tewkesbury Borough Council)
Tewkesbury *p474* 01684 272012
Aylmer, The Hon A J (Reynolds Porter Chamberlain LLP) *Zj Zq*
London E1 *p71* 020 3060 6000
Aylmore, P (Bennett Richmond) *S1 K1 M1 G H E W N P F1 Zc Zk Zl*
Lanchester *p270* 01207 521843
Aylott, R C (ASB Aspire) *N O*
Maidstone *p298* 0845 063 6465
Aylward, J (Neil Millar & Co Solicitors) *C1 E R2 W Zb S1 C2*
Manchester *p307* 0161 870 0177
Aylwin, Miss J M (Kidd Rapinet) *E S1 S2 L*
Farnham *p225* 0845 017 9609
Aynsley, Ms C A (Jones Robertson)
Widnes *p431* 0151 423 3661
Aynsley, P D (McCarthy Bennett Holland) *K1 Q D1 J1 N O*
Wigan *p432* 01942 206060
Ayre, Miss A (Royds LLP) *E S2 R2 S1 L Zh R1*
London EC4 *p74* 020 7583 2222
Ayre, Miss C M M (Browne Jacobson LLP) *N Q O*
Nottingham *p336* 0115 976 6000
Ayre, Ms K (Pinsent Masons LLP)
London EC2 *p67* 020 7418 7000
Ayre, M J (Travers Smith LLP) *R2 Zb*
London EC1 *p87* 020 7295 3000
Ayre, N D (Crosse Wyatt Verney & Ayre) *S1 A1 S2 W A2 J1 Zl*
South Molton *p383* 01769 572157
Ayre, P H (Gordons LLP) *E*
Leeds *p273* 0113 227 0100
Ayre, Ms S (Simon A Holt & Co) *N Q J2 Zr Zq*
Preston *p357* 01772 250871
Ayres, A (Ayres Waters) *K1 W S1 K2*
Stockport *p395* 0161 480 5229
Ayres, Ms J E (Davenport Lyons) *Q L Zq*
London W1 *p25* 020 7468 2600
Ayres, Miss K E (Hill Dickinson LLP) *N O Q Za*
London EC3 *p41* 020 7283 9033
Ayres, Mrs L (Terrells LLP) *K3 K1 N*
Peterborough *p347* 01733 896789
Ayres, Miss L (HC Solicitors LLP) *C1 N E W L F1 X Zc Zk Zv O*
Peterborough *p347* 01733 882800
Ayrton, S (Bristows) *O Ze*
London EC4 *p15* 020 7400 8000
Azam, S M M (Clough & Willis) *C1 S2 E C2*
Bury *p170* 0161 764 5266
Azariah, Ms B S (Beardsells) *N Q*
Cheadle *p185* 0161 477 2288
Azhar, N (Pothecary Witham Weld)
Westminster *p69* 020 7821 8211
Azis, N J (McDermott Will & Emery UK LLP) *C1 C2*
London EC2 *p56* 020 7577 6900
Aziz, I (Unsworth Rose) *S1*
Camden *p89* 020 7483 4411
Aziz, Ms N (Bristol City Council)
Bristol *p451* 0117 922 2000
Aziz, Ms T (Lawrence Lupin) *Zi Zg M1 Q*
Wembley *p426* 020 8733 7200
Azmi, H (Howard Kennedy LLP) *S2 E R2*
London W1 *p48* 020 7636 1616
Azzuri, O (Teacher Stern LLP) *E R2 S2*
London WC1 *p86* 020 7242 3191

B

Babar, Mrs D (Treasury Solicitors Department)
London WC2 *p110* 020 7210 3000
Babar, J (Stokoe Partnership) *G H*
Manchester *p310* 0161 237 5755
Waltham Forest *p83* 020 8558 8884
Babar, Ms N (Walker Morris)
Leeds *p277* 0113 283 2500
Babar, Miss S (Newmans Solicitors) *S1 S2 E W*
Horley *p252* 01293 771521
Babb, P G (Kerman & Co LLP) *J1 K1 Q O*
London WC2 *p49* 020 7539 7272
Babcock, M (Dickinson Dees) *C1*
Newcastle upon Tyne *p324* . 0191 279 9000
Bacchus, S K (Darbys Solicitors LLP) *S1 L*
Oxford *p343* 01865 811700
Bach, D J (National Grid PLC)
Warwick *p471* 01926 653000
Back, Miss F J E (Browne Jacobson LLP)
London EC3 *p16* 020 7539 4900
Backhaus, Mrs J A (Hewitsons) *R1*
Cambridge *p174* 01223 461155
Backhouse, Ms A (Wright Hassall LLP) *O Q R1 A3*
Leamington Spa *p270* 01926 886688
Backhouse, D H (Austin & Carnley) *G H*
Leighton Buzzard *p282* . . . 01525 372140
Backhouse, D M (T A Matthews) *C1 S2 E Zl*
Hereford *p248* 01432 352121
Backhouse, G D (Leeds City Council)
Leeds *p462* 0113 224 3513
Backhouse, J A (Backhouse Jones Ltd) *G I J1 M1 N O P Q Zt*
Clitheroe *p196* 01254 828300
Backhouse, J N (Backhouse Jones Ltd) *G Zt J1 J2 F1 F2 P*
Clitheroe *p196* 01254 828300
Backhouse, M (Backhouse Solicitors)
Chelmsford *p186* 01245 216626
Backhouse, T (Ashurst LLP)
London EC2 *p7* 020 7638 1111
Backler, Mrs C (MFG Solicitors) *K1 D1 P W L V*
Kidderminster *p265* 01562 820181
Backman, F T (Stafford Young Jones) *S1 S2*
London EC4 *p82* 020 7623 9490
Bacon, A (Prettys)
Ipswich *p262* 01473 232121
Bacon, A J (BTMK Solicitors LLP) *N Zr*
Southend-on-Sea *p387* . . . 01702 339222
Bacon, D (Borneo Hughes Martell LLP) *P M1 D1 J1 F1 K1 N B1 G*
Northampton *p331* 01604 624822
Bacon, D C (Standard Chartered Bank)
London EC2 *p109* 020 7457 7500
Bacon, G G D (Simmons & Simmons)
London EC2 *p79* 020 7628 2020
Bacon, G P (Bryan & Armstrong) *N*
Mansfield *p311* 01623 624505
Bacon, Miss H M (Gregory Abrams Davidson LLP) *K1 D1 W*
Liverpool *p288* 0151 494 0777
Bacon, I L (Franklins) *S1 W E L*
Leighton Buzzard *p282* . . . 01525 376611
Bacon, Mrs J (Test Valley Borough Council) *S1 C1 E W*
Andover *p447* 01264 368000
Bacon, T F (Hewitsons)
Cambridge *p174* 01223 461155
Milton Keynes *p317* . 0370 086 8300 / 01908 488300
Bacon-Campbell, Mrs H (Wessex Housing Partnership Ltd)
Basingstoke *p448* 01256 844506
Badain, Miss M R (Healys LLP) *S2 E L S1*
Brighton *p159* 01273 685888
Badcock, Mrs A (Bower & Bailey) *S1*
Oxford *p343* 01865 311133
Badcock, Ms A I (Morgan Cole)
Oxford *p344* 01865 262600
Badcock, Miss J M (Cogent Law) *N G*
Croydon *p204* 0844 245 4452
Baddeley, J (Wake Smith & Tofields) *C1 C2 T1 Ze Zf U1*
Sheffield *p377* 0114 266 6660
Baddeley, P C M (Manches LLP) *C1 J1 Zj*
Oxford *p343* 01865 722106
Baddiel, M S (Howarth Goodman) *E L S1 R1 C1 Zh*
Manchester *p305* 0161 832 5068
Baden, M C J (Gregsons) *C1 E M1 N S1 P J1 Zc Zf*
Liverpool *p288* . . . 0151 924 6444 / 236 6120
Baden-Daintree, J C (Quality Solicitors Burroughs Day) *N*
Bristol *p164* 0117 929 0333
Badenhorst, M (Caversham Solicitors Ltd) *B1 F1 F2 L Zk O Q*
Reading *p360* 0118 947 8638
Badham, C (Osborne Clarke) *Zb M3*
London EC2 *p65* 020 7105 7000
Badham, Ms J (Lloyds TSB Group PLC)
Bristol *p452* 0117 905 5500
Badham, P F D (Peter Badham & Co) *S1 W L Q R1 Zd A1 S2*
London W14 *p9* 020 7603 9798
Badham, Ms S (CMS Cameron McKenna LLP)
Bristol *p162* 0117 930 0200
Badiani, Mrs D (Patrick J Cusack & Co) *S1 S2 R2 E W*
Harrow *p241* 020 8863 3414
Badley, Ms A (Spearing Waite LLP) *J1*
Leicester *p281* 0116 262 4225
Badman, R (Hibberts LLP) *G D1 H K1 Zl*
Crewe *p203* 01270 215117
Badrick, Miss R (Stewarts Law LLP) *J1 Zp*
London EC4 *p83* 020 7822 8000
Baehr, E R (Baehrs) *K1 Q O J1 F1 N Zk*
Bournemouth *p151* 01202 292075
Bafi, A (Herbert Smith LLP) *C1 C2*
London EC2 *p40* 020 7374 8000
Bagby, J M (Russell & Russell) *G H*
Chester *p191* 01244 405700
Bagg, S J (Lewis Silkin LLP) *Zh L*
London EC4 *p53* 020 7074 8000
Baggaley, Miss J (Mills & Reeve) *R2 E*
Cambridge *p175* 01223 364422
Baggallay, R M B (Clifford Chance)
London E14 *p20* 020 7006 1000
Baggley, J D J (West Oxfordshire District Council)
Witney *p477* 01993 861581
Baggott, D R (Machins Solicitors LLP) *M3 C1*
Luton *p295* 01582 514000
Baggott, Mrs J M (The Head Partnership) *S1 W*
Reading *p361* 0118 975 6622
Baggott, M J (MLM Cartwright) *C2 A3 Zi S2 E C3 I F1 Ze C1*
Cardiff *p179* 029 2046 2562
Baggs, C J (Clifton Ingram LLP) *E S1 S2*
Wokingham *p437* 0118 978 0099
Baggs, Mrs E L (CMS Cameron McKenna LLP) *E R2*
London EC3 *p17* 020 7367 3000
Baggs, S J (Wiggin LLP) *O J1 Ze Zf Zk Zw*
Cheltenham *p189* 01242 224114
Bagguley, R J (Baines Bagguley Solicitors) *S1 W K1 D1 S2 L K3 T2 E*
Morecambe *p318* 01524 413294
Bagley, Miss C M (Shoosmiths) *W T2 Zd*
Northampton *p332* . . 0370 086 3000 / 01604 543000
Bagley, P (Shulmans) *O Q A3 Zq L Zl B1*
Leeds *p276* 0113 245 2833
Bagley, R C A (Boys & Maughan) *S1 E W Zx R2 S2 Zd*
Ramsgate *p359* 01843 595990
Bagnall, Miss F R (Browne Jacobson LLP) *N Zj*
Nottingham *p336* 0115 976 6000
Bagnall, G (BLB Solicitors) *S1 E A1 C1 L W R1 B1*
Bradford-on-Avon *p155* . . . 01225 866541
Bagnall, Ms M (Mayer Brown International LLP)
London EC2 *p59* 020 3130 3000
Bagnall, Mrs U M W (Ursula Bagnall Divorce & Family Law Solicitors)
Cowes *p201* 01983 247221
Bagot, K G (Steele & Son) *S1 S2 E W K4 A1 C1*
Clitheroe *p196* 01200 444321
Bagri, M S (Keoghs LLP) *N Zj O Q*
Bolton *p149* 01204 677000
Coventry *p200* 024 7665 8200
Bagshaw, I P (Clifford Chance)
London E14 *p20* 020 7006 1000
Bagshaw, Mrs J (Newcastle Upon Tyne City Council) *F1 G H L N O Q S1 Zc Zq*
Newcastle upon Tyne *p466* . 0191 232 8520
Bagshaw, R M (Amphlett Lissimore) *G K1 H*
Croydon *p6* 020 8771 5254
Bagshaw, S (D C Kaye & Co) *J1 N Q F2 G W L J2*
Great Missenden *p234* . . . .01494 864650 / 862226
Bagshaw, Mrs S J (Pert & Malim)
Grantham *p232* 01476 561631
Bagwell, R (Foot Anstey)
Exeter *p221* 01392 411221
Bahia, Miss S (David Tagg & Co) *D1 K1 L*
London SW6 *p85* 020 7736 0999
Bahra, Mrs A A K (HSR Solicitors) *J1 Q*
London E1 *p37* 020 7791 1111
Baigent, Dr D (Bristows)
London EC4 *p15* 020 7400 8000
Baigent, Miss K (Brachers) *S1 E*
Maidstone *p299* 01622 690691
Baigent, P D (Freeth Cartwright LLP) *C1 C2 Zb*
Nottingham *p337* 0115 936 9369
Baigent, S C (Freeth Cartwright LLP) *O B1 Q J1*
Nottingham *p337* 0115 936 9369
Bailes, A J C (Brindley Twist Tafft & James) *N*
Coventry *p200* 024 7653 1532
Bailes, B (Brian Bailes)
Newcastle under Lyme *p323* . 01782 626214
Bailes, Mrs E M (Stewarts Law LLP) *A3 B2 O Q Zq*
London EC4 *p83* 020 7822 8000
Bailes, Ms R E (LG Lawyers)
London SE1 *p50* 020 7379 0000
Bailey, A (Addleshaw Goddard) *R2*
London EC1 *p4* 020 7606 8855
Bailey, A J (Pearsons) *D2 D1 K3 K1*
Gillingham *p229* 01634 280150
Morley *p319* 0113 252 0331
Bailey, A M (Brighton & Hove Council - Legal Services)
Hove *p461* 01273 290000
Bailey, Mrs A M (Debenhams Ottaway) *N*
St Albans *p390* 01727 837161
Bailey, A P (Knights Solicitors LLP) *Zc E P R1 S1*
Newcastle under Lyme *p323* . 01782 619225
Bailey, Ms B (Charles Russell LLP)
London EC4 *p19* 020 7203 5000
Bailey, Mrs B A (Northumberland County Council) *K1 D1*
Morpeth *p466* 01670 533000
Bailey, C (Sarginsons Law LLP) *G H S1 N E W L M1 D1 P*
Coventry *p201* 024 7655 3181
Bailey, Miss C (Punch Robson) *K1 K2 K3*
Middlesbrough *p315* 01642 230700
Bailey, Mrs C M (Gardner Leader LLP) *K1 D1*
Newbury *p322* 01635 508080
Bailey, C P D (Thompsons (formerly Robin/Brian Thompson & Partners))
Birmingham *p143* 0121 262 1200
Bailey, C S (Fraser Dawbarns) *S1 W P E F1 L M1 C1 Zc*
King's Lynn *p266* 01553 666600

Bailey, D (Taylors) *O Q*
Blackburn *p146* 0844 800 0263
Bailey, D (Brabners Chaffe Street)
Liverpool *p286* 0151 600 3000
Bailey, D A J (SGH Martineau LLP) *O Q Zq L A3*
London EC3 *p75* 020 7264 4444
Bailey, Ms D L (Arora Bailey) *K1 S1 W*
Cheam *p185* 020 8661 0000
Bailey, D W (William Bailey) *J1 K1 L Q S1 S2 W*
Southwark *p9* 020 8693 9615
Bailey, Ms E (Howard Kennedy LLP) *Zb*
London W1 *p48* 020 7636 1616
Bailey, Ms E J (Land Registry - Croydon Office) *E S1 S2 Zd*
Croydon *p456* 020 8388 3288
Bailey, Mrs F J (Haywards) *D1 D2 K1*
Stowmarket *p399* 01449 613631
Bailey, Mrs G M (Fareham Borough Council)
Fareham *p458* 01329 236100
Bailey, I (Irwin Mitchell LLP) *N Zr*
Leeds *p274* 0870 150 0100
Bailey, J (Berry Redmond & Robinson) *D1 K1 K3 V*
Weston-super-Mare *p429* . 01934 513963
Bailey, J K (Bailey & Bailey) *S1 P M1 E L G W*
Middlesbrough *p315* 01642 240991
Bailey, Mrs J M (Andrew & Co LLP) *K1 J1 Zp*
Lincoln *p284* 01522 512123
Bailey, Mrs K (Mosshaselhurst) *K1*
Northwich *p333* 01606 74301
Bailey, Miss K A (Bailey Wright & Co) *X N J1 D1 Zp*
Birmingham *p135* 0845 475 1996
Bailey, Mrs L A (Walker Morris) *Zc*
Leeds *p277* 0113 283 2500
Bailey, Ms L J (City of Bradford Metropolitan District Council)
Bradford *p451* 01274 752236
Bailey, Miss M (Doncaster Metropolitan Borough Council)
Doncaster *p457* 01302 734651
Bailey, M (Bailey Nicholson Grayson) *D1 G H K1 Q*
Woodford Green *p439* 020 8418 2900
Bailey, M (Speechly Bircham LLP) *I U2 C1 Ze U1*
London EC4 *p81* 020 7427 6400
Bailey, Miss M A (Salford City Council)
Swinton *p473* 0161 794 4711
Bailey, M D (ASB Law) *E Zd*
Crawley *p202* 01293 603600
Bailey, M E (Bailey Morgan & Co) *W S2 S1 E R2 L J1 T1 T2*
Skegness *p380* . . .01754 768383 / 763007
Bailey, M P W (Churchers) *B1 J1 F1 N P Zk*
Fareham *p223* 01329 822333
Bailey, M R (Stephens & Son LLP) *W Zm K4*
Chatham *p185* 01634 811444
Bailey, M T (Somerfield Stores Ltd)
Bristol *p452* 0117 935 6135
Bailey, P K (Howes Percival LLP)
Leicester *p280* 0116 247 3500
Bailey, Miss P S (Thomas Magnay & Co) *D1 K1 K3*
Gateshead *p229* 0191 477 3333
Bailey, P W (Brockbank Curwen Cain & Hall) *S1 W E A1 Zm*
Workington *p440* 01900 603563
Bailey, Ms R (Lewis Nedas & Co) *G H*
Camden *p53* 020 7387 2032
Bailey, R (Steeles) *Ze C3 F1 C1*
Norwich *p335* 0870 609 0200
Bailey, R (Bailey Wain & Curzon) *S1 W C1 L*
Stoke-on-Trent *p397* 01782 847934
Bailey, R F (Fullers) *A1 C1 E L M1 N S1 T1 W Zc*
Rugby *p368* 01788 542288
Bailey, R L (Taylor Wessing) *N Q O B1*
London EC4 *p86* 020 7300 7000
Bailey, R S (Graham Coffey & Co) *N*
Manchester *p302* 0161 200 2440
Bailey, Ms S (LG Lawyers)
London SE1 *p50* 020 7379 0000
Bailey, Ms S (Trowers & Hamlins) *L Zh*
London EC3 *p88* 020 7423 8000
Bailey, S A (Hibberts LLP) *L O Q Zk Zl G H*
Crewe *p203* 01270 215117
Bailey, Miss S E (Bower & Bailey) *K1 Q N D1 L J1 O F1*
Oxford *p343* 01865 311133
Witney *p436* 01993 705095
Bailey, Mrs S E (Chubb & Co) *S1 Q Zl E*
Matlock *p313* 01629 581252
Bailey, S G J (Thomas Guise) *S2 E A1 R1 R2 S1*
Worcester *p439* 01905 723131
Bailey, Miss S J (P E S Consulting Ltd)
Borehamwood *p450* . . . .
Bailey, T (Beswicks) *Zw E R2*
Hanley *p239* 01782 205000
Bailey, T J (Bowcock & Pursaill) *W A1 K4*
Leek *p278* 01538 399199
Bailey, Mrs Y S (Baileys) *S1 E*
Brackley *p153* 01280 701166
Bailey-Bradshaw, Mrs R E (Davisons) *S1*
Birmingham *p137* 0121 685 1255
Bailey-Gibbs, C J (Ford & Warren) *J1*
Leeds *p273* 0113 243 6601
Bailhache, E (Bailhache Shaw Marsden) *C1 E F1 W*
Taunton *p408* 01823 351122
Bailham, L S W (Johar & Co) *K3 K1 Zq O Q N*
Leicester *p280* 0116 254 3345
Baillie, Miss E L (B P Collins LLP) *K1 K3*
Gerrards Cross *p229* 01753 889995
Baillie, Ms K M (Field Fisher Waterhouse LLP) *Zo*
London EC3 *p31* 020 7861 4000
Baillie-Hamilton, S J (Mayo Wynne Baxter LLP) *A1 C1 E S2*
Lewes *p283* 01273 477071
Baily, J (Herbert Smith LLP)
London EC2 *p40* 020 7374 8000
Baily, M R H (Stephenson Harwood) *W T1 Zd*
London EC2 *p82* 020 7329 4422
Baily, Ms T K (Boyes Turner) *O Q*
Reading *p360* 0118 959 7711
Bain, R (Tolhurst Fisher LLP)
Southend-on-Sea *p387* . . . 01702 352511
Bainbridge, D J K (Waverley Borough Council)
Godalming *p459* 01483 523333
Bainbridge, Ms J (Blake Lapthorn) *O Q U2 Ze*
Chandlers Ford *p184* 023 8090 8090
Bainbridge, M J (Thompsons (formerly Robin/Brian Thompson & Partners)) *J1 Zp*
Nottingham *p339* 0115 989 7200
Bainbridge, P R (Kenyon Son & Craddock) *N S1 O Q F1 E*
Goole *p231* 01405 720850
Bainbridge, S R (Dickinson Dees) *O*
Newcastle upon Tyne *p324* . 0191 279 9000
Bainbridge, T (Jones Day) *I*
London EC4 *p46* 020 7039 5959
Baines, A (Crombie Wilkinson) *S1 A1*
Malton *p300* 01653 600070
Baines, A W (Ashfords LLP) *A1 E L B1 O Q*
Bristol *p160* 0117 321 8000
Baines, Mrs C (Browne Jacobson LLP)
Nottingham *p336* 0115 976 6000
Baines, Miss C A (Blackpool Borough Council) *E L C1 S1 R1*
Blackpool *p450* 01253 477450
Baines, C S (Glaisyers Solicitors LLP) *E S2*
Manchester *p304* 0161 832 4666
Baines, D W (Baines Bagguley Solicitors) *C1 E L S1 T1*
Morecambe *p318* 01524 413294
Baines, Mrs J (Walker Smith Way) *K1 D1 K2 K3*
Chester *p191* 0844 346 3100
Baines, J H (Arnold Deacon Greene & Co) *E A1 R1*
Sleaford *p381* 01529 414414
Baines, N R (Thompsons (formerly Robin/Brian Thompson & Partners)) *N*
Nottingham *p339* 0115 989 7200
Baines, P W (SA Law) *E Zf Zk Zw Zc*
St Albans *p390* 01727 798000
Baines, Miss R (Rouse Legal (Formerly Willoughby & Partners)) *Ze*
London E14 *p74* 020 7536 4100
Baines, R E (Holman Fenwick Willan)
London EC3 *p42* 020 7264 8000
Baines, T C (B P Collins LLP) *C1 C2*
Gerrards Cross *p229* 01753 889995
Bains, A S (Bains Solicitors) *G H J1 Zl Zt*
Wellingborough *p424* 01933 440000
Bains, Mrs B (Caversham Solicitors Ltd) *N*
Reading *p360* 0118 947 8638
Bains, B S (Lawrence Hamblin) *N Zr*
Henley-on-Thames *p247* . . . 01491 411884
Bains, Miss J (Thompsons (formerly Robin/Brian Thompson & Partners)) *J1*
London WC1 *p87* 020 7290 0000
Bains, Miss K (George Green LLP) *E R1 Zu*
Cradley Heath *p201* 01384 410410
Bains, Mrs M (Chebsey & Co) *K1*
Burnham *p168* 01628 660077
Bains, P N (Hewlett-Packard Ltd)
Bracknell *p451* 01344 360000
Baird, A (Watson Farley & Williams)
London EC2 *p90* 020 7814 8000
Baird, Miss G (Farrer & Co LLP)
London WC2 *p31* 020 3375 7000
Baird, J (Simmons & Simmons)
London EC2 *p79* 020 7628 2020
Baird, J (Wellers Law Group LLP) *Q O L J1*
Bromley *p167* 020 8464 4242
Baird, J A (Persimmon Homes Legal Department)
York *p477* 01904 642199
Baird, J E (James E Baird) *S1 S2 C1 K1 E W J1 N R1 Zl Q Zv*
Sunderland *p401* 0191 514 5888
Baird, J W (Clifford Chance)
London E14 *p20* 020 7006 1000
Baird, Ms K L (Barlow Lyde & Gilbert LLP)
London EC3 *p10* 020 7247 2277
Baird, S (Brabners Chaffe Street) *Zw Zi O*
Manchester *p301* 0161 836 8800
Baiter, C J (EDF Energy Networks Ltd)
Crawley *p456* 01293 656070
Bajaj, Ms A A (Coventry City Council)
Coventry *p456* 024 7683 4863
Bajaj, R (Steele Raymond) *F1 Q L B1 O Zl F2*
Bournemouth *p152* 01202 294566
Bajaria, Mrs P (Clarkson Wright & Jakes Ltd) *J1 Zp*
Orpington *p341* 01689 887887
Bajna, Miss A (Zermansky & Partners) *L*
Leeds *p278* 0113 245 9766
Bajwa, Miss H J (Baily Gibson) *C1*
High Wycombe *p249* 01494 442661
Bakehouse, Miss D A (Bazeley Barnes & Bazeley) *G H*
Bideford *p132* 01237 473122
Baker, A (Kennedys)
Cambridge *p174* 01223 533060
Baker, A C (Baker Gray & Co) *D1 F1 G H J1 K1 L N Q S1 V W*
Blaydon-on-Tyne *p147* 0191 414 4869
Baker, A D J (Boys & Maughan) *N Q O J1 J2 Zp*
Ramsgate *p359* 01843 595990
Baker, A J (Plexus Law (A Trading Name of Parabis Law LLP)) *A3 J2 N Zj*
Leeds *p276* 0844 245 4100
Baker, A M (Taylor Wessing) *C1 J1 F1 T1 I Ze*
London EC4 *p86* 020 7300 7000
Baker, Miss B (Atherton Godfrey) *N*
Doncaster *p211* 01302 320621
Baker, Ms C (Davenport Lyons)
London W1 *p25* 020 7468 2600
Baker, C (Osborne Clarke) *R2*
London EC2 *p65* 020 7105 7000
Baker, C C (DB Law) *S1 W S2 L*
Camborne *p173* 01209 712428
Baker, Ms C D (Blake Lapthorn) *O Q*
Portsmouth *p354* 023 9222 1122
Baker, C G B (Turnbull Garrard) *Q O J1 N E L Zq Zl Zc B1 R1 A1 F1 Ze Zm*
Shrewsbury *p379* . .01743 350851 / 351332
Baker, C J (EDF Energy Networks Ltd)
Crawley *p456* 01293 656070
London SW1 *p106* 020 7242 9050
Baker, Mrs D (Forbes) *K1 G H M1 F1 Zl Zd*
Preston *p356* 01772 220022
Baker, Ms D (Toller Beattie LLP) *D1 K1 P K3 O Q Zq*
Barnstaple *p125* 01271 341000
Baker, D A (Portner & Jaskel LLP) *B1 E J1 L M1 N P T1 Ze Zf Zk*
London W1 *p68* 020 7616 5300
Baker, D G (White & Case LLP)
London EC2 *p91* 020 7532 1000
Baker, D H (Forbes) *N Q O F1 G H*
Preston *p356* 01772 220022
Baker, D J B (Ince & Co Services Ltd)
London E1 *p44* 020 7481 0010
Baker, G R (Hegarty LLP) *W T2 S1 K4 Zo*
Peterborough *p347* 01733 346333
Baker, G S (HMG Law LLP) *E S1 S2 A1*
Bicester *p132* 01869 252244
Oxford *p343* 01865 244661
Baker, Ms H (Sacker & Partners LLP) *Zo*
London EC2 *p76* 020 7329 6699
Baker, H (Skadden Arps Slate Meagher & Flom (UK) LLP)
London E14 *p80* 020 7519 7000
Baker, H J (Linklaters LLP) *Zc*
London EC2 *p54* 020 7456 2000
Baker, I D (Sills & Betteridge LLP) *S1*
Lincoln *p285* 01522 542211
Baker, I P (SGH Martineau LLP) *C1 B1 Zb*
Birmingham *p142* 0870 763 2000
Baker, Ms J (Rothwell & Evans) *K1 G P*
Swinton *p407* 0161 794 1830
Baker, J (Michelmores LLP) *J1 C1*
Exeter *p221* 01392 688688
Baker, Miss J (Wendy Hopkins Family Law Practice LLP) *W K4*
Cardiff *p178* 029 2034 2233
Baker, Mrs J (hlw Keeble Hawson LLP) *Zq Zr*
Sheffield *p375* 0114 272 2061
Baker, Ms J (The College of Law)
London WC1 *p105* 0800 289997
Baker, Ms J C (Ward Hadaway) *C1 I U2 Ze*
Newcastle upon Tyne *p327* . 0191 204 4000
Baker, J D I (Ashford Borough Council)
Ashford *p447* 01233 331111
Baker, J H (Southend-on-Sea Borough Council)
Southend-on-Sea *p472* 01702 215000
Baker, Mrs K (Heyman & Co) *S1 W K1 N D1 Q*
Leigh *p282* 01942 604135
Baker, K (Napthens LLP) *O N Q*
Preston *p357* 01772 888444
Baker, Mrs K J (Newstead & Walker) *N O Q J1 K1 G F1 F2 K3*
Otley *p342* 01943 461414
Baker, Ms L (Halton Borough Council)
Widnes *p476* 0151 424 2061
Baker, Ms L (Forsters LLP) *C1*
Westminster *p33* 020 7863 8333
Baker, Miss L (MKB Solicitors LLP) *C1 D1 E F1 G H J1 K1 L M1 Zo Zp Zs*
Barnsley *p124* 01226 210000
Baker, M (Pinsent Masons LLP)
London EC2 *p67* 020 7418 7000
Baker, M (Powis & Co) *S1 W C1 E L R1 A1 S2 Zd*
Clacton-on-Sea *p195* 01255 233400
Baker, M F (CMS Cameron McKenna LLP) *N O Q Zj*
London EC3 *p17* 020 7367 3000
Baker, Ms M F J (Kingsley Napley) *D1 K1 K2*
London EC1 *p50* 020 7814 1200
Baker, M G B (Richmonds) *S1 E M1 G H P N K1 A1 W*
Newcastle upon Tyne *p326* . 0191 232 2155
Baker, M J (Baker Macdonald) *N Q K1 W F1 J1 L O K3*
Sevenoaks *p374* 01732 457978
Baker, M J (Michael Baker Solicitors Limited) *N*
Farnborough *p224* 01252 744600
Baker, Mrs M M (Humphries Kirk) *K1 N V D1*
Poole *p352* 01202 715815
Baker, N B (Clarke Willmott) *P R1 Zn*
Bristol *p162* 0845 209 1000 / 0117 305 6000
Baker, N D (Irwin Mitchell LLP) *W T2 Zm*
Sheffield *p376* 0870 150 0100
Baker, N G (Green Wright Chalton Annis) *A1 E S1 W L S2 K4*
Steyning *p395* 01903 814190
Baker, O M (Rawlins Davy PLC) *S1 S2 E R1*
Bournemouth *p152* 01202 558844
Baker, P (Hill Dickinson LLP) *W T1 S1 E A1 R1*
Liverpool *p288* 0151 600 8000
Baker, P (OBW Perera) *G H*
Colchester *p197* 01206 541111
Baker, Mrs P A (Pearl Baker) *S1 W C1 E G L P M1 N K1 Zs Zl Ze*
Rayleigh *p359* 01268 745568
Baker, P J (Alban Gould Baker & Co) *S1 W*
Islington *p4* 020 7607 5085
Baker, P J (East Sussex County Council)
Lewes *p463* 01273 481000
Baker, Mrs P J (McCormicks) *O Q B1 F1 L Zb Ze*
Harrogate *p240* 01423 530630
Baker, P M (Hawley & Rodgers) *S2 S1*
Loughborough *p293* 01509 230333
Nottingham *p337* 0115 955 9000
Baker, Q (Cheltenham Borough Council)
Cheltenham *p454* 01242 262626
Baker, R (Buckles Solicitors LLP) *K1 T2 W*
Peterborough *p346* 01733 888888
Baker, R (BHP Law)
Stockton-on-Tees *p396* . . . 01642 672770
Baker, Ms R (Harrison Clark LLP) *W*
Cheltenham *p188* 01242 269198
Worcester *p439* 01905 612001
Worcester *p439* 01905 612001
Baker, Mrs R A (Atherton Godfrey) *N*
Doncaster *p211* 01302 320621
Baker, R G (Department for Business, Enterprise and Regulatory Reform)
London SW1 *p105* 020 7215 0105
Baker, R G (Stephens & Scown) *A1 S2 E*
Exeter *p222* 01392 210700
Baker, R J (Lloyds TSB Group PLC)
London EC2 *p107* 020 7158 2729
Baker, R R (Stephenson Harwood) *Q Zq*
London EC2 *p82* 020 7329 4422
Baker, S (Harris Fowler) *J1 N Q Zr*
Taunton *p408* 01823 251515
Baker, Mrs S B (Field Seymour Parkes) *D1 K1 D2 K3 X*
Reading *p360* 0118 951 6200
Baker, S C (Dacorum Borough Council)
Hemel Hempstead *p460* . . . 01442 228000
Baker, S D (Civil Aviation Authority)
London WC2 *p105* 020 7453 6162
Baker, Mrs S E (Surrey County Council)
Kingston upon Thames *p462* 020 8541 9088
Baker, Miss S E (Wannop Fox Staffurth & Bray) *W S1 S2 K4*
Littlehampton *p285* 01903 721112
Bognor Regis *p148* 01243 864001
Baker, S H (Nottinghamshire County Council Legal Services Division)
West Bridgford *p475* 0115 977 3478
Baker, Miss S J (Forsters LLP) *E*
Westminster *p33* 020 7863 8333
Baker, S J (Lodders Solicitors LLP) *A1 S2*
Stratford-upon-Avon *p400* . . 01789 293259
Baker, S N (Boyes Turner)
Reading *p360* 0118 959 7711
Baker, Ms S R (Larby Williams with Gwyn & Gwyn) *S1 K1 K3 W*
Cowbridge *p201* 01446 775535
Baker, T (Keoghs LLP) *N*
Bolton *p149* 01204 677000
Baker, Mrs T (Woollcombe Yonge) *G H*
Plymouth *p351* 01752 660384
Baker, Ms T A (Manchester City Council)
Manchester *p465* 0161 234 5000
Baker, W G C (Bannister Preston) *S1 S2*
Irlam *p263* 0161 775 0444
Baker, W S (Veale Wasbrough Vizards) *E L R1 R2 S2 Zu*
Bristol *p165* 0117 925 2020
Bakes, M J (Herbert Smith LLP) *O Zj*
London EC2 *p40* 020 7374 8000
Bakewell, Mrs J (Eric Robinson Solicitors) *S1 L E S2 R2*
Hythe *p259* 023 8084 4304
Bakewell, Mrs J K (St Helens Borough Council)
St Helens *p472* 01744 456000
Bakewell, P N (Eric Robinson Solicitors) *S2 E S1 L R2 C1 R1 T1 T2 C2*
Hythe *p259* 023 8084 4304
Bakshi, N (Simman Solicitors) *J1 Zi*
Croydon *p205* 020 8686 1085
Bal, J (Farrer & Co LLP) *C1 I*
London WC2 *p31* 020 3375 7000
Bal, K P S (Debidins) *S1 L K3*
Ealing *p26* . . . .020 8567 1381 / 8567 6343
Balakrishnan, Mrs S (Conway & Co) *S1 W*
Harrow *p241* 020 8863 0535
Balakumar, Ms V (Oaks Solicitors)
Wembley *p426* 020 8970 2159
Balan, A (Howes Percival LLP) *K3 K1 D1*
Norwich *p334* 01603 762103
Balaraman, B (Bala & Co)
London E6 *p9* 020 8548 8808
Balasubramanian, A (Ashurst LLP)
London EC2 *p7* 020 7638 1111
Balch, Mrs H (Dickinson Manser) *D1 K1 G Q V*
Poole *p352* 01202 673071
Balchin, G S (Bolt Burdon) *Zq*
Islington *p14* 020 7288 4700
Balchin, J H C (Quality Solicitors Burroughs Day) *O Q J1*
Bristol *p164* 0117 929 0333
Balderstone, C J L (Persimmon PLC) *E C1 Ze*
Northampton *p467* 01604 884600
Baldock, Ms A E (Allen & Overy LLP)
London E1 *p5* 020 3088 0000

 See p634 for the Key to Work Categories

Baldock, G (Bull & Bull) S1 S2 W L E C1 T1 T2 V
Herne Bay p248 . . . . 01227 742660
Baldock, Ms K (Morgan Cole)
Oxford p344 . . . . 01865 262600
Baldwin, Miss A C (Downs) S1 L E A1
Dorking p212 . . . . 01306 880110
Baldwin, A P d F (Huggins & Lewis Foskett) S2 S1 E B1 O Q W
Redbridge p43 . . . . 020 8989 3000
Baldwin, Ms C (Withers LLP) K1
London EC4 p92 . . . . . . 020 7597 6000
Baldwin, C F (Baldwin & Co) S1
London SE16 p9 . . . . . . 020 7237 3035
Baldwin, C J (Pollard Bower Solicitors) K1 D1 N F1 Q S1 V G H O Zc Zf Zk Zo
Burnley p169 . . . . 01282 457624
Baldwin, C R (Romain Coleman & Co) S2 S1 E C1
Waltham Forest p73 . . . . . 020 8520 3322
Baldwin, D (Withers LLP) A1 E S1
London EC4 p92 . . . . . . 020 7597 6000
Baldwin, Miss D (Springfield Advice & Law Centre) Zm Zg V
London SW17 p109 . . . . . 020 8767 6884
Baldwin, D J (Waddington & Son) K1 S1 N Q W D1 L Zm
Burnley p169 . . . . 01282 426666
Baldwin, Ms E (Horsey Lightly) K1
Newbury p322 . . . . 01635 580858
Baldwin, J (Baldwin Townsend & Co) N S1 Q K1 W L G A1 B1 F1
Cwmbran p206 . . . . 01633 866007
Baldwin, J F (Ellisons) W L E S1
Clacton-on-Sea p195 . . . . 01255 421248
Colchester p197 . . . . . . 01206 764477
Baldwin, Ms J S L (Foys Solicitors) S2 E
Doncaster p211 . . . . 01302 327136
Baldwin, L (Radcliffes Le Brasseur) O
Westminster p70 . . . . . . 020 7222 7040
Baldwin, M (Macfarlanes) C1
London EC4 p56 . . . . . . 020 7831 9222
Baldwin, P (Paris Smith LLP) O Q
Southampton p386 . . . . . 023 8048 2482
Baldwin, P N (Anthony Collins Solicitors LLP) D1 Zm
Birmingham p137 . . . . . . 0121 200 3242
Baldwin, R (Baldwin Wyatt Solicitors) W S1 L E S2 Q N J1 K4
Burnley p169 . . . . 01282 429999
Baldwin, R G (Thompson Smith & Puxon) S1 W L E R1 Zl
Clacton-on-Sea p195 . . . . 01255 221919
Baldwin, Ms S M (Fonseca & Partners) K1 D1
Abergavenny p113 . . . . . 01873 857114
Bale, M D E (Hammond Bale) N B1 P M1 Zg Ze
London W1 p38 . . . . 020 7499 7624
Bale, Mrs S A (Davis Wood) W S1 T1 V Zm
Bristol p162 . . . . 0117 965 3504
Balen, P (Freeth Cartwright LLP) N
Nottingham p337 . . . . . . 0115 936 9369
Balfour-Lynn, Mrs J M (Peters & Peters) G H N O P Q K1
London EC4 p67 . . . . . . 020 7629 7991
Balgobin, A (Rollingsons) J1
London EC1 p73 . . . . . . 020 7611 4848
Bali, Ms R (Wolters Kluwer (UK) Ltd)
Hinckley p461 . . . . 01455 897361
Balkitis, A J (Rothera Dowson) P Zt
Nottingham p338 . . . . . . 0115 910 0600
Ball, Miss A (Lloyds TSB Group PLC)
London EC2 p107 . . . . . . 020 7158 2729
Ball, Ms A P (Hempsons) N Q Zr G
Manchester p305 . . . . . . 0161 228 0011
Ball, C C (Weightmans LLP)
Liverpool p291 . . . . 0151 227 2601
Ball, C J (Charles Lucas & Marshall) S1 W E A1
Wantage p421 . . . . 01235 771234
Ball, Ms C L (Squire Sanders (UK) LLP)
London EC2 p81 . . . . . . 020 7655 1000
Ball, Mrs C V (OMW Solicitors) D2 D1 K1 S1 W
Burton-on-Trent p17001283 563401 / 530333
Ball, D (Fraser Dawbarns) S1 W
Wisbech p435 . . . . 01945 461456
Ball, D R W (Fraser Dawbarns) S1 S2
March p312 . . . . 01354 602880
Ball, E S (Parker Grego Cullen & Ball)
Birmingham p141 . . . . . . 0121 200 3031
Ball, Miss H (Sacker & Partners LLP) Zo
London EC2 p76 . . . . . . 020 7329 6699
Ball, Ms J (Joanne Ball Solicitors)
Liverpool p286 . . . . 0151 724 6645
Ball, J A (Fynmores) S1 P W A1 C1 S2
Bexhill p132 . . . . 01424 732333
Ball, Mrs J E (Barlow Robbins LLP) K3 K1
Guildford p235 . . . . 01483 543200
Ball, J F (Taylor Wessing)
London EC4 p86 . . . . . . 020 7300 7000
Ball, Ms J M (Barlow Lyde & Gilbert LLP) Zj
London EC3 p10 . . . . . . 020 7247 2277
Ball, J R (Kerrier District Council) S1 K1 M1 E R1 W N L C1
Camborne p452 . . . . 01209 614000
Ball, Miss L (Cyngor Sir Ynys Mon (Isle of Anglesey County Council))
Llangefni p463 . . . . 01248 750057
Ball, Ms L H (Blackfords LLP) K1 K2
Croydon p204 . . . . 020 8686 6232
Ball, M K J (Hempsons) Q
Westminster p40 . . . . . . 020 7839 0278
London W1 p76 . . . . 020 7631 4714
Ball, N J (Bridge Sanderson Munro) K1 D1
Doncaster p211 . . . . 01302 321621
Ball, R K (Brewer Harding & Rowe) K1 M1 P N B1 J1 D1 G L V Zp Zl Zd
Barnstaple p125 . . . . . . 01271 342271
Ball, S (Pierre Thomas & Partners) N Q J1 O
London W6 p67 . . . . 020 7602 0305
Ball, Mrs S J (Verisona Solicitors) F1 J1 N Q
Waterlooville p423 . . . . . 023 9226 5251
Ball, Miss S L (Rollits LLP) K1 Q D1 J1 O F1
Hull p258 . . . . 01482 323239
Ball, T (Speechly Bircham LLP) Ze
London EC4 p81 . . . . . . 020 7427 6400
Ballam, J A (Ballam) G H Zm
Birkenhead p134 . . . . . . 0151 647 8977
Birkenhead p134 . . . . . . 0151 647 6000
Ballantyne, Ms J M Q (Barlow Lyde & Gilbert LLP)
London EC3 p10 . . . . . . 020 7247 2277
Ballantyne, Ms J R (Maclaren Warner) K1 V J1 L Zi
Stapleford p394 . . . . . . 0115 939 5252
Ballantyne, S G (North Tyneside Council)
Newcastle upon Tyne p466 . 0191 643 5000
Ballard Scott, Mrs C (Kingsley Napley) K1
London EC1 p50 . . . . . . 020 7814 1200
Ballard, B R (Birkett Long LLP) T2 W
Colchester p197 . . . . . . 01206 217300
Ballard, Ms M M (Buckinghamshire County Council)
Aylesbury p448 . . . . 01296 383653
Ballard, P (Thompsons (formerly Robin/Brian Thompson & Partners)) N
Plymouth p350 . . . . 01752 675810
Ballard, T (Harbottle & Lewis LLP)
London W1 p38 . . . . 020 7667 5000
Ballaster, R T (Carter Lemon Camerons) S2 R2 S1
London EC1 p18 . . . . . . 020 7406 1000
Ballato, Ms L (Kaim Todner Ltd) G H B2
London EC4 p47 . . . . . . 020 7353 6660
Balli, E (DWFM Beckman) L N Q B1 E
Westminster p25 . . . . . . 020 7872 0023
Ballinger, M R (Reynolds Porter Chamberlain LLP) O Q Zj Zq
London E1 p71 . . . . 020 3060 6000
Ballinger, P (Merthyr Tydfil County Borough Council)
Merthyr Tydfil p465 . . . . 01685 725000
Balmain, Ms L A (Murrays Partnership) G H
Southwark p62 . . . . 020 7701 8653
Balme, R D (Wartnabys) W K1 Q L
Market Harborough p312 . . 01858 463322
Balmford, C R (Nyland & Beattie) N W V S1 S2 K1 K3 L Zq
Widnes p432 . . . . 0151 424 5656
Balmforth, Mrs E (Kirbys) P R1 S1 S2 E
Harrogate p240 . . . . 01423 542000
Balneaves, A D (Robin Murray & Co) G H
Chatham p185 . . . . 01634 832332
Balogun, A (E E F South)
Hook p461 . . . . 01256 763969
Balsara, J S (Balsara & Co) B1 E K1 L N P S1 W Zb Zd Zi
London EC1 p9 . . . . 020 7797 6300
Balsham, J S (City of Bradford Metropolitan District Council)
Bradford p451 . . . . 01274 752236
Balsom, D G (Onions & Davies) K1 S1 J1 L N W K3
Market Drayton p312 . . . . 01630 652405
Balsom, G (Brignalls Balderston Warren) E S1 S2
Letchworth p283 . . . . . . 01462 482248
Balson, R (Holman Fenwick Willan)
London EC3 p42 . . . . . . 020 7264 8000
Baltay, Ms E (Bingham McCutchen (London) LLP)
London EC2 p12 . . . . . . 020 7661 5300
Bamber, A (Allen & Overy LLP)
London E1 p5 . . . . 020 3088 0000
Bamber, R J (Mills & Reeve) K1 D1
Cambridge p175 . . . . . . 01223 364422
Bambridge, Ms C J (BAE Systems PLC)
London SW1 p104 . . . . . . 01252 373232
Bambridge, D C (Bambridges Solicitors Limited) Q N K1 J1 O S2 E
Boston p151 . . . . 01205 310510
Bambridge, M E (Shell International Ltd)
London SE1 p109 . . . . . . 020 7934 1234
Bambury, D R (Browne Jacobson LLP) O B1 Q Zj Zq B3
Nottingham p336 . . . . . . 0115 976 6000
Bambury, Ms H (Osborne Clarke) R2
London EC2 p65 . . . . . . 020 7105 7000
Bamford, Ms A E (Squire Sanders (UK) LLP)
Leeds p277 . . . . 0113 284 7000
Bamford, K A (The College of Law Chester)
Chester p454 . . . . 0800 289997
Bamford, K R (Knights Solicitors LLP) E L A1 P R1
Newcastle under Lyme p323 . 01782 619225
Bamford, N (DLA Piper UK LLP)
Birmingham p137 . . . . . . 0870 011 1111
Bamford, R (Archer & Archer) W
Ely p218 . . . . 01353 662203
Bamford, Mrs R (Wilson & Bird) S1 W G K3
Aylesbury p121 . . . . 01296 436766
Bamford, Miss S (Nelsons)
Nottingham p338 . . . . . . 0115 958 6262
Bamford, T (Harbottle & Lewis LLP)
London W1 p38 . . . . 020 7667 5000
Bamforth, Ms D (Ingrams)
York p445 . . . . 01904 520600
Bamforth, E J (E J Bamforth Solicitors) M1 P N G H F1 J1 Zl
Chester p190 . . . . 01244 357209
Bamforth, R J (White & Case LLP)
London EC2 p91 . . . . . . 020 7532 1000
Banahan, M J (Hawkins Hatton LLP) S1 E C1 W N J1 Zl
Dudley p213 . . . . 01384 216840
Banasko, J E (Watson Solicitors) G H B2 W
Warrington p422 . . . . . . 01925 571212
Bancroft, J W D (John Copland & Son) D1 F1 H K1 N Q V G Zg
Sheerness p375 . . . . 01795 664431
Bancroft, R E (Stuart Smith & Burnett) S1 L E C1 S2
Bridlington p158 . . . . . . 01262 678128
Bancroft, Ms S (Radcliffes Le Brasseur)
Westminster p70 . . . . . . 020 7222 7040
Bancroft, T J (John Copland & Son) B1 C1 K1 L M1 N P T1 W Zb Zg Zk
Sheerness p375 . . . . 01795 664431
Band, Ms C (Herbert Smith LLP) O Zb Zq
London EC2 p40 . . . . . . 020 7374 8000
Band, C J (Inghams) S1 W E C1 T1
Thornton Cleveleys p411 . . 01253 824111
Banday, Mrs Z (George Davies Solicitors LLP) S1
Manchester p303 . . . . . . 0161 236 8992
Bandesha, Miss S (Gartmore Investment Management PLC)
London EC3 p106 . . . . . . 020 7782 2000
Bandurka, A (Holman Fenwick Willan)
London EC3 p42 . . . . . . 020 7264 8000
Banerjee, Miss A (Roy Foreman & Co) G H B2
Grimsby p235 . . . . 01472 355262
Leeds p274 . . . . 0113 200 7400
Banerjee, Miss N S (Denison Till) K1 K3 K2
York p444 . . . . 01904 611411
Banerjee, Ms S K (Jones Myers LLP)
Leeds p275 . . . . 0113 246 0055
Banes, A L (Howard Kennedy LLP) C1 C2 F1 J1 W T1 T2 B1 Zd
London W1 p48 . . . . 020 7636 1616
Banfeild, Ms C (Withers LLP) O Q
London EC4 p92 . . . . . . 020 7597 6000
Banfi, J P (JMW Solicitors) R1 R2 S2 C1 C2 E Zc
Manchester p306 . . . . . . 0845 872 6666
Banfield, S J (Tucker Turner Kingsley Wood & Co) C1 J1
London WC1 p88 . . . . . . 020 7242 3303
Banga, R (Field Fisher Waterhouse LLP)
London EC3 p31 . . . . . . 020 7861 4000
Bange, V K (Pinsent Masons LLP) A3 O Zc
Birmingham p141 . . . . . . 0121 200 1050
Bangor-Jones, Miss C L (Hewitsons) O Q L A3 Zb
Northampton p332 . . . . . 01604 233233
Banham-Hall, Mrs M A (Heald Solicitors) D1 K1 T2 W Zh K2
Milton Keynes p317 . . . . . 01908 662277
Banham-Hall, M R (Heald Solicitors) E P R1 R2 S2 Zc Zd
Milton Keynes p317 . . . . . 01908 662277
Banharally, M H (Lee Associates) E F1 G K1 S1 I Zj Zl Zw
Wandsworth p52 . . . . . . 020 8682 9797
Banister Dean, Miss E (Blandy & Blandy) Q O F1 F2 Zk N Zq
Reading p360 . . . . 0118 951 6800
Banister, Mrs H J (Davis Gregory Ltd) S1 S2
Cheltenham p188 . . . . . . 01242 235202
Bankes, C (Simmons & Simmons)
London EC2 p79 . . . . . . 020 7628 2020
Bankes, R (IBB Solicitors) O
Uxbridge p417 . . . . 0845 638 1381
Bankes-Jones, A H M (Clifford Chance)
London E14 p20 . . . . 020 7006 1000
Banks, A (Stone King LLP) G H Zl
Bath p128 . . . . 01225 337599
Banks, Mrs C M (Maxwell Hodge Solicitors) N J2
Huyton p258 . . . . 0151 489 6161
Banks, Ms C S (Kidd Rapinet) K1 D1
High Wycombe p250 . . . . . 0845 017 9607
Banks, Ms D (Keoghs LLP) N Zj O Q
Bolton p149 . . . . 01204 677000
Banks, Ms D M A (LG Lawyers)
London SE1 p50 . . . . 020 7379 0000
Banks, Miss E R (Broomhead & Saul) K1 K3
Taunton p408 . . . . 01823 288121
Banks, G C (Geldards LLP) E S2
Derby p208 . . . . 01332 331631
Banks, G M (Thursfields) K1 D1 V
Kidderminster p266 . . . . . 01562 820575
Banks, Miss G P (Blaenau Gwent Borough Council) K1 D1 N G H S1 V W
Ebbw Vale p458 . . . . 01495 350555
Banks, Mrs H (Buller Jeffries) S1 W E S2
Birmingham p136 . . . . . . 0121 212 2620
Banks, I (Franklins) S1 D1 K1 K3 W D2
Dunstable p214 . . . . 01582 699111
Banks, Ms J (John Hodge Solicitors) K1 K4 N Q T2 V W Zm
Weston-super-Mare p429 . . 01934 623511
Banks, Mrs J L (Blount Hemmings) K4 T2 W S1
Kingswinford p268 . . . . . . 01384 400565
Banks, Ms J M (Rotherham Magistrates Court)
Rotherham p470 . . . . 01709 839339
Banks, Ms K (Hogan Lovells International LLP)
London EC1 p42 . . . . . . 020 7296 2000
Banks, Miss M I (M I Banks) D1 F1 G
Stretford p400 . . . . 0161 864 1961
Banks, Mrs N (Lester Morrill) G H
Leeds p275 . . . . 0113 245 8549
Banks, Miss N (Mogers) A1 C1 E S1
Bath p127 . . . . 01225 750000
Banks, P J (Irwin Mitchell LLP) N
Birmingham p139 . . . . . . 0870 150 0100
Banks, R S (Shell International Ltd)
London SE1 p109 . . . . . . 020 7934 1234
Banks, Miss S A (Roythornes LLP) T2 K4 W
Spalding p389 . . . . 01775 842500
Banks, Mrs S M (Clark Brookes) W S1
West Bromwich p427 . . . . 0121 553 2576
Banks, S W D (Fisher Meredith) S2 S1 E W R1 Zl Ze
Lambeth p32 . . . . 020 7091 2700
Banky, J L (John L Banky Solicitors) S1 Q E B1 O W S2
Reading p359 . . . . 0118 930 4630
Bann, P (Mills & Bann) S1 W L K1 C1 J1 F1 E P
Newbury p322 . . . . 01635 521545 / 32000
Banner, N L (Forshaws Davies Ridgway LLP) S1 E W C1 G H R1 F1 B1
Warrington p422 . . . . . . 01925 230000
Banner, R R (Banner Jones) N
Chesterfield p191 . . . . . . 01246 209773
Banner, S (Howes Percival LLP) W
Northampton p332 . . . . . 01604 230400
Bannister, A (Weightmans LLP) O Q P Zc Zj
Dartford p207 . . . . 020 7822 1900
London EC4 p91 . . . . . . 020 7822 1900
Bannister, A C J (Alsters Kelley) K1 K3
Coventry p199 . . . . 0844 561 0100
Nuneaton p339 . . . . 0844 561 0100
Bannister, A R (Will Harrington & Co) B2 G H
Sutton Coldfield p403 . . . . 0121 321 1999
Bannister, B N (Laytons) C1 C2 F1 T1 Zb
Guildford p236 . . . . 01483 407000
Bannister, Ms C J (Drysdales) K3 K1 K2 D1 D2
Southend-on-Sea p387 . . . 01702 423400
Bannister, C K (Gregory Rowcliffe Milners) C1
London WC1 p37 . . . . . . 020 7242 0631
Bannister, E (Field Fisher Waterhouse LLP)
London EC3 p31 . . . . . . 020 7861 4000
Bannister, J (Hogan Lovells International LLP)
London EC1 p42 . . . . . . 020 7296 2000
Bannister, J P (Bannister & Co) G H
Yeovil p443 . . . . 01935 433133
Bannister, J S (Armitage Sykes LLP) E
Huddersfield p255 . . . . . . 01484 538121
Bannister, Ms K (Russell-Cooke LLP) C2 B1 Zb
London SW15 p74 . . . . . . 020 8789 9111
Bannister, R (Challinors) C1 P
Birmingham p136 . . . . . . 0121 212 9393
Bannister, T (Bingham McCutchen (London) LLP)
London EC2 p12 . . . . . . 020 7661 5300
Bannister, Ms Y (Financial Services Authority)
London E14 p106 . . . . . . 020 7066 1000
Bannon, Ms L F (Withers LLP) T2 W
London EC4 p92 . . . . . . 020 7597 6000
Bansal, Miss B (Paris Smith LLP) K1
Southampton p386 . . . . . 023 8048 2482
Bansal, R T (Bansal & Co) C1 B1 E W J1 L Q S1 T1 T2 Zi Zl Zv
Southall p384 . . . . 020 3118 2063
Bansel, G S (Pattinson & Brewer) J1 W Zp Zk
London WC1 p66 . . . . . . 020 7400 5100
Banting, Mrs D S (W H Darbyshire & Son) S1 E S2 W K4
Blackpool p146 . . . . 01253 346646
Banton, Ms L (Field Fisher Waterhouse LLP)
London EC3 p31 . . . . . . 020 7861 4000
Banwell, Ms C (McLellans) J1
Hertford p249 . . . . 01992 532000
Banyard-Smith, E (K&L Gates LLP)
London EC4 p47 . . . . . . 020 7648 9000
Baptist, Ms A B (Longmores) K1 K3
Hertford p248 . . . . 01992 300333
Baptist, A I (Kidd Rapinet) S2 E S1 R2 L
London WC2 p49 . . . . . . 020 7205 2115
Baptist, Miss K (Staffordshire County Council)
Stafford p472 . . . . 01785 223121
Baptiste, C (Cartwright King)
Leicester p279 . . . . 0116 253 9222
Bar, J W (Preston Redman) E F1 J1 L S1 R1
Bournemouth p152 . . . . . 01202 292424
Baranski, K (Geldards LLP) C1 B1 J1 Ze Zf
Cardiff p178 . . . . 029 2023 8239
Barbeary, S G (Brewer Harding & Rowe) L J2 Q F1 Zq N
Barnstaple p125 . . . . . . 01271 342271
Barber, Mrs A (TBI Solicitors) W
Hartlepool p243 . . . 0800 052 6824 / 01429 264101
Barber, B R (Beetenson & Gibbon) N J1 L Q F1
Grimsby p235 . . . . 01472 240251
Barber, Ms C (Kent County Council)
Maidstone p464 . . . . 01622 694320
Barber, C C (Gregory Rowcliffe Milners) B1 L Q Zc N O K1
London WC1 p37 . . . . . . 020 7242 0631
Barber, D E O (Linklaters LLP)
London EC2 p54 . . . . . . 020 7456 2000
Barber, D P (Raleys) N
Barnsley p125 . . . . 01226 211111
Barber, Ms G A (Aviva PLC)
London EC3 p103 . . 020 7283 7500 / 01603 687905
London EC2 p7 . . . . 020 7638 1111
Barber, G W (Grindrods) E L R1 S1 N O Q
Newton-le-Willows p330 . . . 01925 221321
Barber, Mrs J C (Hempsons) J1 N Q Zq O Zr
Westminster p40 . . . . . . 020 7839 0278
Barber, J D (Glovers Solicitors LLP) E
London W1 p36 . . . . 020 7935 8882
Barber, Mrs J M (Denniss Matthews) W Zv
London SE20 p27 . . 020 8778 7301 / 8778 7631

Barber, J S (Elliot Mather LLP) G
Chesterfield p192 . . . . . . 01246 231288

Barber, Miss L (Bury & Walkers LLP) S1 W
Barnsley p124 . . . . 01226 733533

Barber, Ms L (Button Legal LLP) K1 K3 D1
Coventry p200 . . . . 024 7652 5457

Barber, Miss L J (Forsters LLP) S1
Westminster p33 . . . . 020 7863 8333

Barber, M (Brearleys Solicitors) N C1 F1
Batley p128 . . . . 01924 473065

Barber, P C (DWF) E S2 R2
Liverpool p287 . . . . 0151 907 3000

Barber, P J (Southampton City Council) S1 W
Southampton p472 . . . . . . 023 8022 3855

Barber, P W B (Blake Lapthorn) C1 C3 I Zc Ze Zb
Chandlers Ford p184 . . . . 023 8090 8090

Barber, R (Millington Wallace & Co) K1 L E N
London N14 p61 . . . . 020 8882 1051

Barber, Ms R (Frisby & Co) J2 B2 P G
Stafford p392 . . . . 01785 244114

Barber, R I (Barber & Co) N
Glossop p230 . . . . 0845 803 0991

Barber, R T (Veale Wasbrough Vizards) A1 E L R1 S1 T1 W Zd
London EC4 p89 . . . . 020 7405 1234

Barber-Lomax, P A (Barber-Lomax) S1 W J1 E
Bedford p129 . . . . 01234 721108

Barbier-Emery, R (Ince & Co Services Ltd)
London E1 p44 . . . . 020 7481 0010

Barbone, D M (Sternberg Reed) B2 G H
Barking p123 . . . . 020 8591 3366
Romford p366 . . . . 01708 766155

Barbor, Mrs C M (K&L Gates LLP) N O Zj
London EC4 p47 . . . . 020 7648 9000

Barbour, Ms D (DLA Piper UK LLP)
London EC2 p24 . . . . 0870 011 1111

Barca, R G (Wilson Barca LLP) M1 N P G E B1 L Zk Ze Zl Zf
London W1 p92 . . . . 020 7272 2072

Barcan, R A (Barcan Woodward) N Zr
Bristol p161 . . . . 0117 925 8080

Barcham, Miss G B (Poole Magistrates Court)
Poole p469 . . . . 01202 745309

Barclay, Ms E (Greenwoods) N O Q G Zj
Milton Keynes p317 . . . . . 01908 298200

Barclay, G S (Warner Goodman LLP) K1 K2 K3 D1 D2
Southampton p387 . . . . . . 023 8063 9311

Barclay, J R (Mills & Reeve) W T1 A1 C1
Norwich p335 . . . . 01603 660155

Barclay, Ms J V (Coley & Tilley) K1 P M1 N F1 G
Birmingham p136 . . . . . . 0121 643 5531

Barclay, M R W (Olswang LLP)
London WC1 p64 . . . . 020 7067 3000

Barclay, Ms S J (Sarah Barclay & Co)
Blackpool p146 . . . . 01253 356051

Bard, C (Tolhurst Fisher LLP)
Southend-on-Sea p387 . . . . 01702 352511

Barda, R (Goodwins Family Law Solicitors) K1
Harrow p241 . . . . 020 8423 3525

Bardell, E E (Lewis & Dick) K1 J1 D1 K2
Crawley p202 . . . . 01293 526031

Bardell, M R (Travers Smith LLP) E Zb R2
London EC1 p87 . . . . 020 7295 3000

Barden, G (Jones Day) O
London EC4 p46 . . . . 020 7039 5959

Barden, Mrs J L (Whiting & Mason) K1 W L
New Mills p321 . . . 01663 742432 / 747958

Barden, P T (Devonshires) Q O B2 B1 J1 C1 I Zp Zq Zk Zj Zg
London EC2 p27 . . . . 020 7628 7576

Bardsley, P G (Ross & Craig) E S1 S2
Westminster p73 . . . . 020 7262 3077

Bardswell, C N (Belmont & Lowe) K1 T2 W Zw
London EC1 p11 . . . . 020 7608 4600

Bare, M A (Morrish Solicitors LLP) N Q
Leeds p276 . . . . 0113 245 0733

Barel, Ms S E (LG Lawyers)
London SE1 p50 . . . . 020 7379 0000

Barfield, P F (Thomas Cooper) N Za
London EC3 p22 . . . . 020 7481 8851

Barford, Mrs B C (Clarke Kiernan) D1 K1 N Q
Tonbridge p412 . . . . 01732 360999

Barford, M T (Max Barford & Co) D1 D2 J1 K1 N Zq Zw
Tunbridge Wells p414 . . . . 01892 539379

Bargate, Q D F (Simmons & Simmons) O Q B1 P Za Zj Zb
London EC2 p79 . . . . 020 7628 2020

Barge, R (Aaron & Partners LLP Solicitors) D1 K3 K1 K2
Chester p190 . . . . 01244 405555

Barham, C R (The College of Law) P M1 K1 F1 G J1 L
London WC1 p105 . . . . . . 0800 289997

Barham, Mrs J C (Cumming & Riley) G H B2
Grays p233 . . . . 01375 383691

Barham, Ms K L (Barlow Robbins LLP) K1 K2
Godalming p231 . . . . 01483 417121

Barham, Mrs M (Ginn & Co) S1 W
Cambridge p174 . . . . 01223 358275

Barham, R E C (SNR Denton) C1
London EC4 p75 . . . . 020 7242 1212

Barham, R S (Pemberton Greenish LLP) E L S1
London SW3 p66 . . . . 020 7591 3333

Bari, M (Jeya & Co) S2 E Q L S1
Newham p46 . . . . 020 8552 1999

Baria, Ms P I K (Levenes Solicitors) N
Haringey p53 . . 020 8881 7777 / 8881 6764

Baring, S (Stan Baring Solicitor) E B1 C1 H L N O K1 D1 Q Ze
Godalming p231 . . . . 01483 860986

Bark-Jones, A G (Bark & Co)
London EC4 p9 . . . . 020 7353 1990

Bark-Jones, R (Morecrofts Solicitors LLP) B1 B3 C1 C2 C3 E W T1 R1 R2 S1 S2 T2
Liverpool p290 . . . . 0151 236 8871

Barkas, Ms K (Miller Sands) W T2 K4 Zm
Cambridge p175 . . . . 01223 202345

Barker, A D (Jones Day) Zb
London EC4 p46 . . . . 020 7039 5959

Barker, Miss A L (Crown Prosecution Service Essex)
Chelmsford p454 . . . . . . 01245 455800

Barker, Mrs A M (Birmingham City Council Legal & Democratic Services)
Birmingham p449 . . . . . . 0121 303 2066

Barker, Miss B C (Macfarlanes) C1
London EC4 p56 . . . . 020 7831 9222

Barker, Mrs C A (South Tyneside Magistrates Court)
South Shields p471 . . . . . 0191 455 8800

Barker, C D (Conwy County Borough Council)
Conwy p455 . . . . 01492 576108

Barker, Mrs C E (Laytons) K1 S1 D1 P F1 W
Manchester p306 . . . . . . 0161 834 2100

Barker, C J (Birketts LLP) R2 E S2
Ipswich p262 . . . . 01473 232300

Barker, C J (Tanner & Taylor LLP) K1 D1 N Q F1
Farnham p225 . . . . 01252 733770

Barker, D (Pinsent Masons LLP)
London EC2 p67 . . . . 020 7418 7000

Barker, Mrs D (Advance Legal) Zr N J1
Burton-on-Trent p170 . . . . 01283 544492

Barker, D B (Allen & Overy LLP)
London E1 p5 . . . . 020 3088 0000

Barker, D J (Burnett Barker) K1 F1 W B1 T1 Ze Zq J1 J2 L N Zi Zk Q Zp
Bury St Edmunds p171 . . . 01284 701131

Barker, D J (Carrick Read (Leeds) Solicitors LLP)
Leeds p272 . . . . 0113 246 7878

Barker, D L (Harvey Ingram Borneos)
Bedford p130 . . . . 01234 353221

Barker, D N (East Cambridgeshire District Council)
Ely p458 . . . . 01353 665555

Barker, Ms E (Roythornes LLP)
Spalding p389 . . . . 01775 842500

Barker, F (Squire Sanders (UK) LLP)
Birmingham p142 . . . . . . 0121 222 3000

Barker, Mrs F R (Blocks) J1
Ipswich p262 . . . . 01473 230033

Barker, G W (Mercers) W T2 Zd A1
Henley-on-Thames p247 . . . 01491 572138

Barker, Ms H D (Rochdale Metropolitan Borough Council)
Rochdale p470 . . . . 01706 647474

Barker, I (Pinsent Masons LLP) R2
Leeds p276 . . . . 0113 244 5000

Barker, I B (Watson Burton LLP)
Newcastle upon Tyne p327 . 0845 901 2100

Barker, Ms J (Capsticks Solicitors LLP) N O
London SW19 p18 . . . . . . 020 8780 2211

Barker, J (Osborne Clarke) Zb R2
Bristol p164 . . . . 0117 917 3000
Reading p361 . . . . 0118 925 2000

Barker, J C (Forbes) A1 B1 C1 E F1 J1 L R1 S1 T1 Zc Zd Ze
Blackburn p145 . . . . 01254 54374

Barker, J D (Richmond Anderson Goudie) N Q L J1 F1
Chester-le-Street p191 . . . 0191 388 7884

Barker, J G M (Devonshires) Zb
London EC2 p27 . . . . 020 7628 7576

Barker, J M (Squire Sanders (UK) LLP)
Manchester p310 . . . . . . 0161 830 5000

Barker, J P (Bowling & Co) O L
London E15 p15 . . . . 020 8221 8000

Barker, J R (Morris Orman Hearle) N Zj J2
Cheltenham p188 . . . . . . 01242 257188

Barker, J S (Barkers) K1 D1 W
Bolton p148 . . . . 01204 370011

Barker, J V (Barker Austin) B1 E G K1 L M1 N P R1 S1 Ze Zk Zl
London EC3 p9 . . . . 020 7377 1933

Barker, K (Penningtons) E
London EC2 p66 . . . . 020 7457 3000

Barker, Ms K L (Myer Wolff) D1 K1 D2
Hull p257 . . . . 01482 223693

Barker, Ms L (Caplans) G H
Harrow p241 . . . . 020 8864 0111

Barker, L D (Hacking Ashton LLP) A1 L O Q Zq B1 A2 F1
Newcastle under Lyme p323 . 01782 715555

Barker, M A (Gateshead Metropolitan Borough Council)
Gateshead p458 . . . . 0191 433 3000

Barker, Miss M C (Needham Poulier & Partners) G H
London N17 p63 . . . . 020 8808 6622

Barker, M G (Warwick & Barker) S1 K1 W M1 C1 D1 E F1 J1 L Zc Zd Zl
Rustington p369 . . . . . . 01903 775051

Barker, M J M (Clarke Willmott) C1
Southampton p3850845 209 1000 / 0117 305 6000

Barker, Miss N (DWF) Zj
Liverpool p287 . . . . 0151 907 3000

Barker, Mrs P M (Coole & Haddock) K1
Horsham p253 . . . . 01403 210200

Barker, P R (Andrew Jackson) E C1 S1
Hull p257 . . . . 01482 325242

Barker, Ms R (The College of Law)
London WC1 p105 . . . . . . 0800 289997

Barker, R E (Barker Gotelee Solicitors) A1 R1 T1 W Zd M1 A2 C3 P T2 K4
Ipswich p262 . . . . 01473 611211

Barker, R H (Thompson & Jackson) S2 E L C1
Plymouth p350 . . . 01752 665037 / 221171

Barker, R M (Birmingham City Council Legal & Democratic Services)
Birmingham p449 . . . . . . 0121 303 2066

Barker, S (Janes) B2 G H
London SW1 p46 . . . . 020 7930 5100

Barker, S J (Steele & Son) G H N O Q W F1 J1 L Zl
Clitheroe p196 . . . . 01200 444321

Barker, S J (Barker Gillette) B2 G
London W1 p9 . . . . 020 7636 0555

Barker, Mrs S J (Warners Solicitors) S1 Zl
Tonbridge p412 . . . . 01732 770660

Barker, T (DLA Piper UK LLP)
London EC2 p24 . . . . 0870 011 1111

Barker, V E (Mundays LLP) E S2 R2
Cobham p196 . . . . 01932 590500

Barker, W T (SGH Martineau LLP) Ze
Birmingham p142 . . . . . . 0870 763 2000

Barker-Davies, M E (Richardson & Davies) E C1 S1 W L M1 F1 R1 N J1 Zl Zd Ze
Coventry p201 . . . . 024 7622 2001

Barkham, Miss C J (Smyth Barkham) Zd Zf T1 T2 W
London WC2 p80 . . . . 020 7632 9550

Barklam, J R B (Saunders Roberts) K3 K1
Evesham p220 . . . . 01386 442558

Barkley, P A M (Tozers)
Exeter p222 . . . . 01392 207020

Barlex, P A (Taylor Haldane Barlex LLP) G H
Chelmsford p187 . . . . . . 0845 293 7688

Barley, M (Bond Pearce LLP) O L
Southampton p385 . . . . . . 0845 415 0000

Barley, M D T (Pritchard Englefield) C1
London EC2 p69 . . . . 020 7972 9720

Barley, R A (Norton Peskett) D1 G H K1 Zl
Lowestoft p294 . . . . 01502 533000

Barling, D H (Dean Wilson Laing) C1 E L P R1 S1
Brighton p159 . . . . 01273 327241

Barlow, Ms A E (Margraves)
Llandrindod Wells p291 . . . 01597 825565

Barlow, A P (Pinsent Masons LLP) E B1 Zb
Leeds p276 . . . . 0113 244 5000

Barlow, C (Simmons & Simmons)
London EC2 p79 . . . . 020 7628 2020

Barlow, Mrs C A (Birketts LLP (Wollastons LLP)) J1 O Q J2
Chelmsford p186 . . . . . . 01245 211211

Barlow, C J M (Butcher & Barlow LLP) A1 C1 N O Q W
Sandbach p372 . . . . 01270 762521

Barlow, G J (Charles Coleman LLP) K3
Windsor p434 . . . . 01753 861115

Barlow, G R (Aviva PLC) E S2 R2
London EC3 p103 . . 020 7283 7500 / 01603 687905
Norwich p467 . . . . 01603 622200

Barlow, J K (Tracey Barlow Furniss & Co) A1 E G H J1 M1 L B1 C1 N Zj Zl Zk Q O
Worksop p441 . . . . 01909 472355

Barlow, J M (Clifford Chance)
London E14 p20 . . . . 020 7006 1000

Barlow, Ms J M (Cyril Morris Arkwright) S1 E L C1
Bolton p148 . . . . 01204 535261

Barlow, J T (Barker Son & Isherwood LLP) P L C1 F1 B1 Zc Ze Zj
Andover p118 . . . . 01264 353411

Barlow, Ms K E (Treasury Solicitors Department) Q N O F1 J1
London WC2 p110 . . . . . . 020 7210 3000

Barlow, M R (Leathes Prior) O C1 Ze
Norwich p334 . . . . 01603 610911

Barlow, Mrs M T (Moxons) C1 S2 E S1 W
Pontefract p351 . . . . . . 01977 703215

Barlow, N H (Monro Fisher Wasbrough LLP) W Zd S1 T2 T1
London WC1 p61 . . . . 020 7404 7001

Barlow, P (Hill Dickinson LLP) S1 L E W Zh
Liverpool p288 . . . . 0151 600 8000

Barlow, P (Kennedys) N Q Zr Zm
Cambridge p174 . . . . 01223 533060

Barlow, P M (Hancocks) E C1 S1 W T1 A1 Zd Zc
Banbury p122 . . . . 01295 253211

Barlow, R G (Browne Jacobson LLP) P R1 L Q Zj Zt Zn
Nottingham p336 . . . . . . 0115 976 6000

Barlow, S A (Nelsons) D1 G H J1
Derby p209 . . . . 01332 372372

Barlow, W M (Gosschalks) N P F1 Zj
Hull p256 . . . . 01482 324252

Barnard, Ms A (Russell Jones & Walker)
Manchester p309 . . . . . . 0161 383 3500

Barnard, A (Trowers & Hamlins)
London EC3 p88 . . . . 020 7423 8000

Barnard, A L C (Atkinson Ritson) E S2 S1 R2 Zc Zl A2
Carlisle p181 . . . . 01228 525221

Barnard, C (RHW Solicitors LLP) W K4
Guildford p237 . . . . 01483 302000

Barnard, C D (Herbert Smith LLP) C1 M2 Zb
London EC2 p40 . . . . 020 7374 8000

Barnard, D (Dee & Griffin) K1 K4 S1 T2 W
Gloucester p230 . . . . 01452 617288

Barnard, G P (Dickinson Dees) E S1 A1 R1 W L T1 Zh Zc Zd
Newcastle upon Tyne p324 . 0191 279 9000

Barnard, Miss H L (Hansells) W
Norwich p334 . . . . 01603 615731

Barnard, I J (Ashton KCJ) C1 E S1 S2
Ipswich p262 . . . . 01473 232425

Barnard, I S (Field Fisher Waterhouse LLP)
London EC3 p31 . . . . 020 7861 4000

Barnard, J (Lewis Silkin LLP)
London EC4 p53 . . . . 020 7074 8000

Barnard, Mrs M G (Knocker & Foskett) T1 W
Sevenoaks p374 . . . . 01732 459931

Barnard, N (Stephens Wheeler Cooke & Sons) S1 W
Luton p295 . . . . 01582 720175

Barnard, N G H (Owen White) Zh E L R1
Slough p382 . . . . 01753 876800

Barnard, T J W (Simmons & Simmons) E L S1
London EC2 p79 . . . . 020 7628 2020

Barnard, Miss V L (Chattertons Solicitors) G H S1 W K1 P D1 J1 Zl
Newark p322 . . . . 01636 673731

Barnden, T (Wesley Gryk) Zi
Lambeth p37 . . . . 020 7401 6887

Barnes, A (Morgan Cole)
Oxford p344 . . . . 01865 262600

Barnes, A J (Howes Percival LLP) N B1 L O A3 Zq
Norwich p334 . . . . 01603 762103

Barnes, A W H (Bates N V H)
London WC2 p11 . . . . 020 7936 2930

Barnes, B K (Barnes Harrild & Dyer) G H K1 D1 Zl
Croydon p204 . . . . 020 8681 5128

Barnes, C (Gateley LLP) J1
Manchester p304 . . . . . . 0161 836 7700

Barnes, C G (Fraser Brown) S1 E Zl
Nottingham p337 . . . . . . 0115 988 8777

Barnes, Mrs C L (Taylors) O Ze Q
Blackburn p146 . . . . 0844 800 0263

Barnes, D (Vickers & Co) D1 K1 G B2 X
Ealing p89 . . . 020 8579 2559 / 8840 3999

Barnes, D A (Linklaters LLP)
London EC2 p54 . . . . 020 7456 2000

Barnes, D A (Napthens LLP) N O Q
Preston p357 . . . . 01772 888444

Barnes, D J (Ashton KCJ) C1 C2 C3 J1 B1 Zb Zj Zo Zp Ze
Bury St Edmunds p171 . . . 01284 762331

Barnes, Miss D K (Burnetts) A1 E S1
Carlisle p181 . . . . 01228 552222

Barnes, Mrs D R (Beale and Company Solicitors LLP) W T1 C1 Zc Ze T2 P M1
London WC2 p11 . . . . 020 7240 3474

Barnes, Miss F J (Thompson Smith & Puxon) W K4
Clacton-on-Sea p195 . . . . 01255 221919

Barnes, F J (Blackfords LLP) S1 M1 P W E J1
Croydon p204 . . . . 020 8686 6232

Barnes, G A (Addleshaw Goddard) B1
Manchester p300 . . . . . . 0161 934 6000

Barnes, I L O (Keypoint Law LLP) Q N
Doncaster p212 . . . . 01302 329655

Barnes, Ms J (Carrick Read (Leeds) Solicitors LLP) B1 O Q N
Leeds p272 . . . . 0113 246 7878

Barnes, J C (Herbert Smith LLP) E
London EC2 p40 . . . . 020 7374 8000

Barnes, J E (James E Barnes) S1 W Zh
Ealing p10 . . . . 020 8810 7100

Barnes, J E (Reynolds Porter Chamberlain LLP) O Q Zj Zb
Bristol p164 . . . . 020 3060 6000

Barnes, J M (Widdows Mason) G H M1 P K1 N
Warrington p422 . . . . . . 01925 632267

Barnes, Miss J M (Timms) N J1 F1 Q
Derby p209 . . . . 01332 364436

Barnes, Ms K D (Runnymede Borough Council)
Addlestone p447 . . . . . . 01932 838383

Barnes, Miss K E (Lester Morrill) N K1 Zr
Leeds p275 . . . . 0113 245 8549

Barnes, K G L (Palmers) J1 Q Zp
Basildon p126 . . . . 01268 240000

Barnes, Miss L (Donald Race & Newton) K1 K3 Q N
Colne p198 . . . . 01282 864500

Barnes, Miss L A (Nexus Solicitors) O
Manchester p308 . . . . . . 0161 819 4900

Barnes, M (Brabners Chaffe Street) Zn C1
Manchester p301 . . . . . . 0161 836 8800

Barnes, Mrs M (Furse Sanders & Co) W T2 T1 K4 V Zd Zm A1 S1
South Molton p383 . . . . . 01769 572251

Barnes, Ms M (Family Law Associates LLP) K1
Haringey p30 . . . . 020 8342 7760
London EC2 p66 . . . . 020 7457 3000

Barnes, M G (West Yorkshire Fire & Civil Defence Authority)
Bradford p451 . . . . 01274 682311

Barnes, M N (Kirklees Metropolitan Borough Council)
Huddersfield p461 . . . . . 01484 221421

Barnes, N (Robinsons) Q O B1 N J1 G H F1 Zl
Derby p209 . . . . 01332 291431

Barnes, N G (Ben Hoare Bell & Co) G H
Sunderland p401 . . . . . . 0191 565 3112

Barnes, N V (Thomson Webb & Corfield) D1 N G H Zi
Cambridge p176 . . . . 01223 578068

Barnes, O W A (Travers Smith LLP) C1 C2
London EC1 p87 . . . . 020 7295 3000

Barnes, P (Hugh James) Zr N
Cardiff p179 . . . . 029 2022 4871

See p634 for the Key to Work Categories

Barnes, P D (Haworth & Nuttall) *S1 W*
Blackburn *p145* 01254 272640
Great Harwood *p234*. 01254 884253

Barnes, P M (Martello Professional Risks Limited) *Q Zc*
London EC3 *p108* 020 7337 7500

Barnes, Ms R (Winckworth Sherwood LLP)
London SE1 *p92*. 020 7593 5000

Barnes, R A (Metropolitan Police Directorate of Legal Services)
London SW1 *p108*. 020 7230 7210

Barnes, R A H (David Conway & Co) *C1 S2 E L R1 S1 Zc*
London W1 *p26* 020 7258 3000

Barnes, R T (Biscoes) *C1 E F1 J1 K1 L M1 N P*
Portsmouth *p354*. 023 9266 0261

Barnes, Mrs S D F (Archers Law LLP) *K1 D1*
Stockton-on-Tees *p396* . . . 01642 636500

Barnes, Miss S E (Napthens LLP) *S1*
Preston *p357* 01772 888444

Barnes, Ms S M (Yates Barnes) *E S1 L R1 W T1*
Chorley *p194* 01257 267014

Barnes, S N (Teignbridge District Council)
Newton Abbot *p466* 01626 361101

Barnes, T M (Brewer Harding & Rowe) *S1 E L*
Barnstaple *p125* 01271 342271

Barnes, T W (Simmons & Simmons)
London EC2 *p79*. 020 7628 2020

Barnet, Mrs N (Plexus Law (A Trading Name of Parabis Law LLP)) *N*
Evesham *p220*. 01386 769160

Barnett, Mrs A (Flanagans Solicitors)
Eynsham *p223*. 01865 430040

Barnett, A D (Conway & Co) *C1 E F1 L S1 W*
Harrow *p241*. 020 8863 0535

Barnett, A J (Woolliscrofts) *N*
Hanley *p239*. 01782 204000

Barnett, D E (Drivers) *W S1*
York *p444* 01904 625661

Barnett, E G (Allen & Overy LLP)
London E1 *p5* 020 3088 0000

Barnett, G D R (Simmons & Simmons)
London EC2 *p79*. 020 7628 2020

Barnett, Mrs H (Hadgkiss Hughes & Beale) *K1*
Birmingham *p138* 0121 449 5050

Barnett, I G (Hewitsons) *A1*
Northampton *p332*. 01604 233233

Barnett, J (Coles Miller Solicitors LLP) *S1 W L K1*
Bournemouth *p151*. 01202 293226

Barnett, J E (Burges Salmon) *T2 W T1*
Bristol *p161* 0117 939 2000

Barnett, J R W (Maples Teesdale LLP) *E*
London EC2 *p58*. 020 7600 3800

Barnett, Dr J S (James S Barnett) *O Q E W C1 R1 M1 Zd Ze*
Hungerford *p258*. 01488 658461

Barnett, M (Addleshaw Goddard)
London EC1 *p4* 020 7606 8855

Barnett, Ms M T (Memery Crystal) *E S2 S1*
London WC2 *p60* 020 7242 5905

Barnett, N D (SNR Denton) *Q*
London EC4 *p75*. 020 7242 1212

Barnett, P D (Hadgkiss Hughes & Beale) *E S1 S2 W*
Birmingham *p138* 0121 449 5050

Barnett, R (Goodall Barnett James) *G H K1 D1*
Horley *p252* 01293 414448

Barnett, R A (CKFT) *C1 C2 J1 W Zd Ze*
London NW3 *p17* 020 7431 7262

Barnett, R J C (Halton Borough Council)
Widnes *p476*. 0151 424 2061

Barnett, S (Michelmores LLP) *N O Zq Q*
Exeter *p221* 01392 688688

Barnett, Mrs S D (Freedman Sharman & Co) *A1 B1 C1 D1 F1 G K1 M1 S1*
Borehamwood *p150* 020 8953 9111

Barnett, S P (Fox Williams) *C2 C1*
London EC2 *p33*. 020 7628 2000

Barnett, Miss T O (CooperBurnett) *K1 K2 K3 D1 D2*
Tunbridge Wells *p415* 01892 515022

Barnfather, A P (Pannone LLP) *B2 J2 F2*
Manchester *p308* 0161 909 3000

Barnfield, L T (South Staffordshire Council)
Codsall *p455*. 01902 696000

Barnshaw, F S (Legal Aid Area Office No 7 (North Western))
Manchester *p465* 0845 602 1400

Barnsley, P (Higgs & Sons) *K1 D1 D2*
Brierley Hill *p158*. 0845 111 5050

Barodekar, Ms J F (MBNA Europe Bank Ltd) *C1 I J1 Zb*
Chester *p454* 01244 672002

Baron, Miss A (Richard Griffiths & Co) *G H*
Salisbury *p371*. 01722 329966

Baron, D L (Napthens LLP) *K1*
Preston *p357* 01772 888444

Baron, Mrs K (Stephensons Solicitors LLP) *Zr*
Wigan *p432* 01942 777777

Baron, L R (Painters) *C1 K4 Zd W T1*
Kidderminster *p266* 01562 822295

Baron, P R (Paul R Baron) *G H*
Carshalton *p183*. 020 8401 2251

Baron, R M (Robin Baron Commercial Lawyers) *C1 U2 I C2 Zza F1 J1 F2*
Camden *p11*. 020 7485 4477

Barot, Mrs S (Camerons Jones) *S1*
Harrow *p241*. 020 8423 6666

Barr, Mrs A C (Barr Ellison LLP) *E C1*
Cambridge *p174*. 01223 417200

Barr, Mrs A L (Land Registry - Lancashire Office)
Preston *p469* 01772 836700

Barr, B S (Brian Barr Solicitors) *N Zq Zr Q*
Manchester *p301* 0161 720 6700

Barr, D C J (Brighouses) *W S1 E L*
Southport *p388* . . .01704 534101 / 500151

Barr, E J (Rich & Carr Freer Bouskell) *E S1 Q K1 F1 L W N*
Blaby *p145* 0116 242 6039

Barr, G (Watson Burton LLP) *Zc E Zj Q*
Newcastle upon Tyne *p327* . 0845 901 2100

Barr, H (Clayton Mott) *S1 W E Zi*
Nottingham *p336*. 0115 941 7422

Barr, Ms L (Lewis Silkin LLP)
London EC4 *p53*. 020 7074 8000

Barr, Mrs M (Rollits LLP) *S2 E R2*
York *p445* 01904 625790

Barr, R A (Burges Salmon) *C1 C2 M2 T1*
Bristol *p161* 0117 939 2000

Barr, Miss S (Odeon & UCI Cinemas)
Manchester *p465* 0161 455 4000

Barr, S J (Charsley Harrison LLP) *S1*
Slough *p381*. 01753 517600

Barr, W D W (Mills & Reeve) *A1 C1 E L S1 T1 W Zd Zn Zo*
Cambridge *p175*. 01223 364422

Barr-Smith, A J (SNR Denton) *Zw*
London EC4 *p75*. 020 7242 1212

Barrable, Ms A (EMW) *E*
Milton Keynes *p316* 0845 070 6000

Barraclough, D W M (Lupton Fawcett) *E S2 R2*
Leeds *p275* 0113 280 2000

Barraclough, Mrs H R (DLA Piper UK LLP)
Leeds *p272* 0870 011 1111

Barradale, C R J D (Veale Wasbrough Vizards) *A1 E L S1 W T1 T2 Zd Zv*
London EC4 *p89*. 020 7405 1234

Barran, Mrs V T (Oliver Fisher) *S1 W L*
London W11 *p32*. 020 3219 0145

Barras, Mrs T W (WilmerHale)
London EC2 *p92*. 020 7645 2400

Barratt, A J (Fraser Dawbarns) *S1 E W K4 L R1 T1 T2 A1 C1*
Downham Market *p213* . . . 01366 383171
King's Lynn *p266* 01553 666600

Barratt, J C P (Keene Marsland) *S1 E*
Tunbridge Wells *p415* 01892 526442

Barratt, Mrs J Y (Barratt Goff & Tomlinson) *N*
Nottingham *p335*. 0115 931 5171

Barratt, Ms L (Bindmans LLP) *Zi*
London WC1 *p12* 020 7833 4433

Barratt, M (Friends Provident)
Dorking *p457* 01306 654925

Barratt, N R M (Warners Solicitors) *E S2 S1*
Sevenoaks *p374*. 01732 747900

Barratt, R (Morgan Lewis & Bockius)
London EC4 *p61*. 020 3201 5000

Barratt, Mrs S (Portsmouth City Council)
Portsmouth *p469*. 023 9283 4034

Barratt, S C (Whitbread PLC)
London LU5 *p110* 01582 424200

Barratt, Miss S L (Hay & Kilner) *N L F1 V Q X*
Wallsend *p419*. 0191 262 8231

Barrea, A (Barrea LLP) *Zi K1 W X D1 E L*
High Wycombe *p249*. 01494 537699

Barrell, M G (Mahany & Co Solicitors LLP) *D1 K1 S1*
Horley *p252* 01293 772888

Barrell, M G A (Greene & Greene) *K1 D1 K2 K3*
Bury St Edmunds *p171* . . . 01284 762211

Barrett, Mrs A C (Worsdell & Vintner) *C1 S2 E K4 S1 W*
Harefield *p239*. 01895 824713
Ickenham *p259* 01895 672631

Barrett, A D (Vanderpump & Sykes) *N*
Enfield *p219*. 020 8367 3999

Barrett, Mrs A E (Nottingham City Council (City Sec Dept))
Nottingham *p467*. 0115 915 5555

Barrett, A F (Wortley Byers) *C1 E L P R1 S1 W*
Brentwood *p156* 01277 268368

Barrett, B (Bermans LLP) *B1 O B2 Zb F1 U2*
Liverpool *p286*. 0151 224 0500

Barrett, C (Bird & Bird LLP) *C1 C2*
London EC4 *p13*. 020 7415 6000

Barrett, Miss E (DWF) *O Q*
Manchester *p303* 0161 603 5000

Barrett, Ms E (Tollers LLP) *N*
Northampton *p332*. 01604 258558

Barrett, G N (Pinkney Grunwells Lawyers LLP) *A1 E Ze X J1 R1 S1 W*
Whitby *p430*. 01947 601122

Barrett, G S (Mills & Reeve) *O Q Zj Zq*
London EC3 *p61*. 020 7648 9220

Barrett, Mrs H (Broadbents) *K1 G H W*
Heanor *p246*. 01773 769891

Barrett, H M S (Furley Page LLP) *T2 W Zv*
Canterbury *p176*. 01227 763939

Barrett, H R G (Ross & Craig) *E L R1 S1*
Westminster *p73*. 020 7262 3077

Barrett, Ms J (Lawrence Lupin) *Zi Zg*
Wembley *p426*. 020 8733 7200

Barrett, J (Berwins Solicitors Limited) *T1 T2 W*
Harrogate *p240* 01423 509000

Barrett, J M (Field Fisher Waterhouse LLP)
London EC3 *p31*. 020 7861 4000

Barrett, Ms L (Jackson Brierley Hudson Stoney) *W K4*
Rochdale *p365*. . .01706 644187 / 649214

Barrett, M (Goodman Derrick LLP) *C1 C2*
London EC4 *p36*. 020 7404 0606
London EC1 *p50*. 020 7814 1200

Barrett, M D (Barretts) *C1 E L S1*
London WC1 *p11* 020 7248 0551

Barrett, M E (Blaker Son & Young) *C1 C2 J1 N O Q*
Lewes *p283* 01273 480234

Barrett, M J (Cannock Chase District Council)
Cannock *p453*. 01543 462621

Barrett, O S (Richard Brown & Co) *G H*
Peterborough *p346* 0870 850 3062

Barrett, R A (Horwich Farrelly) *G H K1 L M1*
Manchester *p305* 0161 834 3585

Barrett, R W A (WBW Solicitors) *O C2 Q E Ze Za*
Newton Abbot *p329* 01626 202404

Barrett, Mrs S (George Davies Solicitors LLP) *J1 Zp*
Manchester *p303* 0161 236 8992

Barrett, S A (Barrett & Co Solicitors LLP) *E C1 S1 Zc Zd Zv C2*
Reading *p359* 0118 958 9711

Barrett, S C L (Barrett Nelligan Solicitors) *S1 E H G L C1 W N J1 S2*
Fleetwood *p226* 01253 771664

Barrett, S R (Horsey Lightly) *S2 R2 Zl*
Newbury *p322*. 01635 580858

Barrett, T E (Bennett Griffin) *N Q O F1*
Worthing *p441*. 01903 229925

Barrett, T L (Mills & Reeve) *S1 E*
Norwich *p335* 01603 660155

Barrett-Hague, Ms H P (The Generics Group AG)
Cambridge *p453*. 01223 875200

Barrett-Williams, Ms S (Troutman Sanders LLP)
London EC2 *p88*. 020 7038 6650

Barretto, Mrs M L (Fisher Meredith) *K3 K1*
Lambeth *p32*. 020 7091 2700

Barricella, D (Barricella Hughes Marchant)
Ipswich *p262*. 01473 226225

Barrie Murray, G D (Monro Fisher Wasbrough LLP) *C1 E S1 T1 B1 Zl Zi*
London WC1 *p61* 020 7404 7001

Barrington, C B (Barrington Scholfield) *S1 A1 W E L C1*
Bridgwater *p157* . . .01278 422858 / 422873

Barrington, Ms D A (Barringtons Solicitors) *C1 C2 E F1 F2 J1 S1 S2 W Ze*
Farnham *p224*. 01252 741751

Barrington, Ms H E (Derby City Council)
Derby *p456* 01332 293111
Nottingham *p467*. 0115 901 3901

Barrington, J C J (Thorne Segar) *N Q K1 F1 J1 L*
Minehead *p318* 01643 703234

Barrington, Ms L (London Stock Exchange Ltd)
London EC2 *p107* 020 7797 1000

Barrington, N J F C (Hine Downing Solicitors)
Falmouth *p223*. 01326 316655

Barrington, W J R (Moore Blatch Solicitors) *R1 E*
Southampton *p386*. 023 8071 8000

Barrington-Clark, H (Wessex Solicitors Chambers Ltd) *G H*
Portsmouth *p355*. 023 9238 1114

Barritt, K (Young & Lee) *N Q O C1 Zb Zd*
Birmingham *p143* 0121 633 3233

Barritt-Hayes, Mrs C (Ipswich Borough Council)
Ipswich *p461*. 01473 432000

Barron, Ms A C (Lamb Brooks LLP) *N*
Basingstoke *p126* 01256 844888

Barron, A D (Glazer Delmar)
London SE22 *p35* 020 8299 0021

Barron, A H (Vivash Hunt) *W T2*
Worcester Park *p440* 020 8330 1961

Barron, Miss C (Taylors) *O Q*
Manchester *p310* 0844 800 0263

Barron, C A (Brown Barron) *S1 S2 K3 W K1 O Zl*
Barrow-in-Furness *p125* . . . 01229 828814

Barron, G (Snowball Worthy Lowe) *C1 E J1 O Q C2 B1 S2*
Sunderland *p402*. 0191 565 3221

Barron, R P (Linklaters LLP)
London EC2 *p54*. 020 7456 2000

Barron, Mrs W J (Senior Calveley & Hardy) *K1 S1 W*
Lytham *p297*. 01253 733333

Barrow, A J (Travers Smith LLP) *E L R1 Zc*
London EC1 *p87*. 020 7295 3000

Barrow, J (Gullands) *K1 D1 K3*
Maidstone *p299* 01622 678341

Barrow, K M (Kenneth M Barrow & Co) *S1 W H G K1 L*
Seaham *p373* 0191 513 0333

Barrow, K M (Blake Lapthorn) *C1 F1 J1 B1 Ze Zf*
London EC1 *p13*. 020 7405 2000

Barrow, Miss L L (Rowley Dickinson) *S1 W E*
Manchester *p309* 0161 834 4215

Barrow, M R (M R Barrow) *F1 C1*
Poole *p352* 01202 737745

Barrow, P B (Quinn Melville) *D1 E F1 K1 L C1*
Liverpool *p290*. 0151 236 3340

Barrow, S C J (Jackson Barrett & Gass) *S1 W E A3*
Wilmslow *p433*. 01625 523988

Barrowcliff, N P (Davies & Company) *Q C1 F1 Ze*
Stockport *p395*. 0161 355 5500

Barrowclough, Miss J (Donald Race & Newton) *S1 W R1*
Colne *p198* 01282 864500

Barrowclough, J A (Roberts & Smith) *S1 W L S2*
Nelson *p321*. 01282 619000

Barrowman, Ms K (Judge & Priestley) *E L N Q S1 Zu*
Bromley *p166* 020 8290 0333

Barry, D J (David J Barry) *S1 K1 W*
Ross-on-Wye *p367* 01989 564209

Barry, Miss E (TWM Solicitors LLP) *N L J1 Zl O Q Zq Zp J2*
London SW19 *p85*. 020 8946 6454

Barry, G D S C (Ewings & Co) *W S1 S2*
London SE20 *p30* 020 8778 1126

Barry, Miss H C (Wrexham County Borough Council)
Wrexham *p477* 01978 292000

Barry, I F (Sharpe & Co) *S1 S2 C1 E J1 K1 Q O W L Zl Zc Ze*
Harrow *p242*. 020 8422 4555

Barry, J (Barry & Co) *W N S1 S2*
Pevensey Bay *p348* .01323 766370 / 768382

Barry, J A (Olswang LLP) *O Ze Zf*
London WC1 *p64* 020 7067 3000

Barry, J E (ASB Law) *S1 K1 R1 D1 Zc*
Crawley *p202* 01293 603600

Barry, Miss L P (Lesley P Barry) *G H D1*
Windsor *p434* 01753 860061

Barry, M J (City of Sunderland)
Sunderland *p473*. 0191 520 5555

Barry, M T (Malloy & Barry) *D1 E F1 G H J1 K1 L M1*
Cardiff *p180* 029 2034 3434

Barry, Ms N C (Bishop & Sewell LLP) *S1*
London WC1 *p13* 020 7631 4141

Barry, Ms P E (Lewis Silkin LLP) *O*
London EC4 *p53*. 020 7074 8000

Barry, Ms R (Treasury Solicitors Department)
London WC2 *p110*. 020 7210 3000

Barry, R J (Travers Smith LLP) *C1 C2*
London EC1 *p87*. 020 7295 3000

Barry, R S W (Allen & Overy LLP) *Ze*
London E1 *p5* 020 3088 0000

Barry, S (Michael Simkins LLP) *Zf*
London WC1 *p79* 020 7874 5600

Barry, Miss S C (Bridgend County Borough Council)
Bridgend *p451*. 01656 643643

Barry-Walsh, N M (Ranson Houghton) *E L S1*
Andover *p118* 01264 351533

Barsey, Dr H (Field Fisher Waterhouse LLP)
London EC3 *p31*. 020 7861 4000

Barson, K (Severn Trent Water Ltd)
Birmingham *p450* 0121 722 4000

Barstow, J (Freeclaim Solicitors)
Manchester *p304* 0161 437 9999

Bart, Mrs G O (Makanda Bart) *K1 G H D1 D2 K3 B2 Zi*
London N15 *p58*. 020 8802 0034

Bartalotta, M (Lansdale & Holdsworth) *N*
Bolton *p149* 01204 491111

Barter, Mrs S A (Rootes & Alliott) *K3 K1*
Folkestone *p227*. 01303 851100

Bartfield, Ms S E (Lester Morrill) *N Zr Q*
Leeds *p275* 0113 245 8549

Barth, P (Penningtons) *Zi*
London EC2 *p66*. 020 7457 3000

Bartholomew, D M (Edgar Cule & Evans) *K1 N Q S1 W L*
Pentre *p346* 01443 434179

Bartholomew, J A (Taylor Walton LLP) *E C1 T1 R1 A1 Zc*
Luton *p295* 01582 731161

Bartholomew, M J (Maxwell Winward LLP) *C1 C2 C3*
London EC4 *p59*. 020 7651 0000

Bartholomew, M J (CMS Cameron McKenna LLP)
London EC3 *p17*. 020 7367 3000

Bartholomew, R O (Sparling Benham & Brough) *S1 E C1 L A1 B1*
Manningtree *p311* 01206 392201
Colchester *p198*. 01206 733733

Bartholomew, Miss S (Wains) *S1*
Macclesfield *p297* 01625 429511

Bartle, K (Vingoe Lloyd) *K1 K4 W*
Helston *p246* 01326 555800

Bartlett, Miss A (Bramsdon & Childs) *S2 E S1*
Southsea *p388*. 023 9282 1251

Bartlett, B W (Bartlett Gooding & Weelen) *S1 E W L F1 C1 A1 B1 J1*
Castle Cary *p183* 01963 350888
Shepton Mallet *p378*. 01749 343091

Bartlett, C D (Bartletts Solicitors) *C1 S2 E L*
Liverpool *p286*. 0151 227 3391

Bartlett, Mrs E (Speechly Bircham LLP) *J1*
London EC4 *p81*. 020 7427 6400

Bartlett, G (Jefferies Essex LLP) *G H P Zl Zm B2*
Westcliff-on-Sea *p428* 01702 332311

Bartlett, J (Harthills) *K1*
Rotherham *p367*. 01709 377399

Bartlett, J A (Bartletts Solicitors) *A1 B1 C1 D1 E F1 G H*
Liverpool *p286*. 0151 227 3391

Bartlett, Miss J M (Burrows) *K1 L J1 Q W S1 K2 S2 K3*
Harrow *p241*. . .020 8904 7725 / 8904 4150

Bartlett, J W (J W Bartlett & Co)
Teddington *p408*. 020 8943 9831

Bartlett, Mrs K (Berry Smith LLP)
Cardiff *p177* 029 2034 5511

Bartlett, Mrs L (Humphries Kirk) *Zc E C1*
Poole *p352* 01202 725400

Bartlett, Ms L (Mills & Reeve) *K1*
Cambridge *p175*. 01223 364422

Bartlett, Ms L Y (HallmarkHulme) *K1 G H F1 O Q Zl*
Worcester *p439* 01905 726600

Bartlett, Ms M E (Reynolds Porter Chamberlain LLP) *Zq*
London E1 *p71* 020 3060 6000

Bartlett, P (Simmons & Simmons)
London EC2 *p79*. 020 7628 2020

Bartlett, P N (Bartletts Solicitors)
Chester *p190* 01244 313301

Bartlett, Mrs R A (Lodders Solicitors LLP) *F1 L Q O*
Stratford-upon-Avon *p400* . . 01789 293259

Bartlett, R S (SJ Berwin LLP) *Zb*
London EC4 *p75*. 020 7111 2222

Bartlett, Ms S (The College of Law Guildford)
Guildford *p459*. 01483 460200

Bartlett, T J (Cumberland Ellis Peirs) *A1 E L R1*
London WC1 *p23* 020 7242 0422

Bartley, A J (Jolliffe & Co) *A3 Zb B1 I Ze Zza L Zj U2 Zk O Q Zq*
Chester *p190* 01244 310022

Bartley, J A (Shoosmiths) *C1 I F1 Ze*
Northampton *p332*. . 0370 086 3000 / 01604 543000

Bartley-Smith, T (Thomas Guise) *S2 E S1*
Worcester *p439* 01905 723131

Bartolozzi, Ms S (Trowers & Hamlins)
London EC3 *p88*. 020 7423 8000

Barton, A (Stephens & Scown) *K1*
Exeter *p222* 01392 210700

Barton, Mrs A M (British Waterways Board)
Watford *p475* 01923 226422

Barton, C D (Hague & Dixon) *E S1 W L U2 C1*
York *p444* 01904 627111

Barton, C P (Denison Till)
York *p444* 01904 611411

Barton, D (Sedgwick Kelly LLP)
Watford *p424* 01923 228311

Barton, D A (Williams & Co) *A1 C1 E F1 R1 R2 S1 S2 Zb Zc*
Ampthill *p118* 01525 405566

Barton, D R (Southerns) *S1 S2 W*
Burnley *p169* 01282 422711
Ilkley *p261*. 01943 609969

Barton, Ms G (Penningtons) *Zr*
Godalming *p231*. 01483 791800

Barton, H (Andrew & Co LLP) *A1 C1 E Q N R1 S1*
Lincoln *p284*. 01522 512123

Barton, H D H G (Gardner Croft LLP) *C1 S2 E C2 R1 S1*
Canterbury *p176*. 01227 813400

Barton, Mrs J (Land Registry - Gloucester Office)
Gloucester *p459*. 01452 511111

Barton, J P (Gardner Leader LLP) *E W T2*
Newbury *p322* 01635 508080

Barton, Mrs L (Hunters) *W T2*
London WC2 *p44* 020 7412 0050

Barton, Mrs L (Ramsdens Solicitors) *K3 K1 B2 D1 L V G*
Huddersfield *p256* 01484 821500

Barton, Mrs L C E (Aldridge Brownlee Solicitors LLP) *K1 N D1*
Bournemouth *p151*. 01202 294411

Barton, Miss L K (Graysons) *K1 K3*
Sheffield *p375*. 0114 272 9184

Barton, P D (Field Fisher Waterhouse LLP) *O C1 Q Ze Zf*
London EC3 *p31*. 020 7861 4000

Barton, P D (Gordons LLP)
Leeds *p273* 0113 227 0100

Barton, P J (McBride Wilson & Co) *B1 J1 K1 L N O Q Zc Ze Zq*
London WC2 *p56* 020 7242 1300

Barton, P L (Ashfords LLP) *W T2 Zd*
Tiverton *p412* 01884 203000

Barton, Ms P M (Edwards Duthie) *Zr N*
Ilford *p260*. 020 8514 9000

Barton, R S (Atha Barton & Co) *D1 F1 G H J1 K1 L N Q S1*
Guisborough *p237* 01287 633242
Skelton-in-Cleveland *p381* . . 01287 651521

Barton, Miss S (Berwins Solicitors Limited) *E R1 S1 C1*
Harrogate *p240* 01423 509000

Barton, S (Cyril Morris Arkwright) *K1*
Bolton *p148* 01204 535261

Barton, S L (Thomson Wilson Pattinson) *W S1 G F1 L C1 E Zd Zl H*
Kendal *p264*. 01539 721945

Barton, S P (Bolton-Jones & Co) *K1 S1 W P M1 L F1 J1 B1*
Liverpool *p286*. 0151 733 2241

Barton, S V (Hodge Jones & Allen LLP) *Zg*
London NW1 *p41* 020 7874 8300

Barton, W (William Barton) *S1 R1 L X Zu*
Sutton *p402* 020 8642 4858

Bartram, Mrs J A (Crombie Wilkinson) *A1 W*
Malton *p300* 01653 600070
York *p444* 01904 624185

Bartram, P S (Bartram & Co) *Zi*
Ealing *p11* 020 8840 0444

Bartram, R (Legal Aid Area Office No 7 (North Western))
Manchester *p465* 0845 602 1400

Barty, Miss S C (CMS Cameron McKenna LLP) *O Zq*
London EC3 *p17*. 020 7367 3000

Barun, Ms J (Kaim Todner Ltd) *K1 K4 N Zm*
London EC4 *p47*. 020 7353 6660

Barwick, Ms C (Trowers & Hamlins)
London EC3 *p88*. 020 7423 8000

Barwick, D (Brabners Chaffe Street) *S2 E*
Liverpool *p286*. 0151 600 3000

Barwick, G (Ashurst LLP)
London EC2 *p7* 020 7638 1111

Barwick, T I (Cannings Connolly) *E R2 Zc*
London EC1 *p18*. 020 7329 9000

Barwood, N H (Bond Pearce LLP) *B1 C1 Zd*
Southampton *p385*. 0845 415 0000

Baseley, Miss R L (Mills & Reeve) *W T2 Zd*
Cambridge *p175*. 01223 364422

Bash, G L (Graham Bash & Co) *J1 M1*
Hackney *p11*. 020 8985 8892

Basha, Miss S (Kennedys) *Zj*
London EC3 *p49*. 020 7667 9667

Basheer, T (Sheridans) *I U2 Ze Zf Zw*
London WC1 *p78* 020 7079 0100

Bashforth, Mrs E M (Sheffield City Council)
Sheffield *p471*. 0114 273 4019

Bashforth, R L (Robert L Bashforth & Co) *G H*
Chesterfield *p192* 01246 200204

Bashir, Ms N (Nottinghamshire County Council Legal Services Division)
West Bridgford *p475*. 0115 977 3478

Bashir, R A (Stachiw Bashir Green) *K1 D1 W V Q N F1 L*
Bradford *p155*. 01274 404010

Bashir, Miss S (Berry Smith LLP) *C1 C2 C3 B1 Ze Zf*
Cardiff *p177* 029 2034 5511

Bashir, Mrs S (Sheffield City Council)
Sheffield *p471*. 0114 273 4019

Bashir, Mrs S (Owen White) *E*
Slough *p382*. 01753 876800

Bashir, Z I (Flint Bishop Solicitors) *N Q Zj Zq F2 V*
Derby *p208* 01332 340211

Basi, S (S S Basi & Co) *G H N Q Zi Zk K1 V L*
Ilford *p259*. 020 8518 1236

Baskind, S A (Cohen Cramer Solicitors) *K1 N Q O G E S1 L F1 W Zl Zc Zi Zm*
Leeds *p272* 0800 542 9408

Basnett, K (Goughs) *K1 N Q D1 J1 F1 O V Zl*
Calne *p173* 01249 812086

Basnett, R J G (Woolliscrofts) *A1 E L S1 W*
Hanley *p239*. 01782 204000

Basra, Miss B K (Anthony Collins Solicitors LLP) *Zh L*
Birmingham *p137* 0121 200 3242

Basran, Miss S (Jones Day) *Zb*
London EC4 *p46*. 020 7039 5959

Bass, G W T (Hay & Kilner) *G K1 S1 H W Zl S2*
Wallsend *p419*. 0191 262 8231

Bass, J L (Travers Smith LLP) *E*
London EC1 *p87*. 020 7295 3000

Bass, R (Belron International Ltd) *M2 M1 C2 C3 Q C1 J1 T1 I B1 Ze Zo Zb Zp Zj*
Egham *p470*. 01784 476800

Bassani, R V (Radcliffes Le Brasseur) *B1 G J1 H N O Q*
Westminster *p70*. 020 7222 7040

Bassendine, J S (Ashford Borough Council)
Ashford *p447* 01233 331111

Bassett, A P (Stephens & Scown) *O Q L J1 F1*
St Austell *p391* 01726 74433

Bassett, Mrs C A (Forsters LLP) *O Q*
Westminster *p33*. 020 7863 8333

Bassett, Ms G A (Bonallack & Bishop) *W T2*
Salisbury *p371*. 01722 422300

Bassett, Mrs G M (HC Solicitors LLP) *K3 K1 N K2 Q D1 X*
Peterborough *p347* 01733 882800

Bassett, M P (Atkins Bassett) *C1 E W S1 S2 K4*
Hinckley *p250* 01455 632685

Bassett, M R (Pengelly & Rylands) *S2 C1 S1 J1*
Tenterden *p410* . .01580 762248 / 763008

Bassey, R (Birmingham City Council Legal & Democratic Services)
Birmingham *p449* 0121 303 2066

Bassford, H (DLA Piper UK LLP)
London EC2 *p24*. 0870 011 1111

Bastable, Miss D N (Doreen Neale Bastable Solicitor) *C1 E K1 S1*
Birmingham *p135* 0121 744 3611

Bastable, G R (BCL Burton Copeland) *B2 G J2*
London WC2 *p9* 020 7430 2277

Bastian-Carter, Mrs N (Wellers Law Group LLP) *W*
Bromley *p167* 020 8464 4242

Bastiman, P I L (Colin Brown & Kidson) *S1 W K1 L N G A1 F1 J1*
Whitby *p430*. 01947 603391

Bastin, Miss J (Nigel Davis Solicitors) *A1 A2 A3 E W O K3 R1 Zq*
Belper *p131* 01335 372889

Bastow, Ms G M (Lewis Silkin LLP) *Zh E*
London EC4 *p53*. 020 7074 8000

Bastow, M R (Lyons Davidson) *Q O N L*
Bristol *p163* 0117 904 6000

Bastyan, T A J (Gilbert Stephens) *K1 D1 K2*
Exeter *p221* 01392 424242

Basu, S (Penningtons)
London EC2 *p66*. 020 7457 3000

Basu-Owen, Mrs B R (HM Land Registry - Harrow Sub Office)
Harrow *p460*. 020 8235 1181

Basuta, Ms M (Memery Crystal) *C1 C2*
London WC2 *p60* 020 7242 5905

Baszynska-Kamrowska, Ms R R E (Renata & Co) *F1 K1 N O Q Zw W*
Birmingham *p141* 0121 777 7333

Bata, R (Troutman Sanders LLP)
London EC2 *p88*. 020 7038 6650

Batch, K W (Norton Peskett) *B1 D1 G H J1 L M1 N P F1 Zl*
Great Yarmouth *p234* 01493 849200

Batcheler, Miss L J (Basingstoke & Deane Borough Council)
Basingstoke *p448* 01256 845402

Batchelor, Ms C (Keoghs LLP) *N Zj O Q*
Bolton *p149* 01204 677000

Batchelor, Miss C N (Hill Dickinson LLP) *Zr*
Manchester *p305* 0161 817 7200

Batchelor, D (Ashurst LLP)
London EC2 *p7* 020 7638 1111

Batchelor, Miss E (Herrington & Carmichael LLP)
Camberley *p173*. 01276 686222

Batchelor, G J M (Barlow Lyde & Gilbert LLP)
London EC3 *p10*. 020 7247 2277
London EC3 *p31*. 020 7861 4000

Batchelor, J (Keoghs LLP) *N Q Zj O*
Bolton *p149* 01204 677000

Batchelor, Mrs J A (Batchelor Myddelton) *J1 C1 C2 Zq Ze*
Potters Bar *p355*. 01707 647088

Batchelor, J M (Tates Solicitors)
Leeds *p277* 0113 242 2290

Batchelor, K (Batchelor Sharp) *S1 E C1 W*
Bristol *p161* 01454 319100
Kingswood *p268*. 0117 967 1772

Batchelor, R J (AWB Partnership LLP) *N Q K1 L J1 O G*
Guildford *p235*. 01483 302345

Batchelor, Mrs S M (Abbott & Co) *K1 S1 F1 D1 L N Q W*
Walkden *p419* 0161 799 8003

Bate, D H G (Burnley-Jones Bate & Co) *G S1 E C1 H*
London SW19 *p16*. 020 8542 8101

Bate, J R S (Buglear Bate & Co) *D1 K1 L N O Q Zg*
Woking *p436*. . . . .01483 715527 / 724246

Bate, Ms M (Ashurst LLP)
London EC2 *p7* 020 7638 1111

Bate, R (Bentley Solicitors) *N Zq Zr*
Crewe *p203* 01270 509800

Bate, R J (Brabners Chaffe Street) *S1 W*
Manchester *p301* 0161 836 8800

Bate, R T (Richard T Bate & Co) *C1 Q*
Tetbury *p410*. 01666 503722

Bate, Mrs V A (Berg Legal) *O Q*
Manchester *p301* 0161 833 9211

Bateman, Ms A L (Harrison Clark LLP) *J1*
Cheltenham *p188* 01242 269198

Bateman, A N (Alastair Bateman & Co) *Zm G H*
Bradford *p153* 01274 739973

Bateman, Ms C H (Gordons LLP)
Leeds *p273* 0113 227 0100

Bateman, Miss H C (Metcalfes) *E Zl S2 R2*
Bristol *p164* 0117 929 0451

Bateman, Mrs J A (Shulmans) *S2 E R2*
Leeds *p276* 0113 245 2833

Bateman, J F A (Batemans) *C1 E L M1 N R1 S1 W Zb Zc Zo Zl*
Hemel Hempstead *p246* . . . 01442 834344

Bateman, M D (Davenport Lyons) *J1 O Q Zk*
London W1 *p25* 020 7468 2600

Bateman, Mrs P (Goldstones) *K1 D1 Zl K2*
Swansea *p405*. 01792 643021

Bateman, P R (Glanvilles) *E C1 R1 L S1 B1 Zh*
Newport *p328* 01983 527878

Bateman, R P (Stokes Solicitors) *E C1 J1 S2 S1 Zt*
Portsmouth *p355*. 023 9282 8131

Bates, A J (Gilbert Stephens) *S1 W S2*
Exeter *p221* 01392 424242
Sidmouth *p380*. 01395 512443

Bates, A P (Morris & Bates) *A1 B1 C1 D1 E F1 G H J1 K1 Zb Zc Zd*
Aberystwyth *p114* 01970 625566

Bates, B (Morrison & Foerster (UK) LLP) *Zb*
London EC2 *p62*. 020 7920 4000

Bates, C (Ashurst LLP)
London EC2 *p7* 020 7638 1111

Bates, Ms C A (Northamptonshire County Council)
Northampton *p467*. 01604 236236

Bates, C J (Clifford Chance)
London E14 *p20*. 020 7006 1000

Bates, Ms C L (SGH Martineau LLP) *Q L O*
London EC3 *p75*. 020 7264 4444

Bates, Mrs C W (Newsome Vaughan LLP) *W S1*
Coventry *p200*. 024 7663 3433

Bates, Ms H (Grahame Stowe Bateson) *K1 K3 D1*
Leeds *p274* 0113 246 8163

Bates, Miss H (Oglethorpe Sturton & Gillibrand) *W S1*
Lancaster *p270* 01524 846846

Bates, Ms H (Turner & Wall) *K1 K3 D1*
Keighley *p264* 01535 607831

Bates, I J (J Keith Park & Co) *D1 G H K1 L M1 N P V*
St Helens *p391* 01744 636000

Bates, Miss J A (Plexus Law (A Trading Name of Parabis Law LLP)) *N Q Zj J2*
Evesham *p220*. 01386 769160

Bates, J E N (Arnold Fooks Chadwick LLP) *W S1 T2 X Zd S2 E K4 J1 L*
London W1 *p7*. 020 7499 3007

Bates, J H (Morris & Bates)
Aberystwyth *p114* 01970 625566

Bates, M D (Clifford Chance)
London E14 *p20*. 020 7006 1000

Bates, M R (Taylor Wessing)
London EC4 *p86*. 020 7300 7000

Bates, M S G (Chester City Council)
Chester *p454* 01244 324324

Bates, N J (Nicholas Bates) *G H*
Basingstoke *p126* 01256 331278

Bates, P J (Bannister Bates Property Lawyers) *C1 C2 E S1 T2 Zc*
Morecambe *p318* 01524 416300

Bates, R (Rix & Kay Solicitors LLP) *Zd W T2*
Hove *p255*. 01273 329797

Bates, R A (Kennedys)
London EC3 *p49*. 020 7667 9667

Bates, R D (Sharp & Partners) *Q N*
Nottingham *p339*. 0115 959 0055

Bates, R E (Cramp & Co) *F1 K1 L Q O K3*
Eastbourne *p215* 01323 720581

Bates, R P (Kerman & Co LLP) *T1 T2 W*
London WC2 *p49* 020 7539 7272
Croydon *p205* 020 8686 5000

Bates, Miss S (Mayer Brown International LLP) *C1 C2*
London EC2 *p59*. 020 3130 3000

Bates, Mrs S J (Borough of Telford & Wrekin) *L Q P R1*
Telford *p473*. 01952 380000

Bates, Ms V (Cannings Connolly) *S2 E S1*
London EC1 *p18*. 020 7329 9000

Bateson, A J (Grahame Stowe Bateson) *G H S1 K1 D1 E N T1 J1 Zd Zj Zc*
Leeds *p274* 0113 246 8163

Bateson, D J (Taylor Nelson Sofres PLC)
London W5 *p109* 020 8967 4348

Bateson, D W (Thomas Cooper) *O M2 Za Zj*
London EC3 *p22*. 020 7481 8851

Bateson, Ms J M (Thornton & Co) *K1 J1 Q G E*
Lytham *p297*. 01253 782808

Batey, Miss J (Shell International Ltd)
London SE1 *p109* 020 7934 1234

Bath, S (Cartwright King)
Nottingham *p336*. 0115 958 7444

Batham, Ms E M (Bury Metropolitan Borough Council) *D1 D2 K1*
Bury *p452* 0161 253 7771

Bather, S R (Burley & Geach) *W T1 T2 Zm*
Grayshott *p233* 01428 605355
Haslemere *p243*. 01428 656011

Bathurst, D J C (Chichester & District Magistrates Courts)
Chichester *p455* 01243 817000

Bathurst, N C S (Barlow Lyde & Gilbert LLP)
London EC3 *p10*. 020 7247 2277

Batistich, M E (Barlow Lyde & Gilbert LLP)
London EC3 *p10*. 020 7247 2277

Batko, C (W Davies) *Zl O Q N*
Woking *p436*. 01483 744900

Batley, Miss S (Jones Day) *O*
London EC4 *p46*. 020 7039 5959

Batt, M D (Greene & Greene) *A1 R1 S1 T2 W*
Bury St Edmunds *p171* . . . 01284 762211

Batt, S J L (North Lincolnshire Council) *J1 N O Q Zq K3 Zr*
Scunthorpe *p470*. 01724 296296

Batta, R (Anthony Collins Solicitors LLP) *Zr N*
Birmingham *p137* 0121 200 3242

Battell, J P (DB Law) *D1 K1 S1 W L A1*
Camborne *p173* 01209 712428

Battell, Ms N J (Piper Smith Watton LLP) *E L S1 S2*
London SW1 *p68* 020 7222 9900

Battelley, C (Waldrons) *J1 Zp J2*
Brierley Hill *p158*. 01384 811811

Batten, D H C (Battens) *W T2 I Zb Zv*
Yeovil *p443* 01935 846000

Batten, Ms H (Wise Geary) *S1*
Banbury *p122* 01295 278500

Batten, Miss H L R (Jordans) *Q O N*
Wakefield *p418* 01924 387110

Batten, J H (Bridgend County Borough Council)
Bridgend *p451*. 01656 643643

Batten, Miss S (Shentons) *S1*
Winchester *p434*. 01962 844544

Battersby, Ms C M (City & County of Swansea)
Swansea *p473*. 01792 636000

Battersby, M J (Chafes) *S1 E L W A1 Zd*
Wilmslow *p433*. 01625 531676

Battersby, P (Davies Battersby Ltd) *Q Za Zj*
London EC3 *p26*. 020 7621 1090

Battersby, R (Sutcliffes) *S1 W K1 N E C1 Q V D1 A1*
Rawtenstall *p359* 01706 215107

Battersby, R F (Graham Dack & Company (inc Battersby James)) *N A1 W S1 Zc Zl*
Chatteris *p185*. 01354 695885

Battersby, S J (Jameson & Hill) *G H N D1 J1 Zl*
Hertford *p248* 01992 554881

Batteson, A (Bristows)
London EC4 *p15*. 020 7400 8000

Batteson, Miss M (Simmons & Simmons)
London EC2 *p79*. 020 7628 2020

Batteson, Miss W (Eastleigh Borough Council)
Eastleigh *p457*. 023 8068 8068

Battisby, D K (Lanyon Bowdler LLP) *N O J1 Q Zp*
Wellington *p425* 01952 244721

Battrick, G A (Gordon A Battrick & Co) *S1 L W E N J1 K1 F1*
Bridgend *p157*. 01656 768111

Battrick, R J (Spicketts Battrick Law Practice) *S1 M1 L W A1 E J1 P B1 R1 Zb Zj Zp*
Cardiff *p181* 029 2046 1480

Battu, B K (Huggins & Lewis Foskett) *S1 B1 D1 D2 F1 K1 L N Q*
Redbridge *p43*. 020 8989 3000

Batty, Mrs A (Clarion Solicitors LLP) *E*
Leeds *p272* 0113 246 0622

Batty, C W A (Harold Benjamin) *E S1 R1 C1 L*
Harrow *p241*. 020 8422 5678

Batty, Mrs E J (Reading Borough Council)
Reading *p469* 0118 939 0900

Batty, I C (CMS Cameron McKenna LLP)
London EC3 *p17*. 020 7367 3000

Batty, Mrs K (Henry Hyams) *G H*
Leeds *p274* 0113 243 2288

Batty, M (Roland Robinsons & Fentons LLP)
Lytham *p297*. 01253 734253

Batty, M (Greene & Greene) *Zq O N Q Zl*
Bury St Edmunds *p171* . . . 01284 762211

See p634 for the Key to Work Categories

Batty, Mrs S P (A C B Hurst & Co) *W T1* Henley-on-Thames *p247*. . . 01491 572699

Battye, Ms C (Warner Goodman LLP) *S2 E* Portsmouth *p355*. . . 023 9275 3575

Battye, N J (Brearleys Solicitors) *N Q F1 Zq* Batley *p128* . . . 01924 473065

Baty, R W (Travers Smith LLP) *J1* London EC1 *p87*. . . 020 7295 3000

Bau, Mrs S (Colin Rayner & Co) *K1 D1 V K2 Q Zo N L* Bolton *p149* . . . 01204 591145

Baucher, Mrs H A (Hill Dickinson LLP) *M1 L G J1 P F1 Zm* London EC3 *p41*. . . 020 7283 9033

Bauer, A J (Ashfords LLP) *T1 C1* Exeter *p220* . . . 01392 337000

Baugh, J N (Crown Prosecution Service Dorset) Bournemouth *p450*. . . 01202 498700

Baugh, Ms S J (MFG Solicitors) *S2 E A1* Telford *p409*. . . 01952 641651

Baulf, P J (Gill Akaster) *O Q K1 J1 K3* Plymouth *p349*. . . 01752 203500

Baum, C (Marcus Baum) *S1 E C1 F1 L W Zh* Southend-on-Sea *p387* . . . 01702 346677

Baum, J M (Levi Solicitors LLP) *T2 W* Leeds *p275* . . . 0113 244 9931

Baverstock, D P (Coffin Mew & Clover) *S1 W* Gosport *p232* . . . 023 9252 3111

Baverstock, Mrs H F (Knight Polson Solicitors) *K1 W K3* Eastleigh *p216*. . . 023 8064 4822

Bavinton, M (Ashurst LLP) London EC2 *p7* . . . 020 7638 1111

Bawa, Ms K (HCB Solicitors) Solihull *p382*. . . 0121 705 2255

Bawn, D L (Gibson & Co) *S2 E K4 T2 W* Newcastle upon Tyne *p324* . 0191 273 3817

Bawtree, Ms J (Trowers & Hamlins) London EC3 *p88*. . . 020 7423 8000

Baxandall, Mrs C E (Thistle Hotels PLC) *C1 B1 M1 Zb Zh* Leeds *p463* . . . 0113 243 9111

Baxendale, Miss A L (BUPA) London WC1 *p104*. . . 020 7656 2305

Baxter, B (Reynolds Porter Chamberlain LLP) London E1 *p71* . . . 020 3060 6000

Baxter, C (Baxter & Co) *C1 F1 J1 K1 L N O S1* Bournemouth *p151*. . . 01202 530249

Baxter, C N A (Dowse Baxter) *C1 N E O Q J1 B2* London SW19 *p27*. . . 020 8946 9110

Baxter, Mrs H (George Davies Solicitors LLP) *J1* Manchester *p303* . . . 0161 236 8992

Baxter, Mrs H (Merritt & Co) *F1 L M1 V K1 N O Q* Yarm *p443*. . . 01642 885555

Baxter, Miss J (Lancashire County Council) Preston *p469* . . . 01772 254868

Baxter, Ms J (Simmons & Simmons) London EC2 *p79*. . . 020 7628 2020

Baxter, Ms K E (Lewis Silkin LLP) *J1 Q* London EC4 *p53*. . . 020 7074 8000

Baxter, N (Baxter Brown McArthur) London SW11 *p11* . . . 020 7924 8130

Baxter, N J (Mark & Co) London W14 *p58* 020 7603 3710 / 7602 6942

Baxter, Ms P A (DAC Beachcroft) London EC4 *p24*. . . 020 7242 1011

Baxter, R A (Stevens & Bolton) *C1 J1 T1 I Ze Zo* Guildford *p237*. . . 01483 302264

Baxter, Ms R J (Baxters) *D1 K1 L* Hull *p256* . . . 01482 224011

Baybut, D (Stephensons Solicitors LLP) *C1 C2 E* Wigan *p432* . . . 01942 777777

Bayer, J J (Myers Fletcher & Gordon) *W S2 J1 S1 Zp E* London W6 *p62* . . . 020 7610 4433

Bayes, A M (Layzells) *E S1 C1* London N10 *p52*. . . 020 8444 0202

Bayles, Mrs J D (Smith Roddam) *D2 D1 K1 K3 K2* Bishop Auckland *p144*. . . 01388 603073

Bayles, J F (John Bayles & Co) *B1 C1 D1 E F1 G H J1 K1 L Zm Zo* Birtley *p144* . . . 0191 410 2142; Durham *p214* . . . 0191 386 1161

Bayles, L (Ian N Gunby & Co) *N* Milnthorpe *p316* . . . 01539 562044; Barrow-in-Furness *p125* . . . 01229 811811

Bayles, Miss L S (Male & Wagland) *W T2* Potters Bar *p355*. . . 01707 657171

Bayley, B J (Wolferstans) *Zr N J1 Q G* Plymouth *p351*. . . 01752 663295

Bayley, C R (Pilkington PLC) St Helens *p472* . . . 01744 28882

Bayley, Ms K (Barlow Robbins LLP) *W* Woking *p436*. . . 01483 748500

Bayley, P (British Telecommunications PLC) London EC1 *p104* . . . 020 7356 6181

Bayley, Miss S L (Hillyer McKeown LLP) *C1 C2* Chester *p190* . . . 01244 318131

Baylin, S (Clifford Chance) London E14 *p20*. . . 020 7006 1000

Baylis, N (K&L Gates LLP) *C1* London EC4 *p47*. . . 020 7648 9000

Baylis, R J (Burley & Geach) *Q G H N K1* Grayshott *p233* . . . 01428 605355; Petersfield *p348* . . . 01730 262401

Baylis, S (Langleys) York *p445* . . . 01904 610886

Bayliss, Miss C (Dexter Montague LLP) *W T2* Reading *p360* . . . 0118 939 3999

Bayliss, D A (Frisby & Co) *E O S2* Stafford *p392* . . . 01785 244114

Bayliss, G V (Aubrey David) *W S1 L S2* Westminster *p25*. . . 020 7224 4410

Bayliss, J (Farrer & Co LLP) *Zb* London WC2 *p31* . . . 020 3375 7000; London EC4 *p81*. . . 020 7427 6400

Bayliss, M J (Scaiff LLP) *M1 N P K1 S1 C1 F1 J1* Worcester *p440* . . . 01905 727700

Bayliss, P B (Lloyds & Cooper) *O N P Q Zc Zj Zr* Leominster *p283*. . . 01568 613236

Bayly, P J (Crown Prosecution Service Cumbria) Carlisle *p453*. . . 01228 882900

Bayman, H M I (Sykes Lee & Brydson) *G N Q H F1 J1 Zm Zp B2 F2 Zl* York *p445* . . . 01904 731100

Baynard, Mrs V A (Baynards) *S1 E* Bexleyheath *p132* . . . 020 8304 5113

Baynton, D A (Metcalfes) *J1 N O Q* Bristol *p164* . . . 0117 929 0451

Baynton, G W (ClarksLegal LLP) *E S1* London WC2 *p20* . . . 020 7539 8000; London W1 *p46* . . . 020 7339 7000

Bays, J D (John Bays & Co) *S1 E W L* Haringey *p11* . . . 020 8881 3609; Haringey *p26* . . . 020 8808 3237

Bays, K J (Davenport Lyons) *N P C1 Ze Zf* London W1 *p25* . . . 020 7468 2600

Bazeer, S M (Bazeer & Co) *G L J1 W V* London SW19 *p11*. . . 020 8543 6600

Bazen, M J (Clark Holt) *C1 J1 I U2 Ze Zza* Swindon *p406*. . . 01793 617444

Bazley, P C (Gordon Dean Solicitors) *N W* Norwich *p334* . . . 01603 767671

Bazzard, S R (Blaser Mills) *A1 E C1 S1 W R2 S2* Chesham *p189* . . . 01494 782291

Beabey, B (Farrer & Co LLP) London WC2 *p31* . . . 020 3375 7000

Beach, G A (Bailey & Cogger) *C1 E M1 P R1 S1 W X Zt* Tonbridge *p412* . . . 01732 353305

Beach, P M (Wills Chandler Beach) *S1 W E A1 C1 L K1 P T1 R1 Zc K4* Fleet *p226*. . . 01252 613351; Hook *p252*. . . 01256 764646 / 764647

Beach, S W (Taylor Vinters) *E L* Cambridge *p176*. . . 01223 423444

Beacham, Ms J H (Clausen Miller LLP) *Zj O Zq* London EC3 *p20*. . . 020 7645 7970

Beachley, I K (Moss Beachley Mullem & Coleman) *K1 G L M1 P W D1 J1 H F1 Zi Zk Zl* Westminster *p62*. 020 7402 1401 / 7723 5783

Beadel, D P S (Ashfords LLP) *O* Plymouth *p349*. . . 01752 521500

Beadel, M J S (Stephens & Scown) *S1 E Zc* St Austell *p391* . . . 01726 74433

Beadell, C A (Irwin Mitchell LLP) *Zr F2* Manchester *p306* . . . 0870 150 0100

Beadle, Miss J L (Gullands) *N Q* Maidstone *p299* . . . 01622 678341

Beadman, Ms S (Goodman Derrick LLP) London EC4 *p36*. . . 020 7404 0606

Beadnall, A S (Stephenson Harwood) *O J1 C1* London EC2 *p82*. . . 020 7329 4422

Beadnall, D S J (David Beadnall) *M1 K1 D1 G H J1* Middlesbrough *p315* . . . 01642 311635

Beadsworth, M F (Mercers) *E S1* Henley-on-Thames *p247*. . . 01491 572138

Beagley, J D (Rosling King) *Zq R2 Zc* London EC4 *p73*. . . 020 7353 2353

Beahan, Ms C A (Allen & Overy LLP) London E1 *p5* . . . 020 3088 0000

Beahan, S J (Irwin Mitchell LLP) *F1 O U1 Zj* Sheffield *p376* . . . 0870 150 0100

Beake, H B (Mills Curry) *S1 W* Eastcote *p216* . . . 020 8868 8841

Beal, Ms D J (George Green LLP) *W T2* Cradley Heath *p201* . . . 01384 410410

Beal, Miss K E (Fraser Brown) *K3 K1 D1 D2* Nottingham *p337*. . . 0115 988 8777

Beal, Mrs S E (Southampton City Council) Southampton *p472*. . . 023 8022 3855

Beale, Mrs A M (Pothecary Witham Weld) *Q J1 N F1 L Zd Zl Ze* Westminster *p69*. . . 020 7821 8211

Beale, E C (Edwards Angell Palmer & Dodge) London EC2 *p28*. . . 020 7583 4055

Beale, G W K (Reed Smith LLP) *C1 C2* London EC2 *p71*. . . 020 3116 3000

Beale, Ms J (Wall James Chappell) *B1 K4 J1 Q W* Stourbridge *p399* . . . 01384 371622

Beale, P A E (Reed Smith LLP) London EC2 *p71*. . . 020 3116 3000

Beaman, N W (Nigel W Beaman) *O Q J1 Zc K1 Zp* Cannock *p176*. . . 01543 574474

Beamer, Mrs B J (Everys) *S1 E L* Budleigh Salterton *p168* . . . 01395 442223

Beames, C M (Berry Smith LLP) *S1 W T2* Cardiff *p177* . . . 029 2034 5511

Beames, M A (Rawlison Butler LLP) *W K4* Crawley *p202* . . . 01293 527744

Beamish, S C (The College of Law) *O Zn* London WC1 *p105*. . . 0800 289997

Bean, A (MacLeish Littlestone Cowan) Redbridge *p57*. . . 020 8514 3000

Bean, A S J (Anthony Collins Solicitors LLP) *D1 K1* Birmingham *p137* . . . 0121 200 3242

Bean, C J (Gaby Hardwicke) *S1* Eastbourne *p215*. . . 01323 435900

Bean, R T (Yorkshire Electricity Group PLC) Leeds *p463* . . . 0113 289 2123

Beange, D (Ison Harrison) Leeds *p274* . . . 0113 284 5000

Beanland, C (The College of Law Chester) Chester *p454* . . . 0800 289997

Bear, D L (DAC Beachcroft) *N O Q Zj* London EC4 *p24*. . . 020 7936 2222

Bearcroft, Mrs S M (Mills & Reeve) *E* Cambridge *p175*. . . 01223 364422

Beard, A C W (Tozers) *P E R1 C1 L N* Exeter *p222* . . . 01392 207020

Beard, D P (Higgs & Sons) *C1 C2 Ze C3 J1* Brierley Hill *p158*. . . 0845 111 5050

Beard, M P (Dawson Cornwell) *T1 T2 W* London WC1 *p26* . . . 020 7242 2556

Beard, R J (Thomson Snell & Passmore) *O L Zl* Tunbridge Wells *p415* . . . 01892 510000

Beard, R J (Laytons) *O Q N Ze* London EC4 *p52*. . . 020 7842 8000

Beardmore, I D (Flint Bishop Solicitors) *E* Derby *p208* . . . 01332 340211

Beardmore, M (DLA Piper UK LLP) Birmingham *p137* . . . 0870 011 1111

Beards, J S (Fulchers of Farnborough) *G H J1* Farnborough *p224*. . . 01252 522475

Beardsley, Ms A M (Allen & Overy LLP) London E1 *p5* . . . 020 3088 0000

Beardsmore, D B (Vincent & Co) *S1 K1 Q* Wigan *p432* . . . 01942 241421

Beardsworth, M (Kingsley Napley) *G* London EC1 *p50*. . . 020 7814 1200

Beardwood, M P (DLA Piper UK LLP) *E R2 S2* Liverpool *p287*. . . 0870 011 1111

Beardwood, O J H (Linskills Solicitors) *G H* Liverpool *p289*. . . 0151 236 2224

Beare, S N (Reed Smith LLP) *Za* London EC2 *p71*. . . 020 3116 3000

Bearham, Ms D Y (Deborah Bearham & Co) Tadworth *p407*. . . 01737 812707

Bearman, A (Russell-Cooke LLP) *J1* London SW15 *p74*. . . 020 8789 9111

Bearman, Mrs C M (Ash Clifford) *W S1 A1* Bridgwater *p157* . . . 01278 451327

Bearman, C P (Saunders Bearman LLP) *S2 E R2 S1 L W R1 Zc Zv* London W1 *p76* . . . 020 7224 2618

Bearman, Mrs S L (Nottinghamshire County Council Legal Services Division) West Bridgford *p475*. . . 0115 977 3478

Bearn, Ms K M (LG Lawyers) London SE1 *p50*. . . 020 7379 0000

Bearne, Ms A (HRJ Law LLP) Welwyn Garden City *p425* . . 01707 887700

Bearpark, Miss L E (Hewitsons) *J1* Cambridge *p174*. . . 01223 461155

Beashel, Ms R (Beashel Solicitors) *D1 K1 K3 D2* Warminster *p421*. . . 01985 220680

Beasley, Mrs G R (Peterborough City Council) Peterborough *p468* . . . 01733 747474

Beasley, Ms J (Quality Solicitors Burroughs Day) Bristol *p164* . . . 0117 929 0333

Beasley, S (Beasley Johnson Loyns) *N* Walsall *p419*. . . 01922 644433

Beasley, S M (T A Capron & Co) *K3 A3 J1 K1 L N O Q R1 Zc Ze Zj Zk* Grays *p233* . . . 01375 378331

Beasley, T J (Levenes Solicitors) *G H N* Birmingham *p140* . . . 0121 212 0000; Haringey *p53* . 020 8881 7777 / 8881 6764

Beastall, J R (Clifford Chance) London E14 *p20*. . . 020 7006 1000

Beat, J A (Child & Child) *Q O Zc L A3 J1 Zl* London SW1 *p20* . . . 020 7235 8000

Beaton, M J (Ashton KCJ) *S1 E* Bury St Edmunds *p171* . . . 01284 762331

Beatson, Miss K (Anthony Gold) *K1 K2 D1 K3* London SE1 *p6* . . . 020 7940 4000

Beattie, Miss J J B (Wedlake Bell LLP) *S1 W E L* London WC1 *p91* . . . 020 7395 3000

Beattie, Ms K (Taylor Wessing) London EC4 *p86*. . . 020 7300 7000

Beattie, R H (Toller Beattie LLP) *A1 C1 E F1 K1 L R1 S1 T1 W Zc Zo* Barnstaple *p125* . . . 01271 341000

Beattie, Ms V (Co-operative Insurance Society Ltd) Manchester *p464* . . . 0161 832 8686; Manchester *p311* . . . 0161 832 2500

Beaty, R J G (DAC Beachcroft) London EC3 *p24*. . . 020 7208 6800

Beaumont, C (Scutt Beaumont Solicitors Ltd) Leicester *p281*. . . 0116 254 4200

Beaumont, C S (Kirkland & Lane) *C1 E S1 S2 N* Southwell *p389* . . 01636 813128 / 812180

Beaumont, G (London Borough of Wandsworth) London SW18 *p110* . . . 020 8871 6000

Beaumont, G F (MKB Solicitors LLP) *D1 F1 K1 L Q S1 W V J1 Zl* Barnsley *p124*. . . 01226 210000

Beaumont, M (KBL Solicitors) *E C1 R1 Zc* Bolton *p149* . . . 01204 527777

Beaumont, Ms R (Russell-Cooke LLP) *E* London SW15 *p74*. . . 020 8789 9111

Beaumont, Miss R (Last Cawthra Feather LLP) *O* Bradford *p154* . . . 01274 848800

Beaumont, Ms R J (Reynolds Porter Chamberlain LLP) London E1 *p71* . . . 020 3060 6000

Beaumont, R N (Gordon Lutton) *K1 D1 K2 O N Q* Hereford *p248* . . . 01432 355345

Beaumont, Mrs S J (Borneo Hughes Martell LLP) *K1 P H G M1 F1 D1 S1 N L Zl Zk* Northampton *p331*. . . 01604 624822

Beauvoisin, M A (McNamara Ryan) *S2 E L S1 W* Weybridge *p430*. . . 01932 846041

Beaven, Miss K J (Barker Gotelee Solicitors) *K1 S1 K2 K3* Ipswich *p262*. . . 01473 611211

Beavis, K F (The Beavis Partnership) *S1 W L N E G* Witham *p435* . . . 01376 500255

Beazleigh, G (Plexus Law (A Trading Name of Parabis Law LLP)) London EC3 *p68*. . . 0844 245 4000

Beazley, Mrs E L (Atherton Godfrey) *N* Doncaster *p211* . . . 01302 320621

Bebawi, A (EMI Music Publishing Ltd) London W8 *p106* . . . 020 3059 3059

Bebbington-Plant, Mrs A (Cullimore Dutton) *W S1* Chester *p190* . . . 01244 356789

Bechares, S J (MLM Cartwright) *E S1 S2 U1* Cardiff *p179* . . . 029 2046 2562

Bechelet, J F (Bivonas Limited Solicitors) *E O* London EC3 *p13*. . . 020 7337 2600

Becirevic, A (Paragon Law) *Zi* Nottingham *p338*. . . 0115 964 4123

Beck, A (Walker Morris) *L O Q Zl* Leeds *p277* . . . 0113 283 2500

Beck, B J (Jeffreys & Powell) *S1 L A1 S2 E* Brecon *p156*. . . 01874 622106

Beck, Ms C (Irwin Mitchell LLP) *G H D1 D2 K1* Sheffield *p376* . . . 0870 150 0100

Beck, Ms J (TV Edwards LLP) *K1 K2 D1* London EC3 *p85*. . . 020 7790 7000

Beck, P J (Quinn Melville) *J1 Zm* Liverpool *p290*. . . 0151 236 3340

Beck, Miss S (Ford & Warren) *Zj B2* Leeds *p273* . . . 0113 243 6601

Beck, Mrs S (Taylor Bracewell) Doncaster *p212* . . . 01302 341414

Beck, S (Whitehead Monckton) Maidstone *p299* . . . 01622 698000

Beck, Ms S (King & Spalding International LLP) London EC2 *p49*. . . 020 7551 7500

Beck, Ms S (Simmons & Simmons) London EC2 *p79*. . . 020 7628 2020

Becker, A (J Pearlman) *S1 E S2* London NW11 *p66*. . . 020 8458 9266

Becker, M S (Curtis) *B1 J1 K1 J2 L Zl O Q N Zp* Plymouth *p349*. . . 01752 204444

Becker, S N (Stanley Tee) *G H Zl V* Bishop's Stortford *p144* . . . 01279 755200

Beckerley, P A (Rausa Mumford) *N O* Cardiff *p180* . . . 029 2034 4341

Beckett, Mrs A J (Cooper Sons Hartley & Williams) *S2 S1* Buxton *p172*. . . 01298 77511

Beckett, Miss C A (C R Burton & Co) *G H D1* London SE20 *p16* . 020 8778 4455 / 8659 5775

Beckett, C B (Inghams) *K1 D2 D1* Fleetwood *p226* . . . 01253 873481

Beckett, Mrs D M (Beckett & Co) *N Q O* Preston *p356* . . . 01772 315200

Beckett, Mrs J (Max Gold Law) *W S1* Hull *p257* . . . 01482 224900; Scunthorpe *p373*. . . 01724 871999

Beckett, J G (Parker Bird Gardner) *S2 E* Huddersfield *p256* . . . 01484 825200

Beckett, Mrs M P (Inghams) *N* Blackpool *p146* . . . 01253 626642

Beckett, M R (Dyfed Powys Police Authority) Carmarthen *p453* . . . 01267 226440

Beckett, Miss P L (Wilson & Co) *K1 D2 D1* London N17 *p92*. . . 020 8808 7535

Beckett, R G (DLA Piper UK LLP) *E R1 Zc R2 S2* Manchester *p303* . . . 0870 011 1111

Beckett, S (Magrath LLP) London W1 *p57* . . . 020 7495 3003

Beckford-Stennett, Ms E (Stennett & Stennett) London N14 *p82* . . . 020 8920 3190

Beckitt, J P (CMS Cameron McKenna LLP) *E* London EC3 *p17*. . . 020 7367 3000

Beckman, B C (DWFM Beckman) *W E S1 C1 S2* Westminster *p25*. . . 020 7872 0023

Beckman, N I (DWFM Beckman) *C1 E L S1 Zc Ze S2* Westminster *p25*. . . 020 7872 0023

Beckman, P (DWFM Beckman) *C1 E L S1 S2* Westminster *p25*. . . 020 7872 0023

Beckwith, N J (Gosschalks) *C1 T1 A1* Hull *p256* . . . 01482 324252

Beckwith, S M (Plexus Law (A Trading Name of Parabis Law LLP)) London EC3 *p68*. . . 0844 245 4000

Beckworth, V A (Elliot Mather LLP) *K1 D1 G H* Chesterfield *p192* . . . 01246 231288

Beddoe, Mrs B E C (Ison Harrison) *K1 K3 D1* Garforth *p228* . . . 0113 286 1455

Beddoes, P C (Wright Hassall LLP) *C1 C2* Leamington Spa *p270* . . . 01926 886688

Beddow, Ms H (Powell Eddison Freeman & Wilks) *W T2* Harrogate *p240* . . . 01423 564551

Beddow, S J (Wall James Chappell) *J1 O Q* Stourbridge *p399* . . . 01384 371622

Beddows, Miss J (The Wilkes Partnership LLP) *W* Birmingham *p143* . . . 0121 233 4333

Beddows, Miss K E (Lodders Solicitors LLP) *C1 C2 J1* Stratford-upon-Avon *p400* . . 01789 293259

Bedford, Mrs A L (Pickering & Butters) *K1 N*
Stafford *p393* . . . 01785 603060

Bedford, Mrs C A (HM Land Registry - Plymouth) *S1 E W*
Plymouth *p468* . . . 01752 636000 / 636123

Bedford, J B P A (Stevens & Bolton) *O C1 N Q Zn*
Guildford *p237* . . . 01483 302264

Bedford, P H D (Allen & Overy LLP)
London E1 *p5* . . . 020 3088 0000

Bedford, R (Bedfords) *K1 L O Q N S1 W*
Somerton *p383* . . . 01458 888153

Bedford, R A J (Machins Solicitors LLP) *N J1 Zp Q O Zq*
Luton *p295* . . . 01582 514000

Bedford, R J (Burges Salmon) *A1 N P L F1*
Bristol *p161* . . . 0117 939 2000

Bedford, S (Linklaters LLP)
London EC2 *p54* . . . 020 7456 2000

Bedi, Ms A (Financial Services Authority)
London E14 *p106* . . . 020 7066 1000

Bednarczyk, M S (Hart Brown Solicitors) *N Q Zr*
Guildford *p236* . . . 0800 068 8177

Bee, G P (Harris Cartier LLP) *N*
Slough *p382* . . . 01753 810710

Bee, T J M (Addleshaw Goddard)
London EC1 *p4* . . . 020 7606 8855
Manchester *p300* . . . 0161 934 6000

Beech, Mrs A J (Percy Hughes & Roberts) *N*
Birkenhead *p134* . . . 0151 666 9090

Beech, D W (David W Beech) *T2 W*
Westminster *p11* . . . 020 7493 4932

Beech, Mrs H L (ClarksLegal LLP) *J1 N O Q Zo Zp*
Reading *p360* . . . 0118 958 5321

Beech, M E (Heatons LLP) *M1 A3 B1 C1 O Ze*
Manchester *p305* . . . 0161 835 8010

Beech, R C T (Cocks Lloyd) *A1 C1 E L R1 S1 Zc*
Nuneaton *p339* . . . 024 7664 1642

Beecham, Sir J H (Beecham Peacock) *S1 K1 H W T1 J1 N G C1 E Zk Zl*
Newcastle upon Tyne *p323* . . . 0191 232 3048

Beecham, M (Poole Townsend) *K1 D1 Q L*
Barrow-in-Furness *p125* . . . 01229 811811

Beecham, N C (Field Fisher Waterhouse LLP)
London EC3 *p31* . . . 020 7861 4000

Beechey, J (Clifford Chance)
London E14 *p20* . . . 020 7006 1000

Beeching, Mrs P M H (Stallard March & Edwards) *K1 D1 J1*
Worcester *p440* . . . 01905 613404

Beechinor, Ms G (Sacker & Partners LLP) *Zo*
London EC2 *p76* . . . 020 7329 6699

Beedham, A J (Clarke Willmott) *C1 C2 Zb M2 B1 M1 C3 U2 T1 S2 E*
Birmingham *p136* 0845 209 1000 / 0117 305 6000

Beedham, G (British Telecommunications PLC)
London EC1 *p104* . . . 020 7356 6181

Beeharry, K (Goodman Ray) *K1*
Hackney *p36* . . . 020 7608 1227

Beeharry, Mrs R (Hart Brown Solicitors) *S1*
Woking *p437* . . . 0800 068 8177

Beekarry, Miss D (Attwaters) *K1 D1*
Loughton *p294* . . . 020 8508 2111

Beeley, C A (Millichips) *K1 N F1 J1 L Q Zq*
West Bromwich *p427* . . . 0121 500 6363

Beeley, H W (Machins Solicitors LLP) *S2 A1 S1 E L*
Luton *p295* . . . 01582 514000

Beer, D L L (Essex County Council)
Chelmsford *p454* . . . 0845 743 0430

Beer, M C (Brown Beer Nixon Mallon) *G H*
Redcar *p362* . . . 01642 490202

Beer, P (Taylor Wessing)
London EC4 *p86* . . . 020 7300 7000

Beesley, J M S (Laytons) *R2 S1 S2*
London EC4 *p52* . . . 020 7842 8000

Beesley, M J (Shakespeares) *O J1*
Birmingham *p142* . . . 0121 237 3000

Beesley, P F B (Lee Bolton Monier-Williams) *S1 W R1 E A1 J1 L X Zd Zx*
Westminster *p52* . . . 020 7222 5381

Beesley, Miss S (Plexus Law (A Trading Name of Parabis Law LLP)) *N Q*
Evesham *p220* . . . 01386 769160

Beesley-Hewitt, A (Hegarty LLP) *K4 T2 W*
Peterborough *p347* . . . 01733 346333

Beeson, Miss C (Woodroffes)
Westminster *p93* . . . 020 7730 0001

Beeson, G K (Mayo Wynne Baxter LLP) *S1*
Lewes *p283* . . . 01273 477071

Beeson, P G (Thames Water Utilities Limited)
Reading *p469* . . . 0118 373 8000

Beeson, Ms S C (LG Lawyers)
London SE1 *p50* . . . 020 7379 0000

Beeson, S R (Beesons) *S1 S2 W*
Milton Keynes *p316* . . . 01908 271171

Beevers, Miss L C (Ramsdens Solicitors) *K1 D2 D1 K3*
Huddersfield *p256* . . . 01484 821500

Beevers, P (Atteys) *O Zq B1 F1 A3*
Barnsley *p124* . . . 01226 212345

Beevers, P J (Eastgate Assistance Ltd) *F1 Q N K1 W G S1 Zq*
Colchester *p455* . . . 0870 523 4500

Beezer, T M (Bond Pearce LLP) *O Q Zf Zk Ze*
Southampton *p385* . . . 0845 415 0000

Beg, Mrs A P (RWP Solicitors) *L S2 E S1 J1*
Pangbourne *p345* . . . 0118 984 2266

Beg, Ms F (ML Law Ltd) *O Q K1 S1*
Eastleigh *p216* . . . 023 8060 0661

Beg, Miss U S (Gill & Co) *S1 S2 W*
Ilford *p260* . . . 020 8554 8774

Begbie, A D (Richards Solicitors) *B1 C1 F1 G J1 K1 L N O*
Edgware *p217* . . . 020 8731 5929

Beggs, Ms D (SNR Denton)
London EC4 *p75* . . . 020 7242 1212

Beggs, Miss K (Ashton Bond Gigg) *W*
Nottingham *p335* . . . 0115 947 6651

Begley, W (Speechly Bircham LLP) *W T2*
London EC4 *p81* . . . 020 7427 6400

Begner, L (Howard Kennedy LLP) *R2*
London W1 *p48* . . . 020 7636 1616

Begner, Ms S (Mayer Brown International LLP) *Q*
London EC2 *p59* . . . 020 3130 3000

Begum, Ms P (Bedfordshire County Council)
Bedford *p448* . . . 01234 363222

Begum, Miss R (Bolton Metropolitan Borough Council)
Bolton *p450* . . . 01204 333333

Begum, Miss R (DW Solicitors) *S1 K3 K1*
Northampton *p331* . . . 01604 624222

Begum, R (Painters) *K1 Zo*
Stourport-on-Severn *p399* . . . 01299 822033

Begum, Ms S (Scott Rees & Co) *N Q*
Skelmersdale *p381* . . . 01695 722222

Begum, Miss S (Male & Wagland) *W S1 K1 J1*
Potters Bar *p355* . . . 01707 657171

Begum, Miss U N (Isherwood & Hose) *S1 S2 W*
Heywood *p249* . . . 01706 360032 / 368741

Behal, P (Taylor Phillips)
Hayes *p245* . . . 020 8561 7367

Behan, Miss L (American Express Bank Ltd)
London RH15 *p103* . . . 020 7824 6000

Beharrell, J S K (Gosschalks) *E L*
Hull *p256* . . . 01482 324252

Behr, Mrs S A L B (Behr & Co) *K1 D1 D2 K4*
Brynmawr *p167* . . . 01495 310581

Behrens, P (Ashurst LLP)
London EC2 *p7* . . . 020 7638 1111

Beidas, Mrs C E (Owen White) *S2 E*
Slough *p382* . . . 01753 876800

Beigel, N N (Norman Beigel & Co) *E L*
London NW11 *p11* . . . 020 8455 8183

Beighton, J S (Beightons) *W E S1 L*
Derby *p208* . . . 01332 346430

Beighton, Mrs M P (North Yorkshire County Council)
Northallerton *p467* . . . 01609 780780

Beighton, R (Hamnett Osborne Tisshaw) *G H B2*
Haywards Heath *p245* . . . 01444 443030

Beilby, Miss H M (Rupert Wood & Son) *K1 D1*
Ashton-under-Lyne *p120* . . . 0161 330 9121

Beiley, R (Trowers & Hamlins)
London EC3 *p88* . . . 020 7423 8000

Beirne, K H (Morrison & Foerster (UK) LLP) *O Q*
London EC2 *p62* . . . 020 7920 4000

Beirne, Ms N M (Reed Smith LLP) *Zb Zv*
London EC2 *p71* . . . 020 3116 3000

Belchak, Miss P H (Kingsley Napley) *Zi*
London EC1 *p50* . . . 020 7814 1200

Belcher, Mrs A M (Warwickshire County Council)
Warwick *p475* . . . 01926 410410

Belcher, C (Farrer & Co LLP) *W T2*
London WC2 *p31* . . . 020 3375 7000

Belcher, N G M (Spratt Endicott) *E S2*
Banbury *p122* . . . 01295 204000

Belcher, N J (Nockolds) *A1 W C1 E Zl Zy S2 R1 A2 J1 S1*
Bishop's Stortford *p144* . . . 01279 755777

Belcher, Mrs P D (Driver Belcher Solicitors)
Bishop's Waltham *p144* . . . 01489 892101 / 892102

Belcher, Mrs P D (Driver Belcher Solicitors) *D1 G H J1 K1 L N O Q F1 S1*
Southampton *p385* . . . 01489 785737

Belcher, P L (GSC Solicitors) *S1 E L*
London EC1 *p34* . . . 020 7822 2222

Belcher, Mrs P M (Squire Sanders (UK) LLP) *L*
Leeds *p277* . . . 0113 284 7000

Belcher, W (Ashurst LLP)
London EC2 *p7* . . . 020 7638 1111

Belderbos, J A (Bird Wilford & Sale) *Q G K1 K2 Zl N*
Loughborough *p293* . . . 01509 232611

Belfield, S (Frisby & Co) *G J1 B2 N P J2 F1*
Stafford *p392* . . . 01785 244114

Belfield, Mrs S K (Kingston upon Hull City Council)
Hull *p461* . . . 01482 300300

Belina, Miss S (Over Taylor Biggs) *J1 C2 C1 E*
Exeter *p222* . . . 01392 823811

Bell, A (McDermott Will & Emery UK LLP)
London EC2 *p56* . . . 020 7577 6900

Bell, A (Plexus Law (A Trading Name of Parabis Law LLP)) *N Q*
London EC3 *p68* . . . 0844 245 4000

Bell, Ms A (Department for Business, Enterprise and Regulatory Reform)
London SW1 *p105* . . . 020 7215 0105

Bell, A (Reynolds Porter Chamberlain LLP)
London E1 *p71* . . . 020 3060 6000

Bell, A (Irwin Mitchell LLP) *B1 E Zl S1*
Manchester *p306* . . . 0870 150 0100

Bell, A (Manches LLP) *T1 C2*
London WC2 *p58* . . . 020 7404 4433

Bell, A J (Scott Duff & Co) *S1 W L Zh*
Penrith *p346* . . . 01768 865551

Bell, A J (Barlow Lyde & Gilbert LLP)
London EC3 *p10* . . . 020 7247 2277

Bell, Ms A J (Nelsons) *G*
Nottingham *p338* . . . 0115 958 6262

Bell, Mrs A L (Pannone LLP) *N*
Manchester *p308* . . . 0161 909 3000

Bell, B (Linklaters LLP) *C1 Zb*
London EC2 *p54* . . . 020 7456 2000

Bell, Miss B M (Dickins Shiebert) *S1 S2 W L E*
Potters Bar *p355* . . . 01707 851100

Bell, Mrs C A (Mercers)
Henley-on-Thames *p247* . . . 01491 572138

Bell, Ms C A (LG Lawyers) *O W Zq*
London SE1 *p50* . . . 020 7379 0000

Bell, Mrs C E (Actons) *J1 O Q*
Nottingham *p335* . . . 0115 910 0200

Bell, C J C (Taylor Wessing) *E L R1 B1 O A1 S1 Zh Zs Zn*
London EC4 *p86* . . . 020 7300 7000

Bell, C P (Brabners Chaffe Street) *Ze C1 U2 Zza Zf U1 F1 F2 Zz*
Liverpool *p286* . . . 0151 600 3000

Bell, D (Taylor Wessing)
London EC4 *p86* . . . 020 7300 7000

Bell, D G (Stevens) *G H*
Stoke-on-Trent *p398* . . . 01782 343353

Bell, D G (Evans Powell & Co) *D1 F1 J1 K1 L S1 N Q K3*
Llanelli *p292* . . . 01554 772632

Bell, Miss D J (Hollis & Co) *G H*
Sutton-in-Ashfield *p404* . . . 01623 443344

Bell, D M (Battens) *D1 G H K1 Q F1 Zm*
Dorchester *p212* . . . 01305 250560

Bell, D W (Edell Jones & Lessers) *Q N S1 L W*
London E6 *p28* . . . 020 8548 5700

Bell, Mrs E (Symes Bains Broomer) *K4 T1 W*
Scunthorpe *p373* . . . 01724 281616

Bell, Miss F L (Memery Crystal) *T1 T2 W*
London WC2 *p60* . . . 020 7242 5905

Bell, Ms G (Alderson Dodds) *S2 E S1 L*
Blyth *p147* . . . 01670 352293

Bell, G (Ashurst LLP)
London EC2 *p7* . . . 020 7638 1111

Bell, G (Thomson Snell & Passmore) *N Zr*
Tunbridge Wells *p415* . . . 01892 510000

Bell, G F (Pinsent Masons LLP)
London EC2 *p67* . . . 020 7418 7000

Bell, G J (Stanley Tee) *C1 C2 Ze A1 I F1*
Bishop's Stortford *p144* . . . 01279 755200

Bell, G T (DWF) *E S2 R2 Zc S1*
Liverpool *p287* . . . 0151 907 3000

Bell, Ms H (Bell Lax Litigation) *O N Q A3 Zc Zq K1 K2 K3*
Sutton Coldfield *p403* . . . 0121 355 0011

Bell, Miss H E (Gedye & Sons (Solicitors) Ltd) *W S1 E*
Grange-over-Sands *p232* . . . 01539 532313

Bell, J (Bell Park Kerridge) *N O Q J1 F1 Zm Zr*
Carlisle *p181* . . . 01228 888999

Bell, J (Kirby Sheppard) *J1*
Bristol *p163* . . . 0845 840 0045

Bell, Mrs J (Backhouse Jones Ltd) *C1 E C2 T1 Zb B1 S2*
Clitheroe *p196* . . . 01254 828300

Bell, Miss J (Guest Walker & Co) *S1 W*
York *p444* . . . 01904 624903

Bell, J (Ashurst LLP) *C1 Zo*
London EC2 *p7* . . . 020 7638 1111

Bell, Mrs J (Slough Borough Council) *S1 W*
Slough *p471* . . . 01753 552288

Bell, Mrs J C (Gammon Bell & Co) *S1 E N W K1 C1 F1 L R1 B1 Zv Zl*
Eastleigh *p216* . . . 023 8068 4900

Bell, J D (Mundays LLP)
Cobham *p196* . . . 01932 590500

Bell, Mrs J E (Roach Pittis) *K1*
Newport *p328* . . . 01983 524431

Bell, J H (First National Banks PLC)
Caerphilly *p452* . . . 029 2086 0133

Bell, J N (Joseph N Bell) *W K4 O Q*
Lewes *p283* . . . 01273 897377

Bell, Miss L (TMJ Legal Services LLP) *D2 D1 K3 K1*
Hartlepool *p243* . . . 01429 235616

Bell, Ms L (Bell & Buxton) *K1*
Sheffield *p375* . . . 0114 249 5969

Bell, Miss L D (Pannone LLP) *J1*
Manchester *p308* . . . 0161 909 3000

Bell, Mrs M (SA Law) *K1 D1*
St Albans *p390* . . . 01727 798000

Bell, Mrs M (Frisby & Co) *G B2 J2*
Stafford *p392* . . . 01785 244114

Bell, M A (Harold Bell & Co) *C1 E L M1 R1 S1 T1 A1 J1 N Zv Zi Zj*
Ewell *p220* . . . 020 8393 0231

Bell, M F (Scarborough Borough Council)
Scarborough *p470* . . . 01723 232348

Bell, M G (Osborne Clarke) *T1*
Bristol *p164* . . . 0117 917 3000

Bell, M R (Ben Hoare Bell & Co) *K1 G D1 H F1 V S1*
Sunderland *p401* . . . 0191 516 0466

Bell, M R (Whitehead Monckton) *Zd W T2 T1*
Maidstone *p299* . . . 01622 698000

Bell, N (Stevens) *G H*
Stafford *p393* . . . 01785 250908

Bell, Mrs N (Beswicks) *G*
Hanley *p239* . . . 01782 205000

Bell, N T H (Cherwell District Council) *Q O J1 K1*
Banbury *p448* . . . 01295 252535

Bell, N W (Shentons) *D1 F1 G H J1 K1 L N S1*
Winchester *p434* . . . 01962 844544

Bell, Miss O A (Bromleys Solicitors LLP) *K1 D1 D2*
Ashton-under-Lyne *p120* . . . 0161 330 6821

Bell, Mrs P (Hewitsons) *S2 E S1*
Northampton *p332* . . . 01604 233233

Bell, P B (Irwin Mitchell LLP) *G N O Q J1 Zl Zj Zk B2*
Leeds *p274* . . . 0870 150 0100

Bell, P J (Crutes) *N Q O*
Newcastle upon Tyne *p324* . . . 0191 233 9700

Bell, Ms R (Pengelly & Rylands) *W S1 K1 N J1*
Tenterden *p410* . . . 01580 762248 / 763008

Bell, R (Speechly Bircham LLP) *C3 M1 U2 O C2 U1 I*
London EC4 *p81* . . . 020 7427 6400

Bell, R I (Bedwell Watts & Co) *S1 W A1 E T1 C1 R1 K1 J1 F1*
Scarborough *p372* . . . 01723 373356 / 363553

Bell, R J (Haworth Holt Bell Limited) *O E C1 K1 C3 L B1 J1 T1 Ze N F1*
Altrincham *p116* . . . 0161 928 7136

Bell, R P G (Mullis & Peake) *E L A1 C1 R1 S1 Zl S2*
Romford *p366* . . . 01708 784000

Bell, R S (Darbys Solicitors LLP) *S2 E R1 S1 A1*
Oxford *p343* . . . 01865 811700

Bell, R W (ASB Law) *C1 C2 Zi Ze*
Crawley *p202* . . . 01293 603600

Bell, Ms S (DLA Piper UK LLP)
Liverpool *p287* . . . 0870 011 1111

Bell, Ms S (DWF) *C1 C2 F1*
Liverpool *p287* . . . 0151 907 3000

Bell, Ms S (Stephens & Scown) *K1*
Truro *p414* . . . 01872 265100

Bell, Miss S (Hodge Jones & Allen LLP) *L*
London NW1 *p41* . . . 020 7874 8300

Bell, S (KBL Solicitors) *S1 S2 E R2 R1*
Bolton *p149* . . . 01204 527777
Preston *p357* . . . 01772 888700

Bell, Ms S C (City of Bradford Metropolitan District Council)
Bradford *p451* . . . 01274 752236

Bell, S C (Norfolk County Council - Legal Services)
Norwich *p467* . . . Minicom: 0844 800 8011

Bell, S E (Steadman Jones & Bell) *N D1 F1 J1 K1 Q W S1 Zj Zl Zt*
Ammanford *p118* . . . 01269 592306

Bell, Miss S L (Batchelors Solicitors) *L Q O W Zh K4*
Bromley *p166* . . . 020 8768 7000

Bell, S N (Bhatia Best) *Q N*
Nottingham *p336* . . . 0115 950 3231

Bell, S T (Backhouse Jones Ltd) *Q C2 C1 Zt B1 E*
Clitheroe *p196* . . . 01254 828300

Bell, Ms V (Kennedys)
London EC3 *p49* . . . 020 7667 9667

Bell, W S (North Lincolnshire Council)
Scunthorpe *p470* . . . 01724 296296

Bell, Miss Z E (Isherwood & Hose) *W K4 N*
Rochdale *p365* . . . 01706 359190 / 522225

Bellamy, Miss E J (Drummonds) *S1 S2 E*
Chester *p190* . . . 01244 408300

Bellamy, P A (Linder Myers Solicitors) *E S1 C1 W A1 B1 T1*
Manchester *p307* . . . 0844 984 6400

Bellamy, P J (Gowmans) *S1 S2*
Paignton *p345* . . . 01803 546100

Bellamy, Ms S V (Orange PCS Ltd)
Bristol *p452* . . . 0870 376 8888

Bellau, D M (Hamlins LLP)
London W1 *p38* . . . 020 7355 6000

Bellavia, G A S (Harding Evans LLP) *G L Q O A3 Zb Zq B1 Zw*
Newport *p328* . . . 01633 244233

Bellchamber, D C (David Bellchamber & Co)
Cobham *p196* . . . 01932 702233

Bellenger, G F W (Kidd Rapinet) *J1 J2 Zg Zi O Q Zp*
London WC2 *p49* . . . 020 7205 2115

Bellew, D (Veale Wasbrough Vizards) *C1 C2 T1*
Bristol *p165* . . . 0117 925 2020

Bellhouse, J M H (White & Case LLP)
London EC2 *p91* . . . 020 7532 1000

Bellhouse, J W (Wedlake Bell LLP) *A3 Zc R2 M1 Zj*
London WC1 *p91* . . . 020 7395 3000

Bellhouse, R M (Emsleys) *K1 D1 K3*
Castleford *p183* . . . 01977 550115

Belling, S D (Anthony Collins Solicitors LLP) *Zh C1 L Zd*
Birmingham *p137* . . . 0121 200 3242

Bellis, Miss A C (Henmans LLP) *O B1 Zb Zq Zj A3*
Oxford *p343* . . . 01865 781000

Bellis, Mrs B M (AIB Group (UK) PLC (Legal and Securities Dept))
Uxbridge *p474* . . . 01895 272222

Bellis, Ms J M S (Juliet Bellis & Co) *S2 L O E C1 S1*
Uckfield *p416* . . . 01825 750811

Bellis, M J (Noble) *G H*
Shefford *p377* . . . 01462 814055

Bellis, N D (Dickinson Dees) *C1 I*
Newcastle upon Tyne *p324* . . . 0191 279 9000

Bellis, P (QualitySolicitors C Turner) *S1 S2*
Blackburn *p145* . . . 01254 688400

Belliss, Miss C K (Bridgend County Borough Council)
Bridgend *p451* . . . 01656 643643

Bellman, M A J (Blanchards Bailey LLP) *S1*
Blandford Forum *p147* . . . 01258 459361

Bellringer, S (Fanshaw Porter & Hazlehurst) *B1 F1 K4 K1 Q S1 T2 W*
Birkenhead *p134* . . . 0151 647 4051

See p634 for the Key to Work Categories

Bellshaw, P A (CMHT Solicitors) *G N S1 Q V W H K1 L E Zm*
Brownhills *p167* 01543 372347
Walsall *p420*. 01922 646400

Belsham, Miss G S (Ince & Co Services Ltd)
London E1 *p44* 020 7481 0010

Belsham, Ms J A (Stuart Hurrion & Green) *S1*
Bexleyheath *p132* 020 8298 1595

Benavides, Ms A (MBNA Europe Bank Ltd)
Chester *p454* 01244 672002

Benbow, Ms C (Gloucestershire Magistrates' Courts)
Gloucester *p459*. 01452 420100

Benbow, I P (Molesworths Bright Clegg) *Q O L F1 C1 W Zk*
Rochdale *p365*. 01706 356666

Bendall, Mrs A E (Stallard March & Edwards) *S1 W*
Worcester *p440* 01905 613404

Bendall, Miss E M (Sternberg Reed) *D1 K1 G H Zm D2*
Barking *p123* 020 8591 3366

Bendall, Ms M (Veale Wasbrough Vizards) *O Q Zl Zq*
Bristol *p165* 0117 925 2020

Bendell, D H T (David Bendell & Co) *E F1 G H J1 K1 N Q S1 W Zl*
Hinckley *p250* 01455 619322

Bendell, I P (CMS Cameron McKenna LLP)
London EC3 *p17*. 020 7367 3000

Bendle, Ms C D (Henmans LLP) *W*
Oxford *p343* 01865 781000

Benedek, S P (Benedek Joels Solicitors) *E*
London NW11 *p12*. 020 8458 0005

Benedict, J C (Collins Long) *Zf Ze J1 C1*
Southwark *p21*. 020 7401 9800

Benefield, Ms R M (Davis Wood) *Q K1 G L F1 H N*
Bristol *p162* 0117 965 3504

Benest, Miss E C (Lucas & Wyllys) *K1 D1 V*
Great Yarmouth *p234* 01493 855555
Lowestoft *p294* 01502 500123

Benfield, Mrs E (Edward Hayes LLP) *D1 K1 K2 D2 K3*
Chichester *p192* 01243 781431

Benfield, Mrs S B (Ratcliffe Duce & Gammer LLP) *K1 S1 D1*
Reading *p361* 0118 957 4291

Benger, D J (Ward Benger)
London WC1 *p90* 020 7242 2900

Benger, N B (TWM Solicitors LLP) *C1 E S2 S1 L J1*
Leatherhead *p271* 01372 374148

Bengo, Ms T (Thomas Dunton Solicitors) *K1 D1 Q N W*
Orpington *p342* 01689 822554

Benguigui, M (Barlow Lyde & Gilbert LLP)
London EC3 *p10*. 020 7247 2277

Benhadj, Ms S (Dawson Cornwell) *K1 K3 D1 D2*
London WC1 *p26* 020 7242 2556

Benham, A D (Reed Smith LLP) *O M2 Q Za Zj*
London EC2 *p71*. 020 3116 3000

Benham, Ms A J (PricewaterhouseCoopers Legal LLP)
London SE1 *p69*. 020 7212 1616

Benham, J G (Alistair Keeble) *S1*
Clacton-on-Sea *p195* 01255 818900

Benham, N (Ashurst LLP)
London EC2 *p7* 020 7638 1111

Benison, Ms M A (HBOS PLC)
Halifax *p460*. 0870 600 5000

Benjamin, Mrs C (Teacher Stern LLP) *E S1*
London WC1 *p86* 020 7242 3191

Benjamin, Mrs C J (Durham County Council)
Durham *p457* 0191 383 3513

Benjamin, C R (W A G Davidson & Co) *E W S1 C1 T1 L*
London W3 *p26* 020 8992 4884

Benjamin, D (Berry Smith LLP) *O Q*
Cardiff *p177*. 029 2034 5511

Benjamin, Ms D G (Kingsley Napley) *E*
London EC1 *p50*. 020 7814 1200

Benjamin, J M (GSC Solicitors) *M2 M1 Ze Zf U2 O U1*
London EC1 *p34*. 020 7822 2222

Benjamin, K J (Vauxhall Motors Ltd)
Luton *p464* 01582 721122

Benjamin, M (Shammah Nicholls LLP) *S2 E R2*
Manchester *p309* 0161 832 9272

Benn, Ms M F J (Shelley & Co) *G H*
Cambridge *p175*. 01223 359441

Benn, Miss R (Frisby & Co) *B2 G H*
Stafford *p392* 01785 244114

Bennell, Mrs J E (Band Hatton LLP) *W K4 T2*
Coventry *p200*. 024 7663 2121

Benner, P C (Houseman Benner) *S1 W K1 R1 L S2 E*
Haywards Heath *p246* 01444 414081

Bennet, C (Carter Slater & Co) *G H*
Northampton *p331*. 01604 717505

Bennet, I D (Cadwalader Wickersham & Taft)
London WC2 *p17* 020 7170 8700

Bennett, A (Peter Peter & Wright) *S1 E A1 W C1 S2 K4 Zd Zc*
Bude *p168*. 01288 352101

Bennett, A (Ashfords LLP) *B1 C1 O*
Exeter *p220* 01392 337000

Bennett, Miss A C (Ann C Bennett) *W J1 X Zd Zi*
London SW3 *p12* 020 7352 7494

Bennett, B (Runnymede Borough Council)
Addlestone *p447*. 01932 838383

Bennett, B C (Woodfines LLP) *S2 E S1 A1 L*
Sandy *p372* 01767 680251

Bennett, Miss C (BLB Solicitors) *I N J1*
Trowbridge *p413*. 01225 755656

Bennett, Mrs C (Berry & Berry) *G H B2*
Maidstone *p299* 01622 690777

Bennett, Ms C (EDF Energy plc)
London SW1 *p106*. 020 7242 9050

Bennett, C F C G (Enever Freeman & Co) *B1 C1 E L S1 W F1 J1 O N Zi Zj Zm*
Ruislip *p368* 01895 634031

Bennett, Mrs C M (Coole & Haddock) *S1 W L K1*
Horsham *p253*. 01403 210200

Bennett, C P (Roythornes LLP) *O J1 N Q Ze Zy Zq Zt*
Spalding *p389* 01775 842500

Bennett, C W (Heppenstalls) *K1 K3*
Lymington *p296* 01590 689500
New Milton *p321*. 01425 610078

Bennett, D S (Gardner Croft LLP) *K3 D1 K1*
Canterbury *p176* 01227 813400

Bennett, E (Ashurst LLP)
London EC2 *p7* 020 7638 1111

Bennett, Miss E (Ouvry Creed Solicitors) *K4 Zo W T2 K1*
Tetbury *p410*. 01666 504005

Bennett, Mrs E A (Linklaters LLP)
London EC2 *p54*. 020 7456 2000

Bennett, Miss E D (Olswang LLP)
London WC1 *p64* 020 7067 3000

Bennett, Mrs F M (Wilkin Chapman Grange Solicitors) *C1 E R2 S1 S2*
Louth *p294* 01507 606161

Bennett, G (Bird & Lovibond) *O Q N*
Uxbridge *p417*. 01895 256151

Bennett, G A (Addleshaw Goddard)
Leeds *p271* 0113 209 2000
Manchester *p300* 0161 934 6000

Bennett, G M (Darbys Solicitors LLP) *G H J2 Zv B2*
Oxford *p343* 01865 811700

Bennett, G R (Shoosmiths) *E L B1 Zd*
Fareham *p224*. . . . 0370 086 6800 / 01489 616800

Bennett, G S (James B Bennett & Co) *B1 C1 E L R1 S1 T1 W Zh Zl*
Crawley *p202* 01293 544044

Bennett, Mrs H K (Plexus Law (A Trading Name of Parabis Law LLP)) *N Q*
Evesham *p220*. 01386 769160

Bennett, Miss J (Coffin Mew & Clover) *E L S1 Zh R1 Zs*
Fareham *p223* 01329 825617

Bennett, Miss J A (Askew Bunting Solicitors LLP) *K1*
Middlesbrough *p314* 01642 252555

Bennett, Miss J M (Family Law Consultants) *K1 D1 K3*
Cheltenham *p188* 01242 222201

Bennett, J W (Forbes) *N F1 L Q O Zj Zk Zq Zr*
Accrington *p114* 01254 872111

Bennett, Ms L (City of Sunderland)
Sunderland *p473*. 0191 520 5555

Bennett, Mrs L A (SAS Daniels LLP) *S2 C2 R1 E*
Stockport *p396*. 0161 475 7676

Bennett, L J (Gregory Abrams Davidson LLP) *S2 E*
Liverpool *p288* 0151 733 3353

Bennett, Mrs L J (Wolverhampton City Council)
Wolverhampton *p477* 01902 556556

Bennett, M (Taylor Wessing)
London EC4 *p86*. 020 7300 7000

Bennett, M (Osborne Clarke) *T1*
Bristol *p164* 0117 917 3000

Bennett, Ms M (Speechly Bircham LLP) *E L R2*
London EC4 *p81*. 020 7427 6400

Bennett, M J (Linklaters LLP)
London EC2 *p54*. 020 7456 2000

Bennett, M K G (Douglas Clift & Co) *N Q K1 D1 K3*
Lancaster *p269* 01524 32437

Bennett, M L (Kerman & Co LLP) *C2 C1*
London WC2 *p49* 020 7539 7272

Bennett, M M B (Brecher) *E S1 L S2 R2*
London W1 *p15* 020 7563 1000

Bennett, M P (Charles Russell LLP) *E R2*
London EC4 *p19*. 020 7203 5000

Bennett, M S (Brabners Chaffe Street) *Zw Ze I U2 Zf*
Manchester *p301* 0161 836 8800

Bennett, N (Donnelly McArdle Adamson)
Hartlepool *p243* 01429 274732

Bennett, N (Michael Simkins LLP) *Zf Zw*
London WC1 *p79* 020 7874 5600

Bennett, N A (Thompsons (formerly Robin/Brian Thompson & Partners)) *N Q O M2*
London WC1 *p87* 020 7290 0000

Bennett, N H (Bedfordshire County Council)
Bedford *p448* 01234 363222

Bennett, N J H (Bennetts Law Practice Ltd)
Clacton-on-Sea *p195* 01255 254400

Bennett, Ms P (DLA Piper UK LLP)
London EC2 *p24*. 0870 011 1111

Bennett, P (The Child Law Partnership) *D1 Q Zu*
Guildford *p236*. 01483 543790

Bennett, P G (Insley & Partners) *S1 W E B1 L P R1 J1 C1 M1 O Zl*
Bournemouth *p152*. 01202 510167

Bennett, P G (Bennett Griffin) *C1 O Zc Q J1 F1 F2*
Ferring *p225*. 01903 229999

Bennett, P H E (Dolmans) *N Zu Zw J2*
Cardiff *p178* 029 2034 5531

Bennett, P J (Hutchinson Thomas) *N Zr*
Neath *p320* 01639 645061

Bennett, P J (Treasury Solicitors Department) *B1 F1 J1 K1 L N O Q*
London WC2 *p110*. 020 7210 3000

Bennett, P L (The Endeavour Partnership LLP)
Stockton-on-Tees *p397* . . . 01642 610300

Bennett, P R (George Green LLP) *C1 U2 Zb*
Cradley Heath *p201* 01384 410410

Bennett, Mrs R H (Goughs) *W S1*
Chippenham *p193* 01249 444499

Bennett, R J (Holroyd & Co) *S1 E C1 O Q N W J1 F1 T1 Zc Zl Zp*
Huddersfield *p256* 01484 645464

Bennett, S (Leviten Thompson & Co) *K1 K3 D1 N*
Sheffield *p376* 0114 276 9321

Bennett, S (Blaser Mills) *G H*
High Wycombe *p249*. 01494 450171

Bennett, S (Hogan Lovells International LLP)
London EC1 *p42*. 020 7296 2000

Bennett, Ms S (Brabners Chaffe Street) *Zc E Q R1 S1*
Liverpool *p286*. 0151 600 3000

Bennett, S A (Simon Bennett)
Marlow *p313*. 01628 478088

Bennett, Mrs S A (Gallaher Ltd)
Weybridge *p476* 01932 859777

Bennett, Miss S B (Hempsons) *N Q Zr*
Manchester *p305* 0161 228 0011

Bennett, S C (Reed Smith LLP) *Q*
London EC2 *p71*. 020 3116 3000

Bennett, Miss S L (Smith Llewelyn Partnership) *K1 K3 D2*
Swansea *p405*. 01792 464444

Bennett, Ms S R (Bross Bennett) *K1 M1 S1 W*
London N6 *p16* 020 8340 0444

Bennett, T (Churchers) *W*
Fareham *p223*. 01329 822333

Bennett, Ms V (Department for Business, Enterprise and Regulatory Reform)
London SW1 *p105*. 020 7215 0105

Bennett, W (Stephen Burdon Solicitors) *G H*
Nottingham *p336*. 0115 950 0054

Bennett, W C (Milford & Dormor)
Chard *p184* . . . . . . 01460 65335 / 61000

Bennett, mr W G (Moeran Oughtred & Co) *C1 E L S1 Zi*
Watford *p423* 01923 256263

Bennett, W R (Gregory Rowcliffe Milners) *A1 A2 E R1 S1 Zl*
London WC1 *p37* 020 7242 0631

Bennett-Helps, Mrs A (Duffield Stunt)
Chelmsford *p186*. 01245 262351

Bennett-Matthews, Mrs S (Walsall Metropolitan Borough Council)
Walsall *p475*. 01922 650000

Bennetts, A (City of London Corporation)
London EC2 *p107* 020 7606 3030

Bennetts, D R (Blackhurst Swainson Goodier LLP) *S1 S2 E R2 C1 A1*
Lancaster *p269* 01524 32471

Bennetts, Miss N A (Maclachlan) *K1 K3 D1 D2*
Sherborne *p378* 01935 817736

Benneworth, R J (Turner Coulston) *S1 E Q N W O C1 F1 K1 J1*
Northampton *p333*. 01604 622101

Benney, Miss B (Field Fisher Waterhouse LLP)
London EC3 *p31*. 020 7861 4000

Benning, Miss L K (Blaser Mills) *S1*
High Wycombe *p249*. 01494 450171

Bennington, D (Jefferies Essex LLP) *F1 O Q C2 Zq*
Westcliff-on-Sea *p428* 01702 332311

Bennion, C R (Howes Percival LLP) *B1 C1 Zb*
Leicester *p280*. 0116 247 3500

Bennion, Ms T A (Pinkney Grunwells Lawyers LLP) *D1 K1*
Scarborough *p372*. 01723 352125

Benoy, J (Dar & Co)
Manchester *p303* 0161 225 3777

Benski, P M (Amber Valley Borough Council)
Ripley *p470* 01773 570222

Benskin, A J (Moss Solicitors LLP) *W K4 T2 N*
Loughborough *p293* 01509 217770

Benskin, Mrs L J (Hillyer McKeown LLP) *O C1 Q Zq*
Chester *p190* 01244 318131

Bensley, A W (Risdon Hosegood) *N S1 Q O E W G H L Zd Zj Zr*
Williton *p433*. 01984 632277

Benson, A (Andrew Jackson)
Hull *p257* 01482 325242

Benson, A (Byrne & Partners) *G B2 O*
London EC4 *p16*. 020 7842 1616

Benson, A J (Benson & Co) *A1 C1 E L S1*
Hastings *p243* 01424 433601

Benson, C (Leigh Day & Co) *J1 Zp*
London EC1 *p52*. 020 7650 1200

Benson, C d G (Wragge & Co LLP)
London EC1 *p93*. 0870 903 1000

Benson, C J (Taylor Wessing) *Ze Zf*
London EC4 *p86*. 020 7300 7000

Benson, Ms E M C (Barlow Lyde & Gilbert LLP)
London EC3 *p10*. 020 7247 2277

Benson, E R J (Browne Jacobson LLP) *J1 Zp*
Nottingham *p336*. 0115 976 6000

Benson, G N (Medlicott & Benson) *S1 W E F1 L X N Zd Zm*
London SW1 *p60* 020 7839 2818

Benson, Ms H (Henscott Solicitors) *G H*
London E17 *p40*. 0870 880 0007

Benson, Ms H (Leeds City Council)
Leeds *p462* 0113 224 3513

Benson, J (J A Kemp & Co)
London WC1 *p48* 020 7405 3292

Benson, J C (Burges Salmon) *E Zh L*
Bristol *p161* 0117 939 2000

Benson, J J (James Benson & Co) *G H*
Liverpool *p286*. 0151 236 8755

Benson, J W (Hart Reade) *W V T2 Zd*
Eastbourne *p215*. 01323 727321

Benson, Ms M (Harbottle & Lewis LLP)
London W1 *p38* 020 7667 5000

Benson, M J (Benson Watkins) *L R1 S1 W*
Swansea *p404*. 01792 704320

Benson, M P (Justices Clerks Office)
Stoke-on-Trent *p472*. 01782 845353

Benson, N (Manches LLP) *O E*
London WC2 *p58* 020 7404 4433
Crawley *p202* 01293 527744

Benson, N (Bermans LLP) *J1*
Liverpool *p286*. 0151 224 0500

Benson, Mrs S J (Hawley & Rodgers) *K1 V L N*
Nottingham *p337*. 0115 955 9000

Benson, T (Fletcher Dervish) *G H D1 B2 F1 Q Zq Zi*
Haringey *p33* 020 8800 4615

Benson, T (Tollers LLP) *N*
Corby *p199* 01536 276727

Benstock, A L (The Lister Croft Partnership) *W Zm Zb*
Pudsey *p358*. 0113 257 0526
Wakefield *p418* 0871 220 1333

Bentham, A (J A Kemp & Co)
London WC1 *p48* 020 7405 3292

Bentham, D (Brabners Chaffe Street) *Zw C1 Zf Ze U2 F1 F2 Zza C3 Zl*
Manchester *p301* 0161 836 8800

Bentham, P J (Addleshaw Goddard)
Manchester *p300* 0161 934 6000

Bentley, A D T (Bentley Solicitors) *N Zq Zr*
Crewe *p203* 01270 509800

Bentley, B (DLA Piper UK LLP) *O Zc*
Sheffield *p375* 0870 011 1111

Bentley, Mrs C (Knowles Benning)
Dunstable *p214* 01582 667711

Bentley, D J (Bentley & Co) *C1 C2*
Pudsey *p358*. 0113 236 0550

Bentley, Ms J (Nelsons)
Leicester *p280*. 0116 222 6666

Bentley, J (Michael Simkins LLP) *Zf*
London WC1 *p79* 020 7874 5600

Bentley, J T (Hay & Kilner) *E C1*
Newcastle upon Tyne *p325* . 0191 232 8345

Bentley, Mrs K E (Glaisyers Solicitors LLP) *A3 B1 O*
Manchester *p304* 0161 832 4666

Bentley, M (Anthony Clark & Co) *N Q F1 L J1 W F2 Zv*
Lincoln *p284*. 01522 512321

Bentley, M S (Irwin Mitchell LLP) *C1 Zc*
Sheffield *p376* 0870 150 0100

Bentley, N D (Irwin Mitchell LLP) *C1 I*
Leeds *p274* 0870 150 0100

Bentley, R A (Bentleys) *S1 C1 P M1 G H K1 L W F1 Zl Zf Zk*
Waltham Forest *p12* 020 8521 8751

Bentley, R T (Goad & Butcher) *A1 S1 E S2 W*
Settle *p374* 01729 823500

Bentley, Miss S A (Southerns) *K1 D1 G H L S1 V Zm*
Burnley *p169* 01282 422711

Bentley, S F (Tang Bentley & Jackson) *G H B2*
Fareham *p224*. 01329 220401

Benton, D M (Allen & Overy LLP)
London E1 *p5* 020 3088 0000

Benton, K J (Rollits LLP) *C1 C3 I Ze*
Hull *p258* 01482 323239

Bentzien, S R (Lattice Property Holdings Ltd)
Basingstoke *p448* 01256 308803

Benussi, Mrs D P (Benussi & Co) *K1 K2 M2 K3*
Birmingham *p135* 0121 248 4001

Benwell, G E (Blandy & Blandy) *W T2*
Reading *p360* 0118 951 6800

Benwell, N J O (Simmons & Simmons)
London EC2 *p79*. 020 7628 2020

Benyon-Tinker, Miss E L (Tozers) *K1 K3*
Exeter *p222* 01392 207020

Benz, R L (Kidd Rapinet) *E C1 S2 C2*
Aylesbury *p121* 0845 017 9616

Benzecry, E C (CMS Cameron McKenna LLP) *E R1 P Zb*
London EC3 *p17*. 020 7367 3000

Benzeval, A J (Stewarts Law LLP) *N*
London EC4 *p83*. 020 7822 8000

Beoku-Betts, D S E (Joint Council for the Welfare of Immigrants) *Zi G H*
London EC1 *p107* 020 7251 8708

Beppu, R (Simmons & Simmons)
London EC2 *p79*. 020 7628 2020

Berardi, Miss M (Sheridans) *O Q Zf*
London WC1 *p78* 020 7079 0100

Bercow, A S (Stephenson Harwood) *N J1 B1 Ze*
London EC2 *p82*. 020 7329 4422

Bereford, J (Dicksons Solicitors Ltd) *Zr C1 F1 L O Q N*
Stoke-on-Trent *p397*. 01782 262424

Berens, Ms C W (Kennedys) *Zj Q N C1*
London EC3 *p49*. 020 7667 9667

Berens, D A (Fuglers) *C1 C2 J1 T1 T2 W Zd Ze Zf Zz*
London W1 *p34* 020 7323 6450

Beresford, Ms A (Addleshaw Goddard)
Manchester *p300* 0161 934 6000

Beresford, D W J (Carrick Read Solicitors LLP)
Hull *p256* 01482 211160
Hull *p256* 01482 211160

6

Beresford, Mrs E (Keypoint Law LLP) *N Q*
Doncaster *p212* 01302 329655

Beresford, G M (Gudgeons Prentice) *W T2*
Stowmarket *p399* 01449 613101

Beresford, J (Harcus Sinclair) *Q T2 W*
London WC2 *p38* 020 7242 9700

Beresford, J E (Baxter Caulfield) *W S1*
Huddersfield *p255* 01484 519519

Beresford, M A (Taylor Bracewell) *N Q O*
Doncaster *p212* 01302 341414

Beresford, N (Treasury Solicitors Department)
London WC2 *p110* 020 7210 3000
London EC3 *p31* 020 7861 4000

Beresford, P B (Dicksons Solicitors Ltd) *S1 L C1 R1 W E A1 K1 P Zc Zd Zh*
Stoke-on-Trent *p397* 01782 262424

Beresford, Mrs R E (Dyne Drewett Solicitors Ltd) *W*
Wincanton *p433* 01963 32374

Beresford-Jones, N P (Ellisons) *W K4 T2*
Colchester *p197* 01206 764477

Beresford-Smith, Mrs S J (Wansbroughs) *N Zj Zu Q J2 X*
Devizes *p210* 01380 733300

Beressi, Ms R M (Wigan Borough Council)
Wigan *p476* 01942 244991

Bereza, Miss K E (Maples Teesdale LLP) *E*
London EC2 *p58* 020 7600 3800

Berg, A G J (Watson Farley & Williams)
London EC2 *p90* 020 7814 8000

Berg, J (Eddowes Perry & Osbourne) *G H Zm Zl B2*
Sutton Coldfield *p403* 0121 686 9444

Berg, J P (Vyman Solicitors) *O Q J1 Zp Zq Ze Zk Zb B2 M2 N K1 B1 K3 Zz*
Harrow *p242* 020 8427 9080

Berg, P R (Paul Berg & Taylor) *S1 E C1 W*
Harpenden *p239* 01582 760161

Berg, R (Osborne Clarke) *C2 R2 Zz*
London EC2 *p65* 020 7105 7000

Berg, R L (Berg Legal) *C1 N J1 U2*
Manchester *p301* 0161 833 9211

Berg, R L (Janes) *G H B2*
London SW1 *p46* 020 7930 5100

Berg, T (Short Richardson & Forth LLP) *O B1 Zq*
Newcastle upon Tyne *p326* 0191 232 0283

Berg, W (Crowell & Moring) *C3*
London EC4 *p23* 020 7413 0011

Bergen, C E (Henry Hyams) *G H K1 D1*
Leeds *p274* 0113 243 2288

Bergen, L A (Henry Hyams) *K1 D1 G V*
Leeds *p274* 0113 243 2288

Berger, D (Zatman & Co)
Manchester *p311* 0161 832 2500

Berger, J D (Salans) *Ze Zf Zw*
London EC4 *p76* 020 7429 6000

Bergin, J C (Metropolitan Police Directorate of Legal Services) *N Q J1*
London SW1 *p108* 020 7230 7210

Bergin, S D (Simon Bergin) *S1 E W B1 Zd Q*
Stockport *p395* 0161 432 9945

Bergman, A K (Wilson Browne) *K1 D1 V Zm D2*
Kettering *p265* 01536 410041

Bergson, W Z (Wolfson & Co) *N Q O K1 J1 Zv*
Manchester *p311* 0161 873 8999

Bergum, G S (West Bromwich Magistrates Court)
West Bromwich *p476* 0121 533 3333

Beric, Miss A (Taylor Vinters) *N*
Cambridge *p176* 01223 423444

Beringer, Ms C E M (Pothecary Witham Weld) *Zd*
Westminster *p69* 020 7821 8211

Beringer, G G (Allen & Overy LLP)
London E1 *p5* 020 3088 0000

Berk, A (Wills Chandler) *J1 Q N*
Basingstoke *p127* 01256 322911

Berkeley, A R (Berkeley Solicitors) *C1 O J1 Q C2 K1 T1 T2 N*
Droylsden *p213* 0161 371 0011

Berkeley, C B (Pinsent Masons LLP) *Zo*
London EC2 *p67* 020 7418 7000

Berkeley, Mrs Y (Borough of Telford & Wrekin)
Telford *p473* 01952 380000

Berkner, M (Skadden Arps Slate Meagher & Flom (UK) LLP)
London E14 *p80* 020 7519 7000

Berkoff, Ms J (Reynolds Porter Chamberlain LLP)
London E1 *p71* 020 3060 6000

Berkovitz, Ms J (Shell International Ltd)
London SE1 *p109* 020 7934 1234

Berkson, J (Hill Dickinson LLP) *N M1 P F1 G J1 Zj*
Liverpool *p288* 0151 600 8000

Berman, D J (Daniel Berman & Co) *B2 G H*
London NW5 *p12* 020 7428 7798

Berman, J (Sacker & Partners LLP) *Zo*
London EC2 *p76* 020 7329 6699

Bermingham, Miss M T (May May & Merrimans) *E S2 S1 A1*
London WC1 *p59* 020 7405 8932

Bernard, P D (Wimpey Homes Holdings Ltd)
London W6 *p110* 020 8846 3107

Bernard-Carlin, J F (Nottingham City Council (City Sec Dept))
Nottingham *p467* 0115 915 5555

Berner, T (Radcliffes Le Brasseur)
Westminster *p70* 020 7222 7040

Bernhard, R C (Royal College of Nursing)
London W1 *p109* 020 7409 3333

Berns, R M (Piper Smith Watton LLP) *E S1 R2 T1 T2 S2*
London SW1 *p68* 020 7222 9900

Bernstein, B (Bude Nathan Iwanier) *B1 C1 E L M1 N P S1 T1 W*
London NW11 *p16* 020 8458 5656

Bernstein, Ms L (Levine Mellins Klarfeld) *B1 C1 C2 C3 D1 E F1 G J1 K1 Zl Zv*
Stanmore *p394* 020 8954 7474

Bernstein, R J (Adilsons)
London NW2 *p4* 020 8452 3793

Bernstein, S (Lawrence Stephens) *C1 C2 B1 J1 U1 Ze U2*
London EC1 *p82* 020 7935 1211

Bernstein, Mrs S (OGR Stock Denton) *J1 Zp*
London N3 *p64* 020 8349 0321

Berrange, Ms B (Alexander & Partners) *G H*
Brent *p5* 020 8965 7121

Berresford, P (BRM Solicitors) *N*
Chesterfield *p191* 01246 555111

Berrett, M V (Charles Lucas & Marshall) *Zr N Q*
Wantage *p421* 01235 771234

Berridge, D P (Bray & Bray) *K1 D1 D2 V*
Leicester *p279* 0116 254 8871

Berridge, Miss V E L (Royal Mail Group)
London EC4 *p109* 020 7250 2468

Berriman, Miss C A (Frearsons) *K1 K3*
Skegness *p380* 01754 897600

Berry, A (Lea & Co) *E C1 R2 S2 R1 Zb Zc*
Stockport *p396* 0161 480 6691

Berry, Miss A (Astills) *S1 W*
Leicester *p278* 0116 249 4450

Berry, A G (HM Land Registry - Plymouth)
Plymouth *p468* 01752 636000 / 636123

Berry, A W (Farnworth Shaw) *G H K1 D1 F1*
Nelson *p321* 01282 699996

Berry, C (Harrison Clark LLP) *E*
Cheltenham *p188* 01242 269198
Worcester *p439* 01905 612001
Worcester *p439* 01905 612001

Berry, Mrs C A (Taylor Vinters) *O*
Cambridge *p176* 01223 423444

Berry, C J (Berrys Solicitors) *A1 C1 G K1 L M1 N P S1*
Blackpool *p146* 01253 620022

Berry, C M (Pengillys LLP) *W S1 T1 E C1 A1 Zl*
Weymouth *p430* 01305 768888

Berry, C R (Edwin Coe LLP) *B1 O Q Zd Zj Zw Zk*
London WC2 *p29* 020 7691 4000

Berry, D (Berry & Walton Solicitors) *A1 B1 C1 E F1 K1 M1 N P R1 Zb Zc Zt*
King's Lynn *p266* 01553 764398
King's Lynn *p266* 01485 571366

Berry, D H (Charles Russell LLP) *C1 I C2*
London EC4 *p19* 020 7203 5000

Berry, Mrs E (Wragg Mark-Bell Solicitors) *D1 K3 K1 Q N D2 C1 F1 K2 O Ze Zb*
Carlisle *p182* 01228 711728

Berry, Mrs F (Stewarts Law LLP) *O Q Zq*
London EC4 *p83* 020 7822 8000

Berry, Ms J (Brabners Chaffe Street) *W K4 T2*
Preston *p356* 01772 823921

Berry, J M (Leon Kaye Solicitors) *C1*
London SW11 *p48* 020 7228 2020

Berry, Ms J M (Reed Smith LLP) *P R1*
London EC2 *p71* 020 3116 3000

Berry, J R P (Blaser Mills) *G H*
Aylesbury *p120* 01296 434416

Berry, Ms L (Stone King LLP) *D1 L N*
Bath *p128* 01225 337599

Berry, Ms M (Sacker & Partners LLP) *Zo*
London EC2 *p76* 020 7329 6699

Berry, M J (Thompsons (formerly Robin/Brian Thompson & Partners)) *N J1*
Plymouth *p350* 01752 675810

Berry, N B (Jackamans) *C1 E F1 G J1 L M1 P S1*
Felixstowe *p225* 01394 279636

Berry, N J (Pinsent Masons LLP)
London EC2 *p67* 020 7418 7000

Berry, P A (DWF) *N Zj*
Liverpool *p287* 0151 907 3000

Berry, P A (Teacher Stern LLP) *E C1 R2*
London WC1 *p86* 020 7242 3191

Berry, P G (Berry Redmond & Robinson)
Winscombe *p434* 01934 842811

Berry, R J (Berry Smith LLP) *E C1 L R1*
Cardiff *p177* 029 2034 5511

Berry, R J D (Rowntree & Berry) *S1 K1 P E W G L M1 T1 C1 Zl*
Fleetwood *p226* 01253 872581

Berry, Ms R M S (Berry Redmond & Robinson) *K4 K1 W*
Weston-super-Mare *p429* 01934 513963
Winscombe *p434* 01934 842811

Berry, S (M&A Solicitors LLP) *C1*
Cardiff *p179* 029 2048 2288

Berry, S C (Clarks Legal LLP) *W S1 E*
Reading *p360* 0118 958 5321

Berry, Miss S J (Blackburn with Darwen Borough Council)
Blackburn *p450* 01254 585585

Berry, S N (Atkinson McCall) *G K1 D1 S1 H J1 N L Q Zl*
Harrogate *p240* 01423 501531

Berry, Miss V (Pannone LLP) *K1*
Manchester *p308* 0161 909 3000

Berry, W (Hudgell & Partners) *S1 S2*
Greenwich *p43* 020 8854 1331

Berry, W J C (Nicholls Christie & Crocker) *G H B2*
Uxbridge *p417* 01895 256216

Bertram, Miss A (Harthills) *K1*
Rotherham *p367* 01709 377399

Bertrand, A (Boyes Turner) *S2 E L*
Reading *p360* 0118 959 7711

Berwald, M F (PCB Lawyers LLP) *E S1 S2*
London W1 *p65* 020 7486 2566

Berwick, G K (Freeth Cartwright LLP) *O R1*
Nottingham *p337* 0115 936 9369

Berwin, H B (Darlington Hardcastles) *Q O K3 J1 N B2 C1*
Rickmansworth *p364* 01923 774272
London EC2 *p56* 020 7588 9080

Berwin, P D (Berwins Solicitors Limited) *K1 Zv I Ze C1*
Harrogate *p240* 01423 509000

Besant, I R (Wright Hassall LLP) *J1 Zl Zp J2*
Leamington Spa *p270* 01926 886688

Besch, Miss H C (Fox Williams) *J1*
London EC2 *p33* 020 7628 2000

Beskine, Ms S J M (Hopkin Murray Beskine) *K1 L D1 K2*
London N4 *p42* 020 7272 1234

Besser, A B (Addleshaw Goddard) *B1 C1 Zb*
London EC1 *p4* 020 7606 8855

Best, A R (Prince Evans) *O Zc*
Ealing *p69* 020 8567 3477

Best, A W (HSR Law (Hayes, Son & Richmond)) *C1 S2 R2 C2*
Doncaster *p211* 01302 347800
Gainsborough *p228* 01427 613831

Best, D W (Gillian Radford & Co) *J1*
Westminster *p70* 020 8960 4366

Best, I (Gateshead Metropolitan Borough Council)
Gateshead *p458* 0191 433 3000

Best, I J (Rix & Kay Solicitors LLP) *W T2 S1*
Seaford *p373* 0845 165 8178

Best, M J (Bhatia Best) *G H Zp Zg*
Nottingham *p336* 0115 950 3231

Best, R L (Richard Best & Co) *G N L Q V J1 H K1 D1 X Zm Zq Zi Zd Zp*
Rugby *p368* 01788 571135

Best, Mrs R L (City of London Corporation) *J1 N Q S1 Zp*
London EC2 *p107* 020 7606 3030

Best, R S M (Clifford Chance)
London E14 *p20* 020 7006 1000

Best, Miss S A (Thatcher & Hallam) *K1*
Midsomer Norton *p316* 01761 414646

Best, S J (West Wiltshire District Council) *F1 G H J1 K1 L M1 P R1 Zu R2*
Trowbridge *p474* 01225 770396

Best, Ms W R (Nicholson Portnell) *K1 D1 K3*
Hexham *p249* 01434 603656

Bestley, M R J (SAS Daniels LLP) *O J1 Q F1 P Zb*
Macclesfield *p297* 01625 442100

Bestwick, Miss T E A (Nottingham City Council (City Sec Dept))
Nottingham *p467* 0115 915 5555

Beswetherick, M (Reynolds Porter Chamberlain LLP)
London E1 *p71* 020 3060 6000

Beswick, D J (Squire Sanders (UK) LLP) *J1*
Birmingham *p142* 0121 222 3000

Betambeau, A (Peter Peter & Wright) *S1 L T2 W A1 S2 K4 E*
Okehampton *p340* 01837 52379

Bethell, C (Beesley & Co)
Manchester *p301* 0161 445 3678

Bethell-Jones, Ms J (Trowers & Hamlins)
London EC3 *p88* 020 7423 8000

Bettany, T M C (Speechly Bircham LLP) *J1*
London EC4 *p81* 020 7427 6400

Betteridge, A C (Ashfords LLP) *C2 C1*
Bristol *p160* 0117 321 8000

Betteridge, M A (Betteridges) *A1 B1 D1 E F1 K1 N O Q W*
Hertford *p248* 01992 505406

Betteridge, Miss S L (Kirklees Metropolitan Borough Council)
Huddersfield *p461* 01484 221421

Bettiga, G (Lawrence Lupin) *Zi M1 Zg Q M4*
Wembley *p426* 020 8733 7200

Bettison, O J S (Spratt Endicott) *S1 R1*
Banbury *p122* 01295 204000

Bettosi, Ms F (Harding Evans LLP) *G H*
Newport *p328* 01633 244233

Betts, Mrs C A (Gateley LLP)
Birmingham *p138* 0121 234 0000

Betts, G (Buckles Solicitors LLP) *J1*
Peterborough *p346* 01733 888888
Cambridge *p175* 01223 364422

Betts, J (Irwin Mitchell LLP) *N*
Manchester *p306* 0870 150 0100

Betts, J J (Mybrief Solicitors) *G H B2 N W F1 Zl*
Chatham *p185* 01634 544544

Betts, Mrs J T (Julia T Betts) *E K1 S1 W Q S2 A2*
Nottingham *p336* 01623 499080

Betts, K (Betts & Co Solicitors Ltd) *G H B2*
Ashford *p119* 01304 213172

Betts, Mrs K J (Kim Betts & Co) *S1 E L C1 A1 F1 Zl*
Loughton *p294* 020 8508 5505

Betts, M I (Guillaumes Solicitors) *S1 E W L T1 Zm*
Weybridge *p430* 01932 840111

Betts, R (Hansells) *S1 S2*
Norwich *p334* 01603 615731

Betts, W E (Forster Dean Ltd) *S1*
Widnes *p431* 0151 422 0982

Beuzeval, Miss L J (Larcomes LLP) *W*
Portsmouth *p354* 023 9266 1531

Bevan, A H (Bevans) *J1 O A3 Zp*
Bristol *p161* 0117 923 7249

Bevan, Ms C J (Brockbank Curwen Cain & Hall) *K1 G F1 S1 N V Zl*
Cockermouth *p197* 01900 827222

Bevan, Miss C T (Yorkshire Dales National Park Authority)
Leyburn *p463* 0870 166 6333 / 01969 652323

Bevan, D (Bowcock Cuerden LLP) *M1 K1 S1 G F1 P V W*
Nantwich *p320* 01270 611106

Bevan, Ms E (Penningtons) *Zr N*
Basingstoke *p127* 01256 407100

Bevan, J A (Bevan Kidwell) *S2 E O N W S1 L*
London EC1 *p12* 020 7843 1820

Bevan, J E M (Allen & Overy LLP)
London E1 *p5* 020 3088 0000

Bevan, Miss J R (Bevan Kidwell) *C1 C2 Ze*
London EC1 *p12* 020 7843 1820

Bevan, Mrs J V (Anthony Collins Solicitors LLP) *K1*
Birmingham *p137* 0121 200 3242

Bevan, Miss M D (David Cowan) *K1 G H D1 D2 K3*
Dorking *p212* 01306 886622

Bevan, P (Linklaters LLP)
London EC2 *p54* 020 7456 2000

Bevan, P B P (BP PLC)
London SW1 *p104* 020 7496 4000

Bevan, P L (Beor Wilson Lloyd) *N*
Swansea *p405* 01792 655178

Bevan, R M (Maclaren Warner) *G H K1 J1 M1 P N D1 W Zp*
Stapleford *p394* 0115 939 5252

Bevan, R T G (Overburys & Raymond Thompson) *K1 D1 D2*
Norwich *p335* 01603 610481

Bevan, S (Veale Wasbrough Vizards) *J1 Zp*
Bristol *p165* 0117 925 2020

Bevan, Mrs S J (Brindley Twist Tafft & James) *Zr N*
Coventry *p200* 024 7653 1532

Bevan-Thomas, G (Parker Bullen) *E S2 R1 R2*
Andover *p118* 01264 400500

Beven, R (Ashurst LLP)
London EC2 *p7* 020 7638 1111

Bever, A (Addleshaw Goddard)
Leeds *p271* 0113 209 2000
Manchester *p300* 0161 934 6000

Beveridge, Ms D M (Northumbrian Water Ltd)
Durham *p457* 0870 608 4820

Beverley, Mrs L S (Dorset County Council)
Dorchester *p457* 01305 251000

Beverley, R A (Freeth Cartwright LLP) *F1 Zj Zq Zr*
Nottingham *p337* 0115 936 9369

Bevington, A M (Rootes & Alliott) *S1 E A1 L C1 T1 W F1 R1 Zm*
Folkestone *p227* 01303 851100

Bevington, P E (EMW) *C1 C2*
Milton Keynes *p316* 0845 070 6000

Bevis, J H (Colemans) *S1*
Haywards Heath *p245* 01444 459555

Bevis, M G (Bevis Rowntree) *A1 C1 C2 E L S1 S2 T2 W Zd*
Midhurst *p315* 01730 812201

Bevitt, Ms A (Morrison & Foerster (UK) LLP) *J1 Zza*
London EC2 *p62* 020 7920 4000

Bew, J (Squire Sanders (UK) LLP) *C1 C2 Zb*
London EC2 *p81* 020 7655 1000

Bew, Mrs K A (Wansbroughs) *K1*
Devizes *p210* 01380 733300

Bewley, Mrs C E (Burges Salmon) *C1*
Bristol *p161* 0117 939 2000

Bexfield, Ms C A (Harrison Clark LLP) *E*
Cheltenham *p188* 01242 269198
Worcester *p439* 01905 612001
Worcester *p439* 01905 612001

Beynon, Mrs F M R (Ward & Rider Limited) *N J2*
Coventry *p201* 024 7655 5400

Beynon, Mrs H M (Beynons) *E F1 L S1 R1 W Zh*
Orpington *p341* 01689 861008

Beynon, R W (Beynons Nicholls) *M1 P W B1 E T1 C1 L G Zk Zt*
London EC4 *p12* 020 7353 5860

Bezzant, C D (Reed Smith LLP) *R2 E*
London EC2 *p71* 020 3116 3000

Bhabra, Ms R K (Irwin Mitchell LLP) *N Zr*
Sheffield *p376* 0870 150 0100

Bhachu, A S (Mackenzie & Co) *G H K1 N*
Hounslow *p254* 020 8569 6289

Bhachu, Mrs M (Turner Coulston)
Northampton *p333* 01604 622101

Bhagwandeen, Ms A R (AB Law) *O Q J1 C1 E*
Harrow *p241* 020 8426 5613

Bhaijee, Ms Z (Magrath LLP) *Zi J1*
London W1 *p57* 020 7495 3003

Bhailok, A (Bhailok Fielding) *D1 E G H J1 K1 L N Q S1 Zi Zp Zv*
Preston *p356* 01772 202191

Bhakar, G S (Bhakar Tomlinson) *C1 S2 E J1 L O Q C2 Zq S1*
Wellington *p425* 01952 270555

Bhakta, Miss N (Dass Solicitors) *G B2 S1 N*
Birmingham *p137* 0121 248 4000

Bhalla, Ms S (Massers) *N*
Nottingham *p338* 0115 851 1666

Bhalla, S B (Gordons Solicitors LLP) *S1*
Maidenhead *p298* 0870 777 1122
Marlow *p313* 01628 487487

Bhaloo, Mrs S (Marks & Spencer PLC)
London W2 *p107* 020 7935 4422

Bhambra, Ms P (MacLeish Littlestone Cowan) *D1 K3 K1*
Ilford *p260* 020 8514 3000

Bhamjee, M H (Crowley & Co) *G N J1 W X Zd Zi Zp*
Cardiff *p178* 029 2045 8895

See p634 for the Key to Work Categories

Bhan, N (DAC Beachcroft)
London EC4 *p24*. 020 7242 1011
Bhandal, Ms B R (Thurrock Borough Council)
Grays *p459* 01375 390000
Bhandal, N S (Bhatia Best) *G H*
Nottingham *p336*. 0115 950 3231
Bhandal, S S (Wright Hassall LLP) *E S2 R2*
Leamington Spa *p270* 01926 886688
Bhandari, S (Kirk & Partners) *K3 K1 J1 Q Zp L*
London SE9 *p50*. 020 8850 2484
Bhangal, R (Anthony Collins Solicitors LLP) *E*
Birmingham *p137* 0121 200 3242
Bhangra, M (Hatten Wyatt)
Gravesend *p232*. 01474 351199
Bharaj, Mrs A (Pumfrey & Lythaby) *W*
Orpington *p342* 01689 833657
Bharakhda, V D (J H Hart & Co) *O Q N Zi L S2 E S1*
London E6 *p39* 020 8472 2652
Bhardwaj, Ms S (Equity Solicitors) *K3 Zi S1*
Birmingham *p138* 0121 554 7470
Bhargava, Miss R (Russell-Cooke LLP) *W*
London SW15 *p74*. 020 8789 9111
Bharj, C S (Burton Woolf & Turk) *Q N S1 L W F1 B1 C1 J1 U2 Ze Zq Zi*
London EC1 *p16*. 020 7831 6478
Bharj, Mrs R (South Bucks District Council)
Denham *p456* 01895 837200
Bharya, Mrs R (Eaton Ryan & Taylor) *O Q A3 F1 Zq N F2 Zj J2*
Birmingham *p138* 0121 236 1999
Bhasin, R (Steel & Shamash) *D1 K1 N*
Lambeth *p82*. 020 7803 3999
Bhaskaran, Ms R S (Addleshaw Goddard) *E S1*
Leeds *p271* 0113 209 2000
Bhatia, A K (Bhatia Best) *G H N Q S1 S2*
Nottingham *p336*. 0115 950 3231
Bhatia, Miss P (Sheridans) *Zf Ze J1*
London WC1 *p78* 020 7079 0100
Bhatiani, Miss M (Darlingtons) *Q*
Edgware *p217*. .020 8952 0033 / 8951 6666
Bhatoa, A (Patel & Bhatoa)
Bradford *p154* 01274 669023
Bhatoa, A S (Bullivant & Partners)
London EC4 *p16*. 020 7332 8250
Bhatoa, J (H S Kang & Co)
Barking *p123* 020 8594 5465
Bhatoa, J S (Patel & Bhatoa) *E J1 M1 N S1*
Bradford *p154* 01274 669023
Bhatt, C (Bishop & Sewell LLP) *E L S1 S2*
London WC1 *p13* 020 7631 4141
Bhatt, R (Bhatt Murphy) *Zg*
Hackney *p12*. 020 7729 1115
Bhatta, B S (E Edwards Son & Noice) *S1*
Billericay *p133*. 01277 658551
Bhattacharyya, G (Reed Smith LLP) *O Zb Zk Zf Zj*
London EC2 *p71*. 020 3116 3000
Bhatti, Mrs I (Bracknell Forest Borough Council) *K1 N*
Bracknell *p450*. 01344 424642
Bhatti, Miss N (Heptonstalls LLP) *N*
Pontefract *p351* 01977 602804
Bhatti, Miss N (Rowberrys) *D1 K1 N O Q Zr Zq K3*
Crowthorne *p204* 01344 775311
Bhatti, Ms S K (Everatt's) *S1 S2 E R2 W*
Harrow *p241*. 020 8424 0088
London N3 *p53* 020 8371 7400
Bhavsar, R (Jasvir Jutla & Co) *Zi*
Leicester *p280*. 0116 254 0809
Bhela, Mrs H K (Westminster City Council)
London SW1 *p110*. 020 7641 6000
Bhinder, R (Alexander & Partners)
Brent *p5*. 020 8965 7121
Bhogal, Mrs G K (Gill & Co) *D1 K1 S1 K3 W*
Ilford *p260*. 020 8554 8774
Bhogal, Ms H (Capsticks Solicitors LLP) *N Zr*
London SW19 *p18*. 020 8780 2211
Bhogal, Mrs M K (Bristol City Council)
Bristol *p451* 0117 922 2000
Bhogal, P (Bowling & Co) *C1 S2 E*
London E15 *p15*. 020 8221 8000
Bhogal, Mrs T K (Thames Water Utilities Limited) *N Q Zr J1 K1 L*
Reading *p469* 0118 373 8000
Bhojani, S (Cartwright King)
Leicester *p279*. 0116 253 9222
Bhomra, S S (Mandla Bhomra & Co)
Birmingham *p140* 0121 523 3384
Bhopal, S K (Birmingham City Council Legal & Democratic Services) *G O*
Birmingham *p449* 0121 303 2066
Bhudia, G K (Freemans Solicitors) *E S2 S1*
London W1 *p34* 020 7935 3522
Bhula, D (Gordon Dadds) *C1 J1 Q O*
London W1 *p25* 020 7493 6151
Bhullar, Mrs P (Lawrence Lupin) *Zi Zg Q M1*
Wembley *p426*. 020 8733 7200
Bhuller, T S (Kaim Todner Ltd) *N G H*
London SE17 *p47* 020 7701 4747
Bhurawala, A H (Morgan Hall Solicitors) *O C1 B2 N V R2 Zi Zl*
Ilford *p260*. 020 8514 4448
Bhutta, Mrs P F M (Patricia Bhutta & Ruth Caro LLP) *S1 W E*
Botley *p151* 01865 863128
Bi, F (SNR Denton)
London EC4 *p75*. 020 7242 1212
Bi, S (Kirbys) *D1 K4 K1 V W*
Harrogate *p240* 01423 542000
Biagi, Ms I G (Barlow Lyde & Gilbert LLP)
London EC3 *p10*. 020 7247 2277
Bianchina, Ms C (Nottingham City Council (City Sec Dept)) *K1 D1 D2 K2 V*
Nottingham *p467*. 0115 915 5555
Bibbings, Ms J (Trowers & Hamlins)
London EC3 *p88*. 020 7423 8000
Bibby, C (Smith Jones Solicitors) *N Q*
Kenilworth *p264* 01926 859933
Burnley *p169* 01282 855400
Bibby, Mrs J M L (Lime Pictures Limited) *G J1 Ze*
Liverpool *p463*. 0151 722 9122
Bibby, K (Napthens LLP) *N*
Preston *p357* 01772 888444
Bibby, Mrs K (174 Law) *K1 K3 S1 W*
Birkenhead *p134*. 0151 647 7372
Bibby, P A (George Davies Solicitors LLP)
Manchester *p303* 0161 236 8992
Bibby, P A (Bingham McCutchen (London) LLP)
London EC2 *p12*. 020 7661 5300
Bibby, P J (Keoghs LLP) *C1 C2*
Bolton *p149* 01204 677000
Bibby, P S (MSB Solicitors LLP) *C1 E G K1 L M1 S1 W F1 J1*
Liverpool *p289*. 0151 281 9040
Bibby, Miss S J (Nottingham City Council (City Sec Dept))
Nottingham *p467*. 0115 915 5555
Biber, E (B A A PLC)
London UB3 *p103* 0870 000 0123
Bibi, Ms S (Anthony Gold) *N S1 W*
London SE1 *p6* 020 7940 4000
Bible, E (Brethertons LLP) *O B1*
Banbury *p122* 01295 270999
Bichard, K D (Howard Kennedy LLP) *E C1*
London W1 *p48* 020 7636 1616
Bicheno, Miss J H (Europe Arab Bank PLC) *E*
London EC2 *p106* 020 7315 8500
Bickerdike, Mrs A Y (Telford Magistrates Court)
Telford *p474* 01952 204500
Bickerdike, S (Penningtons)
Godalming *p231* 01483 791800
Bickerstaff, R M (Bird & Bird LLP) *C1*
London EC4 *p13*. 020 7415 6000
Bickerton, D J (Clifford Chance)
London E14 *p20*. 020 7006 1000
Bickerton, Ms P J (Allen & Overy LLP)
London E1 *p5* 020 3088 0000
Bickford, D (Penningtons) *J1*
Basingstoke *p127* 01256 407100
Bickford, D J (Boodle Hatfield) *R2 E S2 L*
Westminster *p14*. 020 7629 7411
Reading *p360* 0118 951 6200
Bickley, J (HM Land Registry - Birkenhead) *S1 W*
Birkenhead *p449*. 0151 473 1110
Bidder, B (Speechly Bircham LLP) *E R1 S1*
London EC4 *p81*. 020 7427 6400
Biddick, L (Kitsons LLP)
Exeter *p221* 01392 455555
Biddle, Miss F (Anthony Collins Solicitors LLP) *J1*
Birmingham *p137* 0121 200 3242
Biddle, P P (Thomas Horton LLP) *S1 E L S2*
Bromsgrove *p167* 01527 871641
Biddle, Miss S M (Pinsent Masons LLP) *C1 U2*
London EC2 *p67*. 020 7418 7000
Biddlecombe, Mrs J E (Paris Smith LLP) *J1 Zp*
Southampton *p386*. 023 8048 2482
Biddulph, Ms A (Ashurst LLP)
London EC2 *p7* 020 7638 1111
Biddulph-Smith, N R (Walters & Plaskitt) *K1 P M1 N S1 E G L C1 J1 Zw Zv Zi*
Stoke-on-Trent *p398*. 01782 819611
Biden, Ms S (Bates Wells & Braithwaite London LLP) *Zd C1*
London EC4 *p11*. 020 7551 7777
Bidwell, C J S (Woolley Bevis Diplock) *E C1 S1 R1*
Brighton *p160* 01273 323231
Bidwell, Mrs J E (National Grid PLC)
Warwick *p471* 01926 653000
Bieber, I R C (Radcliffes Le Brasseur) *C1 D1 E K1 L S1 W Zd*
Westminster *p70*. 020 7222 7040
Biedul, R (Maples Teesdale LLP) *E*
London EC2 *p58*. 020 7600 3800
Biggerstaff, D (Trowers & Hamlins) *C1*
London EC3 *p88*. 020 7423 8000
Biggerstaff, Mrs H L (Bailey & Cogger) *K1*
Tonbridge *p412* 01732 353305
Biggin, S G (Hewitsons) *O Q*
Cambridge *p174*. 01223 461155
Biggs, C I W (Biggs & Co) *Q W K1 S1 L*
Wokingham *p437* 0118 989 4511
Biggs, C M (Lightfoots LLP) *E S2 C1*
Thame *p410*. 01844 212305
Biggs, J (Ince & Co Services Ltd)
London E1 *p44* 020 7481 0010
Biggs, K M (Foot Anstey) *E*
Exeter *p221* 01392 411221
Biggs, Mrs N (Overburys & Raymond Thompson) *E*
Norwich *p335* 01603 610481
Biggs, Ms N (Pritchard Joyce & Hinds) *B1 Q*
Beckenham *p129* 020 8658 3922
Biggs, Mrs N (Charles Lucas & Marshall) *K3 K1 D1*
Newbury *p322* 01635 521212
Biggs, Ms N N (TV Edwards LLP) *K1*
London SE8 *p85*. 020 7790 7000
Biggs, P A (Wains) *W A1 E S1 S2*
Macclesfield *p297* 01625 429511
Biggs, P D (Cadwalader Wickersham & Taft)
London WC2 *p17* 020 7170 8700
Biggs, R A (Over Taylor Biggs) *C1 B1 J1 T1 F1 Ze*
Exeter *p222* 01392 823811
Biggs, R J (DWF) *N Q Zj*
Liverpool *p287*. 0151 907 3000
Biggs, Ms S (Fentimans) *K1 N Q L J1 Zm Zl*
Knowle *p269*. 01564 779459
Biggs, Ms T (Rutters) *K1 K3*
Shaftesbury *p374* 01747 852377
Biginton, W G (The Royal Borough of Kensington & Chelsea)
London W8 *p109* 020 7361 2741
Biglin, Miss H (BHP Law) *W*
Darlington *p206* 01325 466794
Bigmore, D (David Bigmore & Co) *C1 J1 Zb Ze*
Wrexham *p442* 01978 855058
London EC4 *p36*. 020 7404 0606
Bignall, J (Bignalls) *C1 T1 W Ze*
Westminster *p12*. 020 7637 3071
Bignall, Mrs N (Bignalls) *C1 J1 E O P Ze Zc*
Westminster *p12*. 020 7637 3071
Bignell, F G (Just Employment) *C1 J1 J2 N Zp T2*
Guildford *p236*. 01483 303636
Bignell, T (Druces LLP) *B1 O Q*
London EC2 *p27*. 020 7638 9271
Bijlani, R (Asghar & Co) *N*
Southall *p384* 020 8843 0010
Bijmolen-Reed, Ms A J (Roche Products Ltd)
Welwyn Garden City *p475* . . 01707 366000
Bilan, S S (Ess Ess Bilan Solicitors)
Kenton *p265*. 0844 800 1747
Bilas, W (The College of Law)
London WC1 *p105*. 0800 289997
Bilbeisi, A M (Bilbeisi & Co Solicitors) *K3 K1 Zi V W L D1*
Barnet *p12*. 020 8446 7262
Biles, Ms C (Ashurst LLP)
London EC2 *p7* 020 7638 1111
Biles, G (The College of Law York) *O Q J1 F1*
York *p477* 0800 289997
Billing, C D (Camps Solicitors) *N Q K1 J1 S1 F1 O Zv*
Birkenhead *p134*. 0151 201 8080
Billing, M J (Bishopscourt Group Services Ltd)
Brentwood *p451* 01277 247304
Billing, Ms P (DLA Piper UK LLP)
Sheffield *p375*. 0870 011 1111
Billinge, R A (Bennett & Co) *S1 W E*
Liverpool *p286*. 0151 733 2372
Billingham, C N (Devonshires) *L Q Zh*
London EC2 *p27*. 020 7628 7576
Billingham, D G (David Billingham & Partners) *G D1 H S1 W Q N K1 J1 A1 Zl Zm*
Cheltenham *p187* 01242 676224
Billingham, R (Challinors) *G H Zl*
Halesowen *p237*. 0121 550 0481
Stourbridge *p399* . .01384 375437 / 378991
Billingham, Ms S J (Michelmores LLP) *C1 C2*
Exeter *p221* 01392 688688
Billings, D M (Irwin Mitchell LLP) *C1 S2 E C2 S1 R2*
Birmingham *p139* 0870 150 0100
Billingsley, Miss E (Levison Meltzer Pigott) *K1*
London EC4 *p53*. 020 7556 2400
Billington, C L (Dowson Billington) *E S1 W C1 L T2 Q*
Preston *p356* 01772 556807
Billington, C M (Wrigleys Solicitors LLP) *J1 Zd Zp X Zv*
Leeds *p278* 0113 244 6100
Billington, G (CMS Cameron McKenna LLP)
Bristol *p162* 0117 930 0200
London EC3 *p17*. 020 7367 3000
Billington, Miss J (Jones Day) *J1*
London EC4 *p46*. 020 7039 5959
Billins, E G (Solomons Solicitors) *R1 W E C1 T2*
Bournemouth *p152*. 01202 802807
Billyard, P (Charles Lucas & Marshall) *C1 C2 Ze*
Newbury *p322*. 01635 521212
Billyeald, C P (Shakespeares) *C1 C2 Zb*
Nottingham *p339*. 0115 945 3700
Bilous, Miss C (Glaisyers Solicitors LLP) *K1 K3*
Manchester *p304* 0161 224 3311
Bilton, Miss E (Bilton Hammond LLP) *D1 D2 K1 K2*
Mansfield *p311*. 01623 675800
Bilton, G (Bilton Hammond LLP) *G H S1 C1 K1 P D1 E W F1*
Mansfield *p311*. 01623 675800
Bilton, P (Bilton Hammond LLP) *N*
Mansfield *p311*. 01623 675800
Bilton, S M (Bilton Hammond LLP) *C1 E R2 S1 S2 Zq*
Mansfield *p311*. 01623 675800
Biltoo, M A (Waltons & Morse LLP) *Za O A3*
London EC3 *p90*. 020 7623 4255
Bindman, Sir G L (Bindmans LLP) *Q J1 Zg Zk Zp*
London WC1 *p12* 020 7833 4433
Bindman, S L (Bindman & Co) *S1 W K1 N Q L O G H J1 Zi*
Whickham *p430* 0191 488 4950
Bindshedler, R (Howard Kennedy LLP) *T1 C1*
London W1 *p48* 020 7636 1616
Bingham, A (Gallaher Ltd)
Weybridge *p476* 01932 859777
Bingham, A D (Newbys) *Q K1 L N F1 D1 J1*
Middlesbrough *p315* .01642 247717 / 247967
Bingham, A J (Bingham & Co) *S1 W P M1 L K1 G*
Leicester *p279*. 0116 253 0091
Bingham, Ms C M (SNR Denton) *Zf*
London EC4 *p75*. 020 7242 1212
Bingham, J (Sacker & Partners LLP) *Zo*
London EC2 *p76*. 020 7329 6699
Bingham, J (EMW) *Zb C2*
Milton Keynes *p316* 0845 070 6000
Bingham, Ms J (The College of Law)
London WC1 *p105*. 0800 289997
Bingham, N C (Challenor Gardiner) *K1 N Q L O F1*
Oxford *p343*. 01865 721451
Bingham, N I F (Pini Franco LLP) *B1 M2 O Zc Zj*
London EC1 *p67*. 020 7566 3140
Binitie, Mrs J (Reading Borough Council)
Reading *p469* 0118 939 0900
Binks, J S (Legal Services Commission Regional Office (Merseyside)) *Q O N F1 G H J1 K1 M1 P Zl*
Liverpool *p463*. 0151 242 5200
Binnersley, P N (Quality Solicitors HPJV) *K1 S1*
Newport *p329* 01633 242526
Binnie, Ms L (Blandy & Blandy) *J1*
Reading *p360* 0118 951 6800
Binning, P (Corker Binning Solicitors) *G Q M2 Zi*
London WC2 *p22* 020 7353 6000
Binning, S S (Dempster Binning LLP) *E S2 R2*
Chandlers Ford *p184* 023 8062 1790
Binnion, Miss L A (Binnion Lindsay-Veal LLP) *N Zq Zw Zr F1 Q*
Stourport-on-Severn *p399* . . 01299 827860
Binns, A J (Dunham Guest & Lyons) *S1 S2 W E Zm*
Cannock *p176*. 01543 462121
Binns, C A (Irwin Mitchell LLP) *Zm Zg Q*
Manchester *p306* 0870 150 0100
Binns, D R (Walker Foster) *S1 S2 C1*
Silsden *p380*. 01535 653408
Binns, J D (BCL Burton Copeland) *B2 G*
London WC2 *p9* 020 7430 2277
London W1 *p89* 020 7487 2505
Binns, R B (Simmons & Simmons) *O E Ze Zf*
London EC2 *p79*. 020 7628 2020
Binstead, D R (Crown Prosecution Service Cumbria)
Carlisle *p453*. 01228 882900
Birbeck, Mrs J H (Milne Moser) *K1 G H D1 N S1 D2 K3*
Kendal *p264*. . . . .01539 729786 / 725582
Birch, A (hlw Keeble Hawson LLP) *E S2 F1*
Sheffield *p376* 0114 276 5555
Birch, Miss D A (Birmingham City Council Legal & Democratic Services)
Birmingham *p449* 0121 303 2066
Birch, Mrs E L (Enoch Evans LLP) *K1 F1 V Q D1 L B1 Zm A3*
Walsall *p420*. 01922 720333
Birch, G (Harrowells)
York *p444* 01904 558600
Birch, I (Pearson Fielding Polson) *G H*
Liverpool *p290*. 0151 236 3636
Birch, J (Pinsent Masons LLP) *C2 C1*
London EC2 *p67*. 020 7418 7000
Birch, J N (Fieldings Porter) *P M1 N K1 D1 L G C1 J1 F1 Zc Zj Zk*
Bolton *p149* 01204 540900
Birch, J R (Quality Solicitors Mewies) *O J1 C1 Q L*
Skipton *p381*. 01756 799000
Birch, Miss L (T B I Financial Services Ltd)
Reading *p469* 0118 931 3800
Birch, Miss R A (Glynis M Mackie) *W*
Gosforth *p232* 0191 236 5308
Birch, Miss R U I (Wansbroughs) *E*
Devizes *p210* 01380 733300
Birch, Miss R V (Butcher & Barlow LLP) *E W Zd*
Leigh *p281*. 01942 674144
Birch, Mrs S (Nyland & Beattie) *K1 D1*
Widnes *p432*. 0151 424 5656
Birch Reynardson, T H (DLA Piper UK LLP) *M2 A3 O Q Za Zj*
London EC2 *p24*. 0870 011 1111
Birchall, A W (Birchall Ryan Solicitors) *O K1 K2 G J1 H F1 L S1 N V W*
Congleton *p198* 01260 297070
Birchall, C A (Woodfines LLP) *G*
Bletchley *p147*. 01908 366333
Birchall, D (Clarke Willmott) *W T2*
Birmingham *p136* 0845 209 1000 / 0117 305 6000
Birchall, D (SNR Denton) *C1*
London EC4 *p75*. 020 7242 1212
Birchall, Ms D C (Birchall Blackburn LLP) *S1 W M2 N*
Manchester *p301* 0161 236 0662
Preston *p356* 01772 561663
Birchall, Miss D C (Grace & Co) *N J2*
Warrington *p422*. 01925 242488
Birchall, G (Howard Kennedy LLP) *T1 T2 W K4*
London W1 *p48* 020 7636 1616
Birchall, M J (Addleshaw Goddard)
Manchester *p300* 0161 934 6000
Birchall, P (Pinsent Masons LLP) *E S1*
Manchester *p308* 0161 234 8234
Birchall, S J (DAC Beachcroft) *E L R1 S1 Zc*
Manchester *p303* 0161 934 3000
Birchwood, Mrs G S (Bartletts Solicitors) *Q N*
Chester *p190* 01244 313301
Bird, A D (Tayntons LLP Solicitors) *E S1 C1 A1 B1 J1 L Zh*
Gloucester *p230*. 01452 522047
Bird, Ms A E (Chesterfield Law Centre)
Chesterfield *p455* . .01246 550674 / 204570
Bird, A F (Simmons & Simmons)
London EC2 *p79*. 020 7628 2020
Bird, A J (Reed Smith LLP)
London EC2 *p71*. 020 3116 3000

6

Bird, B (Linklaters LLP)
London EC2 *p54*. 020 7456 2000

Bird, Miss C (W Davies) *N Q O J1 Zq*
Woking *p436*. 01483 744900

Bird, C J (Bird & Daniels) *G K1 S1 H D1 L B1 P V Zc Zi Zl*
Shipley *p378*. 01274 580999

Bird, C L (Eric Robinson Solicitors) *W T2 S1 S2 K4*
Hythe *p259* 023 8084 4304

Bird, C P (Glynns Solicitors) *Zr N Q O Zq*
Bristol *p162* 01761 490883

Bird, D I (TLT Solicitors) *T2 W T1 F1 Zo*
Bristol *p165* 0117 917 7777

Bird, D I (Paris Smith LLP) *T1 T2 W K4*
Southampton *p386*. 023 8048 2482

Bird, D J (Veale Wasbrough Vizards) *Zc E P Zo*
Bristol *p165* 0117 925 2020

Bird, D J (Atherton Godfrey) *K1 D1 K2*
Doncaster *p211* 01302 320621

Bird, D N (Hopley Pierce & Bird) *S1 J1 W K4 L T2*
Wrexham *p443* 01978 315100

Bird, D P (Berry Redmond & Robinson) *C1 G H L K1 E D1 M1 S1*
Weston-super-Mare *p429* . . 01934 619000

Bird, D W (Crane & Staples) *W T2 S1*
Welwyn Garden City *p425* . . 01707 329333

Bird, E R W (Maples Teesdale LLP) *E S2*
London EC2 *p58*. 020 7600 3800

Bird, G (Blair Allison & Co) *K1 S1 W*
Birmingham *p135* 0121 233 2904

Bird, Ms H (Kerman & Co LLP) *S2 E L W*
London WC2 *p49* 020 7539 7272

Bird, Miss J (Russell-Cooke LLP) *W M1 M2 K4 Zo*
London SW15 *p74*. 020 8789 9111

Bird, Ms J (Trowers & Hamlins)
London EC3 *p88*. 020 7423 8000

Bird, J C M (Resolution PLC) *C1 J1 B1 Ze*
Birmingham *p450* 01564 828888

Bird, Ms J L (Stables & Co)
Halesowen *p237*. 0121 585 3820

Bird, Ms J M (Kirklees Metropolitan Borough Council) *K1 V Zm*
Huddersfield *p461* 01484 221421

Bird, J R S (Lodders Solicitors LLP) *E S1 A1 L C1*
Stratford-upon-Avon *p400* . . 01789 293259

Bird, J S (Marchant Harries & Co) *G H*
Aberdare *p113*. 01685 885500

Bird, Mrs M L (Allan Jay Paine & Co) *S1 S2*
Enfield *p5* 020 8886 1404

Bird, M S (Freeth Cartwright LLP) *N Q V F1*
Derby *p208* 01332 361000
Nottingham *p337*. 0115 936 9369

Bird, N D (Reynolds Porter Chamberlain LLP) *O Zq*
London E1 *p71* 020 3060 6000

Bird, N M H (Allen & Overy LLP)
London E1 *p5* 020 3088 0000

Bird, Ms P (Simmons & Simmons)
London EC2 *p79*. 020 7628 2020

Bird, P L (Wilson & Bird) *G S1 E C1 H N W Q K1 O S2 R2*
Aylesbury *p121* 01296 436766

Bird, R (Kendall & Davies) *S1 W*
Burford *p168*. 01993 822025

Bird, R G (Yarwood & Stubley) *W S1 E L*
Blyth *p148*. 01670 361211

Bird, Miss S A (Norwich and Peterborough Building Society) *C1 L S1*
Peterborough *p468* 01733 372372

Bird, S D (Birds Solicitors) *G H B2*
Wandsworth *p13*. 020 8874 7433

Bird, S D S (Marchant Harries & Co) *G H N Q Zl*
Aberdare *p113*. 01685 885500

Bird, S M (Mayo Wynne Baxter LLP) *N E Q J1 S1*
East Grinstead *p215*. 01342 310600

Bird, Ms S R A (Metropolitan Police Directorate of Legal Services)
London SW1 *p108*. 020 7230 7210

Bird, T (Wedlake Bell LLP)
London WC1 *p91* 020 7395 3000

Birdi, B S (Teacher Stern LLP) *E S1*
London WC1 *p86* 020 7242 3191

Birdi, K (Plexus Law (A Trading Name of Parabis Law LLP)) *Zj O Q N*
London EC3 *p68*. 0844 245 4000

Bird-Wood, Mrs S (Russell & Co) *W*
Malvern *p300* 01684 892000

Birdy, L R (Birdy & Co) *D1 O Q N E S1 C1 L K1 W Zi*
Wembley *p426*. 020 8900 9112

Biriah, Ms J (Pictons Solicitors LLP) *G H*
Milton Keynes *p317* 01908 663511

Biriyok, Mrs L (Biriyok Show Solicitors) *S2 K3 J1 K1 L Zi Q H S1 W*
London SE16 *p13* 020 7237 4646

Birkbeck, Ms R (Eaton Smith LLP) *E S2*
Huddersfield *p255* 01484 821300
Bolton *p149* 01204 677000

Birkett, G J (FBC Manby Bowdler LLP) *O Q*
Wolverhampton *p437* 01902 578000

Birkett, Mrs J (Muckle LLP) *R2 E*
Newcastle upon Tyne *p325* . 0191 211 7777

Birkett, Mrs N A (Nottinghamshire County Council Legal Services Division)
West Bridgford *p475*. 0115 977 3478

Birkett, P (Howard Kennedy LLP) *E R2*
London W1 *p48* 020 7636 1616

Birkett, R (Cartwright King) *G H Zl*
Nottingham *p336*. 0115 958 7444

Birkinshaw, D C (Schofield Sweeney) *E R1 A1 R2 S1 S2 Zc*
Bradford *p154* 01274 306000

Birkinshaw, Ms J L (East Riding of Yorkshire Council)
Beverley *p449* 01482 887700

Birks, D (BHP Law)
Stockton-on-Tees *p396* . . . 01642 672770

Birnage, Miss S J (Hewitsons) *S1 L*
Saffron Walden *p370*. 01799 522471

Birnie, Mrs J (Machins Solicitors LLP) *W K4*
Luton *p295* 01582 514000

Birt, T D (Osborne Clarke) *F2 R2 U2 C2 F1*
London EC2 *p65*. 020 7105 7000

Birtles, Ms A (Lanyon Bowdler LLP) *A1 E S1 L R1*
Ludlow *p294*. 01584 872333

Birtles, Dr A D (Hewitson & Harker Limited) *S1 A1 W C1 K1 L T1 A2 S2 F1 G J1 Zg N Zr O Q*
Kirkby Stephen *p268*. 01768 371534

Birtles, Miss C E (Heelis Solicitors) *S1 W S2 K4 A1*
Appleby *p118* 01768 351591

Birtles, P J (Hewitson & Harker Limited) *S1 A1 W C1 K1 L T1 P R1 K3 K4 E Zf X Zi*
Kirkby Stephen *p268*. 01768 371534

Birtles, Ms R (Frank Howard) *N Q*
Warrington *p422*. 01925 653481

Birtwell, Miss J (O'Melveny & Myers LLP)
London EC4 *p64*. 020 7088 0000

Birtwell, J C (Fieldings Porter) *G H K1 M1 P Zi*
Bolton *p149* 01204 540900

Birtwistle, G (Shacklocks) *W T2*
Derby *p209* 01332 559281

Birtwistle, Miss K (National Association of Local Councils)
London WC1 *p108*. 020 7637 1865

Bisal, Mrs S (Newsome Vaughan LLP) *W*
Coventry *p200*. 024 7663 3433

Bisatt, D (Tollers LLP)
Northampton *p332*. 01604 258558

Bisgrove, Miss E (Wansbroughs) *G H*
Melksham *p314* 01225 703222

Bish, T G (Prudential PLC)
London EC4 *p108* 020 7220 7588

Bishi, F (Philcox Gray & Co)
London SE15 *p67* 020 7703 2285
Islington *p91*. 020 7251 5533

Bishop, A (Shoosmiths)
Birmingham *p142* 0370 086 4000 / 0121 335 4440

Bishop, A (Williams MacDougall & Campbell) *K1 H G*
Worthing *p442*. 01903 214186

Bishop, A K (Madge Lloyd & Gibson) *S1 W L C1 A1 E K4 S2*
Gloucester *p230*. 01452 520224

Bishop, B (DLA Piper UK LLP)
London EC2 *p24*. 0870 011 1111

Bishop, C W (The College of Law)
London WC1 *p105*. 0800 289997

Bishop, Ms F J (LG Lawyers)
London SE1 *p50*. 020 7379 0000

Bishop, G B M (Howard Kennedy LLP) *Zl O*
London W1 *p48* 020 7636 1616

Bishop, Ms G F (Family Law in Partnership LLP) *K1 K2*
London WC2 *p30* 020 7420 5000

Bishop, J H W (Hipkin & Co) *J1 J2 N Q W L O Zr K4*
Whitley Bay *p431* 0191 253 3509

Bishop, J J H (Moorhead James LLP) *E S2 L S1 R1 P R2 B1*
London EC4 *p61*. 020 7831 8888

Bishop, J M (Pinsent Masons LLP) *O Q C1 Zc Zj*
London EC2 *p67*. 020 7418 7000

Bishop, Ms K (QualitySolicitors Hill & Abbott) *K3 K1 D1 D2*
Chelmsford *p187*. 01245 258892

Bishop, Miss L A (Herrington & Carmichael LLP) *J1 Zp O Q*
Wokingham *p437* 0118 977 4045

Bishop, Ms M (Bishop McBride Olden)
Cardiff *p177* 029 2049 0111

Bishop, M (Pinsent Masons LLP) *Zb*
London EC2 *p67*. 020 7418 7000

Bishop, M R (David Gray Solicitors) *Zm Zg*
Newcastle upon Tyne *p324* . 0191 232 9547

Bishop, N A (Royal Borough of Kingston upon Thames)
Kingston upon Thames *p462*. 020 8546 2121

Bishop, R (Gosport Borough Council)
Gosport *p459* 023 9258 4242

Bishop, R H (Challinors) *K1 P G N S1 B1 W F1 C1 Zc Ze Zl*
West Bromwich *p427* 0121 553 3211

Bishop, S A (BLB Solicitors) *E S2 R2 S1 L C1*
Swindon *p406* 01793 615011

Bishop, S C (Bishop & Sewell LLP) *S1 E L W S2*
London WC1 *p13* 020 7631 4141

Bishop, S J (MFG Solicitors)
Bromsgrove *p167* 01527 831691

Bishop, Mrs S L (Pearson Maddin Solicitors)
New Malden *p321* 020 8949 9500

Bishop, Miss S R (Owen White) *S2 E S1*
Slough *p382*. 01753 876800

Bishop, T A (BLB Solicitors) *E S1 A1 R1 T1 W*
Bath *p127* 01225 462871
Trowbridge *p413*. 01225 755656

Bishop, T J (Bonallack & Bishop) *K1 D1 G H D2 P*
Salisbury *p371*. 01722 422300

Bishton, Mrs J A (Fisher Meredith) *D1 D2*
Lambeth *p32*. 020 7091 2700

Bisla, Mrs S (Anthony Collins Solicitors LLP) *E*
Birmingham *p137* 0121 200 3242

Biss, M S (British American Tobacco)
London WC2 *p104*. 020 7845 1000

Bissett, M (White & Case LLP) *Zb*
London EC2 *p91*. 020 7532 1000

Bissmire, M J (Bissmire Fudge & Co) *B1 E G K1 L M1 N P R1 S1 Zb Zc Zl*
Haverfordwest *p244* 01437 764723
Pembroke Dock *p345* 01646 685501

Bisson, N J (Plumstead Community Law Centre)
London SE18 *p108* 020 8855 9817

Bitel, N A (Max Bitel Greene LLP) *M1 P J1 W B1 Zb Ze Zf Zk Zw*
Islington *p59*. 020 7354 2767

Bitmead, K J (Barlow Lyde & Gilbert LLP) *O Q Zj N*
London EC3 *p10*. 020 7247 2277

Blach, A (CMS Cameron McKenna LLP)
London EC3 *p17*. 020 7367 3000

Blachford, M K (Kerman & Co LLP) *S1 W R1 S2*
London WC2 *p49* 020 7539 7272

Black, A J (Pinsent Masons LLP)
London EC2 *p67*. 020 7418 7000

Black, A W (Linklaters LLP)
London EC2 *p54*. 020 7456 2000

Black, C E (Black & Co) *G B2 H*
Earl Shilton *p214* 01455 844005

Black, D (Zatman & Co)
Manchester *p311* 0161 832 2500

Black, D C (Harrowells) *E C1 L S2*
York *p444*. 01904 690111

Black, D J (Bower & Bailey) *N Zr*
Oxford *p343*. 01865 311133

Black, Mrs E (Norfolk County Council - Legal Services)
Norwich *p467* . . . Minicom: 0844 800 8011

Black, Mrs E P (Taylors) *O Q*
Blackburn *p146* 0844 800 0263

Black, G L (Berg Legal) *C1 C2 Ze*
Manchester *p301* 0161 833 9211

Black, G R (W Davies) *W*
Woking *p436*. 01483 744900

Black, J A (Mayer Brown International LLP) *E S2 R2*
London EC2 *p59*. 020 3130 3000

Black, J S W (North West Hampshire Magistrates Court)
Basingstoke *p448* 01252 366000

Black, K (Morgan Lewis & Bockius)
London EC4 *p61*. 020 3201 5000

Black, Ms K L (Eastleigh Borough Council)
Eastleigh *p457*. 023 8068 8068

Black, Miss K M (Boodle Hatfield)
Westminster *p14*. 020 7629 7411

Black, Ms L (Osborne Clarke) *E*
London EC2 *p65*. 020 7105 7000

Black, Ms L E (Edwin Coe LLP) *E*
London WC2 *p29* 020 7691 4000

Black, M (Salford City Council)
Swinton *p473* 0161 794 4711

Black, Mrs M F (Currey & Co) *W T2 Zd*
Westminster *p24*. 020 7802 2700

Black, P M (Hughmans) *Q O K3 S2 E*
London EC4 *p44*. 020 7246 6560

Black, R (Barlow Robbins LLP)
Guildford *p235*. 01483 562901

Black, R (Barlow Lyde & Gilbert LLP) *Za O A3 Zj M2*
London EC3 *p10*. 020 7247 2277

Black, R A (Russell Jones & Walker) *G H*
Manchester *p309* 0161 383 3500

Black, R D (SJ Berwin LLP)
London EC4 *p75*. 020 7111 2222

Black, S (McDermott Will & Emery UK LLP)
London EC2 *p56*. 020 7577 6900

Black, Ms S E (Herbert Smith LLP) *C1 C3 M1*
London EC2 *p40*. 020 7374 8000

Black, Ms S L (Black Norman) *C1 D1 E G J1 K1 L M1 P R1 O W*
Crosby *p203*. 0151 931 2777

Black, Miss S R (May May & Merrimans) *K3 D1 K1*
London WC1 *p59* 020 7405 8932

Black, S R K (Harrowells) *O J1 Q B1 Zp Zq Zk Zl Zg J2*
York *p444*. 01904 690111

Blackall, Miss M C (Quinn Melville) *N G*
Liverpool *p290*. 0151 236 3340

Blackburn, A J (Grant Saw Solicitors LLP) *K1 D1 Q L J1 O*
Greenwich *p36*. 020 8858 6971

Blackburn, A R (Nash & Co Solicitors LLP) *C1 S2 E Ze U2 Zza I*
Plymouth *p350*. 01752 664444

Blackburn, Ms C (Manches LLP) *C1*
Oxford *p343*. 01865 722106

Blackburn, C (MWR Law Ltd) *C1 O J1 Q B1*
Preston *p357* 01772 254201

Blackburn, C (Swinburne & Jackson LLP) *K1 G H P D1 W V Zl Zm B2 D2*
Gateshead *p229*. 0191 477 2531 / 477 3222

Blackburn, D (Derbyshire County Council)
Matlock *p465* 01629 580000

Blackburn, G (Mulcahy Smith) *S1 E W Q T1 C1 O*
Gateshead *p229* 0191 490 1000

Blackburn, G A (London Borough of Southwark) *L S2 S1 W*
London SE1 *p109* 020 7525 5000

Blackburn, Miss H J (The International Family Law Group) *K1 D1*
London WC2 *p45* 020 3178 5668
London E1 *p71* 020 3060 6000

Blackburn, J D (Ashfords LLP) *S1 A1 W*
Exeter *p220* 01392 337000
Taunton *p408* 01823 232300

Blackburn, J D (Turner Parkinson) *S2 E R2 R1 C1*
Manchester *p310* 0161 833 1212

Blackburn, Mrs J M (Ramsdens Solicitors) *S1*
Elland *p217* 01422 372478

Blackburn, Miss M J (Henry Hughes & Hughes) *W S1 T1*
London SW16 *p40*. 020 8765 2700

Blackburn, M S D (City of York Council)
York *p477* 01904 551045

Blackburn, P (St Helens Borough Council)
St Helens *p472* 01744 456000

Blackburn, Miss R M (Lancashire County Council) *K1 V D1 X*
Preston *p469* 01772 254868

Blackburn, Miss S (Pannone LLP) *E L S1 S2*
Manchester *p308* 0161 909 3000

Blackett, Ms L (TLT Solicitors)
London EC2 *p85*. 020 3465 4000

Blackett, P R (BHP Law) *E W*
Darlington *p206* 01325 466794

Blackham, M J (Barber Titleys) *N M1 B1 J1 C1 C2 Q Zc Zq O Zr F1 Zl*
Harrogate *p240* 01423 502211

Blackhurst, A L (ALB Law) *G H N A2 Zr K3 J1 Zq*
Southport *p388* 01704 500771

Blackhurst, Ms D E (Confreys) *Zm*
Cardiff *p177* 029 2045 8080

Blackhurst, Miss K J (Bannister Preston) *N Q Zq*
Sale *p370* 0161 973 2434

Blackie, Mrs L G (Durham City Council)
Durham *p457* 0191 386 6111

Blackie, N A C (FBC Manby Bowdler LLP) *P R1*
Telford *p409* 01952 292129

Blacklaws, Ms C (TV Edwards LLP) *D1 K1 K2 D2*
London SE8 *p85*. 020 7790 7000
London SE8 *p91*. 020 8479 8000

Blackledge, P L (Tickle Hall Cross) *C1 E L S1 W*
St Helens *p391* 0800 854379

Blackler, A J M (Macfarlanes) *E*
London EC4 *p56*. 020 7831 9222

Blacklidge, M J (Forbes) *F1 G H J1 L M1 P Zi Zl*
Blackburn *p145* 01254 580000

Blacklock, J C (Charles Blacklock & Co)
Monmouth *p318* 01600 714444

Blackman, Miss A (Thomson Webb & Corfield) *D1 Zo K1 S1*
Cambridge *p176*. 01223 578068

Blackman, G (Edwards Duthie) *K1*
London E13 *p29*. 020 8514 9000

Blackman, Ms J (Future Film Financing Ltd) *T1*
London W1 *p106* 020 7009 6600

Blackman, L (Russell-Cooke LLP) *B2 G H*
London SW15 *p74*. 020 8789 9111

Blackman, L F (Lionel Blackman) *G H I*
Epsom *p219*. 01372 728941

Blackmore, D M (Turners Solicitors LLP) *B1 D1 J1 K1 O Q Zp N*
Bournemouth *p153*. 01202 291291

Blackmore, Miss J (Somerset County Council)
Taunton *p473* 0845 345 9166

Blackmore, Ms K C (Leeds City Council)
Leeds *p462* 0113 224 3513

Blackmore, M R (Battens) *S1 W S2*
Dorchester *p212*. 01305 250560
Chard *p184* . . . . . . 01460 65335 / 61000

Blackmore, P A (Olswang LLP) *C1 C2 B1*
London WC1 *p64* 020 7067 3000

Blackmore, P H (First Assist)
Sutton *p473* 020 8652 1313

Blackmore, P N (Patrick Blackmore) *N*
Menai Bridge *p314*. .01248 715987 / 714987

Blackmore, P W (McGrigors LLP)
London EC4 *p56*. 020 7054 2500
Manchester *p307* 0161 935 8337

Blackmore, Ms V K (Allen & Overy LLP)
London E1 *p5* 020 3088 0000

Blacksell, S G (DLA Piper UK LLP) *E R2 S2*
Sheffield *p375* 0870 011 1111

Blackshaw, S M (Linklaters LLP)
London EC2 *p54*. 020 7456 2000

Blackstock, G S C (Pitman Blackstock White) *S1 M1 W*
Lydney *p296*. 01594 842475

Blackwell, Mrs A (McGrigors LLP)
London EC4 *p56*. 020 7054 2500

Blackwell, C A W (C A W Blackwell) *W S1 T2*
Royston *p368* 01763 243803

Blackwell, Mrs H (Capsticks Solicitors LLP) *C1 E R2*
London SW19 *p18*. 020 8780 2211

Blackwell, J (Nabarro LLP)
Sheffield *p376* 0114 279 4000

Blackwell, Ms K (Anthony Collins Solicitors LLP) *E*
Birmingham *p137* 0121 200 3242

Blackwell, Ms L (Pemberton Greenish LLP) *S1 E L*
London SW3 *p66* 020 7591 3333

Blackwell, M (McGrigors LLP)
London EC4 *p56*. 020 7054 2500

Blackwell, N J (Browne Jacobson LLP) *E A1 F1 J1*
Nottingham *p336*. 0115 976 6000

Blackwell, T (Moore Blatch Solicitors) *N*
Southampton *p386*. 023 8071 8000

Blackwell-West, Ms J D (Blackwell-West) *N*
Ferndown *p225* 01202 892300

See p634 for the Key to Work Categories

Blackwood, Miss R H (Housing & Property Law Partnership) L Zh Q
Islington p43 020 7553 9000

Blades, E (Harrow Solicitors & Advocates) B2 G H
Wealdstone p424 020 8863 0788

Blades, G T (Wilkin Chapman Epton Blades) G Zg
Lincoln p285 01522 512345

Blades, Mrs J (Dolmans) N Q L
Cardiff p178 029 2034 5531

Blades, Ms M Y (Thurrock Borough Council)
Grays p459 01375 390000

Blagbrough, W (Ince & Co Services Ltd)
London E1 p44 020 7481 0010

Blagdon, Miss S (Clerk to Sheffield Justices)
Sheffield p470 0114 276 0760

Blain, A B (CKFT) C1 C2 J1 F1 Ze
London NW3 p17 020 7431 7262

Blain, J J (Veale Wasbrough Vizards) E S1 L R1
London EC4 p89 020 7405 1234

Blain, M J H (Blain Boland & Co) C1 E J1 K1 S1 S2 W Zl
Willaston p432 0151 327 1301
Ellesmere Port p217 0151 355 2645

Blain, S (Fisher Meredith) K1
Lambeth p32 020 7091 2700

Blair, A D (Barlow Lyde & Gilbert LLP) Q Zj Zq
London EC3 p10 020 7247 2277

Blair, A P K (Walters & Barbary) G H L N
Camborne p173 01209 712454

Blair, B (Boodle Hatfield)
Westminster p14 020 7629 7411

Blair, J J (Dickinson Dees) B1
Newcastle upon Tyne p324 0191 279 9000

Blair, R J G (WBW Solicitors) Zr N
Torquay p413 0870 701 4321

Blair, S (Farrer & Co LLP)
London WC2 p31 020 3375 7000

Blair, S W (Radcliffes Le Brasseur) S1 E J1 Q L N W C1 K1 Zh Zd
Westminster p70 020 7222 7040

Blair, Mrs T A (Portsmouth City Council)
Portsmouth p469 023 9283 4034

Blake, Ms A (Quastel Midgen LLP) J1 C1 U2 F2 Ze Zza C2
London W1 p70 020 7908 2525

Blake, Ms A E (Coca-Cola Enterprises Ltd)
Uxbridge p474 01895 231313

Blake, C G (Glynnes) J1 J2 N
Ealing p214 020 8997 1437

Blake, Ms C M (Charlotte Blake) C1 J1 Zc
London NW5 p13 020 7485 4010

Blake, C S (Blake Lapthorn) E A1
Chandlers Ford p184 023 8090 8090

Blake, G A J (Somers & Blake) S1 G N Q W J1 Zi
London W7 p80 020 8567 7025

Blake, J (Cowlishaw & Mountford)
Uttoxeter p417 01889 565211

Blake, J A (Bates Wells & Braithwaite London LLP) Zd C1 X
London EC4 p11 020 7551 7777

Blake, J E (SJ Berwin LLP)
London EC4 p75 020 7111 2222

Blake, J W (John Howe & Co) J1 O Q N
Pudsey p358 0113 236 3936

Blake, Ms K (Alexander & Co) E S1 Zc
Derby p208 01332 600005

Blake, Mrs K V (North Somerset District Council)
Weston-super-Mare p476 01934 888888

Blake, Mrs M (Walter Gray & Co) Zd K4 T2 V S1 W L K1
Ryde p369 01983 563765

Blake, M A (Parkinson Wright LLP) F1 J1 O Q Zq
Worcester p440 01905 726789

Blake, Ms M A (DAC Beachcroft) E S2
London EC4 p24 020 7242 1011

Blake, P J (Kennedys) Zj N
London EC3 p49 020 7667 9667

Blake, P L G (Prettys) O F1 Zc A3 M2
Ipswich p262 01473 232121

Blake, P M W (Clifford Chance)
London E14 p20 020 7006 1000

Blake, Ms S (Tolhurst Fisher LLP)
Southend-on-Sea p387 01702 352511

Blake, Mrs S K (Berwins Solicitors Limited) S1
Harrogate p240 01423 509000

Blake, W (Shepherd + Wedderburn LLP)
London EC4 p78 020 7429 4900

Blake, Ms Y (Norton Peskett)
Lowestoft p294 01502 533000

Blake-Barward, V (East Riding of Yorkshire Council)
Beverley p449 01482 887700

Blakebrough, S (Platt Halpern)
Oldham p341 0161 626 4955

Blakely, R (Wilson & Co) Zi
London N17 p92 020 8808 7535

Blakeman, D J E (Howard Kennedy LLP) E L S1 R1 A1
London W1 p48 020 7636 1616

Blakemore, A C (Weightmans LLP) N O P F1 Zc Zk Zq
Liverpool p291 0151 227 2601

Blakemore, Ms C (Kingsley Napley) K1 D1
London EC1 p50 020 7814 1200

Blakemore, Mrs J (CMHT Solicitors) D1 K1 G H X W N Zm C1 S2 E J1
Walsall p420 01922 646400

Blakemore, Mrs N H (Squire Sanders (UK) LLP)
Leeds p277 0113 284 7000

Blakemore, P J (GHP Legal) S1 E W
Wrexham p442 01978 291456

Blakeney, W (William Blakeney) W Q S1 L S2
Westminster p14 020 7717 8510

Blakesley, J F (Gamlins)
Llandudno p291 01492 860420

Blakesley, Miss K (Pritchard Joyce & Hinds) O Q N C1
Beckenham p129 020 8658 3922

Blakey, Ms C (Fitzhugh Gates) S1
Shoreham-by-Sea p378 01273 461381

Blakey, C K (Stapleton Gardner & Co) J1 L
Morley p319 0113 253 8111

Blakey, Miss F (Marks & Spencer PLC)
London W2 p107 020 7935 4422

Blakey, J A (Squire Sanders (UK) LLP)
Leeds p277 0113 284 7000

Blakey, Miss L (Freeman Johnson) K1 D1 N L
Spennymoor p389 01388 814389

Blakey, M R (Hill Dickinson LLP) E R1 R2 S2
Manchester p305 0161 817 7200

Blamire, Miss B L (Trethowans LLP) N Zj
Southampton p387 023 8032 1000

Blamire-Brown, M P (Solihull Metropolitan Borough Council)
Solihull p471 0121 704 6000

Blamires, B H (Cumbria County Council)
Carlisle p453 01228 607374 / 607351

Blanch, Ms J S (McDermott Will & Emery UK LLP) A3 O
London EC2 p56 020 7577 6900

Blanchard, Miss C (Conway & Co)
Henley-on-Thames p247 01491 411122

Blanchette, Ms K (Plexus Law (A Trading Name of Parabis Law LLP)) N
London EC3 p68 0844 245 4000

Bland, Mrs K (Anthony King & Co) L K1 Zh
Basildon p126 01268 240400

Bland, Miss L (Ellisons) N O Q
Colchester p197 01206 764477

Bland, Miss L M (Lupton Fawcett) J1 Zp
Leeds p275 0113 280 2000

Bland, M (Leslie Harris Solicitors & Advocates) Q K1 D1 N
Lytham p297 01253 724974

Bland, M (Linklaters LLP)
London EC2 p54 020 7456 2000

Bland, M H (Percy Hughes & Roberts) J1 L W Q Zp
Birkenhead p134 0151 666 9090

Bland, Miss S H (Gordon Dadds) K1
London W1 p25 020 7493 6151

Blaney, T D (LG Lawyers) E R1
London SE1 p50 020 7379 0000

Blank, J A (Abrahamson & Associates) J1 E S2 S1 C1 W K1 I
London NW11 p3 020 8458 1100

Blank, Mrs K S (Freeth Cartwright LLP) C1 F1 C2 Zw
Leicester p279 0116 248 1100
Leicester p281 0116 262 4225

Blank, M C (Buckles Solicitors LLP) E A1 S2 S1 R2
Peterborough p346 01733 888888

Blankfield, A M (Field Fisher Waterhouse LLP) C1 C2 C3 J1 B1 T1 Zb
London EC3 p31 020 7861 4000

Blanks, Ms H (Cadbury Schweppes PLC)
London W1 p104 020 7409 1313

Blanksby, M A (Pinsent Masons LLP) O Q Zc
London EC2 p67 020 7418 7000

Blanning, J P (Restormel Borough Council)
St Austell p472 01726 223612

Blaquiere, A D (DWF) N Zj O
Liverpool p287 0151 907 3000

Blasdale, Miss D V (Gedling Borough Council)
Nottingham p467 0115 901 3901

Blatcher, Ms P (Coldham Shield & Mace) S1
London E4 p21 020 8524 6323

Blatchford, T J (North Devon District Council)
Barnstaple p448 01271 327711

Blatherwick, I P (Browne Jacobson LLP) C1 C2 B1
Nottingham p336 0115 976 6000

Blatherwick, J D (Tallents Solicitors) S1 L E C1 A1 F1 W Zl
Newark p322 01636 671881

Blatherwick, P (Tallents Solicitors) A1 C1 E L S1 T1 W R1 Zd Zl
Newark p322 01636 671881

Blavo, J (Blavo & Co Solicitors)
London WC1 p14 020 7025 2020

Blaxell, S (More Fisher Brown) C1 Za Zj
London EC4 p61 020 7330 8000

Blay, A J (Seymours) S1 E W C1 L R1 T1 Zh S2
Coventry p201 024 7655 3961

Blay, R A (Magrath LLP) O Q
London W1 p57 020 7495 3003

Blaza, Miss R A (Bailey & Haigh) N Q K3 K1 F1 Zq O Zr D1
Selby p373 01757 705191

Blazey, Miss J R (Taylor Wessing) C1
London EC4 p86 020 7300 7000

Bleakley, Mrs L (Cartwright King) S1 K1 P W F1 M1 V L A1
Nottingham p336 0115 958 7444
Nottingham p338 0115 958 6262

Bleasdale, J (Hill Dickinson LLP) J1 N
Liverpool p288 0151 600 8000

Bledge, Ms L F (Potter Rees (Serious Injury) Solicitors)
Manchester p309 0161 237 5888

Bleetman, Mrs J A (Parkes Wilshire Johnson) S2 W S1 L C1
Barnet p124 020 8441 1556

Bletso, B E (Pritchard Englefield) C1 C2 Zb Ze
London EC2 p69 020 7972 9720

Blewett, M (Pinsent Masons LLP)
London EC2 p67 020 7418 7000

Blezard, R J (Chattertons Solicitors) A1 S2 E A2 M1 O R1 W T1 L A3 S1 Zh
Grantham p232 01476 591550
Northampton p332 01604 233233

Blick, Mrs A J (Blick & Co) K1 Q D1
London EC3 p14 020 7247 9696

Blick, Miss G (Grays) Q L K1 F1
York p444 01904 634771

Blick, M (The Wilkes Partnership LLP) E L R1 S1 Zl S2
Birmingham p143 0121 233 4333

Blick, Miss P S (Solihull Magistrates Court)
Solihull p471 0121 705 8101

Blick, R D (Blick & Co) C1 G M1 N P Za Zb Zf A3 O Q
London EC3 p14 020 7247 9696

Bligh, P (Gullands) G H
Maidstone p299 01622 678341

Bligh, Ms V J (Foot Anstey)
Plymouth p349 01752 675000

Blinkho, I G (Lancashire County Council)
Preston p469 01772 254868

Bliss, A W H (Sidley Austin Brown & Wood) Zb
London EC2 p78 020 7360 3600

Bliss, Miss N K (Metcalfes) O Q B1 Zb
Bristol p164 0117 929 0451

Blizard, Ms L J (Needham Poulier & Partners) G H
London N17 p63 020 8808 6622

Bloch, L M (Halegate Properties Ltd) E L S1
Edgware p458 020 8951 1616

Block, Miss C V (Metcalfes) N
Bristol p164 0117 929 0451

Block, Ms J (Simmons & Simmons)
London EC2 p79 020 7628 2020

Blocker, A (Kennedys)
London EC3 p49 020 7667 9667

Blohm, Ms K E (Hempsons) N Zr
Manchester p305 0161 228 0011

Blois, M (Browne Jacobson LLP) Q Zr Zj
Nottingham p336 0115 976 6000

Blok, A G (Mulcare Jenkins) E L S1 S2 W K4 J1 R2
Haywards Heath p246 01444 459954

Blomfield, D R (Boyes Turner) J1
Reading p360 0118 959 7711

Blomfield, Ms N M (Barlow Lyde & Gilbert LLP)
London EC3 p10 020 7247 2277

Blomstrand, L E (Leonard Blomstrand)
London SE20 p14 020 8776 7707

Blood, D C (Cocks Lloyd) E R2 S1 S2
Nuneaton p339 024 7664 1642

Blood, M J (Cocks Lloyd) F1 C1 J1 Q L
Nuneaton p339 024 7664 1642

Blood, M J (Brabners Chaffe Street) C1 J1 Zw Ze
Manchester p301 0161 836 8800

Bloodworth, A (Fawcett & Pattni) K1 K3 D1
Walsall p420 01922 640424

Bloom, A (Solomon Taylor & Shaw)
London NW3 p80 020 7431 1912

Bloom, A C (Steptoe & Johnson) C1 C2 B1 U2
London EC2 p83 020 7367 8000

Bloom, A H (Richard Pearlman LLP) Zb F1 B1 O Q
London EC2 p66 020 7739 6100

Bloom, B K (J E Baring & Co)
London EC1 p9 020 7242 8966

Bloom, D (Kaim Todner Ltd) G H B2
Islington p47 020 7700 0070

Bloom, F D (Davenport Lyons) Zf
London W1 p25 020 7468 2600

Bloom, Mrs G (Kingsley Napley) K1 D1
London EC1 p50 020 7814 1200

Bloom, G S (E D C Lord & Co) S1 E W C1 L N T1 R1 Zl
Hayes p245 020 8848 9988

Bloom, I E (Ross & Craig) O J1 Ze Zf Zk Zw Zz C2
Westminster p73 020 7262 3077

Bloom, J D (Julian Bloom & Co) C1 E C2 S1 W S2
Bushey p171 020 8950 3001

Bloom, M D (Hegarty LLP) J1 Zk Zp
Peterborough p347 01733 346333

Bloom, Miss N S (Sutton-Mattocks & Co LLP) Q L O B1 F1 J1 Zq
London W4 p84 020 8994 7344

Bloom, R A (Dickinson Dees) J1
Newcastle upon Tyne p324 0191 279 9000

Bloom, S G (Jonas Roy Bloom) N Q Zj O
Birmingham p139 0121 212 4111

Bloom, Ms S L (Capsticks Solicitors LLP) N Zr Zq
London SW19 p18 020 8780 2211

Bloomer, F J (Jonas Roy Bloom) G H
Birmingham p139 0121 212 4111

Bloomer, J (Howes Percival LLP) E S1
Milton Keynes p317 01908 672682

Bloomer, J M (Ison Harrison) S1 S2
Ilkley p261 01943 889100
Ilkley p261 01943 889100

Bloomfield, D J (Hatch Brenner) K1 N J1 D1 F1 L
Norwich p334 01603 660811

Bloomfield, Ms P J (NFLA Ltd) K3 K1
Nottingham p338 0115 945 4555

Bloomfield, Miss T L (Clark Willis) K1 K3 D1 D2
Darlington p206 01325 281111

Bloor, Miss J (Walters & Plaskitt)
Stoke-on-Trent p398 01782 819611

Bloor, Miss J (Derbyshire County Council)
Matlock p465 01629 580000

Bloor, J (Lees Solicitors LLP) C1 S2 E C2
Birkenhead p134 0151 647 9381

Blori, Mrs C C L (Chapmans Solicitors) K1 K2 V Zl Zi
Sutton p402 020 8337 3801

Bloss, Ms J M (Sykes Lee & Brydson) D1 D2 K1 K3
York p445 01904 731100
York p445 01904 529000

Blount, J (Blount Hemmings) S1 Zf S2 E A1
Kingswinford p268 01384 400565

Blow, Miss E L (Wilkin Chapman LLP) E S2 C1 R2 Zc P R1 S1
Grimsby p235 01472 262626

Blow, Miss V A (R J Osborne & Co) G H
Corby p199 01536 204111

Blower, A (Addleshaw Goddard) O
London EC1 p4 020 7606 8855

Blower, B J S (Nicholsons Solicitors LLP) C1 E S1 A1
Lowestoft p294 01502 532300

Blower, P M (Taylor & Emmet LLP) S1 L
Sheffield p377 0114 218 4000

Blower, R H (Charles Russell LLP) W T2
London EC4 p19 020 7203 5000
London EC2 p82 020 7329 4422

Blowers, Miss M (Fladgate LLP) O Q N
London WC2 p32 020 3036 7000

Blowers, M A (Mogers) S1
Bath p127 01225 750000

Blows, Dr M J (Macfarlanes) C1
London EC4 p56 020 7831 9222

Blows, S (Holman Fenwick Willan)
London EC3 p42 020 7264 8000

Bloxham, A (Bartletts Solicitors) J1 J2 N Q
Liverpool p286 0151 521 7333

Bloxham, D C S (Thomson & Bancks LLP) J1 Zp Q Zl K4 N
Tewkesbury p410 01684 299633

Bloxham, J (Bloxhams) S1 S2 E
Leicester p279 0116 222 3302

Bloxsome, G R (Blackfords LLP) G
Croydon p204 020 8686 6232

Bloxwich, Mrs R (William Wright & Son) K1 D1
Dudley p213 01384 255344

Bloxwich, Miss R (Environment Agency (North East Region))
Leeds p462 0870 850 6506

Bluck, Miss L A (Wallace Robinson & Morgan) W
Solihull p383 0121 705 7571

Blue, Mrs K (Scott Duff & Co) K1 S1 W L A1 F1 D1
Penrith p346 01768 865551

Bluestone, S M (Bluestone & Co) G
London E7 p14 020 8470 2266

Bluett, B (Caladashins)
Ealing p17 020 8832 9000

Blum, Ms B F M (Shell International Ltd)
London SE1 p109 020 7934 1234

Blundell, D I (Crown Prosecution Service West Midlands)
Birmingham p449 0121 262 1300

Blundell, N G (Browne Jacobson LLP) Zc O A3 Zq
Nottingham p336 0115 976 6000

Blundell, N S P (Bird & Bird LLP) C1 C2
London EC4 p13 020 7415 6000

Blunden, M (Boyes Turner) C1 C3 Ze
Reading p360 0118 959 7711

Blunden, P L (Alistair Harper & Co) G H
Haywards Heath p245 01444 457890

Blunden, Mrs W (Williams MacDougall & Campbell) K1
Worthing p442 01903 214186

Blunderfield, A (Stanley Tee) L O Q Zq F1
Bishop's Stortford p144 01279 755200

Blundy, A C (Andrew C Blundy Solicitors) O C1 Q L J1 R1 K1 Zl
Greenwich p14 020 8293 3633

Blundy, P H (Royal College of Nursing)
London W1 p109 020 7409 3333

Bluston, D (Lavery Haynes)
London NW3 p51 020 7435 7441

Blyth, G D (Wright Hassall LLP) E S2 R2
Leamington Spa p270 01926 886688

Blyth, J M (Peterborough City Council)
Peterborough p468 01733 747474

Blyth, M (Linklaters LLP)
London EC2 p54 020 7456 2000

Blyth-Cook, Mrs A M (Ann Blyth-Cook & Co) G H
Southend-on-Sea p387 01702 462999

Blythe, Ms D A (Russell-Cooke LLP) N Zr
London SW15 p74 020 8789 9111

Blythe, I (Banks Kelly) N S1 L Q J1 C1 Zs Zw V Zv K1
London EC2 p9 020 7248 4231

Blythe, M (City of York Council) E R1 L
York p477 01904 551045

Blythe, R J (Quality Solicitors Hill & Abbott) K1 D1 D2 K3
Chelmsford p187 01245 258892

Boaden, J H (Mills & Co) O M2 Q Za Zj Zb
Newcastle upon Tyne p325 0191 233 2222

Boag, R J D (Jacobs Solicitors) G H D1 K1 N
Ellesmere Port p217 0151 355 8481

Boahen, Ms C A (Metropolitan Police Directorate of Legal Services)
London SW1 p108 020 7230 7210

Boahene, W N (BWF Solicitors) L Zi
London E8 p9 020 7241 7180

Boakes, S J (Croudace Ltd) C1 J1 E L O W S1
Caterham p454 01883 346464

6

Board, A E (Cornfield Law) *E S1 P G W J1 N C1 B1*
Eastbourne *p215* 01323 412512

Board, Mrs N J (Ranson Houghton) *G K1 N*
Andover *p118* 01264 351533

Boardman, Miss K (Levi Solicitors LLP) *O Q B1*
Leeds *p275* 0113 244 9931

Boardman, Mrs K (Thorneycroft Solicitors Ltd) *K3 K1 Q N W*
Macclesfield *p297* 01625 503444

Boardman, P (Bower & Bailey) *N O K1 K2*
Oxford *p343* 01865 311133

Boardman, P A (Colin Rayner & Co) *N Q S1 W*
Bolton *p149* 01204 591145

Boardman, P R (Lester Aldridge LLP) *L*
Bournemouth *p152* 01202 786161

Boardman, Mrs R J (Bird & Bird LLP) *Ze I U2*
London EC4 *p13* 020 7415 6000

Boardman, T (Cartmell Shepherd) *W*
Penrith *p346* 01768 862326

Boast, J (Jones Day) *Zb*
London EC4 *p46* 020 7039 5959

Boast, M D (Blocks) *W S1 K1 L*
Felixstowe *p225* 01394 283241

Boateng, A (London Borough of Southwark)
London SE1 *p109* 020 7525 5000

Boateng-Ennin, Mrs N A A (Bromley Magistrates Court)
Bromley *p452* 0845 601 3600

Boatswain, C (Hopkin Murray Beskine)
London N4 *p42* 020 7272 1234

Bobak, J (George Ide LLP) *M1 N K1 P J1 B1 D1 F1 Zp*
Chichester *p192* 01243 786668

Bobb, T (Sutovic & Hartigan)
London W3 *p84* 020 8993 5544

Boccali-Vine, Mrs M (DWFM Beckman) *S2 E L R1 R2 S1*
Westminster *p25* 020 7872 0023

Bochenski, A J J (DWF) *Zb F1*
Manchester *p303* 0161 603 5000

Bodalia, Ms R (Coventry City Council)
Coventry *p456* 024 7683 4863

Boddam-Whetham, J D (Gowmans) *D2 K1 Zl*
Paignton *p345* 01803 546100

Boddington, Ms L F (Kingsley Napley) *Zl*
London EC1 *p50* 020 7814 1200

Boddy, Mrs A M (North Yorkshire County Council)
Northallerton *p467* 01609 780780

Boddy, I M (The Johnson Partnership) *G H*
Nottingham *p337* 0115 941 9141

Boddy, J N (HM Revenue & Customs)
Salford *p470* 0870 785 8545

Boddy, K R T (Harold Benjamin) *L S1 P E K1 M1 W*
Harrow *p241* 020 8422 5678

Boddy, N F (Brown Beer Nixon Mallon) *K1 V W J1 N Q L B1 F1 Zi Zp Zr Zv*
Middlesbrough *p315* 01642 254182

Boddy, N F (Wilson & Co Solicitors) *G H*
Middlesbrough *p315* 01642 222292

Boddy, W D C (Max Gold Law)
Hull *p257* 01482 224900

Bode, A (Trowers & Hamlins)
London EC3 *p88* 020 7423 8000

Bode, A F (Trowers & Hamlins) *E L Zh*
Manchester *p310* 0161 211 0000

Boden, D (Ince & Co Services Ltd)
London E1 *p44* 020 7481 0010

Boden, J J (Rothera Dowson) *W E A1 C1 S1 S2 R1 R2 T1 T2*
Nottingham *p338* 0115 910 0600

Boden, Miss K (Salmons) *K1 K3 D1*
Newcastle under Lyme *p323* 01782 621266

Boden, Ms L (Stones Solicitors LLP) *S1*
Exeter *p222* 01392 666777

Boden, M J (Kennet District Council)
Devizes *p457* 01380 724911

Bodenstein, C (Fishburns) *M1 Zj O N Zq*
London EC3 *p32* 020 7280 8888

Bodi, A Y (AYB Law Solicitors) *N Q Zq*
Preston *p356* 01772 250605

Bodkin, P M (Chamberlain Martin Solicitors) *S1 W T1 B1 A1 E F1*
Littlehampton *p285* 01903 713814 / 716548
Bognor Regis *p148* 01243 825211

Bodley, Mrs A E (Batchelors Solicitors) *K1 K3*
Bromley *p166* 020 8768 7000

Bodley, K F (Kevin Bodley) *C1 M1 J1 C3 A3 I Zg M2 O C2 M3*
Holsworthy *p251* 01409 221460
Bournemouth *p152* 01202 558844

Body, D I B (Irwin Mitchell LLP) *N Zr*
Sheffield *p376* 0870 150 0100

Body, R (Richard Body & Co)
St Leonards-on-Sea *p392* 01424 201301

Boehm, Miss M (DW Solicitors) *Q Zl J1 W*
Northampton *p331* 01604 624222

Bogaardt, Ms J M (Battens) *W*
Yeovil *p443* 01935 846000

Bogan, H (Ormerods) *J1 L Q*
Croydon *p205* 020 8686 5000

Bogard, H P (Blatchfords) *S1 G F1 B1 L*
Harrow *p241* 020 8422 1181

Bogle, A (Hill Dickinson LLP) *O Zb B1*
Manchester *p305* 0161 817 7200

Bogle, Mrs L (United Utilities)
Warrington *p475* 01925 237000

Bogle, N H (Pinsent Masons LLP)
London EC2 *p67* 020 7418 7000

Bohanna, Ms L D (FBC Manby Bowdler LLP) *W T2*
Wolverhampton *p437* 01902 578000

Bohill, Mrs J S (Warners Solicitors) *S1*
Sevenoaks *p374* 01732 747900

Bohm, P (Bates Wells & Braithwaite London LLP) *C1 C2 Zd*
London EC4 *p11* 020 7551 7777
London WC2 *p32* 020 3036 7000

Bohuszewicz, J V (A V A Mitchell & Co) *C1 M1 N E P Zc Zj*
Woodford Green *p439* 020 8504 7766

Boileau, Mrs L M (Wilkin Chapman Epton Blades) *K1 D1 K3*
Lincoln *p285* 01522 512345

Bointon, Ms R A (DLA Piper UK LLP) *C1 C3 M1*
Birmingham *p137* 0870 011 1111

Bointon, Ms S (Ashurst LLP)
London EC2 *p7* 020 7638 1111

Bola, Ms A (Allianz Insurance PLC)
Guildford *p459* 01483 552730

Bolam, P J (Crown Prosecution Service Durham)
Durham *p457* 0191 383 5800

Boland, B D (Blain Boland & Co) *S1 K1 L W S2*
Willaston *p432* 0151 327 1301
Ellesmere Port *p217* 0151 355 2645

Boland, N (Stephensons Solicitors LLP) *G H Zt*
Wigan *p432* 01942 777777

Bolas, Mrs J E (Maidstone Borough Council)
Maidstone *p464* 01622 602000

Bolc, A (Cartwright King)
Leicester *p279* 0116 253 9222

Boldon, Ms J (Kennedys)
London EC3 *p49* 020 7667 9667

Bolgar-Smith, Mrs H C E (Ambrose Appelbe) *K1 D1 S1 K2 K3*
London WC2 *p6* 020 7242 7000

Bollington, D (The Stokes Partnership) *Ze J1 N T1 T2 C1 C2 F1*
Crewkerne *p203* 01460 279279

Bolt, Ms C (Environment Agency (North East Region))
Leeds *p462* 0870 850 6506

Bolt, Mrs E (Windeatts) *W*
Kingsbridge *p267* 01548 852727

Bolt, Ms L (Paul Robinson Solicitors) *Q L N O*
Westcliff-on-Sea *p428* 01702 338338

Bolt, R K (Bolt Burdon) *N Zq Zr*
Islington *p14* 020 7288 4700

Bolter, A G (Watkins & Gunn) *C1 G H L S1 W X*
Pontypool *p352* 01495 762244

Bolton, C N (Birchall Blackburn LLP) *N*
Preston *p356* 01772 561663
Blackburn *p146* 01254 672222

Bolton, G S (HM Revenue & Customs)
Salford *p470* 0870 785 8545

Bolton, Ms H (Scanlans) *H G*
Sunderland *p402* 0191 565 2565

Bolton, Ms H M (Mills & Reeve) *C1 Zb C2*
Cambridge *p175* 01223 364422

Bolton, J P (Healys LLP) *S1 S2 E R2 W L*
Brighton *p159* 01273 685888

Bolton, Mrs L V (Fonseca & Partners) *W V S1 N Q O K1 H G D1 S2*
Ebbw Vale *p216* 01495 303124

Bolton, Ms M (Wolferstans)
Plymouth *p351* 01752 663295

Bolton, M R A (Dickins Shiebert) *E L R1 S1 Zd*
Potters Bar *p355* 01707 851100

Bolton, N R (Harvey Roberts) *K1 S1 Q W G H B1 L J1 D1 Zl*
Stockport *p395* 0161 443 2828

Bolton, P (Farnworth Shaw) *S1 W C1 E L*
Colne *p198* 01282 864081

Bolton, R A (Shakespeares) *E R1 S1 Zh*
Birmingham *p142* 0121 237 3000

Bolton-Jones, Mrs M A (Wills Group Ltd)
London EC3 *p110* 020 7488 8111

Bonamy, L (Jones Day) *C1*
London EC4 *p46* 020 7039 5959

Bonar, Ms J C (City of Sunderland)
Sunderland *p473* 0191 520 5555

Bonavia, K L (Stephenson Harwood) *C1*
London EC2 *p82* 020 7329 4422

Bond, A (Shepherd + Wedderburn LLP)
London EC4 *p78* 020 7429 4900

Bond, Mrs A (Torbay Council)
Torquay *p474* 01803 201201

Bond, Ms A J (Pinsent Masons LLP)
Birmingham *p141* 0121 200 1050

Bond, A J (A J Bond & Co) *C1 E S1 B1 K1 W J1 Q*
Bromley *p166* 020 8464 2229

Bond, Ms C L (Gullands) *G H*
Maidstone *p299* 01622 678341

Bond, Ms C L (Davidson Large LLP) *J1*
Harrogate *p240* 01423 727272

Bond, Mrs C M (Evans & Co) *K1 D1 V S1 K3*
Spennymoor *p389* 01388 815317

Bond, D (Field Fisher Waterhouse LLP)
London EC3 *p31* 020 7861 4000

Bond, Mrs D (Acklam Bond Noor)
Accrington *p114* 01254 872272

Bond, D E (Stockton-On-Tees Borough Council)
Stockton-on-Tees *p472* 01642 393939

Bond, Ms E (Ison Harrison) *K1 K3 D1*
Leeds *p274* 0113 284 5000

Bond, Ms F (Bristol City Council)
Bristol *p451* 0117 922 2000

Bond, Miss G (Steven Young & Co) *G H*
Cheltenham *p188* 01242 257269

Bond, G G N (Tozers) *K1 D1 Zl*
Exeter *p222* 01392 207020

Bond, I (Michelmores LLP) *W T2*
Exeter *p221* 01392 688688

Bond, I R (Bond Joseph) *G H*
Canterbury *p176* 01227 453545

Bond, Miss J (Torbay Council)
Torquay *p474* 01803 201201

Bond, J (Glaisyers Solicitors LLP) *C1 J1 N F1 I B1 Ze Zj Zc*
Manchester *p304* 0161 832 4666

Bond, Miss J (Manches LLP) *O*
Oxford *p343* 01865 722106

Bond, Ms J A (Hodge Halsall) *B1 J1 F1 F2 L O Q Zl*
Southport *p388* 01704 531991

Bond, Ms K (ASB Law)
Crawley *p202* 01293 603600

Bond, K J (Moss & Poulson) *F1 J1 N Q O X S1 Zi*
Shrewsbury *p379* 01743 350571

Bond, M A (Latham & Watkins LLP)
London EC2 *p51* 020 7710 1000

Bond, N M (A J Bond & Co) *K3 Q S1 W*
Bromley *p166* 020 8464 2229

Bond, P (Penningtons)
London EC2 *p66* 020 7457 3000

Bond, R E R (CVS Solicitors) *J1 C1*
London W1 *p17* 020 7493 2903

Bond, R T J (Speechly Bircham LLP) *C1 I Zza U2*
London EC4 *p81* 020 7427 6400

Bond, Miss S (Tunbridge Wells Borough Council)
Tunbridge Wells *p474* 01892 526121

Bone, Ms A C (Bendles)
Carlisle *p181* 01228 522215

Bone, H N (Winchester City Council)
Winchester *p476* 01962 840222

Bone, J P (Muckle LLP) *E R2 S2*
Newcastle upon Tyne *p325* 0191 211 7777

Bone, M (Jerman Simpson Pearson & Samuels) *G N H Zm*
Southend-on-Sea *p387* 01702 610071

Bonegal, Ms J M (Thursfields) *W S1*
Worcester *p440* 01905 730450

Boneham, Ms C (Squire Sanders (UK) LLP)
Leeds *p277* 0113 284 7000

Bonehill, M J (H Montlake & Co) *C1 E S1 L J1 N W Ze Zi Zl Zp*
Ilford *p260* 020 8532 4800

Bonell, A P (Bonell & Co) *S1 E L C1 W A1 Zc*
Stratford-upon-Avon *p400* 01789 299115

Bonham, Mrs J B (Winterbotham Smith Penley LLP) *K1 D1 K3*
Stroud *p401* 01453 847200

Bonham-Carter, N J (Kerseys) *W T2 K4*
Ipswich *p262* 01473 213311

Boni, Miss I L (Graham Coffey & Co) *N*
Manchester *p302* 0161 200 2440

Boniface, D (Metcalfes) *N O P Q Zc Zj J2*
Bristol *p164* 0117 929 0451

Boniface, Miss S L (West Sussex County Council)
Chichester *p455* 01243 777100

Bonnaillie-Valmorin, Mrs F (Elizabeth Muirhead Solicitors) *K1*
London WC2 *p62* 020 7936 4445

Bonnar, R (DLA Piper UK LLP) *C1 C2 F1 J1 M1 M2*
Leeds *p272* 0870 011 1111

Bonner, Ms M (Foot Anstey) *K1 D1*
Plymouth *p349* 01752 675000

Bonner, P L (Peter Bonner & Co) *G H D1*
Lewisham *p14* 020 8297 1727

Bonnett, H (Corries Solicitors) *N*
York *p444* 0845 241 5566

Bonney, I D F (Holt & Longworth) *S1 Q K1 G N F1 L V Zl Zq Zr*
Rossendale *p367* 01706 213251 / 229131

Bonney, Mrs S A (Thomas Guise) *S2 E*
Worcester *p439* 01905 723131

Bonning, M (Foot Anstey) *N Q O Zq*
Plymouth *p349* 01752 675000

Bonning, M (Michelmores LLP) *O Zc Za A3*
Exeter *p221* 01392 688688

Bonny, P I (Withers LLP)
London EC4 *p92* 020 7597 6000

Bonsall, R P (Glaisyers) *N Q J1 L F1 W*
Tamworth *p407* 01827 61011

Bonsignore, Miss S (Fladgate LLP) *C1*
London WC2 *p32* 020 3036 7000

Bonsor, A M (SNR Denton) *Zb*
London EC4 *p75* 020 7242 1212

Bonstow, N P (Michael W Pipe) *C1 L S1 T1 V W E B1 P*
Paignton *p345* 01803 559746 / 529797

Bonville-Ginn, Miss M (Corus Group Limited)
London SW1 *p105* 020 7717 4523

Bonwick, Miss S A (Pannone LLP) *E S2 R2 Zh R1*
Manchester *p308* 0161 909 3000

Bonye, M (Herbert Smith LLP) *O*
London EC2 *p40* 020 7374 8000

Boobier, N J (Osborne Clarke) *O*
Bristol *p164* 0117 917 3000

Boobier, P D (Dolmans) *Zf N O J2 Zk Q Zj Zq*
Cardiff *p178* 029 2034 5531

Boobyer, D (Tollers LLP)
Northampton *p332* 01604 258558

Boobyer, D M (Tollers LLP) *K1 N Q O Zk*
Northampton *p332* 01604 258558

Boocock, Miss V H M (East Sussex County Council)
Lewes *p463* 01273 481000

Boodhoo, H D (Harry Boodhoo & Co) *D1 S2 E B2 S1*
Withington *p436* 0161 445 0588

Boodt, P (Streeter Marshall) *S2 E K3 K1 L Q S1*
Croydon *p205* 020 8680 2638

Booker, Ms K L (Wilkinson Woodward) *E S1 W*
Halifax *p238* 01422 339600

Booker, M (Lawrence Lupin) *Zi*
Wembley *p426* 020 8733 7200

Booker, R S (Pinsent Masons LLP) *C1 C2 B1 T1 Zb*
London EC2 *p67* 020 7418 7000

Booker, Mrs S (Henmans LLP) *Zr*
Oxford *p343* 01865 781000

Booker, T J (MWR Law Ltd) *N*
Preston *p357* 01772 254201

Boomla, Mrs V A (London Fire & Emergency Planning Authority)
London SE1 *p107* 020 8555 1200

Boon, D J (Thomas Flavell & Sons) *N Q J1 J2*
Hinckley *p250* 01455 610747

Boon, J A (Roythornes LLP) *K3 K1 K2*
Spalding *p389* 01775 842500

Boon, M J (Somerset County Council)
Taunton *p473* 0845 345 9166

Boon, M T (McCarthy Bennett Holland) *S1 C1 N W Zl B1*
Wigan *p432* 01942 206060

Boon, S D (DLA Piper UK LLP) *O B1 B2 Q J1 Zb Zk*
London EC2 *p24* 0870 011 1111

Boorman, S (Leeds City Council) *N L J1 Q*
Leeds *p462* 0113 224 3513

Booroff, K (Michael Cullen & Partners) *K1*
Billericay *p133* 01277 623132

Boot, D (Timms) *N Q*
Derby *p209* 01332 364436

Booth, Miss A J (Elborne Mitchell LLP) *O Q C1 J1 M1 Zj Zk Zo*
London EC3 *p29* 020 7320 9000

Booth, Miss A K (Eaton Smith LLP) *J1 Zp*
Huddersfield *p255* 01484 821300

Booth, A P (Fasken Martineau LLP) *Ze C1 Zy U2 I F1 F2*
London W1 *p31* 020 7917 8500

Booth, A W (Turner Parkinson) *C1 C2 Zf*
Manchester *p310* 0161 833 1212

Booth, Miss C (DR James & Son)
Pontardawe *p351* 01792 862334

Booth, C D (Pinsent Masons LLP) *B1 C1 J1*
Leeds *p276* 0113 244 5000

Booth, C W (C W Booth & Co) *G H S1 N W Q K1*
Bishop Auckland *p144* 01388 606660

Booth, Ms E (Quastel Midgen LLP) *E S2*
London W1 *p70* 020 7908 2525

Booth, G A (Simmons & Simmons)
London EC2 *p79* 020 7628 2020

Booth, G T (Ascroft Whiteside) *C1 S2 E F1 L S1*
Blackpool *p146* 01253 766866

Booth, Miss H J (Latimer Hinks) *N Q K1 K3*
Darlington *p206* 01325 341500

Booth, J (Canter Levin & Berg)
Liverpool *p287* 0151 239 1000

Booth, Ms J L (Michelin Tyre PLC)
Stoke-on-Trent *p472* 01782 402266

Booth, Mrs J M (John Shirley & Co)
Burnham-on-Sea *p169* 01278 780202

Booth, Ms K (Hogan Lovells International LLP) *Zb*
London EC1 *p42* 020 7296 2000

Booth, Ms L (Starr & Partners LLP)
London EC4 *p82* 020 7199 1450

Booth, Mrs L F (HM Land Registry - Birkenhead (Rosebrae))
Birkenhead *p449* 0151 472 6666

Booth, Ms N (Burton & Co LLP) *D1 K1*
Lincoln *p284* 01522 523215

Booth, N (Bury & Walkers LLP)
Wombwell *p438* 01226 753433

Booth, P S S (Baxter Caulfield) *O J1 P B1 N Zc Ze Zl M1 Zp*
Huddersfield *p255* 01484 519519

Booth, Mrs R (Field Seymour Parkes) *S2 E*
Reading *p360* 0118 951 6200

Booth, R (Maxwell Winward LLP) *Zc A3 Zq O*
London EC4 *p59* 020 7651 0000

Booth, R C (BCL Burton Copeland) *B2 G J2*
London WC2 *p9* 020 7430 2277

Booth, R J (Hammond Bale) *B1 C1 E O Q*
London W1 *p38* 020 7499 7624

Booth, Ms R L (BUPA)
London WC1 *p104* 020 7656 2305

Booth, Ms R M (Macfarlanes) *E*
London EC4 *p56* 020 7831 9222

Booth, S (IBB Solicitors)
Chesham *p189* 0845 638 1381

Booth, Miss S (K&L Gates LLP)
London EC4 *p47* 020 7648 9000

Booth, Miss S A (Irwin Mitchell LLP) *N P Zr*
Sheffield *p376* 0870 150 0100

Booth, S J (Sarginsons Law LLP) *S1 L K1 W R1 H G P E*
Coventry *p201* 024 7655 3181

Booth, S J (S Booth & Co) *Q O S1 E W S2*
Islington *p14* 020 7226 3366

Booth, T R (Wilkin Chapman LLP) *S1*
Beverley *p131* 01482 398398

Boothman, G D (Ashurst LLP) *B1 C1*
London EC2 *p7* 020 7638 1111

Boothroyd, C D (Boothroyds) *G*
London SE6 *p14* 020 8690 4848

Boothroyd, Miss R (K&L Gates LLP)
London EC4 *p47* 020 7648 9000

Boothroyd, Miss S M (West Sussex County Council)
Chichester *p455* 01243 777100

See p634 for the Key to Work Categories

Bootland, E T (Linder Myers Solicitors)
Manchester *p306* 0844 984 6000

Booty, P (McCarthy Stewart & Booty Solicitors) *N*
Bury St Edmunds *p171* . . . 01284 748927

Booz, J (Veale Wasbrough Vizards)
Bristol *p165* 0117 925 2020

Boran, Ms R (Mayer Brown International LLP) *N Zj*
London EC2 *p59*. 020 3130 3000

Bordell, K S (Speechly Bircham LLP) *B1*
London EC4 *p81*. 020 7427 6400
London EC1 *p87*. 020 7295 3000

Borders, I J (First Title Insurance PLC)
London EC4 *p106* 020 7832 3100

Boreham, R W (Ware & Kay LLP) *T1 T2 W C2*
Wetherby *p429* 01937 583210

Boret, Mrs S J (Hess Ltd)
London WC2 *p106*. 020 7331 3000

Borgen, Ms I (Brooke Williams) *K1 D1*
Hull *p256* 01482 610886

Borkowski, A T (Geldards LLP)
Derby *p208* 01332 331631

Borley, A J (Scotts Holt & Sellars) *J1 N Zq Q*
Bromsgrove *p167* 01527 872711

Borley, P W (Thanet District Council)
Margate *p465* 01843 577000

Born, G (WilmerHale) *A3*
London EC2 *p92*. 020 7645 2400

Born, J B (WBW Solicitors) *T2 W S1*
Newton Abbot *p329* 01626 202404

Borneo, K A (Harvey Ingram Borneos) *C1 E B1 R1 Zc Ze*
Bedford *p130* 01234 353221

Borrie, A J S (K&L Gates LLP) *C1*
London EC4 *p47*. 020 7648 9000

Borrie, P (LG Lawyers) *T1 W J1 Za Zi Zd*
London SE1 *p50*. 020 7379 0000

Borrill, Ms F C (Lester Morrill) *N Zr Q*
Leeds *p275* 0113 245 8549

Borrington, Miss E L (Berry Smith LLP) *C1*
Cardiff *p177* 029 2034 5511

Borrini, E (Jones Day) *Zb*
London EC4 *p46*. 020 7039 5959

Borrow, Mrs J A (Ormerods) *N J1*
Croydon *p205* 020 8686 5000

Borrowdale, C J (Grainger Appleyard) *K1 D1 V Zi*
Doncaster *p211* 01302 327257

Borrowdale, P E M (Reed Smith LLP) *C1 C2*
London EC2 *p71*. 020 3116 3000

Borthwick, C O (Taylor Walton LLP) *B1 C1 C2 E T1 T2 Zi Zo Zf*
Luton *p295* 01582 731161

Borthwick, T J (Allen & Overy LLP) *B1 C1 Zc*
London E1 *p5* 020 3088 0000

Bortnik, Miss J A (Bross Bennett) *K1 K2*
London N6 *p16* 020 8340 0444

Bosanquet, Ms J C (Goodman Ray) *D1 D2 K1*
Hackney *p36*. 020 7608 1227

Boscawen, C R (Birketts LLP) *T1 T2 W Zd*
Ipswich *p262*. 01473 232300

Bosher, C J D (Perrins Solicitors LLP) *E S2 R2 S1 R1*
Harpenden *p239*. 01582 466140

Bosher, D S (DS Bosher & Co) *S1 S2 W L Q V K1 C1 G M1 Zi Zl Zp Zr Zq*
Hove *p254*. 01273 721913

Bosher, P S (GH Cornish LLP) *S1 E L R1 T1 C1*
Ilford *p260*. 020 8090 0800

Bosi, G (Penningtons)
Basingstoke *p127* 01256 407100

Bosi, Mrs K (Rushmoor Borough Council)
Farnborough *p458* 01252 398398

Bosiaki, Ms A (Manchester City Council)
Manchester *p465* 0161 234 5000

Bosler, Mrs W (TWM Solicitors LLP) *T2 W*
Reigate *p363* 01737 221212

Bosley, A (Lester Morrill) *Q*
Leeds *p275* 0113 245 8549

Bosomworth, S J (Newbys) *S1 S2 W*
Stockton-on-Tees *p397* . . .01642 673733 / 676666

Bosomworth, S J (Newbys) *S1 W E C1 L F1*
Guisborough *p237*. .01287 632208 / 632209

Boss, S A (Shoosmiths)
Birmingham *p142* 0370 086 4000 / 0121 335 4440

Bostock, A (The Johnson Partnership) *G H*
Mansfield *p311*. 01623 427575

Bostock, P A (Currey & Co) *Zd W T2*
Westminster *p24*. 020 7802 2700

Boston, P (Poole Alcock)
Congleton *p198* 01260 275337

Bostridge, P J (Sanders & Co) *E S1 W A1 L C1 F1 K1 P Zj Zl Zv*
Rainham *p359*. 0844 353 3553

Boswall, R R T (Reynolds Porter Chamberlain LLP) *O Zj*
London E1 *p71* 020 3060 6000

Bosworth, Miss J E (KieranClarkeGreen) *G H*
Chesterfield *p192* 01246 211006

Bosworth, J W (Ashfords LLP) *Zu R1*
Exeter *p220* 01392 337000

Bosworth, M (Russell-Cooke LLP) *G H Zw*
London WC1 *p74* 020 7405 6566

Bosworth, P E J E (Bosworths) *S1 E W K1 P L B1 R1 C1 Zc Zk Zl*
East Molesey *p215* 020 8941 3151

Bosworth, Miss R A (Ashley Smith & Co) *G H B2*
Lewisham *p80*. 020 8463 0099

Botham, A (Cleaver Thompson Ltd) *N Q O J1 F1 V Zl L Zr*
Alfreton *p115* 01773 832193

Botham, A (Harvey Ingram LLP) *N*
Leicester *p280*. 0116 254 5454

Botham, Mrs C (Moorcrofts LLP) *S2 E*
Marlow *p313*. 01628 470000

Bothamley, H L M (DAC Beachcroft) *R2 E S2 R1*
Bristol *p162* 0117 918 2000

Bothamley, I A (Prudential PLC)
London EC4 *p108* 020 7220 7588

Botiuk, Y (RMPI Solicitors)
London W1 *p70* 020 7318 4444

Botkai, R P (Winckworth Sherwood LLP) *E L S1 R1 Zl Zc*
London SE1 *p92*. 020 7593 5000

Bott, A J A (Olswang LLP) *C2 F2 I R2*
London WC1 *p64* 020 7067 3000
London EC2 *p65*. 020 7105 7000

Bott, D (Bott & Company) *N*
Wilmslow *p433*. 01625 415800

Bott, J R (Young & Co) *K1 D1*
Stoke-on-Trent *p398*. 01782 339200

Bottaro, Ms A L (Forsters LLP) *E*
Westminster *p33*. 020 7863 8333

Botterill, Mrs L L (Harvey Ingram LLP) *C1*
Leicester *p280*. 0116 254 5454

Botterill, R (Harvey Ingram LLP) *C1 C2 C3 B1 I Ze*
Leicester *p280*. 0116 254 5454

Bottle, S (Davitt Jones Bould) *R1 E S2*
Taunton *p408* 01823 279279

Bottley, S (DLA Piper UK LLP)
Birmingham *p137* 0870 011 1111

Bottomley, M B (Ewart Price) *E J1 J2 K1 N O Q S1 S2 W*
Welwyn Garden City *p425* . . 01707 332383

Bottomley, S J (Mayer Brown International LLP) *C2*
London EC2 *p59*. 020 3130 3000

Bottomley, W J (Hellewell Pasley & Brewer) *J1 L N S1 S2 T2 W*
Batley *p128* 01924 472596

Bottrill, Ms E A (SAS Daniels LLP) *D1 K1*
Stockport *p396*. 0161 475 7676

Bottrill, M D (Bottrill & Co) *K1 K3*
Pinner *p348* 020 8429 1010

Botwright, Ms G A (Moss & Coleman)
Hornchurch *p252* 01708 446781

Bouch, J (Cartwright King)
Leicester *p279*. 0116 253 9222

Bouch, J C (Scutt Beaumont Solicitors Ltd) *G H*
Leicester *p281*. 0116 254 4200

Boucher, J F (T G Pollard & Co) *S1 A1*
Wells *p425*. 01749 674722

Boucher, N S (Beynons Nicholls) *D1 F1 G J1 K1 M1 N*
London EC4 *p12*. 020 7353 5860

Boucher, P J (Girlings) *S1*
Ashford *p119* 01233 647377

Boucher, R M (Cartwright King) *G H Zm*
Leicester *p279*. 0116 253 9222

Bouchier, D I (Olswang LLP) *Zf*
London WC1 *p64* 020 7067 3000

Bouchier, J (Reston's Solicitors Limited) *O Q F1 N*
Warrington *p422*. 0870 755 8998

Bouda, Miss I (Camden Tribunal Unit) *J1 Q V Zo*
London NW5 *p104*. 020 7267 2424

Boueh, Miss E (Brand & Co) *S2 E R2 S1*
Cheam *p185*. 020 8641 2771

Boughey, Mrs L J (Newport City Council)
Newport *p466* 01633 656656

Bould, Ms D S (Pinsent Masons LLP)
London EC2 *p67*. 020 7418 7000

Bould, S R A (Davitt Jones Bould) *E S2 L O A1*
Taunton *p408* 01823 279279

Boulding, R J (Meade-King) *S1 W*
Bristol *p163* 0117 926 4121

Boulongne, I (Makin Dixon Solicitors) *D1 K1 V*
Harrogate *p240* 01423 500035

Boulter, Ms A (Herrington & Carmichael LLP) *D2 D1 K3*
Camberley *p173*. 01276 686222

Boulter, Miss E (Royds LLP) *C1 F1 F2 Ze Zza M1 U2 Zt C2 Zo*
London EC4 *p74*. 020 7583 2222

Boulter, Mrs J (Pickering & Butters) *N*
Stafford *p393* 01785 603060

Boulter, Mrs M (Boulter & Company) *L N Q S1 Zq*
London N8 *p14* 020 8340 0222

Boulton, A P (DAC Beachcroft)
London EC4 *p24*. 020 7936 2222

Boulton, C J (EAD Solicitors LLP) *S1 G J1 M1 N P K1 W C1 E Zl Zm Zk*
Liverpool *p287*. 0151 291 2500

Boulton, D (Lockett Loveday McMahon) *S2 E R2*
Manchester *p307* 0161 237 3627

Boulton, Ms K (Ashurst LLP)
London EC2 *p7* 020 7638 1111

Boulton, Miss N (Byrne & Partners)
London EC4 *p16*. 020 7842 1616

Boulton, P A (IMI PLC)
Birmingham *p450* 0121 717 3700

Bound, R A (Berry Smith LLP) *C1 C2 C3 B1 Ze Zf*
Cardiff *p177* 029 2034 5511

Bourbonnux, Miss L A (Partridge Allen & Co) *C1 E S2 K3 J1 L Q*
Walsall *p420*. 01922 452860

Bourdages, M (Fisher Meredith)
Lambeth *p32*. 020 7091 2700
Hackney *p36*. 020 7608 1227

Bourgeois, C F (Taylor Wessing) *N P B1 R1 C1 Zc Ze Zk*
London EC4 *p86*. 020 7300 7000

Bouri, H C (Harish C Bouri) *C1 E F1 G H J1 K1 L S1 Zh Zl Zp*
Newcastle upon Tyne *p323* . 0191 281 4860

Bourke, Miss C (Anthony Gold) *Zr N*
London SE1 *p6* 020 7940 4000

Bourke, M (O'Neill Patient) *S1*
Stockport *p396*. 0161 483 8555

Bourn, Mrs C (Buss Murton LLP) *K1*
Tunbridge Wells *p415* 01892 510222

Bourn, Mrs J B L (Rix & Kay Solicitors LLP) *J1 Q O Zk Zl L*
Hove *p255*. 01273 329797

Bourne, B (Ellis-Fermor & Negus)
Beeston *p130* 0115 922 1591

Bourne, Miss C (Buller Jeffries) *N O Zj*
Birmingham *p136* 0121 212 2620

Bourne, J P J (Davies & Partners) *E*
Gloucester *p230*. 01452 612345

Bourne, M (Darbys Solicitors LLP) *G H*
Oxford *p343*. 01865 811700

Bourne, N M (Lamb Brooks LLP) *S1 Zl*
Basingstoke *p126* 01256 844888

Bourne, R E (Philip Moody & Co) *S1 K1 W L E F1*
Kew *p265* 020 8948 6388

Bourns, R H G (TLT Solicitors) *B1 C1 J1 Zo Zl*
Bristol *p165* 0117 917 7777

Boursnell, P J (Edwin Coe LLP) *E R2*
London WC2 *p29* 020 7691 4000
London E1 *p71* 020 3060 6000

Bousfield, D S (Wansbroughs) *A1 W S1 E*
Devizes *p210* 01380 733300

Boustred, C N (Henry Boustred & Sons) *S1 S2 W T2*
London N6 *p14* 020 8348 5223

Boustred, P F (Henry Boustred & Sons) *E S1 W T1 A1 L P C1 M1*
London N6 *p14* 020 8348 5223

Boustred, R K W (Henry Boustred & Sons) *S1 K1 D1 L M1 N P J1*
London N6 *p14* 020 8348 5223

Boutcher, D J (Reed Smith LLP) *C1 C2*
London EC2 *p71*. 020 3116 3000

Bouvet, J P (Elmhirst Parker LLP) *K1 Q N O J1 C1 E Zl D1 K2*
Selby *p374* 01757 703895

Bovell, J P A (Battens) *C1*
Yeovil *p443* 01935 846000
Gillingham *p229* 01747 825432

Bovey, C J (MFG Solicitors) *A1 C1 E F1 L S1*
Bromsgrove *p167* 01527 831691
Kidderminster *p265* 01562 820181

Bovey, P H (Department for Business, Enterprise and Regulatory Reform)
London SW1 *p105*. 020 7215 0105

Bovington, Ms V (Langleys) *E Zb*
York *p445* 01904 610886

Bow, Mrs R L (Merthyr Tydfil County Borough Council)
Merthyr Tydfil *p465* 01685 725000

Bowcock, D N (Brabners Chaffe Street)
Manchester *p301* 0161 836 8800

Bowden, Ms A (Pinsent Masons LLP)
London EC2 *p67*. 020 7418 7000

Bowden, A R (Alker & Ball) *E S1 S2*
Wigan *p432* 01942 246241

Bowden, Mrs C (Anthony Gold) *K1 K2 D1 K3*
London SW16 *p6* 020 7940 4000

Bowden, J R (Clarkson Wright & Jakes Ltd) *C1 C2 S2 W*
Orpington *p341* 01689 887887

Bowden, P (Allen & Overy LLP)
London E1 *p5* 020 3088 0000

Bowden, S (Murrays Solicitors) *N*
Bradford *p154* 01274 304448

Bowden, S R (Dutton Gregory) *R1 J1 P F1 D1 O D2 Q*
Winchester *p433*. 01962 844333

Bowdler, S H (FBC Manby Bowdler LLP) *E*
Wolverhampton *p437* 01902 578000

Bowe, Ms A (Ashurst LLP)
London EC2 *p7* 020 7638 1111

Bowe, K (Russell-Cooke LLP) *W*
Kingston upon Thames *p267*. 020 8546 6111

Bowen, Ms A G (Irwin Mitchell LLP) *B1 F1 O Zk*
Sheffield *p376* 0870 150 0100

Bowen, A J (Challinors) *N*
West Bromwich *p427* 0121 553 3211

Bowen, Mrs C A (Bray & Bray) *S2 E S1*
Leicester *p279*. 0116 254 8871

Bowen, Mrs C J (West Devon Borough Council)
Tavistock *p473*. 01822 615911

Bowen, C M L (Taylor Walton LLP) *N Q*
Luton *p295* 01582 731161

Bowen, D A (Woodford Stauffer) *W S1 Q N E L J1*
Farnborough *p224*. 01252 375376

Bowen, D T (Colborne Coulman & Lawrence) *S1 N W R1 B1 P K3 Zc Zd Zt*
Newport *p328* . . . . .01633 264194 / 264196

Bowen, G C (Everys) *S1 L E W*
Sidmouth *p380*. 01395 577983

Bowen, I R (Pearson Hinchliffe) *K1 D1 V L Q*
Oldham *p341* 0161 785 3500

Bowen, J (FBC Manby Bowdler LLP) *K1*
Shrewsbury *p379* 01743 241551

Bowen, Ms L (The Environment Agency (North West Region [HQ]))
Warrington *p475*. 01925 653999

Bowen, M I (Red Kite Law) *S1 K4 W*
Carmarthen *p183* 01267 239000

Bowen, M J (SJ Berwin LLP)
London EC4 *p75*. 020 7111 2222

Bowen, M J (Stuart Smith & Burnett) *D1 F1 J1 K1 L Q V Zl O K3*
Bridlington *p158* 01262 678128

Bowen, N (Bowen Muscatt) *E S2 S1 C1 C2 F1 Q J1 N B2 G Zi Zp Ze*
London W1 *p14* 020 7908 3800

Bowen, P L (Persimmon PLC)
Warrington *p475*. 01942 277277

Bowen, Ms R (Davies & Partners) *Zr*
Birmingham *p137* 0121 616 4450

Bowen, R J (Guillaumes Solicitors) *S1 E L C1 W*
Weybridge *p430*. 01932 840111

Bowen, S (Francis & Buck) *S1 W L Q N*
Cardiff *p178* 029 2034 4995

Bowen, Miss S L (Meesons) *S2 S1 L E*
Ringwood *p364* 01425 472315

Bowen-Ashwin, D J (Jacksons) *A1 C1 E L S1 T1 W Zm S2 A2*
Fordingbridge *p227* 01425 652110

Bowen-Morris, N V (Stephenson Harwood) *Za*
London EC2 *p82*. 020 7329 4422

Bower, A (Forbes)
Blackburn *p145* 01254 662831

Bower, A D (VHS Fletchers Solicitors) *G H*
Nottingham *p339*. 0115 959 9550

Bower, Miss C E (Christine E Bower) *S1*
Twickenham *p416* 020 8898 1615

Bower, D J G (Bower & Bailey) *C1 E R2*
Oxford *p343* 01865 311133

Bower, Ms E A (Children & Families Law Firm) *D1 K1 D2 K3*
London SW9 *p20* 020 7582 6002

Bower, Ms J (Radcliffes Le Brasseur)
Westminster *p70*. 020 7222 7040

Bower, J (Easthams Solicitors Limited) *N*
Blackpool *p146* 0800 032 1432

Bower, Miss J C (IMI PLC)
Birmingham *p450* 0121 717 3700

Bower, M S (Turner & Wall) *F1 G H J1 Q N O Zr Zq J2*
Keighley *p264* 01535 607831

Bower, R (Bower Harris) *G F1 W H S1 E L C1 R1*
Manchester *p301* 0161 832 9404

Bower, R M (Forbes) *N J1 Q G P*
Blackburn *p145* 01254 54374

Bower, T W (Spearing Waite LLP) *E S2 R2 Zc A1*
Leicester *p281*. 0116 262 4225

Bower-Brown, Mrs K (Sills & Betteridge LLP) *O Zk Zq F1 Zc F2 Zh L*
Lincoln *p285*. 01522 542211

Bowering, M (Hatchers Solicitors LLP) *S1*
Shrewsbury *p379* 01743 248545

Bowerman, Ms L C (Bowermans) *N K1 D1 L Q V*
Port Talbot *p353* 01639 891892

Bowerman, M R (Bowermans) *K1 L Q*
Port Talbot *p353* 01639 891892

Bowers, Ms A (Russell Jones & Walker)
Sheffield *p377* 0114 276 6868

Bowers, A J (Bowers & Jessup)
Folkestone *p227*. 01303 850678

Bowers, C (Rosling King)
London EC4 *p73*. 020 7353 2353

Bowers, C D (Taylors)
Manchester *p310* 0844 800 0263

Bowery, Mrs M (Southern Stewart & Walker) *K1 D1 W V*
South Shields *p384* 0191 427 0770

Bowes, C G (DLA Piper UK LLP) *R1*
Manchester *p303* 0870 011 1111

Bowes, Miss J (St Edmundsbury Borough Council)
Bury St Edmunds *p452* . . . 01284 763233

Bowes, Mrs J L (Trethowans LLP) *O Q Zq*
Southampton *p387*. 023 8032 1000

Bowey, Miss D M (Quality Solicitors Clarke & Son) *S1 S2 E*
Basingstoke *p127* 01256 320555

Bowie, J D (James Bowie Caton & Co) *C1 E G H L P R1 S1 T1 W Za Zb Zc*
Ferndown *p225* . . .01202 875646 / 877225

Bowie, Mrs N M (Darwin Bowie Ltd) *W A1 S1 E K4 S2*
Narberth *p320* 01834 860436

Bowker, Ms D C (Steel & Shamash) *K1 D1 G H*
Lambeth *p82*. 020 7803 3999

Bowker, N D (DLA Piper UK LLP) *O*
Birmingham *p137* 0870 011 1111

Bowker, R H (Calthrops)
Spalding *p389* 01775 724381

Bowler, A (Bristows) *O Ze*
London EC4 *p15*. 020 7400 8000

Bowler, C S (Mercers) *Q N O L F1 C1 Zl*
Henley-on-Thames *p247*. . . 01491 572138

Bowler, I J (Linklaters LLP)
London EC2 *p54*. 020 7456 2000

Bowler, I W (DLA Piper UK LLP) *C2 C1*
Leeds *p272* 0870 011 1111

Bowler, Miss J A (Loughridge Bowler) *V W T2 Zv K4*
Coventry *p200*. 024 7663 1632

Bowler, N (Rotherham Magistrates Court)
Rotherham *p470*. 01709 839339

Bowler, Miss S J (Coffin Mew & Clover) *N*
Fareham *p223*. 01329 825617

Bowler-Reed, Ms S (Sabina Bowler-Reed) *K1 D1 D2*
Bristol *p161* 01275 373111

Bowles, C R G (Sheridan Bowles Solicitors) *G H Zl*
Great Yarmouth *p234* 01493 859848

6

Bowles, G A J (Druces LLP) *O Q A3 I M2 Zc Zq*
London EC2 *p27*. 020 7638 9271
Bowles, Mrs H M (Goughs) *K1 D1*
Chippenham *p193* 01249 444499
Bowles, N (Williamson & Barnes) *W T2*
Deal *p207* 01304 373154
Bowles, Miss S (Simmons & Simmons)
London EC2 *p79*. 020 7628 2020
Bowles, T (Reynolds Porter Chamberlain LLP) *B2 O Zb Zj*
London E1 *p71* 020 3060 6000
Bowley, S D (Austen Whetham & Guest) *A1 J1 K1 N Q S1*
Bridport *p158* 01308 422236
Bowley, W J (The Mersey Docks & Harbour Co)
Liverpool *p463*. 0151 949 6000
Bowling, W B C (Bruce Bowling & Co) *S1 W L A1*
Doncaster *p211* 01302 320607
Bowman, Mrs A (Rothera Dowson) *D1 K1 D2*
Nottingham *p338*. 0115 910 0600
Bowman, Miss A D (Henmans LLP) *O Q B1 L Zd*
Oxford *p343* 01865 781000
Bowman, Ms C A (McGrigors LLP) *E R2 L*
London EC4 *p56*. 020 7054 2500
Bowman, C D (Bell Lax Litigation) *N Zr J2*
Sutton Coldfield *p403* 0121 355 0011
Bowman, Ms C H (Treasury Solicitors Department)
London WC2 *p110*. 020 7210 3000
Bowman, D A (Royds LLP) *O Q R1 Zq B1 E*
London EC4 *p74*. 020 7583 2222
Bowman, H M H (SNR Denton) *A3 O Zc*
Milton Keynes *p317* 01908 690260
Bowman, M (Holman Fenwick Willan)
London EC3 *p42*. 020 7264 8000
Bowman, M A (Figueiredo & Bowman) *Zi W S1*
Hackney *p32*. 020 7739 5599
Bowman, M J (Bowman & Co) *S1 W L N Q E K1 O B1 T1 Zl*
Newquay *p329*. 01637 875065
Bowman, N (Kennedys) *C1 O*
Chelmsford *p186*. 0845 838 4800
Bowman, N (Ison Harrison) *K1 K3 D1 K2*
Leeds *p274* 0113 284 5000
Bowman, Mrs R W (McCarthy & Stone PLC)
Bournemouth *p450*. 01202 292480
Bowman, Mrs S J (Adams & Remers) *S1 S2 K3 K1*
Lewes *p283* 01273 480616
East Grinstead *p215*. 01342 323687
Bown, P J (Yaffe Jackson Ostrin) *F1 G H L N T1 Zl*
Liverpool *p291*. 0151 236 5555
Bownes, G A (Mayer Brown International LLP) *S2*
London EC2 *p59*. 020 3130 3000
Bowness, Lord P S (Streeter Marshall) *E O S1 W*
Warlingham *p421* 01883 622433
Bowry, Ms L (Windsor & Maidenhead Borough Council) *R1 Zu P*
Maidenhead *p464* 01628 798888
Bowser, B R (Bowser Ollard & Bentley) *S1 A1 E W B1 Zc C1 C2 L T1 Zv*
Wisbech *p435* 01945 583194
Bowser, E G (Dunn & Baker) *C1 G H O E S1*
Exeter *p221* 01392 285000
Bowskill, Miss E J (Lester Morrill) *K1 W V D2 L*
Leeds *p275* 0113 245 8549
Bowskill, Miss G M (DBL Talbots LLP) *W K4*
Kidderminster *p265* 01562 749910
Bowtle, G J (Reed Smith LLP) *Za*
London EC2 *p71*. 020 3116 3000
Bowyer, I (Gregory Rowcliffe Milners)
London WC1 *p37* 020 7242 0631
Bowyer, R (Osborne Clarke) *C1 I*
Reading *p361* 0118 925 2000
Bowyer-Jones, Ms C M (Moorhead James LLP) *J1 Zw O A3*
London EC4 *p61*. 020 7831 8888
Box, C (Capsticks Solicitors LLP) *Zr*
London SW19 *p18*. 020 8780 2211
Box, Ms E (Gordon Dadds) *A3 Ze L Zj O Q N*
London W1 *p25* 020 7493 6151
Box, Mrs L M (Dixon Coles & Gill) *S1 W L Zd*
Wakefield *p418* 01924 373467
Box, T (Freeman Box) *N P C1 L K1 J1 F1 B1 Zi Zk Zl*
London W1 *p34* 020 7486 9041
Boxall, Mrs S N (High Peak Borough Council)
Chapel-en-le-Frith *p454* . . . 0845 129 7777
Boyars, A L (Millichips) *S1 E C1 L R1 J1 B1 A1 Zc Zi Zl*
Solihull *p382*. 0121 624 4000
Boyce, C A (Copeland Borough Council)
Whitehaven *p476* 01946 852585
Boyce, Mrs M K (Birchall Blackburn LLP) *N Q*
Preston *p356* 01772 561663
Boyce, P J (Goughs) *K1 D1 V*
Chippenham *p193* 01249 444499
Boyce, R H (Jacobs & Reeves) *S1 E W C1 S2*
Wimborne *p433* 01202 880382
Boyce, Ms S M (Arnold Greenwood) *S1 W*
Kendal *p264*. 01539 720049
Boyd, Ms C E (Vivash Hunt) *E S2 C1 J1*
Worcester Park *p440* 020 8330 1961
Boyd, Miss C M (McGrigors LLP)
London EC4 *p56*. 020 7054 2500
Boyd, Ms E P (Blake Lapthorn) *C1 E R1 S1 Zc*
Portsmouth *p354*. 023 9222 1122
Boyd, M (Carter-Ruck) *Zk O Q Zza Zf*
London EC4 *p18*. 020 7353 5005

Boyd, M E (Alexander & Partners) *G H B2*
Brent *p5* 020 8965 7121
Boyd, M P (Pinsent Masons LLP) *C1*
Leeds *p276* 0113 244 5000
Boyd, N (SANPAOLO IMI SPA)
London EC4 *p109* 020 7214 8000
Boyd, N J W (Berry Redmond & Robinson) *T2 W*
Weston-super-Mare *p429* . . 01934 513963
Winscombe *p434* 01934 842811
Boyd, P R (Saunders Roberts) *A1 A2 Zd C1 S2 E R2 C2*
Evesham *p220*. 01386 442558
Boyd, R C (North Yorkshire Law)
Scarborough *p372* 01723 360001
Boyd, S (Linder Myers Solicitors)
Manchester *p306* 0844 984 6000
Boyd, S (Martello Professional Risks Limited)
London EC3 *p108* 020 7337 7500
Boyd, Mrs T E (Northampton Borough Council)
Northampton *p467* 01604 837837
Boydell, J A (Brabners Chaffe Street) *U2 I C2 C1*
Preston *p356* 01772 823921
Boydell, Mrs N A (Maxwell Hodge Solicitors) *S1*
Maghull *p298* 0151 526 7131
Boydon, Ms R Z (Nowell Meller Solicitors Limited) *K2 D1*
Stafford *p393* 01785 252377
Boyer, Ms V (Beviss & Beckingsale)
Axminster *p120* 01297 630700
Boyes, C R (Warrens Boyes & Archer)
Huntingdon *p258*. 01480 411331
Boyes, Miss J E (Wrigleys Solicitors LLP) *T2 W Zd*
Leeds *p278* 0113 244 6100
Boyes, M G (Goodswens) *S1 W C1 E L R1 S2*
Redcar *p362*. 01642 482424
Boyes, Miss S L L (Fisher Jones Greenwood LLP) *Zi J1 V*
Colchester *p197* 01206 578282
Boyes, W O (Percy Short & Cuthbert) *K1 O L Q N S1 B1 Zj Zc*
Islington *p67*. 020 7700 0265
Boylan, Miss D (Raworths LLP) *J1 B1 A3 O Q*
Harrogate *p240* 01423 566666
Boylan, J A (Sedgwick Phelan & Partners) *Q N J1*
Middleton *p315* 0161 653 5299
Boylan, S (Horwich Farrelly) *M1 P F1 N Zj*
Manchester *p305* 0161 834 3585
Boyland, B G (Davitt Jones Bould) *S2 E L*
Taunton *p408* 01823 279279
Boyle, Miss A (Osborne Clarke) *J1 K1*
Bristol *p164* 0117 917 3000
Boyle, C J (Napthens LLP) *J1*
Preston *p357* 01772 888444
Boyle, D P (Ford Simey LLP) *K1 G H D1 N L*
Exmouth *p222*. . .01395 272241 / 0800 169 3741
Boyle, F J (John Boyle & Co) *G H Zl*
Redruth *p362* 01209 213507
Boyle, I (Graham & Rosen) *K1 K3 D1*
Hull *p257* 01482 323123
Boyle, Ms J (Stone King LLP) *J1*
Bath *p128* 01225 337599
Boyle, Ms J A (G T Stewart Solicitors) *N*
London SE22 *p83* 020 8299 6000
Boyle, J M (Saltley and Nechells Law Centre)
Birmingham *p450* 0121 328 2307
Boyle, K (Tinsdills) *E R1 S1*
Hanley *p239*. 01782 262031
Boyle, Mrs K A (Squire Sanders (UK) LLP) *C1 J1 E S1 W B1 Zj Ze Zo*
Leeds *p277* 0113 284 7000
Boyle, Miss L C (Trethowans LLP) *O Q*
Southampton *p387*. 023 8032 1000
Boyle, Miss M J (SNR Denton) *Zj*
London EC4 *p75*. 020 7242 1212
Boyle, Miss N A (McGrigors LLP)
London EC4 *p56*. 020 7054 2500
Boyle, P (Ashurst LLP)
London EC2 *p7* 020 7638 1111
Boyle, R (Macfarlanes)
London EC4 *p56*. 020 7831 9222
Boyle, Miss S (Derbyshire County Council)
Matlock *p465* 01629 580000
Boyne, P J (Kitsons LLP) *E S1 C1 C2*
Newton Abbot *p329* 01626 203366
Boynton, Mrs M B L (Browns)
Beaconsfield *p128* . .01494 677771 / 677021
Bozier, Mrs R (Gawor & Co)
London E1 *p35* 020 7481 8888
Brabban, W (Crown Prosecution Service Durham)
Durham *p457* 0191 383 5800
Brabbins, E O (Steeles) *J1*
Norwich *p335* 0870 609 0200
Brabbs, I R (Thorpe & Co) *K1 K2 K3 S1 S2 L C1*
Scarborough *p372*. 01723 364321
Brabin, Miss M (Pannone LLP) *O C1 Q F1 Zq*
Manchester *p308* 0161 909 3000
Brabner, M G (Brabners Chaffe Street) *C1 C2*
Liverpool *p286*. 0151 600 3000
Brace, G (Adlams LLP)
St Neots *p392*. 01480 474061
Brace, J J (Baring Asset Management Ltd)
London EC2 *p104* 020 7628 6000
Brace, M D (Anthony & Jarvie) *S1 S2 L C1 E O*
Bridgend *p157*. 01656 652737
Brace, Ms R L (Geldards LLP) *J1*
Cardiff *p178* 029 2023 8239
Bracegirdle, M C (Poole Alcock) *S1 L N Q Zq*
Sandbach *p372* 01270 762325
Bracewell, A J (British Telecommunications PLC)
London EC1 *p104* 020 7356 6181

Bracey, J M (T S Edwards & Son) *Zc F1 F2 L O Q N Zq*
Newport *p328* 01633 257166
Hereford *p248* . . .01432 359261 / 276276
Bracey, M S (Stephen D Brine Solicitors) *B1 C1 D1 F1 G H J1 K1 L P Zc Zh Zs*
Liverpool *p286*. 0151 734 5000
Bracher, A R (Bracher Rawlins LLP) *C1 C2 Ze F1 R2*
London WC1 *p15* 020 7404 9400
Bracher, J H (Downs) *C1 J1 Ze Zh X*
Dorking *p212* 01306 880110
Bracken, J (Bircham Dyson Bell)
Westminster *p13*. 020 7227 7000
Bracken, P J (Tynedale District Council)
Hexham *p461* 01434 652200
Brackenbury, Ms A (Simmons & Simmons)
London EC2 *p79*. 020 7628 2020
Brackenbury, Ms L M (Memery Crystal) *C2 C1*
London WC2 *p60* 020 7242 5905
Brackenbury, R (Shakespeares) *B1 O Zc Q A3*
Nottingham *p339*. 0115 945 3700
Brackett, W B (Wykeham Hurford Sheppard & Son LLP) *S1 W L T1 Zc Zd Zb*
Battle *p128* 01424 775088
Brackfield, A C (The BOC Group PLC)
Guildford *p476*. 01483 579857
Brad, Mrs S E (Rollits LLP) *W*
York *p445* 01904 625790
Bradban, Mrs L (EMW) *E*
Milton Keynes *p316* 0845 070 6000
Bradbeer, Ms C (English Heritage)
London EC1 *p106* 020 7973 3360
Bradbeer, Miss S J (Reading Borough Council)
Reading *p469* 0118 939 0900
Bradbeer, Mrs S J (Singleton Winn McDermott Solicitors) *K1*
Newcastle upon Tyne *p326* . 0191 265 8817
Bradberry, Ms L (Miller Sands) *W K4*
Cambridge *p175*. 01223 202345
Bradburne, Mrs S R (Warners Solicitors) *W K4*
Tonbridge *p412* 01732 770660
Bradbury, A (Bradbury Steed)
Littlehampton *p285*. 01903 717048
Bradbury, Ms C (Osborne Clarke) *J1*
London EC2 *p65*. 020 7105 7000
Bradbury, D G (Bradbury Roberts & Raby) *E S1 C1 A1 Zl S2*
Scunthorpe *p373*. 01724 854000
Bradbury, I (Perry Mason Solicitors) *S1*
Torquay *p413* 01803 299000
Bradbury, Miss J J (Russell Jones & Walker) *J1 Zp*
Cardiff *p180* 029 2026 2800
London WC2 *p74* 020 7657 1555
Bradbury, M J (The Smith Partnership) *P K1 M1 G W C1 D1 N B1 F1 Zt Zj Zl*
Stoke-on-Trent *p398*. 01782 324454
Bradbury, N (London Borough of Southwark)
London SE1 *p109* 020 7525 5000
Bradbury, P A (3i PLC)
London SW1 *p103*. 020 7928 3131
Bradbury, P C (Thompson Leatherdale) *C1 E F1 R1 S1*
Reading *p361* 0118 959 1773
Bradbury, P E (Platt Halpern) *G K1 D1 H Zm*
Oldham *p341* 0161 626 4955
Bradbury, P F (Hill Dickinson LLP) *N Zr*
Liverpool *p288*. 0151 600 8000
Bradbury, R D (Attwood & Co) *N Q K1 D1 J1 F1 K3 Zq*
Grays *p233* . . . .01375 378122 / 378123
Bradbury, Miss S J (Taylor Wessing)
London EC4 *p86*. 020 7300 7000
Bradd, Miss C (Shelley & Co) *G H*
Cambridge *p175*. 01223 359441
Bradd, Miss V L (Cooper Sons Hartley & Williams) *S1*
Chapel-en-le-Frith *p184* . . . 01298 812138
Brader, M H C (Olswang LLP) *C2 C1*
London WC1 *p64* 020 7067 3000
Brader-Smith, Ms C (Barlow Lyde & Gilbert LLP)
London EC3 *p10*. 020 7247 2277
Bradey, Mrs L E (Wrigleys Solicitors LLP) *W T2 K4*
Sheffield *p377* 0114 267 5588
Bradfield, Miss H J (Crown Prosecution Service Northamptonshire)
Northampton *p467*. 01604 823600
Bradford, Ms C A (Rugby Borough Council)
Rugby *p470* 01788 533533
Bradford, I C (John Fowlers LLP Solicitors) *N O Q L F1 B1*
Colchester *p197* 01206 576151
Bradford, Miss K J (Stoffel & Co) *W S1 T2*
Beckenham *p129* 020 8650 8157
Bradford, Ms K J (Linklaters LLP)
London EC2 *p54*. 020 7456 2000
Bradford, Miss M (Doughty Hanson & Co Managers Ltd)
London SW1 *p106*. 020 7663 9300
Bradford, Mrs M A (Bradford & Co) *S1 E W L F1 K1*
Nailsea *p320*. . . . .01275 856302 / 856303
Bradford, P A (Bradford & Co)
Bristol *p161* 0117 963 5261
Bradford, S (Humphries Kirk) *W T2 K4*
Poole *p352* 01202 715815
Brading, Miss J H (Powells) *W K4 T2*
Weston-super-Mare *p429* . . 01934 623501
Bradley, A (LG Lawyers)
London SE1 *p50*. 020 7379 0000
Bradley, A (Aboudi Bradley & Co) *A1 C1 E S1 W*
Macclesfield *p297* 01625 428749

Bradley, Miss A J (Department for Business, Enterprise and Regulatory Reform)
London SW1 *p105*. 020 7215 0105
Bradley, A J (Leech & Co) *N*
Manchester *p306* 0161 279 0279
Bradley, A P (Shulmans) *C2 C1 Zb I Zu*
Leeds *p276* 0113 245 2833
Bradley, Miss A T (Donns) *N Q L*
Manchester *p303* 0161 834 3311
Bradley, B L (Gullands) *B1 N Q F1 L O Zk Zq Zl*
Maidstone *p299* 01622 678341
Bradley, Ms C (Lopian Wagner) *N*
Manchester *p307* 0161 834 2324
Bradley, Miss C K (Kingsley Napley) *D1 K1 K2*
London EC1 *p50*. 020 7814 1200
Bradley, C L (Pinney Talfourd LLP)
Hornchurch *p252* 01708 511000
Bradley, D (Richmond Anderson Goudie) *D1 D2 G H J1 K1*
Chester-le-Street *p191*. . . . 0191 388 7884
Bradley, Miss D A (Morgan Cole) *N Zj Zr*
Bristol *p164* 0117 916 7220
Bradley, D G (Hewitsons) *W T2 Zm*
Cambridge *p174*. 01223 461155
Bradley, D J (DLA Piper UK LLP) *J1*
Sheffield *p375* 0870 011 1111
Bradley, D P (Fentons)
Failsworth *p223* 0161 682 7101
Bradley, D R (The Environment Agency (North West Region [HQ]))
Warrington *p475*. 01925 653999
Bradley, Miss E J (Bells) *K4 W*
Romsey *p366* 01794 513328
Bradley, E L (Clifford Chance)
London E14 *p20*. 020 7006 1000
Bradley, G (DLA Piper UK LLP) *A3 O Zc*
Birmingham *p137* 0870 011 1111
Bradley, Mrs H M (Helen M Bradley) *S1 W*
Stockbridge *p395* 01264 860200
Bradley, I N (Callaghans) *C1 E L S1*
Farnham *p224*. 01252 723477
Bradley, Mrs J (Devonshires) *R2*
London EC2 *p27*. 020 7628 7576
Bradley, J (Browns) *S1 E L*
Princes Risborough *p358* . . 01844 344123
Bradley, J C (PBW Solicitors) *W*
Plymouth *p350*. 01752 222206
Bradley, J E (HSR Law (Hayes, Son & Richmond)) *G H J1 Zl B2*
Doncaster *p211* 01302 347800
Gainsborough *p228* 01427 613831
Bradley, Ms J M (Slater Bradley & Co) *K3 S1 K1 W*
Wandsworth *p80*. 020 8788 1008
Bradley, J P (Browns)
Marlow *p313*. 01628 476988
Bradley, M C (Bradley & Jefferies Solicitors Limited) *Zd C3 I Ze S1 C1 P B1 E*
Derby *p208* 01332 221722
Bradley, M N (Green Williamson Solicitors) *W T1 S1 Zd Zo*
Wakefield *p418* 01924 291400
Bradley, Mrs N J (Miles & Partners) *D1 K1*
London EC3 *p60*. 020 7426 0400
Bradley, N R (Anderson Partnership) *N*
Chesterfield *p191* 01246 220737
Bradley, N S (LG Lawyers)
London SE1 *p50*. 020 7379 0000
Bradley, P A (Charles Hill Hubbard) *P K1 G H M1 N L B1 D1*
Chichester *p192*. 01243 781000
Bradley, P B (RAC Motoring Services)
Bristol *p452* 0870 553 3533
Bradley, P J (Cannings Connolly) *Zc S2 E*
London EC1 *p18*. 020 7329 9000
Bradley, P J (David Cowan) *S1 E W*
Dorking *p212* 01306 886622
Bradley, P M (TWM Solicitors LLP) *W V Zm T2*
Reigate *p363* 01737 221212
Bradley, P P S (Dolmans) *N Zw C1 Zq F1 F2 Q*
Cardiff *p178* 029 2034 5531
Bradley, Ms S E (Geldards LLP) *R2*
Cardiff *p178* 029 2023 8239
Bradley, Mrs S I (BBC)
London W12 *p103*. 020 8752 5734
Bradley, Mrs S M (Bretherton Law) *D1 K1 V*
St Albans *p389* 01727 869293
Bradley, S N (Croftons) *S1 E W C1 Zh Zd Zv*
Manchester *p302* 0161 214 6180
Bradley, W S (The Royal Borough of Kensington & Chelsea)
London W8 *p109* 020 7361 2741
Bradley-Shaw, Mrs V E (Large & Gibson) *W*
Southsea *p388*. 023 9229 6296
Bradshaw, A D (Sacker & Partners LLP) *Zo*
London EC2 *p76*. 020 7329 6699
Bradshaw, A N (Roach Pittis) *W S1 T1 E L R1 A1 C1 Zc Zd*
Newport *p328* 01983 524431
Bradshaw, Ms B J (Humfrys & Symonds) *K1 D1 D2*
Hereford *p248* . . .01432 359261 / 276276
Bradshaw, Miss C L (Manches LLP) *E L S1*
Oxford *p343* 01865 722106
Bradshaw, Miss D (Lancashire County Council) *N Q B1*
Preston *p469* 01772 254868
Bradshaw, D J (Waddington & Son)
Burnley *p169* 01282 426666
Bradshaw, D L M (Hay & Kilner) *G M1 P K1 F1 D1 H N S1 Zi Zl*
Newcastle upon Tyne *p325* . 0191 232 8345

See p634 for the Key to Work Categories

Bradshaw, Mrs E (Foster Harrington) *S1 S2 E*
Camberley *p173* 01276 692233

Bradshaw, Miss E J (Gepp & Sons) *G H*
Colchester *p197* 01206 369889

Bradshaw, H T J (Smyth Barkham) *Zd Zf T1 T2 W*
London WC2 *p80* 020 7632 9550

Bradshaw, I G P (Goodman Derrick LLP) *W T1 Zd*
London EC4 *p36* 020 7404 0606

Bradshaw, J (Howes Percival LLP) *B1 O*
Norwich *p334* 01603 762103

Bradshaw, J P (Cunningtons) *S1*
Croydon *p205* 020 8688 8446

Bradshaw, J R (Tarmac Ltd)
Wolverhampton *p477* 01902 353522

Bradshaw, Ms K (Bristows)
London EC4 *p15* 020 7400 8000

Bradshaw, M (Charles Russell LLP) *J1 Zi*
London EC4 *p19* 020 7203 5000

Bradshaw, R P (Bradshaw Hollingsworth Solicitors)
Leicester *p279* 0116 204 2500

Bradwell, Ms J (Bradwell & Co Solicitors Limited) *P Q R1 Zq*
Leeds *p271* 0113 242 1000

Brady, Ms A (Pinnacle Insurance PLC)
Borehamwood *p450* 020 8207 9000

Brady, G W (Challinors) *D1 K1 G*
West Bromwich *p427* 0121 553 3211

Brady, J E (Holmes & Hills LLP) *N*
Braintree *p155* 01376 320456

Brady, Ms K (Watson Burton LLP)
Newcastle upon Tyne *p327* . 0845 901 2100

Brady, K (Howard & Over) *E L S1*
Plymouth *p350* 01752 405774

Brady, Mrs L S (Ibbotson Brady) *N Q J2*
Leeds *p274* 0113 366 3022

Brady, M P (Davey Franklin Jones) *K3 K1*
Cirencester *p195* 01285 654875

Brady, P (Brady Eastwood Pierce & Stewart)
Lewisham *p15* 020 8692 8181

Brady, P J (Society of Lloyd's)
London EC3 *p107* 020 7327 1000

Brady, R (Financial Services Authority)
London E14 *p106* 020 7066 1000

Brady, Ms R (Crockett & Co)
Leeds *p272* 0113 226 0111

Brafield, M (AWB Partnership LLP) *K1 L Q K3 D2 O*
Guildford *p235* 01483 302345

Brafield, M A (Major & Co) *K1 D1 N Q Zm Zi*
Guildford *p236* 01483 455771

Bragg, Mrs A M (Nicholson Portnell) *W T2 K4*
Hexham *p249* 01434 603656

Bragg, J R (Metcalfes) *B1 C1 E F1 J1 S1 T1 W C2 S2*
Bristol *p164* 0117 929 0451

Braham, M P (Brighouses) *K1 G M1 P H F1 J1 V*
Southport *p388* . . .01704 534101 / 500151

Braham, P S (Seddons) *E R2*
Westminster *p77* 020 7725 8000

Brahams, G (Lewis Silkin LLP) *J1*
London EC4 *p53* 020 7074 8000
London EC4 *p83* 020 7822 8000

Brahams, M H (DWFM Beckman) *E S1 W L R2*
Westminster *p25* 020 7872 0023

Braich, A (Dass Solicitors) *Zb C1 C2*
Birmingham *p137* 0121 248 4000

Brailsford, J W (Vincent Laverys) *G H D1 K1*
Preston *p357* 01772 555176

Brailsford, M R (Allen & Overy LLP)
London E1 *p5* 020 3088 0000

Brain, Mrs M A (Malvern Hills District Council)
Malvern *p464* 01684 862151

Brain, N P (North Somerset District Council)
Weston-super-Mare *p476* . . 01934 888888

Brain, R (Kingsley Napley) *Zr N*
London EC1 *p50* 020 7814 1200

Brain, T P (Brignalls Balderston Warren) *S1 E W S2 L*
Biggleswade *p133* 01767 313813

Brainsby, Ms J E (Paris Smith LLP) *T2 W K4*
Southampton *p386* 023 8048 2482

Braithwaite, A L (Osborne Clarke) *C1 T1 J1 B1 W F1 Za Zf Ze U2*
Bristol *p164* 0117 917 3000

Braithwaite, Miss A S (Lupton Fawcett) *K1 D1 D2 K2*
Leeds *p275* 0113 280 2000

Braithwaite, C M (Simmons & Simmons)
London EC2 *p79* 020 7628 2020

Braithwaite, F (HSR Law (Hayes, Son & Richmond)) *O Q Zq*
Doncaster *p211* 01302 347800
Gainsborough *p228* 01427 613831

Braithwaite, J P (Brice Droogleever & Co) *S1 S2 E O W J1*
Kensington & Chelsea *p15*. 020 7730 9925 / 7730 7231

Braithwaite, M R (Stone King LLP) *W K4 T2*
Bath *p128* 01225 337599

Braithwaite, N E (Dickinson Dees) *E*
Newcastle upon Tyne *p324* . 0191 279 9000

Braithwaite, P (Beetenson & Gibbon)
Grimsby *p235* 01472 240251

Braithwaite, P R C (Beetenson & Gibbon) *A1 C1 E J1 S1 T1 W Zd Zj Zo*
Louth *p294* 01507 600610

Brake, Miss K L (Mortimers) *D1 K1*
Ludlow *p294* 01584 871000

Brall, A (Pictons Solicitors LLP)
Luton *p295* 01582 870870

Bramall, A (Talbot & Co) *W T1 C1 A1 S1 Zo*
Burton-on-Trent *p170* 01283 564716

Bramall, P E (Franklin & Co) *N O Q L K1 T2 S2 E Zd R1*
Bakewell *p121* 01629 814461

Bramall, R (Plexus Law (A Trading Name of Parabis Law LLP))
Leeds *p276* 0844 245 4100

Bramall, R C (Ramsdens Solicitors) *N J1 Zj Zq Zw*
Huddersfield *p256* 01484 821500

Bramall, T J (Talbot & Co) *W T2 T1 A1 Zv Zo Zd*
Burton-on-Trent *p170* 01283 564716

Brame, P F (Morgan Cole) *E S2 B1 C1 S1 Zd*
Oxford *p344* 01865 262600

Bramhall, Mrs J (Vale Royal Borough Council)
Winsford *p476* 01606 862862

Bramley, Miss E C (Follett Stock LLP) *K4*
Truro *p414* 01872 241700

Bramley, G J (Hill Dickinson LLP) *Zc E S1 C1 C2 B1 Q O*
Sheffield *p376* 0114 229 7907

Bramley, G P R (Stanley Tee) *A1 C1 C2 E S2*
Bishop's Stortford *p144* . . . 01279 755200

Bramley, J S (DWF) *J1*
Liverpool *p287* 0151 907 3000

Bramley, L C (The Endeavour Partnership LLP) *Zc Q*
Stockton-on-Tees *p397* . . . 01642 610300

Bramley, Mrs S L (The College of Law Guildford)
Guildford *p459* 01483 460200

Bramley, S W (Tozers) *N Zr*
Exeter *p222* 01392 207020

Brammer, A (Cartwright King) *G J2 F2 P B2*
Nottingham *p336* 0115 958 7444

Brammer, D A (Staffordshire County Council)
Stafford *p472* 01785 223121

Brampton, P (IBB Solicitors)
Uxbridge *p417* 0845 638 1381
London EC4 *p86* 020 7300 7000

Bramwell, Ms J E (Bramwell Browne Odedra) *S1 K1 D1 K3 J1*
Chesham *p189* 01494 782244

Branch, H (LSG Solicitors) *Q N K1 K3 O J1 Zr Zq L Zk Zl Zw T2 Zc B1*
London W1 *p51* 020 7851 0100

Branch, P S (Buckles Solicitors LLP) *L Q O F1*
Peterborough *p346* 01733 888888

Brand, A C N (Andrew CN Brand)
Swindon *p406* 01285 810328

Brand, A H (Brand & Co) *A1 B1 C1 E F1 I L R1 S1 T1 W Zc Ze Zh Zs*
Cheam *p185* 020 8641 2771

Brand, C M (CM Brand) *R1*
Heswall *p249* 0151 342 3081

Brand, G J A (Lyons Davidson) *E L C1*
Bristol *p163* 0117 904 6000

Brand, J (Boodle Hatfield)
Westminster *p14* 020 7629 7411

Brand, J A (ARVAL PHH Ltd)
Swindon *p473* 01793 884671

Brand, K (Kenneth Brand & Co) *S1 N L E Q W O*
London NW4 *p15* 020 8202 6751

Brand, R S (Robert Brand & Co) *L E S2 O Q B1 S1 C1 J1 F1 W Zf Zh Zl*
Westminster *p15* 020 7935 2408

Brandes, Mrs A J R (Fladgate LLP) *E L S1 R1 Zc*
London WC2 *p32* 020 3036 7000

Brandes, S P (CGM) *C1 E L S1*
Southampton *p385* 023 8063 2733

Brandis, M J (B P Collins LLP) *O Q*
Gerrards Cross *p229* 01753 889995

Brandman, G (Simmons & Simmons)
London EC2 *p79* 020 7628 2020

Brandman, H (Henri Brandman & Co) *O Q N F2 G J1 K1 K3 C1 Zp Zf Zk Zw Ze Zz*
London W1 *p15* 020 7224 0616

Brandman, M A (Blake Lapthorn) *B1 C1 E K1 L M1 N P S1 T1 Zl Zo*
London EC1 *p13* 020 7405 2000

Brandon, B (Russell Jones & Walker)
London WC2 *p74* 020 7657 1555

Brandt, K M (Squire Sanders (UK) LLP) *O Zc Zo*
London EC2 *p81* 020 7655 1000

Brandwood, C M (Brabners Chaffe Street) *C1 C2*
Manchester *p301* 0161 836 8800

Brandwood, Mrs F M (NCC Group)
Manchester *p465* 0161 209 5200

Branford, Miss C R (Crown Prosecution Service Dorset) *K1 G M1 P H S1 F1 J1 V W Zl*
Bournemouth *p450* 01202 498700

Branley, A (Galbraith Branley) *G H B2*
London N12 *p34* 020 8446 8474

Branley, Ms C E (North Yorkshire County Council) *K1 D1 V*
Northallerton *p467* 01609 780780

Brannan, G C H (Linklaters LLP)
London EC2 *p54* 020 7456 2000

Brannan, Mrs M N (Hart Jackson Hall Smith) *K1 D1 N F1*
Newcastle upon Tyne *p325* . 0191 261 5181

Brannick, A C (Molesworths Bright Clegg) *K1 D1*
Rochdale *p365* 01706 356666

Brannick, A C (Wrigley Claydon) *K1 D1 K3 D2*
Todmorden *p412* 01706 815712

Brannigan, Ms H (Hogan Lovells International LLP)
London EC1 *p42* 020 7296 2000

Brannigan, Ms K (Weightmans LLP) *N O Q*
Dartford *p207* 020 7822 1900

Brannigan, Mrs S J (HKB Wiltshires) *L Zl S1 W*
Great Yarmouth *p234* 01493 855676

Brannigan, W N (Metropolitan Police Directorate of Legal Services) *N O Q*
London SW1 *p108* 020 7230 7210

Branson, C (Boyes Turner) *B1 Zb*
Reading *p360* 0118 959 7711

Branson, C R (Royal Mail Group) *C1 C2*
London EC4 *p109* 020 7250 2468

Branson, M (Borough of Telford & Wrekin)
Telford *p473* 01952 380000

Branston, Ms N (Taylor Wessing)
London EC4 *p86* 020 7300 7000

Branton, Ms C A (Backhouse Jones Ltd) *Q N*
Clitheroe *p196* 01254 828300

Brar, B S (Brar & Co) *S1 F1 E K1 J1 L W V R1 C1 Zl Zi Zj*
Newcastle upon Tyne *p323* . 0191 276 6880

Brar, T S (Galbraith Branley)
London N12 *p34* 020 8446 8474
Ealing *p84* 020 8840 2572

Brar, Y (Herrington & Carmichael LLP) *C1 C3 F1 F2 Ze U2*
Wokingham *p437* 0118 977 4045

Brasington, J (Hatten Wyatt) *W K4*
Gravesend *p232* 01474 351199

Brass, Ms R (Blandy & Blandy) *B1*
Reading *p360* 0118 951 6800

Brassey, L M (Fladgate LLP) *O Q L*
London WC2 *p32* 020 3036 7000

Brassil, Ms L (Simmons & Simmons)
London EC2 *p79* 020 7628 2020

Brassington, Mrs C J (Walker Smith Way) *W T2 K4*
Chester *p191* 0844 346 3100

Brassington, Mrs J C (Moss Solicitors LLP) *G H*
Loughborough *p293* 01509 217770

Brassington, L (Penningtons)
Godalming *p231* 01483 791800

Brassington, Ms S A (The Paul Rooney Partnership)
Liverpool *p290* 0151 227 2851

Bratherton, M R (Silverbeck Rymer)
Liverpool *p290* 0151 236 9594

Brathwaite, Mrs D A (Mills & Reeve) *N Zr*
Birmingham *p140* 0121 454 4000

Brathwaite, Mrs K E J (Northamptonshire Magistrates Courts)
Northampton *p467* 01604 497000

Bratt, D C (Stevens) *G H*
Wolverhampton *p438* 01902 772776

Bratt, P (Squire Sanders (UK) LLP) *P N*
Manchester *p310* 0161 830 5000

Braun, R H (Cambridgeshire County Council) *E M1 C1 P L S1 K1 J1 Zp Zl*
Cambridge *p453* 01223 717111

Braun, S (Perrins Solicitors LLP) *Zh L O Q Zq*
Harpenden *p239* 01582 466140

Braund, J G (Trethowans LLP) *N Zr*
Southampton *p387* 023 8032 1000

Bravery, S (Paragon Law) *X Zi Q G H B2*
Nottingham *p338* 0115 964 4123

Bravo, Ms A M (Baileys)
Brackley *p153* 01280 701166

Bray, C P (Lewis Francis Blackburn Bray) *E W S1 S2*
Sheffield *p376* 0114 272 9721

Bray, D (K&L Gates LLP) *O Q S1 C1 Zb Ze*
London EC4 *p47* 020 7648 9000

Bray, D G (DWFM Beckman) *G K1 N Q O C1 D1 H V W Zf Zi Zk Zp Ze*
Westminster *p25* 020 7872 0023

Bray, D P (Kidson Bray & Lawson) *S1 W T2*
Hindhead *p251* 01428 605222

Bray, E J H (Heseltine Bray & Welsh) *G H Zl Zt*
Barnsley *p124* 01226 210777

Bray, Miss H (Henry Hyams) *G*
Leeds *p274* 0113 243 2288

Bray, Mrs J (Bone & Payne LLP) *K4 S1 W*
Llandudno *p291* 01492 876354

Bray, Miss L M (Paris Smith LLP) *K3 K1*
Southampton *p386* 023 8048 2482

Bray, M J (Thompsons (formerly Robin/Brian Thompson & Partners)) *N*
Newcastle upon Tyne *p327* . 0191 269 0400

Bray, M P (Clifford Chance)
London E14 *p20* 020 7006 1000

Bray, O (Reynolds Porter Chamberlain LLP)
London E1 *p71* 020 3060 6000

Bray, R M (Bray & Krais Solicitors) *C1 J1 Zf Ze*
London SW6 *p15* 020 7384 3050

Bray, R M (Richard Bray & Co) *S2 S1 R2 E J1 C1 Q W O N*
London WC2 *p15* 020 7497 3561

Bray, R P (Squire Sanders (UK) LLP)
London EC2 *p81* 020 7655 1000

Bray, Miss T L (Harcus Sinclair) *K1 K3*
London WC2 *p38* 020 7242 9700

Braybrook, Ms J M (Telegraph Media Group)
London SW1 *p110* 020 7931 3131

Brayford, B (Forsters LLP)
Westminster *p33* 020 7863 8333

Brayne, J L F (Allen & Overy LLP)
London E1 *p5* 020 3088 0000

Brayshaw, Mrs A M (Hampshire County Council)
Winchester *p476* 01962 841841

Brazel, D F (Knocker & Foskett) *S1 E L*
Sevenoaks *p374* 01732 459931

Brazell, Ms L C (Bird & Bird LLP) *Ze I U2*
London EC4 *p13* 020 7415 6000

Brazier, I F (Ford Simey LLP) *G K1 N*
Sidmouth *p380* . . .01395 577061 / 0800 169 3741

Brazier, J S (TLT Solicitors) *W T2*
Bristol *p165* 0117 917 7777

Brazier, K J (Bull & Bull) *S1 S2 E L A1 C1 V Zl*
Canterbury *p176* 01227 714860

Brazier, Miss L (Hook & Partners) *W S1 S2 E*
Canvey Island *p177* 01268 692255

Brazier, N P (Malcolm Wilson & Cobby) *L S1 T2 W S2 E*
Lancing *p270* 01903 765991

Brazier, S (Willans LLP) *C2 C1 U1 I U2 Ze*
Cheltenham *p189* 01242 514000

Brazil, Ms J (Trowers & Hamlins)
London EC3 *p88* 020 7423 8000

Breakell, D J (DLA Piper UK LLP) *C1 B1 Zb*
London EC2 *p24* 0870 011 1111

Breakwell, A M (Breakwells) *K1*
Birmingham *p136* 0121 222 2606
Birmingham *p136* 0845 209 1000 / 0117 305 6000

Breakwell, Mrs G S (Dudley Metropolitan Borough Council) *E*
Dudley *p457* 01384 815326

Breakwell, Miss S L M (William Sturges & Co) *S2 E*
Westminster *p84* 020 7873 1000

Brealey, M O (The Smith Partnership) *D1 F1 G H*
Stoke-on-Trent *p398* 01782 324454

Brearley, Ms C F N (Stephenson Harwood) *J1*
London EC2 *p82* 020 7329 4422

Brearley, J S (John S Brearley) *P R1*
High Wycombe *p249* 01494 512775

Brearley, P (Peter Brearley & Co) *N O Q S1 Zj*
Leeds *p272* 0113 259 1761

Brearley, T H (Michelmores LLP) *E S2 R2*
Exeter *p221* 01392 688688

Brecher, A J (Brecher) *E L R2 S1 S2*
London W1 *p15* 020 7563 1000

Brecher, D J (Brecher) *R2*
London W1 *p15* 020 7563 1000

Brecher, H A (Brecher) *C1 E W S1 S2*
London W1 *p15* 020 7563 1000

Brecher, Ms V Z (Brecher) *E L R2 S1 S2*
London W1 *p15* 020 7563 1000

Brechin, Miss K (Michelmores LLP) *L Q Zq*
Exeter *p221* 01392 688688

Brecknell, P (Withers LLP) *E L P R1 S1 Zc*
London EC4 *p92* 020 7597 6000

Breckon, M (Lockings)
Beverley *p131* 01482 300500

Breeden, S (Sills & Betteridge LLP)
Lincoln *p285* 01522 542211

Breedon, P H (Clough & Willis) *S2 E S1 C1*
Bury *p170* 0161 764 5266

Breen, E (South Tyneside Metropolitan Borough Council) *D1 F1 G H K1 L N Q S1 W M1*
South Shields *p471* 0191 427 1717

Breen, J S (Breens Solicitors) *J1 O Q N*
Liverpool *p286* 0151 928 6544
Southport *p388* 01704 532890

Breen, P (Clark Brookes) *H K1 N O Q*
West Bromwich *p427* 0121 553 2576

Breen, S C (Hodge Jones & Allen LLP) *D1 K1 D2*
London NW1 *p41* 020 7874 8300

Breese, R D (Dutton Gregory) *E R1 R2 S1 S2 L*
Southampton *p385* 023 8022 1344

Breeze, Ms C T (Hugh James) *N Zq Zr Zg X*
Cardiff *p179* 029 2022 4871

Breeze, M D (Kaslers Solicitors LLP) *B1 C1 E J1 L N O Q S1 Zl Zm Zo*
West Malling *p428* 0845 270 2511

Brehony, P D (Stewarts Law LLP) *O Q*
London EC4 *p83* 020 7822 8000

Breindel, Miss M (Ann Blyth-Cook & Co) *G H K1 D1 D2 Zv*
Southend-on-Sea *p387* . . . 01702 462999

Breislin, M S (Norrie Waite & Slater) *O Q D1 N G Zt*
Sheffield *p377* 0114 276 6166

Bremen, J (Maxwell Winward LLP) *Zc Zn A3*
London EC4 *p59* 020 7651 0000

Bremers, J E (Blackburn with Darwen Borough Council)
Blackburn *p450* 01254 585585
Preston *p469* 01772 906101

Bremner, Ms E (DLA Piper UK LLP)
London EC2 *p24* 0870 011 1111

Brenan, J S (Stockler Brunton) *S2 E L Q R1*
London EC4 *p83* 020 7404 6661

Brenlund, Miss L R (Weightmans LLP) *J1 Zza Q O Zp J2*
Dartford *p207* 020 7822 1900

Brennan, Ms A S (Suffolk County Council)
Ipswich *p462* 01473 583000

Brennan, Mrs B A (Debenhams Ottaway) *K1 D1 K3*
St Albans *p390* 01727 837161

Brennan, Miss C A (Morecrofts Solicitors LLP) *K1 K2 D1 D2*
Crosby *p203* 0151 924 9234

Brennan, Miss I M (Langley Wellington) *X*
Gloucester *p230* 01452 521286

Brennan, Ms J E (Burton & Co LLP) *G H J1 F1 M1 P Zp*
Lincoln *p284* 01522 523215

Brennan, Mrs J L (Steel & Co) *S1 K1 W S2 L E*
Knaresborough *p268* 01423 869977
Wetherby *p429* 01937 845539

Brennan, J S (Carter Lemon Camerons) *E C1 L A1 R1 S1 J1 U2 C2 R2*
London EC1 *p18* 020 7406 1000

Brennan, Mrs K (Thursfields) *K1*
Kidderminster *p266* 01562 820575

6

Brennan, Mrs M D (John Fowlers LLP Solicitors) *K3 D1 K1*
Brightlingsea *p159* 01206 302694
Colchester *p197* 01206 576151
Brennan, Mrs N P (South Wales Police)
Bridgend *p451* 01656 869476
Brennan, Mrs R E (Clarkson Wright & Jakes Ltd) *J1*
Orpington *p341* 01689 887887
Brennan, S (Hodge Jones & Allen LLP) *N*
London NW1 *p41* 020 7874 8300
Brennan, T P (Davies & Partners) *C1 T1 B1 Ze Zb Zo F1 A3 Zd C3 J1 Zf M1 B2 O C2 W*
Almondsbury *p115* 01454 619619
Brennan, Mrs Z C (Warner Goodman LLP) *S1*
Portsmouth *p355* 023 9275 3575
Brennand, Ms J L (Lloyd Brennand) *G H M1 K1 D1*
Brentford *p156* 020 8569 9020
Brennand, P (Lomax Geddes & Co) *G H S1 W K1 E L D1 Zj C1 S2 F1*
Manchester *p307* 0161 834 4722
Brennen, R (Swinburne & Jackson LLP) *C1 D1 K1 L N O B1 S1 W*
Ryton *p370* . . . 0191 413 3468 / 413 2630
Brenninkmeyer, Ms M (M M E Brenninkmeyer) *W*
London W1 *p15* 020 7917 1897
Brent, N J (Druces LLP)
London EC2 *p27* 020 7638 9271
Brent, S (Derbyshire County Council)
Matlock *p465* 01629 580000
Brentnall, J N (Wards Solicitors) *S1 E C1 A1 P R1 Zc Zn S2*
Bristol *p165* 0117 929 2811
Weston-super-Mare *p429* . . 01934 413535
Brentnall, Mrs L (Shakespeares) *S1 S2*
Nottingham *p339* 0115 945 3700
Brentnall, T W B (Elborne Mitchell LLP) *Zj A3 O*
London EC3 *p29* 020 7320 9000
Brereton, Ms K (Jeary & Lewis)
Chippenham *p193* 01249 444484
Brereton, M A (McCormacks) *B2 Q S1 W*
London EC3 *p56* 020 7791 2000
Breslin, Mrs D M K (LG Lawyers)
London SE1 *p50* 020 7379 0000
Breslin, Ms K (Barlow Lyde & Gilbert LLP)
London EC3 *p10* 020 7247 2277
Bresnick, D L (CMS Cameron McKenna LLP)
London EC3 *p17* 020 7367 3000
Bressington, A N (Awdry Bailey & Douglas) *D1 K1*
Devizes *p210* 01380 722311
Bresslaw, J H (Simmons & Simmons)
London EC2 *p79* 020 7628 2020
Bretherick, P R J (Tosswill & Co) *G H*
Lambeth *p87* 020 8674 9494
Bretherton, R J H (BPE Solicitors LLP) *B1 C1 T1 Zc Zb*
London WC1 *p9* 020 7387 1437
Brett, A J (Times Newspapers Ltd)
London E1 *p110* 020 7782 5858
Brett, A K (Hewitsons) *E*
Cambridge *p174* 01223 461155
Brett, C (Barlow Lyde & Gilbert LLP) *O Zq*
London EC3 *p10* 020 7247 2277
Oxford *p342* 01865 336600
Brett, Mrs C (South Lincolnshire Magistrates Courts)
Grantham *p459* 01476 563438
Brett, Mrs C A (R M Brett & Co) *W T2*
Cardiff *p177* 029 2023 0440
Brett, Miss D J (Blandy & Blandy) *O Q F1 J1*
Reading *p360* 0118 951 6800
Brett, G A (Stevens & Bolton) *E R2 S2*
Guildford *p237* 01483 302264
Brett, H M D (White & Case LLP) *C1 N I J1 Ze Zf Zd*
London EC2 *p91* 020 7532 1000
Brett, J (Browns)
Marlow *p313* 01628 476988
Brett, Mrs M H (Stanley Tee LLP) *W Zd*
Saffron Walden *p370* 01799 527299
Brett, M P (Black Graf & Co) *E S2 S1*
London NW3 *p13* 020 7586 1141
Brett, R M (R M Brett & Co) *C1 E J1 L R1 S1 T1 T2 W*
Cardiff *p177* 029 2023 0440
Brett, Ms S C (Bretts Solicitors) *G H*
Chelmsford *p186* 01245 401233
Brett, S S (Gildener Brett)
Penzance *p346* 01736 332533
Brett, Miss V J (Charles Russell LLP) *C1 C2*
London EC4 *p19* 020 7203 5000
Brettell, A D (SJ Berwin LLP)
London EC4 *p75* 020 7111 2222
Bretton, R J (Osborne Clarke) *O*
Bristol *p164* 0117 917 3000
Bretz, O W (Clifford Chance)
London E14 *p20* 020 7006 1000
Brew, J (Harrison Clark LLP) *K1 D1 K2*
Cheltenham *p188* 01242 269198
Worcester *p439* 01905 612001
Worcester *p439* 01905 612001
Brew, S A (Fladgate LLP) *O Q B1 J1 Zj Zb*
London WC2 *p32* 020 3036 7000
Breward, A (Taylor Wessing) *I C1 C3 M1 Ze*
London EC4 *p86* 020 7300 7000
Brewer, A P (Fowler de Pledge) *Zq V Q O L C1 B1 A3*
Cambridge *p174* 01223 311291
Brewer, Ms C L (Ashfords LLP)
Exeter *p220* 01392 337000

Brewer, Miss C M (Reynolds Porter Chamberlain LLP) *Q Zj*
London E1 *p71* 020 3060 6000
Brewer, C W (Kennedys) *Q O K1 Zq*
Chelmsford *p186* 0845 838 4800
Brewer, Mrs G M (Guildford Borough Council)
Guildford *p459* 01483 505050
Brewer, Miss J E (Stone Rowe Brewer LLP) *E S1 W K1 L T1*
Twickenham *p416* 020 8891 6141
Brewer, Miss L (Lancashire County Council)
Preston *p469* 01772 254868
Brewer, M (Mills & Reeve) *J1*
Birmingham *p140* 0121 454 4000
Brewer, P (Armitage Sykes LLP)
Brighouse *p158* 01484 714431
Brewer, P J (Solicitors Property Shop Keighley)
Keighley *p264* 01535 608844
Brewer, P S (John Barkers) *E S2 K4 W T2 S1 C1*
Louth *p294* 01507 604773
Mablethorpe *p297* 01507 477673
Brewin, C (Veale Wasbrough Vizards)
Bristol *p165* 0117 925 2020
Brewin, C A (The Johnson Partnership) *G H*
Nottingham *p337* 0115 941 9141
Brewin, Mrs L (Derbyshire County Council) *K4 K1 Zu Zm V W G H N Q*
Matlock *p465* 01629 580000
Brewin, Ms R (Wilkin Chapman LLP) *E S2 R2 S1*
Grimsby *p235* 01472 262626
Brewins, J D (Howlett Clarke Crowther Wood) *K1 Q G N J1 D1 L O S1 W Zl Zi*
Brighton *p159* . . . .01273 327272 / 326341
Brewis, C R (Crane & Staples) *C1 S2 E*
Welwyn Garden City *p425* . . 01707 329333
Brewster, A (Howes Percival LLP)
Norwich *p334* 01603 762103
Brewster, Ms H (Bracknell Forest Borough Council)
Bracknell *p450* 01344 424642
Brewster, M J (TLT Solicitors)
London EC2 *p85* 020 3465 4000
Brewster, P J (Roythornes LLP) *E S1 R2 S2*
Spalding *p389* 01775 842500
Briam, A M (Clifford Chance)
London E14 *p20* 020 7006 1000
Brian, A (Gordons LLP)
Leeds *p273* 0113 227 0100
Brian, A C (Tinsdills) *S1 W E*
Hanley *p239* 01782 262031
Brian, Mrs J A (Meesons) *L S1 S2 W*
Ringwood *p364* 01425 472315
Briano, Ms J E A (BPE Solicitors LLP) *N*
Cheltenham *p187* 01242 224433
Briant, N A (Taylor Wessing) *C1 F1*
London EC4 *p86* 020 7300 7000
Briars, J J R (Williamson & Soden) *E S2 R2*
Solihull *p383* 0121 733 8000
Brice, Ms H (Ellisons) *L O*
Colchester *p197* 01206 764477
Brice, Mrs J (Brice & Co) *G H*
Bures *p168* 01787 227199
Brice, J J (Brice Droogleever & Co) *B1 C1 E K1 L M1 N P S1 W Zc Zh Ze*
Kensington & Chelsea *p15*. 020 7730 9925 / 7730 7231
Brice, N (Napthens LLP) *N*
Preston *p357* 01772 888444
Brice, O C R (Taylor Wessing)
London EC4 *p86* 020 7300 7000
Brice, Ms R (Howard Kennedy LLP) *R2*
London W1 *p48* 020 7636 1616
Brice, R P J (Gepp & Sons) *G H*
Chelmsford *p186* 01245 493939
Colchester *p197* 01206 369889
Brickles, B (Sills & Betteridge LLP) *G*
Boston *p151* 01205 364615
Bricknell, H G M (Lambe Corner) *A1 S1 W L E T1 R1*
Hereford *p248* 01432 355301
Bricknell, P R (Stanley Tee LLP) *E S2 C1 S1*
Saffron Walden *p370* 01799 527299
Brickwood, R L (Sanders Brickwood) *N Q K1 G Zl O*
Cirencester *p195* 01285 654601
Bridel, Miss V (Debenhams Ottaway) *W*
St Albans *p390* 01727 837161
Bridge, D (Battens) *S1*
Yeovil *p443* 01935 846000
Bridge, J D (Farleys Solicitors LLP) *Q Zr N B1 Zg*
Manchester *p304* 0161 660 4254
Bridge, Mrs K (SFN Solicitors) *S1*
Burnley *p169* 01282 421284
Bridge, Ms L (Burton Copeland LLP) *G H*
Manchester *p302* 0161 827 9500
Bridge, Ms S J (Harbottle & Lewis LLP) *W T2*
London W1 *p38* 020 7667 5000
Bridgeman, F M (Allen & Overy LLP)
London E1 *p5* 020 3088 0000
Bridgen, Mrs M J (The Smith Partnership) *K1 K2*
Swadlincote *p404* 01283 226444
Bridgens, S R D (Wilson Browne) *S1 E W C1 F1 K1 L P Zd Zl*
Northampton *p333* 01604 876697
Bridger, A S (Switalski's)
Bradford *p155* 01274 720314
Bridger, J C (Preston Redman) *P M1 K1 G J1 N H F1 Zl Zk Zi O Q D1 Zr K3*
Bournemouth *p152* 01202 292424
Bridges, Ms A V (Mills & Reeve) *T2 W Zd*
Norwich *p335* 01603 660155
Bridges, J (Coffin Mew & Clover) *O L F1 J1 Zp X Zq Zh*
Fareham *p223* 01329 825617

Bridges, Ms J M (Linder Myers Solicitors) *Zr*
Manchester *p306* 0844 984 6000
Bridges, Miss K (Lodders Solicitors LLP) *S1 E L A1 Zc*
Stratford-upon-Avon *p400* . . 01789 293259
Bridges, K D (Osborne Clarke) *O*
Bristol *p164* 0117 917 3000
Bridges, The Hon M T (Farrer & Co LLP)
London WC2 *p31* 020 3375 7000
Bridges, R D (Kirkwoods) *S1 K1 S2 W E K4 L Q*
Stanmore *p394* 020 8954 8555
Bridgford, T R (Macfarlanes) *C1*
London EC4 *p56* 020 7831 9222
Manchester *p310* 0161 830 5000
Bridgman, G H (Graham Bridgman & Co) *B1 O*
Reading *p360* 0118 933 1818
Bridgman, Ms J E (AWB Charlesworth LLP) *D2 D1 K3 K1*
Keighley *p263* 01535 613678
Bridgman, M N E (Elliott Bridgman) *K1 G H D1 N V Q J1 F1*
Telford *p409* 01952 684544
Bridgwater, Mrs J M (Burges Salmon) *J1 O*
Bristol *p161* 0117 939 2000
Bridgwood, Miss H (MacLaren Britton) *D1 K3 K1*
Nottingham *p338* 0115 941 1469
Bridson, Ms D M (Maxwell Hodge Solicitors) *S1*
West Kirby *p428* 0151 625 9154
Bridson, P J (DWFM Beckman) *O Q R1 Ze B1 L Zq U2*
Westminster *p25* 020 7872 0023
Brien, M J (Millichips) *C1 E S1 N*
Solihull *p382* 0121 624 4000
Brienza-Wooldridge, Ms A (Withers LLP) *E S1*
London EC4 *p92* 020 7597 6000
Brierley, A H R (Turnbull Garrard) *S1 E W A1*
Shrewsbury *p379* . 01743 350851 / 351332
Brierley, A W W (3i PLC)
London SW1 *p103* 020 7928 3131
Brierley, D J (Voice: The Union for Education Professionals)
Derby *p457* 01332 372337
Brierley, I (DLA Piper UK LLP)
London EC2 *p24* 0870 011 1111
Brierley, L D (DLA Piper UK LLP) *C1 I C3 U1 Ze U2 Zw*
Manchester *p303* 0870 011 1111
Brierley, M (Hanne & Co)
London SW11 *p38* 020 7228 0017
Brierley, P N (Broomhead & Saul) *K1 G H Q D1 L Zl*
Taunton *p408* 01823 288121
Brierley, S (Ouvry Goodman & Co) *S1 E C1 T1 L R1 F1 J1 A1 Zd Ze*
Sutton *p403* 020 8642 7571
Briffa, D M (Child & Child) *S1 L*
London SW1 *p20* 020 7235 8000
Briffa, Ms M (Briffa) *O Ze*
Islington *p15* 020 7288 6003
Brigg, Ms J A (Turner & Wall) *K1 D1 D2 V*
Keighley *p264* 01535 607831
Briggs, Mrs A (Stanley Tee) *S1*
Braintree *p155* 01376 552277
Briggs, A (Hogan Lovells International LLP)
London EC1 *p42* 020 7296 2000
Briggs, Mrs A (Tinn Criddle & Co) *S2 E S1 W*
Alford *p115* 01507 462882
Sutton-on-Sea *p404* 01507 443043
Briggs, D (Department for Business, Enterprise and Regulatory Reform)
London SW1 *p105* 020 7215 0105
Briggs, D H (David Briggs & Co) *A1 E L S1*
London SW3 *p15* 020 7823 9040
Briggs, Miss E J (Oglethorpe Sturton & Gillibrand) *K1 N Q D1 L F1 J1 Zi*
Lancaster *p270* 01524 846846
Briggs, G M (Addleshaw Goddard)
Leeds *p271* 0113 209 2000
Manchester *p300* 0161 934 6000
Briggs, J H C (Burges Salmon) *O*
Bristol *p161* 0117 939 2000
Briggs, Ms K (Olswang LLP) *C1 Ze Zf*
London WC1 *p64* 020 7067 3000
Briggs, Mrs L (Royds LLP) *O Q L*
London EC4 *p74* 020 7583 2222
Briggs, Ms L J (Osborne Clarke) *O*
Bristol *p164* 0117 917 3000
Briggs, N J (Shakespeares) *Ze O*
Birmingham *p142* 0121 237 3000
Briggs, P E S (Hayton Winkley) *S1 E C1 W A1 T1 L R1 Zc*
Kendal *p264* 01539 720136
Briggs, S (Bond Pearce LLP)
Southampton *p385* 0845 415 0000
Briggs, Mrs S M (Leeds City Council)
Leeds *p462* 0113 224 3513
Briggs, Mrs T (Lewis Silkin LLP) *C1 C2*
London EC4 *p53* 020 7074 8000
Briggs, T E (Briggs Sayer & Co) *S1 W K1 L*
Belper *p130* 01773 825246
Ripley *p364* 01773 744011
Brigham, R A (Quality Solicitors Copley Clark) *S1*
Banstead *p122* 01737 362131
Brighouse, S G (Brighouse Wolff) *Q N Zm K1 K3*
Ormskirk *p341* 01695 573202
Bright, A (Guthrie Jones & Jones)
Bala *p121* 01678 520428
Bright, Ms A J (Bright & Sons) *W T1 T2 K4*
Maldon *p299* 01621 852323
Witham *p435* 01376 512338
Bright, B K (Keith B Bright) *G H W E S1 Q N*
Sutton Coldfield *p403* 0121 351 6296

Bright, C R (Shearman & Sterling LLP) *N C3*
London EC2 *p78* 020 7655 5000
Bright, J D (Barlow Lyde & Gilbert LLP) *Zj O Q I*
London EC3 *p10* 020 7247 2277
Bright, Ms K L (Bishop & Sewell LLP) *O Q*
London WC1 *p13* 020 7631 4141
Bright, P T (Barnetts) *G H M1 P J1 C1 F1*
Southport *p388* 0870 787 3600
Bright, Miss S (Hogan Lovells International LLP) *N Q*
London EC1 *p42* 020 7296 2000
Brightling, C R (Field Seymour Parkes) *C1 C2 Zw*
Reading *p360* 0118 951 6200
Briginshaw, J (British American Tobacco)
London WC2 *p104* 020 7845 1000
Brigman, Ms S (PCB Solicitors LLP) *G H*
Telford *p409* 01952 403000
Brignull, S R (Lodders Solicitors LLP) *T2 W*
Stratford-upon-Avon *p400* . . 01789 293259
Brigstocke, C T (Squire Sanders (UK) LLP) *E*
London EC2 *p81* 020 7655 1000
Brill, I (Vaughan & Co) *N K1 S1 E Q*
Leeds *p277* 0113 261 1044
Brill, S J (The College of Law) *W*
London WC1 *p105* 0800 289997
Brimacombe, D J (Standard Chartered Bank) *O J1 Q*
London EC2 *p109* 020 7457 7500
Brimble, Mrs J (Brimble & Co) *G H K1 M1 F1 J1 P D1 L*
Halifax *p238* 01422 322121
Brimble, J R (Foot Anstey) *K1 D1 Q G Zl L*
Taunton *p408* 01823 625600
Brimble, N C (Nicholls Brimble & Co) *B1 C1 E F1 J1 K1 L M1 N*
Smethwick *p382* 0121 429 8016
Brimelow, R A P (Lewis Silkin LLP) *J1 Zi Zp*
Oxford *p343* 01865 263070
Brims, N B (Norwich City Council)
Norwich *p467* 01603 212212
Brind, Ms Z A (Bird & Lovibond) *S1 S2 K1*
Uxbridge *p417* 01895 256151
Brindle, Miss D A (Rudd Jepson) *S1 W S2*
Bromley *p167* 020 8313 0555
Brindle, W T F (John Barkers) *W K4 S1 T1 T2 A1*
Louth *p294* 01507 604773
Mablethorpe *p297* 01507 477673
Brindley, Ms J (Hains & Lewis Ltd) *K1 K3 G H D1 W V*
Haverfordwest *p244* 0845 408 0125
Brindley, J D (Symes Robinson & Lee) *S1 S2 W*
Exeter *p222* 01392 270867
Brindley, P A (Loosemores) *N*
Cardiff *p179* 029 2022 4433
Brindley, R G (Hadgkiss Hughes & Beale) *S1 W E C1*
Birmingham *p138* 0121 449 5050
Brindley-Slater, P (Storrar Cowdry)
Chester *p191* 01244 400567
Brine, Ms J (Pannone LLP) *N*
Manchester *p308* 0161 909 3000
Brine, S D (Stephen D Brine Solicitors) *S1 E R1 K1 M1 P J1 F1 W Zl*
Liverpool *p286* 0151 734 5000
Brinicombe, Ms H J (Camerons Jones) *K1 K3 D1 D2 Q*
Harrow *p241* 020 8423 6666
Brink, J (Harbottle & Lewis LLP) *C1*
London W1 *p38* 020 7667 5000
Brink, J (Breeze & Wyles Solicitors LLP)
Bishop's Stortford *p144* . . . 01279 715333
Brinkhurst, R J (Warners Solicitors) *C1 J1 Zza F1*
Tonbridge *p412* 01732 770660
Brinkley, P (Glaisyers) *K1 W*
Tamworth *p407* 01827 61011
Brint, S F (Elliot Mather LLP) *G H B2 Zm*
Chesterfield *p192* 01246 231288
Briody, Mrs C A (Elmbridge Borough Council)
Esher *p458* 01372 474198
Briscoe, B A (BTMK Solicitors LLP) *B1 F1 L O Q Zq*
Southend-on-Sea *p387* . . . 01702 339222
Briscoe, Mrs J (Hertfordshire County Council)
Hertford *p460* 01992 555555
Briscoe, J M (Ewart Price) *S1 W L P N M1 K1 J1 E T1 Zc Zj Zk*
Welwyn Garden City *p425* . . 01707 332383
Brisley, Mrs L P (Buckles Solicitors LLP) *K1 K2 K3 D2 A3*
Peterborough *p346* 01733 888888
Brisley, Mrs R A (Gill Akaster) *N*
Plymouth *p349* 01752 203500
Brison, L P D (C W Booth & Co) *G H K1 S1 D1*
Bishop Auckland *p144* 01388 606660
Bristol, J (Birketts LLP) *A1 E R1 S1 R2 S2*
Ipswich *p262* 01473 232300
Bristow, Mrs A J (Brethertons LLP) *N T1 A1 Zd*
Rugby *p368* 01788 579579
Rugby *p368* 01788 579579
Bristow, D (W H Matthews & Co) *C1 S2 E L R2 S1*
Islington *p59* 020 7251 4942
Bristow, K J (Clarkson Wright & Jakes Ltd) *K3 K1*
Orpington *p341* 01689 887887
Bristow, P R K (Mayo Wynne Baxter LLP) *S1*
Brighton *p160* 01273 775533
Bristow, Ms S M (Beale and Company Solicitors LLP) *O Zj Zq*
London WC2 *p11* 020 7240 3474
Britain, R (McDermott Will & Emery UK LLP) *C2 C1*
London EC2 *p56* 020 7577 6900

See p634 for the Key to Work Categories

Britlin, A P (Walker Smith Way) *N*
Chester *p191* 0844 346 3100
Briton, T (Gateshead Metropolitan Borough Council)
Gateshead *p458* 0191 433 3000
Brittain, N (Sidley Austin Brown & Wood) *Zb*
London EC2 *p78* 020 7360 3600
Brittain, Miss S (Young & Co) *K1*
Stoke-on-Trent *p398* 01782 339200
Brittain, T (Matthew Arnold & Baldwin LLP) *E L S1*
London EC4 *p59* 020 7936 4600
Britten, G (Buckinghamshire County Council)
Aylesbury *p448* 01296 383653
Britten, J C (Actons) *P Zl C1 B2 J2*
Nottingham *p335* 0115 910 0200
Britten, J H (RHW Solicitors LLP) *O Q C1*
Guildford *p237* 01483 302000
Britten, P R (Mears Hobbs & Durrant) *A1 E J1 L R1 S1 W Zl Zn*
Lowestoft *p294* 01502 583621
Brittenden, J (Hogan Lovells International LLP)
London EC1 *p42* 020 7296 2000
Britton, A C (Charles Hoile)
Newbury *p322* 01635 45595
Britton, A J (Wilson & Co)
London N17 *p92* 020 8808 7535
Britton, Miss B (Bury & Walkers LLP) *S1 A1*
Barnsley *p124* 01226 733533
Britton, Mrs C M (Britton & Co) *S1 W E L*
Weston-super-Mare *p429* . . 01934 522000
Britton, D J (Speakman & Co) *K1 W*
Crewe *p203* 01270 214237
Britton, Ms L L (Speakman & Co)
Crewe *p203* 01270 214237
Britton, R J (Civil Aviation Authority)
London WC2 *p105* 020 7453 6162
Britton, S M (MacLaren Britton) *J1 L Zp*
Nottingham *p338* 0115 941 1469
Britton, V (De Maid Solicitors & Advocates) *G H B2*
Cardiff *p178* 029 2023 5575
Britz, H (Hodge Jones & Allen LLP) *L*
London NW1 *p41* 020 7874 8300
Broad, Miss C T (Scott Duff & Co) *N W*
Carlisle *p182* 01228 531054
Broad, K M (Department for Business, Enterprise and Regulatory Reform)
London SW1 *p105* 020 7215 0105
Broad, M D (Dutton Gregory) *J1 Zp J2*
Winchester *p433* 01962 844333
Broadbent, C M (C M Broadbent) *A1 E N O P Q R1 S1 W Zc Zd Zl Zt*
Macclesfield *p297* 01625 500038
Broadbent, F M (Batt Broadbent) *A1 E R1 C1 W*
Salisbury *p371* 01722 411141
Broadbent, G (Goughs) *E*
Devizes *p210* 01380 726913
Broadbent, N J (Lupton Fawcett) *O Zq A3 Zj Zk Zz Zc*
Leeds *p275* 0113 280 2000
Broadberry, A (Speechly Bircham LLP) *T2*
London EC4 *p81* 020 7427 6400
Broadbridge, J N (Crombie Wilkinson) *N Q K1 G S1 F1 O H W P Zl Zc*
Malton *p300* 01653 600070
Broadhead, Miss K (McGrigors LLP)
London EC4 *p56* 020 7054 2500
Broadhead, R W N (NBM Massucco Shelbourne) *S1 E C1 W R1 B1 Zl Zc*
Cambridge *p175* 01223 211992
Chelmsford *p187* 01245 269909
Broadhurst, Miss C L S (Brooke-Taylors) *T1 Q G H F1 L K3 K1*
Buxton *p172* 01298 22741
Broadhurst, Ms D (Sheffield City Council) *Zh L*
Sheffield *p471* 0114 273 4019
Broadhurst, E E (Emerson Developments (Holdings) Ltd)
Alderley Edge *p447* 01625 588420
Broadhurst, J (Ashurst LLP)
London EC2 *p7* 020 7638 1111
Broadhurst, Mrs L R (Tileflair Ltd)
Bristol *p452* 0117 959 8877
Broadhurst, Mrs N J (Mundays LLP) *C1 F1 M1*
Cobham *p196* 01932 590500
Broadhurst, S R (Fairweather Stephenson & Co) *K1 K2 L V K3*
Felixstowe *p225* 01394 277941
Broadie, C R (Cripps Harries Hall LLP) *O Q N Zq A3*
Tunbridge Wells *p415* 01892 515121
Broadley, A (Linder Myers Solicitors) *G H K1 D1*
Manchester *p307* 0844 984 6400
Broadley, Ms J (Bindmans LLP) *K3 K1*
London WC1 *p12* 020 7833 4433
Broadmore, D T (Barlow Lyde & Gilbert LLP)
London EC3 *p10* 020 7247 2277
Broady, R D (Temple Heelis LLP) *P K1 M1 G B1 D1 H J1 R1*
Kendal *p264* 01539 723757
Brock, D M J (Mills & Reeve) *R1*
Cambridge *p175* 01223 364422
Brock, J M (Hatch Brenner) *G H K1 D1 Zl*
Norwich *p334* 01603 660811
Brock, Miss S A (Morgan Cole) *Zj N*
Bristol *p164* 0117 916 7220
Brockbank, A L (Field Fisher Waterhouse LLP) *C1 C2*
London EC3 *p31* 020 7861 4000
Brocken, D J (Wilfred Light & Reid) *S1 W E T2 K4*
Southampton *p387* 023 8077 7817
Brockett, Mrs R E (Turners) *W K4 Q*
Cross Hills *p204* 01535 634149
Brockie, C (McDermott Will & Emery UK LLP)
London EC2 *p56* 020 7577 6900
Brockis, J N (Taylor Walton LLP) *C1 C2 C3 F1 J1 I M1 T1 X*
Luton *p295* 01582 731161
Brocklebank, Ms E (Jordans) *K3 K1*
Dewsbury *p210* 01924 457171
Brocklebank, Miss L M (Bond Pearce LLP) *N Zj*
Southampton *p385* 0845 415 0000
Brocklehurst, Mrs A C (Atkinson & Firth) *D1 K1*
Shipley *p378* 01274 584305
Brocklehurst, D A (Burley & Geach) *M1 K1 S1 P N E W F1 J1*
Haslemere *p243* 01428 656011
Brocklehurst, J (Pinsent Masons LLP) *E R2*
Leeds *p276* 0113 244 5000
Brocklehurst, N J (Bell & Co) *K1 K3 N Q Zq*
Cheam *p185* 020 8642 6099
Brocklehurst, P S (Linder Myers Solicitors) *G H B2*
Manchester *p307* 0844 984 6400
Brockman, Mrs A P (Brockmans) *E L*
Stockbridge *p395* 01264 810910
Brockman, C C (Blake Lapthorn) *N B1 O*
Chandlers Ford *p184* 023 8090 8090
Brockway, Ms C E (Stephen Moore & Co)
Rugby *p368* 01788 535127
Brockwell, Mrs A J (Coffin Mew & Clover) *B1 C1 C2 C3 Zb Ze Zj R2*
Southampton *p385* 023 8033 4661
Brodbent, Mrs D (Lupton Fawcett) *N*
Leeds *p275* 0113 280 2000
Broddle, Ms L J (Stone Rowe Brewer LLP) *K1 W D1 K3*
Twickenham *p416* 020 8891 6141
Broderick, Mrs M J (Doncaster Magistrates Court)
Doncaster *p457* 01302 366711
Broderick, T P (West Lancashire District Council)
Ormskirk *p468* 01695 577177
Brodie, Mrs K A (Chester City Council)
Chester *p454* 01244 324324
Brodie, Ms P A (Cole & Co)
Norwich *p334* 01603 617018
Brodie, P S (Cumbria County Council)
Carlisle *p453* . . . . 01228 607374 / 607351
Brodie, S M (Brabners Chaffe Street) *J1*
Liverpool *p286* 0151 600 3000
Brodie, T J (Lester Aldridge LLP) *O*
Bournemouth *p152* 01202 786161
Brodkin, A I (Adrian & Co) *Zl L W*
London NW5 *p4* . 020 7485 8450 / 7267 1240
Brodkin, Mrs B (Cooper Whiteman) *G J1 O Q*
London WC1 *p22* 020 7831 5222
Brodkin, Mrs D B (Adrian & Co) *S1*
London NW5 *p4* . 020 7485 8450 / 7267 1240
Brodrick, R (Trowers & Hamlins)
London EC3 *p88* 020 7423 8000
Brody, Ms M (Mayer Brown International LLP) *P*
London EC2 *p59* 020 3130 3000
Broe, C (Oldhams Solicitors & Advocates) *G H Zl Zi Zg*
Baldock *p121* 01462 895444
Brogan, C (Crompton Halliwell) *S1 S2 E W R2 A1 Zc*
Bury *p170* 0161 797 9222
Brogan, Miss C A (Brindley Twist Tafft & James) *B1 O Q*
Birmingham *p136* 0121 214 8989
Brogan, P (Howarth Goodman) *W L C1 E S1 Zh*
Manchester *p305* 0161 832 5068
Brogden, J (DAC Beachcroft)
London EC4 *p24* 020 7936 2222
Brogden, Ms L (Arnison & Co Solicitors Limited) *N S1*
Penrith *p346* 01768 862007
Brohier, M R (Barnes Marsland) *W T2*
Broadstairs *p166* 01843 861595
Broker, M C (Barrington Scholfield) *W*
Bridgwater *p157* . . 01278 422858 / 422873
Bromelow, G H (Saunders Law Partnership LLP) *G H*
London WC2 *p76* 020 7632 4300
Bromet, E A (Wrigleys Solicitors LLP) *W*
Leeds *p278* 0113 244 6100
Bromfield, C J B (Wansbroughs) *O C1 B1 J1 N P M1 T1 Zd Zi Zo*
Devizes *p210* 01380 733300
Bromfield, J S (John Bromfield & Company Ltd) *K1 J1 S1 W*
Nuneaton *p339* 024 7638 2343
Bromfield, Ms L (Bevans) *J1*
Bristol *p161* 0117 923 7249
Bromiley, V (Napthens LLP) *C1*
Blackburn *p145* 01254 667733
Bromley, E M (Barlow Lyde & Gilbert LLP)
London EC3 *p10* 020 7247 2277
Bromley, Miss J (Russell & Russell) *S1 W K4*
Bolton *p149* 01204 399299
Bromley, M S (Lichfield Reynolds) *G H*
Stoke-on-Trent *p398* 01782 595599
Bromwich, S (Ashurst LLP) *A3 Q*
London EC2 *p7* 020 7638 1111
Bronstein, M S (Salans) *J1*
London EC4 *p76* 020 7429 6000
Brook, A R (Watson Woodhouse) *N D1 K1 D2 Q*
Stockton-on-Tees *p397* . . . 01642 247656
Brook, A S (Nexus Solicitors) *O N Q Zj Zq F2*
Manchester *p308* 0161 819 4900
Brook, Miss C (Aaron & Partners LLP Solicitors) *J1*
Chester *p190* 01244 405555
Brook, Ms C (Walker Morris) *R1 P*
Leeds *p277* 0113 283 2500
Brook, Miss E A (Ison Harrison) *S1*
Guiseley *p237* 01943 889080
Brook, Ms F (Langleys)
York *p445* 01904 610886
Brook, Dr G W (Copleys) *K1 P W F1 J1 G D1 Zb Zc Zt*
St Ives *p391* 01480 464515
Brook, I M (Brooks Solicitors) *S1 W E L R1 P M1 K1 T1 F1*
Shipley *p378* 01274 596724
Brook, J T (W Brook & Co)
Goldthorpe *p231* 01709 898697
Brook, N (Blake Lapthorn) *Zd*
Oxford *p342* 01865 248607
Brook, N P (Blake Lapthorn) *Q O L*
Chandlers Ford *p184* 023 8090 8090
Brook, P (DLA Piper UK LLP) *C1 C3 F1*
Liverpool *p287* 0870 011 1111
Brook, P W G (Brooks Solicitors) *G H K1 L M1 N P R1 D1*
Chesterfield *p192* 01246 220552
Brook, R V (Browne Jacobson LLP) *C1 T1 Ze*
Nottingham *p336* 0115 976 6000
Brook, S (Howard Kennedy LLP) *S1*
London W1 *p48* 020 7636 1616
Brook, S O (Brook Martin & Co) *E C1 S1 R1 W L J1 T1*
Westminster *p16* 020 7935 8520
Brook, W (W Brook & Co) *K1 G H M1 S1 L P V F1 J1 Zc Zm Zp*
Goldthorpe *p231* 01709 898697
Brooke, A W (Anderson Longmore & Higham) *W T1 S1 V J1*
Petworth *p348* 01798 342391
Brooke, D R (G M Wilson) *E F1 G H J1 K1 L M1 P*
Wakefield *p419* 01924 291111
Brooke, J P (Gamlins)
Llandudno *p291* 01492 860420
Brooke, T J D (Massers) *S1 W*
West Bridgford *p427* 0115 851 1666
Brooker, N C (Rodney King & Partners) *G H*
Bristol *p163* 0117 926 5201
Brooker, R L (Roger Brooker & Co) *E C1 W O*
Chelmsford *p186* 01245 351924
Brooker, Ms S K (Pitmans LLP) *B1 Zb O Zq*
Reading *p361* 0118 958 0224
Brookes, Miss A J (Denbighshire County Council) *K1 D1 O N*
Ruthin *p470* 01824 706000
Brookes, A J (Anthony Gold) *L R1 Zh*
London SE17 *p6* 020 7940 4000
Brookes, Miss A K (Bath & North East Somerset Council)
Bath *p462* 01225 394041
Brookes, D (Holman Fenwick Willan)
London EC3 *p42* 020 7264 8000
Brookes, Miss E J (Robinsons) *E*
Derby *p209* 01332 291431
Brookes, G N (Ceredigion County Council)
Aberaeron *p447* 01545 570881
Brookes, J M (Cox & Hodgetts) *K1 G N Q D1 W B1 Zl Zq D2*
Evesham *p220* 01386 442513
Brookes, Ms K (Sternberg Reed) *G H*
Barking *p123* 020 8591 3366
Brookes, Ms K L (Sternberg Reed) *B2 G H Zg*
London NW1 *p83* 020 7485 5558
Brookes, Mrs M (Brookes & Co) *Za O Zj C1*
London EC3 *p16* 020 7621 0067
Brookes, M (Kingsley Brookes) *G H*
Huddersfield *p256* 01484 302800
Brookes, M A (Lee & Thompson) *O Zf Zk Ze J1 Q*
London W1 *p52* 020 7935 4665
Brookes, M D (Godloves) *S1 S2 E*
Leeds *p273* 0113 225 8811
Brookes, M R (Dacorum Borough Council)
Hemel Hempstead *p460* . . . 01442 228000
Brookes, Miss N (Symes Robinson & Lee) *W K4*
Crediton *p203* 01363 775566
Brookes, R P (Bower & Bailey) *C1 C2 Zb E I J1 Ze Zza*
Banbury *p122* 01295 265566
Brookes, Ms S A (PricewaterhouseCoopers Legal LLP) *C1 J1 M1 B1*
London SE1 *p69* 020 7212 1616
Brookes, S A (Salmons) *N Q J1 Zr*
Stoke-on-Trent *p398* 01782 639827
Brookes, Ms S J (Peter Peter & Wright) *J1 Zp*
Bideford *p133* 01237 472233
Brookes, T (Osborne Clarke) *O*
London EC2 *p65* 020 7105 7000
Reading *p361* . . 0370 086 8800 / 0118 965 8765
Brookes, T H (Brookes & Co) *D1 G H*
Chichester *p192* 01243 780333
Brooke-Smith, A J (Andersons Solicitors) *O Q B1*
Nottingham *p335* 0115 947 0641
Brooke-Taylor, G W (Alsters Kelley) *C1 U2 C2 Ze I F1 Zd F2 E S1 S2 R2*
Leamington Spa *p270* 0844 561 0100
Leamington Spa *p270* 01926 886688
Brooke-Taylor, J D (Bristol City Council)
Bristol *p451* 0117 922 2000
Brooking, Ms A M (Sharon Taylor Associates) *G H*
Poole *p353* 01202 759769
Brooking, C (Wakefield Metropolitan District Council)
Wakefield *p474* 01924 306090
Brookman, P (Parlby Calder Solicitors) *G H*
Plymouth *p350* 01752 600833
Brooks, Miss A (Barratt Goff & Tomlinson) *N Zr*
Nottingham *p335* 0115 931 5171
Brooks, A C (Lamb Brooks LLP) *C1 C2 C3 I J1 Zd*
Basingstoke *p126* 01256 844888
Brooks, A F (A F Brooks & Co) *S1 E C1 K1 G J1 M1 W D1 F1*
Stoke-on-Trent *p397* 01782 415007
Aberdare *p113* 01685 873565
Brooks, A R (Roger Brooks & Co) *S1 S2 W L A1 T2 Zl*
Leek *p278* 01538 385656
Brooks, C (Tollers LLP)
Northampton *p332* 01604 258558
Brooks, C (Tollers LLP) *N*
Northampton *p332* 01604 258558
Brooks, C J (Reading Borough Council) *E S1*
Reading *p469* 0118 939 0900
Brooks, C M (Penningtons)
Basingstoke *p127* 01256 407100
Brooks, D C (Brooks) *N K1 Q O L F1 J1*
Shipston-on-Stour *p378* . . . 01608 664406
Brooks, D G (Maddocks Clarke) *S1 K1 M1 E H C1 W P Zl*
Altrincham *p117* 0844 805 5170
Brooks, D J (Fullagar Brooks) *C1 E O Ze Zf*
Swindon *p406* 01793 777007
Brooks, G (Roberts Moore Nicholas Jones) *S1*
Birkenhead *p134* 0151 647 0000
Brooks, G L (Hatten Wyatt)
Gravesend *p232* 01474 351199
Brooks, G P (Geoffrey Leaver Solicitors LLP) *O Q*
Milton Keynes *p317* 01908 692769
Brooks, Miss H S (Charles Russell LLP) *J1*
London EC4 *p19* 020 7203 5000
Brooks, Mrs I (Civil Aviation Authority) *O*
London WC2 *p105* 020 7453 6162
Brooks, Miss J (Layton & Co)
Haverfordwest *p244* 01437 766671
Brooks, J (Maclay Murray & Spens LLP)
London EC2 *p57* 020 7002 8500
Brooks, J (Osborne Clarke) *A3*
Bristol *p164* 0117 917 3000
Brooks, Mrs J M (Jane Brooks Law) *S2 E K4 S1 W*
Hull *p256* 01482 893366
Brooks, L (Lawrence Brooks) *C1 J1 E Zy*
Cranbrook *p202* 01580 715175
Brooks, M T (Brooks & Partners) *S1 E C1 W L*
Camberley *p173* 01276 681217
Brooks, M W S (Stephenson Harwood) *J1 N Za*
London EC2 *p82* 020 7329 4422
Brooks, N (Almy & Thomas) *G H B2*
Torquay *p412* 01803 299131
Brooks, P (Horsey Lightly) *C1 Za Zj J1 M1 S2*
Westminster *p43* 020 7222 8844
Brooks, P (Howard Solicitors)
Manchester *p305* 0800 876 6749
Brooks, Mrs P J L (Tinn Criddle & Co) *S1 W L E A1 R1 C1 B1 T1 Zc*
Alford *p115* 01507 462882
Sutton-on-Sea *p404* 01507 443043
Brooks, Mrs R (Blake Lapthorn) *W K4*
Oxford *p342* 01865 248607
Portsmouth *p354* 023 9222 1122
Brooks, R (Anthony Collins Solicitors LLP) *Zc M1*
Birmingham *p137* 0121 200 3242
Brooks, R (Debenhams Ottaway) *S1*
St Albans *p390* 01727 837161
Brooks, R J (Masefield Solicitors LLP) *S1 A1 K1 L E J1 N X Zd*
Ledbury *p271* 01531 632377
Brooks, R W (Vincents) *G H J1 K1 N Q Zl*
Poulton-le-Fylde *p355* 01253 810643
Brooks, Ms S E L (Warner Goodman LLP) *S1*
Fareham *p224* 01329 288121
Brooks, Miss S J (Downes & Siddall) *K3 D1 K1 L V*
Lincoln *p284* 01522 543343
Brooks, Ms V (Myers Fletcher & Gordon) *O Q Zq Zr J1*
London W6 *p62* 020 7610 4433
Brooksbank, Miss C (Hibberts LLP) *E N X*
Crewe *p203* 01270 215117
Brookshaw, O C (Shoosmiths)
Nottingham *p339* 0370 086 5000 / 0115 906 5000
Brookshaw, O C (Shoosmiths) *C1*
Milton Keynes *p317* . 0370 086 8300 / 01908 488300
Brooks-Johnson, Mrs C A (Pannone LLP) *N*
Manchester *p308* 0161 909 3000
Brooks-Johnson, Mrs C M (Stephens & Son LLP) *S1 T2 W*
Chatham *p185* 01634 811444
Broom, Mrs L E (Peter Lynn & Partners)
Morriston *p319* 01792 310731
Broom, N W (Gough Clinton & Broom) *C1 E F1 L R1 S1 T1 W*
Welling *p424* 020 8301 9000
Broom, P D (Blake Lapthorn) *B1 J1 N O Q*
Chandlers Ford *p184* 023 8090 8090
Broom, Miss R J (Woollcombe Yonge) *W T2*
Plymouth *p351* 01752 660384
Broome, A W (Frisby & Co) *F1 G J1 N P B2 J2*
Stafford *p392* 01785 244114
Broome, B G (South Tyneside Metropolitan Borough Council)
South Shields *p471* 0191 427 1717
Broomer, C V (Symes Bains Broomer) *F1 K1 L M1 S1 T1 W Zi*
Scunthorpe *p373* 01724 281616

6

Broomfield, A (Dickinson Dees) *E*
Newcastle upon Tyne *p324* . 0191 279 9000

Broomfield, Miss D (Bonallack & Bishop) *Zr N Zq*
Salisbury *p371* . 01722 422300

Broomfield, Ms E (Lanyon Bowdler LLP) *N*
Shrewsbury *p379* . 01743 280280

Broomfield, Ms K S E (LG Lawyers)
London SE1 *p50* . 020 7379 0000

Broomfield, R (Ashurst LLP)
London EC2 *p7* . 020 7638 1111

Broomhall, Ms J (Broomhall & Co) *K1 W*
Birmingham *p136* . 0121 633 4868

Broomhall, S A (Broomhall & Co) *S1 C1 G H K1*
Birmingham *p136* . 0121 633 4868

Brophy, C J (Capsticks Solicitors LLP) *C1 I Zd Ze M1*
London SW19 *p18* . 020 8780 2211

Brophy, Ms M L (Radcliffes Le Brasseur)
Westminster *p70* . 020 7222 7040

Brophy, V (Jones Day) *C3*
London EC4 *p46* . 020 7039 5959

Brosinovich, Ms P (K&L Gates LLP)
London EC4 *p47* . 020 7648 9000

Brosnahan, M J (Clifford Chance)
London E14 *p20* . 020 7006 1000

Brosnan, Miss A M (Environment Agency (Anglian Region))
Peterborough *p468* . 01733 371811

Brosnan, C (Hodge Jones & Allen LLP) *L*
London NW1 *p41* . 020 7874 8300

Brosnan, Mrs D J (Buller Jeffries) *N J2 J1 Q Zq*
Birmingham *p136* . 0121 212 2620

Brosnan, Miss L K (Blake Lapthorn) *Zf Ze C1*
London EC1 *p13* . 020 7405 2000

Bross, Ms R V (Bross Bennett) *K1 K2*
London N6 *p16* . 020 8340 0444

Brostoff, M A (GKN PLC (Legal Dept))
Redditch *p469* . 01527 517715

Brothers, Ms K (Land Registry - Gloucester Office) *P K1 M1 L F1 D1 S1 V W B1 Zk Zs*
Gloucester *p459* . 01452 511111

Brothers, N C (N C Brothers & Co)
Reading *p360* . 0118 958 9966

Brothers, N S (Cunningtons) *S1*
Croydon *p205* . 020 8688 8446
London W1 *p46* . 020 7339 7000

Brotherton, A M (Haworth Brotherton) *S1 W E L R1*
Thornton Cleveleys *p411* . 01253 852356

Brotherton, J E M (Wannop Fox Staffurth & Bray) *G S1 E J1 Zl*
Chichester *p193* . 01243 778844

Brotherton, M G (Stone King LLP) *F1 O Q B1 Zk*
Bath *p128* . 01225 337599

Brotherton, M M (Tozers) *S1 E W A1 L R1 T1 C1 Zn*
Exeter *p222* . 01392 207020

Brothwell, P H (P H Brothwell) *S1 W E*
Folkestone *p227* . 01303 253368

Brothwood, G C (DAC Beachcroft) *E P*
Bristol *p162* . 0117 918 2000

Brothwood, I J (Charles Russell LLP) *E B1*
Cheltenham *p187* . 01242 221122

Brothwood, Ms J S (Hughes Paddison) *K1 D1 K2 K3*
Cheltenham *p188* . 01242 574244

Brough, Mrs D (R Bell & Son) *B1 D1 F1 J1 K1 L M1 P V*
Hartlepool *p242* . 01429 273165
Peterlee *p347* . 0191 586 8646

Brough, K A (O H Parsons & Partners) *J1 N*
London WC2 *p66* . 020 7379 7277

Brough, M J A (Michael Brough and Cohen) *L S1 W E F1 J1 Q T2 B1 A1 Zm Zx Ze Zd Zl*
Beaconsfield *p128* . 01494 680420

Brough, P J (HM Land Registry - Birkenhead) *S1 W K1 L E C1 D1*
Birkenhead *p449* . 0151 473 1110
Gloucester *p459* . 01452 511111

Brough, P R (Brough Hall & Co) *G S1 K1 P M1 L W H E*
Skegness *p380* . 01754 768641
Alford *p115* . 01507 462882
Sutton-on-Sea *p404* . 01507 443043

Brougham, A P (Radcliffes Le Brasseur) *E P S1 Zb*
Westminster *p70* . 020 7222 7040

Broughton, A R (Stephens Wheeler Cooke & Sons) *G H S1 W K1 L F1 J1 Zl*
Luton *p295* . 01582 720175

Broughton, D (Portner & Jaskel LLP)
London W1 *p68* . 020 7616 5300

Broughton, Miss H (Morecrofts Solicitors LLP) *K1 D1 D2*
Liverpool *p290* . 0151 236 8871

Broughton, Ms H K (Bevans)
Bristol *p161* . 0117 923 7249

Broughton, J A (AWB Charlesworth LLP) *S1 E W S2*
Keighley *p263* . 01535 613678

Broughton, Ms L (MBNA Europe Bank Ltd)
Chester *p454* . 01244 672002

Broughton, M (Brecher) *E R1 P*
London W1 *p15* . 020 7563 1000

Broughton, M W (Lees Solicitors LLP) *S1*
Heswall *p249* . 0151 342 6273

Broughton, R A (Headleys) *K1 N M1 W G F1 C1 H S1 O Q L J1 V*
Hinckley *p250* . 01455 637815

Broughton, R F S (Ross Coates) *S1 W Zm*
Ipswich *p263* . 01473 621800

Brousson, R (K&L Gates LLP)
London EC4 *p47* . 020 7648 9000

Brower, S J (Edwin Coe LLP) *E L Zb R2 B1*
London WC2 *p29* . 020 7691 4000

Browett, Mrs N (Bates NVH) *W*
Fleet *p226* . 01252 629292

Brown, A (Jones Day) *O*
London EC4 *p46* . 020 7039 5959

Brown, A (Yarwood & Stubley) *G K1 H P S1 N D1 F1 J1 M1 Zk Zi Zm*
Blyth *p148* . 01670 361211

Brown, A (Forshaws Davies Ridgway LLP) *W Zl S1*
Warrington *p422* . 01925 230000

Brown, A (Simmons & Simmons)
London EC2 *p79* . 020 7628 2020

Brown, A (Herbert Smith LLP) *C1 J1*
London EC2 *p40* . 020 7374 8000

Brown, Miss A (Craig Gee) *D1 K1 L Zl N D2*
Manchester *p304* . 0161 666 9999

Brown, A (Morecrofts Solicitors LLP) *K3 K1 S1*
Liverpool *p290* . 0151 236 8871

Brown, A (Watson Burton LLP)
Newcastle upon Tyne *p327* . 0845 901 2100

Brown, A B (Mills & Co) *B1 C1 E I M1 O Za Zc Ze Zj*
Newcastle upon Tyne *p325* . 0191 233 2222

Brown, Mrs A E (SAS Daniels LLP) *S1*
Stockport *p396* . 0161 475 7676

Brown, Ms A F (Arnold & Porter LLP) *N Q J2*
London EC2 *p7* . 020 7786 6100

Brown, A H (Michael Cullen & Partners) *K1 D1 V D2*
Billericay *p133* . 01277 623132

Brown, A J (P R Scully & Co Solicitors) *Zj B1 K1 L N Q V*
St Helens *p391* . 01744 755800

Brown, A J (NFLA Ltd)
Nottingham *p338* . 0115 945 4555

Brown, A K (Hedleys & Co)
Sunderland *p401* . 0191 567 0101

Brown, Ms A K L (Blackhurst Swainson Goodier LLP) *N K1 Q V F1 K3*
Lancaster *p269* . 01524 32471

Brown, A M (Ashton KCJ) *W T1 T2 Zm*
Bury St Edmunds *p171* . 01284 762331

Brown, Miss A M (Herbert Smith LLP) *Zo*
London EC2 *p40* . 020 7374 8000

Brown, Mrs A M (Anne Brown Solicitors) *Q W J1 C1 F1 O F2 L S1*
London N21 *p16* . 020 8364 2121

Brown, A R (A R Brown & Co) *S1 W K1 P E F1 G L R1 M1 Zl Zc Zs*
Worthing *p441* . 01903 237118

Brown, A T (WBW Solicitors) *S1*
Bovey Tracey *p153* . 01626 833263

Brown, Mrs B (Martin Cray & Co) *N*
Brighton *p159* . 01273 673226

Brown, Miss C (Treasury Solicitors Department)
London WC2 *p110* . 020 7210 3000

Brown, Mrs C (Red Kite Law) *D1 D2 K1*
Haverfordwest *p244* . 01437 763332

Brown, C (SA Law) *E Zc*
St Albans *p390* . 01727 798000

Brown, Miss C (Blake Lapthorn) *P*
Chandlers Ford *p184* . 023 8090 8090

Brown, Miss C A (Finers Stephens Innocent LLP) *N P L J1 C1 F1 Ze Zo Zk*
London W1 *p32* . 020 7323 4000

Brown, C A (Reed Smith LLP) *Za*
London EC2 *p71* . 020 3116 3000

Brown, C G (AMD Solicitors) *K3 L J1 K1*
Bristol *p160* . 0117 923 5562
Bristol *p160* . 0117 962 1460

Brown, C H A (Hannays Solicitors and Advocates) *G H*
South Shields *p383* . 0191 456 7893 / 455 5361

Brown, Mrs C J (Wigan Borough Council)
Wigan *p476* . 01942 244991

Brown, C J (Norfolk County Council - Legal Services)
Norwich *p467* . Minicom: 0844 800 8011

Brown, C M (Hood Vores & Allwood) *S1 S2 W K4 T2 Zd*
Aylsham *p121* . 01263 732123
Dereham *p209* . 01362 692424

Brown, C M (Alban Gould Baker & Co) *K1 L N Q O*
Islington *p4* . 020 7607 5085

Brown, C R (Fosters) *G H J2*
Norwich *p334* . 01603 620508

Brown, D (Dennis Brown Solicitors)
Colchester *p197* . 01206 505060

Brown, D C (Gullands) *Zc O Zj A3 Zq*
Maidstone *p299* . 01622 678341

Brown, D E (Wosskow Brown) *B1 C1*
Sheffield *p377* . 0114 256 1560

Brown, D E (Devonshires) *R2 U2 E Zu Zh*
London EC2 *p27* . 020 7628 7576

Brown, D F (Bevirs) *S1 W A1 E*
Wootton Bassett *p439* . 01793 848900

Brown, D J (Goody Burrett LLP) *B1 K4 S2 W*
Colchester *p197* . 01206 577676

Brown, Mrs D J (Roythornes LLP) *C2 C1*
Spalding *p389* . 01775 842500

Brown, Mrs D J (AWB Charlesworth LLP) *D1 K2 K3*
Skipton *p381* . 01756 793333

Brown, D J (Chivers Easton Brown) *N O B1 J1 Q*
Surbiton *p402* . 020 8390 0081

Brown, D J C (Bristows) *C3 M1 M2 O Ze Zk*
London EC4 *p15* . 020 7400 8000

Brown, D J D (Abbey Law) *L S1 W C1 C2*
Almondsbury *p115* . 01454 202102

Brown, D L (Levi Solicitors LLP) *N F1 Q O L K1 Zi*
Leeds *p275* . 0113 244 9931

Brown, D N (Marsden Rawsthorn LLP) *S1 W*
Preston *p357* . 01772 799600

Brown, D P (Thomas Cooper) *O N Q*
London EC3 *p22* . 020 7481 8851

Brown, D S (Barlows) *Q O N K1 G Zl K3*
Leicester *p278* . 0116 251 8295

Brown, Ms E (Sunderland Magistrates Court) *G H*
Sunderland *p473* . 0191 514 1621

Brown, Mrs E (South Tyneside Metropolitan Borough Council)
South Shields *p471* . 0191 427 1717

Brown, Miss E (Birkett Long LLP) *C1 C2 J1 U2 Zp F1 Ze X*
Colchester *p197* . 01206 217300

Brown, Mrs E A (Brown & Company) *S1 W K4*
Market Harborough *p312* . 01858 434204

Brown, Ms E M (Amphlett Lissimore) *K3 K1*
Croydon *p6* . 020 8771 5254

Brown, E N W (Bircham Dyson Bell)
Westminster *p13* . 020 7227 7000

Brown, E V (Ford & Warren) *E S1 S2 X Zd*
Leeds *p273* . 0113 243 6601

Brown, Mrs F B (Ryedale District Council)
Malton *p464* . 01653 600666

Brown, Mrs F M (HM Land Registry - Leicester)
Leicester *p463* . 0116 265 4000 / 4001

Brown, G (Reed Smith LLP) *Q O B2*
London EC2 *p71* . 020 3116 3000

Brown, Ms G (Phillips Solicitors) *C1 F1 J1 Zi*
Basingstoke *p127* . 01256 460830

Brown, G (Hart Reade) *K3 K1 D1*
Eastbourne *p215* . 01323 727321

Brown, G C (Barlow Lyde & Gilbert LLP)
London EC3 *p10* . 020 7247 2277

Brown, Miss G P (Sefton Metropolitan Borough Council)
Southport *p472* . 01704 533133

Brown, G T (Rentokil Initial PLC)
London SW1 *p108* . 020 7592 2700

Brown, G T (Brown Beer Nixon Mallon) *G H*
Redcar *p362* . 01642 490202

Brown, Ms H (Brabners Chaffe Street) *S2 E R2*
Liverpool *p286* . 0151 600 3000

Brown, Miss H (Ratcliffe & Bibby) *S1 W*
Morecambe *p319* . 01524 410424

Brown, H (Holman Fenwick Willan)
London EC3 *p42* . 020 7264 8000

Brown, Ms H B (Stephensons Solicitors LLP) *D1*
Leigh *p282* . 01942 777777

Brown, Mrs H G (Langleys) *N*
York *p445* . 01904 610886

Brown, Miss H G (Denby & Co) *N S1 W K1*
Ulverston *p416* . 01229 582283

Brown, H S (Law Partners Solicitors Ltd) *G H*
London EC1 *p51* . 0870 600 9444

Brown, Miss H Y (Briggs Sayer & Co) *S1 W*
Belper *p130* . 01773 825246

Brown, I (The Watson Ramsbottom Partnership) *L W S1 E S2 Zc K4 Zh R1*
Blackburn *p146* . 01254 672222

Brown, I C (Clifford Chance)
London E14 *p20* . 020 7006 1000

Brown, I D (Wosskow Brown) *N*
Sheffield *p377* . 0114 256 1560

Brown, I M (Gosschalks) *O*
Hull *p256* . 01482 324252

Brown, Mrs I M (Anthony Collins Solicitors LLP) *N Zr*
Birmingham *p137* . 0121 200 3242

Brown, I R (3M Health Care Ltd) *C1 T1 J1*
Loughborough *p463* . 01509 611611

Brown, J (Shaw & Co) *N*
Newcastle upon Tyne *p326* . 0800 019 1248

Brown, J (The Endeavour Partnership LLP) *E P R1 S1*
Stockton-on-Tees *p397* . 01642 610300

Brown, Ms J (Cornwall County Council) *D1 K1 K2*
Truro *p474* . 01872 322197

Brown, J (Squire Sanders (UK) LLP) *A3 Zc*
Birmingham *p142* . 0121 222 3000

Brown, Mrs J (Aviva PLC)
London EC3 *p103* . 020 7283 7500 / 01603 687905
Eastleigh *p458* . 023 8037 2270

Brown, J (Ince & Co Services Ltd)
London E1 *p44* . 020 7481 0010

Brown, Ms J (Ramsdens Solicitors) *D1 K1 Q*
Huddersfield *p256* . 01484 821500

Brown, J (Dutton Gregory) *C1 C2*
Southampton *p385* . 023 8022 1344

Brown, J (Reynolds Porter Chamberlain LLP)
London E1 *p71* . 020 3060 6000

Brown, Miss J (Bowcock & Pursaill) *K1 K2*
Leek *p278* . 01538 399199
Sandbach *p372* . 01270 766550

Brown, Mrs J (Punch Robson) *D1 K1 D2*
Middlesbrough *p315* . 01642 230700

Brown, Miss J (Straw & Pearce) *W*
Loughborough *p293* . 01509 268931

Brown, Ms J A (Linklaters LLP)
London EC2 *p54* . 020 7456 2000

Brown, Miss J E (Sacker & Partners LLP) *Zo*
London EC2 *p76* . 020 7329 6699

Brown, Ms J E (Financial Services Authority)
London E14 *p106* . 020 7066 1000

Brown, Ms J E (TLT Solicitors) *O B1 Q*
Bristol *p165* . 0117 917 7777

Brown, J G I (Eatons) *Q N K1 J1 F1 G*
Bradford *p153* . 0845 660 0660

Brown, Mrs J S (MLM Cartwright) *O Q N F1 B1*
Cardiff *p179* . 029 2046 2562

Brown, J S (Ray Nixon Brown) *S1 L E W A1 C1 T1 Zc S2*
Leighton Buzzard *p282* . 01525 372247

Brown, J T (Dutton Gregory) *C1 C2 C3 J1 M1 Zw*
Winchester *p433* . 01962 844333

Brown, Mrs K (Kimbells LLP) *J1*
Milton Keynes *p317* . 01908 668555

Brown, K A (Brown & Company) *C1 S2 E L Zl S1 R2*
Market Harborough *p312* . 01858 434204

Brown, Mrs L (Clarke Willmott) *E L P S1*
Bristol *p162* 0845 209 1000 / 0117 305 6000

Brown, Ms L (Hadaway & Hadaway) *S1 W E*
North Shields *p330* . 0191 257 0382

Brown, Mrs L C (Brewer Harding & Rowe) *Zr N*
Barnstaple *p125* . 01271 342271

Brown, L J (Morley Brown & Co) *C1 E L R1 R2 S1 S2*
Boston *p151* . 01205 364986

Brown, Ms L M Z (Forsters LLP) *K1*
Westminster *p33* . 020 7863 8333

Brown, M (Linklaters LLP)
London EC2 *p54* . 020 7456 2000

Brown, M (Eccles Heddon) *A1 S2*
Thirsk *p411* . 01845 522324

Brown, M (Irwin Mitchell LLP) *N*
Leeds *p274* . 0870 150 0100

Brown, M (Brabners Chaffe Street) *C1 Ze U2 F1 I Zza C3*
Liverpool *p286* . 0151 600 3000

Brown, M (Jones Day) *O*
London EC4 *p46* . 020 7039 5959

Brown, M (Pannone LLP) *C1 C2*
Manchester *p308* . 0161 909 3000

Brown, M (CKFT)
London NW3 *p17* . 020 7431 7262

Brown, Ms M (Davenport Lyons)
London W1 *p25* . 020 7468 2600

Brown, M A (Dickinson Dees) *E*
Newcastle upon Tyne *p324* . 0191 279 9000

Brown, Ms M E (ASB Law) *K1 D1 E V*
Maidstone *p298* . 01622 656500

Brown, M F H (D P Roberts Hughes & Denye) *C1 C2 E L S1 W*
Ellesmere Port *p217* . 0151 355 6699

Brown, Miss M J (Williams MacDougall & Campbell) *K1 D1 D2*
Worthing *p442* . 01903 214186

Brown, Mrs M J (William Wright & Son) *W K4*
Dudley *p213* . 01384 255344

Brown, M J (Dickinson Dees) *E Zh L*
Newcastle upon Tyne *p324* . 0191 279 9000

Brown, M L (TBI Solicitors) *W K4 T2*
Hartlepool *p243* . 0800 052 6824 / 01429 264101
Stockton-on-Tees *p397* . 01642 673797

Brown, Miss M P (Marsh Brown & Co) *F1 K1 L N*
Lewisham *p59* . 020 8852 0052

Brown, M P (Mayer Brown International LLP) *C1 F1 B1 Zb*
London EC2 *p59* . 020 3130 3000

Brown, M P (McKenzie Bell Solicitors) *C1 D1 E G H K1 L M1 S1 W*
Sunderland *p401* . 0191 567 4857

Brown, Miss N (Sacker & Partners LLP) *Zo*
London EC2 *p76* . 020 7329 6699

Brown, N A (BRM Solicitors) *O Q L B1 C1 J1*
Chesterfield *p191* . 01246 555111

Brown, N A (CMS Cameron McKenna LLP)
London EC3 *p17* . 020 7367 3000

Brown, Miss N H (Mills & Reeve) *J1 Zp*
Cambridge *p175* . 01223 364422

Brown, N W (Gateley LLP) *Ze T1 C1 C2*
Manchester *p304* . 0161 836 7700

Brown, O (Lyons Wilson) *N Zq*
Manchester *p307* . 0161 830 7777
Manchester *p308* . 0161 909 3000

Brown, P (J W Hughes & Co) *G H K1 F1 W*
Conwy *p199* . 01492 596596

Brown, P (Radcliffes Le Brasseur)
Westminster *p70* . 020 7222 7040

Brown, P (Shepherd Construction Ltd) *C1 E L F1 S1 Zc*
York *p477* . 01904 660400

Brown, P (Gregg Latchams LLP) *E Zu*
Bristol *p162* . 0117 906 9400

Brown, P (Hartlaw LLP) *E S1 C1 Zl Zc R2*
Wetherby *p429* . 01937 547000

Brown, P (Hogan Lovells International LLP)
London EC1 *p42* . 020 7296 2000

Brown, P (MBA Solicitors) *G H*
York *p445* . 01904 666888

Brown, P D C (Broxtowe Borough Council)
Beeston *p449* . 0115 917 7777

Brown, P D R (Radcliffes Le Brasseur) *T1 W Zd Zo*
Westminster *p70* . 020 7222 7040

Brown, P F S (Mossop & Bowser) *S2 W A1 C1 E T1 T2*
Holbeach *p251* . 01406 422651
Long Sutton *p293* . 01406 363212

Brown, P I (Peter Brown & Co Solicitors LLP) *E L S1 W C1 T1 Zl Zb S2 R2*
Barnet *p124* . 020 8447 3277

Brown, Ms P J A (Mills & Reeve) *E*
Norwich *p335* . 01603 660155

Brown, Ms P K M (Nottingham City Council (City Sec Dept)) *J1*
Nottingham *p467* . 0115 915 5555

Brown, P O (Philip Brown & Co)
London W1 *p16* .020 7935 7235 / 7935 7270

See p634 for the Key to Work Categories

Brown, P W (Capsticks Solicitors LLP) *E R2*
London SW19 *p18* 020 8780 2211
Brown, Ms R (Hodders) *B1 F1 J1 Q*
London SW11 *p41* 020 7720 1647
Brown, R (Baxter Brown McArthur)
London SW11 *p11* 020 7924 8130
Brown, R (Woodroffes)
Westminster *p93* 020 7730 0001
Brown, R A (Wilkinson Woodward) *G H K1 N V*
Halifax *p238* 01422 339600
Brown, R A (Mayo Wynne Baxter LLP) *C1 E S2*
Brighton *p160* 01273 775533
Brown, R A (hlw Keeble Hawson LLP) *B1 N O Q*
Leeds *p274* 0113 244 3121
Sheffield *p375* 0114 272 2061
Brown, R A A (Hart Brown Solicitors) *O Q N L J1 B1 R1 F1 Zb Zq Zj*
Guildford *p236* 0800 068 8177
Brown, R C (Travers Smith LLP) *C1 F1 C3*
London EC1 *p87* 020 7295 3000
Brown, R D (Kimbells LLP) *O B1 A3 C3*
Milton Keynes *p317* 01908 668555
Brown, Ms R E (Chennells) *F1 K3 J1 K1 L Q N Zq*
Westcliff-on-Sea *p428* . . . . 01702 349971 / 352195
Brown, R H (Foot Anstey) *O Zb*
Plymouth *p349* 01752 675000
Brown, R I (Lomax Geddes & Co) *G H S1 K1 W D1 F1 C1 Zj L B2*
Manchester *p307* 0161 834 4722
Brown, Mrs R J (Peterborough Magistrates Court)
Peterborough *p468* 01223 314311
Brown, R J (Payne Skillington) *W S1 E L C1*
Coventry *p200* 024 7663 3044
Brown, R M (Hogan Lovells International LLP)
London EC1 *p42* 020 7296 2000
Brown, R M (Allen & Overy LLP)
London E1 *p5* 020 3088 0000
Brown, Miss R P (Canter Levin & Berg) *N Q L F1 J1 P*
St Helens *p391* 01744 634141
Brown, R P (RHW Solicitors LLP) *J1 O Q*
Guildford *p237* 01483 302000
Brown, R S (Dutton Gregory) *S2 E*
Southampton *p385* 023 8022 1344
Winchester *p433* 01962 844333
Brown, R T J (Corker Binning Solicitors) *G H*
London WC2 *p22* 020 7353 6000
Brown, R W (Brown & Co) *W S1*
Chalfont St Giles *p184* 01494 874175
Brown, R W (Richard Brown & Co) *G H*
Peterborough *p346* 0870 850 3062
Brown, R W (Glaisyers Solicitors LLP) *J1 Zp O Q*
Manchester *p304* 0161 832 4666
Brown, Miss S (Careless & Kemp) *W T2*
Sandown *p372* 01983 400456
Brown, Mrs S (Osborne Clarke) *T2 W*
Bristol *p164* 0117 917 3000
Brown, S (Jones Day) *O*
London EC4 *p46* 020 7039 5959
Brown, S (Levenes Solicitors)
Birmingham *p140* 0121 212 0000
Brown, S (NGA)
Colne *p198* 01282 862000
Brown, S (O'Neill Patient)
Stockport *p396* 0161 483 8555
Brown, Ms S (Chichester & District Magistrates Courts)
Chichester *p455* 01243 817000
Brown, S A J (Briffa) *U2 I Ze C1 F1 Zza Zf*
Islington *p15* 020 7288 6003
Brown, S C (Towler Brown) *S1 E W A1 Zd*
Frome *p228* 01373 452955
Brown, Miss S E (Reed Smith LLP) *G H*
London EC2 *p71* 020 3116 3000
Brown, Mrs S E (Boyes Turner) *N*
Reading *p360* 0118 959 7711
Brown, Mrs S E (Rosling King) *N O Zq*
London EC4 *p73* 020 7353 2353
Brown, Ms S J (Elliot Mather LLP) *G H*
Chesterfield *p192* 01246 231288
Brown, S J (Smith Brown & Sprawson) *G H*
Luton *p295* 01582 876900
Brown, S J (Ewings & Co) *S1 W E L Zl*
London SE20 *p30* 020 8778 1126
Brown, Ms S L (HCB Solicitors) *S2 E S1 K3 W*
Lichfield *p284* 01543 414426
Brown, Ms S M (City of Sunderland)
Sunderland *p473* 0191 520 5555
Brown, S M (Thomson Snell & Passmore) *W T2 K4*
Tunbridge Wells *p415* 01892 510000
Brown, Ms S M (Gordons Solicitors LLP)
Marlow *p313* 01628 487487
Brown, Miss S R (Machins Solicitors LLP) *D1 K3 K1*
Luton *p295* 01582 514000
Brown, S V (Pinsent Masons LLP) *E R2*
Birmingham *p141* 0121 200 1050
Brown, Ms S V (Oxford City Council)
Oxford *p468* 01865 249811
Brown, T C (Reynolds Porter Chamberlain LLP) *O Q Zj Zq*
London E1 *p71* 020 3060 6000
Brown, T J (T M Warner & Co) *D1 F1 G H J1 K1 L M1 N P*
Kidlington *p266* 01865 379311
Brown, T L (Thomas Lindsey Brown & Co) *S1 S2 W K1 G D1 J1 L*
Southend-on-Sea *p387* 01702 466266
Brown, T R (Tuckers) *G H*
London SE5 *p88* 020 7703 2324

Brown, Miss V (Field Fisher Waterhouse LLP)
London EC3 *p31* 020 7861 4000
Brown, Miss V (Henmans LLP) *J1*
Oxford *p343* 01865 781000
Brown, W (Kennedys)
London EC3 *p49* 020 7667 9667
Brown, W L (Wallers) *L Q F1 O F2 C1 B1 U2 X Zh Zl Ze Zp Zq Zk A1*
Newcastle upon Tyne *p327* . 0191 261 2281
Brown-Hovelt, Ms L (Corus Group Limited)
London SW1 *p105* 020 7717 4523
Brown-Hovelt, R H (Brown-Hovelt Veale Nelson) *S1 W E K4 S2*
Grayshott *p233* 01428 607433
Browne, A R (Penman Johnson) *E L S1*
Watford *p424* . . . . 01923 225212 / 239566
Browne, Ms B J (Wiseman Lee LLP) *W*
Redbridge *p92* 020 8215 1000
Browne, Mrs C L (Elmbridge Borough Council)
Esher *p458* 01372 474198
Browne, Mrs C L (Buss Murton LLP) *S1 L E*
Cranbrook *p202* 01580 712215
Browne, D (Olswang LLP) *E*
London WC1 *p64* 020 7067 3000
Browne, D J (Parkes Browne) *A1 E L S1 W S2 K4 R1*
Andover *p118* 01264 333336
Browne, D W (Hewitsons) *C1 C2*
Northampton *p332* 01604 233233
London WC1 *p64* 020 7067 3000
Browne, G (Crossmans) *G H V*
Radstock *p358* 01761 431688
Browne, J C (Leo Abse & Cohen) *N*
Cardiff *p179* . . .029 2038 3252 / 2034 5421
Browne, J D (Stones Solicitors LLP)
Exeter *p222* 01392 666777
Browne, Miss J E (Noble) *N*
Shefford *p377* 01462 814055
Browne, J M (Wall James Chappell) *K1 D1*
Stourbridge *p399* 01384 371622
Browne, J R (Bramwell Browne Odedra) *D1 G H K1 L N Q W V S1 Ze Zi Zm K3 Zl*
Chesham *p189* 01494 782244
Browne, K C (The College of Law) *K1 Q S1 W L N F1 B1*
London WC1 *p105* 0800 289997
Browne, Mrs L J A S (Basildon District Council) *G F1 P R1 L Zf Ze Zl*
Basildon *p448* 01268 533333
Browne, L J G (Crossmans MTA) *W T2 C1*
Cambridge *p174* 01223 451442
Browne, Mrs M (Lawson Lewis & Co) *K1*
Eastbourne *p215* 01323 720142
Browne, M C (Gisby Harrison) *S1 E*
Cheshunt *p189* 01707 878300
Browne, M D (Draycott Browne Solicitors) *G H Zi Zl*
Manchester *p303* 0161 228 2244
Browne, M E (Atteys) *S2 S1 A1 E A3*
Retford *p363* 01777 713355
Browne, Ms N M (Blake Lapthorn) *O*
Chandlers Ford *p184* 023 8090 8090
Browne, P (Simmons & Simmons)
London EC2 *p79* 020 7628 2020
Browne, P A (Burges Salmon) *E B1 Zb*
Bristol *p161* 0117 939 2000
Browne, P M (Paul Browne) *S1 T1 L E Zc Ze Zn*
Oakham *p339* 01572 757565
Browne, P W F (Peter Browne) *S1 W S2 L K3 Q J1 Zd*
Bristol *p161* 0117 944 1966
Browne, R J R K (Girlings) *W T1 Zm K4*
Margate *p312* 01843 220274
Browne, T (Pearson Maddin Solicitors) *O Q L Zk Zq*
New Malden *p321* 020 8949 9500
Browne, V M C S (Vincent French & Browne) *C1 N T1 S1 W Za Zb Zl*
London WC1 *p89* 020 7831 4994
Browne, V M N (Vincent French & Browne) *E K1 J1 L N Q S1 W Ze*
London WC1 *p89* 020 7831 4994
Browne, Z (Lyons Davidson)
Bristol *p163* 0117 904 6000
Browning, Ms C (Reynolds Porter Chamberlain LLP)
London E1 *p71* 020 3060 6000
Browning, C P (Browning & Co) *A1 C1 E S1 W Zl*
Looe *p293* . . . . .01503 262119 / 262129
Browning, Miss E A (Keane & Co) *K1 K4 Q S1 T2 V W*
Aldeburgh *p115* 01728 453595
Browning, S (Barlow Lyde & Gilbert LLP) *C1 Zj*
London EC3 *p10* 020 7247 2277
Brownless, D B C (Sills & Betteridge LLP) *N*
Lincoln *p285* 01522 542211
Brownlow, P R (Bird & Bird LLP) *Ze*
London EC4 *p13* 020 7415 6000
Brownlow, T (IBB Solicitors) *G H*
Uxbridge *p417* 0845 638 1381
Brownrigg, J G (Stone King LLP) *K1 K2 K3*
Bath *p128* 01225 337599
Brownson, J M (Allen & Overy LLP)
London E1 *p5* 020 3088 0000
Brownson, R (Mills Chody LLP) *K1 N Q O Zl Zr*
Kenton *p265* 020 8909 0400
Brownsword, Mrs F J (Plexus Law (A Trading Name of Parabis Law LLP)) *N*
Evesham *p220* 01386 769160
Browton, Miss G (SAS Daniels LLP) *W*
Macclesfield *p297* 01625 442100

Broxton, Mrs M (Sandwell Metropolitan Borough Council)
Oldbury *p468* 0121 569 2200
Brozyniak-Siddiqui, E (Ashurst LLP)
London EC2 *p7* 020 7638 1111
Bruce, A J (Linklaters LLP)
London EC2 *p54* 020 7456 2000
Bruce, A R (Walker Smith Way) *N*
Chester *p191* 0844 346 3100
Bruce, Mrs A T (Knights Solicitors LLP) *R1 Zn E P*
Newcastle under Lyme *p323* . 01782 619225
Bruce, D E C (Harrisons Solicitors LLP) *W S1 S2*
Welshpool *p425* 01938 552545
Bruce, Ms E (Trowers & Hamlins)
London EC3 *p88* 020 7423 8000
Bruce, Mrs F C (Fiona Bruce & Co LLP) *W*
Warrington *p421* 01925 263273
Bruce, The Hon H A F (Ungoed-Thomas & King Limited) *W T1 A1 S1 Zi T2*
Carmarthen *p183* 01267 237441
Bruce, Mrs J (Birkett Long LLP) *W*
Chelmsford *p186* 01245 453800
Bruce, Miss J (More Fisher Brown) *O Za*
London EC4 *p61* 020 7330 8000
Bruce, J (Reynolds Porter Chamberlain LLP)
London E1 *p71* 020 3060 6000
Bruce, J A (Larken & Co) *G H D1 N K1 Q V Zl*
Newark *p322* 01636 703333
Bruce, Ms J D (The Endeavour Partnership LLP)
Stockton-on-Tees *p397* 01642 610300
Leeds *p277* 0113 284 7000
Bruce, Mrs K A (Hazell & Co) *A3 J2 N O Q Zc Zq*
Sawbridgeworth *p372* 01279 726604
Bruce, L (Field Fisher Waterhouse LLP)
London EC3 *p31* 020 7861 4000
Bruce, Miss N (Sacker & Partners LLP) *Zo*
London EC2 *p76* 020 7329 6699
Bruce, R (David Rubie Mitchell & Co)
Sutton *p403* 020 8641 0575
Bruce, R M (Woolley Bevis Diplock) *N*
Brighton *p160* 01273 323231
Bruce, R W (Brighton & Hove Council - Legal Services)
Hove *p461* 01273 290000
Bruce, Mrs S E (Franklins) *S1 W*
Abingdon *p114* 01235 553222
Bruce, S J (Farrer & Co LLP)
London WC2 *p31* 020 3375 7000
Bruce-Smith, A (Penningtons)
London EC2 *p66* 020 7457 3000
Bruce-Smith, K J (Harcus Sinclair) *T2 W*
London WC2 *p38* 020 7242 9700
Bruce-Watt, H W D (Pinsent Masons LLP)
London EC2 *p67* 020 7418 7000
Bruce-Watt, Mrs L (British Telecommunications PLC)
London EC1 *p104* 020 7356 6181
Bruder, C E (DWF) *B1 C1 F1 J1 L M1 N P Zh*
Liverpool *p287* 0151 907 3000
Brueggemann, Miss B (Hart Brown Solicitors) *B1 F1 J1 L N O Q Zq Zp*
Guildford *p236* 0800 068 8177
Bruford, J C (Howes Percival LLP) *B1*
Norwich *p334* 01603 762103
Brumby, F (Isadore Goldman Solicitors) *Q B1 C1 O*
London EC4 *p45* 020 7353 1000
Norwich *p334* 01603 610911
Brummell, D (Treasury Solicitors Department)
London WC2 *p110* 020 7210 3000
Brumpton, Mrs S C (Irwin Mitchell LLP) *N Zr*
Leeds *p274* 0870 150 0100
Brumpton, Ms S L (Barlow Lyde & Gilbert LLP)
London EC3 *p10* 020 7247 2277
Brumwell, Mrs S L B (Wilkins & Thompson) *N Q K3 K1 L Zl*
Uttoxeter *p417* 01889 562875
Brunert, M W (Linder Myers Solicitors) *O Q N J1 C1*
Manchester *p307* 0844 984 6400
Brunicki, K J (Clifford Chance)
London E14 *p20* 020 7006 1000
Brunning, Miss E L (Birkett Long LLP) *K1*
Chelmsford *p186* 01245 453800
Brunsdon, P A (Treasury Solicitors Department) *P L N G Zl*
London WC2 *p110* 020 7210 3000
Brunskill, M J (Linskills Solicitors) *G H B2*
Liverpool *p289* 0151 236 2224
Brunskill, P A (Eatons) *N J2 Zr Q G H L*
Bradford *p153* 0845 660 0660
Brunt, H (DLA Piper UK LLP)
London EC2 *p24* 0870 011 1111
Brunt, I C (Haworth & Nuttall) *Q K1 D1 K3*
Blackburn *p145* 01254 272640
Brunt, N C (Heringtons) *P N K1 F1 L G Zp J1 Zl*
Eastbourne *p215* 01323 411020
Brunton, G H S (Stockler Brunton) *M2 N O Q Za Zj*
London EC4 *p83* 020 7404 6661
Brunton, H (Harrowells) *Zr Q N*
York *p444* 01904 558600
Brunton, J N (Nockolds) *O J1*
Bishop's Stortford *p144* . . . 01279 755777
Brunton, P L (Brunton & Co) *S1 G W K1 M1 R1 A1 B1 L J1 Zl Zs Zt*
Aberystwyth *p114* . .01970 612567 / 617931
Machynlleth *p298* . .01654 703110 / 703121
Brunwin, M J (Mercers) *S1 K1 P J1 L M1 R1 G D1 Zc*
Henley-on-Thames *p247* . . . 01491 572138

Brush, P L (Crosse & Crosse) *S1 W*
Exeter *p220* 01392 258451
Bruton, D G (HRJ Law LLP) *W T2 K4*
Welwyn Garden City *p425* . . 01707 887700
Bruton, J M (Wansbroughs) *S2 E S1*
Devizes *p210* 01380 733300
Bryan, A (Churchers) *J1 N Zr*
Portsmouth *p354* 023 9221 0170
Bryan, C J (Glaisyers Solicitors LLP) *E S1 S2 W K4*
Manchester *p304* 0161 224 3311
Bryan, D J (Cheshire County Council)
Chester *p454* 01244 602382
Bryan, Miss J (Bovis Homes Ltd)
Coleshill *p455* 01675 437000
Bryan, J F (Wolverhampton City Council)
Wolverhampton *p477* 01902 556556
Bryan, J F (Whitfields) *B1 C1 D1 F1 K1 L M1 P S1*
Formby *p227* 01704 878501
Bryan, Ms K (Marriott Davies Yapp) *Zb C1*
Sutton *p402* 020 8643 9794
Bryan, M R (Maples Teesdale LLP) *R2 S2 E R1*
London EC2 *p58* 020 7600 3800
Bryan, Mrs P J E (LG Lawyers) *P N M1 F1 B1 C1 L Za Zc Zj*
London SE1 *p50* 020 7379 0000
Bryan, R (Simmons & Simmons)
London EC2 *p79* 020 7628 2020
Bryan, R A (Bryan & Mercer) *C1 E L R1 S1*
St Albans *p389* 01727 861414
Bryan, S (Trowers & Hamlins)
London EC3 *p88* 020 7423 8000
Bryan, S (Hogan Lovells International LLP)
London EC1 *p42* 020 7296 2000
London EC2 *p79* 020 7628 2020
Bryan, Ms S L (McGrigors LLP) *C1*
London EC4 *p56* 020 7054 2500
Bryan, Ms Y (Trowers & Hamlins)
London EC3 *p88* 020 7423 8000
Bryans, N (Ashurst LLP) *C1*
London EC2 *p7* 020 7638 1111
Bryant, A (Gwilym Jones & Davies with Bryant & Co) *N K1 G H*
Mountain Ash *p319* 01443 472206
Bryant, Miss C (Sylvester Mackett) *W*
Trowbridge *p414* 01225 755621
Bryant, Miss C R (Abrams Collyer) *K1 D1 V Q N*
Lymington *p296* 01590 677888
Bryant, D J (Gwilym Jones & Davies with Bryant & Co) *S1 W E C1 A1 G R1*
Mountain Ash *p319* 01443 472206
Bryant, D J (Gwilym Jones & Davies with Bryant & Co)
Mountain Ash *p319* 01443 472206
Bryant, G C (Spratt Endicott) *C1 E S1 N W O B1 F1 J1 Q*
Banbury *p122* 01295 204000
Bryant, Ms H (Farrer & Co LLP)
London WC2 *p31* 020 3375 7000
Bryant, Mrs J (Preston Redman) *J1 Q N*
Bournemouth *p152* 01202 292424
Bryant, J A (Tucker Turner Kingsley Wood & Co) *C1 J1 T1 B1 Ze*
London WC1 *p88* 020 7242 3303
Bryant, Miss J E (Peter Lynn & Partners) *K3 K1 D1*
Morriston *p319* 01792 310731
Bryant, Miss L C P (Coodes) *G H Q*
Newquay *p329* 01637 878111
Bryant, P N (Woking Borough Council)
Woking *p477* 01483 755855
Bryant, Miss S A (Crosse & Crosse) *N Zq Zr J2 E S2*
Exeter *p220* 01392 258451
Bryant, Ms V (Radcliffes Le Brasseur)
Westminster *p70* 020 7222 7040
Bryant, Ms Y E (Surrey County Council)
Kingston upon Thames *p462* . 020 8541 9088
Bryce, A J (Andrew Bryce & Co) *P Zn J2*
Cambridge *p174* 01223 437011
Bryce, J A (Williamson & Soden) *G H K1*
Birmingham *p143* 0121 333 4848
Bryce, J K (Squire Sanders (UK) LLP)
London EC2 *p81* 020 7655 1000
Bryceland, M (Clifford Chance)
London E14 *p20* 020 7006 1000
Brydon, A (Simmons & Simmons)
London EC2 *p79* 020 7628 2020
Brydon, D G (Rothera Dowson) *W Zd*
Beeston *p130* 0115 916 5200
Brydson, Miss L A (Legal Aid Area Office No 6 (West Midland))
Birmingham *p450* 0121 632 6541
Bryer, J S (City of Westminster Magistrates' Court)
London SW1 *p110* 020 7805 1008
Bryers, J R F (Pictons Solicitors LLP) *N Q K1 O G D1 H J1*
Milton Keynes *p317* 01908 663511
Bryers, Ms S (Michelmores LLP) *Zr N J2*
Exeter *p221* 01392 688688
Bryk, J A (Human and Legal Resources)
Aylesbury *p447* 0871 222 3880
Bryk, R A (Howard Kennedy LLP) *S1*
London W1 *p48* 020 7636 1616
Brynmor-Thomas, D (Herbert Smith LLP) *O*
London EC2 *p40* 020 7374 8000
Bryson, Ms E J (Warner Goodman LLP) *E*
Portsmouth *p355* 023 9275 3575
Brzezina, Miss S J (Treasury Solicitors Department)
London WC2 *p110* 020 7210 3000
Buchalter, R L (Richards Solicitors)
Edgware *p217* 020 8731 5929

6

Buchan, Ms A (Olswang LLP) *C1* London WC1 *p64* 020 7067 3000

Buchan, Ms E J (Southend-on-Sea Borough Council) Southend-on-Sea *p472* 01702 215000

Buchan, J A (Rosalind Watchorn) *W* Sheffield *p377* 0114 229 0160

Buchan, Ms M E (Watson Farley & Williams) London EC2 *p90* 020 7814 8000

Buchan, Ms N E (Clifford Chance) London E14 *p20* 020 7006 1000

Buchanan, A M (Southerns) *W S1 J1 T2 C1 G E Zv Zo* Burnley *p169* 01282 422711

Buchanan, C A (Hodgson Coulthard & Co) *D1 F1 G H K1 M1 X* Houghton Le Spring *p253* 0191 584 3333

Buchanan, D A (Clifford Smith & Buchanan) Colne *p198* 01282 860606

Buchanan, D I (Hogan Lovells International LLP) London EC1 *p42* 020 7296 2000

Buchanan, H C S (Morgan Cole) *S1 W L T1 K1 G A1 H D1 M1* Oxford *p344* 01865 262600

Buchanan, I A (Clifford Smith & Buchanan) *W A1 C1 E J1 K1 L N O Q Zc Zl Zb Zl Zj* Nelson *p320* 01282 693182
Colne *p198* 01282 860606

Buchanan, Mrs J (Gardner Leader LLP) *K1 P D1 B1 J1 F1* Newbury *p322* 01635 508080

Buchanan, J D (Rothera Dowson) *J1 J2* Nottingham *p338* 0115 910 0600

Buchanan, J J (Preston Redman) *S1 E A1 T1 W C1 L R1 Zs Zh Zc* Bournemouth *p152* 01202 292424

Buchanan, M (Lupton Fawcett) *Q* Leeds *p275* 0113 280 2000

Buchanan, Ms N (Field Fisher Waterhouse LLP) London EC3 *p31* 020 7861 4000

Buck, B (Skadden Arps Slate Meagher & Flom (UK) LLP) London E14 *p80* 020 7519 7000

Buck, C (Jacobsens) London EC2 *p46* 020 7608 2568

Buck, C (Carillion PLC) Wolverhampton *p477* 01902 422431

Buck, D H (David Buck & Co) *K1 G D1 P N M1 H C1 W L* Brighton *p159* 01273 621745

Buck, G B (Nelsons) *N J1 F1 B1* Nottingham *p338* 0115 958 6262

Buck, M R D (Fussell Wright) *S1 S2 W L* Bristol *p162* 0117 971 3535

Buck, Mrs S M (North Somerset District Council) Weston-super-Mare *p476* 01934 888888

Buckeldee, M S (Herrington & Carmichael LLP) *E S1 L Q* Camberley *p173* 01276 686222

Buckeridge, Ms M (Russell Jones & Walker) *N* Bristol *p164* 0117 374 2222

Buckeridge, R H (Heath Buckeridge) *E S1 S2 C1 J1 W K1 R2 O L Zc Ze Zk* Maidenhead *p298* 01628 671636

Buckett, Mrs C (Hampshire County Council) Winchester *p476* 01962 841841

Buckingham, Miss A J (Bevan Brittan LLP) *E L S1* Bristol *p161* 0870 194 1000

Buckingham, Ms R E (Simmons & Simmons) London EC2 *p79* 020 7628 2020

Buckingham, S (Travers Smith LLP) *C1 Zb* London EC1 *p87* 020 7295 3000

Buckingham, T D (DLA Piper UK LLP) *O Q Zb* Manchester *p303* 0870 011 1111

Buckland, C J (Askews) *B1 E F1 J1 K1 L M1 N P Zc Zf Zk* Redcar *p362* 01642 475252

Buckland, J (Ashurst LLP) London EC2 *p7* 020 7638 1111

Buckland, J M H (Royds LLP) *S1 W* Morden *p318* 020 8542 1067

Buckland, P A (Devonshires) *Zc* London EC2 *p27* 020 7628 7576

Buckland, Ms P J (Peter Peter & Wright) *K1 D1 D2 K3* Bideford *p133* 01237 472233

Buckland, R S (CooperBurnett) *S1 S2 Q W* Tunbridge Wells *p415* 01892 515022

Buckle, D J (Wilkin Chapman LLP) *J1 N F1 O* Grimsby *p235* 01472 262626

Buckle, D M (DMB Law) *C1 E J1 O Q* Sevenoaks *p374* 01732 228800

Buckle, J (HCB Solicitors) *N Q* Walsall *p420* 01922 720000

Buckle, Miss K M (Atherton Godfrey) *N* Doncaster *p211* 01302 320621

Buckle, Mrs S H (Barrett & Co Solicitors LLP) *W K4* Reading *p359* 0118 958 9711

Buckley, A G H (Woodfines LLP) *K1 K3 D1* Bletchley *p147* 01908 366333

Buckley, Mrs B M (Oxfordshire County Council) Oxford *p468* 01865 792422

Buckley, C (Stevens) *G H* Stafford *p393* 01785 250908

Buckley, Miss C (EMW) *C1* Milton Keynes *p316* 0845 070 6000

Buckley, Mrs C J (Nowell Meller Solicitors Limited) *K1 K3* Stafford *p393* 01785 252377

Buckley, Mrs C L (Wrigleys Solicitors LLP) *W* Sheffield *p377* 0114 267 5588

Buckley, Miss C L (Minahan Hirst & Co) *W K4* Cheadle Hulme *p185* 0161 485 8131

Buckley, J D (VHS Fletchers Solicitors) *G H B2* Nottingham *p339* 0115 959 9550

Buckley, Mrs J L (Fraser Brown) *W T2 K4* Bingham *p133* 01949 830812

Buckley, J M (Fladgate LLP) *O B1 Zb* London WC2 *p32* 020 3036 7000

Buckley, J W (Atteys) *S1 C1 E W M1* Wath-upon-Dearne *p424* 01709 872106

Buckley, Mrs K (Inghams) *K1* Blackpool *p146* 01253 626642

Buckley, L J (Squire Sanders (UK) LLP) *E* Manchester *p310* 0161 830 5000

Buckley, M D (East Riding of Yorkshire Council) Beverley *p449* 01482 887700

Buckley, N J J (Pooley Dale & Co) *P G K1 H S1 J1 W F1 D1 C1* Swindon *p406* 01793 488848

Buckley, S (Stockport Metropolitan Borough Council) Stockport *p472* 0161 480 4949

Buckley, Mrs V A (Coventry City Council) Coventry *p456* 024 7683 4863

Buckley, V R (Thompson & Cooke LLP) *Q K1 N J1* Stalybridge *p393* 0161 338 2614

Buckley, W D M (Linklaters LLP) London EC2 *p54* 020 7456 2000

Bucknell, N J (Laytons) *E B1 L O R1 R2* Guildford *p236* 01483 407000

Bucknill, M R (Department for Business, Enterprise and Regulatory Reform) London SW1 *p105* 020 7215 0105

Bucknill, S (Cooper Son & Caldecott) *S1 T1 L W C1 A1 B1 E Zd R1* Henley-on-Thames *p247* 01491 574203

Buckoke, D J (Isadore Goldman Solicitors) *N K1 R1 E O* London EC4 *p45* 020 7353 1000

Buckridge, Ms M (Barcan Woodward) *N* Bristol *p161* 0117 925 8080

Buckthought, Ms S (Wolferstans) *K4 N Q S1 T2 W Zr* Plymouth *p351* 01752 663295

Buckton, Mrs F J M (Langleys) York *p445* 01904 610886

Buckworth, N J R (Shearman & Sterling LLP) *Zn* London EC2 *p78* 020 7655 5000

Buczkiewicz, Ms L (Simmons & Simmons) London EC2 *p79* 020 7628 2020

Buczynsky, Ms H (Russell Jones & Walker) *N J2 V* London WC2 *p74* 020 7657 1555

Budd, Ms E (Speechly Bircham LLP) *Zj* London EC4 *p81* 020 7427 6400

Budd, G L (Cheshire County Council) Chester *p454* 01244 602382

Budd, Ms G S (Cadbury Schweppes PLC) London W1 *p104* 020 7409 1313

Budd, Ms K (MBNA Europe Bank Ltd) Chester *p454* 01244 672002

Budd, N G (Watson Farley & Williams) London EC2 *p90* 020 7814 8000

Bude, A E (Bude Nathan Iwanier) *B1 C1 E F1 J1 L N P S1 Zi* London NW11 *p16* 020 8458 5656

Bude, R (Bude Storz) Hackney *p16* 020 8800 2800

Budge, Miss A G (Ashton KCJ) *W T2* Bury St Edmunds *p171* 01284 762331

Budge, I D R (Brewer Harding & Rowe) *S1 A1 L C1 R1 W E* Barnstaple *p125* 01271 342271

Budge, R G (SNR Denton) *E* London EC4 *p75* 020 7242 1212

Budge, S A C (Cannings Connolly) London EC1 *p18* 020 7329 9000

Budgen, A P B (Irwin Mitchell LLP) *N J2 P* Sheffield *p376* 0870 150 0100

Budgen, R P (Canter Levin & Berg) *J1 Zp* Liverpool *p287* 0151 239 1000

Budhani, S (Bindmans LLP) *Zi* London WC1 *p12* 020 7833 4433

Budibent, Ms S M (Wright Son & Pepper LLP) *W K4* Camden *p93* 020 7242 5473

Budsworth, C (Glaisyers Solicitors LLP) *Q N* Manchester *p304* 0161 832 4666

Buechel, P M M (Alexander Paul) Tiverton *p412* 01884 252361

Bueno de Mesquita, D (Trott & Gentry) *A1 E C1 F1 G L P J1 W N Zc Zl Zi* London N1 *p88* 020 3119 3150

Buffoni, V P (Vincent Buffoni & Co) Islington *p16* 020 7251 8484

Bugden, M R (Gaby Hardwicke) *W S1 T1 V E C1 L B1* Bexhill *p132* 01424 730945

Bugg, A (Linklaters LLP) *B1 N C1 Zb* London EC2 *p54* 020 7456 2000

Bugg, Miss E L (Pictons Solicitors LLP) *K1* Hemel Hempstead *p247* 01442 242441

Bugg, M A G S (Kidd Rapinet) *Q N D1 D2 O J1 L F1 Zp* Reading *p361* 0845 017 8750

Buggle, G J (Penmans) *B1 C1 E F1 J1 L N Q S1 W Zl K1* Corringham *p199* 01375 673968
Stanford-le-Hope *p394* 01375 677777

Bugingo, P (SNR Denton) *C1* London EC4 *p75* 020 7242 1212

Buglear, B O (Buglear Bate & Co) *S1 E B1 L Q* Woking *p436* 01483 715527 / 724246

Bujakowski, P J (Jobling & Knape) *A1 Zb C1 S2 E C3 Ze O T1 C2 R1 R2* Lancaster *p269* 01524 598300

Bukhari, N A S (Bukhari & Co Solicitors Limited) *N Q G H K1 J1 F1 W L Zi* Nelson *p320* 01282 611234

Bukhari, Mrs S (Bukhari & Co Solicitors Limited) *N Q K1 W F1* Nelson *p320* 01282 611234

Bukraba, Miss S L O (Henry Thompson & Sons) *W* Grantham *p232* 01476 563226

Buksmann, Ms J (Lancashire County Council) Preston *p469* 01772 254868

Bulathwela, K A R (Antons) *B1 D1 E G H J1 K1 L N Q Zi Zj Zk Zp* London N8 *p6* 020 8888 6211

Bulathwela, Mrs R M S (Antons) *F1 G H J1 K1 L N S1 S2 V Zi Zl* London N8 *p6* 020 8888 6211

Bulfin, Mrs K J (Bulfin & Co Employment Law Solicitors) *J1 Zp J2* Pinner *p348* 020 8866 0044

Bull, Miss A (Sacker & Partners LLP) *Zo* London EC2 *p76* 020 7329 6699

Bull, C G (Mills & Reeve) *E S2 R2 C1* Birmingham *p140* 0121 454 4000

Bull, G (North Norfolk District Council) Cromer *p456* 01263 513811

Bull, Ms H (Foot Anstey) *K1* Plymouth *p349* 01752 675000

Bull, J R (Atkins Hope Solicitors) *D1 G H R1 F1 K1 L* Croydon *p204* 020 8680 5018

Bull, K B (Lovegrove & Eliot) *K1 K3* Windsor *p434* 01753 851133

Bull, L (Harbottle & Lewis LLP) London W1 *p38* 020 7667 5000
Westminster *p70* 020 7222 7040

Bull, N C (Bull & Co) *S1 E W A1* Andover *p118* 01264 352495

Bull, R (Burges Salmon) *J1 Zp* Bristol *p161* 0117 939 2000

Bull, R A (A H Page) *C3 E L R1 S1 W Zc Ze Zm Zv Zl* Ilford *p260* 020 8554 1985

Bull, Ms S (Bates Wells & Braithwaite London LLP) *J1 J2 Zd* London EC4 *p11* 020 7551 7777

Bull, S J (Bracknell Forest Borough Council) Bracknell *p450* 01344 424642

Bull, T (Reynolds Porter Chamberlain LLP) *Zl Zc* London E1 *p71* 020 3060 6000

Bullbrook, Ms J (Hempsons) *N Zq Zr* Manchester *p305* 0161 228 0011

Bullen, A G S (Hewitsons) *E L S1* Northampton *p332* 01604 233233

Bullen, Ms J (Salans) *J1* London EC4 *p76* 020 7429 6000

Bullen, P V (Paul Bullen & Co) *S1 S2 C1* Doncaster *p211* 01302 819000

Buller, S (Wykeham Hurford Sheppard & Son LLP) Battle *p128* 01424 775088
Chislehurst *p193* 020 8297 0393 / 8467 8307

Bullivant, A (Hamnett Osborne Tisshaw) *G H B2* Haywards Heath *p245* 01444 443030

Bullivant, P W (Hill Dickinson LLP) *E R2 S2 R1 S1 C1 C2* Liverpool *p288* 0151 600 8000

Bullivant, R H F (Hill Dickinson LLP) *O F1 Zy Q Ze* Liverpool *p288* 0151 600 8000

Bullock, J A D (Squire Sanders (UK) LLP) Leeds *p277* 0113 284 7000

Bullock, J F (McGrigors LLP) *T1 T2 B2 P* London EC4 *p56* 020 7054 2500

Bullock, M J (Wiggin LLP) *E L P R1 R2 S1 S2* Cheltenham *p189* 01242 224114

Bullock, P (Hyndburn Borough Council) Lancaster *p447* 01254 388111

Bullock, P C E (Pinsent Masons LLP) *I O Q* London EC2 *p67* 020 7418 7000

Bullock, R (Freeth Cartwright LLP) *Q O J1 Zc Zo Zb* Nottingham *p337* 0115 936 9369

Bullough, J S (Widdows Mason) *O E J1 Q R1 W B1 C1 P S1* Leigh *p282* 01942 673311

Bulman, Mrs D H (Burges Salmon) *J1 Zp* Bristol *p161* 0117 939 2000

Bulman, Miss M (Newcastle Upon Tyne City Council) Newcastle upon Tyne *p466* 0191 232 8520

Bulman, S A (WBW Solicitors) *B1 F1 L N X* Newton Abbot *p329* 01626 202404

Bulman, S C (Davitt Jones Bould) *E* Taunton *p408* 01823 279279
Bristol *p164* 0117 917 3000

Bulmer, Mrs A (HM Land Registry - Durham (Boldon) Office) Durham *p457* 0191 301 2345

Bulmer, Mrs J R (Howells LLP) *D1 D2 K1* Sheffield *p376* 0114 249 6666

Bulmer, L (Napthens LLP) *E* Blackpool *p146* 01253 622305

Bulmer, Ms M (Walker Morris) Leeds *p277* 0113 283 2500

Bulmer, S (Simmons & Simmons) London EC2 *p79* 020 7628 2020

Bulsing, Mrs B E (Eastgate Assistance Ltd) *O Q D1 L F1* Colchester *p455* 0870 523 4500

Bunce, R J R (Simmons & Simmons) London EC2 *p79* 020 7628 2020

Bunce, S (Association of British Travel Agents Ltd) London W1 *p103* 020 7637 2444

Bunce-Linsell, Miss J A (Bunce-Linsell) *W* Wembley *p426* 020 8904 2229

Bunch, A W S (Pinsent Masons LLP) *O Q C1 Zc Zj* London EC2 *p67* 020 7418 7000

Bunch, M C (Bates Wells & Braithwaite London LLP) *J1 J2 Zd* London EC4 *p11* 020 7551 7777

Bundey, Ms R E D (Harrison Bundey) *G H Zi* Leeds *p274* 0113 200 7400

Bunglawala, P (Forshaws Davies Ridgway LLP) Warrington *p422* 01925 230000

Bunker, Miss H E (Piper Smith Watton LLP) *W* London SW1 *p68* 020 7222 9900

Bunn, A D T (David Bunn & Co) Birmingham *p136* 0121 476 8481
Birmingham *p136* 0121 441 3322

Bunn, Mrs C (Greenland Houchen Pomeroy) *S2 E A1 L W* Attleborough *p120* 01953 453143

Bunn, D T (David Bunn & Co) *S1 W* Birmingham *p136* 0121 476 8481
Birmingham *p136* 0121 441 3322

Bunn, J L S (David Bunn & Co) Birmingham *p136* 0121 476 8481
Birmingham *p136* 0121 441 3322

Bunnell, Miss V (Andersons Solicitors) *J1 Zp* Nottingham *p335* 0115 947 0641

Bunney, Miss A I (Coodes) *S1 S2 E L* Truro *p414* 01872 246200

Bunney, M (LDJ Solicitors) *E W S1 A1 C1 L R1 T1* Nuneaton *p339* 024 7674 5000

Bunting, Miss A (Davis Blank Furniss) *J1 Zl* Manchester *p303* 0161 832 3304

Bunting, C J (Clark Willis) *G H B2* Darlington *p206* 01325 281111

Bunting, Mrs D J (Brooke-Taylors) *S1 W* Buxton *p172* 01298 22741

Bunting, Mrs F L (Favell Smith & Lawson Solicitors) *D1 K1 V* Sheffield *p375* 0114 272 4381

Bunting, Ms J (Wright Hassall LLP) *K1 K2* Leamington Spa *p270* 01926 886688

Bunting, Mrs K L (Chattertons Solicitors) *E S1 L A1 C1 Zo* Boston *p151* 01205 351114

Bunting, Mrs L (Arscotts) *S1 W K1* Hove *p254* 01273 735289

Bunting, Miss L E (Birkett Long LLP) *D1 K3 K1* Colchester *p197* 01206 217300

Bunting, P M (Aspinall Wright) *K1 D1 K3 Q N O J1 V L* Glossop *p230* 01457 854645

Bunyan, B R (Farleys Solicitors LLP) *D1 K1* Blackburn *p145* 01254 367854

Burbidge, P C (Gullands) *Zd S2 E S1 R2 R1 Zh A1 L* Maidstone *p299* 01622 678341

Burbidge, P J (Meade-King) *O Q Zc A3* Bristol *p163* 0117 926 4121

Burbidge, S M (Humphreys & Co) Bristol *p163* 0117 929 2662

Burbidge, T (Bond Pearce LLP) Southampton *p385* 0845 415 0000

Burbidge, Miss V (The Endeavour Partnership LLP) Stockton-on-Tees *p397* 01642 610300

Burch, D C S (Burch Phillips & Co) *K1 G J1 O Q Zq* West Drayton *p427* 01895 442141

Burch, Ms J J (Irwin Mitchell LLP) *N X* Sheffield *p376* 0870 150 0100

Burch, J W (Bartletts Solicitors) *Q N* Liverpool *p286* 0151 227 3391

Burch, Ms L F M (Osborne Clarke) *C1* Bristol *p164* 0117 917 3000

Burch, Ms N M A (Addleshaw Goddard) *O Q* London EC1 *p4* 020 7606 8855

Burch, R D (Louis Spragg & Co) *K1 G H D1* Dudley *p213* 01384 211621 / 211622

Burchell, N P (Burchell Williams Limited) *G H* Brighton *p159* 01273 606555

Burchell, Miss S E (Davies Gore Lomax) *D1 K1 D2 K3 V* Leeds *p273* 0113 242 2797

Burcher, D (David Burcher & Co) *S1 N* London NW2 *p16* 020 8452 4127

Burchett, R (Henmans LLP) *A1* Oxford *p343* 01865 781000

Burchfield, J R (Stone King LLP) *W T2 Zd* Bath *p128* 01225 337599

Burd, M (Lewis Silkin LLP) *O J1 Q* London EC4 *p53* 020 7074 8000

Burden, Mrs A J (Adlams LLP) *D1 K1* St Neots *p392* 01480 474061

Burden, C (DLA Piper UK LLP) London EC2 *p24* 0870 011 1111

Burden, J J H (Veale Wasbrough Vizards) *A1 S1 T2 W Zd Zm Zv* London EC4 *p89* 020 7405 1234

Burden, Miss L D (Westminster City Council) London SW1 *p110* 020 7641 6000

Burden, Mrs M (Colemans - CTTS) *N* Manchester *p302* 0161 876 2500

Burden, P A (Howell & Co) *K1 K3* Birmingham *p139* 0121 778 5031

Burden, Miss R (Stevens) *D1 K1 D2* Haverhill *p244* 01440 762511

See p634 for the Key to Work Categories

Burdett, A (Ellen Court Partnership Solicitors)
Preston *p356* 01772 882888

Burdett, C E (Milford & Dormor) *N K1 G H D1 Q*
Chard *p184* 01460 65335 / 61000

Burdett, Miss L O (HSBC Insurance (UK) Ltd)
Brentwood *p448* 01277 842174

Burdett, M F (Hanne & Co) *G H*
London SW11 *p38* 020 7228 0017

Burdett, Miss N (George Davies Solicitors LLP) *O Q*
Manchester *p303* 0161 236 8992

Burdock, R K F (Berry Redmond & Robinson) *S1 S2 W*
Weston-super-Mare *p429* 01934 513963
Winscombe *p434* 01934 842811

Burdon, Ms L C (Bolt Burdon) *E W R1 O T1 T2*
Islington *p14* 020 7288 4700

Burdon, M J (Oxley & Coward Solicitors LLP) *G H*
Rotherham *p367* 01709 510999

Burdon, S M (Stephen Burdon Solicitors) *G H*
Nottingham *p336* 0115 950 0054

Burdon-Cooper, A R (Collyer Bristow LLP) *E L C1 S1 Zw S2*
London WC1 *p22* 020 7242 7363

Burfitt, Ms R K (Bristows) *C1 Ze*
London EC4 *p15* 020 7400 8000

Burford, Ms E (British American Tobacco)
London WC2 *p104* 020 7845 1000

Burford, R A (Callaghans)
Farnham *p224* 01252 723477

Burford, Miss T M (Ford Simey LLP) *W*
Exeter *p221* 01392 274126

Burge, Ms A (Reynolds Porter Chamberlain LLP)
London E1 *p71* 020 3060 6000

Burge, D (SNR Denton)
London EC4 *p75* 020 7242 1212

Burge, Ms H (Withers LLP) *K1 K2 K3*
London EC4 *p92* 020 7597 6000

Burge, Ms K (Merthyr Tydfil Magistrates Court) *K1 M1 P G F1 J1 S1 V H*
Merthyr Tydfil *p465* 01685 721731

Burge, Miss P H (Frearsons) *Q T2 W N*
Skegness *p380* 01754 897600

Burge, S N (Blake Lapthorn) *K1 N*
Chandlers Ford *p184* 023 8090 8090

Burger, P A (Wright Hassall LLP) *E L C1*
Leamington Spa *p270* 01926 886688

Burgerman, B G (Birmingham City Council Legal & Democratic Services)
Birmingham *p449* 0121 303 2066

Burgess, Miss A (Lanyon Bowdler LLP) *A1 S2 E*
Oswestry *p342* 01691 652241

Burgess, Mrs A L V (Charsley Harrison LLP) *W T2*
Windsor *p434* 01753 851591

Burgess, Mrs C (BHP Law) *K1 K3 D1 D2*
Newton Aycliffe *p330* 01325 312534

Burgess, I S (Birmingham City Council Legal & Democratic Services)
Birmingham *p449* 0121 303 2066

Burgess, J (Harvey Roberts) *K1 D1 V W S1 B1 G Q N L Zm*
Stockport *p395* 0161 443 2828

Burgess, Miss J (Catteralls) *K1 S1*
Wakefield *p418* 01924 291122

Burgess, J C A (Field Seymour Parkes) *E L S1 A1 T1 W Zc Zj*
Reading *p360* 0118 951 6200

Burgess, Miss J E (English Heritage)
London EC1 *p106* 020 7973 3360

Burgess, Ms J H (Whiteford Crocker) *S2 E S1*
Plymouth *p350* 01752 550711

Burgess, J P (Emerson Developments (Holdings) Ltd)
Alderley Edge *p447* 01625 588420

Burgess, M C (Bartletts Solicitors)
Liverpool *p286* 0151 521 7333

Burgess, M L (DLA Piper UK LLP) *T1*
Birmingham *p137* 0870 011 1111

Burgess, Ms M L (Metcalfes) *C1 O I U2 C2 Zf Ze*
Bristol *p164* 0117 929 0451

Burgess, N D (Ince & Co Services Ltd)
London E1 *p44* 020 7481 0010

Burgess, Mrs P M (Howard & Co) *K1 S1 W D1*
Barnsley *p124* 01226 215215

Burgess, S T (Stamp Jackson and Procter) *N*
Hull *p258* 01482 324591

Burgess, Ms W A (Reeves & Co) *K1 L F1 K3 Zk O I Q*
Maidstone *p299* 01622 692220
Ramsgate *p359* 01843 592361

Burgess-Smith, M C (Linklaters LLP)
London EC2 *p54* 020 7456 2000

Burgher, Ms C (Anthony Collins Solicitors LLP) *D1 K1*
Birmingham *p137* 0121 200 3242

Burgin, Ms K (Norrie Waite & Slater) *K1 K4 T2 W*
Sheffield *p377* 0114 276 6166

Burgoyne, D E (Thompsons (formerly Robin/Brian Thompson & Partners))
Nottingham *p339* 0115 989 7200

Burgoyne, Miss D E (Bristol City Council) *D1*
Bristol *p451* 0117 922 2000

Burgoyne, P R (Burgoyne & Co) *S1 E L W Q C1 Zv*
Walsall *p420* 01922 616916

Burke, Miss A J (Irwin Mitchell LLP) *Zj N*
Sheffield *p376* 0870 150 0100

Burke, A J (Slee Blackwell) *S1*
Barnstaple *p125* 01271 372128
Braunton *p156* 01271 812019

Burke, B W L (The College of Law) *S1*
London WC1 *p105* 0800 289997

Burke, C G (Pearson Hinchliffe) *O F1 L Q G Zi*
Oldham *p341* 0161 785 3500

Burke, Ms C M (Oxley & Coward Solicitors LLP) *D2 D1 K1*
Rotherham *p367* 01709 510999

Burke, Mrs D (Hartlaw LLP) *K1 D1 K2 K3*
Wetherby *p429* 01937 547000

Burke, D F (Bells Solicitors) *O Q J1 Zq*
Farnham *p224* 01252 733733

Burke, Mrs H (City of Sunderland)
Sunderland *p473* 0191 520 5555

Burke, J (Fisher Meredith) *S1 S2 E*
Lambeth *p32* 020 7091 2700

Burke, J (Read Law Associates) *S1*
Macclesfield *p297* 01625 429131

Burke, J C D (Girlings) *E S2 C1*
Ashford *p119* 01233 664711

Burke, Ms J E (Alan Taylor & Co) *B1 C1 K1 N O Q Zd Zi Zk*
London EC1 *p85* 020 7251 3222

Burke, J M (Gibson & Co) *O*
Newcastle upon Tyne *p324* 0191 273 3817

Burke, Mrs J M (Francis & Co) *W T1 A1 S1*
Chepstow *p189* 01291 622237

Burke, K M (Bennetts Solicitors Attorneys & Notaries) *O N Q J1 M2*
Wrington *p443* 01934 862786

Burke, L (Penningtons) *Ze*
London EC2 *p66* 020 7457 3000

Burke, Ms L A (Beevers Solicitors) *D1 K1*
Ashton-under-Lyne *p119* 0161 339 9697

Burke, Ms L N (Rawlison Butler LLP)
Crawley *p202* 01293 527744

Burke, M P (Bury & Walkers LLP) *E R2 R1 S2 C1 C2 Zc*
Leeds *p272* 0113 244 4227

Burke, N M (Michael W Halsall)
Newton-le-Willows *p330* 01942 727000

Burke, P F (Burke & Co) *S1 W E*
Bristol *p161* 0117 931 4499
Bristol *p164* 0117 962 9978

Burke, P S (Maples Teesdale LLP) *Zb B1 C1 J1 C2*
London EC2 *p58* 020 7600 3800
London EC4 *p86* 020 7300 7000

Burke, R J (Arthur Smiths) *N J1 Q Zl*
Wigan *p432* 01942 242815

Burke, Ms R V (Irwin Mitchell LLP) *N Zj*
Birmingham *p139* 0870 150 0100

Burke, S (Shoosmiths) *E*
Milton Keynes *p317* 0370 086 8300 / 01908 488300
Nottingham *p339* 0370 086 5000 / 0115 906 5000

Burke, S K (Close Thornton) *L N F1 Q*
Darlington *p206* 01325 466461

Burke, Mrs S L (Lincolnshire County Council Resources - Legal Services)
Lincoln *p463* 01522 552222

Burke, W P (Coole & Haddock) *S1 E W*
Worthing *p441* 01903 213511

Burkett, J H (Fisher Jones Greenwood LLP) *O Q*
Colchester *p197* 01206 578282

Burkey, Ms L (Stone King LLP)
Bath *p128* 01225 337599

Burkill, J J (Burkill Govier) *C1 E I L M2 R1 R2 Zb Zc Ze Zn Zw*
Farnham *p224* 01252 717171

Burkill, N C (Taylor Wessing) *N P Zk*
London EC4 *p86* 020 7300 7000

Burkinshaw, A P (Last Cawthra Feather LLP)
Bradford *p154* 01274 848800

Burkitt, R (Birketts LLP) *Q O L N Zc Zq F1*
Ipswich *p262* 01473 232300
Ipswich *p262* 01473 213311
Northampton *p332* 0370 086 3000 / 01604 543000

Burley, K (Rochdale Metropolitan Borough Council)
Rochdale *p470* 01706 647474

Burley, R N (Clifford Chance)
London E14 *p20* 020 7006 1000

Burley, S J (Infields) *S1 W*
Kingston upon Thames *p267* 020 8977 7633 / 8977 1149

Burlingham, I W (Ian Burlingham Solicitor) *F1*
Basingstoke *p126*

Burlinson, Mrs K A (Spearing Waite LLP) *S2 E R2 L*
Leicester *p281* 0116 262 4225

Burman, I A (Laytons) *T1 W Zd*
London EC4 *p52* 020 7842 8000

Burman, J (Heptonstalls LLP) *N P Q Zr*
Goole *p231* 01405 765661

Burman, R B (Robin Burman & Co) *S1 N P E M1 K1 C1 C2 J1 W F1 Ze Zc Zf*
Manchester *p302* 0161 860 7123

Burmeister, N (Ashurst LLP)
London EC2 *p7* 020 7638 1111

Burn, Mrs A (John O'Neill & Co) *W K4 T2*
Gosforth *p232* 0191 246 4000

Burn, A L (Linklaters LLP)
London EC2 *p54* 020 7456 2000

Burn, Mrs G (Burn & Co) *S1 E W K1 F1 N Q V Zv D2 K3*
Wheathampstead *p430* 01438 833446

Burn, G N (Yorklaw Ltd (t/a Burn & Company)) *E S2*
Easingwold *p215* 01347 822188
York *p445* 01904 655442

Burn, Mrs J (FBC Manby Bowdler LLP) *K1 W T2*
Bridgnorth *p157* 01746 761436

Burn, M (Oxford Employment Law Solicitors) *C1 J1 O Zp Q J2 A3*
Oxford *p344* 01865 487136

Burn, N M E (Wilkin Chapman Epton Blades) *Q N G H*
Lincoln *p285* 01522 512345

Burn, R (Burn & Co) *S1 B1 C1 E F1 J1 L N O Q Ze Zv S2*
Wheathampstead *p430* 01438 833446

Burn, R J (Mole Valley District Council)
Dorking *p457* 01306 885001

Burn, S (Simon Burn Solicitors)
Cheltenham *p187* 01242 228444

Burn, S M (Yorklaw Ltd (t/a Burn & Company)) *W K4*
Easingwold *p215* 01347 822188
York *p445* 01904 655442

Burnell, Miss C V (Higgs & Sons) *N Zr*
Brierley Hill *p158* 0845 111 5050

Burnell, E (Veale Wasbrough Vizards) *Zb Zd E*
Bristol *p165* 0117 925 2020

Burnell, R N (Cyngor Sir Ynys Mon (Isle of Anglesey County Council))
Llangefni *p463* 01248 750057

Burnell, S J (Graham Evans & Partners) *G H K1*
Swansea *p405* 01792 655822

Burnet, D H (Pinhorn Burnet) *W*
Hammersmith & Fulham *p67* 020 7385 6688

Burnet, M E (DWF) *W*
Liverpool *p287* 0151 907 3000

Burnett, A (Wilkin Chapman LLP) *A1 B1 C1 E F1 I J2 L N P Q Zc Ze Zj Zk Zl*
Grimsby *p235* 01472 262626

Burnett, C D (Allen & Overy LLP)
London E1 *p5* 020 3088 0000

Burnett, C D (Thorpe & Co) *S1 E L A1 F1 W S2*
Whitby *p430* 01947 603465
Scarborough *p372* 01723 364321

Burnett, D J (Stuart Smith & Burnett) *C1 W L E K4 T2*
Bridlington *p158* 01262 678128

Burnett, Mrs G F (Hewitts) *N Zm G D2 K1 S1*
Newton Aycliffe *p330* 01325 316170

Burnett, J D J (BHP Law) *N*
Durham *p214* 0191 384 0840

Burnett, J J (Mackenzie Jones)
St Asaph *p391* 01745 536030

Burnett, J J (Storrar Cowdry) *J1 Q O K3 K1 N Zp*
Chester *p191* 01244 400567

Burnett, Mrs L E (Thorpe & Co) *W T2 S1*
Scarborough *p372* 01723 364321

Burnett, M (Mills & Reeve) *J1 Zp J2*
Birmingham *p140* 0121 454 4000

Burnett, Mrs M E (Stuart Smith & Burnett) *W S1 K1 D1 F1 K3*
Bridlington *p158* 01262 678128

Burnett, N J (Birketts LLP (Wollastons LLP)) *C1 C2 C3 I M1 M2 Zi Zf Zd Ze*
Chelmsford *p186* 01245 211211

Burnett, N J (CooperBurnett) *C1 E S1 W R1 B1 A1 Ze Zc*
Tunbridge Wells *p415* 01892 515022

Burnett, P (IBB Solicitors) *Zd S1 E S2*
Uxbridge *p417* 0845 638 1381

Burnett, Miss R (Bristows)
London EC4 *p15* 020 7400 8000

Burnett, R (HSR Law (Hayes, Son & Richmond)) *S2 R2 E*
Doncaster *p211* 01302 347800
Gainsborough *p228* 01427 613831

Burnett, Mrs R H A (Paris Smith LLP) *I Ze Zza U1*
Southampton *p386* 023 8048 2482

Burnett, R N R (Burnett Barker) *K1 H D1 L J1 E G W C1 S2 K4 A1*
Bury St Edmunds *p171* 01284 701131

Burnett, R P A (AXA UK PLC) *B1 C1 J1 O Q W Zb Zi*
London E22 *p103* 020 7920 5900

Burnett, S (Mohindra Maini Solicitors LLP)
Manchester *p307* 0161 236 9833

Burnett-Hall, R H (Bristows) *C1 C2 C3 M1 P Ze*
London EC4 *p15* 020 7400 8000

Burnett-Scott, A T (Ashurst LLP) *B1 E*
London EC2 *p7* 020 7638 1111

Burnham, D A (Derek A Burnham) *S1 W E L K1 N Zl*
Leicester *p279* 01664 424517

Burnige, Ms M (Veale Wasbrough Vizards) *X*
London EC4 *p89* 020 7405 1234

Burnip, D W (Forest Heath District Council)
Mildenhall *p466* 01638 719000

Burniston, B H (John Collins & Partners LLP) *C1 Ze U2 I*
Swansea *p405* 01792 773773

Burnley, P A (DLA Piper UK LLP) *N J1 D1 K1 R1 F1 Zd Zm Zs*
Leeds *p272* 0870 011 1111

Burnley-Jones, C L (Burnley-Jones Bate & Co) *B2 G H*
London SW19 *p16* 020 8542 8101

Burns, A (JMW Solicitors) *E L S1 R1 C1 Zc Zn S2 R2*
Manchester *p306* 0845 872 6666

Burns, Ms A (Mary Ward Legal Centre)
London WC1 *p110* 020 7831 7079

Burns, Mrs A (Siddiqui & Co)
Harrow *p242* 020 8423 2400

Burns, A (Mawdsleys) *S1 K1 W S2*
Southport *p388* 01704 537676

Burns, Miss A J (Newcastle Upon Tyne City Council)
Newcastle upon Tyne *p466* 0191 232 8520

Burns, Ms C (Walker & Co) *K1 D1 Q J1 L N*
Rotherham *p367* 01709 817112

Burns, Ms C (Ison Harrison) *K1 K3 D1*
Leeds *p274* 0113 284 5000

Burns, Ms C (Thomson Webb & Corfield) *S1*
Cambridge *p176* 01223 578070

Burns, C A (Lee & Priestley LLP) *K1 D1 G H N*
Leeds *p275* 0845 129 2300

Burns, Miss C E (Glaisyers) *N Q*
Birmingham *p138* 0121 233 2971

Burns, Miss D (Martin Murray & Associates) *G H B2*
Slough *p382* 01753 551313

Burns, Ms E (Geldards LLP) *J1*
Cardiff *p178* 029 2023 8239

Burns, G G (Stephenson Harwood) *Za*
London EC2 *p82* 020 7329 4422

Burns, G J (Wrigley Claydon) *C1 E S2 J1 S1*
Oldham *p341* 0161 624 6811

Burns, Ms H (McKeowns Solicitors Ltd) *N*
St Albans *p390* 0800 032 8328

Burns, I (Sintons LLP) *N*
Newcastle upon Tyne *p326* 0191 226 7878

Burns, Miss L D (Reynolds Porter Chamberlain LLP)
London E1 *p71* 020 3060 6000

Burns, Ms M (Platt Halpern)
Oldham *p341* 0161 626 4955

Burns, M R (Clarion Solicitors LLP) *K1 K2*
Leeds *p272* 0113 246 0622
Harrogate *p240* 01423 530630

6

Burns, P J (Selby District Council)
Selby *p470* 01757 705101

Burns, P J (Chattertons Solicitors) *S1*
Spalding *p389* 01775 768774

Burns, Miss R (Morecrofts Solicitors LLP) *D1 K1 D2*
Liverpool *p290* 0151 236 8871

Burns, R (Squire Sanders (UK) LLP) *C1 C2 C3*
London EC2 *p81* 020 7655 1000

Burns, Miss S (Irwin Mitchell LLP) *N*
Birmingham *p139* 0870 150 0100

Burns, Ms S (Thompsons (formerly Robin/Brian Thompson & Partners)) *Q*
London SW19 *p87* 020 8947 4163

Burns, Mrs Y C (Paul Davidson Taylor)
Horsham *p253* 01403 262333

Burns-Lunt, Ms L (Canter Levin & Berg)
Liverpool *p287* 0151 239 1000

Burquest, Ms M C (DWF) *Q U2 Ze O*
Liverpool *p287* 0151 907 3000

Burr, Miss S E (Mills & Reeve) *E*
Cambridge *p175* 01223 364422

Burraston, R (stevensdrake) *L O Q N*
Crawley *p202* 01293 596900

Burrell, Miss C A (David Auld & Co) *N Zm K1 J1 Q D1 D2*
Morpeth *p319* 01670 505844
Bedlington *p130* 01670 826870

Burrell, C R (Leonard Gray)
Chelmsford *p186* 01245 504904

Burrell, Ms D (David Rubie Mitchell & Co) *G H*
Sutton *p403* 020 8641 0575

Burrell, D R (Keelys LLP) *N Zi*
London EC2 *p48* 020 7422 8686

Burrell, G (BTMK Solicitors LLP) *G H*
Southend-on-Sea *p387* 01702 339222

Burrell, J (Davenport Lyons) *K1 N*
London W1 *p25* 020 7468 2600

Burrell, Miss J K (The Big Food Group PLC)
Deeside *p456* 01244 830100

Burrell, Mrs L A (North Lincolnshire Council)
Scunthorpe *p470* 01724 296296

Burrell, P (Herbert Smith LLP) *O*
London EC2 *p40* 020 7374 8000

Burrell, Ms S A (Birmingham City Council Legal & Democratic Services)
Birmingham *p449* 0121 303 2066

Burrett, T L (Bolt Building Supplies Ltd)
Halstead *p460* 01787 477261

Burridge, M J (Blake Lapthorn) *K1*
Portsmouth *p354* 023 9222 1122

Burridge, S (Park Woodfine Heald Mellows LLP) *S1*
Bedford *p130* 01234 400000

Burridge, S R (Leeds Day) *S1*
Huntingdon *p258* 01480 454301

Burrough, R J (Burroughs) *B2 G Zl Zt Zf Zv*
Maidstone *p299* 01622 676976 / 676982

Burrough, T J A (Burroughs) *J1 N L G H Zl*
Maidstone *p299* 01622 676976 / 676982

Burroughes, J T (Howes Percival LLP) *O P Q*
Norwich *p334* 01603 762103

Burroughs, P A (McGrigors LLP) *E S1 L*
London EC4 *p56* 020 7054 2500

Burroughs, Ms S (FBC Manby Bowdler LLP) *Q*
Shrewsbury *p379* 01743 241551

Burrow, B R (Inghams) *K1 P F1 D1 M1 G N H B1 W Zj Zl Zc*
Blackpool *p146* 01253 626642

Burrow, I N (Girlings) *C1 E S1*
Herne Bay *p248* 01227 367355

Burrow, Ms J A (Ridley & Co) *S1 S2 L*
Westminster *p72* 020 7828 7656

Burrow, M W (Blackhurst Swainson Goodier LLP) *E S1 A1 C1 L R1 J1*
Lancaster *p269* 01524 32471

Burrow, R P (SJ Berwin LLP)
London EC4 *p75* 020 7111 2222

Burrowes, D J B (Shepherd Harris & Co) *G H*
Enfield *p219* 020 8363 8341

Burrowes, J I (PCB Solicitors LLP) *C1 S2 E W S1 A1*
Shrewsbury *p379* 01743 248148

Burrows, A J (Tinsdills) *S2 E S1*
Hanley *p239* 01782 262031
Leek *p278* 01538 399332

Burrows, Miss A J (Tameside Magistrates Court)
Ashton-under-Lyne *p447* . . . 0161 330 2023

Burrows, C (Hempsons)
Harrogate *p240* 01423 522331

Burrows, Mrs D D (Julian Young & Co)
London W1 *p93* 020 7724 8414

Burrows, D J (Glaisyers Solicitors LLP) *A1 E Zh Zn*
Manchester *p304* 0161 832 4666

Burrows, Miss E G (Trowers & Hamlins) *J1 N Zp*
London EC3 *p88*. 020 7423 8000

Burrows, Ms G J (Benussi & Co) *K1 K3*
Birmingham *p135* 0121 248 4001

Burrows, Ms J (Wolferstans) *N Zr*
Plymouth *p351*. 01752 663295

Burrows, J (Howes Percival LLP)
Norwich *p334* 01603 762103

Burrows, Miss J L (Armstrong & Co) *S1 W E L C1 S2*
London SE23 *p7*. 020 8699 3477

Burrows, M (Penningtons) *E*
London EC2 *p66*. 020 7457 3000

Burrows, N C (Blandy & Blandy) *C1 C2 U1 L Zo U2 Ze*
Reading *p360* 0118 951 6800

Burrows, P L (Winters) *S1 S2 A1 E R2*
St Ives *p392*. 01480 377377

Burrows, R (Taylor & Emmet LLP) *Zh*
Sheffield *p377* 0114 218 4000

Burrows, Ms R J (Pellmans) *W T2 K4*
Eynsham *p223*. 01865 884400

Burrows, Ms S D M (Metropolitan Police Directorate of Legal Services)
London SW1 *p108* 020 7230 7210

Burrows, Mrs V (Clark Willis) *K4 N Zm*
Darlington *p206* 01325 281111

Burstall, H P (Burstalls) *E S1 C1 C2 A1 W T1 L S2*
Hull *p256* 01482 621800

Burston, R J (Ernst & Young)
Birmingham *p449* 0121 535 2000

Burt, Ms A (Covent Garden Family Law) *D1 K1 D2*
Camden *p23*. 020 7257 6130

Burt, C (Blake Lapthorn) *O Zc*
Oxford *p342*. 01865 248607

Burt, C (Reynolds Porter Chamberlain LLP)
London E1 *p71* 020 3060 6000

Burt, D R (Plexus Law (A Trading Name of Parabis Law LLP)) *N O Q*
Evesham *p220*. 01386 769160

Burt, J D (Plexus Law (A Trading Name of Parabis Law LLP)) *N*
Evesham *p220*. 01386 769160
Manchester *p309* 0161 214 7933

Burt, J E (Withers LLP) *W T2 Zm*
London EC4 *p92*. 020 7597 6000

Burt, Ms P (Letchers) *W K4 Zm V*
Ringwood *p364* 01425 471424

Burt, S J L (Gudgeons Prentice) *E S1 C1 A1 L S2*
Stowmarket *p399* 01449 613101

Burt, T J (Stallard March & Edwards) *Zd K4 Zq T2 W*
Worcester *p440* 01905 613404

Burtinshaw, Ms C F (Squire Sanders (UK) LLP)
Manchester *p310* 0161 830 5000

Burtoft, A (Oxley & Coward Solicitors LLP) *G H*
Rotherham *p367*. 01709 510999

Burton, Ms A (Portrait Solicitors) *W T2 Zd*
London WC2 *p69* 020 7092 6990

Burton, A (C R Burton & Co) *G H*
London SE20 *p16* . . 020 8778 4455 / 8659 5775

Burton, A C (Simons Muirhead & Burton) *B2 G Zf Zg Zk*
London W1 *p79* 020 7734 4499

Burton, A J (Squire Sanders (UK) LLP)
London EC2 *p81*. 020 7655 1000

Burton, A J W (TLT Solicitors)
London EC2 *p85*. 020 3465 4000

Burton, A R (Bromsgrove District Council)
Bromsgrove *p452* 01527 881288

Burton, A S (Reed Smith LLP) *O Q*
London EC2 *p71*. 020 3116 3000

Burton, B (Reynolds Porter Chamberlain LLP)
London E1 *p71* 020 3060 6000

Burton, Mrs B L (Lefevre & Co) *E S1 W*
Orpington *p342* . . .01689 856835 / 856836

Burton, C J (Gosschalks) *C1 C2 T1 A1*
Hull *p256* 01482 324252

Burton, C R (C R Burton & Co) *G H S1 D1 W*
London SE20 *p16* . . 020 8778 4455 / 8659 5775

Burton, D (Eldridges) *S2 E S1*
Newport *p328* 01983 524741

Burton, G W J (Dale & Newbery LLP) *O W Q A3 B1*
Staines *p393*. 01784 464491

Burton, Ms H C (Ashurst LLP)
London EC2 *p7* 020 7638 1111

Burton, I (Bristows) *Ze*
London EC4 *p15*. 020 7400 8000

Burton, I (Starr & Partners LLP)
London EC4 *p82*. 020 7199 1450

Burton, Ms I (The College of Law Guildford)
Guildford *p459*. 01483 460200

Burton, I R (BCL Burton Copeland) *G B2 J2*
London WC2 *p9* 020 7430 2277

Burton, J (Penningtons)
Basingstoke *p127* 01256 407100

Burton, Ms J A (Burtonwoods) *E S1 C1 W*
London WC1 *p16* 020 7636 2448

Burton, J G (John Burton Solicitors) *S1 W E*
Stone *p398* 01785 814818

Burton, J R (Mansfield District Council)
Mansfield *p465* 01623 463463

Burton, J R (Middleton Dummer)
Oldbury *p340* 0121 544 4788
Dudley *p213*. . . . .01384 253331 / 253771

Burton, J R (Metcalfe Copeman & Pettefar) *S2 E C1*
Peterborough *p347* 01733 865880

Burton, Ms K (LDJ Solicitors) *Q*
Nuneaton *p339* 024 7674 5000

Burton, M (Broadacres Housing Association)
Northallerton *p467*. 01609 767900

Burton, M (Kennedys) *Zj N*
London EC3 *p49*. 020 7667 9667

Burton, M J (DLA Piper UK LLP)
London EC2 *p24*. 0870 011 1111

Burton, Ms M P (North Kensington Law Centre)
London W10 *p108* 020 8969 7473

Burton, M V (MFG Solicitors) *E K1 N O S1 Q A1 D1 J1 Zd Zm Zl Zw*
Kidderminster *p265* 01562 820181

Burton, P (Frettens Solicitors) *J1*
Christchurch *p194* 01202 491777

Burton, P D (Chester & District Housing Trust)
Chester *p454* 01244 305475

Burton, P H (Bullivant & Partners) *G H Zl*
London EC4 *p16*. 020 7332 8250
Lambeth *p90*. 020 7326 7460

Burton, P K (Rice-Jones & Smiths) *L O S2 K3 K1 W*
London EC1 *p72*. 020 7831 2506

Burton, Ms R (Hibberts LLP) *F1 Q W*
Crewe *p203* 01270 215117

Burton, R H (Fairbairn Smith & Co) *S1 S2*
London N17 *p30*. 020 8808 4901

Burton, R J (Hereford Magistrates Court)
Hereford *p460* 01562 514000

Burton, Miss S (Waltons & Morse LLP) *O Za Zj*
London EC3 *p90*. 020 7623 4255

Burton, Ms S C (Hammill Burton Lloyd) *K1 K2*
Kew *p265* 020 8392 6392

Burton, Miss S C N (Jacobs Solicitors) *S1 W L E R1*
Ellesmere Port *p217*. 0151 355 8481

Burton, S J (T G Baynes) *C1 E J1 L C2 R1 R2*
Dartford *p207* 01322 295555

Burton, S P (Squire Sanders (UK) LLP) *Zw Zq Zr*
London EC2 *p81*. 020 7655 1000

Burton, T H (Barber Young Burton & Rind) *K1 S1 S2 W K3*
Westminster *p9* 020 3376 6706

Burton, T J (Pinsent Masons LLP) *Zj*
London EC2 *p67*. 020 7418 7000

Burton, T M (Brabners Chaffe Street) *C1 C2*
Manchester *p301* 0161 836 8800

Burton-Baddeley, I D (Longlands Solicitors) *A1 C1 E F1 K1 L M1 P S1*
Warrington *p422*. 01925 634277

Burton-Howell, Mrs S L (Ieuan Morris & Co) *K1 L N Q S1 V W*
Llandovery *p291*. . .01550 720300 / 720780

Burtwell, D P (Murrays Partnership) *G H*
Southwark *p62*. 020 7701 8653

Bury, C R J (Haworth & Nuttall) *B1 C1 O*
Blackburn *p145* 01254 272640

Bury, Miss J J (Driver Belcher Solicitors) *K1 N Q J1 L F1*
Southampton *p385*. 01489 785737

Bury, J P (The Endeavour Partnership LLP)
Stockton-on-Tees *p397* . . . 01642 610300

Bury, P (KJD)
Stoke-on-Trent *p398*. 01782 202020

Busato, Miss C M (Reed Smith LLP) *C2 C1*
London EC2 *p71*. 020 3116 3000

Busbridge, L B (Wrigleys Solicitors LLP) *W T2*
Leeds *p278* 0113 244 6100

Busby, Miss E (Jones Day) *O*
London EC4 *p46*. 020 7039 5959

Busby, J (Busbys Solicitors) *Q N K1 O F1 J1 L V C1 K3 A3 Zr B1 D1 D2*
Bude *p168*. 01288 359000

Busby, Mrs J A (Shell International Ltd) *E P R1 S1 L*
London SE1 *p109* 020 7934 1234

Busby, Miss L M (Paris Smith LLP) *E S2*
Southampton *p386*. 023 8048 2482

Busby, M (Penningtons) *E*
Godalming *p231* 01483 791800

Busby, Miss S M (Bemrose & Ling) *K1 K3*
Derby *p208* 01332 347300

Buscall, Miss A E (Allen & Overy LLP)
London E1 *p5* 020 3088 0000

Buscombe, R (Thompson & Jackson) *Q N O J1 F1*
Plymouth *p350*. . . .01752 665037 / 221171

Busfield, J (IBB Solicitors) *E S2*
Uxbridge *p417* 0845 638 1381

Bush, G (Marsons Solicitors LLP) *S2 E*
Bromley *p166* 020 8313 1300
Croydon *p205* 020 8686 5000

Bush, Miss J A (Clifford Chance)
London E14 *p20*. 020 7006 1000

Bush, Mrs J M (Ellesmere Port & Neston Borough Council) *K1 M1 F1 G H P*
Ellesmere Port *p458* 0151 356 6789

Bush, M (Plexus Law (A Trading Name of Parabis Law LLP)) *G*
London EC3 *p68*. 0844 245 4000

Bush, M E (Henry Hyams) *S1 E G Q W L V*
Leeds *p274* 0113 243 2288

Bushaway, Ms L L (Teacher Stern LLP) *L*
London WC1 *p86* 020 7242 3191

Bushby, Mrs K (Clark Willis) *L*
Darlington *p206* 01325 281111

Bushell, A (Plexus Law (A Trading Name of Parabis Law LLP)) *Zj N Zr*
Evesham *p220*. 01386 769160
London EC2 *p68*. 020 7763 6103

Bushell, B (R J Osborne & Co) *G H*
Corby *p199* 01536 204111

Bushell, D T (Brown Turner Ross) *G B1 C1 H K1 L M1 N P J1*
Southport *p388* 01704 542002

Bushell, Ms S C (Hague Lambert) *S1 W*
Macclesfield *p297* 01625 616480
Macclesfield *p297* 01625 431111

Bushell, Miss S J (Brown Turner Ross) *K1 L*
Southport *p388* 01704 542002

Bushell, S J (Herbert Smith LLP) *O B1 B2*
London EC2 *p40*. 020 7374 8000

Bushner, D (Ashurst LLP)
London EC2 *p7* 020 7638 1111

Bushner, D (Jones Day) *C1*
London EC4 *p46*. 020 7039 5959

Busk, C E (Department for Business, Enterprise and Regulatory Reform)
London SW1 *p105*. 020 7215 0105

Buss, C T (Watson Farley & Williams)
London EC2 *p90*. 020 7814 8000

Bussell, Ms J M (LG Lawyers)
London SE1 *p50*. 020 7379 0000

Bussell, Ms K L (Nash & Co Solicitors LLP) *J1*
Plymouth *p350*. 01752 664444

Bussell, R (Linklaters LLP)
London EC2 *p54*. 020 7456 2000

Bussell, R (Sills & Betteridge LLP) *K4 W T2 T1*
Lincoln *p285*. 01522 542211

Busst, Ms C L (Coffin Mew & Clover) *D1 G H K1*
Fareham *p223* 01329 825617
Portsmouth *p354*. 023 9238 8021

Bussy, A C W (Stevens & Bolton) *S1 W E*
Guildford *p237*. 01483 302264

Buston, R T D (Asher Prior Bates) *S1 E A1 L W Zc Zd S2 R2*
Colchester *p197* 01206 573089

Bustos Molinero, Mrs S (EMW) *C1 E M2 O Q R1 S1 T2 W S2 K3 Zi K1 J1*
London WC2 *p28* 0845 070 6000

Buswell, Miss K H (Hughes Paddison) *K3 K1 K2*
Cheltenham *p188* 01242 574244

Butchart, Ms J P (Barlow Lyde & Gilbert LLP) *N Q*
Manchester *p301* 0161 829 6400

Butcher, C N (Michelmores LLP) *W Zx T2*
Exeter *p221* 01392 688688

Butcher, D A (Goad & Butcher) *S1 W A1 E Zd*
Settle *p374* 01729 823500

Butcher, J (Manches LLP) *C1 Zb*
London WC2 *p58* 020 7404 4433

Butcher, J E F (Barker Son & Isherwood LLP) *W Zv K4 Zm Zo T2 V*
Andover *p118* 01264 353411

Butcher, MIss J R (Stockton-On-Tees Borough Council)
Stockton-on-Tees *p472* . . . 01642 393939

Butcher, Miss L (Elliot Mather LLP) *K1 K3 D1*
Chesterfield *p192* 01246 231288

Butcher, Mrs M (Wace Morgan) *D1 K1 D2 K3*
Shrewsbury *p379* 01743 280100

Butcher, N (Hansells) *Q Zl F1 J1 L N*
Norwich *p334* 01603 615731

Butcher, N J (DAC Beachcroft) *N O Q Zj*
Bristol *p162* 0117 918 2000

Butcher, T (CMS Cameron McKenna LLP)
London EC3 *p17*. 020 7367 3000

Butcher, T C (Hewetts) *S1*
Reading *p361* 0118 957 5337

Butcher, T G (Charles Russell LLP) *O A3 Zj*
London EC4 *p19*. 020 7203 5000

Butcher, T M (Wilkin Chapman Epton Blades) *N*
Lincoln *p285*. 01522 512345

Butcher, W (Chelmsford Borough Council)
Chelmsford *p454*. 01245 606606

Butera, G (Nabarro LLP)
London WC1 *p63* 020 7524 6000

Buthee, A E (Alan Buthee & Co) *C1 C2 O S1 K1*
Northampton *p331*. 01604 622301

Butler, A (Torbay Council)
Torquay *p474* 01803 201201

Butler, A H (Worthingtons) *C1 S1 W*
Folkestone *p227*. 01303 850206

Butler, A J (Simmons & Simmons)
London EC2 *p79*. 020 7628 2020

Butler, A J (Greene & Greene) *W Zd T2 X*
Bury St Edmunds *p171* . . . 01284 762211
Cambridge *p176*. 01223 423444
Cambridge *p176*. 01223 411421

Butler, A P (Winder Taylor Fallows) *E S2*
Bolton *p150* 01204 498970

Butler, Mrs C (Paul Davidson Taylor) *O C1 B1 F1 Zc Zl*
Horsham *p253*. 01403 262333

Butler, C (RAC Motoring Services) *N*
Bristol *p452* 0870 553 3533

Butler, C I (Speechly Bircham LLP) *K1 K2 T2*
London EC4 *p81*. 020 7427 6400

Butler, C M L P (Kidd Rapinet) *K1 Q O D1*
London WC2 *p49* 020 7205 2115

Butler, Ms D C (Blocks) *K3 K1*
Ipswich *p262*. 01473 230033

Butler, Ms G A (Burtonwoods) *D2 K1*
London WC1 *p16* 020 7636 2448

Butler, H J (Jolliffe & Co) *W T2*
Chester *p190* 01244 310022

Butler, I A (Hanne & Co) *Zh L*
London SW11 *p38*. 020 7228 0017

Butler, I R (Butler Hall & Co) *S1 C1 L E S2 W*
Birmingham *p136* 0121 456 3171

Butler, J (Geldards LLP)
Derby *p208* 01332 331631

Butler, J J F (Howard Kennedy LLP) *E P Zc*
London W1 *p48* 020 7636 1616

Butler, Ms J L (The Stokes Partnership) *D1 G H Zi*
Crewkerne *p203* 01460 279279

Butler, J M (Gaskell & Walker) *G H Zl*
Bridgend *p157*. 01656 653122

Butler, K (Marchant Harries & Co) *S1 L W P E A1 Zh*
Aberdare *p113*. 01685 885500

Butler, Ms K B (Olswang LLP) *T1 T2*
London WC1 *p64* 020 7067 3000

Butler, Ms M (Fellowes Solicitors) *S1 S2 W Zl K4*
London E17 *p31* 020 8520 7392

Butler, M G (Geldards LLP) *J1*
Nottingham *p337*. 0115 983 3650

Butler, M J R (Malcolm Butler & Co) *B1 C1 Q*
Maidstone *p299* 01622 749596

Butler, Miss M S (Bell & Buxton) *W T1*
Sheffield *p375* 0114 249 5969

Butler, P (Knight Polson Solicitors) *G H Zm*
Eastleigh *p216*. 023 8064 4822

Butler, P J (GHP Legal) *C1 O P M1 Q N F1 B1*
Wrexham *p442* 01978 291456

Butler, P M (DLA Piper UK LLP) *Zb*
London EC2 *p24*. 0870 011 1111

Butler, P R (Penman Johnson) *E C1 C2 P*
Watford *p424* . . . .01923 225212 / 239566

Butler, Q H (SGH Martineau LLP) *E A1*
Birmingham *p142* 0870 763 2000

Butler, Ms R (Globecast Northern Europe Ltd)
London WC1 *p106*. 020 7430 4400

Butler, Mrs R (Morgans) *V L*
Cardiff *p180* 029 2072 9888

Butler, R A S (Stone King LLP) *C2 C1 I C3*
Bath *p128* 01225 337599

Butler, R G (Max Bitel Greene LLP) *S1 L W E*
Islington *p59*. 020 7354 2767

Butler, R J O (AWB Partnership LLP) *S1 W L E*
Guildford *p235*. 01483 302345

Butler, Dr S C (Butler & Co) *C1 Ze*
Oakham *p340* 01572 737740

Butler, S M (Butler & Kandler) *K1 D2 S1 W Zi Zl K4 K3*
Ilkley *p261*. 01943 816207

Butler, T J (The National Trust) *E Zc*
Swindon *p475* 01793 817400

Butler, W J (Philcox Gray & Co) *S1 L N W*
London SE15 *p67* 020 7703 2285

Butler, Miss Z M (Bristows) *O C1 Ze*
London EC4 *p15*. 020 7400 8000

Butler-Hunter, Ms C (Birmingham City Council Legal & Democratic Services)
Birmingham *p449* 0121 303 2066

Butler-Smith, Ms B C (Callaghans) *W*
Farnham *p224*. 01252 723477

Butler-Smith, Ms L J (Barlow Lyde & Gilbert LLP) *Zj*
London EC3 *p10*. 020 7247 2277

Butson, M T (T C Smith) *G H J1 N O Zl Q Zq W S1*
Berwick-upon-Tweed *p131*. . 01289 307409

Butt, A (Keoghs LLP) *N Zj O Q*
Bolton *p149* 01204 677000

Butt, Mrs F (Ross & Craig) *J1 Zk O Q N*
Westminster *p73*. 020 7262 3077

Butt, Mrs F (HC Solicitors LLP) *K1 K2 K3 D2*
Peterborough *p347* 01733 882800

Butt, Miss F (A H Page) *S1 S2 E L Q Zl K1 K3*
Ilford *p260*. 020 8554 1985

Butt, F A (Hadfields Butt & Bowyer) *C1 E W S1 L R1 Zl Zm Zv S2*
Farnham *p225*. 01252 716101

Butt, Miss J L (Sharp & Partners) *K1 V D2 D1*
Nottingham *p339*. 0115 959 0055

Butt, N P (Windeatts) *F1 G H N J1 Q*
Totnes *p413* 01803 862233

Butt, Mrs R (Raworths LLP) *J1*
Harrogate *p240* 01423 566666

Butt, Miss S A (Addleshaw Goddard) *F1 L O Zb*
Leeds *p271* 0113 209 2000

Butt, Ms Y M (J A Forrest & Co) *S1 S2 K1 W Zl*
Westminster *p33*. 020 7233 9140

Butt, Ms Z (Edwin Coe LLP) *O Q C3*
London WC2 *p29* 020 7691 4000

Buttaci, Ms G (Guillaumes Solicitors) *W T2 Zm*
Weybridge *p430*. 01932 840111

Butter, Miss S A (Graham Withers & Co) *A1 W T2 S1 Zm*
Market Drayton *p312*. 01630 657222

Butterfield, Mrs A K (Rochdale Metropolitan Borough Council)
Rochdale *p470*. 01706 647474

Butterfield, A R (Walters & Barbary) *S1 W A1 L T1 C1 Zd Zh*
Camborne *p173* 01209 712454

Butterfield, Ms C (HMG Law LLP) *W K4 T2 Zf*
Oxford *p343*. 01865 244661

Butterfield, G (Wills Group Ltd)
London EC3 *p110* 020 7488 8111

Butterfield, P (Gepp & Sons) *G H B2*
Chelmsford *p186*. 01245 493939
Colchester *p197*. 01206 369889

See p634 for the Key to Work Categories

Butterfield, Miss R (Blackhurst Swainson Goodier LLP) *K3 K1*
Lancaster *p269* 01524 32471

Butterfint, Ms L (Wilkin Chapman LLP) *E N Q S1 T2 W*
Beverley *p131* 01482 398398

Butters, Mrs J (Hastings Borough Council)
Hastings *p460* 01424 781066

Butters, J A W (Butters David Grey & Co) *A1 A3 C3 D2 F1 J1 S1 S2*
Hastings *p243* . . . .01424 424949 / 715171

Butters, J S (Clifford Chance)
London E14 *p20* 020 7006 1000

Butterworth, Miss A (Stafford Young Jones) *K3 K1 K2 Q J1 O D1*
London EC4 *p82* 020 7623 9490

Butterworth, A M (Butterworths) *M1 J1 G*
Carlisle *p182* 01228 593939

Butterworth, C J (Raworths LLP) *C1 A3*
Harrogate *p240* 01423 566666

Butterworth, Mrs F A (Scotts Wright) *K1 W K3 S1*
Leyburn *p283* 01966 22227

Butterworth, I (Andrew Jackson) *Za*
Hull *p257* 01482 325242

Butterworth, Mrs J G (J G Butterworth) *S1 E K1 P D1 G W F1 Zs Zl*
Mold *p318* 07984 167453

Butterworth, M C (DAC Beachcroft) *N P J1 Zj Zc*
London EC4 *p24* 020 7936 2222

Butterworth, R H (Bird & Bird LLP) *C1 C2*
London EC4 *p13* 020 7415 6000

Butterworth, Ms S (Squire Sanders (UK) LLP)
London EC2 *p81* 020 7655 1000

Buttle, L (Ranson Houghton) *T2 W*
Andover *p118* 01264 351533

Buttle, R A (Swiss Re Life & Health Ltd)
London EC3 *p109* 020 7933 3000

Buttleman, Ms S A (Bankside Commercial Solicitors) *E A1 L R1*
Southwark *p9* 020 7654 0200

Button, Ms F (Michelmores LLP) *Zc*
Exeter *p221* 01392 688688
London EC2 *p67* 020 7418 7000

Button, J T H (James Button & Co) *Zy Zu Zza J2 Zg Zl*
Matlock *p313* 01629 735566

Button, R N (Button Legal LLP) *C1 E F1 K1 L S1 W*
Coventry *p200* 024 7652 5457

Buttress, Mrs A D (Massucco Buttress) *S1*
Cambridge *p175* 01223 463183

Buttress, Ms C (Gepp & Sons) *W K4*
Chelmsford *p186* 01245 493939
Colchester *p197* 01206 369889

Buttrey, Miss K (Edwards Angell Palmer & Dodge)
London EC2 *p28* 020 7583 4055

Butwick, J (Dechert) *J1*
London EC4 *p26* 020 7184 7000

Buxton, Mrs C J (Blocks) *S1*
Ipswich *p262* 01473 230033

Buxton, E (Shell International Ltd)
London SE1 *p109* 020 7934 1234

Buxton, E (Taylor Wessing)
London EC4 *p86* 020 7300 7000

Buxton, J A (Stapleton & Son) *E C1 L S2 Q S1 J1 O G K1 Zd K4 X*
Stamford *p393* 01780 751226

Buxton, Mrs M E (Hedges) *S1 W*
Didcot *p210* 01235 811888

Buxton, R M (Richard Buxton) *P O R1 M1 Zn Zg M2 Q*
Cambridge *p174* 01223 328933

Buxton, Miss S (McAras Solicitors LLP) *K1 K3*
Leeds *p275* 0113 243 4333

Buys, B (Gartmore Investment Management PLC)
London EC3 *p106* 020 7782 2000

Buys, P (Park Woodfine Heald Mellows LLP) *S2 E*
Northampton *p332* 01604 233200

Buysman, Mrs E L (Philip Ross & Co) *S1 R2*
London W1 *p73* 020 7636 6969

Buzzard, N (The College of Law Chester)
Chester *p454* 0800 289997

Buzzard, Ms R (Russell Jones & Walker) *J1*
Newcastle upon Tyne *p326* . 0191 323 3000

Buzzoni, M (Taylor Wessing)
London EC4 *p86* 020 7300 7000

Bvunzawabaya, R (RBM Solicitors) *J1 Zi*
Coventry *p201* 024 7652 0999

Byam-Cook, D W (Bird & Bird LLP) *B1 C1 C2*
London EC4 *p13* 020 7415 6000

Byam-Cook, Mrs P M (Perry Hay & Co) *W T2 Zm K4*
Richmond upon Thames *p364* 020 8940 8115 / 8332 7532

Byard, Miss L (Woodfines LLP) *C1 J1 O*
Bedford *p130* 01234 270600

Byard, R S (Cripps Harries Hall LLP) *O J1 Q B1 Zp*
Tunbridge Wells *p415* 01892 515121

Byatt, Mrs H E (Jeffrey Mills) *K1 D1*
St Neots *p392* . . . .01480 475871 / 219699

Bye, B (Harbottle & Lewis LLP) *C1 Ze Zf Zw*
London W1 *p38* 020 7667 5000

Byers, Mrs L (Brachers) *Q N L F1 O Zq*
Maidstone *p299* 01622 690691

Byfield, P G (Coffin Mew & Clover) *L O Q*
Southampton *p385* 023 8033 4661

Byford, Ms A (Faegre & Benson LLP)
London EC4 *p30* 020 7450 4500

Byford, C K (Chennells) *N O E Q S2*
Westcliff-on-Sea *p428* . . . .01702 349971 / 352195

Byford, Ms J E (SGH Martineau LLP) *J1 Zp*
Birmingham *p142* 0870 763 2000

Bylett, Miss L (Rawlison Butler LLP) *O*
Crawley *p202* 01293 527744

Byne, J C (Bynes) *S1 S2 W K4 Zl E R1 Zc R2*
Torquay *p412* 01803 295692

Byne, M H (Martin Byne) *L T1 T2*
Bristol *p161* 0117 973 1019

Byng Nelson, R A (Pothecary Witham Weld) *Zd*
Westminster *p69* 020 7821 8211

Bynoe, R W (Charles Russell LLP) *C1 C3 Ze Zf I*
London EC4 *p19* 020 7203 5000

Byram, T S (Cyril Jones & Co) *D1 F1 G H K1 L N Q V S1*
Shotton *p379* 01244 812109

Byrka, Ms M (Anthony Gold) *O*
London SE1 *p6* 020 7940 4000

Byrne, Mrs A A (Perrins Solicitors LLP) *Zh L*
Harpenden *p239* 01582 466140

Byrne, Mrs A D (Linklaters LLP) *E*
London EC2 *p54* 020 7456 2000

Byrne, D J (Scott Rees & Co) *Q N*
Skelmersdale *p381* 01695 722222

Byrne, D K (Byrne & Partners)
London EC4 *p16* 020 7842 1616

Byrne, Mrs E J (Eaton Smith LLP) *W*
Huddersfield *p255* 01484 821300

Byrne, J G (Healds) *C1 E S1 W S2 Zl*
Wigan *p432* 01942 241511

Byrne, J J J (GLP Solicitors) *K1 Q N F1 G H J1 L O*
Manchester *p304* 0161 793 0901

Byrne, Ms J K (Squire Sanders (UK) LLP)
Manchester *p310* 0161 830 5000

Byrne, J O G (Freeth Cartwright LLP) *B1*
Manchester *p304* 0845 634 2540

Byrne, J R (Dorsey & Whitney)
London EC2 *p27* 020 7588 0800

Byrne, L J (Linder Myers Solicitors) *S1 S2*
Manchester *p307* 0844 984 6400

Byrne, Ms M (Squire Sanders (UK) LLP)
London EC2 *p81* 020 7655 1000

Byrne, Miss M A (Leeds City Council) *K1 D1 G H L F1 V*
Leeds *p462* 0113 224 3513

Byrne, P (Clarion Solicitors LLP) *G H B2*
Leeds *p272* 0113 246 0622

Byrne, P K (ClarksLegal LLP) *C1 U1*
Reading *p360* 0118 958 5321

Byrne, R (Brecher) *Zb E*
London W1 *p15* 020 7563 1000

Byrne, S G (Bank of Cyprus UK)
London N14 *p104* 020 8267 7331

Byrne, S H (Thames Water Utilities Limited) *O Q F1 N*
Reading *p469* 0118 373 8000

Byrne, S P (Varley Hibbs LLP) *B1 C1 I M1 Ze*
Coventry *p201* 024 7663 1000

Byrne-Hill, D (Herbert Smith LLP)
London EC2 *p40* 020 7374 8000

Byrnes, Ms N R (E J Moyle) *D1 K3 K1*
Littlehampton *p285* 01903 725143

Byrom, E M (Butcher & Barlow LLP) *W S2 E S1 K4*
Bury *p170* 0161 764 4062

Byrom, Ms S J (Congleton Borough Council) *G H*
Sandbach *p470* 01270 763231

Byrt, Miss S M (Mayer Brown International LLP) *Zc Ze I U2 Zz Zk*
London EC2 *p59* 020 3130 3000

Bysouth, T J (Kenyon Son & Craddock) *S1 W L F1 E R1*
Doncaster *p212* 01405 813108

Bysshe, P J S (Kidd Rapinet) *K1 J1 W K4 S1 E S2*
High Wycombe *p250* 0845 017 9607

Bywater, C L (Lennox Bywater) *C1 M1 C3 M2 C2 Zw Zy*
London NW7 *p53* 020 8906 1206

Bywater, K (Environment Agency (Anglian Region))
Peterborough *p468* 01733 371811

Bywater, Ms M J (Donald Galbraith & Co) *D1 K3 K1*
London N12 *p34* 020 8492 2700

Bywater, R J (Dawson Cornwell) *K3 K1 D1*
London WC1 *p26* 020 7242 2556

Bzowska, Miss M E (Capsticks Solicitors LLP) *C1 Zd Ze M1 E*
London SW19 *p18* 020 8780 2211

C

Cabatbat, Ms L S (Douglass Simon) *K1 D1 Zi*
Brentford *p156* 020 8560 3888

Cabot, Mrs J (Bircham Dyson Bell)
Westminster *p13* 020 7227 7000

Cadbury, Mrs J A (Davisons) *K4 T2 W F1 K1 L P S1*
Birmingham *p137* 0121 685 1248

Caddick, P J (Challinors) *M1 P N K1 J1 B1 C1 D1 F1*
Wolverhampton *p437* 01902 428121

Caddies, A J (Hill Dickinson LLP) *B1 J1 M1 N P Zp*
London EC3 *p41* 020 7283 9033

Caddle, Miss V J (Muckle LLP) *O Q Zq B1 Zk*
Newcastle upon Tyne *p325* . 0191 211 7777

Caddoo, Mrs J H (Rollasons) *W*
Daventry *p207* 01327 301771

Caddy, P S (Laytons) *C1 C2*
Manchester *p306* 0161 834 2100

Cade, Ms N V (Hansen Palomares) *L V*
Lambeth *p38* 020 7640 4600

Cadenhead, S D (Newport City Council)
Newport *p466* 01633 656656

Cadman, Mrs L V (Nyland & Beattie) *K1 D1*
Widnes *p432* 0151 424 5656
Wigan *p432* 01942 244294

Cadman, P H (Russell-Cooke LLP) *G H Zw*
London WC1 *p74* 020 7405 6566

Cadman, T H (Pothecary Witham Weld) *Zd E S2 C1*
Westminster *p69* 020 7821 8211

Cadwallader, D H (DLA Piper UK LLP) *C1 C2 Zw*
Liverpool *p287* 0870 011 1111

Cadywould, A (Ince & Co Services Ltd)
London E1 *p44* 020 7481 0010

Cagney, C (Barnes Marsland) *L N O Q*
Margate *p312* 01843 221466

Cahill, Miss D (Stephens & Scown) *K1 D1*
St Austell *p391* 01726 74433

Cahill, J D (Stewarts Law LLP) *N Zr A3*
London EC4 *p83* 020 7822 8000

Cahill, M P (Clifford Chance)
London E14 *p20* 020 7006 1000

Cahill, Ms M T P (Baileys) *S1 W*
Cheltenham *p187* 01242 514477

Cain, B N (Reed Smith LLP)
London EC2 *p71* 020 3116 3000

Cain, Ms D (Adams & Remers) *O F1 Ze Zq Zl*
Lewes *p283* 01273 480616

Cain, L (Prettys) *S2 E S1*
Ipswich *p262* 01473 232121

Cain, M (Wiggin Osborne Fullerlove) *T1 T2 Zj Zo W*
Cheltenham *p189* 01242 710200
London SW1 *p91* 020 7290 2456

Cain, M F (Brockbank Curwen Cain & Hall) *S1 P K1 F1 D1 L M1 W J1*
Maryport *p313* 01900 813488

Cain, P A (Norton & Co) *N Zr Q Zq Zk*
Prescot *p356* 0151 426 7001

Caine, Ms E S (Radcliffes Le Brasseur) *N Q*
Westminster *p70* 020 7222 7040

Caines, Miss J (Emsleys) *K1 K3 D1 Zh L*
Crossgates *p204* 0113 260 3115

Cains, Miss R S (Wace Morgan) *K1 D1*
Shrewsbury *p379* 01743 280100

Cairaschi, P J J (Portner & Jaskel LLP) *N F1*
London W1 *p68* 020 7616 5300

Caird, Mrs J (Aon Ltd)
London EC2 *p103* 020 7623 5500

Cairns, Ms A (Edwards Angell Palmer & Dodge)
London EC2 *p28* 020 7583 4055

Cairns, C T (McKeag & Co) *W T1 S1*
Gosforth *p231* 0191 213 1010

Cairns, Ms E (Thomson Snell & Passmore) *Zd*
Tunbridge Wells *p415* 01892 510000

Cairns, M D (Rickards & Cleaver) *G K1 S1 N H F1 O E Q J1 Zl L S2 V Zr*
Alfreton *p115* 01773 832204

Cairns, P (Harbottle & Lewis LLP)
London W1 *p38* 020 7667 5000

Cairns, S J (Murray Cairns & Co) *D1 G H J1 K1*
Wellington *p425* 01952 261650

Caisley, A G (Keogh Caisley) *S1 S2 E W*
Tunbridge Wells *p415* 01892 548411

Caisley, C S (Walker Morris) *O*
Leeds *p277* 0113 283 2500

Caisley, L (Hogan Lovells International LLP)
London EC1 *p42* 020 7296 2000

Caisley, L A (Patterson Glenton & Stracey) *S2 S1 E W Q K1 O R2 C1 J1 Zi Zg*
Newcastle upon Tyne *p326* . 0191 232 8628

Cake, Miss C L (Quality Solicitors D'Angibau) *W*
Poole *p353* 01202 708634

Cake, R W A (Dickinson Manser) *S1 C1 E*
Poole *p352* 01202 673071

Cakebread, Mrs M E (Knowles Benning) *K1 N Q S1 G H L F1 W*
Shefford *p377* 01462 814824

Calcara, Ms V (Davenport Lyons) *T1 T2 Zo*
London W1 *p25* 020 7468 2600

Caldecott, T H (Dixon Rigby Keogh) *J1 S1 W K4*
Winsford *p434* 01606 557211

Caldecourt, P (B P Collins LLP) *K1*
Gerrards Cross *p229* 01753 889995

Calder, C A (Freemans) *Zr N Q*
Newcastle upon Tyne *p324* . 0191 222 1030

Calder, K E (Mills & Reeve) *I C1 U1 O Ze Zz*
Cambridge *p175* 01223 364422

Calder, Miss P H (Parlby Calder Solicitors) *G H*
Plymouth *p350* 01752 600833

Calder, Mrs R E (Cambridge City Council)
Cambridge *p452* 01223 457000

Caldera, Ms D (Civil Aviation Authority) *O*
London WC2 *p105* 020 7453 6162

Calderbank, G D (Senior Calveley & Hardy) *S1 E L A1 Zc W*
Lytham *p297* 01253 733333

Calderbank, Ms J (Aviva PLC)
London EC3 *p103* . . 020 7283 7500 / 01603 687905
Norwich *p467* 01603 622200

Calderbank, J R (James Calderbank) *G H Zm*
Cullompton *p205* 01823 680697

Calderwood, A J (Herbert Smith LLP) *C1 M2 Zb*
London EC2 *p40* 020 7374 8000

Calderwood, G D (DB Law) *G K1 H E D1 S1 F1 T1 T2 Zl A1 J1 L*
St Ives *p392* 01736 793883
Penzance *p346* 01736 364261

Calderwood, Ms L (Maxwell Winward LLP) *Zc*
London EC4 *p59* 020 7651 0000

Calderwood, T (Ralph & Co) *N*
Newquay *p329* 01637 872218

Caldicott, A (Harrison Clark LLP) *K1 D1*
Cheltenham *p188* 01242 269198
Worcester *p439* 01905 612001
Worcester *p439* 01905 612001

Caldicott, Mrs R M (Caldicott Gallimore) *S1 E Q O L K1 G J1 D1 Zl*
Leominster *p282* 01568 614168

Caldwell, A (Stevens) *Zl G H*
Saffron Walden *p370* 01799 526849

Caldwell, Ms D K A (Manches LLP) *E*
Oxford *p343* 01865 722106

Caldwell, Miss E (Bracher Rawlins LLP) *C1 C2 C3 F1 Ze*
London WC1 *p15* 020 7404 9400

Caley, Mrs A R (Chapple & Co) *K1 N Q L F1 S1 W J1 V*
March *p312* 01354 652550

Caley, Miss P C F (Barrington & Sons) *F1 S1 J1 K1 L N P W*
Burnham-on-Sea *p169* 01278 782371

Caley, R D (Kerwoods) *E S1 G S2 W*
Redditch *p362* 01527 584444

Calladine, P (Freeth Cartwright LLP)
Manchester *p304* 0845 634 2540

Calladine, P G (Lex Transfleet Ltd) *E C1 Zn R1 Q Zt Zo U2 J1 F1*
Coventry *p456* 024 7669 4494

Callaghan, Ms A (Hempsons) *Zr*
Manchester *p305* 0161 228 0011

Callaghan, E J (Mills & Reeve) *O P Zb Zc*
Cambridge *p175* 01223 364422

Callaghan, Ms L M (MWP Solicitors) *Q N O J1 L*
Basildon *p126* 01268 527131

Callaghan, P A (Taylor Wessing)
London EC4 *p86* 020 7300 7000

Callaghan, P M (Callaghan & Co) *S1 S2 W E C1 L Zl B1*
Westminster *p17* 020 7486 8173

Callaghan, S M (BTMK Solicitors LLP) *N Q*
Southend-on-Sea *p387* . . . 01702 339222

Callaghan, T E (Edward Harte LLP) *W*
Brighton *p159* 01273 662750

Callaway, Miss M (Glanvilles) *W K4 T2*
Havant *p244* 023 9249 2300

Callegari, P (K&L Gates LLP) *J1 O Q Ze*
London EC4 *p47* 020 7648 9000

Calleja, Ms M (The College of Law)
London WC1 *p105* 0800 289997

Caller, R A (Gillhams Solicitors LLP) *S1 E C1 W N J1 C2 S2*
London NW10 *p35* 020 8965 4266

Calligan, D A (SJ Berwin LLP)
London EC4 *p75* 020 7111 2222

Calligas, Ms L (DWFM Beckman) *Q W A3*
Westminster *p25* 020 7872 0023

Calliste, Ms G (Lexica Law) *E S1*
Canterbury *p177* 01227 764141

Callow, Ms F M (Eatons) *D1 D2*
Bradford *p153* 0845 660 0660
Bradford *p155* 01274 305380

Calloway, T (KJD)
Stoke-on-Trent *p398* 01782 202020

Callum, A J (Financial Services Authority)
London E14 *p106* 020 7066 1000

Calman, Miss E J (Edward Pilling & Co)
Oxford *p344* 01865 741122

Calnan, Miss D M (BCL Burton Copeland) *B2 G*
London WC2 *p9* 020 7430 2277

Calnan, Mrs J M (Birkett Long LLP) *E L S2 R2*
Colchester *p197* 01206 217300

Calnan, S C (Christopher Cox Solicitors) *C1 Zy Zza U2*
Northampton *p331* 01604 882287

Calow, D (DLA Piper UK LLP) *E F1*
London EC2 *p24* 0870 011 1111

Calow, D F (Squire Sanders (UK) LLP) *A1 B1 C1 E F1 J1 R1 S1 T1 W Zc Zd Ze*
London EC2 *p81* 020 7655 1000

Calthrop, J F G (Marchants Solicitors)
Mansfield *p312* 01623 655111

Calthrop-Owen, Mrs N M (Actons) *B1 O*
Nottingham *p335* 0115 910 0200

Calthrop-Owen, Miss S I (Morrisons Solicitors LLP) *K1 D1 K3 K2*
Redhill *p362* 01737 854500

Calver, Ms C L (Allen & Overy LLP)
London E1 *p5* 020 3088 0000

Calver, J B (John B Calver & Co)
Westminster *p17* 020 7221 9181

Calverley, J (Edwin Coe LLP) *B1 O*
London WC2 *p29* 020 7691 4000

Calverley, M J B (Bevan Brittan LLP) *S2 E R2*
Bristol *p161* 0870 194 1000

Calvert, G P (Dickinson Dees) *J1*
Newcastle upon Tyne *p324* . 0191 279 9000

Calvert, Mrs J A (Widdows Mason) *S1 W*
Leigh *p282* 01942 673311

Calvert, R (Sharp & Partners) *S1 E M1 P W G H K1 L D1 Zc Zl Zn*
Nottingham *p339* 0115 959 0055

Calvy, Miss M B (Archers Solicitors)
Chelmsford *p186* 01245 216888

Calway, Ms Z F (Cartmell Shepherd) *W*
Penrith *p346* 01768 862326

6

Calzolari, R (Roberts McCracken) *N L Q O B1 K1 J1 G*
Brent *p72* 0870 420 5658

Cambridge, D (Harrison Clark LLP)
Cheltenham *p188* 01242 269198
Worcester *p439* 01905 612001
Worcester *p439* 01905 612001

Cambridge, E (Watson Burton LLP) *E J2 Zl Q N Zo S1*
Newcastle upon Tyne *p327* . 0845 901 2100

Cambridge, Ms S M (Kenneth Bush) *B1 C1 F1 L O Q Zc*
King's Lynn *p266* 01553 692737

Came, R H (Havering Magistrates' Court)
Romford *p470* 0845 601 3600

Cameron, Miss A (Horwich Cohen Coghlan) *N*
Manchester *p305* 0161 830 4600

Cameron, A J (Turbervilles) *C1 K1 L M1 N P W*
Uxbridge *p417* 01895 201700
Uxbridge *p417* 01895 201700

Cameron, A W (Charles Russell LLP) *W T2 Zd*
London EC4 *p19* 020 7203 5000

Cameron, Miss C A (Henmans LLP) *Zr*
Oxford *p343* 01865 781000

Cameron, D (Wayne Leighton)
Edgware *p217* 020 8951 2988

Cameron, I S (Squire Sanders (UK) LLP)
Leeds *p277* 0113 284 7000

Cameron, J (DLA Piper UK LLP)
London EC2 *p24* 0870 011 1111

Cameron, Mrs J (Beers LLP) *J1 E C1 Zb S2 O Q C2*
Kingsbridge *p267* 01548 857000

Cameron, Mrs J (Smith & Copsey) *K1 K3 D1 L Q*
Wallsend *p419* 0191 262 4428

Cameron, J T (Shell International Ltd) *C1 Zf Zd C2 Zv U2*
London SE1 *p109* 020 7934 1234

Cameron, Mrs K (Atherton Godfrey) *Zr*
Doncaster *p211* 01302 320621

Cameron, Ms K (Blandy & Blandy) *A1 B1 C1 C3 N Q Ze Zk*
Reading *p360* 0118 951 6800

Cameron, Mrs K R (Hastings Borough Council)
Hastings *p460* 01424 781066

Cameron, T G (The Merriman Partnership) *A1 E J1 K1 L N O Q S1 W*
Marlborough *p313* 01672 512244

Camfield, P A (May May & Merrimans) *W T2*
London WC1 *p59* 020 7405 8932

Camidge, Mrs H E (Rupert Bear Murray Davies) *K1*
Nottingham *p338* 0115 924 3333

Camidge, Mrs T M (HBOS PLC)
Halifax *p460* 0870 600 5000

Cammack, D J (Birkett Long LLP) *C1 C2 C3 F1 Ze*
Colchester *p197* 01206 217300

Cammack, F (Chattertons Solicitors) *S1 A1 E C1 L R1 W T1*
Boston *p151* 01205 351114

Cammiss, P G (Adams Harrison) *G K1 N O H E F1 W L Zl Zt Zm*
Haverhill *p244* . . . .01440 705731 / 702485

Cammock, Mrs C A (Hand Morgan & Owen) *W K4*
Stafford *p393* 01785 211411

Camp, Mrs J C (Network Rail)
London NW1 *p108* 020 7557 8000

Camp, Ms M A (East Cambridgeshire District Council)
Ely *p458* 01353 665555

Camp, R M (Stephens & Scown) *S2 E*
Exeter *p222* 01392 210700

Campailla, N T (Shell International Ltd)
London SE1 *p109* 020 7934 1234

Campbell, Miss A (Watson Burton LLP)
Newcastle upon Tyne *p327* . 0845 901 2100

Campbell, A (Margraves)
Llandrindod Wells *p291* . . . 01597 825565

Campbell, Ms A C (Taylor Wessing)
London EC4 *p86* 020 7300 7000

Campbell, A L (Behr & Co) *S1 W N Q L S2 J1 V Zq B1*
Brynmawr *p167* 01495 310581

Campbell, Ms A L (Campbell Chambers) *D1 G H J1 K1 N Q Zi Zv*
London EC1 *p18* 020 7691 8777

Campbell, A M (Morgan Cole)
Oxford *p344* 01865 262600

Campbell, Ms B C (Nowell Meller Solicitors Limited) *D2 D1 K1 K3*
Stafford *p393* 01785 252377

Campbell, Ms C (Simmons & Simmons)
London EC2 *p79* 020 7628 2020

Campbell, Mrs C (PCB Solicitors LLP) *Q*
Shrewsbury *p379* 01743 248148

Campbell, C (Canter Levin & Berg)
St Helens *p391* 01744 634141

Campbell, Ms C E (Williams MacDougall & Campbell) *D1 D2 K1*
Worthing *p442* 01903 214186

Campbell, C J (Forster Dean Ltd) *N S1*
St Helens *p391* 01744 755577

Campbell, C J G (HM Land Registry - Durham (Boldon) Office) *E S1*
Durham *p457* 0191 301 2345

Campbell, C N T (Cox & Hodgetts) *Q K1 L F1 Zr Zp O*
Evesham *p220* 01386 442513

Campbell, D (FBC Manby Bowdler LLP) *O Zl J2*
Wolverhampton *p437* 01902 578000

Campbell, D (Michael Simkins LLP) *E*
London WC1 *p79* 020 7874 5600

Campbell, D (IBM United Kingdom Ltd)
London SE1 *p107* 020 7202 3000

Campbell, D A (Sansbury Douglas) *D1 G H K1 V B2*
Bristol *p164* 0117 926 5341

Campbell, D I (Sandwell Metropolitan Borough Council)
Oldbury *p468* 0121 569 2200

Campbell, D L (Malcolm McGuinness) *G H*
Altrincham *p116* 0161 928 7134

Campbell, D S (Hindle Campbell) *G H K1 P N S1 C1 F1 J1*
North Shields *p330* 0191 296 1777

Campbell, D W M (Mogers) *W T2*
Bath *p127* 01225 750000

Campbell, Ms E (Sintons LLP) *C1 I Zu*
Newcastle upon Tyne *p326* . 0191 226 7878

Campbell, Miss E J (West Midlands Police Authority)
Birmingham *p450* 0121 626 5143

Campbell, Ms G (Schneider Page) *N O Q J1*
London E1 *p77* 020 7480 5477

Campbell, G (Reynolds Porter Chamberlain LLP)
London E1 *p71* 020 3060 6000

Campbell, G P (Stephenson Harwood)
London EC2 *p82* 020 7329 4422

Campbell, G W (Australia and New Zealand Banking Group Ltd)
London E14 *p103* 020 3229 2121

Campbell, Ms H A (Dass Solicitors) *Q O Zq Zk*
Birmingham *p137* 0121 248 4000

Campbell, I (Hill Dickinson LLP) *O X J2*
Chester *p190* 01244 896600

Campbell, I C (Campbell Law Solicitors)
Milton Keynes *p316* 0845 226 8118

Campbell, I G R (Charles Hoile) *G H*
Newbury *p322* 01635 45595

Campbell, Ms I L (Dutton Gregory) *E S2 L S1*
Winchester *p433* 01962 844333

Campbell, Ms J (Ison Harrison)
Leeds *p274* 0113 232 6530

Campbell, J (Makin Dixon Solicitors) *D1 K1*
Keighley *p263* 01535 605040

Campbell, Mrs J (Veale Wasbrough Vizards) *N*
Bristol *p165* 0117 925 2020

Campbell, J (Holman Fenwick Willan)
London EC3 *p42* 020 7264 8000

Campbell, Ms J G (Aston Legal Centre)
Birmingham *p449* 0121 523 0965

Campbell, J K (Freeman Johnson) *D1 F1 G H J1 K1 L M1*
Durham *p214* . . . 0191 386 4843 / 386 9619

Campbell, J M (DAC Beachcroft) *O Q Zj*
Bristol *p162* 0117 918 2000

Campbell, J M J (Everett Tomlin Lloyd & Pratt) *K1 G H D1 N W*
Pontypool *p352* 01495 763333
Caldicot *p172* 01291 422753

Campbell, K (Chamberlain Martin Solicitors) *S1 W E L P T1 C1 C2 S2*
Bognor Regis *p148* 01243 825211

Campbell, Mrs K A (Reed Smith LLP) *N O Q*
London EC2 *p71* 020 3116 3000

Campbell, M (Clifford Chance)
London E14 *p20* 020 7006 1000

Campbell, Mrs M (Essex County Council)
Chelmsford *p454* 0845 743 0430

Campbell, Ms M A (John Farr-Davies & Co) *S1 W A1*
Carmarthen *p182* 01267 231818

Campbell, Miss M E (London Borough of Southwark)
London SE1 *p109* 020 7525 5000

Campbell, Ms M E (Reed Smith LLP) *Zj*
London EC2 *p71* 020 3116 3000

Campbell, M R (Taylor Wimpey UK Limited Legal Services) *A1 E K1 L R1 S1 W*
Milton Keynes *p466* 01908 209030

Campbell, Mrs N (Windeatts) *S1*
Totnes *p413* 01803 862233

Campbell, N (Holman Fenwick Willan)
London EC3 *p42* 020 7264 8000

Campbell, N D (Taylor Vinters) *E L P Zn*
Cambridge *p176* 01223 423444

Campbell, N D (Brabners Chaffe Street) *J1*
Liverpool *p286* 0151 600 3000

Campbell, Miss N J (Walsall Metropolitan Borough Council)
Walsall *p475* 01922 650000

Campbell, N J (NGA) *K1 D1 K3*
Colne *p198* 01282 862000
Colne *p198* 01282 868000

Campbell, P (J A Kemp & Co)
London WC1 *p48* 020 7405 3292

Campbell, P A (Hill Dickinson LLP) *M1 P G Zl Zj*
Liverpool *p288* 0151 600 8000

Campbell, P R (Druces LLP) *W T2 A1*
London EC2 *p27* 020 7638 9271

Campbell, R (Faegre & Benson LLP)
London EC4 *p30* 020 7450 4500

Campbell, R (Hart Brown Solicitors) *E S2*
Guildford *p236* 0800 068 8177

Campbell, R (Trowers & Hamlins)
London EC3 *p88* 020 7423 8000

Campbell, R A (Plymouth Justices' Clerk)
Plymouth *p468* 01752 206200

Campbell, R W (Haddock & Company) *G H D1 Zm Zl*
Halifax *p238* 01422 366010

Campbell, Ms S (Leigh Day & Co) *Zr*
London EC1 *p52* 020 7650 1200

Campbell, Ms S (Knocker & Foskett) *W V*
Sevenoaks *p374* 01732 459931

Campbell, Mrs S (Grindeys LLP) *N Q L F1*
Stoke-on-Trent *p397* 01782 846441

Campbell, S G (Taylor Wessing)
London EC4 *p86* 020 7300 7000

Campbell, Miss S H (Heringtons) *W*
Battle *p128* 01424 772401

Campbell, S J (EAD Solicitors LLP)
Liverpool *p287* 0151 291 2500

Campbell, Miss T A (Reynolds Porter Chamberlain LLP) *N Zq Q*
London E1 *p71* 020 3060 6000

Campbell, Miss W P (JWP Solicitors) *D1 D2 K1*
Wakefield *p418* 01924 387171

Campbell-Castle, Mrs K Y (MFG Solicitors) *K1*
Telford *p409* 01952 641651

Campbell-Clause, Mrs S (Wheelers) *N Q J2 Zr*
Aldershot *p115* 01252 316316

Campbell-Taylor, R H (Campbell-Taylor Solicitors) *Zm K4 W Zg*
Hackney *p18* 0845 567 2457

Campion, D J (Humfrys & Symonds)
Hereford *p248* . . . .01432 359261 / 276276

Campion, J (DLA Piper UK LLP) *C2 C1*
Birmingham *p137* 0870 011 1111

Campion, K (McKeowns Solicitors Ltd) *N Q*
St Albans *p390* 0800 032 8328

Campion, P D (Fishburns) *A3 O Q Zc Zj Zq*
London EC3 *p32* 020 7280 8888

Campion, S C (Campion & Co)
Nottingham *p336* 0115 947 6373

Campion, Ms T (Borough Council of King's Lynn and West Norfolk)
King's Lynn *p462* 01553 616270

Campion-Smith, W N (Latham & Watkins LLP)
London EC2 *p51* 020 7710 1000

Camps, G E (Bird & Bird LLP) *W*
London EC4 *p13* 020 7415 6000

Campsall, Ms E (Anthony Collins Solicitors LLP) *Zd*
Birmingham *p137* 0121 200 3242

Camwell, D P (Wilkinson & Butler) *C1 E S1 W*
St Neots *p392* 01480 219229

Canby, M W (Linklaters LLP)
London EC2 *p54* 020 7456 2000

Candey, A D (Blake Lapthorn) *O M1 Ze Zb U2 B1*
London EC1 *p13* 020 7405 2000

Candler, A H B (Gabb & Co) *K1 M1 G J1 D1 F1 H L P N Zi Zm Zt*
Abergavenny *p113* 01873 852432

Candy, T (Griffiths Robertson) *D1 K1*
Reading *p361* 0118 958 5049

Candy, Ms V A (Sarfo Solicitors) *N G H D1 Zi Zl*
Cambridge *p175* 01223 305551

Cane, A (Wortley Byers) *E*
Brentwood *p156* 01277 268368

Cane, A J (Stanley Tee) *C1 S2 E R2*
Bishop's Stortford *p144* . . . 01279 755200

Canham, Miss J (Seddons) *L Q*
Westminster *p77* 020 7725 8000

Canham, Ms S J (Trowers & Hamlins) *Zc*
London EC3 *p88* 020 7423 8000

Canli, Miss G A D (Dawson & Burgess with Bell Dallman & Co) *K1 K3 W S1 Q*
Doncaster *p211* 01302 834744

Cann, J G (Gould & Swayne) *Q O Zq*
Glastonbury *p229* 01458 833700

Cann, S (Stones Solicitors LLP) *T2 W*
Exeter *p222* 01392 666777

Canning, Mrs F G (Gilbert Stephens) *S1*
Exeter *p221* 01392 424242

Canning, L M (Wake Smith & Tofields) *K1*
Sheffield *p377* 0114 266 6660

Canning, L R (Canning & Co) *B1 C1 E G H J1 K1 N P S1 Zc Zj*
Warrington *p421* 01925 630012

Canning, M F (Butcher Burns LLP) *G J1 N O Q F1*
London WC1 *p16* 020 7713 7100

Canning, M P (Garner Canning) *K1 D1 M1 N P G H L*
Birmingham *p138* 0121 749 5577

Canning, Mrs S J (Franklins LLP) *N Zr Zm*
Northampton *p332* 01604 828282

Cannings, Mrs Y (Forbes) *O F1 L N Q Zm*
Accrington *p114* 01254 872111

Cannon, E J (Fladgate LLP) *E R1 S1 L*
London WC2 *p32* 020 3036 7000

Cannon, M (Napthens LLP) *W*
Preston *p357* 01772 888444

Cannon, M J (DAC Beachcroft) *M1 Zc Zu R2*
Birmingham *p137* 0121 698 5200

Cannon, N B (Walker Morris) *E*
Leeds *p277* 0113 283 2500

Cannon, R S (Janes) *G H*
London SW1 *p46* 020 7930 5100

Cannon, Mrs S (Molins PLC)
Milton Keynes *p466* 01908 219000
Milton Keynes *p447* 0870 241 4302

Cannon, S A (Pinney Talfourd LLP)
Hornchurch *p252* 01708 511000

Cannon, Ms S L (London Borough of Bexley)
Bexleyheath *p449* 020 8303 7777

Cant, A (Cartwright King)
Nottingham *p336* 0115 958 7444

Cant, M J (Nabarro LLP)
London WC1 *p63* 020 7524 6000

Cantaris, C (Bretherton Law) *G H*
St Albans *p389* 01727 869293

Cantelli, R (Cantelli & Co) *S1 N K1 Q L W J1*
Bicester *p132* 01869 324899

Canter, J M (The Specter Partnership) *N O F1 Q G H J1*
Birkenhead *p135* 0151 647 3000

Cantlay, W M (Walters & Plaskitt) *D1 F1 G H J1 K1 L P S1*
Stoke-on-Trent *p398* 01782 845807

Cantle, S M (Kennedys) *O Zj Zq*
London EC3 *p49* 020 7667 9667

Cantlon, Ms Z M (Barlow Lyde & Gilbert LLP)
London EC3 *p10* 020 7247 2277

Canton, P M (Royal Mail Group)
London EC4 *p109* 020 7250 2468

Cantoni, C (Moore Blatch Solicitors) *R1 S1 E*
Southampton *p386* 023 8071 8000

Cantor, Mrs A J (Thompson Smith & Puxon) *K1 D1*
Colchester *p198* 01206 574431

Cantor, Miss C (Housing & Property Law Partnership) *O Q L*
Islington *p43* 020 7553 9000

Cantor, J M (Teacher Stern LLP) *O L*
London WC1 *p86* 020 7242 3191

Cantrill, P S (Walker Morris) *C1 O Ze Zf*
Leeds *p277* 0113 283 2500

Cantrill, P T (Albin & Co) *G H*
Reading *p359* 0118 957 4018

Cantwell, Miss R (Linda Stapleton & Co)
Gloucester *p230* 01452 423870

Canty, Ms C R (Canty & Co) *E S1 C1 B1 Zh*
Birmingham *p136* 0121 688 5000

Canty, E (Brabners Chaffe Street) *C1 Ze*
Manchester *p301* 0161 836 8800

Capaldi, J (Runhams) *Q O Zb Zq J1 K1 K3 B1 C1 I U2*
Bradford *p154* 01274 532233

Capeci, B (Allen & Overy LLP)
London E1 *p5* 020 3088 0000

Capes, E (Sills & Betteridge LLP) *C1 C2 Zb*
Gainsborough *p228* 01427 616816
Lincoln *p285* 01522 542211

Caplan, A (Kennedys)
Chelmsford *p186* 0845 838 4800

Caplan, C P (David McLean Legal Services)
Deeside *p456* 01244 283500

Caplan, G (Gary Caplan Solicitors)
Leeds *p272* 0113 216 3118

Caplan, G M (Winston Solicitors LLP) *C1 S2 E I*
Leeds *p278* 0113 320 5000

Caplan, G M (S S Basi & Co) *S2 S1 Q*
Ilford *p259* 020 8518 1236

Caplan, I (Bevan Brittan LLP) *S2 E*
London EC4 *p12* 0870 194 1000

Caplan, M B (Fruhman Davies Livingstones) *N F1 B1*
Manchester *p304* 0161 833 0578

Caplan, M G (Kingsley Napley) *G H Q Zi Zg Zl*
London EC1 *p50* 020 7814 1200

Caplan, R (Caplans) *C1 O E S1 T1 B1 W L J1*
Harrow *p241* 020 8864 0111

Caplan, S J (BTMK Solicitors LLP) *N*
Southend-on-Sea *p387* . . . 01702 339222

Caplen, A H A (Abels) *S1 W E G R1 A1 C1 T1 F1 L Zi Zl Zt*
Southampton *p385* 023 8022 0317

Caplin, D (Cunninghams) *G H*
Manchester *p302* 0161 833 1600

Caplin, I D (Irving Caplin & Co) *S1 W*
Wandsworth *p18* 020 8874 7633

Caplin, M B (Heyman & Co) *M1 N L K1 H F1 D1 C1 W*
Leigh *p282* 01942 604135

Capp, D R (Beecroft Maxwell) *P M1 K1 N G F1 H C1 L B1 Zc*
Canvey Island *p177* 01268 511999

Capper, Dr B S (Penningtons) *E*
Godalming *p231* 01483 791800

Capper, Miss L V (Halton Borough Council)
Widnes *p476* 0151 424 2061

Capper, P D (Risdon Hosegood) *D1 E F1 J1 K1 L P S1 T1 W Zi Zm*
Williton *p433* 01984 632277

Capper, R A (Capper & Jones) *S1 E W*
Mold *p318* 01352 752020

Capper, R M (Harrison Clark LLP) *C1 C2*
Cheltenham *p188* 01242 269198
Worcester *p439* 01905 612001
Worcester *p439* 01905 612001

Capron, D (The College of Law)
London WC1 *p105* 0800 289997

Capstaff, Mrs H A (Wallers) *S1 K1*
Newcastle upon Tyne *p327* . 0191 261 2281

Capstick, J B (Capsticks Solicitors LLP) *C1 Zr*
London SW19 *p18* 020 8780 2211

Capstick, N (Hawkins Ross Limited) *S1 E W L C1 S2 C2 R2*
Stockton-on-Tees *p397* . . .01642 613647 / 678888

Carden, Ms C A (Godwins) *S1 E S2*
Winchester *p433* 01962 841484

Cardew, M F G (Hanne & Co) *G H Zl*
London SW11 *p38* 020 7228 0017

Cardew, S (Penningtons) *T1*
Basingstoke *p127* 01256 407100

Cardozo, H D (Shell International Ltd)
London SE1 *p109* 020 7934 1234

Cardwell, G H (Donnelly McArdle Adamson) *G H P Zq S1 W Q N*
Darlington *p206* 01325 482299

Cardwell, Miss J A (Lyons Wilson) *N Q*
Manchester *p307* 0161 830 7777

Cardy, L (Penningtons) *J1*
Godalming *p231* 01483 791800

See p634 for the Key to Work Categories

Care, Mrs J M (Prestons) *K1 S1 Q*
Poulton-le-Fylde *p355* 01253 882426
Care, J P (Hansells)
North Walsham *p331* 01692 404351
Care, J P (Hansells) *S1 E L*
Cromer *p203* 01263 512003
Care, S (Berry Smith LLP)
Cardiff *p177* 029 2034 5511
Care, T J (Dickinson Dees) *C1*
Newcastle upon Tyne *p324* . 0191 279 9000
Careless, A J (Careless & Kemp) *S1 S2 E L W*
Ventnor *p418* 01983 852626
Careless-Shore, Mrs S (Wannop Fox Staffurth & Bray) *S1 S2*
Bognor Regis *p148* 01243 864001
Carew-Jones, O (Winckworth Sherwood LLP) *X Zx*
London SE1 *p92* 020 7593 5000
Carey, Miss A L (Buckinghamshire County Council)
Aylesbury *p448* 01296 383653
Carey, A P D (Hogan Lovells International LLP)
London EC1 *p42* 020 7296 2000
Carey, Ms B (Clarion Solicitors LLP) *W K4*
Leeds *p272* 0113 246 0622
Carey, Ms C (Sacker & Partners LLP) *Zo*
London EC2 *p76* 020 7329 6699
Carey, Miss C A (Shentons) *D1 K3 K1*
Winchester *p434* 01962 844544
Carey, D (Public Interest Lawyers)
Birmingham *p141* 0121 515 5069
Carey, D A (Taylor Walton LLP) *A1 E L R1 S1 Zh Zs*
Luton *p295* 01582 731161
Carey, Ms E (MSB Solicitors LLP)
Liverpool *p289* 0151 281 9040
Carey, J (Macks Solicitors) *R1 S1*
Middlesbrough *p315* 01642 252828
Carey, J P (Sedgwick Phelan & Partners) *S1 E L Zh*
Middleton *p315* 0161 653 5299
Carey, N J (Forsters LLP) *O Q L*
Westminster *p33* 020 7863 8333
Carey, Mrs P E (Bookers & Bolton) *W T2*
Alton *p116* . . . . 01420 82881 / 88903
Carey, P W (Charles Russell LLP) *C1 I U1 Ze Zf Zk Zw*
London EC4 *p19* 020 7203 5000
Carey, S (Speechly Bircham LLP) *O Q Zc*
London EC4 *p81* 020 7427 6400
Carey, Mrs S A (Michelmores LLP) *L O Q E*
Exeter *p221* 01392 688688
Carey, Ms V J (Withers LLP) *L O Q*
London EC4 *p92* 020 7597 6000
Caris, Mrs B (Caris Robson LLP) *S1 Zv W V*
Newcastle upon Tyne *p324* . 0191 264 6664
Prudhoe *p358* 01661 836851
Caris, P L (Caris Robson LLP) *C1 S2 E O Q N*
Newcastle upon Tyne *p324* . 0191 264 6664
Prudhoe *p358* 01661 836851
Carl, T (Taylor Wessing)
London EC4 *p86* 020 7300 7000
Carle, N N (Browne Jacobson LLP) *N Zj*
Nottingham *p336* 0115 976 6000
Carleton, J (Farrer & Co LLP)
London WC2 *p31* 020 3375 7000
Carley, J P (Massers) *O Zq B1*
Nottingham *p338* 0115 851 1666
Carlile, Miss E (Mason Baggott & Garton) *S1 W*
Scunthorpe *p373* 01724 868611
Carlile, R A (Barnes & Taylor) *O Q N W S1 S2*
Southend-on-Sea *p387* . . . 01702 347300
Carlile, Miss S (Smith Law Partnership) *K4 W J1*
Braintree *p155* 01376 321311
Carlin, C G (Sharp & Partners) *S1 W K1 P L E M1*
Nottingham *p339* 0115 959 0055
Carlin, Mrs D (Brabners Chaffe Street) *S1 S2*
Liverpool *p286* 0151 600 3000
Carlin, Mrs D W (Rawlison Butler LLP)
Crawley *p202* 01293 527744
Horsham *p253* 01403 252492
Carlisle, Ms J (Henmans LLP) *N*
Oxford *p343* 01865 781000
Carlisle, Miss J A (William Sturges & Co) *S2 E S1 L*
Westminster *p84* 020 7873 1000
Carlisle, Ms J C (Russell Jones & Walker)
London WC2 *p74* 020 7657 1555
Carlisle, M A R (Beviss & Beckingsale) *S1 E L A1 S2*
Axminster *p120* 01297 630700
Carlisle, Ms P E (Speakman & Co) *S1 K1 P L*
Crewe *p203* 01270 214237
Carlisle, R A (Atteys) *K1 D1 D2 Zl*
Doncaster *p211* 01302 340400
Carlisle, S (The National Trust)
Swindon *p475* 01793 817400
Carlson, R R (Metcalfe Copeman & Pettefar) *F2 Zy J2*
Wisbech *p435* 01945 464331
Carlton, Miss C A (Belmont & Lowe) *N O*
London EC1 *p11* 020 7608 4600
Carlton, Ms E (Manchester City Council)
Manchester *p465* 0161 234 5000
Carlton, J H (Russell Jones & Walker) *D1 G H J1 K1 N O Q Zk*
London WC2 *p74* 020 7657 1555
Carlton, J M (Wilkin Chapman LLP) *K1 D1 V K2 D2*
Beverley *p131* 01482 398398
Carlton, Ms L (Reynolds Porter Chamberlain LLP)
London E1 *p71* 020 3060 6000
Carman, Mrs A E (Hartlepool Borough Council)
Hartlepool *p460* 01429 266522
Carmen-Davis, Ms N (Lee & Thompson) *Ze Zf*
London W1 *p52* 020 7935 4665
Carmichael, A J (Linklaters LLP)
London EC2 *p54* 020 7456 2000
Carmichael, D J (Pannone LLP) *J1 Zi Zp*
Manchester *p308* 0161 909 3000
Carmichael, Ms F (The College of Law York)
York *p477* 0800 289997
Carmichael, G (Graeme Carmichael) *D1 K1 D2*
Ipswich *p262* 01473 252159
Carmichael, J (The Isaacs Practice)
Bournemouth *p152* 01202 299999
Carmichael, J S (Huggins & Lewis Foskett) *E S2 S1 Q*
Redbridge *p43* 020 8989 3000
Carmichael, N F (Carmichael & Heathfield)
Newcastle upon Tyne *p324* . 0191 230 3010
Carmichael, Ms S J (Squire Sanders (UK) LLP)
Manchester *p310* 0161 830 5000
Carmichael, Miss Z S (Gosschalks) *E L*
Hull *p256* 01482 324252
Carmody, Ms S (Trowers & Hamlins)
London EC3 *p88* 020 7423 8000
Carn, Miss A S (Edwin Coe LLP) *J1*
London WC2 *p29* 020 7691 4000
Carnall, M (HBOS PLC)
Halifax *p460* 0870 600 5000
Carne, Miss P A S (Mylles & Co) *G H J1 W*
Sunninghill *p402* 01344 623388
Carne, Ms V M (R Hancock & Son) *A1 L S1*
Callington *p173* 01579 383101
Carnegie, A J (Clifford Chance)
London E14 *p20* 020 7006 1000
Carnegie, D G R (Rutter & Rutter) *S1 T1 W*
Wincanton *p433* 01963 32224
Carnegie, K (Bovis Homes Ltd) *E S1*
Bishops Cleeve *p450* 01242 662400
Carnegy, C D (Bonallack & Bishop) *N F1 K1 J2 Zk W Q O J1*
Salisbury *p371* 01722 422300
Carneiro, A V (Challinors) *D1 K1*
Birmingham *p136* 0121 212 9393
Carnes, Ms C H (Jewels Solicitors)
Stafford *p393* 01785 602030
Carney, Ms B M (Lewis Silkin LLP) *J1*
London EC4 *p53* 020 7074 8000
Carney, G P (Squire Sanders (UK) LLP)
London EC2 *p81* 020 7655 1000
Carney, G T (Cripps Harries Hall LLP) *C1 C2 B1 T1 J1 O Zd*
Tunbridge Wells *p415* 01892 515121
Carney, M A (Carney Solicitors Ltd) *N*
Hanley *p239* 01782 272999
Carney, P B (DWF) *C1 U2 Ze Zo*
Manchester *p303* 0161 603 5000
Carney, P M (Amber Valley Borough Council)
Ripley *p470* 01773 570222
Carney, T (Terence Carney) *D1 F1 G J1 K1 L S1 V W Zl K4 S2*
Hebburn *p246* . . . 0191 483 5422 / 483 8771
Carolan, Ms L M (DAC Beachcroft) *Zj*
Birmingham *p137* 0121 698 5200
Carolina, R A (PricewaterhouseCoopers Legal LLP) *I*
London SE1 *p69* 020 7212 1616
Carp, J (Speechly Bircham LLP) *J1*
London EC4 *p81* 020 7427 6400
Carpanini, F A G (Olswang LLP) *C1 C2*
London WC1 *p64* 020 7067 3000
Carpanini, P J (Foot Anstey) *E S1 S2 Q N*
Plymouth *p349* 01752 675000
Dartmouth *p207* 01803 833993
Carpenter, Miss A (Mercers) *N O Q*
Henley-on-Thames *p247* . . . 01491 572138
Carpenter, Dr A J (Addleshaw Goddard) *C1*
London EC1 *p4* 020 7606 8855
Carpenter, Ms C M (Kent Law Clinic) *B1 C1 D1 F1 G H J1 K1 L*
Canterbury *p453* 01227 823311
Carpenter, C S (Clifford Chance)
London E14 *p20* 020 7006 1000
Carpenter, C W (Michelmores LLP) *E R2 S2*
Exeter *p221* 01392 688688
Carpenter, J A (Taylor Walton LLP) *O Q Zq*
Luton *p295* 01582 731161
Carpenter, Miss J D (Adams Harrison) *G H J1 L N Q*
Saffron Walden *p370* 01799 523441
Carpenter, J D (Carpenters) *C1 C2 E J1 N O Q S1 W Zc Zd Ze Zk Zl Zp*
Birkenhead *p134* 0870 780 1870
Carpenter, J D (Paton & Carpenter)
Llanelli *p292* . . . . 01554 774760 / 751680
Carpenter, Mrs J L (Kirkland & Lane) *W S1 Zd*
Southwell *p389* . . . 01636 813128 / 812180
Carpenter, P D L (Paton & Carpenter)
Llanelli *p292* . . . . 01554 774760 / 751680
Carpenter, P G (Carpenters Rose) *C1 T1 W Zd Zm Zo*
London NW7 *p18* 020 8906 0088
Carpenter, S C (Crown Prosecution Service Avon & Somerset)
Bristol *p451* 0117 930 2800
Carpenter, Mrs S M (Powell & Co) *S1 W T2 E K1 J1*
Sutton Coldfield *p404* 0121 355 1001
Carr, Miss A (Keoghs LLP) *N Zj Q O*
Bolton *p149* 01204 677000
Carr, A F (Linder Myers Solicitors) *G H M1 P V K1 D1 N R1 S1 Zh Zk Zl*
Manchester *p307* 0844 984 6400
Carr, A M (Kenneth Elliott & Rowe) *N Zt*
Romford *p366* 01708 757575
Carr, A M (Sellafield Ltd)
Warrington *p475* . . . .
Carr, C M (Stephensons Solicitors LLP) *G H J1*
Wigan *p432* 01942 777777
Carr, D J (Malcolm C Foy & Co) *N Q O*
Doncaster *p211* 01302 340005
Carr, D J H (Wedlake Bell LLP)
London WC1 *p91* 020 7395 3000
Carr, E (Fraser Brown) *J1 O Q*
Nottingham *p337* 0115 988 8777
Carr, G R D (Stuckey Carr & Co) *W S1 S2 T2*
Pulborough *p358* 01798 875358
Carr, Ms H (Goughs) *N*
Chippenham *p193* 01249 444499
Carr, J (Towns Needham & Co) *N Q*
Manchester *p310* 0161 832 3721
Carr, J E (Hand Morgan & Owen) *W K4*
Stafford *p393* 01785 211411
Carr, J P (Lewis Silkin LLP) *J1 Zi Zp*
Oxford *p343* 01865 263070
Carr, K (Sternberg Reed) *G H B2 J2 Zg*
London NW1 *p83* 020 7485 5558
Carr, Ms K J (Ince & Co Services Ltd)
London E1 *p44* 020 7481 0010
Carr, Mrs K K (FBC Manby Bowdler LLP) *W T2*
Wolverhampton *p437* 01902 578000
Carr, M J (Dawson Mason & Carr) *S1*
Guildford *p236* 01483 576169
Carr, M R (Sparling Benham & Brough) *W A1 C1*
Colchester *p198* 01206 733733
Carr, P (Hanne & Co)
London SW11 *p38* 020 7228 0017
Carr, P A (Taylor Wimpey UK Limited Legal Services)
Milton Keynes *p466* 01908 209030
Carr, Miss P A (Thomson Webb & Corfield) *E S2*
Cambridge *p176* 01223 578070
Carr, P J (Carr Hepburn Solicitors Ltd) *S1 S2 W Zd Zl*
Hemel Hempstead *p246* . . . 01442 241466
Carr, Ms P L (Over Taylor Biggs) *S2 E R2 S1 L R1*
Exeter *p222* 01392 823811
Carr, R A (Carr & Co) *G H*
Huddersfield *p255* 01484 467860
Carr, R P (Carr & Co) *S1 E L C1 A1 T1 W R1 F1 P Zc Zj Zb*
Banbury *p122* . . . . 01295 275168 / 261744
Carr, S (Burton & Dyson) *E K1 Q N Zm S1*
Gainsborough *p228* 01427 610761
Carr, Ms S A (Ratcliffe & Bibby) *K1 D1 D2 K3*
Lancaster *p270* 01524 39039
Carr, Mrs S A (Beetenson & Gibbon) *K1 Q*
Grimsby *p235* 01472 240251
Carr, S A (S A Carr & Co) *K1 L D1*
Hackney *p18* 020 8986 5438
Carr, Miss S J (Mason & Beer) *K1 D1 V S1*
East Grinstead *p215* 01342 311255
Carr, Mrs S S (Carr & Co) *K1 W K2*
St Albans *p389* 01727 866155
Rugeley *p368* 01889 583871
Carr, W (CMS Cameron McKenna LLP) *C1*
London EC3 *p17* 020 7367 3000
Carr-West, Ms J (Hunters)
London WC2 *p44* 020 7412 0050
Carrel, Mrs S N (Greenland Houchen Pomeroy) *K1 K3 Q*
Norwich *p334* 01603 660744
Carrell, J D P (Farrer & Co LLP) *T1 T2*
London WC2 *p31* 020 3375 7000
Carreras, R M (Knight Polson Solicitors) *G H Zl Zy*
Eastleigh *p216* 023 8064 4822
Carretta, Ms C (Humphries Kirk) *B1 Zc C3 C1 R2*
Dorchester *p212* 01305 251007
Carriage, Mrs R R (Mills & Reeve) *R1 P*
Norwich *p335* 01603 660155
Carrick, B J (Brain Sinnott & Co)
Bristol *p161* 0117 965 1030
Carrick, S (Dickinson Dees) *E*
Newcastle upon Tyne *p324* . 0191 279 9000
Carrick, Mrs S L (Mowbray Woodwards Solicitors) *G H Zm*
Bath *p128* 01225 485700
Carrier, A (Mills & Reeve)
Cambridge *p175* 01223 364422
Carrigan, S (Griffith Smith Conway)
Hove *p254* 01273 821577
Carrington, A M (Banks Carrington & Co) *S1 W E A1 Zl S2*
Blackpool *p146* . . 01253 622269 / 315223
Carrington, A R W (Carrington & Associates) *C1 O B1 Zb M2 Ze*
London EC4 *p18* 020 7822 1855
Carrington, P M (Herbert Smith LLP) *O B1 Zq*
London EC2 *p40* 020 7374 8000
Carritt, Miss D M (Carritt & Co LLP)
London W1 *p18* 020 7323 2765
Carroll, Mrs A (Bonnetts Solicitors LLP) *S1 W Zm*
Hounslow *p253* 020 8570 5286
Carroll, A J (McGrigors LLP)
London EC4 *p56* 020 7054 2500
Carroll, A J (Anthony Carroll & Co) *A1 S1 W*
Lincoln *p284* 01522 544017
Carroll, C J (Travers Smith LLP) *C1 C2*
London EC1 *p87* 020 7295 3000
Carroll, D (Matthew & Matthew Limited) *E S1*
Southbourne *p387* 01202 431943
Carroll, Ms D A (Gamlins)
Llandudno *p291* 01492 860420
Carroll, Mrs D A (J W Hughes & Co) *K1 L W Zo*
Llandudno *p291* 01492 874774
Carroll, D J P (Lovegrove & Eliot) *S1 E W*
Windsor *p434* 01753 851133
Carroll, Miss E J (Walker Morris) *E*
Leeds *p277* 0113 283 2500
Carroll, J (Russell-Cooke LLP) *K1*
London WC1 *p74* 020 7405 6566
Carroll, J D (Forbes Hall LLP) *C1 E L S1 W S2*
London EC2 *p33* 020 7729 9111
Woodford Green *p439* 020 8498 0080
Carroll, J J (Cartmell Shepherd) *A1*
Carlisle *p182* 01228 514077
Carroll, K (Brown & Corbishley) *S1 E K1 G M1 W D1 F1*
Sandbach *p371* 01270 768033
Carroll, Mrs K E (Debenhams Ottaway)
St Albans *p390* 01727 837161
Carroll, Mrs L C (Pickworths) *N Q Zr*
Hemel Hempstead *p247* . . . 01442 261731
Carroll, M (Bevan Brittan LLP) *C1 C2 I Ze*
Bristol *p161* 0870 194 1000
Carroll, M J (Clifford Chance)
London E14 *p20* 020 7006 1000
Carroll, Miss N (Hindle Campbell) *S1*
North Shields *p330* 0191 296 1777
Carroll, S (Enfield Magistrates Court)
London N17 *p106* 020 8808 5411
Carroll, Mrs S (Brown & Corbishley) *K1*
Sandbach *p371* 01270 768033
Carroll, T L (Cuthbertsons) *S2 K1 Q G F1 S1 W N L E Zl*
Blyth *p148* 01670 352121
Carruthers, A J (Mayer Brown International LLP) *O*
London EC2 *p59* 020 3130 3000
Carruthers, A S (Hughes Fowler Carruthers) *D1 K1 K3 K2*
London WC2 *p43* 020 7421 8383
Carruthers, Ms L (Batley & Dewsbury Magistrates Court)
Dewsbury *p457* 01924 468287
Carslake, H B (SGH Martineau LLP) *W T2 Zd Zv*
Birmingham *p142* 0870 763 2000
Carslaw, Ms D P (Sidley Austin Brown & Wood) *Zb R2*
London EC2 *p78* 020 7360 3600
Carson, Mrs E D (Sandersons) *C1 J1*
Hull *p258* 01482 324662
Carson, I (Tollers LLP) *O*
Northampton *p332* 01604 258558
Carson, Ms J W (Simmons & Simmons)
London EC2 *p79* 020 7628 2020
Carson, P (Thompsons (formerly Robin/Brian Thompson & Partners)) *N Zj*
London SW19 *p87* 020 8947 4163
Carson, Ms P M (Bindmans LLP) *Zr W*
London WC1 *p12* 020 7833 4433
Carson, T J (Paul Rudd) *N S1 W Q*
Grimsby *p235* 01472 350881
Carstairs, P (Watson Farley & Williams)
London EC2 *p90* 020 7814 8000
Carswell, A J (Dickinson Manser) *F1*
Poole *p352* 01202 673071
Carter, A C (Anthony C Carter) *E G H K1 L O Q S1 W Zl*
Plymouth *p349* 01752 255000
Carter, A J (Trowers & Hamlins) *C1 Zb*
London EC3 *p88* 020 7423 8000
Carter, A J (Thompsons (formerly Robin/Brian Thompson & Partners)) *N*
Birmingham *p143* 0121 262 1200
Carter, Mrs A L (Martin-Kaye LLP) *N Q*
Telford *p409* 01952 272222
Carter, A M (Woodfines LLP) *O*
Milton Keynes *p317* 01908 202150
Carter, Mrs A M (Eric Wright Group Ltd) *E*
Bamber Bridge *p448* 01772 698822
Carter, A M (HT Legal Limited t/a Harrison Townend & Ormeshers) *C1 S2 E O R1 K3 K1 L N*
Hyde *p259* 0161 368 1559
Carter, Mrs B C (Nottinghamshire County Council Legal Services Division) *D1*
West Bridgford *p475* 0115 977 3478
Carter, B F (Crellins Carter Solicitors) *S1 S2 W Zo Zi*
Weybridge *p429* 01932 858833
Carter, Ms B L (Barbara Carter) *D1 D2 K1*
Birmingham *p136* 0121 441 3238
Carter, Miss C (Trethowans LLP) *N Zr*
Salisbury *p371* 01722 412512
Carter, Mrs C A (Forsters LLP) *R1*
Westminster *p33* 020 7863 8333
Carter, Ms C A (The Lifeboat)
Deal *p456* 01304 374475
Carter, Mrs C J (Oxley & Coward Solicitors LLP) *W T2*
Rotherham *p367* 01709 510999
Carter, Mrs C J (Ashurst LLP) *C1 J1*
London EC2 *p7* 020 7638 1111
Carter, C J (Hall Ward & Fox) *Q E K1 C1 F1 S1 Zl Zf*
Weston-super-Mare *p429* . .01934 626656 / 626657
Carter, D (Ison Harrison) *C1*
Leeds *p274* 0113 284 5000
Carter, D (Ashurst LLP) *C1*
London EC2 *p7* 020 7638 1111
Carter, D G (Warwickshire County Council)
Warwick *p475* 01926 410410
Carter, D G (Bell Park Kerridge) *A1 E J1 L S1 T2 W S2*
Carlisle *p181* 01228 888999
Carter, D M (Berg Legal) *O Q Zq A3 Zk F2*
Manchester *p301* 0161 833 9211

Carter, D M (Denbighshire County Council) *S1 W A1 L Zv*
Ruthin *p470* 01824 706000

Carter, D R (Gepp & Sons) *W T1 E*
Chelmsford *p186*. 01245 493939
Colchester *p197* 01206 369889

Carter, Miss E J (Hegarty LLP) *J1 Zp J2 Zi Zza*
Peterborough *p347* 01733 346333
London EC2 *p71*. 020 3116 3000

Carter, Mrs F M J (Browne Jacobson LLP) *K1 H D1 G P Zl*
Nottingham *p336*. 0115 976 6000

Carter, G (Martello Professional Risks Limited)
London EC3 *p108* 020 7337 7500

Carter, G F (Graeme John Solicitors) *C1 C2 C3 E F1 K1 L M1 P S1*
Aberdare *p113*. 01685 872491

Carter, Ms G M (Coventry City Council)
Coventry *p456*. 024 7683 4863

Carter, Miss H A (Morecrofts Solicitors LLP)
Liverpool *p290*. 0151 236 8871

Carter, Mrs H J (Simmons & Simmons) *W T2*
London EC2 *p79*. 020 7628 2020

Carter, H S (Cooper Sons Hartley & Williams) *L S1 S2*
Buxton *p172*. 01298 77511

Carter, I C S (VHS Fletchers Solicitors) *G H*
Nottingham *p339*. 0115 959 9550

Carter, Ms J (Reed Smith LLP)
London EC2 *p71*. 020 3116 3000

Carter, J (McKeowns Solicitors Ltd) *N*
St Albans *p390* 0800 032 8328

Carter, Mrs J (Hibberts LLP) *K4 T2 W*
Nantwich *p320*. 01270 624225

Carter, J A (Nelsons) *E S1*
Nottingham *p338*. 0115 958 6262

Carter, J B C (Martin Tolhurst Partnership LLP)
Gravesend *p233*. 01474 325531

Carter, J D R (Larby Williams with Gwyn & Gwyn) *S1 W K4 S2 E*
Cowbridge *p201* 01446 775535

Carter, Mrs J M (Human and Legal Resources) *N Q O Zq Zk Zp J1 B1 F1 F2*
Aylesbury *p447* 0871 222 3880

Carter, J S (Farrell Matthews & Weir) *G H*
London W6 *p31* 020 8741 1482

Carter, J W (Speechly Bircham LLP) *T1*
London EC4 *p81*. 020 7427 6400

Carter, Miss K (Green Wright Chalton Annis) *W*
Rustington *p369* 01903 774131
Worthing *p441*. 01903 234064

Carter, K (Derbyshire County Council)
Matlock *p465* 01629 580000

Carter, Mrs K A (Norfolk County Council - Legal Services)
Norwich *p467* . . . Minicom: 0844 800 8011

Carter, K R (Carter Slater & Co) *G H*
Northampton *p331*. 01604 717505

Carter, L (Thompsons (formerly Robin/Brian Thompson & Partners))
Birmingham *p143* 0121 262 1200
London SW19 *p87*. 020 8947 4163

Carter, Ms L (Lewis Silkin LLP)
London EC4 *p53*. 020 7074 8000

Carter, Mrs L J (MacDonald Oates LLP) *K1*
Petersfield *p348* 01730 268211

Carter, M (Addleshaw Goddard)
London EC1 *p4* 020 7606 8855

Carter, M (North Yorkshire Law) *S1 W*
Whitby *p430*. 01947 602131

Carter, M P (Enfield Magistrates Court)
London N17 *p106* 020 8808 5411

Carter, M P (Paul Crowley & Co) *S2 S1*
Liverpool *p287*. 0151 264 7363

Carter, Ms N (Boyes Turner) *Zi*
Reading *p360* 0118 959 7711
London EC2 *p66*. 020 7457 3000

Carter, N A (Anthony Collins Solicitors LLP) *B1 O Q Zc Zq*
Birmingham *p137* 0121 200 3242

Carter, Miss N J E (Reynolds Porter Chamberlain LLP) *O Q Zq Zj*
London E1 *p71* 020 3060 6000

Carter, P (Kennedys) *J1*
London EC3 *p49*. 020 7667 9667

Carter, P A (Finers Stephens Innocent LLP) *C1*
London W1 *p32* 020 7323 4000

Carter, P A R (Gregory Rowcliffe Milners) *W T2 Zd*
London WC1 *p37* 020 7242 0631

Carter, P I (Carter Slater & Co) *G H*
Northampton *p331*. 01604 717505

Carter, R A (Carter Read & Dove) *S1 R1 L B1 W E S2 J1*
Swindon *p406* 01793 617617

Carter, Ms R E (Kerseys) *K1 K2 K3*
Ipswich *p262*. 01473 213311

Carter, R J (Martin Tolhurst Partnership LLP) *S1 S2 R2 W*
Ashford *p119* 01233 505555

Carter, R J (The Specter Partnership) *N Q O*
Birkenhead *p135*. 0151 647 3000

Carter, S (Napthens LLP) *J1*
Preston *p357* 01772 888444

Carter, Ms S (Department for Business, Enterprise and Regulatory Reform)
London SW1 *p105*. 020 7215 0105

Carter, S A (Howell-Jones LLP) *C1 E*
Kingston upon Thames *p267*. 020 8549 5186

Carter, S A (Aaron & Partners LLP Solicitors) *A1 E P L Zu Zn R1*
Chester *p190* 01244 405555

Carter, Ms S E (BHR Law) *S2*
Exeter *p220* 01392 496100

Carter, Miss S K R (Ross Carter) *W T2 K4*
Brockenhurst *p166*. 01590 624422

Carter, S L (Charles Russell LLP) *O Zj*
London EC4 *p19*. 020 7203 5000

Carter, Ms S M (East Sussex County Council)
Brighton *p451* 01273 670888

Carter, Ms S M (Somerset County Council)
Taunton *p473* 0845 345 9166

Carter, Mrs S T (Stockport Metropolitan Borough Council)
Stockport *p472*. 0161 480 4949

Carter, Miss S V (Irvings)
Liverpool *p289*. 0800 954 0243

Carter, T J (Attwaters) *B1 C1 J1 O Q Zp*
Harlow *p239*. 01279 638888

Carter, Ms V (Benson Watkins) *D1 K1 W V*
Swansea *p404*. 01792 704320

Carter, W S C (Underhill Langley & Wright) *W K4*
Wolverhampton *p438* 01902 423431

Carter-Birch, Mrs E (Dollman & Pritchard) *D2 D1 K1 K3*
Caterham *p183* 01883 347823

Carter-Silk, A (Manches LLP) *C1 U1 Ze O U2*
London WC2 *p58* 020 7404 4433
London EC4 *p81*. 020 7427 6400

Cartier, L (Cartier & Co)
London WC2 *p19* 020 7405 7777

Cartier, L I (Harris Cartier LLP) *C1 O B2*
London WC2 *p39* 020 7405 7100

Cartin, P G P (Ewings & Co) *C1 S2 E S1*
London SE20 *p30* 020 8778 1126

Cartledge, Ms A (The College of Law Guildford)
Guildford *p459*. 01483 460200

Cartledge, Ms D (QualitySolicitors Gruber Garratt) *G H B2 Zl Ze*
Oldham *p341* 0161 665 3502

Cartledge, M R (O H Parsons & Partners) *D1 F1 G H K1 L M1 P W Zi Zm*
London WC2 *p66* 020 7379 7277

Cartlidge, H A (Olswang LLP)
London WC1 *p64* 020 7067 3000

Cartmell, A C G (Bates Wells & Braithwaite London LLP) *E S2 R2 Zh L Zd*
London EC4 *p11*. 020 7551 7777

Cartmell, K (Keoghs LLP) *W J1*
Bolton *p149* 01204 677000

Cartmell, R I (DC Kaye & Co) *G H J1 K1 N O Q W V Zq Zp*
Great Missenden *p234*. . . .01494 864650 / 862226

Cartmell, T H (Cartmell Shepherd) *A1 E W L T1 C1*
Carlisle *p182*. 01228 514077

Cartmell, Miss V L (Blackpool Borough Council)
Blackpool *p450* 01253 477450

Cartridge, J G (Cartridges)
Exeter *p220* 01392 256854

Cartwright, A (Clifford Chance)
London E14 *p20*. 020 7006 1000

Cartwright, Ms A (Jones Day) *C1*
London EC4 *p46*. 020 7039 5959

Cartwright, Mrs C (Thorneycroft Solicitors Ltd) *N*
Macclesfield *p297* 01625 503444

Cartwright, Miss C L (Higgs & Sons) *T2 W*
Brierley Hill *p158*. 0845 111 5050

Cartwright, G (G Cartwright & Co) *S1 W K1 L M1 E C1 J1 G*
Chatteris *p185*. 01354 692607

Cartwright, J L (Sandwell Metropolitan Borough Council)
Oldbury *p468* 0121 569 2200

Cartwright, J L (Walsall Metropolitan Borough Council)
Walsall *p475*. 01922 650000

Cartwright, K N (Drummonds) *S1 S2 E*
Chester *p190* 01244 408300

Cartwright, Ms L (Russell Jones & Walker)
Sheffield *p377* 0114 276 6868

Cartwright, M J (Cartwright & Co) *S1 P G M1 K1 H D1 F1 W*
Kirkham *p268* . . . .01772 683116 / 687010

Cartwright, Ms S L (Bevan Brittan LLP)
Birmingham *p135* 0870 194 1000

Cartwright, T (Ashurst LLP)
London EC2 *p7* 020 7638 1111

Cartwright, T J (Squire Sanders (UK) LLP) *C2 C1 Zv*
London EC2 *p81*. 020 7655 1000

Cartwright-Harwood, Mrs S K (Philip Avery & Co) *Q K1 M1 N F1 S1 K2*
Llanelli *p292*. 01554 746295

Cartwright-Terry, Mrs E (Darbys Solicitors LLP) *E*
Oxford *p343*. 01865 811700

Carty, P C (Environment Agency (Thames Region)) *P*
Reading *p469* 0870 850 6506

Caruthers-Little, P G (Camerons Jones) *W*
Harrow *p241*. 020 8423 6666

Carver, Ms A (Michelmores LLP) *C1*
Exeter *p221* 01392 688688

Carver, Mrs L I (Gepp & Sons) *W*
Chelmsford *p186*. 01245 493939
Colchester *p197* 01206 369889

Carver, S J (Parry Carver) *S1 C1 A1 W E Zl*
Wellington *p425* 01952 641291

Carvill, P A (Carvill & Johnson LLP) *K1 D1*
Birmingham *p136* 0121 476 9000

Carville, Miss H (Max Engel & Co LLP) *C1 S2 E J1 W S1*
Northampton *p331*. 01604 887450

Carvis, P M (Godloves) *N O Q*
Leeds *p273* 0113 225 8811

Carwardine, Ms J (Russell-Cooke LLP) *G H*
London SW15 *p74*. 020 8789 9111

Cary, Ms A J (Isadore Goldman Solicitors) *J1 O L*
London EC4 *p45*. 020 7353 1000

Cary, Ms P J (Norfolk County Council - Legal Services)
Norwich *p467* . . . Minicom: 0844 800 8011

Cary, T J (Leathes Prior) *N Zi*
Norwich *p334* 01603 610911

Casagranda, Ms C K (Blandy & Blandy)
Reading *p360* 0118 951 6800

Casanova, J (Sidley Austin Brown & Wood) *Zb*
London EC2 *p78*. 020 7360 3600

Casaru, Mrs J C (Dilwyns) *W*
Llandrindod Wells *p291* . . . 01597 822707
Wadebridge *p418* 01208 812415

Casey, Ms A (Last Cawthra Feather LLP) *E*
Bradford *p154* 01274 848800

Casey, Miss A M (Taunton Deane Borough Council)
Taunton *p473* 01823 356356

Casey, G (MKB Solicitors LLP) *N*
Barnsley *p124* 01226 210000

Casey, Mrs G R (Harcus Sinclair) *K1 K3 Q*
London WC2 *p38* 020 7242 9700

Casey, Mrs H (CB4law) *K1 D1 V K2*
Cambridge *p174*. 01223 316666

Casey, Ms J E (Glaisyers Solicitors LLP) *D1 K1*
Manchester *p304* 0161 224 3311

Casey, Ms L (Lewis Silkin LLP) *J1*
London EC4 *p53*. 020 7074 8000

Casey, R J (Switalski's)
Wakefield *p419* 01924 882000

Casey, R J (British American Tobacco)
London WC2 *p104*. 020 7845 1000

Casey, S (Arnold & Porter LLP) *Ze*
London EC2 *p7* 020 7786 6100

Casey, Miss S M (Caseys) *M1 G P F1 H L D1 K1 J1 N Zl Zm*
Highbridge *p250*. 01278 794495

Casey-Evans, K (Paris Smith LLP) *J1*
Southampton *p386*. 023 8048 2482

Cash, A J (Cartwright King)
Derby *p208* 01332 346111
Derby *p209* 01332 372372

Cash, H (Rooks Rider) *C1 C2 C3 F1*
London EC1 *p73*. 020 7689 7000

Cash, M (Penningtons)
Basingstoke *p127* 01256 407100

Cash, W N P (Radcliffes Le Brasseur)
Westminster *p70*. 020 7222 7040

Cashell, Ms B P M (Wake Smith & Tofields) *W*
Sheffield *p377* 0114 266 6660

Cashman, B J M (Byrne Frodsham & Co) *G H N*
Widnes *p431*. 0151 424 5601

Cashman, J (Holman Fenwick Willan)
London EC3 *p42*. 020 7264 8000

Cashman, Mrs J E (Thomson Snell & Passmore) *Zm W T2*
Tunbridge Wells *p415* 01892 510000

Cashman, M (Morgan Lewis & Bockius) *T1 T2*
London EC4 *p61*. 020 3201 5000

Cashman, O (Hartley & Worstenholme) *Q J1 O N*
Castleford *p183* 01977 732222

Cashman, R (SA Law Chambers) *N*
Ilford *p260*. 020 8554 0012

Cashmore, G (HCB Solicitors) *N P M1 K1 J1 Zl*
Solihull *p382*. 0121 705 2255

Cashmore, P A (McGrigors LLP)
London EC4 *p56*. 020 7054 2500

Casoojee, M R (Strasons) *S2 S1 E W*
London SW16 *p84*. 020 8677 7534

Casotti, M (A F Barker & Co) *E S1 K1 L P W*
Berkhamsted *p131*. 01442 863336

Cass, Miss M C (Bristows) *T1 T2*
London EC4 *p15*. 020 7400 8000

Cass, S (Chabra Cass & Co) *G H*
Brent *p19* . . . .020 8450 9833 / 8452 2200

Cassam, R I (Temple Law Solicitors)
Cardiff *p181* 029 2083 8970

Cassel, R D (Hatch Brenner) *J1 Zm Zl Zp J2*
Norwich *p334* 01603 660811

Cassidy, Ms A (Moore Blatch Solicitors) *Zr*
Richmond upon Thames *p364*020 8744 0766

Cassidy, Mrs A I (McKeag & Co) *D1 K1*
Gosforth *p231* 0191 213 1010

Cassidy, D M (Paul Dodds Solicitors) *Zr O Q N Zq J1 J2 Zj*
Wallsend *p419*. 0191 263 6200

Cassidy, J (Harris Cartier LLP) *O*
London WC2 *p39* 020 7405 7100

Cassidy, M J (Squire Sanders (UK) LLP) *E*
London EC2 *p81*. 020 7655 1000

Cassidy, M O (Pannone LLP) *N*
Manchester *p308* 0161 909 3000

Cassidy, N (Steele Ford & Newton)
Nelson *p321*. 01282 692531

Cassidy, Mrs S L (Field Fisher Waterhouse LLP)
London EC3 *p31*. 020 7861 4000

Cassidy, T M (Mills & Reeve) *E S2 R1 R2 Zv*
Birmingham *p140* 0121 454 4000

Cassidy, Miss V (Butcher Burns LLP) *S1 S2*
London WC1 *p16* 020 7713 7100

Cassidy, Ms V C (Wirral Borough Council)
Wallasey *p475* 0151 638 7070

Cassin, Mrs A J (Midwinters) *S1 E W S2 T2*
Cheltenham *p188* 01242 514674

Casson, M (LD Law) *B1 D1 D2 F1 J1 K1 L N P Q Zo Zk Zl Zy*
Harlow *p239*. 01279 441266

Casson, P (Craig Gee) *G H J1 K1 B2 J2 L Q N Zp*
Manchester *p304* 0161 666 9999

Casstles, A (Devonshires) *E*
London EC2 *p27*. 020 7628 7576
London EC2 *p66*. 020 7457 3000

Castagnino, P (Ashurst LLP)
London EC2 *p7* 020 7638 1111

Castell, J (Faegre & Benson LLP) *S2 E L*
London EC4 *p30*. 020 7450 4500

Castellani, L (Harbottle & Lewis LLP) *Q O J1 Zk*
London W1 *p38* 020 7667 5000

Casterton, Miss D S (TV Edwards LLP) *K1*
London SE8 *p85*. 020 7790 7000

Castiglione, Ms S (Metropolitan Police Directorate of Legal Services)
London SW1 *p108*. 020 7230 7210

Castka, Mrs I A (Wilson Browne) *E A1 S1 L*
Kettering *p265*. 01536 410041

Castle, A L (First Discount Ltd)
London EC2 *p106* 020 7739 5992

Castle, Mrs B E V (Castles) *W K4*
Hurstpierpoint *p258* .01273 836007 / 837107

Castle, Miss D J (Blake Lapthorn) *S1 L*
Portsmouth *p354*. 023 9222 1122

Castle, D T (The Castle Partnership) *G H Zl*
Woking *p436*. 01483 730062
Guildford *p235*. 01483 300905

Castle, Miss J L (Pinsent Masons LLP)
London EC2 *p67*. 020 7418 7000

Castle, J R (Castles) *E C1 S1*
Hurstpierpoint *p258* .01273 836007 / 837107

Castle, N A (Beaumont Legal) *B1 F1 J1 L N O Q Zl*
Wakefield *p418* 0845 122 8100

Castle, Miss N M (Irwin Mitchell LLP) *Zr*
Manchester *p306* 0870 150 0100

Castle, R J (Roland Robinsons & Fentons LLP) *G H*
Blackpool *p147* 01253 621432

Castle, R W (Cambridge City Council) *S1 W L*
Cambridge *p452*. 01223 457000

Castle, Miss S J (Reading Borough Council)
Reading *p469* 0118 939 0900

Castle, W A (Allen & Overy LLP)
London E1 *p5* 020 3088 0000

Castledine, Ms C (Westminster City Council)
London SW1 *p110*. 020 7641 6000

Castley, S J (Shook Hardy & Bacon LLP) *O*
London EC4 *p78*. 020 7332 4500

Castling, S H P (Kent Reliance Building Society)
Chatham *p454*. 01634 848944

Castrey, Ms A J E (Alison Castrey Limited)
Bristol *p162* 0117 962 2356

Castro, G (Teacher Stern LLP) *Zw Ze C1*
London WC1 *p86* 020 7242 3191

Caswell, Mrs A (Carters) *K4 V W T1*
Pontefract *p351* 01977 703224

Cataldo, Miss N S (Solomon Taylor & Shaw) *Q O L*
London NW3 *p80* 020 7431 1912

Catcheside, Ms S E C (Metropolitan Police Directorate of Legal Services) *K1 J1 N D1 Q V Zl*
London SW1 *p108*. 020 7230 7210

Catchpole, D (Mills & Reeve) *O Q B1 F1*
Norwich *p335* 01603 660155

Catchpole, Mrs P J (Penny Catchpole Solicitors) *Zo S1 D1 K1 N Q K2*
Winchester *p433*. 01962 866522

Cater, C J (Spicketts Battrick Law Practice) *N*
Pontypridd *p352* 01443 407221

Cater, Ms L (Lanyon Bowdler LLP) *S2 E*
Shrewsbury *p379* 01743 280280

Cater, Ms S A M (Morgan Cole) *J1 O Zp*
Oxford *p344*. 01865 262600

Cates, S A (Laytons) *J1 C1*
London EC4 *p52*. 020 7842 8000

Cathcart, J B (Cathcarts)
Ickenham *p259* . . .01895 631942 / 675631

Cathcart, Miss J E (Heringtons) *S1 W*
Rye *p370* 01797 222955

Cathcart, Miss K (Collins Solicitors) *K3 B1 B2 K1 N W Zq Zr*
Watford *p423* 01923 223324

Cathcart, P J (Cathcarts) *A3 C1 E M2 S2*
Ickenham *p259* . . .01895 631942 / 675631

Cathcart, T C (Birdsall & Snowball) *A1 C1 E K1 L S1 W*
Filey *p226*. 01723 515151

Catherall, H A (Gotelee) *G H O Zt*
Ipswich *p262*. 01473 211121

Catherall, Ms K E (Aaron & Partners LLP Solicitors) *E J1*
Chester *p190* 01244 405555

Cathie, F A (Barlow Lyde & Gilbert LLP) *O J1 Zq*
London EC3 *p10*. 020 7247 2277

Catlow, Mrs M J (The College of Law)
London WC1 *p105*. 0800 289997

Cato, J (Temple & Co Commercial Solicitors) *O J1 S2*
Daventry *p207*. 0845 241 4045
Northampton *p333*. 01604 622101

Caton, M (Barlow Lyde & Gilbert LLP)
London EC3 *p10*. 020 7247 2277

Caton, M J (Moore Blatch Solicitors) *E*
Southampton *p386*. 023 8071 8000

Caton, P M H (James Bowie Caton & Co) *B1 C1 D1 F1 G H K1 M1 N*
Ferndown *p225* . . .01202 875646 / 877225

Cattell, C V (Hadgkiss Hughes & Beale) *K3 F1 K1 L O Q N Zq V*
Birmingham *p138* 0121 449 5050
Birmingham *p139* 0121 707 8484

Catterall, A R (Taylors) *O C1 Ze Zb*
Manchester *p310* 0844 800 0263

See p634 for the Key to Work Categories

Catterall, Mrs L M (Royal College Of Nursing)
Leeds *p463* 0113 244 3648
Catterall, P (Howard Kennedy LLP) *R2 E*
London W1 *p48* 020 7636 1616
Catterick, Mrs A (Darlington Borough Council)
Darlington *p456* 01325 388055
Catterick, J W (ASB Law) *W*
Maidstone *p298* 01622 656500
Cattermole, S (Powleys) *D1 K1 N Zu*
Lowestoft *p294* 01502 581121
Catterson, Miss R F (Blackhurst Swainson Goodier LLP) *S2 E S1 W*
Lancaster *p269* 01524 32471
Catuara, Miss D (Healys LLP) *Q O Zq Zk*
Brighton *p159* 01273 685888
Caulcrick, Miss F M (TWM Solicitors LLP) *N Q O*
Epsom *p219* 01372 729555
Caulfield, A S (Gaby Hardwicke) *W*
Eastbourne *p215* 01323 435900
Caulfield, B J (Dechert) *O Zj*
London EC4 *p26* 020 7184 7000
Caulfield, Ms H M A (Royal College of Nursing)
London W1 *p109* 020 7409 3333
Caulfield, S (Hodge Jones & Allen LLP) *G H*
London NW1 *p41* 020 7874 8300
Caunt, A (McDermott Will & Emery UK LLP) *C2 C1*
London EC2 *p56* 020 7577 6900
Caunt, I G (Serjeant & Son) *K1 D1 N J1 L Q*
Ramsey *p359* 01487 812325
Causer, C G (K&L Gates LLP) *R2*
London EC4 *p47* 020 7648 9000
Causier, Miss K M (Irwin Mitchell LLP) *Zq O*
Sheffield *p376* 0870 150 0100
Causton, P R (Steele Raymond) *T2 T1 W A1 Zd Zo*
Bournemouth *p152* 01202 294566
Caute, E (Farrell Matthews & Weir) *G H*
London W6 *p31* 020 8741 1482
Cauter, M C (Edridges & Drummonds) *S1 W L E F1 R1 K1 C1*
South Croydon *p383* 020 8651 1218
Cauthery, H A (Hugh A Cauthery) *G H*
Wisbech *p435* 01945 464692
Cava, Miss C R (Glovers Solicitors LLP) *Zb R2*
London W1 *p36* 020 7935 8882
Cavalier, S (Thompsons (formerly Robin/Brian Thompson & Partners)) *J1 M1 Zg Zp*
Plymouth *p350* 01752 675810
Cavalla, M P (Sylvester Mackett) *W K4*
Trowbridge *p414* 01225 755621
Cavanagh, Miss G (Rawlins Davy PLC) *E F1 Ze Q*
Bournemouth *p152* 01202 558844
Cavanagh, Miss H (Lewis Silkin LLP) *C1*
London EC4 *p53* 020 7074 8000
Cavanagh, Mrs K (DWF) *N Q*
Liverpool *p287* 0151 907 3000
Cavanagh, Mrs N (Bradbury Roberts & Raby) *K1 K3*
Scunthorpe *p373* 01724 854000
Cave, A R (HC Solicitors LLP) *Zm Zg G*
Peterborough *p347* 01733 882800
Cave, D (Ashurst LLP)
London EC2 *p7* 020 7638 1111
Cave, H (Watson Burton LLP) *E*
Newcastle upon Tyne *p327* 0845 901 2100
Cave, H G (Mincoffs Solicitors LLP) *E R2*
Newcastle upon Tyne *p325* 0191 281 6151
Cave, J P (J P Cave & Co) *S1*
Thame *p410* 01844 216208
Thame *p410* 01844 212305
Cave, J S C (Bells Solicitors) *E S1 L*
Farnham *p224* 01252 733733
Cave, M A (Harrison Clark LLP)
Cheltenham *p188* 01242 269198
Worcester *p439* 01905 612001
Worcester *p439* 01905 612001
Cave, P J S (Atkinson Cave & Stuart) *G H*
Blackpool *p146* 01253 293151
Cave, S L (Goughs) *S1 W C1 E A1 L R1 Zd Zb*
Calne *p173* 01249 812086
Cave, Miss T (Veale Wasbrough Vizards) *N Zr*
Bristol *p165* 0117 925 2020
Cavell, D G (Environment Agency (Wales))
Cardiff *p453* 0870 850 6506
Cavell, Mrs F H (Stephens & Scown) *K1 D1 D2*
St Austell *p391* 01726 74433
Cavell, J R B (ASB Law) *E*
Maidstone *p298* 01622 656500
Caven, Mrs J L (Wakefield Court House)
Wakefield *p474* 01924 303461
Caveney, M (Middlesbrough Council)
Middlesbrough *p465* 01642 245432
Cavett-Dunsby, Ms E (Clifford Chance)
London E14 *p20* 020 7006 1000
Cavill, D (HM Land Registry - Hull)
Hull *p461* 01482 223244
Cavill, J C J (George Haworth Chappell & Whitworth) *K1 S1 F1 W*
Bury *p170* 01706 824811
Cawkwell, A (Muckle LLP) *B1 Zb*
Newcastle upon Tyne *p325* 0191 211 7777
Cawley, A (Barlow Lyde & Gilbert LLP) *Zj*
London EC3 *p10* 020 7247 2277
Cawley, W L W (Stephenson Harwood)
London EC2 *p82* 020 7329 4422
Cawood, Mrs C (Heptonstalls LLP) *N*
Pontefract *p351* 01977 602804
Cawthorn, E O (Berwick-upon-Tweed Borough Council)
Berwick-Upon-Tweed *p449* . . 01289 330044

Cawthorn, Ms M S (Wilkinson Woodward) *B1 F1 Q O J1 Zl Zp*
Halifax *p238* 01422 339600
Cawthorn, N S (Ashton KCJ) *Q N O*
Ipswich *p262* 01473 232425
Cawthorpe, Miss K (Russell-Cooke LLP) *E R2 S2 L*
London SW15 *p74* 020 8789 9111
Cawthron, M O (Pinsent Masons LLP) *T1 T2*
London EC2 *p67* 020 7418 7000
Caygill, Ms C S (Wyre Forest District Council)
Stourport-on-Severn *p473* . . 01562 820505
Cayless, N (Sacker & Partners LLP) *Zo*
London EC2 *p76* 020 7329 6699
Ceadel, Mrs D J (Darbys Solicitors LLP) *R2*
Oxford *p343* 01865 811700
Cecil, W (Curtis Davis Garrard) *O Za A3*
Uxbridge *p417* 020 8734 2800
Cenizo, Miss A (Darlingtons) *E W K1*
Edgware *p217* . 020 8952 0033 / 8951 6666
Centeleghe, D (Chester City Council) *R1*
Chester *p454* 01244 324324
Cephas, Mrs C (Venters Solicitors) *K1 K3 D1 D2*
London SE5 *p89* 020 7277 0110
Cereghino, Ms K (Lawson West Solicitors Limited) *A1 Zc C1 E P L Zl R1 S1*
Leicester *p280* 0116 212 1000
Cessford, Ms R K (Squire Sanders (UK) LLP)
London EC2 *p81* 020 7655 1000
Cestaro, Mrs J G (Smith Brown & Sprawson) *G H B2*
Luton *p295* 01582 876900
Cha, Ms A (Pinsent Masons LLP) *I Ze*
London EC2 *p67* 020 7418 7000
Cha, Ms S (Kennedys) *Zj*
London EC3 *p49* 020 7667 9667
Cha, W J B (Blake Lapthorn) *C1 Zl*
Portsmouth *p354* 023 9222 1122
Chabra, A (Chabra Cass & Co) *G H*
Brent *p19* . . . 020 8450 9833 / 8452 2200
Chad, D C M (AST Hampsons) *M1 N P G H J1 S1 B1 F1 K1 Zl Zc Zi*
Rochdale *p365* 01706 522311
Chad, Ms J (The Johnson Partnership) *G H*
Nottingham *p337* 0115 941 9141
Chada, R (Hodge Jones & Allen LLP) *B2 Zm G H Zy Zg*
London NW1 *p41* 020 7874 8300
Chadd, R J (Leathes Prior) *C1 C3 I M1 M2 R1 Ze Zf*
Norwich *p334* 01603 610911
Chadder, P A (Henmans LLP) *N Q Zr Zq*
Oxford *p343* 01865 781000
Chadha, Ms K K (Freemans Solicitors) *K1 D1*
London W1 *p34* 020 7935 3522
Chadha, P A (City of London Corporation)
London EC2 *p107* 020 7606 3030
Chadney, S (Herbert Smith LLP)
London EC2 *p40* 020 7374 8000
Chadwell, S L (Anderson Longmore & Higham) *B1 K4 P K1 T2 S1 E C1 W*
Petworth *p348* 01798 342391
Chadwick, C (Widdows Mason) *W S1*
Warrington *p422* 01925 632267
Chadwick, D B (Crown Prosecution Service Durham)
Durham *p457* 0191 383 5800
Chadwick, Ms D E (Olswang LLP) *C1 C2*
London WC1 *p64* 020 7067 3000
Chadwick, D M (Mayer Brown International LLP) *Zj Zq O*
London EC2 *p59* 020 3130 3000
Chadwick, G J (Actons) *N*
Nottingham *p335* 0115 910 0200
Chadwick, G M (The Mersey Docks & Harbour Co)
Liverpool *p463* 0151 949 6000
Chadwick, G W A (Taylor Vinters) *W T2*
Cambridge *p176* 01223 423444
Chadwick, J (Kettering Borough Council)
Kettering *p462* 01536 410333
Chadwick, Miss K L (Pannone LLP) *C1 C2 C3 Ze*
Manchester *p308* 0161 909 3000
Chadwick, Ms L (Pannone LLP) *K1*
Manchester *p308* 0161 909 3000
Chadwick, Ms L (Winston Solicitors LLP) *W K4 C1*
Leeds *p278* 0113 320 5000
Chadwick, N (Tinsdills) *S1 E W G*
Newcastle under Lyme *p323* . 01782 612311
Chadwick, Miss N (Peasegoods) *L N*
Manchester *p308* 0161 205 2772
Chadwick, R E (Awdry Bailey & Douglas) *C1 C2 S1 E J1 S2*
Devizes *p210* 01380 722311
Chadwick, S P (Debenhams Ottaway) *N O Q Zq*
St Albans *p390* 01727 837161
Chadwick, W P (Mander Cruickshank Solicitors LLP) *A1 B1 C1 E S1 W Zl Zv*
Coalville *p196* 01530 510666
Chadwyck-Healey, N G (Chadwyck-Healey & Co) *G H B2*
London EC4 *p19* 020 7353 6900
Chaffee, Miss M J (Brignalls Balderston Warren) *W*
Letchworth *p283* 01462 482248
Chaffer, Miss L R (Biscoes) *K1 K3*
Gosport *p232* 023 9251 2030
Chaffey, M D (Dyne Drewett Solicitors Ltd) *S1*
Sherborne *p378* 01935 813691
Chaggar, R S (LG Lawyers) *E S2*
London SE1 *p50* 020 7379 0000
Chagger, Mrs S (Mullis & Peake) *S1*
Romford *p366* 01708 784000

Chahal, Miss K K (Edward Fail Bradshaw & Waterson) *G B2 H*
London EC3 *p30* 020 7790 4032
Chahal, Mrs R (NFLA Ltd) *D1 K1 K3*
Nottingham *p338* 0115 945 4555
Chahal, S (Bindmans LLP) *L Zm*
London WC1 *p12* 020 7833 4433
Chakrabarti, A M (Allen & Overy LLP)
London E1 *p5* 020 3088 0000
Chakrabarti, Mrs S (Hills Solicitors Limited) *K3 D1 K1 V W*
Bolton *p149* 01204 388300
Chakravortty, Ms S (Jones Day) *Zb*
London EC4 *p46* 020 7039 5959
Chalcraft, D J (Alexander & Partners) *N D1 K1 G Zi Zr H D2 B2*
Brent *p5* 020 8965 7121
Chalfont-Griffin, M (Chubb Bulleid) *E S2 A1 S1*
Street *p400* 01749 836100
Chalk, W A M (Hewitsons) *W*
Cambridge *p174* 01223 461155
Chalkley, A D (Boyes Turner) *O Q*
Reading *p360* 0118 959 7711
Chalkley, R A (Hill Hofstetter LLP) *E L R1 P A1 Zn*
Solihull *p382* 0121 210 6000
Challands, R (Bond Pearce LLP) *Zj Zq*
Plymouth *p349* 0845 415 0000
Challender, B J (Taylors) *S2 R1 E*
Blackburn *p146* 0844 800 0263
Challinor, Mrs S (Leathes Prior) *E S2 Zc R1 L Zm*
Norwich *p334* 01603 610911
Challis, T J (Weightmans LLP) *N O Q*
Dartford *p207* 020 7822 1900
Chalmers, A (DLA Piper UK LLP)
Sheffield *p375* 0870 011 1111
Chalmers, Ms S (Diageo PLC)
London W1 *p105* 020 7927 5300
Chaloner, P M (Adams & Remers) *E J1 S1*
Lewes *p283* 01273 480616
Seaford *p373* 01323 899331
Chalton, S N L (Bird & Bird LLP) *I*
London EC4 *p13* 020 7415 6000
Chamberlain, A (Holman Fenwick Willan)
London EC3 *p42* 020 7264 8000
Chamberlain, Mrs A A (AWB Charlesworth LLP) *O Q L Zq Zl F2 Ze*
Keighley *p263* 01535 613678
Chamberlain, A M J (Addleshaw Goddard)
Manchester *p300* 0161 934 6000
Chamberlain, C (Chamberlains) *S1 E W L C1 Zc Ze Zo S2*
Bishop's Waltham *p144* . . . 01489 896141
Chamberlain, Ms E J M (Morgan Cole) *T1 W Zd*
Oxford *p344* 01865 262600
Chamberlain, Mrs F (Oxfordshire County Council)
Oxford *p468* 01865 792422
Chamberlain, Miss H B (Chamberlains) *S1 R1 W*
Bishop's Waltham *p144* . . . 01489 896141
Chamberlain, K (Chamberlain Thomas & Co) *S1 N L K1 E D1 R1 C1*
Wirral *p435* 0151 633 2800
Chamberlain, Miss M (Travers Smith LLP) *C1*
London EC1 *p87* 020 7295 3000
Chamberlain, Miss N (Kelcey & Hall) *K1 D1*
Bristol *p163* 0117 927 9604
Chamberlain, N J (Gordons LLP)
Leeds *p273* 0113 227 0100
Chamberlain, P (Ashurst LLP)
London EC2 *p7* 020 7638 1111
Chamberlain, P (Brabners Chaffe Street) *J1*
Manchester *p301* 0161 836 8800
Chamberlain, R C (Swayne Johnson Solicitors) *S1 W E C1 A1 T1 L Zd S2*
Denbigh *p208* 01745 812835
St Asaph *p391* 01745 582535
Chamberlain, S T (Field Fisher Waterhouse LLP)
London EC3 *p31* 020 7861 4000
Chamberlain, T K (DAC Beachcroft) *M1 N*
London EC3 *p24* 020 7208 6800
Chamberlain, T R T (EMW) *W*
Milton Keynes *p316* 0845 070 6000
Chamberlain, Mrs V C (Hawley & Rodgers) *K1*
Loughborough *p293* 01509 230333
Chamberlayne, J C (Stewarts Law LLP) *N*
London EC4 *p83* 020 7822 8000
Chamberlin, A M F (Chamberlins) *E C1 W S1 T1 A1 Zm*
Hitchin *p251* 01462 623456
Chamberlin, Ms J (Sansbury Douglas) *G H*
Bristol *p164* 0117 955 2663
Chambers, A P (Seatons Solicitors) *N Q W J1 L F1*
Corby *p199* 01536 276300
Chambers, E B (Campbell Chambers) *B2 G H Zi*
London EC1 *p18* 020 7691 8777
Chambers, G (Gisby Harrison) *Q L*
Cheshunt *p189* 01707 878300
Chambers, Miss J A (Shulmans) *C1 Zd*
Leeds *p276* 0113 245 2833
Chambers, Ms J M (Needham Poulier & Partners) *G H*
London N17 *p63* 020 8808 6622
Chambers, Dr J P (DWF) *J1*
Liverpool *p287* 0151 907 3000
Chambers, Mrs K A (Livingstons) *S1 S2*
Ulverston *p416* 01229 585555
Chambers, M D (Kenwright & Lynch) *K1 K3 D1 D2 K2*
Wandsworth *p49* 020 8767 1211
Chambers, Mrs N (AWB Charlesworth LLP) *S2 S1 A1 C1 E L*
Skipton *p381* 01756 793333

Chambers, Mrs R (Anderson Longmore & Higham) *S1*
Storrington *p399* 01903 745666
Chambers, Ms S T (Colman Coyle LLP) *N Zm*
Islington *p22* 020 7354 3000
Chambers, Ms T (Financial Services Authority)
London E14 *p106* 020 7066 1000
Champaneri, A (Winston Solicitors LLP) *J1 Q S2*
Leeds *p278* 0113 320 5000
Champaneria, K (Gittins McDonald) *K1 G D1 H D2 K3*
Wrexham *p442* 01978 291662
Champkin, J R (J R Champkin) *O C1 S2 Zw Ze J1 B1*
Evesham *p220* 01386 871287
Chan, E (Linklaters LLP)
London EC2 *p54* 020 7456 2000
Chan, Ms E L S L (Squire Sanders (UK) LLP)
London EC2 *p81* 020 7655 1000
Chan, Miss J (Seddons) *N G*
Westminster *p77* 020 7725 8000
Chan, J C P (James Chan & Co) *C1 C2 J1 O E*
London EC4 *p19* 0844 848 9988
Chan, Miss L G (Knowsley Metropolitan Borough Council)
Huyton *p461* 0151 443 3593
Chan, Ms M Y (Lloyds TSB Group PLC) *B1 C1 C2 Zg*
Bristol *p452* 0117 905 5500
Chan, R (Arc Property Solicitors LLP) *S1 S2 E O B1*
Harrogate *p240* 0800 612 9097
Chan, Mrs S L (Wilson Browne) *J1 N O Q*
Kettering *p265* 01536 410041
Chan, Miss S M (Seatons Solicitors) *K1 G H N L Q F1 Zv*
Corby *p199* 01536 276300
Chan, T (Judge & Priestley) *E K4 K1 S1 T2 W*
Bromley *p166* 020 8290 0333
Chan, W Y (Brady Eastwood Pierce & Stewart)
Lewisham *p15* 020 8692 8181
Chana, Miss J (Jones Day) *E*
London EC4 *p46* 020 7039 5959
Chana, Mrs K (Fraser Brown) *B1 O Q Zq*
Nottingham *p337* 0115 988 8777
Chana, Miss S (Vickers & Co) *S1*
Ealing *p89* . . . 020 8579 2559 / 8840 3999
Chanan, Ms S Y (Salehs LLP) *W*
Manchester *p309* 0161 434 9991
Chander, Miss A R (Martin-Kaye LLP) *J1*
Telford *p409* 01952 272222
Chandler, Ms B (Charles Lucas & Marshall) *N Zq*
Swindon *p406* 01793 511055
Chandler, Mrs C (Abney Garsden McDonald) *N*
Cheadle *p185* 0161 482 8822
Chandler, Miss C E (Taylor Wessing) *N O Zj*
London EC4 *p86* 020 7300 7000
Chandler, C H M (Chandler Ray) *A1 C1 E L S1 S2 R2 W C2*
Buckingham *p167* 01280 814040
Chandler, G F (GCA Solicitors (Giffen Couch & Archer)) *K3 K1 L W S1 D2 V*
Luton *p295* 01582 410041
Chandler, Ms H (Shoosmiths)
Milton Keynes *p317* . 0370 086 8300 / 01908 488300
Chandler, J (Neil Myerson LLP) *J1*
Altrincham *p117* 0161 941 4000
Chandler, J R (DLA Piper UK LLP)
London EC2 *p24* 0870 011 1111
Chandler, Miss K S E (Greene & Greene) *K3 K1*
Bury St Edmunds *p171* . . . 01284 762211
Chandler, M J (EJ Winter & Son) *F1 W G H J1 K1 L N S1 Zg Zi Zv Zw Zq*
Reading *p361* 0118 957 4424
Chandler, N (SNR Denton) *Zb*
London EC4 *p75* 020 7242 1212
Chandler, Ms P A (Pannone LLP) *N J2 Zq*
Manchester *p308* 0161 909 3000
Chandler, S A L (Chandler Harris LLP) *C1 M1 W E*
Manchester *p302* 0161 834 2200
Chandler, Mrs S E (Sharman Law) *K1 V*
Bedford *p130* 01234 303030
Chandler, S P (Wortley Byers) *A1 C1 E P Zc*
Brentwood *p156* 01277 268368
Chandler, Miss V A (Blake Lapthorn) *O*
Chandlers Ford *p184* 023 8090 8090
Chandler, W (Hill Dickinson LLP) *E R2 S2 R1 L*
Liverpool *p288* 0151 600 8000
Chandra, P (Parry Law)
Whitstable *p431* 01227 276276
Chandraratna, Mrs S K V (John Fowlers LLP Solicitors) *G*
Colchester *p197* 01206 576151
Chandrasena, Mrs N M (Chands & Co)
Pinner *p348* 020 8933 8332
Chang, Ms H (Pinsent Masons LLP)
London EC2 *p67* 020 7418 7000
Channa, Mrs K K (Slough Borough Council)
Slough *p471* 01753 552288
Channer, G J O (Ashfords LLP) *S1 W A1*
Taunton *p408* 01823 232300
Channer, N (Corby Borough Council)
Corby *p456* 01536 402551
Channer, T N (McMillan Williams) *Zr N*
South Croydon *p383* 020 8253 7600
Chanot, Mrs J E (Hartnell Chanot & Partners Family Law Specialists) *K1 K2 D1 D2 K3*
Exeter *p221* 01392 421777
Chant, D (Ford & Warren) *G Zt*
Leeds *p273* 0113 243 6601

6

Chant, Mrs M L (Blake Lapthorn) *C1 C2 C3 M1*
Chandlers Ford *p184* 023 8090 8090
Chanter, M H (Foot Anstey) *N K1 O F1 D1 B1 Q*
Truro *p414*. 01872 243300
Chantler, Miss H (Morrisons Solicitors LLP) *W K4*
Redhill *p362* 01737 854500
Chantler, M J (Farrer & Co LLP)
London WC2 *p31* 020 3375 7000
Chantler, M J K (George Davies Solicitors LLP) *Zw Ze Zf Zd N Q*
Manchester *p303* 0161 236 8992
Chantrey, Miss F J (Zermansky & Partners) *Q Zp*
Leeds *p278* 0113 245 9766
Chape, P (JMW Solicitors) *S2 E R1 R2 C1*
Manchester *p306* 0845 872 6666
Chapelow, M J (Howard Kennedy LLP) *C1 M2*
London W1 *p48* 020 7636 1616
Chaplin, A J (Chivers Walsh Smith and Irvine & Co) *K1 D1*
Bradford *p153* 01274 740077
Chaplin, Ms J (Hague & Dixon) *W S1*
York *p444* 01904 627111
Chaplin, M P (Chaplin & Co) *C1 E I S1 O Q J1 K1 W L Zc Zf Zl*
Stanmore *p394* 020 8954 8202
Chaplin, Ms R (Reynolds Porter Chamberlain LLP)
London E1 *p71* 020 3060 6000
Chaplin, S P A (Nelsons) *K1 G H S1*
Nottingham *p338*. 0115 958 6262
Chapman, A (Bermans LLP) *B1 C1 E J1 R1 Zl L W Zb S2 C2*
Liverpool *p286*. 0151 224 0500
Chapman, A (Land Law LLP) *A1 S2 E*
Altrincham *p116* 0161 928 8383
Chapman, A (Croftons) *S1 L R1 W Zd Zh*
Manchester *p302* 0161 214 6180
Chapman, Ms A B (Quality Solicitors Chapman & Chubb) *K1 K2 W Zd D2*
Alfreton *p115* 01773 540480
Chapman, A D (Baileys) *C1 E S1 Zc S2*
Cheltenham *p187* 01242 514477
Chapman, A J (Skanska UK PLC)
Rickmansworth *p470*. 01923 776666
Chapman, A P (Treasury Solicitors Department)
London WC2 *p110*. 020 7210 3000
Chapman, Mrs A R (Jameson & Hill) *W J1*
Ware *p421*. 01920 460531
Hertford *p248* 01992 554881
Chapman, B L (Peter Dunn & Co) *G H J1 V*
Sunderland *p401*. 0191 568 9000
Chapman, C (Ellesmere Port & Neston Borough Council)
Ellesmere Port *p458* 0151 356 6789
Chapman, Ms C (DWF)
Liverpool *p287*. 0151 907 3000
Chapman, Ms C (Radcliffes Le Brasseur)
Westminster *p70*. 020 7222 7040
Chapman, Miss C (Radcliffes Le Brasseur) *I G Zr B2 Zk J1 N*
Leeds *p276* 0113 234 1220
Chapman, Miss C (Thompsons (formerly Robin/Brian Thompson & Partners)) *J2 N J1 G Zp*
Plymouth *p350*. 01752 675810
Chapman, C (Thames Water Utilities Limited)
Reading *p469* 0118 373 8000
Chapman, C (Charles Russell LLP) *T1 W*
London EC4 *p19*. 020 7203 5000
Chapman, C G (Linder Myers Solicitors) *S1 W L T1 R1 C1 F1 N Zh Zo*
Manchester *p307* 0844 984 6400
Chapman, C J (Barnes Marsland) *J1*
Margate *p312* 01843 221466
Chapman, D (Leathes Prior) *J1*
Norwich *p334* 01603 610911
Chapman, D A (Wortley Byers) *Q N S1 G E F1 J1 L*
Brentwood *p156* 01277 268368
Chapman, D P (Phillips & Co) *G H*
Salisbury *p371*. 01722 321666
Chapman, Mrs E (Anthony Gold) *K1 K3 D1*
London SE1 *p6* 020 7940 4000
Chapman, E (Kirbys) *K4 K1 S1 T2 W*
Harrogate *p240* 01423 542000
Chapman, Ms E (Ormerods) *K1*
Croydon *p205* 020 8686 5000
Chapman, Mrs E M (Weightmans LLP) *N Q*
Liverpool *p291*. 0151 227 2601
Chapman, Miss F J D (MacDonald Oates LLP) *K1 K3*
Midhurst *p316* 01730 816711
Chapman, G (Warner & Richardson) *S1 W A1 E L K1 T1 M1 G F1*
Winchester *p434*. 01962 868366
Chapman, Ms G (Linklaters LLP)
London EC2 *p54*. 020 7456 2000
Chapman, G H G (Bridge McFarland) *D1 D2 F1 K1 L N Q W Zq*
Grimsby *p235* 01472 311711
Chapman, G H L (Coffin Mew & Clover) *E L S1 S2 Zh*
Fareham *p223*. 01329 825617
Chapman, G K C (Lamberts) *S1 E L W*
Paddock Wood *p344*. 01892 833456
Chapman, G W (Merthyr Tydfil County Borough Council)
Merthyr Tydfil *p465* 01685 725000
Chapman, Ms H (Bradbury Roberts & Raby) *K1 K3*
Scunthorpe *p373*. 01724 854000
Chapman, J (Keoghs LLP) *Q N*
Coventry *p200* 024 7665 8200
Chapman, J (Ashurst LLP)
London EC2 *p7* 020 7638 1111

Chapman, Mrs J (Environment Agency (Wales))
Cardiff *p453* 0870 850 6506
Chapman, Ms J (Bolt Burdon) *N*
Islington *p14*. 020 7288 4700
Chapman, Ms J (Russell-Cooke LLP) *E S2*
London SW15 *p74*. 020 8789 9111
Chapman, J H (Kirklees Metropolitan Borough Council)
Huddersfield *p461* 01484 221421
Chapman, J T (Yates Ardern) *G H B2*
Ashton-under-Lyne *p120*. . . 0161 330 3332
Chapman, J T (Bevan Brittan LLP) *C1 E R2*
London EC4 *p12*. 0870 194 1000
Chapman, J T (Wolferstans) *S1 A1*
Plymouth *p351*. 01752 663295
Chapman, Miss K (Vanderpump & Sykes) *K3 K1 K2 D1 D2*
Enfield *p219*. 020 8367 3999
Chapman, Ms K E (Druces LLP) *E L Zs*
London EC2 *p27*. 020 7638 9271
Chapman, Ms K E (Cadbury Schweppes PLC (Legal Dept))
Birmingham *p449* 0121 625 7000
Chapman, M (Darbys Solicitors LLP) *K1 K3*
Oxford *p343*. 01865 811700
Chapman, M (George Davies Solicitors LLP) *K1*
Manchester *p303* 0161 236 8992
Chapman, M (Venters Solicitors)
London SE5 *p89*. 020 7277 0110
Chapman, M R (Wade & Davies) *S1 A1 E K1 W T1*
Great Dunmow *p233*. 01371 872816
Chapman, N D (Dale & Newbery LLP) *S2 C1 E L S1*
Staines *p393*. 01784 464491
Redhill *p362* 01737 780295
Chapman, O (Reed Smith LLP) *E*
London EC2 *p71*. 020 3116 3000
Chapman, Mrs O A M (Burley & Geach) *S1*
Haslemere *p243*. 01428 656011
Chapman, O J (Russell-Cooke LLP) *R1 R2 S1*
London WC1 *p74* 020 7405 6566
Chapman, P (Clarke Willmott) *N O Q Zq*
Bristol *p162* 0845 209 1000 / 0117 305 6000
Chapman, P (Keith Flower & Co)
Pinner *p348* 020 8868 1277
Chapman, P (Bird & Bird LLP) *I U1*
London EC4 *p13*. 020 7415 6000
Chapman, P A (Mitchells) *K1 J1 D1 Q*
York *p445* 01904 623751
Chapman, Miss P J (Bircham Dyson Bell) *W*
Westminster *p13*. 020 7227 7000
Chapman, P R (Wall James Chappell) *C1 F1 J1*
Stourbridge *p399* 01384 371622
Chapman, Ms R (Bird & Bird LLP) *R2 E L*
London EC4 *p13*. 020 7415 6000
Chapman, R A J (Trethowans LLP) *E S2 R2*
Salisbury *p371*. 01722 412512
Chapman, Miss S (QualitySolicitors C Turner) *N Q*
Blackburn *p145* 01254 688400
Chapman, Mrs S C (Susan Chapman) *S1 E W*
Nailsea *p320*. 01275 401996
Chapman, S J (Laytons) *O Ze*
Guildford *p236*. 01483 407000
Chapman, S J (Pinsent Masons LLP) *O*
Leeds *p276* 0113 244 5000
Chapman, T (Kent County Council)
Canterbury *p453*. 01227 767020
Chapman, T (Kent County Council)
Maidstone *p464* 01622 694320
Chapman, V (Bingham McCutchen (London) LLP)
London EC2 *p12*. 020 7661 5300
Chappel, O H (Grylls & Paige) *S1 S2 W*
Redruth *p363* . . . .01209 215261 / 215357
Chappell, Ms A (Boodle Hatfield)
Westminster *p14*. 020 7629 7411
Chappell, Ms B A (B A Chappell & Co) *D1 K1 N E L P S1 F1 J1 M1*
Chelmsford *p186*. 01245 251650
Chappell, C D (Chappell Pascoe) *Q N F1 O L J1 J2*
Crowborough *p204*. 01892 664348
Chappell, Mrs M T (Hague & Dixon) *S1 S2 W*
Pickering *p348*. 01751 475222
Chappell, N R (Miles & Cash) *G H K1 J1 M1 P F1 V L*
Heanor *p246*. 01773 530000
Chappell, Mrs S M (Burnetts) *N*
Carlisle *p181*. 01228 552222
Carlisle *p182*. 01228 552222
Chapple Gill, S T (Brabners Chaffe Street) *E*
Liverpool *p286*. 0151 600 3000
Chapple, D A (Chapple & Co) *G K1 N E Q O L F1 D1 H Zl K3*
March *p312* 01354 652550
Chapple, J L (Challinors) *K1 G H D1 P M1 N F1 J1 B1 Ze Zl Zp*
Halesowen *p237*. 0121 550 0481
Charalambous, C (Stokoe Partnership) *G H*
Waltham Forest *p83* 020 8558 8884
Charalambous, H (Prince Evans)
Ealing *p69*. 020 8567 3477
Charalambous, L (Simons Muirhead & Burton) *G N P Q*
London W1 *p79* 020 7734 4499
Charan, Ms P K (Treasury Solicitors Department)
London WC2 *p110*. 020 7210 3000
Charandeep, S (JS Law)
Hayes *p245* 020 8817 1004
Chard, A (Adrian Chard & Co)
Basingstoke *p126* 01256 363944
Chard, Miss C R (Allders (Croydon) Ltd)
Croydon *p456* 020 8603 7400

Chard, D (Langleys) *C1 E S1 Zd*
York *p445* 01904 610886
Charity, Mrs A (Paul Davidson Taylor) *O C1 B1 F1 Zc Zl*
Horsham *p253*. 01403 262333
Charles, A B (Bazeley Barnes & Bazeley) *P M1 K1 S1 G H J1 W*
Bideford *p132* 01237 473122
Charles, D W T (Charles Crookes & Jones) *E W A1 S1*
Caerphilly *p172* 029 2086 0628
Charles, G P (Graham Charles & Co)
Tunbridge Wells *p415* 01892 511766
Charles, J A (Sebastians)
London EC4 *p77*. 020 7583 2105
Charles, Miss J C (Mosshaselhurst) *S1 W*
Northwich *p333* 01606 74301
Charles, J M (J M Charles & Co)
Ickenham *p259* 01895 634402
Charles, Mrs K A (Richard Wilson Solicitors Ltd) *K1 L S1*
Goring *p231* 01491 879100
Charles, Ms L (Carey Law)
Alton *p116*. . . . .
Charles, O P (Oliver Charles) *N O Q K1 C1 E F1 D1 W Zd Zl*
Leicester *p279*. 0116 243 1166
Charles, R T (Lyons Davidson) *N O Q*
Bristol *p163* 0117 904 6000
Charles, Ms S (Howard Kennedy LLP) *Q Zf Zk*
London W1 *p48* 020 7636 1616
Charles, S M (Sinclairs)
Penarth *p345* 029 2070 6444
Charles-Jones, P (Waltons & Morse LLP) *Za O Q A3*
London EC3 *p90*. 020 7623 4255
Charles-Ward, Mrs J T (Sternberg Reed) *Zr*
Barking *p123* 020 8591 3366
Charlesworth, M N (Glaisyers Solicitors LLP) *S1 S2 L E W*
Manchester *p304* 0161 832 4666
Charlson, Mrs J (Carillion PLC)
Wolverhampton *p477* 01902 422431
Charlton, Mrs A E (Surrey County Council)
Kingston upon Thames *p462*. 020 8541 9088
Charlton, A H (Fraser Dawbarns) *S1 S2 F1 P E*
Downham Market *p213* . . . 01366 383171
Charlton, C (Clarke Willmott) *R1 Zu P Zh*
Bristol *p162* 0845 209 1000 / 0117 305 6000
Charlton, Ms C I (C&C Family Law) *K1 K3*
Plymouth *p349*. 01752 222211
Charlton, D F (Alliance Boots PLC)
Nottingham *p467*. 0115 950 6111
Charlton, D M (Ward Hadaway) *C1*
Newcastle upon Tyne *p327* . 0191 204 4000
Charlton, Mrs J (Harvey Ingram Borneos)
Newport Pagnell *p329* 01908 613545
Charlton, Ms J (David Gray Solicitors) *Zi*
Newcastle upon Tyne *p324* . 0191 232 9547
Charlton, J C (Terry Jones Solicitors & Advocates) *K3 K1 D1*
Shrewsbury *p379* 01743 285888
Charlton, P J (Clifford Chance)
London E14 *p20*. 020 7006 1000
Charlton, R (Davenport Lyons)
London W1 *p25* 020 7468 2600
Charlton, Ms S P (Dorset County Council)
Dorchester *p457* 01305 251000
Charlton, S R (Weightmans LLP) *D1 C1 K4 K1 N Q Zm Zr*
Birmingham *p143* 0121 632 6100
Charlwood, Ms D (Kennedys)
London EC3 *p49*. 020 7667 9667
Charman, D M (Rich & Carr Freer Bouskell) *N P Q G H K1 L*
Leicester *p281* 0116 253 8021
Charman, Ms L A (Wellers Law Group LLP) *F1 J1 K1 L N Q S1 W Zl*
Bromley *p167* 020 8464 4242
Charmbury, Ms R (Squire Sanders (UK) LLP)
Leeds *p277* 0113 284 7000
Charnley, D R (Sternberg Reed) *G H*
Romford *p366* 01708 766155
Charnley, F B D (Berry Redmond & Robinson) *K1 N Q*
Weston-super-Mare *p429* . . 01934 513963
Charnley, Miss L (MacLaren Britton) *L Q N*
Nottingham *p338*. 0115 941 1469
Charnley, M J (John Boyle & Co) *G H*
Redruth *p362* 01209 213507
Charnley, Mrs R C (SFN Solicitors) *N*
Burnley *p169* 01282 421284
Charnley, Mrs S J (Breens Solicitors) *W*
Liverpool *p286*. 0151 928 6544
Charnley, W F (McDermott Will & Emery UK LLP) *C2 C1*
London EC2 *p56*. 020 7577 6900
Charnock, J H (Butcher & Barlow LLP) *S1 W*
Runcorn *p369* 01928 572268
Charnock-Neal, Ms G M (John O'Neill & Co) *K1 K2 K3 D1 D2 Q N O F1*
Gosforth *p232* 0191 246 4000
Charon, R D (Klimt & Co) *E C1 S1 L*
Westminster *p50*. 020 7486 4432
Charrot, Ms E (Hill Dickinson LLP)
Manchester *p305* 0161 817 7200
Charrot, R C B (George Davies Solicitors LLP) *K3 K1 M2*
Manchester *p303* 0161 236 8992
Manchester *p308* 0161 909 3000
Chart, J D (Barnett Alexander Conway Ingram) *S1 E N C1 P B1 L R1 Ze Zo*
London N3 *p10* 020 8349 7680

Chart, R P (Reynolds Porter Chamberlain LLP) *O Zj Q Zq*
London E1 *p71* 020 3060 6000
Charter, M (Blake Lapthorn) *A1 A2 E*
Chandlers Ford *p184* 023 8090 8090
Charter, P A (Barlow Lyde & Gilbert LLP)
London EC3 *p10*. 020 7247 2277
Charuk, A (Godloves) *N*
Leeds *p273* 0113 225 8811
Charvet, C (Withers LLP) *S1*
London EC4 *p92*. 020 7597 6000
Chase, Ms B (Department for Business, Enterprise and Regulatory Reform)
London SW1 *p105*. 020 7215 0105
Chase, Mrs B M (McCarthy & Stone PLC)
Bournemouth *p450*. 01202 292480
Chase, G J (Clark Ricketts LLP) *M3*
London WC2 *p20* 020 7240 6767
Chase, Miss V (Harvey Ingram LLP) *C1*
Leicester *p280*. 0116 254 5454
Chasmer, Mrs M (Prettys)
Chelmsford *p187*. 01245 295295
Chataway, B T (Hopkin Murray Beskine) *L*
London N4 *p42* 020 7272 1234
Chatburn, Miss S E (Blackhurst Swainson Goodier LLP) *S1 W*
Preston *p356* 01772 253841
Chater, M (Morton Solicitors) *C1 S2 Ze J1 K1 S1 W*
Dunstable *p214* 01582 501240
Chater, Mrs S J (LDJ Solicitors) *K1*
Nuneaton *p339* 024 7674 5000
Chater, S P (Addleshaw Goddard)
London EC1 *p4* 020 7606 8855
London E1 *p5* 020 3088 0000
Chatfield, C (Waltons & Morse LLP) *O M2 Q*
London EC3 *p90*. 020 7623 4255
Chatham, T C (Penmans) *S1 G F1 C1 B1 L H J1*
Kenilworth *p264* 01926 858222
Chatters, N (Lloyd Green Solicitors) *N Q F1 J1 J2 Zj*
Chelmsford *p187*. 01245 294600
Chatterton, A J (Foys Solicitors) *C1 S1 S2 W*
Doncaster *p211* 01302 327136
Chatterton, Mrs J K (Fox Williams) *J1 Zi*
London EC2 *p33*. 020 7628 2000
Chatterton, K (Jordans) *N*
Dewsbury *p210* 01924 457171
Chatterton, Ms T (The College of Law Chester)
Chester *p454* 0800 289997
Chatwell, Ms E J (Green Wright Chalton Annis) *S1*
Worthing *p441*. 01903 234064
Steyning *p395*. 01903 814190
Chaudary, Miss S (Capsticks Solicitors LLP) *S2 E S1 R2*
London SW19 *p18* 020 8780 2211
Chaudhari, P (Lanyon Bowdler LLP) *A1 E P R1 S1*
Telford *p409*. 01952 291222
Chaudhary, Miss A (Harvey Ingram LLP) *E S2*
Leicester *p280*. 0116 254 5454
Chaudhary, M R (Oxley & Coward Solicitors LLP) *O Q J1*
Rotherham *p367*. 01709 510999
Chaudhri, Miss T (Legal and Professional Claims Ltd)
London EC4 *p107* 020 7621 3900
Chaudhry, B S (Owen Nash & Co) *B2 G H*
Walsall *p420*. 01922 746746
Chaudhry, M S (Stokes Solicitors)
Portsmouth *p355*. 023 9282 8131
Chaudhuri, Ms A A (Edwards Angell Palmer & Dodge)
London EC2 *p28*. 020 7583 4055
Chaudri, Ms A (Bristows) *Ze*
London EC4 *p15*. 020 7400 8000
Chaudry, A R (Slough Borough Council) *K1 L N O Q S1 B1 E W G Zi Zl Zp*
Slough *p471*. 01753 552288
Chaudry, N (Dodd Lewis Solicitors) *Q L*
London SE3 *p27*. 020 8852 1255
Chauhan, Miss L (Vickers & Co) *K1*
Ealing *p89*. . . . .020 8579 2559 / 8840 3999
Chauhan, N (Jaffe Porter Crossick)
London NW6 *p46* 020 7625 4424
Chauhan, Mrs Z (Josiah Hincks) *D2 D1 K3 K1*
Blaby *p145* 0116 264 3430
Chavda, H (Henmans LLP) *C1 Ze C2 U2 F1 F2 U1 Zza I M1 Zu*
Oxford *p343*. 01865 781000
Chave-Hill, Mrs L L (Eldridges) *S1*
Freshwater *p227*. 01983 752492
Chawdary, Mrs S (Carvers (Part of the Wilkes Partnership LLP)) *K1*
Birmingham *p136* 0121 784 8484
Chawla, Miss D K (Henmans LLP) *Zr*
Oxford *p343*. 01865 781000
Chawner, Ms J (Shentons) *K3 K1*
Winchester *p434*. 01962 844544
Chayra, S (Howes Percival LLP) *Q*
Leicester *p280*. 0116 247 3500
Cheadle, Mrs C J (EAD Solicitors LLP)
Liverpool *p287*. 0151 734 4339
Cheadle, K (Higgs & Sons) *E S1 S2*
Brierley Hill *p158*. 0845 111 5050
Cheah, Miss E (Vance Harris) *S1 S2*
London E14 *p89*. 020 7538 5232
Cheal, J (Dyne Drewett Solicitors Ltd) *A1 A2*
Shepton Mallet *p378*. 01749 342323
Chebsey, K (Chebsey & Co) *Q Zl G Zza*
Beaconsfield *p128* 01494 670440

Checketts, Ms H A (Band Hatton LLP) *S1 S2*
Coventry *p200* 024 7663 2121

Checkley, Ms L (Pemberton Greenish LLP) *Q*
London SW3 *p66* 020 7591 3333

Checkley, R H (Furse Sanders & Co) *S1 S2 E L A1 W T1 T2 C1 Zl Zd K4*
South Molton *p383* 01769 572251

Chedgy, Mrs C A (Williams Thompson) *K3 K1*
Christchurch *p194* 01202 484242

Cheema, Ms H (G T Stewart Solicitors) *G H B2*
London SE22 *p83* 020 8299 6000

Cheesman, Mrs C A (Kirklees Metropolitan Borough Council)
Huddersfield *p461* 01484 221421

Cheesman, Ms J (The College of Law Guildford)
Guildford *p459* 01483 460200

Cheesman, L E (Cheesman & Co) *K1 D1 M1 P J1 C1 T1 V*
Liverpool *p287* 0151 258 1212

Cheetham, Ms A (Irwin Mitchell LLP) *N Zr*
London EC1 *p45* 0870 150 0100

Cheetham, D N (Claytons) *S1 E C1 G L W M1 K1 Zd*
St Albans *p390* 01727 865765

Cheetham, Ms G (Morgan Cole) *C1 T1 W X Zi Zd*
Oxford *p344* 01865 262600

Cheetham, Miss G E (Brighouses) *K1 D1 G N S1*
Southport *p388* . . .01704 534101 / 500151

Cheetham, J L R (Royal Mail Group)
London EC4 *p109* 020 7250 2468

Cheetham, Mrs L C (Cheethams) *S1 W K4 K1 K3*
Penkridge *p345* 01785 714761

Cheetham, Ms N J (Fentons) *N J1 Q*
Failsworth *p223* 0161 682 7101

Cheetham, N R (Cheethams) *S1 J1 E C1 Zv A1 S2 K4 W*
Penkridge *p345* 01785 714761

Cheetham, R A (Fraser Dawbarns) *A1 E C1 W L C2 S2 J1*
Wisbech *p435* 01945 461456

Cheffings, C N (Hogan Lovells International LLP)
London EC1 *p42* 020 7296 2000

Chen, Mrs C J (Watford Borough Council)
Watford *p475* 01923 226400

Chen, Ms P (Harvey Son & Filby) *E L S1*
Ipswich *p262* 01473 712962

Chen, Miss S M (N C Morris & Co) *S1*
London SW7 *p62* 020 7584 8764

Chenery, F H (Francis H Chenery) *S1 Q C1 E W J1 F1 K1 A1 S2 L K3*
Diss *p210* 01379 644055

Chenery, Mrs I L A (Chenery Maher & Co) *S1 W A1 E K4 S2 L*
Clitheroe *p196* 01200 422264

Chenery, Ms R (Field Seymour Parkes) *S1*
Reading *p360* 0118 951 6200

Cheng, A (Herbert Smith LLP)
London EC2 *p40* 020 7374 8000

Cheng, Ms A (Ashurst LLP)
London EC2 *p7* 020 7638 1111

Cheng, Ms J C L (Taylor Wessing)
London EC4 *p86* 020 7300 7000

Cheng, P K (Tanburghs O'Brien Lahaise) *E S2 L O Q J1*
Camden *p85* 020 7372 6614

Cheong Tung Sing, Ms J C (Clifford Chance)
London E14 *p20* 020 7006 1000

Cheong, K W (Shell International Ltd)
London SE1 *p109* 020 7934 1234

Chequer, J S (Heyes Samuel) *Q N*
Ryde *p369* 01983 615615

Cherrill, J N (Buss Murton LLP) *W T2*
Tunbridge Wells *p415* 01892 510222

Cherry, A J (DAC Beachcroft)
Bristol *p162* 0117 918 2000

Cherry, C T (BTMK Solicitors LLP) *E C1 C2 C3 L S1 T1 T2*
Southend-on-Sea *p387* . . . 01702 339222

Cherry, Miss D (Oxley & Coward Solicitors LLP) *Q O F1 L J1 Zq B1 Zk F2*
Rotherham *p367* 01709 510999

Cherry, R (Ratcliffe Duce & Gammer LLP) *J1 Q N O*
Reading *p361* 0118 957 4291

Cherry, R M (Doncaster Magistrates Court)
Doncaster *p457* 01302 366711

Cherryman, Ms T (Bryan Cave) *T2 W M2*
London EC2 *p19* 020 7207 1100

Cherryson, Miss G M (Everys) *N*
Exmouth *p222* 01395 264384

Chesher, Mrs A E (T A Capron & Co) *S1 W S2 Zm*
Grays *p233* 01375 378331

Chesher, M (Kennedys)
London EC3 *p49* 020 7667 9667

Cheshire, N (Ashurst LLP)
London EC2 *p7* 020 7638 1111

Cheshire, N (Rooks Rider) *E R1*
London EC1 *p73* 020 7689 7000

Cheshire, T (Sutton-Mattocks & Co LLP) *C1 C2*
London SW13 *p84* 020 8876 8811

Chesney, Miss K E (Coffin Mew & Clover) *C1 Zh F1 U2 I U1 Ze F2 Zd C3 M1*
Southampton *p385* 023 8033 4661

Chesney, S R (Duffield Stunt) *K1 W J1 K3*
Chelmsford *p186* 01245 262351

Chess, J M (Wiggin LLP) *I Zf Ze*
Cheltenham *p189* 01242 224114

Chesser, A J S (DAC Beachcroft) *L O Q*
London EC4 *p24* 020 7242 1011

Chesser, Miss R L (Muckle LLP) *O*
Newcastle upon Tyne *p325* . 0191 211 7777

Chessher, S (Beale and Company Solicitors LLP) *O Zq Zj A3 J2 Zc C1*
London WC2 *p11* 020 7240 3474

Chester, Ms C D (Thompsons (formerly Robin/ Brian Thompson & Partners)) *N*
Birmingham *p143* 0121 262 1200

Chester, Mrs G (Elliott Bridgman)
Telford *p409* 01952 684544

Chester, G C (John Whiting & Co)
Launceston *p270* 01566 777677

Chester, Mrs J (Peach Grey & Co) *G H*
Southampton *p386* 023 8033 4695

Chester, Ms J E (Bond Pearce LLP)
London EC3 *p14* 0845 415 0000

Chester, J R (Chester & Co) *S1*
Bournemouth *p151* 01202 395395

Chester, N L (Kingston upon Hull City Council) *K1*
Hull *p461* 01482 300300

Chester, Ms T G (Creighton & Partners)
London WC1 *p23* 020 7976 2233

Chesterfield, H N E (EEF Western) *J1 Zp*
Bristol *p452* 0117 906 4800
Bristol *p162* 0117 968 8148

Chesterman, J D H (Latham & Watkins LLP) *C1 Zb*
London EC2 *p51* 020 7710 1000

Chesterton, J C (Everys) *G H K1 V Zl Q*
Honiton *p252* 01404 41221

Chestnutt, Mrs E M D (Chestnutts) *E S1 W L K1 S2 K3 K4*
Ainsdale *p114* 01704 572221

Chesworth, J G (Harrison Drury & Co) *E O P Q*
Preston *p357* 01772 258321

Chesworth, Miss K J (Carillion PLC)
Wolverhampton *p477* 01902 422431

Chesworth, Mrs S J (SAS Daniels LLP) *K1 D1 K3 D2*
Stockport *p396* 0161 475 7676

Chetland, G A (Paul Robinson Solicitors) *S1 S2 C1 E Zc Zv*
Westcliff-on-Sea *p428* 01702 338338

Chetouani, Ms I (Glazer Delmar) *Zi*
London SE22 *p35* 020 8299 0021

Chetwood, D C (Russell & Co) *S1 E W C1 A1 T2 S2*
Malvern *p300* 01684 892000

Chetwood, I A (Ince & Co Services Ltd)
London E1 *p44* 020 7481 0010

Chetwood, T W (Stephen Morgan & Co) *S1 K1 K3 L C1 N Q W B1*
Exeter *p221* 01392 215121

Chetwood, W J (Bentleys Stokes & Lowless) *N Za*
London EC3 *p12* 020 7782 0990

Chetwynd, Mrs K R (John Copland & Son) *D2 D1 G H K3 K1 N S1 X J1 Q V Zk W Zh*
Sheerness *p375* 01795 664431

Cheung, Ms C (Kennedys)
London EC3 *p49* 020 7667 9667

Cheung, Ms C J (Freemans Solicitors) *Zi*
London W1 *p34* 020 7935 3522

Chevalier, P I (P Chevalier & Co)
Surbiton *p402* 020 3393 8217

Cheveley, P (Travers Smith LLP)
London EC1 *p87* 020 7295 3000

Cheves, Mrs M M (Russell-Cooke LLP) *Zd*
London SW15 *p74* 020 8789 9111

Cheves, R B (Brewer Harding & Rowe) *Q N Zq J1 O Zp J2*
Barnstaple *p125* 01271 342271

Chew, Ms L G S (Duffield Stunt) *S1 L S2 E*
Chelmsford *p186* 01245 262351

Cheyne, D W (Linklaters LLP)
London EC2 *p54* 020 7456 2000

Cheyney, E C (Hill Dickinson LLP) *O A3 Zc Zb Ze B2*
London EC3 *p41* 020 7283 9033

Chhatrisha, Miss R (M M & K Ltd)
London EC3 *p107* 020 7283 7200

Chhokar, J S (Chhokar & Co) *S2 E S1 C1 Ze Zf*
Southall *p384* 020 8574 2488

Chhokar, S S (Chhokar & Co) *B1 E K1 O Q S1 Ze Zd W Zi*
Southall *p384* 020 8574 2488

Chhoker, S (Irwin Mitchell LLP) *N*
Birmingham *p139* 0870 150 0100

Chiappe, P A (Joelson Wilson LLP) *C1 C2 I C3 U2 J1*
Westminster *p46* 020 7580 5721

Chichester, R J (Grant Saw Solicitors LLP) *J1 L N O Q Zq Zp*
Greenwich *p36* 020 8858 6971

Chick, M (Bishop & Sewell LLP) *C1 E S2 L Q*
London WC1 *p13* 020 7631 4141

Chidley, Miss C A (Dickins Hopgood Chidley LLP) *J1 Q S2 C1 W S1*
Hungerford *p258* 01488 683555

Chidley, C J O (Dickins Hopgood Chidley LLP) *C1 E B1 J1 F1 O Q*
Hungerford *p258* 01488 683555

Chidley, M A (DLA Piper UK LLP)
Leeds *p272* 0870 011 1111

Chignell, J B (TWM Solicitors LLP) *O Q N A3 J1 Zp Zr*
Epsom *p219* 01372 729555

Chiko-Radomski, Mrs M (Kingsley Napley) *C1 T1*
London EC1 *p50* 020 7814 1200

Child, A A (DAC Beachcroft) *Zu Zg X*
London EC4 *p24* 020 7242 1011

Child, D S (Gardner Leader LLP) *E S1 W C1 A1 L*
Newbury *p322* 01635 508080

Child, Ms I L (Wheltons) *D1 K3 K1*
Guildford *p237* 01483 537633

Child, Ms K (Franklins LLP) *N Zi*
Milton Keynes *p317* 01908 660966

Child, Miss L C (Burnetts) *Zc O*
Carlisle *p181* 01228 552222

Child, T J P (Field Seymour Parkes) *O L Q F1 Zq Zu Zh Zl*
Reading *p360* 0118 951 6200

Children, S R (Robert C Seeckts) *D1 F1 G H K1 L M1 P S1*
Tunbridge Wells *p415* 01892 537615

Childs, A M (Hamer Childs) *G H*
Worcester *p439* 01905 724565

Childs, C G (MLM Cartwright) *J1 G Zt O Zl J2*
Cardiff *p179* 029 2046 2562

Childs, D R (Clifford Chance)
London E14 *p20* 020 7006 1000

Childs, Ms N (Trowers & Hamlins)
London EC3 *p88* 020 7423 8000

Childs, Mrs S G (Family Matters Solicitors) *K1*
Torquay *p412* 01803 328577

Childs, W (Radcliffes Le Brasseur)
Westminster *p70* 020 7222 7040

Chillery, Ms J L (Aaron & Partners LLP Solicitors) *B1 O G Zt*
Chester *p190* 01244 405555

Chilton, M (The Big Food Group PLC) *C1 B1 E N T1 J1 S1 Zi*
Deeside *p456* 01244 830100

Chilton, V (Hegarty LLP) *Zc E Q S1 S2*
Peterborough *p347* 01733 346333

Chilvers, M D (Wilkin Chapman LLP)
Grimsby *p235* 01472 262626

Chima, Mrs M K (Adams Solicitors) *E S1 W L J1 P Zb*
London E1 *p4* 020 7790 2000

Chima, Mrs S (NFLA Ltd) *K3 K1*
Nottingham *p338* 0115 945 4555

Chima, S S (Adams Solicitors) *E S1 R1 Zi W*
London E1 *p4* 020 7790 2000

Chin, E (Penningtons) *Zi*
London EC2 *p66* 020 7457 3000

Chin, Ms J (Simmons & Simmons)
London EC2 *p79* 020 7628 2020

Chin, K K L (Richmonds)
Newcastle upon Tyne *p326* . 0191 232 2155

Chinery, R M (The Beavis Partnership) *K1 F1 G J1 L Zk Zm Zj*
Chelmsford *p186* 01245 264748

Chinn, D S (Hill Dickinson LLP) *M1 P Zc*
Liverpool *p288* 0151 600 8000

Chipatiso, P M (Abiloye & Co)
London E12 *p3* 020 8478 5678

Chipman, Ms N (Bemrose & Ling) *S2 E S1 C1 Zi*
Derby *p208* 01332 347300

Chipperfield, M (Reynolds Porter Chamberlain LLP) *N*
London E1 *p71* 020 3060 6000

Chipperfield, Ms R F J (Barlow Lyde & Gilbert LLP)
London EC3 *p10* 020 7247 2277

Chipping, Mrs E M (Sedgwick Kelly LLP) *W*
Watford *p424* 01923 228311

Chirag, P (Criminal Defence Solicitors) *G H*
Westminster *p23* 020 7353 7000

Chirnside, Mrs K E (Oxford City Council) *R1 S1*
Oxford *p468* 01865 249811

Chisem, G M (Anthony Walters & Co) *S1 W G H K1 L N D1 F1 E Zl Zm Zv*
Bishop Auckland *p144* 01388 662222

Chisholm, I (G & I Chisholm) *S1 W R1 T1 C1 E Zc Zl*
Bodmin *p148* 01208 74242

Chisholm, J A (Keelys LLP)
Lichfield *p284* 01543 420000

Chisholm, Miss K A (Magrath LLP) *Zi Zg M1*
London W1 *p57* 020 7495 3003

Chisholm, Mrs M (Middlesbrough Council) *E S2*
Middlesbrough *p465* 01642 245432

Chisholm, P H (Sheffield City Council)
Sheffield *p471* 0114 273 4019

Chisholm-Batten, Mrs S (Michelmores LLP) *O*
Exeter *p221* 01392 688688

Chism, Ms D J (Manches LLP) *K3 K1*
London WC2 *p58* 020 7404 4433
London EC4 *p83* 020 7822 8000

Chisman, D (Vickers Chisman & Wishlade) *D1 G H K1 M1*
Stockton-on-Tees *p397* . . . 01642 615439

Chisnall, J S C (David Gist Solicitors)
Bristol *p162* 0117 927 9111

Chisnall, Ms K (St Helens Law Limited)
St Helens *p391* 01744 454433

Chisolm, Ms R A (Sheffield City Council)
Sheffield *p471* 0114 273 4019

Chissick, M P (Field Fisher Waterhouse LLP)
London EC3 *p31* 020 7861 4000

Chittenden, J W (Humphries Kirk) *P J2 R1 Zc E C1 A3*
Poole *p352* 01202 725400

Chittenden, S V (The Smith Partnership) *G H*
Derby *p209* 01332 225225

Chittock, M J (Brewer Harding & Rowe) *S2 E S1*
Bideford *p132* 01237 472666

Chiu, M P C (Chiu & Benson) *B1 C1 E J1 Zi Zj O Q Zp*
London SW1 *p20* 020 7930 1133
London SW1 *p60* 020 7839 2818

Chivers, A J (Meade-King) *B1 O Q C1 Zc Zq*
Bristol *p163* 0117 926 4121

Chivers, Mrs A M (Heringtons) *A1 E L S1*
Battle *p128* 01424 772401

Chivers, P M (Osborne Clarke) *O*
Bristol *p164* 0117 917 3000

Chiverton, S D (A H Brooks & Co) *N Q Zr O*
Leek *p278* 01538 383201

Chiverton, T J (Hansells) *S2*
Norwich *p334* 01603 615731

Chmerling, Miss G A (Reynolds Porter Chamberlain LLP) *N O J1*
London E1 *p71* 020 3060 6000

Chohan, H (Speechly Bircham LLP) *E P R2*
London EC4 *p81* 020 7427 6400

Chohan, I J (EEI Solicitors) *N Q O*
Liverpool *p287* 0151 707 8004

Chohan, P K (Magwells) *C1 E L R1 S1 J1 W F1 Zb Zc Zo*
Islington *p57* 020 7833 2244

Choi, D (Ashurst LLP)
London EC2 *p7* 020 7638 1111

Chonan, Miss M (Solihull Magistrates Court)
Solihull *p471* 0121 705 8101

Chong, E (Palmers) *C1 B1 O T1 Zb*
Grays *p233* 01375 484444

Chong, P (DLA Piper UK LLP)
London EC2 *p24* 0870 011 1111

Chong, Ms P (Wortley Byers) *W T2*
Brentwood *p156* 01277 268368

Chong, P K T (Knipe Woodhouse-Smith) *Q J1 K1 F1 D1 B1 O N L Zc Ze*
Chalfont St Peter *p184* . . . .01753 887877 / 889149

Chopra, Miss N (Garden House Solicitors) *F2 J1 L O Q N W*
Hertford *p248* 01992 422128

Chopra, Ms R (City of London Corporation)
London EC2 *p107* 020 7606 3030

Chorkley, Ms S (Farleys Solicitors LLP) *W Q*
Accrington *p114* 01254 367853
Burnley *p169* 01282 798664

Choudhary, Miss A (George Green LLP) *K3 K1*
Cradley Heath *p201* 01384 410410

Choudhary, C (Hugh James) *S1*
Cardiff *p179* 029 2022 4871

Choudhery, Miss F (Kidd Rapinet) *S2 E*
Slough *p382* 0845 017 9638

Choudhry, M S K (Welwyn Hatfield District Council)
Welwyn Garden City *p475* . . 01707 357000

Choudhry, Miss N (Martin Murray & Associates) *G H B2*
Slough *p382* 01753 551313

Choudhuri, D (Canter Levin & Berg) *K1*
St Helens *p391* 01744 634141

Choudhuri, D (Stephensons Solicitors LLP) *D1 F1 G H J1 K1 L Q V Zj Zo*
Leigh *p282* 01942 777777

Choudhury, A (Kent County Council)
Maidstone *p464* 01622 694320

Choudhury, A (Cartwright Cunningham Haselgrove & Co) *E S1 W*
Waltham Forest *p19* 020 8520 1021

Choudhury, D (QualitySolicitors Jackson & Canter) *E Zi S1*
Liverpool *p290* 0151 282 1700

Choudhury, H (Daybells LLP) *E S2 S1 K3 K1 W Q*
London E15 *p26* 020 8555 4321

Choudhury, H K (McMillan Williams) *Zr*
Croydon *p205* 01689 848311

Choudhury, M K (Farringdons)
London WC1 *p31* 020 7242 0949

Choudhury, P (Department for Business, Enterprise and Regulatory Reform)
London SW1 *p105* 020 7215 0105

Choudhury, R Z (Zaman Choudhury & Co)
London N15 *p20* 020 8881 4511

Choudri, F J (Pitmans LLP) *N Q*
Reading *p361* 0118 958 0224

Choudry, Miss A (Short Richardson & Forth LLP) *J1*
Newcastle upon Tyne *p326* . 0191 232 0283

Choudry, S (Middleweeks Solicitors) *G H Q B2*
Manchester *p307* 0161 839 7255

Choueka, Ms R S (LG Lawyers)
London SE1 *p50* 020 7379 0000

Chowdhary, W (QualitySolicitors C Turner) *N Zi*
Blackburn *p145* 01254 688400

Chowdhry, Mrs L (Howell-Jones LLP)
Cheam *p186* 020 8642 8142

Chowdhury, A A A (Challinors) *G H Zi*
West Bromwich *p427* 0121 553 3211

Chowdhury, Mrs F (Hodge Jones & Allen LLP) *L Q*
London NW1 *p41* 020 7874 8300

Chown, Miss E G (Reed Smith LLP)
London EC2 *p71* 020 3116 3000

Chowne, R F (Whyte & Co) *S1 W E S2*
Gillingham *p229* 01634 852377

Choyce, D G (Financial Services Authority)
London E14 *p106* 020 7066 1000

Chrisfield, Ms C (Foster & Partners)
Bristol *p162* 0117 922 0229

Chrisp, J A R (Serjeant & Son) *Q C1 J1 R1 S1 L Zd Zl K1*
Ramsey *p359* 01487 812325

Christensen, A (Pearson Fielding Polson) *G H B2*
Liverpool *p290* 0151 236 3636

Christensen, Mrs C F (Townshends LLP) *W T2 K4*
Coleshill *p198* 01675 467333

Christensen, J (Bircham Dyson Bell)
Westminster *p13* 020 7227 7000

Christer, B S (Stafford Young Jones) *W T2 S1 S2 Zo*
London EC4 *p82* 020 7623 9490

Christian, Mrs A (Last Cawthra Feather LLP) *W*
Bradford *p154* 01274 848800

Christian, Mrs C M (Scott Duff & Co) *S1 W S2*
Penrith *p346* 01768 865551

Christian, J M S (Pinsent Masons LLP)
Leeds *p276* 0113 244 5000

Christian, Miss L B (Lamb Brooks LLP) *D1 K1 W K3*
Basingstoke *p126* 01256 844888

Christian, Ms L H (Christian Khan Solicitors) *J1 L N P Q V X Zg Zi Zk Zp Zm*
London WC1 *p49* 020 7631 9500

Christian, P (Ward Hadaway) *C1 C2 T1*
Newcastle upon Tyne *p327* 0191 204 4000

Christie, Mrs A (Somerton & Fletcher) *Q L*
Cambridge *p175* 01223 566596

Christie, A J (Harding Evans LLP) *N Q Zl*
Newport *p328* 01633 244233

Christie, D (Thompsons (formerly Robin/Brian Thompson & Partners)) *J1 J2 N Q V Zg Zo Zp Zq Zu*
Plymouth *p350* 01752 675810

Christie, I (Mayer Brown International LLP) *E*
London EC2 *p59* 020 3130 3000

Christie, Miss L (Trethowans LLP) *J1*
Southampton *p387* 023 8032 1000

Christie, L (Finers Stephens Innocent LLP) *C1 J1*
London W1 *p32* 020 7323 4000

Christie, M J (Nicholls Christie & Crocker) *S1 W L Zm*
Harrow *p242* 020 8863 6366

Christie, N (Morrison & Foerster (UK) LLP) *Zb*
London EC2 *p62* 020 7920 4000

Christie, Ms P J (Bird & Bird LLP) *O N J1 Q*
London EC4 *p13* 020 7415 6000

Christie, Mrs S (Cherwell District Council)
Banbury *p448* 01295 252535

Christie, Ms T J (Wolverhampton City Council)
Wolverhampton *p477* 01902 556556

Christie, Mrs V E (TMJ Legal Services LLP) *L K4 S1 W*
Durham *p214* 0191 383 0111

Christie-Miller, R (Schillings) *O Zw Zk*
London WC1 *p77* 020 7034 9000

Christison, Mrs A K (Mander Cruickshank Solicitors LLP) *G H*
Coalville *p196* 01530 510666

Christmas, A M (Downs) *A1 J1 M1 R1*
Dorking *p212* 01306 880110

Christmas, M (DLA Piper UK LLP)
Manchester *p303* 0870 011 1111

Christmas, P (Beardsells) *N J2*
Cheadle *p185* 0161 477 2288

Christmas, Mrs S E (Hedleys Solicitors LLP)
East Horsley *p215* 01483 284567

Christmas, S J M (Russell Worth) *N*
Plympton *p351* 01752 334100

Christodoulou, A (Harris da Silva) *B1 F1 G H J1 K1 L N O Q*
Islington *p39* 020 7713 0700

Christodoulou, C (Watermans)
London N13 *p90* 020 8888 2820

Christofi, C (Healys LLP) *C1 M2 E Zk Zq Zc M1*
London EC4 *p39* 020 7822 4000

Christofi, C I (Andersons) *S1*
Croydon *p204* 020 8680 3131

Christoforou, Ms J (Ashurst LLP)
London EC2 *p7* 020 7638 1111

Christoforou, Ms M A (McMillan Williams) *E*
Coulsdon *p199* 020 8668 4131

Christopher, Ms C (Bird & Co) *N*
Grantham *p232* 01476 591711

Christopher, G (Reilly & Co Solicitors) *E S1 S2*
Birmingham *p141* 0121 744 4090

Christopher, W (RMPI Solicitors)
London W1 *p70* 020 7318 4444

Christopher, W D (Battens) *S1 W L A1 T1*
Sherborne *p378* 01935 814811

Christou, Miss C (Boodle Hatfield)
Westminster *p14* 020 7629 7411

Christou, C (Swinnerton Moore Solicitors) *E S1 R1 L G*
London EC4 *p84* 020 7236 7111

Christou, C H (Nahlis Christou)
London WC1 *p63* 020 7278 6888

Christou, C P (C P Christou LLP) *C1 S1 W B1 E F1 G J1 Ze Zi Zl K3*
London N12 *p20* 020 8446 6777

Christou, Miss S (YVA Solicitors) *S1 S2*
London N12 *p93* 020 8445 9898

Christy, Mrs R V (Blake Lapthorn) *J1*
Chandlers Ford *p184* 023 8090 8090

Christy, S R (Mills & Reeve) *E X*
Cambridge *p175* 01223 364422

Chronias, N J (DAC Beachcroft)
London EC4 *p24* 020 7242 1011

Chrysanthou, C (Fasken Martineau LLP) *C2 M2 C1*
London W1 *p31* 020 7917 8500

Chrystie, Miss J (Field Fisher Waterhouse LLP)
London EC3 *p31* 020 7861 4000
London EC3 *p31* 020 7861 4000

Chu, Ms K S (Barlow Lyde & Gilbert LLP)
London EC3 *p10* 020 7247 2277

Chua, Ms B B Y (Chua's Solicitors) *O S1 Zl Zi W S2*
London EC4 *p20* 020 7242 6789

Chubb, Ms A (Treasury Solicitors Department) *K1 W J1*
London WC2 *p110* 020 7210 3000

Chubb, A H (Child & Child) *W T2 K4*
London SW1 *p20* 020 7235 8000

Chubb, J G (David & Snape) *S1 C1 W L A1 S2*
Porthcawl *p353* 01656 782070 / 785038

Chubb, S J (Clarkson Wright & Jakes Ltd) *S2 E R2*
Orpington *p341* 01689 887887

Chubb, Miss S R (Kidd Rapinet) *S1*
Aylesbury *p121* 0845 017 9616

Chudasama, Ms B (Dobsons) *G H*
Orpington *p341* 01689 886300

Chudleigh, J P (Bonallack & Bishop) *W T2 C1*
Salisbury *p371* 01722 422300

Chudleigh, M G (Sedgwick Detert Moran & Arnold) *A3 Zj M2 O Zq*
London EC3 *p77* 020 7929 1829

Chui, K (Whatley Lane) *L S1*
Newmarket *p327* 01638 561133

Chuku, J N (Butterworths) *K1 D1*
Carlisle *p182* 01228 593939

Chumas, S A (Barlow Lyde & Gilbert LLP) *O Q Za Zj*
London EC3 *p10* 020 7247 2277

Chumber, H L (McGrath Litigation Partnership) *N L Q*
Birmingham *p140* 0121 643 4828

Chumber, Miss N (Cunningtons) *S1*
Ilford *p259* 020 8553 0002

Chun, D (Warner Goodman LLP)
Southampton *p387* 023 8063 9311

Chung, S J P (Chung & Platt) *S2 E C1 S1 Zi R2 L T1 T2 R1 W Zj Zb Zl B1*
Manchester *p302* 0161 228 6777

Chung, Ms S M Y (Atlee Chung & Company)
London W1 *p8* 020 7287 9988

Church, Mrs J D M O (Marshall Hatchick)
Woodbridge *p439* 01394 388411

Church, J F (Stephens & Scown) *C1 B1 E R1 Ze Zn*
St Austell *p391* 01726 74433

Church, Miss K M (Hewitsons) *L E Q O*
Cambridge *p174* 01223 461155

Church, M (Leo Abse & Cohen)
Cardiff *p179* 029 2038 3252 / 2034 5421

Church, R K (Roy Kenneth Church) *C1 C2 C3 E S1*
Gorseinon *p231* 01792 371420

Church, Ms S J (Harvey Ingram Borneos) *N*
Bedford *p130* 01234 353221

Churchard, Mrs C H (Royal Mail Group)
London EC4 *p109* 020 7250 2468

Churchill, Ms A E (Batchelors Solicitors) *Zh L*
Bromley *p166* 020 8768 7000

Churchill-Coleman, Mrs W J (Creston PLC) *E*
London EC1 *p105* 020 7448 8950

Church-Taylor, A (Farleys Solicitors LLP) *G H P B2*
Blackburn *p145* 01254 367854

Churchward, N L W (Wolferstans) *N*
Plymouth *p351* 01752 663295

Ciaffey, C (Ameer Meredith) *N Zr*
Cambridge *p174* 01223 577077

Ciechan, A F (Wansbroughs) *T1 T2 W Zd*
Devizes *p210* 01380 733300

Cioffi, J C (Fitzhugh Gates) *P F1 N Q J1*
Shoreham-by-Sea *p378* 01273 461381

Circus, Mrs T K (Thursfields) *S1 W L*
Stourport-on-Severn *p399* 01299 827517

Cirillo, Mrs K (Preuveneers & Co) *S2 E S1 W*
Mitcham *p318* 020 8646 4885

Citrine, D P (Duffield Harrison LLP) *S1 E C1 W L P M1 N*
Hoddesdon *p251* 01992 442911

Citron, P (H L F Berry & Co) *S2 W K3 Q N S1*
Failsworth *p223* 0161 681 4005
Manchester *p302* 0161 860 7123

Clair, Miss M K (Grant Saw Solicitors LLP) *K3 K1*
Greenwich *p36* 020 8858 6971

Claisse, C H (Kemp Little LLP) *C1 U1 U2 I Zb C2*
London EC2 *p48* 020 7600 8080

Clake, M (Ellis Jones) *E P Zu S1*
Bournemouth *p151* 01202 525333

Clamp, Miss J (Davies Johnson & Co (Shipping & Commercial Solicitors)) *Za A3 Zj O Q C1 J1*
Plymouth *p349* 01752 226020

Clancy, A (Leigh Turton Dixon) *D1 K1 L Q N Zu*
Stockton-on-Tees *p397* 01642 345230

Clancy, D P (Bawtrees LLP) *K1*
Witham *p435* 01376 513491

Clancy, T J B (Watkins & Gunn)
Pontypool *p352* 01495 762244

Clapham, G R C (Guy Clapham & Co) *B1 C1 E J1 L N O Q S1 W Zd Ze Zi S2 K3*
London W1 *p20* 020 7935 1095

Clapham, R A J (Monro Fisher Wasbrough LLP) *E S2 S1 W*
London WC1 *p61* 020 7404 7001

Clapham, Ms T A (Bennett Griffin) *W K4*
Ferring *p225* 01903 229999

Clapp, A E J (Antony Clapp)
Maidstone *p299* 01622 815940

Clapp, G N (Geoffrey Clapp) *G H D1 M1 J1 K1 P V Zg Zi*
Carlisle *p182* 01228 810228

Clare, A (Ashurst LLP)
London EC2 *p7* 020 7638 1111

Clare, A D (Napthens LLP) *C1*
Blackburn *p145* 01254 667733

Clare, Miss E L (Hadfields Butt & Bowyer) *S2*
Farnham *p225* 01252 716101

Clare, Mrs E R (Spencer Davies) *A1 S1 S2 W*
Grassington *p232* 01756 753015

Clare, Mrs J E (Boyes Turner) *E L*
Reading *p360* 0118 959 7711

Clare, J E (Harris & Harris) *C1 E S2 C2 R1 A3 A1*
Frome *p228* 01373 463366

Clare, Mrs J M (Harris & Harris) *S1 L*
Frome *p228* 01373 463366

Clare, P (Muckle LLP) *C1 C2*
Newcastle upon Tyne *p325* 0191 211 7777

Clarey, S K C (Devon County Council)
Exeter *p458* 01392 382000

Claridge, J C M (Ward & Rider Limited) *J2 Zj N*
Coventry *p201* 024 7655 5400

Claridge, Miss L (Gullands) *J1 Zc Q*
Maidstone *p299* 01622 678341

Claridge, T J (Foot Anstey) *Zb B1 Q N*
Truro *p414* 01872 243300
Bristol *p165* 0117 917 7777

Clark, Ms A (Fisher Jones Greenwood LLP) *K1*
Colchester *p197* 01206 578282

Clark, A (Fletchers) *N Q*
Southport *p388* 01704 546919

Clark, Ms A (Winckworth Sherwood LLP) *E S1 S2 Zh*
London SE1 *p92* 020 7593 5000

Clark, A C (Hodgsons & Mortimer) *K3 K1 Q N Zl L*
Richmond *p363* 01748 850950

Clark, A D C (Gosschalks) *C1 T1 B1 Ze Zc*
Hull *p256* 01482 324252

Clark, Ms A G (Crown Prosecution Service Durham)
Durham *p457* 0191 383 5800

Clark, Mrs A H (Hampshire County Council)
Winchester *p476* 01962 841841

Clark, Ms A J (Sedgwick Kelly LLP) *S1*
Watford *p424* 01923 228311

Clark, A J (The Ringrose Law Group - Richard Harwood) *D1 K1 Zm*
Lincoln *p285* 01522 814700

Clark, Ms A J (Monro Fisher Wasbrough LLP) *P M1 K1 N J1 F1 B1*
London WC1 *p61* 020 7404 7001

Clark, A J C (Allen & Overy LLP)
London E1 *p5* 020 3088 0000

Clark, A M (Clark & Weeks) *S1 K1 E S2*
Plymouth *p349* 01752 345311

Clark, A S (Ashurst LLP) *Zb*
London EC2 *p7* 020 7638 1111

Clark, A S J (R N Williams & Co Limited) *S1*
Wolverhampton *p438* 01902 429051

Clark, B S (International Management Group)
London W4 *p107* 020 8233 5000

Clark, Ms C (Leeds Day) *E R1 S1*
Huntingdon *p258* 01480 454301

Clark, C A (Chris Clark Solicitors & Estate Agents) *G H S1 W S2 Zl R1*
Stafford *p392* 01785 241842 / 241944

Clark, C E M (Linklaters LLP)
London EC2 *p54* 020 7456 2000

Clark, D (IBB Solicitors)
Uxbridge *p417* 0845 638 1381

Clark, D (Waltons & Morse LLP) *O A3 Za Zh*
London EC3 *p90* 020 7623 4255

Clark, D A (David Clark & Co) *G H S1 Zi S2*
London NW3 *p20* 020 7433 1562

Clark, D C (Gudgeons Prentice) *S2 R2 E S1 C1*
Stowmarket *p399* 01449 613101

Clark, D E (The Smith Partnership) *B1 F1 G H J1 K1 L M1 N P Zp*
Derby *p209* 01332 225225

Clark, Ms E (Ashurst LLP)
London EC2 *p7* 020 7638 1111

Clark, F (Black Rock)
London EC4 *p104* 020 7743 3000

Clark, Miss F E (Browne Jacobson LLP) *N*
London EC3 *p16* 020 7539 4900

Clark, G (Green Wright Chalton Annis) *W S1*
Worthing *p441* 01903 234064
Arundel *p118* 01903 881122

Clark, G J A (Edwin Coe LLP) *C1 C2 C3 I M1 U2 Ze T1 T2 Zn*
London WC2 *p29* 020 7691 4000

Clark, G M (Pellmans) *A1 A2 S2 C1 E S1 J1*
Eynsham *p223* 01865 884400

Clark, G W (Astwood Law)
Redditch *p362* 01527 892200

Clark, Ms H (Edwards Angell Palmer & Dodge)
London EC2 *p28* 020 7583 4055

Clark, I F (Clark Ricketts LLP) *M3*
London WC2 *p20* 020 7240 6767

Clark, I G (Kent County Council)
Maidstone *p464* 01622 694320

Clark, I H (Pinsent Masons LLP) *E R1 P*
London EC2 *p67* 020 7418 7000

Clark, I J (Portsmouth City Council)
Portsmouth *p469* 023 9283 4034

Clark, Ms I R F (Clifford Chance)
London E14 *p20* 020 7006 1000

Clark, Mrs J (Grainger Appleyard) *K1 D1*
Doncaster *p211* 01302 327257

Clark, Miss J (Kennedys) *Zj N*
London EC3 *p49* 020 7667 9667

Clark, Ms J (Robert Lizar) *G H*
Manchester *p307* 0161 226 2319

Clark, Ms J (Punch Robson) *S1*
Stockton-on-Tees *p397* 01642 754050

Clark, J (Bingham McCutchen (London) LLP)
London EC2 *p12* 020 7661 5300

Clark, J (Walker Smith Way) *O N Q J1 B1*
Chester *p191* 0844 346 3100

Clark, J (Holman Fenwick Willan)
London EC3 *p42* 020 7264 8000

Clark, J (Longden Walker & Renney) *N Q*
Sunderland *p401* 0191 567 7024

Clark, Mrs J E (Bovis Homes Ltd)
Cheadle Hulme *p454* 0161 488 5000

Clark, Ms J J (Black Norman) *E*
Crosby *p203* 0151 931 2777

Clark, Mrs J L (Burt Brill & Cardens) *E S2*
Brighton *p159* 01273 604123

Clark, J N (DLA Piper UK LLP)
London EC2 *p24* 0870 011 1111

Clark, J R (Bury & Walkers LLP) *C1 C2 C3 E A1 F1 L M1 R1 T1 Zb Zc Zd Zn*
Barnsley *p124* 01226 733533

Clark, J S (Gateshead Metropolitan Borough Council) *S1 K1 G M1 P H D1 F1 L W*
Gateshead *p458* 0191 433 3000

Clark, Ms K (Simmons & Simmons)
London EC2 *p79* 020 7628 2020

Clark, Mrs K (Appleby Hope & Matthews) *G K1 D1*
Middlesbrough *p314* 01642 440444

Clark, Miss K (Ford & Warren) *O*
Leeds *p273* 0113 243 6601

Clark, Mrs K (McDermott Will & Emery UK LLP) *J1*
London EC2 *p56* 020 7577 6900

Clark, Miss L (Marsden Rawsthorn LLP) *J1*
Preston *p357* 01772 799600

Clark, Miss L E (Fraser Brown) *W*
Nottingham *p337* 0115 988 8777

Clark, Ms L K (Aviva PLC)
London EC3 *p103* 020 7283 7500 / 01603 687905
Norwich *p467* 01603 622200

Clark, Miss L V (Brooke North LLP) *B1 O*
Leeds *p272* 0113 283 2100

Clark, Miss L Y (Charles Russell LLP) *L O Q Zl*
London EC4 *p19* 020 7203 5000

Clark, M (Elborne Mitchell LLP)
London EC3 *p29* 020 7320 9000

Clark, M (Chanter Ferguson) *S1 E A1 K1 L W P F1 V C1 Zc Zl*
Barnstaple *p125* 01271 342268
Bideford *p132* 01237 478751

Clark, M (Harthills) *G H*
Rotherham *p367* 01709 377399

Clark, M A (BTMK Solicitors LLP) *N J2*
Southend-on-Sea *p387* 01702 339222

Clark, M A (T G Baynes) *F1 B1 Zc O Q*
Bexleyheath *p132* 020 8301 7777

Clark, M A (DWF) *C1 C2 F1 F2*
Manchester *p303* 0161 603 5000

Clark, Mrs M C (Wansbroughs)
Devizes *p210* 01380 733300

Clark, M C C (Davies Battersby Ltd) *O Q Zq*
London EC3 *p26* 020 7621 1090

Clark, Mrs M D (Wrigleys Solicitors LLP) *S1*
Sheffield *p377* 0114 267 5588

Clark, Mrs M M (Segens Blount Petre) *K1 D1*
Westminster *p77* 020 7332 2222

Clark, N (Neil Clark) *M1 N P K1 G H D1 S1 E W Zl Zm*
Northampton *p331* 01604 583684

Clark, N J (Minter Ellison)
London EC2 *p61* 020 7448 4800

Clark, N J R (Peter Peter & Wright) *A1 S1 W E T2 C1 L S2*
Holsworthy *p251* 01409 253262

Clark, P (Taylor Wessing)
London EC4 *p86* 020 7300 7000

Clark, P (Dickinson Dees) *C1 Zw*
Newcastle upon Tyne *p324* 0191 279 9000

Clark, P G (Oxfordshire County Council)
Oxford *p468* 01865 792422

Clark, P M (Graysons) *N Q Zr*
Sheffield *p375* 0114 272 9184

Clark, Ms P S (Legal Aid Area Office No 4 (South Western))
Bristol *p452* 0117 921 4801

Clark, P S (Jeffrey Mills) *S2 E S1*
St Neots *p392* 01480 475871 / 219699

Clark, Ms R (Squire Sanders (UK) LLP) *O Q*
Leeds *p277* 0113 284 7000

Clark, R (Royds LLP) *S1 S2 R2*
London EC4 *p74* 020 7583 2222

Clark, R (Mullis & Peake) *S1 S2 W*
Romford *p366* 01708 784000

Clark, Ms R (Land Law LLP) *B1 E S1*
Altrincham *p116* 0161 928 8383

Clark, R A (Clark Holt) *C1 C2 Zb*
Swindon *p406* 01793 617444

Clark, R E (Chattertons Solicitors) *N Q O Zr Zq*
Grantham *p232* 01476 591550

Clark, R F (Robin F Clark & Co) *S1 E G R1 C1 H W P N Zi Zl D2 Zg B1 D1 S2 F2 K3 K4 J1 K1 B2 L O Q Zp Zw*
Gravesend *p232* 01474 334444

Clark, R J (Ilett & Clark Solicitors) *E S1 W*
Worksop *p441* 01909 500544

Clark, R J (B P Collins LLP) *O Q*
Gerrards Cross *p229* 01753 889995

Clark, R J R (Burges Salmon) *E L*
Bristol *p161* 0117 939 2000

Clark, R M (Irwin Mitchell LLP) *C2 C1 I Ze Zf U2*
Sheffield *p376* 0870 150 0100

Clark, R P (Mullis & Peake) *S1*
Chadwell Heath *p184* 020 8599 2417

Clark, Ms S (Walker Morris)
Leeds *p277* 0113 283 2500

Clark, Mrs S (Rooks Rider)
London EC1 *p73* 020 7689 7000

Clark, Ms S (Norfolk County Council - Legal Services)
Norwich *p467* Minicom: 0844 800 8011

Clark, S A L (RHW Solicitors LLP) *W*
Guildford *p237* 01483 302000

See p634 for the Key to Work Categories

Clark, Miss S C (Neasham Lloyd) *D1 K1 Q*
Bicester *p132* 01869 252161

Clark, S C (Walker Morris) *B1 Zb*
Leeds *p277* 0113 283 2500

Clark, Mrs S E (Last Cawthra Feather LLP) *C1*
Bradford *p154* 01274 848800

Clark, S H T (Linklaters LLP)
London EC2 *p54* 020 7456 2000

Clark, S T (Gould & Swayne) *E A1 L S1 S2*
Glastonbury *p229* 01458 833700

Clark, T (Pitmans LLP) *O Q A3 Zc I Ze U2*
Reading *p361* 0118 958 0224

Clark, T J (Mid Sussex District Council)
Haywards Heath *p460* 01444 458166

Clark, T J (Blandy & Blandy) *J1 O L Q Zl Zp*
Reading *p360* 0118 951 6800

Clark, T W S (Kimbells LLP) *E S2 L*
Milton Keynes *p317* 01908 668555

Clark, Mrs V C (Bristows) *Ze*
London EC4 *p15* 020 7400 8000

Clark, Miss V J (Squire Sanders (UK) LLP) *O Q Zj*
London EC2 *p81* 020 7655 1000

Clarke, A (McGrath & Co) *G H*
Birmingham *p140* 0121 643 4121

Clarke, A (Bentleys Stokes & Lowless) *Za A3 M2 O Q*
London EC3 *p12* 020 7782 0990

Clarke, A (DLA Piper UK LLP)
Leeds *p272* 0870 011 1111

Clarke, A (Eccles Heddon) *S1 S2 E K1 W*
Ripon *p365* 01765 601717
Thirsk *p411* 01845 522324

Clarke, Ms A (Wilkin Chapman Epton Blades) *B1 T1 Zb*
Lincoln *p285* 01522 512345

Clarke, Miss A (Pannone LLP) *W T2*
Manchester *p308* 0161 909 3000

Clarke, A G (H T Argent & Son) *A1 E L S1 T2 W*
Aldeburgh *p115* 01728 452133
Saxmundham *p372* 01728 602323

Clarke, A J J (Speechly Bircham LLP) *C2*
London EC4 *p81* 020 7427 6400

Clarke, A L (Judge & Priestley) *S1 E W S2*
Bromley *p166* 020 8290 0333

Clarke, A L (Taylor Walton LLP) *E S2*
Luton *p295* 01582 731161

Clarke, A M R (Brachers) *Q N Zj*
Maidstone *p299* 01622 690691

Clarke, B (Kirkland & Lane)
Southwell *p389* . . .01636 813128 / 812180

Clarke, B (Lee Bolton Monier-Williams) *T2 W*
Westminster *p52* 020 7222 5381

Clarke, B J (Russell Jones & Walker) *J1 Zp Zg*
Cardiff *p180* 029 2026 2800
London WC2 *p74* 020 7657 1555

Clarke, B R (Capron & Helliwell) *S1 E L Zl S2*
Wroxham *p443* 01603 783818

Clarke, Ms C J (London Fire & Emergency Planning Authority)
London SE1 *p107* 020 8555 1200

Clarke, Mrs C M (Mills & Reeve) *C1 C2 B1*
Cambridge *p175* 01223 364422

Clarke, C R (Thatcher & Hallam) *Q O C1 B1 J1 L N F1 I Ze Zj Zk Zq Zv*
Midsomer Norton *p316* 01761 414646

Clarke, D (Capsticks Solicitors LLP) *E S2 R2*
London SW19 *p18* 020 8780 2211

Clarke, Ms D (Aidan Woods & Co) *G H B2 Zm*
Bristol *p165* 0117 952 2006

Clarke, D E (Cole & Co)
Norwich *p334* 01603 617018

Clarke, Ms D L S (Withers LLP) *W*
London EC4 *p92* 020 7597 6000

Clarke, D M (Morgan Clarke Solicitors) *N S1 W B2 G H*
Cirencester *p195* 01285 650066

Clarke, Ms E (Ashurst LLP)
London EC2 *p7* 020 7638 1111

Clarke, E (Linklaters LLP)
London EC2 *p54* 020 7456 2000

Clarke, F D W (Treasury Solicitors Department)
London WC2 *p110* 020 7210 3000

Clarke, F V (Tozers) *S1 E W L T1 Zd*
Exeter *p222* 01392 207020

Clarke, G B (Pearless de Rougemont & Co) *S1 W T1 E A1 C1 L Zm*
East Grinstead *p215* 01342 323687

Clarke, G L (Stoke-on-Trent City Council)
Stoke-on-Trent *p472* 01782 234567

Clarke, Ms H (Pitmans LLP) *W T2 K4*
Reading *p361* 0118 958 0224

Clarke, Miss H C (Somerset County Council)
Taunton *p473* 0845 345 9166

Clarke, I A (Burnley-Jones Bate & Co)
London SW19 *p16* 020 8542 8101

Clarke, I D (South Somerset District Council)
Yeovil *p477* 01935 462462

Clarke, Mrs I S (Sills & Betteridge LLP) *K1 S1 W*
Sleaford *p381* 01529 302800

Clarke, I W J (The Clarke Partnership) *N*
Stockport *p395* 0161 474 6600

Clarke, J (Merseyside Police)
Liverpool *p463* 0151 777 8080

Clarke, J (Brabners Chaffe Street) *B1 Zc E Zu S1 T1*
Liverpool *p286* 0151 600 3000

Clarke, Mrs J (Aviva PLC) *K1 D1 Zl*
London EC3 *p103* . . 020 7283 7500 / 01603 687905
Settle *p374* 01729 823500

Clarke, Ms J (Sykes Lee & Brydson) *K4 T2 W Zo*
York *p445* 01904 731100

Clarke, Ms J (Calibre Solicitors Limited)
Manchester *p302* 0870 458 4418

Clarke, Miss J (Spearing Waite LLP) *J1*
Leicester *p281* 0116 262 4225

Clarke, J A (Hardy Miles Titterton) *C1 J1 K1 L N Q S1 T2 W Zi Zl*
Duffield *p214* 01332 841115

Clarke, Ms J C (Ashfords LLP) *E*
Bristol *p160* 0117 321 8000

Clarke, J C (Attwaters) *C1 S2 E P C2 R2*
Harlow *p239* 01279 638888

Clarke, J D (Bevan Brittan LLP) *C1 J1 R1 Zl*
Bristol *p161* 0870 194 1000

Clarke, Mrs J E (Harvey Ingram Borneos) *A1 L S1 W*
Newport Pagnell *p329* 01908 613545

Clarke, Ms J E M (Bond Pearce LLP)
Plymouth *p349* 0845 415 0000

Clarke, J F (Metcalfe Copeman & Pettefar) *G H Zg B2*
Wisbech *p435* 01945 464331

Clarke, Ms J H (Crossmans) *K1 N D1 Q V*
Radstock *p358* 01761 431688

Clarke, J M (Bawtrees LLP) *N Q Zl*
Witham *p435* 01376 513491

Clarke, Miss J M (Clifford Chance)
London E14 *p20* 020 7006 1000

Clarke, Mrs J P (Reynolds Johns Partnership) *S2 E S1*
Bishop's Stortford *p144* . . . 01279 508626

Clarke, J R (Gill Akaster) *K4 Q Zo T2 W*
Plymouth *p349* 01752 203500

Clarke, J R M (Mayo Wynne Baxter LLP) *S1 T1 W Zd*
Seaford *p373* 01323 891412

Clarke, Mrs K (Harvey Ingram LLP) *W*
Leicester *p280* 0116 254 5454

Clarke, Mrs K E (Hacking Ashton LLP) *O Q Zq Ze W*
Newcastle under Lyme *p323* . 01782 715555

Clarke, Miss L (Malcolm C Foy & Co) *D1 K3 K1 K2*
Doncaster *p211* 01302 340005

Clarke, Ms L (Osborne Clarke) *J1*
London EC2 *p65* 020 7105 7000

Clarke, M (Clarke Willmott) *A3 M2 Zk O*
Bristol *p162* 0845 209 1000 / 0117 305 6000

Clarke, M D (Freeman Johnson) *G H*
Durham *p214* . . 0191 386 4843 / 386 9619

Clarke, M D A (Powleys) *D2 D1 S2 F1 K3 J1 K1 L Q N W O*
Lowestoft *p294* 01502 581121

Clarke, Ms M F (DLA Piper UK LLP) *J1*
Manchester *p303* 0870 011 1111

Clarke, Miss M J (Field Seymour Parkes) *W K4*
Reading *p360* 0118 951 6200

Clarke, M J (Eccles Heddon) *S1 E A1 W C1 L S2 R1 R2 F1*
Ripon *p365* 01765 601717

Clarke, M J (Whiteford Crocker) *S1 S2 E W*
Plymouth *p350* 01752 550711

Clarke, Ms M M (Bristows) *Ze*
London EC4 *p15* 020 7400 8000

Clarke, N (Aaron & Partners LLP Solicitors) *B1 O Q*
Chester *p190* 01244 405555

Clarke, N A (Harrowells) *W*
York *p444* 01904 558600

Clarke, N M (Northamptonshire Magistrates Courts)
Northampton *p467* 01604 497000

Clarke, Ms P (Ashurst LLP)
London EC2 *p7* 020 7638 1111

Clarke, P (Welsh Development Agency Legal Services)
Cardiff *p453* 029 2082 8681

Clarke, P A (Peter Clarke Solicitors) *G H K1 D1 S1*
Totton *p413* 023 8066 6636

Clarke, P E (South Tyneside Magistrates Court)
South Shields *p471* 0191 455 8800

Clarke, Mrs P M (Welsh Development Agency Legal Services) *C1 F1 C2 I Ze Zf Zz*
Cardiff *p453* 029 2082 8681

Clarke, R D (Keoghs LLP) *B2 N Zj O Q*
Bolton *p149* 01204 677000

Clarke, R E (Buckles Solicitors LLP) *G H N*
Peterborough *p346* 01733 888888

Clarke, R G (Nabarro LLP) *P R1 J2 Zu Zn*
Sheffield *p376* 0114 279 4000

Clarke, R J (Clyde Chappell & Botham) *K1 W*
Stoke-on-Trent *p397* 01782 599577

Clarke, R J A (Croftons) *S1 Zh C1*
Manchester *p302* 0161 214 6180

Clarke, Ms R L (Kemps Solicitors) *G B2 H*
Oldham *p340* 0161 633 0555

Clarke, R L (L A Steel) *N Q O F1 F2 J1 Zp Zr J2*
Barnsley *p125* 01226 770909

Clarke, Ms R M (Squire Sanders (UK) LLP) *Zo*
Leeds *p277* 0113 284 7000

Clarke, R T (QualitySolicitors Hill & Abbott) *N Zr*
Chelmsford *p187* 01245 258892

Clarke, Miss S (West Berkshire Council)
Newbury *p466* 01635 42400

Clarke, Miss S (Cramp & Co) *G H B2 V*
Eastbourne *p215* 01323 720581

Clarke, S (Herbert Smith LLP) *O*
London EC2 *p40* 020 7374 8000

Clarke, Ms S (Birmingham City Council Legal & Democratic Services) *C1*
Birmingham *p449* 0121 303 2066

Clarke, Miss S (EMW) *J1 Zi*
Milton Keynes *p316* 0845 070 6000

Clarke, S (Forsters LLP) *K1*
Westminster *p33* 020 7863 8333

Clarke, S (Clarke & Hartland Solicitors) *G H J1 F1 K1 S1*
Cardiff *p177* 029 2048 3181

Clarke, S (Clarke Willmott) *Zc A3 I Q*
Bristol *p162* 0845 209 1000 / 0117 305 6000

Clarke, Ms S E (Hart Jackson & Sons) *S1 L W A1 R1 F1 E C1 T1 S2 T2*
Ulverston *p416* 01229 583291

Clarke, S J (Crowdy & Rose) *W S1 T1 E*
Lechlade *p271* 01367 252644

Clarke, Mrs S M (The Clarke Partnership) *N*
Stockport *p395* 0161 474 6600

Clarke, S P (Russell-Cooke LLP) *E S2*
London SW15 *p74* 020 8789 9111

Clarke, Miss T (Chancellors Lea Brewer) *W E Q C1 K4 F1*
Bexleyheath *p132* 020 8303 0077

Clarke, W M (Powleys) *D1 F1 G H J1 K1 L N P Zp Zl K3*
Lowestoft *p294* 01502 581121

Clarke, Mrs Y (Sills & Betteridge LLP) *D1 K1 Q N*
Boston *p151* 01205 364615

Clarke Janene, Miss C (Spearing Waite LLP) *B1 O*
Leicester *p281* 0116 262 4225

Clarke-Williams, J C (Russell Jones & Walker) *O Q Zk Zq Zw*
London WC2 *p74* 020 7657 1555

Clarkson Webb, D W (Osborne Clarke) *B1 O Q F1 L*
Bristol *p164* 0117 917 3000

Clarkson, P M (Wrigleys Solicitors LLP) *W T2 Zd*
Sheffield *p377* 0114 267 5588

Clarkson, Ms Z N (Hansen Palomares) *L V Zp Zq N*
Lambeth *p38* 020 7640 4600

Clarson, Mrs S M (Browne Jacobson LLP) *P R1 Zu*
Nottingham *p336* 0115 976 6000

Clarson, Ms V (Bird & Co) *G*
Newark *p322* 01636 650880

Clary, M (Grant Saw Solicitors LLP) *O Q L Zq*
Greenwich *p36* 020 8858 6971

Clasby, N (Watson Burton LLP) *E*
Newcastle upon Tyne *p327* . 0845 901 2100

Clason, A (Charles Russell LLP) *C2 U1 C1 I*
London EC4 *p19* 020 7203 5000

Clasper, Mrs G A (Winston Solicitors LLP) *K1 K2 K3*
Leeds *p278* 0113 320 5000

Classon, Mrs M T (WBW Solicitors) *N Zr*
Newton Abbot *p329* 01626 202404

Claughton, M J (Olliers) *G H B2*
Manchester *p308* 0161 834 1515

Claus, S (Brabners Chaffe Street)
Liverpool *p286* 0151 600 3000

Claxton, J D (Burnetts) *K1 J1 R1*
Carlisle *p181* 01228 552222
Carlisle *p182* 01228 552222

Claxton, Miss K L (TMJ Legal Services LLP) *K3 K1 D1 D2*
Hartlepool *p243* 01429 235616
Wingate *p434* 01429 838225

Clay, A (Squire Sanders (UK) LLP) *C3 I Ze*
Leeds *p277* 0113 284 7000

Clay, C E (Harvey Ingram Borneos) *O P Q Zq Zc*
Milton Keynes *p317* 01908 696002

Clay, D N (DWF) *C1 C2 W*
Liverpool *p287* 0151 907 3000

Clay, I (Tierney & Co) *J1 S2*
Rotherham *p367* 01709 709000

Clay, J M L (Mayer Brown International LLP) *E R2*
London EC2 *p59* 020 3130 3000

Clay, N (John Robinson & Co) *G H A2*
Hull *p258* 01482 324818

Clay, O H (Linklaters LLP)
London EC2 *p54* 020 7456 2000

Clayden, D J (Aviva PLC)
London EC3 *p103* . . 020 7283 7500 / 01603 687905
Norwich *p467* 01603 622200

Clayden, J (Reynolds Porter Chamberlain LLP)
London E1 *p71* 020 3060 6000

Clayden, M J R (Stephens & Scown) *E A1 C1 Zl*
Exeter *p222* 01392 210700

Clayden, P B C (Manches LLP) *Ze*
Oxford *p343* 01865 722106

Claydon, Miss L E (Burges Salmon) *B1 C1*
Bristol *p161* 0117 939 2000

Claydon, R H (Cumbria County Council)
Carlisle *p453* . . . . .01228 607374 / 607351

Clayfield, Mrs R J (ClarksLegal LLP) *N Q J1*
Reading *p360* 0118 958 5321

Clays, J M (Paris Smith LLP) *S2 E*
Southampton *p386* 023 8048 2482

Clayton, A (Osborne Clarke) *E*
Bristol *p164* 0117 917 3000

Clayton, A (Penningtons) *Zr N*
Godalming *p231* 01483 791800

Clayton, Miss A (Clayton) *E*
Staines *p393* 01784 227590

Clayton, B (Crompton Halliwell) *N K1 J1 O Q F2 J2*
Bury *p170* 0161 797 9222

Clayton, Mrs C (Keoghs LLP) *N Zj Q O*
Bolton *p149* 01204 677000

Clayton, D F (Doyle Clayton Solicitors Limited) *J1 Zp*
London E14 *p27* 020 7038 8051
London EC2 *p27* 020 7329 9090

Clayton, G M (Mills & Co) *C1 C2 E*
Newcastle upon Tyne *p325* . 0191 233 2222

Clayton, J D A (Guy Williams Layton) *K1 N J1 Q S1 W V C1 D1*
Wirral *p435* . . . 0151 342 1831 / 342 6144

Clayton, J I (Forsters LLP) *Zc*
Westminster *p33* 020 7863 8333

Clayton, J P (Graham Evans & Partners) *S1 W G H D1 K1 E N C1*
Swansea *p405* 01792 655822

Clayton, J R W (Guardian Royal Exchange PLC)
London EC3 *p106* 020 7283 7101

Clayton, Mrs K (Durham County Council)
Durham *p457* 0191 383 3513

Clayton, Mrs K A (National Grid PLC)
Warwick *p471* 01926 653000

Clayton, Mrs M (Matthew & Matthew Limited) *C1 E S1*
Southbourne *p387* 01202 431943

Clayton, N (Harvey Ingram LLP) *N*
Leicester *p280* 0116 254 5454

Clayton, P M (Pinsent Masons LLP) *O Zc*
Manchester *p308* 0161 234 8234

Clayton, R (Simmons & Simmons)
London EC2 *p79* 020 7628 2020

Clayton, R G (Russell Jones & Walker) *N C1 G J1 J2 K1 O Q E Zk Zw Za Zt Zr*
Sheffield *p377* 0114 276 6868

Clayton, R M (Hillyer McKeown LLP) *D1 K1*
Bebington *p129* 0151 645 4255

Clayton, Miss S F (DWF) *J1 Zp M1 Zg*
Manchester *p303* 0161 603 5000

Clayton, Miss V A (The Johnson Partnership) *G H*
Nottingham *p337* 0115 941 9141

Clayton, W J (Hill Dickinson LLP) *C1 J1 U2 O C2 Zq*
Manchester *p305* 0161 817 7200

Cleal, A A (Allen & Overy LLP)
London E1 *p5* 020 3088 0000

Cleanthous, Ms L (Kaim Todner Ltd) *G*
London SE17 *p47* 020 7701 4747

Clearkin, Miss A M (Brabners Chaffe Street) *E*
Liverpool *p286* 0151 600 3000

Cleary, D W (The Wilkes Partnership LLP) *B1*
Birmingham *p143* 0121 233 4333

Cleary, T (Frisby & Co) *J2 G B2*
Stafford *p392* 01785 244114

Cleaveland, Ms H M (SNR Denton) *C1*
London EC4 *p75* 020 7242 1212

Cleaver, Miss M (Oslers Solicitors) *G H*
Cambridge *p175* 01223 352558

Cleaver, P F J (Billson & Sharp) *S1 E C1 L S2 C2 T1*
Leicester *p279* 0116 255 9911

Cleaver, R (Linklaters LLP)
London EC2 *p54* 020 7456 2000

Cledwyn, D A (Knight Polson Solicitors) *S2 E L S1 W*
Eastleigh *p216* 023 8064 4822

Cleere, A P (Tranter Cleere & Co) *G H K1 D1 N Q W J1 L*
Manchester *p310* 0161 428 1569

Clegg, D (Shoosmiths) *O*
Birmingham *p142* 0370 086 4000 / 0121 335 4440

Clegg, G D (British Telecommunications PLC)
London EC1 *p104* 020 7356 6181

Clegg, G J (Lupton Fawcett) *E T1*
Leeds *p275* 0113 280 2000

Clegg, Miss H S (Gilbert Stephens) *N Q J1*
Exeter *p221* 01392 424242

Clegg, J (Howells LLP) *K3*
Sheffield *p376* 0114 249 6666

Clegg, Mrs J E (Broomhead & Saul) *N L W*
Taunton *p408* 01823 288121

Clegg, Ms J M (Stephenson Harwood)
London EC2 *p82* 020 7329 4422

Clegg, Mrs L (Douglas Wemyss Solicitors) *Q N K1*
Leicester *p281* 0116 299 9199

Clegg, P A (Dickinson Parker Hill) *S1 E C1 W K1 R1 L A1*
Ormskirk *p341* 01695 574201

Clegg, P D (Muckle LLP) *E*
Newcastle upon Tyne *p325* . 0191 211 7777

Clegg, R H M (Clegg Manuel)
Islington *p20* 020 7847 5600

Clegg, Miss V E (DAC Beachcroft) *E R2 S2 L Zc*
Leeds *p272* 0113 251 4700

Cleland, J (Pinsent Masons LLP)
Leeds *p276* 0113 244 5000

Clemence, M E (Edmondson Hall) *K1 K3 K2*
Newmarket *p327* 01638 560556
Ipswich *p262* 01473 232121

Clemens, A S J (Restormel Borough Council)
St Austell *p472* 01726 223612

Clement, Ms E (Chattertons Solicitors)
Lincoln *p284* 01522 814600

Clement, J S (Turbervilles) *N*
Uxbridge *p417* 01895 201700
Uxbridge *p417* 01895 201700

Clement-Evans, J C (Hugh James) *N Q*
Cardiff *p179* 029 2022 4871

Clements, C (SA Law Chambers) *L Q N*
Ilford *p260* 020 8554 0012

Clements, D (Askews) *S1 W*
Redcar *p362* 01642 475252

Clements, Ms J M (Hunters) *W T2 S1 Zv*
London WC2 *p44* 020 7412 0050

Clements, J S (Roger James Clements & Partners) *S1 E R1 J1*
Newport *p329* 01633 257844

Clements, M (South Tyneside Metropolitan Borough Council)
South Shields *p471* 0191 427 1717

Clements, M (Clements and Co) *S1 E S2 K1 L Zl N W F1 F2 R2 O Q Zq J1 C1 B1 Zt K3*
Cardiff *p177* 029 2036 1771
Clements, Miss M J (Rhondda Cynon Taff County Borough Council) *D1*
Pentre *p468* 01443 424300
Clements, R G P (Beaumonts) *Q L O J1 N E Zc*
Hereford *p247* 01432 352345
Clements, Ms S T (Yaffe Jackson Ostrin) *D1 K1 N L G F1 J1 Q S1 W*
Liverpool *p291* 0151 236 5555
Clemo, C L (C L Clemo & Co)
London SW20 *p20* 020 8944 1017
Clemo, Miss P (Pamela Clemo & Co) *S1 W K4*
Kingston upon Thames *p267*. 020 8949 8791
Clennel-White, Mrs J E (Challinors) *K1 D1*
West Bromwich *p427* 0121 553 3211
Cleverdon, D E (Dunn & Baker) *K1 D1 D2*
Exeter *p221* 01392 285000
Cleverdon, Ms J (Cleverdons) *K1 S1 W*
Enfield *p218* 020 8367 5375
Cleverley, Mrs E A (FBC Manby Bowdler LLP) *K1 K3*
Wolverhampton *p437* 01902 578000
Cleverly, Mrs N (Biscoes) *S1 S2 W*
Wickham *p431* 01329 833249
Cleverly, S P C (British American Tobacco)
London WC2 *p104* 020 7845 1000
Clewett, Miss S (Berry Smith LLP)
Cardiff *p177* 029 2034 5511
Clewlow, J (Paul Davidson Taylor) *E L J1 S1 S2*
Horsham *p253* 01403 262333
Clews, S C (Franklins) *D1 G H K1 L*
Leighton Buzzard *p282* . . . 01525 376611
Clibbon, J A (Streathers Solicitors LLP) *O Zq*
London W1 *p84* 020 7034 4200
Cliff, P (Gateley LLP) *C1 C2*
Birmingham *p138* 0121 234 0000
Cliff, R J (Starkie & Gregory) *W S1 S2 T2 Zm*
Long Eaton *p293* 0115 849 9000
Cliff, R M (George Green LLP) *C1 T1*
Cradley Heath *p201* 01384 410410
Cliffe, H (Rushton Hinchy Solicitors) *J1 Zj Q N*
St Helens *p391* 0845 054 0564
Clifford, Ms A C (TLT Solicitors) *E*
Bristol *p165* 0117 917 7777
Clifford, C G (Druitts) *S1 S2 W*
Bournemouth *p151* 01202 551863
Clifford, D I (Devonshires) *Zr K3 Zx K1 O Q N Zq Zs*
London EC2 *p27* 020 7628 7576
Clifford, E (GLP Solicitors) *D1 H E G K1 M1 P S1 J1 W Zl Zp Zl*
Manchester *p304* 0161 795 5531
Clifford, E P (Keelys LLP) *N*
London EC2 *p48* 020 7422 8686
Clifford, G (Manches LLP) *E R2 Zb Zc Zh Zu*
Oxford *p343* 01865 722106
Clifford, H (Ince & Co Services Ltd)
London E1 *p44* 020 7481 0010
Clifford, Mrs J M F (North Tyneside Council)
Newcastle upon Tyne *p466* . 0191 643 5000
Clifford, L (Freeth Cartwright LLP)
Birmingham *p138* 0845 634 2575
Clifford, M (Pickerings LLP) *C1 C2*
Tamworth *p407* 01827 317070
Clifford, M J (Squire Sanders (UK) LLP) *C1 B1 F1 J1*
Birmingham *p142* 0121 222 3000
Clifford, Mrs M P (Gordons) *S1*
Guildford *p236* 01483 451900
Clifford, Mrs S (Wansbroughs) *N Zr*
Melksham *p314* 01225 703222
Clifford, S J (Ellisons)
Colchester *p197* 01206 764477
Clifford, S J (Wansbroughs) *G H B2*
Melksham *p314* 01225 703222
Clift, Ms C P (Lightfoots LLP) *Zq O B2 Q*
Thame *p410* 01844 212305
Clift, Ms H M (Official Solicitor and Public Trustee) *K1 K2 D1*
London WC2 *p108* 020 7911 7127
Clift, I (Jerman Simpson Pearson & Samuels) *N*
Basildon *p126* 01268 820111
Clift, J (City of London Corporation)
London EC2 *p107* 020 7606 3030
Clift, N R (Hill Dickinson LLP) *N Za Zj*
London EC3 *p41* 020 7283 9033
Clift, T P C (EJ Winter & Son) *S1 S2*
Reading *p361* 0118 957 4424
Clifton, D R G (Joelson Wilson LLP) *Zl J2 Zy*
Westminster *p46* 020 7580 5721
Clifton, H (Moore Blatch Solicitors) *Zc J1 S1*
Southampton *p386* 023 8071 8000
Clifton, R W (Taylor Wessing) *C1 C2 J1*
London EC4 *p86* 020 7300 7000
Clifton, S (Page Gulliford & Gregory Limited) *Q O L J1*
Southampton *p386* 023 8022 5821
Clifton-Thompson, Mrs P (Wortley Redmayne Kershaw) *Q O J1*
Chelmsford *p187* 01245 491122
Clinch, L (Hodge Jones & Allen LLP) *N*
London NW1 *p41* 020 7874 8300
Cline, Ms H (Taylor Wessing)
London EC4 *p86* 020 7300 7000
Cline, N A F (Latham & Watkins LLP) *C2 C1*
London EC2 *p51* 020 7710 1000
Clingman, M R (Levenes Solicitors) *N*
Haringey *p53* . 020 8881 7777 / 8881 6764
Clinning, S (Howard Kennedy LLP) *Zb C1 R2*
London W1 *p48* 020 7636 1616
Clinton, A J (ASB Law) *B1 O*
Crawley *p202* 01293 603600
Clinton, A J (Meikles) *H G*
Bishop Auckland *p144* 01388 451122
Clinton, K D (Gough Clinton & Broom) *E S1 W*
Welling *p424* 020 8301 9000
Clinton, S R (Clifford Chance)
London E14 *p20* 020 7006 1000
Clipston, Mrs H (Edwards Angell Palmer & Dodge)
London EC2 *p28* 020 7583 4055
Clipstone, S W S (Neves Solicitors) *C1 E L S1*
Milton Keynes *p317* 01908 304560
Clisby, P W (Newcastle Under Lyme Borough Council)
Newcastle Under Lyme *p466*. 01782 717717
Clish, J L (Clark Willis) *G H*
Darlington *p206* 01325 281111
Clist, Miss A H (Allen & Overy LLP)
London E1 *p5* 020 3088 0000
Clithero, R J (Napthens LLP) *E*
Blackburn *p145* 01254 667733
Clixby, Miss K A (Ralph & Co)
Newquay *p329* 01637 872218
Cloake, Mrs J (Oxfordshire County Council)
Oxford *p468* 01865 792422
Clode, Miss C (FBC Manby Bowdler LLP) *O Q*
Wolverhampton *p437* 01902 578000
Clode, D (Clodes Solicitors) *G H K3 K4 K1 W S1 Zm N Q*
Cardiff *p177* . 029 2076 5050 / 01446 720777
Clode, M C J (Clodes Solicitors) *G H K1 J1 D1 V N Zm Zl Zi*
Cardiff *p177* . 029 2076 5050 / 01446 720777
Clode, Miss V E (Clodes Solicitors) *G H K3 K4 K1 W S1 Zm N Q*
Cardiff *p177* . 029 2076 5050 / 01446 720777
Cloke, G S (Brewer Harding & Rowe) *S2*
Barnstaple *p125* 01271 342271
Cloke, Miss S (Biscoes) *K3 K1*
Portchester *p353* 023 9237 0634
Cloney, V (Cloney & Co) *B1 T1 E W C1 S1 N L R1 Zc Zl*
Lytham *p296* 01253 712116
Close, C B (Sacker & Partners LLP) *Zo*
London EC2 *p76* 020 7329 6699
Close, C J (Michelmores LLP) *A1 S1*
Exeter *p221* 01392 688688
Close, Mrs D M (Davitt Jones Bould) *E A1*
Taunton *p408* 01823 279279
Close, J (Sharp & Partners) *G B2 H*
Long Eaton *p293* 0115 973 4111
Close, N M (Donns) *N Zj*
Manchester *p303* 0161 834 3311
Close, P M W (Morrisons Solicitors LLP) *Q K1 D1 N L F1 C1 J1 Zm K3*
Camberley *p173* 01276 686005
Clossick, A P (Gordons LLP) *K1 K3*
Leeds *p273* 0113 227 0100
Leeds *p277* 0113 222 0022
Clothier, R D (TLT Solicitors) *E*
Bristol *p165* 0117 917 7777
Cloud, Miss S (TWM Solicitors LLP) *K1*
Reigate *p363* 01737 221212
Cloud, Ms S L (The Family Law Partnership LLP)
Leatherhead *p271* 01372 700890
Clough, A J (Herbert Smith LLP) *C1*
London EC2 *p40* 020 7374 8000
Clough, C G (Lindley Clough)
Pudsey *p358* 0113 257 0523
Clough, Miss E (Brearleys Solicitors) *K1 D1 D2*
Batley *p128* 01924 473065
Clough, Ms F V (HM Land Registry - Durham (Boldon) Office)
Durham *p457* 0191 301 2345
Clough, J E (Preston Redman) *E S1 L O Q R2 S2 B1*
Bournemouth *p152* 01202 292424
Clough, M (Addleshaw Goddard) *M1 M2*
London EC1 *p4* 020 7606 8855
Clough, N J (Kelcey & Hall) *G H*
Bristol *p163* 0117 927 9604
Clough, N J (Bromleys Solicitors LLP) *J1 K1 K3*
Ashton-under-Lyne *p120* . . . 0161 330 6821
Clough, P J I (Peter Clough & Co) *S1 K1 W L*
Sheerness *p375* 01795 669299
Clough, P V (Osborne Clarke) *O A3 U2*
Bristol *p164* 0117 917 3000
Clough, R J (Preston Redman) *P N L R1 B1 J1 C1 E O Zc Zk Zl Zs*
Bournemouth *p152* 01202 292424
Clough, Ms V M (Bendles)
Carlisle *p181* 01228 522215
Clover, Mrs A S (Barlow Lyde & Gilbert LLP) *O Zj Zq*
London EC3 *p10* 020 7247 2277
Clovis, Mrs P A (Ferguson Bricknell) *B1 Zc K3 J1 K1 L Q N Zp*
Oxford *p343* 01865 767567
Clowes, Mrs E L A (Martin-Kaye LLP) *E*
Telford *p409* 01952 272222
Cluderay, S P (Tates Solicitors) *G H Zl*
Leeds *p277* 0113 242 2290
Clulee, B (NFLA Ltd) *K3 K1*
Nottingham *p338* 0115 945 4555
Cluley, Mrs J (Samuels Solicitors)
Barnstaple *p125* 01271 343457
Cluley, Mrs M (Cluley & Co) *K1 D1 S1 W N*
Winsford *p434* 01606 553719
Clulow, J A (Barlow Lyde & Gilbert LLP) *A3 Za Zj M2 O*
London EC3 *p10* 020 7247 2277
Clunie, P J H (Howes Percival LLP) *Zb*
Milton Keynes *p317* 01908 672682
Clutterbuck, H (Napthens LLP) *Q*
Preston *p357* 01772 888444
Clutton, B G O (Macfarlanes) *T1 W Zd*
London EC4 *p56* 020 7831 9222
Clyne, H (Hodge Jones & Allen LLP) *K1 K2 D1*
London NW1 *p41* 020 7874 8300
Clyne, J D (Jackson Parton) *Za O A3 Q*
London EC3 *p45* 020 7702 0085
Clyne, Miss L M (Yorkshire Water Services Ltd)
Bradford *p451* 01274 804159
Coad, G (Bernard Chill & Axtell) *D1 K4 K1 V W*
Southampton *p385* 023 8022 8821
Coady, Ms A J (Quality Solicitors Copley Clark) *N*
Sutton *p403* 020 8643 7221
Coaker, Miss F (Griffiths & Hughes Parry) *D1 K1*
Holywell *p252* . . . .01352 711815 / 711945
Coane, J (Pinsent Masons LLP)
London EC2 *p67* 020 7418 7000
Coate, Ms S C (Marshalls)
Godalming *p231* 01483 416101
Coates, Miss A (Irwin Mitchell LLP) *N J2*
Birmingham *p139* 0870 150 0100
Coates, A J (Birchall Blackburn LLP) *E O Q C1 S2 J1 Zg Zk N Zq W*
Manchester *p301* 0161 236 0662
Preston *p356* 01772 561663
Coates, A S (Kennedys)
London EC3 *p49* 020 7667 9667
Coates, Miss C A (Buller Jeffries) *N J2 Q O Zj Zc*
Birmingham *p136* 0121 212 2620
Coventry *p200* 024 7622 8734
Coates, Miss C E (Meikles) *K1 G D1 K3 H Q N S1 W*
Ferryhill *p226* 01740 652811
Coates, C J (Hugh James) *H G Q*
Cardiff *p179* 029 2022 4871
Coates, Miss H E (Wood Sherwood & Co) *S1 W*
Pocklington *p351* 01759 302791
Coates, J W (Loveday & Keighley) *S2 E J1 S1 Q*
Matlock *p313* . . . . . 01629 583142 / 56660
Coates, Mrs K A (Clifford Chance)
London E14 *p20* 020 7006 1000
Coates, N E (Barker Austin) *N M1 P J1 L*
London EC3 *p9* 020 7377 1933
Coates, N H (Russell-Cooke LLP) *S2 S1*
London SW15 *p74* 020 8789 9111
Coates, Mrs N M (Ellisons) *K4 T2 W K1 D1 Q V*
Frinton-on-Sea *p227* 01255 851000
Colchester *p197* 01206 764477
Coates, R (Forrester & Forrester) *E S1*
Chippenham *p193* 01249 444300
Coates, R A (Brain Sinnott & Co) *S1 W E*
Kingswood *p268* 0117 960 6880
Coates, R F (Buller Jeffries) *O Q N Zc Zj Zq*
Coventry *p200* 024 7622 8734
Birmingham *p136* 0121 212 2620
Coates, R M (Ross Coates) *S1 W K1 J1*
Ipswich *p263* 01473 695400
Coates, Miss S (Churchers) *D1*
Portsmouth *p354* 023 9221 0170
Coates, S C (Irwin Mitchell LLP) *J1 O Zp*
Leeds *p274* 0870 150 0100
Coates, T J (Lewis Silkin LLP) *A3 O Q J1*
London EC4 *p53* 020 7074 8000
Coats, A J N (Clifford Chance)
London E14 *p20* 020 7006 1000
Coats, Mrs C M (Caroline Coats Solicitors) *W T2 K4*
Southampton *p385* 023 8089 0919
Coats, P (Radcliffes Le Brasseur)
Westminster *p70* 020 7222 7040
Coats, P J (Squire Sanders (UK) LLP) *C1 C2*
London EC2 *p81* 020 7655 1000
Cobain, A E (Cobains) *G H N Q J1 L O Zl Zv*
Blackpool *p146* 01253 290092
Cobain, Mrs L E (Cobains) *K1 S1 W N E L Q O J1*
Blackpool *p146* 01253 290092
Cobb, Mrs C (Plexus Law (A Trading Name of Parabis Law LLP)) *Zj N Q Zq A3 F2 Zr J2*
London EC3 *p68* 0844 245 4000
Cobb, E (Stone Rowe Brewer LLP) *Zc E Q S1*
Twickenham *p416* 020 8891 6141
Cobb, J M (Heckford Norton)
Saffron Walden *p370* 01799 522636
Cobb, L (Taylor Wessing) *O B1 Q Zc*
London EC4 *p86* 020 7300 7000
Cobb, P A (Rothera Dowson) *K1*
Beeston *p130* 0115 916 5200
Cobb, R (Michelmores LLP) *C1 C2*
Exeter *p221* 01392 688688
Cobb, Miss R M (Hardman & Watson) *W*
Broadstairs *p166* 01843 863479
Cobb, R V (Parker Arrenberg) *S1*
London SE6 *p65* 020 8695 2330
Cobb, S J (Bird & Co) *G H*
Newark *p322* 01636 650880
Cobbett, J R G (Biscoes) *C1 E J1 K1 M1 N P S1 W Ze*
Portsmouth *p354* 023 9266 0261
Cobbett, M S (Ellis-Fermor & Negus) *E A1 C1 W S1 L T1 Zd Zn*
Long Eaton *p293* 0115 972 5222
Cobbold, J (Gross & Co) *E A1*
Bury St Edmunds *p171* . . . 01284 763333
Cobden-Ramsay, R B (Harcus Sinclair) *K1 K3*
London WC2 *p38* 020 7242 9700
Cobley, N A (Cobleys LLP) *G H M1 P N S1 D1 K1 J1 E*
Liverpool *p287* 0151 242 9000
Coburn, Miss C (Olswang LLP) *E*
London WC1 *p64* 020 7067 3000
Cochrane, A (Flint Bishop Solicitors) *Zl J1 O Zp Zc*
Derby *p208* 01332 340211
Cochrane, C (Clifford Chance)
London E14 *p20* 020 7006 1000
Cochrane, C (Briffa) *Ze U2 O*
Islington *p15* 020 7288 6003
Cochrane, J K (Cochranes Law Firm Limited) *S1 W S2 L*
Billingham *p133* 01642 366800
Cochrane, Miss L (Blake Lapthorn) *O Q*
London EC1 *p13* 020 7405 2000
Cochrane, S (Herbert Smith LLP) *C1*
London EC2 *p40* 020 7374 8000
Cochrane, Ms S (Treasury Solicitors Department)
London WC2 *p110* 020 7210 3000
Cockayne, A J (Michelmores LLP) *Q W*
Exeter *p221* 01392 688688
Cockburn, A D (Megsons LLP) *E S1 O Q K1 V W*
Oldham *p340* 0161 633 6131
Cockburn, Miss G E (RHW Solicitors LLP) *W T2 S1 Zd*
Guildford *p237* 01483 302000
Cockburn, Ms J (Hodge Jones & Allen LLP) *Zg Zp*
London NW1 *p41* 020 7874 8300
Cockburn, Ms K (Thorneycroft Solicitors Ltd) *N*
Macclesfield *p297* 01625 503444
Cockcroft, Miss R (Manches LLP) *K1*
London WC2 *p58* 020 7404 4433
Cocker, G G (Inghams) *K1 F1 D1 J1 D2 N H L Q V Zl*
Blackpool *p146* 01253 626642
Cocker, I (North Yorkshire Law) *B1 E F1 F2 G H J1 K1 L N O Q V Zl Zm*
Scarborough *p372* 01723 360001
Whitby *p430* 01947 602131
Cockerton, Ms E (Ashurst LLP)
London EC2 *p7* 020 7638 1111
Cockerton, M R (Cockertons) *A1 E L S1 R1 T2 W Zn K4*
Bakewell *p121* 01629 812613
Cockill-Guy, Mrs C (Butcher & Barlow LLP) *K1 K2*
Northwich *p333* 01606 47523
Cocking, I (Simmons & Simmons)
London EC2 *p79* 020 7628 2020
Cockle, D N (Judge Sykes Frixou) *B1 O K3 K1*
London WC2 *p47* 020 7379 5114
Guildford *p236* 01483 454242
Cockle, P J (Peter J Cockle) *W S1*
Chelmsford *p186*. .01245 225534 / 020 7015 1850
Cockling, J M (Wall James Chappell) *S1 S2 E W K4 L T2 R2 K3 Q*
Stourbridge *p399* 01384 371622
Cockram, P T (Pinney Talfourd LLP)
Brentwood *p156* 01277 268700
Cockram, R A (Addleshaw Goddard)
Leeds *p271* 0113 209 2000
Manchester *p300* 0161 934 6000
Cocks, Miss R (Cheltenham & Gloucester PLC)
Gloucester *p459* 01452 372372
Cocks, Miss V S (Gawor & Co) *S1 S2 L N O Q W K1 J1*
London E1 *p35* 020 7481 8888
Cockx, M J (Amelans) *M1 P J1 K1 S1 W G F1 L*
Manchester *p301* 0161 434 4545
Codd, G R (Irwin Mitchell LLP) *N Zr*
Sheffield *p376* 0870 150 0100
Codd, M (Penningtons) *E*
London EC2 *p66* 020 7457 3000
Codd, Ms N J (The Penhale Practice) *K3*
Morecambe *p319* 01524 401010
Coddington, Ms C (HSR Law (Hayes, Son & Richmond)) *N K1 K3*
Doncaster *p211* 01302 347800
Gainsborough *p228* 01427 613831
Coddington, R G (Knights Solicitors LLP) *E Zn*
Cheltenham *p188* 01242 524654
Code, R A (Mark Jones & Partners) *G H*
Liverpool *p289* 0151 286 9594
Code, Ms S (Charles Russell LLP) *N Q*
London EC4 *p19* 020 7203 5000
Codling, Mrs L (Andrews McQueen) *S1 W*
Bournemouth *p151* 01202 290628
Codling, T H (Barlow Rowland) *A1 B1 C1 E L T1 W C3 Zo C2 T2 Zn K4 S2*
Accrington *p114* 01254 300400
Codrington, I C (Sharman Law)
Bedford *p130* 01234 303030
Coe, Ms N (Backhouse Jones Ltd) *N Zj O Zt Q*
Clitheroe *p196* 01254 828300
Coe, N P (Reston's Solicitors Limited) *B1 N*
Warrington *p422* 0870 755 8998
Coe, P H (Andersons) *S1 E W C1 L A1*
Croydon *p204* 020 8680 3131
Coen, J (Ford & Warren) *J2 Q*
Leeds *p273* 0113 243 6601
Coetzee, H (Bevan Brittan LLP)
London EC4 *p12* 0870 194 1000
Coffee, J K (Rich & Carr Freer Bouskell) *S1 E L W C1*
Syston *p407* 0116 242 6036
Leicester *p281* 0116 253 8021
Coffell, F H (Field Fisher Waterhouse LLP)
London EC3 *p31* 020 7861 4000
Coffer, Mrs J (Coffers) *G H*
Amersham *p117* 01494 727323
Coffey, D J (Taylor Wessing)
London EC4 *p86* 020 7300 7000
Coffey, D P (Graysons) *W K4*
Sheffield *p375* 0114 272 9184

See p634 for the Key to Work Categories

Coffey, G J (Graham Coffey & Co) *N O Q*
Manchester *p302* . . . 0161 200 2440
Coffey, Mrs J (Bishop & Sewell LLP) *S1*
London WC1 *p13* . . . 020 7631 4141
Coffey, Ms J (Reynolds Porter Chamberlain LLP)
London E1 *p71* . . . 020 3060 6000
Coffey, L (Jones Day) *O*
London EC4 *p46* . . . 020 7039 5959
Coffin, C (Withers LLP) *B1 O Q Zq*
London EC4 *p92* . . . 020 7597 6000
Cogan, A T (Tinsdills)
Hanley *p239* . . . 01782 262031
Cogar, R M (Stephens & Scown) *G H A2*
St Austell *p391* . . . 01726 74433
Cogher, Ms P (Speechly Bircham LLP) *Zo Zd J1 C2 T1 T2*
London EC4 *p81* . . . 020 7427 6400
Coghgan, M F (Keith Levin & Co) *K1 S1 S2 D1 E F1 F2 W Q X Zm Zp*
Huyton *p258* . . . 0151 480 5777
Coghlan, B (Horwich Cohen Coghlan) *N*
London EC4 *p43* . . . 020 7332 2230
Manchester *p305* . . . 0161 830 4600
Coghlan, M F (Norton & Co) *E F1 L S1 W Zl*
Prescot *p356* . . . 0151 426 7001
Coghlan, M J (Thorneycroft Solicitors Ltd) *S1 Q N W L K1 O J1 E*
Macclesfield *p297* . . . 01625 503444
Coghlan, S A E (SGH Martineau LLP)
Birmingham *p142* . . . 0870 763 2000
Cohen, A (Fladgate LLP) *L S1 H*
London WC2 *p32* . . . 020 3036 7000
Cohen, A E (W Davies) *P N M1 B1 C1 L J1 E Zl Zb Zc*
Woking *p436* . . . 01483 744900
Cohen, A E C (Cohen Filippini) *C1 D1 E F1 G H J1 K1 M1 L*
Altrincham *p116* . . . 0161 929 9993
Cohen, Ms A J (Pannone LLP) *O Q Zq Zl*
Manchester *p308* . . . 0161 909 3000
Cohen, A L (Clifford Chance)
London E14 *p20* . . . 020 7006 1000
Cohen, Ms E (Bindmans LLP) *Zi*
London WC1 *p12* . . . 020 7833 4433
Cohen, F A (Simmons & Simmons) *E S1 L W T1 R1*
London EC2 *p79* . . . 020 7628 2020
Cohen, H (Fruhman Davies Livingstones)
Manchester *p304* . . . 0161 833 0578
Cohen, H (Grahame Stowe Bateson) *G H K1 S1 W*
Leeds *p274* . . . 0113 274 4611
Leeds *p275* . . . 0113 244 9931
Cohen, H A (Sternberg Reed) *J1*
Barking *p123* . . . 020 8591 3366
Cohen, H P (Livingstone & Co) *W S1 S2 M1 E K1 R1 Zd J1 F1 Zm P*
Manchester *p307* . . . 0161 833 0578
Cohen, H P (Salans) *C1 F1 Zb*
London EC4 *p76* . . . 020 7429 6000
Cohen, H S (Cohen Cramer Solicitors) *E N Q S1 S2 W K1 L F2 B1 Ze Zf Zk Zl Zp*
Leeds *p272* . . . 0800 542 9408
Cohen, I E (Layzells) *S1 S2 W K4*
London N10 *p52* . . . 020 8444 0202
Cohen, J (Collyer Bristow LLP) *C1 C3 U2 F1 Ze Zz Zi O I*
London WC1 *p22* . . . 020 7242 7363
Cohen, J (Kingsley Napley) *W T2 Zo V Zd*
London EC1 *p50* . . . 020 7814 1200
Cohen, J (Pinsent Masons LLP)
London EC2 *p67* . . . 020 7418 7000
Cohen, J D (Davenport Lyons) *W*
London W1 *p25* . . . 020 7468 2600
Cohen, J L (SNR Denton)
London EC4 *p75* . . . 020 7242 1212
Cohen, J S (Duane Morris) *O Q L U1 Ze J1 U2*
London EC1 *p28* . . . 020 7786 2100
Cohen, Miss K A (Jaffe Porter Crossick) *S1 S2 L*
London NW6 *p46* . . . 020 7625 4424
Cohen, L (McDermott Will & Emery UK LLP) *Q Ze*
London EC2 *p56* . . . 020 7577 6900
Cohen, Ms L (Williscroft & Co) *K1 K3 D1*
Bradford *p155* . . . 01274 305380
Cohen, M (Jaffe Porter Crossick) *C1 E O S1 S2 Q*
London NW6 *p46* . . . 020 7625 4424
Cohen, Ms M D (Montague Lambert & Co) *N*
Ealing *p61* . . . 020 8997 2288
Cohen, M J (GLP Solicitors) *S1 E G H W K1 M1 F1*
Manchester *p304* . . . 0161 795 5531
Cohen, N (Trowers & Hamlins) *T1 Zd*
London EC3 *p88* . . . 020 7423 8000
Cohen, N (Fladgate LLP)
London WC2 *p32* . . . 020 3036 7000
Cohen, P (Brian Barr Solicitors) *N Zr Zq Q*
Manchester *p301* . . . 0161 720 6700
Cohen, P G (Jeffrey Green Russell) *N J1 P B1 M1*
London W1 *p46* . . . 020 7339 7000
Cohen, R (Rudds) *S1 S2*
Westcliff-on-Sea *p428* . . . 01702 347853
Cohen, R (Montague Lambert & Co) *S1 C1 T1 E B1 W N P Zc Zi Zl*
Ealing *p61* . . . 020 8997 2288
Cohen, R (Farrer & Co LLP)
London WC2 *p31* . . . 020 3375 7000
Cohen, R A (LG Lawyers)
London SE1 *p50* . . . 020 7379 0000
Cohen, R H (Kennards Wells) *D1 E F1 G J1 K1 L N W S1 Zm*
Redbridge *p362* . . . 020 8550 5103
Cohen, R J (SJ Berwin LLP)
London EC4 *p75* . . . 020 7111 2222

Cohen, R M (Linklaters LLP)
London EC2 *p54* . . . 020 7456 2000
Cohen, Ms S (Lewis Silkin LLP)
London EC4 *p53* . . . 020 7074 8000
Cohen, Miss S (Jaffe Porter Crossick) *E S1 Q S2 Zl*
London NW6 *p46* . . . 020 7625 4424
Cohen, S C (Taylor Wessing) *Ze*
London EC4 *p86* . . . 020 7300 7000
Cohen, S E (Cohen Filippini) *D1 F1 G H J1 K1 M1 N*
Altrincham *p116* . . . 0161 929 9993
London EC4 *p43* . . . 020 7332 2230
Manchester *p305* . . . 0161 830 4600
Cohen, S P (Michael Conn Goldsobel) *R2 Zza Ze I C1 E S2*
London W1 *p60* . . . 020 7580 8902
Cohen, Ms V L (McKinnells) *W L K4*
Lincoln *p284* . . . 01522 541181
Cohoon, Miss K M (Philip J Hammond & Sons) *S1 W E L J1*
Leicester *p280* . . . 0116 251 7171
Coiley, J (Ashurst LLP)
London EC2 *p7* . . . 020 7638 1111
Coish, A J (Andrew Jackson) *Za N O*
Hull *p257* . . . 01482 325242
Coish, S F (Curtis) *S1 W E A1 C1*
Plymouth *p349* . . . 01752 204444
Colabawalla, R (Dass Solicitors) *C1 J1 O Q B2*
Birmingham *p137* . . . 0121 248 4000
Colacicchi, Mrs C E V (Hewitsons) *W Zo*
Northampton *p332* . . . 01604 233233
Colahan, J (Latham & Watkins LLP)
London EC2 *p51* . . . 020 7710 1000
Colas, J N K (Brown Turner Ross) *B1 G H J1 K1 L M1 P S1*
Southport *p388* . . . 01704 542002
Colbert, Miss C L (Blake Lapthorn) *K1*
Oxford *p342* . . . 01865 248607
Colbridge, C (Shearman & Sterling LLP) *O*
London EC2 *p78* . . . 020 7655 5000
Colburn, Mrs C (Towns Needham & Co) *E S1 V W Zd Zo*
Manchester *p310* . . . 0161 832 3721
Colby, Mrs C S (Blandy & Blandy) *T2 W*
Reading *p360* . . . 0118 951 6800
Colby, Ms S (Pollecoff Solicitors Ltd)
London EC2 *p68* . . . 020 7608 2568
Coldbeck, Mrs S E (Society of Lloyd's)
London EC3 *p107* . . . 020 7327 1000
Coldicott, Mrs R L (Irwin Mitchell LLP) *E*
Sheffield *p376* . . . 0870 150 0100
Cole, A J (Ansons LLP) *S1 W S2*
Lichfield *p284* . . . 01543 263456
Cole, A S P (Coles Solicitors) *N Q E O*
Northallerton *p331* . . . 01609 780717
Cole, Ms C (Simon Lacey Law Associates) *K3 K1*
Weymouth *p430* . . . 01305 777711
Cole, C J (John Hodge Solicitors) *S1 W*
Clevedon *p196* . . . 01275 874213
Cole, Miss E (Bindmans LLP) *J1 Zp*
London WC1 *p12* . . . 020 7833 4433
Cole, G (Mander Cruickshank Solicitors LLP) *K1 N*
Coalville *p196* . . . 01530 510666
Cole, G H (Bedfordshire County Council)
Bedford *p448* . . . 01234 363222
Cole, Mrs H (W Evans George & Sons) *S1 S2 W L Zl Zv*
Newcastle Emlyn *p323* . . . 01239 710228
Cole, Mrs J A (Comercrawley) *N*
Diss *p210* . . . 01379 644311
Cole, J H (Slee Blackwell) *O Q J1 Zq L Zc A3 B1 X Zj Zb F1 Zp*
Barnstaple *p125* . . . 01271 372128
Cole, J N (Hogan Lovells International LLP)
London EC1 *p42* . . . 020 7296 2000
Cole, J P O (Morgan Cole)
Oxford *p344* . . . 01865 262600
Cole, Mrs K H (Newark & Sherwood District Council)
Newark *p466* . . . 01636 650000
Cole, Miss L (Rogers & Norton) *C1 S2 E I U2*
Norwich *p335* . . . 01603 666001
Cole, Mrs L A (Bournemouth Borough Council)
Bournemouth *p450* . . . 01202 451178
Cole, M (Prettys) *J1 Zp*
Ipswich *p262* . . . 01473 232121
Cole, M G (Penningtons) *J1*
Godalming *p231* . . . 01483 791800
Cole, Ms M R (White & Case LLP)
London EC2 *p91* . . . 020 7532 1000
Cole, N (Chebsey & Co) *Zu H G B2*
Burnham *p168* . . . 01628 660077
Cole, N J (Beviss & Beckingsale) *S1 E R1 A1 C1 W L A3 S2*
Axminster *p120* . . . 01297 630700
Cole, N J (Verisona Solicitors) *N Q J1*
Waterlooville *p423* . . . 023 9226 5251
Cole, Ms P A (EEF South)
Hook *p461* . . . 01256 763969
Cole, Ms P M (DAC Beachcroft)
Manchester *p303* . . . 0161 934 3000
Cole, R A (Forsters LLP)
Westminster *p33* . . . 020 7863 8333
Cole, S (Hewitsons) *O A3 C3 M2*
Northampton *p332* . . . 01604 233233
Cole, S (Squire Sanders (UK) LLP) *B1 O Zb*
London EC2 *p81* . . . 020 7655 1000
Cole, S B (Glaisyers) *S1 W R1 L E Zc Zd*
Birmingham *p138* . . . 0121 233 2971
Cole, T A (Penningtons) *S1*
Godalming *p231* . . . 01483 791800

Cole, Miss W E (Paul Robinson Solicitors) *S1 S2 C1 E Zv*
Westcliff-on-Sea *p428* . . . 01702 338338
Cole-Marshall, Mrs N (Martin Murray & Associates) *G H B2*
Reading *p361* . . . 0118 950 8577
Colebourne, T (Colebournes Solicitors and Advocates) *G H*
Blackpool *p146* . . . 01253 293195
Coleclough, S D (PricewaterhouseCoopers LLP) *S1 T1 L W R1*
Birmingham *p450* . . . 0121 200 3000
Colegate, P (Russell-Cooke LLP) *E*
London WC1 *p74* . . . 020 7405 6566
Coleman, Miss A (Blaser Mills) *W*
Chesham *p189* . . . 01494 782291
Coleman, Miss B A (Allen & Overy LLP)
London E1 *p5* . . . 020 3088 0000
Coleman, Ms C (Stephens & Scown) *E L C2*
Exeter *p222* . . . 01392 210700
Coleman, C F (Morgan Clarke Solicitors) *G H*
Cirencester *p195* . . . 01285 650066
Coleman, D R (Lincolnshire County Council Resources - Legal Services)
Lincoln *p463* . . . 01522 552222
Coleman, G C (Kenwright Walker Wyllie) *S1 P G M1 W S2 F1 J1 H E Zj Zk Zp*
East Molesey *p215* . . . 020 8979 1131
Coleman, Mrs H (The Dental Law Partnership) *Zr*
Nantwich *p320* . . . 01270 613320
Coleman, Ms J (Farrer & Co LLP)
London WC2 *p31* . . . 020 3375 7000
Coleman, J D (David Phillips & Partners) *G H B2*
Manchester *p308* . . . 0161 860 7354
Coleman, J P (K&L Gates LLP) *E L S1*
London EC4 *p47* . . . 020 7648 9000
Coleman, Mrs M V (Victor Lissack Roscoe & Coleman) *G H Zl B2*
London W1 *p89* . . . 020 7487 2505
Coleman, N (RAC Motoring Services)
Bristol *p452* . . . 0870 553 3533
Coleman, N L (Keoghs LLP) *N Zj O Q A3*
Coventry *p200* . . . 024 7665 8200
Coleman, Mrs P (North Lincolnshire Council)
Scunthorpe *p470* . . . 01724 296296
Coleman, P D (Prester Coleman & Co) *D1 K1 Zm*
Northampton *p332* . . . 01604 633133
Coleman, P H (DLA Piper UK LLP)
London EC2 *p24* . . . 0870 011 1111
Coleman, P J (Higgs & Sons) *A1 E L R1 S2*
Brierley Hill *p158* . . . 0845 111 5050
Coleman, P R (Dickinson Dees)
Newcastle upon Tyne *p324* . 0191 279 9000
Coleman, R J (Capron & Helliwell) *W S1 T1 A1 Zm*
Stalham *p393* . . . 01692 581231
Coleman, R J (Coleman & Betts)
Kingston upon Thames *p267*. 020 8549 4402
Coleman, R J (Colemans - CTTS) *N*
Manchester *p302* . . . 0161 876 2500
Coleman, Miss S M (The National Trust)
Swindon *p475* . . . 01793 817400
Coleman, Miss V E (Weightmans LLP) *Q N*
Liverpool *p291* . . . 0151 227 2601
Coles, Miss A (West Berkshire Council) *Q N K3 G O F1*
Newbury *p466* . . . 01635 42400
Coles, Mrs A (MKB Solicitors LLP) *K1 K4 W*
Barnsley *p124* . . . 01226 210000
Coles, Mrs A M (Fox Williams)
London EC2 *p33* . . . 020 7628 2000
Coles, A R (Jeffrey Green Russell) *E C1 L F1 Zl*
London W1 *p46* . . . 020 7339 7000
Coles, B G S (Stork & Coles) *C1 J1 O Q Zd*
London WC1 *p84* . . . 020 7404 6021
Coles, D C (Hornby Baker Jones & Wood) *G H N Q S1 J1 F1 B1 V E Zl*
Newport *p328* . . . 01633 262848
Coles, Miss H E (Maitland Walker) *O Q C1 C3 M1 E N S1*
Minehead *p318* . . . 01643 707777
Coles, I (Mayer Brown International LLP)
London EC2 *p59* . . . 020 3130 3000
Coles, J M (Brain Chase Coles) *S1 S2 E*
Basingstoke *p126* . . . 01256 354481
Coles, J R (George Green LLP) *O Q A3 Zq*
Cradley Heath *p201* . . . 01384 410410
Coles, P A E (Charles Russell LLP) *C3 Ze Zf*
London EC4 *p19* . . . 020 7203 5000
Coles, P T (Barlow Lyde & Gilbert LLP) *N Q J1*
London EC3 *p10* . . . 020 7247 2277
Coles, R M F (Gateley LLP) *C1 Zb Za*
London EC4 *p35* . . . 020 7653 1600
Coles, S (Hall Smith Whittingham LLP) *S1 R2*
Crewe *p203* . . . 01270 212000
Coles, S D (Curtis) *B1 C1 C2 L*
Plymouth *p349* . . . 01752 204444
Coles, Mrs V (Cardiff County Council)
Cardiff *p453* . . . 029 2087 2000
Colesby, L (DBL Talbots LLP)
Stourbridge *p399* . . . 01384 445850
Coley, C (Penningtons) *J1*
Godalming *p231* . . . 01483 791800
Coley, J D (Pinsent Masons LLP) *J1*
Birmingham *p141* . . . 0121 200 1050
Coley, T L (Worthingtons) *S2 E L S1 W*
Folkestone *p227* . . . 01303 850206
Colgan, Ms L (Smith Law Partnership) *J1*
Braintree *p155* . . . 01376 321311
Colhoun, Ms A H (Bankside Law Ltd) *B2 G*
London SE1 *p9* . . . 0844 745 4000

Coll, Ms B A (Wesley Gryk) *Zi*
Lambeth *p37* . . . 020 7401 6887
Collard, Miss R E (Carter-Ruck) *Q Ze Zk Zz*
London EC4 *p18* . . . 020 7353 5005
Colledge, D J (Seymours) *C1 E S1*
Coventry *p201* . . . 024 7655 3961
Colledge, M (Russell-Cooke LLP) *O Zq A3 B2 F1*
London SW15 *p74* . . . 020 8789 9111
Collen, Ms A J (Mills & Reeve) *E*
Norwich *p335* . . . 01603 660155
Collen, Miss J S (Andrew Markham & Co) *D1 G H K1 Zm*
Carmarthen *p182* . 01267 221550 / 236199
Collen, M R (Sintons LLP) *Zb B1 C2*
Newcastle upon Tyne *p326* . 0191 226 7878
Coller, Miss D F (Metcalfe Copeman & Pettefar) *K1*
Thetford *p410* . . . 01842 756100
Coller, E C (Nichols Marcy Dawson) *K1 N D1 L*
Walton-on-Thames *p420* . . . 01932 219500
Collett, D (Ince & Co Services Ltd)
London E1 *p44* . . . 020 7481 0010
Collett, Mrs L J (McGrigors LLP)
London EC4 *p56* . . . 020 7054 2500
Collett, S (Brookes & Co)
Chichester *p192* . . . 01243 780333
Worthing *p442* . . . 01903 201120
Collett, Mrs V (Treasury Solicitors Department)
London WC2 *p110* . . . 020 7210 3000
Collette, Ms L (Platt & Fishwick) *W S1*
Wigan *p432* . . . 01942 243281
Colley, Miss A (Knight Polson Solicitors) *J1 Zp Q L J2 Zh V*
Eastleigh *p216* . . . 023 8064 4822
Colley, A (Birdsall & Snowball) *S2 E Q S1 W*
Scarborough *p372* . . . 01723 351351
Colley, Miss A S (MFG Solicitors) *E*
Bromsgrove *p167* . . . 01527 831691
Colley, B (Lumsdons Solicitors LLP)
Stourport-on-Severn *p399* . . 01299 827766
Colley, Mrs C L (Graham & Rosen) *N*
Hull *p257* . . . 01482 323123
Colley, D (Bury & Walkers LLP)
Leeds *p272* . . . 0113 244 4227
Colley, Ms J (Ford & Warren) *E X*
Leeds *p273* . . . 0113 243 6601
Colley, Miss L (Painters) *K3 K2 D1 K1*
Kidderminster *p266* . . . 01562 822295
Colley, Ms T (Aviva PLC)
London EC3 *p103* . . 020 7283 7500 / 01603 687905
Norwich *p467* . . . 01603 622200
Collie, P (Fenwick Elliott)
London WC2 *p31* . . . 020 7421 1986
Collier, Ms C R (Atkins Hope Solicitors) *D1 K1*
Croydon *p204* . . . 020 8680 5018
Collier, D A (Archers Law LLP) *C1 E*
Stockton-on-Tees *p396* . . . 01642 636500
Collier, Ms I L (Kennards Wells) *K1 Zh L G H K3 Q*
London E11 *p48* . . . 020 8539 8338
Collier, Mrs I S (HMG Law LLP) *S1 S2*
Oxford *p343* . . . 01865 244661
Collier, Mrs J C (Mark Eisenthal & Co) *K1 S1 F1 J1*
London WC2 *p29* . . . 020 7379 3475
Collier, Mrs L (Harvey Ingram LLP) *N*
Leicester *p280* . . . 0116 254 5454
Collier, M E (Eric Wright Group Ltd)
Bamber Bridge *p448* . . . 01772 698822
Collier, P G (Allan Janes LLP) *S1*
High Wycombe *p249* . . . 01494 521301
Collier, R (Veale Wasbrough Vizards) *Zb C1 M2*
Bristol *p165* . . . 0117 925 2020
Collier, R G (DLA Piper UK LLP) *E*
Birmingham *p137* . . . 0870 011 1111
Collier, Ms T S (Barlow Lyde & Gilbert LLP)
London EC3 *p10* . . . 020 7247 2277
Collier-Jones, Ms B (Stephensons Solicitors LLP) *N*
St Helens *p391* . . . 01942 777777
Collier-Wright, R G (Cumberland Ellis Peirs) *Q L O*
London WC1 *p23* . . . 020 7242 0422
Collin, G K (Chamberlins) *E S1 W L Q S2 R2*
Hitchin *p251* . . . 01462 623456
Colling, R J (Woodfines LLP) *K1 D1 K3*
Bedford *p130* . . . 01234 270600
Colling, Miss Z L (Pinkney Grunwells Lawyers LLP) *S2 S1*
Scarborough *p372* . . . 01723 352125
Collingbourne, A C (Hornby Baker Jones & Wood) *F1 G H J1 N Q O V*
Newport *p328* . . . 01633 262848
Collinge, Ms J (Winckworth Sherwood LLP) *E S1 S2 Zh*
London SE1 *p92* . . . 020 7593 5000
Collingham, S J (McKinnells) *K1 D1 D2 K2*
Lincoln *p284* . . . 01522 541181
Collings, R (Harrison Bundey) *G H*
Leeds *p274* . . . 0113 200 7400
Collingwood, B D (Barlow Robbins LLP) *J1 Zp O*
Woking *p436* . . . 01483 748500
Collingwood, D (Corries Solicitors)
York *p444* . . . 0845 241 5566
Collingwood, M A (Pinsent Masons LLP)
Bristol *p164* . . . 0117 924 5678
Collingwood, M B (Skanska UK PLC) *E Zc*
Rickmansworth *p470* . . . 01923 776666
Hull *p257* . . . 01482 325242
Collingwood, P R (Walker Smith Way) *W T2 K4*
Chester *p191* . . . 0844 346 3100
Collins, A D (SNR Denton) *T1*
London EC4 *p75* . . . 020 7242 1212

6

Collins, A L (Verisona Solicitors) *M1 P G H J1 K1 L N C1 W Zl Zk*
Waterlooville *p423* 023 9226 5251

Collins, Ms A M (EM Collins & Co) *K1 G H N J1 W S1 S2 B1 Zl*
Pinner *p348* 020 8866 1820

Collins, A M (Speechly Bircham LLP) *Zb C2 W*
London EC4 *p81*. 020 7427 6400

Collins, Ms A M (Oliver D'Sa Solicitors) *K1*
Leicester *p279*. 0116 275 5549

Collins, A P (Addleshaw Goddard)
London EC1 *p4* 020 7606 8855
Manchester *p300* 0161 934 6000

Collins, A S (Laytons) *C1 C2 C3 I Ze*
London EC4 *p52*. 020 7842 8000

Collins, A W (Howard Kennedy LLP) *E S1 L B1*
London W1 *p48* 020 7636 1616

Collins, B P (Butters David Grey & Co) *G F1 H J1 Q W S1*
Hastings *p243* . . . .01424 424949 / 715171

Collins, C (Hodge Jones & Allen LLP)
London NW1 *p41* 020 7874 8300

Collins, Ms C (Anthony Gold) *L Zg*
London SE17 *p6*. 020 7940 4000

Collins, Ms C A (Norton Peskett) *S1 E K1 W P G D1 A1 L N Zl*
Great Yarmouth *p234* 01493 849200

Collins, Miss C A (Leeds City Council) *K1 D1*
Leeds *p462* 0113 224 3513

Collins, Mrs C Y (Lattey & Dawe) *Q O Zq*
London EC2 *p51*. 020 7623 2345

Collins, Mrs D (H M Revenue & Customs)
London WC2 *p106*. . . . .

Collins, D A (Blake Lapthorn) *T2 S2 W Zv*
Portsmouth *p354*. 023 9222 1122

Collins, Ms D A (Taylor Wessing)
London EC4 *p86*. 020 7300 7000

Collins, D J (Menneer Shuttleworth) *K1 Q N L G J1 F1 O D1 Zl*
St Leonards-on-Sea *p392* . . 01424 720044

Collins, Ms E (Beviss & Beckingsale) *E P Zl R1 W*
Honiton *p252* 01404 548050

Collins, Ms E (Weightmans LLP) *K1 D1 N*
Knutsford *p269* 01565 634234

Collins, E G L (Jackson Brierley Hudson Stoney) *W*
Rochdale *p365*. . . .01706 644187 / 649214

Collins, Mrs E M (EM Collins & Co) *D1 F1 G H K1 L N Q S1 V Zi Zv*
Pinner *p348* 020 8866 1820

Collins, F G (Mogers) *E A1 W C1 S2*
Bath *p127* 01225 750000

Collins, G E (Green Wright Chalton Annis) *S1*
Worthing *p441*. 01903 234064
Steyning *p395* 01903 814190

Collins, G S (Poole & Co) *A1 E J1 R2 L S1 T2 W S2 K4*
Crewkerne *p203* 01460 279100

Collins, J (Collins Long) *O Q Zf*
Southwark *p21*. 020 7401 9800

Collins, J B (Harold G Walker) *D1 K1 K3 N D2*
Bournemouth *p152*. 01202 203200

Collins, J E (Treasury Solicitors Department)
London WC2 *p110*. 020 7210 3000

Collins, J P (Plexus Law (A Trading Name of Parabis Law LLP)) *Q N Zj*
London EC3 *p68*. 0844 245 4000

Collins, Mrs J W (Derbyshire County Council)
Matlock *p465* 01629 580000

Collins, K (Prince Evans)
Ealing *p69*. 020 8567 3477

Collins, K P (Legal and Professional Claims Ltd)
London EC4 *p107* 020 7621 3900

Collins, Ms L (Van Baaren & Wright) *D1*
Richmond upon Thames *p364*020 8940 2525

Collins, Mrs L F (Collins Solicitors) *D1 L K1 N O Q V Zc F1*
Watford *p423* 01923 223324

Collins, Miss L M (Birkett Long LLP) *K1 K3*
Chelmsford *p186*. 01245 453800

Collins, M (EAD Solicitors LLP)
Liverpool *p287*. 0151 734 4339

Collins, Ms M (Brighouses) *S1 S2 W*
Southport *p388* . . .01704 534101 / 500151

Collins, Mrs M (Hertfordshire County Council) *K1 N W G V L F1*
Hertford *p460* 01992 555555

Collins, M (Forster Dean Ltd) *S1*
Runcorn *p369* 01928 590999

Collins, Mrs M (Cozens-Hardy LLP) *W*
Norwich *p334* 01603 625231

Collins, M J (Goodman Derrick LLP)
London EC4 *p36*. 020 7404 0606

Collins, Ms N (Prisoners' Advice Service)
London EC1 *p108* 020 7253 3323

Collins, N (Ashurst LLP)
London EC2 *p7* 020 7638 1111

Collins, N D (Ford & Warren) *Zj N*
Leeds *p273* 0113 243 6601

Collins, N G (Russell Jones & Walker) *N*
Cardiff *p180* 029 2026 2800

Collins, N J (Nabarro LLP) *B1 E L*
London WC1 *p63* 020 7524 6000

Collins, Ms N S (George Davies Solicitors LLP) *C1 C2*
Manchester *p303* 0161 236 8992

Collins, P D (FBC Manby Bowdler LLP) *J1*
Wolverhampton *p437* 01902 578000

Collins, R (Charles Russell LLP) *K1 D1*
London EC4 *p19*. 020 7203 5000

Collins, Ms R C (Lloyds TSB Asset Finance Division Ltd)
Southampton *p450*. 01489 776880

Collins, R J A (McGrigors LLP) *T1 T2 Q*
London EC4 *p56*. 020 7054 2500

Collins, Miss R L (Warners Solicitors) *K1 Q*
Sevenoaks *p374*. 01732 747900

Collins, S (Anthony King & Co) *G H*
Basildon *p126* 01268 240400

Collins, S (Salans)
London EC4 *p76*. 020 7429 6000

Collins, Mrs S M (Disken & Co) *W S1 K4*
Dewsbury *p210* 01924 464101

Collins, Mrs S M (Harold G Walker) *W K4*
Bournemouth *p152*. 01202 203200

Collins, Ms S M (William Sturges & Co) *S2 E L*
Westminster *p84*. 020 7873 1000

Collins, T J (Weightmans LLP) *B1 I Ze Zk Q*
Liverpool *p291*. 0151 227 2601

Collins, V J (Bakewells) *K1 D1*
Derby *p208* 01332 348791

Collins, W (Collins Solicitors) *D2 D1 Zr K3 K1 N*
Watford *p423* 01923 223324

Collins, W D (Collins Solicitors) *K1 N O Q L D1 V Zc*
Watford *p423* 01923 223324

Collins, W F (Hibbert Lucas Butter) *S1 W K1 A1 C1 S2 E Zl T2*
Whitchurch *p430*. 01948 662231

Collins Rice, Ms R (H M Revenue & Customs)
London WC2 *p106*. . . . .

Collinson, A R (Whiteside & Knowles Ltd) *A1 E S1 W S2*
Morecambe *p319* 01524 416315

Collinson, D (Howard Kennedy LLP) *R2 E*
London W1 *p48* 020 7636 1616

Collinson, D J (Furness & District Petty Sessional Division)
Barrow-in-Furness *p448* . . . 01229 820161

Collinson, I H (Ward Hadaway) *O Zk Zj*
Newcastle upon Tyne *p327* . 0191 204 4000

Collinson, Miss J (City of Sunderland)
Sunderland *p473*. 0191 520 5555

Collinson, P J (J H Powell & Co) *K1 Zd X S1 W L Q S2 D1 Zx*
Derby *p209* 01332 372211

Collinson, R J (The College of Law Chester)
Chester *p454* 0800 289997

Collis, Ms F (Collis & Co) *S1 W E*
Wandsworth *p22*. 020 8767 3332

Collis, Mrs J E (B P Collins LLP) *E S1 S2*
Gerrards Cross *p229*. 01753 889995

Collis, Miss P C N (CKFT) *K1 D1*
London NW3 *p17* 020 7431 7262

Collison, S B (Marathon Oil UK Ltd)
London NW1 *p107*. 020 7298 2500
Southampton *p472*. 023 8022 3855

Colliver, D J (Squire Sanders (UK) LLP) *Zb C1*
London EC2 *p81*. 020 7655 1000

Collyer, Mrs E A (Capron & Helliwell) *S1 W*
Stalham *p393* 01692 581231

Collyer, Mrs J M (Abrams Collyer) *S1 W E L J1 Zh S2*
Lymington *p296* 01590 677888

Collyer, Mrs M (Horsey Lightly) *W*
Newbury *p322* 01635 580858

Collymore, Ms S J (British Telecommunications PLC)
London EC1 *p104* 020 7356 6181

Colman, A M (Pritchard Englefield) *P O M1 Ze Zj*
London EC2 *p69*. 020 7972 9720

Colman, H (Colman Coyle LLP) *Zc O*
Islington *p22*. 020 7354 3000

Colman, J M P (Plexus Law (A Trading Name of Parabis Law LLP)) *Zj O Q Zq E Zr A3*
London EC3 *p68*. 0844 245 4000

Colman, Mrs L (Barlow Robbins LLP) *W*
Guildford *p235*. 01483 543200

Colman, N J (London Borough of Barking & Dagenham) *D1 G J1*
Barking *p448* . .020 8592 4500 / 8252 8233

Colman, P N (Allen Barfields) *S1 L W E C1 T1 S2 Zl*
West Wickham *p428*. 020 8654 2706

Colman, R (Howes Percival LLP) *C1 C2*
Norwich *p334* 01603 762103

Colman, S (WBW Solicitors) *G H*
Newton Abbot *p329* 01626 202404

Colman, S H (George Mitchell Colman & Co) *S1 E*
Birmingham *p137* 0121 427 7700

Colman, Ms S R (George Mitchell Colman & Co) *S1 E W*
Birmingham *p137* 0121 427 7700

Colmer, Miss K (Churchers) *K1*
Portsmouth *p354*. 023 9286 2424

Colombo, A (Badhams Law (A Trading Name of Parabis Law LLP))
Croydon *p204* 0844 245 4000

Colquhoun, E S (Clarke Kiernan) *K1 N S1*
Tonbridge *p412* 01732 360999

Colquhoun, I (Ashurst LLP)
London EC2 *p7* 020 7638 1111

Colquhoun, I T (Mylles & Co) *E C1 S1 W R2 S2*
Sunninghill *p402*. 01344 623388

Colquhoun, Miss S K (Beardsells) *N Q*
Cheadle *p185* 0161 477 2288

Colston, J M (Stewarts Law LLP) *Zb B2 O Q*
London EC4 *p83*. 020 7822 8000

Coltman, L (Coltman Warner Cranston LLP)
Coventry *p200*. 024 7662 7262

Coltman, L (Hill Hofstetter LLP) *O N*
Solihull *p382*. 0121 210 6000

Coludrick, T (Varley Hibbs LLP) *Ze C1 U2 C2*
Coventry *p201*. 024 7663 1000

Colven, Ms S M (Howells LLP) *K1 K3*
Sheffield *p376* 0114 249 6666

Colville, Mrs E (Shepherd + Wedderburn LLP)
London EC4 *p78*. 020 7429 4900
London EC4 *p86*. 020 7300 7000

Colville, I J (Wright Hassall LLP) *O Ze*
Leamington Spa *p270* 01926 886688

Colville, J A K (Stokes Solicitors) *S1 E L R1 Zc Zh*
Portsmouth *p355*. 023 9266 1541

Colville, M (DWF) *N*
Manchester *p303* 0161 603 5000

Colville, S W (Warners Solicitors) *S2 E*
Tonbridge *p412* 01732 770660

Colvin, A J (City of London Corporation)
London EC2 *p107* 020 7606 3030

Colvin, S N (Pinsent Masons LLP)
London EC2 *p67*. 020 7418 7000

Colvin, Mrs V S (Kirwans) *G H*
Birkenhead *p134*. 0151 608 9078

Colwell, Miss F (Paul Robinson Solicitors) *B1 J1 L O Q N*
Westcliff-on-Sea *p428* 01702 338338

Colwell, R (Metcalfe Copeman & Pettefar) *K3 K1*
King's Lynn *p266* 01553 778102

Combe, J W (Muckle LLP) *E L R2 S2*
Newcastle upon Tyne *p325* . 0191 211 7777

Combe, S J (Reynolds Porter Chamberlain LLP)
London E1 *p71* 020 3060 6000

Comben, A F (Simmons & Simmons) *C1 C2*
London EC2 *p79*. 020 7628 2020

Combes, N (Harrowells)
York *p444* 01904 690111

Comer, I R (Comercrawley) *N*
Diss *p210* 01379 644311

Comer, M (Paul Stevens & Co) *Q N*
Bristol *p165* 0117 942 9308

Comiskey, A I (Linklaters LLP)
London EC2 *p54*. 020 7456 2000

Comley, C M (Kidd Rapinet) *K1 O N Q J1*
Slough *p382* 0845 017 9638

Commons, Ms A M (Aviva PLC)
London EC3 *p103* . . 020 7283 7500 / 01603 687905

Compton, G M (Bankside Commercial Solicitors) *G H O Q Zi*
Southwark *p9* 020 7654 0200

Compton, J R (AWB Partnership LLP) *J1 M1 F1 O Q J2*
Guildford *p235*. 01483 302345

Compton, S J (Comptons) *S2 S1 W L*
Camden *p22*. 020 7485 0888

Comrie, Mrs S K (Enoch Evans LLP) *W T2*
Walsall *p420*. 01922 720333

Comstive, Ms L (Blackburn with Darwen Borough Council)
Blackburn *p450* 01254 585585

Comyn, J C C (Watson Farley & Williams)
London EC2 *p90*. 020 7814 8000

Comyn-Platt, J (Platt Halpern) *D1 G H K1 L*
Oldham *p341* 0161 626 4955

Concagh, A N (Stephenson Harwood) *M2 Q Za Zj*
London EC2 *p82*. 020 7329 4422

Concannon, N P (Rotherham Metropolitan Borough Council)
Rotherham *p470*. 01709 382121

Concannon, S T (Walker Morris) *T1*
Leeds *p277* 0113 283 2500

Conder, A J (Macfarlanes) *W T1 M1 B1 Zd Zb Zi*
London EC4 *p56*. 020 7831 9222

Conder, J (Linklaters LLP) *E S1*
London EC2 *p54*. 020 7456 2000

Conder, J H (Morgan Cole) *Zc*
Oxford *p344* 01865 262600

Condron, Ms L M (London Stock Exchange Ltd)
London EC2 *p107* 020 7797 1000

Conduit, J (Sills & Betteridge LLP)
Boston *p151*. 01205 364615

Coneron, Mrs R J (Parker Bird Gardner) *D1 K3 K1 W D2*
Huddersfield *p256* 01484 825200

Confrey, N P (Confreys) *Zm*
Cardiff *p177* 029 2045 8080

Congdon, A (London Underground Ltd)
London SW1 *p107*. 020 7918 3126

Congdon, A J (Chadbourne & Parke)
London EC4 *p19*. 020 7337 8000

Congdon, R J L (Brewer Harding & Rowe) *W*
Barnstaple *p125* 01271 342271

Congdon, S (Holman Fenwick Willan)
London EC3 *p42*. 020 7264 8000

Congreves, Ms J A (B P Collins LLP) *W*
Gerrards Cross *p229*. 01753 889995

Coningham, J P (Coninghams Solicitors) *Zg G H N O Q B2 A3 E T2*
London SW1 *p22* 020 8296 1957

Coningsby, J E R (Nelsons) *K1 C1 C2 E L O R1*
Leicester *p280*. 0116 222 6666

Conlan, Ms S (Capsticks Solicitors LLP) *N Zr*
London SW19 *p18*. 020 8780 2211

Conley, R D (Chadwick-Healey & Co) *G H B2*
London EC4 *p19*. 020 7353 6900

Conlon, C A (Royal Borough of Kingston upon Thames)
Kingston upon Thames *p462*. 020 8546 2121

Conlon, Miss E (NCC Group)
Manchester *p465* 0161 209 5200

Conlon, J (Langleys) *Zu D1 D2 K1*
Lincoln *p284*. 01522 888555
York *p445* 01904 610886

Conlon, J D (A Halsall & Co) *C1 E F1 J1 L P R1 S1 T1*
Birkenhead *p134*. 0151 647 6323

Conlon, J M (Bell & Buxton) *O Q C1 F1 K3 K1 L W T2 D1 D2*
Sheffield *p375* 0114 249 5969
London SW6 *p65* 020 7381 8311

Conlon, Miss M (Department for Business, Enterprise and Regulatory Reform)
London SW1 *p105*. 020 7215 0105

Conlon, M A (Israel Strange & Conlon) *E S1 L S2 Zl*
Islington *p45*. 020 7833 8453

Conn, Ms L (Reynolds Porter Chamberlain LLP)
London E1 *p71* 020 3060 6000

Conn, N S (Avesco Group PLC) *C1 B1 N E J1 T1 Ze*
Crawley *p456* 01293 583400

Conn, Miss R (Stanley Tee LLP) *W T2*
Cambridge *p175*. 01223 311141

Connah, Miss F L (Goodhand and Forsyth Quality Solicitors) *K1 K3*
Redhill *p362*. 01737 773533

Connah, G (E A Harris & Co Ltd) *S1 S2 E L W*
Buckley *p168* 01244 541505
Shotton *p378* 01244 822555

Connal, S A M (Ellisons) *K1 D1 J1*
Clacton-on-Sea *p195* 01255 421248
Colchester *p197*. 01206 764477

Connell, G (hlw Keeble Hawson LLP) *S1 W Zx*
Sheffield *p375* 0114 272 2061

Connell, Mrs J (Cambridge City Council)
Cambridge *p452*. 01223 457000

Connell, K J (Squire Sanders (UK) LLP)
Manchester *p310* 0161 830 5000

Connell, Ms M (Simmons & Simmons)
London EC2 *p79*. 020 7628 2020

Connell, M J (Connell Associates) *B1 C1 E F1 M1 N P W Zb Zc Zj*
Liverpool *p287*. 0151 236 2011

Connell, M S (Hetts) *E C1 J1 K1*
Scunthorpe *p373*. 01724 843287
Scunthorpe *p373*. 01724 270290

Connell, N V (Beecham Peacock) *G H*
Newcastle upon Tyne *p323* . 0191 232 3048

Connell, Mrs P (Broxbourne Borough Council)
Cheshunt *p454* 01992 785555

Connell, P D (Mullis & Peake) *E C1 L A1 T1 R1*
Romford *p366* 01708 784000

Connell, R (Steed & Steed LLP) *K1 K2 V D1 K3*
Braintree *p155*. 01376 552828

Connell, R (Speechly Bircham LLP) *B1*
London EC4 *p81*. 020 7427 6400

Connell, Mrs S E (Scott Duff & Co) *N Q*
Carlisle *p182*. 01228 531054

Connell, Ms S T (Allen & Overy LLP)
London E1 *p5* 020 3088 0000

Connelly, R T (Birmingham City Council Legal & Democratic Services)
Birmingham *p449* 0121 303 2066

Conner, Ms I A (Alen-Buckley & Co) *W T1 T2 C2 S1 Q K4 S2 V B3*
Wandsworth *p4* 020 8767 8336

Conner, L G (Samble Burton & Worth) *S1 W J1 T1 K1*
Burton-on-Trent *p170* 01283 565731

Conner, T (Ashurst LLP)
London EC2 *p7* 020 7638 1111

Connery, M B (Leech & Co) *N*
Manchester *p306* 0161 279 0279

Connick, D A (Fasken Martineau LLP) *E*
London W1 *p31* 020 7917 8500
London W1 *p46* 020 7339 7000

Connick, J A (Clifford Chance)
London E14 *p20*. 020 7006 1000

Connock, A (Eaton Ryan & Taylor) *J1 O Q Ze A3 Zp U1 L Zq*
Birmingham *p138* 0121 236 1999

Connoley, M (Reed Smith LLP) *Zj*
London EC2 *p71*. 020 3116 3000

Connolley, Mrs C (Glovers Solicitors LLP) *Zq Q*
London W1 *p36* 020 7935 8882

Connolly, A J (Bolton Magistrates Court) *G H*
Bolton *p450* 01204 558200

Connolly, Miss A J (Glaisyers Solicitors LLP) *N*
Manchester *p304* 0161 832 4666

Connolly, J (Clifford Chance)
London E14 *p20*. 020 7006 1000

Connolly, Ms J A (Thompsons (formerly Robin/Brian Thompson & Partners)) *N*
Liverpool *p290*. 0151 224 1600

Connolly, J J (Cannings Connolly) *E S2*
London EC1 *p18*. 020 7329 9000

Connolly, J W (Thomas Flavell & Sons) *S2 C1 S1*
Hinckley *p250* 01455 610747

Connolly, Mrs K (Warners Solicitors) *E S1*
Sevenoaks *p374*. 01732 747900

Connolly, K M (McCorry Connolly Solicitors) *E S1 W*
Romford *p366* 01708 727269

Connolly, L (Bells Solicitors) *O Q J1 K1 K3 Zq F1*
Farnham *p224*. 01252 733733

Connolly, Ms L (Russell-Cooke LLP) *K1*
Kingston upon Thames *p267*. 020 8546 6111

Connolly, Mrs L A (Frearsons) *W*
Skegness *p380* 01754 897600

Connolly, Ms M E (Mackesys) *G H D1*
London SE14 *p57* 020 7639 0888

Connolly, Miss P J (Young & Co) *N Q*
Stoke-on-Trent *p398*. 01782 339200

Connolly, P M (Sparling Benham & Brough) *C1 T1 S1 S2 L E*
Colchester *p198* 01206 733733

Connolly, R J F (MFG Solicitors) *S1 E B1 L*
Worcester *p440* 01905 610410

See p634 for the Key to Work Categories

Connolly, Miss S (Hodge Halsall) K1 K3 D1 D2
Southport p388 . . . . 01704 531991

Connolly, S M (Mayer Brown International LLP) Zj O Zq A3
London EC2 p59. . . . . . . 020 3130 3000

Connon, Miss H P N (Somerset County Council)
Taunton p473 . . . . 0845 345 9166

Connor, Mrs A L (Russell & Russell) D1 K1 K3
Bolton p149 . . . . 01204 399299

Connor, Ms C (Dawson Cornwell) K1 K3 D1
London WC1 p26 . . . . . . 020 7242 2556

Connor, Miss C L (Blake Lapthorn) C1 I U2 Ze
Chandlers Ford p184 . . . . 023 8090 8090

Connor, C P (Wells Connor & Co) S1 W R1 C1 A1 E L T1 F1 Zl Zf Zc
Horsforth p253. . . . . 0113 239 0088

Connor, F (The Manchester Airport Group PLC)
Manchester p465 . . . . . . 0871 271 0711

Connor, Miss J E (Duncan Watts LLP) K1 K2 K3
Warwick p422 . . . . 01926 493485

Connor, N W (McLellans) Zl F2 J2 Zy
Hertford p249 . . . . 01992 532000

Connor, Ms R (Jones Day) J1
London EC4 p46. . . . . . . 020 7039 5959

Connor, Miss S A (Hayes & Storr) E S2 S1
Wells-next-the-Sea p425. . . 01328 710210

Connor, V (Pinsent Masons LLP)
London EC2 p67. . . . . . . 020 7418 7000

Connor, Mrs W (Wrigley Claydon) W T1 S1 Zm
Oldham p341 . . . . 0161 624 6811

Conolly, Mrs E M (North East Lincolnshire Borough Council)
Cleethorpes p455 . . . . . . 01472 324001
Grimsby p459 . . . . 01472 313131

Conradi, M (Kemp Little LLP) U1 I U2 C1
London EC2 p48. . . . . . . 020 7600 8080

Conrathe, P A (Ormerods)
Croydon p205 . . . . 020 8686 5000

Conron, Mrs E (Bird & Co) D1 K1 V
Grantham p232 . . . . 01476 591711

Conroy, M C (Gilbert Turner Coomber) S1 E W
Waltham Forest p35 . . . . . 020 8520 5886

Conroy, M J (Kitson & Trotman) A1 D1 G K1 N R1 B1 E H L Zl Zc
Beaminster p129. . . . . . . 01308 862313
Lyme Regis p296 . . . . . . 01297 442580

Conroy, P (Addleshaw Goddard) E
Manchester p300 . . . . . . 0161 934 6000

Conroy, T R (Cadmans Law & Property) S1 W E S2 K4
Cleckheaton p195 . . . . . . 01274 874231

Consiglid, Miss L F (FBC Manby Bowdler LLP) C1 C2 F1 Ze C3
Wolverhampton p437 . . . . 01902 578000

Constable, Mrs A G (Weld & Beavan) W
Enfield p219. . . . . 020 8363 1281

Constable, Mrs J (Davenport Lyons) C1 C2
London W1 p25 . . . . 020 7468 2600

Constable, Mrs J (Environment Agency (South West Region))
Exeter p458 . . . . 0870 850 6506

Constable, R M (Derby City Council)
Derby p456 . . . . 01332 293111

Constable, T C (Weld & Beavan) W S1 K4 S2
Enfield p219. . . . . 020 8363 1281

Constant, G C (Philip Ross & Co) S1 S2
London W1 p73 . . . . 020 7636 6969
London EC1 p82. . . . . . . 020 7935 1211

Constant, R M (PolyGram International Ltd)
London SW1 p108. . . . . . 020 7747 4000

Constantine, Miss G V (Constantine & Summers) K1 S1
Camberley p173. . . . . 01276 23211

Constantine, M (Judge & Priestley) Q Zu
Bromley p166 . . . . 020 8290 0333

Constantinou, C (Constantinou Solicitors) S1
Long Eaton p293 . . . . . . 0115 849 8000

Convery, Mrs L (Lewis Silkin LLP) L R1 R2 S2 E S1 Zh
London EC4 p53. . . . . . . 020 7074 8000

Conway, Ms A (Jones Day) E
London EC4 p46. . . . . . . 020 7039 5959

Conway, A D (Conway & Conway) S2 E W S1 L C2 J2 K2 B1
Westcliff-on-Sea p428 . . . . 01702 710373

Conway, A J (Lawrence Stephens) B1 F1 J1 N O Q Zq L Zp
London EC1 p82. . . . . . . 020 7935 1211

Conway, B (Ince & Co Services Ltd)
London E1 p44 . . . . 020 7481 0010

Conway, D (Hill Dickinson LLP) N
Liverpool p288. . . . . 0151 600 8000

Conway, D P (David Conway & Co) C1 R1 E J1 L S1 W Ze Zw
London W1 p26 . . . . 020 7258 3000

Conway, Ms E (Linklaters LLP)
London EC2 p54. . . . . . . 020 7456 2000

Conway, E F (Chattertons Solicitors) N E O Zq Q L
Boston p151. . . . . 01205 310025

Conway, Miss H M B (Wansbroughs) W
Devizes p210 . . . . 01380 733300

Conway, J E (Winston Solicitors LLP) E S1 S2 W
Leeds p278 . . . . 0113 320 5000

Conway, J L (Conway & Conway) S2 E W R2 S1 L C1 K1 B1 A1
Westcliff-on-Sea p428 . . . . 01702 710373

Conway, Mrs K J (Wrigleys Solicitors LLP) E S1 S2
Leeds p278 . . . . 0113 244 6100

Conway, L R R (Conway & Co) C1 C2 E L R1 S1 W Zc Ze
Henley-on-Thames p247. . . 01491 411122

Conway, Miss N (Kennedys) O Q
Manchester p306 . . . . . . 0161 829 2599

Conway, P I (Davenport Lyons) O Q Zk
London W1 p25 . . . . 020 7468 2600

Conway, R B (Oliver Fisher) L P M1 G K1 J1 F1 H N Zc
London W11 p32. . . . . . . 020 3219 0145

Conway, Mrs S K R (Griffith Smith Conway) A1 B1 C1 E F1 J1 L R1 S1 T1 V W Zd Zl
Hove p254. . . . . 01273 821577

Conway, S P (Plexus Law (A Trading Name of Parabis Law LLP)) J1
Evesham p220. . . . . 01386 769160

Conyers, Miss J (Co-operative Insurance Society Ltd) J1 Zo
Manchester p464 . . . . . . 0161 832 8686

Conyers-Kelly, T (Hethertons LLP) N Q O L Zl Zq A1 B1 J1 F1 J2 W
York p445 . . . . 01904 528200

Cooch, P J (Hewitsons) E R2 S2 S1
Northampton p332. . . . . . 01604 233233

Cook, Ms A (Veale Wasbrough Vizards) J1
Bristol p165 . . . . 0117 925 2020

Cook, Ms A (Wedlake Bell LLP)
London WC1 p91 . . . . . . 020 7395 3000

Cook, Mrs A C (Harvey Ingram LLP) S1
Leicester p280. . . . . 0116 254 5454

Cook, A H A (Cook & Talbot) S1 W A1 T1 L E S2
Southport p388 . . . . 01704 535216

Cook, Ms A J (Girlings) K1 K3
Ashford p119 . . . . 01233 647377

Cook, Ms A M (Aldridge Brownlee Solicitors LLP) P F1 J1 L N R1 B1 O Q Zc
Bournemouth p151. . . . . . 01202 294411

Cook, C (DLA Piper UK LLP) Ze
Birmingham p137 . . . . . . 0870 011 1111

Cook, C (Wiggin Osborne Fullerlove) T1 T2 M2 C1 Zf
Cheltenham p189 . . . . . . 01242 710200
London SW1 p91 . . . . . . 020 7290 2456

Cook, Ms C A E (K&L Gates LLP)
London EC4 p47. . . . . . . 020 7648 9000

Cook, Ms C A E (Forsters LLP) T2 W
Westminster p33. . . . . . . 020 7863 8333

Cook, C B (Amphlett Lissimore)
Croydon p6 . . . . 020 8771 5254

Cook, Ms C E (Jordans) C1
Wakefield p418 . . . . 01924 387110

Cook, C J (Cook & Partners) K1 S1 M1 P L G D1 H F1
Croydon p204 . . . . 020 8655 4466

Cook, C R (Salusburys Harding & Barnett) N Q O K1 D2 G H D1 J1 Zr
Leicester p281. . . 0116 262 9033 / 262 6052

Cook, D (Coffin Mew & Clover) L E S1 R1 Zs
Fareham p223. . . . . 01329 825617

Cook, D A (Henry & Company)
Swindon p406 . . . . 01793 832000

Cook, D A (Daniel & Edwards) K1 D1 Q K3
Ramsgate p359 . . . . 01843 594651

Cook, D C J (Bird & Bird LLP) C1 U1
London EC4 p13. . . . . . . 020 7415 6000

Cook, F (Stones Solicitors LLP) Q N
Exeter p222 . . . . 01392 666777

Cook, Mrs F M E (Blake Lapthorn) S2 E S1 A1 R1 R2 L
Chandlers Ford p184 . . . . 023 8090 8090

Cook, G M (Hannays Solicitors and Advocates) G H
South Shields p383 . . 0191 456 7893 / 455 5361

Cook, I A (Laytons) E L R1 S1 R2
Guildford p236. . . . . 01483 407000

Cook, Ms J (Barnsley Metropolitan Borough Council)
Barnsley p448 . . . . 01226 770770

Cook, Ms J (Gateshead Metropolitan Borough Council) O B2 Q E S2 N C1 B1 G J1 Zw Zr Ze Zf Zj
Gateshead p458. . . . . . . 0191 433 3000

Cook, J C (SAS Daniels LLP) J1
Stockport p396. . . . . 0161 475 7676

Cook, J M C (Ramsdens Solicitors) N J1 O G Q Zj
Huddersfield p256 . . . . . . 01484 821500

Cook, J O (Adur District Council)
Shoreham-by-Sea p471 . . . 01273 263300

Cook, J T G (Tayntons LLP Solicitors) S2 S1
Gloucester p230. . . . . . . 01452 522047

Cook, Miss L (Allen & Overy LLP)
London E1 p5 . . . . 020 3088 0000

Cook, Miss L F (Cook & Talbot) S1 W
Southport p388 . . . . 01704 535216

Cook, Miss L J (Morrish Solicitors LLP) N Q
Leeds p276 . . . . 0113 245 0733

Cook, M (Anthony Collins Solicitors LLP) C1 Zu
Birmingham p137 . . . . . . 0121 200 3242

Cook, M J (Donnelly McArdle Adamson) O Q N S1 W
Sunderland p401. . . . . . . 0191 510 9911

Cook, Mrs M L (Cook & Talbot) S1 W N F1 A1
Southport p388 . . . . 01704 535216

Cook, N (Frisby & Co) G B2 H
Stafford p392 . . . . 01785 244114

Cook, N C S (Paul Davidson Taylor) B1 C1 C2 C3 E F1 J1 M1 S1 Zb Zd Ze Za
Horsham p253. . . . . 01403 262333

Cook, N D (Birketts LLP (Wollastons LLP)) E X Zl R2 S2 R1
Chelmsford p186. . . . . . . 01245 211211

Cook, N E (Cooks) N P
Newcastle under Lyme p323. 01782 611090

Cook, Ms P (Warner Goodman LLP) Zb F1
Southampton p387. . . . . . 023 8063 9311

Cook, P D (Osborne Clarke) A1 B1 C1 F1 J1 M1 N P Za Zc
Bristol p164 . . . . 0117 917 3000

Cook, Miss P D (Waltons & Morse LLP) O M2 A3
London EC3 p90. . . . . . . 020 7623 4255

Cook, Mrs P J (Streeter Marshall)
Purley p358 . . . . 020 8660 6455

Cook, P M (Greenland Houchen Pomeroy) K1 S1 W N Q O C1 E T1 Zl S2
Wymondham p443. . . . . . 01953 606351

Cook, Mrs R E (Foot Anstey) D1 D2 K1
Exeter p221 . . . . 01392 411221
Exeter p221 . . . . 01392 688688

Cook, R J (Michael Hill Partnership) G H N Q K1 J1 Zi Zv
Leicester p280. . . . . 0116 254 1609

Cook, R J (Trethowans LLP) O Zq Ze Q A3
Southampton p387. . . . . . 023 8032 1000

Cook, R J (Robert Cook & Co Solicitors) K1 S1 E C1 Zd Zl
Fleet p226. . . . . 01252 812957

Cook, Ms S (C&C Family Law) K1 K3
Plymouth p349. . . . . 01752 222211

Cook, S (Hanne & Co)
London SW11 p38 . . . . . . 020 7228 0017

Cook, Ms S (Forsters LLP) R2 Zc
Westminster p33. . . . . . . 020 7863 8333

Cook, S (Thompsons (formerly Robin/Brian Thompson & Partners)) N
Leeds p277 . . . . 0113 205 6300

Cook, Miss S (Burley & Geach) K1 D1 V L
Haslemere p243. . . . . . . 01428 656011

Cook, S (SNR Denton) Zb
London EC4 p75. . . . . . . 020 7242 1212

Cook, S C (Thomson & Bancks LLP) W T2 T1 S1 Zm
Tewkesbury p410 . . . . . . 01684 299633

Cook, Mrs S J (Land Registry - Lancashire Office)
Preston p469 . . . . 01772 836700

Cook, S J H (Ormerods) Q
Croydon p205 . . . . 020 8686 5000

Cook, S L D (Thomson & Bancks LLP) O N Q F1 G Zl
Pershore p346. . . . . 01386 562000

Cook, T (Taylor Walton LLP) C1 U2 I
Luton p295 . . . . 01582 731161

Cook, Miss T J E (Warner Goodman LLP) K1 K2 K3 D1 D2
Southampton p387. . . . . . 023 8063 9311

Cook, T M (Bird & Bird LLP) Ze
London EC4 p13. . . . . . . 020 7415 6000

Cook, W (Simmons & Simmons)
London EC2 p79. . . . . . . 020 7628 2020

Cooke, A (Wellers Law Group LLP) C1 S2 E
London WC1 p91 . . . . . . 020 7242 7265

Cooke, A J (Young & Co) G H
Stoke-on-Trent p398. . . . . 01782 339200

Cooke, A N (Hogan Lovells International LLP) Ze
London EC1 p42. . . . . . . 020 7296 2000
London EC1 p93. . . . . . . 0870 903 1000

Cooke, C E C (Rooks Rider) C1 T1 W B1 J1 Zb F1 M1 Zd Ze Zl Zo Zv
London EC1 p73. . . . . . . 020 7689 7000

Cooke, Mrs C L (National Grid PLC)
Warwick p471 . . . . 01926 653000

Cooke, D (Maclay Murray & Spens LLP)
London EC2 p57. . . . . . . 020 7002 8500

Cooke, E (DLA Piper UK LLP)
London EC2 p24. . . . . . . 0870 011 1111

Cooke, Miss E (Last Cawthra Feather LLP) O
Leeds p275 . . . . 0113 244 0876

Cooke, E S E (TLT Solicitors) E A1 P R2
Bristol p165 . . . . 0117 917 7777

Cooke, E W G (Anderson Longmore & Higham) K1 K2 K3 D1 D2
Chichester p192. . . . . . . 01243 787899

Cooke, I J (Charles Russell LLP) S1 E
London EC4 p19. . . . . . . 020 7203 5000

Cooke, J A F (Amphlett Lissimore) W S1 T2
Croydon p6 . . . . 020 8771 5254

Cooke, J C (Wellers Law Group LLP) C1 C2 R2 T1 C3 Zo Zd Zc
London WC1 p91 . . . . . . 020 7242 7265

Cooke, J D (Aviva PLC)
London EC3 p103 . . 020 7283 7500 / 01603 687905

Cooke, Mrs J E (Heckford Norton) W T2 K4
Stevenage p395 . . . . 01438 312211

Cooke, J G (Enoch Evans LLP) C1 C2 S1 S2 W
Walsall p420. . . . . 01922 720333

Cooke, J W (Thomson Wilson Pattinson) A1 H G J1 P R1 S1 S2
Kendal p264. . . . . 01539 721945

Cooke, Ms L A (Barlow Lyde & Gilbert LLP) Zj Zq
London EC3 p10. . . . . . . 020 7247 2277

Cooke, M K (John Barkers) A1 B1 C1 E J1 L S1 S2 W Zi Zv Zl
Grimsby p234 . . . . 01472 358686

Cooke, P S (Salans) J1
London EC4 p76. . . . . . . 020 7429 6000

Cooke, Q G P (Bristows) C1 C2 B1 T1 Zo
London EC4 p15. . . . . . . 020 7400 8000

Cooke, Ms R (Wrigleys Solicitors LLP) Zo
Leeds p278 . . . . 0113 244 6100

Cooke, R (Squire Sanders (UK) LLP) O Zc
London EC2 p81. . . . . . . 020 7655 1000

Cooke, R N (Taylor & Emmet LLP) O L Q Zq
Sheffield p377 . . . . 0114 218 4000

Cooke, R P (Field Fisher Waterhouse LLP) C1 E B1 R1 Zb
London EC3 p31. . . . . . . 020 7861 4000

Cooke, S (Withers LLP) T2 W A1 Zm
London EC4 p92. . . . . . . 020 7597 6000

Cooke, S M (MFG Solicitors) Zc Q W S2 E S1
Bromsgrove p167 . . . . . . 01527 831691

Cooksey, J P (Pontefract Magistrates Court)
Pontefract p468 . . . . 01977 691600

Cooksey, P D (Bower & Bailey) S1 S2 W
Banbury p122 . . . . 01295 265566

Cooksley, Mrs A (Ansons LLP) N K1 Q Zr Zq S2
Lichfield p284 . . . . 01543 263456

Cooksley, Ms K (Bevan Brittan LLP)
London EC4 p12. . . . . . . 0870 194 1000

Cooksley, M W H (Thompson Smith & Puxon) O Q B1 Zb Zc Zk
Colchester p198. . . . . . . 01206 574431

Cookson, C J (Waugh & Co) S1 W
Haywards Heath p246 . . . . 01444 451666

Cookson, Miss H J (Chronnell Hibbert) K1 D1
Stockport p395. . . . . 0161 494 6085

Cookson, J M (Moerans) C1 E W L S2
Edgware p217. . . . . 020 8952 0242

Cookson, J S (Waugh & Co) S1 W A1 L
Haywards Heath p246 . . . . 01444 451666

Cookson, N A (Darlington Borough Council)
Darlington p456 . . . . 01325 388055

Cookson, P (Roythornes LLP) A1 O Q G J1 P J2 Zk Zq
Peterborough p347 . . . . . 01733 558585

Cookson, R (HC Solicitors LLP) E S1
Peterborough p347 . . . . . 01733 882800

Cookson, Mrs R A (Goldstones) Q L N
Swansea p405. . . . . 01792 643021

Cookson, Miss S L (Hellewell Pasley & Brewer) S1 W
Dewsbury p210 . . . . 01924 455515

Cookson, S T (Ashurst LLP) E
London EC2 p7 . . . . 020 7638 1111

Cooles, R J (Abbott Cresswell LLP) E S1 Zh W
London SW14 p3 . . . . . . 020 8876 4478

Cooley, A E (Davies & Partners) S2 E L R1
Gloucester p230. . . . . . . 01452 612345

Coolican, T (Russell Jones & Walker) B2 G
Cardiff p180 . . . . 029 2026 2800

Coombe, A J (hlw Keeble Hawson LLP) B1 C2 F1 J1 T1 T2 W Zb Zd Zo
Sheffield p375 . . . . 0114 272 2061

Coombe, C B (Linklaters LLP)
London EC2 p54. . . . . . . 020 7456 2000

Coombe, J (Birketts LLP (Wollastons LLP)) K1
Chelmsford p186. . . . . . . 01245 211211
Chelmsford p187. . . . . . . 01245 491122

Coombe, R N J (Whitehead Monckton) C1 E J1 Ze
Maidstone p299 . . . . 01622 698000

Coomber, G (DAC Beachcroft) N Zj
London EC4 p24. . . . . . . 020 7936 2222

Coomber, Miss S A (John Fowlers LLP Solicitors) N Zm
Colchester p197. . . . . . . 01206 576151
Brightlingsea p159. . . . . . 01206 302694

Coombes, D A D (Family Law in Partnership LLP) K1 K2
London WC2 p30 . . . . . . 020 7420 5000

Coombes, Ms V (LG Lawyers)
London SE1 p50. . . . . . . 020 7379 0000

Coombs, D J (William Bailey) S1 L S2
Southwark p9 . . . . 020 8693 9615

Coombs, Miss D L (Leeds Day) S1 S2
St Neots p392 . . . . 01480 474661

Coombs, G E (GH Cornish LLP)
Ilford p260. . . . . 020 8090 0800

Coombs, Miss H M (North Tyneside Council)
Newcastle upon Tyne p466 . 0191 643 5000

Coombs, I (Truman-Moore) W S1 L
Verwood p418 . . . . 01202 824677

Coombs, I R (Mayo Wynne Baxter LLP) S1 E W C1 K1 L P M1 R1 G Zl F1
Eastbourne p215. . . . . . . 01323 730543

Coombs, P D (Aaron & Partners LLP Solicitors) W T2
Chester p190 . . . . 01244 405555

Coombs, R G (Foot Anstey) C1
Exeter p221 . . . . 01392 411221
Plymouth p349. . . . . 01752 675000

Cooney, A P (Lockings)
Hull p257 . . . . 0845 075 4197

Cooney, C J (GCL Solicitors) C1 E F1 J1 L N R1 S1 R2
Guildford p236. . . . . 01483 577091

Cooney, C M (Campbell Courtney & Cooney) D1 G H K1 N O Q W Zl Zj J2 Zq Zr
Camberley p173. . . . . 01276 25100

Cooney, D A (Aaron & Partners LLP Solicitors) W T2
Chester p190 . . . . 01244 405555

Cooney, P D O (Fairweather Stephenson & Co) P J1 E L Q N S1 W G H Zl
Felixstowe p225 . . . . 01394 277941

Cooper, Ms A (Rotherham Magistrates Court)
Rotherham p470. . . . . . . 01709 839339

Cooper, A (WBW Solicitors) G H
Torquay p413 . . . . 0870 701 4321

Cooper, A (Blake Lapthorn) J1
Chandlers Ford p184 . . . . 023 8090 8090

Cooper, A J (Weightmans LLP) N J1 Q Zl Zp Zj
Liverpool p291. . . . . 0151 227 2601

Cooper, B D (Bell Lamb & Joynson) K1 D1 L D2 S2 K3 K4 Q N S1 W Zh G
Weaverham p424 . . . . . . 0844 412 4348
Runcorn p369 . . . . 0844 412 4348

Cooper, B D H (B D H Cooper Ltd)
Haywards Heath p245 . . . . 01444 831127

6

Cooper, Miss C (Swinburne Maddison) *K1 Q O N*
Durham *p214* . . 0191 384 2441 / 384 7455

Cooper, C (Wollen Michelmore Solicitors) *T2 W K4*
Newton Abbot *p330* 01626 332266

Cooper, Miss C (Wendy Hopkins Family Law Practice LLP) *K1 K3 D1 D2*
Cardiff *p178* 029 2034 2233

Cooper, Ms C (The Wilkes Partnership LLP) *B1 Zb*
Birmingham *p143* 0121 233 4333

Cooper, C B (Brethertons LLP) *C1 S2 E F1 M1 B1 J1*
Rugby *p368* 01788 551611
Rugby *p368* 01788 579579

Cooper, C J (Bridge McFarland) *M1 K1 P F1 S1 G H L V W Zl*
Grimsby *p235* 01472 311711

Cooper, C L (Lofthouse & Co) *S1 G H K1 D1 J1 F1 N Q L Zm Zl Zc*
Castleford *p183* 01977 603347

Cooper, C L (Plexus Law (A Trading Name of Parabis Law LLP))
Evesham *p220*. 01386 769160

Cooper, C S (Read Cooper) *A2 E*
Thame *p410*. 01844 260038

Cooper, Mrs D (Michelmores LLP) *E R2*
Exeter *p221* 01392 688688

Cooper, D (NFLA Ltd) *K1 K3 D1*
Wellingborough *p424* 01933 222700

Cooper, D A (Paris Smith LLP) *C1 Zb Ze C2*
Southampton *p386*. 023 8048 2482

Cooper, D C (Fullers Family Law Practice LLP) *K1 D1*
Bedford *p130* 01234 343134

Cooper, D C (ASB Law) *O Q Zq*
Crawley *p202* 01293 603600

Cooper, Miss D K (Parkinson Wright LLP) *G H*
Worcester *p440* 01905 726789

Cooper, D M (Cox Cooper Limited) *O J1 Zp Q Ze*
Birmingham *p137* 0121 777 0015

Cooper, D P (BUPA)
London WC1 *p104*. 020 7656 2305

Cooper, D P W (Moss Solicitors LLP) *S1 S2 E Zl L C1*
Loughborough *p293* 01509 217770

Cooper, Ms E (Taylor Walton LLP) *J1*
Luton *p295* 01582 731161

Cooper, E J O (Russell Jones & Walker)
London WC2 *p74* 020 7657 1555

Cooper, E N (Hague Lambert) *E C1 T1 W S1 R1*
Urmston *p417* 0161 747 7321

Cooper, Mrs G (William H Lill & Co) *S1 S2 W*
Altrincham *p116* 0161 928 8111
Lymm *p296* . . . . .01925 753170 / 755668

Cooper, G A (British American Tobacco) *O*
London WC2 *p104*. 020 7845 1000

Cooper, G J (Carpenter & Co)
Wallington *p419* 020 8669 5145

Cooper, G J (Bank of Scotland)
Chester *p454* 01244 690000

Cooper, G J (Trafford Metropolitan Borough Council)
Stretford *p473* 0161 912 1212

Cooper, Mrs G L (Harrogate Borough Council)
Harrogate *p460* 01423 500600

Cooper, G M (Greenwoods Solicitors LLP) *L Zu R1 S1*
Peterborough *p347* 01733 887700

Cooper, I R (Radcliffes Le Brasseur) *Zr Zm Q*
Leeds *p276* 0113 234 1220

Cooper, Mrs J (Squire Sanders (UK) LLP) *E L*
London EC2 *p81*. 020 7655 1000

Cooper, Ms J (Thompsons (formerly Robin/Brian Thompson & Partners)) *N J1 Zr*
Sheffield *p377* 0114 270 3300

Cooper, Miss J (Linklaters LLP)
London EC2 *p54*. 020 7456 2000

Cooper, J (Hogan Lovells International LLP) *C1*
London EC1 *p42*. 020 7296 2000

Cooper, J (Paisleys) *G H*
Workington *p440*. 01900 602235

Cooper, J (The Wilkes Partnership LLP) *B1 Zb*
Birmingham *p143* 0121 233 4333

Cooper, J (Bond Pearce LLP)
Plymouth *p349*. 0845 415 0000

Cooper, Ms J (J Cooper)
London EC3 *p22*. 020 7790 0441

Cooper, Ms J A (MacLaverty Cooper Atkins)
Kingston upon Thames *p267*. 020 8549 9994

Cooper, J B (Eaton Smith LLP) *C1 C3 Ze C2 Zo T1 T2 W*
Huddersfield *p255* 01484 821300

Cooper, Miss J D (Atter Mackenzie & Co) *K1 D1 Q D2 K3*
Evesham *p220*. 01386 425300

Cooper, J E (Barlow Lyde & Gilbert LLP) *A3 Zb B1 Zj M2 O Zq*
London EC3 *p10*. 020 7247 2277

Cooper, Miss J E (Henry Hyams) *G H*
Leeds *p274* 0113 243 2288

Cooper, Mrs K (Cooper Stott) *N K1 W*
Durham *p214* 0191 384 7210

Cooper, K (Ince & Co Services Ltd)
London E1 *p44* 020 7481 0010

Cooper, Mrs K (EMW) *E R2 S2*
Milton Keynes *p316* 0845 070 6000

Cooper, Ms L (Thorneycroft Solicitors Ltd) *N*
Macclesfield *p297* 01625 503444

Cooper, Ms L (Watson Farley & Williams) *C1 C2*
London EC2 *p90*. 020 7814 8000

Cooper, Mrs L C (Cooper Nimmo) *S1*
Blackpool *p146* 01253 626793

Cooper, Ms M (Graysons) *K1 K3*
Sheffield *p375* 0114 272 9184

Cooper, M A (Brindley Twist Tafft & James) *W S1 N*
Coventry *p200*. 024 7653 1532

Cooper, M F (BLB Solicitors) *W*
Trowbridge *p413*. 01225 755656

Cooper, M J (London Borough of Wandsworth)
London SW18 *p110* 020 8871 6000

Cooper, M L (Cooper Whiteman) *N Q O Zk S2*
London WC1 *p22* 020 7831 5222

Cooper, M V (Davitt Jones Bould) *E S2 L A1 R1*
Taunton *p408* 01823 279279

Cooper, Ms N (Fisher Jones Greenwood LLP) *K1*
Colchester *p197* 01206 578282

Cooper, Mrs N (Mid Devon District Council)
Tiverton *p474* 01884 255255

Cooper, Mrs N (Ware & Kay LLP) *C1 E C2 Zb*
York *p445* 01904 716000

Cooper, N (Radcliffes Le Brasseur)
Westminster *p70*. 020 7222 7040

Cooper, N C (Cooper Stott) *N S1 W Q*
Durham *p214* 0191 384 7210

Cooper, Ms O (Gregory Rowcliffe Milners) *W*
London WC1 *p37* 020 7242 0631

Cooper, P (Tozers) *S2 E S1*
Exeter *p222* 01392 207020

Cooper, Mrs P (Knipe Woodhouse-Smith) *N F1 E J1 Q S1 W Zk*
Chalfont St Peter *p184*. . . .01753 887877 / 889149

Cooper, P (CKFT)
London NW3 *p17* 020 7431 7262

Cooper, P R (Paul Cooper & Co) *E S1 W L Zd*
Leicester *p279*. 0116 255 4477

Cooper, P S (The Ringrose Law Group - Paul Cooper) *D1 J1 K1 N Zm Zi Zj O Q X*
Boston *p151*. 01205 311511

Cooper, P V J (Financial Services Authority)
London E14 *p106* 020 7066 1000

Cooper, R (BTMK Solicitors LLP) *G B2*
Southend-on-Sea *p387* . . . 01702 339222

Cooper, Dr R (R T Coopers Solicitors) *C1 E L F1 Ze Zza X J1 M1 M2 Q O C2 Zp Zw*
London E1 *p22* 020 7488 9947

Cooper, Mrs R (Roythornes LLP) *E S2 A1 S1*
Spalding *p389* 01775 842500

Cooper, R A (Buss Murton LLP) *W*
Tunbridge Wells *p415* 01892 510222

Cooper, R D (Lee Bolton Monier-Williams) *O Q J1 A3 Zd Zx*
Westminster *p52*. 020 7222 5381

Cooper, R M (Bell Lax Litigation) *O Zq Q B1 F1 A3 C1 F2*
Sutton Coldfield *p403* 0121 355 0011

Cooper, R M (HRJ Law LLP) *J2 F2 Zl*
Welwyn Garden City *p425* . . 01707 887700

Cooper, R S J (Derbyshire Dales District Council)
Matlock *p465* 01629 761100

Cooper, Mrs S (Infogrames United Kingdom Ltd) *I Ze Zf*
London W6 *p465* 020 8222 9700

Cooper, Miss S A (Derby City Council)
Derby *p456* 01332 293111

Cooper, Miss S J (Wright & McMillan Bennett) *G H*
Telford *p409* 01952 291100

Cooper, S J (Barlow Lyde & Gilbert LLP) *O Q Zj*
London EC3 *p10*. 020 7247 2277

Cooper, S K (Hodge Jones & Allen LLP) *W*
London NW1 *p41* 020 7874 8300

Cooper, Mrs S L (Sheila Cooper LLB) *G W L*
London NW6 *p22* 020 7372 0510

Cooper, Miss T C (Squire Sanders (UK) LLP)
Leeds *p277* 0113 284 7000

Cooper, T E (Cooper & Co) *A2 F1 G J1 K1 O Q N*
York *p444* 01904 626266

Cooper, Miss V (Crellins Carter Solicitors) *K1 D1 Zr N*
Weybridge *p429* 01932 858833

Cooper, W G (Conwy County Borough Council) *D1 G H K1 V*
Conwy *p455* 01492 576108

Cooperman, M M (Mayo Wynne Baxter LLP) *N Q O G Zr*
Brighton *p160* 01273 775533

Coopersmith, Ms L D (Trowers & Hamlins) *L Zh*
London EC3 *p88*. 020 7423 8000

Coopey, C (Mayo Wynne Baxter LLP)
Brighton *p160* 01273 775533

Coopman, P D (Treasury Solicitors Department)
London WC2 *p110*. 020 7210 3000

Coote, Ms D M (Plexus Law (A Trading Name of Parabis Law LLP)) *N*
Evesham *p220*. 01386 769160

Cope, Ms E J (Barlow Lyde & Gilbert LLP)
London EC3 *p10*. 020 7247 2277

Cope, G A (Redrow PLC)
Flint *p458* 01244 520044

Cope, Ms R (Russell Jones & Walker)
Manchester *p309* 0161 383 3500

Cope, R F (Walters & Barbary) *S1 A1 E L*
Camborne *p173* 01209 712454

Cope, R I (SAS Daniels LLP) *S1 L W E R1 T1*
Congleton *p198* 01260 282300

Cope, T J (Richard Freeman & Co) *A1 M1 P S1 W C1 L Zi Zl R2*
Kensington & Chelsea *p34*. 020 7351 5151

Copeland, A A P (Stanley Tee LLP) *Zr*
Cambridge *p175*. 01223 311141

Copeland, Ms E (Trowers & Hamlins)
London EC3 *p88*. 020 7423 8000

Copeland, Miss F (Wedlake Bell LLP) *W T2*
London WC1 *p91* 020 7395 3000

Copeland, G J (BHP Law) *C1*
Darlington *p206* 01325 466794

Copeland, H (Holman Copeland)
Lewisham *p42* . .020 8852 1162 / 8852 2632

Copeland, Mrs J C (Ian N Gunby & Co) *G H N Q Zl Zm*
Milnthorpe *p316* 01539 562044
Barrow-in-Furness *p125* . . . 01229 811811

Copeland, J W J (Symons & Gay)
Romford *p366* 01708 744211

Copeland, M (Howells LLP) *X Zm*
Sheffield *p376* 0114 249 6666

Copeland, R A (Allen Barfields) *S1 W P M1 A1 T1 Zi*
Croydon *p204* 020 8680 2050

Copeman, J (Herbert Smith LLP) *O A3 B2 Zb*
London EC2 *p40*. 020 7374 8000

Copeman, M (Copeman Markham Solicitors) *G H*
Hull *p256* 01482 212979

Copestake, I T (Nelsons) *W S1 T1 Zm*
Derby *p209* 01332 372372

Copestake, M G (Freeth Cartwright LLP) *C1 C2 C3*
Derby *p208* 01332 361000
Nottingham *p337*. 0115 936 9369

Copitch, L M (Lavin Copitch) *N S1 W*
Manchester *p306* 0161 223 5484

Copitch, M H (Copitch) *K1 Q D1 L N O S1 E G*
Haringey *p22* 020 8883 9831

Copithorne, Ms A (Richard Buxton) *P M1 Zg M2 Q R1 Zn O*
Cambridge *p174*. 01223 328933

Copland, Miss B D (Goodman Derrick LLP) *Q J1 Zf*
London EC4 *p36*. 020 7404 0606

Coplestone-Crow, T (The Wilkes Partnership LLP) *E L R1 S1 S2*
Birmingham *p143* 0121 233 4333

Copley, B W (Harrowells)
York *p444* 01904 558600

Copley, D T (Addleshaw Goddard)
Leeds *p271* 0113 209 2000
Manchester *p300* 0161 934 6000

Copley, Ms E (Ingrams) *A1 E R1 S1 Zc*
York *p445* 01904 520600

Copley, Mrs J C P (Copley Davies) *J1 O Q Zp*
St Albans *p390* 01727 764978

Copley, J S (Pickering & Butters) *S1 A1 E W C1 L*
Rugeley *p368* 01889 803080

Copp, Ms C L (Ingrams) *S1*
Hull *p257* 01482 358850
York *p445* 01904 520600

Coppack, Mrs R (Walker Smith Way) *S1*
Chester *p191* 0844 346 3100

Coppard, Mrs P L (Mayo Wynne Baxter LLP) *S1 W*
East Grinstead *p215*. 01342 310600

Coppen, J G W (Bernard Chill & Axtell) *B1 F1 L N Q J1 Zl O*
Southampton *p385*. 023 8022 8821

Coppen, Mrs R (Rosamund Coppen & Company) *S1 E W L*
Bath *p127* 0330 440 1802

Copper, J P (Ginn & Co) *F1 J1 K1 N Zl O Q K3*
Cambridge *p174*. 01223 358275

Coppin, J D S (Shearman & Sterling LLP) *C2*
London EC2 *p78*. 020 7655 5000

Copping, M A (Hamlins LLP) *C1 J1 B1 Zb*
London W1 *p38* 020 7355 6000

Copping, V A (Harvey Copping & Harrison) *S1 E L S2 Zl*
Wickford *p431* . . . .01268 733381 / 763211

Coppinger, J (Buckles Solicitors LLP) *Zc A3 O Zq*
Peterborough *p346* 01733 888888

Coppins, C L (Herrington & Carmichael LLP) *S1*
Wokingham *p437* 0118 977 4045

Copsey, P B (MFG Solicitors) *C1 E Zd I*
Kidderminster *p265* 01562 820181

Copsey, R B (Smith & Copsey) *G H*
Wallsend *p419*. 0191 262 4428

Copson, J (Withers LLP) *K1*
London EC4 *p92*. 020 7597 6000

Coram, R (Michelmores LLP) *E S2 L S1*
Sidmouth *p380*. 01395 512515

Coram, R S (WBW Solicitors) *S1 E A1 L R1 W C1*
Exeter *p222* 01392 202404

Corbally, Miss S L (Telford Magistrates Court)
Telford *p474* 01952 204500

Corben, Miss H (SJ Berwin LLP) *T1*
London EC4 *p75*. 020 7111 2222

Corbett, A C (Maxwell Winward LLP) *O Q E Zq*
London EC4 *p59*. 020 7651 0000

Corbett, E C (Corbett & Co International Construction Lawyers Ltd) *O Zc A3*
Teddington *p409*. 020 8614 6200

Corbett, G (Stevens) *G H*
Stoke-on-Trent *p398*. 01782 343353

Corbett, Miss H L (Nigel Davis Solicitors) *Q A1 K1*
Belper *p131* 01335 372889

Corbett, I (Squire Sanders (UK) LLP) *O N L J1 Zj Zc*
London EC2 *p81*. 020 7655 1000

Corbett, I A (Hopkins) *N Zr*
Mansfield *p311*. 01623 468468

Corbett, K (Faber Maunsell Ltd)
St Albans *p472* .020 8784 5784 / 8639 3579

Corbett, Miss M A (MFG Solicitors)
Kidderminster *p265* 01562 820181

Corbett, P G (Levetts) *C1 F1 K1 L N O Q S1 W Zl*
London SE8 *p53*. 020 7237 7771

Corbett, P W U (Stephenson Harwood) *T1 T2*
London EC2 *p82*. 020 7329 4422

Corbett, Ms S (McMillan Williams) *Zr N*
Croydon *p205* 01689 848311

Corbett, Ms T E (Tania Corbett)
Pinner *p348* 020 8868 6100

Corbin, Miss D L (Donna L Corbin) *N Q K1 S1 S2 W B1 J1 R1 L*
Petersfield *p348* 01730 261288

Corby, Mrs G (Dale & Co Solicitors Lincoln) *K3 K1 D1 D2*
Lincoln *p284*. 01522 513399

Corby, Ms N J (Lincolnshire County Council Resources - Legal Services) *D1 K1 D2 K2*
Lincoln *p463*. 01522 552222

Corcoran, A (Shoosmiths)
Reading *p361* . . 0370 086 8800 / 0118 965 8765

Corcoran, A J (Payne Marsh Stillwell) *S2 E S1 W*
Southampton *p386*. 023 8022 3957

Corcoran, Ms D (Abney Garsden McDonald) *N*
Cheadle *p185* 0161 482 8822

Corcoran, D (Claude Hornby & Cox) *B2 G H*
London EC4 *p20*. 020 7332 8269

Corcoran, Miss E (Aaron & Partners LLP Solicitors) *O Q L*
Chester *p190* 01244 405555

Corcoran, J (Sintons LLP) *Zc E*
Newcastle upon Tyne *p326* . 0191 226 7878

Corcoran, J A (Corcorans) *S1 W Zl*
Worthing *p441*. 01903 824428

Corcoran, J J (Kaim Todner Ltd) *G H*
Islington *p47*. 020 7700 0070

Corcoran, Mrs L A E J (Wace Morgan) *W K4*
Shrewsbury *p379* 01743 280100

Corcoran, M (Kerman & Co LLP) *C2 J1*
London WC2 *p49* 020 7539 7272

Corcoran, Miss S (Lewis Nedas & Co) *G H*
Camden *p53*. 020 7387 2032

Corcut, A (Austin & Carnley) *N*
Leighton Buzzard *p282* . . . 01525 372140

Corcut, Ms S (Reynolds Porter Chamberlain LLP)
London E1 *p71* 020 3060 6000

Cordall, Ms G (Maclay Murray & Spens LLP)
London EC2 *p57*. 020 7002 8500

Cordall, Ms G (Lewis Silkin LLP) *C1 I*
London EC4 *p53*. 020 7074 8000

Cordell, B (Bernard Cordell) *C1 S1 S2 J1 K1 L O Q W G*
London NW3 *p22* 020 8209 3752

Cordell, C P (Cordell & Co) *N*
Dorking *p212* 01306 743003

Cordell, S A (Joelson Wilson LLP) *C1 J1 T1 Ze C2 C3 I Zn Zz*
Westminster *p46*. 020 7580 5721

Corder, Mrs R A (Sema Group UK Ltd)
London NW1 *p109*. 020 7830 4213

Cordery, B D (Bristows) *O Ze*
London EC4 *p15*. 020 7400 8000

Cordery, D J (Maxwell Winward LLP) *Zc*
London EC4 *p59*. 020 7651 0000

Cordiner, M J M (Cheshire County Council)
Chester *p454* 01244 602382

Cordiner, Mrs S A (Denbighshire County Council)
Ruthin *p470* 01824 706000

Cordingley, Miss H S (Hansells) *W T2*
Norwich *p334* 01603 615731

Cordingley, J B (John B Cordingley & Co) *B1 G E H N S1 Zl*
Bradford *p153* 01274 736646

Cordingley, P A B (Chattertons Solicitors) *P N M1 M2 K1 D1 G J1 H Zl Zp*
Horncastle *p252* 01507 522456

Cordon, Ms A C (Eric Bowes & Co) *K4 S1 W*
Solihull *p382*. 0121 744 3691

Cordonnier, Ms S (Waltons & Morse LLP) *Zj M3 O*
London EC3 *p90*. 020 7623 4255

Cordran, R (Olswang LLP)
London WC1 *p64* 020 7067 3000

Cordwell, Ms Y (Stevens Son & Pope) *K1 D1 N F1 J1 L Q V K2*
Burgess Hill *p168* 01444 246377

Cordy, Ms T A (Crown Prosecution Service Dorset)
Bournemouth *p450*. 01202 498700

Core, G V (Norfolk County Council - Legal Services) *C1 C2 I U2 J1*
Norwich *p467* . . . . . Minicom: 0844 800 8011

Corfield, N E (Thomson Webb & Corfield) *C1 E J1*
Cambridge *p176*. 01223 578070

Corfield, S G (FBC Manby Bowdler LLP) *E A1 Zc A2*
Bridgnorth *p157* 01746 761436

Cork, A (Romain Coleman & Co) *E S1 C1*
Waltham Forest *p73* 020 8520 3322

Cork, Mrs K E (Sandwell Metropolitan Borough Council)
Oldbury *p468* 0121 569 2200

Cork, M J (KJD) *O B1 Q L*
Stoke-on-Trent *p398*. 01782 202020

Cork, S J (Sandwell Metropolitan Borough Council)
Oldbury *p468* 0121 569 2200

Corke, A J (Lester Aldridge LLP) *O*
Bournemouth *p152*. 01202 786161

Corke, Mrs J M (Janet M Corke) *S1 W L Zd E*
Liverpool *p287*. 0151 726 0443

Corker, D (Lupton Fawcett)
Sheffield *p376* 0114 276 6607

Corker, D T (Corker Binning Solicitors) *G H N*
London WC2 *p22* 020 7353 6000

See p634 for the Key to Work Categories

Corley, Miss S L (Hillyer McKeown LLP) *O Q Zl*
Chester *p190* 01244 318131

Cormack, A (Coles Miller Solicitors LLP) *N P*
Poole *p352* 01202 673011

Cormack, C (The Grech Gooden Partnership LLP) *B2 G H*
Cardiff *p178* 029 2022 2255

Cormack, Mrs C L (Humphries Kirk) *K1 K3*
Poole *p352* 01202 715815

Cormack, Mrs M P (Luton Borough Council)
Luton *p464* 01582 546000

Cormack, Mrs R (Sansbury Douglas) *G H*
Bristol *p164* 0117 955 2663

Cormican, I (Sacker & Partners LLP) *Zo*
London EC2 *p76* 020 7329 6699

Cornall, D A (Doncaster Magistrates Court)
Doncaster *p457* 01302 366711

Cornall, Miss S (Blake Lapthorn) *S1 E*
Portsmouth *p354* 023 9222 1122

Cornberg, D M (Haswell & Cornberg)
Newcastle upon Tyne *p325* 0191 276 5300

Cornberg, M J (The Beavis Partnership) *C1 O Q N J1 S1 L F1 G C2*
Chelmsford *p186* 01245 264748

Cornelius, B J (W Parry & Co)
Swansea *p405* 01792 470037

Cornelius, J (Squire Sanders (UK) LLP)
London EC2 *p81* 020 7655 1000

Cornell, Mrs E L (Catteralls) *N Q*
Wakefield *p418* 01924 291122

Cornell, K P (Burton Woolf & Turk) *S1 W L*
London EC1 *p16* 020 7831 6478

Cornell, M B (Holmes & Hills LLP) *L O Q J1 F1*
Braintree *p155* 01376 320456

Cornell, P C E (Clifford Chance)
London E14 *p20* 020 7006 1000

Cornell, P J (Cornell & Co) *G H*
Leominster *p282* 01568 612288

Corner, Mrs H (Addleshaw Goddard)
Manchester *p300* 0161 934 6000

Corner, H R (Mills & Reeve) *Ze I U2 O U1*
Cambridge *p175* 01223 364422

Corner, Miss N C (BPE Solicitors LLP) *E S1*
Cheltenham *p187* 01242 224433

Corner, R H G (Alfred Truman) *W*
Buckingham *p167* 01280 822217
Bicester *p132* 01869 252761

Corner, S J (Eaton Ryan & Taylor) *N O J2 Q Zj A3 Zc F2 Zq B2*
Birmingham *p138* 0121 236 1999

Cornes, H (Hill Dickinson LLP) *Zc A3 Zq*
Manchester *p305* 0161 817 7200

Cornes, J (Ramsdens Solicitors) *B1 F1 L Q*
Huddersfield *p256* 01484 821500

Cornes, Ms J (Fisher Meredith) *Zm Zg*
Lambeth *p32* 020 7091 2700

Cornes, Ms S E (TWM Solicitors LLP) *K1 D1 Zm K2*
London SW19 *p85* 020 8946 6454

Cornes, Mrs S R (Ellis & Co) *S1 K1 L W N J1 Zv*
Chester *p190* 01244 319388

Corney, S T (Olswang LLP) *O*
London WC1 *p64* 020 7067 3000

Cornfield, S G (Plexus Law (A Trading Name of Parabis Law LLP)) *Q N*
Evesham *p220* 01386 769160

Cornford, H C T (Chilcotts)
Tavistock *p408* 01822 612535 / 614242

Cornforth, A P (Hextalls) *O Q N Zj*
London EC2 *p41* 020 7382 0700

Cornforth, Ms D H (Piper Smith Watton LLP) *L S1 S2 E*
London SW1 *p68* 020 7222 9900

Cornforth, S (EAD Solicitors LLP) *M1 L D1 H G J1 V F1 Zp Zi*
Liverpool *p287* 0151 291 2500

Cornhouse, M J (Eastgate Assistance Ltd)
Colchester *p455* 0870 523 4500

Cornick, T C (Macfarlanes) *C1*
London EC4 *p56* 020 7831 9222

Cornish, Mrs J (Borlase & Company) *E C1 Q O Zj*
Helston *p246* 01326 574988

Cornish, Miss L J (Hansells) *K3 K1*
Norwich *p334* 01603 615731

Cornish, M (Anthony Gold) *C1 J1 Ze O Q Zq Zp J2*
London SE1 *p6* 020 7940 4000

Cornish, M T (GH Cornish LLP) *E C1 L N R1 T1 B1 J1 Zc Zl Zo*
Ilford *p260* 020 8090 0800

Cornish, Mrs S (Coodes) *W T2*
Liskeard *p285* 01579 347600

Cornish, Ms S (Reynolds Porter Chamberlain LLP)
London E1 *p71* 020 3060 6000

Cornish, Mrs S C (Barlow Lyde & Gilbert LLP) *Zr N*
London EC3 *p10* 020 7247 2277

Cornish, T (Burnetts) *K1*
Carlisle *p181* 01228 552222

Cornish, Ms T J (Glazer Delmar) *L Zh*
London SE22 *p35* 020 8299 0021

Cornthwaite, J P (Wedlake Bell LLP) *C3 Ze F1 F2*
London WC1 *p91* 020 7395 3000

Cornthwaite, R B (Garstangs) *O Q G*
London WC2 *p35* 020 7427 5678

Cornwell, Miss F L (Bhatia Best) *G H*
Nottingham *p336* 0115 950 3231

Cornwell, J (BCL Burton Copeland)
London WC2 *p9* 020 7430 2277

Cornwell, J A (Grove Tompkins Bosworth) *K1 L K3*
Birmingham *p138* 0121 236 9341 / 236 8091

Cornwell, J R (Dawson Cornwell) *K1 K3 K2 W*
London WC1 *p26* 020 7242 2556

Cornwell, N R (Skanska UK PLC) *O Zc*
Rickmansworth *p470* 01923 776666

Cornwell, Ms T M (Teresa M Cornwell) *K1 S1 E W Q N L J1*
Oxted *p344* 01883 712721 / 722594

Coronel, Ms D A (Reigate & Banstead Borough Council)
Reigate *p469* 01737 276000

Corp, D J (Nantes) *J1 Q N K1 L Zr Zq*
Bridport *p158* 01308 422313

Corp, Mrs G A (Goughs) *J1 E S2 C1 Zp*
Calne *p173* 01249 812086

Corr, P H M (Sidley Austin Brown & Wood)
London EC2 *p78* 020 7360 3600

Corran, R S (Weightmans LLP) *O Q B1 F1 Zq*
Manchester *p311* 0161 233 7330

Corrie, B (Corries Solicitors) *Zj N S1 W*
York *p444* 0845 241 5566

Corrigan, Miss A J (Tate & Lyle PLC)
London EC3 *p109* 020 7626 6525

Corrigan, Mrs A V (Treasury Solicitors Department)
London WC2 *p110* 020 7210 3000

Corrigan, Mrs J A (Phillips Solicitors) *Q W K1*
Basingstoke *p127* 01256 460830

Corrigan, J P E (MLM Cartwright) *E S1 U1*
Cardiff *p179* 029 2046 2562

Corrigan, M G (Farleys Solicitors LLP) *N F1 F2 Q Zq Zw*
Blackburn *p145* 01254 367855

Corrigan, P (Farleys Solicitors LLP) *Q N F1*
Burnley *p169* 01282 798664

Corrigan, P (Bray & Bray) *A3 L O Q Zq*
Leicester *p279* 0116 254 8871
Peterborough *p346* 01733 888888

Corrigan, T G (DAC Beachcroft)
Bristol *p162* 0117 918 2000

Corrighan, J (Crown Prosecution Service Durham)
Durham *p457* 0191 383 5800

Corringan, Mrs S V (The Ringrose Law Group - David Thornley) *K1 D1 D2*
Grantham *p232* 01476 590200

Corris, Mrs C (Tanners) *S1 S2*
Cirencester *p195* 01285 659061

Corry, D D (Somerset County Council)
Taunton *p473* 0845 345 9166

Corry, Miss K (Bone & Payne LLP) *K1 D1 K3*
Colwyn Bay *p198* 01492 532385

Corry, S N (British Telecommunications PLC)
London EC1 *p104* 020 7356 6181

Corsellis, D (Stephens & Scown) *R1 E*
Exeter *p222* 01392 210700

Corser, R D R (Challinors) *W E S1 C1*
Birmingham *p136* 0121 212 9393

Corser, Ms S M (Challinors) *N Zq*
Birmingham *p136* 0121 212 9393

Corsi, Ms J (Doyle Clayton Solicitors Limited) *J1 Zp*
London EC2 *p27* 020 7329 9090

Cort, Miss H J (Paris Smith LLP) *K3 K1*
Southampton *p386* 023 8048 2482

Corte, L (Skadden Arps Slate Meagher & Flom (UK) LLP)
London E14 *p80* 020 7519 7000

Corti, Ms T (Nockolds) *C1 C3 I F1 U2 C2*
Bishop's Stortford *p144* 01279 755777

Cortis, Ms V (The College of Law) *K1 D1*
London WC1 *p105* 0800 289997

Cory-Wright, Ms D (Edwards Angell Palmer & Dodge)
London EC2 *p28* 020 7583 4055

Cosby, Ms A (Forsters LLP) *A1 S2*
Westminster *p33* 020 7863 8333

Cosgrave, M B G (Wollen Michelmore Solicitors) *W S1 E T1 C1 T2*
Newton Abbot *p330* 01626 332266

Cosgrove, J S (Peter Dunn & Co) *S1 S2 W Zl C1 E K4 L C2 R2*
Sunderland *p401* 0191 568 9000

Cosgrove, Mrs M C (Widdows Mason) *S1 E*
Warrington *p422* 01925 632267

Coskery, Ms S (Field Fisher Waterhouse LLP)
London EC3 *p31* 020 7861 4000

Cosma, A (Martin Murray & Associates) *G H B2*
West Drayton *p427* 01895 431332

Cosstick, M (Anthony Holden Crofts & Co) *S1 S2 W E K4*
Ealing *p6* 020 8840 7878
Brentford *p156* 020 8568 7768

Costa, E (Taylors Legal)
Ilford *p261* 020 8501 4959

Costa, Mrs G (Shepherd Harris & Co) *S1 S2 E L*
Enfield *p219* 020 8363 8341

Costall, Miss J L (McKinnells) *S1 S2 E*
Lincoln *p284* 01522 541181

Costa-Petrou, Mrs A (Petrou & Co) *S2 S1 Q L*
London N14 *p67* 020 8920 5800

Costello, Mrs A A (Henmans LLP) *Zr*
Oxford *p343* 01865 781000

Costello, A J (Russell & Russell) *G H*
Bolton *p149* 01204 399299

Costello, Miss C L (Edwards Angell Palmer & Dodge)
London EC2 *p28* 020 7583 4055

Costello, Ms J T (Knights Solicitors LLP) *W K4 A3*
Newcastle under Lyme *p323* 01782 619225

Costello, Ms S (Linder Myers Solicitors)
Manchester *p307* 0844 984 6400

Coster, Ms S (Howell-Jones LLP) *W*
Leatherhead *p271* 01372 860650

Costigan, P D (Band Hatton LLP) *E S1 C1 R1 L B1 Zc Ze Zo*
Coventry *p200* 024 7663 2121

Cotes, H N E (Plexus Law (A Trading Name of Parabis Law LLP))
Evesham *p220* 01386 769160

Cotgreave, Ms A (Hallows Associates) *K1 D1 V D2*
Mold *p318* 01352 752773 / 758603 / 0800 525696

Cotgrove, J (Buckles Solicitors LLP)
Peterborough *p346* 01733 888888

Cotran, P (Dale & Newbery LLP) *W*
Staines *p393* 01784 464491

Cottam, A M (Barlow Lyde & Gilbert LLP)
London EC3 *p10* 020 7247 2277

Cottam, Miss D (Higgs & Sons) *Q*
Brierley Hill *p158* 0845 111 5050

Cottell, Ms S (Ashurst LLP)
London EC2 *p7* 020 7638 1111

Cotter, N (Jones Day) *O*
London EC4 *p46* 020 7039 5959

Cotterell, Miss V (Merrony Wall) *S1 W K4*
Twickenham *p416* 020 8898 4700

Cotterhill, M W (Cotterhill Hitchman LLP) *B1 C1*
Sutton Coldfield *p403* 0121 323 1860

Cotterill, Ms P V (Challinors) *W*
West Bromwich *p427* 0121 553 3211

Cotterill, Miss S E (Blake Lapthorn) *E S2 Zl J2*
London EC1 *p13* 020 7405 2000

Cotterill, T C (Colemans) *B1 L F1 J1 C1*
Haywards Heath *p245* 01444 459555

Cottingham, R (Lee Bolton Monier-Williams)
Westminster *p52* 020 7222 5381

Cottingham, R (Reed Smith LLP)
London EC2 *p71* 020 3116 3000

Cottingham, S W (Thompsons (formerly Robin/Brian Thompson & Partners)) *N J1 J2*
Plymouth *p350* 01752 675810

Cottis, M J (Hogan Lovells International LLP)
London EC1 *p42* 020 7296 2000

Cottle, Mrs J (Dolmans) *J1 C1 Zza C2 F1 Zw*
Cardiff *p178* 029 2034 5531

Cotton, A R (The Rank Group PLC)
Maidenhead *p464* 01628 504000

Cotton, Ms C (Bindmans LLP) *Zg*
London WC1 *p12* 020 7833 4433

Cotton, Mrs J E (Broxtowe Borough Council)
Beeston *p449* 0115 917 7777

Cotton, Miss S (Dartford Borough Council)
Dartford *p456* 01322 343434

Cottrell, A J G (Cockshott Peck Lewis) *S1 S2 E W K1*
Ainsdale *p114* 01704 574144
Southport *p388* 01704 534034

Cottrell, Mrs E J (Harold G Walker) *K3 K1*
Bournemouth *p152* 01202 203200

Cottrell, Ms J H (Stephenson Harwood) *T1*
London EC2 *p82* 020 7329 4422

Cottrell, S L (Goldsmith Williams) *N Q*
Liverpool *p288* 0845 373 3737

Cottrill, M E (174 Law) *S1 W*
Birkenhead *p134* 0151 647 7372

Cottrill, S H (Olswang LLP) *O Q I Ze*
London WC1 *p64* 020 7067 3000

Coubrough, Ms L (Bindmans LLP) *K1 D1 Zm*
London WC1 *p12* 020 7833 4433

Couch, G A (Bircham Dyson Bell)
Westminster *p13* 020 7227 7000

Couch, Miss J P (Atkinson & Co) *K1 D1 D2*
Newport *p328* 01633 251118

Couch, Mrs S J (WBW Solicitors) *N Zr*
Newton Abbot *p329* 01626 202404

Coucher, Ms S (DLA Piper UK LLP)
London EC2 *p24* 0870 011 1111

Couchman, F A (TV Edwards LLP) *N*
London EC3 *p85* 020 7790 7000

Couchman, N (Couchmans LLP)
London WC1 *p23* 020 7611 9660

Coughlan, C (Berry Smith LLP)
Cardiff *p177* 029 2034 5511

Coughlan, C J (Bromsgrove & Redditch Magistrates Court)
Kidderminster *p462* 01562 514000

Coughlan, Mrs L (Brecon Beacons National Park Authority)
Brecon *p451* 01874 624437

Coughlan, M K (Langley Wellington) *Q N Zr X Zq*
Gloucester *p230* 01452 521286

Coughlin, Miss J H (Baxter Caulfield) *E S2*
Huddersfield *p255* 01484 519519

Coughtrie, K (Davies Gore Lomax) *Q R1*
Leeds *p273* 0113 242 2797

Coughtrie, Mrs K J (Herefordshire Council)
Hereford *p460* 01432 260000

Coughtrie, Ms K J (County of Herefordshire District Council)
Hereford *p460* 01432 260266

Couldrake, G M (Howes Percival LLP) *B1 C1 Zb Ze I*
Northampton *p332* 01604 230400

Couldrey, N J (Sacker & Partners LLP) *Zo*
London EC2 *p76* 020 7329 6699

Couldrick, T D (Blake Lapthorn) *C1 C2 Ze*
London EC1 *p13* 020 7405 2000

Coules, I (Berry Redmond & Robinson) *K4 S1 W K1*
Weston-super-Mare *p429* 01934 513963

Couling, G A (Austin Ryder & Co) *S1 C1 E S2 W K1 K3 N Q G H Zl*
Enfield *p8* 020 8804 5111

Coull, G P (Reynolds Porter Chamberlain LLP) *O Q Zq Zj*
London E1 *p71* 020 3060 6000

Coulson, Miss A C (Hart Brown Solicitors) *W*
Cranleigh *p202* 0800 068 8177

Coulson, E W H (Squire Sanders (UK) LLP) *O Q Zj*
Leeds *p277* 0113 284 7000

Coulson, G A (Braund & Fedrick) *E L R1 S1*
Sidcup *p380* 020 8300 6515

Coulson, J R (Corries Solicitors) *N Zl Zj J2*
York *p444* 0845 241 5566

Coulson, N K L (Bristows)
London EC4 *p15* 020 7400 8000
London EC4 *p46* 020 7039 5959

Coulter, C (Ashurst LLP) *U2 U1 I Ze*
London EC2 *p7* 020 7638 1111
London EC2 *p62* 020 7920 4000

Coulter, E C (Page Gulliford & Gregory Limited) *K1 S1 N M1 E*
Southampton *p386* 023 8022 5821

Coulter, Ms F I (Page Gulliford & Gregory Limited) *W K1 S1 N Q C1 G L J1 Zl*
Southampton *p386* 023 8022 5821

Coulter, Miss J (Walker Foster with Kennedy Thompson)
Ilkley *p261* 01943 609969

Coulter, Ms T J (Bournemouth Borough Council) *L Q*
Bournemouth *p450* 01202 451178

Coulthard, M (Hodgson Coulthard & Co) *N K1 W Q D1 S1 G H V*
Houghton Le Spring *p253* 0191 584 3333

Coulthard, R H (The National Trust)
Swindon *p475* 01793 817400

Coulthurst, Mrs V J (Forshaws Davies Ridgway LLP)
Warrington *p422* 01925 230000

Coulton, P (Skadden Arps Slate Meagher & Flom (UK) LLP)
London E14 *p80* 020 7519 7000

Councell, Mrs R (Heptonstalls LLP) *Zr N*
Goole *p231* 01405 765661

Counsell, Mrs S (Pardoes) *K1 D1*
Bridgwater *p158* 01278 457891

Coupe, D B S (Coupe Bradbury) *T2 W T1 C1*
Lytham *p296* 01253 736670

Coupe, Mrs J (Raworths LLP) *S1*
Harrogate *p240* 01423 566666

Coupe, S B (Coupe Bradbury) *D1 D2 G H K1 V*
Kirkham *p268* 01772 683000
Lytham *p296* 01253 736670

Coupe, S J (Russell & Russell) *G H*
Chester *p191* 01244 405700

Coupland, C M (Nicholas Bates) *G H*
Basingstoke *p126* 01256 331278

Coupland, Ms E (AXA UK PLC)
London E22 *p103* 020 7920 5900

Coupland, I D (Lupton Fawcett) *O Q B1 L J1*
Leeds *p275* 0113 280 2000

Course, G A (East Dorset District Council)
Wimborne *p476* 01202 886201

Court, Mrs A E (Oadby & Wigston Borough Council)
Wigston *p476* 0116 288 8961

Court, Ms J A (Squire Sanders (UK) LLP)
London EC2 *p81* 020 7655 1000

Court, P G (Plexus Law (A Trading Name of Parabis Law LLP)) *O A3 Zj Zq Q*
London EC3 *p68* 0844 245 4000

Court, S (Blake Lapthorn) *T1 T2*
Oxford *p342* 01865 248607

Courtenay, W (London Stock Exchange Ltd)
London EC2 *p107* 020 7797 1000

Courtenay-Evans, G P (CVS Solicitors) *E S2 R2 S1 C1 C2 O J1 W Ze*
London W1 *p17* 020 7493 2903

Courtenay-Stamp, Mrs B K (Stones Solicitors LLP)
Exeter *p222* 01392 666777

Courtenay-Stamp, D J (Macfarlanes) *C1 Ze*
London EC4 *p56* 020 7831 9222

Courtier, Ms A J (DWF) *T1 T2*
Manchester *p303* 0161 603 5000

Courtneidge, Mrs H A (Hilary A Courtneidge) *S1*
Hertford *p248* 01992 589120

Courtney, Ms C M (The Newspaper Society)
London EC4 *p108* 020 7632 7400

Courtney, J (Forshaws Davies Ridgway LLP)
Warrington *p422* 01925 230000

Courtney, L (Davenport Lyons)
London W1 *p25* 020 7468 2600

Courtney, Miss M C E I (Howell-Jones LLP) *E S1 W J1*
Cheam *p186* 020 8642 8142

Courtney-Stubbs, J (Bird & Bird LLP) *C1 C2*
London EC4 *p13* 020 7415 6000

Courts, S M (BSG Solicitors LLP)
London N3 *p9* 020 8343 4411

Cousal, Ms H (The College of Law Guildford)
Guildford *p459* 01483 460200

Couse, Ms C (Brabners Chaffe Street) *Zw C1*
Manchester *p301* 0161 836 8800

Cousins, C T (Digwa Cousins) *D1 F1 G H J1 K1 L M1 V W Zd Zh Zm*
Leeds *p273* 0113 249 6661

Cousins, Miss E B A (Scannells Hunt) *K1 K3 S1 S2 W J1 L Q E Zx*
Brentwood *p156* 01277 223242

Cousins, Miss H R (Cousins Tyrer) *G H*
Leeds *p272* 0113 247 0400

6

Cousins, Mrs J E (Mowll & Mowll) E C2 C1 S1 S2
Dover p213 . . . 01304 873344
Cousins, J T M (David Gray Solicitors) G H Q
Newcastle upon Tyne p324 . 0191 232 9547
Cousins, M E (Burnetts) O Q F1 Zc Ze Zk
Carlisle p181. . . 01228 552222
Carlisle p182. . . 01228 552222
Cousins, Ms S (Foreman Laws) D2 D1 K3 K1 K2 W Zd K4
Hitchin p251 . . . 01462 458711
Luton p295 . . . 01582 410041
Coutsavlis, S S (Squire Sanders (UK) LLP) E L
Manchester p310 . . . 0161 830 5000
Coutts, A (Allen Barfields)
West Wickham p428. . . 020 8654 2706
Couve, M D (Speechly Bircham LLP) Zj C2
London EC4 p81. . . 020 7427 6400
Couzens, J R (Parrott & Coales LLP) Q O B1 N L
Aylesbury p121 . . . 01296 318500
Covell, R S (King & Co) S1 W L
Cambridge p175. . . 01954 251818
Coveney, N D (Foot Anstey) E R2 S1 S2
Plymouth p349. . . 01752 675000
Coveney, S (HM Land Registry - Hull)
Hull p461 . . . 01482 223244
Coventon, Mrs E A (Pumfrey & Lythaby) Zr K4 K1 Zm S1 W L E
Orpington p342 . . . 01689 833657
Coventry, Ms T V (Lees Solicitors LLP) S1 S2 J1 E
Birkenhead p134. . . 0151 647 9381
Cover, M (Charles Russell LLP) Ze
London EC4 p19. . . 020 7203 5000
Cover, M S (Biscoes) S2 S1 J1 W C1 E I Ze C2 R1 R2
Petersfield p348 . . . 01730 264799
Coverley, Miss C E (The Johnson Partnership) G H
Nottingham p337. . . 0115 941 9141
Cowan, A (Castle Sanderson) O J1 Zi
Leeds p272 . . . 0113 232 1919
Cowan, A J (Devonshires) L R2 Zh Zb Zd C2
London EC2 p27. . . 020 7628 7576
Cowan, B (MacLeish Littlestone Cowan) S1 P K1 G F1 E W Zl
Ilford p260. . . 020 8514 3000
Cowan, D J (David Cowan) S1 S2 G W H E
Dorking p212 . . . 01306 886622
Cowan, Mrs J A (Pearl & Co) S1 S2 E F1 W C1
Stanmore p394 . . . 020 8958 4889
Cowan, M (Olswang LLP) C1
London WC1 p64 . . . 020 7067 3000
Cowan, Mrs S (Horwich Farrelly) N G Q
Manchester p305 . . . 0161 834 3585
Cowan, Ms S E (Lester Aldridge LLP) C1
Bournemouth p152. . . 01202 786161
Cowan, T S (Thornton & Co) E S1 W
Hammersmith & Fulham p87. 020 8743 3000
Cowan-Clark, Mrs J P (Schofield Sweeney) S2 S1 E G I L
Bradford p154 . . . 01274 306000
Cowans, Ms K (Henry Hyams)
Leeds p274 . . . 0113 243 2288
Coward, Mrs A J (Eaton Smith LLP) E
Huddersfield p255 . . . 01484 821300
Coward, Mrs B I (Granville-West) S1 W
Pontypool p352 . . . 01495 751111
Coward, D J (Sampson Coward LLP) F1 J1 Q
Salisbury p371. . . 01722 410664
Coward, M (Lester Aldridge LLP) E L C1 A1
Bournemouth p152. . . 01202 786161
Coward, N (Merritt & Co) C1 L S1 T1 W
Yarm p443. . . 01642 885555
Coward, R F (Hill Dickinson LLP) J1
Liverpool p288. . . 0151 600 8000
Coward, T A B (Geoffrey Leaver Solicitors LLP) O Q B1 C1 J1 Zc Ze I
Milton Keynes p317 . . . 01908 692769
Coward, Mrs T G M H (Sampson Coward LLP) D1 K1 Q W
Salisbury p371. . . 01722 410664
Cowdery, P L (Quality Solicitors Clarke & Son) O Q L N J1 Zq
Basingstoke p127 . . . 01256 320555
Cowdrey, Mrs J E (Anthony King & Co) N J2 Q F2
Basildon p126 . . . 01268 240400
Cowdrey, Ms V E (Henmans LLP) W T2
Oxford p343. . . 01865 781000
Cowdry, Ms A (Charles Hoile) D1 K1
Newbury p322. . . 01635 45595
Cowdry, D M (Storrar Cowdry) S1 K1 W E A1 Zd
Chester p191 . . . 01244 400567
Cowdry, J J A (The London Law Agency Ltd) C1 C2
London WC1 p107. . . 020 7353 9471
Cowell, Mrs A M (Blake Lapthorn) S1
Oxford p342. . . 01865 248607
Cowell, Miss E C (Pannone LLP) K1 K2
Manchester p308 . . . 0161 909 3000
Cowell, J (Taylors) C1 F1 C2
Manchester p310 . . . 0844 800 0263
Cowell, L (DLA Piper UK LLP)
Manchester p303 . . . 0870 011 1111
Cowell, P H (FBC Manby Bowdler LLP) D1 K1 O Q
Bridgnorth p157 . . . 01746 761436
Cowell, R (ASB Law) B1 O
Maidstone p298 . . . 01622 656500
Cowell, R J (Juliet Bellis & Co) L O Q Zq
Uckfield p416 . . . 01825 750811
Cowell, S R (Pigotts) S1 S2
Dover p213 . . . 01304 210614 / 212206
Cowell, W S (Miller Sands) K1 D1 K2 Q O N Zr
Cambridge p175. . . 01223 202345
Cowen, Miss A M (Leech & Co) N Zq Zr
Manchester p306 . . . 0161 279 0279
Cowen, Mrs C L (Olswang LLP)
London WC1 p64 . . . 020 7067 3000
Cowen, Miss L E (Leonie Cowen & Associates) J1 X Zd Zh Zu
London NW6 p23 . . . 020 7604 5870
Cowen, M (Olswang LLP) I
London WC1 p64 . . . 020 7067 3000
Cowen, Mrs M R (Neves Solicitors) S1 E R1 L S2
Harpenden p239. . . 01582 715234
Cowen, R (Crown Prosecution Service Durham)
Durham p457 . . . 0191 383 5800
Cowen, R C (Squire Sanders (UK) LLP) O E C1 Zc Zj
London EC2 p81. . . 020 7655 1000
Cowens, Miss R (Alderson Dodds) G H
Blyth p147. . . 01670 352293
Cowgill, A (Godwins) W T1 K4 T2
Winchester p433. . . 01962 841484
Cowgill, D R (Dixon Rigby Keogh) S1 W A1 E C1 L
Middlewich p315. . . 01606 835736
Cowie, I G (Ian Cowie) G H S1 M1 N P L C1 D1
Guisborough p237. . . 01287 636401
Cowie, Miss J (Swinburne Snowball & Jackson) S1 W A1 K4
Consett p199 . . . 01207 502532
Cowie, R P (Nelsons)
London SE1 p63. . . 020 7403 4000
Cowlard, M J (Thomas Flavell & Sons) S1 W K1 K3 E
Earl Shilton p214 . . . 01455 842297
Cowlard, Miss V V A (Andrews McQueen) G H K1 M1 P D1 J1 L Zl Zl
Bournemouth p151. . . 01202 290628
Cowle, V W (Cowle Smart) O Q N Zr K1 J1 C1 Zc A1 B1 F1 Ze
Cheltenham p188 . .01242 222744 / 570700
Cowles, R A (Cowles) C1 L S1 T1 W
Croydon p23. . . 020 8679 1811
Cowley, Miss A (Ian Cruickshank & Co) K3 K1 D1 L G H W S1 D2
Jarrow p263 . . . 0191 428 0900
Cowley, A G (Goodwin Cowley) S1 W
Lowestoft p294 . . . 01502 532700
Cowley, Ms C (Owen White) L O P Zh
Slough p382. . . 01753 876800
Cowley, Ms H (Hatchers Solicitors LLP)
Shrewsbury p379 . . . 01743 248545
Cowley, Ms H D (Taylor Walton LLP) B1 C1 C2 C3 L J1 P
Luton p295 . . . 01582 731161
Cowley, J (Blake Lapthorn) O F1
Oxford p342. . . 01865 248607
Cowley, J (Lee Chadwick & Co) B1 F1 J1 L O Q S1 W
Witney p436. . . 01993 703272
Cowley, Mrs K C T (Bhatia Best) K1 D1 W
Nottingham p336. . . 0115 950 3231
Nottingham p339. . . 0115 947 4486
Cowley, Ms L (Nockolds) G H N P K1 K2
Bishop's Stortford p144 . . . 01279 755777
Cowley, M J (DLA Piper UK LLP) Zo
London EC2 p24. . . 0870 011 1111
Cowley, P N (Sefton Metropolitan Borough Council)
Southport p472 . . . 01704 533133
Cowley, S (Cowley Di Giorgio & Co) E S1 C1 K3 K1 Zl L Q N W
Bedford p129 . . . 01234 218171
Cowlin, J R (E D C Lord & Co)
Hayes p245 . . . 020 8848 9988
Cowling, M (Cowlings) S1 G H L K1 W D1 N
Mexborough p314 . . . 01709 587538
Cowlishaw, J P (Wedlake Bell LLP) E L S2
London WC1 p91 . . . 020 7395 3000
Cowper, D A (Mills & Reeve) E
Cambridge p175. . . 01223 364422
Cowper, P J (Red Kite Law) G H J1 Zl Zm Zt
Tenby p410 . . . 01834 842122
Cowper, Ms R (Walker Morris) R2
Leeds p277 . . . 0113 283 2500
Cowper, R J (Bryan Cave) O B1 B2 M2
London EC2 p19. . . 020 7207 1100
London EC2 p82. . . 020 7329 4422
Cowsill, E (Eric Cowsill Solicitor)
Ivybridge p263. . . 01752 205202
Cox, A (Ashurst LLP)
London EC2 p7 . . . 020 7638 1111
Cox, A A (Weightmans LLP)
Liverpool p291. . . 0151 227 2601
Cox, A B S (Cox Cooper Limited) J1 C1 I U2 Zp C2
Birmingham p137 . . . 0121 777 0015
Cox, A F (Anthony F Cox) S1 W E S2
Guildford p236. . . 01483 562422
Cox, A G (Boys & Maughan) S1 W E M1 P
Birchington p134. . . 01843 842356
Cox, Miss A J (Irwin Mitchell LLP) S1
Birmingham p139 . . . 0870 150 0100
Cox, Mrs A J (Verisona Solicitors) K1 M1 C1 F1 J1 V D1 W
Waterlooville p423 . . . 023 9226 5251
Cox, A J (Whiteford Crocker) C1 C2 E R2 S2 W
Ivybridge p263. . . 01752 698488
Plymouth p350. . . 01752 550711
Cox, A N (Foster Harrington) K1 L C1 N J1
Camberley p173. . . 01276 692233
Cox, Ms B A (Mayer Brown International LLP) T2 W Zo
London EC2 p59. . . 020 3130 3000
Cox, Ms C (Footner & Ewing) W
Romsey p366 . . . 01794 512345
Cox, C C A (DAC Beachcroft) T1
London EC4 p24. . . 020 7242 1011
Cox, Mrs C D (Swindon Borough Council)
Swindon p473 . . . 01793 463000
Cox, C J (Christopher Cox Solicitors) Zc O Zq Zb A3 Zj J1 P C3
Northampton p331. . . 01604 882287
Cox, Mrs C P (Miles Preston & Co) K1
London EC4 p69. . . 020 7583 0583
Cox, D (Bristol City Council)
Bristol p451 . . . 0117 922 2000
Cox, D (Mackrell Turner Garrett) A1 E R1 S1
Woking p437. . . 01483 755609
Cox, Mrs G (Antony Hodari & Co) N
Manchester p305 . . . 0161 832 4781
Cox, G F (Colemans - CTTS) N Q O
Manchester p302 . . . 0161 876 2500
Cox, G S (Dickinson Manser) P N D1 M1 J1 L B1 O Zd Zl Zk Zp
Poole p352 . . . 01202 673071
Cox, H A (Simpson Duxbury) K1 N D1 Q V
Bradford p155 . . . 01274 734166
Cox, H W (Whitelock & Storr) G H B2
London WC1 p91 . . . 020 7405 3913
Cox, I D G (Sarginsons Law LLP) S1 E K1 L N M1 P R1 F1 B1 Zi
Coventry p201. . . 024 7655 3181
Cox, I J (Herbert Smith LLP) E L R1 R2
London EC2 p40. . . 020 7374 8000
Cox, Miss I L (Cartwright King) G H
Leicester p279. . . 0116 253 9222
Leicester p281. . . 0116 254 4200
Cox, Mrs I M (Archers Law LLP) W
Stockton-on-Tees p396 . . . 01642 636500
Cox, Ms J (Bryan Cave) A3 O
London EC2 p19. . . 020 7207 1100
Cox, J C (Elmhirst Parker LLP) S1 K1 W H G J1 E A1 R1 Zd Ze S2 Zm
Leeds p273 . . . 01977 682219
Cox, J D (Anthony Collins Solicitors LLP) L Zh
Birmingham p137 . . . 0121 200 3242
Cox, J G (Fullers Family Law Practice LLP) K1
Bedford p130 . . . 01234 343134
Cox, J J (Dewar Hogan) O L Zq
London EC4 p27. . . 020 7634 9550
Cox, Mrs J L (Warner Goodman LLP) W
Fareham p224. . . 01329 288121
Cox, J M (Aviva PLC) K2 K1 S1 Q O
London EC3 p103 . 020 7283 7500 / 01603 687905
Harpenden p239. . . 01582 766261
Cox, J P (Maffey & Brentnall) S1 K1 W L J1
Watford p423 . . . 01923 234607
Cox, J R A (Maxwell Winward LLP) J1 Zt Zi
London EC4 p59. . . 020 7651 0000
Cox, Ms K (Taylor Walton LLP)
St Albans p390 . . . 01727 845245
Cox, K A (CB Legal) C1 T1 J1 Zb
Camden p17. . . 020 7323 9192
Cox, Miss M (Tollers LLP) J1
Northampton p332. . . 01604 258558
Cox, M (Trowers & Hamlins)
London EC3 p88. . . 020 7423 8000
Cox, Miss M (Manches LLP) J1
London WC2 p58 . . . 020 7404 4433
Cox, M A (Pearson Hinchliffe) G H M1
Oldham p341 . . . 0161 785 3500
Cox, M B (Moseleys) S1 S2 E W
Lichfield p284 . . . 01543 414100
Cox, M C B (Bridgehouse Partners) S2 C1 E
Bicester p132 . . . 01869 243457
Cox, M D (Woodfines LLP) S1 W T2
Bedford p130 . . . 01234 270600
Cox, Mrs M J (Portsmouth City Council)
Portsmouth p469. . . 023 9283 4034
Cox, N P (Willans LLP) N L P F1 B1 Zc A3 O Q X
Cheltenham p189 . . . 01242 514000
Cox, P B (Jonas Roy Bloom) G H Zg
Birmingham p139 . . . 0121 212 4111
Cox, P G (Bells) K1 K3 S1 Q W K2
Romsey p366 . . . 01794 513328
Cox, P J (Rushcliffe Borough Council)
West Bridgford p476. . . 0115 981 9911
Cox, P R (Waveney District Council)
Lowestoft p464 . . . 01502 562111
Cox, Ms R (Pluck Andrew & Co) N
Hyde p259. . . 0161 368 6311
Cox, R (Bristows) Ze P O
London EC4 p15. . . 020 7400 8000
Cox, R (Stones Solicitors LLP) E S1 W
Exeter p222 . . . 01392 666777
Cox, R C (Browne Jacobson LLP) C1 C2
Nottingham p336. . . 0115 976 6000
Cox, R N (Shakespeares) E S2 P R1
Stratford-upon-Avon p400 . 0845 630 8833
Cox, Mrs S A (Dean Wilson Laing) C1 E S1 S2
Brighton p159 . . . 01273 327241
Cox, S C (Chattertons Solicitors) A1 C1 C2 E R1 S1 T1
Horncastle p252. . . 01507 522456
Cox, S D (K&L Gates LLP) E L S1 Zb
London EC4 p47. . . 020 7648 9000
Cox, T E (Linklaters LLP)
London EC2 p54. . . 020 7456 2000
Cox, T M (Walsall Metropolitan Borough Council)
Walsall p475. . . 01922 650000
Cox, Mrs V A (CMHT Solicitors) D1 F1 G H J1 K1 P M1 S1 V Zl Zm Zt
Walsall p420. . . 01922 646400
Cox-Healey, J P (Granville-West Chivers & Morgan) M1 K1 G H P S1 W F1 D1 J1 Zk Zl
Abertillery p113 . . . 01495 217070
Coxall, D O (Alfred Truman) G H K1 M1 N P C1
Bicester p132 . . . 01869 252761
Coxall, E (Mayo Wynne Baxter LLP) F1 S1 W
Eastbourne p215. . . 01323 730543
Coxhead, E W J (PCB Solicitors LLP) Q O N L J1 W B1 Zc
Shrewsbury p379 . . . 01743 248148
Coxon, Ms C (McClure Naismith)
London EC4 p56. . . 020 7623 9155
Coxon, Mrs E C G (Coxons) W T2 S1 K4 C1 S2 E
West Bridgford p427. . . 0115 981 2000
Coxon, J G (North Yorkshire Law) K1 G H N P L W J1 F1 D1 Zl
Whitby p430. . . 01947 602131
Coxon, T (Wrexham County Borough Council)
Wrexham p477 . . . 01978 292000
Coy, G S (Mundays LLP) K1 D1 D2 K2
Cobham p196 . . . 01932 590500
Coyle, A J (Lennons) A1 C1 C2 E L S1 W S2
Chesham p189 . . . 01494 773377
Coyle, D J (Cocks Lloyd) G H
Nuneaton p339 . . . 024 7664 1642
Coyle, G E (Rollits LLP) O Q Zl F1 F2 Zy
Hull p258 . . . 01482 323239
Coyle, J C (Rowley Dickinson) S1 E L R1 W
Manchester p309 . . . 0161 834 4215
Coyle, Miss K A (Kidd Rapinet) K1 J1
Maidenhead p298 . . . 0845 017 9608
Coyle, Ms L B (Freemans Solicitors) D1 K1
London W1 p34 . . . 020 7935 3522
Coyle, R W (Colman Coyle LLP) S2 R2 E
Islington p22. . . 020 7354 3000
Coyne, A G (Howard Kennedy LLP) E R1 Zc
London W1 p48 . . . 020 7636 1616
Coyne, Mrs D (George Davies Solicitors LLP) J1 Zp
Manchester p303 . . . 0161 236 8992
Coyne, K J (Coyne Learmonth) S1 W C1 E G H J1 F1 M1
Liverpool p287. . . 0845 602 0870
Coyne, Ms L E (Rochdale Metropolitan Borough Council)
Rochdale p470. . . 01706 647474
Coyne, M J (Ralli Solicitors) N Q
Manchester p309 . . . 0870 998 9000
Coyne, Miss N B (Ross & Craig) C1 C2
Westminster p73. . . 020 7262 3077
Coyne, Mrs S (MFG Solicitors) N O Q F1 L
Worcester p440 . . . 01905 610410
Cozens, Miss F M (Nockolds) D2 K3 K1
Bishop's Stortford p144 . . . 01279 755777
Cozens, P F (Waltham Forest Magistrates' Court)
London E17 p110 . . . 0845 601 3600
Cozens, Ms S J (Charles Russell LLP) C1 C2
London EC4 p19. . . 020 7203 5000
Cozeros, D (Donnelly & Elliott Limited) N J1 J2 L Q F1
Gosport p232 . . . 023 9250 5500
Crabb, B L (Austin Ryder & Co) A1 E G R1 S1 W
Enfield p8 . . . 020 8804 5111
Crabbe, P V (Adams Burrows) S1 S2 V
Bristol p160 . . . 0117 970 2246
Crabbe, Ms S (London Borough of Greenwich Legal Services)
London SE18 p106 . . . 020 8921 5123
Crabbie, A R (Forsters LLP) E
Westminster p33. . . 020 7863 8333
Crabtree, A M (Wilkinson Woodward) S1 E R1 L A1
Halifax p238. . . 01422 339600
Crabtree, C J (Crabtree Chadwick) A1 E L S1 W S2
Pudsey p358. . . 0113 290 9499
Crabtree, Mrs L A (Wilkinson Woodward) D1 K1
Halifax p238. . . 01422 339600
Crabtree, M C J (Ford & Warren) E L S1 S2
Leeds p273 . . . 0113 243 6601
Crabtree, M G (Forbes) N O Q
Blackburn p145 . . . 01254 662831
Crabtree, R M (Russell Jones & Walker) N
Manchester p309 . . . 0161 383 3500
Crabtree, W J O (Crabtree Chadwick) W S2 S1
Pudsey p358. . . 0113 290 9499
Crack, S T (Hethertons LLP) S1 S2 E
York p445 . . . 01904 528200
Cracknell, E (Russell-Cooke LLP) L
London WC1 p74 . . . 020 7405 6566
Cracknell, Miss E (Barker Gotelee Solicitors) S2 E R2 S1 L
Ipswich p262. . . 01473 611211
Ipswich p262. . . 01473 232300
Cracknell, R M (Cracknells) E R2 S1 S2 W
Guildford p236. . . 01483 535558
Craddock, R (Lloyds Chemists PLC Legal Services)
Warley p475. . . 0121 553 6633
Craddock, S G (Brethertons LLP) K1 V K2 D1 D2
Banbury p122 . . . 01295 270999
Rugby p368 . . . 01788 579579
Cradick, J S (Gateley LLP) O Q Zj Za N
London EC4 p35. . . 020 7653 1600
Craft, G R (Rollits LLP) E L S1 W Zh
Hull p258 . . . 01482 323239
Craft, M C (Blake Lapthorn) C1 J1
Chandlers Ford p184 . . . 023 8090 8090

See p634 for the Key to Work Categories

Craft, P E (Payne & Payne) *A1 C1 E L R1 S1 W*
Hull *p257* 01482 326446
Hull *p257* 01482 326446

Cragg, A C (Chattertons Solicitors) *K1 D1*
Sleaford *p381* 01529 411500

Cragg, H (Nash & Co Solicitors LLP)
Plymouth *p350* 01752 664444

Cragg, Ms S (Otten Penna Ltd) *Zm*
Northenden *p333* 0161 945 1431

Craggs, Miss A (Blake Lapthorn)
Oxford *p342* 01865 248607
Oxford *p343* 01865 790744

Craggs, A (Hill Dickinson LLP) *N Q Zr*
Liverpool *p288* 0151 600 8000

Craig, A (Bullivant & Partners)
London EC4 *p16* 020 7332 8250

Craig, Mrs A H (Hayes & Storr) *E J1 S1 C1 S2*
King's Lynn *p266* 01553 778900

Craig, Mrs A J (Muckle LLP) *Ze C1 U2 Zc*
Newcastle upon Tyne *p325* . 0191 211 7777

Craig, C (DLA Piper UK LLP)
Sheffield *p375* 0870 011 1111

Craig, E D (Charles Russell LLP) *Zw O Q U1*
London EC4 *p19* 020 7203 5000

Craig, E G (Williamsons) *S1 L W C1 E K1*
Hexham *p249* . . . . 01434 602643 / 606308

Craig, Miss E J M M (The Legal Practice Solicitors) *C1 E F1 J1 L R1 S1 W Zc Zd Zv*
Wembley *p426* 020 8903 7017

Craig, Ms F (Beswicks)
Hanley *p239* 01782 205000

Craig, Mrs G (Gedye & Sons (Solicitors) Ltd) *W*
Grange-over-Sands *p232* . . 01539 532313
Cirencester *p195* 01285 659061

Craig, G (Fisher Jones Greenwood LLP) *V*
Colchester *p197* 01206 578282

Craig, G A (Henneberry & Co)
London NW6 *p40* 020 8830 1907

Craig, G H (Howard Kennedy LLP) *E C1 R1 Zb Zd*
London W1 *p48* 020 7636 1616

Craig, Mrs H B (Quality Solicitors Burroughs Day) *N*
Bristol *p164* 0117 929 0333

Craig, J (Gordons Solicitors LLP)
Marlow *p313* 01628 487487

Craig, J H (Bates Wells & Braithwaite London LLP) *C1 C2 Zd*
London EC4 *p11* 020 7551 7777

Craig, Mrs J I (Manches LLP) *K1*
London WC2 *p58* 020 7404 4433

Craig, K (Christian Khan Solicitors) *Zg N*
London WC1 *p49* 020 7631 9500

Craig, Miss L H (Dibbens) *K1 W*
Wimborne *p433* 01202 882456

Craig, Mrs M S (Melanie Craig Solicitors) *J1 K1 Q*
Leeds *p272* 0113 244 4081

Craig, N C D (Watson Burton LLP) *E A1 W K1 S1 L R1*
Newcastle upon Tyne *p327* . 0845 901 2100

Craig, N S (Hentys LLP) *C1 B1 Zb I*
Waterlooville *p423* 023 9224 6710

Craig, P A (Bracher Rawlins LLP) *C1 E L S1 W S2*
London WC1 *p15* 020 7404 9400

Craig, R D (Finers Stephens Innocent LLP) *C1 T1 W E J1 Zd Ze Zi*
London W1 *p32* 020 7323 4000

Craig, S C (Mills & Reeve) *J1 O Q*
Cambridge *p175* 01223 364422

Craig, T R (Muckle LLP) *A3 O Zc Zn Zq*
Newcastle upon Tyne *p325* . 0191 211 7777

Craigie, Mrs C A (Kennedys) *N*
London EC3 *p49* 020 7667 9667

Craigs, L (Lennons) *K1 Q*
Chesham *p189* 01494 773377

Craik, M J V (SGH Martineau LLP) *Zc*
Birmingham *p142* 0870 763 2000

Cramer, Mrs J (Henry Boustred & Sons) *W N Q O L K1 J1*
London N6 *p14* 020 8348 5223

Cramer, P I (Cramer Pelmont)
London N8 *p23* 020 8340 0091

Cramer, R G (Cohen Cramer Solicitors) *B1 J1 N O Q Zl Zf Zw A3*
Leeds *p272* 0800 542 9408

Cramond, I J (David Gray Solicitors) *L*
Newcastle upon Tyne *p324* . 0191 232 9547

Cramp, Ms C (S V Wadsworth & Co) *N*
Solihull *p383* 0121 745 8550

Cramp, D W (Dudley Cramp & Co) *C1 E O S1 J1 R1 Zt*
Sittingbourne *p380* 01795 420024

Cramp, Mrs S M (Cramp & Co) *C1 E L S1 S2 W K4*
Eastbourne *p215* 01323 720581

Crampton, T (LG Lawyers)
London SE1 *p50* 020 7379 0000

Crane, Miss F M (Vale Royal Borough Council)
Winsford *p476* 01606 862862

Crane, J M (Crane & Walton)
Ashby-de-la-Zouch *p118* . . 01530 414111

Crane, Miss L (Radcliffes Le Brasseur) *J1*
Westminster *p70* 020 7222 7040

Crane, N J (Cranes) *S1 W E L R1 T1 Zc Zh Zv*
Barry *p126* 01446 720444
Cardiff *p178* 029 2034 4995

Crane, R H (S M Reed & Co)
Hove *p255* 01273 727351

Crane, T J (Cranes) *S1 W E L R1 T1 Zc Zh Zj Zv*
Barry *p126* 01446 720444
Cardiff *p178* 029 2034 4995

Craner, Mrs J H (Randle Thomas LLP) *W K4*
Helston *p246* 01326 572951

Cranfield, Miss E (Berry & Berry) *G H B2*
Tonbridge *p412* 01732 355911

Cranfield, R W L (Allen & Overy LLP)
London E1 *p5* 020 3088 0000

Crangle, G P (Crangle Edwards) *G S1 K1 H N W D1 P J1 L Ze*
Cheadle *p185* 0161 428 2331

Crangle, P J (Savage Crangle) *W L B1 E A1 C1 K1 N M1 P*
Skipton *p381* 01756 794611

Cranidge, N A (AgustaWestland Legal Dept - Yeovil)
Yeovil *p477* 01935 702240

Cranshaw, Ms R (Crown Prosecution Service Thames Valley)
Abingdon *p447* 01235 551900

Cranston, Miss H (Kellogg Brown & Root (UK) Ltd)
Leatherhead *p462* 01372 865000

Cranston, I T (Ince & Co Services Ltd) *O Q M1 Za Zj Zc*
London E1 *p44* 020 7481 0010

Cranston, M D (Reed Smith LLP) *M1 Zj O*
London EC2 *p71* 020 3116 3000

Cranton, M (Solomon Taylor & Shaw) *J1 Zi*
London NW3 *p80* 020 7431 1912

Crarer, T J (Parker Bullen) *A1 E L R1 S1 Zc R2*
Salisbury *p371* 01722 412000

Craske, N P (Lucas & Wyllys) *W T2 S1 T1 V*
Great Yarmouth *p234* 01493 855555

Craughan, J (Hogan Lovells International LLP)
London EC1 *p42* 020 7296 2000

Craven, R N (Mayer Brown International LLP) *Zc*
London EC2 *p59* 020 3130 3000

Craven, Ms S (Glanvilles) *E C1 L S2 Zh*
Fareham *p224* 01329 282841

Crawford, A J (Devonshires) *Zd C1 C2 Zh*
London EC2 *p27* 020 7628 7576

Crawford, Miss B E (Jacobs Solicitors) *D1 K1 L N Q S1 W V*
Ellesmere Port *p217* 0151 355 8481

Crawford, B M (QualitySolicitors Hill & Abbott) *K1 D1 X K2 D2 K3*
Chelmsford *p187* 01245 258892

Crawford, Miss E F (Slough Borough Council)
Slough *p471* 01753 552288

Crawford, F A (Glazer Delmar) *K1*
London SE22 *p35* 020 8299 0021

Crawford, G (BHP Law)
North Shields *p330* 0191 257 2213

Crawford, G (Simmons & Simmons)
London EC2 *p79* 020 7628 2020

Crawford, Miss G K (McGrigors LLP)
London EC4 *p56* 020 7054 2500

Crawford, J (Speechly Bircham LLP)
London EC4 *p81* 020 7427 6400

Crawford, J W (Ellis Jones) *S1 S2*
Bournemouth *p151* 01202 525333

Crawford, Ms L (Lloyds TSB Group PLC)
Bristol *p452* 0117 905 5500

Crawford, Ms L (Osborne Clarke) *R2*
London EC2 *p65* 020 7105 7000

Crawford, Mrs L H G (Cheltenham & Gloucester PLC)
Gloucester *p459* 01452 372372

Crawford, L J (Myers Fletcher & Gordon) *C1 O*
London W6 *p62* 020 7610 4433

Crawford, P H (Stitt & Co) *Q O C1 J1 L K1 S1 E Zk Zp Zw Zv*
London EC4 *p83* 020 7832 0840

Crawford, Miss R (Aspinall Wright) *K1 S1 W Q D1 K3*
Glossop *p230* 01457 854645

Crawford, Miss R A (Shell International Ltd)
London SE1 *p109* 020 7934 1234

Crawford, Mrs S (Wiggin LLP) *T1*
Cheltenham *p189* 01242 224114

Crawley, Miss E (Comercrawley) *N*
Diss *p210* 01379 644311

Crawley, Miss F (Bryan Cave) *Ze U2 I U1 C1 C3 C2 F1 F2*
London EC2 *p19* 020 7207 1100

Crawley, P (Mark Gilbert Morse) *S1 S2*
Newcastle upon Tyne *p325* . 0191 261 0096

Crawshaw, Mrs E A (Place Blair & Hatch) *K1 D1 G H S1 W L V N*
Northallerton *p331* 01609 780101

Cray, Miss J L (Beardsells) *N*
Cheadle *p185* 0161 477 2288

Cray, M W (Martin Cray & Co) *P G J1 M1 K1 N C1 S1 W Zi Zm*
Brighton *p159* 01273 673226

Craze, A R (Menneer Shuttleworth) *M1 N P K1 G L S1 W C1 O Zj Zt Zl*
St Leonards-on-Sea *p392* . . 01424 720044

Creamer, R (Radcliffes Le Brasseur)
Westminster *p70* 020 7222 7040

Creamore, M G (Gregsons) *L N J1 Zp*
London SW19 *p37* 020 8946 1173

Creasey, Ms B (Nelsons) *G H*
Nottingham *p338* 0115 958 6262

Creasey, D J (Brómets Jackson Heath) *W S1 Zv*
Tadcaster *p407* 01937 832371

Creasey, D J S (Leeds Metropolitan University) *S1 W C1 K1 M1 L F1 G T1 E Zc Zl Zp*
Leeds *p463* 0113 812 9028

Creasey, R J C (Bedwell Watts & Co) *D1 F1 H K1 L M1 P S1*
Scarborough *p372* . .01723 373356 / 363553

Creed, A W G (Trowers & Hamlins)
London EC3 *p88* 020 7423 8000

Creed, Miss B (Tunbridge Wells Borough Council)
Tunbridge Wells *p474* 01892 526121
London W6 *p110* 020 8846 3107

Creed, R D (Ouvry Creed Solicitors) *W*
Tetbury *p410* 01666 504005

Creed, T (R Bell & Son) *K1 D1 G H S1 M1 W L*
Hartlepool *p242* 01429 273165
Peterlee *p347* 0191 586 8646

Creek, J (DFA Law LLP) *C1 C2 E F1 R1 R2 S2 Zc Ze Zn*
Northampton *p331* 01604 609560

Cregan, M J (Bolitho Way)
Portsmouth *p354* 023 9282 0747

Crehan, M P (MC Law) *C1 B1 O*
Petersfield *p348* 01730 261979

Creighton, Ms L (Creighton & Partners)
London WC1 *p23* 020 7976 2233

Creighton, S R (Bhatt Murphy) *Zg*
Hackney *p12* 020 7729 1115

Crellin, D E (Crellins Carter Solicitors) *E N P S1 S2 R1 T1 C1 B1 J1 K1 R2 Zq O*
Weybridge *p429* 01932 858833

Cremin, M T (Rohan & Co) *S2 S1 C1 W R2*
Haywards Heath *p246* 01444 450901

Cremin, M T (Paul Davidson Taylor) *A1 G E S1 W*
Horsham *p253* 01403 262333

Cresswell, A (Crown Prosecution Service Devon & Cornwall)
Exeter *p458* 01392 288000

Cresswell, A J (Cresswell & Co) *I M1 N O Q C1 C3 J1 F1 B1 Zc Ze*
London W4 *p23* 020 8742 0070

Cresswell, J (BBC)
London W12 *p103* 020 8752 5734

Cresswell, P G (Hannays Solicitors and Advocates) *G H K1 D1*
South Shields *p383* . . 0191 456 7893 / 455 5361

Cresswell, T (J A Kemp & Co)
London WC1 *p48* 020 7405 3292

Creswick, Miss E S (Horsham District Council)
Horsham *p461* 01403 215100

Creswick, Mrs J (Roberts Moore Nicholas Jones) *K1 D1 W S1 K3*
Birkenhead *p134* 0151 647 0000

Crewdson, Mrs A (CVC Solicitors)
Penzance *p346* 01736 362313

Crewe, J (Linder Myers Solicitors) *C1 E S1 L T1 W Zc Zh Zi*
Manchester *p306* 0844 984 6000

Crewe, J (Laytons) *C1 C2*
London EC4 *p52* 020 7842 8000

Crewe, P F (Shammah Nicholls LLP) *B1 O Q*
Manchester *p309* 0161 832 9272

Crews, G R (Bennett Welch & Co) *E S1*
London SE19 *p12* 020 8670 6141

Cribb, Mrs J (Treasury Solicitors Department)
London WC2 *p110* 020 7210 3000

Cribbs, Ms A J (Sacker & Partners LLP) *Zo*
London EC2 *p76* 020 7329 6699

Crichard, M (DLA Piper UK LLP)
London EC2 *p24* 0870 011 1111

Crichton, P J (DLA Piper UK LLP) *C1*
London EC2 *p24* 0870 011 1111

Crichton, Miss S R (Eaton Smith LLP) *C1 C2*
Huddersfield *p255* 01484 821300

Crichton-Stuart, C (Squire Sanders (UK) LLP)
London EC2 *p81* 020 7655 1000

Criddle, P M (Tinn Criddle & Co) *A1 C1 J1 K1 L P R1 S1 T1 W Zc Zl Zj*
Alford *p115* 01507 462882
Sutton-on-Sea *p404* 01507 443043

Cridland, G J (Exeter City Council) *R1 P Zu*
Exeter *p458* 01392 277888

Crier, P B (Blake Lapthorn) *J1*
Chandlers Ford *p184* 023 8090 8090

Crighton, J A (Clifford Harris & Co) *O Q B1 J1 N C1*
London W1 *p21* 020 7486 0031

Crilly, P F P (County of Herefordshire District Council)
Hereford *p460* 01432 260266

Crine, D C (Henmans LLP) *Zq Zj Q*
Oxford *p343* 01865 781000

Crippin, S (Carter Lemon Camerons) *W T2*
London EC1 *p18* 020 7406 1000

Cripps, Ms A C (Squire Sanders (UK) LLP)
London EC2 *p81* 020 7655 1000

Cripps, Ms J A (Morgan Cole) *W L E S1 T2 Zd Zo*
Oxford *p344* 01865 262600

Cripps, J R (Morlings)
Maidstone *p299* 01622 673081

Cripps, R A J (Gullands) *E S2 C1 J1 C2 R2*
Maidstone *p299* 01622 678341

Cripwell, J P (Denison Till) *Q O N*
York *p444* 01904 611411

Criscuolo, L (Ashurst LLP)
London EC2 *p7* 020 7638 1111

Crisp, A C (Mason Bullock Solicitors) *Q J1 B1 F1 O N Zq*
Northampton *p332* 01604 601575

Crisp, H C (Crisp & Co Solicitors) *D1 F1 Q S1 Ze*
Guildford *p236* 01483 570810

Crisp, J M G (Parkes Wilshire Johnson) *C1 S2 E K1 O Q S1 W*
Barnet *p124* 020 8441 1556

Crisp, S H (Powleys) *A1 C1 D1 E J1 L R1 S1 T1 W Zc Zj Zo*
Lowestoft *p294* 01502 581121

Cristie, Ms L (Simmons & Simmons)
London EC2 *p79* 020 7628 2020

Cristofoli, G P (Bookers & Bolton) *O N Q J1 B1 K1 F1 D1 G H Zza*
Alton *p116* . . . . . 01420 82881 / 88903

Critchell, P J (DFA Law LLP) *S1 T1 W T2 Zd*
Northampton *p331* 01604 609560

Critchley, Mrs N P (Horwich Farrelly) *N Q*
Manchester *p305* 0161 834 3585

Critchley, P (Rollingsons)
London EC1 *p73* 020 7611 4848

Critchley, P A (Charles Russell LLP) *E S1*
Guildford *p235* 01483 252525

Critchlow, G H J (Fenwick Elliott) *O A3 Zc*
London WC2 *p31* 020 7421 1986

Crittenden, M I K (Wigan Borough Council)
Wigan *p476* 01942 244991

Crix, P R (Gotelee) *W A1 T2 E*
Ipswich *p262* 01473 211121

Croad, K (Pinney Talfourd LLP)
Upminster *p416* 01708 229444

Croall, D E (Lancashire County Council) *G N D1 K1 J1 H F1 Zl Zf*
Preston *p469* 01772 254868

Crocco, P (PricewaterhouseCoopers Legal LLP) *C1 Zo*
London SE1 *p69* 020 7212 1616

Crocker, J (Earl & Crocker) *K1 D1 Zl D2 V*
Liskeard *p285* 01579 345304

Crocker, J M (Bindmans LLP) *N Zr*
London WC1 *p12* 020 7833 4433

Crocker, N D (Squire Sanders (UK) LLP) *E*
Leeds *p277* 0113 284 7000

Crocker, N J (Young & Co) *E S1 F1 L J1 W*
Bedford *p130* . . . .01234 346411 / 344211

Crocker, P (Appleby Hope & Matthews)
Middlesbrough *p314* 01642 440444

Crocker, R (Taylor Walton LLP) *W*
St Albans *p390* 01727 845245

Crockett, Mrs H (Crockett & Co) *D1 K3 K1 W*
Leeds *p272* 0113 226 0111

Crockford, P R (Dechert) *C1 F1 M1*
London EC4 *p26* 020 7184 7000

Crockford, Mrs S A (Chamberlain Martin Solicitors) *D1 K1 V*
Bognor Regis *p148* 01243 825211

Crocombe, A M (Henmans LLP) *O A3 Zj Zq*
Oxford *p343* 01865 781000

Croft, A C (Druces LLP) *O Q Zq B1*
London EC2 *p27* 020 7638 9271

Croft, B V (Birnberg Peirce & Partners) *Zi*
Camden *p13* 020 7911 0166

Croft, Mrs L M (Crampton Pym & Lewis)
Oswestry *p342* 01691 653301

Croft, R (Maitland Walker)
Cheltenham *p188* 01242 285855

Croft, Mrs S A (Shirley Croft Solicitors) *K1 N Q D1 J1*
Chelmsford *p186* 01245 380019

Croft, Miss S L (Shook Hardy & Bacon LLP) *O*
London EC4 *p78* 020 7332 4500

Crofts, Ms A (DAC Beachcroft)
London EC4 *p24* 020 7242 1011

Crofts, D A (Thornes) *W C1 E S2*
Wolverhampton *p438* 01902 313311

Crofts, G F (Crofts) *S1 E G M1 C1*
Kettering *p265* 01536 518742

Crofts-Turnbull, Mrs D H (Moxons) *K3 D1 K1*
Pontefract *p351* 01977 703215

Croke, Mrs H (Travers Smith LLP) *C2*
London EC1 *p87* 020 7295 3000

Croker, P A J (Kenneth Bush) *G H J1 Zo*
King's Lynn *p266* 01553 692737

Croker, R A D (CMS Cameron McKenna LLP)
London EC3 *p17* 020 7367 3000

Crolla, Ms C (Fuglers) *O Q K3 K1 J1*
London W1 *p34* 020 7323 6450

Cromack, Ms J (Addleshaw Goddard)
Leeds *p271* 0113 209 2000

Cromarty, Miss I M (Department for Business, Enterprise and Regulatory Reform) *C1 Ze Zi*
London SW1 *p105* 020 7215 0105

Crombleholme, D R (Bridge McFarland)
Grimsby *p235* 01472 311711

Cromby, A (Bracher Rawlins LLP) *O Q*
London WC1 *p15* 020 7404 9400

Crome, P (Chadwyck-Healey & Co) *G H B2*
London EC4 *p19* 020 7353 6900

Crompton, Miss J H (Shell International Ltd) *S1 L E Zh*
London SE1 *p109* 020 7934 1234

Crompton, J M (Napthens LLP) *N*
Chorley *p194* 0845 260 2111

Crompton, J R M (Thomson Wilson Pattinson) *S1 E R1 L W C1 K1 P A1 T1 Zd S2*
Windermere *p434* 01539 442233

Crompton, Mrs N J (Garth Rigby & Co)
Ashton-in-Makerfield *p119* . . 01942 717378

Crompton, S G (Russell & Russell) *S1 R1*
Bolton *p149* 01204 399299
Chester *p191* 01244 405700

Crompton, Ms T (Farleys Solicitors LLP) *L N Q*
Burnley *p169* 01282 798664

Crompton-Pell, Ms H M (Boyes Turner) *C1*
Reading *p360* 0118 959 7711

Cronan, Mrs G D (Hampshire County Council)
Winchester *p476* 01962 841841

Crone, J E S (Menneer Shuttleworth) *S1 E W T1 R1 L A1 Zl Zl Zm*
Bexhill *p132* 01424 730630

Cronin, Miss E (Anthony King & Co) *S1 W*
Basildon *p126* 01268 240400

Cronin, N (Southerns) *N Zm*
Burnley *p169* 01282 422711

Cronin, Miss R (Margary & Miller) *A3 F1 O Q N*
Felixstowe *p225* 01394 273333
Norwich *p335* 0870 609 0200

Cronkshaw, N S (Simmons & Simmons)
London EC2 *p79* 020 7628 2020

Cronly-Dillon, Ms M (Olswang LLP) *J1*
London WC1 *p64* 020 7067 3000

Cronshey, Mrs W E (John Fowlers LLP Solicitors)
Colchester *p197* 01206 576151

Croock, J (Dechert) *C2*
London EC4 *p26* 020 7184 7000

Crook, A R (Cirencester Town Council)
Cirencester *p455* 01285 655646

Crook, B C (Barlow Lyde & Gilbert LLP)
London EC3 *p10* 020 7247 2277

Crook, D F (Crown Prosecution Service Durham)
Durham *p457* 0191 383 5800

Crook, Miss H J (Denison Till) *A1 E S2 X R2 Zd*
York *p444* 01904 611411

Crook, Miss L A (Ford & Warren) *J1 Q C2 Zg T1*
Leeds *p273* 0113 243 6601

Crook, N W (Heald Solicitors) *I C1 J1 Ze U2 C3 C2*
Milton Keynes *p317* 01908 662277

Crook, P (Allen & Overy LLP)
London E1 *p5* 020 3088 0000

Crook, P (Husband Forwood Morgan) *S1 W L K1 E F1 T1 C1 J1 Zc Zh Zk*
Liverpool *p289* 0151 236 9626

Crook, S (J Keith Park & Co) *Zr N Q*
St Helens *p391* 01744 636000

Crook, Mrs V S A (Bird & Bird LLP) *C1 Zw U1 I*
London EC4 *p13* 020 7415 6000

Crookes, J (Pinsent Masons LLP)
London EC2 *p67* 020 7418 7000

Crookes, R F (Charles Crookes Limited) *C1 W E S1 T1 R1 A1*
Cardiff *p178* 029 2049 1271

Crooknorth, J (Rowbis Solicitors) *G H B2*
Gloucester *p230* 01452 301903

Crooknorth, Mrs M C (Rowbis Solicitors) *D1 K1 D2*
Gloucester *p230* 01452 301903

Croom, M J (Duncan Watts LLP) *K1 K2 K3*
Warwick *p422* 01926 493485

Croot, D J (Poole Alcock)
Nantwich *p320* 01270 625478

Cropley, P L (Chattertons Solicitors) *M1 B1 G H J1 C1 C2 K1 N F1 L Za Zl Ze*
Boston *p151* 01205 351114

Cropper, G G (Harrow Magistrates Court (Clerks Office))
Wealdstone *p475* 020 8427 5146

Croques, F (Pattichi Hill & Croques) *N*
Ilford *p260* 020 8911 8233

Crosbie, Miss R M (Norwich Union Insurance Group) *D1 K1 S2 W K4*
Norwich *p467* 01603 622200
Cromer *p203* 01263 513355

Crosby, Mrs A (Selby District Council)
Selby *p470* 01757 705101

Crosby, A A (Yarwood Stimpson & Co) *S1 S2 E W T2 T1 Zv*
Whitley Bay *p431* 0191 297 0123

Crosby, D B (Crosby & Moore Solicitors) *N Q K1 F1*
Hove *p254* 01273 863295

Crosby, Mrs S (John Fowlers LLP Solicitors)
Colchester *p197* 01206 576151

Crosfield, S (Simon Crosfield & Co) *G H W S1 Zq N K1 Zr D1 K3 S2 Q J1 F2*
Ripon *p365* 01765 692277

Croshaw, J S (Russell & Co) *S1 J1 S2 C1 L Zl*
Malvern *p300* 01684 892000

Crosley, T C (Memery Crystal) *T1*
London WC2 *p60* 020 7242 5905

Cross, Miss A (Michelmores LLP) *C1 C2*
Exeter *p221* 01392 688688

Cross, A D (Hatchers Solicitors LLP) *A1 E L S1 S2 W*
Shrewsbury *p379* 01743 248545

Cross, A J (Brabners Chaffe Street) *J1*
Liverpool *p286* 0151 600 3000

Cross, B G (Cross Solicitors) *G H K1 L N Q W*
Connah's Quay *p199* 01244 822101

Cross, Miss C (Muckle LLP) *E R2*
Newcastle upon Tyne *p325* 0191 211 7777

Cross, D (David Cross & Co) *C1 E W F1 S2 J1*
Thornbury *p411* 01454 419696

Cross, Ms F M (Field Fisher Waterhouse LLP)
London EC3 *p31* 020 7861 4000

Cross, Miss H (Russell-Cooke LLP) *E*
London SW15 *p74* 020 8789 9111

Cross, Miss H L (Joelson Wilson LLP) *C1 C2 F1 F2 Ze Zn*
Westminster *p46* 020 7580 5721

Cross, I (The College of Law Chester)
Chester *p454* 0800 289997

Cross, Miss J E (Cozens-Hardy LLP) *S1*
Norwich *p334* 01603 625231

Cross, J M G (Kitsons LLP) *O Zl Q J1*
Torquay *p413* 01803 202020

Cross, M E (Stephens & Scown) *N*
Truro *p414* 01872 265100

Cross, Miss M L (Christos Wybrew Kenneth Shaw & Co) *E G K1 L M1 P S1 W*
Enfield *p218* 020 8366 1345 / 8367 0840

Cross, Miss P D (Financial Services Authority)
London E14 *p106* 020 7066 1000

Cross, P W S (Walter Williams) *S1 A1 K1 W H C1 J1 N E Zv Zl*
Fishguard *p226* 01348 873223

Cross, R A (Potter & Co) *A1 C1 E S1 S2 L*
Matlock *p313* 01629 582308

Cross, R F (C R Burton & Co) *G H Zl S1 W Q K1*
London SE20 *p16* 020 8778 4455 / 8659 5775

Cross, S (Stefan Cross Solicitors) *N*
Newcastle upon Tyne *p324* 0191 226 6686

Cross, S D (Humphries Kirk) *K4 T1 T2 W*
Bournemouth *p152* 01202 421111

Cross, Ms S G (Pinsent Masons LLP)
London EC2 *p67* 020 7418 7000

Cross, Mrs S J (Oglethorpe Sturton & Gillibrand) *N F1 L B1 Zr Q*
Lancaster *p270* 01524 846846

Cross, T (Langleys)
York *p445* 01904 610886

Cross, Mrs T A (Band Hatton LLP) *K1*
Coventry *p200* 024 7663 2121

Cross, T D B (Gordons LLP)
Leeds *p273* 0113 227 0100

Cross, Mrs Y (Bearders) *W K1 K4 K3*
Brighouse *p158* 01484 710571
Halifax *p238* 01422 365215 / 343427

Crossan, D J (Derek Crossan) *C1 M1 R1 Zc Ze*
Helmsley *p246* 01439 770070

Crosse, D G (DLA Piper UK LLP)
Leeds *p272* 0870 011 1111

Crosse, J P (Wakefield Metropolitan District Council) *B1 D1 J1 K1 L M1 P*
Wakefield *p474* 01924 306090

Crosse, Ms K L (Clifford Chance)
London E14 *p20* 020 7006 1000

Crossfield, M R (DLA Piper UK LLP)
London EC2 *p24* 0870 011 1111

Crossick, S P (Jaffe Porter Crossick) *S2 C1 E J1 L W S1*
London NW6 *p46* 020 7625 4424

Crosskill, J (Norfolk County Council - Legal Services) *F1 F2 O Q*
Norwich *p467* Minicom: 0844 800 8011

Crossland, Mrs J (Arcadia Group Ltd)
London W1 *p103* 020 7636 8040

Crossland, J P (Irwin Mitchell LLP) *N Zi*
Sheffield *p376* 0870 150 0100

Crossley, A T (Sternberg Reed) *K1*
Barking *p123* 020 8591 3366

Crossley, Ms B M (Field Seymour Parkes) *E L S2*
Reading *p360* 0118 951 6200

Crossley, D (Steeles) *C1 O Zf*
Norwich *p335* 0870 609 0200

Crossley, Ms G (Andrew Keenan & Co) *G H B2*
London SE20 *p48* 020 8659 0332

Crossley, Miss G (Burton Copeland LLP) *G H*
Manchester *p302* 0161 827 9500

Crossley, Ms K A (Winckworth Sherwood LLP) *E S1 S2 Zh*
London SE1 *p92* 020 7593 5000

Crossley, M J (Quality Solicitors Mewies) *N*
Skipton *p381* 01756 799000

Crossley, N A (DLA Piper UK LLP) *J1 Zi*
Manchester *p303* 0870 011 1111

Crossley, P M (Squire Sanders (UK) LLP) *O F1 Q Zb Zk*
Leeds *p277* 0113 284 7000

Crossley, R (Walker Morris)
Leeds *p277* 0113 283 2500

Crossley, R V (Clark Ricketts LLP) *M3*
London WC2 *p20* 020 7240 6767

Crossley, Ms S J (Crown Prosecution Service Dyfed Powys)
Carmarthen *p453* 01267 242100

Crossley-Dawson, P A (Roland Robinsons & Fentons LLP) *S1 W E C2 C1*
Lytham *p297* 01253 734253

Crossling, D (Quality Solicitors Jordans) *G H N Q*
Doncaster *p212* 01302 365374

Crossling, M A (Colin Brown & Kidson) *K1 Q N L J1 G F1 D1 A1 H*
Whitby *p430* 01947 603391

Crossman, H (Maxwell Winward LLP) *Zc A3*
London EC4 *p59* 020 7651 0000

Crossman, P V (Crossmans) *G K1 N H D1 Zi Zm*
Radstock *p358* 01761 431688

Crostan, Ms N (Linder Myers Solicitors)
Manchester *p307* 0844 984 6400

Croston, N E (Bryan & Armstrong) *N J1 L*
Mansfield *p311* 01623 626039

Crotch, A J M (Rogers & Norton) *A1 C1 E L S1 T1 W*
Norwich *p335* 01603 666001

Crothers, A H (Bury & Walkers LLP) *G H K1 P D1 F1 Zl Zt*
Barnsley *p124* 01226 733533

Crothers, Mrs C (Bury & Walkers LLP) *K1 V*
Barnsley *p124* 01226 733533

Crotty, A (Morrison & Foerster (UK) LLP) *Zb*
London EC2 *p62* 020 7920 4000

Crotty, S P (Weightmans LLP) *Zu C1 Ze Zf U1 U2 C2 M1*
Liverpool *p291* 0151 227 2601

Crouch, D J (Taylor Wimpey UK Ltd) *S1*
Cannock *p453* 01543 496766

Crouch, Mrs E (Cartmell Shepherd) *L W S1*
Brampton *p156* 01697 72378

Crouch, Ms J (Cherwell District Council)
Banbury *p448* 01295 252535

Crouch, Mrs J A E (Gaby Hardwicke) *W T2 S1 Zd Zm*
Eastbourne *p215* 01323 435900

Crouch, R (Carter Bells LLP) *W K4*
Kingston upon Thames *p267* 020 8939 4000

Crouch, Mrs R A (Lincolnshire County Council Resources - Legal Services) *S1 E W*
Lincoln *p463* 01522 552222

Crouch, R G (Charles Russell LLP) *E S1*
London EC4 *p19* 020 7203 5000

Croucher, D J (Thomas Simon) *Q B1 C1 F1 F2 Zj O N Zq*
Cardiff *p181* 029 2055 7200

Croucher, Ms Y (Cadwalader Wickersham & Taft)
London WC2 *p17* 020 7170 8700

Crouchman, A C (Akin Gump Strauss Hauer & Feld)
London E1 *p4* 020 7012 9600

Croud, Ms A L D (Hatten Wyatt) *K1 P G S1 F1 L J1 W*
Gravesend *p232* 01474 351199

Crow, Ms L J (Faegre & Benson LLP) *C2 C1*
London EC4 *p30* 020 7450 4500
Birmingham *p141* 0121 200 1050

Crow, Miss M (MacLaren Britton) *K3 K1 D1*
Nottingham *p338* 0115 941 1469

Crow, T (National Institutions of the Church of England, Legal Office) *A1 E*
London SW1 *p108* 020 7898 1000

Crow, Miss T E (Clifton Ingram LLP) *S1*
Wokingham *p437* 0118 978 0099

Crowder, Ms J A (Higgins & Co) *N*
Birkenhead *p134* 0151 653 5222

Crowder, P (Savages)
Corbridge *p199* 01434 632505

Crowe, Ms A J R (Treasury Solicitors Department)
London WC2 *p110* 020 7210 3000

Crowe, Miss A L (Charles Russell LLP) *E*
London EC4 *p19* 020 7203 5000

Crowe, Mrs L S (Brooke-Taylors) *S1 A1 E M1*
Buxton *p172* 01298 22741

Crowe, P (The Affordable Law Co Ltd)
York *p444* 01904 788877

Crowe, S (Ross Green & Crowe) *S1 W E L R1 C1 A1 Zc Zl Zm*
Dartford *p207* 01322 225353

Crowle, J (Rich & Carr Freer Bouskell) *E S1*
Lutterworth *p296* 0116 242 6048

Crowley, J M (Crowley & Co) *B2 G H S1 S2 W*
Cardiff *p178* 029 2045 8895

Crowley, L A (Hogan Lovells International LLP)
London EC1 *p42* 020 7296 2000

Crowley, P F (Paul Crowley & Co) *K3 W S1 N Q S2 K1*
Liverpool *p287* 0151 264 7363

Crowley, Miss R A (Doncaster Magistrates Court)
Doncaster *p457* 01302 366711

Crown, G (Lewis Silkin LLP)
London EC4 *p53* 020 7074 8000

Crown, T H R (Baily Gibson) *O Q N Zk Zq*
High Wycombe *p249* 01494 442661
Beaconsfield *p128* 01494 670440

Crowson, Miss H (Fishers) *W T2 Zo Zm K4 T1*
Ashby-de-la-Zouch *p118* 01530 412167

Crowther, A C (Flint Bishop Solicitors) *E S1 S2*
Ashbourne *p118* 01335 342208
Derby *p208* 01332 340211

Crowther, G M (Sansbury Douglas)
Bristol *p164* 0117 926 5341

Crowther, Ms J (Ashurst LLP)
London EC2 *p7* 020 7638 1111

Crowther, J D G (Bailey Smailes)
Huddersfield *p255* 01484 435543

Crowther, N (Worsdell & Vintner)
Harefield *p239* 01895 824713
Ickenham *p259* 01895 672631

Crowther, R (Grahame Stowe Bateson) *K4 Q Zo W*
Harrogate *p240* 01423 562121

Crowther, Ms S L (Barlow Lyde & Gilbert LLP)
London EC3 *p10* 020 7247 2277

Crowther, Mrs S V (Pitmans LLP) *N P O Zu R1*
Reading *p361* 0118 958 0224

Croxen, Miss F (Norfolk County Council - Legal Services)
Norwich *p467* Minicom: 0844 800 8011

Croxford, A (McDermott Will & Emery UK LLP) *C2 C1*
London EC2 *p56* 020 7577 6900

Croxford, Mrs J (London Stock Exchange Ltd)
London EC2 *p107* 020 7797 1000

Croxon, Miss S V (DLA Piper UK LLP) *Ze I Zz*
London EC2 *p24* 0870 011 1111

Croxton, C J (Mackrell Turner Garrett) *N O Q Zc Zj*
London WC2 *p57* 020 7240 0521

Crozier, J (Linklaters LLP)
London EC2 *p54* 020 7456 2000

Crozier, R (Walker Morris) *Ze Zw*
Leeds *p277* 0113 283 2500

Cruddas, I C (Glandfield & Cruddas) *W A1 S1 L T2*
Uttoxeter *p417* 01889 565657

Cruddas, M I (Glandfield & Cruddas) *K1 D1 Q K3*
Uttoxeter *p417* 01889 565657

Cruden, P A (Stratford-on-Avon District Council)
Stratford-upon-Avon *p473* 01789 267575

Crudgington, R H (Grant Saw Solicitors LLP) *C1 E J1 L B1 Zd Zl S2*
Greenwich *p36* 020 8858 6971

Cruft, B (Ince & Co Services Ltd)
London E1 *p44* 020 7481 0010

Cruickshank, G (Punch Robson)
Middlesbrough *p315* 01642 230700

Cruickshank, I J (Ian Cruickshank & Co) *S1 K1 G H Zd Zl K3 S2 W K4*
Jarrow *p263* 0191 428 0900

Cruickshank, J M (Cruickshanks Solicitors) *S1 E Zb Zi W O*
London W1 *p23* 020 7487 4468

Cruickshank, J W (Geoffrey Hill & Co) *S1 G H W E K1 A1*
Hinckley *p250* 01455 637715

Cruickshank, Ms K (Simmons & Simmons) *E*
London EC2 *p79* 020 7628 2020

Cruickshank, R I S (Kidd Rapinet) *C2 I C1*
London WC2 *p49* 020 7205 2115

Cruise, Mrs J (Bentley Solicitors)
Crewe *p203* 01270 509800

Cruise, R (Derbyshire County Council)
Matlock *p465* 01629 580000

Crumbley, W M (BHP Law) *S1*
Newcastle upon Tyne *p323* 0191 221 0898

Crumley, Miss A J (Goodman Derrick LLP) *B1 O Q Zj*
London EC4 *p36* 020 7404 0606

Crumly, R J (Richard Crumly) *D1 F1 G H J1 K1 L S1 N Q V W*
Thatcham *p410* 01635 866166

Crump, Miss G M (Cullimore Dutton) *E S2 S1 K1 Zn*
Chester *p190* 01244 356789

Crump, N C (Wolferstans) *N*
Plymouth *p351* 01752 663295

Crump, R (Holman Fenwick Willan)
London EC3 *p42* 020 7264 8000

Crumplin, P R (Crumplins)
Camden *p23* 020 7483 0282

Crumplin, R I (Thomas Cooper) *A3 O Za Q M2*
London EC3 *p22* 020 7481 8851

Crutch, A (Elmhirst Parker LLP) *E C1 K1 S1 D1 W T1 B1 L V Zl*
Barnsley *p124* 01226 282238

Crute, G S (Crutes) *N Q Zh*
Newcastle upon Tyne *p324* 0191 233 9700

Crute, G T (Archers Law LLP) *W Zd*
Stockton-on-Tees *p396* 01642 636500

Cruwys, G A L (Ashfords LLP) *S1 A1 T2 W*
Tiverton *p412* 01884 203000

Cryan, Miss R (Butcher & Barlow LLP) *K1 D1 K3 S1*
Tyldesley *p416* 01942 883669

Cryne, A J (Temperley Taylor LLP) *G K1 J1 H L N O S1 Zi*
Middleton *p315* 0161 643 2411

Crystal, C (Cunningtons) *S1*
Croydon *p205* 020 8688 8446

Crystal, C R (Rollits LLP) *E*
Hull *p258* 01482 323239

Crystal, Mrs K (Andrew Jackson) *Zd T2 W*
Hull *p257* 01482 325242

Crystal, P M (Memery Crystal) *C1 C2 Zw*
London WC2 *p60* 020 7242 5905

Cselko, G (McEwen Parkinson) *S1 L O Q E W Zq*
Westminster *p56* 020 7487 4361

Csemiczky, P (Galbraith Branley)
London N12 *p34* 020 8446 8474

Cservenka, Miss L (Hanne & Co) *D1 K1*
London SW11 *p38* 020 7228 0017

Csukas, C J (The Wilkes Partnership LLP) *F1 L O Q R1*
Birmingham *p143* 0121 233 4333

Cubbon, Miss S E (Barlow Lyde & Gilbert LLP) *O Zq*
London EC3 *p10* 020 7247 2277

Cubitt, D (Osborne Clarke) *J1 Zg*
London EC2 *p65* 020 7105 7000

Cucchi, Miss A (Lees Solicitors LLP) *S1 S2 E*
West Kirby *p428* 0151 625 9364

Cuckson, D M (Stephenson Harwood) *E P*
London EC2 *p82* 020 7329 4422

Cudbill, Ms H (Trethowans LLP) *J1*
Southampton *p387* 023 8032 1000

Cudd, J M J (Peter Lynn & Partners) *W K4*
Morriston *p319* 01792 310731

Cudd, Mrs K (Randell Lloyd & Martin) *Q N F1 B1 V L K1*
Llanelli *p292* 01554 772149

Cude, Miss D J (CGM) *K1 N L J1*
Southampton *p385* 023 8063 2733

Cudmore, Mrs B (Dyne Drewett Solicitors Ltd) *K4 W*
Shepton Mallet *p378* 01749 342323

Cuerden, J P (Bowcock Cuerden LLP) *O Q J1 Zc A3 Zq C1*
Nantwich *p320* 01270 611106

Cuerden, S P (Irwin Mitchell LLP) *C1 C2*
Leeds *p274* 0870 150 0100

Cuff, D C (Portland Legal Services)
Portland *p354* 01305 866162

Cuffe, N (Judge & Priestley) *C1*
Bromley *p166* 020 8290 0333

Cugley, J H (Woolwich PLC)
Bexleyheath *p449* 020 8298 5000

Culatto, N (Corbett & Co International Construction Lawyers Ltd) *Zc*
Teddington *p409* 020 8614 6200

Culbert, Miss E C (Brighton & Hove Council - Legal Services)
Hove *p461* 01273 290000

Culbert, M C (Osborne Clarke) *O Q B1*
London EC2 *p65* 020 7105 7000

Cull, P G (Treasury Solicitors Department)
London WC2 *p110* 020 7210 3000

Cull, S M (Shentons) *P N S1 L C1*
Winchester *p434* 01962 844544

Cullen, Miss B (Lancashire County Council)
Preston *p469* 01772 254868

Cullen, C N (Freeth Cartwright LLP) *T1 W Zd Zm*
Nottingham *p337* 0115 936 9369

See p634 for the Key to Work Categories

Cullen, G (Maclay Murray & Spens LLP) London EC2 *p57* 020 7002 8500

Cullen, G K (Parker Grego Cullen & Ball) Birmingham *p141* 0121 200 3031

Cullen, Ms J (Howell-Jones LLP) *F2 Ze J1 Zg Zl O Q* Kingston upon Thames *p267* 020 8549 5186

Cullen, Ms K (Walker Morris) Leeds *p277* 0113 283 2500

Cullen, Miss T E (Rochman Landau LLP) *J1 K1 O F1 Q W Zq Zk K2 B1 K3 Zp D1* London W1 *p72* 020 7544 2424

Cullen, T R (Charles Russell LLP) *E S1* London EC4 *p19* 020 7203 5000

Cullen, W I (Simmons & Simmons) London EC2 *p79* 020 7628 2020

Culleton, J D (Steels) *S1 K1 W J1 M1 F1 G L P H Zl Zk* Warrington *p422* 01925 632676

Culley, H E (Irwin Mitchell LLP) *C1 C2 C3 Zw Zd* Sheffield *p376* 0870 150 0100

Culley, M J (Loosemores) *C1 B1 T1 C3 Ze Zf Zk Zw C2* Cardiff *p179* 029 2022 4433

Culligan, Miss E (Shepway District Council) *K1* Folkestone *p458* 01303 852248

Cullimore, A J (Cooper Sons Hartley & Williams) *W T2* Buxton *p172* 01298 77511

Cullinane, L (Clifford Chance) London E14 *p20* 020 7006 1000

Cullington, R E (Johnson & Gaunt) *S1 W L E* Banbury *p122* 01295 256271 / 271200

Cullis, Ms G (Reynolds Porter Chamberlain LLP) London E1 *p71* 020 3060 6000

Cullis, Ms J (Reed Smith LLP) *Zj* London EC2 *p71* 020 3116 3000

Cullis, Ms R S E (Forsters LLP) *L Q O* Westminster *p33* 020 7863 8333

Culpan, Ms V (Capsticks Solicitors LLP) *C1 M1 Zu* London SW19 *p18* 020 8780 2211

Culpin, T J P (Aaron & Partners LLP Solicitors) *B1 G Zl Zt Zv J2* Chester *p190* 01244 405555

Culshaw, C J (Gould & Swayne) *C1 J1 O Q B1* Burnham-on-Sea *p169* 01278 783272 Street *p400* 01458 442433

Culshaw, H P (Pendle Borough Council) *O G Q* Nelson *p466* 01282 661661

Culshaw, Ms S (Simons Muirhead & Burton) *J1 Zf* London W1 *p79* 020 7734 4499

Culver, Miss L (Michelmores LLP) *E R2* Exeter *p221* 01392 688688

Culverhouse, G J (Diamonds) *K1 Q S1 J1 O L N W E C1 F1 B1* Buckhurst Hill *p167* 020 8559 0778

Culverhouse, Mrs J (Trethowans LLP) *S1* Salisbury *p371* 01722 412512

Culverwell, Ms A M (Hutton's) *M1 P N* Cardiff *p179* 029 2037 8621

Culy, A D (Reynolds Porter Chamberlain LLP) *B2 B3 O Q Zj Zo Zq* London E1 *p71* 020 3060 6000

Cumberbatch, C (Hewitsons) *W T2 K4* Cambridge *p174* 01223 461155 Ipswich *p262* 01473 232121

Cumberbatch, M (Stoke-on-Trent City Council) Stoke-on-Trent *p472* 01782 234567

Cumberbatch, M J (Borough of Telford & Wrekin) Telford *p473* 01952 380000

Cumberland, Miss J (Bolt Burdon) *Zr* Islington *p14* 020 7288 4700

Cumberland, Mrs S J (King & Co) *S1* Cambridge *p175* 01954 251818

Cumberlege, The Hon J F (Carter Lemon Camerons) *Zd E S1 L C1* London EC1 *p18* 020 7406 1000

Cumberlidge, Mrs P J (Prior Cumberlidge & Pugh with Jeffery Parr & Co) *K1 F1 J1 L O Q* Birmingham *p141* 0121 707 9211

Cumberlidge, P J (Prior Cumberlidge & Pugh with Jeffery Parr & Co) *S1 E S2 W* Birmingham *p141* 0121 707 9211

Cumberpatch, M (Taylor Wessing) London EC4 *p86* 020 7300 7000

Cumbers, Mrs S (Anthony Gold) *K3 K1* London SE1 *p6* 020 7940 4000

Cumbley, R J (Linklaters LLP) *C1 Ze* London EC2 *p54* 020 7456 2000

Cuming, Ms F (Fisher Meredith) *J1 Zp* Lambeth *p32* 020 7091 2700

Cuming, Ms F (Russell Jones & Walker) London WC2 *p74* 020 7657 1555

Cumming, A (Lupton Fawcett) *N* Leeds *p275* 0113 280 2000

Cumming, G A (Cumming & Riley) *K1 D1 N J1 F1 L X Zm Zo* Grays *p233* 01375 383691

Cumming, R G (Cumming Hodgkinson Dickinson) *S1 W P M1 K1 L E F1 G* Bolton *p148* 01204 523108 / 528396

Cummings, Mrs D A (Taylor Wimpey UK Ltd) Cannock *p453* 01543 496766 London EC2 *p71* 020 3116 3000

Cummings, Mrs G (O'Keeffe Solicitors) *G* Brent *p64* 020 7644 8800

Cummings, G G (Browne Jacobson LLP) *C1 C2 B1* Nottingham *p336* 0115 976 6000

Cummings, N (Cullimore Dutton) *W C1 E S2 A1 L* Chester *p190* 01244 356789

Cummings, Mrs N C (Wyre Forest District Council) Stourport-on-Severn *p473* 01562 820505

Cummins, Ms C J (CMS Cameron McKenna LLP) *P N M1* London EC3 *p17* 020 7367 3000

Cummins, Ms D (Bobbetts Mackan) *D1 K1 K3 D2* Bristol *p161* 0117 929 9001

Cummins, Mrs J (Wainwright & Cummins) *D1 K1 G H* Lambeth *p90* 020 7737 9330

Cummins, J V (Wainwright & Cummins) *G H S1 W D1 E F1 J1 K1 L Zl Zm Zp* Lambeth *p90* 020 7737 9330

Cummins, M (Freeth Cartwright LLP) Leicester *p279* 0116 248 1100

Cummins, M C (Marchants Solicitors) *S1 W T1 F1 K1 N C1 J1 Q* Mansfield *p312* 01623 655111

Cummins, Miss M W (Mackrell Turner Garrett) *S2 E R2 S1* Woking *p437* 01483 755609

Cumpson, J (Nabarro LLP) London WC1 *p63* 020 7524 6000

Cumway, D R (Barnett Alexander Conway Ingram) *S1 G H M1 W K1 E P* London N3 *p10* 020 8349 7680

Cuncliffe, A P (Lambe Corner) *W S1* Hereford *p248* 01432 355301

Cundy, J P (Barlow Lyde & Gilbert LLP) London EC3 *p10* 020 7247 2277

Cuninghame, N (Ashurst LLP) London EC2 *p7* 020 7638 1111

Cunliffe, D R (hlw Keeble Hawson LLP) *G H M1 N P V* Doncaster *p211* 01302 366831

Cunliffe, J F (Franklins) *E S1 C1 L W T1 G* Abingdon *p114* 01235 553222

Cunliffe, M D (Forsters LLP) *R1 E* Westminster *p33* 020 7863 8333

Cunliffe-Jones, P J (London Borough of Haringey) London N22 *p106* 020 8489 0000

Cunliffe-Lister, Earl of Swinton N (N Cunliffe-Lister) *S1 W Q* Driffield *p213* 01377 236006

Cunnah, M (Cyril Jones & Co) *G H S1 E W* Shotton *p379* 01244 812109

Cunnah, R J (CB4law) *S2 E* Cambridge *p174* 01223 316666

Cunnane, Mrs F (McGrigors LLP) London EC4 *p56* 020 7054 2500

Cunningham, Ms A (Metropolitan Police Directorate of Legal Services) *D1 F1 G J1 K1 N O* London SW1 *p108* 020 7230 7210

Cunningham, A (Andrew Jay & Co (Philip Hanby Limited)) *G H* Gainsborough *p228* 01427 612412

Cunningham, B B (John Bellis & Co) *K1 G H M1 P N F1 S1 L W Zl* Penmaenmawr *p346* 01492 622377

Cunningham, Mrs C (Hertfordshire County Council) Hertford *p460* 01992 555555

Cunningham, Mrs C L (Middlesbrough Council) Middlesbrough *p465* 01642 245432

Cunningham, D B (Hewitts) *G K1 D1 N Zj Zm* Bishop Auckland *p144* 01388 604691

Cunningham, Ms E (Rochdale Metropolitan Borough Council) Rochdale *p470* 01706 647474

Cunningham, J F (Moseleys) *K1 D1 Q N J1* Lichfield *p284* 01543 414100

Cunningham, J O (Bingham & Co) Leicester *p279* 0116 253 0091

Cunningham, K G (Irwin Mitchell LLP) *C1 C2* Birmingham *p139* 0870 150 0100 Leeds *p274* 0870 150 0100

Cunningham, K M C (Cunningham Blake) *C1 D1 E F1 G H J1 K1 L M1* London SE3 *p24* 020 8463 0071

Cunningham, Mrs L J (Leech & Co) *N Q* Manchester *p306* 0161 279 0279

Cunningham, M J (Backhouse Jones Ltd) *Zt G E J1* Clitheroe *p196* 01254 828300

Cunningham, M S (Martin Cunningham Solicitors) Stockport *p395* 0161 456 5857

Cunningham, Miss N (Michelmores LLP) *E Q O L* Exeter *p221* 01392 688688

Cunningham, R (Adlams LLP) St Neots *p392* 01480 474061

Cunnington, Mrs C E (Chattertons Solicitors) *W T1 T2 K4* Spalding *p389* 01775 768774

Cupitt, Miss M E (CMS Cameron McKenna LLP) London EC3 *p17* 020 7367 3000

Curbison, N (Colman Coyle LLP) *O Zc* Islington *p22* 020 7354 3000

Curd, R (CMS Cameron McKenna LLP) *O Q Zj* London EC3 *p17* 020 7367 3000

Cure, J P (Cogent Law) *N O Q Zj* Croydon *p204* 0844 245 4452

Curl, Mrs K (Austin & Carnley) *K4 S1 W* Leighton Buzzard *p282* 01525 372140

Curl, Mrs L E R (Steel & Co) *W S1* Knaresborough *p268* 01423 869977

Curley, D (McDermott Will & Emery UK LLP) *Ze O M1 C3 Q* London EC2 *p56* 020 7577 6900

Curley, M D (Friend & Co) *N G H L J1 O Q Zq* Walton-on-Thames *p420* 01932 242962

Curnin, Miss J M (JWP Solicitors) *D1 D2 K1* Wakefield *p418* 01924 387171

Curnow, A G T (Ashurst LLP) *R1* London EC2 *p7* 020 7638 1111

Curnow, Mrs G E (Berry Redmond & Robinson) *A1 C1 E L S1 T1 W* Weston-super-Mare *p429* 01934 513963

Curnow, Mrs N A (Carrick District Council) Truro *p474* 01872 224400

Currall, F (Mid Sussex District Council) Haywards Heath *p460* 01444 458166

Curran, Mrs A (Burnetts) *Zr N* Carlisle *p181* 01228 552222 Carlisle *p182* 01228 552222

Curran, I K (Stafford Borough Council) Stafford *p472* 01785 619000

Curran, J (Bates Wells & Braithwaite London LLP) *J1 J2 Zd* London EC4 *p11* 020 7551 7777

Curran, J J (Clifford Chance) London E14 *p20* 020 7006 1000

Curran, J P T (Watmores) London WC2 *p90* 020 7430 1512

Curran, Mrs K A (Wigan Borough Council) Wigan *p476* 01942 244991

Curran, K J (The Smith Partnership) *O B1* Derby *p209* 01332 225225

Curran, P (O'Donnells) *K4 N W Zm* Preston *p357* 01772 881000

Curran, P (Abney Garsden McDonald) *N* Cheadle *p185* 0161 482 8822

Curran, R J (Squire Sanders (UK) LLP) London EC2 *p81* 020 7655 1000

Currie, Ms A P (Taylor Wessing) *C2 C1* London EC4 *p86* 020 7300 7000

Currie, Mrs C (Kirwans) *K4 W* Birkenhead *p134* 0151 608 9078

Currie, Mrs D A (SJ Berwin LLP) *C2* London EC4 *p75* 020 7111 2222

Currie, Miss J S (Sefton Metropolitan Borough Council) Southport *p472* 01704 533133

Currie, M J (Irwin Mitchell LLP) *Zj* Birmingham *p139* 0870 150 0100

Curry, D D (Daniel Curry & Co) *S1 E L K1 D1 N O G W C1 Zq Zl K4* Croydon *p205* 020 8680 2188

Curry, Ms G (Morgan Cole) Oxford *p344* 01865 262600

Curry, G P E (Stephens & Scown) *C1 B1 T1 A1 Zs Zd* Exeter *p222* 01392 210700

Curry, K (Maxwell Winward LLP) *C1 C2* London EC4 *p59* 020 7651 0000

Curry, L G (Curry Popeck) *S1 W T1 L E R1* London W1 *p24* 020 7224 6633

Curry, R K (Barr Ellison LLP) *N Q* Cambridge *p174* 01223 417200

Curtin, A J (Belshaw & Curtin) *L N* London SE5 *p11* 020 7708 3311

Curtin, R C (Faegre & Benson LLP) *B1* London EC4 *p30* 020 7450 4500

Curtis, A (Alan Curtis Solicitors) *N Q S1 W* Monmouth *p318* 01600 772288

Curtis, Mrs A (Birkett Long LLP) *I Ze* Chelmsford *p186* 01245 453800

Curtis, A (Land Registry - Gloucester Office) Gloucester *p459* 01452 511111

Curtis, D J (Hewitsons) *W T2 Zd* Cambridge *p174* 01223 461155

Curtis, D J (David Curtis & Co) *S1 W G E K1 N F1 Zc Zf* Leicester *p279* 0116 270 2402

Curtis, Miss E L (Bowcock & Pursaill) *S2 S1* Leek *p278* 01538 399199

Curtis, I (Warner Goodman LLP) Fareham *p224* 01329 288121

Curtis, I K (Chorley Borough Council) Chorley *p455* 01257 515151 Lytham *p464* 01253 658658

Curtis, Miss J (Sills & Betteridge LLP) Boston *p151* 01205 364615 Lincoln *p285* 01522 542211

Curtis, J A (SNR Denton) *E Zb* London EC4 *p75* 020 7242 1212

Curtis, J D G (Pemberton Greenish LLP) *W T2* London SW3 *p66* 020 7591 3333

Curtis, Miss K (Beviss & Beckingsale) Honiton *p252* 01404 548050

Curtis, L (Hopkin Murray Beskine) London N4 *p42* 020 7272 1234

Curtis, Mrs L (QualitySolicitors D'Angibau) *S1 T2* Poole *p353* 01202 708634

Curtis, Ms L F (Manchester City Council) Manchester *p465* 0161 234 5000

Curtis, M (Simmons & Simmons) London EC2 *p79* 020 7628 2020

Curtis, Ms M B (K&L Gates LLP) *E* London EC4 *p47* 020 7648 9000

Curtis, M G (Currey & Co) *S1 E A1* Westminster *p24* 020 7802 2700

Curtis, N (Penningtons) *Zr J1 K1 Q N* London EC2 *p66* 020 7457 3000

Curtis, Miss P (Blackburn & Co) *K1 Q D1* Thornton Cleveleys *p411* 01253 853101

Curtis, P E (Laytons) *C1* Manchester *p306* 0161 834 2100

Curtis, R (Letchers) *C1 E J1 L S1 S2* Ringwood *p364* 01425 471424

Curtis, Miss R E (Stone King LLP) *W T2 K4* Bath *p128* 01225 337599

Curtis, R M (ASB Law) *R1 O Q P Zc* Maidstone *p298* 01622 656500

Curtis, Miss S J (Stilwell & Harby) *W* Dover *p213* 01304 206850

Curtis, S M (Clifford Chance) London E14 *p20* 020 7006 1000

Curtis, S R (Curtis Davis Garrard) *O Za A3* Uxbridge *p417* 020 8734 2800

Curtis, Miss T A (Wortley Redmayne Kershaw) *S1 E* Chelmsford *p187* 01245 491122

Curtlin, Mrs H J (RTP Williams Limited) *A1 R1 S1 W* Haverfordwest *p244* 01437 762321

Curwen, D B (Kirby Sheppard) *E A1 S1 W T1 C1* Bristol *p163* 0845 840 0045

Curzon, A F (Bailey Wain & Curzon) *N O Q W Zl Zq* Stoke-on-Trent *p397* 01782 847934

Cusack, A J (Gill Akaster) *S2 E* Plymouth *p349* 01752 203500

Cusack, G J P (Williamson & Soden) *N Zm* Solihull *p383* 0121 733 8000

Cusack, P J (Patrick J Cusack & Co) *B1 C1 G H J1 L N Q R1 Zi Zk Zl Zm Zt Zv* Harrow *p241* 020 8863 3414

6

Cush, J W (RSPCA) Horsham *p461* 0870 010 1181

Cushion, Miss A (Olswang LLP) *B1 C1 Zb Ze Zf Zh* London WC1 *p64* 020 7067 3000

Cushion, G J S (Poppleston Allen) *Zl* Nottingham *p338* 0115 953 8500

Cuskin, Ms C A (Beale and Company Solicitors LLP) *Zc Zq* London WC2 *p11* 020 7240 3474

Cussell, R J (Chubb Bulleid) *T1 W S1 L E A1 R1 N Zd Zl* Wells *p425* 01749 836100

Cussen, Ms T J (Trobridges) *K1 K3* Plymouth *p350* 01752 664022

Cust, G (De La Rue PLC) Basingstoke *p448* 01256 605000

Custance, T N L (Fox Williams) *O Zq F2 Zj F1 P Ze* London EC2 *p33* 020 7628 2000

Custis, Mrs A J (Clarkson Wright & Jakes Ltd) *W T1 T2* Orpington *p341* 01689 887887

Cusworth, A (Linder Myers Solicitors) *W T2 K4 Zo Zd* Manchester *p306* 0844 984 6000

Cusworth, Miss A E (Oxley & Coward Solicitors LLP) *Q O J1 Zp L* Rotherham *p367* 01709 510999

Cusworth, R (Beaumont Legal) *C1 E P* Wakefield *p418* 0845 122 8100

Cusworth, Miss S L (Wilford Smith Solicitors) *G H* Rotherham *p367* 01709 828044

Cutbill, C D (Withers LLP) *C1 W Zo* London EC4 *p92* 020 7597 6000

Cutbill, D A (SAS Daniels LLP) *W* Macclesfield *p297* 01625 442100

Cuthbert, C K (Everys) *E G H J1 K1 L Q S1 W* Exeter *p221* 01392 477983

Cuthbert, G V (Cuthbert & Co) *K1 S1 N J1 Q V L G H J2 Zk Zl Zp Zq Zr* Peterborough *p347* 01733 564655

Cuthbert, Ms J (Tolhurst Fisher LLP) Chelmsford *p187* 01245 495111

Cuthbert, L (McCormacks) *G H B2 W Zm Zg* Basildon *p126* 01268 525999

Cuthbertson, Miss S (Susan Cuthbertson & Co) *K1* Ilkley *p261* 01943 602811 Ilkley *p261* 01943 889100

Cuthbertson, T P (Blackhams Solicitors) *S1 E W C1 T2 Zd Zm S2* Birmingham *p135* 0121 233 6900

Cutler, Ms H A (Bevis Rowntree) *W S1 E T2 L K4* Midhurst *p315* 01730 812201

Cutler, J C (Lloyds & Cooper) *A1 E S1 S2 W* Leominster *p283* 01568 613236

Cutler, K J (Hibberts LLP) *C1 C2 Ze* Nantwich *p320* 01270 624225

Cutler, M H R (Colemans Solicitors LLP) *S1 T2 W* Maidenhead *p298* 01628 631051

Cutler, M W (ASB Law) *M1 P* Maidstone *p298* 01622 656500

Cutmore, Ms C (Muckle LLP) *A3 Q Zc* Newcastle upon Tyne *p325* 0191 211 7777

Cutmore, S (Coles Miller Solicitors LLP) *Q O B1 N Zq W F1 Zc L Zj R1 C1 J1 Ze Zk* Poole *p352* 01202 673011

Cutting, D (South Yorks Joint Secretariat (Fire, Police, Pensions, Passenger Transport)) Barnsley *p448* 01226 772856

Cutting, Ms G (Rowberry Morris) *S1 S2* Reading *p361* 0118 958 5611

Cutting, M J (Linklaters LLP) London EC2 *p54* 020 7456 2000

Cuttle, M B (Cuttle & Co) *G H K1 D1 W Zt Zl Zj* Manchester *p302* 0161 835 2050

Cutts, D S (Weightmans LLP) *Zr N O Zj* Leicester *p281* 0116 253 9747

Cutts, Ms H K (Browne Jacobson LLP) *N Q* Nottingham *p336* 0115 976 6000

Cutts, Ms H V (Westminster City Council) London SW1 *p110* 020 7641 6000

Cutts, I J (Sykes Lee & Brydson) *K1 G D1 H Zk K3 Q*
York *p445* . . . 01904 529000
Cutts, Miss M (Stewarts Law LLP) *N*
Leeds *p277* . . . 0113 222 0022
Cutts, Ms M L (Bower & Bailey) *C1 S2 E R2 S1*
Swindon *p406* . . . 01793 610466
Cuxson, Mrs J M (Veale Wasbrough Vizards) *T2 W Zv*
London EC4 *p89* . . . 020 7405 1234
Czajka, A M (Roythornes LLP) *Zn S2 E*
Nottingham *p338* . . . 0115 948 4555
Czyzowski, J M (Collyer Bristow LLP)
London WC1 *p22* . . . 020 7242 7363

D

D'Agostino, J J G (Herbert Smith LLP)
London EC2 *p40* . . . 020 7374 8000
D'Aguilar, Ms L (Warner Goodman LLP)
Southampton *p387* . . . 023 8063 9311
D'Aloise, Ms D J (London Fire & Emergency Planning Authority)
London SE1 *p107* . . . 020 8555 1200
D'Ambrogio, P (Law Offices of Paul D'Ambrogio) *Zr K4 J1 N S1 W*
Chester *p190* . . . 0870 442 2654
D'Ambrosio, Ms C (Withers LLP) *E S1 Zc S2*
London EC4 *p92* . . . 020 7597 6000
D'Arcy, Miss A E (Hempsons) *N Q O Zr*
Harrogate *p240* . . . 01423 522331
D'Arcy, Miss L (Burtonwood Brewery PLC)
Warrington *p475* . . . 01902 711811
D'Arcy, P B (Blandy & Blandy) *N O L Q*
Reading *p360* . . . 0118 951 6800
D'Aubney-Abdullah, Miss F M (Fuglers) *S1 W Q C1 J1*
London W1 *p34* . . . 020 7323 6450
D'Costa, I (Sacker & Partners LLP) *Zo*
London EC2 *p76* . . . 020 7329 6699
D'Costa, P (Hill Dickinson LLP) *O B2 J1 Q B1 A3 Zp Zq M2 C1 F1*
London EC3 *p41* . . . 020 7283 9033
D'Costa, S (Healys LLP)
London EC4 *p39* . . . 020 7822 4000
D'este-Hoare, C (Howard Kennedy LLP) *C1*
London W1 *p48* . . . 020 7636 1616
D'Sa, O A (Oliver D'Sa Solicitors) *G H Zi*
Leicester *p279* . . . 0116 275 5549
D'Souza, Ms C (Cumberland Ellis Peirs) *E O Q R1 Zq*
London WC1 *p23* . . . 020 7242 0422
D'Souza, F E (John Smythe & Co)
Kingston upon Thames *p267* 020 8546 1390
Da Costa, A J (DLA Piper UK LLP) *C1 C2*
Leeds *p272* . . . 0870 011 1111
London EC2 *p24* . . . 0870 011 1111
Da Costa, J (Boys & Maughan) *K1*
Margate *p312* . . . 01843 234000
Da Costa, M (Bankside Law Ltd) *B2 G Zq*
London SE1 *p9* . . . 0844 745 4000
Da Costa, M A (Richard Freeman & Co) *E S2 S1 W R2*
Kensington & Chelsea *p34* . 020 7351 5151
da Silva, C J L (Harris da Silva)
Islington *p39* . . . 020 7713 0700
Da Silva, D (HCB Solicitors)
Solihull *p382* . . . 0121 705 2255
Da Silva, Ms L A F (Van Baaren & Wright) *S1*
Richmond upon Thames *p364* 020 8940 2525
Dabbs, Ms J K (Everys) *W V S1 T2 S2*
Taunton *p408* . . . 01823 337636
Dabby-Joory, G (Howard Kennedy LLP)
London W1 *p48* . . . 020 7636 1616
Dabek, Miss A (Anthony Collins Solicitors LLP) *J1*
Birmingham *p137* . . . 0121 200 3242
Daboh, Ms E A (Capsticks Solicitors LLP) *S2 E R2 S1*
London SW19 *p18* . . . 020 8780 2211
Daby, R (Jefferies Essex LLP) *X J1 J2 L O Q N*
Westcliff-on-Sea *p428* . . . 01702 332311
Dabydeen, R (Squire Sanders (UK) LLP)
London EC2 *p81* . . . 020 7655 1000
Dabydeen, R (Wedlake Bell LLP) *T1 T2*
London WC1 *p91* . . . 020 7395 3000
Dacam, P A (Hogan Lovells International LLP)
London EC1 *p42* . . . 020 7296 2000
Dace, N H (Buller Jeffries) *N J2 O Zr Zm Zj Q Zq*
Birmingham *p136* . . . 0121 212 2620
Dack, C (Chichester & District Magistrates Courts)
Chichester *p455* . . . 01243 817000
Dacre, Mrs L J (Livingstons) *G H K1*
Dalton-in-Furness *p206* . . . 01229 462126
Dad, S (Shazad H Dad Solicitors) *K1 N*
Bradford *p153* . . . 01274 731000
Dad, S (Nabarro LLP) *C1 Zu*
London WC1 *p63* . . . 020 7524 6000
Dadak, R E (Lewis Silkin LLP) *Zk Ze Zg Zw*
London EC4 *p53* . . . 020 7074 8000
Dadd, J (Thompsons (formerly Robin/Brian Thompson & Partners)) *N J2 J1 Zr Zw*
London SW19 *p87* . . . 020 8947 4163
Dadge, J W (Barlow Lyde & Gilbert LLP) *N Q*
Manchester *p301* . . . 0161 829 6400
Dadswell, Miss L (Penningtons)
Godalming *p231* . . . 01483 791800
Dadswell, P J (The Smith Partnership) *K1 K2*
Derby *p209* . . . 01332 225225
Daffern, R (Pinsent Masons LLP) *E R2 L*
Leeds *p276* . . . 0113 244 5000

Dagg, S M (Newcastle Upon Tyne City Council)
Newcastle upon Tyne *p466* . 0191 232 8520
Daghlian, J D (O'Melveny & Myers LLP)
London EC4 *p64* . . . 020 7088 0000
Dagley-Morris, J H (Pinkerton Leeke & Co) *F1 J1 K1 M1 N P Ze*
Cheltenham *p188* . . . 01242 237477
Dagnall, G J (DWF) *O Zk Zq*
Liverpool *p287* . . . 0151 907 3000
Dagnall, Ms J E (Mayer Brown International LLP)
London EC2 *p59* . . . 020 3130 3000
Dagnall, Ms V (Broudie Jackson Canter) *G H*
Liverpool *p286* . . . 0151 227 1429
Dagnell, A (Bevan Brittan LLP)
Birmingham *p135* . . . 0870 194 1000
Dagonnot, P (Fishburns) *M1 Zj M2 O Zq*
London EC3 *p32* . . . 020 7280 8888
Dahan-Bouchard, Miss P H M (Bouchard & Associates) *C1 S1 T2 T1 W Zv*
London SW6 *p14* . . . 020 7736 1823
Dahia, Miss H K (Taylor Wessing) *C1 C2*
London EC4 *p86* . . . 020 7300 7000
Dahil, B S (Heer Manak) *G H Zl B2 P Zg Zy*
Coventry *p200* . . . 024 7666 4000
Dahill, Mrs J (Wannop Fox Staffurth & Bray) *K1 D1 D2 K3*
Worthing *p442* . . . 01903 228200
Dahl-Nielsen, N F (Jackson Parton) *O Zj A3 Za*
London EC3 *p45* . . . 020 7702 0085
Dail, J (Rowberry Morris) *K1 D1 D2 K2 Zp*
Reading *p361* . . . 0118 958 5611
Dailly, A (Ashurst LLP)
London EC2 *p7* . . . 020 7638 1111
Daisley, Miss J D (Wragge & Co LLP)
London EC1 *p93* . . . 0870 903 1000
Daji, J A (West Yorkshire Passenger Transport Executive)
Leeds *p463* . . . 0113 251 7436
Daker, J H (Wilson Browne) *S1 W E M1 C1 K1 A1 T1*
Higham Ferrers *p250* . . . 01933 410000
Dakers, M J (Dakers Marriott Solicitors) *Zo C1 E W S2 S1 J1 P Zl R2 Zw T1 T2 B1*
Strood *p400* . . . 01634 813300
Dakers, S (Smith Sutcliffe) *K1 G N Q*
Burnley *p169* . . . 01282 426251
Dakers, T J (Dakers) *B1 C1 E G H L S1 V W Zc Zd Zl*
Brighton *p159* . . . 01273 571685
Dakin, Mrs C L (Underhill Langley & Wright) *A1 C1 O E S1 S2*
Wolverhampton *p438* . . . 01902 423431
Dakin, J E (Nabarro LLP)
London WC1 *p63* . . . 020 7524 6000
Dakin, Miss K (Farnworth Shaw) *N Q J1*
Colne *p198* . . . 01282 865885
Dakin, P J (Iain Nicholson & Co) *S1 C1 C2 L E W N O A1 F1 Zc*
Ponteland *p351* . . . 01661 823863
Dakin, S (Actons)
Nottingham *p335* . . . 0115 910 0200
Dalby, Miss C M (Hatchers Solicitors LLP) *N*
Shrewsbury *p379* . . . 01743 248545
Dalby, M (Holman Fenwick Willan)
London EC3 *p42* . . . 020 7264 8000
Dalby, W J (Gregg Latchams LLP) *O N J1 L B1 F1 C1*
Bristol *p162* . . . 0117 906 9400
Daldorph, M J (Hunters) *K1 K2 Q C1 O J1 Zv D1*
London WC2 *p44* . . . 020 7412 0050
Dale, A G (Pooley Dale & Co) *S1 L W E C1 B1 A1 J1*
Swindon *p406* . . . 01793 488848
Dale, Mrs B (Brooke Williams) *K1 W V*
York *p444* . . . 01904 677888
Dale, J D (Hibberts LLP) *T2 W*
Nantwich *p320* . . . 01270 624225
Dale, J I (Andrew Jackson) *J1 Zi*
Hull *p257* . . . 01482 325242
Dale, Miss J M (Raworths LLP) *E S1 L*
Harrogate *p240* . . . 01423 566666
Dale, J R G (Lee & Priestley LLP) *R2 S2*
Leeds *p275* . . . 0845 129 2300
Dale, M (Dale-Stevens LLP) *Za Zj O*
Felixstowe *p225* . . . 020 7929 2247
Dale, R A (Dale & Co Solicitors Lincoln) *J1 Zg F1 Zm*
Lincoln *p284* . . . 01522 513399
Dale, Ms S (Stephanie Dale & Co) *G H*
Hove *p254* . . . 01273 748333
Dale, Miss Z (Thomson & Bancks LLP) *K4 K1 T2 W*
Pershore *p346* . . . 01386 562000
Dale-Jones, R G L (Hill Dickinson LLP) *C1 Zo C2*
Liverpool *p288* . . . 0151 600 8000
Dale-Lace, Mrs C (Dale-Lace & Co) *S2 S1 W*
Beaconsfield *p129* . . . 01494 675269
Dales, Miss A V (Frearsons) *D1 K1 D2 K3*
Skegness *p380* . . . 01754 897600
Dales, Mrs T E (Harvey Ingram Borneos) *W*
Newport Pagnell *p329* . . . 01908 613545
Daley, B M (Wakefield Magistrates Court)
Wakefield *p474* . . . 01924 303746
Dalgarno, D I (McDermott Will & Emery UK LLP) *J1*
London EC2 *p56* . . . 020 7577 6900
Dalgarno, F (Dalgarno Solicitors) *N J1*
Warrington *p421* . . . 0870 444 1501
Dalgetty, Ms E (BWTLaw LLP) *W K4*
Epsom *p219* . . . 01372 725655
Cheam *p186* . . . 020 8642 8142

Dalkin, Miss J (Watson Burton LLP) *J1*
Newcastle upon Tyne *p327* . 0845 901 2100
Dallas, J A (SNR Denton) *Zn*
London EC4 *p75* . . . 020 7242 1212
Dalley, I C (LG Lawyers)
London SE1 *p50* . . . 020 7379 0000
Dallimore, R J (Gardner Dallimore) *K1 G H N Q O J1 F1 D1 Zl*
Hereford *p248* . . . 01432 263535
Dalling, S J (Anthony Collins Solicitors LLP) *J1*
Birmingham *p137* . . . 0121 200 3242
Dallman, T A (Dawson & Burgess with Bell Dallman & Co) *S1 M1 G H J1 N P W E*
Doncaster *p211* . . . 01302 834744
Dallow, Ms S E (Dickinson Dees) *B1*
Newcastle upon Tyne *p324* . 0191 279 9000
Dally, J (Goodman Ray) *D1 D2 K1*
Hackney *p36* . . . 020 7608 1227
Dally, P (Robin Simon LLP) *N P Zj*
Manchester *p309* . . . 0333 010 0000
Leeds *p277* . . . 0113 284 7000
Dally, P C (Bird & Bird LLP) *Zf C1*
London EC4 *p13* . . . 020 7415 6000
Dalowsky, P M (Walker & Co) *S1 S2 W E*
Rotherham *p367* . . . 01709 817112
Dalrymple, J A C (Grayson Willis Bennett) *G H B2*
Sheffield *p375* . . . 0114 290 9500
Dalton, A (Ben Hoare Bell & Co) *I G H K1 D1*
Sunderland *p401* . . . 0191 565 3112
Dalton, A J (The White Dalton Partnership) *Q N*
Leighton Buzzard *p282* . . . 0800 783 6191
Dalton, C (Mary Ward Legal Centre)
London WC1 *p110* . . . 020 7831 7079
Dalton, G W (Dalton & Hague) *S1 T1 W L A1 F1 J1*
Sedbergh *p373* . . . 01539 620365
Dalton, Ms J (Trowers & Hamlins)
London EC3 *p88* . . . 020 7423 8000
Dalton, Miss L J (Lancashire County Council)
Preston *p469* . . . 01772 254868
Dalton, M (Daltons Solicitors) *E C1 C2 R1 S1 L J1 A1 Zc*
Petersfield *p348* . . . 01730 262816
Dalton, M C (Martin C Dalton) *H G K1 N Q S1 Zt K3*
Horsham *p253* . . . 01403 266642
Dalton, P R (Chubb & Co) *A1 S2 E K3 K4 R2 T2 W*
Matlock *p313* . . . 01629 581252
Dalton, R S (Lupton Fawcett)
Leeds *p275* . . . 0113 280 2000
Daly, Miss B (Sayer Moore & Co) *E K4 J1 W S1*
London W3 *p77* . . . 020 8993 7571
Daly, G (The College of Law)
London WC1 *p105* . . . 0800 289997
Daly, J B (Crompton Halliwell) *G H*
Bury *p170* . . . 0161 797 9222
Daly, Miss J E (Glaisyers Solicitors LLP) *D1 K1*
Manchester *p304* . . . 0161 224 3311
Daly, J M (Chabra Cass & Co) *G H*
Brent *p19* . . . 020 8450 9833 / 8452 2200
Daly, Ms M (Lawrence Davies & Co) *G H*
Hammersmith & Fulham *p26* 020 7381 1171
Daly, M (Rowlinsons) *S2 E W S1*
Frodsham *p227* . . . 01928 735333
Daly, Ms P E (Newcastle Upon Tyne City Council) *D1 X J1*
Newcastle upon Tyne *p466* . 0191 232 8520
Daly, R T (Yorkshire Dales National Park Authority)
Leyburn *p463* 0870 166 6333 / 01969 652323
Daly, S (Dass Solicitors) *G K1 H*
Birmingham *p137* . . . 0121 248 4000
Daly, S N (Simon Daly Solicitors) *O B1 C1 C2 Zc F1*
Stockton-on-Tees *p396* . . . 01642 604074
Dalzell, M (Watson Burton LLP)
Leeds *p278* . . . 0845 901 2100
Dalziel, Ms C (Calderdale Metropolitan BC Corporate Services Directorate)
Halifax *p460* . . . 01422 357257
Damani, S B (Universal Music)
London W14 *p110* . . . 020 8910 5000
Damerell, Miss J M (Michelmores LLP) *E L Zh S2 R2*
Exeter *p221* . . . 01392 688688
Damia Diaz-Plaja, G (Simmons & Simmons)
London EC2 *p79* . . . 020 7628 2020
Damianou, Mrs R L (Wrigley Claydon) *K1 Q N D1 Zi*
Oldham *p341* . . . 0161 624 6811
Dammone, L (Squire Sanders (UK) LLP) *O L Zb*
Manchester *p310* . . . 0161 830 5000
Damon, J (Universal Pictures International Ltd)
London WC1 *p110* . . . 020 7079 6000
Danagher, D K J (National Grid PLC)
Warwick *p471* . . . 01926 653000
Danagher, Ms U M T (ASB Law) *K1 K2 K3*
Maidstone *p298* . . . 01622 656500
London WC2 *p60* . . . 020 7242 5905
Danaher, J (Streathers Solicitors LLP) *S1 S2 E*
London W1 *p84* . . . 020 7034 4200
Danaher, W J (Howells LLP) *G*
Barnsley *p124* . . . 01226 805190
Danby, M P (Maxwell Hodge Solicitors) *Zr N*
Maghull *p298* . . . 0151 526 7131
Danby, P A (Danby & Co) *A1 E L S1 W Zl*
Northampton *p331* . . . 01604 604573
Dance, Ms M (Cyril Morris Arkwright) *G H*
Bolton *p148* . . . 01204 535261
Dancer, Miss E K (Andersons Solicitors) *S1 E S2*
Nottingham *p335* . . . 0115 947 0641

Dancey, E J (Davitt Jones Bould) *E R1 O*
Taunton *p408* . . . 01823 279279
Dancey, Miss H P (Nestle UK Ltd)
Croydon *p456* . . . 020 8667 5260
Dando, G (Ramsdens Solicitors) *J1 Zw*
Huddersfield *p256* . . . 01484 821500
Dandridge, Ms N W (Thompsons (formerly Robin/Brian Thompson & Partners)) *J1 Zp*
Plymouth *p350* . . . 01752 675810
Dandy, Ms K H (Sacker & Partners LLP) *O Zo*
London EC2 *p76* . . . 020 7329 6699
Dandy, R I (WBW Solicitors) *F1 F2 Zh L Q O*
Exeter *p222* . . . 01392 202404
Daneshku, S (Lewis Silkin LLP) *O*
London EC4 *p53* . . . 020 7074 8000
Daneshmand, Mrs N (Fladgate LLP) *C1 C2*
London WC2 *p32* . . . 020 3036 7000
Danger, Ms G S (Tinklin Springall) *K1 Q O J1 N L F1 Zp Zl*
Beckenham *p129* . . . 020 8402 7222
Danher, Ms S C (Bennett Welch & Co)
London SE19 *p12* . . . 020 8670 6141
Daniel, A (Sheridans) *O Q G Zf*
London WC1 *p78* . . . 020 7079 0100
Daniel, B (Ford & Warren) *J1 J2 Zp*
Leeds *p273* . . . 0113 243 6601
Daniel, D (Russell Jones & Walker)
London WC2 *p74* . . . 020 7657 1555
Daniel, D N (Thomas Simon) *J1 G Zp Zg*
Cardiff *p181* . . . 029 2055 7200
Daniel, J (Simmons & Simmons)
London EC2 *p79* . . . 020 7628 2020
Daniel, K (Jeromes) *S1 W S2 K3 L D1 C1 E K4 K1 K2 O Q R1 A3*
Shanklin *p374* . . . 01983 862643
Daniel, Mrs L S (Leona Daniel) *D1 K1*
Hassocks *p243* . . . 01273 845024
Daniel, M R M (Daniel & Edwards) *W S1 T1 C1 Zd*
Ramsgate *p359* . . . 01843 594651
Daniel, P J (Boyes Turner) *E L B1*
Reading *p360* . . . 0118 959 7711
Daniel, R (Boyes Turner) *E*
Reading *p360* . . . 0118 959 7711
Daniel, R D (Roche Products Ltd)
Welwyn Garden City *p475* . . 01707 366000
Daniel, S J (Ward & Rider Limited) *K1*
Coventry *p201* . . . 024 7655 5400
Daniel, S W (Bridgend County Borough Council)
Bridgend *p451* . . . 01656 643643
Daniel, T H (Edwards Angell Palmer & Dodge)
London EC2 *p28* . . . 020 7583 4055
Daniel, T P C (Daniel and Harris) *S1 S2 W E*
Camden *p25* . . . 020 7625 0202
Daniel, W A (Thompson & Jackson) *Zl G H*
Plymouth *p350* . . . 01752 665037 / 221171
Danielian, M (Field Fisher Waterhouse LLP)
London EC3 *p31* . . . 020 7861 4000
Daniell, J P (Hardmans) *S1 W L E C1 T1 A1 K4 S2 T2 Zl*
Deal *p207* . . . 01304 373377
Daniell, Mrs V A (Gregg Latchams LLP)
Bristol *p162* . . . 0117 906 9400
Daniells, I C (Ashfords LLP) *O A3*
Exeter *p220* . . . 01392 337000
Daniels, A R (Levine Mellins Klarfeld) *O Q K1 N J1*
Stanmore *p394* . . . 020 8954 7474
Daniels, Mrs D E (Bird & Daniels) *C1 N P M1 E J1 W T1 F1 Ze Zf Zp*
Shipley *p378* . . . 01274 580999
Daniels, Miss G (Menneer Shuttleworth) *Q*
St Leonards-on-Sea *p392* . . . 01424 720044
Daniels, G H I (LDJ Solicitors) *K1 D1 H G V M1 J1 L P*
Hinckley *p250* . . . 01455 637030
Daniels, J (Steele Raymond) *E L Zh S2*
Bournemouth *p152* . . . 01202 294566
Daniels, J (Browne Jacobson LLP) *T1 W*
Nottingham *p336* . . . 0115 976 6000
Daniels, J G (DF Legal LLP) *C1 E N B1 Q S1 A1 O R1*
Tewkesbury *p410* . . . 01684 850750
Daniels, L (Forster Dean Ltd) *N*
Runcorn *p369* . . . 01928 590999
Daniels, Miss L J (Wolverhampton City Council) *Q L G V P Zn*
Wolverhampton *p477* . . . 01902 556556
Daniels, M J (Dickinson Manser) *E C1 J1 L*
Poole *p352* . . . 01202 673071
Daniels, M J (Heald Nickinson) *L S2 E*
Camberley *p173* . . . 01276 680000
Daniels, P A T (Russell Jones & Walker) *J1 Q Zp Zd Zg Zw*
London WC2 *p74* . . . 020 7657 1555
Daniels, P E (Stephens & Son LLP) *S2 E S1*
Chatham *p185* . . . 01634 811444
Daniels, Mrs R (Taylors) *B1 C1*
Manchester *p310* . . . 0844 800 0263
Daniels, Ms S (W R Joyce Solicitors LLP)
Cannock *p176* . . .
Daniels, Ms S J (Field Fisher Waterhouse LLP)
London EC3 *p31* . . . 020 7861 4000
Daniels, S J (Berg Legal) *S2 E L R2 S1*
Manchester *p301* . . . 0161 833 9211
Daniels, Miss S M (Purcell Parker) *G H*
Birmingham *p141* . . . 0121 236 9781
Danilunas, Ms M (Squire Sanders (UK) LLP) *O M1 M2 I C3 Ze Zf Zg*
London EC2 *p81* . . . 020 7655 1000
Danks, J (Russell-Cooke LLP) *G H Zw*
London WC1 *p74* . . . 020 7405 6566

See p634 for the Key to Work Categories

Danks, Miss M (Cotterhill Hitchman LLP) *N O Q W*
Sutton Coldfield *p403* 0121 323 1860

Dann, Miss E (Copeman Markham Solicitors) *G H*
Hull *p256* 01482 212979

Dann, Ms L M (Treasury Solicitors Department)
London WC2 *p110*. 020 7210 3000

Dann, P J (Bird & Bird LLP) *U1*
London EC4 *p13*. 020 7415 6000

Dannan, G R (Park Woodfine Heald Mellows LLP) *C1 E Ze*
Bedford *p130* 01234 400000

Dannan, Miss R S (Blake Lapthorn) *B1 O Q*
Chandlers Ford *p184* 023 8090 8090

Dannreuther, D I (Withers LLP) *C1 Zb*
London EC4 *p92*. 020 7597 6000

Danskin, D J C (EMW) *E S2*
Milton Keynes *p316* 0845 070 6000

Danter, T A (Dolmans) *N*
Cardiff *p178* 029 2034 5531

Danvers, A (GHP Legal) *S1 T2 W*
Llangollen *p292*. 01978 860313

Danziger, Ms V H (Capsticks Solicitors LLP) *Zr*
London SW19 *p18*. 020 8780 2211

Daodu, A (Thomas Andrew & Daodu Solicitors) *C1 O Q Za Zb Zi*
Westminster *p87*. 020 7224 9522

Daoud, F J (Lawrence & Co) *C2 G S1 Zi*
London W9 *p52* 020 7266 4333

Dapin, H L (Irwin Mitchell LLP) *S1 W*
Leeds *p274* 0870 150 0100

Daplyn, Ms E (Sacker & Partners LLP) *Zo*
London EC2 *p76*. 020 7329 6699

Dar, M Z (Dar & Co) *N*
Manchester *p303* 0161 225 3777

Dar, S (Khan Solicitors) *D1 D2 K1 K2 N V Zi Zp Zr*
Manchester *p306* 0161 256 2100

Darbhanga, Mrs S (Borough of Telford & Wrekin) *K1 M1 N P W L S1 F1*
Telford *p473*. 01952 380000

Darby, A G (Woolley Bevis Diplock)
Hove *p255*. 01273 722532

Darby, C J (Freeth Cartwright LLP) *O*
Leicester *p279*. 0116 248 1100
Nottingham *p337*. 0115 936 9369

Darby, J E (Darby & Darby) *S1 G E H D1 M1 R1 W K1 L Zl Zt*
Torquay *p412* 01803 313656

Darby, K R (Woolley Beardsleys & Bosworth) *S1 S2 W L*
Loughborough *p293* 01509 212266

Darby, M J (M J Darby & Co) *S1 M1 P F1 W K1 G C1 L E Zn Zj*
Halesowen *p237*. 0121 421 7933

Darby, Mrs M L (Bickley Wheatley & Co)
Birmingham *p135* 0121 377 6266

Darby, Mrs R K (Scott Fowler) *C1 S2 E L*
Northampton *p331*. 01604 750506

Darbyshire, Miss A (PolyGram Film Operations) *C1 C3 Zf Ze*
London W1 *p108* 020 7307 1300

Darbyshire, Mrs J M (Baches) *D1 K1 J1 F1 L V*
West Bromwich *p427* . 0121 553 3286 / 553 7076

Darbyshire, Miss K E (Labrums) *Q K1 N D1 V*
St Albans *p390* 01727 858807

Darbyshire, R W (W H Darbyshire & Son) *E S1 W T1 R1 L Zl V T2 S2*
Blackpool *p146* 01253 346646
Lytham *p296*. 01253 736134

Dard, S (Shoosmiths)
Milton Keynes *p317* . 0370 086 8300 / 01908 488300

Dare, Ms C (John Fowlers LLP Solicitors) *Zm*
Colchester *p197*. 01206 576151

Dare, H (Penningtons)
London EC2 *p66*. 020 7457 3000

Dare, Ms J (Ashurst LLP)
London EC2 *p7* 020 7638 1111

Dargan, Mrs T A (Curry Popeck) *K1*
London W1 *p24* 020 7224 6633

Dargan-Cole, Mrs A M (Rochdale Metropolitan Borough Council)
Rochdale *p470*. 01706 647474

Darios, J (Joseph Darios Solicitors) *N*
Southampton *p385*. 023 8023 7575

Dark, A P (Shakespeares) *J1*
Stratford-upon-Avon *p400* . 0845 630 8833

Dark, Mrs M R (Marie Dark Solicitors) *E F1 F2 K1 S1 S2 W K3 K4 L Q*
Chepstow *p189* 01291 621638

Darke, A J (Irwin Mitchell LLP) *N Zj*
Sheffield *p376* 0870 150 0100

Darkwah, Mrs A B (Mellor & Jackson) *S1 S2*
Royton *p368*. 0161 624 0387

Darlaston, G W E (Irwin Mitchell LLP) *N*
London EC1 *p45*. 0870 150 0100

Darley, M L (Skadden Arps Slate Meagher & Flom (UK) LLP)
London E14 *p80*. 020 7519 7000

Darling, Mrs J E (Hellawell & Co) *D1 E F1 K1 L S1 V N W*
Newbiggin-by-the-Sea *p322* . 01670 817223

Darling, M E (DAC Beachcroft) *C1 C2*
London EC4 *p24*. 020 7242 1011

Darlington, C J V (Darlington Hardcastles) *S1 S2 W L J1 F1 E C1 Zl R2*
Rickmansworth *p364*. 01923 774272

Darlington, J (Lyons Davidson)
Bristol *p163* 0117 904 6000

Darlington, M C (H L F Berry & Co) *Zx X S2 E Zd Q S1*
Failsworth *p223* 0161 681 4005

Darlington, Ms S (Linder Myers Solicitors)
Manchester *p306* 0844 984 6000

Darlow, D P (Fairbrother & Darlow) *D1 K1 Q N F1 G J1 H L W*
Bracknell *p153*. 01344 420808

Darlow, Ms T (Boodle Hatfield)
Westminster *p14*. 020 7629 7411

Darnell, J M (Weightmans LLP) *O Q L*
Liverpool *p291*. 0151 227 2601

Darnton, D (Osborne Clarke) *E R2*
Bristol *p164* 0117 917 3000

Darnton, J E (Bircham Dyson Bell) *K1 D1 S1*
Westminster *p13*. 020 7227 7000

Darr, W H (Cooke Painter Limited) *S1 W*
Knowle *p269*. 0117 977 7403

Darrall, J (Reynolds Porter Chamberlain LLP)
London E1 *p71* 020 3060 6000

Dart, A R (Brewer Harding & Rowe) *G H K1 D1 P M1 J1 L Zl*
Barnstaple *p125* 01271 342271

Dart, P R (Paul Finn Solicitors) *W T1 A1 S1 Zm*
Bude *p168*. 01288 356256

Darvill, D J (Bircham Dyson Bell)
Westminster *p13*. 020 7227 7000

Darvill, K E (Kenneth Elliott & Rowe) *R1 E P*
Romford *p366* 01708 757575

Darwin, A D (DLA Piper UK LLP)
London EC2 *p24*. 0870 011 1111

Darwin, Miss B S (Darwin Gray) *A3 B1 C1 J1 O Q*
Cardiff *p178* 029 2082 9100

Darwin, J F (Norrie Waite & Slater) *S1 M1 K1 P G W L J1 F1 T1*
Sheffield *p377*. 0114 276 6166

Darwin, Mrs S (Heptonstalls LLP) *Zr*
Goole *p231* 01405 765661

Darwish, D (Jameson & Hill) *Q L N Zq*
Hertford *p248* 01992 554881

Das, J (Dedicated Accident Solicitors) *Zr N C1*
Derby *p208* 01332 869286

Das, Ms S (Treasury Solicitors Department) *N*
London WC2 *p110*. 020 7210 3000

Das, Miss S (Atherton Godfrey) *J1 O*
Doncaster *p211* 01302 320621

Dasent, Mrs S M (North Devon District Council)
Barnstaple *p448*. 01271 327711
Cardiff *p453* 029 2082 8681

Dasgupta, Ms D (Birnberg Peirce & Partners) *Zg Zp*
Camden *p13*. 020 7911 0166

Dass, A (Dass Solicitors) *O B1 Q J1 M2 Zj*
Birmingham *p137* 0121 248 4000

Dass, D (Premier Solicitors)
Bedford *p130* 01234 358080

Dathi, S (Royds LLP) *K1 K2 D1 K3*
London EC4 *p74*. 020 7583 2222

Dattani, M (Links Legal)
Ilford *p260*. 020 8551 0999

Dattani, Ms S (The Beavis Partnership) *Q J1 Zl F1 B1 N*
Chelmsford *p186*. 01245 264748

Daughtrey, G W (Cooper Burnett) *K1 P D1 V J1*
Tunbridge Wells *p415* 01892 515022

Daultrey, Miss E (Marsden Rawsthorn LLP) *K3 D1 K1 D2 K2*
Preston *p357* 01772 799600

Daultrey, S R (LSG Solicitors) *C1 C2 Zw T1 M2*
London W1 *p51* 020 7851 0100

Dauncey, R O (Anthony Collins Solicitors LLP) *C1 E*
Birmingham *p137* 0121 200 3242

Dauncey, Ms S A (Avon & Somerset Constabulary)
Portishead *p469* 01275 816270

Dautlich, Ms E (Holman Fenwick Willan)
London EC3 *p42*. 020 7264 8000

Dautlich, M C (Olswang LLP) *Ze O M2 L Zf*
London WC1 *p64* 020 7067 3000

Davage, J (Lockett Loveday McMahon) *Zb B1 C1 C2*
Manchester *p307* 0161 237 3627

Davenport, Ms B M (Lewis Silkin LLP) *E C1*
London EC4 *p53*. 020 7074 8000

Davenport, Mrs E (Gepp & Sons) *G H*
Chelmsford *p186*. 01245 493939
Colchester *p197* 01206 369889

Davenport, Ms E M (Leeds City Council)
Leeds *p462* 0113 224 3513

Davenport, Mrs H (Cullimore Dutton) *W K4 S1*
Chester *p190* 01244 356789

Davenport, J A (Jeremy Davenport) *S1 W E A1*
Hockley *p251* 01702 205163

Davenport, Miss J N S (Mills & Reeve) *Zc*
Cambridge *p175*. 01223 364422

Davenport, Ms K (Field Fisher Waterhouse LLP)
London EC3 *p31*. 020 7861 4000

Davenport, N C (Davenport & Scott) *S1 S2 W A1 Zi*
Ambleside *p117* 01539 431919

Davenport, N F (Turner Parkinson) *C1 C2 A3*
Manchester *p310* 0161 833 1212

Davenport, Mrs R (PCB Solicitors LLP) *Q N G H F1 J1 V*
Shrewsbury *p379* 01743 248148

Davenport, S C (South Yorkshire Passenger Transport Executive)
Sheffield *p471* 0114 276 7575

Davenport, Mrs S F (MacDonald Oates LLP) *S1 S2 W*
Petersfield *p348* 01730 268211

Davenport, T J P (Charles Crookes with George Tudor & de Winton) *A1 S1 W X Zd Zx*
Brecon *p156*. 01874 625151

Davern, Miss C (IBB Solicitors) *D1*
Uxbridge *p417*. 0845 638 1381

Davey, A C (Abensons) *S1 J1 W C1 E L R1 F1 G M1 Zl Zd Zt*
Liverpool *p285*. 0151 733 3111

Davey, Mrs A K (Spelthorne Borough Council)
Staines *p472*. 01784 451499

Davey, Ms C (Howells LLP) *G H*
Sheffield *p376* 0114 249 6666

Davey, Miss C E (Jobling & Knape) *C1 S2 E Zza J1 O C2 R1 R2 S1 T1*
Lancaster *p269* 01524 598300

Davey, Ms C F (Stevens & Bolton) *R1 P E S1 Zs*
Guildford *p237*. 01483 302264

Davey, F R (Royds LLP) *S1*
Morden *p318* 020 8542 1067

Davey, J H (Herbert Smith LLP) *C1*
London EC2 *p40*. 020 7374 8000

Davey, J W (Addleshaw Goddard)
Manchester *p300* 0161 934 6000

Davey, Miss K M (Pritchard Joyce & Hinds) *S2 E S1*
Beckenham *p129* 020 8658 3922

Davey, Ms M (John Boyle & Co)
Truro *p414*. 01872 272356

Davey, Ms M J (Davies Parsons Allchurch) *G H K1 L M1 P S1 W F1 V Zh Zl*
Llanelli *p292*. 01554 749144

Davey, M P K (First Assist)
Sutton *p473* 020 8652 1313

Davey, P C (Burges Salmon) *C1 C2*
Bristol *p161* 0117 939 2000

Davey, R (Kitsons LLP)
Torquay *p413* 01803 202020

Davey, S R (Network Rail)
London NW1 *p108*. 020 7557 8000

Davey, Mrs V L (Gordons LLP) *S1 S2 R2 E*
Leeds *p273* 0113 227 0100

Davey-Holpin, Ms S (John Morley & Co) *B1 E K4 J1 K1 Q Zo V W N Zr S1*
Rainham *p359*. 01634 375444

David, Mrs D C (Howell-Jones LLP) *N Q Zr*
Kingston upon Thames *p267*. 020 8549 5186
Walton-on-Thames *p420*. . 01932 234500

David, I S (DWFM Beckman) *Ze Zf Zk*
Westminster *p25*. 020 7872 0023

David, J R O (David & Snape) *G H K1 N*
Bridgend *p157*. 01656 661115

David, Mrs P G (Roy Thomas Begley & Co) *K1 D1*
Swansea *p404*. . . .01792 643797 / 643798
Maesteg *p298* 01656 732911

David, R R (Dolmans) *E R2 R1 Zc*
Cardiff *p178* 029 2034 5531

Davidian, G (EMW) *Zb C1 M2 C2*
London WC2 *p28* 0845 070 6000

Davidoff, P D (B P Collins LLP) *W T2 K4 Zm*
Gerrards Cross *p229*. 01753 889995

Davidovski, Ms M (Salans)
London EC4 *p76*. 020 7429 6000

Davidson, A (National Grid PLC) *N G Q L H B1 W*
Warwick *p471* 01926 653000

Davidson, A (Lupton Fawcett) *X J1 J2 Q N*
Leeds *p275* 0113 280 2000

Davidson, A G F (Knights Solicitors LLP) *O Q J1 B1*
Newcastle under Lyme *p323*. 01782 619225

Davidson, A J (AWB Charlesworth LLP) *N O L J1 F1 F2 Q G*
Skipton *p381*. 01756 793333

Davidson, Ms B (Hewitts)
Bishop Auckland *p144* 01388 604691

Davidson, B H (Gregory Abrams Davidson LLP) *E S1 C1 L B1 W T1 Zo Ze Zc*
Liverpool *p288*. 0151 236 5000

Davidson, C J (Isherwood & Hose) *G N H Q*
Heywood *p249*. . . .01706 360032 / 368741

Davidson, Ms D E (Farrer & Co LLP)
London WC2 *p31* 020 3375 7000

Davidson, D M (Charles Russell LLP) *K1*
London EC4 *p19*. 020 7203 5000

Davidson, Miss F L (Weightmans LLP) *D1 D2 K1*
Liverpool *p291*. 0151 227 2601

Davidson, Miss G (Mitsubishi Securities International PLC)
London EC2 *p108* 020 7577 2804

Davidson, G C (Morecrofts Solicitors LLP) *C1 C2 C3 E L S1 S2 T1 T2*
Liverpool *p290*. 0151 236 8871

Davidson, G L (Spicketts Battrick Law Practice) *N*
Cardiff *p181* 029 2046 1480

Davidson, Mrs G M (Skipton Building Society)
Skipton *p471*. 01756 705000

Davidson, G R G (Hill Dickinson LLP) *N O E Q*
Manchester *p305* 0161 817 7200

Davidson, G W I (Maclay Murray & Spens LLP) *C1 C2 Zo*
London EC2 *p57*. 020 7002 8500

Davidson, Miss H (Land Law LLP) *E*
Altrincham *p116* 0161 928 8383

Davidson, J (Crown Packaging UK PLC)
Wantage *p475*. 01235 402611

Davidson, J (Andrew & Co LLP) *A1 E S1 T2*
Lincoln *p284*. 01522 512123

Davidson, J G (Quality Solicitors Jackson & Canter) *L*
Liverpool *p290*. 0151 282 1700

Davidson, J J S (Davidson Merali & Co) *B1 D1 F1 J1 K1 L M1 N P A1 Ze Zk Zm*
London W8 *p26* 020 7937 2525

Davidson, Ms J S (Potter Rees (Serious Injury) Solicitors)
Manchester *p309* 0161 237 5888

Davidson, K (Environmental Law Consultancy)
Manchester *p304* 0845 860 0595

Davidson, Ms L (Switalski's)
Wakefield *p419* 01924 882000

Davidson, M M (Davidson Broadbent & Co) *C1 E S1*
Harrogate *p240* 01423 561229

Davidson, R (Davidson & Co) *J1 Q O C1 F1*
Edgware *p217*. 020 8951 5656

Davidson, R (Ashurst LLP)
London EC2 *p7* 020 7638 1111

Davidson, R M (Davidson Large LLP) *E L R1 S1 A1 C2 Zl*
Harrogate *p240* 01423 727272

Davidson, Mrs R W (Roberta Davidson) *S1*
Surbiton *p402* 020 8399 6704

Davidson, S B (Davis Davidson) *A1 J1 K1 N O P Q S1*
Beverley *p131*. 01482 881278

Davidson, Mrs S J (Squire Sanders (UK) LLP)
London EC2 *p81*. 020 7655 1000

Davidson, Miss S L (BUPA)
London WC1 *p104*. 020 7656 2305

Davidson, Ms S P (Morecrofts Solicitors LLP)
Birkenhead *p134*. 0151 666 2210

Davidson, S R (Sheldon Davidson Solicitors) *N S1 W L*
Whitefield *p430* 0161 796 5445

6

Davidson Lund, D (DWF) *Zq N O Zj*
Manchester *p303* 0161 603 5000

Davidson-Smith, Mrs M A (Davidson Smith & Co) *K1 D1 Q N F1 B1 J1 V C1*
Bedford *p130* 01234 351971

Davie, F P (DLA Piper UK LLP) *O A3 B2*
Birmingham *p137* 0870 011 1111

Davie, G P (Shakespeares) *C2 C1*
Birmingham *p142* 0121 237 3000

Davies, A (Linklaters LLP)
London EC2 *p54*. 020 7456 2000

Davies, Ms A (Forsters LLP) *T2*
Westminster *p33*. 020 7863 8333

Davies, Ms A (Steeles) *J1*
Norwich *p335* 0870 609 0200

Davies, A (DLA Piper UK LLP)
Leeds *p272* 0870 011 1111

Davies, Ms A (Lamb Brooks LLP) *K1 D1*
Basingstoke *p126* 01256 844888

Davies, Miss A (GHP Legal)
Wrexham *p442* 01978 291456

Davies, A B (Graeme John Solicitors) *D2 S1 S2 W*
Aberdare *p113*. 01685 878563

Davies, A B C (V J G Johns & Son) *W S1 K1 A1 G Zm Zv*
Fishguard *p226* 01348 873671

Davies, Ms A C (Thompson Smith & Puxon) *K1*
Colchester *p198* 01206 574431

Davies, Ms A C (Crowell & Moring) *J2 F2 N*
London EC4 *p23*. 020 7413 0011

Davies, Ms A C (Cartmell Shepherd)
Carlisle *p182*. 01228 516666

Davies, Mrs A D (Smith Llewelyn Partnership) *N O Q*
Swansea *p405*. 01792 464444

Davies, A D (Thompsons (formerly Robin/Brian Thompson & Partners))
Liverpool *p290*. 0151 224 1600
London SW19 *p87*. 020 8947 4163

Davies, Mrs A E C (T R Evans Hughes & Co) *A1 L S1 T1 W*
Holyhead *p251*. 01407 762204

Davies, A G (Pitmans LLP) *E*
Reading *p361* 0118 958 0224

Davies, Miss A H (Foys Solicitors) *K1 D1 P M1 G H J1 L D2 S1 W*
Sheffield *p375* 0114 246 7609

Davies, A I (Gateley LLP) *E L*
Birmingham *p138* 0121 234 0000

Davies, Ms A J (Mills & Reeve) *E R2*
Cambridge *p175*. 01223 364422

Davies, A J (Thanet District Council)
Margate *p465* 01843 577000

Davies, Miss A J (Walker Smith Way) *N*
Chester *p191* 0844 346 3100

Davies, A J (Gomer Williams & Co) *G K1 H N D1 F1 S1 P J1 W Zt Zi*
Llanelli *p292*. 01554 755101

Davies, Miss A J (Sternberg Reed) *G H*
Romford *p366* 01708 766155

Davies, A K (Hugh James) *N Zr*
Cardiff *p179* 029 2022 4871

Davies, Miss A L (Simpson Millar LLP) *N Zq*
London EC1 *p80*. 0844 858 3400

Davies, A M (Gabb & Co) *E S1 W L R1 N A1*
Abergavenny *p113*. 01873 852432

Davies, A M (Richard George & Jenkins) *K1 G H M1 P D1 J1 A1 B1 Zc Zj Zm N*
Newtown *p330*. 01686 626210

Davies, Mrs A M (A M Davies) *O A3 Zq Q C1 L*
Harrogate *p240* 01423 772860

Davies, A M (Davies Parsons Allchurch) *A1 B1 C1 D1 E F1 G H J1 K1 Ze Zf Zg*
Llanelli *p292*. 01554 749144

Davies, A M (Spencer Davies) *S1 S2 N Q O K1 W Zl Zq J1 G F1 P H*
Grassington *p232* 01756 753015

Davies, A P C (Metcalfe Copeman & Pettefar) *S1 S2 A1 L E*
Thetford *p410* 01842 756100

Davies, A R (DWF)
Liverpool *p287*. 0151 907 3000

Davies, Ms B (Chesterfield Borough Council)
Chesterfield *p455* 01246 345345

Davies, B (Prince Evans)
Ealing *p69*. 020 8567 3477

Davies, B (Alletsons Ltd) *G H L K1 V*
Bridgwater *p157*. 01278 456621

Davies, B (Hertz Europe Ltd)
Hounslow *p461* 01895 553500

Davies, B C (Flintshire County Council)
Mold *p466*. 01352 702411

Davies, B K (Hanney Dawkins & Jones) *E S1 W*
Pinner *p348* 020 8866 2144

Davies, Mrs B M D M (Bevis Rowntree) *S1 E W*
Midhurst *p315*. 01730 812201

Davies, Mrs C (Michelmores LLP) *W K4*
Exeter *p221* 01392 688688

Davies, Ms C (Jones Day) *O*
London EC4 *p46*. 020 7039 5959

Davies, C (Pearson Maddin Solicitors) *E S1 L*
New Malden *p321* 020 8949 9500

Davies, Miss C (Smith Llewelyn Partnership) *K1 K3 D2*
Swansea *p405*. 01792 464444

Davies, C (Linder Myers Solicitors) *D1 K1*
Manchester *p306* 0844 984 6000

Davies, C (Pickerings LLP) *C1 C2*
Tamworth *p407* 01827 317070

Davies, C A (Nicholls Henstock & Stevenson)
Altrincham *p117* 0161 980 6099

Davies, Mrs C E (City of Bradford Metropolitan District Council) *D1 Zm*
Bradford *p451*. 01274 752236

Davies, Ms C E (Thompsons (formerly Robin/Brian Thompson & Partners)) *N J1 V K1*
Plymouth *p350*. 01752 675810

Davies, Miss C E (Ince & Co Services Ltd) *N Q O Zq Zj Zr*
London E1 *p44* 020 7481 0010

Davies, Ms C E (Ben Hoare Bell & Co) *K1 D1*
Newcastle upon Tyne *p323* . 0191 275 2626

Davies, C G (Sheehans Solicitors) *D1 K1 N Q W Zq*
Neath *p320* 01639 630844
Port Talbot *p353*. 01639 883237

Davies, Miss C J (Treasury Solicitors Department)
London WC2 *p110*. 020 7210 3000

Davies, C J (Boyes Sutton & Perry) *S1 E C1 W*
Barnet *p123* 020 8449 9155

Davies, C J D (Clifford Chance)
London E14 *p20*. 020 7006 1000

Davies, C L (Gartsides) *G H S2 C1 S1*
Abergavenny *p113*. 01873 857555
Newport *p328* 01633 213411

Davies, Miss C M (Davies & Partners) *R1 S2*
Gloucester *p230*. 01452 612345

Davies, Miss C M (Levi Solicitors LLP) *W*
Leeds *p275* 0113 244 9931

Davies, Miss C M (Equality & Human Rights Commission) *J1*
Manchester *p464* 0161 829 8100

Davies, Mrs C R (Charles Lucas & Marshall) *W K4 T2*
Hungerford *p258*. 01488 682506

Davies, C R (Rubin Lewis O'Brien) *S1 G H W E L C1 M1 P*
Cwmbran *p206* 01633 867000

Davies, Ms C S (W Davies) *S2 E R2 S1*
Woking *p436*. 01483 744900

Davies, C W (John Collins & Partners LLP) *C1 E*
Swansea *p405*. 01792 773773

Davies, C W (Whitehead Monckton) *O Q*
Maidstone *p299* 01622 698000

Davies, Ms D (Wilson Davies & Co)
Harlow *p239*. 01279 426486

Davies, Mrs D (Woodfines LLP) *E S2 W S1 Zd*
Cambridge *p176*. 01223 411421

Davies, D C S (Sanders & Co) *S1 E W L P*
Rainham *p359*. 0844 353 3553

Davies, Mrs D E (Key2Law LLP) *S1*
Ewell *p222*. 020 8393 0941

Davies, D G (Society of Lloyd's)
London EC3 *p107* 020 7327 1000

Davies, D J (Davies & Co) *K1 D1 D2*
Bromley *p166* 020 8460 6668

Davies, Mrs D J (Hancocks) *K1 W D1*
Banbury *p122* 01295 253211

Davies, Mrs D J (Solihull Metropolitan Borough Council)
Solihull *p471*. 0121 704 6000

Davies, D L R (David L R Davies & Co) *A1 C1 E F1 K1 L M1 P S1 W Zc Zk*
Ammanford *p117*. . .01269 593463 / 592119

Davies, D M (Howard Kennedy LLP) *C1 M2*
London W1 *p48* 020 7636 1616

Davies, D M (Flintshire County Council)
Mold *p466*. 01352 702411

Davies, D M (Morton Pugh Welch) *C1 E S1 W S2*
London EC2 *p62*. 020 7374 4141

Davies, D P E (HSR Law (Hayes, Son & Richmond)) *K1 D1 K2*
Doncaster *p211* 01302 347800
Gainsborough *p228* 01427 613831

Davies, Ms E (Bridgend County Borough Council)
Bridgend *p451*. 01656 643643

Davies, Ms E (Keoghs LLP) *N Zj O Q*
Bolton *p149* 01204 677000
Coventry *p200*. 024 7665 8200

Davies, Mrs E (CB4law) *K1*
Cambridge *p174*. 01223 316666

Davies, Ms E (Taylor Wessing)
London EC4 *p86*. 020 7300 7000

Davies, Ms E (Osborne Clarke) *J1*
London EC2 *p65*. 020 7105 7000

Davies, Miss E A (The Woodland Davies Partnership LLP) *A1 A2 S1 W S2*
Hay-on-Wye *p245* 01497 820406
Kington *p268* 01544 230841
Talgarth *p407* 01874 711744

Davies, Ms E A (Hewitsons) *C1 C2*
Cambridge *p174*. 01223 461155

Davies, Mrs E E (Manches LLP) *O Q Zh Zl L E*
Oxford *p343* 01865 722106

Davies, E L (JNP Legal) *K1 F1 M1 S1 J1 P L Zi Zp Zl*
Merthyr Tydfil *p314* 01685 350421

Davies, Miss E M (Brunton & Co) *S1 K1 W D1 N J1 L*
Machynlleth *p298* . .01654 703110 / 703121

Davies, Mrs E M (Gough Davies) *D1 E F1 G H J1 K1 L N Q*
Bargoed *p123* 01443 839393

Davies, E P (Dickinson Dees) *E S1 W L Zh*
Newcastle upon Tyne *p324* . 0191 279 9000

Davies, E P (Lawrence Davies & Co) *G H K1 D1 D2 K3*
Hammersmith & Fulham *p26*. 020 7381 1171

Davies, E R (Pinsent Masons LLP) *Zc*
Manchester *p308* 0161 234 8234

Davies, Ms E R (Brinley Morris Rees & Jones)
Llanelli *p292*. 01554 774241

Davies, E T (Olswang LLP) *O Q P Zd Ze Zf Zw*
London WC1 *p64* 020 7067 3000

Davies, E W F (Price & Kelway) *S1 L A1 C1 R1 E W Zo Zv*
Milford Haven *p316* 01646 695311

Davies, Ms F R (Gordons LLP)
Leeds *p273* 0113 227 0100

Davies, G (Herbert Smith LLP) *C2*
London EC2 *p40*. 020 7374 8000

Davies, Mrs G (Davies Sully Wilkins) *F1 F2 J1 J2 L N O Zr*
Caerphilly *p172* 029 2088 7828

Davies, G (Wright Hassall LLP) *A1 S2 S1*
Leamington Spa *p270* 01926 886688

Davies, G (Davies Battersby Ltd) *Q Za*
London EC3 *p26*. 020 7621 1090

Davies, G (Reynolds Porter Chamberlain LLP)
London E1 *p71* 020 3060 6000

Davies, Miss G (Walker Morris) *O R1*
Leeds *p277* 0113 283 2500

Davies, G A B (Llewellyn Jones & Co) *A1 C1 E S1*
Mold *p318*. 01352 755305

Davies, G d M (Nicholas Morris) *E S1 O R1 W Q Zk*
London W11 *p62*. 020 7792 0890

Davies, G E (Tudur Owen Roberts Glynne & Co) *K1 D1 N S1 G P F1 H W V*
Bangor *p122*. . . .01248 362315 / 355826
Caernarfon *p172*. . .01286 672207 / 672851

Davies, G H (Bone & Payne LLP) *A1 C1 E F1 L S1*
Colwyn Bay *p198* 01492 532385

Davies, G J (T R Harris Arnold & Co) *Q L N F1 Zq S1*
Gorseinon *p231* . . .01792 892166 / 891331

Davies, G K (Howes Percival LLP)
Leicester *p280*. 0116 247 3500

Davies, G L S (Patchell Davies (Trading Name of PD Law Ltd)) *K1 N Q O W G L H V F1 Zf Zk Zo*
Blackwood *p147*. 01495 227128

Davies, G R (Lewis Silkin LLP) *C1 C2 C3 J1 Ze Zv*
London EC4 *p53*. 020 7074 8000

Davies, G R (Geldards LLP) *E S2*
Cardiff *p178* 029 2023 8239

Davies, G R (Gaskell & Walker) *S1 G L H K1 W Zl*
Bridgend *p157*. 01656 653122

Davies, G W (Martin-Kaye LLP) *O Zq*
Telford *p409*. 01952 272222

Davies, Mrs H (Peters Langsford Davies) *F2 S1 S2 P*
Launceston *p270* 01566 772451

Davies, H (Howell Jones & Co) *S1 S2 G O W A1 H J1 Zc Zl*
Abergele *p113*. . . .01745 826282 / 825845
Llanrwst *p292* 01492 640277

Davies, H (Martyn Prowel) *N Q O F1 J1*
Cardiff *p180* 029 2047 0909

Davies, Mrs H A (Cheryl Lewis & Co) *S1 E W L C1 J1 F1 Zl Zd*
Birkenhead *p134*. 0151 652 1451

Davies, H E (Walker Smith Way) *E A1 R2 S2*
Chester *p191* 0844 346 3100

Davies, H G (Kendall & Davies) *A1 E L S1 S2*
Burford *p168*. 01993 822025

Davies, H L L (Hywel Davies & Co) *S1 Q K1 G C1 A1 F1 W H L Zd*
Bala *p121* 01678 520307

Davies, Miss H M (Pritchard Edwards & Co) *K1 D1 K3*
Carmarthen *p182* 01267 234022

Davies, H R A F (Simpson Millar LLP) *M1 N P*
London EC1 *p80*. 0844 858 3400

Davies, I (Lyons Davidson)
Cardiff *p179* 029 2030 3710
Solihull *p382*. 0121 683 8310

Davies, I (Mogers)
Bath *p127* 01225 750000

Davies, I (Conwy County Borough Council)
Conwy *p455* 01492 576108

Davies, I G H (Neath Port Talbot County Borough Council)
Port Talbot *p469*. 01639 763333

Davies, I M (Poole Townsend) *W S1*
Grange-over-Sands *p232* . . 01539 533316

Davies, I M (Iwan Davies & Co) *G H C1 D1 F1 J1 M1 P V K1 Zl Zm*
Pontypridd *p352*. 01443 485566

Davies, J (Wilkinson & Butler)
St Neots *p392*. 01480 219229

Davies, Miss J (Tayntons LLP Solicitors) *S1 W*
Gloucester *p230*. 01452 522047

Davies, Mrs J (Calvert Smith & Sutcliffe) *S1 E R1 A1 C1 W*
Richmond upon Thames *p364* 020 8940 0017

Davies, Mrs J (Marchant Harries & Co) *G H J1 N Q F1 V Zl*
Mountain Ash *p319* 01443 476444

Davies, J (Mullis & Peake) *W T2*
Romford *p366*. 01708 784000

Davies, Mrs J (Mowbray Woodwards Solicitors) *K1*
Bath *p128* 01225 485700

Davies, Miss J (Veale Wasbrough Vizards) *J1 Zp*
Bristol *p165* 0117 925 2020

Davies, J A (Harding Evans LLP) *G H*
Newport *p328* 01633 244233

Davies, J A (Teacher Stern LLP) *O Q Zf Zw*
London WC1 *p86* 020 7242 3191

Davies, J B (Lewis Silkin LLP) *J1*
London EC4 *p53*. 020 7074 8000

Davies, J B (GH Cornish LLP)
Ilford *p260*. 020 8090 0800

Davies, J C (K&L Gates LLP)
London EC4 *p47*. 020 7648 9000

Davies, Miss J C (Cameron Jones Hussell & Howe) *D1*
Port Talbot *p353*. 01639 885261

Davies, J C M (DWF) *C1 Zl*
Liverpool *p287*. 0151 907 3000
Manchester *p303* 0161 603 5000

Davies, J D C (Rhondda Cynon Taff County Borough Council) *L R1 S1*
Pentre *p468* 01443 424300

Davies, Mrs J E (Wigan Borough Council) *X Q J1*
Wigan *p476* 01942 244991

Davies, Mrs J E (Booth Ince & Knowles) *R1 S1 W K4*
Hyde *p259*. 0161 368 2134

Davies, J E (Davies Ingram & Harvey) *W S1 E C1*
Swansea *p405*. 01792 653764

Davies, J E J (Linklaters LLP)
London EC2 *p54*. 020 7456 2000

Davies, Mrs J F (Pembrokeshire County Council)
Haverfordwest *p460* 01437 764551

Davies, J H (Jeremy Davies & Co)
London SW7 *p26* 020 7589 4999

Davies, J J (Fruhman Davies Livingstones) *B1 C1 E F1 J1 K1 M1 R1 S1 W Zi Zj Zo*
Manchester *p304* 0161 833 0578

Davies, J K E (Field Seymour Parkes) *K1*
Reading *p360* 0118 951 6200

Davies, Mrs J L (Bird & Co) *W*
Newark *p322* 01636 650880

Davies, J L (Bromleys Solicitors LLP) *D1 K1 D2*
Ashton-under-Lyne *p120*. . . 0161 330 6821

Davies, J L (J A Hughes) *S1 K1 L N Q W E G H Zl Zv*
Penarth *p345* 029 2070 2449

Davies, Ms J M (Garnett Williams Powell) *K1 S1 W*
Rhyl *p363* 01745 334658

Davies, J M (Pattinson & Brewer) *C1 S1*
London WC1 *p66* 020 7400 5100

Davies, J M (Reynolds Porter Chamberlain LLP) *O Zj Zo Zq*
London E1 *p71* 020 3060 6000

Davies, J N C (Edwin Coe LLP) *E S2 S1 R2 L*
London WC2 *p29* 020 7691 4000

Davies, J N W (Lamb & Holmes) *E C1 S1 L J1*
Corby *p199* 01536 745168

Davies, J P (Milne Moser) *S1 W T1 A1 S2*
Kendal *p264*. . . . .01539 729786 / 725582

Davies, J P (Memery Crystal) *C1 C2 T1 W*
London WC2 *p60* 020 7242 5905

Davies, J R (Vincent Sykes & Higham LLP) *C1 I O Q J1 Ze*
Thrapston *p411* 01832 732161

Davies, J W (Chorley Borough Council)
Chorley *p455* 01257 515151

Davies, J W (Simmons & Simmons)
London EC2 *p79*. 020 7628 2020

Davies, J W H (Davies Murray-White & Co) *B1 C1 E J1 L R1 A1 S1 S2 W*
Stratford-upon-Avon *p400* . . 01789 295544

Davies, J W R (Laytons) *J1 Zi*
London EC4 *p52*. 020 7842 8000

Davies, Mrs K (Everys) *W*
Honiton *p252* 01404 43431

Davies, K A (Roskell Davies & Co) *K1 N S1 L F1 J1 O Q*
Birmingham *p141* 0121 354 1515 / 355 1011

Davies, Ms K L (Teignbridge District Council)
Newton Abbot *p466* 01626 361101

Davies, Ms K M (McGrigors LLP) *O B1 Zb Zc Zj*
London EC4 *p56*. 020 7054 2500

Davies, Mrs L (Durham County Council)
Durham *p457* 0191 383 3513

Davies, Ms L (Judge & Priestley) *N*
Bromley *p166* 020 8290 0333

Davies, Ms L (The College of Law Guildford)
Guildford *p459*. 01483 460200

Davies, Miss L (Wrexham County Borough Council)
Wrexham *p477* 01978 292000

Davies, Mrs L A (Platt & Fishwick) *S2 S1*
Wigan *p432* 01942 243281

Davies, L C (Marriott Davies Yapp) *C1 I C2 J1 P M2 M1 C3 T1 Zb Zd Ze Zf*
Sutton *p402* 020 8643 9794

Davies, Miss L J (Cardiff Magistrates Court) *K1 D1 D2*
Cardiff *p453* 029 2046 3040

Davies, Mrs L M (Harvey Ingram LLP) *C1 Ze*
Leicester *p280*. 0116 254 5454

Davies, L M (Pinsent Masons LLP)
Bristol *p164* 0117 924 5678

Davies, Mrs L M (Vincent Sykes & Higham LLP) *W T1 A1 Zd*
Thrapston *p411* 01832 732161

Davies, Ms L R (Parry Davies Clwyd-Jones & Lloyd) *K1 S2 Q W*
Caernarfon *p172*. 01286 673381
Llangefni *p292*. 01248 723106

Davies, M (Fox Williams) *Zi*
London EC2 *p33*. 020 7628 2000

Davies, M (Poole Townsend)
Barrow-in-Furness *p125* . . . 01229 811811

Davies, Ms M (Wilkin Chapman Grange Solicitors) *A1 E S1*
Grimsby *p235* 01472 262626

Davies, M C (W M Furness & Son) *S1 S2 K4 W*
Irlam *p263*. . . . 0161 775 9962 / 775 6765

Davies, M C (Howard Solicitors)
Manchester *p305* 0800 876 6749

Davies, Mrs M C A (Buckinghamshire County Council)
Aylesbury *p448* 01296 383653

Davies, M C U (Trevor Griffiths & Humphries) *N K1 G H Zl*
Blackwood *p147*. 01495 225236

Davies, M E (Rawlins Davy PLC) *E M1 R1 R2 S2 T1 T2 W Zd*
Bournemouth *p152*. 01202 558844

Davies, M G (Andersons Solicitors) *J1 Zp*
Nottingham *p335*. 0115 947 0641

Davies, M G (Bennett Richmond) *S1 M1 K1 W P G L J1 V Zc Zj Zl*
Lanchester *p270*. 01207 521843

Davies, M H (Barker Gillette) *S1 S2 E*
London W1 *p9*. 020 7636 0555

Davies, M J (DWF) *B1*
Manchester *p303* 0161 603 5000

Davies, M J (Environment Agency (Southern))
Worthing *p477*. 01903 820692

Davies, Mrs M J (Welwyn Hatfield District Council)
Welwyn Garden City *p475* . . 01707 357000

Davies, M J (Sanders & Co) *G H N Q F1 J1 D1 B1*
Stourbridge *p399* . .01384 375437 / 378991

Davies, M J (Wansbroughs) *N Zu Q*
Devizes *p210* 01380 733300

Davies, M J (Rupert Bear Murray Davies) *K1*
Nottingham *p338*. 0115 924 3333

Davies, Mrs M K (AMD Solicitors) *S2 W X E A3*
Bristol *p160* 0117 962 1460

Davies, M K P (Wilson & Co) *Zi*
London N17 *p92*. 020 8808 7535

Davies, Ms M L (FBC Manby Bowdler LLP) *W*
Wolverhampton *p437* 01902 578000

Davies, Ms M M (John Collins & Partners LLP) *N Zr*
Swansea *p405*. 01792 773773

Davies, M N (Backhouse Jones Ltd) *G Zj O Q N Zt*
Clitheroe *p196*. 01254 828300

Davies, M N (Hill Dickinson LLP) *Zu N J2 O Q Zq*
Liverpool *p288*. 0151 600 8000

Davies, Miss M R (Gateley LLP) *O*
Birmingham *p138* 0121 234 0000

Davies, M S (Stevens Lucas) *N Q O S1 S2 W*
Oswestry *p342*. 01691 670999

Davies, M S (Healys LLP) *L O R1*
London EC4 *p39*. 020 7822 4000

Davies, M S (Olswang LLP) *Q*
London WC1 *p64* 020 7067 3000

Davies, M S J (Cleveland Solicitors) *N P*
London EC3 *p20*. 020 7377 8866

Davies, N (Jones Day) *Zb*
London EC4 *p46*. 020 7039 5959

Davies, N (Davenport Lyons)
London W1 *p25* 020 7468 2600

Davies, N J (Mackrell Turner Garrett)
London WC2 *p57* 020 7240 0521

Davies, Mrs N J (Petersons) *N Q O Zq*
Newport *p329* 01633 255151

Davies, N L (Paris Smith LLP) *K1 D2 K2 K3*
Southampton *p386*. 023 8048 2482

Davies, N R (Evans & Davies) *S1 K1 Q W F1 N E J1 C1*
Aberaeron *p113* 01545 570335

Davies, N W (Thursfields) *K1 D1*
Kidderminster *p266* 01562 820575

Davies, P (Emsleys) *J1 Q N*
Leeds *p273* 0113 232 1030

Davies, P (Greenwoods)
Milton Keynes *p317* 01908 298200

Davies, P (Storrar Cowdry) *E S2 S1 R2*
Chester *p191* 01244 400567

Davies, Ms P A (SNR Denton) *E*
London EC4 *p75*. 020 7242 1212

Davies, P A (Wallis Prance)
Basingstoke *p127* 01256 464311

Davies, P B (Hamilton Davies) *N K1 F1 F2 J1 J2 B1 O Q Zp Zw Zq K3 D2*
Stevenage *p394* 01438 315898

Davies, P C (Elwyn Jones & Co) *W S1 E*
Bangor *p122*. 01248 370224

See p634 for the Key to Work Categories

Davies, P D (Bridge Sanderson Munro) *S1 W E A1 Zc*
Wath-upon-Dearne *p424* . . . 01709 873321
Doncaster *p211* 01302 321621

Davies, P G (Gateley LLP) *A3 Zc Zq*
Birmingham *p138* 0121 234 0000

Davies, P G (The Woodland Davies Partnership LLP) *S1 S2 K1 K2 D2 N K3 W*
Hay-on-Wye *p245* 01497 820406
Kington *p268* 01544 230841
Talgarth *p407* 01874 711744

Davies, P H (Davies & Company) *B1 C1 E N P R1 S1 T1 W I Zj*
Stockport *p395*. 0161 355 5500

Davies, P H (The Robert Davies Partnership) *E W S1 T2 K1*
Newport *p329* 01633 413500

Davies, P I (Essex County Council)
Chelmsford *p454*. 0845 743 0430

Davies, P L (Walter Williams) *S1 A1 G K1 W H C1 J1 N E Zv Zl*
Fishguard *p226* 01348 873223

Davies, Miss P M (PCB Solicitors LLP) *W*
Shrewsbury *p379* 01743 248148

Davies, P M (Davey Franklin Jones) *N Q Zl Zr*
Gloucester *p230*. 01452 508800

Davies, P M (Nicholls Brimble & Co) *C1 E L S1*
Smethwick *p382*. 0121 429 8016

Davies, P R (Bircham Dyson Bell) *T2 W*
Westminster *p13*. 020 7227 7000

Davies, Mrs R (Morgans) *K3 K1*
Cardiff *p180* 029 2072 9888

Davies, Mrs R (Clerical Medical Investment Group)
London EC2 *p105* 020 7321 1425

Davies, Ms R (Westminster City Council) *K1 D1 G H*
London SW1 *p110*. 020 7641 6000
Haverfordwest *p244* 01437 763332

Davies, R (Bilton Hammond LLP) *G H Zg Zm*
Mansfield *p311*. 01623 675800

Davies, R (Keoghs LLP) *N Zj O Q*
Bolton *p149* 01204 677000

Davies, R (The Smith Partnership) *O N B1 B2*
Derby *p209* 01332 225225

Davies, Ms R (Addleshaw Goddard)
Manchester *p300* 0161 934 6000

Davies, Ms R (John Pickering & Partners LLP) *N Zr*
Halifax *p238* 0808 144 0959

Davies, R A C (R George Davies & Co) *S1 W L A1*
Abergavenny *p113*. 01873 852535

Davies, R B (Davies Murray-White & Co)
Stratford-upon-Avon *p400* . . 01789 295544

Davies, R B M (RBM Davies & Partners LLP) *K1 K2 D1 K3 S1 W K4*
Neston *p321*. 0151 336 6611

Davies, R C (Barber Titleys) *A1 S2 E S1 R2 L*
Harrogate *p240* 01423 502211

Davies, R G (Stevens) *G H*
Stoke-on-Trent *p398*. 01782 813200

Davies, R G (Anthony & Jarvie) *S1 S2 L C1 E O*
Bridgend *p157*. 01656 652737

Davies, R G (Jacklyn Dawson) *S1 E L W T1 K4 S2*
Newport *p328* 01633 262952

Davies, R H T (The Robert Davies Partnership) *C1 N A1 B1 E*
Newport *p329* 01633 413500

Davies, R J (Bond Pearce LLP) *E P*
Southampton *p385*. 0845 415 0000

Davies, Miss R L (Fraser Brown) *C1 S2 E*
Nottingham *p337*. 0115 988 8777

Davies, R L (Kendall & Davies) *N W K1 J1 R1 Zc Zl K3*
Bourton-on-the-Water *p153* . 01451 820277

Davies, R L (Clifford Chance)
London E14 *p20* 020 7006 1000

Davies, R L (Squire Sanders (UK) LLP)
London EC2 *p81*. 020 7655 1000

Davies, Mrs R L (Humphries Kirk) *O Zj C1*
Poole *p352* 01202 715815

Davies, R M (Geoffrey Morris & Ashton) *A1 B1 C1 D1 E F1 G H J1 K1 Zc Zm Zv S1 S2*
Wrexham *p442* 01978 291322

Davies, R M (Leo Abse & Cohen) *N*
Cardiff *p179* . . .029 2038 3252 / 2034 5421

Davies, Mrs R M (Howells) *N Q*
Cardiff *p178* 029 2040 4020

Davies, R N (GLP Solicitors) *D2 D1 G K3 K1 Zl*
Bury *p170* 0161 764 1818

Davies, R N (Elmbridge Borough Council) *S1*
Esher *p458* 01372 474198

Davies, R S (Richard Stephen Davies) *S1 W A1 J1 C1 R1 L*
Mold *p318* 01352 754468

Davies, R T (Plexus Law (A Trading Name of Parabis Law LLP)) *Zj O Q N*
London EC3 *p68*. 0844 245 4000

Davies, R W (A Halsall & Co) *S1 N W E T2 S2*
Wirral *p435* 0151 678 9090

Davies, Miss S (Burt Brill & Cardens) *L S1*
Brighton *p159* 01273 604123

Davies, Ms S (Geldards LLP) *E S2*
Cardiff *p178* 029 2023 8239

Davies, Ms S (Thompsons (formerly Robin/Brian Thompson & Partners)) *N*
Liverpool *p290*. 0151 224 1600

Davies, Ms S (Cardiff County Council)
Cardiff *p453* 029 2087 2000

Davies, Mrs S (Harrisons Solicitors LLP) *S1 W K4 S2 A1*
Newtown *p330*. 01686 625134

Davies, S (Linklaters LLP)
London EC2 *p54*. 020 7456 2000

Davies, S (Stevens) *G H*
Stoke-on-Trent *p398*. 01782 813200

Davies, Miss S A (Mayer Brown International LLP) *Zc Zq A3 O*
London EC2 *p59*. 020 3130 3000

Davies, S A (Charles Russell LLP) *E*
London EC4 *p19*. 020 7203 5000

Davies, Ms S C (Joelson Wilson LLP) *Zl J2 Zy F2*
Westminster *p46*. 020 7580 5721

Davies, Miss S E (Gateley LLP) *O*
London EC4 *p35*. 020 7653 1600

Davies, S G (Underhill Langley & Wright) *S1 E W*
Wolverhampton *p438* 01902 782606
Wolverhampton *p438* 01902 423431

Davies, S H R (David L R Davies & Co)
Ammanford *p117*. . .01269 593463 / 592119

Davies, Ms S J (Gotelee) *J1*
Ipswich *p262*. 01473 211121

Davies, S J (McGrigors LLP)
London EC4 *p56*. 020 7054 2500

Davies, S J (Pepperells) *N J1 L Zk O Q Zr Zm Zq Zp V*
Scunthorpe *p373*. 01724 871999

Davies, Ms S J (Squire Sanders (UK) LLP)
London EC2 *p81*. 020 7655 1000

Davies, S K (Neath Port Talbot County Borough Council)
Port Talbot *p469*. 01639 763333

Davies, Ms S L (Watson Marshal) *W S1 K4*
London W4 *p90* 020 8987 0100

Davies, Ms S M (Plexus Law (A Trading Name of Parabis Law LLP)) *O Q Zj Zq Zr*
London EC3 *p68*. 0844 245 4000

Davies, Mrs S M (Hempsons) *Zr*
Manchester *p305* 0161 228 0011

Davies, S M (Davies & Gribbin Solicitors)
Ormskirk *p341* 01695 573433

Davies, S P (Paris Smith LLP) *C1 C2 Zw*
Southampton *p386*. 023 8048 2482

Davies, Miss S W (Jacklyn Dawson) *E S1 S2 R2 T2 K4 L W*
Newport *p328* 01633 262952

Davies, T (Muckle LLP) *J1*
Newcastle upon Tyne *p325* . 0191 211 7777

Davies, T (Penningtons) *E Zh*
Basingstoke *p127* 01256 407100

Davies, Miss T A (Stanley Tee) *N Q O*
Bishop's Stortford *p144* . . . 01279 755200

Davies, T J (CMS Cameron McKenna LLP) *Za*
London EC3 *p17*. 020 7367 3000

Davies, T J (Laytons) *J1 Zi*
London EC4 *p52*. 020 7842 8000
Exeter *p221* 01392 688688

Davies, T J (Field Fisher Waterhouse LLP)
London EC3 *p31*. 020 7861 4000

Davies, Miss T J B (Stroud and Swindon Building Society)
Stroud *p473* 01453 757011

Davies, T J E (Kennedys) *Zj Zq N O Q*
London EC3 *p49*. 020 7667 9667

Davies, T L (Bond Pearce LLP) *Zl*
Bristol *p161* 0845 415 0000

Davies, Miss T M (Dolmans) *N*
Cardiff *p178* 029 2034 5531

Davies, Miss V (Harbottle & Lewis LLP)
London W1 *p38* 020 7667 5000

Davies, Ms V N (Edwin Coe LLP) *O A3 M2 Zza*
London WC2 *p29* 020 7691 4000

Davies, Ms Y (Hugh James) *S1 Zh E*
Cardiff *p179* 029 2022 4871

Davies Williams, Miss C E (Patchell Davies (Trading Name of PD Law Ltd)) *W S1 L K4 S2*
Blackwood *p147*. 01495 227128

Davies-Jones, Mrs A (Milwyn Jenkins & Jenkins Limited)
Llanidloes *p292* 01686 412166

Davies-Ratcliff, Ms K (C Brewer & Sons Ltd)
Eastbourne *p457*. 01323 411080

Davin, J (Mary Monson Solicitors Ltd) *G H*
Swinton *p407* . . 0161 794 0088 / 0808 155 4870

Davin, Ms J (AMEC PLC) *O Q Zc*
Knutsford *p462* 01565 683123

Davin, Miss S J (Lawrence Lupin) *Zi Zg M2*
Wembley *p426*. 020 8733 7200

Davis, A (Pinsent Masons LLP) *C3*
London EC2 *p67*. 020 7418 7000

Davis, A (Leigh Davis) *C1 E F1 J1 L S1 R1 T1 W Zf Zi Zl*
London W1 *p26* 020 7631 0302

Davis, Ms A (Sternberg Reed) *G*
Barking *p123* 020 8591 3366

Davis, Ms A C (Nelsons)
Nottingham *p338*. 0115 958 6262

Davis, A T (Fishburns) *A3 O Q F2 Zo Zj Zq*
London EC3 *p32*. 020 7280 8888

Davis, B H (Mayo Wynne Baxter LLP) *Zr Zl Q W G H K1 D1 J1 N*
Eastbourne *p215*. 01323 730543

Davis, Ms C (DLA Piper UK LLP)
London EC2 *p24*. 0870 011 1111

Davis, Miss C (Rubin Lewis O'Brien)
Cwmbran *p206* 01633 867000

Davis, C C (Staffordshire County Council)
Stafford *p472* 01785 223121

Davis, Miss D (Hertfordshire County Council)
Hertford *p460* 01992 555555

Davis, D D (Nicholas & Co) *E S1 S2 W*
London W1 *p63* 020 7323 4450

Davis, Mrs D S (Chandler Ray) *S1 K1 S2 W E J1 K4*
Buckingham *p167* 01280 814040

Davis, Ms E (Davenport Lyons)
London W1 *p25* 020 7468 2600

Davis, E C A (Russell & Co) *F1 K1 N Q S1 S2*
Malvern *p300* 01684 892000

Davis, E H C (AXA UK PLC)
London E22 *p103* 020 7920 5900

Davis, Mrs E J (Blake Lapthorn) *C1 F1 Zd*
Portsmouth *p354*. 023 9222 1122

Davis, Ms F J (Wolverhampton City Council)
Wolverhampton *p477* 01902 556556

Davis, Ms G (Rooks Rider)
London EC1 *p73*. 020 7689 7000

Davis, I D S (Scott Bailey) *S1 E W K1 D1 C1 T1 F1 G*
Lymington *p296* 01590 676933

Davis, I M K (Trowers & Hamlins) *C1 E L I P Zh Zd Zb*
London EC3 *p88*. 020 7423 8000

Davis, I R (Henmans LLP) *A1 E L S1*
Oxford *p343* 01865 781000

Davis, J (Galbraith Branley)
London N12 *p34* 020 8446 8474
London NW1 *p41* 020 7874 8300

Davis, Ms J (Shoosmiths)
Birmingham *p142* 0370 086 4000 / 0121 335 4440

Davis, J (Davis-Law Associates) *G B2*
Chalfont St Peter *p184*. . . . 01753 888776

Davis, J A (Davis Wood) *E S1 C1 J1*
Bristol *p162* 0117 965 3504

Davis, J A (EMW) *C1 I Ze Zza Zf U2*
London WC2 *p28* 0845 070 6000

Davis, J A (Irwin Mitchell LLP) *N Zg*
Sheffield *p376* 0870 150 0100

Davis, Mrs J D (Larcomes LLP) *S1*
Portsmouth *p354*. 023 9266 1531

Davis, J E (SANPAOLO IMI SPA)
London EC4 *p109* 020 7214 8000

Davis, J E M (Hamilton Downing Quinn) *Q O N J1 L B1 C1 Zw*
London WC1 *p38* 020 7831 8939

Davis, J K (Beevers Solicitors) *S1 S2 C1 E*
Ashton-under-Lyne *p119*. . . 0161 339 9697
Stalybridge *p393*. 0161 338 2614

Davis, Mrs J L (B P Collins LLP) *J1*
Gerrards Cross *p229*. 01753 889995

Davis, J R (Davis & Co) *S1 E W*
Ilford *p259* 020 8551 4228

Davis, J R (Clifton Ingram LLP) *J1 J2 N O Q Zi Zp Zq*
Wokingham *p437* 0118 978 0099

Davis, Ms L (SNR Denton) *Zb*
London EC4 *p75*. 020 7242 1212

Davis, M (Battens) *D1 K1 N G H*
Sherborne *p378* 01935 814811

Davis, M (TV Edwards LLP)
London SE8 *p85*. 020 7790 7000

Davis, Mrs M A (Field Fisher Waterhouse LLP) *J1 P*
London EC3 *p31*. 020 7861 4000

Davis, M E (Herbert Smith LLP) *O Zc*
London EC2 *p40*. 020 7374 8000

Davis, M F (Metropolitan Police Directorate of Legal Services) *Q N S1 S2 L W J1 B1 O K1 Zl Zr*
London SW1 *p108*. 020 7230 7210

Davis, M H R (Carter Vincent Jones Davis)
Bangor *p122* 01248 362551

Davis, M J (Charles Hoile) *G H D1 K1 N L J1 F1 B1 R1*
Newbury *p322*. 01635 45595

Davis, M M (DWFM Beckman) *C1 S2 E C2 R1 R2 S1 W*
Westminster *p25*. 020 7872 0023

Davis, M M (Charles Russell LLP) *W T2 Zd*
Cheltenham *p187* 01242 221122

Davis, M O (Warners Solicitors) *E S1 L R2 S2*
Sevenoaks *p374*. 01732 747900

Davis, Ms N (Martin-Kaye LLP) *D1 K1 K3*
Telford *p409* 01952 272222

Davis, N (Browne Jacobson LLP) *N Zq O Zj*
London EC3 *p16*. 020 7539 4900
Nottingham *p336*. 0115 976 6000

Davis, Mrs N (JMD Law Limited) *L Zg O Q N Zq*
Cardiff *p179* 029 2045 6780

Davis, N (Simmons & Simmons)
London EC2 *p79*. 020 7628 2020

Davis, N D C (Albinson Napier & Co) *N O Q F1 Zq J1*
Warrington *p421* 01925 634681

Davis, N J R (Mills & Reeve) *Zq Zj O*
London EC3 *p61*. 020 7648 9220

Davis, Dr N J R (Goughs) *A1 C1 S2 E S1*
Devizes *p210* 01380 726913

Davis, N L (Memery Crystal) *C1 C2 Zn*
London WC2 *p60* 020 7242 5905

Davis, N P (Glaisyers) *G*
Birmingham *p138* 0121 233 2971

Davis, N R (Nigel Davis Solicitors) *A1 A2 P R1 U1 W A3*
Belper *p131* 01335 372889

Davis, P A (Tucker Turner Kingsley Wood & Co) *S1 E K1 L W G C1 Zd Zi Zc*
London WC1 *p88* 020 7242 3303

Davis, P R (Reed Smith LLP) *E*
London EC2 *p71*. 020 3116 3000

Davis, R (Barlow Robbins LLP) *Zr N*
Guildford *p235*. 01483 543200

Davis, R A (Glinert Davis) *C1 O J1 L B1 C2 Zf*
Westminster *p36*. 020 7724 4442

Davis, R E (Squire Sanders (UK) LLP)
London EC2 *p81*. 020 7655 1000

Davis, R G (Ralph Davis) *N O J1 Zq L*
Islington *p26* 020 7253 7200

Davis, R G L (Browne Jacobson LLP) *Q*
Nottingham *p336*. 0115 976 6000

Davis, R J (Buller Jeffries) *N O J1 Q Zj Zc Zh*
Birmingham *p136* 0121 212 2620

Davis, R J (Freeman Box) *E S1 W L J1 Zl*
London W1 *p34* 020 7486 9041

Davis, R J (Peter Bonner & Co) *G H*
Lewisham *p14* 020 8297 1727

Davis, R R (Nicholas & Co)
London W1 *p63* 020 7323 4450

Davis, Mrs S (Adams & Remers) *J1*
Lewes *p283* 01273 480616

Davis, S (Lewis Silkin LLP)
London EC4 *p53*. 020 7074 8000

Davis, Ms S (Trowers & Hamlins)
London EC3 *p88*. 020 7423 8000

Davis, Ms S (Jones Day) *E*
London EC4 *p46*. 020 7039 5959

Davis, Mrs S J (Dixon Ward) *E S1 S2*
Richmond upon Thames *p364* 020 8940 4051

Davis, S J (SJ Berwin LLP)
London EC4 *p75*. 020 7111 2222

Davis, Mrs S J E (Capsticks Solicitors LLP) *N Zq*
London SW19 *p18* 020 8780 2211

Davis, S W (Clifford Chance)
London E14 *p20* 020 7006 1000

Davis, T A (Davis & Co) *O Q M2 Za Zj Ze Zn B1*
London EC3 *p26*. 020 7621 1091

Davis, Miss T M (Thornes) *K1 D1 D2 G H*
Wolverhampton *p438* 01902 313311

Davis, T P (Purcell Parker) *H G*
Birmingham *p141* 0121 236 9781

Davis, W M (Davis Davidson) *K1 N O Q F1 L J1 S1 W Zc Zl*
Beverley *p131* 01482 881278

Davis-Pipe, F J (Davis Priest & Co) *S1 K1 W K4*
Redditch *p362* 01527 69231

Davison, A J (Swinburne Maddison) *S1 A1 L W M1 G H R1 C1 P Zh Zl Zn*
Durham *p214* . . 0191 384 2441 / 384 7455

Davison, A J (Muckle LLP) *C2 C1*
Newcastle upon Tyne *p325* . 0191 211 7777

Davison, B (Ison Harrison) *K1 K3*
Leeds *p274* 0113 284 5000

Davison, G (Housemans)
London EC3 *p43*. 020 3170 6000

Davison, G A (Davisons) *B1 C1 E F1 J1 L N R1 S1 W*
Birmingham *p137* 0121 685 1234

Davison, H (DLA Piper UK LLP)
Leeds *p272* 0870 011 1111

Davison, I A (Ford & Warren) *Zt N*
Leeds *p273* 0113 243 6601

Davison, I R (Horsham District Council)
Horsham *p461* 01403 215100

Davison, Mrs J (Muckle LLP) *C1 C2*
Newcastle upon Tyne *p325* . 0191 211 7777

Davison, J R (Arthur Jackson & Co) *K1 W Zl*
Rotherham *p367*. 01709 363876

Davison, Ms L (Larcomes LLP) *K3 K1 K2*
Portsmouth *p354*. 023 9266 1531

Davison, M D (Hogan Lovells International LLP)
London EC1 *p42*. 020 7296 2000

Davison, N M (Housemans)
Newcastle upon Tyne *p325* . 0191 232 1307

Davison, Miss O M (Latham & Co) *M1 P D1 G H*
Loughborough *p293* 01509 238822

Davison, P C (British American Tobacco)
London WC2 *p104* 020 7845 1000

Davison, R (BTG International Ltd)
London EC4 *p104* 020 7575 0000

Davison, R (Scarborough Borough Council)
Scarborough *p470*. 01723 232348

Davison, Mrs R (Williscroft & Co) *K1 K3 X*
Bradford *p155* 01274 305380

Davitt, Miss M F (Davitt Jones Bould) *E S2 L*
Taunton *p408* 01823 279279

Davitt, O (Davitt & Co)
London NW2 *p26* 020 7566 8244

Davy, A K (Tameside Metropolitan Borough Council)
Ashton-under-Lyne *p447*. . . 0161 342 3028

Davy, C G (British Telecommunications PLC)
London EC1 *p104* 020 7356 6181

Davy, Mrs E (Kitsons LLP) *B1*
Exeter *p221* 01392 455555

Davy, Miss F J (Sprake & Kingsley) *W*
Bungay *p168* 01986 892721

Daw, Miss C (Brachers) *J1 Zp*
Maidstone *p299* 01622 690691

Daw, S W (Heald Solicitors) *O Q Ze J1*
Milton Keynes *p317* 01908 662277

Dawar, Ms R (Dawar & Co) *G K1 Zi Zo Zv L E S1*
Ilford *p259* 020 8550 4741

Dawbarn, M L (Lincoln Financial Group)
Gloucester *p459*. 0845 678 8888

Dawbarn, R (Kennedys)
London EC3 *p49*. 020 7667 9667

Dawbney, M J (Herbert Smith LLP) *E Zs*
London EC2 *p40*. 020 7374 8000

Dawe, Miss J A (Basingstoke & Deane Borough Council)
Basingstoke *p448* 01256 845402

Dawe, M D A (Scott Fowler) *S1 W L R1 F1 E C1*
Northampton *p331*. 01604 750506

Dawe, R J (Everys) *S1 E W C1 L T1 R1 A1 Zd Zc Zm*
Exmouth *p222* 01395 264384

Dawe-Lane, P J (Osborne Clarke) *C1*
Bristol *p164* 0117 917 3000

Dawes, C T (Fidler & Pepper)
Mansfield *p311*. 01623 451111
Kirkby-in-Ashfield *p268*. 01623 451111
Dawes, Miss E (Russell-Cooke LLP) *E*
London SW15 *p74*. 020 8789 9111
Dawes, M (Memery Crystal) *C1 C2*
London WC2 *p60* 020 7242 5905
Dawkins, Miss A L (Dunning & Co) *K1 K3 D1 D2*
London SE5 *p28*. 020 7733 6217
London SE5 *p89*. 020 7277 0110
Dawkins, Miss K (Nicholson Martin Legge & Miller) *K4 K3 K1 S1 W*
Houghton Le Spring *p253* . . 0191 584 2841
Dawkins, L A (Slee Blackwell) *N Q Zq Zr*
Barnstaple *p125*. 01271 372128
Braunton *p156*. 01271 812019
Dawkins, M P (Simmons & Simmons) *O Q M1 B1 Zb Zj Zk*
London EC2 *p79*. 020 7628 2020
Dawkins, Miss P C (Nelsons)
Leicester *p280*. 0116 222 6666
Dawkins, Ms T (British Telecommunications PLC)
London EC1 *p104* 020 7356 6181
Dawrant, Ms F M (Quality Solicitors Burroughs Day) *O Q*
Bristol *p164* 0117 929 0333
Dawson, A G (Sintons LLP) *S1 K1 L W D1 F1*
Newcastle upon Tyne *p326* . 0191 226 7878
Dawson, Ms A M (Waldrons) *C1 E L R1 S1 T1*
Kingswinford *p268*. 01384 811811
Dawson, A M (Thomson Wilson Pattinson) *S1 W G S2*
Windermere *p434* 01539 442233
Dawson, A W (Brunswicks LLP) *J2 G P Zy Zza*
Birkenhead *p134*. 0870 766 8400
Dawson, B (Dawson Lloyd & Co) *Q O K1 E C1 R1 T2 Zq*
Reading *p360* 0118 966 9238
Dawson, B M (Walker Smith Way) *N Zr Zq*
Chester *p191* 0844 346 3100
Dawson, B W (Underwood Solicitors LLP) *O B1 L I Zi Zk Zl*
Westminster *p89*. 020 7526 6000
Dawson, Mrs C (KBL Solicitors) *S1*
Bolton *p149* 01204 527777
Dawson, C E H (Humphrys & Co)
Rhyl *p363* 01745 343158
Dawson, C G (Harrop White Vallance & Dawson) *E S1 T2 W Zd*
Mansfield *p311*. 01623 629221
Dawson, Ms C M (Nicholls Lindsell & Harris and Ingham & Wainwright) *K1 N Q V*
Poynton *p355* 01625 876411
Dawson, C W C (Wilkinson & Butler) *G H L S1 B2*
St Neots *p392*. 01480 219229
Dawson, Ms D M (University of Birmingham) *E S1*
Birmingham *p450* 0121 414 3637
Dawson, Mrs E (Welsh Health Legal Services)
Cardiff *p453* 029 2031 5500
Dawson, G J (Graham Dawson & Co) *E W S1 C1 L T1 Zl*
Bexley *p132*. 01322 558811
Dawson, Miss H E (Trafford Metropolitan Borough Council)
Stretford *p473* 0161 912 1212
Dawson, Mrs H L (Sykes Lee & Brydson) *K1 S1 W*
York *p445* 01904 731100
Dawson, I (Shulmans) *J1 C1 F1 Zp*
Leeds *p276* 0113 245 2833
Dawson, J (Addleshaw Goddard)
London EC1 *p4* 020 7606 8855
Dawson, J F (J F Dawson) *C1 J1 L Zd*
Beaconsfield *p129*. 01494 670566
Dawson, Miss J L (Elliot Mather LLP) *C1 C2 E*
Chesterfield *p192* 01246 231288
Dawson, J N (Fendom Dawson & Partners) *E G K1 L H Q S1 W*
High Wycombe *p250*. 01494 450361
Dawson, J W (Skipton Building Society)
Skipton *p471*. 01756 705000
Dawson, Miss K (Chawner Grey & Co) *W K4 T2*
Weston-super-Mare *p429* . .01934 417768 / 623541
Dawson, Mrs K (Shell International Ltd)
London SE1 *p109* 020 7934 1234
Dawson, Ms K L (Farrell Matthews & Weir) *G K1 H K3*
London W6 *p31* 020 8741 1482
London W6 *p30* 020 8746 3771
Dawson, Mrs K L (Coley & Tilley)
Birmingham *p136* 0121 643 5531
Dawson, Ms K L (Wansbroughs) *N Zu*
Devizes *p210* 01380 733300
Dawson, Mrs L J (Ellisons) *K1 K3 D1*
Colchester *p197*. 01206 764477
Dawson, M (Corries Solicitors) *N*
York *p444* 0845 241 5566
Dawson, Mrs M C (Partridge & Wilson) *S1 L*
Bury St Edmunds *p171* 01284 762281
Dawson, M C (Dawson Mason & Carr) *S1 E*
Guildford *p236*. 01483 576169
Dawson, M P (Ellen Court Partnership Solicitors) *N Q K1 H G B1 V F1*
Preston *p356* 01772 882888
Dawson, Mrs N (Humphrys & Co)
Rhyl *p363* 01745 343158
Dawson, P (City of Lincoln Council)
Lincoln *p463*. 01522 881188
Dawson, P M (Russell-Cooke LLP) *S2 E*
London WC1 *p74* 020 7405 6566

Dawson, R A (Bassetlaw District Council)
Worksop *p477* 01909 533533
Dawson, R E (Nichols Marcy Dawson) *E S1 S2 W*
Walton-on-Thames *p420*. . . 01932 219500
Dawson, R G (Brethertons LLP) *N Zr*
Banbury *p122* 01295 270999
Dawson, R G H (HCB Solicitors) *K1 D1*
Walsall *p420*. 01922 720000
Dawson, R J (Kirwans) *S1 W E S2*
Birkenhead *p134*. 0151 608 9078
Dawson, R P H (Stanley Hays) *G H K1 L S1 S2 W K3*
Heckmondwike *p246*. 01924 403809
Dawson, Ms S (Norwich Union Insurance Group) *J1 Zp C1*
Norwich *p467* 01603 622200
Dawson, S (Hegarty LLP) *D1 K1 K3*
Peterborough *p347* 01733 346333
Dawson, S (MKB Solicitors LLP) *E J1 S1 T2 W*
Barnsley *p124*. 01226 210000
Dawson, Ms S E M (Bristol City Council)
Bristol *p451* 0117 922 2000
Dawson, S J (Forbes) *G H N Q L F1 J1 V K1*
Chorley *p194* 01257 260600
Dawson, Mrs S M (Davey Franklin Jones) *W*
Gloucester *p230*. 01452 508800
Dawson, W (Farrer & Co LLP)
London WC2 *p31* 020 3375 7000
Dawson, W S (Simmons & Simmons)
London EC2 *p79*. 020 7628 2020
Dawson-Asaam, Ms E (Philcox Gray & Co) *L S1 V Ze Zi*
London SE15 *p67* 020 7703 2285
Dawson-Gerrard, R (Stephensons Solicitors LLP) *O C1 A3 Zq L Ze*
Leigh *p282*. 01942 777777
Dawson-Pick, Mrs C L (Gordons Solicitors LLP) *O N P L F1 Zl Zc Zd*
Marlow *p313*. 01628 487487
Dawtrey, J (Blake Lapthorn) *U2 C1*
Oxford *p342* 01865 248607
Day, A (Taylor Wessing)
London EC4 *p86*. 020 7300 7000
Day, D C (CMS Cameron McKenna LLP) *C1 C2*
London EC3 *p17*. 020 7367 3000
Day, G C (DLA Piper UK LLP) *J1 Ze Zp*
London EC2 *p24*. 0870 011 1111
Day, Mrs L K (Palmers Solicitors) *Q K3 K1 O L J1 N Zq B1*
Kingston upon Thames *p267*. 020 8549 7444
Day, M (Langleys)
York *p445* 01904 610886
Day, M J (Leigh Day & Co) *N P*
London EC1 *p52*. 020 7650 1200
Day, M S (Tassells) *P C2 N J1 B1 R1 Zl F1 F2 Zc*
Faversham *p225*. 01795 533337
Day, N G S (Hague Lambert) *J1 O K1*
Manchester *p305* 0161 834 6066
Day, P D (Wilkin Chapman Grange Solicitors) *S1 T2 W A1 E R1*
Louth *p294* 01507 606161
Day, P J (Wedlake Bell LLP) *E S2*
London WC1 *p91* 020 7395 3000
Day, P J (Horsey Lightly Fynn) *Zl Zy J2 Zw*
Bournemouth *p152*. 01202 551991
Day, P M (Langley Wellington) *E S1 C1 W A1 S2 T1 T2*
Gloucester *p230*. 01452 521286
Day, R (Foreman Laws)
Hitchin *p251* 01462 458711
Day, R (SJ Berwin LLP)
London EC4 *p75*. 020 7111 2222
Day, R (Scutt Beaumont Solicitors Ltd) *G H*
Leicester *p281*. 0116 254 4200
Day, R J (Burnand Brazier Tisdall) *K1 Q N F1 L J1*
Hove *p254*. 01273 734022
Day, R J H (Pyms) *W S1 K4 S2 L*
Belper *p131* 01773 822307
Day, S (Joseph Darios Solicitors) *N*
Southampton *p385*. 023 8023 7575
Day, Miss S (Camden Community Law Centre)
London NW5 *p104*. 020 7284 6510
Day, Ms S E (Druces LLP) *S1 E L J1*
London EC2 *p27*. 020 7638 9271
Day, Ms S E (Glazer Delmar) *S2 E S1*
London SE22 *p35* 020 8299 0021
Day, Miss S J (DLA Piper UK LLP) *C2 C1 F1 Zb*
Leeds *p272* 0870 011 1111
Day, Miss S T (Marsons Solicitors LLP) *N Zq*
Bromley *p166* 020 8313 1300
Day, T F (Hartley & Worstenholme) *S1 E W A1 L C1 R1 T1*
Castleford *p183* 01977 732222
Daya, Mrs S (Bristol City Council)
Bristol *p451* 0117 922 2000
Dayal, A (Finers Stephens Innocent LLP)
London W1 *p32* 020 7323 4000
Daycock, D M (City & County of Swansea)
Swansea *p473*. 01792 636000
Dayes, S C C (Taylor Wessing) *C1 Zb*
London EC4 *p86*. 020 7300 7000
Daykin, Mrs A H (Abigail Daykin & Co) *J1 J2 Zp*
Farnham *p225*01252 719155 / 07774 259331
Daykin, J (Weatherhead & Butcher) *S1 W E*
Bingley *p133*. 01274 562322
Dayle, R (Fladgate LLP)
London WC2 *p32* 020 3036 7000
Dayment, Ms S J (Scott Richards) *W*
Teignmouth *p409* 01626 772441
Daymond, A (Wansbroughs) *G H N Q Zm Zp*
Melksham *p314* 01225 703222

De Alwis, C (Charles De Alwis) *C1 E F1 G J1 K1 O Q S1 W Zi Zl*
Chadwell Heath *p183* 020 8597 5717
De Basto, R J C (Allen & Overy LLP)
London E1 *p5* 020 3088 0000
de Bertodano, M R S (Pooley Dale & Co) *A1 C1 G H K1 P T1 V*
Swindon *p406* 01793 488848
de Bono, D (Edwin Coe LLP) *B1 O Ze*
London WC2 *p29* 020 7691 4000
De Bruin, Miss K (Laytons) *E L S1 R2*
Guildford *p236*. 01483 407000
de Bruin, Ms N A (High Peak Borough Council)
Chapel-en-le-Frith *p454* . . . 0845 129 7777
de Candole, Ms S E (Batt Broadbent) *W T2 Zx*
Salisbury *p371*. 01722 411141
De Carvalho, Ms S (Dexter Montague LLP) *Zg Zi Q*
Reading *p360* 0118 939 3999
De Caulaincourt, Ms C D (Ashurst LLP)
London EC2 *p7* 020 7638 1111
De Coninck, R (De Coninck Solicitors) *L S1 W Zv*
Stoke-on-Trent *p397*. 01270 883484
De Ferrars, D K P (Taylor Wessing) *O Q Zj*
London EC4 *p86*. 020 7300 7000
de Ferrars, J K G (Peters Langsford Davies) *W T1 T2 E C1 A1 L R1 S1 Zd S2*
Launceston *p270* 01566 772451
de Ferrars Green, Ms C A (Mills & Reeve) *E S2 R1 R2*
Cambridge *p175*. 01223 364422
de Freitas, G (Penningtons)
London EC2 *p66*. 020 7457 3000
De Freitas, M A (Beale and Company Solicitors LLP) *Zq O Zj*
London WC2 *p11* 020 7240 3474
De Froberville, Ms V (LG Lawyers)
London SE1 *p50*. 020 7379 0000
de Galleani, S C (Cumberland Ellis Peirs) *E S1 S2 L R1 R2 A1 Zi Zs*
London WC1 *p23* 020 7242 0422
De Giovanni, J R (Downie & Gadban) *S1 E*
Alton *p116*. 01420 82879
Guildford *p236*. 01483 407000
De Graeve, M J A (Capsticks Solicitors LLP) *N Zr Zq*
London SW19 *p18*. 020 8780 2211
De Haas, B C (Jones Robertson) *G H K1 N L F1 D1 V W*
Runcorn *p369* 01928 711119
Widnes *p431*. 0151 423 3661
De Jong, Ms L M (Napp Pharmaceutical Holdings Ltd)
Cambridge *p453*. 01223 424444
De Jongh, A (Bates Wells & Braithwaite London LLP) *O Q A3 Zd*
London EC4 *p11*. 020 7551 7777
De La Fuente, Ms H (Abrahams Dresden)
London EC1 *p3* 020 7251 3663
De La Porte, P (Plexus Law (A Trading Name of Parabis Law LLP)) *Q O Zj N*
Evesham *p220*. 01386 769160
de la Rue, C M (Ince & Co Services Ltd)
London E1 *p44* 020 7481 0010
De Lacey, S L (Follett Stock LLP) *J1 Q*
Truro *p414*. 01872 241700
De Lance-Holmes, J (Linklaters LLP)
London EC2 *p54*. 020 7456 2000
De Lausan, Ms L (GH Cornish LLP) *C1 J1 C3 O F1*
Ilford *p260*. 020 8090 0800
de Lisle, Ms L (Reynolds Porter Chamberlain LLP)
London E1 *p71* 020 3060 6000
De Lorenzo, A (Simmons & Simmons)
London EC2 *p79*. 020 7628 2020
De Lorenzo, J (Irwin Mitchell LLP) *M1 M2 N*
London EC1 *p45*. 0870 150 0100
De Loynes, S J (Hewitsons) *E S2 L*
Northampton *p332*. 01604 233233
de Maid, B K (De Maid Solicitors & Advocates) *G H B2*
Cardiff *p178* 029 2023 5575
de Maid, M W (De Maid Solicitors & Advocates) *G H B2*
Cardiff *p178* 029 2023 5575
de Main, J D (Squire Sanders (UK) LLP) *E R1*
Leeds *p277* 0113 284 7000
De Maria, P (Doyle Clayton Solicitors Limited) *J1 Zp*
London EC2 *p27*. 020 7329 9090
De Meese, T (Crowell & Moring) *C3*
London EC4 *p23*. 020 7413 0011
De Mello Kamath, A R P (TLT Solicitors)
London EC2 *p85*. 020 3465 4000
De Mowbray, Ms V (Poole & Co) *S1 W*
Crewkerne *p203* 01460 279100
De Nisi, S (Ray Nixon Brown) *S1 W L A1 C1 E S2*
Leighton Buzzard *p282* . . . 01525 372247
de Pledge, P D (Fowler de Pledge) *B1 C1 E Zc Ze Zq J1 C2 O*
Cambridge *p174*. 01223 311291
De Prez, I S (Suffolk Coastal District Council)
Woodbridge *p477* 01394 383789
de Quidt, Mrs E J (Battens)
Yeovil *p443* 01935 846000
De Ridder, K C M (British Telecommunications PLC)
London EC1 *p104* 020 7356 6181
De Sica, G (Karina Leapman & Co) *D1 K3 K1 L O Q N*
London NW6 *p52* 020 7794 7741

De Silva, Ms D A (Wiggin LLP) *Zk O Zz Ze Zza U2*
Cheltenham *p189* 01242 224114
De Silva, K W E (Edward De Silva & Co) *K1 I N Q S1 V W T2 G Zi Zl Zq*
Southall *p384* 020 8571 2299
De Silva, Ms L (SNR Denton) *C1*
London EC4 *p75*. 020 7242 1212
de Silva, N (Penningtons)
London EC2 *p66*. 020 7457 3000
de Sousa, Miss S (Chadwyck-Healey & Co) *G H B2*
London EC4 *p19*. 020 7353 6900
De Souza, Ms M (Thompsons (formerly Robin/Brian Thompson & Partners)) *J1*
London SW19 *p87*. 020 8947 4163
De Souza, Miss S (Anthony Gold) *N Zr*
London SE1 *p6* 020 7940 4000
De Souza, Mrs S (T G Baynes) *K1 K3 D2*
Dartford *p207* 01322 295555
De Soyza, U (De Soyza & Fernando) *B3 D1 S2 E G H K3 K1 B2*
London SE21 *p26* 020 8670 9918
De Sybel, O (Bentleys Stokes & Lowless) *Za*
London EC3 *p12*. 020 7782 0990
De Tute, Mrs S L (Irwin Mitchell LLP) *O Q*
Leeds *p274* 0870 150 0100
De Val, Mrs S J I (Chelmsford Borough Council)
Chelmsford *p454*. 01245 606606
De Vecchi, I M T (Ines De Vecchi)
London SW12 *p26*. 020 8675 0152
De Vere, Miss L (Gordon de Vere) *S2 E S1*
St Albans *p390* 01727 758126
De Verneuil-Smith, B (McClure Naismith)
London EC4 *p56*. 020 7623 9155
De Viell, Miss M L (Thames Water Utilities Limited)
Reading *p469* 0118 373 8000
de Villiers, P S (Stewarts Law LLP) *O B1*
London EC4 *p83*. 020 7822 8000
de Villiers, T (Williams Gorman LLP)
Haringey *p91* . . . .
de Voil, N M (Rich & Carr Freer Bouskell) *E J1 C1 S1 W A1 L Zi Zc*
Leicester *p281*. 0116 253 8021
De Vos, Ms A L (Donns) *N*
Manchester *p303* 0161 834 3311
De'Ath, G (Gross & Co) *W T2 K4 Zd*
Bury St Edmunds *p171* 01284 763333
De-Friend, R (The College of Law)
London WC1 *p105*. 0800 289997
De-Maine, Ms S (The College of Law)
London WC1 *p105*. 0800 289997
De-Mel, Miss V L (Roebucks) *W G K4 T2*
Blackburn *p145* 01254 274000
de-Souza, M (Luke Kore Solicitors)
London SE17 *p50* 020 7277 3880
Deacon, A A R (Percy Walker & Co) *W K4*
Hastings *p243* 01424 721234
Deacon, A R (Hine Downing Solicitors) *T2 W K4*
Falmouth *p223*. 01326 316655
Deacon, C (Jefferies Essex LLP) *G Zm*
Westcliff-on-Sea *p428* 01702 332311
Deacon, J (Squire Sanders (UK) LLP) *M2 O Zc*
London EC2 *p81*. 020 7655 1000
Deacon, J T (George H Coles & Co) *Q O N F1 G H L J1 Zl Zb*
Hove *p254*. 01273 205101
Deacon, Ms M (LG Lawyers)
London SE1 *p50*. 020 7379 0000
Deacon, Ms S (B P Collins LLP) *E*
Gerrards Cross *p229*. 01753 889995
Deadman, Mrs R E (Oxley & Coward Solicitors LLP) *K1 K2 D1 D2*
Rotherham *p367*. 01709 510999
Deakin, J (Veale Wasbrough Vizards) *X Zw*
Bristol *p165* 0117 925 2020
Deakin, K (Veale Wasbrough Vizards) *J1 Zp*
Bristol *p165* 0117 925 2020
Deal, A M (Barker Gillette) *B2 O Q*
London W1 *p9*. 020 7636 0555
Dean, Miss A (Pinney Talfourd LLP)
Hornchurch *p252* 01708 511000
Dean, A G (Dean & Co) *C1 E S2 K4 L W*
Stourbridge *p399* 01384 352525
Dean, Miss A L (Gepp & Sons) *N*
Chelmsford *p186*. 01245 493939
Colchester *p197* 01206 369889
Dean, B (Ashworths Solicitors) *S2 C1 E R2*
London SW19 *p8* 0845 370 1000
Dean, B E (AWB Partnership LLP) *S1 W E T1 Zh*
Guildford *p235*. 01483 302345
Dean, Miss C (Justices' Clerk's Office)
Worthing *p477*. 01903 210981
Worthing *p477*. 01903 210981
Dean, C E (Geldards LLP) *Zc*
Derby *p208* 01332 331631
Dean, G R (Gordon Dean Solicitors) *J1 N Q W*
Norwich *p334* 01603 767671
Dean, G R B (The Smith Partnership) *D1 K1*
Derby *p209* 01332 225225
Dean, Ms H M (Walsall Metropolitan Borough Council)
Walsall *p475*. 01922 650000
Dean, H M (Irwin Mitchell LLP) *N Zj*
Birmingham *p139* 0870 150 0100
Dean, Mrs J (Dean & Co) *S1 W K1 L R1 E*
Stourbridge *p399* 01384 352525
Dean, J L F (Sutton-Mattocks & Co LLP)
London W4 *p84* 020 8994 7344
Dean, J M (John M Dean & Co) *G H J1 N Q S1 W B1 D1*
Denton *p208*. 0161 337 9665

See p634 for the Key to Work Categories

Dean, Ms K A (Chorley Magistrates' Court) Chorley p455 01257 225000

Dean, K J (Stephenson Harwood) London EC2 p82 020 7329 4422

Dean, Mrs L J (The Head Partnership) S1 W L K4 Reading p361 0118 975 6622

Dean, M (Simmons & Simmons) O J1 London EC2 p79 020 7628 2020

Dean, Ms M S (HCB Solicitors) D2 B1 K3 K4 J1 K1 L Q N W Lichfield p284 01543 414426

Dean, N G (Gosschalks) N P L F1 Zj Hull p256 01482 324252

Dean, P (Holman Fenwick Willan) London EC3 p42 020 7264 8000

Dean, P (Mincoffs Solicitors LLP) Newcastle upon Tyne p325 0191 281 6151

Dean, Mrs R (Clarion Solicitors LLP) C1 C2 Leeds p272 0113 246 0622

Dean, R E (Pinkney Grunwells Lawyers LLP) W A1 V Zm Zd Zo T2 Bridlington p158 01262 673445

Dean, R M (Gordons LLP) Leeds p273 0113 227 0100

Dean, S (Abbey Law Solicitors) N G H Burton-on-Trent p170 01283 539718

Dean, S A (Alker & Ball) C1 E S2 C2 Wigan p432 01942 246241

Dean, Ms S J (Waldrons) S1 Walsall p420 01384 811811

Dean, Ms T (Bates Wells & Braithwaite London LLP) London EC4 p11 020 7551 7777

Dean, Miss V (Prisoners' Advice Service) K1 London EC1 p108 020 7253 3323

Dean, W J (Dean Thomas & Co) N K1 F1 J1 Zq Worksop p441 01909 500511

Deane, Miss S A (Bhatia Best) G H Nottingham p336 0115 950 3231

Deane, Ms W A (Platt Halpern) D1 K1 Manchester p308 0161 224 2555 Manchester p309 0161 834 3114

Deans, A R W (Hextalls) Zj F2 Zq Zw O Q N J2 Zc F1 Zf P Zy London EC2 p41 020 7382 0700

Deans, M S (Paul Robinson Solicitors) C1 E S2 S1 Westcliff-on-Sea p428 01702 338338

Deans, N (Goodman Derrick LLP) London EC4 p36 020 7404 0606

Deans, S J (B P Collins LLP) C1 I Ze C2 Gerrards Cross p229 01753 889995

Dear, A A A (Ashurst LLP) E London EC2 p7 020 7638 1111

Dear, M J (Malcolm Dear Whitfield Evans LLP) S1 W E N K1 O Q Kenton p265 020 8907 4366

Dearden, J (MKB Solicitors LLP) G H K1 D1 Barnsley p124 01226 210000

Dearden, M J (Robson & Co) J1 K1 N Q W K3 Hythe p259 01303 264581 / 267413

Dearden, Ms R (The College of Law York) O York p477 0800 289997

Deards, T J (British Waterways Board) Watford p475 01923 226422 Kingston upon Thames p462 020 8541 9088

Dearing, B (SFN Solicitors) G S1 Burnley p169 01282 421284

Dearing, G G (Brachers) K1 D1 B1 Zt Maidstone p299 01622 690691

Dearing, I B (SFN Solicitors) C1 O E S1 W Q A1 G T1 Zf Zn Ze Zw Burnley p169 01282 421284

Dearing, M (Manchester City Council) Manchester p465 0161 234 5000

Dearing, M G (Knowsley Metropolitan Borough Council) Huyton p461 0151 443 3593

Dearing, N (SFN Solicitors) G H B2 Burnley p169 01282 421284

Dearing, P (Kingston upon Hull City Council) Hull p461 01482 300300

Dearle, Ms J (Withers LLP) T2 W London EC4 p92 020 7597 6000

Dearle, M (Withers LLP) K1 London EC4 p92 020 7597 6000

Dearlove, J R (The National Trust) E Swindon p475 01793 817400

Dearsall, Mrs C (Hart Brown Solicitors) S1 Woking p437 0800 068 8177

Dearsley, K R (DLA Piper UK LLP) Zf London EC2 p24 0870 011 1111

Deas, R (BHP Law) K3 K1 North Shields p330 0191 257 2213

Deasy, P (Taylor Wessing) London EC4 p86 020 7300 7000

Deavall, M (Woolliscrofts) N K1 Q S1 Hanley p239 01782 204000

Deaves, G L G (Holden & Co) G S1 N W K1 E V D1 L Zl Za Zj Hastings p243 01424 722422

Deaville, M (Kennedys) Q N London EC3 p49 020 7667 9667

Deaville, Ms P (Pluck Andrew & Co) Hyde p259 0161 368 6311

Debenham, C J (Debenhams Ottaway) S1 E St Albans p390 01727 837161

Debenham, J M R (James M R Debenham) C1 O P Q S1 S2 W Ze Zq Zy Dorchester p212 0845 230 0644

Debenham, Miss K A (Simmons & Simmons) London EC2 p79 020 7628 2020

Debenham, R E (Debenhams Ottaway) W St Albans p390 01727 837161

Debens, M S (Downs) E C1 L O Q B1 F1 Zl Zc Dorking p212 01306 880110

DeBiase, Ms J (IBB Solicitors) E K1 Q W Uxbridge p417 0845 638 1381

Debidin, D D P (Debidins) K1 S1 P G H L F1 W Q Zi Zk Ealing p26 020 8567 1381 / 8567 6343

Debidin, Ms D S (Debidins) D1 F1 F2 J1 K1 Q Zi V W Ealing p26 020 8567 1381 / 8567 6343

Debnath, T (Solihull Magistrates Court) Solihull p471 0121 705 8101

Debney, Ms F (Challinors) N Q Birmingham p136 0121 212 9393

Debney, P (Challinors) N Q O Zr B2 J2 Zw Zj West Bromwich p427 0121 553 3211

Decardi-Nelson, R (Enfield Magistrates Court) London N17 p106 020 8808 5411

Decesare, J (3i PLC) London SW1 p103 020 7928 3131

Dee, A L (Dee & Griffin) K1 S1 J1 W N C1 D1 E Q F1 Zc Zm Zl Gloucester p230 01452 617288

Deebank, Ms J M (Yorkshire Electricity Group PLC) Leeds p463 0113 289 2123

Deech, Dr J S (Blake Lapthorn) C1 E J1 L A1 B1 Oxford p342 01865 248607

Deegan, T A (T A Deegan) E L P S1 Whitton p431 020 8755 2574

Deehan, Miss H R (Memery Crystal) E S1 S2 London WC2 p60 020 7242 5905

Deehan, Ms R H (Lester Aldridge LLP) E London WC2 p53 0844 967 0785

Deekes, D M (Milford & Dormor) S1 L W Axminster p120 01297 32206 / 32207

Deeley, M (Pearson Rowe) N Q O Birmingham p141 0121 236 7388

Deeming, Ms M J (Browne Jacobson LLP) N Zj Nottingham p336 0115 976 6000

Deeming, N (The BOC Group PLC) Guildford p476 01483 579857

Deeny, Ms L B (Barlow Lyde & Gilbert LLP) London EC3 p10 020 7247 2277

Deepak, Mrs P (Hasan Solicitors) Zi K1 Birmingham p139 0121 778 4003

Deer, Ms S (Plexus Law (A Trading Name of Parabis Law LLP)) N Q Evesham p220 01386 769160

Deerness, Ms Y (Cancer Research UK) London WC2 p104 020 7242 0200

Dees, D C (Heald Solicitors) C1 U2 C2 I Milton Keynes p317 01908 662277

Deeth, Ms A M (Herbert Smith LLP) London EC2 p40 020 7374 8000

DeFeo, M (Crowell & Moring) C2 London EC4 p23 020 7413 0011

Defries, G (Bird & Bird LLP) C1 U1 London EC4 p13 020 7415 6000

Defries, G (Dechert) C2 London EC4 p26 020 7184 7000

Degirmen, E (Wright Son & Pepper LLP) S1 S2 E Camden p93 020 7242 5473

Dehghan, Ms J (Malletts Solicitors) K1 K3 London WC1 p58 020 7061 3760

Deibel, J W (Deibel & Allen) S1 W E C1 K1 L T1 S2 R2 Portslade-by-Sea p354 01273 430999

Deighton, Miss S (Coffin Mew & Clover) L Q Zh Zu Fareham p223 01329 825617

Dejon-Stewart, Miss E (Percy Hughes & Roberts) W O Birkenhead p134 0151 666 9090

Dekany, A (Holman Fenwick Willan) London EC3 p42 020 7264 8000

Del Giudice, Dr C (Claudio Del Giudice) C1 M2 O London EC2 p26 020 7613 2788

Del Medico, G G (BBC) London W12 p103 020 8752 5734

Del-Llano, M (Jacobs & Reeves) C1 R2 S1 E S2 Poole p353 01202 674425

Delafaille, O M (Bristows) O Ze London EC4 p15 020 7400 8000

Delahunty, Ms L M (Peters & Peters) G H J1 M1 N Q O Zp Zg London EC4 p67 020 7629 7991

Delamere, Miss R C (Nestle UK Ltd) Croydon p456 020 8667 5260

Delaney, Miss A M (Torbay Council) Torquay p474 01803 201201

Delaney, Ms C J (CMS Cameron McKenna LLP) London EC3 p17 020 7367 3000

Delaney, Miss C J M (Irwin Mitchell LLP) Zr Sheffield p376 0870 150 0100

Delaney, M J (Matthew Arnold & Baldwin LLP) J1 O Q B1 C1 Zq Watford p423 01923 202020

Delaney, R (Plexus Law (A Trading Name of Parabis Law LLP)) N Q Evesham p220 01386 769160

Delaney, Miss S M (D P Roberts Hughes & Denye) K1 K2 D1 Birkenhead p134 0151 647 6000

Delbourgo, Ms A (The College of Law) London WC1 p105 0800 289997

Delemore, Miss C L (Geldards LLP) Ze Cardiff p178 029 2023 8239

Delgado, Ms A (Ashurst LLP) London EC2 p7 020 7638 1111

Delgado-Bush, Miss N L (Elliot Mather LLP) Mansfield p311 01623 655666

Delin, W (Wyre Forest District Council) Stourport-on-Severn p473 01562 820505

Dell, A B (DLA Piper UK LLP) B1 C1 J1 Zb C2 London EC2 p24 0870 011 1111 London EC2 p81 020 7655 1000

Dell, Mrs A M (South Bucks District Council) Denham p456 01895 837200

Dell, Ms G (McNamara Ryan) W K4 Weybridge p430 01932 846041

Dell, N J (Redrow PLC) S2 E R2 S1 A1 Bristol p452 01275 813350 Bridgwater p158 01278 457891

Dell, R J (Badhams Law (A Trading Name of Parabis Law LLP)) Zj E Zq Croydon p204 0844 245 4000

Dell, Ms S L (Follett Stock LLP) O Q B1 L V Zq Truro p414 01872 241700

Dellar, H (Lee Bolton Monier-Williams) Westminster p52 020 7222 5381

Dellaway, Ms L M (Maxwell Winward LLP) W T2 London EC4 p59 020 7651 0000

Deller, Miss A M (Clifton Ingram LLP) D1 D2 K1 Wokingham p437 0118 978 0099

Deller, Mrs I K (Sandwell Metropolitan Borough Council) Oldbury p468 0121 569 2200

Deller, M (Northrop McNaughtan Deller) London W9 p64 020 7289 7300

Delrio Walker, Ms L M E (Staffordshire County Council) Stafford p472 01785 223121

Delroy, Ms J (Addleshaw Goddard) Manchester p300 0161 934 6000

Deluca, Ms W (Mondial Assistance (UK) Ltd) Croydon p456 020 8681 2525

Delves, C R W (Abbott Cresswell LLP) D1 K1 London SW14 p3 020 8876 4478

Delves, Ms M C (Claire Delves) D1 Northampton p331 01327 831050

Demelo, A (Key2Law LLP) Ewell p220 020 8393 0941

Demery, N P (Society of Lloyd's) London EC3 p107 020 7327 1000

Demetriou, A (Anthony Solicitors) Q N O L S1 W J1 K1 Enfield p6 020 8360 4333

Demetriou, Mrs M (Austin Ryder & Co) A1 E G R1 S1 W Enfield p8 020 8804 5111

Demetriou, Ms R (AMD Solicitors) K1 D1 K3 Bristol p160 0117 962 1460

Demidecki-Demidowicz, M R (Michael Demidecki) G Q London W9 p26 020 7266 3607

Demoily, M R (Atha & Co) N Q Middlesbrough p314 01642 222575

Demosthenous, P (P George & Co) N Q S1 Zj Haringey p35 020 8341 9080

Dempsey, Ms G (Pearson Lowe) B1 C1 E K1 L Q S1 Zc Westminster p66 020 7224 0888

Dempsey, Ms J E (London Fire & Emergency Planning Authority) London SE1 p107 020 8555 1200

Dempsey, P D (Kerman & Co LLP) Zd T1 T2 W London WC2 p49 020 7539 7272

Dempsey, R J (Roythornes LLP) N Q Zr O Spalding p389 01775 842500

Dempsey, S (Shakespeares) Birmingham p142 0121 237 3000

Dempsey, S F (Lewis Silkin LLP) J1 London EC4 p53 020 7074 8000

Dempster, A D R (Herbert Smith LLP) O Zj Zq London EC2 p40 020 7374 8000

Dempster, Miss A J (Persimmon PLC) E S1 Witham p476 01376 518811

Dempster, K R (Kerman & Co LLP) C1 C2 U2 Zb U1 I J1 Zza Zn London WC2 p49 020 7539 7272

Dempster, Mrs P A S (Freeth Cartwright LLP) O B1 J1 Nottingham p337 0115 936 9369

Dempster, P E A (Dempster Binning LLP) E S2 R2 Chandlers Ford p184 023 8062 1790

Denby, R M (Denby & Co) Q W S1 A1 E L O T2 Barrow-in-Furness p125 01229 822366 Ulverston p416 01229 582283

Dench, Ms A (Miles & Partners) D1 F1 G K1 L P M1 V London EC3 p60 020 7426 0400

Dench, R (Edridges & Drummonds) S1 W L P K1 E M1 C1 South Croydon p383 020 8651 1218

Dench, S H (Stewarts Law LLP) N M3 M2 London EC4 p83 020 7822 8000

Dendle, Ms S (Ellis Jones) K1 Bournemouth p151 01202 525333

Denford, R (Bristol City Council) Bristol p451 0117 922 2000

Denham, A (Thompsons (formerly Robin/Brian Thompson & Partners)) N Manchester p310 0161 819 3500

Denham, Ms C (Medlicott Snows) D1 K3 K1 Bishops Castle p145 01588 638425

Denham, D R W (De La Rue PLC) C1 Zb Ze Basingstoke p448 01256 605000

Denham, J A C (Simpson Millar LLP) J1 O Q London EC1 p80 0844 858 3400

Denham, Mrs J M (Stevens) K1 K3 Haverhill p244 01440 762511

Denham, Ms K (Harris Cartier LLP) K1 K3 Slough p382 01753 810710

Denham, S C (Denhams) K1 S1 G Q W Guildford p236 01483 456450

Denham, Miss S J (Turbervilles) K1 D1 D2 Uxbridge p417 01895 201700 Uxbridge p417 01895 201700

Denham, Miss S M (Samantha Denham Solicitors) S1 Hastings p243 01424 718822 / 719111

Denholm, M G (Walker Smith Way) N Wrexham p443 0844 346 3100

Denholm, P M (Essex County Council) Chelmsford p454 0845 743 0430

Denison, J A (Green Williamson Solicitors) N Q O Zk Wakefield p418 01924 291400

Denison, P B (Kenneth Bush) K1 P G M1 F1 S1 D1 L V King's Lynn p266 01553 692737

Denley, Miss G (Mackrell Turner Garrett) K1 D1 K2 S1 Q N G Woking p437 01483 755609

Denley, P (Pinsent Masons LLP) E Birmingham p141 0121 200 1050

Denley, Mrs P (The International Family Law Group) K3 K1 K2 London WC2 p45 020 3178 5668

Denmead, M (Barr Ellison LLP) A1 Q S1 E Cambridge p174 01223 417200

Dennehy, Ms A M (National Grid PLC) Warwick p471 01926 653000

Dennehy, Ms L F (Information Commisioner) Wilmslow p476 01625 545700

Dennehy, Ms S (The Newspaper Society) J1 Q London EC4 p108 020 7632 7400

Dennerly, Miss J E (Sedgwick Phelan & Partners) W Middleton p315 0161 653 5299

Dennerly, R C (Sedgwick Phelan & Partners) N J1 Middleton p315 0161 653 5299

Dennerly, R E (Foot Anstey) E S1 L Plymouth p349 01752 675000 Plymouth p351 01752 663295

Denness, Miss C (Peterborough City Council) Peterborough p468 01733 747474

Dennett, Ms A (Kingston upon Hull City Council) K1 Hull p461 01482 300300

Dennett, Mrs K L (Hewitsons) R1 Cambridge p174 01223 461155

Dennett, R (Green Williamson Solicitors) Wakefield p418 01924 291400

Dennett-Thorpe, Ms L (John Laing) London SW1 p107 020 7901 3200

Dennies, O (Denniss Matthews) London SE20 p27 020 8778 7301 / 8778 7631

Denning, M (Sidley Austin Brown & Wood) Zb London EC2 p78 020 7360 3600

Dennis, Ms A (Russell-Cooke LLP) E London SW15 p74 020 8789 9111

Dennis, Ms A J (Reed Smith LLP) C1 London EC2 p71 020 3116 3000

Dennis, Mrs A M M (Wycombe & Beaconsfield Magistrates Court) High Wycombe p461 01494 651035

Dennis, D R (David Phillips & Partners) B2 G H Bootle p150 0151 922 5525

Dennis, J (Kirwans) W Moreton p319 0151 677 3433

Dennis, J A J (Barlow Lyde & Gilbert LLP) London EC3 p10 020 7247 2277 London EC3 p31 020 7861 4000

Dennis, Ms M (Wiseman Lee LLP) D1 K1 K3 Waltham Forest p92 020 8215 1000

Dennis, M (Shammah Nicholls LLP) O Q C1 B1 Manchester p309 0161 832 9272

Dennis, M J (Bird & Bird LLP) C1 C2 Zw London EC4 p13 020 7415 6000

Dennis, N P A (Hart Reade) D1 K1 K3 Eastbourne p215 01323 727321

Dennis, Mrs R L (Ashfield District Council) Kirkby-in-Ashfield p462 01623 450000

Dennis, Mrs S (Gaby Hardwicke) K1 Hastings p243 01424 438011

Dennis, T D (Drummonds) N K3 Zr Q O L Chester p190 01244 408300

Dennis-Browne, D (Reynolds Porter Chamberlain LLP) London E1 p71 020 3060 6000

Dennison, A L C (Horwich Cohen Coghlan) N P B1 M1 C1 J1 F1 Zc Ze Zb Manchester p305 0161 830 4600

Dennison, G (Simmons & Simmons) London EC2 p79 020 7628 2020

Dennison, Miss J (Armstrong Foulkes) Zr Middlesbrough p314 01642 231110

Denny, A (Faegre & Benson LLP) J1 Zp London EC4 p30 020 7450 4500

Denny, C J (SNR Denton) E Milton Keynes p317 01908 690260

Denny, Miss J (Clarkson Wright & Jakes Ltd) K1 Orpington p341 01689 887887

Denny, J M (Cripps Harries Hall LLP) W Tunbridge Wells p415 01892 515121

Denny, K J (Martin Tolhurst Partnership LLP) S1 K1 Gravesend p233 01474 325531

Denny, Ms K L (Nabarro LLP) London WC1 p63 020 7524 6000

Denny, N (Mogers) Bath p127 01225 750000

Denny, N R (TLT Solicitors) *K1*
Bristol *p165* 0117 917 7777

Denny, Mrs S (Ronaldsons) *K1 K3 K2 D1*
Norwich *p335* 01603 618883

Denovan-Smith, D J (DR Solicitors) *J1 O Q*
Guildford *p236*. 01483 511555

Dent, Mrs H (Keoghs and Nicholls, Lindsell & Harris) *L*
Altrincham *p116* 0161 928 9321

Dent, Ms J L (Simmons & Simmons)
London EC2 *p79*. 020 7628 2020

Dent, L (Home Group Ltd)
Newcastle upon Tyne *p459* . 0845 155 1234

Dent, N A H (Barlow Lyde & Gilbert LLP)
London EC3 *p10*. 020 7247 2277
London EC2 *p79*. 020 7628 2020

Dentith, P J (Almy & Thomas) *G H B2*
Torquay *p412* 01803 299131

Denton, A (Bell Lax Litigation) *N Zr O Q*
Sutton Coldfield *p403* 0121 355 0011

Denton, A (Pinsent Masons LLP) *O Q*
Manchester *p308* 0161 234 8234

Denton, C M (Chris Denton) *A1 B1 C1 D1 E F1 G H J1*
Burley-in-Wharfedale *p168*. . 01943 607828

Denton, L A (Bowcock Cuerden LLP) *P Zu R1*
Nantwich *p320*. 01270 611106
Chester *p190* 01829 773100
Manchester *p311* 0161 233 7330

Denton, Ms S C (Nottingham Law Centre) *L*
Nottingham *p467*. 0115 978 7813

Denton, Z W (Treasury Solicitors Department)
London WC2 *p110*. 020 7210 3000

Denton-Hawkes, Ms M M (Port of Tyne Authority)
South Shields *p471* 0191 455 2671

Denton-Masih, Mrs N (Machins Solicitors LLP) *W K4*
Luton *p295* 01582 514000

Denver, Mrs S (Hempsons) *Zr Zq N*
Manchester *p305* 0161 228 0011
Lancaster *p270* 0844 858 3900

Denvir, Miss A M (Nicol Denvir & Purnell) *D1 K1 D2*
Cardiff *p180* 029 2079 6311

Denye, A J (D P Roberts Hughes & Denye) *C1 E F1 J1 L R1 S1 W Zc Ze Zl*
Birkenhead *p134*. 0151 647 6000

Denyer, S J (DWF) *N Q Zj*
Manchester *p303* 0161 603 5000

Denza, P (Lamb Brooks LLP) *W K4*
Basingstoke *p126* 01256 844888

Depner, J M (Ross Aldridge LLP) *N*
Cheltenham *p187* 01242 707400

Depree, Mrs H (Edwards Angell Palmer & Dodge)
London EC2 *p28*. 020 7583 4055

Derbyshire, A (Birchall Ryan Solicitors) *K1 G H W*
Congleton *p198* 01260 297070

Derbyshire, Dr D W (SJ Berwin LLP) *Zo*
London EC4 *p75*. 020 7111 2222

Derbyshire, Ms H (Shoosmiths)
Fareham *p224*. . . . 0370 086 6800 / 01489 616800

Derbyshire, P A (Ford Simey LLP) *N P Zj*
Exeter *p221* 01392 274126

Derbyshire, Ms S J (Foys Solicitors) *D1 D2 K1*
Doncaster *p211* 01302 327136

Derbyshire, Miss S L (Telford Magistrates Court)
Telford *p474* 01952 204500

Deretic, Ms U (Kerman & Co LLP) *C1 C2*
London WC2 *p49* 020 7539 7272

Derham, Ms M A (Harbottle & Lewis LLP) *C1 F1 Zv*
London W1 *p38* 020 7667 5000

Deritis, Ms V S L (Marrons) *N*
Newcastle upon Tyne *p325* . 0191 281 1304

Dernie, Miss N (Mills & Reeve) *W S1*
Norwich *p335* 01603 660155

Derosaire, Mrs P (Rebecca L Faret Solicitors) *W S1*
Flitwick *p226*. 01525 712112

Derrett-Smith, Miss T (Challinors) *K1 D1*
Birmingham *p136* 0121 212 9393

Derrick, Mrs A D R (Palmers) *S2 E S1*
Basildon *p126* 01268 240000

Derrick, M (AWB Partnership LLP) *W T1 S1*
Guildford *p235*. 01483 302345

Derry, Mrs H (Sills & Betteridge LLP) *K1 K2*
Lincoln *p285*. 01522 542211

Derry, J S (Evans Derry Rennie & Co)
Birmingham *p138* 0121 770 1721

Derry, Mrs M V (Keith Flower & Co) *D1 K1 K2 K3 W*
Pinner *p348* 020 8868 1277

Derry-Evans, R S (CMS Cameron McKenna LLP)
London EC3 *p17*. 020 7367 3000

Dersley, Miss G K (Information Commisioner)
Wilmslow *p476*. 01625 545700

Deru, Ms K (Department for Business, Enterprise and Regulatory Reform)
London SW1 *p105*. 020 7215 0105

Dervan, G P (MSB Solicitors LLP)
Liverpool *p289*. 0151 281 9040

Dervin, Ms D (Magrath LLP) *Zi*
London W1 *p57* 020 7495 3003

Dervish, D (Fletcher Dervish) *N K1 G E S1 B1 H O Q Zi Zl D1 B2 S2*
Haringey *p33* 020 8800 4615

Dervish, E N (Hugh Jones & Co) *E J1 K1 N O Q S1 W Zl Zj Zo Zi*
London N3 *p43* 020 8346 2236

Des Forges, R J (Leeds City Council)
Leeds *p462* 0113 224 3513

Desai, B (Broadway Solicitors)
Wandsworth *p16*. 020 8767 7718

Desai, Ms B (Plexus Law (A Trading Name of Parabis Law LLP)) *N Q*
Evesham *p220*. 01386 769160
London EC3 *p68*. 0844 245 4000

Desai, B K (Allen & Overy LLP) *C1 Zg*
London E1 *p5* 020 3088 0000

Desai, C (Bhatia Best) *K1 K2*
Nottingham *p336*. 0115 950 3231

Desai, D (McGrigors LLP)
London EC4 *p56*. 020 7054 2500

Desai, F B (Surrey County Council)
Kingston upon Thames *p462*. 020 8541 9088

Desai, K S (Mayer Brown International LLP) *M1*
London EC2 *p59*. 020 3130 3000

Desai, L (Aylesbury Vale District Council)
Aylesbury *p447* 01296 585858

Desai, Ms M (McGrigors LLP)
London EC4 *p56*. 020 7054 2500

Desai, N (Ellis Taylor Law LLP) *E L Q S1*
London WC2 *p29* 020 7405 0206

Desai, Miss N D (Barlow Lyde & Gilbert LLP) *L Q G*
London EC3 *p10*. 020 7247 2277

Desbottes, Mrs K J (K J Desbottes & Co)
Caterham *p183* 01883 343460

Desforges, Miss A B (The College of Law) *M1 P K1 S1*
London WC1 *p105*. 0800 289997

Desira, R (Corries Solicitors)
York *p444* 0845 241 5566

Desmond, A C A (Boyes Turner) *N*
Reading *p360* 0118 959 7711

Desmond, L (Blake Lapthorn) *E*
Oxford *p342*. 01865 248607

Desor, K K (Desor & Co) *B1 Zc S2 E F1 F2 L O Q N Zq S1 W*
Hayes *p245* 020 8569 0708

Desor, Mrs N (Desor & Co) *D2 D1 K3 K1 N Zq*
Hayes *p245* 020 8569 0708

Desoutter, N A (Coole & Haddock) *J1 M1 P G H S1 F1 E W A1 Zc Zk Zl*
Horsham *p253*. 01403 210200

Despicht, Miss R (Birnberg Peirce & Partners)
Camden *p13*. 020 7911 0166

Detheridge, C J (Wace Morgan) *O Q Zq*
Shrewsbury *p379* 01743 280100

Dev, Mrs R (Portner & Jaskel LLP) *N*
London W1 *p68* 020 7616 5300

Devall, R (Pitmans LLP) *J1 Zi Zw*
Reading *p361* 0118 958 0224

Devane, J P A (J P A Devane Solicitor)
Woking *p436*. 01483 472760

Devas, H E (Boodle Hatfield) *E P L R1 R2 S2*
Westminster *p14*. 020 7629 7411

Deveney, Ms J E (Jeffreys & Powell) *Q K1 N F1*
Brecon *p156*. 01874 622106

Devenport, Mrs J (Ridley & Hall) *E C1 L*
Huddersfield *p256* 01484 538421

Dever, D M (Leviten Thompson & Co) *K3 D1 D2 G H K1 S1 S2 Q*
Sheffield *p376* 0114 276 9321

Devereaux, A (Ince & Co Services Ltd)
London E1 *p44* 020 7481 0010

Devereux, A T (Borneo Hughes Martell LLP) *E S2 C2 R2 C1 S1*
Northampton *p331*. 01604 624822

Devereux, Ms C (The Endeavour Partnership LLP) *J1*
Stockton-on-Tees *p397* . . . 01642 610300

Devereux, I (Stephenson Harwood) *E L*
London EC2 *p82*. 020 7329 4422

Devereux, M J (Olswang LLP) *C1 Zb Ze Zf*
London WC1 *p64* 020 7067 3000

Devereux, R J (Devereux & Co) *K1*
Bristol *p162* 0117 959 3344
Bristol *p162* 0117 938 0222

Devereux, R J (Friends Provident)
Dorking *p457* 01306 654925

Deverill, Mrs I (Parker Bullen) *W T2 Zd*
Andover *p118* 01264 400500

Devile, J R (Carter Devile) *S1 E L W F1 C1 K1 N Q D1 Zc Zl*
Ilford *p259*. 020 8590 1066

Devine, A N (Swinburne Maddison) *K1 G H D1 M1 N P S1 B1 F1 Zi*
Durham *p214* . . 0191 384 2441 / 384 7455

Devine, Mrs J E (Storrar Cowdry) *K1*
Chester *p191* 01244 400567

Devine, J R (Muckle LLP) *Zw Zd C1*
Newcastle upon Tyne *p325* . 0191 211 7777

Devine, P (Reynolds Porter Chamberlain LLP)
London E1 *p71* 020 3060 6000

Devitt, Ms C L (Information Commisioner)
Wilmslow *p476*. 01625 545700

Devitt, P (Addleshaw Goddard)
Manchester *p300* 0161 934 6000

Devitt, S J (Treasury Solicitors Department)
London WC2 *p110*. 020 7210 3000

Devlia, A (HSBC Legal Department)
Birmingham *p449* 0121 455 2740

Devlin, A J (Owen White) *R2 E Zh*
Slough *p382*. 01753 876800

Devlin, A J M (Horsey Lightly) *K1 L D1 B1 Zk Zl*
Westminster *p43*. 020 7222 8844

Devlin, H (Withers LLP) *C2 C1 Zf*
London EC4 *p92*. 020 7597 6000

Devlin, J R (Grove Tompkins Bosworth) *E F1 G H N L S1*
Birmingham *p138* 0121 236 9341 / 236 8091

Devlin, M B (Cumbria County Council)
Carlisle *p453*. . . . .01228 607374 / 607351

Devlin, M D (Stephensons Solicitors LLP) *D1*
Manchester *p310* 0161 832 8844

Devlin, P J (Hartlepool Borough Council)
Hartlepool *p460* 01429 266522

Devlin, S (Kerman & Co LLP) *K1 O C2*
London WC2 *p49* 020 7539 7272

Devlin, S (DLA Piper UK LLP)
Manchester *p303* 0870 011 1111

Devonald, N (Wilson Devonald Ltd)
Swansea *p406*. 01792 484566

Devoy, J M (Aaron & Partners LLP Solicitors) *B1 O Q Zv Zq Zk*
Chester *p190* 01244 405555

Dew, M P (Abrams Collyer) *W T2 Zd K4*
Lymington *p296* 01590 677888

Dew, Mrs S (Edward Hayes LLP) *K3 D2 K1 G H B2*
London EC4 *p39*. 020 7353 0011

Dewar, A R (DAC Beachcroft)
London EC4 *p24*. 020 7936 2222

Dewar, M A (Simmons & Simmons)
London EC2 *p79*. 020 7628 2020

Dewar, M J (T G Baynes) *S1*
Dartford *p207* 01322 295555

Dewar-Finch, Ms S (Middlesbrough Council)
Middlesbrough *p465* 01642 245432

Dewdney, R O (Leeds Day) *B1 C1 E L S1 Zl*
Huntingdon *p258*. 01480 454301

Dewes, C (Shoosmiths)
Birmingham *p142* 0370 086 4000 / 0121 335 4440

Dewey, A C (Shell International Ltd) *C1 C2 C3 E J1 M1 M2 O P Q Ze Zc*
London SE1 *p109* 020 7934 1234

Dewey, C R (Ward Gethin) *N Q J2 Zr*
King's Lynn *p266* 01553 660033

Dewey, M (Hallett & Co) *S1 W S2*
Ashford *p119* 01233 625711

Dewhurst, C T (Challenor Gardiner) *S1 S2 W E K4*
Oxford *p343*. 01865 721451

Dewhurst, J T (The Watson Ramsbottom Partnership) *G H J1 Zl*
Blackburn *p146* 01254 672222
Darwen *p207* 01254 701111

Dewis, Ms S (Galbraith Branley) *K1 D2 D1 K3*
London N12 *p34*. 020 8446 8474

Dewis, Miss S J F (Freedman Sharman & Co) *K1 D1 M1 J1 F1 P L*
Borehamwood *p150* 020 8953 9111

Dews, R J (Dews Witcomb) *S1 T1 E W C1*
Leicester *p279*. 0116 233 4499

Dewsbury, A (Gillespies) *S1 W C1 E L S2 C2*
Walsall *p420*. 01922 627474

Dewsbury, S P (Thompsons (formerly Robin/Brian Thompson & Partners)) *N J1*
Birmingham *p143* 0121 262 1200

Dewson, Ms F M (Simmons & Simmons) *C1 C2*
London EC2 *p79*. 020 7628 2020

Dewson, Mrs S M (KieranClarkeGreen) *K1 D1*
Staveley *p394* 01246 280099

Dexter, Miss H C (TBI Solicitors) *W*
Barnard Castle *p123*. 01833 638326

Dexter, J (Keoghs LLP) *J1 J2 N*
Bolton *p149* 01204 677000

Dexter, Miss M S (South Tyneside Metropolitan Borough Council)
South Shields *p471* 0191 427 1717

Dey, D (Clifford Chance)
London E14 *p20*. 020 7006 1000

Deygoo, Miss E S (Deygoo & Co Solicitors) *E S1 L Q F1 K3 K4 J1 I R1 Zc S2 V W Zq Zl*
Thornton Heath *p411*. 020 8664 9224

Deyong, Miss E M (Taylor Vinters) *E*
Cambridge *p176*. 01223 423444

Dhaliwal, Mrs A (Bird & Lovibond) *S1 S2 K3 K1 N*
Uxbridge *p417*. 01895 256151

Dhaliwal, H S (Duncan Lewis & Co) *S2 E Zi Zg G H*
Hackney *p53*. 020 7923 4020

Dhaliwal, K S (Simon & Co) *K1 L Q S1 E F1 G N J1 Zi Zv*
Southall *p384* 020 8571 3883

Dhaliwal, Mrs N K (Mackenzie & Co) *G H K1 Zi*
Hounslow *p254* 020 8569 6289

Dhami, Miss M (The International Family Law Group) *K1 K3 D1*
London WC2 *p45* 020 3178 5668

Dhanda, Ms B (Amphlett Lissimore) *G H*
Croydon *p6* 020 8771 5254

Dhanendran, Miss M (Ford & Warren) *E N*
Leeds *p273* 0113 243 6601

Dhanju, P (Dhanju Mclean & Anwar Solicitors)
Iver *p263* 01753 651743

Dhanoa, A K (Hodge Jones & Allen LLP) *G H*
London NW1 *p41* 020 7874 8300

Dhanota-Jones, Mrs T (Bottrill & Co) *K3 K1 K2*
Pinner *p348* 020 8429 1010
London W1 *p34* 020 7486 9041

Dhar, Mrs V (Clerk to Sheffield Justices)
Sheffield *p470* 0114 276 0760

Dharamsi, M (Mundays LLP) *T2 W Zd*
Cobham *p196* 01932 590500

Dhariwal, M (Lawcomm Solicitors) *S1 S2 Zi Q N Zv W O J1*
Fareham *p224*. 01489 864100

Dhesi, K S (Alastair Bateman & Co) *G H*
Bradford *p153* 01274 739973

Dhillon, Miss A (Harrison Clark LLP) *C1 C2*
Cheltenham *p188* 01242 269198
Worcester *p439* 01905 612001
Worcester *p439* 01905 612001

Dhillon, Miss J K (Reynolds Johns Partnership) *W*
Bishop's Stortford *p144* . . . 01279 508626

Dhillon, N (Noble)
Shefford *p377* 01462 814055

Dhillon, Miss R K (Austin & Carnley) *G H*
Leighton Buzzard *p282* . . . 01525 372140

Dhillon, Miss S (Howard Kennedy LLP) *E*
London W1 *p48* 020 7636 1616

Dhillon, Mrs S N (Badhams Law (A Trading Name of Parabis Law LLP)) *N*
Croydon *p204* 0844 245 4000

Dhillon, Mrs S P K (Birmingham City Council Legal & Democratic Services)
Birmingham *p449* 0121 303 2066

Dhillon-Sidhu, Mrs B K (Mills & Reeve) *Zm*
Birmingham *p140* 0121 454 4000

Dhinsa, Miss D (Dawson Hart) *C1 E C2*
Uckfield *p416* 01825 762281

Dhir, K (Holman Fenwick Willan)
London EC3 *p42*. 020 7264 8000

Dhir, S K (Gullands) *W T2*
Maidstone *p299* 01622 678341

Dhirani, Ms S (Northern Rock PLC)
Gosforth *p459* 0191 285 7191

Dhokia, M (HSK Solicitors LLP) *Zi N Q*
Manchester *p305* 0161 795 4818

Dhokia, R (Freedman Green Dhokia) *J1 C1 O Zp C2 Ze*
Camden *p34*. 020 7625 6003

Dhooper, P (TLT Solicitors)
London EC2 *p85*. 020 3465 4000

Dhooper, S (Judge & Priestley) *K1 Zj Q N*
Bromley *p166* 020 8290 0333

Di-Donato, Miss T (GCA Solicitors (Giffen Couch & Archer)) *K3 K1 D1 D2 S1 W J1*
Luton *p295* 01582 410041

Diamond, Miss C (Blandy & Blandy) *W T2 K4*
Reading *p360* 0118 951 6800

Diamond, D C M (Edward Oliver & Bellis) *G H D1*
Ilford *p260*. 020 8500 4168

Diamond, J P (Wiseman Lee LLP) *D1 K1 K2 K3*
Newham *p92* 020 8215 1000

Diamond, Ms L R (Diamonds) *Q K1 S1 E O C1 J1 W L F1 Ze Zk*
Buckhurst Hill *p167* 020 8559 0778

Diamond, P D (Blake Lapthorn)
London EC1 *p13*. 020 7405 2000

Diaper, S J (Crown Prosecution Service Avon & Somerset)
Bristol *p451* 0117 930 2800

Dias, C (Cunningtons) *Zi*
Croydon *p205* 020 8688 8446

Dias, Miss C (Radcliffes Le Brasseur) *E S1 S2*
Westminster *p70*. 020 7222 7040

Dias, J C (Sintons LLP) *N Q O*
Newcastle upon Tyne *p326* . 0191 226 7878

Dibb, Miss R L (Shulmans) *Zc O*
Leeds *p276* 0113 245 2833

Dibben, M P (Brethertons LLP) *S1 L*
Banbury *p122* 01295 270999
Rugby *p368* 01788 551611

Dibble, R D (Watson Farley & Williams)
London EC2 *p90*. 020 7814 8000

DiBianco, G (Skadden Arps Slate Meagher & Flom (UK) LLP)
London E14 *p80*. 020 7519 7000

Dick, C M (Paris Smith LLP) *C1 I F1 Ze Zf Zw F2 U1 U2 Zza*
Southampton *p386*. 023 8048 2482

Dick, Miss K J (Samuel Phillips Law Firm) *J1 J2 Zp Zza A3 Q*
Newcastle upon Tyne *p326* . 0191 232 8451

Dick, Miss Z (BHP Law) *C1*
Darlington *p206* 01325 466794

Dicken, P (Hugh James) *N Q Zj*
Cardiff *p179* 029 2022 4871

Dickens, Mrs G (Graham Evans & Partners) *K1 S1 D1 F1 V W L*
Swansea *p405*. 01792 655822

Dickens, K C (Dickens & Co) *N C1 K1 O G W S1 L E T1 Zm Zl Zj*
Crowthorne *p204* . .01344 772901 / 776151

Dickens, Miss M A L (Bell Lax Litigation) *K3 Q N O K1 Zq Zr*
Sutton Coldfield *p403* 0121 355 0011

Dickens, Ms M T (Dickens & Co) *S1*
Crowthorne *p204* . .01344 772901 / 776151

Dickens, Ms P J (Geldards LLP) *W*
Nottingham *p337*. 0115 983 3650

Dickens, Mrs T J (Birkett Long LLP) *C1 C2 F1 Ze*
Colchester *p197* 01206 217300

Dickenson, G W (Dickenson Martin) *J1 K1 M1 S1 W*
Warrington *p421*. 01925 574748

Dicker, R W (Cornfield Law) *P K1 M1 F1 L J1 G B1 W S1*
Eastbourne *p215*. 01323 412512

Dickerson, J C (Anderson Longmore & Higham)
Petworth *p348*. 01798 342391

Dickie, P J A (Prettys) *O C1 Q Za*
Ipswich *p262*. 01473 232121

Dickins, A R (Thomson Snell & Passmore) *W Q*
Tunbridge Wells *p415* 01892 510000

Dickins, E (Chua's Solicitors) *S1 S2 E J1 K1 O Q W N B2 Zq Zr Zo Zk*
London EC4 *p20*. 020 7242 6789

Dickins, G C (Lloyds TSB Asset Finance Division Ltd)
Southampton *p450*. 01489 776880

Dickins, J G (Dickins Hopgood Chidley LLP) *S1 R1 E L S2 R2 K4 W*
Hungerford *p258*. 01488 683555

See p634 for the Key to Work Categories

Dickins, Mrs J M (Mayer Brown International LLP) *O Q Zl*
London EC2 *p59*. 020 3130 3000

Dickinson, A (Dickinson Dees)
Newcastle upon Tyne *p324* . 0191 279 9000

Dickinson, A E (Tomlinson & Dickinson) *E K1 P S1*
Sudbury *p401* . . . .01787 375189 / 376820

Dickinson, Miss A M (Wains) *D1 K1 K3*
Macclesfield *p297* 01625 429511

Dickinson, C (Hay & Kilner) *E S1 T1 W A1 C1 F1 L R1 Ze Zd Zs*
Newcastle upon Tyne *p325* . 0191 232 8345

Dickinson, Mrs C A (Maxwell Hodge Solicitors) *W K4 T2*
Heswall *p249* 0151 342 6447

Dickinson, C M (Irwin Mitchell LLP)
London EC1 *p45*. 0870 150 0100

Dickinson, D R (Simmons & Simmons)
London EC2 *p79*. 020 7628 2020

Dickinson, Mrs H F (Nottinghamshire County Council Legal Services Division)
West Bridgford *p475*. 0115 977 3478

Dickinson, Miss J (Clarion Solicitors LLP) *O Q*
Leeds *p272* 0113 246 0622

Dickinson, J W (Lee Chadwick & Co) *T2 W*
Witney *p436*. 01993 703272

Dickinson, J W (TLT Solicitors)
London EC2 *p85*. 020 3465 4000

Dickinson, Miss M (Walker Morris) *O*
Leeds *p277* 0113 283 2500

Dickinson, M K (Michelmores LLP) *C1 C2*
Exeter *p221* 01392 688688

Dickinson, M R (Dickinson Wood) *G H S1 W L*
Doncaster *p211* 01302 329504

Dickinson, N J (Dickinsons) *E S1 L R1 A1 B1 C1 O*
Blackpool *p146* 01253 781010

Dickinson, P J G (Mayer Brown International LLP) *C1 C2*
London EC2 *p59*. 020 3130 3000

Dickinson, R (Manches LLP) *Ze I U2 Zf F2 F1 U1 Zza Zs Zz Zw Zk*
London WC2 *p58* 020 7404 4433

Dickinson, R (Yorkshire Electricity Group PLC)
Leeds *p463* 0113 289 2123

Dickinson, R (Keoghs LLP) *Q N*
Bolton *p149* 01204 677000

Dickinson, R M (Dickinson & Co) *S1 E*
Stamford *p393*. 01780 752581

Dickinson, Ms S (Dean Wilson Laing) *J1 Zp O Q N*
Brighton *p159* 01273 327241

Dickinson, T A (Brabners Chaffe Street) *E S2 R2*
Liverpool *p286*. 0151 600 3000

Dickman, A D (GSC Solicitors) *O Ze Zf*
London EC1 *p34*. 020 7822 2222

Dickman, M C (Fussell Wright) *T1 W S1*
Bristol *p162* 0117 927 9117

Dicks, N (Bhatia Best) *G H*
Nottingham *p336*. 0115 950 3231

Dickson, Miss A (Wedlake Bell LLP) *C1 F1 F2 U2 Ze Zn*
London WC1 *p91* 020 7395 3000

Dickson, A I (Nelson Guest & Partners) *G H*
Sidcup *p380*. . .020 8309 5010 / 8309 0558

Dickson, A J R (Russell-Cooke LLP) *T1 W*
Kingston upon Thames *p267*. 020 8546 6111

Dickson, G H (Bury & Walkers LLP) *A1 P R1 S1 S2 E R2*
Leeds *p272* 0113 244 4227

Dickson, J (Linklaters LLP)
London EC2 *p54*. 020 7456 2000

Dickson, J (Gowmans) *W T2*
Paignton *p345*. 01803 546100

Dickson, Ms K F (Sacker & Partners LLP) *Zo*
London EC2 *p76*. 020 7329 6699

Dickson, M J N (Green Wright Chalton Annis) *N*
Worthing *p441*. 01903 234064

Dickson, Ms V (The College of Law Guildford)
Guildford *p459*. 01483 460200

Didizian, Miss M (Linklaters LLP)
London EC2 *p54*. 020 7456 2000

Didsbury, J C (Birchall Blackburn LLP) *G H Zm Zl Zi*
Preston *p356* 01772 561663

Diedrick, Miss J T (Hutchinson & Buchanan) *N Q L J1 S2 S1 F1*
Ripon *p365* 01765 602156

Dieffenthaller, J R (The Mitchell Plampin Partnership) *K1 D1 J1 Q*
Maldon *p299*. 01621 852566

Diez, Mrs S V (Baily Gibson) *S1 S2 Ze K1 N T2 W*
Beaconsfield *p128* 01494 672661

Difelice, M (Brabners Chaffe Street)
Manchester *p301* 0161 836 8800

Digby-Bell, C H (Palmer Capital Partners) *R2 S2 Zc*
London W1 *p108* 020 7409 5500
Westminster *p33*. 020 7863 8333

Diggens, Mrs M V (Caradon District Council)
Liskeard *p463* 01579 341000

Diggle, Ms C J (LG Lawyers) *E S2*
London SE1 *p50*. 020 7379 0000

Dighero, M (Allen & Overy LLP)
London E1 *p5* 020 3088 0000

Dignan, J T (Shelley & Co) *G H*
Cambridge *p175*. 01223 359441

Digva, Mrs J (Fraser Brown) *K1 Q L*
Nottingham *p337*. 0115 988 8777

Digwa, R S (Digwa Cousins) *C1 E S1 W B1 L J1 G K1 P Zc Zi Zl*
Leeds *p273* 0113 249 6661

Digwood, A J (Rollits LLP) *C1 E I Zk Zl O Q Ze U2*
York *p445* 01904 625790

Dilks, Mrs A M (Bray & Dilks) *K1*
Falmouth *p223*. 01326 212021

Dilks, B M (Hine Downing Solicitors) *K1 N Q J1 L F1 O*
Falmouth *p223*. 01326 316655

Dilks, W N (Kidd & Spoor)
Newcastle upon Tyne *p325* . 0191 273 9217
North Shields *p330* 0191 257 3101

Dillabough, Ms E R (K&L Gates LLP)
London EC4 *p47*. 020 7648 9000

Dillarstone, R (Greenwoods Solicitors LLP) *J1 Zp*
Peterborough *p347* 01733 887700

Dilley, Mrs G (Machins Solicitors LLP) *K4 W*
Luton *p295* 01582 514000

Dillon, Miss E M (Osborne Clarke) *R2*
London EC2 *p65*. 020 7105 7000

Dillon, Miss F (Birchall Blackburn LLP)
Southport *p388* 01704 232323

Dillon, F P (Silversmiths)
Bootle *p150* 0151 922 6066

Dillon, Ms J (Stephensons Solicitors LLP) *L*
Leigh *p282*. 01942 777777

Dillon, J (McKeowns Solicitors Ltd) *N*
St Albans *p390* 0800 032 8328

Dillon, J J (Hardman & Watson) *K1 K3 D1*
Broadstairs *p166*. 01843 863479

Dillon, M J (John Laing) *Zc O C1 E*
London SW1 *p107*. 020 7901 3200

Dillon, M L G (Taylor Wessing)
London EC4 *p86*. 020 7300 7000

Dillon, P (Squire Sanders (UK) LLP)
London EC2 *p81*. 020 7655 1000

Dillon, Ms P M (Addleshaw Goddard) *N P M1 O J1 L B1 Zk*
Leeds *p271* 0113 209 2000

Dillon, Ms S H (Congleton Borough Council)
Sandbach *p470* 01270 763231

Dilloway, Ms H J (Boothroyds) *G H*
London SE6 *p14*. 020 8690 4848

Dimelor, Miss E (Spratt Endicott) *Ze U2 O*
Banbury *p122* 01295 204000

Dimelow, A S (Hibberts LLP) *K1 J1 Q N*
Crewe *p203* 01270 215117

Dimitrellou, S (Ince & Co Services Ltd)
London E1 *p44* 020 7481 0010

Dimitriou, A G (Edwards Angell Palmer & Dodge)
London EC2 *p28*. 020 7583 4055

Dimmick, S M (Blandy & Blandy)
Reading *p360* 0118 951 6800

Dimmock, Miss R M (Victor Lissack Roscoe & Coleman) *B2 G H Zm*
London W1 *p89* 020 7487 2505

Dimond, P C (Gullands) *K1 K3 D1*
Maidstone *p299* 01622 678341

Dimsdale Gill, Miss A M (Hogan Lovells International LLP)
London EC1 *p42*. 020 7296 2000

Din, S (Crockett & Co) *D1 K1*
Leeds *p272* 0113 226 0111

Dinamani, Ms K (Ashurst LLP)
London EC2 *p7* 020 7638 1111

Dineen, M (Russell-Cooke LLP) *E R2 S2*
London WC1 *p74* 020 7405 6566

Dineley, Ms R M (DAC Beachcroft)
London EC4 *p24*. 020 7242 1011

Dingemans, Ms A (Martello Professional Risks Limited)
London EC3 *p108* 020 7337 7500

Dingle, Ms J (Land Law LLP) *E*
Altrincham *p116* 0161 928 8383

Dingle, Mrs L J (Ann Pointer) *S1 E A1*
Tavistock *p408*. 01822 614882

Dinkeldein, D (Kaim Todner Ltd) *G H B2*
London EC4 *p47*. 020 7353 6660

Dinnick, S R (Radcliffes Le Brasseur) *M1 P K1 J1 G C1 F1 Ze*
Westminster *p70*. 020 7222 7040

Dinsdale, Mrs A R (Copleys) *S1 K1 W E M1*
Huntingdon *p258*. 01480 456191

Dinsmore, A (Stewarts Law LLP) *N*
London EC4 *p83*. 020 7822 8000

Dinsmore, A D W (Irwin Mitchell LLP) *N*
London EC1 *p45*. 0870 150 0100

Diomede, M W (Mowll & Mowll) *W T1 E S1 B1 Zd*
Dover *p213* 01304 873344

Dionissiou, D (Clifford Harris & Co) *B1 K3 K1 O Q*
London W1 *p21* 020 7486 0031

Dionissiou, D (Moreland & Co Solicitors) *B1 C1 G K3 J1 K1 S2 L O Q Zq Zp*
Haringey *p61* 020 8881 8833

Dionissiou, Mrs S (Moreland & Co Solicitors) *Zi K3 W*
Haringey *p61* 020 8881 8833

Diplock, D J E (Woolley Bevis Diplock)
Hove *p255*. 01273 722532

Diplock, Miss R J (Hallett & Co) *W T2*
Ashford *p119* 01233 625711

Disken, B T (Disken & Co) *S2 L O Q Zq S1 Zw*
Dewsbury *p210* 01924 464101

Disken, T (Disken & Co) *C1 S2 L Zl Zw*
Dewsbury *p210* 01924 464101

Disley, S J (Roythornes LLP) *S2 E Zh A1*
Spalding *p389* 01775 842500

Dismore, Mrs M J (Breeze & Wyles Solicitors LLP) *Q J1 F1*
Hertford *p248* 01992 558411

Disney, C (Howes Percival LLP) *J1*
Norwich *p334* 01603 762103

Diss, P J (SJ Berwin LLP)
London EC4 *p75*. 020 7111 2222

Distin, G H (Squire Sanders (UK) LLP)
London EC2 *p81*. 020 7655 1000

Ditchburn, J (Hough Halton & Soal) *N Zr*
Carlisle *p182*. 01228 524379

Ditchburn, Miss L F (Fitzhugh Gates) *K1 J1 D1*
Brighton *p159* 01273 686811

Ditchfield, Ms C (Lodders Solicitors LLP) *W*
Stratford-upon-Avon *p400* . . 01789 293259

Ditchman, Ms R (Rosemary Ditchman) *S1 W Zd S2*
Dereham *p209*. 01362 683530

Diton, C (Stone Rowe Brewer LLP) *Zr J1 J2 N*
Twickenham *p416* 020 8891 6141

Ditta, B A (Forbes) *G H N V*
Blackburn *p145* 01254 580000

Ditton, S M (South Hams District Council)
Totnes *p474* 01803 861234
Shrewsbury *p464* 0345 678 9000

Ditz, Mrs C (Family Law in Partnership LLP) *K1*
London WC2 *p30* 020 7420 5000

Ditz, G M (Jaffe Porter Crossick) *W E R2 Ze*
London NW6 *p46* 020 7625 4424

Diver, Miss I B (Foot Anstey) *R1 E A1 F1 W P Zc Zs*
Exeter *p221* 01392 411221

Diver, J (Jefferies Essex LLP) *S1 W*
Westcliff-on-Sea *p428* 01702 332311

Divitantonio, Ms M (GC Law) *G H*
Hereford *p248* 01432 275397

Diwan, Miss T S (Lee & Thompson) *Zf C1*
London W1 *p52* 020 7935 4665

Dix, Ms B (Capsticks Solicitors LLP) *N K1 D1 Zr*
London SW19 *p18*. 020 8780 2211

Dix, J T (Hewitsons) *C1 C2*
Cambridge *p174*. 01223 461155

Dix, M T G (Wilkin Chapman LLP) *B1*
Grimsby *p235* 01472 262626

Dix, S C (Legal Services Commission)
Nottingham *p467*. 0115 908 4200

Dixey, Miss G S (Aviva PLC)
London EC3 *p103* . 020 7283 7500 / 01603 687905
London EC3 *p105* 020 7283 7500
Eastleigh *p458*. 023 8037 2270

Dixon, A (Collyer Bristow LLP)
London WC1 *p22* 020 7242 7363

Dixon, Mrs A J (FBC Manby Bowdler LLP) *E S2*
Telford *p409*. 01952 292129

Dixon, Miss A J (Elliot Mather LLP) *E S2 R2 L S1*
Chesterfield *p192* 01246 231288

Dixon, Mrs A J (Brown Beer Nixon Mallon) *G H*
Redcar *p362*. 01642 490202

Dixon, A J (Dixon Stewart) *D1 E F1 G H J1 K1 L N O Q R1 S1 Zc Zl*
New Milton *p321*. 01425 621515

Dixon, A J (Newcastle Upon Tyne City Council)
Newcastle upon Tyne *p466* . 0191 232 8520

Dixon, A J (Askew Bunting Solicitors LLP) *S2 W S1*
Middlesbrough *p314* 01642 252555

Dixon, Ms A L (Barlow Lyde & Gilbert LLP)
London EC3 *p10*. 020 7247 2277

Dixon, B (Lupton Fawcett)
Leeds *p275* 0113 280 2000

Dixon, C (Ashurst LLP)
London EC2 *p7* 020 7638 1111
Horsham *p253*. 01403 252492

Dixon, C (Dixon Law Limited)
Leeds *p273* 0113 204 2470
Bradford *p154* 01274 744405

Dixon, C C (Kenneth Elliott & Rowe) *C1 C2 E L M2 R2 S2*
Romford *p366* 01708 757575

Dixon, C P (Radcliffes Le Brasseur) *E*
Leeds *p276* 0113 234 1220

Dixon, C S J (Everys) *S1 E W A1 L Zc*
Exmouth *p222*. 01395 264384

Dixon, D (Andrew Jackson) *E*
Hull *p257* 01482 325242

Dixon, Miss D (Webster Dixon LLP) *S2 S1 R2 E O Q W K1 F1 N Zi Zn Zq*
London EC1 *p90*. 020 7353 8300

Dixon, Miss D (McKenzie Bell Solicitors) *S1 E J1 K1*
Sunderland *p401*. 0191 567 4857
Washington *p423* 0191 416 2605

Dixon, G (Penningtons) *E*
Basingstoke *p127* 01256 407100

Dixon, G C (Nabarro LLP) *A3 M2 Zc*
London WC1 *p63* 020 7524 6000

Dixon, H B (Everys) *W*
Exmouth *p222*. 01395 264384

Dixon, Mrs H L (Flint Bishop Solicitors) *E S2*
Derby *p208* 01332 340211

Dixon, I (Makin Dixon Solicitors) *D1 K1*
Keighley *p263* 01535 605040

Dixon, J (IBM United Kingdom Ltd)
London SE1 *p107* 020 7202 3000

Dixon, J (BHP Law)
Halifax *p238*. 01422 250650

Dixon, J C (Davisons)
Birmingham *p137* 0121 685 1255

Dixon, Ms J L (Plexus Law (A Trading Name of Parabis Law LLP))
Leeds *p276* 0844 245 4100

Dixon, Miss K (Mander Cruickshank Solicitors LLP) *G K1*
Coalville *p196* 01530 510666

Dixon, K A (Rollits LLP)
Hull *p258* 01482 323239

Dixon, K J (Flint Bishop Solicitors) *N Zq*
Derby *p208* 01332 340211

Dixon, K O (Bruce Lance & Co) *B1 J1 N O Q Zl Zw*
High Wycombe *p250*. 01494 450494

Dixon, Mrs L (Scarborough Borough Council)
Scarborough *p470*. 01723 232348

Dixon, L S (Nicol Denvir & Purnell) *K1 K2 K3*
Cardiff *p180* 029 2079 6311

Dixon, M (MSP Legal Services LLP) *S1 S2 F2 W*
Hartlepool *p243* 01429 232204

Dixon, M E (Serious Law LLP - The Serious Law Practice) *N O*
Bolton *p150* 0800 616 681

Dixon, Miss M E (Humphries Kirk) *C1 Zc*
Poole *p352* 01202 725400

Dixon, Mrs M F (Bryan & Armstrong)
Mansfield *p311*. 01623 624505

Dixon, M R (Rollits LLP)
Hull *p258* 01482 323239

Dixon, M R (hlw Keeble Hawson LLP) *B1*
Sheffield *p376* 0114 276 5555

Dixon, P (Leigh Turton Dixon) *Zi N*
Middlesbrough *p315* 01642 241101

Dixon, P F (Molesworths Bright Clegg) *N Zl*
Rochdale *p365*. 01706 356666

Dixon, P R (Drivers) *N K1 Q Zl B1 J1*
Malton *p300* 01653 600075

Dixon, Ms R (Newcastle Upon Tyne City Council)
Newcastle upon Tyne *p466* . 0191 232 8520

Dixon, Miss R (Stamp Jackson and Procter) *N*
Hull *p258* 01482 324591
Leeds *p277* 0113 222 0022

Dixon, R C (Hague & Dixon) *S1 S2 E W Zm*
York *p444* 01759 371634

Dixon, R P (Turbervilles) *J1 O B1 L N F1 Q Zp*
Uxbridge *p417*. 01895 201700
Uxbridge *p417*. 01895 201700

Dixon, Mrs S (Aldridge Brownlee Solicitors LLP)
Bournemouth *p151*. 01202 527008

Dixon, S (Dean Thomas & Co) *S1 W K1 F1 Q*
Chesterfield *p192* 01246 810050

Dixon, S C (Palmers) *C1*
Basildon *p126* 01268 240000

Dixon, Ms S M (McGrigors LLP)
London EC4 *p56*. 020 7054 2500

Dixon, W R (Field Seymour Parkes) *O A3 B2*
Reading *p360* 0118 951 6200
London EC2 *p67*. 020 7418 7000

Dixon-Lewis, Miss C (Dixon Lewis Solicitors) *B1 L N Q K1 Zl*
Wellington *p425* 01952 245700

Djan-Krofa, Mrs M A (Wainwright & Cummins) *S1 Q L*
Lambeth *p90*. 020 7326 7460

Djanogly, J S (SJ Berwin LLP)
London EC4 *p75*. 020 7111 2222

Djurisic, J (Trowers & Hamlins)
London EC3 *p88*. 020 7423 8000

Dobbie, Ms V J (Swinburne Snowball & Jackson) *K1 G H N F1 D1 J1*
Consett *p199* 01207 502532

Dobbin, C (Paris Smith LLP) *J1*
Southampton *p386*. 023 8048 2482

Dobbin, M S (Sintons LLP) *E S1 S2 Zl Zs*
Newcastle upon Tyne *p326* . 0191 226 7878

Dobbins, A M (Hatch Brenner) *S1 E C1 T1 A1 W R1 L C2 S2 Zc*
Norwich *p334* 01603 660811

Dobbs, Miss A J (Fentons)
Failsworth *p223* 0161 682 7101

Dobbs, C (Chattertons Solicitors) *S1 S2 W K1 G H E D1 C1 Zl*
Newark *p322* 01636 673731

Dobbs, R A E (C Brewer & Sons Ltd)
Eastbourne *p457*. 01323 411080

Dobias, M P (DAC Beachcroft) *M1 N O P Q Zj*
London EC4 *p24*. 020 7936 2222

Dobie, G A (Barcan Woodward) *S1 W*
Bristol *p160* 0117 963 5237

Dobie, J C (Stones Solicitors LLP) *S1*
Exeter *p222* 01392 666777

Dobinson, I (Trowers & Hamlins)
London EC3 *p88*. 020 7423 8000

Doble, Mrs A M (Wiggin LLP) *O Zk Zf Ze U2 Zz*
Cheltenham *p189* 01242 224114

Doble, D P (Allen & Overy LLP)
London E1 *p5* 020 3088 0000

Doble, Ms E (Stephens & Scown) *G*
St Austell *p391* 01726 74433

Dobson, Mrs A (C J Giles & Co) *S1 W K1 J1 Q N S2 Zi*
Wokingham *p437* 0118 978 1017

Dobson, A C (LG Lawyers) *O Ze*
London SE1 *p50*. 020 7379 0000

Dobson, Mrs A J (PCB Solicitors LLP) *W*
Shrewsbury *p379* 01743 248148

Dobson, A S (Lawson West Solicitors Limited) *D1 K1 K2 K3*
Leicester *p280*. 0116 212 1000

Dobson, Mrs C A M (Loughridge Bowler) *W V K4 T2 Zv*
Coventry *p200*. 024 7663 1632

Dobson, D (Sternberg Reed) *K1*
Barking *p123* 020 8591 3366

Dobson, G E (Dobsons) *G H B2 I*
Orpington *p341* 01689 886300

Dobson, G M (Martin Tolhurst Partnership LLP) *K3 Q N S1*
Gravesend *p233* 01474 325531

Dobson, J A H (Blake Lapthorn) *C1 O*
Chandlers Ford *p184* 023 8090 8090

Dobson, J S (Dobson & Sleeman) *G H K1 D1 F1 N W Q J1 S1 Zk Zi Zl Zm Zj*
Middlesbrough *p315* 01642 231707

Dobson, K G (Goughs) *S1 W L E R1*
Chippenham *p193* 01249 444499
Melksham *p314* 01225 703036

Dobson, Mrs K P (Sherrards) *O B1 Q*
St Albans *p390* 01727 832830

Dobson, M (Brabners Chaffe Street) *E S1*
Manchester *p301* 0161 836 8800

Dobson, Ms M K (Barlow Lyde & Gilbert LLP)
London EC3 *p10* 020 7247 2277

Dobson, Miss N (Fishers) *W T2 Zo Zm K4 T1*
Ashby-de-la-Zouch *p118* 01530 412167

Dobson, N (Pinsent Masons LLP) *Zu*
Leeds *p276* 0113 244 5000

Dobson, Mrs N J (Doncaster Metropolitan Borough Council)
Doncaster *p457* 01302 734651

Dobson, R (Napthens LLP) *C1*
Preston *p357* 01772 888444

Dobson, R A (Beightons) *S1 L E Zl S2 Zd Zh J1 Q*
Derby *p208* 01332 346430

Dobson, Mrs R M R (Pannone LLP)
Manchester *p308* 0161 909 3000

Dobson, S N (Speechly Bircham LLP) *O P J1 R1 Ze*
London EC4 *p81* 020 7427 6400

Docherty, Ms J A (Brockmans) *S1*
Stockbridge *p395* 01264 810910

Docherty, K J (Irwin Mitchell LLP) *E R2 S2*
Sheffield *p376* 0870 150 0100

Docherty, P J (Row & Scott) *G H K1 V*
Newcastle upon Tyne *p326* 0191 273 9929

Docking, P J (Smith Gadd & Co) *S1 S2 E L A1*
Horsham *p253* 01403 271222

Docking, P J (Sacker & Partners LLP) *Zo*
London EC2 *p76* 020 7329 6699

Dockrell, H R (Financial Services Authority)
London E14 *p106* 020 7066 1000

Doctors, J (Jeffrey Doctors & Marchant) *E S1 L C1 W A1*
Watford *p423* 01923 231250

Dodd, A J (Ashfords LLP) *D1 K1 D2*
Tiverton *p412* 01884 203000
Plymouth *p350* 01752 206460

Dodd, A L (Churchers) *G H Zl*
Portsmouth *p354* 023 9286 2424

Dodd, C (Leeds Day) *A1 E S1 Zb*
Huntingdon *p258* 01480 454301

Dodd, Ms C E (Byrne Frodsham & Co) *D1 K1*
Widnes *p431* 0151 424 5601

Dodd, C G L (Dodd Lewis Solicitors) *C1 E O*
London SE3 *p27* 020 8852 1255

Dodd, C H (Birketts LLP) *M2 O*
Ipswich *p262* 01473 232300

Dodd, C W (Hall Smith Whittingham LLP) *B1 Q S1 F1 G H K1 L M1 Zm*
Crewe *p203* 01270 212000
Nantwich *p320* 01270 610300

Dodd, G S (Evans Dodd LLP) *C1 T1 Zb Ze C2 M2*
London W1 *p30* 020 7491 4729

Dodd, J (Gill Akaster)
Plymouth *p349* 01752 203500

Dodd, O A (Bartletts Solicitors) *Q N*
Chester *p190* 01244 313301

Dodd, P E (Nockolds) *K1 N Q G H*
Bishop's Stortford *p144* 01279 755777

Dodd, Mrs S (Hart Brown Solicitors) *E S2*
Guildford *p236* 0800 068 8177

Dodden, Miss L (Ash Clifford)
Bridgwater *p157* 01278 451327

Dodds, B J (Dodds & Partners) *G H*
Leicester *p279* 0116 253 8585

Dodds, Mrs C F (Mayo Wynne Baxter LLP) *W S1*
Lewes *p283* 01273 477071

Dodds, G D (DWF)
Manchester *p303* 0161 603 5000

Dodds, Mrs M (Stockport Metropolitan Borough Council)
Stockport *p472* 0161 480 4949

Dodds, N D P (Kenneth Bush) *G M1 N P H K1 A1 C1 F1 L Zl Zp Zc*
King's Lynn *p266* 01553 692737

Dodds, P R (Paul Dodds Solicitors) *B1 D1 G H K1 L S1 V*
Wallsend *p419* 0191 263 6200

Dodds, Mrs S E (Burnetts) *F1 F2 J1 O Q*
Carlisle *p181* 01228 552222
Carlisle *p182* 01228 552222

Dodds, Mrs V A (Newcastle Upon Tyne City Council)
Newcastle upon Tyne *p466* 0191 232 8520

Dodge, J F (Blanchards Bailey LLP) *W T2 K4*
Blandford Forum *p147* 01258 459361

Dodhia, D (Jane Kaim-Caudle & Co) *K2 D1*
Watford *p423* 01923 219061

Dodo, Miss T (Lawrence Lupin) *K3 K1 D1*
Wembley *p426* 020 8733 7200

Dodsley, Mrs C H (Birmingham City Council Legal & Democratic Services)
Birmingham *p449* 0121 303 2066

Dodson, A (Wills Chandler) *C1 S2 E S1*
Basingstoke *p127* 01256 322911

Dodson, C J (Wains) *S1 S2 W E*
Macclesfield *p297* 01625 429511

Dodson, M (London Borough of Southwark)
London SE1 *p109* 020 7525 5000

Dodson, M (Simmons & Simmons)
London EC2 *p79* 020 7628 2020

Dodsworth, Mrs C M (Pinsent Masons LLP) *O Q Zc*
London EC2 *p67* 020 7418 7000

Dodsworth, J R S (Macfarlanes) *C1*
London EC4 *p56* 020 7831 9222

Doe, A M (Everett Tomlin Lloyd & Pratt) *G K1 N H*
Pontypool *p352* 01495 763333

Doerr, Ms M E (Rosling King) *Zq O Zc Zj Q*
London EC4 *p73* 020 7353 2353

Doggett, Miss A (Harold Stock & Co) *N*
Ashton-under-Lyne *p120* 01457 835597 / 835034

Dogra, M (Dogra & Co) *S1 S2 R2 E W L*
Southall *p384* 020 8571 7741

Dogra, R S (Saunders Law Partnership LLP) *G H B2*
London WC2 *p76* 020 7632 4300
London W1 *p89* 020 7487 2505

Dogra, S (Linklaters LLP)
London EC2 *p54* 020 7456 2000

Doherty, C B G (Robson & Co) *E S1 W S2*
Hythe *p259* 01303 264581 / 267413

Doherty, D (Angela Taylor Criminal Solicitors) *N*
Manchester *p310* 0161 256 2233

Doherty, Ms N (Clifford Johnston & Co) *N Zm*
Manchester *p302* 0161 249 2700

Doherty, N F (TV Edwards LLP) *G H*
London N15 *p85* 020 7790 7000

Doherty, Mrs S (Grindeys LLP) *S1*
Stoke-on-Trent *p397* 01782 846441

Doherty, T (EAD Solicitors LLP) *M1 N P J1 G*
Liverpool *p287* 0151 291 2500

Doinik, A (Hallett & Co) *Zb E Zl Q S1*
Ashford *p119* 01233 625711

Dol, Mrs H (Hale & Hopkins) *S1*
Swindon *p406* 01793 522277

Dolan, Miss A L (Brabners Chaffe Street) *O Q L A3 B1 Zq J1*
Preston *p356* 01772 823921

Dolan, C P (Blake Lapthorn) *E L*
Chandlers Ford *p184* 023 8090 8090
Fareham *p224* 0370 086 6800 / 01489 616800

Dolan, G (Ramsdens Solicitors) *C1 S2 E*
Halifax *p238* 01422 330700
Huddersfield *p256* 01484 821500

Dolan, Ms H S (Potter Rees (Serious Injury) Solicitors)
Manchester *p309* 0161 237 5888

Dolan, Ms P (Rochman Landau LLP) *B1 D1 D2 F2 K1 K2 O L Q Zq Zu*
London W1 *p72* 020 7544 2424

Dolasa, Ms S R (Maples Teesdale LLP) *S2 E*
London EC2 *p58* 020 7600 3800

Dolder, A D (Watson Farley & Williams)
London EC2 *p90* 020 7814 8000

Dolding, Miss E A (Warners Solicitors) *C1 C2*
Tonbridge *p412* 01732 770660

Doley, C S (Carter-Ruck) *Zk Zq O Zg*
London EC4 *p18* 020 7353 5005

Dollery, A J (Bates & Mountain) *S1 S2 W E L A1 T1 T2*
Caistor *p172* 01472 851224

Dollery, D I (Glaisyers) *G H Zf Zm*
Birmingham *p138* 0121 233 2971

Dolley, Mrs M A J (Davitt Jones Bould) *S2 E*
Taunton *p408* 01823 279279

Dollimore, Mrs C (Humphries Kirk) *S2 E*
Poole *p352* 01202 725400

Dollimore, D J (Paul Dodds Solicitors) *K1 D1 Q S2 G*
Wallsend *p419* 0191 263 6200

Dollimore, Ms J D (Hempsons)
Westminster *p40* 020 7839 0278

Dollimore, R (Jacobs & Reeves) *W L*
Poole *p353* 01202 674425

Dolman, Ms D J (Irwin Mitchell LLP) *C1*
London EC1 *p45* 0870 150 0100

Dolman, P J (Travers Smith LLP) *C1 C2*
London EC1 *p87* 020 7295 3000

Dolman, R A (Wedlake Bell LLP) *T1 W*
London WC1 *p91* 020 7395 3000

Dolphin, H (DLA Piper UK LLP) *B1 C1 Zb*
Birmingham *p137* 0870 011 1111

Dolphin, Mrs S A (Hibbert Lucas Butter) *K1 L S1 S2 W*
Whitchurch *p430* 01948 662231

Dolties, D A (Romain Coleman & Co) *N L Q Zl*
Waltham Forest *p73* 020 8520 3322

Dolton, C J (Fulton Robertson) *F1 G H J1 K1 L M1 N*
Amersham *p117* 01494 722326

Dom Paul, Ms A (Kingsley Napley) *A3 B2 O Q*
London EC1 *p50* 020 7814 1200

Domb, A J (Davenport Lyons) *C1 C2 C3 I J1 B1 X Zb Ze Zf Zc*
London W1 *p25* 020 7468 2600

Dominey, Ms H (Frettens Solicitors) *K1*
Christchurch *p194* 01202 491777

Don Carolis, F A (AMEC PLC)
Knutsford *p462* 01565 683123

Don, A M W (Blandy & Blandy) *K1 D1 K2*
Reading *p360* 0118 951 6800

Don, R J R (Knocker & Foskett) *C1 E S1 W T1*
Sevenoaks *p374* 01732 459931

Donabie, Mrs J C (Muckle LLP) *J1*
Newcastle upon Tyne *p325* 0191 211 7777

Donaghey, Ms Y (Kerman & Co LLP) *C1*
London WC2 *p49* 020 7539 7272

Donald, I S (Bemrose & Ling) *D1 K1 V H Zm*
Derby *p208* 01332 347300

Donald, M (Hogan Lovells International LLP)
London EC1 *p42* 020 7296 2000

Donald, N S (GCA Solicitors (Giffen Couch & Archer)) *D2 D1 K3 K1 K2 Q S1*
Luton *p295* 01582 410041

Donald, O (Radcliffes Le Brasseur)
Westminster *p70* 020 7222 7040

Donaldson, I C (Matthew Arnold & Baldwin LLP) *W T2 Zm*
Watford *p423* 01923 202020

Donaldson, Miss J (The International Family Law Group) *K3 D1 K1*
London WC2 *p45* 020 3178 5668

Donaldson, J R (Land Registry)
London WC2 *p107* 020 7917 8888

Donaldson, Ms K E (Baxter Caulfield) *C1 E L S1 W*
Huddersfield *p255* 01484 519519

Donaldson, L (Gill Turner Tucker) *K3 K1 K2*
Maidstone *p299* 01622 759051

Donaldson, Miss P (Hempsons) *N Zr*
Harrogate *p240* 01423 522331

Donaldson, P N (Donaldson Dunstall) *W S1 N Q K1 K3 L K4 J1 Zl Zq O*
Bexhill *p131* 01424 216329

Donaldson, P W (Squire Sanders (UK) LLP)
Manchester *p310* 0161 830 5000

Donalson, Miss K (Druitts) *J1 N*
Bournemouth *p151* 01202 551863

Donavan, Mrs M C (Cardiff County Council)
Cardiff *p453* 029 2087 2000

Done, Mrs L A (Trafford Metropolitan Borough Council)
Stretford *p473* 0161 912 1212

Donegan, Ms H (Barlow Lyde & Gilbert LLP)
London EC3 *p10* 020 7247 2277

Donegan, J P (Osler Donegan Taylor) *N J1 Q L O S1 F1 G E Zi Zp Zh*
Brighton *p160* 01273 710712

Donegan, Ms L (Aviva PLC) *C1*
London EC3 *p103* 020 7283 7500 / 01603 687905
Norwich *p467* 01603 622200
York *p477* 01904 452210

Donegan, P G (Taylor Haldane Barlex LLP) *G H*
Chelmsford *p187* 0845 293 7688

Donegan, S P (Barlow Lyde & Gilbert LLP)
London EC3 *p10* 020 7247 2277

Donell, N J (Jacksons) *S1 C1 E L R1 A1 T1 W Zc Zd S2 Zn*
Fordingbridge *p227* 01425 652110

Donen, Mrs A B L (Bryan & Armstrong) *K1*
Mansfield *p311* 01623 624505

Dongray, D M (Wycombe District Council)
High Wycombe *p461* 01494 461002

Donkin, J A (John Donkin & Co)
Gateshead *p228* 0191 495 2896 / 477 1781

Donn, R L (Donns) *M1 P B1 N*
Manchester *p303* 0161 834 3311

Donn, Ms S S (Philcox Gray & Co) *D1 D2 K1*
London SE15 *p67* 020 7703 2285

Donnabella, Miss R (Serious Fraud Office)
London WC1 *p109* 020 7239 7272

Donnan, B (Edward Harte LLP) *F1 J1 L N Q Zv Zc*
Brighton *p159* 01273 662750

Donnellan, M (Trowers & Hamlins) *O Zh*
London EC3 *p88* 020 7423 8000

Donnellan, T H (The Walkers Partnership) *D1 G H J1 K1 L M1 N P W Zm*
Royston *p368* 01763 241121 / 248896
Royston *p368* 01763 248896

Donnelly, A M (Nicol Denvir & Purnell) *D1 K1 S1*
Cardiff *p180* 029 2079 6311

Donnelly, C W M (Donnelly McArdle Adamson) *G S1 H K1 D1 W R1*
Hartlepool *p243* 01429 274732

Donnelly, D (Wake Smith & Tofields) *S2 E S1*
Sheffield *p377* 0114 266 6660

Donnelly, Miss F L (Merthyr Tydfil County Borough Council)
Merthyr Tydfil *p465* 01685 725000

Donnelly, Miss F M (BHP Law) *S1 W K1 E L M1 J1 F1 Zl*
Durham *p214* 0191 384 0840

Donnelly, J B C (Donnelly & Elliott Limited) *O Q J1 C1 L E W Za*
Gosport *p232* 023 9250 5500

Donnelly, Miss L (Glaisyers Solicitors LLP) *K1 K3*
Manchester *p304* 0161 224 3311

Donnelly, M (Donnelly & Elliott Limited) *S1 E C1 W*
Gosport *p232* 023 9250 5500

Donnelly, W S (Churchers) *K1 P N F1 G H L J1 Q Zc Zl*
Lee-on-the-Solent *p271* 023 9255 1500

Donner, Miss L (Hertfordshire County Council)
Hertford *p460* 01992 555555

Donner, R H (Feld McKay & Donner Solicitors) *E L Q S1 W*
Rochdale *p365* 01706 645656

Donnison, C (Howard Kennedy LLP) *J1 O N Q Zf Zq Zk*
London W1 *p48* 020 7636 1616

Donnison, Mrs J (Hempsons) *E L S2 P Zh*
Manchester *p305* 0161 228 0011

Donnithorne, N C (Reed Smith LLP) *Zo*
London EC2 *p71* 020 3116 3000

Donoghue, Ms K (Thomson Snell & Passmore) *K4 W*
Tunbridge Wells *p415* 01892 510000

Donoghue, L (Butcher Burns LLP)
London WC1 *p16* 020 7713 7100

Donoghue, M D (Silverman Sherliker LLP) *J1 J2 Zp*
London EC2 *p78* 020 7749 2700

Donoghue, M D (Hempsons) *J1 Zp*
Westminster *p40* 020 7839 0278

Donoghue, Miss R (Shoosmiths) *N*
Basingstoke *p127* 0370 086 6200 / 01256 696200

Donohue, B K (Quality Solicitors Burroughs Day)
Bristol *p164* 0117 929 0333

Donovan, A D (Diageo PLC) *C1 J1 B1 Zb*
London W1 *p105* 020 7927 5300

Donovan, Ms C M (Squire Sanders (UK) LLP) *E C3 I M1 Q Ze Zt Zw*
London EC2 *p81* 020 7655 1000

Donovan, Miss E M G (McCormacks)
London EC3 *p56* 020 7791 2000

Donovan, J R (Stanley Tee) *N O Q Zj*
Bishop's Stortford *p144* 01279 755200

Donovan, K (Bermans LLP)
Liverpool *p286* 0151 224 0500

Donovan, K P (DWF) *C2 C1*
Liverpool *p287* 0151 907 3000

Donovan, M (Donovan Newton Limited)
Nottingham *p336* 0115 985 6600

Donovan, M J (Crowell & Moring) *C1 C2*
London EC4 *p23* 020 7413 0011

Donovan, Mrs R (John Pickering & Partners LLP) *Zr Zq Zg K4*
Halifax *p238* 0808 144 0959

Donovan, T J (Kingsley Napley) *Zr J2 N Zq*
London EC1 *p50* 020 7814 1200

Donson, V A (Ford Simey LLP) *W T1 S1 A1 L Zd*
Exeter *p221* 01392 274126

Doobay, A (Peters & Peters) *B2 G Zg*
London EC4 *p67* 020 7629 7991

Doody, M J (Wartnabys) *S1 A1 E W L R1 S2*
Market Harborough *p312* 01858 463322

Dooey, Miss K (Hillyer McKeown LLP) *C1 C2 Ze*
Chester *p190* 01244 318131

Dookhun, M Y A (Boyes Sutton & Perry) *S2 E S1*
Barnet *p123* 020 8449 9155

Doolan, Ms H (Crockett & Co) *K1*
Leeds *p272* 0113 226 0111

Doole, Ms N J (Chelmsford Borough Council)
Chelmsford *p454* 01245 606606

Dooley, R J (Kirbys) *E L S1 Zb*
Harrogate *p240* 01423 542000

Dooley, Miss S (Burton Copeland LLP) *G H*
Manchester *p302* 0161 827 9500

Doolittle, I G (Trowers & Hamlins)
London EC3 *p88* 020 7423 8000

Doonan, W E (SNR Denton) *Zo*
London EC4 *p75* 020 7242 1212

Dooris, Mrs R (Redcar and Cleveland Borough Council)
Redcar *p465* 01642 466201

Doorne, D (Bedford Borough Council)
Bedford *p448* 01234 267422

Dootson, G J (Hodge Halsall) *W T2 K4*
Southport *p388* 01704 531991

Doraisamy, J (Squire Sanders (UK) LLP)
London EC2 *p81* 020 7655 1000

Doran, Ms C (Royds LLP) *J1 Zp*
London EC4 *p74* 020 7583 2222

Doran, D F (Stanton & Doran) *S1 W E L*
Upminster *p417* 01708 641781

Doran, E J (Linklaters LLP)
London EC2 *p54* 020 7456 2000

Doran, Ms G (Withers LLP) *D1 K1*
London EC4 *p92* 020 7597 6000

Doran, J C (DAC Beachcroft)
London EC3 *p24* 020 7208 6800

Doran, Ms K (Forsters LLP) *Zb*
Westminster *p33* 020 7863 8333

Doran, K (Askew Bunting Solicitors LLP) *N Q*
Middlesbrough *p314* 01642 252555

Doran, N J L (Macfarlanes) *C1*
London EC4 *p56* 020 7831 9222

Doran, S (McKeowns Solicitors Ltd) *N*
St Albans *p390* 0800 032 8328

Doran, V J (Doran & Co) *W S1 E*
Coulsdon *p199* 020 8660 6947

Doran-Robinson, Miss R A (East Sussex County Council)
Lewes *p463* 01273 481000

Dore, M J (Taylor Wimpey UK Limited Legal Services) *E S1*
Milton Keynes *p466* 01908 209030

Dore, MIss P (Lewis Silkin LLP) *Ze U2 I*
London EC4 *p53* 020 7074 8000

Dorey, H (Punch Robson) *N*
Middlesbrough *p315* 01642 230700

Dorey, Miss S (Toller Beattie LLP) *J1 G L K3*
Barnstaple *p125* 01271 341000

Dorian, F L (Dorians) *G H K1 D1 M1 F1 L P J1*
Derby *p208* 01332 680580

Doring, M (Simmons & Simmons)
London EC2 *p79* 020 7628 2020

Dorkins, Ms J (Shoosmiths)
Northampton *p332* 0370 086 3000 / 01604 543000

Dorling, S (Trowers & Hamlins)
London EC3 *p88* 020 7423 8000

Dorman, B H (Lloyd & Associates) *C1 C2 S1 W L Zc*
London SW7 *p55* 020 7589 9599

 See p634 for the Key to Work Categories

Dorman, G J (Knights) *S1 S2 W*
Tunbridge Wells *p415* 01892 537311

Dorman, J (Harold Benjamin) *E S1 W*
Harrow *p241*. 020 8422 5678

Dorman, Ms N (Pinsent Masons LLP)
London EC2 *p67*. 020 7418 7000

Dorr, A (Alwena Jones & Jones) *S1 S2 W A1*
Tywyn *p416* 01654 711499

Dorr, A W (Morgan & Co) *S1 W T1 S2*
Stourbridge *p399* 01384 440069

Dorrington Ward, Miss A (Sherwood Wheatley) *S2 K4 S1 W*
Kingston upon Thames *p267*. 020 8546 0144

Dosaj, Ms A K (Land Registry - Croydon Office)
Croydon *p456* 020 8388 3288

Dosani, D (Callaghans)
Farnham *p224*. 01252 723477

Dosanj, Mrs K K (Cocks Lloyd) *Q N*
Nuneaton *p339* 024 7664 1642

Dosanjh, Miss A (Jordans) *K1 K2 K3 D1*
Castleford *p183* 01977 518778

Dosanjh, I S (Streeter Marshall) *K1 N L J1 D1 F1*
Croydon *p205* 020 8680 2638

Dosanjh, Miss P K (Anthony Stockton) *S1*
Coventry *p201*. 01676 535790

Dosanjh, S P S (Lester Aldridge LLP) *E S2 S1*
London WC2 *p53* 0844 967 0785

Dossabhoy, Miss Y (AFL Solicitors) *Zb B1 E Ze Zu S1 C1 F1*
Bournemouth *p151*. 01202 729999

Dossani, Ms K (Jones & Duffin Solicitors LLP) *K1 V Zi L*
Leicester *p280*. 0116 222 1555

Double, P (Double & Megson)
Market Deeping *p312* 01778 341494

Douch, Mrs K E (Stevens) *S1 S2 W*
Haverhill *p244* 01440 762511

Dougal-Biggs, Miss T (Unilever PLC)
London EC4 *p110* 020 7822 5252

Dougall, Miss P (Rees Page) *D1 D2 K3 K1*
Bilston *p133* 01902 577776

Dougan, Mrs K (Campion & Co) *N K1*
Nottingham *p336*. 0115 947 6373

Dougan, Ms K (Comercrawley) *N*
Diss *p210* 01379 644311

Dougans, R (Bryan Cave) *O M2 Zk*
London EC2 *p19*. 020 7207 1100

Dougherty, Ms S P (Squire Sanders (UK) LLP)
London EC2 *p81*. 020 7655 1000

Doughty, A R (CMS Cameron McKenna LLP)
London EC3 *p17*. 020 7367 3000

Doughty, C (Withers LLP) *K1 D1 Zk*
London EC4 *p92*. 020 7597 6000

Doughty, J C (Bridge McFarland) *J1 N*
Grimsby *p235* 01472 311711
Lincoln *p284*. 01522 518888

Douglas, A F (Travers Smith LLP) *T1*
London EC1 *p87*. 020 7295 3000

Douglas, A I (Williamsons) *S1 E W*
Whitley Bay *p431* 0191 252 7711

Douglas, A J (Awdry Bailey & Douglas) *N P R1 O J1 E G Q C1 B1 Zp Zi Zj*
Calne *p173* 01249 815110
Devizes *p210* 01380 722311
Wootton Bassett *p439* 01793 853200

Douglas, Miss C L D (Rollits LLP) *S2 E Zh S1*
Hull *p258* 01482 323239

Douglas, Mrs C M (Berry & Berry) *K1 D1 D2 Q S1*
Tunbridge Wells *p414* 01892 526344

Douglas, Miss D A (Lavery Haynes)
London NW3 *p51* 020 7435 7441

Douglas, I J (Cook & Partners) *B1 C1 J1 N O Q Zc Zi Zq Zr*
Croydon *p204* 020 8655 4466

Douglas, Ms J (Stockton-On-Tees Borough Council)
Stockton-on-Tees *p472* . . . 01642 393939

Douglas, Ms J E (SNR Denton) *T1 T2*
London EC4 *p75*. 020 7242 1212

Douglas, M J (Reed Smith LLP) *C1 C2*
London EC2 *p71*. 020 3116 3000

Douglas, N A (Watson Woodhouse)
Stockton-on-Tees *p397* . . . 01642 247656

Douglas, R G (Chancellors Lea Brewer) *S2 S1 W K4 L*
Bexleyheath *p132* 020 8303 0077

Douglas, W M (Wills & Probate Countrywide) *S1 E A1 L W*
Tavistock *p408*. 01626 334455

Douglas-Hughes, J P (Gepp & Sons) *A1 S1 T1*
Chelmsford *p186*. 01245 493939
Colchester *p197* 01206 369889

Douglass, Mrs A A (Brutton & Co) *S2 E S1*
Fareham *p223*. 01329 236171

Douglass, D (Ward Hadaway) *E R2 S2*
Newcastle upon Tyne *p327* . 0191 204 4000

Douglass, J (Linklaters LLP)
London EC2 *p54*. 020 7456 2000

Doull, I (Berry Smith LLP) *O Q N J1*
Cardiff *p177* 029 2034 5511

Dourish, Ms A C (Stephenson Harwood)
London EC2 *p82*. 020 7329 4422

Doval, Miss R M (Pemberton Greenish LLP) *S1*
London SW3 *p66* 020 7591 3333

Dovaston, Miss K (Jefferies Essex LLP) *K1 K2 D1*
Westcliff-on-Sea *p428* 01702 332311

Dove, Mrs C (MacDonald Oates LLP) *S1*
Petersfield *p348* 01730 268211

Dove, Miss P J (Haywards) *D1 D2 K1*
Stowmarket *p399* 01449 613631

Dove, S H (Carter Read & Dove) *A1 B1 C1 E L R1 S1 S2 W*
Swindon *p406* 01793 617617

Dove, S J A (Brewer Harding & Rowe) *A1 C1 E L R1 S1 T1 W*
Barnstaple *p125* 01271 342271

Dover, J P (Berg Legal) *E*
Manchester *p301* 0161 833 9211

Dow, A C (Leech & Co) *N O Q*
Manchester *p306* 0161 279 0279

Dow, D (Simon Crosfield & Co)
Ripon *p365* 01765 692277

Dowd, A C (SAS Daniels LLP) *N Zr*
Stockport *p396*. 0161 475 7676

Dowdall, W P (Yates Ardern) *H B2 G*
Ashton-under-Lyne *p120*. . . 0161 330 3332

Dowden, M (Charles Russell LLP) *E U1 O R2*
London EC4 *p19*. 020 7203 5000

Dowding, Ms A B (Countryside Properties PLC)
Brentwood *p451* 01277 260000

Dowding, N A (Gardner Iliff & Dowding) *N W*
Cannock *p176*. 01543 466941

Dowding, Miss S (Elwyn Jones & Co) *D1 K1 V Zv D2 K2*
Bangor *p122*. 01248 370224

Dowding, Miss S (Kennedys) *Zj N*
London EC3 *p49*. 020 7667 9667

Dowell, Miss J (Marcus Barnett) *L*
London SW1 *p10* 020 7235 9215

Dowen, Ms D (Hill Dickinson LLP) *P*
Manchester *p305* 0161 817 7200

Dowen, Mrs H (Harrowell & Atkins) *S1 S2 L E A1 W T2*
Berkhamsted *p131*. 01442 865671

Dowen, Mrs S N (Michelmores LLP) *K1 K3*
Sidmouth *p380*. 01395 512515

Dowie, A (Steel & Shamash) *K1 D1*
Lambeth *p82*. 020 7803 3999

Dowie, Miss S (Anthony King & Co) *K3 K1 D1 D2*
Basildon *p126* 01268 240400

Dowle, P W (DLA Piper UK LLP)
Manchester *p303* 0870 011 1111

Dowler, Mrs M (Aplin Stockton Fairfax) *A1 E R1 S1*
Banbury *p122* 01295 251234

Dowler, M L (Chelmsford Borough Council)
Chelmsford *p454*. 01245 606606

Dowling, C (Department for Business, Enterprise and Regulatory Reform)
London SW1 *p105*. 020 7215 0105

Dowling, F N (Irwin Mitchell LLP) *Zh J1*
Birmingham *p139* 0870 150 0100

Dowling, Ms J (Milner Elledge)
Dagenham *p206*. 020 8984 0940

Dowling, J D (Runhams) *O C1 E L S1 B1 Q F1 J1 K1 Zf Zl*
Bradford *p154* 01274 532233

Dowling, R (Josiah Hincks) *S2 E C1*
Leicester *p280*. 0116 255 1811

Dowling, Ms S E (Blandy & Blandy) *O Zl Q J1 Zo Zp J2*
Reading *p360* 0118 951 6800

Dowman, Mrs S (Wortley Byers) *C1 C2 C3*
Brentwood *p156* 01277 268368

Down, I K (Hamlins LLP) *C1 J1 B1 Ze Zi*
London W1 *p38* 020 7355 6000

Down, S (K&L Gates LLP)
London EC4 *p47*. 020 7648 9000

Down, S (Harrow Solicitors & Advocates) *G H B2*
Wealdstone *p424* 020 8863 0788

Downes, A M (Mullis & Peake) *E L S1 W Zl*
Romford *p366* 01708 784000

Downes, Ms C (Edwards Angell Palmer & Dodge)
London EC2 *p28*. 020 7583 4055

Downes, Miss D (Collins Solicitors) *D2 D1 K3 K1 S1 W*
Watford *p423* 01923 223324

Downes, D G (Clarks Legal LLP)
Cardiff *p177* 029 2055 7500

Downes, K (Frisby & Co) *K1 N Q D1 F1 V G B2 K3*
Stafford *p392* 01785 244114

Downes, N (Trowers & Hamlins)
London EC3 *p88*. 020 7423 8000

Downes, P R C (Downes & Siddall) *D1 G K1 N Q S1 W L E F1 Zc Ze Zl Zm Zp*
Lincoln *p284*. 01522 543343

Downes, Ms S (Harding Evans LLP) *D1 K1*
Newport *p328* 01633 244233

Downes, S (FBC Manby Bowdler LLP) *C1*
Wolverhampton *p437* 01902 578000

Downey, Ms A C (Nottingham Law Centre)
Nottingham *p467*. 0115 978 7813

Downey, Ms A E (Dickinson Dees) *O*
Newcastle upon Tyne *p324* . 0191 279 9000

Downey, Ms G M P (Diageo PLC)
London W1 *p105* 020 7927 5300

Downey, M J (Charles Crookes & Jones) *P M1 N F1 V W J1 L B1*
Caerphilly *p172* 029 2086 0628

Downey, Ms R (Hogan Lovells International LLP)
London EC1 *p42*. 020 7296 2000

Downhill, C (Freeth Cartwright LLP)
Nottingham *p337*. 0115 936 9369

Downie, M L (Josiah Wedgwood & Sons Ltd)
Stoke-on-Trent *p473*. 01782 282394

Downie, R (Bathurst Brown Downie & Airey LLP) *F1 K1 L N Q S1 W B1 J1 O*
Twickenham *p416* 020 8892 1537

Downie, Mrs R A (Verisona Solicitors) *E S2 C1 S1 Zl C2*
Waterlooville *p423* 023 9226 5251

Downing, Miss E K (Frearsons) *S1*
Skegness *p380* 01754 897600

Downing, Miss H K (Banner Jones) *D1 K3 K1 V*
Chesterfield *p191* 01246 209773

Downing, I (Act Family Law) *K1*
Plymouth *p349*. 01752 226224

Downing, J (Rollits LLP)
Hull *p258* 01482 323239

Downing, J W W (Terence St J Millett) *S1 S2 L W R2 Zc A1*
London SW7 *p82* 020 7581 7500

Downing, N P (Herbert Smith LLP) *O Zc*
London EC2 *p40*. 020 7374 8000

Downing, P W (Frearsons) *S1 S2 G Zl*
Skegness *p380* 01754 897600

Downing, W J L (Manches LLP) *J1*
Oxford *p343* 01865 722106

Downs, Mrs A J (Young & Co) *G H*
Stoke-on-Trent *p398*. 01782 339200

Downs, G (Punch Robson) *K1 K2 Zm J1*
Middlesbrough *p315* 01642 298830
Middlesbrough *p315* 01642 230700

Downs, W N (Squire Sanders (UK) LLP)
Manchester *p310* 0161 830 5000

Downton, C H (C H Downton)
Doncaster *p211* 01302 360060

Downton, D G (David Downton & Co) *J1 O F1 M1 Zp Q Zj Zb*
Milton Keynes *p316* 01908 563030

Downy, P J (Farrer & Co LLP)
London WC2 *p31* 020 3375 7000

Dowsett, Ms K (Faegre & Benson LLP) *E S2*
London EC4 *p30*. 020 7450 4500

Dowsett, R H (British Medical Association)
London WC1 *p104*. 020 7387 4499

Dowsey, P (Reynolds Porter Chamberlain LLP)
London E1 *p71* 020 3060 6000

Dowson, J H (Stanley Tee) *E S1 S2 R2*
Bishop's Stortford *p144* . . . 01279 755200

Dowson, Miss L (Rollits LLP) *C1 C3 I Ze*
Hull *p258* 01482 323239

Doyle, Mrs A (Orange PCS Ltd) *E*
Bristol *p452* 0870 376 8888

Doyle, Ms A M C (IBM United Kingdom Ltd) *C1 M1 C3 I C2 F1 M2 Zb Ze Zg*
London SE1 *p107* 020 7202 3000

Doyle, Mrs C M (Wake Smith & Tofields) *K1 K3 K2*
Sheffield *p377* 0114 266 6660

Doyle, C R (Williamson & Soden) *G H*
Solihull *p383*. 0121 733 8000

Doyle, H T (Harvey Ingram LLP) *S1 E Zh*
Leicester *p280*. 0116 254 5454

Doyle, J (Hogan Lovells International LLP)
London EC1 *p42*. 020 7296 2000

Doyle, J (Barlow Lyde & Gilbert LLP)
London EC3 *p10*. 020 7247 2277

Doyle, L A (Rotherham Metropolitan Borough Council)
Rotherham *p470*. 01709 382121

Doyle, Mrs M P (Lovegrove & Eliot) *W S1 E K1*
Windsor *p434* 01753 851133

Doyle, P C (Doyle Clayton Solicitors Limited) *J1 Zp*
London EC2 *p27*. 020 7329 9090

Doyle, S D (Boyes Turner) *E*
Reading *p360* 0118 959 7711

Doyle, Miss S J (Marrons) *S2 E*
Leicester *p280*. 0116 289 2200

Doylend, R O (Powys County Council)
Brecon *p451*. 01874 624141

Drabble, Ms J (hlw Keeble Hawson LLP) *E S2*
Leeds *p274* 0113 244 3121

Drabble, R A (Lincolnshire County Council Resources - Legal Services)
Lincoln *p463*. 01522 552222

Dracoulis, A (Boodle Hatfield)
Westminster *p14*. 020 7629 7411

Drage, A W (Northamptonshire Magistrates Courts)
Northampton *p467*. 01604 497000

Draisey, D J (Hunters) *Q Zq N Zr O*
London WC2 *p44* 020 7412 0050

Drake, A (Pemberton Greenish LLP) *C1*
London SW3 *p66* 020 7591 3333

Drake, A J (Garnett Williams Powell) *S1 W S2*
Rhyl *p363* 01745 334658

Drake, Ms A V L (Bird & Bird LLP) *W K4 T2*
London EC4 *p13*. 020 7415 6000
St Albans *p390* 01727 832830

Drake, D N (Cunningtons) *N Q O J1*
Braintree *p155*. 01376 326868

Drake, E (Howes Percival LLP)
Norwich *p334* 01603 762103

Drake, J (Reynolds Porter Chamberlain LLP)
London E1 *p71* 020 3060 6000

Drake, J C (Ashurst LLP)
London EC2 *p7* 020 7638 1111

Drake, M J (Collyer Bristow LLP) *K1 D1*
London WC1 *p22* 020 7242 7363

Drake, M J (Rustons & Lloyd) *O N K1 F1 Zk Zq*
Newmarket *p327*. 01638 661221

Drake, M R (Isle of Wight Council) *K1 J1 Zl*
Newport *p466* 01983 823207

Drake, N (Pictons Solicitors LLP) *S1*
Luton *p295* 01582 870870

Drake, P V (Barwells) *W S1*
Peacehaven *p345* 01273 582271

Drake, R W S (Dickins Hopgood Chidley LLP) *A1 S2 E K4 L R2 S1 W*
Hungerford *p258*. 01488 683555

Drake, S K (Steeles) *N K2 K1*
Diss *p211* 01379 652141
Norwich *p335* 0870 609 0200

Drake, S P (Blake Lapthorn) *Zl*
Chandlers Ford *p184* 023 8090 8090

Drake-Brockman, A (Allen & Overy LLP) *C1 Zb*
London E1 *p5* 020 3088 0000

Drakes, Mrs C A (McKinnells) *S2 E*
Lincoln *p284*. 01522 541181

Dransfield, G (Hanson PLC)
London SW1 *p106*. 020 7245 1245

Dransfield, R (Stewarts Law LLP) *Zr*
London EC4 *p83*. 020 7822 8000

Draper, A (Richard Pearlman LLP) *E S1 L O*
London EC2 *p66*. 020 7739 6100

Draper, Miss A C (Hempsons) *E S1 S2*
Manchester *p305* 0161 228 0011

Draper, D (Farleys Solicitors LLP) *O Q A3 Zw*
Blackburn *p145* 01254 367856

Draper, D (Farleys Solicitors LLP) *N Q F1*
Blackburn *p145* 01254 367855

Draper, Mrs F H (Myer Wolff) *K3 K1 K2*
Hull *p257* 01482 223693

Draper, J P M (Draper & Co) *W K1 S1 J1 L*
Farnham *p225*. 01252 727374
Aldershot *p115*. 01252 318151

Draper, Mrs L (Attwells Solicitors) *R1 S1*
Ipswich *p262*. 01473 746000

Draper, L J (Draper & Co) *S1 W L E B1 R1 T1*
Farnham *p225*. 01252 727374

Draper, M G (CMS Cameron McKenna LLP)
London EC3 *p17*. 020 7367 3000

Draper, P (Dechert) *M2*
London EC4 *p26*. 020 7184 7000

Draper, R G (Kendall & Davies) *S1 S2*
Moreton-in-Marsh *p319* . . . 01608 650312

Draper, Ms S L (Berry & Berry) *K1 D1 D2*
Eccles *p216* 0161 789 7414

Draper, Ms W M (Draper & Co) *S1 K1 E F1 W*
Farnham *p225*. 01252 727374

Drasdo, M R (Henmans LLP) *W T2 Zd*
Oxford *p343*. 01865 781000

Dray, C G (Nabarro LLP) *J1 N Zn Zc Zp*
Sheffield *p376* 0114 279 4000

Dray, Ms F (Williams MacDougall & Campbell)
Worthing *p442*. 01903 214186

Draycott, Mrs C A (The College of Law Chester)
Chester *p454* 0800 289997

Draycott, S D (Draycott Browne Solicitors) *G H*
Manchester *p303* 0161 228 2244

Drayson, Mrs N A (Shakespeares) *Q L O Zq Zh*
Stratford-upon-Avon *p400* . 0845 630 8833

Drayton, Miss H M (Hewitsons) *C2 C1*
Cambridge *p174*. 01223 461155

Drazen, P L (Lupton Fawcett) *C1 E O Q J2 F2*
Leeds *p275* 0113 280 2000

Drennan, O (Collyer Bristow LLP)
London WC1 *p22* 020 7242 7363

Drepaul, R S (Vickers & Co) *L N G*
Ealing *p89*. . . .020 8579 2559 / 8840 3999

Dresden, B J C (Lewis Silkin LLP) *C1 O Ze Zw*
London EC4 *p53*. 020 7074 8000

Dresner, J A L (Peter Brown & Co Solicitors LLP) *S2 E Zl W S1*
Barnet *p124* 020 8447 3277

Drew, Mrs A (Farleys Solicitors LLP) *K1*
Blackburn *p145* 01254 367854

Drew, Ms A (Prudential PLC)
London EC4 *p108* 020 7220 7588

Drew, C (Brown & Corbishley) *G H J1 K1 C1 M1 L R1 P S1*
Newcastle under Lyme *p323*. 01782 717888

Drew, Ms C A (Charles Russell LLP) *C1 C2*
Guildford *p235*. 01483 252525

Drew, D P (Shoosmiths) *C2 C1 J1*
Reading *p361* . . 0370 086 8800 / 0118 965 8765

Drew, Miss H M (Brown & Corbishley) *G H*
Newcastle under Lyme *p323*. 01782 717888

Drew, Mrs J (Hewitts)
Bishop Auckland *p144*. . . . 01388 604691

Drew, J (Reynolds Porter Chamberlain LLP)
London E1 *p71* 020 3060 6000

Drew, J R (Akin Gump Strauss Hauer & Feld)
London E1 *p4* 020 7012 9600

Drew, Ms K L (Gardner Leader LLP) *S1*
Newbury *p322*. 01635 508080

Drew, Ms L S (Newsome Vaughan LLP) *S1 W Zh*
Coventry *p200*. 024 7663 3433

Drew, M (Hansell Drew & Co) *G H*
Dartmouth *p207* 01803 834555

Drew, M (Goughs) *K1 D1*
Corsham *p199*. 01249 712193

Drew, Ms N (Mogers) *D1 K3 K1*
Bath *p127* 01225 750000

Drew, N J (DLA Piper UK LLP)
London EC2 *p24*. 0870 011 1111

Drew, Miss N J M (Morgan Cole) *N*
Bristol *p164* 0117 916 7220

Drew, R J P (Jolliffe & Co) *S1*
Chester *p190* 01244 310022

Drew, T (Southcombe & Hayley) *C1 E G L N*
Westminster *p81*. 020 7935 6631

Drewe, D M (Crutes) *N O Q*
Newcastle upon Tyne *p324* . 0191 233 9700

Drewery, Miss H P (Graham & Rosen) *N Q*
Hull *p257* 01482 323123

Drewett, R N F (Osborne Clarke) *Zd S1 R2 A1*
Bristol *p164* 0117 917 3000

Drewitt, B A (Brian Drewitt)
Stockport *p395*. 0845 260 0855

6

Drewitt, J L (Forsters LLP) A1 T2 W Zd
Westminster p33 020 7863 8333

Drewitt, S R (Macfarlanes) C1
London EC4 p56 020 7831 9222

Dreyfuss, Ms N (Simmons & Simmons)
London EC2 p79 020 7628 2020

Dring, G N (Graysons) K3 D1 K1
Sheffield p375 0114 272 9184

Dring, H (Morecrofts Solicitors LLP) K4 K1 T2 V W
Liverpool p290 0151 236 8871

Drinkall, C (Rollits LLP) B1 E N Q S1 Zu
Hull p258 01482 323239

Drinkall, V (Rich & Carr Freer Bouskell) K1 R1 S1 W
Leicester p281 0116 253 8021

Drinkall, V R (Ratcliffe & Bibby) S1 W L N P E F1 J1 Zl
Lancaster p270 01524 39039

Drinkwater, Ms K (Russell Jones & Walker)
Manchester p309 0161 383 3500

Drinkwater, Miss S (Keoghs LLP) J2 N Q
Bolton p149 01204 677000

Drinkwater, S P (East Hertfordshire District Council)
Bishop's Stortford p450 01279 655261

Driscoll, B (Simmons & Simmons)
London EC2 p79 020 7628 2020

Driscoll, Mrs H (SGH Martineau LLP) Ze
Birmingham p142 0870 763 2000

Driscoll, J (Scott Rees & Co) N Q
Skelmersdale p381 01695 722222

Driscoll, P J (Mills & Reeve) Zj Zq
London EC3 p61 020 7648 9220

Driscoll, Mrs R (Widdows Mason)
Leigh p282 01942 673311

Driscoll, Miss S (Pardoes) J1
Yeovil p444 01935 382680

Driscoll, Ms V (Hugh James)
Cardiff p179 029 2022 4871

Driver, A J (Bhatia Best) G H
Nottingham p336 0115 950 3231

Driver, J (Browne Jacobson LLP)
Nottingham p336 0115 976 6000

Driver, J (Hibberts LLP) A1 C1 E F1 G L R1 S1 W Zl
Tarporley p408 01829 733338

Driver, J H G (CGM) G Q K1 L H Zc
Southampton p385 023 8063 2733

Driver, T J (Blake Lapthorn) R1 P E A1 Zl Zn Zs
Chandlers Ford p184 023 8090 8090

Dronfield, H (Hanne & Co)
London SW11 p38 020 7228 0017

Druce, A D (Fitzhugh Gates) E N J1 L O
Brighton p159 01273 686811

Druce, Ms G (Jones Day) O
London EC4 p46 020 7039 5959

Druiff, Ms N D J (Forsters LLP) E
Westminster p33 020 7863 8333
London EC4 p86 020 7300 7000

Drukker, N J B (Curtis Turner & Drukker Ltd) C1 E F1 N R1 Zc Ze Zj Zm
London EC4 p24 020 7353 1770

Drukker, T J (Robert Brand & Co) E Ze C2 R2 C1 Zb Zf J1
Westminster p15 020 7935 2408

Drummond, Miss E (Blake Lapthorn)
Oxford p342 01865 248607

Drury, D M (The Wilkes Partnership LLP) C1 E S1 W J1 R1 A1 N B1 F1 Zy Zl Zb Zc Zq
Birmingham p143 0121 233 4333

Drury, Mrs G (Gwendoline Drury) S1 W E L
Cottingham p199 01482 840201

Drury, M J (BCL Burton Copeland) B2 G Zza I
London WC2 p9 020 7430 2277

Drury, R J (Wansbroughs) A1 E R2 S1 S2
Devizes p210 01380 733300

Drury, S (Holman Fenwick Willan)
London EC3 p42 020 7264 8000

Dry, Miss A C (Hill Dickinson LLP) S2 E R2
Liverpool p288 0151 600 8000

Dryden, Ms E (Michael Baker Solicitors Limited) N
Farnborough p224 01252 744600

Dryden, Miss G R (Harvey Ingram LLP) E
Leicester p280 0116 254 5454

Dryden, Mrs S J (Blake Lapthorn) O Q Zq
Chandlers Ford p184 023 8090 8090

Dryden, W J (Patterson Glenton & Stracey) N J1 Q O K1 W Zl C1 F1
Newcastle upon Tyne p326 0191 232 8628

Dryland, R T (Tilbury Goddard) S1 W K4
Thornton Heath p411 020 8684 5581

du Pre, D R K (David Du Pre & Co) K1
London WC1 p28 020 7430 1950

Du Rocher, Ms K M (Hatten Wyatt) S1 S2 E L
Gravesend p232 01474 351199

Dua, Mrs A (A Dua & Co) D1 F1 G H J1 K1 L N Q S1 V Zh Zi Zl Zp
Greenford p234 0845 430 4086

Dubash, R S (Penningtons) O
London EC2 p66 020 7457 3000

Dubb, S S (Eastwoods Solicitors) Zr G
London EC4 p28 020 3137 4800

Dubbins, R A (Kennedys) C1 E J1 K1 L M1 N P W Zc Zf
London EC3 p49 020 7667 9667

Duberley, Miss H E (James Warry & Co) S1 S2 W
Coleford p198 01594 833184

Dubignon, Ms C (Howard Kennedy LLP) C1
London W1 p48 020 7636 1616

Duce, C W (Dundas & Duce) S1 E
Maidstone p299 01622 681867

Duce, K (Mills & Reeve) Zr N Q
Birmingham p140 0121 454 4000

Duchart, A S (Wrigleys Solicitors LLP) W T2 A1 Zd
Leeds p278 0113 244 6100

Duchenne, C P M (HRJ Law LLP) B1 D1 F1 K1 L Q Zi A3
Hitchin p251 01462 628888

Duchenne, Mrs J M (Duchennes) B1 C1 C2 F1 N O Q K1 Zl
Bedford p130 01234 356678

Duck, M P V (Moore Blatch Solicitors)
Southampton p386 023 8071 8000

Ducker, N (Shammah Nicholls LLP) C1 C2
Manchester p309 0161 832 9272

Duckitt, D N (East Staffordshire Borough Council) A1 E J1 L S1
Burton-on-Trent p452 01283 508000

Duckitt, Mrs J E (Hawley & Rodgers) N W
Loughborough p293 01509 230333

Duckworth, A S (Scott Rees & Co) N Q
Skelmersdale p381 01695 722222
Newcastle upon Tyne p326 0191 323 3000

Duckworth, J P (Whetter Duckworth Fowler) S1 W R1 E Zh Zv
Kidlington p266 01865 842100

Duckworth, Mrs L J (Margary & Miller) K4 T2 W Zd Zm
Woodbridge p439 01394 382777

Duckworth, Mrs M E (Parkes Browne) J1 J2 N O Q
Andover p118 01264 333336

Duckworth, M J (Lees Solicitors LLP) W T2 K4
Birkenhead p134 0151 647 9381

Duckworth, Q J (Russell & Russell) S2 E
Bolton p149 01204 399299

Duckworth, Miss S (Mundays LLP) K1 D1
Cobham p196 01932 590500

Duckworth, T (J A Kemp & Co)
London WC1 p48 020 7405 3292

Duddell, S J (Metcalfes) N J2 Q Zr
Bristol p164 0117 929 0451

Duddles, M R (Oldham Marsh Page Flavell) G H Zl Zm
Melton Mowbray p314 01664 563162

Duddy, Ms G (Michelin Tyre PLC)
Stoke-on-Trent p472 01782 402266

Duderstadt, Miss I (Angel Trains Ltd)
London SW1 p103 020 7592 0500

Dudhia, M I M (Musa Dudhia & Co) C1 S2 E O Q L S1 W C2
London W1 p28 020 7499 5353

Dudley, A P (Shakespeares) E L R1 S1 Zh R2 S2 Zu
Stratford-upon-Avon p400 0845 630 8833

Dudley, Ms C A (Atteys)
Doncaster p211 01302 340400

Dudley, D H (Grove Tompkins Bosworth) G H P
Birmingham p138 0121 236 9341 / 236 8091

Dudley, J A (Mackrell Turner Garrett) O N Q L B1 F1 C1 Zk Ze Zt
Woking p437 01483 755609

Dudley, Ms K (Dickinson Manser)
Poole p352 01202 673071

Dudley, K M (SGH Martineau LLP) T2 W Zd
Birmingham p142 0870 763 2000

Dudley, S W (Weightmans LLP) N O Q
Dartford p207 020 7822 1900

Dudman, N D (Rundlewalker) K1 K2
Exeter p222 01392 209209

Dudson, Ms J (Simpson Millar LLP)
Leeds p276 0844 858 3200

Duff, Ms C E (Mayer Brown International LLP) J1
London EC2 p59 020 3130 3000

Duff, Mrs F S (Butcher Andrews) Q N J1 L
Fakenham p223 01328 863131

Duff, H A S (Scott Duff & Co) N Zr
Keswick p265 01768 774321

Duff, Ms L J (Angel & Co) K1 K3 K2 D1
Coventry p200 024 7625 2211

Duff, P H (Shoosmiths) J1
Nottingham p339 0370 086 5000 / 0115 906 5000

Duff, R J S (Housing & Property Law Partnership) L Q R1 R2 Zh Zl
Islington p43 020 7553 9000

Duff, Mrs S E (Cartmell Shepherd) K1 W
Carlisle p182 01228 516666

Dufficy, S F (CMS Cameron McKenna LLP) Zb Zc
London EC3 p17 020 7367 3000

Duffield, Ms N (The College of Law)
London WC1 p105 0800 289997

Duffield, P (Withers LLP) T2 W Zd
London EC4 p92 020 7597 6000

Duffin, A L (Bury & Walkers LLP) S1 E L W
Barnsley p124 01226 733533

Duffin, Miss J E (Stanley Tee) A1 L O Q N Zq
Bishop's Stortford p144 01279 755200

Duffin, P A (Jones & Duffin Solicitors LLP) K1 J1 W F1 L B1 N
Leicester p280 0116 222 1555

Duffin, R I (Bemrose & Ling) D2 D1 K3 K1
Derby p208 01332 347300

Duffus, P A (Andrew Jackson) N Q
Hull p257 01482 325242

Duffy, Miss E C (Nockolds) O Q
Bishop's Stortford p144 01279 755777

Duffy, J (Public Interest Lawyers)
Birmingham p141 0121 515 5069

Duffy, K G (Hadfields Butt & Bowyer) S1
Farnham p225 01252 716101

Duffy, Ms L (Muckle LLP) Zb C1
Newcastle upon Tyne p325 0191 211 7777

Duffy, M (Ince & Co Services Ltd)
London E1 p44 020 7481 0010

Duffy, M J (LG Lawyers) E
London SE1 p50 020 7379 0000

Duffy, P (DLA Piper UK LLP) E
Manchester p303 0870 011 1111

Duffy, P J (Clark Willis) D2 D1 K3 K1
Darlington p206 01325 281111

Duffy, S (Russell Jones & Walker)
Sheffield p377 0114 276 6868

Duffy, S (Cobains) G H D1 J1 N Q F1
Blackpool p146 01253 290092

Duffy, Mrs S J L (Henmans LLP) E S2 A1 R2
Oxford p343 01865 781000

Duffy, S M (Buckles Solicitors LLP) W T2
Peterborough p346 01733 888888

Dufton, Miss A L B (Ford & Warren) J1 Zp
Leeds p273 0113 243 6601

Dugal, Miss S (Taylor Walton LLP) C1
Luton p295 01582 731161

Dugan, J W (Brockbank Curwen Cain & Hall) G P F1 J1
Whitehaven p431 01946 692194

Dugan, R M (McLoughlin & Company LLP) B1 J1 L A3 Q Zq
Shrewsbury p379 01743 272272

Dugan, Ms S (Bird & Bird LLP) E L
London EC4 p13 020 7415 6000

Dugdale, Ms E (Foot Anstey) F1 J1 K1 N
Truro p414 01872 243300

Dugdale, Miss H L (Keith Levin & Co) G H N K1 L Zr
Huyton p258 0151 480 5777

Dugdale, M J (Kingsley Smith Solicitors LLP) O Q J2 J1 Zl Zq L Zp B1 F1 F2
Chatham p185 01634 811118

Dugdale, Miss N (Blake Lapthorn) Zc
Oxford p342 01865 248607

Dugdale, P A (Forbes) F1 L J1 N O Q Zj Zk Zq Zr
Accrington p114 01254 872111

Dugdale, R J (William Sturges & Co) O Q N Zq Zr J1 L Zp R1 B1 A3
Westminster p84 020 7873 1000

Dugdale, Mrs V A (Abrams Collyer) K1 K3 V
Lymington p296 01590 677888

Duggal, Miss S (Rawlins Davy PLC) Q
Bournemouth p152 01202 558844

Duggan, Mrs F E R (The Littlewoods Organisation PLC)
Liverpool p463 0151 235 3055

Duggan, M F (Addleshaw Goddard) C2 C1
London EC1 p4 020 7606 8855

Duggan, P A (Metcalfes)
Bristol p164 0117 929 0451

Duggan, R P (Bolton-Jones & Co) S1 W
Liverpool p286 0151 733 2241

Duggins, V P (Valentine Duggins) S1 W E L B1 Zv
Wallasey p419 0151 638 4844

Duke, Miss E (Anthony Collins Solicitors LLP) L Zh
Birmingham p137 0121 200 3242

Duke, Mrs S (Moss & Coleman) W
Hornchurch p252 01708 446781

Duke-Cohan, G M (Myers Fletcher & Gordon) B1 M1 N O Q Zj Zb Zw Zq Zr
London W6 p62 020 7610 4433

Dukes, Mrs A E (AMD Solicitors) K1 D1 K3 X K2
Bristol p160 0117 962 1460

Dukes, Ms N A (Bailey & Haigh) F1 O Q N K1 K3 D1
Selby p373 01757 705191

Dukes, R J (Taylor Wessing) Zb
London EC4 p86 020 7300 7000

Dulai, K S (Mills Chody LLP)
Kenton p265 020 8909 0400

Duley, Ms S E (Peterborough Magistrates Court)
Peterborough p468 01223 314311

Dulieu, B (Linklaters LLP)
London EC2 p54 020 7456 2000

Dumaka, A (MacLeish Littlestone Cowan) K1
Ilford p260 020 8514 3000

Dumbleton, Mrs E M (EMD Law LLP)
St Leonards-on-Sea p392 01424 420261

Dumbleton, J (The Rank Group PLC)
Maidenhead p464 01628 504000

Dummer, A R H (Middleton Dummer) N
Oldbury p340 0121 544 4788

Dumolo, Miss K (Bolt Burdon) Zr
Islington p14 020 7288 4700

Dunaway, Miss H E (British American Tobacco)
London WC2 p104 020 7845 1000

Dunbar, B J (Barlow Lyde & Gilbert LLP)
London EC3 p10 020 7247 2277

Dunbar, Mrs J K (Salusburys Harding & Barnett) E S2 S1 L
Leicester p281 0116 262 9033 / 262 6052

Dunbar, Miss L (Sacker & Partners LLP)
London EC2 p76 020 7329 6699

Dunbar, Mrs L J (Nottinghamshire County Council Legal Services Division) K1 D1 V
West Bridgford p475 0115 977 3478

Dunbar, M (Lewis Silkin LLP) E
London EC4 p53 020 7074 8000
London EC4 p78 020 7429 4900

Dunbar, P E (Rochman Landau LLP)
London W1 p72 020 7544 2424

Dunbar, T C (Moss Solicitors LLP) E S2 S1 L Zc
Loughborough p293 01509 217770

Duncan, A G (Whatley Weston & Fox) S1 S2 E L A1 T1 T2 W Zb Zc Zd
Worcester p440 01905 731731

Duncan, A J (Allen & Overy LLP)
London E1 p5 020 3088 0000

Duncan, A M M (Denison Till) C1 J1 T1 Ze Zo Zq Zz
York p444 01904 611411

Duncan, A S (Addleshaw Goddard) E
London EC1 p4 020 7606 8855

Duncan, C (Bank Of Ireland UK Financial Services) E L Q Zb
Bristol p451 0117 979 2222

Duncan, Ms C (Henry Hughes & Hughes) L Q S1
London SW16 p40 020 8765 2700

Duncan, Mrs C I (Warner & Richardson) W C1
Winchester p434 01962 868366

Duncan, G L (Charles Russell LLP) T1 W Zd
London EC4 p19 020 7203 5000

Duncan, I L (Mackintosh Duncan) S2 S1 W J1 Zg Zi
Southwark p57 020 7357 6464

Duncan, I S (Marsden Duncan) S1 S2 E W L
Birchington p134 01843 295743 / 841161

Duncan, K W (Stephenson Harwood) Q L
London EC2 p82 020 7329 4422

Duncan, L (Symes Bains Broomer)
Scunthorpe p373 01724 281616

Duncan, Ms M (Kennedys) N Zm
Cambridge p174 01223 533060

Duncan, Ms M (Henmans LLP) N O
Oxford p343 01865 781000

Duncan, M (Charles Russell LLP) W T2 K4
Guildford p235 01483 252525

Duncan, Miss M (Martin Murray & Associates) G H B2
Slough p382 01753 551313

Duncan, M G (Allen & Overy LLP)
London E1 p5 020 3088 0000

Duncan, M G J (Sidley Austin Brown & Wood) Zb
London EC2 p78 020 7360 3600

Duncan, M N R (Charles Russell LLP) W G Q N Ze Zl
London EC4 p19 020 7203 5000

Duncan, Mrs N (Bond Pearce LLP) J1
Plymouth p349 0845 415 0000
Exeter p221 01392 688688

Duncan, P D H (Northamptonshire County Council)
Northampton p467 01604 236236

Duncan, R (Andrew & Andrew Solicitors) N O Q Zq Zr
Portsmouth p354 023 9266 1381

Duncan, Ms S (Squire Sanders (UK) LLP)
Leeds p277 0113 284 7000

Duncan, S A (Fieldings Porter) S1 W E L Zl
Bolton p149 01204 540900

Duncan, Mrs V A M (Marshalls)
Godalming p231 01483 416101

Duncan, Ms V L (Donnelly McArdle Adamson) K1
Hartlepool p243 01429 274732

Duncan, W M (Wolferstans) Zc C1 Ze C2
Plymouth p351 01752 663295

Duncombe, J W (Lloyd Green Solicitors) N
Chelmsford p187 01245 294600

Duncombe, M N (Rootes & Alliott) S1 S2
Folkestone p227 01303 851100

Duncombe, S B (Dale & Newbery LLP) K1
Staines p393 01784 464491

Dundas, R A S C (Dundas & Duce) S1 E Zf Zl
Maidstone p299 01622 681867

Dunford, M T (North West Surrey Magistrates Court)
Woking p477 01483 714950

Dunger, Mrs F E (IBM United Kingdom Ltd) I C3 J1 C1 C2 M1 Ze Zo
London RG21 p107 020 7202 5935
London SE1 p107 020 7202 3000

Dunham, D W (Sherwood Dunham) B1 D1 C1 E J1 K1
Wellingborough p424 01933 276147

Dunham, Mrs E M (Worcestershire County Council)
Worcester p477 01905 766335

Dunigan, S (Glaisyers) F1 J1 N
Birmingham p138 0121 233 2971

Dunk, Miss M E (The Johnson Partnership) G H
Nottingham p337 0115 941 9141

Dunkerley, Mrs A T W (BLB Solicitors) K1 K2 D1 D2
Swindon p406 01793 615011

Dunkerley, Miss C (TMJ Legal Services LLP) W K4 S1
Hartlepool p243 01429 235616
Wingate p434 01429 838225

Dunkley, Ms F J (Fisher Meredith) G H B2
Lambeth p32 020 7091 2700

Dunkley, J (Toller Beattie LLP) Zd C1 S2 E Zza J1 P U2 C2 Zp
Barnstaple p125 01271 341000

Dunkley, J P (Muckle LLP) K1 G H I D1 F2 Zl
Newcastle upon Tyne p325 0191 211 7777

Dunkley, M K (Harvey Ingram LLP) W T2 S1 Zd Zm
Leicester p280 0116 254 5454

Dunkley, R (Ray Borley & Dunkley) W S1 E Zv
Stony Stratford p399 01908 563232

Dunlavy, A (Teacher Stern LLP) O Q Zf
London WC1 p86 020 7242 3191

Dunleavy, Miss T A (Bemrose & Ling) K1 D1 D2
Derby p208 01332 347300
Derby p209 01332 225225

Dunlop, A A (Burges Salmon)
Bristol p161 0117 939 2000

Dunlop, C M (Barlow Lyde & Gilbert LLP)
London EC3 p10 020 7247 2277

 See p634 for the Key to Work Categories

Dunlop, Mrs J (Friends Provident)
Dorking *p457* 01306 654925

Dunlop, Ms J M (Clifford Poole & Co) *K1 D1 K3*
Salford *p370* 0161 736 0160

Dunlop, Ms K (Shepherd + Wedderburn LLP) *B1 Zl Zu E S2 L Q S1*
London EC4 *p78* 020 7429 4900

Dunlop, Ms L J (Derby City Council)
Derby *p456* 01332 293111

Dunlop, S (Clifford Chance)
London E14 *p20* 020 7006 1000

Dunlop, Miss T M (Taylor Wessing) *N P Ze Zf*
London EC4 *p86* 020 7300 7000

Dunmore, W M (Maxwell Winward LLP) *E L R2 S2 Zh*
London EC4 *p59* 020 7651 0000

Dunn, Mrs A (MacDonald Oates LLP) *S1 S2*
Midhurst *p316* 01730 816711

Dunn, A J (Dunn Simpson & Co) *S1 W A1 E L*
Bridgwater *p158* 01278 424272

Dunn, Mrs B E (Trafford Metropolitan Borough Council)
Stretford *p473* 0161 912 1212

Dunn, Ms C (FWD Law Associates) *N K1 K2*
Newport *p328* 01633 660440

Dunn, C (Waltons & Morse LLP) *N M1 Q Zj Za*
London EC3 *p90* 020 7623 4255

Dunn, Miss C (Archers Law LLP) *N Zr*
Stockton-on-Tees *p396* 01642 636500

Dunn, Mrs C (Austin Ryder & Co) *A1 E G R1 S1 W C1 Q D1 N*
London NW1 *p8* 020 7833 0882
Enfield *p8* 020 8804 5111

Dunn, C C W (Parametric Technology (UK) Ltd)
Fleet *p458* 01252 817600

Dunn, Miss C F (Gosschalks)
Hull *p256* 01482 324252

Dunn, C M (H Vaughan Vaughan & Co) *S1 A1 W R1 L Q T1 T2 J1*
Builth Wells *p168* 01982 552331 / 553571

Dunn, D M (Hadaway & Hadaway) *S1 S2 E*
North Shields *p330* 0191 257 0382

Dunn, D M (Chambers Rutland & Crauford) *G Q N H L D1*
London N12 *p19* 020 8446 2777

Dunn, G R F (Chamberlain Martin Solicitors) *S1 W L T1 E*
Bognor Regis *p148* 01243 825211

Dunn, G S (Forsters LLP) *E*
Westminster *p33* 020 7863 8333

Dunn, Mrs H (Fieldings Porter) *K1 D1*
Bolton *p149* 01204 540900

Dunn, H C H (Linklaters LLP)
London EC2 *p54* 020 7456 2000

Dunn, I H (Bond Pearce LLP) *E*
Bristol *p161* 0845 415 0000

Dunn, J (Hanne & Co)
London SW11 *p38* 020 7228 0017

Dunn, J (Conwy County Borough Council) *E S1 A1 C1 S2 Zh L Zl*
Conwy *p455* 01492 576108

Dunn, Mrs J (Molesworths Bright Clegg) *W K4*
Rochdale *p365* 01706 356666

Dunn, J A (Ford & Warren) *E R2 S2*
Leeds *p273* 0113 243 6601

Dunn, J B (Burges Salmon) *E*
Bristol *p161* 0117 939 2000

Dunn, J H R (Devonshires) *B2 O Q*
London EC2 *p27* 020 7628 7576

Dunn, J M W (Brockbank Curwen Cain & Hall) *S2 E S1 Zl*
Cockermouth *p197* 01900 827222

Dunn, M (Lee Bolton Monier-Williams) *E L S1 W Zd*
Westminster *p52* 020 7222 5381

Dunn, M R (Reed Smith LLP)
London EC2 *p71* 020 3116 3000

Dunn, Mrs N N (Stefanie O'Bryen Solicitor) *E S1 S2 R2 W K4*
Watlington *p424* 01491 614700

Dunn, P (Peter Dunn & Co) *C1 C2 E R1 R2 S1 S2 W*
Sunderland *p401* 0191 568 9000

Dunn, P D (Gilbert Stephens) *S1 W L C1 T1 S2 Zo*
Exeter *p221* 01392 424242

Dunn, P W (Alderson Dodds) *W T1 G H M1 N P B1*
Blyth *p147* 01670 352293

Dunn, R C (Norcliffe & Co) *K1 D1 F1 L N O Q Zl*
Huddersfield *p256* 01484 514907

Dunn, Miss R E (Smith Llewelyn Partnership) *D1 D2 K3*
Swansea *p405* 01792 464444

Dunn, S R (Dunn & Co) *S1 C1 E L W R1*
Kingston upon Thames *p267* 020 8541 1332

Dunnage, Ms P J (Squire Sanders (UK) LLP)
Birmingham *p142* 0121 222 3000

Dunne, Ms C (SA Law) *E*
St Albans *p390* 01727 798000

Dunne, Miss C A (Chebsey & Co) *J2 Zu V G H Q N*
Burnham *p168* 01628 660077

Dunne, D J (Hill Dickinson LLP) *Q Zj N*
Liverpool *p288* 0151 600 8000

Dunne, F (Watson Farley & Williams)
London EC2 *p90* 020 7814 8000

Dunne, Ms M A (ConocoPhillips (UK) Ltd)
London W1 *p105* 020 7408 6000

Dunne, M F G (Fosters) *A1 E R1 S1 T2 W*
Lowestoft *p294* 01502 573307

Dunne, Mrs R A (Crossmans MTA)
Cambridge *p174* 01223 451442

Dunnett, Miss C C (South Cambridgeshire District Council)
Cambridge *p453* 0845 045 0500

Dunnigan, D (Clifford Chance)
London E14 *p20* 020 7006 1000

Dunning, A (Aaron & Partners LLP Solicitors) *J1*
Chester *p190* 01244 405555

Dunning, Ms R D K (Dunning & Co) *D1 K1 G H L Zm*
London SE5 *p28* 020 7733 6217

Dunning, S J (Dunning Anderson) *S1 K1 G H F1 E D1 M1 N P*
Carterton *p183* 01993 840200

Dunning, Mrs S M (B P Collins LLP) *E R2 S2*
Gerrards Cross *p229* 01753 889995

Dunningham, A (Foot Anstey)
Taunton *p408* 01823 625600

Dunphy, D (Burton & Dyson) *W*
Gainsborough *p228* 01427 610761

Dunphy, S (Ashurst LLP)
London EC2 *p7* 020 7638 1111

Dunsdon, T C (Bristol City Council)
Bristol *p451* 0117 922 2000

Dunstall, C T P (Donaldson Dunstall) *S1 S2 W C1 E*
Bexhill *p131* 01424 216329

Dunstan, Ms E F (Kerrier District Council)
Camborne *p452* 01209 614000

Dunstan, J (CVC Solicitors) *S1 L S2 E A1 B1 W C1 F1 J1 N R1 P Zl Zm*
St Ives *p392* 01736 795456

Dunston, C W (Pritchard Englefield) *W*
London EC2 *p69* 020 7972 9720

Dunstone, K (Kitsons LLP)
Exeter *p221* 01392 455555

Dunton, Mrs F C (Knight Polson Solicitors) *J1*
Eastleigh *p216* 023 8064 4822

Dunton, Miss M J (Thomas Dunton Solicitors) *T1 W C1 D1 E K1 L M1 S1 Ze Zb*
Orpington *p342* 01689 822554

Dunton, Ms M V (Thomas Boyd Whyte) *C1 G H D1 K1 M1 S1 B1 N W Zl*
Bexleyheath *p132* 020 8303 7755

Duodu, K (David Price Solicitors & Advocates) *Zk*
London EC4 *p69* 020 7353 9999

Dupre, Ms L (Dawson Cornwell) *K1 K3*
London WC1 *p26* 020 7242 2556

Durairajah, Ms S (Rosemary Smith & Co) *S1 K1 W*
Crowthorne *p204* 01344 777441

Duran, S N K (Mian & Co) *G H*
Birmingham *p140* 0121 684 8000

Durant, I (Terry Jones Solicitors & Advocates) *G B2 H*
Shrewsbury *p379* 01743 285888

Durant, P J C (Truman-Moore) *K1 P S1 C1 F1 L G Zl*
Christchurch *p194* 01425 673994
Verwood *p418* 01202 824677

Durcan, Miss C (Hooper Holt & Co) *G Zl H*
Redhill *p362* 01737 761111

Durcan, J P (Rickards & Cleaver) *K1 D1 G H V Q L*
Alfreton *p115* 01773 832204

Durdant-Hollamby, G (Thomson Snell & Passmore) *S1 S2*
Tunbridge Wells *p415* 01892 510000

Durell, G A A (Simmons & Simmons)
London EC2 *p79* 020 7628 2020

Dures, B (Metcalfe Copeman & Pettefar) *N Q O J1*
Thetford *p410* 01842 756100

Dures, F J (The Dures Partnership LLP)
Liverpool *p287* 0151 242 5111

Durey, Ms S (Capsticks Solicitors LLP) *E Zc R1 R2*
London SW19 *p18* 020 8780 2211

Durgan, Mrs N (The Lister Croft Partnership) *S1 E L W*
Wakefield *p418* 0871 220 1333

Durham Hall, Mrs P H (Everys) *B1 S1*
Exmouth *p222* 01395 264384

Durham, J G (Veale Wasbrough Vizards) *S2 E S1*
London EC4 *p89* 020 7405 1234

Durham, Ms L (Jordans) *K1 K2 K3 Q*
Dewsbury *p210* 01924 457171

Durham, S (Cuttle & Co Solicitors) *K1 D1*
Oldham *p340* 0161 678 7443

Durkan, A (Sills & Betteridge LLP) *N J2*
Lincoln *p285* 01522 542211

Durkin, P P (Abney Garsden McDonald) *N V*
Cheadle *p185* 0161 482 8822

Durkin, S H (Barlow Lyde & Gilbert LLP)
London EC3 *p10* 020 7247 2277

Durkin, T F (Myer Wolff) *K1 S1 Zm W K4*
Hull *p257* 01482 223693

Durling, A J (Blaser Mills) *K1 D1*
Rickmansworth *p364* 01923 776211

Durman, A J (Manchesters)
South Croydon *p383* 020 8651 3118

Durn, D (David Durn & Co) *S1 E W S2*
Ruislip *p368* 01895 612400

Durnin, M (Dollman & Pritchard) *G B2 H*
Caterham *p183* 01883 347823

Durning, J (Rowntree & Berry) *K1 L M1 P S1*
Fleetwood *p226* 01253 872581

Durose, Miss A L (MAN B&W Diesel Ltd)
Stockport *p472* 0161 419 3125

Duroshola, A (Scott Rees & Co) *N Q*
Skelmersdale *p381* 01695 722222

Durrance, P (Withers LLP) *C1 C2 T1*
London EC4 *p92* 020 7597 6000

Durrant, F T (Barr Ellison LLP) *W T1 Zd*
Cambridge *p174* 01223 417200

Durrant, R (Boys & Maughan)
Margate *p312* 01843 234000

Durrant, S R (Gardner Leader LLP) *S1*
Newbury *p322* 01635 508080

Durston-Hillyer, Ms H (DAC Beachcroft)
Winchester *p433* 01962 705500

Dury, A (DLA Piper UK LLP) *J2 N*
Sheffield *p375* 0870 011 1111

Dury, Miss L (John Hodge Solicitors) *S2 A1 S1*
Weston-super-Mare *p429* 01934 623511

Dusad, M (ClarksLegal LLP) *C1*
London WC2 *p20* 020 7539 8000

Dustan, Miss J K (Thomson Wilson Pattinson) *S1 S2 C1 E*
Kendal *p264* 01539 721945

Dusting, S (Gard & Co) *S1*
Plymouth *p349* 01752 668246

Dutch, Ms C (Hogan Lovells International LLP)
London EC1 *p42* 020 7296 2000

Dutch, P (Harold Benjamin)
Harrow *p241* 020 8422 5678

Duthie, A L (Bevan Brittan LLP)
London EC4 *p12* 0870 194 1000

Duthie, Miss H F (Tayntons LLP Solicitors) *D1 K3 K1*
Gloucester *p230* 01452 522047

Duthie, M B (Squire Sanders (UK) LLP) *Zw Q O*
London EC2 *p81* 020 7655 1000

Dutta, M (Reynolds Porter Chamberlain LLP)
London E1 *p71* 020 3060 6000

Dutta, S (Fisher Meredith) *Zg Q*
Lambeth *p32* 020 7091 2700

Dutton, A A (Swatton Taylor Dutton) *N J1 O Q S1 L K3 W*
Tring *p413* 01442 825566

Dutton, Ms C E (Bone & Payne LLP) *W*
Colwyn Bay *p198* 01492 532385

Dutton, Ms F H (Bells Solicitors) *K1 D2*
Farnham *p224* 01252 733733

Dutton, Ms M (Boodle Hatfield)
Westminster *p14* 020 7629 7411

Dutton, R M (Jacobs & Reeves) *N J1 J2 Ze Zr Zk*
Poole *p353* 01202 674425

Duval, M S (Howard Kennedy LLP) *C1*
London W1 *p48* 020 7636 1616

Dux, Miss E E (Russell Jones & Walker)
London WC2 *p74* 020 7657 1555

Duxbury, Mrs A F (Kingston upon Hull City Council) *D1 X Zm*
Hull *p461* 01482 300300

Duxbury, Ms C (Forbes) *L S1 S2*
Preston *p356* 01772 220022

Duxbury, P (HM Land Registry - Hull)
Hull *p461* 01482 223244

Duxbury, Mrs S E (Anglia Ruskin University)
Chelmsford *p454* 01245 493131
Warwick *p475* 01926 410410

Duxbury, Miss W J (Cripps Harries Hall LLP) *J1*
Tunbridge Wells *p415* 01892 515121

Dwek, J V (Horwich Cohen Coghlan) *N*
Manchester *p305* 0161 830 4600

Dwight, Miss S E (Sarah Dwight Solicitor) *S1 W*
Birmingham *p137* 0121 702 2100

Dworakowski, S (Waddington Webber) *D1 F1 G H J1 K1 N Q W*
Keighley *p264* 01535 662644 / 662647

Dwyer, C (Ince & Co Services Ltd)
London E1 *p44* 020 7481 0010

Dwyer, Ms K (Kennedys) *N J2*
London EC3 *p49* 020 7667 9667

Dwyer, N A (Hay & Kilner) *B1 J1 M1 N*
Newcastle upon Tyne *p325* 0191 232 8345

Dwyer, P (City of Bradford Metropolitan District Council)
Bradford *p451* 01274 752236

Dwyer, P A (Crown Prosecution Service Cumbria)
Carlisle *p453* 01228 882900

Dyakowski, J A G (Dyakowski Gafford) *S1 S2 W*
Chipping Norton *p193* 01608 643051

Dyar, P (Black Graf & Co) *E S2 W Zi S1*
London NW3 *p13* 020 7586 1141

Dyde, Mrs G A (Tozers) *W T2*
Exeter *p222* 01392 207020

Dyde, T P (Tozers) *N Zr*
Exeter *p222* 01392 207020

Dye, A (Sintons LLP) *C1 C2*
Newcastle upon Tyne *p326* 0191 226 7878

Dye, C (DAC Beachcroft)
London EC3 *p24* 020 7208 6800

Dye, Miss J B (Pinsent Masons LLP) *C1 C3*
Birmingham *p141* 0121 200 1050

Dyer, A G (Bolsover District Council)
Chesterfield *p455* 01246 240000

Dyer, Miss A V (Lee & Priestley LLP) *K1 Q S1 O N V D1*
Leeds *p275* 0845 129 2300

Dyer, Miss C (Welch & Co) *W K4 S1*
Cardigan *p181* 01239 614070

Dyer, Miss C (Blandy & Blandy) *K1 K2*
Reading *p360* 0118 951 6800

Dyer, Ms C A (W J Williams & Davies) *K1 D1 H N V X*
Cardigan *p181* 01239 612262

Dyer, C D (Osborne Clarke) *R2*
London EC2 *p65* 020 7105 7000

Dyer, Ms H F (DLA Piper UK LLP) *E A1 S1 Zb*
London EC2 *p24* 0870 011 1111

Dyer, J L (Maitland Walker) *W S1*
Minehead *p318* 01643 707777

Dyer, J S (W J Williams & Davies) *S1 K1 W A1 D1 N Q L V B1 Zd Zc Zl*
Cardigan *p181* 01239 612262

Dyer, K M (Tyndallwoods) *G H Q*
Birmingham *p143* 0121 624 1111

Dyer, Mrs L R M (Aviva PLC)
London EC3 *p103* 020 7283 7500 / 01603 687905
Norwich *p467* 01603 622200

Dyer, M D (Barnes Harrild & Dyer) *G H J1*
Croydon *p204* 020 8681 5128

Dyer, M J (Verisona Solicitors) *C1 D1 E F1 G H J1 K1 L Zc Zf Zg*
Waterlooville *p423* 023 9226 5251

Dyer, M W (Eric Robinson Solicitors) *M1 R1 K1 F1 G S1 D1 L H V Zi Zl*
Southampton *p385* 023 8042 5000

Dyer, N J (Stones Solicitors LLP)
Exeter *p222* 01392 666777

Dyer, P N (Ellis Jones) *E L S1 S2 W*
Ringwood *p364* 01425 484848

Dyer, S D (Eaton-Evans & Morris) *D1 G H J1 K1 Q N S1 W*
Haverfordwest *p244* 01437 763383

Dyer, Ms S M (Howard & Over) *N Q F1 L W*
Plymouth *p350* 01752 556606

Dyer, T (Brethertons LLP)
Rugby *p368* 01788 579579

Dyke, E (Forshaws Davies Ridgway LLP) *B1 E S1 T1*
Warrington *p422* 01925 230000

Dyke, Mrs J A (Tyndallwoods) *W N T2 Zd*
Birmingham *p143* 0121 693 2222
Birmingham *p143* 0121 624 1111

Dyke, N (Marshalls) *E C1 O Q S2*
Godalming *p231* 01483 416101

Dyke, Miss R (Gudgeons Prentice) *K4 W*
Stowmarket *p399* 01449 613101

Dykes, S (Stevens) *G H*
Stoke-on-Trent *p398* 01782 813200

Dykins, R (Fox Williams) *O A3*
London EC2 *p33* 020 7628 2000

Dymock, A R (Meade-King) *O Zq*
Bristol *p163* 0117 926 4121

Dymock, P M (Large & Gibson) *O N Q G K1 F1 J1 L H Zl*
Southsea *p388* 023 9229 6296

Dymond, A S (Herbert Smith LLP)
London EC2 *p40* 020 7374 8000

Dymond, N (Rundlewalker) *S1*
Exeter *p222* 01392 209209
Exeter *p222* 01392 210700

Dyne, Ms A (The College of Law Chester)
Chester *p454* 0800 289997

Dyne, J B (Dyne Solicitors Limited) *A1 E Zn Zt S2*
Chester *p190* 01829 773100

Dyson, A (DLA Piper UK LLP) *I*
Leeds *p272* 0870 011 1111

Dyson, A J (Clifford Chance)
London E14 *p20* 020 7006 1000

Dyson, Ms C A (Knights Solicitors LLP) *J1 K1 Zp*
Newcastle under Lyme *p323* 01782 619225

Dyson, Miss J E (Rix & Kay Solicitors LLP) *K1 D1*
Hove *p255* 01273 329797

Dyson, Mrs J H (Dutton Gregory) *D1 K1*
Winchester *p433* 01962 844333

Dyson, J H P (Clifton Ingram LLP) *J1 Q*
Wokingham *p437* 0118 978 0099

Dyson, J M H (Wilkinson Woodward) *B1 J1 L O Q Zc Ze Zl Zp*
Halifax *p238* 01422 339600

Dyson, K (Keith Dyson & Co)
Manchester *p304* 0161 832 9933

Dyson, M E (Ceredigion County Council)
Aberaeron *p447* 01545 570881

Dyson, M J (Badhams Law (A Trading Name of Parabis Law LLP)) *N O Q F1 F2 Zr Zq*
Croydon *p204* 0844 245 4000

Dyson, Miss M L (Eaton Smith LLP) *C1 C2 F1 U2 Ze Zza*
Huddersfield *p255* 01484 821300

Dyson, N R (Hartlaw LLP) *C1 E T1 A1 R1 W J1 F1 Zj Zo Zd*
Wetherby *p429* 01937 547000

Dyson, P R (Scott Richards) *W P N S1 L M1 K1 C1 F1 Zc Zk Zl Zv*
Teignmouth *p409* 01626 772441

Dyson, R H (Leigh Day & Co) *Zr*
London EC1 *p52* 020 7650 1200

Dyson, R J G (Howlett Clarke Crowther Wood) *S1 W Q K1 C1 N E F1 Zd Zn*
Brighton *p159* 01273 327272 / 326341

Dyson, R K (hlw Keeble Hawson LLP) *C1 C2*
Sheffield *p376* 0114 276 5555

Dytch, A (Liefman Rose & Co) *N P L E S1 W Zj S2 T2*
Manchester *p306* 0161 740 7878

Dyton, C J (Essex County Council)
Chelmsford *p454* 0845 743 0430

Dyton, R (Simmons & Simmons)
London EC2 *p79* 020 7628 2020

Dzimitrowicz, A P (Dzimitrowicz York) *C1 Q B1 S1 E*
Croydon *p205* 020 8667 0340

Dziobon, Mrs R (Manches LLP)
London WC2 *p58* 020 7404 4433

E

Eachus, Ms H K (Phillips Solicitors) *K1 Q S1*
Basingstoke *p127* 01256 460830

Ead, Mrs S (Caerphilly County Borough Council)
Hengoed *p460* 01443 815588

Eade, J (Coodes)
St Austell *p391* 01726 874700

Eades, J W (Pemberton Greenish LLP) *S1*
London SW3 *p66* 020 7591 3333

Eady, Ms C S (K&L Gates LLP)
London EC4 *p47*. 020 7648 9000

Eagle, Ms K (Michelmores LLP) *S2 S1*
Exeter *p221* 01392 688688

Eagle, Mrs K H J (Maitland Walker) *J1 M1 C3 O S2 E*
Minehead *p318* 01643 707777

Eagle, R A (Josiah Hincks) *S1 W Zb Zd C1 S2 E C3 K4 C2 Zq T1 T2 Zo*
Leicester *p280*. 0116 255 1811

Eagle, R J (Powys County Council)
Brecon *p451*. 01874 624141

Eagle, T (Hansells) *F1 L N P O*
Norwich *p334* 01603 615731

Eagles, B (Howard Kennedy LLP) *Zf*
London W1 *p48* 020 7636 1616

Eaglesfield, Ms J L (Gordons LLP)
Leeds *p273* 0113 227 0100

Eales, J P (Kenneth Bush) *B1 C1 D1 E F1 G H J1 K1 M1 Zo Zp Zl*
King's Lynn *p266* 01553 692737

Eales, P S (Stafford Eales) *E R1 S2 R2*
Wotton-under-Edge *p442* . . 0117 370 0500

Eames, Miss C M (McLellans) *Zl*
Hertford *p249* 01992 532000
Nottingham *p338*. 0115 953 8500

Eames, Mrs D M (Davies & Partners) *C1 Ze F1 Zd*
Almondsbury *p115*. 01454 619619

Eames, Ms M (Nelsons)
Nottingham *p338*. 0115 958 6262

Eames-Hughes, M (Osborns) *G Q F1 V L J1 H S1 W Zl D1 X R1*
Colwyn Bay *p198* . .01492 532056 / 532820

Eardley, D J L (Skandia Life Assurance Co Ltd) *C1 J1*
Southampton *p472*. 023 8033 4411

Eardley, Miss E (The Johnson Partnership) *G H*
Nottingham *p337*. 0115 941 9141

Earl, A H (Earl & Crocker) *S1 E L A1 R1 W Zd S2*
Liskeard *p285* 01579 345304

Earl, B (Milburns Solicitors) *L S1 W E*
Workington *p440*. 01900 67363

Earl, D M (Wedlake Bell LLP) *E R2 S2*
London WC1 *p91* 020 7395 3000

Earl, Ms J A (Moeran Oughtred & Co) *S1 Q N K1 L O B1 J1 W E Zh Zl Zi*
Watford *p423* 01923 256263

Earl, M (Chesworths) *S1 E S2*
Stoke-on-Trent *p397*. 01782 599993

Earl, T J (Rochdale Metropolitan Borough Council) *K1 W N Q J1 L G*
Rochdale *p470*. 01706 647474

Earlam, Ms B (The College of Law Chester)
Chester *p454* 0800 289997

Earland, R A (Wood's Solicitors) *C1 E F1 J1 R1 S1 T2 W Q K1 Zd Zn*
Disley *p210* 01663 765511

Earle, Mrs A (Pearson Maddin Solicitors) *N J1 Q*
New Malden *p321* 020 8949 9500

Earle, Mrs A (Lincolnshire County Council Resources - Legal Services)
Lincoln *p463*. 01522 552222

Earle, J (Ashurst LLP)
London EC2 *p7* 020 7638 1111

Earle, R L (Bates Wells & Braithwaite London LLP) *O Q A3 C3 Zd*
London EC4 *p11*. 020 7551 7777

Earle-Hutton, Mrs G C C (McMillan Williams Solicitors) *K1 G H B2 K3*
Bexleyheath *p132* 020 8303 0168

Earley, C (Keypoint Law LLP) *W*
Doncaster *p212* 01302 329655

Early, O (Veale Wasbrough Vizards) *K1 D1*
Bristol *p165* 0117 925 2020

Early, Ms R A (Temperley Taylor LLP) *D1 K1*
Middleton *p315* 0161 643 2411

Earnshaw, Mrs A L (Oxley & Coward Solicitors LLP) *G H B2 Zi Ze*
Rotherham *p367*. 01709 510999

Earnshaw, G P (Forbes) *N P F1 G H K1*
Preston *p356* 01772 220022

Earnshaw, Mrs M J (Weymouth & Portland Borough Council) *Q N O D1 K1 L J1 F1 W V Zm Zd Zc*
Weymouth *p476* 01305 838000

Earnshaw, P M (Crutes) *S2 E R2*
Newcastle upon Tyne *p324* . 0191 233 9700

Earnshaw, Ms R A (Fisher Jones Greenwood LLP) *K1 K3*
Colchester *p197* 01206 578282

Earnshaw, Mrs S E (Senior Calveley & Hardy) *K1 K3 N*
Lytham *p297*. 01253 733333

Earnshaw, W R (Heelis Solicitors) *S1 A1 W C1 K1 P L R1 T1 J1 Zl*
Appleby *p118* 01768 351591

Earons, A G (Percy Walker & Co) *S2 S1*
Hastings *p243* 01424 721234

Easdon, A G (Carr & Co) *S1 S2 E*
Blyth *p147*. 01670 351251

Easdown, D (George Davies Solicitors LLP) *C2 C1 Zb*
Manchester *p303* 0161 236 8992

Eason, N P (NBM Eason) *S1 W L*
Ashby-de-la-Zouch *p118*. . . 01530 560545

Eason, R G (Jacksons) *Q N K1 S1 E O J1 L A1 F1 Zl Zc S2 J2 Zq*
Fordingbridge *p227* 01425 652110

East, Miss F M (Weightmans LLP) *N O Q*
Dartford *p207* 020 7822 1900

East, L T (Reed Smith LLP) *Za*
London EC2 *p71*. 020 3116 3000

East, N (Hempsons) *E S2 R2 S1 L P J1*
Westminster *p40*. 020 7839 0278

East, N (Lodders Solicitors LLP) *S2 E*
Stratford-upon-Avon *p400* . . 01789 293259

East, S R (Meade-King) *E S1*
Bristol *p163* 0117 926 4121

Easter, Ms C (Ashurst LLP) *C1 C3 U1*
London EC2 *p7* 020 7638 1111

Easter, C (Robinson Allfree) *S2 E C1 S1*
Ramsgate *p359* 01843 592361

Easter, Mrs F (Lucas & Wyllys) *K1*
Great Yarmouth *p234* 01493 855555

Easter, J J (Rowland Tildesley & Harris) *S2 E G K3 K1 S1*
Willenhall *p433* 01902 366571

Easterbrook, A (Myer Wolff) *W K4 T2*
Hull *p257* 01482 223693

Easterbrook, Ms J L (Bevan Brittan LLP)
London EC4 *p12*. 0870 194 1000

Eastgate, G (Amphlett Chatterton) *S1 S2*
Leamington Spa *p270* 01926 311427

Eastham, Ms J J (Aviva PLC)
London EC3 *p103* . . 020 7283 7500 / 01603 687905
Norwich *p467* 01603 622200

Easthope, D (Lanyon Bowdler LLP) *G H B2 Zl*
Shrewsbury *p379* 01743 280280

Easthope, R (Harrisons Solicitors LLP) *S1 W K1 L P M1 G N D1 T1 Zd Zh Zi K2*
Welshpool *p425* 01938 552545

Eastman, Miss E (Beale and Company Solicitors LLP) *Zq Q O Zj*
London WC2 *p11* 020 7240 3474

Easton, D (Leigh Day & Co) *N*
London EC1 *p52*. 020 7650 1200

Easton, Miss E K (Blake Lapthorn) *B1*
Portsmouth *p354*. 023 9222 1122

Eastwell, N W (Linklaters LLP)
London EC2 *p54*. 020 7456 2000

Eastwood, A G (Goodswens) *B1 F1 H J1 M1 N P*
Redcar *p362*. 01642 482424

Eastwood, D J (Somerfield Stores Ltd)
Bristol *p452* 0117 935 6135

Eastwood, Ms H A (Dixon Ward) *S1 S2 E*
Richmond upon Thames *p364* 020 8940 4051

Eastwood, O (Lewis Silkin LLP) *J1*
London EC4 *p53*. 020 7074 8000

Eastwood, R M (Pearson Hinchliffe)
Oldham *p341* 0161 785 3500

Eastwood, S (Brady Eastwood Pierce & Stewart)
Lewisham *p15* 020 8692 8181

Eastwood, S (Eastwoods Solicitors) *N Q O J1 Zw Zk G Zj*
London EC4 *p28*. 020 3137 4800

Easty, Ms G M (London Borough of Southwark) *K1*
London SE1 *p109* 020 7525 5000

Eatock, Ms J (Wilkin Chapman LLP) *J1 C1*
Grimsby *p235* 01472 262626

Eaton, A (Leeds City Council)
Leeds *p462* 0113 224 3513

Eaton, A A (Nelsons)
Derby *p209* 01332 372372

Eaton, A G (Aviva PLC) *E*
London EC3 *p103* . . 020 7283 7500 / 01603 687905
Norwich *p467* 01603 622200

Eaton, Miss A J (Morecrofts Solicitors LLP) *K1 K2 D1 D2*
Liverpool *p290*. 0151 236 8871

Eaton, Ms C (London Borough of Haringey)
London N22 *p106* 020 8489 0000

Eaton, Mrs C M (Edward Pilling & Co)
Oxford *p344* 01865 741122

Eaton, Ms D J (Sheffield City Council)
Sheffield *p471* 0114 273 4019

Eaton, Mrs E (hlw Keeble Hawson LLP) *W T2*
Sheffield *p376* 0114 276 5555

Eaton, J C J (Lupton Fawcett) *W T2*
Leeds *p275* 0113 280 2000

Eaton, Ms K (Punch Robson) *S1*
Stockton-on-Tees *p397* . . . 01642 754050

Eaton, Mrs L J (Adlams LLP) *S1 W L T1*
St Neots *p392* 01480 474061

Eaton, M (Housing & Property Law Partnership) *Zh O Q E L Zc*
Islington *p43*. 020 7553 9000

Eaton, M W S (Eaton & Few) *N S1 B1 J1 K3 Q O*
St Ives *p391* 01480 301558

Eaton, N D (Eaton Ryan & Taylor) *O N J1 F1 Q Zj Zp Zq Zc A3 J2*
Birmingham *p138* 0121 236 1999

Eaton, P G (Penningtons)
London EC2 *p66*. 020 7457 3000

Eaton, R (Lawrences) *G H*
Wellingborough *p424* 01933 442324

Eaton, Ms S (Fishburns) *Zj O Q N*
London EC3 *p32*. 020 7280 8888

Eaton, Miss T (BLB Solicitors) *N*
Bath *p127* 01225 462871

Eatough, D T (Clifford Chance)
London E14 *p20* 020 7006 1000

Eatough, J A (Napthens LLP) *E*
Blackburn *p145* 01254 667733

Eatough, J M (Kettering Borough Council)
Kettering *p462*. 01536 410333
Manchester *p303* 0870 011 1111

Eatwell, J W (Herrington & Carmichael LLP) *S2 E C1 J1 O S1 L Q R1 Ze Zl Zp Zq*
Wokingham *p437* 0118 977 4045

Eaves, J D (Pilgrim & Webster) *W K1 S1 K3 E*
Hinckley *p250* 01455 634851

Eaves, Miss L (Lodders Solicitors LLP) *Q W*
Stratford-upon-Avon *p400* . . 01789 293259

Eaves, Mrs P (Neville-Jones & Co) *S1 S2 E R2*
Wareham *p421* 01929 552471

Ebanks, Miss J Y (Tyndallwoods) *L Zu Zh*
Birmingham *p143* 0121 624 1111

Ebdon, R A (Longden Walker & Renney) *D1 F1 K1 M1*
Sunderland *p401*. 0191 567 7024

Ebenezer, Mrs M A (DWF) *N Zj*
Preston *p356* 01772 556677

Ebert, D H (David Ebert & Co) *S1 S2 W*
Southampton *p385*. 023 8047 7625

Ebizie, Mrs C (Salford City Council)
Swinton *p473* 0161 794 4711

Ebner, H (Myers Fletcher & Gordon) *C1 E S1 W T1 J1 L F1 K1 R1 Zm Zo*
London W6 *p62* 020 7610 4433

Ebrahim, A (Bowling & Co) *W*
London E15 *p15* 020 8221 8000

Ebrahimi, Miss J Y (HM Land Registry - Harrow Sub Office)
Harrow *p460*. 020 8235 1181

Ebsworth, J R (Devonshires) *C1 Ze C2 Zw*
London EC2 *p27*. 020 7628 7576

Eccles, D N (Bannister Preston) *D1 F1 G H J1 K1 M1*
Sale *p370* 0161 973 2434

Eccles, Miss J L (Charles Platel Solicitors) *E S2 S1 C1 Zc*
Wokingham *p437* 0118 978 4866

Eccles, S P (Pinney Talfourd LLP) *N K1 O Q Zq*
Hornchurch *p252* 01708 511000

Eccleston, Ms L (Ashurst LLP) *C1*
London EC2 *p7* 020 7638 1111

Eccleston, Mrs L (Walker Smith Way) *W T2 K4*
Chester *p191* 0844 346 3100

Eccleston, Miss R (Browne Jacobson LLP) *C1 C2 Zw*
Nottingham *p336*. 0115 976 6000

Eccleston, R K (Howell Hylton) *G H*
Camborne *p173* 01209 613014

Eccleston, S (Sheffield City Council)
Sheffield *p471* 0114 273 4019

Echenagusia, J M (Interval International Ltd) *C1 Zc*
London SW20 *p107* 020 8336 9300

Eddings, G (Holman Fenwick Willan)
London EC3 *p42*. 020 7264 8000

Eddison, Mrs T (South Norfolk District Council)
Long Stratton *p463* 01508 533633

Eddleston, Mrs M E (Grigsby Eddleston & Co) *S1 W S2*
Stevenage *p394* 01438 742525

Eddlestone, W L (Hamilton Downing Quinn) *C1 J1 L M1 N O Q W Ze Zf Zk F2 I U1 U2*
London WC1 *p38* 020 7831 8939

Eddleston-Haynes, G C (Foot Anstey) *E O Q L*
Plymouth *p349*. 01752 675000

Eddon, G H (North Yorkshire County Council) *D1*
Northallerton *p467* 01609 780780

Eddowes, R (Dewes LLP) *G H M1 P K1*
Tamworth *p407* 01827 58391

Eddy, Mrs A (Matthew & Matthew Limited) *S1*
Southbourne *p387* 01202 431943

Eddy, A (Wansbroughs) *G H*
Melksham *p314* 01225 703222

Eddy, Ms A M (Irwin Mitchell LLP) *N*
London EC1 *p45*. 0870 150 0100

Eddy, Ms B J (Simmons & Simmons)
London EC2 *p79*. 020 7628 2020

Eddy, C J (Cole & Co)
Norwich *p334* 01603 617018

Eddy, Miss C J (Darbys Solicitors LLP) *K1 K2*
Oxford *p343*. 01865 811700

Ede, D (David Ede Solicitors)
London SE18 *p28* 020 8316 4758

Ede, S A (Bridge McFarland) *C1 C2 J1 O Q B1 Ze Zv*
Grimsby *p235* 01472 311711

Edelstyn, P (Precision Castparts Corp)
Hereford *p460*. 01432 382200

Eden, J (EMW) *Zb C1*
Milton Keynes *p316* 0845 070 6000

Eden, J W (Eden & Co) *M1 C1 S1 K1 P N*
Manchester *p304* 0161 237 1116

Eden, R E A (Bower & Bailey) *S2 C1 E S1 W*
Oxford *p343*. 01865 311133

Eden, Miss S (Rollingsons)
London EC1 *p73*. 020 7611 4848

Eder, G P (Finers Stephens Innocent LLP) *L E R1 S1 C1 Zo M1*
London W1 *p32* 020 7323 4000

Ederley Harris, Mrs A A (Legal Services Commission)
Reading *p469* 0118 955 8600

Edey, Ms K (Ashurst LLP)
London EC2 *p7* 020 7638 1111

Edgar, A B (Hogan Lovells International LLP)
London EC1 *p42*. 020 7296 2000

Edgar, A C (Edward Harte LLP)
Brighton *p159* 01273 662750

Edgar, A N L (Clifford Chance)
London E14 *p20* 020 7006 1000

Edgar, J (Harbottle & Lewis LLP)
London W1 *p38* 020 7667 5000

Edgar, Mrs L T (Brabners Chaffe Street)
Manchester *p301* 0161 836 8800

Edgar, Mrs P S (Cripps Harries Hall LLP) *S2 E*
Tunbridge Wells *p415* 01892 515121

Edge, L (Leeds City Council)
Leeds *p462* 0113 224 3513

Edge, P L (Thurrock Borough Council)
Grays *p459* 01375 390000

Edge, R (Wilkinson Woodward) *K3 K1 D1*
Huddersfield *p256* 01484 483800

Edge, Miss S M (Cambridgeshire County Council)
Cambridge *p453*. 01223 717111

Edgecombe, P S (Whiteford Crocker) *C1 S2 E S1 W*
Plympton *p351*. 01752 335994

Edgecombe, R J (Carmarthenshire County Council)
Carmarthen *p453* 01267 224010

Edgell, J L (LG Lawyers)
London SE1 *p50*. 020 7379 0000

Edgelow, J (Salans) *C1 C2*
London EC4 *p76*. 020 7429 6000

Edgerley Harris, Mrs A A (Edgerley Harris Solicitors)
Winchester *p433*. 01962 779861

Edgerley Harris, G J (Edgerley Harris Solicitors)
Winchester *p433*. 01962 779861

Edgington, A (LDJ Solicitors) *E S1 R1 C1*
Nuneaton *p339* 024 7674 5000

Edgington, Mrs E (Horsey Lightly) *K1*
Newbury *p322* 01635 580858

Edila, Mrs G (The Royal Borough of Kensington & Chelsea)
London W8 *p109* 020 7361 2741

Edinboro-Wright, Mrs T (Dodd Lewis Solicitors) *E R2 S1 S2*
London SE3 *p27*. 020 8852 1255

Edlin, Miss A B (Cardiff Magistrates Court)
Cardiff *p453* 029 2046 3040

Edlmann, S R R (Linklaters LLP)
London EC2 *p54*. 020 7456 2000

Edmead, Ms K J (Tollers LLP) *K4 W*
Kettering *p265*. 01536 520111

Edmond, J T S (Marrons) *R1 E R2 P O*
Leicester *p280*. 0116 289 2200

Edmondes, N C (Trowers & Hamlins) *E B1*
London EC3 *p88*. 020 7423 8000

Edmonds, MIss C (Steeles) *J1*
London EC2 *p82*. 020 7421 1720
Norwich *p335* 0870 609 0200

Edmonds, C J (Howlett Clarke Solicitors) *S1 W S2*
Hove *p254*. 01273 419728

Edmonds, C W I (David Gist Solicitors) *N*
Bristol *p162* 0117 927 9111
Bristol *p164* 0117 929 0333

Edmonds, J D P (Kingsfords) *S1 E C1 A1 L*
Ashford *p119* 01233 665544

Edmonds, M J (Pengillys LLP) *S1 S2*
Dorchester *p212*. 01305 768888
Weymouth *p430*. 01305 768888

Edmonds, M W (Merchant Investors Assurance Co Ltd)
Bristol *p452* 0117 926 6366

Edmonds, Ms R J (Caldicott Gallimore)
Leominster *p282*. 01568 614168

Edmondson, G (Gavin Edmondson Solicitors) *K4 Q N S1 T2 W*
Northwich *p333* 01606 43762

Edmondson, G A (Amphletts) *L F1 J1 Q E N O K4 Zh*
Colwyn Bay *p198* 01492 532296

Edmondson, J (Farrer & Co LLP)
London WC2 *p31* 020 3375 7000

Edmondson, J (Mellor & Jackson) *S1 E W M1 C1 N G K1 R1 Zb Zl Zt*
Oldham *p340* 0161 624 7081

Edmondson, M A (Edmondson Hall) *B1 C1 J1 K1 N O Q Zk Zl Zc Zj Zw*
Newmarket *p327*. 01638 560556

Edmondson, Miss N (Birkett Long LLP) *N P Zr Zq*
Chelmsford *p186*. 01245 453800

Edmondson, P (CMS Cameron McKenna LLP) *C1 Zj Ze*
London EC3 *p17*. 020 7367 3000

Edmondson, R H (Woolley Bevis Diplock) *E*
Brighton *p160* 01273 323231

Edmondson, S D (Edmondsons) *K1 G P D1 S1 W N J1 F1 M1*
St Albans *p390* 01727 866497

Edmondson, W D B (Coates Allbutt Edmondson & Taylor) *S1*
Tankerton *p407* . . .01227 272617 / 262813

Edmondson-Jones, G E (G E Edmondson-Jones)
Easingwold *p215*. 01347 821615

Edmund, Mrs T (Bristows) *E S1 L R1 P*
London EC4 *p15*. 020 7400 8000

Edmunds, Ms J (Reed Executive PLC)
London WC2 *p108*. 020 7421 1640

Edmunds, K (Carvers (Part of the Wilkes Partnership LLP)) *R2 S1 S2 E*
Birmingham *p136* 0121 784 8484
Sutton Coldfield *p403* 0121 350 0987

Edmunds, Mrs L J (Evans Powell & Co) *K1 K3 D1 Zr Q W L S1*
Llanelli *p292*. 01554 772632

Edmunds, Mrs S B (Rix & Kay Solicitors LLP) *S1*
Seaford *p373* 0845 165 8178

Edmunds, Miss S E (Capsticks Solicitors LLP) *Zr*
London SW19 *p18*. 020 8780 2211

Edmundson, R J (PricewaterhouseCoopers Legal LLP) *C2 C1*
London SE1 *p69*. 020 7212 1616

Edney, S J (S J Edney) *N Zr*
Swindon *p406* 0800 421234

Edon, J A (HM Land Registry - Hull) *E W L C1 T1 S1 R1 B1 A1*
Hull *p461* 01482 223244

Edwardes Jones, J R (Druces LLP) *W C1 J1*
London EC2 *p27*. 020 7638 9271

See p634 for the Key to Work Categories

Edwards, Mrs A (The Johnson Partnership) G H B2
Mansfield p311. . . . . 01623 427575

Edwards, A (Alan Edwards & Co) E L Q S1
Kensington & Chelsea p28. . 020 7221 7644

Edwards, Ms A (Boodle Hatfield)
Westminster p14. . . . . . . 020 7629 7411

Edwards, A D (Reed Smith LLP) E S1
London EC2 p71. . . . . . . 020 3116 3000

Edwards, Mrs A G (Wannop Fox Staffurth & Bray) K4 W
Worthing p442. . . . . 01903 228200

Edwards, Mrs A M (Fladgate LLP) W T2
London WC2 p32 . . . . . . 020 3036 7000

Edwards, Mrs A S (Allen & Overy LLP)
London E1 p5 . . . . 020 3088 0000

Edwards, A T A (TV Edwards LLP) G Zl H B2
London EC3 p85. . . . . . . 020 7790 7000

Edwards, A W C (Farrer & Co LLP) T1 A1 W C1 Zd
London WC2 p31 . . . . . . 020 3375 7000

Edwards, B (Geoffrey Morris & Ashton) S2 E L Zl Zu R1 W
Wrexham p442 . . . . 01978 291322

Edwards, B C (Barrington Charles Edwards & Co)
London SE20 p11020 8659 7228 / 8659 7227

Edwards, B J (Bridge Sanderson Munro) C1 E C2 J1
Doncaster p211 . . . . 01302 321621

Edwards, C (Hanratty & Co) D1 S2 G K3 J1 Q S1 W
Newtown p330. . . . . 01686 626239

Edwards, C (Loosemores) S2 E S1 W
Cardiff p179 . . . . 029 2022 4433

Edwards, Mrs C (Bearders) W K4 S1 K3 K1
Halifax p238 . . . . .01422 365215 / 343427

Edwards, C (Powys County Council)
Welshpool p475 . . . . 01938 552828
Llandrindod Wells p463 . . . 01597 826000

Edwards, C J (Myers Fletcher & Gordon) P K1 G L M1 N J1 H D1 F1 Zi Q
London W6 p62 . . . . 020 7610 4433

Edwards, C J (Henry Hughes & Hughes) E
London SW16 p40. . . . . . 020 8765 2700

Edwards, C O (Johnson & Gaunt) G K1 P M1 F1 H J1 D1 Zl
Banbury p122 . . . .01295 256271 / 271200

Edwards, C R (Stewarts Law LLP) N
London EC4 p83. . . . . . . 020 7822 8000

Edwards, D (Hilary Meredith Solicitors)
Wilmslow p433. . . . . 01625 539922

Edwards, D (Guthrie Jones & Jones) N O G Q K1 S1 W L A1 X Zl Zu Zv Zr Zz
Bala p121 . . . . 01678 520428

Edwards, D E (Waldrons) O Q B1 Zc
Brierley Hill p158. . . . . . 01384 811811

Edwards, D I (Rother District Council)
Bexhill p449. . . . . 01424 787878

Edwards, D J (Burt Brill & Cardens) W S1 T2 Zd
Brighton p159 . . . . 01273 604123

Edwards, D J D (Plexus Law (A Trading Name of Parabis Law LLP)) Zj N
Colchester p198. . . . . . . 0844 245 4950

Edwards, D M (Stanley H Cross & Co) G H
Chorley p194 . . . . 01257 272222

Edwards, D P (Goodman Derrick LLP)
London EC4 p36. . . . . . . 020 7404 0606

Edwards, D R (Bennett Griffin) C1 O Zq
Ferring p225. . . . . 01903 229999

Edwards, D S M (Aaron & Partners LLP Solicitors) B1 C1 C2 C3 J1 M1 O Q T1 Zb Ze Zv
Chester p190 . . . . 01244 405555

Edwards, Ms E A (Amphlett Lissimore) K3 K1 K2
Croydon p6 . . . . 020 8771 5254

Edwards, E E (Hill Dickinson LLP) S1 L E R1 A1 Zl
Liverpool p288. . . . . 0151 600 8000

Edwards, Mrs F M (Ford Simey LLP) O F1 Zc
Exeter p221 . . . . 01392 274126

Edwards, G (Browne Jacobson LLP)
Nottingham p336. . . . . . . 0115 976 6000

Edwards, G (Percy Hughes & Roberts) S2 E S1
Birkenhead p134. . . . . . . 0151 666 9090

Edwards, G (Buss Murton LLP) W
Tunbridge Wells p415 . . . . 01892 510222

Edwards, Miss G B (Pannone LLP) Zr
Manchester p308 . . . . . . 0161 909 3000

Edwards, G J (Reynolds Porter Chamberlain LLP)
London E1 p71 . . . . 020 3060 6000

Edwards, Mrs G J (Lovegrove & Eliot) S1 E L W K1 F1 R1
Windsor p434 . . . . 01753 851133

Edwards, G M (Pinsent Masons LLP) C2 C1
London EC2 p67. . . . . . . 020 7418 7000

Edwards, G R (Crangle Edwards) G H K1 S1 W Zv
Stretford p400. .0161 865 2993 / 865 7816 / 865 5875

Edwards, G W (Everett Tomlin Lloyd & Pratt) N O Q R1 J1 C1 Zl Zc
Pontypool p352 . . . . 01495 763333

Edwards, Ms H (Russell-Cooke LLP) E
London SW15 p74. . . . . . 020 8789 9111

Edwards, H D (Bone & Payne LLP) N G Q Zl J1
Llandudno p291 . . . . 01492 876354

Edwards, H M (Martin Edwards) G K1 S1 J1 W D1 C1 E S2 Zl K3 K4 O Q R1
Shifnal p378. . . . . 01952 462118

Edwards, H M (Langleys) Q N
Lincoln p284. . . . . 01522 888555
York p445 . . . . 01904 610886

Edwards, H R (Reed Smith LLP) E
London EC2 p71. . . . . . . 020 3116 3000

Edwards, I (Addleshaw Goddard)
London EC1 p4 . . . . 020 7606 8855

Edwards, Ms J (Thomson Snell & Passmore) C1
Tunbridge Wells p415 . . . . 01892 510000

Edwards, Ms J (Manches LLP) K1
London WC2 p58 . . . . . . 020 7404 4433

Edwards, J (Ziadies) K1 D1
London SW9 p94 . . . . . . 020 7737 0934

Edwards, Mrs J (Davies & Partners) Zr Q N
Gloucester p230. . . . . . . 01452 612345

Edwards, J C (Preston Goldburn) W T2 K4 J1
Falmouth p223. . . . . 01326 318900

Edwards, J D L (Squire Sanders (UK) LLP)
Manchester p310 . . . . . . 0161 830 5000

Edwards, J I (Peter Edwards Law)
Wirral p435 . . . . 0151 632 6699

Edwards, J L (Widdows Mason) G H N O Q S1 W S2 J1 K1
Warrington p422. . . . . . . 01925 632267

Edwards, J R (Clark Brookes) K1 O Q T1 T2 W
West Bromwich p427 . . . . 0121 553 2576

Edwards, J S P (GHP Legal) A1 B1 D1 G H J1 K1 L M1 N Zl
Wrexham p442 . . . . 01978 291456

Edwards, J W (Edwards Clegg) E S1 W R1 P Zc
Beeston p130 . . . . 0115 922 4537

Edwards, Miss K (Wendy Hopkins Family Law Practice LLP) K1 K3 D1 D2
Cardiff p178 . . . . 029 2034 2233

Edwards, Miss K (Coles Miller Solicitors LLP) W L K4
Bournemouth p151. . . . . . 01202 293226

Edwards, Miss K (George Davies Solicitors LLP) O Q
Manchester p303 . . . . . . 0161 236 8992

Edwards, Miss K A (Wace Morgan) W
Shrewsbury p379 . . . . . . 01743 280100

Edwards, K D (Dudley Metropolitan Borough Council)
Dudley p457. . . . . 01384 815326

Edwards, Miss K L (Sears Tooth) K3 K1
London W1 p77 . . . . 020 7499 5599

Edwards, K M (Weightmans LLP) C1 J1 I Ze Zf Zp
Liverpool p291 . . . . 0151 227 2601

Edwards, Mrs L (Essex County Council)
Chelmsford p454. . . . . . . 0845 743 0430

Edwards, Mrs L (Derbyshire County Council) E P Zu R1 S1
Matlock p465 . . . . 01629 580000

Edwards, L (Wrigleys Solicitors LLP) Zo
Leeds p278 . . . . 0113 244 6100

Edwards, Miss L E (Clarke Willmott) S2
Bristol p162 0845 209 1000 / 0117 305 6000

Edwards, Miss L J (Gosport Borough Council)
Gosport p459 . . . . 023 9258 4242

Edwards, M (Ashurst LLP)
London EC2 p7 . . . . 020 7638 1111

Edwards, Miss M (Salford City Council)
Swinton p473 . . . . 0161 794 4711

Edwards, Miss M A (Field Seymour Parkes) S1 L
Reading p360 . . . . 0118 951 6200

Edwards, Ms M A (Hodders) D2 D1 K3 K1
High Wycombe p250. . . . . 01494 511345

Edwards, M J (Lane & Co) O Q
Walsall p420. . . . . 01922 721259

Edwards, M J (SGH Martineau LLP) N L
Birmingham p142 . . . . . . 0870 763 2000

Edwards, M J (Pinney Talfourd LLP)
Brentwood p156. . . . . . . 01277 268700

Edwards, M J (Clifford Chance)
London E14 p20. . . . . . . 020 7006 1000

Edwards, Ms M K (Pritchard Edwards & Co) K1 D1 Q S1 W N
Carmarthen p182 . . . . . . 01267 234022

Edwards, N G (Berkson Wallace Solicitors) O Q N
Wallasey p419. . . . . 0151 691 6900

Edwards, N L (Nigel Edwards & Co) S1 E L W T1
Maidstone p299 . . . . 01622 690575

Edwards, Mrs N M (Dolmans) N Q J2 Zw
Cardiff p178 . . . . 029 2034 5531

Edwards, N M (Lewis Silkin LLP) C1 C2 B1
London EC4 p53. . . . . . . 020 7074 8000

Edwards, P (Smyth Barkham) Zd Zf T1 T2 W
London WC2 p80 . . . . . . 020 7632 9550

Edwards, P C (Peter Edwards Law)
Wirral p435 . . . . 0151 632 6699

Edwards, Miss P C (Dawson Hart) S1
Uckfield p416 . . . . 01825 762281

Edwards, Miss P C (Edwards Clegg) C1 S2 E S1
Beeston p130 . . . . 0115 922 4537

Edwards, P D (Irwin Mitchell LLP) N Zr Zq
Birmingham p139 . . . . . . 0870 150 0100

Edwards, P J (Capsticks Solicitors LLP) J1 N Q Zp Zg
London SW19 p18. . . . . . 020 8780 2211

Edwards, P W (Tozers) N O Q
Exeter p222 . . . . 01392 207020

Edwards, R (E Rex Makin & Co) N G Q Zq
Liverpool p289. . . . . 0151 709 4491

Edwards, Miss R (Shulmans) E S2 R2 S1
Leeds p276 . . . . 0113 245 2833

Edwards, Ms R (Otten Penna Ltd) Zm W
Northenden p333 . . . . . . 0161 945 1431

Edwards, R B S (Roger Edwards & Co) C1 D1 E F1 G H K1 M1 S1 W Zm Zl
Tredegar p413. . . . . 01495 722865

Edwards, Mrs R E (Thursfields) G H D1 Zi Zl
Worcester p440 . . . . 01905 730450

Edwards, Mrs R E (Gwynedd Council)
Caernarfon p452. . . . . . . 01286 672255

Edwards, Ms R J (Ashfords LLP) K1
Taunton p408 . . . . 01823 232300

Edwards, R J (Barlow Lyde & Gilbert LLP) Zj
London EC3 p10. . . . . . . 020 7247 2277

Edwards, R J (Bridge McFarland) S2 S1 E W N C1 B1 G J1 K1 Zr Zv
Grimsby p235 . . . . 01472 311711

Edwards, R J (Buller Jeffries) J2 N O Q Zj
Birmingham p136 . . . . . . 0121 212 2620

Edwards, R M (Battens) E
Yeovil p443 . . . . 01935 846000

Edwards, Miss R M (William Sturges & Co) S1 Zl S2
Westminster p84. . . . . . . 020 7873 1000

Edwards, R N (Martyn Prowel) D1 S1 K1
Cardiff p180 . . . . 029 2047 0909

Edwards, R W (Rowberry Morris) S1 E W C1 C2 Zl Zf S2
Reading p361 . . . . 0118 958 5611
Staines p393. . . . . 01784 457655

Edwards, Mrs S (Forsters LLP) E R1 R2
Westminster p33. . . . . . . 020 7863 8333

Edwards, S (Reed Smith LLP) Zf
London EC2 p71. . . . . . . 020 3116 3000

Edwards, Miss S E (Keene & Kelly) D1 K3 K1
Mold p318. . . . . 01352 753882

Edwards, Miss S J (Leo Abse & Cohen)
Cardiff p179 . . .029 2038 3252 / 2034 5421

Edwards, Mrs S K (PCB Solicitors LLP) D1 K1 K3
Shrewsbury p379 . . . . . . 01743 248148

Edwards, Mrs S L (Wrexham County Borough Council)
Wrexham p477 . . . . 01978 292000

Edwards, Mrs S L (Harding Evans LLP) K1
Newport p328 . . . . 01633 244233

Edwards, S W (Sumitomo Mitsui Banking Corporation Europe Limited)
London EC4 p109 . . 020 7786 1000 / 1017

Edwards, T A (Cumberland Ellis Peirs) C1 I C2 Ze
London WC1 p23 . . . . . . 020 7242 0422

Edwards, Ms T D (Davies & Partners) N Zr
Birmingham p137 . . . . . . 0121 616 4450

Edwards, Mrs V A (Hatchers Solicitors LLP) S2 R2 E
Shrewsbury p379 . . . . . . 01743 248545

Edwards, Mrs V M (Forsters LLP) Zb
Westminster p33. . . . . . . 020 7863 8333

Edwards, W M H (Pemberton Greenish LLP) W T1
London SW3 p66 . . . . . . 020 7591 3333

Eedle, Miss P R (Ware & Kay LLP) S1 E W L
York p445 . . . . 01904 716000

Eeles, Miss J M (South Cheshire Magistrates Court)
Crewe p456 . . . . 0870 162 6261

Eeles, Mrs M (Dixon Rigby Keogh) S1 W K4 L
Sandbach p372 . . . . 01270 766550

Eels, Miss R L (Stone King LLP) K1 K2 K3
Bath p128 . . . . 01225 337599

Efthymiadis, Miss K M (Molesworths Bright Clegg) S1 E R1 L
Rochdale p365. . . . . 01706 356666

Egan, Miss A (E&K Solicitors & Estate Agents) E N S1 W Q
Manchester p304 . . . . . . 0161 256 3915

Egan, A J (Charles Lucas & Marshall) J1
Swindon p406 . . . . 01793 511055

Egan, Mrs C H (Squire Sanders (UK) LLP) C1 E J1 B1
Birmingham p142 . . . . . . 0121 222 3000

Egan, J (Woodfines LLP) K1 D1 K3
Milton Keynes p317 . . . . . 01908 202150

Egan, J B (Joe Egan Solicitors) G H K1 L M1 S1
Bolton p149 . . . . 01204 386214
Bolton p149 . . . . 01204 368060

Egan, J M (Carlisle City Council)
Carlisle p453. . . . . 01228 817000

Egan, P (Parry Davies Clwyd-Jones & Lloyd) S1 K1 G L D1 Q H N
Amlwch p117 . . . .01407 831777 / 830665

Egan, S W D (Bates Wells & Braithwaite London LLP) Zf
London EC4 p11. . . . . . . 020 7551 7777

Egar, Rev J A (National Institutions of the Church of England, Legal Office)
London SW1 p108. . . . . . 020 7898 1000

Egginton, Miss J M (Sandwell Metropolitan Borough Council) L N P Q Zh Zj Zy
Oldbury p468 . . . . 0121 569 2200

Egglestone, R G (Dutton Gregory) N J1 K1
Winchester p433. . . . . . . 01962 844333

Egner, F G K (Neil McQueen Duncan & Egner) S1 K1 W Zj F1 A1 S2 E L O Q N C2 K4
Newcastle upon Tyne p326 . 0191 232 7469

Egner, M G K (Neil McQueen Duncan & Egner) Q N O Zw S1 S2 W K1 E F1 L Zj K3 C1 J1 K4
Newcastle upon Tyne p326 . 0191 232 7469

Egremont, N J (Saulet & Co) H G
Southsea p389. . . . . 023 9281 9442

Eichler, Ms J (Funnell & Perring)
Hastings p243 . . . . 01424 426287

Eilon, Mrs B A (Fladgate LLP) E L S1 W
London WC2 p32 . . . . . . 020 3036 7000

Eilon, Dr D (Lawrence Stephens) I
London EC1 p82. . . . . . . 020 7935 1211

Eisenberg, Mrs R (Moorcrofts LLP) C1 C2
Marlow p313. . . . . 01628 470000

Eisenthal, M M (Mark Eisenthal & Co) E C1 L S1 W Q O N J1 Ze Zf Zk Zm Zi
London WC2 p29 . . . . . . 020 7379 3475

Eizenberg, J (Beale and Company Solicitors LLP) Zq Zj
London WC2 p11 . . . . . . 020 7240 3474

Ejikeme, Ms I (McKeowns Solicitors Ltd) N Q
St Albans p390 . . . . 0800 032 8328

Eka, Ms N (Cunningtons) S1
Braintree p155. . . . . 01376 326868

Ekanayake, J (Ashurst LLP)
London EC2 p7 . . . . 020 7638 1111

Ekberg, C R (Beetenson & Gibbon) S1 W
Grimsby p235 . . . . 01472 240251

Eke, R J (Wilkin Chapman Epton Blades) B1 Q C1 C2 C3 Ze
Lincoln p285. . . . . 01522 512345

Ekers, Ms K A (Forsters LLP) E
Westminster p33. . . . . . . 020 7863 8333

Ekins, S J (Fladgate LLP) O Q B1 Zk Zj Ze
London WC2 p32 . . . . . . 020 3036 7000

Eklund, J D (Giffen Couch & Archer)
Leighton Buzzard p282 . . . 01525 372681

Ekokobe, Miss J (Jacobs Forbes Solicitors) J1 Zi Zp
London N17 p45. . . . . . . 020 8880 4154

Ekon, Mrs L K (Investec Bank (UK) Ltd)
London EC2 p107 . . . . . . 020 7597 4000

Ekpenyoung, G (Browne Jacobson LLP) L N P Q Zl Zj
Nottingham p336. . . . . . . 0115 976 6000

El-Chamaa, H (Penningtons) Zi
London EC2 p66. . . . . . . 020 7457 3000

El-Imad, N (Seddons) S1 S2 E
Westminster p77. . . . . . . 020 7725 8000

El-Shatoury, Ms N (Surrey County Council)
Kingston upon Thames p462. 020 8541 9088

Eland, Miss D E (Rowlinsons) W K4 S1
Frodsham p227 . . . . 01928 735333

Elcoate, Mrs H L (Northumberland County Council)
Morpeth p466 . . . . 01670 533000

Elcombe, Ms M (Leonard & Co) Zi K1 K3
Southampton p386. . . . . . 023 8023 4433

Elder, H (Gordon Dadds) O
London W1 p25 . . . . 020 7493 6151

Elder, I F (Allen & Overy LLP)
London E1 p5 . . . . 020 3088 0000

Eldergill, Prof A C (Anselm Eldergill) Zm
Twickenham p416 . . . . . . 07971 198742

Elderton, Ms S L (Squire Sanders (UK) LLP)
Manchester p310 . . . . . . 0161 830 5000

Eldred, G R (Thomas Cooper) C1 M2 J1 Zg Zo Zb
London EC3 p22. . . . . . . 020 7481 8851

Eldred, Ms J (Trowers & Hamlins)
London EC3 p88. . . . . . . 020 7423 8000

Eldridge, D J (Howard Kennedy LLP) M1 E G C1 Zj
London W1 p48 . . . . 020 7636 1616

Eldridge, Miss F P M R (Clark Holt) C2 C1 Zb
Swindon p406 . . . . 01793 617444

Eldridge-Hinmers, Mrs T (Veale Wasbrough Vizards) X
London EC4 p89. . . . . . . 020 7405 1234

Eldridge-Hinmons, Mrs T (Ormerods)
Croydon p205 . . . . 020 8686 5000

Eleady-Cole, Mrs R (Lawson Lewis & Co) K1 K3
Eastbourne p215. . . . . . . 01323 720142

Eleanor, N J R (Aviva PLC)
London EC3 p103 . . 020 7283 7500 / 01603 687905
Norwich p467 . . . . 01603 622200
York p477 . . . . 01904 452210

Elek, Ms J K (Southend-on-Sea Borough Council) X D1
Southend-on-Sea p472 . . . 01702 215000

Eley, J (Farrer & Co LLP)
London WC2 p31 . . . . . . 020 3375 7000

Elford, Ms C (Reynolds Porter Chamberlain LLP)
London E1 p71 . . . . 020 3060 6000

Elford, Miss C L (Jolliffe & Co) O Q
Chester p190 . . . . 01244 310022

Elgar, Dr J (Liddell and Company) J1
Billericay p133. . . . . 01277 636426

Elgar, J N (K&L Gates LLP) C1 C2 Zb
London EC4 p47. . . . . . . 020 7648 9000

Elgee, J E (Elgee Pinks Solicitors) S1 W T1 E
Westerham p429. . . . . . . 01959 568100

Elgood, G D A (Debenhams Ottaway) S2 S1 E
Radlett p358. . . . . 01923 857171

Elias, A (Clifford Chance)
London E14 p20. . . . . . . 020 7006 1000

Elias, C (Dollman & Pritchard) W K4
Caterham p183 . . . . 01883 347823
London N12 p93. . . . . . . 020 8445 9898

Elias, C P (Michelmores LLP) S2 E S1 W T2 R2 M2 L Zi
Exeter p221 . . . . 01392 688688
London W1 p60 . . . . 020 7659 7660

Elias, H H (Kenneth Brand & Co) S1 S2 E W Zv L Q
London NW4 p15 . . . . . . 020 8202 6751

Elias, M (Nigel Davis Solicitors) W A1 Q T1 T2 K4 A2
Belper p131 . . . . 01335 372889

Elias, Ms N (Alsters Kelley) K1 K3
Coventry p199. . . . . 0844 561 0100

Elin, Miss T (Elin & Associates)
Basingstoke p126 . . . . . . 01256 358864

Elkin, Mrs N L A (Jefferies LLP) N
Altrincham p116 . . . . 0800 342 3191

Elkington, Mrs L M (McKinnells) G H
Lincoln p284. . . . . 01522 541181

Elkins, Ms J (Field Fisher Waterhouse LLP) Ze U2
London EC3 p31. . . . . . . 020 7861 4000

Elkins, Miss J C (Field Fisher Waterhouse LLP) E
London EC3 p31. . . . . . . 020 7861 4000

Elkins, T C (Johnson & Gaunt) C1 E S1 T1 F1 B1 M1 R1 Zc Zf Zo
Banbury p122 . . . .01295 256271 / 271200

Elks, M J (Radcliffes Le Brasseur) J1 L O Q
Westminster p70. . . . . . . 020 7222 7040

Ellaby, P (Hill Dickinson LLP) C1 C2
Manchester p305 . . . . . . 0161 817 7200

6

Ellam, Miss E (Hampshire County Council)
Winchester *p476* 01962 841841

Ellami, Miss R (Oxley & Coward Solicitors LLP) *W K4 T2*
Rotherham *p367* 01709 510999

Ellard, S C (Peacock Group Ltd) *E R1 S1 P*
Cardiff *p453* 029 2027 0228

Elledge, Ms K (Milner Elledge) *K1*
Dagenham *p206* 020 8984 0940

Ellement, Mrs N G (St Helens Borough Council)
St Helens *p472* 01744 456000
Preston *p357* 01772 555176

Ellenbogen, M J (Andrew Jackson & Co) *K1 D1 Q N W*
Liverpool *p289* 0151 487 8426
Liverpool *p289* 0151 709 5816 / 488 1000

Ellender, M T (Canterbury City Council)
Canterbury *p453* 01227 862000

Eller, Ms N (CMS Cameron McKenna LLP) *Zb*
London EC3 *p17* 020 7367 3000

Ellerbeck, Mrs R (Wolferstans) *K1 K3*
Plymouth *p351* 01752 663295

Ellerman, P D (Herbert Smith LLP) *C2 J1*
London EC2 *p40* 020 7374 8000

Ellery, Ms J Y (Metcalfes) *J1 N Q O Zj J2*
Bristol *p164* 0117 929 0451

Elley, Mrs E M L (The Royal London Mutual Insurance Society Ltd)
London EC3 *p455* 020 7506 6500

Ellicott, M C (Ellicotts) *S1 C1 W E K1 L F1 J1 T1*
London N20 *p29* 020 8445 5257 / 8445 2880

Ellingham, P W J (Kennedys) *J1 O N*
London EC3 *p49* 020 7667 9667

Ellingham, Miss S (Hartnell Chanot & Partners Family Law Specialists) *K1 D1 D2 K3*
Exeter *p221* 01392 421777

Ellingsworth, Ms K (Clarkson Wright & Jakes Ltd) *W K4*
Orpington *p341* 01689 887887

Ellington, Ms S M (Weightmans LLP)
Liverpool *p291* 0151 227 2601

Ellins, H M (Charles Lucas & Marshall) *E C1*
Swindon *p406* 01793 511055

Elliot, A (Hough Halton & Soal) *Q F1 L J1*
Carlisle *p182* 01228 524379

Elliot, G (Addleshaw Goddard)
Leeds *p271* 0113 209 2000

Elliot, J (Wilson & Co) *Zi*
London N17 *p92* 020 8808 7535

Elliot, Ms J L (Fox Williams) *C1 U1 C3 I F1 F2 Ze M1 U2 Zl*
London EC2 *p33* 020 7628 2000

Elliot, N (Reed Smith LLP) *C1 C3 C2*
London EC2 *p71* 020 3116 3000

Elliot, N J (Shacklocks) *E S1 S2 C1*
Belper *p131* 01773 822333

Elliot, N L (Fenwick Elliott)
London WC2 *p31* 020 7421 1986

Elliot, R B (Franklins) *K1 K3 D2*
Abingdon *p114* 01235 553222

Elliott, A (Ashurst LLP)
London EC2 *p7* 020 7638 1111

Elliott, A (Pinsent Masons LLP)
London EC2 *p67* 020 7418 7000

Elliott, Ms A (Graysons)
Sheffield *p375* 0114 272 9184

Elliott, Mrs A E (Latimer Hinks) *W T1 S1*
Darlington *p206* 01325 341500

Elliott, A E (Cumbria County Council)
Carlisle *p453* 01228 607374 / 607351

Elliott, Mrs A L (Brignalls Balderston Warren) *E S2*
Letchworth *p283* 01462 482248

Elliott, A W (LG Lawyers)
London SE1 *p50* 020 7379 0000

Elliott, Mrs C (HCB Solicitors) *T2 W Zm*
Walsall *p420* 01922 720000

Elliott, C (Elliott & Williams)
London N8 *p29* 020 7566 8244

Elliott, C (Hadaway & Hadaway) *E Zl S1*
North Shields *p330* 0191 257 0382

Elliott, Ms C A (LG Lawyers)
London SE1 *p50* 020 7379 0000

Elliott, Mrs C C (Coles Miller Solicitors LLP) *E L S1*
Poole *p352* 01202 673011

Elliott, C P (Hay & Kilner) *S2 S1 E Zl*
Wallsend *p419* 0191 262 8231

Elliott, D A (Worcestershire County Council)
Worcester *p477* 01905 766335

Elliott, Miss E (Morgan Cole) *K1*
Oxford *p344* 01865 262600

Elliott, G (Jones Day) *C1*
London EC4 *p46* 020 7039 5959

Elliott, Miss G R (Reynolds Porter Chamberlain LLP) *J1 O Q X Zp*
London E1 *p71* 020 3060 6000

Elliott, Miss J (South Yorkshire Passenger Transport Executive)
Sheffield *p471* 0114 276 7575

Elliott, J B Y (Brignalls Balderston Warren) *C1 C2 S2 E L W S1*
Letchworth *p283* 01462 482248

Elliott, Mrs J F (Dexter Montague LLP) *N Q J1 Zp*
Reading *p360* 0118 939 3999

Elliott, J O (Edwin Coe LLP) *B1 B2 O Q*
London WC2 *p29* 020 7691 4000

Elliott, L (Herbert Smith LLP)
London EC2 *p40* 020 7374 8000

Elliott, Mrs L M (Sheppersons) *F1 F2 J1 L O Q N Zq Zp*
Horley *p252* 01293 772424

Elliott, M (Pearson Rowe) *Zc C1 S2 E L R2 S1*
Birmingham *p141* 0121 236 7388

Elliott, M A (Walker Smith Way) *N*
Wrexham *p443* 0844 346 3100

Elliott, M D (Henry Thompson & Sons) *C1 E F1 L S1*
Grantham *p232* 01476 563226

Elliott, Mrs M F (May May & Merrimans) *W T2*
London WC1 *p59* 020 7405 8932

Elliott, M G (Martin Elliott & Co) *S1 E W*
Colchester *p197* 01206 767112

Elliott, M G (AgustaWestland Legal Dept - Yeovil)
Yeovil *p477* 01935 702240

Elliott, M J H (Linklaters LLP)
London EC2 *p54* 020 7456 2000

Elliott, Ms P A H (Forsters LLP) *A1 T2*
Westminster *p33* 020 7863 8333
London EC4 *p92* 020 7597 6000

Elliott, P J (Clifford Chance)
London E14 *p20* 020 7006 1000

Elliott, P J (Sharman Law)
Bedford *p130* 01234 303030

Elliott, P M (Charles Russell LLP) *C1 C2*
Oxford *p343* 0845 359 0090

Elliott, R (Davenport Lyons) *C1*
London W1 *p25* 020 7468 2600

Elliott, R J (Linklaters LLP)
London EC2 *p54* 020 7456 2000

Elliott, Miss S (Wedlake Bell LLP) *O Zc*
London WC1 *p91* 020 7395 3000

Elliott, S K (Ward Hadaway) *J1 J2 Zp*
Newcastle upon Tyne *p327* 0191 204 4000

Elliott, Mrs T H (Capsticks Solicitors LLP) *J1 Zp*
London SW19 *p18* 020 8780 2211

Elliott, W J (Barwells) *I S2 S1 W L*
Newhaven *p327* 01273 514213

Ellis, Miss A (Gordon Dadds) *S1 S2 E L R2 A1*
London W1 *p25* 020 7493 6151

Ellis, Miss A (Ronaldsons)
London WC1 *p73* 020 7580 6075

Ellis, A L (Tudur Owen Roberts Glynne & Co) *S1 W L A1 C1 E R1 K1 Zd Zo*
Bangor *p122* 01248 600171
Blaenau Ffestiniog *p147* 01766 830206

Ellis, Miss A L (Kirwans) *K1 D1*
Birkenhead *p134* 0151 608 9078

Ellis, A M (Forbes) *N O B1 Zk*
Blackburn *p145* 01254 662831

Ellis, B K (B K Ellis & Co) *E S1 L S2*
Borehamwood *p150* 020 8386 8686

Ellis, B L (Woolley Bevis Diplock) *W*
Hove *p255* 01273 722532

Ellis, Mrs B M (Friends Provident)
Dorking *p457* 01306 654925

Ellis, B M (Chattertons Solicitors) *Q N G L O H J1*
Sleaford *p381* 01529 411500

Ellis, D A (Thorneycroft Solicitors Ltd) *N*
Macclesfield *p297* 01625 503444

Ellis, D S (Higgs & Sons) *C1 C2 B1 E T1 I Ze Zc Zo*
Brierley Hill *p158* 0845 111 5050

Ellis, D W H (Trevor Griffiths & Humphries) *S1 W L E G F1 C1 Zc*
Blackwood *p147* 01495 225236

Ellis, Miss E M (Beers LLP) *R1 A1 S2 E S1*
Kingsbridge *p267* 01548 857000

Ellis, Ms G (McGrath & Co) *G H*
Birmingham *p140* 0121 643 4121

Ellis, G (Friends Provident)
Dorking *p457* 01306 654925

Ellis, G A J (Thomas Guise) *P N F1 J1 D1 K1 O Q V*
Worcester *p439* 01905 723131

Ellis, G D (Roy Foreman & Co) *G Q H*
Grimsby *p235* 01472 355262

Ellis, G J D (Francis Law LLP) *N E O Zl*
Lydney *p296* 01594 842242

Ellis, Ms J (Gladstone Solicitors)
Nottingham *p337* 0115 955 5050

Ellis, Mrs J (Gladstone Solicitors) *K1 G D1*
Nottingham *p337* 0115 955 5050

Ellis, Miss J (Fraser Brown) *S2 E S1*
Nottingham *p337* 0115 988 8777

Ellis, Ms J (Pinsent Masons LLP) *C2*
Birmingham *p141* 0121 200 1050

Ellis, Mrs J (Waldrons) *K1*
Brierley Hill *p158* 01384 811811

Ellis, Miss J A (Hyndburn Borough Council)
Lancaster *p447* 01254 388111

Ellis, J M (Ellis Lakin & Co) *S1 A1 W L R1 T1 C1 E Zl*
Pickering *p348* 01751 472121

Ellis, J W (Ellis & Co) *S1 K1 L W N J1 Zv Zc*
Chester *p190* 01244 319388

Ellis, K A (Christopher Davidson Solicitors LLP) *C1 E S1 S2 A1 C2 R2*
Cheltenham *p188* 01242 581481

Ellis, L (Blake Lapthorn) *I U2 C1*
Oxford *p342* 01865 248607

Ellis, Miss L J (Steven Young & Co) *G H*
Gloucester *p230* 01452 332882

Ellis, M (Mark Ellis & Co) *A1 B1 C1 E K1 L M1 N P R1 Zv*
Hornchurch *p252* 01708 471808 / 471587

Ellis, M (Coles Miller Solicitors LLP) *O*
Poole *p352* 01202 673011

Ellis, M (Mark Jones & Partners) *H G*
Liverpool *p289* 0151 286 9594

Ellis, M F (Cripps Harries Hall LLP) *E L A1 R2*
Tunbridge Wells *p415* 01892 515121

Ellis, M H (TBI Solicitors) *N O F1 J1 L B1 V Zc*
Hartlepool *p243* 0800 052 6824 / 01429 264101

Ellis, P (Farnfield & Nicholls) *D1 K4 K1 V W*
Gillingham *p229* 01747 825432

Ellis, Miss P (Cardiff County Council)
Cardiff *p453* 029 2087 2000

Ellis, P J (Browne Jacobson LLP) *O Q C1 B1 Ze Zb Zk Zh*
Nottingham *p336* 0115 976 6000

Ellis, P T (KJD) *B1 C1 C2*
Stoke-on-Trent *p398* 01782 202020

Ellis, Ms R (Department for Business, Enterprise and Regulatory Reform)
London SW1 *p105* 020 7215 0105

Ellis, R C (Coldham Shield & Mace) *S2 S1*
London E4 *p21* 020 8524 6323

Ellis, Miss R H (Ison Harrison) *Zr*
Leeds *p274* 0113 284 5000

Ellis, R K (Richard Ellis & Co) *S1 W E*
Leeds *p273* 0113 228 4000

Ellis, S (Darling & Stephensons) *E R1 S1*
Darlington *p206* 01325 489000

Ellis, S (Hugh James)
Cardiff *p179* 029 2022 4871

Ellis, Miss S C (McGrigors LLP)
London EC4 *p56* 020 7054 2500

Ellis, S C S (Parrott & Coales LLP) *S1*
Aylesbury *p121* 01296 318500

Ellis, S D (Barlow Lyde & Gilbert LLP)
London EC3 *p10* 020 7247 2277

Ellis, S E H (Aaron & Partners LLP Solicitors) *Zd A1 E Zx*
Chester *p190* 01244 405555

Ellis, T (Aughton Ainsworth)
Salford *p370* 0161 877 8555

Ellis, T (Bevan Brittan LLP) *O B1 Q C1*
Bristol *p161* 0870 194 1000

Ellis, Mrs T M (J A Hughes) *N Q*
Barry *p126* 01446 411000

Ellis, Miss V J (Moseleys) *W*
Lichfield *p284* 01543 414100

Ellis-Davies, D (Ellis Davies & Co)
Caernarfon *p172* 01286 672437

Ellis-Davies, R H (Ellis Davies & Co) *A1 E G L S1 W Zl*
Caernarfon *p172* 01286 672437

Ellis-Dokubo, B (Beevers Solicitors) *F1 G H J1 N O Zk Zp*
Ashton-under-Lyne *p119* 0161 339 9697

Ellison, Mrs A (Cheshire County Council)
Chester *p454* 01244 602382

Ellison, Ms R (Procter & Gamble UK (Legal Dept))
Weybridge *p476* 01932 896000

Ellison, R C (Pinsent Masons LLP) *Zo*
London EC2 *p67* 020 7418 7000

Elliss, Miss A (Wortley Byers) *S1 S2*
Brentwood *p156* 01277 268368

Elliston, P S (SLP Solicitors) *S1 E C1 N W*
Stanmore *p394* 020 8420 7950

Ellson, Ms S (Field Fisher Waterhouse LLP)
London EC3 *p31* 020 7861 4000

Ellum, P R A (Ellum LLP) *C1 A3 Zc C3 I F1 F2 Ze Zj M2 O Q*
London EC3 *p29* 020 7481 0977

Ellwood, J R (TBI Solicitors) *G H D1 K1 S1 M1 N P V E*
Hartlepool *p243* 0800 052 6824 / 01429 264101

Elly, M N C (ARVAL PHH Ltd)
Swindon *p473* 01793 884671

Elman, J A (Clifford Chance)
London E14 *p20* 020 7006 1000

Elmer, Mrs A E (Burton & Co LLP) *D1 K1 V*
Lincoln *p284* 01522 523215

Elmer, R F (Burton & Co LLP) *E S1 C1*
Lincoln *p284* 01522 523215

Elmhirst, N D (Parker Rhodes Hickmotts) *A1 C1 E L R1 S1*
Rotherham *p367* 01709 365116

Elmore-Jones, M R (Friends Provident)
Dorking *p457* 01306 654925

Elms, R A (Stanley Tee) *A1 E S1 S2*
Bishop's Stortford *p144* 01279 755200

Elmslie, M G (Hewitsons) *Ze O F2 U2*
Cambridge *p174* 01223 461155

Elphee, J (IBB Solicitors) *S2 E*
Uxbridge *p417* 0845 638 1381

Elphick, Miss C A (Gilbert Stephens) *W*
Exeter *p221* 01392 424242

Elphick, R W (LG Lawyers) *C1*
London SE1 *p50* 020 7379 0000

Elphicke, C (Reed Smith LLP) *T1*
London EC2 *p71* 020 3116 3000

Elphicke, Ms N (Addleshaw Goddard)
London EC1 *p4* 020 7606 8855

Elphinston, A (Anthony Collins Solicitors LLP) *W Zm Zd*
Birmingham *p137* 0121 200 3242

Elsden, Miss C R (Stanley H Cross & Co) *G H*
Chorley *p194* 01257 272222

Elsdon, Dr M J (M J Elsdon) *S1 E K1 D1 L N W F1*
North Walsham *p331* 01692 403562

Else, C (The Smith Partnership) *N B1 C1 E J1 L R1 T1 Zc Ze*
Derby *p209* 01332 225225

Elsenaar, M C (DLA Piper UK LLP) *Zc*
London EC2 *p24* 0870 011 1111

Elsey, A E (Elsey & Hodson) *C1 D1 F1 G H K1 M1 N P V Zj Zk Zp*
Peterborough *p347* 01733 314064

Elsey, E (Russell-Cooke LLP) *O*
London SW15 *p74* 020 8789 9111

Elsey, M P (Ashurst LLP) *M1 M2*
London EC2 *p7* 020 7638 1111

Elsey, S K (Davis & Co) *O Q Zn B1 Za Zj*
London EC3 *p26* 020 7621 1091

Elsmore, Ms F A (Hansells) *W V*
North Walsham *p331* 01692 404351

Elson, Miss D T (Blight Skinnard) *S1 W*
Saltash *p371* 01752 842141

Elson, D W (Charles Russell LLP) *O Q B1 Zc Ze Zj Zp*
Guildford *p235* 01483 252525

Elson, S A (Nelsons) *G H*
Nottingham *p338* 0115 958 6262

Elson, Mrs S C (Solicitors Disciplinary Tribunal)
London EC4 *p109* 020 7329 4808

Elstob, Miss H M (Tilly Bailey & Irvine LLP) *N Zr*
Stockton-on-Tees *p397* 01642 673797

Elstow, Ms M (Davenport Lyons) *E S1 L*
London W1 *p25* 020 7468 2600

Elton, Ms C B (Southampton City Council) *F1 J1 K1 L N Q V Zp*
Southampton *p472* 023 8022 3855

Elton, F P (Girlings) *W G H Zl*
Canterbury *p177* 01227 768374

Elton, J A (Salans) *O Q M1 B1 C1 Zg Zj*
London EC4 *p76* 020 7429 6000

Eltringham, Miss M (Eltringham & Co) *L S1 W*
Newcastle upon Tyne *p324* 0191 266 5878

Elverston, N (Herbert Smith LLP)
London EC2 *p40* 020 7374 8000

Elves, Mrs C (Williams MacDougall & Campbell) *D1 K1*
Worthing *p442* 01903 214186

Elvidge, S R (Simmons & Simmons)
London EC2 *p79* 020 7628 2020

Elvin, Mrs J M (Elvin & Co) *S1 W*
Loughborough *p293* 01509 852454

Elvin, Mrs L C (Mills & Reeve) *E*
Cambridge *p175* 01223 364422

Elvin, M A S J (Elvin & Co) *E W C1 A1 S2 R2*
Loughborough *p293* 01509 852454

Elvin, R J (Squire Sanders (UK) LLP) *O Zk Zw*
Manchester *p310* 0161 830 5000

Elvins, Ms K G (Thomas Horton LLP) *S2 S1*
Bromsgrove *p167* 01527 871641

Elvy, M C (Ashurst LLP) *F2*
London EC2 *p7* 020 7638 1111

Elway, J G (LG Lawyers) *C1*
London SE1 *p50* 020 7379 0000

Elwen, J D (McGrigors LLP)
London EC4 *p56* 020 7054 2500

Elwess, Mrs A R (Burton & Dyson) *S1 W K4*
Gainsborough *p228* 01427 610761

Elwess, Mrs E K (Pearsons & Ward) *W T1 T2*
Malton *p300* 01653 692247

Elwood, Mrs C J (Preston Borough Council)
Preston *p469* 01772 906101
Southport *p472* 01704 533133

Elworthy, M N (British Telecommunications PLC)
London EC1 *p104* 020 7356 6181

Elwyn Jones, H (Elwyn Jones & Co) *A1 J1 K1 L O P Q S1 W B1 Zv N*
Bangor *p122* 01248 370224

Ely, J (Lewis Silkin LLP) *E S2 Zh L R2 R1 S1*
London EC4 *p53* 020 7074 8000

Ely, R (Skadden Arps Slate Meagher & Flom (UK) LLP)
London E14 *p80* 020 7519 7000

Emanuel, D (Veale Wasbrough Vizards) *C2 C1*
Bristol *p165* 0117 925 2020

Emanuel, R I (Allan Janes LLP) *C1*
High Wycombe *p249* 01494 521301

Emberton, Miss E M (Embertons) *S1 W T2 E L Zv*
Enfield *p218* 020 8364 4249

Emberton, Miss J L (Radcliffes Le Brasseur) *L O*
Westminster *p70* 020 7222 7040

Embley, Ms J (The College of Law)
London WC1 *p105* 0800 289997

Emden, C A (Howard Kennedy LLP) *O Q B1 J1 L F1 N Zi*
London W1 *p48* 020 7636 1616

Emerson, J R (Gepp & Sons) *N Q O L*
Chelmsford *p186* 01245 493939
Colchester *p197* 01206 369889

Emerson, M (Jones Day) *E*
London EC4 *p46* 020 7039 5959

Emerson, N (Howard Kennedy LLP)
London W1 *p48* 020 7636 1616

Emerson, N M (Bircham Dyson Bell) *Q O*
Westminster *p13* 020 7227 7000

Emerton, A R L (South Bedfordshire District Council)
Dunstable *p457* 01582 472222

Emerton, J (Addleshaw Goddard)
Leeds *p271* 0113 209 2000

Emerton, J A T H (Squire Sanders (UK) LLP) *O B1 J1 Q*
Leeds *p277* 0113 284 7000

Emery, Ms C (Burton & Co LLP) *E S2 C1 S1 Zl Zc J1 A1 L Zh R1 F2 Zd Ze P*
Lincoln *p284* 01522 523215

Emery, Miss C E (Harrison Clark LLP) *C2*
Worcester *p439* 01905 612001

Emery, D (Metropolitan Police Directorate of Legal Services)
London SW1 *p108* 020 7230 7210

Emery, Miss J (Berry Smith LLP) *S1*
Cardiff *p177* 029 2034 5511

Emery, Miss J D (Burrell Jenkins) *G H*
Cannock *p176* 01543 505040

See p634 for the Key to Work Categories

Emery, Ms K L (Emery Johnson Partnership) *D1 G H* Leicester *p279* 0116 255 4855

Emery, Mrs L A (Brabners Chaffe Street) *K4 K1 T1 T2 W* Liverpool *p286* 0151 600 3000

Emery, M C (Atkinson Ritson) *N O Q Zj* Carlisle *p181* 01228 525221

Emery, Ms S E (FDC Law) *A1 L C1 S2 E R1 S1* Frome *p228* 01373 463311

Eminton, D E (Paris Smith LLP) *O Q L E* Southampton *p386* 023 8048 2482

Emmerson, D M (Emmersons Solicitors) *G K1 H V* Sunderland *p401* 0191 567 6667

Emmerson, Miss J (Emmersons Solicitors) *K1 W D1 D2* Sunderland *p401* 0191 567 6667

Emmerson, J D (TV Edwards LLP) *K1 D1 L F2 G H* London EC3 *p85* 020 7790 7000

Emmerson, N J (Dickinson Dees) *S1* Newcastle upon Tyne *p324* 0191 279 9000

Emmerson, S J (Laytons) *G P O Q Zt* Guildford *p236* 01483 407000

Emmett, Mrs B (Hague Lambert) *W* Urmston *p417* 0161 747 7321

Emmett, D J (Milne Moser) *S1 W L E S2 T2* Kendal *p264* 01539 729786 / 725582

Emmett, H (Hal Emmett & Co) *S2 E Q S1* Maghull *p298* 0151 531 7666

Emmett, P D (Walker Morris) *C1* Leeds *p277* 0113 283 2500

Emmison, M G (Goodman Derrick LLP) *C1 C2 Zw* London EC4 *p36* 020 7404 0606

Emmott, E R (Nicholas & Co) *S1 E C1 L N R1* London W1 *p63* 020 7323 4450

Emmott, J F (Reed Smith LLP) *R1 A1* London EC2 *p71* 020 3116 3000

Emmott, T (Gordons LLP) Leeds *p273* 0113 227 0100

Emmott, Ms T (Pictons Solicitors LLP) *Q* Luton *p295* 01582 870870

Emms, Miss F E (Gateley LLP) Birmingham *p138* 0121 234 0000

Emo, Ms N J (Brewer Harding & Rowe) *S1* Bideford *p132* 01237 472666 Leigh *p282* 01942 777777

Emore, Miss K (London Borough of Southwark) *L Zh D1 K1 J1* London SE1 *p109* 020 7525 5000

Emsley, K H (Lupton Fawcett) *C1 E Zc* Leeds *p275* 0113 280 2000

Emslie, A C W (Mullis & Peake) *W T1 S1* Romford *p366* 01708 784000

Emslie, Miss J R (McGrigors LLP) London EC4 *p56* 020 7054 2500

Emslie, Miss M (Pannone LLP) *B1 B2 O* Manchester *p308* 0161 909 3000

Endall, P A J (Warwickshire County Council) Warwick *p475* 01926 410410

Enderby, K I (Gordons LLP) Leeds *p273* 0113 227 0100

Enderby, W K (Coutts & Co) London WC2 *p105* 020 7753 1403

Endfield, A E (Islington Pottery & Housewares Co) Liverpool *p463* 0151 486 1888

Endicott, D (Spratt Endicott) *T2 W Zd* Banbury *p122* 01295 204000

Endlar, I D (Endlars) Manchester *p304* 0161 795 4333

Eneberi, J (Shell International Ltd) *I C3 C2 C1 Ze* London SE1 *p109* 020 7934 1234

Enever, Mrs S A (Clarke & Hartland Solicitors) *K1 D1 G* Cardiff *p177* 029 2048 3181

Enfield, Miss C C M (Winckworth Sherwood LLP) *X S1* London SE1 *p92* 020 7593 5000

Engel, D J (Addleshaw Goddard) *Zk Q* London EC1 *p4* 020 7606 8855

Engel, R E (Max Engel & Co LLP) *C1 E J1 S2 R2 C2 W* Northampton *p331* 01604 887450

Engelsman, S M (Butcher Burns LLP) *B1 Q Zb* London WC1 *p16* 020 7713 7100

Engert, N (Clarke Willmott) *R1 E* Bristol *p162* 0845 209 1000 / 0117 305 6000

England, A (Whatley Lane) Newmarket *p327* 01638 561133

England, Miss E K (Keoghs and Nicholls, Lindsell & Harris) *L* Altrincham *p116* 0161 928 9321

England, Ms M (Mogers) *B1 J1 Q* Bath *p127* 01225 750000

England, M J (Barlow Robbins LLP) *E C1 S1* Woking *p436* 01483 748500

England, P A (Nottinghamshire County Council Legal Services Division) West Bridgford *p475* 0115 977 3478

England, Mrs R I (Rupert Bear Murray Davies) *D1 D2 K1* Nottingham *p338* 0115 924 3333

England, R J (Pickerings LLP) *K3 K1* Tamworth *p407* 01827 317070

England, R W (Arnold Brierley & Robinson) *K1 K3 D2* Oldham *p340* 0161 678 1122

England, S (Napthens LLP) *E S1* Preston *p357* 01772 888444

England, Mrs S L (Gales) *J1 Zp Q* Bournemouth *p152* 01202 512227 / 512446

England-Kerr, A R (England Kerr Hands & Co) *S1 W P G* Birmingham *p138* 0121 427 9898

Englehart, D J (Engleharts) *E S1 C1 L W J1 A1 F1 Zb Zl Zo* Hove *p254* 01273 204411

Engleman, C A (Rollits LLP) *B1 C1 S1 E C2* York *p445* 01904 625790

English, A J (Russells) *C1 Zf Ze* London W1 *p75* 020 7439 8692

English, C W F (Shell International Ltd) London SE1 *p109* 020 7934 1234

English, Mrs E (B A A PLC) London UB3 *p103* 0870 000 0123

English, J (Bates Wells & Braithwaite London LLP) *C1 C2 Zd* London EC4 *p11* 020 7551 7777

English, K (Kidd & Spoor) *S1* Whitley Bay *p431* 0191 297 0011

English, M B (Shakespeares) *Zc N O Q Zq A3* Birmingham *p142* 0121 237 3000

Ennals, A M (Department for Business, Enterprise and Regulatory Reform) London SW1 *p105* 020 7215 0105

Ennals, R J (Sparling Benham & Brough) *A1 C1 E L R1 S1 W Zl* Colchester *p198* 01206 733733

Ennals, S (Essential Rights) *V Zg Zp* Sheffield *p375* 0114 255 4526

Ennis, Mrs E (Farnworth Shaw) *K1 D1 S1* Nelson *p321* 01282 699996

Ennis, J C F (Green Wright Chalton Annis) *J1 K1 L N Q* Worthing *p441* 01903 234064

Ennis, R J (Rees Page) *N O Q J1* Wolverhampton *p438* 01902 577777

Ennis-Gayle, D (Kaim Todner Ltd) *G H B2* Islington *p47* 020 7700 0070

Ennos, N (Wills Chandler Beach) *W S1 K3 J1* Hook *p252* 01256 764646 / 764647

Enoch, P M (Salans) *C1 T1 T2 B1 W Zb Zc Zw* London EC4 *p76* 020 7429 6000

Enock, J R (Vickers & Co) Ealing *p89* 020 8579 2559 / 8840 3999

Enser, J (Olswang LLP) *C1 C3 I M1 Ze Zf* London WC1 *p64* 020 7067 3000

Ensor, Ms M (HCB Solicitors) *E* Walsall *p420* 01922 720000

Enstein, Miss L (BCL Burton Copeland) *B2 G J2* London WC2 *p9* 020 7430 2277

Enstone, J (Faegre & Benson LLP) *C1 U2 U1 I Ze Zza Zl* London EC4 *p30* 020 7450 4500

Enstone, J (Stephenson Harwood) *I U1 U2* London EC2 *p82* 020 7329 4422

Enstone, Miss P J (PJ Legal) *K4 S1 T2 W Q K1 N F1 F2 Zq O X Zr L* Spalding *p389* 01406 420023

Enstone, Mrs R (Harvey Ingram Borneos) Milton Keynes *p317* 01908 696002

Enticott, Mrs I C (Rhondda Cynon Taff County Borough Council) Pentre *p468* 01443 424300

Enticott, R W (George Ide LLP) *A1 C1 E R2 S2 L W* Chichester *p192* 01243 786668

Entwistle, G J (Baines Bagguley Solicitors) *C1* Morecambe *p318* 01524 413294

Entwistle, Ms L (British American Tobacco) London WC2 *p104* 020 7845 1000

Entwistle, M G (Hill Dickinson LLP) *C1 T1* London EC3 *p41* 020 7283 9033

Entwistle, P A (Oldham Metropolitan Borough Council) Oldham *p468* 0161 911 3000

Entwistle, R R (Berkson Wallace Solicitors) *W* Wallasey *p419* 0151 691 6900 Bebington *p129* 0151 645 4255

Entwistle, S R (Lewis Silkin LLP) *C1 C2 C3 J1 Ze Zv* London EC4 *p53* 020 7074 8000

Entwistle, Ms T H (Russell & Russell) *N* Bury *p171* 0161 762 2888

Eppel, T D L (McFaddens LLP) *B1 C1 F1 J1 S1 T1 W Zb Ze Zf* London EC2 *p56* 020 7588 9080

Epps, T A F (Russell Jones & Walker) *H G Zm* London WC2 *p74* 020 7657 1555

Epton, D (Ashurst LLP) London EC2 *p7* 020 7638 1111

Erasmus, J D (Granville-West Chivers & Morgan) *P G S1 K1 Zl* Blackwood *p147* 01495 223161

Ereira, D P (Linklaters LLP) London EC2 *p54* 020 7456 2000

Ericsson, Ms C (Russell Jones & Walker) Manchester *p309* 0161 383 3500

Eriksson-Lee, Ms A J (Memery Crystal) *K1 K2 K3* London WC2 *p60* 020 7242 5905

Eriksson-Lee, C (Warners Solicitors) *W K4* Tonbridge *p412* 01732 770660

Erlam, Mrs J (Prince Evans) Ealing *p69* 020 8567 3477

Errhioui, Miss F H (Steele Raymond) *N J1* Bournemouth *p152* 01202 294566

Erridge, R (Richard Erridge & Co) *E S2 K4 S1 W* Wotton-under-Edge *p442* 01454 418615

Errington, I S (Gordons LLP) Leeds *p273* 0113 227 0100

Errington, J (Hellawell & Co) *B1 G S1 H K1 P J1 L N* Newbiggin-by-the-Sea *p322* 01670 817223

Errington, S T (Ward Hadaway) *E R2 S2* Newcastle upon Tyne *p327* 0191 204 4000

Erskine-Naylor, Ms F (Harbottle & Lewis LLP) London W1 *p38* 020 7667 5000

Erusalimsky, A (Stewarts Law LLP) *O Q M2 Zq A3 B2* London EC4 *p83* 020 7822 8000

Ervin, Miss L K (Lamb Brooks LLP) *O Q* Basingstoke *p126* 01256 844888

Ervine, MIss C (Jeary & Lewis) *D1 E H K1 N Q* Chippenham *p193* 01249 444484

Erwin, A D (Fladgate LLP) *E C1 M1 Zc* London WC2 *p32* 020 3036 7000

Erwin, D J (Colemans - CTTS) *N Q G L* Manchester *p302* 0161 876 2500

Erwin, Ms S L (Browne Jacobson LLP) *J1 N Zj* Nottingham *p336* 0115 976 6000

Esam, D R (DAC Beachcroft) *E S1* Bristol *p162* 0117 918 2000

Esam, P M (Travers Smith LLP) *Zo* London EC1 *p87* 020 7295 3000

Escolme, Miss H (Red Kite Law) *W* Pembroke *p345* 01646 683222

Escolme, Mrs S G (Hayton Winkley) *J1* Kendal *p264* 01539 720136

Escott, Mrs H J (Harvey Escott & Co) *K1 D1 G V S1 W E H N L Q* Burnham-on-Crouch *p169* 01621 784838 / 784839

Escott, J R L (Colemans Solicitors LLP) *S1 S2 E* Maidenhead *p298* 01628 631051

Escott, Mrs R C F (Hatch Brenner) *N* Norwich *p334* 01603 660811

Escritt, Ms S (Russell Jones & Walker) London WC2 *p74* 020 7657 1555

Esdaile, R H (Bowers) *W T1 S1 L C1* London NW2 *p15* 020 8455 9881

Esien, Miss I (IBB Solicitors) *N* Uxbridge *p417* 0845 638 1381

Eskell, G P (Pardoes) *M1 N P* Bridgwater *p158* 01278 457891

Esney, R D (City & County of Swansea) Swansea *p473* 01792 636000

Esplen, S M (Russells) *C1 Ze Zf* London W1 *p75* 020 7439 8692

Espley, A (Espley & Co) *E D1 K1 L S1 W N Q C1 B1 Zh Zl* Liverpool *p288* 01704 830200

Essam, Ms C (Sheffield City Council) Sheffield *p471* 0114 273 4019

Essat, A H (Ashby-de-la-Zouch Petty Sessional Division) Coalville *p455* 01530 810661 Hinckley *p461*

Essen, Mrs A (Ison Harrison) *K1 S1* Ilkley *p261* 01943 889100

Essenhigh, Miss K A (Field Seymour Parkes) *E A1 S2* Reading *p360* 0118 951 6200

Essery, Ms H J (Newsome Vaughan LLP) *O J1 A3 Q C1 Za Zk M2 B1 Zza F1 Zp* Coventry *p200* 024 7663 3433 Birmingham *p142* 0121 222 3000

Essex, W A (McGlennons) *S1 W Q* Merton *p56* 020 8946 6015

Esslinger, Ms A (Bryan Cave) *C1 C3 I F1 F2 Ze G Zza M1 M2 U2 C2* London EC2 *p19* 020 7207 1100

Esterhuizen, G A (Lester Aldridge LLP) Bournemouth *p152* 01202 786161

Esterkin, N J (Betesh Partnership) *N* Manchester *p301* 0161 834 2623

Ete, C (Charles Ete & Co) *G K1 Zi S2 D2 K3 J1 B2 Zh L W* London SE5 *p29* 020 7820 9818

Etheridge, Ms A (Davenport Lyons) *J1* London W1 *p25* 020 7468 2600

Etheridge, R W J (Rogers & Norton) *E C1 L S2* Norwich *p335* 01603 666001

Etherington, K (Mellor & Jackson) *N Zq O Q* Oldham *p340* 0161 624 7081

Etherington, N J (Rothera Dowson) *E* Nottingham *p338* 0115 910 0600

Etim-Gorst, Miss T (Bristol City Council) *K1* Bristol *p451* 0117 922 2000

Ettinger, C B (Irwin Mitchell LLP) *N J2 M1 P* London EC1 *p45* 0870 150 0100

Etuk, J (Johns & Saggar) *Zg S1 G H L Zf Zw* London WC1 *p46* 020 3490 1475

Eustace, Ms V (Owen White) *Q L O N* Slough *p382* 01753 876800

Eva, Ms S (Cumberland Ellis Peirs) *C1 C2 C3 J1* London WC1 *p23* 020 7242 0422

Evagora, K (Reed Smith LLP) *Za* London EC2 *p71* 020 3116 3000

Evans, A (Taylor Wessing) London EC4 *p86* 020 7300 7000

Evans, A (Ashurst LLP) London EC2 *p7* 020 7638 1111

Evans, Miss A (Hillyer McKeown LLP) *N* Chester *p190* 01244 318131

Evans, Mrs A (Rowley Dickinson) *Zr Q N* Manchester *p309* 0161 834 4215

Evans, A (Bristol City Council) Bristol *p451* 0117 922 2000

Evans, A (Geldards LLP) Cardiff *p178* 029 2023 8239

Evans, Ms A (Mills & Reeve) *A1 S1 L* Cambridge *p175* 01223 364422

Evans, A (Sintons LLP) *C1 C2* Newcastle upon Tyne *p326* 0191 226 7878

Evans, Ms A (Osborne Clarke) *R2 E* London EC2 *p65* 020 7105 7000

Evans, Ms A C (Willans LLP) *C1 C2* Cheltenham *p189* 01242 514000

Evans, A D (Brooke North LLP) *T2 W* Leeds *p272* 0113 283 2100

Evans, A D (Hill Dickinson LLP) *J1 Zj Zk O N Zq X* Liverpool *p288* 0151 600 8000

Evans, A D (John Howe & Co) *T2 W* Pudsey *p358* 0113 236 3936

Evans, A G (Field Fisher Waterhouse LLP) *C1 B1 J1 Zb* London EC3 *p31* 020 7861 4000

Evans, Mrs A J (Dolmans) *N* Cardiff *p178* 029 2034 5531

Evans, Miss A J (Mackenzie Jones) *N Q S1* St Asaph *p391* 01745 536030

Evans, A L (Carmarthenshire County Council) Carmarthen *p453* 01267 224010

Evans, A M (Lanyon Bowdler LLP) *S1 A1 L E* Shrewsbury *p379* 01743 280280

Evans, A M (Gateley LLP) *C1 C3 I F1 F2 U1 U2 Ze Zz* Birmingham *p138* 0121 234 0000

Evans, A N (Graham Evans & Partners) *G H K1 N D1 F1 Zl* Swansea *p405* 01792 655822

Evans, B (Ford & Warren) *B1* Leeds *p273* 0113 243 6601

Evans, Ms B (North Devon District Council) Barnstaple *p448* 01271 327711 Plymouth *p468* 01752 668000

Evans, Ms B (Parker Arrenberg) London SE6 *p65* 020 8695 2330

Evans, Ms B (Bevan Brittan LLP) *Zu* Bristol *p161* 0870 194 1000

Evans, Mrs B A (Mackrell & Thomas) *N* Liverpool *p289* 0151 480 3666 Prescot *p356* 0151 426 7001

Evans, Mrs B L (Winterbotham Smith Penley LLP) *D2 D1 K3 K1* Stroud *p401* 01453 847200

Evans, Mrs C (Staffordshire County Council) Stafford *p472* 01785 223121

Evans, Ms C (Woodfines LLP) *G Zt* Milton Keynes *p317* 01908 202150

Evans, Miss C (The College of Law Chester) *P* Chester *p454* 0800 289997

Evans, Ms C (Kaim Todner Ltd) *G H B2* London EC4 *p47* 020 7353 6660

Evans, Miss C A (Walker Smith Way) *G* Chester *p191* 0844 346 3100

Evans, Miss C A (Walker Morris) *B1* Leeds *p277* 0113 283 2500

Evans, Miss C C (Batchelor Myddelton) *S2 E R1 W* Potters Bar *p355* 01707 647088

Evans, Ms C E (Barlow Lyde & Gilbert LLP) London EC3 *p10* 020 7247 2277

Evans, Mrs C E (SFN Solicitors) *K3 K2 K1* Burnley *p169* 01282 421284

Evans, C F (Shepherd Evans Solicitors) *D1 F1 Q N* Macclesfield *p297* 01625 503909

Evans, Mrs C H S (Metcalfes) *E S2* Bristol *p164* 0117 929 0451

Evans, Mrs C J (Clerk to Justices Office) Aberaeron *p447* 01545 570886

Evans, C J (Sharp & Partners) *K1 G F1 H* Long Eaton *p293* 0115 973 4111

Evans, Mrs C L (Chichester & District Magistrates Courts) Chichester *p455* 01243 817000

Evans, Mrs C M (Eric Cowsill Solicitor) *W* Ivybridge *p263* 01752 205202

Evans, C P (Linklaters LLP) London EC2 *p54* 020 7456 2000

Evans, Ms C R (Daimler Chrysler UK Ltd) Milton Keynes *p466* 01908 245000

Evans, D (Trowers & Hamlins) London EC3 *p88* 020 7423 8000

Evans, D (Blake Lapthorn) *O Zc* Oxford *p342* 01865 248607

Evans, Ms D (Evans Main Solicitors) Sevenoaks *p374* 01732 464848

Evans, D (Douglas-Jones Mercer) Swansea *p405* 01792 650000

Evans, D C H (Geoffrey Searle Planning Solicitors) *R1 Zu* Billericay *p133* 01277 633014

Evans, D E (Simmonds Hurford) *K1 D1 G H* Swansea *p405* 01792 462729 / 641070

Evans, Miss D E (Burges Salmon) *A1* Bristol *p161* 0117 939 2000

Evans, D F (PricewaterhouseCoopers Legal LLP) *J1 Zp Zo* London SE1 *p69* 020 7212 1616

Evans, D F (Addleshaw Goddard) *R1* London EC1 *p4* 020 7606 8855

Evans, D G (Manches LLP) *O* Oxford *p343* 01865 722106

Evans, D J (Addlestone Keane Solicitors) *S2 E S1* Leeds *p271* 0113 244 6700

Evans, D J (Ashurst LLP) *E L M1 M2* London EC2 *p7* 020 7638 1111

Evans, D J (Enoch Evans LLP) *C1 J1 B1 E* Walsall *p420* 01922 720333

Evans, Miss D J (Plymouth City Council) *G P R1 L Q* Plymouth *p468* 01752 668000

Evans, Ms D L (Shergill & Co) Hounslow *p254* 020 8570 2323

Evans, D M (Red Kite Law) *N J1*
Carmarthen *p183* . . . 01267 239000

Evans, D M (L G Williams & Prichard) *S2 E O C1 C2*
Cardiff *p181* . . . 029 2022 9716

Evans, D P (Arnold Davies Vincent Evans) *S1 A1 W S2 K4 L R1*
Lampeter *p269* . . . 01570 422233
Tregaron *p413* . . . 01974 298816

Evans, D R (Evans Powell & Co) *A1 C1 E F1 K1 R1 S1 S2 Zl W*
Llanelli *p292* . . . 01554 772632

Evans, D R (Carmarthenshire County Council)
Carmarthen *p453* . . . 01267 224010

Evans, D R C (DWF) *N G*
Liverpool *p287* . . . 0151 907 3000

Evans, D W (Cozens-Hardy LLP) *E S2 L*
Norwich *p334* . . . 01603 625231

Evans, Ms E A (Capsticks Solicitors LLP) *Zr*
London SW19 *p18* . . . 020 8780 2211

Evans, Ms E C (Eaton Ryan & Taylor) *O Q B1 F1 A3 Zq*
Birmingham *p138* . . . 0121 236 1999

Evans, E C (M&A Solicitors LLP) *E R1 R2*
Cardiff *p179* . . . 029 2048 2288

Evans, Miss E J L (Edward Hughes) *G H K1 Zt*
Rhyl *p363* . . . 01745 343661 / 344551

Evans, Miss E M (Mary Evans & Co) *S1 Q K1 N W E L D1*
Carmarthen *p182* . . . 01267 233881

Evans, Ms G (Davies Parsons Allchurch)
Llanelli *p292* . . . 01554 749144

Evans, G (J Charles Hughes & Co) *A1 C1 D1 K1 L R1 S1 T1 W P*
Harlech *p239* . . . 01766 780818
Dolgellau *p211* . . . 01341 422464

Evans, Ms G (Shell International Ltd)
London SE1 *p109* . . . 020 7934 1234

Evans, Ms G (Hugh James)
Cardiff *p179* . . . 029 2022 4871

Evans, G C (Stones) *C1 E N S1 B1 A1 P G Ze Zi*
London W1 *p83* . . . 020 7935 4848

Evans, G E (Abensons) *S1 E L C1 W P R1*
Liverpool *p285* . . . 0151 733 3111

Evans, G H (Dibbens) *N O Q J1 F1 B1 Zc*
Wimborne *p433* . . . 01202 882456

Evans, G J (Monro Fisher Wasbrough LLP) *S1 E K1 P N L*
London WC1 *p61* . . . 020 7404 7001

Evans, G L (Graham Evans & Partners) *G H K1 N S1*
Swansea *p405* . . . 01792 655822

Evans, G R (Evans & Greaves) *C1 D1 E F1 G H K1 L M1 S1 Zl*
Caerphilly *p172* . . . 029 2086 6001

Evans, G S (Bray & Bray) *O Q U2*
Leicester *p279* . . . 0116 254 8871

Evans, G S (Powells) *C1 S2 E F1 J1 L Zl S1*
Weston-super-Mare *p429* . . . 01934 623501

Evans, G S C (Hugh James) *N Q L F2 F1 B1 Zr Zq*
Cardiff *p179* . . . 029 2022 4871

Evans, G W W (Hermer & Evans) *S1 W E L C1 F1*
Cardiff *p178* . . . 029 2038 7766 / 2022 4009

Evans, Miss H A (Tickle Hall Cross) *N L O Q F1 J1 Zc Zj*
St Helens *p391* . . . 0800 854379

Evans, H C (DLA Piper UK LLP) *B1 O Zb*
Leeds *p272* . . . 0870 011 1111

Evans, H D (Richard George & Jenkins) *S1 F1 L J1 H W Q*
Newtown *p330* . . . 01686 626210

Evans, Mrs H E (Carmarthenshire County Council)
Carmarthen *p453* . . . 01267 224010

Evans, Miss H M (Evans + Webb) *S1 W S2 L*
Malvern *p300* . . . 01684 562526

Evans, H N (Wragge & Co LLP)
London EC1 *p93* . . . 0870 903 1000

Evans, Mrs I C (Bird & Bird LLP) *Zb*
London EC4 *p13* . . . 020 7415 6000

Evans, I G D (Gwynedd Council)
Caernarfon *p452* . . . 01286 672255

Evans, I R (Weightmans LLP)
Liverpool *p291* . . . 0151 227 2601

Evans, Ms J (Allen & Overy LLP)
London E1 *p5* . . . 020 3088 0000

Evans, J (Foot Anstey) *C1 C2 Zd*
Exeter *p221* . . . 01392 411221

Evans, Mrs J (Staffordshire County Council) *E F1 J1 L*
Stafford *p472* . . . 01785 223121

Evans, Mrs J (Biscoes) *K1 G H N Q*
Portsmouth *p354* . . . 023 9266 0261

Evans, Ms J (Newport City Council)
Newport *p466* . . . 01633 656656

Evans, Ms J (Lewis Silkin LLP) *C1 C2*
London EC4 *p53* . . . 020 7074 8000

Evans, J (Evans & Davies) *S1 W K1 G O L E F1 J1 R1 Zl Zw Zc Zk Zq*
Aberaeron *p113* . . . 01545 570335

Evans, J (The Paul Rooney Partnership)
Liverpool *p290* . . . 0151 227 2851

Evans, J A (The Gwyn George Partnership) *S1 W S2*
Aberdare *p113* . . . 01685 874629 / 871133

Evans, J A A (Linklaters LLP)
London EC2 *p54* . . . 020 7456 2000

Evans, J C (Newport City Council)
Newport *p466* . . . 01633 656656

Evans, Ms J D (Taylor Walton LLP) *C1 C2 F1 F2*
Luton *p295* . . . 01582 731161

Evans, J D (Sims Cook & Teague) *S1 W L E*
Thornbury *p411* . . . 01454 414342

Evans, Mrs J F (Brains) *Zd C1 S2 E L S1 T1 T2 W K4*
St Austell *p391* . . . 01726 68111
Truro *p414* . . . 01872 276363

Evans, J G (Devonalds) *G H K1 S1 W M1 P B1 C1 D1*
Pontypridd *p352* . . . 01443 404700

Evans, J K (Kerman & Co LLP) *Zf Zk O Q Zq*
London WC2 *p49* . . . 020 7539 7272

Evans, J K (Manchester City Council)
Manchester *p465* . . . 0161 234 5000

Evans, Ms J L (DWF) *N*
Liverpool *p287* . . . 0151 907 3000

Evans, J L (The Castle Partnership) *Zl G H*
Guildford *p235* . . . 01483 300905

Evans, J M (Linklaters LLP)
London EC2 *p54* . . . 020 7456 2000

Evans, Mrs J M (Neil Myerson LLP) *J1*
Altrincham *p117* . . . 0161 941 4000

Evans, Mrs J P (Howell Jones & Co) *C1 C2 E W A1*
Abergele *p113* . . . 01745 826282 / 825845
Llanrwst *p292* . . . 01492 640277

Evans, J P (Field Seymour Parkes) *Zd C1 F1 F2 I Ze*
Reading *p360* . . . 0118 951 6200

Evans, J R P (Stephens & Scown) *G H Zl*
St Austell *p391* . . . 01726 74433

Evans, J T (Treasury Solicitors Department)
London WC2 *p110* . . . 020 7210 3000

Evans, Mrs K (Legal Hobbit)
London EC2 *p52* . . . 020 7194 8400

Evans, Ms K (Beswicks) *D1 K1 Zo*
Hanley *p239* . . . 01782 205000

Evans, Mrs K E (Carillion PLC)
Wolverhampton *p477* . . . 01902 422431

Evans, Miss K J (Atherton Godfrey) *E S1*
Doncaster *p211* . . . 01302 320621

Evans, K N (Davis Blank Furniss) *S1 W E L R1*
Glossop *p230* . . . 01457 860606

Evans, Ms K R (TLT Solicitors) *E*
Bristol *p165* . . . 0117 917 7777

Evans, L (Neil Myerson LLP) *O Q*
Altrincham *p117* . . . 0161 941 4000

Evans, Ms L E (Evans & Greaves)
Caerphilly *p172* . . . 029 2086 6001

Evans, M (Hugh James) *N Zr*
Cardiff *p179* . . . 029 2022 4871

Evans, Mrs M (Buss Murton LLP) *K1*
Tunbridge Wells *p415* . . . 01892 510222

Evans, M (Forshaws Davies Ridgway LLP) *E J1 S1*
Warrington *p422* . . . 01925 230000

Evans, Mrs M (Marion Evans) *K3 K1 W S1*
Bewdley *p131* . . . 01299 402741

Evans, M (Evans Derry Rennie & Co)
Birmingham *p138* . . . 0121 770 1721

Evans, M (Squire Sanders (UK) LLP)
London EC2 *p81* . . . 020 7655 1000

Evans, M (Langley Wellington) *D1 S1 K1 S2*
Gloucester *p230* . . . 01452 521286

Evans, M (RBM Davies & Partners LLP) *K1 K2 K3*
Neston *p321* . . . 0151 336 6611

Evans, M (Jones Day) *C3*
London EC4 *p46* . . . 020 7039 5959

Evans, Mrs M (Glyn Owen & Co) *W S1 L F1 N J1 Q*
Colwyn Bay *p198* . . . 01492 532649

Evans, M (Kaim Todner Ltd) *G H B2*
London EC4 *p47* . . . 020 7353 6660

Evans, Mrs M (Martin & Strain) *D1 W K1 D2*
Pwllheli *p358* . . . 01758 612042

Evans, Mrs M A (Carmarthenshire County Council)
Carmarthen *p453* . . . 01267 224010

Evans, M D (Fentons) *G N*
Failsworth *p223* . . . 0161 682 7101

Evans, M F (Cleggs) *N Q*
Nottingham *p336* . . . 0115 977 5877
Leicester *p280* . . . 0116 212 1000

Evans, Mrs M H (Mayo Wynne Baxter LLP) *W*
Lewes *p283* . . . 01273 477071

Evans, M J (Brains) *B1 O Q Zq C1*
St Austell *p391* . . . 01726 68111
Truro *p414* . . . 01872 276363
Truro *p414* . . . 01872 265100

Evans, M J (Burges Salmon) *T2 W Zd Zl*
Bristol *p161* . . . 0117 939 2000

Evans, M L B (CVC Solicitors) *D1 D2 K1 L Q Zm J1 N Zr*
Penzance *p346* . . . 01736 362313

Evans, M N R (Travers Smith LLP) *Zb Zo*
London EC1 *p87* . . . 020 7295 3000

Evans, M R (Davies Blunden & Evans) *E V S1 K1 W R1 Zl*
Farnborough *p224* . . . 01252 541633

Evans, N (Veale Wasbrough Vizards) *E*
Bristol *p165* . . . 0117 925 2020

Evans, N (Healys LLP) *J1 Zp C1*
London EC4 *p39* . . . 020 7822 4000

Evans, Ms N (Hogan Lovells International LLP)
London EC1 *p42* . . . 020 7296 2000

Evans, Ms N (Horwich Cohen Coghlan) *Q*
Manchester *p305* . . . 0161 830 4600

Evans, N A (Malcolm Dear Whitfield Evans LLP) *S1 W E N C1 Zl*
Kenton *p265* . . . 020 8907 4366

Evans, N A (Jameson & Hill) *T2 W E S2 C1*
Ware *p421* . . . 01920 460531

Evans, Ms N H (Bond Pearce LLP) *C1*
Bristol *p161* . . . 0845 415 0000

Evans, O M (Almy & Thomas) *G K1 N H J1 Zq K3 K4*
Torquay *p412* . . . 01803 299131

Evans, P (Foys Solicitors) *E L M1 S1 S2 W C1 Ze C2 R1 P*
Worksop *p441* . . . 01909 473560

Evans, P (Hugh James) *K1 A3 D1 V N J2*
Cardiff *p179* . . . 029 2022 4871

Evans, P (Peterborough City Council)
Peterborough *p468* . . . 01733 747474

Evans, P (Graham & Rosen) *K4 T2 W*
Hull *p257* . . . 01482 323123

Evans, P (T R Harris Arnold & Co) *W S1*
Gorseinon *p231* . . . 01792 892166 / 891331

Evans, P C (L G Williams & Prichard) *Q N J1 B1 C1 S1 E L K1 K3 Zc*
Cardiff *p181* . . . 029 2022 9716

Evans, P H (Vale of Glamorgan Council)
Barry *p448* . . . 01446 700111

Evans, P J (Doncaster Metropolitan Borough Council) *J1*
Doncaster *p457* . . . 01302 734651
London SW19 *p87* . . . 020 8947 4163

Evans, P J (Flintshire County Council)
Mold *p466* . . . 01352 702411

Evans, P J (Henmans LLP) *Zq O N*
Oxford *p343* . . . 01865 781000

Evans, Mrs P L (Scannell Evans) *K1*
Stanford-le-Hope *p394* . . . 01375 642240

Evans, R (Fanshaw Porter & Hazlehurst)
Birkenhead *p134* . . . 0151 647 4051

Evans, Ms R (Needham Poulier & Partners) *G H Zm*
London N17 *p63* . . . 020 8808 6622

Evans, R (Pearson Hinchliffe) *S2 S1*
Oldham *p341* . . . 0161 785 3500

Evans, R (Collins Benson Goldhill LLP) *S2 E J1 O Q*
Westminster *p21* . . . 020 7436 5151

Evans, R (Walker Morris)
Leeds *p277* . . . 0113 283 2500

Evans, R (Roland Robinsons & Fentons LLP) *J1 O Q N F1 F2 L*
Blackpool *p147* . . . 01253 621432

Evans, R (Clarke Willmott) *Zj Zc N*
Southampton *p385* 0845 209 1000 / 0117 305 6000

Evans, R (Imperial Tobacco Group PLC) *Ze*
Bristol *p452* . . . 0117 963 6636

Evans, R A (LG Lawyers)
London SE1 *p50* . . . 020 7379 0000

Evans, R B (Lanyon Bowdler LLP) *J1 N Q F1 Zp*
Telford *p409* . . . 01952 291222

Evans, R C (DAC Beachcroft)
London EC3 *p24* . . . 020 7208 6800

Evans, R D (Memery Crystal) *O E*
London WC2 *p60* . . . 020 7242 5905

Evans, R D (Eric Robinson Solicitors) *N O Q L J1 F1 B1*
Southampton *p386* . . . 023 8022 6891

Evans, Mrs R E (Wace Morgan) *W*
Shrewsbury *p379* . . . 01743 280100

Evans, R E (Jestyn Jeffreys) *S1 W G H C1 M1 L E K1 R1 Zl*
Neath *p320* . . . 01639 635641

Evans, R G (Evans & Co) *S1 T1 C1 E W A1 Zd Ze*
Ferryhill *p226* . . . 01740 657444
Spennymoor *p389* . . . 01388 815317

Evans, R G B (Colin Brown & Kidson) *S1 W K1 L N G A1 F1 J1*
Whitby *p430* . . . 01947 603391

Evans, R K (John Collins & Partners LLP) *K1*
Swansea *p405* . . . 01792 773773

Evans, Mrs R L (Haworth Holt Bell Limited) *J1*
Altrincham *p116* . . . 0161 928 7136

Evans, Miss R L (Warwickshire County Council)
Warwick *p475* . . . 01926 410410

Evans, Ms R L (Levenes Solicitors)
Birmingham *p140* . . . 0121 212 0000

Evans, R M (Mayer Brown International LLP) *Zo*
London EC2 *p59* . . . 020 3130 3000

Evans, R M T (Rodericks) *S1 W K1 T1 L E Zl*
Llanelli *p292* . . . 01554 773424

Evans, R T B (Parfitt Cresswell) *W T2 S1 V L K1*
London SW6 *p65* . . . 020 7381 8311

Evans, R W (Charles Crookes & Jones) *D1 F1 G H K1 L S1 N Q*
Caerphilly *p172* . . . 029 2086 0628

Evans, Miss S (Coodes) *K1*
Liskeard *p285* . . . 01579 347600

Evans, Ms S (Franklins LLP) *E R1 S1*
Milton Keynes *p317* . . . 01908 660966

Evans, Miss S (Berry Smith LLP)
Cardiff *p177* . . . 029 2034 5511

Evans, S (Dodd Lewis Solicitors) *J1 Q Zp*
London SE3 *p27* . . . 020 8852 1255

Evans, Ms S (The College of Law Chester)
Chester *p454* . . . 0800 289997

Evans, Ms S (Trowers & Hamlins)
London EC3 *p88* . . . 020 7423 8000

Evans, Miss S C (Birchall Blackburn LLP) *J1 O*
Manchester *p301* . . . 0161 236 0662

Evans, S D (Devonalds) *N L G H O Zh Zj Zm*
Pontypridd *p352* . . . 01443 404700

Evans, S E (Birchall Blackburn LLP) *B1 Zc F1 Q*
Chorley *p194* . . . 01257 279011
Preston *p356* . . . 01772 561663

Evans, Mrs S E (Lester Aldridge LLP) *J1 K1*
Bournemouth *p152* . . . 01202 786161

Evans, S J (Birmingham City Council Legal & Democratic Services)
Birmingham *p449* . . . 0121 303 2066

Evans, S J (Rawlison Butler LLP) *O A3 B1 B2 J1 U2 Ze Zg Zk*
Crawley *p202* . . . 01293 527744

Evans, S J (Simmons & Simmons)
London EC2 *p79* . . . 020 7628 2020

Evans, Mrs S L (Stone Milward Rapers) *S1 S2 E L*
Chichester *p193* . . . 01243 602832

Evans, Miss S L (Tomleys) *W S1 A1 S2 L C1*
Newtown *p330* . . . 01686 626641

Evans, Mrs S M (Shirley M Evans) *S1 E W C1 L A1*
Grange-over-Sands *p232* . . . 01539 535208

Evans, S M (Dolmans) *J2 L N Q Zu*
Cardiff *p178* . . . 029 2034 5531

Evans, S N (South Lakeland Magistrates' Court)
Kendal *p462* . . . 01539 720478

Evans, S P (Hempsons) *N Zr Zm*
Harrogate *p240* . . . 01423 522331

Evans, S R (Cocks Lloyd) *W T1 A1 S1*
Nuneaton *p339* . . . 024 7664 1642

Evans, T (Gloucestershire County Council - Legal & Democratic Services)
Gloucester *p459* . . . 01452 425203

Evans, T (Kieran Clarke Green) *K1 D1 D2 K2 K3*
Chesterfield *p192* . . . 01246 211006

Evans, T (James Morgan Solicitors)
Cardiff *p180* . . . 029 2038 2111 / 2022 1600

Evans, Miss T H (Bradford & Bingley PLC)
Bingley *p449* . . . 01274 555555

Evans, Miss V (Percy Hughes & Roberts) *S1 S2*
Birkenhead *p134* . . . 0151 666 9090

Evans, Mrs W J R (BPE Solicitors LLP) *E S2 L S1*
Cheltenham *p187* . . . 01242 224433

Evans, W L H (University of the West of England, Bristol)
Bristol *p452* . . . 0117 965 6261

Evans, W R (Richardson & Davies) *P K1 N G H L S1 F1 M1 E C1 O*
Coventry *p201* . . . 024 7622 2001

Eve, N (Churchers) *E R1 S1*
Fareham *p223* . . . 01329 822333

Eveleigh, G W (Davies Prichard & Weatherill) *K3 K1 S1 S2 W*
Cardiff *p178* . . . 029 2037 7471

Eveleigh, Ms K (Ashurst LLP)
London EC2 *p7* . . . 020 7638 1111

Eveleigh, R J (Winckworth Sherwood LLP) *E S1 S2*
London SE1 *p92* . . . 020 7593 5000

Evenett, Mrs H (Clifford Chance)
London E14 *p20* . . . 020 7006 1000

Everall, Miss D J (Higgs & Sons) *N Q*
Brierley Hill *p158* . . . 0845 111 5050

Everard, Ms K (Downs) *E S1 S2 W L*
Godalming *p231* . . . 01483 861848

Everatt, Miss A M (J R Hobbs & Co) *K1 M1 S1 W D1 L P*
Slough *p382* . . . 01753 524466

Everatt, Mrs K (Hampshire County Council)
Winchester *p476* . . . 01962 841841

Everest, Ms M C (Bird & Lovibond) *K1 N Q K3 J1*
Ruislip *p368* . . . 01895 636037

Everett, A M (Awdry Bailey & Douglas)
Calne *p173* . . . 01249 815110
Devizes *p210* . . . 01380 722311
Wootton Bassett *p439* . . . 01793 853200

Everett, C W (Wortley Byers) *O*
Brentwood *p156* . . . 01277 268368

Everett, Miss F L (Jackson Brierley Hudson Stoney) *S1 W N S2 E*
Rochdale *p365* . . . 01706 644187 / 649214

Everett, Miss J L (Dutton Gregory) *D1 K1*
Southampton *p385* . . . 023 8022 1344

Everett, Mrs N J (Cyril Morris Arkwright) *S1*
Bolton *p148* . . . 01204 535261

Everett, R J C (Financial Services Authority)
London E14 *p106* . . . 020 7066 1000

Everett, S R (United Cooperatives Ltd)
Rochdale *p451* . . . 01706 202020

Everett, S R (Radcliffes Le Brasseur) *C1 E T1 B1 J1 Ze*
Leeds *p276* . . . 0113 234 1220

Everiss, M C (Edwards Angell Palmer & Dodge)
London EC2 *p28* . . . 020 7583 4055

Everitt, C (Simmons & Simmons)
London EC2 *p79* . . . 020 7628 2020

Eversfield, Ms R D (Eversfield & Co) *C1 E L Q S1 T1*
London WC2 *p30* . . . 020 7836 5547

Evershed, W F (The Reece-Jones Partnership)
Sevenoaks *p374* . . . 01732 457575

Everson, Miss J C (Capsticks Solicitors LLP) *Zm Zr N*
London SW19 *p18* . . . 020 8780 2211

Ewan, C A (Ewan & Co Solicitors) *Q S1 W L J1 K3 K1 O N S2 C1 Zr Zq E B1*
Ilford *p260* . . . 020 8514 5687

Ewart, M J (Reed Smith LLP) *Zb*
London EC2 *p71* . . . 020 3116 3000

Ewart, P W (Hewitsons) *W Zd*
Cambridge *p174* . . . 01223 461155

Ewart-James, A W (Whitemans) *E W*
Gloucester *p231* . . . 01452 411601

Ewbank, Ms S (Norrie Waite & Slater) *D1 K1 Zu*
Sheffield *p377* . . . 0114 276 6166

Ewen, Ms J (Ince & Co Services Ltd)
London E1 *p44* . . . 020 7481 0010

Ewen, Miss M M (Henmans LLP) *W T2 T1*
Oxford *p343* . . . 01865 781000

Ewens, J (Penningtons) *E*
Godalming *p231* . . . 01483 791800

See p634 for the Key to Work Categories

Ewens, R A (Solihull Metropolitan Borough Council)
Solihull *p471*. 0121 704 6000

Ewens, S E (HMG Law LLP) *C1 E A1 S1 R1 L Zb Zd*
Oxford *p343*. 01865 244661

Ewin, A H (Durham County Council)
Durham *p457* 0191 383 3513

Ewin, Mrs N J (Spencer Ewin Mulvihill) *S1 Q B1 O Zq B2*
Harrogate *p240* 01423 509826

Ewing, Ms H C (Lewis Silkin LLP) *C1 C2*
London EC4 *p53*. 020 7074 8000

Ewing, S A (David Phillips & Partners) *H G B2*
Bootle *p150* 0151 922 5525

Ewing, S A (Russell-Cooke LLP) *Zza C1 C2 Ze Zl*
London SW15 *p74*. 020 8789 9111

Ewings, Mrs D M (Ewings & Co) *W*
London SE20 *p30* 020 8778 1126

Ewings, P I (Ewings & Co) *D1 G H*
London SE20 *p30* 020 8778 1126

Exell, K B (Lewis Francis Blackburn Bray) *S2 S1 L W E C1 T2 T1*
Sheffield *p376*. 0114 272 9721

Exley, Miss G (Glaisyers Solicitors LLP) *L*
Manchester *p304* 0161 224 3311
Manchester *p308* 0161 205 2772

Exley, P M (Simmons & Simmons)
London EC2 *p79*. 020 7628 2020

Exley, S D H (Davitt Jones Bould) *E S2 L*
Taunton *p408* 01823 279279

Exten-Wright, J (DLA Piper UK LLP)
London EC2 *p24*. 0870 011 1111

Exton, Mrs A E (Taylor Wessing) *W T2 Zd*
London EC4 *p86*. 020 7300 7000

Exton, Ms E J (Forsters LLP) *O*
Westminster *p33*. 020 7863 8333

Eyitene, G O (Wirral Borough Council)
Wallasey *p475*. 0151 638 7070

Eyles, T G (Taylor Wessing) *C1 Zb*
London EC4 *p86*. 020 7300 7000

Eyley, J W (Emmerson Brown & Brown) *K1 D1 B1 F1 J1 L*
Deal *p207* 01304 362146

Eyre, Miss E (Barlow Robbins LLP) *T2 W K4*
Godalming *p231*. 01483 417121

Eyre, Ms J (Wedlake Bell LLP)
London WC1 *p91* 020 7395 3000

Eyre, J M (Savage Crangle) *P S1 M1 J1 K1 L W E F1 Zl Ze*
Skipton *p381*. 01756 794611

Eyre, Ms L D (Woodfines LLP) *S2 E S1*
Bedford *p130* 01234 270600

Eyre, M I (JMW Solicitors) *N P M1 B1 C1*
Manchester *p306* 0845 872 6666

Eyre, M J (Hadgkiss Hughes & Beale) *S1 E L*
Birmingham *p139* 0121 778 2161

Eyre, N A (Co-operative Wholesale Society Ltd)
Manchester *p464* 0161 834 1212

Eyre, P J (Glovers Solicitors LLP) *Zc A3*
London W1 *p36* 020 7935 8882

Eyre, Ms R (Wolferstans) *N Q*
Plymouth *p351*. 01752 663295

Eyre, Mrs S (Brethertons LLP) *K4 W T1 A1 Zd*
Rugby *p368* 01788 579579
Rugby *p368* 01788 579579

Eyriey, D G (Clifton Ingram LLP) *C1 C2 C3 E R2 S2 Zd*
Wokingham *p437* 0118 978 0099

Eyton-Jones, M R (EMW) *N Q*
Milton Keynes *p316* 0845 070 6000

Ezekiel, A (Penningtons) *Zb*
London EC2 *p66*. 020 7457 3000

Ezekiel, E (Penningtons) *O*
London EC2 *p66*. 020 7457 3000

Ezekiel, M (HBOS PLC)
Halifax *p460*. 0870 600 5000

Ezzat, K M A (TV Edwards LLP) *G H*
London N15 *p85*. 020 7790 7000

F

Faber, G M (Higgs & Sons) *O Q L F2 Zl Zk Ze Zq*
Brierley Hill *p158*. 0845 111 5050

Faber, M S D (Faber & Co) *G H Q*
Birmingham *p138* 0121 236 5751

Faber, R M (Faber & Co) *G H K1 D1 K3 Q K2*
Birmingham *p138* 0121 236 5751

Fabre, Miss G (Pritchard Englefield) *C2 C1 Zb C3 M2 J1 U2 O*
London EC2 *p69*. 020 7972 9720

Facchiano, Miss N G (EMW) *J1*
Milton Keynes *p316* 0845 070 6000

Facer, A (Ward Hadaway) *W T2 Zd*
Newcastle upon Tyne *p327* . 0191 204 4000

Facer, Miss S (Lee & Thompson) *J1 Zf Zk*
London W1 *p52* 020 7935 4665

Facey, C L (Merricks Formerly Merrick Kelleher) *K1 K3 Q N J1 W B1 D1 F2 G O V Zq*
Wadebridge *p418* . .01208 812068 / 813104

Fackler, D A J (Mullis & Peake) *S1 E L W*
Romford *p366*. 01708 784000

Fadoju, Mrs N (Miller Parris) *K3 K1*
Worthing *p442*. 01903 205771

Fagade, A O (L Morgan & Co)
Brent *p61* 020 8965 2850

Fagan, D T (Weightmans LLP) *J1*
Liverpool *p291*. 0151 227 2601

Fagan, Miss G M (Newcastle Upon Tyne City Council)
Newcastle upon Tyne *p466* . 0191 232 8520

Fagan, Mrs J L (Brabners Chaffe Street) *K1 T2 W Zd*
Liverpool *p286*. 0151 600 3000

Fagan, N J (Hill Dickinson LLP) *B1 C1 E O Q S1 W*
Liverpool *p288*. 0151 600 8000

Fagan, N K (Knowsley Metropolitan Borough Council) *B1*
Huyton *p461*. 0151 443 3593

Fagan, P W (Forsters LLP) *O*
Westminster *p33*. 020 7863 8333

Fagan, S (Draycott Browne Solicitors)
Manchester *p303* 0161 228 2244

Fagan, Miss V (Bradford & Bingley PLC)
Bingley *p449*. 01274 555555

Fagelman, S B N (GLP Solicitors) *N K1 F1 S1 W Q G H Zq*
Manchester *p304* 0161 793 0901

Fagelson, I B (Reed Smith LLP) *C1 Zb Zj Zh*
London EC2 *p71*. 020 3116 3000

Fagge, N (Simmons & Simmons)
London EC2 *p79*. 020 7628 2020

Fahm, S T (Fahm & Co) *N Q J1 B1 L R1 M2 V K1 F1 Zi Zm Zv Zp Zh*
Blackwood *p147*. 01495 224973

Fahy, Ms A (Leathes Prior) *R1 E A1*
Norwich *p334* 01603 610911

Fahy, Miss A K (Thompsons (formerly Robin/Brian Thompson & Partners)) *N*
Birmingham *p143* 0121 262 1200

Fahy, G (Watson Burton LLP) *J1*
Leeds *p278* 0845 901 2100

Fahy, G (Hanne & Co) *K1 K3*
London SW11 *p38*. 020 7228 0017

Fahy, M P (Steeles) *E*
Norwich *p335* 0870 609 0200

Fahy, R (Matthew Arnold & Baldwin LLP) *O J1 Q Zw*
Milton Keynes *p317* 01908 687880

Fail, J (Marsden Rawsthorn LLP) *K1 D1 Q K3*
Preston *p357* 01772 799600

Fairbairn, B A (Barrie Fairbairn Solicitors) *G H*
Leicester *p279*. 0116 244 8272

Fairbairn, D (Christchurch Borough Council)
Christchurch *p455* 01202 495000

Fairbairn, E (Woodford Stauffer)
Farnborough *p224*. 01252 375376

Fairbairn, J E K (SNR Denton) *O*
Milton Keynes *p317* 01908 690260

Fairbairn, Mrs M (Gregg Latchams LLP) *S1*
Bristol *p162* 0117 906 9400

Fairbairn, Ms N R (Ison Harrison) *Zr*
Leeds *p274* 0113 284 5000

Fairbairn, P J (Avon Rubber PLC)
Melksham *p465* 01225 896800

Fairbairn, R M (Lester Aldridge LLP)
London WC2 *p53* 0844 967 0785

Fairbank, Mrs M E (Akermans) *W T2 S1*
Worthing *p441*. 01903 820413

Fairbrother, A J (Metropolitan Police Directorate of Legal Services)
London SW1 *p108*. 020 7230 7210

Fairbrother, J (Collier Littler)
Altrincham *p116* 0161 980 6046

Fairbrother, Mrs J D (Fairbrother & Darlow) *K1 S1 S2 N D1 W*
Bracknell *p153*. 01344 420808

Fairclough, A N (Smith Roddam) *E C1 A1 S1 W*
Bishop Auckland *p144*. . . . 01388 603073

Fairclough, D (Russell-Cooke LLP) *Zr N*
London SW15 *p74*. 020 8789 9111

Fairclough, Ms E (Mogers) *E*
Bath *p127* 01225 750000

Fairclough, Ms L A (Ward Hadaway) *E L S2 R2*
Newcastle upon Tyne *p327* . 0191 204 4000

Fairclough, Miss L C (Irwin Mitchell LLP)
Sheffield *p376* 0870 150 0100

Fairfax, Mrs G M (Bishop & Sewell LLP) *B1 C1 F1 J1 K1 Q T1 T2 V W Zd Zl Zo Zv*
London WC1 *p13* 020 7631 4141

Fairfax-Cholmeley, C M (Herbert & Cholmeley) *W S1 K4*
Banbury *p122* 01295 263556

Fairfield, D P J (Rosenblatt) *C1 C3 U2*
London EC4 *p73*. 020 7955 0880

Fairfield, Ms G A (Herbert Smith LLP)
London EC2 *p40*. 020 7374 8000

Fairhead, B A (McGrigors LLP)
London EC4 *p56*. 020 7054 2500

Fairhurst, Ms A P (George Davies Solicitors LLP) *E S1 L*
Manchester *p303* 0161 236 8992

Fairhurst, C J (Arthur Smiths) *K3 K1 D1 D2*
Wigan *p432* 01942 242815

Fairhurst, G J (Arthur Smiths) *M1 K1 P N F1 J1*
Wigan *p432* 01942 242815

Fairhurst, R W (Whitbread PLC)
London LU5 *p110* 01582 424200

Fairless, Miss G P (Denniss Matthews) *E S1 S2*
London SE20 *p27* . . 020 8778 7301 / 8778 7631

Fairless, Mrs S (Graham White & Co) *K3 K4 K1 O Q S1 N*
Bushey *p172*. 020 8950 5304

Fairley, A S (Harold G Walker) *S1 L F1*
Bournemouth *p152*. 01202 203200

Fairley, Mrs J A (Foreman Laws) *E W C1 C2*
Hitchin *p251* 01462 458711

Fairley, R (Allen & Overy LLP)
London E1 *p5* 020 3088 0000

Fairley, Mrs V (Blake Lapthorn) *W*
Chandlers Ford *p184* 023 8090 8090

Fairley, Ms V J (Radcliffes Le Brasseur)
Westminster *p70*. 020 7222 7040

Fairlie, A D (Read Roper & Read)
Manchester *p309* 0161 832 6905

Fairlie, Mrs C M (Kirklees Metropolitan Borough Council)
Huddersfield *p461* 01484 221421

Fairman, Mrs M (Derbyshire County Council) *E Zu R1 S1*
Matlock *p465* 01629 580000

Fairman, Ms S A (Squire Sanders (UK) LLP)
Leeds *p277* 0113 284 7000

Fairweather, A C (Clarke Willmott) *N Zq*
Taunton *p408*0845 209 1000 / 0117 305 6000

Fairweather, Ms H J (Ilett & Clark Solicitors) *O J1 Q*
Worksop *p441*. 01909 500544

Fairweather, M P (Fairweather Stephenson & Co) *E C1 A1 L S1 W*
Leiston *p282*. 01728 832832

Fairweather, N (Harman & Harman) *J1 N Q Zp Zr*
London SW2 *p39* 01227 452977

Fairweather, N (Fairweather & Co Solicitors)
Canterbury *p176*. 01227 784337

Fairweather, P S (Warwickshire County Council)
Warwick *p475* 01926 410410

Fairweather, S F (Ilett & Clark Solicitors) *B1 E F1 G H J1 K1 L Q V Zl*
Worksop *p441*. 01909 500544

Faithfull, E P (Hadgkiss Hughes & Beale) *W*
Birmingham *p139* 0121 707 8484
Birmingham *p138* 0121 449 5050

Fakhrai, Miss B (CKFT) *S2 E*
London NW3 *p17* 020 7431 7262

Fakoya, Ms B (Net Employment Solicitors) *J1 Zi W*
Ashford *p119* 020 8906 6804

Falcao, T (Stones Solicitors LLP) *J1*
Exeter *p222* 01392 666777

Falck, A C (Preston Redman) *L R1 S1 S2 E*
Bournemouth *p152*. 01202 292424

Falconer, G M (HSBC Legal Department)
Birmingham *p449* 0121 455 2740

Falconer, Ms H E (Metcalfes) *N Q O J2*
Bristol *p164* 0117 929 0451

Falk, W W (O'Garra's) *G H*
Leeds *p276* 0113 247 1477

Falkner, J M G (Mills & Reeve) *L*
Norwich *p335* 01603 660155

Falkner, R (Morgan Lewis & Bockius)
London EC4 *p61*. 020 3201 5000

Falkus, Ms C D (Bross Bennett) *K1 K2*
London N6 *p16* 020 8340 0444

Fallanca, A (Knowles Benning) *S1 A1 W*
Luton *p295* 01582 798000

Fallen, P D (Edward Fail Bradshaw & Waterson) *G H B2*
London EC3 *p30*. 020 7790 4032
London EC3 *p30*. 020 7264 2016

Faller, Ms C (Farrer & Co LLP)
London WC2 *p31* 020 3375 7000

Faller, Ms C T (Trowers & Hamlins) *E*
London EC3 *p88*. 020 7423 8000

Fallon, Mrs E J (Winchester City Council)
Winchester *p476*. 01962 840222

Fallon, I R (FBC Manby Bowdler LLP) *T1 W*
Wolverhampton *p437* 01902 578000

Fallon, M A (Irwin Mitchell LLP) *N G J2 Zj*
Leeds *p274* 0870 150 0100

Fallon, P F (Reed Smith LLP) *O*
London EC2 *p71*. 020 3116 3000

Fallon, S A (Ford & Warren) *O Zq*
Leeds *p273* 0113 243 6601

Falloon, Ms K (Kennedys) *Zj*
London EC3 *p49*. 020 7667 9667

Fallows, Miss A J (Burnetts) *K1 D1*
Carlisle *p181*. 01228 552222
Carlisle *p182*. 01228 552222

Fallows, J P W (Miles-Pierce Solicitors) *N K1 Q Zq D1 W*
Birmingham *p140* 0800 987 5305

Fallows, P H (Miles-Pierce Solicitors) *B1 C1 G H K1 L P S1 W M1 Zi*
Birmingham *p140* 0800 987 5305

Falvert-Martin, D (Bower & Bailey) *S1*
Oxford *p343*. 01865 311133

Falvey, C D A (Taylor Vinters) *E Zi*
Cambridge *p176*. 01223 423444

Falvey, R M (R M Falvey & Co) *O*
London SW3 *p30* 020 7100 3414

Falvey, Miss S L (Mills & Reeve) *R2 E S2 S1*
Cambridge *p175*. 01223 364422

Fane De Salis, M T (Chichester & District Magistrates Courts)
Chichester *p455* 01243 817000

Fane, Ms E (Trowers & Hamlins)
London EC3 *p88*. 020 7423 8000

Fanner, C J (Herbert Smith LLP) *Zb*
London EC2 *p40*. 020 7374 8000

Fanning, M (Plexus Law (A Trading Name of Parabis Law LLP)) *N F2 A3 Zj Zq*
London EC3 *p68*. 0844 245 4000

Fanning, P J (Colemans - CTTS) *S1 E W L C1 R1 T1 Zc*
Kingston upon Thames *p267*. 020 8296 9966

Fanning, Miss S E (DLA Piper UK LLP)
London EC2 *p24*. 0870 011 1111

Fanning, S J (Brighton Housing Trust) *F1 F2 J1 L O Q*
Brighton *p451* 01273 234737
Brighton *p159* 01273 665470

Fanson, D J (Sansbury Douglas) *G H*
Bristol *p164* 0117 955 2663
Knowle *p269*. 0117 963 5044

Fantham, Mrs L M (Moss Solicitors LLP) *K1*
Loughborough *p293* 01509 217770

Fantham, S A (Stuart Fantham)
Aylesbury *p121* 01296 620300

Fanthorpe, M R (Alexander & Partners) *D1 G H K1*
Brent *p5*. 020 8965 7121

Farahi, Mrs S (Radcliffes Le Brasseur) *Q Zr N K1*
Westminster *p70*. 020 7222 7040

Faraoni, D (Bates Wells & Braithwaite London LLP) *W T2 Zd*
London EC4 *p11* 020 7551 7777

Fardell, E (Thomson Snell & Passmore) *W Zm K4*
Tunbridge Wells *p415* 01892 510000

Fardoe, R J (Seymours) *L F1 B1 C1 S2 E S1 W K4 A1*
Coventry *p201*. 024 7655 3961

Faret, Miss R L (Rebecca L Faret Solicitors) *J1 K1 L S1 W N S2 Zl Zr*
Flitwick *p226*. 01525 712112

Farkas, A C (Pinsent Masons LLP) *C2 C1*
London EC2 *p67*. 020 7418 7000

Farley, A (Horwich Cohen Coghlan) *N*
Manchester *p305* 0161 830 4600

Farley, A H (Watson Farley & Williams)
London EC2 *p90*. 020 7814 8000

Farley, H R (Churchers) *G H*
Portsmouth *p354*. 023 9286 2424
Chatham *p185*. 01634 832332

Farman, Miss R A (Steeles) *E*
Norwich *p335* 0870 609 0200

Farman, Mrs T (Corries Solicitors) *N J2*
York *p444* 0845 241 5566

Farmaner, K I (Foot Anstey) *Zj N Q O A2*
Plymouth *p349*. 01752 675000
Southampton *p387*. 023 8032 1000

Farmar, R N (Kealy Farmar & Co) *C1 E F1 K1 L S1 S2 W J1*
Henley-on-Thames *p247*. . . 01491 410393

Farmer, Miss A (Peter Brown & Co Solicitors LLP) *S1*
Barnet *p124* 020 8447 3277

Farmer, Miss C (WGS Solicitors) *S1 S2 W J1 K1 L Q*
Westminster *p90*. 020 7723 1656

Farmer, C (Ince & Co Services Ltd)
London E1 *p44* 020 7481 0010

Farmer, C M (WGS Solicitors) *C1 S2 Zl S1 B2 J1 E L W*
Westminster *p90*. 020 7723 1656

Farmer, D (Thurstan Hoskin Solicitors) *S1 S2*
Redruth *p363* 01209 213646

Farmer, Ms J (Lewis Silkin LLP)
London EC4 *p53*. 020 7074 8000

Farmer, M (Steptoe & Johnson) *E L R2 S1 S2*
London EC2 *p83*. 020 7367 8000

Farmer, Mrs N L (The Ringrose Law Group - David Thornley) *S1 W*
Grantham *p232* 01476 590200

Farmer, P R (Petty Sessional Divisions of East Penwith, Falmouth and Kerrier Isles)
Truro *p474*. . . . . .01872 274075 / 277375

Farmery, A (Shoosmiths)
Reading *p361* . . 0370 086 8800 / 0118 965 8765

Farndon, Miss C J C (Horsey Lightly) *K1*
Westminster *p43*. 020 7222 8844

Farndon, C L (Andersons Solicitors) *G H S1 Zl S2 B2 L W E*
Harrogate *p239* 01423 527852

Farnell, Ms C (Field Fisher Waterhouse LLP)
London EC3 *p31*. 020 7861 4000

Farnell, J (Briffa) *Ze Zg O*
Islington *p15*. 020 7288 6003

Farnell, M E (Ratcliffe Duce & Gammer LLP) *S1 W T1 R1 L E C1 A1 Zc Ze Zo T2*
Reading *p361* 0118 957 4291

Farnill, Mrs A (Tallents Solicitors) *T1 T2 W*
Southwell *p389* 01636 813411

Farnsworth, D C (Lewis Silkin LLP) *C1 O I Ze Zw*
London EC4 *p53*. 020 7074 8000

Farnsworth, S P (Clarkson Hirst) *G H*
Lancaster *p269* 01524 39760

Farnworth, J (Cumbria County Council) *G H Zm*
Carlisle *p453*. . . . .01228 607374 / 607351

Farooq, M (Wallace McNally) *G H*
Coventry *p201*. 024 7622 0300

Farooq, M (Millerchip Peachey) *G H*
Coventry *p200*. 024 7624 3615

Farooq, V (Shoosmiths)
Birmingham *p142* 0370 086 4000 / 0121 335 4440

Farooqi, Ms S B (Exeter City Council)
Exeter *p458* 01392 277888

Farquhar, A (Munro Solicitors)
London E7 *p62* 020 8503 1718

Farquharson, Ms A (Cozens-Hardy LLP) *S1*
Norwich *p334* 01603 625231

Farquharson, D (Osborne Clarke) *O*
London EC2 *p65*. 020 7105 7000

Farquharson, Miss M A (Simmons & Simmons)
London EC2 *p79*. 020 7628 2020

Farr, D (Kenneth Elliott & Rowe) *E L S1 W S2*
Romford *p366*. 01708 757575

Farr, Miss H J (Fladgate LLP) *J1*
London WC2 *p32* 020 3036 7000
London EC2 *p67*. 020 7418 7000

Farr, Ms J (AWB Partnership LLP) *E S2 S1 C1 L*
Guildford *p235*. 01483 302345

6

To find a wide range of International law firms please refer to International law firms Section 19

Farr, J R (Ince & Co Services Ltd)
London E1 p44 . . . . 020 7481 0010

Farr, J R (Herbert Smith LLP) C1 J1
London EC2 p40. . . . . . . 020 7374 8000

Farr, M D (Max Gold Law) G H
Hull p257 . . . . 01482 224900

Farr, N J (Herbert Smith LLP) C1 C2
London EC2 p40. . . . . . . 020 7374 8000

Farr, T J (Cambridgeshire County Council)
Cambridge p453. . . . . . . 01223 717111

Farr-Davies, Ms A (Gordon Young Solicitors Ltd) G H
Luton p296 . . . . 01582 405577

Farrand, D J (Mills & Reeve) R2
Cambridge p175. . . . . . . 01223 364422

Farrands, S (Minter Ellison) Zb C1 M2 C2 R2 Zv
London EC2 p61. . . . . . . 020 7448 4800

Farrant, S (Johnson Matthey PLC) C1
London EC1 p107 . . . . . . 020 7269 8400

Farrar, P (Hill Dickinson LLP) J1
Liverpool p288. . . . . 0151 600 8000

Farrar, Miss R L (Terrells LLP) K3 K1 N
Peterborough p347 . . . . . 01733 896789

Farrell, A (Alnwick District Council)
Alnwick p447 . . . . 01665 510505

Farrell, A (C Nicholls)
Bodmin p148 . . . . 01208 76969

Farrell, E (Berwins Solicitors Limited) Q
Harrogate p240 . . . . 01423 509000

Farrell, F P T (Farrell & Hobbs) D1 K1 N J1 Q
Manchester p304 . . . . . . 0161 445 1000

Farrell, J (Kennedys) Ze Zk Zj
London EC3 p49. . . . . . . 020 7667 9667

Farrell, J T H (Herbert Smith LLP) O A3 Zn
London EC2 p40. . . . . . . 020 7374 8000

Farrell, Mrs L R (Bristows) O J1 Q N Zp L
London EC4 p15. . . . . . . 020 7400 8000

Farrell, N D (Farrells Solicitors) B1 C1 Q C2 F1 J1 K1 N O G Zc
Bristol p162 . . . . 0117 944 4664

Farrell, Mrs P (Salmons) S1 W S2
Stoke-on-Trent p398. . . . . 01782 639827

Farrell, R A (Hill Dickinson LLP) A3 Zc
Liverpool p288. . . . . 0151 600 8000

Farrell-Knowles, Ms J (Watson Burton LLP) E P S1
Newcastle upon Tyne p327 . 0845 901 2100

Farrelly, Mrs L (George Davies Solicitors LLP)
Manchester p303 . . . . . . 0161 236 8992

Farrelly, P A (Bermans LLP) B1 O Q
Manchester p301 . . . . . . 0161 827 4600

Farren, Ms H (Walkers) K1
Rossendale p367 . . . . . . 01706 213565

Farren, M C (Clarke Willmott) A1
Taunton p4080845 209 1000 / 0117 305 6000

Farren, P S (Linklaters LLP)
London EC2 p54. . . . . . . 020 7456 2000

Farrer, C (Hempsons)
Westminster p40. . . . . . . 020 7839 0278

Farrer, C A (Radcliffes Le Brasseur) E L P R1
Westminster p70. . . . . . . 020 7222 7040

Farrer, R E G (Cozens Moxon & Harts) E W S1 C1
Hampton p238. . . . . 020 8979 4333

Farrier, M J C (Boyes Turner) J1 C1
Reading p360 . . . . 0118 959 7711

Farrier, P J (Tait Farrier Graham) A1 B1 D1 E J1 G H K1
Gateshead p229. . . . . . . 0191 490 0108

Farries, G R (Thomas Solicitors) K1 W S1 J1 L Q V E F1
Long Eaton p293 . . . . . . 0115 946 1061

Farrington, D (Consumers' Association)
London NW1 p105. . . . . . 020 7770 7000

Farrington, D J (Consumers' Association)
London NW1 p105. . . . . . 020 7770 7000
Slough p471. . . . . 01753 771908

Farrington, Ms E (Moorhead James LLP) J1 Zp
London EC4 p61. . . . . . . 020 7831 8888

Farrington, G (Farrington & Co) E K1 S1 W Ze Zf
Reading p360 . . . . 0118 947 8914

Farrington, P M M (Hand Morgan & Owen) C1 O Q B1 F1 L Zq
Stafford p393 . . . . 01785 211411

Farrington, T J (Streeter Marshall) E P R1 S1
Croydon p205 . . . . 020 8680 2638

Farrow, C J (Mark Gilbert Morse) S1 W
Newcastle upon Tyne p325 . 0191 261 0096

Farrow, Ms F E (Virgin Atlantic Airways Ltd)
Crawley p456 . . . . 01293 562345

Farrow, Miss J E (Colemans) S1
Chelmsford p186. . . . . . . 01245 264494

Farrow, Mrs L (Austins Penny & Thorne) S1 S2
Berkhamsted p131. . . . . . 01442 872141

Farrow, M J (Wylie Kay) O W Q N K3
Blackpool p147 . . . . 01253 296297

Farrow, P K (Gales) Q S1 K1 N L F1 W S2 D1 K3
Bournemouth p152. .01202 512227 / 512446

Farrow, R H G (Stephensons) E K1 L S1 W K4 S2
Brierley Hill p158. . . . . . . 01384 79731

Farrow, Ms S (Thorneycroft Solicitors Ltd)
Macclesfield p297 . . . . . . 01625 503444

Farrow, T J (Halliburton) C1 C3 M2 O T1 Ze Zj
Plymouth p468. . . . .

Farry, Miss G (Lee Rigby Partnership) K1 K3 D1
Leyland p283 . . . . 01772 421748
Blackburn p146 . . . . 01254 672222

Farthing, I R (Singleton Saunders Flood Solicitors) S1 W K4 E S2
Dover p213 . . . . 01304 240080

Farthing, N C (Birketts LLP) A1 L Q Zl
Ipswich p262. . . . . 01473 232300

Fashola, Ms N (London Borough of Southwark)
London SE1 p109 . . . . . . 020 7525 5000

Fatemi, C (Michael Simkins LLP) E S1
London WC1 p79 . . . . . . 020 7874 5600

Faulkes, A J (Crombie Wilkinson) E D1 C1 R1 S1 A1 Zc
York p444 . . . . 01904 624185

Faulkner, B W (Rogers & Norton) N O Q L Zl
Norwich p335 . . . . 01603 666001

Faulkner, C J (Yorkshire Building Society)
Bradford p451 . . . .

Faulkner, D (SGH Martineau LLP)
Birmingham p142 . . . . . . 0870 763 2000

Faulkner, Mrs H L (DAC Beachcroft)
Bristol p162 . . . . 0117 918 2000

Faulkner, Miss J (Pearson Rowe) K1 K2 D1
Birmingham p141 . . . . . . 0121 236 7388

Faulkner, K (Geoffrey Morris & Ashton) D1 D2 S1 S2 W K1 E K3
Mold p318 . . . . 01352 754711

Faulkner, S M (Eastgate Assistance Ltd)
Colchester p455 . . . . 0870 523 4500

Faulkner, W (AXA UK PLC)
London E22 p103 . . . . . . 020 7920 5900

Faure Walker, Ms A (Bates Wells & Braithwaite London LLP) Zd C1
London EC4 p11. . . . . . . 020 7551 7777

Fausset, A R (Department for Business, Enterprise and Regulatory Reform)
London SW1 p105. . . . . . 020 7215 0105

Favre, Mrs A B (Pemberton Greenish LLP) E S2 S1
London SW3 p66 . . . . . . 020 7591 3333

Fawcett, Miss E M (Ouvry Goodman & Co) W T1 S1 C1 Zm
Sutton p403 . . . . 020 8642 7571

Fawcett, J (Gordons LLP) C1
Leeds p273 . . . . 0113 227 0100

Fawcett, Mrs J A (Addleshaw Goddard)
Leeds p271 . . . . 0113 209 2000

Fawcett, Mrs J A (Taylor Fawcett)
Harrogate p241 . . . . 01423 538111

Fawcett, N E (Fawcett & Pattni) S1 S2
Walsall p420. . . . . 01922 640424

Fawcett, Ms P M (Bevans) E K1 K4 P R1 S1 Zo
London WC2 p12 . . . . . . 020 7353 9995

Fawcett, R (Bennett Griffin) S2 E S1
Ferring p225. . . . . 01903 229999

Fawcett, R W (Bird & Bird LLP) C1 U1 I
London EC4 p13. . . . . . . 020 7415 6000

Fawcus, S (Doncaster Metropolitan Borough Council)
Doncaster p457 . . . . 01302 734651

Fawden, A C (Simpson Millar LLP) N
London EC1 p80. . . . . . . 0844 858 3400

Fawell, S J K (Edwards Angell Palmer & Dodge)
London EC2 p28. . . . . . . 020 7583 4055

Fazal, Miss S (G T Stewart Solicitors) G H B2
London SE22 p83 . . . . . . 020 8299 6000

Fazaluddin, S M M (Hodge Jones & Allen LLP) L
London NW1 p41 . . . . . . 020 7874 8300

Fazan, Ms C (Leigh Day & Co) Zr
London EC1 p52. . . . . . . 020 7650 1200

Fazio, Miss D T (Milford & Dormor) S1 W S2 T2
Seaton p373. . . . . 01297 20528

Fazio, Miss S (Collyer Bristow LLP) C3 M1 M2
London WC1 p22 . . . . . . 020 7242 7363

Fear, G G (Graham Fear & Co) S1 L
Enfield p218 . . . . 020 8363 3331

Fear, J C (Harvey Ingram LLP) E S1 L
Leicester p280. . . . . 0116 254 5454

Fear, Mrs J M (Higgins & Co) W S1 S2
Birkenhead p134. . . . . . . 0151 653 5222

Fear, Miss N D (North Somerset District Council) G H K1 Q Zm
Weston-super-Mare p476 . . 01934 888888

Fearn, A (Langleys) A1 K4 T2 W
Lincoln p284. . . . . 01522 888555
York p445 . . . . 01904 610886

Fearn, A W (Byron Fearn) A1 C1 E F1 G H J1 K1 L
Dunstable p214 . . . . 01582 605822

Fearn, Mrs B (Erewash Borough Council) S1 G H
Ilkeston p461 . . . . 0115 907 2244

Fearn, B F (Squire Sanders (UK) LLP)
London EC2 p81. . . . . . . 020 7655 1000

Fearn, M (McMillen Hamilton McCarthy) N
London E3 p57 . . . . 020 8980 6060

Fearnley, A A (Fearnley & Co) S1 T1 T2 L Zh E W K1
Ealing p31. . . . . 020 8579 9898

Fearnley, F T K (Fearnley & Co)
Macclesfield p297 . . . . . . 01625 427303

Fearnley, Mrs P A (Thomson Snell & Passmore) N Zr
Tunbridge Wells p415 . . . . 01892 510000

Fearnley, R F T (Knights Solicitors LLP) W T2 A1 K4
Newcastle under Lyme p323. 01782 619225

Fearon, Miss L M (DWF) N Zj
Preston p356 . . . . 01772 556677

Fearon, Ms S E (Roberts Moore Nicholas Jones) G H
Birkenhead p134. . . . . . . 0151 647 0000

Feather, A (Michelmores LLP) C1 C2
Exeter p221 . . . . 01392 688688

Featherstone, Miss S (Winters) S1 S2
St Ives p392. . . . . 01480 377377

Featherstone, Miss T (Goodman Ray) K1
Hackney p36. . . . . 020 7608 1227

Featherstonhaugh, Ms D J (Hamlins LLP) E S1
London W1 p38 . . . . 020 7355 6000

Feaver, L J (LG Lawyers)
London SE1 p50. . . . . . . 020 7379 0000

Fedeski, Ms S (Solihull Magistrates Court)
Solihull p471. . . . . 0121 705 8101

Fedeyko, Ms M A (Thompson Smith & Puxon) C1 F1 Zd Zb
Colchester p198 . . . . 01206 574431

Feehan, J D (United States Air Force)
Bury St Edmunds p452 . . . 01638 543533

Feeley, G (Pothecary Witham Weld) Zd
Westminster p69. . . . . . . 020 7821 8211

Feely, M T (David Barney & Co) S1 W
Stevenage p394 . . . . 01438 314281

Feenan, D P J (Thompsons (formerly Robin/Brian Thompson & Partners)) N
Birmingham p143 . . . . . . 0121 262 1200

Feeney, A (Holman Fenwick Willan)
London EC3 p42. . . . . . . 020 7264 8000

Feeney, Ms E (Woodfines LLP) L Q K1
Sandy p372 . . . . 01767 680251

Feeney, Ms J (JP Morgan Chase Bank)
London EC2 p107 . . . . . . 020 7777 2000

Feeny, E (Hanne & Co)
London SW11 p38 . . . . . . 020 7228 0017

Feeny, H D (Feeny & Co) S1 S2 W
Bristol p162 . . . . 0117 923 9477

Feeny, Miss M N M (Boodle Hatfield) E L R2
Westminster p14. . . . . . . 020 7629 7411

Feeny, M R (Brabners Chaffe Street) T2 W
Liverpool p286. . . . . 0151 600 3000

Fegan, Mrs J V (Newman & Bond) K3 K1
Barnsley p125 . . . . 01226 213434

Fegan, Ms L (Morrisons Solicitors LLP) F1
Redhill p362 . . . . 01737 854500

Fegbemi, O O (Chhokar & Co) S2 E Q S1
Southall p384 . . . . 020 8574 2488

Fehler, Ms C (Michael Simkins LLP) Ze Q Zf Zk O Zm Zq
London WC1 p79 . . . . . . 020 7874 5600

Feild, P R (London Borough of Barking & Dagenham)
Barking p448 . 020 8592 4500 / 8252 8233

Feingold, D (Ross-Brown & Birtwistle) Zm G H S1 D1 M1 P N K1 L J1
Rochdale p365. . . . .

Feinstein, Ms N (Hogan Lovells International LLP)
London EC1 p42. . . . . . . 020 7296 2000

Felce, J (Jones Day) O
London EC4 p46. . . . . . . 020 7039 5959

Felce, S N (Hill Dickinson LLP) E R2 S2 R1 L
Liverpool p288. . . . . 0151 600 8000

Feld, B G (Feld McKay & Donner Solicitors) G H K1 D1
Rochdale p365. . . . . 01706 645656

Feldman, Ms D (Davenport Lyons) W T2 Zd
London W1 p25 . . . . 020 7468 2600

Feldmann, M (Oberman Law) E S2 S1 L W R2 C1
Camden p64. . . . . 020 7242 6154

Felgate, W (Gloucestershire County Council - Legal & Democratic Services)
Gloucester p459. . . . . . . 01452 425203

Fell, Ms C (Stone King LLP) K1
Bath p128 . . . . 01225 337599

Fell, Miss C H (Waddington & Son) G H
Burnley p169 . . . . 01282 426666

Fell, Mrs E (BUPA)
London WC1 p104. . . . . . 020 7656 2305

Fell, G (McMillan Williams) G H
Wallington p419 . . . . 020 8669 4962

Fell, J M (Pinsent Masons LLP) C1 F1 Ze
London EC2 p67. . . . . . . 020 7418 7000

Fell, Mrs N J (Hayton Winkley) S1 W C1 E A1 L Zc
Kendal p264. . . . . 01539 720136

Fell, P (Jerman Simpson Pearson & Samuels) N
Basildon p126 . . . . 01268 820111

Fell, R (Travers Smith LLP)
London EC1 p87. . . . . . . 020 7295 3000

Fellowes, Ms K (Dickinson Dees) K1
Newcastle upon Tyne p324 . 0191 279 9000

Fellowes, S R J (Fellowes Solicitors) S1 S2 W Zl K4
London E17 p31 . . . . 020 8520 7392

Fellows, Ms A A (Dickinson Dees) C1
Newcastle upon Tyne p324 . 0191 279 9000

Fellows, D (Royal Borough of Kingston upon Thames)
Kingston upon Thames p462. 020 8546 2121

Fellows, D C G (Calvert Smith & Sutcliffe) S1 L
Richmond upon Thames p364020 8940 0017

Fellows, M (British Telecommunications PLC)
London EC1 p104 . . . . . . 020 7356 6181

Fellows, P (Coffin Mew & Clover) E L R1 Zh Zs S2
Fareham p223. . . . . 01329 825617

Fellows, Miss S C (Stephenson Harwood)
London EC2 p82. . . . . . . 020 7329 4422

Feltham, A (Hampshire County Council)
Winchester p476. . . . . . . 01962 841841

Feltham, Mrs D F (Gwyn James Solicitors) B1 J1 N V W D1 D2 K1 L K3 Q Zk
Coleford p198 . . . . 01594 833042
Cinderford p195 . . . . 01594 822277

Feltham, Ms K J (Leeds City Council)
Leeds p462 . . . . 0113 224 3513

Felton, C G (Gardner Leader LLP) N O
Newbury p322. . . . . 01635 508080

Felton, Ms K H (Felton & Co) S1 E S2 W
Stanmore p394 . . . . 01923 839599

Felton, Ms L (Windsor & Maidenhead Borough Council)
Maidenhead p464 . . . . . . 01628 798888

Felton, N (Ford & Warren) N V Zq
Leeds p273 . . . . 0113 243 6601

Felton, Ms P (Tollers LLP) W
Northampton p332. . . . . . 01604 258558

Felton, R (Southampton City Council)
Southampton p472. . . . . . 023 8022 3855

Fender, K J (Frank Stimpson & Son) S1 W E
London SE23 p83 . . . . . . 020 8699 7644

Fendick, Miss L (Jones Day) E
London EC4 p46. . . . . . . 020 7039 5959

Fendrich, P B (British Waterways Board) E S1 L
Watford p475 . . . . 01923 226422

Fendt, Ms A (Israel Strange & Conlon) E L S1 S2
Islington p45. . . . . 020 7833 8453

Fendt, T E (Sherrards) E P S2 S1 R2
St Albans p390 . . . . 01727 832830

Fenech-Pisani, C (Ashurst LLP)
London EC2 p7 . . . . 020 7638 1111

Fenlon, K A (Arscotts) S1 S2 E W R1 R2
Hove p254. . . . . 01273 735289

Fenn, I W (Linklaters LLP)
London EC2 p54. . . . . . . 020 7456 2000

Fenn, J L L (Steele Raymond) E L N O Ze B1
Bournemouth p152. . . . . . 01202 294566

Fenn, M (RMPI Solicitors)
London W1 p70 . . . . 020 7318 4444

Fennell, Ms V (Oxford City Council)
Oxford p468 . . . . 01865 249811

Fenny, A J (Andrew J Fenny & Co) S1 C1 E W L P N K1 M1 G Zd Zl Zo
Cramlington p201 . . . . . . 01670 737393

Fenny, J (Irwin Mitchell LLP) G H B2
Sheffield p376 . . . . 0870 150 0100

Fentiman, N P (Fentimans) N C1 K1 G F1 E J1 L Q S2 F2
Knowle p269. . . . . 01564 779459

Fenton, Ms A (Andrew Jackson) E
Hull p257 . . . . 01482 325242

Fenton, A P (Cunningtons) S1 E W L
Braintree p155. . . . . 01376 326868

Fenton, C P (Dyne Drewett Solicitors Ltd) K1 N Q O Zl
Wincanton p433 . . . . 01963 32374

Fenton, D (Teacher Stern LLP) O J1 Q Zp
London WC1 p86 . . . . . . 020 7242 3191

Fenton, J G (DLA Piper UK LLP)
London EC2 p24. . . . . . . 0870 011 1111

Fenton, M T (Farrer & Co LLP) K1 O Q
London WC2 p31 . . . . . . 020 3375 7000

Fenton, N J (Bray & Dilks) S1 S2 E W A1 L C1 R1 Zl
Truro p414. . . . . 01872 271717

Fenton, Miss T M (Birchall Blackburn LLP) B1 O Zb Zq C1
Manchester p301 . . . . . . 0161 236 0662

Fenton, W J T (Howlett Clarke Crowther Wood) K1 S1 M1 P J1 L B1 W G E
Brighton p159 . . .01273 327272 / 326341

Fenwick, J C (AMEC Group Ltd)
London EC1 p103 . . . . . . 020 7089 7350

Fenwick, P (Dickinson Dees) Q
Newcastle upon Tyne p324 . 0191 279 9000

Fenwick, Mrs S (South Lakeland District Council)
Kendal p462. . . . . 01539 733333

Ferdinand, Mrs S C I (Ferdinand Kelly) O Q Zh Zk
Sutton Coldfield p403 . . . . 01827 893526

Fereday, Mrs R M (Awdry Bailey & Douglas)
Devizes p210 . . . . 01380 722311

Ferera, L (Jones Day) C2
London EC4 p46. . . . . . . 020 7039 5959

Ferguson, Miss A (Welsh Health Legal Services) M1 P G
Cardiff p453 . . . . 029 2031 5500

Ferguson, Mrs A B (Knowsley Metropolitan Borough Council)
Huyton p461. . . . . 0151 443 3593

Ferguson, A C (Swindon Borough Council)
Swindon p473 . . . . 01793 463000

Ferguson, Miss A J (Rio Tinto PLC)
London W2 p109 . . . . . . 020 7781 2000

Ferguson, A N E (Environment Agency (Southern)) L
Worthing p477. . . . . 01903 820692

Ferguson, B (Cadge & Gilbert) C1 F1 B1 J1 E L Q N S1 W Ze Zl Zk Zw
Loddon p292. . . . .01508 520361 / 520362

Ferguson, Miss C M (Taylor Wessing) N P
London EC4 p86. . . . . . . 020 7300 7000

Ferguson, D S (Dickinson Dees) E
Newcastle upon Tyne p324 . 0191 279 9000

Ferguson, E (Slade Legal) E S1 L C1 W
Didcot p210 . . . . 01235 511211

Ferguson, G (Ashurst LLP)
London EC2 p7 . . . . 020 7638 1111

Ferguson, H (Norfolk County Council - Legal Services)
Norwich p467 . . . Minicom: 0844 800 8011

Ferguson, H D (Gordons) E S2
Guildford p236. . . . . 01483 451900
London WC1 p36 . . . . . . 020 7421 9421

Ferguson, I J A (Allen & Overy LLP)
London E1 p5 . . . . 020 3088 0000

Ferguson, J A (Grylls & Paige) S1 S2 W K4
Redruth p363 . . . .01209 215261 / 215357

Ferguson, J A (Napthens LLP) E
Preston p357 . . . . 01772 888444

Ferguson, J C C (Ferguson Solicitors) A3 B1 C1 F1 J1 L N O Q Zb Zc Zj Zk Zq Ze
London EC4 p31. . . . . . . 020 7822 2999

See p634 for the Key to Work Categories

Ferguson, Mrs J E (Brookes & Co)
Chichester *p192* 01243 780333

Ferguson, J J (Chanter Ferguson) *K1 Q N D1 F1 J1 G L O A1 Ze Zi Zk Zs Zt*
Barnstaple *p125* 01271 342268
Bideford *p132* 01237 478751

Ferguson, J M (Taylor Wessing)
London EC4 *p86* 020 7300 7000

Ferguson, Miss J M (Joan Ferguson & Co) *K1 K2 K3 D1 D2*
Manchester *p304* 0161 795 5866

Ferguson, Miss J R G (BHP Law) *N*
Newcastle upon Tyne *p323* . 0191 221 0898

Ferguson, Miss K (Jefferies LLP)
Altrincham *p116* 0800 342 3191

Ferguson, Mrs M (Bournemouth Borough Council)
Bournemouth *p450* 01202 451178

Ferguson, M A (Seymours) *T2 W*
Coventry *p201* 024 7655 3961

Ferguson, N (Jones Day) *C1*
London EC4 *p46* 020 7039 5959

Ferguson, P E C (Kellogg Brown & Root (UK) Ltd)
Leatherhead *p462* 01372 865000

Ferguson, Ms R (Davenport Lyons)
London W1 *p25* 020 7468 2600

Ferguson, Mrs S (Widdows Mason) *K1 D1*
Leigh *p282* 01942 673311

Ferguson, Miss S J (Cripps Harries Hall LLP) *E L*
Tunbridge Wells *p415* 01892 515121

Ferguson, S P (Humfrys & Symonds)
Hereford *p248* . . . .01432 359261 / 276276

Ferguson, Ms V (Ashfords LLP) *C1 C3*
Exeter *p220* 01392 337000

Ferguson, Ms V (Jones Day) *B1*
London EC4 *p46* 020 7039 5959

Fergusson, E (Herbert Smith LLP) *Zb*
London EC2 *p40* 020 7374 8000

Fergusson, J R (hlw Keeble Hawson LLP)
Sheffield *p375* 0114 272 2061

Fergusson, Ms L C (Linklaters LLP)
London EC2 *p54* 020 7456 2000

Fergusson, M (Stephensons Solicitors LLP) *G H*
Wigan *p432* 01942 777777

Ferin, G (EMW) *R1*
Milton Keynes *p316* 0845 070 6000

Fermor, A P L (Cripps Harries Hall LLP) *C1 E A1 L A2*
Tunbridge Wells *p415* 01892 515121

Fernandes, Ms A (Financial Services Authority)
London E14 *p106* 020 7066 1000

Fernandes, A P (Rochman Landau LLP) *C2 B1 F1 J1 O U2 Zb Ze Zj Zd Zf*
London W1 *p72* 020 7544 2424

Fernandes, Miss A R (Irwin Mitchell LLP) *K1*
Birmingham *p139* 0870 150 0100

Fernandes, F J (Northampton Borough Council)
Northampton *p467* 01604 837837

Fernandes, J C (The Hillman Partnership) *S1 G H K1 F1 N J1 W*
Swindon *p406* 01793 642100

Fernandes, L (Ince & Co Services Ltd)
London E1 *p44* 020 7481 0010

Fernandes, S A (Fraser Brown) *J1*
Bingham *p133* 01949 830812

Fernandez Lewis, J S (MLM Cartwright) *C1 C2*
Cardiff *p179* 029 2046 2562

Fernandez Moreno, Ms J (Stewarts Law LLP) *K3 K1*
London EC4 *p83* 020 7822 8000

Fernandez, Ms C A R (Wiseman Lee LLP) *S1 S2 E*
Redbridge *p92* 020 8215 1000

Fernandez, G G (Ashurst LLP) *Zb*
London EC2 *p7* 020 7638 1111

Fernandez, I (IBB Solicitors)
Uxbridge *p417* 0845 638 1381

Fernando, C (McKenzies) *G H*
London N9 *p57* 020 8350 4114

Fernando, H S (Fernando & Co) *D1 E F1 G H J1 K1 L N P Zi*
Wandsworth *p31* 020 8767 4611

Fernando, Mrs I (Indira Fernando) *E K1 L Q W Zi*
Southall *p384* 020 8575 6544

Ferneyhough, Mrs G Y (Pickworths) *E C1 S1*
Hemel Hempstead *p247* . . . 01442 261731

Fernie, A W (Freeclaim Solicitors)
Manchester *p304* 0161 437 9999

Fernie, J W D (Aker Kvaerner Engineering Services Ltd)
Stockton-on-Tees *p472* . . . 01642 334142

Ferns, S (Jacobs Solicitors) *N*
Ellesmere Port *p217* 0151 355 8481

Ferns, T (Rosenblatt)
London EC4 *p73* 020 7955 0880
London EC4 *p86* 020 7300 7000

Ferraby, D J (DF Legal LLP) *E K4 J1 T2 W S1 R1 P M1 L K1 H G F1*
Tewkesbury *p410* 01684 850750

Ferrara, Ms S (Cancer Research UK)
London WC2 *p104* 020 7242 0200

Ferrari, Mrs R A (Powells) *A2 D1 K1 D2 Zg Zk*
Weston-super-Mare *p429* . . 01934 623501

Ferraro, G A (Lupton Fawcett) *N*
Leeds *p275* 0113 280 2000

Ferreira, H (Longmores) *E S1 L*
Hertford *p248* 01992 300333

Ferreira, Ms R F (Epping Forest District Council)
Epping *p458* 01992 564000

Ferrera, P (Jones Day) *C1*
London EC4 *p46* 020 7039 5959

Ferris, B J P J (Brian Ferris) *G H*
Tunbridge Wells *p415* 01892 518609

Ferris, D J (Osborne Clarke) *C1*
Bristol *p164* 0117 917 3000

Ferris, Mrs K L (Wallace Robinson & Morgan) *K1 S1 K3*
Solihull *p383* 0121 705 7571

Ferris, L (Jones Robertson) *G H*
Runcorn *p369* 01928 711119

Ferris, R (Roger James Clements & Partners) *N O K1 S1 K3 W E S2 Zi*
Newport *p329* . . . .01633 263316 / 663316

Ferro, Ms A L H (Blaser Mills) *K1 D1*
High Wycombe *p249* 01494 450171

Ferry, Ms M A (Trafford Metropolitan Borough Council)
Stretford *p473* 0161 912 1212

Ferson, Mrs A E E (Thomson Wilson Pattinson) *D1 K3 J1 K1*
Kendal *p264* 01539 721945

Fetherston-Dilke, E (Farrer & Co LLP)
London WC2 *p31* 020 3375 7000

Fetherstone, M J (Napthens LLP) *E*
Preston *p357* 01772 888444

Few, Miss C (Field Seymour Parkes) *C1 Zza*
Reading *p360* 0118 951 6200

Few, D J (Blandy & Blandy) *B1 C1 C2 E F1 J1 T1 X Zb*
Reading *p360* 0118 951 6800

Few, J E (Eaton & Few) *E S2 S1 W*
St Ives *p391* 01480 301558

Fewkes, Mrs C S (Visa Europe)
London W2 *p110* 020 7937 8111

Fiaca, S (B D Laddie) *E L S1 Q O R2 S2*
Westminster *p51* 020 7963 8585

Fiaccavento, MS S (Simmons & Simmons)
London EC2 *p79* 020 7628 2020

Fiamma, S (Allen & Overy LLP)
London E1 *p5* 020 3088 0000

Fiander, Mrs C (Venters Solicitors) *K1 D1 K3 D2*
Reigate *p363* 01737 229610

Ficht, B (Trowers & Hamlins)
London EC3 *p88* 020 7423 8000

Fickling, Mrs R P (Davies Blunden & Evans) *N Q Zi*
Farnborough *p224* 01252 541633

Fiddes, Mrs J (BHP Law) *K1*
Newcastle upon Tyne *p323* . 0191 221 0898

Fiddy, M J (DLA Piper UK LLP)
London EC2 *p24* 0870 011 1111

Fidler, A J (Mullis & Peake) *E L S1 W R2*
Romford *p366* 01708 784000

Fidler, A P (Stephen Fidler & Co) *P M1 K1 S1 W D1 Zl*
London EC1 *p31* 020 7353 8999

Fidler, M D (Stephen Fidler & Co)
London EC1 *p31* 020 7353 8999

Fidler, P J M (Stephenson Harwood) *B1 Zb*
London EC2 *p82* 020 7329 4422

Fidler, S M (Stephen Fidler & Co) *N P M1 K1 L D1 F1 J1 G H Ze Zm Zl*
London EC1 *p31* 020 7353 8999

Fiducia, A N (Bryan Cave) *C2 C1 Zf*
London EC2 *p19* 020 7207 1100

Field, A (Rosenblatt) *O*
London EC4 *p73* 020 7955 0880

Field, A J (A J Field & Co) *K1 N W S1 V Zl*
Sheerness *p375* 01795 580600
Sittingbourne *p380* 01795 436363

Field, C M (Macfarlanes) *E*
London EC4 *p56* 020 7831 9222

Field, C R (Rollits LLP) *C1 S1 B1 E K1 T1 Zb D1 A1 N C2 Zl Zv Zw*
Hull *p258* 01482 323239

Field, Ms E (Stephenson Harwood) *C1 C2*
London EC2 *p82* 020 7329 4422

Field, G H (Graham Withers & Co) *W L S1 C1*
Shrewsbury *p380* 01743 236345

Field, G J (Longmores) *W T1 Zd K4 T2*
Hertford *p248* 01992 300333

Field, G S (Blocks) *A1 W S1 E*
Ipswich *p262* 01473 230033

Field, Ms H (Hanne & Co) *K1 K2 K3*
London SW11 *p38* 020 7228 0017
Kingston upon Thames *p267*. 020 8546 6111

Field, H S (John Barkers) *K1 D1 D2 J1*
Grimsby *p234* 01472 358686

Field, I T (Allen & Overy LLP)
London E1 *p5* 020 3088 0000

Field, J D (Calderdale Metropolitan BC Corporate Services Directorate)
Halifax *p460* 01422 357257
Huddersfield *p461* 01484 221421

Field, J G (Thursfields) *S1 S2 L*
Kidderminster *p266* 01562 820575

Field, J P (Carter Bells LLP) *O N L*
Kingston upon Thames *p267*. 020 8939 4000

Field, L (Barlow Lyde & Gilbert LLP) *Q N*
Manchester *p301* 0161 829 6400

Field, M A (Just Law Ltd)
Chelmsford *p454* 01245 396444

Field, M C (Freemans Solicitors) *G H B2*
London W1 *p34* 020 7935 3522

Field, M J W (Stone Milward Rapers) *W*
Chichester *p193* 01243 602832

Field, Miss R (Russell & Russell) *S1*
Bolton *p149* 01204 399299

Field, R A (Truman-Moore) *C1 E F1 G J1 K1 L N S1 T1 W*
Verwood *p418* 01202 824677

Field, R D (Buss Murton LLP) *W Zd*
Tunbridge Wells *p415* 01892 510222

Field, S (Mills & Reeve) *Zq*
Norwich *p335* 01603 660155

Field, Miss S A (Bristows) *I M1 O Ze Zf*
London EC4 *p15* 020 7400 8000

Field, T (Simmons & Simmons)
London EC2 *p79* 020 7628 2020

Field, T F (DLA Piper UK LLP) *E*
Leeds *p272* 0870 011 1111

Field, Miss V L (West Sussex County Council)
Chichester *p455* 01243 777100

Fielden, Mrs A J (Alison Fielden & Co) *S1 S2 W*
Cirencester *p195* 01285 653261

Fielden, R C (Jackson Parton) *Za O A3 Zj Q*
London EC3 *p45* 020 7702 0085

Fielder, A (Banner Jones) *N*
Sheffield *p375* 0114 275 5266

Fielder, Ms K (B P Collins LLP) *J1 N O F1 B1 Q Zb Zi*
Gerrards Cross *p229* 01753 889995

Fielder, S (Osborne Clarke) *F2 C2 R2 I*
London EC2 *p65* 020 7105 7000

Fieldhouse, D M (Guy Williams Layton) *B1 E F1 J1 K1 L N O Q Zt*
Liverpool *p288* 0151 236 7171

Fieldhouse, J (McClure Naismith) *E*
London EC4 *p56* 020 7623 9155

Fieldhouse, Miss M (Winston Solicitors LLP) *N*
Leeds *p278* 0113 320 5000

Fieldhouse, N J C (Stevens & Bolton) *I Ze G C2*
Guildford *p237* 01483 302264

Fielding, A L (Stewarts Law LLP) *Zr*
London EC4 *p83* 020 7822 8000

Fielding, Ms C (Herbert Smith LLP)
London EC2 *p40* 020 7374 8000

Fielding, J K (Pearson Fielding Polson) *G H*
Liverpool *p290* 0151 236 3636

Fielding, Miss K A (McGrigors LLP) *E S1*
London EC4 *p56* 020 7054 2500

Fielding, M W (Roythornes LLP) *B1 A2 A3 Zr F1 F2 G Zy J2 O Q N Zq A1 P*
Nottingham *p338* 0115 948 4555

Fielding, N (Harrowells)
York *p444* 01904 690111

Fielding, R G S (QualitySolicitors D'Angibau) *Q W T2*
Poole *p353* 01202 708634

Fielding, R M (Bhailok Fielding) *S1 M1 E L B1 F1 P*
Preston *p356* 01772 202191

Fielding, R T (Streeter Marshall) *O Q L B1 N Zb Zc Ze*
Croydon *p205* 020 8680 2638

Fielding, S (Gosschalks) *E R2 S2*
Hull *p256* 01482 324252

Fielding, T (Barker Booth & Eastwood) *J1 Q L*
Blackpool *p146* 01253 362500

Fields, A (Hewitsons) *Ze*
Cambridge *p174* 01223 461155

Fieldsend, J (Bolsover District Council)
Chesterfield *p455* 01246 240000

Fife, J K (Field Fisher Waterhouse LLP)
London EC3 *p31* 020 7861 4000

Fifer, J I (Everett Tomlin Lloyd & Pratt)
Pontypool *p352* 01495 763333

Fifield, D G (Hallett & Co) *S1 S2 W*
Ashford *p119* 01233 625711

Fifield, G N (SNR Denton) *J1*
London EC4 *p75* 020 7242 1212

Figgins, Ms A (Mayo Wynne Baxter LLP) *K1 N*
Seaford *p373* 01323 891412

Figon, H (Hempsons) *E S1 L W Q*
Harrogate *p240* 01423 522331

Figueiredo, A X D R (Figueiredo & Bowman) *A3 C1 E G K1 M1 S1 S2 W Zi*
Hackney *p32* 020 7739 5599

Figueiredo, Miss I M L (Goughs) *S1*
Calne *p173* 01249 812086

Filar, N B (Kenneth Elliott & Rowe) *N Zq J2*
Romford *p366* 01708 757575

Filby, Miss L (Linda Filby Solicitor) *G H K1 L S1 N D1 E F1 Q Zi Zk Zl Zp*
Seaford *p373* 01273 695321

Fildes, Ms S (The Owen-Kenny Partnership)
Chichester *p193* 01243 532777

Filippini, Miss E (Cohen Filippini)
Altrincham *p116* 0161 929 9993

Filkin, M (Ashurst LLP)
London EC2 *p7* 020 7638 1111

Fillery, Ms N (Blake Lapthorn) *C1*
Oxford *p342* 01865 248607

Filleul, Mrs J S (Peter J Fowler)
Wimborne *p433* 01202 849242

Fillmore, T M (Alsters Kelley) *E C1 W J1 S1 Ze*
Leamington Spa *p270* 0844 561 0100

Filton, Ms S (Miller Gardner)
Manchester *p307* 0161 877 4777

Finbow, Ms N (Temperley Taylor LLP) *K4 W*
Middleton *p315* 0161 643 2411

Finbow, R J (Ashurst LLP) *C1 C3 Zw*
London EC2 *p7* 020 7638 1111

Finch, J R (Hertz Europe Ltd)
Hounslow *p461* 01895 553500

Finch, K (Veale Wasbrough Vizards) *E*
Bristol *p165* 0117 925 2020

Finch, P A (Dickinson Dees) *R1 P*
Newcastle upon Tyne *p324* . 0191 279 9000

Finch, Miss S A (Platt & Fishwick) *K1 S1 V L N Q*
Wigan *p432* 01942 243281

Finch, S J (Salans) *B1 C1 E S1 N P J1 L Zb Zj Zo*
London EC4 *p76* 020 7429 6000

Fincham, A L R (CMS Cameron McKenna LLP) *O J1 Zp*
London EC3 *p17* 020 7367 3000

Fincham, Ms N A (TLT Solicitors) *C1 B1 T1 Zb*
London EC2 *p85* 020 3465 4000

Findlay, A (Hayes & Storr)
Fakenham *p223* 01328 863231

Findlay, A G (Chapmans Solicitors) *Q N O D1 L*
Sutton *p402* 020 8337 3801

Findlay, C (Harold G Walker) *K3 K1 D1 D2*
Bournemouth *p152* 01202 203200

Findlay, Mrs D H (Hansells) *K3 K1*
Norwich *p334* 01603 615731

Findlay, D M (Taylor Wessing) *C1 O Zb*
London EC4 *p86* 020 7300 7000

Findlay, Miss E A (Denby & Co) *K3 D1 D2 G H K1 K2*
Barrow-in-Furness *p125* . . . 01229 822366

Findlay, F A (Basingstoke & Deane Borough Council)
Basingstoke *p448* 01256 845402

Findlay, Mrs L (Wansbeck District Council)
Ashington *p447* 01670 532292

Findlay, Miss M (Woodfines LLP) *S1 S2 E*
Bedford *p130* 01234 270600

Findlay, Mrs V A (Woodfines LLP) *Zd C1 C3 I F1 F2 Ze Zp Zza U2 C2 Zo*
Bedford *p130* 01234 270600

Findley, C D (Bircham Dyson Bell) *A1 T1 E C1 W R1 S1 Zc Zd Zn*
Westminster *p13* 020 7227 7000
Oxford *p344* 01865 262600

Findlow, N M (Mark Findlow & Co) *S1 S2 E W L K4 Q*
Macclesfield *p297* 01625 617306

Fine, M (Freedman Green Dhokia) *J1 Zp*
Camden *p34* 020 7625 6003

Finegold, J (Howard Schneider Spiro Steele) *E L R1 S1 S2*
Barnet *p124* 020 8216 2020

Finizio, S P (WilmerHale) *A3*
London EC2 *p92* 020 7645 2400

Fink, R J (Pinsent Masons LLP) *C2 G Zb Zj*
London EC2 *p67* 020 7418 7000

Finlan, P (Faegre & Benson LLP) *C2 C1*
London EC4 *p30* 020 7450 4500

Finlay, A S (Nottinghamshire County Council Legal Services Division) *K1 N Q L D1 J1 F1 G*
West Bridgford *p475* 0115 977 3478

Finlay, C V (Harvey Ingram LLP) *O J1 B1 M1 F1 Q Zc Ze Zj Zp*
Leicester *p280* 0116 254 5454

Finlay, Miss D M (Max Engel & Co LLP) *J1 O Q W E*
Northampton *p331* 01604 887450

Finlayson, Ms L (Taylor Wessing)
London EC4 *p86* 020 7300 7000

Finlayson, Ms L (Hallett & Co) *K1*
Ashford *p119* 01233 625711

Finlayson, R G (Lamb Brooks LLP) *O N J1*
Basingstoke *p126* 01256 844888

Finlayson-Brown, Ms E J E P (Allen & Overy LLP)
London E1 *p5* 020 3088 0000

Finlayson-Brown, N M (Mills & Reeve) *S2 E R2 S1*
Cambridge *p175* 01223 364422

Finn, Mrs A (Gullands) *J1*
Maidstone *p299* 01622 678341

Finn, A (Freers) *D1 G K1 H P F1 J1 I L R1 Zm*
Middlesbrough *p315* 01642 244666

Finn, Mrs J (Lupton Fawcett) *E*
Leeds *p275* 0113 280 2000

Finn, M (EMW) *Ze*
Milton Keynes *p316* 0845 070 6000

Finn, M A (Osborne Clarke) *O*
London EC2 *p65* 020 7105 7000

Finn, P H (Paul Finn Solicitors) *A1 T1 S1 C1 W R1 K1 L Zl Zq Zr Zs D1 O X*
Bude *p168* 01288 356256

Finn, Miss R (Wake Smith & Tofields) *K1 K3*
Sheffield *p377* 0114 266 6660

Finnegan, A J (Osborne Clarke) *U1 U2 C1*
London EC2 *p65* 020 7105 7000
Reading *p361* 0118 925 2000

Finnegan, M G (McGrigors LLP) *C1 C2*
London EC4 *p56* 020 7054 2500

Finneran, K A P (Michelmores LLP) *N Zr*
Exeter *p221* 01392 688688

Finnerty, Miss N (Corker Binning Solicitors) *Q G B2*
London WC2 *p22* 020 7353 6000

Finney, C (Browne Jacobson LLP) *Zq Zj O B2 P*
Nottingham *p336* 0115 976 6000

Finney, R (SNR Denton) *Zb*
London EC4 *p75* 020 7242 1212

Finnigan, K P (Barlow Lyde & Gilbert LLP) *N Q*
Manchester *p301* 0161 829 6400

Finnis, J (Hartnells)
London SE5 *p39* 020 7703 9222

Finnis, Ms S F (Girlings) *K1 D1 V K3*
Canterbury *p177* 01227 768374

Fiore, Miss D (Isle of Wight Council)
Newport *p466* 01983 823207

Fiore, Miss D J (London Borough of Haringey)
London N22 *p106* 020 8489 0000

Firbank, Miss C (Harrogate Borough Council)
Harrogate *p460* 01423 500600

Firby, Miss S (Cripps Harries Hall LLP) *E A1*
Tunbridge Wells *p415* 01892 515121

Firdose, T (Keppe & Partners Solicitors) *O Q Zq A3 F1 F2 L M4 Zk W*
Twickenham *p416* 020 8891 4488

Fireman, D (CKFT) *S2 C1 R2*
London NW3 *p17* 020 7431 7262

For a range of specialised Legal Services please refer to Section 20

Fireson, Ms M (Smith Law Partnership) *W*
Braintree *p155* 01376 321311

Firman, A J L (Carter Lemon Camerons) *J1 C1 C2 Zb Zp Zd*
London EC1 *p18* 020 7406 1000

Firmin, Ms R (Nelsons)
Nottingham *p338* 0115 958 6262

Firn, Ms E (Jones Day) *Zb*
London EC4 *p46* 020 7039 5959

Firoz, Mrs A Y (Moxon & Barker) *S1 W*
Pontefract *p351* 01977 602999

Firth, A (Foys Solicitors) *D1 D2 F2 J1 K1 N O Zp Zq Zr*
Rotherham *p367* 01709 375561

Firth, A D (A D Firth & Co)
Macclesfield *p297* 01625 261840

Firth, Ms A J (Kirby Sheppard) *W*
Bristol *p163* 0845 840 0045

Firth, Mrs A L (Franklins) *S1*
Abingdon *p114* 01235 553222

Firth, A S (PricewaterhouseCoopers Legal LLP)
London SE1 *p69* 020 7212 1616

Firth, Mrs B J (Mills & Reeve) *R1 E Zs*
Cambridge *p175* 01223 364422

Firth, D I (Raleys) *N*
Barnsley *p125* 01226 211111

Firth, D M A (Capsticks Solicitors LLP) *L O P Q R1*
London SW19 *p18* 020 8780 2211

Firth, I G (Ian Rose & Firth)
Whitley Bay *p431* 0191 252 0113

Firth, Mrs J E (Squire Sanders (UK) LLP)
Manchester *p310* 0161 830 5000

Firth, P G (AWG PLC)
Huntingdon *p461* 01480 323140

Firth, P N (DLA Piper UK LLP) *E R2 Zn*
Sheffield *p375* 0870 011 1111

Firth, R F (Firth Lindsay) *S1 E W R1 T2 A1 B1 G L C2 Zc S2*
Sheffield *p375* 0114 276 0586

Firth, S N (Linklaters LLP)
London EC2 *p54* 020 7456 2000

Fisch, N I (Olswang LLP) *E S2*
London WC1 *p64* 020 7067 3000

Fischer, D (Pinsent Masons LLP)
London EC2 *p67* 020 7418 7000

Fischer, Mrs R B (Fischer & Co) *S1 W L E*
Barnet *p32* . . . .020 8346 7036 / 8922 0689

Fischl, N J (Mills & Reeve) *C1 B1*
Norwich *p335* 01603 660155

Fish, Mrs C (Cartmell Shepherd) *N*
Carlisle *p182* 01228 516666

Fish, D G (Fish & Co) *K1 D1 Zm*
Wolverhampton *p438* 01902 826464

Fish, D R (Norwich Union Insurance Group)
Norwich *p467* 01603 622200
York *p477* 01904 452210

Fish, D R L (Aviva PLC)
London EC3 *p103* . . 020 7283 7500 / 01603 687905

Fish, Mrs E (Armitage Sykes LLP) *K1*
Brighouse *p158* 01484 714431

Fish, J (J A Kemp & Co)
London WC1 *p48* 020 7405 3292

Fish, J L (Forresters) *K1 D1 D2*
Barrow-in-Furness *p125* . . . 01229 820297

Fisher, A (Fisher Scoggins Waters LLP) *Q Zj*
London EC4 *p32* 020 7489 2035

Fisher, Mrs A (Rotherham Metropolitan Borough Council) *J1 Q K1 F1 N O Ze Zp*
Rotherham *p470* 01709 382121

Fisher, A (Ashley Fisher & Co) *K1 M1 P F1 D1 G L S1 W C1*
Blackpool *p146* 01253 751585

Fisher, Mrs A E (Hatchers Solicitors LLP) *C1 C2 U2 Ze*
Shrewsbury *p379* 01743 248545

Fisher, A G (Fisher Jones Greenwood LLP) *N O E C1 D1*
Colchester *p197* 01206 578282

Fisher, B W (Bank of Scotland Legal Operations)
London EC2 *p104* 0870 600 5000

Fisher, Miss C (Cambridgeshire County Council)
Cambridge *p453* 01223 717111

Fisher, C A (Lees Solicitors LLP) *N*
Birkenhead *p134* 0151 647 9381

Fisher, Ms C R (Barlow Robbins LLP) *O Q L N F1*
Guildford *p235* 01483 562901

Fisher, D (Osborne Clarke) *O J1 P*
London EC2 *p65* 020 7105 7000

Fisher, Mrs D (Willcox Lewis LLP) *W T2 Zd*
Norwich *p335* 01508 480100

Fisher, D J (Dickinson Dees) *E*
Newcastle upon Tyne *p324* . 0191 279 9000

Fisher, D J W (D Fisher & Co) *B1 C1 E L S1 W*
Borough Green *p150* 01732 884299

Fisher, Miss E (Clerk to Sheffield Justices)
Sheffield *p470* 0114 276 0760

Fisher, Miss H D (Frearsons) *K1 D1 D2 N*
Skegness *p380* 01754 897600

Fisher, I A (Husband Forwood Morgan) *W S1 D1 L E C1 K1 Zd*
Liverpool *p289* 0151 236 9626

Fisher, I M (Lancashire County Council)
Preston *p469* 01772 254868

Fisher, I M (Charles Russell LLP) *S2 E*
London EC4 *p19* 020 7203 5000
Guildford *p236* 01483 511555

Fisher, J (Philip Ross & Co)
London W1 *p73* 020 7636 6969

Fisher, Mrs J (Plexus Law (A Trading Name of Parabis Law LLP)) *N Zj O*
Evesham *p220* 01386 769160

Fisher, Mrs J (Guildford Borough Council)
Guildford *p459* 01483 505050

Fisher, J H (Thomas Horton LLP) *A1 S1 L W*
Bromsgrove *p167* 01527 871641

Fisher, J J (Alexiou Fisher Philipps) *K1 D1 K3*
London W1 *p5* 020 7409 1222

Fisher, Mrs J K (English Heritage)
London EC1 *p106* 020 7973 3360

Fisher, J R (Brookes & Co) *D1 H G K1*
Chichester *p192* 01243 780333

Fisher, J T (Bennett Oakley & Partners) *K1 F1 L M1 P S1 W Zl Zg Ze*
Burgess Hill *p168* 01444 235232

Fisher, J W (British Telecommunications PLC)
London EC1 *p104* 020 7356 6181

Fisher, Ms K L (Borough of Telford & Wrekin)
Telford *p473* 01952 380000

Fisher, Miss L (Fendom Dawson & Partners) *S2 K3 K4 Q Zl S1 W*
High Wycombe *p250* 01494 450361

Fisher, Mrs M (Wallace Robinson & Morgan) *C1 S2 E Zl C2 R2*
Solihull *p383* 0121 705 7571

Fisher, Miss M C (Forshaws Davies Ridgway LLP) *S1*
Warrington *p422* 01925 230000

Fisher, M E (St Helens Borough Council)
St Helens *p472* 01744 456000

Fisher, M L (Graysons) *A2 F2 P M1 Zy J2 L Zj Q N Zm Zw*
Sheffield *p375* 0114 272 9184

Fisher, N (John Pickering & Partners LLP) *N*
Manchester *p308* 0808 144 0957

Fisher, N H (Simmons & Simmons)
London EC2 *p79* 020 7628 2020

Fisher, N J (LG Lawyers) *E S2*
London SE1 *p50* 020 7379 0000

Fisher, Miss N M (Forsters LLP)
Westminster *p33* 020 7863 8333

Fisher, P H (Beecham Fisher Ridley) *D1 K1 Zd X K3*
Southend-on-Sea *p387* . . . 01702 348384

Fisher, Mrs R (Morrisons Solicitors LLP) *W*
London SW19 *p62* 020 8971 1020

Fisher, R (Fishburns) *Zj O Q Zq Zo A3 Zc*
London EC3 *p32* 020 7280 8888

Fisher, R A (Heringtons) *K1 Q B1 F1 L*
Rye *p370* 01797 222955

Fisher, R J H (Charles Crookes Limited) *E S2 S1 W*
Cardiff *p178* 029 2049 1271

Fisher, S (Cyril Jones & Co)
Wrexham *p443* 01978 367830

Fisher, Miss S E (Stitt & Co) *S2 E S1*
London EC4 *p83* 020 7832 0840

Fisher, S J (Davies Blunden & Evans) *K1 K3 Q Zw J1*
Farnborough *p224* 01252 541633

Fisher, S J (Luttons Dunford) *A1 C1 E R1 T1 Ze Zk*
Gloucester *p230* 01452 529751

Fisher, Miss S L (Diageo PLC)
London W1 *p105* 020 7927 5300

Fisher, Ms S L (Barlow Lyde & Gilbert LLP)
London EC3 *p10* 020 7247 2277

Fisher, S P (Maidstone Borough Council)
Maidstone *p464* 01622 602000

Fisher, Ms T (DLA Piper UK LLP)
London EC2 *p24* 0870 011 1111
London EC2 *p81* 020 7655 1000

Fisher, T B (Lees Solicitors LLP) *K1 K3*
West Kirby *p428* 0151 625 9364

Fisher, W D (United Utilities)
Warrington *p475* 01925 237000

Fisher, W H (Andrew Jackson) *E L R1 Zc*
Hull *p257* 01482 325242

Fisher, Miss Y L (Spearing Waite LLP) *O Q*
Leicester *p281* 0116 262 4225

Fisher Crouch, S R (Beviss & Beckingsale) *O Q N Zq*
Honiton *p252* 01404 548050

Fishley, B (Field Fisher Waterhouse LLP)
London EC3 *p31* 020 7861 4000

Fishman, A D (Philip Ross & Co) *E C1 S1 L R1*
London W1 *p73* 020 7636 6969

Fishman, I M D (Fishman & Co Solicitors) *S2 R2 E S1 Q N O L W C1 Zl C2*
London W1 *p32* 020 7935 3500

Fishman, Ms J C (PCB Lawyers LLP) *E S2 L R2*
London W1 *p65* 020 7486 2566

Fishman, Miss K E (Performing Right Society Ltd) *B1 Ze*
London W1 *p108* 020 7580 5544

Fishwick, I (Pearson & Pearson) *S1 W S2 L*
Kirkby Lonsdale *p268* 01524 271222

Fisk, Ms M (Ashurst LLP)
London EC2 *p7* 020 7638 1111

Fissenden, Ms J (Ashurst LLP)
London EC2 *p7* 020 7638 1111

Fitch, Mrs A D (Rix & Kay Solicitors LLP) *C1 S2 E S1*
Hove *p255* 01273 329797

Fitch, M N (Hatch Brenner) *Q O F1 L F2 N*
Norwich *p334* 01603 660811

Fitchett, Ms A J (Thompsons (formerly Robin/Brian Thompson & Partners)) *N*
Nottingham *p339* 0115 989 7200

Fitt, Ms C (Reuters Group PLC)
London E14 *p109* 020 7250 1122

Fitt, R (Bristows)
London EC4 *p15* 020 7400 8000

Fitton, C A (Pinsent Masons LLP)
Birmingham *p141* 0121 200 1050

Fitton, D R F (Winckworth Sherwood LLP) *R1 R2 S1 S2 Zh*
London SE1 *p92* 020 7593 5000

Fitton, H M (Howard Fitton) *S1 W K1 E Q N T2 C1 T1 L Zl Zm Zv Zq Zw*
Lymm *p296* 01925 757565

Fitzgeorge-Balfour, Ms C (Wansbroughs)
Devizes *p210* 01380 733300

Fitzgerald, Miss C A (Barrett & Thomson) *D1 D2 K1 V*
Slough *p381* 01753 437416

Fitzgerald, D (Wainwright & Cummins) *N*
Lambeth *p90* 020 7737 9330

FitzGerald, D C (Ellis Lakin & Co) *S1 J1 L W E K4 Zl*
Pickering *p348* 01751 472121

Fitzgerald, Miss E L (Tayntons LLP Solicitors) *N*
Gloucester *p230* 01452 522047

Fitzgerald, Ms F C (Colemans - CTTS) *A3 F1 F2 J2 N Q Zq Zr*
Kingston upon Thames *p267* 020 8296 9966

FitzGerald, Ms G A (Baileys) *K1 D1 V D2*
Cheltenham *p187* 01242 514477

Fitzgerald, H J B (Atkinson Ritson) *A1 W T1 S1 S2 T2*
Wigton *p432* 01697 343241

Fitzgerald, J (Ince & Co Services Ltd)
London E1 *p44* 020 7481 0010

Fitzgerald, Ms J A (Gregory Rowcliffe Milners) *K1 D1*
London WC1 *p37* 020 7242 0631

FitzGerald, J F (Simmons & Simmons)
London EC2 *p79* 020 7628 2020

Fitzgerald, Ms K M (Barlow Robbins LLP) *Zr N*
Woking *p436* 01483 748500

Fitzgerald, Mrs L E (Robson & Co) *W S1 K4 E*
Hythe *p259* . . . . .01303 264581 / 267413

Fitzgerald, Ms M C (Sylvester Mackett) *W*
Trowbridge *p414* 01225 755621

Fitzgerald, M E (Treasury Solicitors Department) *N P J1 C1 E M1 B1 R1 Ze Zk Zc*
London WC2 *p110* 020 7210 3000

Fitzgerald, Ms R (Bindmans LLP) *K3 K1*
London WC1 *p12* 020 7833 4433

Fitzgerald, R C (Pardoes) *O Q Zq Zc Ze Zf B1 Zj Zo*
Taunton *p408* 01823 446200

Fitzgerald, Ms S (Stephens & Scown) *K1*
St Austell *p391* 01726 74433

Fitzgerald, Ms S (TV Edwards LLP)
London EC3 *p85* 020 7790 7000

Fitzgerald, S C P (Stephenson Harwood) *L O Zq*
London EC2 *p82* 020 7329 4422

Fitzgerald-Hart, M E (Fitzgerald-Harts) *W A1 S1*
Boroughbridge *p150* 01423 322312

Fitzgibbon, J (Horsey Lightly) *K1 J1*
Westminster *p43* 020 7222 8844

Fitz-Gibbon, Miss S L (Whitehead Monckton) *S2 S1*
Maidstone *p299* 01622 698000

Fitzgraham, Mrs R (Lawson Lewis & Co) *Zi*
Eastbourne *p215* 01323 720142

Fitzherbert, I (Stitt & Co) *S1 E L R2*
London EC4 *p83* 020 7832 0840

Fitzmaurice, A (Brabners Chaffe Street) *S2 E R2 Zu*
Manchester *p301* 0161 836 8800

Fitzmaurice, Ms C (Bury Metropolitan Borough Council)
Bury *p452* 0161 253 7771

Fitzmaurice, Mrs C S (Terry Jones Solicitors & Advocates) *K1 K2*
Shrewsbury *p379* 01743 285888

Fitzmaurice, N F (Terry Jones Solicitors & Advocates) *N O Q Zq A3*
Newport *p329* 01952 810307

Fitzmaurice, P C (Borlase & Company) *S1 W L*
Helston *p246* 01326 574988

Fitzpatrick, A J (Rowley Dickinson) *N Zq*
Manchester *p309* 0161 834 4215

Fitzpatrick, A J (Andrew Fitzpatrick) *G H*
Manchester *p304* 0161 248 9799

Fitzpatrick, Miss A M (Pluck Andrew & Co) *G H*
Ashton-under-Lyne *p120* . . . 0161 330 2875

Fitzpatrick, D (Hodge Jones & Allen LLP) *L*
London NW1 *p41* 020 7874 8300

Fitzpatrick, Ms D (Simmons & Simmons)
London EC2 *p79* 020 7628 2020

Fitzpatrick, D (Taylor Wessing)
London EC4 *p86* 020 7300 7000

Fitzpatrick, Ms E (IBB Solicitors) *D1 K1 D2*
Uxbridge *p417* 0845 638 1381

Fitzpatrick, G (Keoghs LLP) *N Zj O Q*
Bolton *p149* 01204 677000

Fitzpatrick, I (Canter Levin & Berg) *N Q*
Liverpool *p287* 0151 239 1000

Fitzpatrick, J (Northern Rock PLC) *E L S2*
Gosforth *p459* 0191 285 7191

Fitzpatrick, J (Hempsons) *N G Zr*
Manchester *p305* 0161 228 0011

Fitzpatrick, Miss J C (Read Dunn Connell) *K1 K3*
Bradford *p154* 01274 723858

Fitzpatrick, K (Tickle Hall Cross) *E S1 W L Zl*
Prescot *p356* 0800 854379
St Helens *p391* 0800 854379

Fitzpatrick, Ms K M (Graysons) *D1 K1*
Sheffield *p375* 0114 272 9184

Fitzpatrick, M (TWM Solicitors LLP)
Guildford *p237* 01483 752700

Fitzpatrick, M B A (P M Hunter & Co) *S1 W E L T1 B1 A1 K1 V Q Zv Zd Zc Zj*
London SE24 *p44* 020 7737 7725

Fitzpatrick, M F (DFA Law LLP) *R1 S2 E C1 A1 Zi*
Northampton *p331* 01604 609560

Fitzpatrick, N (DLA Piper UK LLP) *Zf*
London EC2 *p24* 0870 011 1111

Fitzpatrick, P J (Taylor Walton LLP)
Luton *p295* 01582 731161

Fitzpatrick, Mrs P J (Gadsby Wicks) *N Zr*
Chelmsford *p186* 01245 494929

Fitzpatrick, S J (Boodle Hatfield) *Q O J1 Zi Zp*
Westminster *p14* 020 7629 7411

Fitzsimmons, A J E (Ince & Co Services Ltd) *B1 B2 C3 M1 M2 N Q U2 Za Zj*
London E1 *p44* 020 7481 0010

Fitzsimmons, Miss J M (George Green LLP) *J1*
Cradley Heath *p201* 01384 410410

Fitzsimmons, M (Brockbank Curwen Cain & Hall) *S2 E S1 C1*
Whitehaven *p431* 01946 692194

Fitzsimons, Miss H J (Edward Hayes LLP) *D2 D1 K1 K2 K3*
Chichester *p192* 01243 781431

Fitzsimons, Ms L (Osborne Clarke) *J1*
Bristol *p164* 0117 917 3000

Fitzsimons, S (Nabarro LLP) *E R2*
Sheffield *p376* 0114 279 4000

Fitzwalter, S A (Thompsons (formerly Robin/Brian Thompson & Partners))
Birmingham *p143* 0121 262 1200

Fitzwater, Ms J A (Crellins Carter Solicitors) *E S2 S1 W*
Weybridge *p429* 01932 858833
Weybridge *p429* 01932 858833

Flack, M (Comercrawley) *N*
Diss *p210* 01379 644311

Flack, W (Lawrence Law)
London SW15 *p52* 020 8788 0055

Flaga, Miss M (Haddock & Company) *G N*
Halifax *p238* 01422 366010

Flagg, A (Clarkson Wright & Jakes Ltd) *Q Zk Zq O*
Orpington *p341* 01689 887887

Flaherty, J D (Barlow Lyde & Gilbert LLP) *O Q Za Zj*
London EC3 *p10* 020 7247 2277

Flaherty, Ms K A (Teachers' Building Society)
Wimborne *p476* 01202 843503

Flaherty, P D P (Leigh Bailey Solicitors) *A1 E L S1 W*
Preston *p357* 01772 744719

Flahive, J (Marsh & McLennan Companies, Inc)
London EC3 *p108* 020 7357 1000

Flaig, Miss C A (ClarksLegal LLP) *J1*
Reading *p360* 0118 958 5321

Flanagan, Mrs A J (Barlow Robbins LLP) *E S2*
Woking *p436* 01483 748500

Flanagan, Ms C (Redditch Borough Council)
Redditch *p469* 01527 64252
Leamington Spa *p462* 01926 450000

Flanagan, F J (EBR Attridge LLP) *B2 G H I*
London SW11 *p28* 020 7228 7050

Flanagan, Mrs H A (Country Land and Business Association Ltd) *S1 L E*
London SW1 *p105* 020 7235 0511

Flanagan, Mrs J (Russell & Russell) *D1 K3 K1*
Bolton *p149* 01204 399299

Flanagan, J A P (Goffeys) *F1 S1 Q*
Southport *p388* 01704 531755

Flanagan, J P (Rollits LLP) *C2 C1*
Hull *p258* 01482 323239

Flanagan, Miss K H (British American Tobacco) *O M1 C3 Ze Zf*
London WC2 *p104* 020 7845 1000

Flanagan, P T (Allen & Overy LLP)
London E1 *p5* 020 3088 0000

Flanagan, T D (Pinsent Masons LLP) *J1 Zp*
London EC2 *p67* 020 7418 7000
London EC2 *p82* 020 7329 4422

Flannagan, D A M (Attwaters) *W K4 T2*
Loughton *p294* 020 8508 2111

Flannery, Miss M J (Environment Agency (North East Region)) *S1 W L G H K1 F1 D1 P V Zc Zk Zl*
Leeds *p462* 0870 850 6506

Flannery, S M (Ayres Waters) *K1 W*
Stockport *p395* 0161 480 5229

Flashman, Mrs C J (Barlow Robbins LLP) *Zr N*
Woking *p436* 01483 748500

Flatau, T S (Davenport Lyons) *S1*
London W1 *p25* 020 7468 2600

Flathers, J M (Irwin Mitchell LLP) *E L R1 R2 P*
Birmingham *p139* 0870 150 0100

Flatt, N (NFLA Ltd) *K1 D1 K3*
Nottingham *p338* 0115 945 4555

Flavell, G T (Thomas Flavell & Sons) *C1 E J1 S1 W T1 A1*
Hinckley *p250* 01455 610747

Flavell, K C (Harold Benjamin) *D1 G H K1 N S1 P W Zi Zp*
Harrow *p241* 020 8422 5678

Flavell, L D (PricewaterhouseCoopers Legal LLP)
London SE1 *p69* 020 7212 1616

Fleck, R J H (Herbert Smith LLP) *C1 C3 M1 B3*
London EC2 *p40* 020 7374 8000

Fleet, Miss R B R (Dibbens) *D1 K1 W*
Wimborne *p433* 01202 882456

Fleetwood, Ms B R (Morgan Cole)
Oxford *p344* 01865 262600
London EC2 *p67* 020 7418 7000

Fleetwood, M D (Heatons LLP) *C1 C2*
Manchester *p305* 0161 835 8010

Fleetwood, R G (Addleshaw Goddard)
Manchester *p300* 0161 934 6000

See p634 for the Key to Work Categories

Fleetwood, Ms V A (British American Tobacco UK Ltd)
Aylesbury *p447* . . . 01296 335000

Fleming, A (BTMK Solicitors LLP)
Southend-on-Sea *p387* . . . 01702 339222

Fleming, Miss A M (DAC Beachcroft) *N*
Manchester *p303* . . . 0161 839 8396

Fleming, A R (Blocks) *C1 E B1 Ze Zl J1 I*
Ipswich *p262* . . . 01473 230033

Fleming, D K (Woolf Simmonds) *S1 W L*
Westminster *p93* . . . 020 7262 1266

Fleming, D M (William Heath & Co) *B1 K3 L O Q R1 W*
London SW11 *p40* . . . 020 7350 1068

Fleming, D M (William Heath & Co) *N K1 L Q*
Westminster *p40* . . . 020 7402 3151

Fleming, Miss F (Rosling King) *Q O*
London EC4 *p73* . . . 020 7353 2353

Fleming, Miss F (Heaney Watson) *K1 K3 D1*
Manchester *p305* 0800 567 7597 / 0161 359 3347

Fleming, Ms H J (Forsters LLP) *O*
Westminster *p33* . . . 020 7863 8333

Fleming, Mrs J E (Linder Myers Solicitors) *K1*
Manchester *p306* . . . 0844 984 6000

Fleming, Mrs J H (Brethertons LLP)
Banbury *p122* . . . 01295 270999

Fleming, J M (J H Powell & Co) *O C1 J1 N S1 E M1 W P A1 Zl Zc Zn S2*
Derby *p209* . . . 01332 372211

Fleming, Ms N E (Simons Muirhead & Burton) *B2 G*
London W1 *p79* . . . 020 7734 4499

Fleming, Ms P (LG Lawyers)
London SE1 *p50* . . . 020 7379 0000

Fleming, P J (DLA Piper UK LLP) *B1 Zb*
London EC2 *p24* . . . 0870 011 1111

Fleming, R A (Alfred Newton & Co) *S1 W S2 B1 R1 A1 Zc*
Stockport *p396* . . 0161 480 6551 / 480 1245

Fleming, S M (City of Bradford Metropolitan District Council) *N Q L P B1 Zj Zk Zs Zw Zc*
Bradford *p451* . . . 01274 752236

Fleming, Mrs S P (Aylesbury Vale District Council)
Aylesbury *p447* . . . 01296 585858

Fleming, Mrs Z J (Senior Calveley & Hardy) *W*
Lytham *p297* . . . 01253 733333

Flemington, H M (BUPA)
London WC1 *p104* . . . 020 7656 2305

Flemming, G V (Irwin Mitchell LLP) *G H*
Sheffield *p376* . . . 0870 150 0100

Flemming, G V (Howells LLP) *G H*
Sheffield *p376* . . . 0114 249 6666

Fletcher, Mrs A (Newport City Council) *K1 D1*
Newport *p466* . . . 01633 656656
Newport *p329* . . . 01633 257844

Fletcher, A (Brabners Chaffe Street) *Zh E Zd*
Liverpool *p286* . . . 0151 600 3000

Fletcher, Ms A (Bury & Walkers LLP) *K4 S1 W*
Barnsley *p124* . . . 01226 733533

Fletcher, A E V (EMW) *J1*
Milton Keynes *p316* . . . 0845 070 6000

Fletcher, A H (Davey Franklin Jones) *S1 E L W A1 Zh S2*
Gloucester *p230* . . . 01452 508800

Fletcher, Mrs A L (British Telecommunications PLC)
London EC1 *p104* . . . 020 7356 6181

Fletcher, Miss C (Wannop Fox Staffurth & Bray) *S2 E S1 R2 R1 L C1 B1*
Worthing *p442* . . . 01903 228200

Fletcher, Mrs C (Williamson & Soden) *K1 D1 J1*
Solihull *p383* . . . 0121 733 8000

Fletcher, Miss C L (Gould & Swayne) *W*
Street *p400* . . . 01458 442433

Fletcher, D (Farrer & Co LLP)
London WC2 *p31* . . . 020 3375 7000

Fletcher, D M (Andersons)
Croydon *p204* . . . 020 8680 3131

Fletcher, Ms E (Family Law in Partnership LLP) *K1*
London WC2 *p30* . . . 020 7420 5000

Fletcher, E B (Fletchers) *N*
Southport *p388* . . . 01704 546919

Fletcher, I C M (Barker Gooch & Swailes) *S1 W E C1 L Zl*
Enfield *p218* . . . 020 8366 3161

Fletcher, I M (Stephenson Harwood) *B1 Zb*
London EC2 *p82* . . . 020 7329 4422

Fletcher, J (Ashurst LLP)
London EC2 *p7* . . . 020 7638 1111

Fletcher, Mrs J A (Harding Evans LLP) *K1 D1*
Newport *p328* . . . 01633 244233

Fletcher, J G (Fletcher & Co Solicitors)
Knutsford *p269* . . . 01565 755411

Fletcher, J H (Charles Russell LLP)
London EC4 *p19* . . . 020 7203 5000

Fletcher, J M (Fletchers) *S1 E C1 G H M1 W K1 L J1*
Winsford *p434* . . . 01606 556322 / 556324

Fletcher, K P W (Hewitsons) *C1 I C3 F1 M1 Ze Zf U2 C2 U1 F2 M2*
Northampton *p332* . . . 01604 233233

Fletcher, L (Fletchers) *J2 Q N*
Southport *p388* . . . 01704 546919

Fletcher, L (Bates Wells & Braithwaite London LLP) *Zd C1*
London EC4 *p11* . . . 020 7551 7777

Fletcher, M (Hills Solicitors Limited) *E B1 N S1 W*
Bolton *p149* . . . 01204 388300

Fletcher, M (Linklaters LLP)
London EC2 *p54* . . . 020 7456 2000

Fletcher, Mrs M C (Flintshire County Council)
Mold *p466* . . . 01352 702411

Fletcher, M J G (Lee Bolton Monier-Williams) *L S1 W E A1 Zd*
Westminster *p52* . . . 020 7222 5381

Fletcher, M W (Taylor Wessing) *B1 C1 I Zj Zb*
London EC4 *p86* . . . 020 7300 7000

Fletcher, Miss N (Levison Meltzer Pigott) *K1*
London EC4 *p53* . . . 020 7556 2400

Fletcher, N J (Greathead & Whitelock) *K1 D1 J1 S1 M1*
Pembroke *p345* . . . 01646 682101

Fletcher, N M (Clifford Chance)
London E14 *p20* . . . 020 7006 1000

Fletcher, P C (Somerton & Fletcher) *W S1*
Cambridge *p175* . . . 01223 566596

Fletcher, R (Russell Jones & Walker)
London WC2 *p74* . . . 020 7657 1555

Fletcher, R A (Fletchers) *N O Q*
Southport *p388* . . . 01704 546919

Fletcher, R M (R M Fletcher & Co) *K1 G H M1 P S1*
Redcar *p362* . . . 01642 490400

Fletcher, S (Linklaters LLP)
London EC2 *p54* . . . 020 7456 2000

Fletcher, S (Brignalls Balderston Warren) *S1 E S2*
Stevenage *p394* . . . 01438 359311

Fletcher, S J (Rotherham Metropolitan Borough Council) *N Q O*
Rotherham *p470* . . . 01709 382121

Fletcher, S P (Davies & Partners) *E S2*
Gloucester *p230* . . . 01452 612345

Fletcher, Miss V (Horsey Lightly) *E*
Westminster *p43* . . . 020 7222 8844

Fletcher, W J (Banner Jones) *S1 K3 K1*
Chesterfield *p192* . . . 01246 861250

Fletcher, Mrs Y S (Higgs & Sons) *S1*
Kingswinford *p268* . . . 01384 342100

Fletcher-Wood, C (Burges Salmon) *O N Za Zj*
Bristol *p161* . . . 0117 939 2000

Flett, Ms A (ClarksLegal LLP) *J1*
Cardiff *p177* . . . 029 2055 7500

Flett, R J (Keith Levin & Co) *G H N Q V K1 L J1 F1*
Huyton *p258* . . . 0151 480 5777

Fleury, J (Clifford Chance)
London E14 *p20* . . . 020 7006 1000

Fleury, P A (P A Fleury & Co) *E W S1 L Q T2 A1 T1 J1 C1 Zd Ze Zi Zl*
London EC4 *p33* . . . 020 7329 3405

Flew, S R (Radcliffes Le Brasseur) *G H Zq*
Westminster *p70* . . . 020 7222 7040

Flewitt, J A (Peace Revitt) *K1 G D1 H D2 Q W*
Rotherham *p367* . . . 01709 898454

Flexman, M P F (Sutton-Mattocks & Co LLP) *W*
London SW13 *p84* . . . 020 8876 8811

Flinders, Mrs T J (HSR Law (Hayes, Son & Richmond)) *S1 W*
Doncaster *p211* . . . 01302 347800
Gainsborough *p228* . . . 01427 613831

Flint, A P (Colman Coyle LLP) *S1*
Islington *p22* . . . 020 7354 3000

Flint, B J (Pearson Rowe) *K1 W J1 E A1 L Q O*
Birmingham *p141* . . . 0121 236 7388

Flint, J (Ford & Warren) *N J2 O Q B2 F1*
Leeds *p273* . . . 0113 243 6601

Flint, P J (Barlow Lyde & Gilbert LLP)
London EC3 *p10* . . . 020 7247 2277
London EC2 *p90* . . . 020 7814 8000

Flint, P J (Lanyon Bowdler LLP) *D1 K1*
Shrewsbury *p379* . . . 01743 280280

Flint, S M (Ison Harrison) *S1*
Leeds *p274* . . . 0113 284 5000

Flinton, M J (BUPA)
London WC1 *p104* . . . 020 7656 2305

Flitcroft, Miss J (AstraZeneca)
Macclesfield *p464* . . . 01625 582828

Flood, C T (Lester Aldridge LLP) *S2 E*
London WC2 *p53* . . . 0844 967 0785
London WC2 *p60* . . . 020 7242 5905

Flood, Mrs E F (Singleton Saunders Flood Solicitors) *S1 W E S2 K4*
Dover *p213* . . . 01304 240080

Flood, J C A (McNamara Ryan) *S1 S2 L*
Weybridge *p430* . . . 01932 846041

Flood, P M (Reynolds Porter Chamberlain LLP)
London E1 *p71* . . . 020 3060 6000

Flood, R C (Maplestones)
Ickenham *p259* . . . 01895 632255

Flood, Ms S J (Yorkshire Water Services Ltd)
Bradford *p451* . . . 01274 804159

Flood, S M (Hibberts LLP) *G H*
Crewe *p203* . . . 01270 215117

Flood, T (Jones Day) *C2*
London EC4 *p46* . . . 020 7039 5959

Flor, L S (Lees Solicitors LLP) *Zr*
Birkenhead *p134* . . . 0151 647 9381

Florent, M E (Allen & Overy LLP)
London E1 *p5* . . . 020 3088 0000

Floris, G (Gould & Swayne) *S2 J1 E O Q S1*
Wells *p425* . . . 01749 675535

Flory, P A (Thomson Snell & Passmore) *Zr N*
Tunbridge Wells *p415* . . . 01892 510000

Flower, Ms D J (Reynolds Porter Chamberlain LLP) *N Zr Zq*
London E1 *p71* . . . 020 3060 6000

Flower, Ms H (Osborne Clarke) *C1*
London EC2 *p65* . . . 020 7105 7000

Flower, J M P (Ward Hadaway) *D1 D2 K1 Q V*
Newcastle upon Tyne *p327* . 0191 204 4000

Flower, K D (Keith Flower & Co) *E S1 W Q O*
Pinner *p348* . . . 020 8868 1277

Flower, N G (Overburys & Raymond Thompson) *W T2 K4*
Norwich *p335* . . . 01603 610481

Flower, T E (Preston Redman) *Q O C1 E N*
Bournemouth *p152* . . . 01202 292424

Flowerdew, Ms K E (Massers) *K1 D1 N K2*
Nottingham *p338* . . . 0115 851 1666

Flowerdew, R A (TLT Solicitors) *O J1 Q N*
Bristol *p165* . . . 0117 917 7777

Flowers, Ms E (Aon Ltd)
London EC2 *p103* . . . 020 7623 5500

Flowers, I (Mayer Brown International LLP) *Zo*
London EC2 *p59* . . . 020 3130 3000

Flowers, J (Bell Wright & Co) *O N J1 Zq E Zc*
Gainsborough *p228* . . . 01427 611722

Flowers, Mrs R (Ison Harrison) *K1 K3 D1*
Leeds *p274* . . . 0113 284 5000

Floyd, Mrs A M (Black Rock)
London EC4 *p104* . . . 020 7743 3000

Floyd, A V (Blackfords LLP) *G H*
Croydon *p204* . . . 020 8686 6232

Floyd, K G (HBOS PLC)
Halifax *p460* . . . 0870 600 5000

Floyd, Mrs S E (HMG Law LLP) *T2 W*
Oxford *p343* . . . 01865 244661

Floyd-Walker, D A (Helder Roberts & Co) *E S1 S2 W R2*
Chagford *p184* . . . 01647 433161
Moretonhampstead *p319* . . . 01647 440000

Fluck, N P (Stapleton & Son) *A1 S1 C1 E J1 L W T1 Zd*
Stamford *p393* . . . 01780 751226

Fluet, C G (Lewis Silkin LLP)
London EC4 *p53* . . . 020 7074 8000

Fluker, J R (Wedlake Bell LLP) *E P R1 Zl S2*
London WC1 *p91* . . . 020 7395 3000

Flynn, Ms B (Housemans) *Zr X J1 K1 J2 Zj Q N Zu*
London EC3 *p43* . . . 020 3170 6000

Flynn, D B (Portrait Solicitors) *S1 T2 W Zd*
London WC2 *p69* . . . 020 7092 6990

Flynn, Mrs D H (Cartmell Shepherd) *N Q*
Carlisle *p182* . . . 01228 516666

Flynn, D M (Heald Nickinson) *B1 Zr F1 O Q N Zq*
Camberley *p173* . . . 01276 680000

Flynn, Mrs J (Swinburne Snowball & Jackson) *S1 W L C1 E*
Consett *p199* . . . 01207 502532

Flynn, J (Dickinson Dees) *C1 C2*
Newcastle upon Tyne *p324* . 0191 279 9000

Flynn, J A (Swinburne Snowball & Jackson) *K1 G H Q N J1 S1 W Zl Zh*
Consett *p199* . . . 01207 502532

Flynn, Ms L (Stephensons Solicitors LLP) *K1 V L N D1*
Wigan *p432* . . . 01942 777777

Flynn, Miss L (Scotts Wright) *K3 K1*
Catterick Garrison *p183* . . . 01748 832431

Flynn, Mrs L E (Backhouse Jones Ltd) *Zt J1 O Zj*
Clitheroe *p196* . . . 01254 828300

Flynn, M (Brighouse Wolff) *G H*
Skelmersdale *p381* . . . 01695 722577

Flynn, M A W (Canter Levin & Berg) *N Q J1 G H I K1 O F1 V Zj Zk Zm Zl Zo*
Kirkby *p268* . . . 0151 546 4562

Flynn, M F (Cheshire County Council)
Chester *p454* . . . 01244 602382

Flynn, Miss R (DWF) *N*
Liverpool *p287* . . . 0151 907 3000

Flynn, Miss R E (Taylor Vinters) *O Zw*
Cambridge *p176* . . . 01223 423444

Flynn, T N (Terence Flynn & Co) *E L S1*
Coulsdon *p199* . . . 020 8660 8061

Foat, R (Rowena Foat Solicitors)
Ormskirk *p341* . . .

Foden, A J (Healds) *Q J1 L F1 S2 C1 E B1*
Wigan *p432* . . . 01942 241511

Foden, M R (Blake Lapthorn) *Zb C2 C1 B1*
Chandlers Ford *p184* . . . 023 8090 8090

Foden, S M (Fodens) *F1 O Q Zc Zq*
Much Wenlock *p320* . . . 01952 726111

Fogarty, M (Paul Crowley & Co)
Liverpool *p287* . . . 0151 264 7363

Fogarty, T M (Bevan Brittan LLP)
London EC4 *p12* . . . 0870 194 1000

Fogel, S A (Dechert) *E*
London EC4 *p26* . . . 020 7184 7000

Fogerty, J D (Pannone LLP) *N*
Manchester *p308* . . . 0161 909 3000

Fogg, Ms J E (Environment Agency (North East Region)) *G H*
Leeds *p462* . . . 0870 850 6506

Foggin, Mrs E S (Richard Jacklin & Co) *W T2 K4*
Southport *p388* . . . 01704 500024

Foggo, D (O'Keeffe Solicitors) *G*
Brent *p64* . . . 020 7644 8800

Foggo, G (Fox Williams) *O J1 Q*
London EC2 *p33* . . . 020 7628 2000

Foh, Ms D (Ashurst LLP)
London EC2 *p7* . . . 020 7638 1111

Foinette, Miss E C (Rooks Rider) *E S1 Zc R1 S2 R2 Zv*
London EC1 *p73* . . . 020 7689 7000

Foley, A (Anthony Foley) *S1 L W K1 C1 F1 Q*
Accrington *p114* . . . 01254 391223

Foley, Ms E (Angel Trains Ltd)
London SW1 *p103* . . . 020 7592 0500

Foley, Miss J (John Donkin & Co)
Gateshead *p228* . 0191 495 2896 / 477 1781

Foley, Mrs J C (Lowes) *S1*
Rainham *p359* . . . 01634 371111

Foley, J P (Thompsons (formerly Robin/Brian Thompson & Partners)) *N*
London SW19 *p87* . . . 020 8947 4163

Foley, Mrs M (Boyes Sutton & Perry) *K1 K3*
Barnet *p123* . . . 020 8449 9155

Foley, M (Foley Harrison)
Gateshead *p228* . . . 0191 477 6333

Foley, Mrs M A (HM Land Registry - Durham (Boldon) Office) *S1 K1*
Durham *p457* . . . 0191 301 2345

Foley, M G (Harrison Bundey) *G H*
Leeds *p274* . . . 0113 200 7400

Foley, Ms M R (Gillian Radford & Co) *K1 I L V D1 K3 D2*
Westminster *p70* . . . 020 8960 4366

Foley, N J (Neil Foley & Co) *G H D1 N K1 Q L Zl Zm Zi*
Pontypridd *p352* . . . 01443 406085

Foley, R (Howard Kennedy LLP) *R2*
London W1 *p48* . . . 020 7636 1616

Foley, R (Brockbank Curwen Cain & Hall) *G H*
Workington *p440* . . . 01900 603563

Foley, R E (Pinsent Masons LLP) *A3 O Zc*
Bristol *p164* . . . 0117 924 5678

Foley, V J (Harvey Ingram Borneos) *B1 F1 J1 N O Q*
Bedford *p130* . . . 01234 353221

Foley Jones, A P (Mackenzie Jones)
St Asaph *p391* . . . 01745 536030

Folgate, M S (Scrivenger Seabrook) *N*
St Neots *p392* . . . 01480 214900

Follett, M J (Michelmores LLP) *Zx Zd*
Exeter *p221* . . . 01392 688688

Follett-Carman, Mrs L (Michelmores LLP) *E R2 S2 S1*
Exeter *p221* . . . 01392 688688

Folley, Mrs L (Wortley Byers) *C1 C2 C3*
Brentwood *p156* . . . 01277 268368

Follis, M I (Challinors) *K1 D1*
Birmingham *p136* . . . 0121 212 9393

Follis, R T (Irwin Mitchell LLP) *Zr N P Zm*
Birmingham *p139* . . . 0870 150 0100
Birmingham *p142* 0370 086 4000 / 0121 335 4440

Follows, Ms S J (Abney Garsden McDonald) *N*
Cheadle *p185* . . . 0161 482 8822

Fomina, A (Ince & Co Services Ltd)
London E1 *p44* . . . 020 7481 0010

Fong, Miss A (Martin Tolhurst Partnership LLP) *J1 K1 J2 L O Q N*
Gravesend *p233* . . . 01474 325531

Fong, Ms K (Rouse Legal (Formerly Willoughby & Partners)) *Ze A3*
London E14 *p74* . . . 020 7536 4100

Fong, M H Y F (Antony Hodari & Co) *N*
Manchester *p305* . . . 0161 832 4781

Fongenie, W (Osborne Clarke) *P*
London EC2 *p65* . . . 020 7105 7000

Fonseca, J F A (Fonseca & Partners) *D1 F1 G H K1 L M1 P S1 W Zl Zm*
Ebbw Vale *p216* . . . 01495 303124

Foo, Ms A (SNR Denton) *O*
Milton Keynes *p317* . . . 01908 690260

Foolat, E I (The Watson Ramsbottom Partnership) *N Q S1 F1 V*
Blackburn *p146* . . . 01254 672222

Foong, J (G T Stewart Solicitors) *G H B2*
London SE22 *p83* . . . 020 8299 6000

Foord, R A J (Stephenson Harwood) *O Q Zq B2*
London EC2 *p82* . . . 020 7329 4422

Foort, Miss S M (Foort Tayler) *S1 E W*
Great Dunmow *p233* . . . 01371 875200

Foot, A G (Fitzhugh Gates) *S2 E C1 W K4 Zd Zc A1 A2*
Brighton *p159* . . . 01273 686811
Brighton *p160* . . . 01273 608003

Foot, Miss C (Roger Richards) *S1 S2 W L*
Paignton *p345* . . . 01803 845191

Foot, M (Birnberg Peirce & Partners) *G Zg*
Camden *p13* . . . 020 7911 0166

Foot, M R (Bennett Welch & Co) *S1 E W Zl*
London SE19 *p12* . . . 020 8670 6141

Foot, T (Veale Wasbrough Vizards) *E*
Bristol *p165* . . . 0117 925 2020

Foot, W D (Blake Lapthorn) *J1 O B1 Q Zb Zp*
London EC1 *p13* . . . 020 7405 2000

Foote, C J (Gregg Latchams LLP) *J1 L Q O N*
Bristol *p162* . . . 0117 906 9400

Foote, M A (Derby City Council)
Derby *p456* . . . 01332 293111

Foote, N J (Coodes) *E S2 S1 L*
Penzance *p346* . . . 01736 362294

Foote, P G (Eden District Council)
Penrith *p468* . . . 01768 817817

Foottit, G T W (Mander Hadley & Co) *S1 W E A1 L Zh*
Coventry *p200* . . . 024 7663 1212

Foottit, T G (Roythornes LLP) *E A1 L S1 S2 U1*
Spalding *p389* . . . 01775 842500

Forbat, Mrs J C (Morrisons Solicitors LLP) *W*
Redhill *p362* . . . 01737 854500

Forbes, D I (Forbes) *B1 C1 E L R1 S1 W Zl Zv Zm*
Accrington *p114* . . . 01254 872111

Forbes, Miss D K (Wycombe & Beaconsfield Magistrates Court)
High Wycombe *p461* . . . 01494 651035

Forbes, Ms J J (SGH Martineau LLP) *X*
Birmingham *p142* . . . 0870 763 2000

Forbes, Ms M (Trethowans LLP) *O Q N Zq A3*
Southampton *p387* . . . 023 8032 1000

Forbes, Mrs M (Department for Business, Enterprise and Regulatory Reform)
London SW1 *p105*. 020 7215 0105

Forbes, Miss S (Reuters Group PLC)
London E14 *p109* 020 7250 1122

Forbes, Miss S E M (Burges Salmon) *C1 B1 Zb*
Bristol *p161* 0117 939 2000

Ford, A (Veale Wasbrough Vizards)
Bristol *p165* 0117 925 2020

Ford, A D E (IBM United Kingdom Ltd)
Winchester *p476*. 01962 815000

Ford, A E L (Brockmans) *S2 E S1 R2 L*
Stockbridge *p395* 01264 810910

Ford, A H (Cockshott Peck Lewis) *C1 E J1 K1 L S1*
Southport *p388* 01704 534034

Ford, A J (Withers LLP) *O Q Zf*
London EC4 *p92*. 020 7597 6000

Ford, A M (Andrew M Ford Solicitors) *K1 N*
Leicester *p279*. 0845 075 4059

Ford, D H (Argyles) *A1 C1 C3 E R1 S1 T1 T2 W N*
Tamworth *p407* 01827 56276

Ford, D J (Anthony Clark & Co) *S1 G H K1 L M1 C1 D1 E A1 Zc Zh Zl*
Lincoln *p284*. 01522 512321

Ford, D J T (Mills Chody LLP) *S1 S2 E C1 L R1 R2 Zl W*
Hatch End *p244* 020 8428 2272

Ford, Miss E (Brain Chase Coles) *K1 K3*
Basingstoke *p126* 01256 354481

Ford, Mrs E F (MacLaren Britton) *K1 K3*
Nottingham *p338*. 0115 941 1469

Ford, G C (Fordlittle) *B1 O E C1 Q N S1 W R1 J1 Ze Zl*
Sittingbourne *p380*. 01795 436111

Ford, I R (Russell-Cooke LLP) *S2 E L Zl R1 R2 S1 W*
Kingston upon Thames *p267*. 020 8546 6111

Ford, J (Trowers & Hamlins)
London EC3 *p88*. 020 7423 8000

Ford, J (John Ford Solicitors) *L Zm X Zg Zu Zf Q R1 Zq Zp*
London N4 *p33* 020 8800 6464

Ford, Ms J (Capsticks Solicitors LLP) *Zr*
London SW19 *p18*. 020 8780 2211

Ford, Miss J A E (Hetts Johnson Whiting) *S1 W T1 A1 E*
Brigg *p158*. 01652 655101

Ford, K D (HSBC Legal Department)
Birmingham *p449* 0121 455 2740

Ford, L G (Coodes)
Truro *p414*. 01872 246200

Ford, Miss N (Hopkins) *Q L V*
Mansfield *p311*. 01623 460460

Ford, P (Addison O'Hare) *D2 D1 K3 K1 K2*
Walsall *p419*. 01922 725515

Ford, P C (Nabarro LLP)
London WC1 *p63* 020 7524 6000

Ford, P J (Kirwans) *G H B2*
Birkenhead *p134*. 0151 608 9078

Ford, R (Pinsent Masons LLP)
London EC2 *p67*. 020 7418 7000

Ford, R (Owen White) *N O L Q Ze Zq*
Slough *p382*. 01753 876800

Ford, R D (Hodgson Coulthard & Co) *G H*
Houghton Le Spring *p253* . . 0191 584 3333

Ford, R L (Lindsay Ford Solicitors Ltd) *S1 E C1 W D1 T1 Zc*
Caerphilly *p172* 029 2088 2441

Ford, S A L (Olswang LLP) *Zf Ze*
London WC1 *p64* 020 7067 3000

Ford, T G (Lester Aldridge LLP) *C1 R1 J1 F1 N B1 Zk Ze Zf*
London WC2 *p53* 0844 967 0785

Ford, T P L (The BOC Group PLC)
Guildford *p476*. 01483 579857

Ford, Mrs V M (Heath Sons & Broome) *K1 D1 W K2*
Manchester *p305* 0161 681 1933

Forde, B (Saunders Law Partnership LLP) *J1 Q N*
London WC2 *p76* 020 7632 4300

Forde, Miss C (Hewitsons) *R1 Zu*
Northampton *p332*. 01604 233233

Forde, D (Penningtons) *S1*
Godalming *p231*. 01483 791800

Fordham, D (PCB Lawyers LLP) *S1 L R2*
London W1 *p65* 020 7486 2566

Fordham, D A (Simons Muirhead & Burton) *Q O N L G H E S1 C1 F1*
London W1 *p79* 020 7734 4499

Fordham, D E (Wallace Robinson & Morgan) *S1 W E*
Solihull *p383*. 0121 705 7571

Fordham, G M (Biggs & Co) *Q N K1 D1 L G S1 H J1 W Zx Zq Zi Zk Zp*
Wokingham *p437* 0118 989 4511

Fordham, J M (Stephenson Harwood) *O B2*
London EC2 *p82*. 020 7329 4422

Fordham, T J (Bedford Borough Council)
Bedford *p448* 01234 267422

Fordyce, R P H (Charles Russell LLP) *E C1 L S1 O Zh Zc*
Guildford *p235*. 01483 252525

Foreman, Ms E (Archers Law LLP) *J1 Zl*
Stockton-on-Tees *p396* . . . 01642 636500

Foreman, Mrs H C (Franklins) *W*
Abingdon *p114*. 01235 553222

Foreman, M R (Roy Foreman & Co) *G H Zi*
Grimsby *p235* 01472 355262

Foreman, N J (Nelsons) *S1 W S2*
Leicester *p280*. 0116 222 6666

Foreman, Miss S (RSPCA)
Horsham *p461*. 0870 010 1181

Foreman, T M (MBNA Europe Bank Ltd)
Chester *p454* 01244 672002

Forfar, Ms C B (John Bellis & Co) *S1 K1 E W L J1 P R1 G C1 Zl*
Penmaenmawr *p346*. 01492 622377

Forge, Mrs A (McGrigors LLP)
London EC4 *p56*. 020 7054 2500
London EC2 *p59*. 020 3130 3000

Forman, A P (Horton & Moss) *S1 W E L C1*
Ilkeston *p261* . . 0115 932 1431 / 930 8208

Forman, J B (Ouvry Goodman & Co) *J1 K1 N*
Sutton *p403* 020 8642 7571

Forman, J W S (Tinn Criddle & Co)
Sutton-on-Sea *p404* 01507 443043
Alford *p115* 01507 462882

Forman, Mrs S B (Donns) *Zr N*
Manchester *p303* 0161 834 3311

Forman, T (Andrew Jay & Co (Philip Hanby Limited)) *B1 C1 O Q Zq*
Gainsborough *p228* 01427 612412

Fornasier, V (Hogan Lovells International LLP)
London EC1 *p42*. 020 7296 2000

Forrest, A (Southampton City Council)
Southampton *p472*. 023 8022 3855

Forrest, Mrs A S (Hawley & Rodgers) *K1 D1*
Nottingham *p337*. 0115 955 9000

Forrest, C (Veale Wasbrough Vizards) *E*
Bristol *p165* 0117 925 2020

Forrest, Mrs C (Berg Legal) *J1 Zi Zo Zp*
Manchester *p301* 0161 833 9211

Forrest, C (McDermott Will & Emery UK LLP) *Zb B1*
London EC2 *p56*. 020 7577 6900

Forrest, C B (Yorkshire Electricity Group PLC)
Leeds *p463* 0113 289 2123

Forrest, D B (Solicitor Direct) *D1 G J1 K1 Q S1 W H N*
Leyland *p283* 01772 424999

Forrest, Miss E (Meikles) *K1 S1 W N Q V Zm D1 Zh L*
Stockton-on-Tees *p397* . . . 01740 620255

Forrest, Mrs E (Sacker & Partners LLP) *Zo*
London EC2 *p76*. 020 7329 6699

Forrest, Mrs E S (Howells LLP) *K1 K3*
Sheffield *p376* 0114 249 6666

Forrest, J A (J A Forrest & Co) *S1 W Q E B1 C1 O Ze Zi Zl*
Westminster *p33*. 020 7233 9140

Forrest, J S (Squire Sanders (UK) LLP)
Birmingham *p142* 0121 222 3000

Forrest, Miss K A (Gloucestershire County Council - Legal & Democratic Services)
Gloucester *p459*. 01452 425203

Forrest, L (Hodge Jones & Allen LLP) *D2 D1 K1 K2 K3*
London NW1 *p41* 020 7874 8300

Forrest, Mrs S F A (Pembrokeshire County Council)
Haverfordwest *p460* 01437 764551

Forrester, Mrs C E (Cartmell Shepherd) *L N P B1 F1 J1 Zc Zd Zb*
Haltwhistle *p238* 01434 320362

Forrester, Mrs D J (Graham Withers & Co) *S1 L*
Shrewsbury *p380* 01743 236345

Forrester, D L (Geoffrey Forrester & Co)
Jarrow *p263* 0191 420 0820

Forrester, G M (Geoffrey Forrester & Co) *D1 F1 G H J1 K1 L M1 S1 W*
Jarrow *p263* 0191 420 0820

Forrester, J E (Holman Fenwick Willan)
London EC3 *p42*. 020 7264 8000
London EC2 *p82*. 020 7329 4422

Forrester, Mrs J E (Lodders Solicitors LLP) *W Zd*
Stratford-upon-Avon *p400* . . 01789 293259
Leamington Spa *p270* 01926 886688

Forrester, Miss K S (Williamson & Soden) *Zl U1 S2 E*
Solihull *p383*. 0121 733 8000

Forrester, Mrs N (Young & Co) *Q N Zm*
Stoke-on-Trent *p398*. 01782 339200

Forrester, R D (Aaron & Partners LLP Solicitors) *P A1 C1 C2 E R1 Zn Zv S2*
Chester *p190* 01244 405555

Forrester, T (Davitt Jones Bould) *S2 E A1*
Taunton *p408* 01823 279279

Forret, Miss T (Lupton Fawcett) *O F1 F2 J2 A3 C3 I*
Leeds *p275* 0113 280 2000

Forrow, Miss L (Dakers Marriott Solicitors) *E S2 C1 W*
Strood *p400* 01634 813300

Forryan, A J (Clifford Chance)
London E14 *p20*. 020 7006 1000

Forsdyke, R (Herbert Smith LLP) *E*
London EC2 *p40*. 020 7374 8000

Forshaw, M J (Weightmans LLP)
Liverpool *p291*. 0151 227 2601

Forshaw, S A (Howell-Jones LLP) *S1*
Kingston upon Thames *p267*. 020 8549 5186
Leatherhead *p271* 01372 860650

Forskitt, R D J (DFA Law LLP) *Q N R1 O L Zr*
Northampton *p331*. 01604 609560

Forster Dean, P (Forster Dean Ltd)
Runcorn *p369* 01928 590999
Widnes *p431*. 0151 495 3270

Forster, A J (Actons) *E C1 B1 S1 W Zo*
Nottingham *p335*. 0115 910 0200

Forster, A J B (Metcalfes) *C3 C1 C2 Ze Zb Zd Zf*
Bristol *p164* 0117 929 0451

Forster, Mrs C (Wansbeck District Council)
Ashington *p447* 01670 532292

Forster, Ms C L (Forster & Wheeler)
Birmingham *p138* 0121 421 4888

Forster, Ms D J (Powell Forster) *L N Q Zq*
Lambeth *p69*. 020 7737 8111

Forster, Miss I L (Stewarts Law LLP) *O Q Zq*
London EC4 *p83*. 020 7822 8000

Forster, J C (Andrews Stanton & Ringrose) *K1 D1 S1 C1 A1 E T1 V W J1 Zl Zd*
Bourne *p151*. 01778 422626

Forster, Miss K A (Lyons Wilson) *L E S1*
Manchester *p307* 0161 830 7777

Forster, Miss L (Andersons Solicitors) *J1 Zp*
Nottingham *p335*. 0115 947 0641

Forster, Mrs R D (Metcalfes) *S2 E R2*
Bristol *p164* 0117 929 0451

Forster, S B (City of Sunderland)
Sunderland *p473*. 0191 520 5555

Forster, Miss S L (Muckle LLP) *C1 Zd*
Newcastle upon Tyne *p325* . 0191 211 7777

Forsyth, A J S (Barlow Lyde & Gilbert LLP) *O Q Zj*
London EC3 *p10*. 020 7247 2277

Forsyth, D R (Goodhand and Forsyth Quality Solicitors) *G J1 H Zl*
Redhill *p362* 01737 773533

Forsyth, Miss G (Elmhirst Parker LLP) *K4 T2 K1 W S1 L*
Selby *p374* 01757 703602

Forsyth, Mrs J (Bank of Ireland Home Mortgages Ltd) *E S1*
Reading *p469* 01734 393393

Forsyth, J F (Thursfields) *S1 W A1 E T1 C1 L*
Kidderminster *p266* 01562 820575

Forsyth, K M R (DAC Beachcroft)
London EC3 *p24*. 020 7208 6800

Forsyth, Mrs L (Irwin Mitchell LLP) *Zr N Zm X*
Manchester *p306* 0870 150 0100

Forsyth, N B (Barker Gillette) *O J1 Q L F1 F2 E K1 P Ze Zk Zp*
London W1 *p9*. 020 7636 0555

Forsyth, P (Ellisons) *C1 C2*
Colchester *p197* 01206 764477

Forsythe, K (Reynolds Porter Chamberlain LLP)
London E1 *p71* 020 3060 6000

Forsythe, Ms L (Buckinghamshire County Council)
Aylesbury *p448* 01296 383653

Fort, D (Smith Sutcliffe) *E S2 S1 W O L C1 Zl*
Burnley *p169* 01282 426251

Forte, Ms R M (Hadaway & Hadaway) *K1 D1 W T2 S1 D2 V*
North Shields *p330* 0191 257 0382

Forth, T E (Forth & Co) *S1 E W L A1 Q N*
Yarm *p443*. 01642 784000

Fortin-Lees, B (Taylor Wessing)
London EC4 *p86*. 020 7300 7000

Fortnam, J R (Pinsent Masons LLP) *Q*
Birmingham *p141* 0121 200 1050

Fortune, Ms K (Reynolds Porter Chamberlain LLP)
London E1 *p71* 020 3060 6000

Forward, G A (Kitsons LLP) *A1 B1 C1 E F1 L S1 T1 Zc Zj*
Torquay *p413* 01803 202020

Foskett, A E (Moss & Coleman) *C1 D1 J1 S1*
Hornchurch *p252* 01708 446781

Foskett, N (Russell & Co) *W T2*
Malvern *p300* 01684 892000

Foskett, P W (Gordons LLP)
Leeds *p273* 0113 227 0100

Fosler, Mrs N (Stewarts Law LLP) *N*
London EC4 *p83*. 020 7822 8000

Foss, P W (Barlow Lyde & Gilbert LLP) *Za A3 Zj M2 O*
London EC3 *p10*. 020 7247 2277

Foss, R J (Kingsley Napley) *O Q Zc A3*
London EC1 *p50*. 020 7814 1200

Foss, T F (Gard & Co) *K1 D1 V N K3*
Plymouth *p349*. 01752 668246

Foss-Pedersen, N (Rosenblatt)
London EC4 *p73*. 020 7955 0880

Foster, A (Robert Lizar) *G H*
Manchester *p307* 0161 226 2319

Foster, Miss A (Citi Financial Europe PLC)
London E14 *p469* . . . .

Foster, Ms A (Osborne Clarke) *R2*
London EC2 *p65*. 020 7105 7000

Foster, A C (Rix & Kay Solicitors LLP) *K3 K1 N*
Uckfield *p416* 01825 700177

Foster, Miss A C (Carter-Ruck) *Zk J1 Q*
London EC4 *p18*. 020 7353 5005

Foster, A J (Travers Smith LLP) *C1*
London EC1 *p87*. 020 7295 3000

Foster, A M (Squire Sanders (UK) LLP)
London EC2 *p81*. 020 7655 1000

Foster, Ms B (Darbys Solicitors LLP) *J1*
Oxford *p343* 01865 811700

Foster, C (Ince & Co Services Ltd)
London E1 *p44* 020 7481 0010

Foster, C (Herbert Smith LLP) *O*
London EC2 *p40*. 020 7374 8000

Foster, C S (Walkers) *N P S1 K1 E W B1 J1 Zi*
Rossendale *p367* 01706 213565

Foster, D C (Cadbury Schweppes PLC (Legal Dept)) *C1*
Birmingham *p449* 0121 625 7000

Foster, D C G (Alliance Boots PLC)
Nottingham *p467*. 0115 950 6111

Foster, D G (Barlow Robbins LLP) *Q P L F1 Zc Zj Zq*
Guildford *p235*. 01483 562901

Foster, D G (Charles Hart Solicitors) *K1 D1 D2*
Cheddar *p186* 01934 742315

Foster, D H (GLP Solicitors) *N K1 G H S1 L V D1 J1 F1 Zl*
Middleton *p315* 0161 653 6295

Foster, D J (Baxters) *H J1 K1 L V W G D1*
Tamworth *p407* 01827 899059
Tamworth *p407* . . . . 01827 58333 / 58334

Foster, Mrs E (HM Revenue & Customs)
Salford *p470*. 0870 785 8545

Foster, Miss E L (Paris Smith LLP) *C1 Ze*
Southampton *p386*. 023 8048 2482

Foster, E R (ASB Law) *E K4 R1 S1 W Zc C1 S2 F1 F2 Zh L O Q*
Maidstone *p298* 01622 656500
Herne Bay *p248* 01227 283634

Foster, Mrs E S S (Henry Boot PLC)
Sheffield *p470* 0114 255 5444

Foster, Mrs G A (Wolferstans) *K1 S1*
Plymouth *p351*. 01752 663295

Foster, H (DLA Piper UK LLP)
London EC2 *p24*. 0870 011 1111

Foster, J (LG Lawyers)
London SE1 *p50*. 020 7379 0000

Foster, Ms J (NFLA Ltd) *K3 K1*
Chesterfield *p192* 01246 471900

Foster, J C (Spearing Waite LLP) *K1 D1 D2 V K3*
Leicester *p281*. 0116 262 4225

Foster, J G (Bircham Dyson Bell)
Westminster *p13*. 020 7227 7000

Foster, J M (Gordons LLP) *E A1*
Leeds *p273* 0113 227 0100
Leeds *p276* 0113 245 2833

Foster, Mrs L (Hewitts) *K1 S1 D1 W*
Crook *p203* 01388 762466

Foster, M (Mincoffs Solicitors LLP) *Zl R1*
Newcastle upon Tyne *p325* . 0191 281 6151

Foster, M C (Stephenson Harwood) *C1 B1 Zb*
London EC2 *p82*. 020 7329 4422

Foster, Miss M H (Calvert Smith & Sutcliffe) *G H K1 D1 M1 P F1 J1 Zl*
Richmond upon Thames *p364* 020 8940 0017

Foster, M J (Fynmores) *J1*
Bexhill *p132* 01424 732333

Foster, N (Anthony Collins Solicitors LLP) *K1 D1 W*
Birmingham *p137* 0121 200 3242

Foster, N F (Woodford Robinson) *N K1 Q S1*
Northampton *p333*. 01604 624926

Foster, N J E (Cole & Co) *S1 S2 W R2*
Norwich *p334* 01603 617018

Foster, N N (Dyne Drewett Solicitors Ltd) *D1 F1 G H J1 K1 L M1 P*
Shepton Mallet *p378*. 01749 342323

Foster, P E J (Lewis Silkin LLP) *A3 O Q N Zr*
London EC4 *p53*. 020 7074 8000

Foster, P G (Paul Foster & Co) *S1*
York *p444* 01904 765159

Foster, R C (Churchers) *S1 E C1 W R1 S2*
Fareham *p223*. 01329 822333

Foster, R C H (Sedgwick Kelly LLP) *J1 N O Q*
Watford *p424* 01923 228311

Foster, R E (Henmans LLP) *Zd C1*
Oxford *p343* 01865 781000

Foster, R G E (Linder Myers Solicitors) *G H K1 J1 S1 M1 P W D1 A1 Zp Zl Zm*
Shrewsbury *p379* 0844 984 6002

Foster, Ms S (Clerk to Sheffield Justices)
Sheffield *p470* 0114 276 0760

Foster, Ms S (Worksop Magistrates Court)
Worksop *p477* 01909 486111

Foster, S (Hogan Lovells International LLP)
London EC1 *p42*. 020 7296 2000

Foster, Mrs S A (Henmans LLP) *O Q Zq*
Oxford *p343* 01865 781000

Foster, Mrs S A (West Berkshire Council)
Newbury *p466* 01635 42400

Foster, S A (Berg Legal) *C1 B1 Zb*
Manchester *p301* 0161 833 9211

Foster, Miss S C (Farleys Solicitors LLP) *K1*
Accrington *p114* 01254 367853

Foster, S D (Taylor Woodrow Construction Legal Department) *O Zc Zn*
Watford *p475* 01923 478442

Foster, S G (Stewarts Law LLP) *K3 K1*
London EC4 *p83*. 020 7822 8000

Foster, Mrs S I (Barlow Lyde & Gilbert LLP) *Zq*
London EC3 *p10*. 020 7247 2277

Foster, S J (Tyndallwoods) *L J1 P V Zi Zp*
Birmingham *p143* 0121 624 1111

Foster, S J (DWF) *J1 J2*
Manchester *p303* 0161 603 5000

Foster, Miss S J (Trethowans LLP) *K1*
Salisbury *p371*. 01722 412512

Foster, T G (Reed Smith LLP) *C1 Zb Ze*
London EC2 *p71*. 020 3116 3000

Foster, T R (Foster Harrington) *S1 W*
Camberley *p173* 01276 692233

Foster, V P (Foster & Partners) *K1 D1 K3 D2*
Bristol *p162* 0117 922 0229

Foster-Pegg, J (Blanchards Bailey LLP) *S1 K1 D1 F1 L W*
Stalbridge *p393* 01963 363593

Foston, Ms L (Bridge McFarland)
Grimsby *p235* 01472 311711

Fothergill, A J (Hanney Dawkins & Jones) *E S2 S1 W T2 R2 R1 L P C1 Zc*
Pinner *p348* 020 8866 2144

Fothergill, S (Judge Sykes Frixou)
London WC2 *p47* 020 7379 5114

Fothergill, S D (Palmers) *A1 S2 E R2 S1*
South Woodham Ferrers *p384* 01245 322111

Fotiou, A P (Edmondson Hall) *Q O N Zw L*
Newmarket *p327*. 01638 560556

See p634 for the Key to Work Categories

Fottrell, Miss C (Criminal Defence Solicitors) *G H*
Westminster *p23* 020 7353 7000

Fouad, M (Ziadies) *K1 K4 N Q W*
London SW9 *p94* 020 7737 0934

Foulds, M A (Rothera Dowson) *S1 E W*
Nottingham *p338* 0115 952 0900

Foulke, R J (Calderdale Metropolitan BC Corporate Services Directorate)
Halifax *p460* 01422 357257
Manchester *p310* 0161 830 5000

Foulkes, C M (Plexus Law (A Trading Name of Parabis Law LLP)) *A3 J2 N Zj*
Leeds *p276* 0844 245 4100

Foulkes, D R M (Belmores) *G H W Q L*
Norwich *p334* 01603 499999

Foulkes, E R (Lockett Loveday McMahon) *C1 I F1 Ze Zza U2 C2*
Manchester *p307* 0161 237 3627

Foulkes, H (Skadden Arps Slate Meagher & Flom (UK) LLP)
London E14 *p80* 020 7519 7000

Foulkes, P (Armstrong Foulkes) *Zr*
Middlesbrough *p314* 01642 231110

Foulkes, Mrs R M (Andrew Jackson) *S1 A1*
Hull *p257* 01482 325242

Foulkes-Williams, Ms M T (Biscoes) *S1 W*
Portchester *p353* 023 9237 0634

Foundling, Mrs D J (Warner Goodman LLP) *N*
Southampton *p387* 023 8063 9311

Fountain, A M (A Halsall & Co) *S1 W E S2*
Birkenhead *p134* 0151 647 6323
Wirral *p435* 0151 632 2336

Fountain, Ms C (Wheltons) *S1 W*
Guildford *p237* 01483 537633

Fountain, C J L (Hewitts) *C1 E S2*
Stockton-on-Tees *p397* 01642 673701

Fountain, Mrs J T (Bedwell Watts & Co) *W S2 S1 T2*
Scarborough *p372* .01723 373356 / 363553

Fowell, E M (Foot Anstey) *J1*
Plymouth *p349* 01752 675000

Fowkes, Miss K (The Johnson Partnership) *G H*
Chesterfield *p192* 01246 520930

Fowkes, Mrs L L (Borough of Telford & Wrekin)
Telford *p473* 01952 380000

Fowkes, Miss N E (Milford & Dormor)
Ilminster *p261* 01460 55445

Fowlds, J L (Rich & Carr Freer Bouskell) *C1 D1 F1 G H J1 K1 M1 N P Zl Zt*
Leicester *p281* 0116 253 8021

Fowlds, Mrs R (South Hams District Council)
Totnes *p474* 01803 861234

Fowle, R (Cogent Law)
Croydon *p204* 0844 245 4452
London EC3 *p68* 0844 245 4000

Fowler, Ms A (Wilde & Co) *K1 W K3 S1*
Neston *p321* 0151 353 1899

Fowler, Miss A E (Scott Fowler) *W T2 S1 K4*
Northampton *p331* 01604 750506

Fowler, Ms A J (Dickinson Parker Hill) *K1 D1 F1 N J1 L D2*
Ormskirk *p341* 01695 574201

Fowler, A R (Fowler de Pledge) *N Q L Zq R2*
Cambridge *p174* 01223 311291

Fowler, Mrs A V (TWM Solicitors LLP) *E R2 S2 L*
Epsom *p219* 01372 729555

Fowler, Mrs C E (Blake Lapthorn) *J1*
Chandlers Ford *p184* 023 8090 8090

Fowler, C H (Langley Wellington) *D1 K1 W D2 Zl Q S1*
Gloucester *p230* 01452 521286

Fowler, D C (Tollers LLP) *E S1 S2 R1 R2*
Kettering *p265* 01536 520111

Fowler, E R (Scott Fowler) *C1 S2 E L R2 S1*
Northampton *p331* 01604 750506

Fowler, H F J (Palmers) *E R1 R2 S1 S2*
Bedford *p130* 01234 211161

Fowler, Ms H P (City of London Magistrates Court)
London EC4 *p107* 020 7332 1830

Fowler, P (The Dures Partnership LLP)
Liverpool *p287* 0151 242 5111

Fowler, P F C (PCB Solicitors LLP) *S2 Q W C1 E*
Shrewsbury *p379* 01743 248148

Fowler, Ms P J (Hughes Fowler Carruthers) *K1 D1 K2 K3*
London WC2 *p43* 020 7421 8383

Fowler, P J (Peter J Fowler) *C1 C2 E L M2 S1 W Ze Zi*
Wimborne *p433* 01202 849242

Fowler, R C (Scott Fowler) *F1 M1 C1 B1 S2 E Zc*
Northampton *p331* 01604 750506

Fowler, R J (Whetter Duckworth Fowler) *K1 M1 P G L W F1 D1 S1 Zi Zk*
Kidlington *p266* 01865 842100

Fowler, Mrs R M (Max Engel & Co LLP) *S1 S2 W*
Northampton *p331* 01604 887450

Fowles, A J C (Chubb Bulleid) *G K1 N O Q S1 L W F1 H J1*
Street *p400* 01749 836100

Fowles, A R (Morrisons Solicitors LLP) *S1 W E A1 S2*
Camberley *p173* 01276 686005

Fowles, Mrs J E (Gotelee) *K1 D1*
Ipswich *p262* 01473 211121

Fownes, Miss E L (Borough of Telford & Wrekin)
Telford *p473* 01952 380000

Fox, A N (Davies Johnson & Co (Shipping & Commercial Solicitors)) *O Q Za*
Plymouth *p349* 01752 226020

Fox, A P S (Manches LLP) *O Zb B1 Q B2 J1 U2 Zo Zq A3 Zk Zj N G Zg*
London WC2 *p58* 020 7404 4433

Fox, Miss B J (Read Dunn Connell) *T2 W*
Bradford *p154* 01274 723858

Fox, Ms C (Eastleys) *K1 D1*
Paignton *p345* 01803 559257

Fox, Mrs C (Mills & Reeve) *E*
Cambridge *p175* 01223 364422

Fox, Miss C (Blake Lapthorn) *C2 C1*
London EC1 *p13* 020 7405 2000

Fox, Miss C E F (Sheridans) *C1 C2 J1*
London WC1 *p78* 020 7079 0100

Fox, Ms C J (Rothera Dowson) *S1*
Nottingham *p338* 0115 910 0600

Fox, C R (Hall Smith Whittingham LLP) *M1 K1 Q G H J1 D1 F1 O V Zj Zl*
Nantwich *p320* 01270 610300
Crewe *p203* 01270 212000

Fox, Ms C V (Department for Business, Enterprise and Regulatory Reform)
London SW1 *p105* 020 7215 0105

Fox, D B (Singletons Austin Ryder) *Q N O L K1*
Enfield *p219* 020 8363 0101

Fox, Ms E (Reynolds Dawson)
London WC2 *p71* . 020 7839 2373 / 07659 130481

Fox, Miss F (Squire Sanders (UK) LLP) *E*
London EC2 *p81* 020 7655 1000

Fox, Miss H M (Quality Solicitors Burroughs Day) *J1*
Bristol *p164* 0117 929 0333

Fox, Miss J A (Taylor Vinters) *W*
Cambridge *p176* 01223 423444

Fox, J A (Horsey Lightly) *S1 W*
Westminster *p43* 020 7222 8844

Fox, J J (Herbert Smith LLP) *C1 Zb*
London EC2 *p40* 020 7374 8000

Fox, J N (Noble)
Shefford *p377* 01462 814055

Fox, J R C (Murray Hay Solicitors) *Zb R2 E*
London SW15 *p62* 020 8780 1225

Fox, Mrs L (Appleby Hope & Matthews) *D1 K1 Zm V*
Middlesbrough *p314* 01642 440444

Fox, Ms L J E (Kathy Webb & Co) *D1 D2 K3 K1*
Guisborough *p237* 01287 633331

Fox, Miss M (Weightmans LLP)
Liverpool *p291* 0151 227 2601

Fox, Ms M (Ashfords LLP) *J1*
Taunton *p408* 01823 232300

Fox, M C (Wachtel Fox & Co) *S1 S2 W*
Rickmansworth *p364* 01923 775651

Fox, M P (CMS Cameron McKenna LLP) *O Zj Zc*
London EC3 *p17* 020 7367 3000

Fox, Ms M V (The Head Partnership) *D1 K1 K2 N K3*
Reading *p361* 0118 975 6622

Fox, Mrs N (Surrey County Council)
Kingston upon Thames *p462* 020 8541 9088

Fox, P F J E (H2O Law LLP) *Zk Ze O U2*
London EC4 *p37* 020 7405 4700

Fox, P P (dgb Solicitors) *A3 Zr O Q N Zq B1*
Chatham *p184* 01634 304000

Fox, P R (Lawson Coppock & Hart) *C1 O C2 C3 Ze Q N*
Manchester *p306* 0161 832 5944

Fox, P R (Ashfords LLP) *S1 E C1 A1 W T1 L R1 J1*
Taunton *p408* 01823 232300

Fox, R C (Leathes Prior) *Zza U2*
Norwich *p334* 01603 610911

Fox, R D (Fox Williams) *C1 J1 Zp*
London EC2 *p33* 020 7628 2000

Fox, R M (Kingsley Napley) *O Q J1*
London EC1 *p50* 020 7814 1200

Fox, R S (Shacklocks)
Mansfield *p312* 01623 626141

Fox, S (CMHT Solicitors) *K1 X K3 Zm*
Walsall *p420* 01922 646400

Fox, Ms S (Ashurst LLP) *S2 C1 O Q C1 C1 Zb C1 Zb Zn*
London EC2 *p7* 020 7638 1111

Fox, S C (Ince & Co Services Ltd) *O M1 Zj*
London E1 *p44* 020 7481 0010

Fox, S G (Loosemores) *E S2 S1 L*
Cardiff *p179* 029 2022 4433

Fox, S H (Ralli Solicitors) *G O B2 C1*
Manchester *p309* 0870 998 9000

Fox, Ms S J (Withers LLP) *K1 K2*
London EC4 *p92* 020 7597 6000

Fox, T N (Software AG UK Ltd)
Derby *p456* 01332 611000

Fox, Ms V E (hlw Keeble Hawson LLP) *K1 P G N*
Sheffield *p375* 0114 272 2061

Fox-Edwards, Ms J (LG Lawyers) *L*
London SE1 *p50* 020 7379 0000

Fox-Murphy, Ms K (Taylor Wessing)
London EC4 *p86* 020 7300 7000

Foxall, P I (Burr Sugden) *S1 W E A1*
Keighley *p263* 01535 605407

Foxford, M J (Birchall Blackburn LLP) *P Q S1 T2 W C1 E C2 Ze S2 C3 I F1 Zl R2 T1*
Manchester *p301* 0161 236 0662
Preston *p356* 01772 561663

Foxler, J H (Joseph Foxler & Co) *K1 G N S1 W L H J1 B2*
Bury *p170* 0161 797 4126

Foxley, Miss E R (Muckle LLP) *E R2 S2*
Newcastle upon Tyne *p325* 0191 211 7777

Foxley, Mrs J M (Powys County Council)
Llandrindod Wells *p463* 01597 826000

Foxley, Mrs J M (James Button & Co) *Zy Zu Zza J2 Zg Zl R1*
Matlock *p313* 01629 735566

Foxon, R D (Barlows) *C1 S2 E S1 W L*
Leicester *p278* 0116 251 8295

Foxton, Ms R (The College of Law)
London WC1 *p105* 0800 289997

Foy, Miss C (Brabners Chaffe Street) *S1*
Liverpool *p286* 0151 600 3000

Foy, Miss E (Darbys Solicitors LLP) *K1 D1*
Oxford *p343* 01865 811700

Foy, F (Thompsons (formerly Robin/Brian Thompson & Partners)) *N*
Plymouth *p350* 01752 675810

Foy, J D (Debenhams Ottaway) *S2 E*
St Albans *p390* 01727 837161

Foy, M C (Malcolm C Foy & Co) *E C1 L R1 S1 W S2*
Doncaster *p211* 01302 340005
Rotherham *p367* 01709 836866

Foy, S P (Barker Booth & Eastwood) *N Q*
Blackpool *p146* 01253 362500

Foyster, E (Burton & Dyson) *K4 K1 W*
Gainsborough *p228* 01427 610761

Foyster, R C (Langleys) *Zr E K1 Q S1 W N*
Lincoln *p284* 01522 888555
York *p445* 01904 610886

Foyster, R M (Ashton KCJ) *N Q*
Felixstowe *p225* 01394 277188

Fozard, C R F (Pannone LLP) *C1 C2*
Manchester *p308* 0161 909 3000

Fozard, Ms R (Davidson Large LLP) *E L R1 S1 Zl Zc S2*
Harrogate *p240* 01423 727272

Fraenkel, Miss E M (Newtons) *W S1 T2*
Camden *p63* . .020 7794 9696 / 7435 5351

Frain, J L (Holt & Longworth) *F1 G H J1 K1 N O Q V D1 Zi Zl Zm*
Rossendale *p367* . .01706 213251 / 229131

Fraiser, Miss M (Sherwood Dunham) *G H B2*
Wellingborough *p424* 01933 276147

Frall, Ms M (Radcliffes Le Brasseur)
Westminster *p70* 020 7222 7040

France, Ms A (Forsters LLP) *E*
Westminster *p33* 020 7863 8333

France, Ms D (Holman Fenwick Willan) *C1 C2*
London EC3 *p42* 020 7264 8000

France, Ms I (Linklaters LLP)
London EC2 *p54* 020 7456 2000

France, M N J (Graham Withers & Co) *K1 N V D1 D2*
Shrewsbury *p380* 01743 236345

France, R (Longmores) *W T2 K4*
Hertford *p248* 01992 300333

France-Hayhurst, R C (Ronaldsons)
London WC1 *p73* 020 7580 6075

Francetti, D A (Meade-King) *E*
Bristol *p163* 0117 926 4121

Francey, A (Lupton Fawcett) *T1*
Leeds *p275* 0113 280 2000

Francis, Mrs A S (Percy Walker & Co) *W K4*
Hastings *p243* 01424 721234

Francis, A W (Fenwick Elliott) *C1 N O Q Zc Zj*
London WC2 *p31* 020 7421 1986

Francis, B H (Pinsent Masons LLP)
London EC2 *p67* 020 7418 7000

Francis, Mrs D (Palmers) *J1*
Basildon *p126* 01268 240000

Francis, D B (Lloyds & Cooper) *W S1 T1 A1 E L S2 Zd Zl T2*
Leominster *p283* 01568 613236

Francis, D J (Preston Redman) *S1 E L R1*
Bournemouth *p152* 01202 292424

Francis, Ms E A (Hanne & Co) *K1*
London SW11 *p38* 020 7228 0017

Francis, Miss E S (Coutts & Co)
London WC2 *p105* 020 7753 1403

Francis, G N (Persimmon Homes Legal Department)
York *p477* 01904 642199

Francis, Mrs J A (Francis & Co) *W*
Cranleigh *p202* 01483 267222

Francis, J G (Chebsey & Co) *G H*
Burnham *p168* 01628 660077

Francis, Mrs J M (Nottinghamshire County Council Legal Services Division)
West Bridgford *p475* 0115 977 3478

Francis, Ms K E (DLA Piper UK LLP)
London EC2 *p24* 0870 011 1111

Francis, K M (Davitt Jones Bould) *R1 Zu*
Taunton *p408* 01823 279279

Francis, Ms L (Tonbridge & Malling Borough Council)
West Malling *p476* 01732 876030

Francis, Miss L J (Olswang LLP) *Zf*
London WC1 *p64* 020 7067 3000

Francis, M (Tolhurst Fisher LLP)
Southend-on-Sea *p387* 01702 352511

Francis, M P (Field Seymour Parkes) *A1 S2 E L R1 R2*
Reading *p360* 0118 951 6200

Francis, P (Glovers Solicitors LLP) *C1 C2 Zb*
London W1 *p36* 020 7935 8882

Francis, Mrs P J L (LG Lawyers) *L P N*
London SE1 *p50* 020 7379 0000

Francis, R (Motley & Hope) *K1 J1 Q*
Biggleswade *p133* 01767 600600

Francis, R J (Association of Train Operating Companies)
London WC1 *p103* 020 7841 8000

Francis, R S (Lewis Francis Blackburn Bray)
Sheffield *p376* 0114 272 9721

Francis, Ms S S V (Kirby Sheppard) *K1 D1*
Bristol *p163* 0845 840 0045

Francis, T (Blackfords LLP)
Woking *p436* 01483 723331

Francis, T N (Plexus Law (A Trading Name of Parabis Law LLP)) *Zj Zq*
Colchester *p198* 0844 245 4950

Francis, Ms V (Ford Simey LLP) *G H K1*
Exeter *p221* 01392 274126

Franco, R (Pini Franco LLP) *C1 C2 E F1 M2 S2 U1*
London EC1 *p67* 020 7566 3140

Francois, Ms L N S (Thompsons (formerly Robin/Brian Thompson & Partners)) *N*
London SW19 *p87* 020 8947 4163

Francombe, N D (Clarke Willmott) *S2 E R2*
Taunton *p408*0845 209 1000 / 0117 305 6000

Franey, D F (Russell Jones & Walker) *J1 V Zg Zp*
Manchester *p309* 0161 383 3500

Frangeskides, C (Holman Fenwick Willan)
London EC3 *p42* 020 7264 8000

Frangeskides, Ms M (Orrick Herrington & Sutcliffe LLP)
London EC2 *p65* 020 7862 4600

Frank, Ms E (Childrens Legal Centre) *D1*
Colchester *p455* . . .01206 872466 / 873828
Colchester *p197* 01206 578282

Frank, G M (Frank & Co)
London W1 *p34* 020 7224 3837

Frank, R (Burchell Williams Limited) *G H*
Brighton *p159* 01273 606555

Frank, Ms S (Frank & Co)
London W1 *p34* 020 7224 3837

Frankel, M D (DWFM Beckman) *Zd C1 S2 E S1 T2 W*
Westminster *p25* 020 7872 0023

Frankel, M S D (Mayo Wynne Baxter LLP) *Zj N*
Brighton *p160* 01273 775533

Frankel, Ms T A (Gadsby Wicks) *N Zr*
Chelmsford *p186* 01245 494929

Frankel, W H (Penningtons)
London EC2 *p66* 020 7457 3000

Frankham, Mrs F M (Kent County Council)
Maidstone *p464* 01622 694320

Frankland, E J (Howes Percival LLP) *O Q*
Norwich *p334* 01603 762103

Frankland, Mrs H C (Doncaster Magistrates Court) *S1 W A1 E F1 J1 L R1 C1 K1 Zc Zi Zl*
Doncaster *p457* 01302 366711

Frankland, J A (Howes Percival LLP) *W T2 T1 S1 Zo*
Norwich *p334* 01603 762103

Frankland, Mrs K J (Farleys Solicitors LLP) *K1 D1*
Burnley *p169* 01282 798664

Frankland, M P (Byrne & Partners) *B2 O G*
London EC4 *p16* 020 7842 1616

Frankland, N J (Mills & Reeve) *N Zr Q Zq*
Birmingham *p140* 0121 454 4000

Frankland, R J (Redcar and Cleveland Borough Council)
Redcar *p465* 01642 466201

Franklin, Mrs A (County of Herefordshire District Council)
Hereford *p460* 01432 260266

Franklin, Mrs A (Herefordshire Council)
Hereford *p460* 01432 260000

Franklin, Mrs D J (Howard Outred & Co)
Dartford *p207* 01322 224881

Franklin, Mrs F M (Sacker & Partners LLP) *J1 Zo*
London EC2 *p76* 020 7329 6699

Franklin, Miss J A (Keene Marsland) *K3 K1*
Tunbridge Wells *p415* 01892 526442

Franklin, Ms J M (Canterbury City Council)
Canterbury *p453* 01227 862000

Franklin, M B (DLA Piper UK LLP)
London EC2 *p24* 0870 011 1111

Franklin, M L (Franklins LLP) *C1 E N Zd Zf*
Milton Keynes *p317* 01908 660966
Northampton *p332* 01604 828282

Franklin, N R (Rollits LLP) *A1 B1*
Hull *p258* 01482 323239

Franklin, R P (Wise Geary) *O Q W K3*
Banbury *p122* 01295 278500

Franklin, R T (Edwin Coe LLP) *F1 O Q Zj Zq*
London WC2 *p29* 020 7691 4000

Franklin, Mrs S (Pearlmans Solicitors LLP)
London NW4 *p66* 020 8201 6311

Franklin, Ms S A (Unilever PLC)
London EC4 *p110* 020 7822 5252

Franklin, Mrs S E (Turner Coulston) *N Q S1 K1 W V G J1*
Northampton *p333* 01604 622101

Franklin, S F (Martin Tolhurst Partnership LLP) *N Zr Zq B1 A1 J1 J2 L O Q*
Gravesend *p233* 01474 325531

Franks, D T (Michael Simkins LLP) *Ze Zf*
London WC1 *p79* 020 7874 5600

Franks, Mrs M B (Bradford & Bingley PLC)
Bingley *p449* 01274 555555

Franks, M L B (Debenhams Ottaway) *S1 S2 E*
Radlett *p358* 01923 857171

Franks, M M (William Sturges & Co) *Zd U2 S1 S2*
Westminster *p84* 020 7873 1000

Franks, Ms N (Linklaters LLP)
London EC2 *p54* 020 7456 2000

Franks, R A (Franks & Co) *O Q C1 B1 S1 E K1 L Zk Zc Zv Zl Zq S2*
London EC4 *p34* 020 7242 8008

Franks, Ms W H (Brian Koffman & Co) *S1 E*
Manchester *p306* 0161 832 3852

Franks, Ms Z (Newcastle Upon Tyne City Council)
Newcastle upon Tyne *p466* 0191 232 8520

Frankton, J R (Johns Gilbert & Frankton) *S1 W E S2 K4*
Rugby *p368* 01788 576384

Frankum, Ms A C (Penningtons) *Ze*
London EC2 *p66* 020 7457 3000

Frase, R (Dechert) *Zv Zb*
London EC4 *p26*. 020 7184 7000

Fraser, Mrs A E (Bright & Sons) *W K4*
Maldon *p299*. 01621 852323

Fraser, A I (Weld & Beavan) *S1 W S2 K4*
Enfield *p219*. 020 8363 1281

Fraser, A I (Wilson Barca LLP) *C1 E K1 L S1 W Zl*
London N19 *p92*. 020 7272 2072

Fraser, C A K (Charles Fraser & Co) *E A1 S1 L Zl*
Bury St Edmunds *p171* . . . 01284 750111
Cambridge *p175*. 01223 713300

Fraser, D J (R George Davies & Co) *A1 C1 E F1 J1 L O Q S1 S2 V W Zd Zg Zq*
Abergavenny *p113*. 01873 852535

Fraser, D R (Silverman Livermore) *N Q*
Runcorn *p369* 01928 714121

Fraser, D S (Wortley Redmayne Kershaw) *K1*
Chelmsford *p187*. 01245 491122

Fraser, Ms F (R G Frisby & Small) *K4 W*
Leicester *p279*. 0116 233 5522

Fraser, Ms G (Reynolds Porter Chamberlain LLP)
London E1 *p71* 020 3060 6000

Fraser, G (Clarke Kiernan) *D1 K1 Zo*
Tonbridge *p412* 01732 360999

Fraser, Miss G M (Fraser Wise & Co) *K1 J1 G H*
Grantham *p232* . . .01476 566646 / 561870

Fraser, Ms J (Cooke Painter Limited) *S1 K3 J1 Q W*
Bristol *p162* 01275 835569

Fraser, Miss L M Y (David Phillips & Partners) *D1 K1*
Bootle *p150* 0151 922 5525

Fraser, M (Breeze & Wyles Solicitors LLP)
Bishop's Stortford *p144* . . . 01279 715333

Fraser, P D (OGR Stock Denton) *O J1 L C1 E*
London N3 *p64* 020 8349 0321

Fraser, P H C (Meadows Fraser LLP) *C1 E S1 L R1 N S2 C2 Zc*
Weybridge *p430*. 01932 852057

Fraser, W (LG Lawyers)
London SE1 *p50*. 020 7379 0000

Fraser, W L (Fraser Wise & Co) *S1 K1 G E C1 J1 H D1 Zl*
Grantham *p232* . . .01476 566646 / 561870

Frawley, M W (Taylor Wessing) *B1 C1 N Zb*
London EC4 *p86*. 020 7300 7000

Frayling, J C (Sylvester Mackett) *S2 E*
Trowbridge *p414*. 01225 755621

Frayne, Miss C (Rowlinsons) *S1 S2*
Frodsham *p227* 01928 735333

Freakley, Ms R (Grindeys LLP) *B1 E P L Q R1 S1*
Stoke-on-Trent *p397*. 01782 846441

Freckleton, P J (Mark Jones & Partners) *G H*
Birkenhead *p134*. 0151 647 9594

Freckleton, Ms S J (Tewkesbury Borough Council)
Tewkesbury *p474* 01684 272012

Fredericks, Ms T F (Todmans SRE) *W T2*
Rayleigh *p359* 01268 774073

Free, I C (Ian C Free) *S1 S2 L W*
West Kirby *p428*. 0151 625 0000

Freear, Mrs D E (Doreen Freear Solicitor) *K1 S1*
Macclesfield *p297* 01625 611711

Freedman, C C E M (Freedmans)
London W4 *p34* 020 8987 9155

Freedman, D (Aubrey David) *L E S1 B1 W C1 J1 F1 S2 C2 R2*
Westminster *p25*. 020 7224 4410

Freedman, D (Freedman Sharman & Co) *F1 G H K1 M1 P*
Borehamwood *p150* 020 8953 9111

Freedman, J M (Freedman Green Dhokia) *K1 K3 W T2*
Camden *p34*. 020 7624 2981

Freedman, Ms S (Freedmans)
London W4 *p34* 020 8987 9155

Freeland, M F (Wollen Michelmore Solicitors) *N M1 J1 F1 A1 C1 B1 Zk Zp O Zq A2 Zd*
Newton Abbot *p330* 01626 332266

Freeland, R C B (Simmons & Simmons)
London EC2 *p79*. 020 7628 2020

Freely, P A (W H Matthews & Co) *C1 E F1 J1 K1 S1 N Q O W Zc Zi Zl S2*
Islington *p59*. 020 7251 4942

Freeman, A (Linklaters LLP)
London EC2 *p54*. 020 7456 2000

Freeman, Mrs C (Durham County Council)
Durham *p457* 0191 383 3513

Freeman, D (Bevans) *L*
London WC2 *p12* 020 7353 9995

Freeman, E (Glaisyers Solicitors LLP) *S1 W E S2*
Manchester *p304* 0161 224 3311

Freeman, Ms E (Kundert & Co) *K1*
Coventry *p200*. 024 7668 4928

Freeman, E M (PCB Solicitors LLP) *G H K1 S1 W D1 L Q*
Telford *p409*. 01952 403000

Freeman, G C (The Dures Partnership LLP) *E C1 C2 B1 J1 S1 W I O T2 Zh Zi Zl Zv Ze*
Liverpool *p287*. 0151 242 5111

Freeman, H (Freemans Solicitors) *E S1 O Q L Zb*
London W1 *p34* 020 7935 3522
London SE15 *p67* 020 7703 2285

Freeman, H H (Gilbert Turner Coomber) *S1 S2 W*
Waltham Forest *p35* 020 8520 5886

Freeman, Mrs H M (Hempsons) *Zr*
Manchester *p305* 0161 228 0011

Freeman, H P (B D Laddie) *E S1 W R2 S2*
Westminster *p51*. 020 7963 8585

Freeman, J (Speechly Bircham LLP) *K1 K2*
London EC4 *p81*. 020 7427 6400

Freeman, J (Freeman Box) *E S1 N P L R1 K1 B1 Zi Zl*
London W1 *p34* 020 7486 9041

Freeman, Miss J M (Dickinson Manser)
Poole *p352* 01202 673071

Freeman, K M (Freemans) *Zl E S1 Zr N*
Newcastle upon Tyne *p324* . 0191 222 1030

Freeman, Ms L P S (Reed Smith LLP) *Zc*
London EC2 *p71*. 020 3116 3000

Freeman, M (Trethowans LLP) *Q O N L Ze F1*
Salisbury *p371*. 01722 412512

Freeman, Mrs M (Freeman & Co Solicitors) *K1*
Wetherby *p429* 01937 583111

Freeman, N (Horwood & James LLP) *C1 E S1 R1 Ze Zd*
Aylesbury *p121* 01296 487361

Freeman, N (Freeman & Co)
Manchester *p304* 0161 236 7007
Manchester *p304* 0161 233 2130

Freeman, P (Gates and Partners)
London EC3 *p35*. 020 7220 5950

Freeman, P J (Simmons & Simmons)
London EC2 *p79*. 020 7628 2020

Freeman, P R (Moore & Tibbits) *G H D1 K1 S1 M1 P L*
Warwick *p422* 01926 491181

Freeman, Miss R (Miles Preston & Co) *K1*
London EC4 *p69*. 020 7583 0583

Freeman, R (Hogan Lovells International LLP)
London EC1 *p42*. 020 7296 2000

Freeman, R (Chattertons Solicitors)
Sleaford *p381* 01529 411500

Freeman, R A (King & Co) *S1 W E C1 T1 L V J1 A1*
Cambridge *p175*. . .01223 365432 / 566038

Freeman, R J S (National Grid PLC)
Warwick *p471* 01926 653000

Freeman, R N G (Morecrofts Solicitors LLP) *K1*
Liverpool *p290*. 0151 236 8871

Freeman, S (Gabbs LLP) *E C1 S1 L A1 R1*
Hereford *p248* 01432 353481

Freeman, S (Wedlake Bell LLP)
London WC1 *p91* 020 7395 3000

Freeman, Ms S (Lawrence Lupin) *Zi*
Wembley *p426*. 020 8733 7200

Freeman, S J (Sintons LLP) *S1 K1 L W D1*
Newcastle upon Tyne *p326* . 0191 226 7878

Freeman, S J (LDJ Solicitors) *S2 E S1*
Nuneaton *p339* 024 7674 5000

Freeman, S R T (Freemans Solicitors) *A1 W T2 Zd Zm*
Bath *p127* 01225 330733

Freeman-Wallace, R D (Watson Burton LLP) *E R2 S2*
Newcastle upon Tyne *p327* . 0845 901 2100

Freemantle, J (Ambrose Appelbe) *Q O*
London WC2 *p6* 020 7242 7000

Freemantle, Mrs J (Surrey County Council)
Kingston upon Thames *p462*. 020 8541 9088

Freer, G J (McGrigors LLP)
London EC4 *p56*. 020 7054 2500

Freer, K (Widdows Mason) *C1 E F1 J1 K1 M1 N P S1 W Zl Zt*
Leigh *p282*. 01942 673311
Westhoughton *p429* 01942 816515

Freer, P R (Freer & Archer) *B1 D1 F1 G H J1 K1 L Q O Zl Zj*
Leicester *p279*. 0116 241 3199

Freeston, S T (E C Lidster & Co) *H G*
Grimsby *p235* 01472 348417

Freestone, Miss C M (Bristol City Council) *K1 D1 Zg*
Bristol *p451* 0117 922 2000

Freestone, Miss H (Browne Jacobson LLP) *Q Zr Zq*
Nottingham *p336*. 0115 976 6000

Freestone, Ms L (Herbert Smith LLP)
London EC2 *p40*. 020 7374 8000

Freeth, R (Anthony Collins Solicitors LLP) *X Zu*
Birmingham *p137* 0121 200 3242

Freitas, A A G (McKinnells) *G H*
Lincoln *p284*. 01522 541181

Frempong, Miss D (Campion & Co) *D1 G H K1 L*
Nottingham *p336*. 0115 947 6373

French, A (Stewarts Law LLP) *J1 Zp*
London EC4 *p83*. 020 7822 8000

French, A D (Clifford Chance)
London E14 *p20* 020 7006 1000

French, B A (Blaser Mills) *C1 Ze Zza*
High Wycombe *p249*. 01494 450171

French, B G (Blocks) *K1 N O S1 Q D1 E W Zc*
Ipswich *p262*. 01473 230033

French, Mrs C J (William Wright & Son) *F1 K1 K4 L W S1*
Dudley *p213*. 01384 255344

French, D (Squire Sanders (UK) LLP) *S1*
Birmingham *p142* 0121 222 3000

French, D I (French & Co Solicitors Ltd) *G H K1 D1 N L J1 V*
Sutton Coldfield *p403* 0121 362 7330

French, Mrs D V (French & Co Solicitors Ltd) *S1 K1 L W R1 V J1 D1 E F1*
Sutton Coldfield *p403* 0121 362 7330

French, G A (Alan Edwards & Co) *L G H N Q Zg Zh*
Kensington & Chelsea *p28*. 020 7221 7644

French, Mrs J (French & Co) *S1 E K1 C1 F1 W D1*
Nottingham *p337*. 0115 955 1111

French, J (Band Hatton LLP) *Q O F1 J1 T1 W Zc Zj V Zn Zv Zt Zm M2 M4*
Coventry *p200*. 024 7663 2121

French, J A (Pinsent Masons LLP) *O Q Zc*
London EC2 *p67*. 020 7418 7000

French, Mrs K (Squire Sanders (UK) LLP) *A1 F1*
Leeds *p277* 0113 284 7000

French, K (Dixon & Templeton) *S1 S2 L W A1 C1 R1 E Zc*
Fordingbridge *p227* 01425 652194

French, Ms K M (Barlow Lyde & Gilbert LLP)
London EC3 *p10*. 020 7247 2277

French, M S (Edward Hayes LLP) *G H B2*
London EC4 *p39*. 020 7353 0011

French, M S J (Somerville & Savage) *K1 S1 W*
Torquay *p413* 01803 324500
Torquay *p413* 01803 312700

French, Mrs P (Pannone LLP) *N*
Manchester *p308* 0161 909 3000

French, Ms S (McDermott French) *G H K1 S1*
Newton Abbot *p329* 01626 200177

French, Mrs V V (Birketts LLP) *S1 S2*
Ipswich *p262*. 01473 232300

Fretten, I (Frettens Solicitors) *C1 C2 E J1 L S1 W Zc Zh S2 D1 R2*
Christchurch *p194* 01202 491777

Fretten, Ms K (Frettens Solicitors) *J1*
Christchurch *p194* 01202 491777

Fretten, M I (Frettens Solicitors) *C1 C2 U2 J1*
Christchurch *p194* 01202 491777

Fretwell, Ms K (Blandy & Blandy) *K1*
Reading *p360* 0118 951 6800

Fretwell, P A (Blake Lapthorn) *N Zr X*
Portsmouth *p354*. 023 9222 1122
Chichester *p192* 01243 786668

Fretwell, Mrs S (Shirley Fretwell) *S1 W*
Ilkeston *p261* 0115 932 3623

Frew, A (Lodders Solicitors LLP) *E S2*
Stratford-upon-Avon *p400* . . 01789 293259

Frew, J W (DWF) *Zb*
Manchester *p303* 0161 603 5000

Frey, Ms S (Howard Kennedy LLP) *E*
London W1 *p48* 020 7636 1616

Freyne, Miss M A M (Mayer Brown International LLP) *E O*
London EC2 *p59*. 020 3130 3000

Fribbance, Ms G M (Nantes) *Zd N Zo J1 Zm J2 Zp*
Bridport *p158* 01308 422313

Fricker, D (Jones Day) *Zb*
London EC4 *p46*. 020 7039 5959

Friday, K (Glovers Solicitors LLP) *Zb B1 Q*
London W1 *p36* 020 7935 8882

Friday, Ms M (Vickers & Co)
Ealing *p89*. . . .020 8579 2559 / 8840 3999

Friday, S M (Percy Short & Cuthbert) *S1 E W L S2 R2*
Islington *p67*. 020 7700 0265

Friebe, Miss K E (DLA Piper UK LLP) *E R2 S2*
London EC2 *p24*. 0870 011 1111

Friedlander, R T (Parrott & Coales LLP) *S1 W C1 E A1 T1 L*
Aylesbury *p121* 01296 318500

Friedman, Ms R (Bindmans LLP) *N*
London WC1 *p12* 020 7833 4433

Friend, Mrs C (Peters & Peters) *O*
London EC4 *p67*. 020 7629 7991

Friend, H (Gregory Abrams Davidson LLP) *S1 S2 W*
Liverpool *p288*. 0151 236 5000

Friend, Mrs M J (Eldridges) *S1 W K4*
Freshwater *p227*. 01983 752492
Newport *p328* 01983 524741

Friend, M J (Michael Friend) *N Q O J1 J2 R1 G E Zj Zk Zv Zc Zw Zq Zr*
Esher *p220* 01372 468098

Friend, M W (Allen & Overy LLP)
London E1 *p5* 020 3088 0000

Friend, R S (Greenwood & Co) *E C1 N Q S1 M1 L B1 O W Zb Zl Zc S2*
London EC1 *p37*. 020 7831 8386

Friend, Miss S J (British Olympic Association)
London SW18 *p104* 020 8871 2677

Friend, Mrs V O (Silverman Sherliker LLP) *K1 K2*
London EC2 *p78*. 020 7749 2700

Frieze, Ms J (Russell Jones & Walker)
Manchester *p309* 0161 383 3500

Frieze, S A (Brooke North LLP)
Leeds *p272* 0113 283 2100

Friis, Ms L J (Friis & Radstone) *S1 W L E S2*
Stevenage *p394* 01438 741001

Frimond, Mrs J M (Julia Frimond Solicitors) *K1 K3*
Guildford *p236*. 01483 452224

Frimston, R M (Russell-Cooke LLP) *W T1 Zm Zd*
London SW15 *p74*. 020 8789 9111

Fripp, Mrs E F (Alsters Kelley) *J1*
Leamington Spa *p270* 0844 561 0100
Nuneaton *p339* 0844 561 0100

Frisby, Miss B A (Rix & Kay Solicitors LLP) *C1 S2 E C2 S1*
Hove *p255*. 01273 329797

Frisby, M C (Stevens & Bolton) *N*
Guildford *p237*. 01483 302264

Frith, B (Watson Burton LLP)
Newcastle upon Tyne *p327* . 0845 901 2100

Frith, K (Harrison Bundey) *G H*
Leeds *p274* 0113 200 7400

Frith, L (Ramsdens Solicitors) *S1*
Huddersfield *p256* 01484 821500

Frith, Ms M (Trowers & Hamlins)
London EC3 *p88*. 020 7423 8000

Frith, S (Motley & Hope) *E A1 S1 S2*
Biggleswade *p133* 01767 600600

Fritsche, Miss S E M (Cumberland Ellis Peirs) *F1 L O P Q*
London WC1 *p23* 020 7242 0422

Frixou, Ms B (Judge Sykes Frixou) *C1 E J1 T1 Ze Zf*
London WC2 *p47* 020 7379 5114

Frochot, Ms M (Field Fisher Waterhouse LLP) *Zb*
London EC3 *p31*. 020 7861 4000

Froggatt, Miss H P (Nelsons) *N Q L Zq F1*
Nottingham *p338*. 0115 958 6262

Froggatt, Miss P (LloydLaw LLP)
London SE1 *p55*. 020 7403 5050

Froggatt, P H (Stevenage Borough Council)
Stevenage *p472* 01438 242242

Froggatt, Mrs R (Elliot Mather LLP) *K1*
Mansfield *p311*. 01623 655666

Froggatt, Miss S (CMHT Solicitors) *Zm G K3*
Brownhills *p167* 01543 372347

Frogson, R (Rollits LLP) *C1 C2 Zb*
York *p445* 01904 625790

Frogson, R J (Gordons LLP)
Leeds *p273* 0113 227 0100

From, Miss C D A (C From & Co) *S1 E B1 W F1 O Zc Zb Zd*
London W4 *p34* 020 8995 6153

Fromont, Miss S (IBB Solicitors) *N*
Uxbridge *p417*. 0845 638 1381

Froome, D (Capsticks Solicitors LLP) *Q Zr N*
London SW19 *p18*. 020 8780 2211
London EC3 *p49*. 020 7667 9667

Frosdick, A C (Barnsley Metropolitan Borough Council)
Barnsley *p448* 01226 770770

Frost, Ms A E (Smith Chamberlain) *T2 W T1 Zo*
Wellingborough *p425* 01933 224971

Frost, Miss A J (Solihull Metropolitan Borough Council)
Solihull *p471*. 0121 704 6000

Frost, A N (Woodfines LLP) *N*
Sandy *p372* 01767 680251

Frost, C E (Squire Sanders (UK) LLP)
London EC2 *p81*. 020 7655 1000

Frost, D R (Read Roper & Read) *N Q L F1*
Manchester *p309* 0161 832 6905

Frost, J A C (Belcher Frost) *S1 S2*
Emsworth *p218* 01243 377231

Frost, P G (Calthrops) *S1 A1 W E R1 N L B1 K1*
Spalding *p389*. 01775 724381

Frost, Miss P H (Gregg Latchams LLP)
Bristol *p162* 0117 906 9400

Frost, P J (Pendle Borough Council)
Nelson *p466*. 01282 661661

Frost, P J (Herbert Smith LLP) *C1 J1*
London EC2 *p40*. 020 7374 8000

Frost, R (E J Winter & Son) *S1 W S2 K4*
Reading *p361* 0118 957 4424

Frost, S (O'Neill Patient) *O Q J1 B1*
Stockport *p396*. 0161 483 8555

Frost, Ms S C (Nicholson Portnell) *W K4 T2*
Hexham *p249* 01434 603656

Froster, S K (Juliet Hardick Solicitors)
Bath *p127* 01225 311177

Frostick, N G (Austins Penny & Thorne) *E S2 W*
Berkhamsted *p131*. 01442 872141

Froude, Ms K S (Willans LLP) *O Q*
Cheltenham *p189* 01242 514000

Frowd, C J (Alsters Kelley) *E C2 L*
Leamington Spa *p270* 0844 561 0100

Fruhman, H L (Alphafood Ltd)
Bury *p452*. 0161 797 8600

Fruhman, S H (Fruhman Davies Livingstones)
Manchester *p304* 0161 833 0578

Fry, J C (Hodge Jones & Allen LLP) *N*
London NW1 *p41* 020 7874 8300

Fry, Ms M (Ashurst LLP)
London EC2 *p7* 020 7638 1111

Fry, N (Bindmans LLP) *J1*
London WC1 *p12* 020 7833 4433

Fry, R H P (DAC Beachcroft) *C1 Zf*
London EC4 *p24*. 020 7242 1011

Fryer, Ms C A (Bristol City Council)
Bristol *p451* 0117 922 2000

Fryer, J M (Ramsdens Solicitors) *C1 W E T1 A1 Zd Zc S2 T2 C2*
Huddersfield *p256* 01484 821500

Fryer, L D (Pinsent Masons LLP) *O Q Zc*
London EC2 *p67*. 020 7418 7000

Fryett- Kerr, Mrs V (Hertfordshire County Council)
Hertford *p460* 01992 555555

Fryzer, W A (Dechert) *E*
London EC4 *p26*. 020 7184 7000

Fuchter, C V (Stephens & Son LLP) *J1 L N O Q Zq*
Chatham *p185*. 01634 811444

Fudge, I G (Bissmire Fudge & Co) *B1 E G K1 L M1 N P H S1 Zc Zl*
Haverfordwest *p244* 01437 764723
Pembroke Dock *p345* 01646 685501

Fuff, Mrs H (Field Fisher Waterhouse LLP) *T2 W K4*
London EC3 *p31*. 020 7861 4000

Fugard, R (Linklaters LLP)
London EC2 *p54*. 020 7456 2000

Fuggle, R E (HMG Law LLP) *S1 E C1 A3 L S2*
Oxford *p343*. 01865 244661

Fugler, B M (Fuglers)
London W1 *p34* 020 7323 6450

Fugler, M C (Fugler & Co) *E S1*
Maidenhead *p298* 01628 670935

Fuhrmann, Mrs C (Miller Parris) *K3 K1*
Worthing *p442*. 01903 205771

Fulcher, D S (Fulchers) *S1 K1 O D1 N E W K2*
Woking *p436*. 01483 885522

See p634 for the Key to Work Categories

Fulcher, K (Hayes & Storr) *W K4*
Holt *p251* 01263 712835

Fulda, S (Berg Legal) *N P*
Manchester *p301* 0161 833 9211

Fulford, Mrs S K (Carvill & Johnson LLP) *N W J1*
Birmingham *p136* 0121 476 9000

Fulford, S R G (Barlow Robbins LLP) *L Zq E O Q*
Guildford *p235* 01483 562901

Fullagar, J V S (FullagarBrooks) *J1 O N Zp Zc*
Swindon *p406* 01793 777007

Fullen, Ms A D (Cheltenham & Gloucester PLC)
Gloucester *p459* 01452 372372

Fuller, Mrs A (IBB Solicitors)
Uxbridge *p417* 0845 638 1381

Fuller, Mrs C (Terrells LLP) *K3 K1*
Peterborough *p347* 01733 896789

Fuller, C R S (Simmons & Simmons)
London EC2 *p79* 020 7628 2020

Fuller, Miss E (Edward Hands & Lewis) *K1 K3 O N F1*
Loughborough *p293* 01509 216161

Fuller, G D (Kingsfords) *W T2 Zd K4*
Ashford *p119* 01233 665544
Whitstable *p431* 01227 276276
Maidstone *p299* 01622 698000

Fuller, G W (Allen & Overy LLP)
London E1 *p5* 020 3088 0000

Fuller, Ms J L V (Thompson & Jackson) *K1 D1 K3*
Plymouth *p350* 01752 665037 / 221171
Plymouth *p351* 01752 663295

Fuller, L R (MacLaren Britton) *G H J2*
Nottingham *p338* 0115 941 1469

Fuller, M D (Fullers Family Law Practice LLP)
Bedford *p130* 01234 343134

Fuller, Miss R (Berry & Berry) *D1 K1*
Tunbridge Wells *p414* 01892 526344

Fuller, Ms R E (ClarksLegal LLP) *T2 W*
London WC2 *p20* 020 7539 8000

Fuller, R J (Pictons Solicitors LLP) *G H*
Hemel Hempstead *p247* 01442 242441

Fuller, Miss S A (Derrick Bridges & Co) *K1 Q L N W V S1*
Barnet *p123* 020 8449 7326

Fuller, Miss S J (Austin Ray) *W K4*
Milton Keynes *p316* 01908 769648

Fuller, S J (Harris Cartier LLP) *E B1 C1 S2 T1 M1 R1 Zc C2 R2 C3 O Zo*
London WC2 *p39* 020 7405 7100

Fuller, Miss S M (Lincoln Financial Group) *C1 C2 Zj Zo*
Gloucester *p459* 0845 678 8888

Fuller, Mrs Y M (Barringtons Solicitors) *S1 W*
Farnham *p224* 01252 741751

Fullerlove, M R (Wiggin Osborne Fullerlove) *T1 T2 W Zd Zo*
Cheltenham *p189* 01242 710200
London SW1 *p91* 020 7290 2456

Fullwood, R E (HSR Law (Hayes, Son & Richmond)) *S1 A1 E S2 W*
Epworth *p219* 01427 872206
Doncaster *p211* 01302 347800
Gainsborough *p228* 01427 613831
Doncaster *p212* 01302 341414

Fulton, N A (Stafford Young Jones) *W T2*
London EC4 *p82* 020 7623 9490

Fulton, R A (Goodrich Control Systems)
Solihull *p471* 0121 451 5711

Fung, K T (DLA Piper UK LLP)
London EC2 *p24* 0870 011 1111

Funnell, Ms A (Hart Reade) *D1 K1 K3*
Eastbourne *p215* 01323 727321

Funnell, A (Andrew Jackson) *C1*
Hull *p257* 01482 325242

Furber, D W (Bury Magistrates Court)
Bury *p452* 0161 447 8600

Furber, J (Farrer & Co LLP)
London WC2 *p31* 020 3375 7000

Furber, Miss S L (Aaron & Partners LLP Solicitors) *W T2*
Chester *p190* 01244 405555

Furlong, Ms C A (Burnett Barker) *G H B2*
Bury St Edmunds *p171* 01284 701131

Furman, M A (Macfarlanes) *C1 Zb*
London EC4 *p56* 020 7831 9222

Furman, N R (EC Lidster & Co) *G H*
Grimsby *p235* 01472 348417

Furmston, Mrs N J (Barker Gotelee Solicitors) *K1 K2 K3*
Ipswich *p262* 01473 611211
Ipswich *p262* 01473 232300

Furness, C G (Atkins Hope Solicitors) *G H*
Croydon *p204* 020 8680 5018

Furness, I C (Lupton Fawcett) *N B1 M1 Q J1 O Zw Zr*
Leeds *p275* 0113 280 2000

Furness, Ms K (@Cornwall Law)
Truro *p414* 01872 222688 / 222712

Furness, P J (Clark Willis) *G H K1 K3 J1*
Darlington *p206* 01325 281111

Furness, R A (Mylles & Co) *D1 D2 K1 Q Ze Zk*
Sunninghill *p402* 01344 623388

Furness, R M (Swinburne Maddison) *S1 L E C1 K1 W A1 P J1 F1 Zb Zi Zl*
Durham *p214* 0191 384 2441 / 384 7455

Furnish, Ms C (Thomson Snell & Passmore) *Zr N*
Tunbridge Wells *p415* 01892 510000

Furniss, C J (Gordons LLP)
Leeds *p273* 0113 227 0100

Furniss, Mrs M A (Gabbitas Robins) *K1 Q N*
Marlow *p313* 01628 472600

Furniss, Miss R (Shammah Nicholls LLP) *O Q W A1 F1 J1*
Manchester *p309* 0161 832 9272

Furnivall, P W (Mills & Reeve) *T1 T2 W Zd*
Norwich *p335* 01603 660155

Fursdon, Ms K (Fursdon Knapper) *Zi*
Plymouth *p349* 01752 309090

Fursey, M J (Arnold Thomson Limited) *A1 E S1*
Towcester *p413* 01327 350266

Fursman, P (Collins Dryland & Thorowgood LLP) *W Q L*
Tilehurst *p411* 0118 942 2448

Fursman, W (Collins Dryland & Thorowgood LLP) *S1 E K1 M1 N P B1 C1 F1 J1 L O Q*
Tilehurst *p411* 0118 942 2448

Fuschillo, Miss C (Pothecary Witham Weld) *W*
Westminster *p69* 020 7821 8211

Fusco, Miss A (DWF) *N Q*
Manchester *p303* 0161 603 5000

Fusco, Ms C (Anthony Gold) *K1 K3 D1*
London SE1 *p6* 020 7940 4000

Futter, D (Ashurst LLP)
London EC2 *p7* 020 7638 1111

Fyfe, S (Taylor Walton LLP)
Luton *p295* 01582 731161

Fyles, Miss H E (DWF) *B1 O C1*
Manchester *p303* 0161 603 5000
Manchester *p303* 0161 236 8992

Fynn, L C (Horsey Lightly Fynn) *R1 P Zl Zg Zw*
Bournemouth *p152* 01202 551991

Fyson, A W (Sharp & Partners) *E C1 Zc Ze S2*
Long Eaton *p293* 0115 973 4111

Fyson, Miss L M (Southend-on-Sea Borough Council)
Southend-on-Sea *p472* 01702 215000
St Albans *p472* 01727 866100

Fytch, Miss V J (Max Barford & Co) *S1 S2 W*
Tunbridge Wells *p414* 01892 539379

G

Gabay, N J (Thomson Snell & Passmore) *C1 T1 C2*
Tunbridge Wells *p415* 01892 510000

Gabb, C M (Eddowes Waldron) *K1 D1*
Derby *p208* 01332 348484

Gabb, L H (Bond Pearce LLP) *E Zn*
Plymouth *p349* 0845 415 0000

Gabbie, L (Bracher Rawlins LLP) *J1 Zza Zp*
London WC1 *p15* 020 7404 9400

Gabbitas, A A (Rugby Borough Council)
Rugby *p470* 01788 533533

Gabbitas, Mrs E L (Clerk to Sheffield Justices)
Sheffield *p470* 0114 276 0760

Gabbitas, J G (Gabbitas Robins) *E T1 W L S1 R1 A1 Zn P C1 Zd*
Marlow *p313* 01628 472600

Gabbutt, T J (Barlow Rowland) *N O Q Zl Zq J1 P Zc Zh Zj Zk Zp W*
Accrington *p114* 01254 300400

Gabell, Mrs J M (Shepway District Council)
Folkestone *p458* 01303 852248

Gaborak, Miss R (Leeds City Council) *L M1*
Leeds *p462* 0113 224 3513

Gabrielli, Ms I (British Telecommunications PLC)
London EC1 *p104* 020 7356 6181

Gadd, Miss P S (Pearson Maddin Solicitors) *W F1 T1 Zd*
New Malden *p321* 020 8949 9500

Gaddam, Ms P R (Zaiwalla & Co)
London WC2 *p93* 020 7312 1000

Gaddes, Ms A (Hellewell Pasley & Brewer) *D1 K1 N S1 V Zo K2*
Batley *p128* 01924 472596

Gaddes, L (Hellewell Pasley & Brewer) *S1 S2 E C1 W Q N K3*
Dewsbury *p210* 01924 455515

Gadhia, Mrs H (Trott & Gentry) *K1 N*
London N1 *p88* 020 3119 3150

Gadhia, S (Stephenson Harwood) *Q Zq B1*
London EC2 *p82* 020 7329 4422

Gadsby, Mrs G M (Gadsby Wicks) *N Zr*
Chelmsford *p186* 01245 494929

Gadsby, Ms J K (Hodge Jones & Allen LLP) *N*
London NW1 *p41* 020 7874 8300

Gadsden, Miss E (Coupe Bradbury) *K4 W T2*
Lytham *p296* 01253 736670

Gadsden, Miss J C (Gloucestershire County Council - Legal & Democratic Services) *P K1 G S1 L Zl*
Gloucester *p459* 01452 425203

Gadwah, Ms B A (Bibi Gadwah Solicitors) *K1 K3*
London E14 *p12* 020 7377 6102

Gaff, Ms A (Covent Garden Family Law) *K1 D1 D2*
Camden *p23* 020 7257 6130

Gaffney, D J (Margary & Miller) *A1 E S1 T2 W Zd*
Southwold *p389* 01502 723308

Gaffney, R D (Taylor Vinters) *N*
Cambridge *p176* 01223 423444

Gafford, G (Dyakowski Gafford) *P M1 S1 K1 G L W H J1*
Chipping Norton *p193* 01608 643051

Gagan, H (Rita Sen Solicitors) *K4 K1 Q T2 W*
Bognor Regis *p148* 01243 263658

Gage, Mrs K E (Adams & Remers) *K3 K1*
Lewes *p283* 01273 480616
Brighton *p160* 01273 775533
Tunbridge Wells *p415* 01892 510000

Gage, R (Hoole & Co) *Zi G*
Bristol *p163* 0117 942 8871

Gage, Ms S (Thompsons (formerly Robin/Brian Thompson & Partners))
London SW19 *p87* 020 8947 4163

Gagie, M (Simmons & Simmons)
London EC2 *p79* 020 7628 2020

Gaines, Miss S K (Brachers) *S2 E*
Maidstone *p299* 01622 690691

Gair, Mrs A (Clifton Ingram LLP) *J1 Q*
Wokingham *p437* 0118 978 0099

Gair, R J (Ashton KCJ) *N O*
Ipswich *p262* 01473 232425

Gait, Mrs A (Green Williamson Solicitors)
Wakefield *p418* 01924 291400

Gait, R C C (Osborne Clarke) *R2*
London EC2 *p65* 020 7105 7000

Gaitskell, Mrs Z (Beviss & Beckingsale) *K3 K1 D1*
Honiton *p252* 01404 548050

Gajjar, N (Treasury Solicitors Department)
London WC2 *p110* 020 7210 3000

Gal, Miss C (Watkins & Gunn) *S1 S2*
Pontypool *p352* 01495 762244

Galbraith, Miss C (Jones Day) *C1*
London EC4 *p46* 020 7039 5959

Gale, A (Maurice Smiths) *D1 E K1 K4 N Q S1 T1 T2 W Zl Zu*
Castleford *p183* 01977 557171
Pontefract *p351* 01977 794395

Gale, C D (Loveday & Keighley) *A1 C1 E F1 L S1 W*
Matlock *p313* 01629 583142 / 56660

Gale, C R (RSPCA) *S1 E N G W A1 L Zc*
Horsham *p461* 0870 010 1181

Gale, G (Blanchards Bailey LLP) *D1 K1*
Blandford Forum *p147* 01258 459361

Gale, Miss J L (O'Donnells) *K1 K3*
Preston *p357* 01772 881000

Gale, J S (Stephenson Harwood) *C1 Zo U2*
London EC2 *p82* 020 7329 4422

Gale, Ms M J (Carter Bells LLP) *W T2*
Kingston upon Thames *p267* 020 8939 4000

Gale, Mrs R J (Brown & Company) *S1 W*
Market Harborough *p312* 01858 434204

Gale, Mrs S (Parker Arrenberg)
London SE6 *p65* 020 8695 2330

Gale, S (Herbert Smith LLP) *B1 C1*
London EC2 *p40* 020 7374 8000

Gale, Miss S B (Metropolitan Police Directorate of Legal Services)
London SW1 *p108* 020 7230 7210

Galea, V (Osborne Clarke) *J1*
London EC2 *p65* 020 7105 7000

Galic, Miss D (B P Collins LLP) *E S1 S2*
Gerrards Cross *p229* 01753 889995

Gall, D H (David Gall LLB Solicitor) *S1 L W*
Hawes *p245* 01969 667171

Gall, G R (Howard Pollok & Webb) *B1 D1 K1 L N O Q Zl K3 Zq*
Norwich *p334* 01603 660051
Great Yarmouth *p234* 01493 853725

Gallacher, Ms M (NFLA Ltd) *K1 K3 D1*
Wellingborough *p424* 01933 222700

Gallagher, A (Birchall Blackburn LLP) *J2 N*
Preston *p356* 01772 561663

Gallagher, A (Denby & Co) *G H B2 D1 W Q O A3 J2 Zi Zm Zq Zg*
Ulverston *p416* 01229 582283

Gallagher, A (Denby & Co) *G H O Q N D1 K1 Zl*
Barrow-in-Furness *p125* 01229 822366

Gallagher, A (Hogan Lovells International LLP)
London EC1 *p42* 020 7296 2000

Gallagher, A J (BAE Systems PLC)
London SW1 *p104* 01252 373232

Gallagher, C A (Zermansky & Partners) *L M1 Zp*
Leeds *p278* 0113 245 9766

Gallagher, C J (Birchall Blackburn LLP) *N K1 Q V G H J1 W S1 D1 Zr Zq*
Preston *p356* 01772 744744

Gallagher, C M (Hodge Jones & Allen LLP) *W*
London NW1 *p41* 020 7874 8300

Gallagher, D (Field Fisher Waterhouse LLP)
London EC3 *p31* 020 7861 4000

Gallagher, D B (Burnett Barker) *G H Zt Zl B2*
Bury St Edmunds *p171* 01284 701131

Gallagher, D J (Lawson Coppock & Hart) *N J1 O Q B1 K3 K1 Zk Zq*
Manchester *p306* 0161 832 5944

Gallagher, Ms E A (Hay & Kilner) *K1 D1*
Newcastle upon Tyne *p325* 0191 232 8345
Newcastle upon Tyne *p326* 0191 232 8451

Gallagher, Mrs J (Thomson Snell & Passmore) *C1*
Tunbridge Wells *p415* 01892 510000

Gallagher, J D (Shelter Legal Services) *L*
London EC1 *p109* 020 7505 2000

Gallagher, Mrs J S (British Telecommunications PLC)
London EC1 *p104* 020 7356 6181

Gallagher, Mrs K L (Maples Teesdale LLP) *E S2*
London EC2 *p58* 020 7600 3800

Gallagher, Mrs M (Fursdon Knapper)
Plymouth *p349* 01752 309090

Gallagher, P J (John Boyle & Co) *G H Zl*
Redruth *p362* 01209 213507
Truro *p414* 01872 272356

Gallagher, S D (Neale Turk Rochfort) *K1 D1 K3*
Camberley *p173* 01276 20551
Farnborough *p224* 01252 515155

Gallagher, S J (Morrish Solicitors LLP) *J1*
Leeds *p276* 0113 245 0733

Gallagher, Miss S M (Marsden Rawsthorn LLP) *E L*
Preston *p357* 01772 799600

Gallagher, S P (IBM United Kingdom Ltd)
London SE1 *p107* 020 7202 3000

Gallagher, S R (Atherton Godfrey) *E C1 Zl*
Doncaster *p211* 01302 320621

Gallagher, T (Roberts Moore Nicholas Jones) *G H*
Birkenhead *p134* 0151 647 0000

Gallagher, Miss Y (LG Lawyers) *C1*
London SE1 *p50* 020 7379 0000

Gallaher, Mrs L J (Bird & Co) *K1 D1 W*
Grantham *p232* 01476 591711

Gallardo Garcia, R G F (SJ Berwin LLP)
London EC4 *p75* 020 7111 2222

Gallaway, D M P (Blake Lapthorn) *S1 E L W*
Portsmouth *p354* 023 9222 1122

Galledari, A (Jones Day) *Zb*
London EC4 *p46* 020 7039 5959

Gallen, G (DLA Piper UK LLP)
Sheffield *p375* 0870 011 1111

Galletti, B P L (Purcell Parker)
Birmingham *p141* 0121 236 9781

Gallico, S (Stephen Gallico Solicitors) *K4 T2 W*
Haywards Heath *p245* 01444 411333

Gallier, Mrs V A (Wade Stevens & Co) *O Q K1 W L J1 K3 Zl*
Orpington *p342* 01689 831122

Galliet, Ms M (Plexus Law (A Trading Name of Parabis Law LLP)) *Zj Q*
London EC3 *p68* 0844 245 4000

Gallifant, D W (D W Gallifant) *W S1 S2 K4*
West Mersea *p428* 01206 383050

Gallimore, Miss J (Rowberry Morris) *K1 K2*
Reading *p361* 0118 958 5611
Tadley *p407* 0118 981 2992

Gallimore, Mrs J D (Caldicott Gallimore) *S1 E W*
Leominster *p282* 01568 614168

Gallimore, M (Hogan Lovells International LLP)
London EC1 *p42* 020 7296 2000

Gallington, Miss P L (Thompson & Jackson) *K4 W*
Plymouth *p350* 01752 665037 / 221171

Gallop Mildon, Ms N (Sykes Anderson LLP) *T2 T1 W*
London EC2 *p85* 020 3178 3770

Gallop, Mrs E L (Longmores) *E A1 L*
Hertford *p248* 01992 300333

Gallop, P G B (Burton & Burton Solicitors LLP) *S1 E L C1 W*
Nottingham *p336* 0845 094 2500

Galloway, Mrs C G (Howell Jones & Co) *S1 W*
Abergele *p113* 01745 826282 / 825845
Llanrwst *p292* 01492 640277

Galloway, Ms D (Reed Smith LLP) *Za*
London EC2 *p71* 020 3116 3000

Galloway, Mrs F J (Reed Smith LLP) *A3 O Q Zn*
London EC2 *p71* 020 3116 3000

Galloway, Ms J (IBB Solicitors) *K3*
Chesham *p189* 0845 638 1381

Galloway, Ms K (North Yorkshire County Council)
Northallerton *p467* 01609 780780

Galloway, Miss L (Keoghs LLP) *B2*
Bolton *p149* 01204 677000

Galloway, M L (Skanska UK PLC)
Rickmansworth *p470* 01923 776666

Galloway, R A H (Lester Aldridge LLP) *E S1 L R1 T1 W*
London WC2 *p53* 0844 967 0785

Galloway, T W (Charles Russell LLP)
London EC4 *p19* 020 7203 5000

Galvin, J S (Rogerson Galvin) *G H S1 K1 M1 P*
Ashton-under-Lyne *p120* 0161 344 2027 / 335 9005

Galvin, Mrs L (Vauxhall Motors Ltd)
Luton *p464* 01582 721122

Galvin, M (Anthony Louca Solicitors)
Westminster *p55* 020 7723 9889

Galvin, M P (Warners Solicitors) *W T2 Zd*
Tonbridge *p412* 01732 770660

Gamage, Miss E L (Payne & Gamage) *S1 E*
Newark *p322* 01636 640649

Gamage, M (Payne & Gamage) *Zd S2 E K4 S1 W*
Newark *p322* 01636 640649

Gamble, A (Hogan Lovells International LLP)
London EC1 *p42* 020 7296 2000

Gamble, Miss D M (Forster Dean Ltd) *K1*
Widnes *p431* 0151 422 0982

Gamble, Ms J (Sternberg Reed) *G*
Barking *p123* 020 8591 3366

Gamble, Ms S G (Gateshead Metropolitan Borough Council)
Gateshead *p458* 0191 433 3000

Gambles, R P (Hewetts) *L Zd W S2 S1*
Reading *p361* 0118 957 5337

Gamblin, Mrs C G (Hughes Paddison) *O Q N Zq L*
Cheltenham *p188* 01242 574244

Gamblin, S (Barlow Lyde & Gilbert LLP)
London EC3 *p10* 020 7247 2277

Game, D J (Barnes Sarney & Game) *W L N S1 S2 J1 Zq*
Rayleigh *p359* 01268 773881 / 774785

Game, M (Hayes & Storr) *Q*
Fakenham *p223* 01328 863231

Gameethige, T (Ziadies) *K1*
London SW9 *p94* 020 7737 0934

Gamester, T (Biscoes)
Portsmouth *p354* 023 9266 0261

Gammer, Ms F C (Aviva PLC)
London EC3 *p103* 020 7283 7500 / 01603 687905
Norwich *p467* 01603 622200

Gammie, P J (Paris Smith LLP) *S2 E*
Southampton *p386* 023 8048 2482

Gammon, N J (Gammon Bell & Co) *G H K1 O Q W J1 N D1*
Eastleigh *p216* 023 8068 4900

Gammon, P N (Thursfields) *D1 K1*
Worcester *p440* 01905 730450

Gandecha, P (Gandecha & Pau) *E S1 C1 N Q G K1 W B1 J1 Zc Zb Zl*
Barnet *p34* 020 8905 0900

Ganderton, A P (Bray & Bray) *N J2*
Leicester *p279* 0116 254 8871

6

Ganderton, Mrs E A (Geldards LLP) *E S2*
Cardiff *p178* 029 2023 8239
Ganderton, Mrs V A (Mercy Messenger) *K3 K1*
Birmingham *p140* 0121 770 1221
Gandhi, Mrs S (Charles Russell LLP) *R2 S1 L S2 E C1*
London EC4 *p19*. 020 7203 5000
Gandon, Miss S A (Sheppersons) *D1 K1 K2 V K3*
Reigate *p363* 01737 244987
Horley *p252* 01293 772424
Gandy, Ms L (South Yorkshire Passenger Transport Executive)
Sheffield *p471* 0114 276 7575
Gangani, S N (R W Hemmings & Co) *Zd C1 S2 F1 X J1 K1 L Zi Q Zs S1 V W*
Leicester *p280*. 0116 255 8500
Gangar, S S (Gangar & Co) *G K1 D1 W L F1 H N S1 V Zi Zl*
West Bromwich *p427* 0121 553 4166
Gani, Ms Z (Gani & Co) *G H B2*
Lambeth *p35*. 020 7733 8169
Ganley, Miss S J (Underwood Solicitors LLP) *S2 E R2*
Westminster *p89*. 020 7526 6000
Gannicott, I R (I R Gannicott) *S1 W A1 B1 L R1*
Bourton-on-the-Water *p153* . 01451 820265
Gannon, A C (Staffordshire County Council)
Stafford *p472* 01785 223121
Gannon, Miss C (Gannons Limited) *J1 C1 O U2 C2 Zp T2*
Camden *p35*. 020 7438 1060
Gannon, Miss C A (Hewitsons) *J1*
Cambridge *p174*. 01223 461155
Gannon, Ms C M (Royal Liver Assurance Ltd)
Liverpool *p463*. 0151 236 1451
Gant, Miss P (Collins Benson Goldhill LLP) *C1 J1 S1 W*
Westminster *p21*. 020 7436 5151
Garbett, Ms K (Peters & Peters) *N P J1 F1 Q O B1 Zk*
London EC4 *p67*. 020 7629 7991
Garbett, Miss S M (Garbetts) *E S1 S2*
Taunton *p408* 01984 667506
Garbutt, Ms J (Sintons LLP) *K4 T2 W*
Newcastle upon Tyne *p326* . 0191 226 7878
Garbutt, M (North Lincolnshire Council)
Scunthorpe *p470*. 01724 296296
Garcha, Mrs B (Bains Solicitors) *B2 G H Zl*
Wellingborough *p424* 01933 440000
Garcha, G S (Garcha & Co) *G H Zi Q N W V J1 B2 F1 F2 S2 E Zh L Zg Zl O Zp S1*
London EC3 *p35*. 020 7375 1888
Garcha, J S (Maxwell Winward LLP) *Zc*
London EC4 *p59*. 020 7651 0000
Garcia, Ms N (Tyndallwoods) *Zg Zi*
Birmingham *p143* 0121 624 1111
Garcia-Deleito, A S (Barlow Robbins LLP) *S1 S2 E A1*
Godalming *p231*. 01483 417121
Garde-Evans, Miss A (Coodes) *J1 Q*
Launceston *p270* 01566 770000
Garden, Miss P (Field Seymour Parkes) *C2 C1 Zb*
Reading *p360* 0118 951 6200
Gardener, H P K (Phillips Solicitors) *K1 D1 N L P J1 Zl K2*
Basingstoke *p127* 01256 460830
Gardener, P F (J Garrard & Allen) *Zr F1 J1 Zg Zk O Q N Zq Zp*
Olney *p341* 01234 711215
Gardham, J R (Pepperells) *S2 C1 E*
Hull *p257* 01482 326511
Scunthorpe *p373*. 01724 871999
Gardiner, A (Runnymede Borough Council)
Addlestone *p447*. 01932 838383
Gardiner, Ms A E (Squire Sanders (UK) LLP)
London EC2 *p81*. 020 7655 1000
Gardiner, D N (Royal College Of Nursing)
Leeds *p463* 0113 244 3648
Gardiner, Ms E T (Beale and Company Solicitors LLP) *Zq O Zj*
London WC2 *p11* 020 7240 3474
Gardiner, Mrs F L (West Sussex County Council)
Chichester *p455* 01243 777100
Gardiner, G A W (Barlow Lyde & Gilbert LLP)
London EC3 *p10*. 020 7247 2277
Gardiner, I C (Hill Dickinson LLP) *N Zr*
Liverpool *p288*. 0151 600 8000
Gardiner, N G (Challenor Gardiner) *W S1 E*
Oxford *p343*. 01865 721451
Gardiner, P D (Gardiners Solicitors) *E S1 N G H W*
London W14 *p35* 020 7603 7245
Gardiner, Mrs S (Pritchard Joyce & Hinds) *K1 K3*
Beckenham *p129* 020 8658 3922
Gardiner, W D (Morrish Solicitors LLP) *N Q*
Leeds *p276* 0113 245 0733
Gardiner-Hill, E (Cripps Harries Hall LLP) *C1 F1 Ze Zf U2 C2*
Tunbridge Wells *p415* 01892 515121
Gardner, Ms A (Watson Burton LLP)
Newcastle upon Tyne *p327* . 0845 901 2100
Gardner, A H (ASB Aspire) *E S1 C1 W L T1*
Maidstone *p298* 0845 063 6465
Gardner, Mrs C M (Allen & Overy LLP)
London E1 *p5* 020 3088 0000
Gardner, D A (Curtis Davis Garrard) *O Za A3*
Uxbridge *p417*. 020 8734 2800
Gardner, D H (Gardner Dallimore) *A1 S1 W E B1 L C1 T2 G H Zl Zc*
Hereford *p248* 01432 263535
Gardner, D R (Manchester City Council)
Manchester *p465* 0161 234 5000
Gardner, E P (Marsden Rawsthorn LLP) *W S1 T2*
Preston *p357* 01772 799600
Gardner, I S (Ratcliffe & Bibby) *S1 W T1*
Morecambe *p319* 01524 410424
Gardner, Ms J (Russell-Cooke LLP) *Zr N*
London SW15 *p74*. 020 8789 9111
Gardner, J L (Cyngor Sir Ynys Mon (Isle of Anglesey County Council))
Llangefni *p463*. 01248 750057
Gardner, Miss J R (Parkinson Wright LLP) *K1 D1*
Worcester *p440* 01905 726789
Gardner, J S (Thompsons (formerly Robin/Brian Thompson & Partners)) *J1*
Birmingham *p143* 0121 262 1200
Gardner, Mrs K E (Clarke Willmott) *N J1 Zj*
Bristol *p162* 0845 209 1000 / 0117 305 6000
Gardner, K R (Hampshire County Council)
Winchester *p476*. 01962 841841
Gardner, L R (West Lancashire District Council)
Ormskirk *p468*. 01695 577177
Gardner, M (Wedlake Bell LLP) *O Q B1 Zb*
London WC1 *p91* 020 7395 3000
Gardner, M A (AXA UK PLC)
London E22 *p103* 020 7920 5900
Gardner, N (Ashurst LLP)
London EC2 *p7* 020 7638 1111
Gardner, N J (Herbert Smith LLP) *O Ze*
London EC2 *p40*. 020 7374 8000
Gardner, P (Trowers & Hamlins)
London EC3 *p88*. 020 7423 8000
Gardner, P A (Osborne Clarke) *C1 U2 Zz*
London EC2 *p65*. 020 7105 7000
Gardner, P A (Surrey County Council)
Kingston upon Thames *p462*. 020 8541 9088
Gardner, P J (Gardner Thorpe) *J1 K1 N O Q Zb Zc Zj*
Haslemere *p243*. 01428 661151
Gardner, P R (Parker Bird Gardner) *D1 K1*
Huddersfield *p256* 01484 825200
Gardner, R J (General Mills UK)
Uxbridge *p474*. 01895 201133
Gardner, R M (Miller Gardner) *C1 B1*
Manchester *p307* 0161 877 4777
Gardner, R S J (Hill Dickinson LLP) *N Za Zj*
London EC3 *p41*. 020 7283 9033
Gardner, S W (Gardner Austin) *E R2 S1 S2 W C1*
Westminster *p35*. 020 7831 2600
Gardner, W M (Latimer Hinks) *O B1*
Darlington *p206* 01325 341500
Gardner-Browne, E (Geldards LLP) *E S2*
Nottingham *p337*. 0115 983 3650
Gare, Mrs R (Reynolds Porter Chamberlain LLP) *Zj Zq*
London E1 *p71* 020 3060 6000
Garel, Ms J M (Avon & Bristol Law Centre)
Bristol *p451* 0117 924 8662
Garety, H J (Addleshaw Goddard)
London EC1 *p4* 020 7606 8855
Garfield, I (BPE Solicitors LLP) *C1 U2 I Ze Zf Zza U1 X F1 Zd C3*
Cheltenham *p187* 01242 224433
Garfield, Mrs R F (Clarion Solicitors LLP) *C1 I Ze Zf Zw U2*
Leeds *p272* 0113 246 0622
Harrogate *p240* 01423 530630
Garfinkel, D I (Harter & Loveless) *S1 S2 W*
Islington *p39*. 020 7688 2900
Garfitt, D A (Langleys)
York *p445* 01904 610886
Garford, F S (Squire Sanders (UK) LLP) *E R2 S2*
London EC2 *p81*. 020 7655 1000
Garget, S J (Hunton & Garget) *W S1 S2 E A1*
Richmond *p364* 01748 850400
Garland, A (The Wilkes Partnership LLP) *B1 Zb*
Birmingham *p143* 0121 233 4333
Garland, Mrs D H (Rowe Radcliffe) *S1 S2*
South Croydon *p383*. 020 8680 2070
Garland, N M (William Sturges & Co) *S1*
Westminster *p84*. 020 7873 1000
Garland, P (Kemp Little LLP) *O Q C1 Ze*
London EC2 *p48*. 020 7600 8080
Garland, P J (Radcliffes Le Brasseur) *E R2 S1 S2*
Westminster *p70*. 020 7222 7040
Garland, S H (Kaim Todner Ltd) *G H*
Islington *p47*. 020 7700 0070
Garlick, G (Stockton-On-Tees Borough Council)
Stockton-on-Tees *p472* . . . 01642 393939
Garlick, Ms M M (Weightmans LLP) *Zq*
Manchester *p311* 0161 233 7330
Garlick, Miss S (Keoghs LLP) *N Zj O Q*
Bolton *p149* 01204 677000
Garling, V R H (Brignalls Balderston Warren) *S1*
Letchworth *p283*. 01462 482248
Garner, C (KJD) *W*
Stoke-on-Trent *p398*. 01782 202020
Garner, C A W (Irwin Mitchell LLP) *M2 N Zy*
Sheffield *p376* 0870 150 0100
Garner, D J (Carter-Ruck) *Zk O Zq M2*
London EC4 *p18*. 020 7353 5005
Garner, J R (Stilwell & Harby) *S1 S2 L E*
Dover *p213* 01304 206850
Garner, Mrs J S (Salusburys Harding & Barnett) *N Zr*
Leicester *p281*. . 0116 262 9033 / 262 6052
Garner, Miss K (Garner Hutchings) *E O J1 L*
Westminster *p35*. 020 7932 2400
Garner, K (Garner Canning) *E Q R1 S1 Zu*
Tamworth *p407* 01827 314004
Garner, Miss L (Myer Wolff) *D1 K1 K3*
Hull *p257* 01482 223693
Garner, Mrs M A (Treasury Solicitors Department)
London WC2 *p110*. 020 7210 3000
Garner, P (Metcalfe Copeman & Pettefar) *J1 E S2 W Zt*
Wisbech *p435* 01945 464331
Garner, P (Quality Solicitors C Turner) *F1 N Q Zl*
Blackburn *p145* 01254 688400
Garner, Miss V L (Otten Penna Ltd) *D1 D2 K1*
Northenden *p333* 0161 945 1431
Garner-Patel, Miss A M S (Treasury Solicitors Department)
London WC2 *p110*. 020 7210 3000
Garnett, C (Harrowells)
York *p444* 01904 558600
Garnett, C J (Shoosmiths) *C1 C2*
Nottingham *p339*. 0370 086 5000 / 0115 906 5000
Garnett, Miss H E (Heptonstalls LLP) *O Q*
Goole *p231* 01405 765661
Garnett, Miss H J (Baxter Caulfield) *O Q J1 P R1*
Huddersfield *p255* 01484 519519
Garnett, J (Trowers & Hamlins)
London EC3 *p88*. 020 7423 8000
Garnett, Miss J C (Douglas Clift & Co) *K1 N Q D1 G H K3*
Lancaster *p269* 01524 32437
Garnett, Mrs S R (TBI Solicitors) *E S2*
Hartlepool *p243* . . . 0800 052 6824 / 01429 264101
Garnett, W M M (Bates Wells & Braithwaite London LLP) *J1 J2 Zd X*
London EC4 *p11*. 020 7551 7777
Garnham, Miss C X (Simmons & Simmons)
London EC2 *p79*. 020 7628 2020
Garnier, Mrs S M (Mills & Reeve) *A1 W S1 L*
Norwich *p335* 01603 660155
Garrad, Ms V L (Gateley LLP) *J1*
Birmingham *p138* 0121 234 0000
Garrard, L (WBW Solicitors) *G H*
Torquay *p413* 0870 701 4321
Garrard, Ms S L (T R S Miller Solicitors) *W*
Hythe *p259* 01303 266861
Garrard, Ms S L (Rootes & Alliott) *S1 K3 K1 D1 W D2 S2 J1 L*
Folkestone *p227*. 01303 851100
Garratt, S J (Quality Solicitors Gruber Garratt) *G H N Q J1 B2 Zr Zq Zl*
Oldham *p341* 0161 665 3502
Garrett, Miss A M (Mills & Reeve) *B1 F1 N*
Cambridge *p175*. 01223 364422
Garrett, D (Fanshaw Porter & Hazlehurst)
Birkenhead *p134*. 0151 647 4051
Garrett, Mrs E (Stockton-On-Tees Borough Council) *K1 D1 D2*
Stockton-on-Tees *p472* . . . 01642 393939
Garrett, Mrs J (Swindon Borough Council)
Swindon *p473* 01793 463000
Garrett, Miss K (Bell Lax Litigation) *O Zq J1 Zk*
Sutton Coldfield *p403* 0121 355 0011
Garrett, S J A (Hawkins Hatton LLP) *N Q O Zj B2*
Dudley *p213*. 01384 216840
Garrett, Miss S L (Cripps Harries Hall LLP) *J1 Zp*
Tunbridge Wells *p415* 01892 515121
Garrett, Ms S M (Addleshaw Goddard)
Leeds *p271* 0113 209 2000
Manchester *p300* 0161 934 6000
Garrick, A (Allan Garrick) *C1 E F1 K1 L N S1*
Lancaster *p269* 01524 62985
Garrod, Miss A J (Garrods Solicitors) *K1 D1 N Q J1 S1 W V Zq D2 O C1 S2 E B1*
Chelmsford *p186*. 01245 492494
Garrod, D J (McDermott Will & Emery UK LLP) *C3*
London EC2 *p56*. 020 7577 6900
Garrod, M (Russell-Cooke LLP) *E*
London SW15 *p74*. 020 8789 9111
Garrood, Ms B M (Cartridges) *K1*
Exeter *p220* 01392 256854
Garrood, Ms S (Mills & Reeve) *N*
Norwich *p335* 01603 660155
Garrood, T (Ince & Co Services Ltd)
London E1 *p44* 020 7481 0010
Garrood, T A (Simmons & Simmons)
London EC2 *p79*. 020 7628 2020
Garry, P S (Cripps Harries Hall LLP) *O A3*
Tunbridge Wells *p415* 01892 515121
Garsden, P W A (Abney Garsden McDonald) *N O Q K1 G F1 W C1 B1 J1 Zi Zk Zm*
Cheadle *p185* 0161 482 8822
Garsed, D F (Ramsdens Solicitors) *S1*
Elland *p217* 01422 372478
Huddersfield *p256* 01484 821500
Garside, P A J (Brighouse Wolff) *S1 L E A1 C1 W*
Ormskirk *p341*. 01695 573202
Garson, J M (Garson & Co) *L Q O S1 E J1 B1 F1 W Zl Zc*
Pinner *p348* 020 8429 4111
Garson, M D (Kagan Moss & Co) *C1 E T1 W O Q R2 S2 S1*
Teddington *p409*. 020 8977 6633
Garstang, M E (Garstangs)
Bolton *p149* 01204 531118
Garthwaite, Ms H E (Taylor Wessing) *C1 P M1*
London EC4 *p86*. 020 7300 7000
Gartland, Miss C (The Thrasher Walker Partnership) *C1 S2 O*
Stockport *p396*. 0161 442 6240
Garton, M H M (MHM Solicitors) *O Q Zc Zj*
Leicester *p280*. 0845 234 0230
Garton, R (Mason Baggott & Garton) *E C1*
Epworth *p219* 01427 872661
Scunthorpe *p373*. 01724 868611
Gartshore, D H (Haringey Magistrates Legal Advisers Office)
London N6 *p106*. 0845 601 3600
Garvey, Mrs A (Birchall Blackburn LLP) *K3 K1*
Preston *p356* 01772 561663
Garvey, J W (Hockfield & Co) *E L O Zh*
Lambeth *p41*. 020 7582 8784
Garvey, L (Penningtons)
Godalming *p231* 01483 791800
Garvey, M A (Bray & Bray) *G H Zl*
Leicester *p279*. 0116 254 8871
Garvey, Miss P (Hill Dickinson LLP)
Manchester *p305* 0161 817 7200
Garvey, Ms R K (Edwards Duthie) *K1*
London E13 *p29*. 020 8514 9000
Garvey, Mrs S (Oldham Marsh Page Flavell) *W*
Melton Mowbray *p314* 01664 563162
Market Harborough *p312*. . . 01858 463322
Garvie, C P (Pinsent Masons LLP) *B2 O C1*
London EC2 *p67*. 020 7418 7000
Garvin, M S P (LSG Solicitors) *S2 R2 E L O B1*
London W1 *p51* 020 7851 0100
Garvin, N N P (Garvins Solicitors) *Q N*
Manchester *p304* 0161 495 2880
Garwood, C C (Carrick Read Solicitors LLP)
Hull *p256* 01482 211160
Hull *p256* 01482 211160
Garwood, M (Norfolk County Council - Legal Services)
Norwich *p467* . . . Minicom: 0844 800 8011
Gascoigne, A D (Morrison & Masters Limited) *A1 C1 E S1 J1*
Swindon *p406* 01793 526601
Gascoyne, Ms Z E (Cobleys LLP) *H G*
Liverpool *p287*. 0151 242 9000
Gash, L (Blaser Mills) *J1*
High Wycombe *p249*. 01494 450171
Gash, R (Devon County Council)
Exeter *p458* 01392 382000
Gask, Miss P J (London Borough of Bexley)
Bexleyheath *p449* 020 8303 7777
Gaskell, Mrs A (Bolton Metropolitan Borough Council)
Bolton *p450* 01204 333333
Gaskell, Miss C L (Leeds City Council)
Leeds *p462* 0113 224 3513
Gaskell, E M (Legal Aid Area Office No 12 (Chester & N Wales))
Chester *p454* 01244 315455
Liverpool *p463*. 0151 242 5200
Gaskell, Ms F A (Clough & Willis) *O N F1 B1 Q*
Bury *p170* 0161 764 5266
Gaskell, J D (Flintshire County Council)
Mold *p466* 01352 702411
Gaskell, Miss L C (Leathems Solicitors) *D1 K3 K1 W*
Whaley Bridge *p430*. 01663 733431
Gaskell, M A (Legal Services Commission No 9 (North Eastern))
Leeds *p463* 0113 390 7300
Gaskell, R G (MacRae & Co LLP) *C1 S2 I J1 O Q C2 S1 W*
Southwark *p57*. 020 7378 7716
Gaskins, P M (Kitsons LLP) *E R2 S2 S1*
Torquay *p413* 01803 202020
Gasper, S P (Bruce Lance & Co) *M1 P D1 J1 K1 N L G*
High Wycombe *p250*. 01494 450494
Gasson, W D (Thompsons (formerly Robin/Brian Thompson & Partners)) *N*
Cardiff *p181* 029 2044 5300
Gaston, K R (Plexus Law (A Trading Name of Parabis Law LLP)) *Zj E*
Colchester *p198* 0844 245 4950
Gaston, M (Stafford Young Jones) *E S2 S1*
London EC4 *p82*. 020 7623 9490
Gate, P (Russell-Cooke LLP) *W*
London SW15 *p74*. 020 8789 9111
Gatehouse, Ms M (Ashurst LLP)
London EC2 *p7* 020 7638 1111
Gatenby, J K (Addleshaw Goddard)
Manchester *p300* 0161 934 6000
Gater, J B (Blandy & Blandy) *W T2*
Reading *p360* 0118 951 6800
Gates, C (Wright & Lord) *K1 K3 F1 J1 L Zl O Q N*
Morecambe *p319* 01524 402050
Gates, C J (Larcomes LLP) *J1 Q O*
Portsmouth *p354*. 023 9266 1531
Gates, Ms E (SNR Denton) *Zn*
London EC4 *p75*. 020 7242 1212
Gates, Miss K L (Geldards LLP) *E S2*
Cardiff *p178* 029 2023 8239
Gates, P G (Peter G Gates) *A1 K1 Q S1 W*
Horsham *p253*. 01403 753636
Gates, R J (Gordons Solicitors LLP) *J1 E O Q N G S1 C1 C3 Zp Zw*
Marlow *p313*. 01628 487487
Gates, R R (Red Kite Law) *T2 W*
Haverfordwest *p244* 01437 763332
Gates, S (Gates and Partners)
London EC3 *p35*. 020 7220 5950
Gates, Miss S M (Druitts) *W K4*
Bournemouth *p151*. 01202 551863
Gateshill, Mrs J C (Kingston upon Hull City Council) *W T1*
Hull *p461* 01482 300300
Gatherer, Miss A (Crawley Borough Council)
Crawley *p456* 01293 438000
Gatrell, Miss C (North Yorkshire County Council)
Northallerton *p467* 01609 780780

See p634 for the Key to Work Categories

Gattas, J J N (Gattas Denfield Solicitors) *C1 E F1 G J1 L P S1*
London NW9 *p35* 020 8204 7181

Gauden, Ms S (Maxwell Winward LLP) *E Zl R2 C1*
London EC4 *p59*. 020 7651 0000

Gaudern, Miss E (BHP Law) *W*
Darlington *p206* 01325 466794
Manchester *p308* 0161 909 3000

Gaudion, B J (Thornes) *G H K1*
Wolverhampton *p438* 01902 313311

Gaudion, Miss L J (Isle of Wight Council)
Newport *p466* 01983 823207

Gaughan, Miss L K (Ward Gethin) *N*
King's Lynn *p266* 01553 660033

Gaukroger, Miss C M (Chester City Council)
Chester *p454* 01244 324324

Gaul, P (Weightmans LLP)
Liverpool *p291*. 0151 227 2601

Gaul, S (Clarion Solicitors LLP) *C1*
Leeds *p272* 0113 246 0622

Gault, I T (Herbert Smith LLP) *C1 Zo*
London EC2 *p40*. 020 7374 8000

Gaulter, A M (Citibank National Association)
London E14 *p105* 020 7500 5000

Gaunt, Mrs A M (HBOS PLC)
Halifax *p460* 0870 600 5000

Gaunt, Dr E U (Taylor Wessing) *Zb M2*
London EC4 *p86*. 020 7300 7000

Gaunt, Mrs H K (Jobling Gowler) *K4 W T2*
Macclesfield *p297* 01625 614250

Gaunt, J R T (John Gaunt & Partners) *O Zl Zf*
Sheffield *p375* 0114 266 8664

Gaunt, M A (Brumell & Sample) *L S1 S2 W*
Morpeth *p319* 01670 512336

Gaunt, Ms S (Taylor & Emmet LLP) *S1*
Sheffield *p377* 0114 218 4000

Gauntlett, K R (Thackray Williams) *S1 W E Zl*
Bromley *p167* 020 8290 0440

Gausden, P (The College of Law Chester)
Chester *p454* 0800 289997

Gaut, D M (Poole Alcock) *K1 M1 P G W S1 F1 J1 V*
Crewe *p203* 01270 256665

Gautam, H (Breeze & Wyles Solicitors LLP) *D1 K1*
Cheshunt *p189* 01992 642333
Hertford *p248* 01992 558411

Gavan, J V (Laytons) *C1 T1 F1*
Manchester *p306* 0161 834 2100

Gavens, Ms C M (LG Lawyers)
London SE1 *p50*. 020 7379 0000

Gavin, F (Ince & Co Services Ltd)
London E1 *p44* 020 7481 0010

Gavin, P (KJD) *J1*
Stoke-on-Trent *p398*. 01782 202020

Gavin-Brown, I (William Sturges & Co) *S2 W*
Westminster *p84*. 020 7873 1000

Gawade, J A T (Lee & Thompson) *Zf*
London W1 *p52* 020 7935 4665

Gawler, S (Stephens & Scown) *E Zn*
Exeter *p222* 01392 210700

Gawler, T N (Maclachlan) *S1 S2 A1 R2 E*
Sherborne *p378* 01935 817736

Gawn, Miss B J (Gilbert Stephens) *S1 E A1 W*
Exeter *p221* 01392 424242

Gawne, C (Irwin Mitchell LLP) *Zr*
Manchester *p306* 0870 150 0100

Gawor, M A (Gawor & Co) *E L*
London E1 *p35* 020 7481 8888

Gawthorp, Mrs V A (Wrigleys Solicitors LLP) *A1 L E*
Leeds *p278* 0113 244 6100

Gawthorpe, B J (Gwynne Hughes) *J1 K1 N Q S1 K3 O B1 F1 L Zl*
New Quay *p321* 01545 560525

Gay, D J (Burningham & Brown) *S1 E W S2*
Bath *p127* 01225 320090

Gay, M (Foot Anstey) *C1 E C2*
Taunton *p408* 01823 625600

Gay, M E (DLA Piper UK LLP) *O Zw*
London EC2 *p24*. 0870 011 1111

Gay, N M (Moss Solicitors LLP) *Q O J1 L B1*
Loughborough *p293* 01509 217770

Gay, R J (Hill Dickinson LLP) *O Za Zj*
London EC3 *p41*. 020 7283 9033

Gay, R W (Roger Gay & Co)
Somerton *p383* 01458 273137

Gaye, M (Ford Simey LLP) *E C1 N B1 R1 S1 Zc Ze*
Exeter *p221* 01392 274126

Gaye, M (Kitsons LLP)
Exeter *p221* 01392 455555

Gayer, G I (Cartwright Cunningham Haselgrove & Co) *S2 E W T2 C1*
Woodford Green *p439* 020 8506 5200

Gayer, W P (Broomhead & Saul) *G H Q K1*
Ilminster *p261* 01460 57056

Gayford, R M (Taylor Wessing) *B1 Zb*
London EC4 *p86*. 020 7300 7000

Gayle, Ms C (Children & Families Law Firm) *K1 K3 D1*
London SW9 *p20* 020 7582 6002

Gaymer, Mrs J M (Simmons & Simmons) *J1 N O*
London EC2 *p79*. 020 7628 2020

Gaymer, J M (Bracher Rawlins LLP) *E L R1 Zc Zn Zs*
London WC1 *p15* 020 7404 9400

Gayner, N C D (Squire Sanders (UK) LLP)
London EC2 *p81*. 020 7655 1000

Gaythorpe, D J (Hartley & Worstenholme) *S1 L E W R1*
Pontefract *p351* 01977 732222

Gaythwaite, Dr D M (Bird & Bird LLP) *Ze*
London EC4 *p13*. 020 7415 6000

Gaze, Miss J A (Lamb Brooks LLP) *T2 W*
Basingstoke *p126* 01256 844888

Gazzard, D (FDC Law) *N O Q J2 Zl Zr Zq*
Frome *p228* 01373 465051

Gbadamosi, G (London Borough of Southwark)
London SE1 *p109* 020 7525 5000

Gbaja, Mrs A K (Addie & Co) *S1 E L W Zi Zd P C1 B1 M2*
London WC2 *p4* 020 7395 3740

Gbejuade, Miss H O O (Treasury Solicitors Department)
London WC2 *p110*. 020 7210 3000

Geale, Mrs M E (Tendring District Council)
Clacton-on-Sea *p455* 01255 686567

Geaney, K G P (Kevin Geaney) *S1 M1 W P E A1 F1 J1 L K1 Zc Zg*
Kidlington *p266* 01865 379498

Geaney, Ms S (LG Lawyers) *Zd*
London SE1 *p50*. 020 7379 0000

Gear-Evans, Mrs J (John Mohamed & Co) *K1 P S1 W J1 D1*
Bedworth *p130*. 024 7649 1964

Gearey, H (Penningtons)
Godalming *p231* 01483 791800

Gearing, D L (Sanders & Co) *B1 E S1 K1 O Q C1 W J1*
Harold Wood *p239*. 0844 353 3553

Gearing, M C (Hewitsons) *C1 C2*
Cambridge *p174*. 01223 461155

Gearing, M G P (Allen & Overy LLP)
London E1 *p5* 020 3088 0000

Gearon, P (Charles Russell LLP) *J1 O*
Cheltenham *p187* 01242 221122

Geary, R D (Wise Geary) *C1 C3 I J1 T1 T2 U1 U2 Zb Ze*
Banbury *p122* 01295 278500

Geary, Ms V M (North Tyneside Council)
Newcastle upon Tyne *p466* . 0191 643 5000

Gebhard, M C (Hammond Bale) *C1 E F1 J1 L O Q W Zd Ze Zi*
London W1 *p38* 020 7499 7624

Gecaga, S (Bates Wells & Braithwaite London LLP) *Zd C1*
London EC4 *p11*. 020 7551 7777

Geday, M (Herbert Smith LLP) *C2 Zb*
London EC2 *p40*. 020 7374 8000

Geddes, A J (Bendall & Sons) *S1 E W T1 L R1 J1 A1 B1 C1 Zl Zi Zm*
Newmarket *p327*. 01638 661116

Gedge, Mrs A E S (Foot Anstey)
Plymouth *p349*. 01752 675000

Gee, A G J (Albion Gee & Co) *M2 O W C1 Ze Zf*
London W4 *p4*. 020 8742 7600

Gee, C (Craig Gee) *G H D1 K1 D2 J1 L N W O Zq*
Manchester *p304* 0161 666 9999

Gee, Miss E A (The College of Law) *O Q N Zq*
London WC1 *p105*. 0800 289997

Gee, I J N (Jobling & Knape) *M3 N O J2 F1 E*
Lancaster *p269* 01524 598300

Gee, Miss L M (Capsticks Solicitors LLP) *N Zm Zr*
London SW19 *p18*. 020 8780 2211

Gee, M R (Davis Blank Furniss) *E L R1 S1 W*
Glossop *p230* 01457 860606

Gee, W G F (Currey & Co) *S1 S2 R1 R2 A1 E*
Westminster *p24*. 020 7802 2700

Geen, J (M&A Solicitors LLP) *E R2*
Cardiff *p179* 029 2048 2288

Geeson, M (Darbys Solicitors LLP) *G H B2 J2 Zu Zy*
Oxford *p343* 01865 811700

Geffen, C S H (Ashurst LLP) *C1*
London EC2 *p7* 020 7638 1111

Gegan, P E (Premier Property Lawyers Ltd) *G S1 K1 M1 H V D1 F1 W J1*
Enderby *p218* 0845 234 0217

Geisler, A M (Duane Morris) *O I F1 Zj Ze Zc Zw*
London EC1 *p28*. 020 7786 2100

Geist-Divver, Ms C (Treasury Solicitors Department) *K1 L V X Zm*
London WC2 *p110*. 020 7210 3000

Gelb, S N (Michael Conn Goldsobel) *S2 E L S1 W*
London W1 *p60* 020 7580 8902

Geldard, P D A (Forbes) *M1 P J1 L F1*
Blackburn *p145* 01254 662831

Gelfer, A (Newtons)
Camden *p63*. . .020 7794 9696 / 7435 5351

Gellert, Ms M S (Greenwoods)
London EC3 *p37*. 020 7220 7818

Gelling, P R (DWF) *E L S2 A1 R2*
Manchester *p303* 0161 603 5000

Gellner, Ms D A (Pierce Glynn) *L Q Zi*
Southwark *p67*. 020 7407 0007

Gelshinan, E (Rigby Golding) *S1 E W*
Sunbury-on-Thames *p401* . . 01932 765741

Gelsthorpe, E (BAE Systems PLC)
London SW1 *p104*. 01252 373232

Gelsthorpe, S J (Cartwright King) *G H*
Nottingham *p336*. 0115 958 7444

Gembali, Mrs M (Derbyshire County Council) *D1 K1 Zu*
Matlock *p465* 01629 580000

Gemmell, J (Cunningtons) *S1*
Braintree *p155*. 01376 326868

Gemmell, Mrs R E B (Tewkesbury Borough Council)
Tewkesbury *p474* 01684 272012

Genco, G (McKenzies) *N*
Hertford *p248* 01992 503344

Gengatharan, M (Genga & Co) *G H B2 V L Zi Zh K1 D1 O*
Wembley *p426*. 020 8795 5020

Gennard, Ms N (Waldrons) *C1 Ze C2*
Brierley Hill *p158*. 01384 811811

Genner, Mrs S A (Jewels Solicitors) *D1 K1 K3 D2*
Stafford *p393* 01785 602030

Gent, B (Irwin Mitchell LLP) *Zr*
Sheffield *p376* 0870 150 0100

Gent, Mrs C E (Pinkerton Leeke & Co) *W S1 S2 E*
Cheltenham *p188* 01242 237477

Gent, Miss C L (Atha Barton & Co) *D1 F1 W G H J1 K1 L Q V*
Guisborough *p237*. 01287 633242
Skelton-in-Cleveland *p381* . . 01287 651521

Gent, Ms E (Maxwell Gillott (MG Law Ltd)) *X Zg*
Lancaster *p270* 0844 858 3900

Gent, N H (Trethowans LLP) *C2 C1 Zb*
Southampton *p387*. 023 8032 1000

Gent, Ms S (London Underground Ltd) *O Q Zc*
London SW1 *p107*. 020 7918 3126

Gentilella, M (Smith Brown & Sprawson)
Luton *p295* 01582 876900

Gentle, D B (Goldkorn Mathias Gentle Page LLP) *G S2 E F1 Ze Zf K1*
London WC1 *p36* 020 7631 1811

Gentle, S (Kingsley Napley) *G H B2 Zg*
London EC1 *p50*. 020 7814 1200

Gentles, Ms S (Blake Lapthorn) *I U2*
London EC1 *p13*. 020 7405 2000

Gentry, H E (Meaby & Co Trading as Hart Scales & Hodges)
Dorking *p212* 01306 884432

Geoffrey, W (J A Kemp & Co)
London WC1 *p48* 020 7405 3292

Geoghegan, C (Penningtons) *E*
Basingstoke *p127* 01256 407100

Geoghegan, S (Rosling King) *E L Q R1 S1 Zj*
London EC4 *p73*. 020 7353 2353

George, A (Arnold George & Co) *N K1 J1 C1 E O Q S1 W K3*
Ilford *p259*. 020 8554 5484

George, A D G (Ince & Co Services Ltd) *A3 F1 M2 O U2 Za Zj*
London E1 *p44* 020 7481 0010

George, A V (Bruce Lance & Co)
High Wycombe *p250*. 01494 450494

George, C J (Rothera Dowson) *N Q W*
Nottingham *p338*. 0115 910 0600

George, C R (Lambe Corner) *W S1 T1 L E C1 T2*
Hereford *p248* 01432 355301

George, Mrs D C (Northamptonshire County Council) *D1 P*
Northampton *p467*. 01604 236236

George, D I (Roger James Clements & Partners) *G H J1 N Q*
Newport *p329* 01633 257844

George, D T J (Barwells) *K1 N P S1 E F1 L B1 G J1 Zl Zc*
Eastbourne *p215*. 01323 411505

George, F A (Richard Griffiths & Co) *K1 K3 K2 S1 W G*
Salisbury *p371*. 01722 329966

George, G J (The Gwyn George Partnership) *N K1 G D1 M1 F1 Q V B1 L Zl*
Aberdare *p113*. . . .01685 874629 / 871133

George, Ms H L (Overburys & Raymond Thompson) *S1*
Norwich *p335* 01603 610481

George, Ms K (Wolton & Co) *Zm*
Deal *p207* 01304 389789

George, K G E (Coodes) *S1 E A1 W*
Liskeard *p285* 01579 347600

George, Ms L (Sheppersons) *K1 K3 D1*
Horley *p252* 01293 772424

George, Miss L (The College of Law Guildford)
Guildford *p459*. 01483 460200

George, Miss N M J (London Stock Exchange Ltd) *C1 F1 J1 Zb*
London EC2 *p107* 020 7797 1000

George, N P (George & Co) *C1 S2 J1 C2 Zl E S1 W*
Bury St Edmunds *p171* . . . 01449 737582

George, P (Whiteside & Knowles Ltd) *N Q L F1 B1 J1 S1 W Zi Zr Zp*
Morecambe *p319* 01524 416315

George, Mrs P D (South Tyneside Metropolitan Borough Council) *K1 D1 F1 V M1*
South Shields *p471* 0191 427 1717

George, P M C (Charles Russell LLP) *K1*
London EC4 *p19*. 020 7203 5000

George, P W (Birkett Long LLP) *C1 C2 R2 X*
Colchester *p197* 01206 217300

George, P W (William George & Son) *S1 W N L A1 E S2*
Porthmadog *p354* . .01766 512011 / 512474

George, S (Bobbetts Mackan) *G H*
Bristol *p161* 0117 929 9001

George, Miss S A (Moseley George) *K1 G H Q V Zm*
Cardigan *p181*. 01239 623960

George, S R (Rubin Lewis O'Brien)
Cwmbran *p206* 01633 867000

George, T (Shoosmiths) *W T2 Zd*
Northampton *p332*. . 0370 086 3000 / 01604 543000

George, V S (Wright Hassall LLP) *O Q Zz*
Leamington Spa *p270* 01926 886688

Georgeou, Ms A S (Pinnacle Insurance PLC)
Borehamwood *p450* 020 8207 9000

Georgiou, A T (Paris Smith LLP) *E S2*
Southampton *p386*. 023 8048 2482

Georgiou, C (Berry Redmond & Robinson)
Weston-super-Mare *p429* . . 01934 513963

Georgiou, C K (Ashurst LLP)
London EC2 *p7* 020 7638 1111

Georgiou, G (Mundays LLP) *S2 E*
Cobham *p196* 01932 590500

Georgiou, G C (Lorrells LLP) *B1 C1 E J1 L M1 N S1 T1 W Za Zc Zf*
London EC1 *p55*. 020 7681 8888

Georgiou, G S (Wellers Law Group LLP) *C1 O Q W*
London WC1 *p91* 020 7242 7265

Georgiou, P (Joseph Hill & Co) *G H B2*
London N15 *p41*. 020 8880 3535

Georgiou, Mrs R (Roulla Georgiou)
Barnet *p35*. 020 8368 0220

Georgiou, Ms S E (Daltons) *C1 E F1 G H L M1 N P R1 Zs*
Eastbourne *p215*. 01323 720040

Georgious, Ms S (Harding Evans LLP) *D1 K1*
Newport *p328* 01633 244233

Gerada, C (Jeffrey Green Russell) *C1 C2 C3 I U1 J1*
London W1 *p46* 020 7339 7000

Geraghty, J A (Herbert Smith LLP)
London EC2 *p40*. 020 7374 8000

Geraghty, R (Russell Jones & Walker) *E*
London WC2 *p74* 020 7657 1555

Geraghty, S F (Dechert) *C2*
London EC4 *p26*. 020 7184 7000

Gerakaris, Ms M V A (Jackson Parton) *O A3 Za Zj Q*
London EC3 *p45*. 020 7702 0085

Gerber, J R M (WGS Solicitors) *S1 S2 R2*
Westminster *p90*. 020 7723 1656

Gerdes, Mrs V A (Vance Harris) *W*
Crowborough *p204*. 01892 653434

Gerrard, D N (DLA Piper UK LLP)
London EC2 *p24*. 0870 011 1111

Gerrard, Ms J (Cartwright King)
Nottingham *p336*. 0115 958 7444
Nottingham *p338*. 0115 958 6262

Gerrard, S G (Wiltshire County Council)
Trowbridge *p474*. 01225 713000

Gerrard, T A (Cardiff Magistrates Court)
Cardiff *p453* 029 2046 3040

Gerrard, W A (Bell & Co) *N Q*
Liverpool *p286*. 0151 928 8686

Gerschlick, P (Matthew Arnold & Baldwin LLP)
Watford *p423* 01923 202020

Gershlick, A H (Jefferies Essex LLP) *C1 E S1 T1 W S2 R2*
Westcliff-on-Sea *p428* 01702 332311

Gershon, L (Gershon & Goldstein) *S1 E W*
Edgware *p217* 020 8952 5272

Gershuny, P D (Hogan Lovells International LLP)
London EC1 *p42*. 020 7296 2000

Gershuny, Mrs R M (Collins Solicitors) *Q K1 N D1 V*
Watford *p423* 01923 223324

Gerszt, J M (Hogan Lovells International LLP)
London EC1 *p42*. 020 7296 2000

Gervasio, J E P (hlw Keeble Hawson LLP)
Sheffield *p375* 0114 272 2061

Gething, Miss H (Herbert Smith LLP) *C1 T1 C2*
London EC2 *p40*. 020 7374 8000

Gething, H (Donnelly McArdle Adamson) *C1 D1 E G H K1 L M1 P R1*
Peterlee *p347* 0191 586 3581

Getty, D E (Gaby Hardwicke) *C1 C3 F1 I J1 L O Q N P Ze Zk*
Eastbourne *p215*. 01323 435900

Gewirtz, J (Linklaters LLP)
London EC2 *p54*. 020 7456 2000

Ghafoor, Q (Flint Bishop Solicitors)
Derby *p208* 01332 340211

Ghai, Miss R (Reena Ghai Solicitors) *K3 D1 D2 G H K1 B2*
Hounslow *p253* 020 8759 9959

Ghai, S (Plexus Law (A Trading Name of Parabis Law LLP)) *K1 K4 N Q W*
London EC3 *p68*. 0844 245 4000

Ghani, M (Ismail & Ghani) *S1 P G M1 K1 E W Zi*
Bradford *p154* 01274 737546

Ghebre-Ghiorghis, M (Brighton & Hove Council - Legal Services)
Hove *p461*. 01273 290000

Ghelani, C (Sacker & Partners LLP) *Zo*
London EC2 *p76*. 020 7329 6699

Ghelani, S (H M Revenue & Customs) *C1 D1 G H K1 L N Q S1 W Zi Zl Zm Zp*
London WC2 *p106*.

Ghirardani, P S G (Stephenson Harwood) *N Za Zj B2*
London EC2 *p82*. 020 7329 4422

Ghose, A M (Wokingham District Council)
Wokingham *p477* 0118 974 6000
Slough *p381*. 01753 779637

Ghosh, R (Brady Eastwood Pierce & Stewart)
Lewisham *p15* 020 8692 8181

Ghuman, Mrs T (Alsters Kelley) *W*
Coventry *p199*. 0844 561 0100

Giacon, D A P (Collyer Bristow LLP) *E S2*
London WC1 *p22* 020 7242 7363

Giacon, F P A (Hogan Lovells International LLP)
London EC1 *p42*. 020 7296 2000

Giaretta, B (Ashurst LLP)
London EC2 *p7* 020 7638 1111

Gibb, A (Purdys) *A1 E S1 S2 W Zl A2 C1 K4 T2*
Reepham *p363* 01603 870606

Gibb, A G (DWT Legal Ltd) *S1 S2*
Kidderminster *p265* 0844 770 3799

6

Gibb, Miss G (Norwich Union Insurance Group)
Norwich *p467* 01603 622200

Gibb, Miss S (Norfolk County Council - Legal Services)
Norwich *p467* . . . Minicom: 0844 800 8011

Gibbens, S J (Gibbens Solicitors) *Zj Zo T1 T2 W*
Stockton-on-Tees *p397* . . . 01642 702481

Gibber, R A (Tate & Lyle PLC)
London EC3 *p109* 020 7626 6525

Gibbins, D J S (Wragge & Co LLP)
London EC1 *p93* 0870 903 1000

Gibbins, Ms D K (Deborah Gibbins & Co) *K1 K3 D1*
Billericay *p133* 01268 270866

Gibbins, Miss L A (Adams & Remers) *W K4*
Lewes *p283* 01273 480616

Gibbins, N R (Murrays) *D2 K1 Zm D1*
Bodmin *p148* 01208 72863

Gibbon, Mrs F (The Endeavour Partnership LLP) *T1 Zb*
Stockton-on-Tees *p397* . . . 01642 610300

Gibbon, N (Allen & Overy LLP)
London E1 *p5* 020 3088 0000

Gibbon, N C (DAC Beachcroft)
London EC4 *p24* 020 7242 1011

Gibbon, P A (Draycott Browne Solicitors) *B2 G H*
Manchester *p303* 0161 228 2244

Gibbon, P A (Wake Smith & Tofields) *S2 E L Zc R2*
Sheffield *p377* 0114 266 6660

Gibbon, R (Ansbacher & Co Ltd)
London SE1 *p103* 020 7089 4700
London SE1 *p103* 020 7089 4700

Gibbon, R (Ford & Warren) *C1 C2 Ze F1*
Leeds *p273* 0113 243 6601

Gibbon, R L (Beetenson & Gibbon) *S1 W E L C1 R1 T1 P Zd Zb Ze*
Grimsby *p235* 01472 240251

Gibbon, Miss S (Ashfords LLP) *O Zh L*
Exeter *p220* 01392 337000

Gibbons, A (Hill Dickinson LLP) *N Zr Q J1*
Liverpool *p288* 0151 600 8000

Gibbons, Mrs A C (Fieldings Porter) *B1 C1 E L O R1*
Bolton *p149* 01204 540900

Gibbons, Mrs C E (Burton & Co LLP) *S1 S2*
Lincoln *p284* 01522 523215

Gibbons, G (Graham Smith Property Lawyers) *S1 E W L K1 G P N C1*
Watford *p424* 01923 227212

Gibbons, G D (Bates NVH) *C1 C2 E S1 S2*
Hook *p252* 01256 760074

Gibbons, H M (Lee & Kan)
London W1 *p52* 020 7287 8888

Gibbons, I R (Wiltshire County Council)
Trowbridge *p474* 01225 713000

Gibbons, Ms J (IBB Solicitors) *G H*
Uxbridge *p417* 0845 638 1381

Gibbons, Mrs J (NFLA Ltd) *K3 K1 D1*
Chesterfield *p192* 01246 471900

Gibbons, Mrs J M (Nicholls Lindsell & Harris and Ingham & Wainwright) *K1 L N S1 T2 W*
Poynton *p355* 01625 876411

Gibbons, J R (The Smith Partnership) *C1 S2*
Derby *p209* 01332 225225

Gibbons, J R (Norton Peskett) *K1 Q O G N Zl Zm*
Great Yarmouth *p234* 01493 849200

Gibbons, Ms K (Clifford Chance)
London E14 *p20* 020 7006 1000

Gibbons, Ms L M (Squire Sanders (UK) LLP)
London EC2 *p81* 020 7655 1000

Gibbons, S (Stephenson Harwood) *B2 Za Zj*
London EC2 *p82* 020 7329 4422

Gibbons, T P (Rothera Dowson)
Nottingham *p338* 0115 910 0600

Gibbs, Mrs A C (RSPCA)
Horsham *p461* 0870 010 1181

Gibbs, Miss C (dgb Solicitors) *S1 L S2 E*
Chatham *p184* 01634 304000

Gibbs, Mrs C D (Last Cawthra Feather LLP) *W*
Ilkley *p261* 01943 601020

Gibbs, Mrs C E (Spratt Endicott) *O Q B1 J1 Zk Zp*
Banbury *p122* 01295 204000

Gibbs, D (Birkett Long LLP) *B1 Q*
Colchester *p197* 01206 217300

Gibbs, G (Hart Brown Solicitors) *J1*
Guildford *p236* 0800 068 8177

Gibbs, H W (Brethertons LLP) *S1 L*
Rugby *p368* 01788 551611

Gibbs, Mrs J K (Norfolk County Council - Legal Services) *S1 E H G S2 W F1 K1 V C2 L B2 D1 Q R2*
Norwich *p467* . . . Minicom: 0844 800 8011

Gibbs, Mrs J T (Austins Penny & Thorne) *S2 E R2 S1*
Berkhamsted *p131* 01442 872141

Gibbs, M J C (Jeremy Gibbs & Co) *S1 D1 E G P W K1 M1*
Amersham *p117* 01494 724671

Gibbs, N J (Woodfines LLP) *C1 E J1 S2*
Milton Keynes *p317* 01908 202150

Gibbs, P D (Jacobs & Reeves) *C1 O Q N Zq L J1 F1*
Poole *p353* 01202 674425

Gibbs, R K (Davies & Partners) *C1 E L R1 S1 R2 Zc S2*
Almondsbury *p115* 01454 619619

Gibbs, Miss R L (West Sussex County Council)
Chichester *p455* 01243 777100

Gibbs, Miss S D (Hornby & Levy) *D1 D2 K1 X*
London SW9 *p43* 020 7737 0909

Gibbs, S N (Field Fisher Waterhouse LLP) *O Q*
London EC3 *p31* 020 7861 4000

Giblin, Mrs L (Harthills) *G H*
Rotherham *p367* 01709 377399

Giblin, P J (Clarkson Wright & Jakes Ltd) *L S1 W*
Orpington *p341* 01689 887887

Gibney, J (Tollers LLP)
Northampton *p332* 01604 258558

Gibney, J D (Tollers LLP) *N*
Northampton *p332* 01604 258558

Gibson, Miss A (Butcher & Barlow LLP) *N Q C1*
Runcorn *p369* 01928 576056

Gibson, A (R J Osborne & Co) *N*
Wellingborough *p424* 01933 273400

Gibson, A G (Gibson & Co) *A1 S2 E K3 S1 W*
Hexham *p249* 01434 602131
Newcastle upon Tyne *p324* . 0191 273 3817

Gibson, A P (Hill Dickinson LLP) *N J1 F1 O Q Zc Ze Zo Zp J2*
Chester *p190* 01244 896600

Gibson, A R J (K&L Gates LLP) *C1*
London EC4 *p47* 020 7648 9000

Gibson, C (Short Richardson & Forth LLP) *I C2 C1*
Newcastle upon Tyne *p326* . 0191 232 0283

Gibson, C (Steptoe & Johnson) *M2 U2 Ze M1*
London EC2 *p83* 020 7367 8000

Gibson, C (Field Fisher Waterhouse LLP)
London EC3 *p31* 020 7861 4000

Gibson, Mrs C A (Shoosmiths) *O Q Zb*
Northampton *p332* . . 0370 086 3000 / 01604 543000

Gibson, D (Milburns Solicitors) *S1 W*
Workington *p440* 01900 67363

Gibson, Mrs D (Noble)
Shefford *p377* 01462 814055

Gibson, D M (Crutes) *J1 Zw*
Newcastle upon Tyne *p324* . 0191 233 9700

Gibson, D S C (Gibson & Co)
Hexham *p249* 01434 602131

Gibson, D T (Milburns Solicitors) *S1 W*
Maryport *p313* 01900 813541

Gibson, Ms E (Ashfords LLP)
Exeter *p220* 01392 337000

Gibson, Mrs E B J (Reading Borough Council)
Reading *p469* 0118 939 0900

Gibson, Mrs G M (Donnelly McArdle Adamson) *K1 W*
Hartlepool *p243* 01429 274732

Gibson, J C (Howells LLP) *G H*
Sheffield *p376* 0114 249 6666

Gibson, Ms J E (Lanyon Bowdler LLP)
Telford *p409* 01952 291222

Gibson, Miss J L (Harcus Sinclair) *T2 W*
London WC2 *p38* 020 7242 9700
London EC4 *p92* 020 7597 6000

Gibson, Ms J P (Gibson & Co) *O Q Zq A3 B2 Zk*
Newcastle upon Tyne *p324* . 0191 273 3817

Gibson, Ms L C (Orange PCS Ltd)
Bristol *p452* 0870 376 8888

Gibson, M (Wosskow Brown) *K4 N S1 T2 W*
Sheffield *p377* 0114 256 1560

Gibson, M J (Bailey & Haigh) *F1 J1 L O Q N*
Selby *p373* 01757 705191

Gibson, M J (David Gray Solicitors) *G H B2 Zg*
Newcastle upon Tyne *p324* . 0191 232 9547

Gibson, N (Holroyd & Co) *K1*
Huddersfield *p256* 01484 645464

Gibson, N (Trowers & Hamlins)
London EC3 *p88* 020 7423 8000

Gibson, N C (Stephenson Harwood) *Zb*
London EC2 *p82* 020 7329 4422

Gibson, P A (Coles Solicitors) *N*
Northallerton *p331* 01609 780717

Gibson, Ms R (Trowers & Hamlins)
London EC3 *p88* 020 7423 8000

Gibson, Ms R E (Fentons)
Failsworth *p223* 0161 682 7101

Gibson, R M (Samuel Phillips Law Firm) *M1 K1 J1 P G H D1 S1 N W Zl Zm*
Newcastle upon Tyne *p326* . 0191 232 8451

Gibson, S (Penningtons)
Basingstoke *p127* 01256 407100

Gibson, Miss S C (Andrew Jackson) *E R1 Zc*
Hull *p257* 01482 325242

Gibson, S J (Kennedys)
London EC3 *p49* 020 7667 9667

Gibson, S K (Kirwans) *N*
Liverpool *p289* 0151 229 5600

Gibson, S W (Yarwood & Stubley) *D1 F1 G H J1 K1 M1 P S1*
Blyth *p148* 01670 361211

Gibson, T J (Gibson & Co) *O Q Zq A3 B2*
Hexham *p249* 01434 602131
Newcastle upon Tyne *p324* . 0191 273 3817

Gibson, T W (South Bucks District Council)
Denham *p456* 01895 837200

Gibson, Ms U (Manches LLP) *J1*
Oxford *p343* 01865 722106

Gibson, Mrs Y (Buckinghamshire County Council)
Aylesbury *p448* 01296 383653

Gibson-Birch, N (Machins Solicitors LLP) *W K4 T2 S1*
Luton *p295* 01582 514000
Luton *p296* 01582 723322

Gibson-Bolton, Ms E M (SJ Berwin LLP)
London EC4 *p75* 020 7111 2222

Gibson-Davies, M E (Tendring District Council)
Clacton-on-Sea *p455* 01255 686567

Giddens, P J (Peter Giddens & Co) *E S1 W*
Cambridge *p174* 01954 250089

Giddings, I T (Brindley Twist Tafft & James) *K1 Q Zr D1 D2 K3 K2*
Coventry *p200* 024 7653 1532

Giddins, M P C (Lester Aldridge LLP) *N O Q Zj*
Bournemouth *p152* 01202 786161

Giddy, N (Veale Wasbrough Vizards) *C1 E O Q*
London EC4 *p89* 020 7405 1234

Gidman, P J (DWF) *E S2 R2 L S1*
Manchester *p303* 0161 603 5000

Gidney, D G (Burges Salmon) *E R2 S2*
Bristol *p161* 0117 939 2000

Gidney, S J (Aviva PLC)
London EC3 *p103* . . 020 7283 7500 / 01603 687905
Norwich *p467* 01603 622200

Gidwani, Ms K (Fenwick Elliott)
London WC2 *p31* 020 7421 1986

Giess, M D (Maxwell Winward LLP) *E R2 L*
London EC4 *p59* 020 7651 0000

Gieve, Ms K E (Bindmans LLP) *D1 K1*
London WC1 *p12* 020 7833 4433

Gifford, A C (Dickinson Dees) *W*
Newcastle upon Tyne *p324* . 0191 279 9000

Gifford, J H (Passmore Lewis & Jacobs) *K1 S1 M1 P F1 H G W D1 N*
Barry *p126* 01446 721000

Gifford, N C O (Malcolm Wilson & Cobby) *S1 W S2 E*
Worthing *p442* 01903 237581

Gifford, R D (Sheridans) *O Q Zi K1*
London WC1 *p78* 020 7079 0100

Gigg, C G A (Ashton Bond Gigg) *B1 J1 O Zq*
Nottingham *p335* 0115 947 6651

Gilani, Ms F D (Staffordshire County Council) *D1*
Stafford *p472* 01785 223121

Gilberg, S J (Barlow Lyde & Gilbert LLP)
London EC3 *p10* 020 7247 2277

Gilbert, A F (Kennedys) *Zj J2*
London EC3 *p49* 020 7667 9667

Gilbert, Miss C R (Neil Myerson LLP) *J1*
Altrincham *p117* 0161 941 4000

Gilbert, Mrs D L (Radcliffes Le Brasseur) *N G Zr*
Leeds *p276* 0113 234 1220

Gilbert, G E (Essex County Council)
Chelmsford *p454* 0845 743 0430

Gilbert, I (George H Coles & Co) *S1 E W L J1*
Hove *p254* 01273 205101

Gilbert, I M (Walker Morris) *C1*
Leeds *p277* 0113 283 2500

Gilbert, J A (Aubrey Isaacson Solicitors) *N S1 W J1 Q L K1 F1*
Whitefield *p430* 0161 959 6000

Gilbert, Mrs J M (Cozens-Hardy LLP) *N J1 J2*
Norwich *p334* 01603 625231

Gilbert, K (Howes Percival LLP)
Leicester *p280* 0116 247 3500

Gilbert, M (Addleshaw Goddard) *R2*
London EC1 *p4* 020 7606 8855

Gilbert, M S (Plymouth City Council) *Zu X*
Plymouth *p468* 01752 668000

Gilbert, P W (Hutchins & Co) *L N*
Hackney *p44* 020 8986 3911

Gilbert, Dr P X (Bristows) *C1 O Ze*
London EC4 *p15* 020 7400 8000

Gilbert, R M (Debenhams Ottaway) *K1 K3*
St Albans *p390* 01727 837161

Gilbert, R N (Rollits LLP) *O B1 Q L*
Hull *p258* 01482 323239

Gilbert, Miss S (Streeter Marshall) *K1*
Croydon *p205* 020 8680 2638

Gilbert, S A (Charles Russell LLP) *C1 C2*
London EC4 *p19* 020 7203 5000

Gilbert, S A (Ross & Craig) *E L S1 S2*
Westminster *p73* 020 7262 3077

Gilberthorpe, Miss H L (Foys Solicitors) *O Q N*
Doncaster *p211* 01302 327136

Gilbertson, J (Ince & Co Services Ltd)
London E1 *p44* 020 7481 0010

Gilbertson, Mrs K A F (Greenwoods Solicitors LLP) *J2 Zy F2 P*
Peterborough *p347* 01733 887700

Gilbey, B D (Squire Sanders (UK) LLP) *T1 C2*
London EC2 *p81* 020 7655 1000

Gilbey, I (Shoosmiths) *E R1*
Birmingham *p142* 0370 086 4000 / 0121 335 4440

Gilbey, M C (British American Tobacco) *O Q*
London WC2 *p104* 020 7845 1000

Gilbey, S W (Watkins Stewart & Ross) *W S1 E A1*
Ipswich *p263* 01473 226266

Gilbey, Mrs T H (British American Tobacco UK Ltd)
Aylesbury *p447* 01296 335000

Gilbride, Ms C (Grant Argent & Co) *S1 S2 W C1*
Brent *p7* 020 8452 7651

Gilchrist, R (Glovers Solicitors LLP) *Zb B1 E R1 S1*
London W1 *p36* 020 7935 8882

Gilchrist, R M R (Renshaw Gilchrist & Co) *A1 C1 E L S1 W Zc*
Fleetwood *p226* 01253 873569

Gilchrist, S J (Druces LLP) *B1 O*
London EC2 *p27* 020 7638 9271
London WC2 *p29* 020 7691 4000

Gilchrist, S N (Saunders Law Partnership LLP) *B2 G*
London WC2 *p76* 020 7632 4300

Gildener, P (Gildener Brett) *N Q F1 B1 J1 Zl Zk Zq Zd*
Penzance *p346* 01736 332533

Gildener, S J (Squire Sanders (UK) LLP)
London EC2 *p81* 020 7655 1000

Gilding, Mrs J M (Gard & Co) *W K4 Zm*
Plymouth *p349* 01752 668246

Giles, A (Salans)
London EC4 *p76* 020 7429 6000

Giles, A P (Rawlings Giles)
London SW11 *p71* 020 7223 2765

Giles, B (McGrigors LLP)
London EC4 *p56* 020 7054 2500

Giles, C J (C J Giles & Co) *S1 K1 M1 F1 G J1 W*
Wokingham *p437* 0118 978 1017

Giles, Ms E (Kingsley Napley) *G B2*
London EC1 *p50* 020 7814 1200

Giles, Ms E V (Sparrow & Trieu Solicitors) *E S1*
London W1 *p81* 020 7287 6608

Giles, H P (Treasury Solicitors Department)
London WC2 *p110* 020 7210 3000

Giles, J A (Aldridge Brownlee Solicitors LLP) *K1 W T1*
Bournemouth *p151* 01202 527008

Giles, Miss K (ASB Law) *K1 Q N J1*
Maidstone *p298* 01622 656500

Giles, Miss K (Clerical Medical Investment Group)
London EC2 *p105* 020 7321 1425

Giles, Mrs K D (Hooper Holt & Co) *K1 S1 D1 L Q B1*
Redhill *p362* 01737 761111

Giles, M (Warner Goodman LLP) *Zo*
Fareham *p224* 01329 288121

Giles, Ms M (Giles Wilson)
Leigh-on-Sea *p282* 01702 477106

Giles, M J (Squire Sanders (UK) LLP) *N Q*
Birmingham *p142* 0121 222 3000

Giles, M M V (Guildford Borough Council)
Guildford *p459* 01483 505050

Giles, N P (Edwin Coe LLP) *W Q C1 T2*
London WC2 *p29* 020 7691 4000

Giles, P (Browne Jacobson LLP) *T1*
Nottingham *p336* 0115 976 6000

Giles, P (Giles Wilson)
Leigh-on-Sea *p282* 01702 477106

Giles, R L (Hatten Wyatt) *N Q*
Gravesend *p232* 01474 351199

Giles, S (Tinn Criddle & Co) *S1 L S2 W E*
Alford *p115* 01507 462882

Giles, Miss T M (Walsall Metropolitan Borough Council)
Walsall *p475* 01922 650000

Giles, W M (Nash & Co Solicitors LLP) *K1 D1*
Plymouth *p350* 01752 664444

Gilford, L N (Kennedys) *Q O N Zj*
London EC3 *p49* 020 7667 9667

Gilhooly, Miss S J (Harrison Clark LLP) *C1 C2*
Cheltenham *p188* 01242 269198
Worcester *p439* 01905 612001
Worcester *p439* 01905 612001

Gilkes, R (Carvers (Part of the Wilkes Partnership LLP)) *D1 K1*
Birmingham *p136* 0121 784 8484

Gilks, P (Glovers Solicitors LLP) *C1 C2 Zb*
London W1 *p36* 020 7935 8882

Gill, Ms A (Davenport Lyons) *K1*
London W1 *p25* 020 7468 2600

Gill, A (Trowers & Hamlins)
London EC3 *p88* 020 7423 8000

Gill, Ms A (Speechly Bircham LLP) *E R1 S1 T2 W*
London EC4 *p81* 020 7427 6400

Gill, A J (Forrester & Forrester) *A1 C1 C2 C3 E J1 L S1 T1 W*
Malmesbury *p300* 01666 822671

Gill, Ms A R (Kirby Sheppard) *K3 K1 D1*
Kingswood *p268* 0845 840 0045

Gill, A S (Gill & Co) *B1 C1 D1 F1 G J1 K1 L N S1 W Zl Zp*
Ilford *p260* 020 8554 8774

Gill, B S (Walsall Metropolitan Borough Council)
Walsall *p475* 01922 650000

Gill, Ms C (Raleys) *N*
Barnsley *p125* 01226 211111

Gill, Mrs C F (Carter-Ruck) *Q Ze Zk*
London EC4 *p18* 020 7353 5005

Gill, C H (Bawtrees LLP) *C1 C2 E O S2*
Witham *p435* 01376 513491

Gill, Mrs D E (B P Collins LLP) *C1 C2 Ze*
Gerrards Cross *p229* 01753 889995

Gill, Ms F M A (DAC Beachcroft) *P Ze*
London EC4 *p24* 020 7936 2222

Gill, Ms G (Aviva PLC)
London EC3 *p103* . . 020 7283 7500 / 01603 687905

Gill, G S (Eric Bowes & Co) *L N*
Solihull *p382* 0121 744 3691

Gill, Ms H (John Ford Solicitors) *Zd*
London N4 *p33* 020 8800 6464

Gill, H (Pinsent Masons LLP)
London EC2 *p67* 020 7418 7000

Gill, Mrs H A (Leathes Prior) *W*
Norwich *p334* 01603 610911

Gill, H F (Forsters LLP) *E*
Westminster *p33* 020 7863 8333

Gill, Miss I R E (Halton Borough Council) *D1*
Widnes *p476* 0151 424 2061

Gill, I W (Blake Lapthorn) *E P L*
Portsmouth *p354* 023 9222 1122

Gill, I W (Pemberton Greenish LLP) *E S2*
London SW3 *p66* 020 7591 3333

Gill, J (Wolferstans) *B1 E K1 S1 T1 Zc Zl*
Plymouth *p351* 01752 663295

Gill, J (Pinsent Masons LLP) *E L R1 S1*
Birmingham *p141* 0121 200 1050

Gill, Mrs J A E (Allen & Overy LLP)
London E1 *p5* 020 3088 0000

See p634 for the Key to Work Categories

Gill, J C H (Heptonstalls LLP) *W* Goole *p231* 01405 765661
Gill, Miss J L (Society of Lloyd's) London EC3 *p107* 020 7327 1000
Gill, Miss J L (South Gloucestershire Council) Thornbury *p474* 01454 868686
Gill, J S (Hatten Wyatt) *N Zq Zr J1 J2* Gravesend *p232* 01474 351199
Gill, J S (Dixon Coles & Gill) *N Q S1 J1* Wakefield *p418* 01924 373467
Gill, Mrs K (Environment Agency (Midlands Region)) Solihull *p471* 0121 711 2324
Gill, Miss L M (Bhatia Best) *G H* Nottingham *p336* 0115 950 3231
Gill, Miss M K (Brooke North LLP) *O Q* Leeds *p272* 0113 283 2100
Gill, M S (Addleshaw Goddard) *O* London EC1 *p4* 020 7606 8855
Gill, M S (Sternberg Reed) *N Zr* Barking *p123* 020 8591 3366
Gill, N (Geoffrey Leaver Solicitors LLP) *N* Milton Keynes *p317* 01908 692769
Gill, O S (Gill & Co) *S1* Ilford *p260* 020 8554 8774
Gill, Ms R (Squire Sanders (UK) LLP) London EC2 *p81* 020 7655 1000
Gill, R (Bermans LLP) *C1 E C2* Liverpool *p286* 0151 224 0500
Gill, R (Brabners Chaffe Street) Liverpool *p286* 0151 600 3000
Gill, Miss R K (Derby City Council) Derby *p456* 01332 293111
Gill, S (Solihull Metropolitan Borough Council) Solihull *p471* 0121 704 6000
Gill, Miss S (Robin F Clark & Co) Gravesend *p232* . . . . 01474 334444 Chadwell Heath *p183* 020 8597 5717
Gill, Mrs S A (Elliot Mather LLP) *S1 S2 W* Matlock *p313* 01629 584885
Gill, Ms S F (McGrigors LLP) *S2 E U1* London EC4 *p56* 020 7054 2500
Gill, Ms S J (Bray & Bray) *K1 D1 D2 K3* Hinckley *p250* 01455 639900
Gill, S N (Gateley LLP) *C2 C1* Birmingham *p138* 0121 234 0000
Gill, Mrs S V (Alsters Kelley) *K1 K3* Coventry *p199* 0844 561 0100
Gill, W A (Geldards LLP) *N J1 B1 M1 P R1 K1 Za Zc Zl Zs* Cardiff *p178* 029 2023 8239
Gillam, Miss E (Wortley Redmayne Kershaw) *Q* Chelmsford *p187* 01245 491122
Gillam, Miss K J (CooperBurnett) *W K4* Tunbridge Wells *p415* 01892 515022
Gillan, A C (Bennett Welch & Co) London SE19 *p12* 020 8670 6141
Gillanders, D S (Gillanders) *S1 L E R1 C1 A1 Zd* Cheltenham *p188* 01242 583434
Gillard, Mrs A J (Reading Borough Council) Reading *p469* 0118 939 0900
Gillard, N D (Reed Smith LLP) *C1 Ze Zf* London EC2 *p71* 020 3116 3000
Gillatt, R M (Baxter Caulfield) *S1 E* Huddersfield *p255* 01484 519519
Gillbanks, J A (Brabners Chaffe Street) *E* Liverpool *p286* 0151 600 3000
Gillen, A J (Travers Smith LLP) *C1 C2* London EC1 *p87* 020 7295 3000
Gillen, G A (Leeds City Council) *K1 D1 D2* Leeds *p462* 0113 224 3513
Gillery, B F (Metcalfe Copeman & Pettefar) *S1 S2 Zh R2* King's Lynn *p266* 01553 778102
Gillespie, A J (Hill Dickinson LLP) *Zj N* Liverpool *p288* 0151 600 8000
Gillespie, A N (QualitySolicitors Jackson & Canter) *D1 K1 K3 L W N* Liverpool *p290* 0151 282 1700
Gillespie, A S (Allen & Overy LLP) London E1 *p5* 020 3088 0000
Gillespie, D (DLA Piper UK LLP) London EC2 *p24* 0870 011 1111
Gillespie, Ms J A (Plexus Law (A Trading Name of Parabis Law LLP)) *Q O Zj Zq E* London EC3 *p68* 0844 245 4000
Gillespie, Mrs K (National Grid) Warwick *p475* 01926 653000
Gillespie, Mrs K (National Grid PLC) Warwick *p471* 01926 653000
Gillespie, Ms K A (Samuel Phillips Law Firm) *Zr* Newcastle upon Tyne *p326* . 0191 232 8451
Gillett, Mrs F (Trethowans LLP) *N Zr* Salisbury *p371* 01722 412512
Gillett, F C (Stewarts Law LLP) *A3 O* London EC4 *p83* 020 7822 8000
Gillett, J D (Barnes Gillett) *A1 B1 C1 E L S1 T1 W S2* Brentwood *p156* 01277 226491
Gillette, J F (Barker Gillette) *E S2 C1* London W1 *p9* 020 7636 0555
Gillham, G E A (McGrigors LLP) London EC4 *p56* 020 7054 2500
Gillham, Ms S A (Thomson & Bancks LLP) *S1 E L S2* Pershore *p346* 01386 562000
Gillibrand, D L (Oglethorpe Sturton & Gillibrand) *N C1 J1 F1 Ze Zc L O Q* Lancaster *p270* 01524 846846
Gillibrand, R M N (Oglethorpe Sturton & Gillibrand) *A1 S1 W P R1* Lancaster *p270* 01524 846846
Gillies, J R (Cumming Hodgkinson Dickinson) *E K1 L N O Q S1 W* Bolton *p148* . . . . .01204 523108 / 528396
Gillies, M (Corries Solicitors) *S1 W* York *p444* 0845 241 5566
Gillies, N P (Beale and Company Solicitors LLP) *Q O Zq Zj A3* London WC2 *p11* 020 7240 3474
Gilligan, R (Barlow Lyde & Gilbert LLP) *Q N* Manchester *p301* 0161 829 6400
Gilliland, Mrs E (Towns Needham & Co) *C1 C2 S1 E W R1 Zd Zo* Manchester *p310* 0161 832 3721
Gillingham, G A (RHW Solicitors LLP) *E S2* Guildford *p237* 01483 302000
Gillingham, M E (Mayo Wynne Baxter LLP) *S1 E* Brighton *p160* 01273 775533
Gillings, Miss S J (Simmons & Simmons) London EC2 *p79* 020 7628 2020
Gillings, S P (Bolt Burdon) *N* Islington *p14* 020 7288 4700
Gillion, F (Fenwick Elliott) *O Q Zc Zi A3 P Zj R2* London WC2 *p31* 020 7421 1986
Gillions, J A (Fishers) *T2 W Zd Zm Zo T1* Ashby-de-la-Zouch *p118* . . 01530 412167
Gillis, I F (DWF) *C1 C2* Manchester *p303* 0161 603 5000
Gillman, A J T (Powell Spencer & Partners) *N G H Zg* London NW6 *p69* 020 7604 5600
Gillman, Mrs J M (Willans LLP) *W* Cheltenham *p189* 01242 514000
Gillman, M J (Bishop & Sewell LLP) *K1 G D1 Q D2* London WC1 *p13* 020 7631 4141
Gillott, C R E (Irwin Mitchell LLP) *N Zq Zr* Leeds *p274* . . . . 0870 150 0100 Lancaster *p270* 0844 858 3900
Gillott, R C G (Radcliffes Le Brasseur) *C1 I J1 M1 F1 Ze* Westminster *p70* 020 7222 7040
Gillott, Ms S L (Howells LLP) *K1 K3* Sheffield *p376* 0114 249 6666
Gillson, Ms J L (Punch Robson) *Zm J1* Middlesbrough *p315* 01642 230700
Gilman, G A (Hargreaves Gilman) *E S1 W S2* Manchester *p305* 0161 443 1711
Gilman, T E (Manches LLP) *W K4 T2* Oxford *p343* 01865 722106
Gilmartin, Ms C (Taylor Wessing) London EC4 *p86* 020 7300 7000
Gilmore, A (Janes) *G H B2* London SW1 *p46* 020 7930 5100
Gilmore, L (Hamlins LLP) *Ze Zf* London W1 *p38* 020 7355 6000
Gilmour, C H D (PCB Lawyers LLP) *C1 E K1 L S1 T1 W* London W1 *p65* 020 7486 2566
Gilmour, Mrs E (Steele Raymond) *K4 T1 W C1 C2 F1 Ze U2* Bournemouth *p152* 01202 294566
Gilmour, I A (Edwin Coe LLP) *E S1 S2* London WC2 *p29* 020 7691 4000
Gilmour, Ms M A C (Field Fisher Waterhouse LLP) *E L P* London EC3 *p31* 020 7861 4000
Gilmour, Miss S (Straw & Pearce) *G H* Loughborough *p293* 01509 268931
Gilmour, Ms S E (Male & Wagland) *B1 F1 J1 L N O Q Zc Zk Ze Zq Zr* Potters Bar *p355* 01707 657171
Gilmour, S P N (Shakespeares) *J1 Zp* Birmingham *p142* 0121 237 3000
Gilmour, Miss V I J (Mundays LLP) *K1 D1* Cobham *p196* 01932 590500
Gilpin, Miss R S (Blake Lapthorn) *Zd Zl C1* Portsmouth *p354* 023 9222 1122
Gilroy, C M (John Collins & Partners LLP) *E* Swansea *p405* 01792 773773
Gilroy, N (Davenport Lyons) *Zf Ze O Zw* London W1 *p25* 020 7468 2600
Gilroy-Thomas, Mrs M (Raworths LLP) *T2 W K4* Harrogate *p240* 01423 566666
Gilyott, F H (Andrew Kingston & Co) *W S1 S2 K4* Hull *p257* 01482 216217
Gimblett, R J (Barlow Lyde & Gilbert LLP) *N O Q Zj* London EC3 *p10* 020 7247 2277
Gin, Ms A (Ashurst LLP) London EC2 *p7* 020 7638 1111
Ginesi, Mrs L (Carter Lemon Camerons) *G J1 N O Q* London EC1 *p18* 020 7406 1000
Gingell, M (Doyle Clayton Solicitors Limited) *J1 Zp Zi* London EC2 *p27* 020 7329 9090
Ginger, N J (Machins Solicitors LLP) *E S2 A1 R2* Luton *p295* 01582 514000
Ginn, Mrs A M (Angel Trains Ltd) London SW1 *p103* 020 7592 0500
Ginnaw, Ms J (Badhams Law (A Trading Name of Parabis Law LLP)) Croydon *p204* 0844 245 4000
Ginsburg, Ms E A (London Borough of Haringey) *D1 K1 D2* London N22 *p106* 020 8489 0000
Ginvert, Mrs G B (Weightmans LLP) *N J1 G* Leicester *p281* 0116 253 9747
Gipson, M E (Birketts LLP) *C1 C2 B1 Ze I* Ipswich *p262* 01473 232300
Girach, F M H J (Hatten Wyatt) Gravesend *p232* 01474 351199
Girdlestone, Miss V M (Royal Borough of Kingston upon Thames) Kingston upon Thames *p462*. 020 8546 2121
Girgis, S (Morrison & Foerster (UK) LLP) *T1* London EC2 *p62* 020 7920 4000
Girling, Ms D (Mills & Reeve) *O Q Zb B1* Norwich *p335* 01603 660155
Girling, S (Suffolk County Council) Ipswich *p462* 01473 583000
Girton, Mrs H R (Alfred Truman) *S1 W* Bicester *p132* 01869 252761
Gist, D (David Gist Solicitors) *N K1 D1* Bristol *p162* 0117 927 9111
Gist, S (David Gist Solicitors) *N* Bristol *p162* 0117 927 9111
Gist, Mrs V A (The Merriman Partnership) *S1 W* Marlborough *p313* 01672 512244
Gitlin, M (OGR Stock Denton) *K4 K1 Q W* London N3 *p64* 020 8349 0321
Gittings, S R T (Stamp Jackson and Procter) *E L A1 P C1 Zc R1* Hull *p258* 01482 324591
Gittins, A C (Lanyon Bowdler LLP) *C1 A1 T1 R1 B1 E A2 R2 S2 Ze* Oswestry *p342* 01691 652241
Gittins, B (Gittins McDonald) *S1 O Q N Zr F1 F2 W* Wrexham *p442* 01978 291662
Gittins, Miss D U (Wace Morgan) *S1* Shrewsbury *p379* 01743 280100
Gittins, J A (Gittins McDonald) *S1 S2 E G H Zl L Zl R2 J1* Wrexham *p442* 01978 291662
Gittins, J A (Reynolds Porter Chamberlain LLP) *A3 O J2 Zc* London E1 *p71* 020 3060 6000
Gittins, P (King & Co) *S1 W Q L* Cambridge *p175* . . .01223 365432 / 566038
Gittins, P M (Hatchers Solicitors LLP) *N O F1 Q B1* Shrewsbury *p379* 01743 248545
Gittoes-Davis, Miss A M (Devereux & Co) *K1 K3* Bristol *p162* 0117 938 0222
Gittus, C M I (Gateley LLP) *E* Leicester *p279* 0116 285 9000
Given, A (Goughs) *E P R1 S1* Corsham *p199* 01249 712193
Given, Ms T J (Barlow Lyde & Gilbert LLP) London EC3 *p10* 020 7247 2277
Gizzi, J A (DAC Beachcroft) London EC4 *p24* 020 7242 1011
Gladders, J M (Wallers) *S1 C1* Newcastle upon Tyne *p327* . 0191 261 2281
Gladding, Miss K J (Wilkin Chapman LLP) *J1 O Q J2 N* Grimsby *p235* 01472 262626
Gladdle, T M G (Bray & Bray) *C1 C2 B1 E S2 Ze* Leicester *p279* 0116 254 8871
Gladman, H J C (St James's Place) Cirencester *p455* 01285 640302
Gladman, J W E (Raleys) *Zr N Zq* Barnsley *p125* 01226 211111
Gladwell, K J (Stephens & Son LLP) *K1 K3* Chatham *p185* 01634 811444
Gladwyn, Mrs B A (Caerphilly County Borough Council) Hengoed *p460* 01443 815588
Glaister, Miss L P C (Stanley Tee) *W T2 A1* Bishop's Stortford *p144* 01279 755200
Glancy, Ms M P (Linder Myers Solicitors) *K1 S1 E C1 D1 T1 W J1 F1* Manchester *p307* 0844 984 6400
Glandfield, J E (Glandfield & Cruddas) *G H S1 W* Uttoxeter *p417* 01889 565657
Glansfield, R (Glansfields) *D1 D2 G H K1 K3* Mansfield *p311* 01623 627827
Glanvill, Ms T (Leeds Day) *K1 D1 K3 D2* Huntingdon *p258* 01480 454301
Glanville, Miss K D (Pemberton Greenish LLP) *Q R1 L* London SW3 *p66* 020 7591 3333
Glanville, P (John Pickering & Partners LLP) *N* Halifax *p238* 0808 144 0959
Glasner, D S M (WGS Solicitors) *P K1 N L D1 O Q Zq* Westminster *p90* 020 7723 1656
Glass, Mrs C (Southern Stewart & Walker) *D1 K1* South Shields *p384* 0191 427 0770
Glass, C A (Brightstone Law LLP) *W T2* Elstree *p218* . . . . 020 8731 3080 London WC1 *p86* 020 7242 3191
Glass, D S (Pritchard Englefield) *C1 C2 Zb Ze* London EC2 *p69* 020 7972 9720
Glass, Ms H (London Borough of Lewisham) *S1 W K1 L D1 E F1* London SE6 *p107* 020 8695 6000
Glass, Miss J (BCL Burton Copeland) *B2 G H* London WC2 *p9* 020 7430 2277
Glassberg, Ms E L (Brecher) *S2 E L R2 S1* London W1 *p15* 020 7563 1000
Glasser, C (Sheridans) *O F1 K1* London WC1 *p78* 020 7079 0100
Glassey, N J A (Nigel Glassey Solicitor) Stockport *p395* 0161 443 1395
Glassey, W (Mayer Brown International LLP) London EC2 *p59* 020 3130 3000
Glastonbury, Mrs V (SNR Denton) *Zb* London EC4 *p75* 020 7242 1212
Glaves-Smith, Miss A L (Child & Child) *S1 S2 W* London SW1 *p20* 020 7235 8000
Glazebrook, Ms R J (Barlow Robbins LLP) *C1 C2* Guildford *p235* 01483 562901
Glazebrook, R L (Fraser Dawbarns) *N G H* King's Lynn *p266* 01553 666600
Glazer, M H (Glazer Delmar) *N* London SE22 *p35* 020 8299 0021
Glazier, B E (Lester Aldridge LLP) *T1 W C1 A1 Zd Zo* Bournemouth *p152* 01202 786161
Gleave, Miss A S (Butcher & Barlow LLP) *D1 K3 K1* Sandbach *p372* 01270 762521
Gleave, Miss C E (Wakefield Metropolitan District Council) Wakefield *p474* 01924 306090
Gleave, Ms H (Hunters) *K1 Q K2* London WC2 *p44* 020 7412 0050
Gleave, P (The National Trust) Swindon *p475* 01793 817400
Gledhill, Mrs A B A (Leeds City Council) Leeds *p462* 0113 224 3513
Gledhill, Ms C R (Squire Sanders (UK) LLP) Leeds *p277* 0113 284 7000
Gledhill, D B (Bermans LLP) *E B1 C1 J1 R2 Zb C2 Zl S2* Manchester *p301* 0161 827 4600
Gledhill, I R (Rotherham Metropolitan Borough Council) Rotherham *p470* 01709 382121

6

Gledhill, Miss J (Thompsons (formerly Robin/Brian Thompson & Partners)) *N Zr* Leeds *p277* 0113 205 6300
Gledhill, R M (Finn Gledhill) *S1 L C1 E R1 W A1 Zl* Halifax *p238* . . . . 01422 330000 Hebden Bridge *p246* 01422 842451
Gledhill, S J (Napthens LLP) *K1* Blackpool *p146* 01253 622305
Gleed, D (Treasury Solicitors Department) London WC2 *p110* 020 7210 3000
Gleek, G (Simmons Gleek Solicitors) *E L S1 C1 W T1 R1 B1 Zc* London W1 *p79* 020 7580 9090
Gleeson, Ms J (City of Bradford Metropolitan District Council) Bradford *p451* 01274 752236
Gleeson, M J (Memery Crystal) *C1 C2* London WC2 *p60* 020 7242 5905
Gleeson, Ms N C (British Telecommunications PLC) London EC1 *p104* 020 7356 6181
Gleeson, Miss P (John Swales) *D1 K1 D2* Ashford *p119* 01233 732590
Glen, Ms A (Grahame Stowe Bateson) *G H* Leeds *p274* 0113 246 8163
Glen, Miss L (Derek M Jordan) *W K1 Q T2 N* Settle *p374* . . . . .01729 823589 / 823514
Glen, Miss P H (Watson Farley & Williams) London EC2 *p90* 020 7814 8000
Glen, Miss R (Thomas Cooper) *O C1 M1 Zj Za N* London EC3 *p22* 020 7481 8851
Glenday, Miss F M (Pinkney Grunwells Lawyers LLP) *P M1 K1 G D1 H J1 N F1 Zm* Scarborough *p372* 01723 352125
Glendening, Dr J (Browne Jacobson LLP) *N Zr Q* Nottingham *p336* 0115 976 6000
Glendenning, M (Holden & Co) *G H* Hastings *p243* 01424 722422
Glendinning, D (Ward Hadaway) *K1 D1 G P Zl* Newcastle upon Tyne *p327* . 0191 204 4000
Glendinning, Miss D C (Wrigleys Solicitors LLP) *E R2 S2 X* Leeds *p278* 0113 244 6100
Glenholme, Mrs S (Debenhams Ottaway) *W* St Albans *p390* 01727 837161
Glenister, I (Lanyon Bowdler LLP) *T1 A1 R1 E L A2 C1 C2 P R2 Zd* Oswestry *p342* 01691 652241
Glenister, Mrs J (Hart Brown Solicitors) *S1* Cranleigh *p202* 0800 068 8177
Glenn, J R (Brethertons LLP) *W T1 A1 Zd* Rugby *p368* . . . . 01788 579579 Rugby *p368* 01788 579579
Glenton, Miss A (Blaker Son & Young) *K1 D2 D1 K3* Lewes *p283* 01273 480234
Glenville, M J (Brabners Chaffe Street) *E* Liverpool *p286* 0151 600 3000
Glew, Ms D (Squire Sanders (UK) LLP) London EC2 *p81* 020 7655 1000
Glibbery, P J (Hepburns) *K1 J1 Q L* Oxted *p344* 01883 723712
Glicksman, B J (Stephenson Harwood) London EC2 *p82* 020 7329 4422
Gliddon, Miss J (Davies Johnson & Co (Shipping & Commercial Solicitors)) *Za A3 Zj O Q* Plymouth *p349* 01752 226020
Glinert, D A (Glinert Davis) *E S1 C1 L Zl* Westminster *p36* 020 7724 4442
Glinka, Miss D F (Trafford Metropolitan Borough Council) Stretford *p473* 0161 912 1212
Glithero, R C (Pannone LLP) *B1 Zb C1 F1* Manchester *p308* 0161 909 3000
Globe, D C (Globe Wareing Cropper) Liverpool *p288* 0151 486 8833
Glockler, Miss S A (Abrahams Dresden) *J1 O Q* London EC1 *p3* 020 7251 3663
Glossop, C C A (St Modwen Properties PLC) Birmingham *p450* 0121 222 9400
Glover, A (MKB Solicitors LLP) *K1 Zi* Barnsley *p124* 01226 210000
Glover, Ms A J (Hine Solicitors) *G* Gerrards Cross *p229* 01753 482400

Glover, Miss A J (Kingsfords) *E S1 K1 C1 Q N W J1 Zl L S2 R1*
Ashford *p119* 01233 624545
Glover, D (DLA Piper UK LLP) *C1 C2 I M2 U1 U2*
Birmingham *p137* 0870 011 1111
Glover, Miss E (FBC Manby Bowdler LLP) *O Q*
Wolverhampton *p437* 01902 578000
Glover, Ms G (Alan Edwards & Co) *L Zh Q Zg*
Kensington & Chelsea *p28*. . 020 7221 7644
Glover, J R (Fenwick Elliott) *O Q Zi Zc A3 P Zj R2*
London WC2 *p31* 020 7421 1986
Glover, L (The Ringrose Law Group - Richard Harwood) *D1 K1*
Lincoln *p285*. 01522 814700
Glover, R J (Squire Sanders (UK) LLP)
Leeds *p277* 0113 284 7000
Glover, Miss R S (Wake Smith & Tofields) *C1 S2 E*
Sheffield *p377*. 0114 266 6660
Glover, S G (Squire Sanders (UK) LLP)
Leeds *p277* 0113 284 7000
Glover, Ms S L (E G Arghyrakis & Co) *Za O A3 Zj M2*
London EC4 *p7* 020 7353 2302
Glover, T J (QualitySolicitors D'Angibau) *J1 F1 L Q N*
Boscombe *p151*. 01202 393506
Gluck, L M (Metropolitan Police Directorate of Legal Services)
London SW1 *p108*. 020 7230 7210
Gluyas, L (DLA Piper UK LLP)
London EC2 *p24*. 0870 011 1111
Glynn, Miss A (Robert Lizar) *H G*
Manchester *p307* 0161 226 2319
Glynn, Ms A (Robert Lizar) *G H*
Manchester *p307* 0161 226 2319
Glynn, A D (TLT Solicitors) *E*
Bristol *p165* 0117 917 7777
Glynn, Miss J A (Glynns Solicitors) *N O P Q Zq Zr J2*
Bristol *p162* 01761 490883
Glynn, Ms J H (Zermansky & Partners) *D1 K1 K3*
Leeds *p278* 0113 245 9766
Glynn, L (Ashurst LLP)
London EC2 *p7* 020 7638 1111
Glynn, M (DLA Piper UK LLP)
London EC2 *p24*. 0870 011 1111
Glynn, M R (Blackhurst Swainson Goodier LLP) *S2 E C1*
Preston *p356* 01772 253841
Glynn, Ms P (Charles Russell LLP) *C1 C2*
London EC4 *p19*. 020 7203 5000
Glynn, Ms P (Pierce Glynn) *L V*
Southwark *p67*. 020 7407 0007
Glynn, Miss S (Taylor Wessing)
London EC4 *p86*. 020 7300 7000
Glynne, A S P (Glynnes) *J1 J2 N*
Ealing *p214* 020 8997 1437
Glyn-Owen, Mrs S V (Phillips Solicitors) *W T2*
Basingstoke *p127* 01256 460830
Glynternick, Ms N C (Hewitsons) *J1*
Northampton *p332*. 01604 233233
Goacher, S C (Wirral Borough Council)
Wallasey *p475*. 0151 638 7070
Goadby, A (Pyms) *S1 Zc W S2 L A1*
Belper *p131* 01773 822307
Goalen, I M (Shearman & Sterling LLP)
London EC2 *p78*. 020 7655 5000
Goatley, Mrs H M (Barlow Robbins LLP) *N Q Zr*
Guildford *p235*. 01483 543200
Goaziou, Ms C M (Winterbotham Smith Penley LLP) *N Zr*
Stroud *p401* 01453 847200
Goda, Mrs J M (Henriques Griffiths) *W*
Bristol *p163* 0117 909 4000
Godar, G W (DLA Piper UK LLP) *C1 O C3 A3 Ze*
London EC2 *p24*. 0870 011 1111
Godbolt, J D (Oxford Employment Law Solicitors) *C1 J1 Ze O Zp Q J2*
Oxford *p344* 01865 487136
Godby, P C (British American Tobacco)
London WC2 *p104*. 020 7845 1000
Goddard, D A (Clifton Ingram LLP) *O Q*
Wokingham *p437* 0118 978 0099
Goddard, F (WBW Solicitors) *L Q F1 Zm*
Exeter *p222* 01392 202404
Goddard, J C H (Cullimore Dutton) *C1 E S1*
Chester *p190* 01244 356789
Goddard, K W (Birkett Long LLP) *S1*
Colchester *p197*. 01206 217300
Goddard, N (Ashurst LLP)
London EC2 *p7* 020 7638 1111
Goddard, Mrs R (Crewe & Nantwich Borough Council)
Crewe *p456* 01270 537102
Goddard, Mrs S E (Sutton-Mattocks & Co LLP) *E S1 S2*
London SW13 *p84*. 020 8876 8811
Goddard, Ms V (Pinsent Masons LLP) *E R2 L*
Leeds *p276* 0113 244 5000
Godden, D (Hodge Jones & Allen LLP) *G*
London NW1 *p41* 020 7874 8300
Godden, R W (Linklaters LLP)
London EC2 *p54*. 020 7456 2000
Godfrey, A (Penningtons)
London EC2 *p66*. 020 7457 3000
Godfrey, C H (Atherton Godfrey) *S1 W E C1 L Zl S2*
Doncaster *p211* 01302 320621
Godfrey, C M J (Burges Salmon) *C1 C2 F1 J1 Zb*
Bristol *p161* 0117 939 2000
Godfrey, C R (Veale Wasbrough Vizards) *J1 Q O*
London EC4 *p89*. 020 7405 1234
Godfrey, D J V (Sharp & Partners) *S1 W E L M1 F1 B1 Zi Zm*
Nottingham *p339*. 0115 959 0055
Godfrey, D N (Hill Dickinson LLP) *Zb C1 Zj C2 M2*
London EC3 *p41*. 020 7283 9033
Godfrey, I M (Shepherd Harris & Co) *G H K1 P M1 S1 L D1 J1 W Zi Zl Zt*
Enfield *p219*. 020 8363 8341
Godfrey, Miss N (Lewis Silkin LLP)
London EC4 *p53*. 020 7074 8000
Godfrey, Miss P E (Nabarro LLP)
London WC1 *p63* 020 7524 6000
Godfrey, R J (Bridgend County Borough Council)
Bridgend *p451* 01656 643643
Godfrey, Mrs S M (Cardiff Magistrates Court)
Cardiff *p453* 029 2046 3040
Godfrey, W E M (Simmons & Simmons)
London EC2 *p79*. 020 7628 2020
Godfrey-Payne, J (Horsey Lightly Fynn) *Zi R1 Zu Zy J2 P*
Bournemouth *p152*. 01202 551991
Godhania, H (ABV Solicitors) *N*
Hayes *p245* 0844 587 9996
Godison, Mrs T M (City of Lincoln Council)
Lincoln *p463*. 01522 881188
Godsell, Mrs E J (Paton & Carpenter) *S1 W K1 P L D1*
Llanelli *p292* . . . . .01554 774760 / 751680
Godsiffe, N E (Sylvester Mackett) *K1 K3*
Trowbridge *p414*. 01225 755621
Godson, A (Russell Jones & Walker)
Bristol *p164* 0117 374 2222
Godwin, A G (Blackburn & Co) *G K1 D1 H V Zl*
Fleetwood *p226* 01253 872238
Godwin, D (FBC Manby Bowdler LLP) *A1 E*
Bridgnorth *p157* 01746 761436
Godwin, G R (Dyne Drewett Solicitors Ltd) *S1 W A1 C1 F1 L E J1 P*
Sherborne *p378* 01935 813691
Godwin, J (Brown & Corbishley) *S1 E L A1*
Newcastle under Lyme *p323*. 01782 717888
Godwin, Miss M (Plexus Law (A Trading Name of Parabis Law LLP)) *N Q*
Evesham *p220*. 01386 769160
Godwin, Miss M E (Penman Johnson) *D1 G H K1*
Watford *p424* . . . .01923 225212 / 239566
Godwin, N (Reynolds Porter Chamberlain LLP)
London E1 *p71* 020 3060 6000
Godwin, N J (Thompsons (formerly Robin/Brian Thompson & Partners)) *N*
London WC1 *p87* 020 7290 0000
Godwin-Austen, J R (Hunters) *W T2 Zv*
London WC2 *p44* 020 7412 0050
Goel, P V (hlw Keeble Hawson LLP)
Doncaster *p211* 01302 366831
Goel, Ms R (Grindeys LLP) *S1*
Stoke-on-Trent *p397*. 01782 846441
Goel, Miss S K (GPT Solicitors) *K1 D1 L B1 Q G J1 S1 S2*
Wembley *p426*. .020 8904 6495 / 8904 6598
Goepel, D R (Edwin Coe LLP) *T2 W Zd K4*
London WC2 *p29* 020 7691 4000
Goff, A J (George Ide LLP) *K4 K1 Q W N*
Chichester *p192* 01243 786668
Goff, Ms M A (Morrisons Solicitors LLP) *S1 S2*
Woking *p437*. 01483 726146
Goff, M T A (Barratt Goff & Tomlinson) *N Zr*
Nottingham *p335*. 0115 931 5171
Goffman, R (EMW) *E S2 S1*
Milton Keynes *p316* 0845 070 6000
Gofton, T (Mogers) *J1*
Bath *p127*. 01225 750000
Gogarty, R C A (Holman Fenwick Willan) *O*
London EC3 *p42*. 020 7264 8000
Goggin, T (Hogan Lovells International LLP)
London EC1 *p42*. 020 7296 2000
Goggins, A L (Gardner Leader LLP) *N G H J2 Q F2 Zp Zq*
Newbury *p322* 01635 508080
Gohel, Mrs N (Spearing Waite LLP) *S2 E R2*
Leicester *p281*. 0116 262 4225
Gohil, Ms B (Thomson Snell & Passmore) *J1 Zp*
Tunbridge Wells *p415* 01892 510000
Gohil, Ms K (British Telecommunications PLC)
London EC1 *p104* 020 7356 6181
Going, J M (Hart Jackson & Sons) *S1 L W E A1 T1 J1 F1*
Ulverston *p416*. 01229 583291
Gold, The Hon A N M (Joelson Wilson LLP) *E C2 C1 S1*
Westminster *p46*. 020 7580 5721
Gold, D (Ince & Co Services Ltd)
London E1 *p44* 020 7481 0010
Gold, D L (Herbert Smith LLP) *O M2*
London EC2 *p40*. 020 7374 8000
Gold, D M (John O'Neill & Co)
Gosforth *p232* 0191 246 4000
Gold, H B (Mincoffs Solicitors LLP) *E C1 W S1 L T1 Zb*
Newcastle upon Tyne *p325* . 0191 281 6151
Gold, I H (Veseys Solicitors) *G H N*
Birmingham *p143* 0121 523 1123
Gold, Mrs J R (SJ Berwin LLP) *C1 B1*
London EC4 *p75*. 020 7111 2222
Gold, J S (Sebastians) *C1 E O S1 S2 W*
London EC4 *p77*. 020 7583 2105
Gold, L M (M Gold & Co (Metals) Ltd)
London E9 *p106*. 020 8986 6314
Gold, M J (Max Gold Law) *G H K1 M1 D1 Zg*
Hull *p257* 01482 224900
Gold, R A (Stone King LLP) *X*
Bath *p128* 01225 337599
Gold, Mrs S J (Cheshire County Council) *N*
Chester *p454* 01244 602382
Goldberg, A (Edward Oliver & Co) *S1 G P M1 W H J1 L F1*
Cheshunt *p189* 01992 633491
Goldberg, D H (Gisby Harrison) *O N Q*
Cheshunt *p189* 01707 878300
Goldberg, J P L (Quastel Midgen LLP) *S1 E W L*
London W1 *p70* 020 7908 2525
Goldberg, M L (DAC Beachcroft)
London EC4 *p24*. 020 7936 2222
Goldberg, M P (SJ Berwin LLP)
London EC4 *p75*. 020 7111 2222
Goldberg, P M (Lester Morrill) *G H B2 Zy*
Leeds *p275* 0113 245 8549
Goldberg, Ms S (Chivers Easton Brown) *Q O L J1 Zq*
Surbiton *p402* 020 8390 6155
Goldberg, S (Simons Muirhead & Burton) *C1 Zf*
London W1 *p79* 020 7734 4499
Goldberg, S S (OGR Stock Denton) *C1 E S1 L Zq S2*
London N3 *p64* 020 8349 0321
Goldburn, T J (Preston Goldburn) *Zr N*
Falmouth *p223*. 01326 318900
Golden, Miss B J (Beverley Golden) *S1 P N G C1*
Southampton *p386*. 023 8086 7137
Golden, Mrs C M (Goldens) *N*
Pinner *p348* 020 8429 8282
Golden, D M (Howell & Co) *B2 Zl*
Birmingham *p139* 0121 778 5031
Golden, J (Allen & Overy LLP)
London E1 *p5* 020 3088 0000
Golden, P J (Forsters LLP) *A1 T2*
Westminster *p33*. 020 7863 8333
Goldenberg, P (Michael Conn Goldsobel) *C1 C2*
London W1 *p60* 020 7580 8902
Golder, Q R (Taylor Vinters) *C1 C2*
Cambridge *p176*. 01223 423444
Goldfarb, J (Ince & Co Services Ltd)
London E1 *p44* 020 7481 0010
Goldfinch, Ms M (Thames Water Utilities Limited)
Reading *p469* 0118 373 8000
Goldhill, Ms S S R (Adams Harrison) *K1 V D1*
Saffron Walden *p370*. 01799 523441
Goldie, Miss H E (BUPA)
London WC1 *p104*. 020 7656 2305
Golding, A C (Hewitt Burrough & Co) *S1 W*
Dartford *p207* 01322 273833
Golding, Mrs A M (Gullands) *O Q N Zq Zk Zr F1*
Maidstone *p299* 01622 678341
Golding, Mrs K A (Sparling Benham & Brough) *D1 K1*
Colchester *p198*. 01206 733733
Golding, Ms N (Barlow Lyde & Gilbert LLP)
London EC3 *p10*. 020 7247 2277
Golding, Ms N J (Chichester District Council)
Chichester *p455* 01243 785166
Golding, P J (AMD Solicitors) *W T1 N S1 L J1 T2 K1 K2 Q Zd*
Bristol *p160* 0117 973 8205
Golding, Miss P V (Worcester City Council)
Worcester *p477* 01905 723471
Golding, Mrs R (Forsters LLP) *E*
Westminster *p33*. 020 7863 8333
Golding, S J J (EMI Music Publishing Ltd)
London W8 *p106* 020 3059 3059
Goldkorn, G (Goldkorn Mathias Gentle Page LLP) *O Q*
London WC1 *p36* 020 7631 1811
London SE5 *p36*. 020 7703 1144
Goldman, A A (Arcadia Group Ltd)
London W1 *p103* 020 7636 8040
Goldman, I J (Godloves) *S1 E S2*
Leeds *p273* 0113 225 8811
Goldman, Ms R J (Linklaters LLP)
London EC2 *p54*. 020 7456 2000
Goldman, Ms S (Ahmed & Co) *Zh L V*
Camden *p4* 020 7383 2243
Goldmeier, R (Solomon Taylor & Shaw) *O S2 S1*
London NW3 *p80* 020 7431 1912
Goldreich, N A (Comptons) *N F1 B1 J1 C1 W Zf*
Camden *p22*. 020 7485 0888
Goldring, A P (Greenland Houchen Pomeroy) *E K1 L S1 W O Q S2 K3*
Watton *p424*. 01953 882864
Goldring, S (Goldring & Co) *T2 W C1*
Rainham *p359*. 01634 260012
Goldring, S O (Reynolds Porter Chamberlain LLP) *N Q Zj*
London E1 *p71* 020 3060 6000
Goldsack, Mrs P (Canterbury City Council)
Canterbury *p453*. 01227 862000
Goldsborough, A (Sills & Betteridge LLP)
Boston *p151*. 01205 364615
Goldsborough, P (Pinsent Masons LLP) *C2 C1*
Leeds *p276* 0113 244 5000
Goldsmith, A J (Hill Dickinson LLP)
London EC3 *p41*. 020 7283 9033
Goldsmith, D J (Gardner Leader LLP) *B1 F1 G J1 K1 L M1 N P*
Newbury *p322*. 01635 508080
Goldsmith, E R (Goldsmith Williams) *S1 W S2*
Liverpool *p288*. 0845 373 3737
Goldsmith, I A (Carter Devile) *S2 K3 K1 Q S1 W Zl O*
Ilford *p259*. 020 8590 1066
Goldsobel, H (Michael Conn Goldsobel) *C1 C2*
London W1 *p60* 020 7580 8902
Goldson, S (Jeary & Lewis)
Chippenham *p193* 01249 444484
Goldson, S (Rayners) *S1 S2 N Q J2 W*
Chippenham *p193* 01249 650394
Goldspink, G (Howard Kennedy LLP) *E*
London W1 *p48* 020 7636 1616
Goldspink, R A (Morgan Lewis & Bockius)
London EC4 *p61*. 020 3201 5000
Goldstein, D (Ormerods) *G B2 H*
Croydon *p205* 020 8686 5000
Goldstein, Mrs J E (Samuel Phillips Law Firm) *D1 K1 K2 D2 V Zo*
Newcastle upon Tyne *p326* . 0191 232 8451
Goldstein, J J (JJ Goldstein & Co) *S1 E L W*
London NW4 *p36* 020 8202 1899
Goldstein, K C (Gershon & Goldstein) *S1 E S2 W*
Edgware *p217*. 020 8952 5272
Goldstein, L (Bayley Law Ltd (BYL))
Salford *p370*. 0870 837 3300
Goldstein, S (Howard Kennedy LLP) *Q*
London W1 *p48* 020 7636 1616
Goldstone, A M (Law Partners Solicitors Ltd)
London EC1 *p51*. 0870 600 9444
Goldstone, Mrs H E (Holmes & Hills LLP) *S1 S2 E*
Braintree *p155*. 01376 320456
Goldstone, N K (Magrath LLP) *O Q B1 N J1 Zk Zf Ze Zc Zza*
London W1 *p57* 020 7495 3003
Goldstone, Mrs S H (Sandra Goldstone) *S1 W*
Twickenham *p416* 020 8287 3635
Goldstone, Miss S R (Sally Goldstone Family Law) *W K1 K3 D2*
Swansea *p405*. 01792 456139
Goldstraw, S B (Manches LLP) *T1*
London WC2 *p58* 020 7404 4433
Goldsworthy, Mrs C S (John Collins & Partners LLP) *N Q*
Swansea *p405*. 01792 773773
Goldsworthy, Miss R J (FWD Law Associates) *W S1*
Newport *p328* 01633 660440
Cardiff *p180* 029 2047 0909
Goldthorp, Ms A (Addleshaw Goddard)
London EC1 *p4* 020 7606 8855
Goldthorp, Ms A S (Taylor Wessing) *B1 N P*
London EC4 *p86*. 020 7300 7000
Goldthorp, D (Yorkshire Water Services Ltd)
Bradford *p451* 01274 804159
Goldthorp, Mrs J I (Hillyer McKeown LLP) *S1*
Bebington *p129* 0151 645 4255
Goldup, I F (Hardman & Watson) *S1 S2 K1 K3 D1 W*
Broadstairs *p166*. 01843 863479
Goldwater, M (SLP Solicitors) *P N M1 K1 J1 F1*
Stanmore *p394* 020 8420 7950
Golestani, K (Jennings Perks & Co) *C1 E Zd*
Walsall *p420*. 01922 459000
Golker, H (Manuel Swaden) *S1 E L*
London NW6 *p58* 020 7431 4999
Gollaglee, J (Irwin Mitchell LLP) *B2 G*
Sheffield *p376* 0870 150 0100
Golland, C D (Freeth Cartwright LLP) *T1 W*
Nottingham *p337*. 0115 936 9369
Golledge, Ms J (Segens Blount Petre) *B1 Zb C1 Zq O Q Zj Zc*
Westminster *p77*. 020 7332 2222
Gollogly, B R (Bournemouth Borough Council)
Bournemouth *p450*. 01202 451178
Gollott, C R E (Lester Morrill) *Zr N Zq*
Leeds *p275* 0113 245 8549
Golstein, J (Wayne Leighton) *O Q Zi K3 K1 W N Zk B2 Zq*
Edgware *p217*. 020 8951 2988
Golstein, L (Seddons) *L B2 R1 O*
Westminster *p77*. 020 7725 8000
Golten, D M (Cannings Connolly) *O Q Zq Zh A3*
London EC1 *p18*. 020 7329 9000
Gomersall, J S (Glynns Solicitors) *N O Q Zq Zr*
Bristol *p162* 01761 490883
Gomersall, R V (Onions & Davies) *S1 A1 E W L*
Market Drayton *p312*. 01630 652405
Gomery, Ms K (Heaney Watson) *K1*
Liverpool *p288*. 0151 282 5555
Gomes, C T (Clive Gomes Solicitors) *G H B2*
Wembley *p426*. 020 8904 2614
Gomes, Miss N A S (Jaffe Porter Crossick)
London NW6 *p46* 020 7625 4424
Gomm, J A (Sparling Benham & Brough) *F1 O Q N Zq*
Colchester *p198* 01206 733733
Gomme, J E (dgb Solicitors) *C1 J1 Zl Zp*
Chatham *p184*. 01634 304000
Goncalves, Mrs A (Merritt & Co) *S1 W S2*
Yarm *p443*. 01642 885555
Gondhia, Miss S (Edward Fail Bradshaw & Waterson) *G H B2*
London EC3 *p30*. 020 7790 4032
Gonzalez, Ms A (Wilson & Co)
London N17 *p92*. 020 8808 7535
Goobey, Miss J (Olswang LLP) *O E L B1*
London WC1 *p64* 020 7067 3000
Gooch, C D (Barlows) *E S1 W C1 C2 S2*
Leicester *p278*. 0116 251 8295
Gooch, Ms D A (London Borough of Southwark)
London SE1 *p109* 020 7525 5000
Gooch, J (Kingsley Napley) *E*
London EC1 *p50*. 020 7814 1200
Gooch, Miss N (Knights) *Q L O Zq Ze A1*
Tunbridge Wells *p415* 01892 537311
Gooch, R (Gosschalks) *E L*
Hull *p256* 01482 324252

See p634 for the Key to Work Categories

Good, Mrs D F (Linklaters LLP)
London EC2 *p54* 020 7456 2000
Good, K D (Purcell Parker) *G H*
Birmingham *p141* 0121 236 9781
Good, K D C (Glaisyers) *G H B2 P Zu F2*
Birmingham *p138* 0121 233 2971
Wolverhampton *p438* 01902 710822
Good, Mrs R A (Malcolm McGuinness) *G H*
Altrincham *p116* 0161 928 7134
Goodacre, Mrs S (Ashton Bond Gigg) *A1 S2 E R1 R2*
Nottingham *p335* 0115 947 6651
Goodall, Ms C M (Morgans) *L V Zh Zm*
Cardiff *p180* 029 2072 9888
Goodall, Miss C M H (Herbert Smith LLP) *C1 C2*
London EC2 *p40* 020 7374 8000
Goodall, C P (Simmons & Simmons)
London EC2 *p79* 020 7628 2020
Goodall, Mrs D (Linder Myers Solicitors) *Zr N S1 S2*
Manchester *p307* 0844 984 6400
Goodall, Miss E L (Elliot Mather LLP) *G H*
Mansfield *p311* 01623 655666
Goodall, K (Goodall Barnett James)
St Leonards-on-Sea *p392* . . 01424 444475
Goodall, Mrs M K (Massers)
West Bridgford *p427* 0115 851 1666
Goodall, P A (Max Gold Law) *D1 K3 K1 D2*
Hull *p257* 01482 224900
Goodall, R (QualitySolicitors Gruber Garratt) *K1 Zm G*
Stalybridge *p393* 0161 303 2328
Goodall, Miss S (Shell International Ltd)
London SE1 *p109* 020 7934 1234
Goodbody, C J B (Middleton & Upsall LLP) *K1 D1 J1 L*
Warminster *p421* 01985 214444
Goodbody, Miss S J W (East Sussex County Council) *G D1 H F1*
Brighton *p451* 01273 670888
Goodbody, S W (Thomson Snell & Passmore) *W T2*
Tunbridge Wells *p415* 01892 510000
Goodchild, Ms E (Kennedys)
London EC3 *p49* 020 7667 9667
Goodchild, J C (Pemberton Greenish LLP) *W T2*
London SW3 *p66* 020 7591 3333
Goodchild, P J C (The College of Law) *I Ze*
London WC1 *p105* 0800 289997
Goodchild, R (Warner & Richardson) *W T2*
Winchester *p434* 01962 868366
Goode, Miss F S (John Birkby & Co) *K1 S1 W K3 S2*
Oldham *p340* 0161 626 5686
Goode, Miss J A (Whitehead Monckton) *C1*
Maidstone *p299* 01622 698000
Goode, Ms N (Lewis Silkin LLP) *R1 R2 S2 Zh L Zb Zd*
London EC4 *p53* 020 7074 8000
Goode, T J R (Thomas Cooper) *Q J1 O K1 K3*
London EC3 *p22* 020 7481 8851
Goode, Ms V (Lewis Silkin LLP)
London EC4 *p53* 020 7074 8000
Gooden, Miss M (Ward Gethin) *N W*
King's Lynn *p266* 01553 660033
Gooden, Mrs S M (Trowers & Hamlins) *C1 Zb Zh*
London EC3 *p88* 020 7423 8000
Gooden, S P (Standley & Co) *G K1 F1 D1 E H Zl J1 N O S2*
Knowle *p269* 01564 776287
Goodenough, L E (Haywards)
Stowmarket *p399* 01449 613631
Gooderidge, C J (Harris Cartier LLP) *N Q*
Slough *p382* 01753 810710
Gooderson, Ms P F (Hammersmith & Fulham Community Law Centre)
London W6 *p106* 020 8741 4021
Goodfellow, Mrs J (HM Land Registry - Leicester)
Leicester *p463* . . . . .0116 265 4000 / 4001
Goodfellow, Dr J A (ICI Chemicals & Polymers Ltd)
Redcar *p469* 01642 435629
Goodfellow, P J (Gateshead Metropolitan Borough Council)
Gateshead *p458* 0191 433 3000
Goodfellow, R (Addleshaw Goddard)
Leeds *p271* 0113 209 2000
Goodfellow, R N (RSPCA)
Horsham *p461* 0870 010 1181
Goodfrey, Ms A J (Pleass Thomson & Co) *N Q O W K1 F1 E S1 L*
Clacton-on-Sea *p195* 01255 221133
Goodge, J A (Bazeley Barnes & Bazeley) *K1 G Q S1 W L S2*
Bideford *p132* 01237 473122
Goodger, M (Mills & Reeve) *Ze*
Cambridge *p175* 01223 364422
Goodger, Mrs S (Henmans LLP) *Zq O W*
Oxford *p343* 01865 781000
Goodger, S W (Andrew Keenan & Co) *G H B2*
London SE20 *p48* 020 8659 0332
Goodger, T J (Elborne Mitchell LLP) *O Q Zj Zq*
London EC3 *p29* 020 7320 9000
Goodhand, K F (Goodhand and Forsyth QualitySolicitors) *G W H*
Redhill *p362* 01737 773533
Goodier, Miss J E (Farleys Solicitors LLP)
Accrington *p114* 01254 367853
Goodier, J O (Blackhurst Swainson Goodier LLP) *W S1*
Preston *p356* 01772 253841

Gooding, Miss A E (McNamara Ryan) *K1 Q N O J1 W S1 K3 Zq*
Weybridge *p430* 01932 846041
Gooding, C A (Howard Kennedy LLP) *N Za Zc Zj*
London W1 *p48* 020 7636 1616
Gooding, D J C (Mills & Reeve) *Zq Zj O Q*
Birmingham *p140* 0121 454 4000
Goodinge, O H W (Wills Group Ltd)
London EC3 *p110* 020 7488 8111
Goodings, R G (Wholley Goodings LLP) *K1 D1 Q K3 S1 W S2*
Bedlington *p130* 01670 824080
Goodkind, Ms L (Coca-Cola Enterprises Ltd)
Uxbridge *p474* 01895 231313
Goodlad, R D (Oxfordshire County Council)
Oxford *p468* 01865 792422
Goodlad, Mrs V M S (Currey & Co) *T2 W*
Westminster *p24* 020 7802 2700
Goodman, Miss A F (Goodman King) *J1 S1 K1 Zp W E*
Tavistock *p408* 01822 615510
Goodman, Miss A L (Bhatia Best) *G H*
Nottingham *p336* 0115 950 3231
Goodman, Mrs A R (Franklins) *W*
Abingdon *p114* 01235 553222
Goodman, B G (Kellogg Management Services (Europe) Ltd) *C1 C3 U2 Ze Zt Zw*
Manchester *p465* 0161 869 2000
Goodman, Ms C L (Bristows) *C1 C3 Ze Zf*
London EC4 *p15* 020 7400 8000
Goodman, D (Squire Sanders (UK) LLP) *R1*
Leeds *p277* 0113 284 7000
Goodman, Ms D (Withers LLP) *O W Zd Zg*
London EC4 *p92* 020 7597 6000
Goodman, D M (David Goodman & Co) *C1 O Q M2 B1 S1 S2 N R1 Zb Zc Ze Zq Zj*
Westminster *p36* 020 7323 3369
Goodman, D R (Bircham Dyson Bell) *C1 T1 B1 N Ze Zf Zc*
Westminster *p13* 020 7227 7000
Goodman, E S (Radcliffes Le Brasseur) *T1 T2 W*
Westminster *p70* 020 7222 7040
Goodman, Mrs F (Newmans Solicitors) *S1 W S2 T2*
Horley *p252* 01293 771521
Goodman, Miss F (George Davies Solicitors LLP) *C1 C2 F1*
Manchester *p303* 0161 236 8992
Goodman, Ms J (Foot Anstey) *O Q Zb*
Plymouth *p349* 01752 675000
Goodman, J (Barlow Lyde & Gilbert LLP) *N Q*
London EC3 *p10* 020 7247 2277
Goodman, J A (DAC Beachcroft) *M2 P Zc*
London EC4 *p24* 020 7936 2222
Goodman, Miss J A (Family Law Associates LLP) *K1 K2 K3*
Haringey *p30* 020 8342 7760
Goodman, J A (Sidley Austin Brown & Wood) *R2*
London EC2 *p78* 020 7360 3600
Goodman, J E (Cook Taylor Woodhouse)
London SE9 *p22* 020 8859 0936
Goodman, J L (Pardoes) *N Q*
Bridgwater *p158* 01278 457891
Goodman, M T (Gravesham Borough Council)
Gravesend *p459* 01474 564422
Goodman, Miss N A S (Guest Walker & Co) *D1 G H J1 F1*
York *p444* 01904 624903
Goodman, P (Simmons & Simmons) *O Zj*
London EC2 *p79* 020 7628 2020
Goodman, P W (Jameson & Hill) *B1 C1 E S1 S2 W Zw*
Hertford *p248* 01992 554881
Goodman, R (Pontefract Petty Sessional Division)
Pontefract *p468* 01977 723600
Wakefield *p474* 01924 303461
Goodman, Ms S (Barlow Lyde & Gilbert LLP)
London EC3 *p10* 020 7247 2277
Goodman, Mrs S J (Thompsons (formerly Robin/ Brian Thompson & Partners)) *N J1 Zr*
Plymouth *p350* 01752 675810
Goodman, Ms T (Collyer Bristow LLP) *J1*
London WC1 *p22* 020 7242 7363
Goodrham, S (Gateley LLP) *O Ze Zq Zk U2 A3 F1*
Birmingham *p138* 0121 234 0000
Goodrich, J C (Denison Till) *W A1 Zm Zv T2 V*
York *p444* 01904 611411
Goodrich, L I (Lewis Silkin LLP) *E P*
London EC4 *p53* 020 7074 8000
Goodrich, M G (Lee-Barber Goodrich & Co) *W S1 T1 E C1 B1 Zj*
Torquay *p413* 01803 295535
Goodrich, P A (Lee-Barber Goodrich & Co) *S1 C1 E L R1 W Zl*
Torquay *p413* 01803 295535
Goodrich, R (Reynolds Porter Chamberlain LLP)
London E1 *p71* 020 3060 6000
Goodridge, Ms C (Avon & Bristol Law Centre)
Bristol *p451* 0117 924 8662
Goodridge, M R (Barlow Robbins LLP) *K1 Q O F1 Zk*
Godalming *p231* 01483 417121
Goodrum, N J (McCormicks) *N O J1 Q A3*
Harrogate *p240* 01423 530630
Goodship, R L (Bell & Co) *K1 K3*
Sutton *p402* 020 8661 8611
Goodson, R (Rodney Goodson) *S1 E S2 W*
Norwich *p334* 01603 632832
Goodstone, P (Addleshaw Goddard)
Manchester *p300* 0161 934 6000
Goodway, C C (Grays) *T2 W Zd*
York *p444* 01904 634771

Goodway, Mrs C R (Grays) *W T2 K4 Zm*
York *p444* 01904 634771
Goodwill, C P (Clifford Chance)
London E14 *p20* 020 7006 1000
Goodwill, P (Nabarro LLP) *N*
Sheffield *p376* 0114 279 4000
Goodwin, Mrs A (Gordon Lutton) *K3 J1 K1 O Q*
Hereford *p248* 01432 355345
Goodwin, Ms A M (Squire Sanders (UK) LLP)
London EC2 *p81* 020 7655 1000
Goodwin, A W (Brignalls Balderston Warren) *E S2 R2 L R1*
Letchworth *p283* 01462 482248
Goodwin, Miss B (Hempsons) *Zr N*
Manchester *p305* 0161 228 0011
Goodwin, C A (Graysons) *N*
Sheffield *p375* 0114 272 9184
Goodwin, Miss C J (Dorset County Council) *G H K1 Zl Q Zh L N*
Dorchester *p457* 01305 251000
Goodwin, Mrs C Z (C Z Goodwin) *S1*
Amersham *p117* 01494 724446
Goodwin, D P (Goodwin & Co) *S1*
London SW16 *p36* 020 8677 9554
Goodwin, Mrs E (Staffordshire County Council)
Stafford *p472* 01785 223121
Goodwin, G I (Poole Alcock) *A1 B1 E F1 G J1 K1 L W S1 Zc*
Alsager *p116* 01270 876550
Goodwin, I (Lanyon Bowdler LLP)
Ludlow *p294* 01584 872333
Goodwin, J (Burr Sugden) *Zc E F1 J1 Q N W*
Keighley *p263* 01535 605407
Goodwin, J L (Bridge Sanderson Munro) *W T2*
Doncaster *p211* 01302 321621
Goodwin, J S (Cohen Cramer Solicitors) *M1 G P N S1 E Zi Zp*
Leeds *p272* 0800 542 9408
Goodwin, Ms L (Taylor Wessing)
London EC4 *p86* 020 7300 7000
Goodwin, M (DLA Piper UK LLP)
Liverpool *p287* 0870 011 1111
Goodwin, M (Mark Goodwin & Co)
Wilmslow *p433* 01625 526495
Goodwin, M (Harrison Clark LLP) *O Q Zc*
Cheltenham *p188* 01242 269198
Worcester *p439* 01905 612001
Worcester *p439* 01905 612001
Goodwin, M A F (Taylor Wessing) *T1 W A1 C1 Ze Zf Zo*
London EC4 *p86* 020 7300 7000
Goodwin, M C A (Laytons) *C1 C2 C3*
London EC4 *p52* 020 7842 8000
Goodwin, N J (Goodwins Family Law Solicitors) *K1*
Harrow *p241* 020 8423 3525
Goodwin, P A (SNR Denton) *C1*
London EC4 *p75* 020 7242 1212
Goodwin, P W (Bircham Dyson Bell)
Westminster *p13* 020 7227 7000
Goodwin, S B (Leeds Day) *K1 K4 T2 W Zo*
St Ives *p392* 01480 464600
Goodwin, Mrs S K (Torbay Council)
Torquay *p474* 01803 201201
Goodwin, T P (Parry Law) *W*
Herne Bay *p248* 01227 361131
Whitstable *p431* 01227 276276
Goodwin, W H (AST Hampsons) *S1 G P F1 E K1 C1*
Rochdale *p365* 01706 522311
Goodwyn, E (Pinsent Masons LLP)
London EC2 *p67* 020 7418 7000
Goodyear, Ms M (Davies Gore Lomax) *K1 Zo*
Leeds *p273* 0113 242 2797
Goodyer, Miss M C (Stewarts Law LLP) *N*
London EC4 *p83* 020 7822 8000
Goold, J (Jones Day) *C1*
London EC4 *p46* 020 7039 5959
Goold, Ms K (Bindmans LLP) *N*
London WC1 *p12* 020 7833 4433
Goolden, J T (Wilkin Chapman LLP) *Zu R1 J1 X*
Grimsby *p235* 01472 262626
Goonesena, K R (MacRae & Co LLP) *B1 C1 S2 E C3 I J1 M1 Zj M2 U2 O Q C2 R2 Zv S1 T1*
Southwark *p57* 020 7378 7716
Gopeesingh, Ms G (Westminster City Council)
London SW1 *p110* 020 7641 6000
Gopsill, J (Gateley LLP)
Birmingham *p138* 0121 234 0000
Gora, Miss B W (Knowsley Metropolitan Borough Council)
Huyton *p461* 0151 443 3593
Goral, Miss A (Marsden Rawsthorn LLP) *B1 F1 G Q N Zq S1*
Preston *p357* 01772 799600
Gorczac, Ms J (Field Fisher Waterhouse LLP)
London EC3 *p31* 020 7861 4000
Gordelier, Miss N (Allen Hoole Solicitors) *G H Zm*
Bristol *p160* 0117 942 0901
Gordon, A (Reynolds Porter Chamberlain LLP)
London E1 *p71* 020 3060 6000
Gordon, A F J (Hamlins LLP) *E*
London W1 *p38* 020 7355 6000
Gordon, Ms A H (Actons) *E S1 C1 R1 L W*
Nottingham *p335* 0115 910 0200
Gordon, B C (Farmar Miller Rabin Gordon) *S1 W L F1 G E J1 C1 H S2*
Edgware *p217* 020 8381 3339
Gordon, C (Shrewsbury and Atcham Borough Council)
Shrewsbury *p471* 01743 281000
Gordon, Ms C (Farrer & Co LLP)
London WC2 *p31* 020 3375 7000

Gordon, C A (DLA Piper UK LLP) *O Zj*
London EC2 *p24* 0870 011 1111
Gordon, C D (Gordon Lutton) *S1 E B1 C1 P N W T1 M1*
Hereford *p248* 01432 355345
Gordon, D C (Atteys) *N P O Q J1*
Barnsley *p124* 01226 212345
Gordon, D G S (Mayo Wynne Baxter LLP) *C1 C2 J1 E*
Brighton *p160* 01273 775533
Gordon, D S (Challenor & Son) *W S1 E C1*
Abingdon *p114* 01235 520013
Gordon, Ms E (The College of Law Chester)
Chester *p454* 0800 289997
Gordon, G (Ashurst LLP)
London EC2 *p7* 020 7638 1111
Gordon, G C (Turbervilles) *J1 N Zp*
Uxbridge *p417* 01895 201700
Uxbridge *p417* 01895 201700
Gordon, G R T (Caerphilly County Borough Council)
Hengoed *p460* 01443 815588
Gordon, Miss H (Roberts Moore Nicholas Jones) *D1 K1*
Birkenhead *p134* 0151 647 0000
Gordon, I (JMW Solicitors) *R1 R2 S2 C1 C2 E Zc*
Manchester *p306* 0845 872 6666
Gordon, J (Farrer & Co LLP)
London WC2 *p31* 020 3375 7000
Gordon, J (Dechert)
London EC4 *p26* 020 7184 7000
Gordon, J C D (Global Solutions Ltd)
Broadway *p452* 01386 858585
Gordon, J D S (Gordons) *C1 B1 M1 J1 F1 E S1 Zb*
London WC1 *p36* 020 7421 9421
Gordon, Ms J H (Norwich Union Life)
York *p477* 01904 452210
Gordon, J M (Geldards LLP) *E L R1*
Nottingham *p337* 0115 983 3650
Gordon, K (Charles Russell LLP) *C2 C1 R2 Zw*
London EC4 *p19* 020 7203 5000
Gordon, K W (Gordons Solicitors LLP) *S2 C1 C2 E S1 Zb Zc*
Marlow *p313* 01628 487487
Gordon, Mrs L (Spratt Endicott) *K4 W*
Banbury *p122* 01295 204000
Gordon, Ms L S (Andrew Jackson)
Hull *p257* 01482 325242
Gordon, Ms M (Christian Khan Solicitors) *G H K1 L*
London WC1 *p49* 020 7631 9500
Gordon, Miss M L (Maxwell Hodge Solicitors) *S1 W K4 T2 S2 E*
West Kirby *p428* 0151 625 9154
Gordon, N G (TLT Solicitors) *E L A1 C1 R1 Zc*
London EC2 *p85* 020 3465 4000
Gordon, N R (Fasken Martineau LLP) *C1 C2 Zb*
London W1 *p31* 020 7917 8500
Gordon, P D (McClure Naismith) *O Q*
London EC4 *p56* 020 7623 9155
Cheltenham *p189* 01242 514000
Gordon, Ms R (LG Lawyers)
London SE1 *p50* 020 7379 0000
Gordon, R C P R (Watson Burton LLP) *O Q Zc A3 I*
Newcastle upon Tyne *p327* . 0845 901 2100
Gordon, R K (Silverman Sherliker LLP) *E S1 S2 L R2 R1*
London EC2 *p78* 020 7749 2700
Gordon, S (Banner Jones) *K1 F1 P W*
Chesterfield *p191* 01246 560560
Sheffield *p375* 0114 275 5266
Gordon, S M (Squire Sanders (UK) LLP) *C1 E R1 S1 T1 Zd Zi Zo*
London EC2 *p81* 020 7655 1000
Gordon Brown, Ms D (Shoosmiths) *E*
Milton Keynes *p317* . 0370 086 8300 / 01908 488300
Gordon-Brown, Mrs D (Shoosmiths)
Nottingham *p339*. 0370 086 5000 / 0115 906 5000
Gordon-Lee, A J (Toller Beattie LLP) *A1 C1 E S1 T1 W R1 L B1 N Zc Zs Zt*
Barnstaple *p125* 01271 341000
Gordon-Orr, A (Ashurst LLP)
London EC2 *p7* 020 7638 1111
Gordon-Russell, M (Steptoe & Johnson) *E S2 R2 S1 L Zc*
London EC2 *p83* 020 7367 8000
Gordon-Saker, P D (Stephenson Harwood) *B1 Q O*
London EC2 *p82* 020 7329 4422
Gordon-Smith, P (Woodroffes) *B1 S1 O Q S2*
Westminster *p93* 020 7730 0001
Gore, A J (Wellers Law Group LLP) *K1*
Bromley *p167* 020 8464 4242
Gore, D J (Davenport Lyons) *O Q Zf Ze Zk*
London W1 *p25* 020 7468 2600
Gore, J (Lyons Davidson)
Bristol *p163* 0117 904 6000
Gore, J G (Bayham Solicitors LLP)
Tunbridge Wells *p414* 01892 891999
Gore, J R (Edwin Coe LLP) *E S1 S2*
London WC2 *p29* 020 7691 4000
Gore, Ms P (Davies Gore Lomax) *K1 D1 X D2 K3 K4*
Leeds *p273* 0113 242 2797
Gore, R A (Gregg Latchams LLP) *Q O F1 N Zq B1 Zk*
Bristol *p162* 0117 906 9400

6

Gorecki, A Z (AstraZeneca)
Macclesfield *p464* 01625 582828

Gorham, Ms R M (ConocoPhillips (UK) Ltd)
London W1 *p105* 020 7408 6000

Gori, L (Ashurst LLP)
London EC2 *p7* 020 7638 1111

Gorley, A A (Antony Gorley & Co) *N Zr*
Newbury *p322*. 01635 551321

Gorlov, Mrs A M H (Winckworth Sherwood LLP)
London SE1 *p92*. 020 7593 5000

Gorman, A (Williams Gorman LLP)
Haringey *p91* . . . .

Gorman, C A (Kerman & Co LLP) *C1 F1 J1 S1 S2 W Ze Zf*
London WC2 *p49* 020 7539 7272

Gorman, D (Carey Law)
Alton *p116*. . . . .

Gorman, D J (Pardoes) *W*
Taunton *p408* 01823 446200

Gorman, Ms F (Davies & Partners) *K1 K3*
Almondsbury *p115*. 01454 619619

Gorman, Ms H (Bolton Metropolitan Borough Council)
Bolton *p450* 01204 333333

Gorman, K (Barker Booth & Eastwood) *S1 E C1*
Blackpool *p146* 01253 362500

Gorman, M M (Scotts Holt & Sellars) *W*
Bromsgrove *p167* 01527 872711

Gorman, S (Kerman & Co LLP) *C1 T1 F1 E L S1 Zb Zf Ze*
London WC2 *p49* 020 7539 7272

Gorman, T (Gorman Hamilton) *S1 P M1 G K1 L J1 F1 N B1 Zl*
Newcastle upon Tyne *p324* . 0191 232 1123

Gornall-King, W R W (Boyes Turner) *C1 C3 Zb Ze I*
Reading *p360* 0118 959 7711

Gorner, J S (Gregorys Solicitors) *L A3 Zr Zg Q N Zq*
Stockport *p395*. 0161 456 8125
Altrincham *p116* 0161 928 9321

Gorrie, E D C (Allen & Overy LLP)
London E1 *p5* 020 3088 0000

Gorsia, Mrs S (Stanley & Co)
Wembley *p427*. 020 8903 7864

Gorski, P E (Wiggin LLP) *Zk Zz O*
Cheltenham *p189* 01242 224114

Gorst, J (Bryan Cave) *S2 E*
London EC2 *p19*. 020 7207 1100

Gorst, Mrs L A (Arnold Greenwood) *K3 K1*
Kendal *p264*. 01539 720049

Gorst, L D (Lancaster City Council)
Lancaster *p462* 01524 582000

Gorst-Williams, Ms H H A (Bristows) *O Ze Zk*
London EC4 *p15*. 020 7400 8000

Gorton, Mrs C A (South Tyneside Metropolitan Borough Council)
South Shields *p471* 0191 427 1717

Gorton, Ms K C (DWF) *Q*
Liverpool *p287*. 0151 907 3000

Gosal, S S (Hood Vores & Allwood) *K1 D1 D2 J1 Q*
Dereham *p209*. 01362 692424

Gosden, N (Ashfords LLP) *K1*
Exeter *p220* 01392 337000

Gosling, Ms E S (Forsters LLP) *L Q O*
Westminster *p33*. 020 7863 8333

Gosling, J (Holman Fenwick Willan)
London EC3 *p42*. 020 7264 8000

Gosling, J A (Addleshaw Goddard)
Manchester *p300* 0161 934 6000

Gosling, P G (Higgs & Sons) *T2 W*
Brierley Hill *p158*. 0845 111 5050

Gosling, Mrs S G (Hague Lambert) *W*
Knutsford *p269* 01565 652411

Goss, A P (Bruce Lance & Co) *K1 N J1 F1 L*
Poole *p353* 01202 679379

Goss, Ms J (Abney Garsden McDonald) *K3 K1 D1*
Cheadle *p185* 0161 482 8822
Altrincham *p117* 0161 926 9969

Goss, Ms J A (Palmers) *K1 K3*
Basildon *p126* 01268 240000

Gossage, C (Russells) *C1 Ze Zf*
London W1 *p75* 020 7439 8692

Gossling, Ms M R (Clifford Chance)
London E14 *p20*. 020 7006 1000

Gostick, Mrs C (Buckles Solicitors LLP) *E S2 R2*
Peterborough *p346* 01733 888888

Gotch, P (Reeds Solicitors) *N*
Oxford *p344* 01865 260230

Gotelee, M (Barker Gotelee Solicitors) *N Zt*
Ipswich *p262*. 01473 611211

Gothard, C (Speechly Bircham LLP) *W T2 Zd*
London EC4 *p81*. 020 7427 6400

Gottler, D J (Stafford Young Jones) *S1 K3 S2 W Q J1*
London EC4 *p82*. 020 7623 9490

Gottschalk, P N (Beadle Pitt & Gottschalk) *E C1 S1 W*
Canterbury *p176*. 01227 464481

Gough, A J (Furley Page LLP) *E S2 R1 P*
Canterbury *p176*. 01227 763939

Gough, B (Gough Davies) *D1 E F1 G H J1 K1 L N Q*
Bargoed *p123* 01443 839393

Gough, C (Plexus Law (A Trading Name of Parabis Law LLP)) *N Q*
Manchester *p309* 0844 245 4100

Gough, D J (Harvey Ingram Borneos)
Milton Keynes *p317* 01908 696002

Gough, Miss H (Lodders Solicitors LLP) *A1*
Stratford-upon-Avon *p400* . . 01789 293259

Gough, Mrs J H M (Wards Solicitors) *N K1*
Bristol *p165* 0117 929 2811

Gough, J R (Lynch Hall & Hornby)
Harrow *p242*. 020 8864 0722

Gough, K R (T G Baynes) *S2 E L R2*
Bexleyheath *p132* 020 8301 7777

Gough, Miss L (Enoch Evans LLP) *K1 K3*
Walsall *p420*. 01922 720333

Gough, M (Bedford Borough Council)
Bedford *p448* 01234 267422

Gough, M W (The Clarke Partnership) *N*
Stockport *p395*. 0161 474 6600

Gough, R (DLA Piper UK LLP) *C1 C2*
Sheffield *p375* 0870 011 1111

Gough, R D (Thomson Snell & Passmore) *A1 E S2*
Tunbridge Wells *p415* 01892 510000

Gough, R E N (Wains) *S1 W E*
Congleton *p198* 01260 279414
Macclesfield *p297* 01625 429511

Gough, S G (DLA Piper UK LLP) *T1*
London EC2 *p24*. 0870 011 1111

Goulbourne, Ms J (Brabners Chaffe Street) *P F2 J2*
Preston *p356* 01772 823921

Gould, Ms A (Wedlake Bell LLP) *Ze*
London WC1 *p91* 020 7395 3000

Gould, Miss C (Philip Ross & Co) *E S2 S1*
London W1 *p73* 020 7636 6969

Gould, Miss F E A (W Davies) *W K4*
Woking *p436*. 01483 744900

Gould, Ms H L (Bristol City Council) *G H*
Bristol *p451* 0117 922 2000

Gould, J (Allen & Overy LLP)
London E1 *p5* 020 3088 0000

Gould, J C (Russell-Cooke LLP) *C1 O*
London SW15 *p74*. 020 8789 9111

Gould, Ms K J (McGrigors LLP)
London EC4 *p56*. 020 7054 2500

Gould, N (Fenwick Elliott) *O Q Zi Zc A3 P Zj R2*
London WC2 *p31* 020 7421 1986

Gould, N S B (Ince & Co Services Ltd)
London E1 *p44* 020 7481 0010

Gould, P J (Bankside Commercial Solicitors) *M1 N P J1 G B1*
Southwark *p9* 020 7654 0200

Gould, R (ASB Law)
Crawley *p202* 01293 603600

Gould, T (Nelsons) *B2*
Nottingham *p338*. 0115 958 6262

Gould, Mrs U M S (Pannone LLP) *C1 C2 Zd Zu*
Manchester *p308* 0161 909 3000

Gould, Mrs V (British Standards Institution)
London W4 *p104* 020 8996 7010

Gould, Ms V J (Warwickshire County Council) *D1 N Zm Zu J1 D2 X*
Warwick *p475* 01926 410410

Goulden, C P (TLT Solicitors) *D1 D2 K1*
Bristol *p165* 0117 917 7777

Goulden, H J (Finers Stephens Innocent LLP) *J1 J2*
London W1 *p32* 020 7323 4000

Goulden, Ms J S L (J S L Goulden) *S1 G H W K1*
London NW3 *p36* 020 7435 8887

Goulden, T M (Brabners Chaffe Street) *Zh E S2 R2 R1*
Liverpool *p286*. 0151 600 3000

Goulding, H H J (Farrer & Co LLP)
London WC2 *p31* 020 3375 7000

Goulding, Ms J (Freeth Cartwright LLP) *F1 Zm*
Nottingham *p337*. 0115 936 9369

Goulding, J (Cheyney Goulding) *C1 E J1 S1 P R1 O Q Zb Ze Zl*
Guildford *p236*. 01483 567676

Goulding, K A (Steed & Steed LLP)
Sudbury *p401* 01787 373387

Goulding, N (hlw Keeble Hawson LLP) *C1 C2*
Sheffield *p376* 0114 276 5555
Sheffield *p376* 0870 150 0100

Goulding, Miss S (Woodfines LLP) *S2 E*
Bedford *p130* 01234 270600

Gouldingay, Ms W (Tallents Solicitors) *K2 K1*
Newark *p322* 01636 671881

Gouldingay, Ms W E (Kirkland & Lane) *K1 K2 D1*
Southwell *p389* . . .01636 813128 / 812180

Gouriet, G C (LG Lawyers)
London SE1 *p50*. 020 7379 0000

Gouriet, M (Withers LLP) *K1*
London EC4 *p92*. 020 7597 6000

Gourley, A (Crowell & Moring) *M2 A3*
London EC4 *p23*. 020 7413 0011

Gover, G R (Graham Gover Solicitor) *R1*
Exeter *p221* 01392 423090

Govier, C (Stones Solicitors LLP) *K1 D1*
Exeter *p222* 01392 666777

Govier, Miss E A (Gilbert Stephens) *W K3 T2*
Ottery St Mary *p342*. 01404 812228
Sidmouth *p380*. 01395 512443
Exeter *p221* 01392 424242

Govier, J (IBB Solicitors)
Uxbridge *p417*. 0845 638 1381

Govier, S C G (Symes Robinson & Lee) *S1 S2 W Zd*
Budleigh Salterton *p168* . . . 01395 445581

Govinden, G (Parfitt Cresswell) *C1 E J1 S2 F1*
London SW6 *p65* 020 7381 8311

Gow, Mrs S M (Foys Solicitors) *S1 W*
Rotherham *p367*. 01709 375561

Gowan, D R (DAC Beachcroft) *O B1 E Zc Zj*
London EC4 *p24*. 020 7936 2222

Gowans, A J (Miles Hutchinson & Lithgow) *D1 G H K1 L N Q S1 W Zi Zg*
Middlesbrough *p315* 01642 242698
Saltburn-by-the-Sea *p371* . .01287 623049 / 622056

Gowans, A J (Osborne Clarke) *C1 C2 C3 J1 B1*
Reading *p361* 0118 925 2000

Gowans, Ms R (Stephen Burdon Solicitors) *G H*
Nottingham *p336*. 0115 950 0054

Gowar, A G (Harrowells) *A1 Zd K4 T2 W*
York *p444* 01904 558600

Goward, P J S (Druces LLP) *E S2 R2 R1*
London EC2 *p27*. 020 7638 9271

Gowen, A (Hanne & Co)
London SW11 *p38* 020 7228 0017

Gower, Ms A (Lucas & Wyllys) *C1 S1 S2*
Great Yarmouth *p234* 01493 855555

Gower, N L (Dolmans) *N B1 Zk Q Zu*
Cardiff *p178* 029 2034 5531

Gower, Mrs P M (Parker Bullen) *K1 K2 K3 D1*
Salisbury *p371*. 01722 412000

Gower, Miss R B (Wallace Robinson & Morgan) *W*
Solihull *p383*. 0121 705 7571

Gowing, Ms C M (Hansells)
Norwich *p334* 01603 615731

Gowing, S E (Crosse Wyatt Verney & Ayre) *S1 E W L C1 T1*
South Molton *p383*. 01769 572157

Gowland, J (Belmores)
Norwich *p334* 01603 499999

Gowland, S D (ILS Solicitors)
Durham *p214* 0191 378 2030

Gowler, S D L (Jobling Gowler) *N Zr*
Macclesfield *p297* 01625 614250

Gowlet, D T (Daybells LLP) *N P L K1 B1*
London E15 *p26*. 020 8555 4321

Gowling, Mrs S (MFG Solicitors) *A1*
Worcester *p440* 01905 610410

Gowman, Miss A J (DLA Piper UK LLP) *S2 R2*
London EC2 *p24*. 0870 011 1111

Gowman, Ms L O (LG Lawyers)
London SE1 *p50*. 020 7379 0000

Gowrley, R (DLA Piper UK LLP)
London EC2 *p24*. 0870 011 1111

Gowthorpe, R B (Lansbury Worthington) *G H B2*
London W6 *p51* 020 8563 9797

Gozzett, N (Edward Hayes LLP) *G H B2*
Worthing *p441*. 01903 215999

Grabiner, M S (Nabarro LLP) *E*
Sheffield *p376* 0114 279 4000

Grabowski, Mrs J M (Oglethorpe Sturton & Gillibrand) *C1 C2 Zb*
Lancaster *p270* 01524 846846

Grace, A W (Dicksons Solicitors Ltd) *S1 L C1 R1 W E A1 K1 P Zc Zd Zh*
Stoke-on-Trent *p397*. . . . 01782 262424

Grace, Ms C (Suttons)
London W1 *p84* 020 7935 5279

Grace, Ms C D (Grace & Co) *S1 E W L Zd S2 R2 Zh*
London W1 *p36* 020 7935 7938
London W1 *p39* 020 7935 5541

Grace, Ms E M (British Telecommunications PLC)
London EC1 *p104* 020 7356 6181

Grace, Miss J (Grace & Co) *C1 O F1 Q N J1*
Warrington *p422* 01925 242488

Grace, Miss P D (Chamberlain Martin Solicitors) *S1 S2*
Bognor Regis *p148* 01243 825211

Grace, R H (J B Wheatley & Co) *G*
London SE8 *p91*. 020 8479 8000

Grace, Miss S J (Morgans) *G H B2*
Cardiff *p180* 029 2072 9888

Gracey, Miss C (Aon Consulting) *Zo*
Farnborough *p458* 01252 768000

Gracie, Miss M P (Cyril Morris Arkwright) *K1 D1 K2 K3*
Bolton *p148* 01204 535261

Gradie, Mrs E C (Maxwell Winward LLP) *Q O L Zq*
London EC4 *p59*. 020 7651 0000

Gradon, R M (P&O Legal Dept)
London SW1 *p108*. 020 7930 4343

Gradus, Ms E (Tollers LLP) *E*
Northampton *p332*. 01604 258558

Gradwell, D J (AGH Solicitors) *S2 N*
Bolton *p148* 01204 364433

Grady, A G (David Gist Solicitors) *N*
Bristol *p162* 0117 927 9111

Grady, Ms H (Russell Jones & Walker)
Bristol *p164* 0117 374 2222

Grady, S F (Astrazeneca PLC)
London W1 *p103* 020 7304 5000

Graf, R A S (Black Graf & Co) *E S2 C1 S1*
London NW3 *p13* 020 7586 1141

Graff, Miss S E (Graff & Redfern) *S1 K1*
Richmond upon Thames *p364* 020 8940 0860 / 8948 2815

Grafton, P J (Carmarthenshire County Council)
Carmarthen *p453* 01267 224010

Graham, A (Swinburne & Jackson LLP) *G H K1 K2*
Washington *p423* 0191 416 0004

Graham, Mrs A (The Johnson Partnership) *G H*
Nottingham *p337*. 0115 941 9141

Graham, A J (Smith Jones Solicitors) *N O J1 Q Zj*
Kenilworth *p264* 01926 859933
Burnley *p169* 01282 855400

Graham, A J (Keoghs LLP) *N Zj O Q*
Bolton *p149* 01204 677000

Graham, C (DWF) *N Q Zj Zr*
Liverpool *p287*. 0151 907 3000

Graham, C (Watson Burton LLP) *J1 Zp*
Newcastle upon Tyne *p327* . 0845 901 2100

Graham, Miss C (Walker Smith Way) *N*
Chester *p191* 0844 346 3100

Graham, Mrs C E (Redcar and Cleveland Borough Council)
Redcar *p465*. 01642 466201

Graham, C K C (Blake Lapthorn) *O Q*
Oxford *p342* 01865 248607

Graham, D (Walkers) *S1 S2*
Rossendale *p367* 01706 213565

Graham, D J (Macks Solicitors)
Middlesbrough *p315* 01642 252828

Graham, Mrs E (Collyer Bristow LLP) *K1 D1 D2 K2 W*
London WC1 *p22* 020 7242 7363

Graham, E J (Ince & Co Services Ltd)
London E1 *p44* 020 7481 0010

Graham, Ms F (Boodle Hatfield)
Oxford *p343*. 01865 790744

Graham, Ms F (Boodle Hatfield) *W T2*
Westminster *p14*. 020 7629 7411

Graham, F A (Fitzgrahams) *B1 F1 G H K1 L M1 P S1 W Zi Zk Zl*
St Leonards-on-Sea *p392* . . 01424 446666

Graham, I A (Crown Prosecution Service Dorset)
Bournemouth *p450*. 01202 498700

Graham, I A (Clifton Ingram LLP) *E L S1 S2*
Wokingham *p437* 0118 978 0099

Graham, I D (Fraser Dawbarns)
King's Lynn *p266* 01553 666600

Graham, I D (Trowers & Hamlins) *L Zh*
London EC3 *p88*. 020 7423 8000

Graham, Ms J (Bolt Burdon) *J1*
Islington *p14*. 020 7288 4700

Graham, J (Kennedys) *Zj*
London EC3 *p49*. 020 7667 9667

Graham, Miss J (Massers) *N*
Nottingham *p338*. 0115 851 1666

Graham, Miss J A (Shepherd + Wedderburn LLP) *C1 E P R1*
London EC4 *p78*. 020 7429 4900

Graham, J D (Wythenshawe Law Centre)
Manchester *p465* 0161 498 0905

Graham, Ms J L (Hempsons) *N Zr*
Manchester *p305* 0161 228 0011

Graham, J M H (Fortescue Graham & Lloyd) *S1 W K3 K1*
Leatherhead *p271* 01372 374895

Graham, J R B (DBL Talbots LLP) *Zi K1 J1 Q N*
Dudley *p213*. 01384 252471

Graham, Miss K (Squire Sanders (UK) LLP) *E Zc*
London EC2 *p81*. 020 7655 1000

Graham, K F (Hathaways) *S1 G H W K1 E J1 P R1*
Gateshead *p228*. 0191 477 2288

Graham, Ms K L (Pearson Caulfield) *G H K1 D1 W*
Newcastle upon Tyne *p326* . 0191 261 8878

Graham, M (Gaynham King & Mellor) *D1 D2 K3 K1*
Appleby *p118* 01768 351422
Penrith *p346*. 01768 864651

Graham, M (Mowbray Woodwards Solicitors)
Bath *p128* 01225 485700

Graham, M (Forresters) *G H Zl*
Barrow-in-Furness *p125* . . . 01229 820297

Graham, Miss M (Tameside Metropolitan Borough Council)
Ashton-under-Lyne *p447*. . . 0161 342 3028

Graham, Mrs M M (Blake Lapthorn) *W S1 T2*
Oxford *p342*. 01865 248607

Graham, Miss N (Mills & Reeve) *Zq Zj Q N*
London EC3 *p61*. 020 7648 9220

Graham, N (Oxfordshire County Council)
Oxford *p468* 01865 792422

Graham, Ms N E (Barlow Lyde & Gilbert LLP)
London EC3 *p10*. 020 7247 2277

Graham, Ms P (ASB Law) *O*
Maidstone *p298* 01622 656500

Graham, P F (Charles Lucas & Marshall) *S1*
Newbury *p322*. 01635 521212

Graham, P J (Shaw Graham Kersh)
London W1 *p78* 020 7734 9700

Graham, Mrs P J (Appleby Hope & Matthews) *D1 K1 M1 H G W S1 J1 P F1 Zm*
Middlesbrough *p314* 01642 440444

Graham, R (Swinburne & Jackson LLP) *K3 K1 V L F1 G B1*
Gateshead *p229*. 0191 477 2531 / 477 3222

Graham, R J C (Birnberg Peirce & Partners) *Zg Zi M1 G*
Camden *p13*. 020 7911 0166

Graham, R N (Zermansky & Partners) *E R1 Zc*
Leeds *p278* 0113 245 9766

Graham, S (London Underground Ltd)
London SW1 *p107*. 020 7918 3126

Graham, S (Farrer & Co LLP)
London WC2 *p31* 020 3375 7000

Graham, Mrs S A (Mills & Reeve) *A1 W*
Norwich *p335* 01603 660155

Graham, Mrs S D (Horsey Lightly Fynn) *J1 P G Zl Zw Zy*
Bournemouth *p152*. 01202 551991

Graham, Miss S E (John A Behn Twyford & Co) *M1 P J1 W G F1*
Liverpool *p286*. 0151 236 0367

Graham, S T (Ward Hadaway) *Zl K1 G*
Newcastle upon Tyne *p327* . 0191 204 4000

Graham, T (KJD)
Stoke-on-Trent *p398*. 01782 202020

Graham, T (Farrer & Co LLP)
London WC2 *p31* 020 3375 7000

Graham, T (Taylor Wessing) *O*
London EC4 *p86*. 020 7300 7000

See p634 for the Key to Work Categories

Graham, W J (Thomas Simon) *O Q N J1 F1 B1 Zk Zl*
Cardiff *p181* 029 2055 7200

Graham Wood, Miss C (Birnberg Peirce & Partners) *Zg Zi*
Camden *p13* 020 7911 0166

Graham-Harrison, S A (Darbys Solicitors LLP) *G H*
Oxford *p343* 01865 811700

Graham-Jones, Ms J A (Crutes) *N Q*
Carlisle *p182* 01228 525195

Graham-Smith, D (Penningtons) *E*
Godalming *p231* 01483 791800

Graham-Wilson, Miss J (Reed Smith LLP)
London EC2 *p71* 020 3116 3000

Grainge, Miss K V (Cripps Harries Hall LLP) *O*
Tunbridge Wells *p415* 01892 515121

Grainger, Miss C M (Pannone LLP) *Zc A3 O C1 J2 P M2 U2*
Manchester *p308* 0161 909 3000

Grainger, J P (Grainger Appleyard) *A1 B1 C1 E F1 J1 L R1 S1 W*
Doncaster *p211* 01302 327257

Grainger, T D (Fiona Bruce & Co LLP) *N Q J1*
Warrington *p421* 01925 263273

Granby, Mrs J (Family Law Associates LLP) *K1 K3*
Haringey *p30* 020 8342 7760

Grand, H (Aviva PLC)
London EC3 *p103* 020 7283 7500 / 01603 687905
Norwich *p467* 01603 622200

Grandage, N (SNR Denton)
London EC4 *p75* 020 7242 1212

Grandison, E (Grays) *Zd J1 Q Zp*
York *p444* 01904 634771

Grange, Ms J (Hadaway & Hadaway) *D1 K1 K3 V*
North Shields *p330* 0191 257 0382

Grange, M (Clarion Solicitors LLP) *S2 E*
Leeds *p272* 0113 246 0622
Leeds *p277* 0113 284 7000

Granger, A S (Taylor Wessing) *B1 C1 F1 J1 N P Zb Zi Zp*
London EC4 *p86* 020 7300 7000

Granger, Miss E M (Corby Borough Council) *R1*
Corby *p456* 01536 402551

Granger, Mrs J (Kingsfords) *N*
Ashford *p119* 01233 665544

Granger, Mrs K A (Southampton City Council)
Southampton *p472* 023 8022 3855

Granger, Miss R E (Lincolnshire County Council Resources - Legal Services)
Lincoln *p463* 01522 552222

Granger, W (Speechly Bircham LLP) *J1*
London EC4 *p81* 020 7427 6400

Grant, A (Robert Lizar) *K1 D1*
Manchester *p307* 0161 226 2319

Grant, Mrs A (Grants Solicitors) *S1*
Fleet *p226* 01252 622288

Grant, A (Ballantyne Grant LLP)
Chester *p190* 01244 394230

Grant, A C M (Andre Grant & Co) *S2 S1 W*
Haringey *p36* 020 8800 8802

Grant, A G (Jones Day) *E*
London EC4 *p46* 020 7039 5959

Grant, A M (Duffield Harrison LLP) *M1 N P K1 D1 F1 V B1 Zk Zm Zp*
Hoddesdon *p251* 01992 442911

Grant, Mrs C A (Squire Sanders (UK) LLP) *C1 C2*
Leeds *p277* 0113 284 7000

Grant, C E (Treasury Solicitors Department)
London WC2 *p110* 020 7210 3000

Grant, D (Tracey Barlow Furniss & Co) *G H*
Worksop *p441* 01909 472355

Grant, D J (Baron Grey) *B1 S2 J1 K1 L Zl R1 S1 W*
Twickenham *p416* 020 8891 4311

Grant, Miss D M (Plexus Law (A Trading Name of Parabis Law LLP)) *N*
Evesham *p220* 01386 769160

Grant, F M (Miles Hutchinson & Lithgow) *K1 S1 L V W Zi Zg*
Saltburn-by-the-Sea *p371* 01287 623049 / 622056
Middlesbrough *p315* 01642 242698

Grant, Miss H J (Bird & Bird LLP) *C1 I*
London EC4 *p13* 020 7415 6000

Grant, I S (Kirby Sheppard) *C1 O S1 W S2*
Kingswood *p268* 0845 840 0045

Grant, Ms J (The Royal Borough of Kensington & Chelsea)
London W8 *p109* 020 7361 2741

Grant, Ms J (Langleys) *D1 K1 Zu*
York *p445* 01904 610886

Grant, Miss J (Crompton Halliwell) *G H*
Bury *p170* 0161 797 9222

Grant, J (ASB Law)
Crawley *p202* 01293 603600

Grant, Mrs J D (Stockton-On-Tees Borough Council)
Stockton-on-Tees *p472* 01642 393939

Grant, J M (Cohen Cramer Solicitors) *C1 E F1 J1 K1 L M1 N P S1*
Leeds *p272* 0800 542 9408

Grant, Ms K A E (Clifton Ingram LLP) *K1 K3*
Reading *p360* 0118 957 3425

Grant, L G V (Thursfields) *Zm S1 W*
Kidderminster *p266* 01562 820575

Grant, M S (CMS Cameron McKenna LLP) *Zo*
London EC3 *p17* 020 7367 3000

Grant, Mrs M S (Simmonds Grant) *K1 L J1*
Oakham *p340* 01572 756866

Grant, Ms N (Ballantyne Grant LLP)
Chester *p190* 01244 394230

Grant, N A (Bevan Brittan LLP) *D1 Q V Zg Zm Zu*
London EC4 *p12* 0870 194 1000

Grant, N G (Devonshires) *Zr N Zd*
London EC2 *p27* 020 7628 7576

Grant, Miss N J (Nottingham City Council (City Sec Dept))
Nottingham *p467* 0115 915 5555

Grant, P J A (BSG Solicitors LLP) *N P K1 J1 M1 I Zc Ze Zl*
London N3 *p9* 020 8343 4411

Grant, Miss R M (Hogan Lovells International LLP)
London EC1 *p42* 020 7296 2000

Grant, S (Warner Goodman LLP)
Portsmouth *p355* 023 9275 3575
Portsmouth *p355* 023 9275 3575

Grant, Ms S A (Hill Dickinson LLP) *Zq*
Manchester *p305* 0161 817 7200

Grant, Mrs S M (Montlake & Co) *K4 W*
Banstead *p122* 01737 352211

Grant, S R (Pannone LLP) *C1 C2 Zu*
Manchester *p308* 0161 909 3000

Grant, S U (Samuel Phillips Law Firm) *G H M1 D1 V*
Newcastle upon Tyne *p326* 0191 232 8451

Grant, Ms T (The College of Law)
London WC1 *p105* 0800 289997

Grant, T (Myers Fletcher & Gordon) *S1 S2 W*
London W6 *p62* 020 7610 4433

Grant, T R (The Rank Group PLC)
Maidenhead *p464* 01628 504000
London EC4 *p53* 020 7074 8000

Grantham, D (Ince & Co Services Ltd)
London E1 *p44* 020 7481 0010

Grantham, D R (Gregsons) *K1 G D1 V H F1 N Zp Zi*
Liverpool *p288* 0151 703 2550

Grantham, M (Robin Burman & Co) *C1 E O B1 T1 J1 F1 P S1 W Zb Ze Zo Q*
Manchester *p302* 0161 860 7123

Granville, H S (Freeman Box) *S1 E L C1 W F1*
London W1 *p34* 020 7486 9041

Granville, M P (Carlyon & Son) *N Q O J1 W T1 S1 K3*
Truro *p414* 01872 278641

Grasby, Mrs K E (Warwickshire County Council)
Warwick *p475* 01926 410410

Grassam, P M (Browning & Co) *W S1 K4*
Looe *p293* 01503 262119 / 262129
Plymouth *p349* 01752 675000

Grateley, Mrs J (The College of Law Chester)
Chester *p454* 0800 289997

Gratton, Ms E A (Eden & Co) *M1*
Manchester *p304* 0161 237 1116

Gratton, M J (Morgan & Lamplugh) *K1 D1 F1*
Hastings *p243* 01424 721821

Gravell, D (LG Lawyers)
London SE1 *p50* 020 7379 0000

Gravell, R J B (Morrisons Solicitors LLP) *S1*
London SW19 *p62* 020 8971 1020

Graves, A (Environment Agency (Wales))
Cardiff *p453* 0870 850 6506

Graves, C J L (Fisher Jones Greenwood LLP) *D1 G J1 K1 L N Zl*
Colchester *p197* 01206 578282

Graves, Ms H K (Fisher Jones Greenwood LLP) *M1 Zg Zi V*
Colchester *p197* 01206 578282

Graves, Ms K A L (Withers LLP) *T2 W*
London EC4 *p92* 020 7597 6000

Gravestock, Mrs A E (Bates Wells & Braithwaite London LLP) *E S2 R2 Zh L Zd*
London EC4 *p11* 020 7551 7777

Gravill, R M (Squire Sanders (UK) LLP)
London EC2 *p81* 020 7655 1000

Gray, Miss A (Kirbys) *K1 D1 N Q O*
Harrogate *p240* 01423 542000

Gray, A (The College of Law)
London WC1 *p105* 0800 289997

Gray, Ms A C (Addleshaw Goddard)
Leeds *p271* 0113 209 2000

Gray, A D (Aviva PLC)
London EC3 *p103* 020 7283 7500 / 01603 687905
Norwich *p467* 01603 622200

Gray, Miss A L (Farleys Solicitors LLP) *W*
Blackburn *p145* 01254 367855

Gray, Mrs A R (Dickinson Dees) *Q*
Newcastle upon Tyne *p324* 0191 279 9000

Gray, C (Graham White & Co) *D1 E F1 G H J1 K1 N S1 W*
Bushey *p172* 020 8950 5304

Gray, C J P (Baker Gray & Co) *G H K1 D1 S1 W*
Newcastle upon Tyne *p323* 0191 222 0203

Gray, Mrs C M (Aaron & Partners LLP Solicitors) *C2 C1*
Chester *p190* 01244 405555

Gray, D (Darwin Gray)
Cardiff *p178* 029 2082 9100

Gray, D J (DLA Piper UK LLP) *O Q Zq*
Manchester *p303* 0870 011 1111

Gray, Miss E (Sintons LLP) *K1 K3 S1*
Newcastle upon Tyne *p326* 0191 226 7878

Gray, Mrs E (Symes Robinson & Lee) *W K4*
Exeter *p222* 01392 270867

Gray, Miss E A C (British Telecommunications PLC)
London EC1 *p104* 020 7356 6181

Gray, F (Bradford Magistrates Court)
Bradford *p451* 01274 390111

Gray, G (Holman Fenwick Willan)
London EC3 *p42* 020 7264 8000

Gray, J (Taylor Bracewell) *G H*
Doncaster *p212* 01302 341414

Gray, Mrs J K (Wheelers) *S2 E L*
Aldershot *p115* 01252 316316

Gray, J P (William Sturges & Co) *A1 C1 D1 E J1 K1 L M1 N P Za Zb Zc*
Westminster *p84* 020 7873 1000

Gray, Mrs K (South Ribble Borough Council)
Preston *p469* 01772 421491
Barnsley *p124* 01226 210000

Gray, Miss K (PCB Solicitors LLP) *C1 S2 E S1*
Shrewsbury *p379* 01743 248148

Gray, Ms K L (Pothecary Witham Weld) *W*
Westminster *p69* 020 7821 8211

Gray, M L (Wilmot & Co Solicitors LLP) *S1 A1 S2 E*
Cirencester *p195* 01285 650551

Gray, N (Irwin Mitchell LLP) *Zr*
Manchester *p306* 0870 150 0100

Gray, Miss N E (Northumbrian Water Ltd)
Durham *p457* 0870 608 4820

Gray, N G (Farrell Matthews & Weir) *G H*
London W6 *p31* 020 8741 1482

Gray, R (Gray Hooper Holt LLP) *J1 Q N F1*
Redhill *p362* 01737 761004

Gray, Mrs R P A (Carlisle City Council)
Carlisle *p453* 01228 817000

Gray, R S (Keoghs LLP) *N Zj O Q*
Bolton *p149* 01204 677000

Gray, R S (Plexus Law (A Trading Name of Parabis Law LLP))
London EC3 *p68* 0844 245 4000

Gray, Ms S (Russell Jones & Walker)
Manchester *p309* 0161 383 3500

Gray, Ms S (Langleys) *B1 E S1*
York *p445* 01904 610886

Gray, S (Pinsent Masons LLP)
London EC2 *p67* 020 7418 7000

Gray, Miss S (McGrigors LLP)
London EC4 *p56* 020 7054 2500

Gray, S C (CMHT Solicitors) *G H S1 A1 C1 B1 M1 P N Zk*
Walsall *p420* 01922 646400

Gray, S C (Fiona Bruce & Co LLP) *K4 Zd W*
Warrington *p421* 01925 263273

Gray, T C (FBC Manby Bowdler LLP) *N O Q*
Willenhall *p432* 01902 366566

Gray, T J (Clough & Willis) *N O Q Zj*
Bury *p170* 0161 764 5266

Gray, T R (Sintons LLP) *K1 S1 E D1 C1 W L A1 F1 R1 Zi Zd Zl Zc R2*
Newcastle upon Tyne *p326* 0191 226 7878

Graydon, J R M (Environment Agency (Thames Region)) *O Q J1 N B1 I Zc Zj Zk C3*
Reading *p469* 0870 850 6506

Grayland, Ms T E (Bright & Sons) *N*
Maldon *p299* 01621 852323
Witham *p435* 01376 512338

Grayson, A R (Royal College of Nursing)
Exeter *p458* 0845 456 7829

Grayson, B (Shell International Ltd)
London SE1 *p109* 020 7934 1234

Grayson, J D (Bailey Nicholson Grayson)
Woodford Green *p439* 020 8418 2900

Grayson, Mrs K (Russell & Russell) *N*
Bolton *p150* 01204 375700

Grayson, Ms L (Squire Sanders (UK) LLP) *C1 J1 K1 L N O Q*
Leeds *p277* 0113 284 7000

Grayson, R (Kevill Kirkham & Grayson) *S1 W E A1 C1 L R1*
Chorley *p194* 01257 263676 / 269212

Grayson, R K (Thompsons (formerly Robin/Brian Thompson & Partners)) *N J1*
Bristol *p165* 0117 304 2400

Grayston, Ms J A (Graystons) *Zr N*
Wirral *p435* 0151 645 0055

Grazebrook, A M (Wilmot & Co Solicitors LLP) *W T2*
Cirencester *p195* 01285 650551

Graziani, M R (Amphlett Lissimore) *S2 S1 E*
Croydon *p6* 020 8771 5254

Grazier, Ms E (Bristol City Council)
Bristol *p451* 0117 922 2000

Grazier, Mrs S N J (Gabbs LLP) *C1 S2 E*
Hereford *p248* 01432 353481

Gread, Miss J (West Berkshire Council)
Newbury *p466* 01635 42400

Greager, J (Pritchard Englefield)
London EC2 *p69* 020 7972 9720

Greager, J E (Fox Williams) *O C1 B1 Zk Ze*
London EC2 *p33* 020 7628 2000

Grealis, K B (Stewarts Law LLP) *N Zr*
London EC4 *p83* 020 7822 8000

Greany, D (Adams Solicitors) *E S1 R1*
London E1 *p4* 020 7790 2000

Grearson, N (Hayes & Storr) *K1*
Fakenham *p223* 01328 863231
Diss *p211* 01379 652141

Greatbanks, Miss A (Hall Smith Whittingham LLP) *S1 W*
Crewe *p203* 01270 212000

Greatbatch, P (Nelsons)
Derby *p209* 01332 372372

Greatholder, P M (Russell-Cooke LLP) *L*
London WC1 *p74* 020 7405 6566

Greaves, A (Steptoe & Johnson) *O Q Zb Zj*
London EC2 *p83* 020 7367 8000

Greaves, A C S (Jones Day) *C1*
London EC4 *p46* 020 7039 5959

Greaves, A E (Fritchley Goldsmith) *G H*
Barnsley *p124* 01226 215600

Greaves, Mrs A L (Southampton City Council)
Southampton *p472* 023 8022 3855

Greaves, C J (Christopher J Greaves) *G H J1 K1 P S1*
Rothwell *p368* 0113 282 7988

Greaves, C S (Evans & Greaves) *Q K1 N G H J1 F1 V*
Caerphilly *p172* 029 2086 6001

Greaves, Miss D F M (Coventry City Council) *D1 K1*
Coventry *p456* 024 7683 4863
West Bromwich *p427* 0121 553 3211

Greaves, J A (MWR Law Ltd) *N Q Zj*
Preston *p357* 01772 254201

Greaves, Ms J A (Pinsent Masons LLP) *T1*
Leeds *p276* 0113 244 5000

Greaves, L (Harbottle & Lewis LLP)
London W1 *p38* 020 7667 5000

Greaves, P N (Aviva PLC) *N O Q*
London EC3 *p103* 020 7283 7500 / 01603 687905

Greaves, P N (Norwich Union Insurance Group)
Norwich *p467* 01603 622200

Greaves, P N (Howard & Co) *Q N*
Barnsley *p124* 01226 211888

Greaves, P N (McCormicks) *N O Q*
Harrogate *p240* 01423 530630

Greaves, S (Wrigleys Solicitors LLP) *Zd C1 Zb F1 F2 Ze C2*
Sheffield *p377* 0114 267 5588

Greaves, T R (Hodge Jones & Allen LLP) *G H*
London NW1 *p41* 020 7874 8300

Grebby, Ms S C (David Gray Solicitors) *L*
Newcastle upon Tyne *p324* 0191 232 9547

Grech, F (Berry Smith LLP) *J1*
Cardiff *p177* 029 2034 5511

Grech, S (The Grech Gooden Partnership LLP) *G H*
Cardiff *p178* 029 2022 2255

Greco, Miss M A T (Clerk to Sheffield Justices)
Sheffield *p470* 0114 276 0760

Green, A (Raymond Saul & Co) *Q O L K3 N B1*
London E1 *p76* 020 7480 5840

Green, Ms A (Radcliffes Le Brasseur)
Westminster *p70* 020 7222 7040

Green, A C (Stachiw Bashir Green) *J1 Q O Zp C1 Zk W*
Bradford *p155* 01274 404010

Green, A D (Kingsfords) *K1 K3*
Ashford *p119* 01233 624545

Green, A D (Hewitts) *D1 G H J1 K1 N V W*
Newton Aycliffe *p330* 01325 316170

Green, Mrs A D (Stewarts Law LLP) *K1 K3*
Leeds *p277* 0113 222 0022

Green, A D D (Neale Turk) *B1 C1 G J1 K1 L N O Q R1*
Fleet *p226* 01252 811070

Green, A G (Freedman Green Dhokia) *S1*
Camden *p34* 020 7625 6003

Green, A J (Graham & Rosen) *O N Q J1 B1 Zl*
Hull *p257* 01482 323123

Green, Miss A J (Mackrell Turner Garrett) *B2 D1 G K1 N O Q Zc Zj*
London WC2 *p57* 020 7240 0521

Green, Mrs A J (The Ringrose Law Group - David Thornley) *J2 S1 L N Q*
Grantham *p232* 01476 590200
Sleaford *p381* 01529 301300

Green, A J (DWF) *E L R2 S2 P R1*
Liverpool *p287* 0151 907 3000

Green, A J L (Martin-Kaye LLP) *S1 E W C1 M1 K1 L R1*
Telford *p409* 01952 272222

Green, Miss A L (Teacher Stern LLP) *O Q Ze*
London WC1 *p86* 020 7242 3191

Green, A M (Jones & Co) *W S2 S1*
Retford *p363* 01777 703827

Green, Ms A M (Wirral Borough Council) *N K1 D1 Q O B1 J1*
Wallasey *p475* 0151 638 7070

Green, Ms A M M (Birchall Blackburn LLP) *K1 K3*
Chorley *p194* 01257 279011

Green, A M S (CMS Cameron McKenna LLP)
London EC3 *p17* 020 7367 3000

Green, A Q S (National Grid PLC) *Zv*
Warwick *p471* 01926 653000

Green, B (Salans) *B1*
London EC4 *p76* 020 7429 6000

Green, B R (Squire Sanders (UK) LLP) *E C1 L A1 O R1 S1 T1 Zb Zc*
Leeds *p277* 0113 284 7000

Green, Ms C (Stephens & Scown) *Q*
Exeter *p222* 01392 210700

Green, C (Healys LLP) *Zi*
London EC4 *p39* 020 7822 4000

Green, C (Geoffrey Williams & Christopher Green) *G H Zi*
Cardiff *p181* 029 2034 3377

Green, Miss C A R (Heptonstalls LLP) *W*
Goole *p231* 01405 765661

Green, Mrs C J (Browne Jacobson LLP) *E A1 C1 L*
Nottingham *p336* 0115 976 6000

Green, Mrs C J (Winterbotham Smith Penley LLP) *Zk O Q Zq*
Stroud *p401* 01453 847200

Green, C J (Wokingham District Council)
Wokingham *p477* 0118 974 6000

Green, Ms C M (C M Green & Co)
Aldershot *p115* 01252 326501

Green, Mrs C M (Veale Wasbrough Vizards) *K4 W T2*
London EC4 *p89* 020 7405 1234

6

Green, C N (Ouvry Goodman & Co) *B1 C1 K1 N L J1 D1 G H R1 Zc Zl*
Sutton *p403* 020 8642 7571

Green, D (Stewarts Law LLP) *N M2 M3*
London EC4 *p83* 020 7822 8000

Green, D G (Friends Provident)
Dorking *p457* 01306 654925

Green, D G (Prudential PLC)
London EC4 *p108* 020 7220 7588

Green, D J (Stevens) *G H*
Stoke-on-Trent *p398* 01782 343353

Green, D J S (Charles Russell LLP) *J1 Zi Zo Zp*
London EC4 *p19* 020 7203 5000

Green, D L (Parkinson Wright LLP) *P N J1 F1 B1 V L Zj Q Zq Zr*
Worcester *p440* 01905 726789

Green, Ms D L (The College of Law York)
York *p477* 0800 289997

Green, D R (Blackburn & Co) *K1 S1 P M1 W F1 J1 D1*
Thornton Cleveleys *p411* . . . 01253 853101

Green, Miss E (WBW Solicitors)
Exeter *p222* 01392 202404

Green, Ms E (Symes Robinson & Lee) *K1*
Exeter *p222* 01392 270867

Green, F G (Thomson Snell & Passmore) *E A1 R1 P L Zc*
Tunbridge Wells *p415* 01892 510000

Green, Mrs F J (Green & Co) *G H*
Maidstone *p299* 01622 676769

Green, G (George Green LLP) *C2 C1*
Cradley Heath *p201* 01384 410410

Green, G M (CMS Cameron McKenna LLP)
London EC3 *p17* 020 7367 3000

Green, G M (Fraser Brown) *C1 E S1*
Nottingham *p337* 0115 988 8777

Green, G P (Landons) *S1 W T2 L E S2 Zh Zd*
Brentwood *p156* 01277 210021

Green, G R (Dickson Haslam) *S1 C1 E G W B1 P F1 K1 M1 Zl*
Preston *p356* 01772 883100

Green, G S (Ashurst LLP) *C1*
London EC2 *p7* 020 7638 1111

Green, Mrs H A (Edwards Duthie) *E C1 S1*
Ilford *p260* 020 8514 9000

Green, H A (Whitworth & Green) *D1 F1 G H W K1 L M1 S1 P*
Blackpool *p147* 01253 772912

Green, Ms H C (Hoole & Co) *K1*
Bristol *p163* 0117 969 1436

Green, J (LG Lawyers)
London SE1 *p50* 020 7379 0000

Green, Ms J (Lawson West Solicitors Limited) *T2 W*
Market Harborough *p312* . . . 01858 445480

Green, J (Bell & Buxton) *S2 S1*
Sheffield *p375* 0114 249 5969

Green, J (Reed Smith LLP) *O A3 Zj M2*
London EC2 *p71* 020 3116 3000

Green, Mrs J (South Derbyshire District Council)
Swadlincote *p473* 01283 221000

Green, Miss J (National Westminster Bank PLC)
Telford *p474* 01952 206000

Green, J A (Whetham & Green)
Burgess Hill *p168* 01444 233403

Green, Mrs J A (Blair Allison & Co) *K1 S1 D1 W Zi*
Birmingham *p135* 0121 233 2904

Green, Mrs J C (Brighouse Wolff) *K1 N O F1*
Maghull *p298* 0151 520 2717

Green, J M (KieranClarkeGreen) *S1 W K1 L E T1 F1 C1*
Chesterfield *p192* . 01246 230359 / 234937

Green, Ms J M (Dunn & Baker) *A1 C1 E L R1 S1*
Exeter *p221* 01392 285000

Green, J W L (Kenyon Son & Craddock) *K1 D1 G H*
Doncaster *p212* 01405 813108

Green, K (Foys Solicitors) *F1 F2 J1 L N O P Zc Zh Zi Zk Zo Zp Zq Zr*
Doncaster *p211* 01302 327136

Green, K (IBM United Kingdom Ltd)
London SE1 *p107* 020 7202 3000

Green, K S (Finn Gledhill) *G H K1 M1*
Halifax *p238* 01422 330000
Hebden Bridge *p246* 01422 842451

Green, Mrs L (Barlow Robbins LLP) *E C1 C2*
Guildford *p235* 01483 562901
Hitchin *p251* 01462 458711

Green, Ms L (TV Edwards LLP) *D2 D1 K1*
London EC3 *p85* 020 7790 7000

Green, L S (Lloyd Green Solicitors) *N Q Zj*
Chelmsford *p187* 01245 294600

Green, M (Weightmans LLP) *S1 O Q*
Liverpool *p291* 0151 227 2601

Green, Ms M (Mundays LLP) *K1*
Cobham *p196* 01932 590500

Green, M J (Stephenson Harwood) *Zb U2*
London EC2 *p82* 020 7329 4422

Green, M J (Matthew John Green) *C1 E L S1 T1 W*
Horsham *p253* 01403 210200

Green, M J (Shell International Ltd) *C1 E R1 R2 S1 S2*
London SE1 *p109* 020 7934 1234

Green, M J (Addleshaw Goddard) *P Zc Zj*
London EC1 *p4* 020 7606 8855

Green, M K (Cheryl Lewis & Co) *N K1 Q G O F1 J1 H V Zl*
Birkenhead *p134* 0151 652 1451

Green, M P (Lodders Solicitors LLP) *A1 S1 W T2*
Stratford-upon-Avon *p400* . . . 01789 293259

Green, M T (Short Richardson & Forth LLP) *B1 Ze P Zk O Q Zq*
Newcastle upon Tyne *p326* . 0191 232 0283

Green, M W (E Rex Makin & Co) *D1 G H B2 Zl*
Liverpool *p289* 0151 709 4491

Green, N (Trowers & Hamlins)
London EC3 *p88* 020 7423 8000

Green, Miss N (Perry Hay & Co) *S1 S2*
Richmond upon Thames *p364* 020 8940 8115 / 8332 7532

Green, N C (Robotham & Co) *S1 S2 A1 W*
Derby *p209* 01332 346018

Green, N H (Thomas Cooper) *O C1 M1 Zj Zb Zc Za*
London EC3 *p22* 020 7481 8851

Green, N J (Squire Sanders (UK) LLP) *E*
Birmingham *p142* 0121 222 3000

Green, N S (The Smith Partnership) *W S1 T1 L F1 E C1 R1 V*
Burton-on-Trent *p170* 01283 536471

Green, P (Barlow Robbins LLP) *O B1 Q*
Guildford *p235* 01483 562901

Green, P A (Wannop Fox Staffurth & Bray) *S1 S2*
Bognor Regis *p148* 01243 864001

Green, P D (Bell Lamb & Joynson) *G N H*
Runcorn *p369* 0844 412 4348
Liverpool *p286* 0844 412 4348

Green, P J (Morrison & Foerster (UK) LLP) *Zb*
London EC2 *p62* 020 7920 4000

Green, Ms P M (Spratt Endicott) *A3 Zc Ze L O Q*
Banbury *p122* 01295 204000

Green, Miss P M E (Sheridans) *Q J1 O Ze Zf Zg Zq*
London WC1 *p78* 020 7079 0100

Green, R (Harrison Clark LLP) *J1*
Cheltenham *p188* 01242 269198
Worcester *p439* 01905 612001
Worcester *p439* 01905 612001

Green, R B (Hill Dickinson LLP) *Zw Zk Zt*
Liverpool *p288* 0151 600 8000

Green, Miss R E (Lancashire County Council) *J1 N Q*
Preston *p469* 01772 254868

Green, Mrs R E (Rich & Carr Freer Bouskell) *D1 K1*
Leicester *p281* 0116 253 8021

Green, R G (Gill Turner Tucker) *K1 D1 L S1 Q W G*
Maidstone *p299* 01622 759051

Green, R I (Gardner Leader LLP) *E C1 S1 S2 Zl*
Newbury *p322* 01635 508080

Green, R J (Memery Crystal) *J1 C1*
London WC2 *p60* 020 7242 5905

Green, R L (Gosschalks) *Zl*
Hull *p256* 01482 324252

Green, R M (Bailey Smailes)
Holmfirth *p251* 01484 686000
Huddersfield *p255* 01484 435543
Huddersfield *p256* 01484 645464

Green, Mrs S (Fletchers) *N*
Southport *p388* 01704 546919

Green, Mrs S (The Gwyn George Partnership) *D1 K3 K1 D2 Zm*
Aberdare *p113* . . . .01685 874629 / 871133

Green, Mrs S (Anthony Collins Solicitors LLP) *W*
Birmingham *p137* 0121 200 3242

Green, S (Pinney Talfourd LLP)
Hornchurch *p252* 01708 511000

Green, Mrs S C (VHS Fletchers Solicitors) *H G*
Nottingham *p339* 0115 959 9550

Green, S H W (Waller Needham & Green)
Peterborough *p347* 01733 311422

Green, Miss S L (Gurney-Champion & Co) *K1 Q N O S1 W F1*
Portsmouth *p354* 023 9282 1100

Green, Mrs S M (Vincent Sykes & Higham LLP)
Thrapston *p411* 01832 732161

Green, Mrs S M (Glanvilles) *W K4 T2*
Havant *p244* 023 9249 2300

Green, S M (Muckle LLP) *C1 I U2 C3 Zza Ze*
Newcastle upon Tyne *p325* . 0191 211 7777

Green, S M C (Wiggin Osborne Fullerlove) *W T1 T2 Zd*
Cheltenham *p189* 01242 710200
London SW1 *p91* 020 7290 2456

Green, Mrs S M R (Cripps Harries Hall LLP) *O N Zq*
Tunbridge Wells *p415* 01892 515121

Green, S P (Fosters) *N Zr*
Norwich *p334* 01603 620508

Green, S W (Waldrons) *N O Q Zq Zr Zj*
Brierley Hill *p158* 01384 811811

Green, T L (McCarthy & Stone PLC)
Bournemouth *p450* 01202 292480

Green, T R (DLA Piper UK LLP) *E R1 S1 Zc*
London EC2 *p24* 0870 011 1111

Green, Ms V (Hill Dickinson LLP) *Zr N Q Zm J2*
Liverpool *p288* 0151 600 8000

Green, V J (Taylor & Emmet LLP) *S2 E Zd X*
Sheffield *p377* 0114 218 4000

Greenall, J (The Roland Partnership) *N*
Chester *p191* 01244 659404

Greenaway, N (Berry Smith LLP) *C1 C2 C3 B1 Ze Zf*
Cardiff *p177* 029 2034 5511

Greenbank, D A (Macfarlanes) *C1*
London EC4 *p56* 020 7831 9222

Greenbank, Mrs S (Hewitsons) *E S2 U1 R2*
Cambridge *p174* 01223 461155

Greenberg, J (Quastel Midgen LLP) *E J1 T1 Ze C1 F1 U2 R2*
London W1 *p70* 020 7908 2525

Greenberg, T K (Fuglers) *N Zf Q O S2 W Zk L*
London W1 *p34* 020 7323 6450

Greenbury, S C (Field Fisher Waterhouse LLP) *T2 W*
London EC3 *p31* 020 7861 4000

Greenby, B H (Howard Kennedy LLP) *E S1 L*
London W1 *p48* 020 7636 1616

Greene, D M (Edwin Coe LLP) *B1 B2 O M2 Zb Zc Ze Zg Zw*
London WC2 *p29* 020 7691 4000

Greene, J (The College of Law York)
York *p477* 0800 289997

Greene, J (Mowbray Woodwards Solicitors) *K1 S1 D1 L E*
Bath *p128* 01225 485700

Greene, K J (K&L Gates LLP) *O P Zc*
London EC4 *p47* 020 7648 9000

Greener, C T (Northern Rock PLC)
Gosforth *p459* 0191 285 7191

Greener, S P (Davis Gregory Ltd) *S1 E L R1 W*
Cheltenham *p188* 01242 235202

Greenfield, D A (Carpenter & Co) *W S1 T2 K4*
Wallington *p419* 020 8669 5145

Greenfield, G M (Freeth Cartwright LLP) *Zb B1 L*
Nottingham *p337* 0115 936 9369

Greenfield, G N I (Squire Sanders (UK) LLP)
Leeds *p277* 0113 284 7000

Greenfield, Ms H L (Family Law in Partnership LLP) *K1*
London WC2 *p30* 020 7420 5000

Greenfield, I J (ASB Law) *A1 E S1 W*
Crawley *p202* 01293 603600

Greenhaf, Ms S (Osborne Clarke) *R2*
London EC2 *p65* 020 7105 7000

Greenhaf, Ms S L (The National Trust)
Swindon *p475* 01793 817400

Greenhalgh, Mrs A M (Grant Saw Solicitors LLP) *E W C1 C2 S2 S1 K4*
Greenwich *p36* 020 8858 6971

Greenhalgh, D J K (Clarkson Wright & Jakes Ltd) *N Zr*
Orpington *p341* 01689 887887

Greenhalgh, D M (H2O Law LLP) *J1 Zg O Q D1 G K1 N Zp*
London EC4 *p37* 020 7405 4700

Greenhalgh, F (QualitySolicitors Gruber Garratt) *D1 K1*
Oldham *p341* 0161 665 3502

Greenhalgh, G (Canter Levin & Berg)
St Helens *p391* 01744 634141

Greenhalgh, Mrs J D (Crombie Wilkinson) *D1 K3 K1 K2*
York *p444* 01904 624185

Greenhalgh, P (Taylor Walton LLP) *J1*
Luton *p295* 01582 731161

Greenhalgh, P D (Peter D Greenhalgh) *S1 W T1 E P K1 F1 G J1 M1 Zl*
Glossop *p230* 01457 861319

Greenhalgh, Mrs S (Julia Frimond Solicitors) *K1 K3*
Guildford *p236* 01483 452224

Greenhall, Mrs J (Morrisons Solicitors LLP) *W T2*
Woking *p437* 01483 726146

Greenheld, Miss M G (Kirbys) *K1 D1*
Harrogate *p240* 01423 542000

Greenhough, R (Spicketts Battrick Law Practice)
Cardiff *p181* 029 2046 1480

Greenhouse, G I (Greenhouse Stirton & Co) *A3 K2 T2 W*
London EC1 *p37* 020 7490 3456

Greenidge, I (Hodge Jones & Allen LLP) *L Q*
London NW1 *p41* 020 7874 8300

Greenish, D J W (Pemberton Greenish LLP) *L S1*
London SW3 *p66* 020 7591 3333

Greenlay, Mrs C L (Durham City Council)
Durham *p457* 0191 386 6111

Greenlees, M B (Sacker & Partners LLP) *Zo*
London EC2 *p76* 020 7329 6699

Greenley, S K P T (Reynolds Porter Chamberlain LLP) *O Q Zj Zq*
London E1 *p71* 020 3060 6000

Greeno, E P (Herbert Smith LLP) *O*
London EC2 *p40* 020 7374 8000

Greenough, Miss A (Horsey Lightly) *W*
Newbury *p322* 01635 580858

Greenough, A E (Hogan Lovells International LLP)
London EC1 *p42* 020 7296 2000

Greenshields, I F (Dickinson Dees) *E*
Newcastle upon Tyne *p324* . 0191 279 9000

Greenshields, T F (McKenzie Bell Solicitors) *M1 N P J1 S1 A1 C1 W E B1 Zc Ze Zd*
Sunderland *p401* 0191 567 4857

Greensitt, Mrs J D (Barr Ellison LLP) *K4 W*
Cambridge *p174* 01223 417200

Greenslade, I R (Douglas Clift & Co) *N K1 F1 D1 O L G K3*
Lancaster *p269* 01524 32437

Greensmith, C (Orme & Slade Ltd) *S2 S1 W E*
Ledbury *p271* 01531 632226

Greensmith, T A L (Dickson Haslam) *M1 P N K1 L F1 D1 J1 Zj*
Kirkham *p268* 01772 685109

Greensmith, T H (Knowles Benning) *E N O F1 R1 Zc Zi*
Luton *p295* 01582 798000

Greenspan, Mrs E (Quastel Midgen LLP)
London W1 *p70* 020 7908 2525

Greenstein, M B (Goodge Law) *N*
London W1 *p36* 020 7636 9222

Greenstone, N D A (Fladgate LLP) *C1*
London WC2 *p32* 020 3036 7000

Greenstreet, I A (Squire Sanders (UK) LLP) *Zo*
London EC2 *p81* 020 7655 1000

Greenup, A (Bolt Burdon) *Ze Zf Zza*
Islington *p14* 020 7288 4700

Greenway, K P (Bromsgrove & Redditch Magistrates Court)
Kidderminster *p462* 01562 514000

Greenway, M (Whittinghams) *S1 W E L K1 N C1 Q F1*
Porthcawl *p353* 01656 788823

Greenwell, C R (Nelsons)
Leicester *p280* 0116 222 6666

Greenwell, Mrs G M (Chelsea Building Society)
Cheltenham *p454* . . . .

Greenwell, Mrs K J (Moss Solicitors LLP) *W K4 T2*
Loughborough *p293* 01509 217770
Leicester *p280* 0116 222 6666

Greenwell, Miss N (LDJ Solicitors) *L F1 Q N*
Nuneaton *p339* 024 7674 5000

Greenwood, A L (Emsleys) *N J2 Q O F2 K1 Zq Zl Zw*
Leeds *p273* 0113 232 1030

Greenwood, A L (Kennedys) *N O Q Zj Zq*
London EC3 *p49* 020 7667 9667

Greenwood, A T J (Cooper Son & Caldecott) *S1 E A1 K1 R1 T1 C1 W I Zd*
Henley-on-Thames *p247* . . . 01491 574203

Greenwood, C I (Lewis Silkin LLP) *A3 O Q N*
London EC4 *p53* 020 7074 8000

Greenwood, Ms D (Punch Robson) *D2 X K1 D1*
Middlesbrough *p315* 01642 230700

Greenwood, D A (Jordans) *N*
Dewsbury *p210* 01924 457171

Greenwood, D M (DAC Beachcroft) *N P M1 J1 O Zj*
Leeds *p272* 0113 251 4700

Greenwood, Miss H D (Westminster City Council)
London SW1 *p110* 020 7641 6000

Greenwood, Mrs J (Bolton Magistrates Court)
Bolton *p450* 01204 558200

Greenwood, J D (HBOS PLC)
Halifax *p460* 0870 600 5000

Greenwood, J H (Greenwood & Co) *E C1 N Q S1 M1 L B1 O W Zb Zl Zc S2 T1*
London EC1 *p37* 020 7831 8386

Greenwood, J K (Farnworth Shaw) *S1 S2 C1 E*
Nelson *p321* 01282 699996

Greenwood, J N (Greenwoods)
Knaresborough *p268* 01423 862975

Greenwood, J R S (JGT) *G H M1 S1 K1 P W F1 J1 L Zl Zm*
Burnley *p169* 01282 426722

Greenwood, Mrs K (IBB Solicitors) *S2 S1 Zd E*
Uxbridge *p417* 0845 638 1381

Greenwood, Miss K A (Dickinson Parker Hill) *P R1 V S1*
Ormskirk *p341* 01695 574201

Greenwood, Mrs L (Brockbank Curwen Cain & Hall) *K1 N V Q L F1 D1 D2 S1 B1 Zm*
Cockermouth *p197* 01900 827222

Greenwood, Mrs L D (Greenwoods) *E L S1 S2 W*
Knaresborough *p268* 01423 862975

Greenwood, Ms L D A (The International Family Law Group) *K3 K1*
London WC2 *p45* 020 3178 5668
London E1 *p71* 020 3060 6000

Greenwood, Mrs N (Freeman Box) *K3 K1 K2*
London W1 *p34* 020 7486 9041

Greenwood, P (The Sethi Partnership Solicitors)
Eastcote *p216* 020 8866 6464

Greenwood, R J (Thompsons (formerly Robin/Brian Thompson & Partners)) *N*
Nottingham *p339* 0115 989 7200

Greenwood, R S (Molesworths Bright Clegg) *N E W Zl*
Rochdale *p365* 01706 356666

Greenwood, S (HBOS PLC)
Halifax *p460* 0870 600 5000

Greenwood, S (Farleys Solicitors LLP)
Blackburn *p145* 01254 367856

Greenwood, Miss S J (Hatch Brenner) *S2 C1 A1*
Norwich *p334* 01603 660811

Greenwood, S P (Muckle LLP) *C2 C1 Zo*
Newcastle upon Tyne *p325* . 0191 211 7777

Greenwood, S R (Stone King LLP) *D1 K1*
Bath *p128* 01225 337599

Greer, A D (RAC Motoring Services)
Bristol *p452* 0870 553 3533

Greer, D C (Thomson & Bancks LLP) *S2 E C1 S1 L A1*
Pershore *p346* 01386 562000

Greg, Ms L (Hanover Solicitors)
London SW3 *p38* 0870 383 1974

Gregg, A D M (Gregg Latchams LLP) *G N O P Q H J1 K1 L Zl Zm Zt Zv*
Bristol *p162* 0117 906 9400

Greggs, Mrs A J (TMJ Legal Services LLP) *B1 F1 F2 J2 Zh L Zk Q X N Zq V*
Hartlepool *p243* 01429 235616
Wingate *p434* 01429 838225

Gregor, Ms L (Thompsons (formerly Robin/Brian Thompson & Partners)) *N*
Bristol *p165* 0117 304 2400

Gregorious, Mrs C A (CAG Solicitors) *C1 S2 K3 K4 J1 K1 W S1*
Chobham *p193* 01276 488082

Gregory, Ms A (Farrer & Co LLP)
London WC2 *p31* 020 3375 7000

Gregory, A H (DWF) *B1 Zb C1 O*
Manchester *p303* 0161 603 5000

Gregory, A H (hlw Keeble Hawson LLP) *C1 C2 C3 F1 J1 N O P Q*
Sheffield *p375* 0114 272 2061

See p634 for the Key to Work Categories

Gregory, C (Payne Marsh Stillwell) N
Southampton p386 ...... 023 8022 3957

Gregory, Mrs D A (Hogan Lovells International LLP)
London EC1 p42 ...... 020 7296 2000

Gregory, Mrs F S (Oglethorpe Sturton & Gillibrand) W
Kirkby Lonsdale p268 .... 01524 271388
Grange-over-Sands p232 .. 01539 533316

Gregory, G (Willett & Co)
Bury St Edmunds p171 ... 01284 701323

Gregory, G N (Midwinters) E S1 S2 Zl
Cheltenham p188 ...... 01242 514674

Gregory, Ms J A (GE Capital Solutions) C1
Bristol p452 ...... 0870 241 8899

Gregory, Ms J E (Joelson Wilson LLP) O Q
Westminster p46 ...... 020 7580 5721

Gregory, J R N (Keene & Kelly) S1 W J1 R1 F1 S2 A1 L Zl Zt V
Mold p318 ...... 01352 753882

Gregory, Mrs K (Henmans LLP) N O Q Zj Zq
Oxford p343 ...... 01865 781000

Gregory, Miss K (Fieldings Porter) K1 S1 W D1
Bolton p149 ...... 01204 540900

Gregory, Ms K M (National Air Traffic Services Ltd)
London WC2 p108 ...... 01489 616001

Gregory, K V (CMS Cameron McKenna LLP)
London EC3 p17 ...... 020 7367 3000

Gregory, L (Clarke Kiernan) N
Tonbridge p412 ...... 01732 360999

Gregory, Ms L A (Memery Crystal) C1 C2 Zw Zn
London WC2 p60 ...... 020 7242 5905

Gregory, M R (Johns Gilbert & Frankton) Q K1 O N J1 F1 F2 C1 Zq R1 K3 Zc U2 Zp
Rugby p368 ...... 01788 576384

Gregory, Mrs N J (Crosse & Crosse) Zr N Zq
Exeter p220 ...... 01392 258451

Gregory, P (Wrigley Claydon) S1 E
Oldham p341 ...... 0161 624 6811

Gregory, P (Gordons LLP) E
Leeds p273 ...... 0113 227 0100

Gregory, P D (Stephens & Scown) Zq Q Zi O
Exeter p222 ...... 01392 210700

Gregory, P H (Tuffnells Parcels Express Ltd)
Sheffield p471 ...... 0114 256 1111

Gregory, Miss R (LSG Solicitors) D1 D2 K2 Zq Zr
London W1 p51 ...... 020 7851 0100

Gregory, R C F (Barker Son & Isherwood LLP) N J1 P
Andover p118 ...... 01264 353411

Gregory, S H (Foot Anstey) C1 L E F1 A1 J1 T1 W R1 B1 Zb Zc
Exeter p221 ...... 01392 411221

Gregory, Ms T (Public Interest Lawyers) D1 X Zu
Birmingham p141 ...... 0121 515 5069

Gregory, T A W (Lambert Taylor & Gregory) G H K1 N J1 Zq
Gateshead p228 ...... 0191 477 0616

Gregory, T R (Bowcock & Pursaill) C1 E S2 R1
Leek p278 ...... 01538 399199

Gregory, T W (Ramsdens Solicitors) C1 E R1 S1 Zc S2 R2
Huddersfield p256 ...... 01484 821500

Gregson, A (Travers Smith LLP) Zb
London EC1 p87 ...... 020 7295 3000

Gregson, C J (Ashfords LLP) E
Plymouth p349 ...... 01752 521500

Gregson, Miss J M (Davenport Lyons) C1 C2
London W1 p25 ...... 020 7468 2600

Gregson, M (Anthony Collins Solicitors LLP) J1
Birmingham p137 ...... 0121 200 3242

Gregson, M J (Coodes) G H N P
Newquay p329 ...... 01637 878111

Gregson, P M (Bentleys Stokes & Lowless)
London EC3 p12 ...... 020 7782 0990

Gregson-Murray, Ms S M (Gregsons) G H Q S1 W Zg
Nottingham p337 ...... 0115 941 1999

Greig, D P L (Jeffrey Green Russell)
London W1 p46 ...... 020 7339 7000

Greig, D V (Taylor Wessing)
London EC4 p86 ...... 020 7300 7000

Greig, M C (Rogers & Norton) S1 S2 E
Norwich p335 ...... 01603 666001

Greig, Miss R J S (Painters) K1 D1 K3
Stourport-on-Severn p399 .. 01299 822033

Greig, Ms V (Collyer Bristow LLP) J1
London WC1 p22 ...... 020 7242 7363

Grenfell, M G (Wilmot & Co Solicitors LLP) B1 C1 J1 N O Q Ze Zq Zr
Cirencester p195 ...... 01285 650551

Grenville, A T (Clifford Chance)
London E14 p20 ...... 020 7006 1000

Grenville, Mrs M P (Maureen P Grenville) D1 D2 Zm
Duffield p214 ...... 01332 841789

Gresswell, D G (Allens) C1 C2 C3 F1 J1 I Ze
Portsmouth p354 ...... 023 9282 2411

Greswold, P G (Wrigleys Solicitors LLP) T2 W A1
Leeds p278 ...... 0113 244 6100

Grevatte, Mrs K (Bhatia Best) G H
Nottingham p336 ...... 0115 950 3231

Greves, Mrs M K (Gordon Lutton) S1 L E W
Hereford p248 ...... 01432 355345

Greville, M (Watson Farley & Williams)
London EC2 p90 ...... 020 7814 8000

Grewal, Ms G H (Alsters Kelley) Zr N
Coventry p199 ...... 0844 561 0100

Grewal, Miss P K (Dodd Lewis Solicitors) S1
London SE3 p27 ...... 020 8852 1255

Grewal, Ms S K (London Borough of Greenwich Legal Services)
London SE18 p106 ...... 020 8921 5123

Grewer, Mrs J L (Hegarty LLP) W K4
Peterborough p347 ...... 01733 346333

Grey, C (Penningtons) E
London EC2 p66 ...... 020 7457 3000

Grey, Miss D J K (Taylor Wessing) C1 C2
London EC4 p86 ...... 020 7300 7000

Grey, Miss J (Peach Grey & Co) G
Southampton p386 ...... 023 8033 4695

Grey, J D (Butters David Grey & Co) B1 C1 D1 E F1 G H K1 L N Zp Zs Zw
Hastings p243 ....01424 424949 / 715171

Grey, Ms L (Hill Dickinson LLP)
Liverpool p288 ...... 0151 600 8000

Grey, R L (W A G Davidson & Co) W S1 T1 E C1
London W3 p26 ...... 020 8992 4884

Grey, Mrs S (Gerald Armstrong & Co) H G K1 D1
Sunderland p401 ...... 0191 514 0966

Gribben, Miss K A (Network Rail)
London NW1 p108 ...... 020 7557 8000

Gribbin, Mrs B (Davies & Gribbin Solicitors)
Ormskirk p341 ...... 01695 573433

Gribble, D W (British Telecommunications PLC)
London EC1 p104 ...... 020 7356 6181

Gribble, J (Michelmores LLP) E R2
London W1 p60 ...... 020 7659 7660

Gribble, Ms J E (South Tyneside Metropolitan Borough Council) G D1 Ze Zl
South Shields p471 ...... 0191 427 1717

Gribbon, Mrs M (Cripps Harries Hall LLP) W T2
Tunbridge Wells p415 ...... 01892 515121

Grice, D W (Denison Till) A1 E S1 L R2
York p444 ...... 01904 611411

Grice, J H (Dutton Gregory) E R2 S2
Winchester p433 ...... 01962 844333

Grice, K (RMPI Solicitors) O Q
London W1 p70 ...... 020 7318 4444

Grice, T (NGA) G H S1 K1 E W
Burnley p169 ...... 01282 457295

Gridley, J R (Kirby Sheppard) K1 D1
Bristol p163 ...... 0845 840 0045

Gridley, Mrs R A (Stanley Smith Hill & Co) W S1
Carshalton p183 ...... 020 8669 0044

Grieg, W (McGrigors LLP)
London EC4 p56 ...... 020 7054 2500

Grier, C (Crown Prosecution Service Dorset)
Bournemouth p450 ...... 01202 498700

Grier, I S (SGH Martineau LLP) B1 Q C1
London EC3 p75 ...... 020 7264 4444

Grierson, C K (Hogan Lovells International LLP)
London EC1 p42 ...... 020 7296 2000

Grierson, J S (Grierson Shaw & Co) G S1 H K1 D1 P J1 L F1 M1 Zl Zk Zi
Durham p214 ...... 0191 386 2434

Grieves, Miss H (Grieves Solicitors) J2 N
Huddersfield p255 ...... 01484 300192

Grieveson, Miss L J (MPH Solicitors) N
Manchester p307 ...... 0161 832 7722

Griffen, B (Dickinson Dees) O
Newcastle upon Tyne p324 . 0191 279 9000

Griffin, A J C (Cartridges) N O L F1
Exeter p220 ...... 01392 256854

Griffin, C (Ashurst LLP)
London EC2 p7 ...... 020 7638 1111

Griffin, C R (Skandia Life Assurance Co Ltd)
Southampton p472 ...... 023 8033 4411

Griffin, Miss E (Borough of Telford & Wrekin) G K1
Telford p473 ...... 01952 380000

Griffin, E (Coodes)
St Austell p391 ...... 01726 874700

Griffin, J (Shell International Ltd)
London SE1 p109 ...... 020 7934 1234

Griffin, J (Everys) N F1 Q G H L O V
Honiton p252 ...... 01404 41221

Griffin, J E (Warley Magistrates Court) G H K1 Zl
Oldbury p468 ...... 0121 511 2222

Griffin, Miss K (Curtis Turner & Drukker Ltd)
London EC4 p24 ...... 020 7353 1770

Griffin, K P (Dee & Griffin) K1 S1 J1 W N C1 D1 E Q F1 Zc Zm Zl
Gloucester p230 ...... 01452 617288

Griffin, M (Maclachlan) G H J1 K1 L N O Zl
Sherborne p378 ...... 01935 817736

Griffin, N M (Neil Griffin & Co) K3 K1 D1 K2 N
Honiton p252 ...... 01404 42609

Griffin, P (Crown Prosecution Service Dorset) P K1 M1 G N J1 Zt Zl
Bournemouth p450 ...... 01202 498700

Griffin, P (Neville-Jones & Co) S1 E W
Swanage p404 ....01929 422666 / 423761

Griffin, P A (Aldridge Brownlee Solicitors LLP) S1 W L
Bournemouth p151 ...... 01202 526343

Griffin, P J (Herbert Smith LLP) C1 M2 A3 C3
London EC2 p40 ...... 020 7374 8000

Griffin, S (Linklaters LLP)
London EC2 p54 ...... 020 7456 2000

Griffin, S G (Linklaters LLP)
London EC2 p54 ...... 020 7456 2000

Griffin, T A S (Napthens LLP) N
Preston p357 ...... 01772 888444

Griffith, A (DLA Piper UK LLP)
London EC2 p24 ...... 0870 011 1111

Griffith, D R G (Bone & Payne LLP) E S1 W S2
Llandudno p291 ...... 01492 876354

Griffith, Mrs J M (City of London Magistrates Court)
London EC4 p107 ...... 020 7332 1830

Griffith, M (Pinsent Masons LLP) Zj
London EC2 p67 ...... 020 7418 7000

Griffith, Mrs N (David Gist Solicitors)
Bristol p162 ...... 0117 927 9111

Griffith, P D J (Havant Borough Council) C1 S1
Havant p460 ...... 023 9247 4174

Griffith, Mrs R (Welsh Health Legal Services) N Q L Zh
Cardiff p453 ...... 029 2031 5500

Griffith, Miss S M (Prudential PLC)
London EC4 p108 ...... 020 7220 7588

Griffiths, Ms A (Gateley LLP)
Birmingham p138 ...... 0121 234 0000

Griffiths, A (K&L Gates LLP) B1 J1 M1 N P
London EC4 p47 ...... 020 7648 9000

Griffiths, Miss A (Irwin Mitchell LLP) Zr
Manchester p306 ...... 0870 150 0100

Griffiths, A D (South Gloucestershire Council)
Thornbury p474 ...... 01454 868686

Griffiths, A H M (Klimt & Co) E S1 L R1 W
Westminster p50 ...... 020 7486 4432

Griffiths, Ms C (Russell Jones & Walker)
Birmingham p141 ...... 0121 233 8300

Griffiths, Miss C J (Taylor Wimpey UK Limited Legal Services)
Milton Keynes p466 ...... 01908 209030

Griffiths, Miss C M (Red Kite Law) K1
Carmarthen p183 ...... 01267 239000

Griffiths, D (Russell-Cooke LLP) O
London SW15 p74 ...... 020 8789 9111

Griffiths, D G (Eleri Thomas & Co Ltd) W S1 A1
Newcastle Emlyn p323 ...... 01239 710942

Griffiths, D H (Clifford Chance)
London E14 p20 ...... 020 7006 1000

Griffiths, D H (HCB Solicitors) S1 W
Walsall p420 ...... 01922 720000

Griffiths, D J (Maxwell Hodge Solicitors) C1 S2 E
Liverpool p289 ...... 0151 227 4545

Griffiths, E (DLA Piper UK LLP)
London EC2 p24 ...... 0870 011 1111

Griffiths, Miss E (MacLeish Littlestone Cowan)
Redbridge p57 ...... 020 8514 3000

Griffiths, Ms E L (Oxford City Council)
Oxford p468 ...... 01865 249811

Griffiths, Mrs F (Beviss & Beckingsale)
Chard p184 ...... 01460 269700

Griffiths, Miss F C (Graham Evans & Partners) S1 W D1 G H K1 Zk
Swansea p405 ...... 01792 655822

Griffiths, Mrs F N (Hutchinson Thomas) D1 K1
Neath p320 ...... 01639 645061

Griffiths, G N (Coley & Tilley) E C1 S1 L A1 J1 T1 W Zh Zj
Birmingham p136 ...... 0121 643 5531

Griffiths, H R (Norris & Miles) S1 N O Q E W S2
Tenbury Wells p409 ...... 01584 810575

Griffiths, Mrs H R (Willett & Co) W S1 S2 A1 E B1 C1 Zl C2 Q T2 R2
Bury St Edmunds p171 ... 01284 701323

Griffiths, H R (Welsh Development Agency Legal Services) E S1 S2 R1 R2
Cardiff p453 ...... 029 2082 8681
Kingswood p268 ...... 0117 960 6880

Griffiths, Ms I (Reynolds Porter Chamberlain LLP)
London E1 p71 ...... 020 3060 6000

Griffiths, I D H (Moody & Woolley) E S1 W
Derby p209 ...... 01332 344221

Griffiths, Miss J (Martyn Prowel) N
Cardiff p180 ...... 029 2047 0909

Griffiths, J C (Williamson & Barnes) S1 W E L
Deal p207 ...... 01304 373154

Griffiths, J C (Geldards LLP)
Cardiff p178 ...... 029 2023 8239

Griffiths, Miss J E (Denbighshire County Council)
Ruthin p470 ...... 01824 706000

Griffiths, J L (Red Kite Law) A1 B1 E K1 S1 W
Carmarthen p183 ...... 01267 239000

Griffiths, J L (Edwards Angell Palmer & Dodge) Zc
London EC2 p28 ...... 020 7583 4055
London WC2 p29 ...... 020 7691 4000

Griffiths, J P (Ashton KCJ)
Bury St Edmunds p171 ... 01284 762331

Griffiths, J P (Gladstone Solicitors) K1 G H D1 M1 P W V J1 F1
Nottingham p337 ...... 0115 978 1666

Griffiths, K M (Red Kite Law) S1 S2 W A1 L R1 Zl
Carmarthen p183 ...... 01267 239000

Griffiths, Miss L (Sheridans) O Q U1 Zf A3
London WC1 p78 ...... 020 7079 0100

Griffiths, L A (Hacking Ashton LLP) C1 E F1 I Ze
Newcastle under Lyme p323 . 01782 715555

Griffiths, M D (Shell International Ltd) C1
London SE1 p109 ...... 020 7934 1234

Griffiths, M R W (Henriques Griffiths) E S1
Bristol p163 ...... 0117 909 4000
Winterbourne p435 ...... 01454 854000

Griffiths, M S (Steven Young & Co) G H
Gloucester p230 ...... 01452 332882

Griffiths, M S R (Williamson & Barnes) K1 F1 Q J1
Deal p207 ...... 01304 373154

Griffiths, N (Bank of Scotland Legal Operations)
London EC2 p104 ...... 0870 600 5000

Griffiths, Mrs N (Treasury Solicitors Department) O Zj
London WC2 p110 ...... 020 7210 3000

Griffiths, Mrs N (Barlow Robbins LLP) S1
Guildford p235 ...... 01483 543200

Griffiths, Miss N J (Russell & Russell) N
Middleton p315 ...... 0161 653 6200

Griffiths, N R (SNR Denton) O
London EC4 p75 ...... 020 7242 1212

Griffiths, P F (Challinors) C1 E J1 L N O Q P Zb Zl
West Bromwich p427 ...... 0121 553 3211

Griffiths, P G (Greathead & Whitelock) K1 N Q Zr J1 O S1 D1 D2 F1 Zl
Pembroke p345 ...... 01646 682101

Griffiths, P S (Bentleys Stokes & Lowless) N Za Zj
London EC3 p12 ...... 020 7782 0990

Griffiths, R A (Harrowells)
York p444 ...... 01904 558600

Griffiths, R G (Blandy & Blandy) C1 C2 C3 E J1 Zl
Reading p360 ...... 0118 951 6800

Griffiths, R J M (Walters & Williams)
Carmarthen p183 ...... 01267 236686

Griffiths, R L (Richard Griffiths & Co) G H K1 L S1 W Zl Zm
Salisbury p371 ...... 01722 329966

Griffiths, R M B (Newsome Vaughan LLP) E L R2 S2
Coventry p200 ...... 024 7663 3433

Griffiths, R R G (Penmans) S1 W K1 E G J1 L
Wellesbourne p424 ...... 01789 470022

Griffiths, Ms S (S4C) C1 Zf Ze
Cardiff p453 ...... 029 2074 7444

Griffiths, S (Addleshaw Goddard) C1
London EC1 p4 ...... 020 7606 8855

Griffiths, S (George Green LLP) A3 B1 Ze B2 J2 Zk O Q Zq
Cradley Heath p201 ...... 01384 410410

Griffiths, Mrs S E (Wall James Chappell) K4 T2 W
Stourbridge p399 ...... 01384 371622

Griffiths, Miss S E F (Shirley Griffiths) K1 N W D1 Q S1 T2 S2 Zg K3 Zi Zq K4
Hythe p259 ...... 01303 266689

Griffiths, Ms S F (Stephanie F Griffiths) K1 S1
Kingston upon Thames p267. 020 8546 5986

Griffiths, Ms S G (Eaves) O Q
Milford Haven p316 ...... 01646 695785

Griffiths, Miss S J (Wright & McMillan Bennett) N K1 J2 Q Zq
Telford p409 ...... 01952 291100

Griffiths, S W (Eaves) P
Milford Haven p316 ...... 01646 695785

Griffiths, S W (Taylor Walton LLP) E L S1
Luton p295 ...... 01582 731161

Griffiths, T (Breese-Gwyndaf) S1 E L W J1 S2 N Zc Zr K1 O Zq
Porthmadog p353 .01766 512253 / 514227

Griffiths, T (Mayo Wynne Baxter LLP) W S1 Q
Eastbourne p215 ...... 01323 730543

Griffiths, Mrs T (Hains & Lewis Ltd) K4 S1 W S2
Haverfordwest p244 ...... 0845 408 0125

Griffiths, W E (Devonalds) D1 F1 G H K1 L J1 N
Pontypridd p352 ...... 01443 404700

Griffiths, W G T (Jeffreys & Powell) A1 S1 W
Builth Wells p168 ...... 01982 553224
Brecon p156 ...... 01874 622106

Grigg, J (Clarke Willmott) J1 L O Q
Southampton p3850845 209 1000 / 0117 305 6000

Grigg, J A (Willans LLP) K1 K3
Cheltenham p189 ...... 01242 514000

Grigg, Mrs K M (Preston Goldburn) K1 W C1 K3 Q
Falmouth p223 ...... 01326 318900

Grigg, M (Clifford Chance)
London E14 p20 ...... 020 7006 1000

Grigg, N J (Greene & Greene) E S2 S1
Bury St Edmunds p171 ... 01284 762211

Grigg, Mrs V L (Newsome Vaughan LLP) L Zh
Coventry p200 ...... 024 7663 3433

Griggs, P J S (Ince & Co Services Ltd)
London E1 p44 ...... 020 7481 0010

Grigsby, G (Grigsby Eddleston & Co) S1 E W S2
Stevenage p394 ...... 01438 742525

Grimbaldstone, Ms H (Plexus Law (A Trading Name of Parabis Law LLP)) Q O Zj Zr Zq
London EC3 p68 ...... 0844 245 4000

Grimes, D R (Bury & Walkers LLP) D1 K1 V Zo
Barnsley p124 ...... 01226 733533

Grimes, I R (Fraser Dawbarns) E S1
Downham Market p213 ...... 01366 383171

Grimes, J (Kingsley Napley) G B2
London EC1 p50 ...... 020 7814 1200

Grimes, J A (Drysdales) W E C1 S1 Zc Zd
Southend-on-Sea p387 ... 01702 423400

Grimes, Mrs J J (Bury & Walkers LLP) E C1 C3 L S1 A1 Zc
Barnsley p124 ...... 01226 733533

Grimes, Miss L M (Richard Reed) D1 K1 V K3
Sunderland p402 ...... 0191 567 0465

Grimes, M (Pannone LLP) O Q B1 C1
Manchester p308 ...... 0161 909 3000

Grimm, K (Stone Rowe Brewer LLP) K4 S1 T2 W
Twickenham p416 ...... 020 8891 6141

Grimmett, L (Lanyon Bowdler LLP) K1 Q N
Wellington p425 ...... 01952 244721

Grimmett, Miss L J (Lanyon Bowdler LLP) D1 D2 K1
Telford p409 ...... 01952 291222

Grimsdale, Miss S L (Reed Executive PLC) E S1 L
London WC2 p108 ...... 020 7421 1640

Grimshaw, C (London Borough of Southwark)
London SE1 p109 ...... 020 7525 5000

Grimshaw, I D (Trethowans LLP) J1
Southampton p387 ...... 023 8032 1000

Grimshaw, J A (Barber Titleys) A1 E L S1 S2 R2
Harrogate p240 ...... 01423 502211

Grimshaw, Ms K (Irwin Mitchell LLP) O
Leeds p274 ...... 0870 150 0100

Grimshaw, Mrs K E (FBC Manby Bowdler LLP) *S1*
Wolverhampton *p437* 01902 578000
Wolverhampton *p438* 01902 313311

Grimshaw, Miss M B (Wyre Borough Council)
Poulton-le-Fylde *p469* . . . 01253 891000

Grimshaw, S L (stevensdrake) *E R2*
Crawley *p202* 01293 596900

Grimwade, Ms S (Fisher Jones Greenwood LLP) *S1 W*
Colchester *p197* 01206 578282

Grimwood, P C (Sandersons) *B2 C1 O Q*
Hull *p258* 01482 324662

Grimwood, P J (Hart Brown Solicitors) *N F1 I O Q Zq Zr*
Guildford *p236* 0800 068 8177

Grinbergs, Miss R (Anthony Collins Solicitors LLP) *E*
Birmingham *p137* 0121 200 3242

Grindal, I S (Newsome Vaughan LLP) *E S1 S2 A1 W T2 L*
Coventry *p200* 024 7663 3433

Grindall, D J (Grindall & Hanna Solicitors) *C1 J1*
Southwark *p37* 020 8299 3801

Grindlay, S R (Brindley Twist Tafft & James) *E A1 C1 S1*
Coventry *p200* 024 7653 1532

Grindley, M J (stevensdrake) *E*
Crawley *p202* 01293 596900

Grindley, P J (hlw Keeble Hawson LLP)
Sheffield *p375* 0114 272 2061

Grindrod, Miss C (Backhouse Jones Ltd) *N Zj Q*
Clitheroe *p196* 01254 828300

Grindrod, D P (Roebucks) *E S1 S2 A1*
Blackburn *p145* 01254 274000

Grindrod, P J (BAS Solicitors) *C1 E L S2 W S1 Zc*
Bracknell *p153* 01344 862111

Grindrod, Mrs S L (Grindrod & Co) *E S1 S2 W A1 C1 Zi*
Wellington *p425* 01952 243064

Gringras, C (Olswang LLP) *O I M2 C3 M1 Ze*
London WC1 *p64* 020 7067 3000

Grinstead, D J (Bolitho Way) *M1 G S1 K1 L E W N P*
Portsmouth *p354* 023 9282 0747

Grisdale, Miss N (Denbighshire County Council)
Ruthin *p470* 01824 706000

Grisedale, A S (Muckle LLP) *C1 U1 I Zza Zu U2 X*
Newcastle upon Tyne *p325* . 0191 211 7777

Griston, D H F (CMS Cameron McKenna LLP)
London EC3 *p17* 020 7367 3000

Griver, M R (Portner & Jaskel LLP) *E L R1 S1*
London W1 *p68* 020 7616 5300

Groat, A M (Waughs) *D1 F1 G H J1 K1 L N*
East Grinstead *p215* 01342 323545

Groch, S (DWF) *J1 J2 P N*
Manchester *p303* 0161 603 5000

Grocock, C R (Wilkin Chapman LLP) *B1 Q O*
Grimsby *p235* 01472 262626

Grocock, M D (Freeth Cartwright LLP) *A1 E*
Nottingham *p337* 0115 936 9369

Grocott, Miss P A (Wartnabys) *S1 W A1 E*
Market Harborough *p312* . . . 01858 463322

Grocott, S (Grindeys LLP) *C1 B1 L*
Stoke-on-Trent *p397* 01782 846441

Groeger Wilson, J L (Clarkson Wright & Jakes Ltd) *W T2 Zo*
Orpington *p341* 01689 887887

Grogan, C (Cambridge Constabulary)
Huntingdon *p461* 01480 456111

Grogan, Mrs F K (Hay & Kilner) *W S1*
Newcastle upon Tyne *p325* . 0191 232 8345

Grogan, J D (Dickinson Dees) *O*
Newcastle upon Tyne *p324* . 0191 279 9000

Grogan, P (JMW Solicitors) *G H K1 M1 D1 S1*
Manchester *p306* 0845 872 6666

Gromett, P (Paul Gromett & Co) *A1 B1 C1 D1 E F1 G H J1*
London W1 *p37* 020 7631 2066

Gronow, S D V (Pinsent Masons LLP) *C1 C2*
Birmingham *p141* 0121 200 1050

Groom, Ms L (Slade Legal) *S1*
Abingdon *p114* 01235 521920

Groom, Mrs M (Bates Wells & Braithwaite London LLP) *Zd C1 X*
London EC4 *p11* 020 7551 7777

Groom, S (Osborne Clarke) *F2 Ze U2*
London EC2 *p65* 020 7105 7000

Groom, S W (Osborne Clarke) *U1 U2*
Bristol *p164* 0117 917 3000

Groombridge, J (Aston Clark)
London W3 *p8* 020 8752 1122

Grosberg, R D (Nelsons) *W S1 E*
Nottingham *p338* 0115 958 6262

Grose, J (Dechert) *O E*
London EC4 *p26* 020 7184 7000

Grose, P A (Lester Aldridge LLP) *E C1*
Bournemouth *p152* 01202 786161

Gross, J (Quastel Midgen LLP) *E S2 R2 R1*
London W1 *p70* 020 7908 2525

Gross, N M (Coffin Mew & Clover) *B1 C1 C2 C3 Zb Ze Zj*
Southampton *p385* 023 8033 4661

Gross, R W (Toller Beattie LLP) *R1*
Barnstaple *p125* 01271 341000

Grossbard, D M (Brecher) *Zb*
London W1 *p15* 020 7563 1000

Grosscurth, R D P (Grosscurth & Co) *Zv*
Moreton *p319* 0151 678 8212

Grosse, Miss L M (Winckworth Sherwood LLP) *K1 O Q J1 D1 N*
London SE1 *p92* 020 7593 5000

Grosse, R B (Taylor Wessing) *B1 C1 E J1 L N S1 T1 W Zc Ze*
London EC4 *p86* 020 7300 7000

Grossman, D J (Freedman Green Dhokia) *S1 L S2 E R1*
Camden *p34* 020 7625 6003

Grossman, Ms F (Hodge Jones & Allen LLP) *D1 K1*
London NW1 *p41* 020 7874 8300

Grosz, S E (Bindmans LLP) *Q P J1*
London WC1 *p12* 020 7833 4433

Grounds, A J (Hough Halton & Soal) *K1*
Carlisle *p182* 01228 524379

Grout, R J (East Sussex County Council)
Lewes *p463* 01273 481000

Grove, A W (Andrew Grove & Co) *D1 H J1 K1 L N Q S1 W E*
Cambridge *p174* 01223 367133

Grove, D (FBC Manby Bowdler LLP) *E*
Wolverhampton *p437* 01902 578000

Grove, Ms M (Gill Akaster) *K1 D1 K2*
Plymouth *p349* 01752 203500

Grove, M L (Martin L Grove) *S1 K1 N S2 W V J1 E F2 Q*
Middlesbrough *p315* 01642 456615
Saltburn-by-the-Sea *p371* . . 01287 650675

Grove, Ms N (Ginn & Co) *K3 K1*
Cambridge *p174* 01223 358275

Grove, R (Manches LLP) *L R1 R2 E*
London WC2 *p58* 020 7404 4433
London EC4 *p81* 020 7427 6400

Grove, R C (Braund & Fedrick) *S1 E C1 N R1 J1 Ze Zl*
Sidcup *p380* 020 8300 6515

Grove, R T (Atteys) *F1 J1 M1 N P*
Doncaster *p211* 01302 340400

Grove, S L (Harrison Clark LLP) *Zw C1*
Worcester *p439* 01905 612001

Grover, A (Garstangs)
London WC2 *p35* 020 7427 5678

Grover, Ms E (Nelsons)
Leicester *p280* 0116 222 6666

Grover, N S (Teacher Stern LLP) *O Q F1 B1*
London WC1 *p86* 020 7242 3191

Groves, A B (City of London Corporation)
London EC2 *p107* 020 7606 3030

Groves, C (Reynolds Porter Chamberlain LLP)
London E1 *p71* 020 3060 6000

Groves, C G (Cozens-Hardy LLP) *E C2 A1*
Norwich *p334* 01603 625231

Groves, Ms G L (LG Lawyers)
London SE1 *p50* 020 7379 0000

Groves, K (Liddell and Company) *N G Q*
Romford *p366* 01708 775999

Groves, N K (Wolferstans) *N*
Plymouth *p351* 01752 663295

Groves, P (Harbottle & Lewis LLP) *Zf C1 Zw Ze Zk Q E S2 I C2 K1 T1 M3 Zd Zz*
London W1 *p38* 020 7667 5000

Groves, S P (Brooks & Partners) *D1 K1 G M1 S1 F1 H E C1*
Camberley *p173* 01276 681217

Grower, A H (Magrath LLP) *Zf*
London W1 *p57* 020 7495 3003

Gruber, H P (QualitySolicitors Gruber Garratt) *S2 E C1 S1 C2*
Ashton-under-Lyne *p120* . . . 0161 344 2244

Grumbridge, M C (M C Grumbridge)
London W4 *p37* 020 8994 0929

Grundberg, A O V (McGuireWoods London LLP) *T2 T1 C1 M2 C2*
London EC4 *p57* 020 7632 1600

Grundell, Ms C (Brooke Williams) *K1 D1 K2*
Leeds *p272* 0113 246 8400

Grundy, Ms J K (Hutsby Mees) *S1 W C1 E L*
Stafford *p393* 01785 259211

Grundy, M R (Linder Myers Solicitors) *K1 G H*
Manchester *p307* 0844 984 6400

Grundy, P M (Land Law LLP) *E S1 S2 R2 R1 P A1 Zc Zd*
Altrincham *p116* 0161 928 8383

Grunert, C A (John Gaunt & Partners) *Zl Zf O Q*
Sheffield *p375* 0114 266 8664

Grunewald, J P (Watmores) *M1 P N J1 Zj*
London WC2 *p90* 020 7430 1512

Grunwell, R L (Pinkney Grunwells Lawyers LLP) *E S1 R1 C1 W A1 L Zc Zd*
Scarborough *p372* 01723 352125

Grut, O (The Economist Newspaper Ltd)
London SW1 *p106* 020 7830 7000

Gryk, W C (Wesley Gryk) *Zi Zg*
Lambeth *p37* 020 7401 6887

Grylls, P W (Gullands) *L N O Q Zq Zr*
Maidstone *p299* 01622 678341

Guard, J P (Foot Anstey) *S1 E A1 L W*
Exeter *p221* 01392 411221

Gubbay, D O A (Dechert) *T1 T2*
London EC4 *p26* 020 7184 7000

Gubbins, Mrs J M (Trowers & Hamlins) *C1 Zh*
London EC3 *p88* 020 7423 8000

Gubbins, R S (Ashurst LLP)
London EC2 *p7* 020 7638 1111

Gubbins, Miss S B (Eldridges) *S1 S2 E*
Newport *p328* 01983 524741

Gudgeon, J R (P T Ryan & Co) *K1 W S1 S2 J1 Q A1 Zc Zn Zv E L*
King's Lynn *p266* 01553 761741

Gudgin, Mrs H A (Cambridgeshire County Council) *D1*
Cambridge *p453* 01223 717111

Guedalla, D R (Birnberg Peirce & Partners)
Camden *p13* 020 7911 0166

Guelfi, L (Abels)
Southampton *p385* 023 8022 0317

Guerin, G P (Hooper Holt & Co) *G H P V M1 F1 C1 K1 D1 B1 X J1 Zq*
Redhill *p362* 01737 761111

Guess, Mrs A C (Wise Geary) *E S1*
Banbury *p122* 01295 278500

Guest, Ms A (Atha & Co) *N Q K1 W*
Middlesbrough *p314* 01642 222575

Guest, Mrs A F (Alida Guest) *Zi M1 Zg*
London W11 *p37* 020 7727 6273

Guest, B S (Enoch Evans LLP) *C1 C2 E S1 S2 W B1 Zy Zl*
Walsall *p420* 01922 720333

Guest, D M (hlw Keeble Hawson LLP) *O B1 Q*
Sheffield *p376* 0114 276 5555

Guest, Miss G M (David Ake & Co) *G H D1 K1 Zg Zm*
Leeds *p271* 0113 244 8808

Guest, Miss H A E (Underwood Solicitors LLP) *W E T2 Zd S1 A1 C1 L R1 T1*
Westminster *p89* 020 7526 6000

Guest, Ms J (Harter & Loveless) *L Zg*
Islington *p39* 020 7688 2900

Guest, J A T (Guest & Co) *E T1 L R1 S2 W*
Cuckfield *p205* 01444 413731

Guest, J C (Guest Walker & Co) *A1 C1 E L S1 W*
York *p444* 01904 624903

Guest, J D (Churchers) *E S1 W C1 T1 L F1 S2 Zd*
Fareham *p223* 01329 822333

Guest, M A (Armitage & Guest) *K1 S1 W P M1 F1 E*
Wakefield *p418* 01924 371877

Guest, Ms N (Hethertons LLP) *N Q O L Zq*
York *p445* 01904 528200
Hull *p257* 01482 358850

Guest, N (Veale Wasbrough Vizards) *C1 C2*
Bristol *p165* 0117 925 2020

Guest, R (Plexus Law (A Trading Name of Parabis Law LLP)) *J1 J2 N Q*
London EC3 *p68* 0844 245 4000

Guest, R A (Societe Generale Asset Management) *C1*
London EC2 *p109* 020 7090 2500

Guest, R J T (Keene & Kelly) *C1 S2 K4 A1 W E S1 L*
Mold *p318* 01352 753882

Guest, Ms S (Fishburns) *Zc Zj O Q*
London EC3 *p32* 020 7280 8888

Guest, Mrs T J (SJP Solicitors) *J1*
Hunstanton *p258* 01485 532662

Guida, Ms M E F (Silverman Sherliker LLP) *E Zl R2 S1*
London EC2 *p78* 020 7749 2700

Guild, Prof E H (Kingsley Napley) *Zi Zg*
London EC1 *p50* 020 7814 1200

Guilfoyle, R T C (Guillaumes Solicitors) *E L R1 S1 T1 C1*
Weybridge *p430* 01932 840111

Guillen, J C (Gough Clinton & Broom) *N Q O J1*
Welling *p424* 020 8301 9000

Guinness, S N K (Sylvester Mackett) *C1*
Trowbridge *p414* 01225 755621

Guise, P J (Thomas Guise) *K1 S1 M1 F1 W J1 L V A1 Zl*
Worcester *p439* 01905 723131

Guit, R (Addleshaw Goddard)
London EC1 *p4* 020 7606 8855

Guiver, Ms J E (Rother District Council)
Bexhill *p449* 01424 787878

Gul, Miss Z S (City of Bradford Metropolitan District Council) *Zi S1 K1*
Bradford *p451* 01274 752236

Gulati, A K (A K Gulati & Co) *A3 D1 K1 L S1 W Zv D2 K3 K2 T2*
Sutton *p402* 020 8770 7979

Gulbenkian, B P (Gulbenkian Andonian Solicitors) *Zi*
London WC1 *p37* 020 7269 9590

Gull, Ms R (Massers) *Q J1*
Nottingham *p338* 0115 851 1666

Gulland, A B (Gullands) *E A1 Zd S1 W*
Maidstone *p299* 01622 678341

Gullett, A J (McManus Seddon) *Q N O Zq L*
Bradford *p154* 01274 741841

Gulliford, Miss L J (Thompsons (formerly Robin/Brian Thompson & Partners)) *Q K1 N J1*
Middlesbrough *p315* 01642 554162

Gulliver, B R (Brutton & Co) *S1 E S2*
Fareham *p223* 01329 236171

Gulliver, Mrs S A (Daniel Curry & Co) *D1 D2 K1*
Croydon *p205* 020 8680 2188
Ewell *p220* 020 8393 0941

Gulshan, Ms S E (Romain Coleman & Co) *N L Q*
Waltham Forest *p73* 020 8520 3322

Gumbrell, Mrs C M (Roythornes LLP) *A1 O F1 Q L Zl B1 R1 P Zq*
Spalding *p389* 01775 842500

Gummer, Mrs A J (DWF) *E R2 S2 L*
Manchester *p303* 0161 603 5000

Gummers, E M (Howard Kennedy LLP) *C1 C2 I M2 F1 Ze Zb*
London W1 *p48* 020 7636 1616

Gumpert, A (Jones Day) *E*
London EC4 *p46* 020 7039 5959

Gunaratnam, Mrs E (Laytons) *C1 C2 U2 Ze*
London EC4 *p52* 020 7842 8000

Gunby, I N (Ian N Gunby & Co) *S1 E W L*
Milnthorpe *p316* 01539 562044
Kendal *p264* 01539 721945

Gundry, C (Farnfield & Nicholls) *A1 C1 E S1*
Sturminster Newton *p401* . . 01258 474270

Gunn, A (Greenwoods Solicitors LLP) *C1 C2*
Peterborough *p347* 01733 887700

Gunn, B M (Crown Prosecution Service Derbyshire)
Derby *p456* 01332 614000

Gunn, Ms D E (Banner Jones) *K1 D1 K3*
Chesterfield *p191* 01246 209773

Gunn, N F (Mark Jones & Partners) *G H*
Birkenhead *p134* 0151 647 9594
Liverpool *p289* 0151 236 2224

Gunn, Miss N J (Anthony Gold) *K1 D1 K3*
London SW16 *p6* 020 7940 4000

Gunn, R M (Reed Smith LLP) *Za*
London EC2 *p71* 020 3116 3000

Gunnell, Ms J E (Blandy & Blandy) *E S2 R2 T1 F2*
Reading *p360* 0118 951 6800

Gunning, Miss C M (SGH Martineau LLP) *C1*
Birmingham *p142* 0870 763 2000

Gunning, Mrs E (Red Kite Law) *V L Q*
Haverfordwest *p244* 01437 763332

Gunson, M J (Bates Wells & Braithwaite London LLP) *E S2 R2 Zh L Zd*
London EC4 *p11* 020 7551 7777

Gunson, N P (Whiting & Mason) *S1 W L S2*
Marple *p313* 0161 427 1040

Gunston, W (Osborne Clarke) *Zb*
London EC2 *p65* 020 7105 7000

Guppy, Mrs E A (David Durn & Co) *K1 K3 D1*
Ruislip *p368* 01895 612400

Guppy, T (Pengillys LLP) *K1 P M1 D1 F1 G H Za*
Weymouth *p430* 01305 768888

Gupta, Ms A (Squire Sanders (UK) LLP) *E*
Leeds *p277* 0113 284 7000

Gupta, A S (Duncan Lewis & Co) *Zi G H K1 Q V L*
Hackney *p53* 020 7923 4020

Gupta, D (Clarkson Wright & Jakes Ltd) *E S2*
Orpington *p341* 01689 887887

Gupta, Mrs M (Breeze & Wyles Solicitors LLP)
Bishop's Stortford *p144* . . . 01279 715333

Gupta, R (Bankside Law Ltd) *B2 G Zq*
London SE1 *p9* 0844 745 4000

Gupta, R (LGFL LLP)
Yateley *p443* 01252 877327

Gupta, R (Clarke Willmott) *O*
Bristol *p162* 0845 209 1000 / 0117 305 6000

Gupta, Ms S (Glaisyers Solicitors LLP) *Zi Zg M1*
Manchester *p304* 0161 224 3311

Gupta, Ms S (Robert Lizar) *Zi*
Manchester *p307* 0161 226 2319

Gupta, S (Higgs & Sons) *C1 C2 Zb T1*
Brierley Hill *p158* 0845 111 5050

Gupwell, M J (Gregg Latchams LLP) *G J2 M2 O Q N*
Bristol *p162* 0117 906 9400

Gurluk, B (Heppenstalls) *S1*
Lymington *p296* 01590 689500

Gurluk, B (Heppenstalls) *S1*
Lyndhurst *p296* 023 8028 2885
London EC2 *p78* 020 7749 2700

Gurney, Miss L (Hertfordshire County Council)
Hertford *p460* 01992 555555

Gurney, Miss L F (Gurneys) *N Q K1 O K3 W*
Framlingham *p227* 01728 621372

Gurney-Champion, D R S (Field Fisher Waterhouse LLP) *C1 C2 C3*
London EC3 *p31* 020 7861 4000

Gurney-Champion, N C A (Gurney-Champion & Co) *E C1 S1 Q W K1 L S2 N T2 Zd Zq*
Newport *p328* 01983 522665
Portsmouth *p354* 023 9282 1100

Gurr, S (Lexica Law) *J1 Q S1*
Canterbury *p177* 01227 764141

Gurusinghe, Mrs S C K P (Gurusinghe & Co) *D1 E G H K1 L M1*
Wembley *p426* 020 8903 5349

Guse, V T H (Chandler Ray) *S1 W K1 E T1 A1 L C1 P G Zm Zc Zl*
Winslow *p435* . . . .01296 712204 / 712729

Guthberlet, Ms A (Murrays Partnership) *G H D1*
Southwark *p62* 020 7701 8653

Guthrie, D E (Ashby Family Law Practice) *K1 K3 D2*
Derby *p208* 01332 293293

Guthrie, G (Speechly Bircham LLP) *M2 C2 C1*
London EC4 *p81* 020 7427 6400

Gutteridge, N (Burnetts) *N*
Carlisle *p181* 01228 552222
Carlisle *p182* 01228 552222

Gutteridge, P R D (Hewitsons) *E C1 R1 S1 A1 Zc Zs*
Cambridge *p174* 01223 461155

Guttridge, R J (Blake Lapthorn)
London EC1 *p13* 020 7405 2000

Guy, C J (Basingstoke & Deane Borough Council)
Basingstoke *p448* 01256 845402

Guy, D J (W H Matthews & Co) *S1 S2 L*
Sutton *p402* 020 8642 6677

Guy, Mrs E M (Carter Bells LLP) *K1 Q D1 K3*
Kingston upon Thames *p267*. 020 8939 4000

Guy, M (Greenwoods) *N*
Bristol *p162* 0117 910 0200

Guy, R J (Eyre & Co) *E W S1 S2*
Birmingham *p138* 0121 784 4722

Guy, Ms S C (The Royal London Mutual Insurance Society Ltd)
London EC3 *p455* 020 7506 6500

Guy-Spratt, A M (Royal Borough of Kingston upon Thames)
Kingston upon Thames *p462*. 020 8546 2121

Guyatt, R D (Bond Pearce LLP) *E R1*
Bristol *p161* 0845 415 0000

Guyer, G H (George H Guyer)
Burnley *p169* 01282 773438

Guyer, M (Vickers & Co) *K1 D1 P J1 F1 L W*
Ealing *p89* . . . .020 8579 2559 / 8840 3999

See p634 for the Key to Work Categories

Gvero, R (Longmores) *Q O J1* Hertford *p248* 01992 300333

Gwenlan, S B (Bromleys Solicitors LLP) *D1 K1 D2* Ashton-under-Lyne *p120* 0161 330 6821

Gwilliam, Miss C J T (Jacklyn Dawson) *Q V L O B1 F1 F2 Zc Zq* Newport *p328* 01633 262952

Gwilliam, D J (LG Lawyers) London SE1 *p50* 020 7379 0000

Gwilliam, M J (Plexus Law (A Trading Name of Parabis Law LLP)) *N* London EC2 *p68* 020 7763 6103

Gwilliams, I (Ashurst LLP) London EC2 *p7* 020 7638 1111

Gwilliams, J E (DBL Talbots LLP) *S1* Kidderminster *p265* 01562 749910

Gwillim, D (Speechly Bircham LLP) *Zc Zq E* London EC4 *p81* 020 7427 6400

Gwinn, C H S L (Parker Bullen) *C1 C2 J1 Ze* Andover *p118* 01264 400500

Gwinnell, Ms L (Wansbroughs) *N* Melksham *p314* 01225 703222

Gwyn, Mrs L A (Elwyn Jones & Co) *K1 K2 L V W D1 S1* Bangor *p122* 01248 370224

Gwyn, S (Parry Davies Clwyd-Jones & Lloyd) *K1 D1 D2 W S1 R2 N O Q L* Llangefni *p292* 01248 723106

Gwynne, Ms A (Leo Abse & Cohen) *N* Cardiff *p179* 029 2038 3252 / 2034 5421

Gwynne, R (Stephenson Harwood) *Q A3* London EC2 *p82* 020 7329 4422

Gwynne, S (Linklaters LLP) London EC2 *p54* 020 7456 2000

Gwynne-Hughes, J D (Gwynne Hughes) *A1 S2 E S1 W K4 R1 R2* Aberaeron *p113* 01545 570861 New Quay *p321* 01545 560525

Gwynne-Hughes, J D (Gwynne Hughes) *W S1 S2 Q T2 A1 L Zv Zo Zr Zl* Aberaeron *p113* 01545 570861 New Quay *p321* 01545 560525

Gwyther, Ms K (TLT Solicitors) *K1 N Q G* Bristol *p165* 0117 917 7777

Gyamfi, S (Hanson Woods Solicitors) *N* Ilford *p260* 020 8590 9220

Gyasi, K (Brooke North LLP) *B1 O* Leeds *p272* 0113 283 2100

Gybels, E (Crowell & Moring) *C1* London EC4 *p23* 020 7413 0011

Gyles, Mrs N J (Stuckey Carr & Co) *S1 W S2 Zm* Pulborough *p358* 01798 875358

Gyngell, J (Bird & Bird LLP) *I Ze* London EC4 *p13* 020 7415 6000

Gyte, Ms M (Howells LLP) *Zr* Sheffield *p376* 0114 249 6666

H

Habergham, K J E (Andrew Jackson) *Za* Hull *p257* 01482 325242

Habershon, Ms H (Barlow Robbins LLP) *K1 M2* Godalming *p231* 01483 417121

Hachemi, M (Ison Harrison) Leeds *p274* 0113 284 5000

Hack, Miss A (TV Edwards LLP) *K1* London EC3 *p85* 020 7790 7000

Hack, Ms K (McGrigors LLP) London EC4 *p56* 020 7054 2500

Hackelsberger, R (Field Fisher Waterhouse LLP) London EC3 *p31* 020 7861 4000

Hackenbroch, M (Maurice Hackenbroch & Co) *G M1 N P K1* Edgware *p217* 020 8958 4000

Hacker, D A (Thackray Williams) Bromley *p167* 020 8290 0440

Hackett, A (Lupton Fawcett) Sheffield *p376* 0114 276 6607

Hackett, Miss E (Zatman & Co) *T1* Manchester *p311* 0161 832 2500

Hackett, Mrs J M (Tamworth Borough Council) Tamworth *p473* 01827 709258

Hackett, Ms K (The Wilkes Partnership LLP) *C1 J1 T1* Birmingham *p143* 0121 233 4333

Hackett, Miss M C (MFG Solicitors) Bromsgrove *p167* 01527 831691

Hackett, Ms N (Family Law in Partnership LLP) *K1 K2* London WC2 *p30* 020 7420 5000

Hackett, S B (DWF) *N Q Zj* Preston *p356* 01772 556677

Hackett, T G (J A Hughes) *G H D1 J1 K1 L N* Barry *p126* 01446 411000

Hackfath, M R (E C Lidster & Co) *H G* Grimsby *p235* 01472 348417

Hacking, H M (Geldards LLP) *Q O J1* Nottingham *p337* 0115 983 3650

Hacking, Mrs K (Gateley LLP) *Zb B1 O* Birmingham *p138* 0121 234 0000

Hacking, S M (DWF) *C1 C2* Manchester *p303* 0161 603 5000

Hackney, Ms C B (Eddowes Waldron) *J1 J2 N Q* Derby *p208* 01332 348484

Hackney, C P (Geldards LLP) *N O Zq* Derby *p208* 01332 331631

Hackney, Mrs D F (Nowell Meller Solicitors Limited) *S2 E S1* Stafford *p393* 01785 252377

Hackney, P A (Stoke-on-Trent City Council) Stoke-on-Trent *p472* 01782 234567

Haddadi, L (Farrell Matthews & Weir) London W6 *p31* 020 8741 1482

Hadden, J M (British Telecommunications PLC) London EC1 *p104* 020 7356 6181

Hadden, M M M (Simmons & Simmons) London EC2 *p79* 020 7628 2020

Haddleton, R J (Gowlings) *Q K1 D1 R1 F1 Zl B1 Ze K3 J1 P N* Preston *p357* 01772 251287

Haddock, C (Haddock & Company) Halifax *p238* 01422 366010

Haddock, J K (First Assist) Sutton *p473* 020 8652 1313

Haddock, S A (Allen & Overy LLP) London E1 *p5* 020 3088 0000

Haddon, N R C (SAS Daniels LLP) *Zc* Stockport *p396* 0161 475 7676

Haddon, P (Hill Dickinson LLP) London EC3 *p41* 020 7283 9033

Haddow, C (Saunders Law Partnership LLP) *G H* London WC2 *p76* 020 7632 4300

Haddow, J C (Forbes) *W S1 T1 R1 L A1 E Zm* Blackburn *p145* 01254 54374

Hadfield, A (Jones & Co) Bawtry *p128* 01302 710555 Retford *p363* 01777 703827

Hadfield, Ms C (Leech & Co) *N* Manchester *p306* 0161 279 0279

Hadfield, C G (Nichols Marcy Dawson) *S1 E W* Walton-on-Thames *p420* 01932 219500

Hadfield, D W (Hextalls) *P M1 N L Zj* London EC2 *p41* 020 7382 0700

Hadfield, M T (Hadfield & Co) *C1 Q E S1 W I F1 T1 T2 Zc Zd* Welling *p424* 020 8301 0808

Hadida, Mrs S (Tandridge District Council) Oxted *p468* 01883 722000

Hadida, V F (Thomas Dunton Solicitors) *A3 Q N O F1 F2 J1 K1 B1 C1 W Ze Zk* Orpington *p342* 01689 822554

Hadley, Ms A L (British Medical Association) London WC1 *p104* 020 7387 4499

Hadley, D S (Dudley Metropolitan Borough Council) Dudley *p457* 01384 815326

Hadley, J (The Wilkes Partnership LLP) *S1 W* Birmingham *p143* 0121 233 4333

Hadley, J (Shoosmiths) Fareham *p224* 0370 086 6800 / 01489 616800

Hadley, Miss K M (Irwin Mitchell LLP) *N* Sheffield *p376* 0870 150 0100

Hadley, M B (VHS Fletchers Solicitors) *G H* Nottingham *p339* 0115 959 9550

Hadley, N M (CMS Cameron McKenna LLP) London EC3 *p17* 020 7367 3000

Hadley, R J J (Dyne Drewett Solicitors Ltd) *W K4* Shepton Mallet *p378* 01749 342323

Hadley, R V (K&L Gates LLP) *O J1 Zk Zc* London EC4 *p47* 020 7648 9000

Hadley, S W (KJD) *O* Stoke-on-Trent *p398* 01782 202020

Hadley-Piggin, J M (Ashfords LLP) Exeter *p220* 01392 337000

Hadlow, S (Shammah Nicholls LLP) *C1 C2 C3* Manchester *p309* 0161 832 9272

Hado, Miss A (Richard Pearlman LLP) *E L S1 W R1 A1* London EC2 *p66* 020 7739 6100

Hadwick, Ms L (Michelmores LLP) *E L* Exeter *p221* 01392 688688

Hadzik, Miss L (Aaron & Partners LLP Solicitors) *J1 Zt G H* Chester *p190* 01244 405555

Hafezi, N (Robert Lizar) *L Zi* Manchester *p307* 0161 226 2319

Haffenden, K (Bennett Griffin) *K4 T2 W* Ferring *p225* 01903 229999

Haffner, A N (Zatman & Co) *B1 O Q Zq* Manchester *p311* 0161 832 2500

Hafiaz, M (Leeds Day) *E L N Q* Huntingdon *p258* 01480 454301

Hagan, J A (Harris Hagan) London EC1 *p39* 020 7002 7636

Hagan, P (Ashurst LLP) London EC2 *p7* 020 7638 1111

Hagerty, M G (Brighouse Wolff) *G H N F1 K1 D1 Q J1 Zl Zm* Skelmersdale *p381* 01695 722577

Hagerty-Cross, Ms S (Walker Morris) Leeds *p277* 0113 283 2500

Hagestadt, Ms C L (EEF) London SW1 *p106* 020 7222 7777

Haggar, T (Red Kite Law) *K1* Pembroke *p345* 01646 683222

Haggard, Ms S L (Davenport Lyons) *E R2* London W1 *p25* 020 7468 2600

Hagger, R O (Robert Hagger & Co) Tunbridge Wells *p415* 01892 515795

Haggerty, K (Elmhirst Parker LLP) *H G N S1* Selby *p374* 01757 703895

Haggett, P S N (Burges Salmon) *O B1 Zb Zj* Bristol *p161* 0117 939 2000

Haggett, R W (The College of Law Chester) *O Q N Zq* Chester *p454* 0800 289997

Haggie, T J (Latimer Hinks) *A1 B1 C1 E L R1 S1 T1 W Zn* Darlington *p206* 01325 341500

Hagley, Ms J K (Avon & Somerset Constabulary) Portishead *p469* 01275 816270

Hagopian, Ms S N (Gregsons) *G H* London SW19 *p37* 020 8946 1173

Hagyard, M A (Waddington Webber) *D1 F1 G H J1 K1 N Q W* Keighley *p264* 01535 662644 / 662647

Hahlo, Ms F (Reynolds Porter Chamberlain LLP) London E1 *p71* 020 3060 6000

Hahn, E M (Morrison & Foerster (UK) LLP) *Zb* London EC2 *p62* 020 7920 4000

Haider, A K (Harris Cartier LLP) *N* Slough *p382* 01753 810710

Haider, S (Haider Kennedy Legal Services Ltd) London SE25 *p37* 020 8771 2323

Haidermota, T (Blake Lapthorn) Oxford *p342* 01865 248607

Haig, R A (Martin Adams & McColl) *S1 E N D1 K1 W J1 T1 L Zl K3 K4* Northampton *p332* 01604 634123

Haig, R M (Chafes) *A1 E* Wilmslow *p433* 01625 531676

Haigh, Ms C (LG Lawyers) London SE1 *p50* 020 7379 0000

Haigh, Mrs C (Meikles) *K3 K1 G H S1* Barnard Castle *p123* 01833 690505

Haigh, G (Molesworths Bright Clegg) *G H Zi* Rochdale *p365* 01706 356666

Haigh, G M (KieranClarkeGreen) *G H D1* Chesterfield *p192* 01246 211006

Haigh, J (Shammah Nicholls LLP) *O Q J1* Manchester *p309* 0161 832 9272

Haigh, Mrs J A (Crown Prosecution Service Durham) *K1 G H D1 M1 W F1* Durham *p457* 0191 383 5800

Haigh, Mrs J E (Cockertons) *W S1 K4 S2 E A1* Bakewell *p121* 01629 812613

Haigh, J S (Hempsons) *S1 E L W C1* Harrogate *p240* 01423 522331

Haigh, M A (Alexander Haigh & Co) *K1 D1 G H S1 K3* Brentwood *p156* 01277 216320

Haigh, R S F (Atteys) *G H* Doncaster *p211* 01302 340400

Haigh, S (Punch Robson) *E S1 S2 C1* Middlesbrough *p315* 01642 230700

Hailey, Mrs E A (Barlow Robbins LLP) *E S2 S1* Woking *p436* 01483 748500

Hailey, Miss J A (Coltman Warner Cranston LLP) *F1 Zc O Q Zq* Coventry *p200* 024 7662 7262

Hails-Smith, P (Joelson Wilson LLP) *C1 C2 U2 I* Westminster *p46* 020 7580 5721

Haine, Miss R (BTMK Solicitors LLP) *K1 K3 D1* Southend-on-Sea *p387* 01702 339222

Haines, A (Osborne Clarke) *U1 U2* London EC2 *p65* 020 7105 7000

Haines, Miss A C M (Allen & Overy LLP) London E1 *p5* 020 3088 0000

Haines, A J (Andrew Jackson) *K1 D1 M1 W Zi* Hull *p257* 01482 325242

Haines, D K (Charles Russell LLP) *O Q Zl* Guildford *p235* 01483 252525

Haines, D O (Wrigley Claydon) *A1 W E S1 Zh* Oldham *p341* 0161 624 6811

Haines, Mrs H F (Taylor Walton LLP) *K1 K2 D1* St Albans *p390* 01727 845245

Haines, J (Ashurst LLP) London EC2 *p7* 020 7638 1111

Haines, Miss J M (Mills & Reeve) *O N* Birmingham *p140* 0121 454 4000

Haines, Mrs J M (Lloyds & Cooper) *S1 W L S2* Leominster *p283* 01568 613236

Haines, K P J (Fendom Dawson & Partners) *E F1 K1 L R1 S1 T1 W* High Wycombe *p250* 01494 450361

Haines, L J (Simmons & Simmons) *Ze* London EC2 *p79* 020 7628 2020

Haines, Mrs P (Larby Williams with Gwyn & Gwyn) *S1 K4 W* Cowbridge *p201* 01446 775535

Haines, P H (Adrian Stables) *N O Q* Somerton *p383* 0845 873 6180

Haines, S (Imperial Tobacco Group PLC) Bristol *p452* 0117 963 6636

Haines, Mrs S (Lionel Blackman) Epsom *p219* 01372 728941

Haines, T P (VHS Fletchers Solicitors) Nottingham *p339* 0115 959 9550

Hains, Miss V H (Hains & Lewis Ltd) *D1 K1 Q A1 W G S1 N F1 L Zl Zq* Haverfordwest *p244* 0845 408 0125

Hainsworth, M J (SJ Berwin LLP) *T1 I* London EC4 *p75* 020 7111 2222

Hair, M J (Davitt Jones Bould) *E S2 R1 P L* Taunton *p408* 01823 279279

Hairsine, R I (HWP Limited) *W T2* Hull *p257* 01482 629295

Hajek, S P J (Clutton Cox Solicitors) *E S1 W L* Chipping Sodbury *p193* 01454 312125

Hakes, A (Hamers Solicitors) *E* Hull *p257* 01482 326666

Hakim, M A (Wilson Barca LLP) *S2 S1 E C1 R2 W* London W1 *p92* 020 7272 2072

Halberstam, J (Fisher Meredith) *S1 S2 E* Lambeth *p32* 020 7091 2700

Haldane, Ms L K (Royal Mail Group) London EC4 *p109* 020 7250 2468

Haldane, R D (Taylor Haldane Barlex LLP) *G H* Chelmsford *p187* 0845 293 7688

Haldane, R M J (Stephenson Harwood) *C1* London EC2 *p82* 020 7329 4422

Hale, A (Herbert Smith LLP) London EC2 *p40* 020 7374 8000

Hale, A T W (Inghams) *C1 E F1 G H J1 K1 L M1 N* Knott-End-on-Sea *p269* 01253 810547 Poulton-le-Fylde *p355* 01253 890545

Hale, C G (Travers Smith LLP) *C1 C2* London EC1 *p87* 020 7295 3000

Hale, G K E (Persimmon Homes Legal Department) York *p477* 01904 642199

Hale, I R (French & Co) *N Q O X V L W* Nottingham *p337* 0115 955 1111

Hale, Ms K (Williams Gorman LLP) Haringey *p91*

Hale, Mrs K (Tayntons LLP Solicitors) Gloucester *p230* 01452 522047

Hale, Ms K R (Kirby Sheppard) *K3 K1 D1* Thornbury *p411* 0845 840 0045

Hale, Miss N (Youngs Criminal Defence Services Limited) *G H* Sheffield *p377* 0114 249 5444

Hale, N P (Cheltenham & Gloucester PLC) *O Q B1 Zb* Gloucester *p459* 01452 372372

Hale, P D (Simmons & Simmons) London EC2 *p79* 020 7628 2020

Hale, R A (Whittuck Taylor & Caines) *S1 W E C1 L A1 R1* Keynsham *p265* 0117 986 3504

Hale, S P (Ellis-Fermor & Negus) *N J1 Q Zl* Beeston *p130* 0115 922 1591

Hale-Burt, Ms C (David Gray Solicitors) *Zi* Newcastle upon Tyne *p324* 0191 232 9547

Hales, C (Recompense Solicitors Ltd) *N* Totnes *p413* 0800 037 5817

Hales, Ms C A (Eastleys) *N* Paignton *p345* 01803 559257

Hales, J S (Bond Pearce LLP) *J1 O* Southampton *p385* 0845 415 0000

Hales, J S F (Kenwright & Lynch) *D1 G H K1 L M1 P F1* Wandsworth *p49* 020 8767 1211

Hales, Ms L J I (Bishop & Sewell LLP) *S1 L K1 O J1 C1 W* London WC1 *p13* 020 7631 4141 Reading *p360* 0118 951 6800

Hales, M G (Nabarro LLP) London WC1 *p63* 020 7524 6000

Hales, T (Hodge Jones & Allen LLP) *K1 K2 D1 K3* London NW1 *p41* 020 7874 8300

Halevy, Ms T (Lewis Silkin LLP) *O Q C1 Zq A3 Zg F1* London EC4 *p53* 020 7074 8000

Haley, Miss B M (Marsden Rawsthorn LLP) *C1 E C2 O* Preston *p357* 01772 799600

Haley, D (Preston Borough Council) Preston *p469* 01772 906101

Haley, Ms E (Stone King LLP) *N* Bath *p128* 01225 337599

Haley, Ms E J (Boodle Hatfield) *T2 W* Westminster *p14* 020 7629 7411

Haley, J A (Just Employment) *J1 N Zp C1 T2 J2* Guildford *p236* 01483 303636

Halford, J (Bindmans LLP) London WC1 *p12* 020 7833 4433

Halford, Miss S (Stevens) *D1 K1 D2* Haverhill *p244* 01440 762511

Halil, A H (Pearson Maddin Solicitors) New Malden *p321* 020 8949 9500

Halim, Miss T L (JP Morgan Chase Bank) London EC2 *p107* 020 7777 2000

Hall, A (Grahame Stowe Bateson) *K4 K1 N Zm* Leeds *p274* 0113 276 0044

Hall, A (Alan Hall) *C1 D1 E K1 L M1 P S1 T1* Gateshead *p228* 0191 477 7224

Hall, Ms A (Howarth Scott) *K1* Bexleyheath *p132* 020 8303 4658

Hall, A (Blair Allison & Co) *D1 K1 N* Birmingham *p135* 0121 233 2904

Hall, A (Walker Morris) Leeds *p277* 0113 283 2500

Hall, Ms A (Edmondson Hall) *C1 E J1 S1 W Zd Zl* Newmarket *p327* 01638 560556

Hall, Ms A (Norton Peskett) Great Yarmouth *p234* 01493 849200

Hall, A J (Veale Wasbrough Vizards) *C1* London EC4 *p89* 020 7405 1234

Hall, A J (Birmingham City Council Legal & Democratic Services) Birmingham *p449* 0121 303 2066

Hall, A J (Nowell Meller Solicitors Limited) *K1 K3* Stafford *p393* 01785 252377

Hall, A L (Jackson & Co) *S1 W S2* Lutterworth *p296* 01455 556321

Hall, Miss A M (Ward Gethin) *S1* King's Lynn *p266* 01553 660033

Hall, A M (Mincoffs Solicitors LLP) *C1* Newcastle upon Tyne *p325* 0191 281 6151

Hall, A N (Universal Pictures International Ltd) London WC1 *p110* 020 7079 6000

Hall, A P (George Davies Solicitors LLP) *W T2* Manchester *p303* 0161 236 8992

Hall, B (Clifford Chance) London E14 *p20* 020 7006 1000

Hall, B A (Woodfines LLP) *E L R1 S1 P S2 B1 A1 Zc Zd Zl Zs* Sandy *p372* 01767 680251

Hall, B J C (Laytons) *T2 Zd T1 K1 Zm* London EC4 *p52* 020 7842 8000

6

Hall, B W (Forbes Hall LLP) S1 K4 W Zm T2
London EC2 p33 020 7729 9111
Woodford Green p439 020 8498 0080

Hall, C (Royds LLP) V T2 T1
London EC4 p74 020 7583 2222

Hall, Ms C (Winckworth Sherwood LLP) D1 D2 S1 W
London SE1 p92 020 7593 5000

Hall, Ms C A (Hadaway & Hadaway) K1 D1 D2 G H
North Shields p330 0191 257 0382

Hall, C D K (Mercers) W T2 Zd A1
Henley-on-Thames p247 01491 572138

Hall, C G (Brockbank Curwen Cain & Hall) S1 L G K1 W S2 F1
Maryport p313 01900 813488

Hall, C I J (Stanley H Cross & Co) K1 N D1 G H J1 F1 Zk Zl W
Chorley p194 01257 272222

Hall, Mrs C J (Brough Hall & Co) B1 C1 F1 F2 J1 K1 L Zl O Q N S1 K3 W D1
Skegness p380 01754 768641
Alford p115 01507 462882
Sutton-on-Sea p404 01507 443043

Hall, C M (Norman Saville & Co) N O Q J1 Zq Zc Zj Zk F1 K1 K3
London N10 p76 020 8883 9711

Hall, C S (Knights) A1 A2 W Zw Zd S1
Tunbridge Wells p415 01892 537311

Hall, D (McMillan Williams) W
Carshalton p183 020 8432 2041

Hall, Miss D (Cooper Sons Hartley & Williams) N Q L J1
Buxton p172 01298 77511

Hall, Miss D (Clark Willis) L Zh Q
Darlington p206 01325 281111

Hall, D A (Sedgefield Borough Council)
Spennymoor p472 01388 816166

Hall, D C (Hall Reynolds) C1 E B1 J1 O Q S1 Zv W C2 F1 L
Bidford-on-Avon p133 01789 772955

Hall, D F (Andrew Jackson) Za
Hull p257 01482 325242

Hall, D I J (Anthony Collins Solicitors LLP) C1 E Ze
Birmingham p137 0121 200 3242

Hall, D N (Tustain Jones & Co)
Nuneaton p339 024 7664 1222

Hall, Mrs E H (Dickson Haslam) W S1
Lytham p296 01253 730111

Hall, Ms E L (Hodge Jones & Allen LLP) D1 K1
London NW1 p41 020 7874 8300

Hall, Mrs E L C (United Utilities)
Warrington p475 01925 237000

Hall, Mrs G (Pepperells) D1 K3
Scunthorpe p373 01724 871999

Hall, Miss G (Kelcey & Hall) K1 D1 D2
Bristol p163 0117 927 9604

Hall, G C (Darbys Solicitors LLP) W T2 Zd
Oxford p343 01865 811700

Hall, G L (Rothwell & Evans) K1 Q
Swinton p407 0161 794 1830

Hall, Ms G M (Watson Burton LLP) C1 B1 J1 E N T1 F1 M1 Zb Ze Zd
Newcastle upon Tyne p327 0845 901 2100

Hall, G N (Devonshires) U2 C1 I Zh
London EC2 p27 020 7628 7576

Hall, G P (Radcliffes Le Brasseur) Q Zc Zj Zq
Westminster p70 020 7222 7040

Hall, Ms G R (Prettys) K1 K2 K3
Ipswich p262 01473 232121

Hall, Ms H (DLA Piper UK LLP)
Manchester p303 0870 011 1111

Hall, Mrs H A (Colemans - CTTS) O Q
Manchester p302 0161 876 2500

Hall, I T (Hall & Co)
Warrington p422 01925 245858

Hall, Ms J (Graysons) N
Sheffield p375 0114 272 9184

Hall, J (Patchell Davies (Trading Name of PD Law Ltd)) K3 K1 G
Blackwood p147 01495 227128

Hall, J B (TBI Solicitors) N O L J1 F1 V B1 Zc Zj
Hartlepool p243 0800 052 6824 / 01429 264101

Hall, Mrs J C (David Gray Solicitors) G H B2 Zg
Newcastle upon Tyne p324 0191 232 9547

Hall, J C (Mander Hadley & Co) G H M1
Coventry p200 024 7663 1212

Hall, J E (CMS Cameron McKenna LLP)
London EC3 p17 020 7367 3000

Hall, J J F (Foot Anstey) W T2
Exeter p221 01392 411221

Hall, J J F (Gill Akaster) K4 T2 W
Plymouth p349 01752 203500

Hall, Miss J M (Tosswill & Co) G H
Lambeth p87 020 8674 9494

Hall, Mrs J M (Christies International PLC)
London SW1 p105 020 7839 9060

Hall, J M (Taylor Wessing)
London EC4 p86 020 7300 7000

Hall, J N (Thompsons (formerly Robin/Brian Thompson & Partners)) N J1
Southampton p387 023 8021 2040

Hall, J P (Gordons LLP)
Leeds p273 0113 227 0100

Hall, J S (Birketts LLP) E Zd Zx S1
Ipswich p262 01473 232300

Hall, J S (Behr & Co) K1 K3 D1 Q
Brynmawr p167 01495 310581

Hall, Mrs K (DLA Piper UK LLP) R1
Leeds p272 0870 011 1111

Hall, Mrs K E A (Harvey Ingram LLP) E S1 L
Leicester p280 0116 254 5454

Hall, K G (Southern Water Services Ltd)
Worthing p477 01903 264444

Hall, Ms K J (Lovats)
Brentwood p451 01277 263081

Hall, Miss L (Russell-Cooke LLP) K3 K1 M2
Kingston upon Thames p267 020 8546 6111

Hall, Miss L (Newcastle Under Lyme Borough Council)
Newcastle Under Lyme p466 01782 717717

Hall, Miss L (Gill Akaster) S1 S2
Plymouth p349 01752 203500

Hall, Ms L J (Burnetts) Zr
Carlisle p181 01228 552222
Carlisle p182 01228 552222

Hall, M (Sternberg Reed) L
Barking p123 020 8591 3366

Hall, M (Russells) Ze Zf
London W1 p75 020 7439 8692

Hall, M E (Millichips) K1 G H Q Zl
West Bromwich p427 0121 500 6363

Hall, M F (Cleggs) C1 I Ze Zza U2 C2
Nottingham p336 0115 977 5877
Nottingham p338 0115 851 1666

Hall, M J (Citi Financial Europe PLC)
London E14 p469

Hall, M R (The Owen-Kenny Partnership) S1 W E L
Bognor Regis p148 01243 864865
Chichester p193 01243 532777

Hall, N (Hewitsons) J1
Northampton p332 01604 233233

Hall, N A J (TBI Solicitors)
Hartlepool p243 0800 052 6824 / 01429 264101

Hall, N C D (Black Rock)
London EC4 p104 020 7743 3000

Hall, N J (Layzells) S1 W E N O B1
London N10 p52 020 8444 0202

Hall, N J (J Keith Park & Co) D1 K1 N Q
St Helens p391 01744 636000

Hall, N J (Ralph & Co) R1 O Q L G Zc Zl Zv
Newquay p329 01637 872218

Hall, Ms N J (Robert Lizar) G H
Manchester p307 0161 226 2319

Hall, Ms P (Michelmores LLP) K1
Exeter p221 01392 688688

Hall, Ms P (Clarke Willmott) Zc
Bristol p162 0845 209 1000 / 0117 305 6000

Hall, P A (Anthony Collins Solicitors LLP) N Zm
Birmingham p137 0121 200 3242

Hall, Mrs P A (Mayo Wynne Baxter LLP) L R1 S1 W
Eastbourne p215 01323 730543

Hall, P A (Chiltern District Council)
Amersham p447 01494 729000

Hall, P A (Hart Jackson Hall Smith) C1 S1 E W L A1 Zf
Newcastle upon Tyne p325 0191 261 5181

Hall, P D (Ross Solicitors Ltd) G H
Swindon p406 01793 512960

Hall, Mrs P J R (Butler Hall & Co) C1 E S1 S2 W
Birmingham p136 0121 456 3171

Hall, Ms P M (Burnetts) O Q Zq
Carlisle p181 01228 552222
Carlisle p182 01228 552222

Hall, Miss P M (Alderson Dodds) G H
Blyth p147 01670 352293

Hall, P N (Monro Fisher Wasbrough LLP)
London WC1 p61 020 7404 7001

Hall, R (Terry Jones Solicitors & Advocates) E S1
Shrewsbury p379 01743 285888

Hall, R (Penningtons) Zr N
Godalming p231 01483 791800

Hall, R (Crown Prosecution Service Dorset)
Bournemouth p450 01202 498700

Hall, R A (Aldridge Brownlee Solicitors LLP) W T1
Bournemouth p151 01202 527008

Hall, Mrs R H (Walker & Co) N G H
Rotherham p367 01709 817112

Hall, Mrs R L (Coupe Bradbury) K1 Zl
Lytham p296 01253 736670

Hall, R M (Michael Hall) W S1 N E
Letchworth p283 01462 674767

Hall, R W E (Roebucks) E S1 S2 A1 R1 Zx R2
Blackburn p145 01254 274000
Blackburn p145 01254 503070

Hall, Mrs S (Debenhams Ottaway) D1 K1 K3
St Albans p390 01727 837161

Hall, Ms S (Trowers & Hamlins)
London EC3 p88 020 7423 8000

Hall, Mrs S (Beetenson & Gibbon) K1 Q
Grimsby p235 01472 240251

Hall, Ms S (Boodle Hatfield)
Westminster p14 020 7629 7411

Hall, Miss S (Bristows) C1 C2
London EC4 p15 020 7400 8000

Hall, Miss S (Farleys Solicitors LLP) G H B2
Blackburn p145 01254 367855
Blackburn p145 01254 367854

Hall, Miss S (McClure Naismith)
London EC4 p56 020 7623 9155

Hall, S (Barlow Lyde & Gilbert LLP) O Q Zj Zq
London EC3 p10 020 7247 2277

Hall, Ms S (Devonshires) R2 E S2 L Zh
London EC2 p27 020 7628 7576

Hall, Ms S E (Hewitsons) E S2 U1
Cambridge p174 01223 461155

Hall, Mrs S J (Michael Salt) G H
Rochdale p365 01706 646655

Hall, S J (Mayo Wynne Baxter LLP) Q O C1 D1 K1 W Zd Zj Zl
Brighton p160 01273 775533

Hall, T (Taylor Vinters) Zc
Cambridge p176 01223 423444

Hall, T (Reynolds Porter Chamberlain LLP)
London E1 p71 020 3060 6000

Hall, T D O (Furley Page LLP) L O Zl
Canterbury p176 01227 763939

Hall, Mrs T J (Coles Miller Solicitors LLP) K1
Bournemouth p151 01202 511512

Hall, Mrs V (BBC)
London W12 p103 020 8752 5734

Hall, Ms V (ClarksLegal LLP) J1
Cardiff p177 029 2055 7500

Hall, W (Mills & Reeve) C1 M1 Zu F1 Zc
Birmingham p140 0121 454 4000

Hall-Paterson, K (Patersons Solicitors)
Bolton p149 01204 308889

Hall-Paterson, W (Patersons Solicitors) Zr
Bolton p149 01204 308889

Halladay, S (DLA Piper UK LLP) B1
London EC2 p24 0870 011 1111

Hallam, Mrs A J (Essex County Council)
Chelmsford p454 0845 743 0430

Hallam, Miss A R (BRM Solicitors) C1 J1 O
Chesterfield p191 01246 555111

Hallam, Miss C M (Burges Salmon) K1 A1 T2
Bristol p161 0117 939 2000

Hallam, D C (Hethertons LLP) A1 S2 E L S1
Boroughbridge p150 01423 322940

Hallam, D C (Henry Hyams) G H N S1 E L Zi Zl
Leeds p274 0113 243 2288

Hallam, D E (Collier Littler)
Altrincham p116 0161 980 6046

Hallam, F (Wilsons) Zq Q O N Zj E F1 F2
Horsforth p253 0113 258 6888

Hallam, J A (Sharp & Partners) S1 E A1 C1 T1 L Zp
Nottingham p339 0115 959 0055

Hallam, Miss L (Bedfordshire County Council)
Bedford p448 01234 363222

Hallam, M (Withers LLP) T2 W Zd Zi Zo
London EC4 p92 020 7597 6000

Hallam, M C (DLA Piper UK LLP) E R2 S2
Manchester p303 0870 011 1111

Hallam, M J (Howards) E S1 L C1 T1 W F1 P J1 R1
London NW6 p43 020 7328 1947

Hallam, O L H (Wrigleys Solicitors LLP) W T2 K4
Leeds p278 0113 244 6100

Hallam, Mrs P (Cattles PLC)
Batley p448 01924 444466

Hallam, R H (Turbervilles) W C1 E S1 T1
Uxbridge p417 01895 231311

Hallam, R L (Hogan Lovells International LLP)
London EC1 p42 020 7296 2000

Hallam, R S (Claude Hornby & Cox) G H B2
London EC4 p20 020 7332 8269

Hallam, S (Savage Crangle)
Skipton p381 01756 794611

Hallam, S H (CMS Cameron McKenna LLP)
London EC3 p17 020 7367 3000

Hallam, T G (Russell Jones & Walker)
London WC2 p74 020 7657 1555

Hallam-Peel, D A (Hallam-Peel & Co) K1 L N B1 F1 J1 O Q
London WC2 p38 020 3006 1661

Hallatt, Ms D (DAC Beachcroft)
Leeds p272 0113 251 4700

Hallatt, F D (Lloyds TSB Asset Finance Division Ltd)
Southampton p450 01489 776880

Hallchurch, N C (Oliver D'Sa Solicitors) G H L Zm
Leicester p279 0116 275 5549

Hallchurch, N W (B P Collins LLP) O P L B1 N Q Zb Zc Ze Zj Zk
Gerrards Cross p229 01753 889995

Hallen, D A (A H Brooks & Co) K1 D1 D2 S1 Q V W
Leek p278 01538 383201

Hallen, M S (Hallens Solicitors) J1 Q Zp
Hounslow p253 020 8622 3729

Haller, S M (DLA Piper UK LLP) Zc Za
London EC2 p24 0870 011 1111

Hallett, Ms A M (Risdon Hosegood) K1 D1 F1 V J2 K2
Williton p433 01984 632277

Hallett, J (Kenneth Bush) T1 W
King's Lynn p266 01553 692233

Hallett, Miss L (Marsden Rawsthorn LLP) Zc E O Q
Preston p357 01772 799600

Hallett, T (Henmans LLP) N
Oxford p343 01865 781000

Halliday, D N (Fairchild Greig) S1 W E C1 R1 L
London W3 p30 020 8993 6886

Halliday, G P (Graham Halliday & Co) K1 L S1
London N12 p38 020 8445 4071

Halliday, J G T (Foreman Laws) E Zc Zh R2
Hitchin p251 01462 458711

Halliday, M D (Halliday Reeves) G H S1 D1 K1 Zv
Gateshead p228 0191 477 7728

Halliday, N (Straw & Pearce)
Loughborough p293 01509 268931

Halliday, S G (Rowberrys) E J1 S1 C1 W Q C2 K1 L Zc S2 R2
Crowthorne p204 01344 775311

Halliday, T (The Eric Whitehead Partnership) K1 S1 G H W J1 V Q N L
Cheadle p185 01538 755761

Hallifax, Ms R E M (Kidd Rapinet) E S1 W
London WC2 p49 020 7205 2115

Halligan, Miss J P (Pilkington PLC)
St Helens p472 01744 28882

Halligan, Mrs S M (Henriques Griffiths) K1 V W
Bristol p163 0117 909 4000

Hallinan, L E L (Robertsons) F1 J1 N O Q
Cardiff p180 029 2023 7777

Hallinan, P J (Grant Argent & Co) S1 S2 E W L Zb R1
Brent p7 020 8452 7651

Halling, M (Forsters LLP) E
Westminster p33 020 7863 8333

Halling-Brown, Ms R J (Mowbray Woodwards Solicitors) W
Bath p128 01225 485700

Halliwell, J J (John J Halliwell & Co) S1 W G H E K1 M1 T1 L D1 Zm Zj
Silsden p380 01535 653094

Halliwell, Ms T (Jeffrey Green Russell) C1 J1 Zd Zl
London W1 p46 020 7339 7000

Halliwell, T M (Gabbs LLP) S1 A1 E C1 W K1 M1 N G Ze Zl
Leominster p282 01568 616333

Hallmark, Ms A (The Watson Ramsbottom Partnership)
Blackburn p146 01254 672222

Hallmark, D J S (Hallmark Hulme) A1 C1 G N P R1
Worcester p439 01905 726600

Hallmark, Mrs R (Roythornes LLP) E A1
Spalding p389 01775 842500

Hallott, R (Anthony Collins Solicitors LLP) E S2 R2 Zh L
Birmingham p137 0121 200 3242

Hallows, J (Finers Stephens Innocent LLP) Zc E J2
London W1 p32 020 7323 4000

Hallows, Ms J R (Squire Sanders (UK) LLP)
Leeds p277 0113 284 7000

Hallows, R C (Hallows Associates) A1 B1 C1 E F1 J1 L N Zl Zt S2 Zc F2 O Q
Mold p318 01352 752773 / 758603 / 0800 525696

Halls, Mrs E N J (Sharp & Partners) B1 F1 G J1 K1 L M1 N P Ze Zj Zk
Nottingham p339 0115 959 0055

Hallsworth, C C (Woodfines LLP) G Zt Zl
Milton Keynes p317 01908 202150

Hallworth, Mrs A (Hayes & Storr) N J1
Fakenham p223 01328 863231

Hallworth, Miss A F (Warwickshire County Council)
Warwick p475 01926 410410

Halnan, Ms P A (Treasury Solicitors Department)
London WC2 p110 020 7210 3000

Halon, G M (Antony Hodari & Co) N
Manchester p305 0161 832 4781

Halperin, Ms C (Russell Jones & Walker)
London WC2 p74 020 7657 1555

Halperin, C J S (GSC Solicitors) C1 U1 F1 Ze Zf C2 J1
London EC1 p34 020 7822 2222

Halpern, D J (Platt Halpern) L N
Manchester p308 0161 224 2555
Manchester p309 0161 834 3114

Halpern, D M (Lambe Corner) S2 E C1 J1 B1 S1 Zc Q L O T1
Hereford p248 01432 355301

Halpin, Ms E C (GCA Solicitors (Giffen Couch & Archer)) C1 J1 L R2 S1 F1
Luton p295 01582 410041

Halsall, D A (Halsall David PLC)
Fleetwood p458 01253 778888

Halsall, Mrs D J (Hill Dickinson LLP) E R2 S2 L
Liverpool p288 0151 600 8000

Halsall, G D (DWF) Zb S2 E Zh L R2
Liverpool p287 0151 907 3000

Halsall, M (Stockport Metropolitan Borough Council)
Stockport p472 0161 480 4949

Halsall, M P (The Copyrights Group Ltd)
Banbury p448 01295 672050

Halsall, M W (Michael W Halsall)
Newton-le-Willows p330 01942 727000

Halsey, B (Lewis Silkin LLP) E
London EC4 p53 020 7074 8000

Halsey, Ms F R (Neves Solicitors) K4 W
Harpenden p239 01582 715234

Halsey, J (Edward Hayes LLP) G H B2
Chichester p192 01243 781431

Halstead, I H (Bhakar Tomlinson) S1 S2 W
Wellington p425 01952 270555

Halstead, J D (Beardsells) N Q W S1
Cheadle p185 0161 477 2288

Halstead, P G (Smith Sutcliffe) W S1 T1 C1
Burnley p169 01282 426251

Halstead, T J (Shulmans) R2
Leeds p276 0113 245 2833

Halton, Mrs J M (Gateley LLP) W
Birmingham p138 0121 234 0000

Halton, J S (Cripps Harries Hall LLP) F2 U2 Ze
Tunbridge Wells p415 01892 515121

Ham, J R (Gawor & Co) E
London E1 p35 020 7481 8888

Ham, Miss J S (Vale of Glamorgan Council)
Barry p448 01446 700111

Ham, K (CMS Cameron McKenna LLP)
London EC3 p17 020 7367 3000

Ham, N L (Clarke Willmott) O E Q
Bristol p162 0845 209 1000 / 0117 305 6000

See p634 for the Key to Work Categories

Ham, R G (Barlow Lyde & Gilbert LLP) *B1 C1 E J1 Zb Ze*
London EC3 *p10* 020 7247 2277

Ham, S E (Cardiff County Council)
Cardiff *p453* 029 2087 2000

Ham, W R (Atter Mackenzie & Co) *K3 K1 Q Zg*
Evesham *p220* 01386 425300

Hamandi, T (Clark Ricketts LLP) *M3*
London WC2 *p20* 020 7240 6767

Hamann, R (Hodge Jones & Allen LLP) *G*
London NW1 *p41* 020 7874 8300

Hamblet, Ms S (Wheelers) *J1*
Aldershot *p115* 01252 316316

Hambleton, Mrs J I C (Bevirs) *S1*
Calne *p173* 01249 814536

Hambleton, J L (Kimbells LLP) *C1 C2 C3 Zb*
Milton Keynes *p317* 01908 668555

Hambleton, M S (Charltons Solicitors)
Biddulph *p132* 01782 522111

Hambleton, P C (W T Jones) *C1 O Q S1 S2 W*
London WC1 *p47* 020 7405 4631 / 7242 7767

Hambleton-Grey, V J (Baron Grey) *O Q M1 J1 B1 C1 K1 L E R1 F1 Ze Zi Zl Zq*
Twickenham *p416* 020 8891 4311

Hamblett, A E (Harvey Ingram Borneos) *B1 J1 O Q Zb Zc Ze Zv*
Milton Keynes *p317* 01908 696002

Hamblin, J (WBW Solicitors)
Exeter *p222* 01392 202404

Hamblin, J C K (Bond Pearce LLP) *Zf Ze I*
Southampton *p385* 0845 415 0000

Hamblin, M L (Lawrence Hamblin) *N Zr*
Henley-on-Thames *p247* 01491 411884

Hambling, M (Rogers & Norton) *N O Q Zq J2*
Norwich *p335* 01603 666001

Hambly, Mrs J (Mowbray Woodwards Solicitors) *K1*
Bath *p128* 01225 485700

Hambury, J (Pinsent Masons LLP)
London EC2 *p67* 020 7418 7000

Hameed, H R (Leeds City Council) *K1 L Q F1 D1*
Leeds *p462* 0113 224 3513

Hameed, Dr R (Hameed & Co) *V G H E Q K1 J1 L S1 Zi Zp Zl M2 S2 Zg*
London NW10 *p38* 020 8830 1335

Hamer, A N (Reynolds Porter Chamberlain LLP) *O Q Zj Zq*
London E1 *p71* 020 3060 6000

Hamer, C J (Druces LLP) *S2 E R2*
London EC2 *p27* 020 7638 9271

Hamer, E A (Hamers) *G S1 W M1 P J1 F1 K1*
Rossendale *p367* 01706 222260

Hamer, Mrs F A (Farnfield & Nicholls) *W T2*
Warminster *p421* 01985 214661

Hamer, J J A (Walker Morris) *C1*
Leeds *p277* 0113 283 2500

Hamer, L (Bennetts Solicitors Attorneys & Notaries) *C1 O Q D1*
Wrington *p443* 01934 862786

Hamer, Miss M A (Wendy Hopkins Family Law Practice LLP) *D1 K1 K3 D2*
Cardiff *p178* 029 2034 2233

Hamer, Mrs S (Barnes Marsland) *J1*
Margate *p312* 01843 221466

Hamer, T P (BHP Law) *G H K1*
Darlington *p206* 01325 466794

Hames, M (Sacker & Partners LLP) *Zo*
London EC2 *p76* 020 7329 6699

Hamill, K (Barlow Lyde & Gilbert LLP)
London EC3 *p10* 020 7247 2277

Hamill, P B (Tosswill & Co) *G H*
Lambeth *p87* 020 8674 9494

Hamilton, A J R (Veale Wasbrough Vizards) *K1 K3 W*
London EC4 *p89* 020 7405 1234

Hamilton, D A (Gorman Hamilton) *N Q*
Newcastle upon Tyne *p324* 0191 232 1123

Hamilton, D J F (HSBC Legal Department) *B1 F1 Zb*
Birmingham *p449* 0121 455 2740

Hamilton, G (Field Fisher Waterhouse LLP)
London EC3 *p31* 020 7861 4000

Hamilton, I D (Hamilton Davies) *C1 S2 E L S1 T1 Zd Zf Zl Zv*
Stevenage *p394* 01438 315898

Hamilton, J (Hill Dickinson LLP) *W*
Liverpool *p288* 0151 600 8000
Kendal *p264* 01539 723757

Hamilton, J (Anthony Gold)
London SW16 *p6* 020 7940 4000

Hamilton, J (Squire Sanders (UK) LLP)
London EC2 *p81* 020 7655 1000

Hamilton, Mrs J K (Austin Ray) *W K4 T2*
Milton Keynes *p316* 01908 769648

Hamilton, J S (Hamiltons) *E L S1 W*
Leeds *p274* 0113 244 6455

Hamilton, Miss K (Russell-Cooke LLP) *K1 K3*
London WC1 *p74* 020 7405 6566

Hamilton, Ms K (Stephens & Scown) *E*
Exeter *p222* 01392 210700

Hamilton, Ms L (Basildon District Council)
Basildon *p448* 01268 533333

Hamilton, M (Bourjois Ltd)
Croydon *p456* 020 8688 7131

Hamilton, Ms M M (McMillen Hamilton McCarthy) *K1 D1 D2 K3*
London E3 *p57* 020 8980 6060

Hamilton, Mrs M S (Wrigleys Solicitors LLP) *T2 W Zd*
Leeds *p278* 0113 244 6100

Hamilton, M W (Capsticks Solicitors LLP) *J1 J2 Zp*
London SW19 *p18* 020 8780 2211

Hamilton, N J A (Clifford Chance)
London E14 *p20* 020 7006 1000

Hamilton, P (Hamilton Downing Quinn) *N O Q W J1 B1 K1 L Zl Zf Zk Zr*
London WC1 *p38* 020 7831 8939

Hamilton, P J C (Tinsdills) *K1*
Hanley *p239* 01782 262031

Hamilton, R (Lawson Lewis & Co) *N O Q L J1 Zq Zr*
Eastbourne *p215* 01323 720142

Hamilton, R (Mowll & Mowll) *B1 F1 L N O Q Zq J2 R1*
Dover *p213* 01304 873344

Hamilton, R D (Davis Blank Furniss) *S2 E S1 Zb*
Manchester *p303* 0161 832 3304

Hamilton, Mrs R S (Astills) *S2 S1 W K3 D1 K1 K4*
Leicester *p278* 0116 249 4450

Hamilton, Ms S (Irwin Mitchell LLP) *E R2 S2*
Birmingham *p139* 0870 150 0100

Hamilton, S (Crutes) *W T2*
Newcastle upon Tyne *p324* 0191 233 9700

Hamilton, Mrs S A (Quality Solicitors Burroughs Day) *N*
Bristol *p164* 0117 929 0333

Hamilton, Ms S C (Forsters LLP) *E R2*
Westminster *p33* 020 7863 8333

Hamilton, Miss S I (Peter Brown & Co Solicitors LLP) *E L S1 S2 W*
Barnet *p124* 020 8447 3277

Hamilton, T G (Addleshaw Goddard) *C2*
Manchester *p300* 0161 934 6000

Hamilton Barns, J M (GSC Solicitors) *C1 C2 M2 Zb*
London EC1 *p34* 020 7822 2222

Hamilton Ryan, Mrs K L (Pannone LLP) *O Q*
Manchester *p308* 0161 909 3000

Hamilton-Cole, Ms E (Coles Miller Solicitors LLP) *K1 D1*
Broadstone *p166* 01202 694891

Hamilton-Hislop, Ms A (Gordons LLP)
Leeds *p273* 0113 227 0100

Hamilton-Hislop, Miss A (Irwin Mitchell LLP) *E S2*
Sheffield *p376* 0870 150 0100

Hamir, O (Anthony Collins Solicitors LLP) *Zc C1 Zh Zu*
Birmingham *p137* 0121 200 3242

Hamlen, G E (Goodman Derrick LLP) *E*
London EC4 *p36* 020 7404 0606

Hamlin, E A M (A-Z Law Solicitors)
Wandsworth *p3* 020 8355 0830

Hamlin, Mrs K (Roebucks) *Zd E L R1 S1 X Zx*
Blackburn *p145* 01254 274000

Hamlin, P R P (Withers LLP) *Q W Zd*
London EC4 *p92* 020 7597 6000

Hamlyn, C (Wall James Chappell) *T2 W*
Stourbridge *p399* 01384 371622

Hamlyn, P T (Pearson Lowe) *C1 E S1 L Zc Zh*
Westminster *p66* 020 7224 0888

Hammal, P J (Forster Dean Ltd) *N*
Runcorn *p369* 01928 590999

Hammersley, Miss F S (Challinors) *D1 K1*
Birmingham *p136* 0121 212 9393

Hammersley, J J (Humphries Kirk) *W K4 Zo*
Bournemouth *p152* 01202 421111

Hammersley, Mrs J M (Trethowans LLP) *E S2*
Salisbury *p371* 01722 412512

Hammersley, R R (Stephensons) *D1 E K1 L N O Q K3*
Brierley Hill *p158* 01384 79731

Hammerton, R G (KTP Solicitors) *D1 F1 K1 L*
Bridgend *p157* 01656 869002

Hammett, M G (GoodyBurrett LLP) *S1 E W L C1 A1*
Colchester *p197* 01206 577676

Hammett, S (Howes Percival LLP)
Norwich *p334* 01603 762103

Hammill, Ms J (Van Baaren & Wright) *S1*
Richmond upon Thames *p364* 020 8940 2525

Hammill, Ms J M (Hammill Burton Lloyd) *E S1*
Kew *p265* 020 8392 6392

Hammock, A J (Akermans) *S1 W S2*
Storrington *p399* 01903 745353

Hammon, C (Ashurst LLP)
London EC2 *p7* 020 7638 1111

Hammon, M A (Hammon Oakley) *A1 C1 G H S1 T1*
Coventry *p200* 024 7644 8585

Hammon, W A (Cumberland Ellis Peirs) *E S1*
London WC1 *p23* 020 7242 0422

Hammond, Sir A H (National Institutions of the Church of England, Legal Office)
London SW1 *p108* 020 7898 1000

Hammond, C (Penningtons) *Zh*
London EC2 *p66* 020 7457 3000

Hammond, Mrs C E (Bennett Griffin) *J1 O C1 Q*
Ferring *p225* 01903 229999

Hammond, C J (Hammond Bale) *B1 C1 E F1 J1 L S1 T1 W Zb Zc Ze Zf*
London W1 *p38* 020 7499 7624

Hammond, D J (Andrew Jackson) *C1 C2*
Hull *p257* 01482 325242

Hammond, G W (Thomas Flavell & Sons) *S1 S2 E W*
Market Bosworth *p312* 01455 290203

Hammond, I B (Simmons & Simmons)
London EC2 *p79* 020 7628 2020

Hammond, Miss J A (Rosamund Coppen & Company) *S1 E W L*
Bath *p127* 0330 440 1802

Hammond, J C (CMS Cameron McKenna LLP)
London EC3 *p17* 020 7367 3000

Hammond, J C (Bilton Hammond LLP)
Chesterfield *p192* 01246 232418
Mansfield *p311* 01623 675800

Hammond, Miss J M (Bury Metropolitan Borough Council)
Bury *p452* 0161 253 7771

Hammond, L (Steele Ford & Newton) *Q N*
Nelson *p321* 01282 692531

Hammond, M D (Treasures) *B1 G J1 D1 O Zt Q Zl*
Gloucester *p230* 01452 525351

Hammond, R B (Rothera Dowson) *O Q Ze F2*
Nottingham *p338* 0115 910 0600

Hammond, R D (Philip J Hammond & Sons) *E S1 W L J1 F1 N A1 C1 O Q Ze*
Leicester *p280* 0116 251 7171

Hammond, R S (Farrell Matthews & Weir) *K1 K3*
London W6 *p30* 020 8746 3771

Hammond, Mrs S J (Blackburn with Darwen Borough Council)
Blackburn *p450* 01254 585585

Hammond, Ms S K (Central Networks)
Castle Donington *p454* 0800 096 3080

Hammond, Miss S K (Powergen PLC)
Coventry *p456* 024 7642 4748 / 4000

Hammond, Mrs T M (Whyte & Co) *K1 Q K3 W*
Gillingham *p229* 01634 852377

Hammond, Mrs V L (Nick Hutchinson & Co) *Q J1 K1 N*
Cheltenham *p188* 01242 261515

Hammond, Ms Z K (Barlow Lyde & Gilbert LLP)
London EC3 *p10* 020 7247 2277

Hammond-Chambers-Borgnis, Mrs J A (Butcher Andrews) *N Q*
Fakenham *p223* 01328 863131

Hamor, Ms F J (Pannone LLP) *J1*
Manchester *p308* 0161 909 3000

Hampshire, Miss A C (Eric Robinson Solicitors)
Southampton *p385* 01489 788922

Hampson, I (AST Hampsons) *S1 E C1 W L*
Rochdale *p365* 01706 522311

Hampson, J (Croftons) *K1 N Q D1 L*
Manchester *p302* 0161 214 6180

Hampstead, Ms R A (Hess Ltd)
London WC2 *p106* 020 7331 3000

Hampton, A E H (Pothecary Witham Weld) *W*
Westminster *p69* 020 7821 8211

Hampton, Mrs J (Timms) *W*
Derby *p209* 01332 364436

Hampton, P (Paul Hampton) *P N L B1 J1 Zl*
London SW1 *p38* 020 7932 2450

Hams, R J (Wansbroughs) *N P Zj*
Devizes *p210* 01380 733300

Hamshaw, Mrs S (Charles Lucas & Marshall) *D1 K3 K1*
Newbury *p322* 01635 521212

Hamshaw-Thomas, C W (Imperial Tobacco Group PLC)
Bristol *p452* 0117 963 6636

Hamylton, G S (Bray & Bray) *G H*
Leicester *p279* 0116 254 8871

Hamzavi, A (Andrew C Blundy Solicitors) *L S2 E O Q S1 W J1*
Greenwich *p14* 020 8293 3633

Hamzij, Miss D (WBW Solicitors)
Exeter *p222* 01392 202404

Hanbury, C J (Tozers) *E L S1*
Newton Abbot *p329* 01626 207020

Hanbury, S (Wolferstans) *N Zr*
Plymouth *p351* 01752 663295

Hanby, Mrs K J (Doncaster Magistrates Court)
Doncaster *p457* 01302 366711

Hanby, P (The Ringrose Law Group - Richard Harwood) *F1 J1 M1 N P Zm Zl Zt*
Lincoln *p285* 01522 814700

Hancock, A R T (Garner & Hancock Solicitors LLP) *E S1 T2 W Zd*
Isleworth *p263* 020 8232 9560

Hancock, Miss C (Pannone LLP) *O Q F1 L*
Manchester *p308* 0161 909 3000

Hancock, Mrs F (Bower & Bailey) *S1*
Witney *p436* 01993 705095

Hancock, Miss H M (Simmons & Simmons)
London EC2 *p79* 020 7628 2020

Hancock, Ms I M (Knights Solicitors LLP) *J1 Q Zp*
Newcastle under Lyme *p323* 01782 619225

Hancock, Miss J D (Ramsdens Solicitors) *C1 E S2*
Huddersfield *p256* 01484 821500

Hancock, N (The College of Law Guildford)
Guildford *p459* 01483 460200

Hancock, Mrs N A (Manches LLP) *C2*
Oxford *p343* 01865 722106

Hancock, N P (Colemans) *F1 Zl Zt W T2*
Haywards Heath *p245* 01444 459555

Hancock, R D (Coffin Mew & Clover) *W S1 F1 R1 Zi Zs T2 Zd*
Fareham *p223* 01329 825617

Hancock, Ms S (Stephens & Scown) *R1*
St Austell *p391* 01726 74433

Hancock, S C (Herbert Smith LLP) *C1 C2*
London EC2 *p40* 020 7374 8000

Hancock, Miss V S (Davey Franklin Jones) *S1 W E L T1 A1*
Cirencester *p195* 01285 654875

Hancock, W (Speechly Bircham LLP) *T1 W Zd*
London EC4 *p81* 020 7427 6400

Hancocks, I (East Cornwall Magistrates Courts)
Bodmin *p450* 01208 262700

Hand, Mrs C M (Bircham Dyson Bell) *Zh Zu Zd E J1 L R2*
Westminster *p13* 020 7227 7000

Hand, J (Terry Jones Solicitors & Advocates) *G H B2*
Shrewsbury *p379* 01743 285888

Handel, Mrs K (Paul Crowley & Co) *S1 W*
Liverpool *p287* 0151 264 7363

Handel, N J (Gateley LLP) *E L Zh S2*
Birmingham *p138* 0121 234 0000

Handford, Mrs E (Charnwood Borough Council)
Loughborough *p464* 01509 263151

Handforth, M C (Loveday & Keighley) *K1 P S1 G M1 W J1 F1 B1 L*
Matlock *p313* 01629 583142 / 56660

Handler, Ms J A (Burges Salmon) *C1 C2*
Bristol *p161* 0117 939 2000

Handley, Mrs J A (South Lincolnshire Magistrates Courts)
Grantham *p459* 01476 563438

Handley, M (Squire Sanders (UK) LLP)
London EC2 *p81* 020 7655 1000

Handley, R D (BPE Solicitors LLP) *C1*
Cheltenham *p187* 01242 224433

Handley, Ms S (Plexus Law (A Trading Name of Parabis Law LLP)) *N Q*
Evesham *p220* 01386 769160

Handley, W J (Charles Russell LLP)
London EC4 *p19* 020 7203 5000

Handling, Ms E (Ashurst LLP)
London EC2 *p7* 020 7638 1111

Hands, Ms J (Friends Provident)
Dorking *p457* 01306 654925

Hands, P (Browne Jacobson LLP) *B1 C1*
Nottingham *p336* 0115 976 6000

Handscombe, Miss S E (Fladgate LLP) *C1 C2*
London WC2 *p32* 020 3036 7000

Handy, D (Addleshaw Goddard) *E B1 Zb*
Manchester *p300* 0161 934 6000

Handy, O J (Reynolds Porter Chamberlain LLP)
London E1 *p71* 020 3060 6000

Handzji, M (Turner & Wall) *W Zm*
Keighley *p264* 01535 607831

Hanes, Ms C (Nockolds) *K1 K3*
Bishop's Stortford *p144* 01279 755777

Hanif-Ahmed, Ms N (Pearson Hinchliffe) *B1 F1 Ze Zk Q N T1 T2*
Oldham *p341* 0161 785 3500

Haniff, M (Stephenson Harwood) *E L P*
London EC2 *p82* 020 7329 4422

Haniff, Ms S (Reynolds Porter Chamberlain LLP)
London E1 *p71* 020 3060 6000

Hanison, D (Plexus Law (A Trading Name of Parabis Law LLP)) *O Zj N Zq*
London EC3 *p68* 0844 245 4000

Hankey, M (Svenska Handelsbanken AB (publ) London)
London E1 *p109* 020 7578 8115

Hankey, Ms S P (CMS Cameron McKenna LLP) *C3 M1*
London EC3 *p17* 020 7367 3000

Hankin, Ms F (Reynolds Porter Chamberlain LLP)
London E1 *p71* 020 3060 6000

Hankins, Miss C (Boodle Hatfield)
Westminster *p14* 020 7629 7411

Hanks, Mrs K J (Pinkerton Leeke & Co) *F1 K1 K3 J1 Q*
Cheltenham *p188* 01242 237477

Hanley, Ms C M (Bond Pearce LLP) *O Zc*
Plymouth *p349* 0845 415 0000

Hanley, D (Wilson & Co) *Zi*
London N17 *p92* 020 8808 7535

Hanley, J C (Lincolnshire County Council Resources - Legal Services)
Lincoln *p463* 01522 552222

Hanley, J E (Morrish Solicitors LLP) *N Q Zr*
Leeds *p276* 0113 245 0733

Hanley, M G (Wilson & Co) *Zi*
London N17 *p92* 020 8808 7535

Hanlon, J T (Bendles) *S1 S2 E*
Carlisle *p181* 01228 522215

Hanlon, Ms P (Hill Dickinson LLP) *E*
Liverpool *p288* 0151 600 8000

Hann, M C (Pinsent Masons LLP) *U2 Ze*
London EC2 *p67* 020 7418 7000

Hann, P (Hill Dickinson LLP) *O Zj*
London EC3 *p41* 020 7283 9033

Hanna, Ms S M E (Grindall & Hanna Solicitors) *C1 J1*
Southwark *p37* 020 8299 3801

Hannaford, G R (Wansbroughs)
Devizes *p210* 01380 733300

Hannah, D S (Steels) *S2 E Zh Zl R1 S1*
Warrington *p422* 01925 261354

Hannah, T C (Chawner Grey & Co) *S1 S2 A1*
Weston-super-Mare *p429* 01934 417768 / 623541

Hannam, A J (Foot Anstey) *Zr*
Taunton *p408* 01823 625600

Hannam, D P S (Bower & Bailey) *S1 S2 W*
Oxford *p343* 01865 311133
Swindon *p406* 01793 610466

Hannam, I P (Robin Burman & Co) *W K4 S1 S2 E C1*
Manchester *p302* 0161 860 7123

Hannam, I P (Megsons LLP) *S1 W E*
Oldham *p340* 0161 633 6131
Bradford *p154* 01274 738444

Hannam, P D (Hileys) *S1 W T1 A1 S2*
Easingwold *p215* 01347 821234

Hannam, Ms S L (Peters & Peters) *O Q B1 F1 Zk*
London EC4 *p67* 020 7629 7991

Hannan, Miss L (Anderson Partnership)
Chesterfield *p191* 01246 220737

Hannell, Ms S (Alexiou Fisher Philipps) *K1 D1 K3*
London W1 *p5* 020 7409 1222

6

Hannen, Miss P (Kirklees Metropolitan Borough Council)
Huddersfield *p461* 01484 221421

Hannides, N M (Hannides Hewstone & Co) *K1 C1 S1 J1 F1 L S2*
Southampton *p386*. 023 8078 6770

Hannington, A F (Shakespeares) *N Q Zj Zk*
Birmingham *p142* 0121 237 3000

Hannon, D A (Kennedys) *Zj*
London EC3 *p49*. 020 7667 9667

Hannon, Ms D J (Tarmac Ltd)
Wolverhampton *p477* 01902 353522

Hannon, J (William Sturges & Co) *B1 L O Q*
Westminster *p84*. 020 7873 1000

Hanns, S G (Waldrons) *G H*
Dudley *p213*. 01384 811811

Hanrahan, Ms J (Department for Business, Enterprise and Regulatory Reform)
London SW1 *p105*. 020 7215 0105

Hanrahan, Ms M E (Flintshire County Council)
Mold *p466*. 01352 702411

Hanratty, Mrs C (George Davies Solicitors LLP)
Manchester *p303* 0161 236 8992

Hanratty, C J H (Watson Solicitors) *N O J1 B1 L Zr Q Zq S2 Zl*
Warrington *p422*. 01925 571212

Hanratty, P (Mulcahy Smith) *D1 F1 G H J1 K1 N Q V W Zm*
Gateshead *p229*. 0191 490 1000

Hanratty, R G (Hanratty & Co) *P K1 G B1 D1 J1 L M1 S1 V Zc Zl K3 K2 W*
Newtown *p330*. 01686 626239

Hansel, Ms E S (The College of Law Guildford)
Guildford *p459*. 01483 460200

Hansell, J R (Hansell Drew & Co) *G H*
Dartmouth *p207* 01803 834555

Hansen, C (Hansen Palomares) *L V Q Zq*
Lambeth *p38*. 020 7640 4600

Hansen, Ms N L (Freemans Solicitors) *D1 K1 K2 D2*
London W1 *p34* 020 7935 3522

Hansen, O L (Hansen Palomares) *L N Q Zq Zp*
Lambeth *p38*. 020 7640 4600

Hansford, C M (Hewitsons) *S2 E R2 Zl L*
Northampton *p332*. 01604 233233

Hansford, C M (Cartmell Shepherd) *E*
Penrith *p346*. 01768 862326

Hansford, D G (Crown Prosecution Service Cumbria)
Carlisle *p453*. 01228 882900

Hansford, Miss J (Biscoes) *D1 D2 K1*
Wickham *p431*. 01329 833249
Portsmouth *p354*. 023 9238 8021

Hanslip-Ward, M (SNR Denton) *O*
London EC4 *p75*. 020 7242 1212

Hansom, Miss K J (Andrew Jackson) *C1 Ze Zza U2 I C3*
Hull *p257* 01482 325242

Hansom, R E J (Nicholls Christie & Crocker) *G H D1 D2 B2*
Uxbridge *p417*. 01895 256216

Hansom, T (Guillaumes Solicitors) *E S1*
Weybridge *p430*. 01932 840111

Hanson, Mrs B (Bobbetts Mackan) *D1 K3 K1*
Bristol *p161* 0117 929 9001

Hanson, C (DLA Piper UK LLP)
London EC2 *p24*. 0870 011 1111

Hanson, C P (Kennedys) *Zj*
London EC3 *p49*. 020 7667 9667

Hanson, E A (Billson & Sharp) *W T1 S1 V T2*
Leicester *p279*. 0116 255 9911

Hanson, Miss E J (Reed Executive PLC)
London WC2 *p108*. 020 7421 1640

Hanson, G C (Edell Jones & Lessers) *S1 S2 W E*
London E6 *p28* 020 8548 5700

Hanson, Mrs H (Fraser Dawbarns) *W*
King's Lynn *p266* 01553 666600

Hanson, J (Barlow Lyde & Gilbert LLP) *N Zj O Q*
London EC3 *p10*. 020 7247 2277

Hanson, Ms K C E (Welch & Co) *G H K3 K1 D1*
Cardigan *p181*. 01239 614070

Hanson, M C (Ashurst LLP) *Zc*
London EC2 *p7* 020 7638 1111
London EC3 *p17*. 020 7367 3000

Hanson, P (Freeth Cartwright LLP)
Nottingham *p337*. 0115 936 9369

Hanson, Ms R (HBOS PLC)
Halifax *p460* 0870 600 5000

Hanson, Ms S (Richmond Anderson Goudie) *D1 D2 G H K1*
Chester-le-Street *p191*. . . . 0191 388 7884

Hanson, V P A (Oates Hanson) *S2 W S1 K1 N D1 C1 Q J1 L Zc K3*
Huddersfield *p256* 01484 300609

Hanson, Miss Z (Eaton Ryan & Taylor) *Q O B1 C1 L N*
Birmingham *p138* 0121 236 1999

Hanson-Clerehugh, Dr J (Parker Rhodes Hickmotts) *K3 K1 D1*
Rotherham *p367*. 01709 511100

Hanspaul, Ms S (Howard Kennedy LLP) *E*
London W1 *p48* 020 7636 1616

Hantom, D E (Crompton Halliwell) *S1 S2 C1 E L R2 W A1 A2 R1 Zo Zq*
Bury *p170*. 0161 797 9222

Hanton, B J (Ashurst LLP)
London EC2 *p7* 020 7638 1111

Hanton, R W (London Borough of Barking & Dagenham)
Barking *p448* . .020 8592 4500 / 8252 8233
Dagenham *p456*. 020 8592 4500

Haplin, B A (Halpins)
London SW1 *p38* 020 3286 6041

Haq, S (McGrigors LLP)
London EC4 *p56*. 020 7054 2500

Haq, Ms S (Harrison Clark LLP) *O*
Cheltenham *p188* 01242 269198
Worcester *p439* 01905 612001
Worcester *p439* 01905 612001

Haran, J E P (Battens) *S1 W A1*
Yeovil *p443* 01935 846000

Haras-Gummer, C (Gummer & Singh) *B1 E G H K1 M1 N P S1 W Zi Zl Zp*
Hounslow *p253* 020 8572 6905

Harasym, Mrs B A (Charles Newton & Co) *S1*
Eastwood *p216* 01773 535535

Harbach, J (Linklaters LLP)
London EC2 *p54*. 020 7456 2000

Harbage, J J (Walker Morris) *Zc O Q*
Leeds *p277* 0113 283 2500

Harbinson, M (David Billingham & Partners) *C1 G H J1*
Cheltenham *p187* 01242 676224

Harbord, R (Harbord & Co) *Zr E K1 Q N S1 W G H B2*
Epsom *p219*. 01372 720077

Harbottle, J F (Bromets Jackson Heath) *S1 E K1 N L F1 W A1 Zl*
Tadcaster *p407* 01937 832371

Harbottle, J W T (Birketts LLP) *A1 E A2 L S1 R2*
Ipswich *p262*. 01473 232300

Harbottle, Miss R L (MarstonHarbottle) *K1 S1 W*
Hexham *p249* 01434 602486

Harbour, A G W (Scott-Moncrieff Harbour & Sinclair) *K1*
London NW5 *p77* 020 7485 5588
London SE8 *p85*. 020 7790 7000

Harbour, P (Kingsley Napley) *E*
London EC1 *p50*. 020 7814 1200

Harbridge, J (Trowers & Hamlins)
London EC3 *p88*. 020 7423 8000

Harbron, D (Kenneth M Barrow & Co) *G H*
Seaham *p373* 0191 513 0333

Harbron, Ms R (John O'Neill & Co) *W S1 K4 Zl*
Gosforth *p232* 0191 246 4000

Harcombe, Mrs L (Hamlins LLP)
London W1 *p38* 020 7355 6000

Harcourt, R S W (Shakespeares) *C1 C2*
Nottingham *p339*. 0115 945 3700

Harcus, Mrs G A (Forsters LLP) *W*
Westminster *p33*. 020 7863 8333

Harcus, J B (Harcus Sinclair) *K1 K3*
London WC2 *p38* 020 7242 9700

Hardaker, G (Holman Fenwick Willan)
London EC3 *p42*. 020 7264 8000

Hardaker, Ms W (Department for Business, Enterprise and Regulatory Reform)
London SW1 *p105*. 020 7215 0105

Hardaway, Mrs J M (Dawson Hart) *J1 N*
Uckfield *p416* 01825 762281

Hardcastle, Mrs C M (Rollits LLP)
Hull *p258* 01482 323239

Hardcastle, E (Rouse Legal (Formerly Willoughby & Partners))
London E14 *p74*. 020 7536 4100

Hardcastle, Ms L (Edwin Coe LLP) *C1 C2*
London WC2 *p29* 020 7691 4000

Hardcastle, S G (Cornwells) *S2 W E R2*
Bradford *p153* 01274 675631

Hardcastle, S J (Walker Morris) *C1*
Leeds *p277* 0113 283 2500

Hardee, Ms R J (Kevin Lane & Co) *N S1 W*
Port Talbot *p353*. 01639 893700

Hardesty, T J (Herrington & Carmichael LLP) *S2 E R2 S1*
Camberley *p173*. 01276 686222

Hardick, Miss J B (Juliet Hardick Solicitors) *S1 E L W J1*
Bath *p127*. 01225 311177

Hardie, Miss A M (Edwards Angell Palmer & Dodge)
London EC2 *p28*. 020 7583 4055

Hardiker, J (Thomson Wilson Pattinson) *Q G J1 N L H*
Kendal *p264*. 01539 721945

Harding, A J (Hugh James) *N Zr*
Cardiff *p179* 029 2022 4871

Harding, A K (Buchanan & Llewellyn) *N K1 A3*
Westbourne *p428* 01202 752525

Harding, Ms B (ASB Law) *S1*
Maidstone *p298* 01622 656500

Harding, B C (EJ Moyle) *K4 T2 W S1 Zm*
Littlehampton *p285*. 01903 725143

Harding, C E K D (Charles Harding & Co) *G K1 L N H J1 D1 V S1 W Zi Zl Zh Zj Ze*
Wembley *p426*. 020 8795 0990

Harding, D (Herringtons) *D1 M1 P V F1 L Zm Zi*
Rye *p370* 01797 222955

Harding, D (Jones Day) *C1*
London EC4 *p46*. 020 7039 5959

Harding, Miss G (HRJ Law LLP) *C1 S2 E*
Hitchin *p251*. 01462 628888

Harding, G A (Bennett Welch & Co)
London SE19 *p12* 020 8670 6141

Harding, Ms H (British Telecommunications PLC)
London EC1 *p104* 020 7356 6181

Harding, J (CMS Cameron McKenna LLP)
London EC3 *p17*. 020 7367 3000

Harding, J C (Kingsley Napley) *B2 G H*
London EC1 *p50*. 020 7814 1200

Harding, J P S J (Virgin Atlantic Airways Ltd)
Crawley *p456* 01293 562345

Harding, Miss K A (Alliance Solicitors) *S1*
Kenton *p264*. 020 8204 3000
St Albans *p390* 01727 837161

Harding, Miss L A (Brignalls Balderston Warren) *J1*
Stevenage *p394* 01438 359311

Harding, L J (Forest of Dean District Council)
Coleford *p455* 01594 810000
Haverfordwest *p460* 01437 764551

Harding, M D (Barclays Bank PLC)
London EC3 *p104* 020 7699 5000

Harding, M F (Earle & Waller) *S1 W S2*
London N13 *p28*. 020 8888 7866

Harding, M G (South Tyneside Metropolitan Borough Council)
South Shields *p471* 0191 427 1717

Harding, Mrs N A (Hancocks Solicitors Ltd) *J1*
Nottingham *p337*. 0844 474 3377

Harding, Mrs N J (Tunnard & Co) *D1 D2 K1 K3 Zx*
Ripon *p365* 01765 605629

Harding, N P (TWM Solicitors LLP) *W T2*
Epsom *p219*. 01372 729555

Harding, Ms P (Scott Duff & Co) *K1 K3*
Penrith *p346*. 01768 865551

Harding, P C (Tallents Solicitors) *N O*
Newark *p322* 01636 671881

Harding, S (Everys) *S2 E S1 L*
Exmouth *p222* 01395 264384
Exeter *p221* 01392 411221

Harding-Hill, Ms R (McDermott Will & Emery UK LLP) *J1*
London EC2 *p56*. 020 7577 6900

Hardingham, A C (Gateley LLP) *O C1 Q Za Zb Zj*
London EC4 *p35*. 020 7653 1600

Hardingham, Ms S M (Meade-King) *E S2*
Bristol *p163* 0117 926 4121

Hardington, K (Walker Foster) *Q O N C1 E L F1 A3*
Skipton *p381*. 01756 700200

Hardman, Ms A (Linder Myers Solicitors)
Manchester *p307* 0844 984 6400

Hardman, A T H (Rosling King) *A1 E L R1 S1 Zs*
London EC4 *p73*. 020 7353 2353

Hardman, C (Hogan Lovells International LLP)
London EC1 *p42*. 020 7296 2000

Hardman, C V (Steele Raymond) *C1 T2 W C2 T1 J1*
Bournemouth *p152*. 01202 294566

Hardman, D (Watson Burton LLP) *B1 C1 Zb*
Newcastle upon Tyne *p327* . 0845 901 2100

Hardman, I G (Brabners Chaffe Street) *O Q L B1 Ze*
Liverpool *p286* 0151 600 3000

Hardman, J B (Hansells) *Zc C1 S2 C2 E S1*
Norwich *p334* 01603 615731

Hardman, Ms L (Capsticks Solicitors LLP) *N Zr*
London SW19 *p18*. 020 8780 2211

Hardman, M J (Hardman Wood) *S2 C1 C2 E F1 K4 R1 T1 T2*
Blackburn *p145* 01254 295540

Hardman, P B (Gregg Latchams LLP) *C1 C2 Ze C3 U2 I*
Bristol *p162* 0117 906 9400

Hardman, Ms S (Parker Bird Gardner) *D1 K1 M1 V*
Huddersfield *p256* 01484 825200

Hardman, Ms S (Trowers & Hamlins)
London EC3 *p88*. 020 7423 8000

Hardman, Ms T (Keoghs LLP) *N Zj A3 O Q*
Bolton *p149* 01204 677000

Hards, D N (A C S Hards & Co) *E S1 C1 J1 F1 W S2*
New Malden *p321* 020 8942 2258

Hards, M L (Newbys) *K1 N S1 W J1 T2 L G D2 K3*
Guisborough *p237* . .01287 632208 / 632209

Hardstaff, D A (Ashton Bond Gigg) *J1*
Nottingham *p335*. 0115 947 6651

Hardwick, Ms J (Russell Jones & Walker)
London WC2 *p74* 020 7657 1555

Hardwick, J F (Marsden Rawsthorn LLP) *S1 G K1 H L Zl D1 N*
Chorley *p194* 01257 279511

Hardwick, M J (Linklaters LLP)
London EC2 *p54*. 020 7456 2000

Hardwick, R (K&L Gates LLP) *B1 C1 Zb*
London EC4 *p47*. 020 7648 9000

Hardwick, R A (Adcocks Solicitors Ltd) *L S1 S2*
Lichfield *p284* 0845 470 8081

Hardwick, Mrs S (Wolverhampton City Council)
Wolverhampton *p477* 01902 556556

Hardwicke, Ms R (Walter Gray & Co) *K4 T2 W*
Ryde *p369*. 01983 563765

Hardy, A W (Seymours) *K1 K3 L J1 N O F1*
Coventry *p201*. 024 7655 3961

Hardy, B P (Brooke North LLP) *E S1 S2*
Leeds *p272* 0113 283 2100

Hardy, C D (B P Collins LLP) *E S1 L S2*
Gerrards Cross *p229*. 01753 889995

Hardy, Ms D E (Cohen Cramer Solicitors) *K1 D1*
Leeds *p272* 0800 542 9408
Leeds *p275* 0113 243 4333

Hardy, D R (Jobling & Knape) *G K1 S1 W H Zl*
Lancaster *p269* 01524 598300

Hardy, G (County of Herefordshire District Council)
Hereford *p460*. 01432 260266

Hardy, Ms I (Edwards Angell Palmer & Dodge)
London EC2 *p28*. 020 7583 4055

Hardy, I D (Hardy Miles Titterton)
Duffield *p214* 01332 841115

Hardy, J (Reed Smith LLP) *O*
London EC2 *p71*. 020 3116 3000

Hardy, Ms J (Freeth Cartwright LLP) *Zr*
Nottingham *p337*. 0115 936 9369

Hardy, Mrs J D S (Harvey Ingram Borneos) *K1 D1 D2*
Milton Keynes *p317* 01908 696002

Hardy, Mrs J M (Bishop Akers & Co) *A1 E S1 W C1*
Swanley *p404* 01322 660617

Hardy, Mrs J V (Bates N V H) *O Q J1 Zc Zl*
London WC2 *p11* 020 7936 2930

Hardy, M (Park Woodfine Heald Mellows LLP) *S1*
Bedford *p130* 01234 400000

Hardy, Ms M (Greenwoods) *N Q*
Manchester *p305* 0161 245 6520

Hardy, M H (Yarwood Stimpson & Co) *Q S1 W Zl K1 G H*
Whitley Bay *p431* 0191 297 0123

Hardy, Ms N (Ashurst LLP)
London EC2 *p7* 020 7638 1111

Hardy, P (Bird & Co) *J1 Zp N Zq O Q Zg X*
Grantham *p232* 01476 591711

Hardy, P (Hempsons) *Zr*
Manchester *p305* 0161 228 0011

Hardy, P (Morgan Lewis & Bockius)
London EC4 *p61*. 020 3201 5000

Hardy, P I (Robert Lunn & Lowth) *E S1 L A1 T1 R1 P Zc Zd*
Stratford-upon-Avon *p400* . . 01789 292238

Hardy, P J (Addleshaw Goddard) *E*
Leeds *p271* 0113 209 2000
London EC1 *p4* 020 7606 8855

Hardy, R C (Roger Long & Co) *G H*
Croydon *p205* 020 8668 5071

Hardy, R N (Senior Calveley & Hardy) *W C1 Zd T2*
Lytham *p297*. 01253 733333

Hardy, Miss S (Forbes) *N*
Blackburn *p145* 01254 662831

Hardy, S J (Society of Lloyd's)
London EC3 *p107* 020 7327 1000

Hardy, S P (Ibstock Group Ltd)
London TN32 *p107* 01580 883850

Hardy, S R (Burton & Dyson) *A1 D1 Zr E J1 K1 J2 Zl Q N S1 T2 W G H C1*
Gainsborough *p228* 01427 610761

Hardy, Mrs S S (Irwin Mitchell LLP) *N*
Sheffield *p376* 0870 150 0100

Hardy, T P F (CMS Cameron McKenna LLP)
London EC3 *p17*. 020 7367 3000

Hardy, Ms V C (Boodle Hatfield)
Westminster *p14*. 020 7629 7411

Hardy, Mrs V P (Aviva PLC)
London EC3 *p103* . . 020 7283 7500 / 01603 687905
Norwich *p467* 01603 622200

Hardy, W (Eddowes Waldron) *G H B2*
Derby *p208* 01332 348484

Hardy-McBride, K R T (Hardy McBride & Co) *G*
Bromley *p166* 020 8460 1999

Hare, Mrs A S (Nockolds) *S2 E*
Bishop's Stortford *p144* . . . 01279 755777

Hare, I A (Collard & Co) *S1 W L*
Highworth *p250* 01793 765327

Hare, Ms J M (Hewitts) *S1 A1 W E L*
Darlington *p206* 01325 468573

Hare, R G (McKinnells) *Zl K3 K1*
Lincoln *p284*. 01522 541181

Harfield, Miss R L (Russell Jones & Walker) *J1 Zp*
Cardiff *p180* 029 2026 2800

Harfitt, P F (Paul F Harfitt & Co) *S1 A1 W T1 E G K1 P C1 M1 Zc Zl S2 L*
Wem *p426*. 01939 232775

Hargan, K (Keoghs LLP) *J1 J2 Q N*
Bolton *p149* 01204 677000

Hargan, Mrs S K (South Northamptonshire Council)
Towcester *p474* 01327 322322

Hargreave, Mrs A M (HM Land Registry - Hull)
Hull *p461* 01482 223244

Hargreaves, A (Foot Anstey) *E*
Taunton *p408* 01823 625600

Hargreaves, Mrs C (Terence Carney) *K3 K1 D1*
Hebburn *p246* . . 0191 483 5422 / 483 8771

Hargreaves, C K (Lee Bolton Monier-Williams) *E S1 L*
Westminster *p52*. 020 7222 5381

Hargreaves, Mrs D (Edmondson Hall) *Q N L Zl*
Newmarket *p327*. 01638 560556

Hargreaves, Mrs H J (Brockmans) *S2 E L*
Stockbridge *p395* 01264 810910

Hargreaves, I (Addleshaw Goddard) *O*
London EC1 *p4* 020 7606 8855

Hargreaves, Ms J (Leeds City Council) *J1*
Leeds *p462* 0113 224 3513

Hargreaves, Ms L A (Tameside Metropolitan Borough Council)
Ashton-under-Lyne *p447*. . . 0161 342 3028

Hargreaves, M (J C Bamford Excavators Ltd) *N R1*
Uttoxeter *p474*. 01889 590312

Hargreaves, P (Askew Bunting Solicitors LLP) *Q O N Zc L J2 F1 J1 A3 B1*
Middlesbrough *p314* 01642 252555

Hargreaves, P (BHP Law) *N Q O J1*
Newcastle upon Tyne *p323* . 0191 221 0898

Hargreaves, P (Hewitts) *Q O N Zc L J2 F1 J1 A3 B1*
Bishop Auckland *p144* 01388 604691

Hargreaves, P M (Patterson Glenton & Stracey) *J1 S1 Q W*
South Shields *p384* 0800 011 6487

Hargreaves, P M (Reed Smith LLP)
London EC2 *p71*. 020 3116 3000

See p634 for the Key to Work Categories

Hargreaves, Ms S (Howard Kennedy LLP) *E* London W1 *p48* . . . 020 7636 1616

Hargreaves, Ms S (Michelmores LLP) *W* Exeter *p221* . . . 01392 688688

Hargreaves, Miss S (Mellor Hargreaves Solicitors) *N* Oldham *p341* . . . 0800 811 844

Haringman, M S (Quastel Midgen LLP) *C1 E S2 R2 R1 S1 W* London W1 *p70* . . . 020 7908 2525

Harker, C J (Dickinson Dees) *C1 C2* Newcastle upon Tyne *p324* . 0191 279 9000

Harker, P W (Whiteford Crocker) *K1 N P G L F1 H V Zj Zk* Plymouth *p350*. . . . 01752 550711

Harker, S R (Dawson Cornwell) *E L R1* London WC1 *p26* . . . 020 7242 2556

Harker, S T (Treasury Solicitors Department) London WC2 *p110*. . . . 020 7210 3000

Harkin, P M (Pinsent Masons LLP) *C2* Birmingham *p141* . . . 0121 200 1050

Harkins, P B (Carter Slater & Co) *G H* Northampton *p331*. . . . 01604 717505

Harkness, D (Clifford Chance) London E14 *p20*. . . . 020 7006 1000

Harkness, Mrs M J (Fiona Bruce & Co LLP) *S1* Warrington *p421*. . . . 01925 263273

Harkus, A W (Everett Tomlin Lloyd & Pratt) *G H* Pontypool *p352* . . . 01495 763333

Harland, P F (G U S Home Shopping Ltd) Manchester *p464* . . . 0161 277 4708

Harle, Miss K J (Capsticks Solicitors LLP) *J1 Zp J2* London SW19 *p18*. . . . 020 8780 2211

Harle, P (Hogan Lovells International LLP) London EC1 *p42*. . . . 020 7296 2000

Harley, Mrs C (Beviss & Beckingsale) Chard *p184* . . . 01460 269700

Harley, D (Rothera Dowson) *E* Nottingham *p338*. . . . 0115 910 0600

Harley, J (Clark Willis) *G H L Q* Darlington *p206* . . . 01325 281111

Harley, Mrs K (Fanshaw Porter & Hazlehurst) Birkenhead *p134*. . . . 0151 647 4051

Harley, Ms L E (Marsh Brown & Co) *D1 K1* Lewisham *p59* . . . 020 8852 0052

Harley, Mrs S D (Abbott Lloyd Howorth) *S1 E L W Zm* Maidenhead *p298* . . . 01628 798800

Harling, A C (Painters) *B1 F1 J1 L N O Zq* Kidderminster *p266* . . . 01562 822295

Harling, Miss J N (Bottrills Solicitors) *S1* Barnet *p123* . . . 020 8440 8188 / 8441 1125

Harling, M R (Burges Salmon) *O P Zc* Bristol *p161* . . . 0117 939 2000

Harling, P W (Squire Sanders (UK) LLP) *L E* Leeds *p277* . . . 0113 284 7000

Harlock, D F (Diageo PLC) London W1 *p105* . . . 020 7927 5300

Harlow, A J (Blake Lapthorn) *E* Chandlers Ford *p184* . . . 023 8090 8090

Harlow, Mrs E J (Hawley & Rodgers) *K1 G H* Loughborough *p293* . . . 01509 230333

Harlow, Ms S M (Hanne & Co) *D1 K1* London SW11 *p38* . . . 020 7228 0017

Harlowe, C M (Speechly Bircham LLP) *B1* London EC4 *p81*. . . . 020 7427 6400

Harman, B K E (Harmans) *S1 W R1 E L Zs* Mansfield *p311*. . . . 01623 629224

Harman, Ms L A (Druces LLP) *W T2* London EC2 *p27*. . . . 020 7638 9271

Harman, M J (Pinsent Masons LLP) *O Q Zc Zj* London EC2 *p67*. . . . 020 7418 7000

Harman, S (Thompson & Jackson) *S1 S2 E K4 W L C1* Plymouth *p350*. . . 01752 665037 / 221171

Harman, Ms S M (Harman & Harman) *D1 K1 N Zr* London SW2 *p39* . . . 01227 452977

Harman, Miss V A (Denniss Matthews) *D1 K1* London SE20 *p27* . . 020 8778 7301 / 8778 7631

Harman-Bishop, A P (The National Trust) Swindon *p475* . . . 01793 817400

Harman-Wilson, D G (Reynolds Porter Chamberlain LLP) *P O N* London E1 *p71* . . . 020 3060 6000

Harmer, A E J (Batchelors Solicitors) *L Zh* Bromley *p166* . . . 020 8768 7000

Harmer, A R J (Aviva PLC) London EC3 *p103* . 020 7283 7500 / 01603 687905

Harmer, Mrs C (Nantes) *A1 E Zo S1 K1 D1 Zl L V* Bridport *p158* . . . 01308 422313

Harnby, N (Linklaters LLP) London EC2 *p54*. . . . 020 7456 2000

Harnden, M J (Gotelee) *C1 F1 F2 C2* Ipswich *p262*. . . . 01473 211121

Harne, M V (Stamp Jackson and Procter) *N O J1* Hull *p258* . . . 01482 324591

Harnett, Miss K M (Harnett & Co) *S1 W C1 K4* Bristol *p163* . . . 0117 965 5366

Harney, Mrs C A (Harney & Wells) *D1 K1 K3* Brighton *p159* . . . 01273 684666

Harney, N J (Nightingales Solicitors Limited) *J1 M1 N C1 K1 F1 B1 L G P* Stockport *p396*. . . . 01663 764038

Harney, P F (Forsters LLP) *T2 T1 W* Westminster *p33*. . . . 020 7863 8333

Harold, Mrs S C (B J McKenna & Co Solicitors) *D1 K3 K1* Stockport *p396*. . . . 0161 432 5757

Harpalani, S (Harpers) Camden *p39*. . . . 020 7405 8888

Harper, A (Alistair Harper & Co) *G H* Haywards Heath *p245* . . . 01444 457890

Harper, A J (Brabners Chaffe Street) *C1 C2* Manchester *p301* . . . 0161 836 8800

Harper, C J (Gregory Rowcliffe Milners) *O Q N J1 X Zl* London WC1 *p37* . . . 020 7242 0631

Harper, C M (Stephens & Scown) *O Q N Zb Zq Zc Zj* Exeter *p222* . . . 01392 210700

Harper, D (Joelson Wilson LLP) *C1 C2 Zb Zv* Westminster *p46*. . . . 020 7580 5721

Harper, D A (Hogan Lovells International LLP) London EC1 *p42*. . . . 020 7296 2000

Harper, Miss D C (KSH Law Firm) *O C1 C2 N R1 J1 P B1 Q Zc Ze Zr Zu* Newcastle upon Tyne *p325* . 0191 232 5232

Harper, G S (Hamer Childs) *G H B2* Worcester *p439* . . . 01905 724565

Harper, Mrs H K M (Harper Law) *J1 Q A2* Romsey *p366* . . . 01794 322364

Harper, Miss J (Baily Gibson) *K1* High Wycombe *p249*. . . . 01494 442661

Harper, K A (Kingsfords) *Q Zk V F2 F1* Ashford *p119* . . . 01233 665544

Harper, Ms K L (Forsters LLP) *O* Westminster *p33*. . . . 020 7863 8333

Harper, Miss L (Hurlow & Partners) *G H* Cardiff *p179* . . . 029 2039 6087

Harper, Miss L M (Wade & Davies) *W* Great Dunmow *p233*. . . . 01371 872816

Harper, M A (Abels) *C1 E G H J1 L M1 N P S1 Za Zh Zi* Southampton *p385*. . . . 023 8022 0317

Harper, M J P (Withers LLP) *K1 K2* London EC4 *p92*. . . . 020 7597 6000

Harper, M W (Yates Ardern) *H B2 G* Ashton-under-Lyne *p120*. . 0161 330 3332

Harper, N J (Hepburns) London SE22 *p40* . . . 020 8299 3376

Harper, Miss R E (Brabners Chaffe Street) *K1* Liverpool *p286* . . . 0151 600 3000 Preston *p356* . . . 01772 823921

Harper, Mrs S E (Visa Europe) London W2 *p110*. . . . 020 7937 8111

Harpham, N T (Hewitsons) *C1* Cambridge *p174*. . . . 01223 461155 Northampton *p332*. . . . 01604 233233

Harpur, G R T (Duffield Stunt) *W T2 Zd* Chelmsford *p186*. . . . 01245 262351

Harpur, Ms J A (Simpson Millar LLP) *N Zq* London EC1 *p80*. . . . 0844 858 3400

Harrap, J R (Lupton Fawcett) *C1 C2* Leeds *p275* . . . 0113 280 2000

Harrap, Miss R J (Edwin Coe LLP) *J1* London WC2 *p29* . . . 020 7691 4000

Harrap, R J (Orange PCS Ltd) *O Q Zq* Bristol *p452* . . . 0870 376 8888

Harrar, Ms S K (Wright Hassall LLP) *J1* Leamington Spa *p270* . . . 01926 886688

Harraway, Mrs E L (Metropolitan Police Directorate of Legal Services) London SW1 *p108*. . . . 020 7230 7210

Harray, S M (Allen & Overy LLP) London E1 *p5* . . . 020 3088 0000

Harrel, D T D (SJ Berwin LLP) *O* London EC4 *p75*. . . . 020 7111 2222

Harrett, S J (Hutchinson Thomas) *G H* Neath *p320* . . . 01639 645061

Harrhy, T (Bower & Bailey) Witney *p436* . . . 01993 705095

Harries, Miss A C (Whittinghams) *K1 M1* Bridgend *p157*. . . . 01656 653485

Harries, A C D (TLT Solicitors) London EC2 *p85*. . . . 020 3465 4000

Harries, Miss B M (Marrons) *R1 P* Leicester *p280*. . . . 0116 289 2200

Harries, D A (Aaron & Partners LLP Solicitors) *A3 Zc C1 U1 C3 I Ze Zk O Zq Q* Chester *p190* . . . 01244 405555

Harries, D N (Torfaen Borough Council) Pontypool *p469* . . . 01495 766373

Harries, G R (Addleshaw Goddard) *C1* London EC1 *p4* . . . 020 7606 8855

Harries, H J O (Midwinters) *W T2* Cheltenham *p188* . . . 01242 514674

Harries, I R (Morgan & Richardson) *A1 D1 G H K1 L N Q S1 T2 W* Cardigan *p181*. . . . 01239 612302

Harries, Miss J (Torbay Council) Torquay *p474* . . . 01803 201201

Harries, J A (Pembrokeshire County Council) *K1 N* Haverfordwest *p460* . . . 01437 764551

Harries, Miss N (Nicola Harries Solicitor) *D1 K1 L P S1 V W* Chipping Ongar *p193* . . . 01277 362332

Harries, Miss N J (Collyer Bristow LLP) *D2 D1 K2 K1* London WC1 *p22* . . . 020 7242 7363

Harries, N R (Capron & Helliwell) *S1 E C1 L S2* Stalham *p393* . . . 01692 581231

Harries, R E (Barcan Woodward) *Zr* Bristol *p161* . . . 0117 925 8080

Harries, Miss S M (City & County of Swansea) Swansea *p473*. . . . 01792 636000

Harriman, W P (Charles Russell LLP) *W Zd T2* London EC4 *p19*. . . . 020 7203 5000

Harrington, B P (Denison Till) *J1* York *p444* . . . 01904 611411

Harrington, D (Couchmans LLP) London WC1 *p23* . . . 020 7611 9660

Harrington, G D (Moss & Coleman) *E C1 S1 A1 R1 J1 Zl Ze* Hornchurch *p252* . . . 01708 446781

Harrington, J (Harringtons) *G H* Brighton *p159* . . . 01273 606069

Harrington, Ms J A (Southern Water Services Ltd) Worthing *p477*. . . . 01903 264444

Harrington, J G (Pannone LLP) *J1 Zp* Manchester *p308* . . . 0161 909 3000

Harrington, K G (Beale and Company Solicitors LLP) *E S1 S2 C1* London WC2 *p11* . . . 020 7240 3474

Harrington, P A (MPH Solicitors) *N* Manchester *p307* . . . 0161 832 7722

Harrington, S P J (MPH Solicitors) *N* Bury St Edmunds *p171* . . . 01284 811870 Manchester *p307* . . . 0161 832 7722

Harrington, W M (Will Harrington & Co) *G H N Zl B2* Sutton Coldfield *p403* . . . 0121 321 1999

Harris, A (Alan Harris) *D1 H* Plymouth *p350*. . . . 01752 223655

Harris, Mrs A (Skandia Life Assurance Co Ltd) *D1 K1 L N O Q Zb Zk* Southampton *p472*. . . . 023 8033 4411

Harris, Ms A (Watson Farley & Williams) London EC2 *p90*. . . . 020 7814 8000

Harris, A (Blandy & Blandy) *J1* Reading *p360* . . . 0118 951 6800

Harris, Mrs A C (Harrowells) *E C1 L S2* York *p444* . . . 01904 690111

Harris, A C (Oberman Law) Camden *p64*. . . . 020 7242 6154

Harris, A D (DLA Piper UK LLP) *A3 B2 O* Manchester *p303* . . . 0870 011 1111

Harris, Miss A E (Thomson Snell & Passmore) *S1* Tunbridge Wells *p415* . . . 01892 510000

Harris, A H (Pritchard Englefield) *C1 C2 Zb Ze* London EC2 *p69*. . . . 020 7972 9720

Harris, A J (Anthony Harris & Co) *S1 E W Q L K1 R1 Ze* New Milton *p321*. . . . 01425 638288

Harris, A J B (Harvey Ingram Borneos) *G H Zl Zt* Bedford *p130* . . . 01234 353221

Harris, A J H (Garstangs) *G H B2* London WC2 *p35* . . . 020 7427 5678

Harris, A L (HCB Solicitors) *E S1 C1 W* Solihull *p382*. . . . 0121 705 2255

Harris, A P (Pinsent Masons LLP) Bristol *p164* . . . 0117 924 5678

Harris, Ms B (Hughes-Narborough & Thomas) *D1 K1 P M1 W L F1 V Zl K3* Greenwich *p43*. . . . 020 8854 1291

Harris, Mrs B A (Bridge McFarland) *D1 D2* Grimsby *p235* . . . 01472 311711 Lincoln *p284*. . . . 01522 518888

Harris, B B (Brian Harris & Co) *C1 B2 Zi M2 O T2* London W1 *p39* . . . 020 7935 5541 London W1 *p84* . . . 020 7935 5279

Harris, Ms C (Simmons & Simmons) London EC2 *p79*. . . . 020 7628 2020

Harris, Ms C (Doyle Clayton Solicitors Limited) *J1 Zp* Reading *p360* . . . 0118 959 6839

Harris, Ms C (Wilkin Chapman Epton Blades) *E* Lincoln *p285*. . . . 01522 512345

Harris, C (Curry Popeck) *E N* London W1 *p24* . . . 020 7224 6633

Harris, Miss C (Barlow Lyde & Gilbert LLP) *O J1 Zq* London EC3 *p10*. . . . 020 7247 2277

Harris, C D (Harris & Co) *S1 E W C1 K1 K3 Zi Zg B1 J1 N Q* London N3 *p39* . . . 020 3330 7289

Harris, Mrs C J (Birchall Blackburn LLP) *B1 Zl O Q Zb Zq* Chorley *p194* . . . 01257 279011

Harris, C P (Mole Valley District Council) Dorking *p457* . . . 01306 885001

Harris, D (Darbys Solicitors LLP) *J1* Oxford *p343*. . . . 01865 811700

Harris, D (Thompsons (formerly Robin/Brian Thompson & Partners)) *I P* London WC1 *p87* . . . 020 7290 0000

Harris, Mrs D (Penman Johnson) *N O Q L* Watford *p424* . . 01923 225212 / 239566

Harris, D A (Browne Jacobson LLP) *E* Nottingham *p336*. . . . 0115 976 6000

Harris, D A (Hogan Lovells International LLP) London EC1 *p42*. . . . 020 7296 2000

Harris, D B (Duffield Harrison LLP) Hoddesdon *p251*. . . . 01992 442911

Harris, D C (Foys Solicitors) *G H Zl B2* Doncaster *p211* . . . 01302 327136

Harris, Ms D C (Aviva PLC) London EC3 *p103* . 020 7283 7500 / 01603 687905 Norwich *p467* . . . 01603 622200

Harris, Miss D E (Marriott Davies Yapp) *C1 Zd Zc Ze J1 M1* Sutton *p402* . . . 020 8643 9794

Harris, D J (Pollard Bower Solicitors) *N O Q F1 F2 B1 C1* Burnley *p169* . . . 01282 457624

Harris, D J (Barwells) *B1 D1 G J1 K1 L N O Q V* Newhaven *p327* . . . 01273 514213 Eastbourne *p215*. . . . 01323 411505

Harris, D J (Greenland Houchen Pomeroy) *O N Q J1* Norwich *p334* . . . 01603 660744

Harris, D K (HSR Law (Hayes, Son & Richmond)) *A1 C1 C2 E S1 S2 A2* Doncaster *p211* . . . 01302 347800 Gainsborough *p228* . . . 01427 613831

Harris, D K N (The Crown Estate Office) London W15 *p105*. . . . 020 7851 5168

Harris, D L (Smith Roddam) *K1 S1 P M1 D1 F1 G L E Zj Zn* Crook *p203* . . . 01388 762564

Harris, D M (Chandler Harris LLP) *O N B1 C1 J1 L Q* Manchester *p302* . . . 0161 834 2200

Harris, Miss D M (Olswang LLP) *E S1* London WC1 *p64* . . . 020 7067 3000

Harris, D N (Irwin Mitchell LLP) *N* Manchester *p306* . . . 0870 150 0100

Harris, D P (Birchall Blackburn LLP) *N Zr J2 Zq Zw* Preston *p356* . . . 01772 561663

Harris, D R L (Stephenson Harwood) *E C1 S1 L Ze* London EC2 *p82*. . . . 020 7329 4422

Harris, E (Keoghs LLP) *Zj Q N* Bolton *p149* . . . 01204 677000

Harris, Miss E (EMW) *C1* Milton Keynes *p316* . . . 0845 070 6000

Harris, Mrs E A (Oxley & Coward Solicitors LLP) *E A1 L S2* Rotherham *p367*. . . . 01709 510999

Harris, Miss E E (Stantons) *W S1 K1* Gravesend *p233*. . . . 01474 579940

Harris, Miss E H M (Haringey Magistrates Legal Advisers Office) London N6 *p106*. . . . 0845 601 3600

Harris, Miss E K (Powys County Council) Llandrindod Wells *p463* . . . 01597 826000

Harris, G (Gabriel Harris) Barnet *p39*. . . . 020 8343 1355

Harris, Miss G (MPH Solicitors) *Zr* Manchester *p307* . . . 0161 832 7722

Harris, G (Thomas Cooper) *A3 O Za Q* London EC3 *p22*. . . . 020 7481 8851

Harris, Ms G D (SNR Denton) *O* London EC4 *p75*. . . . 020 7242 1212

Harris, G D (Reed Smith LLP) *Za* London EC2 *p71*. . . . 020 3116 3000

Harris, G J (McKeowns Solicitors Ltd) *X N Q* St Albans *p390* . . . 0800 032 8328

Harris, Miss H (Foster & Partners) *S1 W* Bristol *p162* . . . 0117 961 5300

Harris, Mrs H M (Holmes & Hills LLP) *K1 D1* Braintree *p155*. . . . 01376 320456

Harris, I M (Howard Kennedy LLP) *P N L K1 M1 J1 F1 Zd* London W1 *p48* . . . 020 7636 1616

Harris, J (Solomon Taylor & Shaw) London NW3 *p80* . . . 020 7431 1912

Harris, J (Pinsent Masons LLP) London EC2 *p67*. . . . 020 7418 7000

Harris, Miss J (Andrews McQueen) *K1 K3* Bournemouth *p151*. . . . 01202 290628

Harris, J (Dolmans) *J2 Q N Zu C1 E O* Cardiff *p178* . . . 029 2034 5531

Harris, J A (Jolliffe & Co) *E S2 C1 R2 Zc* Chester *p190* . . . 01244 310022

Harris, J A (Martyn Prowel) *G H B2* Cardiff *p180* . . . 029 2047 0909 Cardiff *p180* . . . 029 2072 9888

Harris, J A (Harris Hagan) London EC1 *p39*. . . . 020 7002 7636

Harris, J B (Department for Business, Enterprise and Regulatory Reform) London SW1 *p105*. . . . 020 7215 0105

Harris, J J (DLA Piper UK LLP) *Zo* Manchester *p303* . . . 0870 011 1111

Harris, Ms J K (Kennedys) *N O Q* Chelmsford *p186*. . . . 0845 838 4800

Harris, Ms J M (Barrett & Co Solicitors LLP) *E S2* Reading *p359* . . . 0118 958 9711

Harris, J M (Brecher) *S2 E R2 S1 L* London W1 *p15* . . . 020 7563 1000

Harris, Ms J M S J (Durrington Corporation Ltd) London SW1 *p106*. . . . 020 7235 6146

Harris, J P (Allen & Overy LLP) London E1 *p5* . . . 020 3088 0000

Harris, Mrs J S (Coffin Mew & Clover) *D1 K1* Southampton *p385*. . . . 023 8033 4661

Harris, J S (Brian Harris & Co) *E G B2 C2 J1 N O Q Ze* London W1 *p39* . . . 020 7935 5541

Harris, Ms K (Reynolds Porter Chamberlain LLP) London E1 *p71* . . . 020 3060 6000 London EC2 *p81* . . . 020 7655 1000

Harris, K (Lumsdons Solicitors LLP) Stourport-on-Severn *p399* . 01299 827766

Harris, Miss K A (Roche Products Ltd) Welwyn Garden City *p475* . . . 01707 366000

Harris, Ms K A (Field Fisher Waterhouse LLP) London EC3 *p31*. . . . 020 7861 4000

Harris, K R (Harris & Co) *L S1 W Q J1 S2 E C1 A1 C2* Crawley *p202* . . . 01293 537551

Harris, L (Edwards Angell Palmer & Dodge) *M3 A3 Zb Zc C1 J1 Zj M2 O Q N Zu C2 Zn R2* London EC2 *p28*. . . . 020 7583 4055

Harris, Mrs L (Bross Bennett) *K1 M1 S1* London N6 *p16* . . . 020 8340 0444

Harris, M (Welsh Health Legal Services) Cardiff *p453* . . . 029 2031 5500

Harris, M (Pinsent Masons LLP) *O Zc Q* Leeds *p276* . . . 0113 244 5000

Harris, M (Oberman Law) *R1 R2 S2 S1 E L C1* Camden *p64*. . . . 020 7242 6154

Harris, M (Addleshaw Goddard)
Manchester *p300* 0161 934 6000
Harris, Mrs M A (Steel & Shamash) *P K1 J1 L M1 N D1 F1 C1 Zb*
Lambeth *p82*. 020 7803 3999
Harris, M A P (Harris & Co) *C1 E F1 K1 L M1 R1 S1 T1 W Zc Zj Zl*
Southsea *p388*. 023 9278 5757
Harris, M E (Williams Beales & Co)
Hay-on-Wye *p245* 01497 820302
Harris, M J (Challinors) *C1 Ze*
West Bromwich *p427* 0121 553 3211
Harris, M L (Howard Kennedy LLP) *C1 C2 T1 J1 I B1 Ze Zb*
London W1 *p48* 020 7636 1616
Harris, P (Squire Sanders (UK) LLP)
London EC2 *p81*. 020 7655 1000
Harris, P (Harris Temperley)
London W6 *p39* 020 8233 2989
Harris, P J (Clifford Johnston & Co) *G H B2 Zm*
Manchester *p302* 0161 975 1900
Harris, P J (Wright Hassall LLP) *Ze A3 E*
Leamington Spa *p270* 01926 886688
Harris, P M (Hamers Solicitors) *K1*
Hull *p257* 01482 326666
Harris, P N (Jeffrey Green Russell) *W T1 Zd*
London W1 *p46* 020 7339 7000
Harris, P S (Edward Fail Bradshaw & Waterson) *G H B2*
London EC3 *p30*. 020 7790 4032
London EC3 *p30*. 020 7264 2016
Harris, P T (Irwin Mitchell LLP) *Zb B1 O Q A3*
Birmingham *p139* 0870 150 0100
Harris, R (Bower Cotton Khaitan) *E L R2 S1 S2 Zc*
London EC4 *p15*. 020 7353 1313
Harris, Ms R (Ashurst LLP)
London EC2 *p7* 020 7638 1111
Harris, R A B (Mundays LLP) *E S1 A1*
Cobham *p196* 01932 590500
Harris, R C (ASB Law) *O K1 C1 Q Zd*
Maidstone *p298* 01622 656500
Harris, R C (Peach Grey & Co) *G H*
Southampton *p386*. 023 8033 4695
Harris, R C (Weightmans LLP) *E R1*
Manchester *p311* 0161 233 7330
Harris, Miss R C (Hodge Jones & Allen LLP) *N*
London NW1 *p41* 020 7874 8300
Harris, R L (Claremont Richards) *E C1 W T1*
London EC4 *p20*. 020 7353 3030
Harris, R M C (Kennedys) *N J1 O Zj Zt*
Chelmsford *p186*. 0845 838 4800
Harris, R N (Holmes & Hills LLP) *E L S1 S2*
Halstead *p238* 01787 475312
Harris, R P (Harvey Ingram LLP) *E W S1 T2 A1 Zd*
Leicester *p280*. 0116 254 5454
Harris, R S (Kennedys)
London EC3 *p49*. 020 7667 9667
Harris, R T (AMD Solicitors) *C1 E L S1 Zn*
Bristol *p160* 0117 974 4100
Harris, Ms S (Russell Jones & Walker)
Manchester *p309* 0161 383 3500
Harris, Ms S (Kennedys)
London EC3 *p49*. 020 7667 9667
Harris, Ms S (T Llewellyn Jones)
Neath *p320* 01639 643635
Harris, S (Stokes Solicitors) *S2 S1 E*
Portsmouth *p355*. 023 9266 1541
Harris, Mrs S A (Greenland Houchen Pomeroy) *M1 P K1 J1 B1 L*
Attleborough *p120* 01953 453143
Harris, Mrs S A (Walker Morris) *O*
Leeds *p277* 0113 283 2500
Harris, Miss S C (Family Law Consultants) *K1 D1 K3*
Cheltenham *p188* 01242 222201
Harris, Mrs S C (Mills & Reeve) *J1*
Cambridge *p175*. 01223 364422
Harris, Ms S J (Thompsons (formerly Robin/Brian Thompson & Partners)) *J1 N G P*
Plymouth *p350*. 01752 675810
Harris, Ms S L (HKB Wiltshires) *S1 S2 E*
Great Yarmouth *p234* 01493 855676
Harris, S M (Ashurst LLP)
London EC2 *p7* 020 7638 1111
Harris, S P (Hand Morgan & Owen) *W T2 T1*
Stafford *p393* 01785 211411
Harris, Miss T J (Wallis Prance)
Basingstoke *p127* 01256 464311
Harris, Miss T K (Taylor Walton LLP) *N O Zj*
Luton *p295* 01582 731161
Harris, T R (Morrish Solicitors LLP) *N Q Zj*
Leeds *p276* 0113 245 0733
Harris, Miss V J (The Royal London Mutual Insurance Society Ltd)
London EC3 *p455* 020 7506 6500
Harris, Miss V K (Pannone LLP) *K1*
Manchester *p308* 0161 909 3000
Harris, Miss V M T (Birketts LLP) *W*
Ipswich *p262*. 01473 232300
Harris, Mrs W (Windeatts)
Totnes *p413*. 01803 862233
Harris-Deans, Mrs M (Blake Lapthorn) *O*
Chandlers Ford *p184* 023 8090 8090
Harris-Hughes, E (Collins Benson Goldhill LLP)
Westminster *p21*. 020 7436 5151
Harrisingh, N (Trowers & Hamlins)
London EC3 *p88*. 020 7423 8000
Harris-James, K M (Irwin Mitchell LLP) *D1 G H K1 V*
Birmingham *p139* 0870 150 0100

Harrison, A (Woking Borough Council)
Woking *p477*. 01483 755855
Harrison, Ms A (Stephensons Solicitors LLP) *N*
Wigan *p432* 01942 777777
Harrison, A (Harrisons)
Reading *p361* 0118 959 8974
Harrison, Mrs A L (Durham County Council)
Durham *p457* 0191 383 3513
Harrison, A P (Kennedys) *N Q O Zr Zq*
Chelmsford *p186*. 0845 838 4800
Harrison, A P (Sternberg Reed) *N*
Barking *p123* 020 8591 3366
Harrison, A S (Alan Harrison & Co) *S1 P E M1 N W G K1 F1*
Wembley *p426*. 020 8900 0262
Harrison, B W (Allen & Overy LLP)
London E1 *p5* 020 3088 0000
Harrison, Miss C (The Beavis Partnership) *W*
Chelmsford *p186*. 01245 264748
Harrison, Mrs C (Bell Park Kerridge) *N Q S1*
Carlisle *p181*. 01228 888999
Harrison, Mrs C (Massers) *W*
Nottingham *p338*. 0115 851 1666
Harrison, C (Granville-West Chivers & Morgan) *S1 W E C1*
Newport *p328* 01495 243268
Harrison, C E (Scotts Wright) *N Q J1 J2 L F1 Zr*
Catterick Garrison *p183* . . . 01748 832431
Harrison, D (Jobling & Knape) *E C1 S1 A1 J1 W T1 F1 B1*
Great Eccleston *p233* 01995 670083
Morecambe *p319* 01524 416960
Harrison, Miss D C (Whitehead Monckton) *K1 K2*
Maidstone *p299* 01622 698000
Harrison, D E (Poole Alcock) *W S1 A1 J1 L C1 E R1 T1 Zt*
Sandbach *p372* 01270 762325
Harrison, D L (Harrison Li Solicitors LLP) *S2 E R1 R2 S1*
Camberley *p173*. 01276 27700
Harrison, E J (Kent County Council)
Maidstone *p464* 01622 694320
Harrison, Miss F A (Hempsons) *N Q J1 D1 Zk Zo Zr*
Manchester *p305* 0161 228 0011
Harrison, Ms G (Harvey Copping & Harrison) *W*
Wickford *p431* . . . .01268 733381 / 763211
Harrison, Mrs H E J (Anthony Collins Solicitors LLP) *L O E A3*
Birmingham *p137* 0121 200 3242
Harrison, J (Watson Burton LLP) *Zc Q*
Newcastle upon Tyne *p327* . 0845 901 2100
Harrison, Ms J (Chattertons Solicitors)
Grantham *p232* 01476 591550
Harrison, J (Preston Mellor Harrison) *W E S1*
Chislehurst *p193*. 020 8468 7025
Harrison, Miss J (Ward Hadaway) *C1 C2 Zb*
Newcastle upon Tyne *p327* . 0191 204 4000
Harrison, Mrs J C (J M Harrison) *G S1*
Bampton *p122*. 01993 852222
Harrison, J C (Labrums) *S1 W K1 C1 E G M1 T1 P J1 Zl Zd Zf Zb Zo*
St Albans *p390* 01727 858807
Harrison, J F (John F Harrison) *Zm G H V*
Ashby-de-la-Zouch *p118*. . . 01530 563655
Harrison, J P (Barrett & Co Solicitors LLP) *C1 S2 E S1*
Reading *p359* 0118 958 9711
Harrison, J R (Edwards Duthie) *L Zm*
London E6 *p29* 020 8514 9000
Harrison, Ms K E (Thomas Cooper) *E S1 L W*
London EC3 *p22*. 020 7481 8851
Harrison, Mrs K L (Shoosmiths) *C1 C3 M1 I Zb Ze*
Nottingham *p339*. 0370 086 5000 / 0115 906 5000
Harrison, Ms L (Denison Till) *O*
York *p444* 01904 611411
Harrison, Ms L (Irwin Mitchell LLP) *Zj N G O P*
Sheffield *p376* 0870 150 0100
Harrison, Mrs L (Clarion Solicitors LLP) *O Zf Zw Q*
Leeds *p272* 0113 246 0622
Harrogate *p240* 01423 530630
Harrison, Mrs L D (Frank Howard) *K1 D1 K3*
Warrington *p422*. 01925 653481
Harrison, Miss L E (Horrocks & Co) *S1 W S2 E B1 J1*
Leeds *p274* 0113 230 7944
Harrison, L S (Waldrons) *O Q N L K1*
Walsall *p420*. 01384 811811
Harrison, L T (Debenhams Ottaway) *Zj*
St Albans *p390* 01727 837161
Harrison, M (Foley Harrison) *D1 K1 G H K2*
Gateshead *p228*. 0191 477 6333
Harrison, M (Robert Lizar) *K1 D1*
Manchester *p307* 0161 226 2319
Harrison, M B (Badhams Law (A Trading Name of Parabis Law LLP)) *N Q Zq*
Croydon *p204* 0844 245 4000
Harrison, M E (Durham County Council)
Durham *p457* 0191 383 3513
Harrison, Mrs M F (Stroud and Swindon Building Society)
Stroud *p473* 01453 757011
Harrison, M J (Hepburns)
London SE22 *p40* 020 8299 3376
Harrison, M J (M J Harrison) *A1 B1 E F1 R1 S1 T1 T2 W*
Scarborough *p372*. 01723 865578
Harrison, M J W (Duffield Harrison LLP) *E S1 W C1 R1 L P M1 N G Zk Zl Zm*
Hoddesdon *p251*. 01992 442911

Harrison, Miss M L (Myers Fletcher & Gordon) *Q L O*
London W6 *p62* 020 7610 4433
Harrison, M N (Faber & Co) *S1 E L R1 Q W S2*
Birmingham *p138* 0121 236 5751
Harrison, M R (Hay & Kilner) *G H*
Wallsend *p419*. 0191 262 8231
Harrison, M W (Harrisons Solicitors) *C1 F1 J1 O Q Zj*
Manchester *p305* 0161 819 2511
Harrison, Ms N (Bingham McCutchen (London) LLP)
London EC2 *p12*. 020 7661 5300
Harrison, N (Dickinson Dees) *Q*
Newcastle upon Tyne *p324* . 0191 279 9000
Harrison, N (Hatchers Solicitors LLP) *J1 L C1 S2*
Shrewsbury *p379* 01743 248545
Harrison, N C (Harvey Copping & Harrison) *W O Q K1 J1*
Wickford *p431* . . . .01268 733381 / 763211
Harrison, P (Clarkes) *D1 G H B2 Zl*
Shrewsbury *p379* 01743 231531
Harrison, P (Taylor Wessing) *B1 C1 Zb*
London EC4 *p86*. 020 7300 7000
Harrison, P (Welton Harrison) *E L*
Hessle *p249*. 01482 627711
Harrison, Miss P A (Allen & Overy LLP)
London E1 *p5* 020 3088 0000
Harrison, P J (Crown Prosecution Service Thames Valley)
Abingdon *p447*. 01235 551900
Harrison, P J (Giffen Couch & Archer) *S1 W E L C1*
Stony Stratford *p399*. 01908 563911
Harrison, P R (Poole Alcock) *A1 N Q O D1 R1 H G J1 F1 Zl*
Sandbach *p372* 01270 762325
Harrison, R C (Winckworth Sherwood LLP) *C1 L M1 K1*
Oxford *p344* 01865 297200
London SE1 *p92*. 020 7593 5000
Harrison, R J (Barlow Lyde & Gilbert LLP) *O Zj Zq*
London EC3 *p10*. 020 7247 2277
Harrison, R J F (Menneer Shuttleworth) *S2 E R2 S1 W*
St Leonards-on-Sea *p392* . . 01424 720044
Harrison, R M (Laytons) *O I U2 E*
London EC4 *p52*. 020 7842 8000
Harrison, R W M (Lloyds TSB Group PLC)
London EC2 *p107* 020 7158 2729
Harrison, Mrs S (Marsden Rawsthorn LLP) *J1 C1*
Preston *p357* 01772 799600
Harrison, Mrs S (R F Tansey) *D2 K3 K1*
Thame *p410*. 01844 218000
Harrison, Mrs S (Bryan & Armstrong) *S1 S2*
Mansfield *p311*. 01623 626039
Harrison, Mrs S A (Preston Borough Council)
Preston *p469* 01772 906101
Harrison, Ms S F (Kingston upon Hull City Council)
Hull *p461* 01482 300300
Harrison, S J (Robinson Allfree) *D1 K1 K3 Zl*
Ramsgate *p359* 01843 592361
Harrison, Ms S R (Kitching Walker) *K1 D1 L S1 S2*
Kirkbymoorside *p268*. 01751 431237
Harrison, Ms S R (Thomas Flavell & Sons) *K1 W*
Hinckley *p250* 01455 610747
Harrison, Ms T (Howells LLP) *Zr*
Sheffield *p376* 0114 249 6666
Harrison, T (Forsters LLP) *O Q*
Westminster *p33*. 020 7863 8333
Harrison, Mrs T A (Harrisons Solicitors) *C1 F1 J1 O Q A3*
Manchester *p305* 0161 819 2511
Harrison, T B (Adams Harrison) *S1 G K1 M1 P E F1 H W L Zl Zk Zm*
Haverhill *p244* . . . .01440 705731 / 702485
Saffron Walden *p370*. 01799 523441
Harrison, T M (Newbys) *B1 J1 Q Zq O*
Middlesbrough *p315* .01642 247717 / 247967
Harrison, W (Galbraith Branley)
London N12 *p34*. 020 8446 8474
Harrison, Mrs W A (DLA Piper UK LLP) *C1 Zb*
Leeds *p272* 0870 011 1111
Harrison-Hall, Mrs H M (Allen & Overy LLP)
London E1 *p5* 020 3088 0000
Harrison-Jones, Mrs A T (Hugh James)
Cardiff *p179* 029 2022 4871
Harrison-Obafemi, J (Newmans Solicitors) *B1 C1 S2 E F1 G J1 L Zl O Q N Zp S1*
Horley *p252* 01293 771521
Harriss, D (Bird & Bird LLP) *Ze*
London EC4 *p13*. 020 7415 6000
Harrod, Mrs A M (Spearing Waite LLP) *E S2 R2*
Leicester *p281*. 0116 262 4225
Harrod, Mrs C M (Beaty & Co)
Wigton *p432*. 01697 342121
Harrold, K H (Test Valley Borough Council)
Andover *p447* 01264 368000
Harrold, N A (Hay & Kilner) *B1 O*
Newcastle upon Tyne *p325* . 0191 232 8345
Harrop, P C (Harrops)
Oxted *p344* 01883 712940
Harrop, Miss S C (Jacobs Solicitors) *K1 D1*
Ellesmere Port *p217*. 0151 355 8481
Harrop, Mrs V (Harrops) *W*
Oxted *p344* 01883 712940
Harrop, W D (Woolliscrofts) *N K1 O Q S1 W G H J1*
Newcastle under Lyme *p323*. 01782 662545

Harrop-Griffths, B (John Morse Solicitors) *S2 S1 W*
Swansea *p405*. 01792 648111
Harrow, Mrs E J (Harrowells) *S1*
York *p444* 01904 558600
Harrow, P (Harlow District Council)
Harlow *p460*. 01279 446611
Harrower, G G (Sidley Austin Brown & Wood) *T1*
London EC2 *p78*. 020 7360 3600
Harrowing, P D (United Bristol Healthcare NHS Trust)
Bristol *p452* 0117 928 3730
Harry, Mrs J (Blake Lapthorn) *W*
Chandlers Ford *p184* 023 8090 8090
Harryman, M A (Maples Teesdale LLP) *E S2 R2*
London EC2 *p58*. 020 7600 3800
Harryman, Miss Z A (Russell & Russell) *S1*
Bolton *p149* 01204 399299
Hart, A (Bryan Cave) *C1*
London EC2 *p19*. 020 7207 1100
Hart, Ms A (Heptonstalls LLP) *N*
Pontefract *p351* 01977 602804
Hart, Ms A (Field Fisher Waterhouse LLP)
London EC3 *p31*. 020 7861 4000
Hart, A N (Stephenson Harwood) *B1 J1 O W*
London EC2 *p82*. 020 7329 4422
Hart, A T L (Batt Broadbent) *E S1 S2 A1 A2 L R1 Zc Zd*
Salisbury *p371*. 01722 411141
Hart, A W (Baileys) *W T2 Zd*
Cheltenham *p187* 01242 514477
Hart, Miss C F (Robertsons) *S1 W E L R1 C1*
Barry *p126*. 01446 745660
Hart, C H (Charles Hart Solicitors) *C1 L O G H*
Cheddar *p186* 01934 742315
Hart, Miss C L (KBL Solicitors) *J1*
Bolton *p149* 01204 527777
Hart, D (Lupton Fawcett) *J1 Zp*
Leeds *p275* 0113 280 2000
Hart, Sir D M (National Association of Head Teachers) *J1*
Haywards Heath *p460* 01444 472472
Wigton *p432*. 01697 342121
Hart, D R (Petty Sessional Divisions of East Penwith, Falmouth and Kerrier Isles)
Truro *p474*. . . . . .01872 274075 / 277375
Hart, G (The Smith Partnership) *G H Zm*
Leicester *p281*. 0116 247 2000
Hart, G A (Ward & Rider Limited) *N*
Coventry *p201* 024 7655 5400
Hart, G N W (Hudgell & Partners) *C1 E S1*
Greenwich *p43*. 020 8854 1331
Hart, J (Pinsent Masons LLP) *O Q Zc*
London EC2 *p67*. 020 7418 7000
Hart, J H (J H Hart & Co) *S1 W E S2*
London E6 *p39* 020 8472 2652
Hart, Miss K (Stockton-On-Tees Borough Council) *K1 D1*
Stockton-on-Tees *p472* . . . 01642 393939
Middlesbrough *p314* 01642 252555
Hart, Mrs K J (Harvey Ingram LLP) *N K1*
Leicester *p280*. 0116 254 5454
Hart, Ms M (Harbottle & Lewis LLP) *Q*
London W1 *p38* 020 7667 5000
Hart, Ms N J (Pinsent Masons LLP) *X*
Birmingham *p141* 0121 200 1050
Hart, P C (Waller & Hart) *K4 E C1 S1 L T1 T2 J1 F1 Zl Zn Zq W A1 S2*
Camborne *p173* . . .01209 714064 / 719871
Hart, P W (Royds LLP) *K1 N Q G D1*
London EC4 *p74*. 020 7583 2222
Hart, R (Addleshaw Goddard)
Manchester *p300* 0161 934 6000
Hart, R (RMPI Solicitors) *E S2*
London W1 *p70* 020 7318 4444
Hart, R (Hay & Kilner) *G H D1*
Wallsend *p419*. 0191 262 8231
Hart, Ms R D (Trowers & Hamlins) *L Zh*
London EC3 *p88*. 020 7423 8000
Hart, S (Official Solicitor and Public Trustee) *T1 T2 V W*
London WC2 *p108*. 020 7911 7127
Hart, Miss S E (Brachers) *A1 E L S2 R2*
Maidstone *p299* 01622 690691
Hart, S F (Davies & Partners) *Q Zq Zb B1*
Gloucester *p230*. 01452 612345
Hart, Ms S L (Oxford Law Group) *K1 D1 D2*
Oxford *p344* 01865 297300
Hart, Ms V (Vyman Solicitors) *G H B2*
Gravesend *p233*. 01474 537270
Hart-Leverton, D A (Dorman Joseph Wachtel) *E L S1 S2 W*
London EC3 *p27*. 020 7680 6300
Harte, Ms A (Invesco)
London EC2 *p107* 020 7065 3057
Harte, Mrs E K (Alexiou Fisher Philipps) *K1 D1 K2 K3*
London W1 *p5*. 020 7409 1222
Harte, Ms M C (Blake Lapthorn) *C1 C2*
Oxford *p342* 01865 248607
Harte-Lovelace, Miss V J (K&L Gates LLP) *O Zb L T1*
London EC4 *p47*. 020 7648 9000
Hartford, R R (Aviva PLC)
London EC3 *p103* . 020 7283 7500 / 01603 687905
Norwich *p467* 01603 622200
Hartgroves, R (Northamptonshire Magistrates Courts)
Northampton *p467*. 01604 497000
Hartigan, Miss L A (Meade-King) *B1*
Bristol *p163* 0117 926 4121

 See p634 for the Key to Work Categories

Hartigan, T (Trethowans LLP) *N Zr Q O*
Salisbury *p371*. 01722 412512

Hartland, T J (Clarke & Hartland Solicitors) *D1 F1 G H J1 K1 L S1*
Cardiff *p177* 029 2048 3181

Hartley, A (DLA Piper UK LLP) *J1 Zp Zw*
Leeds *p272* 0870 011 1111

Hartley, Miss A (East Riding of Yorkshire Council)
Beverley *p449* 01482 887700

Hartley, A (BASF PLC)
Cheadle Hulme *p454*. 0161 488 5634

Hartley, Ms A E (Potter Rees (Serious Injury) Solicitors)
Manchester *p309* 0161 237 5888

Hartley, A J (hlw Keeble Hawson LLP) *C1 C2*
Sheffield *p376* 0114 276 5555

Hartley, D J (The Lister Croft Partnership) *S1 S2 W E*
Wakefield *p418* 0871 220 1333

Hartley, D P (Addleshaw Goddard)
London EC1 *p4* 020 7606 8855

Hartley, Ms E B A (Reynolds Porter Chamberlain LLP) *A3 O Zk*
London E1 *p71* 020 3060 6000

Hartley, Ms H (Walker Morris)
Leeds *p277* 0113 283 2500

Hartley, I (Walker Morris)
Leeds *p277* 0113 283 2500

Hartley, I J (EEF West Midlands Association)
Birmingham *p449* 0121 456 2222

Hartley, J (Malletts Solicitors) *B2 G*
London WC1 *p58* 020 7061 3760

Hartley, J A (Donald Race & Newton) *E S1 S2 W L*
Burnley *p169* 01282 433241

Hartley, J M (Norton Peskett) *G M1 P J1 H N L K1 D1*
Lowestoft *p294* 01502 533000

Hartley, Ms J M (Dudley Metropolitan Borough Council) *F1 J1 N*
Dudley *p457*. 01384 815326

Hartley, K (Pinsent Masons LLP) *O Q M1 M2 Zc*
Leeds *p276* 0113 244 5000

Hartley, M C T (Allen & Overy LLP)
London E1 *p5* 020 3088 0000

Hartley, M G (Duane Morris) *C1 S2 E J1 C2 R2 S1 Zw C3 Zf*
London EC1 *p28*. 020 7786 2100

Hartley, M P (Allen & Overy LLP) *O N Zj*
London E1 *p5* 020 3088 0000

Hartley, M W (Calvert Solicitors) *E S1 L S2*
Southwark *p17*. 020 7234 0707

Hartley, P J (Leech & Co) *N Q*
Manchester *p306* 0161 279 0279

Hartley, P J (Young & Co) *W S1*
Stoke-on-Trent *p398*. 01782 339200

Hartley, P J (Kennedys)
London EC3 *p49*. 020 7667 9667

Hartley, Miss R B (Edwards Angell Palmer & Dodge)
London EC2 *p28*. 020 7583 4055

Hartley, Miss S (KBL Solicitors) *W K4 T2*
Bolton *p149* 01204 527777

Hartley, Ms S J J (Reed Smith LLP) *O*
London EC2 *p71*. 020 3116 3000

Hartley, S P (Reed Smith LLP) *Zo*
London EC2 *p71*. 020 3116 3000

Hartnell, N A (Hartnell Chanot & Partners Family Law Specialists) *D1 D2 K1 K2 K3*
Exeter *p221* 01392 421777

Hartnett, Mrs A L (Visa Europe)
London W2 *p110*. 020 7937 8111

Hartnett, Ms A P M (Taylor Walton LLP) *K1*
Harpenden *p239*. 01582 765111

Hartrick, A K (Hempsons) *N Q Zq Zr Zm*
Harrogate *p240* 01423 522331

Hartridge, Mrs J M (Emmerson Brown & Brown) *K1 D1 L F1 B1 J1 V*
Dover *p212* 01304 211766

Hartshorn, A (Shakespeares)
Birmingham *p142* 0121 237 3000

Hartshorn, Mrs M (Millichips) *N Q Zq Zr*
West Bromwich *p427* 0121 500 6363

Hartshorn, R A (Pinsent Masons LLP) *U2 Ze U1 I*
Birmingham *p141* 0121 200 1050

Hartshorn, T P (Morrison & Masters Limited) *S1 S2 E*
Swindon *p406* 01793 526601

Hartshorne, Ms J L (Gardner Iliff & Dowding) *W K4*
Cannock *p176*. 01543 466941

Hartwell, D G (Gordon Lutton) *A1 A2 T1 T2 W C1 J1 Zl*
Hereford *p248* 01432 355345

Hartwell, J E M (Wessex Housing Partnership Ltd)
Basingstoke *p448* 01256 844506

Hartwell, Mrs S A (Pritchard Joyce & Hinds) *K1 Zl*
Beckenham *p129* 020 8658 3922

Harty, D A (Baines Wilson LLP) *E S2 L*
Carlisle *p181*. 01228 552600

Harvard, J C d J (Forth & Co) *Zl S2 W*
Yarm *p443*. 01642 784000

Harvey, A C (Thomson Snell & Passmore) *S1 L*
Tunbridge Wells *p415* 01892 510000

Harvey, Ms A C (Birmingham City Council Legal & Democratic Services)
Birmingham *p449* 0121 303 2066

Harvey, Mrs A J (Pinkney Grunwells Lawyers LLP) *S1 W*
Bridlington *p158* 01262 673445

Harvey, Ms A L (Devonshires) *J1 O Q*
London EC2 *p27*. 020 7628 7576

Harvey, Ms B (The Gwyn George Partnership) *S1 K1 W S2 D1*
Aberdare *p113*. . . .01685 874629 / 871133

Harvey, Mrs C (United Kingdom Nirex Ltd)
Didcot *p457* 01235 825500

Harvey, Ms C (Scott Rees & Co) *N Q*
Skelmersdale *p381* 01695 722222

Harvey, C (Crown Prosecution Service Dyfed Powys)
Carmarthen *p453* 01267 242100

Harvey, Miss C E (Olswang LLP) *C1 C3 Zf Zw*
London WC1 *p64* 020 7067 3000

Harvey, C J (Lamberts) *C1 E K1 L S1 Zf Ze*
Sevenoaks *p374*. 01732 460565

Harvey, Miss C J Z (Hempsons) *N Q Zq Zr*
Westminster *p40*. 020 7839 0278

Harvey, D (Bridge McFarland)
Grimsby *p235* 01472 311711

Harvey, D S (Ford Simey LLP) *B1 C1 D1 E F1 G H J1*
Exeter *p221* 01392 274126
Newquay *p329*. 01637 872218

Harvey, Ms E L (DWF) *J1 Zp*
Liverpool *p287*. 0151 907 3000

Harvey, G (Penningtons)
Godalming *p231* 01483 791800

Harvey, G (Dickinson Dees)
Newcastle upon Tyne *p324* . 0191 279 9000
London EC4 *p78*. 020 7429 4900

Harvey, G R (Girlings) *S1 E C1 S2 R2*
Canterbury *p177*. 01227 768374

Harvey, Ms J (Taylor Wessing)
London EC4 *p86*. 020 7300 7000

Harvey, Mrs J (Debenhams Ottaway)
St Albans *p390* 01727 837161

Harvey, Miss J (Darbys Solicitors LLP) *G H Zi*
Oxford *p343* 01865 811700

Harvey, J (Elliot Mather LLP) *G H V*
Chesterfield *p192* 01246 231288

Harvey, J (Ashurst LLP)
London EC2 *p7* 020 7638 1111

Harvey, J C H (Kennedys) *Zg B1*
London EC3 *p49*. 020 7667 9667

Harvey, J D (Coodes) *K1 N O Q F1 D1 J1 Zq Zc*
St Austell *p391* 01726 874700

Harvey, J H (Shoosmiths) *N P Zc*
Reading *p361* . . 0370 086 8800 / 0118 965 8765

Harvey, J J K (QualitySolicitors D'Angibau) *Q K1 N O F1 J1 L D1*
Boscombe *p151* 01202 393506

Harvey, J N (Hansells) *E S1 L W F1 Zc*
Sheringham *p378* 01263 822176

Harvey, J R S (Neves Solicitors) *Q*
Milton Keynes *p317* 01908 304560

Harvey, K A (Clarke Willmott)
Bristol *p162* 0845 209 1000 / 0117 305 6000

Harvey, K R (Keith Harvey & Co) *S1 E L J1*
Market Harborough *p312*. . . 01858 464327

Harvey, L (Jones Day) *E*
London EC4 *p46*. 020 7039 5959

Harvey, Mrs L C (Alsters Kelley) *Zi*
Coventry *p199* 0844 561 0100

Harvey, Ms L J (Bristol City Council)
Bristol *p451* 0117 922 2000

Harvey, Mrs M A (Addleshaw Goddard)
Leeds *p271* 0113 209 2000

Harvey, M A (Hugh James) *N P X Zw*
Cardiff *p179* 029 2022 4871

Harvey, M A (Nantes) *J1 T1 T2 E C1 S1 R1 L S2 R2*
Bridport *p158* 01308 422313

Harvey, M C (Milwyn Jenkins & Jenkins Limited) *S1 W*
Llanidloes *p292* 01686 412166

Harvey, M J (SNR Denton) *Zb*
London EC4 *p75*. 020 7242 1212

Harvey, M J (Harveys)
Luton *p295* 01582 458567

Harvey, M K (hlw Keeble Hawson LLP) *N J1*
Sheffield *p375* 0114 272 2061

Harvey, M R (Harveys) *Q O D1 N K1 J1 Zk Zm*
Liss *p285* 01730 895000

Harvey, N (Bermans LLP) *B1 F1 J1 Zl L O Q Zb*
Liverpool *p286*. 0151 224 0500

Harvey, N H (Clifford Chance)
London E14 *p20*. 020 7006 1000

Harvey, P (Harvey Son & Filby) *E W S1 C1 C2 A1 L S2 R2 Zd Zi Zx*
Ipswich *p262*. 01473 712962

Harvey, P A E (Morrisons Solicitors LLP) *O Q N*
London SW19 *p62*. 020 8971 1020

Harvey, P C (Bernard Chill & Axtell) *E K1 S1 W*
Eastleigh *p216*. 023 8061 3197

Harvey, Ms R (Cartwright King)
Nottingham *p336*. 0115 958 7444

Harvey, R (Clerical Medical Investment Group)
London EC2 *p105* 020 7321 1425

Harvey, R (Berwins Solicitors Limited) *Q*
Harrogate *p240* 01423 509000

Harvey, R H (Allen & Overy LLP)
London E1 *p5* 020 3088 0000

Harvey, R H J P (Reed Smith LLP) *Za*
London EC2 *p71*. 020 3116 3000

Harvey, Ms R M (Squire Sanders (UK) LLP) *J1 Q C1 C3 O Zg Zp*
London EC2 *p81*. 020 7655 1000

Harvey, Ms S (Ashfords LLP)
Tiverton *p412* 01884 203000

Harvey, Miss S (Brain Chase Coles) *W K4 T2*
Basingstoke *p126* 01256 354481

Harvey, S (Payne & Payne) *N O Q J1 F1*
Hull *p257* 01482 326446

Harvey, Miss S E (Sally Harvey) *E S1 W*
Newtown *p330*. 01686 621033

Harvey, Mrs S E (Harveys)
Liss *p285* 01730 895000

Harvey, S J (Hillyer McKeown LLP) *C1 C2 Zw*
Chester *p190* 01244 318131

Harvey, Miss V C (Shakespeares) *N O J2*
Nottingham *p339*. 0115 945 3700

Harvey, W J (Photiades) *N Q L*
St Albans *p390* 01727 833134

Harvey-Hills, J (Simmons & Simmons)
London EC2 *p79*. 020 7628 2020

Harvie, Mrs H L (Barlow Robbins LLP) *Zd*
Guildford *p235*. 01483 562901

Harwood, Mrs A B (Oldham Metropolitan Borough Council)
Oldham *p468* 0161 911 3000

Harwood, C W (C W Harwood & Co) *E C1 S1 W B1 R1 C2 R2*
Leeds *p274* 0113 245 7027

Harwood, Ms E C (Barlow Lyde & Gilbert LLP)
London EC3 *p10*. 020 7247 2277

Harwood, Ms J (Walker Morris)
Leeds *p277* 0113 283 2500

Harwood, Mrs J R (Thomson Snell & Passmore) *S1 L W S2*
Tunbridge Wells *p415* 01892 510000

Harwood, Mrs K (Napthens LLP) *W*
Preston *p357* 01772 888444

Harwood, M D (Harwood & Co) *E L R1 S1*
Worcester *p440* 01905 420855

Harwood, R J (The Ringrose Law Group - Nerina Farmer) *N J1 Q L*
Sleaford *p381* 01529 301300

Harwood, R M (Hess Ltd)
London WC2 *p106*. 020 7331 3000

Hashemi, A S (Trowers & Hamlins) *C1*
London EC3 *p88*. 020 7423 8000

Hashim, G (Harrison Bundey) *G Q H*
Leeds *p274* 0113 200 7400

Hashmi, Ms A (Molesworths Bright Clegg) *J1*
Rochdale *p365*. 01706 356666

Hashmi, Z D (Aston Clark) *G Q J1 K1 L*
London W3 *p8*. 020 8752 1122

Haskew, D C (Harold Bell & Co) *T2 W Q*
Ewell *p220*. 020 8393 0231

Haskew, J (Chandler Ray) *W S1 V*
Buckingham *p167* 01280 814040

Haskey, Ms T J (Howes Percival LLP) *E L S2*
Norwich *p334* 01603 762103

Haslam, Mrs K E (Blake Lapthorn) *S2 E R1 R2 S1*
London EC1 *p13*. 020 7405 2000

Haslam, M S C (BCL Burton Copeland) *G B2 H*
London WC2 *p9* 020 7430 2277

Haslam, Ms R (Bindmans LLP) *Zi*
London WC1 *p12* 020 7833 4433

Hasler, Mrs J K L (Tanners) *S1 S2 E A1 L R1 W J1*
Cirencester *p195*. 01285 659061

Hasler, M I J (Beers LLP) *W E S1 A1 T1 Zg L Zd Zo*
Kingsbridge *p267* 01548 857000

Hasler, P B (Terence St J Millett) *S1*
London SW7 *p82* 020 7581 7500

Hasnip, A (The Wilkes Partnership LLP) *T1 T2 W*
Birmingham *p143* 0121 233 4333

Hass, F (Stones) *S1 K1 N O Q W*
London W1 *p83* 020 7935 4848

Hassall, D C (Bartons) *C1 A1 O Q F1 Zl*
Kingsbridge *p267* 01548 855655

Hassall, Miss E J (Gateley LLP) *K1 D2*
Manchester *p304* 0161 836 7700

Hassall, J A (Percy Hughes & Roberts) *N Q Zq*
Birkenhead *p134*. 0151 666 9090

Hassall, L M (Bartons) *Za Ze J1 N*
Plymouth *p349*. 01752 675740

Hassall, Ms N J D (Boodle Hatfield) *W T2 Zd*
Oxford *p343* 01865 790744

Hassan, L (MBA Solicitors) *N*
York *p445* 01904 666888

Hassan, P (Keoghs LLP) *N Zj O Q Zw*
Bolton *p149* 01204 677000

Hassan, S H A (Corbin & Hassan) *S1 S2 Zi*
London EC3 *p22*. 020 7247 6518

Hassan, T M (Goldkorn Mathias Gentle Page LLP) *S2 S1 E L*
London WC1 *p36* 020 7631 1811

Hassells, J (KBL Solicitors) *J1*
Bolton *p149* 01204 527777

Hassett, Miss L D H (Barlow Lyde & Gilbert LLP) *O Q Zq*
London EC3 *p10*. 020 7247 2277

Hassett, M J (Forsters LLP) *E*
Westminster *p33*. 020 7863 8333

Hassett, P (Wigan Borough Council)
Wigan *p476* 01942 244991

Hassett, Ms S (Lloyd Platt & Co) *K1 K2 Q*
London N3 *p55* 020 8343 2998

Hassiall, M (Thompsons (formerly Robin/Brian Thompson & Partners)) *N J1*
Stoke-on-Trent *p398*. 01782 406200

Hast, Mrs C K (TWM Solicitors LLP) *D1 K1 K2 Zi*
Epsom *p219*. 01372 729555

Hast, G C (Alen-Buckley & Co) *S1 W*
Wandsworth *p4* 020 8767 8336

Haste, Miss M (Crowell & Moring) *J1*
London EC4 *p23*. 020 7413 0011
London EC2 *p81*. 020 7655 1000

Hastewell, Miss G (Terrells LLP) *K3 D1 K1 N S1 S2 W*
Huntingdon *p258*. 01480 454987

Hastie, Mrs C L (Barlow Robbins LLP) *S1*
Guildford *p235*. 01483 543200

Hastie, R D (Gosschalks) *N L Zj*
Hull *p256* 01482 324252

Hastie, Miss S M (Osmond & Osmond) *O Q F1 F2 N C2 C1 Zq Zo C3 J1 Zj*
London EC4 *p65*. 020 7583 3434

Hastilow, M S (Bosley & Co) *C1 E S1 W R1 K1*
Brighton *p159* 01273 608181

Hastings, I A W (Addleshaw Goddard)
Leeds *p271* 0113 209 2000
Manchester *p300* 0161 934 6000

Hastings, J (Guardian Royal Exchange PLC)
London EC3 *p106* 020 7283 7101

Hastings, Mrs J C (Ginn & Co) *K4 W*
Cambridge *p174*. 01223 358275

Hastings, Mrs M A (Bayer CropScience Ltd)
Cambridge *p452*. 01223 226500

Hastings, P (Steeles) *O Q C1 Zw*
Norwich *p335* 0870 609 0200

Hastings, Mrs T (The BOC Group PLC)
Guildford *p476*. 01483 579857

Hastings, T M (Nelsons) *N P D1*
Nottingham *p338*. 0115 958 6262

Hastings, W J (Bawtrees LLP) *Q N*
Witham *p435* 01376 513491

6

Haswell, R M (Haswell & Cornberg) *D1 F1 G H K1 S1 W L N Q Zf Zl Zo Zv*
Newcastle upon Tyne *p325* . 0191 276 5300

Hasyn, M J (Gordons LLP)
Leeds *p273* 0113 227 0100

Hatchard, J R (Moore Blatch Solicitors) *C1 E R1 S1 P*
Lymington *p296* 01590 625800

Hatchard, M E (Skadden Arps Slate Meagher & Flom (UK) LLP) *C2 C1*
London E14 *p80*. 020 7519 7000

Hatchick, K A (Marshall Hatchick) *C1 C2 C3 J1 M1 M2 E S1 Zb Zc Zf Zh Zi*
Woodbridge *p439* 01394 388411

Hatchwell, M (Davenport Lyons) *C1 M1 J1 B1 Ze*
London W1 *p25* 020 7468 2600

Hately, K (Hay & Kilner) *W T2 K4*
Newcastle upon Tyne *p325* . 0191 232 8345
Newcastle upon Tyne *p325* . 0191 211 7777

Hatfield, A E (David C Hatfield & Co) *C1 F1 P G H J1 K1*
Jarrow *p263* . . . 0191 489 7639 / 489 9450

Hatfield, D C (David C Hatfield & Co) *C1 D1 F1 G H J1 K1 L M1 P Ze*
Jarrow *p263* . . . 0191 489 7639 / 489 9450

Hatfield, J P (Graysons) *S1 W*
Sheffield *p375* 0114 272 9184

Hatfield, M E J (Weightmans LLP) *J1 P N F1 M1 Zp*
Liverpool *p291*. 0151 227 2601

Hatfield, N R (Clifford Chance)
London E14 *p20*. 020 7006 1000

Hathaway, J M P (Heath & Blenkinsop) *C1 E L R1 S1 T1 W Zc Zd*
Warwick *p422* 01926 492407

Hathaway, Ms K (Blake Lapthorn) *S1*
Oxford *p342*. 01865 248607

Hathaway, Miss S (Coley & Tilley)
Birmingham *p136* 0121 643 5531

Hathaway, S (Government Legal Service) *S1 S2*
London BS1 *p106* 0845 300 0793

Hatherall, P J (Capsticks Solicitors LLP) *Zr N D1*
London SW19 *p18*. 020 8780 2211

Hathway, P E M (Waldrons) *G H Zl*
Dudley *p213*. 01384 811811

Hatley, Ms E (Stewarts Law LLP) *K3 K1*
London EC4 *p83*. 020 7822 8000
London EC4 *p92*. 020 7597 6000

Hatt, A S (Hedges) *W S1 L E T1 A1*
Wallingford *p419*. 01491 839839

Hatter, Ms J A (Rustons & Lloyd) *W*
Newmarket *p327*. 01638 661221

Hatter, Mrs P B (Singletons Austin Ryder) *K1 K2 K3 D1*
Enfield *p219*. 020 8363 0101

Hattersley, C W (Ashfords LLP) *O Zt Zj*
Plymouth *p349*. 01752 521500
Plymouth *p349*. 01752 675000

Hattersley, Mrs R J (HM Land Registry - Plymouth)
Plymouth *p468*. . . .01752 636000 / 636123

Hattersley, S L (Godloves) *N*
Leeds *p273* 0113 225 8811
Leeds *p274* 0113 284 5000

Hatton, A P (Salford City Council)
Swinton *p473* 0161 794 4711

Hatton, Miss B (Geoffrey Borg & Co) *S1 W L E*
Ramsgate *p359* 01843 591378

Hatton, D P (Ison Harrison) *Zr*
Leeds *p274* 0113 284 5000

Hatton, G (Hodge Halsall) *E S1 C1 S2 R2 W T2 K4*
Ainsdale *p115* 01704 577171
Southport *p388* 01704 531991

Hatton, J R (Hatton) *A1 C1 E L N P R1 S1 Zv*
Daventry *p207*. 01327 301201

Hatton, P L (KBL Solicitors) *O Q B1 L A3 Zq Ze F1 F2*
Bolton *p149* 01204 527777

Hatton, R J (Tickle Hall Cross) *S1 S2 W*
St Helens *p391* 0800 854379

Hatton, T A (Reynolds Parry-Jones) *N P C1 E J1 M1 R1 Zc Ze Zr*
High Wycombe *p250*. 01494 525941

Hatton, W (MBNA Europe Bank Ltd)
Chester *p454* 01244 672002

Hattrell, A R (Atteys)
Doncaster *p211* 01302 340400

Hatvany, P B (Mowbray Woodwards Solicitors) *G H Zm*
Bath *p128* 01225 485700

Hatvany, P G (Parker Bullen) *Q L N B1 O*
Salisbury *p371* 01722 412000

Hatwood, Ms M (Anthony Gold) *K1 K2 D1*
London SE1 *p6* 020 7940 4000

Hauer, M H (McFaddens LLP) *C1 M2 W J1 Zd Ze Zf Zi Zz*
London EC2 *p56* 020 7588 9080

Hauff, R L (John Lewis plc) *E L R1 Zc*
London SW1 *p107* 020 7828 1000

Hauge, Mrs J C (East Sussex County Council)
Lewes *p463* 01273 481000

Haughin, Ms E J (Cumbria County Council)
Kendal *p462* 01539 773123

Hauser, P E (Bryan Cave)
London EC2 *p19* 020 7207 1100

Hausmann, G B S (C H Hausmann & Co) *B1 C1 J1 L P S1 T1 W Zb Ze Zf Zi*
London W1 *p39* 020 7436 6333

Hava, Ms E M (DAC Beachcroft) *Zq Zj O X*
London EC4 *p24* 020 7936 2222

Havard, Ms P M (British Midland Airways Ltd)
Castle Donington *p453* 01332 854089

Havard-williams, Miss V (Linklaters LLP)
London EC2 *p54* 020 7456 2000

Havenhand, Miss D C (W H Smith PLC)
London W1 *p110* 020 7851 8809

Havenhand, J B (W H Smith PLC) *N W J1 Zh*
London W1 *p110* 020 7851 8809

Havenhand, M A (MPH Solicitors) *Zr*
Manchester *p307* 0161 832 7722

Haverfield, Miss C L (Moore Blatch Solicitors)
Southampton *p386* 023 8071 8000

Havergal, Dr J B (Pritchard Englefield) *E Zc R2*
London EC2 *p69* 020 7972 9720

Havers, Ms C S O (Salans) *B1 O Q Zb*
London EC4 *p76* 020 7429 6000

Havers, Mrs M A L (Lightfoots LLP) *W K4*
Thame *p410* 01844 212305

Havery, A D (John Barkers) *Q N G H*
Grimsby *p234* 01472 358686

Havord, Ms E C (Copleys) *G H*
Huntingdon *p258* 01480 456191

Hawdon, Ms C (Rogers & Norton) *W*
Norwich *p335* 01603 666001

Hawes, Ms A (TLT Solicitors) *K1 D1*
Bristol *p165* 0117 917 7777

Hawes, M R (Bristows) *C1 C2 Zd Zf*
London EC4 *p15* 020 7400 8000

Hawes, Ms R (The College of Law)
London WC1 *p105* 0800 289997

Hawken, K (Mayer Brown International LLP)
London EC2 *p59* 020 3130 3000

Hawker, Miss A J (Steele Raymond) *S1 E*
Bournemouth *p152* 01202 294566

Hawker, Ms F (Mills & Reeve)
Birmingham *p140* 0121 454 4000

Hawker, P (Windeatts) *S1 S2*
Kingsbridge *p267* 01548 852727

Hawker, Mrs S J (Birchall Blackburn LLP) *Zr J2 N*
Preston *p356* 01772 561663

Hawkes, Mrs L S (Fisher Meredith) *K1*
Lambeth *p32* 020 7091 2700

Hawkes, P W (Furley Page LLP) *J1 C3 O Zc Ze Zk*
Canterbury *p176* 01227 763939

Hawkes, Miss S (Taylor Wessing)
London EC4 *p86* 020 7300 7000

Hawkeswood, J (Cripps Harries Hall LLP) *C1 C2*
Tunbridge Wells *p415* 01892 515121

Hawkings, G (Ince & Co Services Ltd)
London E1 *p44* 020 7481 0010

Hawkings, R W (Wortley Byers) *W S1*
Brentwood *p156* 01277 268368

Hawkins, A (Rawlison Butler LLP) *Zb*
Crawley *p202* 01293 527744

Hawkins, A J (Bruce Lance & Co) *S1 S2 L C1 J1 W E*
High Wycombe *p250* 01494 450494

Hawkins, Ms C (Tollers LLP) *E K1 S1 W*
Northampton *p332* 01604 258558

Hawkins, D J (Nabarro LLP) *E R1 R2 S2 Zs Zu*
London WC1 *p63* 020 7524 6000

Hawkins, D M (George Anthony Andrews Solicitors)
London W3 *p6* 020 8746 0550

Hawkins, D S (Sherwood Wheatley) *G L H F1 M1 P J1 B1 D1 Zl Zk*
Kingston upon Thames *p267* 020 8546 0144

Hawkins, Miss H A (AGR Solicitors) *K3 K1*
Mansfield *p311* 01623 460444

Hawkins, Ms J (Cartwright King) *G H*
Nottingham *p336* 0115 958 7444

Hawkins, J (Tendring District Council)
Clacton-on-Sea *p455* 01255 686567

Hawkins, J (Taylor & Emmet LLP) *S2 E*
Sheffield *p377* 0114 218 4000

Hawkins, J A (Salusburys Harding & Barnett) *S1 E C1 C2 S2*
Leicester *p281* 0116 262 9033 / 262 6052

Hawkins, J N G (Meade-King) *C1 C2*
Bristol *p163* 0117 926 4121

Hawkins, J R (Hunters) *A1 S2 E S1*
London WC2 *p44* 020 7412 0050
London SE1 *p50* 020 7379 0000

Hawkins, J T (Everys) *E C1 S1 L W R1 A1 Zc*
Exmouth *p222* 01395 264384

Hawkins, Mrs K J (Shell International Ltd)
London SE1 *p109* 020 7934 1234
Derby *p209* 01332 372372

Hawkins, K J (Dutton Gregory) *S1 W*
Winchester *p433* 01962 844333

Hawkins, M M J (Arnold Thomson Limited) *A1 S2 W S1 E R1 T2 T1*
Towcester *p413* 01327 350266

Hawkins, M R (Swale Borough Council)
Sittingbourne *p471* 01795 417324

Hawkins, N J (Abels) *K1 D1 V B1 F1 G H N Q*
Southampton *p385* 023 8022 0317

Hawkins, P (The College of Law)
London WC1 *p105* 0800 289997

Hawkins, P H (Hill Dickinson LLP)
London EC3 *p41* 020 7283 9033

Hawkins, P J (Trowers & Hamlins) *L R1 Zh*
London EC3 *p88* 020 7423 8000

Hawkins, Miss R E L (Daltons Solicitors) *K2 K1 K3*
Petersfield *p348* 01730 262816

Hawkins, Miss S J (Berry & Berry) *K1 D1 D2 K2 V W*
Maidstone *p299* 01622 690777

Hawkins, S J (Linder Myers Solicitors) *E L S1 S2*
Manchester *p307* 0844 984 6400

Hawkins, Ms S K (Browne Jacobson LLP) *N Zj*
Nottingham *p336* 0115 976 6000

Hawkins, T (The College of Law)
London WC1 *p105* 0800 289997

Hawkridge, J H (Hawkridge & Co) *S1 E C1 T1 A1 W R1 Zl Zc*
Gillingham *p229* 01634 854381

Hawkridge, R M (George Davies Solicitors LLP) *E*
Manchester *p303* 0161 236 8992

Hawks, E J (Beaty & Co) *J1 L N F1 Zd Zh*
Wigton *p432* 01697 342121

Hawks, J (Taylor Wessing)
London EC4 *p86* 020 7300 7000

Hawks, Mrs S (Donnelly McArdle Adamson) *K1 K3 D1 W*
Darlington *p206* 01325 482299

Hawksley, Mrs R J (R J Hawksley & Co) *K1 W S1 R1 N Q O Zl J1 G C1 D1 B1*
Camberley *p173* 01252 890400

Hawksworth, Ms E (Russell Jones & Walker)
London WC2 *p74* 020 7657 1555

Hawksworth, P (Tinsdills) *A1 C1 E K1 Q S1 T1 T2 W*
Leek *p278* 01538 399332

Hawksworth, P J (Tinsdills) *A1 B1 C1 E F1 J1 L M1 N*
Hanley *p239* 01782 262031

Hawksworth, W D (Napthens LLP) *S1 E*
Chorley *p194* 0845 260 2111

Hawkyard, P M (Hamlins LLP) *E*
London W1 *p38* 020 7355 6000

Hawley, D R (Brindley Twist Tafft & James) *N G H D1 K1 O V Q*
Coventry *p200* 024 7653 1532
Nuneaton *p339* 024 7638 7821

Hawley, J A (Baines Wilson LLP) *C1*
Carlisle *p181* 01228 552600

Hawley, Mrs J A (Martin-Kaye LLP) *S1*
Telford *p409* 01952 272222

Hawley, M R (Pannone LLP) *N*
Manchester *p308* 0161 909 3000

Hawley, N (Wortley Byers) *B1 F1 H J1 K1 L N O Q Zi*
Brentwood *p156* 01277 268368

Haworth, C R (Haworth Brotherton) *K1 C1 E S1 W R1 S2 R2*
Thornton Cleveleys *p411* 01253 852356

Haworth, D (Rupert Wood & Son) *N*
Ashton-under-Lyne *p120* 0161 330 9121

Haworth, Miss D M (Fladgate LLP) *E L S1*
London WC2 *p32* 020 3036 7000

Haworth, J E (Lawson West Solicitors Limited) *K1 K2*
Wigston *p432* 0116 212 1080

Haworth, Ms L (Squire Sanders (UK) LLP)
London EC2 *p81* 020 7655 1000

Haworth, L A (Haworth Brotherton) *W*
Thornton Cleveleys *p411* 01253 852356

Haworth, M C (Gateley LLP) *J1 Zp*
Birmingham *p138* 0121 234 0000

Haworth, R C (Haworth Holt Bell Limited) *E C1 C2 C3 L B1 J1 T1 W S1*
Altrincham *p116* 0161 928 7136

Haworth, Miss S M (Howard Kennedy LLP) *S2 R2*
London W1 *p48* 020 7636 1616

Haworth, T P (Haworth Brotherton) *S1 W E C1 L R1 Zl*
Thornton Cleveleys *p411* 01253 852356

Haworth-Hird, Ms C (Bindmans LLP) *Zg Zm L*
London WC1 *p12* 020 7833 4433

Hawrych, V J (Edwin Coe LLP) *C1 C2*
London WC2 *p29* 020 7691 4000

Hawthorn, G R (Miller Sands) *W T2 K4 Zm*
Cambridge *p175* 01223 202345

Hawthorn, Ms P (Pinsent Masons LLP)
London EC2 *p67* 020 7418 7000

Hawthorne, Ms D L (National Grid PLC)
Warwick *p471* 01926 653000

Hawthorne, P J M (Pothecary Witham Weld) *J1 Q A3 Zc*
Westminster *p69* 020 7821 8211

Haxby, Ms J (Squire Sanders (UK) LLP)
Manchester *p310* 0161 830 5000

Haxton, S (Streeter Marshall) *L Q W*
Croydon *p205* 020 8680 2638

Hay, Ms A (Quastel Midgen LLP) *J1 Ze C1 F1 U2 C2 Zc*
London W1 *p70* 020 7908 2525

Hay, A N (Banner Jones) *C1 S2 E S1*
Chesterfield *p191* 01246 560560

Hay, I D (Murray Hay Solicitors) *S1 E C1 L*
London SW15 *p62* 020 8780 1225

Hay, J W S (Sprake & Kingsley) *S1 W*
Beccles *p129* 01502 713214

Hay, Ms K E (Hempsons) *P N Zr*
Manchester *p305* 0161 228 0011

Hay, Mrs K E (Capsticks Solicitors LLP) *N Zr*
London SW19 *p18* 020 8780 2211

Hay, Miss N M (Manches LLP) *K1*
London WC2 *p58* 020 7404 4433

Hay, P R (Perry Hay & Co) *A3 B3 C1 C2 C3 E J1 R2 S1 S2 T2 W Zw*
Richmond upon Thames *p364* 020 8940 8115 / 8332 7532

Hayat, A (Hayat & Co) *H Zi*
Enfield *p218* 020 8360 4485

Haycock, B (HCB Solicitors)
Walsall *p420* 01922 720000

Haycock, K N (Kidd Rapinet) *E S2 U1*
Maidenhead *p298* 0845 017 9608

Hayden, Mrs D (East Riding of Yorkshire Council)
Beverley *p449* 01482 887700

Hayden, N T (Environment Agency (South West Region))
Exeter *p458* 0870 850 6506

Hayden, S B (Enoch Evans LLP) *E S2*
Walsall *p420* 01922 720333

Hayden, T (Clarke Willmott) *P B2 Zl Q Zt*
Taunton *p408* 0845 209 1000 / 0117 305 6000

Haydn-Williams, J J (Taylor Wessing) *N P C1 B1 W J1 F1 Ze Zb*
London EC4 *p86* 020 7300 7000

Haydon, Mrs D R (Hextalls) *O Zj*
London EC2 *p41* 020 7382 0700
London E1 *p71* 020 3060 6000

Haydon, Ms S J (TLT Solicitors) *Za C1 Zi J1 S2 S1 O*
London EC2 *p85* 020 3465 4000

Hayes, Ms A (Levison Meltzer Pigott) *K1*
London EC4 *p53* 020 7556 2400

Hayes, A (Jefferies Essex LLP) *S1 L S2 E*
Westcliff-on-Sea *p428* 01702 332311

Hayes, Miss A (Hague Lambert) *W*
Knutsford *p269* 01565 652411

Hayes, Miss A (LG Lawyers)
London SE1 *p50* 020 7379 0000

Hayes, B H (Tozers) *Za Zj N O*
Exeter *p222* 01392 207020

Hayes, Miss C (Linklaters LLP)
London EC2 *p54* 020 7456 2000

Hayes, C C E (Edward Hayes LLP) *G H J1 K1 V D1 B2*
Chichester *p192* 01243 781431
London EC4 *p39* 020 7353 0011

Hayes, D T M (AWB Charlesworth LLP) *S1 S2*
Skipton *p381* 01756 793333

Hayes, D W S (Clarke Willmott) *E*
Birmingham *p136* 0845 209 1000 / 0117 305 6000

Hayes, E C (Sacker & Partners LLP) *Zo*
London EC2 *p76* 020 7329 6699

Hayes, J (FBC Manby Bowdler LLP)
Wolverhampton *p437* 01902 578000

Hayes, Ms J (Hayes Clifford & Co) *E S1 W S2*
Tilehurst *p411* 0118 941 8416

Hayes, J (Linklaters LLP)
London EC2 *p54* 020 7456 2000

Hayes, J (BCL Burton Copeland) *B2 G*
London WC2 *p9* 020 7430 2277

Hayes, J (Battens) *K1*
Yeovil *p443* 01935 846000

Hayes, J (Howes Percival LLP) *N Zr*
Norwich *p334* 01603 762103

Hayes, Mrs K E (Lancashire County Council)
Preston *p469* 01772 254868

Hayes, K I (Silverbeck Rymer) *N Q*
Liverpool *p290* 0151 236 9594

Hayes, M (Gordon Lutton) *J1 O S2 E C1*
Hereford *p248* 01432 355345

Hayes, Miss M (Sills & Betteridge LLP) *K1 D1*
Gainsborough *p228* 01427 616816

Hayes, M A (Macfarlanes) *W T1 C1 Zd*
London EC4 *p56* 020 7831 9222

Hayes, M J (Heath Sons & Broome) *N K1 G Zl H*
Failsworth *p223* 0161 682 8535

Hayes, M N (Rix & Kay Solicitors LLP) *K1 D1*
Hove *p255* 01273 329797

Hayes, N D (GSC Solicitors) *E S2 R2*
London EC1 *p34* 020 7822 2222

Hayes, N H (Peel Management Limited)
Manchester *p465* 0161 629 8200

Hayes, P (Debenhams Ottaway) *S1 S2 E*
Radlett *p358* 01923 857171

Hayes, R B (Birketts LLP) *N J2 Zr*
Ipswich *p262* 01473 232300

Hayes, R C S (Bartons) *S1 S2 E*
Salcombe *p370* 01548 843005

Hayes, R J (Manches LLP) *C1*
Oxford *p343* 01865 722106

Hayes, R W (Addleshaw Goddard)
Manchester *p300* 0161 934 6000

Hayes, S (McKeowns Solicitors Ltd) *N*
St Albans *p390* 0800 032 8328

Hayes, Ms S E (Trowers & Hamlins) *L C1 Zh Zb Zd*
London EC3 *p88* 020 7423 8000

Hayes, S J (Fiona Bruce & Co LLP) *K1 D1 K3*
Warrington *p421* 01925 263273

Hayes, T (Capsticks Solicitors LLP) *N Zr Zq*
London SW19 *p18* 020 8780 2211

Haygarth, Miss A V (Gloucestershire County Council - Legal & Democratic Services)
Gloucester *p459* 01452 425203

Hayhurst, D (174 Law) *C1 E S1 R1 S2 Zh*
Birkenhead *p134* 0151 647 7372

Hayhurst, Miss J C (Blackhurst Swainson Goodier LLP) *S1 W*
Preston *p356* 01772 253841

Hayhurst, Ms P S (Environment Agency (Thames Region))
Reading *p469* 0870 850 6506

Hayhurst, Ms P S (The College of Law)
London WC1 *p105* 0800 289997

Hayim, B (Muscatt Walker Hayim) *B1 C1 C2 E L Q S1 W Zl*
London W1 *p62* 020 7486 5131

Hayler, Mrs A (Barwells) *N*
Eastbourne *p215* 01323 411505

Hayler, R (Hamnett Osborne Tisshaw) *G H B2*
Haywards Heath *p245* 01444 443030

Hayles, Mrs C A (Larcomes LLP) *E*
Portsmouth *p354* 023 9266 1531

Hayles, N P (HSR Law (Hayes, Son & Richmond)) *B2 G H J1*
Doncaster *p211* 01302 347800
Gainsborough *p228* 01427 613831

Hayley, C (Southcombe & Hayley) *C1 E F1 L*
Westminster *p81* 020 7935 6631

Hayley, M J (Gravesham Borough Council)
Gravesend *p459* 01474 564422

Hayllar, C F (Alletsons Ltd) *G H D1 K1 D2 K2*
Bridgwater *p157* 01278 456621

Hayllar, Ms L (Forsters LLP) *E*
Westminster *p33* 020 7863 8333

Haylock, Ms P E (Murco Petroleum Ltd)
St Albans *p472* 01727 892494

Haylock, Ms S (Lanyon Bowdler LLP) *E S1 C1 O Q Zp*
Shrewsbury *p379* 01743 280280

Haylor, N A G (Gelson Haylor)
Southwark *p35* 020 7928 0675

Hayman, M J (Bynes) *N Q O G H C1 Zg M1 D1 Zr B1 Zq J1*
Torquay *p412* 01803 295692

Haymes, J (Napthens LLP) *C1*
Preston *p357* 01772 888444

Haynes, C (Herbert Smith LLP)
London EC2 *p40* 020 7374 8000

Haynes, G (Mowlem PLC)
Isleworth *p462* 020 8568 9111

Haynes, M A (Haynes & Co) *K1 P N M1 L G B1 Zc Zi*
London W4 *p39* 020 8987 6076

Haynes, N A (Freeth Cartwright LLP) *E*
Nottingham *p337* 0115 936 9369

Haynes, P A (CMHT Solicitors) *G H L K1*
Walsall *p420* 01922 646400

Haynes, S (Marks & Spencer PLC)
London W2 *p107* 020 7935 4422

Haynes, S J (Martin-Kaye LLP) *C1 C2 E Ze M1 M2*
Telford *p409* 01952 272222

Haynes, Mrs V A (British Telecommunications PLC)
London EC1 *p104* 020 7356 6181

Haynes, Ms V J (Bevan Kidwell) *S2 E Ze L Zl O*
London EC1 *p12* 020 7843 1820

Hayre, B (Hayre & Co) *C1 E J1 S2 Ze Zi S1*
Bradford *p154* 01274 744405
Harrogate *p240* 01423 522331

Hayre, H S (Squire Sanders (UK) LLP)
Leeds *p277* 0113 284 7000

Hayre, J S (Birmingham City Council Legal & Democratic Services) *Q B1 N L F1 J1 Zc*
Birmingham *p449* 0121 303 2066

Hayre, Ms M K (Ahmed & Co) *Zi*
Camden *p4* 020 7383 2243

Hayre, Miss S (Cunningtons) *S1*
Wickford *p431* 01268 732268

Hayre, Miss S (Joseph Hill & Co) *Zi G H*
London N15 *p41* 020 8880 3535

Haysom, Mrs E (Nelsons) *S2 E*
Derby *p209* 01332 372372

Hayter, B N F (Rix & Kay Solicitors LLP) *J1 J2 C2*
Uckfield *p416* 01825 700177

Hayter, Ms M (Frettens Solicitors) *F1 Q S1 W Zc Zk*
Christchurch *p194* 01202 491777

Hayter, N R (Ronaldsons)
London WC1 *p73* 020 7580 6075

Haythorn, J F H (Woollcombe Yonge) *G K1 M1 P F1 L D1 B1 H W*
Plymouth *p351* 01752 660384

Haythornthwaite, P J (Pearson & Pearson) *A1 S1 S2 W*
Kirkby Lonsdale *p268* 01524 271222

Hayton, Miss E M (Eddowes Perry & Osbourne) *G H S1*
Sutton Coldfield *p403* 0121 686 9444

Hayton, Miss G (South Tyneside Metropolitan Borough Council)
South Shields *p471* 0191 427 1717

Hayward, A (Owen White) *J1 C1 C2 C3 F1 Zp*
Slough *p382* 01753 876800

Hayward, A G (AstraZeneca)
Macclesfield *p464* 01625 582828

Hayward, Ms C (Trowers & Hamlins)
London EC3 *p88* 020 7423 8000

See p634 for the Key to Work Categories

Hayward, Ms C A (Hewitsons) *E R2 S2 S1 Zh*
Northampton *p332* 01604 233233

Hayward, C E J (Stone King LLP) *W S1 T1 T2*
Bath *p128* 01225 337599

Hayward, C J (Bright & Sons) *A1 A2 C1 I J1 Zy C2 T1*
Maldon *p299* 01621 852323
Witham *p435* 01376 512338

Hayward, C J (Kingsfords) *S1 E C1 L W R1 A1 T1*
Ashford *p119* 01233 624545

Hayward, D J (Derek J Hayward & Co) *G H*
Chatham *p185* 01634 815651

Hayward, D M (Nockolds) *J1*
Bishop's Stortford *p144* . . . 01279 755777

Hayward, D M (DFA Law LLP) *E S2 L S1*
Northampton *p331* 01604 609560

Hayward, D P (LG Lawyers) *E*
London SE1 *p50* 020 7379 0000

Hayward, D S (London Borough of Wandsworth)
London SW18 *p110* 020 8871 6000

Hayward, G S J (Bower & Bailey) *S1 E L W*
Oxford *p343* 01865 311133

Hayward, J (Kerseys) *E S1 S2*
Ipswich *p262* 01473 213311

Hayward, Mrs J V (Stone King LLP) *S1 W*
Bath *p128* 01225 337599

Hayward, Miss M (Wannop Fox Staffurth & Bray) *G H B2*
Chichester *p193* 01243 778844

Hayward, M (Grindeys LLP) *C1 E Zu S1*
Stoke-on-Trent *p397* 01782 846441

Hayward, Miss M A (Wake Smith & Tofields) *C1 C2 U1*
Sheffield *p377* 0114 266 6660

Hayward, M J (Woodfines LLP) *G B2 Zt*
Bletchley *p147* 01908 366333

Hayward, P A (Gateley LLP) *C1 B1 T1 J1 Zc Ze*
Birmingham *p138* 0121 234 0000

Haywood, A (Penningtons) *J1*
London EC2 *p66* 020 7457 3000

Haywood, Mrs C E (Nottinghamshire County Council Legal Services Division)
West Bridgford *p475* 0115 977 3478

Haywood, D G (Reynolds Porter Chamberlain LLP) *E*
London E1 *p71* 020 3060 6000

Haywood, Miss L (Jones Day) *O*
London EC4 *p46* 020 7039 5959

Haywood, Ms L (Follett Stock LLP) *K1 Q Zl*
Truro *p414* 01872 241700

Haywood, M B (Addleshaw Goddard) *E L*
Manchester *p300* 0161 934 6000

Haywood, M J (Cullimore Dutton) *W T2 K4 T1*
Chester *p190* 01244 356789

Haywood, N (DLA Piper UK LLP)
Birmingham *p137* 0870 011 1111

Hazel, J (McKinnells) *J1 Q O*
Lincoln *p284* 01522 541181

Hazeldine, Ms S A (Allen & Overy LLP)
London E1 *p5* 020 3088 0000

Hazell, N (Taylor Wessing)
London EC4 *p86* 020 7300 7000

Hazell, R C (Unilever PLC)
London EC4 *p110* 020 7822 5252

Hazell, R J (Doncaster Magistrates Court)
Doncaster *p457* 01302 366711

Hazell, Ms S N (Hazell & Co) *N O P Q Zc Zj Zq*
Sawbridgeworth *p372* 01279 726604

Hazelton, B P (Emmerson Brown & Brown) *S1 W L E*
Deal *p207* 01304 362146

Hazelton, G A (Fishburns) *Zc Zj O Q Zq*
London EC3 *p32* 020 7280 8888
London EC2 *p81* 020 7655 1000

Hazelton, M (Haringey Magistrates Legal Advisers Office)
London N6 *p106* 0845 601 3600

Hazelton, W (Grenville J Walker)
Blandford Forum *p147* 01258 459911

Hazlehurst, A D (Roberts Moore Nicholas Jones) *Zg Zh*
Birkenhead *p134* 0151 647 0000

Hazleton, W (C Nicholls)
Bodmin *p148* 01208 76969

Hazlewood, Miss M (Churchers) *K4 K1 N Zo S1 T1 T2 W*
Fareham *p223* 01329 822333

Hazlewood, Miss M (John Gaunt & Partners) *Zl O Zf*
Sheffield *p375* 0114 266 8664

Hazzard, Ms L (Hugh James) *Zj*
Cardiff *p179* 029 2022 4871

Head, A J (Forsters LLP) *B1 O Q Zb Zq*
Westminster *p33* 020 7863 8333

Head, Ms A S L (Frederic Hall) *K1 D1 K3 D2*
Folkestone *p227* 01303 851185

Head, Mrs B M (Ashton KCJ) *K1 F1 L*
Ipswich *p262* 01473 232425

Head, Ms C (Smith Law Partnership) *Q N*
Braintree *p155* 01376 321311

Head, G J (Clerk to Sheffield Justices)
Sheffield *p470* 0114 276 0760

Head, M A (The Head Partnership) *C1 R2 S2 E J1 Ze*
Reading *p361* 0118 975 6622

Head, Miss N A (Aon Ltd)
London EC2 *p103* 020 7623 5500

Head, N D (Josiah Hincks) *C1 E S1 A1 A2 Zb B1 Zc C2 S2 C3 Ze P Zh L R1 R2*
Leicester *p280* 0116 255 1811

Head, Miss R (Pickerings LLP) *W*
Tamworth *p407* 01827 317070

Head, Miss R J (Henriques Griffiths) *E Zl*
Bristol *p163* 0117 909 4000

Head, Ms T L (Kennedys) *N Zj J2*
London EC3 *p49* 020 7667 9667

Headd, B (Headd Solicitors)
London N17 *p39* 020 7566 8244

Headford, Ms C (FWD Law Associates) *K1 K2*
Newport *p328* 01633 660440

Headford, Mrs J W (Tozers) *N P B1 F1 J1 A3 O Q*
Exeter *p222* 01392 207020

Headicar, B M (Wiggin LLP) *C1 C2*
Cheltenham *p189* 01242 224114

Headley, Ms C Y (Newcastle Upon Tyne City Council)
Newcastle upon Tyne *p466* . 0191 232 8520

Headley, J G A (Headleys) *G H K1 M1 W D1 C1 S1 J1 Zl Zm Zb*
Hinckley *p250* 01455 637815

Heads, Mrs S E (Susan Heads & Company) *O S1 S2*
Chislehurst *p193* 020 8467 5544

Heal, J P W (Howes Percival LLP) *A1 T2 E W R1*
Norwich *p334* 01603 762103

Heal, Mrs M (Wright & McMillan Bennett)
Telford *p409* 01952 291100

Heal, Miss R A (Davitt Jones Bould) *E S2 R2 L P*
Taunton *p408* 01823 279279

Heal, T R (Ashfords LLP) *E*
Exeter *p220* 01392 337000

Heald, Miss F L (Caroline Coats Solicitors) *K4 W T2*
Southampton *p385* 023 8089 0919

Heald, S (Veale Wasbrough Vizards) *O B1 Q Zb Za*
Bristol *p165* 0117 925 2020

Heale, A G (A G Heale Ltd) *O A3 C1*
Cardiff *p178* 029 2056 2566

Healey, A J (Bishop & Co) *S1 G H D1 E R1 W K1 Zl Zm Zt Zv Zc*
New Mills *p321* 01663 746730

Healey, D P (The Environment Agency (North West Region [HQ]))
Warrington *p475* 01925 653999

Healey, J F (Bray & Dilks) *F1 L N Q O B1*
Truro *p414* 01872 271717

Healey, M B (Thomas Flavell & Sons) *W T2 K4 C1*
Hinckley *p250* 01455 610747

Healey, R (Hopkins) *S1 E C1 W*
Mansfield *p311* 01623 468468

Healey, R J (Howes Percival LLP) *B1 O*
Norwich *p334* 01603 762103

Healy, Mrs A K (Horsham District Council)
Horsham *p461* 01403 215100

Healy, Ms D (M P Jones & Co) *N J1*
Plymouth *p350* 01752 269007

Healy, Ms D (Pannone LLP) *N*
Manchester *p308* 0161 909 3000

Healy, Mrs D C (Kitsons LLP) *N Zr*
Plymouth *p350* 01752 603040

Healy, D P (Trethowans LLP) *Zr N Zw*
Salisbury *p371* 01722 412512

Healy, J A (Healys LLP) *B1 C1 E J1 K1 L N O S1 W Zc Ze Zl*
Brighton *p159* 01273 685888

Healy, J P L (Skadden Arps Slate Meagher & Flom (UK) LLP) *C1*
London E14 *p80* 020 7519 7000

Healy, K (Turbervilles) *E L R1*
Uxbridge *p417* 01895 201700
Uxbridge *p417* 01895 201700

Healy, K (Turbervilles) *E L R1 Zi*
Uxbridge *p417* 01895 201700
Uxbridge *p417* 01895 201700

Healy, K P (Mundays LLP) *E R1 R2*
Cobham *p196* 01932 590500

Healy, Miss N (Pinney Talfourd LLP) *W K4 S1*
Hornchurch *p252* 01708 511000

Healy, Miss R A (Mayo Wynne Baxter LLP) *D2 D1 K3 J1 K1 Q*
Lewes *p283* 01273 477071
Reigate *p363* 01737 221518

Healy, T G (Skipton Building Society)
Skipton *p471* 01756 705000

Healy-Pratt, J S (Stewarts Law LLP) *N M3 Zj M2*
London EC4 *p83* 020 7822 8000

Heaney, S (Heaney Watson) *K1 D1 K3 D2*
Liverpool *p288* 0151 282 5555

Heanley, R B (Hill Dickinson LLP) *N M1 P Za Zj Zc*
London EC3 *p41* 020 7283 9033

Heap, D A (Norcross Lees & Riches) *S1 E W L N*
Oldham *p341* 0161 624 6034

Heap, M (Serious Law LLP - The Serious Law Practice)
Bolton *p150* 0800 616 681

Heap, T R G (Billson & Sharp) *S1 J1 L Q S2 W E*
Leicester *p279* 0116 255 9911

Heap, Ms V (Osborne Clarke) *Zb*
London EC2 *p65* 020 7105 7000

Heaphy, J (Freeth Cartwright LLP) *Zo*
Nottingham *p337* 0115 936 9369

Heard, D J S (Ashfords LLP) *C1 Zb Zj*
Plymouth *p349* 01752 521500

Heard, Mrs H L F (Mowbray Woodwards Solicitors) *G Zm*
Bath *p128* 01225 485700

Heard, P (Forest Heath District Council)
Mildenhall *p466* 01638 719000

Heard, Miss S E (Stephenson Harwood)
London EC2 *p82* 020 7329 4422

Heard, S G (Bracknell Forest Borough Council)
Bracknell *p450* 01344 424642

Hearle, D J (Morris Orman Hearle) *P M1 N Zj*
Cheltenham *p188* 01242 257188

Hearle, I K (Denbighshire County Council)
Ruthin *p470* 01824 706000

Hearn, A E T (Dechert) *Q C3 Ze*
London EC4 *p26* 020 7184 7000

Hearn, K (Ford & Warren) *J1 Zp*
Leeds *p273* 0113 243 6601

Hearnden, B H (CMS Cameron McKenna LLP) *C1 C2*
London EC3 *p17* 020 7367 3000

Hearne, R J (Hearne & Co) *C1 E F1 J1 K1 L H N P S1*
Bearwood *p129* 0121 420 3636

Heartfield, P A (Fishburns) *A3 Zc C1 B2 Zj M2 O Q N Zq P*
London EC3 *p32* 020 7280 8888

Hearty, N (Kaim Todner Ltd) *G H B2 Zm K1 D1 K3*
London EC4 *p47* 020 7353 6660

Heaselden, Mrs N B (New Forest District Council)
Lyndhurst *p464* 023 8028 5000

Heaselgrave, A W (Thursfields) *S1 C1 E A1 N W R1 L J1 T1 Zl Zk*
Kidderminster *p266* 01562 820575

Heath, Miss A (Stewarts Law LLP) *Zr*
London EC4 *p83* 020 7822 8000

Heath, A M (Metcalfes) *O Q N J1 Zj Zq Zv*
Bristol *p164* 0117 929 0451

Heath, Miss B (Knowsley Metropolitan Borough Council)
Huyton *p461* 0151 443 3593

Heath, Miss B (Preston Borough Council)
Preston *p469* 01772 906101

Heath, E J (Heath Buckeridge) *C1 E S1 S2 W*
Maidenhead *p298* 01628 671636

Heath, G W (Nabarro LLP)
London WC1 *p63* 020 7524 6000

Heath, H C (Beswicks) *W S1*
Hanley *p239* 01782 205000

Heath, J (Keoghs LLP) *B2 N Zj O Q*
Bolton *p149* 01204 677000

Heath, J J M (McCarthy & Stone PLC) *E S1 Zh L*
Bournemouth *p450* 01202 292480
Poole *p352* 01202 725400

Heath, Mrs K (Reed Smith LLP) *C1*
London EC2 *p71* 020 3116 3000

Heath, M (Parkinson Wright LLP)
Worcester *p440* 01905 726789

Heath, M (Grahame Stowe Bateson) *K1*
Leeds *p274* 0113 246 8163

Heath, Miss N (Nestle UK Ltd) *E L S1*
Croydon *p456* 020 8667 5260

Heath, Mrs N F (Morrish Solicitors LLP) *N Q*
Leeds *p276* 0113 245 0733

Heath, P (Hewitsons) *C1 C2 U2 F1 Ze*
Cambridge *p174* 01223 461155

Heath, Mrs P (Graysons) *N*
Sheffield *p375* 0114 272 9184

Heath, P J (Shoosmiths) *L Zd Zh Zu P*
Birmingham *p142* 0370 086 4000 / 0121 335 4440
Leamington Spa *p270* 01926 886688

Heath, Miss S (Davies & Gribbin Solicitors) *L N J1*
Ormskirk *p341* 01695 573433

Heath, Miss S E A (Ansons LLP)
Lichfield *p284* 01543 263456

Heath, Miss S E R (Martin-Kaye LLP) *E R2 S2 A1*
Telford *p409* 01952 272222

Heath-Brown, R M (Burrows) *E J1 L O Q S1 S2 W*
Harrow *p241* . . 020 8904 7725 / 8904 4150

Heath-Saunders, A P H (Wedlake Bell LLP) *F1 F2 Ze*
London WC1 *p91* 020 7395 3000

Heathcock, A E (Paris Smith LLP) *C1 Zb C2 Ze*
Southampton *p386* 023 8048 2482

Heathcote, Ms G (Murrays Partnership) *G H*
Southwark *p62* 020 7701 8653

Heathcote, G E (Cartwright King) *G H*
Nottingham *p336* 0115 958 7444
Nottingham *p338* 0115 958 6262

Heathcote, M R (Hetts) *G F1 H J1 K1 L N Q Zk Zl Zq*
Scunthorpe *p373* 01724 270290

Heathcote, Mrs M T (Taylor & Emmet LLP) *K1 D1*
Sheffield *p377* 0114 218 4000

Heathcote, Miss S E (Rupert Bear Murray Davies) *K1 K2*
Nottingham *p338* 0115 924 3333

Heathcote, Ms T (Forsters LLP) *E*
Westminster *p33* 020 7863 8333

Heather, Dr M A (Ambrose)
Durham *p214* 0191 386 7260

Heather, N R (LG Lawyers) *C1*
London SE1 *p50* 020 7379 0000

Heaton, A J (Reed Smith LLP) *E*
London EC2 *p71* 020 3116 3000

Heaton, Miss C (Irwin Mitchell LLP) *N Zr*
Leeds *p274* 0870 150 0100

Heaton, G (Evans & Co)
Gillingham *p229* 020 7232 1325

Heaton, G R (UFB Group PLC)
Basingstoke *p448* 01256 377377

Heaton, J G (Backhouse Jones Ltd) *Zt Q G*
Clitheroe *p196* 01254 828300
Sale *p370* 0161 973 2434

Heaton, Ms J M (Caunters) *W S1*
Liskeard *p285* . . . 01579 343165 / 343484

Heaton, M (Pinsent Masons LLP)
London EC2 *p67* 020 7418 7000

Heaton, N (Hogan Lovells International LLP)
London EC1 *p42* 020 7296 2000

Heaven, G P (Forshaws Davies Ridgway LLP) *G P H*
Warrington *p422* 01925 230000

Hebbron, Mrs M G (Coca-Cola Enterprises Ltd)
Uxbridge *p474* 01895 231313

Hebden, Ms E A (Harrison Drury & Co) *K1*
Preston *p357* 01772 258321

Heckle, K (Broudie Jackson Canter) *G H*
Liverpool *p286* 0151 227 1429

Hedar, Mrs F J (Atkinson & Firth) *K1 G H D1 D2*
Shipley *p378* 01274 584305

Hedayati, Ms A (Russell Jones & Walker)
Manchester *p309* 0161 383 3500

Hedden, R (Freshwater Group of Companies (Legal Dept))
London WC2 *p106* 020 7836 1555

Hedger, Mrs R F (Humphries Kirk) *K4 T1 W Zd T2*
Dorchester *p212* 01305 251007

Hedger, R M (Michelmores LLP) *W K4*
Exeter *p221* 01392 688688
Sidmouth *p380* 01395 512515

Hedges, Mrs J H (Darbys Solicitors LLP) *E S1 R2 L*
Oxford *p343* 01865 811700

Hedges, N M (Darbys Solicitors LLP) *E C1 C2 I L*
Oxford *p343* 01865 811700

Hedges, Mrs S (Hyndburn Borough Council)
Lancaster *p447* 01254 388111

Hedley, D J (Emerson Developments (Holdings) Ltd)
Alderley Edge *p447* 01625 588420

Hedley, J A (Moore Blatch Solicitors) *N*
Southampton *p386* 023 8071 8000

Hedley, Miss J E (City of Sunderland)
Sunderland *p473* 0191 520 5555

Hedley, R B (Clifford Chance) *N P M1 J1 B1 G F1 L Zc Ze Zp*
London E14 *p20* 020 7006 1000

Hedley, Mrs S L (Harthills) *K1 D1*
Rotherham *p367* 01709 377399

Hedley-Dent, Ms S M A (Farrer & Co LLP)
London WC2 *p31* 020 3375 7000

Hedley-Miller, W (Radcliffes Le Brasseur)
Westminster *p70* 020 7222 7040

Hedley-Saunders, P F (M23LAW Solicitors (Hedley-Saunders & Co)) *G*
Crawley *p202* 0844 264 0999

Heeler, A (Hegarty LLP) *C1 Ze Zl*
Peterborough *p347* 01733 346333

Heeley, Mrs H E (Goughs) *N Zr Q*
Chippenham *p193* 01249 444499

Heelis, Miss R C (Attwaters) *Zr*
Harlow *p239* 01279 638888

Heenan, Ms R (DAC Beachcroft)
Leeds *p272* 0113 251 4700

Heer, Miss A R (Chequers Solicitors Ltd) *S1 S2 W K3 O E B1 L*
Hayes *p245* 020 8606 1000

Heer, R (Heer Manak) *K1 D1 N Q F1 G H J1 L V*
Coventry *p200* 024 7666 4000

Heffer, S (Collyer Bristow LLP)
London WC1 *p22* 020 7242 7363

Heffernan, Ms E (DLA Piper UK LLP)
London EC2 *p24* 0870 011 1111

Hefferon, Mrs S H A (Barr Ellison LLP) *N O W*
Cambridge *p174* 01223 411315

Heffner, R (Financial Services Authority)
London E14 *p106* 020 7066 1000

Hefford, Mrs J (Barlows) *K1 W S1 D1*
Market Harborough *p312* . . . 01858 410040

Heffron, D G (Addleshaw Goddard)
Leeds *p271* 0113 209 2000
Manchester *p300* 0161 934 6000

Heffron, Ms J K (Nottingham City Council (City Sec Dept)) *K1 A3 D1 D2*
Nottingham *p467* 0115 915 5555

Hegarty, B (David Gray Solicitors) *G H B2*
Newcastle upon Tyne *p324* . 0191 232 9547

Hegarty, B C (Ashfords LLP) *E R2*
Exeter *p220* 01392 337000

Hegarty, Ms G T (O'Riordan & Co) *K3 K1 W*
Chorley *p194* 01257 262837

Hegarty, R J (Hegarty LLP) *E J1 A1 B1 C1 T1 Ze*
Peterborough *p347* 01733 346333

Hegarty, S C (CMS Cameron McKenna LLP) *O Zb Zj*
Bristol *p162* 0117 930 0200

Heginbotham, P (Davis Blank Furniss) *B1 C1 J1 N P Zc Ze Zo*
Manchester *p303* 0161 832 3304

Hegoda, A N D (Anooma & Hegoda)
London N8 *p6* 020 8348 7772

Hegoda, R A K (Anooma & Hegoda) *G H Zi*
London N8 *p6* 020 8348 7772

Hehir, J P F (Neath Port Talbot Magistrates' Court)
Neath *p466* 01639 765900

Heighton, M R (CMS Cameron McKenna LLP)
London EC3 *p17* 020 7367 3000

Heilpern, Mrs A E (Treasury Solicitors Department) *T1 W Zd Zo*
London WC2 *p110* 020 7210 3000

Heiman, S G (Armstrong & Co) *E C1 L S1*
London SE23 *p7* 020 8699 3477

Heinemann, S (Howard Kennedy LLP) *C1*
London W1 *p48* 020 7636 1616

Heinl, L J (Law Partners Solicitors Ltd)
London EC1 *p51* 0870 600 9444

Heizler, L A (Wright Hassall LLP) *Ze U2 C1 F2 I Zk Zw*
Leamington Spa *p270* 01926 886688

6

Heley, Miss B S (Goughs) *S1 S2 E*
Corsham *p199* . . . 01249 712193

Hellawell, D J (Armitage Sykes LLP) *W*
Huddersfield *p255* . . . 01484 538121

Helliwell, Mrs E (British Telecommunications PLC)
London EC1 *p104* . . . 020 7356 6181

Helliwell, Ms J F (Ansons LLP) *K1 O Q W S1 D1 J1*
Lichfield *p284* . . . 01543 263456

Helliwell, Mrs K (Calderdale Metropolitan BC Corporate Services Directorate)
Halifax *p460* . . . 01422 357257

Helliwell, Ms S J (Lockett Loveday McMahon) *O Q J1 B1*
Manchester *p307* . . . 0161 237 3627

Hellyar, Ms S J (Mackarness & Lunt) *K3 K1 L Q*
Petersfield *p348* . . . 01730 265111

Helman, D S (Busbys Solicitors) *C1 E L S2 R1 S1 Zh R2*
Bude *p168* . . . 01288 359000

Helmer, M (Field Fisher Waterhouse LLP)
London EC3 *p31* . . . 020 7861 4000

Helps, D (Corbett & Co International Construction Lawyers Ltd) *Zc*
Teddington *p409* . . . 020 8614 6200

Hely, Mrs D (DAC Beachcroft) *B1 F1 J1 L O Q Zb Zc*
Manchester *p303* . . . 0161 934 3000

Hembling, B J (Rosling King) *O Q*
London EC4 *p73* . . . 020 7353 2353

Hemelryk, P R (Moore Brown & Dixon LLP) *S1 C1 E L R1 W F1 T1 P A1*
Tewkesbury *p410* . . . 01684 292341

Heming, D C (HC Solicitors LLP) *N Q Zr*
Peterborough *p347* . . . 01733 882800

Hemingray, J J (Fraser Brown) *S2 E S1 A1 Zb L R2 Zw Zc*
Nottingham *p337* . . . 0115 988 8777

Hemingray, Rev R (Raymond Hemingray) *Zx*
Peterborough *p347* . . . 01733 262523

Hemingway, Ms L A (Rooks Rider) *C1 C2 Zb Ze U2 J1*
London EC1 *p73* . . . 020 7689 7000

Hemingway, Miss R (BTMK Solicitors LLP) *N Zr*
Southend-on-Sea *p387* . . . 01702 339222

Hemingway, R W D O (AWB Partnership LLP) *W T2 K4 S1*
Guildford *p235* . . . 01483 302345

Hemingway, Ms S C (City of York Council)
York *p477* . . . 01904 551045

Hemmin, Ms S (Marsh & McLennan Companies, Inc)
London EC3 *p108* . . . 020 7357 1000

Hemming, Miss C A (Tozers) *Zr Q*
Exeter *p222* . . . 01392 207020

Hemming, Miss C J (Robinsons) *E*
Derby *p209* . . . 01332 291431

Hemming, J S J (Osborne Clarke) *J1 Zg*
Bristol *p164* . . . 0117 917 3000

Hemming, P M (Chris Clark Solicitors & Estate Agents) *G H*
Stafford *p392* . . . 01785 241842 / 241944

Hemmings, Ms R (England & Co) *C1 S2 E S1 W*
Great Yarmouth *p234* 01493 844308 / 844309

Hemmings, R A (Law Offices of Richard Hemmings Solicitor) *J1 Zp*
Ipswich *p262* . . . 01473 833844

Hemmings, R G (Blount Hemmings) *S2 E C1 L R2 S1*
Kingswinford *p268* . . . 01384 400565

Hemmings, R W (R W Hemmings & Co)
Leicester *p280* . . . 0116 255 8500

Hemmings, R W (R W Hemmings & Co) *E L S1 W A1 C1 C2 C3 K1 K3*
Taunton *p408* . . . 01823 325090

Hemmings, Miss S A (Wilkins) *W S1 S2 T1*
Aylesbury *p121* . . . 01296 424681

Hempseed, I D (Hempsons) *C1 C2 C3 Zd Ze I*
Westminster *p40* . . . 020 7839 0278

Hems, S (Ince & Co Services Ltd)
London E1 *p44* . . . 020 7481 0010

Hemsi, D (MPH Solicitors) *N J2*
Manchester *p307* . . . 0161 832 7722

Hemsley, M J (Hemsleys) *G H N K1 Q S1 E C1 W*
Chester *p190* . . . 01244 382400

Hemsley, Ms S (Thompsons (formerly Robin/Brian Thompson & Partners))
Leeds *p277* . . . 0113 205 6300

Hemsted, M (DLA Piper UK LLP)
Manchester *p303* . . . 0870 011 1111

Hemus, Miss F (Carter Bells LLP) *W K1*
Kingston upon Thames *p267* 020 8939 4000

Hemus, Mrs L (Darlington Borough Council) *K1*
Darlington *p456* . . . 01325 388055

Henchie, Mrs M K (Attwaters) *K1 D1*
Harlow *p239* . . . 01279 638888

Henchie, N D J (Mayer Brown International LLP) *O Q Zc*
London EC2 *p59* . . . 020 3130 3000

Henchley, K F (Henchleys) *S1 W E N K1 G F2 L Zl Zm Zq Zr*
Littlehampton *p285* . . . 01903 726477

Henchley, M V (National Grid PLC)
Warwick *p471* . . . 01926 653000

Henchley, Miss S (Henchleys) *N S1 W F1 K3 J1 K1 L O Q Zq Zr S2*
Worthing *p441* . . . 01903 877657

Hender, Ms L (Withers LLP) *T2 W*
London EC4 *p92* . . . 020 7597 6000

Henders-Green, Mrs A (Dolmans) *Zq O Q*
Cardiff *p178* . . . 029 2034 5531

Henderson Nee Grantham, Mrs C F (Thompsons (formerly Robin/Brian Thompson & Partners)) *N Zr*
Birmingham *p143* . . . 0121 262 1200

Henderson, Miss A (Wigan Borough Council)
Wigan *p476* . . . 01942 244991

Henderson, Mrs A J (Steel & Co) *S1 K1 K3*
Wetherby *p429* . . . 01937 845539

Henderson, A V B (Ellicotts) *S1 C1 W E K1 L F1 J1 T1*
London N20 *p29* . 020 8445 5257 / 8445 2880

Henderson, Ms B (Barr Ellison LLP) *S1*
Cambridge *p174* . . . 01223 417200

Henderson, Miss D M (Travers Smith LLP) *J1*
London EC1 *p87* . . . 020 7295 3000

Henderson, G (Allen & Overy LLP)
London E1 *p5* . . . 020 3088 0000

Henderson, Ms H C (Farrell Matthews & Weir) *S1*
London W6 *p30* . . . 020 8746 3771

Henderson, I K (Tonbridge & Malling Borough Council)
West Malling *p476* . . . 01732 876030

Henderson, J (Humphries Kirk) *E Zc C1*
Poole *p352* . . . 01202 725400

Henderson, J (Neil Myerson LLP) *J1*
Altrincham *p117* . . . 0161 941 4000

Henderson, J C (Lupton Fawcett) *S1 E L R1*
Leeds *p275* . . . 0113 280 2000

Henderson, J D (Beale and Company Solicitors LLP) *O B1 N Zc Zn Zg Zq*
London WC2 *p11* . . . 020 7240 3474

Henderson, J G (Aviva PLC) *E R2*
London EC3 *p103* . . 020 7283 7500 / 01603 687905
Norwich *p467* . . . 01603 622200
Norwich *p335* . . . 01603 660155

Henderson, Miss K L (Close Thornton) *N Q L F1 B1*
Darlington *p206* . . . 01325 466461

Henderson, Mrs L (Langley Wellington) *X*
Gloucester *p230* . . . 01452 521286

Henderson, L (Callaghans)
Farnham *p224* . . . 01252 723477

Henderson, M R (Graeme John Solicitors) *D1 D2 E F1 F2 J1 K1 K2 Zl Zm Zr Zt*
Tonypandy *p412* . . . 01443 423797

Henderson, N C (Dickinson Dees) *O*
Newcastle upon Tyne *p324* . 0191 279 9000

Henderson, Ms P (Hatch Brenner) *S1*
Norwich *p334* . . . 01603 660811

Henderson, Miss P F (Treasury Solicitors Department)
London WC2 *p110* . . . 020 7210 3000

Henderson, P J (Williamson Hill) *N*
Middlesbrough *p315* . . . 01642 217961

Henderson, R J (Shell International Ltd)
London SE1 *p109* . . . 020 7934 1234

Henderson, R S (Watson Farley & Williams) *C1 Zb*
London EC2 *p90* . . . 020 7814 8000

Henderson, Ms S (Ashurst LLP)
London EC2 *p7* . . . 020 7638 1111

Henderson, S A (Irwin Mitchell LLP) *N Zr*
Birmingham *p139* . . . 0870 150 0100

Henderson, T L (Overburys & Raymond Thompson) *S2 E*
Norwich *p335* . . . 01603 610481

Hendey, D W (Lindleys) *B1 C1 E J1 L M1 N P R1 S1 Zc Ze Zh*
Bristol *p163* . . . 0117 926 2408
Clevedon *p196* . . . 01275 877277

Hendleman, D (Smith Sutcliffe) *J1 C1 W S1 E T2*
Burnley *p169* . . . 01282 426251

Hendren, Mrs V M (Brockbank Curwen Cain & Hall) *G K1 H L Zl*
Whitehaven *p431* . . . 01946 692194

Hendron, G P (Goldens) *N*
Pinner *p348* . . . 020 8429 8282

Hendry, Ms E (Ashurst LLP)
London EC2 *p7* . . . 020 7638 1111

Hendry, Mrs E J (Whitehead Vizard) *K3 K1 Q L*
Salisbury *p371* . . . 01722 412141

Hendry, Mrs H (Jackamans) *S1*
Ipswich *p262* . . . 01473 255591

Hendry, J B (Duncan Lewis & Co) *Zi*
London W12 *p53* . . . 020 7923 4020

Hendry, Miss M C (Thomas Dunton Solicitors) *K1 V*
Orpington *p342* . . . 01689 822554
London E2 *p84* . . . 020 7739 6927

Heneghan, P (Skadden Arps Slate Meagher & Flom (UK) LLP)
London E14 *p80* . . . 020 7519 7000

Henley, C E (Charles Henley) *S1 A1 E L W*
Market Harborough *p312* . . 01536 771811

Henley, J A (Henleys) *S1 W E*
Basingstoke *p126* . . . 01256 840084

Henley, Miss L E (Ford Simey LLP) *W*
Exeter *p221* . . . 01392 274126

Henley, M S (Squire Sanders (UK) LLP) *O Q*
Leeds *p277* . . . 0113 284 7000

Henley, Ms V C (Rubin Lewis O'Brien) *D1 G F1 H K1 J1 M1 P*
Cwmbran *p206* . . . 01633 867000

Hennah, N J (Hornby Baker Jones & Wood) *N Zr J2 L O Q Zq*
Newport *p328* . . . 01633 262848

Hennell, L S (Harvey Ingram LLP) *E*
Leicester *p280* . . . 0116 254 5454

Hennessey, J (Maxwell Winward LLP) *C1 C2 C3*
London EC4 *p59* . . . 020 7651 0000

Hennessey, J C (Oldhams Solicitors & Advocates) *G H*
Baldock *p121* . . . 01462 895444

Hennessey, Ms S (Sintons LLP) *C1 R1 S1 E L Zc Zb*
Newcastle upon Tyne *p326* . 0191 226 7878

Hennessy, F (Campion & Co) *G H*
Nottingham *p336* . . . 0115 947 6373

Hennessy, Miss M M (Sweeney Miller) *S1 L Q N*
Sunderland *p402* . . . 0191 568 2050

Hennigan, J (Squire Sanders (UK) LLP)
London EC2 *p81* . . . 020 7655 1000

Henniker, C A M (Kidd Rapinet) *C1 C2*
London WC2 *p49* . . . 020 7205 2115

Hennis, C R P (Atteys) *G H*
Doncaster *p211* . . . 01302 340400

Hennity, P M (The Wilkes Partnership LLP) *N*
Birmingham *p143* . . . 0121 233 4333

Henrion, J P (Just Employment) *J1 N Zp C1 T2 J2*
Guildford *p236* . . . 01483 303636

Henry, Ms A (Debenhams Ottaway) *Zj N*
St Albans *p390* . . . 01727 837161

Henry, Ms A (Henry Browne Solicitors) *K1 W*
Birmingham *p136* . . . 0121 765 3332

Henry, B (Jonas Roy Bloom) *G B2*
Birmingham *p139* . . . 0121 212 4111

Henry, Ms E D (Last Cawthra Feather LLP)
Bradford *p154* . . . 01274 848800

Henry, G (Garstangs)
London WC2 *p35* . . . 020 7427 5678

Henry, Miss J M H (Pemberton Greenish LLP) *C1 C2*
London SW3 *p66* . . . 020 7591 3333

Henry, K J (Henrys Solicitors Ltd) *G H N*
Stockport *p395* . . . 0161 477 8558

Henry, Mrs K L (Mulcahy Smith) *V K3 D1 K1*
Gateshead *p229* . . . 0191 490 1000

Henry, M (Stanley Tee) *Q N*
Bishop's Stortford *p144* . . . 01279 755200

Henry, M A (Birketts LLP) *C1*
Ipswich *p262* . . . 01473 232300

Henry, P M (Barber Titleys) *A1 E L S1 S2 A2 R2*
Harrogate *p240* . . . 01423 502211

Henry, S (Gelbergs LLP) *B1 C1 F1 J1 K1 L N O Q Zb Zh Zq Zr*
Islington *p35* . . . 020 7226 0570

Henry, Ms S (Southend-on-Sea Borough Council)
Southend-on-Sea *p472* . . . 01702 215000

Henry, Miss S (Stanley De Leon) *E S2 S1 R2*
Potters Bar *p355* . . . 01707 657277

Henry, T M (The Reece-Jones Partnership) *C1 C2 E S1*
Sevenoaks *p374* . . . 01732 457575
London EC4 *p91* . . . 020 7822 1900

Henry, T S J (Barber Titleys) *E S1 S2*
Harrogate *p240* . . . 01423 502211

Henry, T S J (Hethertons LLP) *E C1 S2 L*
York *p445* . . . 01904 528200

Henry, W E (Berwick-upon-Tweed Borough Council)
Berwick-Upon-Tweed *p449* . . 01289 330044

Henshall, Ms A (Parker Rhodes Hickmotts) *Zi*
Rotherham *p367* . . . 01709 511100

Henshall, C J (Crewe & Nantwich Borough Council)
Crewe *p456* . . . 01270 537102

Henshall, D G (Volks Hedleys)
Kensington & Chelsea *p89* . 020 7584 6733

Henshall, M A (West Sussex County Council)
Chichester *p455* . . . 01243 777100

Henshaw, Mrs D M F (West Sussex County Council)
Chichester *p455* . . . 01243 777100

Henshaw, Mrs J (Cheshire County Council)
Chester *p454* . . . 01244 602382

Henshaw, Mrs J E (Banner Jones) *S1*
Chesterfield *p191* . . . 01246 560560

Henshaw, M W (Ellesmere Port & Neston Borough Council)
Ellesmere Port *p458* . . . 0151 356 6789

Henshaw, R J (Aplin Stockton Fairfax) *W K4*
Banbury *p122* . . . 01295 251234

Hensleigh, M (Preston Redman) *B1 F1 G H J1 K1 L N Q V Zi Zl Zp K3*
Bournemouth *p152* . . . 01202 292424

Hensley, D A (Nicholls Henstock & Stevenson)
Altrincham *p117* . . . 0161 980 6099

Hensman, S S (Heptonstalls LLP) *N*
Pontefract *p351* . . . 01977 602804

Henson, Miss A J (Irwin Mitchell LLP) *N J1*
Leeds *p274* . . . 0870 150 0100

Henson, D I (The Johnson Partnership) *G H B2*
Nottingham *p337* . . . 0115 941 9141

Henson, Mrs H S (Jacobs & Reeves) *E S1 S2 K1*
Poole *p353* . . . 01202 674425

Henson, J R (Squire Sanders (UK) LLP)
Leeds *p277* . . . 0113 284 7000

Henson, J S (HC Solicitors LLP) *G H D1 D2*
Peterborough *p347* . . . 01733 882800

Henson, Ms M J (Taylor Vinters) *E S2 R1*
Cambridge *p176* . . . 01223 423444

Henson, N C (Rowberry Morris) *S2 E S1 W C1*
Reading *p361* . . . 0118 958 5611
Tadley *p407* . . . 0118 981 2992

Henthorn, S (Reynolds Porter Chamberlain LLP)
London E1 *p71* . . . 020 3060 6000

Henwood, E (hlw Keeble Hawson LLP)
Sheffield *p376* . . . 0114 276 5555

Henwood, Miss F (McKenzies) *K1 D2 D1 K3 S1 W*
London N9 *p57* . . . 020 8350 4114

Henwood, Ms M (Judge & Priestley) *S1*
Bromley *p166* . . . 020 8290 0333

Henwood, S (Ince & Co Services Ltd)
London E1 *p44* . . . 020 7481 0010

Hepburn, D (Hepburns) *S1 S2 E*
Oxted *p344* . . . 01883 723712

Hepburn, D C (Clifford Chance)
London E14 *p20* . . . 020 7006 1000

Hepburn, Ms J A (Carr Hepburn Solicitors Ltd) *K1 D1*
Hemel Hempstead *p246* . . . 01442 241466

Hepburn, M R (M R Hepburn) *E K1 S2 L W S1*
Sutton Coldfield *p403* . . . 0121 378 0440

Hepburn, Ms R A (Toussaint & Co)
Wembley *p427* . . . 020 8903 6111

Heppel, E P J (Rollits LLP) *J1*
Hull *p258* . . . 01482 323239

Heppell, M M (O'Neill Patient) *C1 E S2 S1*
Stockport *p396* . . . 0161 483 8555

Heppell, N (Elliot Mather LLP) *Q*
Mansfield *p311* . . . 01623 655666

Heppenstall, C (Ford & Warren) *A3 F1 N Q Zj*
Leeds *p273* . . . 0113 243 6601

Hepplestall, Ms D (Easthams Solicitors Limited) *S1 W E L*
Blackpool *p146* . . . 0800 032 1432

Hepplestone, Miss V L K (Thompsons (formerly Robin/Brian Thompson & Partners)) *N*
Birmingham *p143* . . . 0121 262 1200

Heptinstall, B M C (Walter Gray & Co) *S1 W K4*
Ryde *p369* . . . 01983 563765

Hepworth, A M (Ince & Co Services Ltd)
London E1 *p44* . . . 020 7481 0010

Hepworth, Ms C A (John Pickering & Partners LLP) *N Zg Zr*
Halifax *p238* . . . 0808 144 0959

Hepworth, M A (Ramsdens Solicitors) *S1*
Halifax *p238* . . . 01422 330700
Huddersfield *p256* . . . 01484 821500

Hepworth, M B (Blake Lapthorn) *C1 C2 B1 Zb*
Oxford *p342* . . . 01865 248607
Portsmouth *p354* . . . 023 9222 1122

Hepworth, M G B (Denison Till) *K1 D1 Zl K3*
York *p444* . . . 01904 611411

Heran, D (Rawstorne Heran Solicitors)
Stratford-upon-Avon *p400* . . 01789 267646

Herard, Ms F (Watson Farley & Williams)
London EC2 *p90* . . . 020 7814 8000

Herath, R (Harrow Solicitors & Advocates) *Zi*
Wealdstone *p424* . . . 020 8863 0788

Herberg, L G (Treasury Solicitors Department)
London WC2 *p110* . . . 020 7210 3000

Herbert, A F (Thompsons (formerly Robin/Brian Thompson & Partners)) *J1 N*
Plymouth *p350* . . . 01752 675810

Herbert, C C (Hart District Council)
Fleet *p458* . . . 01252 622122

Herbert, D M (Lester Aldridge LLP) *O N Q Zj Zc*
London WC2 *p53* . . . 0844 967 0785

Herbert, I (Hugh James) *Zb B1 O N Zq I*
Cardiff *p179* . . . 029 2022 4871

Herbert, Mrs K A (Warwick District Council)
Leamington Spa *p462* . . . 01926 450000

Herbert, Mrs K L (Spearing Waite LLP) *E S2 R2 Zc A1*
Leicester *p281* . . . 0116 262 4225

Herbert, Ms N (Hill Dickinson LLP) *W*
Liverpool *p288* . . . 0151 600 8000

Herbert, N A (Ashby Family Law Practice) *K1 D2 K3 S1*
Derby *p208* . . . 01332 293293

Herbert, P A (Hamlins LLP) *O Q Zf Ze Zp*
London W1 *p38* . . . 020 7355 6000

Herbert, P T (Goodman Derrick LLP) *J1 N P Ze Zk*
London EC4 *p36* . . . 020 7404 0606

Herbert, Mrs R (Howard Kennedy LLP) *E*
London W1 *p48* . . . 020 7636 1616

Herbert, R G W (K&L Gates LLP) *C1 Zb*
London EC4 *p47* . . . 020 7648 9000

Herbert, S B H (Wilkins & Thompson) *W A1 E S2 J1*
Uttoxeter *p417* . . . 01889 562875

Herbert, Miss S R (Batchelors Solicitors) *Zh L*
Bromley *p166* . . . 020 8768 7000

Herbert, Ms S S A (Horsham District Council)
Horsham *p461* . . . 01403 215100

Herbertson, Miss L D (Irwin Mitchell LLP) *Zr*
Manchester *p306* . . . 0870 150 0100

Herd, Mrs A P S (Chenery Maher & Co) *S1 S2 K1 L W*
Clitheroe *p196* . . . 01200 422264

Herd, J K C (Howes Percival LLP) *E P R1 Zb Zc*
Leicester *p280* . . . 0116 247 3500

Herga, R D (B A A PLC)
London UB3 *p103* . . . 0870 000 0123

Heritage, Miss G (Land Law LLP) *S1 E C1 L*
Altrincham *p116* . . . 0161 928 8383

Herklots, R W (Blake Lapthorn) *S1*
Chandlers Ford *p184* . . . 023 8090 8090

Herlihy, Mrs J E (Mills & Reeve) *C1 Zu Zm Zg Ze Zd Zr J1*
Birmingham *p140* . . . 0121 454 4000

Herman, A (Berry & Berry) *P N K1 C1 U1 S1 E J1 L Zc Zl*
Tonbridge *p412* . . . 01732 355911
Tunbridge Wells *p414* . . . 01892 526344

Herman, Ms D A (Barlow Lyde & Gilbert LLP)
London EC3 *p10* . . . 020 7247 2277

Herman, Miss D E (Blaser Mills) *K1 D1 Q*
Harrow *p241* . . . 020 8427 6262

Herman, D J (Stewarts Law LLP) *N*
Leeds *p277* . . . 0113 222 0022

See p634 for the Key to Work Categories

Herman, M R (Lewis Nedas & Co) G H
Camden p53. . . . . 020 7387 2032

Hermer, Mrs J L (Lester Aldridge LLP) O
Bournemouth p152. . . . . . 01202 786161

Hermer, S H (Hermer & Evans) C1 F1 J1 K1 L N S1 V
Cardiff p178 . . .029 2038 7766 / 2022 4009

Hermon, R (Conway & Co) B1 D1 C1 S2 E F1 K3 K1 Zl O Q S1 W
Harrow p241. . . . . 020 8863 0535

Hernandez, G (Fishburns) Zc O Q Zq
London EC3 p32. . . . . . 020 7280 8888

Hernandez-Garcia, Ms M (Howard Kennedy LLP) Zn
London W1 p48 . . . . . . 020 7636 1616

Herne, R J (Richard Herne & Co Solicitors) S1 W K1
Staple Hill p394 . . . . . . 0117 957 4508

Herns, Ms H J (Sitters & Co) D1 K1 D2 K3
Plymouth p350. . . . . . . 01752 220464

Heron, Mrs E (Beviss & Beckingsale)
Seaton p373. . . . . 01297 626950

Heron, Mrs L (West Cumbria Magistrates Courts)
Workington p477. . . . . . . .01900 62244

Heron, P R (McKenzie Bell Solicitors) C1 D1 E G H J1 K1 M1 N P Zk Zl Zm
Sunderland p401. . . . . . 0191 567 4857

Heron, R A (Gilbert Stephens) N K1 G M1 P W D1 Zc Zl
Exeter p221 . . . . 01392 424242
Sidmouth p380. . . . . . . 01395 512443

Heron, Miss S (Metropolitan Police Directorate of Legal Services) P M1 K1
London SW1 p108. . . . . . 020 7230 7210

Herricks, A (Keoghs LLP) C1 C2 Ze U2
Bolton p149 . . . . 01204 677000

Herries-Smith, Mrs C J (Wycombe District Council)
High Wycombe p461. . . . . 01494 461002

Herring, A (DLA Piper UK LLP)
Birmingham p137 . . . . . . 0870 011 1111

Herring, J W F (Mills & Reeve) A1 S1 E W Zd
Norwich p335 . . . . 01603 660155

Herring, N J (The Smith Partnership) K1 K3 D1
Leicester p281. . . . . . . 0116 247 2000

Herring, P R (Ince & Co Services Ltd)
London E1 p44 . . . . 020 7481 0010

Herriott, P F (Partridge & Wilson) W T2
Bury St Edmunds p171 . . . 01284 762281

Herrod, Ms K (Tollers LLP)
Northampton p332. . . . . . 01604 258558

Herrod, Ms K (Tollers LLP) K1
Northampton p332. . . . . . 01604 258558

Herschan, P J O (Pothecary Witham Weld) S1 W E A1 C1 L Zd Zh
Westminster p69. . . . . . . 020 7821 8211

Hershkorn, D H (Brecher) R2 S1 L E S2
London W1 p15 . . . . 020 7563 1000

Hershkorn, J M (Magrath LLP)
London W1 p57 . . . . 020 7495 3003

Herson, M (Buckles Solicitors LLP) O B1 Zq Zk Zc F1 A3
Peterborough p346 . . . . . 01733 888888

Hertz, P L (Clifford Chance)
London E14 p20. . . . . . . 020 7006 1000

Hertzell, A (Penningtons) S1
Godalming p231 . . . . . . 01483 791800

Herward, Miss S M (Stoke-on-Trent City Council) G H K1
Stoke-on-Trent p472. . . . . 01782 234567

Hesbrook, Miss C S (Meade-King) W K4
Bristol p163 . . . . 0117 926 4121

Heseltine, A J (Heseltine Bray & Welsh) S1 E A1 L
Barnsley p124 . . . . 01226 210777

Heseltine, Mrs L A M (Morecrofts Solicitors LLP)
Liverpool p290. . . . . . . 0151 236 8871

Heseltine, P J (Bray & Bray) C1 C2 B1 E M1 Zc Ze
Leicester p279. . . . . . . 0116 254 8871

Heselton, M (Vanderpump & Sykes) K1 Q O N
Enfield p219. . . . . 020 8367 3999

Hesford, A (Howarth Goodman) Zh Q L E J1
Manchester p305 . . . . . . 0161 832 5068

Hesford, Miss S C (SAS Daniels LLP) K1 D1
Macclesfield p297 . . . . . 01625 442100

Hesham, S (Harrison Drury & Co) E S2 L O S1
Preston p357 . . . . 01772 258321

Heshon, D (The College of Law Chester)
Chester p454 . . . . 0800 289997

Hesketh, Mrs J (Metcalfe Copeman & Pettefar) S1 S2 W
Peterborough p347 . . . . . 01733 865880

Hesketh, J J R (Squire Sanders (UK) LLP)
London EC2 p81. . . . . . . 020 7655 1000

Hesketh, P (Russell Jones & Walker) N
Manchester p309 . . . . . . 0161 383 3500

Heslehurst, Ms R E (Barlow Lyde & Gilbert LLP)
London EC3 p10. . . . . . . 020 7247 2277

Heslett, R A (DAC Beachcroft) M1 P N J1 G
London EC4 p24. . . . . . . 020 7242 1011

Heslop, J (Nicholson & Morgan) S1 W
Ponteland p351 . . . .01661 871012 / 823381

Heslop, Ms K (Shell International Ltd)
London SE1 p109 . . . . . . 020 7934 1234

Heslop, N F (Norman H Barnett & Co) G K1 H P D1
London E6 p11. . . . . 020 8471 2112

Heslop, R M (Moseleys) N W C1 B1 Zc O Q Zk Zq Ze Zr
Lichfield p284 . . . . 01543 414100

Hesp, Ms S M T (Mills & Reeve) J1 Zo
Norwich p335 . . . . 01603 660155

Hessel, M (EMW) O Q A3 Zq L B1 R1
London WC2 p28 . . . . . . 0845 070 6000
London W1 p70 . . . . 020 7318 4444

Hession, Ms M (Fruhman Davies Livingstones)
Manchester p304 . . . . . . 0161 833 0578

Hession, Ms R A (Barlow Lyde & Gilbert LLP) N Q G Zj
London EC3 p10. . . . . . . 020 7247 2277

Hetheridge, Miss M S (Thursfields) W
Worcester p440 . . . . 01905 730450

Hetherington, A N (Adams Hetherington) D1 F1 G H K1 M1 S1 W
Ashington p119 . . . . 01670 850520
Cramlington p201 . .01670 714622 / 714635

Hetherington, Ms C (Penningtons) S1
Godalming p231 . . . . . . 01483 791800

Hetherington, D (Margetts & Ritchie) F1 F2 J2 Zy
Birmingham p140 . . . . . . 0121 236 5517

Hetherington, D J (Fladgate LLP) J1 Zp Zi
London WC2 p32 . . . . . . 020 3036 7000
Greenwich p36. . . . . . . 020 8858 6971

Hetherington, Miss G (Shepherd Harris & Co) D1 G H J1 K1
Enfield p219. . . . . 020 8363 8341

Hetherington, Ms L (Ashurst LLP)
London EC2 p7 . . . . 020 7638 1111

Hetherington, Ms M B (The Hetherington Partnership)
Wirral p435 . . . . 0151 632 3411

Hetherington, P C (The Hetherington Partnership) L M1 B1 C1 D1 E W G H J1
Wirral p435 . . . . 0151 632 3411

Hetherington, R (MacLaren Britton) G H W
Nottingham p338. . . . . . . 0115 941 1469

Hetherington, R (Weightmans LLP)
Liverpool p291. . . . . . . 0151 227 2601

Hetherington, Miss R C (Forshaws Davies Ridgway LLP) K1 D1 D2 V K3
Frodsham p227 . . . . 01928 739300

Hetherington, W G (Edwards Solicitors) S1 C1 E W A1 S2 K4 Zl K3
Melton Mowbray p314 . . . . 01664 566606

Hetzel, Miss K (Biscoes) K1
Wickham p431. . . . . 01329 833249

Heuvel, J D (Penningtons) J1
London EC2 p66. . . . . . . 020 7457 3000

Heuvels, J (Ince & Co Services Ltd)
London E1 p44 . . . . 020 7481 0010

Hevey, G (Denison Till) Zc
York p444 . . . . 01904 611411

Hew, K H (Pinsent Masons LLP)
London EC2 p67. . . . . . . 020 7418 7000

Hewardine, J (Ison Harrison) Zc E S1
Leeds p274 . . . . 0113 284 5000

Hewens, T M A (Squire Sanders (UK) LLP)
London EC2 p81. . . . . . . 020 7655 1000

Hewes, P L (CMS Cameron McKenna LLP)
London EC3 p17. . . . . . . 020 7367 3000

Hewes, S P (Bond Pearce LLP) C1 C2
Bristol p161 . . . . 0845 415 0000

Hewetson, C M (Reed Smith LLP) O
London EC2 p71. . . . . . . 020 3116 3000

Hewett, D C (British Telecommunications PLC)
London EC1 p104 . . . . . . 020 7356 6181

Hewett, M L (Martyn Hewett Solicitor) G H
Shepherdswell p377 . . . . . 01304 831888

Hewison, C (Hewison & Nixon) S1 W E
Pontefract p351 . . . . 01977 700705

Hewison, C (Rotherys)
Cleckheaton p195 . . . . . . 01274 876785

Hewison, J E (George Davies Solicitors LLP) B1 C1 C2 Zf Zw T1 J1 M1
Manchester p303 . . . . . . 0161 236 8992

Hewison, Miss V (Muckle LLP) C1 C2
Newcastle upon Tyne p325 . 0191 211 7777

Hewitson, Mrs A (BHP Law) K1
Newcastle upon Tyne p323 . 0191 221 0898

Hewitson, C R B (Hewitsons) A1 T1 T2 W
Cambridge p174. . . . . . . 01223 461155

Hewitson, N (English Heritage)
London EC1 p106 . . . . . . 020 7973 3360

Hewitson, N (Howard Kennedy LLP) R1 E
London W1 p48 . . . . 020 7636 1616

Hewitt, A (Lyons Davidson)
Bristol p163 . . . . 0117 904 6000

Hewitt, A J (Dickinson Dees) C1 Zb
Newcastle upon Tyne p324 . 0191 279 9000

Hewitt, A P (Withers LLP) Q W Zd
London EC4 p92. . . . . . . 020 7597 6000

Hewitt, A S (Thompsons (formerly Robin/Brian Thompson & Partners)) G H
Leeds p277 . . . . 0113 205 6300

Hewitt, Miss C S (Barwells) K3 K1 L Q
Seaford p373 . . . . 01323 899331

Hewitt, C T (Ward Hadaway) C1 Ze F1 I O
Newcastle upon Tyne p327 . 0191 204 4000

Hewitt, D J (Cross Ram & Co) S2 E L S1
Halesworth p237. . . . . . . 01986 873636

Hewitt, Mrs F M (Hayes & Storr) W J1
Fakenham p223 . . . . 01328 863231

Hewitt, Mrs J (Keoghs LLP) O Q N Zj
Bolton p149 . . . . 01204 677000

Hewitt, J A (BUPA) E
London WC1 p104. . . . . . 020 7656 2305

Hewitt, J E (Finers Stephens Innocent LLP) N P L J1 C1 M1 B1 E Zc Ze Zj
London W1 p32 . . . . 020 7323 4000

Hewitt, Ms K (Oldham Marsh Page Flavell)
Melton Mowbray p314 . . . . 01664 563162

Hewitt, Ms L E (Chesworths) W S1
Stoke-on-Trent p397. . . . . 01782 599993

Hewitt, Mrs L J (Trowers & Hamlins) Zh L R2 S1 S2 E
Exeter p222 . . . . 01392 217466

Hewitt, M (South Gloucestershire Council)
Thornbury p474 . . . . 01454 868686

Hewitt, M P A (Powell & Young) S2 A1 C1 E L
Pocklington p351 . . . . . . 01759 302113

Hewitt, R C (Blake Lapthorn) E
Chandlers Ford p184 . . . . 023 8090 8090

Hewitt, R J (Wedlake Bell LLP) B1 O Q Zj
London WC1 p91 . . . . . . 020 7395 3000

Hewitt, Miss R L (Darbys Solicitors LLP) Zr N Zw
Oxford p343. . . . . 01865 811700

Hewitt, R P (Hayes & Storr) A1 Zc E P Zl Zu R1 S2 S1
Sheringham p378 . . . . . . 01263 825959

Hewitt, S F (Fisher Meredith) G H K1
Lambeth p32. . . . . 020 7091 2700

Hewitt, T R M (Burges Salmon) A1 W T2
Bristol p161 . . . . 0117 939 2000

Hewitt, Ms W (Equality & Human Rights Commission)
Manchester p464 . . . . . . 0161 829 8100

Hewland, M A (Simmons & Simmons)
London EC2 p79. . . . . . . 020 7628 2020

Hewson, Miss C L (Simmons & Simmons)
London EC2 p79. . . . . . . 020 7628 2020

Hewson, Ms K (Shoosmiths)
Fareham p224. . . . 0370 086 6800 / 01489 616800

Hewstone, Mrs W J (Hannides Hewstone & Co) N K1 Q L W S1
Southampton p386. . . . . . 023 8078 6770

Hextall, D (Rollits LLP) E S2 L Zc R2 S1
Hull p258 . . . . 01482 323239
Hull p258 . . . . 01482 324662

Hey, S (Charles Russell LLP)
London EC4 p19. . . . . . . 020 7203 5000

Heydon, G H (Brian Harris & Co) T1 W
London W1 p39 . . . . 020 7935 5541
Potters Bar p355. . . . . . . 01707 879646

Heyes, Ms C (Kingsley Napley) Zr Zq
London EC1 p50. . . . . . . 020 7814 1200

Heyes, Ms F J (Pinsent Masons LLP) O Zq Zj
London EC2 p67. . . . . . . 020 7418 7000

Heyes, G (Palmer Hodgson & Heyes) K1 M1 P L V F1 J1 G S1
Fleetwood p226 . . . . 01253 778231

Heyes, Ms J C (Osborne Clarke) U1 U2
Bristol p164 . . . . 0117 917 3000

Heyes, J P (Salford City Council)
Swinton p473 . . . . 0161 794 4711

Heyes, M J (Haworth & Nuttall) K4 Zl S1 W
Accrington p114 . . . . 01254 236221
Blackburn p145 . . . . 01254 272640

Heyes, Miss S C (Heyes Samuel) N
Ryde p369. . . . . 01983 615615

Heylen, T (DLA Piper UK LLP)
Leeds p272 . . . . 0870 011 1111

Heylin, Mrs A (Rogerson Galvin) K1 D1
Ashton-under-Lyne p1200161 344 2027 / 335 9005

Heys, D (Lawson West Solicitors Limited) C1 S2 E L R1 Zc
Leicester p280. . . . . 0116 212 1000

Heys, Mrs D (Allen Hoole Solicitors) G H
Bristol p160 . . . . 0117 942 0901

Heys, J A (Brighton & Hove Council - Legal Services)
Hove p461. . . . . 01273 290000

Heys, Miss L F P R (Legal Services Commission No 9 (North Eastern))
Leeds p463 . . . . 0113 390 7300

Heys, Mrs S M (City & County of Swansea)
Swansea p473. . . . . 01792 636000

Heywood, Miss A (Michelmores LLP) W Q
Exeter p221 . . . . 01392 688688

Heywood, C E (Greenland Houchen Pomeroy) E C1 S1 L A1 Zl
Norwich p334 . . . . 01603 660744

Heywood, Mrs E M (Blake Lapthorn) O Zq Zk
Chandlers Ford p184 . . . . 023 8090 8090

Heywood, J (Pope & Co) K1 L F1 J1 N Q W K3
Sittingbourne p380. . . . . . 01795 474004

Heywood, Miss L J (Newsome Vaughan LLP) E S1
Coventry p200. . . . . 024 7663 3433

Heywood, N (Betesh Partnership) E S2 S1 C1 C2 O Zc
Manchester p301 . . . . . . 0161 834 2623

Heywood, T R E (Bevan Brittan LLP) N P M1 J1 C1 B1 F1 K1 Zc Zd
Bristol p161 . . . . 0870 194 1000

Heywood, Miss V L (Eaton Smith LLP) E S1
Huddersfield p255 . . . . . . 01484 821300

Hezseltine, Mrs W (Dawson & Burgess with Bell Dallman & Co) N Q O Zr Zq
Doncaster p211 . . . . 01302 349463

Hiatt, P (Stevens) G H
Wolverhampton p438 . . . . . 01902 772776

Hibbard, Miss A J (Lyons Davidson) E S1 L J1 C1 R1 F1
Bristol p163 . . . . 0117 904 6000

Hibberd, Ms I G (Glinert Davis) E S2 L R2 S1
Westminster p36. . . . . . . 020 7724 4442

Hibbert, A J (Pinsent Masons LLP) A3
London EC2 p67. . . . . . . 020 7418 7000

Hibbert, B (John Robinson & Co)
Hull p258 . . . . 01482 324818

Hibbert, Ms B (Farleys Solicitors LLP) G H B2
Blackburn p145 . . . . 01254 367855

Hibbert, D S (Browne Jacobson LLP) C1 E Zw
Nottingham p336. . . . . . . 0115 976 6000

Hibbert, E (Aaron & Partners LLP Solicitors) A1 C1 E S2
Chester p190 . . . . 01244 405555
Welshpool p425 . . . . 01938 552545

Hibbert, T (Reed Smith LLP) Zb B1
London EC2 p71. . . . . . . 020 3116 3000

Hibbett, Miss J (Arnold Thomson Limited) E S2
Towcester p413 . . . . 01327 350266
Northampton p332. . 0370 086 3000 / 01604 543000

Hibbs, M J (Shakespeares) J1 O B1 Q Zp
Birmingham p142 . . . . . . 0121 237 3000

Hibbs, Miss N C (Devon County Council)
Exeter p458 . . . . 01392 382000

Hicken, D (Maples Solicitors LLP) S1 A1 Zc Zd S2 E R2
Spalding p389 . . . . 01775 722261

Hicken, Mrs J (Environment Agency (Midlands Region))
Solihull p471. . . . . 0121 711 2324

Hickey, Ms A P M (Rees Wood Terry) W T2
Cardiff p180 . . . . 029 2040 8800

Hickey, F H M (Dowse & Co) N Q J2 L J1
Hackney p27. . . . . 020 7254 6205

Hickey, J (Hacking Ashton LLP) S1 S2 W
Newcastle under Lyme p323 . 01782 715555

Hickey, J (Paynes) W S1 P M1 L K1 G H N V Zl
Bedworth p130. . . . . 024 7631 9820

Hickey, Ms S (Batchelors Solicitors) W K4 T2 Zm
Bromley p166 . . . . 020 8768 7000

Hickford, Ms V A (Irena Spence) K1 S1
Cambridge p175. . . . . . . 01223 713300

Hickinbotham, Mrs S (Henriques Griffiths) K1 K3
Winterbourne p435. . . . . . 01454 854000

Hickland, J (Ince & Co Services Ltd)
London E1 p44 . . . . 020 7481 0010

Hicklin, Miss K S (Mander Cruickshank Solicitors LLP) K1 K2
Coalville p196 . . . . 01530 510666

Hicklin, Ms S M (Clive Shepherd & Co)
Walsall p420. . . . . 01922 647797

Hickling, Mrs J (Underwood Solicitors LLP) S1 E S2 R2
Westminster p89. . . . . . . 020 7526 6000

Hickling, Miss R E (Edwin Coe LLP) J1 Zp
London WC2 p29 . . . . . . 020 7691 4000
London W1 p31 . . . . 020 7917 8500

Hickman, E (Linklaters LLP)
London EC2 p54. . . . . . . 020 7456 2000

Hickman, Ms E (Higgs & Sons) N Q Zr
Brierley Hill p158. . . . . . 0845 111 5050

Hickman, H (Harcus Sinclair) Q T2 W Zq
London WC2 p38 . . . . . . 020 7242 9700

Hickman, Miss N (Timms) D1 K1 D2
Derby p209 . . . . 01332 364436

Hickman, Mrs R F (Surrey County Council)
Kingston upon Thames p462. 020 8541 9088

Hickmott, Mrs J (Bright & Sons) N
Maldon p299. . . . . 01621 852323
Witham p435 . . . . 01376 512338

Hickmott, R W (CMS Cameron McKenna LLP) B1 C1 Q Zb Zg
London EC3 p17. . . . . . . 020 7367 3000

Hicks, A T (Muckle LLP) E S2 Zh R1
Newcastle upon Tyne p325 . 0191 211 7777

Hicks, C A (Wedlake Bell LLP) T2 W Zj
London WC1 p91 . . . . . . 020 7395 3000

Hicks, Mrs E (Levy & Co Solicitors LLP) N Zm H G
Witham p436 . . . . 01376 511819

Hicks, G J (GH Cornish LLP) Zc F1 J1 O Q N Zq
Ilford p260. . . . . 020 8090 0800

Hicks, Mrs J (Blake Lapthorn) W T2
Portsmouth p354. . . . . . . 023 9222 1122

Hicks, J P (Lyons Davidson) E R1 L
Bristol p163 . . . . 0117 904 6000

Hicks, J W (Chelmix Concrete)
Cheltenham p454 . . . . 01242 224763
Cheltenham p454 . . . .

Hicks, J W (Waterson Hicks) O Za Zj C1
London EC3 p90. . . . . . . 020 7929 6060

Hicks, K (Sharratts (London) LLP) Zc Zd E R1 S1
Westerham p429. . . . . . . 01959 568000

Hickson, C P (City of London Corporation)
London EC2 p107 . . . . . . 020 7606 3030

Hickson, L (Barlow Lyde & Gilbert LLP)
London EC3 p10. . . . . . . 020 7247 2277

Hidveghy, M (Jefferies Essex LLP) C1 S2 C2 R2 S1
Westcliff-on-Sea p428 . . . . 01702 332311

Hiester, Mrs E M (Clifford Chance)
London E14 p20. . . . . . . 020 7006 1000

Hiett, A (Rowley Dickinson) C1 E S2 R2 T1 W Ze Zc Zo
Manchester p309 . . . . . . 0161 834 4215

Hifzi, M O (Barlow Lyde & Gilbert LLP) O Q N Zj
London EC3 p10. . . . . . . 020 7247 2277

Higbee, J H (Fisher Meredith)
Lambeth p32. . . . . 020 7091 2700

Higbee, Mrs J V (Cripps Harries Hall LLP) E
Tunbridge Wells p415 . . . . 01892 515121

Higdon, J (Russell-Cooke LLP) S2
Kingston upon Thames p267. 020 8546 6111

Higgin, M J (Shoosmiths)
Reading p361 . . 0370 086 8800 / 0118 965 8765

Higgins, B (Howard Kennedy LLP) E R2
London W1 p48 . . . . 020 7636 1616

Higgins, B V (Michael W Halsall)
Newton-le-Willows p330 . . . 01942 727000

Higgins, Ms C (John Pickering & Partners LLP) N
Liverpool p290. . . . . 0808 144 0958

6

Higgins, D (Emsleys) *L Zh*
Crossgates *p204*. 0113 260 3115
Higgins, D C (Prudential PLC)
London EC4 *p108* 020 7220 7588
Higgins, Mrs D E (Shacklocks) *N Zr*
Mansfield *p312* 01623 626141
Higgins, Ms F (Follett Stock LLP) *E S2 R2 Zx Zd F1 C2 U1 U2 Zc*
Truro *p414*. 01872 241700
Higgins, Ms K (Rowlinsons) *J1 K1*
Frodsham *p227* 01928 735333
Higgins, M (Clive G Wood & Co) *K1 L Q D1*
Stockport *p396*. 0161 480 1000
Higgins, Miss M (Keoghs LLP) *N Zj O Q*
Bolton *p149* 01204 677000
Higgins, Miss P (Arthur Smiths) *W M1 P S1 F1 J1 Zl*
Wigan *p432* 01942 242815
Higgins, P F D (Joseph A Jones & Co) *S2 S1 W L E A1*
Lancaster *p269* 01524 63371
Higgins, P J (Higgins & Co) *M1 P N K1 L F1 G H*
Birkenhead *p134*. 0151 653 5222
Higgins, P M (Paul Crowley & Co) *E S2 S1 R2*
Liverpool *p287*. 0151 264 7363
Higgins, P R (MKB Solicitors LLP) *M1 P F1 N B1 J1 L Zj Zk*
Barnsley *p124*. 01226 210000
Higgins, R (T G Baynes) *E C1 S2 L*
Dartford *p207* 01322 295555
Higgins, R (Watson Nevill) *S1 E*
Maidstone *p299* 01622 661177
Higgins, R (W S Atkins Consultants Ltd)
Epsom *p458*. 01372 726140
Higgins, Mrs R M (Burges Salmon) *E*
Bristol *p161* 0117 939 2000
Higgins, Miss S (Hart Brown Solicitors) *W*
Cobham *p196* 0800 068 8177
Higgins, Ms S (National Grid PLC)
Warwick *p471* 01926 653000
Higgins, Ms S D (Charles Russell LLP)
London EC4 *p19*. 020 7203 5000
Higgins, T (Thomas Higgins & Co)
Wallasey *p419*. 0151 630 8006
Higginson, D (Coodes) *Q L J1*
Truro *p414*. 01872 246200
Higginson, M (Trowers & Hamlins)
London EC3 *p88*. 020 7423 8000
Higgott, Ms F (Rawlison Butler LLP)
Horsham *p253*. 01403 252492
Higgs, D G (Osborne Clarke) *O*
Bristol *p164* 0117 917 3000
Higgs, D H (Higgs & Sons) *W T2*
Brierley Hill *p158*. 0845 111 5050
Higgs, D J (Peter Peter & Wright) *S1 S2 A1 E L R1 R2*
Okehampton *p340*. 01837 52379
Higgs, D M (Lee Bolton Monier-Williams)
Westminster *p52*. 020 7222 5381
Higgs, J M (Higgs & Sons) *S1*
Kingswinford *p268*. 01384 342100
Higgs, L (Bindmans LLP) *N*
London WC1 *p12* 020 7833 4433
Higgs, M (Ashurst LLP)
London EC2 *p7* 020 7638 1111
Higgs, R D (ClarksLegal LLP) *E S2 C2 S1*
Reading *p360* 0118 958 5321
Higgs, Ms R J (Mills & Reeve) *O Q Ze Zk*
Norwich *p335* 01603 660155
Higgs, S M (Towns Needham & Co) *N Q*
Manchester *p310* 0161 832 3721
Higham, Ms A (Fletchers) *D1 K1 W Q N V*
Southport *p388* 01704 546919
Higham, A P (Anderson Longmore & Higham) *A1 C1 J1 K1 L M1 P S1 T1 W S2*
Petworth *p348*. 01798 342391
Higham, A R (Butcher & Barlow LLP) *N Q F1 O Zq Zr*
Bury *p170*. 0161 764 4062
Higham, D R G (Blake Lapthorn) *O Q Zj Zk Zq*
Chandlers Ford *p184* 023 8090 8090
Higham, J (Stephenson Harwood) *B1*
London EC2 *p82*. 020 7329 4422
Higham, R J C (O'Neill Patient) *Zb C1 S2 E C2 J1*
Stockport *p396*. 0161 483 8555
Higham, T (Sills & Betteridge LLP) *C1 C2*
Lincoln *p285*. 01522 542211
Higham, T J (Trethowans LLP) *S1*
Salisbury *p371*. 01722 412512
Highams, Ms E R (Winterbotham Smith Penley LLP) *G H*
Stroud *p401* 01453 847200
Highley, R I (DAC Beachcroft)
London EC4 *p24*. 020 7936 2222
Highmore, R (Charles Russell LLP) *Q E O Zq R1 R2*
London EC4 *p19*. 020 7203 5000
Highnam, T E (Allen & Overy LLP)
London E1 *p5* 020 3088 0000
Higson, R I (EDF Energy plc)
London SW1 *p106*. 020 7242 9050
Higson, T P (DWF) *N Q*
Manchester *p303* 0161 603 5000
Higton, Mrs J (Maclay Murray & Spens LLP) *C1 C2*
London EC2 *p57*. 020 7002 8500
Higton, J P (Squire Sanders (UK) LLP) *Zw Zf*
London EC2 *p81*. 020 7655 1000
Hilbery, G J (Forbes Maclean) *L K1 S2 G C1 J1 Zc B1 F1*
Leigh-on-Sea *p282*. 01702 472747

Hildebrand, R (Trowers & Hamlins)
London EC3 *p88*. 020 7423 8000
Hilder, C (Hodge Jones & Allen LLP) *Zg*
London NW1 *p41* 020 7874 8300
Hilder, Miss M C (Bolt Burdon) *N*
Islington *p14*. 020 7288 4700
Hilditch, C (Simmons & Simmons)
London EC2 *p79*. 020 7628 2020
Hilditch, Mrs D (QualitySolicitors Gruber Garratt) *D1 D2 K1 K2 K3 K4*
Oldham *p341* 0161 665 3502
Hildreth, Miss F G (Davitt Jones Bould) *E S2*
Taunton *p408* 01823 279279
Hildrow, R (Fisher Jones Greenwood LLP) *W*
Colchester *p197*. 01206 578282
Hiles, Miss S (Treasury Solicitors Department)
London WC2 *p110*. 020 7210 3000
Hiley, J D (Hileys) *A1 C1 S2 S1 W*
Thirsk *p411* 01845 522278
Hill, A (Alan Harris) *G H*
Plymouth *p350*. 01752 223655
Hill, Ms A C (City of Bradford Metropolitan District Council) *J1 L O Zo*
Bradford *p451* 01274 752236
Hill, A D S (Thomson Wilson Pattinson) *K1 Q W S1 J1 F1 L D1 O K2 V*
Kendal *p264*. 01539 721945
Hill, A E (Muckle LLP) *E R2*
Newcastle upon Tyne *p325* 0191 211 7777
Hill, Mrs A J (Bower & Bailey) *S1 W S2*
Oxford *p343* 01865 311133
Swindon *p406* 01793 610466
Hill, Ms A J (Wolverhampton City Council)
Wolverhampton *p477* 01902 556556
Hill, Mrs A M E (Burnand Brazier Tisdall) *W S1 K4*
Hove *p254*. 01273 734022
Hill, Ms A N R (Ford Simey LLP) *F1 G H K1 L N Q V*
Exmouth *p222*. . .01395 272241 / 0800 169 3741
Hill, A R (Baines Wilson LLP) *C2 C1*
Carlisle *p181*. 01228 552600
Hill, B (J Garrard & Allen) *E A1 R1 Zc*
Olney *p341* 01234 711215
Hill, B A (Nyland & Beattie) *M1 P G K1 F1 J1 H V D1 L Ze Zi Zl*
Widnes *p432*. 0151 424 5656
Hill, Miss C (Fentons)
Failsworth *p223* 0161 682 7101
Hill, Ms C (Withers LLP) *T2 W Zd Zm*
London EC4 *p92*. 020 7597 6000
Hill, Ms C (Ashfords LLP) *S1*
Exeter *p220* 01392 337000
Hill, C (Reynolds Porter Chamberlain LLP)
London E1 *p71* 020 3060 6000
Hill, C A (Hill Hofstetter LLP) *C1*
Solihull *p382*. 0121 210 6000
Hill, Miss C E (The College of Law)
London WC1 *p105*. 0800 289997
Hill, C J G (Jacklyn Dawson) *T1 T2 E S1 S2*
Newport *p328* 01633 262952
Hill, C M (Barlow Lyde & Gilbert LLP)
London EC3 *p10*. 020 7247 2277
Hill, Ms C R (Forsters LLP) *T2 W*
Westminster *p33*. 020 7863 8333
Hill, D (The College of Law) *O Q*
London WC1 *p105*. 0800 289997
Hill, D (Davidson Large LLP) *J1*
Harrogate *p240* 01423 727272
Hill, D (Howard Kennedy LLP)
London W1 *p48* 020 7636 1616
Hill, D (Napthens LLP) *E*
Blackburn *p145* 01254 667733
Hill, D (Herbert Smith LLP)
London EC2 *p40*. 020 7374 8000
Hill, D (Hogan Lovells International LLP)
London EC1 *p42*. 020 7296 2000
Hill, Mrs D A (Gateshead Metropolitan Borough Council)
Gateshead *p458*. 0191 433 3000
Hill, D K (Bristol City Council)
Bristol *p451* 0117 922 2000
Hill, Ms F (William Sturges & Co) *W T2*
Westminster *p84*. 020 7873 1000
Hill, F P G (MFG Solicitors) *S1 W K1 A1 E L Zd C1*
Worcester *p440* 01905 610410
Hill, G (Grindeys LLP) *Zd T1*
Stoke-on-Trent *p397*. 01782 846441
Hill, Mrs G E (NCC Group)
Manchester *p465* 0161 209 5200
Hill, Mrs G L (Sanderson McCreath & Edney) *O Q N S1*
Berwick-upon-Tweed *p131*. . 01289 306724
Hill, Miss H E (Shulmans) *E O*
Leeds *p276* 0113 245 2833
Hill, Mrs H V (National Grid PLC)
Warwick *p471* 01926 653000
Hill, J (Joseph Hill & Co) *D1 G H K1 V Zi Zm*
London N15 *p41*. 020 8880 3535
Hill, Dr J (McDermott Will & Emery UK LLP)
London EC2 *p56*. 020 7577 6900
Hill, J A (J H Powell & Co) *E O N Q S1 W L C1 F1 Zf Zm*
Derby *p209* 01332 372211
Hill, Ms J A (Bristows) *C1 C2 Zd Ze Zo*
London EC4 *p15*. 020 7400 8000
Hill, J C (Shoosmiths) *Ze O Q*
Northampton *p332*. . 0370 086 3000 / 01604 543000
Hill, Ms J E (Treasury Solicitors Department)
London WC2 *p110*. 020 7210 3000

Hill, Mrs J F (British Telecommunications PLC)
London EC1 *p104* 020 7356 6181
Hill, Mrs J K (Luton Borough Council)
Luton *p464* 01582 546000
Hill, Miss J L (Janette Hill & Co Solicitors) *N Zr*
Hay-on-Wye *p245* 01497 821000
Hill, J M (Jones Law Partnership) *S1 N E*
Marple *p313*. 0161 426 0030
Hill, J M T (Michael Hill Partnership) *G E S1 K1 P W N T1 D1 C1 Zd*
Leicester *p280*. 0116 254 1609
Hill, J N (Davies Parsons Allchurch) *K3 K1*
Llanelli *p292*. 01554 749144
Hill, J P (Clifford Chance)
London E14 *p20*. 020 7006 1000
Hill, J P (Hill & Co) *C1 G H K1 L M1 N P R1 S1*
Aldershot *p115*. 01252 319441
Hill, J R (Barlow Lyde & Gilbert LLP)
London EC3 *p10*. 020 7247 2277
Hill, J R B (Quality Solicitors Clarke & Son) *R2 E S1*
Basingstoke *p127* 01256 320555
Hill, Mrs J S (Thompson & Jackson) *W T1 T2*
Plymouth *p350*. . . .01752 665037 / 221171
Hill, Miss K (Radcliffes Le Brasseur) *R1 Zr N Zm*
Westminster *p70*. 020 7222 7040
Hill, Miss K N (Isle of Wight Council)
Newport *p466* 01983 823207
Hill, K R (QualitySolicitors D'Angibau) *G H*
Boscombe *p151* 01202 393506
Hill, Ms L (Stevens Lucas) *K1 N S1 W*
Oswestry *p342*. 01691 670999
Hill, Mrs M (Brutton & Co) *K1 K3*
Fareham *p223* 01329 236171
Hill, M (Josiah Hincks) *K3 K1*
Leicester *p280*. 0116 255 1811
Hill, M (Tollers LLP)
Northampton *p332*. 01604 258558
Hill, M (Williamson Hill) *K1 W*
Middlesbrough *p315* 01642 217961
Hill, Ms M A (Middlesbrough Council)
Middlesbrough *p465* 01642 245432
Hill, Ms M F (Hugh James) *D1 K1*
Cardiff *p179* 029 2022 4871
Hill, M I (Michael Hill Partnership) *K1 N P G M1 W H C1 L R1 Zd Zl Zt*
Leicester *p280*. 0116 254 1609
Hill, Ms M J (Ribble Valley Borough Council) *Zq J1*
Clitheroe *p455*. 01200 425111
Hill, M J (Raworths LLP) *O Q*
Harrogate *p240* 01423 566666
Hill, Miss M J (Burnetts) *Zr*
Carlisle *p181*. 01228 552222
Carlisle *p182*. 01228 552222
Hill, M T (Tollers LLP) *W S1 L T2*
Kettering *p265*. 01536 520111
Hill, M V T (Bray & Bray) *W T2 A1 K4*
Market Harborough *p312*. . . 01858 467181
Hill, Ms N (Tollers LLP) *D1 K1*
Kettering *p265*. 01536 520111
Hill, P (DAC Beachcroft)
London EC3 *p24*. 020 7208 6800
Hill, P (Simmons & Simmons) *Ze*
London EC2 *p79*. 020 7628 2020
Hill, P J (Shaw Graham Kersh)
London W1 *p78* 020 7734 9700
Hill, Mrs P M (Fitzhugh Gates) *S1 W*
Shoreham-by-Sea *p378* . . . 01273 461381
Hill, Miss P S (Farleys Solicitors LLP) *K1*
Blackburn *p145* 01254 367854
Hill, P W A (DBL Talbots LLP) *C1 E S1*
Wolverhampton *p437* 01902 427561
Hill, Ms R (Blandy & Blandy) *J1*
Reading *p360* 0118 951 6800
Hill, Miss R (Lanyon Bowdler LLP) *K1 S1 T2 V K4 Zd W*
Wellington *p425* 01952 244721
Hill, R (Blake Lapthorn) *L O*
Chandlers Ford *p184* 023 8090 8090
Hill, R (Pattichi Hill & Croques) *E Ze J1 K1 Q N S1*
Ilford *p260*. 020 8911 8233
Hill, R J (Gregg Latchams LLP) *S1 E W T2*
Bristol *p162* 0117 906 9400
Hill, R L (South Wales Police)
Bridgend *p451*. 01656 869476
Hill, Miss R L (Needham Poulier & Partners) *Zm Zg G*
London N17 *p63*. 020 8808 6622
Hill, R M (Mossop & Bowser) *C1 E A1 S2 L C2 S1*
Holbeach *p251*. 01406 422651
Hill, R M (Parker Grego Cullen & Ball) *S1 L W C1 Zf*
Birmingham *p141* 0121 200 3031
Hill, R R (Reynolds Parry-Jones) *Q O N J1 L G*
High Wycombe *p250*. 01494 525941
Hill, S (Harrowells)
York *p444* 01904 558600
Hill, Ms S (Keoghs LLP) *B2*
Coventry *p200*. 024 7665 8200
Hill, S (Hogan Lovells International LLP)
London EC1 *p42*. 020 7296 2000
Hill, Miss S (Capsticks Solicitors LLP) *E R2 S2*
London SW19 *p18*. 020 8780 2211
Hill, Miss S C (Clarke Kiernan) *K1*
Tonbridge *p412* 01732 360999
Hill, S D (Bolt Burdon) *N*
Islington *p14*. 020 7288 4700
Hill, S G V (Allen & Overy LLP)
London E1 *p5* 020 3088 0000

Hill, S J (Hodders)
London NW10 *p41*. 020 8965 9862
Hill, S O (Price & Son) *E S1 A1 C1 F1 K1 L N O Q Zk*
Haverfordwest *p244* 01437 765331
Hill, Ms T (Brockbank Curwen Cain & Hall) *K1 G D1 Q W*
Workington *p440*. 01900 603563
Hill, W D (Price & Son) *S1 C1 A1 J1 W B1 E F1 L R1*
Haverfordwest *p244* 01437 765331
Hillier, Miss M L (Blake Lapthorn) *J1 Zp*
Chandlers Ford *p184* 023 8090 8090
Hillier, P A (HilliersHRW Solicitors) *D1 K1 W F1 G H J1 M1 R1 C1 Zl S2 E L B1*
Kempston *p264* 01234 858000
Hillier, P M (Simmons & Simmons)
London EC2 *p79*. 020 7628 2020
Hillier, Mrs R L (DP Law Ltd t/a David Prosser & Co) *O Q L J1*
Bridgend *p157*. 01656 645921
Hillis, T P (Hillis Solicitors) *N*
Manchester *p305* 0161 248 0500
Hillman, Mrs B (Debenhams Ottaway) *R1*
St Albans *p390* 01727 837161
Hillman, B D (Woodroffes)
Westminster *p93*. 020 7730 0001
Hillman, B M G (Mayo Wynne Baxter LLP) *J1 K1 W T1 V Q Zo Zd*
Lewes *p283* 01273 477071
Hillman, D (Lee Chadwick & Co) *S1 E W L B1 A1 R1 T2 V Zm Zd*
Witney *p436* 01993 703272
Hillman, Mrs S (Wigan Borough Council)
Wigan *p476* 01942 244991
Hillman, T F (The Hillman Partnership) *S1 G K1 F1 J1 W C1*
Swindon *p406* 01793 642100
Hills, A S A (Plexus Law (A Trading Name of Parabis Law LLP)) *A3 J2 N Zj*
Leeds *p276* 0844 245 4100
Hills, D (Jefferies Essex LLP) *K1 K2 D1*
Westcliff-on-Sea *p428* 01702 332311
Hills, Miss D M (Windsor & Maidenhead Borough Council)
Maidenhead *p464* 01628 798888
Hills, G S (Elvin & Co) *N O Q J1 J2 Zq K1*
Loughborough *p293* 01509 852454
Hills, Miss M (Whitehead Monckton) *N Zr*
Maidstone *p299* 01622 698000
Hills, Ms N (Taylor Wessing)
London EC4 *p86*. 020 7300 7000
Hills, Miss N E (Blake Lapthorn) *E*
Chandlers Ford *p184* 023 8090 8090
Hills, P (Paul Hills & Co) *E K4 R1 S1 T1 T2 V W*
Chichester *p193*. 01243 671782
Hills, R J (Stafford Young Jones) *S1 W S2 L C2*
London EC4 *p82*. 020 7623 9490
Hills, Ms S (Ison Harrison) *K1 D1 D2*
Leeds *p274* 0113 284 5000
Hills, Mrs S (Knight Polson Solicitors) *J1 Zp*
Eastleigh *p216*. 023 8064 4822
Hills, S (O'Melveny & Myers LLP)
London EC4 *p64*. 020 7088 0000
Hills, Ms S J (Edwards Angell Palmer & Dodge)
London EC2 *p28*. 020 7583 4055
Hills, Miss V (Harris Cartier LLP) *N*
Slough *p382*. 01753 810710
Hill-Smith, Mrs L (Cripps Harries Hall LLP) *S1 E*
Tunbridge Wells *p415* 01892 515121
Hillson, Ms H J (Scrivenger Seabrook) *N Zr*
St Neots *p392*. 01480 214900
Hillson, M D (Barrett Nelligan Solicitors)
Fleetwood *p226* 01253 771664
Hillson, S N (Macfarlanes) *E*
London EC4 *p56*. 020 7831 9222
Hillyer, D M (Laytons) *E R1 S1 L Zc Zl*
London EC4 *p52*. 020 7842 8000
Hilmi, M D (Jeffrey Green Russell)
London W1 *p46* 020 7339 7000
Hilson, C (London Borough of Southwark)
London SE1 *p109* 020 7525 5000
Hilton, Ms C (Squire Sanders (UK) LLP)
Manchester *p310* 0161 830 5000
Hilton, Ms C (Hall Smith Whittingham LLP) *A1 E S1*
Crewe *p203* 01270 212000
Hilton, C M (Atter Mackenzie & Co) *G N Q H V O B1 Zf Zg*
Evesham *p220*. 01386 425300
Hilton, D J (Beaumont Legal) *Zd Zm T1 T2 N Q O W B1*
Wakefield *p418* 0845 122 8100
Hilton, H V (Dallow & Dallow) *S1 K1 W C1 E G T1*
Wolverhampton *p437* 01902 420208
Hilton, M J (Salehs LLP) *O Q B1 Ze Zq*
Manchester *p309* 0161 434 9991
Hilton, M W (Addleshaw Goddard) *O Q Zc*
Leeds *p271* 0113 209 2000
Leeds *p277* 0113 284 7000
Hilton, P R (Hill Dickinson LLP) *O F1 B1 Q*
Liverpool *p288*. 0151 600 8000
Hilton, R I (Davis Blank Furniss) *S1 W E*
Manchester *p303* 0161 832 3304
Hilton, Ms S (Dallow & Dallow) *F1 E K1 O Q S1 W*
Wolverhampton *p437* 01902 420208
Hilton, Ms S (Manches LLP) *C1 Zu Zh R2*
Oxford *p343*. 01865 722106
Hilton, Mrs S J (Thomas Simon) *K1 D1 D2*
Cardiff *p181* 029 2055 7200

See p634 for the Key to Work Categories

Hilton, Miss V L (hlw Keeble Hawson LLP) *N*
Sheffield *p375* 0114 272 2061

Hilton, Miss V S (Hilton Norbury) *W S1 D1 K1 K4 K3*
Wigan *p432* 01942 241424

Hilton-Johnson, J C (McDonalds Restaurants Ltd)
London N2 *p107* 0870 241 3300

Hilton-Tapp, R I (Salusburys Harding & Barnett) *K1 D1 L J1 N V Zl*
Leicester *p281* . . 0116 262 9033 / 262 6052

Hilyer, Miss J (Aaron & Partners LLP Solicitors) *J1*
Chester *p190* 01244 405555

Himelfield, A K (Harold Stock & Co) *E S2*
Ashton-under-Lyne *p120* . . .01457 835597 / 835034

Hims, Mrs C E (QualitySolicitors Jackson & Canter) *Zi*
Liverpool *p290* 0151 282 1700

Hinchcliffe, M H (Fraser Dawbarns) *G H*
King's Lynn *p266* 01553 666600

Hinchley, G R (Mills & Reeve) *E*
Birmingham *p140* 0121 454 4000

Hinchliffe, D W (Walker Morris) *B1*
Leeds *p277* 0113 283 2500

Hinchliffe, Ms E (Potter Owtram & Peck) *K4 W*
Haslemere *p243* 01428 642321

Hinchliffe, G D (Pearson Hinchliffe) *G K1 N M1 H P S1 C1 D1 W*
Oldham *p341* 0161 785 3500

Hinchliffe, J D G (Senior Calveley & Hardy) *S1 W E K1 S2 T2 L K4*
Kirkham *p268* 01772 671177
Lytham *p297* 01253 733333

Hinchliffe, M (Addleshaw Goddard)
London EC1 *p4* 020 7606 8855

Hinchliffe, Miss R A (HBOS PLC)
Halifax *p460* 0870 600 5000

Hinchliffe, R M (Pearson Hinchliffe) *B1 C1 E J1 K1 N R1 S1 T1 W Zb Zc Ze*
Oldham *p341* 0161 785 3500

Hinchy, C (Rushton Hinchy Solicitors) *Q N*
St Helens *p391* 0845 054 0564

Hinckley, Ms G D (Arnison & Co Solicitors Limited)
Penrith *p346* 01768 862007

Hincks, D M (Foot Anstey) *S1 S2 E A1*
Taunton *p408* 01823 625600

Hind, Mrs A M (Dolmans) *Q N*
Cardiff *p178* 029 2034 5531

Hind, C J (Amphletts) *K1 K2 D1 K3*
Colwyn Bay *p198* 01492 532296

Hind, N A (Bennett Griffin) *N Zq Zg*
Worthing *p441* 01903 229925

Hind, Ms S L (LG Lawyers)
London SE1 *p50* 020 7379 0000

Hinde, C R (Coventry City Council)
Coventry *p456* 024 7683 4863

Hinde, Miss J A (Alan Edwards & Co) *G H*
Kensington & Chelsea *p28* . . 020 7221 7644

Hinder, Ms T L (Roberts Moore Nicholas Jones) *G H*
Birkenhead *p134* 0151 647 0000

Hindes, Mrs P (Owen White) *S2 E*
Slough *p382* 01753 876800

Hinde-Smith, Ms M (Memery Crystal) *Ze C1*
London WC2 *p60* 020 7242 5905

Hindhaugh, I (Jones Day) *E*
London EC4 *p46* 020 7039 5959

Hindle, A J (Boodle Hatfield) *Q O*
Westminster *p14* 020 7629 7411

Hindle, C M (Hindle Campbell) *C1 E N P T1 G*
North Shields *p330* 0191 296 1777

Hindle, G M (DAC Beachcroft) *B1 O Q*
Bristol *p162* 0117 918 2000

Hindle, Mrs H I (Middleton & Upsall LLP) *E L S1 A1 S2*
Warminster *p421* 01985 214444

Hindle, Ms K (Martello Professional Risks Limited)
London EC3 *p108* 020 7337 7500

Hindle, R (Farleys Solicitors LLP)
Blackburn *p145* 01254 367856

Hindley, Miss K L (Telford Magistrates Court)
Telford *p474* 01952 204500

Hindley, P J (Hindley & Co) *Zi*
London N5 *p41* 020 7609 1161

Hindmarch, Ms K (Langleys) *J1*
Lincoln *p284* 01522 888555
York *p445* 01904 610886

Hindmarsh, J D (King & Co) *S1 W L E R1 C1 C2 C3 A1 B1 J1 T1 Zc Zl Zo*
Cambridge *p175* . . .01223 365432 / 566038

Hindmarsh, J P (Finers Stephens Innocent LLP) *C1 C2 E I L O S1 T1 W Q Zc Ze Zh Zv Zj*
London W1 *p32* 020 7323 4000

Hindmarsh, Mrs K V L (Steele & Son) *W Q S1 K4*
Barnoldswick *p124* 01282 813385

Hindmarsh, S C (Hill Dickinson LLP) *E S2 R2 S1*
Manchester *p305* 0161 817 7200

Hindmarsh, S J (Tibbits Fisher)
Birmingham *p143* 0121 707 3900

Hindocha, K K (Hindocha & Co) *S1 E L C1 W*
Wembley *p426* 020 8903 1120

Hindocha, Miss S (Henmans LLP) *E*
Oxford *p343* 01865 781000

Hinds, Ms A (Venters Solicitors) *K1 D1 K3 D2*
London SE5 *p89* 020 7277 0110

Hinds, Mrs J G (Moss Solicitors LLP) *G H*
Loughborough *p293* 01509 217770

Hinds, Mrs S K (Raworths LLP)
Harrogate *p240* 01423 566666

Hinds, S M (Pritchard Joyce & Hinds) *B1 C1 C2 N O Q Zc Ze*
Beckenham *p129* 020 8658 3922

Hindsley, Mrs J K (Pollard Bower Solicitors) *N Q W S1*
Burnley *p169* 01282 457624

Hindson, G G (Southern Stewart & Walker) *N V W*
South Shields *p384* 0191 427 0770

Hine, A (Hine Solicitors) *G H B2*
Gerrards Cross *p229* 01753 482400

Hine, A D (Taylor Wessing) *T2 W*
London EC4 *p86* 020 7300 7000

Hine, J D (The John W Davies Partnership) *N G H Q O W*
Newport *p329* 01633 841773

Hine, Mrs L D (Wellers Law Group LLP) *K4 W*
Bromley *p167* 020 8464 4242

Hine, P D (Marsden Rawsthorn LLP) *C1 C2 C3 E S2*
Preston *p357* 01772 799600

Hines, Miss N (Roythornes LLP) *S1 S2*
Spalding *p389* 01775 842500

Hines, P N (Bromsgrove & Redditch Magistrates Court)
Kidderminster *p462* 01562 514000

Hingley, D (Challinors) *W S1 T1 E*
Wolverhampton *p437* 01902 428121

Hingley, P (Challinors) *S1 W E L C1 F1 J1 K1 R1 T1 Zl*
Wolverhampton *p437* 01902 428121

Hingston, T (Wolferstans) *E S1*
Plymouth *p351* 01752 663295

Hinks, Mrs A J (Blackhurst Swainson Goodier LLP) *N Q L B1*
Preston *p356* 01772 253841

Hinson, Mrs A (The Smith Partnership) *L J1 F1 V Zh Zp*
Derby *p209* 01332 225225

Hinton, D L (The Scout Association) *G H*
London E4 *p109* 020 8433 7178

Hinton, Miss I (Unilever PLC)
London EC4 *p110* 020 7822 5252

Hinton, P (London Stock Exchange Ltd) *I U2 Ze Zf Zza*
London EC2 *p107* 020 7797 1000
London EC2 *p48* 020 7600 8080

Hinton, P A R (Barlow Lyde & Gilbert LLP)
London EC3 *p10* 020 7247 2277

Hinton, P J (KTP Solicitors)
Porth *p353* 01443 687222

Hinton, Ms S (Trowers & Hamlins)
London EC3 *p88* 020 7423 8000

Hipkin, M D (Hipkin & Co) *C1 E N O Q W Zq*
Whitley Bay *p431* 0191 253 3509

Hipper, A K (Mills & Reeve) *Zq*
Norwich *p335* 01603 660155

Hipperson, Mrs F E (B P Collins LLP) *K1*
Gerrards Cross *p229* 01753 889995

Hira, Ms S K (Elliott Bridgman)
Telford *p409* 01952 684544

Hird, R W S (John O'Neill & Co) *Zt*
Gosforth *p232* 0191 246 4000

Hirschfield, G A (Bowling & Co) *S1 P K1 E G H W M1 J1 L Zi Zk Zl*
London E15 *p15* 020 8221 8000

Hirschhorn, Ms C (Davies Gore Lomax) *Zg V L X*
Leeds *p273* 0113 242 2797

Hirst, D (Ramsdens Solicitors) *B1 N Q Zk*
Huddersfield *p256* 01484 821500

Hirst, Miss K (Hansells) *J1 C1 C2*
Norwich *p334* 01603 615731

Hirst, K (Wace Morgan) *J1*
Shrewsbury *p379* 01743 280100

Hirst, M J (Bromleys Solicitors LLP) *N J1 O Q B1 F1*
Ashton-under-Lyne *p120* . . . 0161 330 6821

Hirst, M V (DLA Piper UK LLP) *Zj*
Birmingham *p137* 0870 011 1111

Hirst, Ms N (Withers LLP) *B1 O Q*
London EC4 *p92* 020 7597 6000

Hirst, P (Simmons & Simmons)
London EC2 *p79* 020 7628 2020

Hirst, P S (Irwin Mitchell LLP) *W T2 T1*
Sheffield *p376* 0870 150 0100

Hirst, R A (Clarkson Hirst) *G K1 P N R1 S1 C1 B1 E*
Lancaster *p269* 01524 39760

Hirst, R L (Minahan Hirst & Co) *S1 S2 E*
Cheadle Hulme *p185* 0161 485 8131

Hirst, Miss S E (Bradbury Roberts & Raby) *W K4*
Scunthorpe *p373* 01724 854000

Hiscock, J J (Addleshaw Goddard) *C2*
Manchester *p300* 0161 934 6000

Hiscocks, R H S (Parker Bullen) *W A1 T2*
Andover *p118* 01264 400500

Hitch, G R (Charles Hill Hubbard) *S1 E W T1 C1 L*
Chichester *p192* 01243 781000

Hitch, Mrs S (Buss Murton LLP) *N*
Tunbridge Wells *p415* 01892 510222

Hitchcock, Mrs C J S (Crown Prosecution Service Thames Valley)
Abingdon *p447* 01235 551900

Hitchcock, D W (The Ringrose Law Group - Nerina Farmer) *W A1 S2 S1 T2*
Sleaford *p381* 01529 301300

Hitchcock, J C E (Tandridge District Council)
Oxted *p468* 01883 722000

Hitchcock, Mrs T C (DLA Piper UK LLP) *P*
Sheffield *p375* 0870 011 1111

Hitchen, C J G (Allan Janes LLP) *O J1 B1 C1 L N*
High Wycombe *p249* 01494 521301

Hitchin, J D J (Allen & Overy LLP)
London E1 *p5* 020 3088 0000

Hitching, M (Herbert Smith LLP)
London EC2 *p40* 020 7374 8000

Hitchings, M (Davis Wood) *N J2 Zj*
Bristol *p162* 0117 965 3504

Hitchins, J C (Robert Hitchins Ltd)
Cheltenham *p454* 01242 680694

Hitchman, Mrs C G (Worcestershire County Council) *N O Q L F2 A3*
Worcester *p477* 01905 766335

Hitchman, Miss C M (Field Seymour Parkes) *O Q*
Reading *p360* 0118 951 6200

Hitchman, D L (Cotterhill Hitchman LLP) *O N*
Sutton Coldfield *p403* 0121 323 1860

Hitchman, V F (Bath & North East Somerset Council)
Bath *p462* 01225 394041

Hitschmann, Miss R (Edward Hayes LLP) *G H B2 K1 K3 D2*
London EC4 *p39* 020 7353 0011

Ho, D T W (Christine Lee & Co (Solicitors) Ltd)
Birmingham *p140* 0121 666 6228
London W1 *p52* 020 7287 6233

Ho, Mrs F W S (Belmont & Lowe)
London EC1 *p11* 020 7608 4600

Ho, I (Hunters) *S1 S2 E Zd*
London WC2 *p44* 020 7412 0050

Ho, Mrs J (Christine Lee & Co (Solicitors) Ltd)
Birmingham *p140* 0121 666 6228

Ho, Ms J Y (Crown Prosecution Service Durham)
Durham *p457* 0191 383 5800

Ho, W Y (Burton Burton & Ho LLP) *S1 E N Q J1 W G C1 L Zi*
Leeds *p272* 0113 297 8787

Hoad, A M G (Rawlison Butler LLP) *C1 C2*
Crawley *p202* 01293 527744

Hoar, Ms C (Adams & Remers) *J1*
Lewes *p283* 01273 480616

Hoare, A (Goodman Derrick LLP)
London EC4 *p36* 020 7404 0606

Hoare, Ms C L (Girls' Day School Trust)
London SW1 *p106* 020 7393 6666

Hoare, D L (Knapman & Co) *S1 W*
Paignton *p345* 01803 522700

Hoare, Ms G A (Laytons) *S1*
Guildford *p236* 01483 407000

Hoare, J (Ashurst LLP)
London EC2 *p7* 020 7638 1111

Hoare, J A G (Williams Thompson) *E S1*
Christchurch *p194* 01202 484242

Hoare, Ms K (Green Wright Chalton Annis)
Arundel *p118* 01903 881122

Hoare, Ms K L (Green Wright Chalton Annis)
Worthing *p441* 01903 234064

Hoare, Mrs P (Leeds City Council)
Leeds *p462* 0113 224 3513

Hoare, Mrs P B (Hansells) *N Zr*
Norwich *p334* 01603 615731

Hoare, R J (Andrew Jackson) *K1*
Hull *p257* 01482 325242

Hoath, Ms D (Walker Morris)
Leeds *p277* 0113 283 2500

Hoath, S A (Spencer Ewin Mulvihill) *Q B1 O*
Harrogate *p240* 01423 509826

Hobbs, A G M (FBC Manby Bowdler LLP) *J1 Zp*
Wolverhampton *p437* 01902 578000

Hobbs, C D (Painters) *N G H*
Kidderminster *p266* 01562 822295

Hobbs, D (Farrell & Hobbs) *E C1 L S1 W A1 N R1 Zc Zd Zl*
Manchester *p304* 0161 445 1000

Hobbs, Miss F (E E F South)
Hook *p461* 01256 763969

Hobbs, Ms F (Linklaters LLP)
London EC2 *p54* 020 7456 2000

Hobbs, Ms I (Mayer Brown International LLP)
London EC2 *p59* 020 3130 3000

Hobbs, Ms J (Gateley LLP) *O Q Za Zj*
London EC4 *p35* 020 7653 1600

Hobbs, J E (Worcestershire County Council)
Worcester *p477* 01905 766335

Hobbs, Ms M (Turbervilles) *S2*
Uxbridge *p417* 01895 201700
Uxbridge *p417* 01895 201700

Hobbs, N S (British Telecommunications PLC)
London EC1 *p104* 020 7356 6181

Hobbs, T M (Howells) *S1 E W B1 L D1 C1 C2 R1*
Cardiff *p178* 029 2040 4020

Hobby, Mrs S C (Turners Solicitors LLP) *S1 E L*
Bournemouth *p153* 01202 291291

Hobdell, A (Meldrum Young Solicitors) *G H*
St Albans *p390* 01727 840333

Hobden, A C (Stephen Rimmer LLP) *G H*
Eastbourne *p216* 01323 644222

Hobden, Mrs A V (Cornfield Law) *W*
Eastbourne *p215* 01323 412512
Polegate *p351* 01323 487051

Hobden, B D (Andrew Jackson) *O*
Hull *p257* 01482 325242

Hobden, N (Benussi & Co) *K1 K3*
Birmingham *p135* 0121 248 4001

Hobden, N D (Thomson Snell & Passmore) *J1 Zp*
Tunbridge Wells *p415* 01892 510000

Hobkinson, A J (CMS Cameron McKenna LLP) *F1 M2 N O Q Zi Zj*
London EC3 *p17* 020 7367 3000

Hobsley, J C (Reynolds Porter Chamberlain LLP) *O Q Zq Zj*
London E1 *p71* 020 3060 6000

Hobson, A G F (Reynolds Porter Chamberlain LLP) *J1 N Ze Zp*
London E1 *p71* 020 3060 6000

Hobson, Miss C A (Hardmans) *S2 E W S1 T2 L*
Deal *p207* 01304 373377

Hobson, C N F (Olswang LLP) *Zb F1 L O B2*
London WC1 *p64* 020 7067 3000

Hobson, Ms J (Reed Smith LLP) *J1*
London EC2 *p71* 020 3116 3000

Hobson, Mrs J (Martin Tolhurst Partnership LLP) *S1 K1*
Longfield *p293* 01474 706168

Hobson, Ms J A (Mortons) *N Q Zq Zr*
Sunderland *p401* 0191 514 4323

Hobson, J D (Taylor Walton LLP) *D1 F1 G K1 N O Q Zk Zl Zm*
Luton *p295* 01582 731161

Hobson, K D J (East Cornwall Magistrates Courts)
Bodmin *p450* 01208 262700

Hobson, Ms R (Rotherham Metropolitan Borough Council)
Rotherham *p470* 01709 382121

Hockaday, G (Dickinson Dees) *E*
Newcastle upon Tyne *p324* . 0191 279 9000

Hockin, Mrs J L (Atkins Law Solicitors) *Zi*
Exeter *p220* 01392 671657

Hocking, S (DAC Beachcroft)
London EC4 *p24* 020 7242 1011

Hockings, Ms D (ASB Law)
Crawley *p202* 01293 603600

Hockless, P B (Allen & Overy LLP)
London E1 *p5* 020 3088 0000

Hockley, Ms E (Plexus Law (A Trading Name of Parabis Law LLP)) *Q N L*
London EC3 *p68* 0844 245 4000

Hockney, Miss C J (Equality & Human Rights Commission)
Manchester *p464* 0161 829 8100

Hodari, A V (Antony Hodari & Co) *M1 G*
Manchester *p305* 0161 832 4781

Hodby, R A (Challenor Gardiner) *S1 S2 W E K4*
Oxford *p343* 01865 721451

Hodd, Mrs D A (Forshaws Davies Ridgway LLP) *E W*
Warrington *p422* 01925 230000

Hodd, J (Forshaws Davies Ridgway LLP) *E C1 R1 S1 B1 Zc Ze*
Warrington *p422* 01925 230000

Hoddell, P M (Birkett Long LLP) *K1 Q D1*
Colchester *p197* 01206 217300

Hodder, A J (Whitehead Vizard) *C1 A1 E T1 B1 R1*
Salisbury *p371* 01722 412141

Hodder, A R (National House Building Council)
Milton Keynes *p447* 0870 241 4302

Hodder, C J R (Squire Sanders (UK) LLP) *E S2 Zl*
London EC2 *p81* 020 7655 1000

Hodder, Miss E A (Gross & Co) *K1 D1 V B1 D2*
Bury St Edmunds *p171* . . . 01284 763333

Hoddinott, M H (Stephenson Harwood) *C1 W*
London EC2 *p82* 020 7329 4422

Hodge, D (Brethertons LLP) *J1*
Rugby *p368* 01788 579579

Hodge, H R (Mills Chody LLP) *E R1 S1 T1 W*
Kenton *p265* 020 8909 0400

Hodge, Ms J (Biscoes) *D1 K1 V*
Gosport *p232* 023 9251 2030

Hodge, M J (Merriman Waine & Co) *T2 K3 K1*
Pewsey *p348* 01672 563666
Tetbury *p410* 01666 504005

Hodge, Miss S (Shulmans) *O Q*
Leeds *p276* 0113 245 2833

Hodge, T (Napp Pharmaceutical Holdings Ltd) *C1 Zb C2*
Cambridge *p453* 01223 424444

Hodge, Ms Z (Prettys) *K4 Q T2 V W*
Ipswich *p262* 01473 232121

Hodgen, H R (Sansbury Douglas) *G H D1 Zm*
Bristol *p164* 0117 955 2663

Hodges, A J H (Alan Hodge Solicitors) *P D1 K1 G H L J1 B1 W F1 Zl C1*
Bristol *p163* 01454 888098

Hodges, C J (Thorne Segar) *S1 W G H A1 S2*
Minehead *p318* 01643 703234

Hodges, C J S (CMS Cameron McKenna LLP)
London EC3 *p17* 020 7367 3000

Hodges, Ms D (Osborne Clarke) *C1*
London EC2 *p65* 020 7105 7000

Hodges, Ms D (Rowberry Morris) *K3 K1 D1 W*
Tadley *p407* 0118 981 2992

Hodges, D C (Browns)
Marlow *p313* 01628 476988

Hodges, Mrs G (Wythenshawe Law Centre)
Manchester *p465* 0161 498 0905

Hodges, Ms H L (Eaton-Evans & Morris) *N L G Q F1 S1 V W H J1*
Haverfordwest *p244* 01437 763383

Hodges, J A (Staffordshire County Council) *K1 G D1 N F1 V C1 J1 Q S1 Zl Zm*
Stafford *p472* 01785 223121

Hodges, Ms L (Kingsley Napley) *B2 G*
London EC1 *p50* 020 7814 1200

Hodges, N (Reynolds Porter Chamberlain LLP)
London E1 *p71* 020 3060 6000

Hodges, N J Q (Owen & Co) *K1 J1 L Q W D1 F1 V*
Redhill *p362* 01737 760036

Hodges, Ms P (Herbert Smith LLP) *O Zq*
London EC2 *p40* 020 7374 8000

Hodges, P E (Hill Dickinson LLP) *J1 Q Zl*
Liverpool *p288* 0151 600 8000

6

Hodges, P J (Kagan Moss & Co) E S1 W C1 S2 R2 T2
Teddington p409 . . . . 020 8977 6633

Hodges, S (Willans LLP) S1
Cheltenham p189 . . . . . . 01242 514000

Hodges, S J (Bawtrees LLP) D1 D2 K1 K2 Q
Witham p435 . . . . 01376 513491

Hodges, Ms V (Teacher Stern LLP) E S2
London WC1 p86 . . . . . . 020 7242 3191

Hodgetts, Ms J (Harrison Clark LLP) O
Cheltenham p188 . . . . . . 01242 269198
Worcester p439 . . . . 01905 612001
Worcester p439 . . . . 01905 612001

Hodgetts, Ms L (Roythornes LLP) W T2
Spalding p389 . . . . 01775 842500

Hodgetts, T M (Bevan Brittan LLP)
Birmingham p135 . . . . . . 0870 194 1000

Hodgin, M (Cadbury Schweppes PLC (Legal Dept))
Birmingham p449 . . . . . . 0121 625 7000

Hodgins, Ms N (Bryan Cave) C1 C2 Zo
London EC2 p19 . . . . 020 7207 1100

Hodgins, P (Reynolds Porter Chamberlain LLP)
London E1 p71 . . . . 020 3060 6000

Hodgkinson, G (KJD)
Stoke-on-Trent p398 . . . . . 01782 202020

Hodgkinson, G H (Stephenson Harwood)
London EC2 p82 . . . . 020 7329 4422

Hodgkinson, H (Miles-Pierce Solicitors) B1 C1 G H K1 L P S1 W M1 Zi
Birmingham p140 . . . . 0800 987 5305

Hodgkinson, P J (SAS Daniels LLP) S1 A1
Macclesfield p297 . . . . . . 01625 442100

Hodgkinson, S (Hill Dickinson LLP) E S1
Liverpool p288 . . . . 0151 600 8000

Hodgkiss, Ms K (Barlow Lyde & Gilbert LLP)
London EC3 p10 . . . . 020 7247 2277

Hodgson, Mrs A M (Guildford Borough Council) F1 K1 M1 P S1 T1 W
Guildford p459 . . . . 01483 505050

Hodgson, B K (Ward Hadaway) J1 Zp
Newcastle upon Tyne p327 . 0191 204 4000

Hodgson, Miss C (BHP Law) N V
Durham p214 . . . . 0191 384 0840

Hodgson, C A C (Bates NVH) J1 N L Q F1
Fleet p226 . . . . 01252 629292

Hodgson, Miss C M (Larken & Co) W S1
Newark p322 . . . . 01636 703333

Hodgson, Ms E (Cartwright King)
Derby p208 . . . . 01332 346111

Hodgson, G (Ford & Warren) G Zt J2 O Q
Leeds p273 . . . . 0113 243 6601

Hodgson, G J (Mills & Reeve) Zj
Norwich p335 . . . . 01603 660155

Hodgson, Mrs H M (Colin Rayner & Co) K1 D1 D2 O Q Zk
Bolton p149 . . . . 01204 591145

Hodgson, I F (SNR Denton) Zb
London EC4 p75 . . . . 020 7242 1212

Hodgson, J (Butcher & Barlow LLP) C1 S2 C2 E
Bury p170 . . . . 0161 764 4062

Hodgson, Ms J (Department for Business, Enterprise and Regulatory Reform)
London SW1 p105 . . . . . . 020 7215 0105

Hodgson, J S (Fraser Brown) M1 J1 P V F1 R1 Zt
Nottingham p337 . . . . 0115 988 8777

Hodgson, Mrs L M (Everys) G K1 D1 B2
Exeter p221 . . . . 01392 477983

Hodgson, M K (DBL Talbots LLP) E S2 R2 S1 L Zl R1
Stourbridge p399 . . . . . . 01384 445850

Hodgson, M T (Taylor Wessing)
London EC4 p86 . . . . 020 7300 7000

Hodgson, Mrs M T (Palmer Hodgson & Heyes) A1 C1 E L R1 S1 T1
Thornton Cleveleys p411 . . . 01253 824216

Hodgson, N J (Hodgsons & Mortimer) S1 E C1 W L A1 K4
Richmond p363 . . . . 01748 850950

Hodgson, R A (Hodgsons & Mortimer) W S1 E A1
Darlington p206 . . . 01325 250111 / 355956
Richmond p363 . . . . 01748 850950

Hodgson, R N (Hodgson Coulthard & Co) G K1 H N V F1
Houghton Le Spring p253 . . 0191 584 3333

Hodgson, Ms S (Charles Russell LLP) O Q W
London EC4 p19 . . . . 020 7203 5000

Hodgson, S (Penningtons)
Basingstoke p127 . . . . . . 01256 407100

Hodgson, S (Lanyon Bowdler LLP) D1 K1
Shrewsbury p379 . . . . 01743 280280

Hodgson, Mrs S E (Joseph A Jones & Co) W S1 S2
Lancaster p269 . . . . 01524 63371

Hodgson, S J (Marsden Rawsthorn LLP) A1 E S2 S1 A2 T1 C1
Preston p357 . . . . 01772 799600

Hodgson, Ms S L (Atkinsonhodgson LLP)
Manchester p301 . . . . 0870 300 8790

Hodgson, Ms S M (Land Registry - Lytham Office)
Lytham p464 . . . . 01253 849849 / 840012

Hodkin, P D (Hodkin & Co) Q W K1 S1 F1 Zj Zd Ze O N B1 C1 J1 L
East Grinstead p215 . . . . . 01342 325765

Hodkinson, Mrs C P (Haworth Holt Bell Limited) W
Altrincham p116 . . . . 0161 928 7136

Hodkinson, E W (Bowcock & Pursaill) A1 S1 S2 E
Leek p278 . . . . 01538 399199

Hodkinson, Miss L (Essex County Council)
Chelmsford p454 . . . . 0845 743 0430

Hodrien, Mrs W (EMW) E R2 Zl
Milton Keynes p316 . . . . . 0845 070 6000

Hodsman, D T (Crossmans Solicitors Limited) S1 W A1 S2 K4 T2
Thornbury p411 . . . 01454 412278 / 412004

Hodsman, Mrs D W (Crossmans Solicitors Limited) S1 W
Thornbury p411 . . . 01454 412278 / 412004

Hodson, A (FBC Manby Bowdler LLP) N
Willenhall p432 . . . . 01902 366566

Hodson, D M (The International Family Law Group) K1 K3 K2
London WC2 p45 . . . . 020 3178 5668

Hodson, D M (Slade Legal) D1 E J1 K1 Q V G H M1 P C1 S1 N W Zi Zl
Didcot p210 . . . . 01235 511211
Abingdon p114 . . . . 01235 521920

Hodson, J (Slade Legal) S1 W K1 Q C1 L N J1 E
Abingdon p114 . . . . 01235 521920

Hodson, Miss K D (Clifford Chance)
London E14 p20 . . . . 020 7006 1000

Hodson, P (Beardsells) N O Q
Cheadle p185 . . . . 0161 477 2288

Hodson, R D (Elsey & Hodson) A1 B1 E J1 L R1 S1 T1 W Zc Zi Zl
Peterborough p347 . . . . . . 01733 314064

Hodson, S J (DAC Beachcroft)
London EC4 p24 . . . . 020 7242 1011

Hoe, Ms A (Linklaters LLP)
London EC2 p54 . . . . 020 7456 2000

Hoey, Ms C (Russell Jones & Walker)
Manchester p309 . . . . 0161 383 3500

Hoey, J C (TLT Solicitors) O Q B1 Zb Zj
Bristol p165 . . . . 0117 917 7777

Hoffman, Ms C (Ashurst LLP)
London EC2 p7 . . . . 020 7638 1111

Hoffman, Ms J C (Society of Lloyd's)
London EC3 p107 . . . . 020 7327 1000

Hoffman, Ms M (Bilton Hammond LLP) K1 N Zk
Mansfield p311 . . . . 01623 675800

Hofstetter, J M (Hill Hofstetter LLP) O Q N
Solihull p382 . . . . 0121 210 6000

Hofton, D (Ramsdens Solicitors) S1
Halifax p238 . . . . 01422 330700
Huddersfield p256 . . . . 01484 821500

Hogan, G (Hogans) D1 F1 H K1 N Q Zl Zm
Prescot p356 . . . . 0151 430 7529

Hogan, Ms L J (West Berkshire Council)
Newbury p466 . . . . 01635 42400

Hogan, M (Memery Crystal) E S2
London WC2 p60 . . . . 020 7242 5905

Hogan, P R (Henriques Griffiths) S1 C1 E F1 L W B1
Bristol p163 . . . . 0117 909 4000

Hogan, R D (Dewar Hogan) O L Zq
London EC4 p27 . . . . 020 7634 9550

Hogan, S M (Anthony Collins Solicitors LLP) E
Birmingham p137 . . . . 0121 200 3242

Hogarth, G J (Howells LLP) L
Sheffield p376 . . . . 0114 249 6666

Hogarth, Ms I M (Irene Hogarth Criminal Defence) G H
Newton Abbot p329 . . . . . . 01626 337373

Hogarth, Ms J F (EEF) J1
London SW1 p106 . . . . 020 7222 7777

Hogarth, Mrs L (Howells LLP) G H
Sheffield p376 . . . . 0114 249 6666

Hogarth, M J B (The Littlewoods Organisation PLC) E C1 F1 F2 U2 R2
Liverpool p463 . . . . 0151 235 3055

Hogarth, W R J (Reynolds Porter Chamberlain LLP) Q Zj Zc O P
London E1 p71 . . . . 020 3060 6000

Hogarth-Jones, B (Birkett Long LLP) K4 T2 W
Colchester p197 . . . . 01206 217300

Hogarty, Mrs B R L (Foot Anstey) E O
Exeter p221 . . . . 01392 411221

Hogarty, Ms K (Reed Smith LLP) Zt
London EC2 p71 . . . . 020 3116 3000

Hogben, J (Ashurst LLP)
London EC2 p7 . . . . 020 7638 1111

Hogg, Ms A (Nelsons)
Nottingham p338 . . . . 0115 958 6262

Hogg, D (Close Thornton) A1 C1 C2 E L R1 S1 T1 T2 W
Darlington p206 . . . . 01325 466461

Hogg, D A (HM Revenue & Customs)
London WC2 p106

Hogg, Ms D J (Freemans Solicitors) G B2
London W1 p34 . . . . 020 7935 3522

Hogg, Ms H M (Derby City Council) D1 K1 Q
Derby p456 . . . . 01332 293111

Hogg, Mrs I C (Tanner & Taylor LLP) G H D1 Zi Zm
Aldershot p115 . . . . 01252 316565

Hogg, J (Jennings) E L S1 W
Llanelli p292 . . . . 01554 772331

Hogg, Miss J (Guy Williams Layton) S1 W E L
Liverpool p288 . . . . 0151 236 7171

Hogg, Ms J (Badhams Law (A Trading Name of Parabis Law LLP)) Zj O E
Croydon p204 . . . . 0844 245 4000

Hogg, J G (North Lincolnshire Council)
Scunthorpe p470 . . . . 01724 296296

Hogg, Miss N J (Stewarts Law LLP) K3 K1
London EC4 p83 . . . . 020 7822 8000

Hogg, Ms P (Carpenter & Co) K3 K1 D1
Wallington p419 . . . . 020 8669 5145

Hogg, R C (Somerset County Council) Q R1 Zl Zs Zu
Taunton p473 . . . . 0845 345 9166

Hoggett, J M (Stephens & Scown) E A1 Zb Zc Zn R2
Exeter p222 . . . . 01392 210700

Hogue, Ms P (Reynolds Porter Chamberlain LLP)
London E1 p71 . . . . 020 3060 6000

Hogwood, R M (Stewarts Law LLP) K1 K3
London EC4 p83 . . . . 020 7822 8000

Holah, M (Field Fisher Waterhouse LLP)
London EC3 p31 . . . . 020 7861 4000

Holben, D G (Nuffield Hospitals)
Surbiton p473 . . . . 020 8390 1200

Holborn, Ms J (Baines Wilson LLP) J1 Zp
Carlisle p181 . . . . 01228 552600

Holbrook, Miss J (Plexus Law (A Trading Name of Parabis Law LLP))
London EC3 p68 . . . . 0844 245 4000

Holbrook, Ms J (Brabners Chaffe Street) Zc E P R1 S1
Preston p356 . . . . 01772 823921

Holcombe, Ms J (Newport City Council)
Newport p466 . . . . 01633 656656

Holcroft, Miss P A (Forshaws Davies Ridgway LLP) S1 E S2
Warrington p422 . . . . 01925 230000

Holcroft, Ms R (Stephensons Solicitors LLP) B1 C1 F1 Zh O
Wigan p432 . . . . 01942 777777

Holcroft, R M (Bromiley Holcroft & Co) A1 B1 C1 E F1 K1 L M1 N
Southport p388 . . . . 0870 236 0000

Holdaway, Mrs L (Mills & Reeve) R1
Cambridge p175 . . . . 01223 364422

Holdcroft, N (Tolhurst Fisher LLP)
Southend-on-Sea p387 . . . . 01702 352511

Holden, A (Napthens LLP) A1 C1
Preston p357 . . . . 01772 888444

Holden, Miss A (Browne Jacobson LLP) E
Nottingham p336 . . . . 0115 976 6000

Holden, A C (Ellisons) S1 W
Harwich p243 . . . . 01255 502428

Holden, A D B (Herrington & Carmichael LLP) N O Q B1 F1 J1 C1 S1 I E Zq Zp Ze Zl Zw
Wokingham p437 . . . . 0118 977 4045

Holden, Ms A J (Williamson & Soden) S1
Solihull p383 . . . . 0121 733 8000

Holden, A N (Nigel Holden & Co) H N S1 G Q O B2 W T1 T2 R2 R1 Zg
Blackburn p145 . . . . 01254 682424
Burnley p169 . . . . 01282 426722

Holden, B (Verisona Solicitors) W K4 Zm T2
Waterlooville p423 . . . . . . 023 9226 5251

Holden, D (Symes Bains Broomer)
Scunthorpe p373 . . . . 01724 281616

Holden, D (Trowers & Hamlins)
London EC3 p88 . . . . 020 7423 8000

Holden, D C (AST Hampsons (incorporating Warhurst and co)) S1 W R1 C1 E J1 S2
Bury p170 . . . . 0161 764 3317

Holden, Mrs H J (Shakespeares) N Zj Zq A3
Birmingham p142 . . . . 0121 237 3000

Holden, I (Bond Pearce LLP) C2 C1
Southampton p385 . . . . . . 0845 415 0000

Holden, Ms I L (Blanchards Bailey LLP) K1 D2 D1 K2 K3
Blandford Forum p147 . . . . 01258 459361
Shaftesbury p374 . . . . 01747 440447

Holden, J (Holden & Co) L D1 G H J1 K1 M1 N
Hastings p243 . . . . 01424 722422

Holden, J C (John Holden) G H
Keighley p263 . . . . 01535 667826

Holden, J L (Gordons LLP) C1 Ze Zb
Leeds p273 . . . . 0113 227 0100

Holden, J S (Holden Son & Ullock) S1 W L S2
Thornton Cleveleys p411 . . . 01253 852613 / 862606

Holden, Mrs K (H Batra & Co) O Q J1 N C1 S1 E
London SW1 p11 . . . . 0845 017 5588

Holden, Ms K A (ABN Amro Bank NV)
London EC2 p103 . . . . 020 7628 7766

Holden, Ms L A (Northamptonshire County Council)
Northampton p467 . . . . 01604 236236

Holden, P A (Kimbells LLP) C1 C3 M1
Milton Keynes p317 . . . . . . 01908 668555

Holden, P E (Thompson & Cooke LLP) J1 J2 K1 D1 G H Zl Zx
Stalybridge p393 . . . . 0161 338 2614
Stalybridge p393 . . . . 0161 338 2614

Holden, R C T (Linklaters LLP)
London EC2 p54 . . . . 020 7456 2000

Holden, R S (Hansells) C1 J1 Zq Ze B1 C2
Norwich p334 . . . . 01603 615731

Holden, Miss S J N (Rochman Landau LLP) L O Q B1 W
London W1 p72 . . . . 020 7544 2424

Holden-Shah, Miss E (Bracher Rawlins LLP) S2 S1 E L R1 R2
London WC1 p15 . . . . 020 7404 9400
Islington p20 . . . . 020 7847 5600

Holden-White, D (Mowbray City Advocates)
Bath p128 . . . . 01225 400666

Holder, C P (Lawrence & Holder) S1 E
Potters Bar p355 . . . . 01707 645317

Holder, J (SLP Solicitors) E O S2
Stanmore p394 . . . . 020 8420 7950

Holder, J D (Charles Russell LLP) C1 C2
London EC4 p19 . . . . 020 7203 5000

Holder, J K (Stephens & Son LLP) C1 B1 A3
Chatham p185 . . . . 01634 811444

Holder, Mrs L (EMW) J1
Milton Keynes p316 . . . . . . 0845 070 6000

Holder, T J (Dudley Metropolitan Borough Council)
Dudley p457 . . . . 01384 815326

Holder, T M R (Nelsons) G H R1
Leicester p280 . . . . 0116 222 6666
Nottingham p338 . . . . 0115 958 6262

Holdich, A J (Ford Simey LLP) W T1
Sidmouth p380 . . . 01395 577061 / 0800 169 3741

Holdich, Mrs V H (Ford Simey LLP) W
Exmouth p222 . . . 01395 272241 / 0800 169 3741

Holding, Mrs P (Durham County Council)
Durham p457 . . . . 0191 383 3513

Holding, P F (Helphire (UK) Ltd) Q
Bath p448 . . . . 01225 321000

Holding-Parsons, B G C (Stockler Brunton) O Zg I
London EC4 p83 . . . . 020 7404 6661

Holdom, T (Tollers LLP) N
Northampton p332 . . . . 01604 258558

Holdridge, Ms J A (Johns & Saggar) K1 K3 D1 W Zi
London WC1 p46 . . . . 020 3490 1475

Holdstock, Ms E J (Forsters LLP) Zc
Westminster p33 . . . . 020 7863 8333

Holdsworth, Miss C A (Linder Myers Solicitors) S1 W L E F1 R1 C1 P N K1 Zl Zp
Manchester p307 . . . . 0844 984 6400

Holdsworth, Mrs E A (Wace Morgan) W K4
Shrewsbury p379 . . . . 01743 280100

Holdsworth, Miss F (Keoghs LLP) J1 Zp
Bolton p149 . . . . 01204 677000

Holdsworth, I R (On Legal)
Halifax p238 . . . . 01274 608353

Holdway, Mrs S (Moss & Haselhurst) S1 S2
Winsford p435 . . . . 01606 592159

Hole, M (Hewitts) S1 S2 E W
Stockton-on-Tees p397 . . . . 01642 673701

Hole, P D (Gordons) C1 C2 Zb F1 J1 B1 M2
London WC1 p36 . . . . 020 7421 9421

Holey, A S (Barber Titleys) T2 W
Harrogate p240 . . . . 01423 502211

Holford, M D (Thomas Miller & Co)
London EC3 p108 . . . . 020 7283 4646

Holgate, B J M (Wyeth) C1 C2
Maidenhead p464 . . . . 01628 604377

Holgate, Ms G A (Allen & Overy LLP)
London E1 p5 . . . . 020 3088 0000

Holkham, Miss A M (Aviva PLC)
London EC3 p103 . 020 7283 7500 / 01603 687905
Norwich p467 . . . . 01603 622200

Holladay, Miss A F (Currey & Co) Zd W T2
Westminster p24 . . . . 020 7802 2700

Hollamby, S J (Bennett Griffin) D1 D2 Ze Zd C1 B1
Worthing p441 . . . . 01903 229925

Holland, A (Ashurst LLP)
London EC2 p7 . . . . 020 7638 1111

Holland, Miss A E (Charnwood Borough Council)
Loughborough p464 . . . . . . 01509 263151

Holland, A L (Hatchers Solicitors LLP) G H Zl
Shrewsbury p379 . . . . 01743 248545

Holland, A N (HC Solicitors LLP) G Q
Peterborough p347 . . . . . . 01733 882800

Holland, Mrs C (Redmonds Solicitors) N
Oldham p341 . . . . 01457 879500

Holland, C J (Angel & Co) K3 K1 D1
Coventry p200 . . . . 024 7625 2211

Holland, Ms C K (Lawrence Davies & Co) K1 D1 D2 K3
Hammersmith & Fulham p26 . 020 7381 1171

Holland, Miss C L (Humphries Kirk)
Poole p352 . . . . 01202 725400

Holland, Ms C M (The Watson Ramsbottom Partnership) N
Blackburn p146 . . . . 01254 672222

Holland, C R (Barker Son & Isherwood LLP) D1 D2 E A1 A2 S1 R1
Andover p118 . . . . 01264 791156
Whitchurch p430 . . . . 01256 896262
Andover p118 . . . . 01264 353411

Holland, Ms E R (Williamson & Soden) W
Solihull p383 . . . . 0121 733 8000

Holland, Miss G E (The College of Law York) O Q B1 Zl
York p477 . . . . 0800 289997

Holland, Miss H (Brachers) Zr
Maidstone p299 . . . . 01622 690691
Tunbridge Wells p415 . . . . . 01892 510000

Holland, Mrs H P (Cartmell Shepherd) S2 W
Brampton p156 . . . . 01697 72378

Holland, J R (McCarthy Bennett Holland) C1 E S1 W
Wigan p432 . . . . 01942 206060

Holland, J R (Hogan Lovells International LLP)
London EC1 p42 . . . . 020 7296 2000

Holland, K (Jefferies Essex LLP) S1 L S2 E C1
Westcliff-on-Sea p428 . . . . 01702 332311

Holland, M (DLA Piper UK LLP) E R1 R2 P Zn Zc
Sheffield p375 . . . . 0870 011 1111
Sheffield p376 . . . . 0870 150 0100

Holland, Ms M (MFG Solicitors) E
Worcester p440 . . . . 01905 610410

Holland, Ms N A (Anderson Partnership) K3 K1
Chesterfield p191 . . . . 01246 220737

Holland, Mrs N L (Taylor Wessing)
London EC4 p86 . . . . 020 7300 7000

Holland, N R (Stamp Jackson and Procter) N Zr
Hull p258 . . . . 01482 324591

Holland, P (SNR Denton) G H
London EC4 p75 . . . . 020 7242 1212

Holland, P (Bowling & Co) O
London E15 p15 . . . . 020 8221 8000

See p634 for the Key to Work Categories

Holland, Mrs P S (Eastgate Assistance Ltd) *S1 L W* Colchester *p455* 0870 523 4500

Holland, R (Bailey & Cogger) *A1 E L P R1 S1* Tonbridge *p412* 01732 353305

Holland, R (Dass Solicitors) *Q Zq* Birmingham *p137* 0121 248 4000

Holland, R (The Johnson Partnership) *G H* Nottingham *p337* 0115 941 9141

Holland, Mrs S (Philip J Hammond & Sons) *S1 W E L* Leicester *p280* 0116 251 7171

Holland, S D (Butcher & Barlow LLP) *K1 K3 N J1* Bury *p170* 0161 764 5141

Holland, V (Penningtons) Godalming *p231* 01483 791800

Holland, Ms V G (B P Collins LLP) *Zd C1 C2* Gerrards Cross *p229* 01753 889995

Hollands, G C (Kettering Borough Council) *C1 E F1 L M1 N S1 W* Kettering *p462* 01536 410333

Hollebon, G R (Bevans) *J1 Zp C1 A3* Bristol *p161* 0117 923 7249

Hollely, Miss L J (Shentons) *G H N Q* Winchester *p434* 01962 844544

Hollest, D E (Hewitsons) *S1 A1 E T1 C1* Saffron Walden *p370* 01799 522471

Holley, Mrs J A (Larby Williams with Gwyn & Gwyn) *S1 S2 W L A1 E* Cowbridge *p201* 01446 775535

Holliday, A S (Matthews Lewis & Co) *S2 S1 W* Chester *p191* 01244 327750

Holliday, Miss D (Collins Solicitors) *Zr P J2 Q N Zq* Watford *p423* 01923 223324

Holliday, Mrs M (H F T Gough & Co) *K1 Q W* Whitehaven *p431* 01946 692461

Holliday, R J (Olliers) *G H B2* Manchester *p308* 0161 834 1515

Holliday, S A (Rolls-Royce PLC) Derby *p456* 01332 242424

Holling, D (West Berkshire Council) Newbury *p466* 01635 42400

Holling, K (Trowers & Hamlins) London EC3 *p88* 020 7423 8000

Hollingbury, Mrs I A (HMG Law LLP) *T2 W Zm* Oxford *p343* 01865 244661

Hollingdrake, C N (Jobling & Knape) *C3 F1 Zza J1 Zf U2 O Q N C2 Zp* Lancaster *p269* 01524 598300

Hollinghurst, M W (hlw Keeble Hawson LLP) *N O Zr* Doncaster *p211* 01302 366831

Hollingsworth, Ms A J (Bristows) *J1 O* London EC4 *p15* 020 7400 8000

Hollingsworth, D (Kitsons LLP) *C2 C1* Torquay *p413* 01803 202020

Hollingsworth, G M (Bradshaw Hollingsworth Solicitors) *O I Q F1 F2 Ze Zw Zy* Leicester *p279* 0116 204 2500

Hollingsworth, Ms R A (West Sussex County Council) Chichester *p455* 01243 777100

Hollingsworth, T J (Forbes) *S1 E C1 B1 L W R1 Zc Ze* Blackburn *p145* 01254 54374

Hollingsworth, W K (Cartwright King) *G K1 O Q J1 N D1* Derby *p208* 01332 346111 Leicester *p279* 0116 253 9222 Nottingham *p336* 0115 958 7444

Hollington, Miss J P (Ellisons) *W T1 K1 V Zd Zm* Colchester *p197* 01206 764477

Hollingum, Ms L (Berry & Berry) *H B2 G* Tonbridge *p412* 01732 355911

Hollingworth, D J (Andrew & Co LLP) *A1 L R1 S1 T1 W C1 E Zc Zl* Newark *p322* 01636 673743 Lincoln *p284* 01522 512123

Hollingworth, Ms P D (South Staffordshire Council) Codsall *p455* 01902 696000

Hollins Gibson, A J (Denby & Co) *G H B2* Barrow-in-Furness *p125* 01229 822366 Ulverston *p416* 01229 582283

Hollins, Miss L (Myers Fletcher & Gordon) *J1 S1 S2 W* London W6 *p62* 020 7610 4433

Hollinshead, Mrs G P (Wolferstans) Plymouth *p351* 01752 663295

Hollinshead, Miss J (Addleshaw Goddard) *R2* London EC1 *p4* 020 7606 8855

Hollinshead, Miss W (CMHT Solicitors) *X D1 D2* Walsall *p420* 01922 646400

Hollis, A J (Hollis & Co) *D1 G H K1 S1 K3 N Zi* Sutton-in-Ashfield *p404* 01623 443344

Hollis, J (FDC Law) *W K4* Frome *p228* 01373 465051

Hollis, R J G (Stanley Tee) *K1* Bishop's Stortford *p144* 01279 755200

Hollis, S A (Thomson Webb & Corfield) *Q* Cambridge *p176* 01223 578070

Hollis, S J (Staffordshire County Council) Stafford *p472* 01785 223121

Hollis, S J (Livingstons) *K1 D2 D1 K2 V* Barrow-in-Furness *p125* 01229 828300 Ulverston *p416* 01229 585555

Hollist, A (Holls Solicitors) Beckenham *p129* 020 8658 9767

Holloway, A A (Rowbis Solicitors) *W S1* Gloucester *p230* 01452 301903

Holloway, B (Robinsons) *E S1 L A1 R1 P* Derby *p209* 01332 291431

Holloway, Miss E A (Lawson Coppock & Hart) *E S2* Manchester *p306* 0161 832 5944

Holloway, Mrs L H (Linda Holloway & Co) *S1 W K4* St Albans *p390* 01727 841651

Holloway, Miss M (Harvey Ingram LLP) *E* Leicester *p280* 0116 254 5454

Holloway, N C (Treasury Solicitors Department) London WC2 *p110* 020 7210 3000

Holloway, P A (Gregory Rowcliffe Milners) *C1 T1 B1 W Zc Ze Zo* London WC1 *p37* 020 7242 0631

Holloway, Ms T A P (Hague & Dixon) *W* York *p444* 01759 371634

Holly, N A (Humphreys & Co) Bristol *p163* 0117 929 2662

Hollyer, P A (Elliot Mather LLP) *N P C1 J1 Zl* Chesterfield *p192* 01246 231288

Hollywood, Ms S M (Cross Solicitors) Connah's Quay *p199* 01244 822101

Holman, Miss A (Conveyancing Direct Ltd) *S1* St Leonards-on-Sea *p392* 0845 788 8666

Holman, D M (Nantes) *S1 E W S2* Dorchester *p212* 01305 250100

Holman, J M (Weightmans LLP) Liverpool *p291* 0151 227 2601

Holman, M M J (EMW) *C1* Milton Keynes *p316* 0845 070 6000

Holman, N (Hogan Lovells International LLP) London EC1 *p42* 020 7296 2000

Holman, S K (Whitehead Monckton) *N O Q F1 J1 L Zq Zc* Maidstone *p299* 01622 698000

Holman, T R F (Hempsons) *N Zq Zr* Harrogate *p240* 01423 522331

Holme, C R (Barlow Lyde & Gilbert LLP) London EC3 *p10* 020 7247 2277

Holmes, A (Geoffrey Morris & Ashton) *N O W Q R1* Wrexham *p442* 01978 291322

Holmes, A A L (Antony A Holmes) *S1 W L* Broadway *p166* 01386 858107

Holmes, A F (Buchanan & Llewellyn) *W S1 K4* Westbourne *p428* 01202 752525

Holmes, A M (Bennett & Co) *C1 E F1 L W Za Zc* Liverpool *p286* 0151 733 2372

Holmes, A P (Roach Pittis) *A1 S1 T1 J1 W N B1 L Zd Ze Zh A2 S2 Zn R2* Newport *p328* 01983 524431

Holmes, C (Ashurst LLP) London EC2 *p7* 020 7638 1111

Holmes, Miss D (Anthony Collins Solicitors LLP) *W T2 K4* Birmingham *p137* 0121 200 3242

Holmes, D A (Bridge McFarland) *S1 W L T2* Grimsby *p235* 01472 311711

Holmes, D J (David Holmes & Co) *K1 K3* Great Yarmouth *p234* 01493 658291

Holmes, E A (Thomas Guise) *Q Zq B1 O* Worcester *p439* 01905 723131

Holmes, E G (Letchers) *F1 J1 O L Q N Zq* Ringwood *p364* 01425 471424

Holmes, Miss F A (Walker Smith Way) *W T2 K4* Chester *p191* 0844 346 3100

Holmes, Mrs H C (David Gray Solicitors) *K1 D1 K3* Newcastle upon Tyne *p324* 0191 232 9547

Holmes, I R (Bailey Smailes) *W S1 A1 E T1 C1 B1 R1* Huddersfield *p255* 01484 435543

Holmes, J C (Hempsons) *Zr Zm* Westminster *p40* 020 7839 0278

Holmes, J E (Warrington Borough Council) Warrington *p475* 01925 444400

Holmes, Ms K (Reed Smith LLP) *C3 M1* London EC2 *p71* 020 3116 3000

Holmes, Mrs K E (Minahan Hirst & Co) *K1 N* Cheadle Hulme *p185* 0161 485 8131

Holmes, L (Laurence Holmes Solicitors) *K1 N W* Congresbury *p198* 01934 838445

Holmes, Miss L (Wrigleys Solicitors LLP) *Zo* Leeds *p278* 0113 244 6100

Holmes, Mrs M (Cocks Lloyd) *Q N* Nuneaton *p339* 024 7664 1642

Holmes, N (Ashurst LLP) London EC2 *p7* 020 7638 1111

Holmes, N P (Irwin Mitchell LLP) *N* Manchester *p306* 0870 150 0100

Holmes, O J (Tolhurst Fisher LLP) Chelmsford *p187* 01245 495111

Holmes, P D (Macfarlanes) *E* London EC4 *p56* 020 7831 9222

Holmes, Ms P I (Penmans) *K1 D1 V G H M1* Coventry *p200* 024 7622 6575

Holmes, R (KJD) Stoke-on-Trent *p398* 01782 202020

Holmes, R A (Walker Morris) *Zu C1 Zd* Leeds *p277* 0113 283 2500

Holmes, R M B (Travers Smith LLP) *E R1* London EC1 *p87* 020 7295 3000

Holmes, Ms S (Dowson Billington) *K1 N Q V L* Preston *p356* 01772 556807

Holmes, Ms S (Clifford Joseph) *E R1 S1 L* Maidenhead *p298* 01628 823331

Holmes, S E (SJ Berwin LLP) London EC4 *p75* 020 7111 2222

Holmes, S W (Harvey Ingram Borneos) *M1 F1 D1 T1 N Q* Bedford *p130* 01234 353221

Holmes, Miss V J (Mayo Wynne Baxter LLP) *Zr* Brighton *p160* 01273 775533

Holmes, Mrs W E (Collins Dryland & Thorowgood LLP) *S1 W K4* Henley-on-Thames *p247* 01491 572323

Holmes-Siedle, Ms R (Stevens & Bolton) Guildford *p237* 01483 302264

Holmstock, Mrs R M (Debenhams Ottaway) *S1* Radlett *p358* 01923 857171

Holness, Miss B E (Nash & Co Solicitors LLP) *K1* Plymouth *p350* 01752 664444

Holness, Ms K (Ashurst LLP) London EC2 *p7* 020 7638 1111

Holroyd, A S T (Burton Burton & Ho LLP) *C1 E S1 W* Leeds *p272* 0113 297 8787

Holroyd, J G P (Atkinson McCall) *E A1 S1 L R1 W C1 T1* Harrogate *p240* 01423 501531

Holroyd, Mrs M L (Hempsons) *E L S1 W Zd Zh Zm* Harrogate *p240* 01423 522331

Holroyd, N B (Russell Jones & Walker) Manchester *p309* 0161 383 3500

Holroyd, N J (HKB Wiltshires) *C1 D1 F1 G H K1 M1 P J1* Great Yarmouth *p234* 01493 855676

Holroyd, W A M (Quality Solicitors Jackson & Canter) *S2 W Zi* Liverpool *p290* 0151 282 1700

Holt, A (DLA Piper UK LLP) London EC2 *p24* 0870 011 1111

Holt, Mrs A (Armstrong Foulkes) *Zr* Middlesbrough *p314* 01642 231110

Holt, A D (Brabners Chaffe Street) *T2 W* Liverpool *p286* 0151 600 3000

Holt, A D (Wilkin Chapman Epton Blades) *J1 Q Zl N* Lincoln *p285* 01522 512345

Holt, A J N (Nelsons) *S1 A1 C1 W L T1 R1 E Zd Zf Zl* Leicester *p280* 0116 222 6666

Holt, C (Norman H Barnett & Co) London E6 *p11* 020 8471 2112

Holt, D A (Weightmans LLP) *C1 E F1 L M1 N P* Liverpool *p291* 0151 227 2601

Holt, D G (Cockshott Peck Lewis) *K1 L J1 D1 F1 B1 Zl* Southport *p388* 01704 534034

Holt, Mrs E E (Pannone LLP) *N Zq Zr* Manchester *p308* 0161 909 3000

Holt, Miss G S (Hartwell PLC) Oxford *p468* 01865 866000

Holt, Ms J (Cartwright King) *G H Zm* Derby *p208* 01332 346111

Holt, Mrs J (Tracey Barlow Furniss & Co) *D1 K1 N V Q G* Worksop *p441* 01909 472355

Holt, J (Crown Prosecution Service Merseyside) Liverpool *p463* 0151 239 6400 Manchester *p465* 0161 827 4700

Holt, J B (Stevens) *G H* Stoke-on-Trent *p398* 01782 343353

Holt, J M (Clark Holt) *I C1 J1 Ze U2 Zza* Swindon *p406* 01793 617444

Holt, J R (hlw Keeble Hawson LLP) *N Q Zj Zv* Sheffield *p375* 0114 272 2061

Holt, Mrs K S (Matthew Arnold & Baldwin LLP) *S1 L* Watford *p423* 01923 202020

Holt, Ms M (London Underground Ltd) London SW1 *p107* 020 7918 3126

Holt, P J (Stone Rowe Brewer LLP) *N Zr* Twickenham *p416* 020 8891 6141

Holt, R G (Godloves) *S1 G H W L Zi Zm* Leeds *p273* 0113 225 8864 Leeds *p273* 0113 225 8811

Holt, Ms S P (Reed Smith LLP) *N I O* London EC2 *p71* 020 3116 3000

Holtam, J F (The College of Law Guildford) Guildford *p459* 01483 460200

Holter, M (WilmerHale) *C1 C2 M3 U1* London EC2 *p92* 020 7645 2400

Holtham, D M (Merritt & Co) *M1 N P B1 C1 F1 Zk Zc* Yarm *p443* 01642 885555

Holtham, Miss R V (Clarks Legal LLP) Cardiff *p177* 029 2055 7500

Holton, Ms F A (A L Hughes & Co) *S1 W E S2* London SW16 *p43* 020 8769 7100

Holuba, Ms K (Hill Dickinson LLP) *B1 J1 Q T1 Ze* Liverpool *p288* 0151 600 8000

Holwell, C (Freeth Cartwright LLP) *E* Nottingham *p337* 0115 936 9369

Holyer, Miss R T (Parker Bullen) *W K4* Salisbury *p371* 01722 412000

Holyhead, Ms L (HSBC Legal Department) Birmingham *p449* 0121 455 2740

Holyoak, Mrs A S C (Ashfords LLP) *E* Exeter *p220* 01392 337000

Holyoak, G P (Starkie & Gregory) Long Eaton *p293* 0115 849 9000

Holyoak, I D (Michelmores LLP) *C1 C3* Exeter *p221* 01392 688688

Homer, M P (Howard & Co) *S1 K1 W* Barnsley *p124* 01226 215215

Homer, S C (Field Overell) *S1 W A1 E* Leamington Spa *p270* 01926 422101

Homer, S J (Ashfords LLP) *O Zc A3* Exeter *p220* 01392 337000

Homfray, Mrs E H (Birmingham City Council Legal & Democratic Services) Birmingham *p449* 0121 303 2066

Hommel, G (Herbert Smith LLP) *Zb* London EC2 *p40* 020 7374 8000

Hommel, Ms L F (LG Lawyers) London SE1 *p50* 020 7379 0000

Honchen, B (Punch Robson) *J1 Q O* Middlesbrough *p315* 01642 230700

Hone, A N (Wilson & Berry) *K1 N Q O L* Bracknell *p153* 01344 420555

Honess, P D (David Gist Solicitors) *N J1* Bristol *p162* 0117 927 9111

Honey, D (Holman Fenwick Willan) London EC3 *p42* 020 7264 8000

Honey, Mrs E (Michelmores LLP) *E R2 S2 X* Exeter *p221* 01392 688688

Honey, G E (Seddons) *S2 E S1 W* Westminster *p77* 020 7725 8000

Honey, M G (Wykeham Hurford Sheppard & Son LLP) *A1 C1 C3 E F1 F2 J1 K4 P S2 W Zl Zt Zd Zp* Tenterden *p410* 01580 762251

Honey, R J (Rochford District Council) Rochford *p470* 01702 546366

Honey, R W (Michelmores LLP) *E R2 S2* Exeter *p221* 01392 688688

Honeyands, Mrs S V (Knights Solicitors LLP) *C1 Zf* Newcastle under Lyme *p323* 01782 619225

Honeyball, Mrs H M (Stones Solicitors LLP) Exeter *p222* 01392 666777

Honeyben, Mrs M E (Elliot Mather LLP) *Q J1 F1 N L B1 V Zl* Chesterfield *p192* 01246 231288

Honeywood, Miss K T (Clifford Chance) London E14 *p20* 020 7006 1000

Honeywood, Miss S (Campion & Co) *S1* Nottingham *p336* 0115 947 6373

Honke, P E P (Hal-Solicitors) *G H K1 D1 Q N* Uxbridge *p417* 01895 270907 / 270908

Honniball, M P (Honniball & Co) *S1 E K1 M1 W* Thame *p410* 01844 261484

Honychurch, Miss J V (Emerson Developments (Holdings) Ltd) *E* Alderley Edge *p447* 01625 588420

Hood, A (Anthony Walters & Co) *K1 K3* Bishop Auckland *p144* 01388 662222

Hood, Mrs A M (Brearleys Solicitors) *K3 K1* Batley *p128* 01924 473065 South Shields *p383* 0191 456 7893 / 455 5361

Hood, B J (Winckworth Sherwood LLP) *S1 Zd Zx* London SE1 *p92* 020 7593 5000

Hood, C W (William Hood & Co) *K1 D1 C1 M1 B1 E S1 N J1 T1 Zc Zd Zj V* Macclesfield *p297* 01625 611819

Hood, Miss E A (Sylvester Mackett) *D1 K3 K1 Q V* Trowbridge *p414* 01225 755621

Hood, Miss E C (Joelson Wilson LLP) *O Q Ze Zq Zk* Westminster *p46* 020 7580 5721

Hood, H L A (Hunters) *K1 Q H O Zv* London WC2 *p44* 020 7412 0050

Hood, M (Lees Solicitors LLP) *Zr* Birkenhead *p134* 0151 647 9381

Hood, M L (Rees Wood Terry) *S2 E* Cardiff *p180* 029 2040 8800

Hood, Ms R S C (City of Sunderland) Sunderland *p473* 0191 520 5555

Hood, W J H (Forbes) *G H K1 W S1 J1 L D1* Preston *p356* 01772 220022

Hood-Williams, Ms V J (Kirkland & Lane) *S1 S2 M1* Southwell *p389* 01636 813128 / 812180

Hook, C J (Dorians) Derby *p208* 01332 680580

Hook, D J (Hook & Partners) *Zl Q C1 C2* Canvey Island *p177* 01268 692255

Hook, D R (Hook & Partners) *J1 O Q F1 L* Canvey Island *p177* 01268 692255

Hook, Mrs M (Ashworths Solicitors) *S1* London SW19 *p8* 0845 370 1000

Hook, P (Philip Hook) *S1 W E S2* Norwich *p334* 01603 250050

Hook, Ms S (Howard Kennedy LLP) *R2 E* London W1 *p48* 020 7636 1616

Hook, T S H (Toller Beattie LLP) *G H Zl Zt* Barnstaple *p125* 01271 341000

Hooke, D (Trowers & Hamlins) London EC3 *p88* 020 7423 8000

Hooke, Ms S (Hodge Jones & Allen LLP) London NW1 *p41* 020 7874 8300

Hooker, J (McMillan Williams) *S2 S1* South Croydon *p383* 020 8253 7600

Hooker, M M (Bates NVH) *S1 E W C1 R1 L M1 T1 Zc Zj Zb* Fleet *p226* 01252 629292

Hooley, Ms W (Flint Bishop Solicitors) Derby *p208* 01332 340211

Hooper, A J (J E Baring & Co) *O B1 Q J1* London EC1 *p9* 020 7242 8966

Hooper, A J (Mayo Wynne Baxter LLP) *N Zr* Brighton *p160* 01273 775533

Hooper, Mrs C (Barlow Rowland) *E S1 R1 C1 A1 L T1 Zh R2 Zd T2 Zc S2 K4* Accrington *p114* 01254 300400

Hooper, D (Reynolds Porter Chamberlain LLP) London E1 *p71* 020 3060 6000

Hooper, D R (Enodis PLC) London W1 *p106* 020 7304 6000

Hooper, J (Ashurst LLP) London EC2 *p7* 020 7638 1111

Hooper, J F (John Hooper & Co) *K1* Nottingham *p337* 0115 941 5566

Hooper, Miss J L (City & County of Swansea)
Swansea *p473*. 01792 636000
Hooper, Ms K E (Salford City Council)
Swinton *p473* 0161 794 4711
Hooper, Ms R E (Russell Jones & Walker) *N J2*
London WC2 *p74* 020 7657 1555
Hooper, W D (Kerrier District Council)
Camborne *p452* 01209 614000
Hooson, D J (Swayne Johnson Solicitors) *A1 W Zx L S1*
St Asaph *p391*. 01745 582535
Denbigh *p208* 01745 812835
Hooton, M (Ashurst LLP)
London EC2 *p7* 020 7638 1111
Hopcroft, Ms S (Ellis Jones) *E I Ze*
Bournemouth *p151*. 01202 525333
Hope, B (Pannone LLP) *Zr*
Manchester *p308* 0161 909 3000
Hope, Miss E (Gallaher Ltd)
Weybridge *p476* 01932 859777
Hope, Mrs H C (Motley & Hope) *K1 K2 Q N*
Biggleswade *p133* 01767 600600
Hope, J (Simmons & Simmons)
London EC2 *p79*. 020 7628 2020
Hope, J R (Just Law Ltd) *N*
Chelmsford *p454*. 01245 396444
Hope, K A (Glaisyers) *A1 E J1 L S1 W*
Tamworth *p407* 01827 61011
Hope, S W (Mansfield Magistrates Court)
Mansfield *p465* 01623 451500
Hope, Miss V C (Roythornes LLP) *D1 K1 K3 K2 Q*
Spalding *p389* 01775 842500
Hopewell, C (Charles Russell LLP) *C1 C2 U1*
London EC4 *p19*. 020 7203 5000
Hopgood, A G (Harvey Ingram Borneos) *E Zl J1 O S1 C1*
Milton Keynes *p317* 01908 696002
Hopgood, R P (Larcomes LLP) *N*
Portsmouth *p354*. 023 9266 1531
Hopgood, Miss V A (Dickins Hopgood Chidley LLP) *E S1 L W S2 K4 R1*
Hungerford *p258*. 01488 683555
Hopkin, Ms B J (Hopkin Murray Beskine) *D1 K1 D2*
London N4 *p42* 020 7272 1234
Hopkin, C J (Dicksons Solicitors Ltd) *N D1 K1 S1 W F1 Zl*
Stoke-on-Trent *p397*. 01782 262424
Hopkin, E D (Darbys Solicitors LLP) *C1 U1 L F1 F2 Ze Zza Zf U2 Zz Zw*
Oxford *p343*. 01865 811700
Hopkin, R T B (Brethertons LLP) *N Q O*
Rugby *p368* 01788 579579
Hopkin, Miss S G (Powells) *K1 K2*
Weston-super-Mare *p429* . . 01934 623501
Hopkins, Miss A (Anthony Gold) *Zr N J2*
London SE1 *p6* 020 7940 4000
Hopkins, C (Butcher & Barlow LLP) *Q W L J1 N*
Prestwich *p357* 0161 773 2969
Hopkins, Miss C (Kennedys) *Zj N*
London EC3 *p49*. 020 7667 9667
Hopkins, Mrs C L (Gregg Latchams LLP) *W T2*
Bristol *p162* 0117 906 9400
Hopkins, D (Cowlishaw & Mountford)
Uttoxeter *p417*. 01889 565211
Hopkins, D A (Hewitsons) *B1 O A3*
Northampton *p332*. 01604 233233
Hopkins, D M (Norwich Union Insurance Group)
Norwich *p467* 01603 622200
Hopkins, D S (Stokes Solicitors) *S1*
Portsmouth *p355*. 023 9282 8131
Hopkins, Mrs E M (Chattertons Solicitors) *S1 L E T1 C1 A1 S2*
Spalding *p389* 01775 768774
Hopkins, G R (Streeter Marshall) *E J1 K1 L N O S1 W*
Purley *p358* 020 8660 6455
Hopkins, I H (Avery Naylor) *G H Q*
Swansea *p404*. 01792 463276
Hopkins, Ms J (Lawson West Solicitors Limited) *K1*
Market Harborough *p312*. . . 01858 445480
Hopkins, Ms J (Howe & Spender) *K1 D1 D2*
Neath *p320* 01639 881571
Port Talbot *p353*. 01639 881571
Hopkins, J (Eastleys) *S1 W Zo Zv*
Brixham *p166* 01803 853266
Hopkins, J (Osborne Clarke) *R2*
London EC2 *p65*. 020 7105 7000
Hopkins, Miss J E (Wolverhampton City Council)
Wolverhampton *p477* 01902 556556
Hopkins, Miss K (Donns) *N*
Manchester *p303* 0161 834 3311
Hopkins, M (Birkett Long LLP) *J1 Zp J2 Zg*
Chelmsford *p186*. 01245 453800
Hopkins, M (Bovis Homes Ltd)
Cheadle Hulme *p454*. 0161 488 5000
Hopkins, M D (Pinsent Masons LLP) *Q Zc O*
Manchester *p308* 0161 234 8234
Hopkins, N (Needham Poulier & Partners) *G H Zm*
London N17 *p63*. 020 8808 6622
Hopkins, N (Linklaters LLP)
London EC2 *p54*. 020 7456 2000
Hopkins, P (Cowlishaw & Mountford)
Uttoxeter *p417*. 01889 565211
Hopkins, P A W (Mercers) *W T2 Zd A1*
Henley-on-Thames *p247*. . . 01491 572138
Hopkins, P M (Geldards LLP)
Cardiff *p178* 029 2023 8239
Hopkins, R A (David W Harris & Co) *D1 F1 G H J1 K1 L M1 N P*
Talbot Green *p407*. 01443 223265
Pontypridd *p352*. 01443 486666

Hopkins, S (The Wilkes Partnership LLP) *J1 J2*
Birmingham *p143* 0121 233 4333
Hopkins, S C (Holmes & Hills LLP) *R1 Zu P O Q*
Braintree *p155*. 01376 320456
Hopkins, Mrs S H (Crown Prosecution Service Dorset)
Bournemouth *p450*. 01202 498700
Hopkins, Ms W (DAC Beachcroft)
London EC3 *p24*. 020 7208 6800
Hopkinson, I R (MB Solicitors Ltd trading as MB Law) *N Q F1 J1 C1 O Zp Zj Zk J2*
Leeds *p275* 0113 242 4444
Hopkinson, M J (Platt Halpern) *G*
Manchester *p309* 0161 834 3114
Hopkinson, Ms S (Russell Jones & Walker)
London WC2 *p74* 020 7657 1555
Hopkirk, Ms R (Holman Fenwick Willan)
London EC3 *p42*. 020 7264 8000
Hopley, Ms E (High Peak Borough Council)
Chapel-en-le-Frith *p454* . . . 0845 129 7777
Hopley, G J (Churchers) *G H*
Portsmouth *p354*. 023 9286 2424
Hopley, Miss P K (Co-operative Insurance Society Ltd) *M1 N P*
Manchester *p464* 0161 832 8686
Hopley, R M (Edwards Angell Palmer & Dodge) *O Zj*
London EC2 *p28*. 020 7583 4055
Hopley, T M (QualitySolicitors Gruber Garratt) *G H B2 Zl Ze*
Oldham *p341* 0161 665 3502
Hoppe, J K (Gregory Rowcliffe Milners) *C1 C2 O*
London WC1 *p37* 020 7242 0631
Hopper, Ms C J (Allen & Overy LLP) *E L R1*
London E1 *p5* 020 3088 0000
Hopper, M J (Herbert Smith LLP)
London EC2 *p40*. 020 7374 8000
Hopton, Miss J A (Emsleys) *Q N*
Leeds *p273* 0113 232 1030
Hopwell, M (Cartwright King) *B2 J2 P F2*
Nottingham *p336*. 0115 958 7444
Hopwood, Miss E (Robinsons) *K1*
Derby *p209* 01332 291431
Hopwood, R M (Red Kite Law) *N O Q J1 L F1 Zj*
Carmarthen *p183* 01267 239000
Hopwood, S J (Pheby & Co) *Q K1 K3 D1*
York *p445* 01904 789900
Hoque, Ms M (Kent County Council)
Maidstone *p464* 01622 694320
Hoque, R (Bowling & Co) *E S2*
London E15 *p15*. 020 8221 8000
Hoquee, S (Ashurst LLP)
London EC2 *p7* 020 7638 1111
Horada, P D (Peter Horada) *E G J1 K1 L M1 N P S1 W*
London NW2 *p43* 020 8450 0737
Horan, D P (Moore Blatch Solicitors) *N*
Southampton *p386*. 023 8071 8000
Horbury, Miss C P (Wilkin Chapman Grange Solicitors) *E S2*
Louth *p294* 01507 606161
Horder, F G (Carter Bells LLP) *O K1 Q K3*
Kingston upon Thames *p267*. 020 8939 4000
Hore, Ms C (Bristows) *O Ze*
London EC4 *p15*. 020 7400 8000
Horevey, R A (BUPA)
London WC1 *p104*. 020 7656 2305
Horler, J R C (Dixon Ward) *Q N O L J1 B1 F1 C1 Zl*
Richmond upon Thames *p364* 020 8940 4051
Horley, N J (Buckinghamshire County Council) *K1*
Aylesbury *p448* 01296 383653
Horlock, P (Edward Hayes LLP) *E S1 S2*
Bognor Regis *p148* 01243 822655
Horman, Ms R (The Watson Ramsbottom Partnership)
Blackburn *p146* 01254 672222
Horn, A R (Hadaway & Hadaway) *D1 D2 N O Q J1*
North Shields *p330* 0191 257 0382
Horn, K B J (Warner Goodman LLP) *K1 K2 K3 D1 D2*
Portsmouth *p355*. 023 9275 3575
Horn, M A (Plainlaw LLP) *Q*
Oxford *p344*. 01865 240202
Horn, P J (Plainlaw LLP) *E S2*
Oxford *p344*. 01865 240202
Horn, Ms V M (Dawson Hart) *E*
Uckfield *p416* 01825 762281
Hornblow, D J (Jones Day) *Ze*
London EC4 *p46*. 020 7039 5959
Hornby, J H (Macfarlanes) *E S1 L A1 Zl*
London EC4 *p56*. 020 7831 9222
Hornby, J R (Clifford Chance)
London E14 *p20*. 020 7006 1000
Hornby, M D (Penmans) *E S1 W L C1 B1 F1 M1 P Zi*
Stanford-le-Hope *p394*. . . . 01375 677777
Hornby, Miss N (The Johnson Partnership) *G H V*
Nottingham *p337*. 0115 941 9141
Hornby, R W J (Lynch Hall & Hornby)
Harrow *p242*. 020 8864 0722
Hornby, Ms S F (Lynch Hall & Hornby)
Harrow *p242*. 020 8864 0722
Hornby, Mrs S G A (Hornby & Levy) *D1 D2 K1 X*
London SW9 *p43* 020 7737 0909
Horne, Ms A (Hill Dickinson LLP) *J2 N Q Zj Zm Zr*
London EC3 *p41*. 020 7283 9033
Horne, A D (Blanchards Bailey LLP) *S1 K1 L F1*
Blandford Forum *p147* . . . 01258 459361

Horne, A J (Bridge McFarland Haddon Owen) *S1 S2 W A1 E L*
Louth *p294* 01507 605883
Horne, B (Farleys Solicitors LLP) *G H B2*
Accrington *p114* 01254 367853
Horne, J H (Sylvester Amiel Lewin & Horne LLP) *B1 C1 E L O Q S1 F1 W Zb Ze Zh Zv*
London N12 *p85*. 020 8446 4000
Horne, Miss L J (Paris Smith LLP) *W*
Southampton *p386*. 023 8048 2482
Horne, Ms M L L (TV Edwards LLP) *K1 D1 K3*
London SE8 *p85*. 020 7790 7000
Horne, Ms N (Jeffrey Green Russell) *N Q*
London W1 *p46* 020 7339 7000
Horne, Mrs P (Henriques Griffiths) *E S1 W M1*
Winterbourne *p435*. 01454 854000
Horne, R (Trowers & Hamlins)
London EC3 *p88*. 020 7423 8000
Horne, Ms T (Lewis Silkin LLP)
London EC4 *p53*. 020 7074 8000
Horne, T H (Brumell & Sample) *S1 W*
Morpeth *p319* 01670 512336
Horner, B (Alliance Boots PLC) *J1*
Nottingham *p467*. 0115 950 6111
Horner, D J (Charles Russell LLP) *E P*
London EC4 *p19*. 020 7203 5000
Horner, Mrs D M (Ablehomes Ltd)
Newark *p466* 01636 611662
Horner, Miss F M (Bristol City Council)
Bristol *p451* 0117 922 2000
Horner, I P (Bradbury Roberts & Raby) *N J1 O Q F1*
Scunthorpe *p373*. 01724 854000
Horner, I R (Collyer Bristow LLP) *E S1 S2*
London WC1 *p22* 020 7242 7363
Horner, Miss K (Mills & Reeve) *J1*
Birmingham *p140* 0121 454 4000
Horner, M (Harrowells)
York *p444* 01904 690111
Horner, M B (Kellogg Brown & Root (UK) Ltd)
Leatherhead *p462* 01372 865000
Horner, M D (Linder Myers Solicitors) *N J2 Zq Zr Zw Zt Zj*
Manchester *p307* 0844 984 6400
Horner, N B (Whatley Weston & Fox) *B1 C1 T1 W J1 Zb Ze Zt*
Worcester *p440* 01905 731731
Horner, P (Irwin Mitchell LLP) *E S2*
Sheffield *p376* 0870 150 0100
Horner, P J (Langleys) *I S1 E C1 A1 T1*
Lincoln *p284*. 01522 888555
York *p445* 01904 610886
Hornigold, A S (Pinsent Masons LLP) *C2*
Birmingham *p141* 0121 200 1050
Hornsby, Ms A (Backhouse Jones Ltd) *O Q N*
Clitheroe *p196*. 01254 828300
Hornsby, A P (Hegarty LLP) *B1 Zc E C3 I Ze P J2 L N Q V Zr A3 O*
Peterborough *p347* 01733 346333
Hornsby, Mrs H (Wilkin Chapman LLP) *D1 K1 K3*
Grimsby *p235* 01472 262626
Hornsby-Cox, Ms B J (Belmont & Lowe) *W T2*
London EC1 *p11*. 020 7608 4600
Hornsey, P (Ward Hadaway) *O Zk Zq*
Newcastle upon Tyne *p327* . 0191 204 4000
Hornsey, Ms S (Walker Morris)
Leeds *p277* 0113 283 2500
Horovitz, Ms L S (Barlow Lyde & Gilbert LLP)
London EC3 *p10*. 020 7247 2277
Horowitz, Miss C (AMD Solicitors) *W K4*
Bristol *p160* 0117 962 1460
Horrell, Ms A M (Scott Fowler) *C1 E C2 J1*
Northampton *p331*. 01604 750506
Horridge, Ms J (SNR Denton) *Zb*
London EC4 *p75*. 020 7242 1212
Horridge, P D (Aubrey Isaacson Solicitors) *B1 D1 F1 G J1 K1 L M1 S1*
Prestwich *p357* 0161 959 5000
Horrocks, A J (Barlow Lyde & Gilbert LLP) *I Q O Zq Zj*
London EC3 *p10*. 020 7247 2277
Horrocks, Miss C L (Mills & Reeve) *J1 Zp T1 U2*
Cambridge *p175*. 01223 364422
Horrocks, Mrs N J (Burges Salmon) *P A1*
Bristol *p161* 0117 939 2000
Horrocks, S (Horrocks & Co) *E C1 L N O S1 B1 W J1 K1 Zj Zl*
Leeds *p274* 0113 230 7944
Horsewood, Mrs H J (DWF) *N*
Liverpool *p287*. 0151 907 3000
Horsey, Miss C M (Thornleys Limited) *K1 D1 V*
Plymouth *p350*. 01752 406977
Horsey, G A (Horsey Lightly) *S1 S2 E*
Newbury *p322*. 01635 580858
Horsey, J S N J (Horsey Lightly) *E R2 S2*
Newbury *p322*. 01635 580858
Horsey, R D (Ashfords LLP) *L O Zq*
Exeter *p220* 01392 337000
Horsey, Mrs T P (Horsey Lightly) *K1*
Newbury *p322*. 01635 580858
Horsfall, P (DWF) *Ze C1 U2 I F2 F1*
Manchester *p303* 0161 603 5000
Horsfall, R J C (Lee & Thompson)
London W1 *p52* 020 7935 4665
Horsfield, C P (Macfarlanes) *E S1*
London EC4 *p56*. 020 7831 9222
Horsler, Mrs P A (Fareham Borough Council)
Fareham *p458*. 01329 236100
Horsley, Ms K E (Greenwoods Solicitors LLP) *S2 E R2*
Peterborough *p347* 01733 887700

Horsley, P C (Rees Page) *S1 L R1 E W C1 Zl S2*
Bilston *p133*. 01902 577776
Horsley, S F (TBI Solicitors)
Hartlepool *p243* . . . 0800 052 6824 / 01429 264101
Horsman, A (Horsman Solicitors Ltd) *H G V Q Zl*
Lewes *p283* 01273 474743
Horsnell, C L (Volks Hedleys) *B1 C1 E F1 G J1 K1 L M1 N Zo Zs*
Kensington & Chelsea *p89*. . 020 7584 6733
Horspool, Miss V (Zermansky & Partners) *D1 K1 K3*
Leeds *p278* 0113 245 9766
Horstman, J J (Palmers Solicitors) *W K4 T2 Zm Zd*
Kingston upon Thames *p267*. 020 8549 7444
Horth, R A (Richard Horth) *S1 K1 M1 P W G H D1 J1*
Brackley *p153* 01280 703773
Horton, B M (Marrons) *E J1 S1 S2 R2 L*
Leicester *p280*. 0116 289 2200
Horton, Ms C (John Pickering & Partners LLP) *Zr*
Halifax *p238* 0808 144 0959
Horton, Mrs D (HSBC Legal Department)
Birmingham *p449* 0121 455 2740
Horton, Ms J A (Irwin Mitchell LLP) *N Zr*
Leeds *p274* 0870 150 0100
Horton, Miss J G (Dicksons Solicitors Ltd) *K1 W V D1 K3*
Stoke-on-Trent *p397*. 01782 262424
Horton, J M (Brachers) *Q N O*
Maidstone *p299* 01622 690691
Horton, N J (Hatch Brenner) *C1*
Norwich *p334* 01603 660811
Horton, N J (Thomson Snell & Passmore) *Zq O Q B1 F1 J2 P C3 R1*
Tunbridge Wells *p415* 01892 510000
Horton, P J (FBC Manby Bowdler LLP) *N Q O*
Telford *p409*. 01952 292129
Horton, P J (Hague Lambert) *C1 E S2 P X Zd Zx*
Manchester *p305* 0161 834 6066
Horton, R J (Barnes Marsland) *C1 S2 E*
Margate *p312* 01843 221466
Horton, R J (Horton & Moss) *K1 F1 N J1 L R1 D1 Zl S1*
Ilkeston *p261* . . 0115 932 1431 / 930 8208
Horton, Ms T B (Alexander JLO)
London E14 *p5* 020 7537 7000
Horton, T M (Thomas Horton LLP) *S1 E L W R1*
Bromsgrove *p167* 01527 871641
Horton, Mrs V J (Cheshire East Council)
Sandbach *p464* 0300 123 5500
Horwich, A S (Symes Bains Broomer) *N L*
Scunthorpe *p373*. 01724 281616
Horwich, D J (Horwich Cohen Coghlan) *N*
London EC4 *p43*. 020 7332 2230
Manchester *p305* 0161 830 4600
Horwood, M G (Ford Simey LLP) *K1 T1 G M1 D1 H J1 S1 C1 F1 Zl Zk*
Sidmouth *p380*. . .01395 577061 / 0800 169 3741
Horwood, M S (Foot Anstey) *R1*
Plymouth *p349*. 01752 675000
Horwood, R M (Longmores) *Zd T2 W K4 T1*
Hertford *p248* 01992 300333
Horwood, Miss S E (J A Hughes) *K1 D1 M1 F1 P*
Cardiff *p179* 029 2061 9700
Horwood-Smart, A P (Taylor Vinters) *A1 E*
Cambridge *p176*. 01223 423444
Hosford, D J (Pitmans LLP) *Zo*
Reading *p361* 0118 958 0224
Hosie, J P (Squire Sanders (UK) LLP) *A3 O R2 U2 Zc Zn Zq*
London EC2 *p81*. 020 7655 1000
Hosken, Mrs S J (Winterbotham Smith Penley LLP) *K3 K1*
Dursley *p214* 01453 541940
Hosker, D P (United Utilities)
Warrington *p475*. 01925 237000
Hosker, J (Shrewsbury and Atcham Borough Council)
Shrewsbury *p471* 01743 281000
Hosker, P J (Peel Management Limited)
Manchester *p465* 0161 629 8200
Hoskin, Miss J S (Pinsent Masons LLP) *T2*
Leeds *p276* 0113 244 5000
Hoskin, Ms L (FBC Manby Bowdler LLP) *N*
Wolverhampton *p437* 01902 578000
Hoskin, T C (Thurstan Hoskin Solicitors) *C1 S2 E W S1*
Redruth *p363* 01209 213646
Hosking, A L (Leeds City Council)
Leeds *p462* 0113 224 3513
Hosking, Miss D B D (Bath & North East Somerset Council)
Bath *p462* 01225 394041
Hosking, Miss D J C (Stone King LLP) *N*
Bath *p128* 01225 337599
Hosking, Ms H (John Boyle & Co)
Truro *p414*. 01872 272356
Hosking, Ms H A (John Boyle & Co) *S1 K1 S2 W*
Truro *p414*. 01872 272356
Hosking, Mrs J L (Cornwall County Council) *D1 G H K1 N Q Zl*
Truro *p474*. 01872 322197
Hoskins, Mrs C (Dolmans) *J2 Zj Q N Zq Zw Zu*
Cardiff *p178* 029 2034 5531
Hoskins, C P (Andrew & Co LLP) *P M1 N J1 C1 G L E A1 S1 Zc Zd Zl*
Lincoln *p284*. 01522 512123
Hoskins, J P (Bevan Brittan LLP) *J1 Zp*
Bristol *p161* 0870 194 1000

See p634 for the Key to Work Categories

Hoskins, J R (Simmonds Hurford) *S1 W*
Swansea *p405* . . . 01792 462729 / 641070

Hoskinson, Ms J (Maclachlan) *S1 A1 E R2 S2 W*
Sherborne *p378* . . . 01935 817736

Hostick, Ms K (Kingsley Napley) *J1*
London EC1 *p50* . . . 020 7814 1200

Hotchin, Mrs S L (Royal College Of Nursing)
Leeds *p463* . . . 0113 244 3648

Hotchkiss, G N (Hotchkiss Warburton) *A1 G E L R2 S1 S2 W*
Crediton *p203* . . . 01363 774752

Hothersall, Ms G L (Dowson Billington) *W K4 S1 S2*
Preston *p356* . . . 01772 556807

Hothersall, N (Herrington & Carmichael LLP) *C1 C2 F1 C3 U2 Ze Zf I U1 Zza Zb*
Camberley *p173* . . . 01276 686222
Guildford *p236* . . . 01483 407000

Hothi, Miss B (Wannop Fox Staffurth & Bray) *S2 E I F1 F2 Ze Zza U2 J1*
Worthing *p442* . . . 01903 228200

Hothi, Y S (Simon & Co) *Q O L K1 F1 W B1 Zq N*
Southall *p384* . . . 020 8571 3883

Hotson, G J (Ross Solicitors Ltd) *G H*
Swindon *p406* . . . 01793 512960

Hotson, Ms L (Humphreys & Co)
Bristol *p163* . . . 0117 929 2662

Hotten, Mrs H L (Howell-Jones LLP) *W*
Kingston upon Thames *p267*. 020 8549 5186
Leatherhead *p271* . . . 01372 860650

Hough, Miss G (Norwich Union Life)
York *p477* . . . 01904 452210

Hough, R (Brabners Chaffe Street) *Ze C1 F1 Zza U2 F2*
Liverpool *p286* . . . 0151 600 3000

Hough, R I (Allen & Overy LLP)
London E1 *p5* . . . 020 3088 0000

Houghton, Ms A (Galbraith Branley) *G H B2*
London N12 *p34* . . . 020 8446 8474

Houghton, A L (Hill Dickinson LLP) *E M1 B1 C1 D1 L G H J1*
Liverpool *p288* . . . 0151 600 8000

Houghton, C E R (Moore & Tibbits) *C1 E G K1 S1 S2 N H D1 C2 Zd Zr*
Warwick *p422* . . . 01926 491181

Houghton, Ms C J (Farrell Matthews & Weir) *D1 K1*
London W6 *p30* . . . 020 8746 3771

Houghton, D (Parkinson Wright LLP) *K1 H P N M1 L G F1 D1 V Zb Zc Zl*
Droitwich *p213* . . . 01905 775533

Houghton, D M (HBOS PLC)
Halifax *p460* . . . 0870 600 5000

Houghton, D M (Freeth Cartwright LLP) *I U2 Zza Ze*
Nottingham *p337* . . . 0115 936 9369

Houghton, Mrs F (Squire Sanders (UK) LLP)
Manchester *p310* . . . 0161 830 5000

Houghton, H F (Ranson Houghton) *S1 S2 W*
Salisbury *p371* . . . 01722 328871

Houghton, I (W H Smith PLC) *O Q*
London W1 *p110* . . . 020 7851 8809

Houghton, J (Simmons & Simmons) *B1 C1 Zb*
London EC2 *p79* . . . 020 7628 2020

Houghton, J A C (Monro Fisher Wasbrough LLP) *Zd*
London WC1 *p61* . . . 020 7404 7001

Houghton, J E R (Bond Pearce LLP) *E P R1*
Bristol *p161* . . . 0845 415 0000

Houghton, J M (Austins Penny & Thorne) *W E K4*
Berkhamsted *p131* . . . 01442 872141

Houghton, Miss L M (Royal College Of Nursing)
Leeds *p463* . . . 0113 244 3648

Houghton, Miss L M (Douglas Clift & Co) *K1 K3 D1*
Lancaster *p269* . . . 01524 32437

Houghton, Miss M I (Atherton Godfrey) *N*
Doncaster *p211* . . . 01302 320621

Houghton, Miss R (Canter Levin & Berg) *N Q*
St Helens *p391* . . . 01744 634141

Houghton, Ms R A (Pepperells) *D2 D1 K1 K2 Zk Zo R2 Zq*
Scunthorpe *p373* . . . 01724 871999

Houghton, Miss S E (Houghton Pigot & Co) *C1 F1 K1 L R1 S1 T1 T2 W K3 K4*
Ashton-in-Makerfield *p119* . . 01942 270757
Wigan *p432* . . . 01942 241288 / 824424

Houghton, S P (Lupton Fawcett) *O Zj Zc Zk Zq A3*
Leeds *p275* . . . 0113 280 2000

Hougie, A M (Dechert) *Zv*
London EC4 *p26* . . . 020 7184 7000

Houlden, P C (Grimsby Magistrates Court)
Grimsby *p459* . . . 01472 320444

Houlder, N R (Irena Spence) *D1 K1 N O Q*
Cambridge *p175* . . . 01223 713300

Houldsworth, J H (Houldsworths) *P G K1 S1 C1 W E A1 V L Zd Zi Zl*
Clitheroe *p196* . . . 01254 825757

Houlker, R B (Nightingales Solicitors Limited) *E C1 L P S1 M1 N G H*
Stockport *p396* . . . 01663 764038

Houlston-Hope, J T (Clark Holt)
Swindon *p406* . . . 01793 617444

Hoult, J C (Gamlins) *K1 L J1 K3 O Q*
Rhyl *p363* . . . 01745 343500

Hoult, J F (John Hoult & Co) *S1 K1 A1 D1 L S2 W E K3*
Scunthorpe *p373* . . . 01724 281312

Houltby, R M (Wilkin Chapman Grange Solicitors) *A1 K1 N Q S1 S2*
Alford *p115* . . . 01507 466767

Houltby, R W B (Wilkin Chapman Grange Solicitors) *S1 S2 W*
Grimsby *p235* . . . 01472 262626
Sutton-on-Sea *p404* . . . 01507 440400

Houlton Jones, P (Houlton Carr)
Bridlington *p158* . . . 01262 677979

Hounsell, Mrs S M (Dorset County Council) *Q K1 N*
Dorchester *p457* . . . 01305 251000

Hounslow, J H R (Wilks Price Hounslow) *K1 M1 N G H F1 P D1 J1 Zl*
Ryde *p369* . . . 01983 566241

Hounsome, Miss V R (Warner Goodman LLP) *W*
Fareham *p224* . . . 01329 288121

Hourihan, Ms N (Boodle Hatfield)
Westminster *p14* . . . 020 7629 7411

Hourmouzios, P T (Slater Bradley & Co) *E L R1 S1 W S2*
Wandsworth *p80* . . . 020 8788 1008

Housby, Ms C A (CVS Solicitors) *O Q Zj K1 J1 L R1 Zq*
London W1 *p17* . . . 020 7493 2903

Housden, Mrs L (Machins Solicitors LLP) *Zl S1*
Luton *p295* . . . 01582 514000

House, H G M D (TWM Solicitors LLP) *E S1 C1 Zc S2*
Guildford *p237* . . . 01483 752700

House, M D J (Advance Legal) *N S1 Zr J1 Zp*
Burton-on-Trent *p170* . . . 01283 544492

House, Miss R (Herrington & Carmichael LLP) *K1 S1 N*
Camberley *p173* . . . 01276 686222

House, R M (Mitsubishi Securities International PLC) *C1 N B1 J1 F1 E T1 P Zf Ze Zl*
London EC2 *p108* . . . 020 7577 2804

House, T J (Allen & Overy LLP) *O Q B1 Zb Zj Zk*
London E1 *p5* . . . 020 3088 0000

Housego, P S L (Beers LLP) *O E S1 J1 A1 W C1 K1 F1 Zl*
Kingsbridge *p267* . . . 01548 857000

Housego, Ms S E (Borough of Poole)
Poole *p469* . . . 01202 262808

Houshmand, Mrs J L (Calderdale Metropolitan BC Corporate Services Directorate)
Halifax *p460* . . . 01422 357257

Housley, K (Brabners Chaffe Street) *E*
Liverpool *p286* . . . 0151 600 3000

Houston, Miss A E (Whitehead Monckton) *K4 W*
Tenterden *p410* . . . 01580 765722

Houston, Ms A M (Henmans LLP) *W T2 Zd*
Oxford *p343* . . . 01865 781000

Houston, Ms A M (Challinors)
Birmingham *p136* . . . 0121 212 9393

Houston, J A (Gosschalks) *S2 E*
Hull *p256* . . . 01482 324252

Houston, Ms K (Turners Solicitors LLP) *E S1 S2*
Bournemouth *p153* . . . 01202 291291

Houston, S (Addleshaw Goddard) *C1 C2*
Manchester *p300* . . . 0161 934 6000

Houston, W P (Field Fisher Waterhouse LLP) *E L S1*
London EC3 *p31* . . . 020 7861 4000

Hovell, M A (George Davies Solicitors LLP) *B1 C1 C2 E O I Zw Zb Ze*
Manchester *p303* . . . 0161 236 8992

Hovil, Miss S E (Portrait Solicitors) *W T2*
London WC2 *p69* . . . 020 7092 6990

Howard, A (Coles Miller Solicitors LLP) *E C1 L Zd*
Bournemouth *p151* . . . 01202 293226

Howard, Mrs A (Gurney-Champion & Co) *S1 W S2 E L F1*
Portsmouth *p354* . . . 023 9282 1100

Howard, A J P (Robertsons) *D1 F1 G H J1 K1 L M1 P*
York *p445* . . . 01904 658551

Howard, Ms A K (Nabarro LLP)
London WC1 *p63* . . . 020 7524 6000

Howard, B (Trowers & Hamlins)
London EC3 *p88* . . . 020 7423 8000

Howard, B K (Russells) *O Q Zf Ze*
London W1 *p75* . . . 020 7439 8692

Howard, B R (Howard & Company) *C1 J1 S1 Zl*
Westminster *p43* . . . 020 7486 6610

Howard, Ms C (Taylor Wessing)
London EC4 *p86* . . . 020 7300 7000

Howard, Miss C (Watson Farley & Williams) *C1 C2*
London EC2 *p90* . . . 020 7814 8000

Howard, C (Trowers & Hamlins)
London EC3 *p88* . . . 020 7423 8000

Howard, Mrs C (Blake Lapthorn) *N*
Chandlers Ford *p184* . . . 023 8090 8090

Howard, C J (W H Matthews & Co) *S1 Zc S2 E R2 C1*
Kingston upon Thames *p267*. 020 8549 0264

Howard, C P (Russell Jones & Walker) *J1 Zp Ze*
London WC2 *p74* . . . 020 7657 1555

Howard, Ms C R (Mills & Reeve)
Norwich *p335* . . . 01603 660155

Howard, C R (Clifford Howard & Co) *G N Q Zt*
Okehampton *p340* . . . 01837 861455

Howard, D (Taylor Wessing)
London EC4 *p86* . . . 020 7300 7000

Howard, D C (Robert Barber & Sons) *S1 S2 E W*
Hucknall *p255* . . . 0115 955 2299
Nottingham *p335* . . . 0115 878 9000

Howard, D R (HRJ Law LLP) *E C1 Zh S2*
Hitchin *p251* . . . 01462 628888

Howard, D S (Black Norman) *B1 C1 C2 E S1 S2*
Crosby *p203* . . . 0151 931 2777

Howard, F (Frank Howard) *S1 G H J1 C1 E W*
Warrington *p422* . . . 01925 653481

Howard, Ms F A (Ginn & Co) *E S1 S2 C1*
Cambridge *p174* . . . 01223 358275

Howard, Mrs F M (Fiona M Howard) *S1 W E L C1*
London NW1 *p43* . . . 020 7482 2705

Howard, Ms H P (The Howard Partnership Limited) *A3 K1 K2*
Aylesbury *p121* . . . 01296 770372
London WC2 *p43* . . . 020 7831 4511

Howard, I (JMP Solicitors)
Grantham *p232* . . . 01476 568100

Howard, I P R (Forbes) *N Q Zj*
Blackburn *p145* . . . 01254 662831

Howard, Ms J (Reynolds Porter Chamberlain LLP)
London E1 *p71* . . . 020 3060 6000

Howard, J A (Ashworths Solicitors) *S1 S2*
London SW19 *p8* . . . 0845 370 1000

Howard, Ms J A (Howard Kennedy LLP) *E*
London W1 *p48* . . . 020 7636 1616

Howard, Mrs J E (Simmons & Simmons)
London EC2 *p79* . . . 020 7628 2020

Howard, J F (Macfarlanes) *C1*
London EC4 *p56* . . . 020 7831 9222

Howard, J H (IBB Solicitors) *L Zh S1 E S2*
Chesham *p189* . . . 0845 638 1381

Howard, Ms J N (Hinckley and Rugby Building Society)
Hinckley *p461* . . . 01455 894026

Howard, Ms K P (Brighouses) *J1 N O Q*
Southport *p388* . . 01704 534101 / 500151

Howard, L (Ince & Co Services Ltd)
London E1 *p44* . . . 020 7481 0010

Howard, M (Michelmores LLP) *Zj Q P R1*
Exeter *p221* . . . 01392 688688

Howard, M G (Pictons Solicitors LLP) *K1 D1 V*
Milton Keynes *p317* . . . 01908 663511

Howard, M J (Barlow Lyde & Gilbert LLP) *J1*
London EC3 *p10* . . . 020 7247 2277

Howard, N E (DLA Piper UK LLP) *E R1*
Sheffield *p375* . . . 0870 011 1111

Howard, N G (Kirwans) *G H*
Birkenhead *p134* . . . 0151 608 9078

Howard, Ms P (Salans) *O B1 Q*
London EC4 *p76* . . . 020 7429 6000

Howard, P (Penningtons) *E*
London EC2 *p66* . . . 020 7457 3000

Howard, P (Philip & Robert Howard) *G H D1 K1 M1 P N F1 J1 V Zl Zs Zt*
Barnsley *p124* . . . 01226 780840

Howard, P E (Taylor Wimpey UK Ltd)
Cannock *p453* . . . 01543 496766

Howard, P G (Howard & Co) *G H*
Barnsley *p124* . . . 01226 215215

Howard, R (Philip & Robert Howard) *G H K1 D1 J1 M1 L*
Castleford *p183* . . . 01977 551320

Howard, R G (Robert Howard) *N Zj Q*
Plymouth *p350* . . . 01752 251851

Howard, R G (Gill Akaster) *S1 S2 E*
Plymouth *p349* . . . 01752 203500

Howard, R J (Environment Agency (North East Region))
Leeds *p462* . . . 0870 850 6506

Howard, R M (Grahame Stowe Bateson) *D1 D2 G H*
Leeds *p274* . . . 0113 255 8666

Howard, R V (The Howard Partnership Limited) *C1 C2 E J1 Ze Zf Zk M1 R2 S2 T1 Zn Zz*
Aylesbury *p121* . . . 01296 770372
London WC2 *p43* . . . 020 7831 4511

Howard, S (Black Rock)
London EC4 *p104* . . . 020 7743 3000

Howard, Mrs S A (Robertsons) *G H K1 S1 P F1*
York *p445* . . . 01904 658551

Howard, S D (Treasury Solicitors Department)
London WC2 *p110* . . . 020 7210 3000

Howard, Ms S D (Allen & Overy LLP)
London E1 *p5* . . . 020 3088 0000

Howard, Miss S L (City of Bradford Metropolitan District Council)
Bradford *p451* . . . 01274 752236

Howard, S W C (Goughs) *E S1 C1 L A1 R1 Ze*
Chippenham *p193* . . . 01249 444499

Howard, W A (Reed Smith LLP) *O*
London EC2 *p71* . . . 020 3116 3000

Howard, W I (Shoosmiths)
Milton Keynes *p317* . 0370 086 8300 / 01908 488300

Howard-Smith, Ms C (Michelmores LLP) *E R2 S2*
Exeter *p221* . . . 01392 688688

Howard-Smith, G L (Morgan & Lamplugh) *S1 W L E A1*
Hastings *p243* . . . 01424 721821

Howarth, A (Terry Jones Solicitors & Advocates) *Zm K1*
Shrewsbury *p379* . . . 01743 285888

Howarth, C B P (Herbert Smith LLP)
London EC2 *p40* . . . 020 7374 8000

Howarth, C M (Gordons LLP)
Leeds *p273* . . . 0113 227 0100

Howarth, D J (Painters) *P H J1 G C1 Zq Zr N*
Stourport-on-Severn *p399* . . 01299 822033

Howarth, Ms J (Howarth Scott) *L J1 K1*
Bexleyheath *p132* . . . 020 8303 4658

Howarth, J (Plexus Law (A Trading Name of Parabis Law LLP)) *Zj Zr Zq*
London EC3 *p68* . . . 0844 245 4000

Howarth, J (County of Herefordshire District Council) *G*
Hereford *p460* . . . 01432 260266

Howarth, J (Herefordshire Council)
Hereford *p460* . . . 01432 260000

Howarth, Ms K (Reynolds Porter Chamberlain LLP)
London E1 *p71* . . . 020 3060 6000

Howarth, M H (Paris Smith LLP) *A1 E R2 S1 S2*
Southampton *p386* . . . 023 8048 2482

Howarth, N (Forshaws Davies Ridgway LLP) *J1 P J2 Q N Zm*
Warrington *p422* . . . 01925 230000

Howarth, N G (Howarth & Co)
Wetherby *p429* . . . 01937 584020

Howarth, P (Foot Anstey) *J1*
Plymouth *p349* . . . 01752 675000

Howarth, Ms R I (Land Law LLP) *E S2*
Altrincham *p116* . . . 0161 928 8383

Howarth, Ms S (Howarth Scott) *D1 J1 K1*
Bexleyheath *p132* . . . 020 8303 4658

Howarth, Mrs S (Susan Howarth & Co) *K1 N S1 D1 Q V*
Northwich *p333* . . . 01606 48777

Howarth, Mrs S M (Stone King LLP) *E*
Bath *p128* . . . 01225 337599

Howarth, T (Keoghs LLP) *N J2 Zj O Q A3 B2*
Bolton *p149* . . . 01204 677000
Coventry *p200* . . . 024 7665 8200

Howarth, T C (Davis Gregory Ltd) *N Q*
Cheltenham *p188* . . . 01242 235202

Howat, Ms A (Terrells LLP) *E S1 S2 W*
Peterborough *p347* . . . 01733 896789

Howcroft, S (Greenwoods) *N*
London EC3 *p37* . . . 020 7220 7818

Howd, Mrs K (John Donkin & Co) *K1 S1 W*
Gateshead *p228*. 0191 495 2896 / 477 1781

Howden, P D (Morley Brown & Co) *E S1 C1 L W A1 S2 T2 T1 Zc*
Boston *p151* . . . 01205 364986

Howdle, Mrs N J (Ansons LLP) *V W*
Lichfield *p284* . . . 01543 263456

Howe, A (William Sturges & Co) *T2 W*
Westminster *p84* . . . 020 7873 1000

Howe, D F (Goody Burrett LLP) *S1 S2 L E A1*
Colchester *p197* . . . 01206 577676
Colchester *p197* . . . 01206 577676

Howe, D L (Michelmores LLP) *E R2 S2*
Exeter *p221* . . . 01392 688688

Howe, Ms E (Challinors) *K1*
Birmingham *p136* . . . 0121 212 9393

Howe, I T (John B Cordingley & Co) *S1*
Bradford *p153* . . . 01274 736646

Howe, Miss J A (Vanderpump & Sykes) *L Q*
Enfield *p219* . . . 020 8367 3999

Howe, J B (John Howe & Co) *G D1 H K1 N O Q S1 E W Zi Zv*
Pudsey *p358* . . . 0113 236 3936

Howe, J E (The Howe Practice) *S1 E W*
Stockport *p395* . . . 0161 480 2629

Howe, J P (Lester Aldridge LLP) *E C1 L A1 Zc*
Bournemouth *p152* . . . 01202 786161

Howe, Ms L A (TBI Solicitors) *K1*
Hartlepool *p243* . . . 0800 052 6824 / 01429 264101

Howe, M D (Bevan Brittan LLP) *Zc Zq*
Bristol *p161* . . . 0870 194 1000

Howe, M J (Howe & Co) *P N M1 F1 J1 Zc Ze Zj*
Ealing *p43* . . . 020 8840 4688

Howe, Miss N (Dickinson Dees) *J1 Zza Zp*
York *p444* . . . 0844 984 1500

Howe, Mrs N J (Farnfield & Nicholls) *K1 D1*
Gillingham *p229* . . . 01747 825432

Howe, P D (Hart Brown Solicitors) *S1*
Cobham *p196* . . . 0800 068 8177

Howe, R A (Peter Lynn & Partners)
Swansea *p405* . . . 01792 450010

Howe, R S (Cameron Jones Hussell & Howe) *L S1 W E F1 S2 K4*
Port Talbot *p353* . . . 01639 885261

Howe, Mrs S J (Muckle LLP) *O A3*
Newcastle upon Tyne *p325* . . 0191 211 7777

Howe, T (Davitt Jones Bould) *E S2 P R2*
Taunton *p408* . . . 01823 279279

Howell, A V (Barlow Lyde & Gilbert LLP) *A3 F1 O Q Zj*
London EC3 *p10* . . . 020 7247 2277

Howell, D (John Fowlers LLP Solicitors)
Brightlingsea *p159* . . . 01206 302694

Howell, F N (Howell Hylton) *G H*
Camborne *p173* . . . 01209 613014

Howell, G (Charles Russell LLP) *K1*
London EC4 *p19* . . . 020 7203 5000

Howell, J W (Kitsons LLP) *K3 K1 K2*
Newton Abbot *p329* . . . 01626 203366

Howell, Ms K (Geldards LLP) *J1*
Cardiff *p178* . . . 029 2023 8239

Howell, Mrs M E (Lawson Coppock & Hart) *S1 S2 R2*
Manchester *p306* . . . 0161 832 5944

Howell, Mrs P (Marks & Spencer PLC)
London W2 *p107* . . . 020 7935 4422

Howell, P G (John Howe & Co) *S1 K1 M1 G H C1 N P E*
Pudsey *p358* . . . 0113 236 3936

Howell, P J (Addleshaw Goddard) *T2*
Leeds *p271* . . . 0113 209 2000
Manchester *p300* . . . 0161 934 6000

Howell, P J (Howells) *S1 E L*
Cardiff *p178* . . . 029 2040 4020

Howell, Miss R (Beale and Company Solicitors LLP) *Zj O Zq*
London WC2 *p11* . . . 020 7240 3474

Howell, R J (Clifford Chance)
London E14 *p20* . . . 020 7006 1000

Howell, R O (Barcan Woodward) *D1 K1 K2*
Bristol *p161* . . . 0117 923 2141

Howell, S G (Graham Evans & Partners) *G H K1 N W D1 F1 Zl*
Swansea *p405* 01792 655822
Howell, Ms S J (Brindley Twist Tafft & James) *E S1*
Coventry *p200* 024 7653 1532
Howell, S P J (Cumberland Ellis Peirs) *E Zd L X*
London WC1 *p23* 020 7242 0422
Howell-Pryce, J B (Richard Wilson Solicitors Ltd) *S1 C1 L N Zl*
Goring *p231* 01491 879100
Howell-Richardson, D I (Stones Solicitors LLP)
Exeter *p222* 01392 666777
Howells, C (Marchant Harries & Co) *C1 L T2 W S1 E A1*
Aberdare *p113* 01685 885500
Howells, D A (DAS Legal Expenses Insurance & Co Ltd)
Bristol *p451* 0117 934 2000
Howells, Mrs E (Manchester City Council)
Manchester *p465* 0161 234 5000
Howells, I (Dootsons LLP) *K1 K3 S1*
Culcheth *p205* 01925 765212
Howells, Mrs L J (Morgans) *K3 K1 D2*
Cardiff *p180* 029 2072 9888
Howells, P M (Lloyds TSB Group PLC)
Bristol *p452* 0117 905 5500
Howells, P W F (Howells Williams) *S1 K1 W D1 G B1 H Zl Zm N R1 X F1 F2 J1*
Shrewsbury *p379* 01743 241429
Telford *p409* 01952 582631
Howells, Mrs R (The Rank Group PLC) *J1*
Maidenhead *p464* 01628 504000
Howells, Mrs R (Wendy Hopkins Family Law Practice LLP) *K1 D1 D2 K3*
Cardiff *p178* 029 2034 2233
Howells, R (JMD Law Limited) *S1 E R1 L*
Cardiff *p179* 029 2045 6780
Howells, S J (Evans & Ellis) *K1 S1 P M1 W F1 J1 L Zl S2*
Chepstow *p189* 01291 622814
Howells, T (Ashfords LLP) *A1 O Q*
Tiverton *p412* 01884 203000
Howels, B M (Michelmores LLP) *M1 R2 C3*
Exeter *p221* 01392 688688
Howes, Miss C L (Streeter Marshall) *W*
Croydon *p205* 020 8680 2638
Howes, C M (Harbottle & Lewis LLP) *C1 J1 I B1 Zf Zd Zv*
London W1 *p38* 020 7667 5000
Howes, G R (Fasken Martineau LLP) *C1 C3 I Ze Zf*
London W1 *p31* 020 7917 8500
Howes, J (Pinsent Masons LLP)
London EC2 *p67* 020 7418 7000
Howes, J J Q (Cornfield Law)
Eastbourne *p215* 01323 412512
Howes, Mrs L (Wilkin Chapman Epton Blades) *W T1 T2*
Lincoln *p285* 01522 512345
Howes, L (Hamers Solicitors) *J1*
Hull *p257* 01482 326666
Howes, N (Mills & Reeve) *Zq Zj N*
London EC3 *p61* 020 7648 9220
Leeds *p277* 0113 283 2500
Howes, Miss S (Crutes) *N L G*
Stockton-on-Tees *p396* 01642 623400
Howes, T D (West Somerset District Council)
Williton *p476* 01643 703704
Howick, P N (Stephenson Harwood) *O Zj A3*
London EC2 *p82* 020 7329 4422
Howie, D I (Barlow Lyde & Gilbert LLP) *C1 Zj*
London EC3 *p10* 020 7247 2277
Howie, Ms M (Herbert Smith LLP) *R2*
London EC2 *p40* 020 7374 8000
Howitt, Miss R (Langleys)
York *p445* 01904 610886
Howkins, Miss C L (Rich & Carr Freer Bouskell) *K3 K1*
Leicester *p281* 0116 253 8021
Howland, Mrs A (Massers) *K1 K3*
Nottingham *p338* 0115 851 1666
Howland, Mrs L G (Knights Solicitors LLP) *W K4 T2*
Newcastle under Lyme *p323* 01782 619225
Howland, P J (Beswicks) *G H Zl*
Hanley *p239* 01782 205000
Howle, Ms R (Beswicks) *E S1*
Stoke-on-Trent *p397* 01782 205000
Howles, Ms K A (Clifford Chance)
London E14 *p20* 020 7006 1000
Howlett, Mrs A J (Pannone LLP) *C1 F1 Zu*
Manchester *p308* 0161 909 3000
Howlett, I (Blake Lapthorn) *E*
Chandlers Ford *p184* 023 8090 8090
Howlett, N M (Harris & Harris) *J1 O Q C1 F1 F2 Zq Ze*
Frome *p228* 01373 463366
Howlett, P L (Aviva PLC)
London EC3 *p103* 020 7283 7500 / 01603 687905
Norwich *p467* 01603 622200
Howlett, R (Menneer Shuttleworth) *S2 E*
St Leonards-on-Sea *p392* 01424 720044
Howlett, Mrs S M (McGrigors LLP) *J1 Zi C2 Zp*
London EC4 *p56* 020 7054 2500
Howley, Ms V (Lees Solicitors LLP) *Q J1 O*
Birkenhead *p134* 0151 647 9381
Howliston, R (Hayes & Storr) *W K4*
King's Lynn *p266* 01553 778900
Howman, M T (Howman & Co) *S1*
Ruislip *p369* 01895 621777
Howorth, A J R (Footner & Ewing) *S1 S2 E W*
Romsey *p366* 01794 512345
Howorth, B N (Hay & Kilner) *N F1 O Q*
Newcastle upon Tyne *p325* 0191 232 8345
Howorth, C R A (George Davies Solicitors LLP) *Zr Zm*
Manchester *p303* 0161 236 8992
Howorth, N W (Clifford Chance)
London E14 *p20* 020 7006 1000
Howorth, T R (Charles Crookes Limited) *N Q O*
Cardiff *p178* 029 2049 1271
Howson, Mrs A (Neasham Lloyd) *W*
Bicester *p132* 01869 252161
Howson, A (Ashfords LLP) *Zb E*
Exeter *p220* 01392 337000
Hoy, Ms B (Garside & Hoy) *K1 L N Q D1*
Wealdstone *p424* 020 8427 5656
Hoy, Mrs J A (Blocks)
Ipswich *p262* 01473 230033
Hoy, Ms R (DLA Piper UK LLP)
London EC2 *p24* 0870 011 1111
Hoy, T P (DWF) *Zj N Q*
Liverpool *p287* 0151 907 3000
Hoyes, D M (Hill Dickinson LLP) *O Za Zj*
London EC3 *p41* 020 7283 9033
Hoyland, W H M (Pennine Law) *C1 E C2 N O S2 Ze*
Sheffield *p377* 01226 763551
Hoyle, Miss A (John Lewis plc)
London SW1 *p107* 020 7828 1000
Hoyle, C J (Christopher Hoyle & Co) *Q K1 S1 W N E G D1 L O Zl Zi Zo Ze Zm*
Kendal *p264* 01539 822078
Hoyle, Miss J B (Palmers Solicitors) *S1*
Kingston upon Thames *p267* 020 8549 7444
Hoyle, N R (Brooke North LLP)
Leeds *p272* 0113 283 2100
Hoyle, Miss S J (Parry Carver) *K1 W D1 K3*
Wellington *p425* 01952 641291
Hoyle, S T (Pinders) *J1 N P F1 L Zc Zk Zp E*
Derby *p209* 01332 364751
Hoyle, T A (Roebucks) *N Zx O Q Zd Zm*
Blackburn *p145* 01254 503070
Blackburn *p145* 01254 274000
Hoyle, Mrs V L (Walker Morris) *C2 C1*
Leeds *p277* 0113 283 2500
Hrydziuszko, Mrs E C (Franklins LLP)
Milton Keynes *p317* 01908 660966
Hryniewiecki, E S (Edwards Solicitors) *N S1 S2 W O Q K4 L Zx*
Melton Mowbray *p314* 01664 566606
Hrynkiewicz, Z H (The Mersey Docks & Harbour Co)
Liverpool *p463* 0151 949 6000
Hsu, S (Collins Benson Goldhill LLP) *E*
Westminster *p21* 020 7436 5151
Hsu, S (Simon & Co)
Southall *p384* 020 8571 3883
Huang, Ms M (Quality Solicitors Burroughs Day) *O Q Ze Zk*
Bristol *p164* 0117 929 0333
Huard, J (Bates Wells & Braithwaite London LLP) *E S2 R2 Zh L Zd*
London EC4 *p11* 020 7551 7777
Hubball, D J (Hubball & Co) *O Q G F1 N Zl Zb Zk Zy*
Sutton Coldfield *p403* 0121 323 4822
Hubbard, Mrs A V (Muckle LLP) *O Q*
Newcastle upon Tyne *p325* 0191 211 7777
Hubbard, C (Squire Sanders (UK) LLP) *U1 U2 O I J1 Q Ze*
London EC2 *p81* 020 7655 1000
Hubbard, D (Grahame Stowe Bateson) *N*
Leeds *p274* 0113 276 0044
Hubbard, Miss D (Mander Cruickshank Solicitors LLP) *N G H*
Coalville *p196* 01530 510666
Leicester *p280* 0116 222 6666
Hubbard, Miss E (Graysons) *K3 K1*
Sheffield *p375* 0114 272 9184
Hubbard, Miss J J (Tameside Metropolitan Borough Council)
Ashton-under-Lyne *p447* 0161 342 3028
Hubbard, K W (K W Hubbard & Co) *S1 K1 W N Q*
Gloucester *p230* 01452 414406
Hubbard, L S (Chester City Council)
Chester *p454* 01244 324324
Hubbard, P F (Anthony Collins Solicitors LLP) *Zh C1 L*
Birmingham *p137* 0121 200 3242
Hubbard, R (Hopkins) *K1 K3*
Mansfield *p311* 01623 460460
Hubbard, Ms R M (BCL Burton Copeland) *B2 G J2 H*
London WC2 *p9* 020 7430 2277
Hubbard, Mrs S D (Charles Hill Hubbard) *S1 E W T1 C1*
Chichester *p192* 01243 781000
Hubber, K M (Taylor Wessing) *C1 C2*
London EC4 *p86* 020 7300 7000
Hubble, P L (The College of Law York) *C1*
York *p477* 0800 289997
Huber, B (Edwards Duthie) *G H D1 N F Zl Zi Zp*
London E13 *p29* 020 8514 9000
Huber, N J (Nicholas Huber & Co) *S1 K1 W L E J1 B1 O Q S2 N F1*
Tiverton *p412* 01884 255515
Hubert, B J (Brand & Co) *F1 G H I J1 L N O Q*
Cheam *p185* 020 8641 2771
Hubery, Miss S J M (Jordans) *K1 K3*
Castleford *p183* 01977 518778
Hubner, S J (Shepherd + Wedderburn LLP) *Q T1 T2 W E P R1 S1 Zc*
London EC4 *p78* 020 7429 4900
Huck, Ms J M (Sea Containers Services Ltd)
London SE1 *p109* 020 7805 5202
Huckel, Mrs S (Steeles) *C1 C2 E*
Norwich *p335* 0870 609 0200
Huckle, Ms C (LG Lawyers)
London SE1 *p50* 020 7379 0000
Hucknall, Ms J M (Brennans Solicitors)
Wallsend *p419* 0191 262 5133
Hudd, D G T (Hogan Lovells International LLP) *Zb*
London EC1 *p42* 020 7296 2000
Huddert, N (Bond Pearce LLP)
Plymouth *p349* 0845 415 0000
Huddie, P J (London Borough of Barking & Dagenham)
Dagenham *p456* 020 8592 4500
Barking *p448* 020 8592 4500 / 8252 8233
Huddleson, M J (Atkins Law Solicitors) *J1*
Exeter *p220* 01392 671657
Huddleston, D (Browne Jacobson LLP) *E S1 L R1 A1 Zh*
Nottingham *p336* 0115 976 6000
Hudgell, N M (Jane Brooks Law) *N S1 W Zr*
Hull *p256* 01482 893366
Hull *p257* 01482 787771
Hudson, A (Ashurst LLP)
London EC2 *p7* 020 7638 1111
Hudson, Miss A D (Hudsons)
London SE11 *p43* 020 7793 8740
Hudson, A J (Devonshires) *E S2 S1 R2*
London EC2 *p27* 020 7628 7576
Hudson, B M (Gordons LLP)
Leeds *p273* 0113 227 0100
Hudson, Miss C (Howells LLP) *Zi*
Sheffield *p376* 0114 249 6666
Hudson, Ms C E (Reed Smith LLP)
London EC2 *p71* 020 3116 3000
Hudson, Miss C E (Eastleys) *K1*
Paignton *p345* 01803 559257
Hudson, D (Herbert Smith LLP)
London EC2 *p40* 020 7374 8000
Hudson, D (Watson Solicitors) *G H K3 K1 D1*
Warrington *p422* 01925 571212
Hudson, D G V (Hudson & Co) *C1 T1 C2 M1 J1 M2 O Ze Zi Zn*
London WC1 *p43* 020 7405 4812 / 7831 3282
Hudson, D J (Bhatia Best) *S1 S2 W*
Nottingham *p336* 0115 950 3231
Hudson, Mrs D S (Melton Borough Council)
Melton Mowbray *p465* 01664 502502
Hudson, D W (Stamps Family Solicitors)
Hull *p258* 01482 323495
Hudson, E (Mills & Co) *O Q M2 B1 C1 J1 Za*
Newcastle upon Tyne *p325* 0191 233 2222
Hudson, Ms E (Trowers & Hamlins)
London EC3 *p88* 020 7423 8000
Hudson, G J K (Prettys) *C2 C1 Zb U2*
Ipswich *p262* 01473 232121
Hudson, G R F (Penningtons)
London EC2 *p66* 020 7457 3000
Hudson, Miss H (Last Cawthra Feather LLP) *E*
Bradford *p154* 01274 848800
Hudson, Miss I J (Carter-Ruck) *Zk Q*
London EC4 *p18* 020 7353 5005
Hudson, Ms J (Stephensons) *D1 K4 K1 S1 T2 V W*
Brierley Hill *p158* 01384 79731
Hudson, J C R (Speechly Bircham LLP) *L N Q R1 Zl Zk*
London EC4 *p81* 020 7427 6400
Hudson, J D (Hallett & Co) *S1 W S2*
Ashford *p119* 01233 625711
Hudson, J E G (Hudson And Associates Solicitors-Advocates Ltd) *K1 D1 N*
Kirkby Lonsdale *p268* 0800 019 9768
Hudson, J J S (K&L Gates LLP) *C1 Zc*
London EC4 *p47* 020 7648 9000
Hudson, K A (LG Lawyers) *C1*
London SE1 *p50* 020 7379 0000
Hudson, Ms K M (Bridge McFarland)
Grimsby *p235* 01472 311711
Hudson, M D J (O'Melveny & Myers LLP)
London EC4 *p64* 020 7088 0000
Hudson, M H (DWF) *C1 C2 I Zb F1*
Liverpool *p287* 0151 907 3000
Hudson, M J C (Horwich Farrelly) *N O Q B1 F1*
Manchester *p305* 0161 834 3585
Hudson, M R (Harold G Walker) *C1 S2 E*
Bournemouth *p152* 01202 203200
Hudson, Mrs P P (Farrell Matthews & Weir) *K1 D1 K3*
London W6 *p30* 020 8746 3771
Hudson, Ms R (Gordons LLP)
Leeds *p273* 0113 227 0100
Hudson, R J K (AST Hampsons (incorporating Warhurst and co)) *S1 K1 W*
Bury *p170* 0161 764 3317
Hudson, Ms R L (Hague Lambert) *S1*
Knutsford *p269* 01565 652411
Hudson, S J (Gard & Co) *C1 E S1 S2 A1 W Zc Ze*
Plymouth *p349* 01752 668246
Hueston, J D (Lane & Co) *W*
Cheltenham *p188* 01242 524785 / 222421
Hueting, G P (Geoffrey Hueting & Co) *C1 S1 S2 W*
Bath *p127* 01225 465828
Huey, P D (Department for Business, Enterprise and Regulatory Reform)
London SW1 *p105* 020 7215 0105
Huey-Smith, Miss T (Irene Hogarth Criminal Defence) *G H*
Newton Abbot *p329* 01626 337373
Huffer, N D (ClarksLegal LLP) *J1*
Cardiff *p177* 029 2055 7500
Huggins, A P S (Huggins & Lewis Foskett) *E S1 C1 N P K1 R1 T1 W J1 Ze Zc Zf*
Redbridge *p43* 020 8989 3000
Huggins, Miss K S (QualitySolicitors Hill & Abbott) *Q N K3 L*
Chelmsford *p187* 01245 258892
Huggins, P A (Shakespeares) *S2 E R1 S1*
Stratford-upon-Avon *p400* 0845 630 8833
Huggins, S C (Huggins & Lewis Foskett) *J1 N Q W Zr*
Redbridge *p43* 020 8989 3000
Huggon, T (Browne Jacobson LLP) *R1 P Zc Zn Zs*
Nottingham *p336* 0115 976 6000
Hugh-Jones, C (Hempsons) *C1 I Ze M1 U2*
Harrogate *p240* 01423 522331
Hughes, A (Barlow Robbins LLP) *S1 S2*
Woking *p436* 01483 748500
Hughes, A (Linklaters LLP)
London EC2 *p54* 020 7456 2000
Hughes, Ms A (Brighton & Hove Council - Legal Services) *Q L O*
Hove *p461* 01273 290000
Hughes, Miss A C (Jolliffe & Co) *O Q*
Chester *p190* 01244 310022
Hughes, A D (Hughes Enterprise Law Practice) *O C1 Zq J1 I A3 U2 Ze*
Bristol *p163* 0117 959 6424
Hughes, A G (Ellison & Co) *S1 E W*
Cardiff *p178* 029 2038 2508
Hughes, Mrs A J (Squire Sanders (UK) LLP) *Zc O*
London EC2 *p81* 020 7655 1000
Hughes, B (Crown Prosecution Service Cheshire)
Chester *p454* 01244 408600
Hughes, B K (Henry Hughes & Hughes) *E S1 T1 C1 L W*
London SW16 *p40* 020 8765 2700
Hughes, B R J O (Rainer Hughes) *S1 S2 W J1 C1*
Brentwood *p156* 01277 226644
Hughes, Mrs C (Wilson & Co Solicitors) *K1 G D1 L E*
Middlesbrough *p315* 01642 222292
Hughes, C (Wains) *E S2 W S1*
Macclesfield *p297* 01625 429511
Hughes, Mrs C A (Barlows) *N O Q J1 K1*
Leicester *p278* 0116 251 8295
Hughes, C A R (Hedleys Solicitors LLP) *W Zd T2 S1*
East Horsley *p215* 01483 284567
Hughes, C D (Harding Swinburne Jackson & Co) *N Q G H V J1 S1 W F1*
Sunderland *p401* 0191 565 8194
Hughes, C J B (Wirral Borough Council)
Wallasey *p475* 0151 638 7070
Hughes, Mrs C R (GHP Legal) *D1 G K1 Zm*
Wrexham *p442* 01978 291456
Hughes, C V (Lee Bolton Monier-Williams) *E S1 L R1 R2*
Westminster *p52* 020 7222 5381
Hughes, D (Walker Smith Way) *N*
Wrexham *p443* 0844 346 3100
Hughes, D A (Breese-Gwyndaf) *S1 E L W J1 R1 A1 Zl Q S2 N*
Porthmadog *p353* 01766 512253 / 514227
Hughes, D A (Dickinson Martin) *S1 E W L R1 A1*
Warrington *p421* 01925 574748
Hughes, D A (Jackson Parton) *O Za A3 Q Zj Zb*
London EC3 *p45* 020 7702 0085
Hughes, D A (GKN PLC (Legal Dept))
Redditch *p469* 01527 517715
Hughes, D C (Allen & Overy LLP)
London E1 *p5* 020 3088 0000
Hughes, D C (Trevor Thomas Scott & Jenkins)
Swansea *p406* 01792 843821
Hughes, D R (Yaffe Jackson Ostrin) *S1 W G N*
Liverpool *p291* 0151 236 5555
Hughes, D R (D R Hughes) *S1 W S2*
Wootton Bassett *p439* 01793 840077
Hughes, D S (Allen & Overy LLP)
London E1 *p5* 020 3088 0000
Hughes, D W P (Howell Jones & Co) *S1 A1 P Zl J1*
Abergele *p113* 01745 826282 / 825845
Llanrwst *p292* 01492 640277
Hughes, E (Jones Day) *E*
London EC4 *p46* 020 7039 5959
Hughes, Mrs F (Windeatts) *L O Q N*
Totnes *p413* 01803 862233
Hughes, Ms F M T (Hughes Fowler Carruthers) *K1 D1 K2 K3*
London WC2 *p43* 020 7421 8383
Hughes, G (Squire Sanders (UK) LLP)
London EC2 *p81* 020 7655 1000
Hughes, G A (Birchall Blackburn LLP) *M2 T2 T1 W S2 E S1 R2 Zc Ze*
Manchester *p301* 0161 236 0662
Preston *p356* 01772 561663
Hughes, G J (Battens) *Zv*
Yeovil *p443* 01935 846000
Hughes, Miss G K (Brown Barron) *S1 W Q F1 K1 K3 L Zl*
Barrow-in-Furness *p125* 01229 828814
Hughes, G L (Osborne Clarke) *C1*
London EC2 *p65* 020 7105 7000
Hughes, G O (Clifford Chance)
London E14 *p20* 020 7006 1000
Hughes, Ms H E (Tomleys) *K1 G D1 H J1 Q W S1*
Newtown *p330* 01686 626641

See p634 for the Key to Work Categories

Hughes, H J A (Adam Douglas & Son) *S1 K1 W G H F1 D1 L Q B1 C1 S2 E F2 K3 J1 Zk Zl O N Zq*
Alnwick *p115*. 01665 602363
Berwick-upon-Tweed *p131*. . 01289 306479
Hughes, Miss H L (Jordans) *N*
Dewsbury *p210* 01924 457171
Hughes, Ms I (Moore Brown & Dixon LLP) *K1 S1 J1 L W N*
Tewkesbury *p410* 01684 292341
Hughes, I G (Kerwoods) *K1 D2 D1 L Zl*
Redditch *p362*. 01527 584444
Hughes, I R (Calderdale Metropolitan BC Corporate Services Directorate)
Halifax *p460*. 01422 357257
Hughes, Ms J (Edwards Angell Palmer & Dodge)
London EC2 *p28*. 020 7583 4055
Hughes, Miss J (FBC Manby Bowdler LLP) *A1 S1 T1 W*
Shrewsbury *p379* 01743 241551
Hughes, J (Ince & Co Services Ltd)
London E1 *p44* 020 7481 0010
Hughes, J (Graham Withers & Co) *S1 K1 L Q N D1 D2*
Shrewsbury *p380* 01743 236345
Hughes, J (Barricella Hughes Marchant) *N G H D1 Zl*
Ipswich *p262*. 01473 226225
Hughes, J (Quinn Melville) *N J1*
Liverpool *p290*. 0151 236 3340
Hughes, Mrs J A (Russell & Russell) *S1*
Bolton *p149* 01204 399299
Hughes, J B (Shakespeares) *B1 C1 E Zb*
Birmingham *p142* 0121 237 3000
Hughes, J G (Russells)
London E4 *p75* 020 8529 5933
Hughes, Mrs J G (Hughes Paddison) *W E S1 L S2*
Cheltenham *p188* 01242 574244
Hughes, Miss J K (Burt Brill & Cardens) *W S1 E*
Brighton *p159* 01273 604123
Hughes, Ms J M (Conwy County Borough Council)
Conwy *p455*. 01492 576108
Hughes, J M (Hughes Paddison) *N O Q J1*
Cheltenham *p188* 01242 574244
Hughes, J M (Red Kite Law) *W S1 S2*
Carmarthen *p183* 01267 239000
Hughes, J R C (T R Evans Hughes & Co) *A1 C1 D1 F1 G H J1 K1 L N Zg S1 W*
Amlwch *p117* 01407 830400
Holyhead *p251*. 01407 762204
Hughes, Ms K (AMD Solicitors) *E C2 S2 C1 Ze*
Bristol *p160* 0117 962 1460
Hughes, K (Bridge McFarland) *R1*
Grimsby *p235* 01472 311711
Hughes, Miss K (Hughes Solicitors)
Romford *p366* 020 7566 8244
Hughes, Mrs K A (Thomson Wilson Pattinson) *T2 W*
Kendal *p264*. 01539 721945
Hughes, Ms K E (Hogan Lovells International LLP) *C1*
London EC1 *p42*. 020 7296 2000
Hughes, Miss K J (Martin Murray & Associates) *G H B2*
Slough *p382*. 01753 551313
Hughes, K J (Pardoes) *G H B2 O Q*
Bridgwater *p158*. 01278 457891
Hughes, Ms L (Broudie Jackson Canter) *Q Zg*
Liverpool *p286*. 0151 227 1429
Hughes, Ms L A (DAC Beachcroft) *E*
Manchester *p303* 0161 839 8396
Hughes, Mrs L J (The Merriman Partnership) *S1 E*
Marlborough *p313* 01672 512244
Hughes, L W (Jobling & Knape) *Q O K1*
Lancaster *p269* 01524 598300
Hughes, M (Ashurst LLP)
London EC2 *p7* 020 7638 1111
Hughes, Mrs M A (W H Matthews & Co) *W T2*
Sutton *p402* 020 8642 6677
Hughes, Miss M A (Hains & Lewis Ltd) *D1 K1 K3 V*
Haverfordwest *p244* 0845 408 0125
Hughes, M D (Pardoes) *G H K1 N Q*
Yeovil *p444* 01935 382680
Hughes, M E (CMHT Solicitors) *O C1 B1 E J1 Zc*
Walsall *p420*. 01922 646400
Hughes, M Q H (Henry Hughes & Hughes) *S1 E W C1 L K1 Zb Zl*
London SW16 *p40*. 020 8765 2700
Hughes, M R (Browne Jacobson LLP) *C2 C1*
London EC3 *p16*. 020 7539 4900
Hughes, M W (Hugh James) *Zk O N Zq*
Cardiff *p179* 029 2022 4871
Hughes, N (SGH Martineau LLP) *O B1*
London EC3 *p75*. 020 7264 4444
Hughes, N A (Quality Solicitors Copley Clark) *O B1 L F1 Q Zc Zl*
Banstead *p122*. 01737 362131
Hughes, N A R (Painters) *S1 W L T1 E C1 R1 S2*
Kidderminster *p266* 01562 822295
Hughes, N L (Thomas Simon) *C1 S2 E Ze C2 Zl*
Cardiff *p181* 029 2055 7200
Hughes, Mrs N M (Larby Williams with Gwyn & Gwyn) *A1 S1 S2 W R2*
Cowbridge *p201* 01446 775535
Hughes, N M L (Barlow Lyde & Gilbert LLP) *O Q Zj*
London EC3 *p10*. 020 7247 2277
Hughes, Miss N W (Meade-King) *J1 J2 Zl*
Bristol *p163* 0117 926 4121
Hughes, O R (Cyngor Sir Ynys Mon (Isle of Anglesey County Council)) *P M1 S1 W F1 J1 L K1 G D1 Zl Zp*
Llangefni *p463*. 01248 750057
Hughes, P (Mincoffs Solicitors LLP) *C1 E F1*
Newcastle upon Tyne *p325* . 0191 281 6151
Hughes, Mrs P F (Walker Smith Way) *S1*
Wrexham *p443* 0844 346 3100
Hughes, P J F (Hughes Griffiths Partnership) *E S1 C1 R1 P W J1 M1 O Q Ze*
Swansea *p405*. 01792 458275
Hughes, P K (Underwood Solicitors LLP) *O E L C1 S1 J1 S2*
Westminster *p89*. 020 7526 6000
Hughes, P M (Crutes) *N O G Q*
Newcastle upon Tyne *p324* . 0191 233 9700
Hughes, P R (Walker Smith Way) *N*
Ashton-under-Lyne *p120*. . . 0844 346 3100
Hughes, P S (Hughes & Company) *E S1 W T2 K4*
Tring *p413*. 01442 891717
Hughes, P T (Kundert & Co) *W S1 J1 E C1*
Coventry *p200*. 024 7622 7741
Hughes, Mrs R (Davies Parsons Allchurch)
Llanelli *p292*. 01554 749144
Hughes, R (Canter Levin & Berg)
Kirkby *p268* 0151 546 4562
Hughes, R A (Fox Williams) *C1*
London EC2 *p33*. 020 7628 2000
Hughes, R A (Freeth Cartwright LLP) *S1 C1 A1 E L R1 Zc*
Nottingham *p337*. 0115 936 9369
Hughes, Ms R E (PCB Solicitors LLP)
Church Stretton *p194* 01694 723818
Hughes, R E (Milton Francis & Hughes Solicitors) *S1 W C1 A1 M1 Zc Zl A2 L P S2 Zd Zv*
Oswestry *p342*. 01691 654662
Hughes, R J A (Hughes & Company) *W S1 S2*
Tring *p413*. 01442 891717
Hughes, R M (Sidley Austin Brown & Wood) *R2 Zb*
London EC2 *p78*. 020 7360 3600
Hughes, R P (Wallace Robinson & Morgan) *S1 E C1 A1 W P L Zl*
Solihull *p383*. 0121 705 7571
Hughes, R S (Bridgend County Borough Council) *K1 M1 P S1 W*
Bridgend *p451*. 01656 643643
Hughes, R W (Irwin Mitchell LLP) *B1 C1 O Q Zb*
Leeds *p274* 0870 150 0100
Hughes, Miss S (Anthony Gold) *K3 K1*
London SE1 *p6* 020 7940 4000
Hughes, Mrs S (H F T Gough & Co) *W*
Whitehaven *p431* 01946 692461
Hughes, S D (Rees Page) *K1 D1*
Bilston *p133*. 01902 577776
Hughes, S D (Bevan Brittan LLP) *C1 Zu*
Birmingham *p135* 0870 194 1000
Hughes, S D (The Walkers Partnership)
Royston *p368* 01763 248896
Hughes, Ms S E (Commission for Racial Equality) *K1 P M1 L J1 F1*
Birmingham *p449* 0121 710 3000
Hughes, S J L (Bond Pearce LLP)
Bristol *p161* 0845 415 0000
Hughes, Miss S K (Awdry Bailey & Douglas) *S1*
Devizes *p210* 01380 722311
Hughes, Miss S M (Newport City Council)
Newport *p466* 01633 656656
Hughes, Ms S M (Hewitsons) *T2 W Zo*
Saffron Walden *p370*. 01799 522471
Hughes, S R (Olswang LLP) *E L*
London WC1 *p64* 020 7067 3000
Hughes, T D (Banner Jones) *B1 F1 J1 N Q Zl*
Chesterfield *p191* 01246 209773
Hughes, T G (Passmore Lewis & Jacobs) *S1 W K1 C1 E F1 G H M1 T1 Zl Zm Ze*
Barry *p126*. 01446 721000
Hughes, T J B (Downs) *W*
Dorking *p212* 01306 880110
Hughes, Ms T L (Wendy Hopkins Family Law Practice LLP) *K1 D1 D2 K3*
Cardiff *p178* 029 2034 2233
Hughes, T L (Norcross Lees & Riches) *G H D1 Q X N V Zw*
Oldham *p341* 0161 624 6034
Hughes, T W (Haringey Magistrates Legal Advisers Office)
London N6 *p106*. 0845 601 3600
Hughes, W H (Humphrey Roberts & Bott) *S1 W A1 L T1 R1 K1 G Zl Zm Zv*
Aberystwyth *p114* 01970 617618
Hughes, Mrs Y (Frodshams) *W K4*
St Helens *p391* 01744 626600
Hughes Parry, Ms N (Howell Jones & Co) *K1 K3 W S1 K4*
Abergele *p113*. . . .01745 826282 / 825845
Llanrwst *p292* 01492 640277
Hughes Scholes, Miss C (Bristows)
London EC4 *p15*. 020 7400 8000
Hughes-Jones, G R (BPE Solicitors LLP) *W T1 E Zv*
Cheltenham *p187* 01242 224433
Hughes-Parry, Ms S V (The Hughes Parry Partnership) *J1 K1 S1 S2 E W*
Holywell *p252* 01352 712422
Hughes-Young, C (London Borough of Southwark)
London SE1 *p470* 020 7525 5000
Hugheston-Roberts, C J (Rose Williams & Partners) *G H B2*
Wolverhampton *p438* 01902 710822
Hughman, P G (Hughmans) *G*
London EC4 *p44*. 020 7246 6560
Hugill, A S (Davenport Lyons) *J1 Q*
London W1 *p25* 020 7468 2600
Hugill, Miss L P (Clarion Solicitors LLP) *E S2*
Leeds *p272* 0113 246 0622
Harrogate *p240* 01423 530630
Hugill, R (Harrowells)
York *p444* 01904 690111
Hugman, J M (Morecrofts Solicitors LLP)
Liverpool *p290*. 0151 236 8871
Hugo, C J (Knocker & Foskett) *J1 Q O Zq Zp*
Sevenoaks *p374*. 01732 459931
Huish, Miss G (Behr & Co) *K1 D1 K3*
Brynmawr *p167* 01495 310581
Huka, A (Huka & Co) *Q N*
London NW6 *p44* 020 7624 9341
Hulatt, L (Hedleys Solicitors LLP) *K1 K2 L*
East Horsley *p215*. 01483 284567
Hulbert, G (HBOS PLC)
Halifax *p460*. 0870 600 5000
Hulbert, J C G (Isherwood & Hose) *E S1 W*
Heywood *p249*. . . .01706 360032 / 368741
Rochdale *p365*. . . .01706 359090 / 522225
Huleatt-James, R M (Hogan Lovells International LLP)
London EC1 *p42*. 020 7296 2000
Hull, Miss C L (Latham & Co) *K1 S1 V*
Loughborough *p293* 01509 238822
Melton Mowbray *p314* 01664 563012
Hull, D J (Squire Sanders (UK) LLP) *C1*
Birmingham *p142* 0121 222 3000
Hull, J A (Reed Smith LLP) *O*
London EC2 *p71*. 020 3116 3000
Hull, J K (Memery Crystal) *Ze*
London WC2 *p60* 020 7242 5905
Hull, J P C (The Really Useful Group Ltd) *J1 Zf Ze*
London WC2 *p108*. 020 7240 0880
Hull, K E (Pinney Talfourd LLP)
Hornchurch *p252* 01708 511000
Hull, K M (Oswestry Borough Council)
Oswestry *p468*. 01691 671111
Hull, Miss L K (Southampton City Council)
Southampton *p472*. 023 8022 3855
Hull, R A (Thomas Horton LLP) *G H*
Bromsgrove *p167* 01527 871641
Hull, S (Ashurst LLP)
London EC2 *p7* 020 7638 1111
Hull, W J (TLT Solicitors) *C1 C2 C3 F1 T1 T2 Zo Ze Zp Zj*
Bristol *p165* 0117 917 7777
Hullah, Mrs A (Parker Arrenberg)
London SE6 *p65*. 020 8695 2330
Hullah, Mrs H K V (Marks & Spencer PLC)
London W2 *p107* 020 7935 4422
Hulley, C M (DB Law) *G H*
Camborne *p173* 01209 712428
Hulley, J R (Devonshires) *L O Zu Q*
London EC2 *p27*. 020 7628 7576
Hullis, Mrs C M (Bobbetts Mackan) *K1 K3 D1 D2*
Bristol *p161* 0117 929 9001
Hullis, J G (VHS Fletchers Solicitors) *G H*
Nottingham *p339*. 0115 959 9550
Hulls, M A (Ward Hadaway) *C1 T1 C2 Zb*
Newcastle upon Tyne *p327* . 0191 204 4000
Hulme, A J (Alliance Boots PLC)
Nottingham *p467*. 0115 950 6111
Hulme, Miss E (Goodhand and Forsyth QualitySolicitors) *K1 K3 G H*
Redhill *p362*. 01737 773533
Hulme, J (Bower & Bailey) *J1 Q O N L*
Oxford *p343*. 01865 311133
Hulme, J A (GHP Legal) *N Q O F1*
Oswestry *p342*. 01691 659194
Hulmes, Ms C L (Geoffrey Morris & Ashton) *K1 K3 D1*
Wrexham *p442* 01978 291322
Hulmes, J R (Hill Dickinson LLP) *O Q N M1 C1 Za Zj A3 M2*
Liverpool *p288*. 0151 600 8000
Hulmes, Ms K (Rawlison Butler LLP)
Crawley *p202* 01293 527744
Horsham *p253*. 01403 252492
Hulse, Mrs E V (Environment Agency (Midlands Region))
Solihull *p471*. 0121 711 2324
Hulton, Ms V A (Cockshott Peck Lewis) *T2 W Zd Zm K4*
Southport *p388* 01704 534034
Humber, S (Leigh Day & Co) *Zg P*
London EC1 *p52*. 020 7650 1200
Humberston, D N (Hood Vores & Allwood) *W Zo T1 T2 K4*
Dereham *p209*. 01362 692424
Humble, J (Nicholson Portnell) *S1 E K4 W*
Hexham *p249* 01434 603656
Humble, P (Abbott Bailey Solicitors) *J1*
Middlesbrough *p314* 01642 246617
Hume, Mrs C (Neves) *R1 S1*
Northampton *p332*. 01604 814500
Hume, Miss F L (Astle Paterson Ltd) *C1 J1 U2 F1 Zza C2*
Burton-on-Trent *p170* 01283 531366
Hume, Miss Y (BTMK Solicitors LLP) *K1 X*
Southend-on-Sea *p387* 01702 339222
Humes, N J (Nigel J Humes & Co) *K1 G H S1 W*
Chester-le-Street *p191*. . . . 0191 388 8737
Humes, Ms S I (Thursfields) *K1 D1*
Worcester *p440* 01905 730450
Humpage, T J (Gotelee) *N O Zr*
Ipswich *p262*. 01473 211121
Humphery, J H (Trethowans LLP) *J1 A3*
Salisbury *p371*. 01722 412512
Humphray, Miss M R (Isle of Wight Council)
Newport *p466* 01983 823207
Humphrey, A (Bishop & Sewell LLP) *J1*
London WC1 *p13* 020 7631 4141
Humphrey, A R (Allen & Overy LLP)
London E1 *p5* 020 3088 0000
Humphrey, Ms E (Taylor Wessing)
London EC4 *p86*. 020 7300 7000
Humphrey, G H (Harvey Ingram Borneos) *E S1 C1 L A1 R1 Zd Zp*
Bedford *p130* 01234 353221
Humphrey, Mrs H L (Russell-Cooke LLP) *Zr N*
London SW15 *p74*. 020 8789 9111
Humphrey, N M (Powell & Co) *S1 W L T2 E K1 J1*
Sutton Coldfield *p404* 0121 355 1001
Humphrey, P (Bretherton Law) *W J1 K4*
St Albans *p389* 01727 869293
Humphrey, Ms S A (Addleshaw Goddard)
Leeds *p271* 0113 209 2000
Manchester *p300* 0161 934 6000
Humphreys, A M (Robertsons) *E H K1 D1 J1 Q O*
Barry *p126*. 01446 745660
Humphreys, A R (Lancaster City Council)
Lancaster *p462* 01524 582000
Humphreys, D G (Morrisons Solicitors LLP) *W F1 J1 L S1*
Camberley *p173*. 01276 686005
Humphreys, D G (Bircham Dyson Bell) *A1 E L S1 W*
Westminster *p13*. 020 7227 7000
Humphreys, G (Gardner Leader LLP) *C1 E S2*
Newbury *p322*. 01635 508080
Humphreys, Miss G P (Reynolds Parry-Jones) *S1 W E L C1 Zd T2*
High Wycombe *p250*. 01494 525941
Humphreys, H G (Walker Smith Way) *N*
Chester *p191* 0844 346 3100
Humphreys, Miss J (Camps Solicitors) *N L*
Birkenhead *p134*. 0151 201 8080
Humphreys, J O (Charles Coleman LLP) *S1 E W S2*
Windsor *p434* 01753 861115
Humphreys, K A (Carillion PLC) *O Zc Ze Zt*
Wolverhampton *p477* 01902 422431
Humphreys, Mrs L (Peyto Law)
Fleet *p226*. 01252 617119
Humphreys, N (Hill Dickinson LLP)
London EC3 *p41*. 020 7283 9033
Humphreys, N G (Fisher Jones Greenwood LLP) *K1 D1 K2 D2*
Colchester *p197* 01206 578282
Humphreys, P M G (Clark Holt) *C1 C2 Zb*
Swindon *p406* 01793 617444
Humphreys, Ms R (Morgans) *V L*
Cardiff *p180* 029 2072 9888
Humphreys, R A (Humphreys & Co) *C1 C3 U2 Ze Zf*
Bristol *p163* 0117 929 2662
Humphreys, R E (Blake Lapthorn) *O F1*
Oxford *p342*. 01865 248607
Humphreys, R H (Thursfields) *O Q N*
Worcester *p440* 01905 730450
Humphreys, R J T (Walker Smith Way) *K1 K3 D1*
Chester *p191* 0844 346 3100
Humphreys, R M (Flintshire County Council)
Mold *p466*. 01352 702411
Humphreys, S A (Rhondda Cynon Taff County Borough Council)
Pentre *p468* 01443 424300
Humphreys, V L (V L Humphreys & Co)
Guildford *p236*. 01483 574342
Humphries, B S (Stockport Metropolitan Borough Council)
Stockport *p472*. 0161 480 4949
Humphries, Mrs C (PricewaterhouseCoopers LLP)
London EC4 *p108* 020 7583 5000
Humphries, Miss C A (North Tyneside Council) *K1 N F1 D1 Q*
Newcastle upon Tyne *p466* . 0191 643 5000
Humphries, Mrs D (Lanyon Bowdler LLP) *N Zr*
Shrewsbury *p379* 01743 280280
Humphries, Ms D F (Lanyon Bowdler LLP)
Shrewsbury *p379* 01743 280280
Humphries, Mrs L A (Fitzgerald-Harts)
Boroughbridge *p150* 01423 322312
Humphries, M J (Linklaters LLP)
London EC2 *p54*. 020 7456 2000
Humphries, M P (Stewarts Law LLP) *K1 K3*
London EC4 *p83*. 020 7822 8000
Humphries, Miss M S (Trevor Griffiths & Humphries) *S1 W E*
Blackwood *p147* 01495 225236
Humphries, R (IBB Solicitors) *E S2*
Uxbridge *p417*. 0845 638 1381
Humphries, Ms S L (City & County of Swansea)
Swansea *p473*. 01792 636000
Humphris, P A (Abels) *K1 G P L M1 H F1 N W*
Southampton *p385*. 023 8022 0317
Humphrys, Ms C (Humphrys & Co) *D1 K1 N*
Rhyl *p363* 01745 343158
Wrexham *p443* 01978 313399
Humphrys, J C (Humphrys & Co) *G H*
Rhyl *p363* 01745 343158
Wrexham *p443* 01978 313399
Hundal, Ms K K (Dixon Ward) *S1 S2 E*
Richmond upon Thames *p364*020 8940 4051
Hundal, Ms S (Borneo Hughes Martell LLP) *Q L J1 N Zr*
Northampton *p331*. 01604 624822
Hundle, J (Mills & Reeve) *J1 Zp*
Birmingham *p140* 0121 454 4000
Hung, P K (Wright Hassall LLP) *E S2 R2 Zi*
Leamington Spa *p270* 01926 886688

6

Hung, Miss S (Ronald Fletcher Baker LLP) *O Q S2 C1 B1 J1 N W*
London EC1 *p73* 020 7613 1402

Hunjan, R (Clifford Chance)
London E14 *p20* 020 7006 1000

Hunjan, Mrs R (Guillaumes Solicitors) *L O Q*
Weybridge *p430* 01932 840111

Hunka, S J (Alsters Kelley) *G*
Coventry *p199* 0844 561 0100

Hunn, A J (Kennedys) *Zj N*
London EC3 *p49* 020 7667 9667

Hunneyball, Ms S J (Charles Russell LLP) *N O Q Zj*
London EC4 *p19* 020 7203 5000

Hunnings, I (Tollers LLP)
Northampton *p332* 01604 258558

Hunnings, T I M (Tollers LLP) *N*
Northampton *p332* 01604 258558

Hunsley, G (Hewitts) *G H K1 M1 D1 F1 J1*
Darlington *p206* 01325 468573

Hunston, P (Wiggin Osborne Fullerlove) *C1 M2 T1*
Cheltenham *p189* 01242 710200
London SW1 *p91* 020 7290 2456

Hunt, A E (The Mitchell Plampin Partnership) *N Q J1 O*
Maldon *p299* 01621 852566

Hunt, A G (Wolferstans)
Plymouth *p351* 01752 663295

Hunt, Mrs A J (Howells) *K1 S1 S2*
Caerphilly *p172* 029 2086 7111

Hunt, A J (Howard Kennedy LLP) *C1 C2 J1 Zb*
London W1 *p48* 020 7636 1616

Hunt, A J (Bartletts Solicitors) *N Q*
Liverpool *p286* 0151 228 7730

Hunt, A M (Lawson West Solicitors Limited) *N J1*
Leicester *p280* 0116 212 1000

Hunt, A P (Addison O'Hare) *K1 Q O*
Walsall *p419* 01922 725515

Hunt, A P (Nichols Marcy Dawson) *L G H N J1 F1 B1 Zi Zl*
Walton-on-Thames *p420* . . . 01932 219500

Hunt, Mrs A S L (Dyne Drewett Solicitors Ltd) *C1 S2 L S1*
Sherborne *p378* 01935 813691

Hunt, Mrs B L (Gregg Latchams LLP) *S1 E A1 C1 J1*
Bristol *p162* 0117 906 9400

Hunt, Ms C (Trowers & Hamlins)
London EC3 *p88* 020 7423 8000

Hunt, C D (Spelthorne Borough Council)
Staines *p472* 01784 451499

Hunt, C P (Clarion Solicitors LLP) *C1 C2*
Leeds *p272* 0113 246 0622
Leeds *p275* 0113 280 2000

Hunt, D (Farrer & Co LLP)
London WC2 *p31* 020 3375 7000

Hunt, Ms D (McKenzies) *G H*
London N9 *p57* 020 8350 4114

Hunt, D C (David C Hunt) *P N M1 H*
London SE7 *p44* 020 8856 6350

Hunt, D H E (Birketts LLP (Wollastons LLP)) *O Q B1*
Chelmsford *p186* 01245 211211

Hunt, D J F (DAC Beachcroft)
London EC4 *p24* 020 7242 1011

Hunt, D J G (Field Fisher Waterhouse LLP)
London EC3 *p31* 020 7861 4000

Hunt, Ms E (Gateley LLP) *E R1*
Leicester *p279* 0116 285 9000

Hunt, H P (Fitzhugh Gates) *E S1 W C1 L J1 Zt*
Shoreham-by-Sea *p378* . . . 01273 461381

Hunt, I J (Borough Council of King's Lynn and West Norfolk)
King's Lynn *p462* 01553 616270

Hunt, J (Bevirs)
Swindon *p406* 01793 532363

Hunt, J (Martin Tolhurst Partnership LLP)
Gravesend *p233* 01474 325531

Hunt, J B (Dean Wilson Laing) *K1 N Zr V Zq Zw*
Brighton *p159* 01273 327241

Hunt, J C V (Wake Smith & Tofields) *C1 I M1 T1 Zb U1*
Sheffield *p377* 0114 266 6660

Hunt, J D (Allen & Overy LLP)
London E1 *p5* 020 3088 0000

Hunt, J F (Hunt & Lisners) *S1 K1 N Q L Zd Zm*
Northampton *p332* 01604 846705

Hunt, J I (HSBC Legal Department)
Birmingham *p449* 0121 455 2740

Hunt, Miss J M (Standley & Co) *S1*
Knowle *p269* 01564 776287

Hunt, J P (Trowers & Hamlins) *E L S1 S2 Zh*
London EC3 *p88* 020 7423 8000

Hunt, J P (Reed Smith LLP) *Za*
London EC2 *p71* 020 3116 3000

Hunt, J R (Gordons LLP)
Leeds *p273* 0113 227 0100

Hunt, J S (Salusburys Harding & Barnett) *E S2 C1 S1 W T2 C2 F1 A1 Zl Zv*
Leicester *p281* . . 0116 262 9033 / 262 6052

Hunt, Ms K (Cunningtons) *S1*
Wickford *p431* 01268 732268

Hunt, Mrs K (Ellisons) *W*
Colchester *p197* 01206 764477

Hunt, Mrs L (Alsters Kelley) *Zr*
Coventry *p199* 0844 561 0100

Hunt, M S (Hunt & Morgan) *B1 O C1 E Zb*
Cardiff *p179* 029 2034 1234

Hunt, M T F (Reed Smith LLP) *J1 Zp*
London EC2 *p71* 020 3116 3000

Hunt, N J (Thompson Leatherdale) *S1 E C1 L F1*
Reading *p361* 0118 959 1773

Hunt, N P (Hunts)
Cheltenham *p188* 01242 525777

Hunt, O (Onside Law)
London SW6 *p65* 020 7384 6920

Hunt, P (Harvey Ingram LLP) *R1*
Leicester *p280* 0116 254 5454

Hunt, P (Higgs & Sons) *C1 C2 C3 E Ze Zd*
Brierley Hill *p158* 0845 111 5050

Hunt, P F (Kirwans) *K1 D1*
Birkenhead *p134* 0151 608 9078

Hunt, Ms S M (Bhatia Best) *G H*
Nottingham *p336* 0115 950 3231

Hunt, Miss S V (Brookes & Co) *Za O Zj C1*
London EC3 *p16* 020 7621 0067

Hunt, T E (QualitySolicitors Clarke & Son) *J1 O Q J2 A3*
Basingstoke *p127* 01256 320555

Hunt, T J F (Ipswich Borough Council)
Ipswich *p461* 01473 432000

Huntbach, Ms S (Anthony Collins Solicitors LLP) *N Zr*
Birmingham *p137* 0121 200 3242

Hunter, Ms A (Wesley Gryk) *Zi Zg*
Lambeth *p37* 020 7401 6887

Hunter, Mrs A (Moseleys) *E S1 S2 W L*
Lichfield *p284* 01543 414100

Hunter, Mrs A H (Muckle LLP) *E*
Newcastle upon Tyne *p325* . 0191 211 7777

Hunter, Mrs C (Cozens-Hardy LLP) *S1*
Norwich *p334* 01603 625231

Hunter, Ms C (Samuel Phillips Law Firm) *K1 D1 D2 H G*
Newcastle upon Tyne *p326* . 0191 232 8451

Hunter, C C G (Andrew & Co LLP) *E S1 A1 L R1 Zc Ze Zl*
Lincoln *p284* 01522 512123

Hunter, C J (Coodes) *Q N O B1 F2 L Zq Zr*
St Austell *p391* 01726 874700

Hunter, D J (Bevan Brittan LLP) *E L S1 C1 R1*
Bristol *p161* 0870 194 1000

Hunter, D M (North Devon District Council)
Barnstaple *p448* 01271 327711

Hunter, Ms E (Barlow Robbins LLP) *C1*
Guildford *p235* 01483 562901

Hunter, Miss E K (Nottinghamshire County Council Legal Services Division)
West Bridgford *p475* 0115 977 3478

Hunter, G (Levy & Co Solicitors LLP)
Witham *p436* 01376 511819

Hunter, G (Hepburns)
London SE22 *p40* 020 8299 3376

Hunter, Mrs G (Muckle LLP) *I C1 Ze*
Newcastle upon Tyne *p325* . 0191 211 7777

Hunter, G R A (Hunters) *S1 E W K3*
Westcliff-on-Sea *p428* 01702 353093

Hunter, I (Clifford Chance)
London E14 *p20* 020 7006 1000

Hunter, I D (Bird & Bird LLP) *J1 Zp Zi*
London EC4 *p13* 020 7415 6000

Hunter, J (Bishop & Light) *G H*
Brighton *p159* 01273 626288

Hunter, J (Bishop & Light) *G H*
Brighton *p159* 01273 626288

Hunter, J (HCB Solicitors) *S1*
Walsall *p420* 01922 720000

Hunter, Miss J (Bermans LLP) *Zb Q P O B2*
Liverpool *p286* 0151 224 0500

Hunter, Mrs J C (Walker Morris) *E L*
Leeds *p277* 0113 283 2500

Hunter, J G R (Russell-Cooke LLP) *L*
London WC1 *p74* 020 7405 6566

Hunter, J M (Mills & Reeve) *C1 C2*
Norwich *p335* 01603 660155

Hunter, J M (Forster Dean Ltd) *N*
Widnes *p431* 0151 495 3270

Hunter, J S (Southerns) *D1 F1 J1 K1 M1 N P W*
Burnley *p169* 01282 422711

Hunter, M (Forster Dean Ltd)
Liverpool *p288* 0151 259 1717

Hunter, M S W (Stevens & Bolton) *W E S1 C1 T1 L*
Guildford *p237* 01483 302264

Hunter, Ms N (Cartwright King)
Derby *p208* 01332 346111

Hunter, N (Norman Hunter)
Cliftonville *p196* 07766 313613

Hunter, Miss N J (David Gray Solicitors) *K1 K3 D1*
Newcastle upon Tyne *p324* . 0191 232 9547

Hunter, P A (Mackarness & Lunt) *S2 Ze S1 W*
Petersfield *p348* 01730 265111

Hunter, R J (Allen & Overy LLP)
London E1 *p5* 020 3088 0000

Hunter, R M (Penningtons) *E*
London EC2 *p66* 020 7457 3000

Hunter, Ms S (DAC Beachcroft)
London EC4 *p24* 020 7936 2222

Hunter, S (Squire Sanders (UK) LLP)
London EC2 *p81* 020 7655 1000

Hunter, S A (Amphlett Chatterton) *X O N Zl Q*
Leamington Spa *p270* 01926 311427

Hunter, Mrs S J (BHP Law) *E*
Darlington *p206* 01325 466794

Hunter, Mrs S P (Mills & Reeve) *Zq*
Norwich *p335* 01603 660155

Hunter, Mrs T (Moorcrofts LLP) *C1 C2*
Marlow *p313* 01628 470000

Hunter, Ms W (Squire Sanders (UK) LLP) *Zo*
London EC2 *p81* 020 7655 1000

Hunter Smart, A D A (Wrigleys Solicitors LLP) *W T2*
Leeds *p278* 0113 244 6100

Hunter-Yeats, Ms C (Simmons & Simmons)
London EC2 *p79* 020 7628 2020

Huntingdon, Ms E (Wilkin Chapman LLP) *A1 Zd E Zl R1 S1*
Beverley *p131* 01482 398398

Huntingdon, Mrs J S (Northern Rock PLC)
Gosforth *p459* 0191 285 7191

Huntley, G P K (Hogan Lovells International LLP)
London EC1 *p42* 020 7296 2000

Hunton, R C T (Gowmans) *E S1 S2*
Paignton *p345* 01803 546100

Hunwicks, E V (F Barnes & Son) *S1 S2 W E C1 Zl*
Romford *p366* 01708 745183

Hurd, Mrs J E (Co-operative Insurance Society Ltd)
Manchester *p464* 0161 832 8686

Hurd, M P W (Wycombe Hurd & Co) *C1 T1 T2*
London WC2 *p93* 020 7925 0313

Hurford, Mrs H M (Simmonds Hurford)
Swansea *p405* . . . . 01792 462729 / 641070

Hurlbut, J R (Lees Solicitors LLP) *Zr*
Birkenhead *p134* 0151 647 9381

Hurle, B E (K&L Gates LLP)
London EC4 *p47* 020 7648 9000

Hurley, D (Hurleys) *D1 K1 N Zu*
Bournemouth *p152* 01202 436100

Hurley, N S (Charles Russell LLP)
London EC4 *p19* 020 7203 5000

Hurley, W K (Mosshaselhurst) *G H*
Northwich *p333* 01606 74301

Hurlow, Ms C A (Hurlow & Partners) *K1*
Cardiff *p179* 029 2039 6087

Hurn, Mrs E (Taylors) *C1 C2 C3 J1 T1 Ze Zv*
Blackburn *p146* 0844 800 0263

Hurn, P (Hugh James) *E L*
Cardiff *p179* 029 2022 4871

Hurney, Ms L (McMillan Williams) *Zr N*
Croydon *p205* 01689 848311

Hurrell, A P (Andrew Hurrell Solicitors) *S1 E W C1 F1 J1 T1 T2 L*
Benfleet *p131* 01702 558286

Hurrell, Ms C (Parlett Kent) *Zr N*
Exeter *p222* 01392 494455

Hurrell, Miss D A (Dorothy A Hurrell) *S1 E K1 W*
London W8 *p44* 020 7938 5355

Hurrell, Miss J (Maffey & Brentnall) *W S1 S2*
Watford *p423* 01923 234607

Hurren, Ms S (Lewis Silkin LLP) *L N O Q*
London EC4 *p53* 020 7074 8000

Hurrion, C J (C J Hurrion) *C1 E S1 T1 W Zc*
Sevenoaks *p374* 01732 833997

Hurst, A A (Law Hurst & Taylor) *G H D1 K1 E L S1 W M1 N Zl Zm*
Westcliff-on-Sea *p428* 01702 337864

Hurst, A C B (A C B Hurst & Co) *S1 E W L C1*
Henley-on-Thames *p247* . . . 01491 572699

Hurst, Miss C R (Cumbria County Council)
Carlisle *p453* . . . . 01228 607374 / 607351

Hurst, Mrs D (Royds LLP) *W Zd C1 T2*
London EC4 *p74* 020 7583 2222

Hurst, E B (E B Hurst) *S1 E W R1 K1 N*
Worthing *p442* 01903 246818

Hurst, G N (Withers LLP) *A1 S1 E R2 A2*
London EC4 *p92* 020 7597 6000

Hurst, I (Lock & Marlborough) *J1*
London W3 *p55* 020 8993 7231

Hurst, M (Hamlins LLP) *E*
London W1 *p38* 020 7355 6000

Hurst, P (Ashurst LLP)
London EC2 *p7* 020 7638 1111

Hurst, P J (Robinsons) *E L S1 W*
Liverpool *p290* 0151 227 2555

Hurst, R A (Robert A Hurst) *O Q M1 M2 F1 F2 A3 Ze Zf Zg Zb Zj B1 Zq*
London NW11 *p44* 020 8209 1733

Hurton, Mrs A (Sills & Betteridge LLP) *N*
Lincoln *p285* 01522 542211

Hurwood, M A (Grahame Stowe Bateson) *K1 G N Q D1 J1 F1 W V R1 Zm Zl*
Harrogate *p240* 01423 562121

Husband, D C (Husband Saye) *C1 E L P S1 S2 T2 W*
Cardiff *p179* 029 2034 5217

Huseyin, H E (Bowling & Co) *S1*
London E15 *p15* 020 8221 8000

Huskinson, A P (King & Co) *S1 W A1 E*
Cambridge *p175* . . 01223 365432 / 566038

Huskinson, M G (Stallard March & Edwards) *S1*
Worcester *p440* 01905 723561

Huskisson, J (The Wilkes Partnership LLP) *O*
Birmingham *p143* 0121 233 4333

Hussain, A (Forster Dean Ltd) *N*
Crewe *p203* 01270 254064
Runcorn *p369* 01928 590999

Hussain, A (AGH Solicitors) *N Q S1 G*
Bolton *p148* 01204 364433

Hussain, A (Pothecary Witham Weld) *E S2 Zl O*
Westminster *p69* 020 7821 8211

Hussain, A (Redditch Borough Council)
Redditch *p469* 01527 64252

Hussain, A (Atter Mackenzie & Co) *N G F1 H Q V O B1 Zg Zm Zc*
Evesham *p220* 01386 425300

Hussain, A (HSK Solicitors) *E N Q S1 S2 W*
Bolton *p149* 01204 526465
Manchester *p305* 0161 795 4818

Hussain, Ms A H (Charsley Harrison LLP) *K1*
Windsor *p434* 01753 851591

Hussain, B (Plexus Law (A Trading Name of Parabis Law LLP)) *J1 J2 N Q*
Leeds *p276* 0844 245 4100

Hussain, Mrs F (John Pickering & Partners LLP) *N*
Halifax *p238* 0808 144 0959

Hussain, Mrs F I (Luton Borough Council)
Luton *p464* 01582 546000

Hussain, Ms H (Cogent Law)
Croydon *p204* 0844 245 4452

Hussain, I (The Watson Ramsbottom Partnership) *Zi G K1*
Blackburn *p146* 01254 672222

Hussain, I (Roebucks) *G H P*
Blackburn *p145* 01254 274000

Hussain, K (Ali & Co Solicitor)
Bradford *p153* 01274 391197

Hussain, Ms M (Nottingham City Council (City Sec Dept)) *K1 L V W*
Nottingham *p467* 0115 915 5555

Hussain, M (John Holden) *G H*
Keighley *p263* 01535 667826

Hussain, Ms N (Teacher Stern LLP) *Q O L*
London WC1 *p86* 020 7242 3191

Hussain, Miss R (Rozita Hussain Solicitors) *N S1 E Q W L*
Withington *p436* 0161 448 8222

Hussain, R M (HSBC Legal Department)
Birmingham *p449* 0121 455 2740

Hussain, S (Daniel Curry & Co) *L N Q J1 K3 K1 Zq*
Croydon *p205* 020 8680 2188

Hussain, Mrs S (Robert Barber & Sons) *K1 K3*
Hucknall *p255* 0115 955 2299

Hussain, S (Duncan Lewis & Co) *Zi*
London W12 *p53* 020 7923 4020

Hussain, Miss S (Blaser Mills) *S1*
Chesham *p189* 01494 782291

Hussain, S (LG Lawyers)
London SE1 *p50* 020 7379 0000

Hussain, Ms S (ASB Law)
Crawley *p202* 01293 603600

Hussain, S (SJ LAW)
London E17 *p75* 020 8520 6600

Hussain, Miss S (Inesons) *D1 K1 K3*
Cleckheaton *p195* 01274 872202

Hussain, Ms S G (Northumberland County Council)
Morpeth *p466* 01670 533000

Hussain, T (Young & Co) *G H*
Stoke-on-Trent *p398* 01782 339200

Hussain, T (Ford Banks Irwin) *N O Q S1 S2 Zr Zq Zc*
Manchester *p304* 0161 866 8999

Hussain, T P (Petherbridge Bassra Solicitors) *G H*
Bradford *p154* 01274 724114

Hussain, Miss Z H (Churchill Insurance Group)
London EC1 *p105* 020 7656 6838

Hussain-Akhtar, Mrs S (HKH Kenwright & Cox Solicitors) *K1*
Ilford *p260* 020 8553 9600

Hussein, M R (Harper & Odell) *N B1 S1 C1 Zj O Q E S2 Zl*
Islington *p39* 020 7490 0500

Hussein-Doru, L (Jacobs Allen Hammond)
London W1 *p45* 020 7299 9800

Hussell, D A (Cameron Jones Hussell & Howe) *N F1 G D1 W*
Port Talbot *p353* 01639 885261

Hussell, J E (Cameron Jones Hussell & Howe) *D1 K1 K2*
Port Talbot *p353* 01639 885261

Hussell, J G (Cameron Jones Hussell & Howe) *N Q S1 W Zl A3 K4*
Port Talbot *p353* 01639 885261

Hussey, J G W (Joelson Wilson LLP) *E S2 R1 S1 R2 L*
Westminster *p46* 020 7580 5721

Hussey, P N (Bunzl PLC)
London W1 *p104* 020 7725 5000

Hussey, T (Jones Day) *C2*
London EC4 *p46* 020 7039 5959

Hutcheon, A (Watson Farley & Williams)
London EC2 *p90* 020 7814 8000

Hutcheon, R J (R James Hutcheon Solicitors) *C1 E K4 K1 L Q S1 W N Zq Zw*
Prescot *p356* 0151 431 0548

Hutcheson, K C B (Nabarro LLP)
London WC1 *p63* 020 7524 6000

Hutcheson, S A (Hutcheson Forrest) *C1 E S1 W O G Q J1 L F1 Zd Zc Zh*
Bath *p127* 01225 312311

Hutchings, Mrs A E (The College of Law Guildford)
Guildford *p459* 01483 460200

Hutchings, Mrs J (B A A PLC)
London UB3 *p103* 0870 000 0123

Hutchings, Ms J (Adams Harrison) *E S1*
Saffron Walden *p370* 01799 523441

Hutchings, Mrs J M (Goldbergs) *K1*
Plymouth *p349* 01752 660023

Hutchings, J M H (Garner Hutchings)
Westminster *p35* 020 7932 2400

Hutchings, M B (Michael Hutchings) *C3*
Warminster *p421* 07768 105777

Hutchings, N A (Lexica Law) *S1*
Canterbury *p177* 01227 764141

Hutchings, N E (Blakestons) *K1 N Q W J1 F1 S1 K2 E*
Driffield *p213* 01377 253476

Hutchings, R (Pinsent Masons LLP) *C2*
Leeds *p276* 0113 244 5000

Hutchings, R J (Kitsons LLP) *C1 Zl C2*
Torquay *p413* 01803 202020

Hutchings, R K (John Collins & Partners LLP) *A1 A2*
Swansea *p405* 01792 773773

 See p634 for the Key to Work Categories

Hutchins, R (Weightmans LLP) *C1 C2* Liverpool *p291* 0151 227 2601

Hutchinson, A (Dechert) *E* London EC4 *p26* 020 7184 7000

Hutchinson, Ms A (Dawson Cornwell) *K3 K1 D1 D2* London WC1 *p26* 020 7242 2556

Hutchinson, A C (Humphrys & Co) Rhyl *p363* 01745 343158

Hutchinson, A M (Hutchinson & Buchanan) *S1 W C1 A1 E R1 L J1 T1 S2* Ripon *p365* 01765 602156

Hutchinson, A S (Hutchinson Mainprice) *E S1 C1 W R1 Zf Zv* Westminster *p44* 020 7259 0121

Hutchinson, Mrs D E (Ashton Bond Gigg) *W T1 T2 Zd Zo* Nottingham *p335* 0115 947 6651

Hutchinson, J (North Warwickshire Borough Council) Atherstone *p447* 01827 715341

Hutchinson, Mrs J (National Grid PLC) Warwick *p471* 01926 653000

Hutchinson, J (Darbys Solicitors LLP) *E* Oxford *p343* 01865 811700

Hutchinson, Miss J (Sintons LLP) *W S1 K1* Newcastle upon Tyne *p326* 0191 226 7878

Hutchinson, J C (Pitmans LLP) *C1* Reading *p361* 0118 958 0224

Hutchinson, J P (Beale and Company Solicitors LLP) *C2 C1 Ze Zq I U1 U2* London WC2 *p11* 020 7240 3474

Hutchinson, J S (Raworths LLP) *S1 S2 W X* Harrogate *p240* 01423 566666

Hutchinson, Miss K L (Stewarts Law LLP) *O Q Zq A3* London EC4 *p83* 020 7822 8000

Hutchinson, M (Russell-Cooke LLP) *E R2* London SW15 *p74* 020 8789 9111

Hutchinson, M E (Kirbys) *T1 W Zd* Harrogate *p240* 01423 542000

Hutchinson, Mrs M L (Kagan Moss & Co) *W E S1 A3* Teddington *p409* 020 8977 6633

Hutchinson, M P (Mayer Brown International LLP) *P R1* London EC2 *p59* 020 3130 3000

Hutchinson, Miss N (Bolton Magistrates Court) Bolton *p450* 01204 558200

Hutchinson, N (Wansbroughs) Melksham *p314* 01225 703222

Hutchinson, N G (Nick Hutchinson & Co) *S1 S2 W A1 C1 L* Cheltenham *p188* 01242 261515

Hutchinson, R (Foreman Laws) *W K4* Hitchin *p251* 01462 458711

Hutchinson, Ms S J (Crutes) *E* Stockton-on-Tees *p396* 01642 623400

Hutchinson, Miss V L (Withers LLP) *L S1* London EC4 *p92* 020 7597 6000

Hutchison, D S (Sproull Solicitors LLP) *N O Q* Bodmin *p148* 01208 72328

Hutchison, D W (Goldstones) *G H* Swansea *p405* 01792 643021

Hutchison, Ms E (The Wilkes Partnership LLP) *B1* Birmingham *p143* 0121 233 4333

Hutchison, Miss J (Blaser Mills) *K1* High Wycombe *p249* 01494 450171

Hutchison, R (Ford & Warren) *J1* Leeds *p273* 0113 243 6601

Hutchison, R A (Norman Butcher and Jones Holdings Ltd) *C1 J1 E L Ze Zo* Bromley *p452*

Hutsby, H (Hutsby Mees) *A1 S1 W L E* Stafford *p393* 01785 259211

Hutson, A (Thompsons (formerly Robin/Brian Thompson & Partners)) *N* London WC1 *p87* 020 7290 0000

Hutson, C (Fairchild Greig) *O N Q Zq L J1* London W3 *p30* 020 8993 6886

Hutson, J (Napthens LLP) *K1* Preston *p357* 01772 888444

Hutson, J J E (Garner & Hancock Solicitors LLP) *E L S1 W A1 Zl* Isleworth *p263* 020 8232 9560

Hutt, Mrs H L (Barker Son & Isherwood LLP) *W K4* Andover *p118* 01264 353411

Huttley, Mrs E (Gateley LLP) *J1 J2 N Zc Ze* Birmingham *p138* 0121 234 0000

Hutton, Ms A (Petherbridge Bassra Solicitors) *G H* Bradford *p154* 01274 724114

Hutton, A J P (Cunningtons) *S1 S2 W* Solihull *p382* 0121 705 6868

Hutton, C N (Squire Sanders (UK) LLP) Leeds *p277* 0113 284 7000

Hutton, C N R (Clarion Solicitors LLP) *B1 O Q Zb* Leeds *p272* 0113 246 0622; Harrogate *p240* 01423 530630

Hutton, C R (Speechly Bircham LLP) *T2 W K4* London EC4 *p81* 020 7427 6400

Hutton, D A (Bevan Brittan LLP) *Zt Zb E* Bristol *p161* 0870 194 1000

Hutton, Ms J E (Cyril Morris Arkwright) *N Q F1 O Zq* Bolton *p148* 01204 535261

Hutton, N (Holman Fenwick Willan) London EC3 *p42* 020 7264 8000

Hutton, R D (Mills & Reeve) *E* Norwich *p335* 01603 660155

Hutton, S M C (Hutton's) *D1 G H M1 V Zf Zm Zg* Cardiff *p179* 029 2037 8621

Huws, S W (Tudur Owen Roberts Glynne & Co) Caernarfon *p172* 01286 672207 / 672851

Huxley, Ms K (Ashurst LLP) London EC2 *p7* 020 7638 1111

Huxtable, J (ASB Law) *E S2* Crawley *p202* 01293 603600

Huynh, Q C (Daniel and Harris) *K1* Camden *p25* 020 7625 0202

Hyam, Ms N (Crutes) *N S1 K1 W* Newcastle upon Tyne *p324* 0191 233 9700

Hyams, D J (Ware & Kay LLP) *E C1 L J1 F1* York *p445* 01904 716000

Hyams, J (Manches LLP) *D2 S2* London WC2 *p58* 020 7404 4433

Hyams, Miss L D (Metropolitan Police Directorate of Legal Services) London SW1 *p108* 020 7230 7210

Hyams-Parish, A (Rawlison Butler LLP) *J1* Crawley *p202* 01293 527744

Hyatt, Mrs C O (Cullimore Dutton) *E C1 S2 Zn U1* Chester *p190* 01244 356789

Hyatt, J R (Butcher & Barlow LLP) *A1 S2 E W R1 T2 K4* Sandbach *p372* 01270 762521

Hydari, G (Needham Poulier & Partners) *G H* London N17 *p63* 020 8808 6622

Hyde, Miss C J (Sefton Metropolitan Borough Council) Southport *p472* 01704 533133

Hyde, I R (Pinsent Masons LLP) *T1* Birmingham *p141* 0121 200 1050

Hyde, Miss K L (Berg Legal) *O Q* Manchester *p301* 0161 833 9211

Hyde, M R (Clifford Chance) London E14 *p20* 020 7006 1000

Hyde, T W L (Clarke Willmott) Southampton *p385* 0845 209 1000 / 0117 305 6000

Hyde, W J A (DLA Piper UK LLP) *E R2 S2* Manchester *p303* 0870 011 1111

Hydon, Mrs V J (Moore Blatch Solicitors) *N Zr* Southampton *p386* 023 8071 8000

Hyer, C J (Rosenblatt) *O N J1 Q Zq Zc* London EC4 *p73* 020 7955 0880

Hyett, S (Department for Business, Enterprise and Regulatory Reform) London SW1 *p105* 020 7215 0105

Hyland, Miss C N (Cripps Harries Hall LLP) *E S2* Tunbridge Wells *p415* 01892 515121

Hyland, Mrs T (Henmans LLP) *O Q Zq* Oxford *p343* 01865 781000

Hylton, I (Gordons Solicitors LLP) *E* Marlow *p313* 01628 487487; London W1 *p48* 020 7636 1616

Hylton, P R (Howell Hylton) *D1 F1 G H J1 K1 L N S1 V W Zl* Camborne *p173* 01209 613014

Hyman, D K (Clifford Chance) *C1 C2 I U1* London E14 *p20* 020 7006 1000

Hyman, H S (Howard Hyman & Co) *S2 S1 K1* London N12 *p44* 020 8446 5511

Hyman, L L (Bowers) *E L S2 S1* London NW2 *p15* 020 8455 9881

Hyman, N P L (Jacobs & Reeves) *C1 S1 E* Poole *p353* 01202 674425

Hymanson, H (Harbottle & Lewis LLP) *J1* London W1 *p38* 020 7667 5000

Hymanson, M V (Horwich Cohen Coghlan) *G Q J1 J2 N R2 S1 Zp Zw* Manchester *p305* 0161 830 4600

Hynard, S R (Stanley Tee LLP) *W* Saffron Walden *p370* 01799 527299

Hynd, Ms A C (Ison Harrison) *W* Garforth *p228* 0113 286 1455

Hyne, J (Charles Russell LLP) *B1* Guildford *p235* 01483 252525

Hynes, A (Welsh Health Legal Services) Cardiff *p453* 029 2031 5500

Hynes, J (Tinn Criddle & Co) *S1 W S2* Alford *p115* 01507 462882; Sutton-on-Sea *p404* 01507 443043

Hynes, M (West Lancashire District Council) *S1* Ormskirk *p468* 01695 577177

Hynes, Miss S A (Hempsons) *Zr* Westminster *p40* 020 7839 0278

I

I'Anson, A F (Mendip District Council) Shepton Mallet *p471* 01749 343399

I'Anson, J (Brabners Chaffe Street) Liverpool *p286* 0151 600 3000

Iapichino, A (Simmons & Simmons) London EC2 *p79* 020 7628 2020

Iball, Mrs J A (Henmans LLP) *N Q Zq* Oxford *p343* 01865 781000

Ibberson, C D (Bell & Buxton) *S1 S2 T1 W E L* Sheffield *p375* 0114 249 5969

Ibbitson, M E (Withers LLP) *O Q* London EC4 *p92* 020 7597 6000

Ibbotson, J M (Ibbotson Brady) *N Q J2* Leeds *p274* 0113 366 3022

Ibbotson, P C (David Eyres) *S1 E C1 L W* Sheffield *p375* 0114 249 3222; Sheffield *p377* 0114 256 1560

Ibbotson, R W (James Peters & Co) *B1 Q* Sheffield *p377* 0114 278 8900

Ibe, B (Rafina Solicitors) Wembley *p426* 020 8908 6742

Ibe, Mrs G (Sansbury Douglas) *G H* Bristol *p164* 0117 955 2663

Ibrahim, A J (DLA Piper UK LLP) *B1 F1 O Q* Leeds *p272* 0870 011 1111

Ibrahim, S A (Russell & Russell) *D1 K1 K3* Bury *p171* 0161 762 2888

Iceton, Miss G (Carr & Co) *D2 D1 Zr F1 F2 K3 J1 K1 Q W N* Gosforth *p231* 0191 284 0363

Iceton, T F (Tait Farrier Graham) *G H K1 S1 M1 P B1 W F1 J1* Gateshead *p229* 0191 490 0108

Ide, Mrs F M (Martyn Slocombe & Co) *Q N J1 K1 K3 O J2* Malvern *p300* 01684 574001

Idowu, O A O (Andrew Thorne & Co) *D1 D2 F1 J1 K1 K2 Q V Zi Zj* Shaw *p374* 01706 841775; Shaw *p374* 01706 290488

Ife, M A (Herbert Smith LLP) London EC2 *p40* 020 7374 8000

Ifill, Miss G (Miller Evans & Co) *S2 E Zl S1 W* London EC3 *p60* 020 7987 2515

Ifrahim, M (Ifrahim & Co Solicitors) Ilford *p260* 020 8911 9222

Igbiniyesu, A O (Bracknell Forest Borough Council) Bracknell *p450* 01344 424642

Ignatius, Ms N (Withers LLP) *C1 J1* London EC4 *p92* 020 7597 6000

Igoe, Mrs L R (Lodders Solicitors LLP) *W T2* Stratford-upon-Avon *p400* 01789 293259

Ijaz, M (Linklaters LLP) London EC2 *p54* 020 7456 2000

Ijaz, T (Hogan Lovells International LLP) London EC1 *p42* 020 7296 2000

Ikin, Miss H A (Coffin Mew & Clover) *O Q F1 L Zq X Zg* Fareham *p223* 01329 825617

Ikram, R (Mole Valley District Council) Dorking *p457* 01306 885001

Ilersic, R J (Wartnabys) *K1 N Q L J1* Market Harborough *p312* 01858 463322

Ilett, Ms J E (Official Solicitor and Public Trustee) *S1 W D1 K1 Zm* London WC2 *p108* 020 7911 7127

Ilett, W J (Thomas Butler & Son) *S1 W A1 L C1 F1 Zl K4* Broughton-in-Furness *p167* 01229 716336; Millom *p316* 01229 772553

Iley, M (Trowers & Hamlins) London EC3 *p88* 020 7423 8000

Iley, Mrs M R (Northumberland County Council) *K1 M1 P F1 G* Morpeth *p466* 01670 533000

Iliff, Miss C A M (Fosters) *K1 D1* Norwich *p334* 01603 620508

Iliff, C J P (Hamilton Downing Quinn) *E L S1 A1 Zh* London WC1 *p38* 020 7831 8939

Iliff, M (The College of Law Chester) Chester *p454* 0800 289997

Iliff, N P (DLA Piper UK LLP) *E Zh* Birmingham *p137* 0870 011 1111

Iliffe, Mrs K M (Midwinters) *K1 D1 K2* Cheltenham *p188* 01242 514674

Illing, Mrs C L (Cole & Co) Norwich *p334* 01603 617018

Illingworth, Mrs A C (Field Seymour Parkes) *Zb C1 C2* Reading *p360* 0118 951 6200

Illingworth, Mrs A M (Heald Nickinson) *Zq N Q O Zr* Camberley *p173* 01276 680000

Illingworth, Ms L (Scott Rees & Co) *N Q* Skelmersdale *p381* 01695 722222

Illingworth, M (DLA Piper UK LLP) London EC2 *p24* 0870 011 1111; London EC3 *p42* 020 7264 8000

Illingworth, R S H (Adams & Remers) *E S1* Lewes *p283* 01273 480616

Illingworth, S J (Greenwoods Solicitors LLP) *A1 E S2 R2 R1* Peterborough *p347* 01733 887700

Illingworth-Law, N E H (Lewis Silkin LLP) *O Q* London EC4 *p53* 020 7074 8000

Illsley, Ms D (Nexus Solicitors) *O N F2* Manchester *p308* 0161 819 4900

Illston, T M (Burges Salmon) *T1 Zo* Bristol *p161* 0117 939 2000

Ilori, Mrs M A (Amphlett Lissimore) *S1 E* Croydon *p6* 020 8771 5254

Immanuel, H L (Immanuel & Co) *N J1 Zg* London EC4 *p44* 020 7213 9901

Immins, S C H (Turners Solicitors LLP) *K3 K1 W X D2 D1* Bournemouth *p153* 01202 291291

Imperato, M J (Russell Jones & Walker) *N X Zw* Cardiff *p180* 029 2026 2800

Inal, Y R (Inal & Co) Islington *p44* 020 7354 5272

Ince, Mrs E A (Picketts) *W S1 K1 K3* Buxton *p172* 01298 22874

Ince, R (Blake Lapthorn) *S1* Oxford *p342* 01865 248607

Inch, Mrs A (Dyne Drewett Solicitors Ltd) *S1 W S2* Shepton Mallet *p378* 01749 342323

Inch, D H N (Spratt Endicott) *S1* Banbury *p122* 01295 204000

Incles, G C (Stewarts Law LLP) *N* London EC4 *p83* 020 7822 8000

Incoll, D J (West Devon Borough Council) Tavistock *p473* 01822 615911

Ind, Ms L (Bath & North East Somerset Council) *D1 X* Bath *p462* 01225 394041

Ind, Mrs R C (Cook & Talbot) *W T2 S1* Southport *p388* 01704 535216

Indaimo, A (Withers LLP) *E F1 M2 C1* London EC4 *p92* 020 7597 6000

Infante, D A (Jeremy Gibbs & Co) *S1 E W* Amersham *p117* 01494 724671

Infanti, Ms D (Gotelee) *G H* Ipswich *p262* 01473 211121

Ingall, S J (Vickers & Co) *F1 G J1 K1 L P S1 V* Ealing *p89* 020 8579 2559 / 8840 3999

Ingamells, M W (Grove Tompkins Bosworth) *W T1 S1* Birmingham *p138* 0121 236 9341 / 236 8091

Inge, Miss V J (HM Land Registry - Birkenhead) Birkenhead *p449* 0151 473 1110

Inger, Mrs J A (Tierney & Co) Dinnington *p210* 01909 550730

Ingham, Miss H A (DWF) *E R2 S2* Manchester *p303* 0161 603 5000

Ingham, J (Official Solicitor and Public Trustee) *W K1 Q T2 R1 J1 L F1 N Zl Zm Zc* London WC2 *p108* 020 7911 7127

Ingham, Ms J (Withers LLP) *T2 W Zd Zo* London EC4 *p92* 020 7597 6000

Ingham, J D (Pannone LLP) *Zb C1 R2* Manchester *p308* 0161 909 3000

Ingham, Miss K (Last Cawthra Feather LLP) Shipley *p378* 01274 585459

Ingham, T (CMS Cameron McKenna LLP) London EC3 *p17* 020 7367 3000

Ingle, T F (Squire Sanders (UK) LLP) *C2 C1* London EC2 *p81* 020 7655 1000

Ingleby, Ms C G (MB Solicitors Ltd trading as MB Law) *C1 O C2 F2 F1 M3 Ze U2 Zza* Leeds *p275* 0113 242 4444

Ingleby, Miss D E (Rollits LLP) *J1* Hull *p258* 01482 323239

Inglis, A J (Clifford Chance) London E14 *p20* 020 7006 1000

Inglis, A P E (Olswang LLP) *Ze* London WC1 *p64* 020 7067 3000

Inglis, J (Linklaters LLP) London EC2 *p54* 020 7456 2000

Ingram, D E (Darryl Ingram & Co) *G K1 H S1 D1 L F1* London NW4 *p45* 020 8202 0843

Ingram, G J (G & I Chisholm) *G H D1 K1 L Zl Q V K3* Bodmin *p148* 01208 74242

Ingram, J (Grove Tompkins Bosworth) *O Q G H N J1* Birmingham *p138* 0121 236 9341 / 236 8091

Ingram, J M (Barnett Alexander Conway Ingram) *K1 S1 G H M1 P* London N3 *p10* 020 8349 7680

Ingram, K P (Clifford Chance) London E14 *p20* 020 7006 1000

Ingram, L P (Harrisons Solicitors LLP) *S1 W K1 L J1 R2* Welshpool *p425* 01938 552545

Ingram, Mrs M J (Congleton Borough Council) Sandbach *p470* 01270 763231; Winsford *p476* 01606 862862

Ingram, R (Garstangs) London WC2 *p35* 020 7427 5678

Ingram, R G (Hewitsons) *C2 C1* Northampton *p332* 01604 233233

Ingram, Mrs S (Davisons) *S1* Birmingham *p137* 0121 685 1234

Ingram, Ms S (Blake Lapthorn) *O F1* Oxford *p342* 01865 248607

Ingram, S C (EMW) *R2 E S2* Milton Keynes *p316* 0845 070 6000

Ingram, S C (Clarke Willmott) *E S2 R2* Southampton *p385* 0845 209 1000 / 0117 305 6000

Ingram, S G (Russell Jones & Walker) *B2 G* London WC2 *p74* 020 7657 1555

Ingram, T A (Keoghs LLP) *N Zj O Q* Bolton *p149* 01204 677000; Coventry *p200* 024 7665 8200

Ingrey-Counter, M (Avon Rubber PLC) *O* Melksham *p465* 01225 896800; London EC2 *p65* 020 7105 7000

Inguanta, Ms C (SGH Martineau LLP) *L J2 O Q Zq* London EC3 *p75* 020 7264 4444

Inkester, A P (Nabarro LLP) London WC1 *p63* 020 7524 6000

Inkin, A R (GCL Solicitors) *S1 S2 E R1 R2* Guildford *p236* 01483 577091

Inkpin, D H (Wiseman Lee LLP) *K1 G S1 H P D1 M1 E L N* Redbridge *p92* 020 8215 1000

Inman, M (Bradbury Roberts & Raby) *E C1 L S1 S2 O* Scunthorpe *p373* 01724 854000

Inman, P M (Simmons & Simmons) London EC2 *p79* 020 7628 2020

Inman, P R (Paul Inman & Co) *G* Doncaster *p211* 01302 349395

Inman, R J W (Stone King LLP) Bath *p128* 01225 337599

Innes, Ms C (Trowers & Hamlins) London EC3 *p88* 020 7423 8000

Innes, C (Andrew & Andrew Solicitors) *S1 E R1 L R2 S2*
Portsmouth *p354*. 023 9266 1381
Southsea *p388*. 023 9282 1251
Innes, C D (Liss Gulhane Innes & Co) *S1 M1 C1 P K1 E J1 G F1*
Romford *p366*. 01708 764440
Innes, D (Travers Smith LLP) *C1 C2*
London EC1 *p87*. 020 7295 3000
Innes, H J M (SANPAOLO IMI SPA)
London EC4 *p109* 020 7214 8000
Innes, Ms J (Speechly Bircham LLP) *T1*
London EC4 *p81*. 020 7427 6400
Innes, J A (ASB Law) *K1*
Crawley *p202* 01293 603600
Innes, N (Robin Simon LLP)
Manchester *p309* 0333 010 0000
Manchester *p310* 0161 830 5000
Innes, R H R (Walker Morris) *E*
Leeds *p277* 0113 283 2500
Innes, Ms S (Russell Jones & Walker)
Wakefield *p419* 01924 234300
Innes, Ms W S (North Tyneside Council) *C1 C2 I Ze*
Newcastle upon Tyne *p466* . 0191 643 5000
Innes-Ker, R (Lamb Brooks LLP)
Basingstoke *p126* 01256 844888
Basingstoke *p127* 01256 322911
Innes-Taylor, J S (Linklaters LLP)
London EC2 *p54*. 020 7456 2000
Inniss, N M (Suffolk County Council) *G H B2 Zg*
Ipswich *p462*. 01473 583000
Inns, P A (Hanratty & Co) *E K1 N H Q L W F1 Zl G K3*
Newtown *p330*. 01686 626239
Insaidoo, Ms M (Boys & Maughan) *K3 K1*
Margate *p312* 01843 234000
Inskip, K (Pannone LLP) *Zr*
Manchester *p308* 0161 909 3000
Insley, G M (The Gwyn George Partnership) *G H Zl*
Aberdare *p113*. . . .01685 874629 / 871133
Insley, J D (Gepp & Sons) *J1 Q*
Chelmsford *p186*. 01245 493939
Colchester *p197* 01206 369889
Chelmsford *p187*. 01245 491122
Inzani, Miss L M T (Bevan Kidwell) *Zl*
London EC1 *p12*. 020 7843 1820
Portsmouth *p354*. 023 9222 1122
Ioannou, J (GSC Solicitors) *Q N O F1 E C1 Zr Za Zb Zw B1 Zc J1 K1 B2 M2 Zq*
London EC1 *p34*. 020 7822 2222
Ioannou, Ms K A (T G Baynes) *D2 D1 K3 K1*
Dartford *p207* 01322 295555
Iodice, Ms C (Gregory Rowcliffe Milners) *C1 C2*
London WC1 *p37* 020 7242 0631
Ions, J A (Barlow Lyde & Gilbert LLP) *J1*
London EC3 *p10*. 020 7247 2277
Ions, Mrs K (Boodle Hatfield)
Westminster *p14*. 020 7629 7411
Iqbal, A (Birchfields) *E G N S1 S2 Zi*
Manchester *p301* 0161 835 9865
Iqbal, H (Neves) *E S1 S2 M4*
Luton *p295* 01582 725311
Iqbal, M (Morgan Clarke Solicitors) *E N S1*
Cirencester *p195*. 01285 650066
Iqbal, M G (Harrison Bundey) *G H*
Leeds *p274* 0113 200 7400
Iqbal, T (Noble)
Shefford *p377* 01462 814055
Iqbal, Z (Musa A Patel & Co) *G H*
Dewsbury *p210* 01924 437800
Iqbal, Z (Platt Halpern) *G H D1 K1*
Oldham *p341* 0161 626 4955
Irani, Miss V (Jones Day) *C1*
London EC4 *p46*. 020 7039 5959
Iredale, Miss A A (Elliot Mather LLP) *D1 K3 K1*
Chesterfield *p192* 01246 231288
Iredale, A M (Armitage Sykes LLP) *W*
Huddersfield *p255* 01484 538121
Ireland, G F (NGA)
Burnley *p169* 01282 457295
Ireland, G H (Haworth & Nuttall) *S1 L*
Blackburn *p145* 01254 272640
Ireland, J (Tottenham Hotspur PLC)
London N17 *p110* 020 8365 5023
Ireland, J T (St Helens Borough Council)
St Helens *p472* 01744 456000
Ireland, M (Napthens LLP) *F1*
Blackburn *p145* 01254 667733
Ireland, Ms M E (Harlow District Council)
Harlow *p460*. 01279 446611
Ireland, M J (EMW) *O Q B1*
Milton Keynes *p316* 0845 070 6000
Ireland, N J (Button Legal LLP) *S2 E Zl*
Coventry *p200*. 024 7652 5457
Coleshill *p198* 01675 467333
Ireland, P M (Widdows Mason) *K1 D1 D2 G H*
Warrington *p422*. 01925 632267
Ireland, R H (Lester Aldridge LLP) *C1 J1 Zb Ze Zk O*
London WC2 *p53* 0844 967 0785
Ireland, S C F (Burley & Geach) *B1 F1 J1 L N O*
Petersfield *p348* 01730 262401
Ireland, T R (Rowe Radcliffe) *W*
South Croydon *p383*. 020 8680 2070
Ireland, T S (The Paul Rooney Partnership) *N J2 Zq*
Liverpool *p290*. 0151 227 2851
Irish, S A (Nelsons) *E K1 S1 M1 P L W G H D1*
Derby *p209* 01332 372372
Irish, Mrs T (Ellum LLP) *C1 Zj Ze J1 O Q*
London EC3 *p29*. 020 7481 0977

Irlam, B C (Steele Ford & Newton) *S1 G K1 H P W F1 J1 D1 C1 Zi Zl Zv*
Nelson *p321*. 01282 692531
Irlam, M (Steele Ford & Newton) *G N H*
Nelson *p321*. 01282 692531
Irons, E (Wrigleys Solicitors LLP) *W*
Sheffield *p377* 0114 267 5588
Irons, K J (Hall Ennion & Young) *S1*
Ely *p218*. 01353 662918
Irons, R G (Archers Law LLP) *Q O F1 Zq J1*
Stockton-on-Tees *p396* . . . 01642 636500
Irons, S (Brabners Chaffe Street)
Preston *p356* 01772 823921
Irvine, Miss C J (Harrison Clark LLP) *E A1*
Cheltenham *p188* 01242 269198
Worcester *p439* 01905 612001
Worcester *p439* 01905 612001
Irvine, Ms J (Henderson Global Investors)
London EC2 *p106* 020 7818 1818
Irvine, K D (Seddons) *C1 C2*
Westminster *p77*. 020 7725 8000
Irvine, Miss L (Red Kite Law) *G H*
Tenby *p410* 01834 842122
Irvine, M J (Trethowans LLP) *J1*
Southampton *p387*. 023 8032 1000
Irvine, P J (Edwards Duthie) *N Q Zj*
Ilford *p260*. 020 8514 9000
Irvine, R (Wigan Borough Council)
Wigan *p476* 01942 244991
Irvine, R G (Crick & Freeman) *A1 E L S1 T1 W Zh*
Maldon *p299*. 01621 852606
Irvine, S W (Muckle LLP) *O Q*
Newcastle upon Tyne *p325* . 0191 211 7777
Irving, Mrs A (Irvings) *N O X Q*
Liverpool *p289*. 0800 954 0243
Liverpool *p289*. 0800 954 0243
Irving, A W (Thornton & Co) *N G K1 Q*
Lytham *p297*. 01253 782808
Irving, D P (Mundays LLP) *C1 C2*
Cobham *p196* 01932 590500
Irving, Ms E (Starkie & Gregory) *K1 P M1 S1*
Long Eaton *p293* 0115 849 9000
Irving, G (Quality Solicitors Jackson & Canter) *Zi Zg*
Liverpool *p290*. 0151 282 1700
Irving, Mrs H K (Centro (West Midlands Passenger Transport Exec))
Birmingham *p449* 0121 200 2787
Irving, N (DWF) *Zb O Q*
Manchester *p303* 0161 603 5000
Irving, P M C F (Winckworth Sherwood LLP)
London SE1 *p92*. 020 7593 5000
Irving, S T (Irvings) *B1 C1 C2 E O*
Liverpool *p289*. 0800 954 0243
Liverpool *p289*. 0800 954 0243
Irwin, Ms A T (Cottrill Stone Lawless) *S1 E R2 S2*
Manchester *p302* 0161 835 3681
Irwin, Ms D (Shakespeares)
Birmingham *p142* 0121 237 3000
Irwin, D G (Teacher Stern LLP) *E C1 R2 S2*
London WC1 *p86* 020 7242 3191
Irwin, Ms J A (Nottingham City Council (City Sec Dept))
Nottingham *p467*. 0115 915 5555
Irwin, Ms J F (Blandy & Blandy) *N Q L F1*
Reading *p360* 0118 951 6800
Irwin-Singer, J P T (Blake Lapthorn) *K1 P D1 F1 N L V Zg Zp*
Oxford *p342*. 01865 248607
Isaac, D (Pinsent Masons LLP) *T1*
London EC2 *p67*. 020 7418 7000
Isaac, D A (Davies Parsons Allchurch) *G H*
Llanelli *p292*. 01554 749144
Isaac, D M (Pardoes) *Zr J1*
Bridgwater *p158* 01278 457891
Isaac, D P (Withers LLP) *J1 Q Zi*
London EC4 *p92*. 020 7597 6000
Isaac, Ms F S (Davenport Lyons)
London W1 *p25* 020 7468 2600
Isaac, G F W (Trobridges) *S1 W G H K1 M1 P N E F1 Zl Za*
Torpoint *p412* 01752 812787
Isaac, Miss L M (Andrew Markham & Co) *K1 Q N L K3 B1 D1 J1*
Carmarthen *p182* . .01267 221550 / 236199
Isaac, Mrs M C (City & County of Swansea)
Swansea *p473*. 01792 636000
Isaac, R A (Tanners) *W O J1 C1 Q*
Cirencester *p195*. 01285 659061
Isaac, S K (Gloucester City Council)
Gloucester *p459*. 01452 522232
Isaacs, D (Segens Blount Petre) *E N S1 C1 P*
Westminster *p77*. 020 7332 2222
Isaacs, D L (David Isaacs) *E Zf U2 Ze C1 S2 I O*
Henley-on-Thames *p247*. . . 01491 577130
Isaacs, J A (Barlow Lyde & Gilbert LLP) *Zq*
London EC3 *p10*. 020 7247 2277
Isaacs, J E (Hill Dickinson LLP) *N Za Zj*
London EC3 *p41*. 020 7283 9033
Isaacs, Mrs L J (Wokingham District Council)
Wokingham *p477* 0118 974 6000
Isaacs, M P (Addleshaw Goddard) *O*
Manchester *p300* 0161 934 6000
Isaacs, M R (Butcher & Barlow LLP) *W S1*
Tyldesley *p416*. 01942 883669
Isaacs, P J (Inghams) *S1 S2 E L R1 W*
Fleetwood *p226* 01253 873481
Isaacs, R A (Lloyds TSB Group PLC)
London EC2 *p107* 020 7158 2729
Isaacs, S (Kiteleys Solicitors Limited)
Bournemouth *p152*. 01202 299992

Isaacs, Miss S V (Hornby & Levy) *D1 D2 K1 X*
London SW9 *p43* 020 7737 0909
Isaacson, A (Aubrey Isaacson Solicitors) *C1 E G J1 K1 N O Q S1 W Zc Zj*
Prestwich *p357* 0161 959 5000
Isaacson, A M (Russell-Cooke LLP) *C1 E S2*
London SW15 *p74*. 020 8789 9111
Isaacson, A P (Rootes & Alliott) *K1 K2 J1*
Folkestone *p227*. 01303 851100
Isaacson, S D (Aubrey Isaacson Solicitors) *N Q K1 S1 W J1 D1 F1 G L*
Prestwich *p357* 0161 959 5000
Isbell, Ms R (Herrington & Carmichael LLP) *K1 N S1*
Wokingham *p437* 0118 977 4045
Isbister, L J (Lancashire County Council) *F1 G H K1 L*
Preston *p469* 01772 254868
Isenberg, C A (Barnett Alexander Conway Ingram) *S1 E P L N K1 M1 D1 Zp*
London N3 *p10* 020 8349 7680
Iseries, I (Ashurst LLP)
London EC2 *p7* 020 7638 1111
Ishak, Mrs J M (Squire Sanders (UK) LLP) *C1 C3 I M1 Ze Zh*
Birmingham *p142* 0121 222 3000
Isham, R L V (Wedlake Bell LLP) *J1 O Zc Zk Zp*
London WC1 *p91* 020 7395 3000
Ishani, M G H K (Sherrards)
St Albans *p390* 01727 832830
Ishaq, Miss F (Crombie Wilkinson) *D2 D1 K3 K1*
Selby *p374* 01757 708957
Ishaq, Ms S (Berg Legal) *C1 J1 J2 Zp*
Manchester *p301* 0161 833 9211
Isherwood, P G (Moran & Co) *B1 L N O Q*
Tamworth *p407* 01827 54631
Isherwood, S G (Forbes) *S1 S2 C1 E W P L A1 Zl R1*
Preston *p356* 01772 220022
Isitt, A (E D C Lord & Co)
Hayes *p245* 020 8848 9988
Islam, F (Pannone LLP) *N*
Manchester *p308* 0161 909 3000
Islam, M M (Singleton Saunders Flood Solicitors) *Q J1 Ze O S1 N*
Dover *p213* 01304 240080
Islam-Syed, Mrs N F (Healys LLP) *S1*
London EC4 *p39*. 020 7822 4000
Islip, L A G (Eastgate Assistance Ltd) *A1 E L R1 S1 Zc*
Colchester *p455* 0870 523 4500
Ismail, B (Ismail & Ghani) *E F1 G H J1 K1 L M1 R1 S1 Zl*
Bradford *p154* 01274 737546
Ismail, Miss F (Sydney Mitchell) *E F1 G J1 K1 L P R1 T1*
Birmingham *p142* 0121 698 2200 / 0808 166 8827
Ismail, Mrs N (Kent County Council)
Maidstone *p464* 01622 694320
Ismail, Ms S (South Manchester Law Centre)
Manchester *p465* 0161 225 5111
Ismay, D J (Delta Legal) *Zr Q N*
Stockport *p395*. 0870 350 5101
Ismay, Miss E (Crane & Staples) *T2 W*
Welwyn Garden City *p425* . 01707 329333
Ison, Ms A M (Hughes Fowler Carruthers) *K1 K3*
London WC2 *p43* 020 7421 8383
Ison, Miss R A (Badhams Law (A Trading Name of Parabis Law LLP)) *N*
Croydon *p204* 0844 245 4000
Ison-Jacques, L A (Hodge Jones & Allen LLP) *N*
London NW1 *p41* 020 7874 8300
Israel, A S (Israel Strange & Conlon) *W T2 K4*
Islington *p45*. 020 7833 8453
Israel, B M (Bird & Bird LLP) *B1 Zb*
London EC4 *p13*. 020 7415 6000
Israel, D E (Wedlake Bell LLP) *J1*
London WC1 *p91* 020 7395 3000
Ito, S (Hogan Lovells International LLP)
London EC1 *p42*. 020 7296 2000
Ivanec, Ms A A (Rydon Group Ltd)
Forest Row *p458* 01342 825151
Ivanec, R J (Forth & Co) *S1 S2 C1 J1 Q L F1 B1 M1 Zq Ze*
Yarm *p443*. 01642 784000
Ive, D H (Mayer Brown International LLP) *T1*
London EC2 *p59*. 020 3130 3000
Ivens, R J (Marks & Spencer PLC) *C1 F1 J1 Ze*
London W2 *p107* 020 7935 4422
Ives, G (Bates & Mountain) *G H K1 Q D2 D1*
Grimsby *p235* 01472 357291
Ives, J R (Fosters) *N*
Norwich *p334* 01603 620508
Ives, Miss V E (Charsley Harrison LLP) *C1 S2 E*
Windsor *p434* 01753 851591
Ives, Mrs V S (Ives & Co) *S1 W E*
Nottingham *p337*. 0115 937 2408
Ives-Keeler, S R (Ives-Keeler & Co) *E L R2 S1 S2*
Norwich *p334* 01603 219298
Ivey, N C (Bates Wells & Braithwaite London LLP) *E S2 R2 Zh L Zd*
London EC4 *p11* 020 7551 7777
Ivey, N J (Squire Sanders (UK) LLP)
London EC2 *p81*. 020 7655 1000
Ivill, Mrs F (Enfield Magistrates Court)
London N17 *p106* 020 8808 5411
Ivin, Mrs A (Hugh James)
Cardiff *p179* 029 2022 4871
Ivinson, Ms J (Black Rock)
London EC4 *p104* 020 7743 3000
Ivinson, P J (Hilliers HRW Solicitors) *G H L*
Stevenage *p395* 01438 346000

Ivison, A S (CMS Cameron McKenna LLP)
London EC3 *p17*. 020 7367 3000
Ivor-Jones, M (Frederic Hall) *N L Q S1 S2 W O*
Folkestone *p227*. 01303 851185
Ivory, Ms P (Metcalfe Copeman & Pettefar) *W*
Thetford *p410* 01842 756100
Iwanier, N N (Bude Nathan Iwanier) *B1 C1 E J1 L N P S1 T1 W*
London NW11 *p16* 020 8458 5656
Iyama, Ms I (Iyama Solicitors) *H B2 Zi L*
Southwark *p45*. 020 7357 0709
Iyer, M (Ince & Co Services Ltd)
London E1 *p44* 020 7481 0010
Izod, K H R (Fulchers of Farnborough) *S1 E N K1 G R1 H J1 W S2 C1 K3 O Q*
Farnborough *p224* 01252 522475
Izod, P L (HC Solicitors LLP) *A1 E K4 S1 T2 W S2*
Oundle *p342*. 01832 273506
Peterborough *p347* 01733 882800
Izod, S C (Callaghans) *B1 J1 L O P Q R1 Zb Zc Ze Zi*
Farnham *p224* 01252 723477
Izquierdo, M (Lamb Brooks LLP) *S2 E*
Basingstoke *p126* 01256 844888
Izzard, Mrs C M (Stanley Tee) *W T2*
Bishop's Stortford *p144* . . . 01279 755200
Izzard, Ms J (Park Woodfine Heald Mellows LLP) *K1*
Rushden *p369*. 01933 397000
Izzard, Mrs J T (Bells) *W*
Romsey *p366* 01794 513328
Izzett, M D N (Everys) *S1 E L W*
Exmouth *p222* 01395 264384
Izzett, Mrs S L J (Everys) *L S1*
Budleigh Salterton *p168* . . . 01395 442223

J

Jabeen, Miss F (Tyndallwoods) *Zg Zi*
Birmingham *p143* 0121 624 1111
Jabin, Mrs T (Oldham Law Centre)
Oldham *p468* 0161 627 0925
Jack, A (AMD Solicitors) *W K4*
Bristol *p160* 0117 962 1460
Jack, Mrs J (Eaton Ryan & Taylor) *Q O J1 Zp A3 B1 F1 F2*
Birmingham *p138* 0121 236 1999
Jack, Ms S (Mills & Reeve) *W T2*
Norwich *p335* 01603 660155
Jack, S D R (Kennedys) *N G Zj*
London EC3 *p49*. 020 7667 9667
Jackaman, J (Herbert Smith LLP)
London EC2 *p40*. 020 7374 8000
Jacklin, R (Richard Jacklin & Co) *W T2 K4*
Liverpool *p289*. 0151 243 1313
Southport *p388* 01704 500024
Jackman, D C (Jackman Woods) *A1 Zd E K4 S1 T2 W*
Winchcombe *p433*. 01242 602378
Jackman, I P (Arcadia Group Ltd)
London W1 *p103* 020 7636 8040
Jackman, M (Hodge Jones & Allen LLP) *G B2 Zg*
London NW1 *p41* 020 7874 8300
Jackman, M R (Wilson Browne) *E C1 B1 J1 A1 S1 L F1 W R1 Ze Zl Zc*
Kettering *p265*. 01536 410041
Jackman, Miss R (Walker Morris) *Zb B1*
Leeds *p277* 0113 283 2500
Jacks, H (Mills & Reeve) *O D1 F1 G N J2 Zm Zr Ze*
Birmingham *p140* 0121 454 4000
Jacks, P L T (Fraser Brown) *E S1 C1 A1 R2*
Nottingham *p337*. 0115 988 8777
Jackson, A (McGrigors LLP)
London EC4 *p56*. 020 7054 2500
Jackson, A (Ince & Co Services Ltd)
London E1 *p44* 020 7481 0010
Jackson, Ms A C S (Wandsworth & Merton Law Centre Ltd)
London SW17 *p110* 020 8767 2777
Jackson, A G W (Macfarlanes) *R1 P*
London EC4 *p56*. 020 7831 9222
Jackson, Ms A L (Aviva PLC) *S1 W L R1*
London EC3 *p103* . . 020 7283 7500 / 01603 687905
Jackson, Miss A L G (Reed Smith LLP) *C1 C2*
London EC2 *p71*. 020 3116 3000
Jackson, A P (Stokes Solicitors) *S1 E S2 R1 J1 C1*
Portsmouth *p355*. 023 9282 8131
Jackson, A P C (Blaser Mills) *S1 E*
Staines *p393*. 01784 462511
Jackson, A W J (Mohammed & Co Solicitors) *G H B2 V Zp Ze*
Preston *p357* 01772 888700
Jackson, B (Mowlem PLC)
Bracknell *p451*. 01344 426826
Jackson, Mrs B E (Arnold Greenwood) *Zr J1 Q N*
Kendal *p264*. 01539 720049
Penrith *p346*. 01768 864651
Jackson, B S (John Boyle & Co) *K1 D1*
Redruth *p362* 01209 213507
Truro *p414*. 01872 272356
Jackson, Ms C (Kaim Todner Ltd) *G H B2*
Islington *p47*. 020 7700 0070
London N17 *p92*. 020 8808 7535
Jackson, Ms C (Bindmans LLP) *N*
London WC1 *p12* 020 7833 4433

See p634 for the Key to Work Categories

Jackson, Miss C A (Roland Robinsons & Fentons LLP) *K1 L Q N V*
Blackpool *p147* 01253 621432
Jackson, C C (Quality Solicitors Mewies) *W S1 T2 S2 A1 E*
Skipton *p381*. 01756 799000
Jackson, Mrs C C (Howell-Jones LLP) *W T1*
Leatherhead *p271* 01372 860650
Kingston upon Thames *p267*. 020 8549 5186
Jackson, Ms C G P (Pannone LLP) *N*
Manchester *p308* 0161 909 3000
Jackson, C H (Gisby Harrison) *O*
Cheshunt *p189* 01707 878300
London WC2 *p74* 020 7657 1555
Jackson, C J (Field Fisher Waterhouse LLP) *C1*
London EC3 *p31*. 020 7861 4000
Jackson, C J (Forsters LLP) *E*
Westminster *p33*. 020 7863 8333
Jackson, Ms C M (LG Lawyers) *E*
London SE1 *p50*. 020 7379 0000
Jackson, C M (Burges Salmon) *O J1 Zb Zj*
Bristol *p161* 0117 939 2000
Jackson, D (Sternberg Reed) *N G*
Barking *p123* 020 8591 3366
Jackson, D (Shoosmiths)
Birmingham *p142* 0370 086 4000 / 0121 335 4440
Jackson, Mrs D (Walker Morris) *C1*
Leeds *p277* 0113 283 2500
Jackson, D (Buckles Solicitors LLP) *W T1 Zo T2*
Peterborough *p346* 01733 888888
Jackson, Miss D A (Jackson West) *D1*
Stratford-upon-Avon *p400* . . 01789 204020
Jackson, D H (Hart Jackson & Sons) *K1 N G Q*
Ulverston *p416*. 01229 583291
Jackson, D J (Heath Buckeridge)
Maidenhead *p298* 01628 671636
Jackson, Miss D L (Bhatia Best) *K3 K1*
Nottingham *p336*. 0115 950 3231
Jackson, E (Tang Bentley & Jackson) *G H B2*
Fareham *p224*. 01329 220401
Jackson, Mrs E (Finn Gledhill) *K1 D1 D2 K3*
Hebden Bridge *p246*. 01422 842451
Halifax *p238* 01422 330000
Jackson, Ms E A (Network Rail)
London NW1 *p108*. 020 7557 8000
Jackson, Miss G (Speechly Bircham LLP) *Zr K4 Q N Zm W T1 T2 Zd*
London EC4 *p81*. 020 7427 6400
Jackson, G A (Taylor Wessing) *M1 C1 T1 F1 Zi Zl*
London EC4 *p86*. 020 7300 7000
Jackson, G G (Hart Jackson & Sons) *K1 N G D1 Q F1 J1 H R1 V Zl Zd*
Ulverston *p416*. 01229 583291
Jackson, G S (Widdows Mason) *G H Zl B2*
Wigan *p432* 01942 244294
Jackson, Ms H (Inghams)
Poulton-le-Fylde *p355* 01253 890545
Jackson, Ms H E (Pinkney Grunwells Lawyers LLP) *S2 A1 C1 E P S1*
Bridlington *p158* 01262 673445
Scarborough *p372*. 01723 352125
Jackson, H S (Wilkinson Woodward)
Halifax *p238* 01422 339600
Jackson, J (Shoosmiths)
Birmingham *p142* 0370 086 4000 / 0121 335 4440
Jackson, Mrs J (Blanchards Bailey LLP) *C1 S2 E*
Blandford Forum *p147*. . . . 01258 459361
Jackson, J A (Paul Fallon & Co) *F1 G H K1 L M1 P R1 S1 W*
Watford *p423* 01923 226795
Jackson, J D (Gardner Leader LLP) *G H D1 N Q Zl*
Newbury *p322*. 01635 508080
Jackson, J D (Shoosmiths) *C1 E M1 T1 Zb Zf Zl*
Fareham *p224*. . . . 0370 086 6800 / 01489 616800
Jackson, Mrs J M (Taunton Deane Borough Council)
Taunton *p473* 01823 356356
Jackson, K (Hedleys Solicitors LLP) *J1 Zk Q*
East Horsley *p215*. 01483 284567
Jackson, Ms K E (Edwin Coe LLP) *W T2*
London WC2 *p29* 020 7691 4000
Jackson, Ms K J (Cornwall County Council) *D1 G F1 K1 L N Q O*
Truro *p474*. 01872 322197
Jackson, Miss L (David Gray Solicitors) *N Zg Q*
Newcastle upon Tyne *p324* . 0191 232 9547
Jackson, Ms L A (Squire Sanders (UK) LLP)
London EC2 *p81*. 020 7655 1000
Jackson, Ms L A (Hockfield & Co) *N Q Zq*
Lambeth *p41*. 020 7582 8784
Jackson, Ms L F (ML Law Ltd) *D1 K3 F1 J1 K1 O Q Zq*
Eastleigh *p216*. 023 8060 0661
Jackson, L I (Addleshaw Goddard) *C1*
London EC1 *p4* 020 7606 8855
Jackson, M (Machins Solicitors LLP) *C1 S2 E F1*
Luton *p295* 01582 514000
Jackson, Ms M (The College of Law)
London WC1 *p105*. 0800 289997
Jackson, M A (Beetenson & Gibbon) *S1 K1 W V F1 M1 P T1 G*
Grimsby *p235* 01472 240251
Jackson, M R (Sandersons) *B2 C1 O Q*
Hull *p258* 01482 324662
Jackson, M R (William H Lill & Co) *K1 C1 S1 W E B1 L J1 N*
Altrincham *p116* 0161 928 8111
Lymm *p296* . . . . .01925 753170 / 755668
Jackson, Mrs N A (Yorklaw Ltd (t/a Burn & Company)) *Q F1*
York *p445* 01904 655442
Jackson, N S (Jacksons Solicitors)
London W1 *p45* 020 3058 0512
Jackson, O (William H Lill & Co) *C1 Zj U2 N C2 R2 Zw*
Lymm *p296* . . . . .01925 753170 / 755668
Altrincham *p116* 0161 928 8111
Jackson, O J F (Mundays LLP) *O Q B1 B2 A3 Zc F1 F2 L Zk R1 Zq*
Cobham *p196* 01932 590500
Jackson, P (Hill Dickinson LLP)
Liverpool *p288*. 0151 600 8000
Jackson, P A (Taylor Wessing) *T1*
London EC4 *p86*. 020 7300 7000
Jackson, P G (Atter Mackenzie & Co) *K1 N V G B1 H Q O C1 F1 Zc Ze K3*
Evesham *p220*. 01386 425300
Jackson, P H (Marsden Rawsthorn LLP) *D1 K1 Zm X*
Chorley *p194* 01257 279511
Jackson, R (Brabners Chaffe Street) *E*
Liverpool *p286*. 0151 600 3000
Jackson, R A (Jacksons) *S1 W*
Wirral *p435* 0151 632 3386
Jackson, R F H (Hart Jackson & Sons) *S1 W A1 C1 E T1 L R1 B1 J1 Zo Zc Zd*
Ulverston *p416*. 01229 583291
Jackson, Mrs R J (Swinburne & Jackson LLP) *K1 K2*
Washington *p423* 0191 416 0004
Jackson, Miss R J (Reynolds Porter Chamberlain LLP) *Zk*
London E1 *p71* 020 3060 6000
Jackson, R J B (Stevens Son & Pope) *S1 W S2 Zl E*
Burgess Hill *p168* 01444 246377
Jackson, Ms R M (Cyril Morris Arkwright) *K1*
Bolton *p148* 01204 535261
Jackson, R M (Bower & Bailey) *S2 S1 E*
Banbury *p122* 01295 265566
Jackson, R M (Gudgeons Prentice) *S2 S1 E*
Stowmarket *p399* 01449 613101
Jackson, R W W (Bromets Jackson Heath) *N Q J1 O W C1 S1 Zp*
Tadcaster *p407* 01937 832371
Jackson, S (Michael Brough and Cohen) *K3 K1 D1 Q D2 W*
Beaconsfield *p128*. 01494 680420
Jackson, S A (Southerns) *S1 J1 G H W*
Colne *p198* 01282 863113
Jackson, S A (HMG Law LLP) *J1 O Q Zt*
Bicester *p132* 01869 252244
Jackson, S C (Higgs & Sons) *D1 D2 K1 K2 X*
Brierley Hill *p158*. 0845 111 5050
Jackson, S C (Stokoe Partnership) *G H*
Waltham Forest *p83* 020 8558 8884
Jackson, Ms S C (Dunning & Co) *D1 G H K1*
London SE5 *p28*. 020 7733 6217
Jackson, Mrs S J (Oxley & Coward Solicitors LLP) *W*
Rotherham *p367*. 01709 510999
Jackson, Mrs S J (Davies & Partners) *K1*
Almondsbury *p115*. 01454 619619
Jackson, Miss S M (The Ringrose Law Group - Richard Harwood) *S1*
Lincoln *p285*. 01522 814700
Jackson, S M (Shulmans) *E S2 R2*
Leeds *p276* 0113 245 2833
Jackson, S M (Dickinson Dees) *E*
Newcastle upon Tyne *p324* . 0191 279 9000
Jackson, S R B (Simon Jackson Solicitors) *P L M1 J1 N G Zc Zl O Q R1*
Oswestry *p342*. 01691 791439
Jackson, S T (Barlow Lyde & Gilbert LLP)
London EC3 *p10*. 020 7247 2277
Jackson, Ms T A (Welsh Health Legal Services)
Cardiff *p453* 029 2031 5500
Jackson, T K G (Weightmans LLP) *E R1 Zc R2*
Manchester *p311* 0161 233 7330
Jackson, Miss T N (Leeds City Council)
Leeds *p462* 0113 224 3513
Jackson, Mrs V R (Salford City Council)
Swinton *p473* 0161 794 4711
Jackson, W R (Nelsons) *A1 C1 S2 E C2 Zc*
Nottingham *p338*. 0115 958 6262
Jackson-Nichols, Ms A (Aviva PLC)
London EC3 *p103* . . 020 7283 7500 / 01603 687905
Norwich *p467* 01603 622200
Jackson-Thomas, Miss S J (John Collins & Partners LLP) *K1 D1 V K2*
Swansea *p405*. 01792 773773
Jacob, J M (Leelanes Solicitors LLP) *N S1 L F1 K1 E B1 Zk Zm Ze*
London EC3 *p52*. 020 7220 9410
Jacob, M H (Jonas Roy Bloom) *N Zr*
Birmingham *p139* 0121 212 4111
Jacob, M S (Fuglers) *S2 E S1 Zf Zl Zw R2*
London W1 *p34* 020 7323 6450
Jacob, N D G (LG Lawyers)
London SE1 *p50*. 020 7379 0000
Jacobi, N D (John Collins & Partners LLP) *Q A1 Zq L R1 A2*
Swansea *p405*. 01792 773773
Jacobs, A J (Antony Hodari & Co)
Manchester *p305* 0161 832 4781
Jacobs, A J (Seddons) *E L S1 R1 R2 S2*
Westminster *p77*. 020 7725 8000
Jacobs, A M (Anthony Jacobs & Co) *S1 W E*
Cardiff *p179* 029 2048 3509
Jacobs, A S (DLA Piper UK LLP) *J2 Zj N*
Birmingham *p137* 0870 011 1111
Jacobs, C (Linklaters LLP)
London EC2 *p54*. 020 7456 2000
Jacobs, Miss C A (Palmers) *S1 E S2*
Basildon *p126* 01268 240000
Jacobs, Miss D A J (Gary Jacobs & Co) *D1 G H*
London E18 *p45*. 020 8536 4050
Jacobs, D N (Stanley Tee) *D2 D1 K1 N Zr Zq*
Bishop's Stortford *p144* . . . 01279 755200
Jacobs, Miss F (Josiah Hincks) *B1 Zr J1 L O Q N*
Leicester *p280*. 0116 255 1811
Jacobs, J (Healys LLP) *E R2 S1 S2 T1 T2*
London EC4 *p39*. 020 7822 4000
Jacobs, J (Howell-Jones LLP) *W*
Cheam *p186*. 020 8642 8142
Jacobs, Ms L (Pinsent Masons LLP) *T1*
London EC2 *p67*. 020 7418 7000
Jacobs, L L (Redfern & Co) *S1 W E K3 C1 S2*
Birmingham *p141* 0121 236 1801
Jacobs, P S (Powell Spencer & Partners) *L N Q K1 J1 V Zh*
London NW6 *p69* 020 7604 5600
Jacobs, P W (Jacobs Allen Hammond) *E S1 S2 T2 R1 L C1 Zb Zc*
London W1 *p45* 020 7299 9800
Jacobs, Mrs R M (Jobling Gowler) *Zr*
Macclesfield *p297* 01625 614250
Jacobs, S (Public Interest Lawyers)
Birmingham *p141* 0121 515 5069
Jacobs, S G (Stanley Jacobs) *E L O Q S1 W Zb Zc S2*
Barnet *p46*. 020 8349 4241
Jacobs, S P (Seddons) *O B1 Q Ze Zk Zb A3 Zf Zq*
Westminster *p77*. 020 7725 8000
Jacobs, T (Henry Hyams) *Q G N J1*
Leeds *p274* 0113 243 2288
Jacobs, T H (Flint Bishop Solicitors) *Zc O A3*
Nottingham *p337*. 0115 964 4450
Jacobsen, Mrs E (Warrens Boyes & Archer) *K1 Q K3 J1 K2*
Huntingdon *p258*. 01480 411331
Jacobsen, Mrs H V (Jacobsen & Co) *C1 E L S1 W Zf*
London SW6 *p46* 020 7736 6277
Jacobsen, N L (Jacobsens) *C1 C2 E O S2*
London EC2 *p46*. 020 7608 2568
Jacobsen, P T (Bircham Dyson Bell)
Westminster *p13*. 020 7227 7000
Jacobson, P R (Paul R Jacobson & Co) *E F1 G H K1 L N S1 W*
Leeds *p274* 0113 269 3925
Jacoby, J D (DB Law) *S1*
Camborne *p173* 01209 712428
Penzance *p346* 01736 364261
Jacovides, M (Allen & Overy LLP)
London E1 *p5* 020 3088 0000
Jacques, R (Albin & Co) *G H Zm*
Reading *p359* 0118 957 4018
Jaehrig, Mrs S (Sills & Betteridge LLP) *J1*
Gainsborough *p228* 01427 616816
Lincoln *p285*. 01522 542211
Jaffa, A R (Foot Anstey) *O Ze Zf Zk*
Exeter *p221* 01392 411221
Jaffa, R H (Dass Solicitors) *C1 S2 O Q W S1 R2*
Birmingham *p137* 0121 248 4000
Jaffe, G N (Jaffe Porter Crossick) *E L W S1*
London NW6 *p46* 020 7625 4424
Jagannath, V (Odeon & UCI Cinemas) *E*
Manchester *p465* 0161 455 4000
Jagatia, Miss D S (Ray Borley & Dunkley) *K1 G H Q D1 F1 V N J1 B1 Zt Zc Zl*
Stony Stratford *p399*. 01908 563232
Jagatia, S P (Talbots Legal Advice Centre) *G H*
Stourbridge *p399* . .01384 445850 / 447777
Jagdev, H S (Hasan Solicitors) *G H*
Birmingham *p139* 0121 778 4003
Jagger, C E (Addleshaw Goddard)
Leeds *p271* 0113 209 2000
Jagger, Miss H (Blake Lapthorn) *N Q F1 J1 K1*
Portsmouth *p354*. 023 9222 1122
Jagger, Miss J V (Burnetts) *Zr*
Carlisle *p181*. 01228 552222
Carlisle *p182*. 01228 552222
Jagger, Miss K (Painters) *K1 K3*
Kidderminster *p266* 01562 822295
Jago, Miss A L K (stevensdrake) *K1 K3 D1 D2*
Crawley *p202* 01293 596900
Jago, Mrs H A (Palmers) *W K4*
Basildon *p126* 01268 240000
Jago, Ms S C J (RHW Solicitors LLP) *K1 K3*
Guildford *p237*. 01483 302000
Jago, Ms S J (stevensdrake) *K1 V K2 K3*
Crawley *p202* 01293 596900
Jagusch, S (Allen & Overy LLP)
London E1 *p5* 020 3088 0000
Jahangir, Ms S A N (Archer & Archer) *W T2 K4*
Ely *p218*. 01353 662203
Jahreiss, M (Gateley LLP) *T1 T2*
Birmingham *p138* 0121 234 0000
Jaj, B (Lamb Brooks LLP) *E R1 S1*
Basingstoke *p126* 01256 844888
Jakeman, Mrs L M (Williamson & Soden) *E S2 R2 S1*
Solihull *p383*. 0121 733 8000
Leamington Spa *p270* 01926 886688
Jakes, I R (Jakes & Co) *S1 E N Q W G H K1 L D1 Zc Zl Zn*
New Ollerton *p321*. 01623 860581
Jakobi, S R (Fair Trials Abroad Trust) *P K1 M1 L G D1*
Richmond upon Thames *p470* 020 8332 2800
Jallow, Ms M (Gregory Rowcliffe Milners) *W*
London WC1 *p37* 020 7242 0631
Jalota, Ms K (Waldrons) *Zr N*
Brierley Hill *p158*. 01384 811811
Jama, M (Ince & Co Services Ltd)
London E1 *p44* 020 7481 0010
Jamal, D (Eddowes Waldron) *D1 K3 K1*
Derby *p208* 01332 348484
Jamal, Miss T (Blaser Mills) *K1 K2*
Harrow *p241*. 020 8427 6262
Jamali, F (MRH Solicitors) *Q*
Bolton *p149* 01204 535333
Jamdar, Ms S (SGH Martineau LLP) *O*
Birmingham *p142* 0870 763 2000
James, Ms A (Alliance Boots PLC)
Nottingham *p467*. 0115 950 6111
James, A (Thompsons (formerly Robin/Brian Thompson & Partners))
Newcastle upon Tyne *p327* . 0191 269 0400
James, Mrs A (Turnbull Garrard) *S1 E W A1*
Shrewsbury *p379* . .01743 350851 / 351332
James, A C (Goodall Barnett James) *G H*
Horley *p252* 01293 414448
James, A D (Bynes) *G H K1 K3 B2*
Torquay *p412* 01803 295692
James, A H (Andrew Jackson & Co) *N S1 L K1 Q W F1 G J1 E*
Liverpool *p289*. . 0151 709 5816 / 488 1000
James, A L (Network Rail)
London NW1 *p108*. 020 7557 8000
James, A M (Harrison Clark LLP) *O Q Zc Zq*
Cheltenham *p188* 01242 269198
Worcester *p439* 01905 612001
Worcester *p439* 01905 612001
James, B (Linklaters LLP)
London EC2 *p54*. 020 7456 2000
James, B (Bernard James) *S1 K1 N W E O J1 F1 L Q Zl S2 K3*
Bishop Auckland *p144*. . . . 01388 458868
James, Ms C (B P Collins LLP) *K4 W*
Gerrards Cross *p229*. 01753 889995
James, C A B (G Huw Lewis) *S1 W A1 K1 L C1 E*
Neath *p320* 01639 637181
James, C D (Colin D James) *S1*
Guildford *p236*. 01483 303456
West Byfleet *p427* 01932 355433
James, C L (Brindley Twist Tafft & James) *E S1 L O Zq S2 R1*
Coventry *p200*. 024 7653 1532
James, Mrs C M (Max Engel & Co LLP) *S1 W*
Northampton *p331*. 01604 887450
James, D (Grindeys LLP) *Zl G H K1 Zt F1 Zw*
Stoke-on-Trent *p397*. 01782 846441
James, D (Wendy Hopkins Family Law Practice LLP) *K1 D1 D2 K3*
Cardiff *p178* 029 2034 2233
Cardiff *p180* 029 2037 1131
James, D (Sacker & Partners LLP)
London EC2 *p76*. 020 7329 6699
James, D (Wolferstans) *N*
Plymouth *p351*. 01752 663295
James, Miss D (Steele Raymond) *O Q J1 Zc*
Bournemouth *p152*. 01202 294566
James, D A (Dunham Guest & Lyons) *S1 E S2 Q*
Cannock *p176* 01543 462121
James, D A F (Shakespeares) *C1 C2*
Nottingham *p339*. 0115 945 3700
James, D G (Bryan O'Connor & Co)
Southwark *p64*. 020 7407 2643
James, D J (Moorhead James LLP) *C1 C2 Zd Zw Ze Zza Zb B1*
London EC4 *p61*. 020 7831 8888
James, D S (Bennett Richmond) *S1 M1 A1 E C1 N P F1 W Zd Zl*
Lanchester *p270*. 01207 521843
James, D S (Barlow Lyde & Gilbert LLP)
London EC3 *p10*. 020 7247 2277
James, D W (David James & Company) *G H K3 N S1 W S2*
Aberystwyth *p114* 01970 615789
James, Miss E (Gregg Latchams LLP)
Bristol *p162* 0117 906 9400
James, Mrs E M (Lichfield Reynolds) *K1*
Stoke-on-Trent *p398*. 01782 313212
James, Mrs F C (Squire Sanders (UK) LLP)
Birmingham *p142* 0121 222 3000
James, G D (Graham Evans & Partners) *G H D1 K1 N*
Swansea *p405*. 01792 655822
James, Mrs G V (Dean Wilson Laing) *S1 W T2 Zd K4 Zo*
Brighton *p159* 01273 327241
James, Ms H D (Barlow Lyde & Gilbert LLP)
London EC3 *p10*. 020 7247 2277
James, H O (Newsome Vaughan LLP) *C1 F1 F2 Ze C3 I J1 U2 C2 B2*
Coventry *p200*. 024 7663 3433
James, J (James Pearce & Co) *N O Q J1*
Birmingham *p141* 0121 784 1886
James, J (McMillan Williams) *G H*
Croydon *p205* 01689 848311
James, J A (Squire Sanders (UK) LLP)
Birmingham *p142* 0121 222 3000
James, Mrs J A (Jacklyn Dawson) *K4 L S1 S2 W*
Newport *p328* 01633 262952
James, J A W (Hand Morgan & Owen) *A1 E S1 S2*
Stafford *p393* 01785 211411
James, Mrs J C D (Shakespeares) *E S2 P R1*
Stratford-upon-Avon *p400* . . 0845 630 8833
James, J N (Hay & Kilner) *C1 C2 C3 I M1 F1 Zo Ze Zc*
Newcastle upon Tyne *p325* . 0191 232 8345

6

James, J P G (Northumberland County Council) Morpeth *p466* 01670 533000

James, J R (D R James & Son) *W* Pontardawe *p351* 01792 862334

James, J S P (Taylor Walton LLP) *E L S1* St Albans *p390* 01727 845245

James, J W (Ford & Warren) *B2 N O Q Zl* Leeds *p273* 0113 243 6601

James, Ms K (Baily Gibson) *W* Beaconsfield *p128* 01494 672661

James, K (Williamson & Barnes) *E S1 C1 Zl A1 W* Deal *p207* 01304 373154

James, K A (Brabners Chaffe Street) Preston *p356* 01772 823921

James, Miss K D (Ramsdens Solicitors) *S1 S2* Huddersfield *p256* 01484 821500

James, K R (Shakespeares) *T1 T2 W Zd Zh Zj* Birmingham *p142* 0121 237 3000

James, Ms L (Trowers & Hamlins) London EC3 *p88* 020 7423 8000

James, L B (United States Air Force) Bury St Edmunds *p452* 01638 543533

James, Mrs L G (Solihull Magistrates Court) Solihull *p471* 0121 705 8101

James, Ms M A (Margaret James) *S1 W* Westminster *p46* 020 7834 3447

James, M A (Berry & Berry) *G H K1* Manchester *p301* 0161 703 7300

James, M A C (Lansbury Worthington) *G H B2* London W6 *p51* 020 8563 9797

James, Miss M C (Barlow Lyde & Gilbert LLP) *E R2 P S2 A1* London EC3 *p10* 020 7247 2277; London WC1 *p23* 020 7242 0422

James, Ms M D (Simmons & Simmons) London EC2 *p79* 020 7628 2020

James, M H (Gregg Latchams LLP) *W T1 S1 P N M1 L K1 E A1 Zc Zi Zd S2* Bristol *p162* 0117 906 9400

James, M R (Roger James Clements & Partners) *G S1 M1 W Zl* Newport *p329* 01633 257844

James, M R (Davies & Partners) *R2 E L S2 R1 P Zc* Almondsbury *p115* 01454 619619

James, M T S C (Starbuck & Mack) *S1 W K3* Fareham *p224* 01329 285341

James, Mrs N (AXA UK PLC) London E22 *p103* 020 7920 5900

James, N (Napthens LLP) *E S1* Chorley *p194* 0845 260 2111

James, P (Broadbents) *S1 E L C1 G H J1* Heanor *p246* 01773 769891

James, P (Badhams Law (A Trading Name of Parabis Law LLP)) *J2 G N Zj* Croydon *p204* 0844 245 4000

James, P (Hill Dickinson LLP) *Za C3 M1 Zj O Q Zq Zw* Liverpool *p288* 0151 600 8000

James, P C (Hale & Hopkins) *S1* Swindon *p406* 01793 522277

James, P E F (Lewis Silkin LLP) *I Ze Zf* London EC4 *p53* 020 7074 8000

James, P H B (Huw James Solicitor) *K1 S1 G S2 W V L Q K3* Swansea *p405* 01792 643476 / 411600

James, P R (Clark Holt) *Zb C1 S2 E C3 I Ze Zza J1 U2 C2 R2 A1 Zf* Swindon *p406* 01793 617444

James, Miss P S (Mayer Brown International LLP) *Zo* London EC2 *p59* 020 3130 3000

James, R (Richard James) Newcastle Emlyn *p322* 01239 710455

James, R (Geldards LLP) *R2* Cardiff *p178* 029 2023 8239

James, R (Devas Keogh James) *G H* Peterborough *p347* 01733 340666

James, R (Lanyon Bowdler LLP) *Zb Zd C1 Q T1* Wellington *p425* 01952 244721

James, R A (Hill Dickinson LLP) *E R1 S2 L R2* Liverpool *p288* 0151 600 8000

James, R B (Taylor Vinters) *J1 Zp* Cambridge *p176* 01223 423444

James, Mrs R J (Manches LLP) *K1* Oxford *p343* 01865 722106

James, R M (Newmans Solicitors) *S2 E S1 R2 C1 J1 L R1 W* Horley *p252* 01293 771521

James, R S (Dyne Drewett Solicitors Ltd) *C1 Ze C2* Shepton Mallet *p378* 01749 342323

James, Mrs S (Cooperative Bank PLC) *C1* Manchester *p464* 0161 832 3456

James, S (Clarks Legal LLP) *O* Reading *p360* 0118 958 5321

James, S (DLA Piper UK LLP) Leeds *p272* 0870 011 1111

James, S (Squire Sanders (UK) LLP) Birmingham *p142* 0121 222 3000

James, Mrs S (Grayson Willis Bennett) *G H B2* Rotherham *p367* 01709 720287

James, S A (Winterbotham Smith Penley LLP) *G H J1 O Q Zc* Stroud *p401* 01453 847200

James, S C (Walker Smith Way) *J1 N* Chester *p191* 0844 346 3100

James, Mrs S E (Thomas Simon) *K1 S1* Cardiff *p181* 029 2055 7200

James, S H (Thomas Simon) *S2 J1 K1 L Q N S1* Cardiff *p181* 029 2055 7200

James, S M (Faegre & Benson LLP) London EC4 *p30* 020 7450 4500

James, S T (Clifford Chance) London E14 *p20* 020 7006 1000

James, T (Forman Welch & Bellamys) *E S1* Twickenham *p416* 020 8892 8907 / 8892 7733

James, T (Morrison & Foerster (UK) LLP) *T1* London EC2 *p62* 020 7920 4000

James, Mrs V M (Wrigleys Solicitors LLP) *E S2 X Zd Zx* Leeds *p278* 0113 244 6100

James, Ms W A (Colborne Coulman & Lawrence) *Q S1 E C1 B1 W K1 L F1 J1 K3* Newport *p328* 01633 264194 / 264196

James, W K (Addleshaw Goddard) *C1* London EC1 *p4* 020 7606 8855

Jameson, B (Horsey Lightly) *J1* Newbury *p322* 01635 580858

Jameson, C D C (Paris Smith LLP) *W T2 Zd* Southampton *p386* 023 8048 2482

Jameson, D A (hlw Keeble Hawson LLP) *S2 E* Sheffield *p376* 0114 276 5555

Jameson, R A (Jameson & Hill) *R1 E S1 W C1* Hertford *p248* 01992 554881

Jameson, T (Penningtons) London EC2 *p66* 020 7457 3000

Jamieson, A P (Nelsons) *G H D1 Zl* Nottingham *p338* 0115 958 6262

Jamieson, Mrs C A (Fladgate LLP) *J1 B1* London WC2 *p32* 020 3036 7000

Jamieson, Mrs C A (Lightfoots LLP) *O Q A3* Thame *p410* 01844 212305

Jamieson, E (Hogan Lovells International LLP) London EC1 *p42* 020 7296 2000

Jamieson, Ms K (Fladgate LLP) London WC2 *p32* 020 3036 7000

Jamieson, N D (Barlow Lyde & Gilbert LLP) *N Q O L J1 B1 M1 I A1 Zk Zw Zj Ze Zc* London EC3 *p10* 020 7247 2277

Jamieson, Ms S L (McMillen Hamilton McCarthy) *K1 K3 D1* London E3 *p57* 020 8980 6060

Jamil, S (Criminal Defence Solicitors) *G H* Westminster *p23* 020 7353 7000; London N17 *p92* 020 8808 7535

Jamison, N D (Horne Engall & Freeman LLP) *K1 N O Q* Egham *p217* 01784 432292

Janalli-Brown, Ms E (Henry Hughes & Hughes) *K4 W* London SW16 *p40* 020 8765 2700

Janata, D J (Bower & Bailey) *Q O N C1 B1 F1* Swindon *p406* 01793 610466

Janaway, S (Adams & Remers) *Q* Lewes *p283* 01273 480616

Janaway, S (Charles Russell LLP) *T2 W M1* London EC4 *p19* 020 7203 5000

Janday, Ms S (Aviva PLC) London EC3 *p103* 020 7283 7500 / 01603 687905; Norwich *p467* 01603 622200

Jandoo, A S (Clark Willis) *G H Zm* Darlington *p206* 01325 281111

Jandu, N S (Underwood Solicitors LLP) *S2 E S1 R2* Westminster *p89* 020 7526 6000

Jandu, R (Balsara & Co) *Q B1 O Zb S2 R2* London EC1 *p9* 020 7797 6300

Jane, Ms T (Elliott & Allen) *S1 W* Sedgley *p373* 01902 677204

Janes, D K (Janes) *G H B2* London SW1 *p46* 020 7930 5100

Janisch, S A G (Radcliffes Le Brasseur) *N J1 O Q W Zm Zq* Westminster *p70* 020 7222 7040

Janmohamed, N (Speechly Bircham LLP) *C1 B1 Zb Ze Zj* London EC4 *p81* 020 7427 6400

Janney, Ms J (Teacher Stern LLP) *R1 Zc* London WC1 *p86* 020 7242 3191

Janney, M S J (Kingsley Napley) *A3 Zc Zq* London EC1 *p50* 020 7814 1200

Jansari, A D (Nottingham City Council (City Sec Dept)) *Q O J1 B1 L* Nottingham *p467* 0115 915 5555; Leicester *p280* 0116 255 1811

Jansen, K P (Freeth Cartwright LLP) *C1 B1* Nottingham *p337* 0115 936 9369

Jansen, L (Osborne Clarke) *U1 U2* London EC2 *p65* 020 7105 7000

Jansen, N (Addleshaw Goddard) Manchester *p300* 0161 934 6000

Jansen, P (Penningtons) *Zc* London EC2 *p66* 020 7457 3000

Jansz, Miss C (Canter Levin & Berg) *N Q F1* St Helens *p391* 01744 634141

Japal, T (Rafina Solicitors) *B1 C1 S2 G K3 K1 Zi Q N S1 W J1* Wembley *p426* 020 8908 6742

Jappie, R (Kaim Todner Ltd) *G H B2* London EC4 *p47* 020 7353 6660

Jaque, C (DWFM Beckman) *Zq O Q L Zl* Westminster *p25* 020 7872 0023

Jaques, G L (Wake Smith & Tofields) *J1 O Q P I F1 L Zq Zp Zc J2 Zy* Sheffield *p377* 0114 266 6660

Jardella, Mrs R C (Worthingtons) *K1 K2* Folkestone *p227* 01303 850206

Jardine, Ms K F (Tunbridge Wells Borough Council) Tunbridge Wells *p474* 01892 526121

Jardine, S M (Brethertons LLP) *O N B1 Q F1 Zv* Banbury *p122* 01295 270999

Jardine, Miss V L (Anthony Collins Solicitors LLP) *Zb Zd C1 C2* Birmingham *p137* 0121 200 3242

Jardine-Brown, M (Mundays LLP) *C1 F1 Q W Zk Zl* Cobham *p196* 01932 590500

Jardine-Brown, R A (Curtis Davis Garrard) *O* Uxbridge *p417* 020 8734 2800

Jarlett, Mrs S E (Essex County Council) *G N K1* Chelmsford *p454* 0845 743 0430

Jarlett, S R (Steed & Steed LLP) *S1 E L Zc* Braintree *p155* 01376 552828

Jarman, A R (Wright Hassall LLP) *O Ze* Leamington Spa *p270* 01926 886688

Jarman, C (Bevan Brittan LLP) *C1 Zu* Bristol *p161* 0870 194 1000

Jarman, Miss J (Browne Jacobson LLP) *Zq Zj P I O* Nottingham *p336* 0115 976 6000

Jarman, S A (DWF) *C1 C2* Manchester *p303* 0161 603 5000

Jarockyj, H (Makin Dixon Solicitors) *K1* Halifax *p238* 01422 363184

Jarret, Ms A G (Treasury Solicitors Department) London WC2 *p110* 020 7210 3000

Jarret, M (Nelsons) Leicester *p280* 0116 222 6666

Jarrett, A H (Legal Services Commission Wales Office) Cardiff *p453* 0845 608 7070

Jarrett, M (Enoch Evans LLP) *O Q A3 L W Zq* Walsall *p420* 01922 720333

Jarrett, Mrs S A (Poole Alcock) Nantwich *p320* 01270 625478

Jarrold, Ms L M (Beecham Peacock) *K1 D1* Newcastle upon Tyne *p323* 0191 232 3048

Jarvie, T H (Anthony & Jarvie) *S1 L E A1 W* Bridgend *p157* 01656 652737

Jarvis, Miss A (Moss & Coleman) *K1* Hornchurch *p252* 01708 446781

Jarvis, Mrs A E (Anne Jarvis & Co) *K1 D1 D2 K3* Harrogate *p240* 01423 858582

Jarvis, Mrs A L (Emsleys) *S1 W* Rothwell *p368* 0113 201 4900

Jarvis, A L (SNR Denton) *Zo* London EC4 *p75* 020 7242 1212

Jarvis, B H (Overburys & Raymond Thompson) *N Q Zq F2 Zr* Norwich *p335* 01603 610481

Jarvis, Miss H L (Wollen Michelmore Solicitors) *W* Newton Abbot *p330* 01626 332266

Jarvis, Ms J (Bhatia Best) *K1 D1 D2 G K2* Nottingham *p336* 0115 950 3231

Jarvis, J (Trowers & Hamlins) London EC3 *p88* 020 7423 8000

Jarvis, J P (Shakespeares) *T1 O J1* Nottingham *p339* 0115 945 3700

Jarvis, Ms K (Bickley Wheatley & Co) Birmingham *p135* 0121 377 6266

Jarvis, Ms K V (HCB Solicitors) *K1 D1 W S1* Walsall *p420* 01922 720000

Jarvis, Ms M (Morecrofts Solicitors LLP) Liverpool *p290* 0151 428 1911

Jarvis, N R (Blaser Mills) *G H* Aylesbury *p120* 01296 434416

Jarvis, Miss R (Linklaters LLP) London EC2 *p54* 020 7456 2000

Jarvis, R (Penningtons) *Zb* London EC2 *p66* 020 7457 3000

Jarvis, S (Sharratts (London) LLP) *E R1 S1* Westerham *p429* 01959 568000

Jarvis, S (Ince & Co Services Ltd) London E1 *p44* 020 7481 0010

Jarvis, Mrs S (Blake Lapthorn) *Zr* Oxford *p342* 01865 248607

Jarvis, Mrs S A (Jeffrey Green Russell) *A1 E L S1 S2* London W1 *p46* 020 7339 7000

Jarvis, T H (Squire Sanders (UK) LLP) Leeds *p277* 0113 284 7000

Jasani, K (Kennedys) *Zr C1 J2 Q N* London EC3 *p49* 020 7667 9667

Jaskowiak, A M (The Royal Borough of Kensington & Chelsea) London W8 *p109* 020 7361 2741

Jaswal, Ms D (Buss Murton LLP) *C1 S2 E* Tunbridge Wells *p415* 01892 510222

Jaswal, S S (Jaswal Johnston Boyle) *B1 E K1 Q S1 W Zi R2* London W1 *p46* 020 7317 1540

Javaid, M (DLA Piper UK LLP) London EC2 *p24* 0870 011 1111

Javed, I (Duncan Lewis & Co) *Zg Zi* London W12 *p53* 020 7923 4020

Jay, A P (Andrew Jay & Co (Philip Hanby Limited)) *G H K1 M1 S1 D1 P W F1 Zm* Gainsborough *p228* 01427 612412

Jay, K N (Herbert Reeves & Co) *Zf Zw Ze E* London EC2 *p40* 020 7739 6660

Jay, L P (Cumbria County Council) Carlisle *p453* 01228 607374 / 607351

Jay, Ms R P (Pinsent Masons LLP) *Zza Zu* Manchester *p308* 0161 234 8234

Jay, Miss S (Heald Nickinson) *K3 K1 D1 D2* Camberley *p173* 01276 680000

Jayatilaka, M N U P (Ranga & Co) London NW10 *p70* 020 8451 4518

Jayatilaka, Y G (Nathan & Co) London SW19 *p63* 020 8542 1805

Jaycock, Mrs C (Reynolds Porter Chamberlain LLP) *O Q Zr Zq* London E1 *p71* 020 3060 6000

Jayes, Ms N (Blandy & Blandy) *K1 K4 W* Reading *p360* 0118 951 6800

Jayne, Ms J (Newport City Council) Newport *p466* 01633 656656

Jayson, P (DLA Piper UK LLP) London EC2 *p24* 0870 011 1111

Jeacock, D (David Jeacock) *C1 O Ze Zw* Wootton Bassett *p439* 01793 854111

Jeal, Ms J A (Three Rivers District Council) Rickmansworth *p470* 01923 776611

Jean-Baptiste, Ms M (Joseph Hill & Co) *D1 K1 G H* London N15 *p41* 020 8880 3535

Jeary, M A (Jeary & Lewis) *P N M1 G H J1 K1 F1 L Zj Zo Zt* Chippenham *p193* 01249 444484

Jebb, S P (Osborne Clarke) *C2 R2 Zo* Reading *p361* 0118 925 2000

Jeeps, B S (Stephenson Harwood) *E R1* London EC2 *p82* 020 7329 4422

Jeeves, Miss J M H (Cartmell Shepherd) *W T2 Zd* Carlisle *p182* 01228 516666

Jefcott, L J (Berg Legal) *J1* Manchester *p301* 0161 833 9211

Jeff, Ms D (Seddons) *K1* Westminster *p77* 020 7725 8000

Jeffcoate, R A (Wansbroughs) *E L S1 S2* Devizes *p210* 01380 733300

Jeffcott, R B (Reed Smith LLP) *O J1* London EC2 *p71* 020 3116 3000

Jeffels, Mrs S D (Harvey Ingram Borneos) Newport Pagnell *p329* 01908 613545

Jefferies, Miss A E (Financial Services Authority) London E14 *p106* 020 7066 1000

Jefferies, Mrs A J (Bradley & Jefferies Solicitors Limited) *J1* Derby *p208* 01332 221722; Derby *p209* 01332 372372

Jefferies, B (Trowers & Hamlins) London EC3 *p88* 020 7423 8000

Jefferies, D M (Senior Calveley & Hardy) *S1 W A1 S2 Zd T2* Lytham *p297* 01253 733333

Jefferies, J D F (Freeth Cartwright LLP) *O P* Derby *p208* 01332 361000; Nottingham *p337* 0115 936 9369

Jefferies, M A C (Thorpe & Co) *B1 F1 O* Whitby *p430* 01947 603465

Jefferies, M G (Hugh James) *P Zc O A3 Zq* Cardiff *p179* 029 2022 4871

Jefferies, M I (Jefferies LLP) *N* Altrincham *p116* 0800 342 3191

Jefferies, R J (Lound Mulrenan & Jefferies Solicitors) *G H* Southwark *p55* 020 7793 4012

Jefferis, C J Q (Ince & Co Services Ltd) London E1 *p44* 020 7481 0010

Jefferson, D P (Bray & Bray) *G Zl H B2* Hinckley *p250* 01455 639900

Jefferson, J M (Julian Jefferson) *G H* Plymouth *p350* 01752 250850

Jefferson, Ms P (DAC Beachcroft) London EC4 *p24* 020 7242 1011

Jeffery, E C (Robert Lunn & Lowth) *K1 N Q O G H J1 F1 B1* Stratford-upon-Avon *p400* 01789 292238

Jeffery, Ms G (London Borough of Southwark) London SE1 *p109* 020 7525 5000

Jeffery, I R (Lewis Silkin LLP) *O Q I Ze U1* London EC4 *p53* 020 7074 8000

Jeffery, J N (Renault Trucks UK Ltd) *O N J1 Zc* Dunstable *p457* 01582 471122

Jeffery, J W (AGR Solicitors) *S1 W S2 A1* Shirebrook *p378* 01623 748522

Jeffery, P R (Moore Blatch Solicitors) *B1 C1 U1 I C3 Ze Zj U2 C2* Southampton *p386* 023 8071 8000

Jeffery, S D (Carter Slater & Co) *G H* Northampton *p331* 01604 717505

Jeffrey, A B (Stitt & Co) *Q N K1 B1 O C3 S1 L Zw Zk Zc* London EC4 *p83* 020 7832 0840

Jeffrey, G D R (City of London Corporation) London EC2 *p107* 020 7606 3030

Jeffrey, Mrs S (Darbys Solicitors LLP) *W* Oxford *p343* 01865 811700

Jeffreys, J (DLA Piper UK LLP) Birmingham *p137* 0870 011 1111

Jeffries, Miss F A (Rotherham Metropolitan Borough Council) Rotherham *p470* 01709 382121

Jeffries, G D (Bond Pearce LLP) *Zb B1* Southampton *p385* 0845 415 0000

Jeffries, J D (Pinsent Masons LLP) *B1 E N M1* Leeds *p276* 0113 244 5000

Jeffries, Ms M (Taylor Wessing) London EC4 *p86* 020 7300 7000

Jeffries, R M (Mills & Reeve) *C1* Norwich *p335* 01603 660155

Jeffs, Ms A L (DWF) *N Zj B2 Q* Liverpool *p287* 0151 907 3000

Jeffs, M (Geldards LLP) *E S2* Cardiff *p178* 029 2023 8239

Jeffs, N (Sternberg Reed) *L* Barking *p123* 020 8591 3366

Jelf, Dr P M (Bristows) *Ze* London EC4 *p15* 020 7400 8000

Jelley, J C (Pennon Group PLC) *P* Exeter *p458* 01392 446677

Jellis, Ms J (Simmons & Simmons) London EC2 *p79* 020 7628 2020

See p634 for the Key to Work Categories

Jelly, J M (Irwin Mitchell LLP) *C1 C2 C3 Zb Ze*
Sheffield *p376* 0870 150 0100

Jelly, P K (Keene Marsland) *W K4*
Tunbridge Wells *p415* 01892 526442

Jelly, Mrs S E (Keene Marsland) *K1 K2 K3*
Tunbridge Wells *p415* 01892 526442

Jemmett, Ms E (Gartmore Investment Management PLC)
London EC3 *p106* 020 7782 2000

Jenden, Miss S (MLS Solicitors LLP) *S1 W L E Zv*
Stockport *p396* 0161 968 7037

Jenking, D J (TWM Solicitors LLP) *C1 F1 J1*
Guildford *p237* 01483 752700

Jenkins, Mrs A (Brewer Harding & Rowe) *S1 W*
Barnstaple *p125* 01271 342271

Jenkins, Mrs A (Toller Beattie LLP) *W S1*
Barnstaple *p125* 01271 341000

Jenkins, A (Ungoed-Thomas & King Limited) *S1 W A1 C1 E L R1 Zh Zd*
Carmarthen *p183* 01267 237441

Jenkins, A M (Wansbroughs) *B1 F1 G H J1 L N*
Devizes *p210* 01380 733300

Jenkins, B (Harding Evans LLP) *A3 Zb B1 F1 J1 L O Q C2 Zq Zw*
Newport *p328* 01633 244233

Jenkins, Ms C (Withers LLP) *K1*
London EC4 *p92* 020 7597 6000

Jenkins, Ms C H C (Parlett Kent) *N Zr Zq*
London EC1 *p66* 020 7430 0712

Jenkins, Miss C L (Geraint Jones & Co) *G W S1 S2 Q*
Llandrindod Wells *p291* . . . 01597 822244

Jenkins, Miss C M (Francis & Buck) *S1 E*
Cardiff *p178* 029 2034 4995

Jenkins, Ms C N (London Borough of Greenwich Legal Services)
London SE18 *p106* 020 8921 5123

Jenkins, C W (Baileys) *K1 S1 W L T2*
Cheltenham *p187* 01242 514477

Jenkins, C W (Addleshaw Goddard) *E*
London EC1 *p4* 020 7606 8855

Jenkins, D (Department for Business, Enterprise and Regulatory Reform)
London SW1 *p105* 020 7215 0105

Jenkins, D (Watson Burton LLP) *J1 S1*
Newcastle upon Tyne *p327* . 0845 901 2100

Jenkins, D M (Trevor Thomas Scott & Jenkins) *A1 B1 C1 D1 E F1 J1*
Swansea *p406* 01792 843821

Jenkins, E G (Addleshaw Goddard) *T1 C1 C2*
Manchester *p300* 0161 934 6000

Jenkins, E K (Thomas Simon) *W S1 C1 C2*
Cardiff *p181* 029 2055 7200

Jenkins, G (Young & Lee) *O Q Zc*
Birmingham *p143* 0121 633 3233

Jenkins, G C (Suffolk County Council)
Ipswich *p462* 01473 583000

Jenkins, Miss G E (Arnold Davies Vincent Evans) *T2 S1 W S2 A1*
Lampeter *p269* 01570 422233

Jenkins, Ms H A (Gallaher Ltd)
Weybridge *p476* 01932 859777

Jenkins, H B (JNP Legal) *G H J1 L M1 N P R1 S1*
Merthyr Tydfil *p314* 01685 350421

Jenkins, H M (Malcolm C Foy & Co) *K1 Zm*
Doncaster *p211* 01302 340005

Jenkins, I (Lee & Priestley LLP) *J1 O L Zw*
Leeds *p275* 0845 129 2300

Jenkins, I (Crown Prosecution Service Dyfed Powys)
Carmarthen *p453* 01267 242100

Jenkins, I G (JNP Legal) *N Q L D1 F1 K1 B1 C1 A1*
Merthyr Tydfil *p314* 01685 350421

Jenkins, Mrs J (The Ringrose Law Group - David Thornley) *K1 K2 D1 D2*
Grantham *p232* 01476 590200

Jenkins, Ms J A (Memery Crystal) *O A3*
London WC2 *p60* 020 7242 5905

Jenkins, Mrs J C (Steed & Steed LLP) *A1 S2 E L S1 W*
Sudbury *p401* 01787 373387

Jenkins, Mrs J E (Land Registry - Gloucester Office)
Gloucester *p459* 01452 511111

Jenkins, Miss J E (Suffolk County Council)
Ipswich *p462* 01473 583000

Jenkins, J G (Clark Holt) *C1 C2 Zb*
Swindon *p406* 01793 617444

Jenkins, Miss K S (George Ide LLP) *N*
Chichester *p192* 01243 786668

Jenkins, Ms L (Stewarts Law LLP) *O B2 Zq Zb*
London EC4 *p83* 020 7822 8000

Jenkins, Miss L C (Irwin Mitchell LLP) *N*
Sheffield *p376* 0870 150 0100

Jenkins, M (Randell Lloyd & Martin) *G H K1 M1 P D1 Zl*
Llanelli *p292* 01554 772149

Jenkins, M (Hughmans) *Zb C1 Q N S1*
London EC4 *p44* 020 7246 6560

Jenkins, M A J (Leo Abse & Cohen) *N*
Cardiff *p179* . . . 029 2038 3252 / 2034 5421

Jenkins, Ms M E (Mann Jenkins) *A1 C1 E S1 Zb Zd S2 C2*
Moretonhampstead *p319* . . . 01647 440000

Jenkins, M H (Dickinson Dees) *Zo*
Newcastle upon Tyne *p324* . 0191 279 9000

Jenkins, M J (Harding Evans LLP) *C1 E B1 S1*
Newport *p328* 01633 244233

Jenkins, M R (Streeter Marshall) *K3 J1 K1 L Q*
Croydon *p205* 020 8680 2638

Jenkins, Ms N (Wolferstans) *N Q Zr*
Plymouth *p351* 01752 663295

Jenkins, N T (Bird & Bird LLP) *Ze*
London EC4 *p13* 020 7415 6000

Jenkins, P (MacDonald Oates LLP) *Q O L*
Petersfield *p348* 01730 268211

Jenkins, P H (Browne Jacobson LLP) *T1 W Zd*
Nottingham *p336* 0115 976 6000

Jenkins, P L (Barlow Lyde & Gilbert LLP)
London EC3 *p10* 020 7247 2277

Jenkins, P S G (Burrell Jenkins) *S1 G M1 T1 W K1 L N P R1 Zc Zh Zl Zo*
Cannock *p176* 01543 505040

Jenkins, R (Reynolds Porter Chamberlain LLP) *Zj Q*
London E1 *p71* 020 3060 6000
London EC4 *p73* 020 7353 2353

Jenkins, Ms R C (Jackamans) *K1 N Zl Q*
Ipswich *p262* 01473 255591

Jenkins, R H N (Rooks Rider) *W T1*
London EC1 *p73* 020 7689 7000

Jenkins, R J A (Hugh James) *M1 J2 N*
Cardiff *p179* 029 2022 4871

Jenkins, Ms R K (Jones & Co)
Bawtry *p128* 01302 710555
Retford *p363* 01777 703827

Jenkins, Mrs S (Steven Young & Co) *G H*
Gloucester *p230* 01452 332882

Jenkins, Miss S A (DAC Beachcroft) *F1 J1 O K1 R1 E*
Manchester *p303* 0161 934 3000

Jenkins, S M (Geldards LLP) *J1*
Cardiff *p178* 029 2023 8239

Jenkins, T (Charles Russell LLP) *C1 C2 B1*
Guildford *p235* 01483 252525

Jenkins, T (Trowers & Hamlins)
London EC3 *p88* 020 7423 8000

Jenkins, T N (Montague Lambert & Co) *Q L K1 N R1 J1 P Zc*
Ealing *p61* 020 8997 2288

Jenkins, T P (Charles Russell LLP) *C1 C2 E F1 J1 L S1*
Cheltenham *p187* 01242 221122

Jenkins, Ms V J (Barlow Lyde & Gilbert LLP)
London EC3 *p10* 020 7247 2277

Jenkins Jones, Ms D (Geldards LLP)
Nottingham *p337* 0115 983 3650

Jenkinson, A (Reed Smith LLP) *E*
London EC2 *p71* 020 3116 3000

Jenkinson, Miss H C (Glaisyers Solicitors LLP) *C1 S2 E C2*
Manchester *p304* 0161 832 4666

Jenkinson, I M (Milne Moser) *S1 W Q S2*
Kendal *p264* . . . . . 01539 729786 / 725582

Jenkinson, Mrs J (Bawtrees LLP) *A1 E S1 S2*
Witham *p435* 01376 513491

Jenkinson, M M (Nelsons) *C1 E*
Nottingham *p338* 0115 958 6262

Jenkinson, Ms S C (Norfolk County Council - Legal Services)
Norwich *p467* . . . Minicom: 0844 800 8011

Jenkins-Powell, Mrs M M (Donnelly & Elliott Limited) *W Zm K4 T2*
Gosport *p232* 023 9250 5500

Jenks, Ms H (The College of Law Chester) *K1 F1 S1 D2*
Chester *p454* 0800 289997

Jenkyn-Jones, M (Robin Simon LLP) *Q Zj Zq*
Manchester *p309* 0333 010 0000

Jenner, A (Bonallack & Bishop) *J1 O Q Zq Zp C1*
Salisbury *p371* 01722 422300

Jenner, Ms E (British American Tobacco)
London WC2 *p104* 020 7845 1000

Jenner, Ms J (Ashurst LLP)
London EC2 *p7* 020 7638 1111

Jenner, R (Farleys Solicitors LLP)
Blackburn *p145* 01254 367856

Jenneson, E C (Rollits LLP)
Hull *p258* 01482 323239

Jennett, Ms C (Faegre & Benson LLP) *J1*
London EC4 *p30* 020 7450 4500

Jenney, H W (Stephenson Harwood) *T1*
London EC2 *p82* 020 7329 4422

Jennings, Mrs A M (Heppenstalls) *W T2 K4*
Lymington *p296* 01590 689500
New Milton *p321* 01425 610078

Jennings, Miss B (Lionel Blackman) *G H J1 N Q V S1 Zg Zi*
Epsom *p219* 01372 728941

Jennings, C G (Blanchards Bailey LLP) *O Q Zq*
Blandford Forum *p147* 01258 459361

Jennings, C J (Blake Lapthorn) *C1 B1 M1 T1 Zb*
London EC1 *p13* 020 7405 2000

Jennings, Miss D (Walker Morris) *E R2*
Leeds *p277* 0113 283 2500

Jennings, Ms D (Thomson Snell & Passmore) *Zr N*
Tunbridge Wells *p415* 01892 510000

Jennings, Ms E (Doyle Clayton Solicitors Limited) *J1 Zp*
London EC2 *p27* 020 7329 9090

Jennings, F R (Osborne Clarke) *U1 U2*
London EC2 *p65* 020 7105 7000

Jennings, H M (Burley & Geach) *A1 S1 E*
Grayshott *p233* 01428 605355

Jennings, H M (Burley & Geach) *S1*
Petersfield *p348* 01730 262401

Jennings, M (Hodge Jones & Allen LLP) *N*
London NW1 *p41* 020 7874 8300

Jennings, M F (Stephenson Harwood) *T1 T2*
London EC2 *p82* 020 7329 4422

Jennings, N (Faegre & Benson LLP) *C1 C2*
London EC4 *p30* 020 7450 4500

Jennings, Ms N (BLB Solicitors) *Zc O Q*
Swindon *p406* 01793 615011

Jennings, P (Cripps Harries Hall LLP) *C1 F2 O Ze*
Tunbridge Wells *p415* 01892 515121

Jennings, Miss P (Atherton Godfrey) *Zr*
Doncaster *p211* 01302 320621

Jennings, R D Y (R D Y Jennings & Co)
Malton *p300* 01653 691515

Jennings, R J (Prince Evans) *O L Zc J1*
Ealing *p69* 020 8567 3477

Jennings, Miss R M (Atteys) *G H*
Barnsley *p124* 01226 212345

Jennings, Mrs S (Cripps Harries Hall LLP) *O Zq*
Tunbridge Wells *p415* 01892 515121

Jennings, S C (Tozers) *J1 O Q Zp*
Exeter *p222* 01392 207020

Jennings, Miss S J (Williscroft & Co)
Bradford *p155* 01274 305380

Jennings, S P (Jennings Perks & Co) *D1 J1 K1 W*
Walsall *p420* 01922 459000

Jennings, S P (DLA Piper UK LLP) *E R1*
Manchester *p303* 0870 011 1111

Jennings-Mares, J (Morrison & Foerster (UK) LLP) *Zb*
London EC2 *p62* 020 7920 4000

Jensen, P M (Inghams) *N G H*
Blackpool *p146* 01253 626642

Jenvey, Ms N L (Kingsley Napley) *J1*
London EC1 *p50* 020 7814 1200

Jenyns, H B (Forth & Co) *S1 W L*
Yarm *p443* 01642 784000

Jephson, Miss E R (Sharp & Partners) *D1 K1*
Nottingham *p339* 0115 959 0055

Jepsen, Mrs C R (Jepsen & Co) *E L S1 S2 W*
Leatherhead *p271* 01483 281720

Jepson, A (Rudd Jepson) *S1 E N*
Bromley *p167* 020 8313 0555

Jepson, J S (Kingston upon Hull City Council)
Hull *p461* 01482 300300

Jepson, M (Copeland Borough Council)
Whitehaven *p476* 01946 852585

Jepson, R P (Grayson Willis Bennett) *G H B2*
Sheffield *p375* 0114 290 9500

Jepson, T (West Cumbria Magistrates Courts)
Workington *p477* 01900 62244

Jeram, Miss N (Fladgate LLP) *E L R1*
London WC2 *p32* 020 3036 7000

Jeremiah, A J (City & County of Swansea)
Swansea *p473* 01792 636000

Jeremiah, P L (North Wiltshire District Council)
Chippenham *p455* 01249 706111

Jeremy, A W (Anthony Jeremy & May)
Cardiff *p177* 029 2034 0313

Jerman, M C (Jerman Simpson Pearson & Samuels) *G H B2*
Basildon *p126* 01268 820111

Jermine, Ms R E (Irwin Mitchell LLP) *N Zj*
Birmingham *p139* 0870 150 0100

Jerome, D P (Kaim Todner Ltd) *G H*
London EC4 *p47* 020 7353 6660

Jerram, Miss C E (Oxfordshire County Council) *K1 D1*
Oxford *p468* 01865 792422

Jerram, Mrs P J (Steed & Steed LLP) *A1 Zd C1 E S1*
Sudbury *p401* 01787 373387

Jerrard, W L (Hamilton Downing Quinn) *C1 S2 E J1 L Zl C2 R2 S1 W*
London WC1 *p38* 020 7831 8939

Jervois, D R W (WBW Solicitors)
Newton Abbot *p329* 01626 202404

Jess, Ms H (Shoosmiths)
Milton Keynes *p317* . 0370 086 8300 / 01908 488300

Jesse, C (P Lloyd Jones & Co) *K1 S1 G P F1 E C1 J1 W L*
Buckley *p168* . . . . 01244 547119 / 547110
Mold *p318* . . . . . . 01352 758533 / 758534

Jessop, Ms C E (HMG Law LLP) *Q Zq O B1*
Bicester *p132* 01869 252244
Oxford *p343* 01865 244661

Jessop, G O (Pannone LLP) *A3 I O Zc*
Manchester *p308* 0161 909 3000

Jessup, A P (Eldridges) *W T2 K4*
Newport *p328* 01983 524741

Jessup, Ms L J (Bowers & Jessup) *S1 W E R1 L C1 A1 F1 K1*
Folkestone *p227* 01303 850678

Jethwa, Ms R (Rawlison Butler LLP) *J1*
Crawley *p202* 01293 527744

Jetwani, Miss S (Sylvester Mackett) *K3 K1 Q*
Trowbridge *p414* 01225 755621

Jevon, Ms J K (HCB Solicitors) *W T1 T2 C1*
Walsall *p420* 01922 720000

Jew, N (DLA Piper UK LLP) *J1*
Birmingham *p137* 0870 011 1111

Jewell, A (Anthony Jewell & Co) *S1 M1 K1 D1 G W J1 P E F1*
Pontypridd *p352* 01443 493357

Jewell, P (Oldham Law Centre)
Oldham *p468* 0161 627 0925

Jewels, M A (Jewels Solicitors) *D1 G H K1 M1 P E F1 J1 L*
Stafford *p393* 01785 602030

Jewers, Mrs J (Berwins Solicitors Limited) *W T1 T2*
Harrogate *p240* 01423 509000

Jewers, R H (Brian Ruff Angus & Jewers) *B1 C1 E L O S2 W*
Wickford *p431* 01268 761126

Jewitt, Ms D (McKeag & Co) *K1*
Gosforth *p233* 0191 213 1010

Jewitt, Miss H (Manches LLP) *J1*
London WC2 *p58* 020 7404 4433

Jewitt, P A (Nicholson Portnell)
Hexham *p249* 01434 603656

Jewitt, S E (Nicholson Portnell) *A1 S1 S2 A2 E L*
Hexham *p249* 01434 603656

Jewitt, W E (Mayer Brown International LLP) *Zo*
London EC2 *p59* 020 3130 3000

Jeyanantham, Mrs M (Jeya & Co) *S2 E S1 Zi*
Newham *p46* 020 8552 1999

Jeyasselan, Ms A (Kaim Todner Ltd)
London SE17 *p47* 020 7701 4747

Jhalla, Mrs P S (David Rubie Mitchell & Co) *K1 D1 K3*
Sutton *p403* 020 8641 0575

Jhawar, H (Stevens) *G H*
Stafford *p393* 01785 250908

Jhurry-Wright, Mrs D L (George Ide LLP) *E S2 C1 C2 S1*
Chichester *p192* 01243 786668

Jilani, M A (Brachers) *E S2*
Maidstone *p299* 01622 690691

Jinks, Miss B (Rothera Dowson) *J1 N*
Nottingham *p338* 0115 910 0600

Jinks, Mrs L J (Greenwoods Solicitors LLP) *J1 Zp*
Peterborough *p347* 01733 887700

Jinks, M G (Bakewells) *B1 C1 C2 C3 E F1 F2 J1 J2 L M1 P R1 R2 S2*
Derby *p208* 01332 348791

Jinks, Miss N S C (Aldridge Brownlee Solicitors LLP) *G H*
Bournemouth *p151* 01202 294411

Jirbandey, Ms J (Nelsons) *S1 S2 W*
Tenterden *p410* 01580 767100

Joannides, A A (Boulter & Company)
London N8 *p14* 020 8340 0222

Joannou, Miss E (Protopapas) *E S2 K1 O C1*
London W1 *p69* 020 7636 2100

Joannou, E (Cancer Research UK)
London WC2 *p104* 020 7242 0200

Job, J A (Herrington & Carmichael LLP) *C1 E*
Camberley *p173* 01276 686222

Job, M (Pinsent Masons LLP) *Q Zc*
Manchester *p308* 0161 234 8234

Jobanputra, N (Phillips & Phillips) *E L F1 N O Q S1 V W D1 Zi Zo*
Harrow *p242* . . . 020 8422 4435 / 8422 8155

Jobling, B M (Howell & Co) *E G B2*
Birmingham *p139* 0121 778 5031
London EC1 *p51* 0870 600 9444

Jobling, Mrs M H (Jobling Gowler) *N Q W S1 Zq Zr*
Macclesfield *p297* 01625 614250

Jobling, Ms N H (Network Rail)
London NW1 *p108* 020 7557 8000

Jobson, R P (Gardner Leader LLP) *W T2 K4*
Newbury *p322* 01635 508080

Joels, Miss K E (John Welch & Stammers) *K1 H G L K3 K2*
Witney *p436* 01993 703941

Johal, A (Rainer Hughes)
Brentwood *p156* 01227 226644

Johal, A S (Faber & Co)
Birmingham *p138* 0121 236 5751
Wolverhampton *p438* 01902 773666

Johal, Miss K (FBC Manby Bowdler LLP) *C1 C2*
Wolverhampton *p437* 01902 578000

Johal, Mrs L C (Ashton Bond Gigg) *O Q B1 Zq*
Nottingham *p335* 0115 947 6651

Johal, M (The Smith Partnership) *D1*
Derby *p209* 01332 225225

Johal, Mrs M K (Vyman Solicitors) *S1 S2 E B1 Q*
Harrow *p242* 020 8427 9080

Johal, Mrs P (HRJ Law LLP) *K4 W T2*
Hitchin *p251* 01462 628888

Johal, R (The Johnson Partnership) *G H B2*
Nottingham *p337* 0115 941 9141

Johal, Ms R K (Tucker Turner Kingsley Wood & Co) *N O Q Zi*
London WC1 *p88* 020 7242 3303

Johal, R S (Irwin Mitchell LLP) *C1 C2 Zb*
Birmingham *p139* 0870 150 0100

Johal, S S (Mills Chody LLP) *K1 P M1 G W N S1 F1 Zi J1 Q*
Kenton *p265* 020 8909 0400

Johal-Basi, H (Pickup & Scott) *Zi*
Aylesbury *p121* 01296 397794

Johansen, Mrs L A (Clifford Chance)
London E14 *p20* 020 7006 1000

Johar, D K (Johar & Co) *A1 C1 D1 E G H K1 L M1 N Zb Zc Ze*
Leicester *p280* 0116 254 3345

Johar, Ms S (Hughmans) *E Zl Q S1*
London EC4 *p44* 020 7246 6560

Johar, T R (Johar & Co) *B1 C1 D1 E G H K1 L M1 N Zb Zc Ze*
Leicester *p280* 0116 254 3345

John, A (Horsey Lightly Fynn) *E S1 L Zl S2 A1 R1 R2 Zc*
Bournemouth *p152* 01202 551991

John, Miss A K (John Farr-Davies & Co) *S1 S2 W E C1 J1 F1 B1 Zl Zt Zc Zd Zu U2 A1*
Carmarthen *p182* 01267 231818

John, A R (Osborne Clarke) *P R2*
Bristol *p164* 0117 917 3000

John, Mrs C A (Neath Port Talbot County Borough Council)
Port Talbot *p469* 01639 763333

John, D (George Davies & Evans Limited)
Cardigan *p181* 01239 612308

John, D (Blaenau Gwent Borough Council) *E R1 S1 P L I*
Ebbw Vale *p458* 01495 350555

John, D A R (Graham Evans & Partners) *G H K1 N D1*
Swansea *p405* 01792 655822

John, Ms F R (McGrigors LLP)
London EC4 *p56* 020 7054 2500

6

John, G L S (Hewlett-Packard Ltd)
Bracknell *p451* 01344 360000

John, Ms H (Treasury Solicitors Department)
London WC2 *p110* 020 7210 3000

John, Mrs J (Baily Gibson) *W*
Beaconsfield *p128* 01494 672661

John, J L (Rooks Rider) *S2 R2 E*
London EC1 *p73* 020 7689 7000

John, J R G (Gateley LLP) *B1 C2*
Birmingham *p138* 0121 234 0000
Leicester *p279* 0116 285 9000

John, M A (Beale and Company Solicitors LLP) *E C2 C1 J1 S2 Zc R2 S1 L*
London WC2 *p11* 020 7240 3474
London WC2 *p57* 020 7240 0521

John, M A (Alan Edwards & Co) *S1 S2*
Kensington & Chelsea *p28* . . 020 7221 7644

John, N (Fraser Dawbarns)
Wisbech *p435* 01945 461456
King's Lynn *p266* 01553 660033

John, N (The Eric Whitehead Partnership) *K1 S1 G H W J1 V Q N L*
Cheadle *p185* 01538 755761

John, N H H (Benson Watkins & Co Limited) *S1 W E S2 C1*
Cardiff *p177* 029 2038 2486

John, N J (The Eric Whitehead Partnership) *W K4 T2 G Q*
Cheadle *p185* 01538 755761

John, O A (Drummonds) *Q N*
Chester *p190* 01244 408300

John, Mrs P (Cornwall County Council)
Truro *p474* 01872 322197

John, R H (Matthew Arnold & Baldwin LLP) *W T2*
Watford *p423* 01923 202020

John, R S (Alun Thomas & John) *S1 C1 N Q G K1 E O F1 L D1 Zt Zc Zk*
Aberystwyth *p114* 01970 615900

John, S (Penningtons) *Zr N*
Godalming *p231* 01483 791800

John, T M (Mayer Brown International LLP) *T1 T2*
London EC2 *p59* 020 3130 3000

Johns, Miss C L (Lupton Fawcett) *J1*
Leeds *p275* 0113 280 2000

Johns, D (Tonner Johns Ratti) *S1 E W L C1 F1 A1 K1 J1*
Swansea *p406* 01792 643296

Johns, D T (Fonseca & Partners) *D1 F1 G H K1 L M1 P S1 W Zl Zm*
Ebbw Vale *p216* 01495 303124

Johns, Ms E (Mason Baggott & Garton) *O Q Zc M1*
Scunthorpe *p373* 01724 868611

Johns, Ms G D (Coffin Mew & Clover) *K1 D1 V Zm Zp X Zg*
Portsmouth *p354* 023 9238 8021

Johns, Miss J (Chattertons Solicitors) *T2 W*
Grantham *p232* 01476 591550

Johns, Ms K (Howard Kennedy LLP) *E*
London W1 *p48* 020 7636 1616

Johns, M C (Ashurst LLP) *C1 Zn*
London EC2 *p7* 020 7638 1111

Johns, M S M (K&L Gates LLP) *C1*
London EC4 *p47* 020 7648 9000

Johns, N R (Reynolds Johns Partnership) *K1 Q N O J1 L B1 D1 Zq Zl K3*
Bishop's Stortford *p144* . . . 01279 508626

Johns, P (Chivers Easton Brown) *E S1 S2 W*
Surbiton *p402* 020 8390 6155

Johns, Mrs P J (Coodes) *S1 S2 W E A1 L*
Holsworthy *p251* 01409 253425

Johns, S (Blanchards Bailey LLP) *Q N J1*
Dorchester *p212* 01305 251222

Johnson, A (Bristows) *Ze I C3 M1*
London EC4 *p15* 020 7400 8000

Johnson, A (Penningtons) *N Zr*
Basingstoke *p127* 01256 407100

Johnson, A (Hill Dickinson LLP)
Liverpool *p288* 0151 600 8000

Johnson, A (Batt Broadbent) *C1 B1 R1 J1 F1 T1 Zx Zc Ze Zf Zl*
Salisbury *p371* 01722 411141

Johnson, A (GH Cornish LLP) *M2 M1*
Ilford *p260* 020 8090 0800

Johnson, A (Gosschalks) *E A1 R1 S1*
Hull *p256* 01482 324252

Johnson, A (Hill Dickinson LLP) *N Za Zj*
London EC3 *p41* 020 7283 9033

Johnson, A C (Lupton Fawcett) *Zq O*
Leeds *p275* 0113 280 2000

Johnson, A H M (Stephenson Harwood) *O Za*
London EC2 *p82* 020 7329 4422

Johnson, A J (Knowsley Metropolitan Borough Council)
Huyton *p461* 0151 443 3593

Johnson, Mrs A J (Financial Services Authority)
London E14 *p106* 020 7066 1000

Johnson, A J (Humfrys & Symonds) *S1 W K1*
Hereford *p248* . . . 01432 359261 / 276276

Johnson, A L R (Berry & Berry) *S1*
Tonbridge *p412* 01732 355911

Johnson, A M (Herbert Smith LLP) *O M2 Zb*
London EC2 *p40* 020 7374 8000

Johnson, A P (Kingston upon Hull City Council) *W E R1 C1 L*
Hull *p461* 01482 300300

Johnson, B (Stratford-on-Avon District Council)
Stratford-upon-Avon *p473* . . 01789 267575

Johnson, B T (Geldards LLP)
Nottingham *p337* 0115 983 3650

Johnson, Mrs C (Sills & Betteridge LLP) *K3 K1 S2 W G Q*
Spalding *p389* 01775 714874

Johnson, C (Rooks Rider) *T1 T2*
London EC1 *p73* 020 7689 7000

Johnson, Ms C A (London Stock Exchange Ltd)
London EC2 *p107* 020 7797 1000

Johnson, Mrs C D (Turner Parkinson) *S1 S2*
Manchester *p310* 0161 833 1212

Johnson, Ms C E (Squire Sanders (UK) LLP)
Leeds *p277* 0113 284 7000

Johnson, C H (Moss & Haselhurst) *G H*
Winsford *p435* 01606 592159
Northwich *p333* 01606 74301

Johnson, Miss C L (Crampton Pym & Lewis)
Oswestry *p342* 01691 653301

Johnson, C M B (Parkes Wilshire Johnson) *E S1 C1 T1 W L J1 F1 R1 B1 Zc Zm S2 P Zk Zl Zq R2*
Barnet *p124* 020 8441 1556

Johnson, C P (Robinsons) *E A1 S1 R1 L C1 Zc Zh Zp*
Derby *p209* 01332 291431

Johnson, C R (A Halsall & Co) *D1 F1 G H J1 K1 M1 P V Zl Zm Zj*
Birkenhead *p134* 0151 647 6323

Johnson, Mrs C V (Meikles) *K3 K1 S1 L K4 W*
Barnard Castle *p123* 01833 690505

Johnson, C W (Rex Taylor & Meadows) *C1 E L S1 W V*
West Kirby *p428* 0151 625 6414

Johnson, D (Avon & Somerset Constabulary)
Portishead *p469* 01275 816270

Johnson, D (Boodle Hatfield)
Westminster *p14* 020 7629 7411
London EC2 *p28* 020 7583 4055

Johnson, D (Weightmans LLP) *N F2 J2 Zj G*
Dartford *p207* 020 7822 1900

Johnson, D (Emsleys) *S1 W*
Castleford *p183* 01977 550115

Johnson, Ms D (Hodge Jones & Allen LLP) *D1 K1 K3*
London NW1 *p41* 020 7874 8300

Johnson, D J (Gorman Hamilton) *N J1 Q*
Newcastle upon Tyne *p324* . 0191 232 1123

Johnson, D M (The Johnson Partnership) *G H B2*
Nottingham *p337* 0115 941 9141

Johnson, D P (Norwich City Council)
Norwich *p467* 01603 212212

Johnson, D W (KBL Solicitors) *E S2 R2*
Bolton *p149* 01204 527777

Johnson, E (Calibre Solicitors Limited)
Manchester *p302* 0870 458 4418

Johnson, E C (Roythornes LLP) *S2 E R2*
Nottingham *p338* 0115 948 4555

Johnson, E R D (Richard Johnson & Partners) *W S1 A1 C1 P L T1 R1 E K1*
Hawes *p245* 01969 667000

Johnson, G (Gary Johnson & Co) *N S1 W Zr*
Middlesbrough *p315* 01642 222834

Johnson, G (Smith Roddam) *E G H J1 K1 O N P S1*
Bishop Auckland *p144* 01388 603073

Johnson, G A (Wealden District Council)
Crowborough *p456* 01892 653311

Johnson, Miss H L (Emery Johnson Partnership) *G H*
Leicester *p279* 0116 255 4855

Johnson, Mrs H M (Rosemary Smith & Co) *K3 K1 Q S2 S1 J1 V W L*
Crowthorne *p204* 01344 777441

Johnson, H M (Stewarts Law LLP) *Zr N*
London EC4 *p83* 020 7822 8000

Johnson, I (Johnsons Solicitors LLP)
Reading *p361* 0118 922 7220

Johnson, I L (Ashurst LLP) *T1*
London EC2 *p7* 020 7638 1111

Johnson, I W (Bray & Bray) *N*
Leicester *p279* 0116 254 8871

Johnson, J (Clifford Chance)
London E14 *p20* 020 7006 1000

Johnson, J (Trowers & Hamlins)
London EC3 *p88* 020 7423 8000

Johnson, J (Ronald Fletcher & Co) *K1 D1 K2 K3 D2*
London W9 *p33* 020 7624 0041

Johnson, Mrs J (Lancashire County Council)
Preston *p469* 01772 254868

Johnson, J B (The Royal London Mutual Insurance Society Ltd)
London EC3 *p455* 020 7506 6500

Johnson, Mrs J J (James Pearce & Co) *K1 L Q*
Birmingham *p141* 0121 784 1886

Johnson, Miss J L C (Northamptonshire Magistrates Courts)
Northampton *p467* 01604 497000

Johnson, J M M (Davies Johnson & Co (Shipping & Commercial Solicitors)) *O Za Zj*
Plymouth *p349* 01752 226020

Johnson, Ms J T (Baches) *D1 K1 K2*
West Bromwich *p427* . 0121 553 3286 / 553 7076

Johnson, Mrs K J (Lamb Brooks LLP) *J1 Zp*
Basingstoke *p126* 01256 844888
Guildford *p236* 01483 407000

Johnson, K L (SJP Solicitors) *W T1 K1 S1 L C1 E*
Hunstanton *p258* 01485 532662

Johnson, K T (John Pickering & Partners LLP) *N*
Halifax *p238* 0808 144 0959

Johnson, Miss L (John Morse Solicitors) *S2 E K4 S1 W*
Swansea *p405* 01792 648111

Johnson, L (Parker Rhodes Hickmotts) *K3 K1 W*
Rotherham *p367* 01709 511100

Johnson, Mrs L (Thursfields)
Kidderminster *p266* 01562 820575

Johnson, Ms L (Pinsent Masons LLP)
London EC2 *p67* 020 7418 7000

Johnson, Miss L (Bhatia Best) *S1*
Nottingham *p336* 0115 950 3231

Johnson, Ms L A (Williscroft & Co) *K1 K3*
Bradford *p155* 01274 305380

Johnson, L H (Hoben Johnson) *S1 E W K1 L C1 R1 T1 T2 Zv*
Rushden *p369* 01933 411375

Johnson, Miss L K (Lyons Wilson) *C1 J1 O Q C2 Zq Ze C3 Zk*
Manchester *p307* 0161 830 7777

Johnson, Miss M (Rotherham Metropolitan Borough Council) *S1*
Rotherham *p470* 01709 382121

Johnson, Ms M (TV Edwards LLP) *D1 K3 K1 D2*
London SE8 *p85* 020 7790 7000

Johnson, M (Hetts Johnson Whiting) *A1 C1 D1 E F1 H J1 K1 L N Zl Zt*
Brigg *p158* 01652 655101

Johnson, Mrs M C (Gosschalks)
Hull *p256* 01482 324252

Johnson, M J (Bendles) *Q J1 N O L Zl*
Carlisle *p181* 01228 522215

Johnson, Miss N (IBB Solicitors) *Zd Zm*
Chesham *p189* 0845 638 1381

Johnson, Miss N (Wrigleys Solicitors LLP) *Zd C1*
Leeds *p278* 0113 244 6100

Johnson, N (Gosschalks) *S1 L Zs*
Hull *p256* 01482 324252

Johnson, N (Reynolds Porter Chamberlain LLP)
London E1 *p71* 020 3060 6000

Johnson, N (Kitsons LLP) *B1 Zc E Q N*
Torquay *p413* 01803 202020

Johnson, N (Osborne Clarke) *F2 C1 Zk*
London EC2 *p65* 020 7105 7000

Johnson, Ms N (South Tyneside Metropolitan Borough Council)
South Shields *p471* 0191 427 1717

Johnson, N I (British Waterways Board)
Watford *p475* 01923 226422

Johnson, N R (Thompsons (formerly Robin/Brian Thompson & Partners)) *J1*
London SW19 *p87* 020 8947 4163

Johnson, N R (Glaisyers Solicitors LLP) *B1 C1 F1 N M1 P*
Manchester *p304* 0161 832 4666

Johnson, N T (Foot Anstey) *B1 Q*
Exeter *p221* 01392 411221

Johnson, N W T (Allen & Overy LLP)
London E1 *p5* 020 3088 0000

Johnson, P (Oldham Law Centre)
Oldham *p468* 0161 627 0925

Johnson, P (QualitySolicitors D'Angibau) *Q N J1 K1 G H D1 L V*
Boscombe *p151* 01202 393506

Johnson, P (Jameson & Hill) *K1 K3*
Hertford *p248* 01992 554881

Johnson, P B (Gill Akaster) *S1 Zl S2 A1*
Plymouth *p349* 01752 203500

Johnson, P C (Alexander JLO) *B1 C1 C2 C3 G N Q Zc Ze Zf Zk*
London E14 *p5* 020 7537 7000

Johnson, P D (Bright & Sons) *C1 S2 E*
Witham *p435* 01376 512338

Johnson, P D (Massers) *S1 E*
Nottingham *p338* 0115 851 1666

Johnson, Miss P E (Coffin Mew & Clover) *K1*
Southampton *p385* 023 8033 4661

Johnson, Miss P J (Blackburn with Darwen Borough Council) *K1 L V B1 W D1 Zi Zh*
Blackburn *p450* 01254 585585

Johnson, Mrs P K (Pamela K Johnson Solicitor) *S1*
Poulton-le-Fylde *p355* 01253 812400

Johnson, P N (Thomson & Bancks LLP) *G Q N J1 F1 C1 O Zl*
Pershore *p346* 01386 562000

Johnson, P W (Jeffrey Green Russell) *E R1 L A1 Zb Zc Zs*
London W1 *p46* 020 7339 7000

Johnson, R (Healys LLP) *O*
London EC4 *p39* 020 7822 4000

Johnson, R (McGrigors LLP)
London EC4 *p56* 020 7054 2500

Johnson, R (SJ LAW)
London E17 *p75* 020 8520 6600

Johnson, R (Galbraith Branley) *H G B2*
London N12 *p34* 020 8446 8474

Johnson, R D B (Brett Johnson) *S1 W E F1 J1 L Zl*
Brockenhurst *p166* 01590 612731

Johnson, R E (Taylor Walton LLP)
Luton *p295* 01582 731161

Johnson, R G (Carvill & Johnson LLP) *B1 O Q Zc S2 E*
Birmingham *p136* 0121 476 9000

Johnson, R G (Malcolm C Foy & Co) *N*
Doncaster *p211* 01302 340005

Johnson, Mrs R K (Pengelly & Rylands) *W T2*
Tenterden *p410* . . .01580 762248 / 763008

Johnson, Ms R L (Stephensons Solicitors LLP) *N*
Leigh *p282* 01942 777777

Johnson, Ms R M (Bristol City Council)
Bristol *p451* 0117 922 2000

Johnson, Ms S (Lewis Silkin LLP) *O*
London EC4 *p53* 020 7074 8000

Johnson, Miss S (Manches LLP) *J1 Zp*
London WC2 *p58* 020 7404 4433

Johnson, S (Mid Devon District Council)
Tiverton *p474* 01884 255255

Johnson, S (Paul Rudd) *S1 S2 W*
Grimsby *p235* 01472 350881

Johnson, Mrs S (Alderson Dodds) *K1 D1 M1 F1 P J1 W G*
Blyth *p147* 01670 352293

Johnson, S C (Watmores) *Zu Q N*
London WC2 *p90* 020 7430 1512

Johnson, Mrs S C (Cartmell Shepherd)
Carlisle *p182* 01228 516666

Johnson, Ms S C (Molesworths Bright Clegg) *K1 D1*
Rochdale *p365* 01706 356666

Johnson, Mrs S E (McGrigors LLP) *E S2 R2 R1*
London EC4 *p56* 020 7054 2500

Johnson, Mrs S F (Wessex Water Services Ltd) *P N L R1 J1 B1 Ze Zc*
Bath *p448* 01225 526000

Johnson, Mrs S J (Heptonstalls LLP) *N Q Zr*
Goole *p231* 01405 765661

Johnson, Miss S M (Howard Kennedy LLP) *B1 F1 J1 L N O Q Ze Zi*
London W1 *p48* 020 7636 1616

Johnson, T (Pinsent Masons LLP) *E R2 L*
Birmingham *p141* 0121 200 1050

Johnson, T (Ince & Co Services Ltd)
London E1 *p44* 020 7481 0010

Johnson, T A (SJ Berwin LLP)
London EC4 *p75* 020 7111 2222

Johnson, T G (DAC Beachcroft) *P R1 R2*
London EC4 *p24* 020 7936 2222

Johnson, Ms T J (Coffin Mew & Clover) *N*
Fareham *p223* 01329 825617

Johnson, Miss V (Woolliscrofts) *B1*
Hanley *p239* 01782 204000

Johnson, Ms V M (Lancashire County Council)
Preston *p469* 01772 254868

Johnson, W A (Arun District Council)
Littlehampton *p463* 01903 716133

Johnson, W D (Amos Developments Ltd) *S1 W E A1 L T2 Zh Zv Zd*
Leek *p463* 01588 266664

Johnson, W G (Pickering & Butters) *S1 L W*
Stafford *p393* 01785 603060

Johnston, A (Stephens & Son LLP)
Chatham *p185* 01634 811444

Johnston, A (Holman Fenwick Willan)
London EC3 *p42* 020 7264 8000

Johnston, A (Capsticks Solicitors LLP) *C1 Zd I M1*
London SW19 *p18* 020 8780 2211

Johnston, A F (Jaswal Johnston Boyle) *C1 O Q N*
London W1 *p46* 020 7317 1540

Johnston, A T (Elliot Mather LLP) *E C1 A1 L W B1 S1*
Mansfield *p311* 01623 655666

Johnston, B C (GoodyBurrett LLP) *N Q F1 J1 O L B1 F2 C1 Zr*
Colchester *p197* 01206 577676

Johnston, C J A (Bircham Dyson Bell) *W T2 M2 Zd*
Westminster *p13* 020 7227 7000

Johnston, D S (Clifford Johnston & Co) *S1 S2 K4 W*
Manchester *p302* 0161 975 1900

Johnston, Mrs E A (Gateshead Magistrates Court)
Gateshead *p458* 0191 477 5821

Johnston, E C (Mills & Reeve) *I Ze U2 U1*
Cambridge *p175* 01223 364422

Johnston, Mrs H (Hilary Johnston) *S1 W L E*
Beaconsfield *p129* 01494 678230

Johnston, Miss H E (Portrait Solicitors) *S1*
London WC2 *p69* 020 7092 6990

Johnston, I C (Wortley Redmayne Kershaw) *W*
Chelmsford *p187* 01245 491122

Johnston, I C (Metcalfe Johnston McCormick) *S1 G H W D1 T1 C1 E K1 J1 Zl Zj Zo*
Eccles *p216* . . . 0161 789 3481 / 788 9021

Johnston, J (Burnetts) *J2 Zl Zc*
Carlisle *p181* 01228 552222

Johnston, J (Osborne Clarke) *C1*
London EC2 *p65* 020 7105 7000

Johnston, J J (Shammah Nicholls LLP) *S2 E R1 R2*
Manchester *p309* 0161 832 9272

Johnston, L A (Staffordshire County Council)
Stafford *p472* 01785 223121

Johnston, L M (Hedleys & Co) *S1 E L W R1 C1 T1 F1 Zc S2 J1 O*
Sunderland *p401* 0191 567 0101

Johnston, M C (Blanchards Bailey LLP) *S1 A1 R1 E W*
Blandford Forum *p147* 01258 459361

Johnston, P (Buckinghamshire County Council)
Aylesbury *p448* 01296 383653

Johnston, P F (Reed Smith LLP) *E*
London EC2 *p71* 020 3116 3000

Johnston, P R (Beaty & Co) *W S1 E C1 A1 T1 T2 S2*
Wigton *p432* 01697 342121

Johnston, R (Mayo Wynne Baxter LLP) *N Zj*
Lewes *p283* 01273 477071

Johnston, Mrs S (Pritchard Joyce & Hinds) *K1 K3*
Beckenham *p129* 020 8658 3922

Johnston, S (Nabarro LLP)
London WC1 *p63* 020 7524 6000

Johnston, S J (CMS Cameron McKenna LLP) *B1 E F1 Zb*
London EC3 *p17* 020 7367 3000

Johnston, T K (Addleshaw Goddard)
Manchester *p300* 0161 934 6000

Johnstone, A (Stephenson Harwood)
London EC2 *p82* 020 7329 4422

Johnstone, Miss A N (Radcliffes Le Brasseur) *N Zg Zr*
Westminster *p70* 020 7222 7040

 See p634 for the Key to Work Categories

Johnstone, A R (Treasury Solicitors Department)
London WC2 *p110* 020 7210 3000

Johnstone, Miss C L (Warner Goodman LLP) *K1 T2 V W K4*
Fareham *p224* 01329 288121

Johnstone, Mrs D (Prince Evans) *S1 Zh*
Ealing *p69* 020 8567 3477

Johnstone, Mrs G A (Glynis A Johnstone) *S1 W S2*
Oxted *p344* 01883 716894

Johnstone, H E (Harvey Ingram Borneos) *E S1 A1 W L R1 T1*
Bedford *p130* 01234 353221

Johnstone, I S S (AXA UK PLC)
London E22 *p103* 020 7920 5900

Johnstone, Miss L (Beale and Company Solicitors LLP) *Zq Zj O*
London WC2 *p11* 020 7240 3474

Johnstone, M A (AS Law) *Zy J2 G Zg*
Liverpool *p285* 0151 707 1212

Johnstone, P A (Muckle LLP) *J1 O*
Newcastle upon Tyne *p325* . 0191 211 7777

Johnstone, P W (Merritt & Co) *W T2 S1 S2 Zm*
Yarm *p443* 01642 885555

Johnstone, R (IBB Solicitors)
Uxbridge *p417* 0845 638 1381

Johnstone, W J I (Tuckers) *G H D1 K1*
Manchester *p310* 0161 233 4321

Joiner, J (Trowers & Hamlins)
London EC3 *p88* 020 7423 8000

Joint, A J R (Kemp Little LLP) *I U2 U1 C1*
London EC2 *p48* 020 7600 8080

Jojo, Ms C (Barlow Lyde & Gilbert LLP) *O Q*
London EC3 *p10* 020 7247 2277

Jolin, S A (Browne Jacobson LLP) *O*
Nottingham *p336* 0115 976 6000

Joll, Mrs A C (Churchers) *K1 V D2 D1*
Fareham *p223* 01329 822333

Joll, Ms V (Rawlison Butler LLP) *O E*
Crawley *p202* 01293 527744

Jolley, Mrs F M (Wrigley Claydon) *D1 K1 K3*
Oldham *p341* 0161 624 6811

Jolley, Ms I H (Norfolk County Council - Legal Services)
Norwich *p467* . . . . Minicom: 0844 800 8011

Jolley, P A (Bridgend County Borough Council)
Bridgend *p451* 01656 643643

Jolliff, Mrs D C (Andrew & Co LLP) *A1 E*
Lincoln *p284* 01522 512123

Jolliffe, Miss S A (Charsley Harrison LLP) *J1 O Q*
Windsor *p434* 01753 851591

Jolly, Miss K E (Drummonds) *S1*
Chester *p190* 01244 408300

Jolly, P G (Marsden Rawsthorn LLP) *S1 W E L S2*
Chorley *p194* 01257 279511

Jolly, R (Weightmans LLP)
Liverpool *p291* 0151 227 2601

Joly, C R R (N C Morris & Co)
Salisbury *p371* 01722 415215

Jonas, S M (Jonas Roy Bloom) *G H Zg*
Birmingham *p139* 0121 212 4111

Jonckheer, Ms M J (Crown Prosecution Service Thames Valley) *G*
Abingdon *p447* 01235 551900

Joneja, S (Squire Sanders (UK) LLP)
Manchester *p310* 0161 830 5000

Jones, A (Trowers & Hamlins)
London EC3 *p88* 020 7423 8000

Jones, A (DLA Piper UK LLP)
Birmingham *p137* 0870 011 1111

Jones, A (Harrisons Solicitors LLP) *S1 A1 W R1 P K1 M1 G D1 F1 Zl*
Welshpool *p425* 01938 552545

Jones, A (Hugh James) *F1 O N*
Cardiff *p179* 029 2022 4871

Jones, A (Cartwright King) *G H Zl*
Nottingham *p336* 0115 958 7444
Nottingham *p338* 0115 958 6262

Jones, Ms A (The College of Law Chester)
Chester *p454* 0800 289997

Jones, Ms A (Co-operative Insurance Society Ltd)
Manchester *p464* 0161 832 8686

Jones, Miss A (Torfaen Borough Council)
Pontypool *p469* 01495 766373

Jones, Mrs A (Mills & Reeve) *E*
Cambridge *p175* 01223 364422

Jones, Miss A (Woolliscrofts) *N Q*
Hanley *p239* 01782 204000

Jones, A (Linklaters LLP)
London EC2 *p54* 020 7456 2000

Jones, Mrs A (Stewarts Law LLP) *Zr*
London EC4 *p83* 020 7822 8000

Jones, Miss A (Flintshire County Council) *K1 N O Q L D1 F1*
Mold *p466* 01352 702411

Jones, A (Follett Stock LLP) *E S2 R2 R1*
Truro *p414* 01872 241700

Jones, Miss A C (Mayer Brown International LLP) *E S2 R2*
London EC2 *p59* 020 3130 3000

Jones, A D (B P Collins LLP) *O Q I F1 Zc Zk*
Gerrards Cross *p229* 01753 889995

Jones, Ms A D (Brooke North LLP) *W*
Leeds *p272* 0113 283 2100

Jones, A E (Bowles & Co) *E*
Epsom *p219* 01372 725241

Jones, Mrs A E (Whittinghams) *K1 N Q V L*
Porthcawl *p353* 01656 788823

Jones, A J (Hadgkiss Hughes & Beale) *G H*
Birmingham *p138* 0121 449 5050

Jones, A J (Hadgkiss Hughes & Beale) *C1 S1 E L S2*
Birmingham *p138* 0121 449 5050

Jones, A L (MSP Legal Services LLP) *Zr O Q N Zq W F1*
Hartlepool *p243* 01429 232204

Jones, A M (Birketts LLP (Wollastons LLP)) *C1 C2*
Chelmsford *p186* 01245 211211

Jones, A M (Wiggin LLP) *C2 C1*
Cheltenham *p189* 01242 224114

Jones, A M (Clark Willis) *S1 K3 K1 S2 E W*
Catterick Garrison *p183* 01748 830000

Jones, Miss A M (Blaenau Gwent Borough Council) *P R1 L E S1 Zl Zs*
Ebbw Vale *p458* 01495 350555

Jones, Miss A M (Morris & Bates) *D1 D2 G H K1 J1 V*
Aberystwyth *p114* 01970 625566
Llandrindod Wells *p291* . . . 01597 829055

Jones, Mrs A M B (LDJ Solicitors) *K4 K1 S1 T2 W*
Hinckley *p250* 01455 637030
Nuneaton *p339* 024 7674 5000

Jones, A P (Mills & Reeve) *O Q A3 Zc Zq*
Birmingham *p140* 0121 454 4000

Jones, A R (JMD Law Limited) *E S1 L*
Cardiff *p179* 029 2045 6780

Jones, Ms A V (E A Harris & Co Ltd) *K3 K1 W S1*
Shotton *p378* 01244 822555
Shotton *p379* 01244 812109

Jones, A W (Elwyn Jones & Co) *G N S1 Q J1 H W L F1 Zl Zm Zj Zv E S2*
Bangor *p122* 01248 370224

Jones, Miss A W (Alwena Jones & Jones) *S1 W K1 N L A1 C1 S2*
Blaenau Ffestiniog *p147* . . . 01766 831882
Tywyn *p416* 01654 711499

Jones, B (Darlingtons) *J1 C2*
Edgware *p217* . 020 8952 0033 / 8951 6666

Jones, Ms B (Lanyon Bowdler LLP) *J1*
Telford *p409* 01952 291222

Jones, Ms B (Michelmores LLP) *J1 Zp*
Exeter *p221* 01392 688688

Jones, B (Bone & Payne LLP) *G H*
Llandudno *p291* 01492 876354

Jones, Mrs B C (Beardsells) *K1 G H*
Cheadle *p185* 0161 477 2288

Jones, Mrs B J (Williams & Co) *W S1 S2 T2 E A1 L*
Bridgnorth *p157* . . 01746 762157 / 765603

Jones, B N (DWF) *N*
Liverpool *p287* 0151 907 3000

Jones, Mrs B S (Capper & Jones) *D1 K1 J1 Q N*
Mold *p318* 01352 752020

Jones, B W (Farmers Union of Wales) *A1 C1 E F1 G L R1 S1 T1 W Zd Ze Zl*
Aberystwyth *p447* 01970 820820

Jones, B Y (Barrie Y Jones & Co) *S1 K1 P M1 E*
Bridgend *p157* 01656 657929
Llantwit Major *p292* . 01446 793835 / 794542

Jones, Ms C (Hillyer McKeown LLP) *E S1 S2*
Chester *p190* 01244 318131

Jones, C (Knights Solicitors LLP) *W K4*
Newcastle under Lyme *p323* . 01782 619225

Jones, C (Kundert & Co) *N*
Coventry *p200* 024 7668 4928

Jones, Ms C (Darbys Solicitors LLP) *S1 E L A1*
Oxford *p343* 01865 811700

Jones, Ms C (Machins Solicitors LLP) *Q O B1 B2*
Luton *p295* 01582 514000

Jones, C A (Mander Hadley & Co) *C1 E R1 S1 Zi*
Coventry *p200* 024 7663 1212

Jones, Mrs C A (Chubb Bulleid) *S1 W*
Street *p400* 01749 836100

Jones, Ms C A (British Aerospace Airbus)
Bristol *p451* 0117 966 5881

Jones, Miss C A (Thompsons (formerly Robin/Brian Thompson & Partners)) *N*
Cardiff *p181* 029 2044 5300

Jones, C D (Tucker Turner Kingsley Wood & Co) *E A1 R1 Zl Zc Zo*
London WC1 *p88* 020 7242 3303

Jones, C D (Hewitsons) *C1*
Cambridge *p174* 01223 461155

Jones, Mrs C E (Cullimore Dutton) *D1 K1 G Q O A1*
Chester *p190* 01244 356789

Jones, Mrs C E (Gillian Radford & Co) *K1 K3 D2 D1*
Westminster *p70* 020 8960 4366

Jones, Ms C E (Reed Smith LLP) *O Ze Zk Zf*
London EC2 *p71* 020 3116 3000

Jones, Mrs C E (Pannone LLP) *D2 K1*
Manchester *p308* 0161 909 3000

Jones, Mrs C E (The Jones Partnership) *K1 S1 N Q W*
Mold *p318* 01352 753388

Jones, C E B (Weightmans LLP)
Liverpool *p291* 0151 227 2601

Jones, Miss C F (Leonard & Co) *G H*
Southampton *p386* 023 8023 3242

Jones, C H (Furness & District Petty Sessional Division)
Barrow-in-Furness *p448* . . . 01229 820161

Jones, C H (Slee Blackwell) *J1 O G Q N F1 B1*
Braunton *p156* 01271 812019

Jones, C J D (Kundert & Co) *G D1 F1 H K1 M1 P Zm F2 N*
Coventry *p200* 024 7622 7741

Jones, C J E (Slee Blackwell) *G H Zl*
Barnstaple *p125* 01271 372128

Jones, C L (The Dures Partnership LLP)
Liverpool *p287* 0151 242 5111

Jones, Ms C L (Fulchers of Farnborough) *S1 W K4 R2*
Farnborough *p224* 01252 522475

Jones, Mrs C N (Davies Blunden & Evans) *S1 T1 W*
Farnborough *p224* 01252 541633

Jones, Miss C N (Ceredigion County Council)
Aberaeron *p447* 01545 570881

Jones, C R (Jones Robertson) *S1 K1 D1 W L F1 N P G*
Runcorn *p369* 01928 711119
Widnes *p431* 0151 423 3661

Jones, C R V (Fisher Jones Greenwood LLP) *E L S1 S2 C1 C2 J1 Ze Zl*
Chelmsford *p186* 01245 890110

Jones, C T (Crown Prosecution Service Avon & Somerset)
Bristol *p451* 0117 930 2800

Jones, D (Jerman Simpson Pearson & Samuels)
Southend-on-Sea *p387* . . . 01702 610071

Jones, D (Canter Levin & Berg) *N*
Kirkby *p268* 0151 546 4562

Jones, D (Lawrence Davies & Co) *G H*
Hammersmith & Fulham *p26* . 020 7381 1171

Jones, D (Trethowans LLP) *R2 E S2 Zd A1*
Salisbury *p371* 01722 412512

Jones, D (Watson Burton LLP)
London EC3 *p90* 0845 901 2100

Jones, D (Arun District Council)
Littlehampton *p463* 01903 716133

Jones, D (Essex County Council)
Chelmsford *p454* 0845 743 0430

Jones, D (DWF) *O B1 F1 Q*
Manchester *p303* 0161 603 5000

Jones, D A (Granville-West Chivers & Morgan) *K3 Q S1 L W E*
Newport *p328* 01495 243268

Jones, D C (Berry Smith LLP) *E C1 L*
Cardiff *p177* 029 2034 5511

Jones, Ms D C (Deibel & Allen) *W S1*
Portslade-by-Sea *p354* . . . 01273 430999

Jones, D E (Fisher Jones Greenwood LLP) *S1 E W C1 A1*
Colchester *p197* 01206 835300

Jones, Mrs D E (Conwy County Borough Council)
Conwy *p455* 01492 576108

Jones, Ms D E (DBL Talbots LLP) *K1 G N D2 D1 K3*
Codsall *p197* 01902 843427

Jones, D F D (T B I Financial Services Ltd)
Reading *p469* 0118 931 3800

Jones, D G (Jones Knowles Warburton) *G H V*
Stockport *p395* 0161 474 1992

Jones, D G (Shipton Hallewell & Co) *G H K1 S2 D1 S1*
Chesterfield *p192* 01246 232140

Jones, D H (KJD) *E Zh*
Stoke-on-Trent *p398* 01782 202020

Jones, D I (David Jones & Co) *E L S1 W C1*
Llandudno *p291* 01492 874336

Jones, D J (Hatten Wyatt) *W K4*
Gravesend *p232* 01474 351199

Jones, D J (Morgan Jones & Pett) *Zr N*
Norwich *p335* 01603 877000

Jones, D L (R Gordon Roberts Laurie & Co) *G H D2 D1 N*
Llangefni *p292* . . . 01248 722215 / 723312

Jones, D M (Addleshaw Goddard)
Leeds *p271* 0113 209 2000
Manchester *p300* 0161 934 6000

Jones, D M (David Morgan Jones) *S1 W E C1*
Colchester *p197* 01206 766749

Jones, D M (Squire Sanders (UK) LLP)
London EC2 *p81* 020 7655 1000
Newcastle upon Tyne *p327* . 0845 901 2100

Jones, D M (Edward Hughes) *B1 F1 J1 K1 L O Q N*
Rhyl *p363* . . . . . 01745 343661 / 344551

Jones, D N (Ashurst LLP) *N Q*
London EC2 *p7* 020 7638 1111
Sheffield *p375* 0114 272 2061

Jones, D P (Quality Solicitors Copley Clark) *E L S1 S2*
Sutton *p403* 020 8643 7221

Jones, D R (Gwynedd Council)
Caernarfon *p452* 01286 672255

Jones, D R H (Morris & Bates) *F1 G H J1 K1 L M1 N P W Zh*
Aberystwyth *p114* 01970 625566
Llandrindod Wells *p291* . . . 01597 829055

Jones, D R J (Camerons Jones) *E S1 W T1 K1 C1 L O*
Harrow *p241* 020 8423 6666

Jones, D W (Jones Robertson) *D1 F1 G H K1 L N Q W*
Widnes *p431* 0151 423 3661

Jones, Mrs E (Howell Jones & Co) *W K4 S2 C1 S1*
Abergele *p113* . . . 01745 826282 / 825845
Llanrwst *p292* 01492 640277

Jones, Miss E (Mackrell Turner Garrett) *N O*
London WC2 *p57* 020 7240 0521

Jones, E A (Charles Crookes & Jones) *S1 E M1 K1 G B1 C1 A1 R1 D1 Zt Zl Zc*
Caerphilly *p172* 029 2086 0628

Jones, E D E (Hodge Jones & Allen LLP) *G H*
London NW1 *p41* 020 7874 8300

Jones, E E (Brighouse Wolff) *S1 N P K1 C1 L E F1 D1 W Zc*
Skelmersdale *p381* 01695 717000

Jones, Miss E E (Fisher Meredith) *K1*
Lambeth *p32* 020 7091 2700

Jones, E G (Aviva PLC)
London EC3 *p103* . . 020 7283 7500 / 01603 687905

Jones, E H (GHP Legal) *G H Zi*
Wrexham *p442* 01978 291456

Jones, Mrs E J (Hewitsons) *E S2 R2*
Cambridge *p174* 01223 461155

Jones, Miss E M (Birkett Long LLP) *D1 K1*
Colchester *p197* 01206 217300

Jones, E O (Manches LLP) *J1 O Q Zq*
London WC2 *p58* 020 7404 4433

Jones, Mrs E R (Hugh Williams Son & Co) *A1 E F1 K1 L N S1 I W Zc Zf Zj Zm Zv*
Llandeilo *p291* 01558 823417

Jones, Miss E S (Cumberland Ellis Peirs) *Zd S1 S2*
London WC1 *p23* 020 7242 0422

Jones, E W D (Red Kite Law) *D1 K1*
Carmarthen *p183* 01267 239000

Jones, Ms F A (Manches LLP) *C1 C2*
London WC2 *p58* 020 7404 4433

Jones, F A (John O'Neill & Co) *E W S1 S2 C1 T2 Zd R1 Zc Zh*
Gosforth *p232* 0191 246 4000

Jones, Mrs F P (Tudur Owen Roberts Glynne & Co) *G H M1 K1 S1 F1 J1 W D1 L Zl Zp*
Holyhead *p251* 01407 762374
Caernarfon *p172* . . 01286 672207 / 672851

Jones, Ms G (Emyr Thomas & Son) *S1 S2 W K1*
Caernarfon *p172* . . 01286 672307 / 672308

Jones, G (Bond Pearce LLP)
Bristol *p161* 0845 415 0000

Jones, G (Cyril Jones & Co) *D1 F1 G H J1 K1 L M1 P S1 Zi Zl Zm*
Wrexham *p443* 01978 367830

Jones, Mrs G (Sacker & Partners LLP) *Zo*
London EC2 *p76* 020 7329 6699

Jones, Miss G (Wrexham County Borough Council)
Wrexham *p477* 01978 292000

Jones, G (Norwich Union Insurance Group)
Norwich *p467* 01603 622200

Jones, Miss G (Bates N V H) *E S1 L*
London WC2 *p11* 020 7936 2930

Jones, G (Parry Davies Clwyd-Jones & Lloyd) *S1 R1 W K1*
Pwllheli *p358* . . . . 01758 703000 / 701155

Jones, G (Gamlins) *H G D1 P Zl Zt*
Rhyl *p363* 01745 343500

Jones, G A (Gerald Jones & Co)
Thetford *p410* . . . . 01842 754466 / 754467

Jones, G A (Child & Child) *S1 L C1 T1 R1 E A1 W*
London SW1 *p20* 020 7235 8000

Jones, G C (Parry Davies Clwyd-Jones & Lloyd) *A1 B1 D1 F1 G H J1 K1 L M1*
Llangefni *p292* 01248 723106

Jones, G D (Ormerods) *S1 S2 N O L W Zm Zg*
Croydon *p205* 020 8686 5000

Jones, G E (Crutes) *S2 E R2 S1 Zh*
Stockton-on-Tees *p396* . . . 01642 623400
York *p444* 01904 611411

Jones, G E (Geraint Jones & Co) *G N W S1 K1 Q L H A1 T2 Ze Zd Zg*
Newtown *p330* 01686 627935

Jones, G E M (Keene & Kelly) *D2 K1 D1*
Mold *p318* 01352 753882

Jones, G J (Meade & Co) *E S1 W K4*
London N14 *p60* 020 8886 3643
London N14 *p83* 020 8882 1047

Jones, G K (Whitehead Monckton) *K1 K2 D1*
Maidstone *p299* 01622 698000

Jones, G L (G Lloyd Jones & Co) *W S1 S2 A1 K1 L J1 Zl Zm*
Prestatyn *p356* 01745 888666

Jones, G M (Davis Blank Furniss) *C1 E L S1*
Manchester *p303* 0161 832 3304

Jones, G O (Geraint Jones & Co) *G H J1 S1 Q L S2*
Newtown *p330* 01686 627935

Jones, G O (Lloyd Jones & Co) *K1 N S1 Q L E W C1 F1 Zc Zd Zm S2*
Westcliff-on-Sea *p428* 01702 710338

Jones, G R E (Weightmans LLP) *C1 C2 I C3 M1 B1 F1 Zb Ze*
Liverpool *p291* 0151 227 2601

Jones, G R G (Jordans) *Q N*
Wakefield *p418* 01924 387110

Jones, G S (Smith Llewelyn Partnership) *J1 R1 Zm D2*
Swansea *p405* 01792 464444

Jones, G T (Robyns Owen) *S1 W A1 E L S2*
Pwllheli *p358* 01758 613177

Jones, G W (Gwynedd Council)
Caernarfon *p452* 01286 672255

Jones, G W (Nabarro LLP)
London WC1 *p63* 020 7524 6000

Jones, G W (Rushworth & Glyn Owen) *S1 K1 F1 W J1 N*
Rhyl *p363* 01745 343843

Jones, Miss H (Churchers) *G H*
Portsmouth *p354* 023 9286 2424

Jones, H (Toyota (GB) PLC) *C1 C3 F1 J1 M1 Zo Zj*
Epsom *p458* 01737 363633

Jones, Ms H (Hamilton Davies) *W T2 K4*
Stevenage *p394* 01438 315898

Jones, Ms H (Western Division Service Magistrates Court)
Caernarfon *p452* 01286 675200

Jones, Ms H (Grindeys LLP) *K4 L Zm S1 T2 V W*
Stone *p398* 01785 810780

Jones, H (Osborne Clarke) *Zb*
Bristol *p164* 0117 917 3000

Jones, Ms H A J (Forsters LLP) *W T2*
Westminster *p33* 020 7863 8333
Jones, H A S (Pannone LLP) *T2 W Zm Zo Zv Zd*
Manchester *p308* 0161 909 3000
Jones, Mrs H E (B P Collins LLP) *C1 I C2*
Gerrards Cross *p229*. 01753 889995
Jones, Miss H E (Girls' Day School Trust)
London SW1 *p106*. 020 7393 6666
Jones, H K (Russell & Russell) *G H*
Chester *p191* 01244 405700
Jones, H L (Whittinghams) *E F1 K1 L N Q S1*
Bridgend *p157*. 01656 653485
Jones, Mrs H L M (Squire Sanders (UK) LLP)
Birmingham *p142* 0121 222 3000
Jones, H M C (Potter Jones & Co) *G H*
St Helens *p391* 01744 730376
Jones, H R (Band Hatton LLP) *C1 E L W T1 B1 S1 Zd Ze Zo*
Coventry *p200*. 024 7663 2121
Jones, H R (Sheridans) *J1 Zf Ze*
London WC1 *p78* 020 7079 0100
Jones, H R (R Gordon Roberts Laurie & Co) *W S1 L E*
Llangefni *p292*. . . .01248 722215 / 723312
Jones, I (Jestyn Jeffreys)
Neath *p320* 01639 635641
Jones, I B (Chronnell Hibbert) *K1 G N H D1 Zm*
Hyde *p259*. 0161 368 3434
Stockport *p395*. 0161 494 6085
Jones, I K (Backhouse Jones Ltd) *J2 N O Q*
Clitheroe *p196*. 01254 828300
Jones, I M (Atteys) *A1 E R2 S1 S2*
Doncaster *p211* 01302 340400
Jones, I R (T R Harris Arnold & Co) *J1 S1 W F1*
Gorseinon *p231* . . .01792 892166 / 891331
Jones, I R M B (Jones & Duffin Solicitors LLP) *B1 E R1 S1 W Zd R2*
Leicester *p280*. 0116 222 1555
Jones, Ms I Z (MFG Solicitors) *W T1 Zm*
Telford *p409* 01952 641651
Jones, Ms J (Fraser Dawbarns) *K1 D1 V*
Wisbech *p435* 01945 461456
Jones, Mrs J (Smith Llewelyn Partnership) *N Q*
Swansea *p405*. 01792 464444
Jones, Miss J (Heaney Watson) *K1 K3*
Liverpool *p288*. 0151 293 2936
Jones, Mrs J (Treasury Solicitors Department)
London WC2 *p110*. 020 7210 3000
Jones, Ms J (Anthony Collins Solicitors LLP) *O Zq*
Birmingham *p137* 0121 200 3242
Jones, J (Quality Solicitors Burroughs Day) *K4 T2 W*
Bristol *p164* 0117 929 0333
Jones, J A (Carver Jones) *S1 W K3 S2*
Hereford *p247* 01432 274301
Jones, Miss J A (The Roland Partnership) *Zr N S1*
Chester *p191* 01244 659404
Jones, J A H (Humfrys & Symonds) *D1 D2 K1 N Q O G Zr Zq*
Hereford *p248*. . . .01432 359261 / 276276
Jones, J D (Peter Williams & Co) *E S2 S1 W C1 Zd*
Swansea *p406*. 01792 465597
Jones, J D M (Llewellyn Jones & Co) *P N M1 K1 S1 W C1 E G A1 Zc Zl Zm*
Mold *p318*. 01352 755305
Jones, Mrs J E (Louise Stephens & Co)
Risca *p365* . . . . . .01633 614005 / 601144
Jones, J E (Carter Vincent Jones Davis)
Bangor *p122*. 01248 362551
Jones, Mrs J E M (The Owen-Kenny Partnership) *W*
Chichester *p193* 01243 532777
Jones, J G (Clerk to the Justices)
Caernarfon *p452*. . .01286 675200 / 675288
Colwyn Bay *p455* 01492 541573
Jones, J H (Gregorys Solicitors)
Stockport *p395*. 0161 456 8125
Jones, Mrs J H (Ginn & Co) *S1 E W K4 S2*
Cambridge *p174*. 01223 358275
Jones, J J (Squire Sanders (UK) LLP)
Leeds *p277* 0113 284 7000
Jones, J M (Silversmiths)
Bootle *p150*. 0151 922 6066
Jones, J N (Furley Page LLP) *C1 C2 B1 E*
Canterbury *p176*. 01227 763939
Jones, J O (Swayne Johnson Solicitors) *S1 W T1 C1 E G H R1 L A1 Zl S2*
Llandudno *p291* 01492 876271
Jones, J R (Mark Eisenthal & Co) *S1 W K1 E*
London WC2 *p29* 020 7379 3475
Jones, Miss J S (Nockolds) *N*
Bishop's Stortford *p144* . . . 01279 755777
Jones, Mrs J W (Conwy County Borough Council)
Conwy *p455*. 01492 576108
Jones, Miss K (Blandy & Blandy) *R1 R2*
Reading *p360* 0118 951 6800
Jones, Mrs K (Humphries Kirk) *S1 S2*
Dorchester *p212*. 01305 251007
Jones, Miss K (Temple & Co Commercial Solicitors) *C1 J1 E*
Daventry *p207*. 0845 241 4045
Jones, K (Woodfines LLP) *Q N F1 Zm Zg*
Bedford *p130* 01234 270600
Jones, K (Kenneth Jones) *S1 W E*
Kidsgrove *p266* 01782 771113
Jones, K (Clarke Willmott) *J1 Zp*
Bristol *p162* 0845 209 1000 / 0117 305 6000
Jones, K (Lloyd Platt & Co) *K1 J1*
London N3 *p55* 020 8343 2998
Jones, Ms K A (Sookias & Sookias) *S1 S2*
London W1 *p80* 020 7465 8000

Jones, Miss K A (McKinnells) *N*
Lincoln *p284*. 01522 541181
Jones, K A (E A Harris & Co Ltd) *N Q W L*
Buckley *p168* 01244 541505
Shotton *p378* 01244 822555
Jones, Ms K F (The Jones Partnership)
Mold *p318*. 01352 753388
Jones, Mrs K J (Thursfields) *W*
Kidderminster *p266* 01562 820575
Jones, Miss K L (Foys Solicitors) *D1 D2 K1*
Doncaster *p211* 01302 327136
Jones, K M (Weightmans LLP) *N Q Zj*
Liverpool *p291*. 0151 227 2601
Jones, Ms K P (Eastgate Assistance Ltd) *F1 N Q B1 Zb Zq*
Colchester *p455* 0870 523 4500
Jones, Mrs K S (Booth Ince & Knowles) *S1 W K4*
Hyde *p259*. 0161 368 2134
Jones, Mrs L (Gartsides) *J1 L N*
Abergavenny *p113*. 01873 857555
Jones, L (Hugh James) *E S1 S2 L*
Cardiff *p179* 029 2022 4871
Jones, L (Oldham Metropolitan Borough Council)
Oldham *p468* 0161 911 3000
Jones, L (Worcestershire County Council)
Worcester *p477* 01905 766335
Jones, Miss L (Wrexham County Borough Council)
Wrexham *p477* 01978 292000
Jones, Mrs L (Rix & Kay Solicitors LLP) *W*
Uckfield *p416* 01825 700177
Jones, Ms L A (London Borough of Bexley)
Bexleyheath *p449* 020 8303 7777
Jones, Miss L A (Loosemores)
Cardiff *p179* 029 2022 4433
Jones, Miss L A (Brethertons LLP) *K1 D1*
Rugby *p368* 01788 579579
Jones, Miss L A (DF Legal LLP) *E I K1 S1*
Tewkesbury *p410* 01684 850750
Jones, Miss L C (Parametric Technology (UK) Ltd) *M2 O Q A3*
Fleet *p458*. 01252 817600
Jones, Mrs L J (Pinsent Masons LLP) *J1*
Birmingham *p141* 0121 200 1050
Jones, Mrs L M (Stroud District Council)
Stroud *p473* 01453 766321
Jones, Miss L M (Walker Smith Way) *W T2 K4*
Wrexham *p443* 0844 346 3100
Jones, Ms L M (DBL Talbots LLP)
Wolverhampton *p437* 01902 427561
Jones, Miss L S (Haworth Holt Bell Limited) *K1 K3 Q O*
Altrincham *p116* 0161 928 7136
Jones, M (Ashurst LLP) *Q O*
London EC2 *p7* 020 7638 1111
London EC4 *p83*. 020 7822 8000
Jones, M (Hardy McBride & Co) *G H*
Bromley *p166* 020 8460 1999
Jones, M (Ormerods) *J1*
Croydon *p205* 020 8686 5000
Jones, M (Cocks Lloyd) *W T2 S1*
Nuneaton *p339* 024 7664 1642
Jones, M (Solicitor Direct)
Leyland *p283* 01772 424999
Jones, M (Harbottle & Lewis LLP) *C1 Zf Ze Zk Zv*
London W1 *p38* 020 7667 5000
Jones, Ms M (Metropolitan Police Directorate of Legal Services)
London SW1 *p108*. 020 7230 7210
Jones, Ms M (Bond Pearce LLP) *N J2 Q Zq*
London EC3 *p14*. 0845 415 0000
Jones, Mrs M (Thompsons (formerly Robin/Brian Thompson & Partners))
Cardiff *p181* 029 2044 5300
Jones, M (CMS Cameron McKenna LLP) *C1 C2*
London EC3 *p17*. 020 7367 3000
Jones, M (DWF) *C2 C1*
Manchester *p303* 0161 603 5000
Jones, M (Grayson Willis Bennett) *B2 G H J2*
Sheffield *p375*. 0114 290 9500
Jones, M (Gregsons) *E L S1*
London SW19 *p37*. 020 8946 1173
Jones, M (M P Jones & Co) *N*
Plymouth *p350*. 01752 269007
Jones, M A (Darbys Solicitors LLP) *B2 G O H Zl*
Oxford *p343* 01865 811700
Birmingham *p137* 0121 248 4000
Jones, M C (Male & Wagland) *F1 G H K1 Zl Zp J1 L N O Q K3 D1 J2*
Potters Bar *p355*. 01707 657171
Jones, M C (TWM Solicitors LLP) *E C1 J1 R1 B1 T1 P Zc Ze*
Reigate *p363* 01737 221212
Jones, M D (Lloyd Jones & Co) *W S1 E T1 K1 L Q N F1 Zd Zm S2*
Westcliff-on-Sea *p428* 01702 710338
Jones, M D (Stephensons Solicitors LLP) *G H*
Manchester *p310* 0161 832 8844
Jones, M E (Gedye & Sons (Solicitors) Ltd) *S1 W E C1 L*
Grange-over-Sands *p232* . . 01539 532313
Jones, M E (West Lancashire District Council)
Ormskirk *p468*. 01695 577177
Jones, Mrs M E R (Rhondda Cynon Taff County Borough Council)
Pentre *p468* 01443 424300
Jones, M H (Mark Jones & Partners) *G H*
Liverpool *p289*. 0151 286 9594
Jones, M I (Beale and Company Solicitors LLP) *Zq Q Zc O A3*
London WC2 *p11* 020 7240 3474
Jones, M I (The Clarke Partnership) *N*
Stockport *p395*. 0161 474 6600

Jones, Mrs M J (Central & South West Staffordshire Magistrates Court)
Stafford *p472* 01785 223144
Jones, M J O (Harvey Ingram LLP) *C1 C2 C3 E Zc*
Leicester *p280*. 0116 254 5454
Jones, M K (Hill Dickinson LLP) *C1 C2*
Liverpool *p288*. 0151 600 8000
Jones, Miss M L (Brachers)
Maidstone *p299* 01622 690691
Jones, M L (Michael Leighton Jones) *K1 P M1 S1 W E L F1 V D1 Zc Zl*
Bargoed *p123* 01443 830228
Jones, M L M (Douglas-Jones Mercer) *K1 N F1*
Swansea *p405*. 01792 650000
Jones, M L N (Hugh James) *A3 U1 Zc Ze Zk X M1 Zj O I Zu N Zq Zg*
Cardiff *p179* 029 2022 4871
Jones, M N (SNR Denton) *Zb*
London EC4 *p75*. 020 7242 1212
Jones, Mrs M P (H Jenkins & Hughes) *S1 S2 Q L K1 W*
Holyhead *p251*. 01407 762301
Jones, M W (Geldards LLP) *R2*
Cardiff *p178* 029 2023 8239
Jones, M W (Berrys) *S1 C1 E W Zl*
Tilehurst *p411* 0118 942 2333
Jones, Miss N (Plexus Law (A Trading Name of Parabis Law LLP)) *N Q*
Evesham *p220*. 01386 769160
Jones, N (Davisons) *W S1*
Birmingham *p137* 0121 685 1234
Sutton Coldfield *p403* 0121 323 2525
Jones, Ms N A (Thomas Simon) *N Q O L*
Cardiff *p181* 029 2055 7200
Jones, N A (Squire Sanders (UK) LLP) *J1 Zp*
Manchester *p310* 0161 830 5000
Jones, N A (JMD Law Limited) *N O W J1 L Q F1 Zq Zj Zf C1 S2 E Zk*
Cardiff *p179* 029 2045 6780
Jones, N C (Barwells)
Peacehaven *p345* 01273 582271
Jones, N D (Simmons & Simmons)
London EC2 *p79*. 020 7628 2020
Jones, Mrs N E (Gilbert Davies & Partners) *A1 S1 L W R1 J1 K1 C1 E*
Welshpool *p425* 01938 552727
Jones, Ms N E (Hanne & Co) *W*
London SW11 *p38* 020 7228 0017
Jones, N F (Pinsent Masons LLP) *O Zc*
Birmingham *p141* 0121 200 1050
Jones, N G (Maxwell Hodge Solicitors) *S1 S2 E W*
Heswall *p249* 0151 342 6447
Jones, N G (Sheridans) *E Zf C1*
London WC1 *p78* 020 7079 0100
Jones, N H (Linklaters LLP)
London EC2 *p54*. 020 7456 2000
Jones, Mrs N M (Salford City Council)
Swinton *p473* 0161 794 4711
Jones, N P (Milwyn Jenkins) *Q S1 Zl S2 E*
Newtown *p330*. 01686 626218
Jones, N W (Weightmans LLP) *E R2 S2 L*
Liverpool *p291*. 0151 227 2601
Jones, N W S (CVC Solicitors) *S1 W L S2*
Hayle *p245* 01736 752246
Jones, O (Hart Brown Solicitors) *O Q*
Guildford *p236*. 0800 068 8177
Jones, O (Doyle Clayton Solicitors Limited) *J1 Zp Zi*
London EC2 *p27*. 020 7329 9090
Jones, O D (Gamlins) *K1 G H D1 D2 Zh Zl*
Colwyn Bay *p198* 01492 532275
Jones, O G (Emyr Thomas & Son) *S1 K1 W C1 N T1*
Caernarfon *p172*. . .01286 672307 / 672308
Jones, O P (Lewis & Dick) *S1 E L*
Crawley *p202* 01293 526031
Jones, Miss P (Hill Dickinson LLP) *E R2 S2 R1 S1 C1 C2 L*
Liverpool *p288*. 0151 600 8000
Jones, Ms P (Squire Sanders (UK) LLP) *Q*
Manchester *p310* 0161 830 5000
Jones, P (Harbottle & Lewis LLP)
London W1 *p38* 020 7667 5000
Jones, P (Rawlison Butler LLP) *J1 J2*
Crawley *p202* 01293 527744
Jones, P (Dean Thomas & Co) *K1 D1 K3*
Worksop *p441* 01909 500511
Jones, P (Brooke-Taylors) *T2 W*
Buxton *p172*. 01298 22741
Jones, Mrs P A (Freeth Cartwright LLP) *J1*
Manchester *p304* 0845 634 2540
Jones, P A G (Smith Jones Solicitors) *N Q O F1 Zq*
Kenilworth *p264* 01926 859933
Burnley *p169* 01282 855400
Jones, P A P (The Royal Bank of Scotland)
London EC1 *p109* 020 7427 8000
Jones, P E (Barlow Lyde & Gilbert LLP)
London EC3 *p10*. 020 7247 2277
Jones, P G (Jones Myers LLP) *K1 K2*
Leeds *p275* 0113 246 0055
Jones, P H (Charsley Harrison LLP) *C1 E J1 S1 T1 C3*
Windsor *p434* 01753 851591
Jones, P J (Penmans) *S1 S2 W L*
Coventry *p200*. 024 7622 6575
Jones, P L (Loosemores) *E S2*
Cardiff *p179* 029 2022 4433
Jones, P L (P Lloyd Jones & Co) *A1 C1 D1 G L N*
Mold *p318*. . . . . . .01352 758533 / 758534
Jones, P M (Stuckey Carr & Co) *S1 E W A1 C1 R1 Zd*
Storrington *p399* 01903 743201

Jones, P M (Browne Jacobson LLP) *J1*
Nottingham *p336*. 0115 976 6000
Jones, P M (DWF) *F1*
Manchester *p303* 0161 603 5000
Jones, P N (Atteys) *G H B2*
Doncaster *p211* 01302 340400
Rotherham *p367*. 01709 720287
Jones, P R (Andrew Markham & Co) *G H*
Carmarthen *p182* . .01267 221550 / 236199
Jones, P W E (Banner Jones) *N W K1 D1 G Q K3 V H*
Chesterfield *p191* 01246 209773
Jones, Ms R (Hertfordshire County Council)
Hertford *p460* 01992 555555
Jones, Ms R (Bermans LLP) *Q O Zk*
Liverpool *p286*. 0151 224 0500
Jones, R (Weightmans LLP) *Q N*
Manchester *p311* 0161 233 7330
Jones, R (Forbes) *C1 J2 J1*
Blackburn *p145* 01254 54374
Jones, Ms R (Bury & Walkers LLP) *E J1*
Barnsley *p124*. 01226 733533
Jones, R (The College of Law Chester)
Chester *p454* 0800 289997
Jones, R (Beers LLP) *E W S1*
Kingsbridge *p267* 01548 857000
Jones, R (Beers LLP) *S2 W S1*
Plymouth *p349*. 01752 246000
Jones, R (Ellisons)
Colchester *p197* 01206 764477
Jones, R (Ince & Co Services Ltd)
London E1 *p44* 020 7481 0010
Jones, R (Wirral Borough Council)
Wallasey *p475*. 0151 638 7070
Jones, R (Fidler & Pepper)
Kirkby-in-Ashfield *p268*. 01623 451111
Jones, R A (Carter Vincent Jones Davis)
Bangor *p122*. 01248 362551
Jones, R A (Knights Solicitors LLP) *A1 O Q Zl*
Newcastle under Lyme *p323* . 01782 619225
Jones, R A H (Kennedys) *O N F1 Q Zj*
London EC3 *p49*. 020 7667 9667
Jones, Miss R C (Capsticks Solicitors LLP) *N*
London SW19 *p18*. 020 8780 2211
Jones, R D (Mackenzie Jones) *N Q Zq Zr*
St Asaph *p391*. 01745 536030
Jones, R D L (Whiting & Mason) *J1 F1 N C1 Q O*
Marple *p313*. 0161 427 1040
Jones, R D P (Madge Lloyd & Gibson) *S1 W E L A1 Zd*
Newent *p327* 01531 820088
Gloucester *p230*. 01452 520224
Jones, Miss R E (George Davies & Evans Limited) *S1 W L G H*
Cardigan *p181*. 01239 612308
Jones, Miss R E (Bath & North East Somerset Council) *K1 D1 G H N Q J1*
Bath *p462* 01225 394041
Jones, R E (Squire Sanders (UK) LLP) *T1*
Birmingham *p142* 0121 222 3000
Jones, R G (Lupton Fawcett) *S1 E*
Leeds *p275* 0113 280 2000
Jones, Mrs R H (Elborne Mitchell LLP) *O Zj*
London EC3 *p29*. 020 7320 9000
Jones, Ms R H (Brabners Chaffe Street)
Manchester *p301* 0161 836 8800
Jones, R J (Barlow Lyde & Gilbert LLP)
London EC3 *p10*. 020 7247 2277
Jones, R J (Yaffe Jackson Ostrin) *Q N O K1 L D1*
Liverpool *p291*. 0151 236 5555
Jones, R L (Brinley Morris Rees & Jones) *S1 K1 W T1 D1 J1 F1 Q N L Zl*
Llanelli *p292*. 01554 774241
Jones, R M (Cyngor Sir Ynys Mon (Isle of Anglesey County Council)) *G H K1 L V W J1 D1 M1 P Zi Zj Zl*
Llangefni *p463*. 01248 750057
Jones, R M (Barber Titleys) *T2 W T1 K4*
Harrogate *p240* 01423 502211
Jones, R M V (Burnetts) *C1 I C3 C2 Zza*
Carlisle *p181*. 01228 552222
Carlisle *p182*. 01228 552222
Jones, R O (Bury & Walkers LLP) *E L S1 P N C1 T1 W R1 B1 Zc Zd Zs*
Leeds *p272* 0113 244 4227
Jones, R P (Stephens & Scown) *E C1 W A1 S1 T1 Zd*
St Austell *p391* 01726 74433
Jones, R R (Robyns Owen) *Q S1 W D1 G H K1 Zl O N*
Pwllheli *p358* 01758 613177
Porthmadog *p354* 01766 514747
Jones, R T (Addies) *S2 S1 W C1 E*
Fleetwood *p226* 01253 772128
Jones, R W (Ellis Davies & Co) *A1 E F1 G H L D1 R1 S1 W Zl Zt*
Caernarfon *p172*. 01286 672437
Jones, R W (Hill Dickinson LLP) *S1 E W C1 L K1 R1 J1*
Chester *p190* 01244 896600
Jones, R W (Hay & Kilner) *O N J1 Q Zb Zj*
Newcastle upon Tyne *p325* . 0191 232 8345
Jones, Miss R W (The Smith Partnership) *K1 V K2*
Derby *p209* 01332 225225
Jones, Ms S (Saunders Law Partnership LLP) *G H*
London WC2 *p76* 020 7632 4300
Jones, Mrs S (David & Snape) *K1 K3 D1 Q*
Porthcawl *p353* . . .01656 782070 / 785038
Swansea *p405*. 01792 643021
Jones, Mrs S (Heptonstalls LLP) *Zr*
Goole *p231* 01405 765661
Jones, S (Clifford Chance)
London E14 *p20*. 020 7006 1000

See p634 for the Key to Work Categories

Jones, S (KJD)
Stoke-on-Trent *p398* 01782 202020
Jones, Ms S (Flintshire County Council)
Mold *p466* 01352 702411
Jones, Miss S (City & County of Swansea)
Swansea *p473* 01792 636000
Jones, S (Pengillys LLP) *S1 S2 W L E C1 Zd Zm*
Weymouth *p430* 01305 768888
Jones, S (Thompsons (formerly Robin/Brian Thompson & Partners)) *N*
Stoke-on-Trent *p398* 01782 406200
Jones, S (James Pearce & Co) *K1 D1*
Birmingham *p141* 0121 784 1886
Jones, Mrs S (Cardiff County Council)
Cardiff *p453* 029 2087 2000
Jones, Mrs S A (Wakefield Court House)
Wakefield *p474* 01924 303461
Jones, Ms S A (Farnfield & Nicholls) *N O Q J1 J2 K1 L Ze F2 F1 Zk W G*
Gillingham *p229* 01747 825432
Jones, S A (Weightmans LLP) *J1 C1 G F1 Q O Zk Zj Zl Zp*
Liverpool *p291* 0151 227 2601
Jones, Ms S C (Claire Jones & Associates) *K1 D1 W S1*
Wakefield *p418* 01924 290029
Jones, Miss S C (Dewar Hogan) *O Zq L*
London EC4 *p27* 020 7634 9550
Jones, S D (Merthyr Tydfil County Borough Council)
Merthyr Tydfil *p465* 01685 725000
Jones, S D (Bridge McFarland) *S1 S2 E*
Grimsby *p235* 01472 311711
Jones, Ms S E M (Pannone LLP) *C1 C2*
Manchester *p308* 0161 909 3000
Jones, S G (Griffiths & Hughes Parry) *B1 C1 E F1 G K1 L M1 P R1 Zs*
Holywell *p252* 01352 711815 / 711945
Jones, S G (Sanderson McCreath & Edney) *G H K1 P S1 Zl J1 E L S2*
Berwick-upon-Tweed *p131* 01289 306724
Jones, S H (DLA Piper UK LLP) *I U2 U1 Ze Zw Zf*
Birmingham *p137* 0870 011 1111
Jones, Miss S J (Cardiff Magistrates Court)
Cardiff *p453* 029 2046 3040
Jones, S J (Bernard Chill & Axtell) *G H Zl*
Southampton *p385* 023 8022 8821
Jones, S J H (Todmans SRE) *A1 C1 E J1 K1 L P S1 T1 W Zd*
Rayleigh *p359* 01268 774073
Jones, Mrs S J L (Colemans Solicitors LLP) *C1 C2 Ze*
Maidenhead *p298* 01628 631051
Jones, Miss S L (Stevens) *J1 Q Zp F1 L O*
Haverhill *p244* 01440 762511
Jones, S L (Pannone LLP) *Zr Zm Zq Zg*
Manchester *p308* 0161 909 3000
Jones, Ms S M (Bircham Dyson Bell)
Westminster *p13* 020 7227 7000
Jones, S M (Coole & Haddock)
Worthing *p441* 01903 213511
Jones, S N (Shakespeares) *B1 L O Q Zb Zc*
Birmingham *p142* 0121 237 3000
Jones, Miss S R (Tyndallwoods)
Birmingham *p143* 0121 624 1111
Jones, Mrs S R (Neath Port Talbot County Borough Council)
Port Talbot *p469* 01639 763333
Jones, S R (Hearne & Co) *C1 D1 F1 G H K1 M1 N P S1 Zj Zp*
Bearwood *p129* 0121 420 3636
Jones, Miss S V (Mary Evans & Co) *S1 K1 L*
Carmarthen *p182* 01267 233881
Jones, Ms T (QualitySolicitors Jackson & Canter) *K3 D1 K1*
Liverpool *p290* 0151 282 1700
Jones, T (Allen & Overy LLP)
London E1 *p5* 020 3088 0000
Jones, T (Shammah Nicholls LLP) *S2 E S1 C1 W N R1 P G J1 M1 T1 Zl Zf Zc*
Manchester *p309* 0161 832 9272
Jones, T (Aaron & Partners LLP Solicitors) *O Q Zv Zq K1 K3*
Chester *p190* 01244 405555
Jones, T (Lyons Davidson)
Bristol *p163* 0117 904 6000
Jones, Mrs T F L (Morgan Cole) *Zj N*
Bristol *p164* 0117 916 7220
Jones, T G (T G Jones & Associates) *S1 E B1 T1 A1 J1 K1 L P*
Swansea *p405* 01792 469717
Jones, T H L (Terry Jones Solicitors & Advocates) *A1 B1 C1 D1 E G H K1 L M1*
Shrewsbury *p379* 01743 285888
Jones, T M L (Higgs & Sons) *O J1 Zq Q Zp*
Brierley Hill *p158* 0845 111 5050
Kidderminster *p265* 01562 820181
Jones, T P (Dwr Cymru Cyf)
Merthyr Tydfil *p465* 01443 425627
Jones, T P R (Thompsons (formerly Robin/Brian Thompson & Partners)) *N*
Plymouth *p350* 01752 675810
Jones, T S D (Atter Mackenzie & Co) *S1 S2*
Evesham *p220* 01386 425300
Jones, T W (Woolliscrofts) *N B1 C1 M1 E J1 F1 W P Zb Zc*
Hanley *p239* 01782 204000
Jones, Mrs U E (Backhouse Jones Ltd) *N Q O*
Clitheroe *p196* 01254 828300
Jones, Miss V A (Treasury Solicitors Department)
London WC2 *p110* 020 7210 3000
Jones, Mrs V J (Hillyer McKeown LLP) *E S2*
Chester *p190* 01244 318131
Jones, Mrs V L (Jones Law Partnership) *S1 N E*
Marple *p313* 0161 426 0030
Jones, Mrs V N (Lawson West Solicitors Limited) *N*
Leicester *p280* 0116 212 1000
Jones, W (JMW Solicitors) *S1 K1 M1 P W L G D1 H*
Manchester *p306* 0845 872 6666
Jones, W (Langleys)
York *p445* 01904 610886
Jones, W D A (Wynne D A Jones) *S1 W E C1 T1 Zd*
Cardiff *p179* 029 2056 9496
Jones, W D S (East Hampshire District Council)
Petersfield *p468* 01730 266551
Jones, W H (Hutchinson Thomas) *S1 E C1 L A1 Zc Zn S2*
Neath *p320* 01639 645061
Jones, Mrs W M (Parry Davies Clwyd-Jones & Lloyd) *K1 S1 W Q L N*
Llangefni *p292* 01248 723106
Jones, W T (Pritchard Jones Evans Lane) *G H K1 S1*
Caernarfon *p172* 01286 673387
Jones-Evans, M E (Pritchard Jones Evans Lane) *S1 W K1 M1 A1 P B1 C1 F1 H Zd Zf Zh*
Caernarfon *p172* 01286 673387
Jones-King, Mrs N J (McMillan Williams) *K1*
Carshalton *p183* 020 8432 2041
Jones-Parry, D A (Clifford Chance)
London E14 *p20* 020 7006 1000
Jones-Steele, Ms N C (Morris & Bates)
Aberystwyth *p114* 01970 625566
Jonker, J (Trowers & Hamlins)
London EC3 *p88* 020 7423 8000
Jonsberg, Ms L (Malvern Hills District Council)
Malvern *p464* 01684 862151
Jootla, J K (Squire Sanders (UK) LLP)
Leeds *p277* 0113 284 7000
Jopling, Ms C P (Gordon Jopling (Food Ingredients) Ltd)
Barnsley *p448* 01226 733288
Jordan, A R (Gordons LLP) *C1 C2 U2 Zb*
Leeds *p273* 0113 227 0100
Jordan, Mrs B G (Harrison Clark LLP) *K1 Zq D1*
Cheltenham *p188* 01242 269198
Jordan, Miss C A (Towns Needham & Co) *N Q*
Manchester *p310* 0161 832 3721
Jordan, D (Heckford Norton) *N G H Zl*
Letchworth *p283* 01462 682244
Jordan, D J (Coodes) *K1*
Launceston *p270* 01566 770000
Jordan, D M (Derek M Jordan)
Bentham *p131* 01524 261254
Settle *p374* 01729 823589 / 823514
Jordan, Mrs G L (Grant Saw Solicitors LLP) *S1 E*
Greenwich *p36* 020 8858 6971
Jordan, G W (Charles Russell LLP) *E R1 L S1*
Cheltenham *p187* 01242 221122
Jordan, H A (Osborne Clarke) *E*
Bristol *p164* 0117 917 3000
Jordan, J C (Jordans) *S1 W K1 D1 G H Q N V J1*
Rowley Regis *p368* 0121 559 2922
Jordan, Miss L C (Irwin Mitchell LLP) *N Zr*
Birmingham *p139* 0870 150 0100
Jordan, Ms M (Ashurst LLP)
London EC2 *p7* 020 7638 1111
Jordan, M G (Forsters LLP) *E*
Westminster *p33* 020 7863 8333
Jordan, Ms N (Kaim Todner Ltd) *G H B2*
Islington *p47* 020 7700 0070
Jordan, N (Stables & Co) *F1 G H Q J1 K1 N O S1 W*
Stourbridge *p399* 01384 390581
Jordan, P (Slee Blackwell) *K1 V*
Barnstaple *p125* 01271 372128
Braunton *p156* 01271 812019
Jordan, P A (Hague Lambert) *E S1 L S2*
Manchester *p305* 0161 834 6066
Jordan, P C (Challinors) *G H D1 N Zi*
West Bromwich *p427* 0121 553 3211
Jordan, P G (Bradford & Bingley PLC)
Bingley *p449* 01274 555555
Jordan, P G M (Tucker Turner Kingsley Wood & Co) *B1 C1 J1 O N*
London WC1 *p88* 020 7242 3303
Jordan, Mrs S (Ellis-Fermor & Negus) *W K4*
Beeston *p130* 0115 922 1591
Jordan, Miss S A M (Salans) *B1*
London EC4 *p76* 020 7429 6000
Jordan, S R (DLA Piper UK LLP) *O R2 A3 Zc*
London EC2 *p24* 0870 011 1111
Jordan, T F C (Forshaws Davies Ridgway LLP) *S1 S2 E*
Warrington *p422* 01925 230000
Jordan-Fisher, Ms J M (Cross Ram & Co) *A1 E F1 L S1*
Halesworth *p237* 01986 873636
Jordon, Mrs S (Daltons Solicitors) *E S2 S1 A1 A2 L R1 R2 P*
Petersfield *p348* 01730 262816
Jorgensen, R (Clarks Legal LLP) *J1*
Reading *p360* 0118 958 5321
Jorgenson, J (Addies) *K1 N Q K3*
Fleetwood *p226* 01253 772128
Jory, Ms M A L (Memery Crystal) *C1 C2*
London WC2 *p60* 020 7242 5905
Joscelyne, M (Olswang LLP) *T1 T2*
London WC1 *p64* 020 7067 3000
Joseph, Ms C (Hanover Solicitors) *E S1 Zf Ze*
London SW3 *p38* 0870 383 1974
Joseph, C S (Edwards Angell Palmer & Dodge)
London EC2 *p28* 020 7583 4055
Joseph, D (Abrahams Dresden) *S2 S1 E*
London EC1 *p3* 020 7251 3663
Westcliff-on-Sea *p428* 01702 338338
Joseph, Miss E (Tomleys) *W S1 A1 L C1 Zo J1*
Newtown *p330* 01686 626641
Joseph, G (Nelsons)
London SE1 *p63* 020 7403 4000
Joseph, Ms G (Bond Joseph) *K1 D1 Zm*
Canterbury *p176* 01227 453545
Joseph, H (London Borough of Greenwich Legal Services) *R1*
London SE18 *p106* 020 8921 5123
Joseph, Mrs J (Neves Solicitors) *E S1 S2*
Harpenden *p239* 01582 715234
Joseph, Ms K (Barcan Woodward) *D1 K1 K2*
Bristol *p161* 0117 923 2141
Joseph, M H (Loosemores) *S2 S1 W*
Cardiff *p179* 029 2022 4433
Joseph, Ms M J M (LD Law) *D1 K1*
Harlow *p239* 01279 441266
Joseph, Ms M J W (Pritchard Englefield) *K1 N Q*
London EC2 *p69* 020 7972 9720
Joseph, N (Rutland County Council)
Oakham *p468* 01572 722577
Joseph, O S (Hanratty & Co) *S1 S2 Q G J1 E W*
Newtown *p330* 01686 626239
Joseph, P J (Gregory Abrams Davidson LLP) *E S1 C1 W L*
London NW11 *p37* 020 8209 0166 / 8458 9322
Joseph, P S V (Dorman Joseph Wachtel) *O Q*
London EC3 *p27* 020 7680 6300
Joseph, P W (Squire Sanders (UK) LLP) *O Q Zq*
Birmingham *p142* 0121 222 3000
Joseph, Ms R (Howard Kennedy LLP) *E*
London W1 *p48* 020 7636 1616
Joseph, R L (Pinney Talfourd LLP)
Upminster *p416* 01708 229444
Joseph, V G (LG Lawyers)
London SE1 *p50* 020 7379 0000
Josephi, C H (Hewetts) *E R1 S1 S2 W*
Reading *p361* 0118 957 5337
Josephs, J H (Turner Coulston) *P M1 K1 N D1 G H J1 B1 Zk Zl*
Kettering *p265* 01536 523434
Joshi, Ms N (Duncan Lewis & Co) *Zi D1 D2 G H K1 Q V*
Hackney *p53* 020 7923 4020
Joshi, Mrs R (Clifton Ingram LLP) *K1*
Wokingham *p437* 0118 978 0099
Joshi, Ms U (Shelter Legal Services)
London EC1 *p109* 020 7505 2000
Joslin, P F K (Sykes Lee & Brydson) *W S1 L A1 E C1 Zi S2 T2*
York *p445* 01904 731100
Joslyn, Miss S (The Wilkes Partnership LLP) *C1 C2*
Birmingham *p143* 0121 233 4333
Joss, Miss S (Eastleigh Borough Council)
Eastleigh *p457* 023 8068 8068
Josselyn, G H (Bircham Dyson Bell)
Westminster *p13* 020 7227 7000
Jotangia, D C (Dass Solicitors) *G H*
Birmingham *p137* 0121 248 4000
Joubert, Mrs A (Magrath LLP) *Zi*
London W1 *p57* 020 7495 3003
Jourdan, M (Humphries Kirk) *C1*
Poole *p352* 01202 725400
Jowett, B (Institute of Chartered Accountants in England & Wales) *N J1 P F1*
Milton Keynes *p466* 01908 248100
Joy, M D (Kirklands) *D1 F1 J1 K1 L N O Q Zc Zj Zl*
Romsey *p366* 01794 513466
Joy, M R (Universal Music)
London W14 *p110* 020 8910 5000
Joy, R A (Banner Jones) *S1 Q*
Chesterfield *p191* 01246 560560
Sheffield *p375* 0114 275 5266
Joyce, A L (Allen & Overy LLP)
London E1 *p5* 020 3088 0000
Joyce, A L (Wedlake Bell LLP) *O B1 Ze*
London WC1 *p91* 020 7395 3000
Joyce, Ms E M (De La Rue PLC)
Basingstoke *p448* 01256 605000
Joyce, J G (Addleshaw Goddard) *B1*
Manchester *p300* 0161 934 6000
Joyce, J Q (Pritchard Joyce & Hinds) *E S2*
Beckenham *p129* 020 8658 3922
Joyce, Ms L (QualitySolicitors Jackson & Canter) *K4 Zg*
Liverpool *p290* 0151 282 1700
Joyce, M (Norfolk County Council - Legal Services)
Norwich *p467* Minicom: 0844 800 8011
Joyce, Mrs O (Carey Law)
Alton *p116*
Joyce, P R (Ramsdens Solicitors) *C1 E J1 R2 Ze Zw*
Huddersfield *p256* 01484 821500
Joyce, R (W R Joyce Solicitors LLP)
Cannock *p176*
Joyce, R E (Freeth Cartwright LLP) *O A3*
Birmingham *p138* 0845 634 2575
Joyce, S A (Stephensons Solicitors LLP) *G H*
Wigan *p432* 01942 777777
Joyce, S R M (Tucker Turner Kingsley Wood & Co) *S1 E G R1 Zl Zt*
London WC1 *p88* 020 7242 3303
Joyce, T F (Redfearns) *G H R1 Q*
Heckmondwike *p246* 01924 403745 / 404601
Joyner, T R B (Eldridges) *Q O N Zl L J1*
Newport *p328* 01983 524741
Joyson, C (Howell-Jones LLP) *K1 S1*
Kingston upon Thames *p267* 020 8549 5186
Joyston-Bechal, S (Pinsent Masons LLP) *F2 J2 O*
London EC2 *p67* 020 7418 7000
Jubb, Mrs C S (Warner Goodman LLP) *S1*
Fareham *p224* 01329 288121
Jubb, Ms S (Williams Thompson) *K1 K3*
Christchurch *p194* 01202 484242
Juby, J B (Sparling Benham & Brough)
Frinton-on-Sea *p227* 01255 679222
Jucker, Miss A M (Pinsent Masons LLP)
London EC2 *p67* 020 7418 7000
Juckes, W (Clarke Willmott) *L E R2*
Bristol *p162* 0845 209 1000 / 0117 305 6000
Judd, Ms J (ASB Law)
Maidstone *p298* 01622 656500
Judd, Mrs J (ASB Law) *K1 K2*
Maidstone *p298* 01622 656500
Judd, M G (Clifford Chance)
London E14 *p20* 020 7006 1000
Judd, Miss S E (Thomson Snell & Passmore) *D1 K1 K3*
Tunbridge Wells *p415* 01892 510000
Judd, S J F (Keogh Caisley) *B1 C1 E J1 L O R1 P Zc Ze C2 S2 F1*
Tunbridge Wells *p415* 01892 548411
Judge, A J (Travers Smith LLP) *E Zb*
London EC1 *p87* 020 7295 3000
Judge, D L (Whatley Recordon) *A1 A2 L S1 S2 W E Zd Zv R1 R2 T2*
Malvern *p300* 01684 892939
Judge, E C J (SGH Martineau LLP) *B1 O*
London EC3 *p75* 020 7264 4444
Judge, I M (Bristows) *C1 M1 O Ze*
London EC4 *p15* 020 7400 8000
Judge, J (Wilkin Chapman Grange Solicitors) *W T1 T2*
Louth *p294* 01507 606161
Judge, J B (Newsome Vaughan LLP) *N Q O Zr Zq Zj J2*
Coventry *p200* 024 7663 3433
Judge, S (Lawson Lewis & Co) *O Q N Zq K3 K1*
Eastbourne *p215* 01323 720142
Judge, Mrs V (Gotelee) *C1 I F1 F2 Ze Zza U2 C2*
Ipswich *p262* 01473 211121
Judkins, Mrs B J (Archer & Archer) *Q L F1 B1 O*
Ely *p218* 01353 662203
Judkins, Mrs I C (Judkins Solicitors) *K1 D1 K3*
Hertford *p248* 01992 500456
Judkins, M J (Archer & Archer) *Q N J1 G F1 H O*
Ely *p218* 01353 662203
Judkins, P (Judkins Solicitors) *J1 S2 S1*
Hertford *p248* 01992 500456
Judson, A P (Walker Morris) *E*
Leeds *p277* 0113 283 2500
Judson, C (Amphlett Lissimore) *G H*
Croydon *p6* 020 8771 5254
Judt, Miss E (Wiseman Lee LLP) *G H*
Waltham Forest *p92* 020 8215 1000
Juggins, Miss L (Newbys) *N O Q L F1 B1 Zl*
Stockton-on-Tees *p397* 01642 673733 / 676666
Juhanson, Miss T (F Barnes & Son) *K3 K1 S1 K2 J1*
Romford *p366* 01708 745183
Julian, Ms A (Essex County Council) *K1*
Chelmsford *p454* 0845 743 0430
Julian, Miss L H (Petherbridge Bassra Solicitors) *G H*
Bradford *p154* 01274 724114
Julyan, A J (Speechly Bircham LLP) *J1*
London EC4 *p81* 020 7427 6400
Juma, H (Juma Law Practice) *E S2 J1 S1 W*
Harrow *p241* 020 8861 1199
Jump, D W (Jump & Co Solicitors) *E S2 S1 W*
Chichester *p193* 01243 778508
Jump, G K (Weightmans LLP) *C1 B1 M1 N P Zb Zc Ze O*
Liverpool *p291* 0151 227 2601
Manchester *p311* 0161 233 7330
Jung, V (Jung & Co)
Southall *p384* 020 8813 8996
Junor, Ms C A (Higgs & Sons) *G H N*
Brierley Hill *p158* 0845 111 5050
Jupp, J E I (Morrisons Solicitors LLP) *S1*
Woking *p437* 01483 726146
Juras, Ms V A (Virginia Juras & Co) *T2 W S1 Zi*
Bromley *p166* 020 8402 9403
Jury, Ms C D (Clifford Chance)
London E14 *p20* 020 7006 1000
Jury, M D (Ashfords LLP)
Exeter *p220* 01392 337000
Jury, M D (H2O Law LLP) *Zc Q M2 G*
London EC4 *p37* 020 7405 4700
Jury, Miss S N (Rundlewalker)
Exeter *p222* 01392 209209
Juss, W S (Thompsons (formerly Robin/Brian Thompson & Partners)) *N J1*
Birmingham *p143* 0121 262 1200
Justice, M (Symes Robinson & Lee) *W T2*
Crediton *p203* 01363 775566
Justice, M R (Wilkin Chapman LLP) *R1 S1 E R2 S2 C1 Zc*
Beverley *p131* 01482 398398
Justice, R M (Robert M Justice Tax & Trust Consultant) *Zj T1 T2 W*
Reigate *p363* 01737 222700
Jutla, J S (Jasvir Jutla & Co) *Zi*
Leicester *p280* 0116 254 0809
Jutton, N P (Scott Bailey) *Q N J1 K1 O*
Lymington *p296* 01590 676933

K

Kabia, Miss Y C (Bhatia Best) G H
Nottingham p336 . . . 0115 950 3231

Kachikwu, M (Shell International Ltd)
London SE1 p109 . . . 020 7934 1234

Kadri, N (Asghar & Co) Q Zi Zu
Southall p384 . . . 020 8843 0010

Kadri, O S U (Burnley-Jones Bate & Co)
London SW19 p16 . . . 020 8542 8101

Kagan, C G (Bond Pearce LLP)
Plymouth p349 . . . 0845 415 0000

Kagan, K (Kagan & Co)
London SE4 p47 . . . 020 8694 9969

Kaged, D (Welsh Health Legal Services) Zr Zm K1
Cardiff p453 . . . 029 2031 5500

Kahn, Mrs A (Woodroffes) K1 M4
Westminster p93 . . . 020 7730 0001

Kahn, G R (SNR Denton) Zb
London EC4 p75 . . . 020 7242 1212

Kaijo, Ms N (Waltons & Morse LLP) A3 O Zj
London EC3 p90 . . . 020 7623 4255

Kaim, R J (Kaim Todner Ltd) G H
London EC4 p47 . . . 020 7353 6660

Kaim-Caudle, Mrs P J (Jane Kaim-Caudle & Co) K1 N O W B1
Watford p423 . . . 01923 219061

Kainth, G (Hodge Jones & Allen LLP) N
London NW1 p41 . . . 020 7874 8300

Kainth, Mrs J (Swain & Co) K1 K3
Havant p244 . . . 023 9248 3322

Kainth, S (Thomson Webb & Corfield) G H Zi
Cambridge p176 . . . 01223 578068

Kaiser, Ms G T (Barlow Lyde & Gilbert LLP)
London EC3 p10 . . . 020 7247 2277

Kaiser, I (Stephenson Harwood) Za Zj Q
London EC2 p82 . . . 020 7329 4422

Kaiser, Ms L S (J B Wheatley & Co) K1 D1
London SE8 p91 . . . 020 8479 8000

Kaiser, Miss S C (Hertfordshire County Council)
Hertford p460 . . . 01992 555555

Kaiser, Miss S C (J B Wheatley & Co) K1 D1
London SE8 p91 . . . 020 8479 8000

Kakad, J N (Harbans Singh) E S1
Birmingham p139 . . . 0121 551 4496

Kakkad, S (Salans) B2 J2 Q
London EC4 p76 . . . 020 7429 6000

Kakkad, S S (LG Lawyers)
London SE1 p50 . . . 020 7379 0000

Kalber, T M (Kalber Struckley & Co) G
London W1 p47 . . . 020 7734 1102

Kale, D M (Kale & Co) S1 W Zl Zv
Bournemouth p152 . . . 01202 552375

Kale, Miss E (Stephens & Scown) K1 D2
Exeter p222 . . . 01392 210700

Kale, Mrs R S (Kale & Co) S1 K1 E W N G S2 Zl Zl
Wolverhampton p438 . . . 01902 772500

Kaler, S (Howard Kennedy LLP) Q O L Zc Zq
London W1 p48 . . . 020 7636 1616

Kalia, R (Goodge Law)
London W1 p36 . . . 020 7636 9222

Kalia, Mrs S (Goodge Law)
London W1 p36 . . . 020 7636 9222

Kaliari, J (Noble)
Shefford p377 . . . 01462 814055

Kalideen, Ms S R (AXA UK PLC) C1 Ze
London E22 p103 . . . 020 7920 5900

Kalman, J P (Blake Lapthorn) E
Portsmouth p354 . . . 023 9222 1122

Kalp, A (Trowers & Hamlins)
London EC3 p88 . . . 020 7423 8000

Kalra, K (Kalra & Co)
Waltham Forest p48 . . . 020 8539 0123

Kalsi, H K (Squire Sanders (UK) LLP)
Birmingham p142 . . . 0121 222 3000

Kalsi, Miss S (Howell-Jones LLP) K1
Walton-on-Thames p420 . . . 01932 234500

Kalyan, P (The Johnson Partnership) G H B2
Derby p209 . . . 01332 370473

Kalyanji, G (Rich & Carr Freer Bouskell) W
Leicester p281 . . . 0116 253 8021

Kalymnios, T (Steeles) R2 Zv E
Norwich p335 . . . 0870 609 0200

Kamalpour, A (Dechert) M4
London EC4 p26 . . . 020 7184 7000

Kambli, S (Premier Solicitors) K4 T2 W B3 C1
Bedford p130 . . . 01234 358080

Kamerling, A (DLA Piper UK LLP)
London EC2 p24 . . . 0870 011 1111

Kampanella, G (Stuart Miller & Co) G H
Haringey p61 . . . 020 8888 5225

Kamrowski, J L (Renata & Co) Zv Zr J1 Zf J2 Q N Zq S1 Zw W
Birmingham p141 . . . 0121 777 7333

Kamstra, G S (Simmons & Simmons) Ze
London EC2 p79 . . . 020 7628 2020

Kamstra, S P (Addleshaw Goddard) N C1
Leeds p271 . . . 0113 209 2000
Manchester p300 . . . 0161 934 6000

Kan, M K Y (Simmons & Simmons)
London EC2 p79 . . . 020 7628 2020

Kan, T Y C (Lee & Kan) C1 E K1 L S1
London W1 p52 . . . 020 7287 8888

Kanagasingham, J (Jeya & Co) Zi S2 Q L S1
Newham p46 . . . 020 8552 1999

Kanani, A (Fisher Meredith) K1
Lambeth p32 . . . 020 7091 2700

Kanani, R (Richard Kanani & Co) S1 E L R1 W
Hampton p238 . . . 020 8941 8363

Kanani, Miss Z A (Forsters LLP) W T2
Westminster p33 . . . 020 7863 8333

Kanapathipillai, M (Raj & Pillai)
Hounslow p254 . . . 020 8572 7245

Kandler, J B (Bude Nathan Iwanier) N Q O B1 J1 L W Zv
London NW11 p16 . . . 020 8458 5656

Kandler, Dr R (Butler & Kandler) K1 J1 L W S1
Ilkley p261 . . . 01943 816207

Kane, Miss J (Fletchers) N
Southport p388 . . . 01704 546919

Kane, Ms J (Newcastle Upon Tyne City Council)
Newcastle upon Tyne p466 . 0191 232 8520

Kane, Ms R (Nottingham City Council (City Sec Dept)) K1 D1
Nottingham p467 . . . 0115 915 5555

Kang, A S (Fenland District Council)
March p465 . . . 01354 654321
Dunstable p457 . . . 01582 472222

Kang, B S (Challinors) E S1 C1 L R1 Zi
Birmingham p136 . . . 0121 212 9393

Kang, H S (Kangs Solicitors) G H N B2 S1
Birmingham p139 . . . 0121 449 9888

Kang, H S (H S Kang & Co)
Barking p123 . . . 020 8594 5465

Kang, Ms J (McMillan Williams) Zr N
Mitcham p318 . . . 020 8648 4044

Kang, Miss S S (Lodders Solicitors LLP) J1 N O Q Zq
Stratford-upon-Avon p400 . . 01789 293259

Kanias, N (ClarksLegal LLP) Zd E S1
Reading p360 . . . 0118 958 5321

Kanter, J Q (Olswang LLP) E S1 S2 W
London WC1 p64 . . . 020 7067 3000

Kanter, S A (Olswang LLP) B1 C1 C2 C3 E S1 Zb Zc Zd Zw
London WC1 p64 . . . 020 7067 3000

Kanwar, M (Osborne Clarke) U1 U2
London EC2 p65 . . . 020 7105 7000

Kanwar, N (Plexus Law (A Trading Name of Parabis Law LLP)) O N Q J2 F2 Zr Zj
London EC3 p68 . . . 0844 245 4000

Kapadia, Mrs H J (Beale and Company Solicitors LLP) Zq O A3 Zj Zc
London WC2 p11 . . . 020 7240 3474

Kapoor, Mrs L (DWF) J1 Zp
Manchester p303 . . . 0161 603 5000

Kar, Ms C (London Borough of Southwark)
London SE1 p109 . . . 020 7525 5000

Kar, Ms N (Linklaters LLP)
London EC2 p54 . . . 020 7456 2000

Karali, Miss M (Moreland & Co Solicitors) Q O J1 K1 L K3
Haringey p61 . . . 020 8881 8833

Karali, Mrs M A (Barlow Lyde & Gilbert LLP) O M2 Q Zj Za
London EC3 p10 . . . 020 7247 2277

Karavadra, Ms R M (Harehills & Chapeltown Law Centre)
Leeds p462 . . . 0113 249 1100

Karavas, Ms K (Wandsworth & Merton Law Centre Ltd)
London SW17 p110 . . . 020 8767 2777

Karet, I (Linklaters LLP)
London EC2 p54 . . . 020 7456 2000

Karia, Ms L (Bowling & Co) S1
London E15 p15 . . . 020 8221 8000

Karia, Mrs P (Wason & Co) S1 E W
Potters Bar p355 . . . 01707 664888

Karia, P J (CMS Cameron McKenna LLP) E
London EC3 p17 . . . 020 7367 3000

Karim, M J (Dudley Metropolitan Borough Council)
Dudley p457 . . . 01384 815326

Karim, Miss N (Platinum Partnership Solicitors) B1 C1 E K1 Zi Q N S1 S2
Bradford p154 . . . 0845 490 5000

Karim, Miss S (MFG Solicitors) W
Worcester p440 . . . 01905 610410

Karis, N G (Karis Spyris LLP)
Enfield p219 . . . 020 8443 7000

Karkera, Ms P (Manchester City Council)
Manchester p465 . . . 0161 234 5000

Karmakar, S (Morgan Walker)
London WC2 p62 . . . 020 7831 8333

Karow, Miss W M (Mills & Reeve) N Q
Manchester p307 . . . 0844 561 0011

Karter, A J (Simmons & Simmons)
London EC2 p79 . . . 020 7628 2020

Kartikapallil, D (Scott Rees & Co) S1 N Q
Skelmersdale p381 . . . 01695 722222

Karunakaran, D (Ince & Co Services Ltd)
London E1 p44 . . . 020 7481 0010

Kasbia, K S (Nottinghamshire County Council Legal Services Division)
West Bridgford p475 . . . 0115 977 3478

Kashti, Mrs R M (Darbys Solicitors LLP) W
Oxford p343 . . . 01865 811700

Kassam, K H (Kenneth Elliott & Rowe) E L S2
Romford p366 . . . 01708 757575

Kassell, S C (Maclaren Warner) S1 W E L C1
Ilkeston p261 . . . 0115 930 4994
Stapleford p394 . . . 0115 939 5252

Kassi, A (Reed Smith LLP) A3 Q M2
London EC2 p71 . . . 020 3116 3000

Kathirgamanathan, Mrs G (Nathan Suresh & Amirthan)
Wembley p426 . . . 020 8574 1058

Katira, Ms J (Anthony Gold) N
London SE1 p6 . . . 020 7940 4000

Kato, T (Field Fisher Waterhouse LLP) C1 J1 Zb
London EC3 p31 . . . 020 7861 4000

Katsionis, Mrs P (Davies & Partners) Zr N
Birmingham p137 . . . 0121 616 4450

Katwala, S S (Linklaters LLP)
London EC2 p54 . . . 020 7456 2000

Katz, A J S (Moorcrofts LLP) Ze Zza U2 C1 I
Marlow p313 . . . 01628 470000

Katz, F C (Beauchamps) E S2 S1 R1 R2
Westminster p11 . . . 020 7724 7724

Katz, L M (CKFT)
London NW3 p17 . . . 020 7431 7262

Katz, R S (Kaim Todner Ltd) G H
Islington p47 . . . 020 7700 0070
London EC4 p47 . . . 020 7353 6660

Katzenberg, Ms S E (Ross & Craig) K1 K2
Westminster p73 . . . 020 7262 3077

Kaufman, A (Finers Stephens Innocent LLP) K1 O K2
London W1 p32 . . . 020 7323 4000

Kaufman, A C (Fladgate LLP) C1 B1
London WC2 p32 . . . 020 3036 7000

Kaufman, Mrs G L (Brooke North LLP) B1 O
Leeds p272 . . . 0113 283 2100

Kaufman, H (Fladgate LLP)
London WC2 p32 . . . 020 3036 7000

Kaufman, Ms J G (Steel & Shamash) G H M1
Lambeth p82 . . . 020 7803 3999

Kaufman, P M J (Wiseman Lee LLP) D1 G H N Zm B2
Newham p92 . . . 020 8215 1000

Kaufman, R (Fladgate LLP)
London WC2 p32 . . . 020 3036 7000

Kaufman, S A (Kaufmanlegal) G D1 K1 F1 J1 M1 L P H W Zd Zj Zm
Manchester p306 . . . 0161 205 3955

Kaufman, Mrs V J (Bishop & Co) K1 D1 N
New Mills p321 . . . 01663 746730

Kaufmann, Mrs G (Clarion Solicitors LLP) B1 O Q Zb
Leeds p272 . . . 0113 246 0622

Kaur, Ms A (Malcolm Butler & Co) Q
Walsall p420 . . . 01922 704048

Kaur, A (Ward & Rider Limited)
Coventry p201 . . . 024 7655 5400

Kaur, Ms B (Knight Polson Solicitors) S1 S2
Eastleigh p216 . . . 023 8064 4822
Eastleigh p216 . . . 023 8060 0661

Kaur, Ms D (Sternberg Reed) G
Barking p123 . . . 020 8591 3366
Romford p366 . . . 01708 766155

Kaur, Miss G (Doncaster Magistrates Court)
Doncaster p457 . . . 01302 366711

Kaur, Miss G (Dass Solicitors) E S1 S2 W Q Zl
Birmingham p137 . . . 0121 248 4000

Kaur, Miss H (Gore Legal) J1 Zp
Ealing p36 . . . 020 8810 1652

Kaur, K (Cartwright King) D1 K1 K3
Derby p208 . . . 01332 346111
Leicester p279 . . . 0116 253 9222
Nottingham p336 . . . 0115 958 7444

Kaur, Miss K (Harvey Ingram LLP)
Leicester p280 . . . 0116 254 5454

Kaur, Mrs L (RAC Motoring Services)
Bristol p452 . . . 0870 553 3533

Kaur, Mrs L (Loosemores) C1 Ze C2
Cardiff p179 . . . 029 2022 4433

Kaur, Ms M (Vickers & Co) G H D1 K1
Ealing p89 . . . 020 8579 2559 / 8840 3999

Kaur, Ms N (Hillingdon Law Centre)
Hillingdon p461 . . . 020 8561 9400

Kaur, Miss P (Yorkshire Water Services Ltd)
Bradford p451 . . . 01274 804159

Kaur, P (Addleshaw Goddard)
Leeds p271 . . . 0113 209 2000

Kaur, Mrs R (Attwood & Co) K3 K1 L V D1
Grays p233 . . . 01375 378122 / 378123

Kaur Khara, Mrs B (Jordans) D1 K1 L N Q S1 W
Rowley Regis p368 . . . 0121 559 2922

Kaur-Heer, Miss M (Tyndallwoods) F1 N O Q
Birmingham p143 . . . 0121 624 1111

Kaura, Mrs R (Kaura & Co) A1 B1 C1 E S1 S2 W L
London N12 p48 . . . 020 8445 4069

Kausar, Miss R (Dass Solicitors) B2 G H Zi V Zg J1 W N
Birmingham p137 . . . 0121 248 4000

Kauser, Miss R (Blackburn with Darwen Borough Council)
Blackburn p450 . . . 01254 585585

Kavanagh, D (Skadden Arps Slate Meagher & Flom (UK) LLP)
London E14 p80 . . . 020 7519 7000

Kavanagh, D E (Watson Farley & Williams)
London EC2 p90 . . . 020 7814 8000

Kavanagh, G W C (Barlow Lyde & Gilbert LLP)
London EC3 p10 . . . 020 7247 2277

Kavanagh, Mrs J S (Dawson Hart) J1
Uckfield p416 . . . 01825 762281

Kavanagh, J W (Kavanagh & Co) S1 G H
Eckington p216 . . . 01246 432349

Kavanagh, Miss K P (Fentons) N
Failsworth p223 . . . 0161 682 7101

Kavanagh, P A (Dechert) Ze
London EC4 p26 . . . 020 7184 7000

Kavanagh, Ms S (Lamb & Kavanagh) D1
Camden p51 . . . 020 7209 2481

Kavanagh, Ms S (TV Edwards LLP) K1
London SE8 p85 . . . 020 7790 7000

Kavanagh, S J (Watson Farley & Williams) Zb
London EC2 p90 . . . 020 7814 8000

Kavshal, S K (Dodds & Partners) Zi
Leicester p279 . . . 0116 253 8585

Kay, A (Herbert Smith LLP) C1
London EC2 p40 . . . 020 7374 8000

Kay, A (Langleys)
York p445 . . . 01904 610886

Kay, A (Andersons Solicitors) J1 Zp
Nottingham p335 . . . 0115 947 0641

Kay, Ms A B (National Grid PLC) C1
Warwick p471 . . . 01926 653000

Kay, A G (Read Roper & Read) E S1 C1 W J1 L T1 B1 R1
Manchester p309 . . . 0161 832 6905

Kay, A H (Horwich Cohen Coghlan) N
Manchester p305 . . . 0161 830 4600

Kay, A L T (Aviva PLC)
London EC3 p103 . . 020 7283 7500 / 01603 687905
York p477 . . . 01904 452210

Kay, A L T (Norwich Union Insurance Group)
Norwich p467 . . . 01603 622200

Kay, Miss C (George Davies Solicitors LLP) Zc X R2
Manchester p303 . . . 0161 236 8992

Kay, Mrs F S A (Broadbents) F1 M1
Alfreton p115 . . . 01773 832511

Kay, J (CKFT)
London NW3 p17 . . . 020 7431 7262

Kay, J E (George Davies Solicitors LLP) S1 W Zm
Manchester p303 . . . 0161 236 8992

Kay, J F (Molesworths Bright Clegg) A1 C1 E S2
Rochdale p365 . . . 01706 356666

Kay, Ms J L (Freeth Cartwright LLP) O
Nottingham p337 . . . 0115 936 9369

Kay, J M (Baldwin Wyatt Solicitors) N Q O J1 B1 J2 Zq Zw
Burnley p169 . . . 01282 429999

Kay, Mrs M A (Key2Law LLP) K1 W S1 T1 T2 E
Ewell p220 . . . 020 8393 0941

Kay, M R (Greene & Greene) P N J1 F1 B1 O Q Zq
Bury St Edmunds p171 . . . 01284 762211

kay, Miss N (Manches LLP) J1
London WC2 p58 . . . 020 7404 4433

Kay, P A (Speechly Bircham LLP) Zb R2
London EC4 p81 . . . 020 7427 6400

Kay, P A (Ware & Kay LLP) C1 E B1 J1
York p445 . . . 01904 716000

Kay, Ms P J (Whiting & Mason) L S1 S2 W
Marple p313 . . . 0161 427 1040

Kay, P M (Leadbeater & Kay) N W Zv Zl S1 E S2 B2
Stoke-on-Trent p398 . . . 01782 201933

Kay, R N (Cockertons) C1 E S1 S2 Q A1 J1
Bakewell p121 . . . 01629 812613

Kay, S J (EMW) E S2 R1 R2
Milton Keynes p316 . . . 0845 070 6000
Northampton p332 . . . 01604 233233

Kay, S K (Travers Smith LLP) C1 C2
London EC1 p87 . . . 020 7295 3000

Kay Kanagaratnam, P (Aequitas Law LLP) B1 E M2 O G Za Zf
London W1 p4 . . . 020 7495 2776

Kaya, S (Bartletts) S2 E Zi S1 W
Haringey p11 . .020 8340 2202 / 8340 2203

Kayani, J (Coldham Shield & Mace)
London E4 p21 . . . 020 8524 6323

Kaye, D C (D C Kaye & Co) S1 K1 P W E M1 L B1 F1 G Zl Zi Zj A1 C1 S2 K4 Zm R1 R2
Great Missenden p234 . . .01494 864650 / 862226

Kaye, Ms D L (Ramsdens Solicitors) W S1
Huddersfield p256 . . . 01484 821500

Kaye, Mrs F R (Russell-Cooke LLP) O Q Zc
London SW15 p74 . . . 020 8789 9111

Kaye, G (Howard Kennedy LLP) E
London W1 p48 . . . 020 7636 1616

Kaye, G S (CKFT) E S2 S1 R2 Zc L
London NW3 p17 . . . 020 7431 7262

Kaye, Miss I S (Hertfordshire County Council)
Hertford p460 . . . 01992 555555

Kaye, Mrs K M (Rotherham Magistrates Court)
Rotherham p470 . . . 01709 839339

Kaye, L J (Leon Kaye Solicitors) C1 E G K1 L M1 N P S1
London SW11 p48 . . . 020 7228 2020

Kaye, M D (Kaye Tesler & Co Inc Michael D Kaye & Co) C1 I G O W
London N15 p86 . . . 020 8809 6756

Kaye, Ms N (Boyes Turner) B1 Zb
Reading p360 . . . 0118 959 7711

Kaye, P G (Kayes Solicitors) N
Pudsey p358 . . . 0113 290 0380

Kaye, P S (Linder Myers Solicitors) O Q L F1 B1 K1 Zq Zc Zb
Manchester p306 . . . 0844 984 6000

Kaye, Mrs T M (Kaye & Co) S1
Pinner p349 . . . 020 8428 0010

Kaye, Mrs V C (Treasury Solicitors Department)
London WC2 p110 . . . 020 7210 3000

Kaye, W E (O'Neill Patient) S1 S2
Stockport p396 . . . 0161 483 8555

Kaye, W H (Harrowells) K1
York p444 . . . 01904 558600

Kayne, D (Network Rail)
London NW1 p108 . . . 020 7557 8000

Kazimierska, Ms B (Alexandrou & Co) S1 R2 C1 S2 E Q O
Barnet p123 . . . 020 8447 1503

Keady Smith, Mrs A (Merrony Wall) K1 K3
Twickenham p416 . . . 020 8898 4700

Keady, R (Barlow Lyde & Gilbert LLP) Q Ze
London EC3 p10 . . . 020 7247 2277

Keal, A C (Allen & Overy LLP)
London E1 p5 . . . 020 3088 0000

Kealey, Miss J E (Powys County Council)
Llandrindod Wells p463 . . . 01597 826000

Keall, D J H (Amphlett Lissimore) W T2
Croydon p6 . . . 020 8771 5254

See p634 for the Key to Work Categories

Keall, Ms S C (Travers Smith LLP) *J1 Zi Zp* London EC1 *p87* 020 7295 3000

Kealy, L (Lanyon Bowdler LLP) *K4 T2 W* Shrewsbury *p379* 01743 280280

Kealy, R J C (Kealy Farmar & Co) *S1 E C1 T1 W K1 T2 A1 K3* Henley-on-Thames *p247* . . . 01491 410393

Kean, Ms C M (Wiggin LLP) *O Zk Zf Ze U2 Zz* Cheltenham *p189* 01242 224114

Kean, F J (Barlow Lyde & Gilbert LLP) *O Q Zj Zq* London EC3 *p10* 020 7247 2277

Kean, G J (Leeds City Council) *R1 C1 Zd Ze* Leeds *p462* 0113 224 3513

Keane, B D P (Brentwood Borough Council) Brentwood *p451* 01277 261111

Keane, B P G V (Overburys & Raymond Thompson) *A1 E J1 S1* Norwich *p335* 01603 610481

Keane, D J (Keelys LLP) *C1* Lichfield *p284* 01543 420000

Keane, J (Ewings & Co) *G H* London SE20 *p30* 020 8778 1126

Keane, Ms L (Ashurst LLP) London EC2 *p7* 020 7638 1111

Keane, R S (Keane & Co) *S1 K1 L W P G E A1 T1 Zl C1 S2 J1 Zh Zq* Aldeburgh *p115* 01728 453595

Keanneally, S C (Hall Smith Whittingham LLP) Nantwich *p320* 01270 610300

Kear, Miss S E (The John W Davies Partnership) *A1 C1 E L M1 R1 S1 T1 W Zc* Newport *p329* 01633 841773

Kearney, A T (Mowlem PLC) Isleworth *p462* 020 8568 9111

Kearney, Ms C E (Bristows) *U2 Ze* London EC4 *p15* 020 7400 8000

Kearney, C F (Osborne Clarke) *R2* London EC2 *p65* 020 7105 7000

Kearney, Ms C M (Barlow Lyde & Gilbert LLP) London EC3 *p10* 020 7247 2277

Kearney, F (Lawrence Law) London SW15 *p52* 020 8788 0055

Kearney, Miss S K (Crawford-THG Ltd) London EC3 *p105* 020 7265 0611

Kearney, Miss Y M (Yvonne Kearney) *E P S1 W* Witney *p436* 01993 776018

Kearns, L (Rooks Rider) *T2 W* London EC1 *p73* 020 7689 7000

Kearns, Miss R (Heaney Watson) *K1 K3* Liverpool *p288* 0151 293 2936

Kearns, Miss S J (Rees Page) *S1 T2 W* Wolverhampton *p438* 01902 577777

Kearsley, D (Penningtons) *E* London EC2 *p66* 020 7457 3000

Kearsley, Miss J (Farleys Solicitors LLP) *Zg Q N* Burnley *p169* 01282 798664

Keat, K R (Caradon District Council) Liskeard *p463* 01579 341000

Keates, A J (Stephenson Harwood) *Za* London EC2 *p82* 020 7329 4422

Keates, J L (Shoosmiths) *C1 C2 Zb* Birmingham *p142* 0370 086 4000 / 0121 335 4440

Keates, M C (DLA Piper UK LLP) *B1 E C1 O* Manchester *p303* 0870 011 1111

Keating, B G (Worthingtons) *G H J1 K1* Folkestone *p227* 01303 850206

Keating, G J L (London Borough of Lewisham) London SE6 *p107* 020 8695 6000

Keating, M E (Cadbury Schweppes PLC (Legal Dept)) Birmingham *p449* 0121 625 7000

Keating, Miss S L (Mincoffs Solicitors LLP) *O Q J1 N* Newcastle upon Tyne *p325* . 0191 281 6151

Keating, W J (Paul Davidson Taylor) *E L R1 W B1 Zc Zb Zl* Horsham *p253* 01403 262333

Keats, Ms E (Linklaters LLP) London EC2 *p54* 020 7456 2000

Keats, M (Linklaters LLP) London EC2 *p54* 020 7456 2000

Keatt, N J (Thompson & Jackson) *S1 S2* Plymouth *p350* . . . .01752 665037 / 221171

Keck, Ms C A (Allen & Overy LLP) London E1 *p5* 020 3088 0000

Keddie, J R (Midwinters) *O Q N J1 L Zq J2* Cheltenham *p188* 01242 514674

Kedge, Miss N (Pollecoff Solicitors Ltd) London EC2 *p68* 020 7608 2568

Keeble, A (McMillan Williams) *S2 E* Coulsdon *p199* 020 8668 4131

Keeble, A C (Alistair Keeble) *S1 W E L Zl J1* Clacton-on-Sea *p195* 01255 818900

Keeble, J (DFA Law LLP) *C1 C2* Northampton *p331* . . . . 01604 609560 Milton Keynes *p317* 01908 668555

Keeble, J A (Ward Hadaway) *N J2 Zg Zr* Newcastle upon Tyne *p327* . 0191 204 4000

Keeble, Mrs K (Phillips & Phillips) Harrow *p242* . . .020 8422 4435 / 8422 8155

Keeble, R (The Johnson Partnership) *G H* Nottingham *p337* 0115 941 9141

Keech, A (Michael Lewin Solicitors) *P L Q N W* Leeds *p275* 0113 393 0231

Keegan, D D (Debenhams Ottaway) *N J1* St Albans *p390* 01727 837161

Keegan, M J (Wards Solicitors) *O Q B1 Zb* Bristol *p165* 0117 929 2811

Keegan, Mrs R C (Fiona Bruce & Co LLP) *W K4* Warrington *p421* 01925 263273

Keel, A (Girlings) *E C1 S1 L A1 R1 W Zc Zl* Canterbury *p177* 01227 768374

Keeler, M S (Keelers) *C1 C2 E R1* Kenilworth *p264* 01926 853555

Keeley, Ms J A (Fladgate LLP) *O L P Zl* London WC2 *p32* 020 3036 7000

Keeley, M A (Freeth Cartwright LLP) *Q Zp Zq W J1* Nottingham *p337* 0115 936 9369

Keeling, M (MK Legal Solicitors) *K4 K1 T2 W N Zq* Milton Keynes *p317* 01908 577680

Keeling, P (Stones Solicitors LLP) Exeter *p222* 01392 666777

Keely, S M (Keelys LLP) *C1 E B1 T1 W N Zc Zl* Lichfield *p284* 01543 420000

Keem, D R (Brown Holliday & Clements) *S1 W K1 L K3 E K4* North Shields *p330* 0191 257 0431

Keen, A P C (Allens) *E S1 C1 L* Torquay *p474* 01803 324500

Keen, A P C (Somerville & Savage) *E S1 S2* Torquay *p413* . . . . 01803 324500 Torquay *p413* 01803 312700

Keen, A S (Andrew Keen & Co) *K1 G H F1 B2 Q Zg Zp* London E18 *p48* 020 8989 3123

Keen, Ms C (J A Kemp & Co) London WC1 *p48* 020 7405 3292

Keen, R J (Owen White) *A3 L J1 Zh O Zp* Slough *p382* 01753 876800

Keen, Ms S (Hogan Lovells International LLP) *C1* London EC1 *p42* 020 7296 2000

Keen, Ms S J (Procter & Gamble UK (Legal Dept)) Weybridge *p476* 01932 896000

Keenan, A C (Andrew Keenan & Co) *G H B2* London SE20 *p48* 020 8659 0332

Keenan, M (Walker Smith Way) *N J1* Chester *p191* 0844 346 3100

Keenan, Mrs S J (Runnymede Borough Council) Addlestone *p447* 01932 838383

Keene, A B (Carvers (Part of the Wilkes Partnership LLP)) *K1 Q N F1 O L J1 V* Birmingham *p136* . . . . . . 0121 784 8484 Birmingham *p143* 0121 233 4333

Keene, Ms J S (Garner Canning) *D1 K3 K1* Birmingham *p138* 0121 749 5577

Keenleyside, Mrs P R (Burnetts) *Zr* Carlisle *p181* . . . . 01228 552222 Carlisle *p182* 01228 552222

Keepin, A (Charles Russell LLP) *C1* London EC4 *p19* 020 7203 5000

Keeping, Ms H J (Keeping & Co) Alton *p116* 01420 85221

Keer, Mrs M C (Barlow Robbins LLP) *K1 D1 B1* Godalming *p231* 01483 417121

Keer-Keer, P W (Keer-Keer & Co) *K1 S1 P M1 C1 J1 L F1 W* Hemel Hempstead *p246* . . .01442 216755 / 216756

Keevil, T S (Gallaher Ltd) Weybridge *p476* 01932 859777

Kefford, Mrs M C (Trafford Metropolitan Borough Council) Stretford *p473* 0161 912 1212

Kefford, Mrs R M (Preston Redman) *A1 E L R1 S2 P* Bournemouth *p152* 01202 292424

Kehel, G S (Higgs & Sons) *O Q L W B1 Ze* Brierley Hill *p158* 0845 111 5050

Kehler, H D (DB Law) *G H* Camborne *p173* 01209 712428

Kehoe, Mrs C I (Herbert Smith LLP) *O* London EC2 *p40* 020 7374 8000

Kehoe, Mrs C M (Haworth & Gallagher) *C1 D1 E F1 J1 K1 L M1 P R1 Zs* Wallasey *p419* . . 0151 638 5457 / 638 6088

Kehoe, S A (Advance Legal) *N Zc O Q J1 J2 Zp* Burton-on-Trent *p170* 01283 544492

Keighley, A D D (Walker Foster) *K1 D1 J1 S1* Skipton *p381* 01756 700200

Keighley, D G (Herrington & Carmichael LLP) *S1 S2 W T2 K4 T1* Camberley *p173* 01276 686222

Keily, Ms S (Thomson Snell & Passmore) *K1* Tunbridge Wells *p415* 01892 510000

Keir, G M (Hadgkiss Hughes & Beale) *K1 G P D1 H L F1 J1 V* Birmingham *p138* 0121 449 5050

Keir, Miss K J (Kingsley Napley) *D1 K1* London EC1 *p50* 020 7814 1200

Keith, Miss H (Legal Services Commission) *K1 N G Q H* Reading *p469* 0118 955 8600

Keith-Lucas, P (Bevan Brittan LLP) Bristol *p161* 0870 194 1000

Keitley, Mrs J (Hampshire County Council) Winchester *p476* 01962 841841

Keitley, N (Blake Lapthorn) *B1 C1* Chandlers Ford *p184* 023 8090 8090

Kelbie, Ms J (Lyons Davidson) Leeds *p275* 0113 368 6161

Kelcey, I C P (Kelcey & Hall) *D1 G I B2* Bristol *p163* 0117 927 9604

Keleman, Ms R (Russell Jones & Walker) London WC2 *p74* 020 7657 1555

Keliher, J A (Stephens & Scown) *C1 C2 F1* Exeter *p222* 01392 210700

Kell, Mrs M (Andrew Jackson) *O J2* Hull *p257* 01482 325242

Kell, S J (Andrew Jackson) *N L O Q* Hull *p257* 01482 325242

Kelland, N (Davies Sully Wilkins) Caerphilly *p172* . . . . 029 2088 7828 Barry *p126* 01446 411000

Kellas, Ms S (Birnberg Peirce & Partners) *Zi* Camden *p13* 020 7911 0166

Kellaway, Miss J E (JNP Legal) *N Q J2* Merthyr Tydfil *p314* 01685 350421

Kelleher, Mrs E K (CMS Cameron McKenna LLP) London EC3 *p17* 020 7367 3000

Kelleher, J R (Addleshaw Goddard) *O* London EC1 *p4* 020 7606 8855

Kelleher, Mrs K M (City of London Magistrates Court) London EC4 *p107* 020 7332 1830

Kelleher, M J (Layton & Co) *G S1 A1 L K1 F1 W Zt Zl S2 H* Haverfordwest *p244* 01437 766671

Kelleher, T M (Thomas Cooper) *N Za* London EC3 *p22* 020 7481 8851

Keller, S (James Morgan Solicitors) *C1 S1 E W C2 Zc Zq* Cardiff *p180* . . . 029 2038 2111 / 2022 1600

Kellett, J P (Watson Farley & Williams) London EC2 *p90* 020 7814 8000

Kellett, Miss L M (Anthony Clark & Co) *K1 K3* Lincoln *p284* 01522 512321

Kellett, S (The Smith Partnership) *G H* Stoke-on-Trent *p398* 01782 324454

Kellett, Miss S J (Stamp Jackson and Procter) *E S2 R2 S1 A1 C1 W L* Hull *p258* 01482 324591

Kelley, Mrs M E (Calvert Smith & Sutcliffe) *S1 E L C1 J1 K1 W Zc* Richmond upon Thames *p364* 020 8940 0017

Kelley, M J (Chichester District Council) Chichester *p455* 01243 785166

Kelliher, Miss E (Allen & Overy LLP) London E1 *p5* 020 3088 0000

Kellman, Ms E (Fox Williams) *C1 O Ze* London EC2 *p33* 020 7628 2000

Kelly, A F (Pardoes) *Q O Zq Zc Zl F1* Bridgwater *p158* 01278 457891

Kelly, A M (Andersons Solicitors) *D2 D1 K1* Nottingham *p335* 0115 947 0641

Kelly, Miss C (Jones Day) *E* London EC4 *p46* 020 7039 5959

Kelly, Ms C (Anthony Gold) *C1 J1* London SE1 *p6* 020 7940 4000

Kelly, Mrs C H (Sternberg Reed) *G* Barking *p123* 020 8591 3366

Kelly, C M (Pinsent Masons LLP) London EC2 *p67* 020 7418 7000

Kelly, D (Ellis-Fermor & Negus) *J1 N O Q F1 C1 W* Ripley *p364* 01773 744744

Kelly, Mrs D (HT Legal Limited t/a Harrison Townend & Ormeshers) *S1 S2 W* Hyde *p259* 0161 368 1559

Kelly, D (Harding Evans LLP) *N P Zj* Newport *p328* 01633 244233

Kelly, D (Yarwood Stimpson & Co) *D1 F1 J1 K1 L Q* Whitley Bay *p431* 0191 297 0123

Kelly, D G (Russell Jones & Walker) Wakefield *p419* 01924 234300

Kelly, E G (Lawson Coppock & Hart) *S1 E R1 R2 Zb* Manchester *p306* 0161 832 5944

Kelly, Ms F (Nelsons) Nottingham *p338* 0115 958 6262

Kelly, Mrs F C (Tallents Solicitors) *S1 A1 E L W* Newark *p322* 01636 671881

Kelly, G (Forshaws Davies Ridgway LLP) Warrington *p422* 01925 230000

Kelly, G V (Cyril Jones & Co) *D1 F1 G J1 K1 L M1 P S1 W Zi Zl Zp* Wrexham *p443* 01978 367830

Kelly, G V (Ashurst LLP) *E* London EC2 *p7* 020 7638 1111

Kelly, Ms H L (Palmers) *K1 D1* Grays *p233* 01375 484444

Kelly, I (Reynolds Porter Chamberlain LLP) *Zj Zq* London E1 *p71* 020 3060 6000

Kelly, J (Kennedys) London EC3 *p49* 020 7667 9667

Kelly, Miss J (Parkinson Wright LLP) *K1* Worcester *p440* 01905 726789

Kelly, J (Kirbys Solicitors) *Zj Q N* Newcastle upon Tyne *p325* . 01661 867010

Kelly, Ms J (Williscroft & Co) *K1 D1 L D2* Bradford *p155* 01274 305380

Kelly, J C R (Petherbridge Bassra Solicitors) *D1 E S1 H S2 W Zt* Bradford *p154* 01274 724114

Kelly, J L (Lester Aldridge LLP) *O* Bournemouth *p152* 01202 786161

Kelly, J P (Simmons & Simmons) *O* London EC2 *p79* 020 7628 2020

Kelly, J R (Schillings) *B1 C1 C2 C3 I M1 T1 O* London WC1 *p77* 020 7034 9000

Kelly, J S (Paisleys) *G H S1 Zl* Workington *p440* 01900 602235

Kelly, J S (Butcher & Barlow LLP) *J1 N L C1* Bramhall *p155* 0161 439 8228

Kelly, K (Canter Levin & Berg) Liverpool *p287* 0151 239 1000

Kelly, Ms L (Countryside Properties PLC) Brentwood *p451* 01277 260000

Kelly, Miss L A (Hill Dickinson LLP) *L N Q* Liverpool *p288* 0151 600 8000

Kelly, Miss L E (Gordon Dadds) *S1 E* London W1 *p25* 020 7493 6151

Kelly, L P (Lawrence Stephens) *B1 F1 G M1 N Ze Zf F2 Zk B2 J1 O* London EC1 *p82* 020 7935 1211

Kelly, M A R (Thompsons (formerly Robin/Brian Thompson & Partners)) Birmingham *p143* 0121 262 1200

Kelly, M J (Dexter Montague LLP) *K1 D1 K2* Reading *p360* 0118 939 3999

Kelly, M J (Michael Kelly & Co) *D1 E F1 G H J1 K1 L* Hanham *p238* 0117 967 6559

Kelly, M J (Thornes) *K1 W* Wolverhampton *p438* 01902 313311

Kelly, Mrs M M (Actons) *T1 W Zd Zo* Nottingham *p335* 0115 910 0200

Kelly, M P (Taylor Walton LLP) *F1 L R1* Luton *p295* 01582 731161

Kelly, Ms N (WBW Solicitors) *K1 D1* Newton Abbot *p329* 01626 202404

Kelly, N C (Banks Kelly) *Zr Ze J1 K1 O Q N Zq* London EC2 *p9* 020 7248 4231

Kelly, N T (Lynch Hall & Hornby) *C1 E L M1 S1* Harrow *p242* 020 8864 0722

Kelly, P (Leeds City Council) Leeds *p462* 0113 224 3513

Kelly, P (Northumbrian Water Ltd) *N O P Q Zc* Durham *p457* 0870 608 4820

Kelly, P A (Salter Rees & Kelly) Swansea *p405* 01792 470707

Kelly, P A T (Neves) *Q O J1 Zp* Luton *p295* 01582 725311

Kelly, P D (Tozers) *N J1 O Q C1 F1* Exeter *p222* 01392 207020

Kelly, P G (Kelly & Co) *E S1 R1 J1 C1 K1 W T1 B1 Zt Zc Zh* Leeds *p275* 0113 244 2113

Kelly, P L (Sternberg Reed) *G* Barking *p123* 020 8591 3366

Kelly, P R N (Laytons) *C1 F1 M1 Zb M2* London EC4 *p52* 020 7842 8000

Kelly, Mrs R (Clifford Chance) London E14 *p20* 020 7006 1000

Kelly, Ms R (McGrath & Co) *X J1 K1 N* Birmingham *p140* 0121 643 4121

Kelly, R D (Armitage Sykes LLP) *C1 J1* Huddersfield *p255* 01484 538121

Kelly, R M (Gateshead Metropolitan Borough Council) Gateshead *p458* 0191 433 3000

Kelly, Miss S (Bindmans LLP) *J2 N Zr* London WC1 *p12* 020 7833 4433

Kelly, Miss S (Challinors) *K1 D1* West Bromwich *p427* 0121 553 3211

Kelly, S G (Manches LLP) *R2 E* London WC2 *p58* 020 7404 4433

Kelly, S M (Network Rail) London NW1 *p108* 020 7557 8000

Kelly, Mrs S M (Squire Sanders (UK) LLP) *E S2* Manchester *p310* 0161 830 5000

Kelly, Ms T (Ford Simey LLP) Exeter *p221* 01392 274126

Kelly, T A (GLP Solicitors) *N* Manchester *p304* 0161 834 6721

Kelly, T J (Marshall Hall & Levy) *S1 S2 E A1* South Shields *p384* 0191 455 3181

Kelly, T M (Slee Blackwell) Exeter *p222* 01392 423000

Kelly, Mrs T M M (Reed Smith LLP) *O B1 B2 M2 J1 Ze Zb* London EC2 *p71* 020 3116 3000

Kelman, A (Fladgate LLP) *C2 C1 B1 J1* London WC2 *p32* 020 3036 7000

Kelman, Ms J E (Lawrence & Co) *K1 G M1 P L H V Zi Zl Zp* London W9 *p52* 020 7266 4333

Kelsall, J R (Walker Morris) *E R1 A1 Zc* Leeds *p277* 0113 283 2500

Kelsall, Ms N (Addleshaw Goddard) Manchester *p300* 0161 934 6000

Kelsall, S T (Challinors) *S1 E L R1 W A1 K1* Halesowen *p237* 0121 550 0481

Kelsey, C G (MHM Solicitors) *N P M1 L K1 G F1 B1 D1 J1 Ze Zf Zk* Leicester *p280* 0845 234 0230

Kelsey, Miss G (Brethertons LLP) *D1 K1* Rugby *p368* 01788 579579

Kelsey, N R (Davenport Lyons) *L S1 E* London W1 *p25* 020 7468 2600

Kelton, A (Richard Buxton) *P M1 Zg Q R1 Zn* Cambridge *p174* 01223 328933

Kemal, Mrs A (MacLeish Littlestone Cowan) Redbridge *p57* 020 8514 3000

Kembrey, Ms S (Wolverhampton City Council) Wolverhampton *p477* 01902 556556

Kemp, Ms A (Badhams Law (A Trading Name of Parabis Law LLP)) *Zj N* Croydon *p204* 0844 245 4000

Kemp, A C N (Astrazeneca PLC) London W1 *p103* 020 7304 5000

Kemp, C (Bennett Griffin) Worthing *p441* 01903 229925

Kemp, Mrs C (Lewis & Dick) *W* Epsom *p219* 020 8393 0055

Kemp, D J A (Blaser Mills) *S1 S2 L* High Wycombe *p249* 01494 450171

Kemp, Mrs E J (Alsters Kelley) *K1 K3* Coventry *p199* . . . . 0844 561 0100 Leamington Spa *p270* 0844 561 0100

Kemp, Miss F (Lees Solicitors LLP) *Zr N* Birkenhead *p134* 0151 647 9381

Kemp, G C (Anthony & Jarvie) *S1* Bridgend *p157* 01656 652737

Kemp, G M (Kemps Solicitors) *G H B2*
Oldham *p340* 0161 633 0555

Kemp, Ms J H (Barlow Robbins LLP) *K1*
Guildford *p235* 01483 543200

Kemp, Mrs K A (Anthony & Jarvie) *K1 W K3 K4*
Bridgend *p157* 01656 652737

Kemp, Mrs L A (Careless & Kemp) *S1 S2 W Zd K4 L E*
Sandown *p372* 01983 400456
Ventnor *p418* 01983 852626

Kemp, M B (Stephenson Harwood) *O*
London EC2 *p82* 020 7329 4422

Kemp, M F (EJ Moyle) *Q N J1 F1 F2 L Zq*
Littlehampton *p285* 01903 725143

Kemp, Mrs M J (Nabarro LLP)
London WC1 *p63* 020 7524 6000

Kemp, Ms N (Simmons & Simmons)
London EC2 *p79* 020 7628 2020

Kemp, P (Watson Burton LLP) *Zc E Q N*
Newcastle upon Tyne *p327* 0845 901 2100

Kemp, P A (The Worcester Family Law Practice) *K1 K2 K3*
Worcester *p440* 01905 730900

Kemp, P C (Hertfordshire County Council)
Hertford *p460* 01992 555555

Kemp, R H (Kemp Little LLP) *I C3 Ze U1 U2 Zz F1 F2*
London EC2 *p48* 020 7600 8080

Kemp, R J (Capron & Helliwell) *S1 S2 E K4*
Stalham *p393* 01692 581231

Kemp, R P (Richard P Kemp BA Solicitor) *S1 K1 L N Q C1 F1 G E W Zv*
Martock *p313* 01935 822572

Kemp, Miss S R (Kennedys) *Zr N*
London EC3 *p49* 020 7667 9667

Kemp, W (Watson Burton LLP)
Newcastle upon Tyne *p327* 0845 901 2100

Kemp, Ms W M (Crosse & Crosse) *D1 D2 K1*
Exeter *p220* 01392 258451

Kemp, Mrs Y (Riley Langdon)
Durham *p214* 0191 378 7620

Kempe, P B (Taylor Wessing) *C1 T1 B1 J1 Zb Zj Zo*
London EC4 *p86* 020 7300 7000

Kempka, Mrs P M (Sheffield City Council)
Sheffield *p471* 0114 273 4019

Kempkens, C (Ince & Co Services Ltd)
London E1 *p44* 020 7481 0010

Kempner, R A (Addleshaw Goddard)
Leeds *p271* 0113 209 2000
Manchester *p300* 0161 934 6000

Kempner, S (Sheridans) *Ze Zf Zw Zz*
London WC1 *p78* 020 7079 0100

Kempson, D M B (Tozers) *S2 S1 A2*
Exeter *p222* 01392 207020

Kempton, D A (Gordons Solicitors LLP) *S1 E W Zl*
Marlow *p313* 01628 487487

Kempton, Ms J (The College of Law) *K1 D1*
London WC1 *p105* 0800 289997

Kemshall, D (Pepperells) *W*
Scunthorpe *p373* 01724 871999

Kemsley, Miss A K (Chancellors Lea Brewer) *J1 N O Q W Zk Zl K4 F1*
Bexleyheath *p132* 020 8303 0077

Kench, T R (Timothy Kench & Co) *S1 N K1 W*
Great Missenden *p234* 01494 864153

Kendall, A J (Bevan Brittan LLP)
Birmingham *p135* 0870 194 1000

Kendall, Mrs C (Gough-Thomas & Scott) *E S1 L A1 W*
Oswestry *p342* 01691 655600

Kendall, C (Windeatts) *W T1 T2*
Totnes *p413* 01803 862233

Kendall, D (Penningtons)
Godalming *p231* 01483 791800

Kendall, D C (Valentine Duggins) *S1 W L E*
Wallasey *p419* 0151 638 4844

Kendall, D R (Edwards Angell Palmer & Dodge)
London EC2 *p28* 020 7583 4055

Kendall, J I (Oslers Solicitors) *G H*
Stowmarket *p400* 01449 774670

Kendall, M A R (Reynolds Porter Chamberlain LLP) *Q O Zj Zq*
London E1 *p71* 020 3060 6000

Kendall, M J (Gough-Thomas & Scott) *S1 N C1 W A1 F1 L E Zk Zl*
Ellesmere *p217* 01691 622413

Kendall, M P (West Sussex County Council)
Chichester *p455* 01243 777100

Kendall, R (Ashurst LLP) *M1 M2 Zb*
London EC2 *p7* 020 7638 1111

Kendall, R M (174 Law) *D1 D2 S2 K3 K1 S1 W*
Birkenhead *p134* 0151 647 7372

Kenderdine-Davies, M D G (Gartmore Investment Management PLC)
London EC3 *p106* 020 7782 2000

Kendon, C (Lewis Silkin LLP)
London EC4 *p53* 020 7074 8000

Kendrew, D C (Bendles) *G H J1 K1 L N Zd Zm*
Carlisle *p181* 01228 522215

Kendrew, J H (Castle Sanderson) *G H K1 S1 V Zl*
Leeds *p272* 0113 232 1919

Kendrick, A (Squire Sanders (UK) LLP)
London EC2 *p81* 020 7655 1000

Kendrick, Miss A J (Bristol City Council)
Bristol *p451* 0117 922 2000

Kendrick, Mrs L A (Sharman Law) *K1 D1 M1 P J1 W S1*
Ampthill *p118* 01525 750750

Kendrick, M W (Goodman Derrick LLP) *E S1*
London EC4 *p36* 020 7404 0606

Kenealy, Miss N (Bartletts Solicitors) *Q N*
Chester *p190* 01244 313301

Kengington, Ms S (Boodle Hatfield)
Westminster *p14* 020 7629 7411

Kenmir, S J (Whitehead Vizard) *S2 E R2 C1 S1*
Salisbury *p371* 01722 412141

Kennaird-Banner, Mrs S (Go Conveyancing) *S1 S2 W*
Northampton *p467* 01604 636868
Northampton *p332* 01604 601575

Kennar, E J (Rawlins Davy PLC) *B1 C1 C2 E S2 Zb*
Bournemouth *p152* 01202 558844

Kennard, D (Thomas Cooper) *O M1 M2 N B1 C1 F1 Za Zj*
London EC3 *p22* 020 7481 8851

Kennaugh, Miss G (Stokoe Partnership) *G H*
Manchester *p310* 0161 237 5755

Kennaugh, Ms G A (Burton Copeland LLP) *G H*
Manchester *p302* 0161 827 9500

Kennaway, Miss C (Howells LLP) *Zg*
Sheffield *p376* 0114 249 6666

Kennaway, I M (Cornwall County Council)
Truro *p474* 01872 322197

Kennedy, A (Wosskow Brown) *J1 B1 C1 Zp*
Sheffield *p377* 0114 256 1560

Kennedy, A (Howard & Co) *G H*
Barnsley *p124* 01226 215215

Kennedy, A D (J A Hughes) *W K4*
Cardiff *p179* 029 2061 9700

Kennedy, Ms A P (Doncaster Magistrates Court)
Doncaster *p457* 01302 366711

Kennedy, A S (Stewarts Law LLP) *O Zq Zk C3*
Leeds *p277* 0113 222 0022

Kennedy, Ms B (Bass Taverns Ltd) *C1 N*
Birmingham *p449* 0121 558 1481

Kennedy, Miss C M (Merthyr Tydfil County Borough Council)
Merthyr Tydfil *p465* 01685 725000

Kennedy, Miss C M (Treasury Solicitors Department)
London WC2 *p110* 020 7210 3000

Kennedy, C N (Hewetts) *E P C1*
Reading *p361* 0118 957 5337

Kennedy, Ms D Y L (Society of Lloyd's)
London EC3 *p107* 020 7327 1000

Kennedy, Mrs G C (HRJ Law LLP) *F1 K1 N Q K2 Zr*
Hitchin *p251* 01462 628888

Kennedy, G R (Ince & Co Services Ltd) *B1*
London E1 *p44* 020 7481 0010

Kennedy, H (Bentleys Stokes & Lowless)
London EC3 *p12* 020 7782 0990

Kennedy, Ms J (Anthony Gold) *N Zq Zr*
London SE1 *p6* 020 7940 4000

Kennedy, J E (J E Kennedy & Co) *J2 R1 Zp S1 W A3 J1 M1 X Zg*
Harrow *p241* 020 8864 3056

Kennedy, J I (Blake Lapthorn) *S1*
Chandlers Ford *p184* 023 8090 8090

Kennedy, Miss J P (Collyer Bristow LLP) *A3 Zc Zk O Q N*
London WC1 *p22* 020 7242 7363

Kennedy, Miss J R (Denbighshire County Council)
Ruthin *p470* 01824 706000

Kennedy, K (Clarke Willmott)
Taunton *p408*0845 209 1000 / 0117 305 6000

Kennedy, Ms K L (The College of Law Chester)
Chester *p454* 0800 289997

Kennedy, K N R (John Fowlers LLP Solicitors) *G S1 C1 E H*
Brightlingsea *p159* 01206 302694
Colchester *p197* 01206 576151

Kennedy, K S G (Berg Legal) *C1 J1*
Manchester *p301* 0161 833 9211

Kennedy, M (Herbert Reeves & Co) *E S1 L Zw*
London EC2 *p40* 020 7739 6660

Kennedy, Ms N (Sutovic & Hartigan)
London W3 *p84* 020 8993 5544

Kennedy, P (Hannays Solicitors and Advocates) *G H*
South Shields *p383* 0191 456 7893 / 455 5361

Kennedy, P C (Pinsent Masons LLP) *C1 Zo*
Manchester *p308* 0161 234 8234

Kennedy, T (Marriott Davies Yapp)
Sutton *p402* 020 8643 9794

Kennedy, W C (Treasury Solicitors Department)
London WC2 *p110* 020 7210 3000

Kennedy Harper, T J (Shell International Ltd)
London SE1 *p109* 020 7934 1234

Kennerley, J A (Burton Copeland LLP) *G H*
Manchester *p302* 0161 827 9500

Kennett, R J (Laytons) *C1 C2 Ze*
London EC4 *p52* 020 7842 8000

Kenning, S F M (Warwick & Barker) *S1 K1 W M1 C1 D1 E F1 J1 L Zc Zk Zl*
Rustington *p369* 01903 775051

Kennon, N T (Wragg Mark-Bell Solicitors)
Carlisle *p182* 01228 711728

Kenny, Miss A C (British Telecommunications PLC)
London EC1 *p104* 020 7356 6181

Kenny, Mrs A W (Cannock Chase District Council)
Cannock *p453* 01543 462621

Kenny, C R F (Coffin Mew & Clover) *S1 W R1*
Gosport *p232* 023 9252 3111

Kenny, Mrs E (GHP Legal) *G Zl*
Wrexham *p442* 01978 291456

Kenny, Ms F G (Adams & Remers)
Lewes *p283* 01273 480616

Kenny, Miss F M R (Hill Dickinson LLP) *W*
Liverpool *p288* 0151 600 8000

Kenny, M A (Watson Farley & Williams)
London EC2 *p90* 020 7814 8000

Kenny, M B (Barnsley Metropolitan Borough Council)
Barnsley *p448* 01226 770770

Kenny, P (Neil Myerson LLP) *C1 Ze C2*
Altrincham *p117* 0161 941 4000

Kenny, Prof P H (Dickinson Dees)
Newcastle upon Tyne *p324* 0191 279 9000

Kenny, P J (MFG Solicitors) *C1 D1 J1 F1 Zm Zd*
Telford *p409* 01952 641651

Kenny, S P (The Owen-Kenny Partnership) *B1 C1 J1 M1 N P R1 S1 Ze Zl Zk*
Chichester *p193* 01243 532777

Kenny, Mrs T A (Attwaters) *N*
Harlow *p239* 01279 638888

Kenny, Mrs V (The Owen-Kenny Partnership) *S1 W C1*
Chichester *p193* 01243 532777

Kensell, S (Allen & Overy LLP)
London E1 *p5* 020 3088 0000

Kent, Mrs A (John Collins & Partners LLP) *W*
Swansea *p405* 01792 773773

Kent, A D (Mackrell Turner Garrett) *L B1 Zc F1 O Zq*
London WC2 *p57* 020 7240 0521

Kent, A N (Simmons & Simmons) *B1 J1 C1*
London EC2 *p79* 020 7628 2020

Kent, B S (Bretherton Law) *S1 E C1 W G H L T1 Zl Zt Zc*
St Albans *p389* 01727 869293

Kent, Ms C E G (Forsters LLP) *E*
Westminster *p33* 020 7863 8333

Kent, D I P (Seddons) *C1 O Ze Zf Zk I*
Westminster *p77* 020 7725 8000

Kent, D N (Taylor Wessing) *C1 J1 T1 Zi Zb*
London EC4 *p86* 020 7300 7000

Kent, G (BAE Systems PLC)
London SW1 *p104* 01252 373232

Kent, H J (Debenhams Ottaway)
St Albans *p390* 01727 837161

Kent, J (Gill Turner Tucker) *C1 E Ze*
Maidstone *p299* 01622 759051

Kent, Mrs J D (Franklins) *S1 S2*
Abingdon *p114* 01235 553222

Kent, J M (Clayton Mott) *Zl*
Nottingham *p336* 0115 941 7422

Kent, J P B (HSBC Legal Department)
Birmingham *p449* 0121 455 2740

Kent, Ms K (Pictons Solicitors LLP) *N Zr*
Milton Keynes *p317* 01908 663511

Kent, Ms L A (K&L Gates LLP) *C1 Zc*
London EC4 *p47* 020 7648 9000

Kent, M (Linklaters LLP)
London EC2 *p54* 020 7456 2000

Kent, M A (Pembrokeshire County Council) *N*
Haverfordwest *p460* 01437 764551

Kent, N P (Holmes & Hills LLP) *K1 D1*
Braintree *p155* 01376 320456

Kent, P (Pinsent Masons LLP)
Birmingham *p141* 0121 200 1050

Kent, P D (Unisys Insurance Services Limited) *O Q B1 J1 L Zb*
Liverpool *p463* 0151 328 2918

Kent, Mrs P V (Harding Evans LLP) *P N F1 B1 Zj*
Newport *p328* 01633 244233

Kent, Ms R (Hogan Lovells International LLP)
London EC1 *p42* 020 7296 2000

Kent, R H (Wannop Fox Staffurth & Bray) *W C1 K4*
Worthing *p442* 01903 228200

Kent, Mrs S C (Kent & Co Solicitors) *S1 E L C1 A1 W B1 R1 T1 F1 Zc Zd Zj*
Norwich *p334* 01493 751351

Kentish, P B (J W Hughes & Co) *K1 D1 Q V F1 L W N*
Llandudno *p291* 01492 874774

Kenton, M C (Barlow Lyde & Gilbert LLP) *O Q Zr*
London EC3 *p10* 020 7247 2277

Kentsbeer, Ms M J (Osborne Clarke) *C1*
London EC2 *p65* 020 7105 7000

Kenward, Ms L (Clarkson Wright & Jakes Ltd) *K1*
Orpington *p341* 01689 887887

Kenworthy, Ms A P (Howells LLP) *J1*
Sheffield *p376* 0114 249 6666

Kenworthy, J (DLA Piper UK LLP)
Sheffield *p375* 0870 011 1111

Kenworthy, P R (DWF) *N Zj*
Manchester *p303* 0161 603 5000

Kenyon, Miss A (Farleys Solicitors LLP) *Q B2*
Manchester *p304* 0161 660 4254

Kenyon, C S V (Weightmans LLP) *N Q Zj*
Dartford *p207* 020 7822 1900

Kenyon, Ms J (John Hodge Solicitors) *T2 W*
Weston-super-Mare *p429* 01934 623511

Kenyon, Miss K A (Harold Stock & Co) *N*
Ashton-under-Lyne *p120* 01457 835597 / 835034

Kenyon, P (Boyes Turner) *F1 Ze*
Reading *p360* 0118 959 7711

Kenyon, R J (Field Fisher Waterhouse LLP)
London EC3 *p31* 020 7861 4000

Kenyon, S (DLA Piper UK LLP)
Leeds *p272* 0870 011 1111

Keogh, Ms K E (Barlow Lyde & Gilbert LLP)
London EC3 *p10* 020 7247 2277

Keogh, P A (Wheelers) *S1 E S2*
Aldershot *p115* 01252 316316

Keogh, Ms R (Devas Keogh James) *G H*
Peterborough *p347* 01733 340666

Keough, C (Radcliffes Le Brasseur)
Westminster *p70* 020 7222 7040

Keown, P (Hill Dickinson LLP)
Manchester *p305* 0161 817 7200

Keppe, G E (Keppe & Partners Solicitors) *E G H N O R1 R2 S1 S2 W*
Twickenham *p416* 020 8891 4488

Kerai, Miss H (IBB Solicitors) *N*
Uxbridge *p417* 0845 638 1381

Kerfoot, E L (Aaron & Partners LLP Solicitors) *O Q B1*
Chester *p190* 01244 405555

Kerfoot, Mrs H J (Lincolnshire County Council Resources - Legal Services)
Lincoln *p463* 01522 552222

Kerin, Miss L M J (Stephen Rimmer LLP) *A1 E*
Eastbourne *p216* 01323 644222

Kerin, Mrs S M (Farnfield & Nicholls) *E S1 S2*
Warminster *p421* 01985 214661

Kerley, Ms R H (Coles Miller Solicitors LLP) *R1 S1*
Broadstone *p166* 01202 694891

Kerman, A D (Kerman & Co LLP) *Q W K3*
London WC2 *p49* 020 7539 7272

Kernanec, Mrs C J (Sedgwick Kelly LLP)
Watford *p424* 01923 228311

Kernick, P A (Universal Music)
London W14 *p110* 020 8910 5000

Kernohan, Ms A (Wolferstans) *D1 K1 K4 Q S1 T1 T2 W Zo*
Plymouth *p351* 01752 663295

Kernot, Ms H M (Coupe Bradbury) *W*
Lytham *p296* 01253 736670
Blackpool *p146* 01253 622305

Kerns, P W (Cooperative Bank PLC)
Manchester *p464* 0161 832 3456
Manchester *p464* 0161 832 8686

Kernyckyj, S M (Radcliffes Le Brasseur) *N K1 M1 D1*
Leeds *p276* 0113 234 1220

Kerr, A (Aaron & Partners LLP Solicitors) *C1 O Q I U2*
Chester *p190* 01244 405555

Kerr, Miss A L (Humphries Kirk) *C1*
Poole *p352* 01202 725400

Kerr, Ms A M (Russell Jones & Walker) *N*
London WC2 *p74* 020 7657 1555

Kerr, A M (Pinsent Masons LLP) *C1 Zb*
Leeds *p276* 0113 244 5000

Kerr, Ms C (Bolt Burdon) *N*
Islington *p14* 020 7288 4700

Kerr, Ms C J (Wesley Gryk) *Zi Zg*
Lambeth *p37* 020 7401 6887

Kerr, D (Bird & Bird LLP) *C1 U1*
London EC4 *p13* 020 7415 6000

Kerr, Ms G E (Birketts LLP (Wollastons LLP))
Chelmsford *p186* 01245 211211

Kerr, I L M (Reed Smith LLP) *E*
London EC2 *p71* 020 3116 3000

Kerr, Miss J (IBB Solicitors) *W*
Uxbridge *p417* 0845 638 1381

Kerr, Ms L A (Irwin Mitchell LLP) *O*
London EC1 *p45* 0870 150 0100

Kerr, Ms N J (Pannone LLP) *N Zq*
Manchester *p308* 0161 909 3000

Kerr, Mrs N M F (SJ Berwin LLP) *J1*
London EC4 *p75* 020 7111 2222

Kerr, R C (Shentons) *S1 L E A1 R1 Zl Zd Zm*
Winchester *p434* 01962 844544

Kerr, Miss S (Wrigleys Solicitors LLP) *E*
Leeds *p278* 0113 244 6100

Kerr, Miss S A (Swinburne & Jackson LLP) *O Q N B1 L*
Gateshead *p229* 0191 477 2531 / 477 3222

Kerr, Mrs S E (Limbach Banham) *O Q L K1 J1 N Zl F1*
Royston *p368* 01763 242257

Kerr, S P (Portsmouth City Council)
Portsmouth *p469* 023 9283 4034

Kerridge, P N W (Rogers & Norton) *O Q F1 F2 Zt Zj J2 J1*
Norwich *p335* 01603 666001

Kerridge, Ms V A (Russell Jones & Walker) *N J1 Zp Zo*
London WC2 *p74* 020 7657 1555

Kerrigan, Miss A (Lee Rigby Partnership) *K1 L N*
Leyland *p283* 01772 421748

Kerrigan, A (Burton & Co LLP) *J1 N*
Lincoln *p284* 01522 523215

Kerrigan, Mrs J (Lee Rigby Partnership) *B1 F1 J1 L M1 P R1 S1 W C1*
Leyland *p283* 01772 421748

Kerrigan, J E (DLA Piper UK LLP)
Manchester *p303* 0870 011 1111

Kerrigan, J M D (Challinors) *K1 D1*
Birmingham *p136* 0121 212 9393

Kerrigan, Ms M A (Chennells) *K3 K1 W*
Westcliff-on-Sea *p428* 01702 349971 / 352195

Kerrigan, S (Henrys Solicitors Ltd)
Stockport *p395* 0161 477 8558

Kerrigan, S P (Boodle Hatfield) *L E*
Westminster *p14* 020 7629 7411

Kerry, A (Meldrum Young Solicitors) *G H B2*
Watford *p423* 01923 231598

Kerry, C V (Chester City Council)
Chester *p454* 01244 324324

Kerry, D G (Attwaters) *Zr*
Harlow *p239* 01279 638888

Kerry, R (Hatchers Solicitors LLP)
Shrewsbury *p379* 01743 248545

Kersh, D A (Shaw Graham Kersh)
London W1 *p78* 020 7734 9700

See p634 for the Key to Work Categories

Kershaw, Mrs A (Kennedys) *B1 C1 N Q J1 Zc Zj Zk Zv*
Manchester *p306* 0161 829 2599

Kershaw, A J (Barlow Lyde & Gilbert LLP) *Zj*
London EC3 *p10*. 020 7247 2277

Kershaw, A J (West Sussex County Council)
Chichester *p455* 01243 777100

Kershaw, Ms C (Reynolds Porter Chamberlain LLP)
London E1 *p71* 020 3060 6000

Kershaw, D P (Godloves) *N*
Leeds *p273* 0113 225 8811

Kershaw, D R (Ware & Kay LLP) *S1*
York *p445* 01904 716000

Kershaw, G P (Gateley LLP) *O Zj A3 Q*
London EC4 *p35*. 020 7653 1600

Kershaw, Ms H (Hammond Bale) *E S2 S1 Ze W*
London W1 *p38* 020 7499 7624

Kershaw, Ms H (Pannone LLP) *N J1 J2*
Manchester *p308* 0161 909 3000

Kershaw, I G F (Quality Solicitors Clarke & Son) *W J1 J2 O Q N*
Basingstoke *p127* 01256 320555

Kershaw, P J (Addleshaw Goddard)
Manchester *p300* 0161 934 6000

Kershaw, R (Hewitts) *W S1 S2 L E*
Bishop Auckland *p144* 01388 604691

Kershaw, R C (Hunters) *N Q K1*
London WC2 *p44* 020 7412 0050

Kershaw, Miss R L (Barlow Robbins LLP) *J1*
Guildford *p235*. 01483 562901

Kerslake, Mrs R J (Akermans) *K1 S1 W*
Storrington *p399* 01903 745353

Kerslake, Miss S J (Whitelock & Storr)
London WC1 *p91* 020 7405 3913

Kertland-Peake, Mrs G (Borough of Telford & Wrekin)
Telford *p473* 01952 380000

Keshvari, Ms S (Edward Fail Bradshaw & Waterson) *G H B2*
London EC3 *p30*. 020 7790 4032

Kesic, E (Angel & Co) *N Q J1 L*
Coventry *p200*. 024 7625 2211

Kessler, M (Wannop Fox Staffurth & Bray) *G H K1 Zl*
Chichester *p193* 01243 778844

Kesteven, Ms M A (Gateshead Metropolitan Borough Council) *K1 G H D1 J1 S1 P W*
Gateshead *p458*. 0191 433 3000

Keswick, Ms L (Henderson Global Investors)
London EC2 *p106* 020 7818 1818

Ketchley, Mrs A (The Endeavour Partnership LLP)
Stockton-on-Tees *p397* . . . 01642 610300

Ketley, M (Olswang LLP) *C1 Zf Ze*
London WC1 *p64* 020 7067 3000

Ketley, M (Wiggin LLP) *Zf*
Cheltenham *p189* 01242 224114

Ketteley, J (Ashurst LLP)
London EC2 *p7* 020 7638 1111

Ketteley, S (Ashurst LLP)
London EC2 *p7* 020 7638 1111

Kettle, G I M (Higgs & Sons) *W X E*
Brierley Hill *p158*. 0845 111 5050
Kidderminster *p265* 01562 820181

Kettle, Miss J R (Birmingham City Council Legal & Democratic Services)
Birmingham *p449* 0121 303 2066

Kettle, P J (DBL Talbots LLP) *E*
Wolverhampton *p437* 01902 427561

Kettle, Ms S (Ashurst LLP)
London EC2 *p7* 020 7638 1111

Kettle, S T (Bridgeman Kettle) *S2 K3 J1 K1 Q S1 W*
Bletchley *p147*. 01908 376321

Kettle, Miss T (Kennedys)
London EC3 *p49*. 020 7667 9667

Keuls, P (Trowers & Hamlins)
London EC3 *p88*. 020 7423 8000

Keuls, P H (Trowers & Hamlins) *L E S1 Zh*
Exeter *p222* 01392 217466

Keville, A (Ince & Co Services Ltd)
London E1 *p44* 020 7481 0010

Kew, G A (Hewetts) *E C1 J1 N O K1 I*
Reading *p361* 0118 957 5337

Kew, S E (Cunningtons) *S1 E W L*
Braintree *p155*. 01376 326868

Key, Miss A M (DAC Beachcroft) *E S2 R2 L O*
Manchester *p303* 0161 934 3000

Key, C A (Christopher Key & Co)
Boscastle *p150* 01840 250200

Key, Miss J (Lincolnshire County Council Resources - Legal Services)
Lincoln *p463*. 01522 552222

Key, M (Glaisyers Solicitors LLP) *O B1 L*
Manchester *p304* 0161 832 4666

Key, Miss S J S V (Overburys & Raymond Thompson) *D1 D2 K1 K3*
Norwich *p335* 01603 610481

Keyho, Miss K J D (Vincent & Co) *K1 S1 W*
Wigan *p432* 01942 241421
Wigan *p432* 01257 425121

Keyte, Mrs R (Langley Wellington) *K1 K3*
Gloucester *p230*. 01452 521286

Keyworth, R M (Wilkinson & Butler) *E S2 A1 C1 P T1 S1 W*
St Neots *p392* 01480 219229

Khaira, Mrs H K (Nichols Marcy Dawson) *W*
Walton-on-Thames *p420*. . . 01932 219500

Khaira, Miss P (Parry Carver)
Wellington *p425* 01952 641291

Khaitan, A (Bower Cotton Khaitan) *B1 C1 S2 E U1 F1 F2 Ze J1 O Zi Q N S1 T2*
London EC4 *p15*. 020 7353 1313

Khaitan, S (ALMT Legal)
London EC3 *p3* 020 7645 9190

Khak, B S (Dale & Newbery LLP) *N*
Staines *p393*. 01784 464491

Khakhar, R R (Khakhar & Co)
Ilford *p260*. 020 8478 9881

Khalaf, Mrs A (Khalaf & Co)
Lowestoft *p294* 0845 601 9193

Khaled, M S U (Corbin & Hassan) *Zi*
London EC3 *p22*. 020 7247 6518

Khalid, G (Greenwoods) *B1 Zc E Zj Q*
London WC1 *p37* 020 7323 4632

Khalid, Ms T (George Davies Solicitors LLP) *W*
Manchester *p303* 0161 236 8992

Khalid, Miss Z (GPB Solicitors LLP)
Stratford-upon-Avon *p400* . . 01789 261131

Khalifa, Mrs S (Blackburn with Darwen Borough Council)
Blackburn *p450* 01254 585585

Khalil, Mrs N (Ward & Rider Limited) *N*
Coventry *p201* 024 7655 5400

Khalil, O (E E F South)
Hook *p461*. 01256 763969

Khalil, S (BK Solicitors) *N S1 W E Q O*
Birmingham *p135* 0121 440 1881

Khaliq, Ms A (Freeth Cartwright LLP) *E*
Nottingham *p337*. 0115 936 9369

Khaliq, Miss T (Shepherd Harris & Co) *Q N K1 B1 F1 L*
Enfield *p219*. 020 8363 8341

Khallil, M N (Liddys Solicitors)
Wakefield *p418* 01924 780753

Khamisa, Ms N (Southall Rights Ltd)
Southall *p472* 020 8571 4920

Khamma, S (Reynolds Porter Chamberlain LLP)
London E1 *p71* 020 3060 6000

Khan, A (Crowell & Moring) *C1 C2 Q I*
London EC4 *p23*. 020 7413 0011

Khan, A (Blackwells Solicitors) *N*
Keighley *p263* 01535 600005

Khan, Mrs A (Holmes & Hills LLP) *S1*
Braintree *p155*. 01376 320456

Khan, A (Sacker & Partners LLP) *Zo Zq O*
London EC2 *p76*. 020 7329 6699

Khan, A (M & K Solicitors) *K1 Zi Q*
Luton *p295* 01582 732503

Khan, A (Aurangzeb Khan Solicitors) *D2 B1 Zi O Q Zq S1*
Bradford *p153* 01274 548549

Khan, A A (Squire Sanders (UK) LLP) *O Q*
London EC2 *p81*. 020 7655 1000

Khan, A A (Thompson & Co)
Wandsworth *p87*. 020 8767 5005

Khan, A A (Linder Myers Solicitors) *B2 G H J2 N Q*
Manchester *p307* 0844 984 6400

Khan, Ms E (Walker Morris) *S2 R2*
Leeds *p277* 0113 283 2500

Khan, F (Clifford Chance)
London E14 *p20*. 020 7006 1000

Khan, F A (Taylor Wessing)
London EC4 *p86*. 020 7300 7000

Khan, H (Douglass Simon)
Brentford *p156*. 020 8560 3888

Khan, Mrs L (Loosemores) *N*
Cardiff *p179* 029 2022 4433

Khan, M (Mian & Co)
Birmingham *p140* 0121 684 8000

Khan, Miss M (Ford Motor Company Ltd) *E*
Brentwood *p451* 01277 253000

Khan, M (Gateley LLP) *Zh L Q P N Zu*
Birmingham *p138* 0121 234 0000

Khan, M A (Mellor & Jackson)
Oldham *p340* 0161 624 7081

Khan, M N (Abbott Forbes Solicitors) *X J1 Zi G H N K1*
Oxford *p342* 01865 794855

Khan, M O (Khans) *K3 K1 W Zi*
Ilford *p260*. 020 8553 5995

Khan, M S (Khan Solicitors) *D1 E F1 G H J1 K1 L N Q*
Bradford *p154* 01274 301999

Khan, M Z Z (A-Z Law Solicitors) *D1 S2 G K3 J1 K1 L Zg Zi Q S1 W*
Wandsworth *p3* 020 8355 0830

Khan, N (Rochford District Council)
Rochford *p470*. 01702 546366

Khan, N A (Dorsey & Whitney) *E*
London EC2 *p27*. 020 7588 0800

Khan, R B (Moorhead James LLP) *B1*
London EC4 *p61*. 020 7831 8888

Khan, S (Morgan Cole) *G H P*
Oxford *p344* 01865 262600

Khan, Miss S (SFN Solicitors) *G H*
Burnley *p169* 01282 421284

Khan, S (Trowers & Hamlins)
London EC3 *p88*. 020 7423 8000

Khan, S A (Solicitors Direct) *S1 S2 Zi*
Bradford *p155* 01274 776000

Khan, S A (Gordons LLP)
Leeds *p273* 0113 227 0100

Khan, S A (Khan & Co)
Wolverhampton *p438* 01902 424477

Khan, S D (Khans) *G K1 N Q S1 V W Zg Zi*
Ilford *p260*. 020 8553 5995

Khan, Miss Y (Svedberg Law) *S1 W S2 E L*
London SW1 *p84* 020 7368 7000

Khan, Z (Napthens LLP) *N*
Chorley *p194* 0845 260 2111

Khan Hussain, Mrs S (CMHT Solicitors) *F1 J1 L O Q N*
Walsall *p420*. 01922 646400

Khan-Hussain, A (Coltman Warner Cranston LLP)
Coventry *p200*. 024 7662 7262

Khanam, L (Wosskow Brown) *K1 N Q Zr*
Sheffield *p377* 0114 256 1560

Khandhia, N K (BTMK Solicitors LLP) *F1 L Q*
Southend-on-Sea *p387* . . . 01702 339222

Khandke, S (Couchmans LLP)
London WC1 *p23* 020 7611 9660

Khangura, K (Pinsent Masons LLP) *E L*
London EC2 *p67*. 020 7418 7000

Khanna, Mrs K (Wycombe District Council)
High Wycombe *p461*. 01494 461002

Khanna, Ms S (Lewis Silkin LLP) *J1*
London EC4 *p53*. 020 7074 8000

Khanna, S (TWM Solicitors LLP)
Guildford *p237*. 01483 752700

Khanna, S (The Ringrose Law Group - Richard Harwood) *G H Zl Zm*
Lincoln *p285*. 01522 814700

Khanna, Ms T (Ingrams) *S1*
York *p445* 01904 520600

Khanzada, M Q (Barker Gillette) *N O Q B1*
London W1 *p9*. 020 7636 0555

Kharbanda, Miss A (Blaser Mills) *Q N O*
Staines *p393*. 01784 462511

Kharbanda, S K (David Shine & Kharbanda) *G K1 S1 D1 E Zm Zi*
Southall *p384* . .020 8571 6001 / 8571 6002

Kharia, J S (Abbott Lloyd Howorth) *S2 S1*
Maidenhead *p298* 01628 798800

Khatkar, Miss B K (Young & Lee) *K1 D1 D2 Zg Zh Zl Zv*
Birmingham *p143* 0121 633 3233

Khatoon, Miss U (Nottinghamshire County Council Legal Services Division)
West Bridgford *p475*. 0115 977 3478

Khattak, S A (Khattak Solicitors)
Whitefield *p430* 0161 796 5800

Khatter, G S (Aston Bond LLP)
Slough *p381*. 01753 486777

Khatun, Ms M (Miller Evans & Co) *S2 R1 S1 W Q*
London EC3 *p60*. 020 7987 2515

Khatun, Z (Keppe & Partners Solicitors) *G H*
Twickenham *p416* 020 8891 4488

Khawaja, I (Rollingsons)
London EC1 *p73*. 020 7611 4848

Khehar, Miss G (Clifford Chance)
London E14 *p20*. 020 7006 1000

Khela, Mrs P (Aitken Associates) *K1 D1 V K3*
Islington *p4* 020 7700 6006

Khetia, B (Premier Solicitors)
Bedford *p130* 01234 358080

Kho, Ms A (Jones Day) *Zb*
London EC4 *p46*. 020 7039 5959

Khodabocus, S I (Pardoes) *K1 D1 K3 Q L Zo*
Bridgwater *p158* 01278 457891

Khosla, Miss M (Painters) *K1 D2 D1 K3*
Kidderminster *p266* 01562 822295

Khroud, Miss A (Kent County Council)
Maidstone *p464* 01622 694320

Khullar, A K (Taylor Phillips)
Hayes *p245* 020 8561 7367

Khunkhuna, Mrs D (OMW Solicitors) *D1 D2 G H K1 W*
Burton-on-Trent *p170*01283 563401 / 530333

Khurana, Miss D (Wiggin LLP) *Zf*
Cheltenham *p189* 01242 224114

Khurshid, R (E&K Solicitors & Estate Agents) *E S1 W S2 G*
Manchester *p304* 0161 256 3915

Khushal, K (Stuart Miller & Co)
Haringey *p61* 020 8888 5225

Khushal, K (J D Spicer & Co)
London NW6 *p81* 020 7625 5590

Kidby, R J (Hogan Lovells International LLP)
London EC1 *p42*. 020 7296 2000

Kidd, A (Silverman Sherliker LLP) *W T2 K4*
London EC2 *p78*. 020 7749 2700

Kidd, Miss A (Hegarty LLP) *C1 Ze Zl C2*
Peterborough *p347* 01733 346333

Kidd, C J (Ince & Co Services Ltd)
London E1 *p44* 020 7481 0010

Kidd, C M (Montague Lambert & Co) *C1 E K1 L S1 W Zc Zh Zi*
Ealing *p61*. 020 8997 2288

Kidd, D (Webster Dixon LLP) *Q O B1 Zq F2*
London EC1 *p90*. 020 7353 8300

Kidd, Miss E S (Eccles Heddon) *K1 S1 W D1 F1 J1 D2 Zl M3 K2*
Ripon *p365* 01765 601717

Kidd, G (Pothecary Witham Weld) *C1 T1 W Zd*
Westminster *p69*. 020 7821 8211

Kidd, Mrs H (Aaron & Partners LLP Solicitors) *J1 Zp*
Chester *p190* 01244 405555

Kidd, Miss H M (Dudley Metropolitan Borough Council) *Q J1 O N*
Dudley *p457*. 01384 815326
Scarborough *p372*. 01723 352125

Kidd, Mrs L (Hillyer McKeown LLP) *J1*
Chester *p190* 01244 318131

Kidd, P G (Hartley Thomas & Wright) *K1 G H K2 K3 Zl*
Rochdale *p365*. 01706 644118

Kidd, P S (Penningtons)
London EC2 *p66*. 020 7457 3000

Kidd, R A (Gray & Co) *Zf C1 O W Ze Zw B1*
Manchester *p305* 0161 237 3360

Kidd, Mrs S (Carr & Co) *G H*
Huddersfield *p255* 01484 467860

Kiddle Morris, C J (Allianz Insurance PLC)
Guildford *p459*. 01483 552730

Kiddle, A V (DFA Law LLP) *D1 K1 K2 Zl*
Northampton *p331*. 01604 609560

Kiddle-Morris, Mrs S E (Hood Vores & Allwood) *S1 S2 A1 E R1 R2*
Dereham *p209*. 01362 692424

Kidley, Miss R A (Unilever PLC) *J1 Zp*
London EC4 *p110* 020 7822 5252

Kidman, Miss L T (Lambe Corner) *S1 F1 L W E Zh*
Hereford *p248* 01432 355301

Kidner, E G (Risdon Hosegood) *A1 J1 R1 S1 S2 W*
Wiveliscombe *p436* 01984 623203

Kidson, N D L (Kidson Bray & Lawson) *C1 E S1 J1 W L T2*
London SE11 *p49* 020 7582 0111

Kidwell, Ms M L (Mayer Brown International LLP) *M2 O A1 N*
London EC2 *p59*. 020 3130 3000

Kidwell, N M I (Mincoffs Solicitors LLP)
Newcastle upon Tyne *p325* . 0191 281 6151

Kiely, G R (Blaser Mills) *W T2*
Rickmansworth *p364*. 01923 776211

Kiely, M P (LG Lawyers) *E S2*
London SE1 *p50*. 020 7379 0000

Kieran, J A (KieranClarkeGreen) *N Zm*
Chesterfield *p192* 01246 211006

Kieran, J P (Kieran & Co) *G H J1 K1 D1 M1 P V W*
Worcester *p440* 01905 28635

Kiernan, P (Crowell & Moring) *G*
London EC4 *p23*. 020 7413 0011

Kiff, S (Jones Day) *C1*
London EC4 *p46*. 020 7039 5959

Kigonya, Mrs M (Southampton City Council)
Southampton *p472*. 023 8022 3855

Kikkine, Miss N A (Plexus Law (A Trading Name of Parabis Law LLP)) *N*
Evesham *p220*. 01386 769160

Kilbane, M E (Juliet Bellis & Co) *O Q Zq L*
Uckfield *p416* 01825 750811
Stevenage *p395* 01438 312211

Kilbee, M P (Lloyds TSB Asset Finance Division Ltd)
Southampton *p450*. 01489 776880

Kilbey, I C (Eastgate Assistance Ltd)
Colchester *p455* 0870 523 4500

Kilbey, J M (West Midlands Police Authority)
Birmingham *p450* 0121 626 5143

Kilbourne, Mrs S H (Pillsbury Winthrop Shaw Pittman LLP) *I U2 C1 Ze*
London EC2 *p67*. 020 7847 9500

Kilburn, B (Marshalls)
Woking *p437*. 01483 730531
Godalming *p231* 01483 416101

Kilby, A J (Andrew J Kilby) *S1 P E A1 M1 B1 W Zc*
Gravesend *p233*. 01474 355758

Kilby, P (Bennett Griffin) *S1*
Rustington *p369* 01903 777690

Kilby, Ms V L (Russell-Cooke LLP) *S1 S2*
London SW15 *p74*. 020 8789 9111

Kilcoyne, B M G (Lewis Silkin LLP) *Zh O L A3 E R2 B1 Zc P*
London EC4 *p53*. 020 7074 8000

Kilcoyne, Miss E A (Lewis Silkin LLP) *J1*
London EC4 *p53*. 020 7074 8000

Kilduff, D J (Walker Morris) *Zu E P Zg*
Leeds *p277* 0113 283 2500

Kilgallon, N (Blackpool Pleasure Beach Group)
Blackpool *p450* 01253 341033

Kilgannon, M J (Downs)
Dorking *p212* 01306 880110

Kilgour, Ms E M (Davies & Partners) *E S2 R2*
Almondsbury *p115*. 01454 619619

Kilgour, R (Speechly Bircham LLP) *E R2*
London EC4 *p81*. 020 7427 6400

Kilgour, S M (Reynolds Porter Chamberlain LLP) *O Zb Zj Zq*
London E1 *p71* 020 3060 6000

Kilka, Ms S S (Russell Jones & Walker)
London WC2 *p74* 020 7657 1555

Killen, P J (Osborne Clarke) *R2 J1*
Bristol *p164* 0117 917 3000

Killen, P J (Cobleys LLP) *G H*
Liverpool *p287*. 0151 242 9000

Killen, S L (DWFM Beckman) *O N E B1 K1 B2 Zl Zk*
Westminster *p25*. 020 7872 0023

Killer, R (Dickinson Manser) *G H K1 Q*
Poole *p352* 01202 673071

Killey, Miss D M (Inghams) *S1 W E K1 J1 N Q C1 D1 T2 Zl Zq*
Thornton Cleveleys *p411*. . . 01253 824111

Killick, Mrs K (Donnelly McArdle Adamson) *N O Q*
Darlington *p206* 01325 482299

Killick, S (Dawnay Day International Limited)
London SW1 *p105*. 020 7861 0989

Killin, J R (Barlow Lyde & Gilbert LLP)
London EC3 *p10*. 020 7247 2277

Killin, M C A (Fishers) *C1 O J1 C2 Ze B1 P Q Zq*
Ashby-de-la-Zouch *p118*. . . 01530 412167

Killington, J R (Brown & Emery) *S1 G H W*
Watford *p423* 01923 225255

Killip, Miss J A (Davenport Lyons) *O B1 B2 Zb Q*
London W1 *p25* 020 7468 2600

Killip, Ms S (Badhams Law (A Trading Name of Parabis Law LLP))
Croydon *p204* 0844 245 4000

Killough, Miss L J (Henriques Griffiths) *J1*
Bristol *p163* 0117 909 4000

6

Kilmister, J W (Pattinson & Brewer) *Q N*
London WC1 *p66* 020 7400 5100

Kilner, D (Pearson Fielding Polson) *G H Zl*
Liverpool *p290* 0151 236 3636

Kilner, J K (Hay & Kilner) *S1 W E T1 C1 K1 L R1 B1 P Zd Zm Zo*
Newcastle upon Tyne *p325* 0191 232 8345

Kilner, M A (Maples Teesdale LLP) *O Q A3 S2 E L R1 Zq F1 C3 R2*
London EC2 *p58* 020 7600 3800

Kilner, Mrs M J (William Sturges & Co) *S1 C1 F1 C2 J1 Ze F2 Zb U2*
Westminster *p84* 020 7873 1000

Kilpatrick, B (Addleshaw Goddard)
London EC1 *p4* 020 7606 8855

Kilpatrick, J C (Singleton Winn McDermott Solicitors) *G H D1 K1 Zl*
Newcastle upon Tyne *p326* 0191 265 8817

Kilpatrick, R M (Kilpatrick & Co) *N P C1 M1*
Burnham *p168* 07834 258605

Kilroy, C T (Kilroys) *Q N O C1 E S1 S2 W Zk*
Birmingham *p139* 0121 270 1002

Kilshaw, B D (Hamlins LLP) *E S2*
London W1 *p38* 020 7355 6000

Kilshaw, P N (EJ Winter & Son) *S1 S2 W E*
Reading *p361* 0118 957 4424

Kilvert, M J (Rees Page) *Q O C1 E S1 N S2*
Wolverhampton *p438* 01902 577777

Kilvington, Ms A (Pinsent Masons LLP) *O Q Zc*
London EC2 *p67* 020 7418 7000

Kilvington, G (Harrowells)
York *p444* 01904 690111

Kilvington, W A S (Fell Kilvington & Co) *A1 W R1 S1 L T1 Zl*
Kirkby Stephen *p268* 01768 371495

Kim, M (DLA Piper UK LLP) *O A3 M2 Za*
London EC2 *p24* 0870 011 1111

Kimbell, Mrs H (The College of Law Guildford)
Guildford *p459* 01483 460200

Kimbell, S E (Kimbells LLP) *C1 C2*
Milton Keynes *p317* 01908 668555

Kimberley, M J (The Smith Partnership) *G H K1*
Stoke-on-Trent *p398* 01782 324454

Kimberley, P R (Young & Lee) *E S1 C1 R1 L K1 Zb*
Birmingham *p143* 0121 633 3233

Kimble, A (Bond Pearce LLP) *C1*
Southampton *p385* 0845 415 0000

Kime, Miss L (O'Neill Patient) *S1*
Stockport *p396* 0161 483 8555

Kincaid, N J (Hadaway & Hadaway) *D1 D2 G H K1 Zl Zm*
North Shields *p330* 0191 257 0382

Kinch, Mrs C (Stewarts Law LLP) *K1*
London EC4 *p83* 020 7822 8000

Kinch, D P (Edwin Coe LLP) *C1 C2 M1 Zb M2*
London WC2 *p29* 020 7691 4000

Kinch, E (Lees Solicitors LLP) *S1 S2 E C1 F1*
Birkenhead *p134* 0151 647 9381

Kinchin, G (Walker Lahive)
Plymouth *p350* 01752 551722

Kinchin-Smith, D (Cartwright King)
Nottingham *p336* 0115 958 7444

Kinder, Miss A M (Oglethorpe Sturton & Gillibrand) *L S1 E S2 R2*
Lancaster *p270* 01524 846846

Kinder, Mrs S (Dexter Montague LLP) *O N B1 Q*
Reading *p360* 0118 939 3999

King, A A (Travers Smith LLP) *P N J1 L B1 C1 Zi Zb*
London EC1 *p87* 020 7295 3000

King, A B (Anthony King & Co) *D1 D2 K1 E S2 V*
Basildon *p126* 01268 240400

King, A J (Lennons) *Q N Zr Zq*
Chesham *p189* 01494 773377

King, A J (Rawlison Butler LLP) *E R1 R2*
Crawley *p202* 01293 527744

King, A J T (Foster & Partners) *K1 M1 P V D1 J1*
Bristol *p162* 0117 961 5300

King, A M H (Stone King LLP) *Zd*
Bath *p128* 01225 337599

King, A R G (Tozers) *C1 W T1 A1 Zd Zx*
Teignmouth *p409* 01626 772376

King, Ms B (Philcox Gray & Co) *D1 D2 K1*
London SE15 *p67* 020 7703 2285

King, C (Osborne Clarke) *W*
London EC2 *p65* 020 7105 7000

King, C (Withers LLP)
London EC4 *p92* 020 7597 6000

King, Ms C (Ashurst LLP)
London EC2 *p7* 020 7638 1111

King, C A (Eden & Co) *M1 C1 G S1 K1 P N*
Manchester *p304* 0161 237 1116

King, Mrs C A (ASB Law) *E R2 S1 A1 S2*
Maidstone *p298* 01622 656500
Maidstone *p299* 01622 698000
Tenterden *p410* 01580 765722

King, Mrs C E (Hugh James) *S1 E Zh R2 S2*
Cardiff *p179* 029 2022 4871

King, Miss C F (Boodle Hatfield) *E S1 S2 R2*
Westminster *p14* 020 7629 7411

King, Miss C M (Shulmans) *E S2 R2*
Leeds *p276* 0113 245 2833

King, Ms C P (Field Fisher Waterhouse LLP)
London EC3 *p31* 020 7861 4000

King, Mrs D (Farleys Solicitors LLP) *Zb T1 S2 E F2 Ze C1*
Blackburn *p145* 01254 367856

King, D J (Forbes) *F1 G H J1 M1 P*
Blackburn *p145* 01254 580000

King, Miss D J (DJK Solicitors) *S1 S2 W L Zl*
Waltham Abbey *p420* 01992 718880

King, D R (MLM Cartwright) *Zc S2 E U1 L R1 R2 S1 A1*
Cardiff *p179* 029 2046 2562

King, D T (Turners) *K1 N Q S1 E L*
Cross Hills *p204* 01535 634149

King, Mrs E (Squire Sanders (UK) LLP)
Birmingham *p142* 0121 222 3000

King, Miss E M (Marsons Solicitors LLP) *N Zq*
Bromley *p166* 020 8313 1300

King, G M (Reynolds Parry-Jones) *E C1 S1 W S2 C2*
High Wycombe *p250* 01494 525941

King, Miss H J (Hempsons) *B2 Q Zk*
Westminster *p40* 020 7839 0278

King, Mrs J (Atherton Godfrey) *Zr N*
Doncaster *p211* 01302 320621

King, Mrs J (Gaynham King & Mellor) *D1 K1 S1 L V K3 D2*
Appleby *p118* 01768 351422
Penrith *p346* 01768 864651

King, Miss J A (Abbott & Co) *K1 L D1 F1 S1 Q N W*
Walkden *p419* 0161 799 8003

King, J D (Osborne Clarke) *C1*
London EC2 *p65* 020 7105 7000

King, J J (Forshaws Davies Ridgway LLP) *O L B1 Q C1 J1 Zc*
Warrington *p422* 01925 230000

King, Miss J M (Goodman King) *K1 W S1 E*
Tavistock *p408* 01822 615510

King, J P (Oxford City Council) *L V Q Zg S1*
Oxford *p468* 01865 249811

King, J R (Pictons Solicitors LLP) *W*
Hemel Hempstead *p247* 01442 242441

King, J W M (Beetenson & Gibbon) *C1 E A1 B1 N O R1 H T1 L Zi Zf Zc*
Grimsby *p235* 01472 240251

King, Ms L (The College of Law)
London WC1 *p105* 0800 289997

King, Ms L (John Collins & Partners LLP) *S1*
Swansea *p405* 01792 773773

King, Mrs L S (Dale & Newbery LLP) *W*
Staines *p393* 01784 464491

King, Mrs M (Macnamara King Solicitors)
Warwick *p422* 01926 499889

King, M A R (Fullers) *C1 E K1 A1 S1 T1 W Zj*
Rugby *p368* 01788 542288

King, Miss N (Owen White) *Q L Zh*
Slough *p382* 01753 876800

King, Mrs N (Large & Gibson) *S1*
Southsea *p388* 023 9229 6296

King, Mrs N A (Hughes & Company) *K3 K1 Zr N*
Tring *p413* 01442 891717

King, Ms P (King Solicitors) *S2 E Zi L Q W*
Southall *p384* 020 8571 2239

King, P D S (Shearman & Sterling LLP) *C2*
London EC2 *p78* 020 7655 5000

King, Ms P E (City of Bradford Metropolitan District Council)
Bradford *p451* 01274 752236

King, P G (Hammon Oakley) *Q N S1 W O E C1 J1 Zk Zl*
Coventry *p200* 024 7644 8585

King, Mrs P H (Beaumonts) *W*
Hereford *p247* 01432 352345

King, Miss P I (Ormerods) *K1 X*
Croydon *p205* 020 8686 5000

King, P J (Roebucks) *G H*
Blackburn *p145* 01254 274000

King, P J (Nockolds) *W T2 Zd*
Bishop's Stortford *p144* 01279 755777

King, P N A (Hugh Jones & Co) *S1 E C1 W N L M1 G S2 Zl*
London N3 *p43* 020 8346 2236

King, P N E (Thompsons (formerly Robin/Brian Thompson & Partners)) *N J1 Zo*
Plymouth *p350* 01752 675810

King, Mrs R (Forrester & Forrester) *S1 W*
Chippenham *p193* 01249 444300

King, R C (Ashurst LLP) *A3 Zc Zj Zn*
London EC2 *p7* 020 7638 1111

King, R E (Rodney King & Partners) *G H W*
Bristol *p163* 0117 926 5201

King, R J (Kitson & Trotman) *N Q K1 O F1 Zf Zl Zq Zr*
Bridport *p158* 01308 427436
Lyme Regis *p296* 01297 442580

King, R M (Taylor & Emmet LLP) *W T2*
Sheffield *p377* 0114 218 4000

King, R T (Trowers & Hamlins) *O Q Zc*
London EC3 *p88* 020 7423 8000

King, R W M (Stevens & Bolton) *O Q M1 B1 C1 F1 K1 Zc Zb Zk*
Guildford *p237* 01483 302264

King, S (Mills & Reeve) *N Zq Zm*
Norwich *p335* 01603 660155

King, S (Veale Wasbrough Vizards) *E L R2 S2*
Bristol *p165* 0117 925 2020

King, Mrs S (Wrigleys Solicitors LLP) *J1 Zp*
Leeds *p278* 0113 244 6100

King, S C (Pickerings LLP) *J1 O Zq Zt K4 A3*
Tamworth *p407* 01827 317070

King, Miss S E (Steed & Steed LLP) *K3 K1*
Braintree *p155* 01376 552828

King, S G (LG Lawyers)
London SE1 *p50* 020 7379 0000

King, S R J (Elliot Mather LLP) *G H K1*
Mansfield *p311* 01623 655666

King, T (Edwards Duthie) *G H*
London E13 *p29* 020 8514 9000

King, T P (Vingoe Lloyd) *D1 K1 L N O D2 Q Zq*
Helston *p246* 01326 555800

King, V (Pinsent Masons LLP) *C1*
Leeds *p276* 0113 244 5000

King, Miss V A (Hempsons) *N Zr*
Manchester *p305* 0161 228 0011

King, Ms V C (Grant Saw Solicitors LLP) *S1*
Greenwich *p36* 020 8858 6971

King, Mrs V I (The Crown Estate Office)
London W15 *p105* 020 7851 5168

King, Mrs V M (Fullers) *G H K3 J1 K1 B2*
Rugby *p368* 01788 542288

King-Christopher, A (Speechly Bircham LLP) *T1*
London EC4 *p81* 020 7427 6400

King-Farlow, C (Pemberton Greenish LLP) *T2 W*
London SW3 *p66* 020 7591 3333

King-Farlow, D (Pritchard Englefield) *W T1 Zd Zo*
London EC2 *p69* 020 7972 9720

Kingaby, Mrs E J (Sutton Magistrates' Court)
Wallington *p475* 020 8770 5950

Kingdon, Miss D J (Osborne Clarke) *J1 Zg*
Reading *p361* 0118 925 2000

Kingdon, J F (Crown Prosecution Service Dorset)
Bournemouth *p450* 01202 498700

Kingham, D C (Morrisons Solicitors LLP) *W T1 T2 Zd*
Redhill *p362* 01737 854500

Kingham, Mrs K (Oldhams Solicitors & Advocates) *K1 D1*
Baldock *p121* 01462 895444

Kingham, L (Sandwell Metropolitan Borough Council)
Oldbury *p468* 0121 569 2200

Kingham-Slater, Ms J M (Kirklees Metropolitan Borough Council)
Huddersfield *p461* 01484 221421

Kingman, M D (Toller Beattie LLP) *N Zr*
Barnstaple *p125* 01271 341000

Kings, Ms H S (Dawson Cornwell) *K1 D1*
London WC1 *p26* 020 7242 2556

Kings, J C (Lester Aldridge LLP) *N O Q*
London WC2 *p53* 0844 967 0785

Kings, T (Tollers LLP)
Northampton *p332* 01604 258558

Kings, T R (Tollers LLP) *F1 N O B1 Zk*
Kettering *p265* 01536 520111

Kingsbury, Miss E V S A (Manches LLP) *O Q Zq B1*
London WC2 *p58* 020 7404 4433

Kingsbury, Mrs S A (Cameron Jones Hussell & Howe) *K1 N L*
Port Talbot *p353* 01639 885261

Kingsbury, Mrs T (Ashton KCJ) *D1 K1*
Ipswich *p262* 01473 232425

Kingsbury, W (Morgan Clarke Solicitors) *N*
Cirencester *p195* 01285 650066

Kingsford, N M (Dutton Gregory) *Ze S1 E W A1 C1 J1 L P R1 B1 Zc Zj Zl*
Winchester *p433* 01962 844333

Kingsland, Ms J (Crutes) *K1 N*
Newcastle upon Tyne *p324* 0191 233 9700

Kingsley, C (Kingsley Brookes) *G H*
Huddersfield *p256* 01484 302800

Kingsley, Ms J M (Pannone LLP) *S1*
Manchester *p308* 0161 909 3000

Kingsley, Mrs L (Bone & Payne LLP) *K1 K3 J1*
Llandudno *p291* 01492 876354

Kingsley, N P (Sprake & Kingsley) *B1 D1 E F1 J1 K1 N O Q R1 Zc Zv*
Bungay *p168* 01986 892721

Kingsley, P (Capsticks Solicitors LLP) *Zr N*
London SW19 *p18* 020 8780 2211

Kingsley, S A (Thurloe & Lyndhurst LLP) *S2 E R1*
London WC2 *p87* 0333 123 2255

Kingsley-Smith, Ms E (Kingsley Smith Solicitors LLP) *W S1 K4*
Chatham *p185* 01634 811118

Kingsley-Smith, N M (Kingsley Smith Solicitors LLP) *R1 R2 S2 E C1*
Chatham *p185* 01634 811118

Kingsman, Ms A (Greenwoods) *G*
Milton Keynes *p317* 01908 298200

Kingston, A M (Fulchers) *K1 K3 K2 N Q W*
Woking *p436* 01483 885522

Kingston, Ms K (Scott Rees & Co) *N Q*
Skelmersdale *p381* 01695 722222

Kingston, S (Irwin Mitchell LLP) *N*
Sheffield *p376* 0870 150 0100

Kingston, S T (Farrer & Co LLP) *E S1 S2 L*
London WC2 *p31* 020 3375 7000

Kingston-Davies, Ms J (Lees Solicitors LLP)
Birkenhead *p134* 0151 647 9381
Heswall *p249* 0151 342 6273
West Kirby *p428* 0151 625 9364

Kingston-Splatt, A T (Andrew Kingston & Co) *O Q L B1 F1*
Hull *p257* 01482 216217

Kingstone, M A (Linklaters LLP)
London EC2 *p54* 020 7456 2000

Kininmonth, P (Catteralls) *S1 E L W*
Wakefield *p418* 01924 291122

Kinloch, W A A I (Aaron & Partners LLP Solicitors) *P R1 Zv Zn Zu*
Chester *p190* 01244 405555

Kinman, Ms J (Nelsons) *J1*
Nottingham *p338* 0115 958 6262

Kinneon, S (David Gist Solicitors)
Bristol *p162* 0117 927 9111

Kinner Nilson, J (Manches LLP) *Ze Zy I*
Oxford *p343* 01865 722106

Kinnersley, Mrs A (Russell & Co Solicitors and Estate Agents) *S1 S2 J1 N W Zr*
Crawley *p202* 01293 561965 / 0845 300 2809

Kinnison, A K (Greene & Greene) *O B1 Zb B2 M2*
Bury St Edmunds *p171* 01284 762211

Kinrade, W F (Robinson & Kinrade)
Sutton *p403* 020 8770 2020

Kinsella, Ms M (Capsticks Solicitors LLP) *Zr*
London SW19 *p18* 020 8780 2211

Kinsella, N J (Russell Jones & Walker)
Manchester *p309* 0161 383 3500

Kinsey, A (Rosenblatt)
London EC4 *p73* 020 7955 0880

Kinsey, C J M (Bond Pearce LLP) *B1 Zb C1*
Bristol *p161* 0845 415 0000

Kinsey, Miss J M (Kinsey & Co Solicitors) *K3 K1 K2*
Baildon *p121* 01274 589900

Kinsey, Ms S L (Heringtons) *W C1 E S2 S1*
Eastbourne *p215* 01323 411020

Kinsley, O (Ben Hoare Bell & Co) *Zi*
Sunderland *p401* 0191 565 3112

Kinsley, P (East Cornwall Magistrates Courts)
Bodmin *p450* 01208 262700

Kipling, Mrs J M (W H Darbyshire & Son) *W S1 T2 T1 K4*
Blackpool *p146* 01253 346646

Kirby, A (Howes Percival LLP)
Norwich *p334* 01603 762103

Kirby, A D (Allen Barfields) *N E L Zr K3*
Croydon *p204* 020 8680 2050

Kirby, Mrs A S (Butcher Andrews) *E S2 C1 S1 R2*
Fakenham *p223* 01328 863131

Kirby, Miss C A (Farrer & Co LLP)
London WC2 *p31* 020 3375 7000

Kirby, C A (Ungoed-Thomas & King Limited) *S1 S2 E*
Carmarthen *p183* 01267 237441

Kirby, Ms C D (Kirby & Co)
London SW19 *p50* 020 8545 7171

Kirby, Ms F (Aubrey David) *E*
Westminster *p25* 020 7224 4410

Kirby, Ms K (Trowers & Hamlins)
London EC3 *p88* 020 7423 8000

Kirby, K G (W Parry & Co) *S1 E W*
Swansea *p405* 01792 470037

Kirby, Miss M (Kirbys Solicitors) *Q N Zj*
Newcastle upon Tyne *p325* 01661 867010

Kirby, M (Michael Kirby Solicitors) *S1 K1 W N J1 G F1 D1 Zl S2 B1 L*
York *p444* 01904 415932

Kirby, M J (Stanley Tee) *A1 E S1 S2 R1 Zs*
Bishop's Stortford *p144* 01279 755200

Kirby, P H (Lockings) *G H P M1 N F1 D1 J1 K1*
Hull *p257* 0845 075 4197

Kirby, R C (Speechly Bircham LLP) *T2 W*
London EC4 *p81* 020 7427 6400

Kirby, R K (Abels)
Southampton *p385* 023 8022 0317

Kirby, S (Ince & Co Services Ltd)
London E1 *p44* 020 7481 0010

Kirby, S (Cartwright King) *N*
Nottingham *p336* 0115 958 7444

Kirk, Miss A (Blaser Mills)
Harrow *p241* 020 8427 6262

Kirk, A J K (Marriott Davies Yapp) *C1 C2*
Sutton *p402* 020 8643 9794

Kirk, B W (Starkie & Gregory) *G H M1 N J1 K1*
Long Eaton *p293* 0115 849 9000

Kirk, D N (Simons Muirhead & Burton) *B2*
London W1 *p79* 020 7734 4499

Kirk, Ms E J (B P Collins LLP) *J1 Q*
Gerrards Cross *p229* 01753 889995

Kirk, G D (Druces LLP) *Zi M2*
London EC2 *p27* 020 7638 9271
Bury St Edmunds *p171* 01284 763333

Kirk, G P (Barnsley Metropolitan Borough Council)
Barnsley *p448* 01226 770770

Kirk, Miss H R (Rothera Dowson) *W K4*
Nottingham *p338* 0115 910 0600

Kirk, L (Barker & Co)
Hull *p256* 01482 219966

Kirk, Mrs M E (Wrigleys Solicitors LLP) *A1 E*
Leeds *p278* 0113 244 6100

Kirk, M S (Frederic Hall) *K1 S1 W D1 S2*
Dover *p213* 01304 202411

Kirk, Ms N (Pitmans LLP) *O Q B1*
Reading *p361* 0118 958 0224

Kirk, P G (Aldridge Brownlee Solicitors LLP) *Q J1 N K1*
Bournemouth *p151* 01202 294411

Kirkaldy, I R (HBOS PLC)
Halifax *p460* 0870 600 5000

Kirkbride, B (Runhams) *N Q J1 F1 V L X Zi Zj Zl Zv*
Bradford *p154* 01274 532233

Kirkbride, J K (Bevan Brittan LLP) *O Q L Zj*
Bristol *p161* 0870 194 1000

Kirkby, L P (Symes Bains Broomer) *S1 W A1 L E T1 C1 Zc Zd Zh*
Scunthorpe *p373* 01724 281616

Kirkconel, A H (Dutton Gregory) *K1 Q Zl K3 D1*
Southampton *p385* 023 8022 1344

Kirkham, Miss C (Stanley H Cross & Co)
Chorley *p194* 01257 272222

Kirkham, J (Brennans Solicitors)
Wallsend *p419* 0191 262 5133

Kirkham, Mrs J F (Saunders Roberts) *K1 W V Q L J1 F1 Zl*
Evesham *p220* 01386 442558

Kirkham, J R (North West Leicestershire District Council)
Coalville *p455* 01530 454545

See p634 for the Key to Work Categories

Kirkham, Ms L A (HSR Law (Hayes, Son & Richmond)) *N*
Doncaster *p211* 01302 347800
Gainsborough *p228* 01427 613831

Kirkham, Mrs S (Devonshires) *S1 Zh R2*
London EC2 *p27* 020 7628 7576

Kirkland, P D M (Kirklands) *E S1 S2 W C1 R1 C2*
Totton *p413* 023 8066 3313
Romsey *p366* 01794 513466

Kirkman, Ms A (Chapple & Co) *K1 D1 Q K3*
March *p312* 01354 652550

Kirkman, T H (Latham & Co) *E S1 A1 J1 W C1 T1 T2 Zx*
Melton Mowbray *p314* 01664 563012
Loughborough *p293* 01509 238822

Kirkness, Ms L (The College of Law)
London WC1 *p105*. 0800 289997

Kirkpatrick, A J (Hough Halton & Soal) *N Zq*
Carlisle *p182*. 01228 524379

Kirkpatrick, A R M (Clark Holt) *E S2 R2 A1*
Swindon *p406* 01793 617444
Birmingham *p139* 0870 150 0100

Kirkpatrick, J (Potter Shelley & Co) *N D1 F1 G H J1 K1 L M1 P*
Huntingdon *p258*. 01480 459531

Kirkpatrick, P D J (Bates Wells & Braithwaite London LLP) *Zd C1 X*
London EC4 *p11*. 020 7551 7777

Kirkpatrick, S (Reed Smith LLP) *Za*
London EC2 *p71*. 020 3116 3000

Kirkup, Ms L A (Crown Prosecution Service Durham)
Durham *p457* 0191 383 5800

Kirkup, S (Dickinson Dees) *A1*
Newcastle upon Tyne *p324* . 0191 279 9000

Kirkwood, D H (Longden Walker & Renney) *W*
Sunderland *p401*. 0191 567 7024

Kirkwood, Mrs E (Hacking Ashton LLP) *W K4*
Newcastle under Lyme *p323*. 01782 715555

Kirrane, M J P (Royal Liver Assurance Ltd)
Liverpool *p463*. 0151 236 1451

Kirrane, P I (Jordans) *K4 W*
Dewsbury *p210* 01924 457171

Kirsch, Ms S G (HBOS PLC)
Halifax *p460* 0870 600 5000

Kirstein, Ms C F (British Telecommunications PLC)
London EC1 *p104* 020 7356 6181

Kirtley, Ms D (Dickinson Dees) *C1 C2 Zb*
Newcastle upon Tyne *p324* . 0191 279 9000

Kirtley, M J (Morrisons Solicitors LLP) *S1 S2 W T2 T1 E L C1 Zd*
Woking *p437*. 01483 726146

Kirton, L (Keoghs LLP) *N Zj Q O*
Bolton *p149* 01204 677000

Kirton-Darling, E I (Hodge Jones & Allen LLP) *Zg*
London NW1 *p41* 020 7874 8300

Kirvan, M (BKS Solicitors) *S2 L Zh Q*
London SE20 *p9*. 020 8776 9388

Kirwan, D S (Kirwans) *G H B2 O Q Zl*
Moreton *p319* 0151 677 3433

Kirwan, S P (Nowell Meller Solicitors Limited) *K1 K3*
Stafford *p393* 01785 252377

Kischland, J (Judge Sykes Frixou)
London WC2 *p47* 020 7379 5114

Kish, M (Barlow Lyde & Gilbert LLP) *Zj*
London EC3 *p10*. 020 7247 2277

Kissack, N E J (Pinsent Masons LLP) *N Ze Zb Zk*
Leeds *p276* 0113 244 5000

Kissane, Mrs C (Department for Business, Enterprise and Regulatory Reform)
London SW1 *p105*. 020 7215 0105

Kissane, R J (Austins LLP) *Q N L*
Luton *p295* 01582 456222

Kitchen, Ms C (LG Lawyers)
London SE1 *p50*. 020 7379 0000

Kitchen, Ms J (DFA Law LLP) *D1 K1*
Northampton *p331*. 01604 609560

Kitchen, J (KTP Solicitors) *K1 F1 J1 L N Q V W D1*
Pontypridd *p352* 01443 485141

Kitchen, J D (Larken & Co) *S1 W A1 T1 E S2*
Newark *p322* 01636 703333

Kitchen, M P (SNR Denton) *C1*
London EC4 *p75*. 020 7242 1212

Kitchener, Ms J M (Reed Smith LLP)
London EC2 *p71*. 020 3116 3000

Kitchin, A W N (Ashurst LLP)
London EC2 *p7* 020 7638 1111

Kitchin, J E (Rydon Group Ltd)
Forest Row *p458* 01342 825151

Kitching, N H (Kitching Kneale & Co) *A1 N K1 S1 C1 W S2 L J1 Zk Zl*
Great Ayton *p233* 01642 723713

Kitchingman, Ms F (Carillion PLC)
Wolverhampton *p477* 01902 422431

Kitchingman, J M (Pannone LLP) *N Zr*
Manchester *p308* 0161 909 3000

Kitchman, Mrs R (Graham & Rosen) *J1 Q*
Hull *p257* 01482 323123

Kite, C D P (Kite Griffin) *S2 K1 M1 F1 E J1 C1*
Bracknell *p153*. 01344 425637

Kite, G D A (Foys Solicitors) *N O F1 J1 L Zk Zp Zq Zr C1 F2 Ze J2 Zg Q*
Worksop *p441* 01909 473560

Kite, P (IBB Solicitors) *O*
Uxbridge *p417*. 0845 638 1381

Kiteley, Mrs H J (Birmingham City Council Legal & Democratic Services)
Birmingham *p449* 0121 303 2066

Kiteley, M (Kiteleys Solicitors Limited)
Bournemouth *p152*. 01202 299992

Kitson, A B (CMS Cameron McKenna LLP) *R1 E P Zs*
London EC3 *p17*. 020 7367 3000

Kitson, P J (Russell Jones & Walker)
London WC2 *p74* 020 7657 1555

Kittle, J (DLA Piper UK LLP)
Leeds *p272* 0870 011 1111

Kitto, C P (Ansons LLP) *E S1 L C1 W K1 A1 T1 Zd Zx*
Lichfield *p284* 01543 263456

Kitto, J (Carrick District Council)
Truro *p474*. 01872 224400
Camborne *p452* 01209 614000

Kivlehan, K M (Pearson Caulfield) *G H K1 D1*
Newcastle upon Tyne *p326* . 0191 261 8878

Klage, Miss C M (Bolt Burdon) *N*
Islington *p14*. 020 7288 4700

Klarfeld, S B (Levine Mellins Klarfeld) *E C1 S1 W J1 Zd Zf Zk*
Stanmore *p394* 020 8954 7474

Klass, Mrs S (Berg Legal) *E S1 L R1 A1 Zb Zc*
Manchester *p301* 0161 833 9211

Klauber, Ms J E (Russell-Cooke LLP) *Zd J1*
London SW15 *p74*. 020 8789 9111

Kleanthous, A (Gannons Limited) *J1 O Q*
Camden *p35*. 020 7438 1060

Kleiman, H D (K&L Gates LLP) *C1*
London EC4 *p47*. 020 7648 9000

Klein, Mrs A (Maples Teesdale LLP) *S2 E*
London EC2 *p58*. 020 7600 3800

Klein, Ms A J (Durham County Council)
Durham *p457* 0191 383 3513

Klein, J (Penningtons)
London EC2 *p66*. 020 7457 3000

Klein, Mrs J A (MBNA Europe Bank Ltd)
Chester *p454* 01244 672002

Klein, R J (SJ Berwin LLP)
London EC4 *p75*. 020 7111 2222

Klein, Miss V N (Cook Taylor) *G H*
Greenwich *p22*. 020 8854 1166

Kleiner, G (Speechly Bircham LLP) *W Zq*
London EC4 *p81*. 020 7427 6400
London EC4 *p92*. 020 7597 6000

Kliarkina, Ms N (Davies Johnson & Co (Shipping & Commercial Solicitors)) *Za A3 Zj O*
Plymouth *p349*. 01752 226020

Klim, P E (Russell Jones & Walker) *E R2 S2 S1*
London WC2 *p74* 020 7657 1555

Klimaytys, Ms M L (James B Bennett & Co) *K1 K3 D1*
Crawley *p202* 01293 544044

Klimov, Dr P (Unisys European Services Ltd)
Uxbridge *p474*. 01895 862108

Klimowicz, A (Crane & Walton) *E S1 G H J1*
Leicester *p279*. 0116 255 1901

Klimt, Mrs L E (Klimt & Co) *E S1 C1 L*
Westminster *p50*. 020 7486 4432

Klimt, M S (Fishburns) *A3 Zc C1 B2 Zj M2 O Q N Zq P*
London EC3 *p32*. 020 7280 8888

Kling, E (Dechert) *M2*
London EC4 *p26*. 020 7184 7000

Klinger, A M (Sasto & Klinger) *B1 C1 E J1 L R1 S1 T1 W Zc Zi*
London W1 *p76* 020 7631 4714

Klinger, I M (Charles Harding & Co) *S1 E J1 C1 R1 W L*
Wembley *p426*. 020 8795 0990
Wembley *p426*. 020 8903 7017

Klingher, B (Cartwright Cunningham Haselgrove & Co) *E K1 Q R1 S1*
Waltham Forest *p19* 020 8520 1021

Kloosman, G A (Kloosmans) *S2 W S1*
Southend-on-Sea *p387* . . . 01702 600090

Klopenstein, Ms T L (Coffin Mew & Clover) *Zr*
Fareham *p223*. 01329 825617

Kmotrasova, H (Lennons) *S1 S2 C1 E*
Chesham *p189* 01494 773377

Knagg, C D (John A Behn Twyford & Co)
Liverpool *p286*. 0151 236 0367

Knaggs, D (Irwin Mitchell LLP) *Zj*
Leeds *p274* 0870 150 0100

Knaggs, R J (Richard J Knaggs & Co) *J1 S1 E C1 W L A1 B1 F1 R1 Zc Zl*
Redcar *p362*. 01642 487011

Knaggs, S (Thompsons (formerly Robin/Brian Thompson & Partners)) *N*
Manchester *p310* 0161 819 3500

Knapman, J (Keoghs LLP) *Zr N*
Bolton *p149* 01204 677000

Knapman, N (DAC Beachcroft)
Bristol *p162* 0117 918 2000

Knapman, Mrs S B (Taylor Walton LLP) *S2*
Luton *p295* 01582 731161

Knapp, Ms D (Bedford Borough Council)
Bedford *p448* 01234 267422

Knapp, D R W (Barlow Lyde & Gilbert LLP) *O Q N Zj*
London EC3 *p10*. 020 7247 2277

Knapp, D S (Hart Brown Solicitors) *S1 W L*
Woking *p437*. 0800 068 8177

Knapper, Ms A (Fursdon Knapper)
Plymouth *p349*. 01752 309090

Knapper, C (Fursdon Knapper)
Plymouth *p349*. 01752 309090

Knappett, Ms C (Fisher Jones Greenwood LLP) *K1*
Colchester *p197* 01206 578282

Kneale, Ms R (Hempsons) *Zr*
Westminster *p40*. 020 7839 0278

Knee, Miss D (Catteralls) *C1 E S1 S2*
Wakefield *p418* 01924 291122

Kneebone, Ms S L (Browning & Co) *W S1*
Looe *p293*. . . . . .01503 262119 / 262129

Kneen, Ms J M (BP Oil International Ltd)
London SW1 *p103*. 020 7496 4000

Knewstubb, C (Morecrofts Solicitors LLP) *D1 K1*
Liverpool *p290*. 0151 236 8871

Knifton, I R (Brown Turner Ross) *D1 F1 J1 K1 M1 N P S1 V*
Southport *p388* 01704 542002

Knight, A (Skadden Arps Slate Meagher & Flom (UK) LLP) *C2*
London E14 *p80*. 020 7519 7000

Knight, Mrs A (Watson Burton LLP) *O Q F1 Zc Zq*
Newcastle upon Tyne *p327* . 0845 901 2100

Knight, A R (Taylor Walton LLP) *B1 F1 N O Q*
Luton *p295* 01582 731161

Knight, Ms C (City of London Magistrates Court)
London EC4 *p107* 020 7332 1830

Knight, C J (Knight Polson Solicitors) *G H Q B2*
Eastleigh *p216*. 023 8064 4822

Knight, Mrs C L (Warner Goodman LLP) *K1 K2 K3 D1 D2*
Fareham *p224*. 01329 288121

Knight, D (Laytons)
Guildford *p236*. 01483 407000

Knight, Ms D (Anthony Morris Solicitors)
Crawley *p202* 01293 519619

Knight, D G (Winterbotham Smith Penley LLP) *K1 N K3*
Dursley *p214* 01453 541940

Knight, D M G (Field Fisher Waterhouse LLP) *M1 Ze*
London EC3 *p31*. 020 7861 4000

Knight, Miss F O (Coles Miller Solicitors LLP) *S1 E C1 R1 L S2*
Bournemouth *p151*. 01202 293226

Knight, Mrs G A (Atteys) *N*
Barnsley *p124* 01226 212345

Knight, G A C (DAC Beachcroft) *N O*
London EC4 *p24*. 020 7936 2222

Knight, Mrs H A (Olswang LLP) *E R1 S1*
London WC1 *p64* 020 7067 3000

Knight, I D (Bray & Bray) *E W C1 S1 J1 S2 A1 R2 B1 K4 C2 Zp*
Hinckley *p250* 01455 639900

Knight, J (Wake Smith & Tofields) *S2 E S1 C1 L*
Sheffield *p377* 0114 266 6660

Knight, Miss J A (Payne & Payne) *K1 D1*
Hull *p257* 01482 326446

Knight, J A P (The Ringrose Law Group - Nerina Farmer) *N Zr*
Sleaford *p381* 01529 301300

Knight, Mrs J E (Beviss & Beckingsale)
Axminster *p120* 01297 630700

Knight, J L (FBC Manby Bowdler LLP) *C1 C2*
Wolverhampton *p437* 01902 578000

Knight, K (Biscoes)
Portsmouth *p354*. 023 9266 0261

Knight, Ms K J (Orange PCS Ltd)
Bristol *p452* 0870 376 8888

Knight, Ms L (Shoosmiths)
Fareham *p224*. . . . 0370 086 6800 / 01489 616800

Knight, Mrs L F A (Blake Lapthorn)
Chandlers Ford *p184* 023 8090 8090

Knight, Miss L M (Gregorys Solicitors)
Stockport *p395*. 0161 456 8125

Knight, M (Reynolds Porter Chamberlain LLP)
London E1 *p71* 020 3060 6000

Knight, Mrs M (Anthony Collins Solicitors LLP) *S1 S2*
Birmingham *p137* 0121 200 3242

Knight, M D M (Knights) *A2 N O Q Zk A1 Zq Zw Zd R1*
Tunbridge Wells *p415* 01892 537311

Knight, M I (Christopher Green McCarrahers) *K4 T2 W*
Southampton *p386*. 023 8084 2765

Knight, M S (Harold G Walker) *O Q L N*
Bournemouth *p152*. 01202 203200

Knight, M T (Fishburns) *O Q Zj Zc*
London EC3 *p32*. 020 7280 8888

Knight, Miss P (Leigh Day & Co) *N*
London EC1 *p52*. 020 7650 1200

Knight, P A N (Schofield Sweeney) *S1 E A1 L R1*
Bradford *p154* 01274 306000

Knight, P R (Clarke Willmott)
Birmingham *p136* 0845 209 1000 / 0117 305 6000

Knight, R D (DWF) *S2 E R1*
Liverpool *p287*. 0151 907 3000

Knight, R H (Richard Knight & Co) *S1 K1 G J1 F1 W P V C1*
Syston *p407*. 0116 260 0021

Knight, R J (SA Law) *C1 E S1 T1 T2 W*
St Albans *p390* 01727 798000

Knight, R R A (Saulet & Co) *D1 F1 G H K1 K3 K4*
Southsea *p389*. 023 9281 9442

Knight, S A (Norton Peskett)
Lowestoft *p294* 01502 533000

Knight, Ms S M (Tennant & Knight) *K1 D1 W*
Brighton *p160* 01273 202050

Knight, T A K (Gateley LLP) *O Q Zj Za*
London EC4 *p35*. 020 7653 1600

Knight, Ms V M A (Segens Blount Petre) *K1 K3*
Westminster *p77*. 020 7332 2222

Knights, Ms H (Gartsides)
Newport *p328* 01633 213411

Knights, M (Morrisons Solicitors LLP) *Q*
London SW19 *p62*. 020 8971 1020

Knipe, Mrs A (Anthony Gold) *O W*
London SE1 *p6* 020 7940 4000

Knipe, B P (Knipe Woodhouse-Smith) *W S1 K1 F1 L V*
Chalfont St Peter *p184*. . . .01753 887877 / 889149

Knipe, R A (Chattertons Solicitors) *S1 L E G C1 W K1 Q N Zl*
Spalding *p389* 01775 768774

Knock, S W (Brown & Corbishley) *N P K1 E W F1 D1 C1 L*
Newcastle under Lyme *p323*. 01782 717888

Knopp-McCabe, Mrs J L (Staffordshire County Council) *D1 G K1 Zm*
Stafford *p472* 01785 223121

Knorpel, A M D (ASB Law) *J1*
Crawley *p202* 01293 603600

Knott, Mrs J (Towns Needham & Co) *S1 W T1 L*
Manchester *p310* 0161 832 3721

Knott, Ms J L (Chebsey & Co) *W K4*
Beaconsfield *p128* 01494 670440

Knott, M (Hansells) *W*
Norwich *p334* 01603 615731

Knott, S (Shoosmiths) *E*
Fareham *p224*. . . . 0370 086 6800 / 01489 616800

Knowles, A N (Stewarts Law LLP) *N Zr*
London EC4 *p83*. 020 7822 8000

Knowles, Miss C J (Nottingham City Council (City Sec Dept))
Nottingham *p467*. 0115 915 5555

Knowles, C W (Barnes Coleman & Co) *S1 K1 P G M1*
Benfleet *p131* 01702 558211

Knowles, Mrs E (Redbridge Magistrates Court)
Ilford *p461*. 0845 601 3600

Knowles, Miss E B (Pardoes) *W*
Bridgwater *p158* 01278 457891

Knowles, G (Drivers) *S1 W E A1 L P C1 Zc Zl*
York *p444* 01904 625661

Knowles, Miss G (Wigan Borough Council) *G H*
Wigan *p476* 01942 244991

Knowles, J (George Davies Solicitors LLP) *T2 W*
Manchester *p303* 0161 236 8992

Knowles, J (Sternberg Reed) *D1*
Barking *p123* 020 8591 3366

Knowles, J M (Grays) *J1 K1 N O Q Zp Zd*
York *p444* 01904 634771

Knowles, Ms L (Bindmans LLP) *N*
London WC1 *p12* 020 7833 4433

Knowles, Mrs L M (Percy Hughes & Roberts) *J1*
Birkenhead *p134*. 0151 666 9090

Knowles, N G (DLA Piper UK LLP)
London EC2 *p24*. 0870 011 1111

Knowles, P (Shepherd + Wedderburn LLP)
London EC4 *p78*. 020 7429 4900

Knowles, Ms R (Linklaters LLP)
London EC2 *p54*. 020 7456 2000

Knowles, R M (Steele Raymond) *C1 C2 J1 C3 Ze*
Bournemouth *p152*. 01202 294566

Knowles, S (Yorklaw Ltd (t/a Burn & Company)) *C1 C2 J1*
Easingwold *p215*. 01347 822188
York *p445* 01904 655442

Knowles, S D (Reed Smith LLP) *E*
London EC2 *p71*. 020 3116 3000

Knowles, Mrs S J (Vincent Sykes & Higham LLP) *C1 C3 Ze J1 C2 Zt*
Thrapston *p411* 01832 732161

Knowles, S P (Mills & Reeve) *N Zj Zr*
Birmingham *p140* 0121 454 4000

Knowles, T J (DWF) *J1 Zp*
Manchester *p303* 0161 603 5000

Knowlman, Mrs R M (Gloucestershire County Council - Legal & Democratic Services)
Gloucester *p459*. 01452 425203

Knox, D M (Mills Curry) *S1 W T2*
Eastcote *p216* 020 8868 8841

Knox, J (Linklaters LLP)
London EC2 *p54*. 020 7456 2000

Knox, Ms K (RMPI Solicitors)
London W1 *p70* 020 7318 4444

Knox, M C (Hopkins) *E S1 S2 C2 C1*
Mansfield *p311*. 01623 468468

Knox, Miss S I (Hains & Lewis Ltd) *N D1 G W*
Haverfordwest *p244* 0845 408 0125

Knox, S J (Dixon Coles & Gill) *W S1 Q T2 N S2 F1 K4 L C1*
Wakefield *p418* 01924 373467

Knudsen, Miss D C (Bates NVH) *K1 Q N K3 Zl*
Hook *p252*. 01256 760074

Ko, Mrs C (Gregory Rowcliffe Milners) *E S2 S1*
London WC1 *p37* 020 7242 0631

Kobi-Fordah, P (Cedars & Co) *E R2 S1 S2 Zc*
Greenwich *p19*. 020 8331 6161

Kochane, N J (Plexus Law (A Trading Name of Parabis Law LLP)) *Zj O Q N*
London EC3 *p68*. 0844 245 4000

Kochanek, B F (Environment Agency (Thames Region))
Reading *p469* 0870 850 6506

Kochberg, Ms C (Hogan Lovells International LLP)
London EC1 *p42*. 020 7296 2000

Kochhar, A K (Edwards Angell Palmer & Dodge) *C1*
London EC2 *p28*. 020 7583 4055

Koe, D M (Joelson Wilson LLP) *C1 C2*
Westminster *p46*. 020 7580 5721

Koehne, S D (Stephenson Harwood) *E R2*
London EC2 *p82*. 020 7329 4422

Koffman, A R (Salehs LLP) *O B1 F1 J1 Q C1*
Manchester *p309* 0161 434 9991

Koffman, B (Brian Koffman & Co) *G H K1 M1*
Manchester *p306* 0161 832 3852

Koffman, J P (Sweetman Burke & Sinker) *K1 G H B2 K3*
Ealing *p84* 020 8840 2572

Koh, R (Reynolds Porter Chamberlain LLP)
London E1 *p71* 020 3060 6000

Kohler, Mrs J R (Capsticks Solicitors LLP) *C1 M1 R2 C2 Ze I*
London SW19 *p18* 020 8780 2211

Kokkinos, Ms S (Sternberg Reed) *K1*
Barking *p123* 020 8591 3366

Kolapo, Ms M C (Pearson Maddin Solicitors) *K1*
New Malden *p321* 020 8949 9500
London EC3 *p85* 020 7790 7000

Kominsky, Ms A (Pollecoff Solicitors Ltd) *G H*
London EC2 *p68* 020 7608 2568

Komosa, A K (Tandridge District Council)
Oxted *p468* 01883 722000

Kon, S D (SJ Berwin LLP)
London EC4 *p75* 020 7111 2222

Kong, Ms J (Malcolm C Foy & Co) *K1 Q*
Doncaster *p211* 01302 340005

Kong, Miss K (N Legal) *S1 C2 S2 R2 C1 K4 Zb F1 E W*
Sutton Coldfield *p404* 0121 355 8885

Kong, Miss L (ASB Law) *S1*
Crawley *p202* 01293 603600

Kong, R (Harvey Son & Filby) *S1 B1 C1 E J1 K1 Zi Q N T1 T2 W*
London WC2 *p39* 020 3159 4235

Kong, S (Harvey Son & Filby) *B1 E J1 K1 Zi Q S1 W*
Birmingham *p139* 0121 632 6092
London WC2 *p39* 020 3159 4235

Koniarski, M S (Barnsley Metropolitan Borough Council)
Barnsley *p448* 01226 770770

Konsta, S N (Barlow Lyde & Gilbert LLP)
London EC3 *p10* 020 7247 2277

Konynenburg, F (Hill Dickinson LLP) *Za A3 M2 O*
London EC3 *p41* 020 7283 9033

Koolhoven, R D (Wright Hassall LLP) *C1 B1 O Q Zb*
Leamington Spa *p270* 01926 886688

Koon Koon, D (Garden House Solicitors)
Hertford *p248* 01992 422128

Kopitko, A M (Speechly Bircham LLP) *E*
London EC4 *p81* 020 7427 6400

Koranteng, S V (Cedars & Co) *S1 S2 E O Q*
Greenwich *p19* 020 8331 6161

Kordan, J N (Shoosmiths) *E R1 S1 Zc*
Birmingham *p142* 0370 086 4000 / 0121 335 4440

Korff, J P D (Hillyer McKeown LLP) *A1 R1 S1 W T2*
Chester *p190* 01244 318131

Koritsas, Miss X H K (J M Amin & Co) *J1 L N O Q S1 W K1 E F1 Zi*
Wembley *p426* 020 8903 3766

Korman, A J (Squire Sanders (UK) LLP) *Zw C1 J1 Zf*
London EC2 *p81* 020 7655 1000

Kornbluth, P S (Howard Kennedy LLP) *C1 C2 M2 Zb*
London W1 *p48* 020 7636 1616

Kornhauser, D (Allweis & Co) *T1 N R2 S1 E*
Salford *p370* 0161 792 1020

Korzeniowski, J (Gates and Partners)
London EC3 *p35* 020 7220 5950

Koser, Ms R (EEF West Midlands Association)
Birmingham *p449* 0121 456 2222

Koshar, Mrs S (Leeds City Council)
Leeds *p462* 0113 224 3513

Kosky, D (Lawrence Stephens) *C1 E L M1 N R1 S1 T1 W Zc Zd Zh*
London EC1 *p82* 020 7935 1211

Kosky, J M (Ross & Craig) *O Q Zq B2 Ze Zk Zj N F1 Zr B1 Zb C1 Zc*
Westminster *p73* 020 7262 3077
Westminster *p77* 020 7725 8000

Kosky, J P (Clifford Chance)
London E14 *p20* 020 7006 1000

Kosmin-Barr, M A (OGR Stock Denton) *K1 Q L B1 O Zq K3*
London N3 *p64* 020 8349 0321

Kossoff, D J (Clifford Chance)
London E14 *p20* 020 7006 1000

Kostelnyk, Miss J L (Squire Sanders (UK) LLP)
London EC2 *p81* 020 7655 1000

Kostenko, M (Crowell & Moring) *C2 C1 Zza O A3 Q C3*
London EC4 *p23* 020 7413 0011

Kotani, N (Salans) *C1 C2 C3 F1 B1 J1 Zb*
London EC4 *p76* 020 7429 6000

Kotecha, D (McMillan Williams) *Q O L Zq N*
Mitcham *p318* 020 8648 4044

Kotecha, Ms P (Pinnacle Insurance PLC)
Borehamwood *p450* 020 8207 9000

Kotecha, Miss S (Maples Teesdale LLP) *E S2*
London EC2 *p58* 020 7600 3800

Kotecha, Mrs S (Chetty & Patel) *D1 K1 K2*
Leicester *p279* 0116 254 6222
Leicester *p279* 01455 282832

Kotecha-Pau, Ms K D (Freemans Solicitors) *G K1 H D1 P M1 W S1 L Zl Zi Zp*
London W1 *p34* 020 7935 3522

Kotzur, W (Taylor Wessing)
London EC4 *p86* 020 7300 7000

Koucheksarai, N (Canter Levin & Berg) *D1 K1*
St Helens *p391* 01744 634141

Koucheksarai, Ms N (Quality Solicitors Jackson & Canter) *K3 K1 D1*
Liverpool *p290* 0151 282 1700

Kousetta, H (Howard Kennedy LLP) *Zf*
London W1 *p48* 020 7636 1616

Kovacs, G T (Blake Lapthorn) *Q P*
Chandlers Ford *p184* 023 8090 8090

Kovari, I (CMS Cameron McKenna LLP)
London EC3 *p17* 020 7367 3000

Kowalski, R (Kenneth Bush) *G H K1 L M1 N*
King's Lynn *p266* 01553 692737

Kozlowski, A L (CMS Cameron McKenna LLP)
London EC3 *p17* 020 7367 3000

Kpogho, B A (Able Solicitors) *C1 D1 E F1 G H J1 K1 L O Q S1 V W*
London NW9 *p3* 020 8358 3580

Krafft, P (Farrer & Co LLP)
London WC2 *p31* 020 3375 7000

Krais, M J (Bray & Krais Solicitors) *C1 J1 Ze Zf*
London SW6 *p15* 020 7384 3050

Kramer, B P (Kirkwoods) *C1 S2 E K3 K1 Q S1 W*
Stanmore *p394* 020 8954 8555

Kramer, E (Silverman Sherliker LLP)
London EC2 *p78* 020 7749 2700

Kramer, J M (Segens Blount Petre)
Westminster *p77* 020 7332 2222

Kramer, M C (Bates Wells & Braithwaite London LLP) *O Q A3 C3 Zd*
London EC4 *p11* 020 7551 7777

Kramers, T A P (Ashton KCJ) *E S2 R2 P M1*
Ipswich *p262* 01473 232425

Krangle, M A (Gallaher Ltd)
Weybridge *p476* 01932 859777

Kravitz, N S (Fasken Martineau LLP) *C1 Ze E J1 T1 T2 S1 S2*
London W1 *p31* 020 7917 8500
London WC2 *p60* 020 7242 5905

Krebs, S M (Stephen Krebs & Co) *G H*
Oldham *p340* 0161 652 0507

Krell, S G (Krells) *E S1 Zo*
Withington *p436* 0161 445 8649

Krelle, Mrs D C (Colemans - CTTS) *J2 N*
Manchester *p302* 0161 876 2500

Krempel, Mrs D M (D M Krempel) *S1 W*
Buntingford *p168* 01763 288569

Krempel, S J (D M Krempel) *S1 C1 W S2 E*
Buntingford *p168* 01763 288569

Kreppel, Ms W J (Graham Evans & Partners) *Q J1 F1 K1 L D1 B1 N V W Zp Zk Zl*
Swansea *p405* 01792 655822

Kreser, Ms J I (Silverman Sherliker LLP) *Zo*
London EC2 *p78* 020 7749 2700

Kresner, Ms Y (Sternberg Reed) *G*
Barking *p123* 020 8591 3366
Romford *p366* 01708 766155

Krestin, J M (Butcher Burns LLP) *C1 E L P S1*
London WC1 *p16* 020 7713 7100

Krick, P S (Wilkin Chapman Epton Blades) *P N F1 J1 Q*
Lincoln *p285* 01522 512345

Krige, K (Ashurst LLP)
London EC2 *p7* 020 7638 1111

Krikler, A S (Gillhams Solicitors LLP) *N O Q Zq Zc*
London NW10 *p35* 020 8965 4266

Krischer, D S (Allen & Overy LLP)
London E1 *p5* 020 3088 0000

Krishnan, Miss A (Stewarts Law LLP) *N*
London EC4 *p83* 020 7822 8000

Krishnarajah, N (Krish Solicitors)
Southall *p384* 020 8893 6661

Krol, Mrs R S (Clarks Legal LLP) *E S2*
London WC2 *p20* 020 7539 8000
London W1 *p46* 020 7339 7000

Krone, M (Allen & Overy LLP)
London E1 *p5* 020 3088 0000

Krudy, Ms M (G T Stewart Solicitors) *G H B2 J2*
London SE22 *p83* 020 8299 6000

Krumins, Ms R (Canter Levin & Berg) *E K1 W N Q*
Liverpool *p287* 0151 239 1000
Liverpool *p287* 0151 907 3000

Kruzins, Miss S J (Kruzins) *J1 K1 I N Q V W O R1 C1*
Cardiff *p179* 029 2039 0101
Cardiff *p180* 029 2049 0047

Krywald, Ms S H (McBride Wilson & Co) *Q O C1 B1 J1 E N W Ze Zf Zd R2*
London WC2 *p56* 020 7242 1300

Kubba, J (McGrigors LLP)
London EC4 *p56* 020 7054 2500

Kucera, Ms F J (Linklaters LLP)
London EC2 *p54* 020 7456 2000

Kudryl, A J (Birketts LLP (Wollastons LLP)) *C1 C2 F1*
Chelmsford *p186* 01245 211211

Kuenzel, Miss A (Henmans LLP) *S1 A1*
Oxford *p343* 01865 781000

Kuhn, Ms M L (Squire Sanders (UK) LLP)
London EC2 *p81* 020 7655 1000

Kuhn, M P (Hartwig Notary Chambers) *B1 C1 M1 N O Q Zb Ze*
Croydon *p205* 020 8681 2893

Kujawinski, J W (Sheltons) *L S2 S1 W*
Hucknall *p255* 0115 955 3444

Kukielka, Ms C E L (Hurlow & Partners) *D1 K1*
Cardiff *p179* 029 2039 6087

Kularia, Ms K (Field Seymour Parkes) *J1*
Reading *p360* 0118 951 6200

Kulasingam, R (SNR Denton) *C1 Zb*
London EC4 *p75* 020 7242 1212

Kulczykowska, Mrs D (Hodders) *W*
London NW10 *p41* 020 8965 9862
Milton Keynes *p317* 01908 692769

Kulisra, N (AKL Solicitors) *S1 Q K1 N C1 E W G L V Zc Ze Zj*
Luton *p294* 01582 454365

Kumar, B (Henderson Global Investors)
London EC2 *p106* 020 7818 1818

Kumar, Ms M (Eric Wright Group Ltd)
Bamber Bridge *p448* 01772 698822

Kumar, Ms N (Humphreys & Co)
Bristol *p163* 0117 929 2662

Kumar, Mrs N (Riley Hayes & Co) *G H*
Wolverhampton *p438* 01902 773666

Kumar, Mrs N S (N S Kumar)
Ilford *p260* 020 8554 3393

Kumar, S (McGrath Immigration Solicitors Partnership) *Zi*
Birmingham *p140* 0121 643 4124

Kumar, S (Rowland Tildesley & Harris) *W Zl S1 J1 Zm*
Willenhall *p433* 01902 366571

Kumar, S K (Hornby & Levy) *D1 D2 K1 K2 X*
London SW9 *p43* 020 7737 0909

Kumar, V (Michael Hill Partnership) *M1 P E H K1 S1 W J1 F1 Zc Zk Zp*
Leicester *p280* 0116 254 1609

Kumari, Miss A (Ward & Rider Limited) *N J2*
Coventry *p201* 024 7655 5400

Kumari, Miss M (Elsey & Hodson) *D2 D1 K1 K2 L S1 Q W*
Peterborough *p347* 01733 314064

Kumari, Miss N (Ashton KCJ) *K1*
Bury St Edmunds *p171* 01284 762331

Kumrai, Ms A (Whitelock & Storr) *G H B2*
London WC1 *p91* 020 7405 3913

Kuness, A P (Lewis Silkin LLP) *E*
London EC4 *p53* 020 7074 8000

Kunwardia, J (Hodge Jones & Allen LLP) *L Q*
London NW1 *p41* 020 7874 8300

Kunz, Mrs R (Wade Stevens & Co) *S1 W*
Orpington *p342* 01689 831122

Kupitz, A (Allen & Overy LLP)
London E1 *p5* 020 3088 0000

Kurdian, Ms A (Linklaters LLP)
London EC2 *p54* 020 7456 2000

Kurowski, Ms L (Wilkinson Woodward) *E N Q S1*
Halifax *p238* 01422 339600

Kurth, Mrs S L (Nicholls Christie & Crocker) *K1 D1 K3*
Uxbridge *p417* 01895 256216

Kurtha, Mrs S (Wainwright & Cummins) *K1 S1 W*
Lambeth *p90* 020 7737 9330

Kurthausen, P (MBNA Europe Bank Ltd) *N Q O Zi Zr J1*
Chester *p454* 01244 672002

Kurtz, Miss E F (Barrett & Co Solicitors LLP) *W*
Reading *p359* 0118 958 9711
Swindon *p406* 01793 532363
Slough *p382* 01753 810710

Kushner, K (Potter Rees (Serious Injury) Solicitors)
Manchester *p309* 0161 237 5888

Kushnick, J M (The Skemp Partnership) *N*
Manchester *p310* 0800 040 7566 / 0161 238 5400

Kusi-Appauh, Miss A (Cogent Law) *N*
Croydon *p204* 0844 245 4452

Kustow, D H (Olswang LLP) *E L*
London WC1 *p64* 020 7067 3000

Kusturovic, N (Procol & Candor Solicitors)
Ealing *p69* 020 8993 4646

Kutner, M D (Finers Stephens Innocent LLP) *E R2*
London W1 *p32* 020 7323 4000

Kwan, Miss K (Mills & Reeve) *X Zp*
Cambridge *p175* 01223 364422

Kwasnik, S E (Betesh Partnership) *N J2*
Manchester *p301* 0161 834 2623

Kwaw, Ms C (Hodders) *Zh L Q O F1 J1 Zi*
London NW10 *p41* 020 8838 1537

Kwok, J (Matthew Arnold & Baldwin LLP) *S1 S2 W E*
Watford *p423* 01923 202020

Kyle, C J (Hathaways) *F1 G H J1 K1 L M1 P S1 W*
Gateshead *p228* 0191 477 2288

Kynaston, C (Hatchers Solicitors LLP)
Whitchurch *p430* 01948 663361

Kynnersley, J (FBC Manby Bowdler LLP) *W S1*
Bridgnorth *p157* 01746 761436

Kyriacou, Ms G S (Colman Coyle LLP) *C1 F1 J1 B1*
Islington *p22* 020 7354 3000

Kyriacou, J (Penningtons) *Zr*
London EC2 *p66* 020 7457 3000

Kyriakides, A K (Adonis Kyriakides & Co)
Westminster *p50* 020 7229 3800

Kyriakides, R A F (Kyriakides & Braier) *C1 T1 B1 N E K1 J1 O G R1 W Zf Ze Zc*
London W1 *p50* 020 7637 3289

Kyriakou, S (Ashurst LLP)
London EC2 *p7* 020 7638 1111

Kyte, Ms V E (Denbighshire County Council)
Ruthin *p470* 01824 706000

L

L'Estrange, M J (Watson Farley & Williams) *T1 T2*
London EC2 *p90* 020 7814 8000

L'Estrange, P N (Hamnett Osborne Tisshaw) *K1 K3*
Haywards Heath *p245* 01444 443030

La Rocca, F (Tickle Hall Cross) *S1*
St Helens *p391* 0800 854379

Labadie, R M (Blake Lapthorn) *N*
Portsmouth *p354* 023 9222 1122

Laband, J L (Jackamans) *S1 W T2*
Diss *p210* 01379 643555

Labi, R (Hughes Fowler Carruthers) *K1 K3*
London WC2 *p43* 020 7421 8383

Labinjoh, Ms S L (Hodge Jones & Allen LLP) *Zg N Zq Zp*
London NW1 *p41* 020 7874 8300

Labor, Miss S A (Forster Dean Ltd) *K1 N*
Widnes *p431* 0151 422 0982

Labrom, Mrs L (Andrew Jackson) *W K4 T2 Zd*
Hull *p257* 01482 325242

Labrum, M J (Labrums) *S1 E L Q K1 O W N B1*
St Albans *p390* 01727 858807

Labrum, T H (Oglethorpe Sturton & Gillibrand) *A1 S1 W*
Lancaster *p270* 01524 846846

Labuschagne, W (Invesco)
London EC2 *p107* 020 7065 3057

Lace, J D (Bristows) *B1 C1 C2 C3 J1 Zd Zb*
London EC4 *p15* 020 7400 8000

Lacey, Miss E G (Tayntons LLP Solicitors) *K1 K3*
Gloucester *p230* 01452 522047

Lacey, H C (Clifton Ingram LLP) *A1 C1 E S1 S2 T1 T2 W Zd*
Reading *p360* 0118 957 3425

Lacey, Mrs J (BPE Solicitors LLP) *E*
Cheltenham *p187* 01242 224433

Lacey, Miss J M (EMW) *E R2 S2 L Zb*
Milton Keynes *p316* 0845 070 6000

Lacey, Miss K A (Reading Borough Council)
Reading *p469* 0118 939 0900

Lacey, M R A (LG Lawyers) *C1 J1 F1 I Zj*
London SE1 *p50* 020 7379 0000

Lacey, S C (Simon Lacey Law Associates) *K1 G H D1 P Zl*
Weymouth *p430* 01305 777711

Lacey-Eresh, Mrs J J (P B & W Solicitors LLP t/a Pooley Bendall & Watson) *K1 K2 L V D1 K3*
Ely *p218* 01353 666075

Lachlan, G S J (Godloves) *B1 Ze Zb C1*
Leeds *p273* 0113 225 8811

Lachmansingh, Miss A (Rouse Legal (Formerly Willoughby & Partners)) *Ze*
London E14 *p74* 020 7536 4100

Lack, Miss G (William Heath & Co) *S2 E S1*
London SW11 *p40* 020 7350 1068

Lacy Scott, F J (ASB Law) *J1 Zj*
Crawley *p202* 01293 603600

Lacy, J G (Coole & Haddock) *E S1 S2 Zd*
Horsham *p253* 01403 210200

Lad, B (Greenwoods)
Milton Keynes *p317* 01908 298200

Lada-Walicki, Ms J A M (Barlow Robbins LLP) *J1 X*
Guildford *p235* 01483 562901

Ladd, Miss E C (stevensdrake)
Crawley *p202* 01293 596900

Ladds, Miss J J (Roythornes LLP) *E S1 S2 L A1 R2*
Spalding *p389* 01775 842500

Ladell, Ms R A (Milne Moser) *Q N S1 W*
Kendal *p264* 01539 729786 / 725582

Laderman, D A (Ladermans)
London NW4 *p51* 020 8203 6136

Laderman, D C (Laderman & Co) *W T2 S1 S2 T1 Q C1 K3*
Redbridge *p51* 020 8530 7319

Laderman, H (Ladermans)
London NW4 *p51* 020 8203 6136

Laderman, R E (Laderman & Co) *E S1 T1 W C1 L P J1 F1 H Zc Zf Zl*
Redbridge *p51* 020 8530 7319

Ladha, N (Department for Business, Enterprise and Regulatory Reform)
London SW1 *p105* 020 7215 0105

Lado, R (Charles Crookes Limited) *M1 M2 S1 W C1 C2 J1 Ze*
Cardiff *p178* 029 2049 1271

Ladva, Mrs K (Irwin Mitchell LLP) *U1*
Birmingham *p139* 0870 150 0100

Ladwa, R (Wansbroughs) *C1*
Devizes *p210* 01380 733300

Ladwa, Miss V (Frisby & Co) *G B2*
Stafford *p392* 01785 244114

Lafferty, A (Field Fisher Waterhouse LLP)
London EC3 *p31* 020 7861 4000

Laffery, A N (Field Fisher Waterhouse LLP)
London EC3 *p31* 020 7861 4000

Laffey, M (Thompsons (formerly Robin/Brian Thompson & Partners))
Newcastle upon Tyne *p327* 0191 269 0400

Laffey, T V (Terence Carney) *G H N*
Hebburn *p246* 0191 483 5422 / 483 8771

Lafinhan, O (Salehs LLP) *S1*
Manchester *p309* 0161 434 9991

Lafont De Sentenac, J (TLT Solicitors)
London EC2 *p85* 020 3465 4000

Lagar, C M (DWF)
Manchester *p303* 0161 603 5000

Lagergren, Miss S A (McKinnells) *K1 D1*
Lincoln *p284* 01522 541181

Lages, Miss P R (Lages & Co) *W S1 R1 A1 L E Zd T2 Zm*
Wadhurst *p418* 01892 784419

Lagler, M (Unilever PLC) *C1*
London EC4 *p110* 020 7822 5252

Lahaise, A P (Tanburghs O'Brien Lahaise) *K1 K3 Q W L G S1*
Camden *p85* 020 7372 6614

See p634 for the Key to Work Categories

Laher, A H (Blackpool Borough Council)
Blackpool p450 01253 477450
Lahiff, P F (Lahiff & Co) G H
Greenwich p51 020 8855 5656
Lahive, W A (Walker Lahive) G H
Plymouth p350 01752 551722
Lai, Ms S Y (Christine Lee & Co (Solicitors) Ltd) S2 E S1 W Zi
London W1 p52 020 7287 6233
Laidlaw, K J (McKeag & Co) G H
Gosforth p231 0191 213 1010
Laidler, Mrs J (Gregory Rowcliffe Milners) J1 K1 D1 Zp
London WC1 p37 020 7242 0631
Laight, S B (Pinsent Masons LLP) Zo
Birmingham p141 0121 200 1050
Laing, A J H (Brignalls Balderston Warren) E S1 W T2
Baldock p121 01462 490100
Laing, A M (Cheshire County Council)
Chester p454 01244 602382
Laing, I (Pinsent Masons LLP) Zc Zu
London EC2 p67 020 7418 7000
Laing, Mrs N (DWF) J1 N Zp J2
Manchester p303 0161 603 5000
Laing, R E (Cyfraith JRL Law) S1 W E N K4 P A1 Zq Q Zl Zt
Llanrwst p292 01492 641222
Laird Craig, R J (Forsters LLP) T2 W
Westminster p33 020 7863 8333
Laird, B M (Astwood Law)
Redditch p362 01527 892200
Laird, Mrs C A (Shakespeares) W T1 Zd
Birmingham p142 0121 237 3000
Laird, Miss R (Watson Burton LLP) J1 O
Newcastle upon Tyne p327 0845 901 2100
Laird, S (Reynolds Porter Chamberlain LLP)
London E1 p71 020 3060 6000
Laithwaite, Mrs M (Universal Pictures International Ltd)
London WC1 p110 020 7079 6000
Laitner, G (Faegre & Benson LLP) C2 C1
London EC4 p30 020 7450 4500
Lake, A J (Burnetts) E S2
Carlisle p181 01228 552222
Carlisle p182 01228 552222
Lake, Mrs D (ASB Law) J1 Zp
Crawley p202 01293 603600
Lake, G (Funnell & Perring)
Hastings p243 01424 426287
Lake, J (TV Edwards LLP) G H
London EC3 p85 020 7790 7000
Lake, Ms J (Trowers & Hamlins) L O Q J1 Zb
Manchester p310 0161 211 0000
Lake, Ms T L (Severn Trent Water Ltd)
Birmingham p450 0121 722 4000
Lake, T M D (Stepien Lake) E S1
London W1 p83 020 7467 3030
Lake, V (Dickinson Manser) P L F1 J1 N B1 Zp
Poole p352 01202 673071
Lakeland, N C J (Silverman Sherliker LLP) J1 J2 Zp
London EC2 p78 020 7749 2700
Lakeman, C (Magna Housing Group Ltd)
Dorchester p457 01305 216000
Lakhani, Ms N (Lakhani & Co) Q K3 L K1 W O Zq Zi
Brent p51 020 8204 7100
Lakhani, S (Quality Solicitors Clarke & Son) E S1 S2
Basingstoke p127 01256 320555
Lakhani, S (AKL Solicitors) Zi N
Luton p294 01582 454365
Lakhanpaul, Miss A (South Bucks District Council)
Denham p456 01895 837200
Lakin, I M (Placidi & Co) O Q A3 Ze Zq B2 C1 B1 Zc Zk
Southampton p386 01489 579804
Lakin, J A (Equality & Human Rights Commission)
Manchester p464 0161 829 8100
Lakin, Miss J E (Derbyshire County Council) K1 H G Q
Matlock p465 01629 580000
Lal, H (Jones Day) E
London EC4 p46 020 7039 5959
Lal-Sood, Ms S (Beale and Company Solicitors LLP) O Q N M1 R1 L S1 W Zc Zq
London WC2 p11 020 7240 3474
Lala, M (Rowland Tildesley & Harris) S1 K3 L K1 W
Willenhall p433 01902 366571
Lall, A S (Chambers Solicitors) S1 S2 Zl E W
Slough p381 01753 522204
Lall, Mrs P K (Wakefield Metropolitan District Council)
Wakefield p474 01924 306090
Lall, T S (Charles Russell LLP) T1
London EC4 p19 020 7203 5000
Lalli, Ms A K (J B Wheatley & Co) K1
London SE8 p91 020 8479 8000
Lalli, Ms K (Wedlake Bell LLP)
London WC1 p91 020 7395 3000
Lally, Ms H (Morecrofts Solicitors LLP)
Birkenhead p134 0151 666 2210
Lam, Ms P (Bolt Burdon) O
Islington p14 020 7288 4700
Lam-Kee, Miss L (Glovers Solicitors LLP) R2 Zb
London W1 p36 020 7935 8882
Lamb, Ms A D (Lamb & Kavanagh) D1
Camden p51 020 7209 2481
Lamb, D G (Beecham Peacock) G K1 S1 N W J1 T1 Zi Zm
Newcastle upon Tyne p323 0191 232 3048
Lamb, G E (Nicholsons Solicitors LLP) Q B1
Lowestoft p294 01502 532300
Lamb, G M (DLA Piper UK LLP) J1
Leeds p272 0870 011 1111
Lamb, Ms J (Lewis Nedas & Co) D1 F1 G H J1 K1 L M1 P V Zw Zm Zi
Camden p53 020 7387 2032
Lamb, J E (Lamb & Holmes) A1 C1 E L S1 W
Kettering p265 01536 513195
Lamb, J J B (Lamb & Smart) C1 E L S1 T1
New Milton p321 01425 613434
Lamb, J S (Gosschalks) Ze C1
Hull p256 01482 324252
Lamb, L (Scott Richards)
Teignmouth p409 01626 772441
Lamb, M (Morecrofts Solicitors LLP) W T2
Liverpool p290 0151 236 8871
Lamb, N P (Steeles) J1
Norwich p335 0870 609 0200
Lamb, P L (Tinklin Springall) S1 S2 N W L R2 K1 J1 D1 C1
Bromley p167 020 8402 6222
Lamb, P R (Lewis Silkin LLP) C1
London EC4 p53 020 7074 8000
Lamb, R M (Dilworth Lamb & Co) K1 G H S1 D1 N Q W L
Orpington p341 01689 821119
Lamb, Miss S (Shell International Ltd) E
London SE1 p109 020 7934 1234
Lamb, Mrs S A (Briggs Sayer & Co) S1 W
Belper p130 01773 825246
Lamb, S J (Stephen J Lamb) T1 T2
Southwark p51 020 7738 6838
Lambdin, P J (Stevens & Bolton) N P B1 J1 M1
Guildford p237 01483 302264
Lambe, W J (DWF) O C1 E Q J1 B1 Zc Zb Ze Zk Zz
Manchester p303 0161 603 5000
Lambert, A D (Barlow Lyde & Gilbert LLP)
London EC3 p10 020 7247 2277
Lambert, B (Trowers & Hamlins)
London EC3 p88 020 7423 8000
Lambert, D (Penningtons) O
London EC2 p66 020 7457 3000
Lambert, D S (Hague Lambert) C1 C2 W Ze
Manchester p305 0161 834 6066
Lambert, Ms J (Barlow Lyde & Gilbert LLP) O Q Zj
London EC3 p10 020 7247 2277
Lambert, J F J (Stanford & Lambert) S1 W G H C1 F1 E N L D1
Newcastle upon Tyne p327 0191 232 6226
Lambert, J W (Lamberts) E C1 W S1 L K1 M1 N P T1 Zb Zc Zl Zo Zj
Sevenoaks p374 01732 460565
Lambert, Miss K (Martyn Prowel) G
Cardiff p180 029 2047 0909
Lambert, M D (Carlisle City Council)
Carlisle p453 01228 817000
Lambert, M D (Baily Gibson)
Beaconsfield p128 01494 672661
Lambert, M J (Winterbotham Smith Penley LLP) W Zd T2 K4
Stroud p401 01453 847200
Lambert, N T (Wake Smith & Tofields) N L A3 B1 F1 Zc Zq Zj O Q
Sheffield p377 0114 266 6660
Lambert, P B (TWM Solicitors LLP) S2 C1 E L S1 X
London SW19 p85 020 8946 6454
Lambert, R C (Fishburns) Zc O Zj Q Zq
London EC3 p32 020 7280 8888
Lambert, Ms R E M (Maples Teesdale LLP) E S2
London EC2 p58 020 7600 3800
Lambert, R I (Clifford Chance)
London E14 p20 020 7006 1000
Lambert, Ms S E (Bowles & Co) K1 Q L
Epsom p219 01372 725241
Lambert, S J (Bridge McFarland) N Zr
Grimsby p235 01472 311711
Louth p294 01507 605883
Lambert, Mrs T (Tozers) K1 D1 D2
Newton Abbot p329 01626 207020
Lambert, Miss W (Squire Sanders (UK) LLP) Zo
London EC2 p81 020 7655 1000
Lambie, C J B (Allen & Overy LLP)
London E1 p5 020 3088 0000
Lambie, G J R (Glanvilles) E M1 S1 W Za
Newport p328 01983 527878
Lambie, Ms M (Westminster City Council)
London SW1 p110 020 7641 6000
Lamble, P (Coodes) Q O
Truro p414 01872 246200
Lambrou, L (YVA Solicitors)
London N12 p93 020 8445 9898
Laming, Dr G (Mills & Reeve) T2 W
Norwich p335 01603 660155
Lamond, I D (Stephens & Scown) C1 C2 C3 P R1
St Austell p391 01726 74433
Lamond, Miss M (David Auld & Co) G H K1 Q D1 D2
Bedlington p130 01670 826870
Morpeth p319 01670 505844
Lamont, Ms A (Quality Solicitors Burroughs Day) Zm
Bristol p164 0117 929 0333
Lamont, D (Charles Russell LLP) Zk Ze Zf U2 G Zg Zw
London EC4 p19 020 7203 5000
Lamont, J (Cumberland Ellis Peirs) C1 Ze Zw U2 F1 I M2 Zd
London WC1 p23 020 7242 0422
Lamont, Ms S (Bevan Brittan LLP) J1
Bristol p161 0870 194 1000
Lampard, C (Macfarlanes) E
London EC4 p56 020 7831 9222
Lampert, Mrs J M J (Birmingham City Council Legal & Democratic Services)
Birmingham p449 0121 303 2066
Lamster, P W (The Watson Ramsbottom Partnership)
Blackburn p146 01254 672222
Darwen p207 01254 701111
Lanaghan, Miss K (Squire Sanders (UK) LLP)
London EC2 p81 020 7655 1000
Lanaway, Ms S D (Cooper Lingard) K1 D1
Leigh-on-Sea p282 01702 715411
Lancaster, A D (Lancasters) K1 C1 S1 E N Q L J1 W Zi Zj Zk Zl
London W4 p51 020 8742 1314
Lancaster, A J (Anthony Collins Solicitors LLP) P B1 J1 O Q Zc Zk
Birmingham p137 0121 200 3242
Lancaster, Ms B J (Graysons) N
Sheffield p375 0114 272 9184
Lancaster, Miss C M (Bruce Lance & Co) K3 K1 D1
High Wycombe p250 01494 450494
Lancaster, D B (Pinsent Masons LLP) O Q Zi Zc Zj
London EC2 p67 020 7418 7000
Lancaster, Ms H (Castle Morpeth Borough Council)
Morpeth p466 01670 535000
Lancaster, Miss J (Keoghs LLP)
Bolton p149 01204 677000
Lancaster, J A (GHP Legal) K1 S1 W L F1 J1 V T1 Zm
Wrexham p442 01978 291456
Lancaster, Mrs K E (Farrer & Co LLP)
London WC2 p31 020 3375 7000
Lancaster, Ms N J (Shell International Ltd)
London SE1 p109 020 7934 1234
Lancaster, R S (Burton Copeland LLP)
Manchester p302 0161 827 9500
Lancaster, Ms V A L (Lancasters) S1 G K1 W R1 E C1 L P A1 Ze Zf Zl
Bridlington p158 01262 602401
Lancefield, G M (Brabners Chaffe Street) O Zq Zk
Liverpool p286 0151 600 3000
Lanceley, I K (W H Matthews & Co) Zl Q L J1
Kingston upon Thames p267 020 8549 0264
Lanceley, I K (W H Matthews & Co) Zl L J1 N O Q Zk Zv Zy
Islington p59 020 7251 4942
Lanch, I C (Gosschalks) K1 K2
Hull p256 01482 324252
Land, I S (Levi Solicitors LLP) C1 E J1 L O S1 S2 Q
Leeds p275 0113 244 9931
Land, K J (Sintons LLP) J1
Newcastle upon Tyne p326 0191 226 7878
Landa, K S (HSK Solicitors LLP) S2 E S1
Manchester p305 0161 795 4818
Landau, H (H Landau & Co) J1 N W
Edgware p217 020 8959 6991
Landau, J J (K&L Gates LLP) C1 C2 C3 U1
London EC4 p47 020 7648 9000
Landau, P S (Landau Zeffertt Weir) O Q B1 N K1
London SE1 p51 020 7357 9494
Landau, S (Trott & Gentry) D1 E K1 L M1 N S1 W Q
London N1 p88 020 3119 3150
Landcastle, Miss C (J A Hughes) K1 K3
Barry p126 01446 411000
Lander, A J (G & I Chisholm) K1 P N J1 L F1 B1 V D1 K3
Bodmin p148 01208 74242
Lander, Mrs H A M (Salusburys Harding & Barnett) C1 E L S1 W Zd
Leicester p281 0116 262 9033 / 262 6052
Lander, H W (Harborough District Council)
Market Harborough p465 01858 821341
Lander, T J (Harrop White Vallance & Dawson) G H J1 K1 Q
Mansfield p311 01623 629221
Landers, G A (Richard George & Jenkins) A1 E S1 S2 W
Newtown p330 01686 626210
Landes, Mrs C S (McMillan Williams Solicitors) D2 D1 S2 E G H K3 K1 K2 B2 Zv S1 W
Bexleyheath p132 020 8303 0168
Landey, H S M (Ogden Lyles & Fox) G H N J1 F1 D1 K1 L Q
Eccles p216 0161 789 2793
Irlam p263 0161 775 3744
Landi, D P (Streathers Solicitors LLP) C1 J1 B1 E N L Ze Zf
London W1 p84 020 7034 4200
Landis, Ms J (The College of Law Chester)
Chester p454 0800 289997
Lands, R C (Finers Stephens Innocent LLP) U2 Ze
London W1 p32 020 7323 4000
Landsberg, Ms L (Edwards Duthie) K1
Ilford p260 020 8514 9000
London NW4 p66 020 8201 6311
Landy, J D (Miller Sands) C1 E I L S1 S2 Zc
Cambridge p175 01223 202345
Lane, Mrs A (Wholley Goodings LLP) W
Morpeth p319 01670 519714
Lane, A H (AWB Charlesworth LLP) S1 W
Skipton p381 01756 793333
Lane, A H (Forsters LLP) A1 T2
Westminster p33 020 7863 8333
London EC4 p92 020 7597 6000
Lane, Mrs A M (Crown Prosecution Service Avon & Somerset) D1 F1 G H K1 M1
Bristol p451 0117 930 2800
Lane, D (Hogan Lovells International LLP)
London EC1 p42 020 7296 2000
Lane, Ms D (Goodhand and Forsyth QualitySolicitors) G H
Redhill p362 01737 773533
Lane, Miss E C P (Treasury Solicitors Department)
London WC2 p110 020 7210 3000
Lane, G R (Trethowans LLP) N Zq Zw
Southampton p387 023 8032 1000
Lane, Ms H L (J A Hughes) K3 K1
Cardiff p179 029 2061 9700
Cowbridge p201 01446 775535
Lane, J (Linklaters LLP)
London EC2 p54 020 7456 2000
Lane, Ms J A (Belron International Ltd)
Egham p470 01784 476800
Lane, Mrs J M (VFS Financial Services (UK) Ltd)
Warwick p475 01926 498888
Lane, J R (Rollits LLP) T1 W C1 Zd Zm
York p445 01904 625790
Lane, J S (J S Lane & Co) C1 E L R1 S1 W
Bushey p172 020 8950 1782

6

Lane, K A (Kevin Lane & Co) A1 B1 C1 E G H L R1 S1 T1
Port Talbot p353 01639 893700
Lane, K P (South Northamptonshire Council)
Towcester p474 01327 322322
Lane, M A (Pinsent Masons LLP) O Q M1 Zc
London EC2 p67 020 7418 7000
Lane, M P (Gisby Harrison) F1 J1 O Zl
Cheshunt p189 01707 878300
Lane, M R (Jacklyn Dawson) S1 S2 T2 W C1 E K4
Newport p328 01633 262952
Lane, M S (Fladgate LLP) S1
London WC2 p32 020 3036 7000
Lane, N (Michelmores LLP) I U1 U2 Zza Ze
Exeter p221 01392 688688
Lane, Mrs N (Shell International Ltd)
London SE1 p109 020 7934 1234
Lane, P D (Harvey Ingram LLP) E
Leicester p280 0116 254 5454
Lane, P S (W F Smith LLP) K1 M1 N P W S1 E H J1 F1 Zd Zl
Watton p424 01953 880800
Lane, R (Hugh James) C1 I O
Cardiff p179 029 2022 4871
Lane, R (Wright Hassall LLP) O Zc Zq A3 Zw
Leamington Spa p270 01926 886688
Lane, R A (Harold Benjamin) E S1 R1 C1 L
Harrow p241 020 8422 5678
Lane, R C (Young Coles & Langdon) S1 W T1 E P M1 C1 F1 B1 A1 Zb Ze Zm
Bexhill p132 01424 210013
Lane, R C (CMS Cameron McKenna LLP)
London EC3 p17 020 7367 3000
Lane, R T C (Farrer & Co LLP) C1 C2
London WC2 p31 020 3375 7000
Lane, S A (SGH Martineau LLP) E
Birmingham p142 0870 763 2000
Lane, T A (Rio Tinto PLC)
London W2 p109 020 7781 2000
Lang, Mrs C A (Barrett & Thomson) E S1
Slough p381 01753 437416
Lang, Mrs C M (Bank of Scotland)
Chester p454 01244 690000
Lang, D M (Blanchards Bailey LLP) Zd
Blandford Forum p147 01258 459361
Lang, J (Kitsons LLP)
Plymouth p350 01752 603040
Lang, Ms J (Radcliffes Le Brasseur)
Westminster p70 020 7222 7040
Lang, Miss J L (Radcliffes Le Brasseur) Zr Zq Q G J1 Zm N J2
Cardiff p180 029 2034 3035
Lang, J L (Allen & Overy LLP)
London E1 p5 020 3088 0000
Lang, Mrs J M (Blanchards Bailey LLP) K1 K2
Dorchester p212 01305 251222
Lang, M C (Goughs) R2 S1 S2 W
Corsham p199 01249 712193
Lang, S (George Davies Solicitors LLP) O Q Zq
Manchester p303 0161 236 8992
Lang, T M (George Green LLP) Q J1 O
Cradley Heath p201 01384 410410
Liverpool p291 0151 227 2601
Lang, T T (Weightmans LLP) J1 K1 Q Zz Zl
Birmingham p143 0121 632 6100
Lang, Ms Z (Lupton Fawcett) E S1
Leeds p275 0113 280 2000
Langan, C (Howard Kennedy LLP) E R2
London W1 p48 020 7636 1616
Langat, R (Ashurst LLP)
London EC2 p7 020 7638 1111
Langdon, C M F (Young Coles & Langdon) S1 W C1 M1 L J1 A1 Zd S2 E Zx X Zh
Hastings p244 01424 437878
Langdon, M C (Michelmores LLP) O E L Q
Exeter p221 01392 688688
Langdon, P (Mid Devon District Council)
Tiverton p474 01884 255255
Langdown, V L (Sampson Coward LLP)
Salisbury p371 01722 410664
Langers, J J (Southern Stewart & Walker) C1 S2 E F1 L Q W S1
South Shields p384 0191 456 7788

Langfeld, A L F (Maxwell Hodge Solicitors) *S1 W S2 E C1 L R2 R1 A1*
Formby *p227* 01704 872156
Langford, C R (Howard Kennedy LLP) *E R1*
London W1 *p48* 020 7636 1616
Langford, Miss C V (Higgs & Sons) *G H V*
Brierley Hill *p158*. 0845 111 5050
Langford, D (Howard Kennedy LLP) *C1*
London W1 *p48* 020 7636 1616
Langford, E A (Meade-King) *E*
Bristol *p163* 0117 926 4121
Langford, P J D (Goodman Derrick LLP) *C1 B1 T1 J1 Zb Ze*
London EC4 *p36*. 020 7404 0606
Langford, S (Sayers) *S1 E C1 W L F1 J1 K1 Zl*
Harrow *p242*. 020 8861 4191
Langford, T R (Wallace Robinson & Morgan) *S1 E C1 S2*
Solihull *p383*. 0121 705 7571
Langham, G D (Fiona Bruce & Co LLP) *W K4*
Warrington *p421*. 01925 263273
Langlands, G (John Donkin & Co)
Washington *p423* 0191 416 9444
Langleben, A (Rochman Landau LLP) *O Q J1 L Zq A3*
London W1 *p72* 020 7544 2424
Langley White, Mrs J (Addleshaw Goddard)
London EC1 *p4* 020 7606 8855
Manchester *p300* 0161 934 6000
Langley White, Ms J L (Coventry City Council)
Coventry *p456*. 024 7683 4863
Langley, Mrs A J (GLRS Phoenix LLP)
Stonehouse *p398* 01453 825151
Langley, D (Gregg Latchams LLP) *E C1 S1 W S2*
Bristol *p162* 0117 906 9400
Bristol *p162* 0117 906 9400
Langley, R (Muckle LLP) *Zc Zq Zj A3 O*
Newcastle upon Tyne *p325* . 0191 211 7777
Langmead, Mrs A J (Pennon Group PLC)
Exeter *p458* 01392 446677
Langridge, C J (Cripps Harries Hall LLP) *C1 B1 F1 T1 C2*
Tunbridge Wells *p415* 01892 515121
Langridge, Ms K (Keoghs LLP) *N Zj O Q A3*
Bolton *p149* 01204 677000
Coventry *p200*. 024 7665 8200
Langridge, Ms S E (Sharon Langridge Employment Lawyers) *J1*
Newcastle upon Tyne *p325* . 0191 222 1221
Langrishe, P d P (Symes Robinson & Lee) *D1 K1 N Q Zq*
Budleigh Salterton *p168* . . . 01395 445581
Langsford, Ms A J (Linda Stapleton & Co) *K3 K1*
Gloucester *p230*. 01452 423870
Langsford, I J (Peters Langsford Davies) *Q K3 K1 N Zl Zq*
Launceston *p270* 01566 772451
Langton, Ms B S (Broxtowe Borough Council)
Beeston *p449* 0115 917 7777
Langton, R C (Russell Jones & Walker) *N J1 Zw Zk Zd*
Birmingham *p141* 0121 233 8300
Langton, R J (Cartwright King) *G H*
Derby *p208* 01332 346111
Langton, Mrs S K (Morgans) *S1 B1 E F1 J1 K1 L N Q A1 C1 O W Ze*
Abergavenny *p113*. 01873 859993
Langton, T (The BOC Group PLC)
Guildford *p476*. 01483 579857
Langton, T J (Goodman Derrick LLP) *B1 K1 N P Ze Zf Zk*
London EC4 *p36*. 020 7404 0606
Langworthy, I J (Copleys) *A1 C1 E J1 O Q*
St Ives *p391*. 01480 464515
Huntingdon *p258*. 01480 456191
Lank, Ms C (Bristol City Council)
Bristol *p451* 0117 922 2000
Lankester, Ms J C (Hewitsons) *A1 E S1 L S2*
Northampton *p332*. 01604 233233
Lankshear, J T (Streathers Solicitors LLP) *O Q L B1 K1 Ze Zj Zv*
London W1 *p84* 020 7034 4200
Lannagan, Mrs H A (Freeman Johnson) *K1 K3 D1 D2*
Durham *p214* . . 0191 386 4843 / 386 9619
Lanni, V (Charles Russell LLP) *Zw C1 U1*
London EC4 *p19*. 020 7203 5000
Lansbury, B J (Lansbury Worthington) *G H N B2*
London W6 *p51* 020 8563 9797
Lansdell, H P (Hansells) *E S1 W A1 A2 L Zd*
Aylsham *p121* 01263 734313
Lansdown, S (Hill Dickinson LLP) *O C1 B1 Zj J1 C2*
Liverpool *p288*. 0151 600 8000
Lansdowne, Miss R (South Kesteven District Council)
Grantham *p459* 01476 406080
Lansley, S C (Ellisons) *I E W*
Clacton-on-Sea *p195* 01255 421248
Colchester *p197*. 01206 764477
Lapidge, S (Lodders Solicitors LLP) *W T2*
Henley-in-Arden *p247* 01564 792261
Lapite, Mrs A O (Essex County Council)
Chelmsford *p454*. 0845 743 0430
Lapite, L (Essex County Council)
Chelmsford *p454*. 0845 743 0430
Lappage, Miss J (Denhams) *G H K1 S1 W Q*
Guildford *p236*. 01483 456450
Lapraik, J D (Kennedys) *O Zb*
Cambridge *p174*. 01223 533060
Lapraik, Ms N E P (Mills & Reeve) *E S1*
Cambridge *p175*. 01223 364422

Lapsley, Miss S (Chestnutts) *J1 Q N O F1*
Ainsdale *p114* 01704 572221
Lapthorne, S (ClarksLegal LLP) *J1*
London WC2 *p20* 020 7539 8000
Lapworth, Ms R L (Lester Aldridge LLP) *S1*
Bournemouth *p152*. 01202 786161
Larbalestier, Miss K J (Wollen Michelmore Solicitors) *K1 K3*
Newton Abbot *p330* 01626 332266
Larby, A G B (Larby Williams with Gwyn & Gwyn) *E K1 Zl S1 W*
Cowbridge *p201* 01446 775535
Larcombe, M P (B P Collins LLP) *E S1 S2*
Gerrards Cross *p229*. 01753 889995
Larcombe, S J (Limbach Banham) *A1 C1 E F1 J1 L S1*
Royston *p368* 01763 242257
Larder, D M (Pinsent Masons LLP) *C1*
Leeds *p276* 0113 244 5000
Largan, N A (Crombie Wilkinson) *O Q A3 B1 F2 Zc Zl C1 J1 N Zq*
York *p444* 01904 624185
Large, A (Gateley LLP) *O A3 Zj*
London EC4 *p35*. 020 7653 1600
Large, Ms F K (Barlow Lyde & Gilbert LLP)
London EC3 *p10*. 020 7247 2277
Large, M W L (Matthew Wilkinson Solicitors Ltd) *N Zq Q*
Middlesbrough *p315* 01642 218888
Large, P G (Westminster City Council) *N Q*
London SW1 *p110*. 020 7641 6000
Large, P R A (Wilford Smith Solicitors) *G H K1 M1 P L F1 W Zl*
Rotherham *p367*. 01709 828044
Larke, J (Horsey Lightly) *E S1 R2 S2 Zb*
Westminster *p43*. 020 7222 8844
Larkin, A (Larkin & James) *S1 W S2*
West Byfleet *p427* 01932 355433
Larkin, F (Harveys Solicitors) *N*
Flint *p226* 01352 734003
Larkin, Miss J (Healds) *D1 K1 K3*
Wigan *p432* 01942 241511
Larkin, Ms M I (LG Lawyers)
London SE1 *p50*. 020 7379 0000
Larking, R P (Walker Morris) *R2 S2 E U1*
Leeds *p277* 0113 283 2500
Larkins, Mrs L (Bretherton Law) *D2 D1 K3 K1*
St Albans *p389* 01727 869293
Larkman, K H (Birkett Long LLP) *W T2*
Colchester *p197* 01206 217300
Larner, E (Recompense Solicitors Ltd) *Q*
Totnes *p413*. 0800 037 5817
Larner, Ms J R (Teacher Stern LLP) *E S2*
London WC1 *p86* 020 7242 3191
Laroya, Ms A (Magrath LLP) *S2 E*
London W1 *p57* 020 7495 3003
Larrad, K A (Kirklees Metropolitan Borough Council)
Huddersfield *p461* 01484 221421
Larsen, K (McDermott Will & Emery UK LLP)
London EC2 *p56*. 020 7577 6900
Larter, Mrs F (Veale Wasbrough Vizards) *J1*
Bristol *p165* 0117 925 2020
Larter, Ms H C (DAC Beachcroft)
Leeds *p272* 0113 251 4700
Lartey, Ms V (Hounslow Law Centre Ltd)
Hounslow *p461* 020 8570 9505
Larye, S L (Samuel L Larye & Co) *G H*
Brentford *p156*. 020 8568 7022
Lascelles, S (Skadden Arps Slate Meagher & Flom (UK) LLP)
London E14 *p80*. 020 7519 7000
Lasenby, Ms D J (Blake Lapthorn) *D1 D2*
Chandlers Ford *p184* 023 8090 8090
Lashmore, R A (Knights Solicitors LLP) *E Zg Zn R2*
Newcastle under Lyme *p323*. 01782 619225
Lask, P A (Keith Hall Juviler & Co) *C1 E T1 T2 W G L N R1 S1 Zh Zi Zl Zv Zs*
Greenford *p234* .020 8578 3133 / 8578 5373
Laskey, Miss J M (Wilson Browne) *J1 N O Q*
Northampton *p333*. 01604 876697
Laskey, P S (Bowling & Co) *O Q Zq*
London E15 *p15*. 020 8221 8000
Laski, A (The College of Law)
London WC1 *p105*. 0800 289997
Lass, J D (Davenport Lyons) *C1 L B1 Zb*
London W1 *p25* 020 7468 2600
Lass, Ms R (Mills & Reeve) *L Q O*
Cambridge *p175*. 01223 364422
Lassman, K (Howard Kennedy LLP) *C1 C2 F1 J1 T1*
London W1 *p48* 020 7636 1616
Last, J (Broadbents) *M1 N P K1 D1 F1 G H L V Zc Zf Zl*
Heanor *p246*. 01773 769891
Last, Miss M L (JNP Legal) *K1 D1 D2*
Merthyr Tydfil *p314* 01685 350421
Last, R A C (Caversham Solicitors Ltd) *Q O J1 C1 F1 L B1 Zk Zq F2 D2*
Reading *p360* 0118 947 8638
Laszlo, M G (W H Darbyshire & Son) *S1 W S2 E Zl R1 L*
Blackpool *p146* 01253 346646
Lytham *p296*. 01253 736134
Latcham, Miss J A (Lamb Brooks LLP) *O Q*
Basingstoke *p126* 01256 844888
Latchmore, A W (Shulmans) *E L S2 Zc R2 M1 Zu*
Leeds *p276* 0113 245 2833
Latham, A I (Stamp Jackson and Procter) *C1 C2 A1 C3 M1 J1 B1*
Hull *p258* 01482 324591

Latham, Ms A S (MWRLaw Ltd) *K1 D1 H J1*
Preston *p357* 01772 254201
Latham, C D (Tolhurst Fisher LLP)
Southend-on-Sea *p387* . . . 01702 352511
Latham, D A (Hogan Lovells International LLP)
London EC1 *p42*. 020 7296 2000
Latham, E D A (Treasury Solicitors Department)
London WC2 *p110*. 020 7210 3000
Latham, Mrs G R (Geldards LLP) *N*
Cardiff *p178* 029 2023 8239
Latham, Mrs J M (Burnand Brazier Tisdall) *W S1 K4*
Hove *p254*. 01273 734022
Worthing *p441* 01903 502155
Latham, P K (Glanvilles) *C1 G H K1 R1 S1*
Fareham *p224*. 01329 282841
Latham, Ms R (Wall James Chappell) *E P S1*
Stourbridge *p399* 01384 371622
Latham, Ms S L (Clarke Willmott) *J1 O Q Zo*
Bristol *p162* 0845 209 1000 / 0117 305 6000
Lati, Ms M (Grant Saw Solicitors LLP) *S1 S2 E*
Greenwich *p36*. 020 8858 6971
Latif, Ms A (Tyndallwoods) *Zi*
Birmingham *p143* 0121 624 1111
Latif, M A (Neil Myerson LLP) *C1 C2*
Altrincham *p117* 0161 941 4000
Latif, R (Aman Solicitors Advocates (London) Ltd) *J1 Zi Q N T2 W*
Wembley *p426*. 020 8782 3776
Latimer, E J (Bartletts Solicitors) *S1 K1 N W L F1 Q*
Chester *p190* 01244 313301
Latimer, Ms J V (Simpson Millar LLP) *N Q*
London EC1 *p80*. 0844 858 3400
Latimer, Mrs P M (Latimer Lee LLP)
Heywood *p249*. 01706 628008
Latimer, S R (Latimer Lee LLP)
Prestwich *p358* 0161 798 9000
Lattin, P D (Eurotunnel)
Folkestone *p458*. 01303 283900
Latty, Miss A (Reilly & Co Solicitors) *D1 K3 K1*
Birmingham *p141* 0121 744 4090
Latus, Mrs R (Rollits LLP) *O J2 Zj F2 Zq P*
Hull *p258* 01482 323239
Lau, D (The Johnson Partnership) *G H B2*
Nottingham *p337*. 0115 941 9141
Lau, M L (Reed Smith LLP) *C1*
London EC2 *p71*. 020 3116 3000
Laud, S (Stephenson Harwood) *E*
London EC2 *p82*. 020 7329 4422
Lauder, Ms A J (Taylor Walton LLP) *E S2 S1*
Luton *p295* 01582 731161
Lauder, Ms M C K (Richmond Anderson Goudie) *D1 K1*
Chester-le-Street *p191*. . . . 0191 388 7884
Laudy, R B G (Pinsent Masons LLP) *O Q Zc*
London EC2 *p67*. 020 7418 7000
Laugharne, A C (Chanter Ferguson) *K1 N D1 Q O B1 J1 X F1 G Zj Zl Zv Zc*
Barnstaple *p125* 01271 342268
Bideford *p132* 01237 478751
Laugharne, R J (GCL Solicitors) *C1 E F1 L R1 S1 R2*
Guildford *p236*. 01483 577091
Laughton, Miss S (Andersons Solicitors) *J1 Zp*
Nottingham *p335*. 0115 947 0641
Laundy, D J (Paton Walsh Laundy) *S1 W E F1 N Zi*
London SW19 *p66*. 020 8946 2229
Laurella, Ms L G (L G Laurella)
Ealing *p51*. 020 8840 5761
Laurence, B J (Sherrards) *O Q*
St Albans *p390* 01727 832830
Laurence, Miss F M C (London Fire & Emergency Planning Authority)
London SE1 *p107* 020 8555 1200
Laurenson, Ms K M R (British Telecommunications PLC)
London EC1 *p104*. 020 7356 6181
Laurent, Ms R A (Watson Farley & Williams) *C1 I Ze Zf*
London EC2 *p90*. 020 7814 8000
Laurie, E J (Hanson PLC)
London SW1 *p106*. 020 7245 1245
Lauzeral, Mrs I (Pritchard Englefield) *C1 C2*
London EC2 *p69*. 020 7972 9720
Lavelle, D R (Thomson Wilson Pattinson) *D1 K1 K3*
Kendal *p264*. 01539 721945
Lavelle, Ms F (Daniel and Harris) *D1 K1*
Camden *p25*. 020 7625 0202
Lavelle, G J C (John Welch & Stammers) *N O J1 Q B2 R1*
Witney *p436*. 01993 703941
Lavender, Ms R A (HL Legal & Collections) *F1 Q*
Redditch *p362*. 01527 586500
Laver, M H (Stevens & Bolton) *E A1*
Guildford *p237*. 01483 302264
Laver, Ms S (Ashurst LLP)
London EC2 *p7* 020 7638 1111
Laverick, D (Pensions Ombudsman)
London SW1 *p108*. 020 7834 9144
Lavers, M C W (Reynolds Porter Chamberlain LLP) *E S2 R2 L*
London E1 *p71* 020 3060 6000
Lavery, A D (Lavery Haynes) *L O S1*
London NW3 *p51* 020 7435 7441
Lavery, C H (Vincent Laverys) *G H K1 D1 N O*
Preston *p357* 01772 555176
Lavery, J C (DLA Piper UK LLP)
Birmingham *p137* 0870 011 1111
Lavery, P M (Vincent Laverys) *C1 E L T1 W*
Preston *p357* 01772 555176

Lavery, S (Pini Franco LLP) *C1 J1 Zl*
London EC1 *p67*. 020 7566 3140
Lavin, M D S (Macfarlanes) *C1*
London EC4 *p56*. 020 7831 9222
Lavin, T (Lavin Copitch) *N*
Altrincham *p116* 0161 941 6462
Manchester *p306* 0161 223 5484
Lavington, P (Morrisons Solicitors LLP) *N*
London SW19 *p62*. 020 8971 1020
Law, A (Attwood & Co) *W S1 L E K4*
Grays *p233* . . . . .01375 378122 / 378123
Law, Miss A S (Rochford District Council)
Rochford *p470*. 01702 546366
Law, C (WGS Solicitors)
Westminster *p90*. 020 7723 1656
Law, C L (Canty & Co) *Q O K3*
Birmingham *p136* 0121 688 5000
Law, Ms J W (Brachers) *N O Zr*
Maidstone *p299* 01622 690691
Law, Miss K A (Cripps Harries Hall LLP) *K1 D1*
Tunbridge Wells *p415* 01892 515121
Law, K D (Gough-Thomas & Scott)
Ellesmere *p217* 01691 622413
Law, Ms L J (Switalski's) *D1 K1 D2*
Wakefield *p419* 01924 882000
Law, R M (BBC)
London W12 *p103* 020 8752 5734
Law, Miss S (Treasury Solicitors Department) *O Q Zj*
London WC2 *p110*. 020 7210 3000
Law, S (Penningtons) *E*
Godalming *p231* 01483 791800
Reading *p361* . . 0370 086 8800 / 0118 965 8765
Law, T J (Devon County Council)
Exeter *p458* 01392 382000
Law-Riding, Miss A M (SFN Solicitors) *K1 D1 K2 K3*
Burnley *p169* 01282 421284
Lawer, H (Ralph & Co) *D1 K1*
Newquay *p329*. 01637 872218
Lawes, Miss C H (Blake Lapthorn) *C2*
Portsmouth *p354*. 023 9222 1122
Lawford, Ms L (Ashurst LLP)
London EC2 *p7* 020 7638 1111
Lawler, B M (Moore Brown & Dixon LLP) *Q K1 L J1 N O Zl Zf Zw Zr J2*
Upton-upon-Severn *p417* . . 01684 592675
Tewkesbury *p410* 01684 292341
Lawler, Mrs E (Sills & Betteridge LLP) *K1 K3*
Lincoln *p285* 01522 542211
Lawley, C J (Wokingham District Council)
Wokingham *p477* 0118 974 6000
Lawlor, B T (Morecrofts Solicitors LLP) *E S1 W Zl*
Liverpool *p290*. 0151 236 8871
Lawlor, C (Shell International Ltd)
London SE1 *p109* 020 7934 1234
Lawlor, Mrs F M (Houghton Pigot & Co) *S1 W C1 T1 E K4*
Ashton-in-Makerfield *p119* . 01942 270757
Wigan *p432* . . . . .01942 241288 / 824424
Lawlor, Ms S (Squire Sanders (UK) LLP)
Leeds *p277* 0113 284 7000
Lawrance, J W (Lawrance & Holder) *S1 W E*
Potters Bar *p355*. 01707 645317
Lawrence, Mrs A (Land Law LLP) *E R2 S2*
Altrincham *p116* 0161 928 8383
Lawrence, Miss A M (Warwickshire County Council)
Warwick *p475* 01926 410410
Lawrence, Miss A M (Carter Lemon Camerons)
London EC1 *p18*. 020 7406 1000
Lawrence, Mrs B A S (H Lawrence & Co) *S1 W E S2*
London N6 *p52* .020 7482 2613 / 7482 4212
Lawrence, Miss C (Atherton Godfrey) *Zr N*
Doncaster *p211* 01302 320621
Lawrence, Mrs C (Clarkson Wright & Jakes Ltd) *C1 C2*
Orpington *p341* 01689 887887
Lawrence, Ms C A (Squire Sanders (UK) LLP)
Manchester *p310* 0161 830 5000
Lawrence, C J H (Mawdsleys) *S1*
Southport *p388* 01704 537676
Lawrence, Mrs C J M (Stallard March & Edwards) *W K4 Zm T2*
Worcester *p440* 01905 613404
Lawrence, C S (Clarion Solicitors LLP) *T1 T2 C1 Ze Zf Zk Zw Zb C2 C3 I*
Leeds *p272* 0113 246 0622
Harrogate *p240* 01423 530630
Lawrence, D (McKeowns Solicitors Ltd) *N*
St Albans *p390* 0800 032 8328
Lawrence, D P (Eric Robinson Solicitors)
Southampton *p385*. 023 8042 5000
Lawrence, Miss F (Veale Wasbrough Vizards) *O B1*
Bristol *p165* 0117 925 2020
Lawrence, Mrs F V (Cockshott Peck Lewis) *W S1 T2*
Ainsdale *p114* 01704 574144
Southport *p388* 01704 534034
Lawrence, Mrs H (HKB Wiltshires) *K1*
Lowestoft *p294* 01502 582338
Lawrence, H V H P (H Lawrence & Co) *F1 K1 L N O Q Zv*
London N6 *p52* .020 7482 2613 / 7482 4212
Lawrence, I R (Millington Wallace & Co) *S1 E W L K1 T1 J1 Zo*
London N14 *p61*. 020 8882 1051
Lawrence, J (Hewitsons) *C1 C2*
Cambridge *p174*. 01223 461155
Lawrence, J D (Tallents Solicitors) *N K1 S1 W*
Newark *p322* 01636 671881

See p634 for the Key to Work Categories

Lawrence, J S (Lawrence Wood) S1 E S2 W
Wroxham p443 . . . 01603 783711

Lawrence, J T (Mundays LLP) L S1 S2 E
Cobham p196 . . . 01932 590500

Lawrence, J V (Pearman Smith) C1 E W S1 O
Walsall p420 . . . 01922 624164

Lawrence, Miss L M (Brethertons LLP) C1 S2 E F1 M1 B1 J1
Rugby p368 . . . 01788 579579
Rugby p368 . . . 01788 579579

Lawrence, Ms M (HRJ Law LLP) S1
Hitchin p251 . . . 01462 628888

Lawrence, Ms M (Park Woodfine Heald Mellows LLP) S2 E
Bedford p130 . . . 01234 400000

Lawrence, M D S (Alban Gould Baker & Co) S1 S2 K1 L
Islington p4 . . . 020 7607 5085

Lawrence, M J (Quality Solicitors Copley Clark) J1 Q O
Banstead p122 . . . 01737 362131

Lawrence, M J (Spearing Waite LLP) O Zq
Leicester p281 . . . 0116 262 4225

Lawrence, M K (Kennedys) Q O N Zj
London EC3 p49 . . . 020 7667 9667

Lawrence, N (Sternberg Reed) N
Barking p123 . . . 020 8591 3366

Lawrence, P (Taylor Wessing)
London EC4 p86 . . . 020 7300 7000

Lawrence, P J (Owen White) L Zh
Slough p382 . . . 01753 876800

Lawrence, P W (Patrick Lawrence) K1 D1 Q S1
Gravesend p233 . . . 01474 356441

Lawrence, R (W H Matthews & Co) S1 E S2 L
Kingston upon Thames p267 . 020 8549 0264

Lawrence, Ms R A (Bristows) Ze
London EC4 p15 . . . 020 7400 8000

Lawrence, Mrs R A (Edwards Duthie) E S2
Ilford p260 . . . 020 8514 9000

Lawrence, Mrs R J (Hill Dickinson LLP) J1 Zj Zq
Liverpool p288 . . . 0151 600 8000

Lawrence, R M (Newark & Sherwood District Council)
Newark p466 . . . 01636 650000

Lawrence, Ms S (Keelys LLP) E L S2
Lichfield p284 . . . 01543 420000

Lawrence, Miss S J (Talbot Walker LLP) G H
Andover p118 . . . 01264 363354

Lawrence, T (Leathes Prior) W
Norwich p334 . . . 01603 610911

Lawrence, T (Wood Sherwood & Co) K3 K1 D2 D1 F1 O Q N Zl
Pocklington p351 . . . 01759 302791

Lawrence, T D (Brethertons LLP) A1 Zl C1 S2 E F1 M1 B1 J1
Rugby p368 . . . 01788 579579
Rugby p368 . . . 01788 551611
Rugby p368 . . . 01788 579579

Lawrence, T O (Shakespeares) Zq A3 Ze O Q
Birmingham p142 . . . 0121 237 3000

Lawrenson, C D (The Building Societies Association)
London W1 p104 . . . 020 7437 0655

Lawrenson, Ms E (Lawson West Solicitors Limited) Q N
Leicester p280 . . . 0116 212 1000

Lawrenson, G (Osborne Clarke) O
London EC2 p65 . . . 020 7105 7000

Lawrenson, Mrs K (DWF) O B1
Manchester p303 . . . 0161 603 5000

Lawrenson, K R (Godwins) K1 K2 K3
Winchester p433 . . . 01962 841484

Lawrie, Ms A (Merrils Ede Solicitors)
Cardiff p180 . . . 029 2037 1131

Lawrie, D B S (Daniel & Edwards) S1 W E T1 L A1
Ramsgate p359 . . . 01843 594651

Laws, Miss C (Goodhand and Forsyth Quality Solicitors) S1 S2
Redhill p362 . . . 01737 773533

Laws, D A (Rogers & Norton) A3 F1 F2 O Q Ze Zq
Norwich p335 . . . 01603 666001

Laws, J P (Cripps Harries Hall LLP) O Q B1 A3 I
Tunbridge Wells p415 . . . 01892 515121

Laws, K M (Kingsley Napley) E S2 R2
London EC1 p50 . . . 020 7814 1200

Laws, Ms S A (Duane Morris) C1 C2 I F1 Ze Zj Zb M1 M2 U2 Zo Zza
London EC1 p28 . . . 020 7786 2100

Laws, Mrs W (The College of Law York)
York p477 . . . 0800 289997

Lawson, A J (Lee & Priestley LLP) S2 E
Leeds p275 . . . 0845 129 2300
Harrogate p240 . . . 01423 566666

Lawson, C (Linklaters LLP)
London EC2 p54 . . . 020 7456 2000

Lawson, C J (Aviva PLC)
London EC3 p103 . . 020 7283 7500 / 01603 687905

Lawson, Mrs C M (Burtonwood Brewery PLC)
Warrington p475 . . . 01902 711811

Lawson, D A (Favell Smith & Lawson Solicitors) G M1 P H J1 C1 N L F1
Sheffield p375 . . . 0114 272 4381

Lawson, D M G (Thurrock Borough Council) F1 J1 L Q V X N Zh Zi Zm Zp
Grays p459 . . . 01375 390000

Lawson, D V (David V Lawson Solicitors) S1 L C1 W N P J1 G
Ilford p260 . . . 020 8554 8848

Lawson, F J (W Davies) Q O J1 N A3 Zp B1 B2 F1 F2 G M1 L Zs Zk
Woking p436 . . . 01483 744900

Lawson, H (Foys Solicitors) N Q W J1 V B1
Worksop p441 . . . 01909 473560

Lawson, Ms H R (DWF) N J2 Zj
Leeds p272 . . . 0113 261 6000

Lawson, J E S (Hill Dickinson LLP) C1 Za Zj Zq O
London EC3 p41 . . . 020 7283 9033

Lawson, K (Beevers Solicitors) G H
Ashton-under-Lyne p119 . . . 0161 339 9697

Lawson, K P (Wigan Borough Council)
Wigan p476 . . . 01942 244991

Lawson, M H (William Sturges & Co) B1 Zd C1 S2 E Zo S1 W
Westminster p84 . . . 020 7873 1000

Lawson, M J (Watson Farley & Williams) C1 B1 J1 Ze
London EC2 p90 . . . 020 7814 8000

Lawson, P F (Chattertons Solicitors) N K1 Q O F1 A3 J1 F2 Ze Zq Zl Zp
Boston p151 . . . 01205 310025

Lawson, R (Linder Myers Solicitors)
Manchester p306 . . . 0844 984 6000

Lawson, Mrs S (Actons) E B1 C1 P R1 Zn Zc
Nottingham p335 . . . 0115 910 0200

Lawson, S A (Hunton & Garget) S1 W E L C1 Zl A1
Richmond p364 . . . 01748 850400

Lawson, S A (Foot Anstey) B1 Zq
Exeter p221 . . . 01392 411221
Exeter p221 . . . 01392 688688

Lawson, Mrs S G (Leeds Day) E S2 A1 R2 S1 L
Huntingdon p258 . . . 01480 454301

Lawson, S P (Forshaws Davies Ridgway LLP) Q N Zq
Frodsham p227 . . . 01928 739300

Lawson-Cruttenden, A T (Lawson-Cruttenden & Co) O Q N V Zb
London WC1 p52 . . . 020 7405 0833

Lawson-Hughes, Mrs F M R (Thomas Horton LLP) D2 D1 K3 K1
Bromsgrove p167 . . . 01527 871641

Lawson-King, Ms J (Pinsent Masons LLP) E
Birmingham p141 . . . 0121 200 1050

Lawther, M T (Portsmouth City Council)
Portsmouth p469 . . . 023 9283 4034

Lawton, A C (Thompsons (formerly Robin/Brian Thompson & Partners)) N J1
Plymouth p350 . . . 01752 675810

Lawton, A D (Treasury Solicitors Department)
London WC2 p110 . . . 020 7210 3000

Lawton, C H H (Rio Tinto PLC)
London W2 p109 . . . 020 7781 2000

Lawton, D L D (Fisher Jones Greenwood LLP) N G M1 K1 J1 L F1 H V Zc Zi Zl Zp
Chelmsford p186 . . . 01245 890110

Lawton, Mrs H F (Clayton Mott & Lawton) K1 S1 W K3
Sutton-in-Ashfield p404 . . . 01623 556601

Lawton, Miss J (Atherton Godfrey) N J1
Doncaster p211 . . . 01302 320621

Lawton, Miss J N (Clarkson Wright & Jakes Ltd) O Q L Zl Zq
Orpington p341 . . . 01689 887887

Lawton, K O (Owen Lawton) G H K1 D1
Plymouth p350 . . . 01752 201169

Lawton, Miss M (Backhouse Jones Ltd) C1 Ze Zk O Q
Clitheroe p196 . . . 01254 828300

Lawton, M W (Watson Burton LLP) F1 L N P A3 O
Newcastle upon Tyne p327 . 0845 901 2100

Lawton, Ms N (Fitzhugh Gates) K1 D1 V
Brighton p159 . . . 01273 686811

Lawton, P A (Woolliscrofts) K1 S1 Q W
Hanley p239 . . . 01782 204000

Lawton, Mrs R (Wigan Borough Council)
Wigan p476 . . . 01942 244991

Lax, P A (Bell Lax Litigation) O B1 A3 J1 K1 Zk Zq Zc
Sutton Coldfield p403 . . . 0121 355 0011

Laxman, Miss N K (Blaser Mills) W
Staines p393 . . . 01784 462511

Laycock, A E (Sibley & Co)
London WC2 p78 . . . 020 7395 9790

Laycock, A L (Hertfordshire County Council)
Hertford p460 . . . 01992 555555

Laycock, A M (Carrick Read (Leeds) Solicitors LLP)
Leeds p272 . . . 0113 246 7878

Laycock, J P (Lupton Fawcett) O Q
Leeds p275 . . . 0113 280 2000

Layfield, A R (Parker Bird Gardner) K1 K3
Huddersfield p256 . . . 01484 825200

Layfield, C E (Donns) N
Manchester p303 . . . 0161 834 3311

Layton, Miss E M (CMS Cameron McKenna LLP) G
London EC3 p17 . . . 020 7367 3000

Layton, J M (Layton & Co) F1 G H J1 K1 L N Q S1
Haverfordwest p244 . . . 01437 766671

Layton, M R (Clifford Chance)
London E14 p20 . . . 020 7006 1000

Layzell, Mrs K (Stone King LLP) T2 W
Bath p128 . . . 01225 337599

Layzell-Smith, I F (May May & Merrimans) E L A1 S2
London WC1 p59 . . . 020 7405 8932

Lazar, V (Edward De Silva & Co) K3 K1 Zi Q
Southall p384 . . . 020 8571 2299

Lazard, J (Harvey Ingram Borneos)
Milton Keynes p317 . . . 01908 696002

Lazarus, S (Baskin Ross & Co) S1 E K1 J1 B1 F1 L M1 N
London NW11 p11 . . . 020 8458 5688

Lazell, A J (Roythornes LLP) S1 S2 E L
Spalding p389 . . . 01775 842500

Lazenby, Ms F A (Flint Bishop Solicitors) D1 V D2 K1
Derby p208 . . . 01332 340211

Lazenby, M (Watson Burton LLP) Zb B1 E J1 Zo T1
Leeds p278 . . . 0845 901 2100

Lazonby, I A (Hempsons) N Zq Zr
Harrogate p240 . . . 01423 522331

Lazzeri, Ms L (Nelsons)
Nottingham p338 . . . 0115 958 6262

Le Fevre, Ms J L (Trafford Metropolitan Borough Council)
Stretford p473 . . . 0161 912 1212

Le Fleming Shepherd, G (Stephenson Harwood)
London EC2 p82 . . . 020 7329 4422

Le Fleming, P C (Gardner Croft LLP) T2 W K4
Canterbury p176 . . . 01227 813400

Le Fort, M (Wills Chandler) K3 K1 D1
Basingstoke p127 . . . 01256 322911

Le Gouellec De Schwarz, T F M (Barlow Lyde & Gilbert LLP)
London EC3 p10 . . . 020 7247 2277

Le Grice, T C (Robinson Le Grice) A1 W G Zd A2
St Ives p392 . . . 01736 797973

Le Grys, Ms F C (Hogan Lovells International LLP)
London EC1 p42 . . . 020 7296 2000

Le Helloco, Mrs L S (Dorset County Council)
Dorchester p457 . . . 01305 251000

Le Maitre-George, D R (Simmons & Simmons)
London EC2 p79 . . . 020 7628 2020

Le Masurier, Mrs L C (The Royal Borough of Kensington & Chelsea)
London W8 p109 . . . 020 7361 2741

Le Masurier, Miss O J (Parker Bullen) K3 K1
Salisbury p371 . . . 01722 412000

Le Masurier, R P (Parker Bullen) J1 K1 L G Q C1 D1 V F1 H Zl Ze Zk X
Salisbury p371 . . . 01722 412000

Le May, C S (Mayo Wynne Baxter LLP) N Zj
Lewes p283 . . . 01273 477071

Le Petit, Ms K (Russell Jones & Walker)
London WC2 p74 . . . 020 7657 1555

Le Riche, Ms C (Henry Hughes & Hughes) E S1
London SW16 p40 . . . 020 8765 2700

Le Roux, H (Penningtons)
London EC2 p66 . . . 020 7457 3000

Le Vay, Miss J L M (Dutton Gregory) K1 K2
Winchester p433 . . . 01962 844333

Le Vay, J N (Magrath LLP) Zi
London W1 p57 . . . 020 7495 3003

Lea, B G (Napp Pharmaceutical Holdings Ltd)
Cambridge p453 . . . 01223 424444

Lea, D (Hatten Wyatt) W K4
Gravesend p232 . . . 01474 351199

Lea, G J (Hempsons) R1 R2 E S2
Westminster p40 . . . 020 7839 0278

Lea, J C (Bhatia Best) K1 D1 D2 K2
Nottingham p336 . . . 0115 950 3231

Lea, J E (LG Lawyers)
London SE1 p50 . . . 020 7379 0000

Lea, J M (Follett Stock LLP) C1 C2 U2 Zb U1 Ze I Zw
Truro p414 . . . 01872 241700

Lea, M J (Mark Jones & Partners) G H
Liverpool p289 . . . 0151 286 9594
Liverpool p289 . . . 0151 236 2224

Lea, M R (Chancellors Lea Brewer) S1 P W K1 E C1 F1 Zc Zl
Bexleyheath p132 . . . 020 8303 0077

Lea, Mrs N E (Birmingham City Council Legal & Democratic Services)
Birmingham p449 . . . 0121 303 2066

Lea, Mrs R (Rutland County Council)
Oakham p468 . . . 01572 722577

Lea, R J S (Cullimore Dutton) S2 A1 C1 C2 W Zd
Chester p190 . . . 01244 356789

Lea, S H Q (Lea & Co) C1 C2 O U2 Zf Zv Zw Zz
Stockport p396 . . . 0161 480 6691

Leach, Ms A S (Bristol City Council)
Bristol p451 . . . 0117 922 2000

Leach, B (Charsley Harrison LLP) E S2 R2 C1 S1 C2
Windsor p434 . . . 01753 851591

Leach, B (Stephenson Harwood)
London EC2 p82 . . . 020 7329 4422

Leach, Mrs C (Environment Agency (North East Region))
Leeds p462 . . . 0870 850 6506

Leach, D P (Southerns) G V H
Nelson p321 . . . 01282 603663

Leach, D R (Howells LLP) D1 D2 K1
Sheffield p376 . . . 0114 249 6666

Leach, Ms E (Broudie Jackson Canter) G H
Liverpool p286 . . . 0151 227 1429

Leach, G (Howells LLP) L Zh
Rotherham p367 . . . 01709 364000

Leach, Mrs G (Blake Lapthorn) J1
Portsmouth p354 . . . 023 9222 1122

Leach, Ms J (South Tyneside Metropolitan Borough Council)
South Shields p471 . . . 0191 427 1717

Leach, J D (Ware & Kay LLP) K1 N O Q J1 S1 W C1 V F1 Zi Zj Zl
York p445 . . . 01904 716000

Leach, J M S (Bower & Bailey) Q O K3 J1 N
Banbury p122 . . . 01295 265566

Leach, J R (Savage Crangle) K1 K2 K3
Skipton p381 . . . 01756 794611

Leach, J W (Sevenoaks District Council)
Sevenoaks p470 . . . 01732 227000

Leach, J W E (Leach Rawlence & Hart) W S1 K4
Croydon p205 . . . 020 8680 5850

Leach, Mrs K H (SAS Daniels LLP) W K4
Stockport p396 . . . 0161 475 7676

Leach, Mrs K J (Horwood & James LLP) D1 D2 K1 K3
Aylesbury p121 . . . 01296 487361

Leach, M (DLA Piper UK LLP) J1 M1 P
Liverpool p287 . . . 0870 011 1111

Leach, N I (East Hampshire District Council)
Petersfield p468 . . . 01730 266551

Leach, P J C (Downs) E R1 C1 S2 O P L B1 J1
Godalming p231 . . . 01483 861848

Leach, P R (Saunders Roberts) A1 E L R1 S1
Evesham p220 . . . 01386 442558

Leach, Ms S A (Howells LLP) D1
Sheffield p376 . . . 0114 249 6666

Leach, S D (NFLA Ltd) K3 K1 D1
Nottingham p338 . . . 0115 945 4555
Wellingborough p424 . . . 01933 222700

Leach, Miss S J (Benussi & Co) K1 K3
Birmingham p135 . . . 0121 248 4001

Leach, S M J (Margary & Miller) S1 E W L C1 F1 T1 A1 B1
Felixstowe p225 . . . 01394 273333
Woodbridge p439 . . . 01394 382777

Leach, T S (Burnetts) C1 E
Carlisle p181 . . . 01228 552222
Carlisle p182 . . . 01228 552222

Leacock, P H (Howard Kennedy LLP) M2 C1 C2 Zb
London W1 p48 . . . 020 7636 1616

Leadbeater, Miss D J (Leadbeater & Kay) R1 S1 S2 W Zl Zv
Stoke-on-Trent p398 . . . 01782 201933

Leadbeater, E T D (J C Bamford Excavators Ltd)
Uttoxeter p474 . . . 01889 590312

Leadbeater, Miss J E (Pickworths) K1 K3
Hemel Hempstead p247 . . . 01442 261731

Leadbeater, J P (Woodfines LLP) K1 D1
Bedford p130 . . . 01234 270600

Leadbeater, N J (McManus Seddon) B2 G H
Bradford p154 . . . 01274 741841

Leadbetter, A (Cheshire County Council)
Chester p454 . . . 01244 602382

Leadbetter, A (Forster Dean Ltd) S1
Warrington p422 . . . 01925 575566

Leadbetter, Miss J L (Barnsley Metropolitan Borough Council) D1
Barnsley p448 . . . 01226 770770

Leadbetter, Ms K (Linder Myers Solicitors)
Manchester p306 . . . 0844 984 6000

Leadbitter, A H O (Morgan Cole)
Oxford p344 . . . 01865 262600

Leadbitter, Mrs M (BHP Law)
Halifax p238 . . . 01422 250650

Leader, Miss L S B (Eaton & Few) K1 K3 L Q S1
St Ives p391 . . . 01480 301558

Leader, Miss N J (Palmers Criminal Defence Solicitors) G H
Deal p207 . . . 01304 380572

Leader, S J B (Environment Agency (Anglian Region))
Peterborough p468 . . . 01733 371811

Leadercramer, D I (Ross & Craig) N J1 K1 K2 F1 Zc Ze
Westminster p73 . . . 020 7262 3077

Leadsom, P (Hodge Halsall) E S1 S2 R2 C1
Southport p388 . . . 01704 531991

Leah, A M (Birchall Blackburn LLP) K1 D1 J1 Q
Southport p388 . . . 01704 232323

Leah, Mrs E (Rawlison Butler LLP) K1 K3 D1
Crawley p202 . . . 01293 527744

Leahy, D A (South Tyneside Metropolitan Borough Council) D1 F1 G H J1 K1 L M1
South Shields p471 . . . 0191 427 1717

Leahy, J A (Castle Sanderson) E C1 R2 S2 P
Leeds p272 . . . 0113 232 1919
Leeds p277 . . . 0113 264 7603

Leatherland, A (DWF) J1 J2 Zp
Manchester p303 . . . 0161 603 5000

Leake, A J (Addleshaw Goddard)
Leeds p271 . . . 0113 209 2000
Manchester p300 . . . 0161 934 6000

Leaker, Ms A (Quality Solicitors Jackson & Canter) D1 K3 G
Liverpool p290 . . . 0151 282 1700

Leakey, A (Stephensons Solicitors LLP) Q F1 O P
Leigh p282 . . . 01942 777777

Leaman, C S (Turnbull Garrard) K1 D1 N
Shrewsbury p379 . . 01743 350851 / 351332

Leaman, Ms S (Linder Myers Solicitors) K1 D1 K2
Manchester p306 . . . 0844 984 6000

Leamon, Mrs D (South Gloucestershire Council)
Thornbury p474 . . . 01454 868686

Lean, S F (Lean & Co) O S1 E Q
Fleet p226 . . . 01252 816757

Leaney, Ms H A (Kaim Todner Ltd) G H
London EC4 p47 . . . 020 7353 6660

Leaney, Miss I K (K&L Gates LLP) A3 C3 Zc
London EC4 p47 . . . 020 7648 9000

Leaning, J P (John Boyle & Co) G H N
Redruth p362 . . . 01209 213507
Truro p414 . . . 01872 272356

Leapman, Miss K (Karina Leapman & Co) M1 N P
London NW6 p52 . . . 020 7794 7741

Lear, N C (Mayo Wynne Baxter LLP) E
Lewes p283 . . . 01273 477071

6

Learmonth, A C (Coyne Learmonth) *S1 W C1 E G H J1 F1 M1*
Liverpool *p287*. 0845 602 0870

Learoyd, Ms K (McDermott Will & Emery UK LLP)
London EC2 *p56*. 020 7577 6900

Leask, Miss D E (Ellis Jones) *K1*
Bournemouth *p151*. 01202 525333

Leask, E (Keith Levin & Co) *C1 M1 G K1 V W P L F1*
Huyton *p258*. 0151 480 5777

Leask, R (Harrison Clark LLP) *C1 C2*
Cheltenham *p188* 01242 269198
Worcester *p439* 01905 612001
Worcester *p439* 01905 612001

Leason, W A (Hempsons) *Zm Zr*
Manchester *p305* 0161 228 0011

Leasor, J J (Gawor & Co) *S1 S2 E C1 W Ze*
London E1 *p35* 020 7481 8888

Leate, Mrs M J (Birkett Long LLP) *J1 Zi*
Colchester *p197*. 01206 217300

Leathard, D (Birdsall & Snowball) *A1 C1 E F1 L R1 S1 T1 W*
Scarborough *p372*. 01723 351351

Leathem, C W (Leathems Solicitors) *S1 K1 W P L*
Whaley Bridge *p430*. 01663 733431

Leathem, R C (Rowberry Morris) *I G L M1 N J1 Zl Zk Zz*
Reading *p361* 0118 958 5611

Leather, D (Dollman & Pritchard) *E*
Caterham *p183* 01883 347823

Leather, Mrs P F (Rowbis Solicitors) *K1 D1 D2*
Gloucester *p230*. 01452 301903

Leather, T P (Russell & Russell) *G H*
Bolton *p149* 01204 399299

Leatherdale, M C J (Smith Bates) *S2 E Zd C1 S1*
Lyndhurst *p296* 023 8028 3414

Leathers, R L (Knocker & Foskett) *L D1 E F1 J1 K1 M1 P S1*
Sevenoaks *p374*. 01732 459931

Leathley, J (Martello Professional Risks Limited) *C1 L N Zc Zi*
London EC3 *p108* 020 7337 7500

Leathley, Ms S (East Riding of Yorkshire Council)
Beverley *p449* 01482 887700

Leatt, Ms C A (Bond Pearce LLP) *C1 T1 Zo*
Plymouth *p349*. 0845 415 0000

Leaver, C E (Simmons & Simmons)
London EC2 *p79*. 020 7628 2020

Leavesley, Ms S J (3i PLC) *C1 B1 Zb*
London SW1 *p103*. 020 7928 3131

Lebreton-Towell, Mrs S (Lebreton Towell Solicitor)
Tarporley *p408*. 01829 751459

Leccacorvi, D V (Whitelock & Storr) *G H B2*
London WC1 *p91* 020 7405 3913

Lecchi, Ms E (Charles Russell LLP) *C3 U1 M1*
London EC4 *p19*. 020 7203 5000

Leckie, D (Maclay Murray & Spens LLP)
London EC2 *p57*. 020 7002 8500

Leckie, Miss L (Leech & Co) *N O Q B1 C1 C2 E S1 W J1 Ze Zi Zq Zr Zk*
Manchester *p306* 0161 279 0279

Lecoutre, R (Hunters) *W T2 K4*
London WC2 *p44* 020 7412 0050

Lederman, L B (Lawrence & Co) *K1 G S1 P N H F1 D1 L Zc Zi Zl*
London W9 *p52* 020 7266 4333

Ledger, P P (Roach Pittis) *S1 W L E F1 K1 T1 J1 C1 R1 S2 R2*
Newport *p328* 01983 524431

Ledger, Miss S E (Glanvilles)
Newport *p328* 01983 527878

Ledger, T A (Gateley LLP) *S2 R1*
Birmingham *p138* 0121 234 0000

Ledger, Miss T R (JW Law) *Zd C1 Ze*
Wimborne *p433* 01202 690658

Ledran, K J (Bedford Borough Council)
Bedford *p448* 01234 267422

Ledsham, G (Russell-Cooke LLP) *O*
London SW15 *p74*. 020 8789 9111

Ledward, C J (Max Bitel Greene LLP) *E L S1 S2 W*
Islington *p59*. 020 7354 2767

Ledwidge, R (Forsters LLP) *E S2*
Westminster *p33*. 020 7863 8333

Lee, Ms A (Biscoes) *D1 J1 K1 J2 Q N Zo V*
Portchester *p353*. 023 9237 0634

Lee, Mrs A (Last Cawthra Feather LLP) *W*
Ilkley *p261*. 01943 601020

Lee, A C (Balfour Beatty Power Networks Ltd)
Derby *p456* 01332 288537

Lee, A D R (Hill Dickinson LLP)
London EC3 *p41*. 020 7283 9033

Lee, Ms A H (Taylor Vinters) *N*
Cambridge *p176*. 01223 423444

Lee, A J (Nelsons) *O N Zq*
Nottingham *p338*. 0115 958 6262

Lee, A N (DAC Beachcroft) *E B1 C1 L Ze Zs Zc*
London EC4 *p24*. 020 7936 2222

Lee, A T (Ashfords LLP) *O*
Exeter *p220* 01392 337000

Lee, B (Brecher) *J1 N C1*
London W1 *p15* 020 7563 1000

Lee, Miss C (Maples Teesdale LLP) *Zc*
London EC2 *p58*. 020 7600 3800

Lee, Miss C (Cottrill Stone Lawless) *C1 E S2*
Manchester *p302* 0161 835 3681

Lee, C (Latimer Lee LLP)
Prestwich *p358* 0161 798 9000

Lee, Mrs C A (Paris Smith LLP) *E*
Southampton *p386*. 023 8048 2482

Lee, C A (Rawlison Butler LLP) *O Q Zj Zq C1 I Zk*
Crawley *p202* 01293 527744

Lee, Ms C C K (Christine Lee & Co (Solicitors) Ltd)
Birmingham *p140* 0121 666 6228
London W1 *p52* 020 7287 6233

Lee, D J L (Finn Gledhill) *S1 E C1 L R1 A1 Zc*
Halifax *p238* 01422 330000
Hebden Bridge *p246*. 01422 842451

Lee, D K T (Silverman Sherliker LLP) *C1 Ze S1 S2 Q F1 K1 Zp O C3 Zk K3 K2 Zw*
London EC2 *p78*. 020 7749 2700

Lee, D K W (Lee & Kan) *C1 E F1 L S1 W Zb Ze Zi*
London W1 *p52* 020 7287 8888

Lee, D P (Allen & Overy LLP)
London E1 *p5* 020 3088 0000

Lee, E D (Kloosmans) *S1 W*
Southend-on-Sea *p387* 01702 600090

Lee, Ms E E (Platt Halpern) *K1 D1 D2*
Manchester *p308* 0161 224 2555

Lee, Miss E J (T G Baynes) *O Q J1 B1 Zp*
Bexleyheath *p132* 020 8301 7777

Lee, E P (Blake Lapthorn) *C1 C2 C3 I U1 M1*
Oxford *p342*. 01865 248607

Lee, E R (William Heath & Co) *C1 E W S1*
Westminster *p40*. 020 7402 3151

Lee, Mrs F J (Graham Evans & Partners)
Swansea *p405*. 01792 655822

Lee, G (DFA Law LLP)
Northampton *p331*. 01604 609560

Lee, H (Warner Goodman LLP) *O*
Southampton *p387*. 023 8063 9311

Lee, Miss H L (Williamson & Soden) *S2 E*
Solihull *p383*. 0121 733 8000

Lee, I (Forbes) *G H*
Preston *p356* 01772 220022

Lee, Miss J (Kennet District Council)
Devizes *p457* 01380 724911

Lee, Miss J (Lee & Company) *S1 W S2 L E*
Camberley *p173*. 01276 20911

Lee, Mrs J (Lees Solicitors LLP) *W K4*
Birkenhead *p134*. 0151 647 9381

Lee, Miss J A (Manuel Swaden) *O L*
London NW6 *p58* 020 7431 4999

Lee, J A (Myers Lister Price) *E S1 C1*
Altrincham *p117* 0161 926 9969

Lee, J A (Janes) *B2 H G*
London SW1 *p46* 020 7930 5100

Lee, J B (Lee & Company) *K1 N Q D1 F1 J1 G L C1 S1 Zt Zl*
Camberley *p173*. 01276 20911

Lee, J C R B (Symes Robinson & Lee) *A1 C1 E L S1 W*
Crediton *p203* 01363 775566

Lee, J D (Greenwoods Solicitors LLP) *E P L R1 S1*
Peterborough *p347* 01733 887700

Lee, Miss J E (Horsey Lightly Fynn) *Q J1 O Zp*
Bournemouth *p152*. 01202 551991

Lee, J J (Gabbs LLP) *S1 S2 Zl*
Hereford *p248* 01432 353481

Lee, J M (Anderson Longmore & Higham) *V W T2 Zo K4*
Billingshurst *p133* 01403 782710
Petworth *p348*. 01798 342391

Lee, Miss K (Edwin Coe LLP) *Ze*
London WC2 *p29* 020 7691 4000

Lee, K (Alliance Boots PLC)
Nottingham *p467*. 0115 950 6111

Lee, K A (DLA Piper UK LLP) *O J1*
Liverpool *p287*. 0870 011 1111

Lee, L (Morrison & Foerster (UK) LLP) *Zb*
London EC2 *p62*. 020 7920 4000

Lee, Ms L (Torbay Council)
Torquay *p474* 01803 201201

Lee, L M (Laurence Lee & Co) *G H K1 E F1 M1 S1 L P*
Liverpool *p289*. . 0151 259 1211 / 259 2824

Lee, Ms M (Gallaher Ltd)
Weybridge *p476*. 01932 859777

Lee, M (Lodders Solicitors LLP) *S2 E*
Stratford-upon-Avon *p400* . . 01789 293259

Lee, M (Penningtons)
Godalming *p231* 01483 791800

Lee, M (EBR Attridge LLP) *C1 J1 Ze Zf Zk*
London SE16 *p28* 020 7231 5166

Lee, Ms M A (Lee & Company) *S1 W L E S2*
Camberley *p173*. 01276 20911

Lee, M L (Fruhman Davies Livingstones)
Manchester *p304* 0161 833 0578

Lee, M S (Lee Pomeranc) *B1 C1 E F1 J1 L R1 S1*
London NW4 *p68* 020 8201 6299

Lee, P A (Addleshaw Goddard)
Manchester *p300* 0161 934 6000

Lee, P J (DAC Beachcroft) *W T1 C1 A1 Zd Zm Zo*
Leeds *p272* 0113 251 4700

Lee, R (Canter Levin & Berg)
Liverpool *p287*. 0151 239 1000

Lee, R A (Rubin Lewis O'Brien) *F1 J1 K1 L M1 N P S1 V Ze*
Cardiff *p180* 029 2077 9988

Lee, R H G (Clifford Chance)
London E14 *p20*. 020 7006 1000

Lee, R J (DAC Beachcroft) *E L*
London EC4 *p24*. 020 7936 2222

Lee, R J (Wright Hassall LLP) *C1 B1 C2*
Leamington Spa *p270* 01926 886688

Lee, R N F (Addleshaw Goddard)
Manchester *p300* 0161 934 6000

Lee, R W (Reynolds Porter Chamberlain LLP) *O Zc Zj*
London E1 *p71* 020 3060 6000

Lee, R W (Lee & Thompson) *C1 J1 Ze Zf Zk*
London W1 *p52* 020 7935 4665

Lee, S (Howes Percival LLP)
Norwich *p334* 01603 762103

Lee, S (Penningtons)
Basingstoke *p127* 01256 407100

Lee, Ms S (Simmons & Simmons)
London EC2 *p79*. 020 7628 2020

Lee, S (Anthony Collins Solicitors LLP) *Zu Zd*
Birmingham *p137* 0121 200 3242

Lee, Ms S (Carter Lemon Camerons) *E S1 L R2*
London EC1 *p18*. 020 7406 1000

Lee, Mrs S (Chafes) *K1 K2 D1 S1 W*
Wilmslow *p433*. 01625 531676

Lee, Mrs S A (Swain & Co) *D1 D2 K1 K2 K3*
Havant *p244*. 023 9248 3322

Lee, S D (Stevens) *G H*
Stoke-on-Trent *p398*. 01782 813200

Lee, S J (Stewart Lee) *L X S1 Q*
London N3 *p52* 020 8346 2769

Lee, Mrs S J (MFG Solicitors)
Kidderminster *p265* 01562 820181

Lee, S M (Whatley & Co) *S1 E Zv*
Barnet *p91*. . . .020 8205 1411 / 8205 8931

Lee, Miss S P (Laytons) *T1*
London EC4 *p52*. 020 7842 8000

Lee, T (Russell-Cooke LLP) *N Zr*
London SW15 *p74*. 020 8789 9111

Lee, T R (Young & Lee) *C1 I C2*
Birmingham *p143* 0121 633 3233

Lee, Ms V (Rooks Rider) *W T2 Zd*
London EC1 *p73*. 020 7689 7000

Lee, Ms V (North Kensington Law Centre) *L*
London W10 *p108* 020 8969 7473

Lee, Miss V A (E C Lidster & Co) *H G*
Grimsby *p235* 01472 348417

Lee, W D (Agusta Westland Legal Dept - Yeovil)
Yeovil *p477* 01935 702240

Lee, Ms Z (Cartwright King) *N*
Leicester *p279*. 0116 253 9222

Lee-Mills, Mrs J (Anthony Collins Solicitors LLP) *E*
Birmingham *p137* 0121 200 3242

Lee-Nichols, Ms R P (Jeffrey Green Russell) *G J2 N Zy*
London W1 *p46* 020 7339 7000

Leece, J (Newman & Bond) *C1 E J1 S1 S2*
Barnsley *p125* 01226 213434

Leece, Mrs J (Newman & Bond) *E S2 A1 W*
Barnsley *p125* 01226 213434

Leece, Miss R (Peasegoods) *L N S1 W*
Manchester *p308* 0161 205 2772

Leech, Ms C J B (Pannone LLP) *N*
Manchester *p308* 0161 909 3000

Leech, Miss E J (Leech & Co) *B1 C1 C2 E J1 N O Q S1 W Ze Zi Zk Zq Zr*
Manchester *p306* 0161 279 0279

Leech, G P (Laytons) *E S2*
London EC4 *p52*. 020 7842 8000

Leech, J R A (Squire Sanders (UK) LLP) *O Q Zc Zj*
Birmingham *p142* 0121 222 3000

Leech, M J P (Gill Akaster) *K1 D1 D2 K2*
Plymouth *p349*. 01752 203500

Leech, Miss S (Adam Douglas & Son) *W K4 S1*
Alnwick *p115*. 01665 602363

Leech, S A (Walters & Plaskitt) *S1 W K1 P M1 G F1 J1 E N*
Stoke-on-Trent *p398*. 01782 819611

Leedham, D (Speechly Bircham LLP) *E S2 R2*
London EC4 *p81*. 020 7427 6400

Leedham, I P (National Grid PLC)
Warwick *p471* 01926 653000

Leedham, R J (Addleshaw Goddard) *O A3 Q*
London EC1 *p4* 020 7606 8855

Leedham, R M (Coles Miller Solicitors LLP) *L R1 S1*
Poole *p352* 01202 673011

Leeding, J V (Watts & Leeding) *S1 E K1 W N Q L*
London SE9 *p90*. 020 8850 6366

Leeds, Ms C J (Shearman & Sterling LLP) *Zb*
London EC2 *p78*. 020 7655 5000

Leek, C J (Howell & Co) *O Q*
Birmingham *p139* 0121 778 5031

Leek, Mrs E (Kieran & Co) *K1 K3 K2*
Worcester *p440* 01905 28635
Chesterfield *p192* 01246 211006

Leek, R D (Unilever PLC)
London EC4 *p110* 020 7822 5252

Leek, R E (Higgs & Sons) *W T1 T2 Zd*
Brierley Hill *p158*. 0845 111 5050

Leeke, A P (Pinkerton Leeke & Co) *E S1 W L A1 C1 Zc Zd*
Cheltenham *p188* 01242 237477

Leeming, J (J A Kemp & Co)
London WC1 *p48* 020 7405 3292

Leeming, R J (Burges Salmon) *C1 C2 B1 Zb*
Bristol *p161* 0117 939 2000

Lees, Miss F G E (Crown Prosecution Service Durham)
Durham *p457* 0191 383 5800

Lees, Miss F M (Lodders Solicitors LLP) *E S1 L S2*
Stratford-upon-Avon *p400* . . 01789 293259

Lees, Miss H J (VHS Fletchers Solicitors) *G H*
Nottingham *p339*. 0115 959 9550

Lees, Mrs J (Telford Magistrates Court)
Telford *p474* 01952 204500

Lees, J (Stanley Tee LLP) *S1 W*
Cambridge *p175*. 01223 311141

Lees, J C (Wakefield Metropolitan District Council)
Wakefield *p474* 01924 306090

Lees, Mrs J N A (Hannays Solicitors and Advocates) *K3 V K1*
South Shields *p383* . . 0191 456 7893 / 455 5361

Lees, K (Pearson Hinchliffe)
Oldham *p341* 0161 785 3500

Lees, M (Beesley & Co) *B1 Zr C1 E Q N S1*
Manchester *p301* 0161 445 3678

Lees, N (Ashurst LLP)
London EC2 *p7* 020 7638 1111

Lees, Miss P (Ward Gethin) *S1 L E*
King's Lynn *p266* 01553 660033

Lees, Miss P (BBA Aviation PLC)
London W1 *p103* 020 7514 3999

Lees, R P (Wake Smith & Tofields) *N Zr*
Sheffield *p377* 0114 266 6660

Leese, P (Fladgate LLP) *K1 O*
London WC2 *p32* 020 3036 7000

Leese, R G (Clifford Chance)
London E14 *p20*. 020 7006 1000

Leeson, Miss E H (Langleys) *A1 Zr P J2 Zj K1 N Q*
York *p445* 01904 610886

Leeson, Mrs F G (Godwins) *T2 W K4*
Winchester *p433*. 01962 841484

Leeson, Ms H (SGH Martineau LLP) *B1*
Birmingham *p142* 0870 763 2000

Leeson, M A (Max Barford & Co) *K1 D1 V*
Tunbridge Wells *p414* 01892 539379

Leeson, T (Crowell & Moring) *C1 C2 U1 U2 B1 Zb*
London EC4 *p23*. 020 7413 0011

Leete, M C (Denniss Matthews) *C1 S2 T2 W*
London SE20 *p27* . . 020 8778 7301 / 8778 7631

Leete, T (Alistair Harper & Co) *G H*
Haywards Heath *p245* 01444 457890

Leff, J A R (S D Rosser & Co) *K1 J1 Zq Q Zr O N*
London NW10 *p74*. 020 8451 3848

Leftley, M A (Addleshaw Goddard) *J1*
London EC1 *p4* 020 7606 8855
Manchester *p300* 0161 934 6000

Leftwich, Mrs C (Ware & Kay LLP) *S1 S2 E*
Wetherby *p429* 01937 583210

Legezynska, M (Watson Farley & Williams)
London EC2 *p90*. 020 7814 8000

Legg, B (Elmhirst Parker LLP)
Barnsley *p124* 01226 282238

Legg, Miss C (Sacker & Partners LLP) *Zo*
London EC2 *p76*. 020 7329 6699

Legg, J C (LG Lawyers)
London SE1 *p50*. 020 7379 0000

Legg, Miss K (Higgs & Sons) *C1 C2 Ze*
Brierley Hill *p158*. 0845 111 5050

Legg, Mrs M E (Hewitsons) *Zo*
Northampton *p332*. 01604 233233

Legg, M P (Elmhirst Parker LLP) *S2 J1 L Q B1*
Selby *p374* 01757 703602

Legg, P (Saunders Law Partnership LLP) *G H*
London WC2 *p76* 020 7632 4300

Legg, R A S (South Somerset District Council)
Yeovil *p477* 01935 462462

Legge, Ms A (Ashurst LLP)
London EC2 *p7* 020 7638 1111

Legge, M (DAC Beachcroft)
Manchester *p303* 0161 934 3000

Legge, Ms S (George Davies Solicitors LLP) *L N O*
Manchester *p303* 0161 236 8992

Leggett, J (Parrott & Coales LLP) *S1 W C1 E A1 T1 L R1 Zl Zc*
Aylesbury *p121* 01296 318500

Leggett, J (Speechly Bircham LLP) *Zb*
London EC4 *p81*. 020 7427 6400

Legister, M (Huggins & Lewis Foskett)
Redbridge *p43*. 020 8989 3000

Legister, M P (Warner Goodman LLP)
Portsmouth *p355*. 023 9275 3575

Legrand, Ms J (DLA Piper UK LLP) *A3 O Q Zo Zq*
London EC2 *p24*. 0870 011 1111

Lehane, Miss A B (The Royal Borough of Kensington & Chelsea) *D1 F1 G H K1 L M1 P S1*
London W8 *p109* 020 7361 2741

Lehman, Ms J (Shoosmiths)
Milton Keynes *p317* . 0370 086 8300 / 01908 488300

Lehrer, Ms S (Taylor Wessing)
London EC4 *p86*. 020 7300 7000

Leigh, D T (Straw & Pearce) *G H D1 K1 Q F1 J1 V N B1 Zi Zl Zm*
Loughborough *p293* 01509 268931

Leigh, Ms E L (Lewis Silkin LLP) *C1 C2*
London EC4 *p53*. 020 7074 8000

Leigh, G I F (Addleshaw Goddard) *C3 M1 I Ze C1*
London EC1 *p4* 020 7606 8855

Leigh, G S (GLP Solicitors) *B1 C1 D1 E F1 G H J1 K1 M1*
Bury *p170* 0161 764 1818
Manchester *p304* 0161 834 6721

Leigh, J (Haworth & Nuttall) *S1 W T2*
Blackburn *p145* 01254 272640

Leigh, Ms J C (Midwinters) *Q N Zq*
Cheltenham *p188* 01242 514674

Leigh, J E (CKFT) *N Zq Zr O Q J1*
London NW3 *p17* 020 7431 7262

Leigh, M A M S (Hempsons) *N Q Zq Zr*
Westminster *p40*. 020 7839 0278

Leigh, Miss M D (Child & Child) *S1 W S2*
London SW1 *p20* 020 7235 8000

Leigh, R D (Leigh Davis) *C1 E F1 J1 L S1 R1 T1 W Zf Zi Zl*
London W1 *p26* 020 7631 0302

Leigh, R W (Simmons & Simmons)
London EC2 *p79*. 020 7628 2020

Leigh, S J (Brabners Chaffe Street) *O A3 Zq Zk*
Manchester *p301* 0161 836 8800

See p634 for the Key to Work Categories

Leigh, Miss S L (Darbys Solicitors LLP) *E A1 R2 S2*
Oxford *p343* 01865 811700
Leigh, S P (Gill Akaster) *S1 S2 E*
Plymouth *p349* 01752 203500
Leigh-Hunt, D R (David Leigh-Hunt) *Q O N K3 J1 B1 C1 X Zl Zc Zd Zy W Zu*
Leamington Spa *p270* 01926 427400
Leigh-Hunt, Mrs V I (David Leigh-Hunt) *E S1 S2 W*
Leamington Spa *p270* 01926 427400
Leigh-Pollitt, P J (Doyle Clayton Solicitors Limited) *J1 Zp*
Reading *p360* 0118 959 6839
Reading *p361* 0118 925 2000
Leighton, D (Ashurst LLP)
London EC2 *p7* 020 7638 1111
Leighton, Mrs G E (Bells Solicitors) *W K4*
Farnham *p224* 01252 733733
Leighton, P (DAC Beachcroft)
Birmingham *p137* 0121 698 5200
Leighton, R (TV Edwards LLP) *G H*
London N15 *p85* 020 7790 7000
Leighton, Miss S (Clark Willis) *J1 Q*
Darlington *p206* 01325 281111
Leighton, S T (Croftons) *N L Q*
Manchester *p302* 0161 214 6180
Leighton-Jones, Ms G (Hatchers Solicitors LLP) *E F1*
Shrewsbury *p379* 01743 248545
Leiper, A (LGFL LLP)
Yateley *p443* 01252 877327
Leiper, Miss A J (T G Baynes) *W K4*
Dartford *p207* 01322 295555
Leiper, J K (Hough Halton & Soal) *N W*
Carlisle *p182* 01228 524379
Leiper, Ms M N H (Daniel and Harris) *S1 W*
Camden *p25* 020 7625 0202
Leir, A (Holman Fenwick Willan)
London EC3 *p42* 020 7264 8000
Leitch, A (SJ Berwin LLP)
London EC4 *p75* 020 7111 2222
Leitch, J B J (J B Leitch & Co) *O B1 L Zb Zv*
Liverpool *p289* 0151 708 2250
Leite, Mrs A L (Batchelor Myddelton) *C1 F1 J1 O Q*
Potters Bar *p355* 01707 647088
Leith, J D A (EAD Solicitors LLP) *E S1 W L P C1 S2*
Liverpool *p287* 0151 734 4339
Leivers, Ms A L (Davey Franklin Jones) *S2 E R2*
Cirencester *p195* 01285 654875
Leivesley, Miss A (TV Edwards LLP) *K1 D1*
London EC3 *p85* 020 7790 7000
Leiws, Miss A (Manches LLP) *S2 E*
London WC2 *p58* 020 7404 4433
Leland, E (Leland Swaby Clarke & Norris)
Romford *p366* 01708 762227
Leland, E E (Leland Swaby Clarke & Norris) *S1 W C1 T2 E Zd*
Romford *p366* 01708 762227
Lello, J M (Parker Bullen) *C1 C2 M1 Ze Zb Zf Zj*
Salisbury *p371* 01722 412000
Leman, R F (Actons) *B1 O Q J1 C1 Zc*
Nottingham *p335* 0115 910 0200
Leman, T R (Pinsent Masons LLP) *C2*
London EC2 *p67* 020 7418 7000
Leman-Bunkall, G (Ward Gethin) *S1 S2*
Swaffham *p404* 01760 721992
Lemberger, R W (Field Overell) *S1 E J1 T2 W*
Leamington Spa *p270* 01926 422101
Lemco, M D (David Lemco & Co) *C1 E K1 L S1 T1 W Zl B1 S2 J1*
London N13 *p53* 020 8882 1074
Lemer, A J (Arthur & Co) *S1 L E P F1 C1*
Pinner *p348* 020 8866 8282
Lemon, J J (Curry Popeck) *S1 S2 W E*
Kenton *p264*. . .020 8907 2000 / 8907 8896
Lemon, T B (Prince Evans) *S1 S2 E W C1 T1*
Ealing *p69* 020 8567 3477
Lemos, Ms M (Diamantis Lemos Ltd)
London EC2 *p106* 020 7613 1234
Lendrum, B C (Brignalls Balderston Warren) *E S1 S2 C1 C2*
Stevenage *p394* 01438 359311
Lendrum, Mrs C L (Clarks Legal LLP)
Cardiff *p177* 029 2055 7500
Leney, S D (Cripps Harries Hall LLP) *W T2 Zd*
Tunbridge Wells *p415* 01892 515121
Lennaghan, Ms M (Lyons Davidson)
Bristol *p163* 0117 904 6000
Lennie, D (Rupert Wood & Son) *S1 F1 G M1 W J1 Zi Zl*
Ashton-under-Lyne *p120*. . . 0161 330 9121
Lennon, J (Colemans Solicitors LLP) *Q N J1*
Maidenhead *p298* 01628 631051
Lennon, N (Kennedys) *Zc J1 Zj Q*
London EC3 *p49* 020 7667 9667
Lennon, Miss P (Scott Richards) *D1 D2 K1 N K2*
Teignmouth *p409* 01626 772441
Lennon, Miss P A (Taylor & Emmet LLP) *K1 K3*
Sheffield *p377* 0114 218 4000
Lennon, T (Dyne Drewett Solicitors Ltd) *C1 E F1 F2 Ze*
Sherborne *p378* 01935 813691
Lennox, D (Harthills) *D1 Zm*
Rotherham *p367* 01709 377399
Lennox, L P M (Denison Till) *R1 Q Zd P*
York *p444* 01904 611411
Lent, J D (LG Lawyers)
London SE1 *p50* 020 7379 0000
Lentell, Mrs J (Trobridges) *W S1*
Torpoint *p412* 01752 812787

Lenthall, Miss E L (Reed Smith LLP)
London EC2 *p71* 020 3116 3000
Lentin, Mrs M R (Monica Lentin & Co) *G H*
Cambridge *p175* 01223 314452
Leo, J (Coley & Tilley) *O Q J1 N Zq Zk*
Birmingham *p136* 0121 643 5531
Leonard, A (HCB Solicitors) *C1 C2 Zza T1 C3*
Walsall *p420* 01922 720000
Leonard, Ms D (Thompsons (formerly Robin/Brian Thompson & Partners))
Stoke-on-Trent *p398* 01782 406200
Leonard, Miss D M A (Leeds City Council) *Zr N*
Leeds *p462* 0113 224 3513
Leonard, G M (Leonard & Co) *D1 G H N J1 L P Q V Zi Zm Zp*
Southampton *p386* 023 8023 3242
Leonard, G M (Leonard & Co) *D1 K3 K1 L G H Zq*
Southampton *p386* 023 8023 4433
Leonard, Ms G M (Gordons LLP)
Leeds *p273* 0113 227 0100
Leonard, Ms J M (Metropolitan Police Directorate of Legal Services) *M1 N R1 K1 J1*
London SW1 *p108* 020 7230 7210
Leonard, Ms M G (Suffolk County Council) *J1 C1 C2*
Ipswich *p462* 01473 583000
Leonard, N (Allen Barfields) *S2 R2 E C1*
Croydon *p204* 020 8680 2050
Leonard, Ms S (Russell Jones & Walker)
Newcastle upon Tyne *p326* . 0191 323 3000
Leonard, S (Russell-Cooke LLP) *C1 C2*
London WC1 *p74* 020 7405 6566
Leonard, S B (Gordons LLP)
Leeds *p273* 0113 227 0100
Leone, Ms L (Hewitsons) *C3*
Cambridge *p174* 01223 461155
Leota, Mrs S (Belmont & Lowe)
London EC1 *p11* 020 7608 4600
Leport, J S (Leport & Co) *Q O G H N K1 J1 L C1 Zf Zk Zl*
Banbury *p122* . . . .01295 257328 / 268181
Leporte, L A (Cripps Harries Hall LLP) *C1 C2 U1 Zb*
Tunbridge Wells *p415* 01892 515121
Lerman, H A (Anthony Gold) *S2 E S1 R2 R1*
London SE1 *p6* 020 7940 4000
Lerner, Ms S (Hereward & Foster) *G H D1 Zm*
London E16 *p41* 020 7476 6600
Leroy, Ms L (Osborne Clarke) *C1*
London EC2 *p65* 020 7105 7000
Lescure, A (Ince & Co Services Ltd)
London E1 *p44* 020 7481 0010
London EC2 *p90* 020 7814 8000
Lesin-Davis, G S (EAD Solicitors LLP)
Liverpool *p287* 0151 291 2500
Leskin, N (Birnberg Peirce & Partners) *Zi G Zg*
Camden *p13* 020 7911 0166
Lesler, B (W H Matthews & Co) *D1 G H K1 Q K3 Zr F1 Zq J1*
Islington *p59* 020 7251 4942
Leslie, A D (Hill Dickinson LLP) *N Zr*
Liverpool *p288* 0151 600 8000
Leslie, A W (Radcliffes Le Brasseur) *M1 J1 K1 N L P G D1 S1 Zc Zm Zp*
Westminster *p70* 020 7222 7040
Leslie, C (Ince & Co Services Ltd)
London E1 *p44* 020 7481 0010
Leslie, Ms C F (Department for Business, Enterprise and Regulatory Reform)
London SW1 *p105* 020 7215 0105
Leslie, I M (Stone Rowe Brewer LLP) *C1 E S1 L S2*
Twickenham *p416* 020 8891 6141
Leslie, J (Travers Smith LLP) *O Zq*
London EC1 *p87* 020 7295 3000
Leslie, Ms J (TV Edwards LLP) *N*
London EC3 *p85* 020 7790 7000
Leslie, K U (Wilson Browne) *E S2 C1 L S1*
Leicester *p281* 0116 251 7181
Leslie, Ms M (Merseyside Police)
Liverpool *p463* 0151 777 8080
Leslie, R J (Weightmans LLP) *J1 Zp*
Liverpool *p291* 0151 227 2601
Leslie, S (Jones Day) *O*
London EC4 *p46* 020 7039 5959
Leslie, Miss S (Aviva PLC)
London EC3 *p103* . . 020 7283 7500 / 01603 687905
Leslie, S (Derby City Council)
Derby *p456* 01332 293111
Leslie, S C (Reading Borough Council)
Reading *p469* 0118 939 0900
Lesser, M E (Ellum LLP) *C1 J1 Zj C2 I F1 F2*
London EC3 *p29* 020 7481 0977
Lester, A (Frisby & Co) *J1 O Q G B2*
Stafford *p392* 01785 244114
Lester, Ms A P (Gordons LLP)
Leeds *p273* 0113 227 0100
Lester, B C (CKFT)
London NW3 *p17* 020 7431 7262
Lester, Mrs C C (Malvern Hills District Council)
Malvern *p464* 01684 862151
Lester, D M (Milne & Lyall) *D1 K1 G H K3 Zk Zl O Q N*
Bridport *p158* 01308 422362
Lester, J (Wansbroughs)
Devizes *p210* 01380 733300
Lester, J (Curry Popeck) *J1 B1 Zj O Q Zq I*
London W1 *p24* 020 7224 6633
Lester, J M E (Forrester & Forrester) *S1 L A1 W*
Malmesbury *p300* 01666 822671

Lester, M (Freeman Box)
London W1 *p34* 020 7486 9041
Lester, P F (LG Lawyers)
London SE1 *p50* 020 7379 0000
Lester, R C (Cumberland Ellis Peirs) *E S1 Zw*
London WC1 *p23* 020 7242 0422
Lester, R E (Lester Morrill) *G H D1 K1 S1 W Zl D2*
Leeds *p275* 0113 245 8549
Lester, R W (Rossendale Borough Council)
Rawtenstall *p469* 01706 217777
Lester, Ms V L (DWF) *N Q*
Liverpool *p287* 0151 907 3000
Skelmersdale *p381* 01695 722222
Letby, Mrs L C (Elmhirst Parker LLP) *S1 L W*
Leeds *p273* 01977 682219
Leth, Miss M H (Macfarlanes) *C1*
London EC4 *p56* 020 7831 9222
Lethbridge, Mrs A R G (Bristows) *E R1 P L A1 S1 Zd*
London EC4 *p15* 020 7400 8000
Lett, J R J (Kidd Rapinet) *Q J1 O Zq*
Maidenhead *p298* 0845 017 9608
Letters, R J (London Borough of Barking & Dagenham)
Barking *p448* . .020 8592 4500 / 8252 8233
Letts, J R (Letts & Co)
Canterbury *p177* 01227 471555
Letts, Miss K (QualitySolicitors Hill & Abbott) *E S2 L C1 S1*
Chelmsford *p187* 01245 258892
Letwin, Ms I G (Treasury Solicitors Department)
London WC2 *p110* 020 7210 3000
Leung, K (South Manchester Law Centre)
Manchester *p465* 0161 225 5111
Leung, Ms W H A (Leung & Co) *E S1 S2 W J1 K1 F1 P Q C1 Zi Zk Zd Zl Zp*
Bristol *p163* 0117 920 9230
Levaggi, P D M (Charles Russell LLP) *E L O Q Zs*
Guildford *p235* 01483 252525
Levan, B J (Nicholas & Co) *S1 E N R1 C1 L*
London W1 *p63* 020 7323 4450
Levene, A S (Howard Kennedy LLP) *E L S1 W T2*
London W1 *p48* 020 7636 1616
Levene, D (Levenes Solicitors) *N*
Haringey *p53* . .020 8881 7777 / 8881 6764
Levene, D R (Pritchard Englefield) *E S2 R2 Zl*
London EC2 *p69* 020 7972 9720
Levene, Miss K D (Brent Magistrates Court)
London NW10 *p104* 020 8451 7111
Levene, Ms K E (Humphries Kirk) *K1 V K3*
Bournemouth *p152* 01202 421111
Levene, M L (TWM Solicitors LLP) *R2 E S2*
Epsom *p219* 01372 729555
Levene, R C (Park Woodfine Heald Mellows LLP) *Zd*
Bedford *p130* 01234 400000
Leventhal, D (Morrison & Foerster (UK) LLP) *Zb*
London EC2 *p62* 020 7920 4000
Leveque, C (Harbottle & Lewis LLP)
London W1 *p38* 020 7667 5000
Lever, F P (Lynch Hall & Hornby)
Harrow *p242* 020 8864 0722
Lever, H B (Salehs LLP) *S1 E W*
Manchester *p309* 0161 434 9991
Lever, Mrs L R (Mills & Reeve) *Q Zq*
Norwich *p335* 01603 660155
Lever, Mrs L S (Stone King LLP) *K1 J1 K2 K3*
Bath *p128* 01225 337599
Lever, P (Coupe Bradbury) *N*
Lytham *p296* 01253 736670
Lever, R C J (Lee & Thompson) *C1 Zf Ze Zw*
London W1 *p52* 020 7935 4665
Leverton, M (Harbottle & Lewis LLP)
London W1 *p38* 020 7667 5000
Levesley, Mrs K L (Gateley LLP) *O*
Birmingham *p138* 0121 234 0000
Levesley, Mrs L (Walsall Metropolitan Borough Council) *K1 D1*
Walsall *p475* 01922 650000
Levesley, R (South Staffordshire Council)
Codsall *p455* 01902 696000
Levett, P W (Stringer Smith & Levett) *E F1 J1 K1 L M1 P S1 W Zf*
London NW3 *p84* 020 7435 0436
Levey, A D (Blake Lapthorn) *D1 K1*
Portsmouth *p354* 023 9222 1122
Levi, Ms F J (Russell-Cooke LLP) *D1 D2 K1*
Kingston upon Thames *p267*. 020 8546 6111
Levi, P J (Michael Conn Goldsobel) *E L S1 S2 R2 Zc*
London W1 *p60* 020 7580 8902
Levin, A (Dechert) *C2*
London EC4 *p26* 020 7184 7000
Levin, Mrs A E (Herbert Smith LLP) *O Zc*
London EC2 *p40* 020 7374 8000
Levin, D (Mayer Brown International LLP)
London EC2 *p59* 020 3130 3000
Levin, K S (Keith Levin & Co) *N Q G H D1 J1 K1 F1 L W Zv*
Huyton *p258* 0151 480 5777
Levin, Ms M (Fox Williams) *J1*
London EC2 *p33* 020 7628 2000
Levin, Miss M E (Levi Solicitors LLP) *F1 J1 L O Q N*
Leeds *p275* 0113 244 9931
Levine, Ms M (Fisher Levine & Co)
London N2 *p32*
Levine, M A (Levine Mellins Klarfeld) *S1 E S2*
Stanmore *p394* 020 8954 7474
Levine, R J (Maxwell Winward LLP) *E L T1 Zc R2*
London EC4 *p59* 020 7651 0000

Levine, S P (Claremont Richards) *S2 E S1 W C1*
London EC4 *p20* 020 7353 3030
Levine, S R (DLA Piper UK LLP) *O Ze Zf F2 I U1*
London EC2 *p24* 0870 011 1111
Levinger, P D (Butcher Burns LLP) *C1 C2 B1 T1*
London WC1 *p16* 020 7713 7100
Levinson, A M (William Sturges & Co) *S1 W C1 D1 E F1 J1 K1 L R1 Zi Zk Zo*
Westminster *p84* 020 7873 1000
Levinson, J J (Howard Kennedy LLP) *O*
London W1 *p48* 020 7636 1616
Levinson, J M (DAC Beachcroft) *O E L Q J1 R1 B1 N Zl Zw Zb Zk*
Manchester *p303* 0161 934 3000
Levinson, M A (TBI Solicitors) *C1 S1 E D1 J1 R1 T1*
Hartlepool *p243* . . . 0800 052 6824 / 01429 264101
Levinson, S E (Manches LLP) *J1 Zp*
London WC2 *p58* 020 7404 4433
Levison, Mrs G (Zermansky & Partners) *C1 S2 E*
Leeds *p278* 0113 245 9766
Levison, J I (Levison Meltzer Pigott) *K1*
London EC4 *p53* 020 7556 2400
Levison, Miss L R (Pattinson & Brewer) *Q N Zr*
London WC1 *p66* 020 7400 5100
Leviss, Miss C R (Stone King LLP) *C1 Ze*
Bath *p128* 01225 337599
Leviten, D J (Pannone LLP) *E R1 R2 S2*
Manchester *p308* 0161 909 3000
Levitt, A J (Herbert Smith LLP) *C1 Zj C2*
London EC2 *p40* 020 7374 8000
Levitt, Mrs A M (Farrell Matthews & Weir) *K1 D1 D2 K3*
London W6 *p30* 020 8746 3771
Levitt, Miss C A (Steels) *K3 Q K1*
Warrington *p422* 01925 261354
Levontine, C A (Maxwell Winward LLP) *N O Q L B1 E*
London EC4 *p59* 020 7651 0000
Levy, A A (Solomon Levy)
Luton *p295* . . . . . . .01582 425817 / 414948
Levy, A G N (Ince & Co Services Ltd)
London E1 *p44* 020 7481 0010
Levy, A J M (Clifford Chance)
London E14 *p20* 020 7006 1000
Levy, A M (Benson Mazure LLP) *E L S1 T1 S2 R2*
Westminster *p12* 020 7486 8091
Levy, B (Myers Fletcher & Gordon) *C1 T2 C2 W Q*
London W6 *p62* 020 7610 4433
Levy, Mrs D J (WGS Solicitors) *K1*
Westminster *p90* 020 7723 1656
Levy, Mrs D J (Brightstone Law LLP) *K1 S1 W E I*
Elstree *p218* 020 8731 3080
Levy, G D (Olswang LLP) *C1 C2 B1 Zb*
London WC1 *p64* 020 7067 3000
Levy, J (Ashurst LLP)
London EC2 *p7* 020 7638 1111
Levy, J (Lewis Silkin LLP) *O Q*
London EC4 *p53* 020 7074 8000
Levy, J (Lewis Silkin LLP) *E S1 C1 Zh*
London EC4 *p53* 020 7074 8000
Levy, J M (Layzells) *C1 Zw S2 E*
London N10 *p52* 020 8444 0202
Levy, Ms K (Copitch) *S1 W K1 G F1 T2 Q H J1 L*
Haringey *p22* 020 8883 9831
Stoke-on-Trent *p398* 01782 202020
Levy, L (Trowers & Hamlins)
London EC3 *p88* 020 7423 8000
Levy, M (Howard Kennedy LLP) *Q Zc*
London W1 *p48* 020 7636 1616
Levy, N (Ashurst LLP)
London EC2 *p7* 020 7638 1111
Levy, N (Myers Fletcher & Gordon) *C1 M2 T2 W*
London W6 *p62* 020 7610 4433
Levy, P M (OMW Solicitors) *S1 K1 G H P M1 N L E D1 Zd Zh Zl*
Burton-on-Trent *p17001283 563401 / 530333*
Levy, P S (P S Levy & Co) *C1 E L S1 W*
London W1 *p53* 020 7486 7717
Levy, R (Linklaters LLP)
London EC2 *p54* 020 7456 2000
Levy, R A (Leigh Day & Co) *Zr*
London EC1 *p52* 020 7650 1200
Levy, S (Levy & Co Solicitors LLP) *G H*
Witham *p436* 01376 511819
Levy, S P (Pinsent Masons LLP)
London EC2 *p67* 020 7418 7000
Manchester *p310* 0161 830 5000
Lew, S P A (Clifford Chance)
London E14 *p20* 020 7006 1000
Lewarne, R (Keoghs LLP) *N*
Bolton *p149* 01204 677000
Lewin, B C (Sylvester Amiel Lewin & Horne LLP) *B1 C1 E F1 L O Q S1 W Zb Zv*
London N12 *p85* 020 8446 4000
Lewin, J (Pinnacle Insurance PLC)
Borehamwood *p450* 020 8207 9000
Lewin, K M (Brunswicks LLP) *O Zy B2 J2*
Birkenhead *p134* 0870 766 8400
Lewin, M (Michael Lewin Solicitors) *K1 Q N*
Leeds *p275* 0113 393 0231
Lewin, Miss O (Leigh Day & Co) *Zr*
London EC1 *p52* 020 7650 1200
Lewin, S R (Bircham Dyson Bell) *W T2 Zd*
Westminster *p13* 020 7227 7000
Lewington, A D (Pinsent Masons LLP) *C2 C1*
London EC2 *p67* 020 7418 7000
Lewis, A (George Davies Solicitors LLP)
Manchester *p303* 0161 236 8992

6

Lewis, A (Ashurst LLP)
London EC2 *p7* 020 7638 1111
Lewis, Ms A (Newport City Council)
Newport *p466* 01633 656656
Lewis, Miss A (Wilson & Bird) *K1 K3 D1*
Aylesbury *p121* 01296 436766
Lewis, A (Harbottle & Lewis LLP)
London W1 *p38* 020 7667 5000
Lewis, Ms A (Alan Edwards & Co) *G H Q J1 L*
Kensington & Chelsea *p28*. . 020 7221 7644
Lewis, Miss A (Hall Smith Whittingham LLP)
Nantwich *p320*. 01270 610300
Lewis, Miss A A E (Manches LLP) *K1*
Oxford *p343* 01865 722106
Lewis, A B (Linder Myers Solicitors) *N O Q L F1*
Manchester *p306* 0844 984 6000
Lewis, Mrs A E (Cripps Harries Hall LLP) *W T2*
Tunbridge Wells *p415* 01892 515121
Lewis, A I (Bates Wells & Braithwaite London LLP) *S1*
London EC4 *p11* 020 7551 7777
Lewis, A J (Mullis & Peake) *O J1 L F1 Q B1 Zc*
Romford *p366* 01708 784000
Lewis, A J (Green Wright Chalton Annis)
Rustington *p369* 01903 774131
Lewis, A J E (Black Rock)
London EC4 *p104* 020 7743 3000
Lewis, A P M (Broomhead & Saul) *W*
Taunton *p408* 01823 288121
Lewis, A V (Taylor Lewis)
Cardigan *p181*. 01239 621999
Lewis, A W (Arnold Davies Vincent Evans) *W E S1 S2 K4*
Lampeter *p269*. 01570 422233
Tregaron *p413*. 01974 298816
Lewis, Miss A Z (Charles Coleman LLP) *W*
Windsor *p434* 01753 861115
Lewis, Ms B (Mayer Brown International LLP)
London EC2 *p59*. 020 3130 3000
Lewis, B (Graham Evans & Partners) *N Q J1 K1 L O S1 Zj Zk*
Swansea *p405*. 01792 655822
Lewis, Ms B J (Mayer Brown International LLP) *C1 C2*
London EC2 *p59*. 020 3130 3000
Lewis, C (Cyngor Sir Ynys Mon (Isle of Anglesey County Council))
Llangefni *p463*. 01248 750057
Lewis, Mrs C (GHP Legal) *G H*
Wrexham *p442* 01978 291456
Lewis, C (Spicketts Battrick Law Practice) *N*
Pontypridd *p352*. 01443 407221
Lewis, Miss C E (Sheridans) *C1 J1 I Zc Zf*
London WC1 *p78* 020 7079 0100
Lewis, C G (Morgan Cole) *E Zc*
Oxford *p344*. 01865 262600
Lewis, Miss C J (Gowmans) *W K4*
Paignton *p345* 01803 546100
Lewis, C J (Warren Murton) *C1 S2 J1*
London WC1 *p62* 020 7404 5511
Lewis, C J G (Warren Murton) *C1 T1 W Ze Zf*
London WC1 *p62* 020 7404 5511
Lewis, C T (C T Lewis & Co)
Leeds *p275* 0113 245 9726
Lewis, D (Pinsent Masons LLP)
London EC2 *p67*. 020 7418 7000
Lewis, D E (Allen & Overy LLP)
London E1 *p5* 020 3088 0000
Lewis, D G (Richards & Lewis)
Ebbw Vale *p216* 01495 350018
Lewis, D J (Garner Canning) *A1 L S1 S2 W K4 Zm*
Atherstone *p120*. 01827 713543
Lewis, D L (Hamlins LLP) *A1 E L S1 W*
London W1 *p38* 020 7355 6000
Lewis, D L (Weightmans LLP) *J2 N O Q Zi*
Liverpool *p291*. 0151 227 2601
Lewis, D M (Clifford Chance)
London E14 *p20*. 020 7006 1000
Lewis, E (T G Baynes) *N Zr J2*
Bexleyheath *p132* 020 8301 7777
Lewis, E (DAC Beachcroft) *O Zc*
London EC4 *p24*. 020 7936 2222
Lewis, Mrs E C (Berry Smith LLP) *O*
Cardiff *p177* 029 2034 5511
Lewis, E G (Lewis Lewis & Company Ltd) *S1 O K1 Q F1*
St Clears *p391*. 01994 231044
Tenby *p410* 01834 844844
Lewis, E T (LG Lawyers)
London SE1 *p50*. 020 7379 0000
Lewis, Mrs E V P (Peterborough City Council)
Peterborough *p468* 01733 747474
Lewis, Ms F (Blake Lapthorn) *C1 J1*
London EC1 *p13*. 020 7405 2000
Lewis, Miss F A (Howe & Spender) *G H*
Neath *p320* 01639 881571
Lewis, G (Alan Simons & Co) *S1 L W E J1 S2*
Penarth *p345* 029 2070 3991
Lewis, G G (Keppe Rofer) *G H J1 Q N Zq*
Brecon *p156*. 01874 624627
Milford Haven *p316* 01646 695311
Lewis, G J (Buller Jeffries) *F1 F2 J2 N O Q Zj Zc Zq*
Birmingham *p136* 0121 212 2620
Lewis, G R (Burton Copeland LLP) *G*
Manchester *p302* 0161 827 9500
Lewis, Mrs H (Bolton Metropolitan Borough Council)
Bolton *p450* 01204 333333
Lewis, H A (Kirk & Partners) *S1 S2 W T1 E L*
London SE9 *p50*. 020 8850 2484

Lewis, Ms H C (Dickinson Dees) *W*
Newcastle upon Tyne *p324* . 0191 279 9000
Lewis, I (Noble)
Shefford *p377* 01462 814055
Lewis, I B (Walker Smith Way) *S1*
Wrexham *p443* 0844 346 3100
Lewis, I D (Bray & Bray) *C1 C2 J1 F1 Ze Zc Zp*
Leicester *p279*. 0116 254 8871
Lewis, I G (Willcox Lewis LLP) *T2 W Zd*
Norwich *p335* 01508 480100
Lewis, I N (Horwich Cohen Coghlan) *G Q J1 J2 N R2 S1 Zp Zw*
Manchester *p305* 0161 830 4600
Lewis, J (Blake Lapthorn) *W*
Chandlers Ford *p184* 023 8090 8090
Lewis, J (Wolferstans) *N*
Plymouth *p351*. 01752 663295
Lewis, Ms J (Nabarro LLP) *C1 E Zc Zu*
London WC1 *p63* 020 7524 6000
Lewis, J (Brabners Chaffe Street)
Manchester *p301* 0161 836 8800
Lewis, Ms J (George Davies Solicitors LLP) *E R2 S2*
Manchester *p303* 0161 236 8992
Lewis, J (Francis & Co)
Chepstow *p189* 01291 622237
Lewis, J (Alexander JLO) *S1*
London E14 *p5* 020 7537 7000
London E15 *p15*. 020 8221 8000
Lewis, Ms J (Lewis & Lines) *K1 N Q W F1 V D1 L S1 Zq Zv*
Abertillery *p113* 01495 212286
Lewis, Ms J (Brookes & Co) *Za O Zj C1*
London EC3 *p16*. 020 7621 0067
Lewis, Miss J (Steeles) *Q*
Norwich *p335* 0870 609 0200
Lewis, Ms J (Gill Turner Tucker) *D1 K1*
Maidstone *p299* 01622 759051
Lewis, Ms J (Legal Services Commission No 9 (North Eastern))
Leeds *p463* 0113 390 7300
Lewis, Miss J A (Key2Law LLP) *D1 F1 G H J1 K1 L M1 N P Q*
Ewell *p220*. 020 8393 0941
Lewis, J A (Lewis Nedas & Co) *G H W E S1 Zl B2*
Camden *p53*. 020 7387 2032
Lewis, J D R (Lewis Lewis & Company Ltd) *A1 B2 J1 K1 S1 X Zw*
St Clears *p391*. 01994 231044
Tenby *p410* 01834 844844
Lewis, Ms J E (The College of Law)
London WC1 *p105*. 0800 289997
Lewis, Ms J G (Glazer Delmar) *Zh L*
London SE22 *p35* 020 8299 0021
Lewis, J G R (Howard Kennedy LLP) *E S1*
London W1 *p48* 020 7636 1616
Lewis, Mrs J K (Swayne Johnson Solicitors) *W S1 T1*
Denbigh *p208* 01745 812835
Lewis, Mrs J L (Shakespeares) *W T2*
Nottingham *p339*. 0115 945 3700
Lewis, J M (Walker Smith Way) *S1*
Wrexham *p443* 0844 346 3100
Lewis, Miss J M (George Green LLP) *C2*
Cradley Heath *p201* 01384 410410
Lewis, J M (BBC)
London W12 *p103* 020 8752 5734
Lewis, Mrs J M (Howe & Spender) *K1 D1 D2*
Port Talbot *p353* 01639 881571
Lewis, J M (Parker Grego Cullen & Ball)
Birmingham *p141* 0121 200 3031
Lewis, J P (Plexus Law (A Trading Name of Parabis Law LLP)) *N Q Zr O G Zq*
Evesham *p220*. 01386 769160
Lewis, J P (Stallard March & Edwards) *N Q Zr*
Worcester *p440* 01905 613404
Lewis, J R (Red Kite Law) *A1 E R1 C1 Q S2 X J1 O*
Carmarthen *p183* 01267 239000
Lewis, J S (Lewis & Co) *S2 E Q S1 W*
London NW4 *p53* 020 8202 4343
Lewis, J W M (Blackpool Borough Council)
Blackpool *p450* 01253 477450
Lewis, K (GHP Legal) *S1 S2*
Oswestry *p342*. 01691 659194
Lewis, Ms K (The Stokes Partnership) *K1 K2*
Crewkerne *p203*. 01460 279279
Lewis, Mrs K (F Barnes & Son)
Romford *p366* 01708 743727
Lewis, Miss K (Granville-West) *K1*
Pontypool *p352* 01495 751111
Lewis, Ms K E (Joint Council for the Welfare of Immigrants)
London EC1 *p107* 020 7251 8708
Lewis, K J (Cyfraith JRL Law) *Q S1 A1 S2 L W*
Llanrwst *p292* 01492 641222
Lewis, Ms L (Ashurst LLP)
London EC2 *p7* 020 7638 1111
Lewis, Mrs L M (Lightfoots LLP) *W Zm T2*
Thame *p410*. 01844 212305
Lewis, M (Field Fisher Waterhouse LLP)
London EC3 *p31*. 020 7861 4000
Uxbridge *p417*. 0845 638 1381
Lewis, M (LG Lawyers)
London SE1 *p50*. 020 7379 0000
Lewis, M (Adan & Co) *K1 Zu Zm*
Maidstone *p298* 01622 600488
Lewis, M (Osborne Clarke) *C1*
Bristol *p164* 0117 917 3000
Lewis, M (RTL Solicitors)
Bridgend *p157*. 01656 665850
Cardiff *p180* 029 2023 4030

Lewis, Miss M A (Jeffrey Green Russell) *N J2 Q Zj Zq*
London W1 *p46* 020 7339 7000
Lewis, M B (Squire Sanders (UK) LLP) *J1*
London EC2 *p81*. 020 7655 1000
Lewis, M D P (Blanchards Bailey LLP) *T2 W*
Blandford Forum *p147*. . . . 01258 459361
Dorchester *p212*. 01305 251222
Shaftesbury *p374* 01747 440447
Lewis, M H (Finers Stephens Innocent LLP) *W T2 T1*
London W1 *p32* 020 7323 4000
Lewis, M P (Gordons LLP) *O Q E B1 Zc F1 L Zq*
Leeds *p273* 0113 227 0100
Lewis, M R L (Foot Anstey) *C1 B1 Zb*
Plymouth *p349*. 01752 675000
Lewis, M S (Haslam & Payne) *Q L O N S1 W K1 J1*
London SW1 *p39* 020 7828 8725
Lewis, M V (Wright Hassall LLP) *C1 C2*
Leamington Spa *p270* 01926 886688
Lewis, M W (Nottingham Magistrates Court)
Nottingham *p467*. 0115 955 8111
Lewis, Miss N (Environment Agency (Wales))
Cardiff *p453* 0870 850 6506
Lewis, Ms N (Department for Business, Enterprise and Regulatory Reform)
London SW1 *p105*. 020 7215 0105
Lewis, Miss N (Challinors)
Birmingham *p136* 0121 212 9393
Lewis, Ms N (Tedstone George & Tedstone)
Penkridge *p345* 01785 712243
Lewis, N (Bendles) *D1 F1 J1 K1 L M1 P V Zc Zl Zn*
Carlisle *p181*. 01228 522215
Lewis, N W (KBL Solicitors) *K1 Zl*
Bolton *p149* 01204 527777
Lewis, O M (Peachey & Co)
London WC2 *p66* 020 7316 5200
Lewis, Ms P (Hugh James) *O N F1*
Cardiff *p179* 029 2022 4871
Lewis, P (George Ide LLP)
Chichester *p192* 01243 786668
Lewis, P (Herbert Smith LLP) *O Zj Q Zq*
London EC2 *p40*. 020 7374 8000
Lewis, P (Linklaters LLP)
London EC2 *p54*. 020 7456 2000
Lewis, Ms P (Smith Law Partnership) *V K3*
Braintree *p155*. 01376 321311
Lewis, P (Rosling King) *E*
London EC4 *p73*. 020 7353 2353
Lewis, P A (Quality Solicitors HPJV) *G H*
Newport *p329* 01633 242526
Lewis, P G (Lewis Whittle)
Caerphilly *p172* 029 2088 1378
Lewis, P J (Appleby Hope & Matthews) *G H S1 W Q Zl*
Middlesbrough *p314* 01642 440444
Lewis, P M (Cheltenham Borough Council)
Cheltenham *p454* 01242 262626
Lewis, P S (Parkinson Wright LLP) *K1 K2 D1 D2*
Worcester *p440* 01905 726789
Lewis, P V (Lanyon Bowdler LLP) *S1 S2 A1 W*
Hereford *p248* 01432 378379
Wellington *p425* 01952 244721
Lewis, Miss R (Farrer & Co LLP)
London WC2 *p31* 020 3375 7000
Lewis, R (R Miles Richards & Co) *S1 L E W C1 S2 C2*
Pontypridd *p352*. 01443 202237
Lewis, Miss R (Fairbrother & Darlow)
Bracknell *p153*. 01344 420808
Lewis, R (Darwin Gray)
Cardiff *p178* 029 2082 9100
Lewis, R (Hogan Lovells International LLP)
London EC1 *p42*. 020 7296 2000
Lewis, R (Peugeot Citroen Automobiles UK Ltd)
Coventry *p456*. 024 7688 4258
Lewis, R (Lewis Francis Blackburn Bray) *P M1 G K1 H D1 E N S1 L Zc Ze Zb*
Sheffield *p376* 0114 272 9721
Lewis, R (Herbert Smith LLP)
London EC2 *p40*. 020 7374 8000
Lewis, R A J (Ungoed-Thomas & King Limited) *S1 W C1 E L K4*
Carmarthen *p183* 01267 237441
Lewis, R C (Warren Murton) *S1 E L O Q*
London WC1 *p62* 020 7404 5511
Lewis, R D P (Hains & Lewis Ltd) *S1 W Q E F1 A1 I J1 Zd Zo S2*
Haverfordwest *p244* 0845 408 0125
Lewis, R E (J A Stevens & Co)
Epsom *p219*. 01372 745288
Lewis, Ms R K (Dawson Cornwell) *K3 K1*
London WC1 *p26* 020 7242 2556
Lewis, Miss R M (Ashfords LLP) *Zq J1*
Plymouth *p349*. 01752 521500
Lewis, R M (Herbert Smith LLP) *C1 C2*
London EC2 *p40*. 020 7374 8000
Lewis, R W (Maples Solicitors LLP) *A1 C1 E T1 S1 T2 W R1 J1 Zd Zo*
Spalding *p389* 01775 722261
Lewis, R W (Rubin Lewis O'Brien) *S1 W A1 C1*
Cwmbran *p206* 01633 867000
Lewis, R W (WBW Solicitors) *S1 E W L S2*
Torquay *p413* 0870 701 4321
Lewis, Mrs S (Gartsides) *D1 K1*
Newport *p328* 01633 213411
Lewis, S (Brabners Chaffe Street) *C1 U1 I Ze Zza U2 C2 Zw*
Liverpool *p286*. 0151 600 3000

Lewis, Ms S (Grindeys LLP) *R1 C1 E L S1 Zh Zc*
Stoke-on-Trent *p397*. 01782 846441
Stone *p398* 01785 810780
Lewis, Ms S (Gudgeons Prentice) *K1 Q N J1*
Stowmarket *p399* 01449 613101
Lewis, Miss S (Jordans) *Q O N*
Wakefield *p418* 01924 387110
Lewis, S C (City of York Council)
York *p477* 01904 551045
Lewis, Ms S E (Osborne Clarke) *R2*
London EC2 *p65*. 020 7105 7000
Lewis, S G (MacLeish Littlestone Cowan) *O Q L Zq R1*
Redbridge *p57*. 020 8514 3000
Lewis, Miss S J (Philip Avery & Co) *S1 S2 E W*
Llanelli *p292*. 01554 746295
Lewis, Mrs S J (Rutters) *K4 Zm T2 W V*
Shaftesbury *p374* 01747 852377
Lewis, S J (Dickinson Dees) *O*
Newcastle upon Tyne *p324* . 0191 279 9000
Lewis, S J (Lees Solicitors LLP) *Zr*
Birkenhead *p134*. 0151 647 9381
Lewis, Mrs S M (Whatley Weston & Fox) *D2 K1 D1 K3*
Worcester *p440* 01905 731731
Lewis, Miss S R (Saunders Bearman LLP) *E Q S1 S2 Zl*
London W1 *p76* 020 7224 2618
Lewis, S R (T G Pollard & Co) *W S1 T1 A1 Zd Zm Zo*
Wells *p425*. 01749 674722
Lewis, S W (Finers Stephens Innocent LLP) *C1 E R1 T1 L S1 A1 W B1 Zb Zc Zd*
London W1 *p32* 020 7323 4000
Lewis, Ms T (Central London Community Law Centre)
London WC2 *p105*. 020 7839 2998
Lewis, Mrs T (Hertfordshire County Council)
Hertford *p460* 01992 555555
Lewis, T (Green Wright Chalton Annis)
Worthing *p441*. 01903 234064
Lewis, T (Sydney Mitchell) *K1 P L N D1*
Birmingham *p142* 0121 698 2200 / 0808 166 8827
Lewis, T A (Tayntons LLP Solicitors) *W K4*
Gloucester *p230*. 01452 522047
Lewis, T H O (Land Registry - Gloucester Office)
Gloucester *p459*. 01452 511111
Lewis, T J (Macfarlanes)
London EC4 *p56*. 020 7831 9222
Lewis, T M (Travers Smith LLP) *C1*
London EC1 *p87*. 020 7295 3000
Lewis, T M (Johnson & Gaunt) *M1 G P J1 K1 F1 D1 L H V*
Banbury *p122* . . . .01295 256271 / 271200
Lewis, Ms U A (North Kensington Law Centre)
London W10 *p108* 020 8969 7473
Lewis, Ms V (Simmons & Simmons)
London EC2 *p79*. 020 7628 2020
Lewis, V J (Armitage Sykes LLP) *K1*
Brighouse *p158* 01484 714431
Lewis, W (Pinsent Masons LLP) *J1*
London EC2 *p67*. 020 7418 7000
Lewis, W E D (Clarkes) *K1 K2 D1 S1*
Telford *p409*. 01952 291666
Lewis, W R (Rodericks) *K1 L Q S1 W*
Llanelli *p292*. 01554 773424
Lewis Ogden, J P (Harrowells) *C3 C1 C2 E Ze S2 Zd T1*
York *p444* 01904 690111
Lewis-Ethelston, Mrs C A (Hill Dickinson LLP) *E T1 A1 L C1 R1 Zc S2 R2*
Chester *p190* 01244 896600
Lewis-Smith, D W (City of Bradford Metropolitan District Council)
Bradford *p451* 01274 752236
Lewis-Vivas, J (Wedlake Bell LLP) *E S2*
London WC1 *p91* 020 7395 3000
Lewtas, S H (Stephensons Solicitors LLP) *G H D1 K1 J1 P M1 L F1 V Zk Zl Zt*
Leigh *p282*. 01942 777777
Lewzey, G (Jefferies Essex LLP) *G H*
Westcliff-on-Sea *p428* 01702 332311
Leydecker, Miss S V (Herbert Smith LLP) *O Zq*
London EC2 *p40*. 020 7374 8000
Leyland, B (Bailhache Shaw Marsden) *D2 D1 J1 K1 O Q Zq*
Taunton *p408* 01823 351122
Leyland, Mrs J C (Davey Franklin Jones) *K1 K3*
Gloucester *p230*. 01452 508800
Leyland, J F (Hallmark Hulme)
Worcester *p439* 01905 726600
Worcester *p440* 01905 610410
Leyland, S J (Maxwell Hodge Solicitors) *N X*
Kirkby *p268* 0151 548 7370
Leyshon, Ms C (ClarksLegal LLP) *B1 E Zu S1 T1 T2*
Reading *p360* 0118 958 5321
Leyshon, G (Osborne Clarke) *C2 R2*
Reading *p361* 0118 925 2000
Li, Ms A L K (Brown Beer Nixon Mallon) *K1 D1 K3 L N*
Redcar *p362*. 01642 490202
Li, Miss M (Li & Co Solicitor)
Kensington & Chelsea *p54*. . 020 8964 8525
Li, Miss M Y (Smith Llewelyn Partnership) *Q Zr*
Swansea *p405*. 01792 464444
Li, P A (Simmons & Simmons)
London EC2 *p79*. 020 7628 2020
Li, T K M (Harrison Li Solicitors LLP) *S1 S2 E*
Camberley *p173*. 01276 27700
Li-Yan-Hui, D (Hewitsons) *Zt T2 W*
Cambridge *p174*. 01223 461155

See p634 for the Key to Work Categories

Liberatore, F (Jones Day) *C3*
London EC4 *p46* . . . 020 7039 5959
Liburd, Miss J M (Northampton Borough Council)
Northampton *p467* . . . 01604 837837
Liburd, Miss K (Wilsons) *W Q K1 S1 K4 Zp K3 R2 N*
Bradford *p155* . . . 01274 693600
Liburd, Ms S G (Association of Teachers and Lecturers)
London WC2 *p103* . . . 020 7930 6441
Licence, J P W (Furley Page LLP)
Canterbury *p176* . . . 01227 763939
Lichfield, R A (Lichfield Reynolds) *S1 E W G H L C1 R1*
Stoke-on-Trent *p398* . . . 01782 289122
Lidbetter, A W (Herbert Smith LLP) *O*
London EC2 *p40* . . . 020 7374 8000
Liddar, Mrs H A (Oxford City Council)
Oxford *p468* . . . 01865 249811
Liddell, A N (Capstick-Dale & Partners) *O C1 Q B1 F1 F2 J1 N M1 S1 Zk Zq Ze Zt Zp*
Romford *p366* . . . 01708 722466
Liddell, Mrs C M (Enfield Magistrates Court)
London N17 *p106* . . . 020 8808 5411
Liddell, D A (Ware & Kay LLP) *N Q O*
York *p445* . . . 01904 716000
Liddell, D J M (Ashurst LLP) *C1 C3*
London EC2 *p7* . . . 020 7638 1111
Liddell, I D (Liddell and Company) *N*
Romford *p366* . . . 01708 775999
Liddiard, A P J (Attwaters) *W T2 K4*
Loughton *p294* . . . 020 8508 2111
Liddiard, Mrs S J (Machins Solicitors LLP) *C1 I Ze Zza J1 U2 Zp*
Luton *p295* . . . 01582 514000
Liddington, J (Doyle Clayton Solicitors Limited) *J1 Zp*
London E14 *p27* . . . 020 7038 8051
London EC2 *p27* . . . 020 7329 9090
Liddington, O (Clarion Solicitors LLP) *K1 D1 D2 K3*
Leeds *p272* . . . 0113 246 0622
Liddington, S H (Bell & Co) *S2 S1 W E*
Cheam *p185* . . . 020 8642 6099
Liddle, A G (Overburys & Raymond Thompson) *W T1 T2 Zd A1*
Norwich *p335* . . . 01603 610481
Liddle, Mrs C J (Carlisle City Council)
Carlisle *p453* . . . 01228 817000
Liddle, Mrs D J (Goldwaters) *N K1 W Q L V*
Newcastle upon Tyne *p324* . 0191 232 2653
Liddle, Mrs H (TMJ Legal Services LLP) *D1 K1 D2 K3*
Hartlepool *p243* . . . 01429 235616
Wingate *p434* . . . 01429 838225
Liddle, I A (Farleys Solicitors LLP) *Zb B1 Q N C1 C2 S1 L E F2 Ze P*
Blackburn *p145* . . . 01254 367856
Liddle, Mrs J M (Overburys & Raymond Thompson) *L O Zq*
Norwich *p335* . . . 01603 610481
Liddle, P A (Sintons LLP) *F1 S2 L P R2*
Newcastle upon Tyne *p326* . 0191 226 7878
Liddy, K M (Liddys Solicitors) *N O F1 F2*
Wakefield *p418* . . . 01924 780753
Lidster, E C (E C Lidster & Co) *G H*
Grimsby *p235* . . . 01472 348417
Lidstone, Mrs A (Simmons & Simmons)
London EC2 *p79* . . . 020 7628 2020
Lidstrom, T (Linklaters LLP)
London EC2 *p54* . . . 020 7456 2000
Lieb, P (Broudie Jackson Canter) *G H*
Liverpool *p286* . . . 0151 227 1429
Liebeck, D R (Rochman Landau LLP) *B1 O Q J1 Zc Ze Zf Zi Zp Zq L*
London W1 *p72* . . . 020 7544 2424
Liebeschuetz, Miss R E (Law Hurst & Taylor) *G K1 M1 D1 J1 L S1 W*
Westcliff-on-Sea *p428* . . . 01702 337864
Liefman, G (Liefman Rose & Co) *S1 E W L T1 P Zd T2*
Manchester *p306* . . . 0161 740 7878
Life, Ms J E (Edwards Duthie) *G H*
London E13 *p29* . . . 020 8514 9000
Lifely, A M (Osborne Clarke) *I O A3 F2*
London EC2 *p65* . . . 020 7105 7000
Liggett, Miss A (DWF) *N Q*
Liverpool *p287* . . . 0151 907 3000
Liggett, M (Nestle UK Ltd)
Croydon *p456* . . . 020 8667 5260
Liggins, J E (Lovetts PLC) *O*
Guildford *p236* . . . 01483 457500
Light, P C (Pardoes) *N*
Bridgwater *p158* . . . 01278 457891
Light, R A (Stephenson Harwood) *E R2*
London EC2 *p82* . . . 020 7329 4422
Lightbody, B R (Addleshaw Goddard) *E*
Leeds *p271* . . . 0113 209 2000
Manchester *p300* . . . 0161 934 6000
Lightbown, J N (Greenland Houchen Pomeroy) *A1 C1 E L R1 S1 C2 S2 W*
Norwich *p334* . . . 01603 660744
Lightfoot, J C E (Lightfoot O'Brien Westcott) *S1 A1 W*
London W1 *p54* . . . 01394 386336
Woodbridge *p438* . . . 01394 386336
Lightfoot, Miss J K (Henmans LLP) *N Zq*
Oxford *p343* . . . 01865 781000
Lightman, Ms S R I (Treasury Solicitors Department)
London WC2 *p110* . . . 020 7210 3000
Lightowler, A M (Wortley Byers) *C1 J1 E*
Brentwood *p156* . . . 01277 268368
Lightwood, G (Pattinson & Brewer) *Q N P*
Bristol *p164* . . . 0117 917 1100
London WC1 *p66* . . . 020 7400 5100
Liley, Miss S J (Hempsons) *Zr N*
Harrogate *p240* . . . 01423 522331
Lill, J (The College of Law York)
York *p477* . . . 0800 289997
Lilley, A J W (Travers Smith LLP) *J1 J2 M1 Zp*
London EC1 *p87* . . . 020 7295 3000
Lilley, A P (Aldridge Brownlee Solicitors LLP) *G H*
Christchurch *p194* . . . 01425 282150
Lilley, B M J (Woodford Robinson) *G H*
Northampton *p333* . . . 01604 624926
Lilley, E J (Pengillys LLP) *S1 S2 E W L R1 C1 T2*
Weymouth *p430* . . . 01305 768888
Lilley, J (Blaser Mills) *N F1 O Q B1 J1 L Zq*
High Wycombe *p249* . . . 01494 450171
Lilley, Ms R (Coventry City Council)
Coventry *p456* . . . 024 7683 4863
Lilleyman, Ms K (Trowers & Hamlins)
London EC3 *p88* . . . 020 7423 8000
Lilley-Tams, M (Paragon Law) *Zi Q*
Nottingham *p338* . . . 0115 964 4123
Lilliott, Mrs J K (Holmes & Hills LLP) *R1 P Zu*
Braintree *p155* . . . 01376 320456
Lillywhite, I J (Lillywhite Williams & Co)
Dagenham *p206* . . . 020 8593 7471
Lillywhite, Ms P (Heald Nickinson) *L Q J1 Zl*
Camberley *p173* . . . 01276 680000
Lim, M (Lewis Silkin LLP) *O*
London EC4 *p53* . . . 020 7074 8000
Lim, R (Weightmans LLP) *D1 K1*
Liverpool *p291* . . . 0151 227 2601
Lim, Miss S (Civil Aviation Authority)
London WC2 *p105* . . . 020 7453 6162
Lim, Ms Z (Mills & Reeve) *C1 C2 Ze C3 Zb U2 Zv*
Cambridge *p175* . . . 01223 364422
Limb, C J (Fidler & Pepper)
Sutton-in-Ashfield *p404* . . . 01623 451111
Limbachia, Miss S (Birchall Blackburn LLP) *B1 Q*
Chorley *p194* . . . 01257 279011
Limbada, Miss A (Joan Ferguson & Co) *K1 S1 W D1 K3*
Manchester *p304* . . . 0161 795 5866
Limbrey, M S (Moss & Poulson) *C1 E L P R1 S1 Zd Ze Zn*
Shrewsbury *p379* . . . 01743 350571
Limmer, Miss K G (Rushmoor Borough Council)
Farnborough *p458* . . . 01252 398398
Limont, Mrs V A (Berkson Globe Partnership) *G H M1 D1*
Liverpool *p286* . . . 0151 236 1234
Lin, Miss C K L (Lin & Co Solicitors) *S2 K3 Zi Q S1 W*
Birmingham *p140* . . . 0121 244 2300
Sutton Coldfield *p403* . . . 0121 244 2300
Lince, R (Reynolds Porter Chamberlain LLP)
London E1 *p71* . . . 020 3060 6000
Lincoln, R (Lincolns Solicitors) *S1 S2 K1 L Q Zl*
Northwood *p333* . . . 01923 820909
Lincoln, R B (Jeffrey Green Russell) *M1 N P B1 C1 Zj*
London W1 *p46* . . . 020 7339 7000
Lincoln, S F (McKenzie Bell Solicitors) *K1 N Zq*
Sunderland *p401* . . . 0191 567 4857
Lincoln-Lewis, J D (Lincoln-Lewis & Co) *N P K1 L R1 T1 V G H Zc Zi Zl*
Birmingham *p140* . . . 0121 454 7011
Lindemann, C A (Castlemere Properties Ltd)
Altrincham *p447* . . . 0161 941 3499
Lindemann, Ms J (Lawrence Stephens)
London EC1 *p82* . . . 020 7935 1211
Linden, A J R (Gordons LLP) *T1 Zd T2 W Zo*
Leeds *p273* . . . 0113 227 0100
Linden, Miss C (McAras Solicitors LLP) *D1 K3 K1 D2*
Leeds *p275* . . . 0113 243 4333
Linderman, Ms M (Ince & Co Services Ltd)
London E1 *p44* . . . 020 7481 0010
Lindley, M R (Streathers Solicitors LLP) *C1 F1 B1*
London W1 *p84* . . . 020 7034 4200
Lindley, R (Winston Solicitors LLP) *C1 C2 O Zq*
Leeds *p278* . . . 0113 320 5000
Lindley, S R (Jordans) *G H Zl*
Dewsbury *p210* . . . 01924 457171
Lindley, V T (Bailey & Haigh) *W K1 S1 F1 D1 Q*
Selby *p373* . . . 01757 705191
Lindo, Miss P L (Borneo Hughes Martell LLP) *K1 K3*
Northampton *p331* . . . 01604 624822
Lindon-Morris, Mrs C A (Clifton Ingram LLP) *A1 C1 E L S2*
Wokingham *p437* . . . 0118 978 0099
Lindop, Ms J (Field Fisher Waterhouse LLP)
London EC3 *p31* . . . 020 7861 4000
Lindop, J W (Lindops) *Q O N F1 S2 C1 L S1 Zq B1 W J1 E Zv*
Southend-on-Sea *p387* . . . 01702 431791
Lindop, Mrs T R I (Coldham Shield & Mace) *K1 D1 M1 S1 W P*
London E4 *p21* . . . 020 8524 6323
Lindqvist-Jones, Mrs G M (Toller Beattie LLP) *E S2 C1 Zc A1 Zk Zl*
Barnstaple *p125* . . . 01271 341000
Lindsay, A (Allen & Overy LLP)
London E1 *p5* . . . 020 3088 0000
Lindsay, A C (Firth Lindsay) *N G H*
Sheffield *p375* . . . 0114 276 0586
Lindsay, A M (Lindsay Sait & Turner) *C1 F1 K1 L N Q S1 W Zl Zy*
Woking *p437* . . . 01483 604033
Lindsay, C A (Denison Till) *J1 Zb C1 C2 T1*
York *p444* . . . 01904 611411
Lindsay, D R (Crown Prosecution Service Dyfed Powys)
Carmarthen *p453* . . . 01267 242100
Lindsay, Mrs J A (Blackpool Borough Council)
Blackpool *p450* . . . 01253 477450
Lindsay, L (Penningtons)
Basingstoke *p127* . . . 01256 407100
Lindsay, M P (Bird & Bird LLP) *Zb B1*
London EC4 *p13* . . . 020 7415 6000
Lindsay, N (Clarke Willmott) *C1 C2 C3*
Bristol *p162* 0845 209 1000 / 0117 305 6000
Lindsay, P S (DAC Beachcroft) *M1 Zj*
Manchester *p303* . . . 0161 934 3000
Lindsay, R (Telegraph Media Group)
London SW1 *p110* . . . 020 7931 3131
Lindsay, S A (Bevan Brittan LLP) *N Q Zm Zr*
Bristol *p161* . . . 0870 194 1000
Lindsay, S P (Universal Music)
London W14 *p110* . . . 020 8910 5000
Lindsay-Veal, Ms C (Binnion Lindsay-Veal LLP) *N Q Zq Zw Zr F1*
Stourport-on-Severn *p399* . . . 01299 827860
Lindsey, Ms A F P (Taylor Haldane Barlex LLP) *G H*
Chelmsford *p187* . . . 0845 293 7688
Lindsey, M (Geldards LLP) *Ze*
Cardiff *p178* . . . 029 2023 8239
Lindsey, P (Harding Evans LLP) *K4 W T2*
Newport *p328* . . . 01633 244233
Lindstrom, Ms L (Osborne Clarke) *J1*
London EC2 *p65* . . . 020 7105 7000
Lindup, R P (North Yorkshire County Council)
Northallerton *p467* . . . 01609 780780
Linehan, Dr C M (Cornwall County Council) *C1 E P L Ze*
Truro *p474* . . . 01872 322197
Lineker, Miss J C (Birmingham City Council Legal & Democratic Services)
Birmingham *p449* . . . 0121 303 2066
Lines, D (Allen & Overy LLP)
London E1 *p5* . . . 020 3088 0000
Lines, D C (Moran & Co) *N O Q S1*
Tamworth *p407* . . . 01827 54631
Lines, K L (Lewis & Lines) *G H J1 L R1 S1 A1 C1 E N Zl Zv*
Abertillery *p113* . . . 01495 212286
Lines, N C (Millichips) *K1 P J1 M1 F1 L Zl*
West Bromwich *p427* . . . 0121 500 6363
Lines, Miss S (Coles Miller Solicitors LLP) *W T2 Zm*
Poole *p352* . . . 01202 673011
Linford, D (Symes Bains Broomer) *K1 Zi K3*
Scunthorpe *p373* . . . 01724 281616
Linford, Mrs S (Forbes) *N Q F1 L O*
Accrington *p114* . . . 01254 872111
Ling, G S (Speechly Bircham LLP) *O E*
London EC4 *p81* . . . 020 7427 6400
Ling, J P (Lings Solicitors) *W S1 L J1 E Zv F1*
Worthing *p442* . . . 01903 700303
Ling, P (Garden House Solicitors) *Q N*
Hertford *p248* . . . 01992 422128
Ling, Miss R (Squire Sanders (UK) LLP) *O B1 J1*
Leeds *p277* . . . 0113 284 7000
Lingard, C D (Follett Stock LLP) *O Q B1 Zq Zg X*
Truro *p414* . . . 01872 241700
Lingard, Ms M (Cornwall County Council) *B1 O*
Truro *p474* . . . 01872 322197
Lingard, R G (Guildford Borough Council)
Guildford *p459* . . . 01483 505050
Linge, K (Bradley & Jefferies Solicitors Limited) *E Ze*
Derby *p208* . . . 01332 221722
Lingens, M R (Speechly Bircham LLP) *C1*
London EC4 *p81* . . . 020 7427 6400
Lingham, D (Hunters) *T2 W T1*
London WC2 *p44* . . . 020 7412 0050
Lingwood, J R (Mayo Wynne Baxter LLP) *N O Q E*
Brighton *p160* . . . 01273 775533
Lingwood, W E (Aviva PLC)
London EC3 *p103* . . 020 7283 7500 / 01603 687905
Norwich *p467* . . . 01603 622200
Link, G P (Allen & Overy LLP)
London E1 *p5* . . . 020 3088 0000
Linneker, J S (Taylor Wessing) *N C1 Ze*
London EC4 *p86* . . . 020 7300 7000
Linnell, M J (Blake Lapthorn) *S1 W*
Oxford *p342* . . . 01865 248607
Linnett, Ms V (EEF West Midlands Association) *J1*
Birmingham *p449* . . . 0121 456 2222
Linnette, D J (Flynet Ltd) *I C1 O J1 T1 F1 C3 Ze*
Cambridge *p453* . . .
Linnitt, S (Veale Wasbrough Vizards) *E P Zl*
Bristol *p165* . . . 0117 925 2020
Linsell, R D (Addleshaw Goddard) *C1*
London EC1 *p4* . . . 020 7606 8855
Linsell, Ms R S (Rosalind Watchorn) *W T2 S1 K4*
Sheffield *p377* . . . 0114 229 0160
Linskell, R (Speechly Bircham LLP) *J1*
London EC4 *p81* . . . 020 7427 6400
Linskill, J S (Linskills Solicitors) *G H Zv*
Liverpool *p289* . . . 0151 236 2224
Linthwaite, D C (Butcher Andrews) *N O Q Zr Zq J1 J2*
Fakenham *p223* . . . 01328 863131
Holt *p251* . . . 01263 712023
Linton, A J C (Buss Murton LLP) *O J1 Q*
Tunbridge Wells *p415* . . . 01892 510222
Linton, P D (Paul Linton & Co) *S1 E C1 W*
Watford *p423* . . . 01923 230478
Linton, Ms R L (Osborne Clarke) *C1*
Reading *p361* . . . 0118 925 2000
Linton, Ms S (Bryan Cave) *J1 Zi*
London EC2 *p19* . . . 020 7207 1100
Lintott, C J (Penningtons)
London EC2 *p66* . . . 020 7457 3000
Lintott, Mrs L J (Penningtons)
London EC2 *p66* . . . 020 7457 3000
Lintott, P A (Cripps Harries Hall LLP) *S1 L*
Tunbridge Wells *p415* . . . 01892 515121
Lintott, S C (Pannone LLP) *E R1 R2 S2*
Manchester *p308* . . . 0161 909 3000
Linwood, J W (Trowers & Hamlins) *Q O*
London EC3 *p88* . . . 020 7423 8000
Lipman, Ms A J (Geoffrey Lurie) *N S1 W Zr S2 O Q*
Newcastle upon Tyne *p325* . 0191 232 1800
Lipman, J (Degussa UK Services Ltd)
London MK10 *p105* . . . 0845 128 9575
Lipman, P A (Humphreys & Co)
Bristol *p163* . . . 0117 929 2662
Lippell, C S (Addleshaw Goddard)
Manchester *p300* . . . 0161 934 6000
Lipscombe, Ms E (Hughmans) *G H*
London EC4 *p44* . . . 020 7246 6560
Lipscombe, I D (A C S Hards & Co) *Q K1 O W L K2*
New Malden *p321* . . . 020 8942 2258
Lipson, H L (Betesh Partnership) *B1 C1 D1 J1 K1 O Q Zj*
Manchester *p301* . . . 0161 834 2623
Lipson, J D (Withers LLP) *K1*
London EC4 *p92* . . . 020 7597 6000
Liptrot, Mrs C P (Nelsons) *M1 S1 P V L F1*
Nottingham *p338* . . . 0115 958 6262
Liptrot, P W (Thompsons (formerly Robin/Brian Thompson & Partners)) *N*
Stoke-on-Trent *p398* . . . 01782 406200
Lipworth, Ms C H (Peters & Peters) *G B1 N H*
London EC4 *p67* . . . 020 7629 7991
Lisgo, Miss H (BHP Law) *O*
Newcastle upon Tyne *p323* . 0191 221 0898
Lish, Mrs S (Brown Beer Nixon Mallon) *G H*
Redcar *p362* . . . 01642 490202
Lisle, P (Catteralls) *W S1 T1 Zm*
Wakefield *p418* . . . 01924 291122
Lisners, J (Hunt & Lisners) *W S1 Zk Ze Zf Q N Zq K1 Zr L Zp J1 F1 Zi*
London NW4 *p44* . . . 020 8202 3746
Northampton *p332* . . . 01604 846705
Liss, A R (Liss Gulhane Innes & Co) *P K1 M1 G E B1 J1 C1 R1 F1 Zl*
Romford *p366* . . . 01708 764440
Lissett, S W (Legal Aid Area Office No 6 (West Midland))
Birmingham *p450* . . . 0121 632 6541
Lissimore, F H (Amphlett Lissimore) *S1 S2 E*
Croydon *p6* . . . 020 8771 5254
List, K A (Ellisons) *S1 L E*
Colchester *p197* . . . 01206 764477
Lister, Mrs A (Crangle Edwards) *G H D1 W*
Stretford *p400* . 0161 865 2993 / 865 7816 / 865 5875
Lister, E H (Berg Legal) *O*
Manchester *p301* . . . 0161 833 9211
Lister, H D (Forresters) *N Q Zq A2 S2 E L*
Barrow-in-Furness *p125* . . . 01229 820297
Lister, Mrs J C (Wakefield Court House)
Wakefield *p474* . . . 01924 303461
Lister, Ms J R (Gordons LLP)
Leeds *p273* . . . 0113 227 0100
Lister, Mrs J S A (Foot Anstey) *E O*
Plymouth *p349* . . . 01752 675000
Lister, K J (Pannone LLP) *J1 J2 M1 Zp*
Manchester *p308* . . . 0161 909 3000
Lister, M (Harbottle & Lewis LLP)
London W1 *p38* . . . 020 7667 5000
Lister, M A (Gowmans) *W T2 K4*
Paignton *p345* . . . 01803 546100
Lister, M H (Myers Lister Price) *D1 H K1 L M1 N P Zm Zr*
Altrincham *p117* . . . 0161 926 9969
Lister, Miss S (Thomson Snell & Passmore) *S2 E L*
Tunbridge Wells *p415* . . . 01892 510000
Lister, S M (Bond Pearce LLP) *B1 C1 J1 N Ze*
Bristol *p161* . . . 0845 415 0000
Lister, S W (Pannone LLP) *O C3 Ze Zk*
Manchester *p308* . . . 0161 909 3000
Litchfield, Miss C L (Brabners Chaffe Street) *C1 C2*
Manchester *p301* . . . 0161 836 8800
Litchfield, S G (S G Litchfield) *S1 E W L*
London NW8 *p54* . . . 020 7624 2103
Litherland, Miss G M (Stephensons Solicitors LLP) *K1 D1*
Leigh *p282* . . . 01942 777777
Litherland, J R C (Davis Blank Furniss) *B1 F1 J1 K1 N O Q W Zl Zm Zt*
Glossop *p230* . . . 01457 860606
Litherland, K (Shakespeares) *Zq Q*
Nottingham *p339* . . . 0115 945 3700
Lithman, I H (Lithman & Co) *S2 E O Q S1 W N Zq*
Westminster *p55* . . . 020 7935 2212
Litt, J (Boodle Hatfield)
Westminster *p14* . . . 020 7629 7411
Little, A J (Birketts LLP (Wollastons LLP)) *R1 P*
Chelmsford *p186* . . . 01245 211211
Little, Miss C (Brewer Harding & Rowe) *K4 C1 S1 S2 E*
Barnstaple *p125* . . . 01271 342271
Little, Ms C (Hanne & Co)
London SW11 *p38* . . . 020 7228 0017

6

Little, Miss C R (Nicholson Portnell) *K1 V S1 K3*
Hexham *p249* 01434 603656

Little, D A (Magrath LLP)
London W1 *p57* 020 7495 3003

Little, Mrs E M (Fairweather Stephenson & Co) *Q K3 K1 K2 L V*
Felixstowe *p225* 01394 277941

Little, J K (Squire Sanders (UK) LLP) *E O*
London EC2 *p81*. 020 7655 1000

Little, J R (Jones Day) *C2*
London EC4 *p46*. 020 7039 5959

Little, Miss L D (Capron & Helliwell) *W T1 T2 S1*
Wroxham *p443* 01603 783818

Little, M A (H F T Gough & Co) *E S1 S2 A1 C1 L W*
Whitehaven *p431* 01946 692461

Little, Mrs N A (TLT Solicitors) *C2 C1*
Bristol *p165* 0117 917 7777

Little, Ms S (Russell-Cooke LLP) *D1 K1 D2 K2*
Kingston upon Thames *p267*. 020 8546 6111

Little, S (Shoosmiths) *N*
Reading *p361* . . 0370 086 8800 / 0118 965 8765

Little, Ms T B (SJ Berwin LLP) *C1*
London EC4 *p75*. 020 7111 2222

Little, W J (Fordlittle) *S1 S2 W E P R2 Zs*
Sittingbourne *p380*. 01795 436111

Littlefair, Mrs S (HM Land Registry - Hull)
Hull *p461* 01482 223244

Littlefield, Mrs J E (Hadaway & Hadaway) *S1 S2 E*
North Shields *p330* 0191 257 0382

Littlefield, P G (Gepp & Sons) *S1 C1 E O Q*
Chelmsford *p186*. 01245 493939
Colchester *p197* 01206 369889

Littlejohn, Miss J S (Boodle Hatfield) *E S1 L*
Westminster *p14*. 020 7629 7411

Littlemore, Miss J M (SAS Daniels LLP) *K4 Zm W*
Macclesfield *p297* 01625 442100

Littlemore, Mrs S J (Weightmans LLP) *N Q*
Liverpool *p291*. 0151 227 2601

Littler, G C (Guy Littler) *E K1 Q S1 S2*
Kensington & Chelsea *p55*. . 020 7373 3700

Littler, G G (Simmons & Simmons)
London EC2 *p79*. 020 7628 2020

Littler, T (DLA Piper UK LLP)
Sheffield *p375* 0870 011 1111

Littlestone, R P (MacLeish Littlestone Cowan) *S1 E C1 L W*
Barking *p123* 020 8514 3000

Littlewood, Miss S D (Read Dunn Connell) *W K4*
Bradford *p154* 01274 723858

Littner, A (Harbottle & Lewis LLP)
London W1 *p38* 020 7667 5000

Littner, Ms A L (Doyle Clayton Solicitors Limited) *J1 Zp*
London EC2 *p27*. 020 7329 9090

Liu, Ms J C (McCormacks) *B2 G H Zi*
London EC3 *p56*. 020 7791 2000

Liu, Ms M (Howard Kennedy LLP)
London W1 *p48* 020 7636 1616
London EC4 *p56*. 020 7054 2500

Liu, Ms M (Fasken Martineau LLP)
London W1 *p31* 020 7917 8500
London EC4 *p86*. 020 7300 7000

Liu, Y (Field Fisher Waterhouse LLP)
London EC3 *p31*. 020 7861 4000

Liver, Miss S V (Birchall Blackburn LLP) *J1 L N O Q F1*
Preston *p356* 01772 561663

Liveras, S K (Protopapas)
London W1 *p69* 020 7636 2100

Liversedge, Miss A (Thomas Cooper) *Za A3 Zn Zj*
London EC3 *p22*. 020 7481 8851

Livesey, A J (Taylors) *B1 O Zb*
Manchester *p310* 0844 800 0263

Livesey, Ms B M (Calderdale Metropolitan BC Corporate Services Directorate) *Zg*
Halifax *p460*. 01422 357257

Livesey, Miss H D (Milne Moser) *K1 K3*
Kendal *p264*. . . . .01539 729786 / 725582

Livesey, Mrs K A (Bury Magistrates Court)
Bury *p452* 0161 447 8600

Livesey, Mrs K M (Brabners Chaffe Street) *K1 K3*
Liverpool *p286*. 0151 600 3000

Livesey, Mrs T (Farleys Solicitors LLP) *K1*
Blackburn *p145* 01254 367854

Livesley, A W (Birkett Long LLP) *O D1 Q*
Colchester *p197* 01206 217300

Livesley, C J (Blaydon Magistrates Court)
Blaydon-on-Tyne *p450*. . . . 0191 414 4244
Gateshead *p458* 0191 477 5821
South Shields *p471* 0191 455 8800

Livingston, C (Holmes & Hills LLP) *N*
Braintree *p155*. 01376 320456

Livingston, E (Ashfords LLP)
Bristol *p160* 0117 321 8000

Livingston, Mrs S (Pinnacle Insurance PLC)
Borehamwood *p450* 020 8207 9000

Livingstone, A (Osborne Clarke) *R2*
Bristol *p164* 0117 917 3000

Livingstone, H (Holman Fenwick Willan)
London EC3 *p42*. 020 7264 8000

Livingstone, Ms L (Taylor Wessing)
London EC4 *p86*. 020 7300 7000

Livingstone, P H (Clarke Willmott) *N*
Bristol *p162* 0845 209 1000 / 0117 305 6000

Liyanearachchi, Miss A (Pannone LLP) *F1 O Q C1 Zq*
Manchester *p308* 0161 909 3000

Lizar, R S (Robert Lizar) *L Zm Q Zg*
Manchester *p307* 0161 226 2319

Lizra, Ms G (Sweetman Burke & Sinker) *K1 K3*
Ealing *p84*. 020 8840 2572

Llewellin, W O (T O L Llewellin & Co) *S1 E W A1 L R1 T2 S2 K4 Zm*
Haverfordwest *p244* 01437 767140

Llewellyn, Mrs G H (Cadbury Schweppes PLC)
London W1 *p104* 020 7409 1313

Llewellyn, I P (David & Snape) *O Q B1 L*
Bridgend *p157*. 01656 661115

Llewellyn, Mrs M M (Watson Farley & Williams)
London EC2 *p90*. 020 7814 8000

Llewellyn, R (Harbottle & Lewis LLP) *C1 Zf*
London W1 *p38* 020 7667 5000

Llewellyn, R (Gosschalks) *E A1 R1 S1*
Hull *p256* 01482 324252

Llewellyn, R G S (Horsey Lightly Fynn) *K4 S1 W*
Bournemouth *p152*. 01202 551991

Llewellyn, S P (Faegre & Benson LLP) *O Q*
London EC4 *p30*. 020 7450 4500

Llewellyn, Mrs V (Welsh Health Legal Services)
Cardiff *p453* 029 2031 5500

Llewellyn Jones, Miss S E (T Llewellyn Jones) *A1 C1 S1 E G W K1 L M1 N Zc Zj Zt*
Neath *p320* 01639 643635

Llewellyn Williams, G (John Collins & Partners LLP) *Q B1 Zb*
Swansea *p405*. 01792 773773

Llewellyn-Jones, M H (T S Edwards & Son) *J1 N V*
Newport *p328* 01633 257166

Llewellyn-Morgan, H (Radcliffes Le Brasseur) *Zq Zr Q J1 G Zk*
Cardiff *p180* 029 2034 3035
Westminster *p70*. 020 7222 7040

Llewelyn, N P (Douglas-Jones Mercer) *N*
Swansea *p405*. 01792 650000

Llewelyn, W W (Crown Prosecution Service Avon & Somerset) *S1 K1 W L G M1 P H D1 A1*
Bristol *p451* 0117 930 2800

Llewelyn Evans, A (Burges Salmon) *O M2 Q P Zc Zj Zk*
Bristol *p161* 0117 939 2000

Lloyd, Miss A (Dawson Lloyd & Co) *E W S1 Zm*
Reading *p360* 0118 966 9238

Lloyd, Mrs A L (Manches LLP) *S1*
Oxford *p343*. 01865 722106

Lloyd, C A (Macfarlanes) *O Q*
London EC4 *p56*. 020 7831 9222

Lloyd, C C (Taylor Wessing) *Zf Ze*
London EC4 *p86*. 020 7300 7000

Lloyd, C E (CVS Solicitors) *T1 W*
London W1 *p17* 020 7493 2903

Lloyd, C W (Kerman & Co LLP) *O C1*
London WC2 *p49* 020 7539 7272

Lloyd, D (Brighouse Wolff) *G H*
Skelmersdale *p381* 01695 722577

Lloyd, D H (Hallows Associates) *A1 W L S2 S1*
Mold *p318*. . 01352 752773 / 758603 / 0800 525696

Lloyd, D H C (Gabb & Co) *S1 A1 E C1 W L T1*
Abergavenny *p113*. 01873 852432

Lloyd, D J (Wykeham Hurford Sheppard & Son LLP)
Battle *p128* 01424 775088

Lloyd, Ms D J (Nabarro LLP)
London WC1 *p63* 020 7524 6000

Lloyd, D T (H Vaughan Vaughan & Co) *S1 A1 W R1 L Q T1 T2 J1*
Rhayader *p363* 01982 552331
Builth Wells *p168* . .01982 552331 / 553571

Lloyd, E R (GHP Legal) *G H N Q J1*
Oswestry *p342*. 01691 659194

Lloyd, E T A (Swayne Johnson Solicitors) *S1 A1 C1 L E W S2*
Denbigh *p208* 01745 812835
St Asaph *p391*. 01745 582535

Lloyd, Mrs G (David Bunn & Co) *S1*
Birmingham *p136* 0121 441 3322
Birmingham *p136* 0121 476 8481

Lloyd, G R (Drummonds) *S1 S2 E*
Chester *p190*. 01244 408300

Lloyd, G R (Lloyd Brennand) *F1 G H J1 K1 N S1 W Zl*
Brentford *p156*. 020 8569 9020

Lloyd, Ms H W P (Ewings & Co) *G H D1 D2 K1 S1 S2 W E C2 T2 Q*
London SE20 *p30* 020 8778 1126

Lloyd, I a G (Tudur Owen Roberts Glynne & Co) *W S1 E A1 L*
Caernarfon *p172*. . .01286 672207 / 672851
Bangor *p122*. . . . .01248 362315 / 355826

Lloyd, I E (Rowley Dickinson) *S1 T2 W*
Manchester *p309* 0161 834 4215

Lloyd, I H (Camerons Jones) *D1 K1 P Zl*
Harrow *p241*. 020 8423 6666

Lloyd, Mrs J (Brabners Chaffe Street) *O*
Liverpool *p286*. 0151 600 3000

Lloyd, J (Nexus Solicitors) *C1 B1 J1 C2 T1 T2*
Manchester *p308* 0161 819 4900

Lloyd, J (Wilkin Chapman Epton Blades) *A1*
Lincoln *p285*. 01522 512345

Lloyd, J (Harrowells)
York *p444* 01904 558600

Lloyd, J A (EEF West Midlands Association)
Birmingham *p449* 0121 456 2222

Lloyd, J A (T Llewellyn Jones) *S1 W L*
Neath *p320* 01639 643635

Lloyd, Ms J C (Bevan Brittan LLP) *Zr N Zm*
Bristol *p161* 0870 194 1000

Lloyd, J E (LG Lawyers) *E R1*
London SE1 *p50*. 020 7379 0000

Lloyd, J H (Jeff Lloyd) *A1 E J1 K1 L M1 N P S1*
Barry *p126*. 01446 741919

Lloyd, Miss J I (Charles Lucas & Marshall) *E S2 R2 S1*
Swindon *p406* 01793 511055

Lloyd, J N (Stevens & Bolton) *E A1*
Guildford *p237*. 01483 302264

Lloyd, J R (Vingoe Lloyd Solicitors) *E S1 S2 W*
Hayle *p245* 01736 754075

Lloyd, J S (Anthony Collins Solicitors LLP) *K4 K1 S1 T2 V W*
Birmingham *p137* 0121 200 3242
Birmingham *p143* 0121 633 3233

Lloyd, J W (Morrison & Foerster (UK) LLP) *O Q*
London EC2 *p62*. 020 7920 4000

Lloyd, Ms K (Bates Wells & Braithwaite London LLP) *Zd C1*
London EC4 *p11*. 020 7551 7777

Lloyd, Mrs K A (Hogans) *O*
Prescot *p356* 0151 430 7529

Lloyd, K F (Herbert Smith LLP) *O Zq*
London EC2 *p40*. 020 7374 8000

Lloyd, L (Howard Kennedy LLP) *Zf Zw*
London W1 *p48* 020 7636 1616

Lloyd, Miss L (Butcher & Barlow LLP) *S1*
Runcorn *p369* 01928 572268

Lloyd, M (Cogent Law)
Croydon *p204* 0844 245 4452

Lloyd, M (FBC Manby Bowdler LLP) *E*
Telford *p409* 01952 292129

Lloyd, M A (Cook & Talbot) *F1 J1 K1 L N S1*
Southport *p388* 01704 535216

Lloyd, M A (Waltons & Morse LLP) *O Za*
London EC3 *p90*. 020 7623 4255

Lloyd, M D (LloydLaw LLP) *O*
London SE1 *p55*. 020 7403 5050

Lloyd, M G (Charles Hart Solicitors) *E L S1 T1 T2 W*
Cheddar *p186* 01934 742315

Lloyd, M V (M V Lloyd) *E L S1 T2 W*
Fareham *p224*. 023 9228 0944

Lloyd, Mrs N A (Keoghs and Nicholls, Lindsell & Harris) *W*
Altrincham *p116* 0161 928 9321

Lloyd, N G (EMW) *C2 C1*
Milton Keynes *p316* 0845 070 6000

Lloyd, N G (Lloyd Rehman & Co) *Q O N L E S1 B1 W T2 C1 J1 Ze Zj*
London EC4 *p55*. 020 7778 7550

Lloyd, N L (Lloyd & Rowe) *G H*
Cardiff *p179* 029 2045 8999

Lloyd, Ms N W (Parry Davies Clwyd-Jones & Lloyd) *K1 N Q D1 C1 J1 S1 V W M1*
Llangefni *p292*. 01248 723106

Lloyd, P (Whiteheads Solicitors Limited)
Chorley *p194* 01257 266008

Lloyd, P J E (Dutton Gregory) *C1 O Ze Zc*
Winchester *p433*. 01962 844333

Lloyd, P K (Fortescue Graham & Lloyd) *S1 W*
Great Bookham *p233* 01372 456221
Leatherhead *p271* 01372 374895

Lloyd, P L (Crown Prosecution Service Dyfed Powys) *C1 F1 G H J1 K1 M1 N P Zp Zj Zl*
Carmarthen *p453* 01267 242100

Lloyd, Mrs R (DWF) *Zj Zb Q*
Liverpool *p287*. 0151 907 3000

Lloyd, R A (Robertsons) *S1 E W L*
Cardiff *p180* 029 2023 7777

Lloyd, Ms R A (Legal Services Commission No 9 (North Eastern))
Leeds *p463* 0113 390 7300

Lloyd, R E (Birmingham City Council Legal & Democratic Services)
Birmingham *p449* 0121 303 2066

Lloyd, R M (Neil Myerson LLP) *E R2 S2*
Altrincham *p117* 0161 941 4000

Lloyd, R S (Fishburns) *A3 Zc C1 B2 Zj M2 O Q N Zq*
London EC3 *p32*. 020 7280 8888

Lloyd, R W (Birkett Long LLP) *J1 Zp J2*
Colchester *p197* 01206 217300

Lloyd, S (Ashurst LLP)
London EC2 *p7* 020 7638 1111

Lloyd, Ms S A (Brighouse Wolff) *K3 D1 K1 G H*
Skelmersdale *p381* 01695 722577

Lloyd, S A (Randell Lloyd & Martin) *C1 D1 G H J1 K1 L P S1*
Llanelli *p292*. 01554 772149

Lloyd, S C (Lee Rigby Partnership) *G H*
Leyland *p283* 01772 421748

Lloyd, S F (Chambers Fletcher LLP) *W T1*
Northwich *p333* 01606 780400

Lloyd, Ms S J (Gordons LLP)
Leeds *p273* 0113 227 0100

Lloyd, S T (Bates Wells & Braithwaite London LLP) *J1 J2 Zd*
London EC4 *p11*. 020 7551 7777

Lloyd Jones, D I L (Gateley LLP) *A3 Zc*
Birmingham *p138* 0121 234 0000

Lloyd Jones, J J (Piper Smith Watton LLP) *S1 S2 W*
London SW1 *p68* 020 7222 9900

Lloyd Jones, R O (Clarke Willmott) *E*
Taunton *p408*0845 209 1000 / 0117 305 6000

Lloyd Platt, Mrs V (Lloyd Platt & Co) *K1 D1*
London N3 *p55* 020 8343 2998

Lloyd-Davies, Miss H C (Squire Sanders (UK) LLP) *Zw C1 J1 O Q T1 S1 Zd Zi*
London EC2 *p81*. 020 7655 1000

Lloyd-Davies, R J (Royds LLP) *C1 E L R1 S1 W Zd*
London EC4 *p74*. 020 7583 2222

Lloyd-Ellis, Ms S (Potter Rees (Serious Injury) Solicitors)
Manchester *p309* 0161 237 5888

Lloyd-Jones, Mrs C (Scott Rees & Co) *N Q*
Skelmersdale *p381* 01695 722222

Lloyd-Jones, E (Lomax Lloyd-Jones & Co) *G H D1 K1 S1 L P J1 M1 F1*
Southwark *p55*. 020 7703 6461

Lloyd-Jones, Ms I A (Howells LLP) *Zr*
Sheffield *p376* 0114 249 6666

Lloyd-Jones, J (Blake Lapthorn) *P B1 C1 J1 Zc O*
Oxford *p342*. 01865 248607

Lloyd-Jones, Ms M E (North East Lincolnshire Borough Council) *D1 H K1*
Cleethorpes *p455* 01472 324001

Lloyd-Jones, Miss S A (North Cornwall District Council)
Wadebridge *p474* 01208 893259

LLoyd-King, Miss R (Cornwall County Council)
Truro *p474*. 01872 322197

LLoyd-Lewis, E E (Barlow Lyde & Gilbert LLP) *O Q Za Zj*
London EC3 *p10*. 020 7247 2277

Lloyd-Osborne, Miss S E (Wragg Mark-Bell Solicitors) *K4 S1 W A1 A2 S2*
Carlisle *p182*. 01228 711728

Lloyd-Smith, C (Coley & Tilley)
Birmingham *p136* 0121 643 5531

Lloyd-Watts, Ms G E (Alchema Ltd)
Chester *p454* 0151 348 2010

Lloyd-Williams, A M (Herbert Smith LLP)
London EC2 *p40*. 020 7374 8000

Lloyds, Mrs M A (Druitts) *W K4*
Bournemouth *p151*. 01202 551863

Lo, Miss C (Kirwans) *B1 Q S1 Ze Zk*
Liverpool *p289*. 0151 229 5600

Lo, Ms E (DFA Law LLP)
Northampton *p331*. 01604 609560

Lo, E Y M (Wilson Barca LLP) *C1 L P S1*
London N19 *p92*. 020 7272 2072
London W1 *p92* 020 7272 2072

Lo, Ms M (Ashurst LLP)
London EC2 *p7* 020 7638 1111

Loach, C T (Enoch Evans LLP) *G H N J2 P*
Walsall *p420*. 01922 720333

Loader, A J (Horsman Solicitors Ltd) *G H N S1 W Zl Zm Q*
Lewes *p283* 01273 474743

Loadman, Miss C M E (Pinney Talfourd LLP) *K1 D1*
Brentwood *p156* 01277 268700

Loadsman, C D (Theaker Loadsman & Reynolds)
Hove *p255*. 01273 229500

Loasby, D J (P T Ryan & Co) *S1 W*
King's Lynn *p266* 01553 761741

Lobb, Miss A (Morecrofts Solicitors LLP) *N Q Zr X*
Liverpool *p290*. 0151 236 8871

Lobb, A (Nantes) *K4 T2 S1 E W A1*
Bridport *p158* 01308 422313

Lobb, A J (Murrays) *D1 K1 D2 Zm*
Bodmin *p148* 01208 72863

Lobb, N D (HRJ Law LLP) *E O*
Hitchin *p251*. 01462 628888

Lobetta, J H (PCB Lawyers LLP) *E L R2 S2*
London W1 *p65* 020 7486 2566

Loble, S F (Collyer Bristow LLP)
London WC1 *p22* 020 7242 7363

Lobley, Miss L A (Lester Morrill) *G H*
Leeds *p275* 0113 245 8549

Loblowitz, D S H (Manches LLP) *O*
London WC2 *p58* 020 7404 4433
London EC4 *p83*. 020 7822 8000

Lochery, P A (Lawson Coppock & Hart) *W T2 T1 K4 Zq*
Manchester *p306* 0161 832 5944

Lochner, P L (Laytons) *M1*
Guildford *p236*. 01483 407000

Lock, A (DAC Beachcroft)
Bristol *p162* 0117 918 2000

Lock, Miss A B (Warners Solicitors) *S1 S2*
Tonbridge *p412* 01732 770660

Lock, Mrs C M (Marks & Spencer PLC)
London W2 *p107* 020 7935 4422

Lock, E H S (Lock & Marlborough) *N O B1 C1 J1 M1 W T1 L D1 Ze Zc Zb Zj*
London W3 *p55* 020 8993 7231

Lock, I (Stanley De Leon) *B1 C1 E Ze J1 J2 O C2 Zw*
Potters Bar *p355*. 01707 657277

Lock, Mrs J (Heptonstalls LLP) *A1 C1 S2 E*
Goole *p231* 01405 765661

Lock, J D (T Llewellyn Jones)
Neath *p320* 01639 643635

Lock, K J (Official Solicitor and Public Trustee)
London WC2 *p108*. 020 7911 7127

Lock, Miss Z K (Randle Thomas LLP) *K1 D1 Q K3*
Helston *p246* 01326 572951

Locke, D (Veale Wasbrough Vizards) *U2 Ze*
Bristol *p165* 0117 925 2020

Locke, Ms G (CKFT)
London NW3 *p17* 020 7431 7262

Locke, Ms G (Collyer Bristow LLP) *B1 O Zq*
London WC1 *p22* 020 7242 7363

Locke, Miss K (Bevirs) *K1 D1*
Swindon *p406* 01793 532363

Locke, R (Hugh James) *O*
Cardiff *p179* 029 2022 4871

Locke, R A (Robert Locke) *G Q F1 S1 Zt*
Fareham *p224*. 01329 822722

Locke, R B (Birds Solicitors) *B2 G H*
Wandsworth *p13*. 020 8874 7433

See p634 for the Key to Work Categories

Locke, R W (Sharratts (London) LLP) *S1 L E C1 A1 Zh Zc*
Westerham *p429* . . . 01959 568000

Locke, S A (McLellans) *O E T1 W Q C1 L S2*
Hertford *p249* . . . 01992 532000

Locker, Miss E (Goodwin Cowley) *K3 K1 D1 W S1*
Lowestoft *p294* . . . 01502 532700

Lockett, Miss C J (Jackamans)
Felixstowe *p225* . . . 01394 279636

Lockett, Miss D (Young & Co) *K1 D1 D2 K3*
Stoke-on-Trent *p398* . . . 01782 339200

Lockett, J P (Lockett Loveday McMahon) *Zb C1 I Ze J1 U2 C2*
Manchester *p307* . . . 0161 237 3627

Lockhart, D (CKFT)
London NW3 *p17* . . . 020 7431 7262

Lockhart, E T (Davies & Partners) *N P Zq Zr K3*
Almondsbury *p115* . . . 01454 619619

Lockhart, I S (Charles Russell LLP) *T1 W Zd*
London EC4 *p19* . . . 020 7203 5000

Lockhart-Mirams, A R (Lockharts Solicitors) *Q A3 C1 O C2*
London WC1 *p55* . . . 020 7383 7111

Locking, R A (Lockings) *S1 W L E*
Hull *p257* . . . 0845 075 4197

Lockley, A J H (Irwin Mitchell LLP) *O X Zg Zu*
Sheffield *p376* . . . 0870 150 0100

Lockley, C J (Quality Solicitors Clarke & Son) *S2 E R2*
Basingstoke *p127* . . . 01256 320555

Lockley, Miss L (Browne Jacobson LLP)
Nottingham *p336* . . . 0115 976 6000

Lockley, M G (Steels) *S1 W S2 L*
Warrington *p422* . . . 01925 261354

Lockley, S J (hlw Keeble Hawson LLP) *O Q*
Sheffield *p376* . . . 0114 276 5555

Lockwood, C (Ince & Co Services Ltd)
London E1 *p44* . . . 020 7481 0010

Lockwood, Miss C R (Oslers Solicitors) *G H*
Stowmarket *p400* . . . 01449 774670

Lockwood, Miss L J (Birchall Blackburn LLP) *S2 E R2*
Manchester *p301* . . . 0161 236 0662
Preston *p356* . . . 01772 561663

Lockwood, Ms M (Cobains)
Blackpool *p146* . . . 01253 290092

Lockwood, Mrs M A (Clerk to Sheffield Justices)
Sheffield *p470* . . . 0114 276 0760

Lockwood, Mrs S (Burton & Dyson) *K3*
Gainsborough *p228* . . . 01427 610761
Sheffield *p376* . . . 0114 249 6666

Lockwood, Ms S (Lawrences) *G H*
Wellingborough *p424* . . . 01933 442324

Lockwood, Miss S L (Rhys Vaughan) *G H K1 D1 W L F1*
Manchester *p311* . . . 0161 224 1439

Lockwood, Ms S M (East Riding of Yorkshire Council)
Beverley *p449* . . . 01482 887700

Lockyer, Miss H J (Gardner Croft LLP) *Q J1*
Canterbury *p176* . . . 01227 813400

Lockyer, Mrs J (Davenport Lyons) *E L S1*
London W1 *p25* . . . 020 7468 2600
London WC1 *p64* . . . 020 7067 3000

Lodder, D S D (Lodders Solicitors LLP) *A1 C1 E L S1 T1 W Zc*
Stratford-upon-Avon *p400* . . . 01789 293259

Lodder, Ms J (Leeds City Council) *K1 D1 G H V*
Leeds *p462* . . . 0113 224 3513

Lodeto, Mrs J (Liddell and Company) *K1 S1 W*
Benfleet *p131* . . . 01268 565769
Rayleigh *p359* . . . 01268 745406

Lodge, C M (ASB Aspire) *N*
Maidstone *p298* . . . 0845 063 6465

Lodge, J (Bower & Bailey) *S1 L W*
Oxford *p343* . . . 01865 311133

Lodge, Ms J E (Lloyd & Associates) *C1 C2 J1 Zd*
London SW7 *p55* . . . 020 7589 9599

Lodge, Ms L S (Bristol City Council)
Bristol *p451* . . . 0117 922 2000

Lodge, M (Motoringlawyers.com)
Altrincham *p117* . . . 0161 233 0900

Lodge, M S (Browne Jacobson LLP) *Zb*
Nottingham *p336* . . . 0115 976 6000

Lodge, Ms S (Squire Sanders (UK) LLP)
Leeds *p277* . . . 0113 284 7000

Lodh, Miss R (Lees Solicitors LLP) *Zr*
Birkenhead *p134* . . . 0151 647 9381

Lodhi, N (Criminal Defence Solicitors) *G H B2*
Westminster *p23* . . . 020 7353 7000

Lodhi, R A (Arora Lodhi Heath)
London W3 *p7* . . . 020 8993 9995

Lodhi, Ms S (Environment Agency (Midlands Region)) *G H D1 K1 B2 Zi*
Solihull *p471* . . . 0121 711 2324

Lodwick, M J (Frederic Hall) *K1 D1*
Dover *p213* . . . 01304 202411

Loeber, C D (Potter & Co) *G H K1 N Q*
Matlock *p313* . . . 01629 582308

Lofthouse, D (Lofthouse & Co) *M1 P G H K1 J1 D1 W F1 C1 Zm*
Castleford *p183* . . . 01977 603347

Lofthouse, I E (Pennine Law) *E S1 Zl O N W*
Sheffield *p377* . . . 01226 763551

Lofthouse, Miss J A (Pegasi Management Company Ltd) *E L J1 Q*
London SW1 *p108* . . . 020 7245 4500

Lofts, H (Howard Kennedy LLP) *S1*
London W1 *p48* . . . 020 7636 1616

Loftus, C (Martin Murray & Associates) *G H B2*
Slough *p382* . . . 01753 551313

Loftus, J M (Norton Peskett) *S1 W E A1 K1 L T1 R1 C1 M1 Zc Zd Zl*
Lowestoft *p294* . . . 01502 533000

Loftus, M E (Fentons) *N*
Failsworth *p223* . . . 0161 682 7101

Loftus, S J (Ince & Co Services Ltd)
London E1 *p44* . . . 020 7481 0010

Loftus, S R (Wright Hassall LLP)
Leamington Spa *p270* . . . 01926 886688

Logan, A J (HM Land Registry - Durham (Boldon) Office)
Durham *p457* . . . 0191 301 2345

Logan, Mrs C H (Burnetts) *S1 S2*
Carlisle *p181* . . . 01228 552222

Logan, Mrs C L (Cartmell Shepherd) *K1 Q*
Carlisle *p182* . . . 01228 516666

Logan, Ms E (Prescription Medicines Code of Practice Authority)
London SW1 *p108* . . . 020 7930 9677

Logan, G N (Nabarro LLP) *E R2 S2 Zn*
Sheffield *p376* . . . 0114 279 4000

Logan, K (Shepherd + Wedderburn LLP)
London EC4 *p78* . . . 020 7429 4900

Logan, M P (Nabarro LLP)
London WC1 *p63* . . . 020 7524 6000

Logan, P A (Gateshead Magistrates Court)
Gateshead *p458* . . . 0191 477 5821

Logan, S (Canter Levin & Berg) *Zr J2 Q N*
St Helens *p391* . . . 01744 634141

Logan, T D (Ellisons) *W L E J1 T1 A1 Zc Q O C1 S2*
Colchester *p197* . . . 01206 764477

Logg, D (Hannays Solicitors and Advocates) *S1*
South Shields *p383* . . 0191 456 7893 / 455 5361

Logie, M (Ashurst LLP)
London EC2 *p7* . . . 020 7638 1111

Logue, Miss M J (MPH Solicitors) *Zr*
Manchester *p307* . . . 0161 832 7722

Logue, P D (Capstick-Dale & Partners) *E C1 S1 W N Zl*
Romford *p366* . . . 01708 722466

Logue, S F (Baines Wilson LLP) *S2 E L*
Carlisle *p181* . . . 01228 552600

Loh, J (Massers) *S1*
Nottingham *p338* . . . 0115 851 1666

Lohn, Ms K (Jennifer C Margrave) *W V S1*
Guildford *p236* . . . 01483 562722

Lohn, M (Field Fisher Waterhouse LLP)
London EC3 *p31* . . . 020 7861 4000

Lok, X (LG Lawyers)
London SE1 *p50* . . . 020 7379 0000

Lokholm, Ms E S (Watson Farley & Williams)
London EC2 *p90* . . . 020 7814 8000

Lole, D (Walker Morris) *B1*
Leeds *p277* . . . 0113 283 2500

Lomas, Miss E J (Pannone LLP) *Zc A3 O*
Manchester *p308* . . . 0161 909 3000

Lomas, Ms J C (Irwin Mitchell LLP) *W*
London EC1 *p45* . . . 0870 150 0100

Lomas, M M (Ashfords LLP) *C1 Ze*
Exeter *p220* . . . 01392 337000

Lomas, Miss N K (Sheridans) *C1 C2 J1*
London WC1 *p78* . . . 020 7079 0100

Lomas, O (Allen & Overy LLP)
London E1 *p5* . . . 020 3088 0000

Lomas, Miss S A (Ashfords LLP) *E*
Taunton *p408* . . . 01823 232300

Lomas, T R (SAS Daniels LLP) *A1 C1 E L*
Macclesfield *p297* . . . 01625 442100

Lomas Fletcher, Miss S L (Samuel Phillips Law Firm) *J1*
Newcastle upon Tyne *p326* . 0191 232 8451

Lomax, Ms C (Scott Rees & Co) *N Q*
Skelmersdale *p381* . . . 01695 722222

Lomax, J D (Hill Dickinson LLP) *E R1 S2 L O*
Liverpool *p288* . . . 0151 600 8000

Lomax, J R (Backhouse Jones Ltd) *J1 O Q*
Clitheroe *p196* . . . 01254 828300

Lomax, Dr K (Davies Gore Lomax) *G H X L Zg Q N*
Leeds *p273* . . . 0113 242 2797

Lomax, T (Davies Gore Lomax) *L X Zg Q*
Leeds *p273* . . . 0113 242 2797

Lombard, E (Pegden & Co)
London N21 *p66* . . . 020 8360 4715

Lomer, B C R (Druces LLP) *O Q B1*
London EC2 *p27* . . . 020 7638 9271

London, Ms A (Rosenblatt)
London EC4 *p73* . . . 020 7955 0880

London, J (Morrish Solicitors LLP) *N Q*
Leeds *p276* . . . 0113 245 0733

London, J F J (Financial Services Authority)
London E14 *p106* . . . 020 7066 1000

London, Ms K (Kennards Wells) *K3 R2 S1 V W L*
London E11 *p48* . . . 020 8539 8338

London, Ms K J (Russell Jones & Walker) *N*
Manchester *p309* . . . 0161 383 3500

London, M (Devonshires) *J2 O Zh*
London EC2 *p27* . . . 020 7628 7576

London, Ms T (Herbert Smith LLP)
London EC2 *p40* . . . 020 7374 8000

London-Smith, R A (Roberts Moore Nicholas Jones) *Q N*
Birkenhead *p134* . . . 0151 647 0000

Lonergan, M J (DLA Piper UK LLP)
Leeds *p272* . . . 0870 011 1111

Loney, J (Trethowans LLP) *J1*
Southampton *p387* . . . 023 8032 1000

Loney, J M (Foot Anstey) *F1 J1 N Ze Zo Zp*
Plymouth *p349* . . . 01752 675000

Long, Ms A S (Blackpool Borough Council) *L D1 V S1 F1 G H W N Zm*
Blackpool *p450* . . . 01253 477450

Long, B (Larken & Co) *S2 E C1*
Newark *p322* . . . 01636 703333

Long, B A (Oxley & Coward Solicitors LLP) *E S1 S2 L*
Rotherham *p367* . . . 01709 510999

Long, Mrs B J (Cole & Co)
Norwich *p334* . . . 01603 617018

Long, Mrs B M (Blandy & Blandy) *D1 K1 D2*
Reading *p360* . . . 0118 951 6800

Long, Ms C (Capsticks Solicitors LLP) *N Zr D1*
London SW19 *p18* . . . 020 8780 2211

Long, C I (Edward Hayes LLP) *G H B2*
London EC4 *p39* . . . 020 7353 0011

Long, Miss D A (BLB Solicitors) *N J2*
Swindon *p406* . . . 01793 615011

Long, D E (Charles Russell LLP) *W T2 Zd*
London EC4 *p19* . . . 020 7203 5000

Long, I D (Cox & Hodgetts) *A1 E L S1 W*
Evesham *p220* . . . 01386 442513

Long, Miss J C (William Sturges & Co) *C1 K3 C2 D1*
Westminster *p84* . . . 020 7873 1000

Long, Ms J F (Pritchard Joyce & Hinds) *Q O J1 Zb B1 N L F1 Zp*
Beckenham *p129* . . . 020 8658 3922

Long, J L E (Ashton KCJ) *A1 T1 T2 W Zn*
Bury St Edmunds *p171* . . . 01284 762331

Long, Mrs J M (McCarthy Bennett Holland) *K1 N K3*
Wigan *p432* . . . 01942 206060

Long, Mrs J M (Barber Titleys) *T2 W Zd*
Harrogate *p240* . . . 01423 502211

Long, Miss J M (Judith M Long) *E J1 Q*
Southwark *p55* . . . 020 7403 3337

Long, Miss L (Mercy Messenger) *D1 K1 K2 K3*
Birmingham *p140* . . . 0121 770 1221

Long, Mrs M L R (Stokes Solicitors) *C1 C2 A1 R1 Zd S2*
Portsmouth *p355* . . . 023 9282 8131

Long, M T (Napthens LLP) *E*
Blackpool *p146* . . . 01253 622305

Long, P D E (Porter & Co) *N Q L O S1 B1 C1 E F1 K1 Zi Zc Zk Zq Zb*
Sutton *p403* . . . 020 8643 5111

Long, P M (Pitmans LLP) *Zb C1 R2*
Reading *p361* . . . 0118 958 0224

Long, P W (Herbert Smith LLP) *C1 M2 Zb*
London EC2 *p40* . . . 020 7374 8000

Long, Ms R (Last Cawthra Feather LLP) *O Q*
Bradford *p154* . . . 01274 848800

Long, R B (Roger Long & Co) *D1 H K3 B2 G K1*
Croydon *p205* . . . 020 8668 5071

Long, Ms R E (LG Lawyers)
London SE1 *p50* . . . 020 7379 0000

Long, R G (Middlesbrough Council)
Middlesbrough *p465* . . . 01642 245432

Long, R L H (Longs Solicitors) *C1 C2 J1 C3 Ze Zm Zc Zd*
Tonbridge *p412* . . . 01732 360895

Long, S A (Franklins LLP)
Milton Keynes *p317* . . . 01908 660966

Long, S A (Collins Long) *Ze Zf*
Southwark *p21* . . . 020 7401 9800

Long, S J (Funnell & Perring) *D1 K1 G H Zl Q*
Hastings *p243* . . . 01424 426287

Long, Mrs T A (Longs Solicitors) *C1 C2 J1 Zc Ze*
Tonbridge *p412* . . . 01732 360895

Longbottom, Mrs C A (Durham County Council)
Durham *p457* . . . 0191 383 3513

Longbottom, J P (John Barkers) *D2 D1 K1*
Cleethorpes *p195* . . . 01472 695218

Longden, C (ASB Law) *O Q Zq A3 F1 L Zc*
Crawley *p202* . . . 01293 603600
Maidstone *p299* . . . 01622 698000

Longdon, M R (Robinson Allfree) *W K4 T2*
Cliftonville *p196* . . . 01843 228635
Ramsgate *p359* . . . 01843 592361

Longe, D I (TV Edwards LLP) *K1 K3 Q*
London EC3 *p85* . . . 020 7790 7000

Longes, P C (David Cowan) *G H*
Dorking *p212* . . . 01306 886622

Longfield, Ms T (Walker Morris)
Leeds *p277* . . . 0113 283 2500

Longford, N F W (Rustons & Lloyd) *O K1 G N F1 L D1 Zl*
Newmarket *p327* . . . 01638 661221

Longhurst, A W (Wanham Longhurst & Co) *A1 C1 E F1 L S1 S2*
Bury St Edmunds *p171* . . . 01284 735808

Longhurst, Mrs D (Heringtons) *F1 K1 L P B1 Zl*
Hastings *p243* . . . 01424 434192

Longhurst, G W (Ellisons) *S1 S2*
Colchester *p197* . . . 01206 764477

Longhurst, R N (Fawcett & Pattni) *K1 Q S1*
Walsall *p420* . . . 01922 640424

Longland, Mrs C M (Morris Scott & Co) *S1 S2*
Christchurch *p194* . . . 01425 278866

Longland, P D (Steele Raymond) *C1 J1 F1 I M1 M2 Zb Ze Zf B1 C2 C3 F2*
Bournemouth *p152* . . . 01202 294566

Longley, S (G T Stewart Solicitors) *G H B2 J2*
London SE22 *p83* . . . 020 8299 6000

Longley, Ms T (Bates Wells & Braithwaite London LLP) *Zd C1*
London EC4 *p11* . . . 020 7551 7777

Longman, P (Trethowans LLP) *S2 R2*
Southampton *p387* . . . 023 8032 1000

Longmate, Ms K (Harbottle & Lewis LLP) *K1*
London W1 *p38* . . . 020 7667 5000

Longmire, G E (Heringtons) *S1 W E C1 T1*
Hastings *p243* . . . 01424 434192

Longmore, D J (Gillespies) *S1 W Zl E K3 K1*
Walsall *p420* . . . 01922 627474

Longmore, M C J C (Furley Page LLP) *N Zj Zr*
Canterbury *p176* . . . 01227 763939

Longrigg, W F (Charles Russell LLP) *K1*
London EC4 *p19* . . . 020 7203 5000

Longshaw, Mrs A (The College of Law Guildford)
Guildford *p459* . . . 01483 460200

Longshaw, Mrs C M (Knights Solicitors LLP) *K1 K2*
Newcastle under Lyme *p323* . 01782 619225

Longstaff, Miss F J (Masefield Solicitors LLP) *S2 E A1 L S1*
Ledbury *p271* . . . 01531 632377

Longstaff, W J (Longstaff & Midgley) *A1 S1 W*
Scarborough *p372* . . . 01723 351751

Longville, A C (Gard & Co) *S1*
Plymouth *p349* . . . 01752 668246

Longworth, I P (Holt & Longworth) *S1 W E C1 L T1 R1 B1*
Rossendale *p367* . 01706 213251 / 229131

Longworth, Ms J G (J W Hughes & Co) *K1 L K3*
Llandudno *p291* . . . 01492 874774

Longworth, J M (Bromleys Solicitors LLP) *S1 E W C1 S2 K4*
Ashton-under-Lyne *p120* . . 0161 330 6821

Longworth, Mrs M A (Cumbria County Council)
Carlisle *p453* . . . 01228 607374 / 607351

Longworth, P W S (Widdows Mason) *K1 D1*
Westhoughton *p429* . . . 01942 816515

Longworth, S (Stewarts Law LLP) *K3 K1*
London EC4 *p83* . . . 020 7822 8000

Lonnen, Ms J (Wilson & Co)
London N17 *p92* . . . 020 8808 7535

Lonsdale, Ms A (Ashurst LLP)
London EC2 *p7* . . . 020 7638 1111

Lonsdale, D (Hayes & Storr) *W*
Sheringham *p378* . . . 01263 825959

Lonsdale, G J S (SFN Solicitors) *Zl Q*
Burnley *p169* . . . 01282 421284

Lonsdale, Ms K L (Durham County Council)
Durham *p457* . . . 0191 383 3513

Lonsdale, S A (Hunt & Wrigley) *B1 D1 F1 G H J1 K1 L M1 S2 Zr Zq*
Northallerton *p331* . . . 01609 772502

Looby, K J (Warings Solicitors) *S1 K1 E W P L F1 J1 C1 Zl*
Blackpool *p147* . . . 01253 293106

Loomba, A (Sintons LLP) *E*
Newcastle upon Tyne *p326* . 0191 226 7878

Loomba, K (Mincoffs Solicitors LLP) *S2 E S1*
Newcastle upon Tyne *p325* . 0191 281 6151

Loome, S (Birkett Long LLP) *Q B1 C1 O*
Colchester *p197* . . . 01206 217300
London EC4 *p45* . . . 020 7353 1000

Loose, Miss H J E (Ashurst LLP) *C1 P*
London EC2 *p7* . . . 020 7638 1111

Loose, Miss N J C (Muckle LLP) *C1 C2*
Newcastle upon Tyne *p325* . 0191 211 7777

Loose, P (Edwin Coe LLP) *C1 C2 B1 Zd*
London WC2 *p29* . . . 020 7691 4000

Loose, P D (Metropolitan Police Directorate of Legal Services)
London SW1 *p108* . . . 020 7230 7210

Loosemore, S P (Coole & Haddock) *P N L M1 J1 G*
Worthing *p441* . . . 01903 213511

Loosley, P R (Treasury Solicitors Department) *B1 O Q*
London WC2 *p110* . . . 020 7210 3000

Loosley, R J (Fasken Martineau LLP) *C1 I Ze U2 F2 Zf M1 M2*
London W1 *p31* . . . 020 7917 8500

Lopes, Mrs A L (Birmingham City Council Legal & Democratic Services)
Birmingham *p449* . . . 0121 303 2066

Lopez, A N (Palmers Solicitors) *W K4 T2 Zm Zd*
Kingston upon Thames *p267* . 020 8549 7444

Lopez, C R (Birchall Blackburn LLP) *N*
Preston *p356* . . . 01772 561663

Lopez, I D (Allen & Overy LLP)
London E1 *p5* . . . 020 3088 0000

Lopian, M B (Lopian Wagner) *E S1 C1 L T1 W B1 R1 J1 A1 Zo Ze Zc*
Manchester *p307* . . . 0161 834 2324

Lorber, S (Lewis Silkin LLP)
London EC4 *p53* . . . 020 7074 8000

Lord, A C (Fidler & Pepper) *W M1 P E J1 L B1 N F1 C1 Zl Zj*
Sutton-in-Ashfield *p404* . . . 01623 451111

Lord, D A (South Cambridgeshire District Council) *S1 S2*
Cambridge *p453* . . . 0845 045 0500

Lord, Ms G (Maxwell Hodge Solicitors) *N Zr*
Kirkby *p268* . . . 0151 548 7370

Lord, G A (Kennedys) *Zj*
London EC3 *p49* . . . 020 7667 9667

Lord, J E (H Pipes & Co) *S1 E A1 L Zc*
Melbourne *p314* . . . 01332 862113

Lord, J J (Irwin Mitchell LLP) *Zb B1 C1 E F1 Zk Zl Q N R1 S1 O*
Manchester *p306* . . . 0870 150 0100

Lord, J R (Napthens LLP) *W*
Preston *p357* . . . 01772 888444

Lord, Miss K (ASB Law)
Crawley *p202* . . . 01293 603600
Redhill *p362* . . . 01737 854500

Lord, Ms L (Tollers LLP) *Zc E S1*
Milton Keynes *p317* . . . 01908 396230

Lord, Ms L E (Tollers LLP)
Northampton *p332* . . . 01604 258558

Lord, M (Pluck Andrew & Co) *K1 D1 K3*
Hyde *p259*. 0161 368 6311

Lord, M P (Lords) *G H*
Wakefield *p418* 01924 380830

Lord, R J (Nairnsey Fisher & Lewis)
Benfleet *p131* 01268 566655

Lord, S H (Wright & Lord) *W S1 L S2 K4 E*
Morecambe *p319* 01524 402050

Lord, T (Nottingham Magistrates Court)
Nottingham *p467*. 0115 955 8111

Lord-Lynch, Mrs C (Colchester Borough Council)
Colchester *p455* 01206 282222

Lordon, Mrs A J (Taylor Wessing) *O Q*
London EC4 *p86*. 020 7300 7000

Lorenzelli, C J (Kirklees Metropolitan Borough Council)
Huddersfield *p461* 01484 221421

Lorenzo, A (Lewis Silkin LLP) *O J1*
London EC4 *p53*. 020 7074 8000

Lorimer, A C (Stanley Tee LLP) *S2 S1 E U1*
Cambridge *p175*. 01223 311141

Lorimer, M J (Pinnacle Insurance PLC)
Borehamwood *p450* 020 8207 9000

Lorimer, N R T (Lanyon Bowdler LLP) *N J1 Q Zp Zr*
Shrewsbury *p379* 01743 280280
Telford *p409*. 01952 291222

Lorkins, G A (Ison Harrison) *K1*
Leeds *p274* 0113 232 6530

Lorton, C T (Argyles) *K1 G S1 D1 H P J1 M1*
Tamworth *p407* 01827 56276

Lott, J A (Field Seymour Parkes) *O Q C1 Zk A3 Zl B1 Zc L Ze*
Reading *p360* 0118 951 6200

Lott, P D (Association of Teachers and Lecturers) *J1 M1 V E K1 R1*
London WC2 *p103*. 020 7930 6441

Lott, Mrs S L (Geoffrey Milne) *S1 W S2 K4*
Wolverhampton *p438* 01902 373000

Lottari, Ms M (London Borough of Haringey)
London N22 *p106* 020 8489 0000

Louca, Ms L (Anthony Louca Solicitors) *S1 S2 E Zi*
Westminster *p55*. 020 7723 9889

Louden, D W (Newstead & Walker) *E A1 S2 R2 S1*
Otley *p342*. 01943 461414

Louden, R (Reynolds Porter Chamberlain LLP)
London E1 *p71* 020 3060 6000

Loudon, M J (Belmont & Lowe) *A1 E S1 R1 P*
London EC1 *p11*. 020 7608 4600

Loufer, Ms A (ASB Law) *C1*
Crawley *p202* 01293 603600

Lougher, G (Pinsent Masons LLP) *C3*
Birmingham *p141* 0121 200 1050

Lougher, Miss J A (Osborne Clarke) *E R2 L S2*
London EC2 *p65*. 020 7105 7000

Loughlin, Miss H (Shell International Ltd)
London SE1 *p109* 020 7934 1234

Loughlin, J (Freemans Solicitors) *S2 E S1*
London W1 *p34* 020 7935 3522

Loughlin, Miss P (Davies & Partners) *O*
Gloucester *p230*. 01452 612345

Loughran, Ms E M (Bristows)
London EC4 *p15*. 020 7400 8000

Loughrey, Miss F M (Simmons & Simmons)
London EC2 *p79*. 020 7628 2020

Loughrey, S (Carter-Ruck) *Zk Q Zf Ze*
London EC4 *p18*. 020 7353 5005

Loughrey, T P (Thompsons (formerly Robin/Brian Thompson & Partners)) *N*
Birmingham *p143* 0121 262 1200

Loughridge, Miss E J (Loughridge Bowler) *W V T2 Zv K4*
Coventry *p200*. 024 7663 1632

Loughridge, R B (Dutton Gregory) *S1 F1 L W*
Winchester *p433*. 01962 844333

Louis, Ms J (CKFT) *E Q S1*
London NW3 *p17* 020 7431 7262

Lound, Ms M M (Lound Mulrenan & Jefferies Solicitors) *G H*
Southwark *p55*. 020 7793 4012

Lounds, Miss J (Hempsons) *J1 Zp*
Harrogate *p240* 01423 522331

Lousley, C F (Pengillys LLP) *K1 S1 D1 E W L Zj*
Weymouth *p430*. 01305 768888

Louw, D R (Harrowells)
York *p444* 01904 558600

Lovatt, Miss C A (Stoke-on-Trent City Council)
Stoke-on-Trent *p472*. 01782 234567

Lovatt, Mrs H (BPE Solicitors LLP) *C2 C1 C3 Ze*
Cheltenham *p187* 01242 224433

Lovatt, J (stevensdrake) *N O Q*
Crawley *p202* 01293 596900

Lovatt, J C (Addleshaw Goddard) *R2*
London EC1 *p4* 020 7606 8855

Lovatt, J M (Lovatt & Co) *S1 W L E P C1 F1 K1 T1 N*
London EC3 *p55*. 020 7247 9336

Love, Miss A (Farleys Solicitors LLP) *K1 D1*
Blackburn *p145* 01254 367854

Love, Miss A J (Hugh James) *J1*
Cardiff *p179* 029 2022 4871

Love, Mrs C L (Oglethorpe Sturton & Gillibrand) *A1 W S1 T2 E*
Lancaster *p270* 01524 846846

Love, Ms E (Boodle Hatfield) *L*
Westminster *p14*. 020 7629 7411

Love, G (Stephensons Solicitors LLP) *O Q U2*
Leigh *p282*. 01942 777777

Love, J (Arnold Thomson Limited) *A1 E R1 S1*
Towcester *p413* 01327 350266

Love, J C (Irwin Mitchell LLP) *O M1 C3 I Ze Zf Zw Zy Zz*
Leeds *p274* 0870 150 0100

Love, J W (Dickinson Manser)
Poole *p352* 01202 673071

Love, R J (Langley Wellington) *X S1*
Gloucester *p230*. 01452 521286

Love, S (Reynolds Porter Chamberlain LLP) *O Q Zj*
London E1 *p71* 020 3060 6000

Love, S (Costain Engineering & Construction Ltd)
Maidenhead *p464* 01628 842444

Loveday, Mrs A M (Berg Legal) *J1 O*
Manchester *p301* 0161 833 9211

Loveday, B (Fisher Meredith)
Lambeth *p32*. 020 7091 2700

Loveday, Ms E A K (Wedlake Bell LLP) *W T2 Zd*
London WC1 *p91* 020 7395 3000

Loveday, H J C (Loveday & Keighley) *A1 C1 E F1 J1 K1 L M1 S1*
Matlock *p313* . . . . . 01629 583142 / 56660

Loveday, J G (Glaisyers) *N*
Birmingham *p138* 0121 233 2971

Loveday, R E (Lockett Loveday McMahon) *Zb C1 J1 C2*
Manchester *p307* 0161 237 3627

Loveday, S C (Weightmans LLP) *N O Q J2*
London EC4 *p91*. 020 7822 1900

Lovel, W J M (Hempsons) *N Zm Zp Zr*
Harrogate *p240* 01423 522331

Lovelady, M (St Albans District Council)
St Albans *p472* 01727 866100

Loveless, S (Burningham & Brown) *D1 K1 W*
Bath *p127*. 01225 320090

Loveless, S C (Potter Owtram & Peck) *S1 K1 D1 P N E L G C1 J1 Ze Zi Zc*
Haslemere *p243*. 01428 642321

Lovell, Mrs B R (Gedye & Sons (Solicitors) Ltd) *S2 E L S1*
Grange-over-Sands *p232* . . 01539 532313

Lovell, H (Lightfoots LLP)
Thame *p410*. 01844 212305

Lovell, R G F (Fonseca & Partners) *E L S1 W*
Abergavenny *p113*. 01873 857114

Lovell, S W (Taylor Wessing) *Zb*
London EC4 *p86*. 020 7300 7000

Lovelock, G P (Giffen Couch & Archer) *S1 E L Q W Zi*
Leighton Buzzard *p282* . . . 01525 372681

Lovelock, M R (Rushmoor Borough Council)
Farnborough *p458*. 01252 398398

Loveridge, M A (Michael A Loveridge) *S1 N Zz W K1 Zq Zj*
Clitheroe *p196*. 01200 442600

Lovering, Ms K M (W H Matthews & Co) *K1 V S1 Q J1 W*
Staines *p393*. 01784 453154

Lovering, T A (Morrisons Solicitors LLP) *K4 S1 W Zd*
Camberley *p173*. 01276 686005

Lovett, A (Stones Solicitors LLP) *B1*
Exeter *p222* 01392 666777

Lovett, A R (Crown Prosecution Service Cumbria)
Carlisle *p453*. 01228 882900

Lovett, Mrs C L (Everys) *S1*
Honiton *p252* 01404 43431

Lovett, Mrs D (Andrew J Taylor) *S1 W*
Cheadle *p185* 0161 428 1875

Lovett, F J C (Sacker & Partners LLP) *Zo*
London EC2 *p76*. 020 7329 6699

Lovett, G W (Clarke Willmott) *E T1*
Bristol *p162* 0845 209 1000 / 0117 305 6000

Lovett, Ms J (Linklaters LLP)
London EC2 *p54*. 020 7456 2000

Lovewell, L V C (Tinsdills) *Q F1 G H J1 K1 L M1 N P V*
Hanley *p239*. 01782 262031

Loveys, E L (Pinney Talfourd LLP)
Brentwood *p156*. 01277 268700

Lovitt, A M P (Pinsent Masons LLP) *R2 E*
Leeds *p276* 0113 244 5000

Lovitt, J (Rosenblatt)
London EC4 *p73*. 020 7955 0880

Low, A (DLA Piper UK LLP)
London EC2 *p24*. 0870 011 1111

Low, A J W (HKB Wiltshires) *S1 E C1 W B1 Zf Zl*
Great Yarmouth *p234* 01493 855676

Low, Miss C (Kenneth Elliott & Rowe) *K1 K3*
Romford *p366* 01708 757575

Low-Chew-Tung, C (Streathers Solicitors LLP) *B1 S2 E J1 K1 O Q N*
London W1 *p84* 020 7034 4200

Lowde, S R (Wiggin LLP) *I Zf U2 Ze*
Cheltenham *p189* 01242 224114

Lowdell, D K (Richmond upon Thames Magistrates Court)
Richmond upon Thames *p470* 020 8948 2101

Lowdon, Mrs B J (Sintons LLP) *Zx Zd K1 W S1*
Newcastle upon Tyne *p326* . 0191 226 7878

Lowe, A M (Lamb Brooks LLP) *N O Q*
Basingstoke *p126* 01256 844888

Lowe, B (Ford & Warren) *W K4 Zm T2*
Leeds *p273* 0113 243 6601

Lowe, Ms B (Shell International Ltd)
London SE1 *p109* 020 7934 1234

Lowe, Mrs C (Henmans LLP) *Zr*
Oxford *p343*. 01865 781000

Lowe, C (Holman Fenwick Willan)
London EC3 *p42*. 020 7264 8000

Lowe, Ms C (Fraser Brown) *S1*
Nottingham *p337*. 0115 988 8777

Lowe, C C (Watson Farley & Williams)
London EC2 *p90*. 020 7814 8000

Lowe, D M (Field Fisher Waterhouse LLP)
London EC3 *p31*. 020 7861 4000

Lowe, D R (Barker Booth & Eastwood) *N*
Blackpool *p146* 01253 362500

Lowe, Ms F L A (Cendant Relocation) *R2*
Swindon *p473*. 01793 756000

Lowe, Miss F M (Performing Right Society Ltd) *C1 Zf Ze*
London W1 *p108* 020 7580 5544

Lowe, Miss F V (Leach Rawlence & Hart) *C1 S2 E S1 W*
Croydon *p205* 020 8680 5850

Lowe, G F A (Gordon Lowe & Co) *Q N K1 G F1 J1 C1 L O V Zk*
Bristol *p163* 01454 326833

Lowe, J (Trowers & Hamlins)
London EC3 *p88*. 020 7423 8000

Lowe, J (Keoghs LLP) *O Q Zq N*
Bolton *p149* 01204 677000

Lowe, Miss J (Higgs & Sons) *O*
Brierley Hill *p158*. 0845 111 5050

Lowe, Miss J L (Walker Smith Way) *Zr N*
Wrexham *p443* 0844 346 3100

Lowe, J W (Snowball Worthy Lowe) *C1 S2 Zl E O*
Sunderland *p402*. 0191 565 3221

Lowe, K (Wortley Redmayne Kershaw) *A1 E*
Chelmsford *p187*. 01245 491122

Lowe, Ms L (Stroud District Council) *Zl O L Zw*
Stroud *p473* 01453 766321

Lowe, Mrs L (Nicholls Lindsell & Harris and Ingham & Wainwright) *S1 W*
Poynton *p355* 01625 876411

Lowe, M C (David Rubie Mitchell & Co) *G I H Zl*
Sutton *p403* 020 8641 0575

Lowe, Mrs N A (Harold G Walker) *S1 S2*
Bournemouth *p152*. 01202 203200
Wimborne *p433* 01202 881454

Lowe, P B (Lowe Legal Services)
Blandford Forum *p147* 01258 881142

Lowe, P J (Davitt Jones Bould) *E S2*
Taunton *p408* 01823 279279

Lowe, P M (Lowes) *S1 W E G L K1 F1 J1 P V Zl Zp Zd*
Rainham *p359*. 01634 371111

Lowe, P T (Challinors) *M1 P N K1 D1 F1 L C1 J1 B1 Zp Zj Zk*
West Bromwich *p427* 0121 553 3211

Lowe, Ms R A (CMS Cameron McKenna LLP) *B1*
London EC3 *p17*. 020 7367 3000

Lowe, Dr R D (Walker Morris) *Ze C1 Zf U2 Zw*
Leeds *p277* 0113 283 2500

Lowe, R W (Heath Sons & Broome) *G H S1 F1 D1 W Zc S2 E Zf Q N Zq*
Manchester *p305* 0161 681 1933

Lowe, Mrs S (Lowe & Co) *K4 K1 S1 W Zr R1 S2 T2 V*
Bedford *p130* 01234 764731

Lowe, S J (Winters) *W S1*
St Ives *p392*. 01480 377377

Lowe, Ms T (Harrison Clark LLP) *K1 K3*
Cheltenham *p188* 01242 269198
Worcester *p439* 01905 612001
Worcester *p439* 01905 612001

Lowe, T J (Chambers Fletcher LLP) *A1 C1 E L W J1*
Northwich *p333* 01606 780400

Lowe, Ms Z A (Ewart Price) *N O Q*
Welwyn Garden City *p425* . . 01707 332383

Lowe-Petraske, Ms A (Bates Wells & Braithwaite London LLP) *Zd C1*
London EC4 *p11*. 020 7551 7777

Lowens, D A (Norwich City Council)
Norwich *p467* 01603 212212

Lowery, E (Fenwick Elliott) *O Q Zc Zi A3 P Zj R2*
London WC2 *p31* 020 7421 1986

Lowery, P (Mundays LLP) *K1 W T2 K4*
Cobham *p196* 01932 590500

Lowery, R J (Sweeney Miller) *S2 C1 E R2 S1*
Sunderland *p402*. 0191 568 2050

Lowes, Miss C J (Richmonds) *W K1 S1 T1 L P G J1 Zd*
Newcastle upon Tyne *p326* . 0191 232 2155

Lowes, R E (BLB Solicitors) *N*
Bath *p127* 01225 462871

Loweth, J C (Barlow Lyde & Gilbert LLP)
London EC3 *p10*. 020 7247 2277

Loweth, J H (Powergen PLC)
Coventry *p456*. . . . . 024 7642 4748 / 4000

Lowick, M W (Lowick McKay) *K1 P F1 J1 L N D1 O Zl Zm D2*
Cheadle *p185* 0161 491 5588

Lowings, J S (Hallett & Co) *S1 W S2*
Ashford *p119* 01233 625711

Lowless, D M (Red Kite Law) *A1 E L S1 W C1*
Pembroke *p345* 01646 683222

Lowless, P J (Michelmores LLP) *E Zh X R2*
Exeter *p221* 01392 688688

Lowrie, Mrs J C (Lowrie & Co) *S1 K1 N J1 W*
Cobham *p196* 01932 865818

Lowry, Ms E M (W H Matthews & Co)
Staines *p393*. 01784 453154

Lowry, J W (Hine Downing Solicitors) *S1 E L S2 C2 C1*
Falmouth *p223*. 01326 316655

Lowry, M (Addleshaw Goddard)
Leeds *p271* 0113 209 2000

Lowry, M P (Stephens & Scown) *K1 D1 D2*
St Austell *p391* 01726 74433

Lowry, V H (Kingswell Berney) *K1 N Q L Zm J1 M1 V*
Gosport *p232* 023 9258 2211

Lowry-Mullins, K (Dass Solicitors) *G H M1 B2 Zg Zl Q W U2 I*
Birmingham *p137* 0121 248 4000
Westminster *p38*. 020 7233 3999

Lowson, G J (Pinsent Masons LLP) *O Q*
Birmingham *p141* 0121 200 1050

Lowther, Mrs J E (Adlams LLP) *K1 N Q S1 W Zq*
St Neots *p392* 01480 474061

Lowther, K A (Gaynham King & Mellor) *K1 G P M1 S1 V W D1*
Appleby *p118* 01768 351422
Penrith *p346*. 01768 864651

Lowther, P (Adlams LLP) *K4 T2 W Zm*
St Neots *p392* 01480 474061

Lowthian, Ms K (Dickinson Dees) *K1*
Newcastle upon Tyne *p324* . 0191 279 9000

Loxley, Ms M (Birkett Long LLP) *K1*
Colchester *p197* 01206 217300

Loxley, M P (Irwin Mitchell LLP) *K1 K2 D1 D2*
Sheffield *p376* 0870 150 0100

Loxton, Mrs A (Infields) *Q N K3*
Kingston upon Thames *p267* 020 8977 7633 / 8977 1149

Loxton, G C (Leo Abse & Cohen) *S1 W A1 L N Q*
Cardiff *p179* . . .029 2038 3252 / 2034 5421

Loynes, D T (Hartley & Worstenholme) *K1 G H F1 D1 M1 J1*
Pontefract *p351* 01977 732222

Loynes, P (O'Melveny & Myers LLP)
London EC4 *p64*. 020 7088 0000

Loyns, C W (Beasley Johnson Loyns) *N*
Walsall *p419*. 01922 644433

Loynton, Ms J (Loynton & Co) *E S1 Zi Zl*
Birmingham *p140* 0121 327 0118 / 327 0652

Lu, C W (Lu Oliphant Solicitors) *S1 S2 C1 Q J1*
Edgware *p217* 020 8238 2822

Lubar, C (Morgan Lewis & Bockius)
London EC4 *p61*. 020 3201 5000

Lubbock, M A (Ashurst LLP) *I M1 M2 U1*
London EC2 *p7* 020 7638 1111

Lubbock, N C (Steeles) *A1 D1 E F1 G J1 K1 L M1*
Norwich *p335* 0870 609 0200

Lubega, G (Nabarro LLP) *O Zc*
London WC1 *p63* 020 7524 6000

Lucas, A (Field Fisher Waterhouse LLP)
London EC3 *p31*. 020 7861 4000

Lucas, C D (Hill Dickinson LLP) *A3 Za O Zj Zb*
London EC3 *p41*. 020 7283 9033

Lucas, D (BHP Law)
Stockton-on-Tees *p396* . . . 01642 672770

Lucas, D I (Fraser Brown) *Zl*
Nottingham *p337*. 0115 988 8777

Lucas, D W (FBC Manby Bowdler LLP) *E*
Shrewsbury *p379* 01743 241551

Lucas, G (Charles Crookes & Jones) *N K1 G H F1 Q Zh D1*
Caerphilly *p172* 029 2086 0628

Lucas, I C (Stevens Lucas)
Chirk *p193*. 01691 777949

Lucas, Miss J (TLT Solicitors) *L O E Q R1 Zc Zs Zi*
Bristol *p165* 0117 917 7777

Lucas, J F (Zatman & Co) *S1 M1 P W*
Manchester *p311* 0161 832 2500

Lucas, Ms J H (Squire Sanders (UK) LLP)
London EC2 *p81*. 020 7655 1000

Lucas, Miss K K (Storrar Cowdry) *W K4 S1*
Chester *p191* 01244 400567

Lucas, L D (Willans LLP) *E S2 R2*
Cheltenham *p189* 01242 514000

Lucas, M (Dutton Gregory) *Zn*
Southampton *p385*. 023 8022 1344

Lucas, Mrs M E (North Tyneside Council)
Newcastle upon Tyne *p466* . 0191 643 5000

Lucas, M R (Barlow Robbins LLP) *C1 C2 X*
Guildford *p235*. 01483 562901

Lucas, P D (Neale Turk) *E S1 N C1 W M1 L J1 F1 R1 Zk Zl Ze*
Fleet *p226*. 01252 811070

Lucas, P E (Paul Lucas & Co)
Aylesbury *p121* 01296 484022

Lucas, R A (Shulmans) *I Ze U2 Zza Zf Zw*
Leeds *p276* 0113 245 2833

Lucas, Mrs R D (Lester Aldridge LLP) *K1 D1 D2*
Bournemouth *p152*. 01202 786161

Lucas, S (Linklaters LLP)
London EC2 *p54*. 020 7456 2000

Lucas, S (Lucas Law Limited) *N*
London E8 *p55* 020 7812 9067

Lucas, Ms S (Quality Solicitors Burroughs Day) *N*
Bristol *p164* 0117 929 0333

Lucatello, S E M (Max Gold Law) *C1 E S1 M1 M2 K1 N O W J1 Zi Ze Zw S2*
Hull *p257* 01482 224900

Luces, Mrs L C R (Brodie Jackson Canter) *Zg Q Zp*
Liverpool *p286*. 0151 227 1429

Luck, C A (Nabarro LLP)
London WC1 *p63* 020 7524 6000

Luckhurst, G T (Thomas Boyd Whyte) *G H*
Bexleyheath *p132* 020 8303 7755

Luckhurst, H (Speechly Bircham LLP)
London EC4 *p81*. 020 7427 6400

Luckhurst-Matthews, T J (Short Richardson & Forth LLP) *C1 C2 Zh E R2 S2 R1 S1*
Newcastle upon Tyne *p326* . 0191 232 0283

Lucking, Mrs H (Napthens LLP) *K1*
Blackpool *p146* 01253 622305

Lucking, Miss N A L (Capron & Helliwell) *S1 W E L Zl*
Wroxham *p443* 01603 783818

See p634 for the Key to Work Categories

Luckman, S G (Sheridans) *C1 Zf Ze*
London WC1 *p78* 020 7079 0100

Lucy, Miss A (Cumberland Ellis Peirs) *S1*
London WC1 *p23* 020 7242 0422

Lucy, B S (Coles Miller Solicitors LLP) *E S1*
Poole *p352* 01202 673011

Ludford-Thomas, J F (Nottingham City Council (City Sec Dept))
Nottingham *p467*. 0115 915 5555

Ludgate, K D (Ridley & Hall) *S1 W Zc Zv S2*
Huddersfield *p256* 01484 538421

Ludick, Mrs S V (Callaghans) *K1*
Farnham *p224*. 01252 723477

Ludiman, Ms S (Ashurst LLP)
London EC2 *p7* 020 7638 1111

Ludlam, Ms S (Lupton Fawcett) *Ze Q*
Leeds *p275* 0113 280 2000

Ludlow, D C H (Barlow Robbins LLP) *J1 Zp O Zza J2 Zi*
Woking *p436*. 01483 748500

Ludlow, E R (Richard Ludlow & Co) *S2 E R2 S1 W*
Stratford-upon-Avon *p400* . . 01789 552872

Ludlow, H J (Phillips & Phillips)
Harrow *p242*. . .020 8422 4435 / 8422 8155

Ludlow, Ms K E (Linklaters LLP)
London EC2 *p54*. 020 7456 2000

Ludlow, R R (Chattertons Solicitors) *S1 W L E Zo T1 T2 Zv*
Grantham *p232* 01476 591550

Lueder, Ms C (Simmons & Simmons)
London EC2 *p79*. 020 7628 2020

Luff, Ms K (Martello Professional Risks Limited)
London EC3 *p108* 020 7337 7500
London EC3 *p68*. 0844 245 4000

Lugger, A (Stones Solicitors LLP) *A1 S1*
Okehampton *p340*. 01837 650200

Luke, J Y (Hay & Kilner) *A1 E L S1*
Newcastle upon Tyne *p325* . 0191 232 8345

Luke, N (Adam Douglas & Son) *J1 W C1 S2 S1 E*
Alnwick *p115*. 01665 602363

Luker, C C (Osborne Clarke) *C1 F1 Zo Ze*
Bristol *p164* 0117 917 3000

Lukins, E (Morrison & Foerster (UK) LLP) *C1 C2*
London EC2 *p62*. 020 7920 4000

Lukins, E J (Simmons & Simmons)
London EC2 *p79*. 020 7628 2020

Lukoczki, C A (Kirklees Metropolitan Borough Council)
Huddersfield *p461* 01484 221421

Lulic, C (Barlow Lyde & Gilbert LLP)
London EC3 *p10*. 020 7247 2277

Lumb, D J (Lupton Fawcett) *Q S1 W T2*
Leeds *p275* 0113 280 2000

Lumb, E L (Field Fisher Waterhouse LLP)
London EC3 *p31*. 020 7861 4000

Lumb, P S (Reynolds Porter Chamberlain LLP)
London E1 *p71* 020 3060 6000

Lumb, T P (Cartwright King) *G H*
Derby *p208* 01332 346111

Lumby, H (Ashurst LLP) *E*
London EC2 *p7* 020 7638 1111

Lumley, Miss C C (Waughs) *K1 D1 N S1 K2 W V L Q G Zm Zl Zf Zr Zw*
East Grinstead *p215*. 01342 323545

Lumley, Mrs C P (Squire Sanders (UK) LLP) *E*
Leeds *p277* 0113 284 7000

Lumley, M (Shulmans) *C1 I Zu Ze F1 F2 J1 U2 C3 M1 M2 O Zw*
Leeds *p276* 0113 245 2833

Lumley, R W (Waughs) *C1 E L O Q S1 A1 J1 N*
East Grinstead *p215*. 01342 323545

Lumley-Smith, A (Rio Tinto PLC)
London W2 *p109* 020 7781 2000

Lumsden, T A (CooperBurnett) *E C1*
Tunbridge Wells *p415* 01892 515022

Lunat, Y (Ison Harrison) *N O J1 Q*
Leeds *p274* 0113 284 5000

Lund, A (Rees Page) *N Q O*
Wolverhampton *p438* 01902 577777

Lund, Mrs D S (Lopian Wagner) *K1*
Manchester *p307* 0161 834 2324
Manchester *p310* 0161 833 1212

Lund, J R (Manchester City Council)
Manchester *p465* 0161 234 5000

Lund, R M (Turner Parkinson) *B1 O Q Zq*
Manchester *p310* 0161 833 1212

Lundie, A J (LG Lawyers)
London SE1 *p50*. 020 7379 0000

Lundy, D E (Lundys) *W S1 T1 A1 L E*
Driffield *p213* 01377 252831

Lunn, D (Bell & Co) *W K4*
Sutton *p402* 020 8661 8611

Lunn, D C (Windsor & Maidenhead Borough Council)
Maidenhead *p464* 01628 798888

Lunn, D H (Dickinson Parker Hill) *S1 N*
Ormskirk *p341*. 01695 574201

Lunn, Ms T (hlw Keeble Hawson LLP)
Doncaster *p211* 01302 366831

Lunnon, G P (Sherrards) *C1 C2 C3 E L S1 S2 W*
St Albans *p390* 01727 832830

Lunt, J (Cullimore Dutton) *C1 E S1*
Chester *p190* 01244 356789

Lunt, Ms N A (Donns) *N*
Manchester *p303* 0161 834 3311

Lunt, P G (Brabners Chaffe Street) *O*
Liverpool *p286*. 0151 600 3000

Lunt, S D (Walker Smith Way) *E A1 R2 S2*
Chester *p191* 0844 346 3100

Lunt, S W (Gosschalks) *C1 T1 A1 B1 Ze Zc*
Hull *p256* 01482 324252

Lupin, L P R (Lawrence Lupin) *Zi*
Wembley *p426*. 020 8733 7200

Lupson, I F (Jones Day) *O*
London EC4 *p46*. 020 7039 5959

Lupton, D A J (Yaffe Jackson Ostrin) *G H D1 M1 V Zi Zm*
Liverpool *p291*. 0151 236 5555

Lupton, H J (Stevens & Bolton) *E L*
Guildford *p237*. 01483 302264

Lupton, J S (Carrick Read Solicitors LLP)
Hull *p256* 01482 211160
Hull *p256* 01482 211160

Lupton, M (Lockett Loveday McMahon) *F1 J1 C1 C2*
Manchester *p307* 0161 237 3627

Lupton, N (Walker Morris) *O*
Leeds *p277* 0113 283 2500

Lurie, L N (Stamps Family Solicitors) *S1 W*
Hull *p258* 01482 323495

Luscombe, C (Ford & Warren) *O*
Leeds *p273* 0113 243 6601

Luscombe, Miss F L (WBW Solicitors) *W S1*
Newton Abbot *p329* 01626 202404

Luscombe, M A (Hadgkiss Hughes & Beale)
Birmingham *p139* 0121 778 2161

Luscombe, Miss P F B (Penningtons) *N Zr*
Godalming *p231* 01483 791800

Lush, C G (Whitehead Vizard) *S1 W A1*
Salisbury *p371*. 01722 412141

Lush, D N (CVC Solicitors) *S1 W T1 L F2 A1 C1 V P M1 Zm Zd Zl*
Penzance *p346* 01736 362313

Lush, Mrs P M (Whitehead Vizard) *S1 W*
Salisbury *p371*. 01722 412141

Lusher, M J (Horwich Cohen Coghlan) *N*
Manchester *p305* 0161 830 4600

Lusher, R (Cannings Connolly) *E S2*
London EC1 *p18*. 020 7329 9000

Lusingu, Ms L (Kaim Todner Ltd) *K1 D1*
Islington *p47*. 020 7700 0070

Luthra, Miss S (DWF) *U2 Ze C1 I C3 F2 F1 M1*
Manchester *p303* 0161 603 5000

Lutley, A J (A J Lutley) *Zd*
Ashtead *p119* 01372 279066

Luto, A P S (Maxwell Winward LLP) *C1 C3 C2*
London EC4 *p59*. 020 7651 0000

Lutrario, Miss E (HRJ Law LLP) *Zr N*
Hitchin *p251* 01462 628888

Luttman, P (David Street & Company)
Crawley *p202* 01293 616191

Lutton, C A (Luttons Dunford) *A1 C1 E R1 T1 Ze Zk*
Gloucester *p230*. 01452 529751

Luty, N P (Armstrong Luty Solicitors) *N Zr*
Skipton *p381*. 01756 799977

Lux, J S (Ince & Co Services Ltd) *O M1 Za Zj*
London E1 *p44* 020 7481 0010

Luxmoore Styles, R P L (Marsh & McLennan Companies, Inc)
London EC3 *p108* 020 7357 1000

Luxton, Ms S (Simmons & Simmons)
London EC2 *p79*. 020 7628 2020

Lyall, D B (Midwinters) *T2 S1 W*
Cheltenham *p188* 01242 514674

Lyall, G (Dickinson Dees) *T2 W*
Newcastle upon Tyne *p324* . 0191 279 9000

Lycett, Miss J M (Lycett Conveyancing Solicitors) *S1 S2*
Hailsham *p237*. 01323 449552

Lyford, Mrs E M (RHW Solicitors LLP) *E S2 C2*
Guildford *p237*. 01483 302000

Lykiardopoulos, A N (Bristows) *Ze*
London EC4 *p15*. 020 7400 8000

Lyle, Miss S L (Farleys Solicitors LLP) *G H B2*
Burnley *p169* 01282 798664

Lymbourides, Miss C (Joseph Hill & Co)
London N15 *p41*. 020 8880 3535

Lymer, Mrs L A (Davies & Partners) *N Zr Zg*
Gloucester *p230*. 01452 612345

Lymer, P J (Woolliscrofts)
Alsager *p116*. 01270 875915

Lynam, Mrs J (Hounslow Petty Sessions Area)
Feltham *p458* 020 8917 3400

Lynch, Ms A C (British Telecommunications PLC)
London EC1 *p104* 020 7356 6181

Lynch, C E (Capsticks Solicitors LLP) *C1 I M1 Zd Ze*
London SW19 *p18*. 020 8780 2211

Lynch, G J (Hill Dickinson LLP) *G N M1 P J1*
Liverpool *p288*. 0151 600 8000

Lynch, Mrs H S (Perry Hay & Co) *S1*
Richmond upon Thames *p364* 020 8940 8115 / 8332 7532

Lynch, J (Martyn Prowel) *G H Zl*
Cardiff *p180* 029 2047 0909

Lynch, Miss J (Capsticks Solicitors LLP) *J1 Zp J2*
London SW19 *p18*. 020 8780 2211

Lynch, Mrs J (Tennant & Knight) *D1 K1*
Brighton *p160* 01273 202050

Lynch, M (DLA Piper UK LLP)
Leeds *p272* 0870 011 1111

Lynch, Ms M (Farrell Matthews & Weir) *G H*
London W6 *p31* 020 8741 1482

Lynch, Ms M B (Pitmans LLP) *K1 D1 K3 K2*
Reading *p361* 0118 958 0224

Lynch, M J (Wrigleys Solicitors LLP) *C1 T1 J1 I Zd Zb Ze Zh Zv*
Leeds *p278* 0113 244 6100

Lynch, Ms P (Keoghs LLP) *N Zj O Q*
Bolton *p149* 01204 677000

Lynch, R A (DFA Law LLP) *W T2 T1*
Northampton *p331*. 01604 609560

Lynch, R J (Memery Crystal) *O*
London WC2 *p60* 020 7242 5905

Lynch, R M (Kenwright & Lynch)
Wandsworth *p49*. 020 8767 1211

Lynch, Ms S J (Howells LLP) *D1 K1*
Rotherham *p367*. 01709 364000

Lynch, W M (Patrick J Cusack & Co) *B1 C1 E S2 L Q N S1 W*
Harrow *p241*. 020 8863 3414

Lynch, Miss Z (Sacker & Partners LLP) *Zo*
London EC2 *p76*. 020 7329 6699

Lynchehan, M (Linklaters LLP)
London EC2 *p54*. 020 7456 2000

Lyndsey, Ms N (Sternberg Reed) *D1*
Barking *p123* 020 8591 3366

Lyne, A (Penningtons)
London EC2 *p66*. 020 7457 3000

Lyne, Miss A J (Trowers & Hamlins)
London EC3 *p88*. 020 7423 8000

Lyne, Mrs A M (Taylor Vinters) *J1 J2 Zi*
Cambridge *p176* 01223 423444

Lynes, S (Cornwall County Council)
Truro *p474*. 01872 322197

Lyng, Miss T (Royal Mail Group)
London EC4 *p109* 020 7250 2468

Lynham, M (Gillanders) *Q J1 Zp W Zq L N Zl Zr A3*
Cheltenham *p188* 01242 583434

Lynn, Miss A E (Radcliffes Le Brasseur) *N Q J1 Zr Zp*
Leeds *p276* 0113 234 1220

Lynn, J (Levenes Solicitors)
Haringey *p53* . .020 8881 7777 / 8881 6764

Lynn, M (Michael Lynn & Co) *E S1 J1 L F1 Zf*
London SW7 *p55* 020 7225 3681

Lynn, P A (Peter Lynn & Partners) *C1 C2 O Q T1 T2 Zb Zc Zw*
Morriston *p319*. 01792 310731
Swansea *p405*. 01792 450010

Lyon, A (Birnberg Peirce & Partners) *G*
Camden *p13*. 020 7911 0166

Lyon, A (Martello Professional Risks Limited) *L O Zq*
London EC3 *p108* 020 7337 7500

Lyon, A W (Mears Hobbs & Durrant) *N O Q G H V Zg Zk*
Lowestoft *p294* 01502 583621

Lyon, D (Kellogg Brown & Root (UK) Ltd)
Leatherhead *p462* 01372 865000

Lyon, D E (Ellis-Fermor & Negus) *W S1 T2 Zm Zd*
Ripley *p364* 01773 744744

Lyon, Ms E (Rooks Rider) *E R1*
London EC1 *p73*. 020 7689 7000

Lyon, Mrs E A D (Harvey Ingram LLP) *O*
Leicester *p280*. 0116 254 5454

Lyon, M (Barnard & Tomlin) *S1 W*
Luton *p295* 01582 453366
London EC4 *p24*. 020 7353 1770
Benfleet *p131* 01268 565769

Lyon, N (Kimbells LLP) *O L*
Milton Keynes *p317* 01908 668555

Lyon, S J (Burnetts) *C1 S2 E C3*
Carlisle *p181*. 01228 552222
Carlisle *p182*. 01228 552222

Lyon, Ms V (Rich & Carr Freer Bouskell) *E*
Leicester *p281*. 0116 253 8021

Lyon-Small, Mrs K J (Terry Jones Solicitors & Advocates) *S1 Q*
Shrewsbury *p379* 01743 285888

Lyons, Miss C A (Lyons Rounsfell) *A1 C1 E L S1 T1 W*
Bristol *p163* 0117 967 5252

Lyons, E P J F (Lyons Rounsfell) *B1 D1 F1 G H J1 K1 L Q S1 N Zt*
Westbury-on-Trym *p428* . . . 0117 950 6506

Lyons, H (Hogan Lovells International LLP)
London EC1 *p42*. 020 7296 2000

Lyons, J T (John Howe & Co) *S1 Q W Zl*
Pudsey *p358*. 0113 236 3936

Lyons, M (Lyons Solicitor) *A1 E R1 S1 T2 W*
Herne Bay *p248* . . . 01227 360801 / 07906 759286

Lyons, M L P (Stewarts Law LLP) *Zr N*
London EC4 *p83*. 020 7822 8000

Lyons, N H (Foot Anstey) *G H B2 D1 I*
Plymouth *p349*. 01752 675000

Lyons, P (Travers Smith LLP) *Zb R2*
London EC1 *p87*. 020 7295 3000

Lyons, R (Shepherd + Wedderburn LLP)
London EC4 *p78*. 020 7429 4900

Lyons, Miss S E (Mid Bedfordshire District Council) *W*
Shefford *p471* 0845 230 4040

Lyons, S K (Keith Ready & Co) *N K3 Q K1 B1 L Zk J1 Zc F1*
Barton-upon-Humber *p126*. . 01652 632215

Lysaght, W J C (Hugh James) *B1 J1 N O Zq Zr*
Cardiff *p179* 029 2022 4871

Lyttleton, Ms N A (Barlow Lyde & Gilbert LLP)
London EC3 *p10*. 020 7247 2277

Lyttleton, T M (Trevor Lyttleton MBE) *K4 Zm W Ze Zf*
Westminster *p55*. 020 7402 4810

M

Ma, Ms M (Simmons & Simmons)
London EC2 *p79*. 020 7628 2020

Mabane, R (Holman Fenwick Willan)
London EC3 *p42*. 020 7264 8000

Mabbot, Ms S (Browne Jacobson LLP) *K1 D2 D1 Zm Zu*
Nottingham *p336*. 0115 976 6000

Mabbutt, I (EMW) *C2 C1*
Milton Keynes *p316* 0845 070 6000

Mabe, A N (Gateley LLP) *W T2 Zd*
Birmingham *p138* 0121 234 0000

Maberly, A A (Royds LLP) *E S1 L*
London EC4 *p74*. 020 7583 2222

Maberly, G H P (TWM Solicitors LLP) *E C1 A1 X Zf L*
Reigate *p363* 01737 221212

Mabey, J (Hunters) *W T2*
London WC2 *p44* 020 7412 0050

Mabey, P (Keoghs LLP) *N Zj O Q A3*
Coventry *p200*. 024 7665 8200

Mabon, S (Brabners Chaffe Street) *Q*
Manchester *p301* 0161 836 8800

Mabon, W J (Birketts LLP) *J2 N Zr*
Ipswich *p262*. 01473 232300

Mac Brayne, Mrs B L (Fraser Dawbarns) *N*
King's Lynn *p266* 01553 666600

Mac Lua, Ms S (Salans) *B1 O Q Zb*
London EC4 *p76*. 020 7429 6000

Mac Neice, R J J (Ashfords LLP) *Zw*
Exeter *p220* 01392 337000

McAdam, C (Walker Morris) *D2 G H K3 K1 B2 J2*
Leeds *p277* 0113 283 2500

Macadam, Ms M R (Howells LLP) *G H*
Rotherham *p367*. 01709 364000

McAdams, Miss A L (DAC Beachcroft) *N Q P*
London EC4 *p24*. 020 7936 2222

McAfee, Mrs S (Drivers) *S1 S2 W*
York *p444* 01904 625661

McAleavey, Miss C M (Farrer & Co LLP)
London WC2 *p31* 020 3375 7000

McAleer, M (Keoghs LLP) *N*
Bolton *p149* 01204 677000

McAleese, Ms G (Geraldine McAleese & Co)
London W4 *p56* 020 8987 8381

McAlinden, P (Howell Jones & Co) *K1 Q N G H Zc F1 O K3*
Abergele *p113* . . . .01745 826282 / 825845
Llanrwst *p292* 01492 640277

McAlinney, D (McAlinneys Solicitors) *Q N*
Wakefield *p419* 01924 377017

Macalister, I (DWF) *N O P Q Zj*
Liverpool *p287*. 0151 907 3000
Manchester *p303* 0161 603 5000

McAlister, Mrs K A (Rawlison Butler LLP)
Crawley *p202* 01293 527744

McAlister, L J W (National Grid PLC)
Warwick *p471* 01926 653000

McAlister, N S (CMS Cameron McKenna LLP) *C1 C2*
London EC3 *p17*. 020 7367 3000

McAlister, Mrs S C (Cartmell Shepherd)
Carlisle *p182*. 01228 514077

McAllester, A K (Cullimore Dutton) *E S1 A1 W C1 L T1 Zd Zv Zm Zx Zo*
Chester *p190* 01244 356789

McAllister, Ms C (Addleshaw Goddard)
London EC1 *p4* 020 7606 8855

McAllister, D S (Hillyer McKeown LLP) *O Q B1*
Chester *p190* 01244 318131

McAllister, Mrs F R (Mundays LLP) *O Q J1 N B1 F1 Zk*
Cobham *p196* 01932 590500

McAllister, W (Conway & Co) *O Q S1 W E J1*
Henley-on-Thames *p247*. . . 01491 411122

McAlpine, R (SNR Denton)
London EC4 *p75*. 020 7242 1212

McAnaw, Miss F (BTMK Solicitors LLP) *J1*
Southend-on-Sea *p387* . . . 01702 339222

MacAndrew, Mrs H S (Chester City Council)
Chester *p454* 01244 324324

MacAndrew, R A (Hadfields Butt & Bowyer) *W T2 Zv*
Farnham *p225*. 01252 716101

McAnlis, Ms R (Norwich Union Insurance Group)
Norwich *p467* 01603 622200

McAnlis, Mrs R (Aviva PLC)
London EC3 *p103* . . 020 7283 7500 / 01603 687905
York *p477* 01904 452210

McAnulty, G G F (Warings Solicitors)
Blackpool *p147* 01253 293106

Macara, I S (Bennett Griffin) *K4 W*
Rustington *p369* 01903 777690

McAra, Mrs J (McAras Solicitors LLP) *K1 V K2*
Leeds *p275* 0113 243 4333

McAra, R J (McAras Solicitors LLP) *K1 S1 K2 V*
Leeds *p275* 0113 243 4333

McArdle, J (Donnelly McArdle Adamson) *M1 P F1 J1 C1 B1 L Q N*
Darlington *p206* 01325 482299

McArdle, Miss P M (SNR Denton) *J1 O Zp Zo*
London EC4 *p75*. 020 7242 1212

McArdle, S J (KBL Solicitors) *O Q*
Bolton *p149* 01204 527777

McAreavey, J B (Unsworth & Wood) *K1 K3 E S2 L S1 W*
Wigan *p432* 01942 242400

McArthur, A (Doyle Clayton Solicitors Limited) *J1 Zp Zi*
Reading *p360* 0118 959 6839

McArthur, A (Baxter Brown McArthur) *G H B2*
London SW11 *p11* 020 7924 8130

McArthur, C (Field Fisher Waterhouse LLP)
London EC3 *p31*. 020 7861 4000

McArthur, Miss F E (QualitySolicitors D'Angibau) *S2 S1*
Poole *p353* 01202 672598

Macartney, M C (Spratt Endicott) *S1*
Banbury *p122* 01295 204000

MacAskill, I D (Woodfines LLP) *Q K1 N*
Bedford *p130* 01234 270600

Macaulay, A D (Herbert Smith LLP) *C1 C2*
London EC2 *p40*. 020 7374 8000

Macaulay, Mrs A R (Harris & Harris) *K1 K3 D1 D2 X*
Frome *p228* 01373 463366

Macaulay, B (Skadden Arps Slate Meagher & Flom (UK) LLP)
London E14 *p80*. 020 7519 7000

Macaulay, Mrs G A (Squire Sanders (UK) LLP)
London EC2 *p81*. 020 7655 1000

McAulay, Mrs G E (Mullis & Peake) *W*
Chadwell Heath *p184* 020 8599 2417

Macaulay, J (Greenwoods Solicitors LLP) *J1 Zp*
Peterborough *p347* 01733 887700

Macaulay, J G (Thatcher & Hallam) *N O Q C1*
Midsomer Norton *p316*. . . . 01761 414646

Macauley, Ms B (Wandsworth & Merton Law Centre Ltd)
London SW17 *p110* 020 8767 2777

McAuley, C J (Clifford Chance)
London E14 *p20*. 020 7006 1000

McAuley, J D (TWM Solicitors LLP) *S1 S2*
Epsom *p219*. 01372 729555

Macauley, P D (Macauley Smith & Co) *G H*
London SE8 *p56*. 020 8692 4088

Mcauley, Ms S L (Rothera Dowson) *W K4*
West Bridgford *p427*. 0115 914 0077

McAuliffe, J P (Warners Solicitors) *E S1*
Tonbridge *p412* 01732 770660

McAuliffe, Miss M (Stapleton & Son) *D1 K2 K1 L Q*
Stamford *p393*. 01780 751226

Macavoy, P (Barrea LLP) *O Q S2 E C2 Zq R2 B1 F1 J1 N R1 S1 W*
High Wycombe *p249*. 01494 537699

MacBean, J I N (Brian Ruff Angus & Jewers) *F1 J1 W K4*
Wickford *p431*. 01268 761126
Westcliff-on-Sea *p428* 01702 347853

McBean, W (Machins Solicitors LLP) *Q O*
Luton *p295* 01582 514000

McBennett, Mrs E J (Cadmans Law & Property) *N Zr*
Cleckheaton *p195* 01274 874231

MacBrayne, I C (Hayes & Storr)
Fakenham *p223* 01328 863231

McBride, A C A (Linder Myers Solicitors) *N L*
Manchester *p306* 0844 984 6000

McBride, A G (Girlings) *P J1 F1 Zj Zk Zt*
Ashford *p119* 01233 664711

McBride, A K (Kingsley Napley) *B2 G Zg*
London EC1 *p50*. 020 7814 1200

McBride, B E (Thompsons (formerly Robin/Brian Thompson & Partners)) *N J2*
London WC1 *p87* 020 7290 0000

McBride, Miss C (John Donkin & Co) *J1 K1 Q*
Gateshead *p228*. 0191 495 2896 / 477 1781

McBride, Miss C (Prettys) *R2 E S1*
Ipswich *p262*. 01473 232121

McBride, Miss O M (Barker Gooch & Swailes) *W T2 S1*
London N21 *p9* .020 8886 5928 / 8886 5734

McBride, S (TLT Solicitors)
Bristol *p165* 0117 917 7777

McBride, Ms T (Bishop McBride Olden)
Cardiff *p177* 029 2049 0111

McBrien, H J (Penningtons)
London EC2 *p66*. 020 7457 3000

Macbryde, Miss A J (D K Macbryde & Co)
Prestatyn *p356*. 01745 856404

Macbryde, D K (D K Macbryde & Co) *W S2 L S1 R2 T2 Zl*
Prestatyn *p356*. 01745 856404

McBurney, Mrs E J (Weightmans LLP) *A1 C1 C2 E P S1 R1 Zc*
Liverpool *p291*. 0151 227 2601

McBurney, N (Brabners Chaffe Street) *E*
Liverpool *p286*. 0151 600 3000

McCabe, J C (Sintons LLP) *N Q*
Newcastle upon Tyne *p326* . 0191 226 7878

McCabe, Miss K E (Clark Willis) *Zm W K4*
Darlington *p206* 01325 281111

McCabe, Mrs L A (Brown & Corbishley) *D1 K1*
Newcastle under Lyme *p323*. 01782 717888

McCabe, Mrs M (Wards Solicitors) *D1 K1 S1 N*
Portishead *p354*. 01275 850460

McCabe, M K (Kidd Rapinet) *S1 L E S2*
Maidenhead *p298* 0845 017 9608

McCabe, P (Charles Lucas & Marshall) *J1*
Swindon *p406* 01793 511055
Trowbridge *p414*. 01225 755621

McCabe, S (McCormacks) *F1 G L M1 P*
London EC3 *p56*. 020 7791 2000

McCabe, Ms S E (Peter Dunn & Co)
Sunderland *p401*. 0191 568 9000

McCahon, D (Metropolitan Police Directorate of Legal Services)
London SW1 *p108*. 020 7230 7210

McCalister, A J C (BCL Burton Copeland) *G B2 H*
London WC2 *p9* 020 7430 2277

McCall, G (AMD Solicitors) *E S2 C2 Ze C1*
Bristol *p160* 0117 962 1460

McCall, Ms R (Walker Morris)
Leeds *p277* 0113 283 2500

McCallan, Ms M (Mary Monson Solicitors Ltd) *G H*
Swinton *p407* . . 0161 794 0088 / 0808 155 4870

McCallig, Miss C L (Scott Duff & Co) *N*
Keswick *p265* 01768 774321

McCallister, S (Salusburys Harding & Barnett) *K1 Q S1 F1 L J1 G D1*
Leicester *p281*. . 0116 262 9033 / 262 6052

McCallough, R A (Pinsent Masons LLP) *I O Q*
London EC2 *p67*. 020 7418 7000

McCallum, Mrs A L (J Garrard & Allen) *S1 S2 W A1*
Olney *p341* 01234 711215

McCallum, Ms E (Devereux & Co) *K1*
Bristol *p162* 0117 959 3344

McCallum, Ms H (Allen & Overy LLP)
London E1 *p5* 020 3088 0000

McCallum, J I (Russell-Cooke LLP) *E S2 Zc R1*
London SW15 *p74*. 020 8789 9111

McCallum, Mrs P A (Oxfordshire County Council)
Oxford *p468* 01865 792422

Maccallum, Mrs S (Boodle Hatfield) *T1 T2*
Westminster *p14*. 020 7629 7411

McCann, C (Penningtons) *E*
London EC2 *p66*. 020 7457 3000

McCann, M H (Forbes) *S1 Zi W R1*
Preston *p356* 01772 220022

McCann, N M (Joelson Wilson LLP) *O Q Zl F2 L*
Westminster *p46*. 020 7580 5721

McCann, O J (Taylors) *J1 Zp*
Blackburn *p146* 0844 800 0263

McCann, P (South Tyneside Metropolitan Borough Council)
South Shields *p471* 0191 427 1717

McCann, S (Peters & Peters) *O Q*
London EC4 *p67*. 020 7629 7991

McCann, S J (George Davies Solicitors LLP) *A1 E R1 S1*
Manchester *p303* 0161 236 8992

McCarrigle, Ms C C (Manchester City Council)
Manchester *p465* 0161 234 5000

McCarthy, A (Macks Solicitors) *Q N*
Middlesbrough *p315*. 01642 252828

McCarthy, A C (Procter & Gamble UK (Legal Dept))
Weybridge *p476* 01932 896000

McCarthy, Miss A T (K&L Gates LLP) *O Zb*
London EC4 *p47*. 020 7648 9000

McCarthy, B G (DAC Beachcroft)
London EC3 *p24*. 020 7208 6800

McCarthy, Ms C (Rawlison Butler LLP) *O Q*
Crawley *p202* 01293 527744

McCarthy, Miss C (Clarke Kiernan) *G H*
Tonbridge *p412* 01732 360999

McCarthy, Ms C (Howard Kennedy LLP) *E*
London W1 *p48* 020 7636 1616

McCarthy, Ms E (South Gloucestershire Council)
Thornbury *p474* 01454 868686

McCarthy, Mrs E E Z (Clifton Ingram LLP) *W T2 K4*
Reading *p360* 0118 957 3425

McCarthy, Ms F A (McCarthy & White) *S1 W Zm*
Thornbury *p411* 01454 413696

McCarthy, Miss F E (Pattinson & Brewer) *N Q*
London WC1 *p66* 020 7400 5100

McCarthy, Ms G (LG Lawyers)
London SE1 *p50*. 020 7379 0000

McCarthy, J A (Whitemans) *K1 G H*
Gloucester *p231* 01452 411601

McCarthy, Miss J E (Reed Smith LLP) *J1*
London EC2 *p71*. 020 3116 3000

McCarthy, J F (John McCarthy & Co) *S1 E W L C1 A1 Zc Zd*
Newcastle upon Tyne *p325* . 0191 276 9500

McCarthy, Ms J H (Procol & Candor Solicitors) *Zi*
Ealing *p69*. 020 8993 4646

McCarthy, Ms K (Stephen Gallico Solicitors) *J1*
Haywards Heath *p245* 01444 411333

McCarthy, K (McCarthy Stewart & Booty Solicitors) *K1 N G H Q Zl Zm V B2*
Bury St Edmunds *p171* . . . 01284 748927

McCarthy, Miss K J (Harris Cartier LLP) *Zr*
Slough *p382*. 01753 810710

McCarthy, Ms L J (Nottinghamshire County Council Legal Services Division)
West Bridgford *p475*. 0115 977 3478

McCarthy, M P (Reed Smith LLP)
London EC2 *p71*. 020 3116 3000

McCarthy, Ms N (Russells) *O Q Ze Zf Zw*
London W1 *p75* 020 7439 8692

McCarthy, Ms O (Breeze & Wyles Solicitors LLP) *K1 Q Zp*
Hertford *p248* 01992 558411

McCarthy, Ms P A (McMillen Hamilton McCarthy) *K1 G D1 K3*
London E3 *p57* 020 8980 6060

McCarthy, P H (Allen & Overy LLP)
London E1 *p5* 020 3088 0000

McCarthy, P J (Merrils Ede Solicitors)
Cardiff *p180* 029 2037 1131

McCarthy, Mrs P L (Rhondda Cynon Taff County Borough Council)
Pentre *p468* 01443 424300

McCarthy, Ms R (Bates Wells & Braithwaite London LLP) *Zd C1*
London EC4 *p11*. 020 7551 7777

MacCarthy, R J (Addleshaw Goddard) *M3*
London EC1 *p4* 020 7606 8855

McCarthy, Miss R L (MLM Cartwright) *E U1*
Cardiff *p179* 029 2046 2562

McCarthy, Mrs R M (Avery Naylor) *K1 Q*
Swansea *p404*. 01792 463276

McCarthy, S G (Flint Bishop Solicitors) *E S1 C1 S2 L*
Derby *p208* 01332 340211

McCarthy, T (Barker & Co)
Hull *p256* 01482 219966

McCartney, Miss C (Aaron & Partners LLP Solicitors) *J1*
Chester *p190* 01244 405555

McCartney, J P (DAC Beachcroft)
London EC4 *p24*. 020 7936 2222

McCartney, Miss L (Bates Wells & Braithwaite London LLP) *J1 J2 Zd*
London EC4 *p11*. 020 7551 7777

MacCartney, Ms M (Reynolds Porter Chamberlain LLP)
London E1 *p71* 020 3060 6000

McCartney, Miss M (Meade-King) *W T2 K4*
Bristol *p163* 0117 926 4121

McCartney, R W (McCartneys) *F2 G H N S1 S2 W Zl*
Feltham *p225* 020 8751 6051

McCaskie, Ms A G (South Derbyshire District Council)
Swadlincote *p473* 01283 221000

McCauley, Mrs C (Paris Smith LLP) *C3 I F1 Ze J2 C1 C2 B1 Zb T1*
Southampton *p386*. 023 8048 2482

McCauley, Ms H A (Hilary McCauley Solicitors Limited) *S1 W*
Cheadle Hulme *p185*. 0161 485 6723

McCavish, K (Shoosmiths)
Reading *p361* . . 0370 086 8800 / 0118 965 8765

McCheyne, E (Penningtons) *Zr N*
Godalming *p231* 01483 791800

McChlery, Mrs Y (Newcastle Upon Tyne City Council)
Newcastle upon Tyne *p466* . 0191 232 8520

McClarry, Miss C L (Jefferies LLP) *N*
Altrincham *p116* 0800 342 3191

McClay, I S (Fosters) *K1 D1*
Norwich *p334* 01603 620508

McClea, N P D (Pinsent Masons LLP) *E L S1 Zc Zn*
Leeds *p276* 0113 244 5000

McClean, A H (CVS Solicitors) *E L S1*
London W1 *p17* 020 7493 2903

McClellan, L J (Palmers) *W K4*
Basildon *p126* 01268 240000

McClelland, Ms L K (Alletsons Ltd) *K1 G K3 D1*
Bridgwater *p157* 01278 456621

McClenaghan, D T (Laytons) *R2 S1 E L*
Guildford *p236*. 01483 407000

McClenan, M S (Bank of Scotland)
Chester *p454* 01244 690000

McClory, Mrs L J (Wrigleys Solicitors LLP) *Zd C1 C2*
Leeds *p278* 0113 244 6100

McCloud, Ms S (Watson Burton LLP) *Zc Zr E K4 P K1 Zj Q N S1 W*
Newcastle upon Tyne *p327* . 0845 901 2100

McCloy, G R (McCloy Legal) *E S1 W C1 Q N F1 J1 T1 L*
Bradford-on-Avon *p155* . . . 01225 866563

McCloy, Mrs J M (McCloy Legal) *M1 N*
Bradford-on-Avon *p155* . . . 01225 866563

McCloy, M C (McCloy Legal) *C1 N P E M2 S1 K1 J1 F1 L Zd Zw Zf*
Bradford-on-Avon *p155* . . . 01225 866563

McCloy, P J (McCloy Legal) *A1 C1 L E F1 G H J1 K1 D1*
Bradford-on-Avon *p155* . . . 01225 866563

McClung, Ms A (Simmons & Simmons)
London EC2 *p79*. 020 7628 2020

McClung, G E (IBM United Kingdom Ltd) *C1 C3 I U1*
London SE1 *p107* 020 7202 3000

McClure, Ms A (Blake Lapthorn) *N Zr*
Chandlers Ford *p184* 023 8090 8090

McClure, C B (Blake Lapthorn) *C1 C2 C3 Ze U2*
Chandlers Ford *p184* 023 8090 8090

McClure, D S (Hartley & Worstenholme) *O Q N B1 F1 L A3 Zq Zr Ze J1 J2 Zk*
Castleford *p183* 01977 732222

McCluskey, Miss B (Hague Lambert) *K1 K3*
Knutsford *p269* 01565 652411

McCluskey, D R (Peters & Peters) *B2 G Q Zg Zq*
London EC4 *p67*. 020 7629 7991

McCluskey, Ms J L (Sternberg Reed) *Zr*
Barking *p123* 020 8591 3366

McCluskey, Ms L K (Metcalfes) *N Q Za*
Bristol *p164* 0117 929 0451

McCluskey, M W (Barnsley Metropolitan Borough Council)
Barnsley *p448* 01226 770770

McCluskie, Ms G (J A Kemp & Co)
London WC1 *p48* 020 7405 3292

McCole, Mrs S G (R G Frisby & Small) *W T2 K4*
Leicester *p279*. 0116 233 5522

McColgan, Mrs C E (Berry Smith LLP) *K1 D1 V*
Bridgend *p157*. 01656 645525

McColgan, M A (Howells LLP) *G H*
Rotherham *p367*. 01709 364000

McColgan, S E (Davies & Partners) *R2 R1 S2 E S1*
Almondsbury *p115*. 01454 619619

McColl, F R (Maxwell Winward LLP) *C1 C2 J1 Zb*
London EC4 *p59*. 020 7651 0000

McColl, I (Gregg Latchams LLP) *C1 C3*
Bristol *p162* 0117 906 9400

McColl, Mrs P M R (SAS Daniels LLP) *J1 Zza*
Stockport *p396*. 0161 475 7676

McColl, R J (Barwells) *E S1 T1 T2*
Peacehaven *p345* 01273 582271

McCombie, I P (hlw Keeble Hawson LLP) *O Q*
Sheffield *p376* 0114 276 5555

McCombie, P J (Davenport Lyons) *E S1 R1 L*
London W1 *p25* 020 7468 2600

McCondach, I (Rochdale Metropolitan Borough Council)
Rochdale *p470*. 01706 647474

McConkey, I F (DAC Beachcroft)
Manchester *p303* 0161 934 3000

McConnell, Ms A (Squire Sanders (UK) LLP)
Manchester *p310* 0161 830 5000

McConnell, E G (Lupton Fawcett) *C1 C2 Zb*
Leeds *p275* 0113 280 2000

McConnell, T J (Davis Blank Furniss) *S1 E W L*
Manchester *p303* 0161 832 3304

McConway, Ms M (Barlow Lyde & Gilbert LLP)
London EC3 *p10*. 020 7247 2277

McCooey, A E (Andrew McCooey & Co) *G H N Zg A3*
Sittingbourne *p380*. 01795 470686

McCool, Ms G M (MPH Solicitors) *N J2*
Manchester *p307* 0161 832 7722

McCord, P J (EAD Solicitors LLP) *M1 P N J1 O Q*
Liverpool *p287*. 0151 734 4339

McCormack, Miss A (Forster Dean Ltd) *N*
Runcorn *p369* 01928 590999

McCormack, Ms C (Michelmores LLP) *E R2 C3 Zu X*
Exeter *p221* 01392 688688

McCormack, C (Barlow Lyde & Gilbert LLP)
London EC3 *p10*. 020 7247 2277

McCormack, Ms C (Bevan Brittan LLP)
Birmingham *p135* 0870 194 1000

McCormack, F D F T (Balfour Beatty PLC)
London SW1 *p104*. 020 7216 6800

McCormack, Ms G (Gillian Radford & Co) *K1 K3 D1 L*
Westminster *p70*. 020 8960 4366

McCormack, J C (South Gloucestershire Council)
Thornbury *p474* 01454 868686

McCormack, J P (McCormacks) *E G H J1 K1 L M1 N P*
Birmingham *p140* 0121 200 2777

McCormack, Mrs L J (Vale Royal Borough Council)
Winsford *p476*. 01606 862862

McCormack, Ms M (Burkill Govier) *O M2 W C1 Zc Zb*
Farnham *p224*. 01252 717171

McCormack, M E (McCormacks) *D1 D2 K1*
London EC3 *p56*. 020 7791 2000

McCormack, P J (The National Trust) *S1 S2 C1*
Swindon *p475* 01793 817400

McCormack, S A (Kenneth Elliott & Rowe) *N Zr Zj Zq*
Romford *p366* 01708 757575

McCormick Paice, Mrs R (Buss Murton LLP) *S1 S2*
Tunbridge Wells *p415* 01892 510222
London SW3 *p66* 020 7591 3333

Mccormick, Mrs A (Lee Rigby Partnership) *W K4*
Leyland *p283* 01772 421748

McCormick, Miss H (Inghams) *L V J1*
Fleetwood *p226* 01253 873481

McCormick, K (Clifford Chance)
London E14 *p20*. 020 7006 1000

McCormick, M N (Neil McCormick) *Q*
Frome *p228* 01373 455700

McCormick, Ms N J (Squire Sanders (UK) LLP)
London EC2 *p81*. 020 7655 1000

McCormick, P D G (McCormicks) *T1 C1 Zf Zd T2 Ze Zk Zw*
Harrogate *p240* 01423 530630

McCorry, D J (Vickers & Co) *N G H*
Ealing *p89*. . . .020 8579 2559 / 8840 3999

McCorry, Miss R M (McCorry Connolly Solicitors)
Romford *p366* 01708 727269

McCourt, E C (Edward McCourt & Co)
Watford *p423* . . . .01923 448401 / 448402

McCourt, Mrs F J (Solihull Magistrates Court)
Solihull *p471*. 0121 705 8101

McCourt, Miss G S (Wedlake Bell LLP) *E Zb S2*
London WC1 *p91* 020 7395 3000

McCourt, Ms R (ASB Law)
Maidstone *p298* 01622 656500

McCourt, S (Gorman Hamilton) *N Q*
Newcastle upon Tyne *p324* . 0191 232 1123

McCoy, Mrs A (Daniel & Edwards) *W S1*
Ramsgate *p359* 01843 594651

MacCracken, Miss C (Birchall Blackburn LLP) *E C1 W*
Preston *p356* 01772 561663

McCracken, I N d C (Kennedys)
London EC3 *p49*. 020 7667 9667

McCracken, Ms M H (Roberts McCracken) *E S1 S2*
Brent *p72* 0870 420 5658

McCraith, D A (Haworth & Nuttall) *K1 K3 N J1 Zp*
Accrington *p114* 01254 236221

McCready, Mrs C (Greenwoods Solicitors LLP) *S2 E S1 W*
Peterborough *p347* 01733 887700

McCreath, Miss K L (Frisby & Co) *B2 G H*
Stafford *p392* 01785 244114

McCreath, R (Archon Solicitors)
London EC4 *p7* 020 7397 9650

McCredie, M A (Biscoes) *K1 D1 G H L Q Ze Zm*
Portsmouth *p354*. 023 9266 0261

McCree, Ms C (Shell International Ltd) *C1*
London SE1 *p109* 020 7934 1234

See p634 for the Key to Work Categories

McCreery, Ms N J (Hertfordshire County Council)
Hertford *p460* 01992 555555

McCrery, Mrs J (Sharp & Partners) *K1 V*
Nottingham *p339*. 0115 959 0055

McCrimmon, S (Jacobs Solicitors) *N*
Ellesmere Port *p217* 0151 355 8481

McCrone, M (Hockfield & Co) *L*
Lambeth *p41*. 020 7582 8784

McCrum, M H (Wheelers) *B1 F1 J1 L O Q*
Aldershot *p115*. 01252 316316

McCubbin, I (DWF) *N Zj*
Manchester *p303* 0161 603 5000

McCue, J D (H2O Law LLP) *Zf Zg Q Zk O Zz*
London EC4 *p37*. 020 7405 4700

MacCuish, A J (Squire Sanders (UK) LLP) *M2 O Q C1 Zc*
Leeds *p277* 0113 284 7000

McCullagh, G (Bosley & Co) *K1 F1 S1 P J1*
Brighton *p159* 01273 608181

McCulloch, Ms A C (Crutes) *C1*
Newcastle upon Tyne *p324* . 0191 233 9700

McCulloch, A J (Bristows) *Ze*
London EC4 *p15*. 020 7400 8000
London EC4 *p46*. 020 7039 5959

McCulloch, Ms E (Waltons & Morse LLP) *A3 Zj O*
London EC3 *p90*. 020 7623 4255

McCulloch, G P (Lovetts PLC) *B1 O*
Guildford *p236*. 01483 457500

McCulloch, I H (Bircham Dyson Bell)
Westminster *p13*. 020 7227 7000

McCulloch, J (Cozens-Hardy LLP) *Q O F2 F1 B1 N L*
Norwich *p334* 01603 625231

McCulloch, M W B (Meadows Fraser LLP) *L S1 E C1 W S2*
Weybridge *p430* 01932 852057

McCulloch, R C M (Reynolds Parry-Jones) *W T2 Zd*
High Wycombe *p250*. 01494 525941

McCullough, D (Sefton Metropolitan Borough Council)
Southport *p472* 01704 533133

McCullough, J D (Disken & Co) *S1 W S2 L Q*
Dewsbury *p210* 01924 464101

McCullough, P J (Graham Coffey & Co)
Manchester *p302* 0161 200 2440

McCullough, P R (TWM Solicitors LLP) *S1*
Leatherhead *p271* 01372 374148

McCullough, Mrs R J (Henmans LLP) *C1 C2 I*
Oxford *p343*. 01865 781000

McCunn, R A (Davies Johnson & Co (Shipping & Commercial Solicitors)) *O B2 Zj*
Plymouth *p349*. 01752 226020

McCurley, Ms C (Beecham Peacock) *G H K1 Zm D1*
Newcastle upon Tyne *p323* . 0191 232 3048

McCusker, A P M (Field Overell) *O Q N*
Coventry *p200*. 024 7622 9582
Leamington Spa *p270* 01926 422101

McCusker, G (City of York Council)
York *p477* 01904 551045

McCutcheon, Mrs D J L (Rodgers & Burton)
London SW13 *p73*. 020 8939 6300

McCutcheon, Mrs E J G (Kent County Council)
Maidstone *p464* 01622 694320

McCutcheon, Mrs J A (Hampshire County Council)
Winchester *p476*. 01962 841841

McDaid, M (Hurlow & Partners) *K1 D1 D2*
Cardiff *p179* 029 2039 6087

McDairmant, Ms C M (Just Employment) *C1 J1 J2 N Zp T2*
Guildford *p236*. 01483 303636

McDermott, C (Bermans LLP) *E O*
Liverpool *p286*. 0151 224 0500

McDermott, Miss C L (Mackrell Turner Garrett) *J1 Q N Zq*
Woking *p437*. 01483 755609

McDermott, D W (Michael W Halsall)
Newton-le-Willows *p330*. . . 01942 727000

McDermott, F I (Singleton Winn McDermott Solicitors) *D1 G H K1 X Zl*
Newcastle upon Tyne *p326* . 0191 265 8817

McDermott, Miss J (McDermott French)
Newton Abbot *p329* 01626 200177

McDermott, Ms J A (Field Seymour Parkes) *J1*
Reading *p360* 0118 951 6200

McDermott, Miss J E (Russell-Cooke LLP) *K3 K1*
London WC1 *p74* 020 7405 6566

McDermott, P (Trowers & Hamlins)
London EC3 *p88*. 020 7423 8000

McDevitt, J F (Cooper Whiteman) *S2 S1 W*
London WC1 *p22* 020 7831 5222

McDonach, A R (Hill Dickinson LLP)
London EC3 *p41*. 020 7283 9033

McDonagh, B (McDonagh Solicitors) *B1 N S1*
Birkenhead *p134*. 0151 650 2150

McDonagh, Miss C R (Carrick Read Solicitors LLP)
Hull *p256* 01482 211160

McDonagh, G A (Harris Cartier LLP) *C1 Zw C2*
London WC2 *p39* 020 7405 7100

McDonagh, Mrs M (Furley Page LLP) *S1*
Whitstable *p431* 01227 274241

McDonagh, Mrs P (Sanders Brickwood) *W S1 T2*
Cirencester *p195*. 01285 654601

McDonagh, Mrs V (Barlow Robbins LLP) *E S2 R2*
Woking *p436*. 01483 748500

McDonald, Ms A (Luton Borough Council)
Luton *p464* 01582 546000

McDonald, Dr A (Environment Agency (Anglian Region))
Peterborough *p468* 01733 371811

McDonald, A C (Treasury Solicitors Department)
London WC2 *p110*. 020 7210 3000

McDonald, A G (Bittermann & Wood) *G H S1 W K1 P J1 M1 F1 V Zl*
North Shields *p330*0191 257 3211 / 259 6806

Macdonald, A I (Fentons) *Q N L*
Failsworth *p223* 0161 682 7101

McDonald, A J (Thompsons (formerly Robin/Brian Thompson & Partners)) *N*
Newcastle upon Tyne *p327* . 0191 269 0400

McDonald, A J (Uniq PLC)
Gerrards Cross *p459*. 01753 276186

McDonald, A T (Last Cawthra Feather LLP) *O B1*
Leeds *p275* 0113 244 0876

MacDonald, Ms B (Lawson Lewis & Co) *D1 J1 K1*
Eastbourne *p215*. 01323 720142

MacDonald, B (Druces LLP) *C1 C2 Zo J1*
London EC2 *p27*. 020 7638 9271

McDonald, Ms B T (BMD Law) *R2 J1 C1 F1 S2 E L O*
Liverpool *p286*. 0151 222 5777

McDonald, C A (Hallett & Co) *A1 S1 S2 W*
Ashford *p119* 01233 625711

McDonald, C G (Marsden Rawsthorn LLP) *S1 S2 W E*
Preston *p357* 01772 799600

McDonald, Miss C L (Newbys) *E A1 W S1 T2*
Middlesbrough *p315* .01642 247717 / 247967

McDonald, D E J (Stephenson Harwood)
London EC2 *p82*. 020 7329 4422

MacDonald, Mrs F (Russell-Cooke LLP) *W T2*
Kingston upon Thames *p267*. 020 8546 6111

MacDonald, Miss F M (Ferguson Solicitors) *J1 Zp O*
London EC4 *p31*. 020 7822 2999

McDonald, G (SA Law) *C1*
St Albans *p390* 01727 798000

MacDonald, Ms H E (Aitken Associates) *K1 K2 D1 S1 D2 W*
Islington *p4* 020 7700 6006

MacDonald, I C S (Squire Sanders (UK) LLP)
Birmingham *p142* 0121 222 3000

McDonald, I J (Mayer Brown International LLP) *B1 O*
London EC2 *p59*. 020 3130 3000

MacDonald, I N (Bates N V H) *C1 E I P R1 W*
London WC2 *p11* 020 7936 2930

McDonald, J (Hogan Lovells International LLP)
London EC1 *p42*. 020 7296 2000

McDonald, J (Salans) *T1 M2*
London EC4 *p76*. 020 7429 6000

McDonald, Mrs J (Gross & Co) *K1*
Bury St Edmunds *p171* . . . 01284 763333

Macdonald, Mrs J V (Birketts LLP) *E*
Ipswich *p262*. 01473 232300

Macdonald, Miss K (HSR Law (Hayes, Son & Richmond)) *S1 W*
Doncaster *p211* 01302 347800
Gainsborough *p228* 01427 613831

MacDonald, K E (Rotherham Metropolitan Borough Council)
Rotherham *p470*. 01709 382121

McDonald, Ms K M (Gittins McDonald) *D2 K1 D1 K3 L*
Wrexham *p442* 01978 291662

Macdonald, K M (Vance Harris) *C2 E S1 S2*
London E14 *p89*. 020 7538 5232

McDonald, Miss K M (Gilbert Stephens) *N J1 Q*
Exeter *p221* 01392 424242

McDonald, L (Ashurst LLP)
London EC2 *p7* 020 7638 1111

McDonald, Ms L (Kingsley Napley) *G H B2*
London EC1 *p50*. 020 7814 1200

McDonald, L (Ince & Co Services Ltd)
London E1 *p44* 020 7481 0010

McDonald, M (Ashurst LLP)
London EC2 *p7* 020 7638 1111

McDonald, M (Allen & Overy LLP)
London E1 *p5* 020 3088 0000

Macdonald, Ms M (Bird & Bird LLP) *Ze*
London EC4 *p13*. 020 7415 6000

McDonald, M C (Hill Dickinson LLP) *E R1 R2 S2 L*
Liverpool *p288*. 0151 600 8000

Macdonald, Miss P M (Crown Prosecution Service Avon & Somerset)
Bristol *p451* 0117 930 2800

McDonald, Ms R A (Roberta McDonald) *D1 D2*
Birmingham *p140* 0121 449 6821

McDonald, R W (Taylor Wessing) *E S1*
London EC4 *p86*. 020 7300 7000

Macdonald, S H (Farrer & Co LLP)
London WC2 *p31* 020 3375 7000

McDonald, S M (Hallinan Blackburn Gittings & Nott) *G H*
Westminster *p38*. 020 7233 3999

McDonald, W (Jones Day) *C1*
London EC4 *p46*. 020 7039 5959

McDonald, W (McDonald & Co) *D1 E G H K1 L N O Q S1 Zj Zf Zi Zl Zv*
Westminster *p56*. 020 7834 2679

MacDonald Bridge, R (King Prior Macdonald Bridge) *Ze Zf U2 Zk Zz U1 I Zza*
Rochester *p366* 01634 272720

MacDonald-Preston, S (British Midland Airways Ltd)
Castle Donington *p453*. . . . 01332 854089

McDonnell, A K (Hill Dickinson LLP) *E C1*
Liverpool *p288*. 0151 600 8000

McDonnell, J A (John A McDonnell) *W*
Norwich *p335* 01508 570387

MacDonnell, L (Reynolds Porter Chamberlain LLP)
London E1 *p71* 020 3060 6000

McDonnell, M J (Coles Miller Solicitors LLP) *J1 C1 Q O*
Poole *p352* 01202 673011
Westminster *p89*. 020 7526 6000

McDonnell, M J (Cohen Cramer Solicitors) *Q O F1 L N P R1 V Zq Zk Zp Ze*
Leeds *p272* 0800 542 9408

McDonnell, P (Addleshaw Goddard)
Manchester *p300* 0161 934 6000

McDoom, R A (John Bays & Co) *S2 S1 E L Q*
Haringey *p11* 020 8881 3609
Haringey *p26* 020 8808 3237

MacDougald, R H A (Winckworth Sherwood LLP) *W S1 Zd*
London SE1 *p92*. 020 7593 5000

McDougall, A (Ashurst LLP) *N P Zc*
London EC2 *p7* 020 7638 1111

McDougall, A H (Plexus Law (A Trading Name of Parabis Law LLP)) *A3 J2 N Zj*
Leeds *p276* 0844 245 4100

Macdougall, Miss J (Williams MacDougall & Campbell) *G H K1 K2*
Worthing *p442*. 01903 214186

MacDougall, M (Speechly Bircham LLP) *C1 C2*
London EC4 *p81*. 020 7427 6400

MacDougall, Miss R (Beecham Peacock) *G H*
Newcastle upon Tyne *p323* . 0191 232 3048

McDowall, J I (Pearson Rowe) *S1 W E L*
Birmingham *p141* 0121 236 7388

McDowell, Mrs A J (Avril McDowell) *S1 W*
Twickenham *p416* 020 8891 1566

McDowell, Ms H A (CMS Cameron McKenna LLP) *E*
London EC3 *p17*. 020 7367 3000

McDowell, Ms H J (Peters & Peters) *G H N O P Q*
London EC4 *p67*. 020 7629 7991

McDowell, R J (Napthens LLP) *M1 P W*
Preston *p357* 01772 888444

Macduff, D (Silver Fitzgerald) *K1 K3*
Cambridge *p175*. 01223 562001

Mace, A J (Squire Sanders (UK) LLP)
London EC2 *p81*. 020 7655 1000

Mace, Ms J (Quastel Midgen LLP) *K1*
London W1 *p70* 020 7908 2525

Mace, Ms K (Fishburns) *Zj O Q Zq Zo A3 Zc*
London EC3 *p32*. 020 7280 8888

Mace, Miss S (Central Buckinghamshire Magistrates Court)
Aylesbury *p448* 01296 554350

McElhinney, Miss S J (Kemp Little LLP) *C1 C2 U1 U2 I Zb*
London EC2 *p48*. 020 7600 8080

McElhone, S J (Hewitsons) *C1 C2*
Cambridge *p174*. 01223 461155

McElligott, P D P (Penningtons) *E*
London EC2 *p66*. 020 7457 3000

McElvaney, J (Derbyshire County Council)
Matlock *p465* 01629 580000

McEney, Ms E C (Fox Williams) *O*
London EC2 *p33*. 020 7628 2000

Mcerlean, Ms M (Geoffrey Leaver Solicitors LLP) *O Q*
Milton Keynes *p317* 01908 692769

McEvoy, Ms C (Brabners Chaffe Street) *E*
Liverpool *p286*. 0151 600 3000

McEvoy, Miss M T (Neves) *K1 D1 K2 K3 A3*
Luton *p295* 01582 725311

McEwan, K B (Gregg Latchams LLP) *N L O Q*
Bristol *p162* 0117 906 9400

McEwen, G A (Barlow Lyde & Gilbert LLP)
London EC3 *p10*. 020 7247 2277

McEwen, G P (McEwen Parkinson) *C1 O X Zd W Q K1 J1 K3*
Westminster *p56*. 020 7487 4361

McEwen, Ms J C (The College of Law) *E*
London WC1 *p105*. 0800 289997

McEwen, N A (Blake Lapthorn)
London EC1 *p13*. 020 7405 2000

Macey, D (FBC Manby Bowdler LLP) *E*
Telford *p409*. 01952 292129

Macey, D V (Leeds City Council)
Leeds *p462* 0113 224 3513

Macey, T J (Macey & Co) *C1 D1 G H K1 L M1 N P S1*
Greenwich *p56*. 020 8853 2710

Macey-Dare, E J (Lee Bolton Monier-Williams) *J1 O Q N B1 Zr F1 L Zq*
Westminster *p52*. 020 7222 5381

McFadden, J H (McFaddens LLP) *B1 C1 J1 K1 M2 S1 W*
London EC2 *p56*. 020 7588 9080

Macfadyen, M R (Charles Russell LLP) *Zd S1 T2*
London EC4 *p19*. 020 7203 5000

McFadyen, S S (Lupton Fawcett) *N*
Leeds *p275* 0113 280 2000

McFall, Mrs H J (Cullimore Dutton) *Zx W K4 T2*
Chester *p190* 01244 356789

McFall, M (McDermott Will & Emery UK LLP) *C1 C2*
London EC2 *p56*. 020 7577 6900

McFarland, P R E (Bridge McFarland) *E W S1 S2 A1*
Market Rasen *p312* 01673 843723
Louth *p294* 01507 605883

McFarlane, Ms C A (Burges Salmon)
Bristol *p161* 0117 939 2000

McFarlane, Miss C C (West Berkshire Council)
Newbury *p466* 01635 42400

Macfarlane, I (Simmons & Simmons)
London EC2 *p79*. 020 7628 2020

McFarlane, Miss J A (Royal Mail Group)
London EC4 *p109* 020 7250 2468

McFarlane, Ms K F (CMHT Solicitors) *Zm K1*
Walsall *p420*. 01922 646400

McFarlane, Miss K F (CMHT Solicitors) *Zm V K3*
Brownhills *p167* 01543 372347

MacFarlane, Miss M P (Fitzhugh Gates) *E G*
Brighton *p159* 01273 686811

Macfarlane, N R (Hogan Lovells International LLP)
London EC1 *p42*. 020 7296 2000

McFarlane, R G (Dyne Drewett Solicitors Ltd) *W S1 Zd A1*
Sherborne *p378* 01935 813691

McFarlane, S D (Yorkshire Water Services Ltd)
Bradford *p451* 01274 804159

Macfarlane, Mrs V (Roger Brooker & Co) *S1 S2*
Chelmsford *p186*. 01245 351924

McFarlane-Watts, N H (McFarlane Watts & Company Solicitors) *C1 I O Ze Q*
Watlington *p424* 0700 077 7529

Mcgann, Mrs E K (Wortley Redmayne Kershaw) *K1 D1*
Chelmsford *p187*. 01245 491122

McGarrigle, Ms S (David & Snape) *N Zr*
Bridgend *p157* 01656 661115

McGarrity, J J (Geoffrey Leaver Solicitors LLP) *N D1 K1*
Milton Keynes *p317* 01908 692769

6

McGarry, K M (Barker Gooch & Swailes) *S1 W*
London N21 *p9* .020 8886 5928 / 8886 5734

McGarry, M B (Richard Johnson & Partners) *A1 A2 S2 E T1 T2 W S1 R1 L Zl K4*
Hawes *p245* 01969 667000

McGarry, M G (Horwich Cohen Coghlan) *N*
Manchester *p305* 0161 830 4600

McGarva, Miss C L (Bhatia Best) *H G*
Nottingham *p336*. 0115 950 3231

McGarva, J (Hill Dickinson LLP) *J1 Zj G*
Chester *p190* 01244 896600

McGauley, A J (Keelys LLP) *O B1 Q J1*
Lichfield *p284* 01543 420000

McGee Osborne, C M (SNR Denton) *C1*
London EC4 *p75*. 020 7242 1212

McGee, A (Leigh Turton Dixon) *K1 N*
Middlesbrough *p315* 01642 241101

McGee, Miss T (Wace Morgan) *C1 S2 E*
Shrewsbury *p379* 01743 280100

McGeever, B G (Gateley LLP) *B1 J1 M1 N P K1 Zl Zt*
Birmingham *p138* 0121 234 0000

McGeever, Miss C (Telent PLC)
London CV3 *p110* 024 7656 2000

MacGeogh, Ms S (Kennedys) *Zj*
London EC3 *p49*. 020 7667 9667

McGeough, J D (Pemberton Greenish LLP) *E S2*
London SW3 *p66* 020 7591 3333

McGeown, P D (Clifton Ingram LLP) *T2 W Zo V Zd*
Wokingham *p437* 0118 978 0099

McGettigan, J G (Grindeys LLP) *Zj Q N Zr*
Stoke-on-Trent *p397*. 01782 846441

McGhee, Mrs O (Edwards Duthie) *J1*
London E6 *p29* 020 8514 9000

McGhie, Mrs B J (Michelmores LLP) *Zr N*
Exeter *p221* 01392 688688

McGhie, J H (Hewitt Burrough & Co) *G H M1 K1 P Zl*
Dartford *p207* 01322 273833

McGill, D J (Burnetts) *C1*
Carlisle *p181*. 01228 552222
Carlisle *p182*. 01228 552222

McGill, M (Sills & Betteridge LLP) *S1 S2*
Lincoln *p285*. 01522 542211

McGill, Ms N (Howard Kennedy LLP) *Zf*
London W1 *p48* 020 7636 1616

McGillivray, M R (Clifford Chance)
London E14 *p20*. 020 7006 1000

McGillivray, Ms S (AstraZeneca)
Macclesfield *p464* 01625 582828

McGilvray, Mrs P J (Daniel Curry & Co) *K1 D1 D2*
Croydon *p205* 020 8680 2188

McGinley, P (Collins Solicitors) *N J1*
Watford *p423* 01923 223324

McGinn, D J (Hill Dickinson LLP) *O Q F1 B1 Zm*
Liverpool *p288*. 0151 600 8000

McGinn, Miss J L (Addies) *K3 K1 L*
Fleetwood *p226* 01253 772128

McGinn, N S (Cheshire County Council)
Chester *p454* 01244 602382

McGinty, E (Ewings & Co) *G H L S1 V*
London SE20 *p30* 020 8778 1126

McGiue, C D (Coupe Bradbury) *C1 L J1 Q W T1 T2 Zi*
Lytham *p296*. 01253 736670

McGivern, Miss L (David Gray Solicitors) *D1 K1*
Newcastle upon Tyne *p324* . 0191 232 9547

McGiveron, A T (SGH Martineau LLP) *C1*
Birmingham *p142* 0870 763 2000

McGladdery, J (Curtis Davis Garrard) *Za*
Uxbridge *p417*. 020 8734 2800

McGlade, S (Eastgate Assistance Ltd)
Colchester *p455*. 0870 523 4500

McGlennon, Miss D (Edmondson Hall) *K3 K1*
Newmarket *p327*. 01638 560556

McGlinchey, Mrs S L (McGlinchey & Co) *S1*
Cheam *p186*. 020 8330 7979

McGloin, Mrs E (Elaine McGloin) *L R1 S1 S2 W*
East Grinstead *p215*. 01342 328000

McGlone, Miss E M (Neves Solicitors) *J1*
Milton Keynes *p317* 01908 304560

McGlory, Ms E (Cartwright King)
Leicester *p279*. 0116 253 9222

McGlynn, G (Sylvester Mackett) Zr Q Zl J1
Trowbridge p414. . . . . . . 01225 755621

McGoay, Ms S (Bates Wells & Braithwaite London LLP) E S2 R2 Zh L Zd
London EC4 p11. . . . . . . 020 7551 7777

McGoldrick, J (JMW Solicitors) G H K1 M1 D1 S1
Manchester p306 . . . . . . 0845 872 6666

McGoldrick, Mrs J P (Cannock Chase District Council)
Cannock p453. . . . . 01543 462621

McGoldrick, P A (Bond Pearce LLP)
London EC3 p14. . . . . . . 0845 415 0000

McGonagle, G D (Abrahams Dresden) C1 C2 F2 F1 U2 Zf
London EC1 p3 . . . . 020 7251 3663

McGonigal, P (Barlow Lyde & Gilbert LLP) Zj
London EC3 p10. . . . . . . 020 7247 2277

McGonigal, Ms R (Kaim Todner Ltd) K1 D1 K2
Islington p47. . . . . 020 7700 0070

McGonnell, Ms L (Hadaway & Hadaway) N Q K1 B1 L F1 W O
North Shields p330 . . . . . 0191 257 0382

McGorian, Ms S J (Hill Dickinson LLP) E R1 R2 S2 L
Liverpool p288. . . . . 0151 600 8000

McGough, Mrs C M (Mid Sussex District Council)
Haywards Heath p460. . . . 01444 458166

McGovern, Ms J (Stanley De Leon) K1
Potters Bar p355. . . . . . . 01707 657277

McGovern, P J (Farrell Matthews & Weir) G H
London W6 p31 . . . . 020 8741 1482

McGovern, S G (Society of Lloyd's)
London EC3 p107 . . . . . . 020 7327 1000

McGovern, Miss T (North Devon District Council)
Barnstaple p448. . . . . . . 01271 327711

McGowan, Ms A (Langleys) D1 K1 Zu
York p445 . . . . 01904 610886

McGowan, A G (Waugh & Co) W S1 K4 S2
Haywards Heath p246 . . . . 01444 451666

McGowan, Mrs A J (Stallard March & Edwards) O Q N Zq
Worcester p440 . . . . 01905 613404

McGowan, Ms C (Scott Fowler) C1 S2 E
Northampton p331. . . . . . 01604 750506

McGowan, M (Hewitsons) E S2 R2
Cambridge p174. . . . . . . 01223 461155

McGowan, M T (Shearman & Sterling LLP) T1
London EC2 p78. . . . . . . 020 7655 5000

McGowan, P E (Clifford Chance)
London E14 p20 . . . . 020 7006 1000

McGowan, P J (BRM Solicitors) N
Chesterfield p191 . . . . . . 01246 555111

McGowan, W (Bear Stearns)
London E14 p104 . . . . . . 020 7516 6000

McGown, D M (Allen & Overy LLP)
London E1 p5 . . . . 020 3088 0000

McGrane, R J (DLA Piper UK LLP) O
London EC2 p24. . . . . . . 0870 011 1111

McGrath, Ms C A (Taylor Wessing)
London EC4 p86. . . . . . . 020 7300 7000

McGrath, D (Rosleys) K1
Nottingham p338. . . . . . . 0115 958 0584

McGrath, Miss E (Mossop & Bowser) K1 J1 Q K3
Holbeach p251. . . . . 01406 422651

McGrath, G A (Andrew Keenan & Co) G H B2
London SE20 p48 . . . . . . 020 8659 0332

McGrath, G J (McGrath & Co) G H J1 L M1 P V F1 W Zl Zp Zm
Birmingham p140 . . . . . . 0121 643 4121
Birmingham p140 . . . . . . 0121 643 4124
Birmingham p140 . . . . . . 0121 643 4828

McGrath, Mrs J A (J McGrath) S1 W
Sutton Coldfield p403 . . . . 0121 355 4749

McGrath, K T (The Smith Partnership) G H
Leicester p281. . . . . 0116 255 6292

McGrath, M J (DAC Beachcroft)
Winchester p433. . . . . . . 01962 705500

McGrath, P (Taylor Walton LLP)
Luton p295 . . . . 01582 731161

McGrath, P (Calderdale Metropolitan BC Corporate Services Directorate)
Halifax p460. . . . . 01422 357257

McGrath, P G (Withers LLP) C1
London EC4 p92. . . . . . . 020 7597 6000

McGrath, P V (Jackamans) N J1 F1 K1 L
Ipswich p262. . . . . 01473 255591

McGrath, Miss S (Morrison & Foerster (UK) LLP) C1 C2
London EC2 p62. . . . . . . 020 7920 4000

McGrath, S A (Payne Skillington) A1 E F1 L N Q S1
Coventry p200. . . . . 024 7663 3044

McGrath, V H (Vickers & Co) G H
Ealing p89. . . .020 8579 2559 / 8840 3999

McGrath, Mrs Z (Sternberg Reed) K1
Barking p123 . . . . 020 8591 3366

McGraw, T J (Whitfields) C1 E F1 G H K1 P S1 W
Formby p227 . . . . 01704 878501

McGreevy, Ms G (Hogan Lovells International LLP)
London EC1 p42. . . . . . . 020 7296 2000

McGreevy, Miss M (Broudie Jackson Canter) Zm
Liverpool p286. . . . . 0151 227 1429

McGregor, A (Ashurst LLP)
London EC2 p7 . . . . 020 7638 1111

McGregor, Ms C (Maples Solicitors LLP) D1 J1 K1 Q
Spalding p389 . . . . 01775 722261

MacGregor, Ms C (Kennedys) Zj
London EC3 p49. . . . . . . 020 7667 9667

MacGregor, Mrs E M (Ziadies) W
London SW9 p94 . . . . . . 020 7737 0934

MacGregor, Miss E S (Thompsons (formerly Robin/Brian Thompson & Partners)) P N M1 J1 F1 Zc
Bristol p165 . . . . 0117 304 2400

MacGregor, I F (Lees Solicitors LLP) S1 E C1 R2 S2 U2
Birkenhead p134. . . . . . . 0151 647 9381

MacGregor, Ms J A (Lees Solicitors LLP) W K4
Birkenhead p134. . . . . . . 0151 647 9381

McGregor, J R (McGregors) G Q H N F1 E O C1 W
Tamworth p407 . . . . 01827 313999

McGregor, Miss L H (Blake Lapthorn) C1 C2 C3 Ze J1 M1
London EC1 p13. . . . . . . 020 7405 2000

Macgregor, M J (Gibson & Co) A1 K1 S1 W
Hexham p249 . . . . 01434 602131

McGregor, S J (Fraser Dawbarns) O Q G J1 N
March p312 . . . . 01354 602880
Wisbech p435 . . . . 01945 461456

McGregor-Johnson, S (Wansbroughs) Q P O N Zt C2 C1
Devizes p210 . . . . 01380 733300

McGrigor, R I (Barlow Robbins LLP) W
Woking p436. . . . . 01483 748500

McGrorty, C J (The Merriman Partnership) W S1 E A1 Zd Zl Zm
Marlborough p313 . . . . . . 01672 512244

McGrory, K (Shepherd + Wedderburn LLP)
London EC4 p78. . . . . . . 020 7429 4900

McGruer, G (Blake Lapthorn) R1 E P
Oxford p342. . . . . 01865 248607

McGruer, G E (Blake Lapthorn) E R1 Zc
Portsmouth p354. . . . . . . 023 9222 1122

McGuigan, S (Veale Wasbrough Vizards) E S1
Bristol p165 . . . . 0117 925 2020

McGuiness, Ms A M (Moss Solicitors LLP) W K4 T2
Loughborough p293 . . . . . 01509 217770

McGuiness, Mrs J (Beswicks) D1 D2 K1
Hanley p239. . . . . 01782 205000

McGuiness, S D (Persimmon PLC)
Northampton p467. . . . . . 01604 884600

McGuinness, D (Harold Stock & Co) N
Failsworth p223 . . . . 0161 682 2400

McGuinness, J (Forshaws Davies Ridgway LLP) A1 Zb C1 F1 Q N Zu W
Warrington p422. . . . . . . 01925 230000

McGuinness, Mrs S (Bolt Burdon) J1 Zp
Islington p14. . . . . 020 7288 4700

McGuinness, T (Leeds City Council)
Leeds p462 . . . . 0113 224 3513

McGuire, A M (Eddowes Perry & Osbourne) E W S1
Sutton Coldfield p403 . . . . 0121 686 9444

McGuire, Miss C L (Thomas Andrews & Partners) K1 S1 W D1 L F1
Wrexham p442 . . . . 01978 291506

McGuire, Ms F L (Gartmore Investment Management PLC)
London EC3 p106 . . . . . . 020 7782 2000

McGuire, J F (Morrish Solicitors LLP) N
Leeds p276 . . . . 0113 245 0733

McGuire, Mrs J M (Barnsley Magistrates Court)
Barnsley p448. . . . . 01226 320000

McGuire, Miss N J (Addleshaw Goddard)
Manchester p300 . . . . . . 0161 934 6000

McGuire, S P (Henry Hughes & Hughes) E S1
London SW16 p40. . . . . . 020 8765 2700

McGuirk, Ms R (Shoosmiths)
Birmingham p142 0370 086 4000 / 0121 335 4440

McGurk, A (Peasegoods)
Manchester p308 . . . . . . 0161 205 2772

McGurk, Ms A (Harbottle & Lewis LLP)
London W1 p38 . . . . 020 7667 5000

McGurk, Ms R M (Hansells) S1 S2
Norwich p334 . . . . 01603 615731

Macharaga, D T (Mills & Reeve) E R1 S2 A1 P Zh L R2
Birmingham p140 . . . . . . 0121 454 4000

McHardy, D K (Family Law Associates LLP) K1 K2 K3
Haringey p30 . . . . 020 8342 7760

Machell, Miss E (Pannone LLP)
Manchester p308 . . . . . . 0161 909 3000

Macheng, M (Anthony Collins Solicitors LLP) Zb Ze C2
Birmingham p137 . . . . . . 0121 200 3242

Machin, A (Leeds City Council) J1 Zp
Leeds p462 . . . . 0113 224 3513
Leeds p277 . . . . 0113 284 7000

Machin, Ms E A (Squire Sanders (UK) LLP)
Leeds p277 . . . . 0113 284 7000

Machin, I T (Stamp Jackson and Procter) E A1 S2
Hull p258 . . . . 01482 324591

Machin, R J (Co-operative Insurance Society Ltd)
Manchester p464 . . . . . . 0161 832 8686

Machin, Miss S (Barker Son & Isherwood LLP) K1 M1 P N G J1 F1 H B1 W
Andover p118 . . . . 01264 353411

Machin-Jefferies, Ms M (Charles Platel Solicitors) J1 S1 S2 W E
Wokingham p437 . . . . . . 0118 978 4866

Machowski, T (Quality Solicitors Gruber Garratt) N
Oldham p341 . . . . 0161 665 3502

Machray, I E (Field Seymour Parkes) J1
Reading p360 . . . . 0118 951 6200

Machray, M (CVS Solicitors)
London W1 p17 . . . . 020 7493 2903

McHugh, G (McHugh Solicitors) J1 Q S1 N
Newcastle under Lyme p323. 01782 628888

McHugh, Ms L (Bates Wells & Braithwaite London LLP) Zd C1
London EC4 p11. . . . . . . 020 7551 7777

McHugh, P J (Challinors) M1 P N F1
Birmingham p136 . . . . . . 0121 212 9393

McHugh, Miss R (Marsh & McLennan Companies, Inc) Q N
London EC3 p108 . . . . . . 020 7357 1000

McHugo, J H A (Trowers & Hamlins) C1
London EC3 p88. . . . . . . 020 7423 8000

Macias Rial, I (Napthens LLP) E
Preston p357 . . . . 01772 888444

Maciejewski, Ms D E (Radcliffes Le Brasseur) S2 E S1
Westminster p70. . . . . . . 020 7222 7040

McIlveen, Ms H (AMD Solicitors) W T2 T1 K4
Bristol p160 . . . . 0117 962 1460

McIlveen, T (Chesterfield Law Centre)
Chesterfield p455 . .01246 550674 / 204570

McIlveen, W (AstraZeneca)
Macclesfield p464 . . . . . . 01625 582828

McIlwaine, Mrs K (Chester City Council)
Chester p454 . . . . 01244 324324

McIlwaine, S P (Ormerods) N Q B1 K1 Zj Zk
Croydon p205 . . . . 020 8686 5000

McIlwee, R P (Clifford Chance)
London E14 p20. . . . . . . 020 7006 1000

McIndoe, G (Robert Lizar) Zi
Manchester p307 . . . . . . 0161 226 2319

McInerney, B S (Lovegrove & Eliot) S1 E C1 L W R1 M1 B1 S2 Zl C2 R2
Windsor p434 . . . . 01753 851133

MacInnes, Mrs C M (Tina MacInnes) Zm W K4
Swanage p404. . . . . 01929 427227

McInnes, D J (Ince & Co Services Ltd)
London E1 p44 . . . . 020 7481 0010

McInnes, H (Howes Percival LLP)
Norwich p334 . . . . 01603 762103

McInnes, S C (Pritchard Englefield) Q O S2 E S1
London EC2 p69. . . . . . . 020 7972 9720

McIntegart, G T (DWF) C1 C2
Liverpool p287. . . . . 0151 907 3000

McIntosh, Mrs F E (Cripps Harries Hall LLP) S1
Tunbridge Wells p415 . . . . 01892 515121

McIntosh, I W (Addleshaw Goddard) C1 J1 Zb
Leeds p271 . . . . 0113 209 2000
Manchester p300 . . . . . . 0161 934 6000

McIntosh, J R (Ford Simey LLP) G H K1
Exmouth p222. . .01395 272241 / 0800 169 3741

McIntosh, M (K&L Gates LLP)
London EC4 p47. . . . . . . 020 7648 9000

McIntosh, M S (Cripps Harries Hall LLP) Q N G O Zr Zl
Tunbridge Wells p415 . . . . 01892 515121

McIntosh, Miss N (Keoghs LLP) N
Bolton p149 . . . . 01204 677000

Mcintosh, W L (Barlow Lyde & Gilbert LLP) A3 Zza O Q Zo Zq
London EC3 p10. . . . . . . 020 7247 2277

McIntyre Ross, Ms K (Thompsons (formerly Robin/Brian Thompson & Partners))
Plymouth p350. . . . . 01752 675810

McIntyre, Miss E A (Eric Robinson Solicitors) T2 W
Chandlers Ford p184 . . . . 023 8025 4676

McIntyre, G (Clarke Willmott)
Bristol p162 0845 209 1000 / 0117 305 6000

McIntyre, I W R (Maxwell Winward LLP) C1 C2 I J1
London EC4 p59. . . . . . . 020 7651 0000

MacIntyre, S A J (Knocker & Foskett) K1 O N Zr L
Sevenoaks p374. . . . . . . 01732 459931

McIver, Mrs T A (Thomas Higgins & Co) O
Wallasey p419. . . . . 0151 630 8006

McIvor, M (Freemans) S1 S2 E
Newcastle upon Tyne p324 . 0191 222 1030

Mack, I S (Starbuck & Mack) Zc C1 S2 E Zd K3 K4 K1 M2 C2 R1 R2 W
Fareham p224. . . . . 01329 285341

Mack, N (Macks Solicitors) B1 E K4 J1 K1 J2 Zm S1 T2 W N Q O
Middlesbrough p315 . . . . . 01642 252828

McKail, T O (Russell & Russell) G H
Bolton p149 . . . . 01204 399299

Mackarness, S P R (Mackarness & Lunt) E W S1 S2 K4
Petersfield p348 . . . . 01730 265111

Mckay, A (McKays Solicitors) B1 C1 Q O
Liverpool p289. . . . . 0151 702 4858

Mckay, Miss B (Lowick McKay) S1 K1 N W S2 J1 F1 D2 Zl Zh Ze Zr Zy
Cheadle p185 . . . . 0161 491 5588

McKay, B J (Treasury Solicitors Department)
London WC2 p110. . . . . . 020 7210 3000

Mackay, Ms C (LG Lawyers)
London SE1 p50. . . . . . . 020 7379 0000

McKay, Mrs C J (Muckle LLP) E S1
Newcastle upon Tyne p325 . 0191 211 7777

McKay, C J (Wilkin Chapman Grange Solicitors) N
Grimsby p235 . . . . 01472 262626

McKay, D J (Feld McKay & Donner Solicitors) N
Rochdale p365. . . . . 01706 645656

Mackay, D J (Proddow Mackay) B1 K1 M1
Maidenhead p298 . . . . . . 01628 776847

Mackay, Mrs E P (Stewarts Law LLP) K1 K3
London EC4 p83. . . . . . . 020 7822 8000

Mackay, G (Ashfords LLP) C1 U2 Ze Zza C2
Bristol p160 . . . . 0117 321 8000

Mackay, J (Holman Fenwick Willan)
London EC3 p42. . . . . . . 020 7264 8000

McKay, Ms L (IBB Solicitors) E R1 S1
Uxbridge p417. . . . . 0845 638 1381

Mackay, M B (Taylor Wessing) E R1 O A1 Zh
London EC4 p86. . . . . . . 020 7300 7000

McKay, N I (Gilbert Stephens) E S2
Exeter p221 . . . . 01392 424242
Ottery St Mary p342 . . . . . 01404 812228

Mackay, Ms N J (Gordons LLP)
Leeds p273 . . . . 0113 227 0100

Mackay, R I (Mackay & Co)
Birmingham p140 . . . . . . 0121 454 1814

McKay, R J (Berg Legal) C2 C1 Zb
Manchester p301 . . . . . . 0161 833 9211

Mckay, S A (McKay Law)
Leeds p275 . . . . .0845 23 5571

McKay, S J (Squire Sanders (UK) LLP)
London EC2 p81. . . . . . . 020 7655 1000

McKay, T (Jones Day) B1
London EC4 p46. . . . . . . 020 7039 5959

McKay, W (Muckle LLP) E R2 S2 Zc
Newcastle upon Tyne p325 . 0191 211 7777

McKeague, M (Walker Morris) Q L
Leeds p277 . . . . 0113 283 2500

MacKean, A N (Bond Pearce LLP) E
Southampton p385. . . . . . 0845 415 0000

McKeating, Miss C (Co-operative Insurance Society Ltd) N O Q
Manchester p464 . . . . . . 0161 832 8686

Mckechnie, Mrs D (Hamers Solicitors) K4 T2 W S1
Hull p257 . . . . 01482 326666

McKee, Miss J (Taylor Wessing) E
London EC4 p86. . . . . . . 020 7300 7000

Mckee, M (DLA Piper UK LLP)
London EC2 p24. . . . . . . 0870 011 1111

McKee, M A (CIT Group (UK) Ltd)
Bracknell p451. . . . . 01344 827200

McKee, P H (Black Graf & Co) S1 S2 E C1
London NW3 p13 . . . . . . 020 7586 1141

McKee, R J (DWF) N O Q
Liverpool p287. . . . . 0151 907 3000

McKeever, M J (Butcher Burns LLP) L Q O I R1
London WC1 p16 . . . . . . 020 7713 7100

Macken, Ms K (Bindmans LLP) Zr N
London WC1 p12 . . . . . . 020 7833 4433

McKendrick, Ms O (Linklaters LLP)
London EC2 p54. . . . . . . 020 7456 2000

McKendrick, Miss R S (Ashworths Solicitors) S1
London SW19 p8 . . . . . . 0845 370 1000

McKendry, Ms S (Official Solicitor and Public Trustee) X Q Zd
London WC2 p108. . . . . . 020 7911 7127

McKenna, B J (B J McKenna & Co Solicitors) K1 D1 K3 W N
Stockport p396. . . . . 0161 432 5757

McKenna, Ms B M (Unison) J1 N O Q G P K1
London WC1 p110. . . . . . 020 7388 2366

McKenna, Ms C (Robert Lizar) Zm
Manchester p307 . . . . . . 0161 226 2319

McKenna, Miss C M P (Squire Sanders (UK) LLP) Zo
Leeds p277 . . . . 0113 284 7000

McKenna, Miss D (Benussi & Co) K3 K1
Birmingham p135 . . . . . . 0121 248 4001

McKenna, J (Pilkington PLC)
St Helens p472 . . . . 01744 28882

McKenna, J (Paul Crowley & Co) D1 K1
Liverpool p287. . . . . 0151 264 7363

McKenna, J L (Howe & Spender) G H
Neath p320 . . . . 01639 881571

McKenna, M J (Hill Dickinson LLP) P N G J2 B2 Zr
Manchester p305 . . . . . . 0161 817 7200

Mckenna, M L (Bromsgrove & Redditch Magistrates Court)
Kidderminster p462 . . . . . 01562 514000

McKenna, O (Harrison Drury & Co) E S2 L S1
Preston p357 . . . . 01772 258321

Mckenna, P E (Forshaws Davies Ridgway LLP) G H
Warrington p422. . . . . . . 01925 230000

McKenna, Ms S J (Nabarro LLP)
Sheffield p376 . . . . 0114 279 4000

McKenna, Ms Y (London Fire & Emergency Planning Authority)
London SE1 p107 . . . . . . 020 8555 1200

McKenna-Donnelly, Ms E S M (McKenna Donnelly & Co)
Westminster p57. . . . . . . 020 7821 9927

Mackenow, B A (Brian Mackenow & Co) K4 S1 E W C1 L B1 R1 Zd S2 R2
Sunderland p401. . . . . . . 0191 565 6262

Mackenow, Ms J R (Brian Mackenow & Co) O J1 Q Zl C1 Zza Zc
Sunderland p401. . . . . . . 0191 565 6262

McKensie, J (Russell Jones & Walker)
London WC2 p74 . . . . . . 020 7657 1555

MacKenzie, Ms A K (Brighton & Hove Council - Legal Services)
Hove p461. . . . . 01273 290000

McKenzie, A N (Fladgate LLP) W T1 E S1
London WC2 p32 . . . . . . 020 3036 7000

Mackenzie, B (Ford & Warren) O Zt G Zi
Leeds p273 . . . . 0113 243 6601

Mackenzie, Ms C K (Thomson Snell & Passmore) W T2
Tunbridge Wells p415 . . . . 01892 510000

Mackenzie, D P S (Ison Harrison) W
Leeds p274 . . . . 0113 284 5000

McKenzie, G N (Gavin McKenzie) G H
Shrewsbury p379 . . . . . . 01743 235957
Shrewsbury p379 . . . . . . 01743 248148

See p634 for the Key to Work Categories

Mackenzie, Mrs J (Barnes Marsland) *S1 W K4*
Broadstairs *p166* 01843 861595

McKenzie, Miss J (Cartmell Shepherd) *A1 S1 E W*
Carlisle *p182* 01228 514077

MacKenzie, J (Pinsent Masons LLP) *I Ze O*
London EC2 *p67* 020 7418 7000

Mackenzie, Ms J (Stanley M Calvert) *K1 N S1 W F1*
North Shields *p330* 0191 258 1528

MacKenzie, Ms J E (The College of Law Chester)
Chester *p454* 0800 289997

Mackenzie, J K (Mackenzie & Co) *G H Q Zk N*
Hounslow *p254* 020 8569 6289

Mackenzie, Mrs J L (Blake Lapthorn) *D1*
Chandlers Ford *p184* 023 8090 8090
Portsmouth *p354* 023 9221 0170

McKenzie, J L (Vincent French & Browne) *A3 B1 C1 E J1 N P S1 S2 W Za Zb Zc Zd*
London WC1 *p89* 020 7831 4994

McKenzie, J R (Watford Borough Council)
Watford *p475* 01923 226400

Mackenzie, J R (Redferns) *K1 N O Q J1 L S1 F1 E C1 Zc*
Weymouth *p430* 01305 781401 / 782704
Portland *p354* 01305 823636

McKenzie, K S (DAC Beachcroft) *C1 O Zb Zj*
London EC4 *p24* 020 7936 2222

McKenzie, M (Reynolds Porter Chamberlain LLP)
London E1 *p71* 020 3060 6000

McKenzie, Mrs M G (Wigan Borough Council)
Wigan *p476* 01942 244991

MacKenzie, Ms P J (MFG Solicitors) *C1 C2*
Worcester *p440* 01905 610410

McKenzie, Miss R (Stockton-On-Tees Borough Council)
Stockton-on-Tees *p472* 01642 393939

Mackenzie, R (Ashurst LLP)
London EC2 *p7* 020 7638 1111

McKenzie, Mrs S J (Barker Gotelee Solicitors) *A3 Zc F1 F2 Ze O Q Zq*
Ipswich *p262* 01473 611211

Mackenzie, Ms S J (Society of Lloyd's)
London EC3 *p107* 020 7327 1000

McKenzie, T C I (Wright Hassall LLP) *W T2*
Leamington Spa *p270* 01926 886688

McKenzie, Mrs V J (Wace Morgan) *W*
Shrewsbury *p379* 01743 280100

Mackenzie Hill, Ms R (ClarksLegal LLP) *C1*
London WC2 *p20* 020 7539 8000

McKenzie Smith, A (hlw Keeble Hawson LLP) *O Q*
Sheffield *p376* 0114 276 5555

Mackenzie-Grieve, C J (Stephenson Harwood) *E P*
London EC2 *p82* 020 7329 4422

MacKenzie-Ingle, Ms L (Kent County Council)
Maidstone *p464* 01622 694320

McKeon, C (North Yorkshire County Council)
Northallerton *p467* 01609 780780
Richmond *p469* 01748 829100

McKeown, Miss D (McMillan Williams) *N Zr*
Croydon *p205* 01689 848311

McKeown, D (McKeowns Solicitors Ltd) *N*
St Albans *p390* 0800 032 8328

McKeown, H S (Preston Redman) *E S1 A1 P C1 L T1 J1 W Zc Zl B1 R1*
Bournemouth *p152* 01202 292424

McKeown, Ms K (Taylor Wessing)
London EC4 *p86* 020 7300 7000

McKeown, P H (Hillyer McKeown LLP) *E S1 S2 C1 C2*
Bebington *p129* 0151 645 4255
Chester *p190* 01244 318131

McKeown, Miss S (Leport & Co) *N Q O*
Banbury *p122* 01295 257328 / 268181

McKeown, S (SM Solicitors) *N O E B1 Zq S2 R1 J1*
Chester *p191* 01244 314722

Mackereth, E (K&L Gates LLP) *N O*
London EC4 *p47* 020 7648 9000

McKernan, K (Crutes) *N Q O*
Newcastle upon Tyne *p324* 0191 233 9700

McKessy, Mrs E (EEF West Midlands Association)
Birmingham *p449* 0121 456 2222

McKevitt, Miss M A (Neil Foley & Co) *G H*
Pontypridd *p352* 01443 406085

Mackey, C P (Churchers) *D1 V*
Portsmouth *p354* 023 9221 0170

Mackey, D (Sefton Metropolitan Borough Council)
Southport *p472* 01704 533133

Mackey, M P (Burton Copeland LLP) *G*
Manchester *p302* 0161 827 9500

McKibbin, H (Harvey McKibbin Solicitors)
Sutton Coldfield *p403* 0121 240 9115

McKibbin, Ms S (Herbert Smith LLP) *E L*
London EC2 *p40* 020 7374 8000

McKiddie, D J (Catteralls) *S1 E W C1 L T1 R1 Zc Zn Zj*
Wakefield *p418* 01924 291122

Mackie, A (Holman Fenwick Willan)
London EC3 *p42* 020 7264 8000

McKie, Miss A (Lovsey Marsh) *D1 G H K1 S1 Zl Zv*
Birmingham *p140* 0121 212 0255

Mackie, Mrs B M (Thursfields) *N Q*
Kidderminster *p266* 01562 820575

Mackie, C E (Northumbria Probation Board)
Newcastle upon Tyne *p466* 0191 240 7351

Mackie, D A J (Swinburne & Jackson LLP) *E Zl*
Gateshead *p229* 0191 477 2531 / 477 3222

Mackie, D L (Allen & Overy LLP)
London E1 *p5* 020 3088 0000

McKie, D W R (DLA Piper UK LLP) *O Q Za*
London EC2 *p24* 0870 011 1111

Mackie, Mrs G M (Glynis M Mackie) *S1 W J1 L Zd Zv*
Gosforth *p232* 0191 236 5308

Mackie, I H (Macfarlanes) *O Q B1 Ze Zf Zb*
London EC4 *p56* 020 7831 9222

Mackie, J (McCormicks) *O Q Zq*
Harrogate *p240* 01423 530630

Mackie, J W R (McClure Naismith) *O Q Ze Zf Zc*
London EC4 *p56* 020 7623 9155

Mackie, Mrs K F (Draper & Co) *K1*
Farnham *p225* 01252 727374

Mackie, S (John Hodge Solicitors) *Q J1 N*
Weston-super-Mare *p429* 01934 623511

Mackie, W G (Cripps Harries Hall LLP) *E R2 Zc Zh S1*
Tunbridge Wells *p415* 01892 515121

McKiernan, Ms F (Children & Families Law Firm) *K1 D1 V D2*
London SW9 *p20* 020 7582 6002

McKillop, H D (hlw Keeble Hawson LLP) *E L C1 B1 W S1 A1 I C2 Ze*
Leeds *p274* 0113 244 3121

McKillop, I J (Pilkington PLC)
St Helens *p472* 01744 28882

McKimm, D M (Allen & Overy LLP)
London E1 *p5* 020 3088 0000

Mackinder, Ms P (TV Edwards LLP) *K1*
London SE8 *p85* 020 7790 7000

Mackinder, S (Thorpe & Co) *S1 C1 E W A1 K4 S2*
Malton *p300* 01653 694899

McKinlay, I A (Emsleys) *S1 E S2 L*
Rothwell *p368* 0113 201 4900

McKinney, C P (Nelsons) *N Q O J1*
Leicester *p280* 0116 222 6666

McKinney, Miss O B (Frettens Solicitors) *E S1 S2*
Christchurch *p194* 01202 491777
Bournemouth *p152* 01202 786161

McKinney, S J (McKeowns Solicitors Ltd) *N*
St Albans *p390* 0800 032 8328

McKinnon, Ms A S (Windsor & Maidenhead Borough Council)
Maidenhead *p464* 01628 798888

Mackinnon, Ms J (Napthens LLP) *S1 E*
Blackpool *p146* 01253 622305

Mackinnon, Mrs L (H T Argent & Son) *S1 E*
Aldeburgh *p115* 01728 452133
Saxmundham *p372* 01728 602323

Mackinnon, Mrs S J (Cheshire County Council)
Chester *p454* 01244 602382

MacKintosh, Ms A (Martello Professional Risks Limited) *B1 N P*
London EC3 *p108* 020 7337 7500

Mackintosh, J D M (Mackintosh & Co) *T2 W*
Richmond upon Thames *p364* 020 8332 2864

Mackintosh, Ms M B (Freeth Cartwright LLP)
Birmingham *p138* 0845 634 2575

Mackintosh, Ms N A (Mackintosh Duncan) *Zm Q Zg*
Southwark *p57* 020 7357 6464

Mackintosh, Mrs S (Divorce Law Info)
Beaconsfield *p448* 01494 681335

McKirgan, S (Royds LLP) *K1*
London EC4 *p74* 020 7583 2222

McKisack, Ms L (ADT FKE & Security PLC)
Sunbury-on-Thames *p473* 01932 743333

McKittrick, S W (Harvey Ingram LLP) *T2 W*
Leicester *p280* 0116 254 5454

Mackle, J (Clarion Solicitors LLP) *O Q Zq*
Leeds *p272* 0113 246 0622

Mackle, R (Langleys)
York *p445* 01904 610886

Mackley, D (Bolton Metropolitan Borough Council)
Bolton *p450* 01204 333333

Macklin, R J W (SNR Denton)
London EC4 *p75* 020 7242 1212

Mackness, D R (E Wood Holdings PLC)
Northallerton *p467* 01609 788716

McKnight, A (Salans) *B1 C1 Zb*
London EC4 *p76* 020 7429 6000

McKnight, Ms E S (Herbert Smith LLP) *C1 C3 M1*
London EC2 *p40* 020 7374 8000

McKnight, N (Batchelors Solicitors) *Zh L Q*
Bromley *p166* 020 8768 7000

McKno, Miss K S (Breens Solicitors) *N*
Southport *p388* 01704 532890

McKoy, R (London Borough of Southwark)
London SE1 *p109* 020 7525 5000

Mackrell, J A (Mackrell & Thomas) *G H*
Liverpool *p289* 0151 480 3666

Mackreth, Miss J (Carillion PLC)
Wolverhampton *p477* 01902 422431

McLachlan, I (Ian McLachlan) *S1 W*
Redditch *p362* 01527 63883

Mclachlan, Ms J (Plexus Law (A Trading Name of Parabis Law LLP)) *N Q*
Evesham *p220* 01386 769160

Maclachlan, L F (Plexus Law (A Trading Name of Parabis Law LLP)) *Zq Zj O*
London EC3 *p68* 0844 245 4000

McLachlan, Miss M C (Isherwood & Hose) *K1 Q S1 N L J1*
Heywood *p249* 01706 360032 / 368741

Mclaine, Ms E (Archers Law LLP) *B1 I N T1 T2 Zb Ze*
Stockton-on-Tees *p396* 01642 636500

McLardie, L (Penningtons) *J1*
London EC2 *p66* 020 7457 3000

MacLaren, A M (McFaddens LLP) *B1 C3 M2 Zb*
London EC2 *p56* 020 7588 9080

MacLaren, D H (MacLaren Britton) *E C1 W S1 R1 Zl K4 S2*
Nottingham *p338* 0115 941 1469

McLaren, J S (Pentland Group PLC)
London N3 *p108* 020 8346 2600

McLaren, J W B (W H Darbyshire & Son) *N L G J1 O Q H D1 K1 D2 K3*
Blackpool *p146* 01253 346646

McLaren, R I (Robert McLaren Solicitor) *E R1 C1*
Horsham *p253* 01403 823440

McLarney, A P M (Eddowes Perry & Osbourne) *G H N Q Zr K1*
Sutton Coldfield *p403* 0121 686 9444
Sutton Coldfield *p403* 0121 686 9666

McLarney, J (Dodd Lewis Solicitors) *S1 W L S2*
London SE3 *p27* 020 8852 1255

McLauchlan, J (Nelsons) *W*
Leicester *p280* 0116 222 6666
Leicester *p281* 0116 262 4225

McLauchlan, J H (Freeth Cartwright LLP) *E C1 T1 L W Zb Ze Zo*
Nottingham *p337* 0115 936 9369

McLauchlan, P J (Margary & Miller) *E S2 S1 N*
Felixstowe *p225* 01394 273333

McLauchlan, R C (Barlow Lyde & Gilbert LLP) *A3 C1 B2 Zj O Zq*
London EC3 *p10* 020 7247 2277

McLaughlan, Miss C (Stevens & Bolton) *K1 N*
Guildford *p237* 01483 302264

McLaughlin, A J (County of Herefordshire District Council)
Hereford *p460* 01432 260266

Mclaughlin, C (Canter Levin & Berg)
Kirkby *p268* 0151 546 4562

McLaughlin, E (Sills & Betteridge LLP)
Lincoln *p285* 01522 542211

Maclaurin, D (LG Lawyers)
London SE1 *p50* 020 7379 0000

McLay, R I (Parker Bird Gardner) *S1 S2 E*
Huddersfield *p256* 01484 825200

McLean, A P (Nabarro LLP) *Zb*
London WC1 *p63* 020 7524 6000

McLean, Mrs D H (South Tyneside Metropolitan Borough Council)
South Shields *p471* 0191 427 1717

Maclean, Ms F (Richard Rooney & Co)
Merton *p73* 020 8947 8024

McLean, Miss G (Northern Foods PLC)
Leeds *p461* 0113 390 0110

McLean, G (Coles Miller Solicitors LLP) *O Q Zq F1 Ze A1*
Poole *p352* 01202 673011

McLean, G C (Allen & Overy LLP) *C2 C1 U1*
London E1 *p5* 020 3088 0000

McLean, Miss G M (Lupton Fawcett) *J1*
Leeds *p275* 0113 280 2000

Maclean, I (Ince & Co Services Ltd)
London E1 *p44* 020 7481 0010

Maclean, Ms I (Finers Stephens Innocent LLP) *X Zk*
London W1 *p32* 020 7323 4000

McLean, J (Underwood Solicitors LLP) *W Zd C1 T2*
Westminster *p89* 020 7526 6000

McLean, Miss K (Healys LLP) *O Q*
London EC4 *p39* 020 7822 4000

McLean, Ms L C (Laytons) *C1 U2 Ze*
London EC4 *p52* 020 7842 8000

MacLean, M (McGrigors LLP) *Zb Zn C1*
London EC4 *p56* 020 7054 2500

McLean, N L (Dhanju Mclean & Anwar Solicitors) *G H B2*
Iver *p263* 01753 651743

McLean, Ms N M (DLA Piper UK LLP) *E*
Leeds *p272* 0870 011 1111

Maclean, Mrs R (Sills & Betteridge LLP) *D1 D2 K1 K3*
Sleaford *p381* 01529 302800

Maclean, R (Crowell & Moring) *M2*
London EC4 *p23* 020 7413 0011

McLean, Ms S (Morrison & Foerster (UK) LLP) *U1 U2*
London EC2 *p62* 020 7920 4000

McLellan, Ms C A (Telford Magistrates Court)
Telford *p474* 01952 204500

McLellan, R (Hewitsons) *O*
Cambridge *p174* 01223 461155

McLellan, S (Watson Burton LLP) *Zc*
Newcastle upon Tyne *p327* 0845 901 2100

Maclennan, E (Sacker & Partners LLP) *Zo*
London EC2 *p76* 020 7329 6699

McLennan, Miss K (Tozers) *L O Q*
Exeter *p222* 01392 207020

MacLennan, Miss N (Pannone LLP) *A3 C1 E L Zq*
Manchester *p308* 0161 909 3000

Maclennan, P (Anderson & Company) *I Ze C1 U2 Zza*
Shillingford *p378* 01865 858878

McLennan, Ms S (Faegre & Benson LLP) *O*
London EC4 *p30* 020 7450 4500

McLeod, A L (Robin Simon LLP)
Manchester *p309* 0333 010 0000

MacLeod, Mrs G A (David Cowan) *S1*
Dorking *p212* 01306 886622

MacLeod, Miss H (W H Matthews & Co) *A3 Zc O Q N*
Sutton *p402* 020 8642 6677

MacLeod, Ms J (Thackray Williams)
Bromley *p167* 020 8290 0440

Macleod, J R (Weightmans LLP) *N Q*
Manchester *p311* 0161 233 7330

Macleod, Ms K J (Edwin Coe LLP) *O Q B1 L*
London WC2 *p29* 020 7691 4000

McLeod, L (Shepherd + Wedderburn LLP) *Zb E R1 S1 T1*
London EC4 *p78* 020 7429 4900

Mcleod, Mrs M A (Coutts & Co)
London WC2 *p105* 020 7753 1403

Macleod, N R (The Lister Croft Partnership) *O Q Zr N*
Wakefield *p418* 0871 220 1333

McLeod, P (Bhatia Best) *G H*
Nottingham *p336* 0115 950 3231

MacLeod, Ms T (Rosenblatt) *O*
London EC4 *p73* 020 7955 0880

McIlroy, B P (Squire Sanders (UK) LLP)
Manchester *p310* 0161 830 5000

McLoone, I (Taylor Walton LLP) *E*
Luton *p295* 01582 731161

Macloskey, B M (Barry Macloskey Solicitors) *S1 W K1 F1 N L Q S2*
Wrexham *p443* 01978 852485

Macloskey, M C L (Barry Macloskey Solicitors) *G K1 D1 H*
Wrexham *p443* 01978 852485

McLoughin, Miss J (Anthony King & Co) *N J2 Q F2 J1*
Basildon *p126* 01268 240400

McLoughlin, A J (Fieldings Porter) *M1 N P F1 H J1 B1 K1 C1*
Bolton *p149* 01204 540900

Mcloughlin, B (DFA Law LLP) *E R2 S1*
Northampton *p331* 01604 609560

McLoughlin, Ms C B (Surrey County Council)
Kingston upon Thames *p462* 020 8541 9088

McLoughlin, Miss K (Latimer Hinks) *W K4*
Darlington *p206* 01325 341500

McLoughlin, P (Hogan Lovells International LLP)
London EC1 *p42* 020 7296 2000

McLoughlin, P A (McLoughlin & Company LLP) *A3 B1 J2 O P Q Zc Zj Zq*
Shrewsbury *p379* 01743 272272

McLoughlin, Mrs S (B P Collins LLP)
Gerrards Cross *p229* 01753 889995

McLoughlin, Mrs S N (Keoghs LLP) *N Zj O Q*
Bolton *p149* 01204 677000

McLoughlin, T (DWF) *N*
Liverpool *p287* 0151 907 3000

McLynn, Ms L (Bates Wells & Braithwaite London LLP) *J1 J2 Zd*
London EC4 *p11* 020 7551 7777

McMahon, E (Kidd Rapinet) *K1 Q*
Aylesbury *p121* 0845 017 9616

McMahon, E (Forsters LLP) *E S2*
Westminster *p33* 020 7863 8333

McMahon, Ms J E (Stephensons Solicitors LLP) *K1*
Wigan *p432* 01942 777777

McMahon, Miss M (Pillsbury Winthrop Shaw Pittman LLP) *J1*
London EC2 *p67* 020 7847 9500

McMahon, Ms M (Clifford Chance)
London E14 *p20* 020 7006 1000

McMahon, N A C (Reynolds Porter Chamberlain LLP) *O Q Zr Zq*
London E1 *p71* 020 3060 6000

McMahon, Miss O (Broadbents) *G H M1 P*
Alfreton *p115* 01773 832511

MacMahon, P J (Commission for Local Administration in England)
London SW1 *p105* 020 7217 4620

McMahon, T M (Lockett Loveday McMahon) *Zc S2 E R1 R2*
Manchester *p307* 0161 237 3627

McManners, Mrs M A (Grierson Shaw & Co) *E L S1 W*
Durham *p214* 0191 386 2434

McManus, Mrs C A (McManus Seddon) *K1 D1 D2 K3*
Bradford *p154* 01274 741841

McManus, F (Hathaways) *K1 G N H F1 J1 L V W D1*
Gateshead *p228* 0191 477 2288

McManus, Ms S (Newcastle Upon Tyne City Council)
Newcastle upon Tyne *p466* 0191 232 8520

McMaster, Ms L K (Dixon Rigby Keogh) *K1 S1 D1*
Northwich *p333* 01606 48111

McMath, L W T (Collins Dryland & Thorowgood LLP)
Henley-on-Thames *p247* 01491 572323

McMeel, K (Boyes Sutton & Perry) *E S1 W S2*
Barnet *p123* 020 8449 9155

McMenamin, D N (Linklaters LLP)
London EC2 *p54* 020 7456 2000

McMichael, Ms J (Hogan Lovells International LLP)
London EC1 *p42* 020 7296 2000

McMichael, N A (Penningtons) *O*
London EC2 *p66* 020 7457 3000

McMillan, Mrs A (Department for Business, Enterprise and Regulatory Reform)
London SW1 *p105* 020 7215 0105

McMillan, A (Ashurst LLP)
London EC2 *p7* 020 7638 1111

MacMillan, A D (Gateley LLP) *J1 Zp Zw*
Birmingham *p138* 0121 234 0000

McMillan, Miss E (Red Kite Law) *K4 W S1*
Tenby *p410* 01834 842122

Macmillan, E R C (Sonn Macmillan)
London EC3 *p80* 020 7377 8889

6

McMillan, F (Pinsent Masons LLP) *O Zc*
London EC2 *p67*. 020 7418 7000
McMillan, G (Hyndburn Borough Council)
Lancaster *p447* 01254 388111
McMillan, H M (Hamish M McMillan) *B1 E O Q W Zd K4 Zk Zq S1 S2*
London EC4 *p57*. 020 7430 1789
McMillan, J G S (McMillan Williams) *S1*
Coulsdon *p199*. 020 8668 4131
McMillan, J R (Wright & McMillan Bennett) *G H Zl B2 W*
Telford *p409* 01952 291100
Macmillan, Mrs K (Bird & Co) *G H*
Grantham *p232* 01476 591711
McMillan, Ms L J (Peters & Peters) *B2 O*
London EC4 *p67*. 020 7629 7991
Macmillan, P T A (Rolls-Royce PLC)
Derby *p456* 01332 242424
MacMillan, R A S (Wilkin Chapman Epton Blades) *N O Q Zr*
Lincoln *p285*. 01522 512345
Macmillan, R D H (Bhatia Best) *G*
Nottingham *p336*. 0115 950 3231
Grantham *p232* 01476 591711
MacMillan-Scott, A (Ashfords LLP) *E*
Exeter *p220* 01392 337000
McMillin, A P (Sherrards) *E L S1 S2*
St Albans *p390* 01727 832830
McMinn, S (Charles Lucas & Marshall) *C1 C2 Ze*
Newbury *p322* 01635 521212
McMorron, Ms S (Reynolds Porter Chamberlain LLP)
London E1 *p71* 020 3060 6000
McMorrough, Ms A (Layzells) *S2 E R1 S1 W*
London N10 *p52*. 020 8444 0202
McMorrow, Miss M F (DLA Piper UK LLP) *Q Ze*
Birmingham *p137* 0870 011 1111
McMuldroch, J (Pannone LLP) *C1 U2 Ze*
Manchester *p308* 0161 909 3000
Mcmullan, Ms S (Trowers & Hamlins)
London EC3 *p88*. 020 7423 8000
McMullen, Dr J (Wrigleys Solicitors LLP) *J1 Zp X*
Leeds *p278* 0113 244 6100
McMurchie, A (Burnetts) *Zr*
Carlisle *p181*. 01228 552222
Carlisle *p182*. 01228 552222
McMutrie, Ms F (Prettys)
Chelmsford *p187*. 01245 295295
Macnab, A H (Hartlepool Borough Council) *G F1 X P Zi*
Hartlepool *p460* 01429 266522
Macnab, A M (Freeth Cartwright LLP) *C1*
Derby *p208* 01332 361000
Nottingham *p337*. 0115 936 9369
McNab, J (Edward Hands & Lewis) *W S2 S1 K4 Zd*
Loughborough *p293* 01509 216161
McNab, Mrs M (Ross & Craig) *K1 K2*
Westminster *p73*. 020 7262 3077
Macnab, M A (Ellis-Fermor & Negus)
Long Eaton *p293* 0115 972 5222
McNab, S (Travers Smith LLP)
London EC1 *p87*. 020 7295 3000
McNabb, D J (Mark Jones & Partners) *P K1 M1 G H D1 J1 V F1*
Liverpool *p289*. 0151 286 9594
McNabb, J C (SFN Solicitors) *K1 K3 Zm*
Burnley *p169* 01282 421284
McNair, D W (Child & Child) *O Q Zb J1 Zq N Zk K1*
London SW1 *p20* 020 7235 8000
McNair, H L (McNair & Co) *E S1 C1 Q L W I T2 Ze Zk*
Hammersmith & Fulham *p57*. 020 7371 7896
McNair, R D J (Chapmans Solicitors) *S1 W*
Sutton *p402* 020 8337 3801
McNally, I A G (Allan Rutherford) *W C1 T1 S1 E Zd Zm*
Norwich *p333* 01603 621722
McNally, Miss J (Lees Solicitors LLP) *Q J1 O*
Birkenhead *p134*. 0151 647 9381
McNally, Ms J (Wigan Borough Council) *K1 D1 S1 J1 Zh*
Wigan *p476* 01942 244991
McNally, Miss K (Godloves) *S1 K1*
Leeds *p273* 0113 225 8811
Leeds *p273* 0113 286 8822
McNally, Ms K M (Mid Sussex Magistrates Court)
Haywards Heath *p460* 01444 417611
Haywards Heath *p460* 01444 417611
McNally, Mrs K M (Allan Rutherford) *D2 K1 Q V L B1*
Norwich *p333* 01603 621722
McNally, Ms M (Treasury Solicitors Department)
London WC2 *p110*. 020 7210 3000
McNally, M C (Mander Hadley & Co) *G H*
Coventry *p200*. 024 7663 1212
Coventry *p201*. 024 7622 0300
McNally, M P (Knights) *A2 Q O J1 N Zk Zq*
Tunbridge Wells *p415* 01892 537311
McNally, S (Ellis Jones) *D1 K1*
Bournemouth *p151*. 01202 525333
McNally, S V (Hartlaw LLP) *T2 W*
Wetherby *p429* 01937 547000
MacNamara, D R (MMS Solicitors) *S1 K1 W L G R1 Q F1 D1*
Withernsea *p436*. 01964 612318
Mcnamara, Ms J (Field Fisher Waterhouse LLP)
London EC3 *p31*. 020 7861 4000
McNamara, J J M (Rothwell & Evans) *E C1 S1 L W T1*
Sale *p370* 0161 969 7341

McNamara, M C (Rogers & Co) *G H*
Wolverhampton *p438* 01902 310312
McNamara, Miss P A (Fletchers) *D1 K1 N Q Zm*
Southport *p388* 01704 546919
McNamara, Ms R J (Barlow Lyde & Gilbert LLP)
London EC3 *p10*. 020 7247 2277
MacNamara, Mrs S (Keelers)
Kenilworth *p264* 01926 853555
McNamara, S (Bristol City Council)
Bristol *p451* 0117 922 2000
McNamara, Ms U C (Maxwell Winward LLP) *E S2 L R2*
London EC4 *p59*. 020 7651 0000
McNamee, Miss A V (Stockton-On-Tees Borough Council)
Stockton-on-Tees *p472* . . 01642 393939
McNaughtan, Ms C (Northrop McNaughtan Deller) *Ze Zf*
London W9 *p64* 020 7289 7300
McNaughton, G S (Paris Smith LLP) *C1 C2*
Southampton *p386*. 023 8048 2482
McNaull, M (The College of Law York)
York *p477* 0800 289997
McNeany, B (McKenzie Bell Solicitors)
Sunderland *p401*. 0191 567 4857
McNeil, A (Bailey Smailes) *S1 K1 M1 P W L J1 F1 C1 G Zi Zl*
Holmfirth *p251*. 01484 686000
Huddersfield *p255* 01484 435543
McNeil, A (R G Frisby & Small) *Q O N J1 L B1 F1 G H V Zh Zl Zk Zd Zi*
Leicester *p279*. 0116 233 5522
McNeil, Ms A L (Finers Stephens Innocent LLP) *E L O*
London W1 *p32* 020 7323 4000
McNeil, Ms G (Ashurst LLP)
London EC2 *p7* 020 7638 1111
McNeil, J (Paris Smith LLP) *Zb*
Southampton *p386*. 023 8048 2482
McNeil, M (Sills & Betteridge LLP) *G H B2 Zg*
Lincoln *p285*. 01522 542211
McNeil, Miss M B (Kingsfords) *D1 K1 D2*
Ashford *p119* 01233 624545
McNeil, P (Field Fisher Waterhouse LLP) *M1 P*
London EC3 *p31*. 020 7861 4000
McNeil, S A (Bevirs) *K1 J1 N Q F1*
Swindon *p406* 01793 532363
McNeill, A (Peter Peter & Wright) *E L S1 S2 V W R2 C1*
Bideford *p133* 01237 472233
McNeill, Ms C (Brand & Co) *K1 K3*
Cheam *p185*. 020 8641 2771
McNeill, Mrs C A (Thorpe & Co) *S1 L W F1 J1 N V*
Scarborough *p372*. 01723 364321
McNeill, C R (Anthony Gold) *C1 E S1 T1 W T2*
London SE1 *p6* 020 7940 4000
McNeill, S (McGrigors LLP) *O F2 Zk*
London EC4 *p56*. 020 7054 2500
McNeill, S P (Farleys Solicitors LLP) *Q N Zr J1*
Accrington *p114* 01254 367853
McNeill, T A (BCL Burton Copeland) *B2 G J2*
London WC2 *p9* 020 7430 2277
McNeill, T J (City of Salford Magistrates Court)
Salford *p470*. 0161 834 9457
McNeill, Ms V A (Norfolk County Council - Legal Services)
Norwich *p467* . . . Minicom: 0844 800 8011
McNeilly, J (Penningtons) *E*
London EC2 *p66*. 020 7457 3000
McNeish, Ms C D (Terry Jones Solicitors & Advocates) *K3 K1*
Telford *p409* 01952 297979
McNelis, F (Christian Khan Solicitors) *Zg N*
London WC1 *p49* 020 7631 9500
McNerlin, J (Reynolds Porter Chamberlain LLP)
London E1 *p71* 020 3060 6000
McNicholas, Ms A (Paddington Law Centre)
London W10 *p108*. 020 8960 3155
McNicholas, B (Thompsons (formerly Robin/Brian Thompson & Partners)) *N*
London SW19 *p87*. 020 8947 4163
McNicol, A M (Foot Anstey) *Q N L F1 D1 Zk Zl O*
Exeter *p221* 01392 411221
McNicol, S T (Muckle LLP) *B1 C1 Zb*
Newcastle upon Tyne *p325* . 0191 211 7777
MacNish Porter, J A (DAC Beachcroft)
London EC4 *p24*. 020 7242 1011
McNish, A E (Davis Blank Furniss) *C1 C2 O T1 Ze Zza Zb*
Manchester *p303* 0161 832 3304
McNulty, Ms S (Keppe & Partners Solicitors) *K3 K1 Q*
Twickenham *p416* 020 8891 4488
McNulty, S J (Burges Salmon) *E L A1 Zh*
Bristol *p161* 0117 939 2000
McNutt, P L (Stone Rowe Brewer LLP) *N Zr*
Twickenham *p416* 020 8891 6141
Maconald-Brown, C J (Redd) *O Ze*
London EC1 *p71*. 020 7776 4760
McParland, Miss C (Wellers Law Group LLP) *K1*
Bromley *p167* 020 8464 4242
McParland, Ms D (G T Stewart Solicitors) *D1 K1*
London SE22 *p83* 020 8299 6000
McPartland, P (EEI Solicitors)
Liverpool *p287*. 0151 707 8004
McPherson, Miss A F (Quality Solicitors Burroughs Day) *E*
Bristol *p164* 0117 929 0333
McPherson, D S (McPhersons) *S1 E W S2*
Ealing *p57*. 020 8840 9017

Macpherson, Ms E L (Slade Legal) *K1*
Abingdon *p114*. 01235 521920
McPherson, G (J A Hughes)
Barry *p126*. 01446 411000
McPherson, H A (Osborne Clarke) *E*
Bristol *p164* 0117 917 3000
MacPherson, H G (Dodd Lewis Solicitors)
London SE3 *p27*. 020 8852 1255
Macpherson, I C (Rees Page) *S1 W S2*
Wolverhampton *p438* 01902 577777
McPherson, J V (Burchell Williams Limited) *G H*
Brighton *p159* 01273 606555
Macpherson, Ms K (DLA Piper UK LLP)
Birmingham *p137* 0870 011 1111
Macpherson, M C L (Osborne Clarke) *C2*
Reading *p361* 0118 925 2000
Macpherson, R (McGrigors LLP)
London EC4 *p56*. 020 7054 2500
McPherson, Mrs S M (McPhersons) *L S1*
Ealing *p57*. 020 8840 9017
MacPhie, A J W (Hill Dickinson LLP) *S2 R2 R1 W*
Manchester *p305* 0161 817 7200
McPhie, Miss K (The Endeavour Partnership LLP)
Stockton-on-Tees *p397* . . . 01642 610300
McPhie, T (Ellisons) *E Zu R1*
Colchester *p197* 01206 764477
McPhillips, A J N (Muckle LLP) *J1*
Newcastle upon Tyne *p325* . 0191 211 7777
McQuater, G J (Hogan Lovells International LLP)
London EC1 *p42*. 020 7296 2000
McQuater, J (Atherton Godfrey) *N Zr Zq*
Doncaster *p211* 01302 320621
McQuay, Miss E M (Elizabeth McQuay) *K1 K2*
Oxford *p343* 01869 351229
McQueen, D J (CMHT Solicitors) *D1 E F1 G H J1 K1 L M1 P Zl*
Walsall *p420*. 01922 743525
Walsall *p420*. 01922 646400
McQueen-Turner, Ms A (Lawrence Hamblin) *S1*
Henley-on-Thames *p247*. . . 01491 411884
MacQuillan, Ms J A V (MacQuillan & Co)
Ebbw Vale *p216* 01495 304382
Tredegar *p413*. 01495 725031
McQuillan, M (Cuttle & Co) *G H D1 N P Zl*
Manchester *p302* 0161 835 2050
McQuillan, M A (Addleshaw Goddard) *J1*
London EC1 *p4* 020 7606 8855
McQuillen, J P (Barlow Lyde & Gilbert LLP)
London EC3 *p10*. 020 7247 2277
McQuinn, M (Garstangs)
London WC2 *p35* 020 7427 5678
McQuire, Miss J A (Official Solicitor and Public Trustee) *W*
London WC2 *p108*. 020 7911 7127
MacRae, Miss C M (Trethowans LLP) *C1 A1 F1 L J1 W Zf Zb Ze*
Southampton *p387*. 023 8032 1000
MacRae, Miss H (Marks & Spencer PLC)
London W2 *p107* 020 7935 4422
McRae, K I J (Hatchers Solicitors LLP) *S2 E K4 L Zm S1 T2 W*
Whitchurch *p430*. 01948 663361
Northwich *p333* 01606 74301
McRavey-Williams, Ms P (Stratford-on-Avon District Council)
Stratford-upon-Avon *p473* . . 01789 267575
Macready, Miss A (Ison Harrison) *E*
Leeds *p274* 0113 284 5000
McReddie, D C (Freers) *G H K1 K2 N Q V Zm*
Middlesbrough *p315* 01642 244666
Macritchie, K (Shearman & Sterling LLP) *Zn*
London EC2 *p78*. 020 7655 5000
Macro, R (Penningtons)
London EC2 *p66*. 020 7457 3000
McRobert, Ms C (Boodle Hatfield)
Westminster *p14*. 020 7629 7411
Macrory, R H (Hamer Childs) *G H*
Worcester *p439* 01905 724565
Macrory, W J G (Macrory Ward) *B1 C1 S2 E K1 L Zl R2 T2 W*
Barnet *p124* 020 8440 3258
McShane, Mrs C (Shacklocks) *J1 Zp*
Ripley *p365* 01773 743513
McShee, D (Kennedys) *Zj*
London EC3 *p49*. 020 7667 9667
McSheen-Bailey, Mrs C A (Alsters Kelley) *W*
Coventry *p199* 0844 561 0100
McSherry, Miss L E (Cleggs) *C1 S2 E S1*
Nottingham *p336*. 0115 977 5877
McSherry, Miss L J (B P Collins LLP) *K1*
Gerrards Cross *p229*. 01753 889995
MacSherry, Ms O (Macfarlanes)
London EC4 *p56*. 020 7831 9222
McSherry, S (Christian Khan Solicitors) *Zg N*
London WC1 *p49* 020 7631 9500
McSorley, Miss C L (Herrington & Carmichael LLP)
Camberley *p173*. 01276 686222
McSorley, D (The Grech Gooden Partnership LLP) *G H B2 Zc*
Cardiff *p178* 029 2022 2255
McSweeney, J (Howells LLP) *D1 D2 K1*
Sheffield *p376* 0114 249 6666
MacSweeney, N (Martello Professional Risks Limited)
London EC3 *p108* 020 7337 7500
Mactaggart, Miss D J (Jordans) *J1*
Wakefield *p418* 01924 387110
McTavish, Ms C (Fox Williams) *O Q*
London EC2 *p33*. 020 7628 2000
Mactear, Mrs J M (Field Seymour Parkes) *Zc O Q*
Reading *p360* 0118 951 6200

McTernan, Mrs C L (Hague & Dixon) *W S1*
York *p444* 01759 371634
McTier, Mrs G A (Slade Legal) *D1 K1 D2 K2*
Abingdon *p114*. 01235 521920
McTigue, Mrs C (Enoch Evans LLP) *G H*
Walsall *p420*. 01922 720333
Macvay, I C (Steptoe & Johnson) *M2 M1*
London EC2 *p83*. 020 7367 8000
McVean, P J (Footner & Ewing) *S1 S2 W E F1 L A1 J1 Zb Zl*
Romsey *p366* 01794 512345
McVeigh, J M (Teacher Stern LLP) *C2 C1 Ze Zw*
London WC1 *p86* 020 7242 3191
Leamington Spa *p270* 01926 886688
McVeigh, M (Penningtons) *E*
London EC2 *p66*. 020 7457 3000
McVey, Miss K C (Powys County Council)
Llandrindod Wells *p463* . . . 01597 826000
Mcvey, S A (Gordons LLP)
Leeds *p273* 0113 227 0100
MacVicar, R (Clifford Chance)
London E14 *p20*. 020 7006 1000
McWalter, Miss E (McWalter & Co) *K4 P K1 R1 T2 S1 W L*
Cheltenham *p188* 01242 676106
McWatt, Miss R (IBB Solicitors) *D2 D1 K1*
Uxbridge *p417*. 0845 638 1381
Macwhirter, J (Malletts Solicitors) *G H B2 Zl*
King's Lynn *p266* 01553 777744
McWhirter, Ms P (The College of Law Guildford)
Guildford *p459*. 01483 460200
MacWilliam, A H (Lovell Son & Pitfield) *B1 K3 K1 Q S1 W*
Camden *p55*. 020 7242 7883
Macwilliam, C J (Clough & Willis) *M1 S1 H D1 K1 P F1*
Bury *p170* 0161 764 5266
McWilliam, D (Ellis Jones) *N Q F1 L*
Bournemouth *p151*. 01202 525333
McWilliam, Ms J (David Buck & Co) *G H*
Brighton *p159* 01273 621745
McWilliam, S A (Aviva PLC) *C1 U1 I F2 Zza U2 C2 Ze*
London EC3 *p103* . . 020 7283 7500 / 01603 687905
Bury St Edmunds *p171* . . . 01284 762211
McWilliams, Miss H (Berg Legal) *J1*
Manchester *p301* 0161 833 9211
McWilliams, J F (Connell Associates) *O N F1 Zb Zk Zq*
Liverpool *p287*. 0151 236 2011
Leeds *p273* 0113 243 6601
McWilliams, P (Ford & Warren)
Leeds *p273* 0113 243 6601
Madaan, A (Aviva PLC)
London EC3 *p103* . . 020 7283 7500 / 01603 687905
Norwich *p467* 01603 622200
York *p477* 01904 452210
Maddah, Mrs R E G (HRJ Law LLP) *S1*
Hitchin *p251* 01462 628888
Madden, A J (Gateley LLP) *C1 C2 Zb*
Birmingham *p138* 0121 234 0000
Madden, B J (Clarkson Wright & Jakes Ltd) *C1 C2 C3*
Orpington *p341* 01689 887887
Madden, C (Marsden Rawsthorn LLP)
Preston *p357* 01772 799600
Madden, Ms C S G (H F T Gough & Co) *E S1 S2 L W K1*
Whitehaven *p431* 01946 692461
Madden, M (Ashurst LLP) *B1*
London EC2 *p7* 020 7638 1111
Madderson, Ms M (Maddersons)
Broxbourne *p167* 01992 444421
Maddison, Ms S C (Sintons LLP) *N*
Newcastle upon Tyne *p326* . 0191 226 7878
Maddison-White, Mrs H (Hart Reade) *W T2*
Hailsham *p237*. 01323 841481
Maddock, C J (Hay & Kilner) *J1*
Newcastle upon Tyne *p325* . 0191 232 8345
Newcastle upon Tyne *p325* . 0191 211 7777
Maddock, G C (Herbert Smith LLP) *C1 Zj*
London EC2 *p40*. 020 7374 8000
Maddock, M (The College of Law York)
York *p477* 0800 289997
Maddock, P J (Radcliffes Le Brasseur) *C1 C2 I*
Westminster *p70*. 020 7222 7040
Maddocks, G F (Gabb & Co) *N O Q S1 L K1 R1*
Crickhowell *p203*. 01873 810629
Maddocks, N W (Kitsons LLP) *S2 E L O Q S1 Zq*
Plymouth *p350*. 01752 603040
Maddocks, Ms R (Vale Royal Borough Council)
Winsford *p476* 01606 862862
Maddocks, Ms R (Hunters) *K1 C1*
London WC2 *p44* 020 7412 0050
Maddows, Ms C V (Teacher Stern LLP) *E S2*
London WC1 *p86* 020 7242 3191
Maddox, S (Gateley LLP) *E S1*
Manchester *p304* 0161 836 7700
Maddrell, A L (Lester Maddrell)
Cheltenham *p188* 01242 222147
Maddy, Mrs J M (Bray & Bray) *G H*
Leicester *p279*. 0116 254 8871
Madge, D G (South Wales Police)
Bridgend *p451* 01656 869476
Madge, J (Nash & Co Solicitors LLP) *D1 D2 K1*
Plymouth *p350*. 01752 664444
Madgett, R J G (Chamberlins) *E L S1 W*
Lowestoft *p294* 01502 573241
Madichie, Miss A (Plexus Law (A Trading Name of Parabis Law LLP)) *Zj O Q Zq N Zr*
London EC3 *p68*. 0844 245 4000

Madon, Ms A (Penningtons) *E*
London EC2 *p66* 020 7457 3000

Madron, Ms J M L (Royal Mail Group)
London EC4 *p109* 020 7250 2468

Mafham, Ms A E R (Richard Silver) *G B2 H J2*
Manchester *p309* 0161 834 9494

Mafham-Jackson, Mrs J (Clark Willis) *S1*
Darlington *p206* 01325 281111

Magdani, Mrs R (Freeth Cartwright LLP) *J1*
Leicester *p279* 0116 248 1100

Magee, P (Drummonds) *O Q N K1 K2 J1 K3 C1 Zr Zc B1 D2 Zq R1 L*
Chester *p190* 01244 408300

Magee, P J A (Thompsons (formerly Robin/Brian Thompson & Partners)) *G N*
Nottingham *p339* 0115 989 7200

Magell, Miss T (Haworth & Nuttall) *D1 K1*
Accrington *p114* 01254 236221

Maggio, V (Mills & Reeve) *E R2*
Cambridge *p175* 01223 364422

Maggiulli, D M (dgb Solicitors) *K3 D1 K1 K2*
Chatham *p184* 01634 304000

Maggs, D W (Browne Jacobson LLP) *N Zj*
London EC3 *p16* 020 7539 4900
Nottingham *p336* 0115 976 6000

Magill, Miss C C (Wolferstans) *E C1 Zc*
Plymouth *p351* 01752 663295

Maginn, M S (Brown Turner Ross) *N Q*
Liverpool *p287* 0151 236 2233

Maginn, T (Radcliffes Le Brasseur)
Westminster *p70* 020 7222 7040

Magnamara, Mrs S (Macnamara King Solicitors)
Warwick *p422* 01926 499889

Magnay, P (Thomas Magnay & Co) *N C1 G H K1 E J1 W S1 L Zc Zk Zl*
Gateshead *p229* 0191 477 3333
Whickham *p430* . 0191 488 7459 / 488 7766

Magne, D (Magne & Co Solicitors)
Surbiton *p402* 020 8399 3939

Magnin, J D (K&L Gates LLP) *O*
London EC4 *p47* 020 7648 9000

Magnus, A D (Peter Brown & Co Solicitors LLP) *S1*
Barnet *p124* 020 8447 3277

Magnussen, Mrs M (Barlow Robbins LLP) *K1 N Q*
Guildford *p235* 01483 543200

Magrath, C W M (Magrath LLP) *J1 O G Q C1 Zi*
London W1 *p57* 020 7495 3003

Magrath, S A (Alker & Ball) *S1 L R1*
Wigan *p432* 01942 246241

Magrill, Mrs R V (Treasury Solicitors Department)
London WC2 *p110* 020 7210 3000

Maguire, Mrs A (Geoffrey Leaver Solicitors LLP) *N*
Milton Keynes *p317* 01908 692769

Maguire, K J (Fentons) *C1 F1 J1 L M1 N P W*
Failsworth *p223* 0161 682 7101

Maguire, N (Taylor Vinters) *L O Q Zq*
Cambridge *p176* 01223 423444

Maguire, Ms N K (Bird & Bird LLP) *C1 C2*
London EC4 *p13* 020 7415 6000

Maguire, P (CMS Cameron McKenna LLP) *O Zj*
London EC3 *p17* 020 7367 3000

Maguire, R D (DWF) *E R2 P*
Manchester *p303* 0161 603 5000

Maguire, S (Bates & Mountain) *K1 N K3 G H D1*
Grimsby *p235* 01472 357291

Mahaffey, Ms J E (Eaton Smith LLP) *K1 D1 G H K2*
Huddersfield *p255* 01484 821300

Mahajan, Miss V H (Nexus Solicitors) *O Q L Zq*
Manchester *p308* 0161 819 4900

Mahal, R (Wedlake Bell LLP)
London WC1 *p91* 020 7395 3000

Mahany, D S (Mahany & Co Solicitors LLP) *S1 W*
Horley *p252* 01293 772888

Mahapatra, Mrs D E I (MLM Cartwright) *J1 Zp*
Cardiff *p179* 029 2046 2562

Maharaj, V (Weightmans LLP) *S2 R2 E R1*
Manchester *p311* 0161 233 7330

Maher, A (Neil Myerson LLP) *O Q A3 C1 Zq Zk*
Altrincham *p117* 0161 941 4000

Maher, A (Suffolk County Council)
Ipswich *p462* 01473 583000

Maher, Ms C (Kent County Council)
Maidstone *p464* 01622 694320

Maher, C E (Thompson & Cooke LLP) *S1 E R1 J1 S2*
Stalybridge *p393* 0161 338 2614

Maher, Mrs C L (Chenery Maher & Co) *K1 K2 W K3 D1*
Clitheroe *p196* 01200 422264

Maher, C W (Marsden Rawsthorn LLP) *N B1 C3 C2 C1*
Preston *p357* 01772 799600

Maher, Ms J R (Knowsley Metropolitan Borough Council)
Huyton *p461* 0151 443 3593

Maher, P R (Maher & Co) *S1 S2 W*
Maidenhead *p298* 01628 675239

Mahey, Miss S (Elliot Mather LLP) *D1 K3 K1*
Mansfield *p311* 01623 655666

Mahil, Miss S (Jordans) *N*
Dewsbury *p210* 01924 457171

Mahlanglu, N (Calderdale Metropolitan BC Corporate Services Directorate)
Halifax *p460* 01422 357257

Mahmood, A (Amal Solicitors)
Huddersfield *p255* 01484 431999

Mahmood, Miss F (Ford & Warren) *O Q Ze*
Leeds *p273* 0113 243 6601

Mahmood, M (Molesworths Bright Clegg) *S2 E C1*
Rochdale *p365* 01706 356666

Mahmood, R U (Leeds City Council) *N*
Leeds *p462* 0113 224 3513

Mahmood, Ms S (Munro Solicitors) *D1*
London E7 *p62* 020 8503 1718

Mahmood, S (Birmingham City Council Legal & Democratic Services)
Birmingham *p449* 0121 303 2066

Mahmood, T (Arora Lodhi Heath)
London W3 *p7* 020 8993 9995

Mahmood, Y B (K&L Gates LLP) *Zc*
London EC4 *p47* 020 7648 9000

Mahon, Miss J (Clark Willis) *Zh K1 L D1*
Darlington *p206* 01325 281111

Mahoney, Ms A C (Brodie Smith & Mahoney)
Cardiff *p177* . . 029 2022 1848 / 2022 7680

Mahoney, Mrs C (Quality Solicitors Palmers) *W*
Fetcham *p226* 01372 454791

Mahoney, D J (Stanley Smith Hill & Co) *K1 K3 S1 W*
Banstead *p123* 01737 358001

Mahoney, K W (Meade-King) *B1 O*
Bristol *p163* 0117 926 4121

Mahoney, P D (Brodie Smith & Mahoney) *A1 C1 E K1 P S1*
Cardiff *p177* . . .029 2022 1848 / 2022 7680

Mahony, D (Parker Arrenberg) *S1 E R1 Zl L*
London SE6 *p65* 020 8695 2330

Mahy, J H (Clerk to the Justices)
Llandudno *p463* 01492 871333

Mahy, P J (Howells LLP) *Zg*
Sheffield *p376* 0114 249 6666

Maiden, M (Bilton Hammond LLP) *C1 S2 R2 S1 W*
Mansfield *p311* 01623 675800

Maidment, A L (Maidments) *G H*
Salford *p370* 0870 403 4000

Maier, S A (Manches LLP) *O*
Oxford *p343* 01865 722106

Mailer, E (Finers Stephens Innocent LLP) *K4 Q T2 W*
London W1 *p32* 020 7323 4000

Mailer, G J (BCL Burton Copeland) *B2 G*
London WC2 *p9* 020 7430 2277

Maimaris, S R P (London Borough of Wandsworth)
London SW18 *p110* 020 8871 6000

Main, A (Evans Main Solicitors)
Sevenoaks *p374* 01732 464848

Main, D (W Davies) *C1 Ze Zf Zz U2*
Woking *p436* 01483 744900

Main, Miss D J (Cornwall County Council)
Truro *p474* 01872 322197

Main, Miss L C (Sumner & Main) *E S1 W*
Worthing *p442* 01903 239420

Maini, Miss A (Varley Hibbs LLP) *D1 K1 D2*
Coventry *p201* 024 7663 1000

Maini, Ms M (Mohindra Maini Solicitors LLP)
Manchester *p307* 0161 236 9833

Maini, Mrs S (Rich & Carr Freer Bouskell) *K4 K1 S1 T2 W*
Leicester *p281* 0116 253 8021

Mainwaring, H J (Sheridans) *B1 I O U1 Ze Zf Zw*
London WC1 *p78* 020 7079 0100

Mainwaring, M W (The National Library of Wales)
Aberystwyth *p447* 01970 632800

Mainwaring, Mrs P (Moreb Limited) *K1 Q N A1 F1 V B1 A2 A3 Zl K3*
Llandeilo *p291* 01558 822215

Mainwaring, R O (Levenes Solicitors) *N*
Haringey *p53* . .020 8881 7777 / 8881 6764

Mainwaring-Taylor, Miss R (Hunters) *T2 W*
London WC2 *p44* 020 7412 0050

Mair, A S R (Stephenson Harwood) *M1 C1*
London EC2 *p82* 020 7329 4422

Mair, J (Dorset County Council)
Dorchester *p457* 01305 251000

Mair, L (Ashurst LLP) *C1*
London EC2 *p7* 020 7638 1111

Mair, Ms L S (Pierre Thomas & Partners) *N*
London W6 *p67* 020 7602 0305

Maisey, R M A (Davies & Partners) *E L S1*
Gloucester *p230* 01452 612345

Maislish, D M (Duane Morris) *C1 C2 Zn*
London EC1 *p28* 020 7786 2100

Maison, Mrs G E C (Horwood & James LLP) *E A1 L S1*
Aylesbury *p121* 01296 487361

Maitland, B (Bates Wells & Braithwaite London LLP) *Zl Zg*
London EC4 *p11* 020 7551 7777

Maitland, Ms J M (Henmans LLP) *W*
Oxford *p343* 01865 781000

Maitland, Ms L (Gloucestershire County Council - Legal & Democratic Services) *K1 D1*
Gloucester *p459* 01452 425203

Maitland-Walker, J H (Maitland Walker) *C3 C2 C1 M1 O S2 E Ze M2 Q R2*
Minehead *p318* 01643 707777

Maitland-Walker, J H (Clark Holt) *C3*
Swindon *p406* 01793 617444

Majid, Miss A (Williscroft & Co) *K1 K3 V*
Bradford *p155* 01274 305380

Majid, I (Nyland & Beattie) *G H*
Widnes *p432* 0151 424 5656

Majid, S (Solicitors Direct) *S2 E Zi S1 W*
Bradford *p155* 01274 776000

Majid, Miss T N (Cumming & Riley) *G H*
Grays *p233* 01375 383691

Majiyagbe, Ms J J (Wellers Law Group LLP) *S1*
Bromley *p167* 020 8464 4242

Major, A W (Woodhouse & Company) *S1 M1 W G*
Wolverhampton *p438* 01902 773616

Major, C T (K&L Gates LLP) *E R2*
London EC4 *p47* 020 7648 9000

Major, D C (Major & Co) *C1 E S1 K1 W O*
Guildford *p236* 01483 455771

Major, Mrs G M (Wills & Probate Countrywide) *K1 Q J1 F1 O*
Tavistock *p408* 01626 334455

Major, J D (Barlow Lyde & Gilbert LLP) *Zj O Zq*
London EC3 *p10* 020 7247 2277

Major, Miss K E (Bray & Dilks) *K1 D1 J1 K2 K3*
Truro *p414* 01872 271717

Major, M R (Bhatia Best) *G H*
Nottingham *p336* 0115 950 3231

Major, Mrs S M (Global Solutions Ltd)
Broadway *p452* 01386 858585

Maka, Y (DLA Piper UK LLP)
Manchester *p303* 0870 011 1111

Makan, Mrs S (Rich & Carr Freer Bouskell) *K1 D1 D2 V W*
Leicester *p281* 0116 253 8021

Makanda, R C (Makanda & Co) *Zi Zp*
London N19 *p58* 020 7272 8844

Makey, S R (John Barkers) *F1 G K1 K3 L N O Q S1 S2 Zf Zl*
Grimsby *p234* 01472 358686

Makhani, K (S V Wadsworth & Co) *N Zr*
Solihull *p383* 0121 745 8550

Makhani, Miss T (Pickerings LLP) *K1 D1 D2*
Tamworth *p407* 01827 317070

Makin, C (Makin Dixon Solicitors) *D1 K1 Zo S1*
Skipton *p381* 01756 797284

Makin, C (Colman Coyle LLP) *J1*
Islington *p22* 020 7354 3000
Cambridge *p174* 01223 461155

Makin, Mrs D A (Geldards LLP)
Cardiff *p178* 029 2023 8239

Makin, Ms H (Cheshire County Council)
Chester *p454* 01244 602382

Makin, J W G (Pendrigh Makin) *D2 D1 K3 K1 Q W*
Reigate *p363* 01737 221518

Makin, R S G (E Rex Makin & Co) *Ze Zf P M1 Zg Zk Q Zq*
Liverpool *p289* 0151 709 4491

Makinson, P J (Walker Smith Way) *E A1 R2 S2*
Chester *p191* 0844 346 3100

Makol, A (Foys Solicitors) *J1 N O P Zq Zp*
Sheffield *p375* 0114 246 7609

Malamatenios, D (Colman Coyle LLP)
Islington *p22* 020 7354 3000

Malan, F S (N C Morris & Co) *E S1 A1*
London SW7 *p62* 020 7584 8764

Malarby, P A (Bath & North East Somerset Council)
Bath *p462* 01225 394041
Bristol *p451* 0117 922 2000

Malcolm, Ms E A (Marrons) *N*
Newcastle upon Tyne *p325* . 0191 281 1304

Malcolm, Mrs J I (Thomson Snell & Passmore) *S1*
Tunbridge Wells *p415* 01892 510000

Malcolm, S J (LG Lawyers)
London SE1 *p50* 020 7379 0000

Male, R C (Male & Wagland) *E C1 S1 N W J1 O Ze R2 S2 C2 T2*
Potters Bar *p355* 01707 657171

Malekin, P S S A (Malekin Law)
Cardiff *p180* 029 2023 1222

Malekotodjary, Ms R (Gordons LLP)
Leeds *p273* 0113 227 0100

Malhi, R (HCB Solicitors) *T2 W*
Walsall *p420* 01922 720000

Malhotra, Ms S (Boodle Hatfield)
Westminster *p14* 020 7629 7411

Malia, A M (Hadaway & Hadaway) *G K1 H D1*
North Shields *p330* 0191 257 0382

Malia, Ms C A (Irwin Mitchell LLP) *W T2*
Sheffield *p376* 0870 150 0100

Malia, Ms S M C (DWF) *N*
Manchester *p303* 0161 603 5000

Maliakal, Mrs E (Heptonstalls LLP) *Zr*
Goole *p231* 01405 765661

Malik, A (McCormacks) *B2 G H*
London EC3 *p56* 020 7791 2000

Malik, A (HSK Solicitors LLP) *N Q*
Manchester *p305* 0161 795 4818

Malik, A (Edwards Duthie) *J1 G H*
London E6 *p29* 020 8514 9000

Malik, A T (Goldwaters) *C1 E F1 S1 K1 L N P*
Newcastle upon Tyne *p324* . 0191 232 2653

Malik, I K (Muckle LLP) *C2 C1 Zb*
Newcastle upon Tyne *p325* . 0191 211 7777

Malik, M S (Barlow Lyde & Gilbert LLP) *C1*
London EC3 *p10* 020 7247 2277

Malik, P R (Hodge Jones & Allen LLP) *G H*
London NW1 *p41* 020 7874 8300

Malik, Ms S (Birnberg Peirce & Partners) *G Q Zi*
Camden *p13* 020 7911 0166

Malik, S (HSK Solicitors LLP) *Zi N Q*
Manchester *p305* 0161 795 4818

Malik, Ms S (Leigh Day & Co) *N F2 M2 J2 Zg P*
London EC1 *p52* 020 7650 1200

Malik, Miss S (Glaisyers Solicitors LLP) *L*
Manchester *p304* 0161 224 3311

Malik, W (Russell Jones & Walker)
Manchester *p309* 0161 383 3500

Malins, Ms L (Cartwright King)
Nottingham *p336* 0115 958 7444

Malkiel, S (Finers Stephens Innocent LLP) *T1 T2 W*
London W1 *p32* 020 7323 4000

Malla, C (Kennedys) *Zr*
London EC3 *p49* 020 7667 9667

Mallaband, Miss E K (Oglethorpe Sturton & Gillibrand) *E R2 S2*
Lancaster *p270* 01524 846846

Mallalieu, Mrs S F (Shoosmiths) *J1 Zp*
Northampton *p332* . . 0370 086 3000 / 01604 543000

Mallatratt, R S (Hadgkiss Hughes & Beale) *K1 G H Q W*
Birmingham *p138* 0121 449 5050

Mallender, J D R (Bond Pearce LLP) *S2 R2 L A1 S1 C1*
Bristol *p161* 0845 415 0000

Mallet, R G (Wellers Law Group LLP) *J1 Zj Zk O Zq Zp Q N Ze*
London WC1 *p91* 020 7242 7265

Mallett, K G (East Dorset District Council)
Wimborne *p476* 01202 886201

Mallett, R (Malletts Solicitors) *B2 G H Zl Zw*
King's Lynn *p266* 01553 777744
London WC1 *p58* 020 7061 3760

Mallett, Mrs S R (Malletts Solicitors) *K1 N Q V*
King's Lynn *p266* 01553 777744

Malley, C C W (Hansell Wilkes & Co) *W S1*
Dartmouth *p207* 01803 833993

Mallia, P J (Mallia & Co) *G H D1 K1 Zm S1 A1 C1 S2 B2 L Zl N R2 W*
Cardiff *p180* 029 2022 0044

Mallick, Miss C L (Squire Sanders (UK) LLP) *C1 C2*
London EC2 *p81* 020 7655 1000

Mallik, A (Gordons LLP)
Leeds *p273* 0113 227 0100

Mallin, M F (Hill Dickinson LLP) *N Za Zj*
London EC3 *p41* 020 7283 9033

Mallinder, Mrs S (Malcolm C Foy & Co) *N*
Rotherham *p367* 01709 836866

Mallinson, D J (Girlings) *B1 F1 L M1 P*
Ashford *p119* 01233 664711

Mallinson, Miss S J (Wosskow Brown) *N*
Sheffield *p377* 0114 256 1560

Mallinson, S P (Worcestershire County Council)
Worcester *p477* 01905 766335

Mallon, C (Skadden Arps Slate Meagher & Flom (UK) LLP)
London E14 *p80* 020 7519 7000

Mallorie, Ms C J (Barlow Lyde & Gilbert LLP)
London EC3 *p10* 020 7247 2277

Mallorie, Miss S E M (Legal Services Commission Wales Office)
Cardiff *p453* 0845 608 7070

Mallott, Miss C (Barr Ellison LLP) *E S2 C1*
Cambridge *p174* 01223 417200

Malloy, Ms C T (Memery Crystal) *C1 C2*
London WC2 *p60* 020 7242 5905

Malloy, K P (Malloy & Barry) *S1 E W G H F1 C1 B1 L R1 Zd Zl Zj*
Cardiff *p180* 029 2034 3434

Malone, C J (Stephensons Solicitors LLP) *G H*
Manchester *p310* 0161 832 8844

Malone, D (CKM Solicitors) *N*
Durham *p214* 0191 384 9080

Malone, Ms J (The College of Law)
London WC1 *p105* 0800 289997

Malone, M C (Canter Levin & Berg) *B1 J1 O C1 F1 Ze Zf Zk Zo*
Liverpool *p287* 0151 239 1000

Malone, Miss R L (Bray & Bray) *K1*
Leicester *p279* 0116 254 8871

Malone, Mrs S (Plexus Law (A Trading Name of Parabis Law LLP)) *J1*
Evesham *p220* 01386 769160

Maloney, Ms K (TBI Solicitors) *K1*
Hartlepool *p243* . . . 0800 052 6824 / 01429 264101

Maloney, K S (Muckle LLP) *C1 C2 B1*
Newcastle upon Tyne *p325* . 0191 211 7777

Malpas, Mrs E (Crangle Edwards) *K1 N K3 Q*
Cheadle *p185* 0161 428 2331

Malpas, Ms G (Hempsons) *N Zj*
Manchester *p305* 0161 228 0011

Malpass, C (Alan Roberts & Co) *B1 K3 K4 J1 J2 L R1 Zt W*
Chester *p191* 01244 562754

Malseed, Miss L K (Birchall Blackburn LLP) *K4 W*
Preston *p356* 01772 561663

Malsher, Ms A (Anthony Gold) *N Q Zr Zq*
London SE1 *p6* 020 7940 4000

Maltas, Ms E (Maltas & Co) *D1 K1 D2 K3*
Barnsley *p125* 01226 781596

Maltby, J H (Thompson & Cooke LLP) *W C1 E J1 Zo*
Stalybridge *p393* 0161 338 2614

Maltby, N (DLA Piper UK LLP)
Leeds *p272* 0870 011 1111

Malthouse, Ms P (The Child Law Partnership)
Guildford *p236* 01483 543790

Malthouse, Mrs S (Richard Jacklin & Co) *W T2 K4*
Liverpool *p289* 0151 243 1313
Southport *p388* 01704 500024

Malvern-White, Mrs C (Steven Young & Co)
Cheltenham *p188* 01242 257269
Gloucester *p230* 01452 332882

Malyali, C M (McBride Wilson & Co) *C1 E S1 F1 R1 L W Q B1*
London WC2 *p56* 020 7242 1300

Man, D (Jonathan S Rose) *S1 S2 E*
Barnet *p124* 020 8447 4870

Man, Ms M (Kemps Solicitors) *G H B2*
Oldham *p340* 0161 633 0555

Manak, K (Heer Manak)
Coventry *p200* 024 7666 4000

Manan, R (Bhatia Best) *N Q V*
Nottingham *p336* 0115 950 3231

Manches, L S (Manches LLP)
London WC2 *p58* 020 7404 4433
Manchester, J R G (Manchesters)
South Croydon *p383*. 020 8651 3118
Manchester, R G (Manchesters)
South Croydon *p383*. 020 8651 3118
Manchett, J (Cornish Forfar & Allen) *C1 D1 E J1 K1 L M1 P S1*
Liverpool *p287*. 0151 227 1831
Mandair, Miss S (Bhatia Best) *G H*
Nottingham *p336*. 0115 950 3231
Mandalia, Ms M (Vingoe Lloyd)
Helston *p246* 01326 555800
Mandarino, F (Reynolds Porter Chamberlain LLP)
London E1 *p71* 020 3060 6000
Mandel, Ms C (Kennedys)
London EC3 *p49*. 020 7667 9667
Mandelli, M (Keppe & Partners Solicitors) *Zb C1 S2 E J1 C2 R2 Zf O C3*
Twickenham *p416* 020 8891 4488
Mander, B S (LG Lawyers)
London SE1 *p50*. 020 7379 0000
Mander, Ms C (Ashurst LLP)
London EC2 *p7* 020 7638 1111
Mander, C E (Mander Cruickshank Solicitors LLP) *W S1 C1 J1 B1 E L Zo Zv*
Coalville *p196* 01530 510666
Mander, D C (Mander Hadley & Co) *C1 E W S1 R1 T1 A1*
Coventry *p200*. 024 7663 1212
Mander, G S (Vyman Solicitors) *G H B2*
Gravesend *p233*. 01474 537270
Harrow *p242*. 020 8427 9080
Mander, Ms K (McMillan Williams) *K1*
Wallington *p419* 020 8669 4962
Mander, P (Penningtons) *J1*
London EC2 *p66*. 020 7457 3000
Mander, P I (Mander Hadley & Co) *C1 E R1 S1 W Zc Zi*
Coventry *p200*. 024 7663 1212
Mander, S J (Stuart J Mander & Co) *D1 F1 G H J1 K1 L M1 N P Zs Zv Zp*
Walsall *p420*. 01922 642018
Manderfield, E (Pemberton Greenish LLP)
London SW3 *p66* 020 7591 3333
Mandla, S S (Mandla Bhomra & Co) *G H S1 E D1 K1 Zi*
Birmingham *p140* 0121 523 3384
Manek, R (G T Stewart Solicitors) *G H B2 J2 Zg*
London SE22 *p83* 020 8299 6000
Manek, Mrs S (Blaser Mills) *O Q N*
Harrow *p241*. 020 8427 6262
Manek, V M (Walter Wilson Richmond) *S1 E K1 D1 M1 N P J1 L W Zi Zp*
Harrow *p242*. 020 8427 8484
Manfield, Mrs P J (Winckworth Sherwood LLP) *W S1 A1*
London SE1 *p92*. 020 7593 5000
Manfield-Cooke, Mrs C E (Co-operative Insurance Society Ltd)
Manchester *p464* 0161 832 8686
Manfredi-Hamer, J (Wrigleys Solicitors LLP)
Leeds *p278* 0113 244 6100
Mangan, S J (Corbett & Co International Construction Lawyers Ltd) *A3 Zc O*
Teddington *p409*. 020 8614 6200
Mangano, M G (Redfearns) *K1 W G H Zl D1*
Heckmondwike *p246*.01924 403745 / 404601
Mangaroo, Miss S E (Gill Turner Tucker) *K3 K1 K2*
Maidstone *p299* 01622 759051
Mangham, A V (Hawley & Rodgers) *T2 K4 W*
Loughborough *p293* 01509 230333
Manghnani, D L (Evans Dodd LLP) *R2 S2 C1 E S1*
London W1 *p30* 020 7491 4729
Westminster *p70*. 020 7222 7040
Mangnall, Mrs D M A (W H Matthews & Co) *S1 E W R1 L*
Sutton *p402* 020 8642 6677
Manikam, B (HilliersHRW Solicitors) *G H*
Stevenage *p395* 01438 346000
Manir, Miss T (Carters)
Pontefract *p351* 01977 703224
Manita, Ms C M (Harbottle & Lewis LLP) *Ze Zf*
London W1 *p38* 020 7667 5000
Mankabady, M G (LG Lawyers)
London SE1 *p50*. 020 7379 0000
Manktelow, Miss H E (MacDonald Oates LLP) *K1 K3 D1 D2*
Midhurst *p316* 01730 816711
Manku, Ms J (Mitsubishi Securities International PLC)
London EC2 *p108* 020 7577 2804
Manley Topp, Mrs H D (Grenville J Walker) *G K1 Q S1 W*
Blandford Forum *p147*. . . . 01258 459911
Manley, Miss H E (Langley Wellington) *X*
Gloucester *p230*. 01452 521286
Manley, Ms I A (Bradford Law Centre)
Bradford *p451* 01274 306617
Manley, K (Brabners Chaffe Street) *S2 E R2*
Liverpool *p286*. 0151 600 3000
Manley, Miss K M J (Harvey Ingram LLP) *N*
Leicester *p280*. 0116 254 5454
Manley, M J (Brabners Chaffe Street) *O*
Liverpool *p286*. 0151 600 3000
Mann, A R (Alan Mann & Co) *C1 E K1 L M1 P S1 T1*
St Albans *p390* . . .01727 833281 / 846012
Mann, B (Mann & Company) *K1 S1 Q W*
Kettering *p265*. 01536 520025

Mann, Miss B (Cotterhill Hitchman LLP) *S1*
Sutton Coldfield *p403* 0121 323 1860
Mann, D (Haworth & Nuttall) *C1 O*
Blackburn *p145* 01254 272640
Mann, E (Reynolds Porter Chamberlain LLP) *O P Q Zj Zq*
London E1 *p71* 020 3060 6000
Mann, G C (Stoffel & Co) *S1 K1 D1 S2 K3 L*
Beckenham *p129* 020 8650 8157
Mann, H (Rich & Carr Freer Bouskell) *Q*
Leicester *p281*. 0116 253 8021
Mann, Mrs H (Shepherd Harris & Co) *K1 K3*
Enfield *p219*. 020 8363 8341
Mann, I (Pardoes) *A1 E P Q Zu S1*
Bridgwater *p158* 01278 457891
Mann, I A (Temperley Taylor LLP) *S1 C1 E K3 J1 S2 Q O*
Heywood *p249*. 01706 623511
Mann, Ms J E (Fox Williams) *J1 Zi*
London EC2 *p33*. 020 7628 2000
Mann, J W (Mann Jenkins) *B1 C1 J1 L O Zb M3 Zq Zj*
Moretonhampstead *p319*. . . 01647 440000
Mann, Miss K (Greenwoods) *N*
London WC1 *p37* 020 7323 4632
Mann, Ms K K (Chhokar & Co) *K1 Zi Zg*
Southall *p384* 020 8574 2488
Mann, L (Hadaway & Hadaway) *J1*
North Shields *p330* 0191 257 0382
Mann, L (George Mills) *N Q*
Washington *p423* 0191 416 2182
Mann, L N (A L Hughes & Co) *E S1 C1 W R1 S2 R2*
London SW16 *p43*. 020 8769 7100
Mann, Mrs M J (Field Seymour Parkes) *K1 K3*
Reading *p360* 0118 951 6200
Mann, N D (A L Hughes & Co) *C1 E F1 J1 L R1 S1 T1 T2 W S2 Ze*
London SW16 *p43*. 020 8769 7100
Mann, N E (Neil E Mann) *D1 E G H K1 M1 P S1 W Zl*
Prestwich *p358* .0161 832 8806 / 720 8199 / 773 1775
Mann, Ms P K (Veja and Co Solicitors) *G H*
Southall *p385* 020 8574 2626
Mann, R (Baxter Caulfield) *K1*
Huddersfield *p255* 01484 519519
Mann, R (Proffitt & Mann) *Zl N W G H*
Lowestoft *p294* 01502 538582
Mann, R (Robert Mann) *F1 K1 L M1 N S1 P E W S2*
Oswestry *p342*. 01691 671926
Mann, R G (Stoke-on-Trent City Council)
Stoke-on-Trent *p472*. 01782 234567
Mann, R H (Draycott Browne Solicitors)
Manchester *p303* 0161 228 2244
Mann, R M (Bury Metropolitan Borough Council)
Bury *p452* 0161 253 7771
Mann, S (The Smith Partnership) *G H Zl*
Derby *p209* 01332 225225
Mann, S A J (Aviva PLC)
London EC3 *p103* . 020 7283 7500 / 01603 687905
Mann, T G (Jacksons) *W R1 L Zu*
Wirral *p435* 0151 632 3386
Mannakee, Mrs M (Raworths LLP) *E*
Harrogate *p240* 01423 566666
Mannell, M E (Sookias & Sookias) *T1 W T2*
London W1 *p80* 020 7465 8000
Mannering, S J M (Sheltons) *D1 K1*
Nottingham *p339*. 0115 955 3444
Mannering, S N (Stephenson Harwood)
London EC2 *p82*. 020 7329 4422
Manners, A J (Hugh James) *G H N F1 L J1 I O B2 Zq*
Cardiff *p179* 029 2022 4871
Manners, Mrs B T (Granville-West) *K1 D1*
Pontypool *p352* 01495 751111
Manners, The Hon J H R (Macfarlanes) *O J1 L Q Zj*
London EC4 *p56*. 020 7831 9222
Manners-Wood, J P (Reynolds Porter Chamberlain LLP) *Zj*
London E1 *p71* 020 3060 6000
Manning, Mrs C R (Warners Solicitors) *S1*
Sevenoaks *p374*. 01732 747900
Manning, Miss D L V (Moss & Haselhurst) *K1 D1 K2 V*
Winsford *p435* 01606 592159
Manning, Miss D L V (Mosshaselhurst) *K1 D1 D2 K3*
Northwich *p333* 01606 74301
Manning, M C (Ashfords LLP) *A3 O Q Zc Zq*
Exeter *p220* 01392 337000
Manning, Ms N (McMillan Williams)
Carshalton *p183* 020 8432 2041
Manning, N A (Stephen Rimmer LLP) *W T1 S1 Zm Zd*
Eastbourne *p216*. 01323 644222
Manning, P J P (Howes Percival LLP) *N*
Norwich *p334* 01603 762103
Manning, P R (Roland Robinsons & Fentons LLP) *Zl G H*
Blackpool *p147* 01253 621432
Manning, Miss S (Thomson Snell & Passmore) *S1*
Tunbridge Wells *p415* 01892 510000
Manning, T J C (Boodle Hatfield) *E S2*
Westminster *p14*. 020 7629 7411
Mannion, Mrs R N (immigration Appellate Authority) *D1 G H K1*
London EC1 *p107* 020 7353 8060

Mannion, Ms T (Alsters Kelley) *K1 K3*
Coventry *p199*. 0844 561 0100
Nuneaton *p339* 0844 561 0100
Mannix, W (Shoosmiths) *O*
Northampton *p332*. . 0370 086 3000 / 01604 543000
Mannooch, Mrs S (dgb Solicitors) *W T2 K4*
Chatham *p184*. 01634 304000
Manock, Ms P J (Wilkinson Woodward) *D1 K1 K2 K3*
Halifax *p238* 01422 339600
Manock, T P G (Savage Crangle) *A1 E L S1*
Skipton *p381*. 01756 794611
Manoharan, R (Mr Laws Solicitors) *G B1 B2 L N O Q Zl K3*
Wandsworth *p62*.020 8767 9717 / 8672 3447
Mansel, Mrs E C (Welsh Health Legal Services) *N*
Cardiff *p453* 029 2031 5500
Mansell, J J (Paris Smith LLP) *S2 E R2*
Southampton *p386*. 023 8048 2482
Mansell, M J (Allen & Overy LLP)
London E1 *p5* 020 3088 0000
Mansell, Mrs W (Peter Peter & Wright) *W K4*
Bideford *p133* 01237 472233
Manser, P R (Taylor Wessing)
London EC4 *p86*. 020 7300 7000
Mansfield, Miss D A (Harvey Ingram LLP) *E P Zl*
Leicester *p280*. 0116 254 5454
Mansfield, Ms E A (The Smith Partnership) *D1 K1*
Leicester *p281*. 0116 247 2000
Mansfield, Mrs J M (Bristol City Council)
Bristol *p451* 0117 922 2000
Mansfield, M S (Graham Coffey & Co) *N O L*
Manchester *p302* 0161 200 2440
Manski, P L (Jaffe Porter Crossick) *O Q J1 N B1 M1 L R1 K1 E Zf Ze Zc*
London NW6 *p46* 020 7625 4424
Manson, Ms C E (Barlow Lyde & Gilbert LLP)
London EC3 *p10*. 020 7247 2277
Mansouri, Dr C (Mansouri & Son)
Croydon *p205* 020 8401 7352
Mansuri, Ms S (Phillips) *G H K1 K3*
Mansfield *p312* 01623 658556
Mant, J C (John Mant Solicitors) *S1 W L E*
Wantage *p421*. 01235 762900
Mant, J D (Osborne Clarke) *E*
Bristol *p164* 0117 917 3000
Mantell, P D K (Anthony Gold) *S1 W*
London SE17 *p6*. 020 7940 4000
Manthorpe, Ms J (Waltons & Morse LLP) *Q Za*
London EC3 *p90*. 020 7623 4255
Mantion, Miss M L (Quinn Mantion) *S1 B1 K1 N O Q W G E F1 Zd Zk Zl*
London E14 *p70*. 020 7512 2600
Mantle, M (Ashurst LLP)
London EC2 *p7* 020 7638 1111
Mantle, Ms S (Dickinson Dees) *E*
Newcastle upon Tyne *p324* . 0191 279 9000
Manton, Mrs C E (Stokes Solicitors) *K1 D1*
Portsmouth *p355*. 023 9282 8131
Manton, Mrs L M (Dawson Hart) *W K4 Zd T2*
Uckfield *p416* 01825 762281
Brighton *p160* 01273 775533
Manu, M (Maidments) *G H B2*
Birmingham *p140* 0870 403 4000
Manuel, J H (Manuel Swaden) *E L S1 W Zd*
London NW6 *p58* 020 7431 4999
Manuel, Ms L (VHS Fletchers Solicitors) *G H*
Nottingham *p339*. 0115 959 9550
Manuel, S (Clegg Manuel)
Islington *p20*. 020 7847 5600
Manuelides, Y (Allen & Overy LLP)
London E1 *p5* 020 3088 0000
Manville, Miss J (Gelbergs LLP) *J1*
Islington *p35*. 020 7226 0570
Mao, A (Norman Saville & Co) *S1 S2*
London N10 *p76*. 020 8883 9711
Mao, Ms Y (Trowers & Hamlins)
London EC3 *p88*. 020 7423 8000
Maple, T J (Henmans LLP) *O B1 Zq Zw Q*
Oxford *p343* 01865 781000
Maples, D S (Brabners Chaffe Street) *C1*
Liverpool *p286*. 0151 600 3000
Maples, F H (Swindon Borough Council)
Swindon *p473* 01793 463000
Mapletoft, N (Mapletoft & Co) *E B1 C1 J1 L N R1 S1 T1 W Zk Zm Zo*
London SW15 *p58*. 020 8785 2414
Mapplebeck, B H (Thanet District Council)
Margate *p465* 01843 577000
Mapstone, Ms M (DBL Talbots LLP) *C1*
Stourbridge *p399* 01384 445850
Maqbool, A (Trowers & Hamlins)
London EC3 *p88*. 020 7423 8000
Marais, S (DLA Piper UK LLP) *Zb*
London EC2 *p24*. 0870 011 1111
March, R E (Milne Moser) *Q N Zl J1 S1*
Kendal *p264*. . . . .01539 729786 / 725582
Marchant, C S G (Barricella Hughes Marchant) *G H*
Ipswich *p262*. 01473 226225
Marchant, Ms E R (Heald Solicitors) *W*
Milton Keynes *p317* 01908 662277
Ampthill *p118* 01525 750750
Marchant, J L (Jeffrey Doctors & Marchant) *E S1 L C1 W A1 R1*
Watford *p423* 01923 231250
Marchant, R (J Garrard & Allen) *A1 E S1 L S2 Zn C1 T2 R2*
Olney *p341* 01234 711215
Marchant-White, C V (Quality Solicitors Clarke & Son) *S1 E S2 C1 P*
Basingstoke *p127* 01256 320555

Marchbank-Caunce, Mrs C (Simon A Holt & Co) *Q N Zr J2 Zq Zw*
Preston *p357* 01772 250871
Marchese, D L (Davenport Lyons) *C1 Ze*
London W1 *p25* 020 7468 2600
Marchington, Ms S M (Allianz Insurance PLC)
Guildford *p459*. 01483 552730
March-Taylor, Ms R (Howard Kennedy LLP) *E*
London W1 *p48* 020 7636 1616
Marco, A (Collyer Bristow LLP) *K1 D1*
London WC1 *p22* 020 7242 7363
Marcovitch, S I (Benson Mazure LLP) *S1 W Q L E S2*
Westminster *p12*. 020 7486 8091
Marcus, D (London Stock Exchange Ltd)
London EC2 *p107* 020 7797 1000
Marcus, Ms K (Treasury Solicitors Department)
London WC2 *p110*. 020 7210 3000
Marcus, R P A (IBM United Kingdom Ltd)
London RG21 *p107* 020 7202 5935
Marcus, Miss V H (Vaughan & Co) *W S1*
Leeds *p277* 0113 261 1044
Mardarescu, Miss I (Dale & Newbery LLP) *J1 Q*
Staines *p393*. 01784 464491
Mardell, Ms J (The College of Law Guildford)
Guildford *p459*. 01483 460200
Mardling, T R (Crick & Mardling) *S1 G K1 A1 W P F1 J1 M1 C1 Zl Zm Zt*
Stone *p398* . . . . .01785 812650 / 812434
Mardon, Ms C (LG Lawyers)
London SE1 *p50*. 020 7379 0000
Mardon, P E (Simmons & Simmons) *B1 O Q C1*
London EC2 *p79*. 020 7628 2020
Mardon, P R (Winterbotham Smith Penley LLP) *C1 O C2*
Stroud *p401* 01453 847200
Margand, R P (Hood Vores & Allwood) *C1 E F1 J1 L S1 S2 Ze R2 C2 Zb*
Dereham *p209*. 01362 692424
Margarson, J M (Cross Ram & Co) *S1 W E A1 L T1 J1 C1 F1 R1 Zc Zd Zl*
Halesworth *p237*. 01986 873636
Margereson, Ms J K (Pumfrey & Lythaby) *K1 P M1 L V D1*
Orpington *p342* 01689 833657
Margetson, Mrs E A (Anthony Collins Solicitors LLP) *E S2 R2*
Birmingham *p137* 0121 200 3242
Margetts, Ms R (Radcliffes Le Brasseur)
Westminster *p70*. 020 7222 7040
Margey, P (Marsden Rawsthorn LLP) *F1 G H N Q W S1*
Chorley *p194* 01257 279511
Margiotta, Miss S (The Johnson Partnership) *G H*
Derby *p209* 01332 370473
Derby *p209* 01332 372372
Margolis, A S (Cheval Property Finance PLC) *G H C1 F1 N Q*
Watford *p472* 020 8385 3920
Margolis, S H (Future Film Financing Ltd)
London W1 *p106* 020 7009 6600
Margrave, Mrs J C (Jennifer C Margrave) *W T2 V*
Guildford *p236*. 01483 562722
Margrave-Jones, C V (Margraves) *W T2 A1*
Llandrindod Wells *p291* . . . 01597 825565
Margrave-Jones, R D (Dilwyns) *Zl*
Llandrindod Wells *p291* . . . 01597 822707
Margrave-Jones, S R (Dilwyns)
Llandrindod Wells *p291* . . . 01597 822707
Aberystwyth *p114* 01970 624244
Margree, R P (Clifford Chance)
London E14 *p20*. 020 7006 1000
Margrett, Ms S R (Watson Farley & Williams)
London EC2 *p90*. 020 7814 8000
Marham, A T (Carrick Read Solicitors LLP)
Hull *p256* 01482 211160
Hull *p256* 01482 211160
Mariaddan, R R (John Street Solicitors)
London WC1 *p84* 020 7623 8822
Mariani, S G (The Royal Borough of Kensington & Chelsea)
London W8 *p109* 020 7361 2741
Marie-France, J (LD Law)
Harlow *p239*. 01279 441266
Marin Pedreno, C (Dawson Cornwell) *D1 D2 K1 K3*
London WC1 *p26* 020 7242 2556
Marinaccio, R (Palmers Criminal Defence Solicitors) *G H*
Deal *p207* 01304 380572
Marin-Curtoud, B (Jones Day) *T1*
London EC4 *p46*. 020 7039 5959
Marine, S (Saul Marine & Co)
London NW7 *p58* 020 8959 3611
Maring, Miss L (Wright & Lord)
Morecambe *p319* 01524 402050
Marino, L N (Harbottle & Lewis LLP)
London W1 *p38* 020 7667 5000
Marino, P M (Addleshaw Goddard) *O*
London EC1 *p4* 020 7606 8855
Mariscal, Miss S (Hansells) *N Q Zr*
Norwich *p334* 01603 615731
Marjoram, Miss R J (Rotherham Metropolitan Borough Council) *D1 K1*
Rotherham *p470*. 01709 382121
Marjoram, Ms S (Irwin Mitchell LLP)
Sheffield *p376* 0870 150 0100
Mark, J L (Mark Gilbert Morse) *E N C1 P*
Newcastle upon Tyne *p325* . 0191 261 0096
Mark, J N (Richards & Lewis) *N Q G W K1 S1 L H Zi Zq*
Ebbw Vale *p216* 01495 350018

See p634 for the Key to Work Categories

Mark, Miss M G (Mark & Co) *G H K1 D1*
London W14 *p58* 020 7603 3710 / 7602 6942
Markall, Miss K S (Bells Solicitors) *W K4 T2*
Farnham *p224* 01252 733733
Markanday, N (Ashurst LLP)
London EC2 *p7* 020 7638 1111
Mark-Bell, Ms L A (Henmans LLP) *W*
Oxford *p343* 01865 781000
Mark-Bell, W D (Wragg Mark-Bell Solicitors) *G H P Zy B2 A1 J2 A2 Zi Zc Zu C1 S2 E K4 J1 Zl*
Carlisle *p182* 01228 711728
Markbreiter, C P (Department for Business, Enterprise and Regulatory Reform)
London SW1 *p105* 020 7215 0105
Marken, G P A (Coutts & Co)
London WC2 *p105* 020 7753 1403
Markey, D (Ashurst LLP)
London EC2 *p7* 020 7638 1111
Markhah, Miss S J L (Lupton Fawcett) *K3*
Leeds *p275* 0113 280 2000
Markham, A J (Andrew Markham & Co) *G H Zm J1*
Carmarthen *p182* .01267 221550 / 236199
Markham, J (Raleys) *N*
Barnsley *p125* 01226 211111
Markham, Miss J L (Copeman Markham Solicitors) *G H*
Hull *p256* 01482 212979
Markham, L P (DAC Beachcroft)
London EC4 *p24* 020 7242 1011
Markham, Mrs M G (Gullands) *K1 K3*
Maidstone *p299* 01622 678341
Markham, Ms R (Tollers LLP) *A1 E K4 K1 S1 T2 W*
Northampton *p332* 01604 258558
Markham, Ms R E (Gordons LLP) *K1*
Leeds *p273* 0113 227 0100
Leeds *p275* 0113 280 2000
Markham, Mrs S (Chiltern District Council)
Amersham *p447* 01494 729000
Markham, Miss S J L (Hartley & Worstenholme) *W*
Castleford *p183* 01977 732222
Markham, S P (Poole Alcock)
Sandbach *p372* 01270 762325
Nantwich *p320* 01270 625478
Markland, Mrs G (Ingrams) *J1*
York *p445* 01904 520600
Thirsk *p411* 01845 526222
Markland, Ms J (Veale Wasbrough Vizards) *N Zr*
Bristol *p165* 0117 925 2020
Markovitz, Ms J (Withers LLP) *W T2 Zd*
London EC4 *p92* 020 7597 6000
Marks, A A (Aubrey David) *L E J1 W C1 Zl S2 R2*
Westminster *p25* 020 7224 4410
Marks, A C (Taylor Wessing) *E*
London EC4 *p86* 020 7300 7000
Marks, A J (Alexander Marks LLP) *C1 E F1 J1 L N O Q S1 W Zi Zj Zb Zd Zk*
Westminster *p5* 020 7317 1166
Marks, A L (CMS Cameron McKenna LLP)
London EC3 *p17* 020 7367 3000
Marks, B A (Moerans) *S1*
Edgware *p217* 020 8952 0242
Marks, C (Squire Sanders (UK) LLP) *E S1 C1 A1 L*
Leeds *p277* 0113 284 7000
Marks, Miss D C (South Gloucestershire Council)
Thornbury *p474* 01454 868686
Marks, D J (Veja and Co Solicitors) *Q K1 L Zi*
Southall *p385* 020 8574 2626
Marks, Mrs D M (Chambers Fletcher LLP) *W T2*
Northwich *p333* 01606 780400
Marks, D R (CMS Cameron McKenna LLP)
London EC3 *p17* 020 7367 3000
Marks, Ms L (Dawson Cornwell) *K1 K3*
London WC1 *p26* 020 7242 2556
Marks, O M (O M Marks & Co) *C1 S2 E L S1 W*
Barnet *p58* 020 8371 6689
Marks, P (Forshaws Davies Ridgway LLP) *K1 R1 S1 E Zc P Zi*
Warrington *p422* 01925 230000
Marks, S H (Maxwell Winward LLP) *E R2 L*
London EC4 *p59* 020 7651 0000
Marland, G A (Berwins Solicitors Limited) *W T1 T2*
Harrogate *p240* 01423 509000
Marland, Mrs J E (HRJ Law LLP) *W T2*
Hitchin *p251* 01462 628888
Marlborough, S (Lock & Marlborough) *E L S1 W R1 F1 J1 A1 Zl Zi Zs*
London W3 *p55* 020 8993 7231
Marle, Miss K (Pennon Group PLC) *C1 U2 Ze C2 Zza*
Exeter *p458* 01392 446677
Marles, Miss D (Vale of Glamorgan Council)
Barry *p448* 01446 700111
Marles, Mrs W P (GHP Legal) *S1 W*
Wrexham *p442* 01978 291456
Marley, Mrs A (Willson Hawley & Co) *D1 K1 G H J1 N O P S1 V*
Nuneaton *p339* 024 7638 7821
Marley, S E (Stunt Palmer & Robinson)
London E2 *p84* 020 7739 6927
Marlow, C R J (Wiggin Osborne Fullerlove) *C1 M2 T1 T2 W Zd Zo*
Cheltenham *p189* 01242 710200
London SW1 *p91* 020 7290 2456
Marlow, E (Bryan Cave) *Zb*
London EC2 *p19* 020 7207 1100
Marlow, E M (SNR Denton) *Zb*
London EC4 *p75* 020 7242 1212

Marlow, G J (MSB International PLC)
Bromley *p452* 020 8315 9000
Marlow, Miss T (Kingsley Napley) *C1 E Zc*
London EC1 *p50* 020 7814 1200
Marlow-Ridley, S (LDJ Solicitors) *G K1 N Q D1 F1 J1 Zl*
Hinckley *p250* 01455 637030
Marmion, Miss K E (Bower Cotton Khaitan) *S1 T2 W*
London EC4 *p15* 020 7353 1313
Marmor, P D (Sherrards) *A3 B1 I Ze B2 Zk O Q*
St Albans *p390* 01727 832830
Marner, J M (Macaskill's) *C1 E S1 W*
Buckley *p168* 01244 544477
Maroo, A (HM Land Registry - Harrow Sub Office)
Harrow *p460* 020 8235 1181
Marot, Ms M A C J (Veronique Marot & Co) *C1 E J1 Zd S1*
Leeds *p275* 0113 258 2021
Marquand, Dr P B (Capsticks Solicitors LLP) *N Zr Zm*
London SW19 *p18* 020 8780 2211
Marquis Carr, C S (Roland Robinsons & Fentons LLP) *E S1 S2 W Zd*
Blackpool *p147* 01253 621432
Marquis, A R (Merrony Wall) *J1 O Q A3*
Twickenham *p416* 020 8898 4700
Marquis, W A (Cartmell Shepherd) *A1 E J1 L S2*
Penrith *p346* 01768 862326
Marr, D D (Cardiff County Council)
Cardiff *p453* 029 2087 2000
Marr, Ms F (Ashurst LLP)
London EC2 *p7* 020 7638 1111
Marray, N (Quinn Melville) *G H Zl*
Liverpool *p290* 0151 236 3340
Marriott, Ms A (Kennedys)
Chelmsford *p186* 0845 838 4800
Marriott, Miss A J (Davies & Partners) *Zr N*
Almondsbury *p115* 01454 619619
Marriott, A L (Debevoise & Plimpton)
London EC2 *p26* 020 7786 9000
Marriott, D C (Seddons) *E S1 R1 A1 R2 S2*
Westminster *p77* 020 7725 8000
Marriott, Ms H (Brabners Chaffe Street)
Liverpool *p286* 0151 600 3000
Marriott, I L (Warwickshire County Council)
Warwick *p475* 01926 410410
Marriott, J (Charles Russell LLP) *E S1 C1 A1*
Guildford *p235* 01483 252525
Marriott, Ms K (Atherton Godfrey) *K1 D1 D2 K3*
Doncaster *p211* 01302 320621
Marriott, M J (Phillips) *K1 D1 G H*
Mansfield *p312* 01623 658556
Marriott, M S (Dakers Marriott Solicitors) *K1 Q C1 S2 E Ze J1 L Zl O R1 R2 S1 W K3 Zq*
Strood *p400* 01634 813300
Marriott, R R (Marriott Davies Yapp) *C1 I C2 J1 P O M1 M2 C3 Q Ze Zc Zb Za*
Sutton *p402* 020 8643 9794
Marriott, Mrs S J (Charles Russell LLP) *T2 W Zd K4*
Guildford *p235* 01483 252525
London EC4 *p19* 020 7203 5000
Marrison, Ms C R (The Mersey Docks & Harbour Co)
Liverpool *p463* 0151 949 6000
Marron, P A (Marrons) *R1 C1 E O*
Leicester *p280* 0116 289 2200
Marrow, Ms A L (Humphries Kirk) *R1 S2 S1 E L R2 Zh*
Poole *p352* 01202 725400
Marrow, M E (Humphries Kirk) *R1 E L Zc Zh S2*
Poole *p352* 01202 725400
Marrow, P E (Tanners) *O J1 Q N B1 F1*
Cirencester *p195* 01285 659061
Marrs, G (Alan Edwards & Co) *Zh L Q Zg Zu*
Kensington & Chelsea *p28* 020 7221 7644
Marrs, P (Cartmell Shepherd)
Carlisle *p182* 01228 516666
Marsden, A (Haworth Holt Bell Limited) *S2 E L S1*
Altrincham *p116* 0161 928 7136
Marsden, D K (Matthew Arnold & Baldwin LLP) *S1 E S2*
Milton Keynes *p317* 01908 687880
Marsden, Ms E A (Thomas Cooper) *N O Q M1 Za Zj*
London EC3 *p22* 020 7481 8851
Marsden, Mrs E J (Walker Morris) *C1 C2*
Leeds *p277* 0113 283 2500
Marsden, Ms F J (Birchall Blackburn LLP) *N*
Preston *p356* 01772 561663
Marsden, Ms J (Memery Crystal) *O Q Zj Zk M2 Zn*
London WC2 *p60* 020 7242 5905
Marsden, K G (Marsden Duncan) *B1 S2 E K3 J1 K1 R1 L S1 W*
Cliftonville *p196* 01843 295741
Marsden, P (Willetts Marsden) *S1 Q N K1 W F1 P T1 L*
Warrington *p422* 01925 230020
Marsden, P A R B (Brabners Chaffe Street) *E W S2 S1 R1*
Manchester *p301* 0161 836 8800
Marsden, P J (Shaw Marsden) *E S1 C1*
Taunton *p408* 01823 330944
Marsden, R J B (Johnson & Gaunt) *W S1 R1 T1 A1 E M1 B1 Zm*
Banbury *p122* .01295 256271 / 271200
Marsden, R L (The Howe Practice) *S1 S2 W K1 F1 Q G J1 Zl*
Stockport *p395* 0161 480 2629

Marsden, S J (Livingstons) *W T2 V Zv*
Ulverston *p416* 01229 585555
Marsden, Miss S K (Scotts Wright) *S1 S2 W K4*
Leyburn *p283* 01966 22227
Marsden, S P (Dicksons Solicitors Ltd) *K1 S1 J1 N D1 Q L W Zl*
Stoke-on-Trent *p397* 01782 262424
Marsh, A (Hill Dickinson LLP) *O Zj Za*
Manchester *p305* 0161 817 7200
Marsh, Miss A (Metcalfe Copeman & Pettefar) *C1*
Thetford *p410* 01842 756100
Marsh, A B (A B Marsh Solicitors) *D1 G V H K1 B2 D2 Zg C1 S2 E K3*
Salford *p371* 0161 839 2626
Marsh, A C M (DAC Beachcroft) *O Zc*
Leeds *p272* 0113 251 4700
Marsh, Ms A L (Reynolds Porter Chamberlain LLP)
London E1 *p71* 020 3060 6000
London EC2 *p81* 020 7655 1000
Marsh, A L (Fishburns) *O Q Zc Zj Zo Zq*
London EC3 *p32* 020 7280 8888
Marsh, C G (Payne Marsh Stillwell) *O N Zk*
Southampton *p386* 023 8022 3957
Marsh, C J (Marsh Brown & Co) *K1 N J1*
Lewisham *p59* 020 8852 0052
Marsh, D J (Burges Salmon) *C1 C2*
Bristol *p161* 0117 939 2000
Marsh, D J (Wragge & Co LLP)
London EC1 *p93* 0870 903 1000
Marsh, Miss E J (Henmans LLP) *K1 K3*
Oxford *p343* 01865 781000
Marsh, Mrs F M (Scott Duff & Co) *S1 W L A1 E*
Penrith *p346* 01768 865551
Marsh, Mrs H (KBL Solicitors) *S2 E*
Bolton *p149* 01204 527777
Marsh, H S (Pond Marsh) *K1 D1 N Q*
Blackpool *p147* 01253 620466
Marsh, I A (Withers LLP) *T2 W*
London EC4 *p92* 020 7597 6000
Marsh, J (Ashurst LLP)
London EC2 *p7* 020 7638 1111
Marsh, J (Squire Sanders (UK) LLP)
London EC2 *p81* 020 7655 1000
Marsh, J J (Woodfines LLP) *W T2*
Bedford *p130* 01234 270600
Marsh, Ms K (Simmons & Simmons)
London EC2 *p79* 020 7628 2020
Marsh, M W B (Collyer Bristow LLP) *Q L I*
London WC1 *p22* 020 7242 7363
Marsh, P R B (Darbys Solicitors LLP) *E S2*
Oxford *p343* 01865 811700
Marsh, P W (Peter W Marsh & Co) *C1 E F1 G J1 L M1 N P*
Melton Mowbray *p314* 01664 566471
Marsh, R (Financial Services Authority)
London E14 *p106* 020 7066 1000
Marsh, R D (Taylor Wessing)
London EC4 *p86* 020 7300 7000
Marsh, Mrs S (Bobbetts Mackan) *S1 S2 E W K4*
Bristol *p161* 0117 929 9001
Marsh, S F T (Adams Delmar) *S1 E P M1 W F1 L*
Hampton *p238* 020 8941 2097
Marsh, S J (Scott Duff & Co) *N G Q F1 H L V*
Penrith *p346* 01768 865551
Marsh, Mrs S M (Dudley Metropolitan Borough Council) *K1 D1 V F1*
Dudley *p457* 01384 815326
Marsh, Miss V J (Russell & Russell) *K4 W*
Bolton *p149* 01204 399299
Marsh, W (Ince & Co Services Ltd)
London E1 *p44* 020 7481 0010
Marshall, Miss A (Anthony Clark & Co) *K1*
Lincoln *p284* 01522 512321
Marshall, A B (Marsden Rawsthorn LLP) *W T2 K4 Zm*
Preston *p357* 01772 799600
Marshall, Ms A S (Sampson & Co) *K3 K1*
Redditch *p362* 01527 66221
Marshall, A S H (Coodes) *Q O*
Launceston *p270* 01566 770000
Marshall, B (Mills & Reeve) *C1 C2 C3*
Cambridge *p175* 01223 364422
Marshall, Mrs B A (Turnbull Garrard) *S1 W L A1 T1 E C1 R1 Zd*
Shrewsbury *p379* .01743 350851 / 351332
Marshall, B C F (Symes Robinson & Lee) *W S1 S2 A1*
Exeter *p222* 01392 270867
Marshall, Mrs C D (Portsmouth Magistrates Court)
Portsmouth *p469* 023 9281 9421
Marshall, C J G (Burnetts) *Zc O*
Carlisle *p181* 01228 552222
Marshall, Ms C L (Aviva PLC)
London EC3 *p103* . 020 7283 7500 / 01603 687905
Norwich *p467* 01603 622200
Marshall, Mrs C S (Charles Lucas & Marshall) *K3 K1 D1*
Newbury *p322* 01635 521212
Marshall, D (Osborne Clarke) *Zb*
London EC2 *p65* 020 7105 7000
Marshall, D C (Dawson Hart) *A1 C1 E S1 T1 W*
Uckfield *p416* 01825 762281
Marshall, Ms D E (Marshalls) *K1 D1 F1 G H M1 L N P R1 Zi Zm*
Plymouth *p350* 01752 254555
Marshall, D T (Anthony Gold) *N C1 J1 Zr*
London SE1 *p6* 020 7940 4000
Marshall, Mrs E S (London Borough of Haringey)
London N22 *p106* 020 8489 0000
Marshall, Mrs G (Leeds City Council)
Leeds *p462* 0113 224 3513

Marshall, Ms H (Bingham McCutchen (London) LLP)
London EC2 *p12* 020 7661 5300
Marshall, Miss H A (Financial Services Authority)
London E14 *p106* 020 7066 1000
Marshall, Ms H J (Financial Services Authority)
London E14 *p106* 020 7066 1000
Marshall, Mrs H M (Leeds City Council)
Leeds *p462* 0113 224 3513
Marshall, I G (Wychavon District Council)
Pershore *p468* 01386 565000
Marshall, Ms J (Nabarro LLP)
London WC1 *p63* 020 7524 6000
Marshall, J (GHP Legal) *W T1 T2 S1 S2*
Wrexham *p442* 01978 291456
Marshall, J A (T C Smith) *A1 C1 E S1 L*
Berwick-upon-Tweed *p131* 01289 307409
Marshall, J C R (Bell Lamb & Joynson) *G H W S1 F1 Zl K4 Q N*
Runcorn *p369* 0844 412 4348
Marshall, Ms J J (North Bedfordshire Magistrates Court)
Bedford *p449* 01234 319100
Marshall, J M (Taylor Wessing)
London EC4 *p86* 020 7300 7000
Marshall, Mrs J M (Squire Sanders (UK) LLP) *O*
London EC2 *p81* 020 7655 1000
Marshall, J P B (Dickinson Dees) *O*
Newcastle upon Tyne *p324* 0191 279 9000
Marshall, J R (Lupton Fawcett) *B1 O*
Leeds *p275* 0113 280 2000
Marshall, Mrs K E (Waddington & Son) *D2 K1 K3 D1 G H*
Burnley *p169* 01282 426666
Marshall, L J (Shoosmiths) *N*
Northampton *p332* . 0370 086 3000 / 01604 543000
Marshall, M A (Brown & Murray) *S1 G K1 H E L J1 R1 F1 D1*
Millom *p316* 01229 772562
Marshall, Mrs M E (City of Sunderland)
Sunderland *p473* 0191 520 5555
Marshall, Mrs M G (Marsden Rawsthorn LLP) *W T2 K4*
Preston *p357* 01772 799600
Marshall, Miss M L (Hayes & Storr) *W T2 K4*
Wells-next-the-Sea *p425* 01328 710210
Marshall, Mrs M W (Reynolds Parry-Jones) *S1 W T2 Zd*
High Wycombe *p250* 01494 525941
Marshall, Mrs N (Chattertons Solicitors) *S2 E C1 A1 S1 C2*
Boston *p151* 01205 351114
Marshall, N J (Marshall Hatchick) *E L C1 C2 Zf Zl*
Woodbridge *p439* 01394 388411
Marshall, Miss P A (Weightmans LLP) *N*
Liverpool *p291* 0151 227 2601
Marshall, P G (Stephens & Scown) *K1 D1 Zi D2*
St Austell *p391* 01726 74433
Marshall, R (Wolverhampton City Council)
Wolverhampton *p477* 01902 556556
Marshall, R (Royce Marshall & Co) *D1 E G J1 K1 L N Q S1 W*
Retford *p363* 07765 404753
Marshall, Mrs R A (Ashby-de-la-Zouch Petty Sessional Division)
Coalville *p455* 01530 810661
Hinckley *p461*
Marshall, R J (Sills & Betteridge LLP) *G H B2 Zg Zl Zm*
Lincoln *p285* 01522 542211
Marshall, R S J (Henriques Griffiths) *F1 F2 L O Q*
Bristol *p163* 0117 909 4000
Marshall, R W P (Reynolds Porter Chamberlain LLP) *N Q Zq Zr*
London E1 *p71* 020 3060 6000
Marshall, S (Ormerods) *E S1 W C1 R2*
Croydon *p205* 020 8686 5000
Marshall, Miss S E (McCormicks) *C1 Zw Ze*
Harrogate *p240* 01423 530630
Marshall, S F (Robinsons) *C1 E S1 Zd*
Derby *p209* 01332 291431
Marshall, Mrs S L (Aldridge Brownlee Solicitors LLP) *S1 S2*
Christchurch *p194* 01425 282150
Marshall, T (Hogan Lovells International LLP)
London EC1 *p42* 020 7296 2000
Marshall, Miss T (Birmingham City Council Legal & Democratic Services)
Birmingham *p449* 0121 303 2066
Marshall, T J (Brabners Chaffe Street) *W S1 E K4 T2*
Liverpool *p286* 0151 600 3000
Marshall, T J (Hill Dickinson LLP) *A1 E L R1 S1 Zc*
London EC3 *p41* 020 7283 9033
Marshall, T M (Cheyney Goulding)
Guildford *p236* 01483 567676
Marshall, Ms T R (LG Lawyers)
London SE1 *p50* 020 7379 0000
Marshall, T T (DLA Piper UK LLP) *J1*
London EC2 *p24* 0870 011 1111
Marshall, Mrs V L (Shulmans) *S1*
Leeds *p276* 0113 245 2833
Marshall, W (Ince & Co Services Ltd)
London E1 *p44* 020 7481 0010
Marshland, Miss E M C (Blake Lapthorn) *M1 O Q*
Chandlers Ford *p184* 023 8090 8090
Marsland, Ms J P (Hopley Pierce & Bird) *S1 K1*
Wrexham *p443* 01978 315100
Marsland, Miss V G (Clifford Chance)
London E14 *p20* 020 7006 1000

6

Marson, Miss G (Crombie Wilkinson) *K1*
York *p444* 01904 624185

Marston, C B (Hillyer McKeown LLP) *W Zm*
Chester *p190* 01244 318131

Marston, J W (Bone & Payne LLP) *S1 W S2 T2 L*
Colwyn Bay *p198* 01492 532385

Marston, L R (Clough & Willis) *K1 D1 V K3*
Bury *p170* 0161 764 5266

Marston-Jones, D (Lanyon Bowdler LLP) *J1 Q*
Wellington *p425* 01952 244721

Martell, Ms J (ASB Law)
Crawley *p202* 01293 603600

Martil, Mrs M A (Batchelors Solicitors) *Zh L*
Bromley *p166* 020 8768 7000

Martin, Ms A (Downs) *J1*
Dorking *p212* 01306 880110

Martin, A A (Mullis & Peake) *E C1 R1 S1 W L Zi Zl*
Romford *p366* 01708 784000

Martin, A E (Dicksons Solicitors Ltd) *N O Q J1 K1 V W Zr*
Stoke-on-Trent *p397* 01782 262424

Martin, Ms A K (LG Lawyers)
London SE1 *p50* 020 7379 0000

Martin, Miss A K (Greenways) *S1 S2*
Newquay *p329* 01637 872361 / 872251
Wadebridge *p418* 01208 812415

Martin, Mrs A L (Heath & Blenkinsop) *S1 S2 W T2*
Warwick *p422* 01926 492407

Martin, Ms A P (Squire Sanders (UK) LLP)
London EC2 *p81* 020 7655 1000

Martin, B (Clarke Willmott)
Bristol *p162* 0845 209 1000 / 0117 305 6000

Martin, B (Martin & Strain) *S1 S2 W*
Pwllheli *p358* 01758 612042

Martin, B J (John P Martin & Co) *S2 E K4 S1 W*
Scarborough *p372* 01723 500922

Martin, C (Hanne & Co)
London SW11 *p38* 020 7228 0017

Martin, Ms C A (Bircham Dyson Bell)
Westminster *p13* 020 7227 7000

Martin, Mrs C A (Taylor Vinters) *S2 E Zh S1*
Cambridge *p176* 01223 423444

Martin, C D Z (Macfarlanes) *C1*
London EC4 *p56* 020 7831 9222

Martin, C J (Griffith Smith Conway)
Hove *p254* 01273 821577

Martin, Miss C R (George Green LLP) *C1 C2 U1 I*
Cradley Heath *p201* 01384 410410

Martin, Ms D (Stockport Metropolitan Borough Council)
Stockport *p472* 0161 480 4949

Martin, Mrs D (Geldards LLP)
Derby *p208* 01332 331631

Martin, D A (Bishop & Sewell LLP) *S1 W*
London WC1 *p13* 020 7631 4141

Martin, D B (Peter Kandler & Co) *G H*
London W10 *p48* 020 8960 9222

Martin, D E (Paisleys) *G H N*
Workington *p440* 01900 602235

Martin, Miss D J (Royal Mail Group) *L O Zl*
London EC4 *p109* 020 7250 2468

Martin, D K (Cumberland Ellis Peirs) *E L S1 S2 R1 R2 A1 Zh Zs*
London WC1 *p23* 020 7242 0422

Martin, E (DLA Piper UK LLP)
London EC2 *p24* 0870 011 1111

Martin, Ms E (Streathers Solicitors LLP) *S1 L*
London W1 *p84* 020 7034 4200

Martin, Mrs E A (Caradon District Council)
Liskeard *p463* 01579 341000

Martin, Miss E S (Owen White) *E S2 R2 S1*
Slough *p382* 01753 876800

Martin, Miss F (Martin Searle) *J1 O Q F1 B1 Zb Ze Zj*
Brighton *p160* 01273 609911

Martin, F (Stephen Rimmer LLP) *K1*
Eastbourne *p216* 01323 644222

Martin, Ms G (Keppe Rofer)
Brecon *p156* 01874 624627

Martin, Ms G A (Jeffreys & Powell) *K1 D1 D2 V*
Brecon *p156* 01874 622106

Martin, G F (Gateshead Law Centre)
Gateshead *p458* 0191 440 8575

Martin, G F N (Carter-Ruck) *C1 O P Ze Zf Q Zk*
London EC4 *p18* 020 7353 5005

Martin, G M (Memery Crystal) *E S2*
London WC2 *p60* 020 7242 5905

Martin, I A D (I Anthony D Martin) *C1 M2 I M1 U2*
Chorley *p194* 01257 451383

Martin, I C (Macfarlanes) *C1*
London EC4 *p56* 020 7831 9222

Martin, I L (Clifton Ingram LLP) *S1 W Zm K4*
Reading *p360* 0118 957 3425

Martin, J (Linklaters LLP)
London EC2 *p54* 020 7456 2000

Martin, Mrs J A (Kennedys)
Manchester *p306* 0161 829 2599

Martin, Mrs J A (Lancashire County Council) *K1 N G H D1 J1 Zl*
Preston *p469* 01772 254868

Martin, Ms J B (Kerman & Co LLP) *E L S1 R1 P S2*
London WC2 *p49* 020 7539 7272

Martin, Ms J C (Akzo Nobel Ltd)
London SW1 *p103* 020 7009 5000

Martin, J D (Commercial Union PLC)
London EC3 *p105* 020 7283 7500

Martin, J D B (Poole & Co) *S1 A1 E W K1 L R1 C1*
Crewkerne *p203* 01460 279100

Martin, Ms J E (Ashworths Solicitors) *E S2*
London SW19 *p8* 0845 370 1000

Martin, J H (Bartletts) *S1 E W C1 S2*
Haringey *p11* 020 8340 2202 / 8340 2203

Martin, Miss J L (Charles Coleman & Co) *W T2 S2 K4 S1*
Reading *p360* 0118 958 1578

Martin, Ms J L (Bower & Bailey) *Q K1 N*
Oxford *p343* 01865 311133

Martin, J N (Thomson & Bancks LLP) *S1 E W L C1 A1 S2*
Pershore *p346* 01386 562000
Tewkesbury *p410* 01684 299633

Martin, J P (John P Martin & Co) *S1 W E L K4 K3*
Scarborough *p372* 01723 500922

Martin, J R (Laytons) *Ze O U2*
Guildford *p236* 01483 407000

Martin, J S (Carmarthenshire County Council)
Carmarthen *p453* 01267 224010

Martin, Ms K (Hunters) *W T2*
London WC2 *p44* 020 7412 0050

Martin, K (Davies Partnership) *W S1 S2 K4 T2*
St Agnes *p389* 01872 553131

Martin, Mrs K A (Brain Chase Coles) *K3 K1 L*
Basingstoke *p126* 01256 354481

Martin, Mrs L (Blanchards Bailey LLP) *K1 K2*
Blandford Forum *p147* 01258 459361
Dorchester *p212* 01305 251222

Martin, L (Hill Dickinson LLP) *Zm S2 E L A1*
Liverpool *p288* 0151 600 8000

Martin, Ms L (Bristol City Council)
Bristol *p451* 0117 922 2000

Martin, Miss L (Humphries Kirk)
Poole *p352* 01202 725400

Martin, L C (Hodge Jones & Allen LLP) *G H*
London NW1 *p41* 020 7874 8300

Martin, Mrs L J (Brighton & Hove Council - Legal Services) *S1 L*
Hove *p461* 01273 290000

Martin, Ms L M (Mulcahy Smith) *G K1 K3*
Gateshead *p229* 0191 490 1000

Martin, M (Morrisons Solicitors LLP) *K1*
London SW19 *p62* 020 8971 1020

Martin, M (Blake Lapthorn) *B2 O Q Zk*
London EC1 *p13* 020 7405 2000

Martin, Miss M C (Martin-Simms Solicitors) *S1 W C1 E G H L R1 Zl*
London E7 *p59* 020 8552 7042

Martin, M E (Mowbray Woodwards Solicitors) *E S2 C1*
Bath *p128* 01225 485700

Martin, M G (WBW Solicitors) *E J1 L W S1 C1*
Exeter *p222* 01392 202404

Martin, M H J (Manches LLP) *C1 C2*
London WC2 *p58* 020 7404 4433

Martin, M M (Brook Martin & Co) *N P K1 L G C1 F1 J1 Zc*
Westminster *p16* 020 7935 8520

Martin, N A (DFA Law LLP) *B1 N O F1 F2 Q Zq*
Northampton *p331* 01604 609560

Martin, N J (Ward Hadaway) *Zr*
Newcastle upon Tyne *p327* 0191 204 4000

Martin, N J (Bonallack & Bishop) *S1 W S2 K4 Zd A1*
Amesbury *p117* 01980 622992

Martin, O B (Shoosmiths) *E S2*
Birmingham *p142* 0370 086 4000 / 0121 335 4440

Martin, P (Nexus Solicitors) *E S2 S1*
Manchester *p308* 0161 819 4900

Martin, P (David J Foster & Co) *K1 K3*
Tamworth *p407* 01827 58333 / 58334

Martin, Mrs P A (Andrews Martin) *K4 W Zm*
Swindon *p406* 01793 641707

Martin, P A (Society of Lloyd's)
London EC3 *p107* 020 7327 1000

Martin, P D (OGR Stock Denton) *K1 M1 D1 F1 L J1 K2 Zq*
London N3 *p64* 020 8349 0321

Martin, P G (Randell Lloyd & Martin) *A1 B1 C1 D1 E F1 G H J1*
Llanelli *p292* 01554 772149

Martin, P J (Scott Son & Chitty) *Q O S1 E G W S2*
Ashtead *p119* 01372 276211

Martin, P J (Wellers Law Group LLP) *C1 C2 S1 E F1 R1 R2 A3 Zd Zc*
Bromley *p167* 020 8464 4242
London WC1 *p91* 020 7242 7265

Martin, P J (Higgs & Sons) *E S2 R1 P Zd*
Brierley Hill *p158* 0845 111 5050

Martin, P R (Wren Martin) *K1 S1 W*
Stockton-on-Tees *p397* 01642 603609

Martin, P T (McGrigors LLP) *C1 C2*
London EC4 *p56* 020 7054 2500

Martin, R (Ince & Co Services Ltd)
London E1 *p44* 020 7481 0010

Martin, Mrs R (Follett Stock LLP) *Q O Zq N L F1*
Truro *p414* 01872 241700

Martin, R (Speechly Bircham LLP) *J1*
London EC4 *p81* 020 7427 6400

Martin, R (Herbert Smith LLP) *C1*
London EC2 *p40* 020 7374 8000

Martin, R A (Andrews Martin) *S1 S2 W E L C1 O Zl*
Swindon *p406* 01793 641707

Martin, Miss R E S (Reuters Group PLC)
London E14 *p109* 020 7250 1122

Martin, R J (DAC Beachcroft) *E S1 Zh*
London EC4 *p24* 020 7936 2222

Martin, Mrs S (Oldhams Solicitors & Advocates) *D1 K3 K1*
Baldock *p121* 01462 895444

Martin, S (Barlow Lyde & Gilbert LLP)
London EC3 *p10* 020 7247 2277

Martin, S (Greenwoods)
Milton Keynes *p317* 01908 298200

Martin, Mrs S (Boyes Turner) *K4 T2 W Zm*
Reading *p360* 0118 959 7711

Martin, Ms S (Crossmans)
Radstock *p358* 01761 431688

Martin, Miss S A (Pembrokeshire County Council) *N Zu Zj J2 B1*
Haverfordwest *p460* 01437 764551

Martin, S A (Dechert)
London EC4 *p26* 020 7184 7000

Martin, Mrs S A M (Underhill Langley & Wright) *Q O J1 F1 L K1*
Wolverhampton *p438* 01902 423431

Martin, S B (Gartmore Investment Management PLC)
London EC3 *p106* 020 7782 2000

Martin, S C (Carter Read & Dove) *J1*
Swindon *p406* 01793 617617

Martin, Ms S E (Memery Crystal) *J1*
London WC2 *p60* 020 7242 5905

Martin, S E (Treasury Solicitors Department)
London WC2 *p110* 020 7210 3000

Martin, S F (Allen & Overy LLP)
London E1 *p5* 020 3088 0000

Martin, S M (Dickenson Martin) *S1 S2 E W*
Warrington *p421* 01925 574748
Warrington *p422* 01925 571212

Martin, S P (Everys) *D1 F1 K1 L N Q V*
Honiton *p252* 01404 43431

Martin, S R (Macfarlanes) *C1*
London EC4 *p56* 020 7831 9222

Martin, S R (Irwin Mitchell LLP) *S1*
Sheffield *p376* 0870 150 0100

Martin, Mrs S R (Martins) *S1 W K3*
Brockenhurst *p166* 01590 623252

Martin, Miss T (HilliersHRW Solicitors)
Stevenage *p395* 01438 346000

Martin, Mrs T J (North Yorkshire Law)
Scarborough *p372* 01723 360001

Martin, T M (Borough of Poole)
Poole *p469* 01202 262808

Martin, Miss V (Yates Ardern) *H B2 G*
Ashton-under-Lyne *p120* 0161 330 3332

Martin, Miss V E (Bright & Sons) *T2 K4 W*
Maldon *p299* 01621 852323
Witham *p435* 01376 512338

Martin, W A (Curtis Parkinson) *J1 N*
Nottingham *p336* 0115 931 7000

Martin-Moran, Mrs P (C C Bell & Son)
Bedford *p129* 01234 363251

Martin-Summers, P (Higgs & Sons) *S1 W L E A1*
Kingswinford *p268* 01384 342100

Martineau, E C A (Hunters) *W T2*
London WC2 *p44* 020 7412 0050

Martinez, Miss A (The College of Law) *S1 S2 L*
London WC1 *p105* 0800 289997

Martinez, D (Edwards Duthie) *L V*
London E6 *p29* 020 8514 9000

Martini, P F (Cobleys LLP) *G H D1 K1 N S1 S2 E W V*
Liverpool *p287* 0151 242 9000

Martins, Mrs A K (Magrath LLP) *J1 Zp*
London W1 *p57* 020 7495 3003

Martins, Miss S F (Colman Coyle LLP) *J1*
Islington *p22* 020 7354 3000
Norwich *p335* 0870 609 0200

Martland, Ms C L (Graham M Riley & Co)
Southport *p388* 01704 532229

Martyn, C (Fox Williams) *J1*
London EC2 *p33* 020 7628 2000

Martyn, C P (Sumitomo Mitsui Banking Corporation Europe Limited)
London EC4 *p109* 020 7786 1000 / 1017

Martyn, I A (Bond Pearce LLP) *Zj*
Bristol *p161* 0845 415 0000

Martyn, J K (Knight Polson Solicitors) *S1 R2 S2 W*
Eastleigh *p216* 023 8064 4822

Martyn, N (Mundays LLP)
Cobham *p196* 01932 590500

Martynski, M A (Glazer Delmar) *L Zh*
London SE22 *p35* 020 8299 0021

Martyr, C R (Levenes Solicitors)
Birmingham *p140* 0121 212 0000

Maru, Mrs A (London Borough of Haringey)
London N22 *p106* 020 8489 0000

Maru, N (Novell UK Ltd) *C1 I*
Bracknell *p451* 01344 724000

Maruca, Mrs A (Overburys & Raymond Thompson) *K1 K3*
Norwich *p335* 01603 610481

Marven, Miss N (Adams & Remers) *C1 C3 F1 Ze Zza U2 C2 T1*
Lewes *p283* 01273 480616

Marwood, Miss A (Hayton Winkley) *W S1 E*
Kendal *p264* 01539 720136

Marzec, J M (EMW) *O*
London WC2 *p28* 0845 070 6000

Marzheuser-Wood, Ms B (Field Fisher Waterhouse LLP)
London EC3 *p31* 020 7861 4000

Mascarenhas, B C (B C Mascarenhas) *E F1 G H J1 K1 L P S1 W Zd Zi Zl*
Haringey *p59* 020 8889 6246

Mascarenhas, Miss J (Essex County Council) *N Q Zq Zr*
Chelmsford *p454* 0845 743 0430

Mascarenhas, T (PCB Litigation LLP) *B2 O Zq U2 A3 Zb B1 C1 L M2*
London EC1 *p65* 020 7831 2691

Masefield, C W (Masefield Solicitors LLP) *W T1 L A1 S1 C1 E K4*
Ledbury *p271* 01531 632377

Mashall, J (Manches LLP) *Ze U2 I Zza Zf F2 F1 U1*
London WC2 *p58* 020 7404 4433

Masheder, I G (Rotherham Metropolitan Borough Council) *N Q K1 F1 O L G J1 H B1 Zi*
Rotherham *p470* 01709 382121

Mashiter, Miss S D C (Port of London Authority)
London DA12 *p108* 01474 562396

Mashru, Ms H (Williams & Co) *G H V*
Luton *p296* 01582 723322

Masih, B (IBB Solicitors) *N*
Uxbridge *p417* 0845 638 1381

Masih, Mrs J E (Owen White) *C1 C2 C3 J1 I Ze*
Slough *p382* 01753 876800

Masih, S (Glaisyers) *G H I*
Birmingham *p138* 0121 233 2971

Maskell, Ms A C (Aviva PLC)
London EC3 *p103* 020 7283 7500 / 01603 687905
Norwich *p467* 01603 622200

Maskell, Mrs C A (Sherwood-Smith Tilley & Co) *A1 B1 C1 D1 E F1 H J1 K1 Zl Zm Zn*
Houghton Le Spring *p253* 0191 584 3186

Maskell, J S (Department for Business, Enterprise and Regulatory Reform)
London SW1 *p105* 020 7215 0105

Maskery, Miss A (Sintons LLP) *C2 C1 F1 J1*
Newcastle upon Tyne *p326* 0191 226 7878

Maskey, M J (Russell-Cooke LLP) *S2 E*
London WC1 *p74* 020 7405 6566

Maskill, A S L (Addleshaw Goddard) *T1 Zb C1 B3*
Manchester *p300* 0161 934 6000

Maslen, R E A (Stroud District Council) *S1 E L R1 W C1 P*
Stroud *p473* 01453 766321

Masoliver, Y J (Berry & Berry) *D1 K1*
Tonbridge *p412* 01732 355911
Tunbridge Wells *p414* 01892 526344

Mason, A (Shoosmiths) *Zc R1 P J2*
Birmingham *p142* 0370 086 4000 / 0121 335 4440

Mason, A (Ashfords LLP) *S1 S2 R1 L W C1 A1 Zu Zv*
Taunton *p408* 01823 232300

Mason, A D (Davisons) *S1 S2*
Sutton Coldfield *p403* 0121 323 2525

Mason, A F (Dawson Mason & Carr)
Guildford *p236* 01483 576169

Mason, A G (IBM United Kingdom Ltd)
London SE1 *p107* 020 7202 3000

Mason, B (Pickerings LLP) *J1*
Tamworth *p407* 01827 317070

Mason, Mrs C J (Myer Wolff) *K1 K3 D2*
Hull *p257* 01482 223693

Mason, C M (Woolliscrofts) *P N L C1 K1 Zc Ze Zk B1*
Hanley *p239* 01782 204000

Mason, D (Capsticks Solicitors LLP) *N Zr Zm*
London SW19 *p18* 020 8780 2211

Mason, D A (David W Harris & Co) *G H K1 B1 N Q S1 E D1 W Zl*
Pontypridd *p352* 01443 486666

Mason, D E (Financial Services Authority)
London E14 *p106* 020 7066 1000

Mason, D G (Cullimore Dutton) *S1 W A1 A2 R1 L T1 E*
Chester *p190* 01244 356789

Mason, D R (Christopher Davidson Solicitors LLP) *N C1 B1 W J1 R1 L Zc Zk A3 Zd F1 F2 Ze B2 U2 Zl O Q Zq Zp*
Cheltenham *p188* 01242 581481

Mason, Mrs E (Borlase & Company) *S1 L*
Helston *p246* 01326 574988

Mason, Miss E (Green Wright Chalton Annis) *W T2*
Rustington *p369* 01903 774131
Worthing *p441* 01903 234064

Mason, I G (Warrington Borough Council)
Warrington *p475* 01925 444400

Mason, I H R (Redrow PLC)
Flint *p458* 01244 520044

Mason, I J (Financial Services Authority)
London E14 *p106* 020 7066 1000
London EC3 *p10* 020 7247 2277

Mason, I S (MLS Solicitors LLP) *P M1 O C1 I J1 Zd Ze Zg Zi Zk Zp*
Stockport *p396* 0161 968 7037
Northampton *p332* 01604 601575

Mason, Ms J (Kennedys)
London EC3 *p49* 020 7667 9667

Mason, J (Squire Sanders (UK) LLP)
Manchester *p310* 0161 830 5000

Mason, J (Shakespeares) *E*
Birmingham *p142* 0121 237 3000

Mason, Miss J C (Jennifer C Margrave) *W V T2 S1*
Guildford *p236* 01483 562722

Mason, Miss J M (Wannop Fox Staffurth & Bray) *G H*
Bognor Regis *p148* 01243 864001

Mason, J M (Clarkes) *G H B2 Zl*
Telford *p409* 01952 291666

Mason, Mrs J M (Beecroft Maxwell) *W S1 E*
Canvey Island *p177* 01268 511999

Mason, Sir J P (Mason Baggott & Garton) *S1 E W A1 N*
Scunthorpe *p373* 01724 868611

See p634 for the Key to Work Categories

Mason, J R (Simpson Duxbury) *E F1 Q L S1 C1 S2 Zl*
Bradford *p155* 01274 734166

Mason, Miss K N (Boodle Hatfield) *E S1*
Westminster *p14*. 020 7629 7411

Mason, Mrs L (MHM Solicitors) *E C1 S1 W L N R1 A1 T1 V Zc Zd Zh*
Leicester *p280*. 0845 234 0230

Mason, Ms L J (Squire Sanders (UK) LLP)
London EC2 *p81*. 020 7655 1000

Mason, M F (Massers) *W*
Nottingham *p338*. 0115 851 1666

Mason, N (Bevans)
Bristol *p161* 0117 923 7249

Mason, N A (Salmons) *S1 W S2*
Newcastle under Lyme *p323*. 01782 621266

Mason, N C (Hamlins LLP) *E R1*
London W1 *p38* 020 7355 6000

Mason, Miss N J (Humphries Kirk) *W*
Swanage *p404*. 01929 423301

Mason, N P (Squire Sanders (UK) LLP)
London EC2 *p81*. 020 7655 1000

Mason, P (IBB Solicitors) *G H B2*
Uxbridge *p417*. 0845 638 1381

Mason, P (Briffa) *Ze Zf U2 Zza*
Islington *p15*. 020 7288 6003

Mason, P J (Mason Palmer) *K1 Q N W G H D1*
Barnsley *p125* 01226 709100

Mason, P J P (Perry Mason Solicitors) *S1 E L S2 Zl*
Torquay *p413* 01803 299000

Mason, Ms P M (Lester Aldridge LLP)
Bournemouth *p152*. 01202 786161

Mason, P N J (DWF) *S1*
Manchester *p303* 0161 603 5000

Mason, P R (England & Co) *D1 K1 Zm D2*
Great Yarmouth *p234*01493 844308 / 844309

Mason, Miss R (Brown & Corbishley) *G H*
Newcastle under Lyme *p323*. 01782 717888

Mason, Ms R (Mason & Co Solicitors) *Zr Q N Zq*
Hull *p257* 01482 310170

Mason, Mrs R E (Holmes & Hills LLP) *C1 E S2 S1*
Braintree *p155*. 01376 320456

Mason, R J (DWT Legal Ltd) *Q O Zq N B1 A3 F1 Zc Ze L Zk*
Kidderminster *p265* 0844 770 3799

Mason, R J S (Mason Baggott & Garton) *S1 S2 C1 W K4*
Brigg *p158*. 01652 654111
Scunthorpe *p373*. 01724 868611

Mason, Mrs S (Berg Legal) *E S2 S1 R2*
Manchester *p301* 0161 833 9211

Mason, S (Paul Dodds Solicitors) *G H K1 N*
Wallsend *p419*. 0191 263 6200

Mason, Miss S A (Thursfields) *O Q*
Worcester *p440* 01905 730450

Mason, S D (Fishburns) *G H K1 D1 V S1*
London EC3 *p32*. 020 7280 8888

Mason, Mrs S J (George Davies Solicitors LLP) *S2 E R2*
Manchester *p303* 0161 236 8992

Mason, S N (Legal Aid Area Office No 11 (Eastern))
Cambridge *p453*. 01223 366511

Mason, W T (Stanger Stacey & Mason) *K1 N Q O K3*
Witney *p436*. 01993 776491

Mason-Apps, P W (Mason-Apps Smallmans & Co) *S1 K1 E P W S2 N L C1 J1 Zl K3 Zi*
Maidenhead *p298* . .01628 636148 / 636149

Mason-Watts, C (Teifi Law Limited)
Llandysul *p292*. 01559 362744

Masraf, A M (Pinsent Masons LLP) *C1 C2 B1*
London EC2 *p67*. 020 7418 7000

Massam, Mrs R (Warners Solicitors) *K3 K1*
Sevenoaks *p374*. 01732 747900

Massarano, Ms V (DLA Piper UK LLP) *Zo*
Leeds *p272* 0870 011 1111

Massenhove, A (Sykes Anderson LLP) *C1 J1 F1 C2 Zp M3*
London EC2 *p85*. 020 3178 3770
Brentwood *p156* 01277 268368

Masser, I U (Beale and Company Solicitors LLP) *Zq Zj O Q Zc*
London WC2 *p11* 020 7240 3474

Massey, Ms D S (DSM Legal Solicitors)
Warrington *p421*. 0845 009 0863

Massey, Mrs D S (Grace & Co) *J2 N*
Warrington *p422*. 01925 242488

Massey, P (Penningtons) *Zc*
London EC2 *p66*. 020 7457 3000

Massey, P J (British American Tobacco)
London WC2 *p104*. 020 7845 1000

Massey, Ms R (FBC Manby Bowdler LLP) *W*
Wolverhampton *p437* 01902 578000

Massey, S (CGM) *N P J1 M1 K1 D1 O Q*
Southampton *p385*. 023 8063 2733

Massey, W (Farrer & Co LLP)
London WC2 *p31* 020 3375 7000

Massey-Chase, N G (Brain Chase Coles) *K1 D1 K3*
Basingstoke *p126* 01256 354481

Massey-Crow, Miss H V (DAC Beachcroft) *E*
London EC4 *p24*. 020 7936 2222

Massie, Miss K (Wannop Fox Staffurth & Bray) *S1 K1*
Worthing *p442*. 01903 228200

Masson, N J (Alnwick District Council) *G*
Alnwick *p447* 01665 510505

Massucco, M X (Massucco Buttress) *S1*
Cambridge *p175*. 01223 463183

Massy-Collier, J P (Osborne Clarke) *C1*
London EC2 *p65*. 020 7105 7000

Masterman, Mrs L (Clarke & Hartland Solicitors) *S1 E R1 N W L*
Cardiff *p177* 029 2048 3181

Masters, Miss A (Scott Rees & Co) *N Q*
Skelmersdale *p381* 01695 722222

Masters, Mrs A K (Hall Smith Whittingham LLP) *K1 Q S1 D1 F1 J1 N*
Crewe *p203* 01270 212000
Nantwich *p320*. 01270 610300

Masters, A S (Furley Page LLP) *J1 J2*
Canterbury *p176*. 01227 763939

Masters, D C (Penningtons)
London EC2 *p66*. 020 7457 3000

Masters, Mrs F R (OGR Stock Denton) *W*
London N3 *p64* 020 8349 0321

Masters, S J (Dixon Rigby Keogh) *E S1 L W Zl J1 K4*
Middlewich *p315*. 01606 835736

Masters, Miss V J (David Cowan) *K1 G H*
Dorking *p212* 01306 886622

Masterson, A (Pinsent Masons LLP) *O Q F1 N Zo*
Leeds *p276* 0113 244 5000

Mastrominas, G (Forsters LLP) *E*
Westminster *p33*. 020 7863 8333

Matcham, Ms A (Aylesbury Vale District Council)
Aylesbury *p447* 01296 585858

Matcham, P W (Maples Teesdale LLP) *Zc*
London EC2 *p58*. 020 7600 3800

Mateo, Miss M (Curtis Davis Garrard) *O Za A3*
Uxbridge *p417*. 020 8734 2800

Matfin, Mrs E J (Hethertons LLP) *K1*
York *p445* 01904 528200

Mathams, Ms R H (Schofield Sweeney) *C1 J1 C2*
Bradford *p154* 01274 306000

Matharoo, S (Blandy & Blandy) *J1*
Reading *p360* 0118 951 6800

Matharu, A (Harbottle & Lewis LLP)
London W1 *p38* 020 7667 5000

Matharu, Miss B (London Borough of Wandsworth)
London SW18 *p110* 020 8871 6000

Matharu, Miss N (Corbett & Co International Construction Lawyers Ltd) *Zc*
Teddington *p409*. 020 8614 6200

Matharu, Miss R (Crutes) *O Q Zl B2 F1 B1 F2 L*
Newcastle upon Tyne *p324* . 0191 233 9700

Mathe, J (Penningtons) *E*
Godalming *p231* 01483 791800

Matheou, M S (Hogan Lovells International LLP)
London EC1 *p42*. 020 7296 2000

Mather, Ms B (Gateley LLP)
Nottingham *p337*. 0115 983 8200

Mather, B J M (Elliot Mather LLP) *D1 G H K1*
Matlock *p313* 01629 584885

Mather, Mrs G (Mather & Co) *S2 S1 K1 N Q W L J1 F1 B1*
Colchester *p197* 01206 322763

Mather, J S (Berkson Wallace Solicitors) *N S1 W*
Ellesmere Port *p217*. 0151 355 4412
Wallasey *p419*. 0151 691 6900

Mather, R (Burnetts) *R2 S2 E R1*
Carlisle *p181*. 01228 552222

Mather, S P (DWF) *N Zj J2*
Preston *p356* 01772 556677

Mather, Ms V F (DLA Piper UK LLP) *E*
Leeds *p272* 0870 011 1111

Mathers, J D (Greene & Greene) *A1 S1 W*
Bury St Edmunds *p171* . . . 01284 762211

Mathers, Ms M L (Gordons LLP)
Leeds *p273* 0113 227 0100

Mathers, Mrs M L (Ford & Warren) *C1 C2 Zza Ze U2 T1*
Leeds *p273* 0113 243 6601

Matherson, Ms P (Steed & Steed LLP) *K1 V K3 K2*
Sudbury *p401* 01787 373387

Matheson, Ms H L (Corus Group Limited)
London SW1 *p105*. 020 7717 4523

Matheson, K (Penningtons) *E*
London EC2 *p66*. 020 7457 3000

Matheson, Miss N (G T Stewart Solicitors) *G H B2*
London SE22 *p83* 020 8299 6000

Mathews, J B (Tassells) *Q N J1 F1 X R1 O Zg J2 L Zu Zm Zq F2 B1*
Faversham *p225*. 01795 533337

Mathews, J C H (Dickson Haslam) *W S1 E G H N Q*
Preston *p356* 01772 883100

Mathias, A B (Linder Myers Solicitors)
Manchester *p306* 0844 984 6000

Mathias, C (Lewis Lewis & Company Ltd) *S1 W E L*
Tenby *p410* 01834 844844

Mathias, E W (Eryl Mathias) *S1 W*
Llanwrda *p292*. 01588 650664

Mathias, Miss K A (David James & Company) *G H K1 K4 N*
Aberystwyth *p114* 01970 615789
Lampeter *p269*. 01570 423300

Mathias, R (Goldkorn Mathias Gentle Page LLP) *O J1 Q C1*
London WC1 *p36* 020 7631 1811

Mathiason, B J (Traymans) *S1 W E F1 Zl Zd Zm Zv*
Hackney *p88*. 020 7249 9980

Mathie, A J (Cocks Lloyd) *K1 G H D1 Zl*
Nuneaton *p339* 024 7664 1642

Mathieson, Ms J I (Donnelly McArdle Adamson) *J1 J2 Q N*
Darlington *p206* 01325 482299

Mathieson, K A (Reynolds Porter Chamberlain LLP) *O Zk Ze*
London E1 *p71* 020 3060 6000

Matini, A (Rawal & Co)
London N12 *p70*. 020 8445 0303

Matkin, Mrs C (Durham County Council)
Durham *p457* 0191 383 3513

Matlib, Miss N (Percy Short & Cuthbert) *Q S1 W*
Islington *p67*. 020 7700 0265

Matloob, Z (Boys & Maughan) *N*
Margate *p312* 01843 234000

Matloubi, Miss R (Imperial Tobacco Group PLC)
Bristol *p452* 0117 963 6636

Maton, J (Edwards Angell Palmer & Dodge)
London EC2 *p28*. 020 7583 4055

Maton, Miss J E (Bowling & Co) *K1*
London E15 *p15* 020 8221 8000

Matossian, J (Lancasters) *E F1 G L O Q R1 S1 Zi*
London W4 *p51* 020 8742 1314

Matranga, Miss N (Beswicks) *G H*
Hanley *p239*. 01782 205000

Matthams, Ms K (LG Lawyers)
London SE1 *p50*. 020 7379 0000

Matthew, Ms F (Frisby & Co) *M3 K1 Q B2 D1*
Stafford *p392* 01785 244114

Matthew, P (G T Stewart Solicitors) *G H B2 J2*
London SE22 *p83* 020 8299 6000

Matthew, R A (Matthew & Matthew Limited) *S1 E L*
Southbourne *p387*. 01202 431943

Matthew, S R (Matthew & Matthew Limited) *S1 E L*
Southbourne *p387*. 01202 431943

Matthew, Miss T (Blake Lapthorn) *C1 C3 F1 F2 I Ze*
Oxford *p342* 01865 248607

Matthew, Miss W (Wyre Borough Council)
Poulton-le-Fylde *p469* 01253 891000

Matthewman, Miss C (Irwin Mitchell LLP)
Sheffield *p376*. 0870 150 0100

Matthewman, Ms J A (Nowell Meller Solicitors Limited) *S1 W*
Stafford *p393* 01785 252377

Matthews, Ms A (Nicholsons Solicitors LLP) *K4 W*
Lowestoft *p294* 01502 532300

Matthews, A D (Trobridges) *J1 C1 C2 Zp*
Plymouth *p350*. 01752 664022

Matthews, A J (Gateley LLP)
Nottingham *p337*. 0115 983 8200

Matthews, A N (Aviva PLC)
London EC3 *p103* . . 020 7283 7500 / 01603 687905
Norwich *p467* 01603 622200

Matthews, Mrs A R (Tassells) *K1 D1 Zq W T2 K4*
Faversham *p225*. 01795 533337

Matthews, Mrs B (Rawlison Butler LLP)
Horsham *p253*. 01403 252492

Matthews, B R (Wilson Browne) *S1 E F1 A1 R1 W L C1*
Kettering *p265*. 01536 410041

Matthews, Ms C (Ashurst LLP)
London EC2 *p7* 020 7638 1111

Matthews, C (Churchers)
Fareham *p223*. 01329 822333

Matthews, Miss C A (Wright Hassall LLP) *L S2 Zd Zh Zu*
Leamington Spa *p270* 01926 886688

Matthews, C D (A S Matthews & Co) *S1 W*
Manchester *p307* 0161 747 2262

Matthews, Mrs C E (Trethowans LLP) *Zl*
Southampton *p387*. 023 8032 1000

Matthews, C J H (Farrell Matthews & Weir) *D1 K1*
London W6 *p30* 020 8746 3771

Matthews, C W G (Trobridges) *N O Q F1 S1 W J1 L K1 C1 Za Zj Zl*
Plymouth *p350*. 01752 664022
Torpoint *p412* 01752 812787

Matthews, D J (Blaser Mills) *N Q*
Staines *p393*. 01784 462511

Matthews, Mrs D J (Nottingham City Council (City Sec Dept)) *N*
Nottingham *p467*. 0115 915 5555

Matthews, G (Leigh Day & Co) *F2 P M2 N*
London EC1 *p52*. 020 7650 1200

Matthews, Miss G M (Mander Hadley & Co) *S1 E W*
Coventry *p200*. 024 7663 1212

Matthews, G M A (Mark Matthews & Co) *M1 P N K1 G H D1 J1 R1 F1 Zj Zl Zm*
Tamworth *p407* 01827 65765

Matthews, G R (Bond Pearce LLP) *O L Zy*
Southampton *p385*. 0845 415 0000

Matthews, Mrs H F (Bolt Burdon) *O*
Islington *p14*. 020 7288 4700

Matthews, H L (Rutters) *Zd S1 J1 L W*
Shaftesbury *p374* 01747 852377

Matthews, J (Reeds Solicitors) *N*
Oxford *p344* 01865 260230

Matthews, Miss J (Burnett Barker) *K1 D1 D2*
Bury St Edmunds *p171* . . . 01284 701131
London W4 *p51* 020 8742 1314

Matthews, J (DLA Piper UK LLP)
London EC2 *p24*. 0870 011 1111

Matthews, K S (London Borough of Haringey)
London N22 *p106* 020 8489 0000

Matthews, L (David W Harris & Co)
Pontypridd *p352* 01443 486666

Matthews, Miss L E (Harvey Ingram LLP) *N*
Leicester *p280*. 0116 254 5454

Matthews, Ms M (The College of Law)
London WC1 *p105*. 0800 289997

Matthews, Miss N J (Hay & Kilner) *K1 N*
Newcastle upon Tyne *p325* . 0191 232 8345

Matthews, Ms N R (Nottingham City Council (City Sec Dept)) *G H*
Nottingham *p467*. 0115 915 5555

Matthews, N S (Denniss Matthews) *S1 C1*
London SE20 *p27* . . 020 8778 7301 / 8778 7631

Matthews, P (Osborne Clarke) *T2 Zo*
Bristol *p164* 0117 917 3000

Matthews, P (Wedlake Bell LLP) *E P Zb R2 S2*
London WC1 *p91* 020 7395 3000

Matthews, P B J (Withers LLP) *O W M2*
London EC4 *p92*. 020 7597 6000

Matthews, P L J (Crown Prosecution Service Dorset)
Bournemouth *p450*. 01202 498700

Matthews, Mrs P M (Burton & Co LLP) *K1 G H D1*
Sleaford *p381* . . . .01529 306008 / 306009

Matthews, P N (Linder Myers Solicitors) *O Q J1 F1*
Manchester *p307* 0844 984 6400

Matthews, R (City of London Magistrates Court)
London EC4 *p107* 020 7332 1830

Matthews, S (CB4law) *D1*
Cambridge *p174*. 01223 316666

Matthews, S (Neves Solicitors) *C1 Zl Zc E*
Milton Keynes *p317* 01908 304560

Matthews, S (Reeds Solicitors) *P Q N*
Oxford *p344* 01865 260230

Matthews, Ms S (McKeowns Solicitors Ltd) *N*
St Albans *p390* 0800 032 8328

Matthews, Mrs S G (Ward Gethin) *E S2 C1*
King's Lynn *p266* 01553 660033

Matthewson, F (Sintons LLP) *N Q O J2*
Newcastle upon Tyne *p326* . 0191 226 7878

Matthews-Stroud, C W (Bird & Lovibond) *E S1 W*
Greenford *p234* 020 8578 6936

Matthias, Ms B (Follett Stock LLP) *J1 K1 Q*
Truro *p414*. 01872 241700

Matthieson, Mrs S I (Awdry Bailey & Douglas) *N*
Calne *p173* 01249 815110

Mattingley, N R (Greenways) *W S1 A1 E T2*
Newquay *p329*. . . .01637 872361 / 872251

Mattis, C (Shoosmiths)
Milton Keynes *p317* . 0370 086 8300 / 01908 488300

Mattison, R (Salans) *O*
London EC4 *p76*. 020 7429 6000

Mattock, S J (Finn Gledhill) *K1 G D1 H*
Halifax *p238* 01422 330000
Hebden Bridge *p246*. 01422 842451

Mattok, J D (West Cumbria Magistrates Courts)
Workington *p477*. 01900 62244

Matts, V G F (Lodders Solicitors LLP) *C1 J1 E*
Stratford-upon-Avon *p400* . . 01789 293259

Matwala, G (Matwala Vyas LLP)
Ilford *p260*. 020 8597 5097

Maud, N J (Hart Brown Solicitors) *C1 C2 J1*
Guildford *p236*. 0800 068 8177

Maude, G A (Russells) *C1 Ze Zf*
London W1 *p75* 020 7439 8692

Maude, J (Manches LLP) *J1 Zp C1 C2 Q J2 Zg*
London WC2 *p58* 020 7404 4433

Maude, Miss V J (Hartley & Worstenholme) *W*
Castleford *p183* 01977 732222

Maudsley, L S (MWP Solicitors) *K1 D1 S1 E C1*
Basildon *p126* 01268 527131

Mauger, Mrs S (West Dorset District Council)
Dorchester *p457*. 01305 251010

Maughan, A (Morrison & Foerster (UK) LLP) *U1 U2 Zza*
London EC2 *p62*. 020 7920 4000
London EC2 *p67*. 020 7847 9500

Maughan, A L (London Borough of Bexley) *L J1 N G H*
Bexleyheath *p449* 020 8303 7777

Maughan, Mrs D (Squire Sanders (UK) LLP) *N Q*
Birmingham *p142* 0121 222 3000

Maughan, Mrs M (Official Solicitor and Public Trustee)
London WC2 *p108*. 020 7911 7127

Maughan, R D C (Boodle Hatfield) *E S1 L R1*
Westminster *p14*. 020 7629 7411

Maughan, Ms R F (Atha & Co)
Middlesbrough *p314* 01642 222575

Maughan, S (Osborne Clarke) *O*
London EC2 *p65*. 020 7105 7000

Maule, H P (LG Lawyers)
London SE1 *p50*. 020 7379 0000

Mault, Miss N (Cheshire East Council)
Sandbach *p464* 0300 123 5500

Maunder, C (Michelmores LLP) *B1 Zb*
London W1 *p60* 020 7659 7660

Maunder, C (Michelmores LLP) *E Zb*
Exeter *p221* 01392 688688

Maunder, Ms D M (Reynolds Parry-Jones) *E S2 S1*
High Wycombe *p250*. 01494 525941

Maunsell Bower, Mrs C B (Maunsell Bower) *K1 N Q W L O C1 K3 E S1*
Wandsworth *p59*. 020 7378 9592

Maunsell, Mrs A C (Nigel Edwards & Co) *K1 K3 D1*
Maidstone *p299* 01622 690575

Maunsell, J J (Goodman Derrick LLP) *F1 J1 M1 N P R1 Ze Zf Zk*
London EC4 *p36*. 020 7404 0606

Maunsell, M J (Bryan O'Connor & Co)
Southwark *p64*. 020 7407 2643

Maurice, Ms C M (Allen & Overy LLP)
London E1 *p5* 020 3088 0000

Maurice, Miss E A (Vincent Sykes & Higham LLP) *W K4 T2 Zd*
Thrapston *p411* 01832 732161

6

Mauro, M (EMW) *R1 Zu E*
Milton Keynes *p316* 0845 070 6000

Mavrikakis, A (The College of Law)
London WC1 *p105*. 0800 289997

Mavroghonis, P C (Hill Dickinson LLP) *O Q A3*
London EC3 *p41*. 020 7283 9033

Mawbey-Shaw, J (Wilsons) *S1 W R2 Q K1 S2 E L*
Horsforth *p253*. 0113 258 6888

Mawdsley, A P (Carters) *O Q N F1 F2 J1 L Zk C1 A3 S1 S2*
Pontefract *p351* 01977 703224

Mawer, B M (Bywaters Topham Phillips LLP)
Harrogate *p240* 01423 879556

Mawer, Miss J (Maples Solicitors LLP) *C1 S2 E W*
Spalding *p389* 01775 722261

Mawer, Ms L (The College of Law)
London WC1 *p105*. 0800 289997

Mawer, T W (Capsticks Solicitors LLP) *J1 Zp J2*
London SW19 *p18*. 020 8780 2211

Mawhinney, Miss P D (Lumb & Macgill) *G H K1 D1*
Bradford *p154* 01274 730666

Mawhood, J N (Blake Lapthorn) *C1 I O Ze*
London EC1 *p13*. 020 7405 2000

Mawi, Ms G K (Stewarts Law LLP) *N Zr*
London EC4 *p83*. 020 7822 8000

Mawle, M C J (National Union of Students)
London N7 *p108*. 020 7272 8900

Mawson, Mrs S (IBB Solicitors) *E S2*
Uxbridge *p417*. 0845 638 1381

Maxey, J R (Buckles Solicitors LLP) *A3 B1 O Zq Zk*
Peterborough *p346* 01733 888888

Maxey, S J (North Warwickshire Borough Council)
Atherstone *p447*. 01827 715341

Maxfield, Mrs C E E (Eric Robinson Solicitors) *K1 D1*
Chandlers Ford *p184* 023 8025 4676

Maxfield, Mrs C M (Basingstoke & Deane Borough Council)
Basingstoke *p448* 01256 845402

Maxim, Ms R (Brendan Fleming)
Birmingham *p138* 0121 683 5000

Maxton, Miss S L (Elmhirst Parker LLP) *K1 S1 N J1 E W C1 S2 K3*
Leeds *p273* 01977 682219

Maxtone-Smith, M J (Reed Smith LLP) *Zf*
London EC2 *p71*. 020 3116 3000

Maxwell, Mrs A (Michelmores LLP) *Zr N*
Exeter *p221* 01392 688688
Exeter *p222* 01392 202404

Maxwell, Ms A (Bond Pearce LLP)
Bristol *p161* 0845 415 0000

Maxwell, A D (Brice & Co) *S1 E W L N C1 G F1*
Bristol *p161* 0117 973 7484

Maxwell, C (Hamlins LLP) *S2 E S1 R2*
London W1 *p38* 020 7355 6000

Maxwell, D (Seddons) *W T2 K4 Zm*
Westminster *p77*. 020 7725 8000

Maxwell, Mrs E M (Maxwell Gillott (MG Law Ltd)) *X Zg*
Lancaster *p270* 0844 858 3900

Maxwell, J M (Hill Dickinson LLP) *N O Za P*
Liverpool *p288*. 0151 600 8000

Maxwell, K A (Field Fisher Waterhouse LLP)
London EC3 *p31*. 020 7861 4000

Maxwell, Miss K T (Moore Blatch Solicitors) *J1*
Southampton *p386*. 023 8071 8000

Maxwell, P (Housemans) *N*
Newcastle upon Tyne *p325* 0191 232 1307

Maxwell, P L (Dickinson Dees) *B1*
Newcastle upon Tyne *p324* . 0191 279 9000

Maxwell, W (Stewarts Law LLP) *N Q*
Leeds *p277* 0113 222 0022

Maxwell-Harris, Miss J M (Joelson Wilson LLP) *J1 Zi Zp*
Westminster *p46*. 020 7580 5721

May, Ms A (Dickins Hopgood Chidley LLP) *K4 T2 W*
Hungerford *p258*. 01488 683555

May, Mrs A C (Crown Prosecution Service Avon & Somerset)
Bristol *p451* 0117 930 2800

May, Ms C (Taylor Wessing)
London EC4 *p86*. 020 7300 7000

May, Miss C E (Squire Sanders (UK) LLP) *Q P Zj*
London EC2 *p81*. 020 7655 1000

May, C M (Battens) *K1 S1*
Yeovil *p443* 01935 846000

May, D (May & Co) *S1*
Barnet *p59*. 020 8200 6116

May, D A (EBR Attridge LLP) *K3 D1 K1 K2*
London N17 *p28*. 020 8808 0774

May, Ms E J O (Field Fisher Waterhouse LLP)
London EC3 *p31*. 020 7861 4000

May, G R (Mayo Wynne Baxter LLP) *W*
Brighton *p160* 01273 775533

May, Mrs H A (West Sussex County Council)
Chichester *p455*. 01243 777100

May, Ms H J (Royds LLP) *J1*
London EC4 *p74*. 020 7583 2222

May, J (CKFT) *K1*
London NW3 *p17* 020 7431 7262

May, Miss J C (Paris Smith LLP) *R1 R2 Zu Zw*
Southampton *p386*. 023 8048 2482

May, Mrs J C (NBM Massucco Shelbourne) *J1*
Cambridge *p175*. 01223 211992

May, Ms J L (British Telecommunications PLC)
London EC1 *p104* 020 7356 6181

May, J P (Freeth Cartwright LLP) *A3 O Zn Zc Zq Zj*
Nottingham *p337*. 0115 936 9369

May, Miss K J (John Ford Solicitors) *X Zu Zg Zp*
London N4 *p33* 020 8800 6464

May, Miss L A (Thomas Saul & Co) *N*
Whitefield *p430* 0161 773 2833

May, L D (Dover District Council)
Dover *p457* 01304 821199

May, P E (Haringey Magistrates Legal Advisers Office)
London N6 *p106*. 0845 601 3600

May, P N S (TLT Solicitors) *N*
Bristol *p165* 0117 917 7777

May, R (Ashurst LLP)
London EC2 *p7* 020 7638 1111

May, R (DLA Piper UK LLP)
Sheffield *p375*. 0870 011 1111

May, R D B (Royds LLP) *Zd*
London EC4 *p74*. 020 7583 2222

May, S D (Edwards Duthie) *G H*
London E13 *p29*. 020 8514 9000

May, Miss S E (DAC Beachcroft)
Birmingham *p137* 0121 698 5200

May, Miss V (Bower & Bailey) *Zr*
Oxford *p343*. 01865 311133

Mayall, Ms S (Pearson Hinchliffe) *J1*
Oldham *p341* 0161 785 3500

Maybaum, Mrs E T (Alan Smeath & Co) *K1 N F1 G H J1 L V Q*
Woburn Sands *p436* .01908 584307 / 584331

Maybury, Miss K E (Raworths LLP) *W Zm K4*
Harrogate *p240* 01423 566666

Maycock, J d A (Withers LLP) *Ze*
London EC4 *p92*. 020 7597 6000

Maye, G S (Gerard Maye Legal Limited)
Brighton *p160* 01273 560444

Maye, Miss L (Colchester Borough Council)
Colchester *p455*. 01206 282222

Mayer, A (Simmons & Simmons)
London EC2 *p79*. 020 7628 2020

Mayer, A G A (Charles Russell LLP)
Cheltenham *p187* 01242 221122

Mayers, C J (MLM Cartwright) *J1 N J2 Q Zr Zq Zp*
Cardiff *p179* 029 2046 2562

Mayers, Miss D (Corus Group Limited)
London SW1 *p105*. 020 7717 4523

Mayers, I J (Mills & Reeve) *N Zj Zl*
Norwich *p335* 01603 660155

Mayes, C S (Leelanes Solicitors LLP)
London EC3 *p52*. 020 7220 9410

Mayes, Ms F (Irwin Mitchell LLP) *N Zr*
Sheffield *p376* 0870 150 0100

Mayes, Miss K E (HRJ Law LLP) *K1 D1 F1 Zp K3*
Welwyn Garden City *p425* . . 01707 887700

Mayes, W (Kennedys) *Q N*
Chelmsford *p186*. 0845 838 4800

Mayfield, Miss A (Gateley LLP) *Zb C1 C2*
Nottingham *p337*. 0115 983 8200

Mayhead, Ms K E (Epsom & Ewell Borough Council)
Epsom *p458*. 01372 732000

Mayhew, A (Moore Blatch Solicitors) *E R1 S1*
Southampton *p386*. 023 8071 8000

Mayhew, D W (Herbert Smith LLP)
London EC2 *p40*. 020 7374 8000

Mayhew, Mrs J S (Dawson Hart) *W K4*
Uckfield *p416* 01825 762281

Mayhew, Miss L (Attwaters) *K4 W*
Harlow *p239*. 01279 638888

Maylard, Mrs V J (Atteys) *D1 K1 D2*
Barnsley *p124* 01226 212345
Wath-upon-Dearne *p424*. . . 01709 872106

Maylin, T (E Edwards Son & Noice) *N J1 L Zr Zq Q*
Billericay *p133*. 01277 658551

Mayman, S (Ison Harrison)
Leeds *p274* 0113 284 5000

Maynard, A T (Andrew Maynard & Co)
Bath *p127* 01225 461146

Maynard, K P (Jaffe Porter Crossick) *O Q N D1 J1 K1*
London NW6 *p46* 020 7625 4424

Maynard, P A D (Bedwell Watts & Co) *D1 G K1 N H L S1 R1 C1 J1 Zm Zw*
Scarborough *p372* . 01723 373356 / 363553

Maynard, P M (Prudential PLC) *C1 Zb*
London EC4 *p108* 020 7220 7588

Mayne, D (Read Dunn Connell) *E N Q S1*
Bradford *p154* 01274 723858

Mayne, Ms H E (David Gist Solicitors) *N*
Bristol *p162* 0117 927 9111

Mayne, J (Bittermann & Wood) *G K1 M1 P S1 D1*
North Shields *p330*0191 257 3211 / 259 6806

Mayne, Miss K S (Radcliffes Le Brasseur) *S1*
Westminster *p70*. 020 7222 7040

Maynereid, Ms K E (Talbots Legal Advice Centre) *G*
Stourbridge *p399* . 01384 445850 / 447777

Mayo, C J (Simmons & Simmons)
London EC2 *p79*. 020 7628 2020

Mayo, J (Cartwright Cunningham Haselgrove & Co) *K1 K4 Q S1 T2 W*
Waltham Forest *p19* 020 8520 1021

Mayo, Ms N (Linklaters LLP)
London EC2 *p54*. 020 7456 2000

Mayor, A D (Bowling & Co) *S2 S1*
London E15 *p15*. 020 8221 8000

Mayor, Mrs K L (Cripps Harries Hall LLP) *B1 C1 C2 F1 Zb Ze F2*
Tunbridge Wells *p415* 01892 515121

Mays, A (OGR Stock Denton) *S1 E W L S2*
London N3 *p64* 020 8349 0321

Mays, R A (Andrew Jackson) *E R1 Zc*
Hull *p257* 01482 325242

Mayston, W H (Dakers Marriott Solicitors) *O Q J1 Zc L Zq*
Strood *p400*. 01634 813300

Mazarezo, Miss G (Royal College of Nursing)
Exeter *p458* 0845 456 7829

Mazerelo, Miss G (Royal Borough of Kingston upon Thames)
Kingston upon Thames *p462*. 020 8546 2121

Mazharuddin, Miss A (Cousins Tyrer)
Leeds *p272* 0113 247 0400

Mazzier, S M (Richard Freeman & Co) *S1 E W L R2*
Kensington & Chelsea *p34*. . 020 7351 5151

Mbeledogu, Miss O A (Veja and Co Solicitors) *Zi J1*
Southall *p385* 020 8574 2626

Meaby, B W (Meaby & Co) *C1 E G K1 L M1 P S1 J1 W*
London SE5 *p60*. 020 7703 5034

Meaby, R H (Meaby & Co) *K1 S1 P N G J1 W D1 H*
London SE5 *p60*. 020 7703 5034

Meachem, N L (Fraser Dawbarns) *G H Zl Zt*
King's Lynn *p266* 01553 666600

Meachin, A P (Wains) *G H D1 Zl*
Macclesfield *p297* 01625 429511

Meacock, Ms S L (Radcliffes Le Brasseur)
Westminster *p70*. 020 7222 7040

Mead, A (Kennedys) *Zm*
Cambridge *p174*. 01223 533060

Mead, A Y (DWFM Beckman) *C1 M2 R2 T1 T2 E*
Westminster *p25*. 020 7872 0023

Mead, G H (Reed Smith LLP) *J1 Zp*
London EC2 *p71*. 020 3116 3000

Mead, G J (Blocks) *Q B1 F1 F2 Ze Zq O Zl Zk Zj L*
Ipswich *p262*. 01473 230033

Mead, Ms H (ASB Law)
Crawley *p202* 01293 603600

Mead, J H (Carpenters)
Birkenhead *p134*. 0870 780 1870

Mead, J M (Jaffe Porter Crossick) *O Q L N A3 B1 J1 Zc*
London NW6 *p46* 020 7625 4424

Mead, R G (Charles Lucas & Marshall) *W K4 T2*
Newbury *p322*. 01635 521212

Mead, R T (Forsters LLP) *T2 W*
Westminster *p33*. 020 7863 8333

Meade, S J (George Green LLP) *O Q Zq L*
Cradley Heath *p201* 01384 410410

Meade-King, E (Harrow Law Partnership) *G H*
Wealdstone *p424* 020 8863 7888

Meades, Ms A (Robert Lizar) *Zh L*
Manchester *p307* 0161 226 2319

Meadon, S J (Blake Lapthorn) *Zf Ze*
London EC1 *p13*. 020 7405 2000

Meadowcroft, Ms A (Hempsons) *J2 Zr*
Manchester *p305* 0161 228 0011

Meadowcroft, C (Huntingdonshire District Council)
Huntingdon *p461*. 01480 388388

Meadowcroft, Mrs H (Edward Fail Bradshaw & Waterson) *G H B2*
London EC3 *p30*. 020 7790 4032

Meadowcroft, Miss N A (Brabners Chaffe Street) *C2 C1 Zb*
Liverpool *p286*. 0151 600 3000

Meadows, Miss C (Michelmores LLP) *Zr N*
Exeter *p221* 01392 688688

Meadows, F E P (Meadows Fraser LLP) *E S1 L R1 N*
Weybridge *p430* 01932 852057

Meadows, Ms F H (Foot Anstey) *K1*
Plymouth *p349*. 01752 675000

Meadows, J R (Speakman & Co) *W C1 E S1*
Crewe *p203* 01270 214237

Meadows, M J A (Hanne & Co) *G H M1 Zl N*
London SW11 *p38* 020 7228 0017

Meadows, P D (Coca-Cola Enterprises Ltd)
Uxbridge *p474*. 01895 231313

Meadows, Miss R (The Johnson Partnership) *G H B2*
Nottingham *p337*. 0115 941 9141

Meadows, R H (Meadows & Moran) *C1 D1 E L S1 G H R1 M1 K1 Zd Zl Zo*
Romford *p366* 01708 753400

Meadows, R J (Newstead & Walker) *E S2 Zc S1 L*
Otley *p342*. 01943 461414

Meadows, Miss S M (Callaghans) *S1*
Farnham *p224*. 01252 723477

Meads, A (Hill Dickinson LLP) *F1 O Zj*
London EC3 *p41*. 020 7283 9033

Meads, P G (Olswang LLP) *C1 C2 E F1 Ze Zd J1 R2 B1 S1 W Q O Zc*
London WC1 *p64* 020 7067 3000

Meads, Mrs S M (J & S P Pope) *K1 W L D1 V N P F1 Zd Zh Zv*
Exeter *p222* 01392 274006

Meads, W A (Coffin Mew & Clover) *K1 G H D1 K2 F1 Zl L*
Portsmouth *p354*. 023 9238 8021

Meakin, J H D (Alfred Truman) *S1 E K1 P J1 F1 G L Zl*
Bicester *p132* 01869 252761

Meakin, Ms J M (Walker Smith Way) *S1*
Chester *p191* 0844 346 3100

Meakin, N R (TLT Solicitors) *J1 N*
London EC2 *p85*. 020 3465 4000

Meakin, R (Stone King LLP) *Zd*
Bath *p128* 01225 337599

Meakin, W J B (Grant Saw Solicitors LLP) *W S1 T2 K4*
Greenwich *p36*. 020 8858 6971

Meakins, G P (Pengillys LLP) *S1 E L C1 W*
Weymouth *p430* 01305 768888

Meakins, Mrs S (Kidd Rapinet) *J1 K1 D1*
Farnham *p225*. 0845 017 9609

Mealand, S P (Peasegoods) *B1 C1 F1 M1 N P S1 W*
Manchester *p308* 0161 205 2772

Meara, Ms G (Pictons Solicitors LLP)
Luton *p295* 01582 870870

Mears, D (Russell-Cooke LLP) *Zd*
London SW15 *p74*. 020 8789 9111

Mears, J A V (Price Mears & Co) *N S1 E W*
Rochdale *p365*. 01706 653331

Mears, M J P (Mears Hobbs & Durrant) *S1 K1 J1 N O W Zl*
Great Yarmouth *p234* 01493 665413

Mears, P M (Allen & Overy LLP)
London E1 *p5* 020 3088 0000

Measures, Mrs C (Anthony Collins Solicitors LLP) *N*
Birmingham *p137* 0121 200 3242

Measures, J (Barratt Goff & Tomlinson) *N*
Nottingham *p335*. 0115 931 5171
Leicester *p280*. 0116 254 5454

Measures, M H (Hibberts LLP) *B1 E L N S1 O Q*
Nantwich *p320*. 01270 624225

Measures, P (Ince & Co Services Ltd)
London E1 *p44* 020 7481 0010

Measures, P H (Curtis Davis Garrard) *Za*
Uxbridge *p417*. 020 8734 2800

Mecrate-Butcher, R J S (Pinsent Masons LLP) *Zb*
London EC2 *p67*. 020 7418 7000

Medland, F G (Ford Simey LLP) *S1 W E*
Exmouth *p222* . . .01395 272241 / 0800 169 3741

Medlicott, H G (R George Davies & Co) *H K1 D1 G K3 B2*
Abergavenny *p113*. 01873 852535

Medlicott, Mrs J M (Rootes & Alliott) *K3 K1*
Folkestone *p227*. 01303 851100

Medlicott, Mrs K A (R George Davies & Co) *N Q S1*
Abergavenny *p113*. 01873 852535

Medlicott, P J (Medlicott Snows) *S1 A1 W L E Zl*
Knighton *p269*. 01547 528332
Bishops Castle *p145*. 01588 638425

Medlicott, P S (Chubb Bulleid) *A1 E L R1 S1 W T1 C1*
Street *p400* 01749 836100

Medlicott, R C P (Frederic Hall) *G K4 W J1 S1*
Dover *p213* 01304 202411
Folkestone *p227*. 01303 851185

Medlock, L G (Speechly Bircham LLP) *E R2*
London EC4 *p81*. 020 7427 6400

Medyckyj, Ms M M T (Medyckyj & Co) *O Ze C3 M1 Zf Q A3*
Haringey *p60* 020 8442 0000

Mee, J (Reynolds Porter Chamberlain LLP)
London E1 *p71* 020 3060 6000

Mee, Mrs J A (London Underground Ltd)
London SW1 *p107*. 020 7918 3126

Mee, Mrs L M (Marrons) *S2 E R2 L S1*
Leicester *p280*. 0116 289 2200

Mee, P G V (Gillette Management Inc)
Isleworth *p462*. 020 8560 1234

Mee, S (Charles Lucas & Marshall) *W*
Newbury *p322*. 01635 521212

Meech, J R (Justices' Clerk's Office)
Worthing *p477* 01903 210981

Meehan, A (Hudsons Hart & Borrows) *G H K1 D1 W S1 D2 V*
Richmond *p363* 01748 824333

Meehan, Miss A L (Bendall Roberts) *W*
Ely *p218*. 01353 663581

Meehan, K P A (London Borough of Haringey)
London N22 *p106* 020 8489 0000

Meehan, Ms L (Irwin Mitchell LLP) *N Zr*
Leeds *p274* 0870 150 0100

Meek, Ms A F (Harcus Sinclair) *Q W B2 Zq*
London WC2 *p38* 020 7242 9700

Meek, C H (Macfarlanes) *C1*
London EC4 *p56*. 020 7831 9222

Meek, P W D (Furse Sanders & Co) *W T1 T2 Zd K4*
South Molton *p383*. 01769 572251

Meek, S A (Squire Sanders (UK) LLP) *E S1*
Leeds *p277* 0113 284 7000

Meekin, Miss O G (Monro Fisher Wasbrough LLP) *W T1 T2 E R2 S2 S1 Zd C1 J1 Zv K3 K2 N Zl*
London WC1 *p61* 020 7404 7001

Meeks, A S (Pinsent Masons LLP) *Zo*
London EC2 *p67*. 020 7418 7000

Meen, Mrs S (Thornleys Limited) *W*
Plymouth *p350*. 01752 406977

Meer, N M (Squire Sanders (UK) LLP)
London EC2 *p81*. 020 7655 1000

Meer, S M (Meer & Co) *S1 W*
London NW11 *p60*. 020 8458 4554

Meeran, R B (Leigh Day & Co) *N M2 Zg*
London EC1 *p52*. 020 7650 1200

Meere, R (Enoch Evans LLP) *C1 E B1 S1 T1 W J1 L R1 A1 Zc Zn Zo*
Walsall *p420*. 01922 720333

Meerloo, E N (Reynolds Porter Chamberlain LLP) *E L S1 A1*
London E1 *p71* 020 3060 6000

Meers, Mrs C (Penningtons) *S1*
Godalming *p231*. 01483 791800

Mees, D J (Hutsby Mees) *E D1 G N Q S1 K1 J1*
Stafford *p393* 01785 259211

See p634 for the Key to Work Categories

Meese, Miss N (Irwin Mitchell LLP) *N* Sheffield *p376* . . . 0870 150 0100
Meewella, L D (Lakshman Meewella) *D1 G H J1 K1 L N Q S1 V Zi Zl Zp Zg Zq* London SW7 *p60* . . . 020 7370 6595
Megaw, A (Pannone LLP) *O Q B1 Zb* Manchester *p308* . . . 0161 909 3000
Meggitt, E P (Geldards LLP) Cardiff *p178* . . . 029 2023 8239
Meggitt, F W (F W Meggitt & Co) *S1 E R2 S2* Sheffield *p376* . . . 0114 272 7955
Megregian, S (McDermott Will & Emery UK LLP) *C3* London EC2 *p56* . . . 020 7577 6900
Megson, J (Double & Megson) *W S1 S2 E C1 C2 Ze Zi Zl Zv* Bourne *p151* . . . 01778 423376
Mehan, V (Pattinson & Brewer) *N Q U2* London WC1 *p66* . . . 020 7400 5100
Mehdevy, Mrs E R (Field Seymour Parkes) *O Q* Reading *p360* . . . 0118 951 6200
Mehlig, Ms A (Berry Redmond & Robinson) *B1 K1 W X* Weston-super-Mare *p429* . . 01934 513963
Mehlin, Miss A J (Clarkson Wright & Jakes Ltd) *O F1 L Zq* Orpington *p341* . . . 01689 887887
Mehouas, Miss D N L (Pitmans LLP) Reading *p361* . . . 0118 958 0224
Mehrji, Ms G R (Vincent French & Browne) *S1 Q K1 N J1 L W E* London WC1 *p89* . . . 020 7831 4994
Mehta, A (DLA Piper UK LLP) London EC2 *p24* . . . 0870 011 1111
Mehta, Ms A (M&M Solicitors) Leicester *p280* . . . 0116 285 2300
Mehta, Ms A (The Smith Partnership) Leicester *p281* . . . 0116 255 6292
Mehta, C K (Nabarro LLP) London WC1 *p63* . . . 020 7524 6000
Mehta, Ms H (Jones Day) *C1* London EC4 *p46* . . . 020 7039 5959
Mehta, K K (Bromleys Solicitors LLP) *D1 D2 K1* Ashton-under-Lyne *p120* . . . 0161 330 6821
Mehta, Ms N (Tanner & Taylor LLP) *D1 D2 K1 W* Farnborough *p224* . . . 01252 549555
Mehta, S (Wrigley Claydon) *Q N O* Oldham *p341* . . . 0161 624 6811
Mehta, Miss S (Magrath LLP) *Zi* London W1 *p57* . . . 020 7495 3003
Mehta, Ms S (IBB Solicitors) *S1* Chesham *p189* . . . 0845 638 1381
Mehta, Miss U (Essex County Council) Chelmsford *p454* . . . 0845 743 0430
Mehtam, J (Martin-Kaye LLP) *J1 Zi* Telford *p409* . . . 01952 272222
Mei Man, Y (Boodle Hatfield) Westminster *p14* . . . 020 7629 7411
Meighen, A (Thomas & Meighen) *D1 E F1 G H J1 K1 L M1 P Zp Zs Zv* Newcastle upon Tyne *p327* . 0191 214 0355
Meikle, Mrs C (Essex County Council) Chelmsford *p454* . . . 0845 743 0430
Meikle, E (Watson Burton LLP) Newcastle upon Tyne *p327* . 0845 901 2100
Mein, N (Debenhams Ottaway) *S1* Radlett *p358* . . . 01923 857171
Mein, Ms N (Somerset County Council) Taunton *p473* . . . 0845 345 9166
Meir, Miss K M (Ashton Bond Gigg) *J1 O Q* Nottingham *p335* . . . 0115 947 6651
Meisel, Mrs S M (Blair Allison & Co) *K1 D1 T1 P G* Birmingham *p135* . . . 0121 233 2904
Meisels, A (Lewis Nedas & Co) *G H* Camden *p53* . . . 020 7387 2032
Meisner, Mrs J P (Preston Mellor Harrison) *K1 Q N W S1* Chislehurst *p193* . . . 020 8468 7025
Melchior, Miss J (Kingsley Napley) *Q R2* London EC1 *p50* . . . 020 7814 1200
Meldrum, A R J (Meldrum Young Solicitors) *B2 G H* Watford *p423* . . . 01923 231598
Meldrum, N J (Coles Miller Solicitors LLP) *C1 E L* Poole *p352* . . . 01202 673011
Meldrum, P L (Irwin Mitchell LLP) *J1 Zp* Sheffield *p376* . . . 0870 150 0100
Melia, Mrs N A (Greene & Greene) *W T2* Bury St Edmunds *p171* . . . 01284 762211
Melia, P J (Melia & Mumford) *D1 G H K1 M1 P S1* Camberley *p173* . . . 01252 836554
Melin, N D (Judge Sykes Frixou) London WC2 *p47* . . . 020 7379 5114
Mellanby, Ms C A (Ford Simey LLP) *D1 G H K1* Exeter *p221* . . . 01392 274126
Mellersh, M F A (Mellersh & Co) *C1 C2 E S1 T1 J1 L W Zf* Islington *p60* . . . 020 7251 2361
Melles-Sawyers, Miss S (Kitching Walker) *W* Kirkbymoorside *p268* . . . 01751 431237
Mellett, M T (Radcliffes Le Brasseur) Westminster *p70* . . . 020 7222 7040
Melling, K (Napthens LLP) *C1* Preston *p357* . . . 01772 888444
Melling, M B (Machins Solicitors LLP) *N Zq L Q E O S2* Luton *p295* . . . 01582 514000
Mellins, G A (Levine Mellins Klarfeld) *Q L N F1 Zc O Zq* Stanmore *p394* . . . 020 8954 7474
Mellish, M W (Northumberland County Council) Morpeth *p466* . . . 01670 533000
Mellmann, Ms J (Watson Farley & Williams) *C1 C2 U1 U2 Zn* London EC2 *p90* . . . 020 7814 8000
Mellon, Mrs V (Philip Ross & Co) *S1 E L R1 C1* London W1 *p73* . . . 020 7636 6969
Mellor, A M (Allen & Overy LLP) *C1 C2 Zb* London E1 *p5* . . . 020 3088 0000
Mellor, Ms C (Brian Koffman & Co) *G H K1 M1* Manchester *p306* . . . 0161 832 3852
Mellor, Ms C (Thompsons (formerly Robin/Brian Thompson & Partners)) *N Q Zq* London WC1 *p87* . . . 020 7290 0000
Mellor, D (Mellor Hargreaves Solicitors) *N* Oldham *p341* . . . 0800 811 844
Mellor, Miss E G (Forsters LLP) *W T2* Westminster *p33* . . . 020 7863 8333
Mellor, G N (Beswicks) *Zw G* Hanley *p239* . . . 01782 205000
Mellor, I H (George Ide LLP) *Zo T2 W* Chichester *p192* . . . 01243 786668
Mellor, J S T (Allen & Overy LLP) London E1 *p5* . . . 020 3088 0000
Mellor, K W (Kenneth W Mellor) *S1 E W L C1 T1 K1* Rochester *p366* . . . 01634 724951
Mellor, Ms S (Beswicks) *K4 W* Stoke-on-Trent *p397* . . . 01782 205000
Mellors, R T D (Barber Titleys) *K1 D2 Zl K3 D1* Harrogate *p240* . . . 01423 502211
Mellowes, A P D (Dibbens) *S1 E L S2* Wimborne *p433* . . . 01202 882456
Melluish, Miss D A (Eaton Smith LLP) *C1 E O N S1 K1 W Q J1 G Zi Zv Zd Ze Zl* Huddersfield *p255* . . . 01484 821300
Meloy, P (MWR Law Ltd) *N Q Zj* Preston *p357* . . . 01772 254201
Melrose, Mrs B R (Loosemores) *N* Cardiff *p179* . . . 029 2022 4433
Melrose, J (Simmons & Simmons) London EC2 *p79* . . . 020 7628 2020
Melrose, J G (Glanvilles) *W T2 K4* Havant *p244* . . . 023 9249 2300
Melton, A (Matthew Arnold & Baldwin LLP) *K1 Q W* Watford *p423* . . . 01923 202020
Meltzer, D H (Plexus Law (A Trading Name of Parabis Law LLP)) *Zj Q O* London EC3 *p68* . . . 0844 245 4000
Meltzer, J L (Hogan Lovells International LLP) London EC1 *p42* . . . 020 7296 2000
Melville, G A E (Tucker Turner Kingsley Wood & Co) *C1 W T1 J1 B1 Zb Ze Zj* London WC1 *p88* . . . 020 7242 3303
Melville, N J (Quinn Melville) *G H B2* Liverpool *p290* . . . 0151 236 3340
Melville, Ms T (Abbott Lloyd Howorth) *K3 K1* Maidenhead *p298* . . . 01628 798800
Melville-Harris, Ms Z K (Laytons) *E L R1 R2 S1* Guildford *p236* . . . 01483 407000
Melville-Ross, R W (Taylor Vinters) *A1 E S1* Cambridge *p176* . . . 01223 423444
Melville-Shreeve, Mrs A M (WBW Solicitors) *A1 S1 W* Newton Abbot *p329* . . . 01626 202404
Melville-Smith, J D (Seddons) *O Q Zq B1 J1* Westminster *p77* . . . 020 7725 8000
Melville-Walker, T D (MacDonald Oates LLP) *K1 D1 V K3* Midhurst *p316* . . . 01730 816711
Melvin, A L (Hunters) *W T2* London WC2 *p44* . . . 020 7412 0050
Melvin, J M (Quality Solicitors Hill & Abbott) *S1* Chelmsford *p187* . . . 01245 258892
Melvin, R B (Reed Smith LLP) *Za* London EC2 *p71* . . . 020 3116 3000
Melvin, Ms S (Brennans Solicitors) Wallsend *p419* . . . 0191 262 5133
Membery, M C (Pinsent Masons LLP) *O Zj Zq* London EC2 *p67* . . . 020 7418 7000
Memery, Ms J V J (Memery Crystal) *Ze J1* London WC2 *p60* . . . 020 7242 5905
Menaldino, D L (Dorset County Council) Dorchester *p457* . . . 01305 251000
Menard, Miss H (Morgans) *L V K1 C1* Cardiff *p180* . . . 029 2072 9888
Menato, M (Max Gold Law) *R2 Zc W* Hull *p257* . . . 01482 224900
Mendelsohn, G I (Boyes Turner) *A3 O* Reading *p360* . . . 0118 959 7711
Guildford *p236* . . . 01483 407000
Mendelsohn, I C (Berg Legal) *Q O N J1 K1 L P B1 F1 G Ze Zj Zk* Manchester *p301* . . . 0161 833 9211
Mendelsohn, P A (Olswang LLP) *P N M1 F1 B1 J1 L G K1 D1 Zl Zi Zc* London WC1 *p64* . . . 020 7067 3000
Mendelson, Ms T (Howard Kennedy LLP) *Zf* London W1 *p48* . . . 020 7636 1616
Mendelssohn, M C (CMS Cameron McKenna LLP) London EC3 *p17* . . . 020 7367 3000
Mendes da Costa, T (Streeter Marshall) *S1* Croydon *p205* . . . 020 8680 2638
Mendham, A (Gadsby Wicks) *Zr* Chelmsford *p186* . . . 01245 494929
Mendham, S (Debenhams Ottaway) *R1* St Albans *p390* . . . 01727 837161
Mendham, S R (Thames Water Utilities Limited) *R1 P* Reading *p469* . . . 0118 373 8000
Mendoza, Mrs K E (National Counties Building Soc) Epsom *p458* . . . 01372 742211
Mendus, G W B (Oglethorpe & Broatch) *W E S1 A1 T2 Zd K4 Zo* Keswick *p265* . . . 01768 772125
Mendus, Mrs K J (Darbys Solicitors LLP) *G H* Oxford *p343* . . . 01865 811700
Menham, P C (Gordons LLP) Leeds *p273* . . . 0113 227 0100
Menhennet, Ms K E (Cohen Cramer Solicitors) *K1 D1 F1 G L O Q V W N Zi Zj* Leeds *p272* . . . 0800 542 9408
Menhennet, M (Sidley Austin Brown & Wood) *R2* London EC2 *p78* . . . 020 7360 3600
Menhinick, S (Nockolds) Bishop's Stortford *p144* . . . 01279 755777
Menikou, Miss J (Huggins & Lewis Foskett) *W* Redbridge *p43* . . . 020 8989 3000
Mensah, Miss J N (Bennett Griffin) *K1 K3 D1* Worthing *p441* . . . 01903 229925
Mensah, K (Aaskells Solicitors & Advocates) London N14 *p3* . . . 020 8920 2400
Menzies, A (McGrigors LLP) London EC4 *p56* . . . 020 7054 2500
Menzies, C (Anglia Ruskin University) Chelmsford *p454* . . . 01245 493131
Menzies, G G (Mills & Reeve) *O* Cambridge *p175* . . . 01223 364422
Menzies, L (EEF Western) Bristol *p452* . . . 0117 906 4800
Mepham, Mrs J (DB Law) *O K1 N Q J1 L F1 Zc Zk* Camborne *p173* . . . 01209 712428
Mepham, Miss S L (West Sussex County Council) Chichester *p455* . . . 01243 777100
Mepstead, Ms N (Potter Rees (Serious Injury) Solicitors) Manchester *p309* . . . 0161 237 5888
Merali, A (S Merali Solicitor Advocate) Westminster *p60* . . . 020 7724 0508
Merali, A H J (Davidson Merali & Co) *C1 E G J1 K1 L M1 N P S1 Zk Zi* London W8 *p26* . . . 020 7937 2525
Merali, S H J (S Merali Solicitor Advocate) *B1 D1 F1 G J1 K1 L N P Zf Zg* Westminster *p60* . . . 020 7724 0508
Merali, S H J (Davidson Merali & Co) *C1 E G J1 K1 L M1 N P S1 Zk Zi* London W8 *p26* . . . 020 7937 2525
Mercer, A J (Trethowans LLP) *K1 D1 V* Salisbury *p371* . . . 01722 412512
Mercer, Miss B L (Jordans) *N* Dewsbury *p210* . . . 01924 457171
Mercer, Mrs C (Department for Business, Enterprise and Regulatory Reform) London SW1 *p105* . . . 020 7215 0105
Mercer, D F (Jobling Gowler) *N Q Zk Zq Zr Zw* Macclesfield *p297* . . . 01625 614250
Mercer, E P O (Edwin Coe LLP) *U1 U2 O C3 Zza I Ze* London WC2 *p29* . . . 020 7691 4000
London EC4 *p86* . . . 020 7300 7000
Mercer, G A (Blackhurst Swainson Goodier LLP) *S1 W* Preston *p356* . . . 01772 253841
Mercer, G D (Bryan & Mercer) *C1 E L R1 S1* St Albans *p389* . . . 01727 861414
Mercer, Mrs H M (Merseyside Police) Liverpool *p463* . . . 0151 777 8080
Mercer, Ms M A W (Healys LLP) *W T1 R1 S1 C1 L A1 K1 V Zm* Brighton *p159* . . . 01273 685888
Mercer, Miss P J (Vincent Laverys) *K3 K1* Preston *p357* . . . 01772 555176
Mercer, R (Mayo Wynne Baxter LLP) *C1 L* Brighton *p160* . . . 01273 775533
Mercer, T (Ashurst LLP) London EC2 *p7* . . . 020 7638 1111
Mercer, V (Speechly Bircham LLP) *Zb* London EC4 *p81* . . . 020 7427 6400
Mercer, Mrs V M (Luton Borough Council) Luton *p464* . . . 01582 546000
Merchant, Ms C (Michelmores LLP) *Zu E* Exeter *p221* . . . 01392 688688
Merchant, D (Ingrams) *N* York *p445* . . . 01904 520600
Merchant, P D (Radcliffes Le Brasseur) *N O Q Zr Zq Zm Zw Zj* Leeds *p276* . . . 0113 234 1220
Meredith, C J (Powys County Council) Brecon *p451* . . . 01874 624141
Meredith, C J (Powys County Council) Llandrindod Wells *p463* . . . 01597 826000
Meredith, Miss E (Stevens) *G H* Stoke-on-Trent *p398* . . . 01782 813200
Meredith, Miss E L (North Yorkshire County Council) Northallerton *p467* . . . 01609 780780
Meredith, Ms H (Hilary Meredith Solicitors) *N* Wilmslow *p433* . . . 01625 539922
Meredith, Ms H E (Treasures) *K3 K1 D1* Gloucester *p230* . . . 01452 525351
Meredith, Mrs J (Elliott Bridgman) *K1* Telford *p409* . . . 01952 684544
Meredith, J (Aspinall & Co) *K1 O G H F1 N E J1* Bolton *p148* . . . 01204 388200
Meredith, Miss R (Wrigleys Solicitors LLP) *E S2 S1* Leeds *p278* . . . 0113 244 6100
Meredith, R J (Ellis-Fermor & Negus) *S1 S2* Long Eaton *p293* . . . 0115 972 5222
Meredith, S (Terry Jones Solicitors & Advocates) *G H* Telford *p409* . . . 01952 297979
Meredith, S R W (Gabb & Co) *C1 C2 T1* Abergavenny *p113* . . . 01873 852432
Meredith, Ms T (Malletts Solicitors) *G H* King's Lynn *p266* . . . 01553 777744
Meredith, Miss V (Knowsley Metropolitan Borough Council) Huyton *p461* . . . 0151 443 3593
Merifield, Ms F (Sedgwick Kelly LLP) *E S1* Watford *p424* . . . 01923 228311
Merigold, Miss A E (Humphrys & Co) *G H K1 N D1 Q F1 J1 L S1 Zl Zq Zp* Rhyl *p363* . . . 01745 343158
Merkel, A J (Edwin Coe LLP) *B1 B2 O Q Zb Zq* London WC2 *p29* . . . 020 7691 4000
Merrett, J R (ICC United Kingdom) London W2 *p107* . . . 020 7792 8579
Merrett, Ms T (Merrett & Co) *R1 Zu* Bristol *p163* . . . 01275 331228
Merriam, M R (Ashton KCJ) *N P M1 J1 L F1 B1 Zk Zp Q* Bury St Edmunds *p171* . . . 01284 762331
Merrick, D (Rudds) *S1 W L S2 Zm T2 K4* Rayleigh *p359* . . . 01268 778152
Merrick, D M (Crosse & Crosse) *N Zm W T2* Exeter *p220* . . . 01392 258451
Merrick, Miss K A (Russell Jones & Walker) *G H* Wakefield *p419* . . . 01924 234300
Merrick, R F (Merricks Formerly Merrick Kelleher) *S1 K1 W F1 E L A1 P C1 S2 K4 Zl R2 T1 T2* Wadebridge *p418* . .01208 812068 / 813104
Merrick, T F (Merricks Formerly Merrick Kelleher) *W Q Zl K3* Wadebridge *p418* . .01208 812068 / 813104
Merrill, Miss V (Corries Solicitors) York *p444* . . . 0845 241 5566
Merriman, A R (ASB Law) *N* Maidstone *p298* . . . 01622 656500
Merrison, Miss I (Eastleys) *K1* Totnes *p413* . . . 01803 864888
Exeter *p222* . . . 01392 270867
Merritt, C (Paris Smith LLP) *J1* Southampton *p386* . . . 023 8048 2482
Merritt, J C (Matthew & Matthew Limited) *E S1 W C1* Southbourne *p387* . . . 01202 431943
Merritt, Ms S J (Paris Smith LLP) *J1* Southampton *p386* . . . 023 8048 2482
Merry, B R (Merry & Co) *D1 F1 G H J1 L M1 N Q Zv* Ryde *p369* . . . 01983 811722
Merry, I (Merry & Co) *S1 W G S2 H K1* Ryde *p369* . . . 01983 811722
Merry, J G (Lanyon Bowdler LLP) *I J1* Telford *p409* . . . 01952 291222
Wellington *p425* . . . 01952 244721
Merry, Mrs M J (Keelys LLP) *W T2* Lichfield *p284* . . . 01543 420000
Merryweather, C (J A Kemp & Co) London WC1 *p48* . . . 020 7405 3292
Merryweather, M I (Alletsons) *E S1 W N O C1 L Q F1* Burnham-on-Sea *p169* . . . 01278 780151
Merson, D T (Brecher) *E R2* London W1 *p15* . . . 020 7563 1000
Merttens, R W (Lambert Fenchurch Ltd) London EC3 *p107* . . . 020 7560 3000
Mervis, H C (SJ Berwin LLP) London EC4 *p75* . . . 020 7111 2222
Meskimmon, Mrs H L (Wilkinson Woodward) Halifax *p238* . . . 01422 339600
Mesley, Miss L (Michelmores LLP) *E L* Exeter *p221* . . . 01392 688688
Message, W R (Harrison Bundey) *G H* Leeds *p274* . . . 0113 200 7400
Messenger, C A (Messenger & Co) *C1 S2 L O Q R1 R2 S1 W* Henley-on-Thames *p247* . . . 01491 576272
Messenger, D (Matthew Arnold & Baldwin LLP) *D1 K1 V* Watford *p423* . . . 01923 202020
Messenger, D F (Mercy Messenger) *C1* Birmingham *p140* . . . 0121 770 1221
Messenger, Ms M (Mercy Messenger) *K1 K3* Birmingham *p140* . . . 0121 770 1221
Messent, A D (Gateley LLP) *O Q Za Zj* London EC4 *p35* . . . 020 7653 1600
Messent, M J (Trethowans LLP) *N J1 C1 O Zl* Southampton *p387* . . . 023 8032 1000
Messer, Mrs H N (RWP Solicitors) *J1 K1 N O Q* Pangbourne *p345* . . . 0118 984 2266
Messer, L (Collins Benson Goldhill LLP) *S2 E R1 R2* Westminster *p21* . . . 020 7436 5151
Messer, P R (Treasury Solicitors Department) *P K1* London WC2 *p110* . . . 020 7210 3000
Messervy-Whiting, Mrs J E (Plexus Law (A Trading Name of Parabis Law LLP)) *N J2 Q* Evesham *p220* . . . 01386 769160
Messias, S (Lawrence Stephens) *E L S2 R2 S1* London EC1 *p82* . . . 020 7935 1211
Mestre, Miss P (Pritchard Joyce & Hinds) *E C1 Zl* Beckenham *p129* . . . 020 8658 3922
Metcalf, Mrs C A (Stanley Tee) *O N P Q L Zc Zq Zj Zr* Bishop's Stortford *p144* . . . 01279 755200
Metcalf, Miss E C (Wedlake Bell LLP) *W Zj* London WC1 *p91* . . . 020 7395 3000
Metcalf, Mrs G (Sharratts (London) LLP) *L E S1 Zh* Westerham *p429* . . . 01959 568000

6

Metcalf, Mrs J (David Gray Solicitors) *Zm*
Newcastle upon Tyne *p324* . 0191 232 9547

Metcalf, P (Jones Day) *O*
London EC4 *p46* 020 7039 5959

Metcalfe, Miss C L (Shelley & Co) *B2 G H*
Cambridge *p175* 01223 359441
Portsmouth *p355* 023 9282 8131

Metcalfe, D (Metcalfe Johnston McCormick) *N Q C1 E F1 B1*
Eccles *p216* . . . 0161 789 3481 / 788 9021

Metcalfe, D R (Plexus Law (A Trading Name of Parabis Law LLP)) *M1 J2 P O N K1 Q G F1 S1 D1 H J1 Zl Zk Ze*
Leeds *p276* 0844 245 4100

Metcalfe, Ms K E (Middlesbrough Council) *Zr*
Middlesbrough *p465* 01642 245432

Metcalfe, Miss K S (Gaynham King & Mellor) *K1 S1 Zl K3 D2 D1*
Appleby *p118* 01768 351422
Penrith *p346* 01768 864651

Metcalfe, Ms L C (Edwards Angell Palmer & Dodge)
London EC2 *p28* 020 7583 4055

Metcalfe, N T (Baxter Caulfield) *Ze C1 E*
Huddersfield *p255* 01484 519519

Metcalfe, R H (Browne Jacobson LLP) *C1 E B1*
Nottingham *p336* 0115 976 6000

Metcalfe, R J (Leeds Day) *O Q N Ze*
Huntingdon *p258* 01480 454301

Metcalfe, S J (DAC Beachcroft)
Bristol *p162* 0117 918 2000

Metherell, C A J (Bevan Brittan LLP) *O Zq*
Bristol *p161* 0870 194 1000

Methley, A (Atteys) *S1 E C1 L*
Barnsley *p124* 01226 212345

Methold, Mrs K J (Rooks Rider) *T1 W Zd T2*
London EC1 *p73* 020 7689 7000

Methuen, S (Nandy & Co) *D2 F1 K1 L Zg Zi Q N Zp V*
Newham *p63* 020 8536 1800

Metliss, M (SJ Berwin LLP)
London EC4 *p75* 020 7111 2222

Metters, M J W (Miller Parris) *S1 W S2*
Worthing *p442* 01903 205771

Metzger, D S J (Clifford Chance)
London E14 *p20* 020 7006 1000

Mew, D J (Salans)
London EC4 *p76* 020 7429 6000

Mewies, J C (Quality Solicitors Mewies) *G H Zl*
Skipton *p381* 01756 799000

Mewies, Miss S A (Irwin Mitchell LLP) *C1 I*
Birmingham *p139* 0870 150 0100

Meyer, A (Horsey Lightly) *Zd R1 Zr*
Westminster *p43* 020 7222 8844

Meyer, Miss L G (Crown Prosecution Service Avon & Somerset)
Bristol *p451* 0117 930 2800

Meyer, M D (Edwards Angell Palmer & Dodge) *O M1 B1 C1 Q E R1 L F1 T1 Zj Zb Za*
London EC2 *p28* 020 7583 4055

Meyer, Mrs R M (Boyes Turner) *W T2 K4 Zm*
Reading *p360* 0118 959 7711

Meyerhoff, S C (Backhouse Jones Ltd) *J1 O Q N J2*
Clitheroe *p196* 01254 828300

Meyjes, G D C (Clifford Cowling & Co) *S1 A1 C1 E L R1 T1 S2*
Farnham *p224* 01252 725726

Meyler, G (Bank Of Ireland UK Financial Services) *S1*
Bristol *p451* 0117 979 2222

Meyrick, G A L (William Sturges & Co) *C1 E I J1 C2 S1*
Westminster *p84* 020 7873 1000

Mezzetti, A J (Gregory Rowcliffe Milners) *C1 C2 J1 P X Ze*
London WC1 *p37* 020 7242 0631

Miah, B (Gordons LLP)
Leeds *p273* 0113 227 0100

Miah, Mrs G R (Blake Lapthorn) *Q N F1 K1*
Portsmouth *p354* 023 9222 1122

Miah, K (Leach Rawlence & Hart) *S1 E Q L O J1*
Croydon *p205* 020 8680 5850

Miah, S (Blake Lapthorn) *O F1 Zq*
Portsmouth *p354* 023 9222 1122

Miah, S (Stallard March & Edwards) *B1 N O Q Zq*
Worcester *p440* 01905 613404

Mian, A (Mian & Co) *G H*
Birmingham *p140* 0121 684 8000

Mian, K (HKH Kenwright & Cox Solicitors) *B2 D1 H G K1 Zi*
Ilford *p260* 020 8553 9600

Mian, Miss N (Glaisyers) *K1*
Birmingham *p138* 0121 233 2971

Mian, T S (Mian & Co) *F1 G H K1 L P B2 Zg N*
Birmingham *p140* 0121 684 8000

Micah, Ms C (Robert Lizar) *D1 K1*
Manchester *p307* 0161 226 2319

Micciche, A (Borlase & Company) *Q K1 K3*
Helston *p246* 01326 574988

Micciche, A J (Kerrier District Council)
Camborne *p452* 01209 614000

Michael, A (Boys & Maughan) *S2 S1 W*
Broadstairs *p166* 01843 868861

Michael, A (Fuglers) *S1 E L R1 R2*
London W1 *p34* 020 7323 6450

Michael, D (Neath Port Talbot County Borough Council)
Port Talbot *p469* 01639 763333

Michael, S (Pannone LLP) *N*
Manchester *p308* 0161 909 3000

Michaels, M (Michaels & Co) *Q V W D1 L Zw K1*
Woodford Green *p439* 020 8245 1138

Michaelson, Mrs M (Olswang LLP) *C1 C2 E F1 Ze Zd*
London WC1 *p64* 020 7067 3000

Michalowska-Howells, B (Leigh Day & Co) *N P*
London EC1 *p52* 020 7650 1200

Michau, P J (DLA Piper UK LLP)
London EC2 *p24* 0870 011 1111

Michell, J (Cumming & Riley) *S1 W S2*
Grays *p233* 01375 383691

Michelmore, R H G (Gill Akaster) *S1 E C1 R1 A1 T1 Zc C2*
Plymouth *p349* 01752 203500

Michelmore, W F (Michelmores LLP) *S1 A1 W T2*
Exeter *p221* 01392 688688

Michelson, Ms L J (IBM United Kingdom Ltd)
London SE1 *p107* 020 7202 3000

Michie, Ms C (Paddington Law Centre)
London W10 *p108* 020 8960 3155

Michie, Ms I J (Hempsons) *Zr Zm*
Westminster *p40* 020 7839 0278

Micklem, C T (Reynolds Porter Chamberlain LLP) *N Zj Zq*
London E1 *p71* 020 3060 6000

Micklethwait, M S J (Beviss & Beckingsale)
Chard *p184* 01460 269700

Micklewright, Ms M E (London Borough of Southwark)
London SE1 *p109* 020 7525 5000

Micolson, M (Kirklees Metropolitan Borough Council)
Huddersfield *p461* 01484 221421

Middle, K E (Pardoes) *S1 E L W S2*
Yeovil *p444* 01935 382680

Middlecote, B A (Ansons LLP) *G H*
Lichfield *p284* 01543 263456

Middleditch, M S (Linklaters LLP)
London EC2 *p54* 020 7456 2000

Middlehurst, E A (Gregsons) *F1 G M1 J1 K1 N P Zc*
London SW19 *p37* 020 8946 1173

Middlehurst, R H (AWB Partnership LLP) *K1 D1 Q K3 D2 V*
Guildford *p235* 01483 302345

Middlemass, H S W (Brooke North LLP)
Leeds *p272* 0113 283 2100

Middlemass, Ms J A (Addleshaw Goddard)
Leeds *p271* 0113 209 2000

Middlemass, N S G (Brooke North LLP)
Leeds *p272* 0113 283 2100

Middlemost, D J P (Symes Robinson & Lee) *W T2*
Budleigh Salterton *p168* . . . 01395 445581

Middleton, Ms A (Northumberland County Council)
Morpeth *p466* 01670 533000

Middleton, A C (Towns Needham & Co) *W F1 G H J1 C1 N*
Manchester *p310* 0161 832 3721

Middleton, Miss A I E (Williamson & Soden) *C1 C2 Zb Zf U2*
Solihull *p383* 0121 733 8000

Middleton, C (Willans LLP) *S1*
Cheltenham *p189* 01242 514000

Middleton, C (Kemp Little LLP) *J1*
London EC2 *p48* 020 7600 8080

Middleton, Ms C A (Freeman Johnson) *D1 D2 K1*
Durham *p214* . . 0191 386 4843 / 386 9619

Middleton, Miss C A (Blake Lapthorn) *N Zr Q Zj*
Portsmouth *p354* 023 9222 1122

Middleton, C H L (Middleton Dummer) *S1 E C1 W R1 Zc Z2 R2*
Oldbury *p340* 0121 544 4788

Middleton, Mrs C L (Calderdale Metropolitan BC Corporate Services Directorate)
Halifax *p460* 01422 357257

Middleton, Ms E (Boodle Hatfield) *T1 T2 W*
Westminster *p14* 020 7629 7411

Middleton, Mrs E A (Edwards Duthie) *G H*
London E13 *p29* 020 8514 9000

Middleton, Miss J (Manches LLP) *Zc E O A3 C1 R2*
London WC2 *p58* 020 7404 4433

Middleton, J (Lightfoots LLP) *C1 E S2*
Thame *p410* 01844 212305

Middleton, J (Kennedys) *N*
Chelmsford *p186* 0845 838 4800

Middleton, J L (Lincolnshire County Council Resources - Legal Services)
Lincoln *p463* 01522 552222

Middleton, J M (Freeth Cartwright LLP) *F1 J1 L N O Q R1 Zo*
Leicester *p279* 0116 248 1100
Nottingham *p337* 0115 936 9369

Middleton, Mrs K E C (Gordon Lutton) *L S1 W*
Hereford *p248* 01432 355345
Hereford *p248* 01432 352121

Middleton, K S (Morlings) *P N S1 M1 K1 W G B1 L Zc Zk Zm*
Maidstone *p299* 01622 673081

Middleton, Miss L C (Carter-Ruck) *Zk Q Ze Zg U2*
London EC4 *p18* 020 7353 5005

Middleton, Mrs L H (Cooper Sons Hartley & Williams) *S1 L W*
Chapel-en-le-Frith *p184* . . . 01298 812138

Middleton, Mrs L J (Nash & Co Solicitors LLP) *S1 E L*
Plymouth *p350* 01752 664444

Middleton, M (Linklaters LLP)
London EC2 *p54* 020 7456 2000

Middleton, Miss S (Birnberg Peirce & Partners) *G H*
Camden *p13* 020 7911 0166

Middleton, Mrs S F (Steele Raymond) *S1 E S2*
Bournemouth *p152* 01202 294566

Middleton, T S (Hewitsons) *S2 E S1*
Saffron Walden *p370* 01799 522471

Middleton, Mrs V (Divorce & Family Law Practice) *K3 K1*
Birmingham *p137* 0121 200 0890

Middleton Lindsley, Ms S (Druces LLP) *S2 E S1*
London EC2 *p27* 020 7638 9271

Middleton-Cassini, Mrs K K (Environment Agency (Midlands Region))
Solihull *p471* 0121 711 2324

Middleton-Smith, C C (Squire Sanders (UK) LLP) *P*
London EC2 *p81* 020 7655 1000

Midgley, D J (Christine Sharp & Co) *E F1 Q S1 C1 B1 O*
Heywood *p249* 01706 623513

Midgley, J A (Comptons) *N Q L F1*
Camden *p22* 020 7485 0888

Midgley, J P (Longstaff & Midgley) *K1 K3 K4 D2 W*
Scarborough *p372* 01723 351751

Midgley, J P (Gaby Hardwicke) *S1*
Bexhill *p132* 01424 730945

Midgley, Ms S (The Smith Partnership) *D1 K1*
Derby *p209* 01332 225225

Midha, Mrs S (Adams & Remers) *T2 W*
Lewes *p283* 01273 480616

Mifflin, C (Shakespeares) *B1*
Nottingham *p339* 0115 945 3700

Mikolajewski, Miss S J (Plexus Law (A Trading Name of Parabis Law LLP)) *N Q*
London EC3 *p68* 0844 245 4000

Milan, D J (Pope & Co) *J1 K1 Q N V W L K3*
Sittingbourne *p380* 01795 474004

Milan, J (KJD) *Zb F1 T1*
Stoke-on-Trent *p398* 01782 202020

Milburn, B J (Shranks)
London WC1 *p78* 020 7831 6677

Milburn, Miss H L (Watson Burton LLP) *C1 Zb*
Newcastle upon Tyne *p327* . 0845 901 2100

Milburn, Miss P M (Hill Dickinson LLP) *K1 D1 G H S1*
Chester *p190* 01244 896600

Milburn, R J (Talbot & Co) *E C1 A1 L R1 Zc Zl S1*
Burton-on-Trent *p170* 01283 564716

Milburn, S J (HC Solicitors LLP) *G H Zl B2 P*
Peterborough *p347* 01733 882800

Miles, A C (Bobbetts Mackan) *G H Zl*
Bristol *p161* 0117 929 9001

Miles, Miss B J (Lanyon Bowdler LLP) *G H Q Zl N Zt*
Oswestry *p342* 01691 652241

Miles, Miss C S (Petersons)
Newport *p329* 01633 255151

Miles, D (DLA Piper UK LLP)
London EC2 *p24* 0870 011 1111

Miles, D (Latham & Watkins LLP) *E R1*
London EC2 *p51* 020 7710 1000

Miles, Mrs E (The Worcester Family Law Practice) *K1 K3 D2 D1*
Worcester *p440* 01905 730900

Miles, F (TWM Solicitors LLP) *K4 T2 W*
Epsom *p219* 01372 729555

Miles, G (ASB Law) *W*
Maidstone *p298* 01622 656500

Miles, G H (Paris Smith LLP) *K1 K2 D1 K3*
Southampton *p386* 023 8048 2482

Miles, G R (Haldanes) *B1 L N Q O W Zk Zq*
London W1 *p37* 020 7437 5629

Miles, G W (Broxbourne Borough Council)
Cheshunt *p454* 01992 785555

Miles, Ms H (DLA Piper UK LLP)
Birmingham *p137* 0870 011 1111

Miles, Miss H A (Beardsells) *N Q*
Cheadle *p185* 0161 477 2288

Miles, Mrs H E (Isle of Wight Council) *D1 D2 K1*
Newport *p466* 01983 823207

Miles, H R (Bannister Bates Property Lawyers) *G K1 S1 Zl W*
Morecambe *p318* 01524 416300

Miles, Ms J (Barnes Marsland) *W T2*
Broadstairs *p166* 01843 861595

Miles, Ms J (Pannone LLP) *S1*
Manchester *p308* 0161 909 3000

Miles, J C O (Ross & Craig) *C1 C2*
Westminster *p73* 020 7262 3077

Miles, J M (Mayer Brown International LLP) *O*
London EC2 *p59* 020 3130 3000

Miles, Mrs K (Rawlison Butler LLP) *C1 C3 L M1 U2 Ze*
Crawley *p202* 01293 527744

Miles, K D (Torridge District Council)
Bideford *p449* 01237 428700

Miles, M (Batchelors Solicitors) *C1 O Q Zq C2 J1*
Bromley *p166* 020 8768 7000

Miles, Ms R (Dean Wilson Laing) *W S1 K4*
Brighton *p159* 01273 327241

Miles, Miss R (Gill Turner Tucker) *Q J1 L Zp F1*
Maidstone *p299* 01622 759051

Miles, R J (LG Lawyers)
London SE1 *p50* 020 7379 0000

Miles, Ms S (Nockolds) *C1 C2 Ze U2 F1*
Bishop's Stortford *p144* . . . 01279 755777

Miles, Mrs S J (Warner Goodman LLP) *K1 K2 K3 D1 D2*
Southampton *p387* 023 8063 9311

Miles, S J (Edwin Coe LLP) *Ze U2 Zw*
London WC2 *p29* 020 7691 4000
London EC2 *p81* 020 7655 1000
London WC1 *p86* 020 7242 3191

Miles, S J (Pinsent Masons LLP) *Zb*
Birmingham *p141* 0121 200 1050

Miles, Ms S M (Larken & Co) *S2 C1 E*
Newark *p322* 01636 703333

Miles, Mrs S M (Freeth Cartwright LLP) *Q J1 Zl*
Nottingham *p337* 0115 936 9369

Miles, T G (Commercial Union PLC)
London EC3 *p105* 020 7283 7500

Miles, Ms W J (WilmerHale) *A3*
London EC2 *p92* 020 7645 2400

Mileson, C (EMI Music Publishing Ltd)
London W8 *p106* 020 3059 3059
Gravesend *p233* 01474 816517

Milford, C (Hugh James) *K1 D1*
Cardiff *p179* 029 2022 4871

Milk, J (Josiah Hincks) *C1 E J1 W*
Leicester *p280* 0116 255 1811

Milkins, J R (Osborne Clarke) *C1*
Bristol *p164* 0117 917 3000

Mill, J C (Bell & Co) *C1 E S2 C2*
Sutton *p402* 020 8661 8611

Millan, Ms A (Wise Geary) *O Q L B1 F1 Zl Zq*
Banbury *p122* 01295 278500

Millan, Mrs G (Millan Solicitors) *N S1 K1 Zr Zi Q W*
Bradford *p154* 01274 660111

Millan, P S (Noble)
Shefford *p377* 01462 814055

Millane, Ms H (Margaret Reynolds Solicitor) *E S1*
Grays *p233* 01375 390239

Millar, Ms A (Leigh Day & Co) *Zg Zr*
London EC1 *p52* 020 7650 1200

Millar, A D W (Jones Day) *O A3 Zq Q Zk U2*
London EC4 *p46* 020 7039 5959

Millar, A J (Tallents Solicitors) *S1*
Southwell *p389* 01636 813411

Millar, C I (Downs) *B1 C1 O P*
Dorking *p212* 01306 880110

Millar, C J (Pannone LLP) *N*
Manchester *p308* 0161 909 3000

Millar, C T (Simmons & Simmons)
London EC2 *p79* 020 7628 2020

Millar, D P (Cyril Morris Arkwright) *G H*
Bolton *p148* 01204 535261

Millar, Ms E M (Elizabeth M Millar)
London N6 *p60* 020 8348 3228

Millar, Mrs J (Howard & Over) *K1 D1 J1*
Ivybridge *p263* 01752 690123

Millar, Miss J (Bircham Dyson Bell) *W Zd*
Westminster *p13* 020 7227 7000

Millar, J K (Harrowells) *S1*
York *p445* 01904 760237

Millar, Ms L (Maxwell Winward LLP) *T1 T2*
London EC4 *p59* 020 7651 0000
London EC2 *p81* 020 7655 1000

Millar, N M (Neil Millar & Co Solicitors) *C1 O N Q J1 F1 Zc U2 Zq Zp C2*
Manchester *p307* 0161 870 0177

Millar, S (CMS Cameron McKenna LLP)
London EC3 *p17* 020 7367 3000

Millar, Ms S (Cogent Law)
Croydon *p204* 0844 245 4452

Millar Craig, J W R (Royds LLP) *J1 K1 L M1 N P G H D1 Zb Zc Zk*
London EC4 *p74* 020 7583 2222

Millard, Mrs E J (Barlow Robbins LLP) *W Zk*
Guildford *p235* 01483 562901

Millard, Miss F A (Eastgate Assistance Ltd)
Colchester *p455* 0870 523 4500

Millard, Dr R A (Wyeth)
Maidenhead *p464* 01628 604377

Millard, R E (Geoffrey Leaver Solicitors LLP) *O Q Zc A3 B1 Zq Ze U2*
Milton Keynes *p317* 01908 692769

Millband, A (Shakespeares) *J2*
Nottingham *p339* 0115 945 3700

Millbourn, R (Bower & Bailey) *N O Q Zr Zl J2 Zc*
Swindon *p406* 01793 610466

Millen, Ms K K (Laytons) *C1 C2 I F1 J1*
Guildford *p236* 01483 407000

Millen, Mrs L (Roberts Moore Nicholas Jones) *G H*
Birkenhead *p134* 0151 647 0000

Millen, Mrs S (Chattertons Solicitors) *E A1 L S1*
Horncastle *p252* 01507 522456

Millen, Ms V J (Brewer Harding & Rowe) *W*
Barnstaple *p125* 01271 342271

Miller, A (Seddons)
Westminster *p77* 020 7725 8000

Miller, Mrs A (EMW) *E R2*
Milton Keynes *p316* 0845 070 6000

Miller, Mrs A (Perrins Solicitors LLP) *Zc S2 E Zh L R2 S1*
Harpenden *p239* 01582 466140

Miller, Ms A (Withers LLP) *T2 W Zl*
London EC4 *p92* 020 7597 6000

Miller, Ms A (Paul Hills & Co) *S1*
Chichester *p193* 01243 671782

Miller, A D (Miller Clayton) *B1 C1 E J1 K1 L N O Q S1*
Stanmore *p394* 020 8954 5280

Miller, A M (Gullands) *W T1 T2 Zd K4*
Maidstone *p299* 01622 678341

Miller, A W M (Foot Anstey) *W T2 A1 Zd*
Exeter *p221* 01392 411221
Exeter *p221* 01392 688688

Miller, B (DLA Piper UK LLP)
Liverpool *p287* 0870 011 1111

Miller, B L (Davenport Lyons) *C1 I Ze Zf U2*
London W1 *p25* 020 7468 2600

Miller, Mrs C (Treasury Solicitors Department)
London WC2 *p110* 020 7210 3000

See p634 for the Key to Work Categories

Miller, C (Nelsons) *O N J1 Q Zp*
Nottingham *p338*. 0115 958 6262

Miller, C (Taylor Wessing)
London EC4 *p86*. 020 7300 7000

Miller, C G (Clifford Miller) *C3 I Ze Zf*
Beckenham *p129* 020 8663 0044

Miller, Ms C J (Rogerson Galvin) *G H*
Ashton-under-Lyne *p120*0161 344 2027 / 335 9005

Miller, Mrs C J (Sedgwick Kelly LLP)
Watford *p424* 01923 228311

Miller, C M (C M Miller Solicitors) *P N M1*
Barnet *p124* 020 8449 6151

Miller, C M (Barcan Woodward) *K1 D1*
Bristol *p160* 0117 963 5237

Miller, Ms C T (Miller Evans & Co) *S2 E S1 C1 Zl W*
London EC3 *p60*. 020 7987 2515

Miller, Ms D (Max Barford & Co) *A1 E L S1 S2 W*
Tunbridge Wells *p414* 01892 539379

Miller, D (Hamers Solicitors) *D1 K1 Zo*
Hull *p257* 01482 326666

Miller, Ms D (Marks & Spencer PLC)
London W2 *p107* 020 7935 4422
London EC4 *p15*. 020 7400 8000

Miller, D J (Kidd Rapinet) *S1 E S2 L W*
London WC2 *p49* 020 7205 2115

Miller, Mrs D L (Chattertons Solicitors) *K1 D1 F1 M1 P V B1 H G*
Spalding *p389* 01775 768774

Miller, D M A (Official Solicitor and Public Trustee) *T1 T2 V W*
London WC2 *p108*. 020 7911 7127

Miller, D N (Hoole & Co) *G H*
Bristol *p163* 0117 969 1436
Bristol *p163* 0117 942 8871

Miller, D P B (Miller Lyons Solicitors) *W S1 S2 L A1 K4*
Glastonbury *p230* 01458 833660

Miller, D P H (Mulcare Jenkins) *E S1 S2 L R2 W*
Haywards Heath *p246* 01444 459954

Miller, E (Field Fisher Waterhouse LLP)
London EC3 *p31*. 020 7861 4000
London EC3 *p31*. 020 7861 4000

Miller, Mrs E A (Sutton-Mattocks & Co LLP) *S1*
London W4 *p84* 020 8994 7344

Miller, E C G (Olswang LLP) *C1 C2 B1 Zb*
London WC1 *p64* 020 7067 3000

Miller, E S (Reed Smith LLP) *C1 Zb Ze M1*
London EC2 *p71*. 020 3116 3000

Miller, Mrs F (Birmingham City Council Legal & Democratic Services)
Birmingham *p449* 0121 303 2066

Miller, G E P (Miller Law Practice) *N S1 K1 E C1 Q W J1 Zl*
Haringey *p60* 020 8340 2953

Miller, Mrs G K H (Knights Solicitors LLP) *E*
Newcastle under Lyme *p323*. 01782 619225

Miller, Ms H (Manchester City Council)
Manchester *p465* 0161 234 5000

Miller, H (Birnberg Peirce & Partners) *G*
Camden *p13*. 020 7911 0166

Miller, H J (Pembrokeshire County Council)
Haverfordwest *p460* 01437 764551

Miller, Mrs I (Bradford & Co)
Bristol *p161* 0117 963 5261

Miller, I G (Bevan Brittan LLP)
London EC4 *p12*. 0870 194 1000

Miller, I H (Allen Barfields) *Q S1 L W E Zl S2 J1 T1 C1*
West Wickham *p428*. 020 8654 2706

Miller, I N (Wykeham Hurford Sheppard & Son LLP) *A1 C1 E L M1 R1 S1 S2 T1 T2 W Zc Zm Zk Zq*
Tenterden *p410* 01580 762251

Miller, J (DAC Beachcroft) *N I*
London EC3 *p24*. 020 7208 6800

Miller, Mrs J A (Vance Harris) *W*
Crowborough *p204*. 01892 653434

Miller, J C (Miller Clayton) *C2 D1 R1 T1 T2 W*
Stanmore *p394* 020 8954 5280

Miller, Mrs J E (Knowsley Metropolitan Borough Council)
Huyton *p461*. 0151 443 3593

Miller, J L (Whitehead Monckton) *K1 K3*
Maidstone *p299* 01622 698000

Miller, J P (Reynolds Porter Chamberlain LLP) *Zc Zj N*
London E1 *p71* 020 3060 6000

Miller, Mrs J T (Gordons LLP) *O B1 Zb*
Leeds *p273* 0113 227 0100

Miller, Mrs K (Harman & Harman) *K1 D1 Zm*
London SW2 *p39* 01227 452977

Miller, K C (Marks Miller & Co) *E S1 C1 W B1 L K1 S2 O Q N*
Billericay *p133*. 01277 633991

Miller, Ms K M (Finers Stephens Innocent LLP)
London W1 *p32* 020 7323 4000

Miller, Miss M (Kirklees Metropolitan Borough Council)
Huddersfield *p461* 01484 221421

Miller, M (O'Garra's) *B2 G H*
Leeds *p276* 0113 247 1477

Miller, M D (Bolt Burdon) *C1*
Islington *p14*. 020 7288 4700

Miller, M J C (Peter Peter & Wright) *S2 A1 A2 W S1 E L*
Holsworthy *p251*. 01409 253262

Miller, M P (Vaughan & Davies) *W S1 A1 L T1 E S2 T2 K4*
Kington *p268* 01544 230325

Miller, N (Howard Kennedy LLP) *Zf*
London W1 *p48* 020 7636 1616

Miller, N (Fox Williams) *C1 C3 M1 M2 I Ze*
London EC2 *p33*. 020 7628 2000

Miller, N H (Barnard & Co) *Q C1 J1 K1 Zv*
Filton *p226*. 0117 969 2773

Miller, N P (Kidd & Spoor) *G M1 H K1 P D1*
Newcastle upon Tyne *p325* . 0191 273 9217
Whitley Bay *p431* 0191 297 0011

Miller, P (Ashurst LLP)
London EC2 *p7* 020 7638 1111

Miller, P (Sweeney Miller)
Sunderland *p402*. 0191 568 2050

Miller, Ms P (Simmons & Simmons)
London EC2 *p79*. 020 7628 2020

Miller, P D (Birdlife International)
Cambridge *p452*. . . . .

Miller, P J (Howard Kennedy LLP) *C1 C2*
London W1 *p48* 020 7636 1616

Miller, P J (Peter J Miller) *E S2 R2 Zc Zd R1 S1 L W*
Wandsworth *p60*. 0870 321 7561

Miller, P R (Hudson & Taylor) *K1 C1 J1 S1 T1 E*
Rochdale *p365*. 01706 644525

Miller, R (Treasury Solicitors Department)
London WC2 *p110*. 020 7210 3000

Miller, Ms R (Armitage Sykes LLP) *K1 D1*
Huddersfield *p255* 01484 344140

Miller, R F (Harvey Ingram LLP) *E S1 L*
Leicester *p280*. 0116 254 5454

Miller, R H (Akzo Nobel Ltd)
London SW1 *p103*. 020 7009 5000

Miller, R J (Curtis) *M1 N P K1 F1 C1 B1 J1 T1*
Plymouth *p349*. 01752 204444

Miller, R P (Gallaher Ltd)
Weybridge *p476* 01932 859777

Miller, R W (Burnetts) *A1 S2 E*
Carlisle *p181*. 01228 552222
Carlisle *p182*. 01228 552222

Miller, Miss S (Clive G Wood & Co)
Stockport *p396*. 0161 480 1000

Miller, Miss S (DWT Legal Ltd) *K1 Q Zo*
Kidderminster *p265* 0844 770 3799

Miller, S (Squire Sanders (UK) LLP)
Leeds *p277* 0113 284 7000

Miller, S M (Allen & Overy LLP)
London E1 *p5* 020 3088 0000

Miller, Miss S S (Oglethorpe Sturton & Gillibrand) *S1 W*
Kirkby Lonsdale *p268* 01524 271388

Miller, Mrs V E (Eastgate Assistance Ltd) *N B1*
Colchester *p455*. 0870 523 4500

Miller, W F (Sills & Betteridge LLP) *G*
Lincoln *p285*. 01522 542211

Miller Smith, Ms C (Linklaters LLP)
London EC2 *p54*. 020 7456 2000

Millerchip, S J (Millerchip Peachey) *G H*
Coventry *p200*. 024 7624 3615

Millers, L (Ashurst LLP)
London EC2 *p7* 020 7638 1111

Millet, C S G (Morecrofts Solicitors LLP)
Liverpool *p290*. 0151 236 8871

Millett, A (Pemberton Greenish LLP) *C1 Zw*
London SW3 *p66* 020 7591 3333

Millett, Miss E L (Sheltons) *W Zl*
Nottingham *p339*. 0115 955 3444

Millett, P M (Finers Stephens Innocent LLP) *C1 Zb*
London W1 *p32* 020 7323 4000

Millgate, D R (Young Coles & Langdon) *K1 L S1 Q J1 F1 W*
Hastings *p244* 01424 437878

Millichap, Miss S L (Lester Aldridge LLP) *K1*
Bournemouth *p152*. 01202 786161

Milligan, C P (Bird & Co) *G N O H Q Zq*
Grantham *p232* 01476 591711

Milligan, P A (Ford & Warren) *K1 M1 P D1 N F1 J1 Ze*
Leeds *p273* 0113 243 6601

Milligan, S G (Department for Business, Enterprise and Regulatory Reform)
London SW1 *p105*. 020 7215 0105

Milligan, S M (Hodge Jones & Allen LLP) *D2 D1 K1 K2 K3*
London NW1 *p41* 020 7874 8300

Millin, Ms M R (Read Dunn Connell) *E S1*
Bradford *p154* 01274 723858
Bradford *p154* 01274 306000

Millington, Mrs D (Hargreaves Gilman) *W T2 S1*
Manchester *p305* 0161 443 1711

Millington, Ms E (Grindeys LLP) *S1*
Stoke-on-Trent *p397*. 01782 846441

Millington, I D (D P Roberts Hughes & Denye) *C1 E L S1 W*
Birkenhead *p134*. 0151 647 6000

Millington-Jones, Ms Z V (Barlow Lyde & Gilbert LLP)
London EC3 *p10*. 020 7247 2277

Millis, D S (Warners Solicitors) *E S1 S2 L R1*
Tonbridge *p412* 01732 770660

Millis, J (Brachers) *O Q*
Maidstone *p299* 01622 690691

Millman, R G (Arnold Fooks Chadwick LLP) *C1 B1 T1 Zc A3 B3 I Ze J1 C2 Zq*
London W1 *p7*. 020 7499 3007

Millmore, A L (Harbottle & Lewis LLP)
London W1 *p38* 020 7667 5000

Millmore, R G (McCormicks) *B1 O*
Harrogate *p240* 01423 530630

Millross, A A (Anthony Collins Solicitors LLP) *Zd Zh Zn X R1 C1*
Birmingham *p137* 0121 200 3242

Mills, Miss A (Stone King LLP) *K1 K3*
Bath *p128* 01225 337599

Mills, A (Freeth Cartwright LLP) *Ze*
Nottingham *p337*. 0115 936 9369

Mills, Mrs A (Warner Goodman LLP) *S1*
Portsmouth *p355*. 023 9275 3575

Mills, A (Dalgarno Solicitors) *N*
Warrington *p421*. 0870 444 1501

Mills, A D (Middleton Dummer) *S2 S1 W*
Oldbury *p340* 0121 544 4788

Mills, A H W (Mills & Bann) *A1 C1 D1 E K1 L M1 P S1*
Newbury *p322*. . . . 01635 521545 / 32000

Mills, Miss A J (Walton Mills & Co) *Zr N*
Southampton *p387*. 023 8047 7221

Mills, Ms A L (DLA Piper UK LLP) *R2 R1*
Liverpool *p287*. 0870 011 1111

Mills, Mrs A M (Bywaters Topham Phillips LLP) *E L S1 S2 W*
Harrogate *p240* 01423 879556

Mills, Ms B (Wiltshire County Council)
Trowbridge *p474*. 01225 713000

Mills, Mrs C (Longmores) *J1*
Hertford *p248* 01992 300333

Mills, C A (Tozers) *N Zr*
Exeter *p222* 01392 207020

Mills, Mrs C A (Francis Law LLP) *C1 C2 C3 E J1*
Lydney *p296*. 01594 842242

Mills, C J (Donnelly & Elliott Limited) *D1 D2 K1*
Gosport *p232* 023 9250 5500

Mills, D (Mills & Reeve) *J1 Zp*
Cambridge *p175*. 01223 364422

Mills, Ms D E (Howard Kennedy LLP) *J1*
London W1 *p48* 020 7636 1616

Mills, Mrs D L (Howard Kennedy LLP) *C1 C2 F1 I J1 Ze Zn W*
London W1 *p48* 020 7636 1616

Mills, D M (Harvey Ingram Borneos) *S1 W T1 Zd*
Bedford *p130* 01234 353221

Mills, D S (Clarks Legal LLP)
Reading *p360* 0118 958 5321

Mills, Miss D T (Jeffrey Green Russell)
London W1 *p46* 020 7339 7000

Mills, Ms F (Pictons Solicitors LLP) *Zr*
Luton *p295* 01582 870870

Mills, G B (Mills & Co) *B1 C1 E M1 O Za Zc Ze Zj*
Newcastle upon Tyne *p325* . 0191 233 2222

Mills, I D (George Mills) *C1 E J1 L R1 S1 T1 W Zc Zl Zo F1 S2*
Washington *p423* 0191 416 2182

Mills, J (Clarion Solicitors LLP) *O F1*
Leeds *p272* 0113 246 0622

Mills, Mrs J A (Gordon & Penney) *G K1 H D1*
Weston-super-Mare *p429* . . 01934 414161

Mills, J A H (Willans LLP) *E R2 S2*
Cheltenham *p189* 01242 514000

Mills, J T (Jeffrey Mills) *B1 C1 E F1 J1 K1 L M1 P S1 Zi Zl Zw*
St Ives *p392*. . . . 01480 495616 / 494810 / 465757
St Neots *p392*. . . .01480 475871 / 219699

Mills, Mrs L A (Hart Brown Solicitors) *W*
Godalming *p231* 0800 068 8177

Mills, M J (Stokes Solicitors) *K1 D1 W*
Portsmouth *p355*. 023 9282 8131

Mills, N (Bonallack & Bishop) *J1 Q O Zq W Zp L*
Salisbury *p371*. 01722 422300
Bournemouth *p152*. 01202 294566

Mills, N A (Stables & Co) *N O Q J1*
Halesowen *p237*. 0121 585 3820

Mills, N J (Solomon Taylor & Shaw) *S1 E N J1 L W Zh Zd*
London NW3 *p80* 020 7431 1912

Mills, N J (RMPI Solicitors) *M1 P*
London W1 *p70* 020 7318 4444

Mills, P (Morrisons Solicitors LLP) *S1 S2*
Woking *p437*. 01483 726146

Mills, P A (Mills & Co) *S1 W E S2*
Ashton-in-Makerfield *p119* . . 01942 719655

Mills, Ms R (LG Lawyers)
London SE1 *p50*. 020 7379 0000

Mills, Miss R (Robinsons) *J1*
Derby *p209* 01332 291431

Mills, R P (OMW Solicitors) *S1 K1 D1 L M1 N P E F1 W Zi Zl*
Burton-on-Trent *p170*01283 563401 / 530333

Mills, Miss S (Walton Mills & Co) *N Zr*
Southampton *p387*. 023 8047 7221

Mills, S (Ramsdens Solicitors) *E P R1 Zc Zu*
Huddersfield *p256* 01484 821500

Mills, S P (Matthew Arnold & Baldwin LLP) *O Zb Q*
Watford *p423* 01923 202020

Mills, T J (Goffeys) *C1 E F1 J1 L S1 R1*
Southport *p388* 01704 531755

Mills, T M (Garner Canning Vickery) *Zc C1 S2 E C2 R2 S1*
Sutton Coldfield *p403* 0121 323 2646

Millson, A E (Veale Wasbrough Vizards) *W T2 Zd K4 Zo*
London EC4 *p89*. 020 7405 1234

Millward Jones, R (Bevans)
Bristol *p161* 0117 923 7249

Millward, A (Anthony Collins Solicitors LLP) *C1 Ze F1 Zd*
Birmingham *p137* 0121 200 3242

Millward, Miss J H C (Essex County Council)
Chelmsford *p454*. 0845 743 0430

Millward, P L (Straw & Pearce) *G H*
Loughborough *p293* 01509 268931

Milmore, R (Clarion Solicitors LLP) *O B1*
Leeds *p272* 0113 246 0622

Milne, Mrs C R (Girlings Personal Injury Claims Limited) *N Zr*
Canterbury *p177*. 01227 768374

Milne, C S (Onions & Davies) *K4 T2 W*
Market Drayton *p312*. 01630 652405

Milne, D M (Addison O'Hare) *D1 K1 D2*
Walsall *p419*. 01922 725515

Milne, G (Geoffrey Milne) *S1 K1 W A1 L J1 S2 K3*
Wellington *p425* . . .01952 223300 / 223381
Wolverhampton *p438* 01902 373000

Milne, J (Herbert Smith LLP) *C1*
London EC2 *p40*. 020 7374 8000

Milne, J D P (Healys LLP) *C1*
London EC4 *p39*. 020 7822 4000

Milne, Mrs M (iFocus)
East Grinstead *p215*. 020 7566 8244

Milne, Ms N (Esso Petroleum Company Ltd) *O C1*
Leatherhead *p462* 01372 222000

Milne, S G (Memery Crystal) *C1 J1*
London WC2 *p60* 020 7242 5905

Milne, W D (Swale Borough Council)
Sittingbourne *p471*. 01795 417324

Milne-Day, T D (Blake Lapthorn) *S1 W A1 C1 Zd T2 S2*
Oxford *p342* 01865 248607

Milner, H F (Henry Milner & Co) *G H*
London EC1 *p61*. 020 7831 9944

Milner, Miss J E (McCormicks) *G H*
Harrogate *p240* 01423 530630

Milner, Miss M J (Squire Sanders (UK) LLP)
London EC2 *p81*. 020 7655 1000

Milner, Ms P (Withers LLP) *T2 W*
London EC4 *p92*. 020 7597 6000

Milner, P (Marsden Rawsthorn LLP) *S1 W E*
Chorley *p194* 01257 279511

Milner, P D (Lumb & Macgill) *G H*
Bradford *p154* 01274 730666

Milner, S (Clarion Solicitors LLP) *B2 G H*
Leeds *p272* 0113 246 0622

Milner, S J (McCormicks) *B2 G H*
Harrogate *p240* 01423 530630

Milner, S M (Milner Elledge) *N K1 Q V*
Dagenham *p206*. 020 8984 0940

Milner, T (Thomas Milner & Co) *W T2*
Ely *p218*. 01353 860005

Milner-Moore, G (Herbert Smith LLP) *O*
London EC2 *p40*. 020 7374 8000

Milnes, D R (Forbes) *E S2 C1 C2 J1 P L W Zp Ze Zu*
Blackburn *p145* 01254 54374

Milns, C D A (Sills & Betteridge LLP) *K1 Zm*
Lincoln *p285*. 01522 542211

Milns, J W (Burton Copeland LLP) *G*
Manchester *p302* 0161 827 9500

Milns, Miss R J E (May May & Merrimans) *W T2 K4*
London WC1 *p59* 020 7405 8932

Milnthorpe, G (Aviva PLC)
London EC3 *p103* . . 020 7283 7500 / 01603 687905
Norwich *p467* 01603 622200

Milsom, R C (Shelley & Co) *G H*
Cambridge *p175*. 01223 359441

Milson, Miss C (Wigan Borough Council)
Wigan *p476* 01942 244991

Milton, Mrs A K (W Davies) *W K4*
Woking *p436*. 01483 744900

Milton, D A (Jackamans) *W*
Ipswich *p262*. 01473 255591

Milton, Mrs D M (Rushmoor Borough Council)
Farnborough *p458* 01252 398398

Milton, P A (Paul Anthony Milton Solicitors) *C1 F1 I Ze C3 U2*
Maidenhead *p298* 01628 670497

Milton, T G (Segens Blount Petre)
Westminster *p77*. 020 7332 2222

Milton-Downes, Mrs L H (Dyne Drewett Solicitors Ltd) *O Q N*
Shepton Mallet *p378*. 01749 342323

Milton-Jenkins, I (Thorne Segar) *N O Q L W J1 S1*
Minehead *p318* 01643 703234

Milwain, D (Lupton Fawcett) *Zd T1 T2 W*
Leeds *p275* 0113 280 2000

Milward, M D (Stone Milward Rapers) *N K1 G J1 Zm*
Chichester *p193*. 01243 780211

Minahan, M J J (Minahan Hirst & Co) *S1 E S2*
Cheadle Hulme *p185*. 0161 485 8131

Minaides, M G (Minaides Robson) *S1 C1 E N O J1 F1 L M1 Q K1 Zj Zk Zl*
London EC4 *p61*. 020 7831 7761

Minett, Ms K (Russell-Cooke LLP) *J1 Zi*
London SW15 *p74*. 020 8789 9111

Mingay, G F (Edwards Angell Palmer & Dodge)
London EC2 *p28*. 020 7583 4055

Mingham, B P (Lorimers) *S1 W K3 K4 J1 S2*
Buckingham *p168* . .01280 812132 / 813405

Minghella, Ms L C (Financial Services Authority)
London E14 *p106* 020 7066 1000

Minhas, Mrs S K (Christopher Cox Solicitors) *C1 E S1*
Northampton *p331*. 01604 882287

Minifie, R C (Bird Wilford & Sale) *E K1 S1 W Zd*
Loughborough *p293* 01509 232611

Minihan, Miss J C (Cartmell Shepherd) *S2 C1 E*
Carlisle *p182*. 01228 516666

Minihane, Miss A (Quality Solicitors Burroughs Day) *W T2*
Bristol *p164* 0117 929 0333

Minihane, Ms N C (Bird & Lovibond) *W S1 K4*
Uxbridge *p417*. 01895 256151

Minion, R H (MBA Solicitors) *N G H*
York *p445* 01904 666888

Minnighan, Ms M E (Erewash Borough Council)
Ilkeston *p461* 0115 907 2244

Minns, M P (Manches LLP) *J1 L Q*
Oxford *p343* 01865 722106

Minns-Davies, Ms L (Edward Hayes LLP) *G H B2*
Worthing *p441* 01903 215999

Minogue, Ms A (Linklaters LLP)
London EC2 *p54* 020 7456 2000

Minogue, M P (Minogue & Co) *G H*
London W3 *p61* 020 8752 0540

Minors, Mrs S H (Raworths LLP) *K1 K3*
Harrogate *p240* 01423 566666

Minott, D (Ashurst LLP)
London EC2 *p7* 020 7638 1111

Minsky, Mrs S L (Quastel Midgen LLP) *E S2*
London W1 *p70* 020 7908 2525

Minter, Ms M (Mayo Wynne Baxter LLP)
Brighton *p160* 01273 775533

Minto, H C C (Osborne Clarke) *R2 Zc*
London EC2 *p65* 020 7105 7000

Minto, Miss K D (Mayo Wynne Baxter LLP) *S1 E L C1 W R1 T1*
Eastbourne *p215* 01323 730543

Minton, S J (Mintons) *N O*
Leeds *p275* 0113 245 7575

Minty, Ms C (RMPI Solicitors)
London W1 *p70* 020 7318 4444

Minty, Ms H (Russell-Cooke LLP) *K3 K1*
London SW15 *p74* 020 8789 9111

Miotte, L F (McGrigors LLP)
London EC4 *p56* 020 7054 2500

Mir, Ms S (Wilkinsons) *S1*
London E11 *p91* 020 8532 9270

Mirabelli, P W (City of London Corporation)
London EC2 *p107* 020 7606 3030

Miranda, A (Ellisons) *E S1 C1 L*
Colchester *p197* 01206 764477

Miranda, Mrs S (Howard Kennedy LLP) *M2 C1 T1*
London W1 *p48* 020 7636 1616

Mirchandani, N (Hogan Lovells International LLP)
London EC1 *p42* 020 7296 2000

Mireskandari, R (Simons Muirhead & Burton) *B1 J1 L M1 N P W Ze Zk*
London W1 *p79* 020 7734 4499

Mirviss, Ms A S (Copyright Promotions Licensing Group Ltd)
London W6 *p105* 020 8563 6400

Mirwitch, J S (Royal Mail Group)
London EC4 *p109* 020 7250 2468

Mirza, M Y (Mirza & Co)
Waltham Forest *p61* 020 8520 4416

Mirza, R (Lighthouse Solicitors)
Harrow *p242* 020 3170 7588 / 3170 7589

Mirza, Miss S (Osborne Clarke) *O*
London EC2 *p65* 020 7105 7000

Miscampbell, A I F (Blake Lapthorn) *E C1 J1 B1 A1 I S1 L M1 Zd Ze*
Oxford *p342* 01865 248607

Mishra, Miss A J (ClarksLegal LLP) *J1*
London WC2 *p20* 020 7539 8000

Miskella, R (Lewis Silkin LLP)
London EC4 *p53* 020 7074 8000

Misquitta, A (Farrer & Co LLP)
London WC2 *p31* 020 3375 7000

Misra, S V (Riley Hayes & Co) *Q N Zi G H D1 K1*
Bilston *p133* 01902 353300

Missenden, Miss K L (B J McKenna & Co Solicitors) *D1 K1 K3 N*
Stockport *p396* 0161 432 5757

Misson, N J (Foys Solicitors) *G H*
Doncaster *p211* 01302 327136

Mistry, A (Faber & Co) *G H*
Birmingham *p138* 0121 236 5751

Mistry, Ms A P (W Davies) *W*
Woking *p436* 01483 744900

Mistry, Miss D (Price Mistry) *Zo V K1 W Q N*
Birmingham *p141* 0121 200 1577

Mistry, P (Penningtons)
London EC2 *p66* 020 7457 3000

Mistry, Mrs S (West Berkshire Council)
Newbury *p466* 01635 42400

Mitchard, E (Davies & Jones Solicitors) *G H*
Cardiff *p178* 029 2046 5296

Mitchard, Mrs N (Morgans) *B2*
Cardiff *p180* 029 2072 9888

Mitchell, A (stevensdrake) *E P C1 Zc*
Crawley *p202* 01293 596900

Mitchell, Ms A (Watson Solicitors) *K1 W*
Warrington *p422* 01925 571212

Mitchell, A H (Mitchell & Co) *C1 E L N S1 W*
Woodbridge *p439* 01394 386421

Mitchell, Mrs A L (Crombie Wilkinson)
York *p444* 01904 624185
York *p444* 01904 690111

Mitchell, Miss A L (Pemberton Greenish LLP) *E S2*
London SW3 *p66* 020 7591 3333

Mitchell, Ms A V A (Epping Forest District Council) *S1 W E*
Epping *p458* 01992 564000

Mitchell, A W M (Burges Salmon) *T1 W A1 Zd*
Bristol *p161* 0117 939 2000

Mitchell, B J (Grays) *N O Q L K1 K3 Zq*
York *p444* 01904 634771

Mitchell, C (Coles Miller Solicitors LLP) *K1 K3*
Poole *p352* 01202 673011

Mitchell, C A (C Nicholls) *G H*
Bodmin *p148* 01208 76969

Mitchell, C D (Gaynham King & Mellor) *S2 E S1 L*
Appleby *p118* 01768 351422
Penrith *p346* 01768 864651

Mitchell, Miss C E (Irwin Mitchell LLP) *N Zr*
Sheffield *p376* 0870 150 0100

Mitchell, Mrs C E (Beers LLP) *J1*
Kingsbridge *p267* 01548 857000
Plymouth *p349* 01752 246000

Mitchell, C J H (Nichols Marcy Dawson) *E L S1 S2 W*
Walton-on-Thames *p420* 01932 219500

Mitchell, C L (Gateley LLP) *E*
Leicester *p279* 0116 285 9000

Mitchell, Mrs C M (Sutton-Mattocks & Co LLP) *S1 E W L A1 J1 R1 T1 Zm*
London W4 *p84* 020 8994 7344

Mitchell, C R (Charles Coleman LLP) *C1 E S1 S2*
Windsor *p434* 01753 861115

Mitchell, C R (Harbottle & Lewis LLP) *C1 J1 Ze Zf Zw Zv*
London W1 *p38* 020 7667 5000

Mitchell, D J (Blake Lapthorn) *E S1 S2 L*
Portsmouth *p354* 023 9222 1122

Mitchell, D V M (Harvey Ingram LLP) *O N K1 G J1 I Q Zc Ze Zk*
Leicester *p280* 0116 254 5454

Mitchell, E A (Tyndallwoods) *G H S1*
Birmingham *p143* 0121 624 1111

Mitchell, Mrs E C (Emery Johnson Partnership) *K1 D1*
Leicester *p279* 0116 255 4855

Mitchell, I (Anthony Gold) *L Zg*
London SW16 *p6* 020 7940 4000
London NW10 *p41* 020 8838 1537

Mitchell, I M (Terry Jones Solicitors & Advocates) *D1 L Zh*
Shrewsbury *p379* 01743 285888

Mitchell, J (Manches LLP) *Ze Zk O U2 Zz*
Oxford *p343* 01865 722106

Mitchell, J (Squire Sanders (UK) LLP)
London EC2 *p81* 020 7655 1000

Mitchell, J (Dolmans) *N Q J2 Zj Zq Zu*
Cardiff *p178* 029 2034 5531

Mitchell, Ms J (Berkson Wallace Solicitors) *S1*
Wallasey *p419* 0151 691 6900
Bebington *p129* 0151 645 4255

Mitchell, J (Blake Lapthorn) *G Zl B2*
Chandlers Ford *p184* 023 8090 8090

Mitchell, J B (Stevens & Bolton) *E R1*
Guildford *p237* 01483 302264

Mitchell, J E (Sills & Betteridge LLP) *D1 D2 K1 K2 Zg*
Lincoln *p285* 01522 542211

Mitchell, J F (Jones Day) *E*
London EC4 *p46* 020 7039 5959

Mitchell, J P (Squire Sanders (UK) LLP)
Leeds *p277* 0113 284 7000

Mitchell, Ms J S (Manches LLP) *K1*
Oxford *p343* 01865 722106

Mitchell, K (Isadore Goldman Solicitors)
London EC4 *p45* 020 7353 1000

Mitchell, Ms K M (Thompsons (formerly Robin/Brian Thompson & Partners)) *N J1 Zp*
Plymouth *p350* 01752 675810

Mitchell, Ms L (Vickers & Co) *S2 E S1*
Ealing *p89* 020 8579 2559 / 8840 3999

Mitchell, Miss L (Pollard Bower Solicitors) *K1 W*
Burnley *p169* 01282 457624

Mitchell, Miss L E (Rhys Vaughan)
Manchester *p311* 0161 224 1439

Mitchell, M (Graham & Rosen) *D1 F1 K1 L V W*
Hull *p257* 01482 323123

Mitchell, M (Withers LLP) *T2 W Zd*
London EC4 *p92* 020 7597 6000

Mitchell, Miss N (Howard Kennedy LLP) *Zf*
London W1 *p48* 020 7636 1616

Mitchell, Ms N (Knight Polson Solicitors) *K1 K3 D2*
Eastleigh *p216* 023 8064 4822

Mitchell, N P (Herbert Smith LLP) *Zj C2*
London EC2 *p40* 020 7374 8000

Mitchell, P (Canter Levin & Berg) *G H*
Liverpool *p287* 0151 239 1000

Mitchell, P E (Taylor Wessing) *C1 L F1 O Ze Zf*
London EC4 *p86* 020 7300 7000

Mitchell, P G (Donnelly McArdle Adamson) *G H K1 S1*
Darlington *p206* 01325 482299
Hartlepool *p243* 01429 274732

Mitchell, P L R (Druces LLP) *C1 C2 Zb Zj Zo Zv*
London EC2 *p27* 020 7638 9271

Mitchell, Miss P M (Bedfordshire County Council)
Bedford *p448* 01234 363222

Mitchell, R (McDermott Will & Emery UK LLP) *Zo C1 B1 M2 C2*
London EC2 *p56* 020 7577 6900

Mitchell, R (Howard Outred & Co)
Dartford *p207* 01322 224881

Mitchell, S (Stephens & Scown) *E C1 Ze Zb*
St Austell *p391* 01726 74433

Mitchell, S (Overburys & Raymond Thompson)
Norwich *p335* 01603 610481

Mitchell, S (Thompsons (formerly Robin/Brian Thompson & Partners))
Stoke-on-Trent *p398* 01782 406200

Mitchell, Miss S A (Bobbetts Mackan) *D1 K1 D2 K3*
Bristol *p161* 0117 929 9001

Mitchell, Mrs S A (Veale Wasbrough Vizards) *S1 W T2 A1 Zd Zv*
London EC4 *p89* 020 7405 1234

Mitchell, Miss S C (David Rubie Mitchell & Co) *G H*
Sutton *p403* 020 8641 0575

Mitchell, S C (SNR Denton) *C1*
London EC4 *p75* 020 7242 1212

Mitchell, Miss S J (Jefferies Essex LLP) *N O Q Zq*
Westcliff-on-Sea *p428* 01702 332311

Mitchell, S K (Adams & Remers) *W T2 K4*
Lewes *p283* 01273 480616

Mitchell, S P (RAC Motoring Services)
Bristol *p452* 0870 553 3533

Mitchell, T (MB Solicitors Ltd trading as MB Law) *A3 J1 Zj O Q N Zp J2*
Leeds *p275* 0113 242 4444

Mitchell, Ms V (Farleys Solicitors LLP) *E S1 J1 W*
Blackburn *p145* 01254 367856

Mitchell, W (Arc Property Solicitors LLP) *G H*
Harrogate *p240* 0800 612 9097

Mitchell, W H (David Rubie Mitchell & Co) *G H*
Sutton *p403* 020 8641 0575

Mitchell-Innes, C D (William Sturges & Co) *W T2 K4*
Westminster *p84* 020 7873 1000

Mitchem, Miss S E (Tayntons LLP Solicitors) *S1 E L*
Gloucester *p230* 01452 522047

Mitcheson, Mrs C L (HBOS PLC)
Halifax *p460* 0870 600 5000

Mitchiner, J (Field Fisher Waterhouse LLP)
London EC3 *p31* 020 7861 4000

Mitchinson, A N M (Rose Williams & Partners) *G H B2*
Wolverhampton *p438* 01902 710822

Mitchinson, Mrs H M (Gregory Abrams Davidson LLP) *S1 W*
Liverpool *p288* 0151 733 3353

Mitchison, T A (London Borough of Haringey)
London N22 *p106* 020 8489 0000

Mitford, D (Thomas Magnay & Co) *D1 E H M1 P K1 Zl*
Gateshead *p229* 0191 477 3333

Mitson, D R (Gisby Harrison) *W T2*
Cheshunt *p189* 01707 878300

Mitten, M F (Martin Cray & Co) *S1 G J1 M1 K1 N C1*
Brighton *p159* 01273 673226

Mitton, A (Harbottle & Lewis LLP)
London W1 *p38* 020 7667 5000

Mitty, A J (Peter Richbell & Co Solicitors) *N*
Chelmsford *p187* 01245 355300

Mizler, A E (A E Mizler & Co Solicitors) *J1 Q O Zp C1 Ze*
Pinner *p349* 020 8420 1175

Mizon, Miss S (Attwaters) *S2 S1*
Loughton *p294* 020 8508 2111

Mizrahi, E R (Rogers & Co) *E L S1 Zl*
Buckhurst Hill *p167* 020 8498 9910

Moan, F (D P Roberts Hughes & Denye) *N O Q S1 M1 K1 P W F1 G H C1*
Ellesmere Port *p217* 0151 355 6699

Moat, Ms H (Blair Allison & Co) *D1 K1*
Birmingham *p135* 0121 233 2904

Mobbs, Mrs D M (Band Hatton LLP) *K1 V D1*
Coventry *p200* 024 7663 2121

Mobbs, J K (HM Land Registry - Harrow Sub Office)
Harrow *p460* 020 8235 1181

Mobed, Ms J (Mills & Reeve) *C1*
Cambridge *p175* 01223 364422

Mocatta, B S (McGuireWoods London LLP) *S1 E K1 O N W*
London EC4 *p57* 020 7632 1600

Mocatta, Ms G (Howard Kennedy LLP) *O L*
London W1 *p48* 020 7636 1616

Mochrie, G C (Richard Johnson & Partners) *W S1 A1 C1 P L T1 R1 E K1*
Leyburn *p283* 01969 625577

Mockford, Ms C F (Chattertons Solicitors) *W T1 V A1 C1 R1 S1 B1 L J1 Zd*
Lincoln *p284* 01522 814600

Mocklow, M E (DBL Talbots LLP)
Stourbridge *p399* 01384 445850

Modasia, P (Barker Gotelee Solicitors) *C1 C2 F1 J1 Zb Zd*
Ipswich *p262* 01473 611211

Modell, N R (Beale and Company Solicitors LLP) *Zq O Zj*
London WC2 *p11* 020 7240 3474

Modgil, K (Manches LLP) *K1*
London WC2 *p58* 020 7404 4433

Modha, Miss H D (Hodge Jones & Allen LLP) *N*
London NW1 *p41* 020 7874 8300

Mody, A (Spearing Waite LLP) *O B2*
Leicester *p281* 0116 262 4225

Moffat, Ms B A (St Helens Law Limited)
St Helens *p391* 01744 454433

Moffat, Mrs F A (Diageo PLC) *C1 C2*
London W1 *p105* 020 7927 5300

Moffat, Miss F E C (Timms) *K1 D1*
Derby *p209* 01332 364436

Moffat, Ms H (Cumbria County Council) *D1*
Carlisle *p453* 01228 607374 / 607351

Moffat, Ms J (Williams Grand Prix Engineering Ltd)
Wantage *p475* 01235 777700

Moffatt, Miss H (Brockbank Curwen Cain & Hall) *S1 S2 E W R2 R1*
Workington *p440* 01900 603563

Moffatt, Miss J (Swain & Co) *G H*
Havant *p244* 023 9248 3322

Moffitt, Mrs M S (BHP Law) *K1 D2 K2 D1 K3*
Newcastle upon Tyne *p323* 0191 221 0898

Moger, Miss C (Kirby Sheppard) *D1 K1 K3*
Bristol *p163* 0845 840 0045

Moger, S M (Bolitho Way) *G H Zm*
Portsmouth *p354* 023 9282 0747
Portsmouth *p354* 023 9286 2424

Mogg, P J (Cottrill Stone Lawless) *M1 K1 J1 F1 D1 Zj N Q*
Manchester *p302* 0161 835 3681

Moggridge, Mrs V (Wilkin Chapman LLP) *O B1*
Beverley *p131* 01482 398398

Moghadam, F (LG Lawyers)
London SE1 *p50* 020 7379 0000

Moghaddam, Miss M K (Russell & Russell) *K1*
Chester *p191* 01244 405700

Moghal, A (Jeary & Lewis)
Chippenham *p193* 01249 444484

Moghul, J (Ellis Taylor Law LLP)
London WC2 *p29* 020 7405 0206

Mogollon, Ms J C (Devonshires) *L Q O Zh Zg Zc*
London EC2 *p27* 020 7628 7576

Mogridge, P (Stephens & Scown) *E S1 S2*
Exeter *p222* 01392 210700

Mohabir, A H (Mohabirs) *E S1 Zl S2*
London SW4 *p61* 020 7720 5742 / 7622 5495

Mohabir, S S (Mohabirs) *G H B2*
London SW4 *p61* 020 7720 5742 / 7622 5495

Mohamed, J (John Mohamed & Co) *K1 G H M1 P B1 D1 E*
Bedworth *p130* 024 7649 1964

Mohammed, A H (Trowers & Hamlins)
London EC3 *p88* 020 7423 8000

Mohammed, H (Mohammed & Co Solicitors) *E S1 Zi*
Preston *p357* 01772 888700

Mohammed, J (Dowse & Co) *L Q*
Hackney *p27* 020 7254 6205

Mohindra, R (Clarke Willmott) *Ze*
Southampton *p385* 0845 209 1000 / 0117 305 6000

Mohindra, S (Mohindra Maini Solicitors LLP) *Zb I Q N T2 C1 E B1 M1 S1 G W R1 J1 T1 Zi Zj Zp*
Manchester *p307* 0161 236 9833

Moir, A (Herbert Smith LLP)
London EC2 *p40* 020 7374 8000

Moir, A P (Richard Reed) *B1 F1 L Q O*
Sunderland *p402* 0191 567 0465

Moir, C G (Wallers) *S1*
Newcastle upon Tyne *p327* 0191 261 2281

Moir, Mrs D (Goughs) *W K4 T2 V*
Trowbridge *p414* 01225 762683

Moir, P (Mark Gilbert Morse) *A3 O Q Zq*
Newcastle upon Tyne *p325* 0191 261 0096

Moir, R (Pinsent Masons LLP)
London EC2 *p67* 020 7418 7000

Moisidou, Mrs M (Hill Dickinson LLP)
London EC3 *p41* 020 7283 9033

Mok, S (Simmons & Simmons)
London EC2 *p79* 020 7628 2020

Molander, Ms L A (Suffolk County Council) *D1*
Ipswich *p462* 01473 583000

Mole, A G (London Borough of Greenwich Legal Services) *S1 E L P W J1*
London SE18 *p106* 020 8921 5123

Mole, P R (Chanter Ferguson) *S1 W T1 E A1 C1 L J1 R1 K1 Zc Zl Zb*
Barnstaple *p125* 01271 342268
Bideford *p132* 01237 478751

Molesworth, R S H (Performing Right Society Ltd)
London W1 *p108* 020 7580 5544

Molineaux, Miss S (Paul Robinson Solicitors) *N O*
Westcliff-on-Sea *p428* 01702 338338

Molinu, G (Alan Simons & Co) *S1 W S2 K1 K3 D1 L Q Zq*
Penarth *p345* 029 2070 3991

Moll, Miss C E (Thompsons (formerly Robin/Brian Thompson & Partners)) *N J2*
Stoke-on-Trent *p398* 01782 406200

Molla Mohieddin, Ms S (W Davies) *W*
Woking *p436* 01483 744900

Mollaghan, Miss M M (Isadore Goldman Solicitors)
London EC4 *p45* 020 7353 1000

Moller, S H (Simmons & Simmons)
London EC2 *p79* 020 7628 2020

Molloy, K J (East Sussex County Council) *E R1 R2*
Lewes *p463* 01273 481000

Molloy, Mrs S E (The Smith Partnership) *S1 S2 E*
Stoke-on-Trent *p398* 01782 324454

Molloy, W J (Blake Lapthorn) *A3 I O Q U1 Ze*
London EC1 *p13* 020 7405 2000

Molnar, Ms L (Avon & Somerset Constabulary) *N Q L J1 Zl*
Portishead *p469* 01275 816270

Moloney, D J (Alan Taylor & Co) *N P M1 D1 K1 J1 F1 C1 T1 Ze Zf Zi*
London EC1 *p85* 020 7251 3222

Moloney, J B (J B Moloney & Co)
Leicester *p280* 0116 230 1950

Moloney, P H (Barlow Lyde & Gilbert LLP)
London EC3 *p10* 020 7247 2277

Moloney, Ms T (Hutchins & Co) *S1 W E Zl*
Hackney *p44* 020 8986 3911

Moloney, T J (Gregory Rowcliffe Milners) *M1 J1 N O Q*
London WC1 *p37* 020 7242 0631

Molony, R (W F Smith LLP)
Dereham *p209* 01362 852900

Molson, F B (Calthrops) *S1 W A1 T1 L J1 R1 E F1*
Holbeach *p251* 01406 422621

Molter, Miss A (Meade-King) *W K4 T2*
Bristol *p163* 0117 926 4121

Molyneaux, N M (Milburns Solicitors) *K1 D1 Q V N M1 L B1 F1 J1 Zc Zh Zj*
Workington *p440* 01900 67363

Molyneux, N (Farleys Solicitors LLP) *Q N F1*
Burnley *p169* 01282 798664

Molyneux, R J (Everys) *F1 F2 J1 J2 N O Q*
Sidmouth *p380* 01395 577983

See p634 for the Key to Work Categories

Molyneux, Ms S E (Nottingham City Council (City Sec Dept))
Nottingham *p467* 0115 915 5555

Molyneux, W D (MWRLaw Ltd) *E T1 C1 W*
Preston *p357* 01772 254201

Momi, Ms A (Gangar & Co)
West Bromwich *p427* 0121 553 4166

Momi, V (VKM Solicitors)
Wolverhampton *p438* 01902 311155

Monaghan, Miss A A (GHP Legal) *K1*
Oswestry *p342*. 01691 659194

Monaghan, J I (Pinsent Masons LLP) *C1 I B1 T1 Zb Zc Ze*
London EC2 *p67*. 020 7418 7000

Monaghan, Miss M J (Mayo Wynne Baxter LLP) *Q N J1 L B1*
East Grinstead *p215* 01342 310600

Monaghan, P (BHP Law) *J1 O N*
Newcastle upon Tyne *p323* . 0191 221 0898

Monaghan, Miss S (North Lincolnshire Council) *Zi Zg*
Scunthorpe *p470*. 01724 296296

Monaghan, S (Bury Metropolitan Borough Council)
Bury *p452* 0161 253 7771

Monan, Miss M (Edward Hayes LLP) *G H B2*
Chichester *p192* 01243 781431

Monck-Mason, J B R (Hill Dickinson LLP) *Zj N O*
London EC3 *p41*. 020 7283 9033

Monckton, T C (Whitehead Monckton) *S1 W L E C1 M1 N A1 Zb*
Maidstone *p299* 01622 698000
Tenterden *p410* 01580 765722

Monckton-Milnes, Miss H (Smith Roddam) *S1 W L E K1 M1 F1*
Bishop Auckland *p144* 01388 603073

Moncreiffe, M A C (Charles Russell LLP) *C1 U1 U2*
London EC4 *p19*. 020 7203 5000

Moncrieff, Miss E C (Dickinson Dees) *Q L*
Newcastle upon Tyne *p324* . 0191 279 9000

Mondair, N (Riley Hayes & Co) *N*
Bilston *p133* 01902 353300

Mondon, Mrs S J (Borough of Poole)
Poole *p469* 01202 262808

Monds, E B B (Turners Solicitors LLP) *S1 W S2 E R2*
Bournemouth *p153*. 01202 291291

Money, A (Gallaher Ltd)
Weybridge *p476* 01932 859777

Money, Mrs B A (Shakespeares) *S2 E R2 S1*
Birmingham *p142* 0121 237 3000

Money, R A (Kingswell Berney) *S1 W S2 E T1*
Gosport *p232* 023 9258 2211

Money, Miss S J (GoodyBurrett LLP) *S1 S2*
Colchester *p197* 01206 577676

Money-Kyrle, R F (Boyes Turner) *Zr N*
Reading *p360* 0118 959 7711
Oxford *p343* 01865 811700

Monfared, S (Gordons Solicitors LLP) *E I Ze Q R1 S1 T1 T2*
Marlow *p313*. 01628 487487

Mongan, Miss R (George Davies Solicitors LLP) *J1*
Manchester *p303* 0161 236 8992

Monham, Miss A (Berry & Berry) *J1 L Zh Q N*
Tunbridge Wells *p414* 01892 526344

Monighan, Miss K M (Edward Fail Bradshaw & Waterson) *G H B2*
London EC3 *p30*. 020 7790 4032

Monk, A (DLA Piper UK LLP)
London EC2 *p24*. 0870 011 1111

Monk, Miss C A (Hay & Kilner) *W*
Newcastle upon Tyne *p325* . 0191 232 8345

Monk, D T (Matthew & Matthew Limited) *S1 E*
Southbourne *p387*. 01202 431943

Monk, Mrs G (Anthony Collins Solicitors LLP) *Zc C1 M1 Zu X Zh*
Birmingham *p137* 0121 200 3242

Monk, Miss H J (Tanner & Taylor LLP) *G H*
Farnborough *p224*. 01252 549555

Monk, J (Anthony Collins Solicitors LLP) *J1*
Birmingham *p137* 0121 200 3242

Monk, J H (Blaser Mills) *N*
Staines *p393*. 01784 462511

Monk, P N (Allen & Overy LLP)
London E1 *p5* 020 3088 0000

Monk, Mrs V L (Spelthorne Borough Council)
Staines *p472*. 01784 451499

Monkcom, R E (Druces LLP) *J1 T1 T2 C1 W Zd Zp Ze Zo*
London EC2 *p27*. 020 7638 9271

Monkhouse, Miss C (Eaton Smith LLP) *Q O*
Huddersfield *p255* 01484 821300

Monkhouse, J (Alderson Dodds) *G H*
Blyth *p147*. 01670 352293

Monkhouse, Ms L (David Gray Solicitors) *D1 K3 K1*
Newcastle upon Tyne *p324* . 0191 232 9547

Monks, Ms A (Hogan Lovells International LLP)
London EC1 *p42*. 020 7296 2000

Monks, D (Huntingdonshire District Council)
Huntingdon *p461*. 01480 388388

Monks, Mrs J M T (Robin Burman & Co) *Zx S1 S2 X Zd L W Q*
Manchester *p302* 0161 860 7123

Monnes, Miss M M (DBL Talbots LLP) *W K4*
Wolverhampton *p437* 01902 427561

Monnington, J E T (Moore Blatch Solicitors) *N*
Southampton *p386*. 023 8071 8000

Monniot, E (Maples Teesdale LLP)
London EC2 *p58*. 020 7600 3800

Monod, J C R (Robinsons) *S1 S2 E L W A1 T1 T2*
Shoeburyness *p378* 01702 298282

Monod, T J W (Three Valleys Water PLC)
Hatfield *p460* 01707 268111

Monro, C E S (Bray & Bray) *D1 J1 K1 K3*
Market Harborough *p312*. . . 01858 467181

Monro, D D C (Monro Fisher Wasbrough LLP) *W T1 C1 Zd*
London WC1 *p61* 020 7404 7001

Monson, Ms H L (Fox Williams) *J1 Zp*
London EC2 *p33*. 020 7628 2000

Monson, Miss M (Mary Monson Solicitors Ltd) *G H*
Swinton *p407* . 0161 794 0088 / 0808 155 4870

Montagu, F G D (Bennetts Solicitors Attorneys & Notaries) *A1 E R1 S1 T2 W Zd Zo*
Wrington *p443*. 01934 862786

Montague, R (Macks Solicitors) *Q N*
Middlesbrough *p315* 01642 252828

Montague, T M (Brabners Chaffe Street) *C1*
Liverpool *p286*. 0151 600 3000

Montague, W H (Dexter Montague LLP) *N L Q J1 S1 V W*
Reading *p360* 0118 939 3999

Montague-Jones, R R (Reed Smith LLP)
London EC2 *p71*. 020 3116 3000

Montford, Mrs K (Keoghs LLP) *N Zj O Q*
Bolton *p149* 01204 677000

Montgomerie, Miss F J (Reynolds Porter Chamberlain LLP) *N O Q*
London E1 *p71* 020 3060 6000

Montgomery, A (Herbert Smith LLP)
London EC2 *p40*. 020 7374 8000

Montgomery, N (DAC Beachcroft) *B1 Zb*
Bristol *p162* 0117 918 2000

Montgomery, P L G (Humphreys & Co)
Bristol *p163* 0117 929 2662

Montgomery, Ms R E (Last Cawthra Feather LLP) *O Zc*
Bradford *p154* 01274 848800

Montgomery, Ms S (Crane & Staples) *K1*
Welwyn Garden City *p425* . . 01707 329333

Montgomery, Mrs S (Duncan Lewis & Co) *L*
London W12 *p53* 020 7923 4020

Montgomery, S E (Shoosmiths)
Northampton *p332*. . 0370 086 3000 / 01604 543000

Montlake, A S (H Montlake & Co) *C1 E S1 L J1 N G Ze Zl*
Ilford *p260*. 020 8532 4800

Montlake, M L (Fladgate LLP) *E R2 L S2 S1*
London WC2 *p32* 020 3036 7000

Montlake, S (Parrott & Coales LLP) *C1 E*
Aylesbury *p121* 01296 318500

Montorio, M E (DLA Piper UK LLP) *C2 C1 T1 M1 Zb Zf*
Manchester *p303* 0870 011 1111

Montrose, I (Goodman Derrick LLP) *A1 C1 E T1*
London EC4 *p36*. 020 7404 0606

Moodie, A S (Walker Morris) *E*
Leeds *p277* 0113 283 2500

Moody, E (Hamers Solicitors) *B1 E J1 J2 Zk Zl Q Zu S1*
Hull *p257* 01482 326666

Moody, I K (Nockolds) *N Zj Zr Zu Q O J2*
Bishop's Stortford *p144* . . . 01279 755777

Moody, Miss J C (Waugh Moody & Mulcahy) *S1 W S2 E K4*
Newcastle upon Tyne *p327* . 0191 232 8107
Blaydon-on-Tyne *p147*. . . . 0191 414 2967

Moody, P H C (Blake Lapthorn) *O Ze I A3 U2 C1*
London EC1 *p13*. 020 7405 2000

Moody, P H C (Bevan Brittan LLP)
London EC4 *p12*. 0870 194 1000

Moody, P W (P W Moody) *K1 L N Q S1 W Zl*
Barnet *p124* 020 8440 1443

Moody, R P (Reynolds Porter Chamberlain LLP) *Q Zc Ze Zj Zq*
London E1 *p71* 020 3060 6000

Moon, B (Ince & Co Services Ltd)
London E1 *p44* 020 7481 0010

Moon, Miss C A (Wilmot Thompson) *S1 W T1*
Bristol *p165* 0117 927 6583

Moon, D (Barlow Lyde & Gilbert LLP) *N Q*
Manchester *p301* 0161 829 6400

Moon, Ms D J (The Dures Partnership LLP)
Liverpool *p287*. 0151 242 5111

Moon, K G (Moon & Co) *W*
Ashford *p119* 01233 714055

Moon, M W (Bentleys Stokes & Lowless) *A3 O C1 P Za Zn*
London EC3 *p12*. 020 7782 0990

Moon, Miss R (Lancashire County Council)
Preston *p469* 01772 254868

Moon, Ms S (Heald Nickinson) *K1*
Camberley *p173*. 01276 680000

Mooney, E F (DLA Piper UK LLP) *O Q Zj Zk Zc*
Birmingham *p137* 0870 011 1111

Mooney, Miss H J (Gill Turner Tucker) *S1*
Maidstone *p299* 01622 759051

Mooney, K M (Simmons & Simmons) *C1 O M1 Ze Zf Zj*
London EC2 *p79*. 020 7628 2020

Mooney, M (Keoghs LLP) *Zj Q N*
Bolton *p149* 01204 677000

Mooney, Ms N (McMillan Williams) *Zr N*
South Croydon *p383*. 020 8253 7600

Mooney, Ms N (Thomson Snell & Passmore) *N Zr*
Tunbridge Wells *p415* 01892 510000

Moor, Ms J (Wansbroughs)
Devizes *p210* 01380 733300

Moorby, Miss L J (Jordans) *G H*
Wakefield *p418* 01924 387110

Moorcroft, C (Harcus Sinclair) *W T2 Q*
London WC2 *p38* 020 7242 9700

Moorcroft, P J (Squire Sanders (UK) LLP)
Birmingham *p142* 0121 222 3000

Moore, Mrs A (Thomson Wilson Pattinson) *K3 D1 K1*
Kendal *p264*. 01539 721945

Moore, Mrs A A L (Sykes Lee & Brydson) *K4 W*
York *p445* 01904 731100

Moore, A C (Worcestershire County Council)
Worcester *p477* 01905 766335

Moore, Mrs A J (Kingsley Napley) *N Zq Zr*
London EC1 *p50*. 020 7814 1200

Moore, A J (Gateley LLP) *C1 C2*
Nottingham *p337*. 0115 983 8200

Moore, A K (Breeze & Wyles Solicitors LLP) *S1*
Hertford *p248* 01992 558411

Moore, A L (Swinnerton Moore Solicitors) *C1 O N Q B1*
London EC4 *p84*. 020 7236 7111

Moore, A N (AMD Solicitors) *E S2 C2 C1 Ze*
Bristol *p160* 0117 962 1460

Moore, C (Bond Pearce LLP) *B1 Zb O*
Plymouth *p349*. 0845 415 0000

Moore, Miss C A (hlw Keeble Hawson LLP) *Zr*
Sheffield *p375* 0114 272 2061

Moore, Ms C A (Taylor & Emmet LLP) *Zr*
Sheffield *p377* 0114 218 4000

Moore, Miss C E (British Telecommunications PLC)
London EC1 *p104* 020 7356 6181

Moore, C H (Wiggin LLP) *Zf*
Cheltenham *p189* 01242 224114

Moore, C H (Burstalls) *A1 C1 E W S1*
Hull *p256* 01482 621800

Moore, C J (MMS Solicitors) *N Zr*
Withernsea *p436*. 01964 612318

Moore, C L (Waughs) *C1 E L O Q S1 A1 J1 N*
East Grinstead *p215*. 01342 323545

Moore, C L (Krafts Foods UK Ltd)
Cheltenham *p454* 01242 236101

Moore, Ms C L (VHS Fletchers Solicitors) *G H*
Nottingham *p339*. 0115 959 9550

Moore, C L (Hileys) *E S2 S1 A1*
Thirsk *p411* 01845 522278

Moore, C M (dgb Solicitors) *W T1 T2 K4*
Chatham *p184*. 01634 304000

Moore, C R (Tandridge District Council)
Oxted *p468* 01883 722000

Moore, Mrs C S (B P Collins LLP) *W*
Gerrards Cross *p229*. 01753 889995

Moore, D (Harrowells)
York *p444* 01904 558600

Moore, D C (Bailey Wain & Curzon) *K1 J1 D2 Zv D1*
Stoke-on-Trent *p397*. 01782 847934

Moore, D G (Streeter Marshall) *B1 C1 E L R1 S1 T1*
Croydon *p205* 020 8680 2638

Moore, D J (Rodgers & Burton) *L C1 Q N I M1 Zc Zh Ze*
London SW13 *p73*. 020 8939 6300

Moore, D J (Stables & Co) *G H*
Halesowen *p237*. 0121 585 3820

Moore, Miss D L (J Keith Park & Co) *N Q G K1 W*
St Helens *p391* 01744 636000

Moore, D M J (Herbert Smith LLP) *C1 Zb*
London EC2 *p40*. 020 7374 8000

Moore, D R (David Jones & Co) *E N P S1 W L M1*
Llandudno *p291* 01492 874336

Moore, E (DB Law) *G H L*
Penzance *p346* 01736 364261

Moore, Miss E A (HM Land Registry - Leicester) *S1 L E W*
Leicester *p463*. . . . .0116 265 4000 / 4001

Moore, Miss E A (Morrisons Solicitors LLP) *B1 E K1 L Q S1*
Redhill *p362*. 01737 854500

Moore, Miss E I (Johnson Matthey PLC)
London EC1 *p107* 020 7269 8400

Moore, Miss E J (Edwards Angell Palmer & Dodge)
London EC2 *p28*. 020 7583 4055

Moore, Ms F A (Quality Solicitors Chapman & Chubb) *S1 S2 E*
Alfreton *p115* 01773 540480

Moore, Miss F J (Wilson Browne) *K1 D1 Q*
Wellingborough *p425* 01933 279000

Moore, Miss F L (Crombie Wilkinson) *S2 E S1*
York *p444* 01904 624185

Moore, G (Bristows)
London EC4 *p15*. 020 7400 8000

Moore, G (Linklaters LLP)
London EC2 *p54*. 020 7456 2000

Moore, I C (DAC Beachcroft) *M1 P N G Zj*
Manchester *p303* 0161 934 3000

Moore, I C (Squire Sanders (UK) LLP)
London EC2 *p81*. 020 7655 1000

Moore, Miss J (Olswang LLP) *Zf*
London WC1 *p64* 020 7067 3000

Moore, Ms J (Gepp & Sons) *K1 D1 V*
Chelmsford *p186*. 01245 493939
Colchester *p197* 01206 369889

Moore, Miss J A (Scott Fowler) *S2 E C1*
Northampton *p331*. 01604 750506

Moore, J A (Dixon & Templeton) *A1 E S1 W T2*
Ringwood *p364* 01425 476231
Verwood *p418* 01202 824677

Moore, J C (Milburns Solicitors) *D1 K3 K1 N J1*
Maryport *p313* 01900 813541
Workington *p440*. 01900 67363

Moore, J D (Walker Morris) *B1 E Zb R2*
Leeds *p277* 0113 283 2500

Moore, J F (Squire Sanders (UK) LLP) *C3 I M1 M2 Ze Zk*
Birmingham *p142* 0121 222 3000

Moore, J G (KJD) *C1 T1*
Stoke-on-Trent *p398*. 01782 202020

Moore, J G (Sharman Law) *E S1 T2 W J1 R1 Zh Zi Ze*
Bedford *p130* 01234 303030

Moore, J J (Streeter Marshall) *S1 E C1 L R1 Zc*
Croydon *p205* 020 8680 2638

Moore, K (Tinsdills) *M1 P L K1*
Hanley *p239*. 01782 262031

Moore, Miss K A (Scotts Wright)
Catterick Garrison *p183* . . . 01748 832431

Moore, L (Blaser Mills) *S1 E W C1 L T2 R1 T1 C2 Zd Zh Zs Zn*
Harrow *p241*. 020 8427 6262

Moore, L (Jones Day) *Zb*
London EC4 *p46*. 020 7039 5959

Moore, Ms L A (Capsticks Solicitors LLP) *Zr*
London SW19 *p18*. 020 8780 2211

Moore, Miss L S (Bridge McFarland) *D1 K1*
Grimsby *p235* 01472 311711

Moore, Mrs M A (Travers Smith LLP) *C1 C3*
London EC1 *p87*. 020 7295 3000

Moore, M J (Gales) *K1 D1 J1 L Q F1 K3*
Bournemouth *p152*. .01202 512227 / 512446

Moore, M R (ML Law Ltd) *E C1 J1 L B1 Q R1 S1 Zi W S2*
Eastleigh *p216*. 023 8060 0661

Moore, M W (Paris Smith LLP) *C1 C2 Zb*
Southampton *p386*. 023 8048 2482

Moore, N C (CMS Cameron McKenna LLP)
London EC3 *p17*. 020 7367 3000

Moore, N E (Buckles Solicitors LLP) *C1 C2 I U2 Zz*
Peterborough *p346* 01733 888888

Moore, N R (Stephens & Scown) *J1 O*
Exeter *p222* 01392 210700

Moore, O E (Bristol City Council)
Bristol *p451* 0117 922 2000

Moore, Ms P (Keoghs LLP) *B2 N Zj O Q*
Bolton *p149* 01204 677000

Moore, P G (DWF) *O A3 Zq B2 L*
Manchester *p303* 0161 603 5000

Moore, Miss P J (Nabarro LLP) *E N P Zj Zc*
London WC1 *p63* 020 7524 6000
London WC1 *p63* 020 7524 6000

Moore, P J (Robinson Allfree) *S1 E W A1 S2*
Ramsgate *p359* 01843 592361

Moore, Ms R (Pannone LLP) *N*
Manchester *p308* 0161 909 3000

Moore, R (Geldards LLP)
Cardiff *p178* 029 2023 8239

Moore, R (Walker Morris) *R1*
Leeds *p277* 0113 283 2500

Moore, R (Thompson & Cooke LLP) *O Q J1 N*
Stalybridge *p393*. 0161 338 2614

Moore, R G (Aaron & Partners LLP Solicitors) *S1 Zv*
Chester *p190* 01244 405555

Moore, R J (Temple Heelis LLP) *Q O N B1 F1 L*
Kendal *p264*. 01539 723757

Moore, R W (Duffield Harrison LLP) *B1 G K1 M1 N P S1 Zi*
Hoddesdon *p251*. 01992 442911

Moore, R W (Clifford Chance)
London E14 *p20*. 020 7006 1000

Moore, R W C (Taylor & Emmet LLP) *O*
Sheffield *p377* 0114 218 4000

Moore, Miss S (Barber Titleys) *O Q L Zc A3 Zq*
Harrogate *p240* 01423 502211

Moore, S (Herbert Smith LLP)
London EC2 *p40*. 020 7374 8000

Moore, Ms S (Sheila Moore) *G H*
Durham *p214* 0191 386 5621

Moore, Ms S C (Leigh Day & Co) *N*
London EC1 *p52*. 020 7650 1200

Moore, Mrs S C (O'Neill Patient) *K3 K1 D1 D2*
Stockport *p396*. 0161 483 8555

Moore, S D (HBOS PLC)
Halifax *p460* 0870 600 5000

Moore, Miss S J (BCL Burton Copeland) *B2 G*
London WC2 *p9* 020 7430 2277

Moore, S J (Field Fisher Waterhouse LLP)
London EC3 *p31*. 020 7861 4000

Moore, S J (Oglethorpe & Broatch) *S1 S2 W E*
Keswick *p265* 01768 772125

Moore, S J (Furness Evans)
Manchester *p304*

Moore, Miss S J K (Druitts) *K3 K1*
Bournemouth *p151*. 01202 551863
Christchurch *p194* 01202 484242

Moore, Mrs S M (Northumberland County Council)
Morpeth *p466* 01670 533000

Moore, S P (Stephen Moore & Co)
Rugby *p368* 01788 535127

Moore, S R (Bevan Brittan LLP)
Bristol *p161* 0870 194 1000

Moore, T (Burstalls) *S1 W R1 C1 L T2*
Hull *p256* 01482 621800

Moore, T (Gregory Rowcliffe Milners) *Q O Zd Zl*
London WC1 *p37* 020 7242 0631

Moore, T C (Streeter Marshall) *B1 C1 E J1 K1 L N*
Croydon *p205* 020 8680 2638

Moore, T F (Trevor F Moore & Co)
Leicester *p280*. 01530 261719

Moore, W (Berry & Berry) *K1 S1 S2 E L C1*
Maidstone *p299* 01622 690777
Tunbridge Wells *p414* 01892 526344

Moore, W R (Crosby & Moore Solicitors)
Hove *p254*. 01273 863295

6

Moores, Miss C M (Lawson Coppock & Hart) *E S1 S2 R2*
Manchester *p306* 0161 832 5944

Moores, Ms K (Sydney Mitchell) *K1 D1*
Birmingham *p142* 0121 722 2969 / 0808 166 5638

Moorhead, B R K (Moorhead James LLP) *C1 C2 Zw Zz Zd*
London EC4 *p61*. 020 7831 8888

Moorhead, H C D (Henry Moorhead & Co) *S1 W A1 T1 C1 E R1 Zc Zd L*
Hythe *p259* 01303 262525

Moorhead, Mrs R W T (Moorhead James LLP)
London EC4 *p61*. 020 7831 8888

Moorhouse, A (Penningtons)
London EC2 *p66*. 020 7457 3000

Moorhouse, D L (Trowers & Hamlins) *N Zc*
London EC3 *p88*. 020 7423 8000

Moors, D (Teignbridge District Council)
Newton Abbot *p466* 01626 361101

Moors, Miss K E (The Child Law Partnership) *D1 K1 Zu*
Guildford *p236*. 01483 543790

Mooruth, N (Adan & Co) *Zm*
Maidstone *p298* 01622 600488

Moothia, V (Massers) *E*
Nottingham *p338*. 0115 851 1666

Moppett, Ms A J (Craven District Council)
Skipton *p471*. 01756 700600

Moraghan, Ms M R (City of Bradford Metropolitan District Council)
Bradford *p451* 01274 752236

Morallee, A O (K&L Gates LLP)
London EC4 *p47*. 020 7648 9000

Moran, C X (MWRLaw Ltd) *C1 F1 G H J1 O Q*
Preston *p357* 01772 254201

Moran, C X (Nexus Solicitors) *J1*
Manchester *p308* 0161 819 4900

Moran, Mrs E (Field Seymour Parkes) *Zb C1 C2*
Reading *p360* 0118 951 6200

Moran, E A (Lightfoots LLP) *Zq Q O Zb F1*
Thame *p410*. 01844 212305

Moran, G (Merritt & Co) *S1 E L C1 J1 A1 R1 Zh*
Yarm *p443*. 01642 885555

Moran, G T (Hunters) *E R2 S2*
London WC2 *p44* 020 7412 0050

Moran, J (Walker Morris)
Leeds *p277* 0113 283 2500

Moran, Ms M (Leeds City Council)
Leeds *p462* 0113 224 3513

Moran, Ms M (Linklaters LLP)
London EC2 *p54*. 020 7456 2000

Moran, M (Askews) *N C1 Zj*
Redcar *p362*. 01642 475252

Moran, Ms M J M (Invesco)
London EC2 *p107* 020 7065 3057

Moran, N J (Freemans Solicitors) *O Q*
London W1 *p34* 020 7935 3522
London EC2 *p78*. 020 7749 2700

Moran, P G (Moran & Co) *F1 L O Q Zb Zq*
Tamworth *p407* 01827 54631

Moran, P M (Bridge McFarland Haddon Owen) *T1 W A1 C1 B1 R1 J1 K1 E G Zk Zo*
Louth *p294* 01507 605883

Moran, R J (Clarion Solicitors LLP) *C1 C2 C3 M1 Zw Ze Zf*
Leeds *p272* 0113 246 0622
Harrogate *p240* 01423 530630

Moran, S P (Harvey Ingram LLP) *O Q L G*
Leicester *p280*. 0116 254 5454

Moran, T J (Paul Crowley & Co)
Liverpool *p287*. 0151 264 7363

Moran, T J (Speechly Bircham LLP) *S1 A1 L E*
London EC4 *p81*. 020 7427 6400

Moran, Miss V L (Taylor Vinters) *N*
Cambridge *p176*. 01223 423444

Moran-Watson, Ms N (Nina Moran-Watson) *C1*
Clacton-on-Sea *p195* 0845 241 5633

Morcom, H C (Mary Evans & Co) *A1 B1 F1 G K1 M1 P S1*
Carmarthen *p182* 01267 233881

Morcowitz, I A (Colemans) *S1 S2 J1 W C1*
Haywards Heath *p245*. . . . 01444 459555

Mordaunt, C C (Butcher Andrews) *A1 S1*
Fakenham *p223* 01328 863131

Mordecai, Ms L (Osborne Clarke) *U1 U2*
London EC2 *p65*. 020 7105 7000

Mordey, Mrs K A (Hopkins Law LLP) *K1 S1 D1 R1 V H W*
Cardiff *p178* 029 2073 3000

Mordey, S D (Last Cawthra Feather LLP)
Shipley *p378*. 01274 585459

Mordsley, B I (Salans) *J1 C1 Zo*
London EC4 *p76*. 020 7429 6000

Mordue, C (Pinsent Masons LLP) *J1 Zp*
Leeds *p276* 0113 244 5000

More, G R (Serious Fraud Office) *O Zb Zq*
London WC1 *p109*. 020 7239 7272

More, R (Anthony Collins Solicitors LLP) *C1 I Zc*
Birmingham *p137* 0121 200 3242

Moreira, B (Butcher Burns LLP)
London WC1 *p16* 020 7713 7100

Moreland, J M (Swinburne Maddison) *N O Q J1 G H Zr Zi*
Durham *p214* . . 0191 384 2441 / 384 7455

Moreland, R (Stevens) *G H*
Stoke-on-Trent *p398*. 01782 813200

Moremon, Miss V A (Latimer Hinks) *W K4 S1*
Darlington *p206* 01325 341500

Moreno, Ms N (Speechly Bircham LLP) *U1 I C1 Zza M1 U2*
London EC4 *p81*. 020 7427 6400

Moreton, J (Chadwyck-Healey & Co) *B2 G Q*
London EC4 *p19*. 020 7353 6900

Moreton, J C (Bankside Law Ltd) *B2 G Zq*
London SE1 *p9* 0844 745 4000

Moreton, Mrs J M (DBL Talbots LLP) *Q*
Kidderminster *p265* 01562 749910

Moreton, T S (EDF Energy plc)
London SW1 *p106*. 020 7242 9050

Moreton, Ms V J S (TBI Solicitors) *K3 D1 D2 K1*
Hartlepool *p243* . . . 0800 052 6824 / 01429 264101
Stockton-on-Tees *p397* . . . 01642 673797

Morfee, R (Clarke Willmott) *Zo O*
Bristol *p162* 0845 209 1000 / 0117 305 6000

Morgan, A (Red Kite Law) *G H*
Pembroke Dock *p345* 01646 681529

Morgan, A (The College of Law Chester)
Chester *p454* 0800 289997

Morgan, A D (John Morgan & Partners) *S1 K1 N W Q Zl K3 K4*
Mountain Ash *p319* 01443 473708

Morgan, Mrs A E (Three Rivers District Council)
Rickmansworth *p470*. 01923 776611

Morgan, A G (Field Fisher Waterhouse LLP)
London EC3 *p31*. 020 7861 4000

Morgan, A R M (Reed Smith LLP) *C1 Zb*
London EC2 *p71*. 020 3116 3000

Morgan, Mrs A W (Morgans) *S1 M1 P K1 L W J1 R1 F1 A1 Zm C1*
Abergavenny *p113*. 01873 859993

Morgan, A W (Nicholson & Morgan) *A1 E J1 K1 L M1 N P S1 W Zc Zl*
Ponteland *p351* . . .01661 871012 / 823381

Morgan, Ms B (Nairnsey Fisher & Lewis)
Benfleet *p131* 01268 566655

Morgan, Ms C (Linklaters LLP)
London EC2 *p54*. 020 7456 2000

Morgan, Mrs C (Barker Booth & Eastwood) *K1 D1 K2 K3*
Blackpool *p146* 01253 362500

Morgan, Ms C (Lee Bolton Monier-Williams) *C1 Ze O*
Westminster *p52*. 020 7222 5381

Morgan, Ms C A (Kundert & Co) *C1 S2 E G H K3 K4 J1 K1 N R2 S1 W*
Coventry *p200*. 024 7668 4928

Morgan, C H (King Davies & Partners) *S1 L W S2*
Maesteg *p293* 01656 732911

Morgan, Mrs C J (Anthony Clark & Co) *K1 D1 G V*
Lincoln *p284*. 01522 512321

Morgan, Ms C L (Sian Thomas & Daughter Solicitors) *S2 E L S1*
Bridgend *p157*. 01656 645439

Morgan, Ms C M (GoodyBurrett LLP)
Colchester *p197* 01206 577676

Morgan, Miss C M (GoodyBurrett LLP) *K3 K1 Q N*
Colchester *p197* 01206 577676

Morgan, Ms C M (GLRS Phoenix LLP) *K1 D1*
Stroud *p400* 01453 757381

Morgan, D (Harrison Clark LLP) *O*
Worcester *p439* 01905 612001

Morgan, D (Trowers & Hamlins)
London EC3 *p88*. 020 7423 8000

Morgan, D C (Hunt & Morgan) *B1 C1 E O Zb Zl*
Cardiff *p179* 029 2034 1234

Morgan, D F (Greenwoods Solicitors LLP) *B1 O Zq Zk*
Peterborough *p347* 01733 887700

Morgan, D J L (MLM Cartwright) *U1 E S2 L R2 S1*
Cardiff *p179* 029 2046 2562

Morgan, D J V (Higgs & Sons) *E S2 S1 A1 L X Zd*
Brierley Hill *p158*. 0845 111 5050

Morgan, Mrs D M (Red Kite Law) *W*
Pembroke *p345* 01646 683222

Morgan, Mrs D M (Bourne Jaffa) *K1 L N S1 W*
Birmingham *p135* 0121 443 3486 / 444 8440

Morgan, D R (Dyne Drewett Solicitors Ltd) *A1 C1 E R1 S1 T1 T2 W*
Wincanton *p433*. 01963 32374

Morgan, Miss E (Kimbells LLP) *J1*
Milton Keynes *p317* 01908 668555

Morgan, Miss E L (Nicol Denvir & Purnell) *K3 K1 D1*
Cardiff *p180*. 029 2079 6311

Morgan, Miss E M B (Ceredigion County Council)
Aberaeron *p447* 01545 570881

Morgan, Miss E R (Pinsent Masons LLP) *T1*
Birmingham *p141* 0121 200 1050

Morgan, F (Kennedys)
London EC3 *p49*. 020 7667 9667

Morgan, G (Michelmores LLP) *Zc O*
Exeter *p221* 01392 688688

Morgan, G (Wannop Fox Staffurth & Bray)
Worthing *p442*. 01903 201120

Morgan, G (Merthyr Tydfil County Borough Council)
Merthyr Tydfil *p465* 01685 725000

Morgan, Ms G (The College of Law Chester)
Chester *p454* 0800 289997

Morgan, G (Metropolitan Police Directorate of Legal Services)
London SW1 *p108*. 020 7230 7210

Morgan, Ms G (Bindmans LLP) *Zg Zp M2 A2 K4 Zza Q*
London WC1 *p12* 020 7833 4433

Morgan, Ms G (Ofcom)
London SE1 *p108* 020 7981 3040

Morgan, G A (The College of Law Chester) *B1 E J1*
Chester *p454* 0800 289997

Morgan, G C W (Taylor Wessing) *I N Ze Zf*
London EC4 *p86*. 020 7300 7000

Morgan, G H R (Godfrey Morgan)
Norwich *p335* 01603 595700

Morgan, G M (Hugh James) *N P Zn Zq*
Cardiff *p179* 029 2022 4871

Morgan, G W (Thomas Horton LLP) *G H N D1 K1*
Bromsgrove *p167* 01527 871641

Morgan, H D (Cardiff Magistrates Court)
Cardiff *p453* 029 2046 3040

Morgan, H G (Red Kite Law) *S1*
Pembroke *p345* 01646 683222

Morgan, Ms H J (Fletchers) *K1 D1 D2*
Southport *p388* 01704 546919

Morgan, Mrs H S (Harrowells) *W*
York *p444* 01904 558600

Morgan, J (Ince & Co Services Ltd)
London E1 *p44* 020 7481 0010
London EC2 *p82*. 020 7329 4422

Morgan, Ms J (Brent Magistrates Court)
London NW10 *p104* 020 8451 7111

Morgan, J A (Morgan Cole) *N J1 O Q*
Bristol *p164* 0117 916 7220

Morgan, Ms J C (Darlington Borough Council)
Darlington *p456* 01325 388055

Morgan, Mrs J E (Leech & Co) *S1 W*
Manchester *p306* 0161 279 0279

Morgan, J K (Hayes & Storr) *T2 W Zi A1*
King's Lynn *p266* 01553 778900

Morgan, J K (John Morgan Solicitors) *G H K1 M1 P D1 L F1 J1*
Birmingham *p140* 0121 233 1852

Morgan, J S (Portsmouth Magistrates Court)
Portsmouth *p469*. 023 9281 9421

Morgan, Miss K (Southerns) *S1 S2 W*
Colne *p198* 01282 863113

Morgan, K I (TMJ Legal Services LLP) *N O J1 F1*
Hartlepool *p243* 01429 235616
Wingate *p434* 01429 838225

Morgan, K P (Lyons Davidson) *N F1 Q*
Bristol *p163* 0117 904 6000

Morgan, Ms L (Irwin Mitchell LLP) *N*
Sheffield *p376* 0870 150 0100

Morgan, Miss L (John Collins & Partners LLP) *N*
Swansea *p405*. 01792 773773

Morgan, Ms L B (L Morgan & Co) *S1 W L*
Brent *p61* 020 8965 2850

Morgan, Ms L C (Birmingham City Council Legal & Democratic Services)
Birmingham *p449* 0121 303 2066

Morgan, Ms L H (Follett Stock LLP) *Zk O Zf Ze U2 Q Zg*
Truro *p414*. 01872 241700

Morgan, Ms L J (Pannone LLP) *N Zr*
Manchester *p308* 0161 909 3000

Morgan, L R (Davenport Lyons) *C1 T1 W Ze Zf*
London W1 *p25* 020 7468 2600

Morgan, M (Howard Kennedy LLP) *E*
London W1 *p48* 020 7636 1616

Morgan, Miss M (Henmans LLP) *J1*
Oxford *p343*. 01865 781000

Morgan, Ms M A (LD Law) *K1 D1 G H D2*
Harlow *p239*. 01279 441266
Harlow *p239*. 01279 441266

Morgan, M E (O'Neill Morgan Solicitors Limited) *K1 N G Zr*
Stockport *p396*. 0161 429 8383

Morgan, Ms M E (Nicol Denvir & Purnell) *S1 W S2*
Cardiff *p180* 029 2079 6311

Morgan, M J (DLA Piper UK LLP)
Manchester *p303* 0870 011 1111

Morgan, Mrs M J (Osborne Clarke) *T1 T2 W*
Bristol *p164* 0117 917 3000

Morgan, M P (DBL Talbots LLP) *T1 C1 E K1 O S1*
Stourbridge *p399* 01384 445850
Stourbridge *p399* .01384 445850 / 447777

Morgan, M S (Robert Hitchins Ltd) *R1 P*
Cheltenham *p454* 01242 680694

Morgan, N C (Hugh James) *L O Q N*
Cardiff *p179* 029 2022 4871

Morgan, N L T (MLM Cartwright) *S2 E R2 S1 W*
Cardiff *p179* 029 2046 2562

Morgan, N U (Morgan & Co)
Swindon *p406* 01793 512982

Morgan, P B (Girlings) *N*
Canterbury *p177*. 01227 768374

Morgan, Miss P E (Leathes Prior) *D1 K1 V*
Norwich *p334* 01603 610911

Morgan, P J (K&L Gates LLP) *C1 C2*
London EC4 *p47*. 020 7648 9000

Morgan, P R (Hutchinson Thomas) *N Q V L*
Neath *p320* 01639 645061

Morgan, R (Band Hatton LLP) *E S2 C1*
Coventry *p200*. 024 7663 2121

Morgan, Ms R (Morgan Cole)
Oxford *p344* 01865 262600

Morgan, R A (Morgans) *G H D1 K1 S1 F1 J1 V*
Cardiff *p180* 029 2072 9888

Morgan, R C (Harrison Clark LLP) *O Q*
Cheltenham *p188* 01242 269198
Worcester *p439* 01905 612001
Worcester *p439* 01905 612001

Morgan, R C (Richard C Morgan) *N W*
London NW6 *p61* 020 8459 0646

Morgan, R G (Department for Business, Enterprise and Regulatory Reform) *Q O*
London SW1 *p105*. 020 7215 0105

Morgan, R J R (Morgan & Co) *S1 K1 W P*
Basingstoke *p127* 01256 329888

Morgan, R L (Hugh James) *C1 C2 Zb*
Cardiff *p179* 029 2022 4871

Morgan, R W (Foot Anstey) *E A1 S1 S2*
Taunton *p408* 01823 625600

Morgan, Ms S (Withers LLP) *T2 W*
London EC4 *p92*. 020 7597 6000

Morgan, S (Aviva PLC)
London EC3 *p103* . . 020 7283 7500 / 01603 687905
York *p477* 01904 452210

Morgan, S G (Norwich Union Insurance Group)
Norwich *p467* 01603 622200

Morgan, S J (Stephen Morgan & Co) *S1 S2 E C1 W*
Exeter *p221* 01392 215121

Morgan, Mrs S M (Morgan & Co) *K1 D1 S1 W L*
Stourbridge *p399* 01384 440069

Morgan, S R (Simmons & Simmons)
London EC2 *p79*. 020 7628 2020

Morgan, T (MFG Solicitors) *E S1 Zd*
Bromsgrove *p167* 01527 831691
Kidderminster *p265* 01562 820181

Morgan, T J (Barwells) *S1 W E T1 A1 L C1 P J1*
Eastbourne *p215*. 01323 411505

Morgan, Mrs V A C (Bromley Magistrates Court)
Bromley *p452* 0845 601 3600

Morgan, Mrs Y M (Hewitsons) *E S1*
Cambridge *p174*. 01223 461155

Morgan, Ms Z L (Morgan Cole) *N Zj*
Bristol *p164* 0117 916 7220

Morgan-Barrett, Ms A (Barlow Lyde & Gilbert LLP) *Zq*
Manchester *p301* 0161 829 6400

Morgan-Harris, Miss L (Reed Smith LLP) *E O*
London EC2 *p71*. 020 3116 3000

Morgan-Jones, R P (Nile Arnall Solicitors) *G H*
Bristol *p164* 0117 909 8898

Morgan-McGovern, Mrs S (Redbridge Magistrates Court)
Ilford *p461*. 0845 601 3600

Morgan-Platt, Mrs C A L (Denbighshire County Council)
Ruthin *p470* 01824 706000

Morgans, Mrs C (Rees Wood Terry) *W Zi*
Cardiff *p180* 029 2040 8800

Morgans, Miss R (Bone & Payne LLP) *S1 W*
Llandudno *p291* 01492 876354

Morgan-Wynne, D J (Wollen Michelmore Solicitors) *E S2 C1 S1*
Newton Abbot *p330* 01626 332266

Morgan-Wynne, R J (Hall Smith Whittingham LLP) *A1 E L S1 R1 C1 W*
Crewe *p203* 01270 212000
Nantwich *p320*. 01270 610300

Moriarty, J G (Swayne Johnson Solicitors) *K1 Q*
Denbigh *p208* 01745 812835

Morillas-Paredes, I (Colman Coyle LLP) *Q O C1*
Islington *p22*. 020 7354 3000

Morison, D R (BLB Solicitors) *E C1 S1 W T1 R1 L*
Bath *p127* 01225 462871

Morjana, R (M&M Solicitors)
Leicester *p280*. 0116 285 2300

Morjaria, R (The Smith Partnership)
Leicester *p281*. 0116 255 6292

Morley, Ms A (Capsticks Solicitors LLP) *N Zr*
London SW19 *p18*. 020 8780 2211

Morley, Mrs A (Freeth Cartwright LLP) *O*
Nottingham *p337*. 0115 936 9369

Morley, Miss A C (GoodyBurrett LLP) *K3 K1*
Colchester *p197* 01206 577676

Morley, Ms B (Maxwell Hodge Solicitors) *K1 F1 D1 F2 Q K3*
Heswall *p249* 0151 342 6447

Morley, Ms C (Ison Harrison) *K4 W*
Leeds *p274* 0113 284 5000

Morley, Mrs C (Reed Smith LLP) *O Q Zq*
London EC2 *p71*. 020 3116 3000

Morley, Ms C A (Barker Booth & Eastwood) *K1 D1 K3*
Blackpool *p146* 01253 362500

Morley, Miss C L (Department for Business, Enterprise and Regulatory Reform)
London SW1 *p105*. 020 7215 0105

Morley, C R (Morley Brown & Co) *E K1 L S1 W Q J1 J2 N O Zq*
Boston *p151*. 01205 364986

Morley, D A (Shoosmiths) *E*
Milton Keynes *p317* . 0370 086 8300 / 01908 488300
Nottingham *p339*. 0370 086 5000 / 0115 906 5000

Morley, D H (Allen & Overy LLP)
London E1 *p5* 020 3088 0000

Morley, D P (Sharp & Partners) *Q B1 L G H F1 Zl*
Nottingham *p339*. 0115 959 0055

Morley, G (Finers Stephens Innocent LLP) *E Zk*
London W1 *p32* 020 7323 4000

Morley, J (Laytons) *E B1 L O R1 R2*
Guildford *p236*. 01483 407000

Morley, J (London Borough of Southwark)
London SE1 *p109* 020 7525 5000

Morley, J F (John Morley & Co) *A1 C1 B1 L S1 W*
Rainham *p359*. 01634 375444

Morley, Mrs J M (Pattmans) *S1 E S2*
Bromsgrove *p167* 01527 872947
Bromsgrove *p167* 01527 872711

Morley, Ms K (Jones Day) *B1*
London EC4 *p46*. 020 7039 5959

Morley, Ms K H (LG Lawyers)
London SE1 *p50*. 020 7379 0000

See p634 for the Key to Work Categories

Morley, S I (John Morley & Co) *S1 S2 L*
Rainham *p359* 01634 375444

Morley, Mrs V T (Metropolitan Police Directorate of Legal Services)
London SW1 *p108* 020 7230 7210

Morlham, C (Jerman Simpson Pearson & Samuels) *N*
Basildon *p126* 01268 820111

Morling, B A (Morlings) *A1 E S1*
Maidstone *p299* 01622 673081

Moroney, L A J (Moroneys) *S1 W*
Attleborough *p120* 01953 455806
Wymondham *p443* 01953 607042

Morony, Ms E R A (Clifford Chance)
London E14 *p20* 020 7006 1000

Morony, M L (Shell International Ltd) *C1*
London SE1 *p109* 020 7934 1234

Morovic, Mrs K E (John Fowlers LLP Solicitors) *J1*
Colchester *p197* 01206 576151

Morrall, J S (Hunters) *C1 Zb C2 J1 M2 Zd Zo*
London WC2 *p44* 020 7412 0050

Morram, Ms I (Crangle Edwards) *D1 K3 K1*
Stretford *p400* . .0161 865 2993 / 865 7816 / 865 5875

Morrell, M (Brabners Chaffe Street) *C1 C2*
Manchester *p301* 0161 836 8800

Morrell, M A (Holroyd & Co)
Huddersfield *p256* 01484 645464

Morrell, T (Land Registry - Lancashire Office)
Preston *p469* 01772 836700

Morrill, Ms J M (Lester Morrill) *K1 C1 E S1 Zr N Q*
Leeds *p275* 0113 245 8549

Morris, Ms A (Leo Abse & Cohen)
Cardiff *p179* . . .029 2038 3252 / 2034 5421

Morris, A (Bolton Metropolitan Borough Council) *G H P J1 K1 Zl Zm*
Bolton *p450* 01204 333333

Morris, A (DLA Piper UK LLP)
Sheffield *p375* 0870 011 1111

Morris, A (Anthony Morris Solicitors)
Crawley *p202* 01293 519619

Morris, A C (Donnelly McArdle Adamson) *G H*
Hartlepool *p243* 01429 274732

Morris, A C (Hague & Dixon) *S1 S2 E L W*
Pickering *p348* 01751 475222

Morris, Miss A C (Blake Lapthorn) *O L Q*
Chandlers Ford *p184* 023 8090 8090

Morris, A D (Okell & Stewart) *Q K1 D1 S1 A1 C1 H T2 J1*
Ross-on-Wye *p367* 01989 762009

Morris, A D (Merrils Ede Solicitors) *S1 T2 W L Zd*
Penarth *p345* 029 2037 1131

Morris, Mrs A G (Letchers) *W K4*
Ringwood *p364* 01425 471424

Morris, Mrs A G (Forrester & Forrester) *K1 D1 V*
Chippenham *p193* 01249 444300

Morris, A G L (Clarks Legal LLP) *A3 B1 L O P Q Zq*
Reading *p360* 0118 958 5321

Morris, A J (Scotts Holt & Sellars) *C1 E L S1 W*
Bromsgrove *p167* 01527 872711

Morris, Mrs A L (Warners Solicitors) *W K4*
Tonbridge *p412* 01732 770660

Morris, A L (Linklaters LLP)
London EC2 *p54* 020 7456 2000

Morris, A T (Clifford Chance)
London E14 *p20* 020 7006 1000

Morris, A W (Julian Bloom & Co) *S1 E C1 B1 W L F1*
Bushey *p171* 020 8950 3001

Morris, A W (BSG Solicitors LLP)
London N3 *p9* 020 8343 4411

Morris, A W (Geldards LLP) *C1 C2*
Cardiff *p178* 029 2023 8239

Morris, Mrs B H (Mid Bedfordshire District Council)
Shefford *p471* 0845 230 4040

Morris, Miss B J (Divorce & Family Law Practice) *K1 K3*
Birmingham *p137* 0121 200 0890

Morris, Miss B M (Beverley Morris & Co) *S1 W L F1 R1 E*
Lewisham *p62* 020 8852 4433

Morris, B M (Erewash Borough Council) *E F1 G L R1 S1 W Zl*
Ilkeston *p461* 0115 907 2244

Morris, Mrs C (Bermans LLP) *E S1 R1 L*
Liverpool *p286* 0151 224 0500

Morris, C D N (Hempsons) *N Zq Zr*
Westminster *p40* 020 7839 0278

Morris, C G (Paris Smith LLP) *Q F1 G J2 Zl F2 Zq*
Southampton *p386* 023 8048 2482

Morris, C S (Fieldings Porter) *F1 G H N Q*
Bolton *p149* 01204 540900

Morris, D J (William Sturges & Co) *E C1 P R1 U1 A1 L I N T2*
Westminster *p84* 020 7873 1000

Morris, D M (KJD) *E Zh*
Stoke-on-Trent *p398* 01782 202020

Morris, D P (Humphreys & Co) *S2 E C1 S1 R1*
Bristol *p163* 0117 929 2662

Morris, Miss E (Langleys) *Zu K1 D1*
York *p445* 01904 610886

Morris, Mrs E C (Fraser Dawbarns) *K1 K4 T2 W*
Wisbech *p435* 01945 461456

Morris, Ms E G (Geldards LLP)
Cardiff *p178* 029 2023 8239

Morris, Mrs E J (Crombie Wilkinson) *Q Zl L*
York *p444* 01904 624185

Morris, Miss F (Field Seymour Parkes) *J1*
Reading *p360* 0118 951 6200

Morris, G (Gamlins) *A1 B1 C1 E F1 Zl Zm Zn R1 S1*
Rhyl *p363* 01745 343500

Morris, G (Wilkin Chapman LLP) *Q O*
Grimsby *p235* 01472 262626

Morris, G (DLA Piper UK LLP)
Birmingham *p137* 0870 011 1111

Morris, G J (London Underground Ltd)
London SW1 *p107* 020 7918 3126

Morris, Mrs H (Patchell Davies (Trading Name of PD Law Ltd)) *S1 K1 W Q D1 F1*
Blackwood *p147* 01495 227128

Morris, Mrs H A (AST Hampsons) *G H*
Rochdale *p365* 01706 522311

Morris, H M (Frodshams) *S1 S2 C1 E L R2*
St Helens *p391* 01744 626600

Morris, H P (SNR Denton) *Zb*
London EC4 *p75* 020 7242 1212

Morris, H R M (Austins LLP) *K1 K3 D1*
Luton *p295* 01582 456222

Morris, I (EMW) *C1 C2 C3 Zb*
Milton Keynes *p316* 0845 070 6000

Morris, I (Stephensons Solicitors LLP) *G H*
St Helens *p391* 01942 777777

Morris, J (Stevens) *G H*
Stoke-on-Trent *p398* 01782 343353

Morris, Miss J (Beswicks) *E*
Stoke-on-Trent *p397* 01782 205000

Morris, Miss J (Hugh James) *E S2 C1 R1*
Cardiff *p179* 029 2022 4871

Morris, J (Neil Myerson LLP) *J1*
Altrincham *p117* 0161 941 4000

Morris, J (Treasury Solicitors Department)
London WC2 *p110* 020 7210 3000

Morris, J (Plexus Law (A Trading Name of Parabis Law LLP))
London EC3 *p68* 0844 245 4000

Morris, J D (Keoghs LLP) *N Zj O Q*
Bolton *p149* 01204 677000

Morris, J D (Frank Howard)
Warrington *p422* 01925 653481

Morris, J E (Burnetts) *J1 C1 X Zd*
Carlisle *p181* 01228 552222
Carlisle *p182* 01228 552222

Morris, Ms J E (Russell Jones & Walker) *C1 J1*
London WC2 *p74* 020 7657 1555

Morris, Mrs J F (Land Law LLP) *Q R1 E R2*
Altrincham *p116* 0161 928 8383

Morris, Mrs J R (Metropolitan Police Directorate of Legal Services)
London SW1 *p108* 020 7230 7210

Morris, J S (DAC Beachcroft) *M1*
Bristol *p162* 0117 918 2000

Morris, Miss J S (Marchant Harries & Co) *W D1 F1 G H J1 K1 L M1*
Aberdare *p113* 01685 813655
Aberdare *p113* 01685 885500

Morris, Mrs K (Pinkney Grunwells Lawyers LLP) *Q J1*
Scarborough *p372* 01723 352125

Morris, Ms K A (Hillyer McKeown LLP) *N Q O*
Chester *p190* 01244 318131

Morris, Miss M (B D Laddie) *J1 K1 O Q Zp K3*
Westminster *p51* 020 7963 8585

Morris, Miss M C (HM Revenue & Customs)
Salford *p470* 0870 785 8545

Morris, M G (Philips Electronics UK Ltd)
Guildford *p459* 01483 298623

Morris, N (Pinsent Masons LLP) *O Q Zc*
London EC2 *p67* 020 7418 7000

Morris, N C (N C Morris & Co) *E F1 J1 L S1 W*
London SW7 *p62* 020 7584 8764

Morris, N D (Penningtons)
London EC2 *p66* 020 7457 3000

Morris, Miss N L (Russell & Russell) *K1*
Bury *p171* 0161 762 2888

Morris, O J (Stanley Tee) *E S2 R2 S1 C1*
Bishop's Stortford *p144* . . . 01279 755200

Morris, P (BCL Burton Copeland) *B2 G H J2*
London WC2 *p9* 020 7430 2277

Morris, P (Last Cawthra Feather LLP) *N Q G F1 K1*
Bradford *p154* 01274 848800

Morris, P C E (Winckworth Sherwood LLP) *S1 S2 X Zx*
London SE1 *p92* 020 7593 5000

Morris, P D (Kennedys) *Zj N*
London EC3 *p49* 020 7667 9667

Morris, P D F (Berkson Wallace Solicitors) *L F1 W Zr N*
Ellesmere Port *p217* 0151 355 4412
Wallasey *p419* 0151 691 6900

Morris, P H A (Burges Salmon)
Bristol *p161* 0117 939 2000

Morris, P S G (Legal Alliances Worldwide Ltd) *O R1*
Kidderminster *p265* 01562 756830

Morris, Miss R (Hempsons) *N Zr Zj*
Manchester *p305* 0161 228 0011

Morris, Miss R (Howell Jones & Co) *E S2 A1 W S1*
Abergele *p113* . . . .01745 826282 / 825845
Llanrwst *p292* 01492 640277

Morris, R (Thomas Cooper) *Za N*
London EC3 *p22* 020 7481 8851

Morris, R (Leigh Davis)
London W1 *p26* 020 7631 0302
London E1 *p44* 020 7481 0010

Morris, Ms R (Clifton Ingram LLP) *E S1 S2*
Wokingham *p437* 0118 978 0099
Marlow *p313* 01628 470000

Morris, Dr R (Hewitsons) *Zc*
Cambridge *p174* 01223 461155

Morris, R A (Morris Read & Co) *S1 E K1 L N F1 W C1 O V Zi Zl*
Wolverhampton *p438* 01902 420973 / 710004

Morris, R G (Butcher & Barlow LLP) *A1 C1 E S1 W Zc*
Bramhall *p155* 0161 439 8228

Morris, R J (Cozens Moxon & Harts) *W K4 S1*
Teddington *p409* .020 8977 8486 / 8977 4424

Morris, R J (Morris & Bates) *A1 E S1 S2 W Zd*
Llandrindod Wells *p291* . . . 01597 829055
Aberystwyth *p114* 01970 625566

Morris, R J L (R Gordon Roberts Laurie & Co) *W S1 S2 A1 A2 R1*
Llangefni *p292* . . .01248 722215 / 723312

Morris, R W A (Hutchinson Thomas) *S1 L J1 P C1 F1 Zl Zj Zm S2 E*
Neath *p320* 01639 645061

Morris, S (Raworths LLP) *C1 C2 C3 E U2*
Harrogate *p240* 01423 566666

Morris, S (Howell-Jones LLP) *S1 S2*
Kingston upon Thames *p267*. 020 8549 5186

Morris, Miss S A (MFG Solicitors)
Kidderminster *p265* 01562 820181

Morris, Mrs S C (Jeffreys & Powell) *W K1 L*
Brecon *p156* 01874 622106

Morris, S H (Mundays LLP) *O Q*
Cobham *p196* 01932 590500

Morris, S J (CMS Cameron McKenna LLP) *C1*
London EC3 *p17* 020 7367 3000

Morris, S J (Patchell Davies (Trading Name of PD Law Ltd)) *D1 F1 G H J1 K1 Za*
Blackwood *p147* 01495 227128

Morris, Mrs S K (Waller & Hart) *E C1 R2 T1 J1 W S1 O Q K4*
Camborne *p173* . . .01209 714064 / 719871

Morris, S M (Dodds & Partners) *G H K1 S1*
Leicester *p279* 0116 253 8585

Morris, S N (Howard Kennedy LLP) *N O Q Za Ze Zp*
London W1 *p48* 020 7636 1616

Morris, S P (Steadman Jones & Bell) *S1 M1 K1 P G F1 L B1 V C1 Zj Zo Zl*
Ammanford *p118* 01269 592306

Morris, Miss S R (Davies Parsons Allchurch) *K1 Q*
Llanelli *p292* 01554 749144

Morris, Ms T M (Billson & Sharp) *S2 E K4 S1 T2 W*
Leicester *p279* 0116 255 9911

Morris, T R (Bartletts Solicitors) *N Q O F1 Zi*
Chester *p190* 01244 313301

Morris, Mrs U M (Wartnabys) *E S1 S2*
Market Harborough *p312* . . . 01858 463322

Morris, Miss V E (Weightmans LLP)
Liverpool *p291* 0151 227 2601

Morris, W G (Morris & Bates) *A1 B1 C1 D1 E F1 G H J1 K1 Zb Zc Zd*
Aberystwyth *p114* 01970 625566
Knighton *p269* 01547 520130

Morris, W R (Fraser Dawbarns) *W T1 S1 E L*
Wisbech *p435* 01945 461456

Morrisey, Ms D S (Blaser Mills) *W S1*
Chesham *p189* 01494 782291

Morrisey, S (Lewis Silkin LLP)
London EC4 *p53* 020 7074 8000

Morrish, C J (Trowers & Hamlins)
London EC3 *p88* 020 7423 8000

Morrish, D C (Anthony & Jarvie) *W K4 S1*
Bridgend *p157* 01656 652737

Morrish, Miss K J (Bond Pearce LLP) *Q O*
London EC3 *p14* 0845 415 0000

Morrish, T W (Morrish Solicitors LLP) *W K4*
Yeadon *p443* 0113 250 7792

Morris-Jones, Ms L M (PCB Solicitors LLP) *G H N Zy*
Telford *p409* 01952 403000

Morrison, A (Pinsent Masons LLP) *A3 Zc O*
London EC2 *p67* 020 7418 7000

Morrison, A C (Burges Salmon) *A1 E L S1*
Bristol *p161* 0117 939 2000

Morrison, A R (Davitt Jones Bould) *R1*
Taunton *p408* 01823 279279

Morrison, C (DLA Piper UK LLP) *N O Q C1*
London EC2 *p24* 0870 011 1111

Morrison, D (MBA Solicitors) *N G H B2*
York *p445* 01904 666888

Morrison, D (Mackarness & Lunt) *W S1 C1 E Zd T2 S2*
Petersfield *p348* 01730 265111

Morrison, D F (Pearson Maddin Solicitors) *E S1 C1 R1 J1 L*
New Malden *p321* 020 8949 9500

Morrison, Mrs G L (Rollits LLP) *Zd X*
York *p445* 01904 625790

Morrison, I (MFG Solicitors) *A1 E P C1 S1*
Worcester *p440* 01905 610410

Morrison, I A G (Kennedys) *A3 M2 N O Q Zj*
London EC3 *p49* 020 7667 9667

Morrison, Ms J (Morrison Spowart)
London SE6 *p62* 020 8698 9200

Morrison, J J (Manches LLP) *E O*
Oxford *p343* 01865 722106

Morrison, J K (T R S Miller Solicitors) *S1 G F1 E M1 J1 H Zl N*
Hythe *p259* 01303 266861
Folkestone *p227* 01303 851100

Morrison, K G (Eurotunnel)
Folkestone *p458* 01303 283900

Morrison, Miss L (Laytons)
Manchester *p306* 0161 834 2100

Morrison, Ms L (Walker Morris)
Leeds *p277* 0113 283 2500

Morrison, Miss L E (Land Registry - Lancashire Office)
Preston *p469* 01772 836700

Morrison, Ms M (Hogan Lovells International LLP)
London EC1 *p42* 020 7296 2000

Morrison, M (Holman Fenwick Willan)
London EC3 *p42* 020 7264 8000

Morrison, Ms M A (M A Morrison) *E F1 L S1*
Shrewsbury *p379* 01743 874986

Morrison, M E (West Yorkshire Passenger Transport Executive)
Leeds *p463* 0113 251 7436

Morrison, M J (Hill Dickinson LLP) *J1 Zw Zf O Q Zk Zg Ze A3 Zp*
Manchester *p305* 0161 817 7200

Morrison, M W E (Clifford Chance)
London E14 *p20* 020 7006 1000

Morrison, N (Allan Janes LLP) *C1 E*
High Wycombe *p249* 01494 521301

Morrison, Mrs P (Salans) *J1*
London EC4 *p76* 020 7429 6000

Morrison, Mrs S (George Davies Solicitors LLP) *O Q M2 Zq*
Manchester *p303* 0161 236 8992

Morrison, Mrs S K (Hill Dickinson LLP) *J1 Zp M1 Zw*
Manchester *p305* 0161 817 7200

Morrison, T W (Rollits LLP) *C1 U2 Ze I C3*
Hull *p258* 01482 323239

Morrissey, Miss E L (Roebucks) *G*
Blackburn *p145* 01254 274000

Morrissey, J (The Jonathan Morrissey Practice)
Bournemouth *p152* 01202 310999

Morrissy, Ms J (DLA Piper UK LLP)
Sheffield *p375* 0870 011 1111

Morrissy, Miss S A (Thursfields) *S1 C1 A1 R1 W E*
Kidderminster *p266* 01562 820575

Morron, B (Gotelee) *R1 J1 Zu P Zp*
Ipswich *p262* 01473 211121

Morrow, M J R (Henry Hyams) *G H*
Leeds *p274* 0113 243 2288

Morse, J B (Mark Gilbert Morse) *K1 M1 S1 P F1 J1*
Newcastle upon Tyne *p325* . 0191 261 0096

Morse, J F (John Morse Solicitors) *A1 B1 C1 L M1 N P W Zl*
Swansea *p405* 01792 648111

Morse, Mrs N J (Shentons) *G H K3 K1*
Winchester *p434* 01962 844544

Morse, S A (Michelmores LLP) *C1 C2*
Exeter *p221* 01392 688688

Morse, S J (Bartletts Solicitors) *Q N*
Liverpool *p286* 0151 227 3391

Morse, T M (Humphreys & Co)
Bristol *p163* 0117 929 2662

Morse, W T (Willans LLP) *J1*
Cheltenham *p189* 01242 514000

Morshead, J E (Squire Sanders (UK) LLP) *E R2 S2 L*
London EC2 *p81* 020 7655 1000

Morshead, J P (Lees Solicitors LLP) *S2 E R2 S1*
Birkenhead *p134* 0151 647 9381

Morshead, Ms S P A (Shelter Legal Services) *L*
London EC1 *p109* 020 7505 2000

Mort, Miss C (George Green LLP) *E S2*
Cradley Heath *p201* 01384 410410

Mort, S G (Tetrosyl Ltd) *E S1 Zl*
Bury *p452* . . . .

Mortcock, Miss J A (HM Revenue & Customs)
Salford *p470* 0870 785 8545

Mortenson, Mrs A L S (Greene & Greene) *E*
Bury St Edmunds *p171* . . . 01284 762211

Mortimer, A J (Stone King LLP) *T2 W*
Bath *p128* 01225 337599

Mortimer, Mrs A K (Coles Solicitors) *S1 W E K4*
Northallerton *p331* 01609 780717

Mortimer, Ms C (Winterbotham Smith Penley LLP) *G H*
Stroud *p401* 01453 847200

Mortimer, J (Raworths LLP) *O A3 Q Zk F1 F2 Ze Zq*
Harrogate *p240* 01423 566666

Mortimer, Mrs J H C (Surrey County Council)
Kingston upon Thames *p462*. 020 8541 9088

Mortimer, K A M (Bevan Brittan LLP) *L E Zh*
Bristol *p161* 0870 194 1000

Mortimer, N (Colemans - CTTS) *N M2*
Kingston upon Thames *p267*. 020 8296 9966

Mortimer, S A (Birmingham City Council Legal & Democratic Services)
Birmingham *p449* 0121 303 2066

Mortimer, S N (Burnetts) *K1 D1*
Carlisle *p181* 01228 552222
Carlisle *p182* 01228 552222

Mortimer, T W (Ashford Borough Council)
Ashford *p447* 01233 331111

Mortimer-Tracey, Ms J (Lewis Silkin LLP) *E*
London EC4 *p53* 020 7074 8000

Mortimor, Miss L F (Goughs) *D1 K3 K1*
Trowbridge *p414* 01225 762683

Mortlock, Miss M (Burnett Barker) *S1 W*
Bury St Edmunds *p171* . . . 01284 701131

Mortlock, T R (Robinson & Co) *B1 J1 K1 M1 N O P Q S1 Zl*
London EC1 *p72* 020 7405 5180

Mortlock, Ms V (Roythornes LLP) *A1 E L S1 S2 U1*
Spalding *p389* 01775 842500

Morton, A P (Williams & Co) *F1 G H K1 L Q V*
Luton *p296* 01582 723322

6

Morton, C J (Husband Forwood Morgan) *Q S1 K4 W S2*
Liverpool *p289* 0151 236 9626
Morton, D R (Morton Solicitors) *S2 C1 Q S1*
Dunstable *p214* 01582 501240
Morton, G (Stockton-On-Tees Borough Council)
Stockton-on-Tees *p472* . . . 01642 393939
Morton, Mrs J (Stockport Metropolitan Borough Council)
Stockport *p472*. 0161 480 4949
Morton, Mrs J (Network Rail)
London NW1 *p108*. 020 7557 8000
Morton, J A (Mundays LLP) *C1 C2 F1 J1 C3 M1 U1 U2 Ze Zi Zy Zz*
Cobham *p196* 01932 590500
Morton, J S (Simmons & Simmons)
London EC2 *p79*. 020 7628 2020
Morton, J W (Clarke Willmott) *A1 E*
Birmingham *p136* 0845 209 1000 / 0117 305 6000
Morton, Miss K (Cyril Morris Arkwright) *G H Zm*
Bolton *p148* 01204 535261
Morton, N J (Charles Russell LLP) *E S1 L*
Cheltenham *p187* 01242 221122
Morton, P (Brabners Chaffe Street) *O Q*
Manchester *p301* 0161 836 8800
Morton, P (K&L Gates LLP) *N O*
London EC4 *p47*. 020 7648 9000
Morton, R (Morton Price) *C1 C2 J1 Ze Zf*
Sheffield *p376* 0114 266 4141
Morton, R (Herbert Smith LLP)
London EC2 *p40*. 020 7374 8000
Morton, R D (Glaisyers Solicitors LLP) *D1 K1 D2*
Manchester *p304* 0161 224 3311
Morton, R J (Dean Thomas & Co) *S1 L W S2*
Retford *p363*. 01777 703100
Morton, R S (Calvert Smith & Sutcliffe) *A1 B1 C1 E F1 L R1 S1 T1 W*
Richmond upon Thames *p364* 020 8940 0017
Morton, S E (Mortons)
Stockport *p396*. 0161 477 1121
Morton, Miss S L (FBC Manby Bowdler LLP) *K1*
Telford *p409* 01952 292129
Morton-Curtis, R J M (Godwins) *S1*
Winchester *p433*. 01962 841484
Mortor, D G (Crombie Wilkinson) *S2 S1*
York *p444* 01904 624185
Moruzzi, R (Withers LLP) *B1 O*
London EC4 *p92*. 020 7597 6000
Moscisker, A D (Howard Schneider Spiro Steele) *E L R1 S1 S2*
Barnet *p124* 020 8216 2020
Moscow, N S (Curry Popeck) *S1 E W L S2*
Kenton *p264*. . .020 8907 2000 / 8907 8896
Moseby, A (Kemp Little LLP) *C1 C2 U1 U2 I Zb*
London EC2 *p48*. 020 7600 8080
Moseley, Ms B (Nockolds) *J1*
Bishop's Stortford *p144* . . . 01279 755777
Moseley, Ms C G (Moseley George) *S1 S2 W E L R1 R2 Zd*
Cardigan *p181*. 01239 623960
Moseley, K (Marsden Rawsthorn LLP) *D1 G H K3 K1 K2*
Chorley *p194* 01257 279511
Moseley, M M (CMS Cameron McKenna LLP)
London EC3 *p17*. 020 7367 3000
Moseley, R (Berry & Berry) *S2 E L S1*
Tunbridge Wells *p414* 01892 526344
Moser, N S (Taylor Wessing) *O B1 Q Zb*
London EC4 *p86*. 020 7300 7000
Moser, R H S (Hugh Cartwright & Amin) *S1 E M1 W G K1 P*
London WC1 *p43* 020 7632 4200
Moses, J D B (Strick & Bellingham) *C1 E L S1 W*
Swansea *p405*. 01792 641201
Mosey, D (Trowers & Hamlins) *C1 Zc*
London EC3 *p88*. 020 7423 8000
Mosley, D P (DLA Piper UK LLP) *B1 C1 Zb*
Sheffield *p375* 0870 011 1111
Mosley, Mrs K E (City of Bradford Metropolitan District Council) *D1*
Bradford *p451* 01274 752236
Moss, A (Harbottle & Lewis LLP)
London W1 *p38* 020 7667 5000
Moss, Ms A (DLA Piper UK LLP) *N Zj*
Sheffield *p375* 0870 011 1111
Moss, A M (Bristows) *E R2 R1 S2*
London EC4 *p15*. 020 7400 8000
London WC2 *p60* 020 7242 5905
Moss, Miss C E (McKeag & Co) *K1*
Gosforth *p231* 0191 213 1010
Moss, Ms C H (Withers LLP) *T2 Zd W*
London EC4 *p92*. 020 7597 6000
Moss, C J (Pinsent Masons LLP)
London EC2 *p67*. 020 7418 7000
Moss, D (E Rex Makin & Co) *Zb B1 F1 Zj O Q Zq*
Liverpool *p289*. 0151 709 4491
Moss, D J (Hogan Lovells International LLP)
London EC1 *p42*. 020 7296 2000
Moss, D J (Squire Sanders (UK) LLP) *N B1 M1 J1 Zc Ze Zk*
Manchester *p310* 0161 830 5000
Moss, D P (Kingsley Napley) *C1 J1 Zb*
London EC1 *p50*. 020 7814 1200
Moss, G (Taylor Wessing) *I N Ze Zk*
London EC4 *p86*. 020 7300 7000
Moss, G W (Foster & Partners) *D1 K1 K3*
Bristol *p162* 0117 961 5300
Moss, H (Ashurst LLP)
London EC2 *p7* 020 7638 1111
Moss, J (Robert Lizar) *G H*
Manchester *p307* 0161 226 2319

Moss, Ms J (Rochdale Metropolitan Borough Council)
Rochdale *p470*. 01706 647474
Moss, J C (Fishburns) *M2 Zc Zj O Q*
London EC3 *p32*. 020 7280 8888
Moss, Miss J D (Lee Rigby Partnership) *G H K1*
Leyland *p283* 01772 421748
Moss, J H (Nicholls Henstock & Stevenson) *S2 E C1 W S1*
Altrincham *p117* 0161 980 6099
Moss, Miss J V (Moore Brown & Dixon LLP) *W T2*
Tewkesbury *p410* 01684 292341
Moss, Mrs M (Mowbray Woodwards Solicitors) *K1 K3*
Bath *p128* 01225 485700
Moss, Miss M (Russell & Russell) *K1 G H*
Bury *p171* 0161 762 2888
Moss, Mrs M I (Fitzgerald-Harts)
Boroughbridge *p150* 01423 322312
Moss, Miss N (Clark Willis) *W S1 S2 K4 E*
Darlington *p206* 01325 281111
Moss, N A (TLT Solicitors) *C1 B1 Ze*
Bristol *p165* 0117 917 7777
Moss, P G S (Osborne Clarke) *T1*
Bristol *p164* 0117 917 3000
Moss, R J (DAC Beachcroft) *N P M1*
Manchester *p303* 0161 934 3000
Moss, Ms V E (Pinkney Grunwells Lawyers LLP) *K4 K1 V W*
Scarborough *p372*. 01723 352125
Mossman, S (Brighouse Wolff) *P N K1 J1 G F1 H Zj Zl*
Skelmersdale *p381* 01695 722577
Mossop, C P (Howard & Over) *K1 S1 W G H N J1 L Q V*
Ivybridge *p263*. 01752 690123
Mossop, Mrs S E (Hockfield & Co) *L Zh*
Lambeth *p41*. 020 7582 8784
Mostyn, F E T (Francis Mostyn & Co)
Slough *p382*. 01753 545322
Motani, H N (Clifford Chance)
London E14 *p20*. 020 7006 1000
Motegherie, M (TV Edwards LLP) *G H*
London EC3 *p85*. 020 7790 7000
Motherway, Ms H (Watson Burton LLP)
Newcastle upon Tyne *p327* . 0845 901 2100
Mothew, A P (Stapley & Co) *S1 W G E S2 Zm*
Loughton *p294*. 020 8502 1934
Mothew, I D B (Stapley & Co) *S1 S2 W*
Loughton *p294*. 020 8502 1934
Motley, P J (Motley & Hope) *N P K1 J1 D1 Zl*
Biggleswade *p133* 01767 600600
Mott, A (DLA Piper UK LLP) *O*
Sheffield *p375* 0870 011 1111
Mott, Ms E B J (Southwell Mott)
Lichfield *p284* . . . .01543 252102 / 251484
Mott, G R (W Davies) *Zc S2 E R1*
Woking *p436*. 01483 744900
Mott, J C (Southwell Mott)
Lichfield *p284* . . . .01543 252102 / 251484
Mott, L A (BLB Solicitors) *G H*
Swindon *p406* 01793 615011
Swindon *p406* 01793 512960
Mott, N E A (SNR Denton) *S1 K1 W P E L F1*
London EC4 *p75*. 020 7242 1212
Mott, R M (Clayton Mott) *K1 S1 G C1 W Zl Zd Zc*
Nottingham *p336*. 0115 941 7422
Mott, Mrs S M (Clayton Mott) *A1 B1 C1 D1 E F1 J1 K1 K2 L O Q S2 S1 W*
Nottingham *p336*. 0115 941 7422
Sutton-in-Ashfield *p404* . . . 01623 556601
Mottershead, P D (Blackpool Borough Council) *O Q C1 F1 P J1 R1 E B1 Zc Ze Zj*
Blackpool *p450* 01253 477450
Mottershead, Ms S (Hogan Lovells International LLP)
London EC1 *p42*. 020 7296 2000
Mottram, C J G (Severn Trent Water Ltd) *C1 C2 C3 P F1 R1 J1 M1 Q O*
Birmingham *p450* 0121 722 4000
Mouland, D G (Luttons Dunford) *N Q W Zj Zq Zr*
Gloucester *p230*. 01452 529751
Mould, Miss A J (Fladgate LLP) *P M1 N G J1 K1 F1 Zk Zl*
London WC2 *p32* 020 3036 7000
Moulden, Ms V J (Cooperative Bank PLC)
Manchester *p464* 0161 832 3456
Moulder, Ms C (Linklaters LLP)
London EC2 *p54*. 020 7456 2000
Moulding, I R (Clifford Chance)
London E14 *p20*. 020 7006 1000
Moule, Ms J H (Osborne Clarke) *C1 P D1 Zd*
Bristol *p164* 0117 917 3000
Mouls, Ms H S (Fisher Meredith)
Lambeth *p32*. 020 7091 2700
Moulsdale, R C B (Boys & Maughan) *C1 E W S2 K4 R2 S1*
Margate *p312* 01843 234000
Mounce, Miss L W (Eddowes Perry & Osbourne) *G H Zl B2*
Sutton Coldfield *p403* 0121 686 9666
Sutton Coldfield *p403* 0121 686 9444
Mounce, P (Graham & Rosen) *W K4 T2*
Hull *p257* 01482 323123
Mounsey, Ms S (Langleys) *E P R1 S1*
York *p445* 01904 610886
Mounsey, Miss S C (Mowll & Mowll) *K1 K3 D1*
Dover *p213* 01304 873344
Mount, J D (Humphries Kirk) *Zd K4 K1 S1 W T2*
Swanage *p404*. 01929 423301

Mount, P J (Woodfines LLP) *C1 C2 C3 F1 M1 T1 Zd Ze*
Sandy *p372* 01767 680251
Mountain, P (SGH Martineau LLP) *O Zc*
Birmingham *p142* 0870 763 2000
Mountford, Mrs I B (Silverman Sherliker LLP) *Ze C1*
London EC2 *p78*. 020 7749 2700
Mountford, J F (Bonnetts Solicitors LLP) *C1 E L S1 W S2*
Whitton *p431* 020 8898 2022
Mour, Miss L J (Savage Crangle)
Skipton *p381*. 01756 794611
Mourton, P (Lodders Solicitors LLP) *E S2*
Stratford-upon-Avon *p400* . . 01789 293259
Mousavi, Miss N F (Eaton Smith LLP) *N Zr Q*
Huddersfield *p255* 01484 821300
Mousdale, P (Pendle Borough Council)
Nelson *p466*. 01282 661661
Moussalli, R S (Burton Copeland LLP) *G H*
Manchester *p302* 0161 827 9500
Mouton, N (London Borough of Southwark)
London SE1 *p109* 020 7525 5000
Moutrey, Mrs R S (West Sussex County Council)
Chichester *p455* 01243 777100
Mowat, A R (Hill Dickinson LLP) *N M1 Zr Q*
Liverpool *p288*. 0151 600 8000
Mowat, Miss C E (Stanley Tee) *W*
Bishop's Stortford *p144* . . . 01279 755200
Mowat, C J R (Palmers) *E S1 W T2 K4*
Basildon *p126* 01268 240000
Mowat, Ms D M O B (Newcastle Upon Tyne City Council)
Newcastle upon Tyne *p466* . 0191 232 8520
Mowat, R P (Bolt Burdon) *C1 O*
Islington *p14*. 020 7288 4700
Mowberry, Ms M (B P Collins LLP) *E S2 L*
Gerrards Cross *p229*. 01753 889995
Mowbray, J (IBB Solicitors)
Uxbridge *p417*. 0845 638 1381
Mowle, Mrs L F (Irvings Solicitors) *K3 K1 D2 D1*
Derby *p209* 01332 346036
Mowll, B N B (Furley Page LLP) *S2 S1 R2 A1 W*
Canterbury *p176*. 01227 763939
Moxley, P J (Howells LLP) *Zm*
Sheffield *p376* 0114 249 6666
Moxon, A (Claude Hornby & Cox) *G H B2*
London EC4 *p20*. 020 7332 8269
Moxon, N (Higgs & Sons) *W T2 T1 Zd*
Brierley Hill *p158*. 0845 111 5050
Moxon, R L (Davenport Lyons) *Ze Zf Zk*
London W1 *p25* 020 7468 2600
Moxon-Smith, Ms K (Norrie Waite & Slater) *N*
Sheffield *p377* 0114 276 6166
Moynihan, Ms D (Morrison & Foerster (UK) LLP) *U2 U1 Ze*
London EC2 *p62*. 020 7920 4000
Moyse, R M (Boodle Hatfield) *T2 W*
Westminster *p14*. 020 7629 7411
Mozzi, H (Howard Kennedy LLP) *E R2*
London W1 *p48* 020 7636 1616
Msimang, Ms T L (Whitbread PLC)
London LU5 *p110* 01582 424200
Mubarak, S T (Pearson Maddin Solicitors)
New Malden *p321* 020 8949 9500
Mucklow, P (Stallard March & Edwards) *S1 E L W*
Worcester *p440* 01905 613404
Mudd, P J (Walker Morris) *B1 C1 Zb*
Leeds *p277* 0113 283 2500
Mudge, Miss S L (Wollen Michelmore Solicitors) *S2 E S1 L*
Newton Abbot *p330* 01626 332266
Muffitt, Mrs A R (Newcastle Upon Tyne City Council)
Newcastle upon Tyne *p466* . 0191 232 8520
Mugford, R J (Mugford & Co) *E F2 J1 L O Q S1 S2 W Zj Zq Zr*
Fareham *p224*. 01329 844555
Muggeridge, T C (Ray Borley & Dunkley) *S2 E S1 Zv*
Stony Stratford *p399*. 01908 563232
Muglia, R (Skadden Arps Slate Meagher & Flom (UK) LLP)
London E14 *p80*. 020 7519 7000
Muhammad, Mrs J E A Y (Charles De Alwis)
Chadwell Heath *p183* 020 8597 5717
Muir, Miss A M (Metcalfe Copeman & Pettefar) *G H F2 J2*
King's Lynn *p266* 01553 778102
Muir, A S (West Dorset District Council)
Dorchester *p457*. 01305 251010
Muir, Ms C (Stilwell & Harby) *W*
Dover *p213* 01304 206850
Muir, Miss E (AMD Solicitors) *K1 D1 K3*
Bristol *p160* 0117 962 1460
Muir, Miss G M K (Samuel Phillips Law Firm) *Zr N*
Newcastle upon Tyne *p326* . 0191 232 8451
Muir, G S (Nabarro LLP)
London WC1 *p63* 020 7524 6000
Muir, J P (Inghams) *K1 G N H D1 D2 Q F1*
Fleetwood *p226* 01253 873481
Muir, Ms N C (Spratt Endicott) *E S2*
Banbury *p122* 01295 204000
Muir, Ms P S (Lewis Nedas & Co) *G H*
Camden *p53*. 020 7387 2032
Muir, R W (Fladgate LLP) *E L R1 S1*
London WC2 *p32* 020 3036 7000
Muir-Little, J A (Furley Page LLP) *K1 D1 K2*
Canterbury *p176*. 01227 763939
Muirhead, Mrs C J (Farnfield & Nicholls)
Shaftesbury *p374* 01747 854244

Muirhead, Mrs E M (Elizabeth Muirhead Solicitors) *K1 K2 K3*
London WC2 *p62* 020 7936 4445
Muirhead, J (Thorburn & Co) *E S1 C1 K1 B1 L N O W Zi Zk Zl*
Henley-on-Thames *p247*. . . 01491 577625
Muirhead, J D C (Borlase & Company) *W S1*
Helston *p246* 01326 574988
Mukherjee, Ms D (Heather Mains & Co) *Q O K1 J1 W Ze S1*
London NW7 *p40* 020 8906 6660
Mukhtar, Mrs R (Rochdale Metropolitan Borough Council)
Rochdale *p470*. 01706 647474
Mulcahy, Ms H (Reed Smith LLP) *Q O*
London EC2 *p71*. 020 3116 3000
Mulcahy, Ms V (Burton Copeland LLP) *G H*
Manchester *p302* 0161 827 9500
Mulcare, J (Mayo Wynne Baxter LLP)
Lewes *p283* 01273 477071
Mulcare, P A (Spratt Endicott) *K1 K3 D1*
Banbury *p122* 01295 204000
Muldoon, Ms F (Roythornes LLP) *E Zn S1 S2*
Nottingham *p338*. 0115 948 4555
Muldoon, S (Stevens) *H G*
Stoke-on-Trent *p398* 01782 343353
Mulhern, J (Kitsons LLP) *E Zu S1*
Newton Abbot *p329* 01626 203366
Mulhern, Ms K (Hogan Lovells International LLP)
London EC1 *p42*. 020 7296 2000
Mulhern, P A (Thompsons (formerly Robin/Brian Thompson & Partners)) *N Zr J1*
Plymouth *p350*. 01752 675810
Mulholland, P A (Kent County Council)
Maidstone *p464* 01622 694320
Mulkis, I P (Howard Kennedy LLP) *N J1 Q Zf S1 O Zq Zk W*
London W1 *p48* 020 7636 1616
Mulla, Z (Squire Sanders (UK) LLP) *O Zc*
Leeds *p277* 0113 284 7000
Mullan, H (McCormacks) *B2 G H*
London EC3 *p56*. 020 7791 2000
Mullan, Miss L D (Brabners Chaffe Street) *J1*
Liverpool *p286*. 0151 600 3000
Mullan, Miss S E T C (Morrish Solicitors LLP) *Zl F2*
Leeds *p276* 0113 245 0733
Mullane, Mrs C (Birmingham Settlement)
Birmingham *p449* 0121 250 3000
Mullaney, E (Mullaney & Co) *S1 S2 W*
Eastbourne *p215*. 01323 431292
Mullaney, J F (Mullaney & Co) *S1 K1 L G H J1 D1 Zl F1 W Q*
Eastbourne *p215*. 01323 431292
Mullarkey, D C P (A B Marsh Solicitors) *G H K1 Zg Q N J1 Zp*
Salford *p371*. 0161 839 2626
Mullarkey, M P (Pinsent Masons LLP) *Zc*
London EC2 *p67*. 020 7418 7000
Mullarkey, S (Stephen Mullarkey Solicitors) *D1 G H K1 Q W N S1*
Flint *p226* 01352 733770
Mullem, A J (Moss Beachley Mullem & Coleman) *S1 L P W K1 M1 D1 E J1 G Zc Zi Zk*
Westminster *p62*. 020 7402 1401 / 7723 5783
Mullen, A J (Lockett Loveday McMahon) *N Q O F1 B1 M1*
Manchester *p307* 0161 237 3627
Mullen, C P (Pinsent Masons LLP) *Zo*
London EC2 *p67*. 020 7418 7000
Mullen, D J (Anthony Collins Solicitors LLP) *J1*
Birmingham *p137* 0121 200 3242
Mullen, Miss J (Richard Reed) *W S1*
Sunderland *p402*. 0191 567 0465
Mullen, J M (Thompsons (formerly Robin/Brian Thompson & Partners)) *N*
London SW19 *p87*. 020 8947 4163
Mullen, P (Hogan Lovells International LLP)
London EC1 *p42*. 020 7296 2000
Mullender, M J (Fosters) *S1 L E A1 S2 R1*
Lowestoft *p294* 01502 573307
Mullender, R G (Mullenders) *S1 G H J1 K1*
Woking *p437*. 01483 771733
Mulley, G (Herbert Smith LLP)
London EC2 *p40*. 020 7374 8000
Mulley, H (Debenhams Ottaway) *C1*
St Albans *p390* 01727 837161
Mulligan, Ms C M (Plexus Law (A Trading Name of Parabis Law LLP)) *N Q O Zj*
London EC3 *p68*. 0844 245 4000
Mullins, Miss A L (Cheyney Goulding)
Guildford *p236*. 01483 567676
Mullins, D (Watmores)
London WC2 *p90* 020 7430 1512
Mullins, H K (Barlow Lyde & Gilbert LLP) *Zr Zj Q N*
Manchester *p301* 0161 829 6400
Mullins, P (Robert Barber & Sons) *K1 K2 S1 S2 Q*
Nottingham *p335*. 0115 878 9000
Mullins, P M (Stallard March & Edwards) *A2 S1 S2 W*
Worcester *p440* 01905 723561
Mullins, R K (Watmores) *Q*
London WC2 *p90* 020 7430 1512
Mullins, Ms S J E (Redditch Borough Council)
Redditch *p469* 01527 64252
Mullins, Miss T J (Camberwell Green Magistrates Court)
London SE5 *p104* 0845 601 3600
Mullins, Miss V J (Ramsdens Solicitors) *W K4*
Halifax *p238* 01422 330700
Huddersfield *p256* 01484 821500

See p634 for the Key to Work Categories

Mullion, J (Janes) *G H B2*
London SW1 *p46* 020 7930 5100

Mullis, C (NFLA Ltd) *K1 K3*
Chesterfield *p192* 01246 471900

Mullis, J E (Thorne Segar) *S1 E T1 A1 T2*
Minehead *p318* 01643 703234

Mullock, J J (Osborne Clarke) *U1 Ze*
Bristol *p164* 0117 917 3000
London EC2 *p65* 020 7105 7000

Mulrenan, A W (Lound Mulrenan & Jefferies Solicitors) *G H*
Southwark *p55* 020 7793 4012

Mulroney, Miss S E P (Forsters LLP) *S1*
Westminster *p33* 020 7863 8333

Mulvaney, Ms J M (TLT Solicitors) *J1*
Bristol *p165* 0117 917 7777

Mulvihill, E R (Spencer Ewin Mulvihill) *S1*
Harrogate *p240* 01423 509826

Mumford, S (Pinsent Masons LLP) *C1*
London EC2 *p67* 020 7418 7000

Mumford, S A R (Rausa Mumford) *G H K1 J1*
Cardiff *p180* 029 2034 4341

Mumford, S A R (Hains & Lewis Ltd) *G H Zm Zl F1 A3 J2*
Haverfordwest *p244* 0845 408 0125

Mumford, Miss S G (Wakefield Metropolitan District Council)
Wakefield *p474* 01924 306090

Mumford, S H (Wilmot & Co Solicitors LLP) *W A1 Zd T2 K4*
Cirencester *p195* 01285 650551

Mumford, Ms S J (Bevan Brittan LLP)
Bristol *p161* 0870 194 1000

Mumford, Miss S J (TLT Solicitors) *O B1 Q*
Bristol *p165* 0117 917 7777

Mumford, T C (Rotherham Metropolitan Borough Council)
Rotherham *p470* 01709 382121

Munby, Mrs L R (Cozens Moxon & Harts) *K1 K3*
Teddington *p409* 020 8977 8486 / 8977 4424

Muncer, Ms A J (Frettens Solicitors) *C1 C2*
Christchurch *p194* 01202 491777
Basingstoke *p127* 01256 320555

Muncey, J R (Wedlake Bell LLP) *O L*
London WC1 *p91* 020 7395 3000

Munday, C T (Trowers & Hamlins) *L*
London EC3 *p88* 020 7423 8000

Munday, Ms J (Howells LLP) *D1 D2 K1*
Sheffield *p376* 0114 249 6666

Munday, N C (Clifford Chance)
London E14 *p20* 020 7006 1000

Munday, S G (Northamptonshire Magistrates Courts)
Northampton *p467* 01604 497000

Munden, A J (Warner Goodman LLP) *N*
Southampton *p387* 023 8063 9311

Munden, Ms J A (Newman & Bond) *K1 D1 V*
Barnsley *p125* 01226 213434

Mundy, D (Bircham Dyson Bell) *A2 C3 M1 P R1 Zf Zg Zl Zu*
Westminster *p13* 020 7227 7000

Mundy, H E (Chamberlains) *S1 E R1 A1 J1 Zh Zl Zj S2 A2*
Bishop's Waltham *p144* 01489 896141

Mundy, Miss J A (Venters Solicitors) *K1 K3 D1 D2*
Reigate *p363* 01737 229610

Mundy, M P (Clarke Willmott)
Southampton *p385* 0845 209 1000 / 0117 305 6000

Mundy, R S (Roger James Clements & Partners) *S1 S2 E W K1 K3 K4*
Risca *p365* 01633 614166
Newport *p329* 01633 263316 / 663316

Munford, I R (Bermans LLP) *B1 J1 Q Zb C1 O F1 B2*
Manchester *p301* 0161 827 4600

Mungol, Ms R S (Pragesh & McKenzie Solicitors) *C1 S2 F1 G H J1 K1 L Zl S1 W K3*
Thornton Heath *p411* 020 8689 0089

Mungovan, J (Memery Crystal) *C1 C2*
London WC2 *p60* 020 7242 5905

Muniandy, Miss C L (ASB Aspire) *S1 S2 W E*
Maidstone *p298* 0845 063 6465

Munn, T (Trevor Munn) *E R2 S1 S2 W*
Walton-on-Thames *p420* 01932 269153

Munnery, R W (London Borough of Wandsworth)
London SW18 *p110* 020 8871 6000

Munraknah, Miss S D (Wilkins) *K1*
Aylesbury *p121* 01296 424681

Munro, Miss A F (Ison Harrison) *N*
Leeds *p274* 0113 284 5000

Munro, A R (Squire Sanders (UK) LLP)
Manchester *p310* 0161 830 5000

Munro, E C (Munro Solicitors) *D1*
London E7 *p62* 020 8503 1718

Munro, Ms J (Field Fisher Waterhouse LLP)
London EC3 *p31* 020 7861 4000

Munro, Ms L E (Blake Lapthorn) *S1*
Chandlers Ford *p184* 023 8090 8090

Munro, M J (Barlow Lyde & Gilbert LLP) *Zj Q*
London EC3 *p10* 020 7247 2277

Munro, M R (Hatchers Solicitors LLP) *K1 N K2 S1 W K3 D2 K4*
Shrewsbury *p379* 01743 467641

Munro, Miss P L (Pinsent Masons LLP)
Leeds *p276* 0113 244 5000

Munro, R T I (Chubb Insurance Company of Europe S.A.)
London EC3 *p105* 020 7956 5000

Munro, S (Ince & Co Services Ltd)
London E1 *p44* 020 7481 0010

Munroe, Ms R (Rawlison Butler LLP) *S1*
Crawley *p202* 01293 527744

Munsey, Mrs E J (Harvey Ingram LLP) *E L S1*
Leicester *p280* 0116 254 5454

Munsey, J R (National Grid PLC)
Warwick *p471* 01926 653000

Munson, S H (Blake Lapthorn) *C1 T1 Ze Zf*
London EC1 *p13* 020 7405 2000

Murden, T (Corries Solicitors) *N Zj*
York *p444* 0845 241 5566

Murdoch, G I (Stephens & Scown) *W T1 S1 C1*
Truro *p414* 01872 265100

Murdoch, P (Ashurst LLP)
London EC2 *p7* 020 7638 1111

Murfin, A R (Bakewells) *S1 S2 E W C1 C2*
Derby *p208* 01332 348791

Murfitt, S E (Blake Lapthorn) *O Q Zc A3 B2 I*
Chandlers Ford *p184* 023 8090 8090

Murgatroyd, Miss C D (Atherton Godfrey) *Zr*
Doncaster *p211* 01302 320621

Murgatroyd, S (Wilsons) *W J1 N K1 K3*
Pudsey *p358* 0113 236 2333

Muriel, A J W (DLA Piper UK LLP)
London EC2 *p24* 0870 011 1111
London EC2 *p90* 020 7814 8000

Muriel-Sanchez, Mrs M T (Wandsworth & Merton Law Centre Ltd)
London SW17 *p110* 020 8767 2777

Murillo, Miss A (Fenland District Council) *N Q R1*
March *p465* 01354 654321

Murphie, Miss H (Royds LLP) *J1 K1 K3 D1 O*
London EC4 *p74* 020 7583 2222

Murphy, Miss A (Aaron & Partners LLP Solicitors) *Q O Zj K2 Zq*
Chester *p190* 01244 405555

Murphy, A (John Delaney & Co) *G H*
Leeds *p273* 0113 246 8151

Murphy, Ms A C M (Bindmans LLP) *N Zr*
London WC1 *p12* 020 7833 4433

Murphy, A J (David Phillips & Partners) *H G B2*
Bootle *p150* 0151 922 5525

Murphy, Ms B (Osborne Clarke) *M1 P O*
Bristol *p164* 0117 917 3000

Murphy, B (Ashurst LLP)
London EC2 *p7* 020 7638 1111

Murphy, C (Fanshaw Porter & Hazlehurst)
Birkenhead *p134* 0151 647 4051

Murphy, C P (Whiteheads) *K1 S1 G H W J1 V Q N L*
Newcastle under Lyme *p323* 01782 615278

Murphy, D (Russell-Cooke LLP) *S1*
London SW15 *p74* 020 8789 9111

Murphy, Ms D A (St Helens Law Limited)
St Helens *p391* 01744 454433

Murphy, D F (Shell International Ltd)
London SE1 *p109* 020 7934 1234

Murphy, D P (DLA Piper UK LLP)
London EC2 *p24* 0870 011 1111

Murphy, Ms E (Field Fisher Waterhouse LLP)
London EC3 *p31* 020 7861 4000

Murphy, E (Bower & Bailey) *S1 S2 W E*
Oxford *p343* 01865 311133
Swindon *p406* 01793 610466

Murphy, Miss E D (Greenwoods Solicitors LLP) *C1 C2 U2 Ze Zza*
Peterborough *p347* 01733 887700

Murphy, Ms F (Bhatt Murphy) *Zg*
Hackney *p12* 020 7729 1115

Murphy, F (Jones Day) *C3*
London EC4 *p46* 020 7039 5959

Murphy, Ms F M (Mayer Brown International LLP) *C3*
London EC2 *p59* 020 3130 3000

Murphy, Mrs G I (North East Derbyshire District Council)
Chesterfield *p455* 01246 231111

Murphy, G J (Sebastians) *E C1 S1 L W S2*
London EC4 *p77* 020 7583 2105

Murphy, G V (Cyril Jones & Co) *K1 P M1 G F1 L J1 N D1 H Zl Zj Zk*
Wrexham *p443* 01978 263131

Murphy, J (Jamieson & Co) *N Q K3 O B1 W F1*
Newcastle upon Tyne *p325* 0191 281 0063

Murphy, J (Rees Page) *L E C1 Zl S1 S2*
Wolverhampton *p438* 01902 577777

Murphy, Mrs J (Linskills Solicitors) *K1 D1*
Liverpool *p289* 0151 236 2224

Murphy, J A (Whiteheads) *S1 W E*
Newcastle under Lyme *p323* 01782 615278

Murphy, J C (3i PLC)
London SW1 *p103* 020 7928 3131

Murphy, Mrs J L (Coole & Haddock) *K4 W T2*
Horsham *p253* 01403 210200

Murphy, Mrs J L (Reuters Group PLC)
London E14 *p109* 020 7250 1122

Murphy, J P (J Murphy & Sons Ltd)
London NW5 *p108* 020 7267 4366

Murphy, Ms K L (Newcastle Upon Tyne City Council)
Newcastle upon Tyne *p466* 0191 232 8520

Murphy, Ms L (Devonalds) *D1 K1 L M1 P S1*
Pontypridd *p352* 01443 404700

Murphy, Miss L V (Nicholson Portnell) *W S1*
Hexham *p249* 01434 603656

Murphy, Miss M (Luton Borough Council)
Luton *p464* 01582 546000

Murphy, Mrs M (Cornwells) *K1 Q O*
Bradford *p153* 01274 675631

Murphy, M B (LG Lawyers) *C1*
London SE1 *p50* 020 7379 0000

Murphy, M E (Ilett & Clark Solicitors) *C1 E S1 W J1 A1*
Worksop *p441* 01909 500544

Murphy, M J (M J Murphy) *S1*
Pinner *p349* 020 8866 8929

Murphy, M J (Murphy & Co) *O B1 I C1 C2*
Watford *p423* 01923 288043

Murphy, N (Shoosmiths)
Fareham *p224* 0370 086 6800 / 01489 616800

Murphy, Ms N (Leeds City Council) *O Q Zr*
Leeds *p462* 0113 224 3513

Murphy, N S J (Eaton Smith LLP) *L K1 G H D1 F1 Q*
Huddersfield *p255* 01484 821300

Murphy, P (Mawdsleys) *K1 D1*
Southport *p388* 01704 537676

Murphy, Miss P A (Schubert Murphy) *E W S1*
London N21 *p77* 020 8360 2599

Murphy, Mrs P G (Geldards LLP) *S1*
Cardiff *p178* 029 2023 8239

Murphy, P J (Knowsley Metropolitan Borough Council)
Huyton *p461* 0151 443 3593

Murphy, Mrs P M (Phillips Green & Murphy) *S1 W K1 N Q J1 F1 B1 L*
Swansea *p405* 01792 468684

Murphy, P R (Sacker & Partners LLP) *Zo Zq O*
London EC2 *p76* 020 7329 6699

Murphy, S (Cartwright Cunningham Haselgrove & Co) *E K4 S1 W*
Woodford Green *p439* 020 8506 5200

Murphy, Miss S H (Whiteheads) *S1 W*
Newcastle under Lyme *p323* 01782 615278

Murphy, Miss S L (Gedye & Sons (Solicitors) Ltd) *W*
Grange-over-Sands *p232* 01539 532313

Murphy, S P (Edwards Duthie) *G H J1 D1 Zl Zi Zp*
London E13 *p29* 020 8514 9000

Murphy, S P (Carmarthenshire County Council)
Carmarthen *p453* 01267 224010

Murphy, S Q (Stuart Q Murphy) *S1 W S2 K3*
West Byfleet *p427* 01932 355755

Murphy, T M (Jones Robertson)
Widnes *p431* 0151 423 3661

Murphy, V J (G Huw Lewis) *G H S1 N K1 V W A1 Q J1 Zm Zw Zq*
Neath *p320* 01639 637181

Murr, R C (Mackay & Co) *N P E M1 C1 S1 B1 A1 Zg Zc Zj*
Faversham *p225* 01795 536061

Murrall, R (Lanyon Bowdler LLP) *C1 C2 C3 J1 Ze*
Telford *p409* 01952 291222

Murratt, C A (Actons) *O B1 L Q Zh*
Nottingham *p335* 0115 910 0200

Murray, A (Francis & How) *S1 W E L*
Chesham *p189* 01494 782541

Murray, A J (Winckworth Sherwood LLP) *L R1 R2 S1 S2 Zb Zh*
London SE1 *p92* 020 7593 5000

Murray, A M (Harold Stock & Co) *N O Q Zl J1 Zp G H*
Ashton-under-Lyne *p120* 01457 835597 / 835034

Murray, A P D (Francis & How) *E C2 W L S1 U2*
Chesham *p189* 01494 782541

Murray, A R (TLT Solicitors)
London EC2 *p85* 020 3465 4000

Murray, A R E T (Bishop & Sewell LLP) *W*
London WC1 *p13* 020 7631 4141

Murray, Miss C (Neil Myerson LLP) *C1 Ze U2*
Altrincham *p117* 0161 941 4000

Murray, Miss C (Northumberland County Council)
Morpeth *p466* 01670 533000

Murray, C (Barlow Lyde & Gilbert LLP) *N Q*
Manchester *p301* 0161 829 6400

Murray, C (London Borough of Southwark)
London SE1 *p109* 020 7525 5000

Murray, Miss C E (Birmingham City Council Legal & Democratic Services)
Birmingham *p449* 0121 303 2066

Murray, C G (Kemp Little LLP) *U2 I C1 Zf U1 Zz C3 Ze F1 F2 Zza*
London EC2 *p48* 020 7600 8080

Murray, C M (Kingsley Napley) *B2 G H*
London EC1 *p50* 020 7814 1200

Murray, C P (Murray Hay Solicitors) *E S1 S2 R2*
London SW15 *p62* 020 8780 1225

Murray, D T J (Allen & Overy LLP)
London E1 *p5* 020 3088 0000

Murray, E (Allen & Overy LLP)
London E1 *p5* 020 3088 0000

Murray, F G (Everys) *W S1 E A1*
Taunton *p408* 01823 337636

Murray, Ms F J (Temperley Taylor LLP) *K1 N G H J1 V W F1 S1 Q*
Middleton *p315* 0161 643 2411

Murray, Ms G (IBB Solicitors) *W T2 Zm*
Chesham *p189* 0845 638 1381

Murray, H (Herbert Smith LLP) *T1*
London EC2 *p40* 020 7374 8000

Murray, Mrs H B R (Robert Lunn & Lowth) *K1 W Q J1*
Stratford-upon-Avon *p400* 01789 292238

Murray, I P (Lancashire County Council) *N D1 O Q C1 K1 S1 W Zi*
Preston *p469* 01772 254868

Murray, Ms J (Addleshaw Goddard)
Leeds *p271* 0113 209 2000

Murray, J A (North East Lincolnshire Borough Council)
Cleethorpes *p455* 01472 324001

Murray, J J (Ferguson Solicitors) *J1 Zp O Q N*
London EC4 *p31* 020 7822 2999

Murray, Miss J M (Murray Cairns & Co) *S1 W S2 K1*
Wellington *p425* 01952 261650

Murray, J N (Emsleys) *Zh L*
Crossgates *p204* 0113 260 3115

Murray, J R (Murrays) *D1 D2 K1 Zm*
Bodmin *p148* 01208 72863

Murray, J R F (Brown & Murray) *S1 K1 R1 A1 N L P C1 E G Zc Zl Zj*
Millom *p316* 01229 772562

Murray, J V H (Stevens & Bolton) *C1 T1*
Guildford *p237* 01483 302264

Murray, K (Wright & Lord)
Morecambe *p319* 01524 402050

Murray, Mrs L M (Hertfordshire County Council)
Hertford *p460* 01992 555555

Murray, M J (Shoosmiths) *N O Q Zj Zq*
Northampton *p332* 0370 086 3000 / 01604 543000

Murray, N J (Wards Solicitors) *S1 W Zd*
Yate *p443* 01454 316789
Bristol *p165* 0117 929 2811

Murray, O (Ince & Co Services Ltd)
London E1 *p44* 020 7481 0010

Murray, P (Pitmans LLP) *Zb E*
Reading *p361* 0118 958 0224

Murray, Ms P (Murrays Solicitors) *N D1 G H*
Bradford *p154* 01274 304448

Murray, P C (DAC Beachcroft)
Birmingham *p137* 0121 698 5200

Murray, P I (Murray Roach Solicitors) *S1 E W C1 L B1 R1 T1*
Nailsea *p320* 01275 858266 / 852705

Murray, R (Crowell & Moring) *C1 M1 M2 O*
London EC4 *p23* 020 7413 0011

Murray, R A (Millerchip Peachey) *G H*
Coventry *p200* 024 7624 3615

Murray, R J (Robin Murray & Co) *G H*
Chatham *p185* 01634 832332

Murray, Ms R K (Ashfords LLP)
Exeter *p220* 01392 337000

Murray, R R (Wards Solicitors) *S1 K1 W J1 Q E F1 G L T1 Zk Zl*
Clevedon *p196* 01275 850470

Murray, Miss S (Coffin Mew & Clover) *J1 Zp*
Fareham *p223* 01329 825617

Murray, S (Derby Hospitals NHS Foundation Trust)
Derby *p456* 01332 785419

Murray, S (Herbert Smith LLP) *C2*
London EC2 *p40* 020 7374 8000

Murray, S (Stephen Murray & Co) *S1 E W Zl*
Perivale *p346* 020 8997 9669

Murray, S C (British Telecommunications PLC)
London EC1 *p104* 020 7356 6181

Murray, S J (Kirwans) *N*
Liverpool *p289* 0151 229 5600

Murray, S L (The Lister Croft Partnership) *S1 E L C1 W T1 B1 Zl Zc*
Pudsey *p358* 0113 257 0526

Murray, Ms T (North Yorkshire Law)
Scarborough *p372* 01723 360001

Murray, Mrs T J (Alderson Dodds) *K1 B1 F1 N Q J1*
Blyth *p147* 01670 352293

Murray, Ms V M (Hopkin Murray Beskine) *K1 D1*
London N4 *p42* 020 7272 1234

Murray-Hinde, Miss S J (Moorhead James LLP) *J1 Zp*
London EC4 *p61* 020 7831 8888

Murray-Jones, A G (Skadden Arps Slate Meagher & Flom (UK) LLP) *C2*
London E14 *p80* 020 7519 7000

Murray-Jones, R J (Thornleys Limited) *S1 E W L C1 Zv*
Plymouth *p350* 01752 406977

Murray-Lacey, Mrs K A (Gudgeons Prentice) *W T2*
Stowmarket *p399* 01449 613101

Murray-Peters, R J (Pattmans) *S1 S2*
Bromsgrove *p167* 01527 872947

Murray-White, N J (Davies Murray-White & Co)
Stratford-upon-Avon *p400* 01789 295544

Murrell, A D (Drysdales) *Q N O R1 J1 L B1 F1 C1 X*
Southend-on-Sea *p387* 01702 423400

Murrells, P G (Surveyors Indemnity Management Services)
Tunbridge Wells *p474* 01892 528333

Murrills, N (Gateley LLP) *J1*
Manchester *p304* 0161 836 7700

Murrin, P J (DAC Beachcroft)
London EC4 *p24* 020 7936 2222

Murrison, R (Jerman Simpson Pearson & Samuels) *N*
Basildon *p126* 01268 820111

Murtagh, B (Chelsea Building Society)
Cheltenham *p454*

Murtagh, Ms J (Hegarty LLP) *G H*
Peterborough *p347* 01733 346333

Murtagh, Ms M (AWB Partnership LLP) *C1 E L Zh S2 S1*
Guildford *p235* 01483 302345

Musannif, S (Foot Anstey) *D1 K1*
Exeter *p221* 01392 411221

Muscat, L B G (Leonard B G Muscat) *S1 Q B1 F1 L N W T1 K1 J1 Zc Zj Zs*
Gosforth *p232* 0191 285 8510

Muscatt, S (Bowen Muscatt) *E F1 G J1 L N Q S1 W Zl Zr Zc J2 O R1*
London W1 *p14* 020 7908 3800

6

Muscroft, Ms J (Irwin Mitchell LLP) *C1*
Birmingham *p139* 0870 150 0100
Leeds *p277* 0113 283 2500

Musgrave, B P L (Booth Ince & Knowles) *L S1 Q O S2 K3*
Denton *p208* 0161 336 7011

Musgrave, C G (Oxley & Coward Solicitors LLP) *K3 K1*
Rotherham *p367* 01709 510999

Musgrave, C J (BAE Systems PLC)
London SW1 *p104* 01252 373232

Musgrave, G T C (Key2Law LLP) *S1 E W R2 R1 S2 Zd Zu*
Ewell *p220* 020 8393 0941

Musgrave, Miss J (Pepperells) *S1 S2 E L W*
Scunthorpe *p373* 01724 871999

Musgrave, M J (Speechly Bircham LLP) *Zd T2 W*
London EC4 *p81* 020 7427 6400

Musgrave, R J P (Whatley Weston & Fox) *O B1 N J1 Q Zc Zq*
Worcester *p440* 01905 731731

Musgreaves, Miss J (Noble) *G H*
Shefford *p377* 01462 814055

Musgrove, N (CKM Solicitors) *N*
Durham *p214* 0191 384 9080

Mushtaq, A (Isherwood & Hose) *K1 S1 S2 W Zi*
Rochdale *p365* 01706 359090 / 522225

Mushtaq, Miss R S (Mushtaq & Co) *D1 J1 Q N*
Birmingham *p140* 0121 622 1786

Musker, G H R (Astrazeneca PLC)
London W1 *p103* 020 7304 5000

Mussenden, Dr P J (BTG International Ltd)
London EC4 *p104* 020 7575 0000

Musson, S W R (Fishers) *E L S2 P Zn R1 R2 Zc*
Ashby-de-la-Zouch *p118* 01530 412167

Mustafa, Ms H (Pearson Maddin Solicitors) *S1*
New Malden *p321* 020 8949 9500

Mustafa, M I (Mustafa Solicitors) *M1 P B1 F1*
Levenshulme *p283* 0161 248 0400

Mustafa, P (Davenport Lyons) *Zf*
London W1 *p25* 020 7468 2600

Mustafa, Miss S C (Legal and Professional Claims Ltd)
London EC4 *p107* 020 7621 3900

Musters, P H A (Andrew Keenan & Co) *G H B2*
London SE20 *p48* 020 8659 0332

Musto, Miss L M A (Wakefield Metropolitan District Council)
Wakefield *p474* 01924 306090

Mustoe, J K (Weymouth & Portland Borough Council) *S1 W A1 B1 C1*
Weymouth *p476* 01305 838000

Muston, Miss E L (Downs) *W S1*
Dorking *p212* 01306 880110

Mutawi, A (Trowers & Hamlins)
London EC3 *p88* 020 7423 8000

Mutimear, Ms J M (Bird & Bird LLP) *Ze*
London EC4 *p13* 020 7415 6000

Mutter, J (Carillion PLC) *O Q*
Wolverhampton *p477* 01902 422431

Mutti, T J (Traymans) *N Q G F1*
Hackney *p88* 020 7249 9980

Muttock, R M (DLA Piper UK LLP) *N Zj Zq*
Manchester *p303* 0870 011 1111

Mutum, Ms A J (Department for Business, Enterprise and Regulatory Reform)
London SW1 *p105* 020 7215 0105

Muxlow, Ms F T (Taylor Wessing)
London EC4 *p86* 020 7300 7000

Myatt, J W (Lyons Davidson) *K1*
Bristol *p163* 0117 904 6000

Mychalkiw, Miss A (Forbes) *N Q Zj*
Blackburn *p145* 01254 662831

Myddelton, R H (Grand Metropolitan PLC (Legal Dept))
London W1 *p106* 020 7321 6000

Myddelton, R H H (Batchelor Myddelton) *E C1 N Zc W R1 S1 J1 K1 L*
Potters Bar *p355* 01707 647088

Mydlowski, S T (Gordons LLP)
Leeds *p273* 0113 227 0100

Myer, R J (Horwich Cohen Coghlan) *N*
Manchester *p305* 0161 830 4600

Myers, A J (Wolfe Myers & Co) *S1 W E C1 L F1 J1 P M1 N Zi Zl*
London NW4 *p93* 020 8202 8546
London W1 *p93* 020 7580 7426

Myers, C O (Forsters LLP) *S1*
Westminster *p33* 020 7863 8333

Myers, D (Rollits LLP) *E R1 S1*
Hull *p258* 01482 323239

Myers, D D (LG Lawyers)
London SE1 *p50* 020 7379 0000

Myers, Mrs D M (Robin Burman & Co) *Zx S1 Zd*
Manchester *p302* 0161 860 7123

Myers, E E (Barratt Goff & Tomlinson) *N J2 Zw*
Nottingham *p335* 0115 931 5171

Myers, J (The Dures Partnership LLP) *O Q J1 Zc L N Zq B1*
Liverpool *p287* 0151 242 5111

Myers, J (Clifford Chance)
London E14 *p20* 020 7006 1000

Myers, J (Clerical Medical Investment Group)
London EC2 *p105* 020 7321 1425

Myers, J L (Oglethorpe Sturton & Gillibrand) *A1 S1*
Lancaster *p270* 01524 846846

Myers, Ms K (Ward Hadaway) *Zr*
Newcastle upon Tyne *p327* 0191 204 4000

Myers, L N R (SJ Berwin LLP)
London EC4 *p75* 020 7111 2222

Myers, Mrs M (EMW) *C1 C2*
Milton Keynes *p316* 0845 070 6000

Myers, R H (Myers Lister Price) *E S1 L W*
Altrincham *p117* 0161 926 9969

Myers, S A (Allen & Overy LLP)
London E1 *p5* 020 3088 0000

Myerscough, Ms S E C (Gardner Leader LLP) *D1 K1 K2*
Newbury *p322* 01635 508080

Myerson, A A J (Andrew Myerson & Co) *C1 E F1 K1 N P S1 T1 V*
Worthing *p442* 01903 700961

Myerson, Ms D S (Berwins Solicitors Limited) *S1*
Harrogate *p240* 01423 509000

Myerson, N E (Neil Myerson LLP) *C2 C1 Zq*
Altrincham *p117* 0161 941 4000

Myles, A (Levison Meltzer Pigott) *K1*
London EC4 *p53* 020 7556 2400

Myles, D C (Crombie Wilkinson) *K1 K3 K2 D1*
York *p444* 01904 624185

Myles, J J (Forbes) *N*
Blackburn *p145* 01254 662831

Myles, Mrs K (Rollits LLP) *K1 D1 D2 K2*
York *p445* 01904 625790

Myles, Ms P (Chiltern District Council)
Amersham *p447* 01494 729000

Mylrea, Ms K P (Simmons & Simmons)
London EC2 *p79* 020 7628 2020

Mynard, S A (Nigel Broadhead Mynard) *P C1 W R1 K1 B1 G Zl Zc Zi*
Chelmsford *p187* 01245 269909

Mynes, Ms S A (Tameside Metropolitan Borough Council) *D1 G H K1 V Zi Zl Zm*
Ashton-under-Lyne *p447* 0161 342 3028

Myska, Miss H (English Heritage)
London EC1 *p106* 020 7973 3360

Myska, Ms H (Stanley Tee) *J1 Q Zp*
Bishop's Stortford *p144* 01279 755200

Mytton, D L (Boyes Turner) *R1 Zu*
Reading *p360* 0118 959 7711

N

Naaman, Miss D (Reynolds Dawson)
London WC2 *p71* 020 7839 2373 / 07659 130481

Nabozny, M A (Morrish Solicitors LLP) *N Q*
Leeds *p276* 0113 245 0733

Naccarato, J R (CMS Cameron McKenna LLP)
London EC3 *p17* 020 7367 3000

Nadarajah, Ms P (Clegg Manuel) *S1*
Islington *p20* 020 7847 5600

Nadel, Miss D (Kingsley Napley) *N Zr Zq*
London EC1 *p50* 020 7814 1200

Nadel, Ms G (Eatons) *N*
Bradford *p153* 0845 660 0660

Naderi, Mrs D (Lancashire County Council)
Preston *p469* 01772 254868

Nadin, J (Penningtons) *E*
London EC2 *p66* 020 7457 3000

Nadkarni, S (Steele & Son) *S1 S2 L*
Barnoldswick *p124* 01282 813385

Nadler, Ms S (Field Fisher Waterhouse LLP)
London EC3 *p31* 020 7861 4000

Nagel, D (Edwards Angell Palmer & Dodge) *M3 A3 Zb Zc C1 J1 Zj M2 O Q N Zu C2 Zn R2*
London EC2 *p28* 020 7583 4055

Naghen, D J (Maples Solicitors LLP) *G H Zl*
Spalding *p389* 01775 722261

Nagle, A (Morrison & Foerster (UK) LLP) *U1 U2 Zza*
London EC2 *p62* 020 7920 4000
London EC2 *p67* 020 7847 9500

Nagle, K R (Shakespeares) *E L R1 Zh*
Birmingham *p142* 0121 237 3000

Nagle, M A (Colin Ashworth & Co)
Oldham *p340* 01706 845002

Nagle, M A (Hudson & Taylor) *S1 S2 K1 O Q N W*
Rochdale *p365* 01706 644525

Nagle, Mrs N L (Montague Harris) *S1 W E K4 L*
Bristol *p164* 01454 322722 / 313362

Nagle, Miss S (Anna Arthur Associates) *W K1 D1 Q J1*
Woking *p436* 01483 222499

Nagler, Mrs E (McGrigors LLP)
London EC4 *p56* 020 7054 2500

Nagra, A S (Ward & Rider Limited) *N*
Coventry *p201* 024 7655 5400

Nagra, Ms M K (Edward Harte LLP) *E S1 L*
Brighton *p159* 01273 662750

Nahal, H (Herbert Smith LLP) *O Zq*
London EC2 *p40* 020 7374 8000

Nahar, B (Royds LLP) *E S2 S1 R2*
London EC4 *p74* 020 7583 2222

Nahar, R (G J Templeman Solicitors) *S1 S2 W Zl*
Ealing *p86* 020 8566 1200

Nahlis, A (Nahlis Christou)
London WC1 *p63* 020 7278 6888

Nahon, C (Solomon Taylor & Shaw) *C1*
London NW3 *p80* 020 7431 1912

Naidu, G (Henscott Solicitors) *G H*
London E17 *p40* 0870 880 0007

Naik, Mrs S (Percy Short & Cuthbert) *K1 L K3 S1*
Islington *p67* 020 7700 0265

Nainthy, P J (Jackamans) *G H J1 Zl*
Felixstowe *p225* 01394 279636

Nair, Mrs M A (Kirwans) *C1 J1 F2 Ze O*
Liverpool *p289* 0151 229 5600

Nair, Miss N (Gepp & Sons) *G H*
Chelmsford *p186* 01245 493939
Colchester *p197* 01206 369889

Nair, Mrs P (Evans & Ellis) *W S1 L K1 V C1 T2 F1 J1*
Chepstow *p189* 01291 622814

Nair, Ms R (Boodle Hatfield)
Westminster *p14* 020 7629 7411

Nairn, K (Skadden Arps Slate Meagher & Flom (UK) LLP)
London E14 *p80* 020 7519 7000

Naish, R (Walker Morris) *C1 C2*
Leeds *p277* 0113 283 2500

Najran, J (Challinors) *S1*
Wolverhampton *p437* 01902 428121

Nakada, K (Rochman Landau LLP) *J1 Zi Q C2*
London W1 *p72* 020 7544 2424

Nakarja, H (First Title Insurance PLC)
London EC4 *p106* 020 7832 3100

Nalbantian, E (Jones Day) *Zb*
London EC4 *p46* 020 7039 5959

Nall, Mrs S K (Christine Lee & Co (Solicitors) Ltd)
Birmingham *p140* 0121 666 6228

Nally, E (Fieldings Porter) *E S1 C1 L R1 W T1*
Bolton *p149* 01204 540900

Nam, K (Ince & Co Services Ltd) *Q*
London E1 *p44* 020 7481 0010

Nanavita, Miss B (Turners Solicitors LLP) *Q L O C1 Zq*
Bournemouth *p153* 01202 291291

Nandhra, D (The Sethi Partnership Solicitors) *S2 E R2 S1*
Eastcote *p216* 020 8866 6464

Nanji, R (Memery Crystal) *C1 C2*
London WC2 *p60* 020 7242 5905

Nankervis, Ms M V (Osborne Clarke) *B1 K1 M1 N P Ze Zl Zk*
Bristol *p164* 0117 917 3000

Nankervis, R J (Ward Hadaway) *E R2*
Newcastle upon Tyne *p327* 0191 204 4000

Nanner, B (Derbyshire County Council) *Q N Zu S1*
Matlock *p465* 01629 580000
Melton Mowbray *p465* 01664 502502

Nanovski, Ms A (Venters Solicitors) *K1 K3 D1 D2*
London SE5 *p89* 020 7277 0110

Napier, Miss E A (Pickerings LLP) *S2 E*
Tamworth *p407* 01827 317070

Napier, R J (Albinson Napier & Co) *K1 J1 C1 W*
Warrington *p421* 01925 634681

Napier, R M (Albinson Napier & Co) *E C1 W S1 Zk Zg*
Warrington *p421* 01925 634681

Napier, T M (Irwin Mitchell LLP) *N Zr*
Birmingham *p139* 0870 150 0100
Sheffield *p376* 0870 150 0100

Napper, Miss I J S (Mills & Reeve) *I C3 Ze*
Cambridge *p175* 01223 364422

Narayan, D D (Ferns)
London SW4 *p31* 020 7498 9537

Narbeth, I A (Fladgate LLP)
London WC2 *p32* 020 3036 7000

Nari, P R (Engleharts) *E K1 L M1 P S1 Zi*
Hove *p254* 01273 204411

Narraway, N W (Moorhead James LLP) *C1 C2*
London EC4 *p61* 020 7831 8888

Narsi, Ms M (Kaim Todner Ltd) *G H B2*
Islington *p47* 020 7700 0070

Naseem, Miss A (Graysons) *K3 D1 D2 K1 K2*
Sheffield *p375* 0114 272 9184
Rotherham *p367* 01709 373000

Naser, P A (Ellis Jones) *C1 E S1 T1 W Zm Zd*
Ringwood *p364* 01425 484848

Nash, A (Towers & Hamlins)
London EC3 *p88* 020 7423 8000

Nash, D (Pinsent Masons LLP)
London EC2 *p67* 020 7418 7000

Nash, Mrs D (Bartlett Gooding & Weelen) *B1 K3 J1 K1 Q N S1 W L*
Glastonbury *p229* 01458 832510
Castle Cary *p183* 01963 350888
Shepton Mallet *p378* 01749 343091

Nash, D B (Owen Nash & Co) *S1 G H L P F1 M1 W E C1 Zi Zl*
Walsall *p420* 01922 746746

Nash, Miss E (Blaser Mills) *N Q*
Harrow *p241* 020 8427 6262

Nash, E (Hodge Jones & Allen LLP) *N*
London NW1 *p41* 020 7874 8300

Nash, Ms F L E (Fearon & Co) *S1 W*
Guildford *p236* 01483 540840

Nash, Mrs H M (Walker Smith Way) *E A1 R2 S2*
Chester *p191* 0844 346 3100

Nash, Ms J (North Kensington Law Centre) *J1 K1 Q D1 Zp*
London W10 *p108* 020 8969 7473

Nash, Ms J A (Adams Delmar)
Hampton *p238* 020 8941 2097

Nash, Mrs J G (J G Nash)
Stroud *p400* 01453 833652

Nash, Ms M (Davies Battersby Ltd) *Q O B1*
London EC3 *p26* 020 7621 1090

Nash, M A (Simmons & Simmons)
London EC2 *p79* 020 7628 2020

Nash, Ms P H (Lanyon Bowdler LLP) *N Zr O Q Zq*
Shrewsbury *p379* 01743 280280

Nash, Mrs P H (Poole Alcock) *N O Q Zr*
Nantwich *p320* 01270 625478

Nash, P S (Wrigleys Solicitors LLP) *S2 S1 E A1 L*
Leeds *p278* 0113 244 6100

Nash, S C (McGrigors LLP) *Zc A3 O M2 E R2*
London EC4 *p56* 020 7054 2500

Nash, S G (Bird & Lovibond) *L E S1 C1 W T1 S2 Zl*
Uxbridge *p417* 01895 256151

Nash, Mrs S L (Robinsons) *W K4 T2*
Derby *p209* 01332 291431

Nash, S R (Mobil Oil Company Ltd)
Milton Keynes *p466* 01908 853000

Nash, W (Speechly Bircham LLP) *Zb C2*
London EC4 *p81* 020 7427 6400

Nash-Harding, Mrs A (Harding Evans LLP) *G H*
Newport *p328* 01633 244233

Nasir, C (Nasir & Co Law Firm)
London WC2 *p63* 020 7405 3818

Nasir, Miss N (Globecast Northern Europe Ltd)
London WC1 *p106* 020 7430 4400

Nateghi, Ms M (Squire Sanders (UK) LLP)
London EC2 *p81* 020 7655 1000

Nathan, A C (Hextalls) *N P Zc Zj*
London EC2 *p41* 020 7382 0700

Nathan, D (Russell-Cooke LLP) *Zd*
London SW15 *p74* 020 8789 9111

Nathan, Ms M (Teacher Stern LLP) *C1 C2 Zf*
London WC1 *p86* 020 7242 3191

Nathan, M J (Finers Stephens Innocent LLP) *C1 E T1 S1 L W J1 B1 O Zc Ze Zb*
London W1 *p32* 020 7323 4000

Nathan, P N R (Denniss Matthews) *B1 N O*
London SE20 *p27* 020 8778 7301 / 8778 7631

Nathan, R B (Osborne Clarke) *J1 N P F1 Zp Zk*
London EC2 *p65* 020 7105 7000

Nathan, T G (Abrahamson & Associates) *C1 E J1 L S1 W Zb*
London NW11 *p3* 020 8458 1100

Nathanson, Miss M (Jefferies LLP) *N*
Altrincham *p116* 0800 342 3191

Nathasingh, Mrs C (South Northamptonshire Council) *J1 L O G X P Zp*
Towcester *p474* 01327 322322

Nathoo, H D (Gavins Solicitors) *S1 E C1 W L Zb Zi Zl*
London N6 *p35* 020 8374 4459

Nathoo, M S (Allen & Overy LLP)
London E1 *p5* 020 3088 0000

Nathwani, Miss J (Parlett Kent) *Zr N Zq*
Exeter *p222* 01392 494455

Nation, Mrs M J (Charlesworth Nicholl & Co) *S1 A1 E L T2 W J1 C1 S2 R1*
Crediton *p203* 01363 774706

Nation, Ms V D (Staffordshire County Council) *S1 W L E F1 C1 G J1 M1 K1 Ze Zl*
Stafford *p472* 01785 223121

Nation-Dixon, F (Adams & Remers) *T2 W*
Lewes *p283* 01273 480616

Nattrass, A G (Hewitts) *A1 C1 S2 E K4 R1 R2 S1 T1 T2 W*
Bishop Auckland *p144* 01388 604691

Nattrass, J A (Hills Solicitors Limited)
Altrincham *p116* 0161 928 0961

Natzler, Ms C A (London Borough of Greenwich Legal Services)
London SE18 *p106* 020 8921 5123

Naumann, Ms M (Foot Anstey)
Exeter *p221* 01392 411221

Naunton Davies, J V (Currey & Co) *Zd W T2*
Westminster *p24* 020 7802 2700

Navani, J (Criminal Defence Solicitors) *G H B2*
Westminster *p23* 020 7353 7000

Nawaz, F (RMPI Solicitors)
London W1 *p70* 020 7318 4444

Nawaz, Mrs I (Wycombe District Council)
High Wycombe *p461* 01494 461002

Nawaz, Miss Y B (Kirklees Metropolitan Borough Council)
Huddersfield *p461* 01484 221421

Nawrozzadeh, A (Johns & Saggar) *G H B2 Zg*
London WC1 *p46* 020 3490 1475

Nayak, P (Gateshead Metropolitan Borough Council)
Gateshead *p458* 0191 433 3000

Nayee, Ms U (Thorneycroft Solicitors Ltd) *N*
Macclesfield *p297* 01625 503444

Nayler, Miss L F (Robinsons) *W K4 T2*
Derby *p209* 01332 291431

Naylor, D (Roberts & Smith) *S1 W S2*
Nelson *p321* 01282 619000

Naylor, D M (North Yorkshire Law)
Whitby *p430* 01947 602131

Naylor, G (Challinors) *G H*
Birmingham *p136* 0121 212 9393

Naylor, I C (Bowcock & Pursaill) *S1 W T2 S2*
Leek *p278* 01538 399199

Naylor, Ms J (Martin Cunningham Solicitors)
Stockport *p395* 0161 456 5857

Naylor, Miss L (Avery Naylor) *G H D1 K1 N J1 Zp*
Swansea *p404* 01792 463276

Naylor, R H (Gosschalks) *E R1 S1*
Hull *p256* 01482 324252

Naylor, Miss S (Malcolm C Foy & Co) *D1 K3 K1*
Rotherham *p367* 01709 836866

Naylor, Ms S J (Hill Dickinson LLP) *N Q P O Zj*
Liverpool *p288* 0151 600 8000

Naylor, Miss S L (Atherton Godfrey) *J1 N Zq*
Doncaster *p211* 01302 320621

Naylor, Mrs T (Seddons)
Westminster *p77* 020 7725 8000

Naylor, T B (Lyons Davidson)
Bristol *p163* 0117 904 6000

Naylor, Miss Z (Phillips Solicitors) *S1*
Basingstoke *p127* 01256 460830

Nayyar, Mrs A H (Donns) *N*
Manchester *p303* 0161 834 3311

Naz, Miss F (Birdy & Co)
Wembley *p426* 020 8900 9112

See p634 for the Key to Work Categories

Nazam, S (Cadmans Law & Property) *S1 S2*
Cleckheaton *p195* 01274 874231
Nazar, S (Hanratty & Co) *D1 S2 K3 K1 K2 S1 W*
Newtown *p330* 01686 626239
Nazareth, Ms V C (BBC)
London W12 *p103* 020 8752 5734
Nazeem, M (Corbin & Hassan) *Zi*
London EC3 *p22* 020 7247 6518
Nazeer, M M (Malik & Malik Solicitors)
Brent *p58* 020 8830 3050
Nazhat, J (Trowers & Hamlins)
London EC3 *p88* 020 7423 8000
Nazia, Ms S (Cadmans Law & Property)
Cleckheaton *p195* 01274 874231
Nazir, M (Wosskow Brown) *Zi S1 S2 M4*
Sheffield *p377* 0114 256 1560
Nazir, Miss N (Scotts Holt & Sellars) *K3 K1*
Bromsgrove *p167* 01527 872711
Ndungu, Miss E W (Clerk to Sheffield Justices)
Sheffield *p470* 0114 276 0760
Neagle, Ms S (Quality Solicitors Burroughs Day) *K4 T2 V W Zm*
Bristol *p164* 0117 929 0333
Neal, A J (MFG Solicitors) *V*
Halesowen *p237* 0121 550 0777
Neal, A J K (Godwins) *W T2 K4 A1 Zd*
Winchester *p433* 01962 841484
Neal, C B (Bell & Buxton) *W*
Sheffield *p375* 0114 249 5969
Neal, Miss E A (Edwards Duthie) *G H*
London E13 *p29* 020 8514 9000
Neal, J C (Harris Cartier LLP) *C1 S2 E*
Slough *p382* 01753 810710
Neal, M P (South Lakeland District Council)
Kendal *p462* 01539 733333
Neal, N G (Welsh Development Agency Legal Services)
Cardiff *p453* 029 2082 8681
Neal, Q M (Haworth & Gallagher) *G H K1 L N Q*
Birkenhead *p134* 0151 647 8624
Wallasey *p419* 0151 638 5457 / 638 6088
Neal, R (Freeth Cartwright LLP) *T1 T2*
Nottingham *p337* 0115 936 9369
Neale, Ms A (Simmons & Simmons)
London EC2 *p79* 020 7628 2020
Neale, Ms A L (Comptons) *S1 W*
Camden *p22* 020 7485 0888
Neale, L D (England Stickland & Neale) *G H B2*
Birmingham *p138* 0121 377 7773
Neale, M (Nuneaton and Bedworth Borough Council)
Nuneaton *p468* 024 7637 6376
Neale, Miss R L (Rees Page) *J1 Zq Q*
Wolverhampton *p438* 01902 577777
Neale, Miss S (Elliot Mather LLP) *G H*
Mansfield *p311* 01623 655666
Neale, S G (T S Edwards & Son)
Newport *p328* 01633 257166
Neale, S M (Ison Harrison) *E S2*
Leeds *p274* 0113 284 5000
Neame, C (Holman Fenwick Willan)
London EC3 *p42* 020 7264 8000
Neary, Ms J M (Squire Sanders (UK) LLP)
Manchester *p310* 0161 830 5000
Neary, N H (SAS Daniels LLP) *C1 E S2 C2*
Stockport *p396* 0161 475 7676
Neasham, S M (Neasham Lloyd) *K1 M1 P G L W F1 D1 S1 Zi Zk*
Bicester *p132* 01869 252161
Neate, Miss A (The Smith Partnership) *L N Q Zl Zp*
Leicester *p281* 0116 247 2000
Neave, G H (Crown Prosecution Service Dyfed Powys) *S1 K1 W G H P F1 E B1 T1 Zl Zi Zm*
Carmarthen *p453* 01267 242100
Neave, Ms R R (Chelmsford Borough Council)
Chelmsford *p454* 01245 606606
Nedas, Ms S E K (Lewis Nedas & Co) *S1 E G H W S2*
Camden *p53* 020 7387 2032
Neden, Miss S (Walker Smith Way) *N*
Chester *p191* 0844 346 3100
Neea, R F (Enoch Evans LLP) *W T2 K4*
Walsall *p420* 01922 720333
Needham, Mrs A G (Warwickshire County Council)
Warwick *p475* 01926 410410
Needham, D (Max Engel & Co LLP) *B1 Zl O Q F1 F2*
Northampton *p331* 01604 887450
Needham, E A (DWF) *C1 C2*
Manchester *p303* 0161 603 5000
Needham, Ms E L (Needham Poulier & Partners) *G H Zm*
London N17 *p63* 020 8808 6622
Needham, G N E (Paton Walsh Laundy) *L S1 Q W*
London SW19 *p66* 020 8946 2229
Needham, Miss H (Derbyshire County Council)
Matlock *p465* 01629 580000
Needham, M A (Olswang LLP) *E L*
London WC1 *p64* 020 7067 3000
Needham, M J C (Crane & Walton) *W T2 S2*
Coalville *p196* 01530 834466
Needham, P C (Needhams)
Bradford *p154* 01274 371088
Needham, P J E (Davies Prichard & Weatherill) *E S1 S2 W*
Cardiff *p178* 029 2037 7471
Needham, T P (Waller Needham & Green) *G H*
Peterborough *p347* 01733 311422
Needle, Ms S L (hlw Keeble Hawson LLP)
Leeds *p274* 0113 244 3121
Needley, J L (John Barkers) *W S1 K4 T2 T1 S2 C2 E C1*
Louth *p294* 01507 604773
Mablethorpe *p297* 01507 477673
Needof, M (Howard Kennedy LLP) *E*
London W1 *p48* 020 7636 1616
Needs, G (Pardoes) *G L Q*
Bridgwater *p158* 01278 457891
Needs, K L (Risdon Hosegood) *G H N Q K1 S1 J1 O W Zc Zl Zk*
Minehead *p318* 01643 703123 / 700008
Neely, R G D (Mansfield District Council)
Mansfield *p465* 01623 463463
Neenan, P K (Stewarts Law LLP) *M3 N*
London EC4 *p83* 020 7822 8000
Neeve, C (Girlings)
Herne Bay *p248* 01227 367355
Neeves, Mrs M F (Atteys) *S1 W*
Retford *p363* 01777 713355
Negus, Mrs D M (Follett Stock LLP) *J1*
Truro *p414* 01872 241700
Negus, D P (Ellis-Fermor & Negus) *O Q R1 P C1*
Long Eaton *p293* 0115 972 5222
Negus-Fancey, Mrs P M (Rochman Landau LLP) *E P S2 Zd L S1 Zl*
London W1 *p72* 020 7544 2424
Negyal, Ms J (Boodle Hatfield)
Westminster *p14* 020 7629 7411
Nehammer, Mrs K E (Francis Thatcher & Co) *F1 Zl O Q Zr*
Leigh-on-Sea *p282* 01702 471000
Nehammer, M A F (Francis Thatcher & Co) *C1 E F1 J1 L S1 T1 W*
Leigh-on-Sea *p282* 01702 471000
Neidle, P D (Robert Brand & Co) *S2 S1 L W Zl*
Westminster *p15* 020 7935 2408
Neighbour, Ms S (Martin Murray & Associates) *G H B2*
Reading *p361* 0118 950 8577
Neil, D M (Coffin Mew & Clover) *E S1 R1 Zh Zc Zs*
Southampton *p385* 023 8033 4661
Neil, J A (John A Neil) *N J2 Zj Zq Zr*
Bristol *p164* 0117 344 5003
Neilan, J (Quastel Midgen LLP) *E S2 R2*
London W1 *p70* 020 7908 2525
Neiland, M (Bradley & Jefferies Solicitors Limited) *E S1*
Derby *p208* 01332 221722
Neiland, T G (Fishers) *C1 E Zn C2*
Ashby-de-la-Zouch *p118* 01530 412167
Neild, G (Martins) *M1 K1 D1 S1 P W G H N C1 Zc Zj Zo*
Eccles *p216* 0161 707 3660
Neild, R J (BTMK Solicitors LLP) *G H*
Southend-on-Sea *p387* 01702 339222
Neill, Miss A (B J McKenna & Co Solicitors) *K1 D1 K3*
Stockport *p396* 0161 432 5757
Neill, C B (Prince Evans) *N*
Ealing *p69* 020 8567 3477
Neill, Ms H F (Nantes) *E K4 K1 W T1 T2 Zd Zm S1*
Weymouth *p430* 01305 771000
Neilson, Mrs J D (Orme & Slade Ltd) *S1 S2 W L*
Ledbury *p271* 01531 632226
Neilson, Mrs N H (Latimer Hinks) *E S2 S1*
Darlington *p206* 01325 341500
Neilson-Clark, S A (DLA Piper UK LLP) *B1 Zb*
London EC2 *p24* 0870 011 1111
Nel, Mrs S (Bright & Sons) *J1 Zp Q*
Witham *p435* 01376 512338
Nelhams, M (Kellogg Brown & Root (UK) Ltd)
Leatherhead *p462* 01372 865000
Nelken, S J (Freemans Solicitors) *Zb E S2 B1 W*
London W1 *p34* 020 7935 3522
Nellar, S F (Hethertons LLP) *K1 K3*
York *p445* 01904 528200
Nellen, G A L (Nellen) *C1 C2*
Westminster *p63* 020 7499 8122
Nelligan, P M (Barrett Nelligan Solicitors) *G H S1 Q N K1 L W*
Fleetwood *p226* 01253 771664
Nellist, P (Clarke Willmott) *W T1 T2 Zo*
Taunton *p408* 0845 209 1000 / 0117 305 6000
Nellthorp, Mrs A E (Burley & Geach) *S1*
Grayshott *p233* 01428 605355
Petersfield *p348* 01730 262401
Nelson, A (Michael Simkins LLP) *E S1 S2 W*
London WC1 *p79* 020 7874 5600
Nelson, A (David Durn & Co)
Ruislip *p368* 01895 612400
Nelson, Mrs A H (East Sussex County Council) *A1 C1 E F1 L R1 S1*
Lewes *p463* 01273 481000
Nelson, A J (Haworth & Gallagher) *B1 C1 D1 E F1 G K1 M1 S1 W Zl Zt Zh*
Birkenhead *p134* 0151 647 8624
Wallasey *p419* 0151 638 5457 / 638 6088
Nelson, Mrs A M (Butterworths)
Carlisle *p182* 01228 593939
Nelson, Miss A P (Birchall Blackburn LLP) *S1 E S2 L*
Manchester *p301* 0161 236 0662
Nelson, C L (Glovers Solicitors LLP) *R2*
London W1 *p36* 020 7935 8882
Nelson, Ms E (Osborne Clarke) *J1*
London EC2 *p65* 020 7105 7000
Nelson, Miss E (Wrigleys Solicitors LLP) *Zd*
Sheffield *p377* 0114 267 5588
Nelson, Ms E L (Bartletts Solicitors) *S1 W E L*
Liverpool *p286* 0151 227 3391
Nelson, Mrs E L (Tilly Bailey & Irvine LLP) *K1 D1 K3 D2*
Stockton-on-Tees *p397* 01642 673797
Nelson, G (Rooks Rider) *S2 E R2*
London EC1 *p73* 020 7689 7000
Nelson, G (Allen Hoole Solicitors) *G H*
Bristol *p160* 0117 942 0901
Nelson, G J (North Yorkshire County Council) *O*
Northallerton *p467* 01609 780780
Nelson, Ms H (Sheffield Law Centre)
Sheffield *p471* 0114 273 1501
Nelson, I K (Nelson Nichols) *S1 W E L*
Portsmouth *p355* 023 9265 0623
Nelson, Mrs J M R (Cartmell Shepherd) *K1*
Carlisle *p182* 01228 516666
Nelson, J P H (Nelsons) *S1 E C3 S2 J1*
Tenterden *p410* 01580 767100
Nelson, J W R (Moss Solicitors LLP) *G H Zm*
Loughborough *p293* 01509 217770
Nelson, Ms K A (Hewitts) *D2 K3 D1 K1*
Newton Aycliffe *p330* 01325 316170
Nelson, Miss K E (MacDonald Oates LLP) *D1 D2 K1*
Petersfield *p348* 01730 268211
Nelson, Mrs L E (Hedges) *W V T2*
Didcot *p210* 01235 811888
Nelson, Miss M (Bywaters Topham Phillips LLP) *W T1 T2*
Harrogate *p240* 01423 879556
Nelson, O (Ford & Warren) *B1 O Zb*
Leeds *p273* 0113 243 6601
Nelson, P J (Wrigleys Solicitors LLP) *W T1*
Leeds *p278* 0113 244 6100
Nelson, P M (Linklaters LLP)
London EC2 *p54* 020 7456 2000
Nelson, P W (Hand Morgan & Owen) *N Q J1*
Stafford *p393* 01785 211411
Nelson, R (Department for Business, Enterprise and Regulatory Reform)
London SW1 *p105* 020 7215 0105
Nelson, R G (Nicholson Portnell) *J1 S1 Zl G*
Hexham *p249* 01434 603656
Nelson, S (Nelson Guest & Partners) *F1 G H L N O Q*
Sidcup *p380* 020 8309 5010 / 8309 0558
Nelson-Jones, R M (Field Fisher Waterhouse LLP)
London EC3 *p31* 020 7861 4000
Nelson-Wehrmeyer, Mrs S L (Crawley Borough Council)
Crawley *p456* 01293 438000
Nelson-Wehrmeyer, Mrs S L (Wokingham District Council)
Wokingham *p477* 0118 974 6000
Nembhard, Ms I (Birnberg Peirce & Partners) *Zg*
Camden *p13* 020 7911 0166
Neocleous, A C (Bird & Lovibond) *K1 D1 L Q*
Uxbridge *p417* 01895 256151
Neocleous, C (Christos Wybrew Kenneth Shaw & Co) *C1 E F1 G S1 W L Zl*
Enfield *p218* 020 8366 1345 / 8367 0840
Neocleous, N (RMPI Solicitors) *O Q J1 B1 Zk Ze Zl*
London W1 *p70* 020 7318 4444
Neocleous, N (Edwin Coe LLP) *O Q Zq B2 M2 J1 Zk A3 Zc T1 W*
London WC2 *p29* 020 7691 4000
Nertney, J M (Stockton-On-Tees Borough Council)
Stockton-on-Tees *p472* 01642 393939
Nerwan, J (JS Law)
Hayes *p245* 020 8817 1004
Nesbitt, D (Longden Walker & Renney) *N F1*
Sunderland *p401* 0191 567 7024
Nesbitt, G M (Hewitsons) *C1 C2*
Northampton *p332* 01604 233233
Nesbitt, S (Hogan Lovells International LLP)
London EC1 *p42* 020 7296 2000
Ness, P (Steels) *K1 M1 P S1 G H N J1 W F1 Zl Zp Zf*
Warrington *p422* 01925 632676
Nestor, Miss C D (Green Wright Chalton Annis)
Worthing *p441* 01903 234064
Nethercott, S J (Harold G Walker) *E S2*
Bournemouth *p152* 01202 203200
Netherway, S J (CMS Cameron McKenna LLP) *O Q Zj*
London EC3 *p17* 020 7367 3000
Netting, Mrs J H (Wrigleys Solicitors LLP) *Zi*
Sheffield *p377* 0114 267 5588
Nettleship, G R (Irwin Mitchell LLP) *S1*
Sheffield *p376* 0870 150 0100
Nettleship, P (Sutovic & Hartigan) *Zi*
London W3 *p84* 020 8993 5544
Nettleton, G W (Max Gold Law) *W T2 K4*
Hull *p257* 01482 224900
Neuberger, J (Ashurst LLP)
London EC2 *p7* 020 7638 1111
Neuborn, Mrs D J (Wilson Browne) *K1*
Leicester *p281* 0116 251 7181
Neuhoff, Ms T (Greenwoods) *N Zj J2*
Milton Keynes *p317* 01908 298200
Nevill, P H (Henry Nevill & Co) *E L S1 S2 W*
Burnham-on-Sea *p169* 01278 793936
Nevill, Miss Y (Watson Nevill) *K1 K3*
Maidstone *p299* 01622 661177
Neville, Ms C O H (Metropolitan Police Directorate of Legal Services)
London SW1 *p108* 020 7230 7210
Neville, Miss L M (Roebucks) *J1 G Q*
Blackburn *p145* 01254 274000
Neville, P J (Forsters LLP) *A1 L S1*
Westminster *p33* 020 7863 8333
Neville, W J W (Burges Salmon) *A1 L P*
Bristol *p161* 0117 939 2000
Neville-Jones, D J E (Preston Redman) *E A1 W T1 S1 C1 R1 L Za Zc Zd P Zx*
Bournemouth *p152* 01202 292424
Newall, A (The Littlewoods Organisation PLC) *S2 E L*
Liverpool *p463* 0151 235 3055
Chester *p190* 01244 310022
Newall, J (Grainger Appleyard) *K1 G H*
Doncaster *p211* 01302 327257
Newberry, Miss A C (Farnworth Shaw) *N Q*
Colne *p198* 01282 865885
Newberry, Mrs C A (Squire Sanders (UK) LLP)
Leeds *p277* 0113 284 7000
Newbery, A (Herbert Smith LLP)
London EC2 *p40* 020 7374 8000
Newbery, I R (Ian Newbery & Co) *C1 E I J1 K1 L N O Q S1 Zc Ze Zj*
Poole *p353* 01202 669986
Newbery, J A (Stephens & Scown) *H G Zl*
St Austell *p391* 01726 74433
Newbery, M (Herbert Smith LLP)
London EC2 *p40* 020 7374 8000
Newbery, Mrs M J (The Stokes Partnership) *W*
Crewkerne *p203* 01460 279279
Newbold, Mrs E (Graysons)
Sheffield *p375* 0114 272 9184
Sheffield *p376* 0114 213 3888
Newbold, Mrs G B (Newbold & Co) *K1 N S1 W J1 L S2 Q B1 D2*
Cwmbran *p206* 01633 874715
Newbold, Miss G S (Surrey County Council) *K1 D1*
Kingston upon Thames *p462* 020 8541 9088
Newbold, M J (Aldridge Brownlee Solicitors LLP) *K4 W*
Bournemouth *p151* 01202 527008
Newbold, M W (Royds LLP) *S2 E S1*
London EC4 *p74* 020 7583 2222
Newbold, S A C (GPB Solicitors LLP) *J1 N E C1 S2*
Stratford-upon-Avon *p400* 01789 261131
Newbon, P A B (Andrew Jackson) *Za*
Hull *p257* 01482 325242
Newbould, Ms F A (Morton Price) *S2 E S1*
Sheffield *p376* 0114 266 4141
Newbould, Miss S (Lloyds & Cooper) *J1 S2 E S1*
Leominster *p283* 01568 613236
Newboult-Robertson, Mrs K M (Boston Borough Council)
Boston *p450* 01205 314200
Newbury, A R (Pannone LLP) *K1*
Manchester *p308* 0161 909 3000
Newbury, Miss H C (Havant Borough Council)
Havant *p460* 023 9247 4174
Newbury, Ms W L (Backhouse Jones Ltd) *E S2 R1 S1 W R2*
Clitheroe *p196* 01254 828300
Newby, Miss C E (Young & Co) *S1 W*
Stoke-on-Trent *p398* 01782 339200
Newby, M (Quality Solicitors Jordans) *N G H Q O F1 V L W Zl*
Sheffield *p377* 01909 773627
Newcomb, Ms L (Addleshaw Goddard)
London EC1 *p4* 020 7606 8855
Newcombe, Ms C (Field Fisher Waterhouse LLP)
London EC3 *p31* 020 7861 4000
Newcombe, D A Z (Foreman Laws) *O Q N J1 Zc Zk*
Hitchin *p251* 01462 458711
Newcombe, Mrs L M (Straw & Pearce) *K1 D1 K3 D2 G*
Loughborough *p293* 01509 268931
Newcombe, S C (The Smith Partnership) *G H M1 P F1 D1 J1 K1 Zp Zm Zi*
Leicester *p281* 0116 255 6292
Newcombe, Ms S M (Scrivenger Seabrook) *Zr*
St Neots *p392* 01480 214900
Newcombe, T (Royds LLP) *B1 Q*
London EC4 *p74* 020 7583 2222
Newdall, S (Levi Solicitors LLP) *C1 J1 N O Q*
Leeds *p275* 0113 244 9931
Newdick, Ms L (The College of Law Guildford)
Guildford *p459* 01483 460200
Newell, D P (Roland Robinsons & Fentons LLP) *G H K1*
Blackpool *p147* 01253 621432
Newell, D R (The Newspaper Society)
London EC4 *p108* 020 7632 7400
Newell, H A (T S Barkes & Son) *A1 C1 E G K1 L P S1 T1 W Zl*
Moreton-in-Marsh *p319* 01608 650332
Newell, K F (Martin Tolhurst Partnership LLP) *S1 S2*
Ashford *p119* 01233 505555
Newell, K J (James B Bennett & Co) *A1 C1 E J1 L R1 S1 W Zh Zl*
Crawley *p202* 01293 544044
Newell, M (DLA Piper UK LLP)
London EC2 *p24* 0870 011 1111
Newell, P (Napthens LLP) *Q*
Preston *p357* 01772 888444
Newell, P S (Scarborough Borough Council)
Scarborough *p470* 01723 232348
Newey, Ms K J (Gardiners Solicitors) *G H B2*
London W14 *p35* 020 7603 7245
London W6 *p51* 020 8563 9797
Newey, M E (Taylor Wessing)
London EC4 *p86* 020 7300 7000
Newey, R H J (Robert Newey & Co) *T1 T2*
London SE1 *p63* 020 7407 9434
Newey, T J A (Howard Kennedy LLP) *O*
London W1 *p48* 020 7636 1616

Newhall, R E P (Infields) *C1 E S1 W*
Kingston upon Thames *p267* 020 8977 7633 / 8977 1149

Newham, P A (Northampton Borough Council)
Northampton *p467* 01604 837837

Newham, W J L (Hayes & Storr) *W K4*
Wells-next-the-Sea *p425* . . . 01328 710210

Newhouse, D S M (Meadows & Moran) *N C1 Zc*
Romford *p366* 01708 753400

Newick, M (Clifford Chance)
London E14 *p20* 020 7006 1000

Newing, M (Speechly Bircham LLP) *R2 E S2 Zc*
London EC4 *p81* 020 7427 6400

Newman, A (Squire Sanders (UK) LLP)
Leeds *p277* 0113 284 7000

Newman, Miss A C (Davis Gregory Ltd) *N*
Cheltenham *p188* 01242 235202

Newman, Mrs C E (Cambridgeshire County Council) *D1 N X Zm*
Cambridge *p453* 01223 717111

Newman, C F (Edwards Duthie) *E S1 C1 T1 N*
Ilford *p260* 020 8514 9000

Newman, C H (DAC Beachcroft) *C1 J1*
London EC4 *p24* 020 7242 1011

Newman, Miss E L (Guillaumes Solicitors) *K1 K3*
Weybridge *p430* 01932 840111
Weybridge *p430* 01932 840111

Newman, Mrs H (Simmons & Simmons)
London EC2 *p79* 020 7628 2020

Newman, Miss H M (Pritchard Joyce & Hinds) *D1 K1 N O Q Zc*
Beckenham *p129* 020 8658 3922

Newman, I B (Nabarro LLP)
London WC1 *p63* 020 7524 6000

Newman, J (Plexus Law (A Trading Name of Parabis Law LLP)) *Zc Zj Zq E Q O*
London EC3 *p68* 0844 245 4000

Newman, J (Rouse Legal (Formerly Willoughby & Partners)) *Ze F2*
London E14 *p74* 020 7536 4100

Newman, J (Brightstone Law LLP) *F1 S1 E Zb*
Elstree *p218* 020 8731 3080

Newman, Miss J (Warwickshire County Council)
Warwick *p475* 01926 410410

Newman, Miss J E (Simmons & Simmons)
London EC2 *p79* 020 7628 2020

Newman, J H (Bower & Bailey) *S1 S2 E*
Oxford *p343* 01865 311133

Newman, J R (Luton Borough Council)
Luton *p464* 01582 546000

Newman, J R (Dunn & Baker) *K1*
Cullompton *p205* 01884 33818

Newman, Mrs K N (Colemans Solicitors LLP) *K1 D1 V*
Maidenhead *p298* 01628 631051

Newman, M R (Weightmans LLP) *N O Q*
Dartford *p207* 020 7822 1900

Newman, N (Ford & Warren) *J1*
Leeds *p273* 0113 243 6601

Newman, Mrs N M (BWTLaw LLP) *S1 S2 E L K4*
Epsom *p219* 01372 725655

Newman, Miss P A (JNP Legal) *K1 D1 M1 S1 W G H J1 L*
Merthyr Tydfil *p314* 01685 350421

Newman, P M (Patrick Newman & Co) *S1 E W L C1*
Lewes *p283* 01273 479991

Newman, R (Galbraith Branley)
London N12 *p34* 020 8446 8474

Newman, R D (Kitsons LLP) *G M1 K1 D1 J1 P F1 Zl Zt Zd*
Torquay *p413* 01803 202020

Newman, R J (Stephenson Harwood) *E L B1 R2*
London EC2 *p82* 020 7329 4422

Newman, S G (Baxter Caulfield) *C1 T1 B1 Ze I*
Huddersfield *p255* 01484 519519

Newman, Miss S J (Newman Law) *N S1 L K1 J1 B1 W G Zi*
Barnet *p63* 020 8349 2655

Newman, Miss V A (Clarion Solicitors LLP) *K1 D1 K2 D2*
Leeds *p272* 0113 246 0622
Harrogate *p240* 01423 530630

Newnes, A N (Humphrys & Co) *G H K1 Q N*
Wrexham *p443* 01978 313399
Rhyl *p363* 01745 343158

Newnham, J S (Royal Borough of Kingston upon Thames)
Kingston upon Thames *p462*. 020 8546 2121

Newnham, Ms R (Saunders Law Partnership LLP) *G H B2*
London WC2 *p76* 020 7632 4300

Newns, Mrs R (Trowers & Hamlins) *T1 T2*
London EC3 *p88* 020 7423 8000

Newport, Mrs A M (TLT Solicitors) *C1 C2 J1 I Za Zb Zi Ze*
London EC2 *p85* 020 3465 4000

Newport, A P (Purcell Parker) *H G*
Birmingham *p141* 0121 236 9781

Newport, Miss C V (Trethowans LLP) *J1*
Southampton *p387* 023 8032 1000

Newsam, C (MKB Solicitors LLP) *N B1 C1 L O*
Barnsley *p124* 01226 210000

Newsam, S (The Smith Partnership) *G H*
Derby *p209* 01332 225225

Newsham, Miss S J (Teacher Stern LLP) *E S2*
London WC1 *p86* 020 7242 3191

Newsholme, C (Reynolds Porter Chamberlain LLP) *C1 C2*
London E1 *p71* 020 3060 6000

Newsome, T (Radcliffes Le Brasseur) *C1 I T2 M2 Zi*
Westminster *p70* 020 7222 7040

Newsome, T J (Linder Myers Solicitors) *Q O N J1*
Shrewsbury *p379* 0844 984 6002

Newson, B R (Allianz Insurance PLC)
Guildford *p459* 01483 552730

Newson, Ms H (Andrew & Co LLP) *W T2*
Lincoln *p284* 01522 512123

Newson, J M H (QualitySolicitors Hill & Abbott) *N Zr*
Chelmsford *p187* 01245 258892

Newson, S T (Lester Aldridge LLP) *E R1 R2*
London WC2 *p53* 0844 967 0785

Newstead, Miss J A (Hogan Lovells International LLP)
London EC1 *p42* 020 7296 2000

Newth, Ms I S (Mary Ward Legal Centre) *O L V F1 B1*
London WC1 *p110* 020 7831 7079

Newth, J F (Carter Lemon Camerons) *C1 C2 C3 E S1 W R1 K1 Q*
London EC1 *p18* 020 7406 1000

Newton, A (Yorkshire Water Services Ltd)
Bradford *p451* 01274 804159

Newton, A D (Maxwell Hodge Solicitors) *Q K1 N J1 K3 D1*
West Kirby *p428* 0151 625 9154

Newton, Mrs A G M (Carrick District Council)
Truro *p474* 01872 224400

Newton, Miss C (William Sturges & Co) *D1 K1 V*
Westminster *p84* 020 7873 1000

Newton, C C (Charles Newton & Co) *A1 C1 E F1 L S1 T1 W Zc Zl*
Eastwood *p216* 01773 535535

Newton, C E (Neil Myerson LLP) *C1 C2*
Altrincham *p117* 0161 941 4000

Newton, C H (Maxwell Hodge Solicitors) *X N*
Kirkby *p268* 0151 548 7370

Newton, C J (Thomas Flavell & Sons) *S1 S2 E*
Hinckley *p250* 01455 610747

Newton, Mrs C R (Vale Royal Borough Council)
Winsford *p476* 01606 862862

Newton, D (Wakefield Metropolitan District Council)
Wakefield *p474* 01924 306090

Newton, D G (Bailey & Haigh) *S1 L A1 G H N F1 E C1 K1 Zl Zc J1*
Selby *p373* 01757 705191

Newton, G R (Charles Newton & Co) *S1 W T2 Zm K4*
Eastwood *p216* 01773 535535

Newton, Ms J (Children & Families Law Firm) *D1 K1 D2*
London SW9 *p20* 020 7582 6002

Newton, Ms J E (Martins)
Eccles *p216* 0161 707 3660

Newton, J P (Richmond Anderson Goudie) *E S1 W*
Chester-le-Street *p191* 0191 388 7884

Newton, Mrs J R (Parkinson Wright LLP) *S1 E W A1 T1 C1 L*
Worcester *p440* 01905 726789

Newton, J R (North Yorkshire Law)
Whitby *p430* 01947 602131

Newton, Ms K (Tracey Barlow Furniss & Co) *D1 D2 K1*
Retford *p363* 01777 707677

Newton, Ms K (Higgs & Sons)
Brierley Hill *p158* 0845 111 5050

Newton, Mrs K (Kitsons LLP)
Plymouth *p350* 01752 603040

Newton, Ms K J (Rothwell & Evans) *G K1*
Sale *p370* 0161 969 7341

Newton, L (Ashworths Solicitors) *S1 S2*
London SW19 *p8* 0845 370 1000

Newton, Mrs L C (Harvey Ingram LLP) *C1*
Leicester *p280* 0116 254 5454

Newton, Miss L J (Thomas Dunton Solicitors) *N*
Orpington *p342* 01689 822554

Newton, Ms M (Child & Child) *S2 E S1 R2*
London SW1 *p20* 020 7235 8000

Newton, Mrs M A (David W Harris & Co) *K1 D1 D2 K2*
Pontypridd *p352* 01443 486666

Newton, Mrs M J (Barkers) *D1 D2 K1*
Bolton *p148* 01204 370011

Newton, M P (Metcalfe Copeman & Pettefar) *G H*
Peterborough *p347* 01733 865880

Newton, M S (Watts & Leeding) *F1 G H J1 K1 L N S1 W Q*
London SE9 *p90* 020 8850 6366

Newton, P R (BUPA)
London WC1 *p104* 020 7656 2305

Newton, R J (Dairy Crest Group PLC)
Esher *p458* 01372 472285

Newton, S (Donovan Newton Limited)
Nottingham *p336* 0115 985 6600

Newton, S J (Donald Race & Newton) *S2 E W C1 S1 L Zt Zi Ze*
Burnley *p169* 01282 433241

Newton, S K (Redcar and Cleveland Borough Council)
Redcar *p465* 01642 466201

Neyt, G (Beswicks) *O Q J1*
Stoke-on-Trent *p397* 01782 205000

Ng, Mrs H M (Tanburghs O'Brien Lahaise) *S1 S2 G*
Camden *p85* 020 7372 6614

Ng, Ms K (Rawlison Butler LLP)
Horsham *p253* 01403 252492

Ng, Ms K F I (North Tyneside Council)
Newcastle upon Tyne *p466* . 0191 643 5000

Ng, Y (Linklaters LLP)
London EC2 *p54* 020 7456 2000

Ngan, W (Brabners Chaffe Street) *C1 T1 C2*
Liverpool *p286* 0151 600 3000

Nguyen, K (Bournemouth Borough Council)
Bournemouth *p450* 01202 451178

Ni Charthaig, Ms E M (Hayes & Storr) *S1 S2 R1*
King's Lynn *p266* 01553 778900

Nias, P M W (McDermott Will & Emery UK LLP) *T1 T2*
London EC2 *p56* 020 7577 6900

Niblock, A (Tollers LLP)
Milton Keynes *p317* 01908 396230
Northampton *p332* 01604 258558

Nice, Miss A M (Miles Preston & Co) *K1*
London EC4 *p69* 020 7583 0583

Nichol, F J (TV Edwards LLP) *G H*
London EC3 *p85* 020 7790 7000

Nichol, G L (Ison Harrison)
Leeds *p274* 0113 284 5000

Nichol, J (TV Edwards LLP)
London N15 *p85* 020 7790 7000

Nicholaides, M (Mayer Brown International LLP)
London EC2 *p59* 020 3130 3000

Nicholas, Ms A (Gordons LLP)
Leeds *p273* 0113 227 0100

Nicholas, Miss J (Eric Robinson Solicitors) *W T2 Zd K4*
Hythe *p259* 023 8084 4304

Nicholas, K (Nicholas & Co)
London W1 *p63* 020 7323 4450

Nicholas, K M (Nicholas & Partners) *G H N S2 S1 W Zl*
Manchester *p308* 0161 202 4999

Nicholas, Miss L S (Duffield Stunt) *S1 L S2*
Chelmsford *p186* 01245 262351

Nicholas, L S (Caerphilly County Borough Council)
Hengoed *p460* 01443 815588

Nicholas, Miss M (Radcliffes Le Brasseur) *K1*
Westminster *p70* 020 7222 7040

Nicholas, N C K (Nicholas & Co)
London W1 *p63* 020 7323 4450

Nicholas, O (PCB Solicitors LLP) *G H*
Telford *p409* 01952 403000

Nicholas, P L G (Wilmot & Co Solicitors LLP) *E L A1 S1 S2*
Cirencester *p195* 01285 650551

Nicholas, P W (Terry Jones Solicitors & Advocates) *G H*
Shrewsbury *p379* 01743 285888

Nicholas, R W (Roberts Moore Nicholas Jones) *G H Zm*
Birkenhead *p134* 0151 647 0000

Nicholas, S (Tyndallwoods) *K1*
Birmingham *p143* 0121 624 1111

Nicholas, X J (Forsters LLP) *T2 W*
Westminster *p33* 020 7863 8333

Nicholas, Ms Y A (Nicholas & Co)
London W1 *p63* 020 7323 4450

Nicholes, Ms S J (Leigh Day & Co) *Zr*
London EC1 *p52* 020 7650 1200

Nicholl, Miss C S (Charlesworth Nicholl & Co) *D1 K1 Q K3*
Crediton *p203* 01363 774706

Nicholl, J B (George Davies & Evans Limited) *G S1 P M1 D1 H W R1 A1 L*
Cardigan *p181* 01239 612308

Nicholl, Mrs V L (Travers Smith LLP) *T1 T2*
London EC1 *p87* 020 7295 3000

Nicholls, Mrs A H L (Stephens & Scown) *S1 S2 L R1*
St Austell *p391* 01726 74433

Nicholls, C (C Nicholls) *K1 S1 P G M1 H D1 F1 W J1 Zc Zl Zm*
Bodmin *p148* 01208 76969

Nicholls, C E (Nicholls & Sainsbury) *K1 S1 S2 D1 F1 L W V J1 E Zl*
Saltash *p371* 01752 846116

Nicholls, Mrs C L (Dixon Ward) *S1 E S2*
Richmond upon Thames *p364* 020 8940 4051

Nicholls, D C (Harris Cartier LLP) *N O Q*
London WC2 *p39* 020 7405 7100

Nicholls, Miss G G (Henmans LLP) *K3 K1*
Oxford *p343* 01865 781000

Nicholls, G J M (Nicholls & Co) *S1 W N L C1 K1*
Harrogate *p240* 01423 530103

Nicholls, G P (Nicholls Henstock & Stevenson)
Altrincham *p117* 0161 980 6099

Nicholls, Miss H E (Wallace Robinson & Morgan) *K3 K1*
Solihull *p383* 0121 705 7571

Nicholls, H J H (Hegarty LLP) *E Zc*
Peterborough *p347* 01733 346333

Nicholls, Miss J L (Howes Percival LLP) *E S2 L*
Norwich *p334* 01603 762103

Nicholls, J M (Brignalls Balderston Warren) *S1 W T2 E S2 C1 A1 R1*
Stevenage *p394* 01438 359311

Nicholls, M (Lawrences) *G H*
Wellingborough *p424* 01933 442324

Nicholls, M (Michelmores LLP) *C1*
Exeter *p221* 01392 688688

Nicholls, M (J A Kemp & Co)
London WC1 *p48* 020 7405 3292

Nicholls, M A (Mark Nicholls)
Kettering *p265* 01536 502843

Nicholls, P (Brabners Chaffe Street) *E S2 R2*
Manchester *p301* 0161 836 8800

Nicholls, P J (Rhondda Cynon Taff County Borough Council)
Pentre *p468* 01443 424300

Nicholls, S J (Belmores) *Zl G H*
Norwich *p334* 01603 499999

Nicholls, T D (LG Lawyers)
London SE1 *p50* 020 7379 0000

Nicholls, Miss V E (EEF)
London SW1 *p106* 020 7222 7777

Nicholls, W (George Davies Solicitors LLP) *Zw Q N*
Manchester *p303* 0161 236 8992

Nichols Marcy, Miss C A (Nichols Marcy Dawson) *S1*
Walton-on-Thames *p420* . . . 01932 219500

Nichols, C D (Godwins) *S2 E R1 R2 S1 L*
Winchester *p433* 01962 841484

Nichols, M B (CMS Cameron McKenna LLP)
London EC3 *p17* 020 7367 3000

Nichols, P (David Gray Solicitors) *S1 S2 W E*
Newcastle upon Tyne *p324* . 0191 232 9547

Nichols, Mrs P J (Sandom Robinson) *S1*
South Croydon *p383* 020 8651 7020

Nichols, Ms S (David Gist Solicitors) *N*
Bristol *p162* 0117 927 9111

Nichols, S M (Quality Solicitors Clarke & Son) *N Q F1 Zj Zq Zr*
Basingstoke *p127* 01256 320555

Nichols, Mrs T M (Russell-Cooke LLP) *F1*
Kingston upon Thames *p267*. 020 8546 6111

Nicholson, Miss A (Nicholsons) *S1 W K1 Q*
Chorley *p194* 01772 601700

Nicholson, Mrs C (Uttlesford District Council)
Saffron Walden *p470* 01799 510510

Nicholson, D (Tollers LLP)
Northampton *p332* 01604 258558

Nicholson, Mrs D A (Stephens & Son LLP) *K1 K2 K3*
Chatham *p185* 01634 811444

Nicholson, D M (Bailey Nicholson Grayson)
Woodford Green *p439* 020 8418 2900

Nicholson, Ms E A (Fox Williams) *J1*
London EC2 *p33* 020 7628 2000

Nicholson, Mrs E A A (Chattertons Solicitors) *W T1 S1 L*
Boston *p151* 01205 351114

Nicholson, E M (Nicholson & Morgan) *A1 E J1 K1 L M1 N P S1 W Zc Zl*
Ponteland *p351* . . .01661 871012 / 823381

Nicholson, G J (SJ Berwin LLP) *C2*
London EC4 *p75* 020 7111 2222

Nicholson, I H (Iain Nicholson & Co) *C1 Q E W T1 T2 A1 S1 L R1 Zc*
Ponteland *p351* 01661 823863

Nicholson, J (Hughes Fowler Carruthers) *K1*
London WC2 *p43* 020 7421 8383

Nicholson, J A (Barker Gotelee Solicitors) *A1 E S1 S2 M1 C3*
Ipswich *p262* 01473 611211

Nicholson, Ms J A (Avis Management Services Ltd)
Bracknell *p450* 01344 462644

Nicholson, J C (Anthony Gold) *N Zr*
London SE1 *p6* 020 7940 4000

Nicholson, Mrs J M (Knowsley Metropolitan Borough Council) *D1*
Huyton *p461* 0151 443 3593

Nicholson, J P (Mincoffs Solicitors LLP) *C1 C2 E F1 J1*
Newcastle upon Tyne *p325* . 0191 281 6151

Nicholson, Miss K A (Olswang LLP) *C1 C2 I C3 J1 Ze Zl*
London WC1 *p64* 020 7067 3000

Nicholson, Ms K M (London Borough of Lewisham)
London SE6 *p107* 020 8695 6000

Nicholson, Miss L (Eastleys) *T2 W*
Brixham *p166* 01803 853266

Nicholson, Miss L J (East Riding of Yorkshire Council) *G H Zl*
Beverley *p449* 01482 887700

Nicholson, M (Burnley-Jones Bate & Co)
London SW19 *p16* 020 8542 8101

Nicholson, M A (Birmingham City Council Legal & Democratic Services)
Birmingham *p449* 0121 303 2066

Nicholson, M J (Nicholsons Solicitors LLP) *B1 O J1 Q N F1 Ze*
Lowestoft *p294* 01502 532300

Nicholson, Ms M J (Hipkin & Co) *K3 K1 D1 D2 K4 W*
Whitley Bay *p431* 0191 253 3509

Nicholson, M L (North Somerset District Council)
Weston-super-Mare *p476* . . . 01934 888888

Nicholson, P (Milburns Solicitors) *K1 Q N S1 W*
Workington *p440* 01900 67363

Nicholson, P (Russell-Cooke LLP) *S2 E*
London SW15 *p74* 020 8789 9111

Nicholson, R (Michelmores LLP) *O E Zq*
Exeter *p221* 01392 688688

Nicholson, R J (Nicholsons Solicitors LLP) *T1 W*
Lowestoft *p294* 01502 532300

Nicholson, T C (The National Trust)
Swindon *p475* 01793 817400

Nicholson, Ms V K (Kevills) *K1*
Chorley *p194* 01257 265711

Nicholson, Miss Z O (Newman & Bond)
Barnsley *p125* 01226 213434

Nickalls, P (Crutes) *W*
Stockton-on-Tees *p396* 01642 623400

Nickel, E (Ince & Co Services Ltd)
London E1 *p44* 020 7481 0010

Nickels, A J (Brignalls Balderston Warren) *E L S1 S2*
Baldock *p121* 01462 490100

Nickless, Miss K (Telford Magistrates Court)
Telford *p474* 01952 204500

See p634 for the Key to Work Categories

Nickless, R S (Jacobs & Reeves) D1 S2 E G K1 K3 O Q N S1 Zq
Poole p353 01202 731849

Nicklinson, A K (Glovers Solicitors LLP) E
London W1 p36 020 7935 8882

Nickolds, Ms C (Manches LLP) K1 K2
London WC2 p58 020 7404 4433

Nickolls, M L (Berry & Berry) G H B2
Tonbridge p412 01732 355911
Tunbridge Wells p414 01892 526344

Nicks, W A (Hoole & Co) M1 P G K1 Zi
Bristol p163 0117 969 1436

Nickson, Ms D (Stockport Metropolitan Borough Council)
Stockport p472 0161 480 4949

Nickson, Mrs J C (Birdsall & Snowball)
Filey p226 01723 515151
Filey p226 01723 515555

Nickson, J H (Thompsons (formerly Robin/Brian Thompson & Partners)) E W S1 S2
Plymouth p350 01752 675810

Nickson, M P (K J Commons & Co) D1 G H K1 S1 B1 F1
Carlisle p182 01228 822666
Whitehaven p431 01946 66699
Workington p440 01900 604698

Nickson, Ms S C (Squire Sanders (UK) LLP) J1 Zi Zp
Manchester p310 0161 830 5000

Nicol, Ms A G (Edward Fail Bradshaw & Waterson) G H B2
London EC3 p30 020 7790 4032
London EC3 p30 020 7264 2016

Nicol, Miss C J (Dickinson Dees) J1
Newcastle upon Tyne p324 0191 279 9000

Nicol, G F D (Nicol Denvir & Purnell) D1 D2 K1
Cardiff p180 029 2079 6311

Nicol, G K (East Sussex County Council)
Lewes p463 01273 481000

Nicol, Ms J (Doyle Clayton Solicitors Limited) J1 Zp
London EC2 p27 020 7329 9090

Nicol, Ms J (Brighton & Hove Council - Legal Services)
Hove p461 01273 290000

Nicol, Mrs M R (HCB Solicitors) S2 E
Walsall p420 01922 720000

Nicol, Ms T C (Irwin Mitchell LLP) C1 C2
Birmingham p139 0870 150 0100

Nicolaides, M (Mayer Brown International LLP)
London EC2 p59 020 3130 3000

Nicolaou, Ms C (Nicolaou Solicitors) C1 E J1 U2 Zf Zv
Hertford p249 01707 877707

Nicolaou, Ms E (Steeles) R2
Norwich p335 0870 609 0200

Nicolaou, Ms N (B P Collins LLP) Ze J1 Zk Q
Gerrards Cross p229 01753 889995

Nicolet, Mrs L F (Forsters LLP) S1
Westminster p33 020 7863 8333

Nicoll, Miss L (Treasury Solicitors Department)
London WC2 p110 020 7210 3000

Nicoll, Miss P J (Overburys & Raymond Thompson) K1 K3
Norwich p335 01603 610481

Nicoll, R C (Reed Smith LLP) E
London EC2 p71 020 3116 3000

Nicoll, Miss S M (Orange PCS Ltd)
Bristol p452 0870 376 8888

Nicolls, D V (Levenes Solicitors) G
Haringey p53 020 8881 7777 / 8881 6764

Nicolson, S T (Dickinson Dees) C1 C2
Newcastle upon Tyne p324 0191 279 9000

Niebuhr, Mrs H (Darbys Solicitors LLP) N Q J2 Zr
Oxford p343 01865 811700

Nield, Mrs L E (Rowley Dickinson) C1 S2 E L R2 S1 W
Manchester p309 0161 834 4215

Nielson, G A D (Black Rock)
London EC4 p104 020 7743 3000

Nieto, P (Howells LLP) Zm
Sheffield p376 0114 249 6666

Nigh, Miss D (Summers Nigh Law LLP) S1 O B1 J1 Q
Northampton p332 01604 771136

Nightingale, Ms C (Somerfield Stores Ltd)
Bristol p452 0117 935 6135

Nightingale, D S (Southerns) G H
Colne p198 01282 863113

Nightingale, J (Watson Burton LLP) C1 C2
Leeds p278 0845 901 2100

Nightingale, Ms J (HSBC Legal Department) B1 C1 T1
Birmingham p449 0121 455 2740

Nightingale, J A (Citi Financial Europe PLC)
London E14 p469

Nightingale, Ms J C (Lazard & Co Ltd)
London W1 p107 020 7187 2000

Nightingale, Mrs M B (HM Revenue & Customs)
Salford p470 0870 785 8545

Nightingale, P (HM Land Registry - Plymouth)
Plymouth p468 01752 636000 / 636123

Nightingale, S C (Horsey Lightly Fynn) A1 T2 W K4 Zd
Bournemouth p152 01202 551991

Nightingale, Miss S E (Godloves) N
Leeds p273 0113 225 8811

Nightingdale, S (Kennedys)
London EC3 p49 020 7667 9667

Nijjar, Ms B (London Underground Ltd)
London SW1 p107 020 7918 3126

Nilaweera, R H W (Carpenter & Co) S1 E L S2
Wallington p419 020 8669 5145

Nile, R J (Nile Arnall Solicitors) G H
Bristol p164 0117 909 8898

Nilsen, J (Dowse & Co) K1 D1 K3
Hackney p27 020 7254 6205

Niman, G (Niman & Co) S1 E S2 W N
Haringey p63 020 8809 4923

Nimmo, J (Cooper Nimmo) K1
Blackpool p146 01253 626793

Nimmo, M C H (Sims Cook & Teague) K1 G V F1 L B1 Q N J1
Thornbury p411 01454 414342

Niranjanan, Miss R (Anthony Gold) N Zr
London SE1 p6 020 7940 4000

Nisar, F (Boodle Hatfield)
Westminster p14 020 7629 7411

Nisbet, Ms L (TV Edwards LLP)
London EC3 p85 020 7790 7000

Nissen, D E J (Department for Business, Enterprise and Regulatory Reform)
London SW1 p105 020 7215 0105

Niven, B W (Clifton Ingram LLP) B1
Wokingham p437 0118 978 0099

Niven, D M (Penningtons)
London EC2 p66 020 7457 3000

Niven, M S (Brabners Chaffe Street) E R1 R2 S1
Manchester p301 0161 836 8800
Manchester p310 0844 800 0263

Nix, Miss J (Venters Solicitors) K1 D1 K3 D2
London SE5 p89 020 7277 0110

Nixon, Mrs A E (Challinors) L Q Zh
West Bromwich p427 0121 553 3211

Nixon, Ms C S (Taylor Walton LLP) W
Harpenden p239 01582 765111

Nixon, J (Hewison & Nixon) G K1 H S1 F1 J1 W V D1 Zl Zf
Pontefract p351 01977 700705

Nixon, Ms J E C (Overburys & Raymond Thompson) A1 B1 C1 E Q S1
Norwich p335 01603 610481

Nixon, J N V (Brown Beer Nixon Mallon) G H
Redcar p362 01642 490202

Nixon, Mrs K H (Hacking Ashton LLP) S1
Newcastle under Lyme p323 01782 715555

Nixon, M (Forsters LLP) R1 E
Westminster p33 020 7863 8333

Nixon, M P (Downs) J1
Dorking p212 01306 880110

Nixon, Ms P A (Ralph Davis) K1 X Q
Islington p26 020 7253 7200

Nixon, P J M (Westminster City Council)
London SW1 p110 020 7641 6000

Nixon, R (Muckle LLP) E R2 S2 S1
Newcastle upon Tyne p325 0191 211 7777

Nixon, Mrs R J (Dickinson Manser) W
Poole p352 01202 673071

Nixon, R W (Austin Ray) C1 S2 E S1 Zp J1 R2 C2 L F1 A1
Milton Keynes p316 01908 769648

Nixon, S (Enoch Evans LLP) O Q J1
Walsall p420 01922 720333

Niyazi, N (McKenzies) G H
London N9 p57 020 8350 4114

Njindou, C P (Fletcher Dervish) D2 A3 D1 K3 K1
Haringey p33 020 8800 4615

Njoku, Mrs C T (Watford Borough Council)
Watford p475 01923 226400

Nkafu, A J (Quinn Mantion) J1 Zi G W Zp Q
London E14 p70 020 7512 2600

Nkontchou, Mrs A (Addie & Co) C1 S1 W Q O J1 Zq Zp Ze
London WC2 p4 020 7395 3740

Noakes, Ms H (The College of Law)
London WC1 p105 0800 289997

Noakes, Ms H (Hugh James) D1 K1
Cardiff p179 029 2022 4871

Nobbs, C (Pritchard Joyce & Hinds) C1 O Q
Beckenham p129 020 8658 3922

Nobbs, R D (Reynolds Porter Chamberlain LLP)
London E1 p71 020 3060 6000

Nobbs, T S (Rogers & Norton) N O Q Zj Zr
Norwich p335 01603 666001

Noble, Mrs A (BHP Law)
Halifax p238 01422 250650

Noble, B (Rawlison Butler LLP) E R2
Crawley p202 01293 527744

Noble, C J G (Atherton Godfrey) Zr N
Doncaster p211 01302 320621

Noble, D F (Noble) S1 G K1 D1 W M1
Shefford p377 01462 814055

Noble, D P (Cheshire County Council)
Chester p454 01244 602382

Noble, G H (Eldridges) N Q K1 K3 D1 D2
Ryde p369 01983 562241

Noble, Mrs G M (John Welch & Stammers) W K4 T2
Witney p436 01993 703941

Noble, Mrs H M (Berry & Berry) K1 D1 D2
Tonbridge p412 01732 355911
Tunbridge Wells p414 01892 526344

Noble, J (Forsters LLP) E
Westminster p33 020 7863 8333

Noble, Miss K (David Porter & Co)
Hull p257 01482 325863

Noble, M D (National Grid PLC)
Warwick p471 01926 653000

Noble, M H W (MFG Solicitors) A1 B1 C1 E L S1
Bromsgrove p167 01527 831691

Noble, N (Stephenson Harwood)
London EC2 p82 020 7329 4422

Noble, N R (Field Fisher Waterhouse LLP)
London EC3 p31 020 7861 4000

Noble, R T J (Mills & Reeve) A1 T2
Cambridge p175 01223 364422

Noble, Miss S (Boodle Hatfield)
Westminster p14 020 7629 7411

Noblet, Ms C (Squire Sanders (UK) LLP)
London EC2 p81 020 7655 1000

Noblet, M J (Hopkins) C1 S2 E J1
Nottingham p337 0115 910 5555

Noce, Ms A (DWF) N J2
Liverpool p287 0151 907 3000

Nock, K J (Underhill Langley & Wright) P K1 C1 S1 D1 M1 W N E G Zb Zg Zo
Wolverhampton p438 01902 423431

Nock, M (Higgs & Sons) O Q L G H Zl Zk F2 Ze Zq
Brierley Hill p158 0845 111 5050

Nock, T G (Michael Oerton) P W G S1 K1 H L T1 F1 Zl
Barnstaple p125 01271 378686

Nocton, N (Salans) Zl
London EC4 p76 020 7429 6000

Noctor, J (Burnetts) C1 E C2 Zu C3
Carlisle p181 01228 552222
Carlisle p182 01228 552222

Nodder, E J (Bristows) C1 I M1 O Ze Zf Zk C3
London EC4 p15 020 7400 8000

Noel-Smith, Ms K (Forsters LLP) T1 T2 W
Westminster p33 020 7863 8333
Westminster p70 020 7222 7040

Noke, Miss C (AXA UK PLC)
London E22 p103 020 7920 5900

Nokes, J G (Anthony Gold) E S1 W
London SE1 p6 020 7940 4000

Nokes, Mrs S (Veale Wasbrough Vizards) Ze V
Bristol p165 0117 925 2020

Nolan, Miss A (Roebucks) K1 D1
Blackburn p145 01254 274000

Nolan, Mrs A J (Ray Nixon Brown) D1 K1
Leighton Buzzard p282 01525 372247

Nolan, B (Hill Dickinson LLP) Q Zj
Manchester p305 0161 817 7200

Nolan, Ms F (Pini Franco LLP) S2 E
London EC1 p67 020 7566 3140
London EC2 p81 020 7655 1000

Nolan, Miss L V M (Magwells) E
Islington p57 020 7833 2244

Nolan, Miss M (Thompsons (formerly Robin/Brian Thompson & Partners)) N
Nottingham p339 0115 989 7200

Nolan, M J (Winston Solicitors LLP)
Leeds p278 0113 320 5000

Nolan, R C (University of Cambridge) T1 W Zd
Cambridge p453 01223 338600

Nolan, R T (Squire Sanders (UK) LLP) O Q A3 Zb I
Leeds p277 0113 284 7000

Nolan, S A (David Phillips & Partners) B2 G H
Bootle p150 0151 922 5525

Nolte- Conlon, Mrs N M (Warwickshire County Council)
Warwick p475 01926 410410

Noon, A (DLA Piper UK LLP)
Liverpool p287 0870 011 1111

Noon, Ms J A (McGrigors LLP)
London EC4 p56 020 7054 2500

Noon, Ms S J (LG Lawyers)
London SE1 p50 020 7379 0000

Noonan, B J (Johnson McCabe) S1 E L C1 W
Brighton p159 01273 822500

Noonan, J O P (Oldham Marsh Page Flavell) E S1 S2
Melton Mowbray p314 01664 563162

Noonan, L (Rushton Hinchy Solicitors) Zr J1 Q N
St Helens p391 0845 054 0564

Noor, Ms J K (Wolverhampton City Council) K1
Wolverhampton p477 01902 556556
Nottingham p338 0115 958 0584

Noor, M (Taylor Wessing)
London EC4 p86 020 7300 7000

Noor, W I (Acklam Bond Noor) N O Q Zi Zr
Accrington p114 01254 872272

Noorani, A (Noorani Law) C1 J1 L S1 S2 W E
London W1 p63 020 7486 1131

Noor-Khan, Mrs S (Hodge Jones & Allen LLP) G H
London NW1 p41 020 7874 8300

Noormohamed, R (Michelmores LLP) I U1 U2 Zza Ze C3
Exeter p221 01392 688688

Norat, Miss S (EMW) E R2 S2
Milton Keynes p316 0845 070 6000

Norcliffe, J A (Norcliffe & Co) J1 N E C1 G S1 Zl Ze
Huddersfield p256 01484 514907

Norcross Webb, Mrs S (Clarke Willmott) C1 C2
Southampton p385 0845 209 1000 / 0117 305 6000

Norcross, M D (Wrigley Claydon) S1 W S2 E
Oldham p341 0161 624 6811

Nordlinger, D (Skadden Arps Slate Meagher & Flom (UK) LLP)
London E14 p80 020 7519 7000

Nordmann, Mrs B (McGrigors LLP)
London EC4 p56 020 7054 2500

Noreen, Miss A (Wrigleys Solicitors LLP) S1 W
Sheffield p377 0114 267 5588

Norfolk, G (Maclay Murray & Spens LLP) C1
London EC2 p57 020 7002 8500

Norgate, A J (Walter Gray & Co)
Ryde p369 01983 563765

Norgate, Ms C (Mander Hadley & Co) D1 K1
Coventry p200 024 7663 1212

Norgate, D (Crombie Wilkinson) E S1 T2 W S2
Selby p374 01757 708957
York p444 01904 624185

Norman, A J (Pinsent Masons LLP) J1
Birmingham p141 0121 200 1050

Norman, Mrs A S (Butcher & Barlow LLP) S1 S2 W K4
Northwich p333 01606 47523

Norman, D R (Dell Computer Corporation Ltd)
Bracknell p451 01344 860456

Norman, Miss E (Tinsdills) K1 Zo
Hanley p239 01782 262031

Norman, G J (Dollman & Pritchard) W S1 S2 C1
Caterham p183 01883 347823

Norman, G T D (Clifford Chance)
London E14 p20 020 7006 1000

Norman, H S (Black Norman) S1 K1 G C1 H M1 W P F1
Crosby p203 0151 931 2777

Norman, I A (Rushcliffe Borough Council)
West Bridgford p476 0115 981 9911

Norman, I M (Lightfoots LLP) S1 O Q S2 E
Thame p410 01844 212305

Norman, J D (David Phillips & Partners) G H S1 S2
Bootle p150 0151 922 5525

Norman, Ms J M (John Barkers) W K4 T2
Grimsby p234 01472 358686

Norman, Mrs K (KieranClarkeGreen) S2 E S1
Chesterfield p192 01246 211006

Norman, P J (Rawlins Davy PLC) S2 E
Bournemouth p152 01202 558844

Norman, R (DLA Piper UK LLP)
Sheffield p375 0870 011 1111

Norman, R J (Leo Abse & Cohen) M1 N P Zb
Cardiff p179 029 2038 3252 / 2034 5421

Norman, Miss S (Norfolk County Council - Legal Services) N
Norwich p467 Minicom: 0844 800 8011

Norman, Miss S A (Bower & Bailey) Q O N J1 F2 F1 Zr L Zq
Banbury p122 01295 265566
Oxford p343 01865 311133

Norman, T E (Neil Myerson LLP) O Q J1 N B1 L F1 Zi A3 Zc
Altrincham p117 0161 941 4000

Norman, Mrs V L (Maddocks Clarke) N
Altrincham p117 0844 805 5170

Normandale, P T (Inesons) Q O K1 D1 C1 L B1 J1 S1 Zk
Cleckheaton p195 01274 872202

Norman-Thorpe, Miss H S (Buckinghamshire County Council) K1 K2 D1
Aylesbury p448 01296 383653

Normington, A (Pinsent Masons LLP)
London EC2 p67 020 7418 7000

Norrie, Ms A (Plexus Law (A Trading Name of Parabis Law LLP)) Zj Q E Zq
London EC3 p68 0844 245 4000

Norrington, R H (Sackvilles) W S1 K1 E N T2 L Zl
Rainham p359 01708 552804

Norris, A (Donald Race & Newton) C1 S2 E F1 K4 J1 L P S1 W
Burnley p169 01282 433241

Norris, A (Kidd Rapinet) W K4 S1 T2
Maidenhead p298 0845 017 9608

Norris, A J (Geldards LLP) S2 E
Cardiff p178 029 2023 8239

Norris, D (Fulchers) K1 D1 D2 K3
Woking p436 01483 885522

Norris, D (Hogan Lovells International LLP) B1 E S1
London EC1 p42 020 7296 2000

Norris, Ms H (Kimbells LLP) J1
Milton Keynes p317 01908 668555

Norris, Ms J C (Memery Crystal) K1 K2 K3
London WC2 p60 020 7242 5905

Norris, J M (Lupton Fawcett) C1 F1 Zl Zt G B2
Leeds p275 0113 280 2000

Norris, M (Simmons & Simmons)
London EC2 p79 020 7628 2020

Norris, M (The College of Law)
London WC1 p105 0800 289997

Norris, M T (Gibb Ltd)
Reading p469 0118 963 5000

Norris, R H F (Carter Bells LLP) C1 E W C2
Kingston upon Thames p267 020 8939 4000

Norris, R J (DLA Piper UK LLP)
Birmingham p137 0870 011 1111

Norris, R W (Birmingham City Council Legal & Democratic Services)
Birmingham p449 0121 303 2066

Norris, T J (LSG Solicitors) C1 J1 B2 C2 Ze O Zw Zk Zo
London W1 p51 020 7851 0100

Norris, W (Barlow Lyde & Gilbert LLP)
London EC3 p10 020 7247 2277

Norriss, Ms C L (Capsticks Solicitors LLP) J1
London SW19 p18 020 8780 2211

North Lewis, J S (Dickinson Dees) W
Newcastle upon Tyne p324 0191 279 9000

North, C F J (Maxwell Winward LLP) C1 C2 J1
London EC4 p59 020 7651 0000

North, D L (Osborne Clarke) E
London EC2 p65 020 7105 7000

North, G M (Dixon Coles & Goddard) S1 W E
Leicester p279 0116 236 4708

North, J (Radcliffes Le Brasseur)
Westminster p70 020 7222 7040

North, J D (Royds LLP) C1 Ze C2 Zz
London EC4 p74 020 7583 2222

North, L W F (Sparling Benham & Brough) *K1 P M1 G D1*
Colchester *p198* 01206 733733

North, M A (Clarkson Wright & Jakes Ltd) *E C1 S2 R2*
Orpington *p341* 01689 887887

North, P J L (Poole & Co) *A1 C1 E L R1 S1 T1 W*
Crewkerne *p203* 01460 279100

North, R M (Clifford Chance)
London E14 *p20* 020 7006 1000

North, Ms S M (Treasury Solicitors Department)
London WC2 *p110* 020 7210 3000

Northall, A D (Wansbroughs) *K1*
Devizes *p210* 01380 733300

Northam, B F (Kellock & Johnson) *K1 Q N P L G H F1 J1 Zc Zq*
Totnes *p413* 01803 862414

Northcott, M J (Stephens & Scown) *S1 R2 E*
Exeter *p222* 01392 210700

Northey, A W (Sharman Law) *A1 C1 E R1 S1 T2 W*
Ampthill *p118* 01525 750750

Northey, J D (LG Lawyers)
London SE1 *p50* 020 7379 0000

Northover, Ms A E (Forsters LLP) *K1*
Westminster *p33* 020 7863 8333

Northover, B (Veale Wasbrough Vizards) *Zd X C1*
Bristol *p165* 0117 925 2020

Northover, G J (Mowbray Woodwards Solicitors) *S2 G C2 R1 R2 T1 Zc*
Bath *p128* 01225 485700

Northrop, T (Northrop McNaughtan Deller) *Q Zf*
London W9 *p64* 020 7289 7300

Northwood, P (Manches LLP) *O*
Oxford *p343* 01865 722106

Norton, C J (Hogan Lovells International LLP) *E P*
London EC1 *p42* 020 7296 2000

Norton, D (Ince & Co Services Ltd)
London E1 *p44* 020 7481 0010

Norton, D I (Peter Williams & Co) *N*
Swansea *p406* 01792 465597

Norton, Miss E (Russell-Cooke LLP) *W*
London SW15 *p74* 020 8789 9111

Norton, Miss H J L (Gates & Moloney) *K1 W L S1 K3 K4*
Lancing *p270* 01903 766046

Norton, Miss J (Berry Smith LLP) *J1*
Cardiff *p177* 029 2034 5511

Norton, J C (Robin Murray & Co) *G O N L H B2*
Chatham *p185* 01634 832332

Norton, J T (Hadgkiss Hughes & Beale) *S1 W S2*
Birmingham *p138* 0121 449 5050
Birmingham *p139* 0121 707 8484

Norton, Miss L (Boyes Turner) *N Zr*
Reading *p360* 0118 959 7711

Norton, N G (Rogers & Norton) *E C1*
Norwich *p335* 01603 666001

Norton, P A J E (Max Gold Law) *Zq R2 K1*
Hull *p257* 01482 224900

Norton, P E (Paul Norton & Co)
Luton *p295* 01582 494970

Norton, P R (Hansells) *Zd T2 W*
Norwich *p334* 01603 615731

Norton, R W F (Charles Russell LLP) *C1 C2 Zb*
Cheltenham *p187* 01242 221122

Nosek, Miss A T J (ASB Law) *C1 C2*
Crawley *p202* 01293 603600

Nossel, Miss E (Martin Nossel & Co)
Basildon *p126* 01268 289555

Nossel, M I (Martin Nossel & Co) *N K1 D1 J1 V S1 L F1 Q X*
Basildon *p126* 01268 289555

Nosworthy, G E (Cree Godfrey & Wood) *E R2 S1 S2 W K4*
London N2 *p23* 020 8883 9414

Nosworthy, S G (Cree Godfrey & Wood) *S1 Q S2 K1 L K3 J1 N E*
London N2 *p23* 020 8883 9414

Noton, R L (Rollits LLP)
Hull *p258* 01482 323239

Noton, Mrs S J (Swayne Johnson Solicitors) *W T2 A1 L Zd*
Denbigh *p208* 01745 812835

Nott, C R (Hallinan Blackburn Gittings & Nott) *G H*
Westminster *p38* 020 7233 3999

Nottage, Ms V E (Gordon Dadds) *K1 K3*
London W1 *p25* 020 7493 6151

Nottidge, J E (Quality Solicitors Burroughs Day) *N J2*
Bristol *p164* 0117 929 0333

Nottridge, S J (Moss Solicitors LLP) *N J2*
Loughborough *p293* 01509 217770

Nourry, Ms A R M (Clifford Chance)
London E14 *p20* 020 7006 1000

Novak, R J F (Speechly Bircham LLP) *O A3 B2*
London EC4 *p81* 020 7427 6400

Novell, Mrs S A (London Borough of Wandsworth)
London SW18 *p110* 020 8871 6000

Nowell, D R G (Carver Jones) *S1 W K3*
Hereford *p247* 01432 274301

Nowell, M C (Finn Gledhill) *G H N Zl Zt*
Halifax *p238* 01422 330000
Hebden Bridge *p246* 01422 842451

Nowers, G A (Percy Holt & Nowers)
Croydon *p205* 020 8688 3603

Nowinski, R S (Reed Smith LLP) *Za*
London EC2 *p71* 020 3116 3000

Noyce, C D (Lovell Son & Pitfield) *E L S1 S2 W Zl*
Camden *p55* 020 7242 7883

Noyce, R C (Crowdy & Rose) *S1 K1 P M1 G*
Faringdon *p224* 01367 240285

Nugent, Ms A (Bristol City Council)
Bristol *p451* 0117 922 2000

Nugent, Ms C (Trowers & Hamlins)
London EC3 *p88* 020 7423 8000

Nugent, Ms G (Suttons)
London W1 *p84* 020 7935 5279

Nugent, J E (Mayer Brown International LLP) *Ze U2 I*
London EC2 *p59* 020 3130 3000

Nugent, J G (Gisby Harrison) *C1 C2*
Cheshunt *p189* 01707 878300

Nulty, H J (St Helens Law Limited) *N Q L F1 W X*
St Helens *p391* 01744 454433

Nunes de Souza, Miss H (London Borough of Haringey)
London N22 *p106* 020 8489 0000

Nunes, Mrs C V (Crossmans MTA) *S1 E Zl*
Cambridge *p174* 01223 451442

Nunn, Ms A (Sternberg Reed) *N*
Barking *p123* 020 8591 3366

Nunn, A R (A R Nunn) *A1 L S1 W*
Bridgnorth *p157* 01746 768400

Nunn, D P (Simmons & Simmons)
London EC2 *p79* 020 7628 2020

Nunn, G R (Stanley Smith Hill & Co) *S1 C1 W S2*
Carshalton *p183* 020 8669 0044

Nunn, G R (Kerseys) *C1 Ze J1 U2 C2*
Ipswich *p262* 01473 213311

Nunn, Miss K E (Squire Sanders (UK) LLP) *O Q Zc*
London EC2 *p81* 020 7655 1000

Nunn, Mrs L J (Lightfoots LLP) *Q*
Thame *p410* 01844 212305

Nunn, Ms N J (Freeman Johnson)
Spennymoor *p389* 01388 814389

Nunn, Mrs N J (Havering Magistrates' Court)
Romford *p470* 0845 601 3600

Nunn, P T (Simmons & Simmons)
London EC2 *p79* 020 7628 2020

Nunn, S A (Wrigleys Solicitors LLP) *Zd*
Leeds *p278* 0113 244 6100

Nunn, Miss S R (Cozens-Hardy LLP) *D1 D2 K1 V*
Norwich *p334* 01603 625231

Nunney, Ms G G (London Borough of Lewisham)
London SE6 *p107* 020 8695 6000

Nurcombe, Miss S (Banks Kelly) *B1 L O Q N Zq A3*
London EC2 *p9* 020 7248 4231

Nurney, S N (Macfarlanes) *Q*
London EC4 *p56* 020 7831 9222

Nurse, A (Judge & Priestley) *E L R1*
Bromley *p166* 020 8290 0333

Nurse, D C H (Henry Hyams) *F1 J1 L N Q S1 C1*
Leeds *p274* 0113 243 2288

Nurse-Marsh, A R (Barlow Lyde & Gilbert LLP)
Oxford *p342* 01865 336600
London EC3 *p10* 020 7247 2277

Nurse-Marsh, Ms I G (Pinsent Masons LLP) *O Q J1 N B1*
London EC2 *p67* 020 7418 7000

Nutley, Ms N F (Dickinson Dees) *C1*
Newcastle upon Tyne *p324* . 0191 279 9000

Nutley, P (Graham Withers & Co) *B1 E J1 L Zc Zl C1 S2 O Q Zq*
Shrewsbury *p380* 01743 236345

Nutt, Mrs C E (Hewitsons) *W*
Northampton *p332* 01604 233233

Nuttall, Ms A (Keoghs LLP) *N Zj O Q B2*
Bolton *p149* 01204 677000

Nuttall, Ms A (Molesworths Bright Clegg) *N*
Rochdale *p365* 01706 356666

Nuttall, Mrs C J (Sevenoaks District Council)
Sevenoaks *p470* 01732 227000

Nuttall, C L (Gateley LLP) *E S1 R2*
Birmingham *p138* 0121 234 0000

Nuttall, D (HT Legal Limited t/a Harrison Townend & Ormeshers) *E W S1 K4*
Hyde *p259* 0161 368 1559

Nuttall, Mrs D L (Ribble Valley Borough Council)
Clitheroe *p455* 01200 425111

Nuttall, G J (Field Fisher Waterhouse LLP)
London EC3 *p31* 020 7861 4000

Nuttall, M H (Ramsdens Solicitors) *K1 K4 W*
Huddersfield *p256* 01484 821500

Nuttall, Miss L (McGrigors LLP)
London EC4 *p56* 020 7054 2500

Nuttall, S G (Bury & Walkers LLP) *N B1 R1 P L*
Leeds *p272* 0113 244 4227

Nuttall, S P (Jeffrey Green Russell) *C2 C1 U1 U2 I Zf Zw Zza*
London W1 *p46* 020 7339 7000

Nutting, A R (Linder Myers Solicitors) *S2 L E*
Manchester *p307* 0844 984 6400

Nuttman, E (Ford & Warren) *J1*
Leeds *p273* 0113 243 6601

Nwakodo, R (Steptoe & Johnson) *Ze I U2*
London EC2 *p83* 020 7367 8000

Nwoko, Ms L (Ned Nwoko)
Ealing *p63* 020 8997 6733

Nye, M (PCB Solicitors LLP) *K1 Q*
Shrewsbury *p379* 01743 248148

Nyiri, J A (Mills Chody LLP) *S2 S1 E*
Hatch End *p244* 020 8428 2272
Kenton *p265* 020 8909 0400

Nyman, B M (BM Nyman & Co) *Ze Zk Zz I Zf U2*
Haringey *p64* 020 8365 3060

Nyman, L (CKFT)
London NW3 *p17* 020 7431 7262

Nystrom, J S (LG Lawyers)
London SE1 *p50* 020 7379 0000

O

O'Beirne, Miss J (Hogans) *K1 D1 V*
Prescot *p356* 0151 430 7529

O'Beirne, Miss J E (Warrens Boyes & Archer) *W*
Huntingdon *p258* 01480 411331

O'Boyle, Miss C R (Epping Forest District Council)
Epping *p458* 01992 564000

O'Brady, Ms N M (Pattinson & Brewer) *N Q*
London WC1 *p66* 020 7400 5100

O'Brien, A (Brian Ruff Angus & Jewers) *N B1 Q*
Wickford *p431* 01268 761126

O'Brien, Mrs A C (Everett Tomlin Lloyd & Pratt) *K1 S1 W*
Pontypool *p352* 01495 763333

O'Brien, A M (Blackburn & Co) *E G H J1 L S1 S2*
Fleetwood *p226* 01253 872238

O'Brien, B (Breeze & Wyles Solicitors LLP)
Bishop's Stortford *p144* . . . 01279 715333

O'Brien, B R (Lightfoot O'Brien Westcott) *K1 K3*
London W1 *p54* 01394 386336
Woodbridge *p438* 01394 386336

O'Brien, D (Penningtons)
London EC2 *p66* 020 7457 3000

O'Brien, D T (Solomon Taylor & Shaw) *E S1 L S2*
London NW3 *p80* 020 7431 1912

O'Brien, G (Gordon O'Brien) *D1 F1 J1 K1 L N Q S1 V W*
Huyton *p258* 0151 489 4899

O'Brien, H J (Thomas Simon) *W E S1*
Cardiff *p181* 029 2055 7200

O'Brien, Miss J (Reed Smith LLP) *C1 U2*
London EC2 *p71* 020 3116 3000

O'Brien, Ms J L (Leo Abse & Cohen) *J1 L N O P Q Zj*
Cardiff *p179* . . 029 2038 3252 / 2034 5421

O'Brien, J R (Rubin Lewis O'Brien) *B1 E S1 C1 W L*
Cwmbran *p206* 01633 867000

O'Brien, Ms J S (Cunningtons)
Braintree *p155* 01376 326868

O'Brien, K (John Collins & Partners LLP) *C1*
Swansea *p405* 01792 773773

O'Brien, Mrs K (Pardoes) *K1 K2 A3*
Taunton *p408* 01823 446200

O'Brien, Mrs K L (Solomon Taylor & Shaw) *S2 S1 C1*
London NW3 *p80* 020 7431 1912

O'Brien, Ms M (Platt Halpern) *D1 K1*
Manchester *p308* 0161 224 2555

O'Brien, Miss M (SGH Martineau LLP) *O N*
Birmingham *p142* 0870 763 2000

O'Brien, Miss M F (Swiss Re Life & Health Ltd)
London EC3 *p109* 020 7933 3000

O'Brien, Miss N (Needham Poulier & Partners) *G H Zm*
London N17 *p63* 020 8808 6622

O'Brien, P (W Parry & Co) *Q N B1 K1 O*
Swansea *p405* 01792 470037

O'Brien, P A (Cyril Morris Arkwright) *S1 E*
Bolton *p148* 01204 535261

O'Brien, P A (J Esner & Co) *Zi*
Bolton *p149* 01204 522562

O'Brien, P A (Thomas Simon) *E S1 W*
Cardiff *p181* 029 2055 7200

O'Brien, P J (Hill Dickinson LLP) *E S2 R2 S1 L*
London EC3 *p41* 020 7283 9033

O'Brien, Ms P M (Webster O'Brien LLP)
Stockport *p396* 0161 283 3750

O'Brien, S (Sacker & Partners LLP) *Zo*
London EC2 *p76* 020 7329 6699

O'Brien, Miss S (Pitmans LLP) *O Q*
Reading *p361* 0118 958 0224

O'Brien, Mrs S E (Charles Crookes & Jones) *K1*
Caerphilly *p172* 029 2086 0628

O'Brien, Miss S E (Norcross Lees & Riches) *G H N*
Oldham *p341* 0161 624 6034

O'Brien, S J (Henderson Global Investors)
London EC2 *p106* 020 7818 1818

O'Brien, S R (DLA Piper UK LLP) *B1 E C1 I Zb*
London EC2 *p24* 0870 011 1111

O'Brien-Quinn, Mrs H (FBC Manby Bowdler LLP) *L O Q*
Telford *p409* 01952 292129

O'Bryen, Miss S A (Stefanie O'Bryen Solicitor) *K1 K2 W K3 T2*
Watlington *p424* 01491 614700

O'Byrne, E (Russell-Cooke LLP) *J1*
London SW15 *p74* 020 8789 9111

O'Byrne, R (Gateley LLP) *R2 Zh*
Birmingham *p138* 0121 234 0000

O'Byrne, Mrs S (Wace Morgan) *K1 D1 K4*
Shrewsbury *p379* 01743 280100

O'Callaghan, A M (David W Harris & Co)
Pontypridd *p352* 01443 486666

O'Callaghan, Miss E (British American Tobacco)
London WC2 *p104* 020 7845 1000

O'Callaghan, Miss H M (Taylor Walton LLP) *E S2*
Luton *p295* 01582 731161

O'Callaghan, J (Ronald Fletcher Baker LLP) *D1 K1 N W*
London EC1 *p73* 020 7613 1402

O'Callaghan, J K (Callaghans) *E S1 L T1 R1 C1*
Farnham *p224* 01252 723477

O'Callaghan, M P (Cogent Law)
Croydon *p204* 0844 245 4452

O'Callaghan, N D (Machins Solicitors LLP) *O Q B1 L*
Luton *p295* 01582 514000

O'Callaghan, P J (O'Callaghan & Co) *P K1 M1 N S1 J1 L G Zi Zk Zl*
London WC1 *p64* 020 7831 3455

O'Callaghan, T C (Arnold Fooks Chadwick LLP) *C1 Ze Zza U2 C2*
London W1 *p7* 020 7499 3007

O'Cleirigh, F R (Bermans LLP) *B1 C1 E Zb Zl R2 W F1 L*
Liverpool *p286* 0151 224 0500

O'Connell, Ms A (Steel & Shamash) *Zm J1 L*
Lambeth *p82* 020 7803 3999

O'Connell, Mrs A M (West Yorkshire Passenger Transport Executive) *Zq Zr*
Leeds *p463* 0113 251 7436

O'Connell, B J N (Stallard March & Edwards) *N*
Worcester *p440* 01905 723561

O'Connell, C G (Nottingham City Council (City Sec Dept))
Nottingham *p467* 0115 915 5555

O'Connell, C P (Barlow Lyde & Gilbert LLP) *Q O Zj*
London EC3 *p10* 020 7247 2277

O'Connell, D G (Kerman & Co LLP) *C1 C2 J1*
London WC2 *p49* 020 7539 7272

O'Connell, J R (Jeffrey Green Russell) *C1 J1*
London W1 *p46* 020 7339 7000

O'Connell, J V (Howells) *S1 E W B1 L Zm X T1 T2*
Cardiff *p178* 029 2040 4020

O'Connell, L (CMS Cameron McKenna LLP)
London EC3 *p17* 020 7367 3000

O'Connell, Ms R A (Just Employment) *J1 N Zp C1 T2 J2*
Guildford *p236* 01483 303636

O'Conner, C (Prince Evans)
Ealing *p69* 020 8567 3477

O'Connor, A (McGrigors LLP) *E*
London EC4 *p56* 020 7054 2500

O'Connor, B S (BS O'Connor & Co) *E N S1 S2 W K1 K2 L O*
Romford *p366* 01708 700042

O'Connor, B T K (Farleys Solicitors LLP) *Q T2 W O A3*
Blackburn *p145* 01254 367856

O'Connor, D (Grant Saw Solicitors LLP)
Greenwich *p36* 020 8858 6971

O'Connor, Ms D E A (Hadgkiss Hughes & Beale) *S1 S2 W K4*
Birmingham *p138* 0121 449 5050
Birmingham *p139* 0121 707 8484

O'Connor, Mrs E (Boyes Turner) *J1*
Reading *p360* 0118 959 7711

O'Connor, Miss E A (Wyre Borough Council)
Poulton-le-Fylde *p469* 01253 891000

O'Connor, Ms G J (Wandsworth & Merton Law Centre Ltd)
London SW17 *p110* 020 8767 2777

O'Connor, Miss G M (Kent County Council)
Canterbury *p453* 01227 767020
Maidstone *p464* 01622 694320

O'Connor, Ms H P (SJ Berwin LLP)
London EC4 *p75* 020 7111 2222

O'Connor, J (Marshall Hatchick)
Woodbridge *p439* 01394 388411

O'Connor, J B (Kitsons LLP) *S2 E S1*
Exeter *p221* 01392 455555

O'Connor, J B (John O'Connor Solicitors) *S1 K1 E F1 M1 W P C1 T1 L Zl*
Nottingham *p338* 0115 958 6848

O'Connor, J C (Dewes LLP) *C1 E L R1 S1 T1*
Tamworth *p407* 01827 58391

O'Connor, J K (Pothecary Witham Weld) *E S1 L*
Westminster *p69* 020 7821 8211

O'Connor, J M (The Compass Group)
Chertsey *p454* 01932 573000

O'Connor, K (Jefferies Essex LLP) *D1 D2*
Westcliff-on-Sea *p428* 01702 332311

O'Connor, L (Birnberg Peirce & Partners) *Zi*
Camden *p13* 020 7911 0166

O'Connor, Ms M (London Borough of Haringey)
London N22 *p106* 020 8489 0000

O'Connor, Ms M (Thompsons (formerly Robin/Brian Thompson & Partners)) *J1*
London SW19 *p87* 020 8947 4163

O'Connor, M G (Addleshaw Goddard)
Manchester *p300* 0161 934 6000

O'Connor, Ms N (Russell-Cooke LLP) *G*
London SW15 *p74* 020 8789 9111

O'Connor, R G (Furley Page LLP) *J1 J2 Zp*
Canterbury *p176* 01227 763939

O'Connor, S (Harris Cartier LLP) *Zb Zc S1 T1 C1 E S2*
Slough *p382* 01753 810710

O'Connor, S (Sean O'Connor) *C1 S1*
Tonbridge *p412* 01732 365378

O'Connor, S (Talbot & Co) *O Q N J1 F1 K1 D1*
Burton-on-Trent *p170* 01283 564716

O'Conor, J G T (Allen & Overy LLP)
London E1 *p5* 020 3088 0000

O'Conor, M J (Bird & Bird LLP) *I C1*
London EC4 *p13* 020 7415 6000
London EC2 *p24* 0870 011 1111

O'Dea, Miss C M (Heppenstalls) *W S1 T2 L E*
Lymington *p296* 01590 689500

O'Donnell, B (Hutcheson Forrest)
Bath *p127* 01225 312311

O'Donnell, Miss C (Janes) *G H B2*
London SW1 *p46* 020 7930 5100

O'Donnell, D (Thomson Snell & Passmore) *K1 D1 K3*
Tunbridge Wells *p415* 01892 510000

See p634 for the Key to Work Categories

O'Donnell, J A (Harold Stock & Co) *S1 S2 C1 O Q*
Ashton-under-Lyne *p120*. . .01457 835597 / 835034

O'Donnell, J J (O'Donnells) *Zm*
Preston *p357* 01772 881000

O'Donnell, K F (Wykes O'Donnell Williams) *G M1 K1 J1 F1 S1 D1 N W H Q V*
Ilkeston *p261* 0115 932 8776

O'Donnell, K W (Winterbotham Smith Penley LLP) *S1*
Dursley *p214* 01453 541940

O'Donnell, M D (Watson Farley & Williams)
London EC2 *p90*. 020 7814 8000

O'Donnell, P S (Brown Barron) *S1 N K1 Zl S2 K3 Q O W P J1 J2*
Barrow-in-Furness *p125* . . . 01229 828814

O'Donnell, R (Ward Hadaway) *N Zr*
Newcastle upon Tyne *p327* . 0191 204 4000

O'Donnell, T J P (Sharpe & Co)
Ashford *p119* 01784 247376

O'Donoghue, Miss C A (Harry Boodhoo & Co) *D1 F1 G H K1 W*
Withington *p436* 0161 445 0588

O'Donoghue, G T (EMW) *C1 C2 Zb*
Milton Keynes *p316* 0845 070 6000

O'Donogue, A (Tolhurst Fisher LLP)
Southend-on-Sea *p387* . . . 01702 352511

O'Donovan, Ms F (David Durn & Co) *N O Q J1 L*
Ruislip *p368* 01895 612400

O'Donovan, Mrs M E B (Bell Lamb & Joynson) *K1 K3 K4 D1 Q N S1 W B1*
Liverpool *p286*. 0844 412 4348
Tarporley *p408*. 01829 751459

O'Donovan, R (Watson Burton LLP)
Newcastle upon Tyne *p327* . 0845 901 2100

O'Donovan, R V (Radcliffes Le Brasseur) *C1 C2 J1 O*
Westminster *p70*. 020 7222 7040

O'Donovon, R (Watson Burton LLP)
London EC3 *p90*. 0845 901 2100

O'Dowd, C G (Rotherham Magistrates Court)
Rotherham *p470*. 01709 839339

O'Dowd, R (Carpenter & Co) *W K4 T2*
Wallington *p419* 020 8669 5145

O'Dowd-Booth, J A (Tanner & Taylor LLP) *M1 G H K1 P N S1 L F1 W*
Farnborough *p224*. 01252 549555

O'Driscoll, B D (Nexus Solicitors) *E S1 A1 L*
Manchester *p308* 0161 819 4900

O'Driscoll, N (The Smith Partnership) *G H*
Burton-on-Trent *p170* 01283 536471

O'Dwyer, D S (Memery Crystal) *E S2*
London WC2 *p60* 020 7242 5905

O'Dwyer, Ms J M (Metropolitan Police Directorate of Legal Services)
London SW1 *p108*. 020 7230 7210

O'dwyer, Ms L (Russell Jones & Walker)
London WC2 *p74* 020 7657 1555

O'Dwyer, Ms S (Allen Barfields) *K3 D1 K1 K2*
West Wickham *p428*. 020 8654 2706

O'Dwyer, Ms T (Boyes Turner) *K1 K2*
Reading *p360* 0118 959 7711

O'Farrell, Miss L M (Gordon Dadds) *S1 S2*
London W1 *p25* 020 7493 6151

O'Flinn, J P (Mundays LLP) *O Ze Zw Zc Zt Zl M3*
Cobham *p196* 01932 590500

O'Flynn, P (Daltons Solicitors) *S2 E S1 L J1*
Petersfield *p348* 01730 262816

O'Garra, M J (O'Garra's) *B2 G H*
Leeds *p276* 0113 247 1477

O'Gorman, Ms F M (Thompsons (formerly Robin/Brian Thompson & Partners)) *J1 S1 Zp N*
Plymouth *p350*. 01752 675810

O'Gorman, K C (O'Gorman & Co) *G H Q S1 M3*
Warwick *p422* 01926 409900

O'Gorman, T (Tyndallwoods) *Zg Q Zl*
Birmingham *p143* 0121 624 1111

O'Grady, Ms C (Gill Turner Tucker) *K1 D1*
Maidstone *p299* 01622 759051

O'Grady, W (Thomas Magnay & Co) *D1 K1 K3 N*
Gateshead *p229*. 0191 477 3333

O'Hagan, A R (Brittons) *C1 K2 E S2 K4 S1 W Q O N Zf K3 F2 Zq J2 K1 B1 A2 J1 Zw Zk D1*
Beaconsfield *p128* 01494 730722

O'Hagan, Miss B (Churchers) *G H*
Portsmouth *p354*. 023 9286 2424

O'Hagan, P (Horwich Farrelly) *G H K1 M1*
Manchester *p305* 0161 834 3585

O'Hagan, R (Bathurst Brown Downie & Airey LLP) *N Q O Zf Zw B1 J1*
Twickenham *p416* 020 8892 1537

O'Haire, M J (Osborne Clarke) *E*
Bristol *p164* 0117 917 3000

O'Halloran, M (stevensdrake) *C1 I U2 C3*
Crawley *p202* 01293 596900

O'Halloran, R D (Hunters) *N Q O Zq Zr*
London WC2 *p44* 020 7412 0050

O'Hanlon, Ms M (DLA Piper UK LLP) *E R2 S2 Zu*
Liverpool *p287*. 0870 011 1111

O'Hanlon, S P (BBC)
London W12 *p103*. 020 8752 5734

O'Hara, G T (The Wilkes Partnership LLP) *C1 C2 Zb*
Birmingham *p143* 0121 233 4333

O'Hara, Ms H M (Denison Till) *B1 C1 O*
York *p444* 01904 611411

O'Hara, K J (O'Hara Solicitors)
Waterlooville *p423* 023 9225 9822

O'Hara, Ms L C (HBOS PLC) *J1*
Halifax *p460* 0870 600 5000
Manchester *p308* 0161 909 3000

O'Hara, Miss M E A (WGS Solicitors) *A3 B1 Zc J1 O*
Westminster *p90*. 020 7723 1656

O'Hara, Ms M G (Hewitsons) *J1*
Northampton *p332*. 01604 233233

O'Hara, N T (Thursfields) *K1 N Q S1 S2*
Stourport-on-Severn *p399* . . 01299 827517

O'Hara, R (John Pickering & Partners LLP)
Halifax *p238* 0808 144 0959

O'Hara, Mrs S (Forster Dean Ltd) *N*
Runcorn *p369* 01928 590999

O'Hara, S A (Cookson Group PLC)
London EC4 *p105* 020 7822 0000

O'Hare, Mrs E C (Keoghs and Nicholls, Lindsell & Harris) *L*
Altrincham *p116* 0161 928 9321

O'Hare, P (Kemp Little LLP) *C1 U1 I F2 Ze Zza U2 F1*
London EC2 *p48*. 020 7600 8080

O'Hare, P (The Paul Rooney Partnership)
Liverpool *p290*. 0151 227 2851

O'Hare, R (Ashurst LLP)
London EC2 *p7* 020 7638 1111

O'Hare, S J A (South Tyneside Magistrates Court)
South Shields *p471* 0191 455 8800

O'Hare, Mrs T A (Theresa O'Hare Solicitor) *S1 S2 W L V*
Wimborne *p433* 01202 840153

O'Higgins, Ms M (Silverman Sherliker LLP)
London EC2 *p78*. 020 7749 2700

O'Higgins, Ms N G (LG Lawyers)
London SE1 *p50*. 020 7379 0000

O'Hora, Ms J (Levenes Solicitors) *N Q*
Birmingham *p140* 0121 212 0000
Worcester *p440* 01905 613404

O'Kane, Miss F T (Bond Pearce LLP) *A1 E L R1*
Bristol *p161* 0845 415 0000

O'Kane, M C (Peters & Peters) *B2 C3 G*
London EC4 *p67*. 020 7629 7991

O'Kane, M P (Sandersons) *C1 E J1 L M1 R1 S1*
Hull *p258* 01482 324662

O'Keefe, K J (County of Herefordshire District Council)
Hereford *p460* 01432 260266

O'Keefe, K J (Herefordshire Council)
Hereford *p460* 01432 260000

O'Keeffe, A P (Simmons & Simmons)
London EC2 *p79*. 020 7628 2020

O'Keeffe, D (Russell-Cooke LLP) *N Zr*
London SW15 *p74*. 020 8789 9111

O'Keeffe, E A (Lester Aldridge LLP) *E S1 C1 B1 L W R1 A1 Zc*
London WC2 *p53* 0844 967 0785

O'Keeffe, E A (Memery Crystal) *E S1 S2 R1 R2 X*
London WC2 *p60* 020 7242 5905

O'Keeffe, J (Ince & Co Services Ltd)
London E1 *p44* 020 7481 0010

O'Keeffe, J A T (O'Keeffe Solicitors) *G H B2*
Brent *p64* 020 7644 8800

O'Keeffe, Miss M A (O'Keeffe & Co) *S1 W E L*
Woking *p437*. 01483 740734

O'Leary, B A (Wesley Gryk) *Zi Zg*
Lambeth *p37*. 020 7401 6887

O'Leary, Ms H (Jacklyn Dawson) *K1*
Monmouth *p318* 01600 716660

O'Leary, J (E Rex Makin & Co)
Liverpool *p289*. 0151 709 4491

O'Leary, Miss J C (Hay & Kilner) *N Q K1*
Newcastle upon Tyne *p325* . 0191 232 8345

O'Leary, Dr L (Armitage Sykes LLP) *J1*
Huddersfield *p255* 01484 538121

O'Leary, Ms S (Dobsons) *G H*
Orpington *p341* 01689 886300

O'Loughlin, A B P (TWM Solicitors LLP) *W T2*
Guildford *p237*. 01483 752700

O'Loughlin, C N (Ward Hadaway) *M2 O Q Zb*
Newcastle upon Tyne *p327* . 0191 204 4000

O'Loughlin, P H (Addleshaw Goddard)
Leeds *p271* 0113 209 2000
Manchester *p300* 0161 934 6000

O'Loughlin, S P (Hodge Jones & Allen LLP) *N Zg*
London NW1 *p41* 020 7874 8300

O'Mahoney, Ms C (Fosters Law Limited) *S1 A3 S2 E K3 J1 K1 K2 Zh*
Herne Bay *p248* 01227 283634

O'Mahony, A J (Brabners Chaffe Street) *C1 C2*
Liverpool *p286*. 0151 600 3000

O'Mahony, C (Simon Crosfield & Co)
Ripon *p365* 01765 692277

O'Mahony, D (HSBC Insurance (UK) Ltd)
Brentwood *p448* 01277 842174

O'Mahony, F J F (Bryan O'Connor & Co)
Southwark *p64*. 020 7407 2643

O'Mahony, Mrs M (Browne Jacobson LLP) *E*
Nottingham *p336*. 0115 976 6000

O'Mahony, Ms S (Michael Simkins LLP) *C1 C2 J1*
London WC1 *p79* 020 7874 5600

O'Malley, Ms C L (Farrells Solicitors) *S1 Ze*
Bristol *p162* 0117 944 4664

O'Malley, Ms C L (Cooke Painter Limited) *S1 S2*
Bristol *p162* 01275 835569

O'Malley, Ms L (Prettys) *N*
Ipswich *p262*. 01473 232121

O'Malley, S P J (Challinors) *G H*
West Bromwich *p427* 0121 553 3211

O'Maoileoin, M B (Moorhead James LLP) *B1 O Q L A3*
London EC4 *p61*. 020 7831 8888

O'Maoileoin, T (Davenport Lyons) *Zl*
London W1 *p25* 020 7468 2600

O'Mara, Ms K (Lansbury Worthington) *G H B2*
London W6 *p51* 020 8563 9797

O'May, N D (Bindmans LLP) *G*
London WC1 *p12*. 020 7833 4433

O'Meara, Mrs A M (Squire Sanders (UK) LLP) *R2 S2 E P*
Birmingham *p142* 0121 222 3000

O'Meara, Ms C M (Solihull Magistrates Court)
Solihull *p471*. 0121 705 8101

O'Meara, J R (Blake Lapthorn) *C1 C2*
Portsmouth *p354*. 023 9222 1122

O'Neil, D A (Trowers & Hamlins) *C1 E*
London EC3 *p88*. 020 7423 8000

O'Neil, S (Crutes) *N O Q J1 F1*
Carlisle *p182*. 01228 525195

O'Neil, S (Coley & Tilley) *N*
Birmingham *p136* 0121 643 5531

O'Neil, V H (Town & Country Lawyers) *S1 W E L A1 Zh Zc*
Cheltenham *p188* 01242 587900

O'Neil, W (Rosenblatt)
London EC4 *p73*. 020 7955 0880

O'Neill, D (Ashurst LLP)
London EC2 *p7* 020 7638 1111

O'Neill, F (The BOC Group PLC)
Guildford *p476*. 01483 579857

O'Neill, F (Winston Solicitors LLP) *N Zr*
Leeds *p278* 0113 320 5000

O'Neill, G J (Squire Sanders (UK) LLP)
London EC2 *p81*. 020 7655 1000

O'Neill, G N D (Clifford Chance)
London E14 *p20*. 020 7006 1000

O'Neill, J (James O'Neill) *S1 W S2 L*
Morden *p318* 020 8648 1631

O'Neill, Mrs J (Birchall Blackburn LLP) *S1 W S2*
Preston *p356* 01772 744744

O'Neill, Miss J C (J Keith Park & Co) *N K1 K3 W*
St Helens *p391* 01744 636000

O'Neill, J M (John O'Neill & Co) *S1 C1 S2 E*
Gosforth *p232* 0191 246 4000

O'Neill, K J (Andrews McQueen) *G K1 H Q S1 N*
Bournemouth *p151*. 01202 290628

O'Neill, K M J (O'Neill Solicitors) *D1 G H K1 Q B1*
Newcastle upon Tyne *p326* . 0191 232 9008

O'Neill, L (AWB Charlesworth LLP) *W T2 K4*
Keighley *p263* 01535 613678

O'Neill, M B (Allen & Overy LLP)
London E1 *p5* 020 3088 0000

O'Neill, N J (The Specter Partnership) *Q N L P G H Zd Zh*
Birkenhead *p135*. 0151 647 3000

O'Neill, Ms P (Ashurst LLP)
London EC2 *p7* 020 7638 1111

O'Neill, T (Clifford Chance)
London E14 *p20*. 020 7006 1000

O'Neill, T P (Blackhurst Swainson Goodier LLP) *S1*
Lancaster *p269* 01524 32471

O'Neill, Miss V L (HSBC Insurance (UK) Ltd)
Brentwood *p448* 01277 842174

O'Neill, W (Linder Myers Solicitors) *C1 F1 J1 L N P R1 Zv*
Manchester *p307* 0844 984 6400

O'Reilly, Ms C L (Squire Sanders (UK) LLP)
Manchester *p310* 0161 830 5000

O'Reilly, Miss J (PCB Solicitors LLP) *G H K1 D1*
Telford *p409* 01952 403000

O'Reilly, J K (Treasury Solicitors Department)
London WC2 *p110*. 020 7210 3000

O'Reilly, Miss L (Fishburns) *Zc Zj O Q Zq*
London EC3 *p32*. 020 7280 8888

O'Reilly, M (Bates Wells & Braithwaite London LLP) *Zd C1*
London EC4 *p11*. 020 7551 7777

O'Reilly, Miss M (Salford City Council)
Swinton *p473* 0161 794 4711

O'Reilly, Ms P (Kennedys)
Chelmsford *p186*. 0845 838 4800

O'Reilly, S (Russell-Cooke LLP) *Zd*
London SW15 *p74*. 020 8789 9111

O'Reilly, Ms S L (Lewis Silkin LLP) *J1*
London EC4 *p53*. 020 7074 8000

O'Riordan, Miss C L (Spratt Endicott) *C1 Ze*
Banbury *p122* 01295 204000

O'Riordan, J M (O'Riordan & Co) *S1 K1 G M1 P R1 H C1 L*
Chorley *p194* 01257 262837

O'Rourke, G (New Forest District Council)
Lyndhurst *p464* 023 8028 5000

O'Rourke, K (Howe & Co)
Ealing *p43*. 020 8840 4688

O'Rourke, Miss K (Wills Group Ltd)
London EC3 *p110* 020 7488 8111

O'Rourke, Ms P L (Ward & Rider Limited) *K3 K1*
Coventry *p201*. 024 7655 5400

O'Ryan, J I (Birmingham City Council Legal & Democratic Services)
Birmingham *p449* 0121 303 2066

O'Shea, Miss G A (British Waterways Board)
Watford *p475* 01923 226422

O'Shea, J (IMI PLC)
Birmingham *p450* 0121 717 3700

O'Shea, J (Greenwoods)
London EC3 *p37*. 020 7220 7818

O'Shea, Ms J (Pinsent Masons LLP) *C2 Zb*
London EC2 *p67*. 020 7418 7000

O'Shea, J F (Kidd Rapinet) *W K4 N Q S1 S2*
Aylesbury *p121* 0845 017 9616

O'Shea, L T J (Astle Paterson Ltd) *K1 Q L*
Burton-on-Trent *p170* 01283 531366

O'Shea, Miss M C (Leeds City Council)
Leeds *p462* 0113 224 3513

O'Shea, M D (Addleshaw Goddard) *B1 Zb*
Manchester *p300* 0161 934 6000

O'Shea, M N (Rawlison Butler LLP) *C1 I C3 M1 U2 Ze*
Crawley *p202* 01293 527744

O'Shea, M P (CVS Solicitors) *E S1 W*
London W1 *p17* 020 7493 2903

O'Sullivan, Miss A (Bhatia Best) *K1 D1*
Nottingham *p336*. 0115 950 3231

O'Sullivan, A (Gates and Partners)
London EC3 *p35*. 020 7220 5950

O'Sullivan, Ms A M (Turbervilles) *W*
Uxbridge *p417*. 01895 201700
Uxbridge *p417*. 01895 201700

O'Sullivan, B (Byrne & Partners)
London EC4 *p16*. 020 7842 1616

O'Sullivan, D S (Mapletoft & Co) *N W E K1 S1 Q O L C1 F1 Zv Zj*
London SW15 *p58*. 020 8785 2414

O'Sullivan, Miss E M (Bournemouth Borough Council)
Bournemouth *p450*. 01202 451178

O'Sullivan, Ms F M (Challinors) *D1 K1 V K2 K3*
Birmingham *p136* 0121 212 9393

O'Sullivan, Ms J (Hill Dickinson LLP)
Manchester *p305* 0161 817 7200

O'Sullivan, Ms K A (Nelsons) *N*
Derby *p209* 01332 372372

O'Sullivan, K M (Levenes Solicitors) *N J2 Zg*
Haringey *p53* . . .020 8881 7777 / 8881 6764

O'Sullivan, K S (Hepburns) *S1 S2 C1 E C2*
Oxted *p344* 01883 723712

O'Sullivan, M J (Avon & Bristol Law Centre) *L J1 V Zi Zo*
Bristol *p451* 0117 924 8662

O'Sullivan, N (Cartwright King) *G H*
Nottingham *p336*. 0115 958 7444
Nottingham *p338*. 0115 958 6262

O'Sullivan, N (JMD Law Limited) *W K4*
Cardiff *p179* 029 2045 6780

O'Sullivan, Mrs O (Maxwell Winward LLP) *E L R2 S2*
London EC4 *p59*. 020 7651 0000

O'Sullivan, Ms S (Mogers)
Bath *p127* 01225 750000

O'Sullivan, T D J (Crown Prosecution Service Dorset)
Bournemouth *p450*. 01202 498700

O'Sullivan, T P (Owen & O'Sullivan) *B2 D1 J1 K1 L N O Q S1 S2 W*
Ystrad Mynach *p446*. 01443 862263

O'Sullivan, T P (Vickers & Co) *G H*
Ealing *p89*. . . .020 8579 2559 / 8840 3999

O'Toole, I W (Squire Sanders (UK) LLP)
Leeds *p277* 0113 284 7000

O'Toole, J (John Fowlers LLP Solicitors) *G H L Q*
Colchester *p197* 01206 576151

O'Toole, M J (Bana Vaid & Associates) *S1 S2 K4*
Uxbridge *p417*. 01895 272481

O'Toole, Mrs M S A (Nigel S Pullen) *Q N S1 K1 W B1 E L F1 J1 Zl*
Perranporth *p346* 01872 571046
Truro *p414*. . . . .01872 274404 / 276456
Truro *p414*. . . . .01872 274404 / 276456

O'Tuama, Miss C M (Cliona O'Tuama) *T2 W Zd*
London EC4 *p64*. 020 7489 2015

O'Vel, Miss J A (Davis & Co) *K1 G H J1 F1 D1 N Q O*
Ilford *p259*. 020 8551 4228

Oades, Miss M V (South Yorks Joint Secretariat (Fire, Police, Pensions, Passenger Transport))
Barnsley *p448* 01226 772856

Oakdene, Miss R (Paul Crowley & Co) *G H*
Liverpool *p287*. 0151 264 7363

Oake, Ms S L (The Newspaper Society)
London EC4 *p108* 020 7632 7400

Oakes, Ms C A (Lees Solicitors LLP) *W K4*
Birkenhead *p134*. 0151 647 9381

Oakes, Miss N (Bromleys Solicitors LLP) *K1 K3 D1*
Ashton-under-Lyne *p120*. . . 0161 330 6821

Oakes, P (Hill Dickinson LLP) *N Q*
Manchester *p305* 0161 817 7200

Oakes, R A B (Manches LLP) *Zc A3 O*
London WC2 *p58* 020 7404 4433

Oakes, Mrs R M (Henmans LLP) *K3 K2 K1*
Oxford *p343* 01865 781000

Oakes, W (Attwells Solicitors) *A1 Q S1*
Ipswich *p262*. 01473 746000

Oakford, Mrs J (Portsmouth Magistrates Court)
Portsmouth *p469*. 023 9281 9421

Oakland, D A (Kerman & Co LLP) *J1*
London WC2 *p49* 020 7539 7272

Oakland, Mrs J C (Clarke Willmott) *C1 J1 Zo Zp*
Bristol *p162* 0845 209 1000 / 0117 305 6000

Oakley, A J (Bennett Oakley & Partners) *E S1 C1 A1 B1 R1 T1 W N P Zd Zo Zc*
Burgess Hill *p168* 01444 235232

Oakley, Ms B A (Wills Group Ltd)
London EC3 *p110* 020 7488 8111

Oakley, Dr C A (Hough Halton & Soal) *N*
Carlisle *p182*. 01228 524379

Oakley, C H A (Clifford Chance)
London E14 *p20*. 020 7006 1000

Oakley, E A (The Oakley Shee Partnership) *E L S1*
London SE1 *p64*. 020 7089 9066

Oakley, G J (Marks & Spencer PLC)
London W2 *p107* 020 7935 4422

Oakley, J L (Hammon Oakley) *K1 G S1 N Q W E H A1 J1 Zl D1*
Coventry *p200*. 024 7644 8585

Oakley, J R T M (Leonard Gray) *E C1 S1 L A1 W T1 R1*
Chelmsford *p186*. 01245 504904

Oakley, M D (Judge & Priestley) *O Q L J1*
Bromley *p166* 020 8290 0333

Oakley, Miss R (Terry Jones Solicitors & Advocates) *G H Zg Q*
Telford *p409* 01952 297979

Oakley, R (Bates Wells & Braithwaite London LLP) *O Q A3 Zd*
London EC4 *p11*. 020 7551 7777

Oakley, R J (Crown Prosecution Service Dorset)
Bournemouth *p450*. 01202 498700

Oakley, Mrs R M (Nicholls Christie & Crocker) *W*
Harrow *p242*. 020 8863 6366

Oaks, T J (Brooke-Taylors) *G N H Q*
Buxton *p172*. 01298 22741

Oates, Ms H J (Vincent Laverys) *G H*
Preston *p357* 01772 555176

Oates, J (Oates Hanson) *E S1 W S2 T1 T2 L C1*
Huddersfield *p256* 01484 300609

Oates, J M (CooperBurnett) *B1 N Q*
Tunbridge Wells *p415* 01892 515022

Oates, M J (Ian N Gunby & Co) *W Zo*
Milnthorpe *p316* 01539 562044
Barrow-in-Furness *p125* . . . 01229 811811

Oates, R P (Sharp & Partners) *M1 N C1 P J1 F1 K1 Zl Zk Zd*
Nottingham *p339*. 0115 959 0055

Oatham, Ms D Y (Warner Goodman LLP) *E*
Southampton *p387*. 023 8063 9311

Oatham, M (Brachers) *N*
Maidstone *p299* 01622 690691

Oats, Ms M (Simmons & Simmons)
London EC2 *p79*. 020 7628 2020

Obank, R C (DLA Piper UK LLP) *C1 B1*
Leeds *p272* 0870 011 1111

Obayelu, O (Goshen Solicitors) *Zi*
Birmingham *p138* 0121 686 3170

Oberoi, A (Housing & Property Law Partnership) *Zc S2 E Zh L Q*
Islington *p43*. 020 7553 9000

Oberoi, J (Powells) *K1 D1*
Weston-super-Mare *p429* . . 01934 623501

Obertelli, Miss C (Kennedys)
London EC3 *p49*. 020 7667 9667

Obeyesekere, S C A (Stanley & Co) *S2 K3 K1 L Zg Zi M2 O Q N S1 W*
Wembley *p427*. 020 8903 7864

Obhi, Dr H S (Bristows)
London EC4 *p15*. 020 7400 8000

Obhi, Miss M K (Dodds & Partners) *K1 D1*
Leicester *p279*. 0116 253 8585

Obhrai, A (Pearson Maddin Solicitors) *C2 C1 U2 Ze F1 Zza*
New Malden *p321* 020 8949 9500

Obioha, E (Edward Leonards Solicitors) *N Zi S1*
London SE17 *p53* 020 7252 7676

Oborne, Mrs S (Stuart Hurrion & Green) *W K4*
Bexleyheath *p132* 020 8298 1595

Obradovic, Mrs S E (Reading Borough Council)
Reading *p469* 0118 939 0900

Obrart, D A (David A Obrart) *C1 T1 S1 E L W B1 Zi*
London WC2 *p64* 020 7379 4441

Obrey, Mrs L J (Higgs & Sons)
Brierley Hill *p158*. 0845 111 5050

Odaka, Miss G H (Ellesmere Port & Neston Borough Council)
Ellesmere Port *p458*. . . . 0151 356 6789

Oddy, A (Herbert Smith LLP) *O*
London EC2 *p40*. 020 7374 8000

Oddy, J (Veale Wasbrough Vizards) *C1*
London EC4 *p89*. 020 7405 1234

Oddy, Ms L M (Angel Trains Ltd) *F1 B1*
London SW1 *p103*. 020 7592 0500

Odedra, D (Bramwell Browne Odedra) *K1 S1 S2 W G H K3 Zl*
Chesham *p189* 01494 782244

Odedra, Miss N (Chandler Ray) *S1 E*
Buckingham *p167* 01280 814040

Odell, Mrs G (Borough of Telford & Wrekin)
Telford *p473*. 01952 380000

Odell, M C (Harper & Odell) *S1 E G W*
Islington *p39*. 020 7490 0500

Oduyoye, J (London Borough of Southwark)
London SE1 *p109* 020 7525 5000

Oehlert, S (Pritchard Englefield)
London EC2 *p69*. 020 7972 9720

Oelrichs, K W (Greenland Houchen Pomeroy) *E C1 S1 A1 W T1 Zd Zh*
Norwich *p334* 01603 660744

Oerton, M T (Michael Oerton) *S1 P K1 M1 W G B1 H L Zl*
Barnstaple *p125* 01271 378686

Offen, G (Michelmores LLP) *Zc O Q*
Exeter *p221* 01392 688688

Offenbach, Miss D L (Olswang LLP) *C1 C2*
London WC1 *p64* 020 7067 3000

Offer, S (Motorola PCS)
Basingstoke *p448* 01256 790790

Offord, D M N (Browne Jacobson LLP) *Q B1 A3*
Nottingham *p336*. 0115 976 6000

Ogbonnaya, D (Hertfordshire County Council)
Hertford *p460* 01992 555555

Ogden, B (Ince & Co Services Ltd)
London E1 *p44* 020 7481 0010

Ogden, Mrs B A (Beverley Ogden & Co) *S1 W*
Lewes *p283* 01273 474159

Ogden, J J (Barclays Bank PLC) *O B1 Q F1*
London EC3 *p104* 020 7699 5000

Ogden, Mrs M E (Wakefield Metropolitan District Council)
Wakefield *p474* 01924 306090

Ogden, N (McGrigors LLP) *C1 C2*
Manchester *p307* 0161 935 8337

Ogden, S A (East Sussex County Council)
Lewes *p463* 01273 481000

Ogden, Mrs Y S (Reigate & Banstead Borough Council)
Reigate *p469* 01737 276000

Ogg, R S (Wright Hassall LLP) *A1 S1*
Leamington Spa *p270* 01926 886688

Oghoetuoma, H O (McMillan Williams) *G H D1*
Croydon *p205* 01689 848311

Ogilvie, G D (Hunters) *W T2 Zv*
London WC2 *p44* 020 7412 0050

Ogilvie, H M (Shepherd Harris & Co) *G H*
Enfield *p219*. 020 8363 8341

Ogilvie, J S (Herbert Smith LLP) *O Zq*
London EC2 *p40*. 020 7374 8000

Ogilvy Watson, R E (Ashurst LLP) *C1 Zb*
London EC2 *p7* 020 7638 1111

Ogilvy, D M (Mills & Reeve) *E Zh*
Cambridge *p175*. 01223 364422

Ogle, Miss D J (WBW Solicitors) *A1 E L S1*
Exeter *p222* 01392 202404

Ogle, T (Birkett Long LLP) *J1 Zp J2 Zg*
Colchester *p197* 01206 217300

Ogley, A J (Oxley & Coward Solicitors LLP)
Rotherham *p367*. 01709 510999

Ogley, J A (CMS Cameron McKenna LLP)
London EC3 *p17*. 020 7367 3000
London EC2 *p24*. 0870 011 1111

Ogley, J H (Jonathan Ogley & Associates - Spanish Property Lawyers) *J2 N*
Exeter *p222* 01392 462282

Oguejiofor, Ms C (Freemans Solicitors) *Zi*
London W1 *p34* 020 7935 3522

Ogunrinde, Ms R (London Borough of Bexley)
Bexleyheath *p449*. 020 8303 7777

Ogunshakin, I O (Newsome Vaughan LLP) *J1 Q O C1 L Zh Zd M1 Zza F1*
Coventry *p200*. 024 7663 3433

Ogus, I S (Kerman & Co LLP) *E S1 W R1*
London WC2 *p49* 020 7539 7272

Ohbi, Miss K (McGrigors LLP)
London EC4 *p56*. 020 7054 2500

Ohdedar, Miss D (Solihull Metropolitan Borough Council)
Solihull *p471*. 0121 704 6000

Okafor, Miss A (Nottingham City Council (City Sec Dept)) *N Q*
Nottingham *p467*. 0115 915 5555

Oke, P J (Gill Akaster) *Q L*
Plymouth *p349*. 01752 203500

Okebu, P (Stokoe Partnership) *G H*
Waltham Forest *p83* 020 8558 8884

Okeke, Miss C (Grant Saw Solicitors LLP) *S1*
Greenwich *p36*. 020 8858 6971

Okenla, O O (Mountain Partnership) *Zi L G*
Lewisham *p62*. 020 7732 3737

Oki, Ms D E (Wakefield Metropolitan District Council)
Wakefield *p474* 01924 306090

Olaide, F (Doves Solicitors)
London SE1 *p27*. 020 7232 5100

Olaniyan, O O (Glazer Delmar) *Zh L*
London SE22 *p35* 020 8299 0021

Olanrewaju, Ms O (Lawrence Davies & Co) *D1 K3 K1 D2*
Hammersmith & Fulham *p26*. 020 7381 1171

Olarou, D (Jones Day) *O*
London EC4 *p46*. 020 7039 5959

Olavesen, Mrs N M (Oxfordshire County Council)
Oxford *p468* 01865 792422

Oldcorn, P J (First Title Insurance PLC)
London EC4 *p106* 020 7832 3100

Olden, D M (Rausa Mumford) *G H D1 M1 Zi Zm*
Cardiff *p180* 029 2034 4341

Olden, M (Bishop McBride Olden)
Cardiff *p177* 029 2049 0111

Oldershaw, P W (Leathes Prior) *E L*
Norwich *p334* 01603 610911

Oldfield, C (Kennedys)
Manchester *p306* 0161 829 2599

Oldfield, D J (Laytons) *C1 M1 C3 M2 Zb*
London EC4 *p52*. 020 7842 8000

Oldfield, Miss E K (Davis Blank Furniss) *N Q*
Manchester *p303* 0161 832 3304

Oldfield, J (Michael Baker Solicitors Limited) *N*
Farnborough *p224*. 01252 744600

Oldfield, Miss J E (Coles Solicitors) *S1 W*
Northallerton *p331*. 01609 780717

Oldfield, Ms K (Plexus Law (A Trading Name of Parabis Law LLP)) *N Q*
London EC3 *p68*. 0844 245 4000

Oldham, D J (F Barnes & Son) *O B1 K1 N Q S1 S2*
Romford *p366* 01708 745183

Oldham, Mrs E A (Machins Solicitors LLP) *D1 K1 D2*
Luton *p295* 01582 514000

Oldham, Ms H (Fishburns) *Zc Zj A3 O Q*
London EC3 *p32*. 020 7280 8888

Oldham, Mrs L J (Holroyd & Co) *E S1*
Huddersfield *p256* 01484 645464
Sheffield *p376* 0870 150 0100

Oldham, M D (Oldhams Solicitors & Advocates) *G H D1 K1*
Baldock *p121* 01462 895444

Oldham, N H (Towns Needham & Co) *S1 W L C1 E T1 K1 R1 M1 P Zd*
Manchester *p310* 0161 832 3721

Oldham, N P S (Reynolds Porter Chamberlain LLP) *O A3 Q N*
London E1 *p71* 020 3060 6000

Oldman, P A (Hogan Lovells International LLP)
London EC1 *p42*. 020 7296 2000

Oldnall, T M J (Taylor Wimpey UK Ltd)
Cannock *p453*. 01543 496766

Oldridge, S T (Bridge McFarland)
Grimsby *p235* 01472 311711

Oldridge, T J R (Taylor Wessing) *C1 B1 T1 J1 Zb*
London EC4 *p86*. 020 7300 7000

Oldroyd, Ms A E (Leeds City Council) *J1*
Leeds *p462* 0113 224 3513

Oldroyd, A J (The Smith Partnership) *H G*
Derby *p209* 01332 225225

Oldroyd, D R (The Smith Partnership) *G H D1 M1 P K1 W F1 S1 V*
Stoke-on-Trent *p398*. . . . 01782 324454

Oldroyd, G (Bond Pearce LLP) *Zj*
Bristol *p161* 0845 415 0000

Oldroyd, J N (Hayton Winkley) *K1 D1 N Q G J1 O F1 H L Zl*
Kendal *p264*. 01539 720136

Olins, A (IBB Solicitors) *O*
Uxbridge *p417*. 0845 638 1381

Oliphant, A D (Lu Oliphant Solicitors) *S2 K1 O Q S1 W*
Edgware *p217*. 020 8238 2822

Oliva, Ms C M (Uttlesford District Council)
Saffron Walden *p470*. . . . 01799 510510

Olive, D H (DWF) *N Q*
Manchester *p303* 0161 603 5000

Olivelle, Miss R S (Harris Cartier LLP) *C1 J1 C2*
London WC2 *p39* 020 7405 7100

Oliver, A (Hill Dickinson LLP) *Q N*
Liverpool *p288*. 0151 600 8000

Oliver, A C (Andrew Jackson) *Za*
Hull *p257* 01482 325242

Oliver, A P (Dolmans) *N O B1 Q J1 Zj Zk*
Cardiff *p178* 029 2034 5531

Oliver, Ms C (Nottingham City Council (City Sec Dept))
Nottingham *p467*. 0115 915 5555

Oliver, C C (Symes Robinson & Lee) *F1 J2 L N O Q J1 R1 Ze Zf Zc Zp Zq Zr*
Exeter *p222* 01392 270867

Oliver, Miss C J (Sandwell Metropolitan Borough Council)
Oldbury *p468* 0121 569 2200

Oliver, D C (Blake Lapthorn) *N B1 F1 J1 Zc Ze Zk O Q Zd*
Chandlers Ford *p184* 023 8090 8090

Oliver, Miss D E (Harrison Clark LLP) *W*
Cheltenham *p188* 01242 269198
Worcester *p439* 01905 612001
Worcester *p439* 01905 612001

Oliver, D R (Rollits LLP) *S2 E Zh*
York *p445* 01904 625790

Oliver, G C (Hamlins LLP) *B1 C1 J1 T1 Zi Zo*
London W1 *p38* 020 7355 6000

Oliver, Ms H (Lewis Silkin LLP)
London EC4 *p53*. 020 7074 8000

Oliver, I (Ison Harrison) *N*
Leeds *p274* 0113 284 5000

Oliver, I P (George Ide LLP)
Chichester *p192* 01243 786668

Oliver, Ms J (Edwards Duthie) *K1*
London E6 *p29* 020 8514 9000

Oliver, Mrs J (Radcliffes Le Brasseur)
Westminster *p70*. 020 7222 7040

Oliver, Mrs J E (Atteys) *K1 D1 W V*
Doncaster *p211* 01302 340400

Oliver, Miss K (Thomas Horton LLP) *G H Q J1*
Bromsgrove *p167* 01527 871641

Oliver, K E (Peters & Peters) *J1 P N G H O Q Zb Zg Zp*
London EC4 *p67*. 020 7629 7991

Oliver, L M (Vickers & Co) *G H J1 W*
Ealing *p89*. . . .020 8579 2559 / 8840 3999

Oliver, M (Challinors) *Q O L Zq N*
West Bromwich *p427* 0121 553 3211

Oliver, M L (Hewitts) *S1 K1 W G V*
Newton Aycliffe *p330*. . . . 01325 316170

Oliver, N R (Arthur Jackson & Co) *S1 E W L C1*
Rotherham *p367*. 01709 363876

Oliver, N R (Blake Lapthorn) *B1*
Portsmouth *p354*. 023 9222 1122

Oliver, P J (Oldham Metropolitan Borough Council)
Oldham *p468* 0161 911 3000

Oliver, P J R (North Warwickshire Borough Council)
Atherstone *p447*. 01827 715341

Oliver, Miss R J C (Neville-Jones & Co) *N K3 Zr K1 Q F1*
Wareham *p421* 01929 552471

Oliver, R M (Pannone LLP) *C1 C2 F1*
Manchester *p308* 0161 909 3000

Oliver, S (Chesterfield Borough Council)
Chesterfield *p455* 01246 345345

Oliver, S (Woodfines LLP) *J1 C3 I Ze U2*
Bedford *p130* 01234 270600

Oliver, Mrs S J (Barlow Lyde & Gilbert LLP) *Zq O Q Zj*
London EC3 *p10*. 020 7247 2277

Oliver, S W (Sidley Austin Brown & Wood) *C2 C1*
London EC2 *p78*. 020 7360 3600

Oliver, T G (Plexus Law (A Trading Name of Parabis Law LLP)) *N Q O Zj A3 C1 Zu*
London EC3 *p68*. 0844 245 4000

Oliver, V (Gamlins) *S1 S2 W T2 T1 Zh*
Colwyn Bay *p198* 01492 532275

Oliver, V J (Burton Copeland LLP) *G H*
Manchester *p302* 0161 827 9500

Oliver, V J (Stewarts Law LLP) *N*
London EC4 *p83*. 020 7822 8000

Oliver, W H J (Pinsent Masons LLP) *Zb*
London EC2 *p67*. 020 7418 7000

Oliver, Mrs Z D (Wace Morgan) *S2 E A1*
Shrewsbury *p379* 01743 280100

Oliver-Bellasis, J (Woodroffes)
Westminster *p93*. 020 7730 0001

Oliviero, Miss D (Clough & Willis) *E L R1 R2 S1*
Bury *p170* 0161 764 5266

Ollerenshaw, A J (Tayntons LLP Solicitors) *N*
Gloucester *p230*. 01452 522047

Ollett, Mrs J A (Leeds Day) *W K4 T2*
St Neots *p392*. 01480 474661

Olley, A (Lovats)
Brentwood *p451* 01277 263081

Olley, A (Adlams LLP)
St Neots *p392*. 01480 474061

Olley, D R (Blake Lapthorn) *E*
Chandlers Ford *p184* 023 8090 8090

Olley, Ms H (LG Lawyers)
London SE1 *p50*. 020 7379 0000

Olley, N (The College of Law York)
York *p477* 0800 289997

Olley, N M (Burges Salmon) *C1 C2 I P*
Bristol *p161* 0117 939 2000

Ollier, M E (Beviss & Beckingsale) *S1 E W L C1 S2*
Seaton *p373*. 01297 626950

Olliffe, Ms J L (Hal-Solicitors) *D1 E G K1 L N Q S1 S2 W*
Uxbridge *p417*. . . .01895 270907 / 270908

Ollis, Miss K M (Brethertons LLP) *C1 C2 S2 I U2 C3 Zd Ze Zh*
Rugby *p368* 01788 579579

Ollis, R W (Lodders Solicitors LLP) *C1 A1 E L T1 S1 W*
Stratford-upon-Avon *p400* . . 01789 293259

Olmer, P H (Nabarro LLP)
London WC1 *p63* 020 7524 6000

Olmos-Serrano, Miss N (Lawrence Lupin) *M1 Zg Zi*
Wembley *p426*. 020 8733 7200

Olney, Miss L (Derbyshire County Council)
Matlock *p465* 01629 580000

Olsen, J R (Field Fisher Waterhouse LLP) *Ze*
London EC3 *p31*. 020 7861 4000

Olswang, S M (Olswang LLP) *C1 T1 Zf Zk*
London WC1 *p64* 020 7067 3000

Olubajo, T (Ince & Co Services Ltd)
London E1 *p44* 020 7481 0010

Olubisose, M (M Olubi Solicitors) *G J1 K1 L Zi Q*
Lambeth *p64*. 020 7737 3400 / 07956 394567

Oluwole, O (Whitecross Solicitors) *S1 Zi J1 Q*
Islington *p91*. 020 7251 5533

Om, Miss E E H (Osborne Clarke) *T1*
Bristol *p164* 0117 917 3000

OM, Miss G (Britvic Soft Drinks Ltd)
Chelmsford *p454*. 01245 261871

Om, T (Pritchard Jones Evans Lane) *C1 S2 E J1 L R2 Zv S1 W*
Caernarfon *p172*. 01286 673387

Omar, H (Bromptons) *E G K1 S1 L D1 H C1*
London W8 *p16* 020 7937 0005

Ongley, P R (Hayes Clifford & Co) *B1 O D1 N K1 L J1 G F1*
Tilehurst *p411* 0118 941 8416

Onnie, D R (Harold Benjamin)
Harrow *p241*. 020 8422 5678

Onoufriou, G O (Eric Robinson Solicitors) *S1 E L G C1 W R1 H N K1 Zi Zl*
Southampton *p386*. 023 8022 6891

Onoufriou, Ms K (Minaides Robson) *W S1 Q N O Zl L K1 J1 S2 E D1 F1 F2 J2*
London EC4 *p61*. 020 7831 7761

Onoufriou, Miss V (Paris Smith LLP) *S1 R2*
Southampton *p386*. 023 8048 2482

Onourah, Ms A (London Borough of Greenwich Legal Services)
London SE18 *p106* 020 8921 5123

Onslow-Cole, Ms J E (CMS Cameron McKenna LLP) *Zj*
London EC3 *p17*. 020 7367 3000

Onuma, D (Galbraith Branley) *G H B2*
London N12 *p34*. 020 8446 8474

Onwukwe, Ms A (Levenes Solicitors) *J1*
Haringey *p53* . .020 8881 7777 / 8881 6764

Onyett, Ms L (Stones Solicitors LLP)
Exeter *p222* 01392 666777

Onyett, R P (Harrowells) *Q O L B1 X W*
York *p444* 01904 558600

Ooi, Ms Y (Trowers & Hamlins)
London EC3 *p88*. 020 7423 8000

Openshaw, N H F (Openshaws) *C1 C2 M2 C3 Zb Ze*
Bideford *p132* 01237 478900

Openshaw-Blower, A M J (Turner Parkinson) *I Ze C1 U2*
Manchester *p310* 0161 833 1212

Oppal, G S (Charles Simmons)
Ilford *p261*. 020 8514 0000

Opperman, A (Terry Jones Solicitors & Advocates) *S2 S1*
Telford *p409*. 01952 297979

Oppler, M D (Michael Oppler & Co) *Q O L J1 K1 B1 C1 E W S1 Zc Zk Zq Zl*
London SW14 *p65*. . 020 8878 4195 / 8878 4180

Oram, Mrs C (Howlett Clarke Solicitors)
Hove *p254*. 01273 419728

See p634 for the Key to Work Categories

Oram, D R M (Hill Dickinson LLP) *O A3 Zc*
Liverpool *p288* 0151 600 8000

Oran, Miss H (Coles Miller Solicitors LLP) *K3 J1 K1 L O Q N Zh Zl*
Bournemouth *p151* 01202 293226

Orange, P J (Simmons & Simmons)
London EC2 *p79* 020 7628 2020

Orange, S J (Crown Prosecution Service Durham) *K1 M1 P F1 V S1 D1 G*
Durham *p457* 0191 383 5800

Orbell, J H (Bowser Ollard & Bentley) *S1 W K3 S2 A1 K1 Zl*
Wisbech *p435* 01945 583194

Orbell, J H (Bowser Ollard & Bentley) *K1 G S1 S2 H W A1 D1*
March *p312* 01354 652606

Orchard, J A (Vine Orchards) *W S1 T1 L E A1*
Exmouth *p223* 01395 273035 / 264646

Orchard, Miss J D (E Edwards Son & Noice) *S1 W*
Billericay *p133* 01277 658551

Orchard, R H (British Telecommunications PLC)
London EC1 *p104* 020 7356 6181

Orchison, G W E (DLA Piper UK LLP) *Ze Zf Zk*
Manchester *p303* 0870 011 1111

Orcott, M (Walsall Metropolitan Borough Council)
Walsall *p475* 01922 650000

Ord, Miss E C (Espilon Solicitors) *P N Q R1 J2 S1 O*
Ormskirk *p341* 01704 894945

Ord, Ms H M (Newcastle Upon Tyne City Council)
Newcastle upon Tyne *p466* 0191 232 8520

Ord, I S (McKeag & Co) *N Q*
Gosforth *p231* 0191 213 1010

Ord, M (Watson Burton LLP)
Newcastle upon Tyne *p327* 0845 901 2100

Ord, Mrs S M (Hutchinson & Buchanan) *J1 N Q K1 F1*
Ripon *p365* 01765 602156

Ord-Hume, I D (Caversham Solicitors Ltd) *W K4*
Reading *p360* 0118 947 8638

Oren, R (Flint Bishop Solicitors) *Zb C2*
Derby *p208* 01332 340211

Orengo, A (Plexus Law (A Trading Name of Parabis Law LLP)) *Q O Zj E Zq*
London EC3 *p68* 0844 245 4000

Organ, A M (GPB Solicitors LLP) *K1*
Stratford-upon-Avon *p400* 01789 261131

Organ, C D (Russells) *C1 Zf Ze*
London W1 *p75* 020 7439 8692

Organ, Miss H D (Alderson Dodds) *K1 D1 D2*
Blyth *p147* 01670 352293

Orgev, E (Fletcher Dervish) *D1 K1 Zi*
Haringey *p33* 020 8800 4615

Orgill, D (Mayo Wynne Baxter LLP) *Q N O*
Brighton *p160* 01273 775533

Orlebar-Reid, Miss J J (Carritt & Co LLP)
London W1 *p18* 020 7323 2765

Orlik, M F (Lodders Solicitors LLP) *R1 E*
Stratford-upon-Avon *p400* 01789 293259

Orluta, Mrs S A (Bovis Homes Ltd)
Coleshill *p455* 01675 437000

Ormai, Ms G (CMS Cameron McKenna LLP)
London EC3 *p17* 020 7367 3000

Orman, Miss E J (Baily Gibson) *K1*
High Wycombe *p249* 01494 442661

Orman, M R (Morris Orman Hearle) *B1 J1 L M1 N*
Cheltenham *p188* 01242 257188

Ormand, J R (Forbes) *N*
Blackburn *p145* 01254 54374

Orme, D J (Risdon Hosegood) *S1 E C2 C1 A1 Zl*
Taunton *p408* 01823 251571

Orme, R P (DLA Piper UK LLP) *C1 C2*
Birmingham *p137* 0870 011 1111

Orme, Ms S (Gregg Latchams LLP) *K1 K2*
Bristol *p162* 0117 906 9400

Ormerod, Ms L (Jones Day) *E*
London EC4 *p46* 020 7039 5959

Ormes, Mrs V (Rowley Dickinson) *N Q Zr*
Manchester *p309* 0161 834 4215

Ormond, Ms E (Roberts Moore Nicholas Jones) *Q*
Birkenhead *p134* 0151 647 0000

Ormond, Ms J L (DAC Beachcroft)
Bristol *p162* 0117 918 2000

Ormonde, Miss D L (Wiseman Lee LLP) *W*
Redbridge *p92* 020 8215 1000

Ormonde, Mrs F E (Wiseman Lee LLP) *K1 K2 D1*
Redbridge *p92* 020 8215 1000

Ormrod, A (Heaney Watson) *K1 D1 K3*
Liverpool *p288* 0151 256 7777

Ormrod, D (Fynmores) *D1 K1 D2 K2*
Bexhill *p132* 01424 732333

Ormrod, G A (Christopher Harris & Co) *Zc C1 S2 E S1*
Sheerness *p375* 01795 661521

Ornolfsson, J (Ashurst LLP)
London EC2 *p7* 020 7638 1111

Orosz, N E (Carter Lemon Camerons) *Zd C1*
London EC1 *p18* 020 7406 1000

Orpwood, Ms A (Edwards Duthie) *G H*
London E13 *p29* 020 8514 9000

Orr, A J W (Simmons & Simmons)
London EC2 *p79* 020 7628 2020

Orr, Mrs L (Sefton Metropolitan Borough Council)
Southport *p472* 01704 533133

Orr, Ms P A (Barlow Lyde & Gilbert LLP)
London EC3 *p10* 020 7247 2277

Orr, Ms S L (Aviva PLC)
London EC3 *p103* 020 7283 7500 / 01603 687905
Norwich *p467* 01603 622200

Orrell, Ms S (Leonard Gray)
Chelmsford *p186* 01245 504904

Orrell, Mrs S A (Manchester City Council)
Manchester *p465* 0161 234 5000

Orrett, L J R (Freemans Solicitors) *G H B2*
London W1 *p34* 020 7935 3522

Orriss, A C (Neves) *S1 E C1 L T1 Zc*
Luton *p295* 01582 725311

Orsborn, B (Fritchley Goldsmith)
Barnsley *p124* 01226 215600

Orsborn, J G (Downie & Gadban) *A1 B1 C1 C2 E L P R1 S1 T1 T2 W*
Alton *p116* 01420 82879

Orton, M D (Finers Stephens Innocent LLP)
London W1 *p32* 020 7323 4000

Orton, S (Jones Day) *C1*
London EC4 *p46* 020 7039 5959

Orviss, Ms K (Pinsent Masons LLP)
London EC2 *p67* 020 7418 7000

Ory, B C R (AGR Solicitors) *L S1 W C1 E*
Mansfield *p311* 01623 460444

Osbaldeston, Mrs B M (S A Carr & Co) *D1 K1 N O Q Zi W S1 E*
Hackney *p18* 020 8986 5438

Osborn, A N (Mason & Beer) *K1 W E N G D1 Q L S1 H*
East Grinstead *p215* 01342 311255

Osborn, Mrs A T (Thompsons (formerly Robin/ Brian Thompson & Partners)) *N Zr*
Manchester *p310* 0161 819 3500

Osborn, Miss K J (Crosse & Crosse) *N Zq Zr*
Exeter *p220* 01392 258451

Osborn, Miss L M (OBW Perera) *G H*
Colchester *p197* 01206 541111

Osborn, N J (Derrick Bridges & Co) *S1 W E L T1*
Barnet *p123* 020 8449 7326

Osborn, R (Freeth Cartwright LLP) *R2 E S2 L Zc*
Birmingham *p138* 0845 634 2575
Leicester *p279* 0116 248 1100

Osborn, S J (Fisher Jones Greenwood LLP) *K1*
Colchester *p197* 01206 578282

Osborn, T J (Nexus Solicitors) *C1 C3 Ze I W Zf U2*
Manchester *p308* 0161 819 4900

Osborne, A (Shell International Ltd)
London SE1 *p109* 020 7934 1234

Osborne, A (McMillan Williams) *S1*
Coulsdon *p199* 020 8668 4131

Osborne, A J (Windeatts) *S1 L A1 Zl S2 E*
Totnes *p413* 01803 862233

Osborne, C (Wannop Fox Staffurth & Bray) *S1 S2 E*
Worthing *p442* 01903 228200

Osborne, D (Hamnett Osborne Tisshaw) *B2 G H*
Haywards Heath *p245* 01444 443030

Osborne, D N (Watson Farley & Williams)
London EC2 *p90* 020 7814 8000

Osborne, D P (Fraser Dawbarns) *O Q*
King's Lynn *p266* 01553 666600

Osborne, J (WBW Solicitors) *B1 F1 J1 L O Q Zp*
Newton Abbot *p329* 01626 202404

Osborne, Mrs J H A (Edwin Coe LLP) *O Q I F1 F2 Zc Ze Zk Zq*
London WC2 *p29* 020 7691 4000

Osborne, J L (Bosworths) *S1 E W K1 P L G R1 C1 B1 Zc Zk Zl*
East Molesey *p215* 020 8941 3151

Osborne, Mrs J V (Dawson Hart) *W S1 T2 K4*
Uckfield *p416* 01825 762281

Osborne, J W (Clifford Chance)
London E14 *p20* 020 7006 1000

Osborne, Mrs K S (Chivers Easton Brown)
Surbiton *p402* 020 8390 0081

Osborne, Miss L M (Somerville & Savage) *W K4 T2*
Torquay *p413* 01803 312700

Osborne, M (Tollers LLP) *W*
Kettering *p265* 01536 520111

Osborne, M F (Field Fisher Waterhouse LLP)
London EC3 *p31* 020 7861 4000

Osborne, P D (Barrie Y Jones & Co) *N X S2 E G H Q W C1 Zd Zq Zr Zt Zv*
Llantwit Major *p292* 01446 793835 / 794542

Osborne, P F (Stanley Tee) *S1 S2 W*
Great Dunmow *p233* 01371 872166

Osborne, P L (Fox Williams) *C1 C2*
London EC2 *p33* 020 7628 2000

Osborne, P R (Roythornes LLP) *E A1 Zc R2 S2*
Spalding *p389* 01775 842500

Osborne, R (Holman Fenwick Willan)
London EC3 *p42* 020 7264 8000

Osborne, R G (Reynolds Porter Chamberlain LLP)
London E1 *p71* 020 3060 6000

Osborne, Miss R G (David Du Pre & Co) *K1*
London WC1 *p28* 020 7430 1950

Osborne, Mrs S A (Plymouth City Council) *N O Q L G*
Plymouth *p468* 01752 668000

Osborne, S C (Forsters LLP) *C1*
Westminster *p33* 020 7863 8333

Osborne, T W (Wiggin Osborne Fullerlove) *T1 T2 M2 Zf C1*
Cheltenham *p189* 01242 710200
London SW1 *p91* 020 7290 2456

Osbourne, Miss A L P (David Tagg & Co) *D1 K3 K1*
London SW6 *p85* 020 7736 0999

Osbourne, K (Eddowes Perry & Osbourne) *S1 W L E S2*
Sutton Coldfield *p403* 0121 686 9444

Osgerby, Mrs H F (Burrell Jenkins) *D1 K1 W N O Q F1 J1 Zc Ze Zk*
Cannock *p176* 01543 505040

Osgood, M R (Moore Blatch Solicitors)
Southampton *p386* 023 8071 8000

Osgood, Mrs R B (Paris Smith LLP) *K3 K1*
Southampton *p386* 023 8048 2482

Oshry, R (Harold Benjamin)
Harrow *p241* 020 8422 5678

Oshunniyi, Mrs T (Addie & Co)
London WC2 *p4* 020 7395 3740

Osibona, O A A (Freemans Solicitors) *Zi*
London W1 *p34* 020 7935 3522

Osler, H R (Osler Donegan Taylor) *B1 L N O Q S1 W*
Brighton *p160* 01273 710712

Osler, J (Ashurst LLP)
London EC2 *p7* 020 7638 1111

Osman, C (Veale Wasbrough Vizards) *E S1*
Bristol *p165* 0117 925 2020

Osman, C C (Clifford Chance)
London E14 *p20* 020 7006 1000

Osman, J D (Wansbroughs) *N Zu*
Devizes *p210* 01380 733300

Osman, Ms L (Morris Scott & Co) *G H Q*
Christchurch *p194* 01425 278866

Osman, Ms M L (Whitfields) *C1 D1 E K1 M1 P S1*
Formby *p227* 01704 878501

Osmend, E (Rita Sen Solicitors) *E K4 K1 S1 T2 W*
Bognor Regis *p148* 01243 263658

Osmond, W J G (Osmond & Osmond) *B1 Zr S2 E J1 K1 L Zk O Q N R1 Zq Zp S1 A3*
London EC4 *p65* 020 7583 3434

Ospedale, Miss G E D (Royds LLP) *J1 Q*
London EC4 *p74* 020 7583 2222

Ost, Ms J (Wansbroughs) *W K4 T2*
Melksham *p314* 01225 703222

Ost, S D (Squire Sanders (UK) LLP)
Manchester *p310* 0161 830 5000

Ostanek, A M (Clement Hughes & Co) *E L Q S1 W*
Prestatyn *p356* 01745 852121

Oster Warriner, Mrs C (Blake Lapthorn) *N L*
Oxford *p342* 01865 248607

Ostrin, A (Thornton & Co)
Hammersmith & Fulham *p87* 020 8743 3000

Ostrom, J (Bennett Griffin)
Ferring *p225* 01903 229999

Ostrovsky, S (Ashurst LLP)
London EC2 *p7* 020 7638 1111

Osuch-Goodhead, Mrs W M (Nigel Davis Solicitors) *A1 E S2*
Belper *p131* 01335 372889

Osuntokun, S (DLA Piper UK LLP)
London EC2 *p24* 0870 011 1111

Oswin, Ms M S (Nelsons)
Leicester *p280* 0116 222 6666

Othen, Ms V J (Linskills Solicitors) *Q N J1 F1 Zp*
Liverpool *p289* 0151 236 2224

Ottal, A (Maples Teesdale LLP) *E*
London EC2 *p58* 020 7600 3800

Otter, R G (Moore Brown & Dixon LLP) *P K1 J1 A1 S1 W*
Tewkesbury *p410* 01684 292341

Otterwell, Ms L (K&L Gates LLP)
London EC4 *p47* 020 7648 9000

Ottley, A A (Ince & Co Services Ltd)
London E1 *p44* 020 7481 0010

Ottley, R J (Morgan Cole) *N Zj*
Bristol *p164* 0117 916 7220

Ottman, J E (Jeremy Simon & Co) *C1 D1 E W K1 L M1 N P S1 Zm*
Watford *p424* 01923 219292

Otto, A M (Brown Turner Ross) *G D1 H J1 K1 L M1 N P V Zi Zk*
Southport *p388* 01704 542002

Otty, Mrs S (Sustrans Ltd) *E R1 S1 Zn*
Bristol *p452* 0117 926 8893

Otudeko, Mrs F M (Southampton City Council)
Southampton *p472* 023 8022 3855

Otvos, P N J (Teacher Stern LLP) *S2*
London WC1 *p86* 020 7242 3191

Otway, Ms K A (Wiggin LLP) *Zf*
Cheltenham *p189* 01242 224114

Ouazzani, Ms S (Russell-Cooke LLP) *K1 K2 K3 D1*
London SW15 *p74* 020 8789 9111

Oukellou, Miss N (HM Land Registry - Leicester)
Leicester *p463* 0116 265 4000 / 4001

Oulton, J (Mayer Brown International LLP) *Zj*
London EC2 *p59* 020 3130 3000

Oury, J (Oury Clark)
London WC1 *p65* 020 7607 4300

Oury, J E (Oury Clark) *B2 B3 C1 C2 G H J1 T1 T2 W Zg Zq*
London WC1 *p65* 020 7607 4300

Outen, J A (Ashton KCJ) *N J1 J2 Zp*
Ipswich *p262* 01473 232425

Outram, Mrs G (IBB Solicitors) *S1*
Chesham *p189* 0845 638 1381

Outram, J V (Taylor & Emmet LLP) *S1*
Sheffield *p377* 0114 218 4000

Outram, R (IBB Solicitors) *E S2*
Chesham *p189* 0845 638 1381

Outram, S R (S R Outram & Co) *S1 K1 G Q W T1 F1 J1 L*
Boston *p151* 01205 365342

Outten, J E (Caunters) *S2 S1 W*
Liskeard *p285* 01579 343165 / 343484

Outten, S B (Steele Raymond) *J1 O F1 Q Ze Zk B1 J2 F2*
Bournemouth *p152* 01202 294566

Outwaite, R J (Walker Morris) *E R2*
Leeds *p277* 0113 283 2500

Ovens, J H (Lightfoots LLP) *E S1 W A1*
Thame *p410* 01844 212305

Ovens, S R (Newcastle Upon Tyne City Council)
Newcastle upon Tyne *p466* 0191 232 8520

Over, C J (Over Taylor Biggs) *F1 N O Q C1 L T1*
Exeter *p222* 01392 823811

Over, J D N (Moore Blatch Solicitors)
Southampton *p386* 023 8071 8000

Over, J L (Yorkshire Electricity Group PLC)
Leeds *p463* 0113 289 2123

Overend, M C (Charles Lucas & Marshall) *C1 E W Zd*
Swindon *p406* 01793 511055

Overland, Mrs J L (Bird & Co) *S1 S2 L W*
Grantham *p232* 01476 591711

Overton, D V (Wilkin Chapman Grange Solicitors) *E C1 R1 L S1 J1 B1 Zl*
Grimsby *p235* 01472 262626

Overton, Ms E J (Wilkin Chapman Grange Solicitors) *K3 Q J1*
Grimsby *p235* 01472 262626

Overton, J (TV Edwards LLP) *G H*
London EC3 *p85* 020 7790 7000

Overton, M A (Edwin Coe LLP) *C1 C2*
London WC2 *p29* 020 7691 4000

Overy, Miss K J (Skipton Building Society) *O F1*
Skipton *p471* 01756 705000

Overy, Miss S J (Stanley Tee) *K1 N B1 D1 Q*
Bishop's Stortford *p144* 01279 755200

Ovington, M R (BPE Solicitors LLP) *N*
Cheltenham *p187* 01242 224433

Owa, Mrs O (London Borough of Haringey)
London N22 *p106* 020 8489 0000

Owen, Miss A (Rawlison Butler LLP) *C2 C1*
Crawley *p202* 01293 527744

Owen, Mrs A (Blackhurst Swainson Goodier LLP) *K4 T2 W*
Lancaster *p269* 01524 32471

Owen, A (Martello Professional Risks Limited) *O N Q J1 L Zl*
London EC3 *p108* 020 7337 7500
London EC3 *p68* 0844 245 4000

Owen, Mrs A C (Ungoed-Thomas & King Limited)
Carmarthen *p183* 01267 237441

Owen, Miss A E (Moreb Limited) *A1 Q K1 E S1 W C1 R1 L S2 K3 J1*
Llandeilo *p291* 01558 822215

Owen, A J (Leo Abse & Cohen) *N Q O F1 Ze*
Cardiff *p179* 029 2038 3252 / 2034 5421

Owen, A R (Red Kite Law) *G H Zy Zl V*
Carmarthen *p183* 01267 239000

Owen, Miss C (Owen & O'Sullivan)
Ystrad Mynach *p446* 01443 862263

Owen, Mrs C A M (Owen & Co) *S1 W E O*
Redhill *p362* 01737 760036

Owen, Miss C E (R Gordon Roberts Laurie & Co) *K3 K1 S1 V Q*
Llangefni *p292* 01248 722215 / 723312

Owen, Miss C I E (Bolton Metropolitan Borough Council)
Bolton *p450* 01204 333333

Owen, Mrs C M (Brabners Chaffe Street) *S1*
Liverpool *p286* 0151 600 3000

Owen, C M (Manches LLP) *C1 C2*
London WC2 *p58* 020 7404 4433

Owen, D (Layton-Law.com) *K1 S1 W*
Blackpool *p146* 01253 399311

Owen, D (Ashurst LLP)
London EC2 *p7* 020 7638 1111

Owen, D A (British Midland Airways Ltd)
Castle Donington *p453* 01332 854089

Owen, D C H (Molesworths Bright Clegg) *G H*
Rochdale *p365* 01706 356666

Owen, E J (HC Solicitors LLP) *K1 K2 D1 D2 K3*
Peterborough *p347* 01733 882800

Owen, G (Mark Gilbert Morse) *S1 R2 S2 E*
Newcastle upon Tyne *p325* 0191 261 0096

Owen, G (Crowell & Moring) *G*
London EC4 *p23* 020 7413 0011

Owen, Miss G (Thompsons (formerly Robin/Brian Thompson & Partners)) *N*
Plymouth *p350* 01752 675810

Owen, G (Glyn Owen & Co) *S1 E A1 M1 R1 C1 G W T1 V Zl*
Colwyn Bay *p198* 01492 532649

Owen, G D (Gee & Edwards) *M1 N K1 W S1 T1 C1 P Zj Zl Zc*
Swansea *p405* 01792 465806 / 464937

Owen, Mrs G F (Staffordshire County Council) *D1*
Stafford *p472* 01785 223121

Owen, Miss G O (Gwyneth O Owen Solicitor) *S1 T2 W*
Hereford *p248* 01544 318738

Owen, G R (hlw Keeble Hawson LLP) *E C1 R1 Zd*
Sheffield *p375* 0114 272 2061

Owen, H A (Allen & Overy LLP)
London E1 *p5* 020 3088 0000

Owen, I (Geldards LLP) *E S2*
Cardiff *p178* 029 2023 8239

Owen, I E (Robyns Owen) *A1 A3 B1 D1 S2 E G H J1 P K1 K2 O Q N*
Pwllheli *p358* 01758 613177
Porthmadog *p354* 01766 514747

Owen, J (The Dental Law Partnership)
Nantwich *p320* 01270 613320

Owen, J E (Gordons LLP)
Leeds *p273* 0113 227 0100

Owen, J H (Hunters) *W T2*
London WC2 *p44* 020 7412 0050

Owen, J M (Legal Services Commission Wales Office)
Cardiff *p453* 0845 608 7070

Owen, J T (Tudor Owen Roberts Glynne & Co) G S1 H K1 M1 D1 E V N P
Caernarfon p172 . . . 01286 672207 / 672851

Owen, L (Reynolds Porter Chamberlain LLP)
London E1 p71 . . . 020 3060 6000

Owen, Mrs L A (HM Land Registry - Leicester)
Leicester p463 . . . 0116 265 4000 / 4001

Owen, Mrs L G (Baily Gibson) C1 C2 C3 E J1 L S1 T1 T2 W
Beaconsfield p128 . . . 01494 672661

Owen, L P (Baily Gibson) C1 C2 C3 E J1 L S1 T1 T2 W
High Wycombe p249 . . . 01494 442661

Owen, Miss M (Brockbank Curwen Cain & Hall) S1 S2 W E
Whitehaven p431 . . . 01946 692194

Owen, M J (Owen & Co) S1 W S2 E
London NW10 p65 . . 020 8459 4836 / 8459 7263

Owen, Mrs M L (Gomer Williams & Co) S1 W A1 Zh
Llanelli p292 . . . 01554 755101

Owen, M R (Pinsent Masons LLP) E S1
Leeds p276 . . . 0113 244 5000

Owen, M W (Harbottle & Lewis LLP) F1 C1 I Ze W
London W1 p38 . . . 020 7667 5000

Owen, Mrs N (Wansbroughs) K1 D2 D1 V
Devizes p210 . . . 01380 733300

Owen, N S R L (Leo Abse & Cohen) Q N O
Cardiff p179 . . . 029 2038 3252 / 2034 5421
Cardiff p181 . . . 029 2055 7200

Owen, N V (Nigel Owen & Co) S1 O Q S2 B1
Chislehurst p193 . . . 020 8295 1989

Owen, Ms P (DLA Piper UK LLP)
Manchester p303 . . . 0870 011 1111

Owen, P A (Machins Solicitors LLP) K1 D1
Luton p295 . . . 01582 514000

Owen, P M R (KJD) C2 C1 C3 M1 Zb
Stoke-on-Trent p398 . . . 01782 202020

Owen, P R (Charsley Harrison LLP) O Q J1 L F1 S2 C2
Windsor p434 . . . 01753 851591

Owen, P R (Alfred Newton & Co) M1 P N W B1 F1 J1 K1 L S1 Zh Zl Ze
Stockport p396 . 0161 480 6551 / 480 1245

Owen, Mrs R A (Caerphilly County Borough Council) Q P L R1
Hengoed p460 . . . 01443 815588

Owen, R J (Robinson Allfree) N Q O J1 J2 Zq Zc Zr F1 Zk
Ramsgate p359 . . . 01843 592361

Owen, R J H (Derbyshire Building Society)
Duffield p457 . . . 01332 841000

Owen, R J V (Bircham Dyson Bell) R1 P
Westminster p13 . . . 020 7227 7000

Owen, R K (Owen Nash & Co) K1 G M1 P F1 H
Walsall p420 . . . 01922 746746

Owen, Mrs R M (Challinors) D1 K1
West Bromwich p427 . . . 0121 553 3211

Owen, R S (Burges Salmon) E
Bristol p161 . . . 0117 939 2000

Owen, S A (Stallard March & Edwards) C1 C2 E S2 U2 J1 F1
Worcester p440 . . . 01905 613404

Owen, S M (Squire Sanders (UK) LLP)
Leeds p277 . . . 0113 284 7000

Owen, Miss S M (Kellogg Brown & Root (UK) Ltd)
Leatherhead p462 . . . 01372 865000

Owen, T H (Ungoed-Thomas & King Limited) N K1 R1 J1 D1 Zk Zl Zm
Carmarthen p183 . . . 01267 237441

Owen, W J (Moreb Limited) A1 E S1 W T1 C1 R1 P L N
Llandeilo p291 . . . 01558 822215

Owens, A (Morrison & Foerster (UK) LLP)
London EC2 p62 . . . 020 7920 4000

Owens, Miss A (Newbys) K1 D1
Stockton-on-Tees p397 . . . 01642 673733 / 676666

Owens, Mrs A (Terence Carney) K3 D1 D2 K1
Hebburn p246 . . 0191 483 5422 / 483 8771
Hexham p249 . . . 01434 602486

Owens, A J (Irwin Mitchell LLP) O Zq
Sheffield p376 . . . 0870 150 0100

Owens, D J (Bevan Brittan LLP) C1 J1 O Zu
Bristol p161 . . . 0870 194 1000

Owens, Mrs E J (Peterborough Magistrates Court)
Peterborough p468 . . . 01223 314311

Owens, J G (Lewis & Dick) S1 S2 E C1
Epsom p219 . . . 020 8393 0055

Owens, J T E (John Owens Solicitor) B1 C1 S2 E F1 J1 K1 L Zk O Q N S1 W K3
St Asaph p391 . . . 01745 582333

Owens, Miss K M (Mackenzie Jones)
St Asaph p391 . . . 01745 536030

Owens, Ms L E (Davies Parsons Allchurch) Q N L
Llanelli p292 . . . 01554 749144

Owens, M R (Hamways Walker Owens) B1 C1 C2 E N O S1 W
Edenbridge p216 . . . 01732 866666

Owens, N D (Blake Lapthorn) S1
Oxford p342 . . . 01865 248607

Owens, Mrs S (Turner Coulston)
Northampton p333 . . . 01604 622101

Owens, T P (National Institutions of the Church of England, Legal Office)
London SW1 p108 . . . 020 7898 1000

Owens, Miss W (Goodswens) N Q K1 D1 D2 K3
Redcar p362 . . . 01642 482424

Owers, Ms J (Charles Russell LLP) J1
London EC4 p19 . . . 020 7203 5000

Owers, T (Jackamans) K1 Q G L F1 N D1 H
Felixstowe p225 . . . 01394 279636

Ownsworth, Mrs J (Ridley & Hall) W
Huddersfield p256 . . . 01484 538421

Owoso-Yianoma, Mrs N (Essex County Council)
Chelmsford p454 . . . 0845 743 0430

Owst, Miss A R (Kingston upon Hull City Council)
Hull p461 . . . 01482 300300

Owusu, B (BWF Solicitors) M2 K1 Zi Q
London E8 p9 . . . 020 7241 7180

Owusu-Yaw, D (Afrifa & Partners)
London SW9 p4 . . . 020 7820 9177

Oxburgh, Ms M (Fladgate LLP)
London WC2 p32 . . . 020 3036 7000

Oxbury, Ms C N (Milton Keynes Council)
Milton Keynes p466 . . . 01908 691691

Oxbury, Ms C N (Buckinghamshire County Council)
Aylesbury p448 . . . 01296 383653

Oxenham, A M (Lanyon Bowdler LLP) W
Ludlow p294 . . . 01584 872333

Oxley, G A (Oxley & Walsh) G H F1 M1 N S1 W
Weston-super-Mare p429 . . . 01934 517500

Oxley, J M H (Lee & Priestley LLP) C1 C2 J1 C3 M1 Ze Zf Zv
Leeds p275 . . . 0845 129 2300

Oxley, S (Linder Myers Solicitors) K1
Manchester p307 . . . 0844 984 6400

Oxley, S J G (W Davies) E S2 A1 Zc Zd R1 R2
Woking p436 . . . 01483 744900

Oxnard, J P (Pearson Caulfield) G H D1 K1 V
Newcastle upon Tyne p326 . 0191 261 8878

Oxnard, P A (Squire Sanders (UK) LLP) O
London EC2 p81 . . . 020 7655 1000

Oxtoby, Miss D E M (Leeds City Council)
Leeds p462 . . . 0113 224 3513

Oxtoby, E (Squire Sanders (UK) LLP) Q
Leeds p277 . . . 0113 284 7000

Oyetti, O T (Magrath LLP) Zi
London W1 p57 . . . 020 7495 3003

Ozoran, D (Ozoran Turkan & Co) I K1 L Zi V
London N16 p65 . . . 020 7354 0802

P

Pabla, H S (Yates & Co) S1 S2 W
Nottingham p339 . . . 0115 947 4486

Pabst, M (Jones Day) Zb
London EC4 p46 . . . 020 7039 5959
London EC2 p59 . . . 020 3130 3000

Pace, M J (Andrew & Co LLP) N Q G Zm
Lincoln p284 . . . 01522 512123

Pacey, F J (Newbys) A1 E S1 W C1 T1 Zi
Stockton-on-Tees p397 . . . 01642 673733 / 676666

Pacey, Ms G K (Maxwell Winward LLP) C1 Ze Zf C2
London EC4 p59 . . . 020 7651 0000

Pachter, G F (Roberts Moore Nicholas Jones) G H
Birkenhead p134 . . . 0151 647 0000

Pacifico, Ms J (Byrne & Partners) N
London EC4 p16 . . . 020 7842 1616

Paciorek, S (Pinsent Masons LLP)
London EC2 p67 . . . 020 7418 7000

Packer, Ms B (Fulchers of Farnborough) Q W N J1
Farnborough p224 . . . 01252 522475

Packer, E (Wimbledon Magistrates Court)
London SW19 p110 . . . 020 8946 8622

Packer, J V (Taylor Vinters) Zo
Cambridge p176 . . . 01223 423444

Packer, N R (T R Harris Arnold & Co) S1 K2 W
Gorseinon p231 . 01792 892166 / 891331

Packer, Miss P D (Blackhurst Swainson Goodier LLP) K1 J1 K2
Lancaster p269 . . . 01524 32471

Packwood, Ms D N (Wace Morgan) S1 E
Shrewsbury p379 . . . 01743 280100

Paddison, D F (Robertsons) C1 E G S1 Zl
Cardiff p180 . . . 029 2023 7777

Paddison, G (DLA Piper UK LLP)
London EC2 p24 . . . 0870 011 1111

Paddison, M S (Hughes Paddison) K1 D1 L B1 Q K2 O K3
Cheltenham p188 . . . 01242 574244

Paddle, Ms P (Follett Stock LLP) C2 Ze I C1
Truro p414 . . . 01872 241700

Paddock, D (Brabners Chaffe Street) Zb E S2
Liverpool p286 . . . 0151 600 3000

Paddock, Ms J M (Fasken Martineau LLP) C1 C2 C3 B1 J1 M1
London W1 p31 . . . 020 7917 8500

Paddock, Miss L R (Shepherd Harris & Co) W
Enfield p219 . . . 020 8363 8341

Padgett, J (Burr Sugden) C1 E R1
Keighley p263 . . . 01535 605407

Padgett, M E (Coffin Mew & Clover) B1 Zj Ze C1 C2 C3
Fareham p223 . . . 01329 825617

Padmore, I M (Hay & Kilner) N O Q
Newcastle upon Tyne p325 . 0191 232 8345

Padmore, Ms S (Fox Williams) O Q
London EC2 p33 . . . 020 7628 2000

Padovan, D C A (Gateley LLP) Zj Za C1
London EC4 p35 . . . 020 7653 1600

Padwell, Miss M (Treasury Solicitors Department)
London WC2 p110 . . . 020 7210 3000

Paganuzzi, B (Kennedys) Zg B1
London EC3 p49 . . . 020 7667 9667

Paganuzzi, R D P (Forbes Hall LLP) B1 J1 N O Q Zb
London EC2 p33 . . . 020 7729 9111
Woodford Green p439 . . . 020 8498 0080

Paganuzzi, Ms S D (Forbes Hall LLP) S1
London EC2 p33 . . . 020 7729 9111

Page, A (Corus Group Limited)
London SW1 p105 . . . 020 7717 4523

Page, Ms A (DLA Piper UK LLP)
Leeds p272 . . . 0870 011 1111

Page, Ms A (Dixon Rigby Keogh) S1
Winsford p434 . . . 01606 557211

Page, Mrs A C (Stratford-on-Avon District Council)
Stratford-upon-Avon p473 . . . 01789 267575

Page, A D S (Squire Sanders (UK) LLP)
Manchester p310 . . . 0161 830 5000

Page, C C (Ford Motor Company Ltd)
Brentwood p451 . . . 01277 253000

Page, C J (Charles Russell LLP) A1 T2 W
Cheltenham p187 . . . 01242 221122

Page, C J (Girlings) Zd F1 Zl S1 C1 M1 P B1 Ze Zc Zf C2 S2 E R2
Ashford p119 . . . 01233 664711

Page, Mrs C L (Ward Gethin) W T2
King's Lynn p266 . . . 01553 660033

Page, D R S (Lester Aldridge LLP) S1 E S2
London WC2 p53 . . . 0844 967 0785
London WC2 p60 . . . 020 7242 5905

Page, D W (Ashurst LLP) C1 T1 Zb Zj
London EC2 p7 . . . 020 7638 1111

Page, E M H (SJ Berwin LLP)
London EC4 p75 . . . 020 7111 2222

Page, Miss F J (Aviva PLC)
London EC3 p103 . . 020 7283 7500 / 01603 687905
Norwich p467 . . . 01603 622200

Page, Ms G M (Norrie Waite & Slater) N
Rotherham p367 . . . 01709 523983

Page, Miss H (Parrott & Coales LLP) K1
Aylesbury p121 . . . 01296 318500

Page, Miss J L (Elliot Mather LLP) G H K1 Q N D1 F1
Matlock p313 . . . 01629 584885

Page, Ms J M (Allen & Overy LLP)
London E1 p5 . . . 020 3088 0000

Page, Miss K (Withers LLP) C1
London EC4 p92 . . . 020 7597 6000

Page, M (Ashurst LLP)
London EC2 p7 . . . 020 7638 1111

Page, Ms M H (Geoffrey Leaver Solicitors LLP) S2 E
Milton Keynes p317 . . . 01908 692769

Page, N J (Bond Pearce LLP) C1 M1 M2
Southampton p385 . . . 0845 415 0000

Page, R A (Goldkorn Mathias Gentle Page LLP) Zf C1 J1 O Q K3 B1 Zc
London WC1 p36 . . . 020 7631 1811

Page, R E (Mayer Brown International LLP) C1 C2
London EC2 p59 . . . 020 3130 3000

Page, R J (Geraint Jones & Co) D1 D2 F1 G H K3 J1 K1 Zl Q
Newtown p330 . . . 01686 627935

Page, R J (Woollcombe Yonge) G H
Plymouth p351 . . . 01752 660384

Page, S (Grahame Stowe Bateson) L Zi Q N
Leeds p274 . . . 0113 246 8163

Page, S F (Schneider Page) B1 C1 I O Ze Zj
London E1 p77 . . . 020 7480 5477

Page, Ms S K (British American Tobacco)
London WC2 p104 . . . 020 7845 1000

Page, T A C (Clifford Chance)
London E14 p20 . . . 020 7006 1000

Page-Jones, R F A (Robert Kyle & Co) S1 C1 E W S2
Marlow p313 . . . 01628 475751

Paget Skelin, M (Capsticks Solicitors LLP) E R2 Zc
London SW19 p18 . . . 020 8780 2211

Paget, Mrs C (Blake Lapthorn) E O L
Chandlers Ford p184 . . . 023 8090 8090

Paget, C (Hanne & Co)
London SW11 p38 . . . 020 7228 0017

Paget, P J (Gordons LLP) J1 O
Leeds p273 . . . 0113 227 0100

Paget, Miss T A (Macmillans) S1 S2 A1 W
Wadebridge p418 . . . 01208 812415

Paget-Brown, S J (Travers Smith LLP) O A3 B2 Q Zj
London EC1 p87 . . . 020 7295 3000

Pagett, Ms A (Red Kite Law) G O
Haverfordwest p244 . . . 01437 763332

Pagett-Wright, D J (Moss Solicitors LLP) Q O J1 L F1 B1 F2 Zp Zq
Loughborough p293 . . . 01509 217770

Pahljina, C J (Cadence Design Systems Ltd)
Bracknell p451 . . . 01344 865445

Pain, Ms A C (EJ Moyle) K3 K1
Littlehampton p285 . . . 01903 725143

Pain, A J (HM Land Registry - Plymouth)
Plymouth p468 . . . 01752 636000 / 636123

Pain, Miss C (Coley & Tilley)
Birmingham p136 . . . 0121 643 5531

Paine, A J (Fishers) A1 E L S1 S2 A2 Zl
Ashby-de-la-Zouch p118 . . . 01530 412167

Paine, G E H (SNR Denton) Zb
London EC4 p75 . . . 020 7242 1212

Paine, Miss L G (British Telecommunications PLC)
London EC1 p104 . . . 020 7356 6181

Paines, Ms A (Withers LLP) Zd W T2
London EC4 p92 . . . 020 7597 6000

Painter, Mrs B J (Dickinson Dees)
Newcastle upon Tyne p324 . 0191 279 9000

Painter, J R (Painters) S1 E W A1 R1 C1
Kidderminster p266 . . . 01562 822295

Painter, S (Bircham Dyson Bell)
Westminster p13 . . . 020 7227 7000

Painter, Mrs S L (Walsh & Company) W K4 S1
Truro p414 . . . 01872 870923

Painter, W R (Painters) S1 W L A1 C1 E S2
Stourport-on-Severn p399 . . . 01299 822033

Paisley, Ms B L (Reed Smith LLP) O
London EC2 p71 . . . 020 3116 3000

Paisley, Ms K (Reynolds Porter Chamberlain LLP)
London E1 p71 . . . 020 3060 6000

Pajak, S C (T M Warner & Co) S1 E C1 K1 F1 P
Kidlington p266 . . . 01865 379311

Pal, P S (Sidley Austin Brown & Wood) Zb
London EC2 p78 . . . 020 7360 3600

Palazzo, A (McCormacks) B2 G H I
London EC3 p56 . . . 020 7791 2000

Palazzo, U R (McCormacks) B2 G H
London EC3 p56 . . . 020 7791 2000

Palca, Miss J C (Olswang LLP) J1 O Zk Ze Zf Zp
London WC1 p64 . . . 020 7067 3000

Paleokrassas, G (Watson Farley & Williams)
London EC2 p90 . . . 020 7814 8000

Palfreman, A B (Fraser Brown) S1 E Zd
Nottingham p337 . . . 0115 988 8777

Palfreman, Miss A J (Finn Gledhill) N K1 Q D1 Zq D2 Zr
Halifax p238 . . . 01422 330000
Hebden Bridge p246 . . . 01422 842451

Palfrey, J (Lansbury Worthington) G H B2
London W6 p51 . . . 020 8563 9797

Palihawadana, P (Allan Rutherford) G H V Zi B2
Norwich p333 . . . 01603 621722

Palin, S J (Sanderson McCreath & Edney) S1 W Q K3 C1
Berwick-upon-Tweed p131 . . 01289 306724

Palka, S G (Blake Lapthorn) E R1 Zc
Portsmouth p354 . . . 023 9222 1122

Pall, A K (Vyman Solicitors) E S2 Zl R2 S1
Harrow p242 . . . 020 8427 9080

Pall, Miss S (Dexter Montague LLP) S1 E
Reading p360 . . . 0118 939 3999

Pallant, Miss D J (Janette Hill & Co Solicitors) N Zj
Hay-on-Wye p245 . . . 01497 821000

Pallett, Miss H E (Cartwright King) G K1 Zm
Derby p208 . . . 01332 346111
Leicester p279 . . . 0116 253 9222
Nottingham p336 . . . 0115 958 7444

Pallikarou, Miss A (Meade & Co) S1 E W K4
London N14 p60 . . . 020 8886 3643
London N14 p83 . . . 020 8882 1047

Pallister, J F T (Hayes & Storr) S1 A1
Holt p251 . . . 01263 712835

Pallister, K (Calthrops) S1 L E C1 W
Spalding p389 . . . 01775 724381

Pallister, S (Charles Russell LLP) Zd T1 T2 W
Cheltenham p187 . . . 01242 221122
Cheltenham p189 . . . 01242 710200

Pallot, C B (Ashfords LLP)
Exeter p220 . . . 01392 337000

Palman, Ms J (The College of Law)
London WC1 p105 . . . 0800 289997

Palmann, Mrs M I (Pirie Palmann) E F1 J1 P S1 A1 L W R1 C1
Peterborough p347 . . . 01733 427799

Palmer, Miss A D (Rydon Group Ltd) S1 E R1 A1 C1 W T1 L Zh Zs
Forest Row p458 . . . 01342 825151

Palmer, Miss A G (Kennedys) N
London EC3 p49 . . . 020 7667 9667

Palmer, A J (Blaser Mills) S1 E L S2
Chesham p189 . . . 01494 782291

Palmer, Mrs A J (Eaton Smith LLP) C1 C2
Huddersfield p255 . . . 01484 821300

Palmer, A S (Brachers) W Zv Zd T2
Maidstone p299 . . . 01622 690691

Palmer, B (Charles Russell LLP) J1 O Zw X
London EC4 p19 . . . 020 7203 5000

Palmer, Ms C (Leigh Day & Co) J1 Zp Zg
London EC1 p52 . . . 020 7650 1200

Palmer, C (Colin Palmer & Co) S1 W C1
Lowestoft p294 . . . 01502 589277

Palmer, C D (Speechly Bircham LLP) E C1 R1 Zc
London EC4 p81 . . . 020 7427 6400

Palmer, C J (Palmer Hodgson & Heyes) K1 G H D1 P J1 F1 V L
Fleetwood p226 . . . 01253 778231
Thornton Cleveleys p411 . . . 01253 824216

Palmer, D A (BLB Solicitors) S1 E A1 L W C1 R1
Trowbridge p413 . . . 01225 755656

Palmer, Ms E A (Finers Stephens Innocent LLP) W T1 T2
London W1 p32 . . . 020 7323 4000

Palmer, Mrs E J (Davitt Jones Bould) E S2 L
Taunton p408 . . . 01823 279279

Palmer, Mrs E R (Stantons) K1
Gravesend p233 . . . 01474 579940

Palmer, G H (Ford Simey LLP) P M1 K1 R1 N L F1 G J1 D1 Zh Zl
Exeter p221 . . . 01392 274126

Palmer, Mrs H (Mason Palmer) K1 Q V W S1
Barnsley p125 . . . 01226 709100

Palmer, Mrs H E J (Robson Palmer) S2 L R1 S1
South Shields p384 . . . 0191 455 4561

Palmer, Ms I E (Trobridges) W
Plymouth p350 . . . 01752 664022

Palmer, Ms J (Rhodia UK Ltd)
Watford p475 . . . 01923 485758

Palmer, J (Kennedys) E
London EC3 p49 . . . 020 7667 9667

Palmer, Ms J (Palmers) S1
Bedford p130 . . . 01234 211161

See p634 for the Key to Work Categories

Palmer, J E (Herbert Smith LLP) *C1 C2*
London EC2 *p40* 020 7374 8000

Palmer, Mrs J F (Daimler Chrysler UK Ltd)
Milton Keynes *p466* 01908 245000

Palmer, J P (Croftons) *N J1 O*
Manchester *p302* 0161 214 6180

Palmer, J S A (Alletsons) *N Q O S1 L F1*
Burnham-on-Sea *p169* 01278 780151

Palmer, K J (Birketts LLP (Wollastons LLP)) *O J1 J2*
Chelmsford *p186* 01245 211211

Palmer, L (Farnworth Shaw) *F1 N Q Zq*
Colne *p198* 01282 865885

Palmer, Miss L (SAS Daniels LLP) *K1*
Congleton *p198* 01260 282300

Palmer, Mrs L A (Quality Solicitors Palmers) *E S1 W F1 X Q S2 V K4 B1*
Fetcham *p226* 01372 454791

Palmer, Mrs M E (Millington Wallace & Co) *S1 E W L K1 T1*
London N14 *p61* 020 8882 1051

Palmer, M E O (Gregory Rowcliffe Milners) *S1 E*
London WC1 *p37* 020 7242 0631

Palmer, N (Field Fisher Waterhouse LLP)
London EC3 *p31* 020 7861 4000

Palmer, N G (Barker Gotelee Solicitors) *W K4 T2 Zd V*
Ipswich *p262* 01473 611211
Diss *p211* 01379 652141
Luton *p295* 01582 731161

Palmer, N J (Palmers Solicitors) *W K4*
Kingston upon Thames *p267* . 020 8549 7444

Palmer, P A (Clifford Chance)
London E14 *p20* 020 7006 1000

Palmer, P G (Fisher Meredith) *K1*
Lambeth *p32* 020 7091 2700

Palmer, P J (Quality Solicitors Palmers) *S1 K1 A3 W Zq K4*
Fetcham *p226* 01372 454791

Palmer, P W (Dixon Rigby Keogh) *J1 W K4*
Sandbach *p372* 01270 766550

Palmer, R (CMS Cameron McKenna LLP)
London EC3 *p17* 020 7367 3000

Palmer, R B D (Davies Partnership) *S1 E C1 A1 W K1 L P F1 Zk Zo Zl K3*
Helston *p246* 01326 573767

Palmer, R C S (Ashurst LLP) *T1*
London EC2 *p7* 020 7638 1111

Palmer, R F (Graham & Rosen) *C1 S1 A1 T1 E W*
Hull *p257* 01482 323123

Palmer, R J (Watson Burton LLP) *O Q F1 Zq Zc Zj*
Newcastle upon Tyne *p327* . 0845 901 2100

Palmer, R J (Hill Dickinson LLP) *B1 C1 M1*
London EC3 *p41* 020 7283 9033

Palmer, Miss R L (Pardoes) *K1*
Bridgwater *p158* 01278 457891

Palmer, R M (Palmers) *E A1 L R1 T1 S2 T2*
Bedford *p130* 01234 211161

Palmer, Ms S (Leonard & Co) *G H*
Southampton *p386* 023 8023 3242

Palmer, S (Russell-Cooke LLP) *E L S1*
London SW15 *p74* 020 8789 9111

Palmer, Ms S (Palmers) *E S2*
Bedford *p130* 01234 211161

Palmer, Ms S (Salans) *O Q Zq*
London EC4 *p76* 020 7429 6000

Palmer, Miss S A (Blake Lapthorn) *D1 K1 D2*
Chandlers Ford *p184* 023 8090 8090

Palmer, Mrs S C (Palmers Criminal Defence Solicitors) *K1 V N S1*
Deal *p207* 01304 380572

Palmer, S D (Addleshaw Goddard)
Leeds *p271* 0113 209 2000
Leeds *p277* 0113 284 7000

Palmer, Miss S E (Brain Chase Coles) *W K4 T2*
Basingstoke *p126* 01256 354481

Palmer, Mrs S L (Bailey Smailes) *W S1*
Holmfirth *p251* 01484 686000

Palmer, S T H (Bower & Bailey) *C1 S2 E Zl S1 W*
Oxford *p343* 01865 311133
Witney *p436* 01993 705095

Palmer, T D (Welsh Development Agency Legal Services)
Cardiff *p453* 029 2082 8681

Palmer, T H (Olswang LLP) *C1 C2 I*
London WC1 *p64* 020 7067 3000

Palmer, T M (Penningtons) *N Zr*
Basingstoke *p127* 01256 407100

Palmer, Miss V (Shell International Ltd)
London SE1 *p109* 020 7934 1234

Palmer, W E (Speakeasy Advice Centre)
Cardiff *p453* 029 2045 3111

Palomares, Ms M M (Hansen Palomares) *L Zg V X Zi*
Lambeth *p38* 020 7640 4600

Palos, G (Lawrence Stephens) *B1 Zc C1 S2 E L Zl O Q R1 R2 S1 T1 T2*
London EC1 *p82* 020 7935 1211

Paltnoi, Mrs L J (Philip Ross & Co) *C1 C2 F1 U2*
London W1 *p73* 020 7636 6969

Paltridge, S R (The College of Law Guildford)
Guildford *p459* 01483 460200

Paluch, Ms R M (A Kay Pietron & Paluch) *L Q Zi*
Ealing *p3* 020 8992 9997

Pamar, R (Birmingham City Council Legal & Democratic Services)
Birmingham *p449* 0121 303 2066

Panambalana, D M C (Hogan Lovells International LLP)
London EC1 *p42* 020 7296 2000

Panasar, Miss J (Criminal Defence Solicitors) *H G B2*
Westminster *p23* 020 7353 7000

Panayides, A (Clifford Chance)
London E14 *p20* 020 7006 1000

Panayiotou, M I (Squire Sanders (UK) LLP) *C1 C2*
London EC2 *p81* 020 7655 1000

Panayiotou, Ms P (Van Baaren & Wright) *E K1 N S1 W*
Richmond upon Thames *p364* 020 8940 2525

Panayotopoulou, E (Hill Dickinson LLP)
London EC3 *p41* 020 7283 9033

Pancholi, Miss T (Cotterhill Hitchman LLP) *S1 E*
Sutton Coldfield *p403* . . . 0121 323 1860

Pandal, S (The Endeavour Partnership LLP) *E*
Stockton-on-Tees *p397* . . . 01642 610300

Pandelis, Ms M (Edwin Coe LLP) *C1 C2*
London WC2 *p29* 020 7691 4000

Pandit, D (Kaim Todner Ltd) *N G H*
Islington *p47* 020 7700 0070
London EC4 *p47* 020 7353 6660

Pandit, P K (Sintons LLP) *E L S2*
Newcastle upon Tyne *p326* . 0191 226 7878

Pandya, Mrs S (Bradly Trimmer) *W T2*
Alton *p116* 01420 88024

Panesar, G S (Wiggin LLP) *Ze I Zf U2*
Cheltenham *p189* 01242 224114

Panesar, S S (Rainer Hughes)
Brentwood *p156* 01227 226644

Pang, B (The Stokes Partnership) *C1*
Crewkerne *p203* 01460 279279

Pang, W Y (Bassets) *W S1 K4*
Gillingham *p229* 01634 575464

Pangu, S S (Alfred Truman) *N J1 K1 F1 G O Q Zp*
Bicester *p132* 01869 252761

Panizzo, Mrs S E (Penningtons)
London EC2 *p66* 020 7457 3000

Pankhania, K C (KCP Law)
Hounslow *p254* 020 8572 1212

Pankhania, S (George Anthony Andrews Solicitors)
London W3 *p6* 020 8746 0550

Pannone, R J (Pannone LLP) *N Zg Zq Zr*
Manchester *p308* 0161 909 3000

Pantelia, Ms D (Clifford Chance)
London E14 *p20* 020 7006 1000

Panto, B N (Westminster City Council)
London SW1 *p110* 020 7641 6000

Panton, E N (Gladstones) *K1 S1 W*
Crowborough *p204* 01892 610260

Panton, Mrs R J (Kidd Rapinet)
Farnham *p225* 0845 017 9609

Papadakis, J J (Jones Day) *J1*
London EC4 *p46* 020 7039 5959

Papadopulo, P (Philip Ross & Co) *C1 E*
London W1 *p73* 020 7636 6969

Papakyriacou, A A (Briffa) *Ze Zf U2 J1 Zza C1 O Zk Zw M1 C3*
Islington *p15* 020 7288 6003

Papanicolaou, A (Nicos & Co) *K1 G L W Q Zi Zl*
Haringey *p63* 020 8888 1166

Papanicolaou, C (Jones Day) *E*
London EC4 *p46* 020 7039 5959

Papantoniou, K (Healys LLP) *C1*
London EC4 *p39* 020 7822 4000

Pape, Ms F S (Irwin Mitchell LLP) *N Zj*
Sheffield *p376* 0870 150 0100

Papenfus, K L B (Alan Harris) *G H*
Plymouth *p350* 01752 223655

Papworth, Ms K (K&L Gates LLP)
London EC4 *p47* 020 7648 9000

Papworth, R N (Addleshaw Goddard)
Leeds *p271* 0113 209 2000
Manchester *p300* 0161 934 6000

Paradise, Miss N E (Nabarro LLP)
London WC1 *p63* 020 7524 6000

Paradise, P (Taylor Wessing)
London EC4 *p86* 020 7300 7000

Paramesuaran, M (Wilson & Co)
London N17 *p92* 020 8808 7535

Paramjorthy, Mrs M (Philip Ross & Co) *S1 Zi*
Bushey *p172* 020 8090 9191
London W1 *p73* 020 7636 6969

Paramore, S J (Foys Solicitors) *G H B2*
Doncaster *p211* 01302 327136

Parapagga, Miss B K (Levenes Solicitors) *N*
Birmingham *p140* 0121 212 0000

Paravicini, J V R (Forsters LLP) *E*
Westminster *p33* 020 7863 8333

Parbat, V (The Royal Borough of Kensington & Chelsea)
London W8 *p109* 020 7361 2741

Parbery, L A (Dickinson Dees) *T1*
Newcastle upon Tyne *p324* . 0191 279 9000

Parden, N B (Hogan Lovells International LLP)
London EC1 *p42* 020 7296 2000

Parekh, H (Hewitsons) *Ze U2 C1 C3 M1 F1*
Cambridge *p174* 01223 461155

Parekh, S (Greenwoods)
Milton Keynes *p317* 01908 298200

Paremain, R M (Sarginsons Law LLP) *N O Q*
Coventry *p201* 024 7655 3181

Parffrey, F A (Cartridges) *C1 E L R1 S1 W*
Exeter *p220* 01392 256854

Parfitt, D A (Coles Miller Solicitors LLP) *W T2 Zd Zm Zo Zv*
Poole *p352* 01202 673011

Parfitt, Ms E J (Radcliffes Le Brasseur)
Westminster *p70* 020 7222 7040

Parfitt, Mrs E W A (St Edmundsbury Borough Council) *R1*
Bury St Edmunds *p452* . . . 01284 763233

Parfitt, Ms N C (Lee & Thompson) *Ze*
London W1 *p52* 020 7935 4665

Parfitt, Mrs S (Michelmores LLP) *W T2*
Exeter *p221* 01392 688688

Parford, S W (Wolferstans) *N Zr*
Plymouth *p351* 01752 663295

Parham, H G (HM Land Registry - Plymouth)
Plymouth *p468* . . . .01752 636000 / 636123

Pari, O G (Bone & Payne LLP) *G H K1 L Q V K3*
Llandudno *p291* 01492 876354

Parillon, Miss C A (Jacobs Forbes Solicitors) *S2 K1 O Q S1*
London N17 *p45* 020 8880 4154

Paris, S W (Paris & Co)
Stratford-upon-Avon *p400* . . 01789 298177

Paris, S W (Anthony Clark & Co) *S1 R1 Zl S2 E*
Lincoln *p284* 01522 512321

Parish, A J (Sitters & Co) *N Q K3 K1*
Plymouth *p350* 01752 220464

Parish, Mrs J B (Judith Parish Solicitor) *S1 W E L*
Weybridge *p430* 01932 842022

Parish, Mrs L S (Spicketts Battrick Law Practice) *D1 K1*
Pontypridd *p352* 01443 407221

Parish, Mrs N (Financial Services Authority)
London E14 *p106* 020 7066 1000

Parish, P (Hogan Lovells International LLP)
London EC1 *p42* 020 7296 2000

Parisi, Mrs L (Pinsent Masons LLP) *T1 T2*
Birmingham *p141* 0121 200 1050

Park, A W D (Lawrence Stephens) *K1 S1 P N M1 G J1 L E W Ze Zf Zc*
London EC1 *p82* 020 7935 1211

Park, C (Bracher Rawlins LLP)
London WC1 *p15* 020 7404 9400

Park, C E (Pinsent Masons LLP) *C1*
London EC2 *p67* 020 7418 7000

Park, C J (Potter & Co) *K1 G D1 Q O Zl*
Matlock *p313* 01629 582308

Park, D E (Oglethorpe Sturton & Gillibrand) *E C1 C2 J1*
Lancaster *p270* 01524 846846

Park, I G (Park Law) *C1 C2 C3 D1 J1 K1 M2 Zc Zl Zv*
Camberley *p173* 01276 804788

Park, J G (H L F Berry & Co) *W S1 G*
Failsworth *p223* 0161 681 4005

Park, J K (J Keith Park & Co) *S1 C1 E W T1 L B1 R1 A1 Zc Zo*
St Helens *p391* 01744 636000

Park, Mrs J M (Ashfords LLP) *S1*
Exeter *p220* 01392 337000

Park, Mrs J M (Shakespeares) *N Zj*
Birmingham *p142* 0121 237 3000

Park, Ms K S (Kirklees Metropolitan Borough Council) *K1 D1*
Huddersfield *p461* 01484 221421

Park, M A (Gateley LLP)
Birmingham *p138* 0121 234 0000

Park, M T (Addleshaw Goddard) *Zb*
Leeds *p271* 0113 209 2000

Park, Mrs P (DWF) *C1 C2 F1 F2 Zy*
Liverpool *p287* 0151 907 3000

Parkar, Mrs F (Lawrence Lupin) *K3 K1 Zi*
Wembley *p426* 020 8733 7200

Parkash, R (Clifford Chance)
London E14 *p20* 020 7006 1000

Parke, P F (DAC Beachcroft) *P M1 G Zj*
Bristol *p162* 0117 918 2000

Parker, Miss A (The Johnson Partnership) *G H*
Nottingham *p337* 0115 941 9141

Parker, A A (D S Bosher & Co) *O K1 D1 F1 K3 K4 J1 K2 L N Zq W S1*
Hove *p254* 01273 721913

Parker, A B (Hempsons) *C1 M1 F2*
Harrogate *p240* 01423 522331

Parker, A D (Edwards Duthie) *G H B2*
London E13 *p29* 020 8514 9000
London WC2 *p76* 020 7632 4300

Parker, A G (Lightfoots LLP) *E C1*
Thame *p410* 01844 212305

Parker, A J (British Telecommunications PLC)
London EC1 *p104* 020 7356 6181

Parker, A J (Glovers Solicitors LLP) *R2 E Zb*
London W1 *p36* 020 7935 8882

Parker, A J (Smith & Tetley) *S1 S2 W L E T1 R1 C1 A1 Zt*
Ashton-under-Lyne *p120* . . . 0161 330 2865

Parker, A J C (DAC Beachcroft) *N O*
London EC4 *p24* 020 7242 1011

Parker, A S (Forsters LLP) *Zc*
Westminster *p33* 020 7863 8333

Parker, C (Taylor Woodrow Construction Legal Department)
Watford *p475* 01923 478442

Parker, C (Anthony Collins Solicitors LLP) *E S2*
Birmingham *p137* 0121 200 3242

Parker, C A (Patersons) *E L S1 W*
Lancaster *p270* 01524 843336

Parker, Mrs C E (Wilkin Chapman Grange Solicitors) *K1 E D1 W*
Horncastle *p252* 01507 527521

Parker, C J (Eatons) *W S1 L E*
Bradford *p153* 0845 660 0660

Parker, C M (David Lees & Co) *S1 E K1 W N C1 J1 L*
Knowle *p269* 0117 972 1261

Parker, D (Thomson Webb & Corfield) *W S1*
Cambridge *p176* 01223 578070
Cambridge *p176* 01223 518317

Parker, Ms D (Withers LLP) *K1*
London EC4 *p92* 020 7597 6000

Parker, Ms D (Atherton Godfrey) *N J1 Q*
Doncaster *p211* 01302 320621

Parker, D J (Harcus Sinclair) *Q W B2 Zq*
London WC2 *p38* 020 7242 9700
London EC4 *p92* 020 7597 6000

Parker, Mrs E A (Forbes) *G Zm*
Preston *p356* 01772 220022

Parker, G (Russell & Co Solicitors and Estate Agents) *Zr K1 N J1 Zq Q W*
Crawley *p202* 01293 561965 / 0845 300 2809

Parker, Mrs H A (Sintons LLP) *S1 W E L K1 D1 C1 F1 J1 G Zl Zm X*
Newcastle upon Tyne *p326* . 0191 226 7878

Parker, Miss H L (Spearing Waite LLP) *C1 C2 Ze Zd*
Leicester *p281* 0116 262 4225

Parker, Ms H L (Wansbroughs)
Devizes *p210* 01380 733300

Parker, I A (Moss & Coleman) *S1*
Hornchurch *p252* 01708 446781

Parker, I R (Ash Clifford) *N K1 Q S1 E G L F1 O*
Bridgwater *p157* 01278 451327

Parker, Ms J (Kimbells LLP) *E R2*
Milton Keynes *p317* 01908 668555

Parker, J B (Parker Arrenberg) *C1 Zd*
London SE6 *p65* 020 8695 2330

Parker, J R (Burkill Govier) *E R2 S2 C1 Zc L A1*
Farnham *p224* 01252 717171

Parker, Ms J R (Merck Sharp & Dohme Ltd)
Hoddesdon *p461* 01992 452509

Parker, J R (Widdows Pilling & Co) *G N P J1 K1 L F1 H M1 C1 Zb Ze Zp K2 K3 I*
Walkden *p419* 0161 790 1825

Parker, J S (Barlow Lyde & Gilbert LLP)
London EC3 *p10* 020 7247 2277

Parker, J T (MFG Solicitors)
Kidderminster *p265* 01562 820181

Parker, J V (HM Land Registry - Leicester)
Leicester *p463* . . . . .0116 265 4000 / 4001

Parker, J W J (Plexus Law (A Trading Name of Parabis Law LLP)) *A3 J2 N Zj*
Leeds *p276* 0844 245 4100

Parker, Ms K (Clarks Legal LLP) *Q O F1 F2 Zq*
Reading *p360* 0118 958 5321

Parker, Mrs L L (Kerseys) *W K4*
Ipswich *p262* 01473 213311

Parker, L M C (Charles Lucas & Marshall) *C1 I Ze U2 C2*
Newbury *p322* 01635 521212

Parker, Ms L S (The Royal Borough of Kensington & Chelsea)
London W8 *p109* 020 7361 2741

Parker, M (Northumbrian Water Ltd)
Durham *p457* 0870 608 4820

Parker, M A (Bircham Dyson Bell)
Westminster *p13* 020 7227 7000

Parker, M G (Parkers) *O C1*
Stockport *p396* 0161 477 9451

Parker, N (Berry Smith LLP) *O Q*
Cardiff *p177* 029 2034 5511

Parker, N M (Stone Rowe Brewer LLP) *S1 W S2 T2*
Twickenham *p416* 020 8891 6141

Parker, Mrs O J (O'Neill Patient) *W S1*
Stockport *p396* 0161 483 8555
Stockport *p396* 0161 477 9451

Parker, P (Brabners Chaffe Street) *A1 Zc E P J2 Q R1*
Liverpool *p286* 0151 600 3000

Parker, Mrs P E R (Limbach Banham) *W T1*
Royston *p368* 01763 242257

Parker, P J (Watmores) *N O Q J2 Zj*
London WC2 *p90* 020 7430 1512

Parker, Miss R (Oxley & Coward Solicitors LLP) *K3 K1*
Rotherham *p367* 01709 510999

Parker, R (DWF) *N Zj J2*
Leeds *p272* 0113 261 6000

Parker, R (Purcell Parker) *G H L V*
Birmingham *p141* 0121 236 9781

Parker, Ms R (Martello Professional Risks Limited)
London EC3 *p108* 020 7337 7500

Parker, R H (Thorp Parker LLP) *E C1 S1 J1 W S2*
Stokesley *p398* 01642 711354

Parker, R J (Phillips Solicitors)
Basingstoke *p127* 01256 460830

Parker, R J (Reed Smith LLP) *J1 O Q Zc*
London EC2 *p71* 020 3116 3000

Parker, Ms S (Wilkinson & Butler)
St Neots *p392* 01480 219229

Parker, S E (Barnsley Metropolitan Borough Council)
Barnsley *p448* 01226 770770

Parker, Miss S K (DWF) *C1 C2*
Manchester *p303* 0161 603 5000
Stockport *p396* 0161 477 9451

Parker, S R (Kirby Sheppard) *S1 E S2*
Kingswood *p268* 0845 840 0045

Parker, T C (Harbottle & Lewis LLP) *C2 U2 C1*
London W1 *p38* 020 7667 5000

Parker, T G (Davies & Partners) *E S2 Zh*
Gloucester *p230* 01452 612345

Parker, Miss T J (Foot Anstey) *L*
Exeter *p221* 01392 411221

Parker, T M (Cullimore Dutton) *S1 E K4 W*
Chester *p190* 01244 356789

Parker, W G B (Maxwell Winward LLP) *J1*
London EC4 *p59* 020 7651 0000

Parker, W M (Pinsent Masons LLP)
Leeds *p276* 0113 244 5000

6

Parker-Fuller, G (Watson Burton LLP) *R2 S2 E*
Newcastle upon Tyne *p327* . 0845 901 2100

Parker-Gray, Mrs K F (Rotherham Magistrates Court)
Rotherham *p470* 01709 839339

Parkes, D (Harry Boodhoo & Co) *D1 K3 K1*
Withington *p436* 0161 445 0588

Parkes, D A (SJ Berwin LLP)
London EC4 *p75* 020 7111 2222

Parkes, Mrs D P (Hatch Brenner) *W*
Norwich *p334* 01603 660811

Parkes, Ms E (Elaine Parkes Solicitors)
Rye *p370* 01424 883183

Parkes, J A W (Keelys LLP) *C1 E T1 B1 A1 L S1 Zc Ze*
Lichfield *p284* 01543 420000

Parkes, J G (Field Seymour Parkes) *C1 C2 B1 P*
Reading *p360* 0118 951 6200

Parkes, Ms K J (Thompsons (formerly Robin/Brian Thompson & Partners)) *N*
Cardiff *p181* 029 2044 5300

Parkes, Mrs L D (Cross Ram & Co) *S1 E*
Framlingham *p227*. 01728 724111

Parkes, Miss N E (Aaron & Partners LLP Solicitors) *E Q*
Chester *p190* 01244 405555

Parkes, N T (Wiggin LLP) *Zf O Ze Zn*
Cheltenham *p189* 01242 224114

Parkes, R (William Dawes & Co) *S1 W L R1 E A1 T1 C1*
Rye *p370* 01797 223177

Parkes, R (Heringtons) *G H P R1 B1 V Zl*
Hastings *p243* 01424 434192

Parkes, R E (Parkes Browne) *E S1 L W K1 N O Q J1 F1 Zl Zd Zc*
Andover *p118* 01264 333336

Parkes, Mrs S C (Brain Chase Coles) *K2 K1 K3*
Basingstoke *p126* 01256 354481

Parkes, T C (Herbert Smith LLP) *O*
London EC2 *p40*. 020 7374 8000

Parkhill, J A (Larken & Co) *A1 C1 E S2 R1 S1*
Newark *p322* 01636 703333

Parkhouse, A C (Farrer & Co LLP)
London WC2 *p31* 020 3375 7000

Parkhouse, D B (A V Hawkins & Co) *S1 W E G H*
Harrow *p241*. . .020 8422 2364 / 8422 2466

Parkhouse, D L (Lester Aldridge LLP) *T1*
Bournemouth *p152*. 01202 786161

Parkhouse, D L (Parkhouse & Co) *C1 E F1 K1 L P S1 T1 W O Zc Zf Zj*
Bristol *p164* 0117 962 9978

Parkhouse, J R O (Thompsons (formerly Robin/ Brian Thompson & Partners))
Birmingham *p143* 0121 262 1200

Parkhouse, N W (E D C Lord & Co)
Hayes *p245* 020 8848 9988

Parkin, G T (Henry Hyams) *G H*
Leeds *p274* 0113 243 2288

Parkin, Miss H L (Hewitts) *K1 D1 H G Zl Zv J1 F1 F2*
Newton Aycliffe *p330*. 01325 316170

Parkin, J (The Wilkes Partnership LLP) *C1 C2 Ze I*
Birmingham *p143* 0121 233 4333

Parkin, Ms R A (Lockharts Solicitors) *C1*
London WC1 *p55* 020 7383 7111

Parkington, Ms C (Linder Myers Solicitors)
Manchester *p307* 0844 984 6400

Parkins, A S (Percy Hughes & Roberts) *O Q F1 L*
Birkenhead *p134*. 0151 666 9090

Parkinson, Mrs A (Network Rail)
London NW1 *p108*. 020 7557 8000

Parkinson, Mrs A M (Lancaster City Council)
Lancaster *p462* 01524 582000

Parkinson, C (Brabners Chaffe Street)
Liverpool *p286*. 0151 600 3000

Parkinson, Ms C A (Calderdale Metropolitan BC Corporate Services Directorate)
Halifax *p460* 01422 357257

Parkinson, D J M (N Legal)
Sutton Coldfield *p404* 0121 355 8885

Parkinson, D K (Darlington Hardcastles) *S2 E L S1*
Rickmansworth *p364*. 01923 774272

Parkinson, G (Boyes Turner) *O Q L B1*
Reading *p360* 0118 959 7711

Parkinson, Miss G (Dodd Lewis Solicitors) *W*
London SE3 *p27*. 020 8852 1255

Parkinson, Miss G M (Gloucestershire County Council - Legal & Democratic Services)
Gloucester *p459* 01452 425203

Parkinson, G T (Forbes) *G H F1 L*
Accrington *p114* 01254 872111

Parkinson, M (Russell-Cooke LLP) *W*
London SW15 *p74*. 020 8789 9111

Parkinson, M C L (Chattertons Solicitors) *W T2 T1 Zd*
Horncastle *p252* 01507 522456

Parkinson, Ms M E (Butterworths)
Carlisle *p182*. 01228 593939

Parkinson, N (Shelter Legal Services)
London EC1 *p109* 020 7505 2000

Parkinson, P (Stockport Metropolitan Borough Council)
Stockport *p472*. 0161 480 4949

Parkinson, P M (Ewings & Co) *D1 G H J1 K1 Zl Zm*
London SE20 *p30* 020 8778 1126

Parkinson, R C W (Turner Parkinson) *C1 C2*
Manchester *p310* 0161 833 1212

Parkinson, R M (Taylor Bracewell) *K1 M1 P G D1 C1 B1 F1 N J1 Zl*
Doncaster *p212* 01302 341414

Parkinson, T J (Rowlinsons) *S1 S2 E*
Frodsham *p227* 01928 735333

Parkinson, T J (McEwen Parkinson) *E S1 L W C1 S2*
Westminster *p56*. 020 7487 4361

Parkman, Mrs R E E (Wards Solicitors (Family Law Enquiries)) *W L S1*
Weston-super-Mare *p429* . . 01934 428800

Parks, R D (Barlow Robbins LLP) *Q O B1 Zq*
Guildford *p235*. 01483 562901

Parlby, G H (Parlby Calder Solicitors) *G H*
Plymouth *p350*. 01752 600833

Parlett, Mrs M (Foys Solicitors) *D2 D1 K3 K1*
Worksop *p441* 01909 473560

Parmar, Miss A (Bedfordshire County Council)
Bedford *p448* 01234 363222

Parmar, D (Parmars) *S1 C1 E F1 L P Q W N Zi*
Leicester *p280*. 0116 255 5155

Parmar, H (Sharp & Partners)
Nottingham *p339*. 0115 959 0055

Parmar, Ms I S (Capita Group Plc)
Bristol *p451* 01275 840840

Parmar, Ms R (Shelter Legal Services)
London EC1 *p109* 020 7505 2000

Parmar, Ms S (Taylor Walton LLP) *S1*
Luton *p295* 01582 731161

Parmenter, B M G (Birkett Long LLP) *W*
Chelmsford *p186*. 01245 453800

Parnall, J R B (Parnalls Solicitors Limited) *A1 E L S1 W T2*
Launceston *p270* 01566 772375

Parnall, Mrs K S (Parnalls Solicitors Limited) *G H I N O P Q X J1 Zi Zj Zm Zp*
Launceston *p270* 01566 772375

Parnall, R M B (Parnalls Solicitors Limited) *A1 C1 E P S1 R2*
Launceston *p270* 01566 772375

Parnell, A K (Sidley Austin Brown & Wood) *C1 C2*
London EC2 *p78*. 020 7360 3600

Parnell, R J (Bridge McFarland) *J1*
Grimsby *p235* 01472 311711
Lincoln *p284*. 01522 518888

Parnell, Mrs S G T (MLM Cartwright) *S2 Zc E F1 K4 L Zl Zm R1 R2 W Zb*
Cardiff *p179* 029 2046 2562

Parnell-King, M (Gregory Rowcliffe Milners) *W T2*
London WC1 *p37* 020 7242 0631

Parr, Mrs C (Shacklocks) *W T2*
Belper *p131* 01773 822333

Parr, C M (Collyer Bristow LLP)
London WC1 *p22* 020 7242 7363

Parr, Mrs E (Hardman Wood) *S1 W K4 S2*
Blackburn *p145* 01254 295540

Parr, G J (Bolton Metropolitan Borough Council)
Bolton *p450* 01204 333333

Parr, J (Allen & Overy LLP)
London E1 *p5* 020 3088 0000

Parr, Ms J (Information Commisioner)
Wilmslow *p476*. 01625 545700

Parr, J G (Linklaters LLP)
London EC2 *p54*. 020 7456 2000

Parr, K G (Blackhurst Swainson Goodier LLP) *N Q O J1 B1 F1 Zq*
Preston *p356* 01772 253841

Parr, M (The Wilkes Partnership LLP) *W*
Birmingham *p143* 0121 233 4333

Parr, N (Ashurst LLP) *C1*
London EC2 *p7* 020 7638 1111

Parrett, C G J (Isadore Goldman Solicitors) *B1 O Q*
London EC4 *p45*. 020 7353 1000

Parrett, Miss C V E (Maples Teesdale LLP) *O*
London EC2 *p58*. 020 7600 3800

Parrinder, Miss A (Watson Farley & Williams)
London EC2 *p90*. 020 7814 8000

Parrington, S H (Hill Dickinson LLP) *Zj N J1 Zl O C1*
Chester *p190* 01244 896600

Parris, Ms E (Field Fisher Waterhouse LLP)
London EC3 *p31*. 020 7861 4000

Parrott, M K (Clarke Willmott) *Zy F1*
Bristol *p162* 0845 209 1000 / 0117 305 6000

Parrott, P A (Mackrell Turner Garrett) *S1 W E L*
Woking *p437*. 01483 755609

Parrott, R J (Donnelly & Elliott Limited) *D1 D2 K1 L S1 W*
Gosport *p232* 023 9250 5500

Parry, A (Hunters) *T2 W Zd*
London WC2 *p44* 020 7412 0050

Parry, Mrs A E (Dolmans) *N L*
Cardiff *p178* 029 2034 5531

Parry, Miss A M (Brabners Chaffe Street) *W T2*
Liverpool *p286*. 0151 600 3000

Parry, A R (Hill Dickinson LLP) *E R2 S2*
Liverpool *p288* 0151 600 8000

Parry, Mrs C (Western Division Service Magistrates Court)
Caernarfon *p452*. 01286 675200

Parry, Miss C (Watson Solicitors) *D1 K1 K3*
Warrington *p422*. 01925 571212

Parry, Mrs C J (British Vita PLC)
Middleton *p465* 0161 643 1133

Parry, C S (Woollcombe Yonge) *W*
Plymouth *p351*. 01752 660384

Parry, Miss C W (Western Division Service Magistrates Court)
Caernarfon *p452*. 01286 675200

Parry, D H (Darbys Solicitors LLP) *J1 Zp*
Oxford *p343* 01865 811700

Parry, D R (Whatley Recordon) *S1 W S2 R2 L*
Malvern *p300* 01684 892939

Parry, Ms D S (Nabarro LLP)
London WC1 *p63* 020 7524 6000

Parry, E J (Bond Pearce LLP) *E R1 P*
Bristol *p161* 0845 415 0000

Parry, Miss E S (Edward Hughes) *G H*
Rhyl *p363* . . . . . . .01745 343661 / 344551

Parry, G (Parry Davies Clwyd-Jones & Lloyd)
Llangefni *p292*. 01248 723106

Parry, G A (Terry Jones Solicitors & Advocates) *E J1 S2 A1 W C1 C2*
Shrewsbury *p379* 01743 285888

Parry, G H (Hughes Paddison) *W T2 K4*
Cheltenham *p188* 01242 574244

Parry, G M (Allen & Overy LLP)
London E1 *p5* 020 3088 0000

Parry, G M (Vaughan & Davies) *W S1 A1 L T1 E S2 T2*
Kington *p268* 01544 230325

Parry, J (Ashurst LLP)
London EC2 *p7* 020 7638 1111

Parry, J E L (Linder Myers Solicitors) *N*
Manchester *p307* 0844 984 6400

Parry, J G (J W Hughes & Co) *Q M1 J1 K1 L P S1 V W Zg Zm Zn*
Conwy *p199*. 01492 596596

Parry, J N R (Whitfields)
Formby *p227* 01704 878501

Parry, Ms J S (Irwin Mitchell LLP) *N Zg Zr*
London EC1 *p45*. 0870 150 0100

Parry, Ms K (Brabners Chaffe Street) *E S2 S1 Zb A1*
Manchester *p301* 0161 836 8800

Parry, K T (George Davies Solicitors LLP) *A3 Zc Zk O*
Manchester *p303* 0161 236 8992

Parry, Miss M (J Keith Park & Co) *Q A3 N*
St Helens *p391* 01744 636000

Parry, M A (Shelter Legal Services)
London EC1 *p109* 020 7505 2000

Parry, M J (Michael J Parry) *S1 W K1 L*
Criccieth *p203* 01766 523114

Parry, Miss N C (Darlington Borough Council)
Darlington *p456* 01325 388055

Parry, R (R Gordon Roberts Laurie & Co) *K1 A1 S1 Q W*
Llangefni *p292*. . . .01248 722215 / 723312

Parry, R L (Watson Farley & Williams) *Zb Za*
London EC2 *p90*. 020 7814 8000

Parry, R W J (Farrer & Co LLP)
London WC2 *p31* 020 3375 7000

Parry, S (United Cooperatives Ltd)
Rochdale *p451*. 01706 202020

Parry, S (Hewitsons) *E S2 S1 R2*
Northampton *p332*. 01604 233233

Parry, S L (Parry Law) *E L S1 S2 C1 C2*
Herne Bay *p248* 01227 361131
Whitstable *p431* 01227 276276

Parry, Mrs V A (Osborne Clarke) *J1 F2*
London EC2 *p65*. 020 7105 7000

Parry, W T (W Parry & Co) *B1 C1 F1 J1 L N P Zl Zt*
Swansea *p405*. 01792 470037

Parry-Davies, W A (Dowse & Co) *L J1 Zd Zh Zp*
Hackney *p27*. 020 7254 6205

Parry-Jones, D B (Pembrokeshire County Council)
Haverfordwest *p460* 01437 764551

Parry-Jones, S D (Hart Brown Solicitors) *W Zd*
Godalming *p231* 0800 068 8177

Parsley, Miss J M (Hansells) *K1 D1 W*
Norwich *p334* 01603 615731

Parsloe, Ms S (Hodge Jones & Allen LLP) *D2 D1 K1 K2 K3*
London NW1 *p41* 020 7874 8300

Parson, N G (Dixon Rigby Keogh) *C1 E O Q S1*
Northwich *p333* 01606 48111

Parsons, A E (Radcliffes Le Brasseur) *N Q L O B1 Zm Zl Zj*
Westminster *p70*. 020 7222 7040

Parsons, Mrs A J (Dyne Drewett Solicitors Ltd) *S2 E S1*
Shepton Mallet *p378*. 01749 342323

Parsons, A M (Almy & Thomas) *G H B2*
Torquay *p412* 01803 299131

Parsons, Ms B (Staffordshire County Council)
Stafford *p472* 01785 223121

Parsons, Ms C (Lyons Davidson)
Bristol *p163* 0117 904 6000

Parsons, Miss C (Whitehead Vizard) *S1*
Salisbury *p371*. 01722 412141

Parsons, C J (Co-operative Insurance Society Ltd)
Manchester *p464* 0161 832 8686

Parsons, C J H (Herbert Smith LLP) *C1 C2*
London EC2 *p40*. 020 7374 8000

Parsons, Mrs D A (hlw Keeble Hawson LLP) *N Q*
Sheffield *p375* 0114 272 2061

Parsons, Ms F H B (Lambe Corner) *S1 S2 E L R1 W Zc A1 C1 Zh*
Hereford *p248* 01432 355301

Parsons, Ms F S (Cunningtons)
Wickford *p431* 01268 732268

Parsons, J B O (Greathead & Whitelock)
Pembroke *p345* 01646 682101

Parsons, J E (Foot Anstey) *N Q Zw*
Plymouth *p349*. 01752 675000
Southampton *p387*. 023 8032 1000

Parsons, K R (Photiades) *W*
St Albans *p390* 01727 833134

Parsons, Ms L A (Radcliffes Le Brasseur) *Q*
Westminster *p70*. 020 7222 7040

Parsons, M (Judge & Priestley) *W*
Bromley *p166* 020 8290 0333

Parsons, Mrs M (Avon & Somerset Constabulary)
Portishead *p469* 01275 816270

Parsons, M D (Higgs & Sons) *N*
Brierley Hill *p158*. 0845 111 5050

Parsons, M R (Shell International Ltd)
London SE1 *p109* 020 7934 1234

Parsons, N S (Browne Jacobson LLP) *Q P Zj*
Nottingham *p336*. 0115 976 6000

Parsons, P (Trowers & Hamlins)
London EC3 *p88*. 020 7423 8000

Parsons, P T S (Greenwoods) *M1 N P Zj*
Milton Keynes *p317* 01908 298200

Parsons, R E (Sidley Austin Brown & Wood) *B1 F1 Zb*
London EC2 *p78*. 020 7360 3600

Parsons, Mrs S (Nicholson Martin Legge & Miller) *D1 K1 S2 E K3 K4 K2 S1 W*
Stanley *p394*. 01207 232277

Parsons, Mrs S B J (Attwaters) *N*
Harlow *p239*. 01279 638888

Parsons, S J (C Nicholls) *N Q W Zw*
Bodmin *p148* 01208 76969

Parsons, Ms T (Pengillys LLP) *D1 K1 K2*
Dorchester *p212*. 01305 768888

Parsons, T H (Coutts & Co)
London WC2 *p105*. 020 7753 1403

Parsons, T J (Lucas & Wyllys) *N O Q*
Lowestoft *p294* 01502 500123
Great Yarmouth *p234* 01493 855555

Parsons, T L (Green Wright Chalton Annis) *S1 S2 N O Q*
Worthing *p441*. 01903 234064

Parsons, T N (Barlow Lyde & Gilbert LLP)
London EC3 *p10*. 020 7247 2277

Parsonson, R J (Gardner Leader LLP) *S1 L*
Newbury *p322* 01635 508080

Partington, A D (Ogden Lyles & Fox) *S1 W D1 L S2*
Eccles *p216* 0161 789 2793
Irlam *p263*. 0161 775 3744

Partington, I K (Blaser Mills) *W*
Chesham *p189* 01494 782291

Partington, Miss J A (Druitts) *W K4*
Bournemouth *p151*. 01202 551863
Christchurch *p194* 01202 484242

Partington, M (MGN Ltd)
London E14 *p107* 020 7293 3934

Partington, M (Trinity Mirror PLC)
London E14 *p110* 020 7293 3934

Parton, D (Shoosmiths) *S1*
Northampton *p332*. . 0370 086 3000 / 01604 543000

Parton, N G (Jackson Parton) *O Za N A3 Zj*
London EC3 *p45*. 020 7702 0085

Partridge, Ms A (The College of Law Guildford)
Guildford *p459*. 01483 460200

Partridge, D C (Straw & Pearce) *E L S1*
Loughborough *p293* 01509 268931

Partridge, H P (Oldham Marsh Page Flavell) *O C1 G E A1 J1 S1 Q N K1*
Melton Mowbray *p314* 01664 563162

Partridge, J (Brabners Chaffe Street) *C2 C1 F1 Ze I*
Manchester *p301* 0161 836 8800

Partridge, M L J (The Smith Partnership) *G H*
Derby *p209* 01332 225225

Partridge, N (Lyons Davidson) *M1*
Bristol *p163* 0117 904 6000

Partridge, R (Charles Russell LLP) *W T2 Zd*
London EC4 *p19*. 020 7203 5000

Partridge, S J (Sykes Lee & Brydson) *Zl O Q N J1*
York *p445* 01904 731100
York *p445* 01904 529000

Partridge, W M J (Thomson Snell & Passmore) *C1 T1 I Ze Zb C2 C3*
Tunbridge Wells *p415* 01892 510000

Parveen, Ms S (Howells LLP) *G H*
Sheffield *p376* 0114 249 6666

Parviez, Ms S (Stokoe Partnership) *G H*
Waltham Forest *p83* 020 8558 8884

Parys, R (Davisons)
Birmingham *p137* 0121 685 1234

Pascalides, C C (Pascalides & Co) *E S1 M1 G L C1 B1 J1 K1 N Zb Zi Zl*
London WC1 *p66* 020 7837 0049

Pascall, R G (Mander Hadley & Co) *S1 W*
Coventry *p200*. 024 7663 1212

Paschalis, P (Howard Kennedy LLP) *E S1*
London W1 *p48* 020 7636 1616

Pascoe, Miss A L (Simmons & Simmons)
London EC2 *p79*. 020 7628 2020

Pascoe, A W (Sergeant & Collins) *G H D1 S1 E P Zl Zi*
Scunthorpe *p373*. 01724 864215

Pascoe, H R (Loosemores) *N F1*
Cardiff *p179* 029 2022 4433

Pascoe, L O (Chappell Pascoe) *K1 D1 K3*
Crowborough *p204*. 01892 664348

Pasha, N (NP Solicitors) *Q*
Hounslow *p254* 020 8577 7799

Pasha, T (Joint Council for the Welfare of Immigrants)
London EC1 *p107* 020 7251 8708

Pashen, L (Charles Platel Solicitors) *K1 Q Zl K3 O*
Wokingham *p437* 0118 978 4866

Pashley, Mrs A (Malcolm C Foy & Co) *D2 D1 K3 K1*
Doncaster *p211* 01302 340005

Pask, Miss S J (Knowsley Metropolitan Borough Council)
Huyton *p461*. 0151 443 3593

Paskell, F C (Greene & Greene) *E C1 S1 S2 Zc*
Bury St Edmunds *p171* 01284 762211

Pasquill, Ms S (Memery Crystal) *O A3*
London WC2 *p60* 020 7242 5905

See p634 for the Key to Work Categories

Pasquini, N E (Radcliffes Le Brasseur) *C1 C2 M1 M2*
Westminster *p70*. 020 7222 7040
Pass, J H (Dickinson Dees) *C1 J1 B1 Zb Ze*
Newcastle upon Tyne *p324* . 0191 279 9000
Pass, R J L (Woodhouse & Company) *S1 E L W A1 F1 R1 T1 C1 P Zc Zj Zh*
Wolverhampton *p438* 01902 773616
Pass, Ms S A (Forsters LLP) *E*
Westminster *p33*. 020 7863 8333
Passam, Miss D L (East Staffordshire Borough Council)
Burton-on-Trent *p452* 01283 508000
Passemard, Ms S V (Paris Smith LLP) *K1 K3 K2*
Southampton *p386*. 023 8048 2482
Passey, N R J (J W Hughes & Co) *E R1 S1 W C1 L*
Conwy *p199* 01492 596596
Passfield, Miss Z (Meikles) *J1 N*
Bishop Auckland *p144*. . . . 01388 451122
Passi, Miss S (Marsden Rawsthorn LLP) *K3 K1*
Preston *p357* 01772 799600
Passley, Mrs K (Lees Solicitors LLP) *N*
Birkenhead *p134*. 0151 647 9381
Passman, J (Devonshires) *R2 S2 E Zh*
London EC2 *p27*. 020 7628 7576
Passmore, A E (Adams & Remers) *A3 F2 Zc P J2 O Q Zq F1 Ze*
Lewes *p283* 01273 480616
Horsham *p253*. 01403 210200
Passmore, A M L (Beightons) *E S1 W L Zd*
Derby *p208* 01332 346430
Passmore, C J (Simmons & Simmons)
London EC2 *p79*. 020 7628 2020
Passmore, J C (Thomson Snell & Passmore) *W Zd T2 K4*
Tunbridge Wells *p415* 01892 510000
Paszek, N (Ford & Warren) *O*
Leeds *p273* 0113 243 6601
Patankar, Miss S (Harris Cartier LLP) *S2 E*
Slough *p382*. 01753 810710
Patch, M J (HKH Kenwright & Cox Solicitors) *W K1 D1*
Ilford *p260*. 020 8553 9600
Patchell, Mrs E M (Patchell Davies (Trading Name of PD Law Ltd)) *K1 F1 S1 W*
Blackwood *p147*. 01495 227128
Patchell, H (Patchell Davies (Trading Name of PD Law Ltd)) *C1 S1 E K1 G J1 P T1 W*
Blackwood *p147*. 01495 227128
Patchett, Ms E C M (Squire Sanders (UK) LLP)
Manchester *p310* 0161 830 5000
Pate, Miss A E (Vallelys) *K1*
Letchworth *p283*. 01462 483800
Patefield, S M (Napthens LLP) *S1*
Blackburn *p145* 01254 667733
Patel, A (Pearson Rowe) *N J1*
Birmingham *p141* 0121 236 7388
Patel, A (MPH Solicitors) *N*
Manchester *p307* 0161 832 7722
Patel, Miss A (EMW) *Zb C2*
Milton Keynes *p316* 0845 070 6000
Patel, Miss A (Sweetman Burke & Sinker) *K1 K3*
Ealing *p84*. 020 8840 2572
Patel, A (Fladgate LLP) *E R2 S2*
London WC2 *p32* 020 3036 7000
Maidstone *p299* 01622 698000
Patel, Ms A (Amy & Co) *E S1 Zd S2 C1 F1 K3 W*
London EC3 *p6* 020 7539 3535
Patel, Miss A (Needham Poulier & Partners) *G H*
London N17 *p63*. 020 8808 6622
Patel, Miss A (Enoch Evans LLP) *S1 S2 E*
Walsall *p420*. 01922 720333
Patel, A (Chetty & Patel) *S1 E C1 K1 G H L P W T1 Zi Zl Zj*
Leicester *p279*. 0116 254 6222
Patel, A H (HSK Solicitors LLP) *S2 S1*
Manchester *p305* 0161 795 4818
Patel, A K (Balsara & Co) *Q B1 C1 E G L O N T1 T2 Ze Zi Zl*
London EC1 *p9* 020 7797 6300
Patel, A M (Manis) *S1 S2 K1 Q N W*
Thornton Heath *p411*. 020 8239 7111
Patel, Miss A M (McGrigors LLP)
London EC4 *p56*. 020 7054 2500
Patel, A S (Rippon Patel & French)
Westminster *p72*. 020 7323 0404
Patel, A Y (MWRLaw Ltd) *N O J1 F1 L*
Preston *p357* 01772 254201
Patel, B (The Mitchell Plampin Partnership) *W K4*
Maldon *p299*. 01621 852566
Patel, Mrs B (Heather Mains & Co) *N Q K1 S1 E C1 J1 W Zi Zv Ze*
London NW7 *p40* 020 8906 6660
Patel, Mrs B (Cotswold District Council)
Cirencester *p455*. 01285 623000
Patel, Miss B (Gattas Denfield Solicitors) *Q W L N*
London NW9 *p35* 020 8204 7181
Patel, Ms B (Panesar & Co) *G K1 K2 K3 H D1*
Grays *p233* 01375 383283
Patel, D (Fisher Meredith) *L Zg Zi*
Lambeth *p32*. 020 7091 2700
Patel, D (Ferns)
London SW4 *p31* 020 7498 9537
Patel, D C (Bell & Co) *B1 F1 O Q Zq*
Sutton *p402* 020 8661 8611
Patel, Mrs G (Geeta Patel & Company)
London N11 *p66*. 020 8365 7377
Patel, H (Mills & Reeve) *Ze U2 I C1*
Cambridge *p175*. 01223 364422
Patel, H (Harrow Law Partnership)
Wealdstone *p424* 020 8863 7888

Patel, H A (Ganpate) *S1 C1 E L W Q O B1 F1 Zb Zc Zi Zl Zo Zp*
London NW4 *p35* 020 8202 5092
Patel, H G R (Spratt Endicott) *C1 C2*
Banbury *p122* 01295 204000
Patel, J (P K P French) *E S2*
Harrow *p241*. 020 8861 8832
Patel, J (CKFT)
London NW3 *p17* 020 7431 7262
Patel, J (Brethertons LLP)
Rugby *p368* 01788 579579
Patel, J (Links Legal)
Ilford *p260*. 020 8551 0999
Patel, Ms J (Bowling & Co) *E S1 L*
London E15 *p15*. 020 8221 8000
Patel, Miss J (Harvey Ingram Borneos)
Milton Keynes *p317* 01908 696002
Patel, J C (J C Patel) *E K1 L N S1 W*
Wembley *p426*. 020 8903 3519
Patel, J D (Hamer Childs) *G H*
Worcester *p439* 01905 724565
Patel, Miss K (SGH Martineau LLP) *C1*
Birmingham *p142* 0870 763 2000
Patel, K (Child & Child)
London SW1 *p20* 020 7235 8000
Patel, Ms K (Blake Lapthorn) *O Zq*
Chandlers Ford *p184* 023 8090 8090
Patel, Mrs L (Radcliffes Le Brasseur) *W*
Westminster *p70*. 020 7222 7040
Patel, Miss M (Fish & Co) *K1 D1 D2 Zm*
Wolverhampton *p438* 01902 826464
Patel, Miss M (Talbots Legal Advice Centre) *K1*
Stourbridge *p399* . .01384 445850 / 447777
Patel, Mrs M (Wychavon District Council)
Pershore *p468*. 01386 565000
Patel, M (Allansons LLP)
Bolton *p148* 0161 220 8484
Patel, M (Jasvir Jutla & Co)
Leicester *p280*. 0116 254 0809
Patel, M (MRH Solicitors) *Q N*
Bolton *p149* 01204 535333
Patel, Ms M (Ince & Co Services Ltd)
London E1 *p44* 020 7481 0010
Patel, M (Freeth Cartwright LLP) *O Q Zj Zq J2 Ze A3 U2 Zk N*
Leicester *p279*. 0116 248 1100
Patel, M (Norwich Union Insurance Group)
Norwich *p467* 01603 622200
Patel, M A (Duane Morris) *E P R2 S2*
London EC1 *p28*. 020 7786 2100
Patel, M A (Musa A Patel & Co) *S1 G H Zi*
Dewsbury *p210* 01924 437800
Patel, M C (Peterborough City Council)
Peterborough *p468* 01733 747474
Patel, M K (stevensdrake) *E P C1 Zc*
Crawley *p202* 01293 596900
Patel, M R (The Law Partnership) *K1 Q N Zq K3 F1 B1 L W*
Harrow *p242*. 020 8416 7004
Patel, Ms N (Eastgate Assistance Ltd)
Colchester *p455* 0870 523 4500
Patel, Miss N (Evans Dodd LLP) *C1 C2 M2 E S2*
London W1 *p30* 020 7491 4729
Patel, Miss N (Turbervilles) *J1 Q*
Uxbridge *p417*. 01895 201700
Uxbridge *p417*. 01895 201700
Patel, Miss N (Arora Lodhi Heath) *G H V B2*
London W3 *p7*. 020 8993 9995
Patel, Miss N (QualitySolicitors Jackson & Canter) *L*
Liverpool *p290*. 0151 282 1700
Patel, Mrs N (Martin-Kaye LLP) *S1*
Telford *p409* 01952 272222
Patel, N D (GPT Solicitors) *C1 E N S1 W L H O Q Zl Zl Zv*
Wembley *p426*. .020 8904 6495 / 8904 6598
Patel, N T (Enoch Evans LLP) *G H Zl*
Walsall *p420*. 01922 720333
Patel, P (Magwells) *O Q G K1 N L B1 J1 F1 D1 Zc Zi Zb*
Islington *p57*. 020 7833 2244
Patel, P (P K P French)
Harrow *p241*. 020 8861 8832
Patel, Mrs P (Abbott Lloyd Howorth) *S1 S2*
Maidenhead *p298* 01628 798800
Patel, P K (P K P French) *C1 E L S1 I B1 J1 G Zb Zl Zi*
Harrow *p241*. 020 8861 8832
Patel, R (Harvey Ingram LLP) *Q O*
Leicester *p280*. 0116 254 5454
Patel, R (Thompsons (formerly Robin/Brian Thompson & Partners)) *J1*
London WC1 *p87* 020 7290 0000
Patel, Miss R (Radcliffes Le Brasseur)
Westminster *p70*. 020 7222 7040
Patel, Miss R (Solomon Taylor & Shaw)
London NW3 *p80* 020 7431 1912
Patel, R J (Rakkani Solicitors) *S1 W S2*
Leicester *p281*. 0116 299 2999
Patel, S (AXA UK PLC)
London E22 *p103* 020 7920 5900
Patel, Ms S (Bishop & Sewell LLP) *E S2 S1*
London WC1 *p13* 020 7631 4141
Patel, S (Patel & Co) *K1 N Q S1 S2 V O W J1 Zi F1 F2 G Zp D1*
Daventry *p207*. 01327 311213
Patel, S A (Forbes) *Q N F1 Zi Zc*
Blackburn *p145* 01254 54374
Patel, S D (BWTLaw LLP)
Epsom *p219*. 01372 725655
Patel, T (George Ide LLP)
Chichester *p192* 01243 786668

Patel, Mrs T (TWM Solicitors LLP)
Reigate *p363* 01737 221212
Patel, U D (Chetty & Patel)
Leicester *p279*. 0116 254 6222
Patel, V (Hodge Jones & Allen LLP) *N*
London NW1 *p41* 020 7874 8300
Patel, V (Key2Law LLP)
Ewell *p220*. 020 8393 0941
Patel, Y (Edward Hayes LLP) *G H Q N Zr J1 Zq B2*
London EC4 *p39*. 020 7353 0011
Patel, Y K (Freemans Solicitors) *E L R1 Zb S1 S2 R2*
London W1 *p34* 020 7935 3522
Paterson, D S (Herbert Smith LLP) *C1 C2*
London EC2 *p40*. 020 7374 8000
Paterson, J (Leigh Day & Co) *F1 F2 N M2*
London EC1 *p52*. 020 7650 1200
Paterson, Miss J C (Astle Paterson Ltd) *S2 C1 W J1 R1 E*
Burton-on-Trent *p170* 01283 531366
Paterson, J S (Gosport Borough Council)
Gosport *p459* 023 9258 4242
Paterson, M A (Burges Salmon)
Bristol *p161* 0117 939 2000
Paterson, M J (Forrester & Forrester) *Q K1 J1 L N O F1*
Malmesbury *p300* 01666 822671
Paterson, N (British Telecommunications PLC)
London EC1 *p104* 020 7356 6181
Paterson, S (Herbert Smith LLP)
London EC2 *p40*. 020 7374 8000
Paterson-Morgan, Mrs R M (Brice Droogleever & Co) *A1 W C1 E F1 K1 J1 L P*
Kensington & Chelsea *p15*. 020 7730 9925 / 7730 7231
Patez, Mrs J (Hallam-Peel & Co) *N*
London WC2 *p38* 020 3006 1661
Pathak, Miss M B (Keoghs LLP) *N Zj O Q A3*
Bolton *p149* 01204 677000
Coventry *p200*. 024 7665 8200
Pathan, Miss S (Waldrons) *G H*
Brierley Hill *p158*. 01384 811811
Dudley *p213*. 01384 811811
Pathirana, H D M (M M Patel & Co) *E L S1 W*
London NW8 *p66* 020 7722 7673
Pathmanathan, J (LG Lawyers)
London SE1 *p50*. 020 7379 0000
Pathmanathan, K K (ELC Solicitors)
Ealing *p28*. 020 8566 4045
Pathmanathan, P (S Satha & Co) *S1 S2 E Zi Q N G K3 W K1 Zl Zg L O*
Newham *p76* 020 8471 9484
Patience, I W (Roger James Clements & Partners) *N O Q*
Newport *p329* 01633 257844
Patient, D M (Travers Smith LLP) *C1 C2*
London EC1 *p87*. 020 7295 3000
Patient, L J (O'Neill Patient) *S1*
Stockport *p396*. 0161 483 8555
Patmore, Ms L (Pinsent Masons LLP)
London EC2 *p67*. 020 7418 7000
Paton, A J (Pinsent Masons LLP) *A3 O Zj Zq*
Birmingham *p141* 0121 200 1050
Paton, R J (Hill Dickinson LLP) *C1 C2*
Liverpool *p288*. 0151 600 8000
Paton, Miss V J (Clerical Medical Investment Group) *C1 C2 B1*
London EC2 *p105* 020 7321 1425
Patouchas, D (Walsall Metropolitan Borough Council) *E H K1*
Walsall *p475*. 01922 650000
Patrice, Miss S L (Anthony Collins Solicitors LLP) *Zd C1 Zu*
Birmingham *p137* 0121 200 3242
Patricio, D (TWM Solicitors LLP)
Reigate *p363* 01737 221212
Patrick, C J (Howells LLP) *D1 K1*
Rotherham *p367*. 01709 364000
Patrick, Miss J (Lodders Solicitors LLP) *A1*
Stratford-upon-Avon *p400* . . 01789 293259
Patrick, Miss K (Buckles Solicitors LLP) *L Zh Q*
Peterborough *p346* 01733 888888
Patrick, Miss L S (Duncan Watts LLP) *K3 K1*
Warwick *p422* 01926 493485
Patrick, N B (Wilkin Chapman LLP) *Q N O*
Beverley *p131* 01482 398398
Patrick, N R (Portsmouth City Council)
Portsmouth *p469*. 023 9283 4034
Patrinos, A R (Jackson Parton) *O A3 Q Zj Za*
London EC3 *p45*. 020 7702 0085
Patros, G C (Charles Ross Solicitors) *E S2 S1 R2 W*
Barnet *p124* 020 8216 2300
Pattard, E (Ince & Co Services Ltd)
London E1 *p44* 020 7481 0010
Patten, A J (Harbottle & Lewis LLP) *E L S1 R1 P Zc Zv*
London W1 *p38* 020 7667 5000
Patten, D (Mills & Reeve) *E R2*
Cambridge *p175*. 01223 364422
Patten, K (Thompsons (formerly Robin/Brian Thompson & Partners)) *N*
Newcastle upon Tyne *p327* . 0191 269 0400
Patten, Mrs V (Pleass Thomson & Co) *K1 F1 J1 D1 G V N Zl Zq*
Clacton-on-Sea *p195* 01255 221133
Patter, Mrs J (Harris Cartier LLP) *C1 S2 E C2*
London WC2 *p39* 020 7405 7100
Pattern, K (Thompsons (formerly Robin/Brian Thompson & Partners))
Plymouth *p350*. 01752 675810

Patterson, B (The BOC Group PLC)
Guildford *p476*. 01483 579857
Patterson, B (Steptoe & Johnson) *E P S1 S2 Zc*
London EC2 *p83*. 020 7367 8000
Patterson, C (Davies Johnson & Co (Shipping & Commercial Solicitors)) *Za A3 Zj O Q*
Plymouth *p349*. 01752 226020
Patterson, D A (Percy Holt & Nowers)
Croydon *p205* 020 8688 3603
Patterson, Ms E (Cartwright King) *K1 N*
Derby *p208* 01332 346111
Patterson, Miss E (Eastleys) *Q N H*
Paignton *p345*. 01803 559257
Patterson, E B (Hodgsons & Mortimer) *D1 R1 S1 W*
Darlington *p206* . . .01325 250111 / 355956
Patterson, F P (MPH Solicitors) *N Zr J2*
Manchester *p307* 0161 832 7722
Patterson, I D (Thompsons (formerly Robin/Brian Thompson & Partners)) *N*
Stoke-on-Trent *p398*. 01782 406200
Patterson, J M (Hewlett-Packard Ltd)
Bracknell *p451*. 01344 360000
Patterson, K (Yarwood & Stubley)
Blyth *p148*. 01670 361211
Patterson, Mrs M P (Margaret Patterson) *K1*
Altrincham *p117* 0161 941 4862
Patterson, N D (Wansbroughs) *S1 E L A1*
Devizes *p210* 01380 733300
Patterson, P H (Ormerods) *E S1*
Croydon *p205* 020 8686 5000
Patterson, R (Knapman & Co) *S1 W L E S2 T2*
Paignton *p345*. 01803 522700
Patterson, R J H (Chiltern District Council) *L R1 Q S1 G P J1 I Zc Zd Ze Zl Zs*
Amersham *p447*. 01494 729000
Pattichis, N (Widdows Pilling & Co) *N*
Walkden *p419* 0161 790 1825
Pattihis, Miss A (Philip Ross & Co) *E S1 R2*
London W1 *p73* 020 7636 6969
Pattihis, H (Philip Ross & Co) *S1 C1 E L T1*
London W1 *p73* 020 7636 6969
Pattihis, M K (Healys LLP) *A1 C1 E J1 K1 L M1 N R1*
London EC4 *p39*. 020 7822 4000
Pattinson, A E (DLA Piper UK LLP) *E R1 L*
Manchester *p303* 0870 011 1111
Pattinson, Ms A H (Rodgers & Burton)
London SW13 *p73*. 020 8939 6300
Pattinson, K (Harris Cartier LLP) *N*
London WC2 *p39* 020 7405 7100
Pattinson, M (Trowers & Hamlins) *C1 C2 C3 Zb Ze*
London EC3 *p88*. 020 7423 8000
Pattison, A J (Nelsons) *N J1 O Q*
Nottingham *p338*. 0115 958 6262
Pattison, D C (Hewitts) *N J1 K1 P B1 R1 D1 F1 G Zc Zt Zl*
Bishop Auckland *p144* 01388 604691
Pattison, G (Bermans LLP) *Zc E S1*
Liverpool *p286*. 0151 224 0500
Pattison, I N (The Lister Croft Partnership) *S1 W*
Pudsey *p358*. 0113 257 0526
Pattison, J A (Hampshire County Council)
Winchester *p476*. 01962 841841
Pattison, S (Magrath LLP)
London W1 *p57* 020 7495 3003
Pattison, S R (SAS Daniels LLP) *S1*
Bramhall *p155*. 0161 475 7680
Pattman, N E J (Sumitomo Mitsui Banking Corporation Europe Limited)
London EC4 *p109* . . . 020 7786 1000 / 1017
Pattni, Ms B S (Fawcett & Pattni) *K1 D1 N G*
Walsall *p420*. 01922 640424
Pattni, Ms V A (Lockharts Solicitors) *E*
London WC1 *p55* 020 7383 7111
Patton, Miss C E (Taylor & Emmet LLP) *W T2 Zm*
Sheffield *p377* 0114 218 4000
Patton, C N (Sintons LLP) *N*
Newcastle upon Tyne *p326* . 0191 226 7878
Patton, Ms C V (Cambridge City Council) *L P G H Zi*
Cambridge *p452*. 01223 457000
Patton, J (Birchall Blackburn LLP) *B1 J1 O F1 Zq J2 Q N*
Manchester *p301* 0161 236 0662
Pattullo, M J (Bemrose & Ling) *Q O L J1*
Derby *p208* 01332 347300
Derby *p208* 01332 348484
Patwa, Ms F F (Patwa Solicitors) *Zd S2 E Zg Zu R1 S1 F1*
Bearwood *p129* 0121 429 8666
Pau, A C (Gandecha & Pau) *B1 C1 D1 E G J1 K1 L N O Zi Zl*
Barnet *p34*. 020 8905 0900
Paul, A D (Allen & Overy LLP)
London E1 *p5* 020 3088 0000
Paul, C (Trowers & Hamlins)
London EC3 *p88*. 020 7423 8000
Paul, I C D (stevensdrake) *K4 T2 W*
Crawley *p202* 01293 596900
Paul, I N (Martin Murray & Associates) *B2 G H*
West Drayton *p427* 01895 431332
Paul, Ms K S (Harold Benjamin) *E S1 R1 C1 L*
Harrow *p241*. 020 8422 5678
Paul, N W (CMS Cameron McKenna LLP) *C3*
London EC3 *p17*. 020 7367 3000
Paul, Ms P (Michael Simkins LLP) *S2 E S1*
London WC1 *p79* 020 7874 5600
Paul, R (Withers LLP) *T2 W Zv*
London EC4 *p92*. 020 7597 6000
Paul, R A (Battens) *F1 M1 N P Zj Zk*
Yeovil *p443* 01935 846000

6

Paul, Ms S (Hodge Jones & Allen LLP) *G H B2*
London NW1 *p41* 020 7874 8300
Paul, Ms S (Trowers & Hamlins)
London EC3 *p88*. 020 7423 8000
Paull, S (Holman Fenwick Willan)
London EC3 *p42*. 020 7264 8000
Paul-Roberts, Ms B E (Winckworth Sherwood LLP) *S1 S2 Zh*
London SE1 *p92*. 020 7593 5000
Paulson, G (AXA UK PLC)
London E22 *p103* 020 7920 5900
Pauw, K M (London Borough of Wandsworth)
London SW18 *p110* 020 8871 6000
Pavin, D (Taylor Wessing) *I O C1 M1 Ze*
London EC4 *p86*. 020 7300 7000
Pavitt, Ms A E (Hartnells) *G H I B2*
London SE5 *p39*. 020 7703 9222
Pavitt, M G J (Blake Lapthorn) *O Q A3 F1 M1 Zf Zb Zc Zg Zk*
Chandlers Ford *p184* 023 8090 8090
Pavitt, N (Essex County Council)
Chelmsford *p454*. 0845 743 0430
Pavlides, Miss R (Protopapas) *Q O L A3 B1 F1 F2 J1 K3 Zi W*
London W1 *p69* 020 7636 2100
Pavlou, Miss M (C P Christou LLP) *E L S1 S2*
London N12 *p20*. 020 8446 6777
Pavlovic, A N (Russell-Cooke LLP) *O Q B1 B2 A3 Zq*
London SW15 *p74*. 020 8789 9111
Pawlik, A J (ASB Law) *P Q N O*
Crawley *p202* 01293 603600
Maidstone *p298* 01622 656500
Lewes *p283* 01273 480616
Pawson, N (Ashurst LLP)
London EC2 *p7* 020 7638 1111
Paxton, P A (Stewarts Law LLP) *N*
London EC4 *p83*. 020 7822 8000
Pay, A C (MLM Cartwright) *O C1 Q B1 A3 B2 F1 Zc Ze C3 C2 Zq*
Cardiff *p179* 029 2046 2562
Paydon, R (Edwards Angell Palmer & Dodge)
London EC2 *p28*. 020 7583 4055
Payiataki, Ms V (Reed Smith LLP) *A3 M2 Q*
London EC2 *p71*. 020 3116 3000
Payne, A (Butcher Andrews) *P N K1 G H D1 B1 W J1 T1 Zl Zk Zj*
Holt *p251* 01263 712023
Fakenham *p223* 01328 863131
Payne, A C (Wright Hassall LLP) *L Zu Zh*
Leamington Spa *p270* 01926 886688
Payne, A G (Sills & Betteridge LLP) *C1 C2 C3 R2 Ze Zw*
Lincoln *p285*. 01522 542211
Payne, Miss A J (Harbottle & Lewis LLP) *C1 Zf Ze Zk Zv*
London W1 *p38* 020 7667 5000
Payne, A J (Farnworth Shaw) *N Q J1*
Colne *p198* 01282 865885
Payne, Ms C (Harbottle & Lewis LLP)
London W1 *p38* 020 7667 5000
Payne, D (Ward Gethin) *W*
King's Lynn *p266* 01553 660033
Payne, Miss D (Blackfords LLP) *F1 G H J1 K1 L N Q V Zl*
Croydon *p204* 020 8686 6232
Payne, D (Paynes Solicitors) *A1 E K1 Q N S1 W*
Deal *p207*. 01304 372441
Payne, D A J (Jaffe Porter Crossick) *S1 S2*
London NW6 *p46* 020 7625 4424
Payne, D R (Payne & Gamage) *G Q A2*
Newark *p322* 01636 640649
Payne, G P W (Eric Robinson Solicitors) *W E S1 L*
Chandlers Ford *p184* 023 8025 4676
Payne, H (West Sussex County Council)
Chichester *p455* 01243 777100
Payne, I P M (Freeth Cartwright LLP) *C1 E T1 W R1 B1 A1 L Zc Ze Zo*
Nottingham *p337*. 0115 936 9369
Payne, J H (Steven Dean Magac & Co)
Barnet *p124* 020 8441 3399
Payne, J H (Tarbox Robinson & Partners) *P K1 N M1 G F1 B1 J1 D1 H Zl Zc Zk*
Northwood *p333*. 01923 836595
Payne, Mrs J M (Ross & Craig) *W*
Westminster *p73*. 020 7262 3077
Payne, Ms K (DLA Piper UK LLP)
Leeds *p272* 0870 011 1111
Payne, Miss K C (Elborne Mitchell LLP) *C1 J1*
London EC3 *p29*. 020 7320 9000
Payne, K F (Lewis Silkin LLP) *C1 J1*
London EC4 *p53*. 020 7074 8000
Payne, Mrs L M (Harman & Harman) *Zr N*
London SW2 *p39* 01227 452977
Payne, M H D (Wiggin Osborne Fullerlove) *T2 W T1 M2 Zo*
Cheltenham *p189* 01242 710200
London SW1 *p91* 020 7290 2456
Payne, M J (MFG Solicitors) *A1 E C1 F1 S1 R1*
Telford *p409* 01952 641651
Payne, M J (Jackson & Co) *S1 S2 W*
Birstall *p143* 0116 267 6263
Payne, Ms M L (Brethertons LLP) *D1 K1*
Banbury *p122* 01295 270999
Payne, Mrs M P (Margaret Payne) *G H Zm J2 B2 Zt*
Carlisle *p182*. 01228 521383
Payne, N D T (Actons) *N*
Nottingham *p335*. 0115 910 0200
Payne, P A H (Stephens & Scown) *K1 D1 D2*
Exeter *p222* 01392 210700

Payne, P J (Aston Bond LLP) *B1 F1 J1 K1 L M1 N P R1 Zc*
Slough *p381*. 01753 486777
Payne, Miss R C (Clark Willis) *K1 K3*
Darlington *p206* 01325 281111
Payne, R G (Pannone LLP) *S1*
Manchester *p308* 0161 909 3000
Payne, R J (Birketts LLP (Wollastons LLP)) *C2 C1 Zb C3 Zo U2 F1*
Chelmsford *p186*. 01245 211211
Payne, Miss S (Barr Ellison LLP) *O Q Zl Zq Zk*
Cambridge *p174*. 01223 417200
Payne, Miss S (Zermansky & Partners) *K1 D1*
Leeds *p278* 0113 245 9766
Payne, Miss S (Bristows) *O*
London EC4 *p15*. 020 7400 8000
Payne, S P (Gepp & Sons) *K1 D1*
Chelmsford *p186*. 01245 493939
Colchester *p197* 01206 369889
Payne, Ms T J (Parfitt Cresswell) *K3 O Q K1*
London SW6 *p65* 020 7381 8311
Payne, Miss T J (Cardiff Magistrates Court)
Cardiff *p453* 029 2046 3040
Payne, W R S (Haslam & Payne) *S2 E S1*
London SW1 *p39* 020 7828 8725
Paynter, Miss L (Colemans) *K1*
Chelmsford *p186*. 01245 264494
Payton, Miss K (Payton's Solicitors) *G*
London EC4 *p66*. 020 7405 1999
Payton, Ms M J (M J Payton & Co) *K1 S1 E C1 W Q O N Zc Zv*
Malvern *p300* 01684 563318
Payton, Miss R (Plexus Law (A Trading Name of Parabis Law LLP)) *N*
Evesham *p220*. 01386 769160
Payton, Mrs V (Dobsons) *G H*
Orpington *p341* 01689 886300
Pazir, D (Sterling Solicitors)
Birmingham *p142* 0121 772 0777
Peace, Ms C A (Howells LLP) *G H*
Sheffield *p376* 0114 249 6666
Peace, Ms C J (Berwins Solicitors Limited) *E L S1*
Harrogate *p240* 01423 509000
Peace, C M R (Peace Revitt) *S1 G H K1 C1 E F1 W N*
Barnsley *p125* . . . . 01226 341111 / 210077
Peace, Miss L (Sintons LLP) *E S2 R2 S1 L*
Newcastle upon Tyne *p326* . 0191 226 7878
Peacey, N J (Bond Pearce LLP)
Bristol *p161* 0845 415 0000
Peach, M N (Ware & Kay LLP) *N S1 W Q E T2 L*
Wetherby *p429* 01937 583210
Peach, R A (Peach Grey & Co) *G B2 H*
Southampton *p386*. 023 8033 4695
Peach, Miss S (Anderson Partnership) *K1 Q W V D1 B1 N K2*
Chesterfield *p191* 01246 220737
Peachey, A (Steed & Steed LLP) *K1 K2 V D1 K3*
Braintree *p155*. 01376 552828
Peachman, Ms T J E (Essex County Council)
Chelmsford *p454*. 0845 743 0430
Peacock, Miss A M (Russell Jones & Walker) *N Q V*
London WC2 *p74* 020 7657 1555
Peacock, Ms B (Dell Computer Corporation Ltd)
Bracknell *p451*. 01344 860456
Peacock, Miss G (Wards Solicitors) *K1 D1*
Weston-super-Mare *p429* . . 01934 413535
Weston-super-Mare *p429* . . 01934 428800
Peacock, G D (Hargreaves & Co)
Manchester *p305* 0161 445 6461
Peacock, I D (Bond Pearce LLP) *Zj*
Bristol *p161* 0845 415 0000
Peacock, J (Wilkin Chapman LLP) *K1 D1 K2 D2 K3*
Grimsby *p235* 01472 262626
Peacock, J (Irwin Mitchell LLP) *N Zr*
Birmingham *p139* 0870 150 0100
Peacock, M A P (Lupton Fawcett) *O*
Leeds *p275* 0113 280 2000
Peacock, N (Herbert Smith LLP)
London EC2 *p40*. 020 7374 8000
Peacock, N D (Beecham Peacock) *N*
Newcastle upon Tyne *p323* . 0191 232 3048
Peacock, P J (Radcliffes Le Brasseur) *C1 C3*
Westminster *p70*. 020 7222 7040
Peacock, S (Weightmans LLP) *N Q J1*
Liverpool *p291*. 0151 227 2601
Peacock, S C (Ray Nixon Brown) *B1 D1 J1 K1 L N O Q Zp F1 V*
Leighton Buzzard *p282* . . . 01525 372247
Peacock, Miss S V (Blake Lapthorn) *J1*
Portsmouth *p354*. 023 9222 1122
Pead, N (Wills Group Ltd) *C1 J1*
London EC3 *p110* 020 7488 8111
London EC1 *p12*. 020 7843 1820
Peak, C G (Madge Lloyd & Gibson) *K1 D1 D2 W Zx*
Gloucester *p230*. 01452 520224
Peak, Ms H (GPB Solicitors LLP)
Stratford-upon-Avon *p400* . . 01789 261131
Peake, D R (TMJ Law Solicitors)
Northampton *p332*. 01604 608111
Peake, Mrs L (Charltons Solicitors) *K1 P M1*
Biddulph *p132* 01782 522111
Peake, R H (Esso Petroleum Company Ltd)
Leatherhead *p462* 01372 222000
Peake, Mrs S E F (Rix & Kay Solicitors LLP) *E R1 S1 S2*
Hove *p255*. 01273 329797
Peaker, G (Anthony Gold) *L Zg*
London SE17 *p6*. 020 7940 4000

Peaker, R M (Jones Myers LLP) *K1 D1*
Leeds *p275* 0113 246 0055
Pearce, D (Paris Smith LLP) *Ze Zk Q N*
Southampton *p386*. 023 8048 2482
Pearce, D P H (Tucker Turner Kingsley Wood & Co) *W T1 Zd Zo Zf*
London WC1 *p88* 020 7242 3303
Pearce, D W (Pearce West Solicitors) *E S1 S2 W*
Oxford *p344*. 01865 812020
Pearce, Mrs E (MPH Solicitors) *N M3*
Manchester *p307* 0161 832 7722
Pearce, E J F (James Pearce & Co) *W E S1 A1 C1 L*
Birmingham *p141* 0121 360 1300
Sutton Coldfield *p404* 0121 351 5575
Birmingham *p141* 0121 784 1886
Pearce, Mrs F I (Bennetts Solicitors Attorneys & Notaries) *W Zd T2*
Wrington *p443*. 01934 862786
Pearce, G E (Streeter Marshall) *N*
Croydon *p205* 020 8680 2638
Pearce, G M (Pearcelegal LLP) *C1 C2 T2 W Zd*
Solihull *p383*. 0844 412 7899
Pearce, H D (Stone King LLP) *E P R1 R2 S2*
Bath *p128* 01225 337599
Pearce, Miss H J (Robinsons) *O Q L F1 Zq*
Derby *p209* 01332 291431
Pearce, Miss J (Crowley & Co) *G H*
Cardiff *p178* 029 2045 8895
Pearce, Ms J C (DWF) *J1 Zp*
Manchester *p303* 0161 603 5000
Pearce, Mrs J E (Halton Borough Council)
Widnes *p476*. 0151 424 2061
Pearce, Ms J M (Hanne & Co) *K1 D1*
London SW11 *p38* 020 7228 0017
Pearce, Mrs K (Pickerings LLP) *E S2 S1*
Tamworth *p407* 01827 317070
Pearce, L (Ellisons) *Zb B1 E F1 Q N S1*
Colchester *p197* 01206 764477
Pearce, Miss L (Morrisons Solicitors LLP) *K1 K3*
Redhill *p362* 01737 854500
Pearce, Mrs M A M (Bernard Pearce & Co) *E S1 K4 W J1 K1 Q T2*
Enfield *p219* 020 8804 5271
Pearce, M D (Dickinson Dees) *O Ze*
Newcastle upon Tyne *p324* . 0191 279 9000
Pearce, M R (David W Harris & Co) *N G L H*
Pontypridd *p352* 01443 486666
Pearce, R E (R E Pearce & Co) *K1 M1 P G D1 J1 N*
Wallington *p419* 020 8652 3574
Pearce, Mrs R K (Bobbetts Mackan) *G H*
Bristol *p161* 0117 929 9001
Pearce, Ms S (Alwena Jones & Jones) *J1 N Q W S1*
Blaenau Ffestiniog *p147* . . . 01766 831882
Pearce, Ms S E (Varley Hibbs LLP) *D1 G H K1*
Coventry *p201* 024 7663 1000
Pearce, Ms S H (Mary Ward Legal Centre) *L M1 P F1*
London WC1 *p110*. 020 7831 7079
Pearce, T (Thornleys Limited) *K1 J1 S1 L F1 O Q A1 B1*
Plymouth *p350*. 01752 406977
Pearce, T J (Hart Brown Solicitors) *S1*
Cobham *p196* 0800 068 8177
Pearce, Mrs T J (WBW Solicitors) *S1 W S2 E*
Torquay *p413* 0870 701 4321
Pearce, W (Herbert Smith LLP)
London EC2 *p40*. 020 7374 8000
Pearce, W M (Kerrier District Council)
Camborne *p452* 01209 614000
Pearce, W S (Cannings Connolly) *E S2 Zc*
London EC1 *p18*. 020 7329 9000
Pearcy, Miss R E (Wise Geary) *C1 J1*
Banbury *p122* 01295 278500
Pearcy, T R (IFPI Secretariat)
London W1 *p107* 020 7878 7900
Pearl, D (Pearl & Co) *S1 N O W L F1 B1 G E J1 K1 T1 T2 Zo Zm*
London NW4 *p66* 020 8202 6202
Pearl, S J (DAC Beachcroft) *N O Zj Zk*
London EC4 *p24*. 020 7936 2222
Pearl, V (Russell & Russell) *N*
Bury *p171* 0161 762 2888
Pearlman, Mrs D F (Pearlmans Solicitors LLP) *B1 C1 J1 S1 S2 W*
London NW4 *p66* 020 8201 6311
Pearlman, J (J Pearlman) *S2 S1 E W C1 Zd*
London NW11 *p66*. 020 8458 9266
Pearlman, K C (Ross & Craig) *L O Q N Zr*
Westminster *p73*. 020 7262 3077
Pearlman, R H (Silverman Sherliker LLP) *N C1 L B1 Zb Zc*
London EC2 *p78*. 020 7749 2700
Pearlman, R K (Richard Pearlman LLP) *A1 E L R1 S1 W Zv*
London EC2 *p66*. 020 7739 6100
Pearman, S A (Reed Smith LLP) *E*
London EC2 *p71*. 020 3116 3000
Pearman, T (Ashurst LLP)
London EC2 *p7* 020 7638 1111
Pearn, J A G (Slee Blackwell) *E A1 S1 W C1 R1 T1 L P M1 Zl Zc*
Braunton *p156*. 01271 812019
South Molton *p383*. 01769 573771
Pearn, M G (T Llewellyn Jones) *M1 N P G H K1 S1 W J1 E Zf Zl Zt*
Swansea *p405*. 01639 842235
Pearn, M J (T Llewellyn Jones) *G H N O Q Zl*
Neath *p320* 01639 643635
Pearne, Mrs H (Pearne & Co) *C1 Ze Zza U2*
Cheltenham *p188* 01242 530622

Pearne, S (Pearne & Co) *C1 Ze Zza U2*
Cheltenham *p188* 01242 530622
Pears, I G (Park Woodfine Heald Mellows LLP) *N Zr*
Bedford *p130* 01234 400000
Northampton *p332*. 01604 233200
Pears, J D (Shakespeares) *W T2 A1 Zo*
Nottingham *p339*. 0115 945 3700
Pears, Mrs M C (Field Seymour Parkes) *J1 C1 C2*
Reading *p360* 0118 951 6200
Pearse, M J (Follett Stock LLP) *O Q Ze A3 E U1 F1 C1 U2 Zq L Zm*
Truro *p414*. 01872 241700
Pearshouse, Miss J (Keelys LLP) *E S2 L R2*
Lichfield *p284* 01543 420000
Pearson, A (Hogan Lovells International LLP)
London EC1 *p42*. 020 7296 2000
Pearson, Ms A (Ashurst LLP)
London EC2 *p7* 020 7638 1111
Pearson, A J (Pearson Hinchliffe) *A1 C1 E R1 S1 T1 W*
Oldham *p341* 0161 785 3500
Pearson, A J (Pearson Fielding Polson) *G H B2*
Liverpool *p290*. 0151 236 3636
Pearson, A J (Muckle LLP) *Ze C1 O U2*
Newcastle upon Tyne *p325* . 0191 211 7777
Pearson, A J K (Geldards LLP)
Cardiff *p178* 029 2023 8239
Pearson, Mrs A L (Marsden Rawsthorn LLP) *D1 K1 N K3*
Chorley *p194* 01257 279511
Pearson, A M (Runnymede Borough Council)
Addlestone *p447*. 01932 838383
Pearson, A M (Everys) *Q N G H K1 D1 J1 F1 V W Zm*
Exmouth *p222*. 01395 264384
Pearson, A W (Davis-Law Associates) *S2 E S1 R1*
Chalfont St Peter *p184*. . . . 01753 888776
Pearson, Ms C (LG Lawyers)
London SE1 *p50*. 020 7379 0000
Pearson, Ms C (Keoghs LLP) *N Zj O Q*
Bolton *p149* 01204 677000
Pearson, Ms C A (Forsters LLP) *C1*
Westminster *p33*. 020 7863 8333
London EC4 *p92*. 020 7597 6000
Pearson, C J (Allen & Overy LLP) *Ze I Zf*
London E1 *p5* 020 3088 0000
Pearson, C R O N (Balfour Beatty PLC) *C1 F1*
London SW1 *p104*. 020 7216 6800
Pearson, Mrs D (Luttons Dunford) *B1 K1 S1 W*
Gloucester *p230*. 01452 529751
Pearson, D A (Manchester City Council)
Manchester *p465* 0161 234 5000
Pearson, D E (McKenzie Bell Solicitors) *S1 L Zi W J1*
Sunderland *p401*. 0191 567 4857
Pearson, D J (Kirklees Metropolitan Borough Council)
Huddersfield *p461* 01484 221421
Pearson, D R (Clifford Chance)
London E14 *p20*. 020 7006 1000
Pearson, Mrs E I (Hamilton Davies) *S2 S1 W R1 T2 L*
Stevenage *p394* 01438 315898
Pearson, E J (Moxon & Barker) *E A1 S1 L C1 N W M1 J1 Zl*
Pontefract *p351* 01977 602999
Pearson, G (McKenzie Bell Solicitors) *D1 G H K3 K1*
Sunderland *p401*. 0191 567 4857
Pearson, Ms H (Pearson Hinchliffe) *K4 K1 S1 T2 W*
Oldham *p341* 0161 785 3500
Pearson, Miss H (Radcliffes Le Brasseur)
Leeds *p276* 0113 234 1220
Pearson, Ms H E (Bird & Bird LLP) *I C3 O Ze*
London EC4 *p13*. 020 7415 6000
Pearson, Ms H J (Hempsons) *N Zr*
Harrogate *p240* 01423 522331
Pearson, J (Pearson Lowe) *C1 E J1 R1 S1 T1 W Zc Zi*
Westminster *p66*. 020 7224 0888
Pearson, Miss J (Clarion Solicitors LLP) *C1 Zw Zf Ze Zq*
Leeds *p272* 0113 246 0622
Pearson, J B (Ouvry Goodman & Co) *W T1 S1 C1 Zm*
Sutton *p403* 020 8642 7571
Pearson, Ms J E (Pictons Solicitors LLP) *K1*
Luton *p295* 01582 870870
Pearson, K (Blight Skinnard) *K1 N D1 L J1 F1 Q*
Saltash *p371*. 01752 842141
Pearson, L F (Pearson Caulfield) *D1 G H K1 M1 N P S1*
Newcastle upon Tyne *p326* . 0191 261 8878
Pearson, M (Penningtons) *E*
London EC2 *p66*. 020 7457 3000
Pearson, M (Jerman Simpson Pearson & Samuels) *N G H K1 Zl*
Basildon *p126* 01268 820111
Pearson, Ms M (MacLaverty Cooper Atkins)
Kingston upon Thames *p267*. 020 8549 9994
Pearson, M J (Mackesys)
London SE14 *p57* 020 7639 0888
Pearson, Ms P A P (Norris & Miles) *K1 K2 K3*
Tenbury Wells *p409* 01584 810575
Pearson, P W (The Automobile Association)
Cheadle *p454* 0161 485 6188
Pearson, R A N (Hart Jackson & Sons) *S1 W L E A1 T1 C1 F1*
Ulverston *p416*. 01229 583291
Pearson, Miss S (Official Solicitor and Public Trustee)
London WC2 *p108*. 020 7911 7127

See p634 for the Key to Work Categories

Pearson, S (Turner Pearson) *E L S1 W A1 J1 R1 F1 Zl Ze*
Preston *p357* 01772 751775

Pearson, Mrs S (Newcastle Upon Tyne City Council)
Newcastle upon Tyne *p466* 0191 232 8520

Pearson, Ms S A (Capsticks Solicitors LLP) *N Zr*
London SW19 *p18* 020 8780 2211

Pearson, Mrs S M (Stockton-On-Tees Borough Council)
Stockton-on-Tees *p472* 01642 393939

Pearson, Mrs S M (Bowser Ollard & Bentley) *C1 K3 K1*
Wisbech *p435* 01945 583194

Pearson, S T (Freeth Cartwright LLP) *C1 Zv C3*
Nottingham *p337* 0115 936 9369

Pearson, Mrs T L (QualitySolicitors Gruber Garratt) *S1*
Oldham *p341* 0161 665 3502

Pearson, Mrs V (Humphries Kirk) *Zl Q N O J1 L*
Poole *p352* 01202 715815

Pearson-Kendall, M A (Andrew Jackson)
Hull *p257* 01482 325242

Pearson-Smith, A (Reed Smith LLP)
London EC2 *p71* 020 3116 3000

Peart, Miss E T (BCL Burton Copeland) *B2 G H*
London WC2 *p9* 020 7430 2277

Peart, Miss S E (Howells LLP) *D1 D2 K1*
Sheffield *p376* 0114 249 6666

Pease, A M (Allen & Overy LLP)
London E1 *p5* 020 3088 0000

Pease, C E (Longmores) *S1*
Hertford *p248* 01992 300333

Pease, I P B (Taylor Wessing) *O B1 Q J1 Zc*
London EC4 *p86* 020 7300 7000

Peasland, Ms L J (DLA Piper UK LLP) *O*
London EC2 *p24* 0870 011 1111

Peat, A G M (Unilever PLC)
London EC4 *p110* 020 7822 5252

Peat, Mrs K (Gordon Dadds) *K3 K1*
London W1 *p25* 020 7493 6151
London WC2 *p38* 020 7242 9700

Peat, P G (Derbyshire County Council)
Matlock *p465* 01629 580000

Peatfield, Ms L (Edwards Angell Palmer & Dodge)
London EC2 *p28* 020 7583 4055

Peatfield, L (Ince & Co Services Ltd)
London E1 *p44* 020 7481 0010

Peck, A (Tollers LLP)
Northampton *p332* 01604 258558

Peck, A D (Blake Lapthorn) *E C1 B1 R1 S1 J1 T1 A1 Zc Ze*
Chandlers Ford *p184* 023 8090 8090

Peck, A T (Tollers LLP) *K1 K2 D1 D2*
Kettering *p265* 01536 520111

Peck, Mrs J L (Tollers LLP) *E C1 C2 S1 S2 R2 A1*
Kettering *p265* 01536 520111

Peck, Mrs K M (Greenwoods Solicitors LLP) *E*
Peterborough *p347* 01733 887700

Peck, Ms T J (AIB Group (UK) PLC (Legal and Securities Dept))
Uxbridge *p474* 01895 272222

Peckett, Miss V M (CMS Cameron McKenna LLP)
London EC3 *p17* 020 7367 3000

Peckham, L R (Roach Pittis) *G H*
Newport *p328* 01983 524431

Peckmore, Mrs S (Frisby & Co) *G B2*
Stafford *p392* 01785 244114

Peddar-Adams, R (Wace Morgan) *K1 K3*
Shrewsbury *p379* 01743 280100

Pedder, C (Trowers & Hamlins)
London EC3 *p88* 020 7423 8000

Peddie, A D (Pitmans LLP) *C2 C1*
Reading *p361* 0118 958 0224

Peden, D (Osborne Clarke) *O*
Bristol *p164* 0117 917 3000

Pedler, Ms K S (Pritchard Englefield) *Zr*
London EC2 *p69* 020 7972 9720

Pedley, Ms J C (Capsticks Solicitors LLP) *Zr*
London SW19 *p18* 020 8780 2211

Pedley, J R (Whitfields) *C1 F1 G H N Q Zb Ze Zq Zr*
Formby *p227* 01704 878501

Pedley, S G (Pannone LLP) *B1 O Q Zq W*
Manchester *p308* 0161 909 3000

Pedreschi, Miss L (Flintshire County Council) *K1 G H N S1 S2 W E L V Zi Zm Zr Zv Zq*
Mold *p466* 01352 702411

Pedro, M (Manches LLP) *C1 C2*
London WC2 *p58* 020 7404 4433

Peebles, G J (Hegarty LLP) *E S1*
Peterborough *p347* 01733 346333
Stamford *p393* 01780 752066

Peel, Ms A J (Arnold Greenwood) *W S1*
Kendal *p264* 01539 720049

Peel, D G (Fraser Brown) *O Zh L Ze*
Nottingham *p337* 0115 988 8777

Peel, J D (Rollits LLP) *C1 Ze U1 F1 C3 F2 U2*
Hull *p258* 01482 323239

Peel, Miss J E (Mills & Reeve) *E Zd*
Cambridge *p175* 01223 364422

Peel, N J (Weightmans LLP) *Q Zg*
Liverpool *p291* 0151 227 2601

Peel, T (Infogrames United Kingdom Ltd)
London W6 *p465* 020 8222 9700

Peel, T M (Walker Morris) *O*
Leeds *p277* 0113 283 2500

Peeling, Z (Fruhman Davies Livingstones)
Manchester *p304* 0161 833 0578

Peerless, B G (Charles Russell LLP) *T2 W Zd*
London EC4 *p19* 020 7203 5000

Peermohamed, F (Ince & Co Services Ltd)
London E1 *p44* 020 7481 0010

Peermohamed, Ms S (Harbottle & Lewis LLP)
London W1 *p38* 020 7667 5000

Peet, A (Shoosmiths)
Birmingham *p142* 0370 086 4000 / 0121 335 4440

Peet, G B (Healds) *N Zq*
Wigan *p432* 01942 241511

Peet, J C (Squire Sanders (UK) LLP)
London EC2 *p81* 020 7655 1000

Peet, M (Malcolm Peet & Co) *S1 E W*
Wigan *p432* 01257 427867

Peeters, M P D (Pinsent Masons LLP) *Ze*
Leeds *p276* 0113 244 5000

Pegg, A (Lanyon Bowdler LLP) *C1 E S1 O Q*
Shrewsbury *p379* 01743 280280

Pegg, Mrs C A (North Yorkshire County Council)
Northallerton *p467* 01609 780780

Pegg, D J (Pickering & Butters) *S1 S2 E R2*
Rugeley *p368* 01889 803080

Pegg, G L (Pickerings LLP) *K1 D1 D2 K3*
Tamworth *p407* 01827 317070

Peggs, R (Williamson & Soden) *G H P Q B2*
Solihull *p383* 0121 733 8000

Pegler, Miss S (Dale & Newbery LLP) *W*
Staines *p393* 01784 464491

Pegna, J J (Parkers) *K1 G H D1 M1 N Q*
Stockport *p396* 0161 477 9451

Pegram, S C (Challenor & Son)
Abingdon *p114* 01235 520013

Pegram, T J (Challenor & Son)
Abingdon *p114* 01235 520013

Pegrum, R L (Brachers) *E A1 C1 S2 R2*
Maidstone *p299* 01622 690691

Pegrum, Ms V A (K&L Gates LLP)
London EC4 *p47* 020 7648 9000

Peirce, Mrs G (Birnberg Peirce & Partners) *G H R1 V Zi Zg Zp*
Camden *p13* 020 7911 0166

Peirse, Miss R A (Family Law in Partnership LLP) *K3 K1 D1 D2*
London WC2 *p30* 020 7420 5000

Peirson, A M (Williamson Hill) *N*
Middlesbrough *p315* 01642 217961

Pelentrides, S C (S C Pelentrides & Co) *C1 E F1 K1 L M1 N P S1 W Zi Zj Zk*
London N17 *p66* 020 8365 1688

Pell, R M (Brethertons LLP) *N C1 M1 P B1 J1 E Ze Zf Zk*
Rugby *p368* 01788 579579

Pellman, A J G (Pellmans) *A1 A2 K1 Q O C1 E J1 W S1 S2 T1 T2*
Eynsham *p223* 01865 884400

Pellman, I D (Pellmans) *Q O C1 S1 S2 W*
Eynsham *p223* 01865 884400

Pellman, Ms J (Pellmans) *K4 S1 T2 W*
Eynsham *p223* 01865 884400

Pells, Ms H M (B P Collins LLP) *S1*
Gerrards Cross *p229* 01753 889995

Pelmont, N (Cramer Pelmont)
London N8 *p23* 020 8340 0091

Pelopida, M E (Machins Solicitors LLP) *C1 C3 I C2*
Luton *p295* 01582 514000

Pemberton, A (Prince Evans)
Ealing *p69* 020 8567 3477

Pemberton, Ms A J (BUPA) *Ze O C1 U2 C3*
London WC1 *p104* 020 7656 2305

Pemberton, Mrs C W (English Heritage)
London EC1 *p106* 020 7973 3360

Pemberton, G E (Pemberton Greenish LLP) *E L S1 S2*
London SW3 *p66* 020 7591 3333

Pemberton, N (Veale Wasbrough Vizards) *E*
Bristol *p165* 0117 925 2020

Pemble, S (Mills & Reeve) *O A3 Q Zk*
Cambridge *p175* 01223 364422

Pembridge, Ms E M (Fisher Meredith) *K1*
Lambeth *p32* 020 7091 2700

Pembroke, R S (National House Building Council)
Milton Keynes *p447* 0870 241 4302

Penasar, Mrs T (McAras Solicitors LLP) *K3 K1 D1 D2*
Leeds *p275* 0113 243 4333

Penaser, T K (Patrick Lawrence) *K1*
Gravesend *p233* 01474 356441

Pender, J R (Phillips Solicitors) *C1 C2 E R1 I J1 T1 T2 Ze Zc*
Basingstoke *p127* 01256 460830

Pender, Miss M (M Pender) *S1 W S2*
Woking *p437* 01932 352653

Pender, R J (Chris Harrison Law) *N Q W Zr*
Truro *p414* 01872 241408

Pender, S J (E E F South) *C1*
Hook *p461* 01256 763969

Pendlebury Cox, Mrs L P (Gregory Rowcliffe Milners) *O K1 D1 Q Zb Zi*
London WC1 *p37* 020 7242 0631

Pendlebury, Ms A E (Eaton Smith LLP) *N Q O F1 J1*
Huddersfield *p255* 01484 821300

Pendrigh, Miss N D G (Pendrigh Makin) *S1 W S2 T2 K4 E*
Reigate *p363* 01737 221518

Penfold, B (Blake Lapthorn) *G H*
Chandlers Ford *p184* 023 8090 8090

Penfold, C G (Ellisons) *E C1 S1 W L*
Colchester *p197* 01206 764477

Penfold, Ms C S (Radcliffes Le Brasseur) *K1 D1 D2*
Westminster *p70* 020 7222 7040

Penfold, Mrs J (Hart Reade) *Q F1 B1 J1 L O N*
Eastbourne *p215* 01323 727321

Penfold, Ms L (Withers LLP) *C1 I Ze Zf*
London EC4 *p92* 020 7597 6000

Penfold, S D (Moss Beachley Mullem & Coleman)
Westminster *p62* 020 7402 1401 / 7723 5783

Pengelly, Ms V (Faegre & Benson LLP)
London EC4 *p30* 020 7450 4500

Pengilley, Miss S (L G Williams & Prichard) *S1 W K4*
Cardiff *p181* 029 2022 9716

Penhaligan, Ms L (H2O Law LLP) *Ze Zf Zz W*
London EC4 *p37* 020 7405 4700

Peniket, Miss S J (Rees Page) *L S2 E C1 O S1*
Wolverhampton *p438* 01902 577777

Penley, J F (Winterbotham Smith Penley LLP) *A1 W S1 T1 E C1 L Zd*
Dursley *p214* 01453 541940

Penman, A (Alfred Newton & Co) *C1 D1 E G H L T1 N Zl K3 D2*
Stockport *p396* 0161 480 6551 / 480 1245
Wilmslow *p433* 01625 523647

Penman, Ms J (Beecroft Maxwell) *K1 K3 D1 W*
Canvey Island *p177* 01268 511999

Penman, Mrs J A (Russell & Russell) *N*
Middleton *p315* 0161 653 6200

Penman, Miss J J (Alfred Newton & Co) *D1 K3 K1 Zh W*
Stockport *p396* 0161 430 8831

Penman, Mrs S A (Alfred Newton & Co) *D1 G H K1 D2 K3 V W*
Wilmslow *p433* 01625 523647
Stockport *p396* 0161 480 6551 / 480 1245
Stockport *p396* 0161 430 8831

Penn, Miss E M S (James Morgan Solicitors) *S1 S2 W*
Cardiff *p180* 029 2038 2111 / 2022 1600

Penn, G A (Sidley Austin Brown & Wood) *Zb*
London EC2 *p78* 020 7360 3600

Penn, G P (stevensdrake) *F1*
Crawley *p202* 01293 596900

Penn, J F W (Watson Farley & Williams)
London EC2 *p90* 020 7814 8000

Penn, R H (QualitySolicitors Hill & Abbott) *B1 F1 J1 K1 L N Q O*
Chelmsford *p187* 01245 258892

Penn, Miss S (Parkinson Wright LLP) *W T2 K4*
Droitwich *p213* 01905 775533

Penn, T J (Penn Sassoli) *S1 E D1 W M1 G P L K1 B1 Zl Zc*
Royston *p368* 01763 245234 / 245957

Penna, C E (Hewitts)
Bishop Auckland *p144* 01388 604691

Penna, K G (GLRS Phoenix LLP) *N Q O L*
Stroud *p400* 01453 757381

Pennal, P J (Blake Lapthorn) *A3 O Q*
London EC1 *p13* 020 7405 2000

Pennant, Ms A (Reynolds Porter Chamberlain LLP)
London E1 *p71* 020 3060 6000

Pennant, C R (Everett Tomlin Lloyd & Pratt) *E S1 A1 W L O J1 R1 T1 C1 Zd Zl Ze*
Newport *p328* 01633 251801

Pennant, Ms J (Boodle Hatfield) *W*
Westminster *p14* 020 7629 7411

Pennant-Williams, Mrs C (Bowcock Cuerden LLP) *O Q J1*
Nantwich *p320* 01270 611106

Pennelegion, Ms H (Kirby Sheppard) *K3 K1 D1*
Bristol *p163* 0845 840 0045

Pennell, M D (CMS Cameron McKenna LLP)
London EC3 *p17* 020 7367 3000

Penney, C D S (Addleshaw Goddard)
London EC1 *p4* 020 7606 8855

Penney, J P (Gordon & Penney) *G H*
Weston-super-Mare *p429* 01934 414161

Penney, P J (Stanley Tee LLP) *S1*
Saffron Walden *p370* 01799 527299

Pennicott, Mrs S L (Warner Goodman LLP) *K1 K2 K3 D1 D2*
Portsmouth *p355* 023 9275 3575

Pennie, J A (Dickinson Dees) *B1 M1*
Newcastle upon Tyne *p324* 0191 279 9000

Pennington, Mrs D S (Wrexham County Borough Council)
Wrexham *p477* 01978 292000

Pennington, E B (Bells Solicitors) *W K4 V Zm*
Farnham *p224* 01252 733733

Pennington, Miss K H M (Lucas & Wyllys) *W S1*
Great Yarmouth *p234* 01493 855555

Pennington, M T (hlw Keeble Hawson LLP) *M1 N S1 W F1 R1 B1 C1 A1 E Ze Zi Zj*
Doncaster *p211* 01302 366831

Pennington, P R (hlw Keeble Hawson LLP) *E S1 R1 T1 C1 A1 L B1 W Zc Zs Zo*
Doncaster *p211* 01302 366831

Pennington, P R (Kenyon Son & Craddock) *G W E A1 C1 P S1 N V Zl Zd Zn*
Doncaster *p212* 01405 813108

Pennington, R W (Ward Gethin) *O N J1 B1 L Q F1 Zc Zj Zp Zo A3 J2 K1 K3 D1 D2*
King's Lynn *p266* 01553 660033

Pennington, Miss S J (Raworths LLP) *W K4*
Harrogate *p240* 01423 566666

Pennock, Ms J A (Bridge McFarland) *K1 D1 D2 V W*
Grimsby *p235* 01472 311711

Penny, A H (Forsters LLP) *W Zd*
Westminster *p33* 020 7863 8333

Penny, Ms J (Goodall Barnett James)
Horley *p252* 01293 414448

Penny, J J (Hampshire County Council)
Winchester *p476* 01962 841841

Penny, M (Hill Dickinson LLP) *Zj Za*
London EC3 *p41* 020 7283 9033

Penny, S R (John Collins & Partners LLP) *E S1 W L C1*
Swansea *p405* 01792 773772

Penny, T (Clarke Kiernan)
Tonbridge *p412* 01732 360999

Penrose, R P S (Andrew Jackson) *Za*
Hull *p257* 01482 325242

Penrose-Stevens, Ms J A (Kennedys) *N Q*
Chelmsford *p186* 0845 838 4800

Penson, C N (Norton & Co) *K1 N S1 P W F1 G D1 B1*
Hyde *p259* 0161 366 8333

Pentecost, I E (dgb Solicitors) *C1 S2 E C2 R2*
Chatham *p184* 01634 304000

Pentecost, N A (Rawlison Butler LLP) *E L S1*
Crawley *p202* 01293 527744

Penticost, R F (Cripps Harries Hall LLP) *T2 W*
Tunbridge Wells *p415* 01892 515121

Penwell, N (Dunn & Baker) *W K4 T2*
Exeter *p221* 01392 285000

Penzer, N C H (Stephen Murray & Co) *S1 E W*
Perivale *p346* 020 8997 9669

Peplow, Ms A E (Sefton Metropolitan Borough Council) *K1 G J1 L S1*
Southport *p472* 01704 533133

Peppard, Mrs T P (Hancocks) *S1 W*
Banbury *p122* 01295 253211

Pepper, A G T (Carter-Ruck) *Zk O Ze*
London EC4 *p18* 020 7353 5005

Pepper, Ms C (Bryan Cave) *T2 W M2*
London EC2 *p19* 020 7207 1100

Pepper, Miss M E (Whiteford Crocker) *S1 E W*
Saltash *p371* 01752 843134

Pepper, M H (Maples Solicitors LLP) *S1 W L T1 E C1 A1 R1 B1 V Zc Zd Zm*
Spalding *p389* 01775 722261

Pepper, N R (Hand Morgan & Owen) *N O Q J1 G P Zl J2 Zq*
Stafford *p393* 01785 211411

Pepperdine, A (Paul Browne) *E K4 R1 S1*
Oakham *p339* 01572 757565

Pepperell, B S (Pepperells) *S2 E K3 K1 L S1 W*
Scunthorpe *p373* 01724 871999

Pepperell, Mrs J A (Wakefield Metropolitan District Council)
Wakefield *p474* 01924 306090

Pepperell, S W (Pepperells) *C1 F1 J1 K1 N P R1 W Zj Zk Zp*
Scunthorpe *p373* 01724 871999

Peppiatt, S D E (Bingham McCutchen (London) LLP) *Zn*
London EC2 *p12* 020 7661 5300
London EC2 *p78* 020 7655 5000

Peramunagama, Miss S I (Ranga & Co)
London NW10 *p70* 020 8451 4518

Perara, Mrs M (City of York Council)
York *p477* 01904 551045

Percival, D J (Weightmans LLP) *Zu E L O R1 C1 C2 B1 S1 W J1 Zh Zl Zc Zv S2*
Liverpool *p291* 0151 227 2601

Percival, G X (Allen Hoole Solicitors) *G H M1*
Bristol *p160* 0117 942 0901

Percival, J (Straw & Pearce) *N*
Loughborough *p293* 01509 268931

Percival, J C (Hall Smith Whittingham LLP) *A1 C1 E L R1 S1 T1*
Crewe *p203* 01270 212000
Nantwich *p320* 01270 610300

Percival, Miss K (Lanyon Bowdler LLP) *A1 S2 E W*
Oswestry *p342* 01691 652241

Percival, M (W S Atkins Consultants Ltd)
Epsom *p458* 01372 726140

Percival, R (Greenland Houchen Pomeroy) *E K4 R1 S1 W*
Long Stratton *p293* 01508 530033

Percy, Miss C M (Reynolds Porter Chamberlain LLP)
London E1 *p71* 020 3060 6000

Percy, Miss J (Mahany & Co Solicitors LLP) *D1 K1 K3*
Horley *p252* 01293 772888

Pereira, M (Fox Williams) *C1 C2*
London EC2 *p33* 020 7628 2000

Perera, A (OBW Perera) *N Zm*
Colchester *p197* 01206 541111

Perera, Ms C (Perera & Co) *Zi V*
London E7 *p67* 020 8503 0030

Perera, Ms E (Howard Kennedy LLP) *E*
London W1 *p48* 020 7636 1616

Perera, Ms E D (Lewis Silkin LLP) *J1*
London EC4 *p53* 020 7074 8000

Perera, M M D (Perera & Co) *V Zi*
London E7 *p67* 020 8503 0030

Perera, Miss N (McGrigors LLP) *C1 C2*
London EC4 *p56* 020 7054 2500

Perez, C (Stephenson Harwood) *Za*
London EC2 *p82* 020 7329 4422

Peri, H (Whitehead Monckton) *C1 Zb*
Maidstone *p299* 01622 698000

Periklis, M (Mark & Co) *S1 E W S2*
London N13 *p58* 020 8920 9999

Perischine, Ms S (Paul Crowley & Co)
Liverpool *p287* 0151 264 7363

Perkins, A S (Kitsons LLP) *J1 B1 L Q Zp*
Exeter *p221* 01392 455555

Perkins, D (Caerphilly County Borough Council)
Hengoed *p460* 01443 815588

Perkins, Mrs E (Elmhirst Parker LLP) *Q N K1 J1 W O K3*
Leeds *p273* 01977 682219

Perkins, Mrs E S A (Wilkins) *E S1 S2*
Aylesbury *p121* 01296 424681

6

Perkins, Miss G E (Latimer Hinks) *W S1 K4 T2*
Darlington *p206* 01325 341500
Perkins, G R (TWM Solicitors LLP) *N O L J1 F1 Q B1 Zc Zl*
Guildford *p237* 01483 752700
Perkins, Ms J (Irwin Mitchell LLP) *E*
Leeds *p274* 0870 150 0100
Perkins, J D (J Garrard & Allen) *S2 S1 C1*
Olney *p341* 01234 711215
Perkins, Ms J E (D R James & Son) *S1 S2*
Pontardawe *p351* 01792 862334
Perkins, J L (Berg Legal) *C2 C1*
Manchester *p301* 0161 833 9211
Perkins, N J P (Dean Wilson Laing) *P N L K1 R1 Zl O Q Zw*
Brighton *p159* 01273 327241
Perkins, Miss S J (Andersons Solicitors) *K1 K3*
Nottingham *p335* 0115 947 0641
Perks, E R H (Currey & Co) *W T2 Zd*
Westminster *p24* 020 7802 2700
Perks, Ms S (Cunningtons)
Braintree *p155* 01376 326868
Perks, T J (Jennings Perks & Co) *S1 E L W C1*
Walsall *p420* 01922 459000
Perl, N (Sharpe & Perl) *E S1 D1 C1 Q*
Dartford *p207* . . . .01474 872576 / 873359
Perlmutter, A D (Hamlins LLP) *O Q N L A3 J1 E*
London W1 *p38* 020 7355 6000
Perons, Ms K J (Worcestershire County Council)
Worcester *p477* 01905 766335
Perot, N S (McMillan Williams) *K1 D1*
Thornton Heath *p411* 020 8653 8844
Perraton, Ms S L (Squire Sanders (UK) LLP)
Birmingham *p142* 0121 222 3000
Perrett, A L (Harrison Clark LLP)
Ross-on-Wye *p367* 01989 562377
Perrigo, A J F (Morecrofts Solicitors LLP)
Birkenhead *p134* 0151 666 2210
Perriman, R D (W H Matthews & Co) *S1 W S2*
Sutton *p402* 020 8642 6677
Perrin, C C (Clifford Chance)
London E14 *p20* 020 7006 1000
Perrin, Mrs C I (Roger Brooker & Co)
Chelmsford *p186* 01245 351924
Perrin, F (Perrins Solicitors LLP) *E C1 L R1 S1 W Zh*
Harpenden *p239* 01582 466140
Perrin, L C (Osborne Clarke) *B1 M1 N*
Bristol *p164* 0117 917 3000
London EC2 *p65* 020 7105 7000
Perrin, R A (Bircham Dyson Bell)
Westminster *p13* 020 7227 7000
Perrins, G H (RWPS LLP) *C1 E F1 G K1 L M1 P S1 W Ze*
Poole *p353* 01202 466669
Perritt, Mrs J G (Neil Myerson LLP) *E R2*
Altrincham *p117* 0161 941 4000
Perrott, B S (Holman Fenwick Willan)
London EC3 *p42* 020 7264 8000
Perrott, E F V (Taylor Vinters) *O Zq*
Cambridge *p176* 01223 423444
Perrott, J (Cadbury Schweppes PLC (Legal Dept))
Birmingham *p449* 0121 625 7000
Perry, A D (Robert Hitchins Ltd)
Cheltenham *p454* 01242 680694
Perry, The Hon A M (Edwards Angell Palmer & Dodge)
London EC2 *p28* 020 7583 4055
Perry, B (Burningham & Brown) *S2 S1 W E K1*
Bath *p127* 01225 320090
Perry, C J (Bryan & Armstrong) *G H Zm*
Mansfield *p311* 01623 624505
Perry, C J (R A Savage & Co) *K3 K1 D1*
Welwyn Garden City *p425* . . 01707 373037
Perry, Ms C M (Robert Hitchins Ltd)
Cheltenham *p454* 01242 680694
Perry, D A (Waltons & Morse LLP) *Zj Za M2*
London EC3 *p90* 020 7623 4255
Perry, D B (Wortley Redmayne Kershaw) *O Q*
Chelmsford *p187* 01245 491122
Perry, D N (Clifford Chance)
London E14 *p20* 020 7006 1000
Perry, E (Daniel Berman & Co) *G H B2*
London NW5 *p12* 020 7428 7798
Perry, Ms E J (Parry Law)
Whitstable *p431* 01227 276276
Perry, G (Sykes Anderson LLP) *T2 T1 W C1 E Q*
London EC2 *p85* 020 3178 3770
Perry, G J C (Shoosmiths)
Birmingham *p142* 0370 086 4000 / 0121 335 4440
Perry, G R (DWF) *N Zr F1*
Liverpool *p287* 0151 907 3000
Perry, Ms H (Reed Smith LLP) *J1 Zp O*
London EC2 *p71* 020 3116 3000
Perry, H B D (Radcliffes Le Brasseur) *Ze C1 C2*
Westminster *p70* 020 7222 7040
Perry, Miss H L (Leeds City Council) *J1 Zp O*
Leeds *p462* 0113 224 3513
London EC2 *p71* 020 3116 3000
Perry, Miss J (Taylor Wessing) *O*
London EC4 *p86* 020 7300 7000
Perry, Ms J A (Principality Building Society)
Cardiff *p453* 029 2038 2000
Perry, J H (Ashurst LLP) *C1 Zj Zo*
London EC2 *p7* 020 7638 1111
Perry, J S (Palmers Solicitors) *S1 K4 C1 E K1 K3 Q N L O F1 Zl W Zd Zc*
Kingston upon Thames *p267* . 020 8549 7444
Perry, K J (Edwards Angell Palmer & Dodge)
London EC2 *p28* 020 7583 4055

Perry, Ms M (Squire Sanders (UK) LLP) *J1*
London EC2 *p81* 020 7655 1000
Perry, M (Symes Robinson & Lee) *N Q*
Exeter *p222* 01392 270867
Perry, M J (Uttlesford District Council) *E S1 N M1 R1 W P J1 G Zl*
Saffron Walden *p470* 01799 510510
Perry, M K (Capstick-Dale & Partners) *E C1 J1 G L N S1 W*
Romford *p366* 01708 722466
Perry, Mrs N (Bartletts Solicitors) *Q N*
Liverpool *p286* 0151 227 3391
Perry, N C (Sharp & Partners) *E S2 C1 L S1*
Nottingham *p339* 0115 959 0055
Perry, N J (Bird & Bird LLP) *C1 U1*
London EC4 *p13* 020 7415 6000
Perry, P (Trowers & Hamlins)
London EC3 *p88* 020 7423 8000
Perry, P G (DLA Piper UK LLP) *E R2 S2 Zc*
London EC2 *p24* 0870 011 1111
Perry, P I (Barlow Lyde & Gilbert LLP) *Q O Zq Zj*
London EC3 *p10* 020 7247 2277
Perry, R (Simmons & Simmons)
London EC2 *p79* 020 7628 2020
Perry, R A (Davies & Partners) *R2 S2 E I F1 F2 Zza Zg*
Gloucester *p230* 01452 612345
Perry, R C V D (Hart Reade) *K1 N D1 J1 W Zp*
Eastbourne *p215* 01323 727321
Perry, R E (Veale Wasbrough Vizards) *S1 W E C1 T1 L A1 J1 R1 F1 Zd*
London EC4 *p89* 020 7405 1234
Perry, R L (CMHT Solicitors) *G Zy*
Walsall *p420* 01922 646400
Perry, Ms S (Druces LLP) *C1 T1 T2 Zo*
London EC2 *p27* 020 7638 9271
Perry, Mrs S A (Paris Smith LLP) *J1*
Southampton *p386* 023 8048 2482
Perry, Mrs S J (Wright Hassall LLP) *O Q Zq A3*
Leamington Spa *p270* 01926 886688
Perry, Ms S J (Pitmans LLP) *C1*
Reading *p361* 0118 958 0224
Perry, W J (Charles Russell LLP) *O Zj*
London EC4 *p19* 020 7203 5000
Perryman, A M (Morrisons Solicitors LLP) *K1*
Woking *p437* 01483 726146
Perryman-Best, Ms K J (Judge Sykes Frixou)
London WC2 *p47* 020 7379 5114
Persaud, H R (Mackenzie & Co) *G H D1 K1 F1 P Zi N*
Hounslow *p254* 020 8569 6289
Persson, G H H (Pardoes) *W Q*
Bridgwater *p158* 01278 457891
Pert, Mrs S J (Pert & Malim) *S1 A1 E G K1 M1 H L*
Grantham *p232* 01476 561631
Pertoldi, Miss A C (Herbert Smith LLP) *O Zb B2 Zq*
London EC2 *p40* 020 7374 8000
Pertwee, R J C D (Taylor Wessing) *C1 F1 J1 O T1 Zo*
London EC4 *p86* 020 7300 7000
Perugini, Mrs K J (Trethowans LLP) *W*
Salisbury *p371* 01722 412512
Perusko, P (Harvey Ingram Borneos) *D1 K1*
Milton Keynes *p317* 01908 696002
Pervazova, Mrs M (Max Gold Law)
Hull *p257* 01482 224900
Perveen, S (Sterling Solicitors)
Birmingham *p142* 0121 772 0777
Pescott, Miss K M (Swinburne & Jackson LLP) *K1 D2 D1*
Gateshead *p229* . 0191 477 2531 / 477 3222
Ryton *p370* . . . 0191 413 3468 / 413 2630
Pestell, H A J (Clarke Willmott) *B1 Zb E*
Bristol *p162* 0845 209 1000 / 0117 305 6000
Pestelle, N (Wintle & Co) *C1 S1 L W E*
Bognor Regis *p148* 01243 863021
Selsey *p374* 01243 605947
Pester, D P L (TLT Solicitors) *C1 J1*
Bristol *p165* 0117 917 7777
Pester, N (Reynolds Porter Chamberlain LLP)
London E1 *p71* 020 3060 6000
Pestill, J (Royds LLP) *O Q N P U2 C3 Ze*
London EC4 *p74* 020 7583 2222
Petch, Ms E (Bates Wells & Braithwaite London LLP) *O Q A3 C3 Zd*
London EC4 *p11* 020 7551 7777
Petch, J H (Chilcotts) *D1 K1 K3*
Tavistock *p408* . . .01822 612535 / 614242
Plymouth *p350* . . .01752 665037 / 221171
Petch, Mrs K E (Brown Beer Nixon Mallon) *D1 K1 K3*
Redcar *p362* 01642 490202
Petch, R K (Mackarness & Lunt) *S1 W S2*
Petersfield *p348* 01730 265111
Petchey, Mrs J B (Howell-Jones LLP) *J1 O Q*
Kingston upon Thames *p267* . 020 8549 5186
Petchey, P R S (Schofield Sweeney) *C1 C2 E R2*
Bradford *p154* 01274 306000
Peter, C P (Berkson Globe Partnership) *G H L M1 P F1 C1*
Liverpool *p286* 0151 236 1234
Peter, W (Pinsent Masons LLP)
London EC2 *p67* 020 7418 7000
Peterkin, I B (Bennett Griffin) *A1 C1 E F2 L S1 T2 W*
Ferring *p225* 01903 229999
Peters, A (Keoghs LLP) *N Zj O Q Zw Zq*
Bolton *p149* 01204 677000
Peters, A (Martin Smith & Co) *K1 K3 N*
Borehamwood *p150* 020 8953 0636

Peters, Ms A A (LG Lawyers)
London SE1 *p50* 020 7379 0000
Peters, A N (Barlow Robbins LLP) *J1*
Woking *p436* 01483 748500
Peters, Ms C (Reynolds Porter Chamberlain LLP) *O Zq*
London E1 *p71* 020 3060 6000
Peters, Mrs C (Johns & Saggar) *S1*
London WC1 *p46* 020 3490 1475
Peters, D E (Hine Downing Solicitors)
Falmouth *p223* 01326 316655
Peters, Mrs D L (Crane & Staples) *K3 Q Zu K1 D1 D2*
Welwyn Garden City *p425* . . 01707 329333
Peters, E (Addleshaw Goddard)
London EC1 *p4* 020 7606 8855
Peters, G F (Hadgkiss Hughes & Beale) *G*
Birmingham *p138* 0121 449 5050
Peters, G J R (Scott Rowe) *S2 G K4 R1 S1 T2 W*
Lyme Regis *p296* 01297 443777
Peters, I (Anthony Gold) *N*
London SE1 *p6* 020 7940 4000
Peters, Ms J (Faegre & Benson LLP) *C1 C2*
London EC4 *p30* 020 7450 4500
Peters, Ms K J (Capsticks Solicitors LLP) *N Zr*
London SW19 *p18* 020 8780 2211
Peters, M A (Sherrards) *E*
St Albans *p390* 01727 832830
Peters, P D (Trowers & Hamlins)
London EC3 *p88* 020 7423 8000
Peters, R M (Gordon Dadds) *Zd T1*
London W1 *p25* 020 7493 6151
Peters, R O (Broomhead & Saul) *A1 E G H L S1 S2*
Ilminster *p261* 01460 57056
Petersen, Mrs E L M (Fisher Jones Greenwood LLP) *R2 E*
Colchester *p197* 01206 578282
Peterson, A (Penningtons) *J1*
London EC2 *p66* 020 7457 3000
Peterson, D (Petersons) *C1 N O Q W*
Newport *p329* 01633 255151
Peterson, J (Gill Akaster) *S1 Q E*
Plymouth *p349* 01752 203500
Peterson, Ms K R (Potter Rees (Serious Injury) Solicitors)
Manchester *p309* 0161 237 5888
Peterson, R (Wansbroughs)
Devizes *p210* 01380 733300
Peterson, R (Petersons) *C1 E O Q J1 K1*
Newport *p329* 01633 255151
Pether, Miss S J (Andrew Jackson) *N Q O*
Hull *p257* 01482 325242
Petheram, Ms C B (Linklaters LLP)
London EC2 *p54* 020 7456 2000
Petherbridge, A (Petherbridge Bassra Solicitors) *G H*
Bradford *p154* 01274 724114
Petillion, F (Crowell & Moring) *Ze*
London EC4 *p23* 020 7413 0011
Petley, M (The College of Law Guildford)
Guildford *p459* 01483 460200
Peto, Miss L M (Institute of Chartered Accountants in England & Wales)
Milton Keynes *p466* 01908 248100
Peto, Mrs V R (Pellmans) *K1 Q J1 K3 O*
Eynsham *p223* 01865 884400
Petricca-Riding, Mrs C (Aaron & Partners LLP Solicitors) *G H P R1 Zt*
Chester *p190* 01244 405555
Petrie, C A (Newcastle Building Society)
Newcastle upon Tyne *p466* . 0191 244 2000
Petrie, Mrs D (Midwinters) *W T2*
Cheltenham *p188* 01242 514674
Petrie, G W (Gary Caplan Solicitors) *Zi Zl O Q B1*
Leeds *p272* 0113 216 3118
Petrie, Ms J E (Sheffield Law Centre) *G H K1 L M1 P Zp*
Sheffield *p471* 0114 273 1501
Petritz, Mrs S (Sue Petritz) *K1 K3 D1 A2*
Horsham *p253* 01403 790218
Petrou, A C (Petrou & Co) *E S1 S2 C1 F1 J1 R2*
London N14 *p67* 020 8920 5800
Petrou, Mrs D (Petrou Law Partnership)
London N4 *p67* 020 8802 9393
Petrou, J S (Rice-Jones & Smiths) *E K1 S1 Zb S2 W*
London EC1 *p72* 020 7831 2506
Petrou, P (Petrou Law Partnership)
London N4 *p67* 020 8802 9393
Petrou, S (Petrou Law Partnership)
London N4 *p67* 020 8802 9393
Petrou, T (Charles Ross Solicitors)
Barnet *p124* 020 8216 2300
Petrovic, Ms O (Linklaters LLP)
London EC2 *p54* 020 7456 2000
Petry, A (Addleshaw Goddard)
London EC1 *p4* 020 7606 8855
Pett, D J (Pinsent Masons LLP) *T1 T2*
Birmingham *p141* 0121 200 1050
Pett, D R (Morgan Jones & Pett) *N J2 Zq O K1*
Norwich *p335* 01603 877000
Petters, L D (Rodney King & Partners) *G H*
Bristol *p163* 0117 926 5201
Petters, R D (Gamlins) *L P S1 T1 W E*
Llandudno *p291* 01492 860420
Pettersen, A C (Ward & Rider Limited)
Coventry *p201* 024 7655 5400
Petterson, L A (Meikles) *Q G K1 N H D1 S1 W J1*
Ferryhill *p226* 01740 652811

Pettifer, I (Tayntons LLP Solicitors) *J1*
Gloucester *p230* 01452 522047
Pettifer, M J (North Norfolk District Council)
Cromer *p456* 01263 513811
Pettifor, R J (Gateley LLP) *E S2 R2*
Birmingham *p138* 0121 234 0000
Pettingell, M A (Clarke Willmott) *J2*
Bristol *p162* 0845 209 1000 / 0117 305 6000
Pettinger, A (Addleshaw Goddard)
Leeds *p271* 0113 209 2000
Pettingill, Miss J E (Gordons LLP) *J1*
Leeds *p273* 0113 227 0100
Sheffield *p376* 0114 276 5555
Pettit, J E (Ashfords LLP) *W*
Exeter *p220* 01392 337000
Pettit, K J (Darlington Hardcastles) *W*
Rickmansworth *p364* 01923 774272
Pettit, M G (Taylor Walton LLP) *B1 C1 C2 E I J1 T1 T2 X Zc Zo*
Luton *p295* 01582 731161
Pettit, R J (Clifford Chance)
London E14 *p20* 020 7006 1000
Pettitt, A C (Hague Lambert) *E S1 S2*
Knutsford *p269* 01565 652411
Pettitt, Mrs K (Hertfordshire County Council)
Hertford *p460* 01992 555555
Petts, Miss C L (Barlow Lyde & Gilbert LLP) *Zr N*
London EC3 *p10* 020 7247 2277
Petty, S G (Bywaters Topham Phillips LLP) *E L S2 W*
Harrogate *p240* 01423 879556
Peyman, Miss M (Nockolds) *K1*
Bishop's Stortford *p144* . . . 01279 755777
Pezzack, Ms S D (Eli Lilly UK Ltd)
Basingstoke *p448* 01256 315000
Pfeffer, J P (GLP Solicitors) *C1 F1 S1*
Manchester *p304* 0161 795 5531
Pfister, C H (AWB Partnership LLP) *C1 E W S1 R1*
Guildford *p235* 01483 302345
Pheby, J D (Pheby & Co) *N K1 L S1 X W*
York *p445* 01904 789900
Phelan, Miss A M (Richardson Smith & Co) *Q G H K1 D1*
Chesham *p189* 01494 772773
Phelan, C C L (Rollasons) *K1 Q L D1 V J1 N F1 X R1 Zl Zm Zc*
Daventry *p207* 01327 301771
Phelan, Ms C M (Pattinson & Brewer) *N Q*
London WC1 *p66* 020 7400 5100
Phelan, J J (Financial Services Authority)
London E14 *p106* 020 7066 1000
Phelan, Ms P M (David Rubie Mitchell & Co) *S1*
Sutton *p403* 020 8641 0575
Phelan, Miss S (Harvey Ingram Borneos)
Bedford *p130* 01234 353221
Phelops, W L (K&L Gates LLP) *C1 Zw*
London EC4 *p47* 020 7648 9000
Phelps, Mrs C B (Frearsons) *N*
Skegness *p380* 01754 897600
Phelps, J (Harrison Clark LLP) *B1 O Q*
Worcester *p439* 01905 612001
Phelps, J (Michelmores LLP) *C3 M1*
Exeter *p221* 01392 688688
Phelps, J C (DAC Beachcroft)
London EC4 *p24* 020 7242 1011
Phelps, Miss L R L (London Borough of Wandsworth) *K1*
London SW18 *p110* 020 8871 6000
Phelps, M R (Frearsons) *N*
Skegness *p380* 01754 897600
Phelps, Mrs N (Haworth & Nuttall) *E S2 R2*
Blackburn *p145* 01254 272640
Phelps, R (Jones Day) *C2*
London EC4 *p46* 020 7039 5959
Phelps, Miss R J C (Bates Wells & Braithwaite London LLP) *W T2 Zd*
London EC4 *p11* 020 7551 7777
Phelps, Ms S (Thorneycroft Solicitors Ltd) *N Q*
Macclesfield *p297* 01625 503444
Phelps, T (Veale Wasbrough Vizards) *O*
London EC4 *p89* 020 7405 1234
Philbin, D W (Latimer Lee LLP)
Prestwich *p358* 0161 798 9000
Philcox, Ms C A (ASB Law) *N Q J2*
Crawley *p202* 01293 603600
Philip, D (Kennedys) *Zj*
London EC3 *p49* 020 7667 9667
Philip, J J N (Julian Philip & Co) *C1 S1 W E*
Shepperton *p377* 01932 254354
Philip, Ms S (Crown Prosecution Service Avon & Somerset)
Bristol *p451* 0117 930 2800
Philip, Ms T A (Principality Building Society)
Cardiff *p453* 029 2038 2000
Philipp, Ms J (Philipp & Co)
London N2 *p67* 020 7566 8244
Philippon-Thomas, Ms S (Freeth Cartwright LLP)
Leicester *p279* 0116 248 1100
Philippou, Miss A (Stitt & Co) *S2 E S1*
London EC4 *p83* 020 7832 0840
Philippou, Ms H (Nicholas & Co) *D1 J1 K1 N O Q S1 S2 W L Zp Zv*
London W1 *p63* 020 7323 4450
Philippou, Ms H (Philippou & Co) *K1 J1 E S2 C1 D1 L O Q W D2 M3 K3 X S1*
London N13 *p67* 020 8882 4222
Philippou, P (Nicholas & Co) *Q O N W Zr*
London W1 *p63* 020 7323 4450
Philipps, R P S (Reed Smith LLP) *Zf*
London EC2 *p71* 020 3116 3000

See p634 for the Key to Work Categories

Philipps, Mrs S (Alexiou Fisher Philipps) *K1 D1 K2 K3*
London W1 *p5* 020 7409 1222

Philippsohn, S N (PCB Litigation LLP) *B1 L J1 Zb Zc I B2 U2 O Zq A3 M2*
London EC1 *p65* 020 7831 2691

Philips, Ms A (ASB Law) *S1*
Maidstone *p298* 01622 656500

Philips, D (Howard Kennedy LLP) *E S2*
London W1 *p48* 020 7636 1616

Philips, D J (North Lincolnshire Council)
Scunthorpe *p470* 01724 296296

Philips, Ms L (McMillan Williams) *Zr N*
South Croydon *p383* 020 8253 7600

Philips, M J M (Howard Kennedy LLP) *E S1 Zb*
London W1 *p48* 020 7636 1616

Philips, Miss S (Berry & Berry) *D1 K3 K1*
Tonbridge *p412* 01732 355911

Phillip, H A J (Reed Smith LLP) *C1 C2*
London EC2 *p71* 020 3116 3000

Phillip, J C (Walker Foster) *S1 S2 E A1 R2 W*
Skipton *p381* 01756 700200

Phillips, Mrs A (First National Banks PLC)
Caerphilly *p452* 029 2086 0133

Phillips, A (Harbottle & Lewis LLP)
London W1 *p38* 020 7667 5000

Phillips, Ms A (Horne Engall & Freeman LLP)
Egham *p217* 01784 432292

Phillips, Mrs A (Stone King LLP) *Zd*
London EC1 *p83* 020 7796 1007

Phillips, Miss A (McMillan Williams) *K1*
Thornton Heath *p411* 020 8653 8844

Phillips, Ms A (ASB Law) *S2 S1 W K4*
Maidstone *p298* 01622 656500

Phillips, Mrs A (Lewis Lewis & Company Ltd) *S1 W S2 K1 C1*
St Clears *p391* 01994 231044

Phillips, Miss A C (HSBC Legal Department)
Birmingham *p449* 0121 455 2740

Phillips, A J (Fearon & Co) *C1 E L S1 W S2*
Guildford *p236* 01483 540840

Phillips, A J (Wessex Water Services Ltd)
Bath *p448* 01225 526000

Phillips, A M (The Smith Partnership) *E F1 J1 K1 S1 W Zl*
Burton-on-Trent *p170* 01283 548282

Phillips, A R (Moorcrofts LLP) *C2 C1*
Marlow *p313* 01628 470000

Phillips, A R (Mowbray Woodwards Solicitors) *G H N Zl Zm*
Bath *p128* 01225 485700

Phillips, A W (Bates Wells & Braithwaite London LLP) *Zd C1*
London EC4 *p11* 020 7551 7777

Phillips, B G (Clifford Chance)
London E14 *p20* 020 7006 1000

Phillips, B S (Herbert Smith LLP) *C1 T1 C2*
London EC2 *p40* 020 7374 8000

Phillips, Ms C (Osborne Clarke) *C1*
London EC2 *p65* 020 7105 7000

Phillips, Miss C (Lewis Lewis & Company Ltd)
St Clears *p391* 01994 231044

Phillips, Ms C (Reynolds Porter Chamberlain LLP)
London E1 *p71* 020 3060 6000

Phillips, C I G (Davies Ingram & Harvey) *S1 S2*
Swansea *p405* 01792 653764

Phillips, Mrs C M (South Norfolk District Council)
Long Stratton *p463* 01508 533633

Phillips, D A (Harold G Walker) *S1 S2*
Wimborne *p433* 01202 881454
Bournemouth *p152* 01202 203200

Phillips, Ms D A (Gwynedd Council)
Caernarfon *p452* 01286 672255

Phillips, D C S (Teacher Stern LLP) *E S1 L*
London WC1 *p86* 020 7242 3191

Phillips, D D (Phillips) *F1 G H S1 V Zl Zk W Zl O Q*
Mansfield *p312* 01623 658556

Phillips, D G (London Borough of Southwark) *Ze Zf*
London SE1 *p109* 020 7525 5000

Phillips, D H (David Phillips & Partners) *G H B2 Zl*
Bootle *p150* 0151 922 5525

Phillips, D L (Max Barford & Co)
Tunbridge Wells *p414* 01892 539379

Phillips, D M (Phillips & Co) *K1 G C1 N O Q R1 Zl Zm Zj*
Salisbury *p371* 01722 321666

Phillips, D N (Hill Dickinson LLP) *Za*
London EC3 *p41* 020 7283 9033
London EC2 *p82* 020 7329 4422

Phillips, D W (Jestyn Jeffreys) *D1 F1 G H J1 K1 L M1 N P*
Neath *p320* 01639 635641

Phillips, Mrs E (Gabbs LLP) *K1 K2 K3 D1*
Hereford *p248* 01432 353481

Phillips, Miss E F (Fuglers) *N Zj Q*
London W1 *p34* 020 7323 6450

Phillips, Miss E M (MLM Cartwright) *W K4*
Cardiff *p179* 029 2046 2562

Phillips, G (Andrew Jackson) *E S2*
Hull *p257* 01482 325242

Phillips, G D (Price & Kelway) *D1 G H K1 L Q S1 V W Za*
Milford Haven *p316* 01646 695311

Phillips, G I (Sills & Betteridge LLP) *B1 C1 C2 M1 T1 T2 W Zn Zo*
Lincoln *p285* 01522 542211

Phillips, G M (Solomon Taylor & Shaw) *A1 C1 E J1 N P S1*
London NW3 *p80* 020 7431 1912

Phillips, Miss H (Burnetts) *J1*
Carlisle *p181* 01228 552222
Carlisle *p182* 01228 552222

Phillips, H D (Ward & Rider Limited) *N J2 Zj*
Coventry *p201* 024 7655 5400

Phillips, Miss H E (Quality Solicitors Burroughs Day) *C1 Ze I U2 Zw*
Bristol *p164* 0117 929 0333

Phillips, Ms H J (Memery Crystal) *C1 C2*
London WC2 *p60* 020 7242 5905

Phillips, Miss H J (Bells) *E S1 S2 L Zl R1*
Romsey *p366* 01794 513328

Phillips, Ms H M (Glazer Delmar) *W K4*
London SE22 *p35* 020 8299 0021

Phillips, I L (V J G Johns & Son) *S1 W L A1 G H S2*
Fishguard *p226* 01348 873671

Phillips, J (Taylor Wimpey UK Ltd)
Cannock *p453* 01543 496766

Phillips, J (Donnelly McArdle Adamson) *D1 G H K1 S1*
Sunderland *p401* 0191 510 9911
Darlington *p206* 01325 482299

Phillips, Miss J (Morrish Solicitors LLP)
Leeds *p276* 0113 245 0733

Phillips, Miss J (Smith Llewelyn Partnership) *D1 K1*
Swansea *p405* 01792 464444

Phillips, J (Jones Day) *C2*
London EC4 *p46* 020 7039 5959

Phillips, J (Darbys Solicitors LLP) *Zr N Zm*
Oxford *p343* 01865 811700

Phillips, J D (Crosse Wyatt Verney & Ayre) *N Q J1*
South Molton *p383* 01769 572157

Phillips, Miss J E (Irwin Mitchell LLP) *O Zl Zf*
Sheffield *p376* 0870 150 0100

Phillips, J H (Blaenau Gwent Borough Council) *C1 R1 S1 P L I*
Ebbw Vale *p458* 01495 350555

Phillips, J P (Pinsent Masons LLP) *C2 C1 H*
London EC2 *p67* 020 7418 7000

Phillips, Miss K (Wiseman Lee LLP) *G H*
Newham *p92* 020 8215 1000

Phillips, Miss K J (Sprake & Kingsley) *K1 N Q J1 F1 K3*
Bungay *p168* 01986 892721

Phillips, Miss L (Bristows)
London EC4 *p15* 020 7400 8000

Phillips, L S (Blake Lapthorn)
London EC1 *p13* 020 7405 2000

Phillips, Miss M (Lupton Fawcett) *C1 C2 Zb*
Leeds *p275* 0113 280 2000

Phillips, M B (Ward Gethin) *W K4*
King's Lynn *p266* 01553 660033

Phillips, M D (DLA Piper UK LLP)
London EC2 *p24* 0870 011 1111

Phillips, M D (Harbottle & Lewis LLP) *C1 I M1 J1 Zf Zv*
London W1 *p38* 020 7667 5000

Phillips, Mrs M G (Howells) *K1 D1 S1*
Cardiff *p178* 029 2040 4020

Phillips, M H (Tyndallwoods) *G H J1 K1 L P V D1 Zi Zm Zd*
Birmingham *p143* 0121 624 1111

Phillips, M J (Ison Harrison) *S1 W T2 K4*
Garforth *p228* 0113 286 1455

Phillips, M J G (Keelys LLP) *C1 Zb*
Lichfield *p284* 01543 420000

Phillips, M P (GSC Solicitors) *S2 E S1 Zl Zc*
London EC1 *p34* 020 7822 2222

Phillips, N (Biscoes) *K3 L B1 K1 Q*
Portsmouth *p354* 023 9266 0261

Phillips, N D (Beswicks) *J1*
Stoke-on-Trent *p397* 01782 205000

Phillips, N D (William Sturges & Co) *C1 J1 C2 Ze F1 F2 U2 Zd*
Westminster *p84* 020 7873 1000

Phillips, N P (Barlow Robbins LLP) *Ze U2 I O F2*
Guildford *p235* 01483 562901

Phillips, P (Allen & Overy LLP)
London E1 *p5* 020 3088 0000

Phillips, P (Sacker & Partners LLP) *Zo*
London EC2 *p76* 020 7329 6699

Phillips, R (Bowcock Cuerden LLP)
Nantwich *p320* 01270 611106

Phillips, Mrs R (Hess Ltd)
London WC2 *p106* 020 7331 3000

Phillips, R A (Matthew Arnold & Baldwin LLP) *C1 C2 C3*
London EC4 *p59* 020 7936 4600

Phillips, R J (Cooper Lingard) *C1 S2 E K3 J1 K1 O Q S1 W C2 L N*
Leigh-on-Sea *p282* 01702 715411

Phillips, R J (CMS Cameron McKenna LLP)
London EC3 *p17* 020 7367 3000

Phillips, R J (Muckle LLP) *C1 C2 C3*
Newcastle upon Tyne *p325* . 0191 211 7777

Phillips, R J (Treasury Solicitors Department)
London WC2 *p110* 020 7210 3000

Phillips, R M (J & S P Pope) *S1 W L K1 G D1 H V Zv*
Exeter *p222* 01392 274006

Phillips, R Q (Skandia Life Assurance Co Ltd) *C1 Q I J1 Zj Zo Zb*
Southampton *p472* 023 8033 4411

Phillips, Ms S (Berry & Berry) *K1 Q*
Tunbridge Wells *p414* 01892 526344

Phillips, Miss S (Sacker & Partners LLP) *Zo*
London EC2 *p76* 020 7329 6699

Phillips, S (Plexus Law (A Trading Name of Parabis Law LLP)) *A3 P J2 Zj Q N*
London EC3 *p68* 0844 245 4000

Phillips, Mrs S (Oldhams Solicitors & Advocates) *N Q J1*
Baldock *p121* 01462 895444

Phillips, Miss S C (Russell & Co) *S1 S2 W*
Malvern *p300* 01684 892000

Phillips, S H (Burch Phillips & Co) *S1 S2 L W*
West Drayton *p427* 01895 442141

Phillips, T (Heckford Norton) *E S2 R1 S1 A1*
Stevenage *p395* 01438 312211

Phillips, Ms V L (Lewis Silkin LLP) *C1 C2*
London EC4 *p53* 020 7074 8000

Phillips, Ms V M (Thompsons (formerly Robin/Brian Thompson & Partners)) *N J1*
London WC1 *p87* 020 7290 0000

Phillipson, Mrs J (Lichfield Reynolds) *K4 N T2 S1 S2 W*
Stoke-on-Trent *p398* 01782 313212

Phillipson, Ms K R (Hampshire County Council)
Winchester *p476* 01962 841841

Phillipson, P (Simmons & Simmons)
London EC2 *p79* 020 7628 2020

Phillpotts, Miss B A (Peel Management Limited)
Manchester *p465* 0161 629 8200

Philp, Miss N (Devonshires) *J1*
London EC2 *p27* 020 7628 7576

Philpot, D J (Warners Solicitors) *S1 S2 E*
Sevenoaks *p374* 01732 747900

Philpot, D J (Pinsent Masons LLP) *E R2 S2 M1*
Birmingham *p141* 0121 200 1050

Philpott, D (Olliers) *G H*
Manchester *p308* 0161 834 1515

Philpott, G (Veale Wasbrough Vizards) *E L C1 Zb R2 S2*
Bristol *p165* 0117 925 2020

Philpott, J W (Rudds) *K3 K1 J1 N Q L O*
Rayleigh *p359* 01268 778152
Westcliff-on-Sea *p428* 01702 347853

Philpott, P (Quality Solicitors HPJV) *G H K1 N S1 Q D1 L V W Zm Zr Zi Zq Zh*
Newport *p329* 01633 242526

Phippen, C P (Macfarlanes) *O Q*
London EC4 *p56* 020 7831 9222

Phiri, N M (Barlow Lyde & Gilbert LLP)
London EC3 *p10* 020 7247 2277

Phizackerley, Miss K A (Oxfordshire County Council)
Oxford *p468* 01865 792422

Phoenix, R M (Roebucks) *G H*
Blackburn *p145* 01254 274000

Phoenix, Miss S (Paul J Watson) *K3 D1 D2 K1 N W K4*
Middlesbrough *p315* 01642 293427

Photiades, J G P (Photiades) *S1 E C1 W*
Harpenden *p239* 01582 766261

Phull, J (Martin Murray & Associates) *G H B2*
West Drayton *p427* 01895 431332

Phull, Ms J (MFG Solicitors)
Kidderminster *p265* 01562 820181

Phythian, R (Thomson & Bancks LLP)
Pershore *p346* 01386 562000
Tewkesbury *p410* 01684 299633

Phythian-Adams, J (Reynolds Porter Chamberlain LLP)
London E1 *p71* 020 3060 6000

Picard, Mrs A (Moorcrofts LLP) *C1 C2*
Marlow *p313* 01628 470000

Picardo, C E (Carter Lemon Camerons) *E S1 L S2*
London EC1 *p18* 020 7406 1000

Piccos, Miss D J (Wilson & Co) *K1 D2 D1*
London N17 *p92* 020 8808 7535

Pick, G M (Dickinson Manser) *W T2 V Zm Zd*
Poole *p352* 01202 673071

Pickard, A D (Bosworths) *S2 E J1 K1 O Q N S1 W L*
East Molesey *p215* 020 8941 3151

Pickard, G (Field Fisher Waterhouse LLP)
London EC3 *p31* 020 7861 4000

Pickard, Ms H M (Forsters LLP)
Westminster *p33* 020 7863 8333

Pickard, Ms M J (Tameside Metropolitan Borough Council)
Ashton-under-Lyne *p447* . . . 0161 342 3028

Pickard, S C (Lupton Fawcett) *S1 E C1 N Q K1 V W F1 D1 Zi Zm Zc*
Leeds *p275* 0113 280 2000

Pickard, Miss S V (B A A PLC)
London UB3 *p103* 0870 000 0123

Pickburn, Mrs G L F (Coffin Mew & Clover) *S1 W*
Fareham *p223* 01329 825617

Picken, A R (Irvings Solicitors) *S1 W L E K4 S2*
Derby *p209* 01332 346036

Picken, J M (William Sturges & Co) *S1*
Westminster *p84* 020 7873 1000

Picken, R A (Trowers & Hamlins) *C1 Zb*
London EC3 *p88* 020 7423 8000

Pickerin, Ms S M (Tinsdills) *E S1*
Hanley *p239* 01782 262031

Pickering, Mrs A J (Amphlett Lissimore) *W T2*
Croydon *p6* 020 8771 5254

Pickering, A R (Streeter Marshall) *E J1 K1 L N O Q S1 W*
Purley *p358* 020 8660 6455

Pickering, D (DLA Piper UK LLP)
London EC2 *p24* 0870 011 1111

Pickering, G J (stevensdrake) *B1 I O*
Crawley *p202* 01293 596900

Pickering, I (Capsticks Solicitors LLP) *Zr N Zq*
London SW19 *p18* 020 8780 2211

Pickering, J (Irwin Mitchell LLP) *N Zr*
Sheffield *p376* 0870 150 0100

Pickering, J D (Monro Fisher Wasbrough LLP) *S1 W E S2*
London WC1 *p61* 020 7404 7001

Pickering, Ms K F (Squire Sanders (UK) LLP)
Manchester *p310* 0161 830 5000

Pickering, P E (Birchall Blackburn LLP) *Q O Zq Zg Ze Zk*
Manchester *p301* 0161 236 0662

Pickering, S (Michelmores LLP) *B1 C1*
Exeter *p221* 01392 688688

Pickersgill, M D (Walker Morris) *J1 O*
Leeds *p277* 0113 283 2500

Pickersgill, N S D (Perrins Solicitors LLP) *E S2 Zh R2*
Harpenden *p239* 01582 466140

Pickersgill, R (Watson Burton LLP) *B1 E S1 N O Q J1*
Newcastle upon Tyne *p327* . 0845 901 2100

Pickett, J (Linklaters LLP)
London EC2 *p54* 020 7456 2000

Pickford, D (Forbes) *N*
Blackburn *p145* 01254 662831

Pickford, R W G (hlw Keeble Hawson LLP) *S1 W E T1 A1*
Sheffield *p375* 0114 272 2061

Pickin, A J (Shoosmiths) *B1 C1 C3*
Milton Keynes *p317* . 0370 086 8300 / 01908 488300
Nottingham *p339*. 0370 086 5000 / 0115 906 5000

Pickles, Miss A (Whiteside & Knowles Ltd) *A1 S2 E S1 W*
Morecambe *p319* 01524 416315

Pickles, A G (Wrigley Claydon) *S1 G W E K1 P C1 M1 L Zc Zh Zl*
Todmorden *p412* 01706 815712

Pickles, H (Silk Solicitors) *Q N*
Blackburn *p146* 01254 266616

Picknell, J (Mundays LLP)
Cobham *p196* 01932 590500

Pickston, J F (Clifford Chance)
London E14 *p20* 020 7006 1000

Pickstone, J E (Nottingham City Council (City Sec Dept))
Nottingham *p467* 0115 915 5555

Pickthorn, T (Mills & Reeve) *C1 C2 C3 Zb Zz*
Cambridge *p175* 01223 364422

Pickup, B J (SJ Berwin LLP)
London EC4 *p75* 020 7111 2222

Pickup, Ms C (Flint Bishop Solicitors) *E*
Derby *p208* 01332 340211

Pickup, D R (Pickup & Scott) *Zl Zm*
Aylesbury *p121* 01296 397794

Pickup, D S (Farleys Solicitors LLP) *G H B2*
Blackburn *p145* 01254 367854

Pickup, Miss H (Irwin Mitchell LLP) *N*
Birmingham *p139* 0870 150 0100

Pickup, J B (Mosshaselhurst) *S1 W A1 L*
Northwich *p333* 01606 74301

Pickup, Mrs K (Freeth Cartwright LLP) *F2*
Nottingham *p337* 0115 936 9369

Pickup, Mrs M (Blackpool Borough Council)
Blackpool *p450* 01253 477450

Pickup, R J C (Mills & Reeve) *Zc*
Cambridge *p175* 01223 364422

Pickwell, Ms C E (The Ringrose Law Group - Richard Harwood) *K1 D1 J1 K2*
Lincoln *p285* 01522 814700

Pickwick, C A (YVA Solicitors) *H G*
London N12 *p93* 020 8445 9898

Pickworth, J C (DLA Piper UK LLP)
London EC2 *p24* 0870 011 1111

Pickworth, J S (Hartlaw LLP) *Q N F1 O J1 B1 P Zj Zk Zb J2 L Zq Zp A2*
Wetherby *p429* 01937 547000

Picton-Howell, T (Penningtons)
London EC2 *p66* 020 7457 3000

Picton-Turbervill, G (Ashurst LLP) *C1 Zn*
London EC2 *p7* 020 7638 1111

Piddock, A C (Coley & Tilley) *C1 D1 E G H J1 K1 P S1*
Birmingham *p136* 0121 643 5531

Pidduck, J P A (Girlings Personal Injury Claims Limited) *N*
Canterbury *p177* 01227 768374

Pidgeon, A (BTMK Solicitors LLP)
Southend-on-Sea *p387* 01702 339222

Pidgeon, D M (Heckford Norton) *J1 O Q Zq F1 Zc*
Stevenage *p395* 01438 312211

Pidgeon, N (Oldham Marsh Page Flavell) *S1 E W A1*
Melton Mowbray *p314* 01664 563162

Pidgeon, N J (Charles Russell LLP) *E S1 R2*
Guildford *p235* 01483 252525

Pierce, E (Emyr Pierce & Co) *S1 S2 E W L*
Cardiff *p180* 029 2061 6002

Pierce, Ms F (Thomson Snell & Passmore) *N Zr*
Tunbridge Wells *p415* 01892 510000

Pierce, Ms H M (Barlow Lyde & Gilbert LLP)
London EC3 *p10* 020 7247 2277

Pierce, J (Holman Fenwick Willan)
London EC3 *p42* 020 7264 8000

Pierce, J (Brady Eastwood Pierce & Stewart)
Lewisham *p15* 020 8692 8181

Pierce, Ms J J (Charles Russell LLP) *Ze*
London EC4 *p19* 020 7203 5000

Pierce, N (Metropolitan Police Directorate of Legal Services)
London SW1 *p108* 020 7230 7210

Pierce, R T W (Charles Russell LLP) *E S1 W U1*
Guildford *p235* 01483 252525

Pierce, S (Bond Pearce LLP) *C1 C2*
Southampton *p385* 0845 415 0000

Pierce, S E (Pierce Glynn) *L V*
Southwark *p67* 020 7407 0007

Piercy, N (Coley & Tilley) *E L S1 Zl*
Birmingham *p136* 0121 643 5531

6

Pieros, Ms L (Farrell Matthews & Weir) *G H*
London W6 *p31* 020 8741 1482

Pierson, A (Trowers & Hamlins)
London EC3 *p88* 020 7423 8000

Piesse, F W R (Francis Piesse)
London W6 *p67* 020 8748 0010

Pietron, Ms I M (A Kay Pietron & Paluch) *W*
Ealing *p3* 020 8992 9997

Pietrowski, R W J (Richard Pietrowski & Co) *S1 E W*
Guildford *p237* 01483 505398

Piff, Ms E J (Alsters Kelley) *K1 K3*
Leamington Spa *p270* 0844 561 0100

Pigden, S J (Pinsent Masons LLP) *C1*
Birmingham *p141* 0121 200 1050

Pigg, L (Rollits LLP)
Hull *p258* 01482 323239

Piggin, Ms M M (McGrigors LLP)
London EC4 *p56* 020 7054 2500

Piggott, C (Clarke Willmott)
Birmingham *p136* 0845 209 1000 / 0117 305 6000

Piggott, J T L (University of Birmingham) *E S1 L C1 J1 T1 Zl*
Birmingham *p450* 0121 414 3637

Pighills, R (HC Solicitors LLP) *T2 W Zd K4*
Peterborough *p347* 01733 882800

Pigott, J R (Furley Page LLP) *S1*
Canterbury *p176* 01227 763939

Pigott, S C (Levison Meltzer Pigott) *K1 K2*
London EC4 *p53* 020 7556 2400

Pigula, R W (Downie & Gadban) *J1 O Q N*
Alton *p116* 01420 82879

Pike, A (Howard Kennedy LLP)
London W1 *p48* 020 7636 1616

Pike, A (Squire Sanders (UK) LLP)
Leeds *p277* 0113 284 7000

Pike, Ms B (Clarke Willmott) *E R2 S2 R1 L*
Bristol *p162* 0845 209 1000 / 0117 305 6000

Pike, C (Withers LLP) *T2 W*
London EC4 *p92* 020 7597 6000

Pike, C L (Forsters LLP) *W T2*
Westminster *p33* 020 7863 8333

Pike, Ms C M E (University of Birmingham)
Birmingham *p450* 0121 414 3637

Pike, D R (Mayo Wynne Baxter LLP) *S1 S2 E*
East Grinstead *p215* 01342 310600

Pike, Ms E A (Cheltenham & Gloucester PLC)
Gloucester *p459* 01452 372372

Pike, G (West Berkshire Council) *P K1 S1 V R1 J1 F1 L E*
Newbury *p466* 01635 42400

Pike, J (Farrer & Co LLP)
London WC2 *p31* 020 3375 7000

Pike, J D (Addleshaw Goddard) *E*
Leeds *p271* 0113 209 2000
Manchester *p300* 0161 934 6000

Pike, J G (Stephenson Harwood) *E*
London EC2 *p82* 020 7329 4422

Pike, Mrs J M (Walker Morris) *E R2*
Leeds *p277* 0113 283 2500

Pike, J R (Reed Smith LLP) *E*
London EC2 *p71* 020 3116 3000

Pike, J V (Moore & Tibbits) *S1 W E L A1 J1 Zm Zv*
Warwick *p422* 01926 491181

Pike, M J (Addleshaw Goddard)
Manchester *p300* 0161 934 6000

Pike, R G (Barlow Lyde & Gilbert LLP)
London EC3 *p10* 020 7247 2277
London EC4 *p86* 020 7300 7000

Pike, Miss S G (Coffin Mew & Clover) *K2*
Southampton *p385* 023 8033 4661

Pikett, S F (GLRS Phoenix LLP) *K3 J1 K1 J2 Zj O Q N*
Stroud *p400* 01453 763433

Pilcher, S M (CMS Cameron McKenna LLP)
London EC3 *p17* 020 7367 3000

Pilgrim, T (Penningtons) *E*
London EC2 *p66* 020 7457 3000

Piliero, Ms A (Pearson Maddin Solicitors) *K1 K3*
New Malden *p321* 020 8949 9500

Pilkington, A E (Flint Bishop Solicitors) *C1 C2 J1*
Derby *p208* 01332 340211

Pilkington, G K (McFaddens LLP) *C1 C2 Ze*
London EC2 *p56* 020 7588 9080

Pilkington, J E (Redfearns) *S1 W C1 T1 L E B1 A1 J1 F1 Zb Zd Zi*
Heckmondwike *p246* 01924 403745 / 404601

Pilkington, M S (Association of Teachers and Lecturers) *J1 P M1 Zp*
London WC2 *p103* 020 7930 6441

Pilkington, M W (Fletchers) *N*
Southport *p388* 01704 546919

Pilkington, O (K&L Gates LLP)
London EC4 *p47* 020 7648 9000

Pilkington, Miss R L (Russell & Russell) *N*
Bolton *p150* 01204 375700

Pillar, M G (Gill Akaster) *N M1 J1 F1 Zj Zk*
Plymouth *p349* 01752 203500

Pilling, A G D W (Alister Pilling) *S1 K1 G H Q F1 D1 L J1 W Zl*
Camborne *p173* 01209 613800

Pilling, Miss C J (Widdows Pilling & Co) *K4 S1 W*
Walkden *p419* 0161 790 1825

Pilling, D C S (Widdows Pilling & Co) *A1 C1 D1 E G H J1 M1 N P*
Walkden *p419* 0161 790 1825

Pilling, E C H (Edward Pilling & Co) *S1 E W R1 C1*
Oxford *p344* 01865 741122

Pilling, Ms G M (Bonnetts Solicitors LLP) *N*
Hounslow *p253* 020 8570 5286

Pilling, J N (Markand & Co) *G*
London E7 *p58* 020 8470 1422

Pilling, S M (Addleshaw Goddard)
Manchester *p300* 0161 934 6000

Pillman, J C (Morgan Cole) *C1 C2*
Oxford *p344* 01865 262600
London EC2 *p92* 020 7645 2400

Pilmore-Bedford, Ms C A (Bexley Magistrates Court)
Bexleyheath *p449* 020 8304 5211

Pilsworth, I L (Three Valleys Water PLC) *C1 F1*
Hatfield *p460* 01707 268111

Pimblett, T H S (Lloyds & Cooper) *W K4 S1*
Leominster *p283* 01568 613236

Pimloit, W G (Eldridges) *S1 W K4*
Newport *p328* 01983 524741

Pimlott, N (Field Fisher Waterhouse LLP)
London EC3 *p31* 020 7861 4000

Pimstone, A S (Armstrong & Co) *K1 L C1*
London SE23 *p7* 020 8699 3477

Pinch, F R (Irwin Mitchell LLP) *Zr N*
Birmingham *p139* 0870 150 0100
Leeds *p277* 0113 222 0022

Pinchbeck, A S (Heptonstalls LLP) *G P J1 F1 H*
Goole *p231* 01405 765661

Pinches, J (Carter Bells LLP) *C1 S2 E R2 S1*
Kingston upon Thames *p267* 020 8939 4000

Pinchin, Ms C (Quality Solicitors Burroughs Day) *E S2*
Bristol *p164* 0117 929 0333

Pincott, Miss S (Peter Lynn & Partners) *K1 V K3 Q N S1 W*
Morriston *p319* 01792 310731

Pindard, J (Foot Anstey)
Plymouth *p349* 01752 675000

Pinder, I (Gardner Croft LLP) *O Q J1 L*
Canterbury *p176* 01227 813400

Pinder, Mrs J (Berry Smith LLP) *J1*
Cardiff *p177* 029 2034 5511

Pinder, Mrs N (E Rex Makin & Co) *W*
Liverpool *p289* 0151 709 4491

Pine-McLarty, Mrs D (Myers Fletcher & Gordon) *C1 E M2 S1 W*
London W6 *p62* 020 7610 4433

Pinfold, Ms C E (Field Fisher Waterhouse LLP)
London EC3 *p31* 020 7861 4000

Pini, D A (Pini Franco LLP) *B1 C1 F1 C2 Zi*
London EC1 *p67* 020 7566 3140

Pinidiya, T (Bowling & Co) *Zi*
London E15 *p15* 020 8221 8000

Pink, R H (Navy Army & Air Force Institutes)
Amesbury *p447* 01980 627000

Pinkerfield, H A (Hamilton Downing Quinn) *N S1 E C1 B1 Zc S2 Ze F1 Zk J1 Zf Zl O Q Zw T1 C2*
London WC1 *p38* 020 7831 8939

Pinkney, Ms L (Cartwright King)
Nottingham *p336* 0115 958 7444

Pinks, Miss A E (Legal Services Commission)
Reading *p469* 0118 955 8600

Pinks, N H (Elgee Pinks Solicitors) *W T1*
Westerham *p429* 01959 568100

Pinkstone, K C (Canter Levin & Berg) *N Q G H J1 Zj*
Liverpool *p287* 0151 239 1000

Pinn, M D (Eastgate Assistance Ltd) *Q J1*
Colchester *p455* 0870 523 4500

Pinnell, C P (Abbott Cresswell LLP) *S1 E W*
London SW14 *p3* 020 8876 4478

Pinnell, D W (Clarke & Hartland Solicitors) *G H*
Cardiff *p177* 029 2048 3181

Pinner, D R (The Crown Estate Office)
London W15 *p105* 020 7851 5168

Pinney, Ms C (George Davies Solicitors LLP)
Manchester *p303* 0161 236 8992

Pinney, R C (Powys County Council) *N O Q J1*
Llandrindod Wells *p463* 01597 826000

Pinniger, W J R (Coffin Mew & Clover) *D1 K1 V*
Fareham *p223* 01329 825617

Pinning, Ms H M (Clark Brookes) *G H*
West Bromwich *p427* 0121 553 2576

Pinning, R J (Clark Brookes) *C1 E L S1 N P*
West Bromwich *p427* 0121 553 2576

Pinnington, Mrs M (Grant Saw Solicitors LLP) *S1*
Greenwich *p36* 020 8858 6971

Pinnington, S D (Butcher & Barlow LLP) *K1*
Bury *p170* 0161 764 5141

Pinnion, C P (Christopher Pinnion & Co)
Southend-on-Sea *p387* 01702 338218

Pinsent, J (DLA Piper UK LLP) *Zc O*
Liverpool *p287* 0870 011 1111

Pinsent, J C (Weightmans LLP)
Liverpool *p291* 0151 227 2601

Pinto, D F (Pinto Potts LLP) *E L S1 W Zv*
Aldershot *p115* 0800 316 4434

Pinto, Miss L M (Gregorys Solicitors) *W*
Stockport *p395* 0161 456 8125

Pinto, R J (Maurice Smiths) *G H K1 N Q Zl*
Castleford *p183* 01977 557171
Pontefract *p351* 01977 794395

Pintus, M D (Macfarlanes) *W*
London EC4 *p56* 020 7831 9222

Pinwell, G D (Plymouth City Council) *E L S1*
Plymouth *p468* 01752 668000
Exeter *p221* 01392 411221

Pipe, M W (Michael W Pipe) *S1 K1 L W G P H F1 R1 Zl*
Paignton *p345* . . . . 01803 559746 / 529797

Pipe, Miss P (Thomson & Bancks LLP) *K4 T2 W*
Tewkesbury *p410* 01684 299633

Pipe, S F (Morrison & Masters Limited) *K1 S1 T2 W K4*
Swindon *p406* 01793 526601

Piper, Ms A (Farrer & Co LLP) *Zd*
London WC2 *p31* 020 3375 7000

Piper, Ms L (Greenwoods Solicitors LLP) *O Q J1 N*
Peterborough *p347* 01733 887700

Piper, R D S (Gordons LLP)
Leeds *p273* 0113 227 0100

Piper-Thompson, Ms J (Follett Stock LLP) *E K1 K4 Q S1 W X*
Truro *p414* 01872 241700

Pipkin, Mrs J A (Enfield Magistrates Court)
London N17 *p106* 020 8808 5411

Pirani, Mrs M L (Bishop & Sewell LLP) *K1 D1 D2*
London WC1 *p13* 020 7631 4141

Pirie, A H T (Browne Jacobson LLP) *C1 T1 B1 Ze Zb*
Nottingham *p336* 0115 976 6000

Pirie, Ms M F (Ashurst LLP)
London EC2 *p7* 020 7638 1111

Pirinen, T (W H Matthews & Co) *Q S1 T2 W K4*
Islington *p59* 020 7251 4942

Pirozzolo, L R (Eastgate Assistance Ltd) *Q O L E*
Colchester *p455* 0870 523 4500

Pirrie, J M (Family Law in Partnership LLP) *K2 K1*
London WC2 *p30* 020 7420 5000

Pitcairn, A D K (Child & Child)
London SW1 *p20* 020 7235 8000

Pitcher, Mrs D (Blaser Mills) *X V K1 D1 K3*
Aylesbury *p120* 01296 434416

Pitchers, C D (Rustons & Lloyd) *S1 E L P*
Newmarket *p327* 01638 661221

Pitchford, S N (Macfarlanes) *E*
London EC4 *p56* 020 7831 9222

Pithouse, Miss G (Bevirs) *S2 E Zo S1*
Wootton Bassett *p439* 01793 848900

Pitlarge, D C (Hill Dickinson LLP)
London EC3 *p41* 020 7283 9033

Pitman, G C (Pitman Blackstock White) *S2 F1 K3 J1 K1 S1 W Q*
Lydney *p296* 01594 842475

Pitman, S (Blake Lapthorn) *S1*
Oxford *p342* 01865 248607

Pitman, Mrs S A (Bobbetts Mackan) *G H*
Bristol *p161* 0117 929 9001

Pitroff, Ms V (Holman Fenwick Willan)
London EC3 *p42* 020 7264 8000

Pitt, A B (Henriques Griffiths) *Zd W*
Bristol *p163* 0117 909 4000

Pitt, A N (Aldridge Brownlee Solicitors LLP) *G H D1*
Bournemouth *p151* 01202 294411

Pitt, E (Gregg Latchams LLP)
Bristol *p162* 0117 906 9400

Pitt, E B (Addleshaw Goddard) *U1 C3 M1 I C1 F2 F1 Ze Zf*
London EC1 *p4* 020 7606 8855

Pitt, Mrs F E (Rees Wood Terry) *S2 S1 Zi*
Cardiff *p180* 029 2040 8800

Pitt, J A (Lane & Co) *O Q*
Walsall *p420* 01922 721259

Pitt, J R (Headley Brothers Ltd)
Ashford *p447* 01233 623131

Pitt, M (Pearson Hinchliffe) *J1 Zc C1 S2 E*
Oldham *p341* 0161 785 3500

Pitt, P F (Glovers Solicitors LLP) *J1 O*
London W1 *p36* 020 7935 8882

Pitt, R A (Beadle Pitt & Gottschalk) *K1 N*
Canterbury *p176* 01227 464481

Pitt, S (Edwards Angell Palmer & Dodge)
London EC2 *p28* 020 7583 4055

Pitt, T J (E J Moyle) *S1 W L E R1*
Littlehampton *p285* 01903 725143

Pittal, J A (SJ Berwin LLP)
London EC4 *p75* 020 7111 2222

Pittalis, M R (Pittalis & Co) *B1 C1 E S2 S1 W*
London N12 *p68* 020 8446 9555

Pittalis, R R (Pittalis & Co) *J1 O Q L*
London N12 *p68* 020 8446 9555

Pittard, Ms H L (174 Law) *D1 K3 K1 K2 L S1 W*
Birkenhead *p134* 0151 647 7372

Pittaway, I M (Sacker & Partners LLP) *Zo*
London EC2 *p76* 020 7329 6699

Pittaway, M (Thursfields) *G H*
Kidderminster *p266* 01562 820575

Pittordis, Ms M (Hill Dickinson LLP) *M1 P Za*
London EC3 *p41* 020 7283 9033

Pittordou, C (C Pittordou & Co) *E C1 S1 W M1 N*
Potters Bar *p355* 01707 663760

Pitts, Ms L M J (Fisher Meredith) *X Zg N*
Lambeth *p32* 020 7091 2700

Pitts, S F (Thursfields) *W T2 S1 A1 Zd Zm*
Kidderminster *p266* 01562 820575

Pixton, B L (Crown Prosecution Service Avon & Somerset)
Bristol *p451* 0117 930 2800

Pizzey, M S (Stephensons Solicitors LLP) *G H*
Manchester *p310* 0161 832 8844

Place, Ms A F (Browne Jacobson LLP) *A3*
Nottingham *p336* 0115 976 6000

Place, D J (Mortons) *K1 D1 D2 K3*
Sunderland *p401* 0191 514 4323

Placidi, S L (Placidi & Co)
Southampton *p386* 01489 579804

Plane, Mrs J (Hilliers HRW Solicitors) *D2 D1 K1 K2*
Stevenage *p395* 01438 346000

Plane, R A (Harvey McKibbin Solicitors) *S1 E W C1*
Sutton Coldfield *p403* 0121 240 9115

Plank, Ms C M (London Borough of Wandsworth)
London SW18 *p110* 020 8871 6000

Plank, Ms M (Hewison & Nixon) *N K1 F1 L B1 D1 G H Zl Zf*
Pontefract *p351* 01977 700705

Plant, D J (Damian J Plant & Co) *M1 K1 G S1 P D1 L H F1 J1 Zp*
Kenilworth *p264* . . . 01926 847741 / 854677

Plant, J S F (DLA Piper UK LLP)
Manchester *p303* 0870 011 1111

Plant, Mrs M A (M A Plant) *S1 W*
Southminster *p388* . 01621 773185 / 772794

Plant, M A (PBW Solicitors) *E C1 S2 B1 S1 W K4 R1 R2*
Plymouth *p350* 01752 222206

Plant, N D (Clausen Miller LLP) *Zj Zq*
London EC3 *p20* 020 7645 7970
London EC3 *p68* 0844 245 4000

Plant, P G A (Linklaters LLP)
London EC2 *p54* 020 7456 2000

Plant, Miss S J (Peter Lynn & Partners) *K1 D1 D2 V W Q L N*
Morriston *p319* 01792 310731
Swansea *p405* 01792 450010

Plantard, Ms C (British Telecommunications PLC)
London EC1 *p104* 020 7356 6181

Plascow, R H (Mills & Reeve) *Zc*
Cambridge *p175* 01223 364422

Plaskitt, M (Walters & Plaskitt) *G S1 H M1 W L D1 P C1*
Stoke-on-Trent *p398* 01782 830038
Stoke-on-Trent *p398* 01782 819611

Plaskitt, Miss P (Bristows)
London EC4 *p15* 020 7400 8000

Platel, C D (Charles Platel Solicitors) *C1 E L W S2 Ze R1 R2*
Wokingham *p437* 0118 978 4866

Platman, A W (Rochman Landau LLP) *E S1*
London W1 *p72* 020 7544 2424

Platt, Ms C (Stephensons Solicitors LLP) *G H*
Wigan *p432* 01942 777777

Platt, D J E (Adams & Remers) *E R2 S2 S1 Zc*
Lewes *p283* 01273 480616

Platt, Miss H S (Wedlake Bell LLP) *Zb R2*
London WC1 *p91* 020 7395 3000

Platt, Miss M M (Lambert Taylor & Gregory) *S1 W*
Gateshead *p228* 0191 477 0616

Platt, Mrs N A (Hibberts LLP) *E S2 S1*
Nantwich *p320* 01270 624225

Platt, R (Curtis Davis Garrard) *O Za*
Uxbridge *p417* 020 8734 2800

Platt, Miss S A (Blackburn & Co) *W T2*
Fleetwood *p226* 01253 872238

Platten, Mrs V M (Heptonstalls LLP) *K1 D1*
Goole *p231* 01405 765661

Platts, C (Rollits LLP) *N O*
Hull *p258* 01482 323239

Platts, Mrs J C B (Robin Burman & Co) *S1 W L R1 E C1 B1 T1 A1 J1 Zb Ze Zj*
Manchester *p302* 0161 860 7123

Platts, K A G (Bromleys Solicitors LLP) *D1 K1 D2*
Ashton-under-Lyne *p120* . . . 0161 330 6821

Plaut, N D F (Horsey Lightly) *E S1 R2 S2 Zb*
Westminster *p43* 020 7222 8844

Plaw, Miss S (Squire Sanders (UK) LLP)
Leeds *p277* 0113 284 7000

Playfair, Ms J L (Davies & Partners) *S2 E*
Gloucester *p230* 01452 612345

Playford, G (John Morley & Co) *N*
Rainham *p359* 01634 375444

Playford, J D (David Playford & Co) *K1 N Q G D1 J1 F1 O H W Zk Zl Zp*
Portishead *p354* 01275 840111

Playford, Mrs S (Telegraph Media Group)
London SW1 *p110* 020 7931 3131

Playford, Ms S (GLRS Phoenix LLP) *N K1 L Q V D1*
Dursley *p214* 01453 547221

Playle, Ms A (Andersons Solicitors) *T2 W K4*
Nottingham *p335* 0115 947 0641

Pleace, R (Eckford Rands) *S1 W T2 E T1 L S2 R1 K4 R2*
Northampton *p331* 01604 621001

Pleass, Miss J C (Pleass Thomson & Co) *W S1 Q N E Zl Zw Zm Zp Zq*
Clacton-on-Sea *p195* 01255 221133

Plenderleith, M (Ashurst LLP)
London EC2 *p7* 020 7638 1111

Plessier, G (Gordon Lowe & Co) *K1 Q G H J1 N L F1 B2 Zg F2 B1*
Bristol *p163* 01454 326833

Plewa, C (Shepherd + Wedderburn LLP) *E*
London EC4 *p78* 020 7429 4900

Plews, Mrs C (Blake Lapthorn) *D1 F1 J1 K1 M1 N P L Zp*
Oxford *p342* 01865 248607

Plews, Miss E A (Hardmans) *K1 D1 S1 Q D2 F1 L V*
Deal *p207* 01304 373377

Plews, G T (Clifford Chance)
London E14 *p20* 020 7006 1000

Plews, M (Denison Till) *Zc*
York *p444* 01904 611411

Pliener, A M (hlw Keeble Hawson LLP) *E R2 S2*
Leeds *p274* 0113 244 3121

Plomp, Miss H (Gepp & Sons)
Chelmsford *p186* 01245 493939
Colchester *p197* 01206 369889

Plotnek, S G (Ince & Co Services Ltd)
London E1 *p44* 020 7481 0010

Plowman, M C (Leathes Prior) *J1 F1 Zg Zp Q A3*
Norwich *p334* 01603 610911

Pluck, A C (Hart Reade) *S1 E R1 A1 C1 S2*
Eastbourne *p215* 01323 727321

See p634 for the Key to Work Categories

Plum, Miss A M (Miles Preston & Co) *K1*
London EC4 *p69* 020 7583 0583

Plumbley, M B (Powell Eddison Freeman & Wilks) *S1 A1 L S2 Zl W*
Harrogate *p240* 01423 564551

Plumbley-Jones, Ms K M (Taylor Walton LLP) *J1 C1*
Luton *p295* 01582 731161

Plumbly, R C S (Greenland Houchen Pomeroy) *S1 W A1 C1 L E H G K1 B1 Zc Zh Zl*
Attleborough *p120* 01953 453143

Plumley, I J (Barlow Lyde & Gilbert LLP) *Zj*
London EC3 *p10* 020 7247 2277

Plummer, A J (Roythornes LLP) *A1 O L A3 R1 Zq Zs*
Spalding *p389* 01775 842500

Plummer, J (ACT Solicitors) *G N H Zu D1 K1*
Norwich *p333* 01603 610611

Plummer, Ms J (Buckles Solicitors LLP) *A1 E*
Peterborough *p346* 01733 888888

Plummer, Miss S L (Ward Gethin) *K1 K3 D1 D2*
King's Lynn *p266* 01553 660033

Plumridge, D (Kennedys)
London EC3 *p49* 020 7667 9667

Plumridge, Miss S (Parrott & Coales LLP) *S1 E L*
Aylesbury *p121* 01296 318500

Plumtree, Mrs S E (Wilkin Chapman Grange Solicitors)
Grimsby *p235* 01472 262626

Plunkett, G P (Hill Dickinson LLP) *E Zj N A3 F2 P J2 O Zq*
Liverpool *p288* 0151 600 8000

Plunkett, S (Pinsent Masons LLP)
London EC2 *p67* 020 7418 7000

Pluss, H (A Kay Pietron & Paluch) *W S1*
Ealing *p3* 020 8992 9997
Amersham *p117* 01494 724671

Plytas, A J (Environment Agency (Thames Region))
Reading *p469* 0870 850 6506

Pobjoy, G P (Heald Solicitors) *O N Q J1 B1 F1 Ze Zk Zl*
Milton Keynes *p317* 01908 662277

Pocock, Miss E V (Shell International Ltd)
London SE1 *p109* 020 7934 1234

Pocock, Ms R L (East Devon District Council)
Sidmouth *p471* 01395 516551

Poddington, D M (Squire Sanders (UK) LLP) *C1 C2 O J1 A3 Zc*
Leeds *p277* 0113 284 7000

Podger, A J (Pennon Group PLC)
Exeter *p458* 01392 446677

Podger, C J (Davies Blunden & Evans) *J1 K4 S1 T2 W*
Farnborough *p224* 01252 541633

Podolska, Ms A (Farrell Matthews & Weir) *G H*
London W6 *p31* 020 8741 1482

Pointer, Mrs A (Ann Pointer) *S1 S2 W E*
Tavistock *p408* 01822 614882

Pointer, G C (Tynedale District Council)
Hexham *p461* 01434 652200

Pointon, A L P (Enoch Evans LLP) *B1 D1 F1 K1 L M1 N P V Zm Q*
Walsall *p420* 01922 720333

Pointon, C (Aaron & Partners LLP Solicitors) *W T2 Zv*
Chester *p190* 01244 405555

Pointon, N (Doncaster Metropolitan Borough Council)
Doncaster *p457* 01302 734651
Sheffield *p376* 0114 279 4000

Pointon, R (Hill Dickinson LLP)
Liverpool *p288* 0151 600 8000

Polglase, T (Allen & Overy LLP) *Zb*
London E1 *p5* 020 3088 0000

Poli, Miss D (Henry Hyams) *G*
Leeds *p274* 0113 243 2288

Poli, M B (Palmers) *C1 C2 E*
Basildon *p126* 01268 240000

Polin, J (Salans) *C1 Zl*
London EC4 *p76* 020 7429 6000

Politz, M (Thomson Snell & Passmore) *T2 W*
Tunbridge Wells *p415* 01892 510000

Pollacchi, D (LSG Solicitors) *B1 C1 C2 C3 M1 Zb Zd Ze*
London W1 *p51* 020 7851 0100

Pollack, C (SJ Berwin LLP)
London EC4 *p75* 020 7111 2222

Pollard, A (John Delaney & Co) *G H*
Leeds *p273* 0113 246 8151

Pollard, Miss A (Leeds City Council)
Leeds *p462* 0113 224 3513

Pollard, Mrs A M (Derby City Council)
Derby *p456* 01332 293111

Pollard, Mrs E L (Shentons) *W K4*
Winchester *p434* 01962 844544

Pollard, Ms F (Gadsby Wicks) *N Zr*
Chelmsford *p186* 01245 494929

Pollard, Miss H J (Warwickshire County Council)
Warwick *p475* 01926 410410

Pollard, Miss J L (Environment Agency (Southern))
Worthing *p477* 01903 820692

Pollard, J M (Southerns) *K1 O V*
Burnley *p169* 01282 422711

Pollard, Miss L (Wilsons) *W Q K1 S1 K4 K3 C1 S2 R1 Zd O N*
Leeds *p278* 0113 264 3444

Pollard, M (Lawrence Hamblin) *N Zr*
Reading *p361* . . . . 0118 951 6180 / 951 6190

Pollard, Mrs S (Marsh & Co) *K1 D1 S1 D2 W K3*
Lancaster *p269* 01524 68102

Pollard, S B (Kingsley Napley) *B2 G H P Zg Zi*
London EC1 *p50* 020 7814 1200

Pollard, S K (Alexander & Partners) *D2 D1 Zr K1 Zi N*
Brent *p5* 020 8965 7121

Pollard-Levron, Ms X (Richard Freeman & Co) *C1 C2 Zd J1*
Kensington & Chelsea *p34* . . 020 7351 5151

Pollecoff, P K (Pollecoff Solicitors Ltd) *C1 N J1 F1 L E*
London EC2 *p68* 020 7608 2568

Pollen, M J (DLA Piper UK LLP)
London EC2 *p24* 0870 011 1111

Pollen, Mrs R (Hollis & Co) *W N*
Sutton-in-Ashfield *p404* . . . 01623 443344

Polley, Ms J (Surrey County Council)
Kingston upon Thames *p462* . 020 8541 9088

Polley, Mrs R D (Quality Solicitors Chapman & Chubb) *W K4*
Alfreton *p115* 01773 540480

Polli, C H (Pinney Talfourd LLP)
Upminster *p416* 01708 229444

Polling, M L (Simmons & Simmons)
London EC2 *p79* 020 7628 2020

Pollins, J H (Waller Pollins) *S1 E S2 W*
Edgware *p217* 020 8238 5858

Pollitt, D E (DAC Beachcroft)
Bristol *p162* 0117 918 2000

Pollitt, J M (Pearson Hinchliffe) *Zr*
Oldham *p341* 0161 785 3500

Pollitt, Miss S J (The Watson Ramsbottom Partnership) *K1 D1 K3*
Blackburn *p146* 01254 672222

Pollitt, S J (Eaton Smith LLP) *N O Q P G H J1 B1*
Huddersfield *p255* 01484 821300

Pollock, Mrs E E (Brooke North LLP) *J1*
Leeds *p272* 0113 283 2100

Pollock, J (Herbert Smith LLP) *E*
London EC2 *p40* 020 7374 8000

Pollock, Ms K (Stewarts Law LLP) *O A3 Zq B2*
Leeds *p277* 0113 222 0022

Pollock, Ms K Y (Reynolds Porter Chamberlain LLP) *N O Q*
London E1 *p71* 020 3060 6000

Pollock, Mrs L M (Henmans LLP) *E S2 R2*
Oxford *p343* 01865 781000

Pollock, The Hon R C S (Simmons & Simmons) *E*
London EC2 *p79* 020 7628 2020

Pollock, R M (Coodes) *W T2 Zd*
Liskeard *p285* 01579 347600

Pollock, T J (Stroud District Council)
Stroud *p473* 01453 766321

Polmear, Ms M (Morag Polmear Commercial Lawyer) *E*
Newcastle upon Tyne *p326* . 0191 281 8050

Polpitiya, Mrs P (Polpitiya & Co)
Southall *p384* 020 8813 9282

Polson, A G (Pearson Fielding Polson) *G H*
Liverpool *p290* 0151 236 3636

Polson, G (Canter Levin & Berg)
Liverpool *p287* 0151 239 1000

Polson, S J (Pearson Fielding Polson) *G H*
Liverpool *p290* 0151 236 3636

Polsue, J G (Allen-Buckley & Co) *Q O K1 B1 Zc Ze J1 Zn Zq*
Wandsworth *p4* 020 8767 8336

Polycarpou, P (Pepi & Co)
London N14 *p67* 020 8886 0500

Polychronakis, J (Dudley Metropolitan Borough Council)
Dudley *p457* 01384 815326

Pomeranc, S (Lee Pomeranc) *E S1 L C1 N T1 B1 W J1*
London NW4 *p68* 020 8201 6299

Pomeroy, D A W (Ashfords LLP) *B1 O*
Bristol *p160* 0117 321 8000

Pomfret, C M (RHW Solicitors LLP) *E S2 C2*
Guildford *p237* 01483 302000

Pomfret, G D (Atkins Bassett) *N O Q K1 J1 F1 K3*
Hinckley *p250* 01455 632685

Pond, H C (Pond Marsh) *C1 F1 G H J1 K1 L M1 P W*
Blackpool *p147* 01253 620466

Pond, J (Osborne Clarke) *U1 U2*
London EC2 *p65* 020 7105 7000

Pond, Mrs J J (Ellis Jones) *K4 K1 T2 V S1 S2 W*
Swanage *p404* 01929 422233

Pond, Mrs L A (Key2Law LLP) *E S1 W Zm*
Ewell *p220* 020 8393 0941
Banstead *p122* 01737 352211

Ponnampalam, Mrs K (Jeya & Co) *S1 S2 Zi E*
Newham *p46* 020 8552 1999

Pontin, D W (Roberts Moore Nicholas Jones) *S1 S2 W Zc*
Birkenhead *p134* 0151 647 0000

Ponting, Ms A (Farrell Matthews & Weir)
London W6 *p31* 020 8741 1482

Pook, G A (Rutland County Council)
Oakham *p468* 01572 722577

Pool, Miss E (Morecrofts Solicitors LLP)
Liverpool *p290* 0151 236 8871

Pool, O (Veale Wasbrough Vizards) *C1*
Bristol *p165* 0117 925 2020

Poole, A (Poole & Co) *J1*
Crewkerne *p203* 01460 279100

Poole, A (Sternberg Reed) *Zm*
Barking *p123* 020 8591 3366

Poole, A D (Trowers & Hamlins) *C1 C2*
London EC3 *p88* 020 7423 8000

Poole, Miss C (Sackvilles) *S1 W L R1*
Hornchurch *p252* 01708 446704

Poole, D (Royal Mail Group)
London EC4 *p109* 020 7250 2468

Poole, Dr D N J (Bolt Burdon) *Zr N*
Islington *p14* 020 7288 4700

Poole, F J S (George Ide LLP) *K1 K2 N L Zq*
Chichester *p192* . . . .

Poole, I T (Morgan Cole) *N Zj*
Bristol *p164* 0117 916 7220

Poole, I W (National Association of Head Teachers)
Haywards Heath *p460* 01444 472472

Poole, Ms L (Chebsey & Co) *Q Zl*
Beaconsfield *p128* 01494 670440

Poole, M J (Clifford Poole & Co) *N S1 W*
Salford *p370* 0161 736 0160

Poole, N J V (Latimer Hinks) *C1 F1 J1*
Darlington *p206* 01325 341500

Poole, Mrs N Y (Hedges) *K1*
Wallingford *p419* 01491 839839

Poole, R N L (Gregory Rowcliffe Milners) *E S1 C1 L Zd*
London WC1 *p37* 020 7242 0631

Poole, Ms S (Devon County Council)
Exeter *p458* 01392 382000

Poole, Miss S (Greene & Greene) *J1 C1 Zp*
Bury St Edmunds *p171* 01284 762211

Poole, Mrs S (Painters) *S1 S2 C1*
Stourport-on-Severn *p399* . . 01299 822033

Poole, S (DWF) *N Zj*
Liverpool *p287* 0151 907 3000

Poole, Ms S M (Barber Titleys) *S2 E*
Harrogate *p240* 01423 502211

Poole, Miss S P (Bournemouth Borough Council)
Bournemouth *p450* 01202 451178

Pooley, Miss J M (P B & W Solicitors LLP t/a Pooley Bendall & Watson) *A1 C1 E S1 S2 W*
Ely *p218* 01353 666075

Pooley, M J (Penningtons) *E*
Basingstoke *p127* 01256 407100

Pooley, S (Arnold Greenwood) *S1 E W S2*
Kendal *p264* 01539 720049

Pooley, Miss S L (Fox Williams) *O*
London EC2 *p33* 020 7628 2000

Pooley, Mrs S L (The College of Law Guildford)
Guildford *p459* 01483 460200

Poolman, Miss T E (Harold Bell & Co) *G E W L C1 R1 T1 P Zl*
Ewell *p220* 020 8393 0231

Poore, A D (Mills & Reeve) *Ze*
Cambridge *p175* 01223 364422

Poore, M (Dickinson Dees) *C1 Zo*
Newcastle upon Tyne *p324* . 0191 279 9000

Popat, Mrs D (Birdy & Co)
Wembley *p426* 020 8900 9112

Popat, R K (Buckinghamshire County Council)
Aylesbury *p448* 01296 383653

Popat, Mrs T A (Salusburys Harding & Barnett) *S1 W*
Leicester *p281* . . . 0116 262 9033 / 262 6052

Pope, A (Fox Williams) *J1*
London EC2 *p33* 020 7628 2000

Pope, Mrs A C (Archers Law LLP) *K1*
Stockton-on-Tees *p396* . . . 01642 636500

Pope, Ms B (Walker Morris)
Leeds *p277* 0113 283 2500

Pope, C A (HM Land Registry - Birkenhead)
Birkenhead *p449* 0151 473 1110

Pope, C A (Julian Young & Co)
London W1 *p93* 020 7724 8414

Pope, C C (Reed Smith LLP) *Zi*
London EC2 *p71* 020 3116 3000

Pope, Miss E R (Churchers) *S2*
Fareham *p223* 01329 822333

Pope, G V (Pope & Co) *K3 Q S2 K1 J1 L W*
Cromer *p203* 01263 513355

Pope, I (Bishop & Sewell LLP) *O Q*
London WC1 *p13* 020 7631 4141

Pope, Miss J (Shakespeares) *E R2 S2 S1*
Nottingham *p339* 0115 945 3700

Pope, J J R (Eldridge Pope & Co PLC)
Dorchester *p457* 01305 251251

Pope, J L (SNR Denton) *Zc*
London EC4 *p75* 020 7242 1212

Pope, J M (Cobham PLC)
Wimborne *p476* 01202 857552

Pope, Mrs L H (Peak District National Park Authority) *S1*
Bakewell *p448* 01629 816200

Pope, Miss L L (Lock & Marlborough) *K3 W L*
London W3 *p55* 020 8993 7231

Pope, M (Keoghs LLP) *N Zj O Q*
Bolton *p149* 01204 677000

Pope, M (Mike Pope Solicitor) *N*
Workington *p441* 01900 608363

Pope, N (Kitsons LLP)
Exeter *p221* 01392 455555

Pope, Ms N (Bolton Metropolitan Borough Council)
Bolton *p450* 01204 333333

Pope, Ms N P M (Dacorum Borough Council)
Hemel Hempstead *p460* 01442 228000

Pope, T (Simmons & Simmons)
London EC2 *p79* 020 7628 2020

Pope, U G (Pannone LLP) *C1 C2 Zu*
Manchester *p308* 0161 909 3000

Pope, Miss V (Park Woodfine Heald Mellows LLP) *W K4*
Bedford *p130* 01234 400000

Popeck, P I (Curry Popeck) *S1 E W L S2*
Kenton *p264* . . . . 020 8907 2000 / 8907 8896

Popham, C F J (Horsey Lightly) *K1 W L*
Westminster *p43* 020 7222 8844

Popham, E G (Holmes & Hills LLP) *W*
Halstead *p238* 01787 475312

Popham, S G (Clifford Chance)
London E14 *p20* 020 7006 1000

Popiolek, Mrs H J (Childrens Legal Centre)
Colchester *p455* . . .01206 872466 / 873828

Pople, J N (Hill Dickinson LLP) *N Za Zb*
London EC3 *p41* 020 7283 9033

Popplewell, N F M (Burges Salmon) *T1*
Bristol *p161* 0117 939 2000

Porritt, R W (Gowmans) *G H Zm*
Paignton *p345* 01803 546100

Port, J (Port & Co)
Leeds *p276* 0113 242 1212

Porteous, J R (Stevens & Bolton)
Guildford *p237* 01483 302264

Porter, A F (British American Tobacco)
London WC2 *p104* 020 7845 1000

Porter, A J (Thackray Williams) *B1 E F1 L O Q*
Bromley *p167* 020 8290 0440

Porter, A R M (Porter & Co) *S1 E W L C1 R1*
Sutton *p403* 020 8643 5111

Porter, C (Neil Myerson LLP) *S2*
Altrincham *p117* 0161 941 4000

Porter, C (Addleshaw Goddard) *O*
Leeds *p271* 0113 209 2000

Porter, C (Russell Jones & Walker) *N*
Manchester *p309* 0161 383 3500

Porter, C J (England & Co) *K1 K2 V D1 D2*
Great Yarmouth *p234* 01493 604990
Great Yarmouth *p234*01493 844308 / 844309

Porter, C J (Farleys Solicitors LLP) *C1 E S2 F2 Ze*
Blackburn *p145* 01254 367856

Porter, Miss C L (Russell & Russell) *K3 K1*
Chester *p191* 01244 405700

Porter, D (David Porter & Co) *M1 S1 K1 G H V J1 W P F1 Zj Zl Ze*
Hull *p257* 01482 325863

Porter, Miss D (Worcester City Council)
Worcester *p477* 01905 723471

Porter, D M (Porter Associates) *K1 N Q S1*
Prescot *p356* 0151 430 9160

Porter, D S (Fieldings Porter) *C1 S1 T1 W E R1 Zd*
Bolton *p149* 01204 540900

Porter, E (Grahame Stowe Bateson) *D1 K1 Zu*
Leeds *p274* 0113 255 8666

Porter, G J (Underwood & Co) *S1 S2 W*
Totton *p413* . . . .023 8087 1479 / 8086 0827

Porter, G L (Butcher & Barlow LLP) *L N O Q Zq Zr J1*
Northwich *p333* 01606 47523

Porter, Ms H (Warner Goodman LLP) *E O L*
Southampton *p387* 023 8063 9311

Porter, J (Mayo Wynne Baxter LLP) *W*
Eastbourne *p215* 01323 730543

Porter, J A C (Wrigley Claydon) *B1 C1 C2 E F1 J1 L O Q S1 Zl Zp*
Oldham *p341* 0161 624 6811

Porter, J D (Hill Dickinson LLP) *Zq Zj A3 O Zc*
Manchester *p305* 0161 817 7200

Porter, J E (Vanderpump & Sykes) *E C1 S2 O R2 R1 L Zc*
Enfield *p219* 020 8367 3999

Porter, Ms J E H (Lester Aldridge LLP) *K1 D1 D2*
Bournemouth *p152* 01202 786161

Porter, K L (John Robertson) *S1 K1 D1 F1*
Widnes *p432* 0151 423 6500

Porter, Mrs L (DAC Beachcroft) *C1*
Manchester *p303* 0161 934 3000

Porter, Miss L (Arthur Smiths) *D1 K1 P S1 V*
Wigan *p432* 01942 242815

Porter, Miss L (Brindley Twist Tafft & James) *W T2*
Coventry *p200* 024 7653 1532

Porter, N (Buckles Solicitors LLP) *O B1 Zq Q A3*
Peterborough *p346* 01733 888888

Porter, N (Linklaters LLP)
London EC2 *p54* 020 7456 2000

Porter, Ms N (Tinsdills) *E*
Newcastle under Lyme *p323* . 01782 612311

Porter, N H (Stephenson Harwood) *Za*
London EC2 *p82* 020 7329 4422

Porter, N R (Crombie Wilkinson) *S2 S1 E N*
Selby *p374* 01757 708957

Porter, P A (Fiona Bruce & Co LLP) *K1 D1 K3*
Warrington *p421* 01925 263273

Porter, Mrs P J (Thompsons (formerly Robin/Brian Thompson & Partners)) *G*
Manchester *p310* 0161 819 3500

Porter, R (Harbottle & Lewis LLP) *C1 Zf Zv*
London W1 *p38* 020 7667 5000

Porter, R A (Archers Law LLP) *D1 K1 D2*
Stockton-on-Tees *p396* . . . 01642 636500

Porter, R A (The College of Law)
London WC1 *p105* 0800 289997

Porter, R S (Thompson Smith & Puxon) *J1*
Clacton-on-Sea *p195* 01255 221919

Porter, Ms S (DLA Piper UK LLP)
London EC2 *p24* 0870 011 1111

Porter, S (Shoosmiths)
Fareham *p224* . . . . 0370 086 6800 / 01489 616800

Porter, Ms S (Cockertons) *K4 W*
Bakewell *p121* 01629 812613

Porter, S D (Blake Lapthorn) *C2*
Chandlers Ford *p184* 023 8090 8090

Porter, S G (Cooke Painter Limited) *S1 S2*
Knowle *p269* 0117 977 7403

Porter, S J (Colman Coyle LLP) *C1*
Islington *p22* 020 7354 3000

6

Porter, S J (Bower & Bailey) *S1 S2 Zl*
Banbury *p122* 01295 265566
Oxford *p343* 01865 311133

Porter, S K (McGuireWoods London LLP) *C1 C2 J1 S2*
London EC4 *p57*. 020 7632 1600

Porter, S N (Jaffe Porter Crossick) *E S1 W L O Q C1 Zh Zl Zd S2*
London NW6 *p46* 020 7625 4424

Porter, Ms Z (Michelmores LLP) *K3*
Exeter *p221* 01392 688688

Porter, Ms Z R (Archer & Archer) *W T2 K4*
Ely *p218*. 01353 662203

Porter-Gayle, S (Prince Evans)
Ealing *p69*. 020 8567 3477

Porteus, S M (Marrons) *N*
Newcastle upon Tyne *p325* . 0191 281 1304

Portlock, R A (Blake Lapthorn) *Q O Zq*
Chandlers Ford *p184* 023 8090 8090

Portman, Mrs N (3i PLC)
London SW1 *p103*. 020 7928 3131

Portman, S (Hewitsons) *C1 Ze C3 U2 Zz Zy U1*
Cambridge *p174*. 01223 461155

Portman, S (Walsall Metropolitan Borough Council)
Walsall *p475*. 01922 650000

Portner, B (Portner & Jaskel LLP) *E C1 R1 L*
London W1 *p68* 020 7616 5300

Portrait, Ms J S (Portrait Solicitors) *W Zd*
London WC2 *p69* 020 7092 6990

Portsmouth, Miss A L (Laytons) *E S2 R2 S1*
Manchester *p306* 0161 834 2100

Posener, H D (GSC Solicitors) *S2 E S1 L W R2 B1 R1*
London EC1 *p34*. 020 7822 2222

Posnansky, J (Farrer & Co LLP)
London WC2 *p31* 020 3375 7000

Posner, R H (Bhatia Best) *G H*
Nottingham *p336*. 0115 950 3231

Post, Ms M J (Hallett & Co) *S1 S2 L T1 T2*
Ashford *p119* 01233 625711

Postings, Mrs J (Bournemouth Borough Council)
Bournemouth *p450*. 01202 451178

Postle, Mrs R M (Wrigley Claydon) *K3 K1 D1*
Oldham *p341* 0161 624 6811

Potentier, Miss J M (Inesons) *S1 W*
Cleckheaton *p195* 01274 872202

Potgieter, Mrs D C (Cardiff Magistrates Court)
Cardiff *p453*. 029 2046 3040

Pothecary, Ms J M (The College of Law)
London WC1 *p105*. 0800 289997

Pothos, Miss M (Visa Europe)
London W2 *p110*. 020 7937 8111

Potter, A J (Burnand Brazier Tisdall) *W S1 L E*
Hove *p254*. 01273 734022
Worthing *p441*. 01903 235002

Potter, Ms C M (Simmons & Simmons)
London EC2 *p79*. 020 7628 2020

Potter, D M J (Freeth Cartwright LLP) *O J1 B1 L Q C1 Zp Ze*
Nottingham *p337*. 0115 936 9369

Potter, Miss E J (Barlow Robbins LLP) *J2 N*
Guildford *p235*. 01483 543200

Potter, G W P (J H Powell & Co) *S1 E W L R1 Zm A1*
Derby *p209* 01332 372211

Potter, Ms J (Boodle Hatfield)
Westminster *p14*. 020 7629 7411

Potter, Miss J (Maidments) *G H B2*
Bolton *p149* 0870 403 4000

Potter, J (Platt Halpern) *G D1 H K1 Zl*
Manchester *p309* 0161 834 3114

Potter, J C (TWM Solicitors LLP) *S1 S2 E*
London SW19 *p85*. 020 8946 6454

Potter, J H C (Potter Rees (Serious Injury) Solicitors)
Manchester *p309* 0161 237 5888

Potter, J M (Spencer Skuse) *K1 N W L O Q Zq S1 F1 Zr S2*
Cardiff *p181* 029 2034 3993

Potter, K W (Stevens & Bolton) *J1 J2 Zp*
Guildford *p237*. 01483 302264

Potter, M (Ashton KCJ) *J1*
Ipswich *p262*. 01473 232425

Potter, N F (Bishop & Sewell LLP) *E S1 L W R1 J1 S2*
London WC1 *p13* 020 7631 4141

Potter, P H (Potter Jones & Co) *N J1 G Q K1 H L V Zk Zm*
St Helens *p391* 01744 730376

Potter, R W D (V J G Johns & Son) *K1 K2 W G D1*
Fishguard *p226* 01348 873671

Potter, Miss S (Olswang LLP) *C1 Zf Ze*
London WC1 *p64* 020 7067 3000

Potter, T (Ince & Co Services Ltd)
London E1 *p44* 020 7481 0010

Potter, Ms V (Doyle Clayton Solicitors Limited) *J1 Zp*
Reading *p360* 0118 959 6839

Pottinger, Mrs C L (Higgs & Sons)
Brierley Hill *p158*. 0845 111 5050

Potts, Miss C (Portrait Solicitors) *S1*
London WC2 *p69* 020 7092 6990

Potts, C D C (Blake Lapthorn) *Zc O A3 Zq B2 U2*
Oxford *p342*. 01865 248607

Potts, C E (Patterson Glenton & Stracey) *S1 E M1 G P K1 C1 H W F1 Zh Zl Zm*
South Shields *p384* 0800 011 6487

Potts, D W (Browne Jacobson LLP) *O L Zn*
Nottingham *p336*. 0115 976 6000

Potts, Mrs H (Doncaster Metropolitan Borough Council)
Doncaster *p457* 01302 734651

Potts, Miss J C (Whiting & Mason) *L S1 W K1 F1*
New Mills *p321* . . .01663 742432 / 747958

Potts, Miss L M (Hunton & Garget) *S2 E S1 K4 L W J1*
Richmond *p364* 01748 850400

Potts, M (Byrne & Partners)
London EC4 *p16*. 020 7842 1616

Potts, Mrs M (Pritchard Joyce & Hinds) *K1 K3*
Beckenham *p129* 020 8658 3922

Potts, Miss M A (Bradleys) *W S1 K4*
Dover *p212* 01304 204080

Potts, S C (T G Baynes)
Bexleyheath *p132* 020 8301 7777

Poulier, S S R (Needham Poulier & Partners) *G H Zm*
London N17 *p63*. 020 8808 6622

Poulston, M (DWF) *Zo*
Liverpool *p287*. 0151 907 3000

Poulten, J H (Mullis & Peake) *S1 E C1 R1 W T1 A1 D1*
Romford *p366* 01708 784000

Poulter, A (Field Fisher Waterhouse LLP)
London EC3 *p31*. 020 7861 4000

Poulter, Miss B J (Crombie Wilkinson) *W*
York *p444* 01904 624185

Poulter, Mrs G A (Bright & Sons) *S1 E A1 S2*
Maldon *p299*. 01621 852323

Poulter, G G (Whittuck Taylor & Caines) *K1 K3 S1 J1 F1 D1 B1 Zl O Q N*
Keynsham *p265* 0117 986 3504

Poulter, Mrs J (South Tyneside Metropolitan Borough Council)
South Shields *p471* 0191 427 1717

Poulter, Ms J A (Lewis Silkin LLP) *E C1*
London EC4 *p53*. 020 7074 8000

Poultney, B G (Coley & Tilley) *C1 E S1 L*
Birmingham *p136* 0121 643 5531

Poulton, M (Stephen Rimmer LLP) *E S1*
Eastbourne *p216*. 01323 644222

Poulton, R M (Clifford Chance)
London E14 *p20*. 020 7006 1000

Poulton, Miss S M (Co-operative Insurance Society Ltd) *B1 D1 F1 G H J1 K1 M1 N P Zl Zt*
Manchester *p464* 0161 832 8686

Pound, Ms L (Coupe Bradbury) *W*
Lytham *p296*. 01253 736670
Liverpool *p290*. 0151 932 0333

Pound, T J (Barker Gotelee Solicitors) *A1 S1 L S2*
Ipswich *p262*. 01473 611211

Pounder, J (Sproull Solicitors LLP)
Bodmin *p148* 01208 72328

Pounds, F (Ince & Co Services Ltd)
London E1 *p44* 020 7481 0010

Pountney, J (Hetts Johnson Whiting) *K1 J1 B1 F1 G N O Q S1 Zl*
Brigg *p158*. 01652 655101

Pountney, Mrs J A (Hopkins) *S1*
Mansfield *p311*. 01623 468468

Poupart, N K (Wannop Fox Staffurth & Bray) *A1 C1 C2 E L P R1 S1 W Zc Zd Zh Zs*
Bognor Regis *p148* 01243 864001

Pourgourides, P K (Hill Dickinson LLP) *Za*
London EC3 *p41*. 020 7283 9033

Povey, Mrs L (Derby City Council)
Derby *p456* 01332 293111

Povey, Miss L J (Charles Russell LLP) *E*
London EC4 *p19*. 020 7203 5000

Povey, P J (Plexus Law (A Trading Name of Parabis Law LLP)) *N Zw*
Evesham *p220*. 01386 769160

Pow, D (Monro Fisher Wasbrough LLP) *W T1 C1 S1*
London WC1 *p61* 020 7404 7001

Powe, Mrs C E (Walter Gray & Co) *S1 G F1 P M1 L W*
Ryde *p369*. 01983 563765

Powell, A C (Silverman Sherliker LLP) *C1 C2 B1*
London EC2 *p78*. 020 7749 2700

Powell, A E (Buller Jeffries) *N J2*
Birmingham *p136* 0121 212 2620

Powell, A M (Squire Sanders (UK) LLP) *Zo*
London EC2 *p81*. 020 7655 1000

Powell, B (Parfitt Cresswell) *E S2 S1 C1 L*
London SW6 *p65* 020 7381 8311

Powell, Ms C (Test Valley Borough Council)
Andover *p447* 01264 368000

Powell, C (Freeth Cartwright LLP) *Zj*
Nottingham *p337*. 0115 936 9369

Powell, C A (Powells) *S1 K1 D1 W*
Walton-on-the-Naze *p421* . . 01255 675698

Powell, Miss C E (Harrisons Solicitors LLP) *D1 K3 J1 O Q N*
Welshpool *p425* 01938 552545

Powell, C G (Beaumonts) *W A1*
Hereford *p247* 01432 352345

Powell, D (Julian Young & Co) *G H*
London W1 *p93* 020 7724 8414

Powell, Miss D M (Red Kite Law) *L O Q*
Carmarthen *p183* 01267 239000

Powell, E (Ellisons) *N*
Colchester *p197* 01206 764477

Powell, E (Mills & Reeve) *T1*
Cambridge *p175*. 01223 364422

Powell, G (Bird & Bird LLP) *C1 U1*
London EC4 *p13*. 020 7415 6000

Powell, Mrs G A (Ratcliffe Duce & Gammer LLP) *S1 W E K4 S2*
Wokingham *p437* 0118 978 3681

Powell, G D K (Powell Spencer & Partners) *G Zg*
London NW6 *p69* 020 7604 5600

Powell, G L (Trevor Thomas Scott & Jenkins)
Swansea *p406*. 01792 843821

Powell, I S (BTMK Solicitors LLP) *A1 C1 C2 E L R1 R2 W S1 S2 Zb Zc Zd Zh*
Southend-on-Sea *p387* . . . 01702 339222

Powell, J (BTMK Solicitors LLP)
Southend-on-Sea *p387* . . . 01702 339222

Powell, Miss J A (Glaisyers) *G H*
Birmingham *p138* 0121 233 2971

Powell, Miss J D A (Pemberton Greenish LLP) *T2 W*
London SW3 *p66* 020 7591 3333

Powell, J O (Powell Davies Solicitors) *G M1 S1 P N D1 F1 W K1*
Aberystwyth *p114* 01970 636599

Powell, K (hlw Keeble Hawson LLP) *A1 C1 E L S1 T1 W*
Doncaster *p211* 01302 366831

Powell, K M (Charles Russell LLP) *E L Zd*
London EC4 *p19*. 020 7203 5000

Powell, Mrs L J (Everys) *K1 G Q Zi*
Exeter *p221* 01392 477983

Powell, L J (Davenport Lyons) *T1 T2*
London W1 *p25* 020 7468 2600

Powell, Mrs M (Milne Moser) *K3 S1 K1 W*
Kendal *p264*. . . . .01539 729786 / 725582

Powell, Miss N (Tozers) *S1 S2*
Exeter *p222* 01392 207020

Powell, N R (Laytons) *E R2 S1 S2*
Manchester *p306* 0161 834 2100

Powell, N R D (Currey & Co) *W Zd T2*
Westminster *p24*. 020 7802 2700

Powell, P (Wakefield Metropolitan District Council)
Wakefield *p474* 01924 306090

Powell, P D (Ellisons) *E S1 L A1*
Colchester *p197* 01206 764477

Powell, Mrs P J (Land Registry - Gloucester Office)
Gloucester *p459*. 01452 511111

Powell, Mrs P M (Thatcher & Hallam)
Midsomer Norton *p316*. . . . 01761 414646

Powell, Mrs P S (Bristol City Council)
Bristol *p451* 0117 922 2000

Powell, R D (Squire Sanders (UK) LLP)
London EC2 *p81*. 020 7655 1000

Powell, R N A B (Evans Powell & Co) *E F1 G H S1 W Zc*
Llanelli *p292*. 01554 772632

Powell, Mrs S (Jacobs & Reeves) *W*
Poole *p353* 01202 674425

Powell, Miss S J (Stanley Tee) *K1 K3*
Bishop's Stortford *p144* . . . 01279 755200

Powell, S J (Lucas Law Limited) *N E S1 W L R2 S2*
London E8 *p55* 020 7812 9067
Congleton *p198* 01206 292592

Powell, S W (Powell Davies Solicitors) *A1 W S1 J1 L Zd*
Aberystwyth *p114* 01970 636599

Powell, T (Bristows) *C1 M1 O M2 Ze*
London EC4 *p15*. 020 7400 8000

Powell, T J (Powell Forster) *L N Q Zq*
Lambeth *p69*. 020 7737 8111

Powell, Ms V (Osborne Clarke) *U1 U2*
London EC2 *p65*. 020 7105 7000

Powell, W M (Gloucestershire County Council - Legal & Democratic Services)
Gloucester *p459*. 01452 425203

Powell-Evans, Ms R (Russell Jones & Walker)
London WC2 *p74* 020 7657 1555

Power, A (Devonshires) *R2 E*
London EC2 *p27*. 020 7628 7576

Power, A W (Power Scott Solicitors) *S1 K1 W L D1*
Stanley *p394*. 01207 230125

Power, Mrs C L (Walker Morris) *O Q Zl L*
Leeds *p277* 0113 283 2500

Power, D M (Matthew Arnold & Baldwin LLP) *E L S1*
Milton Keynes *p317* 01908 687880

Power, D R (Maples Teesdale LLP) *R2 S2 E L R1*
London EC2 *p58*. 020 7600 3800

Power, Ms E (Clarion Solicitors LLP) *C1 C2*
Leeds *p272* 0113 246 0622

Power, Mrs E J (Paris Smith LLP) *K1 W T2*
Southampton *p386*. 023 8048 2482

Power, E R (Paris Smith LLP) *E*
Southampton *p386*. 023 8048 2482

Power, Ms J E (Diamonds)
Buckhurst Hill *p167* 020 8559 0778

Power, Ms L J (HCB Solicitors) *S1 W*
Solihull *p382*. 0121 705 2255

Power, N D (IBM United Kingdom Ltd)
London SE1 *p107* 020 7202 3000

Power, R F (Harrogate Borough Council)
Harrogate *p460* 01423 500600

Power, R T (London Borough of Greenwich Legal Services)
London SE18 *p106* 020 8921 5123

Power, Ms S (Ashurst LLP)
London EC2 *p7* 020 7638 1111

Power, Ms S (T G Baynes) *S1*
Orpington *p341* . . . .01689 886000 / 886042

Power, Miss S C (London Borough of Southwark)
London SE1 *p109* 020 7525 5000

Power, W (Bevans) *W S1 S2 E R2*
Bristol *p161* 0117 923 7249

Power, W R (Kirklees Metropolitan Borough Council)
Huddersfield *p461* 01484 221421

Powles, A (Clarke Willmott) *C2 C1 O S2 E S1 Ze Zc*
Birmingham *p136* 0845 209 1000 / 0117 305 6000

Powles, R A (Farrer & Co LLP)
London WC2 *p31* 020 3375 7000

Powles, T J J (Rodney King & Partners) *K3 K1*
Bristol *p163* 0117 926 5201

Powlesland, Mrs D (Harris Cartier LLP) *Zr*
Slough *p382*. 01753 810710

Powleson, I L (Kerwoods) *S1 W P*
Redditch *p362*. 01527 584444

Pownall, A (Bonallack & Bishop) *N Zr*
Salisbury *p371*. 01722 422300

Pownall, Miss A L (Hillyer McKeown LLP) *J1*
Chester *p190* 01244 318131

Pownall, J (Oxford City Council)
Oxford *p468* 01865 249811

Powner, M (Charles Russell LLP) *J1 Zp Zw Zg Q O*
London EC4 *p19*. 020 7203 5000

Poxelaris, Miss M (John Laing)
London SW1 *p107*. 020 7901 3200

Poyner, R J (Barlows) *K1 K3*
Leicester *p278*. 0116 251 8295

Poyner, S M (Forshaws Davies Ridgway LLP) *B1 F1 I J1 N O Q Zk Ze Zc*
Warrington *p422*. 01925 230000

Poynter, A C (Swinnerton Moore Solicitors) *Za A3 C1*
London EC4 *p84*. 020 7236 7111

Poynter, M S C (Charles Lucas & Marshall) *E S2 R2 R1 Zc*
Newbury *p322*. 01635 521212

Poyser, J (John Poyser Solicitors) *N Q G Zq*
Manchester *p309* 0161 860 7354

Pracy, Ms L (Pearson Hinchliffe) *O Q N*
Oldham *p341* 0161 785 3500

Prado, A B (Dixon & Templeton) *Q K2 N G H*
Fordingbridge *p227* 01425 652194

Prager, Mrs B I (Regal Investments Ltd) *S1*
Edgware *p458*. . . . .

Prance, Ms D S (Brooks & Partners) *Q O K3 J1 Zq Zl L Zp N B1 F1*
Camberley *p173*. 01276 681217

Prandy, Ms H (Mills & Reeve) *O*
Cambridge *p175*. 01223 364422

Prasad, D (Prasad Solicitors) *E C1 S1 L*
Dewsbury *p210* 01924 464949

Prashant, D (Jeffrey Green Russell)
London W1 *p46* 020 7339 7000

Prashar, S (Torbay Council)
Torquay *p474* 01803 201201

Pratlett, Miss M F (Adams Harrison) *W Zm*
Saffron Walden *p370*. 01799 523441

Pratley, J (Foster & Partners)
Bristol *p162* 0117 922 0229

Pratley, S G (Brockbank Curwen Cain & Hall) *E S1 S2 L W Zh Zd*
Cockermouth *p197*. 01900 827222

Pratt, A G (Austins LLP) *N Q J1 L O*
Luton *p295* 01582 456222

Pratt, A J (DAC Beachcroft)
Bristol *p162* 0117 918 2000

Pratt, Miss A V (Clarion Solicitors LLP) *B1 O Q Zb*
Leeds *p272* 0113 246 0622

Pratt, Ms E (Carillion PLC) *C1 C2*
Wolverhampton *p477* 01902 422431
London EC4 *p53*. 020 7074 8000

Pratt, Miss F J (Quality Solicitors Burroughs Day) *K1*
Bristol *p164* 0117 929 0333

Pratt, Miss J (Christopher Harris & Co)
Sittingbourne *p380*. 01795 437268

Pratt, J A (BHP Law) *C1 D1 E L S1 W*
Durham *p214* 0191 384 0840

Pratt, Mrs J A (Cox & Hodgetts) *A1 L S1 W Zm*
Evesham *p220*. 01386 442513

Pratt, Miss J L (Thomson Snell & Passmore) *D1 K3 K2*
Tunbridge Wells *p415* 01892 510000

Pratt, Ms K L (Winterbotham Smith Penley LLP) *E*
Stroud *p401* 01453 847200

Pratt, Miss K M (Horwood & James LLP) *D1 D2 K1 K3*
Aylesbury *p121* 01296 487361

Pratt, K R (Meesons) *W Zm Zd T2 K4*
Ringwood *p364* 01425 472315

Pratt, Mrs K S (BHP Law) *W*
Darlington *p206* 01325 466794

Pratt, M J (Lindops) *C1 E L O Q S1 W*
Southend-on-Sea *p387* . . . 01702 431791

Pratt, R R (Hopkins) *W S1 S2 E*
Nottingham *p337*. 0115 910 5555

Pratt, T (Bates Wells & Braithwaite London LLP) *Zd C1*
London EC4 *p11*. 020 7551 7777

Pratt, Miss T A (Waldrons) *W S1*
Brierley Hill *p158*. 01384 811811

Pratts, C (Waltons & Morse LLP) *Q Za Zj*
London EC3 *p90*. 020 7623 4255

Precious, Mrs P J (Powell & Young) *N Q O J1 J2 K4 T2 W*
Pocklington *p351* 01759 302113

Preddy, D S (DAC Beachcroft)
Bristol *p162* 0117 918 2000

Preece, Miss C (Milwyn Jenkins) *K1 W N Zh L Q K3 K4 Zk*
Newtown *p330*. 01686 626218

Preece, D (FBC Manby Bowdler LLP) *C1*
Wolverhampton *p437* 01902 578000

Preece, D (Fox Williams) *C2 C1*
London EC2 *p33*. 020 7628 2000

Preece, Ms D C W (Hugh James) *S1 L S2*
Cardiff *p179* 029 2022 4871

See p634 for the Key to Work Categories

Preece, J (Hill Dickinson LLP)
Liverpool *p288* 0151 600 8000
Preece, Ms L (Nelsons) *N*
Nottingham *p338* 0115 958 6262
Preece, Mrs L M (Anthony Jewell & Co) *S1 K1*
Pontypridd *p352* 01443 493357
Preece, M R (Farnfield & Nicholls) *E S1 S2 L A1*
Sturminster Newton *p401* . . 01258 474270
Bournemouth *p152* 01202 551991
Preece, R D (Kenwright Walker Wyllie) *C1 C2 E F1 J1 S2 L O S1 W Zg Zv*
East Molesey *p215* 020 8979 1131
Preece, Miss S N (Kent County Council)
Canterbury *p453* 01227 767020
Preece, Ms V J (Hodders) *K1 D2 D1 K3*
High Wycombe *p250* 01494 511345
Prees, T J (Wansbroughs) *Q O F1 G H J1 K1 L M1 N Zc Zb*
Devizes *p210* 01380 733300
Preet-Ryatt, Miss J (Swindon Borough Council)
Swindon *p473* 01793 463000
Preiskel, D (Preiskel & Co LLP) *U1 U2 C2 C1 I Zza C3 Ze F2 Zf*
London EC4 *p69* 020 7583 2120
Preiskel, R (Preiskel & Co LLP) *U1 U2 C1 C2 I Zza C3 Ze F2 Zf*
London EC4 *p69* 020 7583 2120
Preisner, J (Field Seymour Parkes) *E R2 S2*
Reading *p360* 0118 951 6200
Preisner, N F (Brewer Harding & Rowe) *S1 S2*
Ilfracombe *p261* 01271 863495
Prendergast, Ms A E (Berry Smith LLP) *E L*
Cardiff *p177* 029 2034 5511
Prendergast, S A C (DWF) *Zb R2 C2*
Manchester *p303* 0161 603 5000
Prentice, Miss L E (Dover District Council)
Dover *p457* 01304 821199
Prentice, Miss M L (Hill Dickinson LLP)
London EC3 *p41* 020 7283 9033
Prentice, M P M (Gudgeons Prentice) *A1 C1 E S1 W S2*
Stowmarket *p399* 01449 613101
Prentice, Miss Z M (Heald Nickinson) *O Q F1 Zu N B1 Zl Zq Ze*
Camberley *p173* 01276 680000
Prescott, D T (Prescotts) *M1 B1 S1 E W N P C1 T1 R1 Zc Ze Zh*
Kidderminster *p266* 01562 829982
Prescott, Mrs K E (Co-operative Insurance Society Ltd)
Manchester *p464* 0161 832 8686
Prescott, L (Arthur Smiths) *S1 S2 N*
Wigan *p432* 01942 242815
Prescott, R B C (William Sturges & Co) *Q C1 J1 W A3*
Westminster *p84* 020 7873 1000
Preshaw, A G (Phillips Solicitors) *E C1 S1 A1 W*
Basingstoke *p127* 01256 460830
Presland, M (Howard Kennedy LLP) *E*
London W1 *p48* 020 7636 1616
Presley, Mrs C (Ware & Kay LLP) *W*
York *p445* 01904 716000
Pressdee, S H (Davis Wood) *J1 N Zr Q*
Bristol *p162* 0117 965 3504
Pressler, G J (Parcton Law Chambers Solicitors) *C1 G H J1 K1 N Q R1 S1 W Zc Zg Zk Zl*
Scunthorpe *p373* 01724 847711
Pressley, J (Modus Legal) *C1 C2 C3 I F1 F2 Ze Zza J1 Zt U2*
Chester *p191* 01244 372584
Prest, M D (Dixon Ward) *W T2 K4*
Richmond upon Thames *p364* 020 8940 4051
Preston, A (Platt Halpern)
Oldham *p341* 0161 626 4955
Preston, Ms A J (Platt Halpern) *G H Zg B2*
Manchester *p309* 0161 834 3114
Preston, Mrs A M (Reorient Legal) *C1 C2*
London EC3 *p71* 020 7645 8255
Preston, C A L (Watson Farley & Williams)
London EC2 *p90* 020 7814 8000
Preston, C J (Zermansky & Partners) *K1 K3*
Leeds *p278* 0113 245 9766
Preston, C M C (Miles Preston & Co) *K1 K2*
London EC4 *p69* 020 7583 0583
Preston, Ms D (Ashurst LLP)
London EC2 *p7* 020 7638 1111
Preston, Ms E (Osborne Clarke) *U1 U2*
London EC2 *p65* 020 7105 7000
Preston, E A (Edward Fail Bradshaw & Waterson) *G H B2*
London EC3 *p30* 020 7790 4032
Preston, H S (Preston Goldburn) *S1 L E R1 C1 A1*
Falmouth *p223* 01326 318900
Preston, J M (Prestons) *S1 S2 W*
Poulton-le-Fylde *p355* 01253 882426
Preston, K F (Farleys Solicitors LLP) *G H B2*
Blackburn *p145* 01254 367855
Preston, M (Everys) *J1 K1*
Exmouth *p222* 01395 264384
Preston, R (Beswicks) *O Q*
Stoke-on-Trent *p397* 01782 205000
Preston, R (Boyes Turner) *C1*
Reading *p360* 0118 959 7711
Preston, R E (Rowberry Morris) *E S2 C1 C2 Zl S1*
Staines *p393* 01784 457655
Preston, R E (Rowberry Morris) *S2 E C1 S1*
Reading *p361* 0118 958 5611
Preston, S D (Gordons LLP) *K1 K3*
Leeds *p273* 0113 227 0100
Leeds *p277* 0113 222 0022

Preston, T B (Bray & Bray) *C1 C2 E S2 Ze R2 Zza*
Leicester *p279* 0116 254 8871
Preston, T J N (Lightfoots LLP) *Q L J1*
Thame *p410* 01844 212305
Prestt, G M D (Walker Smith Way) *E A1 R2 S2*
Chester *p191* 0844 346 3100
Pretorius, A (Herbert Smith LLP)
London EC2 *p40* 020 7374 8000
Pretorius, R (Reynolds Porter Chamberlain LLP)
London E1 *p71* 020 3060 6000
Pretorius, Ms R M (SNR Denton) *C1 M2 Zb Zv*
London EC4 *p75* 020 7242 1212
Pretswell-Walker, Mrs K (Cartmell Shepherd)
Carlisle *p182* 01228 514077
Prettyjohn, Mrs H (Robinson Allfree) *S1 S2 E*
Ramsgate *p359* 01843 592361
Preuveneers, B (Preuveneers & Co) *E S1 W S2*
Mitcham *p318* 020 8646 4885
Prew, C A (Roach Pittis) *N O Q B1 F1 J1 L V G H Zc Zk Zj*
Newport *p328* 01983 524431
Prew, R M (QualitySolicitors C Turner) *G H*
Blackburn *p145* 01254 688400
Price, Ms A (Clifford Chance)
London E14 *p20* 020 7006 1000
Price, A (Ison Harrison) *A1 Zb E L*
Leeds *p274* 0113 284 5000
Price, A B (Addleshaw Goddard) *C1 C2 Zw*
Leeds *p271* 0113 209 2000
Price, A M A (Montpellier Group PLC)
London EC3 *p108* 020 7522 3200
Price, Ms A V (Russell & Russell) *K1 K3*
Bolton *p149* 01204 399299
Price, A W (Gordons LLP)
Leeds *p273* 0113 227 0100
Price, Ms B (Trowers & Hamlins)
London EC3 *p88* 020 7423 8000
Price, Mrs C (Kerseys) *K1*
Ipswich *p262* 01473 213311
Price, Ms C (Blair Allison & Co) *D1 K1*
Birmingham *p135* 0121 233 2904
Price, C (Country Land and Business Association Ltd)
London SW1 *p105* 020 7235 0511
Price, Miss C A (Salusburys Harding & Barnett) *K1 K3 Q F2*
Leicester *p281* . . 0116 262 9033 / 262 6052
Price, Ms C A (Wilkinson Woodward) *K3 K1 D1*
Halifax *p238* 01422 339600
Price, C J (The College of Law Chester) *O Q F1 B1*
Chester *p454* 0800 289997
Price, Miss C M (Levenes Solicitors)
Birmingham *p140* 0121 212 0000
Price, Miss C M (Harding Evans LLP) *K1 D1*
Newport *p328* 01633 244233
Price, C M (Tayntons LLP Solicitors) *K1*
Gloucester *p230* 01452 522047
Price, C R (Langleys) *N*
Lincoln *p284* 01522 888555
Price, D (Paris Smith LLP) *K4 T2 V W*
Southampton *p386* 023 8048 2482
Price, Ms D A (Kingsley Napley) *G*
London EC1 *p50* 020 7814 1200
Price, D J (David Price Solicitors & Advocates) *Zk*
London EC4 *p69* 020 7353 9999
Price, Ms D M (Swale Borough Council)
Sittingbourne *p471* 01795 417324
Price, Mrs E (MB Solicitors Ltd trading as MB Law) *O Q N A3 Zj*
Leeds *p275* 0113 242 4444
Price, Ms E M (ConocoPhillips (UK) Ltd)
London W1 *p105* 020 7408 6000
Price, F E (David Tagg & Co) *L O Q J1 Zq*
London SW6 *p85* 020 7736 0999
Price, F H C (The College of Law) *N J1 Q Zm Zq*
London WC1 *p105* 0800 289997
Price, F R (Jeffrey Green Russell) *N P E R1 L B1 Zh Zs Zc*
London W1 *p46* 020 7339 7000
Price, Ms G (The College of Law)
London WC1 *p105* 0800 289997
Price, G D (Newport City Council)
Newport *p466* 01633 656656
Price, Mrs G D (B P Collins LLP) *E S2*
Gerrards Cross *p229* 01753 889995
Price, Miss G M (Myers Lister Price) *F1 G H J1 K1 L M1 V*
Altrincham *p117* 0161 926 9969
Price, G R (Guest Pritchard & Co) *S1 W L E A1*
Old Colwyn *p340* 01492 515371
Price, Miss H (Lewis Silkin LLP) *J1 Zp*
Oxford *p343* 01865 263070
Price, Miss H E (McGrigors LLP)
London EC4 *p56* 020 7054 2500
Price, H M (Hugh James) *N Q L Zh Zj Zt*
Cardiff *p179* 029 2022 4871
Price, I (stevensdrake) *N O Q*
Crawley *p202* 01293 596900
Price, I T (South Oxfordshire District Council) *R1*
Wallingford *p475* 01491 823345
Price, J (Farrer & Co LLP)
London WC2 *p31* 020 3375 7000
Price, Miss J (Graystons) *Zr N Zq*
Wirral *p435* 0151 645 0055
Price, Miss J C (Divorce & Family Law Practice) *K1 K3*
Birmingham *p137* 0121 200 0890
Price, J C (Birdsall & Snowball) *G K1 H N D1 W*
Scarborough *p372* 01723 351351
Price, Miss J H (Portsmouth City Council)
Portsmouth *p469* 023 9283 4034

Price, Miss L C (KieranClarkeGreen) *N Q F1 L Zl J1*
Chesterfield *p192* 01246 211006
Price, M (Hurleys)
Bournemouth *p152* 01202 436100
Price, M C (Walker Morris) *J1*
Leeds *p277* 0113 283 2500
Price, M J S (Thompson Smith & Puxon) *K1 D1 V*
Colchester *p198* 01206 574431
Price, Miss M R (Dale Parkinson & Co)
Aldeburgh *p115* 01728 453338
Price, N C (Ford & Warren) *E S2 R2 Zb*
Leeds *p273* 0113 243 6601
Price, N G (Frederic Hall) *Q K1 J1 Zl Zg G H*
Folkestone *p227* 01303 851185
Price, Ms N J (Cunningtons) *S1*
Braintree *p155* 01376 326868
Price, O G (Wansbroughs) *J1 O L F1 C1 A1 Q Zp Zq*
Devizes *p210* 01380 733300
Price, Mrs P (Spratt Endicott) *J1*
Banbury *p122* 01295 204000
Price, P C (FBC Manby Bowdler LLP) *S1*
Bridgnorth *p157* 01746 761436
Price, R (Symes Bains Broomer) *C1*
Scunthorpe *p373* 01724 281616
Price, R A (Wilks Price Hounslow) *E C1 L S1 R1 W J1 F1 N P Zc Zp Zs*
Ryde *p369* 01983 566241
Price, R A (Pickering & Butters) *O J1 Zt Zl*
Stafford *p393* 01785 603060
Price, R C (Taylor Wessing) *Ze Zc*
London EC4 *p86* 020 7300 7000
Price, Miss R E (Walker Smith Way) *Zc F1 Zk O Q Zq*
Chester *p191* 0844 346 3100
Price, R E (Challinors) *S1 W E L C1 T1 R1 A1 Zl*
Halesowen *p237* 0121 550 0481
Price, R J (Pannone LLP) *M1 O Q B2 E*
Manchester *p308* 0161 909 3000
Price, R P J (Radcliffes Le Brasseur) *C1 E S1 B1 J1 O Zk Zl Ze*
Westminster *p70* 020 7222 7040
Price, R S (CMS Cameron McKenna LLP)
London EC3 *p17* 020 7367 3000
Price, S (Shoosmiths) *C1 C2 C3*
Milton Keynes *p317* . 0370 086 8300 / 01908 488300
Northampton *p332* . . 0370 086 3000 / 01604 543000
Price, S (Young & Lee) *Zf K2 Ze*
Birmingham *p143* 0121 633 3233
Price, Mrs S A (Trowers & Hamlins) *L R1*
London EC3 *p88* 020 7423 8000
Price, S C (Price Mears & Co) *N Q O*
Rochdale *p365* 01706 653331
Price, S J (Herbert Smith LLP)
London EC2 *p40* 020 7374 8000
Price, S J (Morton Price) *S2 E R1 R2 L*
Sheffield *p376* 0114 266 4141
Price, S L (Squire Sanders (UK) LLP) *O Zk*
London EC2 *p81* 020 7655 1000
Price, S T (J Keith Park & Co) *K1 Q G H J1 D1 F1 N O V Zl*
St Helens *p391* 01744 636000
Price, T P (Arnison & Co Solicitors Limited) *N*
Penrith *p346* 01768 862007
Price-Jones, Mrs G (Cyffraith JRL Law) *N K1 Q W V J1 F1 D2*
Llanrwst *p292* 01492 641222
Price-Jones, J H (Northamptonshire County Council) *B1 O*
Northampton *p467* 01604 236236
Prichard, J M W (John Bellis & Co) *S1 E A1 L W G J1 K1 R1 Zl*
Penmaenmawr *p346* 01492 622377
Priddis, Miss V (Michelmores LLP) *D1 K1 D2*
Exeter *p221* 01392 688688
Priddis, Mrs V M L (Foot Anstey) *G H K1 N D1 V Zl Zk*
Exeter *p221* 01392 411221
Priddle, Ms T (Russell-Cooke LLP) *Zd*
London SW15 *p74* 020 8789 9111
Priddle, W J (Burnetts) *E Zh S2*
Carlisle *p181* 01228 552222
Carlisle *p182* 01228 552222
Prideaux, W (Blake Lapthorn) *W*
Chandlers Ford *p184* 023 8090 8090
Pridmore, D A (Gordons LLP) *E S2 R2 Zc R1 S1*
Leeds *p273* 0113 227 0100
Pridmore, Mrs J (Goughs) *K1*
Melksham *p314* 01225 703036
Priest, Ms E (Harrison Clark LLP) *O*
Cheltenham *p188* 01242 269198
Worcester *p439* 01905 612001
Worcester *p439* 01905 612001
Priest, J C (Williams & Co) *R1 S1 A1 E R2 S2*
Ampthill *p118* 01525 405566
Priest, Ms K S (Birmingham City Council Legal & Democratic Services)
Birmingham *p449* 0121 303 2066
Priest, S L (Davis Priest & Co) *K1 S1 D2 W D1 K3*
Redditch *p362* 01527 69231
Priestley, B (Serious Law LLP - The Serious Law Practice)
Bolton *p150* 0800 616 681
Priestley, C S S (Withers LLP) *C1 C2 F1 Zd T1*
London EC4 *p92* 020 7597 6000
Priestley, Ms K M (Emerson Developments (Holdings) Ltd)
Alderley Edge *p447* 01625 588420
Priestley, N (Hattersleys) *N Q O F1 Zj Zq*
Mexborough *p314* 01709 582434

Priestley, N J (Ridley & Hall) *K1 D1 N*
Huddersfield *p256* 01484 538421
Priestley, Mrs V (Central & South West Staffordshire Magistrates Court)
Stafford *p472* 01785 223144
Priestley, V M (L V Priestley & Son) *A1 C1 E K1 L P S1 T1*
Church Stretton *p195* 01694 722254
Prigg, C M (Twomlows) *L S1*
Caldicot *p172* 01291 422753
Prigg, R M (Parry Carver) *D1 F1 G J1 K1 L N Q W Zi Zp Zq K3*
Wellington *p425* 01952 641291
Prikryl, P (D C Kaye & Co) *J1 G Zi O Q N Zc Zr E F1 F2 Ze H Zza P M1 D2 J2 Zg Zk Zj Zw*
Great Missenden *p234* . . . .01494 864650 / 862226
Primhak, Mrs B H (Peak District National Park Authority)
Bakewell *p448* 01629 816200
Primmer, J E (Keelys LLP) *C1 E S1 T1*
Lichfield *p284* 01543 420000
Prince, Mrs B F (TV Edwards LLP) *K1*
London SE8 *p85* 020 7790 7000
Prince, Miss C (Jaffe Porter Crossick) *S1 W L S2*
London NW6 *p46* 020 7625 4424
Prince, Miss D (Bretherton Law) *D1 K1 K2 D2 K3*
St Albans *p389* 01727 869293
Prince, D N (Irwin Mitchell LLP) *K1 D1*
Sheffield *p376* 0870 150 0100
Prince, D T (Pearson Hinchliffe) *K1 K2*
Oldham *p341* 0161 785 3500
Prince, Mrs F L (HRJ Law LLP) *W T2 K4*
Welwyn Garden City *p425* . . 01707 887700
Prince, Ms K P (Alexander Forbes Financial Services)
Croydon *p456* 020 8686 0660
Prince, Miss L (Harbottle & Lewis LLP) *O Q Zk Zf*
London W1 *p38* 020 7667 5000
Prince, M J (DLA Piper UK LLP) *C1 C2 M2 Zw Zb*
Liverpool *p287* 0870 011 1111
Prince, Miss S L (Eldridges) *W T2 K4*
Newport *p328* 01983 524741
Pring, S J (Farrer & Co LLP)
London WC2 *p31* 020 3375 7000
Pringle, Miss C (Gibson & Co) *O Q A3 Zq B2*
Newcastle upon Tyne *p324* . 0191 273 3817
Pringle, H J Y (Wessex Solicitors Chambers Ltd) *H G*
Portsmouth *p355* 023 9238 1114
Pringle, I J (Muscatt Walker Hayim) *B1 C1 E F1 L O Q S1 W Zl*
London W1 *p62* 020 7486 5131
Pringle, Miss J (Turners Solicitors LLP) *W K4*
Bournemouth *p153* 01202 291291
Pringle, Mrs J M (Windsor & Maidenhead Borough Council)
Maidenhead *p464* 01628 798888
Pringle, K H (Stokoe Partnership) *G H B2*
Waltham Forest *p83* 020 8558 8884
Pringle, N M (County of Herefordshire District Council)
Hereford *p460* 01432 260266
Pringle, R (Thompsons (formerly Robin/Brian Thompson & Partners)) *N*
Birmingham *p143* 0121 262 1200
London SW19 *p87* 020 8947 4163
Pringle, R N (Wilson & Berry) *W S1 E L C1*
Bracknell *p153* 01344 420555
Prins, Ms H E (Chambers & Hind (Stapleford)) *K1*
Nottingham *p336* 0115 949 1141
Prinsley, M A (Mayer Brown International LLP) *I Ze U2*
London EC2 *p59* 020 3130 3000
Print, Ms M (Bevan Brittan LLP)
Birmingham *p135* 0870 194 1000
Prior, A W (Davitt Jones Bould) *E S2 R1 P*
Taunton *p408* 01823 279279
Prior, Ms C (Speechly Bircham LLP) *P R1*
London EC4 *p81* 020 7427 6400
Prior, F (Paris Smith LLP) *K1 K3*
Southampton *p386* 023 8048 2482
Prior, Mrs J (South Tyneside Metropolitan Borough Council)
South Shields *p471* 0191 427 1717
Prior, Ms R (Blake Lapthorn) *K1*
Portsmouth *p354* 023 9222 1122
Prior, R D (King Prior Macdonald Bridge) *S1 E W*
Gravesend *p233* 01474 325678
Prior, Miss S K (Anthony Gold) *N Zr*
London SE1 *p6* 020 7940 4000
Pritam, S K (Reynolds Porter Chamberlain LLP) *C1 C2 I J1*
London E1 *p71* 020 3060 6000
Pritchard, B J (Pritchard & Co) *G H K1 S1 W Q L J1 Zi Zl Zm Zs*
Bangor *p122* 01248 370017
Pritchard, D R (B P Collins LLP) *O Q G B1 F1 Zj Zk*
Gerrards Cross *p229* 01753 889995
Pritchard, D V (Segens Blount Petre)
Westminster *p77* 020 7332 2222
Pritchard, E (Pritchard Edwards & Co) *Q N A1 S1 W C1 Zm*
Carmarthen *p182* 01267 234022
Pritchard, E (Machins Solicitors LLP) *S1*
Luton *p295* 01582 514000
Pritchard, Mrs E B (Leonard & Co) *D1 K3 K1 L*
Southampton *p386* 023 8023 4433
Pritchard, J (Swansea Magistrates Court) *G H*
Swansea *p473* 01792 655171
Swansea *p405* 01792 643021

6

Pritchard, J M (Birkett Long LLP) *A1 E S1* Chelmsford *p186*. 01245 453800

Pritchard, Ms K (Burnley-Jones Bate & Co) *G H* London SW19 *p16*. 020 8542 8101

Pritchard, Ms K (DAC Beachcroft) London EC4 *p24*. 020 7936 2222

Pritchard, Ms K L (Cambridge House Legal Centre) *K1 K3 J1 Q Zp X* London SE5 *p104* . . 020 7703 3051 / 7701 9499

Pritchard, K W (Knowsley Metropolitan Borough Council) Huyton *p461*. 0151 443 3593

Pritchard, Ms L (Peter Peter & Wright) *Q N L O F1* Bude *p168*. 01288 352101

Pritchard, L P (DWF) *C1 C3 M1 F1 M2 Ze Zw Zz* Liverpool *p287*. 0151 907 3000

Pritchard, N D (East Northamptonshire District Council) Thrapston *p474* 01832 742000

Pritchard, N D M (TLT Solicitors) *A1 Ze Zb Zc* Bristol *p165* 0117 917 7777

Pritchard, N J (Allen & Overy LLP) London E1 *p5* 020 3088 0000

Pritchard, S (Russell-Cooke LLP) *Zd* London SW15 *p74*. 020 8789 9111

Pritchard, T P (LG Lawyers) London SE1 *p50*. 020 7379 0000

Pritchard-Jones, J D (Pritchard Jones Evans Lane) *S1 W C1 E A1 T1 R1 Zs* Caernarfon *p172*. 01286 673387

Pritty, Miss E (Harbottle & Lewis LLP) London W1 *p38* 020 7667 5000

Privett, Miss P J (Akzo Nobel Ltd) *C1 C2 U2* London SW1 *p103*. 020 7009 5000

Privett, R (Radcliffes Le Brasseur) *N J1 O Q G Zq Zm* Westminster *p70*. 020 7222 7040

Probert, Ms C M E (Trethowans LLP) *E S1 R2 S2* Salisbury *p371*. 01722 412512

Probert, E A W (Foot Anstey) *C1 C2 O T1 T2 I M1 M2 Zb Ze Zo* Exeter *p221* 01392 411221

Probert, Mrs J (Michelmores LLP) *C1 C2* Exeter *p221* 01392 688688

Probert, J P (Robinson & Murphy) *N Zq K1 O* Newcastle upon Tyne *p326* . 0191 230 5023

Probert, Miss K E (Higgs & Sons) *W* Brierley Hill *p158*. 0845 111 5050

Probert, M (Probert & Gray) *S1 W E P G K1 F1 M1 R1* Neath *p320* 01639 643501

Procopi, P (YVA Solicitors) *S1 E L* London N12 *p93*. 020 8445 9898

Procopi, Miss S N (YVA Solicitors) *D1 K1 K3* London N12 *p93*. 020 8445 9898

Procter, A C T (Stamp Jackson and Procter) *C1 C2 C3 A1 O T1 T2 W E B1 Ze Zo Zd J1 A2 M1* Hull *p258* 01482 324591

Procter, I M (Quality Solicitors C Turner) *N J1* Blackburn *p145* 01254 688400

Procter, Ms J (DLA Piper UK LLP) *C1 C2* Leeds *p272* 0870 011 1111

Procter, M W (SJP Solicitors) *S1 P W L M1 K1 G H* Hunstanton *p258*. 01485 532662

Proctor, M B (Aldridge Brownlee Solicitors LLP) *G* Bournemouth *p151*. 01202 294411

Proctor, N C (Addleshaw Goddard) *O Q Zc* Manchester *p300* 0161 934 6000

Proctor, Ms R (Red Kite Law) *N* Milford Haven *p316* 01646 698008

Proctor, R (Barlow Lyde & Gilbert LLP) London EC3 *p10*. 020 7247 2277

Proctor, Mrs R S (Watkins Stewart & Ross) *S1 E S2 W* Ipswich *p263*. 01473 226266

Proctor, Ms S E (Max Bitel Greene LLP) *O Q Zw J1 B1 L C1* Islington *p59*. 020 7354 2767

Proctor, S T (Jordans) *E S2* Wakefield *p418* . . . . 01924 387110 Harrogate *p240* 01423 530630

Proddow, C W N (Bevan Brittan LLP) London EC4 *p12*. 0870 194 1000

Proddow, S K (Proddow Mackay) *M1 S1* Maidenhead *p298* 01628 776847

Proffitt, E (Proffitt & Mann) *N G H L Q* Lowestoft *p294* 01502 538582

Profit, M D J (Blake Lapthorn) *S1 W* Portsmouth *p354*. 023 9222 1122

Propert, Mrs J E (Properts) *S1 S2 E K3 K1 W L R2* Caldicot *p172* 01633 882282

Propert, J P (Properts) *E S2 S1 R2 L* Caldicot *p172* 01633 882282

Prosser, D (Geoffrey Morris & Ashton) *S2 E S1* Wrexham *p442* 01978 291322

Prosser, D L (Ashley Smith & Co) *G H B2* Lewisham *p80*. 020 8463 0099

Prosser, D P (DP Law Ltd t/a David Prosser & Co) *D1 K1 D2* Bridgend *p157*. 01656 645921

Prosser, Mrs H A (South Gloucestershire Council) Thornbury *p474* 01454 868686

Prosser, J (Veale Wasbrough Vizards) *O Q Zc* Bristol *p165* 0117 925 2020

Prosser, Mrs R E (Cancer Research UK) *J1* London WC2 *p104*. 020 7242 0200

Prosser, Miss S (Squire Sanders (UK) LLP) *O* Leeds *p277* 0113 284 7000

Prosser, S J (Harrogate Borough Council) Harrogate *p460* 01423 500600

Prothero, L (Penningtons) *Zr* Godalming *p231*. 01483 791800

Protheroe, Miss A B (Harding Evans LLP) *J1* Newport *p328* 01633 244233

Protheroe, Ms C (Barlow Lyde & Gilbert LLP) London EC3 *p10*. 020 7247 2277

Protopapas, X S (Protopapas) *M1 N P G B1 C1 E J1 K1 L Ze Zi Zk* London W1 *p69* 020 7636 2100

Protopapas, Mrs Z (Protopapas) *S1 E W* London W1 *p69* 020 7636 2100

Proud, Ms M (Tinsdills) *B1 D1 K1 V Zo* Hanley *p239*. 01782 262031

Proudfoot, A (Rogerson Galvin) *S1 W E C1 L A1 R1* Ashton-under-Lyne *p120*0161 344 2027 / 335 9005

Proudler, Miss G A (Olswang LLP) *Ze Zk* London WC1 *p64* 020 7067 3000

Proudley, C (Trowers & Hamlins) *E* London EC3 *p88*. 020 7423 8000

Prout, M J (Gard & Co) *W S1 T2 E C1 Zm Zd S2 K4* Plymouth *p349*. 01752 668246

Provan, G (Tolhurst Fisher LLP) Chelmsford *p187*. 01245 495111

Proven, Mrs K (Cooper Sons Hartley & Williams) *S1 S2 E L W K4* Chapel-en-le-Frith *p184* . . . 01298 812138

Proven, Ms K J (Cooper Sons Hartley & Williams) *S1 W K4 E* Buxton *p172*. 01298 77511

Provins, K J (Mackrell Turner Garrett) London WC2 *p57* 020 7240 0521

Prowel, W M (Martyn Prowel) *G H Zl* Cardiff *p180* 029 2047 0909

Prowle, Miss A L (Barcan Woodward) *N* Bristol *p161* 0117 925 8080

Prowse, A B (Prowse Thomas) *S1 W L E A1 R1 T1 Zd T2* Brixham *p166* 01803 882210

Prowse, P A (Salans) London EC4 *p76*. 020 7429 6000

Pruce, A S (Severn Trent Water Ltd) Birmingham *p450* 0121 722 4000

Prudham, B M (Thompsons (formerly Robin/Brian Thompson & Partners)) *N* Newcastle upon Tyne *p327* . 0191 269 0400

Prusinski, A J (Prusinski Solicitors) *F1 J1 K1 N O Q* Loughborough *p293* 01509 233622

Prusinski, M W (Prusinski Solicitors) *S1 W E L B1 T1 C1* Loughborough *p293* 01509 233622

Pryce, A N (Eastleys) *K1 D1 Zl* Paignton *p345* 01803 559257

Pryce, Mrs G (T A Matthews) *W S1 T2 T1 S2* Hereford *p248* . . . . 01432 352121 Leominster *p283*. 01568 615905

Pryce, Mrs P J (Keith Harvey & Co) *E L S1* Market Harborough *p312*. . . 01858 464327

Pryer, M G L (Wilkins) *K1 D1 J1 Q O L* Aylesbury *p121* 01296 424681

Pryke, O C P (Taylor Vinters) *J1 J2* Cambridge *p176*. 01223 423444

Prymak, Miss A E (Clifton Ingram LLP) *W* Wokingham *p437* 0118 978 0099

Pryn, R J (Domino Printing Sciences PLC) Cambridge *p453*. 01954 781888

Pryor, M D (Tracey Barlow Furniss & Co) *G H S1 M1 P W F1 C1 D1 J1 Zl Zh Zk* Retford *p363*. . . . . 01777 707677 Worksop *p441* 01909 472355

Pryor, S R (Torbay Council) Torquay *p474* 01803 201201

Pryse-Davies, Ms S G (Amphlett Lissimore) *L K1 D1* Croydon *p6* 020 8771 5254

Prytherch, J D (United Utilities) Warrington *p475*. 01925 237000

Przedborski, A A (Peterborough Magistrates Court) Peterborough *p468* 01223 314311

Pucci, Miss S (Stones Solicitors LLP) Exeter *p222* 01392 666777

Puddicombe, A (Gloucester Law Centre) Gloucester *p459*. 01452 423492

Puddicombe, N (Veale Wasbrough Vizards) *O Q Zc* Bristol *p165* 0117 925 2020

Pudge, D J (Clifford Chance) London E14 *p20*. 020 7006 1000

Pudner, Mrs R (Hutchinson Thomas) *D1 K1* Neath *p320* 01639 645061

Puech, M G (Marshall Hall & Levy) *N Q K1 F1 L J1 G D1 H V Ze Zk Zi Zl* South Shields *p384* 0191 455 3181

Pufulete, Mrs H (Terence St J Millett) *S1 L* London SW7 *p82* 020 7581 7500

Pugh, Miss A (Warwickshire County Council) Warwick *p475* 01926 410410

Pugh, A I (Anthony Pugh) Barry *p126*. 01446 751493

Pugh, A J (Hill Dickinson LLP) *Zc P O Q A3 R1 Zq* Liverpool *p288*. 0151 600 8000

Pugh, Ms C (FBC Manby Bowdler LLP) *J1* Wolverhampton *p437* 01902 578000

Pugh, C (Morton Pugh Welch) *N Zk J1 X O Q Ze Zp Zq Zr A3* London EC2 *p62*. 020 7374 4141

Pugh, C C (Nexus Solicitors) *N O Q Zj Zq F2* Manchester *p308* 0161 819 4900

Pugh, Ms C S (LG Lawyers) London SE1 *p50*. 020 7379 0000

Pugh, Ms E (Aaron & Partners LLP Solicitors) *K1 D1* Chester *p190* 01244 405555

Pugh, I C (Hallmark Hulme) *S1 G H J1 N Zl* Worcester *p439* 01905 726600

Pugh, K W (Nabarro LLP) *J1 Zp* Sheffield *p376* 0114 279 4000

Pugh, N (Aplin Stockton Fairfax) *S2 E S1 A1* Banbury *p122* 01295 251234

Pugh, Miss N S (Squire Sanders (UK) LLP) *Zw O C1* London EC2 *p81*. 020 7655 1000

Pugh, R (McKenzies) *N G H* London N9 *p57* 020 8350 4114

Pugh, Mrs R H (Runnymede Borough Council) Addlestone *p447*. 01932 838383

Pugh, S (Wilson & Co) London N17 *p92*. 020 8808 7535

Pugh, Mrs S E (Hawkins Hatton LLP) *J1* Dudley *p213*. . . . . 01384 216840 Dudley *p213*. 01384 216920

Pugh, S R (Cambridge City Council) Cambridge *p452*. 01223 457000

Pugsley, C F (Hole & Pugsley) *S1 W L A3 Zd* Tiverton *p412* 01884 252827

Pugsley, I L (Hole & Pugsley) *S1 W L A1 S2 E* Tiverton *p412* 01884 252827

Pugsley, Miss M J (Hole & Pugsley) *S1 W L* Tiverton *p412* 01884 252827

Pugsley, N W (Askew Bunting Solicitors LLP) Middlesbrough *p314*. 01642 252555

Pugsley, R J L (Hole & Pugsley) Tiverton *p412* 01884 252827

Pugsley, S A P (Pennon Group PLC) Exeter *p458* 01392 446677

Pulford, M A (RMPI Solicitors) *A3 B1 O Zq* London W1 *p70* 020 7318 4444

Pulham, C (Rosenblatt) London EC4 *p73*. 020 7955 0880

Pulham, C (Steeles) *C1* Norwich *p335* 0870 609 0200

Pulham, J S (Pulham & Co) *K4 S1 W T2 E Zd* Saxmundham *p372* 01728 602084

Pullan, Ms M M (Marsh & McLennan Companies, Inc) *N B1 Zj Za* London EC3 *p108* 020 7357 1000

Pullan, Mrs S J (Heppenstalls) New Milton *p321*. . . . . . . 01425 610078 Lymington *p296* 01590 689500

Pullan, T R (LG Lawyers) London SE1 *p50*. 020 7379 0000

Pullen, D M (Reed Smith LLP) *Za* London EC2 *p71*. 020 3116 3000

Pullen, K (Herbert Smith LLP) *C1 Zb* London EC2 *p40*. 020 7374 8000

Pullen, Miss K H L (Bennett Oakley & Partners) *S1* Burgess Hill *p168* 01444 235232

Pullen, M R (DLA Piper UK LLP) London EC2 *p24*. 0870 011 1111

Pullen, N S (Nigel S Pullen) *S1 K4 L S2 W E* Perranporth *p346* 01872 571046

Pullen, S (Howard Kennedy LLP) *Zb R2* London W1 *p48* 020 7636 1616

Pullinger, Ms A C (Rooks Rider) *J1 O Q* London EC1 *p73*. 020 7689 7000

Pulman, R (Hugh James) *O* Cardiff *p179* 029 2022 4871

Pulsford, P J (E D C Lord & Co) *S1 E W C1 L N T1 R1 Zc Zl* Hayes *p245* 020 8848 9988

Pumfrey, Mrs D W (MBNA Europe Bank Ltd) Chester *p454* 01244 672002

Pumfrey, Mrs J (Gepp & Sons) *G H* Chelmsford *p186*. . . . . . . 01245 493939 Colchester *p197* 01206 369889

Pumfrey, R T (Horton & Moss) *K1 N Q F1 D1 J1* Ilkeston *p261* . . 0115 932 1431 / 930 8208

Punatar, T (Punatar & Co Solicitors) *G* London N19 *p69*. 020 7272 3330

Pung, K (KSP Solicitors) *N* Hatfield *p244* 01707 264277

Punjabi, Ms S I (Olswang LLP) *C1 I* London WC1 *p64* 020 7067 3000

Punpher, Miss A (Rainer Hughes) *G Q O* Brentwood *p156*. 01227 226644

Punt, C F J (Crosse Wyatt Verney & Ayre) *D1 D2 F1 F2 G H K1 N Q Zt Zu* South Molton *p383*. 01769 572157

Purbrick, Mrs S A (Red Kite Law) *S1 W* Haverfordwest *p244* 01437 763332

Purcell, Mrs D C (Purcell Parker) *B1 C1 E F1 K1 L R1 S1* Birmingham *p141* 0121 236 9781

Purcell, D W R (Capsticks Solicitors LLP) *O B2 A3 Ze Zk* London SW19 *p18*. 020 8780 2211

Purcell, M T (Purcell Parker) *D1 G H J1 K1 L M1 N P V Zm* Birmingham *p141* 0121 236 9781

Purcell, Ms N J (McDermott Will & Emery UK LLP) *T1* London EC2 *p56*. 020 7577 6900

Purcell, Miss S A (Consolidated Financial Insurance) *C1 Zj* London W4 *p451* 020 8380 3000

Purchas, S R (Ison Harrison) *Q Zg* Leeds *p274* 0113 284 5000

Purches, Miss N (Whiting & Purches) *G H Zm Zl* Solihull *p383*. 0121 605 5050

Purday, Ms D A (Colemans - CTTS) Barnet *p124* 020 8441 1213

Purdue, M C (Verisona Solicitors) *C1 E L S1 T1 W F1* Waterlooville *p423*. 023 9226 5251

Purdy, F (Frank Purdy) Westminster *p69*. 020 7408 6190

Purdy, G (The Manchester Airport Group PLC) Manchester *p465* 0871 271 0711

Purewal, A (Ashurst LLP) London EC2 *p7* 020 7638 1111

Puri, A (VKM Solicitors) *S1 Q Zi S2 W N* Wolverhampton *p438* 01902 311155

Puri, Mrs M (Humfrys & Symonds) *W* Hereford *p248* . . . .01432 359261 / 276276

Puri, Miss R (Alexander Lawyers LLP) London W1 *p5*. 01245 216050

Purkis, Miss S R (Kingsley Napley) *O* London EC1 *p50*. 020 7814 1200

Purkiss, H F (Harter & Loveless) *L Zg S1 S2* Islington *p39*. 020 7688 2900

Purnell, Ms J (Nicol Denvir & Purnell) *K1 D1 V S1 W* Cardiff *p180* 029 2079 6311

Purrier, T J (Barlow Lyde & Gilbert LLP) *B1 F1 J1 L M1 N P R1 Zc Ze Zl O Q* Manchester *p301* 0161 829 6400

Pursall, M L (Berry Smith LLP) *E L* Cardiff *p177* 029 2034 5511

Purser, B L (Heckford Norton) *E S1 L C1 R1 A1 B1 J1 T1 W Zc Ze Zl* Letchworth *p283*. 01462 682244

Purser, Mrs C N K (Barlow Robbins LLP) *K1 K2 M2 D1* Godalming *p231* 01483 417121

Purser, N J E (McKenzies) *K1 D1 D2 S1 Q* London N9 *p57* 020 8350 4114

Pursey, C R (Cardiff County Council) Cardiff *p453* 029 2087 2000

Pursglove, Miss S M (Dixon Rigby Keogh) *K1 Q N* Winsford *p434* 01606 557211

Purslow, Miss A L (Stanley Tee) *S1* Bishop's Stortford *p144* . . . 01279 755200

Purslow, N (Reed Smith LLP) *Q O U2* London EC2 *p71*. 020 3116 3000

Pursell, A (Waltons & Morse LLP) *O Zj Za* London EC3 *p90*. 020 7623 4255

Purtill, Ms M (O'Rourke Reid & Co) Leeds *p276* 0113 245 7811

Purton, T B T (Singhania & Co Ltd) *S1* London SW1 *p80* 020 7799 1688

Purton, T E (Travers Smith LLP) *C1* London EC1 *p87*. 020 7295 3000

Purushothaman, D (Jones Day) *Zb* London EC4 *p46*. 020 7039 5959

Purves, J (Brabners Chaffe Street) *E* Manchester *p301* 0161 836 8800

Purves, P M (Bridge McFarland) *S1 S2 W A1 L E* Grimsby *p235* 01472 311711

Purves, R (Financial Services Authority) London E14 *p106* 020 7066 1000

Pusey, J (Franklins LLP) *E R1 S1* Milton Keynes *p317* 01908 660966

Putin, A (Quality Solicitors Burroughs Day) *O Q* Bristol *p164* 0117 929 0333

Putnam, P S (Wilson Browne) *Q N O J1* Higham Ferrers *p250* 01933 410000

Putnam, Mrs S (London Borough of Bexley) Bexleyheath *p449* 020 8303 7777

Putt, C (Speechly Bircham LLP) *C2* London EC4 *p81*. 020 7427 6400

Puttock, R E (Sherwood Wheatley) *S1 E R1 C1 W A1 F1 L T1 J1 Zc Zl Zj* Kingston upon Thames *p267*. 020 8546 0144

Puvirajasingham, J (Squire Sanders (UK) LLP) Leeds *p277* 0113 284 7000

Puxley, J (HKB Wiltshires) *N K3 K1 D1 D2* Great Yarmouth *p234* 01493 855676

Puxon, P B (Ferguson Solicitors) *C1 J1 U1 Zp* London EC4 *p31*. 020 7822 2999

Puzio, Miss I (Stockport Metropolitan Borough Council) Stockport *p472*. 0161 480 4949

Pyatt, Miss T (Pickering & Butters) *S2 E* Stafford *p393* 01785 603060

Pybus, E J (Samuel Phillips Law Firm) *E S2 W T2 A1 S1 Zn* Newcastle upon Tyne *p326* . 0191 232 8451

Pye, N G (Hill Dickinson LLP) *E C1 S1* Liverpool *p288*. 0151 600 8000

Pye-Smith, C J (Bird & Co) *G H* Grantham *p232* 01476 591711

Pyke, Ms J (Herbert Smith LLP) London EC2 *p40*. 020 7374 8000

Pyke, R (Rogers & Norton) *S2 E C1* Norwich *p335* 01603 666001

Pyne, A R J (Saulet & Co) *G N Q F1 F2 J1 H Zl* Southsea *p389*. 023 9281 9442

Pyne, Mrs S (Ian N Gunby & Co) *E S1 S2* Milnthorpe *p316* . . . . . . 01539 562044 Barrow-in-Furness *p125* . . . 01229 811811

Pyper, T E (TLT Solicitors) *C1 Zd* Bristol *p165* 0117 917 7777

Pyrke, J C (BPE Solicitors LLP) *E L* Cheltenham *p187* 01242 224433

See p634 for the Key to Work Categories

Q

Qamruddin, A (MRH Solicitors) *N*
Bolton *p149* 01204 535333
Qasim, M (Brindley Twist Tafft & James) *Zb B1 Zk Q*
Coventry *p200* 024 7653 1532
Birmingham *p136* 0121 214 8989
Qayyum, A (Bazeer & Co) *Zi K1 S2*
London SW19 *p11* 020 8543 6600
Quaid, Ms O M (Squire Sanders (UK) LLP)
Manchester *p310* 0161 830 5000
Quailey, Mrs M J (Birmingham City Council Legal & Democratic Services)
Birmingham *p449* 0121 303 2066
Quain, J E (Bentleys Stokes & Lowless) *Za Zo Zq*
London EC3 *p12* 020 7782 0990
Quain, Mrs M (Meesons) *S1 W K1 K3 K4 Zm*
Fordingbridge *p227* 01425 655251
Ringwood *p364* 01425 472315
Qualtrough, J R (Simmons & Simmons) *R1 E Zs*
London EC2 *p79* 020 7628 2020
Quantick, G (Myer Wolff) *G H B2*
Hull *p257* 01482 223693
Hull *p257* 01482 326446
Quantick, Mrs H (Foot Anstey) *W T2*
Taunton *p408* 01823 625600
Quantrell, R (Wilkin Chapman Grange Solicitors) *S1 W E A1 K1 L T1 N C1 Q Zd Zm*
Alford *p115* 01507 466767
Quarmby, Mrs L (Woodfines LLP) *Q L N Zq*
Sandy *p372* 01767 680251
Quartermain, J M (Larcomes LLP) *W*
Portsmouth *p354* 023 9266 1531
Quartly, Mrs J (Oxfordshire County Council)
Oxford *p468* 01865 792422
Quastel, D A (Quastel Midgen LLP) *E S2 R2 R1*
London W1 *p70* 020 7908 2525
Quayle, D M (Vale of White Horse District Council)
Abingdon *p447* 01235 520202
Quayle, Ms J R (Muckle LLP) *W*
Newcastle upon Tyne *p325* 0191 211 7777
Quayle, S M (Slough Borough Council)
Slough *p471* 01753 552288
Quearney, Ms B M (Kaim Todner Ltd) *G H*
London EC4 *p47* 020 7353 6660
Quelch, C J (Parque Securities Ltd)
Farnham *p458* 01252 781470
Quelch, S J (Maldon District Council)
Maldon *p464* 01621 854477
Quenby, Ms G (McDermott Will & Emery UK LLP)
London EC2 *p56* 020 7577 6900
Querelle, R E (Hibberts LLP) *S1 W J1 A1 K4*
Tarporley *p408* 01829 733338
Quibell, J B (Laytons) *C1 C2 F1 T1 Zb*
Guildford *p236* 01483 407000
Quick, A R (Stevens & Bolton)
Guildford *p237* 01483 302264
Quick, Miss R (Treasury Solicitors Department)
London WC2 *p110* 020 7210 3000
Quieros, M J (Brignalls Balderston Warren) *N Zr Q Zq G*
Stevenage *p394* 01438 359311
Quigley, D L (J Keith Park & Co) *N E O*
St Helens *p391* 01744 636000
Quigley, Ms D M E (Squire Sanders (UK) LLP)
London EC2 *p81* 020 7655 1000
Quigley, G R (Waugh & Musgrave) *A1 B1 C1 D1 E F1 G H J1 K1 Zc Zj Zl Zt*
Cockermouth *p197* 01900 823127
Quigley, J (Rice-Jones & Smiths) *Zb C1 J1 K1 Zp W*
London EC1 *p72* 020 7831 2506
Quigley, M (Beecham Peacock) *N J1*
Newcastle upon Tyne *p323* 0191 232 3048
Quigley, M (Sintons LLP) *N J1 Zr*
Newcastle upon Tyne *p326* 0191 226 7878
Quigley, P F (Blake Lapthorn) *S1 S2*
Oxford *p342* 01865 248607
Quill, Ms M A M (Routledge Quill & Co) *E S1 A1 B1 C1 C2 L Zc Zj Ze Zk*
Wormley *p441* 01428 682589
Quinan, P D (Bird & Bird LLP) *A3 O Za*
London EC4 *p13* 020 7415 6000
Quincey, A H (Tanburghs O'Brien Lahaise) *S1 S2 E W*
Camden *p85* 020 7372 6614
Quinlan, A (Pinsent Masons LLP) *E*
Leeds *p276* 0113 244 5000
Quinlan, Ms C J (Park Woodfine Heald Mellows LLP) *K1*
Rushden *p369* 01933 397000
Quinlivan, H (Beviss & Beckingsale)
Honiton *p252* 01404 548050
Quinn, Miss A M (Celador Productions Ltd) *S1 W L*
London WC2 *p105* 020 7240 8101
Warwick *p471* 01926 653000
Quinn, Miss C (Linskills Solicitors) *N Q J1 Zq*
Liverpool *p289* 0151 236 2224
Quinn, C (Keoghs LLP) *Q N*
Bolton *p149* 01204 677000
Quinn, Miss G (Willson Hawley & Co)
Nuneaton *p339* 024 7638 7821
Quinn, G A (Quinn & Co) *S1 W*
Chorley *p194* 01257 241818
Quinn, G P (Charltons Solicitors) *W S1 S2 E*
Biddulph *p132* 01782 522111
Quinn, Ms J M (Allen & Overy LLP)
London E1 *p5* 020 3088 0000
Quinn, J S C (MFG Solicitors) *A1 C1 C2 W E R1*
Kidderminster *p265* 01562 820181
Worcester *p440* 01905 610410
Quinn, Ms L M (Colman Coyle LLP) *J1*
Islington *p22* 020 7354 3000
Quinn, M H (Quinn Mantion) *O S1 L F1 E J1 B1 C1 K1 Q Zd Zh Zk Zl*
London E14 *p70* 020 7512 2600
Quinn, M J (Hill Dickinson LLP) *C1 T1 W*
Liverpool *p288* 0151 600 8000
Quinn, N P (Woodfines LLP) *G B2*
Bletchley *p147* 01908 366333
Quinn, P A (Stephensons Solicitors LLP)
Leigh *p282* 01942 777777
Quinn, P C (Quinn Melville) *G H J1 B2*
Liverpool *p290* 0151 236 3340
Quinn, P J (Gregg Latchams LLP) *E C1 S1*
Bristol *p162* 0117 906 9400
Quinn, R D (Kaim Todner Ltd) *N G H*
Ashford *p119* 01233 662002
Quinn, Mrs R J (ClarksLegal LLP) *Zb F1 F2 Zl O Q*
Reading *p360* 0118 958 5321
Quinn, T (Goldbergs) *N Zq*
Plymouth *p349* 01752 660023
Quinn, W A (Weightmans LLP) *Q N Zj*
Liverpool *p291* 0151 227 2601
Quinney, J M (Herbert Smith LLP) *M2 M1*
London EC2 *p40* 020 7374 8000
Quinney, N J (W H Matthews & Co) *K3 K1 N Q F1 J1 G L S1 B1 C1*
Sutton *p402* 020 8642 6677
Quint, Ms S M (British Nuclear Fuels PLC)
Warrington *p475* 01925 832000
Quint, T K (Lawrence Wood) *S2 E L S1 W*
Wroxham *p443* 01603 783711
Quirk, Mrs A E (St Helens Borough Council)
St Helens *p472* 01744 456000
Quirk, E (Glaisyers Solicitors LLP) *E C1 R2*
Manchester *p304* 0161 832 4666
Quirke, Mrs G (Atkinson Cave & Stuart) *Zh L Q B1 V*
Blackpool *p146* 01253 293151
Quirolo, D (Ashurst LLP)
London EC2 *p7* 020 7638 1111
Quli, D R (Reed Smith LLP) *Zf*
London EC2 *p71* 020 3116 3000
Qureshi, F A (Thomas Solicitors) *K1 W G L D1*
Loughborough *p293* 01509 611061
Qureshi, N (London Borough of Southwark)
London SE1 *p109* 020 7525 5000
Qureshi, S (Bindmans LLP)
London WC1 *p12* 020 7833 4433
Qureshi, T A (Mellor & Jackson)
Oldham *p340* 0161 624 7081
Quy, S J (Vanderpump & Sykes) *E S1 C1 T1 L R1*
Enfield *p219* 020 8367 3999
Quy, T J (Bury & Walkers LLP) *J1 F1 N Q Zj Zo Zp*
Barnsley *p124* 01226 733533

R

Rabagliati, D M (Hill Dickinson LLP) *C1 Zb Zc R2*
London EC3 *p41* 020 7283 9033
Rabaiotti, S A F (Marchant Harries & Co) *E F1 L Q S1 W*
Mountain Ash *p319* 01443 476444
Rabani, Mrs N (George Green LLP) *E S2 R2*
Cradley Heath *p201* 01384 410410
Rabbett, M C (Buckles Solicitors LLP) *S1 E S2 A1 R2*
Peterborough *p346* 01733 888888
Rabey, R J (Carlyon & Son) *W E*
Truro *p414* 01872 278641
Rabheru, Mrs S (TWM Solicitors LLP) *S1*
Guildford *p237* 01483 752700
Rabin, P J (Farmar Miller Rabin Gordon) *S1 W L F1 G E J1 C1 H S2*
Edgware *p217* 020 8381 3339
Rabinowicz, J I (Teacher Stern LLP) *M1 O Q Zq X Zr*
London WC1 *p86* 020 7242 3191
Rabinowitz, Mrs L G (Marshalls)
Godalming *p231* 01483 416101
Raby, A S (Thackray Williams) *Q L O J1 B1 Zh Zk*
Beckenham *p129* 020 8663 0503
Raby, C J (Bradbury Roberts & Raby) *K1 V K3*
Scunthorpe *p373* 01724 854000
Raby, Mrs P J (Penny Raby & Co) *K1*
Pershore *p346* 01386 555114
Raby, R E J (Walters & Plaskitt) *S1 W M1 H*
Stoke-on-Trent *p398* 01782 845807
Stoke-on-Trent *p398* 01782 819611
Race, D W (K&L Gates LLP) *C1 Zc*
London EC4 *p47* 020 7648 9000
Race, Mrs E M (Department for Business, Enterprise and Regulatory Reform)
London SW1 *p105* 020 7215 0105
Race, M (Ashurst LLP)
London EC2 *p7* 020 7638 1111
Rackham, Mrs D E (Surrey County Council) *K1*
Kingston upon Thames *p462* 020 8541 9088
Rackstraw, D I (Sedgefield Borough Council)
Spennymoor *p472* 01388 816166
Rackstraw, M (Bindmans LLP) *G H B2*
London WC1 *p12* 020 7833 4433
Radam, Mrs P R (Bell & Co) *S1 W*
Liverpool *p286* 0151 928 8686
Radcliffe, Mrs E J (Rowe Radcliffe) *E S1 W K1 S2 K3*
South Croydon *p383* 020 8680 2070
Radcliffe, Ms J (Pattinson & Brewer) *Zr N Zq*
London WC1 *p66* 020 7400 5100
York *p445* 01904 680000
Radcliffe, M J (Freeth Cartwright LLP) *L C1 E C2 O R1*
Leicester *p279* 0116 248 1100
Nottingham *p337* 0115 936 9369
Radcliffe, Mrs S M (Garner & Hancock Solicitors LLP) *E L*
Isleworth *p263* 020 8232 9560
Radford, Ms A (Birkett Long LLP) *E P R1 S1 Zc Zu*
Chelmsford *p186* 01245 453800
Radford, A J H (Browne Jacobson LLP) *N*
Nottingham *p336* 0115 976 6000
Radford, D N G (GKN PLC (Legal Dept))
Redditch *p469* 01527 517715
Radford, Ms G M (Gillian Radford & Co) *D1 K1 L D2 K3 W K4*
Westminster *p70* 020 8960 4366
Radford, Mrs I J (Freeth Cartwright LLP) *E*
Nottingham *p337* 0115 936 9369
Radford, J (Wilmot Thompson) *W S1 T1 E*
Bristol *p165* 0117 927 6583
Radford, M (Kent County Council) *F1 J1*
Maidstone *p464* 01622 694320
Radford, P J (Bissmire Fudge & Co) *S1 E L A1 W C1 S2*
Haverfordwest *p244* 01437 764723
Pembroke Dock *p345* 01646 685501
Radford, P J (BPE Solicitors LLP) *O Q*
Cheltenham *p187* 01242 224433
Radford, Ms S (DP Law Ltd t/a David Prosser & Co) *K1 D1 D2*
Bridgend *p157* 01656 645921
Radford, W (Berry & Walton Solicitors) *A1 C1 E R1 S1 T1 W*
King's Lynn *p266* 01553 764398
King's Lynn *p266* 01485 571366
Radia, Mrs J (Irvings) *C1 E G H J1 K1 P S1 W N Ze Zi Zl*
Harrow *p241* 020 8427 6600
Radia, M (Radia & Co) *C1 E N P S1*
Harrow *p242* 020 8424 2261
Radia, R (Campbell Courtney & Cooney) *N Zr O Q Zq*
Camberley *p173* 01276 25100
Radia, S K (Alliance Solicitors) *S2 E F1 R1 S1 K1 Zd Zi*
Kenton *p264* 020 8204 3000
Radia, S K G (Alliance Solicitors) *E F1 L N O S1 Zl S2*
Kenton *p264* 020 8204 3000
Radia, U M (Irvings) *C1 E G H J1 K1 P S1 W N Ze Zi Zl S2*
Harrow *p241* 020 8427 6600
Radice, J H (EMI Records Ltd)
London W8 *p106* 020 7795 7000
Radigois, Miss C G C (Parker Bullen) *K4 Zm W*
Andover *p118* 01264 400500
Radiven, D B (Pannone LLP) *N*
Manchester *p308* 0161 909 3000
Radley, L J (Reed Smith LLP) *E L C1*
London EC2 *p71* 020 3116 3000
Radovic, Miss I (Gotelee) *K1*
Ipswich *p262* 01473 211121
Radula-Scott, P J (Thomson Snell & Passmore) *O Q B1 F1 Ze Zk Zl Zi J2 B2*
Tunbridge Wells *p415* 01892 510000
Rae Smith, A F (Allen & Overy LLP)
London E1 *p5* 020 3088 0000
Rae, A (Trowers & Hamlins)
London EC3 *p88* 020 7423 8000
Rae, C A (Clifton Ingram LLP) *Q O N L F1 B2 Zc C1*
Wokingham *p437* 0118 978 0099
Horsham *p253* 01403 262333
Rae, C W (Ascroft Rae) *S1*
Leyland *p283* 01772 434488
Rae, D T (Ross & Son) *S1 E L C1 W R1 A1 S2*
Horley *p252* 01293 782425
Rae, Miss E (Bartlett Gooding & Weelen) *S1 S2 W G H Zl L A1 E*
Castle Cary *p183* 01963 350888
Rae, Mrs F (Horsham District Council)
Horsham *p461* 01403 215100
Rae, S F (Mark Jones & Partners) *G H Zm*
Liverpool *p289* 0151 286 9594
Raeburn, Ms S (Silverbeck Rymer) *N J2 Zr*
Liverpool *p290* 0151 236 9594
Rafe, Miss M (GH Cornish LLP)
Ilford *p260* 020 8090 0800
Raff, D (DLA Piper UK LLP)
London EC2 *p24* 0870 011 1111
Rafferty, A J (Bramsdon & Childs) *Q K1 J1 G H N V W*
Southsea *p388* 023 9282 1251
Rafferty, Ms J (Thompson & Co)
Sunderland *p402* 0191 565 6290
Rafferty, M J (Russell Jones & Walker)
Manchester *p309* 0161 383 3500
Rafferty, O T (Rosling King) *A1 P E L R1 S1 T1 Zj Zs Zb*
London EC4 *p73* 020 7353 2353
Rafferty, P (McKeag & Co) *M1 P*
Gosforth *p231* 0191 213 1010
Rafferty, Ms S K (CMS Cameron McKenna LLP) *C2 C1*
London EC3 *p17* 020 7367 3000
Rafiq, M (Rafiq & Co) *G H I R1 S1 L*
Leeds *p276* 0113 240 7556
Rafiq, Ms S (Appleby Hope & Matthews) *K1 W*
Middlesbrough *p314* 01642 440444
Rafiq, Miss T (Pannone LLP) *J1*
Manchester *p308* 0161 909 3000
Rafique, S T H (Duncan Lewis & Co) *B1 C1 E J1 L M1 N P S1 W*
Hackney *p53* 020 7923 4020
Rafter, Miss N J (Bournemouth Borough Council) *N M1 B1 J1 P F1 K1 C1*
Bournemouth *p450* 01202 451178
Rafter, T S (Penningtons) *S1*
Godalming *p231* 01483 791800
Raftery, P M (Weightmans LLP) *C1 Ze C2*
Manchester *p311* 0161 233 7330
Raggett, M C E (Eaton-Evans & Morris) *K1 M1 G H P J1 V W S1 D1*
Haverfordwest *p244* 01437 763383
Raghudati, A (DWF) *N Zj G*
Preston *p356* 01772 556677
Ragunathan, Miss T (Carillion PLC)
Wolverhampton *p477* 01902 422431
Rahaman-Rahim, Mrs B R (Rafina Solicitors) *S1 Q K1 J1 G E L I C1 O Zi Zp Zm Ze Zk*
Wembley *p426* 020 8908 6742
Rahi, Mrs K K (Dale & Newbery LLP) *K1*
Staines *p393* 01784 464491
Rahim, Miss R B (Ronald Fletcher Baker LLP) *G H*
London EC1 *p73* 020 7613 1402
Rahman, Miss A (Rollingsons)
London EC1 *p73* 020 7611 4848
Rahman, A (Rahman & Co)
London N15 *p70* 020 8809 4643
Rahman, Ms H (Duncan Lewis & Co)
Hackney *p53* 020 7923 4020
Rahman, K (Maples Teesdale LLP) *E S2*
London EC2 *p58* 020 7600 3800
Rahman, L (McCormacks)
London EC3 *p56* 020 7791 2000
Rahman, Miss R (City of London Corporation)
London EC2 *p107* 020 7606 3030
Rahman, Miss S (Glaisyers Solicitors LLP) *S1 W*
Manchester *p304* 0161 224 3311
Rahman, Ms T (Ison Harrison) *K1 K3*
Leeds *p274* 0113 284 5000
Rahman, Z (Nelsons)
Nottingham *p338* 0115 958 6262
Rahman-Cook, F (TV Edwards LLP) *G H*
London EC3 *p85* 020 7790 7000
Rai, Ms A (Lloyd Brennand)
Brentford *p156* 020 8569 9020
Rai, Mrs C A (Foot Anstey) *Zb Zu R1 S1 E*
Plymouth *p349* 01752 675000
Plymouth *p351* 01752 663295
Rai, G (Metropolitan Police Directorate of Legal Services)
London SW1 *p108* 020 7230 7210
Rai, Ms M (Martin Murray & Associates) *G H B2*
Slough *p382* 01753 551313
Rai, Ms R (John Morley & Co) *E S1 L B1 K1 F1 Q*
Rainham *p359* 01634 375444
Rai, Ms R (Whitemans) *K3 K1*
Gloucester *p231* 01452 411601
Rai, R S (Veja and Co Solicitors) *D1 K1 J1*
Southall *p385* 020 8574 2626
Rai, R S (Winckworth Sherwood LLP) *O Q Zq*
London SE1 *p92* 020 7593 5000
Rai, Miss S (Vallelys) *K1 S1 W*
Letchworth *p283* 01462 483800
Rai, Z S (Rai Solicitor) *S2 K3 Q N J1 K1 L Zi S1 W V D1 G Zl E*
Slough *p382* 01753 576800
Raikes, D C (Department for Business, Enterprise and Regulatory Reform)
London SW1 *p105* 020 7215 0105
Railton, G (HC Solicitors LLP) *C1 E Ze J1*
Peterborough *p347* 01733 882800
Railton, Miss J M (Lockings)
Hull *p257* 0845 075 4197
Railton, T J (LG Lawyers)
London SE1 *p50* 020 7379 0000
Raimes, R T (R Toby Raimes) *E R1 S1 C1 Zl*
Newcastle upon Tyne *p326* 0191 230 8086
Raine, D (Debenhams Ottaway)
St Albans *p390* 01727 837161
Raine, D J (Penningtons)
London EC2 *p66* 020 7457 3000
Raine, H B (Herbert Smith LLP) *C1 C2 O*
London EC2 *p40* 020 7374 8000
Raines, M J (Shearman & Sterling LLP) *Zb*
London EC2 *p78* 020 7655 5000
Rainford, Dr D (Taylor Vinters) *I O U2 Ze Zf*
Cambridge *p176* 01223 423444
Rainford, K C (Hannays Solicitors and Advocates) *A1 Zc Zd C1 S2 K4 L Zk Zl Zq R2 S1 T1 T2 W*
South Shields *p383* 0191 456 7893 / 455 5361
Rainford, M J (Burton Copeland LLP) *G H D1 M1 F1 J1 Zl B2*
Manchester *p302* 0161 827 9500
Manchester *p309* 0870 998 9000
Rainger, Ms E (Reynolds Porter Chamberlain LLP)
London E1 *p71* 020 3060 6000
Raingold, D (Oury Clark)
London WC1 *p65* 020 7607 4300
Rainhartz, A (Preiskel & Co LLP) *U1 U2 C1 Zza I F2 C3 Ze C2 Zf*
London EC4 *p69* 020 7583 2120
Raisbeck, Ms J (Nelsons)
Leicester *p280* 0116 222 6666

6

Raiseborough, N (Alsters Kelley) *K4 K1 N T2 W*
Leamington Spa *p270* 0844 561 0100
Nuneaton *p339* 0844 561 0100

Raison, Ms K (Gordons LLP)
Leeds *p273* 0113 227 0100

Raistrick, A S (Christopher Davidson Solicitors LLP) *S1 E L W C1 A1 R1 S2 R2*
Cheltenham *p188* 01242 581481

Raizon, Mrs M C (Gillhams Solicitors LLP) *S1 S2 E*
London NW10 *p35*. 020 8965 4266

Raj, J (Grahame Stowe Bateson) *J1 N*
Leeds *p274* 0113 246 8163

Raja, A R (Quist Solicitors) *G K1 O S1 V C1 E Q I Zb Zl Zk Zj*
London EC2 *p70*. 020 7596 2813

Raja, D D (Bowling & Co) *E L S1 S2*
London E15 *p15*. 020 8221 8000

Raja, Mrs R (Matthew Arnold & Baldwin LLP) *Q*
Watford *p423* 01923 202020

Raja, Ms S (Radcliffes Le Brasseur) *J1 Q O Zp Ze*
Westminster *p70*. 020 7222 7040

Rajagopal, A (G Singh)
Ealing *p80*. 020 8567 2661

Rajakariyar, J A (Nathan Suresh & Amirthan) *V W Zl Ze*
Wembley *p426*. 020 8574 1058

Rajani, A (IBB Solicitors) *G H B2*
Uxbridge *p417*. 0845 638 1381

Rajani, Miss N (Collins Benson Goldhill LLP) *E S2 C1 L J1 O S1*
Westminster *p21*. 020 7436 5151

Rajani-Shah, Mrs A (Squire Sanders (UK) LLP)
London EC2 *p81*. 020 7655 1000

Rajaratnam, Miss M (Hertfordshire County Council)
Hertford *p460* 01992 555555
St Albans *p390* 01727 837161

Rajdev, S (The Sethi Partnership Solicitors)
Eastcote *p216* 020 8866 6464

Rajendra, Mrs A (Rouse Legal (Formerly Willoughby & Partners)) *Ze*
London E14 *p74*. 020 7536 4100

Rajput, A T (Rajput Solicitors) *S2 K3 Zi M4 S1 W*
Birmingham *p141* 0121 777 0300

Rajput, P (Lewis Silkin LLP)
London EC4 *p53*. 020 7074 8000

Rajput-Driver, Mrs M (Hague Lambert) *O J1*
Manchester *p305* 0161 834 6066

Rajshakha, M (Noble)
Shefford *p377* 01462 814055

Rake, P J V (RMPI Solicitors)
London W1 *p70* 020 7318 4444

Rakison, R B (McGuireWoods London LLP) *C1 C2 Zb U1 U2 Ze I J1 Zw Zv E*
London EC4 *p57*. 020 7632 1600

Ralls, Ms C L (Warner Goodman LLP) *N*
Southampton *p387*. 023 8063 9311

Ralph, J D (Dickinson Dees) *E Zb*
Newcastle upon Tyne *p324* . 0191 279 9000

Ralph, J P (Kidd Rapinet) *S2 S1 E*
London WC2 *p49* 020 7205 2115

Ralph, N J (Archon Solicitors)
London EC4 *p7* 020 7397 9650

Ralph, S (Penningtons)
London EC2 *p66*. 020 7457 3000

Ralphs, S J T (Forsters LLP) *E*
Westminster *p33*. 020 7863 8333

Ralston, J B (DAC Beachcroft) *Zw*
Birmingham *p137* 0121 698 5200

Ralston, M D (Orange PCS Ltd) *S1 E L R1 A1 J1 C1 W Zl*
Bristol *p452* 0870 376 8888

Ramage, C J (Irwin Mitchell LLP) *O*
Leeds *p274* 0870 150 0100

Ramage, R W (KJD) *Zo*
Stoke-on-Trent *p398*. 01782 202020

Rambard, Ms S (Howard Kennedy LLP) *E*
London W1 *p48* 020 7636 1616

Rambaud, Ms S (Howard Kennedy LLP) *E*
London W1 *p48* 020 7636 1616

Rambhai, N K (Coventry Building Society)
Coventry *p456*. 024 7665 3516

Ramjeet, Ms J R (Julian Young & Co) *G H B2*
London W1 *p93* 020 7724 8414

Ramm, A R (Symes Bains Broomer) *S1 S2 C1*
Scunthorpe *p373*. 01724 281616

Ramnarine, H (Pragesh & McKenzie Solicitors) *Q N K3 S1*
Thornton Heath *p411*. 020 8689 0089
Thornton Heath *p411*. 020 8684 5581

Ramnarine, Ms J A (Treasury Solicitors Department)
London WC2 *p110*. 020 7210 3000

Ramon, Miss M E (Anthony Collins Solicitors LLP) *K3 D1 K1*
Birmingham *p137* 0121 200 3242

Rampal, Ms M (Park Woodfine Heald Mellows LLP)
Bedford *p130* 01234 400000

Ramphul, Ms M R (SNR Denton) *O*
London EC4 *p75*. 020 7242 1212

Ramprakash, Ms Z (Stephenson Harwood) *B1 O Q Zq*
London EC2 *p82*. 020 7329 4422

Rampton, J N (Royds LLP) *B1 C1 J1*
London EC4 *p74*. 020 7583 2222

Ramsay, B (DLA Piper UK LLP) *Zf*
London EC2 *p24*. 0870 011 1111

Ramsay, Ms J K (Anglia Ruskin University)
Chelmsford *p454*. 01245 493131

Ramsbottom, D (Overburys & Raymond Thompson) *W T2 K4*
Norwich *p335* 01603 610481

Ramsbottom, D A (Ramsbottom & Co Solicitors Limited) *S2 E I J1 O Q N Zq S1 L*
Hayling Island *p245* 023 9246 5931

Ramsbottom, S J (Spencer Ewin Mulvihill) *S1 S2 W E*
Harrogate *p240* 01423 509826

Ramsbottom, W (H Pipes & Co) *K1 S1 J1 F1 E W*
Melbourne *p314* 01332 862113

Ramsden, A H (Potter Owtram & Peck) *K1 D1 Q S1 L N W G H J1 Zl Zd Zm*
Haslemere *p243*. 01428 642321

Ramsden, C R H (Ipswich Borough Council)
Ipswich *p461*. 01473 432000

Ramsden, Miss L (Radcliffes Le Brasseur) *E S2 R2*
Westminster *p70*. 020 7222 7040

Ramsden, Mrs M (Jefferies LLP) *N*
Altrincham *p116* 0800 342 3191

Ramsden, S A (DAC Beachcroft) *B1 C1 Zb*
London EC4 *p24*. 020 7242 1011

Ramsden, Mrs S C (Crombie Wilkinson) *D1 D2*
York *p444* 01904 624185

Ramsden, S M (Gill Akaster) *N Zr*
Plymouth *p349*. 01752 203500

Ramsey, A P (J P Waterhouse & Co) *S1 K1 G H M1 P D1 J1 W T1 Zl Zj Zc*
Banbury *p122* 01295 267555

Ramsey, Mrs C M (Carr Hepburn Solicitors Ltd) *K1 D1*
Hemel Hempstead *p246*. . . 01442 241466

Ramsey, R E (Kenneth Elliott & Rowe) *K1 Q O L D1 K2 E J1 Zq Zi R1 W*
Romford *p366* 01708 757575

Ramsey, W A (Matthew Arnold & Baldwin LLP) *E B1*
Watford *p423* 01923 202020

Ramshaw, Mrs D (Dickinson Dees) *C1*
Newcastle upon Tyne *p324* . 0191 279 9000

Ramshaw, S (Anthony Collins Solicitors LLP) *Zd C1*
Birmingham *p137* 0121 200 3242

Ramshaw, S J (Stamp Jackson and Procter) *N Zr*
Hull *p258* 01482 324591

Ramsumair, Miss L M (St Helens Borough Council)
St Helens *p472* 01744 456000

Ramtohul-Brindle, Ms S (Gillian Radford & Co) *K1 L K3 D1*
Westminster *p70*. 020 8960 4366

Ramzan, Ms R (Scott Rees & Co) *N Q*
Skelmersdale *p381* 01695 722222

Rana, A (Park Woodfine Heald Mellows LLP) *S2 J1*
Bedford *p130* 01234 400000

Rana, H S (HSR Solicitors) *G H S1 S2 Zi*
London E1 *p37* 020 7791 1111

Rance, G (Fellowes Solicitors) *H G B2*
London E17 *p31*. 020 8520 7392

Rance, J R (Buchanan & Llewellyn)
Ferndown *p225* 01202 873355

Rance, Miss L (Russell & Russell) *W K4*
Bolton *p150* 01204 707926

Rand, Ms L A (Tyrer Roxburgh & Co) *K1 D1 W*
Haringey *p89* 020 8889 3319

Rand, Miss M (R L Edwards & Partners)
Bridgend *p157*. 01656 656861

Randall, Mrs A (Williams Thompson) *K3 K1*
Christchurch *p194* 01202 484242

Randall, Ms A E (W S Atkins Consultants Ltd)
Epsom *p458*. 01372 726140

Randall, B N (Leport & Co) *S1 E L W*
Banbury *p122* . . . .01295 257328 / 268181

Randall, C J (Mayo Wynne Baxter LLP) *Q N G O L J1*
Lewes *p283* 01273 477071

Randall, C W (Bates Wells & Braithwaite London LLP) *Zl Zg*
London EC4 *p11*. 020 7551 7777

Randall, Ms D (BUPA)
London WC1 *p104*. 020 7656 2305

Randall, Mrs E (Cornwall County Council)
Truro *p474*. 01872 322197

Randall, G T (Henmans LLP) *W T2 K4*
Oxford *p343* 01865 781000

Randall, Ms H (Trowers & Hamlins)
London EC3 *p88*. 020 7423 8000

Randall, Miss J (Langleys) *E S1*
York *p445* 01904 610886

Randall, J J (Barlow Lyde & Gilbert LLP) *O Q Zq Zj*
London EC3 *p10*. 020 7247 2277

Randall, J R (Blake Lapthorn) *W*
Portsmouth *p354*. 023 9222 1122

Randall, M (stevensdrake) *C1 C2*
Crawley *p202* 01293 596900

Randall, M J (Houghton Pigot & Co) *N G H K1 J1 O Q K3 L*
Wigan *p432* . . . . .01942 241288 / 824424
Ashton-in-Makerfield *p119* . . 01942 270757

Randall, P N (Ashurst LLP) *J1*
London EC2 *p7* 020 7638 1111

Randall, R M (Leonard Gray) *D1 R1 G H K1 Zl P*
Chelmsford *p186*. 01245 504904

Randall, S (Howard & Over) *K1 D1*
Plymouth *p350*. 01752 556606

Randall, Ms W (Percy Hughes & Roberts) *W*
Birkenhead *p134*. 0151 666 9090

Randel, J P G (Lee Bolton Monier-Williams) *C1 E S1 W T2 K4 Zd*
Westminster *p52*. 020 7222 5381

Randhawa, Ms K K (Chhokar & Co) *K1 Zi W*
Southall *p384* 020 8574 2488

Randle, A F (R N Williams & Co Limited) *G H S1 J1 S2 E F1 L N W*
Wolverhampton *p438* 01902 429051

Randle, A R (DLA Piper UK LLP) *Zu*
Birmingham *p137* 0870 011 1111

Randle, A W (Redferns) *D1 J1 K1 L N F1 Zp*
Harrow *p242*. 020 8424 7070

Randle, Mrs R (Painters) *K4 W*
Stourport-on-Severn *p399* . . 01299 822033

Randle, T (Fenwick Elliott) *O Q Zi A3 P Zj R2*
London WC2 *p31* 020 7421 1986

Randles, Miss P A (Walker Smith Way) *E A1 R2 S2*
Chester *p191* 0844 346 3100

Rands, D H (Memery Crystal) *A3 O Q B2 C1 G Zj U2 Ze Zc Zk Zq Zv*
London WC2 *p60* 020 7242 5905

Rands, Mrs S A (Bradbury Roberts & Raby) *K1 D1 V K3*
Scunthorpe *p373*. 01724 854000

Ranford, L P (Russell-Cooke LLP) *Q O B1 Zc*
London SW15 *p74*. 020 8789 9111

Rani, Miss N (Harvey Ingram LLP) *O*
Leicester *p280*. 0116 254 5454

Ranken, N (Harold Stock & Co) *S2 S1*
Ashton-under-Lyne *p120* . . .01457 835597 / 835034

Rankin, Ms C (Colemans - CTTS) *Q N*
Kingston upon Thames *p267*. 020 8296 9966

Rankin, Ms C A (Clarke Willmott) *J1 P Zo*
Bristol *p162* 0845 209 1000 / 0117 305 6000

Rankin, Ms G A (Squire Sanders (UK) LLP)
Birmingham *p142* 0121 222 3000

Rann, D A (Sandersons) *C1 C2 J1 Zw T1 T2*
Hull *p258* 01482 324662

Rannie, A (Hart Reade) *S1 E S2*
Eastbourne *p215*. 01323 727321

Ransford, Mrs S (Russell-Cooke LLP) *Zd*
London SW15 *p74*. 020 8789 9111

Ransley, A (Pritchard Joyce & Hinds) *S1*
Beckenham *p129* 020 8658 3922

Ransley, Mrs O T P C (Manchester City Council)
Manchester *p465* 0161 234 5000

Ransome, C B (Linklaters LLP)
London EC2 *p54*. 020 7456 2000

Ranson, C S (Ransons) *C1 C2 Ze Zv Zw J1 I*
Walton-on-Thames *p421*. . . 01932 269448

Ranson, F N C (Gamlins) *N K1 Q S1 W*
Conwy *p199* 01492 593201

Ranson, I (Hilton Norbury) *S2 E S1 W K4 Q K3*
Wigan *p432* 01942 241424

Ranson, I D (Birchall Blackburn LLP) *W*
Preston *p356* 01772 561663

Ranson, Ms S J (Aviva PLC)
London EC3 *p103* . . 020 7283 7500 / 01603 687905

Ranton, D (Kingsley Napley) *K1 Zg D2 D1*
London EC1 *p50*. 020 7814 1200

Rao, Miss F (Squire Sanders (UK) LLP) *C1 C2*
London EC2 *p81*. 020 7655 1000
London EC2 *p83*. 020 7367 8000

Rao, Mrs P R (Cambridge City Council)
Cambridge *p452*. 01223 457000

Rao, Miss S (Clive Gomes Solicitors) *G H*
Wembley *p426*. 020 8904 2614

Raper, A J (Cripps Harries Hall LLP) *O Q F1*
Tunbridge Wells *p415* 01892 515121

Raper, B H (Gosschalks) *C1 E S1 A1 R1 B1 T1 J1*
Hull *p256* 01482 324252

Raper, T A (Speechly Bircham LLP) *O E Zc*
London EC4 *p81*. 020 7427 6400

Raphael, Miss H (BCL Burton Copeland) *B2 G*
London WC2 *p9* 020 7430 2277

Raphael, Miss N C (Edward Fail Bradshaw & Waterson) *G H B2*
London EC3 *p30*. 020 7790 4032
London EC3 *p30*. 020 7264 2016

Raphael, P M (Peters & Peters) *G T1 N P J1 K1 D1 M1 B1 H Zp Zl Zb Zk*
London EC4 *p67*. 020 7629 7991

Raphael, R J (Teacher Stern LLP) *E L R2*
London WC1 *p86* 020 7242 3191

Rapinet, C W (Hogan Lovells International LLP)
London EC1 *p42*. 020 7296 2000

Rapley, Miss L (Hotchkiss Warburton) *S1 S2 W E*
Crediton *p203* 01363 774752

Rapozo, W (Dechert)
London EC4 *p26*. 020 7184 7000

Rapport, P S (Olswang LLP) *C1 C2 C3 E S1*
London WC1 *p64* 020 7067 3000

Rapps, M J (Gregg Latchams LLP) *T1 W S1*
Bristol *p162* 0117 906 9400

Rasaratnam, P (Ashurst LLP)
London EC2 *p7* 020 7638 1111

Rashid, A (AR Legal Solicitors) *Q O N K1 Zq Zi G*
London W4 *p3*. 020 8747 9090

Rashid, Ms S (Essex County Council)
Chelmsford *p454*. 0845 743 0430

Rasiah, N (Rasiah & Co) *S1 B1 Q K1 Zl Zi*
London SW19 *p70*. 020 8543 4040

Rasool, Ms L (Lewis Nedas & Co)
Camden *p53*. 020 7387 2032

Rasool, N K (Runhams) *S2 E S1 C1 L R2*
Bradford *p154* 01274 532233

Rasool, Miss Z (Jones Day) *Ze*
London EC4 *p46*. 020 7039 5959

Rastall, Miss I E (Isabelle E Rastall) *S1*
Chelmsford *p187*. 01245 349966

Rastrick, J S (Squire Sanders (UK) LLP)
Leeds *p277* 0113 284 7000

Rata, C W (Wessex Water Services Ltd)
Bath *p448* 01225 526000

Rataj, R (Pierre Thomas & Partners) *N O Q G*
London W6 *p67* 020 7602 0305

Ratchford, Ms Y J (Hatten Wyatt) *W K4*
Gravesend *p232*. 01474 351199

Ratcliff, M (SNR Denton) *T1*
London EC4 *p75*. 020 7242 1212

Ratcliff, M J (Plexus Law (A Trading Name of Parabis Law LLP))
London EC3 *p68*. 0844 245 4000

Ratcliffe, A C (Credit Suisse Private Banking)
London E14 *p105* 020 7888 8888

Ratcliffe, D (Great Yarmouth Magistrates Court)
Great Yarmouth *p459* 01493 849800

Ratcliffe, D F (Hall Reynolds) *N O Q Zb Zl Zc Zv K1*
Bidford-on-Avon *p133* 01789 772955

Ratcliffe, J F (Neale Turk) *E S1 A1 C1 C2 R1 W L*
Basingstoke *p127* 01256 473013
Fleet *p226*. 01252 811070

Ratcliffe, R M (Brighouses) *N O Q L F1*
Southport *p388* . . .01704 534101 / 500151

Ratcliffe, S (Greene & Greene) *C1 C2 Ze*
Bury St Edmunds *p171* . . . 01284 762211

Ratcliffe, T H (Gordons LLP)
Leeds *p273* 0113 227 0100

Rathbone, J (Veale Wasbrough Vizards) *C1 C2*
Bristol *p165* 0117 925 2020

Rathbone, M E (Brabners Chaffe Street) *C1*
Liverpool *p286*. 0151 600 3000

Rathe, S M (Forster Dean Ltd) *S1 S2 Zi*
Warrington *p422*. 01925 575566

Rathmell, Mrs A C (Thorp Parker LLP) *K1 S1 O Q W K3*
Stokesley *p398* 01642 711354
Stockton-on-Tees *p397* . . . 01642 676000

Rathod, Mrs R (Moss Solicitors LLP) *K1 D2*
Loughborough *p293* 01509 217770

Rathore, W S (Fraser Brown) *Zl*
Nottingham *p337*. 0115 988 8777

Ratip, A (Ratip Solicitors) *G H I S1 V K1 Q F1 J1*
London SW16 *p70*. 020 8677 0625

Ratnakumar, Mrs C (Ratnakumar & Co) *E S1 Zl*
Ilford *p260*. 020 8551 1411

Ratnam, V (Krish Solicitors)
Southall *p384* 020 8893 6661

Ratnapalan, Mrs K (Ratna & Co)
London E6 *p70* 020 8470 8818

Ratnapalan, M (Ratna & Co)
London E6 *p70* 020 8470 8818

Ratnasekera, Mrs I K (Leslie & Co) *Zi G Zg K3*
Hounslow *p254* .020 8577 5491 / 8572 7252

Ratnasekera, T D L (Leslie & Co) *Zi G M2 Zg*
Hounslow *p254* .020 8577 5491 / 8572 7252

Ratnasingham, D (Krish Ratna)
Southall *p384* 020 8574 6303

Ratnasingham, V (Krish Ratna)
Southall *p384* 020 8574 6303

Rattan, A D (Hodge Jones & Allen LLP) *N*
London NW1 *p41* 020 7874 8300

Rattenberry, A H (Hedleys) *B1 C1 D1 E F1 G H J1 K1 L Zc Zh Zj*
Nottingham *p337*. 0115 947 3506

Rattenbury, M K (Morgan & Richardson) *A1 D1 G H K1 L N Q S1 T2 W*
Cardigan *p181*. 01239 612302

Ratti, S L (Tonner Johns Ratti) *K1 N J1 F1 B1 C1 D1 Q O*
Swansea *p406*. 01792 643296

Rattray, Ms C (Batchelors Solicitors) *E S2*
Bromley *p166* 020 8768 7000

Rattray, C (Addleshaw Goddard)
London EC1 *p4* 020 7606 8855

Rattray, Ms C J (Krafts Foods UK Ltd)
Cheltenham *p454* 01242 236101

Rattray, Ms F (Steel & Shamash) *Zm*
Lambeth *p82*. 020 7803 3999

Rausa, S (Rausa Mumford) *M1 N*
Cardiff *p180* 029 2034 4341

Raval, Ms D (The College of Law)
London WC1 *p105*. 0800 289997

Raval, Miss K (Hewitsons) *Zo*
Northampton *p332*. 01604 233233

Raval, Miss R (Aston Clark)
London W3 *p8*. 020 8752 1122

Ravalde, J C (Coles Solicitors) *N*
Northallerton *p331*. 01609 780717

Ravalia, K (Spearing Waite LLP) *E S2*
Leicester *p281*. 0116 262 4225

Raven, A (Ashurst LLP)
London EC2 *p7* 020 7638 1111

Raven, P M (Freeth Cartwright LLP) *C1 M1*
Nottingham *p337*. 0115 936 9369

Raven, S J (Birketts LLP) *S2 E R2 S1*
Ipswich *p262*. 01473 232300

Ravenscroft, S (Ashurst LLP)
London EC2 *p7* 020 7638 1111

Ravenscroft, S H (Stone King LLP) *N P C1 Za*
Bath *p128* 01225 337599

Ravindran, Mrs C (Charmini Ravindran & Co) *S2 K3 K1 W S1 D1*
Sutton *p403* 020 8770 7874

Raw, Ms J L (Kennedys) *Zj*
London EC3 *p49*. 020 7667 9667

Rawal, N (Rawal & Co)
London N12 *p70*. 020 8445 0303

Rawcliffe, Mrs J L (Cullimore Dutton) *K3 K1 Q O L N*
Chester *p190* 01244 356789

See p634 for the Key to Work Categories

Rawcliffe, Miss L C (The College of Law) *K1*
London WC1 *p105*. 0800 289997
Rawkins, J W D (Taylor Wessing)
London EC4 *p86*. 020 7300 7000
Rawlings, A B (Paul Bullen & Co) *K1 K3*
Doncaster *p211* 01302 819000
Rawlings, C J (Kidd Rapinet) *C1 C2 E O J1 I M1 S1 Q N Ze Zl Zb*
High Wycombe *p250*. 0845 017 9607
Rawlings, Ms D S (Treasury Solicitors Department)
London WC2 *p110*. 020 7210 3000
Rawlings, Miss J E (Andrew Jackson) *E R1 Zc*
Hull *p257* 01482 325242
Rawlings-Smith, Miss K P (Eaton Ryan & Taylor) *Q O B1 F2 Ze Zq*
Birmingham *p138* 0121 236 1999
Rawlins, Miss D U (Fullers Family Law Practice LLP) *K1*
Bedford *p130* 01234 343134
Rawlins, E J (Wilson Browne) *K1*
Leicester *p281*. 0116 251 7181
Rawlins, S R (Bracher Rawlins LLP) *O Q Zw F1 Zc Ze A2 Zq Zk*
London WC1 *p15* 020 7404 9400
Rawlinson, C J (Squire Sanders (UK) LLP)
Leeds *p277* 0113 284 7000
Rawlinson, D J (Hill Dickinson LLP) *N B1 P Zc Ze*
Liverpool *p288*. 0151 600 8000
Rawlinson, P A (Wake Smith & Tofields) *C1 C2 Ze Zf U1*
Sheffield *p377* 0114 266 6660
Rawnsley, Ms R M (Addleshaw Goddard)
Leeds *p271* 0113 209 2000
Manchester *p300* 0161 934 6000
Rawson, Ms E (Charles Russell LLP) *Zr*
London EC4 *p19*. 020 7203 5000
Rawson, J D (Bell Lamb & Joynson)
Liverpool *p286*. 0844 412 4348
Rawson, Ms L J (Howells LLP) *L*
Sheffield *p376* 0114 249 6666
Rawson, N (Radcliffes Le Brasseur)
Westminster *p70*. 020 7222 7040
Rawson, N D A (Radcliffes Le Brasseur) *G K1 M1 N Zk*
Leeds *p276* 0113 234 1220
Rawsthorn, Mrs F C (Bendles) *A1 R2 S1*
Carlisle *p181*. 01228 522215
Rawsthorn, M (Chafes) *S1 W E*
Wilmslow *p433*. 01625 531676
Rawsthorn, R (Lawson Coppock & Hart) *E T1 W Zo R1 R2*
Manchester *p306* 0161 832 5944
Rawstorne, J R (Rawstorne Heran Solicitors) *G K1 D1 H J1 Q V F1 Zl Zm*
Stratford-upon-Avon *p400* . . 01789 267646
Rawstron, C D (DLA Piper UK LLP) *C1 C2*
Birmingham *p137* 0870 011 1111
Rawstron, Mrs D M (Goodman Derrick LLP) *W Zd*
London EC4 *p36*. 020 7404 0606
Ray, A (Northamptonshire Magistrates Courts)
Northampton *p467*. 01604 497000
Ray, A K (Mills & Reeve) *Zb C1 C2 Zc C3*
Cambridge *p175*. 01223 364422
Ray, I (Southampton City Council)
Southampton *p472*. 023 8022 3855
Ray, M H (Eastbourne Borough Council)
Eastbourne *p457*. 01323 410000
Ray, O P (Gotelee) *E S2*
Ipswich *p262*. 01473 211121
Ray, Ms P R (Goodman Ray) *K1 D1 D2*
Hackney *p36*. 020 7608 1227
Raybould, D (Wilford Smith Solicitors) *N S1 W*
Rotherham *p367*. 01709 828044
Raybould, M H (DWFM Beckman) *E C1 C2 O Q S1 J1 L*
Westminster *p25*. 020 7872 0023
Raybould, P (The Wilkes Partnership LLP) *C1 C2*
Birmingham *p143* 0121 233 4333
Rayman, Miss R (FDR Ltd)
Basildon *p448* 01268 296431
Rayment, A S (Walker Morris)
Leeds *p277* 0113 283 2500
Rayment, Ms G (Prettys) *K1*
Ipswich *p262*. 01473 232121
Raymond, C E W (Reynolds Porter Chamberlain LLP) *A3 O Zj Zo*
London E1 *p71* 020 3060 6000
Raymond, J (Russell-Cooke LLP) *O*
London SW15 *p74*. 020 8789 9111
Raymond, J R (Steele Raymond) *C1 E Zb Zc C2*
Bournemouth *p152*. 01202 294566
Raymond, P J (Cripps Harries Hall LLP) *W T2*
Tunbridge Wells *p415* 01892 515121
Raymond, S D (Raymond & Co) *S1 E Q W L F1 C1 T1 T2 B1 Ze Zv Zl Zq*
Islington *p71*. 020 7359 0422
Raymond, Miss Y M (Hamlins LLP) *E L S1 W*
London W1 *p38* 020 7355 6000
Raymont, Ms M C (Brachers) *K1 D1 K2*
Maidstone *p299* 01622 690691
Rayner, Miss A (Swain & Co) *K1 D1 D2 K3*
Havant *p244*. 023 9248 3322
Southampton *p386*. 023 8063 1111
Rayner, Miss A W (Taylor Wimpey UK Limited Legal Services)
Milton Keynes *p466* 01908 209030
Rayner, C (Colin Rayner & Co) *C1 S2 E L S1 W*
Bolton *p149* 01204 591145
Rayner, Mrs C E (Rayners) *K1 S1 S2 W*
Chippenham *p193* 01249 650394
Rayner, D (Birkett Long LLP) *E R1*
Chelmsford *p186*. 01245 453800
Chandlers Ford *p184* 023 8090 8090
Rayner, Miss H E A (Alliance Boots PLC)
Nottingham *p467*. 0115 950 6111
Rayner, Ms K (Phillips Solicitors) *J1*
Basingstoke *p127* 01256 460830
Rayner, K E J (Rayners) *P M1 K1 J1 G H D1 L N*
Chippenham *p193* 01249 650394
Rayner, Mrs V (National Grid PLC)
Warwick *p471* 01926 653000
Raynes, J (Ashurst LLP)
London EC2 *p7* 020 7638 1111
Raynes, Ms V (Birkett Long LLP) *K4 T2 W Zm*
Colchester *p197*. 01206 217300
Raynes, Mrs Z E (Keoghs and Nicholls, Lindsell & Harris) *S1*
Altrincham *p116* 0161 928 9321
Raynor, K N A (Torfaen Borough Council)
Pontypool *p469* 01495 766373
Rayson, Ms C (Ashurst LLP)
London EC2 *p7* 020 7638 1111
Razzaq, S (Anderson Fidler)
Enfield *p218*. 020 8804 6596
Rea, Ms E (Thomas Simon)
Cardiff *p181* 029 2055 7200
Rea, Miss E (Russell Jones & Walker) *G H Q B2*
London WC2 *p74* 020 7657 1555
Rea, Ms G (Thomas Higgins & Co) *O*
Wallasey *p419*. 0151 630 8006
Rea, J G (Hamers Solicitors) *N*
Hull *p257* 01482 326666
Rea, Ms M (Irwin Mitchell LLP) *N P*
London EC1 *p45*. 0870 150 0100
Rea, S A (FBC Manby Bowdler LLP) *C1 C2 Ze U2 Zd*
Shrewsbury *p379* 01743 241551
Read, A (Memery Crystal) *C1 C2*
London WC2 *p60* 020 7242 5905
Read, C (Reynolds Porter Chamberlain LLP)
London E1 *p71* 020 3060 6000
Read, Mrs C L Z (Birkett Long LLP) *W T2*
Chelmsford *p186*. 01245 453800
Read, C S J (SGH Martineau LLP) *X*
Birmingham *p142* 0870 763 2000
Read, D J (Bowles & Co) *C1 E J1 K1 L M1 P S1 Zt*
Epsom *p219*. 01372 725241
Read, Ms F B (Russell-Cooke LLP) *K1 D1 K2 D2*
London SW15 *p74*. 020 8789 9111
Read, F N (Francis Read) *E C1 M1*
London W1 *p71* 020 7499 4055
Read, H (GLRS Phoenix LLP) *A1 D1 E K1 L S1 W Zl*
Stonehouse *p398* 01453 825151
Read, J C (Friend & Co) *S1 E N K1 G H W S2 Zl*
Walton-on-Thames *p420*. . . 01932 242962
Read, K (Just Law Ltd)
Chelmsford *p454*. 01245 396444
Read, M J (Lees Solicitors LLP) *E S1 W C1 L K1 J1*
West Kirby *p428*. 0151 625 9364
Read, N P L (Hogan Lovells International LLP)
London EC1 *p42*. 020 7296 2000
Read, N R (Read Law Associates) *S1 E C1*
Macclesfield *p297* 01625 429131
Read, P A (Read & Co) *E F1 J1 K1 L D1 N W Zl Zq Zk Zy*
Twickenham *p416* 020 8892 8063
Read, P J (Read Cooper) *E S2*
Thame *p410*. 01844 260038
Read, S (Angela Rogan) *W Zd S2 C1 E S1*
Kendal *p264*. 01539 724140
Read, Ms S I K (Key2Law LLP)
Ewell *p220*. 020 8393 0941
Read, S P B C (Bower & Bailey) *S1 K1 E P N B1 C1 Zl Zi S2 D2 D1*
Swindon *p406* 01793 610466
Read, T (Clarke Willmott) *K1 K2 D1*
Birmingham *p136* 0845 209 1000 / 0117 305 6000
Read, T C (Clifton Ingram LLP) *A1 E R2 S1 S2*
Reading *p360* 0118 957 3425
Reader, Ms C (Shell International Ltd)
London SE1 *p109* 020 7934 1234
Reader, Ms L J (Taylor Haldane Barlex LLP) *G H*
Chelmsford *p187*. 0845 293 7688
Reader, P (Berry & Berry) *Q J1 B1 L N*
Tunbridge Wells *p414* 01892 526344
Readett, Ms H A (SGH Martineau LLP) *B1 C1 Zb*
Birmingham *p142* 0870 763 2000
Reading, P (Anthony Collins Solicitors LLP) *E*
Birmingham *p137* 0121 200 3242
Reading, S (Coffin Mew & Clover) *S1*
Portsmouth *p354*. 023 9238 8021
Readman, T G (T G Readman) *S1 E S2*
Plymouth *p350*. 01752 880238
Ready, A C (Fraser Brown) *S1 E W R1 L*
Nottingham *p337*. 0115 933 5311
Ready, H K (Keith Ready & Co) *K4 Zm S2 T2 W S1*
Barton-upon-Humber *p126*. . 01652 632215
Real, M (Bowling & Co) *K1 K2 D1*
London E15 *p15*. 020 8221 8000
Real, Miss S (Phillips Solicitors) *K1 T2 W*
Basingstoke *p127* 01256 460830
Reaney, M E (Wirral Borough Council)
Wallasey *p475*. 0151 638 7070
Rearden, S J (George Davies Solicitors LLP) *Zb F1 R2*
Manchester *p303* 0161 236 8992
Reardon, J A (Pinsent Masons LLP) *C1*
London EC2 *p67*. 020 7418 7000
Reardon, Miss L (South Bucks District Council)
Denham *p456* 01895 837200
Reardon, Mrs M (DWT Legal Ltd) *W K4*
Kidderminster *p265* 0844 770 3799
Reason, A D (McGrigors LLP)
London EC4 *p56*. 020 7054 2500
Reason, M (Michael Reason & Partners LLP) *M2 C1 T2*
London EC4 *p71*. 020 7489 2048
Reavey, C (Stones Solicitors LLP) *Q N*
Exeter *p222* 01392 666777
Reavill, D R (Travers Smith LLP) *Ze I U2*
London EC1 *p87*. 020 7295 3000
Reay, K (Raymond Saul & Co) *L R1 R2 S1 S2 W Zd Zh*
London E1 *p76* 020 7480 5840
Reback, M I (Gabbitas Robins) *W T2 S1*
Marlow *p313*. 01628 472600
Rebello, A F A (Farleys Solicitors LLP) *D1 K1*
Blackburn *p145* 01254 367854
Rebus, P (McDermott Will & Emery UK LLP) *Zb*
London EC2 *p56*. 020 7577 6900
Receveur, Miss K Y M (Stewarts Law LLP) *O U1*
London EC4 *p83*. 020 7822 8000
Rechnic, G L (Rochman Landau LLP) *J1 B1 O Q C1*
London W1 *p72* 020 7544 2424
Rechnitzer, G (Berg Legal) *E C1 S1*
Manchester *p301* 0161 833 9211
Rechtman, F (London Borough of Southwark)
London SE1 *p109* 020 7525 5000
Reckitt, Miss M H V (Kerseys) *K1 K3*
Ipswich *p262*. 01473 213311
Record, Ms M (Trowers & Hamlins)
London EC3 *p88*. 020 7423 8000
Record, Mrs S E (Girlings) *K1 D1 K3*
Herne Bay *p248* 01227 367355
Recordon, B (Whatley Recordon) *A1 C1 E J1 N Q S1 W Zo*
Malvern *p300* 01684 892939
Recordon, Miss M (Whatley Recordon) *K1 N D1*
Malvern *p300* 01684 892939
Redden, Ms K (LG Lawyers)
London SE1 *p50*. 020 7379 0000
Reddick, Ms S (Barlow Lyde & Gilbert LLP)
London EC3 *p10*. 020 7247 2277
Reddie, G C (Commonwealth War Graves Commission)
Maidenhead *p464* 01628 507137
Redding, J S (Druces LLP) *E O Q Zl*
London EC2 *p27*. 020 7638 9271
Redding, N (Barrington & Sons) *Q K1 S1 W E A1 Zl S2*
Burnham-on-Sea *p169*. . . . 01278 782371
Reddington, Miss C (Davis Blank Furniss) *C1 Zb J1*
Manchester *p303* 0161 832 3304
Reddington, J (Horwood & James LLP) *A1 C1 S2 E F1 L C2 S1 W*
Aylesbury *p121* 01296 487361
Reddy, Ms C L (Lewis Silkin LLP)
London EC4 *p53*. 020 7074 8000
Reddy, Mrs M (M Selvi Reddy) *S1*
Caterham *p183* 01883 340578
Reddy, Miss P (Hodge Jones & Allen LLP) *G H B2*
London NW1 *p41* 020 7874 8300
Redfern, A (Ison Harrison) *O*
Leeds *p274* 0113 284 5000
Redfern, D I (Stanley Tee) *F1 F2 J2 K1 N Q Zj*
Bishop's Stortford *p144* . . . 01279 755200
Redfern, Miss G (Dass Solicitors) *B2 G*
Birmingham *p137* 0121 248 4000
Redfern, J F (Parkinson Wright LLP) *C1 B1 E N F1 J1 R1 Zc Zd*
Worcester *p440* 01905 726789
Redfern, P A (Underwood Solicitors LLP) *O Q Zq C1*
Westminster *p89*. 020 7526 6000
Redfern, P W L (Beale and Company Solicitors LLP) *Zj O Zq*
London WC2 *p11* 020 7240 3474
Redfern, Miss R (Robert Hitchins Ltd) *S2 E*
Cheltenham *p454* 01242 680694
Redfern, Ms V (Kirklees Metropolitan Borough Council)
Huddersfield *p461* 01484 221421
Redford, I P (Bristows) *C1*
London EC4 *p15*. 020 7400 8000
Redford, Miss K I (John Gaunt & Partners) *O Zl Zf*
Sheffield *p375* 0114 266 8664
Redford-Crowe, D C (Orange PCS Ltd)
Bristol *p452* 0870 376 8888
Redgate, Mrs A J (Rothera Dowson) *E S1 S2*
Nottingham *p338*. 0115 910 0600
Redgate, T C W (Rothera Dowson) *E*
Nottingham *p338*. 0115 910 0600
Redgrave, P C (Blake Lapthorn) *N*
Portsmouth *p354*. 023 9222 1122
London EC4 *p83*. 020 7822 8000
Redgrave, T M O (Field Fisher Waterhouse LLP) *O Q*
London EC3 *p31*. 020 7861 4000
Redhead, Miss C (Quality Solicitors Clarke & Son) *K4 W*
Basingstoke *p127* 01256 320555
Redhead, Mrs C A B (Burnetts) *C1 Zd Zza U2*
Carlisle *p181*. 01228 552222
Carlisle *p182*. 01228 552222
Redhead, N J (Richard Griffiths & Co) *G H*
Salisbury *p371*. 01722 329966
Redhouse, Mrs S (Red Kite Law) *K1 W S1*
Milford Haven *p316* 01646 698008
Redikin, Ms L J (Squire Sanders (UK) LLP)
Leeds *p277* 0113 284 7000
Redman, Mrs H (Kendall & Davies) *W T2*
Stow-on-the-Wold *p399* . . . 01451 830295
Oxford *p344*. 01865 262600
Redman, M R P (Ford Simey LLP) *K1 J1 Zl*
Exeter *p221* 01392 274126
Redman, Ms S E M (Anthony Clark & Co) *S1 W*
Lincoln *p284*. 01522 512321
Redmayne, J H (Taylor Wessing) *S1 L*
London EC4 *p86*. 020 7300 7000
Redmond, Ms B L (Willans LLP) *S1*
Cheltenham *p189* 01242 514000
Redmond, Ms M E S (Poole Townsend) *W*
Barrow-in-Furness *p125* . . . 01229 811811
Redmond, M W (Stephensons Solicitors LLP) *C1 C2 Ze Zl Zb E*
Leigh *p282*. 01942 777777
Redmore, Ms G M (Petersons) *N Q K1 W*
Newport *p329* 01633 255151
Redpath, S J (Kennards Wells) *K1 P S1 D1 M1 W L F1 N C1 Ze Zb K4*
London E11 *p48* 020 8539 8338
Redrup, N (Jefferies Essex LLP) *G H*
Westcliff-on-Sea *p428* 01702 332311
Redston, Mrs S L (Societe Generale Asset Management) *C1*
London EC2 *p109* 020 7090 2500
Redstone, D M (Addleshaw Goddard) *Ze Zf*
London EC1 *p4* 020 7606 8855
Redstone, D M (Chichester & District Magistrates Courts)
Chichester *p455* 01243 817000
Redstone, Ms G (Portsmouth Magistrates Court)
Portsmouth *p469*. 023 9281 9421
Redzikowska, Ms C (West Oxfordshire District Council)
Witney *p477*. 01993 861581
Reeback, A J (Finers Stephens Innocent LLP) *C1 C2*
London W1 *p32* 020 7323 4000
Reece, Ms E (Meadows & Moran) *K3 K1 Q*
Romford *p366* 01708 753400
Reece, J M (Howard & Co) *D1 K1*
Barnsley *p124* 01226 211888
Reece, O P S (Squire Sanders (UK) LLP) *O Q Zq Zo*
London EC2 *p81*. 020 7655 1000
Reece-Jones, Miss S P (The Reece-Jones Partnership) *D1 E S1 K1 L W*
Sevenoaks *p374*. 01732 457575
Reed, Ms A (Dwyers) *S2*
Ashton-under-Lyne *p120*. . . 0161 308 3928
Reed, A B (Bath & North East Somerset Council)
Bath *p462* 01225 394041
Reed, Ms A G (Bennetts Solicitors Attorneys & Notaries) *W T2*
Wrington *p443*. 01934 862786
Reed, Miss A J (Dilworth Lamb & Co) *D1 E K3 K1 Q S1 W*
Orpington *p341* 01689 821119
Reed, A J T (Squire Sanders (UK) LLP)
London EC2 *p81*. 020 7655 1000
Reed, A M (Morgan & Richardson) *A1 D1 G H K1 L N Q S1 T2 W*
Cardigan *p181* 01239 612302
Reed, A R (Bennetts Solicitors Attorneys & Notaries) *B1 C1 J1 N T1 Zb Zc*
Wrington *p443*. 01934 862786
Reed, C (Gateley LLP) *C1*
Birmingham *p138* 0121 234 0000
Reed, C S (Kathy Webb & Co) *D1 D2 K1*
Guisborough *p237*. 01287 633331
Reed, D (Ashurst LLP)
London EC2 *p7* 020 7638 1111
Reed, D S (WBW Solicitors) *N Zl Zr*
Newton Abbot *p329* 01626 202404
Reed, E C H (Travers Smith LLP) *C1 C2*
London EC1 *p87*. 020 7295 3000
Reed, G C (Browne Jacobson LLP) *N Zq Zj*
Nottingham *p336*. 0115 976 6000
Reed, G D (Financial Services Authority)
London E14 *p106* 020 7066 1000
Reed, G M (Sternberg Reed) *G D1 H K1*
Barking *p123* 020 8591 3366
Reed, I D (Berry & Berry) *G H M1 N P K1 J1 V*
Maidstone *p299* 01622 690777
Tonbridge *p412* 01732 355911
Reed, I G (Ashton KCJ) *W T1 S1 A1 Zm Zo*
Ipswich *p262*. 01473 232425
Reed, J (Mid Suffolk District Council)
Ipswich *p462*. 01449 720711
Reed, J (Lupton Fawcett) *C1 Zl B1 F2*
Leeds *p275* 0113 280 2000
Reed, J (Lee Bolton Monier-Williams) *E*
Westminster *p52*. 020 7222 5381
Reed, J C (LG Lawyers)
London SE1 *p50*. 020 7379 0000
Reed, J C (Kirby Sheppard) *S1 W E A1 C1 K4*
Kingswood *p268*. 0845 840 0045
Reed, L (Reeds Solicitors) *K1 N V*
Oxford *p344*. 01865 260230
Reed, M (Gibson & Co) *O Q A3 B2*
Newcastle upon Tyne *p324* . 0191 273 3817
Reed, Mrs M G (South Oxfordshire District Council)
Wallingford *p475*. 01491 823345
Reed, M J (Michael J Reed Ltd) *G*
Carmarthen *p183* 01267 281675
Reed, M P (Lamb & Holmes) *A1 C1 E S1*
Kettering *p265*. 01536 513195

6

Reed, M S (Stephenson Harwood) *B1 Zb*
London EC2 *p82*. 020 7329 4422

Reed, N J (Ashworths Solicitors) *S2 E S1*
London SW19 *p8* 0845 370 1000

Reed, P H (Stephens & Scown) *W S1 S2 L A1 T2 Zd*
St Austell *p391* 01726 74433

Reed, R S (Grahame Stowe Bateson) *D1 K1 G H N Q V Zm*
Harrogate *p240* 01423 562121
Leeds *p274* 0113 246 8163

Reed, R T (H F T Gough & Co) *K1 G H Q N F1 B1*
Whitehaven *p431* 01946 692461

Reed, S (Horsey Lightly)
Westminster *p43*. 020 7222 8844

Reed, Mrs S A (S M Reed & Co)
Hove *p255*. 01273 727351

Reed, S M (S M Reed & Co)
Hove *p255*. 01273 727351

Reedy, B J (PCB Solicitors LLP) *G H Zl*
Ludlow *p294*. 01584 878456

Reekie, W P (Ward Hadaway) *Zc*
Newcastle upon Tyne *p327* . 0191 204 4000

Reel, Ms T (Douglass Simon)
Brentford *p156*. 020 8560 3888

Rees, Miss A J (John Collins & Partners LLP) *B1 O Zb*
Swansea *p405*. 01792 773773

Rees, C (Nelsons)
Nottingham *p338*. 0115 958 6262

Rees, Mrs C A (Gordon Dadds) *Q O J1 Zq*
London W1 *p25* 020 7493 6151

Rees, C A (DAC Beachcroft) *A1 E L R1*
London EC4 *p24*. 020 7936 2222

Rees, Ms C H (Irwin Mitchell LLP) *Zj*
Leeds *p274* 0870 150 0100

Rees, C R (Byrne Frodsham & Co) *A1 C1 E S1 W*
Widnes *p431*. 0151 424 5601

Rees, C W (Herbert Smith LLP) *C2 I Ze U2*
London EC2 *p40*. 020 7374 8000

Rees, D (Environment Agency (Midlands Region)) *G H*
Solihull *p471*. 0121 711 2324

Rees, D A (Scott Rees & Co) *N J1 K1 L S1 W O*
Skelmersdale *p381* 01695 722222

Rees, Ms D A (M&A Solicitors LLP) *C1*
Cardiff *p179* 029 2048 2288

Rees, D A P (Neath Port Talbot County Borough Council)
Port Talbot *p469*. 01639 763333

Rees, D C H (Davies & Jones Solicitors)
Cardiff *p178* 029 2046 5296

Rees, D E (David Edward Rees & Co) *D1 F1 G H J1 K1 M1 P S1*
Treorchy *p413*. 01443 776361

Rees, D J (Gloucestershire County Council - Legal & Democratic Services)
Gloucester *p459*. 01452 425203

Rees, D M (Provident Personal Credit Ltd)
Bradford *p451* 01274 733321

Rees, D P (Purcell Parker) *G H*
Birmingham *p141* 0121 236 9781

Rees, D V (Kundert & Co) *Q O L N G*
Coventry *p200*. 024 7622 7741

Rees, E G (Lanyon Bowdler LLP) *W T2 K4*
Shrewsbury *p379* 01743 280280

Rees, Ms F (Blake Lapthorn) *S1*
Oxford *p342*. 01865 248607

Rees, G B A (Beor Wilson Lloyd) *N O B1 L Q Zc Zb Zk*
Swansea *p405*. 01792 655178

Rees, H (Howe & Spender) *G H*
Neath *p320* 01639 881571
Port Talbot *p353*. 01639 881571

Rees, I (Howes Percival LLP)
Norwich *p334* 01603 762103

Rees, I (Leo Abse & Cohen)
Cardiff *p179* . . .029 2038 3252 / 2034 5421

Rees, I (Red Kite Law) *N Q*
Tenby *p410* 01834 842122

Rees, J (Bond Pearce LLP)
Bristol *p161* 0845 415 0000

Rees, J (Local Government Association)
London SW1 *p107*. 020 7664 3000

Rees, J B (Hugh James) *J2 O Zn X N*
Cardiff *p179* 029 2022 4871

Rees, Miss J M (Welsh Development Agency Legal Services)
Cardiff *p453* 029 2082 8681

Rees, Ms K (Reynolds Porter Chamberlain LLP) *O Zq*
London E1 *p71* 020 3060 6000

Rees, Ms K J (Pinsent Masons LLP)
Birmingham *p141* 0121 200 1050

Rees, Ms L (Terry Jones Solicitors & Advocates)
Newport *p329*. 01952 810307

Rees, L G (Reed Smith LLP) *O J1*
London EC2 *p71*. 020 3116 3000

Rees, Mrs L J (Harvey Ingram LLP)
Leicester *p280*. 0116 254 5454
Devizes *p210* 01380 733300

Rees, Mrs L W (Harrisons Solicitors LLP) *E R1 S2 S1 A1*
Welshpool *p425* 01938 552545

Rees, M (DF Legal LLP) *E S1*
Ledbury *p271* 01531 633222
Tewkesbury *p410* 01684 850750

Rees, M (Bell Lax Litigation) *Zq O Q*
Sutton Coldfield *p403* 0121 355 0011

Rees, M E (E D C Lord & Co) *E L*
Ealing *p55*. 020 8579 9292

Rees, M H (DLA Piper UK LLP)
London EC2 *p24*. 0870 011 1111

Rees, Miss N (Forsters LLP) *O Q L*
Westminster *p33*. 020 7863 8333

Rees, N (Fullers Family Law Practice LLP) *K1*
Bedford *p130* 01234 343134

Rees, N W (Linklaters LLP)
London EC2 *p54*. 020 7456 2000

Rees, O J (DAC Beachcroft) *N Zj J2*
Leeds *p272* 0113 251 4700

Rees, P M (TLT Solicitors) *S1*
Bristol *p165* 0117 917 7777

Rees, P R (Squire Sanders (UK) LLP)
London EC2 *p81*. 020 7655 1000

Rees, Ms R (Hugh James) *Zh Zj N*
Cardiff *p179* 029 2022 4871

Rees, Ms R (Trowers & Hamlins)
London EC3 *p88*. 020 7423 8000

Rees, Ms R (Welsh Health Legal Services)
Cardiff *p453* 029 2031 5500

Rees, Miss R C (Dolmans) *W K4*
Cardiff *p178* 029 2034 5531

Rees, R E (Adams Harrison) *S1 K1 G A1 W L F1 J1 P*
Haverhill *p244* . . . .01440 705731 / 702485

Rees, Ms R S (Potter Rees (Serious Injury) Solicitors)
Manchester *p309* 0161 237 5888

Rees, S J (DLC Solicitors Limited) *K1 N D1 L G H V W S1 Zm Zg Zt Zl Zi*
Darwen *p207* 01254 761234

Rees, T (Martyn Prowel) *N K3 G Zr E J1 W B2 C1 H P O Q*
Cardiff *p180* 029 2047 0909

Rees, T D (Graham Dawson & Co) *N O*
Bexley *p132* 01322 558811

Rees, V J H (Winckworth Sherwood LLP) *O S1 S2 Zd Zx*
London SE1 *p92*. 020 7593 5000

Reese, G D (Reynolds Porter Chamberlain LLP) *N Zj*
London E1 *p71* 020 3060 6000

Rees-Howell, S C (Jeffrey Green Russell) *J1 O E K1*
London W1 *p46* 020 7339 7000

Rees-Jones, Mrs L O (Carmarthenshire County Council)
Carmarthen *p453* 01267 224010

Rees-Jones, N M (Clifford Chance)
London E14 *p20*. 020 7006 1000

Rees-Knowlden, Mrs C (Barlow Robbins LLP) *Zr N*
Guildford *p235*. 01483 543200

Rees-Roberts, P (Rees-Roberts Solicitors) *E Ze P Zu R1 S1*
Liverpool *p290*. 0151 255 1300

Rees-Williams, Miss L (Field Seymour Parkes) *K3 K1*
Reading *p360* 0118 951 6200

Reeve, A J (Gamlins) *W*
Rhyl *p363* 01745 343500

Reeve, Ms E S J (Lincolnshire County Council Resources - Legal Services)
Lincoln *p463*. 01522 552222

Reeve, Miss F A (Bird & Bird LLP) *C1 Zw*
London EC4 *p13*. 020 7415 6000

Reeve, Mrs N E (DBL Talbots LLP) *E U1 S2*
Stourbridge *p399* 01384 445850

Reeve, P E (The Smith Partnership) *O Q C1*
Derby *p209* 01332 225225

Reeve, Miss P L (Forsters LLP) *A1 S2*
Westminster *p33*. 020 7863 8333

Reeve, Ms S (Johnson & Gaunt) *N Q O J1 L R1 Zj Zq*
Banbury *p122* . . . .01295 256271 / 271200

Reeves, A A (KJD) *C1 Zn Zf*
Stoke-on-Trent *p398*. 01782 202020

Reeves, A M (Squire Sanders (UK) LLP)
Leeds *p277* 0113 284 7000

Reeves, C J (Battens) *Zc J2 O A3*
Yeovil *p443* 01935 846000
Poole *p352* 01202 725400

Reeves, C P (Jacobs & Reeves) *S2 E S1*
Poole *p353* 01202 674425

Reeves, Miss D (Edwards Duthie) *J1 Zp J2 Q X*
London E6 *p29* 020 8514 9000

Reeves, K B (Dyfed Powys Police Authority)
Carmarthen *p453* 01267 226440

Reeves, M A (Myer Wolff)
Hull *p257* 01482 223693

Reeves, M D (Halliday Reeves) *G H B2*
Gateshead *p228*. 0191 477 7728

Reeves, P L (Boys & Maughan) *B1 O Q L F1 J1 N Zq*
Margate *p312* 01843 234000

Reeves, Ms S (Wedlake Bell LLP) *O Zc A3*
London WC1 *p91* 020 7395 3000

Reeves, Mrs S E (Pemberton Greenish LLP) *S1*
London SW3 *p66* 020 7591 3333

Reeves, W R (Tendring District Council)
Clacton-on-Sea *p455* 01255 686567

Reeves-Perrin, L A (CooperBurnett) *Q Zl Zq*
Tunbridge Wells *p415* 01892 515022

Reevey, M A (Addleshaw Goddard)
Leeds *p271* 0113 209 2000
Manchester *p300* 0161 934 6000

Regan, Ms A (Russell-Cooke LLP) *O*
London SW15 *p74*. 020 8789 9111

Regan, A N (Darbys Solicitors LLP) *O Q A3*
Oxford *p343*. 01865 811700

Regan, D J (Mundays LLP) *J1*
Cobham *p196* 01932 590500

Regan, M D (Mayer Brown International LLP) *O Zj Zc Zq A3 Q*
London EC2 *p59*. 020 3130 3000

Regan, M J (Coffin Mew & Clover) *E S1 S2*
Southampton *p385*. 023 8033 4661

Regan, N (James Mason Tucker) *K1 K2 D1 N L Q*
Newton Abbot *p329* 01626 204060

Regan, P C (Berry & Berry) *K1 G H S1 M1 L W D1 P J1 Zp*
Eccles *p216* 0161 789 7414

Regan, Miss S L (Mason Baggott & Garton) *K1 J1 V D1 W L J2 Q Zp*
Scunthorpe *p373*. 01724 868611

Regler, B S (Colemans Solicitors LLP) *E S2 S1*
Maidenhead *p298* 01628 631051

Regnard-Weinrabe, Ms S D (Lewis Silkin LLP) *J1*
London EC4 *p53*. 020 7074 8000

Rehder, S C (Martin Smith & Co) *S1 W S2*
Borehamwood *p150* 020 8953 0636

Rehnema, Ms S (Julian Young & Co) *G H*
London W1 *p93* 020 7724 8414

Reich, L J (HM Land Registry - Harrow Sub Office)
Harrow *p460*. 020 8235 1181

Reich, O (Roche Products Ltd)
Welwyn Garden City *p475* . . 01707 366000

Reid, A (Ashurst LLP)
London EC2 *p7* 020 7638 1111

Reid, A C (Ben Sherman Group Limited)
London EC1 *p104* 020 7812 5300

Reid, A G (Menneer Shuttleworth) *S1 E A1 W C1 L*
St Leonards-on-Sea *p392* . . 01424 720044

Reid, Mrs A K G (East Sussex County Council)
Lewes *p463* 01273 481000

Reid, Miss A M (Birchall Blackburn LLP) *K1 D1*
Preston *p356* 01772 561663

Reid, A P (Irwin Mitchell LLP) *E L S1 W*
Sheffield *p376* 0870 150 0100

Reid, A S (RMPI Solicitors) *N M1 C1 E P T1 B1 S1 K1 A1 Za Zc Zk*
London W1 *p70* 020 7318 4444

Reid, B (Environment Agency (North East Region))
Leeds *p462* 0870 850 6506

Reid, Miss B (Sandwell Metropolitan Borough Council) *L Zh Q O Zu*
Oldbury *p468* 0121 569 2200

Reid, C (Morrison & Foerster (UK) LLP) *Zb*
London EC2 *p62*. 020 7920 4000

Reid, Ms C (Manches LLP) *I*
Oxford *p343*. 01865 722106

Reid, C (May May & Merrimans) *E S2 S1*
London WC1 *p59* 020 7405 8932

Reid, Mrs C A (M A Plant) *K1 K3 Q*
Southminster *p388*. .01621 773185 / 772794

Reid, Miss C E (Bury Magistrates Court)
Bury *p452* 0161 447 8600

Reid, D (Watson Burton LLP)
Newcastle upon Tyne *p327* . 0845 901 2100

Reid, Mrs D G N (London Borough of Greenwich Legal Services)
London SE18 *p106* 020 8921 5123

Reid, D M (Nalders Quality Solicitors) *A1 E S1 S2 W*
Helston *p246* 01326 574001

Reid, Ms E (K&L Gates LLP)
London EC4 *p47*. 020 7648 9000

Reid, Miss E H (Hogan Lovells International LLP)
London EC1 *p42*. 020 7296 2000

Reid, E M (Max Bitel Greene LLP) *B1 K1 L W C1 N P*
Islington *p59*. 020 7354 2767

Reid, Mrs F (Ascroft Whiteside) *Q N O K3 K1 L J1 Zq Zr Zp*
Blackpool *p146* 01253 766866

Reid, F (Couchmans LLP)
London WC1 *p23* 020 7611 9660

Reid, G (Linklaters LLP)
London EC2 *p54*. 020 7456 2000

Reid, G M (Reed Smith LLP) *E L R1 S1*
London EC2 *p71*. 020 3116 3000

Reid, G W (Barlow Robbins LLP) *E R1 S2 L Zc Zh*
Guildford *p235*. 01483 562901

Reid, H (Martin Tolhurst Partnership LLP) *J1*
Gravesend *p233*. 01474 325531

Reid, Ms H K (Ware & Kay LLP) *K3 K1*
Wetherby *p429* 01937 583210

Reid, J (Penningtons) *O*
London EC2 *p66*. 020 7457 3000

Reid, J (O'Rourke Reid & Co)
Leeds *p276* 0113 245 7811

Reid, J (Russells) *Q O Ze Zf Zk Zw J1*
London W1 *p75* 020 7439 8692

Reid, J A (Thomson Snell & Passmore) *O S1 E A1 Zq*
Tunbridge Wells *p415* 01892 510000

Reid, J D (Stockdale & Reid Ltd) *C1 C2 C3 D1 G M1 M2 N Q S1 Zc Ze Zf Zq Zt*
North Shields *p331* 0191 257 1341

Reid, Ms J M (Irwin Mitchell LLP) *S1*
Sheffield *p376* 0870 150 0100

Reid, Miss K (Blandy & Blandy) *P R1*
Reading *p360* 0118 951 6800

Reid, Ms K (London Borough of Greenwich Legal Services)
London SE18 *p106* 020 8921 5123

Reid, Mrs K (Cadmans Law & Property) *D1 D2 K1 L S1*
Cleckheaton *p195* 01274 874231

Reid, Ms L (Underwood Solicitors LLP) *E C1 S2 J1 C2*
Westminster *p89*. 020 7526 6000

Reid, Miss L M (Speakeasy Advice Centre) *N Q L J1 B1 F1 Zh V O Zq*
Cardiff *p453* 029 2045 3111

Reid, M (Oury Clark)
London WC1 *p65* 020 7607 4300

Reid, Mrs M (Beaumonts) *K1*
Hereford *p247* 01432 352345

Reid, M A (Mackesys)
London SE14 *p57* 020 7639 0888

Reid, N W (Linklaters LLP)
London EC2 *p54*. 020 7456 2000

Reid, R F (Shoosmiths) *P G Q K1 Zl Zt*
Northampton *p332*. . 0370 086 3000 / 01604 543000

Reid, Miss R K (MacDonald Oates LLP) *W T2 K4*
Petersfield *p348* 01730 268211

Reid, R N (Darlington Hardcastles) *S1 W L*
Rickmansworth *p364*. 01923 774272
Harrow *p242*. 020 8863 6366

Reid, Mrs S J (Richard Reed) *D1 K1 K3 V*
Sunderland *p402*. 0191 567 0465

Reid, S J P (Rialto Homes PLC)
Hertford *p460* 01992 823589

Reid, T M C (Ashurst LLP) *A3 Zc*
London EC2 *p7* 020 7638 1111

Reid, W (Foys Solicitors) *E L R1 S1 P*
Worksop *p441* 01909 473560

Reid, Mrs Y (Inesons) *N Q*
Cleckheaton *p195* 01274 872202

Reilly, Ms J (Pannone LLP) *N*
Manchester *p308* 0161 909 3000

Reilly, Ms M K (Rotherham Metropolitan Borough Council)
Rotherham *p470*. 01709 382121

Reilly, P J (Thanet District Council) *N Q J1 F1*
Margate *p465* 01843 577000

Reilly, R K (Harbottle & Lewis LLP) *E S1 R1 L P Zc Zv*
London W1 *p38* 020 7667 5000

Reimann, Mrs C A P (Martin Smith & Co) *S1 R2 S2 W K4 J1 F1 E Zc*
Borehamwood *p150* 020 8953 0636

Reingold, Ms J (Simmons & Simmons)
London EC2 *p79*. 020 7628 2020

Reis, M S (Beauchamps) *E S2 S1 R2*
Westminster *p11*. 020 7724 7724

Reisbach, S C (Clifford Chance)
London E14 *p20*. 020 7006 1000

Reisenthel, Miss A L E (Reuters Group PLC)
London E14 *p109* 020 7250 1122

Reisman, S Z (Lee Bolton Monier-Williams) *S1 W R1 L*
Westminster *p52*. 020 7222 5381

Reissner, D H (Charles Russell LLP) *O*
London EC4 *p19*. 020 7203 5000

Relf, D (Holman Fenwick Willan)
London EC3 *p42*. 020 7264 8000
London EC2 *p82*. 020 7329 4422

Relton, J (Donnelly McArdle Adamson)
Hartlepool *p243* 01429 274732

Remi, Mrs L (Julian Young & Co) *G H*
London W1 *p93* 020 7724 8414

Remington, S A (Olswang LLP)
London WC1 *p64* 020 7067 3000

Renaudon, Ms C (Hibberts LLP)
Crewe *p203* 01270 215117

Renaudon, Miss L E (Waverley Borough Council)
Godalming *p459*. 01483 523333

Rench, R C W (William Sturges & Co) *E S2*
Westminster *p84*. 020 7873 1000

Rendell, Miss A (Pannone LLP) *N*
Manchester *p308* 0161 909 3000

Rendell, Mrs S A (B P Collins LLP) *W*
Gerrards Cross *p229*. 01753 889995

Render, J B D (Renders)
Cardiff *p180* 029 2054 4900

Renfree, R P (Mills & Reeve) *Zq*
Cambridge *p175*. 01223 364422

Renger, M (Nabarro LLP) *P R1 Zn*
Sheffield *p376* 0114 279 4000

Rengger, Ms J (Russell-Cooke LLP) *E*
London SW15 *p74*. 020 8789 9111

Renison, D I (Brabners Chaffe Street) *W A1 S2 K4 Zo S1 T2*
Liverpool *p286*. 0151 600 3000

Renison, M C (Laytons) *O Q N J1 Zw*
Manchester *p306* 0161 834 2100

Renney, Mrs C (Newcastle Upon Tyne City Council) *K3 K1*
Newcastle upon Tyne *p466* . 0191 232 8520

Rennie, A (Plexus Law (A Trading Name of Parabis Law LLP)) *J1 N O Zp Zq*
Evesham *p220*. 01386 769160

Rennie, N (Brachers) *W T2*
Maidstone *p299* 01622 690691

Rennison, C J (Davies Blunden & Evans) *S1 S2 W L*
Farnborough *p224*. 01252 541633

Renouf, Ms S J (Bevan Brittan LLP) *R2 E*
Bristol *p161* 0870 194 1000

Renshaw, N (Renshaws) *S1 M1 N P D1 K1 W A1 C1 G Zg Zi Zt*
Kendal *p264*. 01539 740666

Renshaw, P D S (Potter Rees (Serious Injury) Solicitors)
Manchester *p309* 0161 237 5888

Rentoul, Ms A (Simmons & Simmons)
London EC2 *p79*. 020 7628 2020

Rentoul, Ms B (Linklaters LLP)
London EC2 *p54*. 020 7456 2000

Rest, Ms B J (David Gray Solicitors) *Zi Zg M1*
Newcastle upon Tyne *p324* . 0191 232 9547

See p634 for the Key to Work Categories

6

Restell, Mrs G (Mole Valley District Council) Dorking *p457* 01306 885001

Reston, C J (Reston's Solicitors Limited) *B1 C1 N Zb* Warrington *p422* 0870 755 8998

Reston, D C (Herbert Smith LLP) *O Zj* London EC2 *p40* 020 7374 8000

Reston, Mrs S C (Reston's Solicitors Limited) *S1 E W R1 C1* Warrington *p422* 0870 755 8998

Reuben, J B (Lewis Silkin LLP) *E* London EC4 *p53* 020 7074 8000

Reuben, R M E (Macfarlanes) *E Zc* London EC4 *p56* 020 7831 9222

Reuvecamp, Ms I (Capsticks Solicitors LLP) *Q O* London SW19 *p18* 020 8780 2211

Revell, J W (Crown Prosecution Service Dorset) Bournemouth *p450* 01202 498700

Revell, P (Lyons Davidson) Bristol *p163* 0117 904 6000

Revelle, P C (Rolls-Royce PLC) Bristol *p452* 0117 979 7149 Derby *p456* 01332 242424

Revenico, Ms H E (The College of Law Guildford) Guildford *p459* 01483 460200

Revitt, A J (Peace Revitt) *C1 E F1 J1 K1 L N Q S1* Barnsley *p125* 01226 341111 / 210077

Revitt, C J (Favell Smith & Lawson Solicitors) *K1 Q L N F1* Sheffield *p375* 0114 272 4381

Revitt, D J (Irwin Mitchell LLP) *L O Q* Sheffield *p376* 0870 150 0100

Revitt, Ms K (Mayfair Treasury Ltd) *E* Chorley *p455* 01257 269400

Rewane, Miss E (A H Page) *L Zi S1 V S2 W* Ilford *p260* 020 8554 1985

Rewcastle, D (Dickinson Dees) *C1* Newcastle upon Tyne *p324* 0191 279 9000

Rex, N P (Milford & Dormor) *S1 S2 W* Chard *p184* 01460 65335 / 61000

Rexhepaj, Ms B (Johns & Saggar) *Zd Za* London WC1 *p46* 020 3490 1475

Reyersbach, Mrs S M (Wheelers) *K1 Q N D1 K2* Aldershot *p115* 01252 316316

Reynard, J A (Harrowells) *K1 K2* York *p444* 01904 558600

Reynard, M V (Eastbourne Borough Council) Eastbourne *p457* 01323 410000

Reynolds, Miss A (Barrett & Thomson) *K1 N* Slough *p381* 01753 437416

Reynolds, Ms A (Russell-Cooke LLP) *G B2 S1* London SW15 *p74* 020 8789 9111

Reynolds, A W (Robertsons) *S1 B1 C1 E Zi* Cardiff *p180* 029 2023 7777

Reynolds, B W B (Shearman & Sterling LLP) *Zo* London EC2 *p78* 020 7655 5000

Reynolds, C D E (Reynolds Dawson) *G H J1 L* London WC2 *p71* 020 7839 2373 / 07659 130481

Reynolds, Mrs C S (Hartnell Chanot & Partners Family Law Specialists) *K1 K3* Exeter *p221* 01392 421777

Reynolds, Mrs D (Hill Hofstetter LLP) *Q O* Solihull *p382* 0121 210 6000

Reynolds, D C (Warwickshire County Council) Warwick *p475* 01926 410410

Reynolds, Mrs D D (Brunswick Law) *W J1 Q F1 K1 K3* Westerham *p428* 01959 561515 / 563163

Reynolds, Miss D J L (Deborah Reynolds) Pentre *p346* 01443 440888

Reynolds, D M (Neale Turk Rochfort) *S2 E S1 L Zl* Camberley *p173* 01276 20551

Reynolds, Mrs E C (Glanvilles) *T2 W K4* Havant *p244* 023 9249 2300

Reynolds, E M (Bristol City Council) Bristol *p451* 0117 922 2000

Reynolds, Ms F M (LG Lawyers) London SE1 *p50* 020 7379 0000

Reynolds, G (Bartlett Gooding & Weelen) *C1 S2 K3 K1 Q S1 W T1 T2* Castle Cary *p183* 01963 350888 Shepton Mallet *p378* 01749 343091

Reynolds, G C (Lichfield Reynolds) *K1* Stoke-on-Trent *p398* 01782 313212

Reynolds, G R (Freeth Cartwright LLP) *E R1 A1 L* Nottingham *p337* 0115 936 9369

Reynolds, J B (Calderdale Metropolitan BC Corporate Services Directorate) Halifax *p460* 01422 357257

Reynolds, J C (Cargill PLC) Cobham *p455* 01932 861000

Reynolds, J D B (Capsticks Solicitors LLP) *N Q Zr* London SW19 *p18* 020 8780 2211

Reynolds, Miss J E (Cardiff County Council) Cardiff *p453* 029 2087 2000

Reynolds, J J (Gillette Management Inc) Isleworth *p462* 020 8560 1234

Reynolds, Ms K E (Freeth Cartwright LLP) *Zr* Nottingham *p337* 0115 936 9369

Reynolds, Mrs K M (MFG Solicitors) *K1 D1 P V* Worcester *p440* 01905 610410

Reynolds, Mrs L M (Bristows) *C1 O M1 M2 Ze* London EC4 *p15* 020 7400 8000

Reynolds, Mrs M (Margaret Reynolds Solicitor) *E L S1* Grays *p233* 01375 390239

Reynolds, M (Horsey Lightly) *O Q B1* Newbury *p322* 01635 580858

Reynolds, M J (Kirwans) *G H* Birkenhead *p134* 0151 608 9078

Reynolds, M J (Squire Sanders (UK) LLP) Leeds *p277* 0113 284 7000

Reynolds, M P (Jeffrey Green Russell) *M1 N P Zc* London W1 *p46* 020 7339 7000

Reynolds, O D (Rowberry Morris) *K1 K2* Reading *p361* 0118 958 5611

Reynolds, Ms O M (Co-operative Insurance Society Ltd) Manchester *p464* 0161 832 8686

Reynolds, Ms P (Morecrofts Solicitors LLP) Crosby *p203* 0151 924 9234

Reynolds, Miss P A (Bank of Scotland) Chester *p454* 01244 690000

Reynolds, P B (Rowberry Morris) *K1 K2 D1* Reading *p361* 0118 958 5611

Reynolds, P J (Donald Race & Newton) *N Q K1 J1 G H F1 L O D1 Zi Zl* Colne *p198* 01282 864500

Reynolds, Mrs P M (Pauline Reynolds and Co) *K1 K3* Kirkby *p268* 0151 546 4583

Reynolds, Mrs R I (Norris & Miles) *K1 V* Tenbury Wells *p409* 01584 810575

Reynolds, Mrs S (Terry Jones Solicitors & Advocates) *D1 K3 K1* Telford *p409* 01952 297979

Reynolds, S E (Hempsons) *J1 Zm Zg Zp* Manchester *p305* 0161 228 0011

Reynolds, Mrs S L (Reynolds & Hawkes) *S1 L F1 P W G Zc Zh Zl* Milton Keynes *p317* 01908 366521

Reynolds, T G (Verisona Solicitors) *D1 F1 G H J1 K1 L M1 N Za Zl Zp* Waterlooville *p423* 023 9226 5251

Reynolds, T J D (TLT Solicitors) *P Zc* London EC2 *p85* 020 3465 4000

Reynolds, Z M (Streathers Solicitors LLP) *S1 S2 E R2 L C1* London W1 *p84* 020 7034 4200

Reynolds, Miss Z V (Lee & Thompson) *Zf Ze* London W1 *p52* 020 7935 4665

Rhatigan, M V (Lockett Loveday McMahon) *E Zh S2 R2 W* Manchester *p307* 0161 237 3627

Rhead, A J (County of Herefordshire District Council) *G H J1 K1 L D1 M1 V Zm* Hereford *p460* 01432 260266

Rhead, Ms L A (Gartsides) *G H* Newport *p328* 01633 213411

Rhodes, Ms A (Tyne & Wear Passenger Transport Executive) Newcastle upon Tyne *p466* 0191 203 3333

Rhodes, Ms C (Kidd Rapinet) *E S2 A1 S1 U1 Zf* Maidenhead *p298* 0845 017 9608

Rhodes, Ms C (Trowers & Hamlins) London EC3 *p88* 020 7423 8000

Rhodes, Miss C A (John Bromfield & Company Ltd) *K1 D1 S1 W* Nuneaton *p339* 024 7638 2343

Rhodes, C D (Runhams) *S1 W S2 L E* Bradford *p154* 01274 532233

Rhodes, C D (Zermansky & Partners) *W* Leeds *p278* 0113 245 9766

Rhodes, C E R C (Gichard & Co) *F1 G H J1 K1 L N O Q R1 T1 V W Zl Zt* Rotherham *p367* 01709 365531

Rhodes, D C (Andrew Jackson) *W T2 K4* Hull *p257* 01482 325242

Rhodes, D G (Ridley & Hall) *S1 W C1 L S2* Huddersfield *p256* 01484 538421

Rhodes, J G (Macfarlanes) *T1 W C1 Zd* London EC4 *p56* 020 7831 9222

Rhodes, K (Switalski's) *L S1 W Zi* Halifax *p238* 01422 284350

Rhodes, Miss N L (Zermansky & Partners) *K1 K3 D1* Leeds *p278* 0113 245 9766

Rhodes, P (Molesworths Bright Clegg) *J1 J2 B1* Rochdale *p365* 01706 356666

Rhodes, P E H (MFG Solicitors) *W S1* Telford *p409* 01952 641651

Rhodes, S J (Dudley Metropolitan Borough Council) Dudley *p457* 01384 815326

Rhodes, S J (Trethowans LLP) *J1 Zq J2 Zi Zg* Southampton *p387* 023 8032 1000

Rhodes, T (City of London Corporation) London EC2 *p107* 020 7606 3030

Rhodes-Kemp, Mrs R H D (Bolt Burdon) *Zk* Islington *p14* 020 7288 4700

Rhone, Ms S (Department for Business, Enterprise and Regulatory Reform) London SW1 *p105* 020 7215 0105

Rhydderch, Ms L (Harding Evans LLP) *K1 D1* Newport *p328* 01633 244233

Riad, A (Cartwright King) Nottingham *p336* 0115 958 7444

Riaz, Mrs O (HSK Solicitors LLP) *N Q O* Manchester *p305* 0161 795 4818

Riaz, Miss R (Calderdale Metropolitan BC Corporate Services Directorate) Halifax *p460* 01422 357257

Riaz, Mrs S (Gregory Rowcliffe Milners) *C1 J1* London WC1 *p37* 020 7242 0631

Ribbans, Ms M (Jackamans) Felixstowe *p225* 01394 279636

Ribchester, E (Challinors) *E S1 C1 W* West Bromwich *p427* 0121 553 3211

Ribet, D P L (Forsters LLP) *W T2* Westminster *p33* 020 7863 8333

Ribet, J (Levison Meltzer Pigott) *K1* London EC4 *p53* 020 7556 2400

Ricca, A (McKenzies) *N* Hertford *p248* 01992 503344

Riccio, Miss M C (Blake Lapthorn) *Zo* Chandlers Ford *p184* 023 8090 8090

Rice, A M (Mayo Wynne Baxter LLP) *W T1 Zd Zx* Lewes *p283* 01273 477071

Rice, Mrs D E (Ribble Valley Borough Council) Clitheroe *p455* 01200 425111

Rice, J C (SGH Martineau LLP) *E B1 Zb* Birmingham *p142* 0870 763 2000

Rice, J E (Gullands) *S1 W A1 K1 S2* Maidstone *p299* 01622 678341

Rice, J J E (Linklaters LLP) London EC2 *p54* 020 7456 2000

Rice, Miss K J (Coventry City Council) Coventry *p456* 024 7683 4863

Rice, P (Pinsent Masons LLP) London EC2 *p67* 020 7418 7000

Rice, P H (John Lewis plc) London SW1 *p107* 020 7828 1000

Rice, R A (SNR Denton) London EC4 *p75* 020 7242 1212

Rice, R C (Boyes Turner) *C1 C2* Reading *p360* 0118 959 7711

Rice, Ms S (Michelmores LLP) *E S2 L S1 Zu R2* Exeter *p221* 01392 688688

Rice, S (Akin Gump Strauss Hauer & Feld) London E1 *p4* 020 7012 9600

Rich, Miss A (North Somerset District Council) *E S1* Weston-super-Mare *p476* 01934 888888

Rich, A J E (South Ribble Borough Council) Preston *p469* 01772 421491

Rich, A M T (Herbert Smith LLP) *O Ze* London EC2 *p40* 020 7374 8000

Rich, D S (Shammah Nicholls LLP) *S1 S2 R2 Zh* Manchester *p309* 0161 832 9272

Rich, J (Pardoes) *N* Yeovil *p444* 01935 382680

Rich, M W (CMS Cameron McKenna LLP) London EC3 *p17* 020 7367 3000

Richard, J (Addleshaw Goddard) London EC1 *p4* 020 7606 8855

Richards, Ms A E F (McKenzie Richards) *Q W S1 E* Mayfield *p314* 01435 872025

Richards, B W D (LG Lawyers) *N P* London SE1 *p50* 020 7379 0000

Richards, C (Barbock Energy Ltd) Crawley *p456* 01293 584974

Richards, Miss C (Hart Reade) *K1 D1* Hailsham *p237* 01323 841481

Richards, C E (Fox Williams) *J1 Zp* London EC2 *p33* 020 7628 2000

Richards, Miss C J (R N Williams & Co Limited) *N Q F1 W S1 K4 V Zr* Wolverhampton *p438* 01902 429051

Richards, Miss C M (Barker Gotelee Solicitors) *C1 C2 Zb Zd* Ipswich *p262* 01473 611211

Richards, D (Ince & Co Services Ltd) London E1 *p44* 020 7481 0010

Richards, Mrs D (Hutchinson Thomas) *D1 K1 K2 D2* Neath *p320* 01639 645061

Richards, D G (Caerphilly County Borough Council) Hengoed *p460* 01443 815588

Richards, D L (Beale and Company Solicitors LLP) *O A3 Zc Zq* London WC2 *p11* 020 7240 3474

Richards, Ms E (stevensdrake) *B1 I O* Crawley *p202* 01293 596900

Richards, Mrs E (Morgan Cole) Oxford *p344* 01865 262600

Richards, E M J (Hine Downing Solicitors) Falmouth *p223* 01326 316655

Richards, G (The College of Law) London WC1 *p105* 0800 289997

Richards, G (J R Brown & Co) *S1 K1 W L D1 C1 E J1 N O Q R1 Zc* Clevedon *p195* 01275 879292

Richards, G H (Martyn Prowel) *G H Zl* Cardiff *p180* 029 2047 0909

Richards, G W (Farrer & Co LLP) *J1 Ze Zg Zi Zp Zw C1* London WC2 *p31* 020 3375 7000

Richards, H J (Claremont Richards) *E C1 S1 S2 Zo* London EC4 *p20* 020 7353 3030

Richards, I V (Morris Scott & Co) *K1 O Q N G H J1 L D1* Christchurch *p194* 01425 278866

Richards, J (DLA Piper UK LLP) London EC2 *p24* 0870 011 1111

Richards, J (Linklaters LLP) London EC2 *p54* 020 7456 2000

Richards, Ms J E (DAC Beachcroft) London EC4 *p24* 020 7242 1011

Richards, J G G (J G Richards) Larkfield *p270* 01732 870377

Richards, J H (Pinsent Masons LLP) *O* Birmingham *p141* 0121 200 1050

Richards, J L (Cohen Cramer Solicitors) *S1 W K1 M1 C1 C2 C3 E* Leeds *p272* 0800 542 9408

Richards, Miss J L (May May & Merrimans) *W T2 K4* London WC1 *p59* 020 7405 8932

Richards, J M (Hambleton District Council) Northallerton *p467* 01609 779977

Richards, J N (Rowland Tildesley & Harris) *B1 C1 E F1 L S1 T1 W* Willenhall *p433* 01902 366571

Richards, J S (Travers Smith LLP) *R2 Zb* London EC1 *p87* 020 7295 3000

Richards, Ms K (Withers LLP) *K1* London EC4 *p92* 020 7597 6000

Richards, Miss K (Coles Miller Solicitors LLP) *Zr N* Poole *p352* 01202 673011

Richards, Miss K A (Raleys) *N J1* Barnsley *p125* 01226 211111

Richards, Mrs K L (Shentons) *Q O L N K3 K1* Winchester *p434* 01962 844544

Richards, Miss L (Enoch Evans LLP) *E C1 S2* Walsall *p420* 01922 720333

Richards, L (West Midlands Travel Ltd) Birmingham *p450* 0121 254 7200

Richards, L J (Peter Lynn & Partners) *S1 W T2 T1 A1 A2 S2 E L R1 Zv* Morriston *p319* 01792 310731

Richards, M (EDF Energy plc) London SW1 *p106* 020 7242 9050

Richards, M D (Pinsent Masons LLP) *O P M1 B1 Zc Q* Leeds *p276* 0113 244 5000

Richards, M H (Rhondda Cynon Taff County Borough Council) *E L S1 S2 W* Pentre *p468* 01443 424300

Richards, N (Davies Parsons Allchurch) *N G F1 S1* Llanelli *p292* 01554 749144

Richards, Miss N (Macfarlanes) *C1 J1* London EC4 *p56* 020 7831 9222

Richards, N A (Richards & Lewis) Ebbw Vale *p216* 01495 350018

Richards, Mrs N S (Trethowans LLP) *S1 E* Salisbury *p371* 01722 412512

Richards, P W (Wilson Browne) *T2 W* Leicester *p281* 0116 251 7181

Richards, R (DAC Beachcroft) Birmingham *p137* 0121 698 5200

Richards, Mrs R (Stoke-on-Trent City Council) Stoke-on-Trent *p472* 01782 234567

Richards, R F (Napthens LLP) *Q O N* Blackpool *p146* 01253 622305

Richards, R W V (Legal Aid Area Office No 4 (South Western)) Bristol *p452* 0117 921 4801

Richards, Ms S (City & County of Swansea) Swansea *p473* 01792 636000

Richards, Ms S (Thompsons (formerly Robin/Brian Thompson & Partners)) *N Zq* Harrow *p242* 020 8872 8600

Richards, S (George Ide LLP) Chichester *p192* 01243 786668

Richards, S (Jones Day) *O* London EC4 *p46* 020 7039 5959

Richards, S (Gateley LLP) *C2* London EC4 *p35* 020 7653 1600

Richards, Ms S (Wirral Borough Council) Wallasey *p475* 0151 638 7070

Richards, S D (Fasken Martineau LLP) *C1 Ze F1 Zy C3* London W1 *p31* 020 7917 8500

Richards, Ms S K F (Consumers' Association) London NW1 *p105* 020 7770 7000

Richards, S L (Barnes Richards Rutter) *S1 K1 G M1 P H F1 L J1* Chepstow *p189* 01291 628898

Richards, Ms T (Capsticks Solicitors LLP) *N Zr* London SW19 *p18* 020 8780 2211

Richards, T C (Michelmores LLP) *O A3 Ze K2 Zza C1 Zk* Exeter *p221* 01392 688688

Richards, T J (Hewitsons) *Zc R2 A3* Cambridge *p174* 01223 461155

Richards, W R (Hine Downing Solicitors) *W K4* Falmouth *p223* 01326 316655

Richards Bond, S A (Alletsons Ltd) *K1 D1 G H L E* Bridgwater *p157* 01278 456621

Richards-Clarke, Ms T (Philcox Gray & Co) *V L* London SE15 *p67* 020 7703 2285

Richardson, A E F (LG Lawyers) London SE1 *p50* 020 7379 0000

Richardson, Mrs A K (Tozers) *K3 K1* Plymouth *p350* 01752 206460 Plymouth *p350* 01752 550711

Richardson, A P (3i PLC) London SW1 *p103* 020 7928 3131

Richardson, Ms A V (Adams & Remers) *J1 Zp J2* Lewes *p283* 01273 480616

Richardson, B (Arnison & Co Solicitors Limited) *A1 M1 R1 W Q L S1 E* Penrith *p346* 01768 862007

Richardson, Miss B L (Arnold Greenwood) *K3 K1* Kendal *p264* 01539 720049

Richardson, Mrs C (Hewitts) Bishop Auckland *p144* 01388 604691

Richardson, C E (Hunters) *W T2* London WC2 *p44* 020 7412 0050

Richardson, D (Manches LLP) *J1* Oxford *p343* 01865 722106

Richardson, D M (Short Richardson & Forth LLP) *E S2 L R2 S1* Newcastle upon Tyne *p326* 0191 232 0283

Richardson, Ms E E (Storrar Cowdry) *K1 D1 D2* Chester *p191* 01244 400567

Richardson, G A (Williams & Co) *C1 E N L S1 J1 B1 Zl* Luton *p296* 01582 723322

Richardson, Ms H J (Brian Koffman & Co) Manchester *p306* 0161 832 3852

Richardson, I G (Sparling Benham & Brough) *K3 K1 K2 D1*
Colchester *p198* 01206 733733

Richardson, J (Chester City Council)
Chester *p454* 01244 324324

Richardson, J (Archers Law LLP) *C1 L F1 U2*
Stockton-on-Tees *p396* 01642 636500

Richardson, Mrs J A (Henry Hyams)
Leeds *p274* 0113 243 2288

Richardson, J C (Hunters) *W T2*
London WC2 *p44* 020 7412 0050

Richardson, J F (Stephen Rimmer LLP) *K1 K3 D1 D2*
Eastbourne *p216* 01323 644222

Richardson, J I (Lyons Davidson) *N Zl*
Bristol *p163* 0117 904 6000

Richardson, J M (Arnison & Co Solicitors Limited) *W T2 K4*
Penrith *p346* 01768 862007

Richardson, J S (Christopher Davidson Solicitors LLP) *N C1 P B1 Zc Zd Ze Zj Zk O Zq B2 A1 F1*
Cheltenham *p188* 01242 581481

Richardson, J W (Bradly Trimmer) *S1 S2*
Alton *p116* 01420 88024

Richardson, K (Mackrell & Thomas) *G H*
Liverpool *p289* 0151 480 3666

Richardson, Mrs L W (Blaenau Gwent Borough Council)
Ebbw Vale *p458* 01495 350555

Richardson, M (Stephens & Scown) *Q O L F1 Zq*
Exeter *p222* 01392 210700

Richardson, Mrs M (Hodgsons & Mortimer) *K1 S1 W M1 P*
Darlington *p206* 01325 250111 / 355956

Richardson, M A (Platt & Fishwick) *N Q O F1 B1 J1*
Wigan *p432* 01942 243281

Richardson, Ms M L (Charles Coleman LLP) *W S1*
Windsor *p434* 01753 861115

Richardson, N E (RHW Solicitors LLP) *C1 C2*
Guildford *p237* 01483 302000

Richardson, N J (Hamers Solicitors) *K1 D1*
Hull *p257* 01482 326666

Richardson, N J (Hodge Jones & Allen LLP) *G H B2*
London NW1 *p41* 020 7874 8300

Richardson, P (Birdsall & Snowball)
Scarborough *p372* 01723 351351

Richardson, Miss P (Cancer Research UK)
London WC2 *p104* 020 7242 0200

Richardson, P (Sansbury Douglas) *G H*
Bristol *p164* 0117 926 5341

Richardson, P A D (Ray Nixon Brown) *G H J1 P N S1 E F1 Zi Zl S2*
Leighton Buzzard *p282* 01525 372247

Richardson, R J (The National Trust)
Swindon *p475* 01793 817400

Richardson, Mrs S (R F Tansey)
Thame *p410* 01844 218000

Richardson, Miss S (Crombie Wilkinson) *W*
York *p444* 01904 624185

Richardson, S (Bond Pearce LLP) *J1 O A3*
Southampton *p385* 0845 415 0000

Richardson, S D (The Smith Partnership) *F1 M1 P Zm*
Derby *p209* 01332 225225

Richardson, S G (Irwin Mitchell LLP) *E R2 S2*
Sheffield *p376* 0870 150 0100

Richardson, Miss S L (Crombie Wilkinson) *K1 K2 K3*
Malton *p300* 01653 600070

Richardson, Mrs S L (Hague Lambert) *K1 K3*
Knutsford *p269* 01565 652411

Richardson, Ms S L (Pearsons & Ward) *D1*
Malton *p300* 01653 692247
Kingston upon Thames *p267* 020 8546 6111

Richardson, T (Kidd Rapinet) *S1 E S2*
High Wycombe *p250* 0845 017 9607

Richardson, Mrs V J (Maxwell Hodge Solicitors) *K1 D1 K3*
Huyton *p258* 0151 489 6161

Richbell, P L (Peter Richbell & Co Solicitors) *N*
Chelmsford *p187* 01245 355300

Riches, J (Withers LLP) *T2 W*
London EC4 *p92* 020 7597 6000

Riches, Ms S M (George Ide LLP) *Zr*
Chichester *p192* 01243 786668

Richetta, Mrs A (Spicketts Battrick Law Practice) *D1 S2 C1 K3 J1 K1 K2 Zh L N S1 V W*
Cardiff *p181* 029 2046 1480

Richeux, Mrs S (Nottinghamshire County Council Legal Services Division)
West Bridgford *p475* 0115 977 3478

Richman, C (Teacher Stern LLP) *L B1 R1 Zb Ze Zq*
London WC1 *p86* 020 7242 3191

Richmond, C (Middleweeks Solicitors) *G H Q B2*
Manchester *p307* 0161 839 7255

Richmond, Mrs E (Stallard March & Edwards) *W T2 S1*
Worcester *p440* 01905 723561

Richmond, H R (Royal College of Nursing)
London W1 *p109* 020 7409 3333

Richmond, Miss M J (Lovell Son & Pitfield) *S1 W*
Camden *p55* 020 7242 7883

Richmond, M R (The Wood Glaister Partnership)
Solihull *p383* 0121 705 8151

Richmond, N (Brecher) *B1 E R1 S1 Zb Zj*
London W1 *p15* 020 7563 1000

Richmond, P (Napthens LLP) *S1 S2*
Chorley *p194* 0845 260 2111

Richmond, Mrs R E (Richmond & Co) *C1 S2 E S1 K1 W L Zl O Q N*
Horsforth *p253* 0113 259 1188

Richmond, R F (Ascroft Whiteside) *K4 S1 W*
Blackpool *p146* 01253 766866

Richmond-Sterry, Mrs S J (Oxley & Coward Solicitors LLP) *S2 E*
Rotherham *p367* 01709 510999

Richmond-Sterry, T G (Thompsons (formerly Robin/Brian Thompson & Partners)) *N*
Sheffield *p377* 0114 270 3300

Rickaby, Miss A (Berry Smith LLP) *O Q*
Cardiff *p177* 029 2034 5511

Rickard, I F (Mid Suffolk District Council)
Ipswich *p462* 01449 720711

Rickard, Ms J M (Nabarro LLP) *P L J1 F1 R1*
London WC1 *p63* 020 7524 6000

Rickard, M H (Slade Legal) *S1 W*
Abingdon *p114* 01235 521920

Rickard, Ms T (Ashurst LLP)
London EC2 *p7* 020 7638 1111

Rickard, W J (Lester Aldridge LLP) *K1 D1 M1 P E L G J1 N*
London WC2 *p53* 0844 967 0785

Rickards, Ms J E (Peters & Peters) *M1 G N*
London EC4 *p67* 020 7629 7991

Rickatson, Mrs L (Grays) *A1 C1 S1 W E Zd Zx Zn R2 S2*
York *p444* 01904 634771

Rickenberg, Miss C J (Stewarts Law LLP) *N*
London EC4 *p83* 020 7822 8000

Ricketts, P M C (Will Harrington & Co) *G H N B2*
Sutton Coldfield *p403* 0121 321 1999

Ricketts, R A (Clark Ricketts LLP) *M3*
London WC2 *p20* 020 7240 6767

Ricketts, S (SJ Berwin LLP)
London EC4 *p75* 020 7111 2222

Rickitt, S E (Northumberland County Council)
Morpeth *p466* 01670 533000

Ricklow, H I (Collyer Bristow LLP) *Zf Ze I Zw C1 U2 U1 Zz M3 C3 M1 C2*
London WC1 *p22* 020 7242 7363

Rickman, Miss D (Penningtons) *E*
London EC2 *p66* 020 7457 3000

Ricks, Miss H F (Hanne & Co) *G H*
London SW11 *p38* 020 7228 0017

Ricks, P J (Roach Pittis) *K3 K1 D1 D2*
Newport *p328* 01983 524431

Rickwood, Mrs K A (Fareham Borough Council)
Fareham *p458* 01329 236100

Riddell, A J S (Leonie Cowen & Associates) *E S2 C1 Zu*
London NW6 *p23* 020 7604 5870

Riddell, Miss K L (Sintons LLP) *N Q*
Newcastle upon Tyne *p326* 0191 226 7878

Riddett, J D (Blocks) *W*
Ipswich *p262* 01473 230033

Riddle, A (Trowers & Hamlins)
London EC3 *p88* 020 7423 8000

Riddle, Mrs C (Morrison & Masters Limited) *K3 K1 V*
Swindon *p406* 01793 526601

Riddle, P N (Morrison & Masters Limited) *K1 Q N E C1 S1 O J1 Zl*
Swindon *p406* 01793 526601

Riddleston, C H (Saunders Goodin Riddleston Solicitors) *G H D1*
Ipswich *p263* 01473 225600

Riddy, J E (LG Lawyers)
London SE1 *p50* 020 7379 0000

Ridehalgh, P A (Marsden Rawsthorn LLP) *N Zr O Q A3 Zq L*
Preston *p357* 01772 799600

Rideough, P (Rollingsons) *N*
London EC1 *p73* 020 7611 4848

Rider, A T B (Field Fisher Waterhouse LLP)
London EC3 *p31* 020 7861 4000

Rider, M E (Parry Law)
Whitstable *p431* 01227 276276

Ridge, A P (Denison Till) *J1 B1 Zb Ze C1 C2 M1 M2 T1 I*
York *p444* 01904 611411

Ridge, C D (FBC Manby Bowdler LLP) *O Q*
Wolverhampton *p437* 01902 578000

Ridge, Ms H E (Pinsent Masons LLP)
London EC2 *p67* 020 7418 7000

Ridge, P (Bindmans LLP) *Zg L*
London WC1 *p12* 020 7833 4433

Ridgeon, Mrs M C (Prince Evans) *S1 Zh*
Ealing *p69* 020 8567 3477

Ridgway, C P (Hopley Pierce & Bird) *S1 W E L S2 K4*
Wrexham *p443* 01978 315100

Ridgway, Mrs E A (Burton Copeland LLP) *G H*
Manchester *p302* 0161 827 9500

Ridgway, G D (LDJ Solicitors) *S1 T2 W*
Nuneaton *p339* 024 7674 5000

Ridgway, I C (Rogerson Galvin) *G H L S1 W*
Ashton-under-Lyne *p120* 0161 344 2027 / 335 9005

Ridgway, R (Aaron & Partners LLP Solicitors) *W T2*
Chester *p190* 01244 405555

Ridgwell, R M (Browne Jacobson LLP) *P L N Zc Zj*
Nottingham *p336* 0115 976 6000

Riding, Miss E M (Draycott Browne Solicitors) *G H*
Manchester *p303* 0161 228 2244

Riding, J H (Underwood Solicitors LLP) *Q B1 N F1*
Westminster *p89* 020 7526 6000

Ridings, A (Holman Fenwick Willan) *O Za A3 Zj*
London EC3 *p42* 020 7264 8000

Ridings, M D (SAS Daniels LLP) *D1 F1 F2 K1 K2 Q N*
Congleton *p198* 01260 282300

Ridler, M P (Squire Sanders (UK) LLP) *Zo*
Leeds *p277* 0113 284 7000

Ridley, Ms A D (Rich & Carr Freer Bouskell) *W*
Leicester *p281* 0116 253 8021

Ridley, Miss J (Birkett Long LLP) *S1*
Chelmsford *p186* 01245 453800

Ridley, Ms K (Ashurst LLP)
London EC2 *p7* 020 7638 1111

Ridley, M E (Band Hatton LLP) *J1 Zp*
Coventry *p200* 024 7663 2121
Bromley *p167* 020 8290 0440

Ridley, M F (DLA Piper UK LLP) *Zf*
London EC2 *p24* 0870 011 1111

Ridley, Mrs M H (Beecham Fisher Ridley) *K1 K2 L M1 V W Zh K3*
Southend-on-Sea *p387* 01702 348384

Ridley, M W (Ridley & Co) *C1 S2 S1*
Westminster *p72* 020 7828 7656

Ridley, R J (Ridley's) *E S2 S1*
Witney *p436* 01993 776341

Ridout, A J (H M Revenue & Customs)
London WC2 *p106*
London WC2 *p110* 020 7210 3000

Ridout, M D (Smith Chamberlain) *B2 C3 D1 E F1 G H J1 K1 N O Q Ze Zk Zl Zr*
Wellingborough *p425* 01933 224971

Ridpath, S (Speechly Bircham LLP) *B1 O*
London EC4 *p81* 020 7427 6400

Ridsdale, M (Wedlake Bell LLP)
London WC1 *p91* 020 7395 3000

Riedel, Ms P (Linklaters LLP)
London EC2 *p54* 020 7456 2000

Riem, A J (PCB Litigation LLP) *B2 O A3 Zq L Zb B1 M2 U2 Zc*
London EC1 *p65* 020 7831 2691

Ries, Miss E (Squire Sanders (UK) LLP) *J1 Zi*
London EC2 *p81* 020 7655 1000

Ries, Ms E R (Cumberland Ellis Peirs)
London WC1 *p23* 020 7242 0422

Rieveley, Ms K G (Hodders) *S1 S2*
London SW11 *p41* 020 7720 1647

Rifkin, S I (Butcher Burns LLP) *S1 S2*
London WC1 *p16* 020 7713 7100

Rigby, Miss A (Metcalfes) *N Zm J1 Zr Q*
Bristol *p164* 0117 929 0451

Rigby, Ms C M (Bates Wells & Braithwaite London LLP) *Zd C1*
London EC4 *p11* 020 7551 7777

Rigby, G L (Garth Rigby & Co) *S1 R1 L C1 E B1 W M1 F1 P*
Ashton-in-Makerfield *p119* 01942 717378

Rigby, M (Lee Rigby Partnership) *N G H Q S1 V W K1 J1 D1 Zl*
Leyland *p283* 01772 421748

Rigby, M J (Chesworths) *B1 D1 F1 G H J1 K1 M1 P*
Stoke-on-Trent *p397* 01782 599992

Rigby, S C (Stewarts Law LLP) *N*
London EC4 *p83* 020 7822 8000

Rigby, Ms V (Garner Canning) *S1 S2 E*
Tamworth *p407* 01827 314004

Rigg, Ms B A (Bond Pearce LLP) *N Zj*
Plymouth *p349* 0845 415 0000

Rigg, Mrs C T (Pontefract Magistrates Court)
Pontefract *p468* 01977 691600

Rigg, M E (Morrish Solicitors LLP)
Leeds *p276* 0113 245 0733

Rigg, Ms S A (Watson Farley & Williams) *O M1 Q B1 Za Zk Zb*
London EC2 *p90* 020 7814 8000

Rigg, W P (Pickering & Butters) *E C1 C2 P*
Stafford *p393* 01785 603060

Riley, A (Clifford Smith & Buchanan) *S1 Q K1 N W L J1 Zv*
Burnley *p169* 01282 452611

Riley, Mrs A J (Barlows) *W S1 S2*
Leicester *p278* 0116 251 8295

Riley, B (Watson Burton LLP) *R1 P Zs*
Newcastle upon Tyne *p327* 0845 901 2100

Riley, C (Cheshire County Council)
Chester *p454* 01244 602382

Riley, Miss E (Anthony Collins Solicitors LLP) *O Q*
Birmingham *p137* 0121 200 3242

Riley, F W (Osborne Clarke) *C1*
London EC2 *p65* 020 7105 7000

Riley, G M (Graham M Riley & Co) *N O Zq*
Southport *p388* 01704 532229

Riley, J (Michelmores LLP) *W T2 A1*
Exeter *p221* 01392 688688

Riley, J (Pinsent Masons LLP)
London EC2 *p67* 020 7418 7000

Riley, J D (Sylvester Mackett) *E S2 S1 W*
Warminster *p421* 01985 217464 / 217114
Trowbridge *p414* 01225 755621

Riley, Mrs J E (Kerseys) *S1*
Ipswich *p262* 01473 213311

Riley, J J (Haworth & Nuttall) *E*
Blackburn *p145* 01254 272640

Riley, J J A (LG Lawyers) *C1*
London SE1 *p50* 020 7379 0000

Riley, J M (Mercers) *S1 E W*
Henley-on-Thames *p247* 01491 572138

Riley, Ms K (Guest Walker & Co) *S1 E W*
York *p444* 01904 624903

Riley, Mrs K (Henmans LLP) *Zq O*
Oxford *p343* 01865 781000

Riley, Mrs K D (Derbyshire County Council)
Matlock *p465* 01629 580000

Riley, Mrs L B (Rooks Rider) *E L S1*
London EC1 *p73* 020 7689 7000

Riley, Ms M (Riley Langdon)
Durham *p214* 0191 378 7620

Riley, M H C (The Bank of Tokyo Mitsubishi UFJ Ltd)
London EC2 *p104* 020 7330 5000

Riley, Ms N (Field Fisher Waterhouse LLP)
London EC3 *p31* 020 7861 4000

Riley, N D (Ewings & Co) *G H L*
London SE20 *p30* 020 8778 1126

Riley, O J D (LG Lawyers)
London SE1 *p50* 020 7379 0000

Riley, P A (Hartley Thomas & Wright) *G H Zl N Q Zq Zt Zp O Zj Zi Zg L B1 F1*
Rochdale *p365* 01706 644118

Riley, Ms P R (Terence St J Millett) *S1*
London SW7 *p82* 020 7581 7500

Riley, P W (Daybells LLP) *C1 E R1 S1 T1 W*
London E15 *p26* 020 8555 4321

Riley, R (National Grid PLC)
Warwick *p471* 01926 653000

Riley, R (Addleshaw Goddard)
Leeds *p271* 0113 209 2000

Riley, Mrs T A (Shell International Ltd)
London SE1 *p109* 020 7934 1234

Riley, W R C (Leathes Prior) *A1 E L R1 S1 T1 W Zd Zh*
Norwich *p334* 01603 610911

Riley, Miss Z L (Wright & Lord) *Q W K4 N E S1 J1*
Morecambe *p319* 01524 402050

Rimell, Mrs E H (Scaiff LLP) *N Zr J1 J2 Q S1*
Worcester *p440* 01905 727700

Rimmer, Ms A J (Stephensons Solicitors LLP) *K1 D1 D2*
Wigan *p432* 01942 777777

Rimmer, Miss B M (Morecrofts Solicitors LLP) *K4 Q S1 T2 W*
Crosby *p203* 0151 924 9234
Liverpool *p290* 0151 236 8871

Rimmer, E B (Sharp & Rimmer) *S1 W A1 L E C1 R1 F1 J1 K1 Zd Zl*
St Mawes *p392* 01326 270291

Rimmer, J R (Vincent Laverys) *G H K3 K1 D2 B2*
Preston *p357* 01772 555176

Rimmer, K M (Volks Hedleys) *B1 C1 E F1 G J1 K1 L M1 N Zo Zs*
Kensington & Chelsea *p89* 020 7584 6733

Rimmer, P (DLA Piper UK LLP)
Manchester *p303* 0870 011 1111

Rimmer, Mrs P K (HilliersHRW Solicitors) *C1 E O S2 Q Ze Zq Zc X Zi A1 B1 B2 J1 Zl*
Kempston *p264* 01234 858000

Rimmer, S (Stephen Rimmer LLP) *C1 E R1*
Eastbourne *p216* 01323 644222

Rimmer, Mrs V (IBB Solicitors) *E S2*
Uxbridge *p417* 0845 638 1381

Rimmington, A R (Eyre & Co) *S1 W E K4 S2*
Birmingham *p138* 0121 784 4722

Rimola, B P (Quality Solicitors HPJV) *G H K1 N*
Newport *p329* 01633 242526

Rinaldi, Ms S (Howells LLP) *N*
Sheffield *p376* 0114 249 6666

Rind, H J (Barber Young Burton & Rind) *S1 S2 W*
Westminster *p9* 020 3376 6706

Ring, A A (Ross & Craig) *B1 B2 G N O Q*
Westminster *p73* 020 7262 3077

Ring, M S H (Taylor Wessing) *E C1 B1 Zb Zh*
London EC4 *p86* 020 7300 7000

Ring, Ms S (Richard Buxton) *P O R1 M1 Zn Zg M2 Q*
Cambridge *p174* 01223 328933

Rinta-Suksi, Ms P (Bevan Brittan LLP)
Birmingham *p135* 0870 194 1000

Rintoul, D A J (ClarksLegal LLP) *O A3 Zq*
Reading *p360* 0118 958 5321

Riordan Nicholas, D (Gardner Croft LLP) *Q Zq O L R1 R2 B1*
Canterbury *p176* 01227 813400

Riordan, Miss K (Cheshire East Council)
Sandbach *p464* 0300 123 5500

Riordan, Ms M (Russell Jones & Walker)
London WC2 *p74* 020 7657 1555

Riordan, Ms S C (McGrigors LLP)
London EC4 *p56* 020 7054 2500

Riossi, N C (Cheltenham & Gloucester PLC) *M1 N P B1 F1 C1 Ze*
Gloucester *p459* 01452 372372

Riozzi, Miss C M (Moss Solicitors LLP) *G H*
Loughborough *p293* 01509 217770

Ripley, Mrs C F (Field Seymour Parkes) *C1 Ze*
Reading *p360* 0118 951 6200

Ripley, D (Cleaver Thompson Ltd) *S1 W K1 K3 S2*
Clay Cross *p195* 01246 865048

Ripley, R (Langleys)
York *p445* 01904 610886

Ripley, Ms T (Hart Reade) *J1 N Q*
Eastbourne *p215* 01323 727321

Ripman, J (Gotelee) *O Q G L*
Ipswich *p262* 01473 211121

Ripman, J J P (Mills & Reeve) *T2 W*
Norwich *p335* 01603 660155

Ripman, J W (Gotelee) *P N Zt Zq*
Ipswich *p262* 01473 211121

Rippon, A (Rooks Rider)
London EC1 *p73* 020 7689 7000

Rippon, A B (McGrigors LLP) *C1 Zj*
London EC4 *p56* 020 7054 2500

Rippon, P D W (Blake Lapthorn) *B1*
Oxford *p342* 01865 248607

Risbridger, J A H (W Davies) *S1*
Woking *p436* 01483 744900

See p634 for the Key to Work Categories

Riseam, C F (Riseam Sharples)
London WC2 *p72* 020 7836 9555

Riseborough, Ms N (Lucas & Wyllys) *K1*
Great Yarmouth *p234* 01493 855555

Rishko, Mrs M R (Gwynne Hughes)
Aberaeron *p113* 01545 570861

Rispin, P W (Lockings) *S1 W A1 C1 E F1 R1*
Hull *p257* 0845 075 4197

Rissbrook, Ms A (Brabners Chaffe Street) *S1*
Liverpool *p286* 0151 600 3000

Ritchie, A J A (Transco)
Gloucester *p459* 01452 307307

Ritchie, Mrs C (Martyn Prowel) *C1 S2 E K3 K1 C2 S1*
Cardiff *p180* 029 2047 0909

Ritchie, D F (Shepherd Harris & Co) *S1 E S2 W C1 F1 L*
Enfield *p219* 020 8363 8341

Ritchie, G D (British Telecommunications PLC) *C3*
London EC1 *p104* 020 7356 6181

Ritchie, G R (Margetts & Ritchie) *S1 W S2*
Birmingham *p140* 0121 236 5517

Ritchie, J E (Margetts & Ritchie) *F1 F2 Zy S1 W*
Birmingham *p140* 0121 236 5517

Ritchie, Mrs J E M (Kitsons LLP) *K1 K2 K3*
Newton Abbot *p329* 01626 203366

Ritchie, Ms M S (Squire Sanders (UK) LLP) *C1 I C3 Ze Zf*
London EC2 *p81* 020 7655 1000

Ritson, F J (Addleshaw Goddard) *O Q B1*
London EC1 *p4* 020 7606 8855

Ritson, N C (Austin Ray) *S1*
Milton Keynes *p316* 01908 769648

Ritter, S (Phillips & Co) *G H K1 D1*
Salisbury *p371* 01722 321666

Ritzema, G (BHP Law) *O J1*
Newcastle upon Tyne *p323* 0191 221 0898

Rivero, Ms D (Radcliffes Le Brasseur)
Westminster *p70* 020 7222 7040

Rivers, C H (Treasures) *S1 W A1 Zv*
Gloucester *p230* 01452 525351

Rivers, C J (HFC Legal Department)
Windsor *p476* 01344 892435

Rivers, Miss E (Dutton Gregory) *N*
Winchester *p433* 01962 844333

Rivers, Ms G (Collyer Bristow LLP)
London WC1 *p22* 020 7242 7363

Rivers, Mrs P A (Robertson Rivers) *K1 W J1 K3 L*
East Molesey *p215* 020 8979 6077

Rivers, T (Bells Solicitors) *C1 E Q I B1 C2*
Farnham *p224* 01252 733733

Rivett, J (Rodney Warren & Co) *G H*
Eastbourne *p216* 01323 430430

Rivett-Carnac, Ms L (Radcliffes Le Brasseur) *J1*
Westminster *p70* 020 7222 7040

Rix, C (Hogan Lovells International LLP)
London EC1 *p42* 020 7296 2000

Rix, D C W (Rix Mclaren) *D1 F1 G H J1 L M1 N S1*
Scunthorpe *p373* 01724 872038

Rix, R H (Hallett & Co) *S1 W A1 Zl*
Ashford *p119* 01233 625711

Rixon, J R (Rich & Carr Freer Bouskell) *K1 L S1 W*
Leicester *p281* 0116 253 8021

Rixon, P (Chevron Texaco)
London E14 *p105* 020 7719 3000

Rixon, R N E (Bramsdon & Childs) *C1 E L*
Southsea *p388* 023 9282 1251

Riza, Miss A (T R Taner & Co) *S1 G H K1 W C1 E L M1 Zl*
Haringey *p85* 020 8348 1267

Rizvi, R (Manches LLP) *Ze Zk F2 O C1 Zf I Zj Zg Zq Zw M4 Q U1*
London WC2 *p58* 020 7404 4433

Roach, D A (Murray Roach Solicitors) *Q K1 N O L F1 G*
Nailsea *p320* 01275 858266 / 852705

Roach, D M (Maitland Walker) *N S1 Q K1 L O W C1 B1*
Minehead *p318* 01643 707777

Roach, Ms N (Taylor Walton LLP) *J1*
Luton *p295* 01582 731161

Roach, W D A (DAC Beachcroft) *N J2 Zw Zy B2 Zp*
Birmingham *p137* 0121 698 5200

Roache, P J (Philip Roache) *S1 S2 W E*
Pembroke Dock *p345* 01646 682603

Roantree, Mrs C E (Colemans - CTTS) *N Zr*
Kingston upon Thames *p267* 020 8296 9966

Roath, D S (Paris Smith LLP) *J1*
Southampton *p386* 023 8048 2482

Robathan, E (The College of Law)
London WC1 *p105* 0800 289997

Robb, D S (Frank Howard) *G H*
Warrington *p422* 01925 653481

Robb, P (Hogan Lovells International LLP)
London EC1 *p42* 020 7296 2000

Robb, S J G (Shakespeares) *N P J2 Q*
Nottingham *p339* 0115 945 3700

Robb, Miss S M (Decca Music Group Ltd) *O Q*
London W4 *p105* 020 8742 5420
London W1 *p52* 020 7935 4665

Robb-John, A (Celador Productions Ltd) *Zf*
London WC2 *p105* 020 7240 8101

Robbins, A (Whitehead Monckton) *M1 O Q C3 Zc*
Maidstone *p299* 01622 698000

Robbins, Ms A (Bond Pearce LLP) *E S1*
Southampton *p385* 0845 415 0000

Robbins, J N (Marshall Hatchick) *R2 S2 S1 E L R1 Zh*
Woodbridge *p439* 01394 388411

Robbins, Miss K (Roythornes LLP) *B1 F1 F2 Ze U2 O Q*
Nottingham *p338* 0115 948 4555

Robbins, Miss L (Squire Sanders (UK) LLP)
Manchester *p310* 0161 830 5000

Robbins, Ms P (Rooks Rider) *O J1*
London EC1 *p73* 020 7689 7000

Robbins, Q (Broadbents) *Q K1 N G*
Sutton-in-Ashfield *p404* 01623 441123

Roberson, A (Magrath LLP) *Zf O Q C1 F1 Zk Ze B2 Zd*
London W1 *p57* 020 7495 3003

Roberson, Mrs L (3i PLC)
London SW1 *p103* 020 7928 3131

Robert, D A (Wigan Borough Council)
Wigan *p476* 01942 244991

Robert, G (Linklaters LLP)
London EC2 *p54* 020 7456 2000

Roberton, T W (James Mason Tucker) *S1 K1 M1 W E L F1 P C1 J1 Zm*
Newton Abbot *p329* 01626 204060

Roberts, A (Edward Hands & Lewis) *C1 S1 S2 E C2*
Loughborough *p293* 01509 216161

Roberts, A (Alan Roberts & Co) *J1 N F1 J2 K1 L Q O C1 Zl Zk Zq Zp*
Chester *p191* 01244 562754

Roberts, Ms A (Pinsent Masons LLP)
London EC2 *p67* 020 7418 7000

Roberts, Mrs A (Enfield Magistrates Court)
London N17 *p106* 020 8808 5411

Roberts, A (DLA Piper UK LLP)
Liverpool *p287* 0870 011 1111

Roberts, A (Poole Alcock) *N Q*
Nantwich *p320* 01270 625478

Roberts, A C (Lanyon Bowdler LLP) *G H*
Shrewsbury *p379* 01743 280280

Roberts, A J (Leeds Day) *J1 E*
St Ives *p392* 01480 464600

Roberts, A J (Travers Smith LLP) *C2*
London EC1 *p87* 020 7295 3000

Roberts, A J (Marks & Spencer PLC)
London W2 *p107* 020 7935 4422

Roberts, A P (Linklaters LLP)
London EC2 *p54* 020 7456 2000

Roberts, B (Middlesbrough Council) *R1 Zu*
Middlesbrough *p465* 01642 245432

Roberts, B (Evans-Roberts) *A1 D1 G H K1 N Q S1 S2 W*
Machynlleth *p298* 01654 702335 / 702336

Roberts, B J (Jackson Parton) *Za A3 O Q*
London EC3 *p45* 020 7702 0085

Roberts, Ms B J (Bendall Roberts) *S1 W*
Ely *p218* 01353 663581

Roberts, Mrs C (Wychavon District Council)
Pershore *p468* 01386 565000

Roberts, C C B (Reckitt Benckiser PLC)
Slough *p471* 01753 217800

Roberts, C J L (Sansbury Douglas) *G H*
Bristol *p164* 0117 926 5341

Roberts, D (Hempsons) *N Zr*
Harrogate *p240* 01423 522331

Roberts, Mrs D (Stephensons Solicitors LLP) *D1 K1*
Manchester *p310* 0161 832 8844

Roberts, D A (Jones Day) *E*
London EC4 *p46* 020 7039 5959

Roberts, Mrs D A (Barnsley Metropolitan Borough Council)
Barnsley *p448* 01226 770770

Roberts, D C (J W Hughes & Co) *G K1 M1 F1 H D1 N P Zk Zm*
Conwy *p199* 01492 596596

Roberts, D J E (CMS Cameron McKenna LLP)
London EC3 *p17* 020 7367 3000

Roberts, D L (H F T Gough & Co) *G H K1 N Q J1 J2 F1 L Zm Zl*
Whitehaven *p431* 01946 692461

Roberts, D L (Hugh James) *E L Zh R2 S2*
Cardiff *p179* 029 2022 4871

Roberts, D M (Cardiff County Council)
Cardiff *p453* 029 2087 2000

Roberts, D M (Rich & Carr Freer Bouskell) *N G H Q Zl*
Leicester *p281* 0116 253 8021

Roberts, D M (DAC Beachcroft) *E L Zb*
London EC4 *p24* 020 7936 2222

Roberts, D M (Sandersons) *D1 K1 N Q D2 Zi Zq*
Hull *p258* 01482 324662

Roberts, Ms D S (KBL Solicitors) *E*
Bolton *p149* 01204 527777

Roberts, D T (Cardiff County Council)
Cardiff *p453* 029 2087 2000

Roberts, Miss E M (Newark & Sherwood District Council)
Newark *p466* 01636 650000

Roberts, E W (Lees Solicitors LLP) *N Zr*
Birkenhead *p134* 0151 647 9381

Roberts, F (Ingrams) *S1 W E L M1 N P T1*
Thornton Cleveleys *p411* 01253 824111

Roberts, G (Pinsent Masons LLP)
London EC2 *p67* 020 7418 7000

Roberts, Ms G (Freeth Cartwright LLP) *E*
Nottingham *p337* 0115 936 9369

Roberts, G (Benjamin Roberts Solicitors)
Halifax *p238* 01422 356633

Roberts, G D (Thompsons (formerly Robin/Brian Thompson & Partners)) *J1 M1 N Zo*
Plymouth *p350* 01752 675810

Roberts, G J (Herbert Smith LLP) *C1 C2*
London EC2 *p40* 020 7374 8000

Roberts, G L P (Spratt Endicott) *S2 E*
Banbury *p122* 01295 204000

Roberts, H (Canter Levin & Berg) *D1 K1*
Liverpool *p287* 0151 239 1000

Roberts, Miss H (Denbighshire County Council)
Ruthin *p470* 01824 706000

Roberts, Ms H A R (Aventis Pharma Limited T/A Sanofi-Aventis) *C1 C3 M1 C2 I T1 M2 J1 E Ze Zo Zj*
Guildford *p459* 01483 505515

Roberts, Mrs H C (Mayo Wynne Baxter LLP) *T2 W*
Lewes *p283* 01273 477071

Roberts, H G (Tudur Owen Roberts Glynne & Co) *G H M1 K1 S1 F1 J1 V D1 L Zl Zp*
Blaenau Ffestiniog *p147* 01766 830206
Caernarfon *p172* 01286 672207 / 672851
Holyhead *p251* 01407 762374

Roberts, H G B (BKRW Limited) *G H M1 P K1 D1*
Folkestone *p226* 01303 255369

Roberts, H S (Darbys Solicitors LLP) *B1 O G Ze*
Oxford *p343* 01865 811700
Leeds *p277* 0113 284 7000

Roberts, Ms I (Simmons & Simmons)
London EC2 *p79* 020 7628 2020

Roberts, I M (SNR Denton) *F1 Zh*
London EC4 *p75* 020 7242 1212

Roberts, I M V (Breese-Gwyndaf) *S1 W Q N L T2 F1 A1*
Porthmadog *p353* 01766 512253 / 514227

Roberts, J (Barlow Lyde & Gilbert LLP)
London EC3 *p10* 020 7247 2277

Roberts, Miss J (Paris Smith LLP)
Southampton *p386* 023 8048 2482

Roberts, J (Simmons & Simmons)
London EC2 *p79* 020 7628 2020

Roberts, Ms J (Bristol City Council) *Q Zi*
Bristol *p451* 0117 922 2000

Roberts, J (Department for Business, Enterprise and Regulatory Reform)
London SW1 *p105* 020 7215 0105

Roberts, J (Meikles) *S1 A1 W L E S2 K4*
Barnard Castle *p123* 01833 690505

Roberts, Ms J (Thomson & Bancks LLP) *N Q O*
Tewkesbury *p410* 01684 299633

Roberts, J A (Ronald Fletcher Baker LLP) *C1 L B1 O Zi Zl Ze*
London EC1 *p73* 020 7613 1402

Roberts, Mrs J A (Nowell Meller Solicitors Limited) *K1 K3*
Stafford *p393* 01785 252377

Roberts, J D (Lee Rigby Partnership) *G H N Q*
Leyland *p283* 01772 421748

Roberts, J D (Springfield Advice & Law Centre)
London SW17 *p109* 020 8767 6884

Roberts, Mrs J E (Jane E Roberts) *D1 K1*
Northampton *p332* 01604 494431

Roberts, J G (Cyngor Sir Ynys Mon (Isle of Anglesey County Council))
Llangefni *p463* 01248 750057

Roberts, J H (Salford City Council)
Swinton *p473* 0161 794 4711

Roberts, J H (Harvey Roberts) *S1 K1 M1 P W F1 G J1 C1*
Stockport *p395* 0161 443 2828

Roberts, J H A (Bendall Roberts) *S1 W*
Ely *p218* 01353 663581

Roberts, J J (Powis & Co) *Q N O K1 F1*
Clacton-on-Sea *p195* 01255 233400

Roberts, J L (Gullands) *G H B2*
Maidstone *p299* 01622 678341

Roberts, J M (Jeremy Roberts & Co) *K1 M1 G H J1 N P D1 F1 V Zf*
Peterborough *p347* 01733 343943 / 342172

Roberts, J M (Waldrons)
Brierley Hill *p158* 01384 811811

Roberts, J M (Warners Solicitors) *C1 J1 C2 Ze*
Tonbridge *p412* 01732 770660

Roberts, Ms J M P (English Partnerships)
Milton Keynes *p466* 01908 692692

Roberts, Mrs J P (Crombie Wilkinson) *C1 C2*
York *p444* 01904 624185
York *p444* 01904 690111

Roberts, J P (Chafes) *K1 P G F1 D1 M1 J1 V H W Zh Zi Zj*
Wilmslow *p433* 01625 531676

Roberts, Mrs J R (Cannings Connolly) *E S2*
London EC1 *p18* 020 7329 9000

Roberts, Mrs J S (Granville-West Chivers & Morgan) *K1 M1 D1 W S1 P*
Newport *p328* 01495 243268

Roberts, J T (Plexus Law (A Trading Name of Parabis Law LLP)) *N O Q Zj A3 Zu E*
London EC3 *p68* 0844 245 4000

Roberts, J T P (Goodman Derrick LLP) *C1 C2*
London EC4 *p36* 020 7404 0606

Roberts, Mrs J V (Terry Jones Solicitors & Advocates) *S1 W*
Newport *p329* 01952 810307

Roberts, J W (Collins Benson Goldhill LLP) *B1 Zb J1 O*
Westminster *p21* 020 7436 5151

Roberts, J W (Bradbury Roberts & Raby) *N J1 F1 O Q*
Scunthorpe *p373* 01724 854000

Roberts, J W V (Nelsons) *P N*
Nottingham *p338* 0115 958 6262

Roberts, Miss K (Pickerings LLP) *O Q*
Tamworth *p407* 01827 317070

Roberts, K (Thompsons (formerly Robin/Brian Thompson & Partners)) *N*
London SW19 *p87* 020 8947 4163

Roberts, Miss K (Drysdales) *S1 W K4 L*
Southend-on-Sea *p387* 01702 423400

Roberts, K (Morrison & Foerster (UK) LLP)
London EC2 *p62* 020 7920 4000

Roberts, Ms K (Herbert Smith LLP)
London EC2 *p40* 020 7374 8000

Roberts, Mrs L (Russell-Cooke LLP) *S2*
London SW15 *p74* 020 8789 9111

Roberts, Miss L (Terrells LLP) *K1 K3 D1*
Peterborough *p347* 01733 896789

Roberts, Miss L (Fletchers) *N Q*
Southport *p388* 01704 546919

Roberts, L (G T Stewart Solicitors) *N*
London SE22 *p83* 020 8299 6000

Roberts, Mrs L J (Wrexham County Borough Council) *K1 V F1*
Wrexham *p477* 01978 292000

Roberts, L W (Guildford Borough Council) *R1 Q O C1*
Guildford *p459* 01483 505050

Roberts, Mrs M (Foot Anstey)
Taunton *p408* 01823 625600

Roberts, Ms M (Hugh James)
Cardiff *p179* 029 2022 4871

Roberts, Mrs M (Phillips Solicitors) *C1 E R1 S1 Zl*
Basingstoke *p127* 01256 460830

Roberts, M C (Pinsent Masons LLP) *O Q Zc*
London EC2 *p67* 020 7418 7000

Roberts, Ms M J (Edwards Angell Palmer & Dodge)
London EC2 *p28* 020 7583 4055

Roberts, M J (Ramsdens Solicitors) *W T2 Zd R2 S1 E*
Huddersfield *p256* 01484 821500

Roberts, M O (The Ringrose Law Group - Paul Cooper) *F1 M1 N O Q*
Boston *p151* 01205 311511

Roberts, M R (Irwin Mitchell LLP) *Zj*
Sheffield *p376* 0870 150 0100

Roberts, M W (Tinsdills) *Q*
Hanley *p239* 01782 262031

Roberts, N (Jones Day) *E*
London EC4 *p46* 020 7039 5959

Roberts, N J (Kieran & Co) *P M1 N G H J1 K1 F1*
Worcester *p440* 01905 28635

Roberts, N J (Gloucestershire County Council - Legal & Democratic Services)
Gloucester *p459* 01452 425203

Roberts, N S (Abels)
Southampton *p385* 023 8022 0317

Roberts, Mrs N W (Howell Jones & Co) *W T1 L S1 A1 C1 E T2 Zd*
Abergele *p113* 01745 826282 / 825845
Llanrwst *p292* 01492 640277

Roberts, O (Guthrie Jones & Jones) *N O G Q K1 S1 W L A1 X Zl Zu Zv Zr Zz*
Dolgellau *p211* 01341 422604
Bala *p121* 01678 520428

Roberts, P (Ellisons) *E*
Colchester *p197* 01206 764477

Roberts, P A (Cowley Di Giorgio & Co) *W S1 S2 E K1 K3 Q K4*
Bedford *p129* 01234 218171

Roberts, P A (Forsters LLP) *E L*
Westminster *p33* 020 7863 8333

Roberts, P E (Clarkes) *A1 C1 C2 E L R1 S1 S2 W*
Telford *p409* 01952 291666

Roberts, Miss P J (Fentons)
Failsworth *p223* 0161 682 7101

Roberts, P K (Keelys LLP)
Lichfield *p284* 01543 420000

Roberts, P S (O'Donnells) *Zm*
Preston *p357* 01772 881000

Roberts, R (Roberts Buckley)
Manchester *p309* 0161 835 1234

Roberts, Mrs R (Edwards Duthie) *L V*
London E6 *p29* 020 8514 9000

Roberts, R (Brabners Chaffe Street)
Liverpool *p286* 0151 600 3000

Roberts, R A (Gedye & Sons (Solicitors) Ltd) *W Zd K4 Zm S2 E L S1*
Grange-over-Sands *p232* 01539 532313

Roberts, Ms R D (Leeds City Council)
Leeds *p462* 0113 224 3513

Roberts, Ms R J (Derbyshire County Council)
Matlock *p465* 01629 580000

Roberts, R L (Loveday & Keighley) *S1 L W S2 E Q F1 Zi*
Matlock *p313* 01629 583142 / 56660

Roberts, R M (Sheridans) *C1 Zf Ze*
London WC1 *p78* 020 7079 0100

Roberts, Miss R M L (Myer Wolff) *S1 S2*
Hull *p257* 01482 223693

Roberts, R P N (Peter Roberts Solicitor) *S1 W R2 R1 L E S2 Zc T2 Zd K4 A1 F1 C1*
Alrewas *p116* 01283 790045

Roberts, Miss S (Holman Fenwick Willan)
London EC3 *p42* 020 7264 8000

Roberts, Mrs S (Dean Wilson Laing) *K1 V K3*
Brighton *p159* 01273 327241

Roberts, Miss S (Larken & Co) *V K1*
Newark *p322* 01636 703333

Roberts, S (IBB Solicitors) *K1 K3 K2*
Chesham *p189* 0845 638 1381

Roberts, Miss S (Darbys Solicitors LLP) *C2 C1 Zb Zd*
Oxford *p343* 01865 811700

Roberts, S (Allen & Overy LLP)
London E1 *p5* 020 3088 0000

Roberts, Miss S (Derbyshire County Council)
Matlock *p465* 01629 580000

Roberts, S (Penningtons) *J1*
London EC2 *p66* 020 7457 3000

Roberts, S (Stephenson Harwood) *O Zq*
London EC2 *p82* . . . 020 7329 4422
Roberts, S (The College of Law)
London WC1 *p105* . . . 0800 289997
Roberts, Mrs S (Harborough District Council)
Market Harborough *p465* . . . 01858 821341
Roberts, Mrs S (FDC Law) *W*
Frome *p228* . . . 01373 465051
Roberts, Ms S A (Mincoffs Solicitors LLP) *O Q L*
Newcastle upon Tyne *p325* . 0191 281 6151
Roberts, S D (Cripps Harries Hall LLP) *C2 C1 U2 F2*
Tunbridge Wells *p415* . . . 01892 515121
Roberts, Mrs S E (Gwynedd Council)
Caernarfon *p452* . . . 01286 672255
Roberts, S J (Pemberton Greenish LLP) *L Q*
London SW3 *p66* . . . 020 7591 3333
Roberts, S J (Bird Wilford & Sale) *K1 Q J1 G Zi*
Loughborough *p293* . . . 01509 232611
Roberts, S J (Stephen Roberts & Co) *K1 D1 G H S1 W*
Tilbury *p411* . . . 01375 841841
Roberts, Ms T (Charles Russell LLP) *K1*
London EC4 *p19* . . . 020 7203 5000
Roberts, T B (Ian N Gunby & Co) *D1 G H J1 K1 L*
Milnthorpe *p316* . . . 01539 562044
Barrow-in-Furness *p125* . . . 01229 811811
Roberts, T I (Irwin Mitchell LLP) *C1 C2*
Sheffield *p376* . . . 0870 150 0100
Roberts, T P (Heringtons) *W E S1 L C1 A1 T1 Zl Zm*
Battle *p128* . . . 01424 772401
Roberts, T R (Geoffrey Leaver Solicitors LLP) *C1*
Milton Keynes *p317* . . . 01908 692769
Roberts, T S (Field Seymour Parkes) *E S2 S1 C1*
Reading *p360* . . . 0118 951 6200
Roberts, Ms V (Herbert Smith LLP)
London EC2 *p40* . . . 020 7374 8000
Roberts, Ms V (Malcolm C Foy & Co) *J1 L Q*
Doncaster *p211* . . . 01302 340005
Roberts, W (Roberts Solicitors)
Macclesfield *p297* . . . 01625 431111
Roberts, Ms Y L (Max Bitel Greene LLP) *Ze O Zw Zf J1 Q B1 U2 Zza*
Islington *p59* . . . 020 7354 2767
Robertshaw, J M (Kirbys) *Q J1 N O Zq F1 F2 L A1 B1 Zl Zr Zc C3 C1*
Harrogate *p240* . . . 01423 542000
Robertshaw, N A (Zermansky & Partners) *K1 K3*
Leeds *p278* . . . 0113 245 9766
Roberts-Jenkins, Ms R (DAC Beachcroft)
Bristol *p162* . . . 0117 918 2000
Robertson, Ms A J (Tameside Metropolitan Borough Council)
Ashton-under-Lyne *p447* . . . 0161 342 3028
Robertson, A J (T G Baynes) *W K4 T2*
Bexleyheath *p132* . . . 020 8301 7777
Robertson, Ms A M (Squire Sanders (UK) LLP)
Birmingham *p142* . . . 0121 222 3000
Robertson, B (Davenport Lyons) *B1 O B2*
London W1 *p25* . . . 020 7468 2600
Robertson, C (Seddons)
Westminster *p77* . . . 020 7725 8000
Robertson, Ms D (DR Solicitors) *C1 I*
Guildford *p236* . . . 01483 511555
Robertson, D (Fenwick Elliott) *O Q Zi Zc A3 P Zj R2*
London WC2 *p31* . . . 020 7421 1986
Robertson, D B (Robertson Rivers) *S1 W E S2*
East Molesey *p215* . . . 020 8979 6077
Robertson, D F (Lupton Fawcett)
Leeds *p275* . . . 0113 280 2000
Robertson, Ms E M (Addleshaw Goddard) *C1 J1 Q*
London EC1 *p4* . . . 020 7606 8855
London EC4 *p67* . . . 020 7629 7991
Robertson, Miss F A (North Somerset District Council)
Weston-super-Mare *p476* . . . 01934 888888
Robertson, G (J Sainsbury PLC)
London EC1 *p109* . . . 020 7695 6000
Robertson, Mrs H (Veale Wasbrough Vizards) *W T2 Zd*
Bristol *p165* . . . 0117 925 2020
Robertson, I (Pinders) *S1 W E C1 L R1 T1 A1 B1 Zc*
Derby *p209* . . . 01332 364751
Robertson, I C (Howell-Jones LLP) *S1 S2 E*
London SW20 *p43* . . . 020 8947 7991
East Molesey *p215* . . . 020 8979 6077
Robertson, I M (Abrahams Dresden) *O B1 F1 A3*
London EC1 *p3* . . . 020 7251 3663
Horsham *p253* . . . 01403 262333
Robertson, J (Stephenson Harwood) *I U2*
London EC2 *p82* . . . 020 7329 4422
Robertson, J V A (Silverman Sherliker LLP) *O Q A3 Zk*
London EC2 *p78* . . . 020 7749 2700
Robertson, Mrs K J (John Welch & Stammers) *K3 K1*
Witney *p436* . . . 01993 703941
Robertson, Miss L (John Hodge Solicitors) *N Q Zq Zr*
Weston-super-Mare *p429* . . . 01934 623511
Robertson, Ms L (Jones Day) *C2*
London EC4 *p46* . . . 020 7039 5959
Robertson, Ms M (Withers LLP) *O J1 Q C3 M1 Zo Zp*
London EC4 *p92* . . . 020 7597 6000
Robertson, M (Jones Robertson) *G H J1 K1 E F1 P R1 S1 W*
Widnes *p431* . . . 0151 423 3661
Robertson, Mrs M (Lopian Wagner) *J1 L*
Manchester *p307* . . . 0161 834 2324
Robertson, M A (Drysdales) *C1 S2 E L R2 S1*
Southend-on-Sea *p387* . . . 01702 423400
Robertson, N (Hunters) *T2 W*
London WC2 *p44* . . . 020 7412 0050
Robertson, Miss N L (Wolferstans) *K1*
Plymouth *p351* . . . 01752 663295
Robertson, N R (Mayer Brown International LLP) *J1*
London EC2 *p59* . . . 020 3130 3000
Robertson, P C B (Hampshire County Council)
Winchester *p476* . . . 01962 841841
Robertson, R A (Lester Aldridge LLP) *E L S1 C1 Zj Zc*
Bournemouth *p152* . . . 01202 786161
Robertson, Ms S (Ashurst LLP)
London EC2 *p7* . . . 020 7638 1111
Robertson, S (Stephenson Harwood)
London EC2 *p82* . . . 020 7329 4422
Robertson, Mrs S A (The Manchester Airport Group PLC)
Manchester *p465* . . . 0871 271 0711
Robertson, Miss V H (BTMK Solicitors LLP) *K1*
Southend-on-Sea *p387* . . . 01702 339222
Robertson, W (Howlett Clarke Solicitors) *S1*
Hove *p254* . . . 01273 419728
Robeson, S P T (Kidd Rapinet) *O Q N J1 L*
London WC2 *p49* . . . 020 7205 2115
London EC4 *p77* . . . 020 7583 2105
Robins, A G (Strick & Bellingham) *E L S1 W S2 T2*
Swansea *p405* . . . 01792 641201
Robins, A J (Keoghs LLP) *C1 C2 W*
Bolton *p149* . . . 01204 677000
Robins, Miss C A (Pinsent Masons LLP) *T1*
Birmingham *p141* . . . 0121 200 1050
Robins, I J N (Carlsons) *S1 S2 E C1 W*
London N20 *p18* . 020 8445 3331 / 8445 5752
Robins, J A (Bond Pearce LLP) *Zj N*
Southampton *p385* . . . 0845 415 0000
Robins, Mrs K (Parlett Kent) *Zr N X*
Exeter *p222* . . . 01392 494455
Robins, M G (Ashurst LLP) *Zb*
London EC2 *p7* . . . 020 7638 1111
Robins, P D (Sackvilles) *S1 E C1 L W R1 Zl*
Hornchurch *p252* . . . 01708 446704
Robins, S J (Gabbitas Robins) *S1 F1 C1 E P R1 W L*
Marlow *p313* . . . 01628 472600
Robinson, A (Brutton & Co) *W S1 T1*
Fareham *p223* . . . 01329 236171
Robinson, A (Fishers) *K1 K3 D1 Q D2*
Ashby-de-la-Zouch *p118* . . . 01530 412167
Robinson, A (Linder Myers Solicitors)
Manchester *p306* . . . 0844 984 6000
Robinson, A C (Unisys Insurance Services Limited)
Liverpool *p463* . . . 0151 328 2918
Robinson, Mrs A E (Shakespeares) *S2 E A1*
Nottingham *p339* . . . 0115 945 3700
Robinson, Miss A K (Blake Lapthorn) *J1*
Oxford *p342* . . . 01865 248607
Robinson, A M (Emmerson Solicitors) *B2 G H N O Q F1 J1 Zq Zg Zr*
Gosforth *p231* . . . 0191 284 6989
Robinson, A W R (Berry Redmond & Robinson) *E K1 L S1 S2*
Weston-super-Mare *p429* . . . 01934 513963
Robinson, A W S (Robinson Le Grice) *W S1 N Za Zn K4*
St Ives *p392* . . . 01736 797973
Robinson, B (Penningtons)
London EC2 *p66* . . . 020 7457 3000
Robinson, B (TPC Solicitors) *N G L*
Manchester *p310* . . . 0161 832 8867
Robinson, Miss C (Fisher Meredith) *Zi*
Lambeth *p32* . . . 020 7091 2700
Robinson, Mrs C (Batchelor Myddelton) *E R1 S1 W L*
Potters Bar *p355* . . . 01707 647088
Robinson, Miss C A L (Stamp Jackson and Procter) *C1 C2 W E*
Hull *p258* . . . 01482 324591
Robinson, C B (Weightmans LLP) *C1 C2 C3 E S2*
Liverpool *p291* . . . 0151 227 2601
Robinson, C J (Robinsons) *E S1 W*
Shoeburyness *p378* . . . 01702 298282
Robinson, C J A (Temple Heelis LLP) *S1 W L A1 T2 C1*
Kendal *p264* . . . 01539 723757
Robinson, Ms C L (Osborne Clarke) *Zb O*
Bristol *p164* . . . 0117 917 3000
Robinson, C M (C M Robinson) *A1 E L S1 W Zc*
Deal *p207* . . . 01304 363236
Robinson, C M A (Kerman & Co LLP) *O Q*
London WC2 *p49* . . . 020 7539 7272
Robinson, D (Holman Fenwick Willan)
London EC3 *p42* . . . 020 7264 8000
Robinson, D (Ince & Co Services Ltd)
London E1 *p44* . . . 020 7481 0010
Robinson, D (Robinson & Kinrade) *C1 E F1 J1 K1 L S1*
Sutton *p403* . . . 020 8770 2020
Robinson, Mrs D (Muckle LLP) *Zc Zn O A3 Q*
Newcastle upon Tyne *p325* . 0191 211 7777
Robinson, D C (Robinsons) *D1 K1*
Liverpool *p290* . . . 0151 227 2555
Robinson, D H (Tonbridge & Malling Borough Council)
West Malling *p476* . . . 01732 876030
Robinson, Ms D J (The British Council)
London SW1 *p104* . . . 020 7389 4385
Robinson, D J R (Forsters LLP) *T2 W Zd*
Westminster *p33* . . . 020 7863 8333
Robinson, D N (FCE Bank PLC)
Brentwood *p451* . . 01277 692280 / 692281
Brentwood *p451* . . . 01277 253000
Robinson, D P (Fladgate LLP) *C1 C3 Ze*
London WC2 *p32* . . . 020 3036 7000
Robinson, D S (FBC Manby Bowdler LLP) *E S2*
Willenhall *p432* . . . 01902 366566
Robinson, Mrs E (Harthills) *K1 D1*
Rotherham *p367* . . . 01709 377399
Robinson, E F M (McGrath & Co) *G H*
Birmingham *p140* . . . 0121 643 4121
Birmingham *p140* . . . 0121 643 4124
Birmingham *p140* . . . 0121 643 4828
Robinson, G D (Lamb & Holmes) *N Q F1 Zq*
Kettering *p265* . . . 01536 513195
Robinson, G K (Hodgson & Angus) *K1 K3 S1 T2 W*
Stanhope *p394* . . . 01388 528517
Robinson, H (Mills & Reeve) *E*
Cambridge *p175* . . . 01223 364422
Robinson, H (Clifford Chance)
London E14 *p20* . . . 020 7006 1000
Robinson, I (John Barkers) *Q N L B1 Zc Zq*
Grimsby *p234* . . . 01472 358686
Robinson, Mrs I (Nottinghamshire County Council Legal Services Division)
West Bridgford *p475* . . . 0115 977 3478
Robinson, I J (Stanley Tee) *N B1 Q O*
Bishop's Stortford *p144* . . . 01279 755200
Robinson, J (Lancashire Magistrates Courts Committee)
Garstang *p458* . . . 01995 601596
Robinson, J (Ashurst LLP)
London EC2 *p7* . . . 020 7638 1111
Robinson, J (Christian Khan Solicitors) *N Zr*
London WC1 *p49* . . . 020 7631 9500
Robinson, J (Robinson Allfree) *K4 W T2*
Ramsgate *p359* . . . 01843 592361
Robinson, Mrs J (Anthony Collins Solicitors LLP) *E S2 Zh S1 L Zd*
Birmingham *p137* . . . 0121 200 3242
Robinson, Ms J (Cartwright King)
Leicester *p279* . . . 0116 253 9222
Robinson, J C (Norcliffe & Co) *S1 S2 E*
Huddersfield *p256* . . . 01484 514907
Robinson, J D (Roberts Moore Nicholas Jones) *N*
Birkenhead *p134* . . . 0151 647 0000
Robinson, J E (Robinson Allfree) *S1 W E C1 L T1*
Cliftonville *p196* . . . 01843 228635
Robinson, Ms J K (Wigan Borough Council)
Wigan *p476* . . . 01942 244991
Robinson, J T (R A W Clark & Co) *S1 L Zl*
Morpeth *p319* . . . 01670 512391
Robinson, Ms K (Cripps Harries Hall LLP) *E R2*
Tunbridge Wells *p415* . . . 01892 515121
Robinson, Miss K (Hartlaw LLP) *K3 K1 D1 Q*
Wetherby *p429* . . . 01937 547000
Robinson, K (Irwin Mitchell LLP)
London EC1 *p45* . . . 0870 150 0100
Robinson, K J (Irwin Mitchell LLP) *B2*
Sheffield *p376* . . . 0870 150 0100
Robinson, Mrs L (CVC Solicitors) *E K1 L Zl Q Zu Zm S1*
Penzance *p346* . . . 01736 362313
Robinson, Miss L (George Davies Solicitors LLP) *E R2 S2*
Manchester *p303* . . . 0161 236 8992
Robinson, Mrs L (Stewarts Law LLP) *N*
London EC4 *p83* . . . 020 7822 8000
Robinson, Miss L A (Bates Wells & Braithwaite London LLP) *E S2 R2 Zh L Zd*
London EC4 *p11* . . . 020 7551 7777
Robinson, Mrs L B (Levine Mellins Klarfeld) *S1 K1 W D1 T1 V J1*
Stanmore *p394* . . . 020 8954 7474
Robinson, L C (Hague Lambert) *W S1*
Macclesfield *p297* . . . 01625 616480
Robinson, Ms L J (Burton & Co LLP)
Lincoln *p284* . . . 01522 523215
Robinson, Mrs L J (Coodes) *E S1 S2*
Launceston *p270* . . . 01566 770000
Robinson, M (Hodge Halsall) *J1 O Q N Zk J2 C1 Zq*
Southport *p388* . . . 01704 531991
Robinson, M (Simmons & Simmons)
London EC2 *p79* . . . 020 7628 2020
Robinson, M (Wilkin Chapman Grange Solicitors) *Q N L J1 G*
Louth *p294* . . . 01507 606161
Robinson, Ms M (Thomson Snell & Passmore) *K4 W*
Tunbridge Wells *p415* . . . 01892 510000
Robinson, M (Robinsons Solicitors) *N*
Hull *p258* . . . 01482 212401
Robinson, M A (Harlow District Council)
Harlow *p460* . . . 01279 446611
Robinson, M A (County of Herefordshire District Council)
Hereford *p460* . . . 01432 260266
Robinson, M A (Boyes Turner) *O Q K1 P Zl Zi Zq*
Reading *p360* . . . 0118 959 7711
Robinson, M A H (Steven Dean Magac & Co)
Barnet *p124* . . . 020 8441 3399
Robinson, M A H (Tarbox Robinson & Partners) *C1 E J1 L M1 S1 Zc*
Northwood *p333* . . . 01923 836595
Robinson, M D J (Askews) *N J1*
Redcar *p362* . . . 01642 475252
Robinson, M E (Treasury Solicitors Department)
London WC2 *p110* . . . 020 7210 3000
Robinson, Mrs M E (John Fowlers LLP Solicitors) *S1 W*
Brightlingsea *p159* . . . 01206 302694
Colchester *p197* . . . 01206 576151
Robinson, Ms M G (R P Robinson) *D1 D2 G H K1 V*
Leicester *p281* . . . 0116 262 1462
Robinson, M L B (Michael Robinson) *B1 C1 M2 O Q Zj*
London SW7 *p72* . . . 020 7584 5038
Robinson, N (Redrow PLC) *S2 S1 W Q C1 B1*
Flint *p458* . . . 01244 520044
Robinson, N (Nowell Meller Solicitors Limited) *D1 K2 Zm*
Stafford *p393* . . . 01785 252377
Robinson, N (Awdry Bailey & Douglas) *N W Q J1 F1*
Calne *p173* . . . 01249 815110
Wootton Bassett *p439* . . . 01793 853200
Robinson, Miss N (The Dental Law Partnership)
Nantwich *p320* . . . 01270 613320
Robinson, N (Robinson & Murphy) *G H K1 S1 E C1 D1 F1 J1*
Newcastle upon Tyne *p326* . 0191 230 5023
Robinson, Ms N J (Anderson Partnership) *Q L J1*
Chesterfield *p191* . . . 01246 220737
Robinson, N R (Sandom Robinson) *L C1 A3 S2 E W R2 Zd Zw*
South Croydon *p383* . . . 020 8651 7020
Robinson, Ms N V (Barlow Lyde & Gilbert LLP)
London EC3 *p10* . . . 020 7247 2277
Robinson, P (Linklaters LLP)
London EC2 *p54* . . . 020 7456 2000
Robinson, Ms P (Kent County Council)
Maidstone *p464* . . . 01622 694320
Robinson, P (Hunters)
London WC2 *p44* . . . 020 7412 0050
Robinson, P (Langleys) *A1 E K4 R1 S1 T2 W*
York *p445* . . . 01904 610886
Robinson, Miss P A (Laytons) *K1 D2*
Manchester *p306* . . . 0161 834 2100
Robinson, P A (Paul Robinson Solicitors) *S1 E W Zc C2 Zv*
Westcliff-on-Sea *p428* . . . 01702 338338
Robinson, P C (Burges Salmon) *E*
Bristol *p161* . . . 0117 939 2000
London EC2 *p40* . . . 020 7374 8000
Robinson, P H (Muckle LLP) *C1 C2*
Newcastle upon Tyne *p325* . 0191 211 7777
Robinson, P J (Kent County Council)
Canterbury *p453* . . . 01227 767020
Robinson, P N (Marrons) *C1 P A1 E Ze R2 S2 W*
Leicester *p280* . . . 0116 289 2200
Robinson, P S (Devonalds) *S1 E W L G H J1 R1 Zl*
Pontypridd *p352* . . . 01443 404700
Robinson, Miss R (Berwins Solicitors Limited) *S1*
Harrogate *p240* . . . 01423 509000
Robinson, R (Peter Brown & Co Solicitors LLP) *O Q S2 E R2 S1*
Barnet *p124* . . . 020 8447 3277
Robinson, R I (Churchers) *G H K1 Q N Zl Zy*
Portsmouth *p354* . . . 023 9286 2424
Robinson, R P (R P Robinson) *G H S1 S2 W*
Leicester *p281* . . . 0116 262 1462
Robinson, Mrs S (Langleys) *N*
Lincoln *p284* . . . 01522 888555
Robinson, Miss S (Kidd & Spoor) *N*
Whitley Bay *p431* . . . 0191 297 0011
Robinson, Mrs S (Last Cawthra Feather LLP) *S1*
Ilkley *p261* . . . 01943 601020
Robinson, S (BHP Law)
Stockton-on-Tees *p396* . . . 01642 672770
Robinson, Miss S A (Denison Till) *E L R2*
York *p444* . . . 01904 611411
Robinson, Mrs S A (Cumbria County Council)
Carlisle *p453* . . . 01228 607374 / 607351
Robinson, S A (Kevills) *Q N O F1 Ze Zl J1 B1*
Chorley *p194* . . . 01257 265711
Robinson, S A J (Ford & Warren) *J1*
Leeds *p273* . . . 0113 243 6601
Robinson, S C (Macfarlanes) *C1 I*
London EC4 *p56* . . . 020 7831 9222
Robinson, S H (Patrick Smith & Co) *S1 W E K1 C1*
Wantage *p421* . . . 01235 772212
Robinson, Miss S J (Geraint Jones & Co) *Q J1 W Zm B1 L N*
Newtown *p330* . . . 01686 627935
Robinson, Ms S J (JPS Law Solicitors) *E J1 K1 L O*
Westminster *p45* . . . 020 7935 9955
Robinson, S M (Squire Sanders (UK) LLP) *E*
London EC2 *p81* . . . 020 7655 1000
Robinson, S P (Paul Robinson Solicitors) *S2 Zv S1*
Westcliff-on-Sea *p428* . . . 01702 338338
Robinson, S T (Browne Jacobson LLP) *N Zj A2*
Nottingham *p336* . . . 0115 976 6000
Robinson, T J L (Sheridans) *Q J1 K1 O Ze Zf Zw*
London WC1 *p78* . . . 020 7079 0100
Robinson, Ms V (Vivienne Robinson) *C3 M1 M2*
London E11 *p72* . . . 020 8279 8899
Robinson, Mrs V M (MFG Solicitors) *V*
Kidderminster *p265* . . . 01562 820181
Robinson, Mrs Y E (John Morley & Co) *K1*
Rainham *p359* . . . 01634 375444
Robinson, Mrs Z R (Raworths LLP) *K1 V D1*
Harrogate *p240* . . . 01423 566666
Robinson-Bradley, Mrs N E (Sheltons) *K1 Q V*
Nottingham *p339* . . . 0115 955 3444
Robinson-Smith, M (EMW) *Zb C1 C2*
Milton Keynes *p316* . . . 0845 070 6000

 See p634 for the Key to Work Categories

Robison, Mrs B L (Story & Robison) *K1 D1 W D2*
Norwich *p335* 01603 626355

Robley, Ms L (Ashurst LLP)
London EC2 *p7* 020 7638 1111

Roblin, C E (Passmore Lewis & Jacobs) *K1 P*
Barry *p126*. 01446 721000

Robotham, T C (Robotham & Co) *S1 S2 W T2 E*
Derby *p209* 01332 346018

Robson, Mrs A (Edwards Angell Palmer & Dodge)
London EC2 *p28*. 020 7583 4055

Robson, Mrs A J (AJR Solicitors) *Zr K3 Q N O W*
Kingswinford *p268* 0875 500 1201

Robson, B (Harding Swinburne Jackson & Co) *J1 K1 N*
Sunderland *p401*. 0191 565 8194

Robson, Ms C (Norwich Union Insurance Group)
Norwich *p467* 01603 622200

Robson, Mrs C A (Newcastle Upon Tyne City Council)
Newcastle upon Tyne *p466* . 0191 232 8520

Robson, Miss C L (Aviva PLC) *W S1*
London EC3 *p103* . . 020 7283 7500 / 01603 687905

Robson, C R (Bond Pearce LLP)
Bristol *p161* 0845 415 0000
London EC1 *p42*. 020 7296 2000

Robson, D L (Robson Palmer) *E R1 S1 W*
South Shields *p384* 0191 455 4561

Robson, D W (Payne & Payne) *N G H*
Hull *p257* 01482 326446

Robson, F A (Stuart Smith & Burnett) *S1 W E Zd*
Bridlington *p158* 01262 678128

Robson, G L (Middlesbrough Council) *K1 M1 P F1 G J1 S1*
Middlesbrough *p465* 01642 245432

Robson, G R J (Davis Blank Furniss) *K1 D1 Zi Zl*
Manchester *p303* 0161 832 3304

Robson, H (Warner Goodman LLP) *J1*
Southampton *p387*. 023 8063 9311

Robson, Miss H K (Caris Robson LLP) *K1 D1 J1 N D2 Q S1*
Newcastle upon Tyne *p324* . 0191 264 6664
Prudhoe *p358* 01661 836851

Robson, I (Close Thornton) *W S1*
Darlington *p206* 01325 466461

Robson, Mrs I A (Andrew Jackson) *D1 F1 G H J1 K1 L M1 N R1 Zp Zt*
Hull *p257* 01482 325242

Robson, Ms J A (Birmingham City Council Legal & Democratic Services)
Birmingham *p449* 0121 303 2066

Robson, Ms J D (Environment Agency (Midlands Region))
Solihull *p471*. 0121 711 2324

Robson, J D (Ison Harrison) *O Q J1*
Leeds *p274* 0113 284 5000

Robson, Mrs K (Norwich Union Life)
York *p477* 01904 452210

Robson, Mrs L (Blake Lapthorn)
Oxford *p342* 01865 248607

Robson, L W G (Hudson & Co) *E S1 X W L Zd Zi Zl*
London WC1 *p43* 020 7405 4812 / 7831 3282

Robson, Ms M (Barlow Lyde & Gilbert LLP) *O*
London EC3 *p10*. 020 7247 2277

Robson, M (Ford & Warren) *J2 N Q V Zq Zr*
Leeds *p273* 0113 243 6601

Robson, M K (Crutes) *S2 Q K1 J1*
Newcastle upon Tyne *p324* . 0191 233 9700

Robson, M K (Crutes) *S2 Q K1 J1*
Carlisle *p182*. 01228 525195

Robson, M P (Bates Wells & Braithwaite London LLP) *O Q A3 Zd*
London EC4 *p11*. 020 7551 7777

Robson, N (Ward Hadaway)
Newcastle upon Tyne *p327* . 0191 204 4000

Robson, P (Daltons) *A1 C1 E K1 N S1 S2 T2 W Zd Zl*
Oakham *p340* . . . .01572 722002 / 724343
Stamford *p393*. 01780 762526

Robson, R M (Footner & Ewing)
Romsey *p366* 01794 512345

Robson, R S (Warner & Richardson) *E C1 L S1 Zv*
Winchester *p434*. 01962 868366

Robson, Mrs S (Slee Blackwell) *N*
Exeter *p222* 01392 423000

Robson, Miss S (Roebucks) *K3 K1 D1*
Blackburn *p145* 01254 274000

Robson, Mrs S (Michael Anderson & Co) *E S1 W*
Whickham *p430* 0191 488 1221

Robson, S C R (Bristol Water PLC) *O*
Bristol *p451* 0117 966 5881

Robson, S M (Brachers) *J1 O Zp*
Maidstone *p299* 01622 690691

Robson, S P (Swinburne Maddison) *S1 K1 M1 G H W R1 P N F1 Zf Zk Zt*
Durham *p214* . . 0191 384 2441 / 384 7455

Robson-Hemmings, G D (Collins Dryland & Thorowgood LLP) *E S1*
Henley-on-Thames *p247*. . . 01491 572323

Robyns, R O (Roberts & Robyns) *S1 W Q A1 L K4 E*
Pwllheli *p358* 01758 612362

Roche, Ms E (Simmons & Simmons)
London EC2 *p79*. 020 7628 2020

Roche, J F (Walker Morris) *Q B1*
Leeds *p277* 0113 283 2500

Roche, J M (Underwood Solicitors LLP) *E C1 S1 T1 W L R1 Zb Zd*
Westminster *p89*. 020 7526 6000

Roche, N A (Pritchard Englefield)
London EC2 *p69*. 020 7972 9720

Roche, P M (Roche & Co) *B2*
London EC4 *p72*. 020 7831 2209

Rocher, R P (Clifford Chance) *Zj*
London E14 *p20*. 020 7006 1000

Rochester, V (Ince & Co Services Ltd)
London E1 *p44* 020 7481 0010

Rochfort, Miss E D B (Neale Turk Rochfort) *S1 W E L*
Camberley *p173*. 01276 20551

Rochman, J H (Rochman Landau LLP) *O E J1 W Q R1 B1 L Ze Zk Zq Zj S1 S2*
London W1 *p72* 020 7544 2424

Rock Perring, Mrs M (Russell-Cooke LLP) *L*
London WC1 *p74* 020 7405 6566

Rock, Mrs A J (Teacher Stern LLP)
London WC1 *p86* 020 7242 3191

Rocker, R (R&H Law) *Zr J1 Q N*
Croydon *p205* 0800 046 1472
London WC2 *p74* 020 7657 1555

Rockey, Ms C (Martyn Prowel) *N O L B1 F1*
Cardiff *p180* 029 2047 0909

Rockwood, Ms C I (Miller Parris) *K1 Q L*
Worthing *p442*. 01903 205771

Rodak, Mrs M (Jackson Brierley Hudson Stoney) *N W K1 K2 K3 K4*
Rochdale *p365*. . . .01706 644187 / 649214

Rodd, P J (Boys & Maughan) *S1 E R1 Zd S2 Zq R2*
Margate *p312* 01843 234000

Rodda, C B (Royds LLP) *O Q N*
London EC4 *p74*. 020 7583 2222

Roddan, M G J (Eastleys) *J1 L N Zp*
Totnes *p413* 01803 864888

Roddy, Ms R (Hodge Jones & Allen LLP) *D1 K1*
London NW1 *p41* 020 7874 8300

Rode, R C (Clarion Solicitors LLP) *G H B2*
Leeds *p272* 0113 246 0622
Harrogate *p240* 01423 530630

Rodell, Mrs A L (The College of Law Guildford)
Guildford *p459*. 01483 460200

Rodemark, T J (Mulcare Jenkins) *S1 S2 W*
Haywards Heath *p246* 01444 459954

Roden, I G (CKFT) *N Q J1 L O Zl Ze*
London NW3 *p17* 020 7431 7262

Roderick, A W (Neath Port Talbot County Borough Council)
Port Talbot *p469* 01639 763333

Rodger, Miss L J (Allan Rutherford) *K1 D1 V Zl*
Norwich *p333* 01603 621722

Rodger, W M (Simmons & Simmons) *O J1*
London EC2 *p79*. 020 7628 2020

Rodgers, Prof C P (Margraves) *A1*
Llandrindod Wells *p291* . . . 01597 825565

Rodgers, D (Gardner Leader LLP) *C3 J1 T1*
Newbury *p322*. 01635 508080
Sheffield *p375* 0114 272 2061

Rodgers, Mrs E (Andersons Solicitors) *K3 K1*
Nottingham *p335*. 0115 947 0641
Nottingham *p338*. 0115 945 4555

Rodgers, Ms F C (Silverman Sherliker LLP)
London EC2 *p78*. 020 7749 2700

Rodgers, Miss H A (Forsters LLP) *K1*
Westminster *p33*. 020 7863 8333

Rodgers, Mrs J A (Alderson Dodds) *W*
Blyth *p147* 01670 352293
Machynlleth *p298* . .01654 702335 / 702336

Rodgers, K (Ince & Co Services Ltd)
London E1 *p44* 020 7481 0010

Rodgers, Ms L (Howells LLP) *K1 K3*
Sheffield *p376* 0114 249 6666

Rodgers, M E (Bell & Buxton) *S2 E R2*
Sheffield *p375* 0114 249 5969

Rodgers, S P (Cogent Law)
Croydon *p204* 0844 245 4452

Rodgerson, Ms A (Mansfield Magistrates Court)
Mansfield *p465* 01623 451500

Rodgerson, Ms A (Nottingham Magistrates Court)
Nottingham *p467*. 0115 955 8111

Rodrigues, C (Hawkins Hatton LLP) *C1 C2 Zb*
Dudley *p213*. 01384 216840

Rodrigues, Ms M (Taylor Wessing)
London EC4 *p86*. 020 7300 7000

Rodriguez, N J (Ratcliffe Duce & Gammer LLP) *D1 K1 K2 D2 K3*
Wokingham *p437* 0118 978 3681

Rodriguez Marin, F J (Stephenson Harwood) *E R1 R2 Zb*
London EC2 *p82*. 020 7329 4422

Rodriguez-Moreno, G (Aviva PLC)
London EC3 *p103* . . 020 7283 7500 / 01603 687905

Rodway, R P (The Head Partnership) *K1 K3*
Reading *p361* 0118 975 6622

Rodwell, G (Southerns) *S1 W F1 L C1 Zi*
Nelson *p321*. 01282 603663

Rodwell, J V (Duane Morris) *C2 C1 Zza U1 U2 I F1*
London EC1 *p28*. 020 7786 2100

Rodwell, N J (hlw Keeble Hawson LLP) *N P Zc*
Sheffield *p375* 0114 272 2061

Roe, A J (Ashton KCJ) *E Zc*
Bury St Edmunds *p171* . . . 01284 762331

Roe, A J (Tony Roe Solicitors) *K1*
Reading *p361* 0118 930 2360

Roe, F A (Frank Roe Solicitors) *G K1 D1*
St Helens *p391* 01744 24218

Roe, G P (Hewitsons) *T2 W T1*
Northampton *p332*. 01604 233233

Roe, H G (Bishop & Co) *S1 S2 E R2 W*
New Mills *p321* 01663 746730

Roe, M R (Pinsent Masons LLP) *O Q Zc Zj*
London EC2 *p67*. 020 7418 7000

Roebuck, Mrs K A E (Bridge McFarland) *D1 G H*
Grimsby *p235* 01472 311711
Lincoln *p284*. 01522 518888

Roer, C F M (Barker Gooch & Swailes) *W Q J1 L S1 S2*
London N21 *p9* .020 8886 5928 / 8886 5734

Rofe, D J (Reed Smith LLP) *C1 C2 C3*
London EC2 *p71*. 020 3116 3000

Rofer, G (Keppe Rofer)
Brecon *p156*. 01874 624627

Roff, Ms S (DAC Beachcroft)
Bristol *p162* 0117 918 2000

Roffey, K (Hamlins LLP) *C1 O L*
London W1 *p38* 020 7355 6000

Roffey, N P (Nestle UK Ltd)
Croydon *p456* 020 8667 5260

Rogan, Miss A (Angela Rogan) *S1 W*
Kendal *p264*. 01539 724140

Rogan, Mrs I C (Skipton Building Society) *S1 L*
Skipton *p471*. 01756 705000

Rogan, Mrs M (Roberts Moore Nicholas Jones) *S1 W*
Birkenhead *p134*. 0151 647 0000

Rogan, P J H (Ince & Co Services Ltd)
London E1 *p44* 020 7481 0010

Rogers, A (Brabners Chaffe Street) *Zb B1 Zd F1 Ze Q T1*
Liverpool *p286*. 0151 600 3000

Rogers, Ms A M (Mayer Brown International LLP) *Zo*
London EC2 *p59*. 020 3130 3000

Rogers, Ms A N J (Aviva PLC)
London EC3 *p103* . . 020 7283 7500 / 01603 687905
Norwich *p467* 01603 622200

Rogers, B (Tollers LLP)
Northampton *p332*. 01604 258558

Rogers, B C (Tollers LLP) *T2 Zv Zo W*
Kettering *p265*. 01536 520111

Rogers, B T (Stewarts Law LLP) *N*
London EC4 *p83*. 020 7822 8000

Rogers, Miss C (Pluck Andrew & Co)
Hyde *p259*. 0161 368 6311

Rogers, C (Ellisons) *C1*
Colchester *p197* 01206 764477

Rogers, C P (Dickinson Dees) *T1 T2 O W*
York *p444* 0844 984 1500

Rogers, D (Kennedys) *Zj N*
Chelmsford *p186*. 0845 838 4800

Rogers, Mrs D C (Stitt & Co) *S1 E L W Zh R2*
London EC4 *p83*. 020 7832 0840

Rogers, D J (Blaser Mills) *G H*
Aylesbury *p120* 01296 434416

Rogers, F (Penningtons)
London EC2 *p66*. 020 7457 3000

Rogers, F M (Pinney Talfourd LLP)
Hornchurch *p252* 01708 511000

Rogers, G A (McCormicks) *B2 G O*
Harrogate *p240* 01423 530630

Rogers, Mrs G L (Trevor Griffiths & Humphries) *S1 W*
Blackwood *p147*. 01495 225236

Rogers, G P (Chesterfield Borough Council)
Chesterfield *p455* 01246 345345

Rogers, Ms H (Department for Business, Enterprise and Regulatory Reform)
London SW1 *p105*. 020 7215 0105

Rogers, Mrs H L (Aitken Associates) *K1 Q N*
Islington *p4* 020 7700 6006

Rogers, Miss J (The Johnson Partnership) *G H*
Nottingham *p337*. 0115 941 9141
Chesterfield *p192* 01246 211006

Rogers, J (Green Wright Chalton Annis) *S1*
Worthing *p441*. 01903 234064
Arundel *p118* 01903 881122

Rogers, J C (F B Jevons Riley & Pope) *S1 W S2 E*
Edenbridge *p216*. 01732 864411

Rogers, J C (Caerphilly County Borough Council)
Hengoed *p460*. 01443 815588

Rogers, J G (Pluck Andrew & Co) *B1 D1 F1 G H K1 N*
Hyde *p259*. 0161 368 6311

Rogers, Miss J M (Osborne Clarke) *L O*
Bristol *p164* 0117 917 3000

Rogers, J P (Cockertons) *Q C1 A1 E J1 O*
Bakewell *p121*. 01629 812613

Rogers, J W A (Lumsdons Solicitors LLP) *K1 J1 K3 N M1 F1 Zl*
Stourport-on-Severn *p399* . . 01299 827766

Rogers, Ms K (Stone King LLP) *T2 W*
Bath *p128* 01225 337599

Rogers, M C (Ashurst LLP) *Zb*
London EC2 *p7* 020 7638 1111

Rogers, Ms M C (Cumming & Riley) *K1 V Q F1*
Grays *p233* 01375 383691

Rogers, M H (Keoghs LLP) *N Zj O Q*
Bolton *p149* 01204 677000

Rogers, M M (Ames Kent)
Frome *p227* 01373 462017

Rogers, M R (Hawkins Hatton LLP) *N Zr J1 P J2 Zq*
Dudley *p213*. 01384 216840
Dudley *p213*. 01384 216920

Rogers, Ms N (Wolferstans) *J1 K1 Q W*
Plymouth *p351*. 01752 663295

Rogers, Ms N (Johnson & Gaunt) *K1 D1 G H V*
Banbury *p122* . . . . .01295 256271 / 271200

Rogers, Miss N C (Ashfield District Council)
Kirkby-in-Ashfield *p462*. . . . 01623 450000
London N22 *p106* 020 8489 0000

Rogers, O A (Riley Langdon)
Durham *p214* 0191 378 7620

Rogers, P (Hugh James) *N Q G H Zj*
Cardiff *p179* 029 2022 4871

Rogers, Ms P (Michelmores LLP) *K3 D1 K1 K2*
Exeter *p221* 01392 688688

Rogers, P (Davies Ingram & Harvey) *S1 W S2*
Swansea *p405*. 01792 653764

Rogers, R (Harrowells)
York *p444* 01904 558600

Rogers, Mrs R C R (George Ide LLP) *N*
Chichester *p192* 01243 786668

Rogers, R P (Whitehead Monckton) *S1 A1 E*
Maidstone *p299* 01622 698000

Rogers, Mrs S (Red Kite Law)
Tenby *p410* 01834 842122

Rogers, Mrs S (Clarion Solicitors LLP) *W T2*
Leeds *p272* 0113 246 0622
Harrogate *p240* 01423 530630

Rogers, S (Edward Hayes LLP) *D1 K1 V D2 K3*
Worthing *p441*. 01903 215999

Rogers, S (T G Baynes) *B1 F1 Q L Zc*
Bexleyheath *p132* 020 8301 7777

Rogers, S (Fishburns) *Zc Zj O Q Zq*
London EC3 *p32*. 020 7280 8888

Rogers, Mrs S F (Marks & Spencer PLC)
London W2 *p107* 020 7935 4422

Rogers, S F (Brains) *S1 E R2 S2*
Truro *p414*. 01872 276363

Rogers, S J (Broudie Jackson Canter) *G H*
Liverpool *p286*. 0151 227 1429

Rogers, S L (Austin & Carnley) *J1 L R1 S1*
Leighton Buzzard *p282* . . . 01525 372140

Rogers, Mrs T (Lamb Brooks LLP) *W T2*
Basingstoke *p126* 01256 844888

Rogers, Ms T A (Olswang LLP) *Ze Zf*
London WC1 *p64* 020 7067 3000

Rogers, Mrs T A (Gamlins) *K1 D1 D2*
Rhyl *p363* 01745 343500

Rogerson, C (Dawson Cornwell) *D1 D2 K1 K3*
London WC1 *p26* 020 7242 2556

Rogerson, Ms C M (Rogerson Galvin) *G H K1 S1 D1 W L*
Ashton-under-Lyne *p120*0161 344 2027 / 335 9005

Rogerson, D S (Chattertons Solicitors) *J1 L O N Q Zq K1*
Newark *p322* 01636 673731

Rogerson, F A (Hargreaves Gilman) *G H S1 N*
Manchester *p305* 0161 443 1711

Rogerson, Mrs J (Aubrey Isaacson Solicitors) *Q S1 W N*
Prestwich *p357* 0161 959 5000

Rogerson, Miss J S (Trethowans LLP) *E*
Southampton *p387*. 023 8032 1000

Rogerson, Ms K (Jones Day) *E*
London EC4 *p46*. 020 7039 5959

Rogerson, M (Barlow Lyde & Gilbert LLP) *E L S1 R1*
London EC3 *p10*. 020 7247 2277

Rogerson, M (Terry Jones Solicitors & Advocates) *G H Zl*
Shrewsbury *p379* 01743 285888

Rogerson, Mrs M (Bird & Co) *K1 K3 D1*
Grantham *p232* 01476 591711
Newark *p322* 01636 650880

Rogerson, R (Morrish Solicitors LLP) *N Q*
Leeds *p276* 0113 245 0733

Rohan, R F (Rohan & Co)
Haywards Heath *p246* 01444 450901

Rohde, Miss K L (Kingsley Napley) *N Zr*
London EC1 *p50*. 020 7814 1200

Rohl, Dr C L (Manches LLP) *Ze C1 Zz U2*
Oxford *p343* 01865 722106

Rohr, Mrs A L (Morris Scott & Co) *S1 S2 E W*
Christchurch *p194* 01425 278866

Rohsler, C A (Squire Sanders (UK) LLP)
London EC2 *p81*. 020 7655 1000

Roiser, Mrs A R (Hunters) *K3 K1*
London WC2 *p44* 020 7412 0050

Roland, Ms K G N (The Roland Partnership) *Zr N*
Chester *p191* 01244 659404

Roland, T R (The Roland Partnership) *Zr N*
Chester *p191* 01244 659404

Roles, Mrs P J (Field Seymour Parkes) *T1 T2 J1 C1*
Reading *p360* 0118 951 6200

Rolfe, A J (Clifford Chance)
London E14 *p20*. 020 7006 1000

Rolfe, C C (Ellison & Thomas)
Stretford *p400* 0161 865 3827

Rolfe, Mrs C C G (Henmans LLP) *W*
Oxford *p343* 01865 781000

Rolfe, C J (West Midlands Travel Ltd)
Birmingham *p450* 0121 254 7200

Rolfe, Mrs D P (EMW) *Zc Zn*
Milton Keynes *p316* 0845 070 6000

Rolfe, Mrs M S (London Fire & Emergency Planning Authority)
London SE1 *p107* 020 8555 1200

Rolfe, Mrs S (Machins Solicitors LLP) *K1 K3 D2 D1*
Luton *p295* 01582 514000

Rolf-McGregor, E (Cooper Sons Hartley & Williams) *S2 S1 L W*
Buxton *p172*. 01298 77511

Rollason, Miss L (Thompsons (formerly Robin/Brian Thompson & Partners)) *N*
London WC1 *p87* 020 7290 0000

Rollason, Ms N (Bristol City Council)
Bristol *p451* 0117 922 2000

Rollason, N W (Kingsley Napley) *M1 Zi Zg*
London EC1 *p50*. 020 7814 1200

Rollason, P J (Rollasons) *S1 C1 L A1 B1 E R1 Zh Zd Ze*
Daventry *p207*. 01327 301771

Rollason, Ms P R (Aidan Woods & Co) G H B2 Zm
Bristol p165 0117 952 2006

Rollin, Ms B (Gordons LLP)
Leeds p273 0113 227 0100

Rollin, Mrs B (Squire Sanders (UK) LLP)
Leeds p277 0113 284 7000

Rollingson, G (Rollingsons) N Zj J2 Zw
London EC1 p73 020 7611 4848

Rollo, A (Shepherd + Wedderburn LLP)
London EC4 p78 020 7429 4900

Rollo, Ms C (Butcher Burns LLP) C1 J1 Ze
London WC1 p16 020 7713 7100

Rolph, P C A (Steele Raymond) Q J1 K1 O Zl Zp A2 J2 A3
Bournemouth p152 01202 294566

Rolston, Mrs C (Levi Solicitors LLP) J1
Leeds p275 0113 244 9931

Roma, L (Osborne Clarke) R2 C2
London EC2 p65 020 7105 7000

Romain, C O (NUT Solicitors)
London WC1 p62 020 7380 4734

Rome, Miss P S (Lewis Silkin LLP) J1 Zp
Oxford p343 01865 263070

Romney, C D A (CMS Cameron McKenna LLP) E
London EC3 p17 020 7367 3000

Romney, J (R N Williams & Co Limited) K1 K3 C1 O Q W B1 L S1
Wolverhampton p438 01902 429051

Ronald, J R A (Dollman & Pritchard) W S1 K4 T2
Caterham p183 01883 347823

Ronaldson, R W (Ronaldsons) K1 K2 D1 K3
Norwich p335 01603 618883

Ronaldson, S F (Ronaldsons)
London WC1 p73 020 7580 6075

Ronan, M M (South Bedfordshire District Council)
Dunstable p457 01582 472222

Ronayne, R (Blaser Mills) R2 S1 S2 E
Rickmansworth p364 01923 776211

Ronayne, R J (Turbervilles) S1 E
Uxbridge p417 01895 201700
Uxbridge p417 01895 201700

Rondel, M R d C (EMW) B1 F1 O Zq M3 Zb
London WC2 p28 0845 070 6000

Roney, Mrs K E (Hanney Dawkins & Jones) W K1 D1 T1 T2
Pinner p348 020 8866 2144

Roodyn, Ms J (Olswang LLP) E S1
London WC1 p64 020 7067 3000

Rooke, Ms E (ASB Law) N
Maidstone p298 01622 656500

Rooke, Ms Y L (Foot Anstey) K3 K1
Plymouth p349 01752 675000
Southampton p387 023 8032 1000

Rooks, Ms H R V (The Johnson Partnership) G H
Nottingham p337 0115 941 9141

Room, Miss A (Anthony Collins Solicitors LLP) C1
Birmingham p137 0121 200 3242

Roome, J H D (Bingham McCutchen (London) LLP) C1 B1
London EC2 p12 020 7661 5300

Roome, M S (Toller Beattie LLP) C1 S2 E S1 R2 R1 J1 I Ze U2 O Zd L Zj A1
Barnstaple p125 01271 341000

Rooney, Ms A E (Thompsons (formerly Robin/ Brian Thompson & Partners)) Zk Ze
London WC1 p87 020 7290 0000

Rooney, Miss C F M (The Paul Rooney Partnership)
Liverpool p290 0151 227 2851

Rooney, C M (Edward Oliver & Bellis) S1 K1 W Q D1 L C1 N E
Ilford p260 020 8500 4168

Rooney, G M P (Mosshaselhurst) F1 J1 N Q Zl
Northwich p333 01606 74301

Rooney, Miss H M (Hill Dickinson LLP) O B1 Q A3 Zb
Manchester p305 0161 817 7200

Rooney, P (The Paul Rooney Partnership) N G S1 H B2
Liverpool p290 0151 227 2851

Rooney, P J (DLA Piper UK LLP) E R2 S2
Liverpool p287 0870 011 1111

Rooney, P M S (Olswang LLP) C1 C2 Zc
London WC1 p64 020 7067 3000

Rooney, R F (Richard Rooney & Co)
Merton p73 020 8947 8024

Roopra, B (Links Legal)
Ilford p260 020 8551 0999

Rooprai, R (Gordons LLP)
Leeds p273 0113 227 0100

Roos, A (Brabners Chaffe Street) Zh S1 S2 R2 C1
Liverpool p286 0151 600 3000

Roost, A M (Chawner Grey & Co) T2 W Zv K4
Weston-super-Mare p429 01934 417768 / 623541

Root, D L (John Fowlers LLP Solicitors) S1 W S2
Brightlingsea p159 01206 302694
Colchester p197 01206 576151

Root, S M (Berwins Solicitors Limited) A1 B1 D1 F1 K1 L N Q S1
Harrogate p240 01423 509000

Rooth, A (Watson Farley & Williams) O Zj
London EC2 p90 020 7814 8000

Roots, I A (Cripps Harries Hall LLP) O Zq
Tunbridge Wells p415 01892 515121

Roots, L R (Hopkin Murray Beskine) L
London N4 p42 020 7272 1234

Roots, M (Mary Ward Legal Centre)
London WC1 p110 020 7831 7079

Roots, N P P (Henmans LLP) Zd T2 W
Oxford p343 01865 781000

Roox, K (Crowell & Moring) Ze
London EC4 p23 020 7413 0011

Roper, A (Howell-Jones LLP) N J1 B1 F1 W Zc Ze Zj Zq Zr
Kingston upon Thames p267 020 8549 5186
Walton-on-Thames p420 01932 234500

Roper, J (McKinnells) S2 E
Lincoln p284 01522 541181

Roper, J J (DAC Beachcroft) J1 B1 C1 Ze
Bristol p162 0117 918 2000

Roper, Ms N (Trowers & Hamlins)
London EC3 p88 020 7423 8000

Roper, N J (Wolferstans) O I J1 Zw
Plymouth p351 01752 663295

Roper, S (Brabners Chaffe Street) C1 F1 Zb Zza C3 U2
Liverpool p286 0151 600 3000

Roper, S C W (British American Tobacco) O
London WC2 p104 020 7845 1000

Roper, T J (Wolferstans) N Zr
Plymouth p351 01752 663295

Roques, Ms S (J A Kemp & Co)
London WC1 p48 020 7405 3292

Rosa, Mrs M J L (Trafford Metropolitan Borough Council)
Stretford p473 0161 912 1212

Rosbottom, S (Lane & Co) S1 S2
Cheltenham p188 01242 524785 / 222421

Roscoe, R S (Victor Lissack Roscoe & Coleman) B2 G H
London W1 p89 020 7487 2505

Rose, A G (Robinsons) K1 K2
Derby p209 01332 291431

Rose, A J W (Anthony Rose & Co) Ze Zj C2 M1
Rendcomb p363 01242 870040

Rose, A M C (Marks Miller & Co) S1 W L S2 T2 Zd
Billericay p133 01277 633991

Rose, A P (Carpenters Rose) E S1 L W S2 Zd
London NW7 p18 020 8906 0088

Rose, Ms C (Reed Smith LLP) J1
London EC2 p71 020 3116 3000

Rose, C A (Christopher Rose & Co) K4 L S1 W
Penryn p346 01326 372461 / 374430

Rose, D (Michael Conn Goldsobel) A3 K3 J1 K1 L O Q N Zq Zs
London W1 p60 020 7580 8902

Rose, Miss D (Colemans - CTTS) N
Manchester p302 0161 876 2500

Rose, Mrs D A (T G Baynes) K1 K2 D1 K3 D2
Bexleyheath p132 020 8301 7777

Rose, D A W (Hood Vores & Allwood) D1 D2 K1 L Q
Dereham p209 01362 692424

Rose, Dr D J (Lamb & Holmes) K1
Kettering p265 01536 513195

Rose, D P (SJ Berwin LLP)
London EC4 p75 020 7111 2222

Rose, Ms D S (Wiseman Lee LLP) S1 S2 E C1
Redbridge p92 020 8215 1000

Rose, E H (Trowers & Hamlins) C1 M2 R2 U1 Zn Zc
London EC3 p88 020 7423 8000

Rose, Mrs I D (Lichfield Reynolds) D2 D1 G H K1
Stoke-on-Trent p398 01782 313212

Rose, Mrs I L (Redbridge Magistrates Court)
Ilford p461 0845 601 3600

Rose, I M (Poole Alcock) S1 W L K1 G H E N D1 F1 Zc Zl Zh
Crewe p203 01270 256665

Rose, J R (Johnson & Gaunt) G H F1 J1 V N Zl Zt Zk
Banbury p122 01295 256271 / 271200

Rose, J S (Jonathan S Rose) E S1 L C1 J1 W
Barnet p124 020 8447 4870

Rose, Mrs K A (Rees Page) K3 K1
Wolverhampton p438 01902 577777

Rose, Mrs L A (Daltons) S1
Stamford p393 01780 762526

Rose, L J (C C Bell & Son) G H P W D1 M1 N K1 C1 Zl
Bedford p129 01234 363251

Rose, Mrs L M (Davis Blank Furniss) D1 G K1 V H F1 Q
Glossop p230 01457 860606

Rose, Ms M (London Borough of Southwark)
London SE1 p109 020 7525 5000

Rose, Ms M (Veale Wasbrough Vizards) O Q Zq F1
Bristol p165 0117 925 2020

Rose, M S (Liefman Rose & Co) S1 E W L T1 P Zd T2
Manchester p306 0161 740 7878

Rose, Ms N (Aon Ltd)
London EC2 p103 020 7623 5500

Rose, N P (Field Fisher Waterhouse LLP)
London EC3 p31 020 7861 4000

Rose, P M A (Gateley LLP) D1 T1 B1
Manchester p304 0161 836 7700

Rose, P R (JP Morgan Chase Bank) Zg
London EC2 p107 020 7777 2000

Rose, R A (Morrisons Solicitors LLP) C1
Redhill p362 01737 854500

Rose, R E (Harvey Ingram LLP) N Zj
Leicester p280 0116 254 5454

Rose, R I L (Robin Rose)
Northampton p332 01604 760168

Rose, Miss S A (Clifton Ingram LLP) W
Wokingham p437 0118 978 0099

Rose, Ms S E (Clifford Chance)
London E14 p20 020 7006 1000

Rose, S J (Milne Moser) E L T2 S1 W
Milnthorpe p316 01539 562263
Kendal p264 01539 729786 / 725582

Rose, T J (Sansbury Douglas) G H
Bristol p164 0117 955 2663
Knowle p269 0117 963 5044

Rose, T S (Gellhorns) S1 N K1 W S2
Bordon p150 01420 205032

Rose-Smith, B M (Saunders Law Partnership LLP) H G
London WC2 p76 020 7632 4300

Roseblade, E (Roseblade & Co) S1 K1 N R1 W F1 G H L O Zl
Burntwood p170 01543 898591

Roseby, S (Brabners Chaffe Street) B1 E S1
Liverpool p286 0151 600 3000

Roseman, R M (Howard Kennedy LLP) Q
London W1 p48 020 7636 1616

Rosen, D (Herbert Smith LLP)
London EC2 p40 020 7374 8000

Rosen, D J (Darlingtons) Q O N G H B2 B1 Zk Zp Zr
Edgware p217 020 8952 0033 / 8951 6666

Rosen, Mrs L V (Lynne V Rosen) S1
Loughton p294 020 8508 0804

Rosen, P (Norman H Barnett & Co) E S1 W Zb Zc
London E6 p11 020 8471 2112

Rosen, R A (R A Rosen & Co) N P B1 C1 E R1 Ze Zk Zg
London W1 p73 020 7629 6566

Rosen, S A (Collyer Bristow LLP) N B1 P M1 J1 L M3 A3 Zb B2 O
London WC1 p22 020 7242 7363

Rosen, W D (DLA Piper UK LLP) C1 C2
London EC2 p24 0870 011 1111

Rosenak, Ms A O H E (Legal Services Commission)
Reading p469 0118 955 8600

Rosenberg, D (Speechly Bircham LLP) C1 C2
London EC4 p81 020 7427 6400
London EC4 p86 020 7300 7000

Rosenberg, D (Trott & Gentry) S1 E C1 W T1 B1 F1 R1 P Zb Zc Zd
London N1 p88 020 3119 3150

Rosenberg, D J (Burstalls) K1 D1 Zl X
Hull p256 01482 621800

Rosenberg, G H (Corbett & Co International Construction Lawyers Ltd) Zc A3
Teddington p409 020 8614 6200

Rosenblatt, D S (Ronald Fletcher & Co) L N O Q Zq Zr
London W9 p33 020 7624 0041

Rosenblatt, I I (Rosenblatt) C1 O C2 Q C3 Zk Ze Zj Zf
London EC4 p73 020 7955 0880

Rosenblatt, L T (Salans) B1 O Q Zb
London EC4 p76 020 7429 6000

Rosenbloom, Mrs J L (MFG Solicitors) V
Halesowen p237 0121 550 0777

Rosenburg, R B (Fasken Martineau LLP) E Zf
London W1 p31 020 7917 8500

Rosenfield, Mrs R (Birchall Blackburn LLP) D2 D1 K1
Preston p356 01772 561663

Rosenheim, J F (SNR Denton) O
London EC4 p75 020 7242 1212

Rosenthal, R H (Birkett Long LLP) S2 E S1 L Zl
Colchester p197 01206 217300

Rosenthal, S (Saunders Bearman LLP)
London W1 p76 020 7224 2618

Roseveare, M (Ashurst LLP)
London EC2 p7 020 7638 1111

Roskell, I (Roskell Davies & Co) S1 E W
Birmingham p141 0121 354 1515 / 355 1011

Roskell, M W (Pemberton Greenish LLP) L S1
London SW3 p66 020 7591 3333
London EC2 p79 020 7628 2020

Roskill, The Hon J W (Mayer Brown International LLP) J1 Zi J2
London EC2 p59 020 3130 3000

Rosley, J A (Rosleys) D1 E K1 S1 W M2 V X L
Nottingham p338 0115 958 0584

Rosling, A J (Addleshaw Goddard) C1
London EC1 p4 020 7606 8855

Rosling, Ms K T A (Dawson Hart) S2 E R2 R1 S1 Zb L A1
Uckfield p416 01825 762281

Rosmarin, D B (Cambridgeshire County Council) E
Cambridge p453 01223 717111

Ross, A (Williamsons) C1 E F1 J1 N P W Zc
Whitley Bay p431 0191 252 7711

Ross, A D (Bell & Buxton) E C1 C2 S2 Zl S1
Sheffield p375 0114 249 5969

Ross, A H (Muckle LLP) Zc
Newcastle upon Tyne p325 0191 211 7777

Ross, A N (Hawkins Ross Limited) K1 N Q D1 G W X J1 B1 Zc Zl Zq Zv
Stockton-on-Tees p397 01642 613647 / 678888

Ross, Miss C (Collyer Bristow LLP) O B1
London WC1 p22 020 7242 7363

Ross, C (George Davies Solicitors LLP) C2 C1
Manchester p303 0161 236 8992

Ross, Mrs C A R (Forsters LLP) L Q O
Westminster p33 020 7863 8333

Ross, D (Darlingtons) E Q S1
Edgware p217 020 8952 0033 / 8951 6666

Ross, D (Simpson Millar LLP) N
London EC1 p80 0844 858 3400

Ross, D (Taylor Wessing)
London EC4 p86 020 7300 7000

Ross, D R (Watkins Stewart & Ross) E L S1
Ipswich p263 01473 226266

Ross, F B (Hart Brown Solicitors)
London SW19 p39 0800 068 8177

Ross, G (Penningtons)
Basingstoke p127 01256 407100

Ross, Ms G (Walsall Metropolitan Borough Council) D1 F1 J1 K1 L S1 T1 V W P Zf Zl Zp
Walsall p475 01922 650000

Ross, Mrs G (Treasury Solicitors Department)
London WC2 p110 020 7210 3000

Ross, Miss G Z (Stewarts Law LLP) Zr
Leeds p277 0113 222 0022

Ross, Ms H (Gregory Rowcliffe Milners) J1 C1
London WC1 p37 020 7242 0631

Ross, Miss H A (Bond Pearce LLP) Zy F2
London EC3 p14 0845 415 0000

Ross, H A (Claremont Richards) E S2 S1
London EC4 p20 020 7353 3030

Ross, Ms H E (Henmans LLP) S1
Oxford p343 01865 781000

Ross, I P (Borough of Telford & Wrekin)
Telford p473 01952 380000

Ross, I P (Ross Green & Crowe) S1 C1 D1 E K1 N R1 W Zl
Dartford p207 01322 225353

Ross, J (Manches LLP) E S2 L R1 R2 S1
London WC2 p58 020 7404 4433

Ross, J (Lewis Silkin LLP) J1 Zi
London EC4 p53 020 7074 8000

Ross, J I B E (John Ross)
London NW11 p73 020 8458 1924

Ross, J M H (Forsters LLP) L O Q
Westminster p33 020 7863 8333

Ross, K (Chesterfield Borough Council)
Chesterfield p455 01246 345345

Ross, K A (Brown Turner Ross) S1 W
Liverpool p287 0151 236 2233

Ross, K J (Copleys) S1 S2 W E L C1 A1 R1 Ze Zf Zl
Huntingdon p258 01480 456191

Ross, Ms K M (Thompsons (formerly Robin/Brian Thompson & Partners)) J1 N
Plymouth p350 01752 675810

Ross, L P (Laurence Ross & Associates) J1 K1 K3 L O Q Zp W Zq
Radlett p358 01923 850099

Ross, M E (Daniel and Harris) D1 K1 K2
Camden p25 020 7625 0202

Ross, M J (Brown Turner Ross) S1 G H W C1 K1 J1 E M1 P Zk Zi
Liverpool p287 0151 236 2233

Ross, N S (Russell & Russell) G H
Bolton p149 01204 399299

Ross, P J (Paul Ross & Company) O S1 B1 C1 C2 K1 M1 N Q M2 Zb Zd Ze Zj Zq
Manchester p309 0161 832 0706

Ross, R B (Ross Solicitors Ltd) G H
Swindon p406 01793 512960

Ross, S A G (Seddons) S1 E S2
Westminster p77 020 7725 8000

Ross, S T (Brecher) O Q F1 B1 Zq N L
London W1 p15 020 7563 1000

Ross, W M (Pearless de Rougemont & Co) E C1 W S1 A1 R1 T1 Zd
East Grinstead p215 01342 323687

Ross-Appleby, Mrs A M (Kingston upon Hull City Council)
Hull p461 01482 300300

Ross-Macdonald, R (Rouse Legal (Formerly Willoughby & Partners)) Ze
London E14 p74 020 7536 4100

Rossell-Evans, S (Mills & Reeve) Zq Q
Norwich p335 01603 660155

Rosser, A (RTL Solicitors) S1 E W C1
Bridgend p157 01656 665850
Cardiff p180 029 2023 4030

Rosser, Ms C (Juliet Bellis & Co) G L Zg B1 E
Uckfield p416 01825 750811

Rosser, Miss C E (Robinsons)
Derby p209 01332 291431

Rosser, J P (Leo Abse & Cohen) N J2
Cardiff p179 029 2038 3252 / 2034 5421

Rosser, M (Hugh James) K1 V D1
Cardiff p179 029 2022 4871

Rosser, M H (Warners Solicitors) C1 C2 E I J1
Sevenoaks p374 01732 747900

Rosser, S (Clarke Willmott) S2 E R2
Bristol p162 0845 209 1000 / 0117 305 6000

Rosser, S D (S D Rosser & Co) F1 S1 W L Q J1 K1 T1 Zi Zl C1 S2 R1
London NW10 p74 020 8451 3848

Rosshandler, J H (Speechly Bircham LLP) N P M1 J1 Zc Zk Zl
London EC4 p81 020 7427 6400

Rossi, Mrs A J (Farleys Solicitors LLP) G H B2
Blackburn p145 01254 367854

Rossin, C (Larken & Co) D1 G H S1 S2 V W Zl Zm Zw
Newark p322 01636 703333

Rossiter, P S (Peter Rossiter & Co) S1 S2
Burnham-on-Sea p452 01278 780143

Rossiter, T W (Lamb Brooks LLP) E S2
Basingstoke p126 01256 844888

Rostamlou, Miss S N (Chestnutts)
Ainsdale p114 01704 572221
Southport p388 01704 535216

Rostance, N P (1st Solicitors) A1 Q S1 N K1
Stafford p392 01785 213234

Rostron, Miss D J (Linder Myers Solicitors) N Zr
Manchester p307 0844 984 6400

Rostron, J B (Higgs & Sons) W T2
Brierley Hill p158 0845 111 5050

Rostron, M C (Hunt & Morgan) B1 O J1 C1
Cardiff p179 029 2034 1234

Rote, Mrs S (The College of Law)
London WC1 p105 0800 289997

See p634 for the Key to Work Categories

Rotenberg, A (Jones Day) *B1*
London EC4 *p46* . . . 020 7039 5959

Rothburn, Mrs M L (Salehs LLP) *E S2 R2 S1*
Manchester *p309* . . . 0161 434 9991

Rothery, Ms C (Milburns Solicitors) *K1 D1 K3 Q*
Workington *p440* . . . 01900 67363

Rothery, Ms F (FBC Manby Bowdler LLP) *K1*
Wolverhampton *p437* . . . 01902 578000

Rothnie, I A (Herbert Smith LLP) *E*
London EC2 *p40* . . . 020 7374 8000

Rothstein, Miss E D (Hadfields Butt & Bowyer) *K1 K3*
Farnham *p225* . . . 01252 716101

Rothwell, A C (Ashfords LLP) *E*
Exeter *p220* . . . 01392 337000

Rothwell, Ms A L (Thompsons (formerly Robin/Brian Thompson & Partners)) *N Zr*
Sheffield *p377* . . . 0114 270 3300

Rothwell, C E S (hlw Keeble Hawson LLP) *O Q Zb Zj Zk*
Sheffield *p375* . . . 0114 272 2061

Rothwell, G (Saunders Law Partnership LLP) *G H*
London WC2 *p76* . . . 020 7632 4300

Rothwell, Miss L (East Northamptonshire District Council)
Thrapston *p474* . . . 01832 742000

Rothwell, M R G P (Hacking Ashton LLP) *W S2 S1 A1*
Newcastle under Lyme *p323* . 01782 715555

Rothwell, P L (Martin Tolhurst Partnership LLP) *W K4*
Gravesend *p233* . . . 01474 325531

Rothwell, P S (Martin Tolhurst Partnership LLP) *Q O E S1 J1 C1 K1 Zb*
Gravesend *p233* . . . 01474 325531

Rought-Brooks, A C (Hodge Jones & Allen LLP) *L*
London NW1 *p41* . . . 020 7874 8300

Roughton, T J (Morrison & Foerster (UK) LLP) *U1 U2*
London EC2 *p62* . . . 020 7920 4000
London EC2 *p67* . . . 020 7847 9500

Rouine, A P (Pearson Rowe) *A3 Zc C1 E Zh L O Q R1 Zq*
Birmingham *p141* . . . 0121 236 7388

Roulston, J (Forshaws Davies Ridgway LLP) *K1*
Warrington *p422* . . . 01925 604713

Round, Ms C (Brabners Chaffe Street)
Manchester *p301* . . . 0161 836 8800

Round, Ms G (Howells LLP) *K3*
Rotherham *p367* . . . 01709 364000

Round, P J (George Green LLP) *C2 C1*
Cradley Heath *p201* . . . 01384 410410

Rounding, S L (Elmhirst Parker LLP) *W S1 A1 Zd E S2 T2 K4 R2*
Selby *p374* . . . 01757 703895

Rous, S R (Ashfords LLP) *T1 C1 C2*
Exeter *p220* . . . 01392 337000

Rouse, J A I (Wright Hassall LLP) *W S1 T2 Zd*
Leamington Spa *p270* . . . 01926 886688

Rouse, Ms J (Penningtons) *O Zh*
Basingstoke *p127* . . . 01256 407100

Rouse, N (Kennedys) *Q Zj*
London EC3 *p49* . . . 020 7667 9667

Rouse, P D (Shell International Ltd)
London SE1 *p109* . . . 020 7934 1234

Rouse, R (Oxford Law Group) *K1 D1 D2*
Oxford *p344* . . . 01865 297300

Rouse, R J (Morgan Cole) *D1 K1 F1 L M1*
Oxford *p344* . . . 01865 262600

Rousell, J (Wall James Chappell) *K4 T2 W*
Stourbridge *p399* . . . 01384 371622

Rousell, Ms M (Lewis Silkin LLP)
London EC4 *p53* . . . 020 7074 8000

Rout, P J (DLA Piper UK LLP) *C1 Zc*
Manchester *p303* . . . 0870 011 1111

Routen, Mrs J C (Lamb & Holmes) *T1 W*
Corby *p199* . . . 01536 745168

Routledge, A R (Routledge Quill & Co) *C1 C2 B1 T1 T2 Zb Ze Zf*
Wormley *p441* . . . 01428 682589

Routledge, Ms C G (David Gray Solicitors) *D1 N Zg*
Newcastle upon Tyne *p324* . 0191 232 9547

Routledge, Miss H (Samuel Phillips Law Firm) *Zr N*
Newcastle upon Tyne *p326* . 0191 232 8451

Routledge, Ms S (Birnberg Peirce & Partners) *Zi*
Camden *p13* . . . 020 7911 0166

Roveri, A C (South Devon Magistrates' Courts)
Torquay *p474* . . . 01803 612211

Row, B T (Row & Scott) *B1 D1 G H J1 K1 M1 P S1 W Zm Zj Zk*
Consett *p199* . . . 01207 591810
Newcastle upon Tyne *p326* . 0191 273 9929

Rowan, A (Boyes Turner) *Q O*
Reading *p360* . . . 0118 959 7711

Rowan, Ms J (Field Fisher Waterhouse LLP)
London EC3 *p31* . . . 020 7861 4000

Rowan, Miss S (Blake Lapthorn) *O*
London EC1 *p13* . . . 020 7405 2000

Rowan, V B (Pinsent Masons LLP)
London EC2 *p67* . . . 020 7418 7000

Rowberry, A L (Rowberry Morris) *S1 A1 C1 L W E Zc Zj S2*
Reading *p361* . . . 0118 958 5611

Rowberry, Miss C C (Robin Murray & Co) *G H*
Chatham *p185* . . . 01634 832332

Rowberry, Mrs L J R (Carver Jones) *K3 S1 W*
Hereford *p247* . . . 01432 274301

Rowbotham, G W H (McDermott Will & Emery UK LLP) *C1 B1 M1 F1 P Zh Zj Zc*
London EC2 *p56* . . . 020 7577 6900

Rowbotham, Ms M A (Lawsmiths)
Sale *p370* . . . 0161 972 7700

Rowcliffe, S (Hegarty LLP) *N*
Peterborough *p347* . . . 01733 346333

Rowden, J (hlw Keeble Hawson LLP)
Sheffield *p375* . . . 0114 272 2061

Rowden, Mrs W H (Eastleys) *K1 D1*
Paignton *p345* . . . 01803 559257

Rowe, Ms A (Brady Eastwood Pierce & Stewart) *N*
Lewisham *p15* . . . 020 8692 8181
London SE8 *p85* . . . 020 7790 7000

Rowe, A (Bindmans LLP) *K4 W*
London WC1 *p12* . . . 020 7833 4433

Rowe, Mrs A J (Warners Solicitors) *S1 S2*
Sevenoaks *p374* . . . 01732 747900

Rowe, B V (Lyons Davidson) *N Zl Zt Zj*
Bristol *p163* . . . 0117 904 6000

Rowe, C (Aaron & Partners LLP Solicitors) *E S2 R2 Zc*
Manchester *p300* . . . 0161 935 8334
Chester *p190* . . . 01244 405555

Rowe, Miss C M (Shoosmiths) *N F1 M1 P B1 Zc Zk*
Reading *p361* . . 0370 086 8800 / 0118 965 8765

Rowe, D G (Bazeley Barnes & Bazeley) *G H*
Bideford *p132* . . . 01237 473122

Rowe, D P (Davies Blunden & Evans) *S1 S2 K1 W D1 L J1 E*
Farnborough *p224* . . . 01252 541633

Rowe, Ms D R (Lloyd & Rowe) *G H*
Cardiff *p179* . . . 029 2045 8999

Rowe, Miss G C (McPhersons) *A1 A2 E S1*
Stockbridge *p395* . . . 01794 389002

Rowe, Mrs G L (West Lancashire District Council)
Ormskirk *p468* . . . 01695 577177

Rowe, Mrs H (Howlett Clarke Solicitors) *S1*
Hove *p254* . . . 01273 419728

Rowe, I (Horwich Cohen Coghlan) *N*
Manchester *p305* . . . 0161 830 4600

Rowe, Ms J (ClarksLegal LLP) *J1*
Reading *p360* . . . 0118 958 5321

Rowe, Mrs J A (Palmers Solicitors) *W K4 Zm K1*
Kingston upon Thames *p267* . 020 8549 7444

Rowe, J B (CooperBurnett) *E*
Tunbridge Wells *p415* . . . 01892 515022

Rowe, Mrs K J (Muckle LLP) *J1*
Newcastle upon Tyne *p325* . 0191 211 7777

Rowe, Mrs L (Trethowans LLP) *Zr N*
Southampton *p387* . . . 023 8032 1000

Rowe, Ms M (Staffordshire County Council)
Stafford *p472* . . . 01785 223121

Rowe, M J (Vivash Hunt) *Zc S2 E C1 Zh L*
Worcester Park *p440* . . . 020 8330 1961

Rowe, N D (Cripps Harries Hall LLP) *S1 E L A1*
Tunbridge Wells *p415* . . . 01892 515121

Rowe, N F (Maitland Walker) *J1 C1 O*
Cheltenham *p188* . . . 01242 285855

Rowe, N F (Maitland Walker) *O Q J1*
Minehead *p318* . . . 01643 707777

Rowe, R A (G J Hendra Ltd)
Truro *p474* . . . 01872 277212

Rowe, R A (Dodd Lewis Solicitors) *L S1 S2*
London SE3 *p27* . . . 020 8852 1255

Rowe, R D (Radcliffes Le Brasseur) *S2 S1 W Zd*
Westminster *p70* . . . 020 7222 7040

Rowe, S (Williamson & Soden) *O Q B1*
Solihull *p383* . . . 0121 733 8000

Rowe, S A (Howlett Clarke Crowther Wood) *D1 F1 G H K1 L N O Q*
Brighton *p159* . . 01273 327272 / 326341

Rowe, S M (Maitland Walker) *O Q N*
Cheltenham *p188* . . . 01242 285855

Rowe, T J H (Wright Hassall LLP) *E R2 S2*
Leamington Spa *p270* . . . 01926 886688

Rowell, A J (Nelsons) *J1 Zp*
Leicester *p280* . . . 0116 222 6666
Leicester *p281* . . . 0116 262 4225

Rowell, Miss K (Ronaldsons) *K1 K3 K2 D1*
Norwich *p335* . . . 01603 618883

Rowell, M (Brockbank Curwen Cain & Hall) *N G Q Zj*
Whitehaven *p431* . . . 01946 692194

Rowell, P (Mayer Brown International LLP) *Zo*
London EC2 *p59* . . . 020 3130 3000

Rowland, Miss A (Staffordshire County Council)
Stafford *p472* . . . 01785 223121

Rowland, A J (Capsticks Solicitors LLP) *J1 Zp*
London SW19 *p18* . . . 020 8780 2211

Rowland, H R (Gotelee) *G H Zl B2 N J2*
Ipswich *p262* . . . 01473 211121

Rowland, J M (Peter Peter & Wright)
Holsworthy *p251* . . . 01409 253262

Rowland, Mrs J M (Field Seymour Parkes) *W*
Reading *p360* . . . 0118 951 6200

Rowland, M D (Angel & Co) *S1 W S2 L K4 E*
Coventry *p200* . . . 024 7625 2211

Rowland, M L (Large & Gibson) *S1 E C1 L*
Southsea *p388* . . . 023 9229 6296

Rowland, P D (Adams & Remers) *E L S1*
Lewes *p283* . . . 01273 480616

Rowland, R A P (Allen & Overy LLP)
London E1 *p5* . . . 020 3088 0000

Rowland, R C (Humphries Kirk) *S1 E*
Wareham *p421* . . . 01929 552141

Rowland, Mrs R M (Vincent Sykes & Higham LLP) *N W J1*
Thrapston *p411* . . . 01832 732161

Rowland, R P J (Aidan Woods & Co)
Bristol *p165* . . . 0117 952 2006

Rowland, Ms S (Cheshire County Council)
Chester *p454* . . . 01244 602382

Rowland, Mrs S (Ashley Wilson) *N S1 C1 E W J1 L F1 T1 Zh*
London SW1 *p92* . . . 020 7802 4802

Rowland, Miss S F (Alistair Harper & Co) *S1*
Haywards Heath *p245* . . . 01444 457890

Rowland, S J (Davies & Partners) *E*
Gloucester *p230* . . . 01452 612345

Rowland, S W (Walker Foster) *S1 W K4*
Silsden *p380* . . . 01535 653408

Rowland, T J (Peter Peter & Wright) *Q N O J1 L Zq Zp W F1*
Bude *p168* . . . 01288 352101

Rowlands, Ms A (Linder Myers Solicitors) *N Zr*
Manchester *p307* . . . 0844 984 6400

Rowlands, D (Herbert Smith LLP) *E*
London EC2 *p40* . . . 020 7374 8000

Rowlands, I R (Ajilon Group Ltd)
London W6 *p103* . . . 020 8600 6875

Rowlands, J F (Wigan Borough Council)
Wigan *p476* . . . 01942 244991

Rowlands, M (Cripps Harries Hall LLP) *K1 K2*
Tunbridge Wells *p415* . . . 01892 515121

Rowlands, Ms M J (The BOC Group PLC)
Guildford *p476* . . . 01483 579857

Rowlands, M R (Jackamans) *E*
Diss *p210* . . . 01379 643555

Rowlands, P (John Mohamed & Co) *G H N Zl*
Bedworth *p130* . . . 024 7649 1964

Rowlands, S A (Crown Prosecution Service Dyfed Powys)
Carmarthen *p453* . . . 01267 242100

Rowlands, T A (Wrexham County Borough Council) *K1 N Q S1 D1 D2 S2 G*
Wrexham *p477* . . . 01978 292000

Rowles, Ms C (Eastgate Assistance Ltd)
Colchester *p455* . . . 0870 523 4500

Rowles, M J (Bristows) *E R1 P T2 W S1 L Zd*
London EC4 *p15* . . . 020 7400 8000

Rowles-Davies, J N (Bridgehouse Partners) *O Q K3 Ze C1*
Bicester *p132* . . . 01869 243457

Rowley, Ms E (Grayson Willis Bennett) *G H B2*
Rotherham *p367* . . . 01709 720287

Rowley, Ms G (Hempsons) *Zr*
Manchester *p305* . . . 0161 228 0011

Rowley, M (Baxters) *W K1 S1*
Tamworth *p407* . . . 01827 899059
Tamworth *p407* . . 01827 58333 / 58334

Rowley, N (Mackrell Turner Garrett) *N Q G K1 B1 Ze Zj Zb*
London WC2 *p57* . . . 020 7240 0521

Rowley, R G (Freeth Cartwright LLP) *E L S1 T1 W Zc Zl*
Leicester *p279* . . . 0116 248 1100
Nottingham *p337* . . . 0115 936 9369

Rowley, R H (R H Rowley) *E K1 L N O Q S1 W S2*
Coventry *p201* . . . 024 7630 1996

Rowley, S (The Smith Partnership) *H G F1 K1 M1*
Derby *p209* . . . 01332 225225

Rowley, S N (Challinors) *S1 W*
West Bromwich *p427* . . . 0121 553 3211

Rowlinson, Mrs L B (Rowlinsons) *A1 E L R1 S1 W Zi Zv*
Frodsham *p227* . . . 01928 735333

Rowlinson, N H (WBW Solicitors) *W T2 S1*
Newton Abbot *p329* . . . 01626 202404

Rowntree, C H (Bevis Rowntree) *E L S1 T2 W*
Midhurst *p315* . . . 01730 812201

Rowntree, D J (Rutters) *W S1 T1 A1 C1 V F1 L K1 P Zm Zl S2*
Gillingham *p229* . . . 01747 822005
Shaftesbury *p374* . . . 01747 852377

Rowsell, Ms C A (Reuters Group PLC)
London E14 *p109* . . . 020 7250 1122

Rowsell, Miss L (Humphries Kirk) *C1*
Dorchester *p212* . . . 01305 251007

Rowson, B D (Peter Peter & Wright) *F1 K1 L N O Q S1 W K3 S2*
Bideford *p133* . . . 01237 472233

Rowson, G P (British Telecommunications PLC)
London EC1 *p104* . . . 020 7356 6181

Rowson, I C (Freeth Cartwright LLP) *E*
Nottingham *p337* . . . 0115 936 9369

Rowson, J M (City of Sunderland)
Sunderland *p473* . . . 0191 520 5555

Rowson, S (Linklaters LLP)
London EC2 *p54* . . . 020 7456 2000

Rowswell, J (Maxwell Winward LLP) *E S2 L R2*
London EC4 *p59* . . . 020 7651 0000

Roxborough, I D (Clifford Chance)
London E14 *p20* . . . 020 7006 1000

Roxborough, Mrs S E E (Salford City Council) *J1 L P Q*
Swinton *p473* . . . 0161 794 4711

Roxburgh, B O (Osborne Clarke) *C1*
Bristol *p164* . . . 0117 917 3000

Roy, Miss A (Adrianne Roy) *S1 W*
Enfield *p219* . . . 020 8292 9101

Roy, B (Bristows) *U2 U1 C3 M1 I Ze*
London EC4 *p15* . . . 020 7400 8000

Roy, G (GPB Solicitors LLP) *N O Zr B1 F1 G Zw Zza*
Stratford-upon-Avon *p400* . . 01789 261131

Roy, I A (Roys) *S1 W C1*
Carlisle *p182* . . . 01228 526385

Roy, Miss J (Mills & Reeve) *J1*
Cambridge *p175* . . . 01223 364422

Roy, J P (Paris Smith LLP) *C1 C2*
Southampton *p386* . . . 023 8048 2482

Roy, N G (Jonas Roy Bloom) *G H*
Birmingham *p139* . . . 0121 212 4111

Roy, Ms S (Ashurst LLP) *Zb*
London EC2 *p7* . . . 020 7638 1111

Roy, S R (Aviva PLC)
London EC3 *p103* . 020 7283 7500 / 01603 687905
Norwich *p467* . . . 01603 622200

Royan, Ms S M (Metropolitan Police Directorate of Legal Services)
London SW1 *p108* . . . 020 7230 7210

Royce, A D J (Oglethorpe Sturton & Gillibrand) *N Q S2 E O*
Lancaster *p270* . . . 01524 846846

Royce, Mrs A V (Royce & Co) *S1 W E F1 G L*
London SW6 *p74* . . . 020 7736 9103

Royde, Miss M C (Olswang LLP) *C1 I Ze Zf Zw*
London WC1 *p64* . . . 020 7067 3000

Roylance, D (Simmons & Simmons)
London EC2 *p79* . . . 020 7628 2020

Royle, A A J (QualitySolicitors Hill & Abbott) *E C1 J1 M1 T1 R1 C2 S2*
Chelmsford *p187* . . . 01245 258892

Royle, C A (Forshaws Davies Ridgway LLP) *A1 C1 E L R1 S1 T1 W*
Warrington *p422* . . . 01925 230000

Royle, C P (Glaisyers) *G H Zl*
Birmingham *p138* . . . 0121 233 2971

Royle, J M (Eaton Smith LLP) *E S1 C1*
Huddersfield *p255* . . . 01484 821300

Royou, P (Simmons & Simmons)
London EC2 *p79* . . . 020 7628 2020

Royston, Mrs M A (Carpenters Rose) *W*
London NW7 *p18* . . . 020 8906 0088

Ruane, Ms C B (Environment Agency (North East Region))
Leeds *p462* . . . 0870 850 6506

Ruane, Mrs N (Burnetts) *J1*
Carlisle *p181* . . . 01228 552222
Carlisle *p182* . . . 01228 552222

Rubens, Ms M (Alan Edwards & Co) *Zh L Q Zg Zu*
Kensington & Chelsea *p28* . . 020 7221 7644

Rubens, P D (Finers Stephens Innocent LLP)
London W1 *p32* . . . 020 7323 4000

Rubenstein, J L (Lawrence Stephens) *C1 C2 B1 J1 Ze*
London EC1 *p82* . . . 020 7935 1211

Rubie, D A (David Rubie Mitchell & Co) *G H S1 E Zl*
Sutton *p403* . . . 020 8641 0575

Rubie, M A (Procol & Candor Solicitors)
Ealing *p69* . . . 020 8993 4646

Rubin, H J (Bird & Bird LLP) *I*
London EC4 *p13* . . . 020 7415 6000

Rubin, J M (Rubin Lewis O'Brien) *S1 E C1 L R1 T1 W B1 F1 A1 Zc*
Cwmbran *p206* . . . 01633 867000

Rubin, R A (Shammah Nicholls LLP) *O Q*
Manchester *p309* . . . 0161 832 9272

Rubinstein, J R (James Rubinstein & Co) *Ze Zf*
London NW6 *p109* . . . 020 7431 5500

Rubython, E (Goughs)
Devizes *p210* . . . 01380 726913

Ruchniewicz, P W (Collins Benson Goldhill LLP) *E R1*
Westminster *p21* . . . 020 7436 5151

Ruck, D (Gordon Dadds) *K1 K2*
London W1 *p25* . . . 020 7493 6151

Rucker, N P H (LG Lawyers)
London SE1 *p50* . . . 020 7379 0000

Ruckin, Mrs H (Male & Wagland) *U1 U2 V T1 T2*
Potters Bar *p355* . . . 01707 657171

Rudd, A H R (Dover District Council)
Dover *p457* . . . 01304 821199

Rudd, C (JMP Solicitors) *N Q J2*
Warrington *p422* . . . 0845 680 1895

Rudd, D C (Walker Smith Way) *Zr N*
Wrexham *p443* . . . 0844 346 3100

Rudd, Mrs D E (Michael Cullen & Partners) *W Zm*
Billericay *p133* . . . 01277 623132

Rudd, J (Molesworths Bright Clegg) *N*
Rochdale *p365* . . . 01706 356666

Rudd, J M (Rudd Jepson) *S1 E W R1*
Bromley *p167* . . . 020 8313 0555

Rudd, L (Judge & Priestley) *E Zu R1 S1 W*
Bromley *p166* . . . 020 8290 0333

Rudd, Ms P (Cozens-Hardy LLP) *E S1*
Norwich *p334* . . . 01603 625231

Rudd, P R F (Paul Rudd) *N S1 O Q E*
Grimsby *p235* . . . 01472 350881

Rudd, S J (Malcolm Peet & Co)
Atherton *p120* . . . 01942 876115

Ruddick, J C (Brindley Twist Tafft & James) *E C1 T1 S1 R1 W A1 L Zl Zd*
Coventry *p200* . . . 024 7653 1532

Ruddock, D R (Wycombe District Council)
High Wycombe *p461* . . . 01494 461002

Ruddock, G J (FBC Manby Bowdler LLP) *O Q*
Wolverhampton *p437* . . . 01902 578000

Ruddock, K A (Shell International Ltd)
London SE1 *p109* . . . 020 7934 1234

Ruddocks, Mrs J (Coley & Tilley)
Birmingham *p136* . . . 0121 643 5531

Ruddock-West, J (East Sussex County Council)
Lewes *p463* . . . 01273 481000

Ruddy, N E (Paul Davidson Taylor) *C1 B1 C2 J1 Ze Zb*
Horsham *p253* . . . 01403 262333

Rudgard, Mrs S E (Information Commisioner)
Wilmslow *p476* . . . 01625 545700

Rudge, A A D N (BPE Solicitors LLP) *C2 C1 Ze C3 U2*
Cheltenham *p187* . . . 01242 224433

Rudge, A M (Rudge & Co) *C1 E N P S1 J1 B1 O Q F2 S2*
Birmingham *p141* 0121 200 1775

Rudge, C T (Lloyds & Cooper) *K4 T2 W*
Leominster *p283*. 01568 613236

Rudkin, A (Tollers LLP)
Northampton *p332*. 01604 258558

Rudkin, A M (Tollers LLP) *A1 E S1 S2 R2*
Northampton *p332*. 01604 258558

Rudland, Mrs N J (Taylor Fawcett) *S1*
Harrogate *p241* 01423 538111

Rudman, A (Wansbroughs)
Melksham *p314* 01225 703222

Rudman, Miss S (Nottingham City Council (City Sec Dept))
Nottingham *p467*. 0115 915 5555

Rudolph, Ms A (Russell-Cooke LLP) *Ze Zk F1 F2*
London WC1 *p74* 020 7405 6566

Rudston, N (Hodge Jones & Allen LLP)
London NW1 *p41* 020 7874 8300

Ruebain, D E (Levenes Solicitors) *X Zg Zm*
Haringey *p53* . .020 8881 7777 / 8881 6764

Rufai, J M (HSR Solicitors) *S1 S2 Zl*
London E1 *p37* 020 7791 1111

Ruff, M A (Thompsons (formerly Robin/Brian Thompson & Partners)) *N*
Birmingham *p143* 0121 262 1200

Ruffel, Ms A M (LG Lawyers)
London SE1 *p50*. 020 7379 0000

Rugg, A J (Andrew Rugg) *E A1 S1 C1 L W Zd S2*
Taunton *p408* 01823 326822

Rughani, Ms C L (ClarksLegal LLP) *J1*
Reading *p360* 0118 958 5321

Ruis, S V (Fisher Meredith) *Zg*
Lambeth *p32*. 020 7091 2700

Ruiz, R J (Birketts LLP (Wollastons LLP)) *C1 C2 Zb C3 Zo F1 I U2*
Chelmsford *p186*. 01245 211211

Rule, Ms E J (Thornton & Co)
Hammersmith & Fulham *p87*. 020 8743 3000

Rumary, Ms P L (Henmans LLP) *T2 W Zd*
Oxford *p343* 01865 781000

Rumbelow, M N (Fladgate LLP) *J1 Zi*
London WC2 *p32* 020 3036 7000

Rumbold, Ms A (Bates Wells & Braithwaite London LLP) *Zd C1*
London EC4 *p11*. 020 7551 7777

Rumboll, A (Bristows)
London EC4 *p15*. 020 7400 8000

Rumens, I (Howard Kennedy LLP) *W*
London W1 *p48* 020 7636 1616

Rumistrzewicz, A S (Nelson Guest & Partners) *S1 E W C1 J1 L R1 A1 B1 T1 Zc Zh Zl*
Sidcup *p380*. . .020 8309 5010 / 8309 0558

Rumjahn, Miss Y (Wellers Law Group LLP) *S1*
Bromley *p167* 020 8464 4242

Rumke, C M (Gregory Abrams Davidson LLP) *E L S1 W Zl*
London NW11 *p37*. . 020 8209 0166 / 8458 9322

Rumley, Ms J (Bond Pearce LLP)
Bristol *p161* 0845 415 0000

Rumley, P (Russell Jones & Walker)
Bristol *p164* 0117 374 2222

Rummins, M S (Kent County Council)
Maidstone *p464* 01622 694320

Rumney, J L (South Tyneside Metropolitan Borough Council) *B1 F1 G J1 K1 L Zl Q N R1*
South Shields *p471* 0191 427 1717

Rumsby, N (Linklaters LLP)
London EC2 *p54*. 020 7456 2000

Rumsby, Mrs S L (Rio Tinto PLC)
London W2 *p109* 020 7781 2000

Rundall, F R S (Charles Russell LLP) *C1 C2*
Cheltenham *p187* 01242 221122

Rundle, C (Stones Solicitors LLP)
Exeter *p222* 01392 666777

Rundle, C A (Bray & Dilks) *K1 S1*
Truro *p414*. 01872 271717

Rundle, Ms T (Parker Bullen) *J1 Zi*
Salisbury *p371*. 01722 412000

Runham, J S (Runhams) *W S1 C1*
Bradford *p154* 01274 532233

Runnicles, J (Jones Day) *C2*
London EC4 *p46*. 020 7039 5959

Rupal, Y R (Linklaters LLP)
London EC2 *p54*. 020 7456 2000

Rupping, Mrs D A (Machins Solicitors LLP) *O Q L B1 F1*
Luton *p295* 01582 514000

Rusbridge, Mrs A K (Shoosmiths) *Zr N Zq*
Northampton *p332*. .0370 086 3000 / 01604 543000

Rusbridge, P D (Broadbents) *K1 V*
Alfreton *p115* 01773 832511

Rusby, R W (Cowling Swift & Kitchin) *A1 C1 E L M1 R1 S1 T1*
York *p444* . . . . . . .01904 625678 / 625679
Boroughbridge *p150*. 01423 322312

Ruse, P N (Bassets) *G H N Q*
Gillingham *p229*. 01634 575464

Rush, S E (Memery Crystal) *Zn C1*
London WC2 *p60* 020 7242 5905

Rushby, Ms R (Murrays Partnership) *G H*
Southwark *p62*. 020 7701 8653

Rushby, Ms R (John Barkers) *K3 K1*
Grimsby *p234* 01472 358686

Rushford, Miss G (Shirley Griffiths) *K1 N W D1 B2 Q S1 T2 Zg K3 Zi Zq K4*
Hythe *p259* 01303 266689

Rushforth, W C (Chisholms) *S1 S2 K1 L W D1 K3 K4 T2 A1*
Wadebridge *p418* . .01208 812470 / 814205

Rushmer, Mrs J J (Fraser Dawbarns) *C1 S2 E*
Wisbech *p435* 01945 461456

Rushmer, J S (Overburys & Raymond Thompson) *W K4 T2*
Norwich *p335* 01603 610481

Rushton, A S (Knights Solicitors LLP) *C1 Zb C2*
Newcastle under Lyme *p323*. 01782 619225

Rushton, C (Allen & Overy LLP)
London E1 *p5* 020 3088 0000

Rushton, Ms D (Michelmores LLP) *P R1 Zu*
Exeter *p221* 01392 688688

Rushton, D A (Orme & Slade Ltd) *S1 G K1 E W L S2*
Ledbury *p271* 01531 632226

Rushton, D G (Grindeys LLP)
Stoke-on-Trent *p397*. 01782 846441

Rushton, Ms L (Girlings) *W T2 K4*
Canterbury *p177*. 01227 768374

Rushton, Miss S (Veale Wasbrough Vizards) *K1*
Bristol *p165* 0117 925 2020

Rushton, Ms S (Oldham Metropolitan Borough Council)
Oldham *p468* 0161 911 3000

Rushton, S (Rushton Hinchy Solicitors) *N O Q S1*
St Helens *p391* 0845 054 0564

Rushton, Mrs W B (Worcester City Council)
Worcester *p477* 01905 723471

Rushworth, M J (Rushworth & Glyn Owen) *S1 W L J1 E*
Rhyl *p363* 01745 343843

Rusius, J H (Southerns) *G N K1 S1 H C1 E J1 Q F1 Zc Zi Zt*
Nelson *p321*. 01282 603663

Rusling, Miss D C (Graham & Rosen) *E S2 C1*
Hull *p257* 01482 323123

Russ, Ms K A (Travers Smith LLP) *T1 T2*
London EC1 *p87*. 020 7295 3000

Russ, T (Clarke Willmott) *A1 A2 A3 M1 O*
Taunton *p408*0845 209 1000 / 0117 305 6000

Russell, A (Camden Community Law Centre)
London NW5 *p104*. 020 7284 6510

Russell, A (South Tyneside Metropolitan Borough Council)
South Shields *p471* 0191 427 1717

Russell, A C (Donnelly McArdle Adamson) *O Q N*
Darlington *p206* 01325 482299

Russell, A C (Fraser Brown) *J1*
Nottingham *p337*. 0115 988 8777

Russell, A D (Russells) *C1 Ze Zf*
London W1 *p75* 020 7439 8692

Russell, B (Bingham McCutchen (London) LLP)
London EC2 *p12*. 020 7661 5300

Russell, Mrs C H (Allens) *W K4*
Portsmouth *p354*. 023 9282 2411

Russell, C J (Reynolds Porter Chamberlain LLP)
London E1 *p71* 020 3060 6000

Russell, C P (Charles Russell LLP) *W T2 Zd*
Cheltenham *p187* 01242 221122

Russell, D (Russell Jones & Walker)
London WC2 *p74* 020 7657 1555

Russell, D M (Carlsons) *Q O N K3 K1 B1 Zr Zq*
London N20 *p18*.020 8445 3331 / 8445 5752

Russell, Mrs F L (Walker Morris) *E*
Leeds *p277* 0113 283 2500

Russell, Mrs G A (Gardner Croft LLP) *E Q S1*
Canterbury *p176*. 01227 813400

Russell, H (Trowers & Hamlins)
London EC3 *p88*. 020 7423 8000

Russell, Ms H C (Heptonstalls LLP) *N*
Goole *p231* 01405 765661

Russell, Ms H J (Harthills) *G H*
Rotherham *p367*. 01709 377399

Russell, I M R (Nottingham City Council (City Sec Dept))
Nottingham *p467*. 0115 915 5555

Russell, J (Ashurst LLP)
London EC2 *p7* 020 7638 1111

Russell, Miss J (Mullenders) *G H*
Woking *p437*. 01483 771733

Russell, J (Sidley Austin Brown & Wood) *M2 Zb*
London EC2 *p78*. 020 7360 3600

Russell, Miss J (Kidd & Spoor) *K1 G H K3*
Newcastle upon Tyne *p325* . 0191 273 9217

Russell, J C C (Godwins) *W Zd*
Winchester *p433*. 01962 841484

Russell, J E (Clarke Willmott) *E*
Southampton *p385*0845 209 1000 / 0117 305 6000

Russell, Mrs J F (Lennons) *K1 N D1*
Amersham *p117* 01494 433177

Russell, J M (GLRS Phoenix LLP) *O J1 Q B1 N C1 E S1 Zl*
Stroud *p400* 01453 763433

Russell, Miss L (Ison Harrison) *K1 K3 D1*
Leeds *p274* 0113 284 5000

Russell, Miss L (Norfolk County Council - Legal Services)
Norwich *p467* . . . Minicom: 0844 800 8011

Russell, Miss L (TWM Solicitors LLP) *S2 E S1*
London SW19 *p85*. 020 8946 6454

Russell, Mrs L R (DWF) *N*
Liverpool *p287*. 0151 907 3000

Russell, Ms M (Edwin Coe LLP) *W T2*
London WC2 *p29* 020 7691 4000

Russell, M A (Stephenson Harwood) *Za*
London EC2 *p82*. 020 7329 4422

Russell, Mrs M A H (Olswang LLP) *J1 Zp*
London WC1 *p64* 020 7067 3000

Russell, M L C (Bells) *W*
Romsey *p366* 01794 513328

Russell, N S (B D Laddie) *J1 K1 Zp O Q K3*
Westminster *p51*. 020 7963 8585

Russell, P (HSR Law (Hayes, Son & Richmond)) *E S2 R2 C1 C2*
Doncaster *p211* 01302 347800
Gainsborough *p228* 01427 613831

Russell, Ms P (Irwin Mitchell LLP) *K1 D1 V*
Sheffield *p376* 0870 150 0100

Russell, P C (P Russell & Co) *C1 Ze Zf Zw*
London W6 *p74* 020 8233 2943

Russell, P J (Charles Russell LLP) *O Q Zw*
London EC4 *p19*. 020 7203 5000

Russell, P J (Russell Worth) *N Q*
Plympton *p351*. 01752 334100

Russell, R D (Morgan Cole) *S1*
Oxford *p344* 01865 262600

Russell, Miss S (Kingsley Napley) *N Zr*
London EC1 *p50*. 020 7814 1200

Russell, Ms S (Norrie Waite & Slater)
Sheffield *p377* 0114 276 6166

Russell, Mrs S (Irwin Mitchell LLP) *F1 F2 O Q*
Sheffield *p376* 0870 150 0100

Russell, Ms S (Cresswell & Co)
London W4 *p23* 020 8742 0070

Russell, Ms S J (Hill Dickinson LLP) *C1 B1 N Zo*
Liverpool *p288*. 0151 600 8000

Russell, T (PCB Solicitors LLP) *N Q*
Shrewsbury *p379* 01743 248148

Russell, Miss V E (Fenwick Elliott) *O Q Zi Zc A3 P Zj R2*
London WC2 *p31* 020 7421 1986

Russell, Ms V J (Silverman Sherliker LLP) *J1 J2 Zp*
London EC2 *p78*. 020 7749 2700

Russell, W (G T Stewart Solicitors) *G H B2*
London SE22 *p83* 020 8299 6000

Russell-Smith, M R (Ranson Houghton) *W E S1 L C1 O B1 J1 N P Zl Zh Zc*
Salisbury *p371*. 01722 328871
Andover *p118* 01264 351533

Russen, T M S (Jacklyn Dawson) *S1 W E C1 L S2*
Newport *p328* 01633 262952

Russo, Ms M G (Birkett Long LLP) *E S1*
Chelmsford *p186*. 01245 453800

Rust, C M (Rust & Co)
Accrington *p114* 01254 390015

Rust, Ms S (Bhatia Best) *G H*
Nottingham *p336*. 0115 950 3231

Rustem, T D (Rustem Guardian Solicitors) *G H*
London EC4 *p75*. 020 7936 8000

Rustemeyer, A (Burt Brill & Cardens) *Za A3 B1 Zc F1 L Zj O Q Zq*
Brighton *p159* 01273 604123
Uckfield *p416* 01825 762281

Ruston, R (Bowser Ollard & Bentley) *W Q G N K1 J1 F1 O V Zl Zv*
Wisbech *p435* 01945 583194
Chelmsford *p186*. 0845 838 4800

Rutherford, B (Osborne Clarke) *Zb*
London EC2 *p65*. 020 7105 7000

Rutherford, D R (Ince & Co Services Ltd) *Zq Zj*
London E1 *p44* 020 7481 0010

Rutherford, J C (Hine Downing Solicitors) *S2 E S1*
Falmouth *p223*. 01326 316655

Rutherford, Ms L M (Dickinson Dees) *K1*
Newcastle upon Tyne *p324* . 0191 279 9000

Rutherford, M J (Gateley LLP)
Nottingham *p337*. 0115 983 8200

Rutherford, Mrs N (Andrew & Andrew Solicitors) *K1 Q N J1*
Portsmouth *p354*. 023 9266 1381

Rutherford, Miss S (Chamberlain Martin Solicitors) *S2 K4 W C1 T2*
Bognor Regis *p148* 01243 825211

Rutherford, S P (Walters & Barbary) *K1 D1 L N Q G H*
Camborne *p173* 01209 712454

Rutherford, T (IBB Solicitors) *O Q Zq*
Uxbridge *p417*. 0845 638 1381

Rutherford, Ms V (Cartwright King)
Nottingham *p336*. 0115 958 7444

Rutherford, Mrs V (Cornwall County Council)
Truro *p474*. 01872 322197

Rutman, S A (Travers Smith LLP) *E S2*
London EC1 *p87*. 020 7295 3000

Rutstein, M (Jones Day) *B1*
London EC4 *p46*. 020 7039 5959

Rutstein, M (SNR Denton)
London EC4 *p75*. 020 7242 1212

Rutter, C F (Rutter & Rutter) *A1 B1 G K1 L Q S1 S2 W*
Mere *p314*. 01747 860295
Wincanton *p433* 01963 32224

Rutter, Ms C L (Yorklaw Ltd (t/a Burn & Company)) *K3 K1 K2*
Easingwold *p215*. 01347 822188
York *p445* 01904 655442

Rutter, D S (DAC Beachcroft) *N O*
Winchester *p433*. 01962 705500

Rutter, Mrs F A (Elmbridge Borough Council)
Esher *p458* 01372 474198

Rutter, H A (Lupton Fawcett) *O Zq Zc A3*
Leeds *p275* 0113 280 2000

Rutter, Miss J (Beale and Company Solicitors LLP) *Zq Zj A3 J2 Zc O Q*
London WC2 *p11* 020 7240 3474

Rutter, P A (Collyer Bristow LLP) *K1*
London WC1 *p21* 020 7242 7363

Rutter, P D S (Barnes Richards Rutter) *K1 M1 N P G H C1 E S1 T1 Zl*
Chepstow *p189* 01291 628898

Rutter, Ms R (The College of Law Guildford)
Guildford *p459*. 01483 460200

Rutter, Mrs S A (CVS Solicitors) *E S1 L W I J1 Zl*
London W1 *p17* 020 7493 2903

Ruttledge, J (Stones Solicitors LLP) *C1 N Q Zj J2 X P Zv Zg*
Exeter *p222* 01392 666777

Ryabchuk, I (Ropemakers Solicitors)
London E6 *p73* 020 8586 8500

Ryait, Mrs G (Batchelors Solicitors) *Zh L*
Bromley *p166* 020 8768 7000

Ryall, R E J (SA Law) *O*
St Albans *p390* 01727 798000

Ryall, Ms T D d C (Williams Beales & Co) *Q K1 K3 N*
Hay-on-Wye *p245* 01497 820302

Ryan, A (Brabners Chaffe Street) *C1 C2*
Liverpool *p286*. 0151 600 3000

Ryan, Miss A (Thomas Dunton Solicitors) *K1 K3*
Orpington *p342* 01689 822554

Ryan, Ms A (North Warwickshire Borough Council)
Atherstone *p447*. 01827 715341

Ryan, A G (Davis Blank Furniss) *O Q Zq A3 B1 Ze Zk C1*
Manchester *p303* 0161 832 3304

Ryan, B (The Royal Borough of Kensington & Chelsea)
London W8 *p109* 020 7361 2741

Ryan, B P (Dixon Stewart)
New Milton *p321*. 01425 621515

Ryan, Ms C (Fletcher Dervish) *K1 K3 D1 D2*
Haringey *p33* 020 8800 4615

Ryan, Miss C (Hartnell Chanot & Partners Family Law Specialists) *K1 K3*
Exeter *p221* 01392 421777

Ryan, Miss C E (Bailey Smailes) *J2 E S1*
Huddersfield *p255* 01484 435543

Ryan, D F (Miller Lyons Solicitors) *S2 S1 W*
Glastonbury *p230* 01458 833660

Ryan, D G (Charles Hill Hubbard) *G H J1 L M1 N P*
Chichester *p192* 01243 781000

Ryan, Mrs D K (Larken & Co) *S1 W*
Newark *p322* 01636 703333

Ryan, D P (Pinsent Masons LLP) *T2*
Birmingham *p141* 0121 200 1050

Ryan, F M R (Barker Gillette) *O J1 Q Zq Zp A3 Ze F2 P*
London W1 *p9*. 020 7636 0555

Ryan, Ms G M (Hill Dickinson LLP) *O B1 Zb A3*
Manchester *p305* 0161 817 7200

Ryan, Ms H A (Brabners Chaffe Street) *A1 R2*
Preston *p356* 01772 823921

Ryan, J (Morrison & Foerster (UK) LLP) *Ze*
London EC2 *p62*. 020 7920 4000

Ryan, K F (Eaton Ryan & Taylor) *N O Q F1 Zj J2 Zc F2 Ze Zq U1 U2 A3*
Birmingham *p138* 0121 236 1999

Ryan, Miss L (Brian Barr Solicitors) *N Zr Zq J1*
Manchester *p301* 0161 720 6700

Ryan, Mrs L M (TMJ Legal Services LLP) *N*
Hartlepool *p243* 01429 235616
Wingate *p434* 01429 838225

Ryan, Miss M (Ormerods) *X*
Croydon *p205* 020 8686 5000

Ryan, M J (Quality Solicitors Burroughs Day) *N*
Bristol *p164* 0117 929 0333

Ryan, M L (Harold Stock & Co) *N K4 O Q W Zq*
Ashton-under-Lyne *p120*. . .01457 835597 / 835034

Ryan, Ms M T (Family Rights Group)
London E8 *p106*. 020 7923 2628

Ryan, N (Furley Page LLP) *N Zr*
Canterbury *p176*. 01227 763939

Ryan, Mrs R M (Quality Solicitors Jackson & Canter) *K1*
Liverpool *p290*. 0151 282 1700

Ryan, S F (P R Scully & Co Solicitors) *J1 J2 Q N S1*
St Helens *p391* 01744 755800

Ryan, S J (SA Law) *E L C1 Zc*
St Albans *p390* 01727 798000

Ryan, S M (Rawlison Butler LLP)
Crawley *p202* 01293 527744

Ryan, T (Mills & Reeve) *E S2 R2 L S1*
Norwich *p335* 01603 660155

Ryan, T J (Knights) *G A2 Zl B2 Q*
Tunbridge Wells *p415* 01892 537311

Ryan, Miss T M (Russell Jones & Walker)
London WC2 *p74* 020 7657 1555

Ryan, W K (Smith Chamberlain) *B1 D1 F1 G J1 K1 L N O Q V Zi*
Wellingborough *p425* 01933 224971

Ryans, M G (Freemans) *Zl R1*
Newcastle upon Tyne *p324* . 0191 222 1030

Ryatt, H (City of Bradford Metropolitan District Council)
Bradford *p451* 01274 752236

Ryatt, M (Quastel Midgen LLP) *E S1*
London W1 *p70* 020 7908 2525

Rycroft, D A (Bailey Smailes)
Huddersfield *p255* 01484 435543

Rycroft, G F (Joseph A Jones & Co) *W T2 S1 A1*
Lancaster *p269* 01524 63371

Rydeheard, Miss C D (Lyons Wilson) *S1 W*
Manchester *p307* 0161 830 7777

Ryder, Mrs C A (Midwinters) *K1 D1*
Cheltenham *p188* 01242 514674

Ryder, C J (Arnison & Co Solicitors Limited) *E S1 M1*
Penrith *p346*. 01768 862007

Ryder, D (McDermott Will & Emery UK LLP)
London EC2 *p56*. 020 7577 6900

See p634 for the Key to Work Categories

Ryder, D M (Hatchers Solicitors LLP) *K1 N Q S1 K2* Whitchurch *p430* 01948 663361

Ryder, E (Harrowells) York *p444* 01904 558600

Ryder, Miss L J (Shammah Nicholls LLP) *Q O C1 J1* Manchester *p309* 0161 832 9272

Ryder, P (ASB Law) Maidstone *p298* 01622 656500

Rye, Ms C (Watson Burton LLP) Newcastle upon Tyne *p327* . 0845 901 2100

Rylah, F H T (Kenneth Elliott & Rowe) *S2 E C1 S1* Romford *p366* 01708 757575

Ryland, D S (SJ Berwin LLP) London EC4 *p75* 020 7111 2222

Ryland, Miss H J (Cripps Harries Hall LLP) *O Q P M1 Zc E Zh* Tunbridge Wells *p415* 01892 515121

Rylands, K (Pengelly & Rylands) *S1 S2* Tenterden *p410* . . 01580 762248 / 763008

Rylatt, S (Boodle Hatfield) *T2 W* Westminster *p14* 020 7629 7411

Rylatt, Ms V (Withers LLP) *O* London EC4 *p92* 020 7597 6000

Ryle, Miss W (Burt Brill & Cardens) *K3 K1 K2* Brighton *p159* 01273 604123

Ryles, Miss C (Butcher & Barlow LLP) *S1* Prestwich *p357* 0161 773 2969

Ryley, M D (Pinsent Masons LLP) *J1 C1 C2 M2 Zi Zp* London EC2 *p67* 020 7418 7000

Ryley, P (Michelmores LLP) *Zo Zq* Exeter *p221* 01392 688688

Ryman, Ms J C (Ferguson Bricknell) *N K1 Q J1* Oxford *p343* 01865 241814

Rymarz, M A (Nicholsons Solicitors LLP) *S1* Lowestoft *p294* 01502 532300

Rymell, Ms E (Garner Canning) *K1 D1 D2 K2 K3* Atherstone *p120* 01827 713543

Rymer, C A (Silverbeck Rymer) Liverpool *p290* 0151 236 9594

Rymer, J (Silverbeck Rymer) *G H J1 K1 L M1 N P S1 W* Liverpool *p290* 0151 236 9594

Rymer, P R (Reed Smith LLP) *Ze Zf Zw* London EC2 *p71* 020 3116 3000

S

Saade, G (Brecher) *E S2 S1 L* London W1 *p15* 020 7563 1000

Saayman, K (Reed Executive PLC) London WC2 *p108* 020 7421 1640

Sabaa, F (William Heath & Co) London SW11 *p40* 020 7350 1068

Sabalot, Ms D (Deborah A Sabalot Regulatory Consulting) *Zb Zo* St Albans *p390* 01727 859434

Sabberton, D R (Hewitsons) *S1* Cambridge *p174* 01223 461155

Sabberton-Coe, R (The Rank Group PLC) Maidenhead *p464* 01628 504000

Sabharwal, N (Underwood Solicitors LLP) Westminster *p89* 020 7526 6000

Sabine, Ms C (The College of Law) *D1 K1* London WC1 *p105* 0800 289997

Sabine, M D (Warners Solicitors) *S1* Tonbridge *p412* 01732 770660

Sabzwari, Miss R (Pannone LLP) *Zb E* Manchester *p308* 0161 909 3000

Saccaggi, Miss A L M (Rosalind Watchorn) *W* Sheffield *p377* 0114 229 0160

Sacco, Miss G (Cowley Di Giorgio & Co) *E Q N S1 W* Bedford *p129* 01234 218171

Sacco, Miss J L N (Newcastle Upon Tyne City Council) Newcastle upon Tyne *p466* . 0191 232 8520

Sacha, C (Ince & Co Services Ltd) London E1 *p44* 020 7481 0010

Sachdev, R (Payne Skillington) *B1 Q O C1 Zi* Coventry *p200* 024 7663 3044

Sachs, M (Thomas Cooper) *M2 Za* London EC3 *p22* 020 7481 8851

Sacker, A (Kingsley Napley) *C1 T1 W F1 J1 Zd* London EC1 *p50* 020 7814 1200

Sacker, Miss J E (David Sacker & Co) *Zq J1 S1 O B1 E Zw T1* London NW3 *p76* 020 7433 1437

Sacks, A H (Horwich Cohen Coghlan) *S1 E L M1 R1 W K1 P C1 F1 Zl* Manchester *p305* 0161 830 4600

Sacks, Ms T (Hart Brown Solicitors) *O Q* Guildford *p236* 0800 068 8177

Sacranie, F (Cartwright King) Leicester *p279* 0116 253 9222

Sadd, Ms C (Hornby & Levy) *D1 D2 K1 K2 V* London SW9 *p43* 020 7737 0909

Saddiq, Mrs Z (Farleys Solicitors LLP) *K1* Accrington *p114* 01254 367853

Sadek, Miss R (Burnett Barker) *S1* Bury St Edmunds *p171* 01284 701131

Sadiq, K H (Oxley & Coward Solicitors LLP) *N O* Rotherham *p367* 01709 510999

Sadiq, M A (Fork Truck Hire Ltd) Blackburn *p450* 01254 691303

Sadiq, T (Henrys Solicitors Ltd) Stockport *p395* 0161 477 8558

Sadiq, U (Davisons) Birmingham *p137* 0121 685 1248

Sadka, T D (Rawlison Butler LLP) *C1 C2 J1* Crawley *p202* 01293 527744

Sadka-Surowiak, D M (Epsom & Ewell Borough Council) Epsom *p458* 01372 732000

Sadler, Mrs D E (Clarion Solicitors LLP) *K1 G H* Leeds *p272* . . . . 0113 246 0622; Harrogate *p240* 01423 530630

Sadler, Mrs D J (Blake Lapthorn) *J1* Oxford *p342* 01865 248607

Sadler, Mrs E L (Paris Smith LLP) *C1 C2 F1 Ze* Southampton *p386* 023 8048 2482

Sadler, Mrs H E (Frank Howard) *K1 D1 K3* Warrington *p422* 01925 653481

Sadler, I D (Radcliffes Le Brasseur) Westminster *p70* 020 7222 7040

Sadler, J R (Barrett & Co Solicitors LLP) *J1 Q O B1* Reading *p359* 0118 958 9711

Sadler, Mrs K N (Leeds City Council) *R1 X N J1* Leeds *p462* 0113 224 3513

Sadler, Miss L (GoodyBurrett LLP) *K3 K1* Colchester *p197* 01206 577676

Sadler, M (Denby & Co) *S2 S1 R2 W L F1 A1 R1 C1 Zl* Ulverston *p416* 01229 582283

Sadler, M B (Kenneth Elliott & Rowe) *S1 E L W S2 R2* Romford *p366* 01708 757575

Sadler, M D (Henmans LLP) *C1 B1 I E Zd Zf* Oxford *p343* 01865 781000

Sadler, W J (Lamb Brooks LLP) *C1 C2 C3 I J1 Zd* Basingstoke *p126* 01256 844888

Saeed, Ms F K (Birmingham City Council Legal & Democratic Services) Birmingham *p449* 0121 303 2066

Saeed, S (Aman Solicitors Advocates (London) Ltd) *J1 Zi Q* Wembley *p426* 020 8782 3776

Saeedi, Mrs T L (Squire Sanders (UK) LLP) *Zo* Leeds *p277* 0113 284 7000

Safdar, Ms T (South Ribble Borough Council) Preston *p469* 01772 421491

Saffer, S (Trott & Gentry) London N1 *p88* 020 3119 3150

Saffin, Mrs I J (Mundays LLP) *E L A1 B1* Cobham *p196* 01932 590500

Saffman, M (Olliers) *G H B2* Manchester *p308* 0161 834 1515

Saffron, P R (Hewitsons) *O Q Zq B2* Cambridge *p174* 01223 461155

Sagar, B C (Gaby Hardwicke) *E* Hastings *p243* 01424 438011

Sagar, R M (Walker Morris) *R1* Leeds *p277* 0113 283 2500

Sage, C J (Edwards Angell Palmer & Dodge) London EC2 *p28* 020 7583 4055

Sage, J E (FBC Manby Bowdler LLP) *C1 C2* Wolverhampton *p437* 01902 578000

Sage, Ms J E (Lyons Davidson) Bristol *p163* 0117 904 6000

Sage, M (Harding Evans LLP) *G* Newport *p328* 01633 244233

Saggar, S (Johns & Saggar) *L Q N J1 G S1 Zi Zp* London WC1 *p46* 020 3490 1475

Saggers, Mrs H (Barr Ellison LLP) *K3* Cambridge *p174* 01223 417200

Saghir, Miss R (Blackburn with Darwen Borough Council) Blackburn *p450* 01254 585585

Sagoo, N (Maples Teesdale LLP) *E S2* London EC2 *p58* 020 7600 3800

Sagoo, N V (Reynolds Porter Chamberlain LLP) London E1 *p71* 020 3060 6000

Sahni, H S (Sahni & Co) *D1 F1 G H K1 M1 N S1 W Zi Zp* Smethwick *p382* 0121 558 5222

Sahota, B S (Sahota Solicitors) *Zk* London WC2 *p76* 0845 630 2095

Sahota, Ms S (Hodge Jones & Allen LLP) *L Q Zg* London NW1 *p41* 020 7874 8300

Sahu, Miss N (Pannone LLP) *N Zr* Manchester *p308* 0161 909 3000

Saiban, J A (Charles Russell LLP) *Zw I U1 C1 Ze* London EC4 *p19* 020 7203 5000

Sa'id, G (George Anthony Andrews Solicitors) *S1 S2 E K1 N Q L G Zi Zk* London W3 *p6* 020 8746 0550

Saideman, J (Bryan Cave) *O C1 Zk* London EC2 *p19* 020 7207 1100

Saifuddin, Mrs R (R Saifuddin) *D1 G H J1 K1 M1 P R1* Bromley *p167* 020 8466 1266

Saigal, Mrs B (Borneo Hughes Martell LLP) *P K1 M1 L G H F1 B1 J1 W* Northampton *p331* 01604 624822

Saigal, P (Harvey Ingram Borneos) *G H J1 L Zi N Q Zg Zh Zk Zp* Milton Keynes *p317* 01908 696002

Saika, Mrs H S S (Daniel Curry & Co) *K1 D1 D2* Croydon *p205* 020 8680 2188

Saimbhi, Miss M (S S Basi & Co) *S1 S2 Q* Ilford *p259* 020 8518 1236

Saini, P (Penningtons) *Zi* London EC2 *p66* 020 7457 3000

Saini, S (Pictons Solicitors LLP) Luton *p295* 01582 870870

Sainsbury, Ms J L (Nicholls & Sainsbury) *K1 S1 W D1 V D2* Saltash *p371* 01752 846116

Sainsbury, Mrs L E (Maples Teesdale LLP) *E S2 R2* London EC2 *p58* 020 7600 3800

Sainsbury, M F (Sainsburys) *S1 K1 N E W F1 L Q Zd Zh* Denton *p208* 0161 336 7027

Sainsbury, P J (Lockings) *S1 W K1 N C1 F1 L* Hull *p257* 0845 075 4197

Saint, Miss B (Rolls-Royce PLC) Derby *p456* 01332 242424

Saint, P J (Reynolds Porter Chamberlain LLP) *Zj Zq* London E1 *p71* 020 3060 6000

Saint, Miss R (Paris Smith LLP) *E R2 S2 Zl* Southampton *p386* 023 8048 2482

Sainty, H J (Farrer & Co LLP) London WC2 *p31* 020 3375 7000

Sainty, Ms S (Simmons & Simmons) London EC2 *p79* 020 7628 2020

Sait, W E (Lindsay Sait & Turner) *S1 E C1 R1 L W J1* Woking *p437* 01483 604033

Saiyed, T (King Solicitors) *B1 K1 J1 Zj N K3 S1 E S2* Southall *p384* 020 8571 2239

Sakaria, S (Harris Cartier LLP) *S2 E* Slough *p382* 01753 810710

Sakran, Ms S (Manuel Swaden) *S1 S2* London NW6 *p58* 020 7431 4999

Sakrouge, A (Russell-Cooke LLP) *J1* London SW15 *p74* 020 8789 9111

Sal, Mrs D K (Sal & Co) London N18 *p76* 020 8807 5888

Sal, H (Sal & Co) *S2 E Zl S1* London N18 *p76* 020 8807 5888

Sal, I (Sal & Co) *E S1 Zl* London N18 *p76* 020 8807 5888

Salaman, Mrs C M (Amphlett Lissimore) *D1 K1* Croydon *p6* 020 8771 5254

Salamat, Ms A (Edwards Angell Palmer & Dodge) London EC2 *p28* 020 7583 4055

Salamon, T (LSG Solicitors) *C1 M1 M2* London W1 *p51* 020 7851 0100

Salamons, D L P (Cubism Limited) *E S1 C1 Ze* London WC2 *p23* 020 7831 0101

Saldanha, Dr K E (Pannone LLP) *E P R2* Manchester *p308* 0161 909 3000

Sale, J E (Bird Wilford & Sale) *W S1 T2 L Zd Zh K4* Loughborough *p293* 01509 232611

Sale, Mrs R S (Russell & Russell) *K1* Bolton *p150* 01204 707926

Sale, S A (Squire Sanders (UK) LLP) London EC2 *p81* 020 7655 1000

Sale, Mrs S C (Adur District Council) *L Q O V F1 G* Shoreham-by-Sea *p471* . . . 01273 263300

Sale, Mrs S M (Gedling Borough Council) Nottingham *p467* 0115 901 3901

Saleem, M (London Borough of Barking & Dagenham) Barking *p448* . 020 8592 4500 / 8252 8233

Saleem, M M (Malik & Malik Solicitors) Brent *p58* 020 8830 3050

Saleem, Ms N (Ahmed & Co) *Za J1* Camden *p4* 020 7383 2243

Saleh, Miss N F (Metropolitan Police Directorate of Legal Services) London SW1 *p108* 020 7230 7210

Saleh, R I (Salehs LLP) *C1 E T1* Manchester *p309* 0161 434 9991

Salen, W P (Hugh James) *N Zq O Q* Cardiff *p179* 029 2022 4871

Sales, Miss E J (Pemberton Greenish LLP) *E S2* London SW3 *p66* 020 7591 3333

Sales, Miss L (Lancashire County Council) Preston *p469* 01772 254868

Sales, Miss R (Blake Lapthorn) Oxford *p342* 01865 248607

Sales, Miss V N (Dixon Ward) *K1 K3 J1 Q Zl* Richmond upon Thames *p364* 020 8940 4051

Salford, J (Addleshaw Goddard) London EC1 *p4* 020 7606 8855

Salhan, T (Salhan & Company) Birmingham *p142* 0121 605 6000

Salida, M A (Martin Shepherd & Co) *B1 C1 C2 E S1 F1 G L Zv* Enfield *p219* 020 8367 3230

Saliheen, Miss S (McManus Seddon) *K1 D1 K3* Bradford *p154* 01274 741841

Salim, Miss A (CKFT) London NW3 *p17* 020 7431 7262

Salim, Ms F (London Borough of Haringey) London N22 *p106* 020 8489 0000

Salim, I (Davies & Company) *N J2 F2 Zw* Stockport *p395* 0161 355 5500

Salim, M M (M & K Solicitors) Luton *p295* 01582 732503

Salinger, P K (Salinger Solicitors & Notary Public) *S2 E J1 L M2 S1 W K4* Kensington & Chelsea *p76* . 020 7937 8524

Salisbury, Mrs C L (Molesworths Bright Clegg) *S1 W* Rochdale *p365* 01706 356666

Salisbury, D (Teacher Stern LLP) *B1 C1 F1 J1 Zf Zl C2* London WC1 *p86* 020 7242 3191

Salisbury, Miss H (The Royal Borough of Kensington & Chelsea) London W8 *p109* 020 7361 2741

Salisbury, M P (Gamlins) Conwy *p199* . . . . 01492 593201; Llandudno *p291* 01492 860420

Salisbury, R A (Gamlins) *C1 E R1 W Zl* Rhyl *p363* 01745 343500

Salisbury, Ms V R (Mohabirs) *K1 L D1 D2 W* London SW4 *p61* 020 7720 5742 / 7622 5495

Sall, D S (Mackrell Turner Garrett) *C1 F2 J2 J1 Zp* Woking *p437* 01483 755609

Sallabank, Ms C L (Jones Day) *T1* London EC4 *p46* . . . . 020 7039 5959; London EC4 *p75* 020 7242 1212

Sallangou, K (Fuglers) *S1 E L R1 R2* London W1 *p34* 020 7323 6450

Sallis, Mrs P (Ellis-Fermor & Negus) *K1* Ripley *p364* 01773 744744

Sallustio, R (Allen & Overy LLP) London E1 *p5* 020 3088 0000

Sallybanks, R (BCL Burton Copeland) *B2 G* London WC2 *p9* 020 7430 2277

Salmon, A J (Appleby Hope & Matthews) *K1 D1 S1 M1 P R1 L W G H* Middlesbrough *p314* 01642 440444

Salmon, Miss C L (Stewarts Law LLP) *N* London EC4 *p83* 020 7822 8000

Salmon, D A (Speechly Bircham LLP) *N J1 Zc Zf Q* London EC4 *p81* 020 7427 6400

Salmon, J (Pinsent Masons LLP) London EC2 *p67* 020 7418 7000

Salmon, J B (Jacksons) Wirral *p435* 0151 632 3386

Salmon, Miss J F (Eastgate Assistance Ltd) *J1* Colchester *p455* 0870 523 4500

Salmon, Mrs J M (Surrey Heath Borough Council) Camberley *p452* 01276 707100

Salmon, K T (Weightmans LLP) *Zc A3 J2 Zq Zj* Manchester *p311* 0161 233 7330

Salmon, P (Salans) *C1 C2* London EC4 *p76* 020 7429 6000

Salomon, Ms E C (Ofcom) London SE1 *p108* 020 7981 3040

Salsbury, P A (Addleshaw Goddard) *C1 B1 S1 Zb* London EC1 *p4* 020 7606 8855

Salt, Ms J A (Allen & Overy LLP) London E1 *p5* 020 3088 0000

Salt, N M (LSG Solicitors) *E L R1 R2 S1 S2* London W1 *p51* 020 7851 0100

Salt, P P M (Heppenstalls) *S1 W S2 L* Lymington *p296* 01590 689500

Salt, S P (Rolls-Royce PLC) *B1 F1 J1 N C1* Derby *p456* 01332 242424

Salt, S R (Linklaters LLP) London EC2 *p54* 020 7456 2000

Salt, T D (Chattertons Solicitors) *W T1 S1 S2* Grantham *p232* 01476 591550

Salter, A (Woodfines LLP) *W J1 K1 K3 Q* Sandy *p372* 01767 680251

Salter, G C (Stallard March & Edwards) *J1 L O Zq Q Zp* Worcester *p440* 01905 723561

Salter, G E (East Devon District Council) Sidmouth *p471* 01395 516551

Salter, H A (Suttons) *E S2 S1 R1 Zi W* London W1 *p84* 020 7935 5279

Salter, I K (Burges Salmon) *R1 P Zn Zs Zt* Bristol *p161* 0117 939 2000

Salter, Mrs K M (Salter Rees & Kelly) *B1 C1 D1 F1 K1 L S1 W* Swansea *p405* 01792 470707

Salter, N (Wake Smith & Tofields) *E L A1 Zc R1 R2 Zh Zs S2* Sheffield *p377* 0114 266 6660

Salter, Mrs N P (HM Land Registry - Birkenhead (Rosebrae)) Birkenhead *p449* 0151 472 6666

Salter, Miss Z (Forbes) *H G* Preston *p356* 01772 220022

Salthouse, T B (Weightmans LLP) *N* Liverpool *p291* 0151 227 2601

Saltrese, C J (Chris Saltrese Solicitors) Southport *p388* 01704 535512

Salvati, Miss L M (Brooke North LLP) *O Q* Leeds *p272* 0113 283 2100

Salvatore, Mrs C E (Dunn & Baker) *K1 G N* Exeter *p221* 01392 285000

Salvest, Ms D (Mayer Brown International LLP) London EC2 *p59* 020 3130 3000

Salvetti, R S (Biscoes) *E C1 O Q S1 W N F1 G B1 Zq Zc Zd Zf Zb* Wickham *p431* 01329 833249

Salvidge, Mrs T P J (Henriques Griffiths) Bristol *p163* 0117 909 4000

Salvidge, Miss Z (Pritchard Joyce & Hinds) *C1 Q O N* Beckenham *p129* 020 8658 3922

Salvini, R M (Plexus Law (A Trading Name of Parabis Law LLP)) *A3 J2 N Zj* Leeds *p276* 0844 245 4100

Salway, Miss G E (Everys) *K1 N Q L V K2 D1* Exmouth *p222* 01395 264384

Salway, J (Pinsent Masons LLP) London EC2 *p67* 020 7418 7000

Salway, J S (Richards & Morgan LLP) *F1 J1 K1 L S1 Q Zl* Bournemouth *p152* 01202 424234

Samad, A (DLA Piper UK LLP) London EC2 *p24* 0870 011 1111

Samaha, Ms H (DLA Piper UK LLP) London EC2 *p24* 0870 011 1111

Samani, V (Linklaters LLP) London EC2 *p54* 020 7456 2000

Samarasinghe, S V A R A (Sam & Co) *G O Zl C1 K1 N Q S1 V L Zb Zf Ze Zi Zj* London N15 *p76* 020 8808 0020

Samaraweera, Miss P S (Samars Solicitors) *K1 G Q L D1 V H J1 N F1 Zi Zl*
Hounslow *p254* 020 8570 4716

Samaroo, Miss S C D (Morrish Solicitors LLP) *N*
Leeds *p276* 0113 245 0733

Sambreen, Ms A (Ross Solicitors Ltd)
Swindon *p406* 01793 512960

Sambrook, Ms M (Squire Sanders (UK) LLP)
Birmingham *p142* 0121 222 3000

Sami, F (Ashurst LLP) *Zo J1*
London EC2 *p7* 020 7638 1111
London EC2 *p76*. 020 7329 6699

Sampat, Ms S (IBB Solicitors) *E*
Uxbridge *p417*. 0845 638 1381

Sampson, A M (Lloyd & Rowe)
Cardiff *p179* 029 2045 8999

Sampson, D C (David Sampson & Co)
London N2 *p76* 020 8458 0345

Sampson, Mrs G (Coodes) *W*
Launceston *p270* 01566 770000

Sampson, G B (Hewitsons) *E L*
Cambridge *p174*. 01223 461155

Sampson, G C (Pictons Solicitors LLP)
Luton *p295* 01582 870870

Sampson, G M (Atteys)
Doncaster *p211* 01302 340400

Sampson, Ms H (Saunders Law Partnership LLP) *G H*
London WC2 *p76* 020 7632 4300

Sampson, I C (Addleshaw Goddard) *Ze*
Manchester *p300* 0161 934 6000

Sampson, J R (Sampson Coward LLP) *D1 K1 Q S1 W*
Salisbury *p371*. 01722 410664

Sampson, J S (Wright & Wright) *S1 W T2 S2 E*
Guildford *p237*. 01483 531264

Sampson, Mrs K (Hadfield & Co) *S1 E Zl S2*
Welling *p424*. 020 8301 0808

Sampson, N (Rosenblatt) *O N M2 W Q S1 C1 Zf*
London EC4 *p73*. 020 7955 0880

Sampson, P (Veale Wasbrough Vizards) *C1 U2 Ze*
Bristol *p165* 0117 925 2020

Sampson, S (Edward Hayes LLP) *W*
Bognor Regis *p148* 01243 822655

Sampson, S J (Squire Sanders (UK) LLP) *O B1 Ze Zf*
London EC2 *p81*. 020 7655 1000

Sampson, Miss V L (CooperBurnett) *C1 C2 E*
Tunbridge Wells *p415* 01892 515022

Samrai, P S (Bhatia Best) *G H*
Nottingham *p336*. 0115 950 3231

Sams, P (Eric Robinson Solicitors) *L S1*
Southampton *p386*. 023 8022 6891

Samsworth, Mrs J M (Hogan Lovells International LLP)
London EC1 *p42*. 020 7296 2000

Samuda, Miss F (Walsall Metropolitan Borough Council) *Q O*
Walsall *p475*. 01922 650000
Coventry *p199*. 0844 561 0100

Samuel, A P (Rohan & Co) *K3 K1 Q N J1*
Haywards Heath *p246* 01444 450901

Samuel, Ms J M (Samuels Solicitors) *J1 K1 E N O Q R2 S1 S2 Zb Zc Zk Zg Zm Zq*
Barnstaple *p125* 01271 343457

Samuel, M A (Heyes Samuel) *K1 D1 Q V L*
Ryde *p369*. 01983 615615

Samuel, S (G Spilsbury & Co) *N G H S1 K3*
Mountain Ash *p319* 01443 473213

Samuels, A C (Blatchfords) *E S1 Q F1 C1 L J1*
Harrow *p241*. 020 8422 1181

Samuels, A C (Alan Samuels & Co) *S2 E S1*
London N3 *p76* 0845 900 0116

Samuels, B L (Chandler Harris LLP) *J1 O C1 Zq F1*
Manchester *p302* 0161 834 2200

Samuels, B R (Kingsley Napley) *O Q L Zq*
London EC1 *p50*. 020 7814 1200

Samuels, J (Samuels & Co Solicitors) *S1*
Leeds *p276* 0113 394 4117

Samuels, Ms L (International Family Law Chambers) *K1 M2 K2 K3 M1*
London WC2 *p45* 020 7583 5040

Samuels, L C (Lawrence C Samuels LLB Solicitor) *S1 W S2 E*
Northwood *p333*. 01923 824708

Samuels, L D (Ascroft Whiteside) *E S2 S1 C1*
Blackpool *p146* 01253 766866

Samuels, P J (Scotts Holt & Sellars) *E L S1 W*
Bromsgrove *p167* 01527 872711

Samuels, Miss R (Tilly Bailey & Irvine LLP) *K1 K3 D1 D2*
Stockton-on-Tees *p397* . . . 01642 673797

Samuels, S (Jerman Simpson Pearson & Samuels) *N G H*
Southend-on-Sea *p387* . . . 01702 610071

Samuelson, C K (Glanvilles) *Q K1 L B1 D1 R1 Za Zq*
Newport *p328* 01983 527878

Samworth, Miss P A (Lodders Solicitors LLP) *A1 S2 E S1*
Cirencester *p195*. 01285 659535

Samy, Miss L (Berry & Berry) *K4 W T1*
Tunbridge Wells *p414* 01892 526344

Sana, Ms A (Barlow Lyde & Gilbert LLP)
London EC3 *p10*. 020 7247 2277

Sanchetti, A (Morgan Walker)
London WC2 *p62* 020 7831 8333

Sandal, A J (Treasury Solicitors Department)
London WC2 *p110*. 020 7210 3000

Sandall, A V (Anthony Sandall and Co) *E C1 O R1 J1*
Reading *p361* 0118 958 5505

Sandall, Mrs D (Buckles Solicitors LLP) *K3 K1 A1*
Peterborough *p346* 01733 888888

Sandars, G R (SNR Denton)
London EC4 *p75*. 020 7242 1212

Sandars, J E (Mercers) *C1 E F1 J1 S1 Ze Zc*
Henley-on-Thames *p247*. . . 01491 572138

Sandars, Mrs R E (Official Solicitor and Public Trustee)
London WC2 *p108*. 020 7911 7127

Sandbach, C (HC Solicitors LLP) *Q M1 O*
Peterborough *p347* 01733 882800

Sandel, Miss K A (Everys) *Q O*
Exeter *p221* 01392 477983
Exeter *p221* 01392 455555

Sandelands, Mrs E C (H F T Gough & Co) *K1 Q N K2 D1 D2*
Whitehaven *p431* 01946 692461

Sandelands, M T (H F T Gough & Co) *R1 S1 S2 W*
Whitehaven *p431* 01946 692461

Sandelson, D A (Clifford Chance)
London E14 *p20*. 020 7006 1000

Sandelson, J V (Clifford Chance)
London E14 *p20*. 020 7006 1000

Sandeman, Ms G H (Everett Tomlin Lloyd & Pratt) *S1 W E*
Pontypool *p352* 01495 763333

Sander, Ms V R (Linklaters LLP)
London EC2 *p54*. 020 7456 2000

Sandercock, G G M (Granville-West) *Q D1 C1 S1 W E B1 Zl*
Pontypool *p352* 01495 751111

Sanders, Ms A (McKeowns Solicitors Ltd) *N*
St Albans *p390* 0800 032 8328

Sanders, A C (Markand & Co) *S1 E G H W K1 M1 P N J1 Zl*
London E7 *p58* 020 8470 1422

Sanders, A W (Hogan Lovells International LLP)
London EC1 *p42*. 020 7296 2000

Sanders, Mrs B J (Barlow Robbins LLP) *W T2*
Godalming *p231* 01483 417121

Sanders, Ms C (Official Solicitor and Public Trustee)
London WC2 *p108*. 020 7911 7127

Sanders, Mrs C A (Hart Brown Solicitors) *K1*
Godalming *p231* 0800 068 8177

Sanders, D (Linklaters LLP)
London EC2 *p54*. 020 7456 2000

Sanders, D I (Macfarlanes) *E*
London EC4 *p56*. 020 7831 9222

Sanders, D S (Paris Smith LLP) *K3 K1*
Southampton *p386*. 023 8048 2482

Sanders, I (Woodcock & Thompson) *A1 C1 E S1 S2 W Zi Zc*
Northampton *p333*. 01604 758855

Sanders, I J (Marrons) *E R2 S1*
Leicester *p280*. 0116 289 2200

Sanders, Mrs J (Ashurst LLP) *Zn*
London EC2 *p7* 020 7638 1111

Sanders, Mrs J H (North Shropshire District Council)
Wem *p475*. 01939 232771

Sanders, Mrs J K (Pengillys LLP) *K1 K2*
Weymouth *p430* 01305 768888

Sanders, M (SJ Berwin LLP)
London EC4 *p75*. 020 7111 2222

Sanders, M (DFA Law LLP) *K1 S1 W V*
Northampton *p331*. 01604 609560

Sanders, M (Linklaters LLP)
London EC2 *p54*. 020 7456 2000

Sanders, N J (Mayo Wynne Baxter LLP) *C1 E S2*
Lewes *p283* 01273 477071

Sanders, P R B (Sanders & Co)
Rainham *p359*. 0844 353 3553

Sanders, R H (Sanders Brickwood) *E C1 S1 A1 T1*
Cirencester *p195*. 01285 654601

Sanders, Mrs S (Ellis-Fermor & Negus) *K1*
Ripley *p364* 01773 744744

Sanders, T (Dawson & Burgess with Bell Dallman & Co) *J1 S1 E A1 S2 C1*
Doncaster *p211* 01302 349463

Sanders, T S (Skadden Arps Slate Meagher & Flom (UK) LLP) *T1*
London E14 *p80*. 020 7519 7000

Sanders-Key, Ms J (Harbottle & Lewis LLP)
London W1 *p38* 020 7667 5000

Sanderson, A J (Bird & Bird LLP) *O U1 Q*
London EC4 *p13*. 020 7415 6000

Sanderson, Mrs A M (St Helens Borough Council)
St Helens *p472* 01744 456000

Sanderson, Mrs C (Stone King LLP) *E S2 C1 Zd S1*
Bath *p128* 01225 337599

Sanderson, Miss C (Christine Sanderson) *S1 W*
Gosforth *p232* 0191 285 9633

Sanderson, Ms E S (Withers LLP) *J1*
London EC4 *p92*. 020 7597 6000

Sanderson, Mrs J E L (Wrigleys Solicitors LLP) *J1 C1 Zd C2 Zo*
Leeds *p278* 0113 244 6100

Sanderson, Ms L (Simmons & Simmons)
London EC2 *p79*. 020 7628 2020

Sanderson, Miss L J (Sleigh Son & Booth) *Zm W K4 S1*
Droylsden *p213* 0161 370 9524

Sanderson, M A (Walker Morris)
Leeds *p277* 0113 283 2500

Sanderson, P (Mitchell Dodds & Co) *C1 E K1 N Q S1 W Zc Zm*
Whitley Bay *p431* 0191 252 2396 / 252 9557

Sanderson, P A (Travers Smith LLP) *C1*
London EC1 *p87*. 020 7295 3000

Sanderson, Mrs P E (Downes & Siddall) *S1 S2 L*
Lincoln *p284*. 01522 543343

Sandford, J M (Stanley Tee) *F1 F2 B1 N O Q Zj*
Bishop's Stortford *p144* . . . 01279 755200

Sandford, J W (Orange PCS Ltd)
Bristol *p452* 0870 376 8888

Sandford, K (Taylor Wessing) *C1 J1 B1 Ze*
London EC4 *p86*. 020 7300 7000

Sandford, P D (Lancashire County Council)
Preston *p469* 01772 254868

Sandford, R (Walker Morris) *O*
Leeds *p277* 0113 283 2500

Sandford-Pike, J W S (TWM Solicitors LLP) *J1 K1 O Q X Zl*
Guildford *p237*. 01483 752700

Sandham, M S (Guest Pritchard & Co) *S1 S2 W*
Old Colwyn *p340* 01492 515371

Sandham, Ms R L (Forsters LLP) *C1*
Westminster *p33*. 020 7863 8333

Sandhu, Miss B (Russell & Co) *K1*
Malvern *p300* 01684 892000

Sandhu, Miss H (Hawkins Hatton LLP) *O Zq Zr N*
Dudley *p213*. 01384 216840

Sandhu, H (Shakespeares) *C1 Ze Zza I U2 F1 F2*
Nottingham *p339*. 0115 945 3700

Sandhu, J (Ashurst LLP)
London EC2 *p7* 020 7638 1111

Sandhu, P S (Sandhu & Shah) *S1 N Q K1 L E G F1 O W Zc Zj Zl*
London E7 *p76* 020 8552 4100

Sandhy, Miss R (Piper Smith Watton LLP) *M3 C1 C3 Ze J1 M1 Zi C2*
London SW1 *p68* 020 7222 9900

Sandiford, D H (EAD Solicitors LLP) *S2 C1 E J1 O*
Liverpool *p287*. 0151 734 4339

Sandiford, J (Russell-Cooke LLP) *D1*
Kingston upon Thames *p267*. 020 8546 6111

Sandiford, P (Pannone LLP) *O F1*
Manchester *p308* 0161 909 3000

Sandilands, I A (Churchers) *W T1 H G C1 D1 S1*
Gosport *p232* 023 9260 3400

Sandison, H R (Bird & Bird LLP) *I C1*
London EC4 *p13*. 020 7415 6000

Sandison, Ms J A G (Wessex Housing Partnership Ltd)
Basingstoke *p448* 01256 844506

Sandland, A G (Butcher & Barlow LLP) *Q C1 S1 B1 S2 E F1 L O N W*
Runcorn *p369* 01928 576056

Sandlant, D (Reed Smith LLP) *J1*
London EC2 *p71*. 020 3116 3000

Sandler, M H (Gregorys Solicitors) *W K4*
Stockport *p395*. 0161 456 8125
Altrincham *p116* 0161 928 9321

Sandler, Ms N (Jones Day) *Zb*
London EC4 *p46*. 020 7039 5959

Sando, T (Reed Smith LLP) *Zb O*
London EC2 *p71*. 020 3116 3000

Sands, Mrs A B (Wilkinson Woodward)
Halifax *p238* 01422 339600

Sands, Mrs C (Jordans) *N*
Castleford *p183* 01977 518778

Sands, J (Canter Levin & Berg) *K1 W*
Liverpool *p287*. 0151 239 1000

Sands, J D (Linder Myers Solicitors) *O Q K1 C1 B1 F1 R1 L J1*
Manchester *p307* 0844 984 6400

Sands, R J U (Foot Anstey)
Plymouth *p349*. 01752 675000
Plymouth *p351*. 01752 663295

Sands, S B (JMW Solicitors) *C1 Ze U2 O C2*
Manchester *p306* 0845 872 6666

Sandu, L (Phillips & Co) *D1 G K3 K1 K2 L Q D2 M1*
Salisbury *p371*. 01722 321666

Sandy, D J (Simmons & Simmons)
London EC2 *p79*. 020 7628 2020

Sandys, M (Kirwans) *C1 O F2*
Liverpool *p289*. 0151 229 5600
Liverpool *p290*. 0151 282 1700

Saner, J D (Collyer Bristow LLP) *W T1*
London WC1 *p22* 020 7242 7363

Sanford, F R (Reed Smith LLP) *Za*
London EC2 *p71*. 020 3116 3000

Sang, Ms S (The College of Law)
London WC1 *p105*. 0800 289997

Sangar, S (Radcliffes Le Brasseur)
Westminster *p70*. 020 7222 7040

Sanger-Anderson, S J (Ford Simey LLP) *J1 C1 O*
Exeter *p221* 01392 274126
Exeter *p222* 01392 207020

Sangha, H S (William Heath & Co) *J1 K1 L P S1*
Westminster *p40*. 020 7402 3151

Sangha, Ms K (Reed Smith LLP)
London EC2 *p71*. 020 3116 3000

Sangha, T (Seymours) *K3 J1 K1*
Coventry *p201*. 024 7655 3961

Sanghavi, Ms N (P K P French)
Harrow *p241*. 020 8861 8832

Sanghera, G S (EMW) *Zb C1 C2*
Milton Keynes *p316* 0845 070 6000

Sanghera, Mrs H K (Gill & Co) *K1 K3*
Ilford *p260*. 020 8554 8774

Sanghera, Miss S (Josiah Hincks) *W*
Leicester *p280*. 0116 255 1811

Sanghvi, R R (R R Sanghvi & Co) *C1 E G M1 N P S1*
Harrow *p242*. 020 8515 0490

Sangra, S S (Solicitors Active) *E N O S2 S1 R2 L Q Zi*
Leeds *p277* 0113 248 9805

Sangster, D (Red Kite Law) *S1 S2 G H W*
Milford Haven *p316* 01646 698008

Sanichara, D (Ashurst LLP)
London EC2 *p7* 020 7638 1111

Sanig, Mrs M D (Neil Myerson LLP) *S1*
Altrincham *p117* 0161 941 4000

Sankar, Mrs P (Mills & Allen Ltd) *E L O Q C3 T1*
London W2 *p108* 020 7298 8000

Sankey, B (Flint Bishop Solicitors)
Derby *p208* 01332 340211
Nottingham *p337*. 0115 964 4450

Sankhla, B (Quality Solicitors Clarke & Son) *K1 K3 D1 D2*
Basingstoke *p127* 01256 320555

Sansom, Mrs L (Wilkins) *W K4 T2*
Aylesbury *p121* 01296 424681

Sant, Miss E V (The Specter Partnership) *K1 N*
Birkenhead *p135*. 0151 647 3000

Santa-Olalla, M R (Gordons Solicitors LLP) *S1 E M1 P N C1 K1 W G L Zl*
Marlow *p313*. 01628 487487

Santer, M H (Santers Solicitors) *E F1 C1 C2 C3 N Q B1 G S1 Zc Zl Zq Zj Zv*
Barking *p123* 020 8594 7542

Santer, W (Nabarro LLP) *J1 Ze*
London WC1 *p63* 020 7524 6000

Santos, Ms E M (Aviva PLC)
London EC3 *p103* . . 020 7283 7500 / 01603 687905

Santra, Ms K (Colman Coyle LLP) *J1*
Islington *p22*. 020 7354 3000
Watford *p423* 01923 202020

Saperia, M (Fruhman Davies Livingstones)
Manchester *p304* 0161 833 0578

Sapsed, N (Guillaumes Solicitors) *K4 Zm T2 W*
Weybridge *p430*. 01932 840111
Weybridge *p430*. 01932 840111

Sarabia, Mrs M S (Benussi & Co) *K1 K3*
Birmingham *p135* 0121 248 4001

Sarandou, Ms G (Duncan Lewis & Co) *Zi*
London W12 *p53* 020 7923 4020

Saras, J M (Preiskel & Co LLP)
London EC4 *p69*. 020 7583 2120

Sarbjit, Mrs N (Varley Hibbs LLP) *C1 S2 E*
Coventry *p201*. 024 7663 1000

Sardo, R J (Thomas Dunton Solicitors) *N J1*
Orpington *p342* 01689 822554

Sarfas, Ms R N A (Thompsons (formerly Robin/ Brian Thompson & Partners)) *N*
London WC1 *p87* 020 7290 0000

Sarfo-Akrade, E (Sarfo Solicitors) *N*
Cambridge *p175*. 01223 305551

Sargeant, Ms L (Needham Poulier & Partners) *G H*
London N17 *p63*. 020 8808 6622

Sargent, Mrs A (FBC Manby Bowdler LLP) *R1*
Telford *p409* 01952 292129

Sargent, Mrs H V (Jewels Solicitors) *W S1*
Stafford *p393* 01785 602030

Sargent, M M (Fraser Brown) *S1*
Nottingham *p337*. 0115 988 8777

Sargent, P R (Peter R Sargent) *S1 W E L R2 R1 S2*
Grimsby *p235* 01472 887670

Sargent, S (J W Hughes & Co) *S1 S2 N W E L*
Conwy *p199*. 01492 596596

Sarginson, D R (Sarginsons Law LLP) *C1 E G K1 L M1 N P S1*
Coventry *p201*. 024 7655 3181

Sargologo, R J P (Field Fisher Waterhouse LLP) *B1 C1 E L P R1*
London EC3 *p31*. 020 7861 4000

Sarker, Ms E (Trowers & Hamlins)
London EC3 *p88*. 020 7423 8000

Sarkis, Miss A A (May May & Merrimans) *W C1 T2*
London WC1 *p59* 020 7405 8932

Sarma, Ms A (Hopkin Murray Beskine) *K1 D1 L*
London N4 *p42* 020 7272 1234

Sarney, B N (Roger Dean & Co) *S1 Q W J1 E F1 C1 S2*
Biggin Hill *p133* 01959 542872

Sarnowski, M T (Charles Lucas & Marshall) *E C1 W P R1 A1 M1 Zc Zj*
Hungerford *p258*. 01488 682506

Saroop, R (Read Dunn Connell) *F1 J1 L N O Zp Q*
Bradford *p154* 01274 723858

Sarsfield-Hall, Mrs A B (Morgan Cole) *Ze*
Oxford *p344*. 01865 262600

Sartin, Mrs J M (Burnand Brazier Tisdall) *W S1 E K4*
Worthing *p441*. 01903 502155
Hove *p254*. 01273 734022

Sarwar, A H (Forbes) *G H*
Preston *p356* 01772 220022

Sarwar, N (T G Baynes) *N Zr J2*
Bexleyheath *p132* 020 8301 7777

Sarwar, Mrs N (Swinburne & Jackson LLP) *J1*
Gateshead *p229*. 0191 477 2531 / 477 3222

Sassoli, O N (Penn Sassoli) *S1 E D1 W M1 G P L K1 B1 Zl Zc*
Royston *p368* . . . .01763 245234 / 245957

Sasto, S G (Sasto & Klinger) *E L C1 F1 S1 W T1 J1 Zb Zi Ze*
London W1 *p76*. 020 7631 4714

Satchell, Ms P M (Paul Crowley & Co)
Liverpool *p287*. 0151 264 7363

Satchell, Mrs S K (Withers LLP) *L O Zc*
London EC4 *p92*. 020 7597 6000

Sathananthan, S (S Satha & Co) *G H K1 L F1 Q J1 D1 N V Zk Zp Zq Zh*
Newham *p76* 020 8471 9484

Satsavia, Mrs K (Anthony Stockton) *S1 S2*
Coventry *p201*. 01676 535790

See p634 for the Key to Work Categories

Sattar, Miss F (MacLeish Littlestone Cowan)
Barking *p123* 020 8514 3000

Satterly, Mrs E J (Cumberland Ellis Peirs) *W T1 T2*
London WC1 *p23* 020 7242 0422

Satterthwaite, Ms P (LG Lawyers)
London SE1 *p50*. 020 7379 0000

Satyanadhan, R (J Garrard & Allen) *O Q*
Olney *p341* 01234 711215

Saujani, J V (J V Saujani & Co) *E S2 K3 K1 L ZI Q S1 W Zi J1*
Harrow *p242*. 020 8861 2606

Saujani, V (SJ LAW)
London E17 *p75*. 020 8520 6600

Saul, A J (Osborne Clarke) *R2 C2*
London EC2 *p65*. 020 7105 7000

Saul, A P (Fosters) *K1 C1*
Bungay *p168* 01986 895251
Norwich *p334* 01603 620508

Saul, C T (Harvey Ingram LLP) *B1 F1 L O Q*
Leicester *p280*. 0116 254 5454

Saul, K (Walker Smith Way) *Zr N*
Chester *p191* 0844 346 3100

Saul, R (Raymond Saul & Co) *E S1 W L M1 N P*
London E1 *p76* 020 7480 5840

Saul, Miss S A (Camps Solicitors) *N Q*
Birkenhead *p134*. 0151 201 8080

Saul, T J (Thomas Saul & Co) *N S1 W X O*
Whitefield *p430* 0161 773 2833

Saulet, J R (Saulet & Co) *E F1 L R1 P S1 N D1 G K1 H ZI Q W S2 C1*
Southsea *p389*. 023 9281 9442

Saum, R J (Robinsons) *E S1 R2 A1 S2 Zd*
Derby *p209* 01332 291431

Saunby, C (Tollers LLP)
Northampton *p332*. 01604 258558

Saunby, C C (Tollers LLP) *A3 O J1 Zc Ze Zq Zp*
Northampton *p332*. 01604 258558

Saunders, A W (Vivash Hunt) *E S1 C1*
Worcester Park *p440* . . . 020 8330 1961

Saunders, C (Kennedys)
London EC3 *p49*. 020 7667 9667

Saunders, C D (Blake Lapthorn) *W T2 Zd*
Portsmouth *p354*. 023 9222 1122

Saunders, C J (Allan Jay Paine & Co) *L S1 W*
Enfield *p5* 020 8886 1404

Saunders, Ms C L (Taylor Wessing)
London EC4 *p86*. 020 7300 7000

Saunders, C M (The Johnson Partnership) *G H*
Nottingham *p337*. 0115 941 9141

Saunders, C M (Saunders & Co) *E S1*
Richmond upon Thames *p364* 020 8332 2995

Saunders, C P (BP Chemicals Ltd)
Sunbury-on-Thames *p473* . 01932 738320

Saunders, C R (Coca-Cola Enterprises Ltd) *J1 Q Zp*
Uxbridge *p474*. 01895 231313

Saunders, D (Hatchers Solicitors LLP) *C1 E P S1 T1 W Ze Zo*
Shrewsbury *p379* 01743 248545

Saunders, D (Sacker & Partners LLP) *Zo*
London EC2 *p76*. 020 7329 6699

Saunders, D (Sanders & Co) *O Q N J1 B1 K1 G H L F1 ZI Zk Zo*
Rainham *p359*. 0844 353 3553

Saunders, D A (Male & Wagland) *K1 G Q N F1 H J1 L O E S1 W*
Potters Bar *p355*. 01707 657171

Saunders, D W (Wise Geary) *W S1*
Banbury *p122* 01295 278500

Saunders, E (Ashurst LLP)
London EC2 *p7* 020 7638 1111

Saunders, Mrs E A (Canter Levin & Berg) *N Q*
Kirkby *p268* 0151 546 4562

Saunders, E J (Leo Abse & Cohen) *N*
Cardiff *p179* . . .029 2038 3252 / 2034 5421

Saunders, Mrs H M E (Tanners) *A1 A2 S2 E L S1*
Cirencester *p195*. 01285 659061

Saunders, Ms J A (British Telecommunications PLC)
London EC1 *p104* 020 7356 6181

Saunders, J C (Phillips & Co) *N Q F1 K1 W Zq*
Salisbury *p371*. 01722 321666

Saunders, Mrs J M (Allan Jay Paine & Co) *S2 E ZI S1 W*
Enfield *p5* 020 8886 1404

Saunders, J N (Saunders Law Partnership LLP) *G H Q*
London WC2 *p76* 020 7632 4300

Saunders, J S (Blake Lapthorn)
Oxford *p342* 01865 248607

Saunders, Mrs K (Langleys) *Zo S1 D1 K1 X*
Lincoln *p284*. 01522 888555
York *p445* 01904 610886

Saunders, Mrs K E R (Singleton Winn McDermott Solicitors) *K1 D1 D2*
Newcastle upon Tyne *p326* . 0191 265 8817

Saunders, Mrs K S A (Trowers & Hamlins) *R2 Q M2 Zc Zh*
London EC3 *p88*. 020 7423 8000

Saunders, Ms L A (Aaron & Partners LLP Solicitors) *K1 K3*
Chester *p190* 01244 405555

Saunders, L G (Anderson Partnership) *D1 G H E S1 W ZI*
Chesterfield *p191* 01246 220737

Saunders, M (Clifford Chance) *C1*
London E14 *p20*. 020 7006 1000

Saunders, M D (Simmons & Simmons) *S1 L W*
London EC2 *p79*. 020 7628 2020

Saunders, M D (DLA Piper UK LLP) *O*
London EC2 *p24*. 0870 011 1111

Saunders, M J (Mark Saunders & Co) *D1 K1 S1 W*
Gorseinon *p231* 01792 892692

Saunders, M T (Jeffrey Green Russell) *E R2 S2*
London W1 *p46* 020 7339 7000

Saunders, Mrs N (Berwins Solicitors Limited) *J1*
Harrogate *p240* 01423 509000
Leeds *p275* 0113 244 9931

Saunders, N (Thompsons (formerly Robin/Brian Thompson & Partners)) *N G*
Plymouth *p350*. 01752 675810

Saunders, N R (Saunders Goodin Riddleston Solicitors) *H G*
Ipswich *p263*. 01473 225600

Saunders, P (Newsome Vaughan LLP) *Q O C1 J1*
Coventry *p200*. 024 7663 3433

Saunders, P J (Saunders Bearman LLP) *S2 S1 E R2 O B1 ZI Zm*
London W1 *p76* 020 7224 2618

Saunders, R (ACT Solicitors) *N*
Norwich *p333* 01603 610611

Saunders, Miss R M (Davey Franklin Jones) *W K4*
Cirencester *p195*. 01285 654875

Saunders, Ms S A M (Crown Prosecution Service Thames Valley)
Abingdon *p447*. 01235 551900

Saunders, S P (Otten Penna Ltd) *K1 D1 D2*
Northenden *p333* 0161 945 1431

Saunders, W (Jones Day) *C2*
London EC4 *p46*. 020 7039 5959

Saunders, W A (Stephenson Harwood) *Zo C1*
London EC2 *p82*. 020 7329 4422

Saunders, Ms W D (Memery Crystal) *Zv*
London WC2 *p60* 020 7242 5905

Saunders-Jerrom, Mrs L E M (Hewitts) *G H ZI Zm*
Darlington *p206* 01325 468573

Saunt, N H (Kevill Kirkham & Grayson) *K1 P S1 D1 W C1 R1*
Chorley *p194* . . . .01257 263676 / 269212

Sautter, E M (Mayer Brown International LLP) *O A3 B2*
London EC2 *p59*. 020 3130 3000

Sauvain, R P (Parrott & Coales LLP) *K1 K2*
Aylesbury *p121* 01296 318500

Savage, Miss A (Birkett Long LLP) *A1 E S1 T1 T2 W*
Colchester *p197* 01206 217300

Savage, D (Charles Russell LLP) *O Zq Zc*
Guildford *p235*. 01483 252525

Savage, D (R A Savage & Co) *K1 K2 D1 D2*
Welwyn Garden City *p425* . . 01707 373037

Savage, D J (Squire Sanders (UK) LLP)
London EC2 *p81*. 020 7655 1000

Savage, Mrs E P (Savages) *Zd A1 S1 E W*
Corbridge *p199* 01434 632505

Savage, Mrs I (Carillion PLC)
Wolverhampton *p477* 01902 422431

Savage, Mrs J (Stoke-on-Trent City Council)
Stoke-on-Trent *p472*. 01782 234567

Savage, Mrs J M (Wilkin Chapman LLP) *Q N O C1 K1 M1 V X Zq*
Grimsby *p235* 01472 262626

Savage, Mrs K L (Lester Aldridge LLP) *Q*
Bournemouth *p152*. 01202 786161

Savage, M P (Anthony King & Co) *G H J1*
Basildon *p126* 01268 240400

Savage, P (Harrison Clark LLP) *N Zm*
Cheltenham *p188* 01242 269198
Worcester *p439* 01905 612001
Worcester *p439* 01905 612001

Savage, P (Morrisons Solicitors LLP)
Woking *p437*. 01483 726146

Savage, Mrs R A (R A Savage & Co) *D1 K1 K2 D2*
Welwyn Garden City *p425* . . 01707 373037

Savage, R L (Savages) *C1 C2 E J1 N Q F1 Ze Zj Zd Zk*
Corbridge *p199* 01434 632505

Savage, Ms S A (Reed Smith LLP)
London EC2 *p71*. 020 3116 3000

Savage, S J (Wilkin Chapman LLP) *E P S1 J1 M1 C1 F1 T1*
Grimsby *p235* 01472 262626

Savage, Ms T (The College of Law Chester)
Chester *p454* 0800 289997

Savani, S S (Judge Sykes Frixou)
London WC2 *p47* 020 7379 5114

Saverymuttu, Ms C L (Barlow Lyde & Gilbert LLP)
London EC3 *p10*. 020 7247 2277

Savic, Ms J S (Sutovic & Hartigan)
London W3 *p84* 020 8993 5544

Saviker, Ms M Y (Mackrell Turner Garrett) *S1 W*
Addlestone *p114*. 01932 342181

Savill, Ms L J G (Olswang LLP) *C1 F1 E Zb*
London WC1 *p64* 020 7067 3000

Savill, Ms L R (Squire Sanders (UK) LLP)
London EC2 *p81*. 020 7655 1000

Savill, M (Lyons Davidson) *O F1 L J1 ZI Zt Ze*
Bristol *p163* 0117 904 6000

Saville, D J (Reynolds Porter Chamberlain LLP) *O N A3 Q M2 Zj Zq*
London E1 *p71* 020 3060 6000

Saville, Mrs G M (Corries Solicitors) *N*
York *p444* 0845 241 5566

Saville, Mrs M C (Reynolds Parry-Jones) *N Q Zr*
High Wycombe *p250*. 01494 525941

Saville, N (Norman Saville & Co) *W*
London N10 *p76*. 020 8883 9711

Saville, N P (Cannings Connolly) *L O Q J1 Zh A3 Zp Zc*
London EC1 *p18*. 020 7329 9000

Savin, Ms Z (Mercers) *W*
Henley-on-Thames *p247*. . . 01491 572138

Savitt, J (Lawrence Law) *G H K1 D1 L M1 P N S1 E Zc Zi Zp*
London SW15 *p52*. 020 8788 0055

Savjani, S (Savjani & Co) *E S1 S2 C1 Ze W O Q Zi L F1*
London NW10 *p77*. 020 8961 3352

Savva, Miss M (Jameson & Hill)
Hertford *p248* 01992 554881

Savvides, M (Grant Saw Solicitors LLP) *C1 S2 E*
Greenwich *p36*. 020 8858 6971

Savvides, T A (Osborne Clarke) *O Ze Zk*
London EC2 *p65*. 020 7105 7000

Saward, Ms K (Babergh District Council)
Hadleigh *p459* 01473 822801

Sawbridge, Ms R (Shoosmiths)
Birmingham *p142* 0370 086 4000 / 0121 335 4440

Sawers, J A (MacDonald Oates LLP) *S2 E W S1*
Midhurst *p316* 01730 816711

Sawers, R J (MacDonald Oates LLP) *W T2 K4 S1*
Petersfield *p348* 01730 268211

Sawford, Ms F A (Staffordshire County Council) *N P Zj Zk*
Stafford *p472* 01785 223121

Sawicki, Ms S (Pinsent Masons LLP)
London EC2 *p67*. 020 7418 7000

Sax, R N (Manches LLP) *K1*
London WC2 *p58* 020 7404 4433

Saxl, Ms M (Ford Simey LLP) *N*
Exeter *p221* 01392 274126

Saxon, M (James Benson & Co)
Liverpool *p286*. 0151 236 8755

Saxon, P S (BHP Law) *N O*
Newcastle upon Tyne *p323* . 0191 221 0898

Saxon, Ms V A L (Doyle Clayton Solicitors Limited) *J1 Zp*
Reading *p360* 0118 959 6839

Saxton, Ms E (Jones Day) *C1 Zb B1*
London EC4 *p46*. 020 7039 5959

Say, Ms J (Parlett Kent) *Zr N Zq*
London EC1 *p66*. 020 7430 0712

Say, J (Hodge Jones & Allen LLP) *Zr*
London NW1 *p41* 020 7874 8300

Sayani, N R (Beale and Company Solicitors LLP) *C1 E O M1 T1 Q Zb Zi M2*
London WC2 *p11* 020 7240 3474

Sayce, K (Straw & Pearce) *G H*
Loughborough *p293* 01509 268931

Saye, N (Husband Saye) *J1 N W E K1 C1 L O Q*
Cardiff *p179* 029 2034 5217

Sayer, C (Aon Ltd)
London EC2 *p103* 020 7623 5500

Sayer, M B (Briggs Sayer & Co) *C1 D1 F1 G H J1 K1 L N Q P ZI*
Ripley *p364* 01773 744011
Belper *p130* 01773 825246

Sayer, N T (Hewitsons) *J1 Zp*
Cambridge *p174*. 01223 461155

Sayer, P W (Addleshaw Goddard) *T1*
London EC1 *p4* 020 7606 8855

Sayer, R (Sayer Moore & Co) *E W K4 S2*
London W3 *p77* 020 8993 7571

Sayers, Ms D L (Plexus Law (A Trading Name of Parabis Law LLP))
London EC3 *p68*. 0844 245 4000

Sayers, Mrs J (Kennedys)
London EC3 *p49*. 020 7667 9667

Sayers, Ms K (Prettys) *J1 Zp*
Ipswich *p262*. 01473 232121

Sayers, Ms P E (Stilwell & Harby) *D1 K1 V K3*
Dover *p213* 01304 206850

Sayers, S (Kennedys)
London EC3 *p49*. 020 7667 9667

Saynor, J C (Wilson Browne) *C1 E R1 A1 P T1 M1 Ze*
Northampton *p333*. 01604 876697

Saynor, J P (Frederic Hall) *N O F1 L Q J1*
Dover *p213* 01304 202411

Saywell, M (Simmons & Simmons)
London EC2 *p79*. 020 7628 2020

Scaife, T J (Baines Wilson LLP) *J1 C1*
Carlisle *p181*. 01228 552600

Scaiff, P C (Scaiff LLP) *C1 P N M1 S1 E B1 T1 W J1 Zc Ze ZI*
Worcester *p440* 01905 727700

Scale, H G (Bissmire Fudge & Co) *N Zr*
Haverfordwest *p244* 01437 764723
Pembroke Dock *p345* 01646 685501

Scales, A (Radcliffes Le Brasseur)
Westminster *p70*. 020 7222 7040

Scales, A H (Osborne Clarke) *E*
London EC2 *p65*. 020 7105 7000

Scales, Miss G H (E Rex Makin & Co) *D1 K3 K1 D2*
Liverpool *p289*. 0151 709 4491

Scales, J A (Stephenson Harwood) *C1*
London EC2 *p82*. 020 7329 4422

Scales, Miss S (Swinburne & Jackson LLP) *K1*
Chester-le-Street *p191*. . . . 0191 388 7221

Scales, T M C (Allen & Overy LLP)
London E1 *p5* 020 3088 0000

Scally, Ms A C (Paris Smith LLP) *W T2*
Southampton *p386*. 023 8048 2482

Scally, Dr D (Hewitsons) *C1 Ze*
Cambridge *p174*. 01223 461155

Scally, Mrs J R (Greenwoods Solicitors LLP) *J1 Zp*
Peterborough *p347* 01733 887700

Scally, Ms L (Colman Coyle LLP) *C1 B1*
Islington *p22*. 020 7354 3000

Scammell, Miss T (Kitson & Trotman) *K1 S1 Q F1 L W D1 E*
Beaminster *p129*. 01308 862313
Lyme Regis *p296* 01297 442580

Scampton, P M (Dean Wilson Laing) *S2 S1 E*
Brighton *p159* 01273 327241

Scandrett, P D (Charles Russell LLP) *O J1 C1*
Cheltenham *p187* 01242 221122

Scanlan, Ms F (Raworths LLP) *C1 U2 C2*
Harrogate *p240* 01423 566666

Scanlan, W T (Scanlans) *H G S1 S2*
Sunderland *p402*. 0191 565 2565

Scanlon, Ms H (Aletta Shaw Solicitors) *K1 K3 D1*
Bexleyheath *p132* 020 8301 4884

Scannell, Mrs E A (Scannell Evans) *K4 J1 K1 L Q N Zp V W*
Stanford-le-Hope *p394*. . . . 01375 642240

Scannell, Ms J L (Avery Naylor) *G H D1 K1 X*
Swansea *p404*. 01792 463276

Scarborough, J H (Cherwell District Council)
Banbury *p448* 01295 252535

Scarfe, R (Penningtons) *E*
London EC2 *p66*. 020 7457 3000

Scargill, M P (Allen & Overy LLP)
London E1 *p5* 020 3088 0000

Scarisbrick, Mrs R (Bell Lamb & Joynson) *D1 F1 K1 D2 Q K3 K4 V W*
Runcorn *p369* 0844 412 4348

Scarlett, Ms S E (Penningtons)
Godalming *p231* 01483 791800

Scarpa, V P M (Wealden District Council)
Crowborough *p456*. 01892 653311

6

Scarrott, A (Jones Day) *B1*
London EC4 *p46*. 020 7039 5959

Scarrott, D J (Wollen Michelmore Solicitors) *A3 F1 J1 J2 L O Q N Zq*
Newton Abbot *p330* 01626 332266

Scarth, Ms D (Thompsons (formerly Robin/Brian Thompson & Partners)) *N*
London WC1 *p87* 020 7290 0000

Scawin, A (Ralph & Co) *A1 E K4 K1 Zm S1 T2 W*
Newquay *p329*. 01637 872218

Sceats, D R (D R Sceats Solicitor)
Surbiton *p402* 020 8399 5457

Schady, Ms B (Ashurst LLP)
London EC2 *p7* 020 7638 1111

Schaefer, Mrs S M (Society of Lloyd's)
London EC3 *p107* 020 7327 1000

Schaffer, D M (Isadore Goldman Solicitors) *B1 O*
London EC4 *p45*. 020 7353 1000

Schamroth, J M (Stapletons Solicitors) *S1*
London N13 *p82*. 020 8886 6876

Scharfer, J J (Fladgate LLP) *E S1 W*
London WC2 *p32* 020 3036 7000

Schaverien, P R (Howlett Clarke Crowther Wood) *P M1 N K1 G F1 R1 D1 S1*
Brighton *p159* . . . .01273 327272 / 326341

Scheepers, M A (Severn Trent Water Ltd)
Birmingham *p450* 0121 722 4000

Scheiwiller, H R (DLA Piper UK LLP) *E*
Manchester *p303* 0870 011 1111

Scheland, Mrs A (Beswicks) *C2 C1*
Stoke-on-Trent *p397*. 01782 205000

Schilling, K (Schillings) *O Q I K1 Zk Zf Ze Zw*
London WC1 *p77* 020 7034 9000

Schindler, Ms M (Withers LLP) *J1 O Q Zi Zp*
London EC4 *p92*. 020 7597 6000

Schirmer, R W (B J McKenna & Co Solicitors) *S1 W*
Stockport *p396*. 0161 432 5757

Schmid, Miss J M (Penmans) *D1 D2 K1*
Coventry *p200*. 024 7622 6575

Schmidt, Mrs A (Levison Meltzer Pigott) *K1*
London EC4 *p53*. 020 7556 2400

Schmit, Ms K F E (Squire Sanders (UK) LLP)
Manchester *p310* 0161 830 5000

Schmittzehe, Mrs N (Hamlins LLP) *C1 C3 Ze Zf O*
London W1 *p38* 020 7355 6000

Schnadhorst, C F (Lovegrove & Eliot) *S1 S2*
Windsor *p434* 01753 851133

Schneck, Miss C E (Clarkson Wright & Jakes Ltd) *K1*
Orpington *p341* 01689 887887

Schneeberger, C (Tyndallwoods) *Zg Q*
Birmingham *p143* 0121 624 1111

Schneider, E (Schneider Page) *C1 O M1 Ze Zf*
London E1 *p77* 020 7480 5477

Schneider, H D (Darlington Hardcastles) *S2 E S1 C1*
Rickmansworth *p364*. 01923 774272

Schneider, T H (Pritchard Englefield)
London EC2 *p69*. 020 7972 9720

Schnider, Ms J (Taylor Wessing) *C1 C2*
London EC4 *p86*. 020 7300 7000

Schofield, Miss B A (CMS Cameron McKenna LLP) *O Q Zj*
London EC3 *p17*. 020 7367 3000

Schofield, C E (Schofield Sweeney) *C1 C2 J1 Zb Ze*
Bradford *p154* 01274 306000

Schofield, Mrs E (Roland Robinsons & Fentons LLP) *K3 D1 D2 K1*
Blackpool *p147* 01253 621432

Schofield, G P (Taylors Solicitors) *N Q O L Zq*
Braunton *p156*. 01271 812811

Schofield, J (Meikles) *K4 K1 L Zo S1 V W*
Stockton-on-Tees *p397* . . . 01740 620255

Schofield, J (Wilkin Chapman LLP) *N*
Beverley *p131* 01482 398398

Schofield, J A (Waldron & Schofield)
Heywood *p249*. 01706 624029

Schofield, Miss J M (Eaton Smith LLP) *N L J1 Q*
Huddersfield *p255* 01484 821300

Schofield, P R (Farleys Solicitors LLP) *G H B2*
Blackburn *p145* 01254 367855

Schofield, R A (Khan Solicitors) *C1 E J1 T1 B1 R2 N S1*
Manchester *p306* 0161 256 2100

Schofield, S (May May & Merrimans) *E S1 S2 A1 L Zn P*
London WC1 *p59* 020 7405 8932

Scholar, A C (Keoghs LLP) *Zj N O Q*
Bolton *p149* 01204 677000

Scholefield, Mrs K (Keoghs LLP) *O Q N Zj*
Bolton *p149* 01204 677000

Scholefield, Ms S (Pinsent Masons LLP)
London EC2 *p67*. 020 7418 7000

Scholes, Ms L (DWF) *W Zd*
Liverpool *p287*. 0151 907 3000

Scholes, P A (Forbes) *A1 C1 E J1 L R1 S1 W Zo*
Blackburn *p145* 01254 54374
Preston *p356* 01772 220022

Scholes, R J (Crick & Mardling) *S1 W C1 E K1*
Stone *p398* . . . . .01785 812650 / 812434

Scholey, Ms E (Harbottle & Lewis LLP)
London W1 *p38* 020 7667 5000

Scholey, P A (Morrish Solicitors LLP) *N Q J1*
Leeds *p276* 0113 245 0733

Scholey, P D (Thorpe & Co) *K1 D1 D2 K3 Q N J1*
Filey *p226*. 01723 515555

Scholl, P (Peter Scholl & Co) *E S1 L R1 C1 Zl*
London WC1 *p77* 020 7025 2292

Schollar, Ms V T (Blake Lapthorn)
Oxford *p342*. 01865 248607

Schollenberger, D K (Manches LLP) *I C1 Zl U2 Ze Zw F2 M1*
London WC2 *p58* 020 7404 4433

Schomberg, Ms V P (J Garrard & Allen) *T2 W K4*
Olney *p341* 01234 711215

Schon, R L (Simmons & Simmons)
London EC2 *p79*. 020 7628 2020

Schooler, G (Forshaws Davies Ridgway LLP) *H G*
Warrington *p422*. 01925 230000

Schooling, S (Barlow Lyde & Gilbert LLP) *Zq O Q*
London EC3 *p10*. 020 7247 2277

Schoop, J (Prettys)
Ipswich *p262*. 01473 232121

Schoorlemmer, A (Allen & Overy LLP)
London E1 *p5* 020 3088 0000

Schopflin, Ms J (Reynolds Porter Chamberlain LLP) *Zk Zf*
London E1 *p71* 020 3060 6000

Schorah, J A (Weightmans LLP) *C1 E I Ze*
Liverpool *p291*. 0151 227 2601

Schrader, Mrs C (Society of Lloyd's)
London EC3 *p107* 020 7327 1000

Schram, Ms T (Houlton Carr)
Bridlington *p158* 01262 677979

Schreiber, D P (Liss Gulhane Innes & Co) *Zd E S1 S2*
Romford *p366* 01708 764440

Schrire, J R (SJ Berwin LLP) *C1 F1 M2 U2 Ze*
London EC4 *p75*. 020 7111 2222

Schroder, T (Osborne Clarke) *C1*
London EC2 *p65*. 020 7105 7000

Schroedel, Miss M (Henmans LLP) *O Q Zq A3*
Oxford *p343*. 01865 781000

Schroeder, Mrs N L (Olswang LLP) *Q Ze Zk*
London WC1 *p64* 020 7067 3000

Schuck, A (The Wilkes Partnership LLP) *W T2*
Birmingham *p143* 0121 233 4333

Schulz, P F (Allen & Overy LLP)
London E1 *p5* 020 3088 0000

Schulze, Ms S (Ashurst LLP)
London EC2 *p7* 020 7638 1111

Schwarz, D (Druces LLP) *S2*
London EC2 *p27*. 020 7638 9271

Schwarz, D (Lawrence Stephens)
London EC1 *p82*. 020 7935 1211

Schwarz, M (Bindmans LLP)
London WC1 *p12* 020 7833 4433

Schwarz, T (Linklaters LLP)
London EC2 *p54*. 020 7456 2000

Schwer, C P (Birketts LLP) *S2 E T1*
Ipswich *p262*. 01473 232300

Sclater, W P (Trethowans LLP) *O E L A1*
Southampton *p387*. 023 8032 1000

Scobbie, I (Godloves) *Q N K1 G F1 B1 L*
Leeds *p273* 0113 225 8811

Scobie, B J W (Chubb Bulleid) *S1 W L A1 E*
Wells *p425*. 01749 836100

Scoffham, T W (Treasures) *W*
Gloucester *p230*. 01452 525351

Scoggins, M (Fisher Scoggins Waters LLP) *P J2*
London EC4 *p32*. 020 7489 2035

Scoon, I (Shearman & Sterling LLP) *T1*
London EC2 *p78*. 020 7655 5000

Scorah, I A (Aviva PLC) *C1*
London EC3 *p103* . . . 020 7283 7500 / 01603 687905

Score, G C A (Hart Brown Solicitors) *S1*
Godalming *p231* 0800 068 8177

Score, Mrs P (Mackrell Turner Garrett) *S1 W S2 L*
Addlestone *p114*. 01932 342181

Scorer, R (Pannone LLP) *J2 N F2*
Manchester *p308* 0161 909 3000

Scorer, T (Thomas Cooper) *M3 Zj N*
London EC3 *p22*. 020 7481 8851

Scorer, T (Ince & Co Services Ltd)
London E1 *p44* 020 7481 0010

Scotney, D (Double & Megson) *E F1 K1 L N O Q R2 S1 W*
Market Deeping *p312* 01778 341494

Scott, A (Hodge Jones & Allen LLP) *N Zr*
London NW1 *p41* 020 7874 8300

Scott, Ms A (Harrison Clark LLP) *C1 C2*
Cheltenham *p188* 01242 269198
Worcester *p439* 01905 612001
Worcester *p439* 01905 612001

Scott, Ms A (Trowers & Hamlins)
London EC3 *p88*. 020 7423 8000

Scott, Mrs A G (Williamson & Soden) *S1 W L E F1*
Solihull *p383*. 0121 733 8000

Scott, A J (Barlow Lyde & Gilbert LLP) *O Zj Zq*
London EC3 *p10*. 020 7247 2277

Scott, Miss A J (Thomson & Bancks LLP) *W T2*
Pershore *p346*. 01386 562000

Scott, A J (Rustons & Lloyd) *K1 D1 N Zq*
Newmarket *p327*. 01638 661221

Scott, Ms A M (Ramsdens Solicitors) *N*
Halifax *p238* 01422 330700
Huddersfield *p256* 01484 821500

Scott, A P (Andersons Solicitors) *F1 K1 O Q N Zq K3 Zk*
Nottingham *p335*. 0115 947 0641

Scott, A P (Sidley Austin Brown & Wood) *T1*
London EC2 *p78*. 020 7360 3600

Scott, A W H (DAC Beachcroft) *N O P Zj*
Leeds *p272* 0113 251 4700

Scott, A W J (Southcote Scott) *S2 E L Zl S1*
London W1 *p81* 020 7034 7035

Scott, B T (South Tyneside Metropolitan Borough Council)
South Shields *p471* 0191 427 1717

Scott, C D (GHP Legal) *S2 S1 E W C1*
Llangollen *p292* 01978 860313

Scott, C G (Taylors) *Zc C1 J1 O Q C2 Zq B1*
Blackburn *p146* 0844 800 0263
Manchester *p310* 0844 800 0263

Scott, C J H (Mills & Reeve) *Zo*
Norwich *p335* 01603 660155

Scott, Mrs C M (Lanyon Bowdler LLP) *Q N L O F1*
Oswestry *p342*. 01691 652241

Scott, Miss C S J (Howes Percival LLP) *A1 E*
Norwich *p334* 01603 762103

Scott, D (Harbottle & Lewis LLP)
London W1 *p38* 020 7667 5000

Scott, D (Speechly Bircham LLP) *C1 C2*
London EC4 *p81*. 020 7427 6400

Scott, Mrs D A (Eastgate Assistance Ltd) *Q*
Colchester *p455* 0870 523 4500

Scott, D A (Hill Dickinson LLP) *X P Zj Q*
Liverpool *p288*. 0151 600 8000

Scott, D A (ABN Amro Bank NV)
London EC2 *p103* 020 7628 7766

Scott, Ms D E (Cancer Research UK)
London WC2 *p104*. 020 7242 0200

Scott, D H (Stapleton Gardner & Co) *E S1*
Morley *p319* 0113 253 8111

Scott, D J (Palmers Solicitors) *S2 E S1 C1*
Kingston upon Thames *p267*. 020 8549 7444

Scott, D J (Squire Sanders (UK) LLP)
Manchester *p310* 0161 830 5000

Scott, D J M (Mackrell Turner Garrett) *N O Q*
Woking *p437*. 01483 755609

Scott, D L (Mitchells) *J1 N Zp Zq*
York *p445* 01904 623751

Scott, D P (Swayne Johnson Solicitors) *N L Q K1 G H D1 Zr Zq*
Denbigh *p208* 01745 812835

Scott, Ms E J (Lewis Silkin LLP) *O Q*
London EC4 *p53*. 020 7074 8000

Scott, Mrs E M (Winchester City Council)
Winchester *p476*. 01962 840222

Scott, G (Gabbs LLP) *W S1 T2*
Leominster *p282*. 01568 616333

Scott, G A (Barrington Charles Edwards & Co)
London SE25 *p11*020 8656 8318 / 8656 8319

Scott, G J (Philip Ross & Co) *A3 B1 L O Q N Zq*
London W1 *p73* 020 7636 6969

Scott, Mrs G L (Lawson Coppock & Hart) *W K4 T2*
Manchester *p306* 0161 832 5944

Scott, G P (Memery Crystal) *C1 C2*
London WC2 *p60* 020 7242 5905

Scott, G S (Langleys)
York *p445* 01904 610886

Scott, Ms H (Watson Burton LLP) *J1*
Newcastle upon Tyne *p327* . 0845 901 2100

Scott, I (Ashurst LLP)
London EC2 *p7* 020 7638 1111

Scott, I (Charles Russell LLP) *C1*
Oxford *p343*. 0845 359 0090
London W1 *p48* 020 7636 1616

Scott, I A (Hugh James)
Cardiff *p179* 029 2022 4871

Scott, I C (Scotts Wright) *A1 S1 T1 W R1*
Leyburn *p283* 01966 22227

Scott, Mrs J (Ellisons) *J1 Q L*
Colchester *p197*. 01206 764477

Scott, J (Langleys)
York *p445*. 01904 610886

Scott, J (Withers LLP) *B1 O M2 Ze*
London EC4 *p92*. 020 7597 6000

Scott, Mrs J (Archon Solicitors) *J1 Zp A3 X*
London EC4 *p7* 020 7397 9650

Scott, J (Taylor Wessing)
London EC4 *p86*. 020 7300 7000

Scott, J C (Harrowells) *S1 S2 E A1 C1 L*
York *p444* 01904 690111

Scott, Mrs J H (Barcan Woodward) *E S2 R2 S1*
Bristol *p161* 0117 923 2141

Scott, Mrs J L (Swinburne & Jackson LLP) *K1 D1 K3*
Ryton *p370* . . . 0191 413 3468 / 413 2630
Washington *p423* 0191 416 0004

Scott, J M E (Charles Russell LLP) *C1 Zd*
London EC4 *p19*. 020 7203 5000

Scott, J P (Denby & Co) *D1 K1 Q G H N Zm*
Barrow-in-Furness *p125* . . . 01229 822366
Ulverston *p416*. 01229 582283

Scott, J P R (Mark & Co) *G H K1 D1*
London W14 *p58* 020 7603 3710 / 7602 6942

Scott, J R (Row & Scott) *D1 G H J1 K1 M1 P B1 S1 W Zm Zj Zk*
Consett *p199* 01207 591810
Newcastle upon Tyne *p326* . 0191 273 9929

Scott, J W (Herbert Smith LLP) *C3 M1*
London EC2 *p40*. 020 7374 8000

Scott, Ms K (The College of Law) *J1 N*
London WC1 *p105*. 0800 289997

Scott, Ms K (McGrigors LLP)
London EC4 *p56*. 020 7054 2500

Scott, Ms K A (Beecham Peacock) *N*
Newcastle upon Tyne *p323* . 0191 232 3048

Scott, K D (Scott Hyman & Co) *E F1 J1 L M1 N P S1*
Oldham *p340* 0161 628 7018

Scott, Ms K J (Plexus Law (A Trading Name of Parabis Law LLP)) *Zj O Q N*
London EC3 *p68*. 0844 245 4000

Scott, Miss K L (Downs) *W*
Dorking *p212* 01306 880110

Scott, K P (Pickup & Scott) *S1 W Zi*
Aylesbury *p121* 01296 397794

Scott, Miss L (Ford Simey LLP) *D1 G H K1 L N Q*
Exmouth *p222*. . .01395 272241 / 0800 169 3741

Scott, Mrs L (Andersons Solicitors) *K1*
Nottingham *p335*. 0115 947 0641
Leicester *p280*. 0116 222 6666

Scott, L (Shepherd + Wedderburn LLP)
London EC4 *p78*. 020 7429 4900

Scott, L R (Carter Lemon Camerons) *Q J2 Za A3 Zr C1 I F2 Zg U2 O N R1 Zq*
London EC1 *p18*. 020 7406 1000

Scott, M (Bhatt Murphy) *Zg*
Hackney *p12*. 020 7729 1115

Scott, M A (Anami Law Incorporating Kirkwoods) *S1 E W L*
Bushey *p171*. 020 8950 1155

Scott, Miss M F E (Halton Borough Council)
Widnes *p476*. 0151 424 2061

Scott, M J (Moxon & Barker) *N K1 E S1 W*
Pontefract *p351* 01977 602999

Scott, M J R (United Kingdom Atomic Energy Authority) *O Zc*
Didcot *p457* 01235 436984

Scott, M K (University and College Union Solicitors Office) *J1 M1 Ze Zi Zk Zo Zp*
London NW1 *p110*. 020 7756 2500

Scott, M L (Walker Morris) *L O Zc*
Leeds *p277* 0113 283 2500

Scott, Mrs M L (Maxwell Hodge Solicitors) *E S2 C1*
Liverpool *p289*. 0151 227 4545

Scott, M L (Cripps Harries Hall LLP) *E L O Q R1 Zg*
Tunbridge Wells *p415* 01892 515121

Scott, M W (Scotts Wright) *S1 S2 E K4 W Zc A1 Zl*
Catterick Garrison *p183* . . . 01748 832431

Scott, M W D (Coupe Bradbury)
Lytham *p296*. 01253 736670

Scott, N (Memery Crystal) *O A3 Zv Zn*
London WC2 *p60* 020 7242 5905

Scott, Miss N (Steele Ford & Newton) *S1 S2 W K4*
Nelson *p321*. 01282 692531

Scott, N E (Foot Anstey) *G H Q V*
Taunton *p408* 01823 625600

Scott, N J (Andrew Jackson) *Zb C1 C2*
Hull *p257* 01482 325242

Scott, N S (Geoffrey Leaver Solicitors LLP) *W S1*
Milton Keynes *p317* 01908 692769

Scott, Mrs P (Gateley LLP)
Birmingham *p138* 0121 234 0000

Scott, P (Black Graf & Co) *S1 E S2*
London NW3 *p13* 020 7586 1141

Scott, P (Canter Levin & Berg)
Kirkby *p268* 0151 546 4562

Scott, Ms P A (Cartridges) *D1 K1 D2*
Exeter *p220* 01392 256854

Scott, P A (Scott Rees & Co) *N O D1 S1 W*
Skelmersdale *p381* 01695 722222

Scott, P G (Parkinson Wright LLP)
Worcester *p440* 01905 726789

Scott, P J (Andersons Solicitors) *G H S1 S2 B2 K1 J1 W D1 Q Zl Zm Zr Zu Zv*
Harrogate *p239* 01423 527852

Scott, P J M (Cripps Harries Hall LLP) *T1 T2 W Zd*
Tunbridge Wells *p415* 01892 515121

Scott, P M (Salford City Council)
Swinton *p473* 0161 794 4711

Scott, R A (Everys) *G H J1 K1 L N O Q V Zw*
Exeter *p221* 01392 477983

Scott, R H (Power Scott Solicitors) *D1 F1 G H J1 K1 L V S1*
Stanley *p394*. 01207 230125

Scott, R I (Waugh & Musgrave) *E R1 S1 S2 Zs*
Cockermouth *p197*. 01900 823127

Scott, R M (Wilkinson Woodward) *N Q D1*
Halifax *p238* 01422 339600

Scott, Miss R M (Lodders Solicitors LLP) *E S2*
Stratford-upon-Avon *p400* . . 01789 293259

Scott, R N (Bird & Bird LLP) *E P S1 A1 R1*
London EC4 *p13*. 020 7415 6000

Scott, R P (Pearsons & Ward) *S1 S2*
Malton *p300*. 01653 692247

Scott, S (Oxley & Coward Solicitors LLP) *K1 K3*
Rotherham *p367*. 01709 510999

Scott, S (Metcalfe Copeman & Pettefar) *N Q W*
King's Lynn *p266* 01553 778102

Scott, S C (LG Lawyers)
London SE1 *p50*. 020 7379 0000

Scott, S D (MWR Law Ltd) *G H J1 Zt*
Preston *p357* 01772 254201

Scott, S D (Wellers Law Group LLP) *S1 S2 K1 W O E F1 L R1 Zd Zq Zo Zl*
Bromley *p167* 020 8464 4242
London WC1 *p91* 020 7242 7265

Scott, Miss S L (Ward Gethin) *N Q V B1 L F1 J2*
King's Lynn *p266* 01553 660033

Scott, S M (Kaslers Solicitors LLP) *S2 E U1 S1*
West Malling *p428*. 0845 270 2511

Scott, T (DWF) *J1 Zp M1 Zg*
Liverpool *p287*. 0151 907 3000

Scott, Mrs V A (Mowll & Mowll) *T2 V W*
Dover *p213* 01304 873344

Scott, W J (Reed Ryder & Meikle) *W S1 E L Zv*
North Shields *p331* 0191 257 3222

Scott Andrews, A (Aplin Stockton Fairfax) *D1 J1 K1 O Q*
Banbury *p122* 01295 251234

Scotter, R G (J B Wheatley & Co) *G H*
London SE8 *p91*. 020 8479 8000

Scott-Goldstone, S J (Aaron & Partners LLP Solicitors) *Ze U2 C1 C2*
Chester *p190* 01244 405555
Manchester *p306* 0161 834 2100

Scott-Jones, M G (Crane & Walton) *K1 P M1 L N S1 W G*
Ashby-de-la-Zouch *p118*. . . 01530 414111

Scott-Lawler, Miss H J (Burges Salmon)
Bristol *p161* 0117 939 2000

Scott-Malden, Miss A L R (Charles Hoile) *K1*
Newbury *p322*. 01635 45595

Scott-Moncrieff, Ms L A (Scott-Moncrieff Harbour & Sinclair) *Zm Zg*
London NW5 *p77* 020 7485 5588

Scott-Patel, Ms K (Radcliffes Le Brasseur)
Westminster *p70*. 020 7222 7040

Scott-Russell, Miss J (Squire Sanders (UK) LLP) *E*
London EC2 *p81*. 020 7655 1000

Scott-Tucker, M (Kitsons LLP) *E S2 T1 R2 C1 S1*
Exeter *p221* 01392 455555

Scougall, S (Watson Burton LLP)
Newcastle upon Tyne *p327* . 0845 901 2100

Scoular, Miss D M (Maxwell Hodge Solicitors) *W K4*
Liverpool *p289*. 0151 526 9321
West Kirby *p428*. 0151 625 9154

Scoular, Mrs G P L (Mills & Reeve) *J1*
Norwich *p335* 01603 660155

Scouller, Miss A (CGM) *L N K1 Q S1 W Za C1 M1 V Zg*
Southampton *p385*. 023 8063 2733

Scourfield, D (David Scourfield) *K1 Zl N*
Middlesbrough *p315* 01642 874999

Scourfield, Miss E (Hugh James) *N Zr*
Cardiff *p179* 029 2022 4871

Scourfield, Mrs G (Red Kite Law) *K1*
Pembroke *p345* 01646 683222

Scourfield, P T (British American Tobacco)
London WC2 *p104*. 020 7845 1000

Scowen, Miss J E (Lyons Davidson) *Zr*
Bristol *p163* 0117 904 6000

Scrace, J R (Reynolds Parry-Jones) *K1 N G F1 H J1 Q Zr*
High Wycombe *p250*. 01494 525941

Scragg, C J (Blake Lapthorn) *T2 W Zm*
Portsmouth *p354*. 023 9222 1122

Scragg, J K (Barlow Lyde & Gilbert LLP)
London EC3 *p10*. 020 7247 2277

Scrambler, Mrs A R (Warners Solicitors) *K1*
Sevenoaks *p374*. 01732 747900

Scrase, R S (Follett Stock LLP) *O Q X R1 Zl*
Truro *p414*. 01872 241700

Screech, Miss J (WBW Solicitors) *K1 K3*
Exeter *p222* 01392 202404

Screene, Ms Y (Radcliffes Le Brasseur)
Westminster *p70*. 020 7222 7040

Scriven, Mrs B (Higgs & Sons) *Q O K1 L*
Brierley Hill *p158*. 0845 111 5050

Scrivenger, M J (Scrivenger Seabrook) *Zr*
St Neots *p392* 01480 214900

Scrivens, N (Morris Orman Hearle) *N*
Cheltenham *p188* 01242 257188

Scrivens, S N (Bristol Water PLC)
Bristol *p451* 0117 966 5881

Scudamore, Ms C (Tollers LLP)
Northampton *p332*. 01604 258558

Scudamore, Mrs C B (Tollers LLP) *N*
Northampton *p332*. 01604 258558

Scully, Ms D (Carpenters) *N*
Birkenhead *p134*. 0870 780 1870

Scully, Miss E (ASB Law) *B1 O Q*
Crawley *p202* 01293 603600

Scully, P (P R Scully & Co Solicitors) *Zc Zr F1 J1 Zj Q N V*
St Helens *p391* 01744 755800

Scully, Miss P (Derbyshire County Council)
Matlock *p465* 01629 580000

Sculpher, Miss M (Watson Nevill) *K1 K3*
Maidstone *p299* 01622 661177

Scutt, D J (Crown Prosecution Service Durham)
Durham *p457* 0191 383 5800

Scutt, Ms L (Taylor Wessing)
London EC4 *p86*. 020 7300 7000

Seaborne, Ms J A (Howells LLP) *G H*
Sheffield *p376* 0114 249 6666

See p634 for the Key to Work Categories

Seabourne, Mrs M (Seabourne Lawleys) *C1 S2 S1 O W K1 Q* Northwood *p333* 01923 820639
Seabridge, M (Jewels Solicitors) *K1* Stafford *p393* 01785 602030
Seabrook, Miss V (Scrivenger Seabrook) *Zr* St Neots *p392* 01480 214900
Seaford, S D (Geoffrey Leaver Solicitors LLP) *N* Milton Keynes *p317* 01908 692769
Seager, Ms A (The College of Law York) York *p477* 0800 289997
Seager, A (Taylor Wessing) London EC4 *p86* 020 7300 7000
Seager, Ms N J (Clarke Willmott) Bristol *p162* 0845 209 1000 / 0117 305 6000
Seagrave, J P (Barker & Co) *G H B2* Hull *p256* 01482 219966; Hull *p257* 01482 326446
Seagrove, R H (Buller Jeffries) *N O Q Zj* Birmingham *p136* 0121 212 2620
Seaka, M (Fletcher Dervish) *Zi Zg M1* Haringey *p33* 020 8800 4615
Seakens, K (Seakens Solicitors) *S1 E C1 W S2 K4* Virginia Water *p418* 01344 843666
Seal, D A (W Parry & Co) *B1 F1 J1 L N O Q S1 W* Swansea *p405* 01792 470037
Seal, D S (Lawrence Stephens) *S1 E P N C1* London EC1 *p82* 020 7935 1211
Seal, Ms K (Memery Crystal) *E O* London WC2 *p60* 020 7242 5905
Seal, T C (Hattersleys) *K1 W* Mexborough *p314* 01709 582434
Seal-Coon, R F M (Hansells) *S1 W S2 E* North Walsham *p331* 01692 404351
Seal-Coon, Mrs S J (Hansells) *K1 S1 W K2* North Walsham *p331* 01692 404351
Sealy, A W (George Davies Solicitors LLP) *W Zd* Manchester *p303* 0161 236 8992
Sealy, Mrs L J (Hempsons) *N Zr* Manchester *p305* 0161 228 0011
Sealy-Jones, D C (Bulcraigs) *T2 W* Wandsworth *p16* 020 8870 2207 / 8877 0531
Seaman, Ms L M (Matthew Arnold & Baldwin LLP) *O* Watford *p423* 01923 202020
Seaman, Ms M K (Landons) *K1 V D1* Brentwood *p156* 01277 210021
Seaman, Miss N L (Warner Goodman LLP) *J1 Zp* Southampton *p387* 023 8063 9311
Sear, Ms E J M (Maxwell Winward LLP) *L S2 E* London EC4 *p59* 020 7651 0000
Sear, Ms L K (Rothera Dowson) *K1 D1 D2* Nottingham *p338* 0115 910 0600
Searl, Mrs C L (Crutes) *O Zr N* Newcastle upon Tyne *p324* 0191 233 9700
Searl, R (Crutes) *Q N G* Newcastle upon Tyne *p324* 0191 233 9700
Searle, C (Ince & Co Services Ltd) London E1 *p44* 020 7481 0010
Searle, Mrs C (AWB Partnership LLP) *R1 E S2 R2* Guildford *p235* 01483 302345
Searle, C (Penningtons) Basingstoke *p127* 01256 407100
Searle, G J (Geoffrey Searle Planning Solicitors) *R1 Zu* Billericay *p133* 01277 633014
Searle, I R (Barker Gillette) *B1 B2 O Q Zb* London W1 *p9* 020 7636 0555; London EC2 *p27* 020 7638 9271
Searle, Ms J A (Squire Sanders (UK) LLP) London EC2 *p81* 020 7655 1000
Searle, M R (Adams & Remers) *C1 C2 I J1 E F1 W* Lewes *p283* 01273 480616
Searles, Ms D (Dempster Binning LLP) *E S2 S1* Chandlers Ford *p184* 023 8062 1790
Searles, J G (Thorn Drury & Searles) *S1 K1 L W J1 N Q* Ramsgate *p359* 01843 593381
Sears, A M (Andrew & Andrew Solicitors) *N K1 D1 J1 G H C1 B1 L D2* Portsmouth *p354* 023 9266 1381
Sears, G R W (Financial Services Authority) *B1 C1 N P* London E14 *p106* 020 7066 1000
Sears, T P R (Davenport Lyons) *N M1 K1 B1 G P F1 Zk* London W1 *p25* 020 7468 2600
Seary, W P (Shoosmiths) *C1* Milton Keynes *p317* 0370 086 8300 / 01908 488300; Nottingham *p339* 0370 086 5000 / 0115 906 5000
Seath, P (Bates Wells & Braithwaite London LLP) *J1 J2 Zd* London EC4 *p11* 020 7551 7777
Seath, Miss R (Carr Hepburn Solicitors Ltd) *D1 K1 K3* Hemel Hempstead *p246* 01442 241466
Seaton, Ms A (CMS Cameron McKenna LLP) London EC3 *p17* 020 7367 3000
Seaton, Ms C (Glovers Solicitors LLP) *Zq O* London W1 *p36* 020 7935 8882
Seaton, C S T (Burges Salmon) *J1 O Q Zo* Bristol *p161* 0117 939 2000
Seaton, D R (Howard Kennedy LLP) *W* London W1 *p48* 020 7636 1616
Seaton, J W (Fiona Bruce & Co LLP) *C1 N W* Warrington *p421* 01925 263273
Seaton, P W (Seatons Solicitors) *H S1 W E G Q V* Corby *p199* 01536 276300
Seaton, R (Clarke Willmott) *S2 E R2* Bristol *p162* 0845 209 1000 / 0117 305 6000
Seaton, R G C (Harrowells) *S1 A1* York *p444* 01904 558600
Seaton, S N (Jones Day) *C1* London EC4 *p46* 020 7039 5959
Seaton-Fry, Ms M (Hampshire County Council) Winchester *p476* 01962 841841
Seavor, Ms J (Ingrams) *N* York *p445* 01904 520600
Seay, N (Travers Smith LLP) London EC1 *p87* 020 7295 3000
Sebastian, A C P (Sebastians) London EC4 *p77* 020 7583 2105
Seborg, E (Byrne & Partners) *O B2 Q* London EC4 *p16* 020 7842 1616
Secker, J F (Luton Borough Council) *D1 F1 G H K1 L M1 P Zl* Luton *p464* 01582 546000
Secker, Miss T (Trowers & Hamlins) *P Zh* London EC3 *p88* 020 7423 8000
Sedacca, N (Hodge Jones & Allen LLP) *Zg* London NW1 *p41* 020 7874 8300
Seddiki, Miss L (Edwards Angell Palmer & Dodge) London EC2 *p28* 020 7583 4055
Seddon, A (Gowlings) *S1 E A1 L W R1 J1 Zm K4 S2 R2* Preston *p357* 01772 251287
Seddon, A (Winder Taylor Fallows) *S1 W S2 E K1 K3 F1 L J1 K4* Bolton *p150* 01204 697467
Seddon, A H (East Devon District Council) Sidmouth *p471* 01395 516551
Seddon, Miss C A (Seddon Thomson) *K1 K2 D1 S1 S2 W Zl D2 K3* Manchester *p309* 0161 720 8000
Seddon, C C (Pinsent Masons LLP) *O Q I M1 N Ze Zj* London EC2 *p67* 020 7418 7000
Seddon, Miss J (Walker Morris) *E R2* Leeds *p277* 0113 283 2500
Seddon, Ms J (Russell Jones & Walker) London WC2 *p74* 020 7657 1555
Seddon, N (Russell & Russell) *N S1 W* Atherton *p120* 01942 884469
Seddon, R F (McManus Seddon) *Q Zq N D1 D2 O* Bradford *p154* 01274 741841
Sedgley, R N (Richard Sedgley & Co) *S1 W S2 C2 K1 L N J1* Bournemouth *p152* 01202 556222
Sedgwick, C (Miles & Cash) *D1 E G H K1 L M1 N P S1 Zt* Heanor *p246* 01773 530000
Sedgwick, D K (Linder Myers Solicitors) *N Q K1 F1 W S1 Zc Zk* Shrewsbury *p379* 0844 984 6002
Sedgwick, N P (Kirwans) *S1* Birkenhead *p134* 0151 608 9078
Sedgwick, R M (Buss Murton LLP) *C1 C2 E I* Tunbridge Wells *p415* 01892 510222
Sedgwick, Ms S (Myer Wolff) *K1 D1 K3* Hull *p257* 01482 223693
Seear, P J (Wannop Fox Staffurth & Bray) *S1 W C1 E K4* Worthing *p442* 01903 228200
Seeboruth, J (Amphlett Lissimore) *G H* Croydon *p6* 020 8771 5254
Seed, Ms H R (Squire Sanders (UK) LLP) *E* Leeds *p277* 0113 284 7000
Seed, Ms M (Potter Rees (Serious Injury) Solicitors) Manchester *p309* 0161 237 5888
Seed, N R (Wintle & Co) *L S1 T2 W* Bognor Regis *p148* 01243 586611; Selsey *p374* 01243 605947
Seed, Mrs S (Mills & Reeve) *C1* Cambridge *p175* 01223 364422
Seedat, R (Henry Hyams) Leeds *p274* 0113 243 2288
Seedat, Y (Addleshaw Goddard) *C1 C2* Leeds *p271* 0113 209 2000
Seehra, Mrs A (HM Revenue & Customs) Salford *p470* 0870 785 8545
Seel, A C (Elliot Mather LLP) *W K4* Chesterfield *p192* 01246 231288
Seeley, Miss E S (Elizabeth Seeley) *J1 Zp Zza* Ealing *p77* 020 8840 2788
Seeley, I (Ipswich Borough Council) *Zc* Ipswich *p461* 01473 432000
Seeley, N R (Stanley Tee) *G H* Bishop's Stortford *p144* 01279 755200
Seelhoff, A C (Duncan Lewis & Co) *Zi* London W12 *p53* 020 7923 4020
Seema, Mrs S (Veja and Co Solicitors) *Zi K1 W* Southall *p385* 020 8574 2626
Seenath, Miss U (Bowling & Co) *K1 K2* London E15 *p15* 020 8221 8000
Seeney, Miss J (Williamson & Soden) *S1 W* Solihull *p383* 0121 733 8000
Seers, G (E D C Lord & Co) *S1* Hayes *p245* 020 8848 9988
Seery, Ms J (Hill Dickinson LLP) *Zr* Manchester *p305* 0161 817 7200
Seevaratnam, Ms T S (Blake Lapthorn) *Q O N B1 K1 L* Portsmouth *p354* 023 9222 1122
Sefton, D W (Laytons) *C1 F1* Manchester *p306* 0161 834 2100
Sefton, O (Holman Fenwick Willan) London EC3 *p42* 020 7264 8000
Segal, D A (Solomon Taylor & Shaw) *C1* London NW3 *p80* 020 7431 1912
Segall, E R (Conway & Co) *W S2 E S1 T2* Harrow *p241* 020 8863 0535
Segall, M (Ashurst LLP) London EC2 *p7* 020 7638 1111
Segar, D M (Thorne Segar) *S1 W E A1 K4 S2 Zl Zc* Minehead *p318* 01643 703234
Segen, M K (Segens Blount Petre) *C1 E N Q S2 Zq Zr B1* Westminster *p77* 020 7332 2222
Sehgal, M S (Sehgal & Co) *N V* Birmingham *p142* 0121 772 2226
Sehgal, S (Coca-Cola Enterprises Ltd) Uxbridge *p474* 01895 231313
Sehmbi, T (ClarksLegal LLP) *O Q J1* Reading *p360* 0118 958 5321
Sehmi, D S (Gary Jacobs & Co) London E18 *p45* 020 8536 4050
Sehra, Ms G (Kidd Rapinet) *W K4* High Wycombe *p250* 0845 017 9607
Seibert, Ms M (Attwaters) *Zr N* Harlow *p239* 01279 638888
Seifert, L C (Seifert & Co) *C1 F1 J1 K1 L Q R2 S1 S2 W* Cobham *p196* 01932 866788
Seiger, R (DLA Piper UK LLP) Birmingham *p137* 0870 011 1111
Sejas, D (SGH Martineau LLP) *B1* London EC3 *p75* 020 7264 4444
Sekhon, J (Kerman & Co LLP) *C2* London WC2 *p49* 020 7539 7272
Sekhon, Mrs K K (Capsticks Solicitors LLP) *Zr N Zq* London SW19 *p18* 020 8780 2211
Sekhri, Mrs A (BTG International Ltd) London EC4 *p104* 020 7575 0000
Selby Bennett, J S (Humphries Kirk) *Q A1 P Zg Ze O C1* Poole *p352* 01202 725400
Selby, Mrs C R (Shakespeares) *O Zq Q Zc Zj* Nottingham *p339* 0115 945 3700
Selby, C W (Reynolds Parry-Jones) *E C1 S1 S2 C2* High Wycombe *p250* 01494 525941
Selby, Mrs E M (Ingrams) *N* York *p445* 01904 520600
Selby, I C (Selby & Co) *S1 W K1 S2 N L T2 Zo* Highworth *p250* 01793 762327
Selby, J F (Percy Short & Cuthbert) *G H K1 S1 S2* Islington *p67* 020 7700 0265
Selby, M B (Laytons) *T1* London EC4 *p52* 020 7842 8000
Selby, R A (Newtons) *C1 T1 F1 W Ze Zf Zn Zd* Camden *p63* 020 7794 9696 / 7435 5351
Selby-Lowndes, W (Darbys Solicitors LLP) *K1 D1 D2* Oxford *p343* 01865 811700
Seldon, M J (Hartlaw LLP) *S2 C1 E C2 U2* Wetherby *p429* 01937 547000
Selfridge, Ms E K (Howells) *S1 W* Caerphilly *p172* 029 2086 7111
Selig, Ms Y (Davenport Lyons) *K1* London W1 *p25* 020 7468 2600
Sell, K M (Beale and Company Solicitors LLP) *O Q A3 Zj N* London WC2 *p11* 020 7240 3474
Sellahewa, Miss S (Burroughs) *K3 D1 J1* Maidstone *p299* 01622 676976 / 676982
Sellahewa, Miss T (Barlow Robbins LLP) *E S2* Guildford *p235* 01483 562901; Guildford *p236* 01483 407000
Sellar, D A H (Sheffield City Council) Sheffield *p471* 0114 273 4019
Sellar, N P (Challinors) *N Q O A3 V Zr* Birmingham *p136* 0121 212 9393
Sellar-Elliott, Ms C D (Fishman & Co Solicitors) *F1 J1 O Q N Zq Zp* London W1 *p32* 020 7935 3500
Sellars, C J (Banner Jones) *B1 C1 J1 C2 N Q* Chesterfield *p191* 01246 560560
Sellars, Ms E L (Gordons LLP) Leeds *p273* 0113 227 0100
Sellars, Ms H (Hodge Jones & Allen LLP) London NW1 *p41* 020 7874 8300
Sellars, J D (John D Sellars & Co) *G H K1 P M1 D1 Zm* Sutton *p403* 020 8661 7014
Sellars, P C (Stanley Tee) *S1 S2 E A1* Bishop's Stortford *p144* 01279 755200
Sellars, Mrs S (Henmans LLP) *Zr N* Oxford *p343* 01865 781000
Sellek, Ms R L (M&A Solicitors LLP) *C1* Cardiff *p179* 029 2048 2288
Sellers, M (Field Fisher Waterhouse LLP) London EC3 *p31* 020 7861 4000
Selley, T P (Crosse & Crosse) *N F1 R1 Zj L* Exeter *p220* 01392 258451
Sellick, S C (Bracknell Forest Borough Council) Bracknell *p450* 01344 424642
Sellors, J (Finers Stephens Innocent LLP) *Q Ze Zf I U2* London W1 *p32* 020 7323 4000
Sell-Peters, Ms T (Radcliffes Le Brasseur) Westminster *p70* 020 7222 7040
Sells, Ms C (Richard Thorn & Co) *G H* Brighton *p160* 01273 625600
Sels, C R (Cumberland Ellis Peirs) *O Q C1 C2 F1 F2 J1 J2 Zb Zc Zp Zq* London WC1 *p23* 020 7242 0422
Selvamuruganantham, S (Selva & Co) London NW6 *p77* 020 7328 3330
Selvarajah, C (Selvarajah & Co) *C1 E G H J1 K1 M1 N P* Barnet *p77* 020 8204 7884
Selwood, M F (Clifford Harris & Co) London W1 *p21* 020 7486 0031
Selwood, R M (Winterbotham Smith Penley LLP) *W T2 K4* Stroud *p401* 01453 847200
Selwyn, C (Brecher) *S1* London W1 *p15* 020 7563 1000
Selwyn, M (DWF) *S2 E S1* Liverpool *p287* 0151 907 3000
Selwyn, M D (Selwyn & Co) *E S1 O B1 W C1 L R1 J1 Ze Q Zf S2* London N15 *p77* 020 8881 2272
Selwyn, P R (Forsters LLP) *E* Westminster *p33* 020 7863 8333
Selwyn, R (Selwyn & Co) *E S2 L Zf R1 S1 Zl Ze Zza R2 W F1 O Q P* London N15 *p77* 020 8881 2272
Sembi, Mrs N (Gawor & Co) *S1 E S2* London E1 *p35* 020 7481 8888
Semmens, D (Trowers & Hamlins) London EC3 *p88* 020 7423 8000
Sen, Miss R (Rita Sen Solicitors) *Zr K4 K1 Zm V S1 T2 W* Bognor Regis *p148* 01243 263658
Senat, R (Warner Bros) London WC1 *p110* 020 7984 5000
Seneque, Ms G (Bristol City Council) Bristol *p451* 0117 922 2000
Senior, A (J A Kemp & Co) London WC1 *p48* 020 7405 3292
Senior, J (Ashurst LLP) London EC2 *p7* 020 7638 1111
Senior, Ms J A (Wright Hassall LLP) *O L Q R1 A3* Leamington Spa *p270* 01926 886688
Senior, J S (Irwin Mitchell LLP) *Zq* Sheffield *p376* 0870 150 0100
Senior, P (Philip Senior & Co) *A1 C1 E R1 S1 W* Retford *p363* 01777 869545
Senior, R (Berry Smith LLP) *E* Cardiff *p177* 029 2034 5511
Senior, R F (Coles Miller Solicitors LLP) *D1 Q O Ze J1 Zc* Poole *p352* 01202 673011
Senior, R M W (Wakefield Metropolitan District Council) Wakefield *p474* 01924 306090
Senkbeil, Ms S (Willans LLP) *T2 W* Cheltenham *p189* 01242 514000
Senter, B L (Brian L Senter) *B1 L N Q S1 W Zc C1 S2 F1 G J1 K1 Zl R2* Stourbridge *p399* 01384 375649
Senthoorselvan, K (Raja & Co) Wandsworth *p70* 020 8772 4900
Sentongo, Miss L (Manches LLP) *E* London WC2 *p58* 020 7404 4433
Sepanski, Mrs E (Boodle Hatfield) Oxford *p343* 01865 790744
Sephton, Ms C (North Kensington Law Centre) London W10 *p108* 020 8969 7473; London EC1 *p109* 020 7505 2000
Serby, M R D (Wake Smith & Tofields) *J1 O Ze Zl A3 Zc* Sheffield *p377* 0114 266 6660
Serby, T (Reynolds Porter Chamberlain LLP) London E1 *p71* 020 3060 6000
Sereni, G C (Hacking Ashton LLP) *S2 E* Newcastle under Lyme *p323* 01782 715555
Seres, J S D (Sacker & Partners LLP) *Zo* London EC2 *p76* 020 7329 6699
Serfozo, Mrs K (The College of Law Guildford) Guildford *p459* 01483 460200
Serfozo, M J (BAE Systems PLC) *C1* London SW1 *p104* 01252 373232
Sergeant, J P (Lee Bolton Monier-Williams) *O Q M1 J1 P R1 C1 X* Westminster *p52* 020 7222 5381
Sergeant, M G (Maxwell Winward LLP) *Zc A3 Zq O* London EC4 *p59* 020 7651 0000
Sergeant, Mrs M O (Wilson Browne) *W* Kettering *p265* 01536 410041
Sergent, F (Squire Sanders (UK) LLP) London EC2 *p81* 020 7655 1000
Sergison, Mrs A N (Muckle LLP) *J1* Newcastle upon Tyne *p325* 0191 211 7777
Serjeant, Ms E (Ramsdens Solicitors) *C1 F1 L Q* Huddersfield *p256* 01484 821500
Serota, Ms D (Darlingtons) *E Q* Edgware *p217* 020 8952 0033 / 8951 6666
Serr, H J (Emsleys) *N* Leeds *p273* 0113 232 1030
Servian, Dr M S (KJD) *Ze I* Stoke-on-Trent *p398* 01782 202020
Servian, P D (AWB Partnership LLP) *S1 W* Guildford *p235* 01483 302345
Serwanga, Mrs G (Hodge Jones & Allen LLP) *W K4* London NW1 *p41* 020 7874 8300; South Croydon *p383* 020 8253 7600
Setford, G M D (TWM Solicitors LLP) *R2* Epsom *p219* 01372 729555
Sethi, K (E J Winter & Son) *Q O S1 S2 G H W Zl Zi* Reading *p361* 0118 957 4424
Sethi, Mrs R (Sethi & Co) *K1 Q D1 W S1* Sunbury-on-Thames *p401* 01932 772121
Sethi, Mrs R (The Sethi Partnership Solicitors) *G H* Eastcote *p216* 020 8866 6464
Sethi, S (Sethi & Co) *K1 D1 N Q L S1 V W* Sunbury-on-Thames *p401* 01932 772121
Sethi, S (Bone & Payne LLP) *K3 J1 Q N* Colwyn Bay *p198* 01492 532385

6

Sethna, P (Parry Law) *K1*
Herne Bay *p248* 01227 361131

Seton, A (Manches LLP) *E*
London WC2 *p58* 020 7404 4433

Setter, M A (WBW Solicitors) *S1 E W A1*
Newton Abbot *p329* 01626 202404

Seun, A (Doves Solicitors) *L S2 E Q S1 Zi K1 J1 G*
London SE1 *p27* 020 7232 5100

Severin, Mrs M E (Wokingham District Council)
Wokingham *p477* 0118 974 6000

Severn, R E (Straw & Pearce) *G H K1 D1 M1 J1 P N F1 L Zl Zm Zi*
Loughborough *p293* 01509 268931

Severs, C (DLA Piper UK LLP) *C1*
London EC2 *p24*. 0870 011 1111

Severs, D J A (Co-operative Insurance Society Ltd)
Manchester *p464* 0161 832 8686

Seville, Mrs C G (Jewels Solicitors) *D1 K1*
Stafford *p393* 01785 602030

Sevin, Mrs I (Criminal Defence Solicitors) *G H B2*
Westminster *p23*. 020 7353 7000

Seward, Ms K E (Allen & Overy LLP) *J1 J2 O Zi*
London E1 *p5* 020 3088 0000

Seward, Mrs K E (Andrew Jackson) *E*
Hull *p257* 01482 325242

Sewell, D P (Napthens LLP) *C1 C2*
Preston *p357* 01772 888444

Sewell, Mrs E C (Baines Wilson LLP) *S2 E*
Carlisle *p181*. 01228 552600

Sewell, Mrs J (Rollits LLP) *O J2 F2 Zq P*
Hull *p258* 01482 323239

Sewell, J D (Hallam-Peel & Co) *N*
London WC2 *p38* 020 3006 1661

Sewell, M D (Martin Sewell Family Law Solicitor & Advocate) *D1 K1 D2*
Gravesend *p233*. 01474 323251

Sewell, N J (Bevirs) *Zd K4 Zm T2 W*
Calne *p173* 01249 814536
Swindon *p406* 01793 532363

Sewell, P A (McClure Naismith) *Q Zj O*
London EC4 *p56*. 020 7623 9155

Sewell, P B (Fishburns) *A3 Zc C1 B2 Zj M2 O Q N Zq*
London EC3 *p32*. 020 7280 8888

Sewell, V E (Bentleys Stokes & Lowless) *N Za*
London EC3 *p12*. 020 7782 0990

Sexton, Ms D (Field Fisher Waterhouse LLP)
London EC3 *p31*. 020 7861 4000

Sexton, Ms J (J A Kemp & Co)
London WC1 *p48* 020 7405 3292

Sexton, S J E (MSB Solicitors LLP) *B2 D1 G K1 N Q Zf Zg Zq Zw*
Liverpool *p289*. 0151 281 9040

Seymour, A B (Seymours + Solicitors) *Q K1 S1 P N M1 H G E D1 B1 Zm Zk Zi*
Brighton *p160* 01273 628808

Seymour, B F (Linder Myers Solicitors) *O Q J1 L N R1 C1 B1 Ze Zl Zi*
Manchester *p306* 0844 984 6000

Seymour, C N H (Frearsons) *S1 S2 W*
Skegness *p380* 01754 897600

Seymour, Mrs K (Hayton Winkley) *C1 S2 E S1*
Kendal *p264*. 01539 720136

Seymour, M J (Hogan Lovells International LLP)
London EC1 *p42*. 020 7296 2000

Seymour, N (Stones Solicitors LLP) *P*
Exeter *p222* 01392 666777

Seymour, N J (Pricketts) *S1 S2 E W L Zd Zl*
Stockport *p396*. 0161 429 8000

Seymour, P (Ince & Co Services Ltd)
London E1 *p44* 020 7481 0010

Seymour, P J (Actons) *N Zj*
Nottingham *p335*. 0115 910 0200

Seymour, P R H (Field Seymour Parkes) *S2 E A1 X*
Reading *p360* 0118 951 6200

Seymour, Mrs R L (Forsters LLP) *Zc*
Westminster *p33*. 020 7863 8333

Sfar-Gandoura, Ms E (Shoosmiths)
Fareham *p224*. . . 0370 086 6800 / 01489 616800

Shaah, Miss T (Judge & Priestley) *D1 K1 T2 Zo*
Bromley *p166* 020 8290 0333

Shacklady, B M (RHW Solicitors LLP) *E S2*
Guildford *p237*. 01483 302000

Shacklady, B R (Forsters LLP) *O*
Westminster *p33*. 020 7863 8333

Shacklady, Mrs C A (RHW Solicitors LLP) *S1*
Guildford *p237*. 01483 302000

Shackleston, G (Maples Solicitors LLP) *G H J1 Zl*
Spalding *p389*. 01775 722261

Shackleton, A (Pricketts) *O Q J1 N A3 Zb Zq C1 E B2 M2 M1 P B1*
Buxton *p172*. 01298 22874

Shackleton, Miss A (Larcomes LLP) *D1 Q*
Portsmouth *p354*. 023 9266 1531

Shackleton, D A (Eccles Heddon) *S1 W S2 C1 J1*
Ripon *p365* 01765 601717

Shackleton, J F (Squire Sanders (UK) LLP) *O P Zc*
London EC2 *p81*. 020 7655 1000

Shackson, Mrs D (Stevens) *G H*
Stoke-on-Trent *p398*. 01782 343353

Shadbolt, Mrs J E (Mid Devon District Council)
Tiverton *p474* 01884 255255

Shaddock, Mrs K K (Nuneaton and Bedworth Borough Council)
Nuneaton *p468* 024 7637 6376

Shadi, Miss S (Davis Blank Furniss) *J1 Zi*
Manchester *p303* 0161 832 3304

Shadwell, Miss D A (Paul Davidson Taylor) *C1 B1 C2 J1 Ze Zb*
Horsham *p253*. 01403 262333

Shaer, J (Weightmans LLP) *N O Q*
Dartford *p207* 020 7822 1900

Shafeeque, M (Central Law Practice) *I Zi N*
London WC1 *p19* 020 3051 2187

Shaffer, S J (Moerans) *K4 W S1 T2*
Edgware *p217*. 020 8952 0242

Shaffron, Miss A (Edward Hayes LLP) *B2 G H*
London EC4 *p39*. 020 7353 0011

Shafiq, T (Longfords) *B2 Zg G H L N O Q S1 D1 V Zi*
Oldham *p340* 0161 665 4400

Shafqut, Miss A (John Poyser Solicitors) *N*
Manchester *p309* 0161 860 7354

Shah, Miss A (Rochdale Metropolitan Borough Council)
Rochdale *p470*. 01706 647474

Shah, A (Atul Shah) *S1 N O K1 L F1 E C1 W J1 Zi*
Wealdstone *p424* 020 8861 5000

Shah, A G (Frank Forney & Partners LLP) *C1 E R2 S1 S2 W Ze Zi*
Haringey *p33* . .020 8889 1971 / 8888 5481

Shah, A M (McGrigors LLP)
London EC4 *p56*. 020 7054 2500

Shah, A M (CVS Solicitors) *C1 C2 C3 M1 E J1 I M2 T1 T2 Zb Zc Zd Ze Zf*
London W1 *p17* 020 7493 2903

Shah, Mrs B (Everatt's) *B1 Q O L W Zi*
Harrow *p241*. 020 8424 0088

Shah, H (Christian Khan Solicitors)
London WC1 *p49* 020 7631 9500

Shah, J (Stephen Rimmer LLP) *N*
Eastbourne *p216*. 01323 644222

Shah, Mrs K (McKenzies) *K1 K3 D2 D1*
London N9 *p57* 020 8350 4114

Shah, Miss K (Mills Chody LLP) *K1 V D1*
Kenton *p265*. 020 8909 0400

Shah, K (Yugin & Partners) *S1 S2 E C1*
Stanmore *p394* 020 8954 2410

Shah, Ms M (Pittalis & Co) *S2 E S1 W*
London N12 *p68*. 020 8446 9555

Shah, Ms P (Black Rock)
London EC4 *p104* 020 7743 3000

Shah, Ms P (OGR Stock Denton) *W T2*
London N3 *p64* 020 8349 0321

Shah, P V (Awdry Bailey & Douglas)
Calne *p173* 01249 815110
Devizes *p210* 01380 722311
Wootton Bassett *p439* . . . 01793 853200

Shah, R (Darlingtons) *E S1 S2*
Edgware *p217*. .020 8952 0033 / 8951 6666

Shah, R (McKenzies) *S1*
London N9 *p57* 020 8350 4114

Shah, R (Galbraith Branley) *G H B2*
London N12 *p34*. 020 8446 8474

Shah, R S (Wayne Leighton) *C1 S2 S1 R2 E*
Edgware *p217*. 020 8951 2988

Shah, R U (Appleby Shaw)
Windsor *p434* 01753 860606

Shah, Miss S (Speechly Bircham LLP) *T2 W Zd*
London EC4 *p81*. 020 7427 6400

Shah, Mrs S (Gudsons Solicitors) *E S1 L S2 W Zl J1*
London N3 *p37* 020 8371 8389

Shah, S H (Lewis Silkin LLP) *E*
London EC4 *p53*. 020 7074 8000

Shah, S N (Everatt's) *C1 E Q J1 L M1 N P S1 W Zi Ze Zl*
Harrow *p241*. 020 8424 0088

Shah, Mrs T (Oldhams Solicitors & Advocates) *K1*
Baldock *p121* 01462 895444

Shah, V M (Freemans Solicitors) *W*
London W1 *p34* 020 7935 3522

Shah, Z (Molesworths Bright Clegg) *Zl Q N Zu*
Rochdale *p365*. 01706 356666

Shah, Z H (McKenzies) *N G H*
Hertford *p248* 01992 503344

Shahbaz, Mrs P A (HSK Solicitors LLP) *Zi S1*
Manchester *p305* 0161 795 4818

Shahim, Mrs A (Carter Lemon Camerons) *E S1*
London EC1 *p18*. 020 7406 1000

Shaidy, A (Shaidy & Co) *Q C1 B1 S1 E G Zi Zl*
Westminster *p77*. 020 7229 6703

Shaikh, Ms S (Reed Smith LLP) *J1*
London EC2 *p71*. 020 3116 3000

Shaine, N R (Commercial Union PLC)
London EC3 *p105* 020 7283 7500

Shakespeare, Ms E J (Teacher Stern LLP) *C1 C2*
London WC1 *p86* 020 7242 3191

Shakespeare, Ms K (Shoosmiths)
Milton Keynes *p317* . 0370 086 8300 / 01908 488300

Shakespeare, Miss M A (MFG Solicitors)
Kidderminster *p265* 01562 820181

Shakespeare, Miss S (Russell Jones & Walker)
Newcastle upon Tyne *p326* . 0191 323 3000

Shakkour, Miss S (AR Legal Solicitors) *Zg Zi Zl Q S1 W*
London W4 *p3*. 020 8747 9090

Shale, C A (Bird & Lovibond) *W S2 S1 E K4*
Uxbridge *p417*. 01895 256151

Shalet, A D (Rooks Rider) *E R2 S2 S1 L R1*
London EC1 *p73*. 020 7689 7000

Shallcross, J S (Blake Lapthorn) *A1 E*
Chandlers Ford *p184* 023 8090 8090

Shallcross, R A (Shallcross & Co) *E C1*
St Albans *p390* 01727 847804

Shalom, S L L (Davis Blank Furniss) *C1 E J1 L R1 S1 T2 Ze*
Manchester *p303* 0161 832 3304

Shamash, G D (Steel & Shamash) *P N M1 K1 J1 S1 E D1 W Zd*
Lambeth *p82*. 020 7803 3999

Shammah, J E (Shammah Nicholls LLP) *J1 K1 N P M1 G D1 F1 Zb Zc Ze*
Manchester *p309* 0161 832 9272

Shamo, Miss H R (Berry Smith LLP) *S1*
Cardiff *p177* 029 2034 5511

Shamsadeen, Miss B (MBNA Europe Bank Ltd)
Chester *p454* 01244 672002

Shamsolahi, R (Trobridges) *G K1 V*
Plymouth *p350*. 01752 664022

Shangari, S (Charsley Harrison LLP) *S1 S2 E*
Slough *p381*. 01753 517600

Shankland, L (Addleshaw Goddard)
Leeds *p271* 0113 209 2000

Shankland, M D (Cripps Harries Hall LLP) *E S2 R2*
Tunbridge Wells *p415* 01892 515121

Shanmuganathan, N (Taylor Wessing)
London EC4 *p86*. 020 7300 7000

Shanmuganathan, V S (Nathan & Co) *S1 N P G E L*
London SW19 *p63*. 020 8542 1805

Shanmugarajah, K (Shan & Co)
Harrow *p242*. 020 8864 7070

Shann, Miss A (John Lewis plc)
London SW1 *p107*. 020 7828 1000

Shannon, G (Alderson Dodds) *F1 J1 Zr Zq A3 Q*
Blyth *p147*. 01670 352293

Shannon, Ms J A M (Akzo Nobel Ltd)
London SW1 *p103*. 020 7009 5000

Shannon, Ms M E (Shell International Ltd)
London SE1 *p109* 020 7934 1234

Shaoul, J M (J M Shaoul)
Altrincham *p117* 0161 819 1133

Shapiro, J (WGS Solicitors) *S2 E Q S1 C1 J1 R2 N B1 L F2 T1 W Zl*
Westminster *p90*. 020 7723 1656

Shapiro, R H (Gelbergs LLP) *S1 W E*
Islington *p35*. 020 7226 0570

Shardlow, A (Browne Jacobson LLP) *N Zj*
Nottingham *p336*. 0115 976 6000

Shardlow, Mrs J B (Squire Sanders (UK) LLP)
Birmingham *p142* 0121 222 3000

Sharf, N (Rollits LLP) *C1 C2 T1 T2*
Hull *p258* 01482 323239

Sharif, K (Child & Child) *S1 E R2*
London SW1 *p20* 020 7235 8000

Sharif, R (Fountain Solicitors Limited) *Zi N K1 J1*
Walsall *p420*. 01922 645429

Sharif, S (Hadgkiss Hughes & Beale) *S2 E Zl S1 W*
Birmingham *p139* 0121 707 8484

Shariff, Mrs S (Shariff & Co) *E S1 W*
Kenton *p265*. 020 8907 1817

Shariff, T (Hodge Jones & Allen LLP) *Zr*
London NW1 *p41* 020 7874 8300

Sharkey, Miss L (Poppleston Allen) *Zl*
Nottingham *p338*. 0115 953 8500

Sharkey, T M (Kirby Sheppard) *K1 K2 D1 D2*
Kingswood *p268*. 0845 840 0045

Sharland, Ms S B (Bristol City Council)
Bristol *p451* 0117 922 2000

Sharma, Miss A (Hodge Jones & Allen LLP) *Q N Zq*
London NW1 *p41* 020 7874 8300

Sharma, B (Esso Petroleum Company Ltd)
Leatherhead *p462* 01372 222000

Sharma, B D (Arthur & Co) *K1 S1 E Q W D1 D2*
Pinner *p348* 020 8866 8282

Sharma, H (MB Law Limited) *N*
Hounslow *p254* 020 8863 3666

Sharma, Mrs J (Sanders & Co) *N W K1 K3*
Stourbridge *p399* .01384 375437 / 378991

Sharma, K (DLA Piper UK LLP)
London EC2 *p24*. 0870 011 1111

Sharma, M (Millichips)
West Bromwich *p427* 0121 500 6363

Sharma, Miss M (Derbyshire County Council)
Matlock *p465* 01629 580000

Sharma, Ms N (Staffordshire County Council)
Stafford *p472* 01785 223121

Sharma, Mrs N (Keoghs LLP)
Bolton *p149* 01204 677000

Sharma, Mrs N (Sandwell Metropolitan Borough Council)
Oldbury *p468* 0121 569 2200

Sharma, Mrs N (Royal Borough of Kingston upon Thames)
Kingston upon Thames *p462*. 020 8546 2121
Exeter *p458* 0845 456 7829

Sharma, N R (Crowell & Moring) *Zj*
London EC4 *p23*. 020 7413 0011

Sharma, R (Sternberg Reed) *E S1 W Zl*
Barking *p123* 020 8591 3366

Sharma, R D (Taylor Wessing) *E C1 B1 L R1 Zb*
London EC4 *p86*. 020 7300 7000

Sharma, S (Shoosmiths)
Milton Keynes *p317* . 0370 086 8300 / 01908 488300

Sharma, S (J M Wilson Solicitors) *Zi S1 G K3 Zg*
Birmingham *p143* 0121 356 4556

Sharma, Miss S (Reading Borough Council) *D1 K1*
Reading *p469* 0118 939 0900

Sharma, S M (DLA Piper UK LLP)
London EC2 *p24*. 0870 011 1111

Sharma, Ms U (Brown Turner Ross) *S1 S2*
Liverpool *p287*. 0151 236 2233

Sharma, V K (BKS Solicitors) *K1 D1 K2 D2*
London SE20 *p9*. 020 8776 9388

Sharman, I G (Blandy & Blandy) *S1 S2*
Reading *p360* 0118 951 6800
Keswick *p265* 01768 774321

Sharman, J (Freedman Sharman & Co) *S1 E W L*
Borehamwood *p150* 020 8953 9111

Sharman, J R (Bird & Bird LLP) *O*
London EC4 *p13*. 020 7415 6000

Sharman, Ms K (Bawtrees LLP) *W*
Witham *p435* 01376 513491
Braintree *p155*. 01376 326868

Sharman, M (Martin Adams & McColl) *S1 S2 E L W T1 T2 Zl K4*
Northampton *p332*. 01604 634123

Sharman, M D (Sharman & Son) *S1 K1 W P N F1 J1 M1 T1 E*
Liverpool *p290*. 0151 932 0333

Sharman, P G (Sharman & Company Ltd)
Peterborough *p468* 01733 555300

Sharp, A (Davies & Jones Solicitors) *H G*
Cardiff *p178* 029 2046 5296

Sharp, Mrs A (Foot Anstey) *K1*
Exeter *p221* 01392 411221

Sharp, A W (Mander Hadley & Co) *G H*
Coventry *p200*. 024 7663 1212

Sharp, B T J (DMB Law) *S1 W K1 M1 G H L P T1*
Sevenoaks *p374*. 01732 228800

Sharp, Mrs C (Mayer Brown International LLP)
London EC2 *p59*. 020 3130 3000

Sharp, Ms C (Debenhams Ottaway) *W*
St Albans *p390* 01727 837161

Sharp, Mrs C E (Varley Hibbs LLP) *D1 G H K1*
Coventry *p201*. 024 7663 1000

Sharp, Ms C E (Christine Sharp & Co) *F1 K1 W K3 S1*
Heywood *p249*. 01706 623513

Sharp, Ms C F (Mayer Brown International LLP) *P C1*
London EC2 *p59*. 020 3130 3000

Sharp, G (Simmons & Simmons)
London EC2 *p79*. 020 7628 2020

Sharp, I M (Reynolds Porter Chamberlain LLP)
London E1 *p71* 020 3060 6000

Sharp, J (Hartley & Worstenholme) *B1 E Ze R1 S1 T1 T2*
Pontefract *p351* 01977 732222

Sharp, J D (H E Thomas & Co) *S1 E K1 N Q*
Greenwich *p87*. 020 8854 3036

Sharp, L (Girlings) *E S2 C1*
Ashford *p119* 01233 664711

Sharp, P A (Brown Barron) *K1 K3 N D1 D2 Q Zq S1*
Barrow-in-Furness *p125* . . . 01229 828814

Sharp, Ms R (Cottrill Stone Lawless) *K4 K1 W*
Manchester *p302* 0161 835 3681

Sharp, Mrs R (Quality Solicitors Jordans) *S1 W E A1 C1 J1 K1 Zd S2 K4 L T2*
Doncaster *p212* 01302 365374

Sharp, R H (Prettys) *O Zk Zw*
Ipswich *p262*. 01473 232121

Sharp, R V G (Sharp & Rimmer) *S1 W A1 L E C1 R1 F1 J1 K1 Zd Zl*
St Mawes *p392* 01326 270291

Sharp, Miss S F (Woolf Simmonds) *S1 W*
Westminster *p93*. 020 7262 1266

Sharp, Ms S J (Barlow Lyde & Gilbert LLP)
London EC3 *p10*. 020 7247 2277

Sharp, Ms S L (Pitmans LLP) *E S2*
Reading *p361* 0118 958 0224

Sharp, S R (Bivonas Limited Solicitors) *G B2*
London EC3 *p13*. 020 7337 2600

Sharpe, Ms A (Jackamans) *K1*
Diss *p210* 01379 643555

Sharpe, A C (Penmans) *M1 P N D1 K1 G Zh*
Coventry *p200*. 024 7622 6575

Sharpe, C C (TWM Solicitors LLP) *S1 S2*
Reigate *p363* 01737 221212

Sharpe, E A (Sills & Betteridge LLP) *W K4*
Lincoln *p285*. 01522 542211

Sharpe, G (Olswang LLP) *O Q Ze Zf Zk*
London WC1 *p64* 020 7067 3000

Sharpe, G N (Sharpe & Co) *E C1 R2 S1 W L Q G J1 B1 Zh Zl Zq Zv Zc*
Harrow *p242*. 020 8422 4555

Sharpe, G N (The MLT Partnership) *C1 S2 E S1*
Ruislip *p369* 01895 676251

Sharpe, M (Jones & Co)
Bawtry *p128*. 01302 710555
Retford *p363*. 01777 703827

Sharpe, Mrs N (Thompsons (formerly Robin/Brian Thompson & Partners)) *N*
Sheffield *p377* 0114 270 3300

Sharpe, N S (Cooper Sons Hartley & Williams) *O Q B1*
Buxton *p172*. 01298 77511

Sharpe, P (Wilmot & Co Solicitors LLP) *O Q C1 J1*
Cirencester *p195*. 01285 650551

Sharpe, R S (Perrins Solicitors LLP) *R2*
Harpenden *p239*. 01582 466140

Sharpe, S R (Penmans) *N Q G H K1 S1 D1 J1*
Coventry *p200*. 024 7622 6575

Sharpe, T J (Gregory Rowcliffe Milners) *C1 C2 E J1 N X Ze Zo*
London WC1 *p37* 020 7242 0631

Sharples, A P (Mayer Brown International LLP) *C1 C2 U2 U1*
London EC2 *p59*. 020 3130 3000

Sharples, C A (Riseam Sharples) *S1 S2 L*
London WC2 *p72* 020 7836 9555

Sharples, Mrs D J (Hewitsons) *R1 P Zt G*
Cambridge *p174*. 01223 461155

Sharples, J (Walker Smith Way) *N*
Wrexham *p443* 0844 346 3100

Sharples, R (Clifford Chance)
London E14 *p20*. 020 7006 1000

Sharples, S M (Sharples & Co) *E S1 S2 Zx*
Bristol *p165* 0117 942 8214

See p634 for the Key to Work Categories

Sharpley, Ms D A (The College of Law)
London WC1 *p105* 0800 289997

Sharratt, J J (Lexica Law) *S1*
Canterbury *p177* 01227 764141

Sharrock, C S K (Kennedys) *Za Zj O*
London EC3 *p49* 020 7667 9667

Sharrock, Ms J (Ashurst LLP)
London EC2 *p7* 020 7638 1111

Sharrock, Ms L M (MPH Solicitors) *N*
Manchester *p307* 0161 832 7722

Sharron, Ms V S (Nicholas & Co) *S1 W*
London W1 *p63* 020 7323 4450

Shaughnessy, Ms M (John Ford Solicitors) *X Zg Zp Zu R1*
London N4 *p33* 020 8800 6464

Shaw, Ms A (Trowers & Hamlins)
London EC3 *p88* 020 7423 8000

Shaw, Miss A (Massers) *J1*
Nottingham *p338* 0115 851 1666

Shaw, Miss A (Farleys Solicitors LLP) *G H B2*
Blackburn *p145* 01254 367855

Shaw, A J (Manches LLP) *O Q A3 J1 B2 M2 Zq Zk*
London WC2 *p58* 020 7404 4433

Shaw, A J (Higgs & Sons) *N*
Brierley Hill *p158* 0845 111 5050

Shaw, Mrs A M (Land Registry - Croydon Office)
Croydon *p456* 020 8388 3288

Shaw, A W (Stewarts Law LLP) *Q O*
London EC4 *p83* 020 7822 8000

Shaw, Ms B (Coltman Warner Cranston LLP)
Coventry *p200* 024 7662 7262

Shaw, Ms B (TBI Solicitors) *K1 N*
Barnard Castle *p123* 01833 638326

Shaw, B M H (Solomon Taylor & Shaw) *E S1 L S2*
London NW3 *p80* 020 7431 1912

Shaw, C (Howes Percival LLP)
Norwich *p334* 01603 762103

Shaw, Ms C (Serious Fraud Office)
London WC1 *p109* 020 7239 7272

Shaw, Ms C A (Spratt Endicott) *J1 O Q Zk Ze Zc*
Banbury *p122* 01295 204000

Shaw, Mrs C E (Simmons & Simmons)
London EC2 *p79* 020 7628 2020

Shaw, Ms C J (Barlow Lyde & Gilbert LLP)
London EC3 *p10* 020 7247 2277

Shaw, D (Addleshaw Goddard)
Leeds *p271* 0113 209 2000

Shaw, D G (Lyons Rounsfell) *N*
Westbury-on-Trym *p428* . . . 0117 950 6506

Shaw, D T (FBC Manby Bowdler LLP) *E S2*
Telford *p409* 01952 292129

Shaw, Miss E A (Wake Smith & Tofields) *B1 L O Zq Q*
Sheffield *p377* 0114 266 6660

Shaw, G (J Keith Park & Co) *K1 S1 W*
St Helens *p391* 01744 636000

Shaw, G (Sternberg Reed) *G*
Barking *p123* 020 8591 3366
Romford *p366* 01708 766155

Shaw, G (TLT Solicitors) *J1 Zp*
Bristol *p165* 0117 917 7777

Shaw, G G (Booth Ince & Knowles) *K4 W Zm*
Denton *p208* 0161 336 7011

Shaw, H (Parker Rhodes Hickmotts) *S1 T2 W*
Rotherham *p367* 01709 365116

Shaw, H (Andrew & Co LLP) *K1*
Lincoln *p284* 01522 512123

Shaw, Ms H (Potter Rees (Serious Injury) Solicitors)
Manchester *p309* 0161 237 5888

Shaw, Ms H (TV Edwards LLP) *K1*
London SE8 *p85* 020 7790 7000

Shaw, Ms J E (Milburns Solicitors)
Workington *p440* 01900 67363

Shaw, Mrs J M (Scaiff LLP) *N Zj*
Worcester *p440* 01905 727700

Shaw, J S (Grierson Shaw & Co) *G H S1 K1 M1 D1 J1 L F1 W Zl Zk Zi*
Durham *p214* 0191 386 2434

Shaw, J W (Kennedys)
London EC3 *p49* 020 7667 9667

Shaw, Ms K M (Radcliffes Le Brasseur) *K1*
Westminster *p70* 020 7222 7040

Shaw, K R (Jaffe Porter Crossick)
London NW6 *p46* 020 7625 4424

Shaw, Miss L (Plexus Law (A Trading Name of Parabis Law LLP)) *Q F1*
Manchester *p309* 0844 245 4100

Shaw, Mrs L A (Nash & Co Solicitors LLP) *K1 K3 D1 N W S1 E C1 S2 J1 O Q Zq K4 M3*
Plymouth *p350* 01752 664444

Shaw, Mrs L D (Pennon Group PLC) *C1 U1*
Exeter *p458* 01392 446677

Shaw, Miss L N (Kerseys) *W K4*
Ipswich *p262* 01473 213311

Shaw, Ms L V (Wirral Borough Council)
Wallasey *p475* 0151 638 7070

Shaw, M (Pinsent Masons LLP) *C1 B1 J1 F1 E T1 S1 Zb Zc*
Leeds *p276* 0113 244 5000

Shaw, Mrs M A (Dutton Gregory) *W*
Winchester *p433* 01962 844333

Shaw, M A (Hempsons) *Zk Zr*
Westminster *p40* 020 7839 0278

Shaw, Ms M C (David Gray Solicitors) *K3 D1 K1 D2*
Newcastle upon Tyne *p324* . 0191 232 9547

Shaw, M D (Herbert Smith LLP) *C1 C2*
London EC2 *p40* 020 7374 8000

Shaw, Ms M V (Buss Murton LLP) *K3 K1 K4 W D1*
Tunbridge Wells *p415* 01892 510222
London SE3 *p27* 020 8852 1255

Shaw, N (Last Cawthra Feather LLP) *O*
Leeds *p275* 0113 244 0876

Shaw, N (Reed Smith LLP) *Za*
London EC2 *p71* 020 3116 3000

Shaw, N J (Addleshaw Goddard) *W T1 S1*
Manchester *p300* 0161 934 6000

Shaw, N J (Thorpe & Co) *E L Zl Zm B1 S1 S2 J1 O Q*
Filey *p226* 01723 515555

Shaw, N P S (Franklins) *B1 F1 L N O Q S1 J1 Zh Zl*
Abingdon *p114* 01235 553222

Shaw, P R (Taylor Wessing) *N P C1 B1 E R1 T1 S1 L J1 Zc Zi Zn*
London EC4 *p86* 020 7300 7000

Shaw, R (Sheppersons) *Zi D1*
Horley *p252* 01293 772424

Shaw, Ms R (Trowers & Hamlins)
London EC3 *p88* 020 7423 8000

Shaw, R D (Shaw Graham Kersh)
London W1 *p78* 020 7734 9700

Shaw, R E (Rundlewalker) *B1 F1 G L N Q W Zi Zj*
Exeter *p222* 01392 209209

Shaw, R H L (Davenport Lyons) *P N K1 Ze Zf*
London W1 *p25* 020 7468 2600

Shaw, Miss R L (Archer & Archer) *N Q V F1 L Zh Zq Zr K1*
Ely *p218* 01353 662203

Shaw, R M (Manches LLP) *E*
Oxford *p343* 01865 722106

Shaw, R P G (Challinors) *N Q Zr Zj*
West Bromwich *p427* 0121 553 3211

Shaw, R W H (HM Revenue & Customs)
Salford *p470* 0870 785 8545

Shaw, S (Boodle Hatfield) *T2 W*
Westminster *p14* 020 7629 7411

Shaw, Ms S (The Environment Agency (North West Region [HQ]))
Warrington *p475* 01925 653999

Shaw, S C I (Shaw Gillis) *E L S2 S1 W*
Morley *p319* 0113 252 0331

Shaw, Miss S J (Hethertons LLP) *W*
York *p445* 01904 528200

Shaw, S J (Scaiff LLP) *N C1 E Q S2 S1 B1 K1 W Zr*
Worcester *p440* 01905 727700

Shaw, S J (Cleaver Thompson Ltd) *K1 K3 D1 K2*
Alfreton *p115* 01773 832193
Burton-on-Trent *p170* 01283 536471

Shaw, Mrs S M F (BBA Aviation PLC)
London W1 *p103* 020 7514 3999

Shaw, T D (Shaw & Ashton) *S1 P N W T1 M1 L E C1*
Pontefract *p351* 01977 703232

Shaw, Mrs T E (The Environment Agency (North West Region [HQ]))
Warrington *p475* 01925 653999

Shaw, T J (Nabarro LLP)
Sheffield *p376* 0114 279 4000

Shaw, T J B (British Telecommunications PLC)
London EC1 *p104* 020 7356 6181

Shaw, T P (Speechly Bircham LLP) *C1 I C2*
London EC4 *p81* 020 7427 6400

Shaw, Miss V A (The Watson Ramsbottom Partnership) *D1 D2 K1*
Blackburn *p146* 01254 672222

Shaw, Mrs W J (Ashton Bond Gigg) *E S1 A1 S2 C2*
Nottingham *p335* 0115 947 6651

Shawcross, Ms K E (Jobling & Knape) *O Q Zl*
Lancaster *p269* 01524 598300

Shawcross, K R (Harrison Clark LLP) *S1 W E C1 A1 R1 F1 L J1 Zb Zd Zn*
Ross-on-Wye *p367* 01989 562377

Shawe, B (King Davies & Partners) *G H M1 K1 P S1 D1 F1 J1 W Zj Zl Zs*
Maesteg *p298* 01656 732911

Shawe, J D E (Bennetts Law Practice Ltd) *Q K1 W*
Clacton-on-Sea *p195* 01255 254400

Shawley, D M (British Telecommunications PLC)
London EC1 *p104* 020 7356 6181

Shawyer, I K (Travers Smith LLP) *C1 C2*
London EC1 *p87* 020 7295 3000

Shawyer, R J (Silver Shemmings LLP) *A1 Zc A3 Zq O Q C1*
London SW1 *p78* 0845 345 1244

Shaya, M (DAC Beachcroft) *O Q Za Zj*
London EC4 *p24* 020 7936 2222

Shayle, M (Wiggin Osborne Fullerlove) *T2 W T1 C1*
Cheltenham *p189* 01242 710200
London SW1 *p91* 020 7290 2456

Shea, S E (Clifford Chance)
London E14 *p20* 020 7006 1000

Sheach, A J (CMS Cameron McKenna LLP) *C1 C2*
London EC3 *p17* 020 7367 3000

Sheahan, D (Paragon Law) *Zi*
Nottingham *p338* 0115 964 4123

Shear, G J (Teacher Stern LLP) *O Q Ze Zf Zk*
London WC1 *p86* 020 7242 3191

Shear, R C (Edwin Coe LLP) *C1 C2 F1 C3 J1 P Zb Ze Zf Zw*
London WC2 *p29* 020 7691 4000

Sheard, I (Salford City Council)
Swinton *p473* 0161 794 4711

Shearer, Miss A C (GHP Legal) *G H*
Wrexham *p442* 01978 291456

Shearer, Ms L (Ashurst LLP)
London EC2 *p7* 020 7638 1111

Shearing, Miss L T (DWF) *E S2 R2*
Manchester *p303* 0161 603 5000

Shearmur, Miss R A (Michelmores LLP) *D1 D2 K1 K2*
Exeter *p221* 01392 688688

Shears, Miss A (Gard & Co) *S1*
Plymouth *p349* 01752 668246

Shears, G D (Thompsons (formerly Robin/Brian Thompson & Partners)) *J1 J2 N*
Plymouth *p350* 01752 675810

Shears, Ms S D (Crown Prosecution Service Thames Valley)
Abingdon *p447* 01235 551900

Sheath, J C (Brachers) *N O Q Zr*
Maidstone *p299* 01622 690691

Sheather, M K (Gill Akaster)
Plymouth *p349* 01752 203500

Shebon, Mrs H (Forbes) *K1 D1 V*
Blackburn *p145* 01254 580000

Shebson, J (Barlow Lyde & Gilbert LLP) *Zj O*
London EC3 *p10* 020 7247 2277

Shebson, V L (Howard Kennedy LLP) *E R2 S1 S2 W*
London W1 *p48* 020 7636 1616

Shedlow, J R O (Walker Morris) *E*
Leeds *p277* 0113 283 2500

Shedlow, P (Castle Sanderson) *K1 S1 F1 G H N W*
Leeds *p272* 0113 232 1919
Leeds *p277* 0113 264 7603

Shedlow, Ms R (Henry Hyams) *Zm*
Leeds *p274* 0113 243 2288

Shee, F J (The Oakley Shee Partnership) *E S2 S1*
London SE1 *p64* 020 7089 9066

Sheehan, Mrs A (Derby City Council) *K1*
Derby *p456* 01332 293111

Sheehan, A J (BRM Solicitors) *E S2*
Chesterfield *p191* 01246 555111

Sheehan, C (Shoarns Solicitors Christopher Sheehan LLB) *S1 L E W A1 C1 R2 S2*
Blandford Forum *p147* 01258 880214

Sheehan, Ms E (Wilkinson & Butler)
St Neots *p392* 01480 219229

Sheehy-Smith, D J (Sheehy-Smith) *S1 L C1 A1 W*
Derby *p209* 01332 755409

Sheen, J H (Burton & Co LLP) *D1 G H K1*
Sleaford *p381* . . . . 01529 306008 / 306009

Sheen, R J (Bentleys Stokes & Lowless) *O Q N M2 Za Zj Zl*
London EC3 *p12* 020 7782 0990

Sheer, Miss N (Perrins Solicitors LLP) *S2 E Zh S1 R2*
Harpenden *p239* 01582 466140

Sheeran, Ms C F (Thompson Smith & Puxon) *N*
Colchester *p198* 01206 574431

Sheerin, Mrs C (Warner Goodman LLP) *C1*
Southampton *p387* 023 8063 9311

Sheerin, J (Lake District National Park Authority)
Kendal *p462* 01539 724555

Sheffield, C M (Peter Kingshill & Co) *S1 N Q E L W S2 O*
Worthing *p442* 01903 218210

Sheibani, Ms S (Faegre & Benson LLP) *C1 C2*
London EC4 *p30* 020 7450 4500

Sheiham, M (Simmons & Simmons)
London EC2 *p79* 020 7628 2020

Sheikh Collins, Mrs R (DAC Beachcroft) *N P Zj Zc*
Leeds *p272* 0113 251 4700

Sheikh, F R (Daybells LLP) *C1 S2 R2 S1 E*
London E15 *p26* 020 8555 4321
London EC1 *p34* 020 7822 2222

Sheikh, Mrs R (Darbys Solicitors LLP) *B1*
Oxford *p343* 01865 811700

Sheikh, Miss S (Kirklees Metropolitan Borough Council)
Huddersfield *p461* 01484 221421

Sheikh, S A (Sandhu & Shah) *Zi*
London E7 *p76* 020 8552 4100

Sheikh, S A (West Berkshire Council)
Newbury *p466* 01635 42400

Sheikh, S R (GSC Solicitors) *S1 C1 E N P F1 J1 L B1 H Zc Zb*
London EC1 *p34* 020 7822 2222

Sheikh, Ms Y (Barlow Lyde & Gilbert LLP)
London EC3 *p10* 020 7247 2277

Shelbourne, M G J (Waller Needham & Green) *G H*
Peterborough *p347* 01733 311422

Sheldon, Mrs C E (City of Bradford Metropolitan District Council) *K1 D1 D2*
Bradford *p451* 01274 752236

Sheldon, D J (Carvill & Johnson LLP) *G H*
Birmingham *p136* 0121 476 9000

Sheldon, E M (Raworths LLP) *E S1 S2*
Harrogate *p240* 01423 566666

Sheldon, J B (Ashurst LLP) *C1 Zn*
London EC2 *p7* 020 7638 1111

Sheldon, J N (Ashurst LLP) *C1 Zo*
London EC2 *p7* 020 7638 1111

Sheldon, S B (Chris Clark) *G H W S1*
Cannock *p176* 01543 573004

Sheldon, T (Fishburns) *A3 Q Zc Zj Zo Zq*
London EC3 *p32* 020 7280 8888

Sheldrake, Ms C (Ramsdens Solicitors) *K1 K3*
Huddersfield *p256* 01484 821500

Sheldrick, B (Magrath LLP) *Zi*
London W1 *p57* 020 7495 3003

Sheldrick, J (Comptons) *C1 S2 E S1*
Camden *p22* 020 7485 0888
Ruislip *p368* 01895 612400

Sheldrick, Ms K (Hempsons) *Zr N G B2*
Manchester *p305* 0161 228 0011

Shell, E (Jacobs Solicitors) *D1 K1*
Ellesmere Port *p217* 0151 355 8481

Shell, P (John Laing)
London SW1 *p107* 020 7901 3200

Shellard, Ms J A (Addleshaw Goddard) *R2*
London EC1 *p4* 020 7606 8855

Shelley, C J G (Manches LLP) *M1 C1 C3 Zi*
Oxford *p343* 01865 722106

Shelley, D W (Pinsent Masons LLP) *Zo*
Birmingham *p141* 0121 200 1050

Shelley, Mrs J C (Hillyer McKeown LLP) *C1 Ze Zk I O*
Chester *p190* 01244 318131

Shelley, M F (Shelley & Co) *G H*
Cambridge *p175* 01223 359441

Shelley, S (TWM Solicitors LLP) *S1 S2*
Epsom *p219* 01372 729555

Shellien, M (Gregory Abrams Davidson LLP) *N Q*
Liverpool *p288* 0151 733 3353

Shelmerdine, J M (Butcher & Barlow LLP) *S1 E W C1 L A1 Zd*
Sandbach *p372* 01270 762521

Shelston, J J (Brabners Chaffe Street) *J1 Zp Zd*
Liverpool *p286* 0151 600 3000

Shelton, Miss D (Mullis & Peake) *C1 C2*
Romford *p366* 01708 784000

Shelton, Ms E A (Charles Russell LLP) *K1*
London EC4 *p19* 020 7203 5000

Shelton, M H (Caplans) *C1 N M1 K1 D1 G R1 H S1 E Zf Zl Zk*
Harrow *p241* 020 8864 0111

Shelton, R D (The Paragon Group of Companies PLC)
Solihull *p471* 0121 711 3333

Shemar, Miss S (Enoch Evans LLP) *E S2 C1 Zb*
Walsall *p420* 01922 720333

Shemmings, Mrs S A (Silver Shemmings LLP)
London SW1 *p78* 0845 345 1244

Shenk, M D (Steptoe & Johnson) *U2 U1 Ze*
London EC2 *p83* 020 7367 8000

Shenton, Mrs A (Keppe & Partners Solicitors) *Q L Zc Zr J1 N*
Twickenham *p416* 020 8891 4488

Shepard, Miss R D L (Eastleys) *W K4*
Paignton *p345* 01803 559257

Shepard, Mrs S J (Harvey Copping & Harrison) *K1 W J1 Q*
Chelmsford *p186* 01245 322956

Shepard, Mrs S J (Harvey Copping & Harrison) *K1 D1*
Wickford *p431* . . . . 01268 733381 / 763211

Shephard, Ms C (The College of Law Chester)
Chester *p454* 0800 289997

Shephard, J (Hewitsons) *Q L Zr*
Northampton *p332* 01604 233233

Shepherd, Miss A (Drivers) *S1 S2 W*
York *p444* 01904 625661

Shepherd, Miss A M (Macks Solicitors) *W N Q D1 K1*
Middlesbrough *p315* 01642 252828

Shepherd, Miss A M (Glaisyers Solicitors LLP) *K1 K3*
Manchester *p304* 0161 224 3311

Shepherd, Ms C (Squire Sanders (UK) LLP) *Zb C1*
Manchester *p310* 0161 830 5000

Shepherd, Miss C D (Kirby Sheppard) *D1 K1 K3 D2*
Bristol *p163* 0845 840 0045

Shepherd, C J (Clive Shepherd & Co) *P G H D1 F1 M1 S1 V W J1 Zh Zk Zm*
Walsall *p420* 01922 647797

Shepherd, C T (Commercial Union PLC)
London EC3 *p105* 020 7283 7500

Shepherd, D A (FBC Manby Bowdler LLP) *S1*
Shrewsbury *p379* 01743 241551

Shepherd, D G (Wake Smith & Tofields) *C1 C2 U1*
Sheffield *p377* 0114 266 6660

Shepherd, G (Healds) *B1 E L O Zc C1 Q R1 S2 C2*
Wigan *p432* 01942 241511

Shepherd, Mrs G J (Buckinghamshire County Council)
Aylesbury *p448* 01296 383653

Shepherd, I P (Clerk to the Justices)
Beverley *p449* 01482 861607

Shepherd, Miss J (Nottinghamshire County Council Legal Services Division)
West Bridgford *p475* 0115 977 3478

Shepherd, J A (Guy Williams Layton) *E S1 W*
Wirral *p435* . . . 0151 342 1831 / 342 6144

Shepherd, M (Shoosmiths)
Reading *p361* . . 0370 086 8800 / 0118 965 8765

Shepherd, M (Simmons & Simmons)
London EC2 *p79* 020 7628 2020

Shepherd, M A (M A Shepherd & Co) *Zo J1 Zj W*
London N3 *p78* 020 8343 2346

Shepherd, M D (Clive Shepherd & Co)
Walsall *p420* 01922 647797

Shepherd, M L (Squire Sanders (UK) LLP) *P O Q Zy Zw*
Manchester *p310* 0161 830 5000

Shepherd, N (Shoosmiths) *O L Zb*
Northampton *p332* . . 0370 086 3000 / 01604 543000

Shepherd, N P (DLA Piper UK LLP)
Manchester *p303* 0870 011 1111

Shepherd, Ms P (Squire Sanders (UK) LLP) Birmingham *p142* 0121 222 3000

Shepherd, Ms P (ASB Law) Crawley *p202* 01293 603600

Shepherd, P (Tait Farrier Graham) *D1 F1 G H J1 K1 L M1 P* Gateshead *p229*. 0191 490 0108

Shepherd, P M (Blake Lapthorn) *C1 C2 Zb* Chandlers Ford *p184* 023 8090 8090

Shepherd, P W C (Taylor Wessing) *C1 N Zb* London EC4 *p86*. 020 7300 7000

Shepherd, Mrs S (Higgs & Sons) Brierley Hill *p158*. 0845 111 5050

Shepherd, S R (Shepherd Evans Solicitors) *Zr K4 T2 G H N D1 Q J1 K1 S1 W F1 Zm Zv* Macclesfield *p297* 01625 503909

Shepherd, S W (Ince & Co Services Ltd) London E1 *p44* 020 7481 0010

Shepherd, T D (Barlow Lyde & Gilbert LLP) London EC3 *p10*. 020 7247 2277

Shepley, Ms A M (Carillion PLC) Wolverhampton *p477* 01902 422431

Shepley, C R (Crispian Shepley) *J1* Walton-on-Thames *p421*. . . . 01923 221122

Sheppard, A J (Barlow Lyde & Gilbert LLP) *Q N* London EC3 *p10*. 020 7247 2277

Sheppard, A W (Clifford Chance) London E14 *p20*. 020 7006 1000

Sheppard, B D (Walker Morris) *Zu* Leeds *p277* 0113 283 2500

Sheppard, Mrs B J (Dorset County Council) Dorchester *p457*. 01305 251000

Sheppard, Ms C S (Addleshaw Goddard) London EC1 *p4* 020 7606 8855

Sheppard, D A (MLM Cartwright) *J1 Zp Q* Cardiff *p179* 029 2046 2562

Sheppard, G (Wiggin LLP) *Zf Ze C1 Zb T1* Cheltenham *p189* 01242 224114

Sheppard, Ms K (Langleys) *E* York *p445* 01904 610886

Sheppard, R M (EEF West Midlands Association) Birmingham *p449* 0121 456 2222

Sheppard, Miss S (Kemp Little LLP) *C3 M1* London EC2 *p48*. 020 7600 8080

Sheppard, Miss S M (Warner Goodman LLP) *K4 W* Fareham *p224*. 01329 288121

Sheppard, S R (Oxley & Coward Solicitors LLP) *N Q* Rotherham *p367*. 01709 510999

Shepperson, Ms L J (Barlow Lyde & Gilbert LLP) London EC3 *p10*. 020 7247 2277

Shepperson, S H (Sheppersons) *S1 C1 E K1 W O L F1 N P Q* Horley *p252* 01293 772424

Shepperson, Ms T J (T J Shepperson) *L* Norwich *p335* 01603 763096

Sher, G R (Shammah Nicholls LLP) *C1 C2 C3* Manchester *p309* 0161 832 9272

Sher, I (Norman H Barnett & Co) *S1 G K1 Zi Zm E W L* London E6 *p11*. 020 8471 2112

Sherahilo, J I (Brain Sinnott & Co) *K1 K3 K2* Bristol *p161* . . . . 0117 965 1030 Tewkesbury *p410* 01684 299633

Sherborne, D (BPE Solicitors LLP) *J1 Zp M1 Zi Zza C2* Cheltenham *p187* 01242 224433

Sherbrooke, A (Lee Bolton Monier-Williams) *E* Westminster *p52*. 020 7222 5381

Sherburn, I (Wilkin Chapman LLP) *C1 C2 C3 Zy* Grimsby *p235* 01472 262626

Sheret, Mrs R (Plexus Law (A Trading Name of Parabis Law LLP)) *N Q* Evesham *p220*. 01386 769160

Shergill, G S (Shergill & Co) *S1 E P K1 W* Hounslow *p254* 020 8570 2323

Shergill, K (Ashurst LLP) London EC2 *p7* 020 7638 1111

Shergill, Ms M (Vickers & Co) *G H* Ealing *p89*. . . .020 8579 2559 / 8840 3999

Shergill, R (Cartwright King) Nottingham *p336*. 0115 958 7444

Shergill, Mrs S (Jordans) *G H D1 K1* Wakefield *p418* 01924 387110

Sheridan, B B (LDJ Solicitors) *G H D1 P M1 N L* Nuneaton *p339* 024 7674 5000

Sheridan, D J (Wards Solicitors) *K1* Bristol *p165* 0117 929 2811

Sheridan, D R (D R Sheridan & Co) *M1 P N S1 K1 D1 C1 J1 G* Bushey *p172*. 020 8950 6768

Sheridan, I M (Sheridan & Co) *N Q O W S1 M2 Zq Zr K4* Kingston upon Thames *p267*. 020 8541 1181

Sheridan, M J (Squire Sanders (UK) LLP) London EC2 *p81*. 020 7655 1000

Sheridan, M S (Sheridan & Stretton) *S1 E O Q S2 W Zl X C1 L* London W6 *p78* 020 8748 7340

Sheridan, P F (CMS Cameron McKenna LLP) *P* London EC3 *p17*. 020 7367 3000

Sheridan, P R (Wilkin Chapman Grange Solicitors) *Zi Zm Q Zl N* Grimsby *p235* 01472 262626

Sheridan, T (CVC Solicitors) Penzance *p346* 01736 362313

Sheriff, Ms M (Mayo Wynne Baxter LLP) *O* Brighton *p160* 01273 775533

Sheril, J I (Yugin & Partners) *C1 J1 C2 Zb* Stanmore *p394* 020 8954 2410

Sherliker, C J (Silverman Sherliker LLP) *C1 C2 C3 F1 I M2 N Q S1 Ze Zq Zt Zw Zl U1 U2 Zz* London EC2 *p78*. 020 7749 2700

Sherlock, D (Girlings) *B1 F1 L M1 P* Ashford *p119* 01233 664711

Sherlock, Mrs M R (Anthony & Jarvie) *K1 W D1 K3* Bridgend *p157*. 01656 652737

Sherlock, Ms S P K (Squire Sanders (UK) LLP) London EC2 *p81*. 020 7655 1000

Sherman, H C (CMS Cameron McKenna LLP) London EC3 *p17*. 020 7367 3000

Sherman, Miss L (North Somerset District Council) Weston-super-Mare *p476* . . 01934 888888

Sherr, Prof A H (Sherrs) London WC1 *p78* 020 7862 5859

Sherrard, H (Sherrards) *J1* Haywards Heath *p246*. . . . 01444 473344

Sherrard, P P T (Geraint Jones & Co) *G H Q J1 O Zl* Newtown *p330*. 01686 627935

Sherratt, Mrs G A (Staffordshire Moorlands District Council) Leek *p463* 01538 483483

Sherratt, J (Mullis & Peake) *O Q* Romford *p366* 01708 784000

Sherratt, J R (Lichfield Reynolds) *S1 W* Stoke-on-Trent *p398*. 01782 313212

Sherratt, P S (Nowell Meller Solicitors Limited) *K1 D1 D2 K3* Stafford *p393* 01785 252377

Sherratt, Ms V J (Barlow Lyde & Gilbert LLP) *O Q P Zj* London EC3 *p10*. 020 7247 2277

Sherred, P W (Bradleys) *S1 R1 W L J1 E B1 Zd* Dover *p212* 01304 204080

Sherriff, A W G (Bell & Co) *S1 E L W J1 R1 C1 Zc Zh* Cheam *p185*. 020 8642 6099

Sherriff, Ms C A (Wright Hassall LLP) *A1 S2 S1* Leamington Spa *p270* 01926 886688

Sherriff, R K (Gardner Iliff & Dowding) *E H S1 A1 W* Cannock *p176*. 01543 466941

Sherrin, R M (Druces LLP) *O Q A3 L Zq Ze Zk Zj* London EC2 *p27*. 020 7638 9271

Sherrington, Ms E (Hopkin Murray Beskine) *D1 K1* London N4 *p42* 020 7272 1234

Sherrington, J H (Serious Law LLP - The Serious Law Practice) *N O* Bolton *p150* 0800 616 681

Sherrington, P P (Hogan Lovells International LLP) London EC1 *p42*. 020 7296 2000

Sherrington, R M (Brightstone Law LLP) *F1 M1 N P C1 Zb Zd* Elstree *p218*. 020 8731 3080

Sherrott, Mrs S N (Royal Mail Group) London EC4 *p109* 020 7250 2468

Sherry, Ms C A (Glazer Delmar) *S1* London SE22 *p35* 020 8299 0021

Sherville-Payne, Mrs K (DWF) *Zj Zq* Manchester *p303* 0161 603 5000

Sherville-Payne, R (AstraZeneca) Macclesfield *p464* 01625 582828

Sherwin, D (Silver Fitzgerald) *J1 Q F1 L N* Cambridge *p175*. 01223 562001

Sherwin, M M (McMillan Williams) *K1 D1* Thornton Heath *p411*. . . . 020 8653 8844

Sherwin, N A (Clifford Chance) *T1 Zo* London E14 *p20*. 020 7006 1000

Sherwin, Ms R (Gateley LLP) Birmingham *p138* 0121 234 0000

Sherwood, A R (Sherwood Dunham) *G H N J1 Zl* Wellingborough *p424* 01933 276147

Sherwood, C F S (DAC Beachcroft) Leeds *p272* 0113 251 4700

Sherwood, D (Act Legal) *S1* Brighton *p159* 01273 565656

Sherwood, D (Sherwood Solicitors) *S1 W E* Brighton *p160* 01273 608221

Sherwood, J E (Wood Sherwood & Co) *A1 E L S1 S2 W* Pocklington *p351* 01759 302791

Sherwood, M R (Thornleys Limited) *E S1 A1 L* Plymouth *p350*. 01752 406977

Sherwood, N J H (Winterbotham Smith Penley LLP) *S1 E S2 L* Stroud *p401* 01453 847200

Sherwood, Ms S (Davies Gore Lomax) *K1 L Q* Leeds *p273* 0113 242 2797

Sherwood, T A F (Hallmark Hulme) *S1 W* Worcester *p439* 01905 726600

Sherwood-Smith, D K (Sherwood-Smith Tilley & Co) *S1 E G J1 C1 F1 M1 N R1* Houghton Le Spring *p253* . . 0191 584 3186

Shestopal, N J (Barnett Alexander Conway Ingram) *L S1 W Ze Zl* London N3 *p10* 020 8349 7680

Sheward, M (Thursfields) *G H Q N* Worcester *p440* 01905 730450

Shicluna, Miss J A (Stephens & Son LLP) *N Q B1* Chatham *p185*. 01634 811444

Shiebert, D A (Photiades) *N O Q S1 K3 C1 E J1 K1 L* St Albans *p390* 01727 833134

Shiebert, Ms T T (Dickins Shiebert) *C1 E L S1 Zc S2 W R1* Potters Bar *p355*. 01707 851100

Shiel, A (Ward Hadaway) Newcastle upon Tyne *p327* . 0191 204 4000

Shield, Miss A (BPE Solicitors LLP) *E* Cheltenham *p187* 01242 224433

Shield, J L (JST Lawyers) *C1 E G H K1 M1 S1 W Zf Zl* Liverpool *p289*. 0151 282 2828

Shield, M (Varley Hibbs LLP) *Ze C1 O Q* Coventry *p201* 024 7663 1000

Shield, T A (John Gaunt & Partners) *O Zl Zf Q* Sheffield *p375* 0114 266 8664

Shields, Miss D M (McGrigors LLP) London EC4 *p56*. 020 7054 2500

Shields, G J (Forster Dean Ltd) *S1 S2* St Helens *p391* . . . . 01744 755577 Runcorn *p369* 01928 590999

Shields, Ms M (Faegre & Benson LLP) London EC4 *p30*. 020 7450 4500

Shields, Mrs M R (Edwards Duthie) *D1 K1* London E13 *p29*. 020 8514 9000

Shiels, Mrs M C (Royal College of Nursing) London W1 *p109* 020 7409 3333

Shiels, M P (Damian J Plant & Co) *F1 J1 N O Q S1 Zf Zp* Kenilworth *p264* . . .01926 847741 / 854677

Shiels, Mrs P (Cumbria County Council) Kendal *p462*. 01539 773123

Shiers, M R (Nash & Co Solicitors LLP) *N Q L O* Plymouth *p350*. 01752 664444

Shiers, R (McGrigors LLP) *T1 T2 Q* London EC4 *p56*. 020 7054 2500

Shiers, R A (BRM Solicitors) *E C1 S1 S2 J1 Zl* Chesterfield *p191* 01246 555111

Shihab, Z (Max Bitel Greene LLP) Islington *p59*. 020 7354 2767

Shillabeer, T M (Taylor Walton LLP) *E L S1* St Albans *p390* 01727 845245

Shilling, T (Allen & Overy LLP) London E1 *p5* 020 3088 0000

Shillingford, Ms T (Goodman Derrick LLP) *C1 C2 I Ze Zl Zz* London EC4 *p36*. 020 7404 0606

Shillito, C S (Bradshaws Hamer Park & Haworth) *S1 W K1 B1* Blackpool *p146* 01253 621531

Shillito, M R (Herbert Smith LLP) *O Ze* London EC2 *p40*. 020 7374 8000

Shillito, R A (Farrer & Co LLP) *Zk Ze* London WC2 *p31* 020 3375 7000

Shimell, G C (Cardiff County Council) Cardiff *p453* 029 2087 2000

Shimmin, Miss K J (Blake Lapthorn) *C1 B1 C2 Zb* Chandlers Ford *p184* 023 8090 8090

Shimmin, L D (Lansdale & Holdsworth) Bolton *p149* 01204 491111

Shindler, A (SJ Berwin LLP) London EC4 *p75*. 020 7111 2222

Shine, D (David Shine & Kharbanda) *K1 L M1 E G S1 W Zi Zm* Southall *p384* . .020 8571 6001 / 8571 6002

Shine, J N (Gordon Shine & Co) *K1 L M1 G H N P B1 D1 J1* London NW10 *p78*. 020 8969 7033

Shine, R (Reed Smith LLP) *C1* London EC2 *p71*. 020 3116 3000

Shine, R (Brabners Chaffe Street) *E L A1 Zl* Preston *p356* 01772 823921

Shiner, P J (Public Interest Lawyers) Birmingham *p141* 0121 515 5069

Shingadia, D N (Southall Rights Ltd) Southall *p472* 020 8571 4920

Shingari, V K (Birmingham City Council Legal & Democratic Services) *W C1 B1 J1 T2 C2 F1 O I E* Birmingham *p449* 0121 303 2066

Shingler, V (Middleton Dummer) *B1 C1 E G S2 L P S1* Oldbury *p340* 0121 544 4788

Shinner, Mrs M F A C (Parker Rhodes Hickmotts) *N J1 Q* Rotherham *p367*. 01709 511100

Shipley, A (Nelsons) *A3 I B2 M2 O Zq Q N* Nottingham *p338*. 0115 958 6262

Shipley, C C (Downs) *C1 I* Dorking *p212* 01306 880110

Shipman, D G R (Willett & Co) *K1 P N G M1 H D1 F1 J1 V Zi Zj Zk* Bury St Edmunds *p171* . . . 01284 701323

Shipp, Ms E J (SGH Martineau LLP) *C1 B1 J1 U2 C2* London EC3 *p75*. 020 7264 4444

Shipton, I D (Powells) *W T2 Zo* Weston-super-Mare *p429* . . 01934 623501

Shipton, J D (Saunders Roberts) *A1 C1 E F1 L R1 S1* Evesham *p220*. 01386 442558

Shipton, J M (Goughs) *K1 Q L F1 B1* Devizes *p210* 01380 726913

Shipton, M M (Mullis & Peake) *S1 W* Chadwell Heath *p184* . . . 020 8599 2417 Romford *p366* 01708 784000

Shipton, T J M (Linklaters LLP) London EC2 *p54*. 020 7456 2000

Shipway, R R H (Radcliffes Le Brasseur) *M1 G J1* Westminster *p70*. 020 7222 7040

Shiramba, C (LG Lawyers) London SE1 *p50*. 020 7379 0000

Shire, A (Holman Fenwick Willan) *C1 Za Zb* London EC3 *p42*. 020 7264 8000

Shire, Ms P J (LG Lawyers) London SE1 *p50*. 020 7379 0000

Shireby, Mrs C H (Lamberts) *S1 S2 W* Paddock Wood *p344*. 01892 833456

Shires, Mrs K E (Potter Owtram & Peck) *T2 W* Haslemere *p243*. 01428 642321

Shirlaw, Mrs S B (Havering Magistrates' Court) Romford *p470* 0845 601 3600

Shirley, A E (Bawtrees LLP) *C1 S2 E* Witham *p435* 01376 513491

Shirley, M J (Stuart Hurrion & Green) *W C1 S1* Bexleyheath *p132* 020 8298 1595

Shirley, W (Howes Percival LLP) Norwich *p334* 01603 762103

Shirley, W J (John Shirley & Co) Burnham-on-Sea *p169*. . . . 01278 780202

Shirtcliffe, C S (Shirtcliffe & Reston Solicitors) *N K1 G S1 D1 J1 W Q H B1 Zv Zm Zl T1 T2 Zk L B2 S2* Thirsk *p411* 01845 526222

Shirtcliffe, Ms E (Shoosmiths) Nottingham *p339*. 0370 086 5000 / 0115 906 5000

Shmuel, G (CKFT) London NW3 *p17* 020 7431 7262

Shock, T G (Geldards LLP) *M1 N P G H J1* Nottingham *p337*. 0115 983 3650

Shockley, D J (Howlett Clarke Crowther Wood) *F1 G N O Q Zl* Brighton *p159* . . . .01273 327272 / 326341

Shoeb, S (Jefferies Essex LLP) *K1 K2 D1* Westcliff-on-Sea *p428* 01702 332311

Shoheth, Ms R E (Gard & Co) *S1 W K1 K3* Plymouth *p349*. 01752 668246

Shokar, Mrs K K (T G Baynes) *W* Bexleyheath *p132* 020 8301 7777

Shokunbi, A (Havillands) Romford *p366* 01708 766559

Shone, Miss D (Environment Agency (Anglian Region)) Peterborough *p468* 01733 371811

Shone, Miss J A (Anthony Collins Solicitors LLP) *Zr N X* Birmingham *p137* 0121 200 3242

Shone, M J (Hamilton Downing Quinn) *B1 C1 F1 G M1 N P T1 W Zb Ze Zi Zj* London WC1 *p38* 020 7831 8939

Shone, S D (CMS Cameron McKenna LLP) London EC3 *p17*. 020 7367 3000

Shopland, Ms E K (Squire Sanders (UK) LLP) Manchester *p310* 0161 830 5000

Shore, A (Zatman & Co) *C1 G K1 M1 N P J1 Zc Zj Zk* Manchester *p311* 0161 832 2500

Shore, V W (MMS Solicitors) *N* Withernsea *p436*. 01964 612318

Shori, R (Manches LLP) *R2* London WC2 *p58* 020 7404 4433

Shorney, Miss K (Hugh James) Cardiff *p179* 029 2022 4871

Shorrock, Mrs J H (Bury & Walkers LLP) *K3* Barnsley *p124*. 01226 733533

Shorrock, J R (KBL Solicitors) *C1 C2 Ze* Bolton *p149* 01204 527777

Short, Mrs A C (Andrew & Co LLP) Lincoln *p284*. 01522 512123

Short, Mrs A M (Forsters LLP) Westminster *p33*. 020 7863 8333

Short, Ms C S (Richmonds) *K1 D1 N V* Newcastle upon Tyne *p326* . 0191 232 2155

Short, D J (Cozens-Hardy LLP) *N L* Norwich *p334* 01603 625231

Short, G A (Blake Lapthorn) *E S1* Chandlers Ford *p184* 023 8090 8090

Short, Ms H (ABN Amro Management Services) London EC2 *p103* 020 7601 0101

Short, Mrs H (Pannone LLP) *E* Manchester *p308* 0161 909 3000

Short, J F (Franklin & Co) *S1 W T2 A1* Bakewell *p121*. 01629 814461

Short, J R (Taylor Vinters) *C1 C2* Cambridge *p176*. 01223 423444

Short, M G (FDC Law) *S2 E* Frome *p228* 01373 463311

Short, M J (Keoghs LLP) *N Q G* Bolton *p149* 01204 677000

Short, M R (Powell & Young) *S1 W A1 E L* Pocklington *p351* 01759 302113

Short, R N T (Clifford Chance) London E14 *p20*. 020 7006 1000

Short, T (Plexus Law (A Trading Name of Parabis Law LLP)) *N* Manchester *p309* 0844 245 4100

Short, Miss T A (Gregsons) *V L Q G Zh* Nottingham *p337*. 0115 941 1999

Shortall, Miss C L (DWF) *N Q J2 Zj* Liverpool *p287*. 0151 907 3000

Shorthouse, S T (Forbes) *E S1 L C1 W J1 A1 O R1 T2 Zl* Preston *p356* 01772 220022

Shortland, Ms D (The College of Law) London WC1 *p105*. 0800 289997

Shortland, Ms J L (Oliver Fisher) *L P S1 K1 M1 D1 F1 J1 G V Zh Zl Zp* London W11 *p32*. 020 3219 0145

Shortman, S L (South Norfolk District Council) Long Stratton *p463* 01508 533633

Shotnes, S J (Simons Muirhead & Burton) *Q Zk Ze* London W1 *p79* 020 7734 4499

Shotter, P (Glovers Solicitors LLP) *E Zl* London W1 *p36* 020 7935 8882

Shotton, Mrs E J (Darbys Solicitors LLP) *N Q G V Zh Zq Zr* Oxford *p343*. 01865 811700

Shovlin, I D (Higgs & Sons) *N Zr* Brierley Hill *p158*. 0845 111 5050

See p634 for the Key to Work Categories

Showan, R N (Forsters LLP) *S1*
Westminster *p33*. 020 7863 8333

Showell, S V (First Assist)
Sutton *p473* 020 8652 1313
Sutton *p403* 020 8661 7605

Shpaizer, M (Michael & Company)
Merton *p60* 020 8944 0877

Shrago, I C (Druces LLP) *E Zc C1 S2 R2 S1*
London EC2 *p27*. 020 7638 9271
London WC2 *p29* 020 7691 4000

Shreeves, M J (Barker Gooch & Swailes) *M1 N P K1 G H E S1 L*
Enfield *p218* 020 8366 3161

Shrimpton, Mrs E A (Keoghs LLP) *N Zj O Q A3 B2*
Coventry *p200*. 024 7665 8200

Shrimpton, H E (Robin Murray & Co) *D1 G J1 M1 W K1 H N P*
Chatham *p185*. 01634 832332

Shrimpton, J (Kennedys) *N Zq Zr*
London EC3 *p49*. 020 7667 9667

Shrimpton, Ms J E W (Tozers) *D1 D2 K1*
Plymouth *p350*. 01752 206460

Shrimpton, Mrs K J (Lumsdons Solicitors LLP)
Stourport-on-Severn *p399* . 01299 827766

Shrimpton, Mrs L (Keoghs LLP)
Bolton *p149* 01204 677000

Shrimpton, P (Kundert & Co) *S1 S2 E J1 L N R1 W B1*
Coventry *p200*. 024 7622 7741

Shrives, R M (Squire Sanders (UK) LLP) *J1 Zp Zi*
Leeds *p277* 0113 284 7000

Shropshall Clarke, Mrs A E D (Eastleys) *Q N J1*
Paignton *p345* 01803 559257

Shropshire, Miss A (Cancer Research UK)
London WC2 *p104*. 020 7242 0200

Shuba, F M (Taylor Walton LLP) *S1*
Luton *p295* 01582 731161

Shuff, S R (Cooper Sons Hartley & Williams) *N Zr K1 Zq J1*
Chapel-en-le-Frith *p184* . . . 01298 812138

Shufflebotham, A M (Addleshaw Goddard) *R2*
London EC1 *p4* 020 7606 8855

Shufflebottom, Ms K (Beswicks) *G H*
Stoke-on-Trent *p397*. 01782 205000

Shugar, D R (Macfarlanes) *C1*
London EC4 *p56*. 020 7831 9222

Shuja, Miss S (ELS Solicitors) *J1*
Ilford *p260*. 020 8262 5010

Shuker, M (Watson Burton LLP) *E S1*
Newcastle upon Tyne *p327* . 0845 901 2100

Shulman, E R (Chesham & Co) *K1 G M1 P H J1 N D1 L*
Barnet *p20*. 020 8205 3656

Shulman, H B (GH Cornish LLP) *C1 E L N P S1 T1 W Zc Zf Zl*
Ilford *p260*. 020 8090 0800

Shulman, J I (Shulmans) *C2 J1 C1 Zp M1 M2 W*
Leeds *p276* 0113 245 2833

Shurman, D J (Allen & Overy LLP)
London E1 *p5* 020 3088 0000

Shute, Mrs C (Eastleys) *W T2*
Paignton *p345*. 01803 559257

Shute, Mrs C (Osborne Clarke) *T1*
Bristol *p164* 0117 917 3000

Shute, J D (Torbay Council)
Torquay *p474* 01803 201201

Shutkever, Ms C M (Herbert Smith LLP) *C1 C2*
London EC2 *p40*. 020 7374 8000

Shutler, Ms K A (LG Lawyers)
London SE1 *p50*. 020 7379 0000

Shutler, M J (Turners Solicitors LLP) *N Zl C1 O Q Zq J1 Zr*
Bournemouth *p153*. 01202 291291

Shutler, T M (Rydon Group Ltd)
Forest Row *p458* 01342 825151

Shuttari, Ms F A (Shuttari Paul & Co) *D1 K1 G H J1 L N Q S1 W Zl Zc Zm*
Southall *p384* 020 8574 7151

Shuttleworth, A C (Menneer Shuttleworth) *S1 W E T1 J1 A1 R1 L Zd Zl Zx*
Bexhill *p132*. 01424 730630

Shuttleworth, C C (Jones Day) *O*
London EC4 *p46*. 020 7039 5959

Shuttleworth, Ms C W (DWF) *Zq Zj O Q C1 I F1 P B2 U2 Zu T2 T1 F2 Zg*
Manchester *p303* 0161 603 5000

Shuttleworth, I (Hodgson & Angus) *E S2 R1 Zc*
Stanhope *p394* 01388 528517
Harrogate *p240* 01423 566666

Shuttleworth, I R (Gordons LLP) *S2 S1 L E R1 R2 Zc*
Leeds *p273* 0113 227 0100

Shuttleworth, Miss L (Harthills) *G H*
Rotherham *p367*. 01709 377399

Sian, Ms D (Addleshaw Goddard)
London EC1 *p4* 020 7606 8855

Sian, H (Osborne Clarke) *C1*
Bristol *p164* 0117 917 3000

Siaw, K (Mountain Partnership) *L Zl G K1 Q K3 S1 V W*
Lewisham *p62*. 020 7732 3737

Sibbald, J (Wallers) *S1 K1*
Newcastle upon Tyne *p327* . 0191 261 2281

Sibbit, Miss P E (Sacker & Partners LLP) *Zo*
London EC2 *p76*. 020 7329 6699

Sibeon, R (Canter Levin & Berg) *N Q*
Liverpool *p287*. 0151 239 1000

Sibley, R (Leathes Prior) *E L*
Norwich *p334* 01603 610911

Sichel, D (Woolf Simmonds) *K3 K1 Zl O Q*
Westminster *p93*. 020 7262 1266

Siddall, Ms A L (Howells LLP) *K1 K3*
Sheffield *p376* 0114 249 6666

Siddall, B (Bray & Krais Solicitors)
London SW6 *p15* 020 7384 3050

Siddall, J A (VHS Fletchers Solicitors) *N*
Nottingham *p339*. 0115 959 9550

Siddique, F (DLC Solicitors Limited)
Darwen *p207* 01254 761234

Siddiqui, Mrs F (Siddiqui & Co) *G H*
Harrow *p242*. 020 8423 2400

Siddiqui, S (Bankside Law Ltd) *B2 G*
London SE1 *p9* 0844 745 4000

Siddiqui, Miss Z I (George Davies Solicitors LLP) *W*
Manchester *p303* 0161 236 8992

Siddle, P (Howard Kennedy LLP) *C1*
London W1 *p48* 020 7636 1616

Siddons, M A (Girlings) *K1 K3 W*
Margate *p312* 01843 220274

Siddons, P L B (Humphreys & Co)
Bristol *p163* 0117 929 2662

Side, Ms T (Scotts Holt & Sellars) *W*
Bromsgrove *p167* 01527 872711

Sidebottom, M B (Hegarty LLP) *N*
Peterborough *p347* 01733 346333

Sidell, Ms R L (Brighton & Hove Council - Legal Services)
Hove *p461*. 01273 290000

Siderfin, R (Hopkins) *Ze J1 C2 C1*
Mansfield *p311*. 01623 468468

Sideris, I (Simmons & Simmons)
London EC2 *p79*. 020 7628 2020

Sidey, Ms A (Stephenson Harwood) *Zb*
London EC2 *p82*. 020 7329 4422

Sidey, C P (Lupton Reddish) *S1 K1 E W L M1 P R1 A1 C1 Zc*
Rugby *p368* . . . . .01788 542241 / 565163

Sidgwick, B J B (Coodes) *Q*
Penzance *p346* 01736 362294

Sidhu, G S (Sidhu & Co) *S1 E C1 L B1 W F1 R1 N T1 Zi Zj Zl*
Birmingham *p142* 07831 293903

Sidhu, Ms M (MKS Solicitors) *S1 Zi W*
Southampton *p386*. 023 8039 6952

Sidhu, S (Penningtons) *Zi*
London EC2 *p66*. 020 7457 3000

Sidhu, S (Gross & Co) *Zi*
Bury St Edmunds *p171* . . . 01284 763333

Sidhu, T S (Birmingham City Council Legal & Democratic Services)
Birmingham *p449* 0121 303 2066

Sidiqui, S (Field Fisher Waterhouse LLP)
London EC3 *p31*. 020 7861 4000

Sidkin, S L (Fox Williams) *C1 C3 M1 M2 I Ze*
London EC2 *p33*. 020 7628 2000

Sidnick, J A (William Heath & Co) *S1 W C1 L*
Westminster *p40*. 020 7402 3151

Sidoli, P (Russell-Cooke LLP) *O*
London SW15 *p74*. 020 8789 9111

Sidwell, T J (Kerwoods) *W E C1 K4 Zm Zd*
Redditch *p362*. 01527 584444

Sieber, Miss F J (Pritchard Englefield) *K1*
London EC2 *p69*. 020 7972 9720

Siemonek, Mrs L C (Robert Lunn & Lowth) *S1 S2*
Stratford-upon-Avon *p400* . 01789 292238

Sierra, J (Ince & Co Services Ltd)
London E1 *p44* 020 7481 0010

Siew, Ms Y E M (Allen & Overy LLP)
London E1 *p5* 020 3088 0000

Siggs, Miss K (Chubb Bulleid) *D1 K1 K3*
Street *p400* 01749 836100

Sigler, P J (Michelmores LLP) *O M2*
Exeter *p221* 01392 688688
London W1 *p60* 020 7659 7660

Signey, G M (Roland Bardsley Homes Ltd)
Dukinfield *p457* 0161 330 5555

Signy, A (Clifford Chance)
London E14 *p20*. 020 7006 1000

Sigre, S (Turbervilles) *E W S1 T1 L F1 C1 J1 Zc Zn*
Uxbridge *p417*. 01895 201700
Uxbridge *p417*. 01895 201700

Sigsworth, M J (Clark Willis) *V Q F1 B1*
Darlington *p206* 01325 281111

Sigurdsson, R B (Howard Kennedy LLP) *O Q L*
London W1 *p48* 020 7636 1616

Sijuwade, A (Alfred James & Co)
Croydon *p204* 020 8681 4627

Siklos, Ms T (Harbottle & Lewis LLP) *Q*
London W1 *p38* 020 7667 5000

Silburn, Mrs J M (Jeanette Silburn) *S1 E W*
Alresford *p116* 01962 773777

Silcock, R (Mogers)
Bath *p127* 01225 750000

Silk, A (WBW Solicitors) *K3 K1*
Torquay *p413* 0870 701 4321

Silk, A M (Harveys) *K1 J1 Q D2 G F1*
Liss *p285* 01730 895000

Silk, Mrs H S D (Buckinghamshire County Council)
Aylesbury *p448* 01296 383653

Silke, T J (British Telecommunications PLC)
London EC1 *p104* 020 7356 6181

Sillett, A E W (Reading Borough Council)
Reading *p469* 0118 939 0900

Sillett, M (Cannings Connolly) *C1 C2 Zb*
London EC1 *p18*. 020 7329 9000

Sillis, P J (Collyer Bristow LLP) *C1 B1 I U2 C2*
London WC1 *p22* 020 7242 7363

Sillito, Miss J (Aaron & Partners LLP Solicitors) *J1*
Chester *p190* 01244 405555

Sillitto, Miss H E (Environment Agency (Anglian Region))
Peterborough *p468* 01733 371811

Sills, D G (Lee Bolton Monier-Williams) *E W C1 Ze Zl*
Westminster *p52*. 020 7222 5381

Sills, T M (Woodfines LLP) *S2 A1 E L W S1*
Sandy *p372* 01767 680251

Silman, G N (Finers Stephens Innocent LLP) *E C1 R1 T1 L I A1 W Zc Zd Zb*
London W1 *p32* 020 7323 4000

Silva, Mrs A S (Hodders)
London NW10 *p41*. 020 8965 9862

Silva, D (IBB Solicitors) *E R2 S2*
Uxbridge *p417*. 0845 638 1381

Silver, A S (Leonard Cheshire Disability) *C1 J1 F1 M1 Q T1 O B1 P Ze Zc Zb*
London SW1 *p105*. 020 7802 8200

Silver, D M (Rochman Landau LLP) *S2 C1 E R2*
London W1 *p72* 020 7544 2424

Silver, R (Silver Fitzgerald) *D1 D2 Q*
Cambridge *p175*. 01223 562001

Silver, R (Richard Silver) *G H J2 B2*
Manchester *p309* 0161 834 9494

Silver, R (Silver Shemmings LLP)
London SW1 *p78* 0845 345 1244

Silver, Miss S (Fishburns) *Q Zj N*
London EC3 *p32*. 020 7280 8888
London EC3 *p49*. 020 7667 9667

Silver, S R (United Cooperatives Ltd) *E S1 A1 R1 P L*
Rochdale *p451*. 01706 202020

Silverblatt, I J (Pritchard Englefield) *E L P R1 S1 S2*
London EC2 *p69*. 020 7972 9720

Silverman, Mrs F J (Frances J Silverman) *E J1 L S1 Zp Zq S2*
Billingshurst *p133* 01403 783696

Silverman, J T R (Silverman Sherliker LLP) *C1 C2 F1 I W Ze U1 F2*
London EC2 *p78*. 020 7749 2700

Silverman, Ms K (Lewis Silkin LLP)
London EC4 *p53*. 020 7074 8000

Silverman, M (IBB Solicitors) *Zv Zo*
Chesham *p189* 0845 638 1381

Silverman, M C (Streathers Solicitors LLP) *O Q N Ze*
London W1 *p84* 020 7034 4200

Silverman, S I (OGR Stock Denton) *N F1 H F2 G Zq M1 Zf*
London N3 *p64* 020 8349 0321

Silverman, T (Freedman Green Dhokia) *T2 W*
Camden *p34*. 020 7624 2981

Silverstein, R M (Browne Jacobson LLP) *O J1*
London EC3 *p16*. 020 7539 4900

Silverthorne, Miss V A (WBW Solicitors) *S1 E A1 W L Zd*
Exeter *p222* 01392 202404

Silverwood-Cope, T (Heald Solicitors) *O Q*
Milton Keynes *p317* 01908 662277

Silvester, Ms K A (Gateley LLP) *C1 C2*
Birmingham *p138* 0121 234 0000

Silvester, Mrs L K A (Environment Agency (North East Region))
Newcastle upon Tyne *p466* . 0191 203 4000

Silvestro, A W (Payne Marsh Stillwell) *Q J1 O*
Southampton *p386*. 023 8022 3957

Sim, C R (Hay & Kilner) *S1 P E L K1 W C1 Zi*
Newcastle upon Tyne *p325* . 0191 232 8345

Sim, I S (Howells LLP) *J1*
Sheffield *p376* 0114 249 6666

Sim, J A (Temple Heelis LLP) *B1 C1 D1 F1 J1 K1 L M1 N P Zp*
Windermere *p434* 01539 442455
Kendal *p264*. 01539 723757

Simanowitz, L (Bates Wells & Braithwaite London LLP) *Zd C1 Ze X*
London EC4 *p11*. 020 7551 7777

Simcox, Ms J L (AXA UK PLC)
London E22 *p103* 020 7920 5900

Simcox-Parry, Ms E (Stafford Borough Council)
Stafford *p472* 01785 619000

Sime, Ms J (Walkers) *G H Q N*
Rossendale *p367* 01706 213565

Simister, J (Alsters Kelley) *O Q*
Leamington Spa *p270* 0844 561 0100

Simister, Ms T J (Haworth Holt Bell Limited) *J1 K3 K1 J2 Q S1 C1 F1 O*
Altrincham *p116* 0161 928 7136

Simkins, Mrs C A (Arnold Thomson Limited) *E L A1 S1*
Towcester *p413* 01327 350266

Simkins, T A G (Simkins) *C1 E S1 S2 W*
Baldock *p121* 01462 892221

Simm, Mrs C P (May May & Merrimans) *W T2 Zd*
London WC1 *p59* 020 7405 8932

Simm, G (Stones Solicitors LLP)
Exeter *p222* 01392 666777

Simm, I D C (BBA Aviation PLC)
London W1 *p103* 020 7514 3999

Simm, P (Liverpool 8 Law Centre) *Zi*
Liverpool *p463*. 0151 709 7222
Liverpool *p285*. 0151 707 1212

Simmonds, B B (Aubrey Isaacson Solicitors) *N Q G J1 K1 F1*
Whitefield *p430* 0161 959 6000

Simmonds, Ms C (Grindeys LLP) *S1*
Stoke-on-Trent *p398*. 01782 846441

Simmonds, D J (DBL Talbots LLP)
Kidderminster *p265* 01562 749910

Simmonds, Ms J (East Sussex County Council)
Lewes *p463* 01273 481000

Simmonds, J F C (Simmonds Grant) *S1 S2 W N*
Oakham *p340* 01572 756866

Simmonds, J P (Simmonds Grant) *W S1 Zl*
Oakham *p340* 01572 756866

Simmonds, M (Beswicks) *Ze Q O*
Stoke-on-Trent *p397*. 01782 205000

Simmonds, M O (Simmonds Hurford)
Swansea *p405*. . . .01792 462729 / 641070

Simmonds, N R (Stephenson Harwood) *C1 Zo*
London EC2 *p82*. 020 7329 4422

Simmonds, R (Beswicks) *O E*
Stoke-on-Trent *p397*. 01782 205000

Simmonds, Miss R (Simmonds Solicitors) *D1 S2 E K3 K4 K1 S1 W*
Poole *p353* 01202 666417

Simmonds, W F C (Woolf Simmonds) *E S1 C1 L W N*
Westminster *p93*. 020 7262 1266

Simmons, Miss A (Samuel Phillips Law Firm) *D1 K1*
Newcastle upon Tyne *p326* . 0191 232 8451

Simmons, A (DWFM Beckman) *L S1 W S2*
Westminster *p25*. 020 7872 0023

Simmons, Ms C L (Dyne Solicitors Limited) *Zn S2 E P R2*
Chester *p190* 01829 773100

Simmons, G S (Simmons Stein) *E L S1 S2 D1*
Stanmore *p394* 020 8954 8080

Simmons, J A (Collyer Bristow LLP) *C1 Ze Zw Zf I U2*
London WC1 *p22* 020 7242 7363

Simmons, Ms J B (GH Cornish LLP) *J1 L*
Ilford *p260*. 020 8090 0800

Simmons, J K (ASB Law) *J1 O*
Maidstone *p298* 01622 656500

Simmons, J S (Simmons Gleek Solicitors) *E S1 L R1 B1 O W N G Zk Zv Zf*
London W1 *p79* 020 7580 9090

Simmons, N D (B K Ellis & Co) *S1 W E*
Borehamwood *p150* 020 8386 8686

Simmons, R P (Sacker & Partners LLP) *Zo*
London EC2 *p76*. 020 7329 6699

Simmons, S (Redferns) *C1 C2 E L R1 S1 Zc Zh Zl*
Harrow *p242*. 020 8424 7070

Simmons, S A (Kirwans) *G H*
Birkenhead *p134*. 0151 608 9078

Simmons, S B (Brightstone Law LLP) *O Q N J1 G B1 C2 C3 W Zj Ze Zc Zk Zb*
Elstree *p218*. 020 8731 3080

Simmons, T J (Gullands) *S2 E R2 A1 Zc S1 C1*
Maidstone *p299* 01622 678341

Simms, Mrs B (Flint Bishop Solicitors) *E*
Derby *p208* 01332 340211

Simms, J (Clarion Solicitors LLP) *C1*
Leeds *p272* 0113 246 0622

Simms, Miss J (Hewitsons) *A1*
Cambridge *p174*. 01223 461155

Simms, Mrs J A (Environment Agency (Wales)) *G H*
Cardiff *p453* 0870 850 6506

Simms, J F (Bower & Bailey) *S2 E W L Zl S1*
Oxford *p343*. 01865 311133

Simms, Mrs K (Sintons LLP) *I Ze C1 Zb C2 C3 F1 M1 B1 U2*
Newcastle upon Tyne *p326* . 0191 226 7878

Simner, P L (MFG Solicitors) *S1 L*
Kidderminster *p265* 01562 820181

Simoes, S A (Moorhead James LLP) *E S1 S2 Zl L B1*
London EC4 *p61*. 020 7831 8888

Simon, D (Collyer Bristow LLP) *W T2 Zd*
London WC1 *p22* 020 7242 7363

Simon, Mrs D M (Hertfordshire County Council)
Hertford *p460* 01992 555555

Simon, D P (Glaisyers) *K1 D1 N Zk Zl Zp*
Birmingham *p138* 0121 233 2971

Simon, J A (J A Simon & Co) *S1 P M1 L K1 F1 W J1*
Liverpool *p290*. 0151 256 6669

Simon, J N (Harvey Ingram LLP) *C1 J1 B1 O Q Ze Zp*
Leicester *p280*. 0116 254 5454

Simon, L (Radcliffes Le Brasseur)
Westminster *p70*. 020 7222 7040

Simon, P J (Wards Solicitors) *K1*
Staple Hill *p394* 0117 943 4800

Simon, P N (Thomas Simon)
Cardiff *p181* 029 2055 7200

Simon, P N (Thomas Simon) *C1 S2 E S1*
Cardiff *p181* 029 2055 7200

Simon, R F J (Moorhead James LLP) *C1 J1 Zza*
London EC4 *p61*. 020 7831 8888

Simon, Mrs S E (Burton Woolf & Turk) *Q K1 O W J1 T2 L B1 Zd Zl K3 Zc S1 Zq*
London EC1 *p16*. 020 7831 6478

Simonds, Mrs A E (Baches) *K1 D1 S1 W*
West Bromwich *p427* . 0121 553 3286 / 553 7076

Simone, N J (Geldards LLP) *O N Q B1 F1 Zc*
Derby *p208* 01332 331631

Simons, A M (Simons Levine & Co) *N Q K1 L S1 K3 W*
Barnet *p79*. 020 8446 4273

Simons, Ms M (The Johnson Partnership) *G H B2*
Derby *p209* 01332 370473

Simons, M (Blake Lapthorn) *R2*
London EC1 *p13*. 020 7405 2000

Simons, M (Seddons) *N O Q Zr Zi Zk*
Westminster *p77*. 020 7725 8000

Simons, Ms S A (Crossmans MTA) *K1 S1*
Cambridge *p174*. 01223 451442

6

Simons, Mrs S L (Harbottle & Lewis LLP) *Q Zf Ze O Zv*
London W1 *p38* 020 7667 5000

Simpkin, A G (Pannone LLP) *E R1 R2 S2 Zu*
Manchester *p308* 0161 909 3000

Simpkin, J R (Cunningtons) *S1 E L W*
Ilford *p259* 020 8553 0002

Simpkins, Ms N (Ellisons) *N*
Colchester *p197* 01206 764477

Simpson, A (Plexus Law (A Trading Name of Parabis Law LLP)) *N Q*
Evesham *p220* 01386 769160

Simpson, A D K (Northern Foods PLC)
Leeds *p461* 0113 390 0110

Simpson, A J (Alan Simpson & Co) *C1 S1 W K1 J1 N T2 L R1*
Rayleigh *p359* 01268 745406

Simpson, A J (Addleshaw Goddard) *C1 J1*
London EC1 *p4* 020 7606 8855

Simpson, A M (DWF) *E S2 S1 Zw*
Liverpool *p287* 0151 907 3000

Simpson, Mrs A T (Hudgell & Partners) *K1 N D1*
Greenwich *p43* 020 8854 1331

Simpson, B (Withers LLP) *C1 C2*
London EC4 *p92* 020 7597 6000

Simpson, Ms B M (Boodle Hatfield) *K1*
Oxford *p343* 01865 790744

Simpson, B R (Cripps Harries Hall LLP) *Q N O L Zh Zl*
Tunbridge Wells *p415* 01892 515121

Simpson, Mrs C A (Swinburne & Jackson LLP) *E S2 L*
Gateshead *p229* . 0191 477 2531 / 477 3222

Simpson, Miss C H (HM Land Registry - Durham (Boldon) Office) *S1*
Durham *p457* 0191 301 2345

Simpson, C J (Hayes & Storr) *W*
Fakenham *p223* 01328 863231

Simpson, C O (Holmes & Hills LLP) *N*
Braintree *p155* 01376 320456

Simpson, Mrs C R (Lincolnshire County Council Resources - Legal Services)
Lincoln *p463* 01522 552222

Simpson, D (Howells LLP) *G H*
Sheffield *p376* 0114 249 6666

Simpson, Ms D (Bristol City Council)
Bristol *p451* 0117 922 2000

Simpson, D B C (Coles Miller Solicitors LLP) *Zr N*
Poole *p352* 01202 673011

Simpson, Miss D L (Northamptonshire County Council) *E S1 L K1 Q V N*
Northampton *p467* 01604 236236

Simpson, E C F (BTG International Ltd)
London EC4 *p104* 020 7575 0000

Simpson, Miss E R (Andrew Jackson) *O Q*
Hull *p257* 01482 325242

Simpson, F (Stone King LLP) *Zd I*
Bath *p128* 01225 337599

Simpson, Ms F A (Crowell & Moring) *O Q B2 Zq B1*
London EC4 *p23* 020 7413 0011

Simpson, Miss F C (JWP Solicitors) *D1 D2 K1*
Wakefield *p418* 01924 387171

Simpson, Miss F J (Morrish Solicitors LLP) *N*
Leeds *p276* 0113 245 0733

Simpson, G (Harrow Solicitors & Advocates) *K1 L D1 K3*
Wealdstone *p424* 020 8863 0788

Simpson, G (York Magistrates)
York *p477* 01757 293500

Simpson, G J (Hayes & Storr) *Q N J1*
Fakenham *p223* 01328 863231

Simpson, G J (Laytons)
London EC4 *p52* 020 7842 8000
Milton Keynes *p317* . 0370 086 8300 / 01908 488300

Simpson, Miss H (DAC Beachcroft) *E*
Bristol *p162* 0117 918 2000

Simpson, I H (Ian Simpson & Co) *C1 E R1 C2 W T2 Zc*
Oldham *p341* 0161 622 4939

Simpson, J C (Hewitsons) *E*
Cambridge *p174* 01223 461155

Simpson, J F H (Henmans LLP) *J1*
Oxford *p343* 01865 781000

Simpson, Ms J H (Holmes & Hills LLP) *W*
Halstead *p238* 01787 475312

Simpson, Mrs J J (Manches LLP) *K1*
London WC2 *p58* 020 7404 4433

Simpson, J M (Sydney Mitchell)
Birmingham *p142* 0121 698 2200 / 0808 166 8827

Simpson, Mrs K M (Pemberton Greenish LLP) *L S1*
London SW3 *p66* 020 7591 3333

Simpson, Mrs L (Meikles) *K1 G H Q*
Bishop Auckland *p144* 01388 451122

Simpson, Ms L J (Fosters) *D1 D2 K1*
Norwich *p334* 01603 620508

Simpson, M (Bevans) *J1 J2 Q Zc*
Bristol *p161* 0117 923 7249

Simpson, M A (Walker Morris) *A3 E O Zq*
Leeds *p277* 0113 283 2500

Simpson, M A (Browne Jacobson LLP) *N Zj*
Nottingham *p336* 0115 976 6000

Simpson, M C (Squire Sanders (UK) LLP) *T1*
Leeds *p277* 0113 284 7000

Simpson, M J (Cadge & Gilbert) *D1 G H J1 K1 L N S1 V W*
Bungay *p168* 01986 893134

Simpson, N A (CVC Solicitors) *S1 S2 W Zl E L*
St Ives *p392* 01736 795456

Simpson, N C (Dunn Simpson & Co) *B1 C1 D1 E F1 J1 K1 M1 N*
Bridgwater *p158* 01278 424272

Simpson, N W (Hudgell & Partners)
Greenwich *p43* 020 8854 1331

Simpson, P (Paul Dodds Solicitors) *S1 S2 L V*
Wallsend *p419* 0191 263 6200

Simpson, P F (Squire Sanders (UK) LLP) *C2 C1*
London EC2 *p81* 020 7655 1000

Simpson, Mrs R (SAS Daniels LLP) *E L S1 A1*
Congleton *p198* 01260 282300

Simpson, R (Blake Lapthorn) *G H*
Chandlers Ford *p184* 023 8090 8090

Simpson, R (Salehs LLP) *C1 F1*
Manchester *p309* 0161 434 9991

Simpson, R I (Neves Solicitors) *S1 E W A1 C1 T1 L*
Harpenden *p239* 01582 715234

Simpson, Ms S (Squire Sanders (UK) LLP)
Manchester *p310* 0161 830 5000

Simpson, Mrs S (Watkins Stewart & Ross) *S1 R2 K3*
Ipswich *p263* 01473 226266

Simpson, S (Skadden Arps Slate Meagher & Flom (UK) LLP)
London E14 *p80* 020 7519 7000

Simpson, T (Ashurst LLP)
London EC2 *p7* 020 7638 1111

Simpson, Mrs T J (Lupton Fawcett) *N*
Leeds *p275* 0113 280 2000

Simpson, Ms V (Shakespeares)
Birmingham *p142* 0121 237 3000
Stratford-upon-Avon *p400* . . 0845 630 8833

Simpson, W (Irwin Mitchell LLP) *Zj*
Birmingham *p139* 0870 150 0100

Simpson-Scott, G (Colemans - CTTS) *Zr*
Kingston upon Thames *p267*. 020 8296 9966

Sims, B A (Sims Cook & Teague) *E C1 W T1 S1 A1 J1 R1 L Zd Zc Ze*
Thornbury *p411* 01454 414342

Sims, D (Treasury Solicitors Department) *O Q Zc I*
London WC2 *p110* 020 7210 3000

Sims, Miss H (Oxfordshire County Council)
Oxford *p468* 01865 792422

Sims, J D W (Sterratt & Co) *S1 K1 W L S2 K3 K4 J1*
Barnoldswick *p124* 01282 813731

Sims, J J (Waverley Borough Council)
Godalming *p459* 01483 523333

Sims, M S J (DLA Piper UK LLP) *C2 C1 B1 Zj*
London EC2 *p24* 0870 011 1111

Sims, N (Hibberts LLP) *A1 K4 T2 W*
Nantwich *p320* 01270 624225

Sims, P J (T R Harris Arnold & Co) *S1 L W S2 T2*
Gorseinon *p231* . . .01792 892166 / 891331

Sims, P R (Bazeley Barnes & Bazeley) *C1 S1 Q Zd*
Bideford *p132* 01237 473122

Sims, Miss R E (Norwich Union Insurance Group)
Norwich *p467* 01603 622200

Sims, R K (Denniss Matthews) *N Q E*
London SE20 *p27* . . 020 8778 7301 / 8778 7631

Sims, Miss Z C (Peter Peter & Wright) *S1 S2 E*
Bideford *p133* 01237 472233

Simson, C (Andrew & Co LLP) *E S1*
Lincoln *p284* 01522 512123

Sinclair Taylor, J (Russell-Cooke LLP) *Zd*
London SW15 *p74* 020 8789 9111

Sinclair, A (Stone Milward Rapers) *J1 K1 Q*
Chichester *p193* 01243 780211

Sinclair, Ms C (Resolution PLC)
Birmingham *p450* 01564 828888

Sinclair, Ms C M R (Financial Services Authority)
London E14 *p106* 020 7066 1000

Sinclair, F M (Tuckers) *G H*
Manchester *p310* 0161 233 4321

Sinclair, Mrs G (South Gloucestershire Council) *S1*
Thornbury *p474* 01454 868686

Sinclair, I P (Terence St J Millett) *E S1*
London SW7 *p82* 020 7581 7500

Sinclair, J (Stewarts Law LLP) *O C3 Q Zq A3*
Leeds *p277* 0113 222 0022

Sinclair, Ms J N (Bevan Brittan LLP) *J1 Zp*
London EC4 *p12* 0870 194 1000

Sinclair, J T (Brown & Emery) *G H*
Watford *p423* 01923 225255

Sinclair, Mrs L C (Country Land and Business Association Ltd)
London SW1 *p105* 020 7235 0511

Sinclair, P O (BRB (Residuary) Ltd)
London N1 *p104* 020 7904 5087

Sinclair, Miss R (City of Lincoln Council)
Lincoln *p463* 01522 881188

Sinclair, R J (Ellis-Fermor & Negus) *S1 W L Zd*
Ripley *p364* 01773 744744

Sinclair, Ms S (SAS Daniels LLP) *K1 D2 D1 K3*
Bramhall *p155* 0161 475 7680
Stockport *p396* 0161 475 7676

Sinclair, S (Clifford Chance)
London E14 *p20* 020 7006 1000

Sinclair, Ms T (Slee Blackwell) *K1 D1 D2 V*
Barnstaple *p125* 01271 372128

Sinclaire, N D (Boothroyds) *H G D1 M1 P K1 J1 L F1 Zp*
London SE6 *p14* 020 8690 4848

Sinden, Mrs J S (Janet Sinden & Co) *S1*
Hastings *p243* 01424 425285

Sinfield, G J (Hogan Lovells International LLP)
London EC1 *p42* 020 7296 2000

Sinfield, Ms O (Osborne Clarke) *J1*
London EC2 *p65* 020 7105 7000

Singer, Ms C (TV Edwards LLP) *K1*
London SE8 *p85* 020 7790 7000

Singer, Ms D (Barlow Lyde & Gilbert LLP) *N Q*
London EC3 *p10* 020 7247 2277

Singer, J R C (Onside Law) *Zw C1 C2*
London SW6 *p65* 020 7384 6920

Singer, L M (Laurence Singer Solicitor) *K1 K2 K3 D1*
Amersham *p117* 01494 431400

Singh, A (Dutton Gregory) *O Q Zq A3 Zj*
Southampton *p385* 023 8022 1344

Singh, A P (Jameson & Hill)
Hertford *p248* 01992 554881
Ware *p421* 01920 460531

Singh, D (Irwin Mitchell LLP) *B1*
Birmingham *p139* 0870 150 0100
Birmingham *p142* 0121 222 3000

Singh, D (Sydney Mitchell) *J1 B1 C1 C2 C3 E T1 R1*
Birmingham *p142* 0121 698 2200 / 0808 166 8827

Singh, G (G Singh) *D2 S2 E K3 K1 Zg Zi S1 W*
Ealing *p80* 020 8567 2661

Singh, G (Nandy & Co) *Zl Zg L Q F1 F2 V K1 Zp J1*
Newham *p63* 020 8536 1800

Singh, G L (HSK Solicitors) *E Q S1 S2 W*
Bolton *p149* 01204 526465
Manchester *p305* 0161 795 4818

Singh, H (Harbans Singh) *C1 E G H J1 K1 M1 S1 T1 V Zi Zl Zp*
Birmingham *p139* 0121 551 4496

Singh, H (Premier Solicitors)
Bedford *p130* 01234 358080

Singh, J (Royal Mail Group)
London EC4 *p109* 020 7250 2468

Singh, J (Davies & Partners) *J1 Q*
Birmingham *p137* 0121 616 4450

Singh, J (Gummer & Singh) *E G K1 L M1 N P S1 W Zi*
Hounslow *p253* 020 8572 6905

Singh, J (Howes Percival LLP) *C1*
Leicester *p280* 0116 247 3500

Singh, J N (John Neville & Co)
London SW9 *p63* 020 3372 4071

Singh, K (Hegarty LLP) *B1 Zr E K1 Q S1 F1 L N Zi*
Peterborough *p347* 01733 346333

Singh, Ms K (Singh Karran & Co) *W S2 S1*
Hounslow *p254* 020 8570 5776

Singh, K (Kerseys) *E S2*
Ipswich *p262* 01473 213311

Singh, Ms K (Coventry City Council)
Coventry *p456* 024 7683 4863

Singh, M (Thompsons (formerly Robin/Brian Thompson & Partners)) *N*
London SW19 *p87* 020 8947 4163

Singh, N (Judge & Priestley) *L N Zu R1 S1*
Bromley *p166* 020 8290 0333

Singh, Ms N P (Slater Bradley & Co) *K1 W D1 D2*
Wandsworth *p80* 020 8788 1008

Singh, R (Oldhams Solicitors & Advocates) *N Q Zq V*
Baldock *p121* 01462 895444

Singh, R (Petherbridge Bassra Solicitors) *G H M1 N B1 D1 F1 K1 L*
Bradford *p154* 01274 724114

Singh, R (Aubrey David) *B1 L O Q*
Westminster *p25* 020 7224 4410

Singh, R (Hoole & Co) *G H*
Bristol *p163* 0117 942 8871

Singh, S (Leport & Co) *G H Q*
Banbury *p122* . . . .01295 257328 / 268181

Singh, S (Davis Blank Furniss)
Manchester *p303* 0161 832 3304

Singh, Mrs S (Birmingham City Council Legal & Democratic Services)
Birmingham *p449* 0121 303 2066

Singh, S G (Ramsdens Solicitors)
Huddersfield *p256* 01484 821500

Singh, T R (Fisher Meredith) *Zi*
Lambeth *p32* 020 7091 2700

Singh-Dalal, Ms S (LG Lawyers)
London SE1 *p50* 020 7379 0000

Singh-Dalal, Ms S (Osborne Clarke) *C1*
London EC2 *p65* 020 7105 7000

Singh-Takhar, S (GCA Solicitors (Giffen Couch & Archer)) *E J1 K4 S1 W Zc C1 S2 Zh L R2 V*
Luton *p295* 01582 410041

Singleton, Miss A J (Singletons Austin Ryder) *E S1 L A1 M1 Zv Q O S2 N*
Enfield *p219* 020 8363 0101

Singleton, D H (Hadaway & Hadaway) *Zm*
North Shields *p330* 0191 257 0382
Newcastle upon Tyne *p326* . 0191 265 8817

Singleton, Mrs E S (Singletons) *C3 I*
Pinner *p349* 020 8866 1934

Singleton, J (Gordons LLP) *Q L Zq*
Leeds *p273* 0113 227 0100

Singleton, J H (Howard Kennedy LLP) *S1*
London W1 *p48* 020 7636 1616

Singleton, K I (Trethowans LLP) *M1 K1 P G H F1 L B1 Zl*
Salisbury *p371* 01722 412512

Singleton, Mrs M (Eatons) *C1 J1*
Bradford *p153* 0845 660 0660

Singleton, M J J (Singletons Austin Ryder) *S1 E W C1 L R1 M1 P Zv S2*
Enfield *p219* 020 8363 0101

Singleton, P A (Kevills) *S1 E W C1 L*
Chorley *p194* 01257 265711

Singleton, P J (Singleton Saunders Flood Solicitors) *S1 K1 Q F1 R2 J1 K3*
Dover *p213* 01304 240080

Singnagra, M (Boyes Turner) *B1 Zb*
Reading *p360* 0118 959 7711

Sinha, Ms A (Lomax Lloyd-Jones & Co) *G H K1*
Southwark *p55* 020 7703 6461

Sinker, Ms C L (DAC Beachcroft) *N J1*
Manchester *p303* 0161 934 3000

Sinker, Ms S (Sweetman Burke & Sinker) *S1 S2*
Ealing *p84* 020 8840 2572

Sinnamon, Miss M E (Tynedale District Council)
Hexham *p461* 01434 652200

Sinnerton, G J (Sinnertons) *S1 Zo J1 E S2 C1*
Banstead *p123* 01737 212000

Sinnett, A J (The Wood Glaister Partnership) *K1 E N P*
Solihull *p383* 0121 705 8151

Sinnett, Miss K R (David Rubie Mitchell & Co) *G H*
Sutton *p403* 020 8641 0575

Sinnett, P A (Bermans LLP) *C1 O F1 Zb B2 U2*
Liverpool *p286* 0151 224 0500

Sinnott, Miss C L (Birmingham City Council Legal & Democratic Services)
Birmingham *p449* 0121 303 2066

Sinnott, J V (Brain Sinnott & Co) *G H M1 K1 N P W J1 C1 B1*
Kingswood *p268* 0117 960 6880

Sinnott, M E (Russells) *C1 Ze Zf Zw*
London W1 *p75* 020 7439 8692

Sippitt, M A (ClarksLegal LLP) *C1 C3 J1 M1*
Reading *p360* 0118 958 5321

Sira, G S (G S Sira) *C1 E F1 G H K1 L M1 P*
Lichfield *p284* . . . .01543 254382 / 254383

Sirrell, J R L (Palmers) *G H J2*
Basildon *p126* 01268 240000

Sirs, J (Simmons & Simmons)
London EC2 *p79* 020 7628 2020

Sisson, D R (Hansells) *K1 D2 K3*
Norwich *p334* 01603 615731

Sisson, P J M (Barlow Robbins LLP) *Zq O Q Zb L B1*
Guildford *p235* 01483 562901

Sisson, T (Ashton Bond Gigg) *C1 Ze C3 I*
Nottingham *p335* 0115 947 6651

Sisson-Pell, M W (Carr & Co) *G H*
Huddersfield *p255* 01484 467860

Sit, Miss Y F (Irwin Mitchell LLP) *Zm*
Manchester *p306* 0870 150 0100

Sita-Lumsden, Mrs A R (Hextalls) *K1 D1 J1 Zg Zp*
London EC2 *p41* 020 7382 0700

Sitlani, D (Linklaters LLP)
London EC2 *p54* 020 7456 2000

Sitton, Ms S P E (Harrops) *S1 W*
Oxted *p344* 01883 712940

Siva, A (Marsh & McLennan Companies, Inc)
London EC3 *p108* 020 7357 1000

Sivadasan, S (Nathan & Co)
London SW19 *p63* 020 8542 1805

Sivakumar, P S (Samy & Co) *L M1 P S1 V Zc Zi Zl Zv Zh H N O Q*
Harrow *p242* 020 8861 2424

Sivanesan, Miss K (Robinsons) *Zd C1 Ze Zza*
Derby *p209* 01332 291431

Sivertsen, A P (John Morse Solicitors) *Q K1 S1 O E Zl W D1 N*
Swansea *p405* 01792 648111

Sivia, Miss R P (Levenes Solicitors) *G H*
Birmingham *p140* 0121 212 0000

Sivil, M R (Plexus Law (A Trading Name of Parabis Law LLP)) *N O Q*
Evesham *p220* 01386 769160

Sivill, Miss C E (Maples Teesdale LLP) *E*
London EC2 *p58* 020 7600 3800

Sivyer, J D (Simmons & Simmons)
London EC2 *p79* 020 7628 2020

Sivyour, Ms S (Ashurst LLP)
London EC2 *p7* 020 7638 1111

Skaanild, Ms L D (Barlow Lyde & Gilbert LLP)
London EC3 *p10* 020 7247 2277

Skanthabalan, Mrs I (Skanthabalan Solicitors) *S1 S2 E W L R1 R2*
London E15 *p80* 020 8555 2710

Skate, A (W R Joyce Solicitors LLP)
Cannock *p176* . . . .

Skeens, J M (Jeffrey Green Russell) *Zl*
London W1 *p46* 020 7339 7000

Skeggs, Ms A (Reynolds Porter Chamberlain LLP)
London E1 *p71* 020 3060 6000

Skehan, Miss L (Irwin Mitchell LLP) *O*
Birmingham *p139* 0870 150 0100

Skelding, B H (Lester Aldridge LLP) *E R1 L S1*
London WC2 *p53* 0844 967 0785

Skellorn, J J (Barker Gotelee Solicitors) *T2 W A1 T1 K4*
Ipswich *p262* 01473 611211

Skelton, D J (Bond Pearce LLP)
Plymouth *p349* 0845 415 0000

Skelton, J C (BRM Solicitors) *J1 O Q L*
Chesterfield *p191* 01246 555111

Skelton, J M (Macfarlanes) *C1*
London EC4 *p56* 020 7831 9222

Skelton, Ms J R (Bridge McFarland) *K1 K2*
Grimsby *p235* 01472 311711
Lincoln *p284* 01522 518888

Skelton, P J (Devonshires) *S2 E*
London EC2 *p27* 020 7628 7576

Skelton, R N E (Travers Smith LLP) *C1 C2*
London EC1 *p87* 020 7295 3000

See p634 for the Key to Work Categories

Skerrett, P E (Maclay Murray & Spens LLP) *C1 C2 Zj Zo*
London EC2 *p57* 020 7002 8500

Sketchley, Mrs C A (Carol Sketchley Solicitor) *J1 S1 W E A1 Zp Zv*
Coventry *p201* 01676 530514

Sketchley, P D (Dewes LLP) *A1 C1 E L R1 W*
Tamworth *p407* 01827 58391

Skiba, S J (Shakespeares) *O Q B1 Ze Zk*
Nottingham *p339* 0115 945 3700

Skilbeck, J (Fosters Law Limited) *E J1 K1 K4 L R1 S1 W Zi B1 F1 F2 S2 O Q*
Herne Bay *p248* 01227 283634

Skilbeck, P R (Terence St J Millett) *E S1*
London SW7 *p82* 020 7581 7500

Skill, Mrs J (Elliot Mather LLP)
Chesterfield *p192* 01246 231288

Skilton, D (Thomson Snell & Passmore) *Q*
Tunbridge Wells *p415* 01892 510000

Skilton, Ms N (Hutsby Mees) *D1 K3 K1*
Stafford *p393* 01785 259211

Skinnard, N P W (Blight Broad & Skinnard) *C1 A1 S1 T1 W R1 Zc Zn Zt E*
Callington *p173* 01579 382213

Skinner, A P (Palmers)
Grays *p233* 01375 484444

Skinner, Ms A P (L W Cole (Distributors) Ltd)
Birmingham *p449* 0121 351 2299

Skinner, C F (Great Yarmouth Borough Council)
Great Yarmouth *p459* 01493 856100

Skinner, D A P (Pillsbury Winthrop Shaw Pittman LLP) *I U2 C1*
London EC2 *p67* 020 7847 9500

Skinner, D E (Healys LLP) *N J1 Zj Q O*
Brighton *p159* 01273 685888

Skinner, D J (Batchelors Solicitors) *L Zh*
Bromley *p166* 020 8768 7000

Skinner, Ms E A (Drummonds) *N Q Zr*
Chester *p190* 01244 408300

Skinner, Ms H J (Lindops) *K3 D1*
Southend-on-Sea *p387* 01702 431791

Skinner, J (Armitage Sykes LLP) *D1 K1*
Huddersfield *p255* 01484 344140

Skinner, J W D (R W Skinner & Son) *G H K3 W*
Burton-on-Trent *p170* 01283 561694

Skinner, L (Kimbells LLP) *E S2*
Milton Keynes *p317* 01908 668555

Skinner, M (Farleys Solicitors LLP) *B1 Q N*
Manchester *p304* 0161 660 4254

Skinner, M (Kennedys) *N*
London EC3 *p49* 020 7667 9667

Skinner, Miss M C (Batemans) *F1 G H J1 L S1 W Zi*
Hemel Hempstead *p246* 01442 834344

Skinner, M E (McGrigors LLP)
London EC4 *p56* 020 7054 2500

Skinner, Ms N (Plexus Law (A Trading Name of Parabis Law LLP)) *Zj Zq*
London EC3 *p68* 0844 245 4000

Skinner, P A (Shell International Ltd)
London SE1 *p109* 020 7934 1234

Skinner, R (Challinors) *G H*
Birmingham *p136* 0121 212 9393

Skinner, R C V (R W Skinner & Son) *S1 G H M1 W P L K1 J1*
Burton-on-Trent *p170* 01283 561694

Skinner, S (Travers Smith LLP) *C1*
London EC1 *p87* 020 7295 3000

Skinner, W (Chambers & Hind (Stapleford)) *E K4 S1 T2 W S2*
Nottingham *p336* 0115 949 1141

Skinns, Ms J (Bindmans LLP) *N*
London WC1 *p12* 020 7833 4433

Skippen, G R (Fison & Co) *S1 W G H P M1 E K1 Zl*
Ipswich *p262* 01473 280900

Skipper, A D (Hogan Lovells International LLP)
London EC1 *p42* 020 7296 2000

Skipper, R J (Metropolitan Police Directorate of Legal Services)
London SW1 *p108* 020 7230 7210

Skipworth, T L (Manchester City Council)
Manchester *p465* 0161 234 5000

Skirrow, I G (Morrish Solicitors LLP) *N Q Zj*
Leeds *p276* 0113 245 0733

Skivington, G (Gordons Solicitors LLP)
Marlow *p313* 01628 487487

Skrein, S P M (Reed Smith LLP) *N Zf*
London EC2 *p71* 020 3116 3000

Skudra, A D (Hammon Oakley) *G H*
Coventry *p200* 024 7644 8585

Skulnick, J A (W M Furness & Son) *K1 G N J1 F1 V*
Irlam *p263* . . . . 0161 775 9962 / 775 6765

Skuse, G M (Spencer Skuse) *K1 N D1 L*
Cardiff *p181* 029 2034 3993

Skuse, I G (Piper Smith Watton LLP) *J1 M3 C1 Zi C2*
London SW1 *p68* 020 7222 9900

Skyers, Ms S E (British Telecommunications PLC)
London EC1 *p104* 020 7356 6181

Slack, A (LG Lawyers)
London SE1 *p50* 020 7379 0000

Slack, B (Speechly Bircham LLP)
London EC4 *p81* 020 7427 6400

Slack, J (Colemans - CTTS) *N*
Manchester *p302* 0161 876 2500

Slack, S (National Institutions of the Church of England, Legal Office)
London SW1 *p108* 020 7898 1000

Slack, Mrs S J (Ellis-Fermor & Negus) *K1*
Beeston *p130* 0115 922 1591

Sladdin, V A (Atteys)
Doncaster *p211* 01302 340400

Slade, Mrs A R (Peter Peter & Wright) *W K4*
Bideford *p133* 01237 472233

Slade, A T (Fidler & Pepper) *A1 C1 E L S1 W Zc Zn*
Sutton-in-Ashfield *p404* 01623 451111

Slade, B J B (Maitland Walker) *S2 C1 C3 Q E S1*
Minehead *p318* 01643 707777

Slade, D H (Slade Legal) *E S1 L C1 W F1 T1*
Wallingford *p419* 01491 839346

Slade, J R (J R Slade) *S1 G H D1 K2 N Q W T2 V Zv Zr Zl Zy*
Maldon *p300* 01621 828397

Slade, K (Thompsons (formerly Robin/Brian Thompson & Partners)) *N Q*
Liverpool *p290* 0151 224 1600

Slade, M A (Fidler & Pepper) *S1 L A1*
Kirkby-in-Ashfield *p268* 01623 451111

Slade, M J (Gordons) *S1 E*
Guildford *p236* 01483 451900

Slade, R J (Stephenson Harwood) *Za*
London EC2 *p82* 020 7329 4422

Sladen, G G (Scott Hyman & Co) *C1 E F1 L S1 T1*
Oldham *p340* 0161 628 7018

Slanickova, Ms S (Blake Lapthorn) *J1 Zp J2*
London EC1 *p13* 020 7405 2000

Slater, A (Geldards LLP)
Nottingham *p337* 0115 983 3650

Slater, A R (Roland Robinsons & Fentons LLP) *G H Zl*
Blackpool *p147* 01253 621432

Slater, C (Walker Morris) *K1*
Leeds *p277* 0113 283 2500

Slater, Ms D E (Robin Murray & Co)
Chatham *p185* 01634 832332

Slater, Mrs H (Suffolk Coastal District Council)
Woodbridge *p477* 01394 383789

Slater, Ms H J (Equality & Human Rights Commission)
Manchester *p464* 0161 829 8100

Slater, I (DWF) *N Zj J2*
Manchester *p303* 0161 603 5000

Slater, J A (Slater Bradley & Co) *G H K1 L O Q S1*
Wandsworth *p80* 020 8788 1008

Slater, Ms J C (Hay & Kilner) *D1 K1 L W Zm*
Wallsend *p419* 0191 262 8231

Slater, Mrs M (Conway & Co) *D1 K3 K1*
Harrow *p241* 020 8863 0535

Slater, M E (KBL Solicitors) *O*
Bolton *p149* 01204 527777

Slater, N D (DLA Piper UK LLP) *E S2 R2*
Sheffield *p375* 0870 011 1111

Slater, P (Addleshaw Goddard)
London EC1 *p4* 020 7606 8855

Slater, P D S (Hand Morgan & Owen) *S2 S1 E L*
Stafford *p393* 01785 211411

Slater, Mrs R E (Pannone LLP) *K1*
Manchester *p308* 0161 909 3000

Slater, R E H (Simmons & Simmons)
London EC2 *p79* 020 7628 2020

Slater, Miss V (Follett Stock LLP) *Q O J1*
Truro *p414* 01872 241700

Slater, Mrs V L (Croftons) *N*
Manchester *p302* 0161 214 6180

Slater, W A J L (Laytons) *O Q Ze L Zq*
London EC4 *p52* 020 7842 8000

Slater-Reay, Ms R (Higgs & Sons)
Kingswinford *p268* 01384 342100

Slaters, M (Bryan Cave) *Zo*
London EC2 *p19* 020 7207 1100

Slater-Williams, Mrs J (Salmons) *K3 K1 D1*
Stoke-on-Trent *p398* 01782 639827

Slatner, Miss N (Darlingtons) *E S1 S2*
Edgware *p217* . . 020 8952 0033 / 8951 6666

Slatter, A K (Charles Russell LLP) *S1 E S2*
London EC4 *p19* 020 7203 5000

Slattery, Mrs E (Corbett & Co International Construction Lawyers Ltd) *Zc*
Teddington *p409* 020 8614 6200

Slattery, Miss E T (Hogan Lovells International LLP)
London EC1 *p42* 020 7296 2000

Slattery, Miss K (Russell-Cooke LLP) *Zd*
London SW15 *p74* 020 8789 9111

Slattery, M B (Haworth & Nuttall) *S1 W S2*
Great Harwood *p234* 01254 884253
Blackburn *p145* 01254 272640

Slavin, B M (Barry Slavin & Co) *E C1 G H*
London W1 *p80* 020 7612 9010

Slavin, Ms J (Guillaumes Solicitors) *K1 K3*
Weybridge *p430* 01932 840111

Slavin, R (Irwin Mitchell LLP) *Q*
Leeds *p274* 0870 150 0100

Slawinski, J M (Carr & Co) *G H*
Huddersfield *p255* 01484 467860

Sledge, D (Property Law Partners)
Woking *p437* 01483 768629

Sledmore, Miss C R (Rollits LLP) *O Q K3 K1*
Hull *p258* 01482 323239

Sleeman, C (Dobson & Sleeman)
Middlesbrough *p315* 01642 231707

Sleeman, Mrs L (Ambrose Appelbe) *W*
London WC2 *p6* 020 7242 7000

Sleigh, C T (Sleigh & Son) *L S1 S2 W K4*
Droylsden *p213* 0161 370 2198
Droylsden *p213* 0161 370 9524

Sleigh, S T (Sleigh Son & Booth) *L S1 S2 W J1*
Droylsden *p213* 0161 370 9524

Sleight, T (Prettys)
Chelmsford *p187* 01245 295295

Sleightholme, J (Elborne Mitchell LLP)
London EC3 *p29* 020 7320 9000
London EC4 *p86* 020 7300 7000

Sless, Ms T (DAC Beachcroft) *N Zj*
London EC4 *p24* 020 7242 1011

Slettengren, Miss C L (Dairy Crest Group PLC)
Esher *p458* 01372 472285

Slight, A (Fanshaw Porter & Hazlehurst) *N*
Birkenhead *p134* 0151 647 4051

Slight, Miss C E (Cable & Wireless)
London WC1 *p104* 020 7315 4000

Slimming, M P (Powell Eddison Freeman & Wilks) *N Q S2 K1 L G J1 H A1 Zc Zl Zq Zr Zv Zk*
Harrogate *p240* 01423 564551

Slinger, I (Harvey Ingram LLP) *S1 E*
Leicester *p280* 0116 254 5454

Slinger, Miss I (Frettens Solicitors) *K1 D1 K3*
Christchurch *p194* 01202 491777

Slingo, Ms C (DAC Beachcroft)
Bristol *p162* 0117 918 2000

Slingsby, C A (Howard Kennedy LLP) *C1 B1 E M2 M1 J1 T2 W Zi Ze Zc Zj*
London W1 *p48* 020 7636 1616

Sloan, Ms C A (Sloan & Co) *L N O S1*
London W1 *p80* 020 7917 2865

Sloan, D S (Allen & Overy LLP)
London E1 *p5* 020 3088 0000

Sloan, G J D (Leelanes Solicitors LLP) *A1 C1 E L S1 W*
London EC3 *p52* 020 7220 9410

Sloan, S T (Derrick Bridges & Co) *K1 S1 Q G M1 E L F1 C1 D1*
Barnet *p123* 020 8449 7326

Sloane, Mrs C (Berry & Berry) *D1 K3 K1*
Maidstone *p299* 01622 690777

Sloane, N (Roy Foreman & Co) *G Q H*
Grimsby *p235* 01472 355262

Slocombe, M (Martyn Slocombe & Co) *C1 C2 C3 E J1 F1 F2 Zc A1 S2 X R2 R1 Zz W*
Malvern *p300* 01684 574001

Slomski, P (Calderdale Metropolitan BC Corporate Services Directorate)
Halifax *p460* 01422 357257

Sloper, Miss K (Bristows) *Ze Q*
London EC4 *p15* 020 7400 8000

Slorick, M A (Mackrell Turner Garrett) *C1 E R1*
Woking *p437* 01483 755609

Slosarska, Miss K M (Nottinghamshire County Council Legal Services Division)
West Bridgford *p475* 0115 977 3478

Slot, P (Burt Brill & Cardens) *E S2 Zl C1 J1*
Brighton *p159* 01273 604123

Slough, P J (The Grech Gooden Partnership LLP)
Cardiff *p178* 029 2022 2255

Slough, S (Clarke Willmott) *K1 S1 W E*
Bristol *p162* 0845 209 1000 / 0117 305 6000

Slowe, R (SJ Berwin LLP)
London EC4 *p75* 020 7111 2222

Sly, S (DLA Piper UK LLP) *O A3 Q Zc Zq*
Sheffield *p375* 0870 011 1111

Slynn, R M (Allen & Overy LLP)
London E1 *p5* 020 3088 0000

Smale, C E S (Peter Peter & Wright) *W T2 Zd K4 Zo*
Bideford *p133* 01237 472233

Smales, Mrs A L (Hartley & Worstenholme) *S1 E W*
Castleford *p183* 01977 732222

Small, C G (Glanvilles) *W T2 K4*
Havant *p244* 023 9249 2300

Small, D C (Chattertons Solicitors) *K1 G Q M1 P N D1 H J1 L Zl Zi Zj*
Stamford *p393* 01780 764145

Small, D R (The Owen-Kenny Partnership) *K1 Zl*
Chichester *p193* 01243 532777

Small, Miss E A F P (Forsters LLP)
Westminster *p33* 020 7863 8333

Small, Miss E J (Fraser Brown) *Q O W*
Bingham *p133* 01949 830812

Small, G P (Horwich Cohen Coghlan) *Q*
Manchester *p305* 0161 830 4600

Small, Ms J (Woolwich PLC)
Bexleyheath *p449* 020 8298 5000

Small, Ms L (Wallers) *S1*
Newcastle upon Tyne *p327* . 0191 261 2281

Small, Miss L (Harrison Clark LLP) *N Zm*
Cheltenham *p188* 01242 269198
Worcester *p439* 01905 612001

Small, Ms L A (Barlow Lyde & Gilbert LLP)
London EC3 *p10* 020 7247 2277

Small, S (Russell-Cooke LLP) *L*
London WC1 *p74* 020 7405 6566

Small, T P (Spearing Waite LLP) *F1 L N Zk Q Zm Zr*
Leicester *p281* 0116 262 4225

Smallcombe, A K (Hannays Solicitors and Advocates) *G H*
South Shields *p383* . . 0191 456 7893 / 455 5361

Smallcombe, Ms L A F (Birkett Long LLP) *N*
Colchester *p197* 01206 217300

Smalley, Miss E (Williscroft & Co)
Bradford *p155* 01274 305380

Smalley, M D (Martin Smalley & Co) *G H J1*
Nottingham *p339* 0115 955 6555

Smalley, Mrs P A (Alcock & Smalley) *S1 W*
Macclesfield *p297* 01625 431530

Smalley, W A (Huntingdonshire District Council)
Huntingdon *p461* 01480 388388

Smallman, G J (Wrigleys Solicitors LLP) *Zd*
Sheffield *p377* 0114 267 5588

Smallman, J P B (Paul Davidson Taylor) *S1 E*
Horsham *p253* 01403 262333
Worthing *p441* 01903 234064

Smallwood, C S C (Watson Farley & Williams)
London EC2 *p90* 020 7814 8000

Smallwood, Mrs E A (Lancashire County Council)
Preston *p469* 01772 254868

Smallwood, Mrs L J (Michelmores LLP) *E R2 S2 X Zx*
Exeter *p221* 01392 688688

Smallwood, Ms M A (SNR Denton) *C1 E L R1 S1 A1 Zc Zd*
London EC4 *p75* 020 7242 1212

Smallwood, R C (T A Matthews) *S1 A1 S2*
Hereford *p248* 01432 352121

Smark, D (Freeman Johnson) *K1 D1 M1 P N S1 W G H*
Durham *p214* . . 0191 386 4843 / 386 9619

Smart, Mrs C F (HM Land Registry - Plymouth)
Plymouth *p468* . . . .01752 636000 / 636123

Smart, Mrs D M (Taylor & Emmet LLP) *W T2 T1 K4*
Sheffield *p377* 0114 218 4000

Smart, J A (Hodge Jones & Allen LLP) *G H*
London NW1 *p41* 020 7874 8300

Smart, J A (Freeth Cartwright LLP) *E*
Nottingham *p337* 0115 936 9369

Smart, Miss J B (Metcalfes) *K1 K2 S1*
Bristol *p164* 0117 929 0451

Smart, J R (Lamb & Smart) *C1 E L S1 T1*
New Milton *p321* 01425 613434

Smart, K (Keith Smart & Co)
Cwmbran *p206* 01633 872031

Smart, M J (North Devon District Council) *S1 W T1 K1 P M1 D1 L R1*
Barnstaple *p448* 01271 327711

Smart, P C (Walker Morris) *C1*
Leeds *p277* 0113 283 2500

Smart, P J (Blackhams Solicitors) *S1 E W C1 T2 Zm S2*
Birmingham *p135* 0121 233 6900

Smart, R J (Wilson Browne) *S1 E L C1 A1 W Zl*
Wellingborough *p425* 01933 279000

Smartt, Ms F (Russell-Cooke LLP) *J1*
London SW15 *p74* 020 8789 9111

Smeath, Mrs G M (Alan Smeath & Co) *W S1 T1 A1 K1 E C1 L*
Woburn Sands *p436* .01908 584307 / 584331

Smeath, R J (Clarke Willmott)
Taunton *p408*0845 209 1000 / 0117 305 6000

Smedley, D A (Walker Morris) *J1 O Q Zo*
Leeds *p277* 0113 283 2500

Smedley, Mrs L J (Blake Lapthorn) *C1 I*
Chandlers Ford *p184* 023 8090 8090

Smedley, O (Clarke Willmott)
Bristol *p162* 0845 209 1000 / 0117 305 6000

Smee, Ms A N (Gates & Moloney) *K4 W*
Lancing *p270* 01903 766046

Smee, C A (Jaswal Johnston Boyle) *S1 S2 E C1 O Q N*
London W1 *p46* 020 7317 1540

Smee, H (Henry Smee & Co) *O N S1 C1 E J1 B1 K1 L S2*
London N20 *p80* 020 8446 3131

Smeed, M B (Streeter Marshall) *D1 K1*
Croydon *p205* 020 8680 2638

Smellie, D C (Farrer & Co LLP)
London WC2 *p31* 020 3375 7000

Smellie, D J (B P Collins LLP) *C1 J1 T1 B1 Zb Zf Zj*
Gerrards Cross *p229* 01753 889995

Smellie, R (Fenwick Elliott) *O Q Zc Zi A3 P Zj R2*
London WC2 *p31* 020 7421 1986

Smerdon, E (Reynolds Porter Chamberlain LLP) *O N Q Zj*
London E1 *p71* 020 3060 6000

Smerdon, Ms K E (Boyes Turner) *N*
Reading *p360* 0118 959 7711

Smethurst, J D (Russell & Russell) *N*
Bolton *p150* 01204 375700

Smillie, A C (Underhill Langley & Wright) *J1 S1 S2*
Bridgnorth *p157* 01746 764171
Wolverhampton *p438* 01902 423431

Smirles, Ms M C (DWF) *E S2*
Liverpool *p287* 0151 907 3000

Smith, A (Lester Morrill) *G H*
Leeds *p275* 0113 245 8549

Smith, A (Reynolds Porter Chamberlain LLP)
London E1 *p71* 020 3060 6000

Smith, Mrs A (Hopkins) *S1 W*
Nottingham *p337* 0115 910 5555

Smith, Mrs A (Wannop Fox Staffurth & Bray) *W K4*
Worthing *p442* 01903 228200

Smith, Mrs A (Kimbells LLP) *J1*
Milton Keynes *p317* 01908 668555

Smith, A (Longmores) *K1*
Hertford *p248* 01992 300333

Smith, A (Ashfords LLP) *C2 Zb*
Bristol *p160* 0117 321 8000

Smith, A (Kitsons LLP)
Exeter *p221* 01392 455555

Smith, Miss A (Debenhams Ottaway)
St Albans *p390* 01727 837161

Smith, A (QualitySolicitors Gruber Garratt)
Oldham *p341* 0161 665 3502

Smith, A (Beale and Company Solicitors LLP) *O Q N G I Zc Ze A3 Zq J2*
London WC2 *p11* 020 7240 3474

Smith, A (CMS Cameron McKenna LLP)
London EC3 *p17* 020 7367 3000

6

Smith, Mrs A C (Butcher & Barlow LLP) *K1 K3*
Bury *p170* 0161 764 5141

Smith, A C (Smith Brown & Sprawson) *G H D1*
Luton *p295* 01582 876900

Smith, A C (Child & Child) *O Q C1 J1 L A3*
London SW1 *p20* 020 7235 8000

Smith, Mrs A C (Crangle Edwards) *D1 G H K1 W S1*
Stretford *p400* . 0161 865 2993 / 865 7816 / 865 5875

Smith, A C (British Telecommunications PLC)
London EC1 *p104* 020 7356 6181

Smith, A D (Squire Sanders (UK) LLP) *B1*
Leeds *p277* 0113 284 7000

Smith, A D (The Smith Partnership) *F1 J1 K1 Zm S1 N Zl*
Burton-on-Trent *p170* 01283 548282

Smith, A F (Eastwoods Solicitors) *G Zr*
London EC4 *p28*. 020 3137 4800

Smith, A F (The Endeavour Partnership LLP) *C1*
Stockton-on-Tees *p397* . . . 01642 610300

Smith, A G (Davies & Partners) *E*
Gloucester *p230*. 01452 612345

Smith, A H (Simmons & Simmons) *O C1 Ze Zf*
London EC2 *p79*. 020 7628 2020

Smith, Mrs A J (Cumbria County Council)
Carlisle *p453*. . . . .01228 607374 / 607351

Smith, A J (DB Law) *B1 F1 K1 N D1 Q J1 V*
Camborne *p173* 01209 712428

Smith, A J (Grindeys LLP) *A1 C1 E R1 Zb Zc Zd Zh*
Stoke-on-Trent *p397*. 01782 846441

Smith, Ms A J (Harrisons Solicitors LLP) *F1 F2 G H J1 L N O Q S1 S2 A3*
Welshpool *p425* 01938 552545

Smith, A J (Ashley Smith & Co) *G H B2*
Lewisham *p80*. 020 8463 0099

Smith, A K (Archers Law LLP) *N*
Stockton-on-Tees *p396* . . . 01642 636500

Smith, A M (Pillsbury Winthrop Shaw Pittman LLP) *I U1 Ze U2 C1*
London EC2 *p67*. 020 7847 9500

Smith, A M (Bircham Dyson Bell)
Westminster *p13*. 020 7227 7000

Smith, A P (Rich & Carr Freer Bouskell)
Leicester *p281*. 0116 253 8021

Smith, A R (Castle Point Borough Council)
Benfleet *p449* 01268 882200

Smith, B (Ford & Warren) *M1 O Q Zr*
Leeds *p273* 0113 243 6601

Smith, Miss B A (Stanford & Lambert) *S1 K1 D1 W E C1 L J1 F1*
Newcastle upon Tyne *p327* . 0191 232 6226

Smith, B H (Reed Smith LLP) *Zf*
London EC2 *p71*. 020 3116 3000

Smith, B M (Browne Jacobson LLP) *R1 P Zs*
Nottingham *p336*. 0115 976 6000

Smith, B W (Durham County Council)
Durham *p457* 0191 383 3513

Smith, C (Ashurst LLP) *C1*
London EC2 *p7* 020 7638 1111

Smith, Miss C (Derek Smith & Co) *D1 F1 K1 S1 N*
Bolton *p150* 01204 389089

Smith, Ms C (Bartletts Solicitors) *Q N*
Liverpool *p286*. 0151 227 3391

Smith, Ms C (Scott Rees & Co) *N Q*
Skelmersdale *p381* 01695 722222

Smith, Ms C (Squire Sanders (UK) LLP)
London EC2 *p81*. 020 7655 1000

Smith, Mrs C (Sykes Anderson LLP) *J2 Q N S1*
London EC2 *p85*. 020 3178 3770

Smith, Ms C (Linklaters LLP)
London EC2 *p54*. 020 7456 2000

Smith, C (Maclay Murray & Spens LLP)
London EC2 *p57*. 020 7002 8500

Smith, Miss C (Davis Blank Furniss) *N Q K1 J1*
Glossop *p230* 01457 860606

Smith, Mrs C A (Knights Solicitors LLP) *W T2 Zd*
Newcastle under Lyme *p323*. 01782 619225

Smith, C A (Barlow Lyde & Gilbert LLP)
London EC3 *p10*. 020 7247 2277

Smith, C A (Lewes Smith) *S1 W*
Lewes *p283* 01273 483455

Smith, C A (Leonard Gray) *K1 G I V L*
Chelmsford *p186*. 01245 504904

Smith, Mrs C F (Foot Anstey) *B1 D1 F1 J1 K1 L M1 P V*
Exeter *p221* 01392 411221

Smith, C G (Law Brand) *B1 C1 E J1 K1 L Zc Zv*
Stevenage *p395*. 01438 367373

Smith, Miss C H (Penningtons) *E*
London EC2 *p66*. 020 7457 3000

Smith, Mrs C J (Knowles Benning) *G H Zl*
Luton *p295* 01582 798000

Smith, C J (Wilson Browne) *M1 N P B1 F1 J1 Ze Zl*
Leicester *p281*. 0116 251 7181

Smith, C J (Blaser Mills) *J1 C1 O Q E*
High Wycombe *p249*. 01494 450171

Smith, C J (McMillan Williams) *Zr N*
Croydon *p205* 01689 848311

Smith, Ms C L (Crutes) *O*
Newcastle upon Tyne *p324* . 0191 233 9700

Smith, Mrs C L P (Jennings) *K1 V D1 Q*
Llanelli *p292*. 01554 772331

Smith, Ms C M (Allen & Overy LLP)
London E1 *p5* 020 3088 0000

Smith, C R J (SAS Daniels LLP) *Q F2 F1*
Stockport *p396*. 0161 475 7676

Smith, D (Field Fisher Waterhouse LLP)
London EC3 *p31*. 020 7861 4000

Smith, Miss D (Thomas Simon) *D1 D2 K1*
Cardiff *p181* 029 2055 7200

Smith, D (PCB Solicitors LLP) *K1 N V*
Telford *p409*. 01952 403000

Smith, D (Hill Hofstetter LLP) *N Zq*
Solihull *p382*. 0121 210 6000

Smith, D (Anthony Gold) *L Zg*
London SW16 *p6* 020 7940 4000

Smith, D (Fasken Martineau LLP) *C1 C2 B1*
London W1 *p31* 020 7917 8500

Smith, D (Jacklyn Dawson) *S1 W K4*
Newport *p328* 01633 262952

Smith, D (Jones Day) *E*
London EC4 *p46*. 020 7039 5959

Smith, D (Pumfrey & Lythaby) *S1 W L E S2*
Orpington *p342* 01689 833657

Smith, Ms D (Pattinson & Brewer) *N Q*
London WC1 *p66* 020 7400 5100

Smith, D C (Turbervilles)
Uxbridge *p417*. 01895 201700
Uxbridge *p417*. 01895 201700

Smith, D C (Turbervilles) *G H D1 K1 Zl*
Uxbridge *p417*. 01895 201700
Uxbridge *p417*. 01895 201700

Smith, D F (Thomas Solicitors) *S1 E L W C1 Zv*
Long Eaton *p293* 0115 946 1061

Smith, D H (Fairbairn Smith & Co) *Q N L K1 D1 Zl*
London N17 *p30*. 020 8808 4901

Smith, D I (Over Taylor Biggs) *E R2 S2 Zc*
Exeter *p222* 01392 823811

Smith, D J (JWP Solicitors) *G H*
Wakefield *p418* 01924 387171

Smith, D J (Barlow Lyde & Gilbert LLP) *Zq Zj O*
London EC3 *p10*. 020 7247 2277

Smith, D J (Harvey Roberts) *S1 K1 N W Q E D1 O J1 L Zk Zc Zl*
Stockport *p395*. 0161 443 2828

Smith, D J (Blake Lapthorn) *T2 W*
London EC1 *p13*. 020 7405 2000

Smith, D K F (Cartwright King) *C1 E J1 T1 B1*
Nottingham *p336*. 0115 958 7444
Nottingham *p338*. 0115 958 6262

Smith, D M (Oxford City Council)
Oxford *p468* 01865 249811

Smith, D M (Harvey Ingram LLP) *E S2*
Leicester *p280*. 0116 254 5454

Smith, D M W (Allen & Overy LLP)
London E1 *p5* 020 3088 0000

Smith, D R (Beetenson & Gibbon) *K1 H G D1 M1 P V F1 L*
Grimsby *p235* 01472 240251

Smith, Mrs D W (SAS Daniels LLP) *W*
Bramhall *p155*. 0161 475 7680

Smith, E (Linklaters LLP)
London EC2 *p54*. 020 7456 2000

Smith, Mrs E (Bennett Griffin) *C1 J1 Zl O Q*
Ferring *p225*. 01903 229999

Smith, Miss E (Beswicks) *E C1*
Stoke-on-Trent *p397*. 01782 205000

Smith, Miss E (Dunn & Baker) *D1 K3 K1*
Exeter *p221* 01392 285000

Smith, Ms E (Ingrams) *K4 T2 W*
York *p445* 01904 520600

Smith, Ms E (Paul Crowley & Co) *G H*
Liverpool *p287*. 0151 264 7363

Smith, Mrs E A (Curtis) *C1 C2 E*
Plymouth *p349*. 01752 204444

Smith, E M M (Glaisyers) *G H M1 Zg*
Birmingham *p138* 0121 233 2971

Smith, Mrs E S (Howard Kennedy LLP) *N Q O Zq Zf Zk Ze*
London W1 *p48* 020 7636 1616

Smith, Miss F A (Forsters LLP) *W T2*
Westminster *p33*. 020 7863 8333

Smith, F J (Smith & Copsey) *K1 G H S1 V W D1 L N Q*
Wallsend *p419*. 0191 262 4428

Smith, Ms F J (MSP Legal Services LLP) *S1 W E C1 R1 S2*
Hartlepool *p243* 01429 232204

Smith, F R (Harrison Clark LLP) *A1 A2 S2 E S1 R1 R2*
Cheltenham *p188* 01242 269198

Smith, G (Nockolds)
Bishop's Stortford *p144* . . . 01279 755777

Smith, G (Prince Evans)
Ealing *p69*. 020 8567 3477

Smith, G (Lawsmiths)
Sale *p370* 0161 972 7700

Smith, Mrs G (Foot Anstey) *B1 Zq*
Exeter *p221* 01392 411221
Exeter *p221* 01392 688688

Smith, Mrs G A (Davies & Partners) *E*
Gloucester *p230*. 01452 612345

Smith, G C H (Roythornes LLP) *A1 A2 T1 T2 W Zo*
Newmarket *p327*. 01638 561320

Smith, G G (Thomas Magnay & Co) *E K4 K1 Q R1 S1 W*
Gateshead *p229*. 0191 477 3333

Smith, G H (Hansells) *W S1*
Norwich *p334* 01603 615731

Smith, G J H (Bird & Bird LLP) *O I Q Ze*
London EC4 *p13*. 020 7415 6000

Smith, G M (Steele & Son) *E G H Q S1 S2 W*
Colne *p198* 01282 868000

Smith, G Q (Graham Smith Property Lawyers) *C1 F1 J1 L M1 P S1*
Watford *p424* 01923 227212

Smith, G R E (Allen & Overy LLP)
London E1 *p5* 020 3088 0000

Smith, G S (Bircham Dyson Bell)
Westminster *p13*. 020 7227 7000

Smith, Ms H (The College of Law Chester)
Chester *p454* 0800 289997

Smith, Miss H (Boyes Turner) *O Q Zq L Zk*
Reading *p360* 0118 959 7711

Smith, Mrs H (Clarkson Wright & Jakes Ltd) *K1*
Orpington *p341* 01689 887887

Smith, Ms H A (Glaisyers) *K1 D1*
Birmingham *p138* 0121 233 2971

Smith, H C (Lynch Hall & Hornby)
Harrow *p242*. 020 8864 0722

Smith, Miss H D (Hart Reade) *T2 W*
Eastbourne *p215*. 01323 727321

Smith, H E (Andrew Jackson) *N P M1 J1 C1*
Hull *p257* 01482 325242

Smith, H M (Fladgate LLP)
London WC2 *p32* 020 3036 7000

Smith, Miss H M (Heptonstalls LLP) *Zr*
Scunthorpe *p373*. 01724 289959

Smith, I (Canter Levin & Berg) *Q N*
St Helens *p391* 01744 634141
Birkenhead *p134*. 0870 780 1870

Smith, I A D (Middle Level Commissioners)
March *p465* 01354 653232

Smith, I G (Bevirs) *E Zo S2 S1*
Calne *p173* 01249 814536

Smith, I J (Dixon Ward) *T2 S1 W E S2*
Ham *p238* . . .020 8546 0225 / 8549 2615

Smith, I P (Crane & Staples) *C1 E S1 S2 C2*
Welwyn Garden City *p425* . . 01707 329333

Smith, I S (HM Coroners Chambers) *S1 W*
Stoke-on-Trent *p472*. 01782 234777

Smith, J (Whitfields) *G B2 H*
Formby *p227* 01704 878501

Smith, J (Brabners Chaffe Street) *C1*
Manchester *p301* 0161 836 8800

Smith, Ms J (Bircham Dyson Bell)
Westminster *p13*. 020 7227 7000

Smith, Ms J (Anthony Collins Solicitors LLP) *Zd*
Birmingham *p137* 0121 200 3242

Smith, J (JS Law)
Market Harborough *p465*. . . 0870 380 4000

Smith, J (Smith-Rahman Associates)
London N10 *p80*. 020 7566 8244

Smith, Miss J (The Endeavour Partnership LLP)
Stockton-on-Tees *p397* . . . 01642 610300

Smith, Miss J (Palmers) *S1 S2 E*
Basildon *p126* 01268 240000

Smith, Ms J (British Waterways Board)
Watford *p475* 01923 226422

Smith, Miss J A (Percy Hughes & Roberts) *N O Zq B2 Zj*
Birkenhead *p134*. 0151 666 9090

Smith, J A (JSP Solicitors) *D2 D1 K1 K3 J1 K2 Q N S1 V W*
Skegness *p380* . . . 01754 762252 / 01522 537353

Smith, Miss J A (Capsticks Solicitors LLP) *N Zr D1*
London SW19 *p18*. 020 8780 2211

Smith, J A (Wiseman Lee LLP) *G H*
Waltham Forest *p92* 020 8215 1000

Smith, J A V (Farrer & Co LLP)
London WC2 *p31* 020 3375 7000

Smith, J B (Herbert Smith LLP) *O*
London EC2 *p40*. 020 7374 8000

Smith, J B (Tuckers) *G H V*
Manchester *p310* 0161 233 4321

Smith, J C (Sheltons) *K1 J1*
Nottingham *p339*. 0115 955 3444

Smith, Miss J C (William Sturges & Co) *O Q J1*
Westminster *p84*. 020 7873 1000

Smith, J C (Bower & Bailey) *E C1 S2 S1*
Oxford *p343* 01865 311133
Witney *p436* 01993 705095

Smith, J D (DAC Beachcroft) *N O Q Zj*
London EC4 *p24*. 020 7936 2222

Smith, J D (Derek Smith & Co) *S1 W E*
Bolton *p150* 01204 389089
Bury *p171* 01706 829750

Smith, J D (Wrigley Claydon) *S2 S1 Zl R1*
Oldham *p341* 0161 624 6811

Smith, J D F (Dickinson Dees) *T1*
Newcastle upon Tyne *p324* . 0191 279 9000

Smith, Mrs J E (Rothera Dowson) *E L S1 W*
Nottingham *p338*. 0115 916 5200

Smith, Miss J E (Thompsons (formerly Robin/Brian Thompson & Partners)) *N G*
Leeds *p277* 0113 205 6300

Smith, J E (Keelys LLP) *S1 W E K1 L*
Lichfield *p284* 01543 420000

Smith, J G (Betts & Co Solicitors Ltd) *G H*
Ashford *p119* 01304 213172

Smith, J G (Thos R Jones & Son) *E S1 W N P C1 D1 K1 L B1 Zh Zi Zj*
Liverpool *p289*. 0151 928 0715

Smith, J H (J H Smith) *G H*
Carlisle *p182*. 01228 521383

Smith, J J (Broxtowe Borough Council)
Beeston *p449* 0115 917 7777

Smith, J M (Potter Rees (Serious Injury) Solicitors)
Manchester *p309* 0161 237 5888

Smith, J M (Poppleston Allen) *Zl*
Nottingham *p338*. 0115 953 8500

Smith, Mrs J M (Adam Douglas & Son) *W A1 S2 S1 K4*
Alnwick *p115*. 01665 602363

Smith, J M W (Moseleys) *D1 D2 J1 J2 K1 K2 F1 V Zl*
Lichfield *p284* 01543 414100

Smith, J O (Blandy & Blandy) *O A3 Zc J1 Ze B1 Zz Zq*
Reading *p360* 0118 951 6800

Smith, Miss J P (Blaser Mills) *W T2*
High Wycombe *p249*. 01494 450171

Smith, J P (Symes Bains Broomer) *S1 S2 W*
Scunthorpe *p373*. 01724 281616

Smith, Miss J P (Rawlins Davy PLC) *S1 W*
Bournemouth *p152*. 01202 558844
Christchurch *p194* . .01202 473413 / 473414

Smith, J R (Darwin Gray)
Cardiff *p178* 029 2082 9100

Smith, J R S (Chivers Walsh Smith and Irvine & Co) *S1 E A1 C1 W T1 L F1 R1 B1 Zi Zl*
Bradford *p153* 01274 740077
Baildon *p121*. 01274 583106

Smith, J S (SJ Berwin LLP)
London EC4 *p75*. 020 7111 2222

Smith, J S (Thomson & Bancks LLP) *E L S1 S2*
Tewkesbury *p410* 01684 299633

Smith, Mrs J S (EMI Music Publishing Ltd) *C1 Zf Ze*
London W8 *p106* 020 3059 3059

Smith, J S (Nantes) *E K4 A1 S1 T1 T2 W*
Bridport *p158* 01308 422313

Smith, J S (Ashfords LLP) *G K1 N Q*
Tiverton *p412* 01884 203000

Smith, J S (Bartletts Solicitors) *Q N*
Liverpool *p286*. 0151 227 3391

Smith, Mrs K (Stewarts Law LLP) *N*
London EC4 *p83*. 020 7822 8000

Smith, Mrs K (Worksop Magistrates Court)
Worksop *p477* 01909 486111

Smith, Mrs K (Hains & Lewis Ltd) *S1 S2 V*
Haverfordwest *p244* 0845 408 0125

Smith, K (Andrew & Co LLP) *F1 J1 Q*
Lincoln *p284*. 01522 512123

Smith, K (Favell Smith & Lawson Solicitors) *S1 W A1 L R1*
Sheffield *p375* 0114 272 4381

Smith, Mrs K (First Title Insurance PLC)
London EC4 *p106* 020 7832 3100

Smith, K (Barlow Rowland) *W T1 S1 C1 E A1 L T2 Zm Zd K4*
Accrington *p114* 01254 300400

Smith, K (AMEC PLC)
Knutsford *p462* 01565 683123

Smith, Mrs K (Oxford Law Group) *K1 D1 D2*
Oxford *p344* 01865 297300

Smith, Ms K A (Babergh District Council)
Hadleigh *p459* 01473 822801

Smith, Miss K A (Jameson & Hill) *Q O J1 W L N*
Hertford *p248* 01992 554881

Smith, K C (DAC Beachcroft) *L Q O*
London EC4 *p24*. 020 7936 2222

Smith, Miss K L (Jacklyn Dawson) *K1 K3 Zl D1*
Newport *p328* 01633 262952

Smith, Miss K L (Pickworths) *S1 S2 L*
Hemel Hempstead *p247* . . . 01442 261731

Smith, K M (MacDonald Oates LLP) *S1 S2*
Midhurst *p316* 01730 816711

Smith, Ms K M (Cumbria County Council)
Kendal *p462*. 01539 773123
Manchester *p465* 0161 234 5000

Smith, Mrs K M (Larken & Co) *W S1*
Newark *p322* 01636 703333

Smith, K R (MacDonald Oates LLP) *A3 C2 E S1 S2 Zc C1*
Petersfield *p348* 01730 268211

Smith, Ms L (Freeth Cartwright LLP) *Zr*
Nottingham *p337*. 0115 936 9369

Smith, L (Laderman & Co) *K3 W S1 S2 E K1 K4 L D1*
Redbridge *p51*. 020 8530 7319

Smith, Miss L (Preston Borough Council)
Preston *p469* 01772 906101
Birmingham *p450* 0121 626 5143

Smith, Ms L (Dickinson Dees) *J1*
Newcastle upon Tyne *p324* . 0191 279 9000

Smith, Miss L (Wortley Redmayne Kershaw) *J1 O Q Zl*
Chelmsford *p187*. 01245 491122

Smith, L (Red Kite Law) *Q N*
Haverfordwest *p244* 01437 763332

Smith, Ms L (Kitsons LLP) *T1 T2 V W*
Torquay *p413* 01803 202020

Smith, Ms L (Walker Morris)
Leeds *p277* 0113 283 2500

Smith, L C (Brunswicks LLP) *Q O Zm J1 Zq L A3*
Birkenhead *p134*. 0870 766 8400

Smith, Mrs L C (Bowcock Cuerden LLP) *J1 O Q J2 B1 A3 Zq*
Nantwich *p320*. 01270 611106

Smith, L D (Boys & Maughan) *W*
Ramsgate *p359* 01843 595990

Smith, Mrs L J (Blight Broad & Skinnard) *W Zm K4 S1*
Callington *p173* 01579 382213

Smith, Mrs L K (Treasury Solicitors Department)
London WC2 *p110*. 020 7210 3000

Smith, Mrs L N (Ramsdens Solicitors) *C1 S2 E*
Huddersfield *p256* 01484 821500

Smith, Ms L S (Eastgate Assistance Ltd) *G H Zl*
Colchester *p455*. 0870 523 4500

Smith, Miss L S (Owen White) *L J1 Q*
Slough *p382*. 01753 876800

Smith, M (MSP Legal Services LLP) *S1 W E C1 T2 R1 B1 O F1 K4 Zd Zj*
Hartlepool *p243* 01429 232204

Smith, Mrs M (Rogers & Norton) *W*
Norwich *p335* 01603 666001

Smith, M (Stephens & Scown) *K1 D1*
Exeter *p222* 01392 210700

See p634 for the Key to Work Categories

Smith, M (Underwood Solicitors LLP)
Westminster *p89* 020 7526 6000

Smith, M (Cartwright King)
Derby *p208* 01332 346111

Smith, M (Field Fisher Waterhouse LLP)
London EC3 *p31* 020 7861 4000

Smith, M (Cartwright King) *G H*
Nottingham *p336* 0115 958 7444
Nottingham *p338* 0115 958 6262

Smith, M (Plexus Law (A Trading Name of Parabis Law LLP))
Manchester *p309* 0844 245 4100

Smith, M (Colman Coyle LLP) *O Q Zq*
Islington *p22* 020 7354 3000

Smith, Ms M (Doyle Clayton Solicitors Limited) *J1 Zp*
London E14 *p27* 020 7038 8051
London EC2 *p27* 020 7329 9090

Smith, Ms M (Fraser Dawbarns) *K1 D1 Q*
Wisbech *p435* 01945 461456

Smith, M (Ashurst LLP) *Zb Zc*
London EC2 *p7* 020 7638 1111

Smith, M (Mincoffs Solicitors LLP) *K1 K2*
Newcastle upon Tyne *p325* 0191 281 6151

Smith, M (Michael Smith & Co) *S1 L G C1 J1 N W*
Ipswich *p263* 01473 226231

Smith, Miss M A (Capron & Helliwell) *W K4 T2*
Stalham *p393* 01692 581231

Smith, M A (Hayes & Storr) *W*
Fakenham *p223* 01328 863231

Smith, Mrs M A (Lodders Solicitors LLP) *R1 E*
Stratford-upon-Avon *p400* 01789 293259

Smith, M A (Coventry City Council)
Coventry *p456* 024 7683 4863

Smith, M A (Simons Muirhead & Burton)
London W1 *p79* 020 7734 4499

Smith, M A (Coles Miller Solicitors LLP)
Bournemouth *p151* 01202 293226

Smith, M A (Kitsons LLP) *S1 L S2*
Newton Abbot *p329* 01626 203366

Smith, Ms M C (City of Bradford Metropolitan District Council)
Bradford *p451* 01274 752236

Smith, M D (Owen White) *R2 N*
Slough *p382* 01753 876800

Smith, Mrs M E (Mincoffs Solicitors LLP) *K1 D1 G*
Newcastle upon Tyne *p325* 0191 281 6151

Smith, M E (K&L Gates LLP) *O Q J2 A3 N R1 Zq Zc Zj*
London EC4 *p47* 020 7648 9000

Smith, M E (Forbes) *C1 E L S1*
Blackburn *p145* 01254 54374

Smith, M G (dgb Solicitors) *C1 S2 E Zh L R2 S1*
Chatham *p184* 01634 304000

Smith, M J (Squire Sanders (UK) LLP) *Zo*
London EC2 *p81* 020 7655 1000

Smith, M J (Ashurst LLP)
London EC2 *p7* 020 7638 1111

Smith, M J (Mills & Co) *O M2 Q Za Zj Zb*
Newcastle upon Tyne *p325* 0191 233 2222

Smith, M J (Wallers) *E S1 J1 P K1 G Zl*
Newcastle upon Tyne *p327* 0191 261 2281

Smith, M M (Gill Turner Tucker) *C1 E S1 W J1 P Ze Zd Zc*
Maidstone *p299* 01622 759051

Smith, M N S (Biscoes) *N E S2 J1 Q L*
Waterlooville *p423* 023 9225 1257

Smith, M P (Bassets) *K1 M1 H G F1 J1 N P W S1 Zp Ze Zb*
Gillingham *p229* 01634 575464

Smith, M R (DLA Piper UK LLP)
Leeds *p272* 0870 011 1111

Smith, M R (Muckle LLP) *Zc O Q A3*
Newcastle upon Tyne *p325* 0191 211 7777

Smith, M R (Simmons & Simmons)
London EC2 *p79* 020 7628 2020

Smith, M S (Spearing Waite LLP) *C1 C2*
Leicester *p281* 0116 262 4225
Leeds *p277* 0113 284 7000

Smith, M T (Speechly Bircham LLP) *E*
London EC4 *p81* 020 7427 6400

Smith, M T (Martin T Smith) *S1 W E S2*
Leighton Buzzard *p282* 01525 374183

Smith, M W (Shell International Ltd) *E S1 Zh*
London SE1 *p109* 020 7934 1234

Smith, Ms N (Franklins LLP) *K1*
Milton Keynes *p317* 01908 660966

Smith, N (Veale Wasbrough Vizards) *C1 C2*
Bristol *p165* 0117 925 2020

Smith, N F (Alexander & Co) *D1 P H F1 J1 M1 G K1 N O Q Zl*
Derby *p208* 01332 600005
Derby *p208* 01332 600011

Smith, N I (Veale Wasbrough Vizards) *S1 S2 W*
London EC4 *p89* 020 7405 1234

Smith, Miss N J (Trethowans LLP) *A1 E S1*
Salisbury *p371* 01722 412512

Smith, Miss N J (Salford City Council)
Swinton *p473* 0161 794 4711

Smith, Miss N J (Weightmans LLP)
Liverpool *p291* 0151 227 2601

Smith, N J (Forbes) *N O Q*
Blackburn *p145* 01254 54374

Smith, N M (Taylor Wessing)
London EC4 *p86* 020 7300 7000

Smith, N P (Cartwright Cunningham Haselgrove & Co) *O C1 C2 J2*
Waltham Forest *p19* 020 8520 1021
Woodford Green *p439* 020 8506 5200

Smith, N R (Ellis Jones) *N Q O F1 Zl*
Bournemouth *p151* 01202 525333

Smith, N R P (Shacklocks) *W T2*
Mansfield *p312* 01623 626141

Smith, Mrs N S (North East Derbyshire District Council)
Chesterfield *p455* 01246 231111

Smith, Miss N S (Winterbotham Smith Penley LLP) *K3 K1 W*
Dursley *p214* 01453 541940

Smith, N S (George Ide LLP) *E S2 S1*
Chichester *p192* 01243 786668

Smith, N S (Smith Gadd & Co) *K1 D1 F1 J1 L N Q O*
Horsham *p253* 01403 271222

Smith, N W (Currey & Co) *T2 W Zd*
Westminster *p24* 020 7802 2700

Smith, Miss P (Bird & Bird LLP) *W Zd T2*
London EC4 *p13* 020 7415 6000
London WC1 *p59* 020 7405 8932

Smith, P (Hill Dickinson LLP) *E S1 L*
Liverpool *p288* 0151 600 8000

Smith, P (Holman Fenwick Willan)
London EC3 *p42* 020 7264 8000

Smith, P (Richmonds) *K1 S1 M1 P N G D1 E B1*
Newcastle upon Tyne *p326* 0191 270 1711
Newcastle upon Tyne *p326* 0191 232 2155

Smith, P A (Warners Solicitors) *C1 C2 J1 F1 F2 Ze Zw*
Tonbridge *p412* 01732 770660

Smith, P A (Oxley & Coward Solicitors LLP) *N*
Rotherham *p367* 01709 510999

Smith, Mrs P A (Belcher Frost) *W*
Emsworth *p218* 01243 377231

Smith, P A (Crown Prosecution Service Durham) *G H D1 S1 K1 W L M1*
Durham *p457* 0191 383 5800

Smith, P A (Manches LLP)
London WC2 *p58* 020 7404 4433

Smith, P A (Thompsons (formerly Robin/Brian Thompson & Partners)) *N*
Plymouth *p350* 01752 675810

Smith, P D (McKinnells) *N L Q O Zl*
Lincoln *p284* 01522 541181

Smith, P H (The Smith Partnership) *E C1 R1 A1 L S1*
Derby *p209* 01332 225225

Smith, P J (Patrick Smith & Co) *D1 F1 G H K1 M1 P*
Wantage *p421* 01235 772212

Smith, P J (Smith Jones Solicitors) *N O Q*
Kenilworth *p264* 01926 859933
Burnley *p169* 01282 855400

Smith, Ms P J (DWF) *C1 C2 Zd*
Manchester *p303* 0161 603 5000

Smith, P J (Eldridges) *W N*
Ryde *p369* 01983 562241

Smith, P J (E Smith & Co) *S1 S2 W*
Kington *p268* 01544 231010

Smith, P J (Eastgate Assistance Ltd)
Colchester *p455* 0870 523 4500

Smith, P J E (Boyes Turner) *B1*
Reading *p360* 0118 959 7711

Smith, Capt P J M (The Salvation Army)
London EC4 *p109* 020 7236 5222

Smith, P J M (Smith Llewelyn Partnership) *S1 W A1 B1 C1 E T1 S2*
Swansea *p405* 01792 464444

Smith, P M (Beaumont Legal) *S1 S2*
Wakefield *p418* 0845 122 8100
Wakefield *p418* 01924 373467

Smith, P M (SAS Daniels LLP) *S2 S1*
Stockport *p396* 0161 475 7676

Smith, P N (Lanyon Bowdler LLP) *S1 E*
Wellington *p425* 01952 244721

Smith, P N (CMS Cameron McKenna LLP)
London EC3 *p17* 020 7367 3000

Smith, P P W (Buss Murton LLP) *E S2 S1 C1*
Tunbridge Wells *p415* 01892 510222

Smith, P R (Harvey Escott & Co) *S2 W S1 C1*
Burnham-on-Crouch *p169* 01621 784838 / 784839
Brentwood *p156* 01277 210021

Smith, P R (Richardson Smith & Co) *G H K1 L Q W X Zi Zl*
Chesham *p189* 01494 772773

Smith, P R C (Crown Prosecution Service Avon & Somerset)
Bristol *p451* 0117 930 2800

Smith, P T B (Preston Redman) *W T2 K4 K1*
Bournemouth *p152* 01202 292424

Smith, P W (Russells) *W*
London W1 *p75* 020 7439 8692

Smith, P W C (Pearson & Pearson) *S1 W A1 C1 K1 E N*
Kendal *p264* 01539 729555
Kirkby Lonsdale *p268* 01524 271222

Smith, Ms R (Hartlaw LLP) *B1 Q O*
Wetherby *p429* 01937 547000

Smith, R (John Boyle & Co)
Redruth *p362* 01209 213507

Smith, Mrs R (Pontefract Magistrates Court)
Pontefract *p468* 01977 691600

Smith, Miss R A (Ayres Waters)
Stockport *p395* 0161 480 5229

Smith, R A (Barlow Lyde & Gilbert LLP) *T1*
London EC3 *p10* 020 7247 2277

Smith, R A (Addleshaw Goddard) *T1*
London EC1 *p4* 020 7606 8855

Smith, R A (Manches LLP) *P E M1 R1 Zn*
Oxford *p343* 01865 722106

Smith, R A (Roy Smith & Co) *S1 W L E*
Christchurch *p194* 01202 473413 / 473414

Smith, Mrs R A L (Rhondda Cynon Taff County Borough Council)
Pentre *p468* 01443 424300

Smith, R D (Walter Jennings & Sons) *S2 E S1 W*
London NW5 *p46* 020 7485 8626

Smith, R E (Clifford Chance)
London E14 *p20* 020 7006 1000

Smith, R F (Scott Rees & Co) *N Q O J1 P F1 K1*
Skelmersdale *p381* 01695 722222

Smith, R G (Myer Wolff) *G H B2*
Hull *p257* 01482 223693

Smith, R G (Bolt Burdon) *W*
Islington *p14* 020 7288 4700

Smith, R G (Barlow Robbins LLP) *S2 E*
Woking *p436* 01483 748500

Smith, R H (Chattertons Solicitors) *K1*
Horncastle *p252* 01507 522456

Smith, R H (Thompsons (formerly Robin/Brian Thompson & Partners)) *J1 N*
Nottingham *p339* 0115 989 7200

Smith, R J (hlw Keeble Hawson LLP)
Sheffield *p376* 0114 276 5555

Smith, R J (Allen & Overy LLP)
London E1 *p5* 020 3088 0000

Smith, R J (LG Lawyers) *C1 Zo Zj*
London SE1 *p50* 020 7379 0000

Smith, R J (Robert Smith & Co)
Stroud *p401* 01453 757435

Smith, R J E (K&L Gates LLP) *A1 E L*
London EC4 *p47* 020 7648 9000

Smith, Miss R L (Baily Gibson) *K1*
High Wycombe *p249* 01494 442661

Smith, R L (Orange PCS Ltd) *O*
Bristol *p452* 0870 376 8888

Smith, R L (Network Rail) *M1 P N L Zg*
London NW1 *p108* 020 7557 8000

Smith, R L (Goldbergs) *Q J1 L O B1 F2 N Zq F1 Zk Zp*
Plymouth *p349* 01752 660023

Smith, R M J (Smith Bates) *Q N G L S1 W F1 J1 Zl*
Lyndhurst *p296* 023 8028 3414

Smith, R T (Wilkins) *N L F1 O*
Aylesbury *p121* 01296 424681

Smith, R W R (Smith Law Partnership) *A1 C1 S2 E S1*
Braintree *p155* 01376 321311

Smith, Ms S (Tollers LLP) *K1*
Milton Keynes *p317* 01908 396230
Northampton *p332* 01604 258558

Smith, S (J A Kemp & Co)
London WC1 *p48* 020 7405 3292

Smith, Miss S (PCB Solicitors LLP) *K1*
Shrewsbury *p379* 01743 248148

Smith, S (Berwins Solicitors Limited) *K1*
Harrogate *p240* 01423 509000

Smith, Mrs S (Cumberland Ellis Peirs) *K1 K2 N Q L O D1*
London WC1 *p23* 020 7242 0422

Smith, Ms S (Sintons LLP) *Zl*
Newcastle upon Tyne *p326* 0191 226 7878

Smith, S (AZrights Solicitors) *Ze U2*
Islington *p3* 020 7700 1414

Smith, S (Blake Lapthorn) *U2 C3 U1 C1*
Oxford *p342* 01865 248607

Smith, Ms S (Greenland Houchen Pomeroy) *K1 K3*
Norwich *p334* 01603 660744

Smith, S (G T Stewart Solicitors) *N*
London SE22 *p83* 020 8299 6000

Smith, S (Bindmans LLP) *Zg Zm L*
London WC1 *p12* 020 7833 4433

Smith, S (Trowers & Hamlins)
London EC3 *p88* 020 7423 8000

Smith, Ms S (Department for Business, Enterprise and Regulatory Reform)
London SW1 *p105* 020 7215 0105

Smith, Miss S A (Doncaster Magistrates Court)
Doncaster *p457* 01302 366711

Smith, Ms S A (Parkinson Wright LLP) *L S1 W*
Worcester *p440* 01905 726789

Smith, S A (National Institutions of the Church of England, Legal Office) *S1 W*
London SW1 *p108* 020 7898 1000

Smith, S A (Principality Building Society)
Cardiff *p453* 029 2038 2000

Smith, Miss S C (South Western Magistrates Court)
London SW11 *p109* 020 7805 1447

Smith, S D (Wilford Smith Solicitors) *G H M1 L F1 W Zi Zl*
Rotherham *p367* 01709 828044

Smith, Ms S E (Blake Lapthorn) *N*
Oxford *p342* 01865 248607

Smith, Mrs S G (Carr & Co) *N Q L J1 K4 W*
Blyth *p147* 01670 351251
Gosforth *p231* 0191 284 0363

Smith, S H (Slade Legal) *K1 P N J1 F1 L D1 Zl Zm*
Wallingford *p419* 01491 839346

Smith, Mrs S J (Thames Water Utilities Limited)
Reading *p469* 0118 373 8000

Smith, Miss S J (Sidley Austin Brown & Wood) *Zb*
London EC2 *p78* 020 7360 3600

Smith, S J (Machins Solicitors LLP) *S1 Zl*
Luton *p295* 01582 514000

Smith, Miss S J (Dickinson Manser)
Poole *p352* 01202 673071

Smith, S J L (Bower & Bailey) *S1 S2 C1 E L*
Oxford *p343* 01865 311133
Swindon *p406* 01793 610466

Smith, Miss S L (Tollers LLP) *K1 K2 D1 D2*
Northampton *p332* 01604 258558

Smith, Miss S L (McAras Solicitors LLP) *K1 D1*
Leeds *p275* 0113 243 4333

Smith, Mrs S L (Wintle & Co) *T2 W S1 L*
Bognor Regis *p148* 01243 586611

Smith, Mrs S L (Thomson Snell & Passmore) *W K4*
Tunbridge Wells *p415* 01892 510000

Smith, Mrs S M (Crosse & Crosse) *D1 D2 K1*
Exeter *p220* 01392 258451

Smith, S M (O'Garra's) *B2 G H Zr Q N*
Leeds *p276* 0113 247 1477

Smith, S M (Irwin Mitchell LLP) *O*
Sheffield *p376* 0870 150 0100

Smith, S M (Eric H Smith) *S1 W R1*
Burnley *p169* 01282 432141

Smith, Miss S N (B P Collins LLP) *O Q Zk A3 I U2 Zq*
Gerrards Cross *p229* 01753 889995

Smith, S P (Peters & Peters) *B2 G*
London EC4 *p67* 020 7629 7991

Smith, S P (Walker Smith Way) *E A1 R2 S2*
Chester *p191* 0844 346 3100

Smith, Miss S P (Bevan Brittan LLP) *C1 M1 Zu*
Bristol *p161* 0870 194 1000

Smith, Mrs S P (Law Brand) *B1 C1 E J1 K1 L Zc Zv*
Hitchin *p251* 01462 457167

Smith, Mrs S R (Kieran Clarke Green) *S1 W E S2*
Chesterfield *p192* 01246 211006

Smith, S T J (Nelsons)
Leicester *p280* 0116 222 6666

6

Smith, S V (Mackrell Turner Garrett) *K1 K2 K3*
Woking *p437* 01483 755609
Richmond upon Thames *p364* 020 8940 8115 / 8332 7532

Smith, S W B (Clark Holt) *C1 I U2 J1 Ze Zza*
Swindon *p406* 01793 617444

Smith, T (Sintons LLP) *N Q*
Newcastle upon Tyne *p326* 0191 226 7878

Smith, T (Epsom & Ewell Borough Council)
Epsom *p458* 01372 732000
Godalming *p459* 01483 523333

Smith, T (Hart Jackson Hall Smith) *S1 D1 J1 K1 Q W F1 N*
Newcastle upon Tyne *p325* 0191 261 5181

Smith, Ms T A (Mowbray Woodwards Solicitors) *K1 D1 D2 X Q*
Bath *p128* 01225 485700

Smith, T A M (Plymouth Justices' Clerk)
Plymouth *p468* 01752 206200

Smith, T J (The Johnson Partnership) *G H*
Derby *p209* 01332 370473

Smith, T P (Godloves) *S1 S2 W E R1 K4*
Leeds *p273* 0113 225 8874
Leeds *p273* 0113 225 8811

Smith, Miss U (Reading Borough Council)
Reading *p469* 0118 939 0900

Smith, V H P (Northamptonshire County Council)
Northampton *p467* 01604 236236

Smith, Miss V L (Darbys Solicitors LLP) *K1 D1 D2*
Oxford *p343* 01865 811700

Smith, W (K&L Gates LLP) *R2 C2*
London EC4 *p47* 020 7648 9000

Smith, Ms W (Mills & Reeve) *Zd C1 M1 Zu Zy*
Birmingham *p140* 0121 454 4000

Smith, Z (Ince & Co Services Ltd)
London E1 *p44* 020 7481 0010

Smith-Wilds, J (Lawrences)
Wellingborough *p424* 01933 442324

Smitheman, J P (Jonas Roy Bloom) *G H*
Birmingham *p139* 0121 212 4111

Smithers, Miss E J (Clarke Willmott) *W T2 Zo*
Bristol *p162* 0845 209 1000 / 0117 305 6000

Smithers, J R S (Cooper Burnett) *S1 L W*
Tunbridge Wells *p415* 01892 515022

Smithers, S W (George H Coles & Co) *K1 S1 E F1 L Q O N J1*
Hove *p254* 01273 205101

Smithers, T (Veale Wasbrough Vizards) *E P R1 Zn L R2 S2 Zs*
Bristol *p165* 0117 925 2020

Smithers, Mrs V (Kennedys)
Chelmsford *p186* 0845 838 4800

Smithies, R D (Bearders) *W K4 S1 S2*
Brighouse *p158* 01484 710571

Smithson, P D (Howard Kennedy LLP) *C1*
London W1 *p48* 020 7636 1616

Smithson, S (Smithson Hinds Morris) *H G*
Leeds *p276* 0113 245 0456

Smurthwaite, Mrs J (Dickinson Dees) *Q L*
Newcastle upon Tyne *p324* 0191 279 9000

Smy, Miss D (Palmers) *W S2 E S1*
Basildon *p126* 01268 240000

Smy, Miss S R (Norfolk County Council - Legal Services)
Norwich *p467* Minicom: 0844 800 8011
Norwich *p334* 01603 617018

Smyllie, D A (Gordons LLP) *B1 C1 E*
Leeds *p273* 0113 227 0100

Smyth, C (Cheltenham & Gloucester PLC)
Gloucester *p459* 01452 372372

Smyth, C J (England & Co) *B1 Zd C1 S2 E C3 F1 F2 K4 J1 O Q R2 S1*
Great Yarmouth *p234* 01493 844308 / 844309

Smyth, C J W (BLB Solicitors) *G J1 N H Q*
Swindon *p406* 01793 615011

Smyth, D G (Barlow Lyde & Gilbert LLP) *O Q Zj*
London EC3 *p10* 020 7247 2277

Smyth, D H (May May & Merrimans) *T2 W*
London WC1 *p59* 020 7405 8932

Smyth, I (Department for Business, Enterprise and Regulatory Reform)
London SW1 *p105* 020 7215 0105

Smyth, Mrs J A (Smyth Barkham) *Zf T1 T2 W*
London WC2 *p80* 020 7632 9550

Smyth, J S S (Carter Lemon Camerons) *N P J1 M1 W Zk Zj Zq*
London EC1 *p18* 020 7406 1000

Smyth, K G (Burt Brill & Cardens) *K3 K1 J1 Q Zq O A3 K2*
Brighton *p159* 01273 604123

Smyth, Ms L A (Field Seymour Parkes) *J1 Zd*
Reading *p360* 0118 951 6200

Smyth, M T (Clifford Chance)
London E14 *p20* 020 7006 1000

Smyth, N (Kennedys) *B1 Zj Q*
London EC3 *p49* 020 7667 9667

Smyth, N (Taylor Wessing)
London EC4 *p86* 020 7300 7000

Smyth, R (DLA Piper UK LLP) *B2 I T1 G C3*
Manchester *p303* 0870 011 1111

Smyth, R B (Duane Morris) *C1 C2 Ze J1 Zf C3 I Zw U2*
London EC1 *p28* 020 7786 2100

Smyth, S (McKenzies) *G H*
London N9 *p57* 020 8350 4114

Smyth, Miss T P A (Weightmans LLP) *N Q*
Liverpool *p291* 0151 227 2601

Smythe, D (Kingsley Napley) *N M1 B1 F1 J1 B2 Zg*
London EC1 *p50* 020 7814 1200

Snabaitis, Ms J A (Christopher Green McCarrahers) *D1 K1 K3 V*
Southampton *p386* 023 8084 2765

Snadden, Mrs G A (Kirklees Metropolitan Borough Council)
Huddersfield *p461* 01484 221421

Snaith, J E (Paris Smith LLP) *E R1 R2 S1 S2*
Southampton *p386* 023 8048 2482

Snaith, Miss N J (Thompsons (formerly Robin/Brian Thompson & Partners))
Nottingham *p339* 0115 989 7200

Snape, J (Nabarro LLP) *L S1*
London WC1 *p63* 020 7524 6000

Snape, N E (Malvern Hills District Council)
Malvern *p464* 01684 862151

Snatt, D P (Brutton & Co) *F1 P J1 B1 N Za F2 J2 Zk O Q Zq Zp*
Fareham *p223* 01329 236171

Snedden, B N (Peterborough City Council)
Peterborough *p468* 01733 747474

Sneddon, A (Trowers & Hamlins)
London EC3 *p88* 020 7423 8000

Sneddon, B (HC Solicitors LLP) *K1 D1 K3*
Peterborough *p347* 01733 882800

Sneezum, D F (Steed & Steed LLP) *K1 S1 W D1 C1 T1 A1*
Sudbury *p401* 01787 373387

Snelgrove, M A (Browne Jacobson LLP) *C1 Ze I*
Nottingham *p336* 0115 976 6000

Snell, Ms E (Jobling & Knape) *E Q*
Lancaster *p269* 01524 598300

Snell, Ms H (Murrays Partnership) *H G D1*
Southwark *p62* 020 7701 8653

Snell, P G (Stephens & Scown) *N J1 O Q*
St Austell *p391* 01726 74433

Snell, Ms R E (Addleshaw Goddard)
Leeds *p271* 0113 209 2000
Manchester *p300* 0161 934 6000

Snelson, S J (Geoffrey Leaver Solicitors LLP) *J1*
Milton Keynes *p317* 01908 692769

Snipe, I M (Snipelaw) *S1 B1 P M1 N E K1 W G J1*
Blackpool *p147* 01253 844444

Snodgrass, C J A I (Kaim Todner Ltd) *G H*
London SE17 *p47* 020 7701 4747

Snodgrass, P M (Shakespeares) *A1 T1 T2 S1*
Stratford-upon-Avon *p400* 0845 630 8833

Snodin, C J (Harold Benjamin)
Harrow *p241* 020 8422 5678

Snook, Miss H (Morgan Cole) *N Zj*
Bristol *p164* 0117 916 7220

Snook, Ms N (British American Tobacco) *C1 I Ze*
London WC2 *p104* 020 7845 1000

Snow, Miss C (Morgan Cole) *O Q F2 B1 A3 W Ze Zq*
Oxford *p344* 01865 262600

Snow, Ms S (TV Edwards LLP) *G H*
London EC3 *p85* 020 7790 7000

Snow, Miss Y (Anthony King & Co) *K3 K1*
Basildon *p126* 01268 240400

Snowball, N (Whatley Weston & Fox) *W T2 S1 Zd Zm*
Worcester *p440* 01905 731731

Snowden, P R (Stevens & Bolton) *T1 W*
Guildford *p237* 01483 302264

Snowdon, Miss F (Freedman Green Dhokia) *K3 K1*
Camden *p34* 020 7624 2981

Snowdon, Ms H (Hewitts)
Darlington *p206* 01325 468573

Snowdon, Miss L (Stanford & Lambert) *W T2 G S1 H K4 L N Q J1*
Newcastle upon Tyne *p327* 0191 232 6226

Snowdon, M J (Douglas-Jones Mercer) *E F1 S1 T1*
Swansea *p405* 01792 650000

Snowdon, R J (Maclachlan) *S1 Zd S2*
Sherborne *p378* 01935 817736

Snowdon, W D (Hugh James) *C1 I Ze Zw*
Cardiff *p179* 029 2022 4871

Soakell, Mrs C (Lewis Silkin LLP) *J1*
London EC4 *p53* 020 7074 8000

Soar, Mrs J (Tustain Jones & Co) *D1 K1*
Bedworth *p130* 024 7664 3222

Soar, Ms R (Fraser Brown) *S1*
Nottingham *p337* 0115 988 8777

Soares, R A T (McGrigors LLP)
London EC4 *p56* 020 7054 2500

Sobti, P S (Stevenage Borough Council)
Stevenage *p472* 01438 242242

Soccard, Mrs J (Lamb Brooks LLP) *N Q O*
Basingstoke *p126* 01256 844888

Sockanathan, Mrs P (Wimal & Co) *K1 L F1 S1 Zi Zl E W S2*
Thornton Heath *p411* 020 8689 7503

Sockanathan, W (Wimal & Co) *S1 K1 L F1 E W Zi Zl S2*
Thornton Heath *p411* 020 8689 7503

Soden, J S (Williamson & Soden) *S1 E C2 C1 F1*
Solihull *p383* 0121 733 8000

Soden, Miss N M (Brabners Chaffe Street) *J1 Zp*
Manchester *p301* 0161 836 8800

Soden-Bird, C (Veale Wasbrough Vizards) *O Q Zq*
London EC4 *p89* 020 7405 1234

Soderstrom, J (T A Matthews) *N Q J1 O B1 F1 Zt Zl*
Hereford *p248* 01432 352121

Sofaer, G C (Denniss Matthews) *P N K1 D1 M1 E*
London SE20 *p27* 020 8778 7301 / 8778 7631

Soffin, D B (Gates and Partners) *N Q Zj*
London EC3 *p35* 020 7220 5950

Sofi, K M (Johns & Saggar) *G H J1 Zi Zq*
London WC1 *p46* 020 3490 1475

Softly, J R (Newcastle Upon Tyne City Council)
Newcastle upon Tyne *p466* 0191 232 8520

Sogno, J H (Lawson Lewis & Co) *K1 P J1 M1 L V D1 B1 F1 Zc*
Eastbourne *p215* 01323 720142

Sohail, G N (Challinors) *G H*
West Bromwich *p427* 0121 553 3211

Sohal, J S (Gordons LLP) *E S2 R2*
Leeds *p273* 0113 227 0100

Sohal, K J S (Lincolns Solicitors)
Northwood *p333* 01923 820909

Sohal, R (Squire Sanders (UK) LLP)
London EC2 *p81* 020 7655 1000

Sohal, Mrs S (Pearcelegal LLP) *S1 S2 E*
Solihull *p383* 0844 412 7899

Sohanpal, Miss H (Smith Brown & Sprawson) *K1 K2*
Luton *p295* 01582 876900

Sohi, J S (Squire Sanders (UK) LLP)
Birmingham *p142* 0121 222 3000

Sohpal, Mrs K (Armitage Sykes LLP) *W*
Huddersfield *p255* 01484 538121

Sokhal, J (Thomas Boyd Whyte) *G H*
Bexleyheath *p132* 020 8303 7755

Sokhi, R (Ashurst LLP)
London EC2 *p7* 020 7638 1111

Solanki, Miss N (Windeatts)
Kingsbridge *p267* 01548 852727

Solanki, Miss S (Heckford Norton) *W T2 V Zm K4*
Saffron Walden *p370* 01799 522636

Sole, S (Kenwright Walker Wyllie) *S1 S2 J1 W Zl*
East Molesey *p215* 020 8979 1131

Soley, Ms L (Bates Wells & Braithwaite London LLP) *W T2 Zd C1*
London EC4 *p11* 020 7551 7777

Solly, Ms G C (Russell Jones & Walker) *N Zq*
Bristol *p164* 0117 374 2222

Soloman, R M (Hay & Kilner) *N P M1 E R1 C1 B1 J1 L F1 Zc Ze Zh*
Newcastle upon Tyne *p325* 0191 232 8345

Solomides, Mrs J (Maxwell Winward LLP) *E L S2 R2*
London EC4 *p59* 020 7651 0000

Solomon, Mrs A (Charles Russell LLP) *T1*
London EC4 *p19* 020 7203 5000

Solomon, Sir H (Solomon Taylor & Shaw)
London NW3 *p80* 020 7431 1912

Solomon, J (Solomon Levy)
Luton *p295* 01582 425817 / 414948

Solomon, J D (Clifford Chance) *E L*
London E14 *p20* 020 7006 1000

Solomon, Mrs M D (W Davies) *W T2 Zd*
Woking *p436* 01483 744900

Solomon, P J (Juliet Bellis & Co) *B1 C1 D1 F1 G H J1 K1 L E*
Uckfield *p416* 01825 750811

Solomon, S E (W Davies) *C1 C2 S2 E R2 J1 C3 P R1*
Woking *p436* 01483 744900

Solomon, Mrs V (Derrick Bridges & Co)
Barnet *p123* 020 8449 7326

Solomon, Mrs V (Treasures) *N Q Zr*
Gloucester *p230* 01452 525351

Solomons, E B (Official Solicitor and Public Trustee)
London WC2 *p108* 020 7911 7127

Solomons, E B (Metropolitan Police Directorate of Legal Services)
London SW1 *p108* 020 7230 7210

Solomons, S M (Piper Smith Watton LLP) *E L S1*
London SW1 *p68* 020 7222 9900

Somaiya, Miss S (Spearing Waite LLP) *K1 D1 D2 K3*
Leicester *p281* 0116 262 4225

Somarakis, P (Blake Lapthorn) *Zl*
Chandlers Ford *p184* 023 8090 8090
Oxford *p342* 01865 248607

Somasuntharam, Mrs C (Soma & Co Solicitors)
Harrow *p242* 020 8423 0203

Somekh, P A N (DLA Piper UK LLP) *B1 C1 Zb*
Manchester *p303* 0870 011 1111

Somerfield, P W (Charity Commission)
Liverpool *p463* 0151 703 1500

Somers, Mrs A (Irwin Mitchell LLP) *O Zk*
Sheffield *p376* 0870 150 0100

Somers, Mrs H J (North Yorkshire County Council) *D1 D2 G H K1*
Northallerton *p467* 01609 780780

Somers, W A (Somers & Blake) *G H S1 P M1 W C1 K1 J1 L*
London W7 *p80* 020 8567 7025

Somerton, J M (Somerton & Fletcher) *E S1*
Cambridge *p175* 01223 566596

Sommer, Mrs J M (Chebsey & Co) *K1*
Burnham *p168* 01628 660077

Sommerlad, Dr H A K (Leeds Metropolitan University)
Leeds *p463* 0113 812 9028

Sommerville, J A (Thomas Horton LLP) *Q O N G J1 Zk Zq Zr*
Bromsgrove *p167* 01527 871641

Sond, Mrs A K (Curry Popeck) *C1*
London W1 *p24* 020 7224 6633

Sondermann, Ms A (Field Fisher Waterhouse LLP)
London EC3 *p31* 020 7861 4000

Soneji, J S (Sheridans) *A1 E L R1 S1 Zc*
London WC1 *p78* 020 7079 0100

Songhurst, K (Birkett Long LLP) *O Q L*
Colchester *p197* 01206 217300

Sonley, Ms C (Hamers Solicitors) *K4 K1 S1 T2 W*
Hull *p257* 01482 326666

Sonn, D J (Sonn Macmillan)
London EC3 *p80* 020 7377 8889

Sonneborn, Ms K (Ashurst LLP)
London EC2 *p7* 020 7638 1111

Sonola, Ms A O (Hertfordshire County Council)
Hertford *p460* 01992 555555

Soo, Miss S S (McKinnells) *W K4*
Lincoln *p284* 01522 541181

Sood, A (Soods Solicitors)
Ilford *p261* 020 8597 0000

Sood, Ms V (Trott & Gentry) *C1 E S1 P M1 K1 G W*
London N1 *p88* 020 3119 3150

Soodi, J (Dorians) *G H*
Derby *p208* 01332 680580

Sookias, M J (Sookias & Sookias) *O Q T1 C1*
London W1 *p80* 020 7465 8000

Sookias, R J (Sookias & Sookias) *E S1 W L Zg Zi S2*
London W1 *p80* 020 7465 8000

Soomro, N (LG Lawyers)
London SE1 *p50* 020 7379 0000

Soor, S (Cartwright King) *G H*
Nottingham *p336* 0115 958 7444

Soper, S J (Powells) *S2 E R2*
Weston-super-Mare *p429* 01934 623501

Sophocleous, M (Garstangs) *B2 G H O Q*
London WC2 *p35* 020 7427 5678

Sorby, M (Kirklees Metropolitan Borough Council)
Huddersfield *p461* 01484 221421

Sorby, T D (Ilett & Clark Solicitors) *W Zd K4*
Worksop *p441* 01909 500544

Sore, Ms J (Nelsons)
Derby *p209* 01332 372372

Sore, Miss J M C (Northern Foods PLC) *J1*
Leeds *p461* 0113 390 0110
Nottingham *p336* 0115 977 5877

Soren, H (Stockport Metropolitan Borough Council)
Stockport *p472* 0161 480 4949

Sorensen, D P (Morrish Solicitors LLP) *G J1 M1 Q N Zp H*
Leeds *p276* 0113 245 0733

Sorfleet, S R (Hibbert Lucas Butter) *A1 L S1 W*
Ellesmere *p217* 01691 622408
Whitchurch *p430* 01948 662231

Sorrell, Mrs A G (Craigen Wilders & Sorrell) *K1*
London N8 *p23* 020 8888 2255

Sorrell, J R (Craigen Wilders & Sorrell) *S2 C1 S1 Zl Zj*
London N8 *p23* 020 8888 2255

Sorrell, Ms M A (Aviva PLC)
London EC3 *p103* 020 7283 7500 / 01603 687905

Sou, Ms J (Bury Metropolitan Borough Council) *W*
Bury *p452* 0161 253 7771

Soughton, W J E (The Johnson Partnership) *G H*
Nottingham *p337* 0115 941 9141

Soul, J (Harvey Ingram Borneos)
Milton Keynes *p317* 01908 696002

Soul, M (Michael Soul & Associates) *M2 T2 T1 C1*
London WC2 *p80* 020 7353 3358

Soulsby, A W (Northern Rock PLC)
Gosforth *p459* 0191 285 7191

Souper, R J (J D Spicer & Co)
London NW6 *p81* 020 7625 5590

Souter, J (Speechly Bircham LLP)
London EC4 *p81* 020 7427 6400

South, C G (West of England Insurance Services (Luxembourg)) *Za*
London SE1 *p110* 020 7716 6000

South, Ms K T (KPM Solicitors) *K1 Q O S1 J1 F1 W N L G D1 Ze Zi*
London WC2 *p47* 020 7404 1995

Southall, G A L (FBC Manby Bowdler LLP) *C1 C2 S2*
Wolverhampton *p437* 01902 578000

Southby, Ms K M (Gordons LLP)
Leeds *p273* 0113 227 0100

Southby, P D (Browne Jacobson LLP) *O Q P Zk*
Nottingham *p336* 0115 976 6000

Southcote-Want, K D (Southcote Scott) *Q N O Zl*
London W1 *p81* 020 7034 7035

Southcott, W (Russell Jones & Walker) *B2 G T1*
Manchester *p309* 0161 383 3500

Southern, Ms J (Andrew Jackson) *C2 B3*
Hull *p257* 01482 325242

Southern, Mrs L (Camps Solicitors)
Birkenhead *p134* 0151 201 8080

Southern, N D (Keoghs LLP) *J1 Q N*
Bolton *p149* 01204 677000

Southern, P D (J B Wheatley & Co) *G H*
London SE8 *p91* 020 8479 8000

Southern, S M (Squire Sanders (UK) LLP) *Zo*
Manchester *p310* 0161 830 5000

Southern, T R (Blake Lapthorn) *E L*
London EC1 *p13* 020 7405 2000

Southerton, Mrs K A (Dudley Metropolitan Borough Council)
Dudley *p457* 01384 815326

Southey, V G (Barlow Lyde & Gilbert LLP) *C2 Zj*
London EC3 *p10* 020 7247 2277

Southgate, Ms K (Wiggin LLP) *C1 C2*
Cheltenham *p189* 01242 224114

Southgate, S (McClure Naismith)
London EC4 *p56* 020 7623 9155

Southgate, S M (Lester Aldridge LLP) *C1 M1 T1 W J1 Zi*
Bournemouth *p152* 01202 786161

Southon, Miss H L (Harcus Sinclair) *W Zm K4 Zq*
London WC2 *p38* 020 7242 9700

Southorn, A T (McCarthy & Stone PLC) *S2*
Bournemouth *p450* 01202 292480
Carlisle *p181* 01228 552222
Carlisle *p182* 01228 552222

Southorn, C (CMS Cameron McKenna LLP)
London EC3 *p17* 020 7367 3000

Southorn, Mrs E M (Reed Smith LLP)
London EC2 *p71* 020 3116 3000

Southwell, Miss L A (Coodes) *K4 W Zm*
Penzance *p346* 01736 362294

Southwell, N E (Verisona Solicitors) *C1 S2 E Q J1 L C2*
Waterlooville *p423* 023 9226 5251

Southworth, J (Hill Dickinson LLP)
Liverpool *p288* 0151 600 8000

Soutter, I D (The Roland Partnership) *N Zr S1*
Chester *p191* 01244 659404

Sowah, Ms V (Luton Borough Council)
Luton *p464* 01582 546000

Sowden, S J (Hartnell Chanot & Partners Family Law Specialists) *K1 K3 D2 D1*
Exeter *p221* 01392 421777

Sower, G D H (FBC Manby Bowdler LLP) *E S2*
Telford *p409* 01952 292129

Sowerbutts, K J (Paribas Ltd)
London NW1 *p108* 020 7595 2000

Sowerbutts, P (Scully & Sowerbutts Solicitors) *E L Zh*
London N3 *p77* 020 8346 2804

Sowerby, Mrs H J (Cumbria County Council)
Kendal *p462* 01539 773123

Sowerby, Miss J R (DWF) *E S2*
Manchester *p303* 0161 603 5000

Sowerby, T (Lancasters) *S1 W E K1 M1 P D1 C1 G T1 Zc Zl Zj*
Bridlington *p158* 01262 602401

Sowler, T R H (Watson Burton LLP) *T1 C2 Zb Zo M2 O T2 Zd W*
Newcastle upon Tyne *p327* 0845 901 2100

Sowton, O (Blake Lapthorn) *A1 E P S2 R1 Zd*
Chandlers Ford *p184* 023 8090 8090

Soyer, Ms A (Wilson & Co) *K1 D1 D2*
London N17 *p92* 020 8808 7535

Spacey, P M (Hamlins LLP) *E*
London W1 *p38* 020 7355 6000

Spacie, D M (SNR Denton)
London EC4 *p75* 020 7242 1212

Spafford, I (Leeds City Council)
Leeds *p462* 0113 224 3513

Spain, Mrs B V (Harrison Clark LLP) *K1 D1*
Cheltenham *p188* 01242 269198
Worcester *p439* 01905 612001
Worcester *p439* 01905 612001

Spalding, D (Norton Peskett) *N O Zl*
Lowestoft *p294* 01502 533000

Spalding-Siracusa, Mrs W C (Sills & Betteridge LLP)
Lincoln *p285* 01522 542211

Spanner, C M (Lanyon Bowdler LLP) *J1 K1 K3 Q L Zl O*
Ludlow *p294* 01584 872333

Spanner, Ms L J (Coffin Mew & Clover) *G K1 H*
Portsmouth *p354* 023 9238 8021

Spanton, M A (Metropolitan Police Directorate of Legal Services) *J1 L Zp Ze*
London SW1 *p108* 020 7230 7210

Spark, Mrs V J (Thomas Magnay & Co) *S2 K3 K4 J1 K1 W S1 E*
Whickham *p430* 0191 488 7459 / 488 7766

Sparkes, Mrs A E (Welsh Health Legal Services)
Cardiff *p453* 029 2031 5500

Sparkes, S (Sternberg Reed) *G*
Barking *p123* 020 8591 3366

Sparkes, S (Sternberg Reed) *N*
Romford *p366* 01708 766155

Sparks, F M (Squire Sanders (UK) LLP)
London EC2 *p81* 020 7655 1000

Sparks, G (Charles Russell LLP) *C1 I U2 C2*
Guildford *p235* 01483 252525

Sparks, Mrs J (Arnold Greenwood) *S1 K1*
Kendal *p264* 01539 720049

Sparks, Ms L (Family Law Associates LLP) *K3 K1*
Haringey *p30* 020 8342 7760

Sparks, P D J (Bassets) *F1 G K1 L N Q*
Gillingham *p229* 01634 575464

Sparks, R E (Magrath LLP) *Zi Zg*
London W1 *p57* 020 7495 3003

Sparling, G J (London Borough of Bexley)
Bexleyheath *p449* 020 8303 7777

See p634 for the Key to Work Categories

Sparrow, A J (Shell International Ltd) *C1 B1 J1*
London SE1 *p109* 020 7934 1234

Sparrow, A P (Rochman Landau LLP) *U2 I C1 Ze Zza Zf*
London W1 *p72* 020 7544 2424

Sparrow, Mrs D (Hayes & Storr) *W K4*
King's Lynn *p266* 01553 778900

Sparrow, D G (Sparrow & Trieu Solicitors) *K1 L N S1 W Zi Zl*
London W1 *p81* 020 7287 6608

Sparrow, E C A (Ashurst LLP) *B1 O Zj*
London EC2 *p7* 020 7638 1111

Sparrow, Ms H (Panesar & Co) *K3 K1 L*
Grays *p233* 01375 383283

Sparrow, M G (Marshall Hatchick)
Woodbridge *p439* 01394 388411

Sparrow, M T (Fentons) *N*
Failsworth *p223* 0161 682 7101

Sparrow, Miss R K (Hay & Kilner) *N O*
Newcastle upon Tyne *p325* . 0191 232 8345

Sparrow, Mrs T (West Lancashire District Council)
Ormskirk *p468* 01695 577177

Sparshott, S D (Aylesbury Vale District Council)
Aylesbury *p447* 01296 585858

Spash, M D (Piper Smith Watton LLP) *W S1 T2*
London SW1 *p68* 020 7222 9900

Spatz, Mrs A (Trobridges) *N Q O*
Plymouth *p350*. 01752 664022

Spavin, Mrs J L (Gordons LLP) *E S2 R2*
Leeds *p273* 0113 227 0100

Speake, A C (Barlow Lyde & Gilbert LLP) *Za Zj*
London EC3 *p10*. 020 7247 2277

Speake, Mrs C L (Sharples & Co) *E S1*
Bristol *p165* 0117 942 8214

Speake, W R (AgustaWestland Legal Dept - Yeovil)
Yeovil *p477* 01935 702240

Spear, B A (Bulcraigs) *S1 E W C1 L T1 T2 S2 Zc R2*
Wandsworth *p16*. 020 8870 2207 / 8877 0531

Spear, Ms K (Howard Kennedy LLP) *E*
London W1 *p48* 020 7636 1616

Spearey, E A (Bevirs) *Q K1 G H N B1 L O C1*
Calne *p173* 01249 814536

Spearing, Miss L J (Carter-Ruck) *O Zk*
London EC4 *p18*. 020 7353 5005

Spearman, A F (Wortley Byers) *W*
Brentwood *p156* 01277 268368

Spears, Ms R (Brabners Chaffe Street) *E S2*
Liverpool *p286*. 0151 600 3000

Specter, K L (The Specter Partnership) *N O S1 J1 Q*
Birkenhead *p135*. 0151 647 3000

Spedding, Miss D J (Harding Evans LLP) *O Q L F1 F2 Zq*
Newport *p328* 01633 244233

Spedding, Ms J (Withers LLP) *C1 C2*
London EC4 *p92*. 020 7597 6000

Spedding, K H (Shakespeares) *C1 C2*
Birmingham *p142* 0121 237 3000

Spedding, Dr L S (Dr Linda S Spedding) *P C1 C2 C3*
London SW6 *p81* 020 7610 2025

Spedding, R R (Travers Smith LLP) *C1 C2*
London EC1 *p87*. 020 7295 3000

Speechly, G A G (W A G Davidson & Co) *C1 E J1 K1 L M1 N P O Q Zf Zh Zj*
London W3 *p26* 020 8992 4884

Speed, A (Francis Alexander Solicitors) *E S1*
Stockport *p395*. 0161 432 3633

Speed, A W (Hill Dickinson LLP) *A3 O C1 Za Zj*
London EC3 *p41*. 020 7283 9033

Speed, Miss J L (Chattertons Solicitors) *K1 Q O N B1*
Lincoln *p284*. 01522 814600

Speed, Miss J M (Freeth Cartwright LLP) *K1 D1*
Nottingham *p337*. 0115 936 9369

Speed, Ms J S (Martin Murray & Associates) *N*
West Drayton *p427* 01895 431332

Speed, Mrs M (Hague Lambert) *S1*
Macclesfield *p297* 01625 616480

Speed, N P (Reed Smith LLP) *N Zc O Zj*
London EC2 *p71*. 020 3116 3000

Speed, S A (BAS Solicitors) *N Q K1 K3 W Zq O*
Bracknell *p153*. 01344 862111

Speed, T P (Orange PCS Ltd) *C1 C2 Zo*
Bristol *p452* 0870 376 8888

Speedie, Miss K L (Whitehead Monckton) *W T2*
Maidstone *p299* 01622 698000

Speer, P R (Thomson Webb & Corfield) *C1 E P T1 B1 J1 Ze*
Cambridge *p176*. 01223 578070

Speight, Mrs J E (Wakefield Court House)
Wakefield *p474* 01924 303461

Speight, M R (T A Matthews) *S2 S1 L C1 A1*
Hereford *p248* 01432 352121

Speirs, J R (Magnox Electric PLC)
Berkeley *p449* 01452 652222 / 01453 813484

Speirs, S J (Osborne Clarke) *R2*
Bristol *p164* 0117 917 3000

Speker, B N (Samuel Phillips Law Firm) *N D1 J1 K1 O Q W E C1 Zi Zk Zm Zl Zp*
Newcastle upon Tyne *p326* . 0191 232 8451

Speker, D M (Kingsley Napley) *K1 M1 N O Q*
London EC1 *p50*. 020 7814 1200

Speller, P J W (Allen & Overy LLP)
London E1 *p5* 020 3088 0000

Spence, Ms A A M (Spence & Horne) *E S1 L R1 Zc D1 K3 M1 K1 Zg Zi V W S2*
Hackney *p81*. 020 8985 2277

Spence, A M (Metcalfe Copeman & Pettefar) *G H*
King's Lynn *p266* 01553 778102

Spence, Mrs A S (Fletchers) *K1 K3 D1 J1*
Southport *p388* 01704 546919

Spence, Mrs C E (Denniss Matthews) *S1 E*
London SE20 *p27* . . 020 8778 7301 / 8778 7631

Spence, Miss C R (Cowling Swift & Kitchin)
York *p444* ...... 01904 625678 / 625679

Spence, Ms D E (Ward Hadaway) *W T2 Zo*
Newcastle upon Tyne *p327* . 0191 204 4000

Spence, Mrs I J (Charles Fraser & Co) *E S1 W*
Bury St Edmunds *p171* ... 01284 750111
Cambridge *p175*. 01223 713300

Spence, J (Thomson Snell & Passmore) *O L R1*
Tunbridge Wells *p415* 01892 510000

Spence, J (Blandy & Blandy) *E S1*
Reading *p360* 0118 951 6800

Spence, Miss K (J B Wheatley & Co) *G H*
London SE8 *p91*. 020 8479 8000

Spence, P (Dowse & Co) *J1 N G M1 Q J2*
Hackney *p27*. 020 7254 6205

Spence, R (Napthens LLP) *J1*
Preston *p357* 01772 888444

Spence, Mrs S (Dodds & Partners) *N*
Leicester *p279*. 0116 253 8585

Spencer Robb, Mrs R (Clarion Solicitors LLP) *K1 D1*
Leeds *p272* 0113 246 0622
Harrogate *p240* 01423 530630

Spencer, Dr A (CIPIT Solicitors) *I Ze J1 Zz U2 C1 S2 E*
London NW3 *p17* 020 8457 7457

Spencer, Mrs A C (Humphries Kirk) *J1*
Poole *p352* 01202 725400

Spencer, A J (Cozens-Hardy LLP) *J1 Q*
Norwich *p334* 01603 625231

Spencer, Miss A L (Godwins) *S1 L E A1 S2*
Winchester *p433*. 01962 841484

Spencer, B R (Wortley Byers) *E R1 S1 L*
Brentwood *p156* 01277 268368

Spencer, C (Sedgemoor District Council) *R1 Zu Zl*
Bridgwater *p451* . . .01278 424391 / 435435
Stroud *p473* 01453 766321
Taunton *p408* 01823 279279

Spencer, C J (Pardoes) *K1 D1 Q*
Bridgwater *p158* 01278 457891

Spencer, Miss D (Welsh Health Legal Services) *N Zr*
Cardiff *p453* 029 2031 5500
Manchester *p305* 0161 228 0011

Spencer, D C (Bower & Bailey) *S1 S2*
Oxford *p343* 01865 311133

Spencer, D J H (Wollen Michelmore Solicitors)
Newton Abbot *p330* 01626 332266

Spencer, Ms E M (Godloves) *S2 R2 R1 C1 E P S1 L B1 Zb Zf*
Leeds *p273* 0113 225 8811

Spencer, E P G (Barlow Lyde & Gilbert LLP) *O Q Zj*
London EC3 *p10*. 020 7247 2277

Spencer, Miss G M (Spencer Skuse) *S1 W K1 L*
Cardiff *p181* 029 2034 3993

Spencer, G N (Gloucester City Council)
Gloucester *p459* 01452 522232

Spencer, I R (Ian Spencer & Co) *E S1 W S2*
Newbury *p322* 01635 528424

Spencer, J (Hill Dickinson LLP)
Liverpool *p288*. 0151 600 8000

Spencer, Ms J (Penningtons) *Zr N*
Basingstoke *p127* 01256 407100

Spencer, J A (Mills & Reeve) *J1*
Cambridge *p175*. 01223 364422

Spencer, Mrs J E (Southend-on-Sea Borough Council)
Southend-on-Sea *p472* ... 01702 215000

Spencer, J L C (Middleweeks Solicitors) *G H K1 M1 B2*
Manchester *p307* 0161 839 7255

Spencer, Mrs J R (Bendall & Sons) *S1 E W T1 L R1 J1 A1 B1 C1 Zl Zi Zm*
Newmarket *p327*. 01638 661116

Spencer, J S (Spencer Davies) *S1 A1 E W K1 P G H Zd Zl Zw S2*
Grassington *p232* 01756 753015

Spencer, Mrs K N (Robinsons) *K4 W T2*
Ilkeston *p261* 0115 932 4101
Long Eaton *p293* 0115 849 9000

Spencer, Ms L (Portsmouth City Council)
Portsmouth *p469*. 023 9283 4034

Spencer, M J (Actons) *C1 O Q*
Nottingham *p335*. 0115 910 0200

Spencer, P (Laytons) *C1 J1 B1*
Manchester *p306* 0161 834 2100

Spencer, P A (Cox & Hodgetts) *W T2 Zm*
Evesham *p220*. 01386 442513

Spencer, Ms P A (Jeffrey Green Russell) *E Zp*
London W1 *p46* 020 7339 7000

Spencer, R (Hogan Lovells International LLP)
London EC1 *p42*. 020 7296 2000

Spencer, R E (Vine Orchards) *S1 E L W*
Exmouth *p223* . . . .01395 273035 / 264646

Spencer, R J (R T Steele & Spencer) *S1 S2 W L K1 N Q E K3*
Chester *p191* . . . .01244 318016 / 314531

Spencer, S (Morgan Lewis & Bockius)
London EC4 *p61*. 020 3201 5000

Spencer, S D (Hart Brown Solicitors) *S1 W E L J1 A1 T1 F1*
Cranleigh *p202* 0800 068 8177

Spencer, S L (Bambridges Solicitors Limited)
Boston *p151*. 01205 310510

Spencer, Mrs S L H (Burnetts) *F1 F2 O Q*
Carlisle *p181*. 01228 552222

Spencer, T P (East Riding of Yorkshire Council)
Beverley *p449*. 01482 887700

Spencer, Miss Y M (Childrens Legal Centre) *X*
Colchester *p455* . . .01206 872466 / 873828

Spender, J I (Howe & Spender) *G H S1 W*
Neath *p320* 01639 881571
Port Talbot *p353*. 01639 881571

Spender, J R (Howe & Spender) *S1 E W A1 R1 C1 Zl L*
Neath *p320* 01639 881571
Port Talbot *p353*. 01639 881571

Spenser Underhill, D P (Mayer Brown International LLP) *O*
London EC2 *p59*. 020 3130 3000

Spensley, Mrs M (Forbes) *W S1*
Blackburn *p145* 01254 54374

Sperotto, M (Ashurst LLP)
London EC2 *p7* 020 7638 1111

Sperring, D (Clement Hughes & Co) *E L S1 S2 W*
Prestatyn *p356*. 01745 852121

Sperring, I (Clement Hughes & Co) *E L S1 S2 W*
Prestatyn *p356*. 01745 852121

Sperring, J N (William Dawes & Co) *S1 W A1 E G K1 L T1*
Rye *p370* 01797 223177

Sperring, Miss R M (Clement Hughes & Co) *K1 S1 W S2 L*
Prestatyn *p356*. 01745 852121

Spibey, P A (Kennedys) *Zj*
London EC3 *p49*. 020 7667 9667

Spicer, J (Stuart Miller & Co)
Haringey *p61* 020 8888 5225

Spicer, J D (J D Spicer & Co) *S1 P M1 W K1 D1 L J1 H G Zi Zk*
London NW6 *p81* 020 7625 5590

Spicer, N S (Godwins) *Q O J1 K1 K3*
Winchester *p433*. 01962 841484
Winchester *p434*. 01962 868366

Spicer, P (Stuart Miller & Co)
Haringey *p61* 020 8888 5225

Spicer, P W (J D Spicer & Co) *G K1 P M1 H D1 W S1 L J1 Zi Zk*
London NW6 *p81* 020 7625 5590

Spicker, R H (Aviva PLC)
London EC3 *p103* . . 020 7283 7500 / 01603 687905
Norwich *p467* 01603 622200

Spiers, Mrs D (Bookers & Bolton) *E S1*
Alton *p116* ...... 01420 82881 / 88903

Spiers, Ms J (LG Lawyers)
London SE1 *p50*. 020 7379 0000

Spiers, Mrs K J (Warrington Borough Council)
Warrington *p475*. 01925 444400

Spikes, D R (Barlow Lyde & Gilbert LLP)
London EC3 *p10*. 020 7247 2277

Spillane, T A (Stewarts Law LLP) *J1*
London EC4 *p83*. 020 7822 8000

Spiller, G (Geoffrey Spiller Solicitors)
Eastbourne *p216*. 01323 419566

Spiller, R J (Edwards Angell Palmer & Dodge)
London EC2 *p28*. 020 7583 4055

Spilsbury, G (G Spilsbury & Co)
Mountain Ash *p319* 01443 473213

Spilsbury, Miss T S (Irena Spence) *C1 E J1 L S1*
Cambridge *p175*. 01223 713300

Spinetto, S A (Pickering & Butters) *S2 E A2 R2 S1*
Stafford *p393* 01785 603060

Spink, M A (Catteralls) *C1 S1 E W T1 Zd*
Wakefield *p418* 01924 291122

Spink, Ms R (South Devon Magistrates' Courts)
Torquay *p474* 01803 612211

Spink, R A B (Burges Salmon) *C2 C1 T1*
Bristol *p161* 0117 939 2000

Spinks, D G (Squire Sanders (UK) LLP)
London EC2 *p81*. 020 7655 1000

Spinks, Ms J P (Anthony Gold) *N Zr*
London SE1 *p6* 020 7940 4000

Spires, D (Watson Burton LLP) *Zc C1 E Q*
Newcastle upon Tyne *p327* . 0845 901 2100

Spires, P D (Society of Lloyd's)
London EC3 *p107* 020 7327 1000

Spirit, C R A (Charles Hill Hubbard) *A1 W S1 E G H J1 M1 N R1 Ze Zm Zl*
Chichester *p192* 01243 781000

Spirit, Miss D A J (Burley & Geach) *X Zo V K1 M1 P J1 G D1*
Grayshott *p233* 01428 605355
Petersfield *p348* 01730 262401

Spiro, B (BCL Burton Copeland) *G H B2 J2*
London WC2 *p9* 020 7430 2277

Spiteri, A J (O'Keeffe Solicitors) *G H*
Brent *p64* 020 7644 8800

Spittal, P (Linklaters LLP)
London EC2 *p54*. 020 7456 2000

Spittle, J B (Forshaws Davies Ridgway LLP) *S1 W L J1 E C1 G F1 R1*
Warrington *p422*. 01925 604713

Spittle, Ms J C (Denison Till) *O Q A3 A2 Zq Zc Ze Zk*
York *p444* 01904 611411

Spittles, Ms J (Paris Smith LLP) *E S2 R2*
Southampton *p386*. 023 8048 2482

Spitz, G (Salans) *C1 F1 C2 Zl*
London EC4 *p76*. 020 7429 6000

Spitz, Mrs L R (Manches LLP) *K1*
London WC2 *p58* 020 7404 4433

Spivey, J R (Keelys LLP)
Lichfield *p284* 01543 420000

Splaine, Miss L M (Atkinson Cave & Stuart) *K1 F1 G Zm H D1 J1*
Blackpool *p146* 01253 293151

Splaine, Ms V A (Hempsons) *Zr*
Manchester *p305* 0161 228 0011

Spooner, A (Squire Sanders (UK) LLP) *Zy Ze C3 M1 C1 F1 F2*
London EC2 *p81*. 020 7655 1000

Spooner, Mrs C M (W H Matthews & Co) *S1*
Kingston upon Thames *p267*. 020 8549 0264

Spooner, Ms K M (Allen & Overy LLP)
London E1 *p5* 020 3088 0000

Spooner, P A (Charsley Harrison LLP) *D1 K1 K2 Q*
Windsor *p434* 01753 851591

Spoor, N C O (Fairchild Dobbs) *S1 W C1 L E Zd*
Gerrards Cross *p229*. 01753 883127

Spoors, M (Jeromes) *K1 K3 D1 J1 Q*
Newport *p328* 01983 522664
Newport *p328* 01983 524431

Spowart, Ms A (Morrison Spowart)
London SE6 *p62*. 020 8698 9200

Spragg, Miss E J (Baxter Caulfield) *C1*
Huddersfield *p255* 01484 519519

Spragg, L S (Louis Spragg & Co) *G H K1 D1 N S1 W J1 F1 V Zi Zm Zd*
Dudley *p213*. . . . .01384 211621 / 211622

Spragg, M R (Jeffrey Green Russell) *J1 O G N Q B1 Zo Zp*
London W1 *p46* 020 7339 7000

Spragge, C P (CMS Cameron McKenna LLP) *N Za Zj*
London EC3 *p17*. 020 7367 3000

Spraggon, P B (SSB Solicitors) *Ze Zf Zk*
London SW6 *p75* 020 7348 7630

Sprake, A D (Squire Sanders (UK) LLP)
Leeds *p277* 0113 284 7000

Sprake, D J (Sprake & Kingsley) *W L S1*
Bungay *p168* 01986 892721

Sprakes, I C (Bridge McFarland) *Zr*
Grimsby *p235* 01472 311711

Sprakes, S J (Andrew Jackson) *C3 M1 M2 O Ze*
Hull *p257* 01482 325242

Spratt, J E (Spratt Endicott) *C1 C2 J1 Ze*
Banbury *p122* 01295 204000

Sprawson, Ms E (Harding Evans LLP) *V Q B1 L*
Newport *p328* 01633 244233

Sprawson, R (RMPI Solicitors)
London W1 *p70* 020 7318 4444

Sprawson, R (Davenport Lyons)
London W1 *p25* 020 7468 2600

Sprawson, S A (Smith Brown & Sprawson) *G H*
Luton *p295* 01582 876900

Spread, Ms S (Fox Williams) *C1 C2*
London EC2 *p33*. 020 7628 2000

Sprecher, D (SGH Martineau LLP) *C1 B1 O Q J1 T1*
London EC3 *p75*. 020 7264 4444

Spreckley, J E (SGH Martineau LLP) *R1 R2 S2*
Birmingham *p142* 0870 763 2000

Sprenger, J A L (Squire Sanders (UK) LLP)
Leeds *p277* 0113 284 7000

Spriggs, Miss A E (HC Solicitors LLP) *S2 E A1 Zd Zx*
Peterborough *p347* 01733 882800

Spriggs, Ms S E (Weightmans LLP) *N O Q*
Dartford *p207* 020 7822 1900

Spring, T D M (Moore Blatch Solicitors) *Zr*
Southampton *p386*. 023 8071 8000

Springall, I C (Tinklin Springall) *E S1 W*
Beckenham *p129* 020 8402 7222

Springall, P R (Howard Kennedy LLP) *E P R1 S1*
London W1 *p48* 020 7636 1616

Springett, Miss A J (Farrer & Co LLP)
London WC2 *p31* 020 3375 7000

Sproston, Ms L (Reynolds Porter Chamberlain LLP)
London E1 *p71* 020 3060 6000

Sproston, R J (Horwich Cohen Coghlan) *N*
Manchester *p305* 0161 830 4600

Sproull, D (Sproull Solicitors LLP) *B1 E J1 L S1 S2 W*
Camelford *p176* 01840 212315
Port Isaac *p353* 01840 212315

Sproull, D M (Sproull Solicitors LLP) *S1 S2 W E A1*
Bodmin *p148* 01208 72328

Sproull, Ms Z (Foster & Partners) *D1 K1 K3*
Bristol *p162* 0117 922 0229

Spruce, S J (Levi Solicitors LLP) *N*
Leeds *p275* 0113 244 9931

Spruce, T A J (Clerk to Sheffield Justices)
Sheffield *p470* 0114 276 0760

Spurling, J (Spurlings Solicitors) *W S1 S2 T2 Zd*
Christchurch *p194* 01202 473321

Spurling, M (Irwin Mitchell LLP) *N Q J2 Zj Zq*
Birmingham *p139* 0870 150 0100

Spurr, A I (Hewitts) *K4 S1 W S2*
Darlington *p206* 01325 468573

Spurrier, N R (Gregory Rowcliffe Milners) *K1 E L Q O R1 S1 W Zc Zh*
London WC1 *p37* 020 7242 0631

Spyris, T (Karis Spyris LLP) *C1 O S1 Q S2*
Enfield *p219*. 020 8443 7000

Squire, A W (E Edwards Son & Noice) *C1 S2 E J1 S1*
Billericay *p133*. 01277 658551

Squire, D B (Mundays LLP) *S2*
Cobham *p196* 01932 590500

Squire, Miss G (Rosling King) *B1 O Q Zc Zj*
London EC4 *p73*. 020 7353 2353

Squire, G (Osborne Clarke) *O Q J1 L Zc Zq*
Bristol *p164* 0117 917 3000

Squire, J S (Ashfords LLP) *N O*
Taunton *p408* 01823 232300

Squire, Ms L E (Anglia Ruskin University)
Chelmsford *p454*. 01245 493131

6

Squire, N J (Plexus Law (A Trading Name of Parabis Law LLP)) *N M1 Zc Zj A3*
London EC3 *p68*. 0844 245 4000

Squire, P (Ashurst LLP)
London EC2 *p7* 020 7638 1111

Squire, R J (Lyons Davidson) *C1 J1 T1 B1 Zb*
Bristol *p163* 0117 904 6000

Squires, Ms E L (Heaney Watson) *K1 D1 D2 K3*
Liverpool *p288*. 0151 282 5555

Squires, Miss S (Lamb Brooks LLP) *J2 K1 K4 T2 W Ze*
Basingstoke *p126* 01256 844888

Squires, Ms S J (Clifford Chance)
London E14 *p20*. 020 7006 1000

Sriharan, A (Sriharans)
Southall *p384* 020 8843 9974

Sriharan, R S (Sriharans)
Southall *p384* 020 8843 9974

Srikanthalingam, S (Sri Kanth & Co) *K1 N Q V B1 Zi*
Wembley *p426*. 020 8795 0648

Srinivasan, R (J A Kemp & Co)
London WC1 *p48* 020 7405 3292

Srinivasan, Ms S (Leigh Day & Co) *M2 F2*
London EC1 *p52*. 020 7650 1200

Srivastava, V A (Wrigley Claydon) *P M1 K1 J1 F1*
Oldham *p341* 0161 624 6811

Sriwardene, S (Ross Aldridge LLP)
Cheltenham *p187* 01242 707400

Srodon, Miss L B (Davis Gregory Ltd) *K1*
Cheltenham *p188* 01242 235202

St Clair Evans, Ms J (Vickers & Co)
Ealing *p89*. . . .020 8579 2559 / 8840 3999

St Clair, Ms T M (Clifford Chance)
London E14 *p20*. 020 7006 1000

St Clair-Haslam, S (Cumming & Riley) *K1 J1 L Q S1 W V*
Grays *p233* 01375 383691

St John James, S (Wiggin LLP) *V Zf Ze*
Cheltenham *p189* 01242 224114

St John-Smith, C (CMS Cameron McKenna LLP) *B1*
London EC3 *p17*. 020 7367 3000

St Luce, Ms S (St Luce & Co) *D1 G K1*
London SE15 *p82* 020 7635 9131

St Prix, Ms B (Sternberg Reed) *G H*
Barking *p123* 020 8591 3366
Romford *p366*. 01708 766155

Staal, Miss D S (Sherrards) *E L R1*
London W1 *p78* 020 7478 9010

Staal, R J (Sherrards) *E L R1 Zc*
London W1 *p78* 020 7478 9010

Stabler, Mrs S L (Taylor Vinters)
Cambridge *p176*. 01223 423444

Stables, P G (Howard & Co) *G H*
Barnsley *p124* 01226 215215

Stacey, D J (Wills & Probate Countrywide) *W*
Tavistock *p408*. 01626 334455
Newton Abbot *p330* 01626 332266

Stacey, Miss E J (Spratt Endicott) *W*
Banbury *p122* 01295 204000

Stacey, H (Michael Simkins LLP) *K1*
London WC1 *p79* 020 7874 5600

Stacey, Mrs L D (Stanger Stacey & Mason) *S1 W L E Zv S2*
Witney *p436*. 01993 776491

Stacey, Ms L S (Keoghs and Nicholls, Lindsell & Harris) *L*
Altrincham *p116* 0161 928 9321

Stacey, M G F (LG Lawyers) *E Zc*
London SE1 *p50*. 020 7379 0000

Stacey, M W (Stanger Stacey & Mason) *K1 D1 D2 V K3*
Witney *p436*. 01993 776491

Stacey, N J (Ashurst LLP) *C1 T1 Zb*
London EC2 *p7* 020 7638 1111

Stachiw, J N (Stachiw Bashir Green) *N Q*
Bradford *p155* 01274 404010

Stack, Miss C (Brooks & Partners)
Camberley *p173*. 01276 681217

Staddon, Mrs L C (Ford & Warren) *J2 N O*
Leeds *p273* 0113 243 6601

Stader, R W (Blake Lapthorn) *O B2 U2 Zl Zq A3*
London EC1 *p13*. 020 7405 2000

Staff, Mrs J S (Salmons) *K1 K2 D1 D2 K3*
Stoke-on-Trent *p398*. 01782 639827

Stafford, C (Penningtons) *J1*
Godalming *p231*. 01483 791800

Stafford, D L (Kenneth Bush) *A1 C1 E L R1 S1 T1 W*
King's Lynn *p266* 01553 692737

Stafford, G (Jones Day) *C1*
London EC4 *p46*. 020 7039 5959

Stafford, G E (Bright & Sons) *D1 D2 N K1 Q K3*
Maldon *p299*. 01621 852323

Stafford, G E (Sheridans) *E L S1*
London WC1 *p78* 020 7079 0100

Stafford, Mrs G L D (Newport City Council)
Newport *p466* 01633 656656

Stafford, Miss J L (Cambridgeshire County Council) *D1 X*
Cambridge *p453*. 01223 717111

Stafford, L P (Rosling King) *Zj O N Zq*
London EC4 *p73*. 020 7353 2353

Stafford, N J (Maxwell Winward LLP) *E L R2 S2*
London EC4 *p59*. 020 7651 0000

Stafford, P (Jones Day) *C1*
London EC4 *p46*. 020 7039 5959

Stafford, P J (Cartmell Shepherd) *Q O*
Carlisle *p182*. 01228 516666

Stafford, P T (HallmarkHulme)
Worcester *p439* 01905 726600

Stafford, Mrs R (Fendom Dawson & Partners) *W*
High Wycombe *p250*. 01494 450361

Stafford, Mrs R V (High Peak Borough Council)
Chapel-en-le-Frith *p454* . . . 0845 129 7777

Stagg, G P (McMillan Williams) *Q O L Zq A3 N*
Coulsdon *p199*. 020 8668 4131
Reigate *p363* 01737 221212

Stagg, Ms J (Fenwick Elliott) *Zc R2*
London WC2 *p31* 020 7421 1986

Staiano, L A (Carter-Ruck) *Zk Q O M2*
London EC4 *p18*. 020 7353 5005

Staines, Ms H C (DAC Beachcroft) *N J1 M1 P*
Bristol *p162* 0117 918 2000

Staines, Ms J (Charles Russell LLP) *O Q N*
London EC4 *p19*. 020 7203 5000

Staines, Mrs R J (Girlings) *S1*
Ashford *p119* 01233 647377

Stainton, Ms T (Milburns Solicitors) *J1 S1*
Workington *p440*. 01900 67363

Stait, Mrs B G (Tameside Metropolitan Borough Council)
Ashton-under-Lyne *p447*. . . 0161 342 3028

Stait, J (DLA Piper UK LLP)
London EC2 *p24*. 0870 011 1111

Staite, S A (Nabarro LLP)
London WC1 *p63* 020 7524 6000

Staite, Miss Z (Lamb & Holmes) *Q N E F1 L*
Corby *p199* 01536 745168

Stakes, J A (Gordons LLP) *K1 K2 L D1 D2 P Zl*
Leeds *p273* 0113 227 0100

Stakim, Ms C (Morrison & Foerster (UK) LLP) *J1*
London EC2 *p62*. 020 7920 4000

Stalbow, N (Ashurst LLP)
London EC2 *p7* 020 7638 1111

Stallard, Miss E (Welsh Health Legal Services) *F1 G H K1 L N*
Cardiff *p453* 029 2031 5500

Stallard, Miss H (Field Fisher Waterhouse LLP)
London EC3 *p31*. 020 7861 4000

Stallard, J H (Whitehead Monckton) *E S2 S1 R2 L C2*
Maidstone *p299* 01622 698000

Stallard, N C M (Bishop & Sewell LLP) *S1 L K1 O J1 C1 W*
London WC1 *p13* 020 7631 4141

Stallard, R F W (Stallard March & Edwards) *N O Q F1*
Worcester *p440* 01905 613404

Stallard, R J (James Stallard & Co) *C1 E O Q J1 B1 S1 W T1 Zb Ze Zf*
London WC2 *p82* 020 7430 1861

Stallard, W B (Stallard March & Edwards) *S1 C1 E W S2 Zd*
Worcester *p440* 01905 613404

Stallebrass, P (CMS Cameron McKenna LLP) *I1 I2*
London EC3 *p17*. 020 7367 3000

Stambouleiu, H N (Foster & Partners) *N O Q Zl*
Bristol *p162* 0117 922 0229

Stamm, Mrs S A (Vine Orchards)
Exmouth *p223*. . . .01395 273035 / 264646

Stammers, Ms S (Hertfordshire County Council)
Hertford *p460* 01992 555555

Stamp, Mrs K J C (Everys) *C1 E*
Honiton *p252* 01404 43431

Stamp, M A (Linklaters LLP)
London EC2 *p54*. 020 7456 2000

Stanbanks, E J (Cartwright King) *G H D1*
Derby *p208* 01332 346111
Leicester *p279*. 0116 253 9222
Nottingham *p336*. 0115 958 7444

Stanborough, Ms V E (Hamlins LLP) *E*
London W1 *p38* 020 7355 6000

Stanbrook, N (Lawrence Hamblin) *E S1 S2 R2*
Henley-on-Thames *p247*. . . 01491 411884

Stanbrough, D A (Bradly Trimmer) *W*
Alton *p116*. 01420 88024

Stanbury, C C (Herrington & Carmichael LLP)
Camberley *p173*. 01276 686222

Stancliffe, D (Southcombe & Hayley) *O Q B1 C1 Ze*
Westminster *p81*. 020 7935 6631

Stancliffe, E A (Burton Stancliffe & Co) *S1*
Thatcham *p410* 01635 867967

Stancliffe, Mrs M (Pritchard Englefield) *W*
London EC2 *p69*. 020 7972 9720

Stancombe, M F (Hogan Lovells International LLP)
London EC1 *p42*. 020 7296 2000

Stanczyk, Miss J M (Miles Preston & Co) *K1*
London EC4 *p69*. 020 7583 0583

Standen, Mrs D (Hine Downing Solicitors) *C1 E S1 S2*
Falmouth *p223*. 01326 316655

Standen, E (HilliersHRW Solicitors) *S2 C1 E L O Q*
Kempston *p264* 01234 858000

Standen, T (Radcliffes Le Brasseur)
Westminster *p70*. 020 7222 7040

Standish, Ms T A (Bolton Magistrates Court)
Bolton *p450* 01204 558200

Standley, Mrs M (Dolmans) *Q*
Cardiff *p178* 029 2034 5531

Stanfield, A T (Guildford Borough Council)
Guildford *p459*. 01483 505050
Sevenoaks *p470*. 01732 227000

Stanfield, S J (Colemans - CTTS) *N*
Manchester *p302* 0161 876 2500

Stanford, Miss A (Tustain Jones & Co)
Bedworth *p130*. 024 7664 3222

Stanford-Tuck, M D (Taylor Wessing) *T1 W K1 S1 L G A1 D1 Zd Zf Zo*
London EC4 *p86*. 020 7300 7000

Stanger, R A N (Judge & Priestley) *S1 E W C1 J1 L R1 A1 B1 T1 Zl*
Bromley *p166* 020 8290 0333

Stangoe, K M (Geoffrey Leaver Solicitors LLP) *O*
Milton Keynes *p317* 01908 692769

Stanhope, Miss J (J D Spicer & Co) *G*
London NW6 *p81* 020 7625 5590

Stanier, S J (Kelly & Co) *S2 E R2 S1*
Leeds *p275* 0113 244 2113

Staniforth, D P (Norrie Waite & Slater) *G H V J1*
Sheffield *p377* 0114 276 6166

Staniland, R (Nelsons)
Nottingham *p338*. 0115 958 6262

Stanion, S P (Marrons) *F1 J1 N O Q Zl Zp*
Leicester *p280*. 0116 289 2200

Stanley, Ms A J (Bindmans LLP) *Zi Zg*
London WC1 *p12* 020 7833 4433

Stanley, C G A (MFG Solicitors) *N J1 Q O F1 L Zk*
Kidderminster *p265* 01562 820181

Stanley, Miss D (Cox Cooper Limited) *E J1*
Birmingham *p137* 0121 777 0015

Stanley, E A E (Elborne Mitchell LLP)
London EC3 *p29*. 020 7320 9000

Stanley, Mrs H M (Sherrards) *E S2*
St Albans *p390* 01727 832830

Stanley, I G (Allen & Overy LLP)
London E1 *p5* 020 3088 0000

Stanley, J (Hague Lambert) *K1 K3 Q J1*
Urmston *p417* 0161 747 7321

Stanley, J A (Brighouses) *S1 W L*
Southport *p388* . .01704 534101 / 500151

Stanley, J M (Department for Business, Enterprise and Regulatory Reform)
London SW1 *p105*. 020 7215 0105

Stanley, Ms L (LG Lawyers)
London SE1 *p50*. 020 7379 0000

Stanley, P R (O H Parsons & Partners) *G H J1 M1*
London WC2 *p66* 020 7379 7277

Stanley, R (DLC Solicitors Limited) *Zi*
Darwen *p207* 01254 761234

Stannard, A G (Stephen Rimmer LLP) *G H*
Eastbourne *p216*. 01323 644222

Stannard, C (TMJ Legal Services LLP) *Q L N J1 B1 V F1 F2*
Wingate *p434* 01429 838225
Hartlepool *p243* 01429 235616

Stannard, D C (The Dental Law Partnership) *Zr*
Nantwich *p320*. 01270 613320

Stannard, Ms J (Bird & Bird LLP) *C1 U1*
London EC4 *p13*. 020 7415 6000

Stannard, N (Eric Cowsill Solicitor)
Ivybridge *p263*. 01752 205202

Stannard, P A C (Travers Smith LLP) *Zo*
London EC1 *p87*. 020 7295 3000

Stanners, B (TV Edwards LLP) *N Q Zq*
London EC3 *p85*. 020 7790 7000

Stanning, D R (B P Collins LLP) *C1 C2 J1 F1 Zp*
Gerrards Cross *p229*. 01753 889995

Stansfield, C (Nelsons) *N Zw*
Nottingham *p338*. 0115 958 6262

Stansfield, Ms J M (Blake Lapthorn) *S1 W P F1*
Oxford *p342* 01865 248607

Stansfield, Miss L M (Sparling Benham & Brough) *W*
Colchester *p198* 01206 733733

Stansfield, Mrs T (SFN Solicitors) *N*
Burnley *p169* 01282 421284

Stansfield-Glass, M (Hurleys)
Bournemouth *p152*. 01202 436100

Stanton, Ms A M (Beverley Morris & Co) *S1 W S2 E*
Lewisham *p62* 020 8852 4433

Stanton, B M A (Boyes Turner) *J1*
Reading *p360* 0118 959 7711

Stanton, C (Hill Dickinson LLP) *O Q Zq*
Liverpool *p288*. 0151 600 8000

Stanton, D N (QualitySolicitors D'Angibau) *C1 E S1 S2*
Poole *p353* 01202 672598

Stanton, Miss E (Kennedys) *N O J1*
Manchester *p306* 0161 829 2599

Stanton, Mrs J E (Stantons) *D1 K1 E D2 K3*
Gravesend *p233*. 01474 579940

Stanton, Miss J J (Stanton & Doran) *S1 W E L*
Upminster *p417* 01708 641781

Stanton, P J (Michael W Halsall) *N*
Newton-le-Willows *p330* . . . 01942 727000

Stanton, R H (Fladgate LLP) *W*
London WC2 *p32* 020 3036 7000

Stanton, Mrs S L (Capsticks Solicitors LLP) *N*
London SW19 *p18*. 020 8780 2211
Richmond upon Thames *p364* 020 8744 0766

Stanton, T G (Wintle & Co) *N K1 D1 L J1 F1 Q*
Bognor Regis *p148* 01243 863021
Selsey *p374* 01243 605947

Stanway, Ms S (Morecrofts Solicitors LLP)
Liverpool *p290*. 0151 236 8871

Stanwell, C (Nabarro LLP) *R1 Zl Zu*
London WC1 *p63* 020 7524 6000

Stanwix, Ms S (Watson Burton LLP) *Zc Q*
Newcastle upon Tyne *p327* . 0845 901 2100

Stanyer, Miss A F (Cumberland Ellis Peirs) *K4 W T1 T2 Zd*
London WC1 *p23* 020 7242 0422

Staple, Ms D (Hodge Jones & Allen LLP) *D1 K1*
London NW1 *p41* 020 7874 8300

Staples, Miss K T (Allen & Overy LLP)
London E1 *p5* 020 3088 0000

Staples, Ms M (Ashurst LLP)
London EC2 *p7* 020 7638 1111

Staples, N (Noble) *G H*
Shefford *p377* 01462 814055

Stapleton, Ms A P (Hertfordshire County Council)
Hertford *p460* 01992 555555

Stapleton, D P (Sills & Betteridge LLP) *C1 S1 E S2*
Coningsby *p199* 01526 344444
Spilsby *p389*. 01790 752277

Stapleton, G (Stapletons Solicitors) *S1 K1*
London N13 *p82*. 020 8886 6876

Stapleton, M A (Dechert) *T1 T2*
London EC4 *p26*. 020 7184 7000

Stapleton, T (Kennedys) *Zj*
London EC3 *p49*. 020 7667 9667

Starck, J C E (Baron Grey) *G Zg O Q Zq*
Twickenham *p416* 020 8891 4311

Stark, Miss E (Granville-West Chivers & Morgan) *K1 S1 W*
Risca *p365* 01633 612353

Stark, Ms F S (Powergen PLC)
Coventry *p456*. . . . 024 7642 4748 / 4000

Stark, M S (Nockolds) *S1 W C1 A1 L E F1 J1 K1 P*
Bishop's Stortford *p144* . . . 01279 755777

Stark, R (Granville-West Chivers & Morgan) *K1 W D1 F1 J1 Zl Zj Zi*
Risca *p365* 01633 612353

Stark, Mrs S (Teacher Stern LLP) *E S2 L*
London WC1 *p86* 020 7242 3191

Stark, W A (Chivers Easton Brown) *S2 E*
Surbiton *p402* 020 8390 6155

Starkey, D M (Pardoes) *K1 A1 Q W P L*
Bridgwater *p158* 01278 457891

Starkey, P (Costain Engineering & Construction Ltd)
Maidenhead *p464* 01628 842444

Starkey, P M (Mowlem PLC)
Isleworth *p462*. 020 8568 9111

Starkey, T (Brabners Chaffe Street) *Zh R2 E S2 R1*
Liverpool *p286*. 0151 600 3000

Starkie, J E (Harrison Drury & Co) *K1 R1 N P M1 C1 E D1 L S1 O X Zj*
Preston *p357* 01772 258321

Starks, G C (Environment Agency (Southern))
Worthing *p477*. 01903 820692

Starling, Ms J A (TV Edwards LLP) *V Zm*
London EC3 *p85*. 020 7790 7000

Starr, I C (Ashurst LLP) *A3 M1 M2 Ze*
London EC2 *p7* 020 7638 1111

Starr, R I (Salans) *C1 C2 M2*
London EC4 *p76*. 020 7429 6000

Starr, R L (Greenwoods Solicitors LLP) *Q N B2 G*
Peterborough *p347* 01733 887700

Starr, T (Starr & Partners LLP)
London EC4 *p82*. 020 7199 1450

Starrs, Mrs D C (Stevens) *G H*
Wolverhampton *p438* 01902 772776

Start, P (Chattertons Solicitors) *K1 G H F1 N J1 D1 B1 Q K3*
Spalding *p389* 01775 768774

Startin, J P (Clausen Miller LLP) *Zj O A3*
London EC3 *p20*. 020 7645 7970

Statham, Ms A (Taylor Wessing)
London EC4 *p86*. 020 7300 7000

Statham, P M (Pattinson & Brewer) *M1 J1 Zk Zp*
London WC1 *p66* 020 7400 5100

Statham, R J H (Inghams) *E L Q S1 W Zl*
Blackpool *p146* 01253 353308
Poulton-le-Fylde *p355* 01253 890545

Staton, C (DLA Piper UK LLP)
Sheffield *p375* 0870 011 1111

Staton, J M (Schofield Sweeney) *N O Q J1 Zq Zl J2*
Bradford *p154* 01274 306000

Statton, Mrs J (Southern Water Services Ltd)
Worthing *p477*. 01903 264444

Stauffer, Miss V S (Woodford Stauffer) *M1 N P C1 B1 F1 L R1 J1 Ze Zc Zj*
Farnborough *p224*. 01252 375376

Staunton, Miss C J (Bower & Bailey) *K1 J1 Q W*
Witney *p436*. 01993 705095

Staunton, H C T (Hugh Staunton) *C1 W*
Grantham *p232* 01476 861972

Staunton, Ms P (Osborne Clarke) *C1 I U2 Ze*
London EC2 *p65*. 020 7105 7000

Staunton, R M (TLT Solicitors) *C1 B1 Zd Ze Zf*
Bristol *p165* 0117 917 7777

Staveley, C G S (Squire Sanders (UK) LLP) *E L S1 A1*
London EC2 *p81*. 020 7655 1000

Staveley, S A E (SJP Solicitors) *S1 K1 L G P M1 J1 H A1 Zl*
Hunstanton *p258*. 01485 532662

Stawell, K F (Bassets) *G H J1 K1 M1*
Gillingham *p229* 01634 575464

Stead, D (Mills & Reeve) *E R2*
Cambridge *p175*. 01223 364422

Steadman, Mrs G A C (Steadmans) *S1 S2 W E*
Tunbridge Wells *p415* 01892 511102

Steadman, Ms J H (Christopher Harris & Co) *B1 Zc C1 S2 F1 F2 J1 J2 Zh L Zg Zj O Q N*
Sheerness *p375* 01795 661521
Sittingbourne *p380*. 01795 437268

Steadman, Miss N (Hayton Winkley) *W*
Kendal *p264*. 01539 720136

Steadman, T J (Herbert Smith LLP) *C1 C2*
London EC2 *p40*. 020 7374 8000

Steadman, T R (Clifford Chance)
London E14 *p20*. 020 7006 1000

Stear, D E (Kirwans) *S1 L*
Birkenhead *p134*. 0151 608 9078

See p634 for the Key to Work Categories

Stear, P J A (Travers Smith LLP) *Zo*
London EC1 *p87* 020 7295 3000

Stebbing, J A (Stephen Rimmer LLP) *G H K1 D1 F1 L M1 N P V Zl*
Eastbourne *p216* 01323 644222

Stebbings, Miss A (Durham County Council)
Durham *p457* 0191 383 3513

Stebbings, A J F (Pemberton Greenish LLP) *T2 W Zd*
London SW3 *p66* 020 7591 3333

Stebbings, Miss J K (Hewitsons) *W*
Northampton *p332* 01604 233233

Stebbings, R W (R W Stebbings) *G H*
Plymouth *p350* 01752 202287

Stedman, D (Penningtons)
Godalming *p231* 01483 791800

Stedman, Miss G S (Commonwealth War Graves Commission)
Maidenhead *p464* 01628 507137

Stedman, P (Zatman & Co)
Manchester *p311* 0161 832 2500

Steed, D R (BWTLaw LLP) *S2 S1*
Epsom *p219* 01372 725655

Steed, J (Mills & Reeve) *L*
Norwich *p335* 01603 660155

Steed, N H C (Jackamans) *S1 W E A1 T1 R1 L C1*
Ipswich *p262* 01473 255591

Steedman, Mrs J (Stroud and Swindon Building Society)
Stroud *p473* 01453 757011

Steel, A (Plexus Law (A Trading Name of Parabis Law LLP))
Manchester *p309* 0844 245 4100

Steel, A H (Stafford Young Jones) *S1 S2 W Zd*
London EC4 *p82* 020 7623 9490

Steel, C (Canter Levin & Berg) *Q N*
St Helens *p391* 01744 634141

Steel, Ms C (LG Lawyers)
London SE1 *p50* 020 7379 0000

Steel, C J (Steel & Co) *S1 S2 C1 A1 W Zl K1 E L N*
Knaresborough *p268* 01423 869977
Wetherby *p429* 01937 845539

Steel, Miss D S (Beaty & Co) *W Q*
Wigton *p432* 01697 342121

Steel, Ms F (Watson Farley & Williams)
London EC2 *p90* 020 7814 8000

Steel, J R (Blake Lapthorn) *A1 E P Zd X*
Chandlers Ford *p184* 023 8090 8090

Steel, Miss L (Harvey Ingram Borneos)
Milton Keynes *p317* 01908 696002

Steel, L A (L A Steel) *N Q O F1 F2 J1 Zp Zr R1 Zw*
Barnsley *p125* 01226 770909

Steel, M G (Ewart Price) *S1 W L P N M1 K1 J1 E T1 Zc Zj Zk*
Welwyn Garden City *p425* . . 01707 332383

Steel, Ms R (Salans) *J1*
London EC4 *p76* 020 7429 6000

Steele, Miss A (JWP Solicitors) *K1 D1*
Wakefield *p418* 01924 387171

Steele, Miss A E (Eatons) *K1 K3*
Bradford *p153* 0845 660 0660
Bradford *p154* 01274 741841

Steele, C B (Ashfords LLP) *Ze O Zw*
Exeter *p220* 01392 337000

Steele, D R (Steele Raymond) *C1 I J1 C2*
Bournemouth *p152* 01202 294566

Steele, Mrs G (Flint Bishop Solicitors) *T1 V W*
Derby *p208* 01332 340211

Steele, J (Barlow Robbins LLP) *C2 C1*
Guildford *p235* 01483 562901

Steele, Ms J M (Bentleys Stokes & Lowless)
London EC3 *p12* 020 7782 0990

Steele, K J (Coffin Mew & Clover) *E L R1 R2 S2 Zh*
Fareham *p223* 01329 825617

Steele, L H (Rotherham Metropolitan Borough Council) *S1 G K1 M1 W F1 P H*
Rotherham *p470* 01709 382121

Steele, M J (Pannone LLP) *O W F2 Zq*
Manchester *p308* 0161 909 3000

Steele, Mrs N (Stevens) *G H*
Stafford *p393* 01785 250908

Steele, N J (Morlings)
Maidstone *p299* 01622 673081

Steele, P M (Reed Smith LLP) *Za*
London EC2 *p71* 020 3116 3000

Steele, Ms S J (The Lister Croft Partnership) *S1 W*
Wakefield *p418* 0871 220 1333

Steele, Ms S P (Treasury Solicitors Department)
London WC2 *p110* 020 7210 3000

Steele, T C (Palmers) *W S1 T2 L*
South Woodham Ferrers *p384* 01245 322111

Steele, T D (Macfarlanes) *E*
London EC4 *p56* 020 7831 9222

Steele, T M (Sefton Metropolitan Borough Council)
Southport *p472* 01704 533133

Steele-Williams, S T (Coles Miller Solicitors LLP) *E S1 J1 N Q*
Bournemouth *p151* 01202 293226

Steemson, Miss A J (Lodders Solicitors LLP) *S2 E R2*
Stratford-upon-Avon *p400* . . . 01789 293259

Steen, Ms L C (Lynne Steen Commercial Solicitor) *C1 J1 C2 E C3 F1 M1 M2 O P Ze Zd Zy*
Chorley *p194* 01257 452044

Steen, R L H (May May & Merrimans) *W T2 Zd*
London WC1 *p59* 020 7405 8932

Steen, S (Steen & Co Employment Solicitors) *J1*
Oxford *p344* 01865 784101

Steene, Mrs D K (Steene & Co) *W*
Elstree *p218* 020 8953 7707

Steer, B M J (Holley & Steer)
Burnham-on-Sea *p169* 01278 788991

Steer, J (Potter & Co) *E Q R1 S1*
Matlock *p313* 01629 582308

Steer, M (RHW Solicitors LLP) *O Q A3 B1 Zq*
Guildford *p237* 01483 302000

Steer, R A (West Midlands Probation Board)
Birmingham *p450* . 0121 631 3484 ext: 2007

Steer, R A (Richard Steer & Co) *S1 Q O N L K1 E C1 G*
Teddington *p409* 020 8977 8621

Steggles, H (Howes Percival LLP) *Ze*
Leicester *p280* 0116 247 3500

Steggles, M (Thomson Snell & Passmore) *L Q*
Tunbridge Wells *p415* 01892 510000

Steggles, Ms S M (Taylor Haldane Barlex LLP) *G H*
Chelmsford *p187* 0845 293 7688

Stein, J H (Simmons Stein) *E L S1 S2*
Stanmore *p394* 020 8954 8080

Stein, R (Leigh Day & Co) *R1 V X M1 Zu Zg*
London EC1 *p52* 020 7650 1200

Stein, T (Financial Services Authority)
London E14 *p106* 020 7066 1000

Steinberg, B H (Steinbergs) *S1 N Q O F1 K1 W J1 Zl Zs Zi*
Liverpool *p290* 0151 521 4491

Steinberg, D J (Clifford Chance)
London E14 *p20* 020 7006 1000

Steinberg, Miss L M (Meikles) *K1 S1 W G H*
Spennymoor *p389* 01388 814336

Steiner, Ms K J (Howells LLP) *G H*
Sheffield *p376* 0114 249 6666

Steiner, P (Mayer Brown International LLP) *T1 T2*
London EC2 *p59* 020 3130 3000

Steiner, Dr S (Pritchard Englefield) *C1 J1 Q*
London EC2 *p69* 020 7972 9720

Steinfeld, M R (Dechert) *C1 C2*
London EC4 *p26* 020 7184 7000

Stell, S R B (Last Cawthra Feather LLP) *O K1 Q B1 Zl Zw*
Bradford *p154* 01274 848800

Stendall, T (Hopkins) *C1 C2 E S2*
Mansfield *p311* 01623 468468

Stenger, K A (Longden Walker & Renney) *S1 E C1 L R1*
Sunderland *p401* 0191 567 7024

Stenner-Evans, J (Gabbs LLP) *A1 S1 W T1 L E F1 J1 K1*
Hay-on-Wye *p245* 01497 820312

Stenner-Evans, T (Michelmores LLP) *J1 Zi*
Exeter *p221* 01392 688688

Stennett, Mrs C M I (CGM) *S1 E K1 B1 Zl Zb*
Southampton *p385* 023 8063 2733

Stennett, M (Stennett & Stennett) *E K1 M1 N P S1*
London N14 *p82* 020 8920 3190

Stennett, R H M (CGM) *J1 L N O Q Za Zj*
Southampton *p385* 023 8063 2733

Stennett, Ms S (SSB Solicitors) *Zf*
London SW6 *p75* 020 7348 7630

Stenning, Mrs J L (Watson Marshal) *W S1 S2 L E K4*
London W4 *p90* 020 8987 0100

Stenson, Miss F P (Wills Group Ltd)
London EC3 *p110* 020 7488 8111

Stenson, G (Langleys)
Lincoln *p284* 01522 888555

Stenson, G W (The Ringrose Law Group - Richard Harwood) *O J1 B1*
Lincoln *p285* 01522 814700

Stenson, L M (O'Neill Patient) *S1*
Stockport *p396* 0161 483 8555

Stephen, I J (Parker Rhodes Hickmotts) *W*
Rotherham *p367* 01709 511100

Stephen, Ms J (Cripps Harries Hall LLP) *E*
Tunbridge Wells *p415* 01892 515121

Stephen, K G (Mobil Oil Company Ltd)
Milton Keynes *p466* 01908 853000

Stephen, Mrs L (Emsleys) *W T2*
Rothwell *p368* 0113 201 4900

Stephen, N A (BUPA)
London WC1 *p104* 020 7656 2305

Stephens, A C (Williamson & Soden) *G H*
Solihull *p383* 0121 733 8000

Stephens, A G (Benson Watkins) *M1 P H G*
Swansea *p404* 01792 464564

Stephens, A P (Greenways) *S1 E L K1 D1 W Zl Zc K2 S2 C1*
Newquay *p329* . . . .01637 872361 / 872251

Stephens, Mrs B R (Hethertons LLP) *W T2*
York *p445* 01904 528200

Stephens, Miss C A (Peter Lynn & Partners) *K1*
Swansea *p405* 01792 450010

Stephens, Ms C A (Battens)
Yeovil *p443* 01935 846000

Stephens, C G (Follett Stock LLP) *A1 S2 E*
Truro *p414* 01872 241700

Stephens, D (Ashurst LLP)
London EC2 *p7* 020 7638 1111

Stephens, D A (Renders)
Cardiff *p180* 029 2054 4900

Stephens, D C (Battens) *R1 K1 P Zc*
Yeovil *p443* 01935 846000

Stephens, D H (Sydney G Thomas & Co) *S1 E W A1 L T1 K1 Zl*
Builth Wells *p168* 01982 553289

Stephens, G B (Stephens McDonald & Robson) *G W S1 E N H L F1 J1 Q Zl*
Newcastle upon Tyne *p327* . 0191 232 0675

Stephens, G J (Martyn Prowel) *K1 D2 D1*
Cardiff *p180* 029 2047 0909

Stephens, G S (Phillips & Co) *S1 S2 W T1 T2 A1*
Ludlow *p294* 01584 873156

Stephens, H O P (Pinsent Masons LLP) *C1 E L R2 Zb Zd Zh Zu*
Birmingham *p141* 0121 200 1050

Stephens, Miss H R (Langley Wellington) *K1 K3*
Gloucester *p230* 01452 521286

Stephens, J (Ince & Co Services Ltd)
London E1 *p44* 020 7481 0010

Stephens, J L (Clarke Willmott) *E S2 R2*
Southampton *p385*0845 209 1000 / 0117 305 6000

Stephens, J M H (Jonathan Stephens & Co) *A1 A2 S2 S1 W M1*
Usk *p417* 01291 673344

Stephens, Mrs K J (Bird & Bird LLP) *Ze*
London EC4 *p13* 020 7415 6000

Stephens, Miss L (Louise Stephens & Co) *K1 G H N Q S1 W V D1 L Zv Zl Zh*
Risca *p365* . . . . .01633 614005 / 601144

Stephens, L D (Andrew Jackson) *J1*
Hull *p257* 01482 325242

Stephens, L D (Shulmans) *J1*
Leeds *p276* 0113 245 2833

Stephens, M (Hugh James)
Cardiff *p179* 029 2022 4871

Stephens, M (Rooks Rider) *S2 E*
London EC1 *p73* 020 7689 7000

Stephens, M H (Finers Stephens Innocent LLP) *F1 E P G S1 N M1 H C1 B1 Zd Ze Zf Zk*
London W1 *p32* 020 7323 4000

Stephens, M J (L G Williams & Prichard) *N Q O Zc L R1 Zr*
Cardiff *p181* 029 2022 9716

Stephens, M P (Hill Dickinson LLP) *E R1 R2 S2 L*
Liverpool *p288* 0151 600 8000

Stephens, P A (Weightmans LLP)
Liverpool *p291* 0151 227 2601

Stephens, P J (Phillips & Co) *S1 S2 W L E A1 T2*
Ludlow *p294* 01584 873156

Stephens, R (Ceredigion County Council) *G H K1 D1 Q N J1 L Zm*
Aberaeron *p447* 01545 570881

Stephens, R B (Hine Downing Solicitors) *W T2 K4*
Falmouth *p223* 01326 316655

Stephens, R M M (Vanderpump & Sykes) *J1 Q O Zp*
Enfield *p219* 020 8367 3999

Stephens, Ms S (Anthony Gold) *L Zg*
London SE17 *p6* 020 7940 4000

Stephens, Ms S (G T Stewart Solicitors) *D1 K1*
London SE22 *p83* 020 8299 6000

Stephens, S M (Purcell Parker) *D1 G H L S1 V W Zv*
Birmingham *p141* 0121 236 9781

Stephens, S R (LG Lawyers) *E S2*
London SE1 *p50* 020 7379 0000

Stephens, T (Holman Fenwick Willan)
London EC3 *p42* 020 7264 8000

Stephenson, Mrs A (Norton Peskett)
Great Yarmouth *p234* 01493 849200

Stephenson, A J (Carter-Ruck) *Q Ze Zk O*
London EC4 *p18* 020 7353 5005

Stephenson, C J (Stephensons Solicitors LLP) *C1 C2 C3*
Leigh *p282* 01942 777777

Stephenson, Ms C M (Countryside Properties PLC) *E W S1 S2*
Brentwood *p451* 01277 260000

Stephenson, G C (Spratt Endicott) *S1 S2 R2 L*
Banbury *p122* 01295 204000

Stephenson, Ms H (Davitt Jones Bould) *R1*
Taunton *p408* 01823 279279

Stephenson, I W (Darling & Stephensons) *E C1 C2 S2 T2 T1 W S1 A1 Zd X J1 Zl*
Barnard Castle *p123* 01325 489000
Darlington *p206* 01325 489000

Stephenson, J (KSH Law Firm) *C1 J1 O Q Zq*
Newcastle upon Tyne *p325* . 0191 232 5232

Stephenson, J (Winston Solicitors LLP) *J1 Zp*
Leeds *p278* 0113 320 5000

Stephenson, J (Howard Kennedy LLP) *Zf*
London W1 *p48* 020 7636 1616
London EC2 *p81* 020 7655 1000

Stephenson, J C (Stephenson Reynell) *S1 W*
Windermere *p434* 01539 488622

Stephenson, J M (John Stephenson & Co) *E G J1 K1 L N O Q S1 W Zv*
St Albans *p390* 01727 847983

Stephenson, J M (Bircham Dyson Bell) *E L R2 S2*
Westminster *p13* 020 7227 7000

Stephenson, M F (Fairweather Stephenson & Co) *S1 W C1 G H J1 Zl*
Felixstowe *p225* 01394 277941

Stephenson, M J (Beswicks) *G H*
Hanley *p239* 01782 205000

Stephenson, P (Barlow Robbins LLP) *C1 C2*
Guildford *p235* 01483 562901

Stephenson, Miss P (Ashton KCJ) *F1 F2 B1 L O Q N Zq*
Bury St Edmunds *p171* . . . 01284 762331

Stephenson, P M J (KBL Solicitors) *C1 Zw C2*
Bolton *p149* 01204 527777

Stephenson, P S G (Darling & Stephensons) *E K4 J1 K1 Zl T2 W N Zr Zq Q S1 L F1*
Darlington *p206* 01325 489000

Stephenson, Miss R M (Cartmell Shepherd) *W*
Brampton *p156* 01697 72378

Stephenson, S P (Marsden Rawsthorn LLP) *S1 S2 E C1 R2*
Chorley *p194* 01257 279511

Stephenson, Miss T C (Brent Magistrates Court)
London NW10 *p104* 020 8451 7111

Stephenson, T C (Hill Dickinson LLP)
London EC3 *p41* 020 7283 9033

Stepien, K J (Stepien Lake) *E S1 R1 Zc*
London W1 *p83* 020 7467 3030

Stepien, Miss T A (Wall James Chappell) *S1*
Stourbridge *p399* 01384 371622

Sterling, M (Scott Duff & Co) *K1 K3 D1*
Carlisle *p182* 01228 531054

Sterling, M C (Arnison & Co Solicitors Limited) *K1 D1*
Penrith *p346* 01768 862007

Sterling, T (Thompsons (formerly Robin/Brian Thompson & Partners))
London SW19 *p87* 020 8947 4163

Sterlini, L (Tyrer Roxburgh & Co) *L S1 E*
Haringey *p89* 020 8889 3319

Stern, Ms C K (Lewis Silkin LLP) *J1*
London EC4 *p53* 020 7074 8000

Stern, N (Edwards Angell Palmer & Dodge)
London EC2 *p28* 020 7583 4055

Stern, S S W (Teacher Stern LLP)
London WC1 *p86* 020 7242 3191

Stern, Miss V C (Vivien Stern Solicitor) *S1 W*
Camden *p83* 020 7328 5532

Sternberg, G J (Sternberg Reed) *E S1 W*
Barking *p123* 020 8591 3366

Sternberg, J (Sony Music Entertainment (UK) Ltd)
London SW6 *p109* 020 7384 7500

Sternberg, Mrs S E A (Bolsover District Council)
Chesterfield *p455* 01246 240000

Sternfeld, Ms D (Rouse Legal (Formerly Willoughby & Partners)) *Ze A3*
London E14 *p74* 020 7536 4100

Sterratt, M C (Sterratt & Co) *S1 W K4 L S2*
Skipton *p381* 01756 795069

Sterrett, D T (Hughes Paddison) *D1 K1 K3*
Cheltenham *p188* 01242 574244

Stetzel, C (Ince & Co Services Ltd)
London E1 *p44* 020 7481 0010

Stevens, Mrs A (Charles Russell LLP) *N*
Guildford *p235* 01483 252525

Stevens, A G B (Taylor Wessing) *Zb*
London EC4 *p86* 020 7300 7000

Stevens, Ms B C (Bower & Bailey) *W T2*
Oxford *p343* 01865 311133

Stevens, Ms C (Rosleys) *K1 L V*
Nottingham *p338* 0115 958 0584

Stevens, D (Maples Teesdale LLP) *A3 B2 O Q Zq L*
London EC2 *p58* 020 7600 3800

Stevens, Ms D (Ellis Jones) *Q J1 F1*
Bournemouth *p151* 01202 525333

Stevens, Ms D I (Bromsgrove District Council)
Bromsgrove *p452* 01527 881288

Stevens, Ms E (Radcliffes Le Brasseur)
Westminster *p70* 020 7222 7040

Stevens, Mrs E R (Stevens Lucas) *W S1*
Chirk *p193* 01691 777949

Stevens, G R (Hethertons LLP) *J1*
York *p445* 01904 528200

Stevens, Mrs H (Ware & Kay LLP)
York *p445* 01904 716000

Stevens, Mrs J (Collins Dryland & Thorowgood LLP) *S1 W S2*
Tilehurst *p411* 0118 942 2448

Stevens, J A (J A Stevens & Co) *A1 C1 E L R1 S1 T1*
Epsom *p219* 01372 745288

Stevens, J A C (Shacklocks) *W*
Ripley *p365* 01773 743513

Stevens, Miss J L E (Stamp Jackson and Procter) *E S2 L A1 R2 C1 S1 W*
Hull *p258* 01482 324591

Stevens, Ms J M (Thompsons (formerly Robin/Brian Thompson & Partners)) *N V G J1 H*
London WC1 *p87* 020 7290 0000

Stevens, J R (Legal Aid Area Office No 4 (South Western))
Bristol *p452* 0117 921 4801

Stevens, M (Debenhams Ottaway) *W*
St Albans *p390* 01727 837161

Stevens, M (Walker Morris) *C1 Zu*
Leeds *p277* 0113 283 2500

Stevens, M D (Hallett & Co) *J1 N*
Ashford *p119* 01233 625711

Stevens, M D R (Yorkshire Water Services Ltd)
Bradford *p451* 01274 804159

Stevens, M F (Cripps Harries Hall LLP) *E P L R1 R2 S2*
Tunbridge Wells *p415* 01892 515121

Stevens, N (London Borough of Southwark)
London SE1 *p109* 020 7525 5000

Stevens, N J (Bath & Wansdyke Magistrates Court)
Bath *p448* 01225 463281

Stevens, P (Judge & Priestley) *O Q W*
Bromley *p166* 020 8290 0333

Stevens, P (David Rubie Mitchell & Co)
Sutton *p403* 020 8641 0575

Stevens, P A (Olswang LLP) *Ze O I Zf Zw*
London WC1 *p64* 020 7067 3000

Stevens, P B (Jackamans) *O Q*
Ipswich *p262* 01473 255591

Stevens, P B M (Paul Stevens & Co) *G H S1 W T1 D1 P*
Bristol *p165* 0117 942 9308

Stevens, P E (Eddowes Perry Adams Roberts & Co) *C1 E J1 S1 W*
Birmingham *p138* 0121 373 7395

6

Stevens, P H H (Neville-Jones & Co) *W K4 T2*
Swanage *p404*. . . .01929 422666 / 423761
Wareham *p421* 01929 552471

Stevens, P J (Stevens Lucas) *S2 E J1 S1*
Chirk *p193*. 01691 777949

Stevens, P J (Wade Stevens & Co) *C1 B1 Zj S2 E Zf*
Orpington *p342* 01689 831122

Stevens, P J (ClarksLegal LLP) *R1*
London WC2 *p20* 020 7539 8000
Reading *p360* 0118 958 5321
London W1 *p46* 020 7339 7000

Stevens, Ms R E (Sefton Metropolitan Borough Council)
Southport *p472* 01704 533133

Stevens, R J (Luton Borough Council)
Luton *p464* 01582 546000

Stevens, S (Eddowes Waldron) *G H*
Derby *p208* 01332 348484

Stevens, Ms S A M (Allen Hoole Solicitors) *G H*
Bristol *p160* 0117 942 0901

Stevens, Ms S L (Taylor Walton LLP) *K1*
St Albans *p390* 01727 845245

Stevens, Miss V (Huntingdonshire District Council)
Huntingdon *p461*. 01480 388388

Stevens, Ms W M (Anthony Clark & Co) *K3 K1*
Lincoln *p284*. 01522 512321

Stevenson, A (Hopkins) *W*
Mansfield *p311*. 01623 468468

Stevenson, A (Mills & Reeve)
London EC3 *p61*. 020 7648 9220

Stevenson, A (Prime & Co) *E L C1 R1 S1 S2*
Rugby *p368* 01788 576289

Stevenson, A J (Bendles) *A1 C1 I L S1 W*
Carlisle *p181*. 01228 522215

Stevenson, Mrs C (Finn Gledhill) *E S1 C1 L W Zc*
Halifax *p238* 01422 330000
Hebden Bridge *p246*. 01422 842451

Stevenson, C (Penningtons)
Basingstoke *p127* 01256 407100

Stevenson, Ms C (Kennedys)
Chelmsford *p186*. 0845 838 4800

Stevenson, Miss C (Trethowans LLP) *K3 K1*
Southampton *p387*. 023 8032 1000

Stevenson, C L (Chris Stevenson) *S2 D1 E G H K1 S1 W*
Doncaster *p212* 01302 341243

Stevenson, D (Pinsent Masons LLP)
London EC2 *p67*. 020 7418 7000

Stevenson, D (The Wilkes Partnership LLP) *N*
Birmingham *p143* 0121 233 4333

Stevenson, D (Rowlinsons) *S1 E M1 L P F1 W J1 C1 K1 Zc Zj Zb*
Frodsham *p227* 01928 735333

Stevenson, Miss G L (Nelsons) *O Q Zq Ze*
Nottingham *p338*. 0115 958 6262

Stevenson, G N (Stevensons Solicitors) *L S1 C1 E J1 W Zi*
Dereham *p209*. 01362 860300

Stevenson, H J (Bowcock & Pursaill) *S1 E W S2*
Leek *p278* 01538 399199

Stevenson, J D (RWPS LLP) *C1 E K1 N*
Poole *p353* 01202 466669

Stevenson, Mrs J E (Prime & Co) *S1 W*
Rugby *p368* 01788 576289

Stevenson, J H (Parlett Kent) *Zr Zq N*
London EC1 *p66*. 020 7430 0712

Stevenson, Mrs J L (John Hodge Solicitors) *W T2*
Weston-super-Mare *p429* . . 01934 623511

Stevenson, Mrs J M (Mary Smith Solicitor) *E S1 W L Zd*
Lowestoft *p294* 01502 511977

Stevenson, M A (TWM Solicitors LLP) *E S1 S2 R1*
Leatherhead *p271*. 01372 374148

Stevenson, Mrs M S (Brain Chase Coles) *N L Q Zh*
Basingstoke *p126* 01256 354481

Stevenson, P E (Hetts) *K1 M1 G P D1 F1 H J1 N L*
Scunthorpe *p373*. 01724 843287

Stevenson, P N (Latimer Hinks) *E A1*
Darlington *p206* 01325 341500

Stevenson, P R (Colemans) *E C1 W T1 S1 A1 L*
Haywards Heath *p245* 01444 459555

Stevenson, Ms R (Clifford Chance)
London E14 *p20*. 020 7006 1000

Stevenson, Mrs S D (Nicholls Henstock & Stevenson) *N Zr*
Altrincham *p117* 0161 980 6099

Stevenson, S J (Thornleys Limited) *S1 S2 E*
Plymouth *p350*. 01752 406977

Stevenson, T W (Metcalfe Copeman & Pettefar) *A1 C1 E W B1*
Thetford *p410*. 01842 756100

Stevenson, Mrs V (Iain Nicholson & Co) *S1 C1 L E W Q*
Ponteland *p351* 01661 823863

Stevenson, Ms V A R (Roythornes LLP) *N Q Zq*
Spalding *p389* 01775 842500

Steventon, Miss A (Weightmans LLP) *C1 E S1 S2 C2*
Manchester *p311* 0161 233 7330

Stevinson, R J (Crosse & Crosse) *N Zq Zr J2*
Exeter *p220* 01392 258451

Steward, D W (Ince & Co Services Ltd)
London E1 *p44* 020 7481 0010

Steward, G (Macfarlanes) *Q*
London EC4 *p56*. 020 7831 9222

Steward, L C (London Borough of Haringey) *L N Q F1*
London N22 *p106* 020 8489 0000

Steward, M J (Hansells) *C1 C2 S2 W*
Norwich *p334* 01603 615731

Steward, P D (Peter Steward & Co) *N*
Great Yarmouth *p234* 01493 332277

Stewart, A K (Mayer Brown International LLP) *C1 C2*
London EC2 *p59*. 020 3130 3000

Stewart, A P (Clifford Chance)
London E14 *p20*. 020 7006 1000

Stewart, B L (Kettering Borough Council) *N P F1 L K1 Zc Zj*
Kettering *p462*. 01536 410333
Wellingborough *p475* 01933 229777

Stewart, Ms B M (Martin Tolhurst Partnership LLP) *K1 S1*
Longfield *p293*. 01474 706168

Stewart, Mrs C (Pannone LLP) *O F1 Zl L U2*
Manchester *p308* 0161 909 3000

Stewart, Mrs C A (Goldstones) *S1 W*
Swansea *p405*. 01792 643021

Stewart, D (Adams & Remers) *C1 C2*
Lewes *p283* 01273 480616

Stewart, D J (Faegre & Benson LLP) *C1 C2 U1*
London EC4 *p30*. 020 7450 4500

Stewart, D L (FWD Law Associates) *J1 Q O*
Newport *p328* 01633 660440

Stewart, D M C (McCarthy Stewart & Booty Solicitors) *G H Zl*
Stowmarket *p400* 01449 612343

Stewart, Mrs E (HM Revenue & Customs)
Salford *p470*. 0870 785 8545

Stewart, Miss E J (Watts & Leeding) *S1 W K1 N Q J1 S2 Zp Zv*
London SE9 *p90*. 020 8850 6366

Stewart, Mrs F (Reed Smith LLP) *O Zc*
London EC2 *p71*. 020 3116 3000

Stewart, F J (Stewarts Law LLP) *O Q B2*
London EC4 *p83*. 020 7822 8000

Stewart, G (Reed Smith LLP)
London EC2 *p71*. 020 3116 3000

Stewart, G (Squire Sanders (UK) LLP) *Zg*
London EC2 *p81*. 020 7655 1000

Stewart, G C (Allen & Overy LLP)
London E1 *p5* 020 3088 0000

Stewart, G T (G T Stewart Solicitors) *G H B2 J2*
London SE22 *p83* 020 8299 6000

Stewart, Miss H (Thomson Snell & Passmore) *W K4*
Tunbridge Wells *p415* 01892 510000

Stewart, Ms H A (Dixon Stewart) *W S1 K1 Q N G Zl*
New Milton *p321*. 01425 621515

Stewart, I (Southern Stewart & Walker) *S1 G H K1 L N Q W V*
South Shields *p384* 0191 456 7788

Stewart, I E F (CIBA Specialty Chemicals PLC)
Macclesfield *p464* 01625 421933

Stewart, I M A (Heringtons) *S1 W E T1 A1 C1 B1 G K1 M1*
Eastbourne *p215*. 01323 411020

Stewart, J (Howard Kennedy LLP) *O Q P M2*
London W1 *p48* 020 7636 1616

Stewart, Mrs J M (Warings Solicitors) *K1 D1 D2*
Blackpool *p147* 01253 293106

Stewart, Ms K (Shoosmiths) *S1*
Northampton *p332*. . 0370 086 3000 / 01604 543000

Stewart, Mrs K (HSBC Legal Department)
Birmingham *p449* 0121 455 2740

Stewart, M (Holls Solicitors)
Beckenham *p129* 020 8658 9767

Stewart, M A (Arnold Davies Vincent Evans) *N Q K1 O L K3*
Lampeter *p269*. 01570 422233

Stewart, M C (Linder Myers Solicitors) *N Q J1*
Manchester *p307* 0844 984 6400

Stewart, Miss M F (Northumberland County Council) *K1 K2 D1 W*
Morpeth *p466* 01670 533000

Stewart, M R O (Clifford Chance)
London E14 *p20*. 020 7006 1000

Stewart, N (Blake Lapthorn) *O Q*
Chandlers Ford *p184* 023 8090 8090

Stewart, N (Howard Kennedy LLP) *E*
London W1 *p48* 020 7636 1616

Stewart, Ms N (Rooks Rider) *O Q L*
London EC1 *p73*. 020 7689 7000

Stewart, Miss N L (Myer Wolff) *J1 N Q Zq Zk O*
Hull *p257* 01482 223693

Stewart, P D (TWM Solicitors LLP) *O Q J1 L N Zl*
Guildford *p237*. 01483 752700

Stewart, P J (Charles Hoile) *S2 E W S1*
Newbury *p322* 01635 45595

Stewart, P J R (Field Fisher Waterhouse LLP)
London EC3 *p31*. 020 7861 4000

Stewart, Mrs R (Russell-Cooke LLP) *S1 S2*
London SW15 *p74*. 020 8789 9111

Stewart, Miss R A (Max Engel & Co LLP) *Q O Zq Zk*
Northampton *p331*. 01604 887450
Cheltenham *p188* 01242 574244

Stewart, R J (Bryan Cave) *E C1 N Zc*
London EC2 *p19*. 020 7207 1100

Stewart, R S (Winston Solicitors LLP) *S1 W*
Leeds *p278* 0113 320 5000

Stewart, Miss S (Tameside Metropolitan Borough Council)
Ashton-under-Lyne *p447*. . . 0161 342 3028

Stewart, Ms S E (Howarth Scott) *K1*
Bexleyheath *p132* 020 8303 4658

Stewart, Miss S F M (Stewarts Law LLP) *N M2 M3*
London EC4 *p83*. 020 7822 8000

Stewart, S M (Wallace Robinson & Morgan) *B1 Zc F1 J1 L Zk O Q Zq*
Solihull *p383*. 0121 705 7571

Stewart, Mrs V (Derby Hospitals NHS Foundation Trust)
Derby *p456* 01332 785419

Sthalekar, R (Levine Mellins Klarfeld) *S2 S1 Q O E L N K1 C1 F1 Zl Zq Ze Zi*
Stanmore *p394* 020 8954 7474
Harrow *p242*. 020 8515 0490

Stibbs, Miss N (Bristol City Council) *J1*
Bristol *p451* 0117 922 2000

Stickland, A K (England Stickland & Neale) *S1 B1 C1 D1 E G H K1 N*
Birmingham *p138* 0121 377 7773

Stileman, Miss T P E (Kidson Bray & Lawson)
Hindhead *p251* 01428 605222

Stiles, D R (Ashurst LLP)
London EC2 *p7* 020 7638 1111

Still, P (Whitehead Monckton) *S1 E*
Maidstone *p299* 01622 698000

Still, T A (Lyons Davidson) *J1 M1*
Bristol *p163* 0117 904 6000

Stillman, Ms A C (EMW) *O A3 J2*
Milton Keynes *p316* 0845 070 6000

Stillwell, K (Payne Marsh Stillwell) *C1 E*
Southampton *p386*. 023 8022 3957

Stillwell, R J (Randle Thomas LLP) *S1 L E A1 S2*
Helston *p246* 01326 572951

Stilton, A J (SGH Martineau LLP) *C1*
Birmingham *p142* 0870 763 2000

Stilwell, Ms E M (Davies & Partners) *W*
Almondsbury *p115* 01454 619619

Stimpson, B (Reynolds Porter Chamberlain LLP)
London E1 *p71* 020 3060 6000

Stimpson, K (Nabarro LLP)
London WC1 *p63* 020 7524 6000

Stimson, G (Financial Services Authority)
London E14 *p106* 020 7066 1000

Stimson, Miss S (Sacker & Partners LLP) *Zo*
London EC2 *p76*. 020 7329 6699

Stinton, Ms M J (Kingsley Napley) *Zr N*
London EC1 *p50*. 020 7814 1200

Stirk, J R (Tarmac Ltd)
Wolverhampton *p477* 01902 353522

Stirk, R I (Rollits LLP) *L S1 Zh E S2*
York *p445* 01904 625790

Stirling, D A J D (Stirling & Co) *K1 S1 W N L Q J1 V Ze*
Bristol *p165* 0117 931 4435

Stirling, Mrs E (Henmans LLP) *Zq O*
Oxford *p343* 01865 781000

Stirling, Ms J (Healys LLP) *J1*
London EC4 *p39*. 020 7822 4000

Stirling, Mrs J E (Squire Sanders (UK) LLP)
Birmingham *p142* 0121 222 3000

Stirling, Ms J J (Nottingham City Council (City Sec Dept)) *K1 D1 D2*
Nottingham *p467*. 0115 915 5555
Lambeth *p32*. 020 7091 2700

Stirling, Ms M E (Stirling & Co) *K1 S1 W D1 L N*
Bristol *p165* 0117 931 4435

Stirmey, T (Cramp & Co) *G H K1 Q V*
Eastbourne *p215*. 01323 720581

Stirrett, A D (Hillyer McKeown LLP) *C1 Ze C2*
Chester *p190* 01244 318131

Stirton, M J (Greenhouse Stirton & Co) *A3 K2 O*
London EC1 *p37*. 020 7490 3456

Stirzaker, I R (Stallard March & Edwards) *Q*
Worcester *p440* 01905 723561

Stirzaker, M R (British Vita PLC)
Middleton *p465* 0161 643 1133

Stisted, W J (Anderson Longmore & Higham) *S1 C1 L T1 W E S2*
Chichester *p192* 01243 787899

Stitson, R B (The Stroud Stitson Partnership) *S1 W P E*
Plymouth *p350*. 01752 660066

Stittle, J M (Taylor & Emmet LLP) *Zl Q N Zr*
Sheffield *p377* 0114 218 4000

Stoate, N M (Taylor Wessing) *O Q M1 M2 C3 C1 Ze*
London EC4 *p86*. 020 7300 7000

Stobart, A (Samuel Phillips Law Firm) *N O P*
Newcastle upon Tyne *p326* . 0191 232 8451

Stobart, Mrs E S (Kidd & Spoor) *D1 K1 L S1 W E S2*
Newcastle upon Tyne *p325* . 0191 273 9217
Whitley Bay *p431* 0191 297 0011

Stobart, J (Harvey Ingram LLP)
Leicester *p280*. 0116 254 5454

Stobbart, A J (Bird & Bird LLP) *C1 U1*
London EC4 *p13*. 020 7415 6000

Stobirski, Ms E (Bright & Sons) *S2 E*
Witham *p435* 01376 512338

Stock, A P (Harold Stock & Co) *Q C1 R2 S2 E*
Ashton-under-Lyne *p120*. . .01457 835597 / 835034

Stock, J M A (QualitySolicitors Hill & Abbott) *C1 E J1 P C2 R1 S2*
Chelmsford *p187*. 01245 258892

Stock, M J (Gabb & Co) *C1 T1 W A1 R1*
Abergavenny *p113*. 01873 852432

Stock, M R (OGR Stock Denton) *C1 E R2 L S1 W*
London N3 *p64* 020 8349 0321

Stock, S R (Thurloe & Lyndhurst LLP) *E O*
London WC2 *p87* 0333 123 2255

Stockall, N R (Higgs & Sons) *E L S1*
Brierley Hill *p158*. 0845 111 5050

Stockdale, Mrs C (Goodwin Cowley) *D1 D2 K1 K2 K3*
Lowestoft *p294* 01502 532700

Stockdale, C (John Barkers) *B1 L Q N*
Grimsby *p234* 01472 358686

Stockdale, Ms E (Blake Lapthorn) *O I A3 Ze*
London EC1 *p13*. 020 7405 2000

Stockdale, P (Speechly Bircham LLP) *E R2*
London EC4 *p81*. 020 7427 6400

Stockdale, R L (Brooke North LLP)
Leeds *p272* 0113 283 2100

Stockdale, Miss S (Irwin Mitchell LLP)
Birmingham *p139* 0870 150 0100

Stockdale, Miss S J (T C Smith) *K1 G H Q V*
Berwick-upon-Tweed *p131*. . 01289 307409

Stockdale-Garbutt, J W (Recompense Solicitors Ltd) *Q M1 P N K1 B1 F1 L G J1 W*
Totnes *p413* 0800 037 5817

Stocken, M G A (Letchers) *Q N K1 G H D1 F1 K2 K3*
Ringwood *p364* 01425 471424

Stocker, C H R (Stocker & Co) *S1 E K1 C1 L M1 G R1 F1*
Thame *p410*. 01844 216995

Stocker, Miss E C (Trethowans LLP) *E R2 S1*
Southampton *p387*. 023 8032 1000

Stockings, Miss J L (Hansells) *Zr N*
Norwich *p334* 01603 615731

Stockler, W T (Stockler Brunton) *M1 N P O Q C1 T1 E A1 L F1 D1 Ze Zf Zk*
London EC4 *p83*. 020 7404 6661

Stockley, Ms A E (Sternberg Reed) *W*
Barking *p123* 020 8591 3366

Stockley, D (Russell-Cooke LLP) *R1 R2 S1*
London WC1 *p74* 020 7405 6566

Stockley, P J (Bond Pearce LLP) *C1 C2 C3*
Bristol *p161* 0845 415 0000

Stockman, D H (Healys LLP) *E S1 S2*
Brighton *p159* 01273 685888

Stocks, A (Morgans) *V L F1*
Cardiff *p180* 029 2072 9888

Stocks, M (Broadbents) *G H Zg*
Sutton-in-Ashfield *p404* . . . 01623 441123

Stocks, M G M (Blackhams Solicitors) *S1 W E C1 S2*
Birmingham *p135* 0121 233 6900

Stocks, R A (Travers Smith LLP) *C1*
London EC1 *p87*. 020 7295 3000

Stocks, T (Taylor Wessing) *C2 C1*
London EC4 *p86*. 020 7300 7000

Stockton, A D (Dootsons LLP) *E C1 J1 A1 R1 T1*
Leigh *p282*. 01942 673431

Stockton, Mrs C M (Worcestershire County Council) *D1 K1*
Worcester *p477* 01905 766335

Stockton, Miss J (Eddowes Perry & Osbourne) *G H*
Sutton Coldfield *p403* 0121 686 9444

Stockton, M A (Anthony Stockton) *S1 S2 W*
Coventry *p201*. 01676 535790

Stockton, M J (Widdows Mason) *K1 D1 D2 N Q W S1 Zr Zq*
Leigh *p282*. 01942 673311

Stockwell, A H (Stephenson Harwood) *Zb*
London EC2 *p82*. 020 7329 4422

Stockwell, J (Reynolds Porter Chamberlain LLP)
London E1 *p71* 020 3060 6000

Stockwood, M D (Ince & Co Services Ltd)
London E1 *p44* 020 7481 0010
London EC2 *p82*. 020 7329 4422

Stodart, Ms V (Blake Lapthorn) *C1*
Oxford *p342*. 01865 248607

Stoddern, Miss K (Maxwell Hodge Solicitors) *N*
Kirkby *p268* 0151 548 7370

Stogdon, R (Whitehead Monckton) *W T2 A1 R1 Zd*
Maidstone *p299* 01622 698000

Stokeld, J J (Linklaters LLP)
London EC2 *p54*. 020 7456 2000

Stoker, Ms S (Gordons LLP)
Leeds *p273* 0113 227 0100

Stoker, Mrs T A (AMEC PLC)
Knutsford *p462* 01565 683123

Stokes, A G H (W F Smith LLP) *O K1 N Q J1 G H D1 F1*
Dereham *p209*. 01362 852900

Stokes, A M (DAC Beachcroft) *N J2 F2*
Bristol *p162* 0117 918 2000

Stokes, A M (Blake Lapthorn) *I U1 Zj Q N*
London EC1 *p13*. 020 7405 2000

Stokes, Mrs A R (Dedicated Accident Solicitors) *Q N Zr*
Derby *p208* 01332 869286

Stokes, D (The Stokes Partnership) *K1*
Crewkerne *p203*. 01460 279279

Stokes, D C (Davies & Partners) *E S2 Zh*
Birmingham *p137* 0121 616 4450

Stokes, G (Frank Howard) *S1 W E T1 L R1 F1*
Warrington *p422*. 01925 653481

Stokes, G (Plexus Law (A Trading Name of Parabis Law LLP))
London EC3 *p68*. 0844 245 4000

Stokes, Miss H A (Coodes) *K1 S1 W E D1 Q V F1 L J1 Zd Zk Zl*
Penzance *p346* 01736 362294

Stokes, H R (Visa Europe)
London W2 *p110*. 020 7937 8111

Stokes, J (The Stokes Partnership) *A1 C1 E J1 R1 S1 S2 T1 T2 W Zh Zl Zw*
Crewkerne *p203*. 01460 279279

Stokes, Ms K (Heaney Watson) *K1 D1 K3 D2*
Liverpool *p288*. 0151 282 5555

Stokes, M (Kerrier District Council)
Camborne *p452* 01209 614000

 See p634 for the Key to Work Categories

Stokes, M (Plexus Law (A Trading Name of Parabis Law LLP)) *J1*
Evesham *p220*. 01386 769160
London SW19 *p87*. 020 8947 4163

Stokes, Miss R A (Hodders) *L P W K1 D1*
London NW10 *p41*. 020 8965 9862

Stokes, R I (Bovis Homes Ltd) *E*
Bishops Cleeve *p450* 01242 662400

Stokes, R W (Everys) *A1 E L R1 S1*
Seaton *p373*. 01297 21105

Stokes, S J (Blake Lapthorn) *C1 Ze*
London EC1 *p13*. 020 7405 2000

Stokes, Ms V (IBB Solicitors)
Uxbridge *p417*. 0845 638 1381

Stokey, P M (Gordons LLP)
Leeds *p273* 0113 227 0100

Stokoe, A (Guile Nicholas) *Zm Zg*
Kingston upon Thames *p267*. 020 8549 4282

Stokoe, A D (Michael Anderson & Co) *S1 E L W J1*
Whickham *p430*. 0191 488 1221

Stokoe, Miss N (Parry Law) *K1*
Herne Bay *p248* 01227 361131
Whitstable *p431* 01227 276276

Stokoe, Mrs N J (Gateshead Metropolitan Borough Council)
Gateshead *p458*. 0191 433 3000

Stoll, M (DWF) *O*
Liverpool *p287*. 0151 907 3000

Stoll, Ms S J (Browns) *S1 S2*
Beaconsfield *p128* . .01494 677771 / 677021

Stolworthy, Mrs D J (Cornwall County Council) *B1 C1 O Zb*
Truro *p474*. 01872 322197

Stolzenewbung, Ms F J (FWD Law Associates) *C1 S2 E Ze Q*
Newport *p328* 01633 660440

Stone, A (Reynolds Porter Chamberlain LLP) *Zj*
London E1 *p71* 020 3060 6000

Stone, A J (Metcalfes) *N Zr O Zq*
Bristol *p164* 0117 929 0451

Stone, A J (Collins Dryland & Thorowgood LLP) *H J1 N*
Tilehurst *p411* 0118 942 2448

Stone, A M (Cooke Painter Limited) *S1 W S2 E*
Bristol *p162* 0117 971 4074
Bristol *p162* 01275 400037

Stone, A P (Manches LLP) *Q*
Oxford *p343*. 01865 722106

Stone, A S G (Land Law LLP) *E S2 R2*
Altrincham *p116* 0161 928 8383

Stone, D C (Adams & Remers) *B1*
Lewes *p283* 01273 480616

Stone, Miss D J (Rodney King & Partners) *S1 W*
Bristol *p163* 0117 926 5201

Stone, D M (Gill Akaster) *S2 E*
Plymouth *p349*. 01752 203500

Stone, E B (Legal Services Commission)
Nottingham *p467*. 0115 908 4200

Stone, E R M (Withers LLP) *W T2 M2 C1 E*
London EC4 *p92*. 020 7597 6000

Stone, G S (Mayo Wynne Baxter LLP)
Eastbourne *p215*. 01323 730543

Stone, H V (Howard Stone) *Q O E C1 T1 T2 W S1 A3 B1 Zq*
London EC1 *p43*. 020 7490 5900

Stone, I D (Philip Ross & Co) *S1 S2 J1 K1 L Q*
London W1 *p73* 020 7636 6969

Stone, J F (Addleshaw Goddard)
Leeds *p271* 0113 209 2000
Manchester *p300* 0161 934 6000

Stone, J P (Stephens & Scown) *K1 D1*
Truro *p414*. 01872 265100

Stone, J R (Crown Prosecution Service Thames Valley) *K1*
Abingdon *p447*. 01235 551900

Stone, K F (Fox Williams) *U2 I Ze C1 C2 F2*
London EC2 *p33*. 020 7628 2000

Stone, K P (Memery Crystal) *C1 C2*
London WC2 *p60* 020 7242 5905

Stone, L (Lee & Thompson) *C1 Zf*
London W1 *p52* 020 7935 4665

Stone, M M (Colemans Solicitors LLP) *A1 C2 E R1 S1 L R2 S2*
Maidenhead *p298* 01628 631051

Stone, N (Mills & Reeve) *K1*
Norwich *p335* 01603 660155

Stone, N C (Streathers Solicitors LLP)
London W1 *p84* 020 7034 4200

Stone, N P (Boodle Hatfield) *C1 C2 Zb*
Westminster *p14*. 020 7629 7411

Stone, P A (Bond Pearce LLP) *C1 C2*
Bristol *p161* 0845 415 0000

Stone, P B (DLA Piper UK LLP)
Leeds *p272* 0870 011 1111

Stone, R E (Allens) *W T2 A1*
Portsmouth *p354*. 023 9282 2411

Stone, R H (Beardsells) *N*
Cheadle *p185* 0161 477 2288
Manchester *p307* 0161 834 2324

Stone, R J (Stone Milward Rapers) *E C1 K1 L S1 W R1 T1 M1*
Chichester *p193* 01243 780211

Stone, Ms S (K&L Gates LLP)
London EC4 *p47*. 020 7648 9000

Stone, Mrs S C (Bolton Metropolitan Borough Council)
Bolton *p450* 01204 333333

Stone, S F (Stone & Stone) *E J1 K1 L S1 W Q T2*
Morden *p318* 020 8540 2202

Stone, Mrs S G (Brockmans) *W K4*
Stockbridge *p395* 01264 810910

Stone, S N (Lester Aldridge LLP) *E*
London WC2 *p53* 0844 967 0785

Stone, T P C (Steele Raymond) *C1 J1 C2 C3*
Bournemouth *p152*. 01202 294566

Stonebanks, Ms S (Plymouth Justices' Clerk)
Plymouth *p468*. 01752 206200

Stonehill, C (Linklaters LLP)
London EC2 *p54*. 020 7456 2000

Stonehouse, D M (Hine Downing Solicitors)
Falmouth *p223*. 01326 316655

Stonehouse, P B (Hine Downing Solicitors) *S1*
Falmouth *p223*. 01326 316655

Stonehouse, Ms R (Swain & Co) *K1 K3*
Havant *p244*. 023 9248 3322

Stoner, J (3i PLC)
London SW1 *p103*. 020 7928 3131

Stones, G (Wheelers) *W*
Aldershot *p115*. 01252 316316

Stones, J C (John Barkers) *C1 S2 E S1 U2 C2*
Grimsby *p234* 01472 358686

Stoney, Ms M C (Bolton Metropolitan Borough Council)
Bolton *p450* 01204 333333

Stoney, Miss S M (Jackson Brierley Hudson Stoney) *S1 W K4 Zd*
Rochdale *p365*. . . .01706 644187 / 649214

Stoodley, Ms V (Cripps Harries Hall LLP) *E R1*
Tunbridge Wells *p415* 01892 515121

Stookes, P A (Richard Buxton) *P O R1 M1 Zn Zg M2 Q*
Cambridge *p174*. 01223 328933

Stopford, Mrs R C (Oxley & Coward Solicitors LLP) *C1 I Ze C2 U2*
Rotherham *p367*. 01709 510999
Sheffield *p377* 0114 266 6660

Storah, C M (Savage Crangle)
Otley *p342*. 01943 465050

Storch, A J (Andrew Storch) *G H*
Reading *p361* 0118 958 4407

Storer, A (TWM Solicitors LLP)
Reigate *p363* 01737 221212

Storer, Ms C A (Shelter Legal Services) *L K1 Q*
London EC1 *p109* 020 7505 2000

Storer, Mrs J A (Thompsons (formerly Robin/Brian Thompson & Partners)) *N*
Birmingham *p143* 0121 262 1200

Storer, R A (Harbottle & Lewis LLP) *C1 Ze Zf*
London W1 *p38* 020 7667 5000

Storey, A (Marrons)
Newcastle upon Tyne *p325* . 0191 281 1304

Storey, A J (Hutchinson & Buchanan) *N K1 G J1 B1 Q O F1 Zq Zr*
Ripon *p365* 01765 602156

Storey, C (Watson Burton LLP)
Newcastle upon Tyne *p327* . 0845 901 2100

Storey, Mrs K L (Disken & Co) *S1 K4 K3 K1 W*
Dewsbury *p210* 01924 464101

Storey, Miss L (Legal Services Commission)
Nottingham *p467*. 0115 908 4200

Storey, Mrs L A (Penningtons) *Zh*
Basingstoke *p127* 01256 407100

Storey, M A (Samuel Phillips Law Firm) *S1 E S2 L*
Newcastle upon Tyne *p326* . 0191 232 8451

Storey, Miss M J (Hartlaw LLP) *S1 S2 E A1 Zl O*
Wetherby *p429* 01937 547000

Storey, Mrs M P (Storey & Co) *K1 W S1*
Stokesley *p398* 01642 712132

Storey, R J (Hutchinson & Buchanan) *W K4*
Ripon *p365* 01765 602156

Storey, Ms T (Russell Jones & Walker)
London WC2 *p74* 020 7657 1555

Storie, D C P (Norfolk County Council - Legal Services)
Norwich *p467* . . . Minicom: 0844 800 8011

Stork, P D (Stork & Coles) *E S1 L C1*
London WC1 *p84* 020 7404 6021

Stormann, Ms E (Secretan Troyanov)
London WC1 *p77* 020 7404 1199

Storr, Miss D T (South Lakeland District Council)
Kendal *p462*. 01539 733333

Storrar, C J (Storrar Cowdry) *C1 Zl Zb*
Chester *p191* 01244 400567

Storrar, Mrs D D (Storrar Cowdry) *K1 J1 W K3*
Chester *p191* 01244 400567

Storrs, N (Jones Day) *O*
London EC4 *p46*. 020 7039 5959

Storry Deans, H (Harold G Walker) *Q O N Zq J1 J2 Zk Zj*
Bournemouth *p152*. 01202 203200

Storry, D A W (Driver Belcher Solicitors) *G H K1*
Southampton *p385*. 01489 785737

Storry, D A W (Eric Robinson Solicitors) *K1 G H*
Chandlers Ford *p184* 023 8025 4676

Story, Ms J L (Story & Robison) *W K1*
Norwich *p335* 01603 626355

Stotesbury, N P S (Batchelors Solicitors) *C1 K4 J1 W*
Bromley *p166* 020 8768 7000

Stothard, D I (Thompsons (formerly Robin/Brian Thompson & Partners)) *N J2 J1 Zq*
Sheffield *p377* 0114 270 3300

Stothard, Ms T C (Matthew Arnold & Baldwin LLP) *O Ze I U2*
Watford *p423* 01923 202020

Stott, Mrs A M (Cooper Stott) *S1 K1 M1 W D1 P J1 F1 Zl*
Durham *p214* 0191 384 7210

Stott, Ms C (Surrey County Council)
Kingston upon Thames *p462*. 020 8541 9088

Stott, D J (Brignalls Balderston Warren) *G H N Zl*
Stevenage *p394*. 01438 359311

Stott, E (Talbot Walker LLP) *G H B2*
Basingstoke *p127* 01256 332404

Stott, J R (Evans Dodd LLP) *C1 J1 B1*
London W1 *p30* 020 7491 4729

Stott, N (The Paul Rooney Partnership)
Liverpool *p290*. 0151 227 2851

Stott, P (Ingrams) *N Q Zq*
Hull *p257* 01482 358850
York *p445* 01904 520600

Stott, P (Stephensons Solicitors LLP) *Zm Zr N*
Wigan *p432* 01942 777777

Stott, P R K (Mercers) *W Zd Zh Zo T2*
Henley-on-Thames *p247*. . . 01491 572138

Stott, Mrs R (Veale Wasbrough Vizards) *E*
Bristol *p165* 0117 925 2020

Stout, Ms J (DLA Piper UK LLP) *C1 C2*
Sheffield *p375* 0870 011 1111

Stout, L A (Fitzgerald-Harts) *S2 S1 W*
Boroughbridge *p150* 01423 322312

Stovin, A P (Claytons) *E S1 L W Zd*
St Albans *p390* 01727 865765

Stow, Mrs R L (Thorneycroft Solicitors Ltd) *S1 Q N W L K1 O J1 E*
Macclesfield *p297* 01625 503444

Stowbridge, Ms C P (Hutton's) *P M1 K1 F1 N W C1 B1 R1 D1 Zc Zk Zi*
Cardiff *p179* 029 2037 8621

Stowe, G C (Grahame Stowe Bateson) *G H K1 D1 N J1 P Q V Zm*
Leeds *p274* 0113 246 8163

Stowe, M I (Fuglers) *C1 Zf A3 B1 S2 E Ze L M2 O Q C2 R2 S1 W*
London W1 *p34* 020 7323 6450

Stowe, S (Stowe Simon) *S1 K1 G P M1 W E J1 T1 Zc Zj Zl*
Hednesford *p246* 01543 877131

Stowell, Miss S A (Bircham Dyson Bell) *W T1 Zd Zm Zi*
Westminster *p13*. 020 7227 7000

Stowell, Ms V (The Wilkes Partnership LLP) *O Q Zq L*
Birmingham *p143* 0121 233 4333

Stowers, D J (Cartwright King) *B2 O*
Sheffield *p375* 0114 321 1000
Sheffield *p376* 0870 150 0100

Strachan, Miss A (Doyle Clayton Solicitors Limited) *J1*
Reading *p360* 0118 959 6839

Strachan, A M (A M Strachan & Co) *G H N Q L Zl*
Hackney *p84*. 020 7729 0003

Strachan, D A (Brignalls Balderston Warren) *W T2*
Letchworth *p283* 01462 482248

Stradling, Miss K J (Everys) *K1 D1 V G H N F1 Q*
Exmouth *p222*. 01395 264384

Stradling, Miss L S (Gepp & Sons) *W T2*
Chelmsford *p186*. 01245 493939
Colchester *p197* 01206 369889

Strahl, Miss N R G (Osborne Clarke) *R2*
London EC2 *p65*. 020 7105 7000

Strain, A J (Goodman Derrick LLP) *S2 E C1 S1 L W R2*
London EC4 *p36*. 020 7404 0606

Strain, A J (Strain Keville)
Westminster *p84*. 020 7323 5000

Strain, W M (Martin & Strain) *G H N Zl*
Pwllheli *p358* 01758 612042

Straker, H (Dickinson Dees) *S1*
Newcastle upon Tyne *p324* . 0191 279 9000

Strang, D I (Barlow Lyde & Gilbert LLP) *C1 C3 I M1 Ze*
London EC3 *p10*. 020 7247 2277

Strange, C (Rawlison Butler LLP)
Horsham *p253*. 01403 252492

Strange, Ms G E (Bernard Chill & Axtell) *K1 D1 K3 V F1*
Southampton *p385*. 023 8022 8821

Strange, I R (Israel Strange & Conlon) *C1 E S1 L C2 S2*
Islington *p45*. 020 7833 8453

Strange, Ms J (Cartridges) *S1*
Exeter *p220* 01392 256854

Strange, R J (Thomas Cooper) *N Q Za Zj*
London EC3 *p22*. 020 7481 8851

Strangwood, C (Glaisyers Solicitors LLP) *N*
Manchester *p304* 0161 832 4666

Strangwood, Miss J (Martin Edwards) *K3 J1 K1 O Q N W*
Shifnal *p378*. 01952 462118

Stratford, C J (Thomas Flavell & Sons) *S1 S2 E W*
Hinckley *p250* 01455 610747

Stratford, J T (Black Rock)
London EC4 *p104* 020 7743 3000

Strathdee, Mrs C A P (Stone King LLP) *G H*
Bath *p128* 01225 337599

Strathdee, M C (Bevan Brittan LLP) *C1 C2 I*
Bristol *p161* 0870 194 1000

Stratton, C (Linder Myers Solicitors) *E L S2*
Manchester *p307* 0844 984 6400

Stratton, D (Linder Myers Solicitors) *E L Zb*
Manchester *p307* 0844 984 6400

Stratton, N (Berry & Berry) *W S1 Zd Zm Zo*
Tunbridge Wells *p414* 01892 526344

Stratton, Ms N S (Salehs LLP) *O*
Manchester *p309* 0161 434 9991

Stratton, R J (Travers Smith LLP) *T1*
London EC1 *p87*. 020 7295 3000

Stratton, S P (Manches LLP) *E L R1*
Oxford *p343*. 01865 722106

Stratton-Webb, Mrs L (Clough & Willis) *S1*
Bury *p170* 0161 764 5266

Straub, Ms K (Aitken Associates) *K1 W*
Islington *p4* 020 7700 6006

Straughan, Ms J (Pierre Thomas & Partners) *N Q O Zj M2*
London W6 *p67* 020 7602 0305

Straughton, Mrs C L (Peel Management Limited)
Manchester *p465* 0161 629 8200

Strauss, Mrs M (Pothecary Witham Weld) *X Q*
Westminster *p69*. 020 7821 8211

Straw, Mrs A A V (Irwin Mitchell LLP)
Sheffield *p376* 0870 150 0100
Doncaster *p212* 01302 341414

Straw, Miss H M (Alliance Boots PLC) *N O Q Zj*
Nottingham *p467*. 0115 950 6111

Straw, Miss L V (Burton Copeland LLP) *G H B2*
Manchester *p302* 0161 827 9500

Straw, M K (Sills & Betteridge LLP) *W S1 A1 E*
Sleaford *p381* 01529 302800

Streat, R L (Peter Brown & Co Solicitors LLP) *S2 R2 E L S1*
Barnet *p124* 020 8447 3277

Streatfeild, Mrs J F (Messenger & Co) *C1 F1 K1 N Q Zl K3*
Henley-on-Thames *p247*. . . 01491 576272

Streather, B G (Streathers Solicitors LLP) *A1 B1 C1 D1 E F1 J1 K1 L M1 Zn Zo Zp Zs Zt*
London W1 *p84* 020 7034 4200

Street, Ms A (Edwards Angell Palmer & Dodge)
London EC2 *p28*. 020 7583 4055

Street, D L (David Street & Company) *G H E Zl*
Crawley *p202* 01293 616191

Street, Miss L M (Aviva PLC)
London EC3 *p103* . . 020 7283 7500 / 01603 687905
York *p477* 01904 452210

Street, R H (Brabners Chaffe Street) *C1 C2*
Manchester *p301* 0161 836 8800

Street, Mrs T (Borough of Telford & Wrekin)
Telford *p473* 01952 380000

Streeton, Ms H (Boodle Hatfield)
Westminster *p14*. 020 7629 7411

Streeton, Ms H E (Fox Williams) *R2*
London EC2 *p33*. 020 7628 2000

Stretton, Mrs M C (Sheridan & Stretton) *K1 S1 D1 W J1 X*
London W6 *p78* 020 8748 7340

Strevens, Ms C (Stokes Solicitors) *O J1 Q Zg*
Portsmouth *p355*. 023 9282 8131

Strevens, Miss H (DAC Beachcroft)
London EC3 *p24*. 020 7208 6800

Stribling, C R M (Carver Jones) *Q*
Hereford *p247* 01432 274301

Strickland, C E S (Gordons LLP)
Leeds *p273* 0113 227 0100

Strickland, Mrs C L (Awdry Bailey & Douglas) *N*
Wootton Bassett *p439* 01793 853200

Strickland, H (Geldards LLP)
Nottingham *p337*. 0115 983 3650

Strickland, O C L (Berry Redmond & Robinson) *L J1 G H F1 Zl Q*
Weston-super-Mare *p429* . . 01934 619000

Strickland, Miss S J (Thomas Guise) *S2 E*
Worcester *p439* 01905 723131

Strickland, Ms V (Andrew Jackson) *B1 O*
Hull *p257* 01482 325242
Leeds *p277* 0113 283 2500

Stride, A W (John Lewis plc) *S1 W E L B1 A1 C1 R1 V Zm Zi*
London SW1 *p107*. 020 7828 1000

Stride, Ms E J (Forshaws Davies Ridgway LLP)
Warrington *p422*. 01925 604713

Stride, Mrs S R (Coldham Shield & Mace)
London E4 *p21* 020 8524 6323

Strigner, Ms C E (WBW Solicitors) *D1 K1*
Newton Abbot *p329* 01626 202404

Strike, Mrs A L (Hewitts)
Darlington *p206* 01325 468573

Stringer, Ms J (Symons & Gay)
Romford *p366* 01708 744211

Stringer, J (Platt Halpern) *L N*
Manchester *p308* 0161 224 2555

Stringer, Miss J V (Leeds City Council) *F1 O Q*
Leeds *p462* 0113 224 3513

Stringer, P (Stewarts Law LLP) *N*
Leeds *p277* 0113 222 0022

Stringer, Ms R (Whitelock & Storr) *G H B2*
London WC1 *p91* 020 7405 3913

Stringfellow, Miss B J (Calthrops) *N K1 O D1 Q*
Spalding *p389* 01775 724381

Stringfellow, Ms D J (Sookias & Sookias) *O B1 C1 F1 J1*
London W1 *p80* 020 7465 8000

Strogen, C J (Thompsons (formerly Robin/Brian Thompson & Partners)) *N*
Manchester *p310* 0161 819 3500

Stroh, C T (Druces LLP) *J1 C1 C2 C3 M1 T2 J2 Ze Zp Zd*
London EC2 *p27*. 020 7638 9271

Stronach, Mrs J D (Burnetts) *J1*
Carlisle *p181*. 01228 552222
Carlisle *p182*. 01228 552222

Strong, A D (Stafford Young Jones) *Q N*
London EC4 *p82*. 020 7623 9490

Strong, Mrs H D (Lodders Solicitors LLP) *W T2*
Stratford-upon-Avon *p400* . . 01789 293259

Strong, Mrs J (Bevirs) *D1 G H K1 M1 F1 J1 L P*
Swindon *p406* 01793 532363

Strong, N (Atha Strong & Co)
Redcar *p362*. 01642 482421

Strong, Miss R T (Hegarty LLP) *D1 K1 K3*
Peterborough *p347* 01733 346333
Stamford *p393*. 01780 752066

Strong, Miss S J (Harding Evans LLP) *C1 E L R1*
Newport *p328* 01633 244233

Strong, T S (Barlow Lyde & Gilbert LLP) *O U2 Zq Zj*
London EC3 *p10* 020 7247 2277

Strong, Mrs Z C I (Russell-Cooke LLP) *E S2 R2*
London SW15 *p74* 020 8789 9111

Stroud, A P (Thompson & Jackson) *S1 S2*
Plymouth *p350* . . . .01752 665037 / 221171

Stroud, D (Pinsent Masons LLP) *C1 C2*
London EC2 *p67* 020 7418 7000

Stroud, G B (The Stroud Stitson Partnership) *Q K1 N C1 Zl*
Plymouth *p350* 01752 660066

Stroud, Mrs M M (Godwins) *S1 S2 W*
Winchester *p433* 01962 841484

Strouts, E M (Environment Agency (South West Region))
Exeter *p458* 0870 850 6506

Strube, P J (Strube & Co) *S1 E W*
London SE26 *p84* 020 8659 3020

Struckley, Ms K (Kalber Struckley & Co)
London W1 *p47* 020 7734 1102

Strudwick, Mrs C (McPhersons) *S1 S2*
Stockbridge *p395* 01794 389002

Struel, M (Smith Llewelyn Partnership) *C1 E G H K1 M1 P S1 W*
Swansea *p405* 01792 464444

Strunk, Mrs A A (London Borough of Greenwich Legal Services)
London SE18 *p106* 020 8921 5123

Struthers, A (Ashworths Solicitors) *E C1 S2 R2*
London SW19 *p8* 0845 370 1000

Strutt, C G (Mayo Wynne Baxter LLP) *S1 K1 L W E J1 F1 C1 Zi Zl*
Eastbourne *p215* 01323 730543

Struve, A N (Heald Nickinson) *E S1 L R1 A1 C1 J1 Zi Zl*
Camberley *p173* 01276 680000

Struve, M E (Heald Nickinson) *O Q J1 B1 L*
Camberley *p173* 01276 680000

Strycharczyk, K Z B (Burnetts) *D1 J1*
Carlisle *p181* 01228 552222
Carlisle *p182* 01228 552222

Stuart, Ms A (Bretherton Law) *K1 K3*
St Albans *p389* 01727 869293

Stuart, Mrs A M (Crowley & Co) *S2 S1 W Zl K1*
Cardiff *p178* 029 2045 8895

Stuart, E (Ashurst LLP)
London EC2 *p7* 020 7638 1111

Stuart, E (Jones Day) *C1*
London EC4 *p46* 020 7039 5959

Stuart, Miss F (Isadore Goldman Solicitors) *B1 O*
London EC4 *p45* 020 7353 1000

Stuart, G (Atkinson Cave & Stuart) *K1 O G H D1 F1 N B1 J1 Zm*
Blackpool *p146* 01253 293151

Stuart, H (Withers LLP) *A1 S1 P R1 Zn*
London EC4 *p92* 020 7597 6000

Stuart, Miss H M (Gotelee) *D1 K1 D2 K2*
Ipswich *p262* 01473 211121

Stuart, Mrs L A (Cullimore Dutton) *S1 W*
Chester *p190* 01244 356789

Stuart, Ms L E (Clifford Chance)
London E14 *p20* 020 7006 1000

Stuart, N A (Bond Pearce LLP) *E*
Plymouth *p349* 0845 415 0000

Stuart, Mrs P J (Geoffrey Leaver Solicitors LLP) *N J1*
Milton Keynes *p317* 01908 692769

Stuart-Smith, J D (Humphries Kirk) *B1 C1 C2 C3 F1 J1 M2 Ze*
Poole *p352* 01202 725400

Stuart-Taylor, Sir N R (Biscoes) *E R2 S1 S2 W*
Portsmouth *p354* 023 9266 0261

Stubbert, G D (Chua's Solicitors) *O Ze Zf Q Zl E*
London EC4 *p20* 020 7242 6789

Stubbings, R E (C C Bell & Son) *S1 E W C1 A1 K1 G H L M1 Zc Zl*
Bedford *p129* 01234 363251

Stubbins, B F (Shacklocks) *K1 K2*
Belper *p131* 01773 822333

Stubbs, Miss E (Morgans) *D2 D1 K3 K1*
Cardiff *p180* 029 2072 9888

Stubbs, Ms K (McMillen Hamilton McCarthy) *G H*
London E3 *p57* 020 8980 6060

Stubbs, Mrs K A (Aylesbury Vale District Council)
Aylesbury *p447* 01296 585858

Stubbs, M (Stephens & Scown) *O K1 Za Q Zc*
Truro *p414* 01872 265100

Stubbs, M S (KPM Solicitors) *S2 E S1 W*
London WC2 *p47* 020 7404 1995

Stubbs, N (Hansells) *K1 D1 V*
North Walsham *p331* 01692 404351

Stubbs, N G (Aviva PLC)
London EC3 *p103* . . 020 7283 7500 / 01603 687905

Stubbs, P J M (Norrie Waite & Slater)
Sheffield *p377* 0114 276 6166

Stubbs, T J (Salans)
London EC4 *p76* 020 7429 6000

Stucchi, A (Morrison & Foerster (UK) LLP) *Zb*
London EC2 *p62* 020 7920 4000

Studd, A (Russell-Cooke LLP) *Zd*
London SW15 *p74* 020 8789 9111

Studd, L A (Bates & Mountain) *K1 D1 J1 G H F1 V D2*
Grimsby *p235* 01472 357291

Studd, S G (Bishop & Sewell LLP) *S1 L K1 O J1 C1 W*
London WC1 *p13* 020 7631 4141

Studdert-Kennedy, D A (Coleman & Betts)
Kingston upon Thames *p267*. 020 8549 4402

Stueck, B (Jones Day) *O*
London EC4 *p46* 020 7039 5959

Sturdy, J W (Blake Lapthorn) *E*
Chandlers Ford *p184* 023 8090 8090
Southampton *p386* 023 8071 8000

Sturge, A (Turner Parkinson) *C2 C1*
Manchester *p310* 0161 833 1212

Sturge, Mrs C A (RHW Solicitors LLP) *W T2*
Guildford *p237* 01483 302000

Sturge, C A (Laytons) *Zb C1 S2 E Zx L S1*
Guildford *p236* 01483 407000

Sturge, W J (LG Lawyers)
London SE1 *p50* 020 7379 0000

Sturgess, Mrs D E (D E Sturgess) *S1 E*
Romsey *p367* 01794 830791

Sturgess, G H (Blake Lapthorn) *C1 Ze*
Chandlers Ford *p184* 023 8090 8090

Sturley, Ms L M (Newport City Council) *K1 D1 M1 F1 W G N B1*
Newport *p466* 01633 656656
Newport *p329* 01633 257844

Sturman, D C (Holmes & Hills LLP) *S2 E S1*
Braintree *p155* 01376 320456

Sturman, Mrs E G (BUPA)
London WC1 *p104* 020 7656 2305

Sturman, Miss K (Saunders Law Partnership LLP) *G H*
London WC2 *p76* 020 7632 4300

Sturrock, A D (Addleshaw Goddard) *W*
Manchester *p300* 0161 934 6000

Sturrock, Miss L F (Addleshaw Goddard)
Leeds *p271* 0113 209 2000
London EC1 *p4* 020 7606 8855

Sturt, A J (Reed Smith LLP) *O U2*
London EC2 *p71* 020 3116 3000

Sturt, Miss P B (Joelson Wilson LLP) *C2 C1 Zb U1 U2 F1 F2 Ze Zza*
Westminster *p46* 020 7580 5721

Sturt, R H B (Mowll & Mowll) *C1 E R1 T1 Za Zc Zd Ze Zo*
Dover *p213* 01304 873344

Sturzaker, J N (Russell Jones & Walker)
London WC2 *p74* 020 7657 1555

Style, C J D (Linklaters LLP)
London EC2 *p54* 020 7456 2000

Styler, Mrs J S (Baches) *S1 W E L R1 Zl*
West Bromwich *p427* . 0121 553 3286 / 553 7076

Styles, Ms A (Hayes & Storr) *K4 W*
King's Lynn *p266* 01553 778900

Styles, J (Travers Smith LLP) *E S2*
London EC1 *p87* 020 7295 3000

Styles, Ms K (Edwards Duthie) *G H*
London E13 *p29* 020 8514 9000

Styles, K A (FBC Manby Bowdler LLP) *E L*
Wolverhampton *p437* 01902 578000
Cradley Heath *p201* 01384 410410

Stylianou, Miss H (Myers Fletcher & Gordon) *Q O L*
London W6 *p62* 020 7610 4433
Manchester *p308* 0161 819 4900

Styring, Ms J M P (Ewings & Co) *D1 K1 G H*
London SE20 *p30* 020 8778 1126

Su, P K (Edwin Coe LLP) *B1 O Q Zc Zj B2 A3*
London WC2 *p29* 020 7691 4000

Suadwa, F (City of Bradford Metropolitan District Council)
Bradford *p451* 01274 752236

Suarez-Martinez, A V (Edwards Angell Palmer & Dodge)
London EC2 *p28* 020 7583 4055

Suarez-Neves, A (Penningtons) *Zi*
London EC2 *p66* 020 7457 3000

Subbiani, M J (Red Kite Law) *G H*
Pembroke Dock *p345* 01646 681529

Subrero, A (Pollecoff Solicitors Ltd)
London EC2 *p68* 020 7608 2568

Suchak, P M (P M Suchak & Co) *Q O S1 V N K1 B1 J1 W L Zp Zq Zi Zl Ze*
Leicester *p281* 0116 299 0007

Suchak, S (Barlow Lyde & Gilbert LLP)
London EC3 *p10* 020 7247 2277

Suchett-Kaye, C F E (Reynolds Porter Chamberlain LLP) *T1 W Zo*
London E1 *p71* 020 3060 6000

Suchy, A R S (Ince & Co Services Ltd) *C1 M1 Zb Za*
London E1 *p44* 020 7481 0010

Sudbury, Ms K L (Browne Jacobson LLP) *F1 N Q*
Nottingham *p336* 0115 976 6000

Sudbury, R G (AWG PLC) *C3 M1 Ze*
Huntingdon *p461* 01480 323140

Sudweeks, R J (Brett Holt Solicitors) *K1 N O Q S1 W R1*
Worcester Park *p440* 020 8337 0174

Suen, Mrs W Y (Beardsells) *N S1*
Cheadle *p185* 0161 477 2288

Sue-Patt, Ms J P (JPS Law Solicitors) *B1 C1 E J1 L O Q S1 S2*
Westminster *p45* 020 7935 9955

Suergiu, G (Manches LLP) *Ze C1 C2*
London WC2 *p58* 020 7404 4433

Suffield, Ms H A (Broomhead & Saul) *G H*
Ilminster *p261* 01460 57056

Sugden, Mrs L (Gedling Borough Council)
Nottingham *p467* 0115 901 3901

Sugden, M J (Thomson Snell & Passmore) *S1 A1 S2*
Tunbridge Wells *p415* 01892 510000

Sugden, W A (Eaton Smith LLP) *D1 I G H K1*
Huddersfield *p255* 01484 821300

Suggett, J A (Eldridges) *W S1 S2 K4 J1*
Freshwater *p227* 01983 752492

Sugiyama, S H T (Sugiyama & Co) *O Q J1 C1 Zf*
Farnham *p225* 01252 820500

Sugrue, J (Austin & Carnley) *N*
Leighton Buzzard *p282* . . . 01525 372140

Sugrue, J (Noble) *H G*
Shefford *p377* 01462 814055

Suleman, M A (Bromptons) *B1 C1 C2 E L O Q S1 W Zj*
London W8 *p16* 020 7937 0005

Suleman, N (Farleys Solicitors LLP) *Q N*
Blackburn *p145* 01254 367855

Suleman, S (Reed Smith LLP) *C1*
London EC2 *p71* 020 3116 3000

Suleman, S (QualitySolicitors C Turner) *S1 S2*
Blackburn *p145* 01254 688400

Sulh, Mrs S K (Bassets) *W S1 K4 S2 K3 K1*
Gillingham *p229* 01634 575464

Sulkin, Ms E H (Levine Mellins Klarfeld) *K1 D1 W K2*
Stanmore *p394* 020 8954 7474

Sulkowski, D (Doyle Clayton Solicitors Limited) *J1 Zp*
London EC2 *p27* 020 7329 9090

Sullivan, Miss A (Hague Lambert) *W C1*
Manchester *p305* 0161 834 6066

Sullivan, Mrs A (IBM United Kingdom Ltd)
London SE1 *p107* 020 7202 3000

Sullivan, Mrs B (Richard J Knaggs & Co) *S1 S2*
Redcar *p362* 01642 487011
Whitby *p430* 01947 601122

Sullivan, B J (Marcus Barnett) *N J1*
London SW1 *p10* 020 7235 9215

Sullivan, Miss C (Cozens-Hardy LLP) *K1 D1*
Norwich *p334* 01603 625231

Sullivan, Mrs C S A (Minahan Hirst & Co) *S1 W*
Cheadle Hulme *p185* 0161 485 8131

Sullivan, D (Speechly Bircham LLP) *Zb*
London EC4 *p81* 020 7427 6400

Sullivan, D J (Hogan Lovells International LLP)
London EC1 *p42* 020 7296 2000

Sullivan, D J (Kennedys) *Zj*
London EC3 *p49* 020 7667 9667

Sullivan, Miss G (Darbys Solicitors LLP) *E S2 A1 R1*
Oxford *p343* 01865 811700

Sullivan, G (Sullivans Solicitors LLP) *B1 Zj Q N*
Enfield *p219* 020 8363 3888

Sullivan, Ms J (Bright & Sons) *W*
Maldon *p299* 01621 852323

Sullivan, Ms J A (Marchants Solicitors)
Mansfield *p312* 01623 655111

Sullivan, J C P (DLA Piper UK LLP)
Birmingham *p137* 0870 011 1111

Sullivan, K J (Birkett Long LLP) *O*
Colchester *p197* 01206 217300

Sullivan, K M (Warners Solicitors) *C1 C2 J1 Ze*
Sevenoaks *p374* 01732 747900

Sullivan, Miss L (Stewarts Law LLP) *J1*
London EC4 *p83* 020 7822 8000

Sullivan, M A (Linklaters LLP)
London EC2 *p54* 020 7456 2000

Sullivan, Miss S E (Thomson Snell & Passmore) *Zq Q*
Tunbridge Wells *p415* 01892 510000

Sullivan, S J (Legal and Professional Claims Ltd)
London EC4 *p107* 020 7621 3900

Sullivan, S J (Kemps Solicitors) *G H B2*
Oldham *p340* 0161 633 0555

Sullivan, Mrs S L (Blake Lapthorn) *C1*
Chandlers Ford *p184* 023 8090 8090

Sully, M J (Chichester District Council)
Chichester *p455* 01243 785166

Sulston, A (Allen & Overy LLP) *C1 Zb*
London E1 *p5* 020 3088 0000

Sultoon, J A (Ashurst LLP) *Zb*
London EC2 *p7* 020 7638 1111

Sumby, Mrs K M (Nottinghamshire County Council Legal Services Division)
West Bridgford *p475* 0115 977 3478

Sumerling, R W (Radcliffes Le Brasseur) *N C1 Zk Zm*
Westminster *p70* 020 7222 7040

Summerbell, P (Christopher Harris & Co) *F1 F2 X J1 J2 Zg Zj O Q N Zr Zq Zp D2 D1 K1*
Sheerness *p375* 01795 661521
Sittingbourne *p380* 01795 437268

Summerfield, M (Solomon Taylor & Shaw) *B1 A3 J1 L O Q Zq*
London NW3 *p80* 020 7431 1912

Summerfield, N (Lightfoots LLP) *O N Zq*
Thame *p410* 01844 212305

Summerfield, S R (Travers Smith LLP) *C1 C2 U1*
London EC1 *p87* 020 7295 3000

Summers, A J (Wellers Law Group LLP) *S1 T1 L E F1 C1 N C2 C3 T2 Zh Zr Zq*
Bromley *p167* 020 8464 4242
London WC1 *p91* 020 7242 7265

Summers, A M H (Eastleys) *E W S1 Zd*
Paignton *p345* 01803 559257

Summers, F N (Sandwell Metropolitan Borough Council)
Oldbury *p468* 0121 569 2200

Summers, Ms H E (JST Lawyers) *E S1 L J1 Zd*
Liverpool *p289* 0151 282 2828

Summers, J (Howard Kennedy LLP) *W*
London W1 *p48* 020 7636 1616

Summers, Ms J E (Constantine & Summers) *N K1*
Camberley *p173* 01276 23211

Summers, J N (Pitmans LLP) *Zw Ze Zf F2 Zk*
London EC2 *p68* 020 7634 4620

Summers, Mrs K C (Summers Nigh Law LLP) *O Q N B1 F1 J1 Zb*
Northampton *p332* 01604 771136

Summers, M (Speechly Bircham LLP) *T2 W*
London EC4 *p81* 020 7427 6400

Summers, M W (Pinkney Grunwells Lawyers LLP) *S2 G L S1 W*
Filey *p226* 01723 890634
Scarborough *p372* 01723 352125

Summers, P E (Herbert Reeves & Co) *S1 E L Zw*
London EC2 *p40* 020 7739 6660

Summers, Mrs S V (Fraser Dawbarns) *K1 D1*
March *p312* 01354 602880

Summers, Miss Z (Hart Reade) *K3 K1*
Eastbourne *p215* 01323 727321

Summerscales, D J (Redferns) *D1 K3 K1*
Portland *p354* 01305 823636

Sumner, A H (Napthens LLP) *E*
Preston *p357* 01772 888444

Sumner, C E (Kennedys)
London EC3 *p49* 020 7667 9667

Sumner, D (Larcomes LLP) *A1 C1 S2 P*
Portsmouth *p354* 023 9266 1531

Sumner, Mrs D E (Cooks) *K1 D1 S1*
Newcastle under Lyme *p323*. 01782 611090

Sumner, G C E (Sumner & Tabor) *E C1 S2 J1 Q*
Berkhamsted *p131*. .01442 862797 / 872311

Sumner, J (England Stickland & Neale) *N F1 O Q*
Birmingham *p138* 0121 377 7773

Sumner, K W (Marrons) *C1 E J1 O R1 S1*
Leicester *p280* 0116 289 2200

Sumner, Ms M E (W A G Davidson & Co) *S1 W K1 L F1*
London W3 *p26* 020 8992 4884

Sumner, Miss M K (Dixon Rigby Keogh) *K1 D1*
Northwich *p333* 01606 48111

Sumner, Mrs R L (Sumner & Main) *E S1 W*
Worthing *p442* 01903 239420

Sumon, B (Gangar & Co) *G K1 N F2 F1 L Q J1 V S1 Zi Zj*
West Bromwich *p427* 0121 553 4166

Sumpton, S H (Stephenson Harwood) *E C2 S2 R2*
London EC2 *p82* 020 7329 4422

Sumputh, Ms V (Duncan Lewis & Co)
Hackney *p53* 020 7923 4020

Sumputh, Ms V K (Glazer Delmar) *K1*
London SE22 *p35* 020 8299 0021

Sunderland, J C (Sutton Magistrates' Court)
Wallington *p475* 020 8770 5950

Sunderland, J P (Risdon Hosegood) *A1 J1 R1 S1 S2 W*
Dulverton *p214* 01398 322100

Sundram, Ms H (Covent Garden Family Law) *K1 K3*
Camden *p23* 020 7257 6130

Suneja, A (LG Lawyers)
London SE1 *p50* 020 7379 0000

Sunter, C B (Laytons) *C1 C2*
London EC4 *p52* 020 7842 8000

Sunter, T G (Newcastle Upon Tyne City Council)
Newcastle upon Tyne *p466* . 0191 232 8520

Suotton, Mrs L A (South Tyneside Magistrates Court)
South Shields *p471* 0191 455 8800

Suresh, Mrs P (Nathan Suresh & Amirthan)
Wembley *p426* 020 8574 1058

Surgenor, Ms S (Childrens Legal Centre) *D1 K1*
Colchester *p455* . . .01206 872466 / 873828
Colchester *p197* 01206 578282

Surgeoner, S J (Clifford Chance)
London E14 *p20* 020 7006 1000

Suringar, Ms M (Manchester City Council)
Manchester *p465* 0161 234 5000

Surma, R (Geldards LLP)
Derby *p208* 01332 331631

Surridge, R (AXA UK PLC)
London E22 *p103* 020 7920 5900

Surzyn, M H (PCB Solicitors LLP) *G H Zl*
Telford *p409* 01952 403000

Susman, A M (Department for Business, Enterprise and Regulatory Reform)
London SW1 *p105* 020 7215 0105

Sussens, Ms N J (Gordons LLP)
Leeds *p273* 0113 227 0100

Sutch, A L (Stephenson Harwood) *C1 Zo*
London EC2 *p82* 020 7329 4422

Sutcliffe, D I (Heseltine Bray & Welsh) *S1 E N Q C1 F1 K1*
Barnsley *p124* 01226 210777

Sutcliffe, F (Ford & Warren) *J1 J2 M1 X Zg Zu*
Leeds *p273* 0113 243 6601

Sutcliffe, Miss J (Pannone LLP) *T2 W V*
Manchester *p308* 0161 909 3000

Sutcliffe, N J (Foot Anstey) *E S1 S2 A1 W*
Taunton *p408* 01823 625600

Sutcliffe, Mrs S A (Turnbull Garrard) *S1 D1 W K1 G L Zd*
Shrewsbury *p379* . .01743 350851 / 351332

Sutcliffe, T R (Powell Eddison Freeman & Wilks) *W S1 S2 L*
Harrogate *p240* 01423 564551

Sutcliffe, Ms V (Hogan Lovells International LLP)
London EC1 *p42* 020 7296 2000

Sutherland, D (Rodgers & Burton)
London SW13 *p73* 020 8939 6300

Sutherland, Miss F (Winchester City Council)
Winchester *p476* 01962 840222

Sutherland, Miss H B (Guildford Borough Council)
Guildford *p459* 01483 505050

Sutherland, Ms J (Nelsons) *W*
Nottingham *p338* 0115 958 6262

Sutherland, J F (Atherton Godfrey) *S1 L W S2 E*
Doncaster *p211* 01302 320621

Sutherland, Miss M D (Squire Sanders (UK) LLP)
Birmingham *p142* 0121 222 3000

Sutherland, Miss N L (Levison Meltzer Pigott) *K1*
London EC4 *p53* 020 7556 2400

See p634 for the Key to Work Categories

Sutherland, N W (Hansells)
North Walsham p331 . . . . . 01692 404351

Sutherland, P D (Andersons Solicitors) E S1 C1 S2 R2 U2
Nottingham p335 . . . . 0115 947 0641

Sutherland, P W (Batt Broadbent) S1 S2 R2
Salisbury p371 . . . . 01722 411141

Sutherland, P W (Rutters) S1 S2 E
Gillingham p229 . . . . 01747 822005

Sutherland, Ms R H (Clifford Chance)
London E14 p20 . . . . 020 7006 1000

Sutherland, Mrs S L (Scott Bailey) K1 V
Lymington p296 . . . . 01590 676933

Sutherland, T E F (Boodle Hatfield) E P
Westminster p14 . . . . 020 7629 7411

Suthers, M W (Fraser Brown) W S2 S1 E Zi
Bingham p133 . . . . 01949 830812

Suthi, H S (Faber & Co)
Birmingham p138 . . . . . . 0121 236 5751
Wolverhampton p438 . . . . 01902 773666

Sutovic, S (Sutovic & Hartigan)
London W3 p84 . . . . 020 8993 5544

Suttie, F I (DAC Beachcroft)
Leeds p272 . . . . 0113 251 4700

Suttill, Miss C A (Parrott & Coales LLP) N Q
Aylesbury p121 . . . . 01296 318500

Sutton, A J (Ashton Bond Gigg) C1 Ze C3 I
Nottingham p335 . . . . 0115 947 6651

Sutton, A P (Colemans - CTTS) B1 F1 O Q
Kingston upon Thames p267. 020 8296 9966

Sutton, Ms B (Rawlison Butler LLP) E S1
Crawley p202 . . . . 01293 527744

Sutton, Miss C (Guy Williams Layton)
Liverpool p288 . . . . 0151 236 7171

Sutton, Mrs E J (Gardner Croft LLP) D1 K3 K1 D2
Canterbury p176 . . . . 01227 813400

Sutton, E J A (South Bedfordshire District Council)
Dunstable p457 . . . . 01582 472222

Sutton, G (Hay & Kilner) O Zc
Newcastle upon Tyne p325 . 0191 232 8345

Sutton, G R (Kerseys) W K4
Ipswich p262 . . . . 01473 213311

Sutton, Mrs H E (Blackhurst Swainson Goodier LLP) K1 D1 D2
Lancaster p269 . . . . 01524 32471

Sutton, J A (Calthrops) N M1 P R1 B1 F1 G
Spalding p389 . . . . 01775 724381

Sutton, Ms J A (Brevitts) W
Birmingham p136 . . . . . . 0121 472 4131

Sutton, J P (Blake Lapthorn) S1
Oxford p342 . . . . 01865 248607

Sutton, K D (Herrington & Carmichael LLP) N Q K1 B1 C1 C2 G J1 L Zv Zr Zq Zi
Camberley p173 . . . . 01276 686222

Sutton, Mrs K S (Muckle LLP) E R2 S2 Zb
Newcastle upon Tyne p325 . 0191 211 7777

Sutton, Miss L C (Maidments) G H
Salford p370 . . . . 0870 403 4000

Sutton, M (Reynolds Porter Chamberlain LLP) Zj
London E1 p71 . . . . 020 3060 6000

Sutton, M (Berry Smith LLP) C1 C2
Cardiff p177 . . . . 029 2034 5511

Sutton, Ms M J (Kennedys) J1
Chelmsford p186 . . . . . . 0845 838 4800

Sutton, M J (Shakespeares) C1 I Ze Zb
Birmingham p142 . . . . . . 0121 237 3000

Sutton, Ms M L (Linskills Solicitors) G H K1
Liverpool p289 . . . . 0151 236 2224

Sutton, M P (Black Graf & Co) O Q N Zr Zq
London NW3 p13 . . . . . . 020 7586 1141

Sutton, N A (Baches) G H
West Bromwich p427 . 0121 553 3286 / 553 7076

Sutton, Ms N H (Westminster City Council)
London SW1 p110 . . . . . . 020 7641 6000

Sutton, P (Stone King LLP) Zc E Q W B1 F1 O L P
Bath p128 . . . . 01225 337599

Sutton, P (Squire Sanders (UK) LLP)
Birmingham p142 . . . . . . 0121 222 3000

Sutton, P R (McGrigors LLP) C1 C2
London EC4 p56 . . . . 020 7054 2500

Sutton, P W (Reed Smith LLP)
London EC2 p71 . . . . 020 3116 3000

Sutton, R H (Macfarlanes) C1
London EC4 p56 . . . . 020 7831 9222

Sutton, R M (Wrigleys Solicitors LLP)
Leeds p278 . . . . 0113 244 6100

Sutton, R P (Foot Anstey) E L
Plymouth p349 . . . . 01752 675000

Sutton, S (Robson Palmer) C1 E L S1 W Ze Zf S2
South Shields p384 . . . . . 0191 455 4561

Sutton, S D (Brian Harris & Co) Q O J1 Zf M2 Zq A3
London W1 p39 . . . . 020 7935 5541
London W1 p84 . . . . 020 7935 5279

Sutton, Mrs S J (Jefferies LLP) N
Altrincham p116 . . . . 0800 342 3191

Sutton-Mattocks, Miss A J (Sutton-Mattocks & Co LLP) W T2
London SW13 p84 . . . . . . 020 8876 8811

Sutton-Mattocks, R G (Clifford Chance)
London E14 p20 . . . . 020 7006 1000

Svedberg, Mrs A V (Svedberg Law) C1 F1 J1 T1 W Zb Zv
London SW1 p84 . . . . 020 7368 7000

Swabey, S J (Thomas Cooper) C1 C2 J1 M1 M2 O Q
London EC3 p22 . . . . 020 7481 8851

Swaby, A A (Howells LLP) G H
Sheffield p376 . . . . 0114 249 6666

Swaby, J (Eric Robinson Solicitors) D1 K1 Zu
Southampton p385 . . . . . . 023 8042 5000

Swaby, N G (Swaby Clarke & Norris) S1 W Zd S2
Barking p123 . . . . 020 8507 1882

Swaden, M F (Manuel Swaden) B1 O Q W J1
London NW6 p58 . . . . . . 020 7431 4999

Swaffer, P L J (Goodman Derrick LLP) N P Ze Zf Zk
London EC4 p36 . . . . 020 7404 0606

Swaffield, D R (Hill Dickinson LLP) E L C1 O Zj R2 S2
Liverpool p288 . . . . 0151 600 8000

Swain, D (Rawlison Butler LLP) C1
Horsham p253 . . . . 01403 252492

Swain, G F (Swain & Co) N O Q V X Zr
Havant p244 . . . . 023 9248 3322
Southampton p386 . . . . . . 023 8063 1111

Swain, Miss R A (Thomson Snell & Passmore) S1
Tunbridge Wells p415 . . . . 01892 510000

Swain, R A (Paris Smith LLP) C1 C2
Southampton p386 . . . . . . 023 8048 2482

Swainbank, Miss E (Antony Hodari & Co) N
Manchester p305 . . . . . . 0161 832 4781

Swaine, A D (Bishop & Sewell LLP) S1 L
London WC1 p13 . . . . . . 020 7631 4141

Swaine, Miss F M (Leigh Day & Co) Zr Zg
London EC1 p52 . . . . 020 7650 1200

Swainston, M P (Forsters LLP) E
Westminster p33 . . . . 020 7863 8333

Swales, J I (Andrew Jackson) N Q Zi
Hull p257 . . . . 01482 325242

Swallow, L (Lanyon Bowdler LLP) B1 C1 Zj Q N
Shrewsbury p379 . . . . . . 01743 280280

Swallow, M (First Title Insurance PLC)
London EC4 p106 . . . . . . 020 7832 3100

Swallow, M A (The Water Companies Association)
London SW1 p110 . . . . . . 020 7222 0644

Swallow, M S J (Aviva PLC)
London EC3 p103 . . 020 7283 7500 / 01603 687905
Norwich p467 . . . . 01603 622200

Swallow, R P B (ConocoPhillips Ltd)
Warwick p475 . . . . 01926 404000

Swalwell, I M (Coole & Haddock) A1 B1 C1 E S1 T1 W Zb
Worthing p441 . . . . 01903 213511

Swan, A (Freeman Johnson) G Zl B2 J2 Zy F2 P Zt
Spennymoor p389 . . . . . . 01388 814389
Newcastle upon Tyne p326 . 0191 232 0283

Swan, Mrs C E (Wace Morgan) D1 D2 K1 K2
Shrewsbury p379 . . . . . . 01743 280100

Swan, K (Patterson Glenton & Stracey)
South Shields p384 . . . . . 0800 011 6487

Swan, Ms K A (Russell Jones & Walker) G H
London WC2 p74 . . . . 020 7657 1555

Swan, Ms N J (Great Yarmouth Borough Council)
Great Yarmouth p459 . . . . 01493 856100

Swan, Ms V M (Buckinghamshire County Council) D1 K1
Aylesbury p448 . . . . 01296 383653

Swan, W L G (Currey & Co) Zd W T2
Westminster p24 . . . . 020 7802 2700

Swanbury, J B (Mears Hobbs & Durrant) S1 K1 E W N L Q
Beccles p129 . . . . 01502 715818

Swann, D K (David K Swann) E K1 S1 W
Rochdale p365 . . . . 01706 366557

Swann, Ms F (Swanns) E J1 S1 W B1 C1
King's Lynn p266 . . . . . . 01553 811747

Swann, G (Beetenson & Gibbon)
Grimsby p235 . . . . 01472 240251
Louth p294 . . . . 01507 600610

Swann, Ms N (Linklaters LLP)
London EC2 p54 . . . . 020 7456 2000

Swann, W C (Borough of Telford & Wrekin) D1 G H J1 V K1
Telford p473 . . . . 01952 380000

Swannack, Ms K A (Foys Solicitors) D1 D2 K1
Sheffield p375 . . . . 0114 251 1702

Swanney, J (The Watson Ramsbottom Partnership) D1 K3 K1 W
Great Harwood p234.01254 884422 / 883020
Blackburn p146 . . . . 01254 672222

Swansey, Miss J (Muckle LLP) C1 C2 F1 Ze
Newcastle upon Tyne p325 . 0191 211 7777

Swanston, R R (Lucas & Wyllys) C1 D1 E S1 K1 L W Zl K2
Great Yarmouth p234 . . . . 01493 855555

Swanton, Ms G (SGH Martineau LLP) X
Birmingham p142 . . . . . . 0870 763 2000

Swanton, Miss L E (Morgan Cole) N J2 O Zj Zq B2
Bristol p164 . . . . 0117 916 7220

Swanton, S J (Astills) K1 S1 W K4 F1 K3 Zl
Leicester p278 . . . . 0116 249 4450

Swanwick, Ms D (Howard Kennedy LLP) E
London W1 p48 . . . . 020 7636 1616

Swarbrick, J A (Horwich Cohen Coghlan) G H
Manchester p305 . . . . . . 0161 830 4600

Swart, C (Holman Fenwick Willan)
London EC3 p42 . . . . 020 7264 8000

Swash, M (OBW Perera) G H
Colchester p197 . . . . .01206 541111

Swatts, Ms A L (Mark Gilbert Morse)
Newcastle upon Tyne p325 . 0191 261 0096

Swede, D S (Darlingtons) C1 C2
Edgware p217 . .020 8952 0033 / 8951 6666

Swede, J R (Darlingtons) E S2
Edgware p217 . .020 8952 0033 / 8951 6666

Sweeney, B A (DP Law Ltd t/a David Prosser & Co) N J1 Q O W
Bridgend p157 . . . . 01656 645921

Sweeney, Mrs H (Steele & Son) W K4
Barnoldswick p124 . . . . . . 01282 813385

Sweeney, Miss J (Bradleys) S1
Dover p212 . . . . 01304 204080

Sweeney, J A (Devon County Council)
Exeter p458 . . . . 01392 382000

Sweeney, Ms K (Stephensons Solicitors LLP) Zr
Wigan p432 . . . . 01942 777777

Sweeney, Ms L (DLA Piper UK LLP)
Manchester p303 . . . . . . 0870 011 1111

Sweeney, M N (Schofield Sweeney) C1 C2 J1 Zb Ze
Bradford p154 . . . . 01274 306000

Sweeney, Miss N (Latimer Hinks) T2 W
Darlington p206 . . . . 01325 341500

Sweeney, P J (Sweeney Miller) N J1 O Q A3 Zy J2 Zr Zq Zp
Sunderland p402 . . . . 0191 568 2050

Sweeney, P J R (Petherbridge Bassra Solicitors) S1 K1 G H M1 P W
Bradford p154 . . . . 01274 724114

Sweeney, Ms S (DLA Piper UK LLP)
Liverpool p287 . . . . 0870 011 1111

Sweeney, Ms S (Atteys) N Zr
Retford p363 . . . . 01777 713355

Sweet, R (Moorhead James LLP) E S2 S1
London EC4 p61 . . . . 020 7831 8888

Sweet-Escott, Mrs E R (Aviva PLC)
London EC3 p103 . . 020 7283 7500 / 01603 687905
Norwich p467 . . . . 01603 622200

Sweeting, D F (Stratford-on-Avon District Council)
Stratford-upon-Avon p473 . . 01789 267575

Sweeting, Ms F (Osborne Clarke) C2
Bristol p164 . . . . 0117 917 3000

Sweeting, Ms J (Trowers & Hamlins)
London EC3 p88 . . . . 020 7423 8000

Sweeting, M J (Clifford Chance)
London E14 p20 . . . . 020 7006 1000

Sweetman, Ms D (Tuckers) N
Manchester p310 . . . . . . 0161 233 4321

Sweetman, Ms M (South Gloucestershire Council)
Thornbury p474 . . . . 01454 868686

Sweetman, P D (Sweetman Burke & Sinker) L N O Q W
Ealing p84 . . . . 020 8840 2572

Swensson, M (The Environment Agency (North West Region [HQ])) Q N Za
Warrington p475 . . . . 01925 653999

Swerling, L F (Horwich Cohen Coghlan) Q
Manchester p305 . . . . . . 0161 830 4600

Swerner, J S (BSG Solicitors LLP) C1 E
London N3 p9 . . . . 020 8343 4411

Swetman, Ms V (Steeles) C1
Norwich p335 . . . . 0870 609 0200

Swientozielskyj, Miss D (Isherwood & Hose) K1 D1 K3
Heywood p249. . . .01706 360032 / 368741

Swift, Miss C (Follett Stock LLP) A3 Zc O Q Zq Zm
Truro p414 . . . . 01872 241700

Swift, Ms C (Martello Professional Risks Limited)
London EC3 p108 . . . . . . 020 7337 7500

Swift, D C (Halton Magistrates Court)
Runcorn p470 . . . . 01928 716130

Swift, D M (Browne Jacobson LLP) E Zn
Nottingham p336 . . . . 0115 976 6000

Swift, Miss J C (Horwood & James LLP) K1 F1 N O W
Aylesbury p121 . . . . 01296 487361

Swift, Ms J E (Aylesbury Vale District Council)
Aylesbury p447 . . . . 01296 585858

Swift, M (HBOS PLC)
Halifax p460 . . . . 0870 600 5000

Swift, N T (Peters & Peters) B2 G
London EC4 p67 . . . . 020 7629 7991

Swift, R Z (Linklaters LLP)
London EC2 p54 . . . . 020 7456 2000

Swift, Ms S M (Billson & Sharp) E J1 R1 T2 S1 S2 W N
Leicester p279 . . . . 0116 270 2260

Swift, S W (Sills & Betteridge LLP) E A1 C1 W S1
Sleaford p381 . . . . 01529 302800

Swimer, D (Curry Popeck) Q O
London W1 p24 . . . . 020 7224 6633

Swinburn, Mrs D A (Evans & Co) F1 C1 G J1 S1 K1 L O N Zl
Spennymoor p389 . . . . . . 01388 815317

Swinburn, Ms E J (Hewitsons) J1
Cambridge p174 . . . . 01223 461155

Swinburn, R G (Reed Smith LLP) Za
London EC2 p71 . . . . 020 3116 3000

Swinburne, C H S (Swinburne & Jackson LLP) N J1 Q K1 W E Zl S2 K4
Gateshead p229. 0191 477 2531 / 477 3222
Ryton p370 . . . 0191 413 3468 / 413 2630
Washington p423 . . . . . . 0191 416 0004

Swinburne, Miss L L (Swinburne & Jackson LLP) S1 W
Gateshead p229. 0191 477 2531 / 477 3222
Gosforth p233 . . . . 0191 285 7544

Swinburne, Mrs R (Swinburne & Jackson LLP) D1 K3 K1 Zu Zm
Ryton p370 . . . 0191 413 3468 / 413 2630

Swindall, H (Russell-Cooke LLP) E
London SW15 p74 . . . . . . 020 8789 9111

Swindell, J (John Swindell and Co Solicitors)
Blackburn p146 . . . . 01254 52400

Swindell, M R (DLA Piper UK LLP)
London EC2 p24 . . . . 0870 011 1111

Swindells, Mrs J (Muckle LLP) Zb
Newcastle upon Tyne p325 . 0191 211 7777

Swindells, T (Walker Foster) C1 C2
Skipton p381 . . . . 01756 700200

Swinden, M B (Skipton Building Society)
Skipton p471 . . . . 01756 705000

Swindlehurst, Ms F (Roland Robinsons & Fentons LLP) N
Blackpool p147 . . . . 01253 621432

Swingewood, Miss A (BRM Solicitors) E S2 S1
Chesterfield p191 . . . . . . 01246 555111

Swingler, D (Straw & Pearce) G H
Loughborough p293 . . . . . 01509 268931

Swinhoe, C R (Muckle LLP) C1
Newcastle upon Tyne p325 . 0191 211 7777

Swinn, Miss K E (Hutchinson & Buchanan) F1 Q N
Ripon p365 . . . . 01765 602156

Swinnerton, A R (Swinnerton Moore Solicitors) Za O Q C1
London EC4 p84 . . . . 020 7236 7111

Swinscoe, Miss M T (Wrigley Claydon) D1 K1 K3 D2
Oldham p341 . . . . 0161 624 6811

Swire, Miss K (Sacker & Partners LLP) Zo
London EC2 p76 . . . . 020 7329 6699

Swirski, Ms C (Clifford Chance)
London E14 p20 . . . . 020 7006 1000

Swistak, C (Young Swistak Solicitors) G H
Melton Mowbray p314 . . . . 01664 501801

Switalski, S J T (Switalski's) D1 G H
Wakefield p419 . . . . 01924 882000

Sword, J S G (McKenzie Bell Solicitors) K1 D1 E N J1 G H S1 F1 W
Washington p423 . . . . . . 0191 416 2605
Sunderland p401 . . . . 0191 567 4857

Swynnerton, M (DLA Piper UK LLP)
London EC2 p24 . . . . 0870 011 1111

Syddall, J (Serious Law LLP - The Serious Law Practice)
Bolton p150 . . . . .0800 616 681

Sydenham, Mrs P A (Birketts LLP) A1 A2
Ipswich p262 . . . . 01473 232300

Sydenham, R (Hogan Lovells International LLP)
London EC1 p42 . . . . 020 7296 2000

Sydney, A J (Dutton Gregory) E R2 S2
Winchester p433 . . . . 01962 844333

Syed, Miss M C B (Charles Russell LLP) T2 W Zd
London EC4 p19 . . . . 020 7203 5000

Syed, Mrs N (Springfield Advice & Law Centre)
London SW17 p109 . . . . . 020 8767 6884

Syed, Ms S (Clerk to Sheffield Justices)
Sheffield p470 . . . . 0114 276 0760

Syed, Ms S (Morrisons Solicitors LLP) E J1
Woking p437 . . . . 01483 726146

Sykes, Mrs A J (Pannone LLP) W T2
Manchester p308 . . . . . . 0161 909 3000

Sykes, C J (Sykes Anderson LLP) O N J1 K1 E C1
London EC2 p85 . . . . 020 3178 3770

Sykes, Ms C L (Irwin Mitchell LLP) O W Zd Zq
Sheffield p376 . . . . 0870 150 0100

Sykes, D (Foot Anstey) C1 C2 Ze
Exeter p221 . . . . 01392 411221

Sykes, Mrs G (Buckles Solicitors LLP) Zh L O
Peterborough p346 . . . . . 01733 888888

Sykes, J H (Jacobs Allen Hammond) K1 Q O Zd Zk
London W1 p45 . . . . 020 7299 9800

Sykes, J P (Levi Solicitors LLP) C1 Zg O Q N
Leeds p275 . . . . 0113 244 9931

Sykes, J R H (Charles Russell LLP) O Q U1
London EC4 p19 . . . . 020 7203 5000

Sykes, J R H (Lupton Fawcett) O Ze Zw A3
Leeds p275 . . . . 0113 280 2000

Sykes, P (Broomhead & Saul) K1 D1 G H Q L N K2
Taunton p408 . . . . 01823 288121

Sykes, Ms P A (Hunters) W T2 S1 E A1
Towcester p413 . . . . 01327 830895
London WC2 p44 . . . . 020 7412 0050

Sykes, Ms R (Ramsdens Solicitors) J1 W Zl
Huddersfield p256 . . . . . . 01484 821500

Sykes, R W (Parker Bullen) W T1 Zd
Salisbury p371 . . . . 01722 412000

Sykes, T V (Cartmell Shepherd) C1 B1 T1 E S1 F1
Carlisle p182 . . . . 01228 516666

Sylvester Jones, T J (Davitt Jones Bould) E S2 P R1 L R2
Taunton p408 . . . . 01823 279279

Sylvester, Miss C A (Treasury Solicitors Department)
London WC2 p110 . . . . . . 020 7210 3000

Sylvester, M (Motoringlawyers.com)
Altrincham p117 . . . . 0161 233 0900

Sylvester, P B (P B Sylvester & Co)
Wandsworth p85 . . . . 020 8769 6767

Sylvester, Ms S (Carillion PLC)
Wolverhampton p477 . . . . . 01902 422431

Syme, K F (Juliet Hardick Solicitors)
Bath p127 . . . . 01225 311177

Symes, B (Shell International Ltd)
London SE1 p109 . . . . . . 020 7934 1234

Symes-Thompson, P H (Willans LLP) C1 C2 C3 F1 Ze
Cheltenham p189 . . . . 01242 514000

Symington, J (Financial Services Authority)
London E14 p106 . . . . . . 020 7066 1000

Symonds, Ms H (Simmons & Simmons)
London EC2 p79 . . . . 020 7628 2020

Symonds, Mrs L A (Welsh Health Legal Services) N O Q
Cardiff p453 . . . . 029 2031 5500

Symons, A (CMS Cameron McKenna LLP) O
London EC3 p17 . . . . 020 7367 3000

Symons, B M (Pitmans LLP) *N P J1 R1 F1 B1 L C1 Zl*
Reading *p361* 0118 958 0224
Symons, C W (Jennings) *S1 E K1 W*
Llanelli *p292* 01554 772331
Symons, J R (Brewer Harding & Rowe) *A1 L S1 S2 W*
Barnstaple *p125* 01271 342271
Symons, Ms K (Boodle Hatfield) *E L R1*
Westminster *p14* 020 7629 7411
Symons, Miss L (Brains) *K3 K1 D1 Q*
St Austell *p391* 01726 68111
Symons, M J (Helphire (UK) Ltd) *S1 E C1 T1*
Bath *p448* 01225 321000
Symons, P J (Gilbert Stephens) *S1 S2 W Zd*
Exeter *p221* 01392 424242
Symons, T J (G & I Chisholm) *S1 K1 P E W L*
Bodmin *p148* 01208 74242
Symons, Miss V J (Boodle Hatfield) *C2 C1 C3*
Westminster *p14* 020 7629 7411
Syms, H C A (Swain & Co) *L N P Q V X Zm Zr*
Southampton *p386* 023 8063 1111
Synnott, T (TMJ Law Solicitors)
Northampton *p332* 01604 608111
Syson, K G (Stevens & Bolton) *C1 J1 B1 Ze Zi*
Guildford *p237* 01483 302264
Syson, N (Linklaters LLP)
London EC2 *p54* 020 7456 2000
Szabo, P (Graysons) *D1 K1*
Sheffield *p375* 0114 272 9184
Szerdy, J C (DWF) *Zb C1 B1*
Liverpool *p287* 0151 907 3000
Szlezinger, S E (SNR Denton) *C3 M1*
London EC4 *p75* 020 7242 1212
Szolcek, Mrs S G (Legal Moves (Braddon & Snow Limited)) *S1 E*
Hertford *p248* 01992 536503
Szoltysek, P (David Gray Solicitors) *L Zh*
Newcastle upon Tyne *p324* . 0191 232 9547
Szostek, L A (Allsopp & Co) *S1 G K1 P M1 N D1 W C1 H Zl*
Solihull *p382* 0121 705 9020
Szyszko, P G (Universal Pictures International Ltd)
London WC1 *p110* 020 7079 6000

T

Taber, P E (Simpson Duxbury) *S1 W L Zi G H*
Bradford *p155* 01274 734166
Taberner, Mrs C A (Bolton Magistrates Court)
Bolton *p450* 01204 558200
Taberner, M J (Angel & Co) *N O Q J1 F1 B1 C1 L Zp*
Coventry *p200* 024 7625 2211
Tabinor, D (Weightmans LLP) *E R1 S1*
Liverpool *p291* 0151 227 2601
Tabor, Mrs G M (Sumner & Tabor) *S1 K1 W M1 F1 P L V D1*
Berkhamsted *p131* . 01442 862797 / 872311
Tackley, M O (Blake Lapthorn) *Q O Zj C1 Ze M2 C3*
Portsmouth *p354* 023 9222 1122
London EC4 *p57* 020 7632 1600
Tadeusz, Mrs C (Burnley-Jones Bate & Co) *G H*
London SW19 *p16* 020 8542 8101
Tadhunter, Miss S J (Bassets) *K1 D2 D1 V*
Gillingham *p229* 01634 575464
Tadros, R (Ince & Co Services Ltd)
London E1 *p44* 020 7481 0010
Taebi, Mrs V (Barker Gooch & Swailes) *S1 S2 L*
London N21 *p9* . 020 8886 5928 / 8886 5734
Taff, K (Wosskow Brown) *N Q*
Sheffield *p377* 0114 256 1560
Taffs, N J (Streathers Solicitors LLP) *S1 P*
London W1 *p84* 020 7034 4200
Taft, C M (M J Darby & Co) *G H V S1 W D1 F1 D2 Zl K1*
Halesowen *p237* 0121 421 7933
Tager, Ms N (Harbottle & Lewis LLP) *J1*
London W1 *p38* 020 7667 5000
Tagg, C (Bobbetts Mackan) *N Zr*
Bristol *p161* 0117 929 9001
Tagg, D L (David Tagg & Co) *K1 O W F1 Zq*
London SW6 *p85* 020 7736 0999
Taggart, A (Herbert Smith LLP)
London EC2 *p40* 020 7374 8000
Taggart, Mrs A J (Kennedys) *O Zq*
London EC3 *p49* 020 7667 9667
Tague, Miss E (Warners Solicitors) *T1 T2 W K4*
Tonbridge *p412* 01732 770660
Taher, J (Mullis & Peake) *J1 O Q*
Romford *p366* 01708 784000
Tahir, Miss A (Widdows Mason) *O Q J1 F1 E*
Westhoughton *p435* 01942 816515
Tahourdin, A R S C (Herrington & Carmichael LLP) *W T2 Zm Zd*
Camberley *p173* 01276 686222
Tahsin, O H (Cogent Law)
Croydon *p204* 0844 245 4452
Tai, A C B (Levi Solicitors LLP) *E S1 S2*
Leeds *p275* 0113 244 9931
Tailor, Mrs H (Gillhams Solicitors LLP) *W*
London NW10 *p35* 020 8965 4266
Tait, Miss A (S V Wadsworth & Co) *S1*
Solihull *p383* 0121 745 8550
Tait, Ms E M (Stephensons Solicitors LLP) *D1 K1*
Leigh *p282* 01942 777777
Tait, G (Tollers LLP)
Northampton *p332* 01604 258558
Tait, G R (Tollers LLP) *J1 Q O Zq Zp*
Northampton *p332* 01604 258558
Tait, Ms J (McGregors) *G H*
Tamworth *p407* 01827 313999
Tait, M (Powell Spencer & Partners) *K1 D1 Zm*
London NW6 *p69* 020 7604 5600
Tait, N G T M (Carter-Ruck) *J1 P Q Zk Ze O Zf*
London EC4 *p18* 020 7353 5005
Tait, Ms P J R (Australia and New Zealand Banking Group Ltd)
London E14 *p103* 020 3229 2121
Tait, R (Tait Farrier Graham) *D1 F1 G H J1 K1 L M1 P*
Gateshead *p229* 0191 490 0108
Tait, S J W (Browne Jacobson LLP)
Nottingham *p336* 0115 976 6000
Takeuchi, H (J A Forrest & Co) *C1 S1 W E*
Westminster *p33* 020 7233 9140
Takhar, J (Paris Smith LLP) *E*
Southampton *p386* 023 8048 2482
Takhar, R S (Tavistock Law Limited) *Zb R2*
London EC4 *p85* 0845 260 6034
Takiar, N (Muckle LLP) *F2 K3 P O J2*
Newcastle upon Tyne *p325* . 0191 211 7777
Talabi, Mrs A (Lucas Law Limited) *N J2 G H Zk Zj*
London E8 *p55* 020 7812 9067
Talbot, Mrs A (Blake Lapthorn)
Oxford *p342* 01865 248607
Talbot, C E (Painters) *S1 W C1 E*
Kidderminster *p266* 01562 822295
Talbot, D A (Burnley Borough Council)
Burnley *p452* 01282 425011
Talbot, Ms E C (Bonell & Co) *J1 K1 N K3 Q*
Stratford-upon-Avon *p400* . . 01789 299115
Talbot, Miss M (Royal Mail Group)
London EC4 *p109* 020 7250 2468
Talbot, M (Harvey Ingram LLP) *O*
Leicester *p280* 0116 254 5454
Talbot, M B J (Department for Business, Enterprise and Regulatory Reform)
London SW1 *p105* 020 7215 0105
Talbot, M H (Pearson Hinchliffe) *G H Zl Zt*
Oldham *p341* 0161 785 3500
Talbot, Miss M J (Cartwright King) *G H*
Nottingham *p336* 0115 958 7444
Nottingham *p338* 0115 958 6262
Talbot, M J (Nockolds) *E L Zh S2*
Bishop's Stortford *p144* . . . 01279 755777
Talbot, R G (Pictons Solicitors LLP)
Luton *p295* 01582 870870
Talbot, Mrs R L (The College of Law Guildford)
Guildford *p459* 01483 460200
Talboys, P S (Herbert Smith LLP) *C2*
London EC2 *p40* 020 7374 8000
Talfourd, P E (Pinney Talfourd LLP) *E S2 W C1 R1*
Hornchurch *p252* 01708 511000
Talisman, Mrs N (Pinnacle Insurance PLC)
Borehamwood *p450* 020 8207 9000
Tall, N (Speechly Bircham LLP)
London EC4 *p81* 020 7427 6400
Tallon, K (Cook Taylor) *D1 K1 G H*
Greenwich *p22* 020 8854 1166
Talog Davies, R I (GHP Legal) *N O*
Wrexham *p442* 01978 291456
Talpade, A (Fox Williams) *J1*
London EC2 *p33* 020 7628 2000
Talukdar, Miss S (Clough & Willis) *S1 L W E R1*
Bury *p170* 0161 764 5266
Talwar, S (Colemans - CTTS) *Zc Zq F1*
Kingston upon Thames *p267* . 020 8296 9966
Tamana, Ms G (Martin Murray & Associates) *G H*
West Drayton *p427* 01895 431332
Tamber, J (Anthony Collins Solicitors LLP) *D1 D2 K3 K1*
Birmingham *p137* 0121 200 3242
Tamboo, Miss S O (Powys County Council)
Llandrindod Wells *p463* . . . 01597 826000
Tame, S J (Dale & Newbery LLP) *N Q Zr*
Staines *p393* 01784 464491
Tamlyn, A (DLA Piper UK LLP) *C1 C2*
London EC2 *p24* 0870 011 1111
Tamplin, D (Fairweather & Co Solicitors)
Canterbury *p176* 01227 784337
Tamplin, D P (Harman & Harman) *Zr J2 N V*
London SW2 *p39* 01227 452977
Tams, S (Lyons Wilson) *E L S1*
Manchester *p307* 0161 830 7777
Tan, Ms C A L (Guillaumes Solicitors) *K3 K1*
Weybridge *p430* 01932 840111
Tan, Ms E (Beale and Company Solicitors LLP) *Zq Zj O Q A3*
London WC2 *p11* 020 7240 3474
Tan, K B T (Wosskow Brown) *C1 E*
Sheffield *p377* 0114 256 1560
Tan, K G (Oxford Law Group) *Zm*
Oxford *p344* 01865 297300
Tan, R (Phillips & Co)
Salisbury *p371* 01722 321666
Tan, Mrs T (Bookers & Bolton) *D1 D2 K1 K3 Zl N*
Alton *p116* . . . . 01420 82881 / 88903
Tan, W (Tanburghs) *G B2 Zi*
London W12 *p85* 020 8749 8902
Camden *p85* 020 7372 6614
Tandon, Ms T (Trowers & Hamlins)
London EC3 *p88* 020 7423 8000
Tandy, D F (Penmans) *G H M1 F1 D1 K1 N P V*
Coventry *p200* 024 7622 6575
Tandy, Miss S (Davenport Lyons) *O Zk*
London W1 *p25* 020 7468 2600
Taner, T R (T R Taner & Co) *S1 G H K1 L M1 P E J1 W Zi*
Haringey *p85* 020 8348 1267
Tang, Miss C Y (Cruickshanks Solicitors) *S1 S2 E W K3*
London W1 *p23* 020 7487 4468
Tang, D (David Tang & Co) *M3 S2 K1 Zi Q S1*
London W1 *p85* 020 7439 4675
Tang, Miss J (Redbridge Magistrates Court)
Ilford *p461* 0845 601 3600
Tang, Miss T P (Tang Bentley & Jackson) *G H B2*
Fareham *p224* 01329 220401
Tangen, Mrs L (Royds LLP) *O Q*
London EC4 *p74* 020 7583 2222
Tankel, Mrs A (Leigh Davis) *S1 W E K3*
London W1 *p26* 020 7631 0302
Tann, A (Tann & Tann Solicitors) *S2 K3 K1 L Zi S1 W*
Wembley *p427* 020 8902 6810
Tann, Mrs S P L R (Tann & Tann Solicitors) *K3 L J1 Q Zi S1*
Wembley *p427* 020 8902 6810
Tanna, D N (Tanna & Co) *E F1 K1 L N O Q G S1 W Zi*
Leicester *p281* 0116 268 2500
Tanner, Mrs A F R (Burges Salmon) *O Zj*
Bristol *p161* 0117 939 2000
Tanner, G D (Collins Dryland & Thorowgood LLP) *P M1 G J1 D1 F1 S1 L W*
Henley-on-Thames *p247* . . . 01491 572323
Tanner, K (HM Land Registry - Birkenhead)
Birkenhead *p449* 0151 473 1110
Tanner, K (Paragon Law) *Zi*
Nottingham *p338* 0115 964 4123
Tanner, M J (Abbott Lloyd Howorth) *W K4*
Maidenhead *p298* 01628 798800
Burnham *p168* 01628 660077
Tanner, N S (Tanners) *C1 C2 E R1 Zc Zj*
Cirencester *p195* 01285 659061
Tanner, P M R (Shell International Ltd)
London SE1 *p109* 020 7934 1234
Tanner, P R (Leach Rawlence & Hart) *B1 J1 K1 Q O L K3 Zc*
Croydon *p205* 020 8680 5850
Tanner, Ms R C (K&L Gates LLP)
London EC4 *p47* 020 7648 9000
Tansey, A P (A P Tansey) *S1 W E*
Hatfield *p244* 01302 843859
Tansey, Ms J A (Atherton Godfrey) *Zr*
Doncaster *p211* 01302 320621
Tansey, Mrs R F (R F Tansey) *D2 K1 K3*
Thame *p410* 01844 218000
Tansey, S (Scott Rees & Co) *S1 W*
Skelmersdale *p381* 01695 722222
Tansley, Miss Z (Punch Robson) *K1 D1 K3*
Stockton-on-Tees *p397* . . . 01642 754050
Tant, C W (Palmers) *O C1 Ze Zc Zq*
Basildon *p126* 01268 240000
Taplin, Ms J (Oxfordshire County Council) *E R1*
Oxford *p468* 01865 792422
Taplin, M J (Freeth Cartwright LLP) *E*
Derby *p208* 01332 361000
Nottingham *p337* 0115 936 9369
Tapner, P (Taylor Vinters) *N Zr*
Cambridge *p176* 01223 423444
Tapp, R F (Carillion PLC)
Wolverhampton *p477* 01902 422431
Tarbox, J P (Steven Dean Magac & Co)
Barnet *p124* 020 8441 3399
Tarbox, J P (Tarbox Robinson & Partners) *S1 E C1 R1 A1 B1 W L Zc*
Northwood *p333* 01923 836595
Tarbuck, Miss D (Hawkins Hatton LLP) *C1 C2 Zb*
Dudley *p213* 01384 216840
Tarbutt, Miss C M (Andrew Jackson)
Hull *p257* 01482 325242
Tarbutt, Ms K (Taylor Wessing)
London EC4 *p86* 020 7300 7000
Tardivat, C (Stewarts Law LLP) *M3 A3 O Q N M2*
London EC4 *p83* 020 7822 8000
Target, L (Trowers & Hamlins)
London EC3 *p88* 020 7423 8000
Tariq, M (Pearson Hinchliffe) *N R1*
Oldham *p341* 0161 785 3500
Tarleton, Ms S R (Department for Business, Enterprise and Regulatory Reform)
London SW1 *p105* 020 7215 0105
Tarling, J P (Steeles) *I M1 C2 C1*
Norwich *p335* 0870 609 0200
Tarlton-Weatherall, Ms S (Bird & Co) *D1 K1*
Grantham *p232* 01476 591711
Tarne, Mrs J E (Aaron & Partners LLP Solicitors) *W*
Chester *p190* 01244 405555
Tarpey, D J (Taylor Wessing) *C1 B1 Zb*
London EC4 *p86* 020 7300 7000
Tarr, Miss J L (Moss Solicitors LLP) *E S2 R2 C1 S1*
Loughborough *p293* 01509 217770
Tarran, Mrs H A (Robert Barber & Sons) *K4 K1 S1 T1 T2 W*
Nottingham *p335* 0115 878 9000
Tarrant, J (Wilson Devonald Ltd)
Swansea *p406* 01792 484566
Tarrant, J H (Highfields Law Practice)
Cambridge *p174* 01954 210363
Tarrant, J N (Avery Naylor) *G H Q*
Swansea *p404* 01792 463276
Tarrant, Ms L (Mayo Wynne Baxter LLP) *O*
Brighton *p160* 01273 775533
Tarrant, N A (Colemans - CTTS) *S1 S2 E W*
Kingston upon Thames *p267* . 020 8296 9966
Tarrant, Mrs T (Pillsbury Winthrop Shaw Pittman LLP)
London EC2 *p67* 020 7847 9500
Tarrant-Smith, Mrs M J (Trethowans LLP) *W T2*
Salisbury *p371* 01722 412512
Tarring, B W (Cartwright Cunningham Haselgrove & Co) *T2 W*
Woodford Green *p439* 020 8506 5200
Tarry, Ms C (Boodle Hatfield)
Westminster *p14* 020 7629 7411
Tarry, Ms K M (RWP Solicitors) *T2 W*
Pangbourne *p345* 0118 984 2266
Tart, P (Dudley Metropolitan Borough Council)
Dudley *p457* 01384 815326
Tash, S (CKFT)
London NW3 *p17* 020 7431 7262
Tasker, Ms M E (Wiltshire County Council)
Trowbridge *p474* 01225 713000
Tasker, M M B J (Fox Williams) *C2 C1 Zj*
London EC2 *p33* 020 7628 2000
Tasou, Mrs E S (Shulmans) *E S1 S2 R2*
Leeds *p276* 0113 245 2833
Tassell, R G M (Blake Lapthorn) *C1 C2 E*
Portsmouth *p354* 023 9222 1122
Tasselli, J S (Ellis Taylor Law LLP) *Zc C1 O*
London WC2 *p29* 020 7405 0206
Tate, C (HM Land Registry - Harrow Sub Office)
Harrow *p460* 020 8235 1181
Tate, C R (Imperial Tobacco Group PLC) *N O Q*
Bristol *p452* 0117 963 6636
Tate, M (Veale Wasbrough Vizards) *E P Zu R1*
Bristol *p165* 0117 925 2020
Tate, Miss W (Volex Group PLC)
Warrington *p475* 01925 830101
Tatham, Miss S C (Bolt Burdon) *J1 Zp*
Islington *p14* 020 7288 4700
Tatham, S R (Bentleys Stokes & Lowless) *Za*
London EC3 *p12* 020 7782 0990
London EC2 *p82* 020 7329 4422
Tatlock, Ms J E (Hegarty LLP) *K1 D1 Q K3*
Peterborough *p347* 01733 346333
Tatlow, D V (Birmingham City Council Legal & Democratic Services)
Birmingham *p449* 0121 303 2066
Tatnall, B K (Calthrops) *L E S1 W A1 C1 Zl*
Spalding *p389* 01775 724381
Tattam, C S R (Pannone LLP) *C1 C2 C3 M1 Zb Ze*
Manchester *p308* 0161 909 3000
Tatten, J (SNR Denton) *O*
London EC4 *p75* 020 7242 1212
Tattersall, J (Addleshaw Goddard) *O N Zc*
Manchester *p300* 0161 934 6000
Leeds *p277* 0113 284 7000
Tattersall, J P (Thomas Butler & Son) *S2 S1 T2 E L W A1*
Broughton-in-Furness *p167* . 01229 716336
Millom *p316* 01229 772553
Rochdale *p365* 01706 644118
Tattersall, R J (Duffield Stunt) *N Q Zq*
Chelmsford *p186* 01245 262351
Tattersall, S (Bell Park Kerridge) *E S1 S2*
Carlisle *p181* 01228 888999
Tatton-Brown, S (Davenport Lyons) *Zf*
London W1 *p25* 020 7468 2600
Tattum, Ms W (Keoghs and Nicholls, Lindsell & Harris) *K3 K1*
Altrincham *p116* 0161 928 9321
Tatum, N S (Gisby Harrison) *K1*
Cheshunt *p189* 01707 878300
Taub, B H (Brian H Taub & Co) *S1 S2 T1 T2*
London N6 *p85* 020 8340 4471
Taube, M Q N (Sternberg Reed) *G H Zm Zg B2*
London NW1 *p83* 020 7485 5558
Taunt, C J (Blake Lapthorn) *E*
Chandlers Ford *p184* 023 8090 8090
Taunton, A J (Belmores) *G H Q*
Norwich *p334* 01603 499999
Tavener, N J W (Birketts LLP) *E A1 S1 L S2 R2*
Ipswich *p262* 01473 232300
Taverner, P S (Bevan Brittan LLP) *F2 N J2 P Zj Zr*
Bristol *p161* 0870 194 1000
Taverner, S G (Land Registry - Gloucester Office)
Gloucester *p459* 01452 511111
Tavroges, Miss H F (Dickinson Dees)
Newcastle upon Tyne *p324* . 0191 279 9000
Tawana, Mrs J K (FBC Manby Bowdler LLP) *N*
Willenhall *p432* 01902 366566
Tawn, M A (BLB Solicitors) *N L Q*
Swindon *p406* 01793 615011
Tawn, P R (Fisher Jones Greenwood LLP) *G H Zl*
Colchester *p197* 01206 578282
Tawn, Mrs S C (Bright & Sons) *W T1 T2*
Maldon *p299* 01621 852323
Taylaur, K (Manches LLP) *A2 Zc*
London WC2 *p58* 020 7404 4433
Tayler, Ms S A (Foort Tayler) *S1*
Great Dunmow *p233* 01371 875200
Tayleur, T N L (The College of Law) *A1 E*
London WC1 *p105* 0800 289997
Taylforth, Mrs R (Lancashire County Council)
Preston *p469* 01772 254868
Tay-Lodge, Mrs A L (Humfrys & Symonds) *K1 D1 D2*
Hereford *p248* . . . 01432 359261 / 276276
Tay-Lodge, G S (Davies & Partners) *N O Q*
Almondsbury *p115* 01454 619619
Taylor Wilson, Mrs C M W (Denison Till) *W K4*
York *p444* 01904 611411
Taylor, A (Waller Pollins) *S1 E S2 W*
Edgware *p217* 020 8238 5858
Taylor, Ms A (Taunton Deane Borough Council)
Taunton *p473* 01823 356356
Taylor, A (BPE Solicitors LLP) *Zb C1 O*
Cheltenham *p187* 01242 224433

See p634 for the Key to Work Categories

Taylor, A (Hogan Lovells International LLP)
London EC1 *p42* 020 7296 2000

Taylor, Mrs A (North Lincolnshire Council)
Scunthorpe *p470* 01724 296296

Taylor, Ms A (Rochdale Metropolitan Borough Council)
Rochdale *p470* 01706 647474

Taylor, Mrs A (Irwin Mitchell LLP) *Zo*
Leeds *p274* 0870 150 0100

Taylor, A C (ASB Law) *B1 N P C1 M1 L J1 K1 F1 Zl*
Crawley *p202* 01293 603600

Taylor, A D (Hamilton Downing Quinn) *E L S1 S2*
London WC1 *p38* 020 7831 8939

Taylor, A D (Reed Smith LLP) *Za*
London EC2 *p71* 020 3116 3000

Taylor, A D (Fentons)
Failsworth *p223* 0161 682 7101

Taylor, Ms A E L (Christopher Cox Solicitors) *A3 B2 O Q Zq*
Northampton *p331* 01604 882287
Northampton *p332* 0370 086 3000 / 01604 543000

Taylor, A G (Davis Blank Furniss) *S1 E A1 W R1*
Glossop *p230* 01457 860606

Taylor, Ms A J (Davis Gregory Ltd) *N*
Cheltenham *p188* 01242 235202

Taylor, Mrs A J (Wrigley Claydon) *K3 D1 K1*
Oldham *p341* 0161 624 6811

Taylor, A J (Birchall Blackburn LLP) *N J2 Zr Zq*
Chorley *p194* 01257 279011

Taylor, A J (Andrew J Taylor) *E S1 W A1 C1 L R1 T1 Zd Zb Zm Zv*
Cheadle *p185* 0161 428 1875

Taylor, A J M (Butcher Andrews) *W T2 K4 Zd*
Fakenham *p223* 01328 863131

Taylor, A J R (Manches LLP) *Ze Zk O U2*
Oxford *p343* 01865 722106

Taylor, Miss A L (Birchall Blackburn LLP) *S1 S2 E*
Manchester *p301* 0161 236 0662

Taylor, Ms A L (Irwin Mitchell LLP) *J1 O*
Birmingham *p139* 0870 150 0100

Taylor, A M (Giffen Couch & Archer) *C1 E L A1 S1 W*
Leighton Buzzard *p282* 01525 372681

Taylor, A P (Heckford Norton) *G H*
Letchworth *p283* 01462 682244

Taylor, A R M (Alan Taylor & Co) *B1 E F1 M1 N P T1 Zb Zi*
London EC1 *p85* 020 7251 3222

Taylor, A W (CKFT) *B1 O Q Zb Zq*
London NW3 *p17* 020 7431 7262

Taylor, Ms B (Memery Crystal) *O B1*
London WC2 *p60* 020 7242 5905

Taylor, B C (Rustons & Lloyd) *W T1 T2*
Newmarket *p327* 01638 661221

Taylor, B E (Glaisyers Solicitors LLP) *L*
Manchester *p304* 0161 224 3311

Taylor, Mrs B J (Official Solicitor and Public Trustee)
London WC2 *p108* 020 7911 7127

Taylor, Ms C (Mayer Brown International LLP)
London EC2 *p59* 020 3130 3000

Taylor, Miss C (Olswang LLP) *J1 Q Ze Zf Zk Zp Zw*
London WC1 *p64* 020 7067 3000

Taylor, Ms C (Harris Fowler) *N*
Taunton *p408* 01823 251515

Taylor, C (Holman Fenwick Willan)
London EC3 *p42* 020 7264 8000

Taylor, Ms C (Russell & Russell) *N*
Atherton *p120* 01942 884469

Taylor, C (Clarke Willmott) *L O F1*
Bristol *p162* 0845 209 1000 / 0117 305 6000

Taylor, C (Eaton Smith LLP) *C1 C2 Zw Ze U2*
Huddersfield *p255* 01484 821300

Taylor, C (Hains & Lewis Ltd) *D2 K3 J1 K1 Q*
Haverfordwest *p244* 0845 408 0125

Taylor, Mrs C (Norwich Union Insurance Group)
Norwich *p467* 01603 622200

Taylor, Ms C (Pinsent Masons LLP) *O Q*
London EC2 *p67* 020 7418 7000

Taylor, C (Northern Rock PLC)
Gosforth *p459* 0191 285 7191

Taylor, C (Dale & Newbery LLP) *N Q*
Staines *p393* 01784 464491

Taylor, C A (KBL Solicitors) *N*
Bolton *p149* 01204 527777

Taylor, C A (Greene & Greene) *S2*
Bury St Edmunds *p171* 01284 762211

Taylor, Ms C E (Hammersmith & Fulham Community Law Centre)
London W6 *p106* 020 8741 4021

Taylor, Mrs C E (Cardiff County Council)
Cardiff *p453* 029 2087 2000

Taylor, Mrs C E F (Charnwood Borough Council)
Loughborough *p464* 01509 263151

Taylor, Ms C F (Caro Taylor Solicitors) *K3 K1 D1 K2 W*
Poole *p352* 01202 678444

Taylor, C J (Sternberg Reed) *G H*
Barking *p123* 020 8591 3366
Romford *p366* 01708 766155

Taylor, Ms C L (Watson Farley & Williams)
London EC2 *p90* 020 7814 8000

Taylor, Ms C M (Bevan Brittan LLP) *E A1 L B1 S2*
Bristol *p161* 0870 194 1000

Taylor, C M M (Kellogg Brown & Root (UK) Ltd)
Leatherhead *p462* 01372 865000

Taylor, Ms C S (TV Edwards LLP) *G H Zm*
London EC3 *p85* 020 7790 7000

Taylor, Miss C V (Healys LLP) *K3 K1*
Brighton *p159* 01273 685888

Taylor, D (Hanne & Co) *F1 J1 N Q*
London SW11 *p38* 020 7228 0017

Taylor, Ms D (Martin Smalley & Co) *K1 W*
Nottingham *p339* 0115 955 6555

Taylor, Miss D (Mackrell Turner Garrett) *W*
London WC2 *p57* 020 7240 0521

Taylor, D (Creighton & Partners)
London WC1 *p23* 020 7976 2233

Taylor, D A (Penningtons) *E*
London EC2 *p66* 020 7457 3000

Taylor, Miss D F (Allen & Overy LLP)
London E1 *p5* 020 3088 0000

Taylor, Mrs D G S (MacDonald Oates LLP) *K1 K3 V*
Petersfield *p348* 01730 268211

Taylor, D J (Paul Berg & Taylor) *C1 E S1*
Harpenden *p239* 01582 760161

Taylor, D J (Nelsons) *C1 C2*
Nottingham *p338* 0115 958 6262

Taylor, Miss D L (Hague & Dixon) *J1 K1 K3*
York *p444* 01904 627111

Taylor, Miss D L (Richard Pearlman LLP) *A1 E L R1 S1 W Zv*
London EC2 *p66* 020 7739 6100

Taylor, D M (Vauxhall Community Law Centre)
Liverpool *p463* 0151 482 2001

Taylor, D N (Crutes) *N Q J1 F1 L Zc Zl Zj*
Newcastle upon Tyne *p324* 0191 233 9700

Taylor, D W (Thursfields) *G N H Q F1 L J1 Zm Zl*
Worcester *p440* 01905 730450

Taylor, Mrs E (Colin Rayner & Co) *W S1*
Bolton *p149* 01204 591145

Taylor, Miss E (Martin Murray & Associates) *G H B2*
Slough *p382* 01753 551313

Taylor, Miss E (Bradshaws Hamer Park & Haworth) *W K4*
Blackpool *p146* 01253 621531
Lytham *p295* 01253 724251 / 728451

Taylor, Miss E E (Darbys Solicitors LLP) *B1 O Q Ze*
Oxford *p343* 01865 811700

Taylor, E J (Teacher Stern LLP) *C1 C2*
London WC1 *p86* 020 7242 3191

Taylor, Miss E L (Mills & Reeve) *Zq*
Manchester *p307* 0844 561 0011

Taylor, Mrs E M (Dorset County Council)
Dorchester *p457* 01305 251000

Taylor, Mrs E M (Edward Harte LLP) *D1 K1 G D2 K2*
Brighton *p159* 01273 662750

Taylor, Ms F (Stephen Gallico Solicitors) *R1 S1 S2 E*
Haywards Heath *p245* 01444 411333

Taylor, F D (AST Hampsons) *N S1 W Q E*
Manchester *p300* 0161 681 1169

Taylor, Ms F K I (Harrison Bundey) *G H*
Leeds *p274* 0113 200 7400

Taylor, Ms F L (Colemans) *E A1 L S1 C1 R1*
Haywards Heath *p245* 01444 459555

Taylor, Mrs F R (Warners Solicitors) *W*
Tonbridge *p412* 01732 770660

Taylor, Miss G (EEF)
London SW1 *p106* 020 7222 7777

Taylor, G (IFPI Secretariat)
London W1 *p107* 020 7878 7900

Taylor, G (DAC Beachcroft)
Bristol *p162* 0117 918 2000

Taylor, G A (Southerns) *W S1 S2*
Burnley *p169* 01282 422711

Taylor, G D (Nabarro LLP) *C1 C2 T1 Zf*
London WC1 *p63* 020 7524 6000

Taylor, G E (Freeth Cartwright LLP) *A1 C1 E L R1 S1 Zh*
Nottingham *p337* 0115 936 9369

Taylor, G H (Gelbergs LLP) *B1 C1 E F1 J1 L O S1 Q W Zf Zk Zl Zd Zb*
Islington *p35* 020 7226 0570

Taylor, G W (Crown Prosecution Service Durham)
Durham *p457* 0191 383 5800

Taylor, H (Michelmores LLP) *C1 C2*
Exeter *p221* 01392 688688

Taylor, H C (Shell International Ltd) *E L S1 C1 Zc*
London SE1 *p109* 020 7934 1234

Taylor, Mrs H J (Henmans LLP) *K3 K1*
Oxford *p343* 01865 781000

Taylor, Ms H P M (Franklins LLP) *K1 D1*
Northampton *p332* 01604 828282

Taylor, I (Coodes) *K1 D1 V J1 Zm*
St Austell *p391* 01726 874700

Taylor, Ms I (Irwin Mitchell LLP) *Zr*
Birmingham *p139* 0870 150 0100
London EC3 *p49* 020 7667 9667

Taylor, I G (Gard & Co) *E S2 S1 C1*
Plymouth *p349* 01752 668246

Taylor, I J (Philip J Hammond & Sons) *S2 S1 W C1 J1*
Leicester *p280* 0116 251 7171

Taylor, J (Simmons & Simmons)
London EC2 *p79* 020 7628 2020

Taylor, J (Donnelly McArdle Adamson)
Hartlepool *p243* 01429 274732

Taylor, J (Stephens McDonald & Robson) *G H B2*
Newcastle upon Tyne *p327* 0191 232 0675

Taylor, J (Canter Levin & Berg)
Liverpool *p287* 0151 239 1000

Taylor, Mrs J (Palmers) *K1 K3*
South Woodham Ferrers *p384* 01245 322111

Taylor, J (Dixon Lewis Solicitors) *N Q K3 W S1*
Wellington *p425* 01952 245700
Craven Arms *p202* 01588 672399

Taylor, J (Tanners) *W*
Cirencester *p195* 01285 659061

Taylor, Ms J (Trowers & Hamlins)
London EC3 *p88* 020 7423 8000

Taylor, Miss J (Shell International Ltd)
London SE1 *p109* 020 7934 1234

Taylor, J (EMW) *J1 Zp*
Milton Keynes *p316* 0845 070 6000

Taylor, J (Farleys Solicitors LLP) *B2 G H*
Blackburn *p145* 01254 367854

Taylor, J (Squire Sanders (UK) LLP) *Zw O C3 Ze*
London EC2 *p81* 020 7655 1000

Taylor, Ms J (Gardner Leader LLP) *E J1*
Newbury *p322* 01635 508080

Taylor, J A (Gaskell & Walker) *S1 W A1 L*
Cowbridge *p201* 01446 772212

Taylor, J C (Jackamans) *A1 C1 E J1 K1 L Q R1 S1 Zc Zl Zq K3 W*
Harleston *p239* 01379 854455

Taylor, J C (H F T Gough & Co) *R1 S1 S2 E W L A1*
Whitehaven *p431* 01946 692461

Taylor, Mrs J E (Nelsons)
Derby *p209* 01332 372372

Taylor, J F (Blake Lapthorn) *E L R1 R2 S1 S2 Zc*
London EC1 *p13* 020 7405 2000

Taylor, J H (Barlow Lyde & Gilbert LLP) *Q O L R1 Zq*
London EC3 *p10* 020 7247 2277

Taylor, J J L (Hentys LLP) *J1 N B1 R1 O Q*
Waterlooville *p423* 023 9224 6710

Taylor, Mrs J L (Holt & Longworth) *K1 N G*
Rossendale *p367* 01706 213251 / 229131

Taylor, Miss J M (Levenes Solicitors) *G H*
Birmingham *p140* 0121 212 0000

Taylor, J M (Steele & Son) *S1 A1 E L W C1 T1 F1 R1 Zc S2*
Clitheroe *p196* 01200 444321

Taylor, J M A (Manches LLP) *O J1*
Oxford *p343* 01865 722106

Taylor, J N (Honley Law Practice) *B1 K1 F1 K3 J1 L Q*
Holmfirth *p251* 01484 667853

Taylor, Ms J P (Anthony Stockton)
Coventry *p201* 01676 535790

Taylor, J P (Wace Morgan) *J1 N O Q Zr*
Shrewsbury *p379* 01743 280100

Taylor, J R (Environment Agency (Midlands Region))
Solihull *p471* 0121 711 2324

Taylor, J R (Kingston upon Hull City Council)
Hull *p461* 01482 300300

Taylor, J S (Barlow Lyde & Gilbert LLP)
London EC3 *p10* 020 7247 2277

Taylor, J T (CGM) *K1 G H M1 D1 S1 P F1 L V*
Southampton *p385* 023 8063 2733

Taylor, Ms K (Bright & Sons) *K1 K3*
Maldon *p299* 01621 852323

Taylor, Ms K (Bright & Sons) *K1 K3 X*
Witham *p435* 01376 512338

Taylor, Ms K (Langleys) *J1*
York *p445* 01904 610886

Taylor, Ms K F (Wessex Solicitors Chambers Ltd) *S2 S1 E G*
Portsmouth *p355* 023 9238 1114

Taylor, Mrs K L (Fisher Jones Greenwood LLP) *K1 D1 K2*
Colchester *p197* 01206 578282

Taylor, Ms K M (Blandy & Blandy) *E*
Reading *p360* 0118 951 6800

Taylor, K S (Rothwell & Evans) *S1 W E L R1 C1*
Swinton *p407* 0161 794 1830

Taylor, L (Linklaters LLP)
London EC2 *p54* 020 7456 2000

Taylor, Miss L (Rosling King) *O Q L Zq*
London EC4 *p73* 020 7353 2353

Taylor, Mrs L (Peak District National Park Authority)
Bakewell *p448* 01629 816200

Taylor, L (Derbyshire County Council)
Matlock *p465* 01629 580000

Taylor, Mrs L (Fishers) *C1 J1 O Q C2 Ze B1 Zq*
Ashby-de-la-Zouch *p118* 01530 412167

Taylor, L (Hart Brown Solicitors) *W*
Cranleigh *p202* 0800 068 8177

Taylor, Mrs L E (Bower & Bailey) *S1*
Witney *p436* 01993 705095

Taylor, Miss L R (George Green LLP) *W T2 K4*
Cradley Heath *p201* 01384 410410

Taylor, Miss L S (Wilkin Chapman Epton Blades) *Q Zo K1 D1 K3*
Lincoln *p285* 01522 512345

Taylor, M (Stephensons Solicitors LLP) *E*
Wigan *p432* 01942 777777

Taylor, Miss M (Hempsons) *N Zr*
Manchester *p305* 0161 228 0011

Taylor, M (DLA Piper UK LLP)
London EC2 *p24* 0870 011 1111

Taylor, M (Darbys Solicitors LLP) *E S2 R2 A1 C1 Zd*
Oxford *p343* 01865 811700

Taylor, M (Hogan Lovells International LLP)
London EC1 *p42* 020 7296 2000

Taylor, M (Jones Day) *J1*
London EC4 *p46* 020 7039 5959

Taylor, M (Taylor Haldane Barlex LLP) *G H*
Chelmsford *p187* 0845 293 7688

Taylor, M (Magna Housing Group Ltd)
Dorchester *p457* 01305 216000

Taylor, M (Michael Taylor & Associates) *B1 C1 E G M1 N P R1 S1 W*
Bromley *p167* 020 8437 0707
Urmston *p417* 0161 746 7776

Taylor, M (Walker Morris) *C1 B1 Zb*
Leeds *p277* 0113 283 2500

Taylor, M (HM Land Registry - Birkenhead (Rosebrae))
Birkenhead *p449* 0151 472 6666

Taylor, M A (Eaton Ryan & Taylor) *F1 I L O P Q Zb A3 Zc B1 Zj Zk*
Birmingham *p138* 0121 236 1999

Taylor, M A H (Swayne Johnson Solicitors) *S1 W C1 E P R1 G A1 B1*
Ruthin *p369* 01824 703833

Taylor, Mrs M E (Hayes & Storr) *W T2 V Zd Zm*
King's Lynn *p266* 01553 778900

Taylor, M I (Shacklocks) *S2 S1 W K4 L*
Belper *p131* 01773 822333

Taylor, Mrs M J (Kingston upon Hull City Council)
Hull *p461* 01482 300300
Hull *p257* 01482 325242

Taylor, M L (Gowlings) *W S1 L E A1 J1 C1 Zm S2 T2 K4*
Preston *p357* 01772 251287

Taylor, M R (Hill Dickinson LLP) *C1 N P Za Zj*
London EC3 *p41* 020 7283 9033

Taylor, Ms M T (SAS Daniels LLP) *K1 K3 D2 D1*
Stockport *p396* 0161 475 7676

Taylor, Mrs M V (Farleys Solicitors LLP) *G H B2*
Blackburn *p145* 01254 367854

Taylor, Miss N (Essex County Council)
Chelmsford *p454* 0845 743 0430

Taylor, Mrs N (Hart Reade) *S2 S1 E*
Eastbourne *p215* 01323 727321

Taylor, N (DAC Beachcroft) *O Zc*
London EC4 *p24* 020 7936 2222

Taylor, Miss N (Taylors Legal)
Ilford *p261* 020 8501 4959

Taylor, N (Field Fisher Waterhouse LLP)
London EC3 *p31* 020 7861 4000

Taylor, N A (Higgs & Sons) *C1 C2 C3 B1 F1 Ze*
Brierley Hill *p158* 0845 111 5050

Taylor, N J (Healys LLP) *Q O N G J1 K1 L B1 F1 D1*
Brighton *p159* 01273 685888

Taylor, N J (Ellis Jones) *E S1 C1 J1 Zc*
Bournemouth *p151* 01202 525333

Taylor, N S (Jones Myers LLP) *K1 K3*
Leeds *p275* 0113 246 0055

Taylor, P (DLA Piper UK LLP)
Birmingham *p137* 0870 011 1111

Taylor, P (Wilkins & Thompson) *W S1 A1*
Uttoxeter *p417* 01889 562875

Taylor, P (Russell Jones & Walker)
Manchester *p309* 0161 383 3500

Taylor, P A B (Paris Smith LLP) *Q Zq O*
Southampton *p386* 023 8048 2482

Taylor, P C (Clifford Chance)
London E14 *p20* 020 7006 1000

Taylor, P D (Badhams Law (A Trading Name of Parabis Law LLP)) *N O Q Zj*
Croydon *p204* 0844 245 4000

Taylor, P D (Kidd Rapinet) *C1 E L S2 S1*
London WC2 *p49* 020 7205 2115

Taylor, P D (Stanley Tee LLP) *Zr N*
Cambridge *p175* 01223 311141

Taylor, P D (Clifford Chance)
London E14 *p20* 020 7006 1000

Taylor, P E (Ellis Taylor Law LLP) *Zc O Q*
London WC2 *p29* 020 7405 0206

Taylor, P H (Hotchkiss Warburton)
Crediton *p203* 01363 774752

Taylor, P J (Bridge McFarland) *J1 N Zq*
Grimsby *p235* 01472 311711
Lincoln *p284* 01522 518888

Taylor, P J (Wychavon District Council)
Pershore *p468* 01386 565000

Taylor, P J (Hay & Kilner) *E L R1 S1 W C1 A1 G*
Newcastle upon Tyne *p325* 0191 232 8345

Taylor, P J (Pannone LLP) *B2 F2 G H I P Zg Zy*
Manchester *p308* 0161 909 3000

Taylor, P J (Information Commisioner)
Wilmslow *p476* 01625 545700

Taylor, P J (Lancashire County Council)
Preston *p469* 01772 254868

Taylor, P J (Farleys Solicitors LLP) *W*
Blackburn *p145* 01254 367855

Taylor, P J (Ford & Warren) *E S1 W L Za Zp*
Leeds *p273* 0113 243 6601

Taylor, P J A (Hewitsons) *R1 P*
Northampton *p332* 01604 233233

Taylor, P L (Hogan Lovells International LLP) *O M1 Q P C1 B1 Za Zj*
London EC1 *p42* 020 7296 2000

Taylor, P L (AST Hampsons) *S1 E G H M1 D1 C1 K1 P L Zi Zl*
Rochdale *p365* 01706 522311

Taylor, P M (Cree Godfrey & Wood) *S1 S2 Q K1 W*
London N2 *p23* 020 8883 9414

Taylor, Miss P M (HM Revenue & Customs)
Salford *p470* 0870 785 8545

Taylor, P M (Glaisyers) *W S1*
Birmingham *p138* 0121 233 2971

Taylor, P M (Reed Smith LLP) *C1 C2*
London EC2 *p71* 020 3116 3000

Taylor, P P (Co-operative Insurance Society Ltd)
Manchester *p464* 0161 832 8686

6

For a range of specialised Legal Services please refer to Section 20

Taylor, P P (Nightingales Solicitors Limited) *E S1 C1 L R1 W K1*
Stockport *p396*. 01663 764038
Taylor, P R J (North Wiltshire District Council)
Chippenham *p455* 01249 706111
Taylor, P W (Gaby Hardwicke) *A1 B1 C1 E S1 T1 W Zc*
Bexhill *p132* 01424 730945
Taylor, P W (McKenzie Bell Solicitors) *S1 E C1 W M1 K1 P N F1 L Zc Zj Zo*
Sunderland *p401*. 0191 567 4857
Taylor, P W (Taylors Solicitors) *S1 S2 E L A1 W T1 T2 C1 K4 Zd*
Braunton *p156*. 01271 812811
Taylor, Miss R (Butcher & Barlow LLP) *K2*
Frodsham *p227* 01928 733871
Taylor, Miss R (Wilkin Chapman Epton Blades) *G H*
Lincoln *p285*. 01522 512345
Taylor, Miss R (FBC Manby Bowdler LLP) *E*
Wolverhampton *p437* 01902 578000
Taylor, R (Michael Simkins LLP) *C1 I Ze Zf*
London WC1 *p79* 020 7874 5600
Taylor, R (Walker Morris) *O Q Zq L*
Leeds *p277* 0113 283 2500
Taylor, R (Langleys) *A1 C1 C2 E S1 Zc*
York *p445* 01904 610886
Taylor, R (Linder Myers Solicitors) *Q O J1 Zl Zp Zc*
Manchester *p307* 0844 984 6400
Taylor, R A (Simmons & Simmons)
London EC2 *p79*. 020 7628 2020
Taylor, Miss R C (Thomson Snell & Passmore) *S1 S2*
Tunbridge Wells *p415* 01892 510000
Taylor, R C (Solomon Taylor & Shaw) *A1 C1 E J1 N P S1*
London NW3 *p80* 020 7431 1912
Taylor, R D (HCB Solicitors) *E C1 A1 S2 W Zc*
Lichfield *p284* 01543 414426
Taylor, R D (Roland Taylor & Co) *N Q O L K1 S1 J1 B1 G S2 Zq Zc Zk*
Braintree *p155*. 01376 330099
Taylor, R F (Gosschalks) *N P F1 Zj*
Hull *p256* 01482 324252
Taylor, R G (Southerns) *G H*
Burnley *p169* 01282 438446
Taylor, Mrs R H (Daltons) *W S1*
Oakham *p340* . . . .01572 722002 / 724343
Taylor, R I (Taunton Deane Borough Council)
Taunton *p473* 01823 356356
Taylor, Mrs R J (Forster Dean Ltd) *K1 N Q J1 F1 W Zq*
Widnes *p431*. 0151 495 3270
Chorley *p194* 01257 262960
Taylor, R J (Gosschalks) *Zl*
Hull *p256* 01482 324252
Taylor, R J (Beor Wilson Lloyd) *C1 E J1 S2*
Swansea *p405*. 01792 655178
Taylor, R J J (CMS Cameron McKenna LLP)
London EC3 *p17*. 020 7367 3000
Taylor, R J N (Osler Donegan Taylor)
Brighton *p160* 01273 710712
Taylor, R J R (Cubism Limited) *B1 C1 C2 E L M2*
London WC2 *p23* 020 7831 0101
Taylor, Ms R M (Garner Canning) *A1 E J1 R1 S1*
Atherstone *p120*. 01827 713543
Taylor, R M (Mark Taylor & Co) *C1 C2 E J1*
London SW10 *p86*. 020 7349 7373
Taylor, R M (Hill Dickinson LLP) *E L*
London EC3 *p41*. 020 7283 9033
Taylor, R M (Bradbury Roberts & Raby) *A1 E L S1 W*
Scunthorpe *p373*. 01724 854000
Taylor, R N (Longmores) *E A1 L S2 C1*
Hertford *p248* 01992 300333
Taylor, R N (TBI Solicitors) *G H N*
Hartlepool *p243* . . . 0800 052 6824 / 01429 264101
Taylor, R O (Lanyon Bowdler LLP) *A1 Ze Zu W C1 E J1 S1*
Ludlow *p294*. 01584 872333
Taylor, R P (Brockbank Curwen Cain & Hall) *S1 S2 W E*
Workington *p440*. 01900 603563
Taylor, R P (May May & Merrimans) *S1 E L S2*
London WC1 *p59* 020 7405 8932
Taylor, R S (Hedleys Solicitors LLP) *S1 W E T1 C1 K1 L R1 F1 A1 Zl*
East Horsley *p215* 01483 284567
Taylor, Miss R S (Eastgate Assistance Ltd)
Colchester *p455* 0870 523 4500
Taylor, Miss S (Edward Harte LLP) *L K3 J1 Q K1*
Brighton *p159* 01273 662750
Taylor, Mrs S (Lancaster City Council)
Lancaster *p462* 01524 582000
Taylor, Ms S (Holman Fenwick Willan)
London EC3 *p42*. 020 7264 8000
Taylor, S (Beswicks) *O Q*
Stoke-on-Trent *p397*. 01782 205000
Taylor, S (Judge & Priestley) *E C1 B1 L T1 Ze*
Bromley *p166* 020 8290 0333
Taylor, Ms S (Bowcock Cuerden LLP) *S1 K1 K2*
Nantwich *p320*. 01270 611106
Taylor, Mrs S (Wigan Borough Council)
Wigan *p476* 01942 244991
Taylor, Miss S A (Watson Solicitors) *S2 E S1*
Warrington *p422* 01925 571212
Taylor, Ms S A (Sharon Taylor Associates) *G H*
Poole *p353* 01202 759769
Taylor, S A (Sheridans) *O B1 J1 Zb Ze Zj Zk Zv*
London WC1 *p78* 020 7079 0100

Taylor, S C B (Darbys Solicitors LLP) *S2 E R2 S1*
Oxford *p343* 01865 811700
Taylor, Mrs S E (Russell-Cooke LLP) *E*
London SW15 *p74*. 020 8789 9111
Taylor, Mrs S E (Taylor Fawcett)
Harrogate *p241* 01423 538111
Taylor, Ms S J (Gould & Swayne) *C1 J1*
Wells *p425*. 01749 675535
Taylor, S J (Freeth Cartwright LLP) *Zw*
Nottingham *p337*. 0115 936 9369
Taylor, Mrs S J (Philcox Gray & Co) *D1 K1 L N*
London SE15 *p67* 020 7703 2285
Taylor, S J R (Flint Bishop Solicitors) *E S1 L Zh Zc S2*
Derby *p208* 01332 340211
Taylor, S O M (CKFT) *Q O Zb*
London NW3 *p17* 020 7431 7262
Taylor, S P (Michael W Halsall)
Newton-le-Willows *p330* . . . 01942 727000
Taylor, S P (Swindon Borough Council)
Swindon *p473* 01793 463000
Taylor, S P (Atteys)
Doncaster *p211* 01302 340400
Taylor, Miss S P (Howard Kennedy LLP) *E S1 L*
London W1 *p48* 020 7636 1616
Taylor, Ms S R (K&L Gates LLP)
London EC4 *p47*. 020 7648 9000
Taylor, S W (Andrew Jackson) *Za*
Hull *p257* 01482 325242
Taylor, T (Hodge Jones & Allen LLP) *D1 K1*
London NW1 *p41* 020 7874 8300
Taylor, T (Barlow Lyde & Gilbert LLP) *A3 M2 Za O Zj*
London EC3 *p10*. 020 7247 2277
Taylor, T (Withers LLP) *C1 C2 J1*
London EC4 *p92*. 020 7597 6000
Taylor, T A (Mulalley)
Woodford Green *p477* 020 8551 9999
Taylor, Miss T D (Askews) *D1 K1*
Redcar *p362*. 01642 475252
Taylor, T H C (SJ Berwin LLP)
London EC4 *p75*. 020 7111 2222
Taylor, T J (T A Capron & Co) *B1 C1 K1 N P S1 W Zm*
Grays *p233* 01375 378331
Taylor, Ms T J (Kidd Spoor Taylor)
North Shields *p330* 0191 257 3101
Taylor, T J J (Forsters LLP) *R1 E*
Westminster *p33*. 020 7863 8333
Taylor, V (Suffolk County Council)
Ipswich *p462*. 01473 583000
Taylor, Mrs V L (Neil Myerson LLP) *W*
Altrincham *p117* 0161 941 4000
Taylor, Mrs W R (Birmingham City Council Legal & Democratic Services)
Birmingham *p449* 0121 303 2066
Taylor, Ms Y M (Crutes) *E S2*
Stockton-on-Tees *p396* . . . 01642 623400
Taylor-Moran, Ms E (Gelbergs LLP) *J1*
Islington *p35*. 020 7226 0570
Taylorson, I M (TLT Solicitors) *B1 C1 E F1 J1 L M1 N S1 W Zb Zc Ze*
London EC2 *p85*. 020 3465 4000
Taylor-True, Mrs C A (Jordans) *N*
Dewsbury *p210* 01924 457171
Tayton, C (Clarks Legal LLP) *O A3 I Zk*
Reading *p360* 0118 958 5321
Tayton, Mrs S L (Lodders Solicitors LLP) *W K4*
Stratford-upon-Avon *p400* . . 01789 293259
Teacher, A (Teacher Stern LLP) *E S1*
London WC1 *p86* 020 7242 3191
Teacher, D S (Teacher Stern LLP)
London WC1 *p86* 020 7242 3191
Teacher, J S (Edwards Angell Palmer & Dodge)
London EC2 *p28*. 020 7583 4055
Teague, G J (Clifford Chance)
London E14 *p20*. 020 7006 1000
Teague, G R (Sims Cook & Teague) *E J1 L*
Bristol *p165* 0117 927 2141
Teague, Mrs L (Shakespeares) *J1*
Birmingham *p142* 0121 237 3000
Teal, M (Gosschalks) *E L S1*
Hull *p256* 01482 324252
Teale, Mrs S (Cripps Harries Hall LLP) *O Zq*
Tunbridge Wells *p415* 01892 515121
Teall, J (Prince Evans) *L*
Ealing *p69*. 020 8567 3477
Teanby, Miss J (J C Bamford Excavators Ltd)
Uttoxeter *p474*. 01889 590312
Tear, A M (Duncan Lewis & Co) *Zi*
London W12 *p53* 020 7923 4020
Tear, D (AWB Charlesworth LLP) *F2 Ze L Zl O Q Zq B1*
Keighley *p263* 01535 613678
Tear, D A (Gordons LLP)
Leeds *p273* 0113 227 0100
Teasdale, K (Silk Solicitors) *Zj Q N S1*
Blackburn *p146* 01254 266616
Teasdale, Miss K J (Parry Law) *Q*
Herne Bay *p248* 01227 361131
Teasdale, N (DWF)
Preston *p356* 01772 556677
Teasdale, Miss S T (Pannone LLP) *B2 G*
Manchester *p308* 0161 909 3000
Teasdale, S W (Derby City Council)
Derby *p456* 01332 293111
Teather, Ms J C (Barlow Lyde & Gilbert LLP)
London EC3 *p10*. 020 7247 2277
Tedstone, A J A (Tedstone George & Tedstone) *K1 N W A1 G S1 T1*
Penkridge *p345* 01785 712243

Tee, J R (Stanley Tee) *A1 T2 W Zd*
Bishop's Stortford *p144* . . . 01279 755200
Teece, Mrs A A (Alison Teece Solicitor) *S1 C1 S2 C2 J1*
Preston *p357* 01772 877238
Teepe, A (Redditch Borough Council)
Redditch *p469* 01527 64252
Teinert, M J (Frodshams) *S1 E*
St Helens *p391* 01744 626600
Tejani, F B (GPT Solicitors) *E F1 L N O Q S1 W Zc Zi Zl Zv*
Wembley *p426*. .020 8904 6495 / 8904 6598
Telang, J M (Granville-West) *S2 E J1 K1 Q N S1 W*
Caldicot *p172* 01291 423999
Telford, D M (Milburns Solicitors) *A1 B1 W L R1 N S1*
Maryport *p313*. 01900 813541
Workington *p440*. 01900 67363
Teli, Y H (Chequers Solicitors Ltd) *S1 S2 E W O K3 B1 J1*
Hayes *p245* 020 8606 1000
Temperley, A (Keoghs LLP) *N Zj O Q A3*
Coventry *p200*. 024 7665 8200
Temperley, P S (Temperley Taylor LLP) *S1 W C1 B1 E Zl*
Middleton *p315* 0161 643 2411
Temperton, D J (Birkett Long LLP) *E S1*
Colchester *p197* 01206 217300
Tempest, I J (Freeth Cartwright LLP) *L E*
Nottingham *p337*. 0115 936 9369
Tempest, M P (Matthew Arnold & Baldwin LLP) *B1*
Watford *p423* 01923 202020
Tempest, Mrs S (Forbes) *D1 K1*
Blackburn *p145* 01254 580000
Temple, E M F (Temple & Co Commercial Solicitors) *A3 C1 M1*
Daventry *p207*. 0845 241 4045
Temple, J C (Shoosmiths) *E A1 R1 C1 T1 Zc Zn*
Northampton *p332*. . 0370 086 3000 / 01604 543000
Temple, Mrs K L (Kitching Walker) *W S1 A1 L S2*
Kirkbymoorside *p268*. 01751 431237
Temple, R A G (Cole & Co) *S1 S2 E*
Norwich *p334* 01603 617018
Temple, R M (CMS Cameron McKenna LLP)
London EC3 *p17*. 020 7367 3000
Temple, S G (Kitching Walker) *S1 S2 K1 W F1 Q*
Kirkbymoorside *p268*. 01751 431237
Templeman, Ms R (Broudie Jackson Canter) *G H*
Liverpool *p286*. 0151 227 1429
Templeton, J D (Grant Saw Solicitors LLP) *W S1 S2*
Greenwich *p36*. 020 8858 6971
Templeton, Miss K D (Forresters) *G H Zl*
Barrow-in-Furness *p125* . . . 01229 820297
Templeton, S (Canter Levin & Berg) *Zj N*
St Helens *p391* 01744 634141
Templeton, W S (Dixon & Templeton) *E C1 S1 M1 A1 L R1*
Fordingbridge *p227* 01425 652194
Ten Caten, Ms L (Hansen Palomares) *V N L*
Lambeth *p38*. 020 7640 4600
Ten Hove, S (Ross & Craig) *J1 N O Q*
Westminster *p73*. 020 7262 3077
Teng, Mrs E G (Forbes Hall LLP) *S1 S2 E R2*
Woodford Green *p439* 020 8498 0080
Tengroth, A J (Harman & Harman) *Zr N*
London SW2 *p39* 01227 452977
Tennakoon, M A (Tennakoons) *K1 L Q J1 F1 G Zi S2*
Edgware *p217*. 020 8442 8484
Tennant, A (Hawkins Hatton LLP) *S1 W E L R1*
Dudley *p213*. 01384 216840
Tennant, C D S (Max Barford & Co) *K3 K1 Q*
Tunbridge Wells *p414* 01892 539379
Sevenoaks *p374*. 01732 747900
Tennant, D B (SNR Denton) *C1 Zn*
London EC4 *p75*. 020 7242 1212
Tennant, Mrs G M (Tennant & Knight) *K1 D1*
Brighton *p160* 01273 202050
Tennant, Mrs J A (Rees Page) *W S1 E S2*
Wolverhampton *p438* 01902 577777
Tennant, Ms S (Howard Kennedy LLP) *S1*
London W1 *p48* 020 7636 1616
Tennant, S (Colman Coyle LLP) *E S1*
Islington *p22*. 020 7354 3000
Tennekoon, R (ABN Amro Bank NV)
London EC2 *p103* 020 7628 7766
Tennent, A (Hugh Cartwright & Amin) *E S1 L K1 W*
London WC1 *p43* 020 7632 4200
Tennyson, J D (Hart Jackson & Sons) *N Q O F1 Zr Zq*
Ulverston *p416*. 01229 583291
Tenquist, I R (Keoghs LLP)
Bolton *p149* 01204 677000
Tepper, Mrs J (HM Revenue & Customs)
Salford *p470*. 0870 785 8545
Terrar, M (The Wilkes Partnership LLP) *O Q Zq A3 L*
Birmingham *p143* 0121 233 4333
Terras, N C (McDermott Will & Emery UK LLP)
London EC2 *p56*. 020 7577 6900
Terras, N C (Withers LLP)
London EC4 *p92*. 020 7597 6000
Terrell, Mrs F (Worcestershire County Council)
Worcester *p477* 01905 766335
Terrell, G (Wolferstans) *C1 E I Zq*
Plymouth *p351*. 01752 663295

Terrell, Miss L (Terrells LLP) *K3 D1 K1 S1 S2 W N*
Stamford *p394*. 01780 481129
Terrell, Miss L (Terrells LLP) *K3 K1 N*
Peterborough *p347* 01733 896789
Terrell, Mrs M S (Cripps Harries Hall LLP) *E*
Tunbridge Wells *p415* 01892 515121
Terrell, N H (Pictons Solicitors LLP) *S1 L*
Luton *p295* 01582 870870
Terrell, R (Terrells LLP) *D1 K1 K2 K3 N W Q S1 S2 Zl Zo C1*
Peterborough *p347* 01733 896789
Territt, Ms H (Jones Day) *O*
London EC4 *p46*. 020 7039 5959
Terry, Miss C A (Pumfrey & Lythaby) *K1 D1 D2 K3 V*
Orpington *p342* 01689 833657
Terry, Ms C J (Squire Sanders (UK) LLP)
London EC2 *p81*. 020 7655 1000
Terry, C R (Hewitts) *G H N Q O Zl K1*
Crook *p203* 01388 762466
Terry, D A (Terry & Co)
Ingatestone *p261* 01277 354518
Terry, Miss E L (The Manchester Airport Group PLC)
Manchester *p465* 0871 271 0711
Terry, Miss F (Thursfields) *S1 L A1 E*
Worcester *p440* 01905 730450
Terry, J (Bingham McCutchen (London) LLP)
London EC2 *p12*. 020 7661 5300
Terry, M R J C (Cadbury Schweppes PLC (Legal Dept))
Birmingham *p449* 0121 625 7000
Testar, Mrs S K (Perry Hay & Co) *S2 E S1 R2*
Richmond upon Thames *p364* 020 8940 8115 / 8332 7532
Tester, S K (CMS Cameron McKenna LLP) *O Zj Zc*
London EC3 *p17*. 020 7367 3000
Tether, T C G (Bird & Bird LLP) *B1 Zb*
London EC4 *p13*. 020 7415 6000
Tetley, I W F (T G Pollard & Co) *K1 L S1 V C1 B1 J1 F1 N Zl Zd*
Wells *p425*. 01749 674722
Tetley, J L B (Plexus Law (A Trading Name of Parabis Law LLP)) *A3 J2 N Zj*
Leeds *p276* 0844 245 4100
Tetley, M J (Smith & Tetley) *K1 M1 P J1 F1 D1 L Zl Zm*
Ashton-under-Lyne *p120*. . . 0161 330 2865
Tetlow, J R (Country Land and Business Association Ltd) *S1*
London SW1 *p105*. 020 7235 0511
Tetlow, S E (Attwaters) *S1 E S2*
Loughton *p294*. 020 8508 2111
Tetstall, Ms C R (Winchester City Council) *E S1 W*
Winchester *p476*. 01962 840222
Tettmar, V S D (Bond Pearce LLP) *B1 Zb C1*
Bristol *p161* 0845 415 0000
Tevendale, C (Herbert Smith LLP)
London EC2 *p40*. 020 7374 8000
Tew, Mrs H E (Sharp & Partners) *S1*
Nottingham *p339*. 0115 959 0055
Tewksbury, P R (Crown Prosecution Service Dorset)
Bournemouth *p450*. 01202 498700
Thacker, Miss E (Darbys Solicitors LLP) *G H*
Oxford *p343* 01865 811700
Thacker, J H (Gabbs LLP) *S1*
Leominster *p282*. 01568 616333
Thacker, P (MLM Cartwright) *S2 E U1 R2*
Cardiff *p179* 029 2046 2562
Thackeray, Ms S (Finers Stephens Innocent LLP) *B1 Zk Q N*
London W1 *p32* 020 7323 4000
Thackeray, Ms S (Brabners Chaffe Street) *E S2 R2*
Liverpool *p286*. 0151 600 3000
Thackray, J (Penningtons) *K1*
London EC2 *p66*. 020 7457 3000
Thackray, S T E (Thackray Williams) *S1 E W K1 N C1 T1 J1*
Beckenham *p129* 020 8663 0503
Thain, Mrs C (Christina Thain & Co) *S1 W*
Hunstanton *p258*. 01485 525458
Thain, Ms K A (Westminster City Council)
London SW1 *p110*. 020 7641 6000
Thair, S S W (Clarke Willmott) *E P L R1 Zd Zn*
Southampton *p385*0845 209 1000 / 0117 305 6000
Thake, Ms M (Humphries Kirk) *K4 W*
Poole *p352* 01202 715815
Thakerar, D B (D B Thakerar & Co)
Edgware *p217*. 020 8951 3113
Thakker, Mrs D (Wadesons Solicitors) *Q N L*
London SW6 *p90* 020 7384 3333
Thakker, Mrs D (Thakker & Co) *K1 S1 W L*
Harrow *p242*. 020 8424 0571
Thakrar, J (Thakrar & Co) *E G*
Southall *p385* . .020 8571 5851 / 8843 1599
Thakrar, M (Blaser Mills) *N*
Rickmansworth *p364*. 01923 776211
Thakyr, Ms D (Taylor Walton LLP) *J1*
Luton *p295* 01582 731161
Thangavel, Miss T (Kerseys) *W K4*
Ipswich *p262*. 01473 213311
Thapar, Miss J (Alsters Kelley) *K1 K3*
Coventry *p199*. 0844 561 0100
Huddersfield *p256* 01484 825200
Tharmarajah, Ms M (National Association of Local Councils) *L Zh*
London WC1 *p108*. 020 7637 1865

See p634 for the Key to Work Categories

Thatcher, Mrs V A L M T (Children & Families Law Firm) *H D1*
London SW9 *p20* 020 7582 6002

Thatcher, W G H (Hewitsons) *C1 C3 F1 I M1 Ze Zf*
Cambridge *p174* 01223 461155

Thavaraja, R (Raja & Co) *E G J1 K1 L M1 S1 W Zi Zl*
Wandsworth *p70* 020 8772 4900

Theaker, A H (Theaker Loadsman & Reynolds)
Hove *p255* 01273 229500

Theakston, A J (Glaisyers Solicitors LLP) *D1 K1*
Manchester *p304* 0161 224 3311

Theeman, C M (Fisher Jones Greenwood LLP) *L S1 N E R1 P F1 Zh*
Colchester *p197* 01206 578282

Thelwall, J (Park Woodfine Heald Mellows LLP) *S2 E*
Bedford *p130* 01234 400000

Themistocli, M (Davenport Lyons) *S1 S2 E R2 C1 L J1 O Q*
London W1 *p25* 020 7468 2600

Theobald, Miss C M (The Woodland Davies Partnership LLP) *S1 W K1 Q N L K3 Zl*
Hay-on-Wye *p245* 01497 820406
Kington *p268* 01544 230841
Talgarth *p407* 01874 711744

Theobald, Miss L (Coodes) *K1*
St Austell *p391* 01726 874700

Theobald, R J (CooperBurnett) *W K4*
Tunbridge Wells *p415* 01892 515022

Theobald, S C (Thomson Wilson Pattinson) *W S1 T2 Zd*
Kendal *p264* 01539 721945

Theobald, Ms T L (Squire Sanders (UK) LLP)
London EC2 *p81* 020 7655 1000

Theobold, Ms J (The College of Law Guildford)
Guildford *p459* 01483 460200

Theodosiou, C (B D Laddie) *S2 E L S1 W*
Westminster *p51* 020 7963 8585

Theodoulou, Miss M (Stokoe Partnership) *H G*
Waltham Forest *p83* 020 8558 8884

Theofanous, Ms C (Sills & Betteridge LLP)
Skegness *p381* 01754 610101

Theofilopoulos, Mrs Z T (Knights Solicitors LLP) *A1 E L R1 S1 W Zd U1*
Newcastle under Lyme *p323* . 01782 619225

Theophani, F (Swinnerton Moore Solicitors)
London EC4 *p84* 020 7236 7111

Theophilus, Mrs K (Coodes) *A1 S2 E S1*
St Austell *p391* 01726 874700

Thevarajah, Mrs S V (Theva & Co)
London SW19 *p86* 020 8542 6667

Thew, J R (Kirwans) *G H Q*
Moreton *p319* 0151 677 3433

Thew, M A (Marshall Hatchick)
Woodbridge *p439* 01394 388411

Thewlis, Miss H E (Ramsdens Solicitors) *K1 D1 D2 K2 K3*
Huddersfield *p256* 01484 821500

Theyer, N A (Bond Pearce LLP) *E*
Bristol *p161* 0845 415 0000

Thiara, Mrs C (FBC Manby Bowdler LLP) *E*
Wolverhampton *p437* 01902 578000
Birmingham *p139* 0870 150 0100

Thiara, J (Alsters Kelley) *G H*
Coventry *p199* 0844 561 0100

Thiara, R S (Lightfoots LLP) *O Q Zq S1*
Thame *p410* 01844 212305

Thickett, Mrs R (Leathes Prior) *D1 K1 V K2*
Norwich *p334* 01603 610911

Thickins, D R G (Fonseca & Partners) *G H P S1 D1*
Ebbw Vale *p216* 01495 303124

Thierbach, S A (Linklaters LLP)
London EC2 *p54* 020 7456 2000

Thind, I S (Burrell Jenkins) *K1 H K3 D2 D1 G*
Cannock *p176* 01543 505040

Thinzar, T (Boyes Turner) *J1*
Reading *p360* 0118 959 7711

Thirlway, Ms H M W (SA Law) *J1 Zi*
St Albans *p390* 01727 798000

Thirsk, Mrs J L (Raworths LLP) *E R2 S2*
Harrogate *p240* 01423 566666
Leeds *p277* 0113 284 7000

Thirsk, Mrs N R (Guthrie Jones & Jones) *S1 K3 W Zl K1*
Bala *p121* 01678 520428

Thiruketheeswaran, Mrs M (Thirus) *S1 S2 Zi Zl*
London SW19 *p87* 020 8542 3358

Thistlethwaite, Miss A L (AMD Solicitors) *D1 K3*
Bristol *p160* 0117 962 1460

Thistlethwaite, B W (Emrys Jones & Co) *S1 A1 W K1 E B1 G Q N L Zj Zl Zq K3*
Welshpool *p425* 01938 552510

Thom, Ms A (John O'Neill & Co) *W V*
Gosforth *p232* 0191 246 4000

Thom, I R (Kerseys) *C1 C2 E J1 A3 O R2 S2 Zc*
Ipswich *p262* 01473 213311

Thom, R G (LG Lawyers)
London SE1 *p50* 020 7379 0000

Thomas, Miss A (MLM Cartwright) *N Zr Q*
Cardiff *p179* 029 2046 2562

Thomas, Ms A (The International Family Law Group) *K1 K3 K2*
London WC2 *p45* 020 3178 5668

Thomas, Ms A (Reynolds Porter Chamberlain LLP)
London E1 *p71* 020 3060 6000

Thomas, Ms A (Boodle Hatfield)
Westminster *p14* 020 7629 7411

Thomas, A (Thomas & Co) *K1 D1 Q*
Birmingham *p143* 0121 444 0030

Thomas, Miss A C (Taylor Walton LLP) *C1 E L R1 S1*
Luton *p295* 01582 731161

Thomas, Miss A C (West Berkshire Council) *E P N*
Newbury *p466* 01635 42400

Thomas, Ms A E (Kirby Sheppard) *W K4*
Thornbury *p411* 0845 840 0045

Thomas, Mrs A E (Eleri Thomas & Co Ltd) *F1 G J1 K1 P S1 W Zv*
Newcastle Emlyn *p323* 01239 710942

Thomas, A L J (British Standards Institution)
London W4 *p104* 020 8996 7010

Thomas, A M (AMEC PLC)
Knutsford *p462* 01565 683123

Thomas, A P (Morgan & Richardson) *A1 D1 G H K1 L N Q S1 T2 W*
Cardigan *p181* 01239 612302

Thomas, A P (Alun Thomas & John) *A1 C1 W L R1 V E S1 Zl*
Aberystwyth *p114* 01970 615900

Thomas, A P C (Derby City Council)
Derby *p456* 01332 293111

Thomas, A R (Davenport Lyons) *G Zy B2 P Zl U2 R1*
London W1 *p25* 020 7468 2600

Thomas, A W (J W Hughes & Co) *M1 P S1 N K1 F1 W J1 L E*
Conwy *p199* 01492 596596
Llandudno *p291* 01492 874774

Thomas, A W L (Mayo Wynne Baxter LLP) *E S1 S2*
Lewes *p283* 01273 477071

Thomas, Miss B (M&A Solicitors LLP) *C1*
Cardiff *p179* 029 2048 2288

Thomas, Miss B H (Arnold Davies Vincent Evans) *W K4 S1 S2 E A1*
Tregaron *p413* 01974 298816
Lampeter *p269* 01570 422233

Thomas, B M (Clifford Chance)
London E14 *p20* 020 7006 1000

Thomas, Ms C (Howells LLP) *Zi*
Sheffield *p376* 0114 249 6666

Thomas, C (Ambrose Appelbe) *K1 K3*
London WC2 *p6* 020 7242 7000

Thomas, Ms C (North Yorkshire Law)
Whitby *p430* 01947 602131

Thomas, Ms C (Robert Lizar) *H G*
Manchester *p307* 0161 226 2319

Thomas, Miss C (Addleshaw Goddard) *C1 C2*
London EC1 *p4* 020 7606 8855

Thomas, Mrs C E (Hampshire County Council)
Winchester *p476* 01962 841841

Thomas, C E (Allen Barfields) *Q O N F1 Zq B1 J1*
Croydon *p204* 020 8680 2050

Thomas, Mrs C E (Dolmans) *O Q Zq*
Cardiff *p178* 029 2034 5531

Thomas, Ms C E (Clare Thomas & Co)
Newport *p329* 01952 820050

Thomas, Mrs C F (Kerseys) *K1 K3 D1*
Ipswich *p262* 01473 213311

Thomas, Miss C J (Parry Carver) *J1 N W*
Wellington *p425* 01952 641291

Thomas, C J A (Devon County Council)
Exeter *p458* 01392 382000

Thomas, Ms C L (Barlow Lyde & Gilbert LLP)
London EC3 *p10* 020 7247 2277

Thomas, Ms C L (Bells) *S2 E S1 R2*
Romsey *p366* 01794 513328

Thomas, C L (Oxford City Council)
Oxford *p468* 01865 249811

Thomas, Ms C M (Powergen PLC)
Coventry *p456* . . . . 024 7642 4748 / 4000

Thomas, C M (Braikenridge & Edwards) *E K1 L N P S1*
Barnet *p123* . . . 020 8449 1171 / 8441 7862

Thomas, C M (Cripps Harries Hall LLP) *W T2*
Tunbridge Wells *p415* 01892 515121

Thomas, C N (Wollen Michelmore Solicitors) *K2 K1*
Newton Abbot *p330* 01626 332266

Thomas, C R (Watkins & Gunn) *N J1 Q Zr Zq*
Pontypool *p352* 01495 762244

Thomas, Miss D (Berry & Berry) *Q N L J1*
Tunbridge Wells *p414* 01892 526344

Thomas, D A (Roy Thomas Begley & Co) *F1 J1 K1 K2 L N Q S1 S2 W Zc Zk Zo Zr*
Swansea *p404* . . . . 01792 643797 / 643798

Thomas, D B B (Sternberg Reed) *G H B2*
Barking *p123* 020 8591 3366
Romford *p366* 01708 766155

Thomas, D G (Gilbert Davies & Partners) *E C1 S1 W A1 R1 L T1 B1 J1*
Welshpool *p425* 01938 552727

Thomas, D J (Charles Lucas & Marshall) *A1 E S1 L*
Wantage *p421* 01235 771234

Thomas, D K (Lanyon Bowdler LLP) *S1 W Zv T1 T2*
Oswestry *p342* 01691 652241

Thomas, D L (Prowse Thomas) *S1 K1 C1 M1 G H N P*
Brixham *p166* 01803 882210

Thomas, D L (Carmarthenshire County Council)
Carmarthen *p453* 01267 224010

Thomas, D P D (Barker Gotelee Solicitors) *O N J1 Q B1 Zt*
Ipswich *p262* 01473 611211

Thomas, D P J (Kennedys) *Zq Zj Q P*
London EC3 *p49* 020 7667 9667

Thomas, Ms E (DLA Piper UK LLP)
London EC2 *p24* 0870 011 1111

Thomas, Miss E D (Bray & Bray) *G H P*
Leicester *p279* 0116 254 8871

Thomas, E D (Rausa Mumford) *N*
Cardiff *p180* 029 2034 4341

Thomas, E G (Bretherton Law) *D1 G H K1 Zi Zm*
St Albans *p389* 01727 869293

Thomas, E R (Edward Hughes) *G H K1 D1 V Zl Zt*
Rhyl *p363* . . . . . 01745 343661 / 344551

Thomas, Ms E S (Barnes Marsland) *K3 K1*
Margate *p312* 01843 221466
Ramsgate *p359* 01843 592361

Thomas, F (Farnfield & Nicholls)
Gillingham *p229* 01747 825432

Thomas, Miss F (Centro (West Midlands Passenger Transport Exec))
Birmingham *p449* 0121 200 2787

Thomas, Mrs G (Heald Nickinson) *S1 W*
Camberley *p173* 01276 680000

Thomas, Dr G (Mills & Reeve) *C1 I Ze*
Cambridge *p175* 01223 364422

Thomas, Ms G B (Hogan Lovells International LLP)
London EC1 *p42* 020 7296 2000

Thomas, G D (Lester Aldridge LLP) *K1 P B1 N G H D1 Zl Zt*
Bournemouth *p152* 01202 786161

Thomas, G D (Laytons) *O N*
London EC4 *p52* 020 7842 8000

Thomas, G F (Passmore Lewis & Jacobs) *A1 C1 E F1 G J1 M1 N P R1 Zl*
Barry *p126* 01446 721000

Thomas, G R (Watkins & Gunn) *G H J1 N Zf Zl Zr Zq*
Pontypool *p352* 01495 762244

Thomas, Miss G R M (Lester Aldridge LLP) *E*
London WC2 *p53* 0844 967 0785

Thomas, H (Anthony Collins Solicitors LLP) *Zl*
Birmingham *p137* 0121 200 3242

Thomas, Miss H (DWF) *E S2 S1 R2*
Liverpool *p287* 0151 907 3000

Thomas, Ms H (Plexus Law (A Trading Name of Parabis Law LLP)) *Zj*
Colchester *p198* 0844 245 4950

Thomas, Ms H A (R L Edwards & Partners)
Bridgend *p157* 01656 656861

Thomas, H C (Price & Kelway) *A1 C1 E L S1 T2 W X Zd Ze Zo Zv*
Milford Haven *p316* 01646 695311

Thomas, Ms H C (Blake Lapthorn) *G H*
Chandlers Ford *p184* 023 8090 8090

Thomas, H C (Ashurst LLP) *E*
London EC2 *p7* 020 7638 1111

Thomas, H G (Abney Garsden McDonald) *N*
Cheadle *p185* 0161 482 8822

Thomas, Ms H K (The John W Davies Partnership)
Newport *p329* 01633 841773

Thomas, H L (T S Edwards & Son) *M1 S1 W C1 E N Zn Zc Zo Ze*
Hengoed *p247* 01443 814161
Newport *p328* 01633 257166

Thomas, Ms H M (John Boyle & Co) *N K1 D1 G H Q*
Redruth *p362* 01209 213507
Truro *p414* 01872 272356

Thomas, H W (Hewitsons) *N O Q*
Cambridge *p174* 01223 461155

Thomas, I V (Mayer Brown International LLP) *E*
London EC2 *p59* 020 3130 3000

Thomas, I W (Clerk to the Justices)
Caernarfon *p452* . . 01286 675200 / 675288

Thomas, Ms J (Hill Hofstetter LLP) *C1*
Solihull *p382* 0121 210 6000

Thomas, Ms J (Steeles) *L*
Norwich *p335* 0870 609 0200

Thomas, J (Graeme John Solicitors) *J1 J2 N Q Zi Zq Zr*
Aberdare *p113* 01685 872491

Thomas, Mrs J (Childrens Legal Centre) *S1 K1 P L D1 G H E F1 M1 Zh Zn Zp*
Colchester *p455* . . 01206 872466 / 873828

Thomas, J (DB Law)
Penzance *p346* 01736 364261

Thomas, Miss J A (Charles Coleman & Co) *K1 N D1 Q*
Reading *p360* 0118 958 1578

Thomas, J A (Ashurst LLP)
London EC2 *p7* 020 7638 1111

Thomas, Mrs J D (Footner & Ewing) *W S1 A1 E S2*
Romsey *p366* 01794 512345

Thomas, J E K (Read Dunn Connell) *W K4 T2*
Bradford *p154* 01274 723858

Thomas, J G (Humphrys & Co) *K1 D1 F1 G H J1 L N S1 W Zq*
Rhyl *p363* 01745 343158

Thomas, J J (TLT Solicitors)
London EC2 *p85* 020 3465 4000

Thomas, J J (Oxford City Council)
Oxford *p468* 01865 249811

Thomas, J M (Walker Smith Way) *S1*
Chester *p191* 0844 346 3100

Thomas, J M (Financial Services Authority)
London E14 *p106* 020 7066 1000

Thomas, J M (Chebsey & Co) *K1 D1*
Beaconsfield *p128* 01494 670440

Thomas, Mrs J M (Norton Peskett) *S1 W*
Lowestoft *p294* 01502 533000

Thomas, Ms J P (Steeles) *Q L K1 F1*
London EC2 *p82* 020 7421 1720

Thomas, J R (Doncaster Metropolitan Borough Council) *D1 Zm*
Doncaster *p457* 01302 734651

Thomas, J S M (Crown Prosecution Service Durham) *D1 F1 G H J1 K1 L M1 S1*
Durham *p457* 0191 383 5800

Thomas, J W (Penningtons)
London EC2 *p66* 020 7457 3000

Thomas, K (Loosemores) *J1 O C1 Q*
Cardiff *p179* 029 2022 4433

Thomas, Miss K (Horsey Lightly) *S2 E*
Newbury *p322* 01635 580858

Thomas, K (John Collins & Partners LLP) *N Q Zr*
Swansea *p405* 01792 773773

Thomas, K (Manches LLP) *O Q C1 Ze U1 U2 F1 A3*
London WC2 *p58* 020 7404 4433

Thomas, Mrs K E (Reading Borough Council)
Reading *p469* 0118 939 0900

Thomas, K G M (Stewarts Law LLP) *O A3 Zb U1 Ze B2 M2 Q*
London EC4 *p83* 020 7822 8000

Thomas, Miss K M (Environment Agency (Wales)) *G N Q K1 L Zv*
Cardiff *p453* 0870 850 6506

Thomas, K M (Harding Evans LLP) *Zr N*
Newport *p328* 01633 244233

Thomas, L (Butcher Burns LLP)
London WC1 *p16* 020 7713 7100

Thomas, Miss L A (Montague Lambert & Co) *F1 S1 E J1 L B1*
Ealing *p61* 020 8997 2288

6

Thomas, Miss L A (Pannone LLP) *K1*
Manchester *p308* 0161 909 3000

Thomas, L L (Spratt Endicott) *S2 E*
Banbury *p122* 01295 204000

Thomas, L R (Davies Parsons Allchurch) *N Q*
Llanelli *p292* 01554 749144

Thomas, M (Addleshaw Goddard)
London EC1 *p4* 020 7606 8855

Thomas, M (Gartsides)
Newport *p328* 01633 213411

Thomas, M (Charles Lucas & Marshall)
Wantage *p421* 01235 771234

Thomas, M A (Arthur Jackson & Co) *K1 D1 J1 N F1 W Zc Zm*
Rotherham *p367* 01709 363876
Rotherham *p367* 01709 547284

Thomas, M A (Hallmark Hulme) *S1 E W L P*
Worcester *p439* 01905 726600

Thomas, M C P (Treasury Solicitors Department)
London WC2 *p110* 020 7210 3000

Thomas, M H (Sheridans) *E Zf C1*
London WC1 *p78* 020 7079 0100

Thomas, M K (Squire Sanders (UK) LLP) *C1*
London EC2 *p81* 020 7655 1000

Thomas, Miss M K (Alan Edwards & Co) *L S1 W Zj Zh*
Kensington & Chelsea *p28* . . 020 7221 7644

Thomas, Miss M M (Robyns Owen) *K1 S1 W H G L N D1 R1 Q*
Pwllheli *p358* 01758 613177

Thomas, Miss M R (Clifford Chance)
London E14 *p20* 020 7006 1000

Thomas, M R (Sema Group UK Ltd)
London NW1 *p109* 020 7830 4213

Thomas, M R (Hearne & Co)
Bearwood *p129* 0121 420 3636

Thomas, M V (Varley Hibbs LLP) *Q O N Zq Zr S1 K1 K4 L R2 W B1 T2 T1 Zk*
Coventry *p201* 024 7663 1000

Thomas, M W (Stepien Lake) *S1 E*
London W1 *p83* 020 7467 3030

Thomas, N (Blackwell-West) *N*
Ferndown *p225* 01202 892300

Thomas, N A (Bell Lax Litigation) *O Q Zq J1 F1 E B1 Zk A3*
Sutton Coldfield *p403* 0121 355 0011

Thomas, N D W (Blain Boland & Co) *S1 W C1 E L Zd Zx*
Willaston *p432* 0151 327 1301
Ellesmere Port *p217* 0151 355 2645

Thomas, N J P (Atkins Hope Solicitors) *K1 L N*
Croydon *p204* 020 8680 5018

Thomas, N P G (Kennedys)
London EC3 *p49* 020 7667 9667

Thomas, N V (John Collins & Partners LLP) *C1 E*
Swansea *p405* 01792 773773

Thomas, P C (Battens) *S1 L A1 E W*
Dorchester *p212* 01305 250560

Thomas, Miss P E (SJ Berwin LLP)
London EC4 *p75* 020 7111 2222

Thomas, P F (RTL Solicitors)
Bridgend *p157* 01656 665850
Cardiff *p180* 029 2023 4030

Thomas, P M (Thackray Williams)
West Wickham *p428* 020 8777 6698

Thomas, P S (Pierre Thomas & Partners) *N Zj M2*
London W6 *p67* 020 7602 0305

Thomas, P W (Thomas Guise) *S1 P N M1 W J1 G H K1 C1 Zj Ze*
Worcester *p439* 01905 723131

Thomas, R (Gateley LLP)
Birmingham *p138* 0121 234 0000

Thomas, Ms R (Quality Solicitors Burroughs Day) *J1*
Bristol *p164* 0117 929 0333

Thomas, R (Trowers & Hamlins)
London EC3 *p88* 020 7423 8000

Thomas, R (Addison O'Hare) *W S1*
Walsall *p419* 01922 725515

Thomas, R (Addleshaw Goddard)
Manchester *p300* 0161 934 6000

Thomas, R (Speechly Bircham LLP) *J1*
London EC4 *p81* 020 7427 6400

Thomas, R (Harrison Clark LLP) *C1 C2 Zb*
Cheltenham *p188* 01242 269198
Worcester *p439* 01905 612001
Worcester *p439* 01905 612001

Thomas, Mrs R A (Straw & Pearce) *D1 K1*
Loughborough *p293* 01509 268931

Thomas, R C T (Walker Smith Way) *G*
Chester *p191* 0844 346 3100

Thomas, Mrs R E (Carmarthenshire County Council)
Carmarthen *p453* 01267 224010

Thomas, R E (Jones Day) *O*
London EC4 *p46*. 020 7039 5959

Thomas, R E J (Trowers & Hamlins) *E*
London EC3 *p88*. 020 7423 8000

Thomas, Miss R H (Gartmore Investment Management PLC)
London EC3 *p106* 020 7782 2000

Thomas, Miss R J (Coley & Tilley)
Birmingham *p136* 0121 643 5531

Thomas, Ms R J (Seddons) *N O Q Zl*
Westminster *p77*. 020 7725 8000

Thomas, R J (Thomas Simon) *E S1 L R1 A1 C1 Zc Zh Zn*
Cardiff *p181* 029 2055 7200

Thomas, R J M (RWP Solicitors) *W*
Pangbourne *p345* 0118 984 2266

Thomas, R J M (Thomas Andrews & Partners) *S1 L E W C1 R1 B1 F1 G H Zc Ze Zl*
Bala *p121* 01678 520893
Wrexham *p442* 01978 291506

Thomas, R L (Salans) *C1 C2 J1 Zb Ze*
London EC4 *p76*. 020 7429 6000

Thomas, Ms R L (Rose Thomas & Co) *A1 F1 G J1 K1 N Q S1 S2 W*
Lampeter *p269*. 01570 423300

Thomas, Mrs R M (Humphrey Roberts & Bott)
Aberystwyth *p114* 01970 617618

Thomas, R M E (Hutchinson Thomas) *S1 A1 E L R1 Zc*
Neath *p320* 01639 645061

Thomas, R R (T G Baynes) *S1 E W C1 L Zl S2*
Bexleyheath *p132* 020 8301 7777

Thomas, R V (David & Roy Thomas & Co) *S1 W E T1 L A1*
Pontardulais *p351* 01792 882410

Thomas, R V (Thomas & Edge) *S1 W S2*
Derby *p209* 01332 346681

Thomas, S (Chhokar & Co) *O Q L Zq S2 Zj E S1*
Southall *p384* 020 8574 2488

Thomas, Miss S (Sebastians) *D2 B1 D1 K3 K1 B2 O Q N Zl*
London EC4 *p77*. 020 7583 2105

Thomas, Ms S (Armitage Sykes LLP) *K1 D1*
Huddersfield *p255* 01484 344140

Thomas, S (Hibberts LLP) *K1 N Zo V*
Nantwich *p320*. 01270 624225

Thomas, Mrs S (Sian Thomas & Daughter Solicitors) *S1 W S2 L*
Bridgend *p157*. 01656 645439

Thomas, S (Clarke Willmott)
Bristol *p162* 0845 209 1000 / 0117 305 6000

Thomas, S (Hutchinson Thomas) *G N P K1 M1 L F1 S1 W C1 Zl Zt Zc*
Neath *p320* 01639 645061

Thomas, S (The Wilkes Partnership LLP) *O*
Birmingham *p143* 0121 233 4333

Thomas, Mrs S (Radcliffes Le Brasseur) *O Q L*
Westminster *p70*. 020 7222 7040

Thomas, S (ASB Law) *D1 G H M1 L*
Maidstone *p298* 01622 656500

Thomas, S (Steve Thomas & Co) *A1 E K4 J1 Q S1 W*
Haverfordwest *p244* 01437 890500

Thomas, S (O'Neill Patient) *E*
Stockport *p396*. 0161 483 8555

Thomas, S (Dyne Drewett Solicitors Ltd) *Q J1 Zq N G O*
Sherborne *p378* 01935 813691

Thomas, S (Linklaters LLP)
London EC2 *p54*. 020 7456 2000

Thomas, S D (DP Law Ltd t/a David Prosser & Co) *S1 S2*
Bridgend *p157*. 01656 645921

Thomas, Miss S E (Downs) *S1 L*
Dorking *p212* 01306 880110

Thomas, Ms S J (Pinsent Masons LLP)
London EC2 *p67*. 020 7418 7000

Thomas, Mrs S J (Broxtowe Borough Council) *S2 E S1*
Beeston *p449* 0115 917 7777
Nottingham *p338*. 0115 941 1469

Thomas, S J L (Gloucester City Council)
Gloucester *p459*. 01452 522232

Thomas, S M (Wiggin LLP) *E S2 R2 T1 P S1 Zs*
Cheltenham *p189* 01242 224114

Thomas, S M (Michelmores LLP) *D1 K1 K3*
Exeter *p221* 01392 688688

Thomas, S M A (Milton Francis & Hughes Solicitors) *S2 L E W S1*
Oswestry *p342*. 01691 654662

Thomas, S P (GHP Legal) *N*
Wrexham *p442* 01978 291456

Thomas, Mrs S R (Thomas & Co) *K1 S1 Q D1 W L*
Birmingham *p143* 0121 444 0030

Thomas, S R (National Association of Head Teachers) *N Q G H*
Haywards Heath *p460* 01444 472472

Thomas, S R W (Leeds Day) *K3 D1 K1 D2*
Huntingdon *p258*. 01480 454301

Thomas, Ms T C (Gotelee) *G H Zl Zm*
Ipswich *p262*. 01473 211121

Thomas, Mrs T H (Davies Sully Wilkins) *K1 D1 D2 L*
Caerphilly *p172* 029 2088 7828

Thomas, Ms T L (Hewitsons) *J1*
Northampton *p332*. 01604 233233

Thomas, Mrs V A (Bank of Scotland Legal Operations)
London EC2 *p104* 0870 600 5000

Thomas, W G G (Thatcher & Hallam) *S1 S2 E*
Midsomer Norton *p316*. . . . 01761 414646

Thomas, W L (Granville-West Chivers & Morgan) *K1 W P S1*
Risca *p365* 01633 612353

Thomas, W N (The Gwyn George Partnership) *D1 H K1 P V W*
Aberdare *p113*. . . .01685 874629 / 871133

Thomlinson, Mrs A R (Reading Borough Council)
Reading *p469* 0118 939 0900

Thompsell, N P (Field Fisher Waterhouse LLP)
London EC3 *p31*. 020 7861 4000

Thompson, A (Cook Taylor) *E G H S1 Zl*
Greenwich *p22*. 020 8854 1166

Thompson, A (Andrew Thompson & Co)
Leeds *p277* 0113 383 5314

Thompson, A (Howard Kennedy LLP) *C1*
London W1 *p48* 020 7636 1616

Thompson, Miss A (Michelmores LLP) *C1 B1*
Exeter *p221* 01392 688688

Thompson, Miss A (Leslie Harris Solicitors & Advocates) *D1 K1 N*
Lytham *p297*. 01253 724974

Thompson, Ms A (Hopkin Murray Beskine)
London N4 *p42* 020 7272 1234

Thompson, A (Withers LLP) *T2 W*
London EC4 *p92*. 020 7597 6000

Thompson, Ms A (Badhams Law (A Trading Name of Parabis Law LLP)) *Zj*
Croydon *p204* 0844 245 4000

Thompson, A A (Cook Taylor) *G H*
Greenwich *p22*. 020 8854 1166

Thompson, A C (Act Legal) *C1 S2 E R2 S1*
Brighton *p159* 01273 565656
Brighton *p160* 01273 608003

Thompson, A C (Weightmans LLP) *C1 C2 E Ze*
Manchester *p311* 0161 233 7330

Thompson, A C P (Underhill Langley & Wright) *S1 W*
Wolverhampton *p438* 01902 423431

Thompson, A D (Zermansky & Partners) *Q O J1*
Leeds *p278* 0113 245 9766

Thompson, A G (Macfarlanes) *J1 O Q*
London EC4 *p56*. 020 7831 9222

Thompson, Mrs A H (Battens) *S1*
Yeovil *p443* 01935 846000

Thompson, Miss A H (Freeman Johnson) *W K4 T2*
Darlington *p206* 01325 466221

Thompson, A I (LG Lawyers) *T2 T1*
London SE1 *p50*. 020 7379 0000

Thompson, A J (Lee & Thompson) *A3 Zf Zw*
London W1 *p52* 020 7935 4665

Thompson, A L (Devonshires) *Zc*
London EC2 *p27*. 020 7628 7576

Thompson, A R (Langley Wellington) *S1 W S2 L T2*
Churchdown *p195* 01452 856846

Thompson, Mrs C (Roythornes LLP) *E S2 S1*
Peterborough *p347* 01733 558585

Thompson, Ms C (Harrison Clark LLP) *J1*
Cheltenham *p188* 01242 269198
Worcester *p439* 01905 612001
Worcester *p439* 01905 612001

Thompson, C (Howard Kennedy LLP) *C1*
London W1 *p48* 020 7636 1616
London WC1 *p64* 020 7067 3000

Thompson, C D (Simmons & Simmons)
London EC2 *p79*. 020 7628 2020

Thompson, C I (Battens) *S1 W*
Weymouth *p430*. 01305 774666

Thompson, Mrs C L (Squire Sanders (UK) LLP) *J1*
Birmingham *p142* 0121 222 3000

Thompson, Mrs C S L (Mackarness & Lunt) *W T2 K4*
Petersfield *p348* 01730 265111

Thompson, D (Forster Dean Ltd)
Widnes *p431*. 0151 495 3270

Thompson, D (DLA Piper UK LLP) *C1*
Manchester *p303* 0870 011 1111

Thompson, D (Shoosmiths)
Milton Keynes *p317* . 0370 086 8300 / 01908 488300

Thompson, Mrs D (Taylor & Emmet LLP) *D1 D2 K1*
Sheffield *p377* 0114 218 4000

Thompson, D A (Thompsons (formerly Robin/ Brian Thompson & Partners)) *N J1 Zp*
Plymouth *p350*. 01752 675810

Thompson, D C (Moore Blatch Solicitors) *J2 N Zt*
Southampton *p386*. 023 8071 8000

Thompson, D E (Warner Goodman LLP) *N*
Southampton *p387*. 023 8063 9311

Thompson, D G (Marrons) *N*
Newcastle upon Tyne *p325* . 0191 281 1304

Thompson, D I (Michelmores LLP) *C1 Ze F1 U2*
Exeter *p221* 01392 688688

Thompson, D J (Langleys) *N*
York *p445* 01904 610886

Thompson, D J B (City of Sunderland)
Sunderland *p473*. 0191 520 5555

Thompson, D M (The National Trust) *S2 E*
Swindon *p475* 01793 817400

Thompson, D M (Ian N Gunby & Co) *W S1 T2 A1*
Milnthorpe *p316* 01539 562044

Thompson, D W (Quality Solicitors Copley Clark)
Sutton *p403* 020 8643 7221

Thompson, Ms E A (David & Snape) *S1 E C1 A1 W*
Bridgend *p157*. 01656 661115

Thompson, Miss E A (Frisby & Co) *E W L S2 S1*
Stafford *p392* 01785 244114

Thompson, Ms E J (Blackfords LLP) *K1 D1 P V G H L*
Croydon *p204* 020 8686 6232

Thompson, Mrs E M (Birchall Blackburn LLP) *S1 F1 O Q Zq Zj*
Chorley *p194* 01257 279011

Thompson, Ms F H (Boyes Sutton & Perry) *W K4 T2 S1*
Barnet *p123* 020 8449 9155

Thompson, G (Widdows Mason)
Warrington *p422*. 01925 632267

Thompson, Dr G (Blake Lapthorn)
London EC1 *p13*. 020 7405 2000
Chelmsford *p187*. 01245 295295

Thompson, G B (DWT Legal Ltd) *N O Q C1 J1 K1 G Zc Ze Zl*
Kidderminster *p265* 0844 770 3799

Thompson, Mrs G E (AWB Partnership LLP) *S1 S2*
Guildford *p235*. 01483 302345

Thompson, G J (Legal Aid Area Office No 7 (North Western))
Manchester *p465* 0845 602 1400

Thompson, Miss H (Freemans) *Zr N*
Newcastle upon Tyne *p324* . 0191 222 1030

Thompson, Ms H E (SAS Daniels LLP) *J1 Zk O Q*
Macclesfield *p297* 01625 442100

Thompson, Mrs H J (Gregorys Solicitors) *D2 K1 D1*
Stockport *p395*. 0161 456 8125

Thompson, J (Henmans LLP) *O Q*
Oxford *p343* 01865 781000

Thompson, Ms J (Tayntons LLP Solicitors) *N Q Zr*
Gloucester *p230*. 01452 522047

Thompson, J (Thompson & Co) *G K1 L V Zl Zg Zm*
Wandsworth *p87*. 020 8767 5005

Thompson, Miss J A (Cowles) *S1 E W Zm*
Croydon *p23*. 020 8679 1811

Thompson, J B (Cleaver Thompson Ltd) *N D1 Q O F1 Zq Zm D2*
Alfreton *p115* 01773 832193

Thompson, Ms J D (Kerwoods) *L N Q O*
Redditch *p362*. 01527 584444

Thompson, Ms J L (Middlesbrough Council)
Middlesbrough *p465* 01642 245432

Thompson, J L (Thompson Allen LLP) *S2 E R2 S1 L C1*
Brighton *p160* 01273 608003

Thompson, J M (Leviten Thompson & Co) *G H K1 N Q F1 W C1 J1 O Zj Zc*
Sheffield *p376* 0114 276 9321

Thompson, J S (Grahame Stowe Bateson) *W T1 S1 C1 Zm*
Harrogate *p240* 01423 562121

Thompson, K D (Vanderpump & Sykes) *E L R1 C1 Zc P*
Enfield *p219*. 020 8367 3999

Thompson, Mrs K E (Lester Aldridge LLP) *N*
Bournemouth *p152*. 01202 786161

Thompson, K G (Clifford Chance)
London E14 *p20*. 020 7006 1000

Thompson, Miss K J (Kirbys) *K4 K1 S1 W T2*
Harrogate *p240* 01423 542000

Thompson, K J (Alker & Ball) *Q O*
Wigan *p432* 01942 246241

Thompson, K R (Keith R Thompson & Co) *N Q G H F1*
Immingham *p261* 01469 510510

Thompson, K S (Keith S Thompson Solicitor)
Amble *p117* 01665 713723

Thompson, Miss L (Trethowans LLP) *C1 C2*
Southampton *p387*. 023 8032 1000

Thompson, Ms L A M (LG Lawyers)
London SE1 *p50*. 020 7379 0000

Thompson, Miss L J (Clarkson Wright & Jakes Ltd) *E L S1*
Orpington *p341* 01689 887887

Thompson, M (Harvey Ingram Borneos) *C1 E F1 I M1 Ze*
Bedford *p130* 01234 353221

Thompson, M (MBA Solicitors) *N*
York *p445* 01904 666888

Thompson, Mrs M (Bowcock Cuerden LLP) *E S2*
Nantwich *p320*. 01270 611106

Thompson, M C (Steptoe & Johnson) *C1 C2 Zb U2 I*
London EC2 *p83*. 020 7367 8000

Thompson, M D (South Tyneside Metropolitan Borough Council)
South Shields *p471* 0191 427 1717

Thompson, M G (Thompson & Co) *N*
Sunderland *p402*. 0191 565 6290

Thompson, M H (Armitage Sykes LLP) *E*
Huddersfield *p255* 01484 538121

Thompson, M J (Thompson Leatherdale) *W T2 K4 Q T1*
Reading *p361* 0118 959 1773

Thompson, Mrs M L (Wallace Robinson & Morgan) *S1 W*
Solihull *p383*. 0121 705 7571

Thompson, N (Smith Roddam) *D1 E F1 G H J1 K1 L N Q S1 W*
Bishop Auckland *p144* 01388 603073

Thompson, Miss N (Bottrills Solicitors) *S2 E*
Barnet *p123* . . 020 8440 8188 / 8441 1125

Thompson, Miss N (Hethertons LLP) *S1*
York *p445* 01904 528200

Thompson, Miss N (Sherrards) *S2 E*
St Albans *p390* 01727 832830

Thompson, Miss N C (Forresters) *W S1*
Barrow-in-Furness *p125* . . . 01229 820297

Thompson, N H (Birketts LLP (Wollastons LLP)) *C1 C2 C3 I Ze Zi U2 F1*
Chelmsford *p186*. 01245 211211

Thompson, N J (Shearman & Sterling LLP) *Zn*
London EC2 *p78*. 020 7655 5000

Thompson, P (Inghams) *S1 S2*
Blackpool *p146* 01253 626642

Thompson, P (Broudie Jackson Canter) *G H*
Liverpool *p286*. 0151 227 1429

Thompson, P (Radcliffes Le Brasseur)
Westminster *p70*. 020 7222 7040

Thompson, P (Department for Business, Enterprise and Regulatory Reform)
London SW1 *p105*. 020 7215 0105

Thompson, P (EMW) *J1*
Milton Keynes *p316* 0845 070 6000

Thompson, P C (Thompson & Co)
Sunderland *p402*. 0191 565 6290

Thompson, P D (Kennedys) *N Zj Q*
London EC3 *p49*. 020 7667 9667

Thompson, P D (The Watson Ramsbottom Partnership) *J1 F1 O C1 Q S1 E*
Blackburn *p146* 01254 672222
Darwen *p207* 01254 701111

Thompson, P H (Bircham Dyson Bell)
Westminster *p13*. 020 7227 7000

Thompson, P J (Henmans LLP) *T2 W*
Oxford *p343* 01865 781000

Thompson, P J (Butcher & Barlow LLP) *K1 K3 Q*
Bramhall *p155* 0161 439 8228

Thompson, P K (DLA Piper UK LLP) *J1*
Birmingham *p137* 0870 011 1111

Thompson, P S (Radcliffes Le Brasseur)
Westminster *p70*. 020 7222 7040

Thompson, Miss R (Gordons LLP) *G H*
Leeds *p273* 0113 227 0100
Stoke-on-Trent *p398*. 01782 343353

Thompson, R (Pattinson & Brewer) *Q N*
York *p445* 01904 680000

Thompson, R A (Sandersons) *B2 G H*
Hull *p258* 01482 324662

Thompson, R A (Ward Hadaway) *C1 C2*
Newcastle upon Tyne *p327* . 0191 204 4000

Thompson, R A R N (Godwins) *W T2*
Winchester *p433*. 01962 841484

Thompson, R C (WBW Solicitors) *S1 T2 W*
Newton Abbot *p329* 01626 202404

Thompson, R D (Morris Read & Co) *P K1 G S1 M1 F1 R1 W L Zd Zl*
Wolverhampton *p438* 01902 420973 / 710004

Thompson, Miss R H (Anthony Collins Solicitors LLP) *Zd*
Birmingham *p137* 0121 200 3242

Thompson, R J (Breeze & Wyles Solicitors LLP) *K1*
Enfield *p218*. 020 8366 6411

Thompson, Mrs R J (Margaret M Frame & Co) *C1 D1 E F1 G J1 K1 L R1 S1*
Ilford *p260*. 020 8518 6767

Thompson, R P (Mayo Wynne Baxter LLP) *S1 K1 L D1*
Seaford *p373* 01323 891412

Thompson, R P W (Taylor Wessing)
London EC4 *p86*. 020 7300 7000

Thompson, R S (BRM Solicitors) *C1 E T2 F1 I J1 S1 T1*
Chesterfield *p191* 01246 555111

Thompson, Ms S (Magrath LLP)
London W1 *p57* 020 7495 3003

Thompson, Miss S J (Wollen Michelmore Solicitors) *S1*
Newton Abbot *p330* 01626 332266

Thompson, Ms S J (Financial Services Authority)
London E14 *p106* 020 7066 1000

Thompson, Mrs S J (Aviva PLC)
London EC3 *p103* . . 020 7283 7500 / 01603 687905
Norwich *p467* 01603 622200

Thompson, Miss S J (DAC Beachcroft) *Zm Zr N*
Bristol *p162* 0117 918 2000

Thompson, T A (Hegarty LLP) *E C1 J1 S2 Zl*
Peterborough *p347* 01733 346333

Thompson, Mrs V S (Hatchers Solicitors LLP) *D1 K1 K2*
Shrewsbury *p379* 01743 248545

Thompson, Mrs W J (Browne Jacobson LLP) *T2 W*
Nottingham *p336*. 0115 976 6000

Thompson-Haughton, Miss B (Dixon Ward) *W T2 K4*
Richmond upon Thames *p364* 020 8940 4051

Thompstone, D C (Quality Solicitors Copley Clark) *K1 D1*
Sutton *p403* 020 8643 7221

Thomsen, Mrs S E (Burstalls) *Q O N Zq F1 Zg J1*
Hull *p256* 01482 621800

Thomson, Ms A E (FBC Manby Bowdler LLP) *K1 D1*
Telford *p409* 01952 292129

Thomson, A J (Barlow Lyde & Gilbert LLP) *Zj*
London EC3 *p10*. 020 7247 2277

Thomson, Miss A L (Forsters LLP) *J1*
Westminster *p33*. 020 7863 8333

See p634 for the Key to Work Categories

Thomson, Miss B (Butcher Andrews) *W*
Fakenham *p223* 01328 863131

Thomson, Ms C (United Utilities)
Warrington *p475* 01925 237000

Thomson, Miss C F (Seddon Thomson) *N Q K1 G H K3*
Manchester *p309* 0161 720 8000

Thomson, C H (Paris Smith LLP) *O B1 N Q Zl A3 Zq*
Southampton *p386* 023 8048 2482

Thomson, C J (Greene & Greene) *C1 C2 C3 J1 T1 Ze E*
Bury St Edmunds *p171* . . . 01284 762211

Thomson, D (Barrett & Thomson) *C1 F1 J1 L Zc Ze N O*
Slough *p381* 01753 437416

Thomson, Miss E (Parry Law)
Whitstable *p431* 01227 276276

Thomson, Ms E (David Gray Solicitors) *K1 D1 K3 D2*
Newcastle upon Tyne *p324* . 0191 232 9547

Thomson, G A (GKN PLC (Legal Dept))
Redditch *p469* 01527 517715

Thomson, H N M (Thomsons) *O F1 Q*
Northampton *p467* 020 8913 5364

Thomson, Ms J E L (Pierce Glynn) *K1 L*
Southwark *p67* 020 7407 0007

Thomson, J M (J H Powell & Co) *C1 E T1 L S1 W P A1 Zc*
Derby *p209* 01332 372211

Thomson, K J (Linklaters LLP)
London EC2 *p54* 020 7456 2000

Thomson, Mrs K S (Nottingham City Council (City Sec Dept)) *K1 P D1*
Nottingham *p467* 0115 915 5555

Thomson, M A (Freeth Cartwright LLP) *Zj*
Nottingham *p337* 0115 936 9369

Thomson, M A (Arnold Thomson Limited) *A1 A2 E W T1*
Towcester *p413* 01327 350266

Thomson, Mrs M E (Marrons) *R1 E P A1 Zn Zu R2*
Leicester *p280* 0116 289 2200

Thomson, M S (DAC Beachcroft) *J1 O Q Zj Zk*
Bristol *p162* 0117 918 2000

Thomson, M S (Fentons)
Failsworth *p223* 0161 682 7101

Thomson, P (Ashurst LLP)
London EC2 *p7* 020 7638 1111

Thomson, P A A (Forbes Hall LLP) *S2 E S1 L*
London EC2 *p33* 020 7729 9111

Thomson, P D (Peter Thomson) *L K1 W J1 S2 K3 E*
Lambeth *p87* 020 7733 6196

Thomson, P M (Essex County Council)
Chelmsford *p454* 0845 743 0430

Thomson, R B (Saunders Goodin Riddleston Solicitors) *G H*
Ipswich *p263* 01473 225600

Thomson, R J (LG Lawyers)
London SE1 *p50* 020 7379 0000

Thomson, R O (Gosschalks) *N P L F1 Zj*
Hull *p256* 01482 324252

Thomson, T J (Thomson Webb & Corfield) *S1 R2 W*
Cambridge *p176* 01223 578070

Thomson-Hall, Miss P (Wills Group Ltd)
London EC3 *p110* 020 7488 8111

Thomson-Smith, C (Denison Till) *K1 D1 L O Q U2*
York *p444* 01904 611411

Thonger, N J (Heringtons) *A1 E L S1 W T1 C1*
Battle *p128* 01424 772401

Thorburn, W H (Ashurst LLP) *A3 O Q*
London EC2 *p7* 020 7638 1111

Thorby, J F (Collins Benson Goldhill LLP) *C1 C2*
Westminster *p21* 020 7436 5151

Thorn, A E (Neale Turk) *S1 S2 E*
Fleet *p226* 01252 811070

Thorn, J E (Careless & Kemp) *K1 K3 J1 N Q D1 D2*
Ventnor *p418* 01983 852626

Thorn, P R (Wake Smith & Tofields) *D1 K1 Zm K2*
Sheffield *p377* 0114 266 6660

Thorn, R L H (Richard Thorn & Co) *H G N Q O D1 K1*
Brighton *p160* 01273 625600

Thorn, S G (Drivers) *A1 L S1 W C1 E J1 R1 Zc*
Malton *p300* 01653 600075

Thornber, B (SGH Martineau LLP)
Birmingham *p142* 0870 763 2000

Thornberry, J J (Taunton Deane Borough Council)
Taunton *p473* 01823 356356

Thorne, A J R (Andrew Thorne & Co) *B1 C1 I J1 K1 L P R1 S1 W*
Shaw *p374* 01706 841775
Shaw *p374* 01706 290488

Thorne, A N (Carter Bells LLP) *E C1*
Kingston upon Thames *p267*. 020 8939 4000

Thorne, Miss B J (Chambers Rutland & Crauford) *K1 S1 W L E*
London N12 *p19* 020 8446 2777

Thorne, B J (Dechert) *E*
London EC4 *p26* 020 7184 7000

Thorne, Miss C (Anthony King & Co) *D1 D2*
Basildon *p126* 01268 240400

Thorne, C G (Foot Anstey) *N Zr Q O Zq*
Exeter *p221* 01392 411221
Taunton *p408* 01823 625600

Thorne, Mrs C L (Mills & Reeve) *J1*
Cambridge *p175* 01223 364422

Thorne, D A (Reynolds Porter Chamberlain LLP) *A3 O Q Zc Zj Zq*
London E1 *p71* 020 3060 6000

Thorne, G A (Thornes) *G H K1 D1*
Wolverhampton *p438* 01902 313311

Thorne, J (Farrer & Co LLP)
London WC2 *p31* 020 3375 7000

Thorne, J H (Marriott Davies Yapp) *C1 I C2 Ze*
Sutton *p402* 020 8643 9794

Thorne, Miss K J (Borough of Poole)
Poole *p469* 01202 262808

Thorne, Ms L (Davies Sully Wilkins) *F1 F2 J1 J2 L N O*
Caerphilly *p172* 029 2088 7828

Thorne, Mrs L A (Rodericks) *S1 W K1*
Llanelli *p292* 01554 773424

Thorne, L F (Thorne & Co Solicitors) *S2 J1 S1 W N J2*
Dorchester *p212* 01305 251166

Thorne, N M (Shoosmiths) *C1 C2*
Reading *p361* . . 0370 086 8800 / 0118 965 8765

Thorne, S (Clarke Willmott) *T1 T2 Zo*
Taunton *p408*0845 209 1000 / 0117 305 6000

Thorneloe, Miss H (Thorneloe & Co) *S1 W S2 K4 L*
Maidstone *p299* 01622 859416

Thorneloe, M J (Thorneloe & Co) *J1 W C1 E T1 A1 R1 K1 L Zk Zj*
Maidstone *p299* 01622 859416

Thornes, C (Allen & Overy LLP)
London E1 *p5* 020 3088 0000

Thornes, J A (David Webb & Co) *S1 S2 W*
Westcliff-on-Sea *p428* 01702 392939

Thorneycroft, D (Hallett & Co) *J1 Q N R1*
Ashford *p119* 01233 625711

Thorneycroft, M B (Jones Day) *C2*
London EC4 *p46* 020 7039 5959

Thorneycroft, P M (Wolferstans) *K1 K2 D1 V*
Plymouth *p351* 01752 663295

Thorneycroft, R C (Tozers) *C1 F1 E*
Exeter *p222* 01392 207020

Thorneycroft, R P (Thorneycroft Solicitors Ltd) *S1 Q N W L K1 O J1 E Zc*
Macclesfield *p297* 01625 503444

Thornham, C J (Taylor Wessing) *Ze*
London EC4 *p86* 020 7300 7000

Thornhill, J (Ward Hadaway) *J1 Q*
Newcastle upon Tyne *p327* . 0191 204 4000

Thorniley-Walker, M (Radcliffes Le Brasseur)
Westminster *p70* 020 7222 7040

Thorniley-Walker, M J (Radcliffes Le Brasseur) *E C1 S1 T1 R1 P L*
Leeds *p276* 0113 234 1220

Thornley, D G (The Ringrose Law Group - David Thornley) *N G Q O J1 L F1 C1 Zl*
Grantham *p232* 01476 590200

Thornley, J (EAD Solicitors LLP) *N J1 K1 P Zk Zp*
Huddersfield *p255* 01484 437448

Thornley, P (Thornleys Limited) *A1 C1 E F1 S1 W T1 T2*
Plymouth *p350* 01752 406977

Thornley, P A (Fraser Brown) *E S2 C1*
Nottingham *p337* 0115 988 8777

Thornley-Gibson, Mrs R (ASB Law) *J1 N O Q Zp*
Crawley *p202* 01293 603600

Thornton, Mrs A (Martin-Kaye LLP) *N*
Telford *p409* 01952 272222

Thornton, Miss A J (Kelcey & Hall) *G H*
Bristol *p163* 0117 927 9604

Thornton, A J (Wrigleys Solicitors LLP) *Zu Zw V*
Sheffield *p377* 0114 267 5588

Thornton, Miss C L (Claire Jones & Associates) *K1 K3 D1*
Wakefield *p418* 01924 290029

Thornton, Ms C R (Russell-Cooke LLP) *K3 K1*
London WC1 *p74* 020 7405 6566

Thornton, Mrs E S (Chattertons Solicitors) *D1 K1*
Sleaford *p381* 01529 411500

Thornton, Miss F I (Vale of Glamorgan Council)
Barry *p448* 01446 700111

Thornton, Miss F M (Winterbotham Smith Penley LLP) *K1*
Stroud *p401* 01453 847200

Thornton, Ms H K (Newstead & Walker) *S1 W*
Otley *p342* 01943 461414

Thornton, Mrs J (Hertfordshire County Council)
Hertford *p460* 01992 555555

Thornton, J M (Russell-Cooke LLP) *C1*
London SW15 *p74* 020 8789 9111

Thornton, J R C (Maples Teesdale LLP) *E*
London EC2 *p58* 020 7600 3800

Thornton, K E (Wrigleys Solicitors LLP) *W*
Leeds *p278* 0113 244 6100

Thornton, Ms L (Billson & Sharp) *E K1 K4 L S1 T2 V W*
Leicester *p279* 0116 255 9911

Thornton, P J (Douglas Clift & Co) *S1 L E W*
Lancaster *p269* 01524 32437

Thornton, Miss R S (Harrison Clark LLP) *C1 C2*
Worcester *p439* 01905 612001

Thornton-Smith, Miss C J (Harrison Clark LLP) *C1 C2*
Cheltenham *p188* 01242 269198
Worcester *p439* 01905 612001
Worcester *p439* 01905 612001

Thornton-Swan, Ms C A (Mills & Reeve) *E L Zh*
Cambridge *p175* 01223 364422

Thornycroft, B (DAC Beachcroft)
Bristol *p162* 0117 918 2000

Thorogood, J T N (Archer & Archer) *A1 E L R1 S1 S2*
Ely *p218* 01353 662203

Thorogood, M (Information Commisioner)
Wilmslow *p476* 01625 545700

Thorogood, P D (Freeth Cartwright LLP) *C1 B1 T1 R1 Zb*
Nottingham *p337* 0115 936 9369

Thorowgood, N J C (Clifton Ingram LLP) *O Q*
Reading *p360* 0118 957 3425

Thorp, C (Barlow Lyde & Gilbert LLP) *O Za*
London EC3 *p10* 020 7247 2277

Thorp, D C (Bowcock Cuerden LLP) *S1 E A1 S2*
Nantwich *p320* 01270 611106

Thorp, O (CVC Solicitors)
St Ives *p392* 01736 795456

Thorp, R (Parkes Wilshire Johnson) *T2 W Zm*
Barnet *p124* 020 8441 1556
Barnet *p124* 020 8364 9955

Thorp, Ms V J (LG Lawyers)
London SE1 *p50* 020 7379 0000

Thorpe, A (The Clarke Partnership) *N*
Stockport *p395* 0161 474 6600

Thorpe, Miss A K M (Horwood & James LLP) *A1 E L S1*
Aylesbury *p121* 01296 487361

Thorpe, Mrs B (Tierney & Co) *K4 T2 W*
Rotherham *p367* 01709 709000

Thorpe, Mrs C (Dwr Cymru Cyf)
Merthyr Tydfil *p465* 01443 425627

Thorpe, Ms C H (Reynolds Porter Chamberlain LLP) *J1 O X*
London E1 *p71* 020 3060 6000

Thorpe, C J (Howell-Jones LLP) *B1 C1 E S1 T1 W L*
Cheam *p186* 020 8642 8142

Thorpe, J A (Clark Holt) *C2 C1*
Swindon *p406* 01793 617444

Thorpe, J L B (Heringtons) *S1 E L W C1 F1*
Eastbourne *p215* 01323 411020

Thorpe, K G M (Magrath LLP) *Zk O Q*
London W1 *p57* 020 7495 3003

Thorpe, M (Blake Lapthorn) *J1 C1 F1 Zb Zw*
Portsmouth *p354* 023 9222 1122

Thorpe, M P (Harrowells) *R2 S1*
York *p444* 01904 690111

Thorpe, M S (Trethowans LLP) *W S1 T2*
Salisbury *p371* 01722 412512

Thorpe, N J (West Yorkshire Probation Board)
Wakefield *p474* 01924 885300

Thorpe, R G (J Arnold Hancock & Co)
Stretford *p400* 0161 865 2267

Thorpe, S (Onside Law)
London SW6 *p65* 020 7384 6920

Thorpe, S J H (Gardner Thorpe)
Haslemere *p243* 01428 661151
Petworth *p348* 01798 342581

Thorpe-Anderson, Ms J (Stephen Fidler & Co)
London EC1 *p31* 020 7353 8999

Threipland, M P M (Financial Services Authority)
London E14 *p106* 020 7066 1000

Threlfall, Mrs K J (G Cartwright & Co) *S1 S2 A1 E*
Chatteris *p185* 01354 692607

Threlfall, S D (Fletchers) *N*
Southport *p388* 01704 546919

Throp, J (Chapmans Solicitors) *S1 E W L*
Sutton *p402* 020 8337 3801

Throssell, Mrs J (Universal Pictures International Ltd)
London WC1 *p110* 020 7079 6000

Throup, Ms H (Norrie Waite & Slater) *K1*
Sheffield *p377* 0114 276 6166

Thrower, Miss J (Sternberg Reed) *K1*
Barking *p123* 020 8591 3366

Thrower, S (Ashurst LLP) *Zb*
London EC2 *p7* 020 7638 1111

Thubron, Miss C H S (Bailey Smailes) *B1 F1 J1 L O Q C1 Zz C2 Zn Zt S1 Zl Zk M4*
Huddersfield *p255* 01484 435543

Thubron, P (Peter Thubron & Co) *G H K1 S1 E M1 P F1 N W*
Sunderland *p402* 0191 510 1221

Thurkettle, Miss H M (Rosling King) *Zq O*
London EC4 *p73* 020 7353 2353

Thurlby, Miss E M (Rothera Dowson) *D1 K3 K1*
Nottingham *p338* 0115 910 0600

Thurlow, C (Hart Brown Solicitors) *W*
Guildford *p236* 0800 068 8177

Thurlow, M (Birkett Long LLP) *Q*
Chelmsford *p186* 01245 453800

Thurlow, R S (Clarks Legal LLP)
London WC2 *p20* 020 7539 8000

Thurnhill, A J (Thurnhills) *K4 W T2 S1 S2 A1*
Preston *p357* 01772 251762

Thurnhill, J A (Thurnhills) *S1 W L T1 R1 E A1 C1 F1 P Zc Zd Zs*
Garstang *p228* 01995 603142
Preston *p357* 01772 251762

Thurnhill, M G (Thurnhills) *D1 Zr E K1 J2 Zl Q N S1 W K3 O*
Garstang *p228* 01995 603142
Preston *p357* 01772 251762

Thurstan, T M (Chamberlins) *S1 K1 Zi W L E S2 O Q N B1*
Hitchin *p251* 01462 623456

Thurston, J M R (Bird & Co) *W T2*
Newark *p322* 01636 650880

Thurston, J P (Morrison & Foerster (UK) LLP) *Ze*
London EC2 *p62* 020 7920 4000

Thurston, M G (Cartwright King) *B2 J2 F2 P*
Nottingham *p336* 0115 958 7444

Thurston, M R (Blake Lapthorn) *W T2*
Chandlers Ford *p184* 023 8090 8090

Thurston, Mrs S (Overburys & Raymond Thompson) *W T2 K4*
Norwich *p335* 01603 610481

Thwaites, Ms A (Hodge Jones & Allen LLP) *N Q Zg*
London NW1 *p41* 020 7874 8300

Thwaites, G (Salans) *E R2 S2*
London EC4 *p76* 020 7429 6000

Tibb, Mrs R D (Tibb & Co) *S1 E W L*
Barnet *p87* 020 8905 0486

Tibber, C (Anthony Gold) *O Q*
London SE1 *p6* 020 7940 4000

Tibbett, Mrs R H (Percy Hughes & Roberts) *K1 D1*
Birkenhead *p134* 0151 666 9090

Tibbits, A (Tibbits Fisher) *S1 L W*
Birmingham *p143* 0121 707 3900

Tice, R P (Flint Bishop Solicitors) *J1*
Derby *p208* 01332 340211

Ticehurst, P R (Mayo Wynne Baxter LLP) *S1 W S2 L*
East Grinstead *p215* 01342 310600

Tickell, A D (Rex Taylor & Meadows) *C1 E F1 G H J1 K1 L S1 W V N*
West Kirby *p428* 0151 625 6414

Tickell, S C (Sean C Tickell) *E S1 C1 L O W J1*
London N6 *p87* 020 8341 1000

Tickle, Miss D (Parker Rhodes Hickmotts) *K3 D1 D2 K1*
Rotherham *p367* 01709 511100

Tickner, J (Peters & Peters) *O Q Zj*
London EC4 *p67* 020 7629 7991

Ticktum, J P (Bakers) *B1 C1 E L M1 N P S1 W Zc S2*
Mitcham *p318* 020 8648 0363
London WC1 *p78* 020 7831 6677

Tidbury, Miss L (Keer-Keer & Co) *K1 D1 D2 V*
Hemel Hempstead *p246* . . .01442 216755 / 216756

Tidd, A R (Yaffe Jackson Ostrin) *Q N K1 G S1 J1 D1 F1 H L Zl Za*
Liverpool *p291* 0151 259 2666

Tideswell, Ms L C (LG Lawyers)
London SE1 *p50* 020 7379 0000

Tidswell, B J C (Ashurst LLP) *B1 O Q*
London EC2 *p7* 020 7638 1111

Tidswell, T K (Morrish Solicitors LLP) *N*
Leeds *p276* 0113 245 0733

Tier, J J (Phillips & Co) *K1 K3 D1 Q*
Salisbury *p371* 01722 321666

Tier, Ms S J (Sacker & Partners LLP) *Zo*
London EC2 *p76* 020 7329 6699

Tiernan, N (Nicola J Tiernan Solicitors) *K1 Zo*
Bramhall *p156* 0161 439 5286

Tierney, A D P (Tierney & Co) *D1 F1 J1 K1 N O Q*
Dinnington *p210* 01909 550730

Tierney, Ms C (Manchester City Council)
Manchester *p465* 0161 234 5000

Tierney, Miss C M (Knights Solicitors LLP) *S2 E R2*
Newcastle under Lyme *p323*. 01782 619225

Tierney, D (Balfour Beatty Civil Engineering Ltd) *O Q*
Thornton Heath *p474* 020 8684 6922

Tierney, Ms F J (Herrington & Carmichael LLP) *K1 N O D1 Q F1 J1*
Camberley *p173* 01276 686222

Tierney, G (Tierney & Co) *S1 N W K1 Q J1 H D1 F1 L Zl*
Dinnington *p210* 01909 550730

Tierney, P D (Fox Williams) *E*
London EC2 *p33* 020 7628 2000

Tierney, S D G (Tierney & Co) *B1 C1 F1 G H K1 N Q S1 S2*
Dinnington *p210* 01909 550730

Tierney-Jones, G (Bone & Payne LLP) *W S1 S2 E*
Llandudno *p291* 01492 876354

Tighe, D P (Manches LLP) *C1 I C2*
Oxford *p343* 01865 722106

Tighe, Ms F (Gardner Leader LLP) *S1*
Newbury *p322* 01635 508080

Tighe, Ms M E (Leeds Metropolitan University)
Leeds *p463* 0113 812 9028

Tighe, M R (Stewarts Law LLP) *O C3*
Leeds *p277* 0113 222 0022

Tilbrook, R C W (Tilbrook's) *P N M1 J1 F1 B1 R1 Zc Ze*
Chipping Ongar *p193* 01277 896000

Tilbury, A M (Peter Dunn & Co) *L K1 N Q S1*
Sunderland *p401* 0191 568 9000

Tildesley, M A (Rich & Carr Freer Bouskell) *N P C1 M1 F1 B1 L Zl Zc*
Leicester *p281* 0116 253 8021

Tillcock, D J (Freeth Cartwright LLP) *O*
Nottingham *p337* 0115 936 9369

Tillcock, Mrs P E (Dean Thomas & Co) *S1 E W T1 A1 C1 Zv*
Worksop *p441* 01909 500511

Tilley, A C (Dutton Gregory) *J1 N O Q M2 Zc Ze Zj*
Winchester *p433* 01962 844333

Tilley, D F (Tilley & Co) *K1 D1 P N M1 G H B1 L C1 Zk Zm*
St Albans *p390* 01727 840467

Tilley, Ms H S (Kennedys) *Zj N B2*
London EC3 *p49* 020 7667 9667

Tilley, Ms J (Andrew & Co LLP) *E R1 S1*
Lincoln *p284* 01522 512123

Tilley, Miss J (Thorne Segar) *W*
Minehead *p318* 01643 703234

6

Tilley, Mrs J C (Colemans - CTTS) *N Q Zj Zr*
Kingston upon Thames *p267*. 020 8296 9966

Tilley, Mrs J J (North Wiltshire District Council)
Chippenham *p455* 01249 706111

Tilley, Mrs L W (Central & South West Staffordshire Magistrates Court)
Stafford *p472* 01785 223144

Tilley, P W (Kingsley Napley) *E W*
London EC1 *p50*. 020 7814 1200

Tilley, Miss R (Michelmores LLP) *E R2*
Exeter *p221* 01392 688688

Tilley, R (Michelmores LLP) *A1 E S1 S2*
Exeter *p221* 01392 688688

Tilley, Mrs S L (Downs) *S2*
Dorking *p212* 01306 880110

Tilling, S (Plexus Law (A Trading Name of Parabis Law LLP)) *Zj*
Colchester *p198* 0844 245 4950

Tillman, Mrs C M (East Sussex County Council) *K1 D1*
Lewes *p463* 01273 481000

Tillotson, J (John Tillotson)
Stockton-on-Tees *p397* . . . 01642 676000

Tillott, N G (Davies & Partners) *O Q J1*
Gloucester *p230*. 01452 612345

Tilly, Ms C J (TBI Solicitors) *K1 D1 V*
Hartlepool *p243* . . . 0800 052 6824 / 01429 264101

Tilly, D W (Browne Jacobson LLP)
Nottingham *p336*. 0115 976 6000
Nottingham *p337*. 0115 983 3650

Tillyard, Mrs J L (Merrils Ede Solicitors) *N K1 Q P V I M1 Za Zl*
Cardiff *p180* 029 2037 1131

Tilsley, A R (Ellisons) *E C1 R1 L S2*
Colchester *p197* 01206 764477

Tilsley, J R (Essex County Council)
Chelmsford *p454*. 0845 743 0430

Tilson, P (Northumberland County Council) *M1 G H P F1 V D1 J1 N B1 Zm Zp Zi*
Morpeth *p466* 01670 533000

Tilson, Mrs S (Heptonstalls LLP) *N*
Pontefract *p351* 01977 602804

Tiltman, E H (Edward T Davies Sons & Tiltman) *S1 W*
Pontyclun *p352* 01443 225446

Timbrell, A C (Gloucestershire County Council - Legal & Democratic Services)
Gloucester *p459*. 01452 425203

Timmings, Ms C (Field Fisher Waterhouse LLP)
London EC3 *p31*. 020 7861 4000

Timmins, Ms J (Pinsent Masons LLP)
London EC2 *p67*. 020 7418 7000

Timmins, S (Horwich Farrelly) *F1 N O Q J1*
Manchester *p305* 0161 834 3585

Timmis, J M (DB Law) *S2 S1 W*
Camborne *p173* 01209 712428
Penzance *p346* 01736 364261

Timmis, M A (Boyes Sutton & Perry) *B1 Q J1 L G V*
Barnet *p123* 020 8449 9155

Timmis, R (Blick & Co) *Zl*
London EC3 *p14*. 020 7247 9696

Timms, C P (Romain Coleman & Co) *N J1 O*
Waltham Forest *p73* 020 8520 3322

Timms, G (Paul Davidson Taylor) *O C1 B1 F1 Zc Zl*
Horsham *p253*. 01403 262333

Timms, G J (Legal & General Group PLC)
Tadworth *p473*. 01737 370370

Timms, H (Fishman & Co Solicitors) *J1 Zl Q*
London W1 *p32* 020 7935 3500
London W1 *p83* 020 7935 4848

Timms, Miss M (Field Fisher Waterhouse LLP) *O*
London EC3 *p31*. 020 7861 4000
London EC3 *p31*. 020 7861 4000

Timms, M R (M R Timms & Co Limited) *E L S1 W S2*
Dudley *p213*. 01384 458848

Timon, V (Olswang LLP) *C1 I C3 F1 M1 Ze Zf*
London WC1 *p64* 020 7067 3000

Timothy, J V (Land Registry)
London WC2 *p107*. 020 7917 8888

Timothy, P J (HM Land Registry - Durham (Boldon) Office)
Durham *p457* 0191 301 2345

Timperley, R J (Ison Harrison) *O Q*
Leeds *p274* 0113 284 5000

Timson, Mrs H E (MFG Solicitors) *W*
Telford *p409*. 01952 641651

Timson, T P T (Browne Jacobson LLP) *O*
Nottingham *p336*. 0115 976 6000

Tindal, Ms C (Nexus Solicitors) *C1 C2*
Manchester *p308* 0161 819 4900

Tindall, G S (JGT) *G H K1 M1 P S1 F1 J1 W L*
Burnley *p169* 01282 426722

Tindall, Mrs S A (Tyne & Wear Passenger Transport Executive) *Q*
Newcastle upon Tyne *p466* . 0191 203 3333

Tindle, Ms A J (South Tyneside Metropolitan Borough Council)
South Shields *p471* 0191 427 1717

Tingle, Mrs E C (Derbyshire County Council)
Matlock *p465* 01629 580000

Tinker, Miss J E (Cannings Connolly) *O Q*
London EC1 *p18*. 020 7329 9000

Tinker, M D (DLA Piper UK LLP)
Manchester *p303* 0870 011 1111

Tinkler, Mrs H (Buller Jeffries) *N Zj Zr*
Birmingham *p136* 0121 212 2620

Tinkler, K J (Reed Smith LLP)
London EC2 *p71*. 020 3116 3000

Tinkler, S (Clifford Chance)
London E14 *p20* 020 7006 1000

Tinklin, R F (Tinklin Springall) *B1 C1 E F1 K1 L M1 N P*
Bromley *p167* 020 8402 6222

Tinman, J (Rowley Dickinson) *N Zq Zr*
Manchester *p309* 0161 834 4215

Tinn, R (Sills & Betteridge LLP)
Boston *p151*. 01205 364615

Tinning, A R (Grahame Stowe Bateson) *N Zm*
Harrogate *p240* 01423 562121
Leeds *p274* 0113 246 8163

Tinning, M T (MLM Cartwright) *C1 C2 Ze B1 O*
Cardiff *p179* 029 2046 2562

Tinsley, Miss F R (The Roland Partnership) *Zr*
Chester *p191* 01244 659404

Tinsley, Miss J (FBC Manby Bowdler LLP) *K1*
Telford *p409*. 01952 292129

Tippett, G (Bobbetts Mackan) *G H*
Bristol *p161* 0117 929 9001

Tippetts, Miss K (Walker Smith Way) *K1 K3 D1*
Chester *p191* 0844 346 3100

Tippetts, Miss R M (BBC)
London W12 *p103*. 020 8752 5734

Tipping, Miss S (Berkson Wallace Solicitors) *S1 W*
Ellesmere Port *p217*. 0151 355 4412

Tipple, Ms L (Harrison Clark LLP) *K1 K3*
Cheltenham *p188* 01242 269198
Worcester *p439* 01905 612001
Worcester *p439* 01905 612001

Tipple, P J (Bovis Construction Ltd)
Harrow *p460*. 020 8422 3488

Tipton, G S (JMW Solicitors)
Manchester *p306* 0845 872 6666

Tish, Ms R (TV Edwards LLP) *K1*
London SE8 *p85*. 020 7790 7000

Tish, Ms R S (Roberta Tish Solicitors) *K1 K2*
Wandsworth *p87*. 020 7223 6966

Tishler, Miss A S (Barlow Robbins LLP) *J1*
Guildford *p235*. 01483 562901

Tisshaw, Miss G D J (Hamnett Osborne Tisshaw) *K1 K3*
Haywards Heath *p245* 01444 443030

Titchener, J M (ClarksLegal LLP) *J1 O Q*
London WC2 *p20* 020 7539 8000

Titchmarsh, I H (DWF) *P N F1 Zj Zk F2 O Q Zw Zq*
Liverpool *p287*. 0151 907 3000

Titcombe, Ms A D (Portsmouth Magistrates Court)
Portsmouth *p469*. 023 9281 9421

Titcombe, Miss H S C (The Royal Borough of Kensington & Chelsea)
London W8 *p109* 020 7361 2741

Tite, C C (LG Lawyers)
London SE1 *p50*. 020 7379 0000

Tite, Ms L J (Hunters) *W T1 Zd*
London WC2 *p44* 020 7412 0050

Tithecott, Mrs A (Osborne Clarke) *N Q*
Bristol *p164* 0117 917 3000

Titley, E J (Winder Taylor Fallows) *B1 C1 E J1 M1 W P S1 T1 Zb Ze Zj*
Bolton *p150* . . . . .01204 389908 / 522888

Titmas, A (Memery Crystal) *C1 C2*
London WC2 *p60* 020 7242 5905

Titt, J C (Abels) *W S1 L V T1 E Zm*
Southampton *p385*. 023 8022 0317

Titterton, A (Hardy Miles Titterton)
Duffield *p214* 01332 841115

Titterton, Mrs J (Northamptonshire County Council) *D1 G H K1 L R1*
Northampton *p467*. 01604 236236

Titterton, S D (St James's Place)
Cirencester *p455*. 01285 640302

Tiwana, Mrs N (Northwood Law Practice) *K1 Q K3 L N Zq S1 V J1 D2 F1 D1 W Zl Zm Zi*
Northwood *p333* 01923 826208

Tizley, Ms C (Grindeys LLP) *S1*
Stoke-on-Trent *p398*. 01782 846441

Tizzard, J (Farrer & Co LLP)
London WC2 *p31* 020 3375 7000

Tmaira, Ms M (Punatar & Co Solicitors) *G*
London N19 *p69*. 020 7272 3330

Toal, Mrs A L (Maples Solicitors LLP) *D1 G H K1 F1 L N Q*
Spalding *p389* 01775 722261

Toal, Miss L C (Wellers Law Group LLP) *K3 K1 Zi*
Bromley *p167* 020 8464 4242

Tobey, A B (Michelmores LLP) *J1*
Exeter *p221* 01392 688688

Tobias, P A (Hart Brown Solicitors) *W T2 Zv Zo*
Guildford *p236*. 0800 068 8177

Tobin, A C (Bevan Brittan LLP)
London EC4 *p12*. 0870 194 1000

Tobin, Ms B M (Thompsons (formerly Robin/Brian Thompson & Partners)) *Ze*
London WC1 *p87* 020 7290 0000

Tobin, C H (Luton Borough Council)
Luton *p464* 01582 546000

Tobin, R (Kennedys) *Zr K1 Q N Zm*
London EC3 *p49*. 020 7667 9667

Tocher, D R (Wholley Goodings LLP) *A1 C1 C2 E K4 L R1 S1 W*
Bedlington *p130* 01670 824080
Morpeth *p319* 01670 519714

Tocher, Ms J (Taylor Wessing)
London EC4 *p86*. 020 7300 7000

Toczek, L R (The College of Law York) *G P F1 N M1*
York *p477* 0800 289997

Todd, A H (William Sturges & Co) *K1 D1 K3 D2*
Westminster *p84*. 020 7873 1000

Todd, A J (Squire Sanders (UK) LLP)
Leeds *p277* 0113 284 7000

Todd, C D (Archers Law LLP) *E R2 Zl*
Stockton-on-Tees *p396* . . . 01642 636500

Todd, D M (J R Hobbs & Co)
Slough *p382*. 01753 524466

Todd, Mrs E (Davies Gore Lomax) *L Zg*
Leeds *p273* 0113 242 2797

Todd, G (Boodle Hatfield)
Westminster *p14*. 020 7629 7411

Todd, Mrs J (City of Manchester Magistrates' Courts)
Manchester *p465* 0161 832 7272

Todd, J S (Ince & Co Services Ltd)
London E1 *p44* 020 7481 0010

Todd, L (Newcastle Building Society)
Newcastle upon Tyne *p466* . 0191 244 2000

Todd, Mrs M A (Bannister Preston) *K1 P T2*
Sale *p370* 0161 973 2434

Todd, P (Hodge Jones & Allen LLP) *N Q O Zq Zg P Zr Zh J2 Za*
London NW1 *p41* 020 7874 8300

Todd, P J (Hopkins) *N L Q*
Mansfield *p311*. 01623 460460

Todd, R (Bhatia Best) *K1 K2 D2 S1 V W N*
Nottingham *p336*. 0115 950 3231

Todd, R C W (Cattles PLC)
Batley *p448* 01924 444466

Todhunter, Ms S (FBC Manby Bowdler LLP) *N*
Wolverhampton *p437* 01902 578000

Todman, W H D (Todmans SRE) *S1 W S2 Q E C1 L N O K1 Zd Zv Ze Zu*
Rayleigh *p359* 01268 774073

Todner, Ms K E (Kaim Todner Ltd) *G H B2*
London EC4 *p47*. 020 7353 6660

Tofalides, Mrs M (Addleshaw Goddard)
London EC1 *p4* 020 7606 8855
Manchester *p300* 0161 934 6000

Tofayel-Sattar, M (Equity Solicitors) *Zr Q N Zq W J1 L*
Birmingham *p138* 0121 554 7470

Toffis, Miss N (Pascalides & Co)
London WC1 *p66* 020 7837 0049

Toft, Ms B J (William H Lill & Co) *S2 S1*
Altrincham *p116* 0161 928 8111

Toft, I M (Thompsons (formerly Robin/Brian Thompson & Partners)) *N*
Nottingham *p339*. 0115 989 7200

Toft, Ms K (Squire Sanders (UK) LLP)
London EC2 *p81*. 020 7655 1000

Togher, Ms A H (May May & Merrimans) *O Zq A3 Q L J1 Zk*
London WC1 *p59* 020 7405 8932

Togher, Mrs S K (Raworths LLP) *J1*
Harrogate *p240* 01423 566666

Tohani, P (SA Law Chambers) *N S1*
Ilford *p260*. 020 8554 0012

Tolaini, Mrs L K (Barlow Lyde & Gilbert LLP) *C1 Zo Zq*
London EC3 *p10*. 020 7247 2277

Tolan, Miss L (Abrahams Dresden) *S2 E S1*
London EC1 *p3* 020 7251 3663

Tolhurst, P (Tolhurst Fisher LLP)
Chelmsford *p187*. 01245 495111

Tolladay, M J (HKB Wiltshires) *S1 E C1 L T1 A1 W Zc*
Great Yarmouth *p234* 01493 855676

Tollerton, P R (Wilkin Chapman LLP) *E S2 A1 R2*
Grimsby *p235* 01472 262626

Tollett, P (Toller Beattie LLP)
Barnstaple *p125* 01271 341000

Tolley, D N (Addleshaw Goddard) *E*
Leeds *p271* 0113 209 2000
Manchester *p300* 0161 934 6000

Tollinton, D A (Blaser Mills) *N Q*
Harrow *p241*. 020 8427 6262

Tollitt, M J S (Thompsons (formerly Robin/Brian Thompson & Partners)) *N*
Plymouth *p350*. 01752 675810

Toloczko, Ms J M (Mullis & Peake) *K1 P*
Romford *p366* 01708 784000

Tolson, R M (Cooke Painter Limited) *S1 W E S2*
Bristol *p162* 01275 400037

Tolson, S J A (Fenwick Elliott) *O Q Zc Zi A3 P Zj R2*
London WC2 *p31* 020 7421 1986

Tolvas-Vincent, Mrs C E (Bond Pearce LLP) *J1 F1 O*
Southampton *p385*. 0845 415 0000

Tom, M N (Blake Lapthorn) *J1 Zp J2*
London EC1 *p13*. 020 7405 2000

Tomalin, Ms J A (Channel Four Television)
London SW1 *p105*. 020 7396 4444

Toman, Miss R D (Carter-Ruck) *O Zk J1*
London EC4 *p18*. 020 7353 5005

Tomasin, Miss J M (Gateley LLP) *Ze U2 U1 I C1 O M1 Zf Zz*
Nottingham *p337*. 0115 983 8200

Tomaszewska, Ms J M (Pictons Solicitors LLP) *G H*
Milton Keynes *p317* 01908 663511

Tomaszewski, A (Walker Tomaszewski Solicitors) *S2 S1 Zm Za Zi*
Camden *p90*. 020 7722 7740

Tombolis, G (Charles Russell LLP) *U1 C1 C2*
London EC4 *p19*. 020 7203 5000

Tombolis, S (DAC Beachcroft) *E S1*
London EC4 *p24*. 020 7242 1011

Tombs, R S (Turners Solicitors LLP) *E S1*
Bournemouth *p153*. 01202 291291

Tomes, R (Financial Services Authority)
London E14 *p106* 020 7066 1000

Tomiak, Mrs S J (Suffolk Coastal District Council)
Woodbridge *p477* 01394 383789

Tomkins, G R A (Harold Benjamin) *E N S1 W Q*
Harrow *p241*. 020 8422 5678

Tomley, J E C (Tomleys) *A1 W S1 C1 B1 H F1 M1 R1 V Zd Ze Zi*
Newtown *p330*. 01686 626641

Tomlin, B B J (Stephens Wheeler Cooke & Sons) *S1 M1 W E K1 Zl*
Luton *p295* 01582 720175

Tomlin, R L (Dollman & Pritchard) *K1 W D1 L*
Caterham *p183* 01883 347823

Tomlinson, A (Coodes) *S1*
Liskeard *p285* 01579 347600

Tomlinson, A C (DAC Beachcroft)
London EC4 *p24*. 020 7936 2222

Tomlinson, Ms B J (Flintshire County Council)
Mold *p466* 01352 702411

Tomlinson, C (Weightmans LLP)
Manchester *p311* 0161 233 7330

Tomlinson, D A R (Barratt Goff & Tomlinson) *N*
Nottingham *p335*. 0115 931 5171

Tomlinson, D E (Sheltons) *N Q*
Hucknall *p255* 0115 955 3444

Tomlinson, D J (J H Powell & Co) *O J1 Ze Zf U2 Zz Zl I*
Derby *p209* 01332 372211

Tomlinson, G R (Napthens LLP) *A1 C1*
Preston *p357* 01772 888444

Tomlinson, Ms H (Awdry Bailey & Douglas)
Wootton Bassett *p439* 01793 853200

Tomlinson, K P (KieranClarkeGreen) *G D1 H*
Chesterfield *p192* 01246 211006

Tomlinson, Mrs L A (Sheltons) *D1 K1*
Hucknall *p255* 0115 955 3444

Tomlinson, M (Rees Page) *W S1*
Wolverhampton *p438* 01902 577777

Tomlinson, P F (Peter F Tomlinson & Co) *C1 E J1 N Q T1 M1 L B1 W Ze Zo*
Bath *p128* 01225 484232

Tomlinson, R (Gardner Leader LLP) *E S1*
Thatcham *p410* 01635 508080
Newbury *p322* 01635 508080

Tomlinson, Ms S (Anthony Collins Solicitors LLP) *Zd C1 S1 S2*
Birmingham *p137* 0121 200 3242

Tomlinson, S (Hamers Solicitors) *C1 S2*
Hull *p257* 01482 326666

Tomlinson, Ms S A C (Orange PCS Ltd)
Bristol *p452* 0870 376 8888

Tomlinson, S S (Gullands) *S1 R1 S2*
Maidstone *p299* 01622 678341

Tomlinson, Ms T (Stephensons) *E P S1 T2 W*
Brierley Hill *p158*. 01384 79731

Tompkin, N C (P R Vince Solicitors) *C1 C2 E S1 S2 B1 L R1 R2*
Forest Row *p227* 01342 822112

Tompkins, Ms A S (Talbots Legal Advice Centre) *G H*
Stourbridge *p399* . .01384 445850 / 447777

Tompkins, J L P (Williams Beales & Co) *S2 S1 K1 K3 W*
Hay-on-Wye *p245* 01497 820302

Tompkins, J M (Hodders) *Zh L Q O F1 J1*
London NW10 *p41*. 020 8838 1537

Tompkins, P (Dickinson Dees)
Newcastle upon Tyne *p324* . 0191 279 9000

Tompkinson, G F (Redcar and Cleveland Borough Council) *K1 D1 G H M1 Zl*
Redcar *p465*. 01642 466201

Toms, G A (Charsley Harrison LLP) *W*
Windsor *p434* 01753 851591

Toms, R L (Goldbergs) *Q O F1 J1 L Zc Zk Zq*
Plymouth *p349*. 01752 660023
Plymouth *p350*. 01752 675810

Toms-Wilson, Mrs M J (Rootes & Alliott) *K1 D1 D2 K3 S1*
Folkestone *p227*. 01303 851100

Toner, N A (Lewis Silkin LLP) *E R2 S2 P*
London EC4 *p53*. 020 7074 8000

Tonge, D (Langleys) *B1 O Zo*
Lincoln *p284*. 01522 888555

Tonge, D R (Keoghs LLP) *N Zj O Q*
Bolton *p149* 01204 677000

Tonge, Ms L (Lisa Tonge Solicitors) *S1 W S2*
Worsley *p441* 0161 241 6118

Tonge, P G (Cyril Morris Arkwright) *G H*
Bolton *p148* 01204 535261

Tonge, Ms V (Russell Jones & Walker)
Manchester *p309* 0161 383 3500

Tonkinson, Ms J A (Irwin Mitchell LLP) *C1 C2 Zc*
Leeds *p274* 0870 150 0100

Tonks, J M J (Pinsent Masons LLP)
Birmingham *p141* 0121 200 1050

Tonks, J P (Higgs & Sons) *C1 E T1 W Ze*
Brierley Hill *p158*. 0845 111 5050

Tonks, K (Fentons) *N*
Failsworth *p223* 0161 682 7101

Tonner, C J (Legal and Professional Claims Ltd)
London EC4 *p107* 020 7621 3900

Tonner, J H (Tonner Johns Ratti) *B1 C1 D1 G K1 N O Q W X Zb Zf Zm*
Swansea *p406*. 01792 643296

Toogood, A A J (Sheffield City Council)
Sheffield *p471* 0114 273 4019

Toohig, M (Myers Fletcher & Gordon) *O Zf Zw C1*
London W6 *p62* 020 7610 4433

Tooke, M (Department for Business, Enterprise and Regulatory Reform)
London SW1 *p105*. 020 7215 0105

Tooker, J (Holman Fenwick Willan)
London EC3 *p42*. 020 7264 8000

Tookey, Miss C F (Mills & Co) *O Q B1 J1 Za*
Newcastle upon Tyne *p325* . 0191 233 2222

See p634 for the Key to Work Categories

Toolan, P A (Davenport Lyons) *C1 C2* London W1 *p25* 020 7468 2600
Tooley, M (Larcomes LLP) *K1 D2* Portsmouth *p354* 023 9266 1531
Toomey, P D (AST Hampsons) *S1 E W C1 L* Rochdale *p365* 01706 522311
Toomey, T (Ward Hadaway) Newcastle upon Tyne *p327* 0191 204 4000
Toon, Ms E (Partridge Allen & Co) *S1 E J1 C1 Q R1* Walsall *p420* 01922 452860
Toon, J T (Addleshaw Goddard) *C1 T1* Manchester *p300* 0161 934 6000
Toon, Ms V A (Mundays LLP) *B1 F1 L Ze U2* Cobham *p196* 01932 590500
Tootell, Miss A (Wilson & Co) *Zi* London N17 *p92* 020 8808 7535
Tootell, Ms E L (Aviva PLC) London EC3 *p103* 020 7283 7500 / 01603 687905 Norwich *p467* 01603 622200 York *p477* 01904 452210
Tooth, R C (Sears Tooth) *K1* London W1 *p77* 020 7499 5599
Tootle, G R (Roebucks) *N Q O Zq* Blackburn *p145* 01254 274000
Toovey, N C (Stanley Tee LLP) *S2 S1 E* Cambridge *p175* 01223 311141
Topham, Ms A (Squire Sanders (UK) LLP) Manchester *p310* 0161 830 5000
Topham, A J J (John Hodge Solicitors) *N L J1 F1 Q W S1 O Zq* Weston-super-Mare *p429* 01934 623511
Topham, Ms L (Kennedys) Cambridge *p174* 01223 533060
Topiwala, A (Dodds & Partners) *K1 V K2* Leicester *p279* 0116 253 8585
Toppin, R E (Widdows Mason) *G H K1 M1 S1* Wigan *p432* 01942 244294
Topping, C P (Broudie Jackson Canter) *Zg Zq* Liverpool *p286* 0151 227 1429
Topping, G Q (Wellers Law Group LLP) *E S1 W A1 L* London WC1 *p91* 020 7242 7265
Topping, S K (Bird & Bird LLP) *C1 C3 M1* London EC4 *p13* 020 7415 6000
Torah, Ms A A (Talbot Walker LLP) *W K4 T2* Andover *p118* 01264 363354
Tordoff, F (Simpson Duxbury) *K1 D1 Q N G J1 H V* Bradford *p155* 01274 734166
Tordoff, Mrs M A (Environment Agency (Anglian Region)) Peterborough *p468* 01733 371811
Torkar, T (Michelmores LLP) *I U1 U2 Zza Ze C3* Exeter *p221* 01392 688688
Torkisz, Miss J (Beardsells) *N* Cheadle *p185* 0161 477 2288
Tormann, Ms K (Field Fisher Waterhouse LLP) London EC3 *p31* 020 7861 4000
Tormey, Ms S (Barlow Lyde & Gilbert LLP) London EC3 *p10* 020 7247 2277
Tornari, Ms K (Edwards Angell Palmer & Dodge) London EC2 *p28* 020 7583 4055
Tornbohm, P N (Nelsons) *E C1 N R1 Zs Zc* Derby *p209* 01332 372372
Torr, I (Cleggs) *C1 E L R1 S1* Nottingham *p336* 0115 977 5877
Torr, Mrs R (Tinsdills) *E* Hanley *p239* 01782 262031
Torrance, Miss A K (Archers Law LLP) *N J2* Stockton-on-Tees *p396* 01642 636500
Torrance, I M (Oberman Law) *Q O N B1 L W R1 Zp Zq* Camden *p64* 020 7242 6154
Toseland, M J (Dawson & Burgess with Bell Dallman & Co) *W E L S1* Doncaster *p211* 01302 349463
Tossell, M (Hugh James) *S1 E L R1 Zh R2 S2* Cardiff *p179* 029 2022 4871
Tosswill, T M S (Tosswill & Co) *G H* Lambeth *p87* 020 8674 9494
Tostivin, Miss M (Fox Williams) *J1* London EC2 *p33* 020 7628 2000
Toth, J E G (Druces LLP) *Zd W T2* London EC2 *p27* 020 7638 9271 London W1 *p72* 020 7544 2424
Totic, Ms E (Russell-Cooke LLP) *W* London SW15 *p74* 020 8789 9111
Tott, N P (Herbert Smith LLP) *C1 M2 Zb* London EC2 *p40* 020 7374 8000
Tottman, I T (Pickworths) *J1 W* Hemel Hempstead *p247* 01442 261731
Toubkin, M D (Banque Nationale de Paris London Branch) London EC4 *p104* 020 7895 7293
Tough, D R (David Barney & Co) *K1 D1 G H L M1* Stevenage *p394* 01438 314281
Tougher, J (MFG Solicitors) Kidderminster *p265* 01562 820181
Toulson, A (Breeze & Wyles Solicitors LLP) Bishop's Stortford *p144* 01279 715333
Toulson, A (Cunningtons) *S1* Braintree *p155* 01376 326868
Tour, S (Sandwell Metropolitan Borough Council) *C1 B1 F1 O Q Zq* Oldbury *p468* 0121 569 2200
Tournafond, D J (Brabners Chaffe Street) *W E C1 Zd* Liverpool *p286* 0151 600 3000
Toussaint, A M (Toussaint & Co) Wembley *p427* 020 8903 6111
Toussaint, Miss M M (Toussaints) *W E A1 T1 F1* Birmingham *p143* 0121 523 5050
Tout, Miss E J (SNR Denton) *O* London EC4 *p75* 020 7242 1212
Tovey, Mrs S J (Test Valley Borough Council) Andover *p447* 01264 368000
Towell, J O (Cripps Harries Hall LLP) *Zu P R1 E* Tunbridge Wells *p415* 01892 515121
Towell, Ms V (Hartley & Worstenholme) *S1 E L* Pontefract *p351* 01977 732222
Towers, Ms C (DFA Law LLP) Northampton *p331* 01604 609560
Towers, Ms D (Squire Sanders (UK) LLP) London EC2 *p81* 020 7655 1000
Towers, Mrs M (Association of Teachers and Lecturers) London WC2 *p103* 020 7930 6441
Towers, R P (Peasegoods) *N L* Manchester *p308* 0161 205 2772
Towers, Mrs V E (Forsters LLP) *E* Westminster *p33* 020 7863 8333 London EC3 *p88* 020 7423 8000
Towey, G P (Salford City Council) Swinton *p473* 0161 794 4711 Manchester *p310* 0161 832 8844
Towey, J R (Russell & Russell) *G H* Bolton *p149* 01204 399299
Towey, P A (Tozers) *K1 D1* Newton Abbot *p329* 01626 207020
Towler, D P (Thompsons (formerly Robin/Brian Thompson & Partners)) *N J1* Leeds *p277* 0113 205 6300
Towler, D W (Askew Bunting Solicitors LLP) *S1 W A1 E S2* Guisborough *p237* 01287 635151
Towler, J (Langleys) York *p445* 01904 610886
Towler, Ms S (Russell-Cooke LLP) *N Zr* London SW15 *p74* 020 8789 9111
Town, P F (Freeman Johnson) *A1 E J1 L S1 T1 W Zl* Durham *p214* 0191 386 4843 / 386 9619 Northallerton *p331* 01609 772160
Towndrow, Miss J (Friends Provident) *C1 I Ze* Dorking *p457* 01306 654925
Townend, J D (Temple Heelis LLP) *S2 E S1 W* Kendal *p264* 01539 723757
Towner, Ms E J (Kerman & Co LLP) *T2 W* London WC2 *p49* 020 7539 7272
Towner, R N (Fendom Dawson & Towner) *S1 M1 G H K1 N P W E* Marlow *p313* 01628 477808
Townley, Ms A (Salans) *Zb* London EC4 *p76* 020 7429 6000
Townley, Miss H (Percy Hughes & Roberts) *N* Birkenhead *p134* 0151 666 9090
Townley, M D (Bates Wells & Braithwaite London LLP) *Zw Zd* London EC4 *p11* 020 7551 7777
Townley, S (Squire Sanders (UK) LLP) *Zw C1 N Ze Zf* London EC2 *p81* 020 7655 1000
Townroe, M R (Nottingham City Council (City Sec Dept)) *L E Q* Nottingham *p467* 0115 915 5555
Towns, J M (Towns Needham & Co) *O Q P J1 N G Zk* Manchester *p310* 0161 832 3721
Towns, R P (Colemans) *W* Haywards Heath *p245* 01444 459555
Townsend, A (Smith & Graham) *G H D1* Peterlee *p348* 0191 517 3393
Townsend, A (Blake Lapthorn) *E* Chandlers Ford *p184* 023 8090 8090
Townsend, B H (Stewarts Law LLP) *N* Leeds *p277* 0113 222 0022
Townsend, C J (Mills & Reeve) *T1* Cambridge *p175* 01223 364422
Townsend, J (B P Collins LLP) *J1* Gerrards Cross *p229* 01753 889995
Townsend, Ms L A (Steeles) *J1* Norwich *p335* 0870 609 0200
Townsend, Mrs L Y (Horwich Cohen Coghlan) *G S2 P Zt* Manchester *p305* 0161 830 4600
Townsend, Ms L Y (British Telecommunications PLC) London EC1 *p104* 020 7356 6181
Townsend, Miss M J (EBR Attridge LLP) *K1 D1 X Zg L V N* London N17 *p28* 020 8808 0774
Townsend, P (Lewis Silkin LLP) *C1 C2* London EC4 *p53* 020 7074 8000
Townsend, R N I (Saulet & Co) *G H N F1 S1 J1 Q O Zj Zl Zq W K4* Southsea *p389* 023 9281 9442
Townsend, Ms T (Trowers & Hamlins) London EC3 *p88* 020 7423 8000
Townsend, T L (Gardner Croft LLP) *Zt Zl S1 S2 C1 E* Canterbury *p176* 01227 813400
Townshend, P D (Townshends LLP) Coventry *p201* 024 7644 8606 Coleshill *p198* 01675 467333
Townsley, Ms J A (City & County of Swansea) *N* Swansea *p473* 01792 636000
Townson, R (Chorley Borough Council) Chorley *p455* 01257 515151 Skipton *p471* 01756 700600 Nelson *p466* 01282 661661
Toyn, D N (Graysons) *N* Sheffield *p375* 0114 272 9184
Tozer, Mrs R (Field Seymour Parkes) *J1 J2 Zp* Reading *p360* 0118 951 6200
Tozer, R (DLA Piper UK LLP) Birmingham *p137* 0870 011 1111
Tozzi, R P (Burley & Geach) *K4 K1 R1 E T2 W Zm S1 S2 Zd* Liphook *p285* 01428 722334
Tracey, D A (Redferns) *B1 C1 C2 E F1 G H J1 L M1 N Zq* Harrow *p242* 020 8424 7070
Tracy Kelly, J C (Ferdinand Kelly) Sutton Coldfield *p403* 01827 893526
Tracy Phillips, J H (Llys Cennen Solicitors) *S1 G H K1 M1 P N L F1* Ammanford *p117* 01269 592658 / 592790
Tracy Phillips, Ms K A (Llys Cennen Solicitors) *J1 Zp* Ammanford *p117* 01269 592658 / 592790
Tracy, P J E (Willson Hawley & Co) *J1 N O V Q G H P S1 X* Nuneaton *p339* 024 7638 7821
Tradewell, J K (Halton Borough Council) Widnes *p476* 0151 424 2061
Trager-Lewis, A J (C H Hausmann & Co) *C1 O Q J1* London W1 *p39* 020 7436 6333
Trahair, J E R (Foot Anstey) *B1* Plymouth *p349* 01752 675000
Traill, A B G (Battens) *K4 W* Sherborne *p378* 01935 814811 Sherborne *p378* 01935 817736
Traill, N D (Wortley Byers) *C1* Brentwood *p156* 01277 268368
Trainer, M R (Squire Sanders (UK) LLP) *E* Birmingham *p142* 0121 222 3000
Tramnor, D (South Tyneside Metropolitan Borough Council) South Shields *p471* 0191 427 1717
Tran, Miss C C T (Davis & Co) *O Q Zn Zj Za B1* London EC3 *p26* 020 7621 1091
Tranah, Mrs E R (Dempster Binning LLP) *E R1 S2* Chandlers Ford *p184* 023 8062 1790
Tranah, N J (Parker Bullen) *C1 E F1 S1 B1 T1* Salisbury *p371* 01722 412000
Tranter, S (Freeclaim Solicitors) Manchester *p304* 0161 437 9999
Trapnell, Mrs L K (Bonallack & Bishop) *U2 I Ze Zza Zf* Salisbury *p371* 01722 422300
Trask, M A (SJ Berwin LLP) London EC4 *p75* 020 7111 2222
Travell, D G (Jefferies Essex LLP) *Zc B1 C1 E F1 O C2 Zq R2* Westcliff-on-Sea *p428* 01702 332311
Travers, D (Jones Day) *O* London EC4 *p46* 020 7039 5959
Travers, H A (BCL Burton Copeland) *G B2 O J2* London WC2 *p9* 020 7430 2277
Travers, I P H (Nabarro LLP) *A3 O L* London WC1 *p63* 020 7524 6000
Travers, Ms S J (Bournemouth Borough Council) Bournemouth *p450* 01202 451178
Traves, K (Keith Traves) *A1 A2 Zc C1 S2 E F1 F2 Ze G J1 P J2 L Zg* Newport *p328* 01983 525988
Travis, D R (Citi Financial Europe PLC) London E14 *p469*
Travis, Ms K V A (London Borough of Greenwich Legal Services) *K1* London SE18 *p106* 020 8921 5123
Travis, Miss R (Heaney Watson) *K1 D1 K3 D2* Liverpool *p288* 0151 282 5555
Travis, Mrs S (Biscoes) *N* Portsmouth *p354* 023 9266 0261
Traxler, Miss M J (Barlow Lyde & Gilbert LLP) *N Q* London EC3 *p10* 020 7247 2277
Trayford, M J (Waller Needham & Green) *S1 C1 W K1 M1 G P H L F1 Zi Zc Zk* Peterborough *p347* 01733 262182
Trayhurn, N M (Bond Pearce LLP) *Zj* London EC3 *p14* 0845 415 0000
Trayman, C P (Traymans) *G H M1 P S1 D1 K1* Hackney *p88* 020 7249 9980
Traynor, A (Sedgefield Borough Council) *O Q F1 Zl F2 B1* Spennymoor *p472* 01388 816166
Traynor, Mrs A (KBL Solicitors) *C1 C2* Bolton *p149* 01204 527777
Traynor, D (Ronaldsons) London WC1 *p73* 020 7580 6075
Traynor, M (Bates Wells & Braithwaite London LLP) *E S2 R2 Zh L Zd* London EC4 *p11* 020 7551 7777
Treacy, Ms E J (Manchester City Council) Manchester *p465* 0161 234 5000
Treacy, Ms J (Invesco) London EC2 *p107* 020 7065 3057
Treacy, Miss P M (Bristows) *C3 M1* London EC4 *p15* 020 7400 8000
Treagust, G (Trethowans LLP) *E C1 S1* Salisbury *p371* 01722 412512
Treanor, B S (Stephensons Solicitors LLP) *N P V* Leigh *p282* 01942 777777
Treasaden, N H (Brewer Harding & Rowe) *B1 C1 D1 F1 G H J1 K1 L M1 Za Zk Zm* Ilfracombe *p261* 01271 863495
Trebacz, R T (Belvederes) London WC2 *p12* 020 7404 5262 / 7405 0046
Trebble, J M (Scarborough Borough Council) Scarborough *p470* 01723 232348
Treble, Ms A (Mogers) *R1 S1* Bath *p127* 01225 750000
Tredgett, R P (Allen & Overy LLP) London E1 *p5* 020 3088 0000
Tree, M D (Swayne Johnson Solicitors) *S1 S2 E* Denbigh *p208* 01745 812835
Trefny, R (Clifford Chance) London E14 *p20* 020 7006 1000
Tregear, S M (Russells) *O N Ze Zf Zw* London W1 *p75* 020 7439 8692
Tregidga, P R (Cornwall County Council) *S1 L E C1 A1 W P B1 K1* Truro *p474* 01872 322197
Treharne, G (David W Harris & Co) *N G L* Pontypridd *p352* 01443 486666
Treharne, Ms J M (Nicol Denvir & Purnell) *K1 V D1 K2 W D2* Cardiff *p180* 029 2079 6311
Treharne, Miss L J (The Johnson Partnership) *G H* Mansfield *p311* 01623 427575
Treharne, S (Mogers) *S1 W E R1* Bath *p127* 01225 750000
Trehearne, J D (Horsey Lightly) *E S2 S1* Newbury *p322* 01635 580858
Treherne, S G (Blake Lapthorn) *C1 C2* Portsmouth *p354* 023 9222 1122
Treherne, T D (Beaumonts) *K1 D1 S1* Hereford *p247* 01432 352345
Trehy, Ms W (Reynolds Porter Chamberlain LLP) London E1 *p71* 020 3060 6000
Treisman, M J (Bana Vaid & Associates) *W K4* Uxbridge *p417* 01895 272481 Ruislip *p369* 01895 676251
Trelfa, Miss J M (Trelfa & Co) *K1* Hampton *p238* 020 8941 1249
Trelfer, C (ASB Law) *S1 W T1 C1* Maidstone *p298* 01622 656500
Treloar, D A (Hodge Jones & Allen LLP) *Zr* London NW1 *p41* 020 7874 8300
Treloar, Ms V (England Kerr Hands & Co) *S2 S1 W* Birmingham *p138* 0121 427 9898
Tremaine, R T (Clifford Chance) London E14 *p20* 020 7006 1000
Tremlett, R C (Ronnie Tremlett & Co) *G H* Brighton *p160* 01273 696132
Trenchard, Ms G (DBL Talbots LLP) *D1 K3 K1 K2 D2* Kidderminster *p265* 01562 749910
Trenchard, Ms G S (MFG Solicitors) Bromsgrove *p167* 01527 831691
Trenerry, M J W (Mullis & Peake) *F1 M1 J1 P* Romford *p366* 01708 784000
Trenor, J A (WilmerHale) *A3* London EC2 *p92* 020 7645 2400
Trent, Ms A C (Alison Trent & Co) *O Q E C1 L J1 Zp R1 Zq S2 Zc Zl Zb Zd Zk* London EC4 *p88* 020 7583 3350
Trenton, A (Taylor Wessing) London EC4 *p86* 020 7300 7000
Treppass, N J (Howard Kennedy LLP) *P J1 L M1 N Zc* London W1 *p48* 020 7636 1616
Treszka, Miss S (Prince Evans) *S1 Zh* Ealing *p69* 020 8567 3477
Trevelyan-Thomas, Mrs C (Symes Robinson & Lee) *E S1 C1 L* Crediton *p203* 01363 775566
Trevethan, J (Pinsent Masons LLP) *E* London EC2 *p67* 020 7418 7000
Trevitt, Miss D A (Grindeys LLP) *K1 Zi N D1* Stoke-on-Trent *p397* 01782 846441
Trevor, L W (Burtons) *S1 S2 W K4 E* Pembury *p345* 01892 824577
Trevor, Mrs S (Fraser Dawbarns) *D1 K1* King's Lynn *p266* 01553 666600
Trewin, Ms J (Hill Dickinson LLP) *Zr* Liverpool *p288* 0151 600 8000
Triantafillou, Miss M (Briffa) *Ze Zf* Islington *p15* 020 7288 6003
Tribble, Ms L (Michelmores LLP) *W A1 S2 K4 S1* Exeter *p221* 01392 688688
Tribe, Miss A (Hallam-Peel & Co) *K3 K1* London WC2 *p38* 020 3006 1661
Tribe, P J (Elborne Mitchell LLP) *A3 F1 Za Zj* London EC3 *p29* 020 7320 9000
Tribick, A (W H Matthews & Co) *J1 Q N* Staines *p393* 01784 453154
Trick, J F (Stockslegal Ltd) *Zj N Q* Manchester *p310* 0800 988 9055
Tricker, Ms K L (Portsmouth Magistrates Court) Portsmouth *p469* 023 9281 9421
Tricot, D (Skadden Arps Slate Meagher & Flom (UK) LLP) London E14 *p80* 020 7519 7000
Trier, Mrs A (The Family Law Partnership LLP) *K1 K2* Leatherhead *p271* 01372 700890
Trieu, Mrs M T (Sparrow & Trieu Solicitors) *E K1 L S1 W Zi Zl* London W1 *p81* 020 7287 6608
Trigg, M J (Gill Turner Tucker) *O N J1 R1 L F1 Zp* Maidstone *p299* 01622 759051
Triggs, G J (Brewer Harding & Rowe) *S1 E S2 A1* Braunton *p156* 01271 812033 Barnstaple *p125* 01271 342271 Ilfracombe *p261* 01271 863495
Trikha, N (Colemans - CTTS) *E S1* Kingston upon Thames *p267* 020 8296 9966
Trillo, J M (Staffordshire Moorlands District Council) Leek *p463* 01538 483483

6

Trim, C L (Girlings) *S1*
Margate *p312* 01843 220274
Trim, P B H (Howell-Jones LLP) *S1 S2 W J1 E F1 B1 O Q Zq Zr Ze Zl Zv*
Cheam *p186* 020 8642 8142
Trimmer, Mrs S (Max Bitel Greene LLP) *K1 K3 O Q C1*
Islington *p59* 020 7354 2767
Trincas, P (Charles Lucas & Marshall) *N Zl Q G*
Newbury *p322* 01635 521212
Trinder, M S J (Bevan Brittan LLP) *Zr N Zm*
London EC4 *p12* 0870 194 1000
Tring, G J (Sharp & Partners) *S1*
Nottingham *p339* 0115 959 0055
Trinh, Ms N (Forsters LLP) *C1*
Westminster *p33* 020 7863 8333
Trinh, Miss T Y (Clarkson Wright & Jakes Ltd) *C1 C2*
Orpington *p341* 01689 887887
Trippitt, M R (Copleys) *D1 G H K1 N M1 P S1*
Huntingdon *p258* 01480 456191
Tristram, D (Harrison Clark LLP) *A1 R2 S1*
Ross-on-Wye *p367* 01989 562377
Tristram, T H (Greater Manchester Passenger Transport Executive)
Manchester *p465* 0161 242 6000
Tritschler, P (Richard Griffiths & Co) *G H K1 K2 K3 D1 F1 N Q Zl L W J1 S2 D2 E P*
Salisbury *p371* 01722 329966
Trivedi, P (Skadden Arps Slate Meagher & Flom (UK) LLP)
London E14 *p80* 020 7519 7000
Trivedy, V (Trivedy Solicitors) *R1 G Q S1 W Zi Zl*
Wembley *p427* 020 8904 5615
Trobridge, G C (Ashfords LLP) *Zd*
Exeter *p220* 01392 337000
Trood, D P (Bird & Lovibond) *N Q O J1*
Uxbridge *p417* 01895 256151
Troop, I J (Canter Levin & Berg) *Q N*
Liverpool *p287* 0151 239 1000
Trott, D A (Hornby Baker Jones & Wood) *K1 S1 W D1 L Zk S2 D2 K2*
Newport *p328* 01633 262848
Trott, Ms E J (Northamptonshire County Council) *D1 P K1 Zl*
Northampton *p467* 01604 236236
Trott, Mrs H C (Coutts & Co)
London WC2 *p105* 020 7753 1403
Trott, Mrs L (Challinors) *S1 S2 W*
West Bromwich *p427* 0121 553 3211
Trott, Miss L (Edwin Coe LLP) *J1 N O Q*
London WC2 *p29* 020 7691 4000
Trott, P D A (Bates Wells & Braithwaite London LLP) *Zl Zg J1*
London EC4 *p11* 020 7551 7777
Trott, T F (Scott Rowe) *S1 W E*
Lyme Regis *p296* 01297 443777
Trotter, Miss C E (Lester Aldridge LLP) *K1*
Bournemouth *p152* 01202 786161
Trotter, J G (Hogan Lovells International LLP) *O Zj Zk*
London EC1 *p42* 020 7296 2000
Trotter, J M (Bates Wells & Braithwaite London LLP) *O Q A3 C3 Zd*
London EC4 *p11* 020 7551 7777
Trotter, P D (Bray & Bray) *G P H Zl*
Leicester *p279* 0116 254 8871
Troup, A D (TLT Solicitors) *B1 N O*
Bristol *p165* 0117 917 7777
Troup, D S F (Bennett Welch & Co) *W T1 S1 E*
London SE19 *p12* 020 8670 6141
Troup, J E A (Simmons & Simmons)
London EC2 *p79* 020 7628 2020
Troup, Ms K L (Speechly Bircham LLP) *Zv*
London EC4 *p81* 020 7427 6400
Trovato, Mrs H (OGR Stock Denton) *K1 K3*
London N3 *p64* 020 8349 0321
Trowbridge, Mrs K L (Carillion PLC)
Wolverhampton *p477* 01902 422431
Troy, M D (Miller Parris) *W T2*
Worthing *p442* 01903 205771
Troy, Ms P M (Blackfords LLP) *D1 K1 L M1 P*
Croydon *p204* 020 8686 6232
Troyna, N (Last Cawthra Feather LLP) *K4 Zm Zo T1 T2 V W*
Leeds *p275* 0113 244 0876
Trubshaw, J C (Astle Paterson Ltd) *K1 W D1 Q S1 K3*
Burton-on-Trent *p170* 01283 531366
Trudgill, P G (hlw Keeble Hawson LLP) *N Q*
Sheffield *p375* 0114 272 2061
Truefitt, Ms H S (North Yorkshire Law) *D1 D2 G H K1 K2 L Q S1 S2 W*
Whitby *p430* 01947 602131
Scarborough *p372* 01723 360001
Truelove, M C (TWM Solicitors LLP) *E S2 C1*
Guildford *p237* 01483 752700
Trueman, Mrs C L (Yorklaw Ltd (t/a Burn & Company)) *W K4*
York *p445* 01904 655442
Trueman, I K (Maidstone Borough Council) *S1 W E L C1 F1 R1*
Maidstone *p464* 01622 602000
Truex, D (International Family Law Chambers) *K1 M2 K3 M1*
London WC2 *p45* 020 7583 5040
Truman, M (Truelegal Solicitors)
Exeter *p222* 01392 879414
Trump, S F (Russell Jones & Walker)
Bristol *p164* 0117 374 2222
Trundle, Ms J (TV Edwards LLP)
London EC3 *p85* 020 7790 7000
Trundle, P (Martello Professional Risks Limited) *Q O L Zq*
London EC3 *p108* 020 7337 7500
London EC3 *p68* 0844 245 4000
Trundley, Miss C (Park Woodfine Heald Mellows LLP) *K1*
Bedford *p130* 01234 400000
Truong, Ms C (Hodge Jones & Allen LLP) *Q L Zq F1*
London NW1 *p41* 020 7874 8300
Trup, D (Redbridge Magistrates Court)
Ilford *p461* 0845 601 3600
Truran, M G (Treasury Solicitors Department)
London WC2 *p110* 020 7210 3000
Truscott, Ms C L (Hedleys & Co) *S1 R1 N Q L K1 F1 B1 K3*
Sunderland *p401* 0191 567 0101
Truscott, J C (DWF) *C1 C2 U1 U2*
Manchester *p303* 0161 603 5000
Trustram Eve, Ms M C (Withers LLP) *W*
London EC4 *p92* 020 7597 6000
Trynka, S J (Rollits LLP) *C1 T1 E W A1 B1 Zb Zl Zo*
Hull *p258* 01482 323239
Trythall, Mrs J M (Harrison Bundey) *K1 K3 D1 D2*
Leeds *p274* 0113 200 7400
Tsai, Miss R (DWF) *N*
Liverpool *p287* 0151 907 3000
Tsang, D (McDermott Will & Emery UK LLP) *Zo*
London EC2 *p56* 020 7577 6900
Tsang, Ms G S Y (James Tsang & Co)
London W1 *p88* 020 7287 0451
Tsang, Miss H A (Amie Tsang & Co) *G J1 K1 L N O Q S1 S2 W Zi Zl*
Manchester *p310* 0161 236 8821
Tsang, J P M (James Tsang & Co) *C1 E F1 G J1 K1 L N Q S1 Zw Zi Zj Zl*
London W1 *p88* 020 7287 0451
Tschentscher, F (Geldards LLP)
Nottingham *p337* 0115 983 3650
Tsiattalou, H (Stokoe Partnership) *G H B2*
Waltham Forest *p83* 020 8558 8884
Tsindides, S C (Pinney Talfourd LLP)
Hornchurch *p252* 01708 511000
Tsoi, Miss J Y Y (South Derbyshire District Council)
Swadlincote *p473* 01283 221000
Tsoukkas, J (Dollman & Pritchard) *J1 Q B1*
Caterham *p183* 01883 347823
London N12 *p93* 020 8445 9898
Tsui, A (Bracher Rawlins LLP)
London WC1 *p15* 020 7404 9400
Tubb, N D C (Challinors) *N Zr Zq*
Birmingham *p136* 0121 212 9393
Tubb, P M (Black & Co) *G H*
Earl Shilton *p214* 01455 844005
Coalville *p196* 01530 510666
Tubbs, Miss J V (Framlington Group Ltd)
London EC2 *p106* 020 7374 4100
Tuck, Miss D (Bates Wells & Braithwaite London LLP) *O Q A3 C3 Zd X*
London EC4 *p11* 020 7551 7777
Tuck, D C (Weightmans LLP)
Liverpool *p291* 0151 227 2601
Tuck, Mrs K L (Everett Tomlin Lloyd & Pratt) *N Q F2 S1 V W L*
Pontypool *p352* 01495 763333
Tuck, Mrs L E (Bywaters Topham Phillips LLP) *W*
Harrogate *p240* 01423 879556
Tuck, Ms S R (Sue Tuck & Co) *J1 N O Q Zb Zc Zj Zl Zq*
Kensington & Chelsea *p88* . . 020 7385 7733
Tucker, A (Orange PCS Ltd)
Bristol *p452* 0870 376 8888
Tucker, A (Irwin Mitchell LLP) *Zr N P F2*
Sheffield *p376* 0870 150 0100
Tucker, Miss A S (Radcliffes Le Brasseur) *Zr Q J1*
Westminster *p70* 020 7222 7040
Tucker, F E (Morrison & Masters Limited) *K1 Q N F1 B1 L O J2 K3 Zl Zc*
Swindon *p406* 01793 526601
Tucker, G H (Bower & Bailey) *S1*
Witney *p436* 01993 705095
Tucker, Mrs H J (Anthony Collins Solicitors LLP) *L Zh*
Birmingham *p137* 0121 200 3242
Tucker, J A (Allen & Overy LLP)
London E1 *p5* 020 3088 0000
Tucker, J C (Linklaters LLP)
London EC2 *p54* 020 7456 2000
Tucker, J S C (Bray & Bray) *W T2 K4*
Leicester *p279* 0116 254 8871
Tucker, J S C (Harvey Ingram LLP) *W K4*
Leicester *p280* 0116 254 5454
Tucker, Ms K (Morrison & Masters Limited) *K1 Q N J2 Zc*
Swindon *p406* 01793 526601
Tucker, Miss M M (Barr Ellison LLP) *K1 D2*
Cambridge *p174* 01223 417200
Tucker, P J (Dolmans) *S1 S2 E C1 L*
Cardiff *p178* 029 2034 5531
Tucker, Mrs R A (Warwickshire County Council)
Warwick *p475* 01926 410410
Tucker, S (Debenhams Ottaway)
St Albans *p390* 01727 837161
Tucker, Ms S (FBC Manby Bowdler LLP) *E*
Telford *p409* 01952 292129
Tucker, W M (The College of Law Guildford) *N J1 Q O*
Guildford *p459* 01483 460200
Tucker, W P (Nicol Denvir & Purnell) *K1*
Cardiff *p180* 029 2079 6311
Tuckett, Mrs S A (Kenneth Elliott & Rowe) *E L S2 R2*
Romford *p366* 01708 757575
Tuckey, Ms K M (The Merriman Partnership) *K1 K3 D1 D2*
Marlborough *p313* 01672 512244
Tuckley, Ms J (Travers Smith LLP) *C1 C2*
London EC1 *p87* 020 7295 3000
Tuckley, O W H (Henry Cane & Son) *S1 W E L C1*
Brighton *p159* 01273 604091
Tuckley, Ms P A (Bromsgrove & Redditch Magistrates Court)
Kidderminster *p462* 01562 514000
Tuckley, Miss R (Dudley Metropolitan Borough Council)
Dudley *p457* 01384 815326
Tuckman, Ms P (Bolt Burdon) *N Zr*
Islington *p14* 020 7288 4700
Tudball, Ms H C (Harding Evans LLP) *O Q Zq Zb B1 C1 F2*
Newport *p328* 01633 244233
Tudin, A L (SAS Daniels LLP) *W T1 Zm*
Macclesfield *p297* 01625 442100
Tudor, A (Carter-Ruck) *Zk O J1*
London EC4 *p18* 020 7353 5005
Tudor, J (Red Kite Law) *S1*
Milford Haven *p316* 01646 698008
Tudor, Ms M (Barlow Robbins LLP) *J1*
Guildford *p235* 01483 562901
Tudor, M W (Matthew Arnold & Baldwin LLP) *O I Ze*
Watford *p423* 01923 202020
Tudor, Ms N (SGH Martineau LLP)
Birmingham *p142* 0870 763 2000
Tudor, N G (Bell & Buxton) *S1 K4*
Sheffield *p375* 0114 249 5969
Tudor, P (Ince & Co Services Ltd)
London E1 *p44* 020 7481 0010
Tudor-Price, S T (Angel Trains Ltd)
London SW1 *p103* 020 7592 0500
London EC2 *p79* 020 7628 2020
Tudur, M (Tudur Owen Roberts Glynne & Co) *D1 K1 X*
Caernarfon *p172* . . 01286 672207 / 672851
Tufail, F (Mohammed & Co Solicitors) *N O K1 D1 D2 J1 F1 F2 Q Zp*
Preston *p357* 01772 888700
Tufail, Ms R (Clifton Ingram LLP) *K1*
Wokingham *p437* 0118 978 0099
Tufail, Mrs S (Chebsey & Co) *K1*
Burnham *p168* 01628 660077
Tuff, M A (Harris Cartier LLP) *N*
London WC2 *p39* 020 7405 7100
Tuffnell, K D (Macfarlanes) *C1*
London EC4 *p56* 020 7831 9222
Tuffuor, Miss T A (Metropolitan Police Directorate of Legal Services)
London SW1 *p108* 020 7230 7210
Tuft, D M (Carter Lemon Camerons) *E S1 L Zd Zh*
London EC1 *p18* 020 7406 1000
Tugal, Dr B (Shell International Ltd)
London SE1 *p109* 020 7934 1234
Tugbobo, Mrs R (Wandsworth & Merton Law Centre Ltd)
London SW17 *p110* 020 8767 2777
Tull, Mrs S J (Wollen Michelmore Solicitors) *W T2*
Newton Abbot *p330* 01626 332266
Tullett, Miss A M D (Squire Sanders (UK) LLP) *E L*
Leeds *p277* 0113 284 7000
Tulley, C T (DLA Piper UK LLP)
Leeds *p272* 0870 011 1111
Tullo, R K (Aviva PLC) *C1 Zj*
London EC3 *p103* . . 020 7283 7500 / 01603 687905
London EC3 *p105* 020 7283 7500
Tulloch, M G (Wright Son & Pepper LLP) *K1 K2 K3*
Camden *p93* 020 7242 5473
Tulloch, R I (Pearsons & Ward) *E S1 S2*
Malton *p300* 01653 692247
Tully, Ms G (Harter & Loveless) *L Zg*
Islington *p39* 020 7688 2900
Tully, J (Halton Borough Council)
Widnes *p476* 0151 424 2061
Tully, J M (Addleshaw Goddard)
Manchester *p300* 0161 934 6000
Tully, Mrs V E (The College of Law Chester) *Zj*
Chester *p454* 0800 289997
Tumber, Ms T (Solihull Magistrates Court)
Solihull *p471* 0121 705 8101
Tun, T (Herbert Smith LLP)
London EC2 *p40* 020 7374 8000
Tunbridge, M J (Wake Smith & Tofields) *W T2 Zo Zd*
Sheffield *p377* 0114 266 6660
Tunbridge, Mrs R E (Ormerods) *S1 E W*
Croydon *p205* 020 8686 5000
Tungate, Miss W J (Wallace Robinson & Morgan) *E S2 S1 C1 W*
Solihull *p383* 0121 705 7571
Tunkel, D (SJ Berwin LLP)
London EC4 *p75* 020 7111 2222
Tunn, Miss J (Poole Townsend) *G H*
Barrow-in-Furness *p125* . . . 01229 811811
Tunnard, C T (Tunnard & Co) *S1 W L E C1 Zx Zd*
Ripon *p365* 01765 605629
Tunney, V W (Bosworths) *K1 N S1 W L J1 G H F1 X*
East Molesey *p215* 020 8941 3151
Tunnicliffe, Mrs R S (Gordons LLP) *W T1*
Leeds *p273* 0113 227 0100
Tunstall, R (Environment Agency (Wales))
Cardiff *p453* 0870 850 6506
Tunstill, P A (Breeze & Wyles Solicitors LLP) *Q O*
Hertford *p248* 01992 558411
Tuohy, Miss K E (Harvey Ingram LLP) *C1*
Leicester *p280* 0116 254 5454
Tupman, J E C (Woolwich PLC)
Bexleyheath *p449* 020 8298 5000
Tupman, P N (Milburns Solicitors) *K1 N Q F1 V L J1 Zl*
Whitehaven *p431* 01946 694818
Workington *p440* 01900 67363
Turcan, Ms S J (Charles Russell LLP) *J1 Zi Zp*
Cheltenham *p187* 01242 221122
Turek, A T (Treasury Solicitors Department)
London WC2 *p110* 020 7210 3000
Turing, J D (Clifford Chance)
London E14 *p20* 020 7006 1000
Turk, I A (Keeping & Co) *S1 E C1 R1 G H*
Alton *p116* 01420 85221
Turkson, Ms N A (Taylor Wessing)
London EC4 *p86* 020 7300 7000
Turle, A G (Richards & Morgan LLP) *S1 S2 R2 F1 W*
Bournemouth *p152* 01202 424234
Turle, M (Field Fisher Waterhouse LLP)
London EC3 *p31* 020 7861 4000
Turley, C J (Taylor Wessing) *E L*
London EC4 *p86* 020 7300 7000
Turna, Miss D (Norfolk County Council - Legal Services)
Norwich *p467* . . . Minicom: 0844 800 8011
Turnball, S H (LG Lawyers)
London SE1 *p50* 020 7379 0000
Turnbull, Mrs A (Boys & Maughan)
Margate *p312* 01843 234000
Turnbull, A D C (Walker Morris) *T1 W Zo Zm Zd T2*
Leeds *p277* 0113 283 2500
Turnbull, Miss A K (Russell Jones & Walker) *Q N Zj*
Bristol *p164* 0117 374 2222
Turnbull, Mrs C (North Tyneside Council)
Newcastle upon Tyne *p466* . 0191 643 5000
Turnbull, C S (Stewarts Law LLP) *O Zq A3 B2 Zk*
London EC4 *p83* 020 7822 8000
Turnbull, D (Stewarts Law LLP) *N Q V*
London EC4 *p83* 020 7822 8000
Turnbull, D P (Plexus Law (A Trading Name of Parabis Law LLP)) *Zj N Zq*
London EC3 *p68* 0844 245 4000
Turnbull, G A (Freeman Johnson) *S1 K1 E W A1 C1*
Durham *p214* . . 0191 386 4843 / 386 9619
Turnbull, I N (Barlow Lyde & Gilbert LLP)
London EC3 *p10* 020 7247 2277
Turnbull, J A (MacRae & Co LLP) *A3 B1 C3 I Ze J1 M1 Zj U2 O Q C2 Zo R2 S1 Zv T1 W*
Southwark *p57* 020 7378 7716
Turnbull, J C (Bircham Dyson Bell)
Westminster *p13* 020 7227 7000
Turnbull, J W (Linklaters LLP)
London EC2 *p54* 020 7456 2000
Turnbull, K (Muckle LLP) *O Q Zq B2 J1 F2*
Newcastle upon Tyne *p325* . 0191 211 7777
Turnbull, K B (Marshall Hall & Levy) *K1 D1 C1 E J1 B1 N O Q Zc Ze Zi Zk Zl*
South Shields *p384* 0191 455 3181
Turnbull, M (Hamer Childs) *G H*
Worcester *p439* 01905 724565
Turnbull, M C (Thompsons (formerly Robin/Brian Thompson & Partners)) *J1 N*
Manchester *p310* 0161 819 3500
Turnbull, M F (Craven District Council)
Skipton *p471* 01756 700600
Turnbull, M J (Leeds City Council) *E*
Leeds *p462* 0113 224 3513
Turnbull, N H (Walker Smith Way) *N*
Wrexham *p443* 0844 346 3100
Turnbull, P L (Martin Murray & Associates) *G H B2*
Slough *p382* 01753 551313
Turnbull, S (Shepherd + Wedderburn LLP)
London EC4 *p78* 020 7429 4900
Turnbull, Ms S T (Newcastle Upon Tyne City Council)
Newcastle upon Tyne *p466* . 0191 232 8520
Turner, Mrs A (QualitySolicitors D'Angibau) *S1 W*
Poole *p353* 01202 672598
Turner, A (Mills & Reeve) *Zj*
Birmingham *p140* 0121 454 4000
Turner, Mrs A B (Mander Hadley & Co) *D1 F1 J1 K1 L M1 N P Zm*
Coventry *p200* 024 7663 1212
Turner, A C R (Larcomes LLP) *S1 E C1 R1 S2*
Portsmouth *p354* 023 9266 1531
Turner, Mrs A F (Malcolm C Foy & Co) *C1 S2 E*
Doncaster *p211* 01302 340005
Turner, Ms A J (Cleaver Thompson Ltd) *S1 W S2 K4 E*
Alfreton *p115* 01773 832193
Turner, B E (Mills & Reeve) *C2 C1 C3*
Cambridge *p175* 01223 364422
Turner, B R (Gordons) *O Q F1 J1 N C1 L Ze Zf Zk*
London WC1 *p36* 020 7421 9421
Turner, Ms C (Bracher Rawlins LLP) *Q N O Zr J2 P Ze*
London WC1 *p15* 020 7404 9400

See p634 for the Key to Work Categories

Turner, Ms C (Nabarro LLP) *C1 E Zc Zu*
London WC1 *p63* 020 7524 6000
Turner, Miss C F (Harbottle & Lewis LLP)
London W1 *p38* 020 7667 5000
Turner, Mrs C J (Hartnell Chanot & Partners Family Law Specialists) *K1 K3*
Exeter *p221* 01392 421777
Turner, Miss C J A (TMJ Legal Services LLP) *S1 W L R1 K4*
Hartlepool *p243* 01429 235616
Wingate *p434* 01429 838225
Turner, C J A (Newcastle Upon Tyne City Council)
Newcastle upon Tyne *p466* . 0191 232 8520
Turner, C S (St Albans District Council)
St Albans *p472* 01727 866100
Turner, Mrs D (Fiona Bruce & Co LLP) *D1 K1 K3*
Warrington *p421* 01925 263273
Turner, D (Foot Anstey)
Exeter *p221* 01392 411221
Turner, D (Gilbert Turner Coomber) *S1 E W C1 L R1 T1*
Waltham Forest *p35* 020 8520 5886
Turner, D M (Blaser Mills) *S1 E S2*
Rickmansworth *p364*. 01923 776211
Turner, E D (Taylor Vinters) *N*
Cambridge *p176* 01223 423444
Turner, Mrs E E H (Anthony Collins Solicitors LLP) *Zd*
Birmingham *p137* 0121 200 3242
Turner, Miss F C (CKFT)
London NW3 *p17* 020 7431 7262
Turner, G (Trowers & Hamlins)
London EC3 *p88*. 020 7423 8000
Turner, G (Easthams Solicitors Limited)
Blackpool *p146* 0800 032 1432
Turner, G F (Trowers & Hamlins) *E L Zh*
Manchester *p310* 0161 211 0000
Turner, Ms H (Mills & Reeve) *N O*
Cambridge *p175*. 01223 364422
Turner, Miss H F (Archers Law LLP) *A1 E L*
Stockton-on-Tees *p396* . . . 01642 636500
Turner, I C (Meesons) *K1 K3 L G J1 F1 D1 V N Q*
Ringwood *p364* 01425 472315
Turner, J (Watson Burton LLP)
Newcastle upon Tyne *p327* . 0845 901 2100
Turner, Mrs J (Stevens) *S1*
Saffron Walden *p370*. 01799 526849
Turner, J A (Emmerson Brown & Brown)
Sandwich *p372* 01304 612444
Turner, J A (Hewitts) *D1 G H K1 N Q S1 V W L*
Bishop Auckland *p144* 01388 604691
Turner, J C (The Johnson Partnership) *G H*
Nottingham *p337*. 0115 941 9141
Turner, J D (Federal-Mogul Corporation) *M1 K1 P*
Manchester *p464* 0161 955 5200
Turner, J J W (Maples Solicitors LLP) *S2 C1 S1 A1*
Spalding *p389* 01775 722261
Turner, J L (Lindsay Sait & Turner) *W S2 S1*
Woking *p437*. 01483 604033
Turner, J L (Keer-Keer & Co) *K1 D1 W N J1 F1*
Hemel Hempstead *p246* . . .01442 216755 / 216756
Turner, J L (Reed Smith LLP) *C1*
London EC2 *p71*. 020 3116 3000
Turner, K (Turner Coulston) *C1 O E B1 Q J1 T1 N L K1 Zh Ze Zc*
Northampton *p333*. 01604 622101
Turner, Mrs K E (Cumbria County Council)
Carlisle *p453*. . . . .01228 607374 / 607351
Turner, K W (Max Gold Law) *G H J1 X L Zh*
Hull *p257* 01482 224900
Turner, L A (Alan Turner & Co) *S1 E W T2 A1 Zc C1 S2 K4 L*
Bath *p127* 01225 336260
Turner, Ms L M (Ellis Lakin & Co) *Q K1 F1 J1 G V N W L S1 Zl Zk*
Pickering *p348*. 01751 472121
Turner, M (AGR Solicitors)
Mansfield *p311*. 01623 460444
Turner, Ms M (Foot Anstey) *E*
Plymouth *p349*. 01752 675000
Turner, M A (Thames Water Utilities Limited) *L Q C1 J1*
Reading *p469* 0118 373 8000
Turner, M M (Challinors) *G H D1 N Zi*
West Bromwich *p427* 0121 553 3211
Turner, M M (Herbert Smith LLP) *O Ze*
London EC2 *p40*. 020 7374 8000
Turner, M R (Brown & Murray) *A1 J1 N Q S1 W*
Millom *p316* 01229 772562
Turner, Miss N (Alan Edwards & Co) *L E S1 S2*
Kensington & Chelsea *p28*. . 020 7221 7644
Turner, N (Herbert Smith LLP) *E*
London EC2 *p40*. 020 7374 8000
Turner, N A G (Debenhams Ottaway) *W*
St Albans *p390* 01727 837161
Turner, N C (Russell & Co) *Q F1 J1 N D1 O K1*
Malvern *p300* 01684 892000
Turner, N D (Monro Fisher Wasbrough LLP) *W*
London WC1 *p61* 020 7404 7001
Turner, N E (Cumberland Ellis Peirs) *N E F1 J1 L P Q*
London WC1 *p23* 020 7242 0422
Turner, N G (Ziadies) *L*
London SW9 *p94* 020 7737 0934
Turner, N J (Parker Bullen) *A1 T1 W T2 K4 Zd*
Salisbury *p371*. 01722 412000
Turner, N K (Rosamund Coppen & Company) *C1 E L S1 S2 W*
Bath *p127* 0330 440 1802

Turner, N M B (QualitySolicitors C Turner) *N O Q G H Zj Zt*
Blackburn *p145* 01254 688400
Turner, N S (LG Lawyers) *C1 Zb*
London SE1 *p50*. 020 7379 0000
Turner, P (Field Fisher Waterhouse LLP)
London EC3 *p31*. 020 7861 4000
Turner, P (Nexus Solicitors) *Ze O Zq I U2 Q*
Manchester *p308* 0161 819 4900
Turner, P A (Ipswich Borough Council)
Ipswich *p461*. 01473 432000
Ashton-under-Lyne *p447*. . . 0161 342 3028
Turner, P A (Clifford Chance)
London E14 *p20*. 020 7006 1000
Turner, P B (Forbes) *G H K1*
Preston *p356* 01772 220022
Turner, P B (Quality Solicitors Clarke & Son) *C1 C2 Zl E*
Basingstoke *p127* 01256 320555
Turner, P D (Fladgate LLP)
London WC2 *p32* 020 3036 7000
Turner, Mrs P J (Lancashire County Council)
Preston *p469* 01772 254868
Turner, P J (Waddington & Son) *G K1 P M1 J1 H S1 V L W Zl Zi*
Burnley *p169* 01282 426666
Turner, Ms R (Cartwright King)
Nottingham *p336*. 0115 958 7444
Turner, R (Prince Evans)
Ealing *p69*. 020 8567 3477
Turner, R (Simmons & Simmons)
London EC2 *p79*. 020 7628 2020
Turner, Mrs R (HM Land Registry - Plymouth)
Plymouth *p468*. . . .01752 636000 / 636123
Turner, R E (K&L Gates LLP)
London EC4 *p47*. 020 7648 9000
Turner, R J (Girlings) *E C1 S1 L A1 R1 Zc*
Ashford *p119* 01233 664711
Turner, R J (QualitySolicitors D'Angibau) *S1 E C1 W S2*
Poole *p353* 01202 672598
Turner, Miss R L (Pengillys LLP) *Q*
Weymouth *p430*. 01305 768888
Turner, R M (Armitage Sykes LLP) *C1 E C2*
Huddersfield *p255* 01484 538121
Turner, R P (SNR Denton) *O*
London EC4 *p75*. 020 7242 1212
Turner, Mrs S (Bournemouth Borough Council)
Bournemouth *p450*. 01202 451178
Turner, S D (Kingston upon Hull City Council) *A1 D1 F1 G H J1 K1 L N*
Hull *p461* 01482 300300
Turner, S W (Cannock Chase District Council)
Cannock *p453*. 01543 462621
Turner, S W (Stafford Borough Council)
Stafford *p472* 01785 619000
Turner, T J M (Fuller Smith & Turner PLC)
London W4 *p106* 020 8996 2000
Turner, T R (Aviva PLC) *S1 E L A1*
London EC3 *p103* . 020 7283 7500 / 01603 687905
Norwich *p467* 01603 622200
Turner, Ms V J (Sunderland Magistrates Court) *G H K1 D1*
Sunderland *p473*. 0191 514 1621
Turner, W (Ince & Co Services Ltd)
London E1 *p44* 020 7481 0010
Turner, W D R (Birketts LLP) *E L S1 R2 Zd S2*
Ipswich *p262*. 01473 232300
Turner-Johnson, Mrs M (Irwin Mitchell LLP) *O W Zq*
Sheffield *p376* 0870 150 0100
Turnock, A (Beswicks) *G H*
Hanley *p239*. 01782 205000
Turnock, S A (Leeds City Council)
Leeds *p462* 0113 224 3513
Turnor, R W C (Allen & Overy LLP)
London E1 *p5* 020 3088 0000
Turofsky, J M (Landau & Cohen) *P S1 K1 L M1 E*
Elstree *p218*. 0845 331 2477
Turpie, M E (Gordons Solicitors LLP)
Marlow *p313*. 01628 487487
Turpin, Mrs K (HC Solicitors LLP) *E L Zu S1 Zc*
Peterborough *p347* 01733 882800
Turpin, K A (Henriques Griffiths) *S1 E S2*
Bristol *p163* 0117 909 4000
Bath *p128*. 01225 337599
Turrington, Ms F (Spratt Endicott) *O Q L*
Banbury *p122* 01295 204000
Turtle, T W (Herbert Smith LLP) *C1*
London EC2 *p40*. 020 7374 8000
Turton, A (Leigh Turton Dixon) *D1 G H K1*
Middlesbrough *p315* 01642 241101
Turton, K J B (Boodle Hatfield) *E R2*
Westminster *p14*. 020 7629 7411
Turton, S D W (Redfearns) *D1 E G H K1 W S1*
Heckmondwike *p246*.01924 403745 / 404601
Turvey, N A (Appleby Hope & Matthews) *S1 E L W G H K1 M1 J1 D1 Zl Zi Zj*
Middlesbrough *p314*. 01642 440444
Tuson, A F L (Barlow Lyde & Gilbert LLP)
London EC3 *p10*. 020 7247 2277
Tuson, J J F (Kirwans) *E R2 R1 Zc Zb A1 P C1 C2*
Liverpool *p289*. 0151 229 5600
Tuson, N P M (Drummonds) *S1 S2 E*
Chester *p190* 01244 408300
Tussaud, M (Gordon Dadds) *T2 R2 W E*
London W1 *p25* 020 7493 6151
Tustain, P (Tustain Jones & Co) *S2 W*
Bedworth *p130*. 024 7664 3222

Tustian, Miss J S (O H Parsons & Partners) *N J1*
London WC2 *p66* 020 7379 7277
Tustin, P N (GCL Solicitors) *S2 E R1 R2 S1*
Guildford *p236*. 01483 577091
Tutchener-Ellis, J (PCB Solicitors LLP) *N*
Telford *p409*. 01952 403000
Tuthill, A K (William Sturges & Co) *E L S2 R2 S1*
Westminster *p84*. 020 7873 1000
Tuthill, Miss K H (Dobsons) *G H*
Orpington *p341* 01689 886300
Tutt, Ms J C (Wannop Fox Staffurth & Bray) *K1 K3 K4*
Worthing *p442*. 01903 228200
Tuttle, G J (Treasury Solicitors Department)
London WC2 *p110*. 020 7210 3000
Tuttle, P I (HKB Wiltshires) *D1 G H J1 N O Q R1 S1 W*
Lowestoft *p294* 01502 582338
Tutton, Miss N C (FDR Ltd)
Basildon *p448* 01268 296431
Tuvey, M W (Inspire Law) *W N Q Zj*
Banbury *p122* 01295 298211
Twaite, Ms A (Fisher Meredith) *K1 D1 D2*
Lambeth *p32*. 020 7091 2700
Twaite, D (Sheffield City Council)
Sheffield *p471* 0114 273 4019
Twaites, S (Martello Professional Risks Limited) *O Zc Ze Zi*
London EC3 *p108* 020 7337 7500
Twaits, C (Trethowans LLP) *E*
Southampton *p387*. 023 8032 1000
Twambley, A (Amelans) *P K1 G S1 F1 B1 D1 Zm Zh Zj*
Manchester *p301* 0161 434 4545
Twambley, F (Land Registry)
London WC2 *p107*. 020 7917 8888
Tweddle, A (Hewitts) *K1 P L R1 S1 W Zh Zj Zk*
Crook *p203* 01388 762466
Tweddle, G (MB Solicitors Ltd trading as MB Law) *O Q N A3 Zj*
Leeds *p275* 0113 242 4444
Tweddle, Mrs R (Wrigleys Solicitors LLP) *A1*
Leeds *p278* 0113 244 6100
Tweddle, Miss V (Hewitsons) *E L*
Cambridge *p174*. 01223 461155
Tweeddale, A G (Corbett & Co International Construction Lawyers Ltd)
Teddington *p409*. 020 8614 6200
Tweedie, C J (Addleshaw Goddard) *J1*
Leeds *p271* 0113 209 2000
Manchester *p300* 0161 934 6000
Tweedie, D T (Lees Solicitors LLP) *Zr*
Birkenhead *p134*. 0151 647 9381
Twemlow, C M (Society of Lloyd's)
London EC3 *p107* 020 7327 1000
Twemlow, W A (Hill Dickinson LLP) *B1 W S1 E*
Liverpool *p288*. 0151 600 8000
Twidale, W P (Farrer & Co LLP)
London WC2 *p31* 020 3375 7000
Twigden, S C H (Addleshaw Goddard) *E R2*
London EC1 *p4* 020 7606 8855
Manchester *p300* 0161 934 6000
Twigg, D A B (O'Gorman & Co) *G H Zw*
Warwick *p422* 01926 409900
Twiggs, Mrs B L (Crane & Staples) *E S2 C1 S1 R2*
Welwyn Garden City *p425* . . 01707 329333
Twine, D H (Osborns) *C1 N S1 W S2*
Colwyn Bay *p198* . .01492 532056 / 532820
Twine, J (Wolferstans) *J1 Q*
Plymouth *p351*. 01752 663295
Twiney, Mrs R F (Large & Gibson) *S1*
Southsea *p388*. 023 9229 6296
Twining, R P (Warners Solicitors) *A3 F1 F2 J1 K1 L N O Q Zl Zq*
Sevenoaks *p374*. 01732 747900
Twist, G P A (Pinsent Masons LLP)
Birmingham *p141* 0121 200 1050
Twist, Miss P A (P A Twist & Co) *S1 T1 W K1 E R1 C1*
Poole *p353* 01202 709050
Twomey, B F (Sheffield City Council) *V X*
Sheffield *p471* 0114 273 4019
Twomey, P (Underwood Solicitors LLP) *L O Zq*
Westminster *p89*. 020 7526 6000
Twomlow, A J (Twomlows) *K1 P G M1 H F1 W J1 L V Zl*
Caldicot *p172* 01291 422753
Twomlow, Mrs M A (Twomlows) *F1 G H J1 K1 L M1 P S1*
Caldicot *p172* 01291 422753
Twort, Miss G E (Morgan Cole) *N*
Bristol *p164* 0117 916 7220
Twose, S C (Kirby Sheppard) *W S1 K4*
Kingswood *p268*. 0845 840 0045
Twyford, P (Paisleys) *Zr S1 N*
Workington *p440*. 01900 602235
Twyford, R (Adam Douglas & Son)
Berwick-upon-Tweed *p131*. . 01289 306479
Twyman, C J (Edell Jones & Lessers) *S1 S2 W E*
London E6 *p28* 020 8548 5700
Twyman, R C (Piper Smith Watton LLP) *B1 F1 J1 K1 L N Zc O Zp*
London SW1 *p68* 020 7222 9900
Twynam, Miss L (Michael Simkins LLP) *C1 C2 Zf*
London WC1 *p79* 020 7874 5600
Tyas, Ms R (Rothera Dowson) *K1 K3*
Beeston *p130* 0115 916 5200
Tye, S P (Eastgate Assistance Ltd)
Colchester *p455*. 0870 523 4500
Tyerman, J (Pinsent Masons LLP)
London EC2 *p67*. 020 7418 7000

Tyers, Ms E J (Duncan Lewis & Co) *K1 K3 D1*
Hackney *p53*. 020 7923 4020
Tyfield, Ms K S (Bross Bennett) *K1 K3*
London N6 *p16* 020 8340 0444
Tyler, G C (DLA Piper UK LLP)
London EC2 *p24*. 0870 011 1111
Tyler, G R (Pinsent Masons LLP) *O J1 P Zf Zk Zo Zp*
London EC2 *p67*. 020 7418 7000
Tyler, G R (Punch Robson) *B1 F1 O Q Zc*
Middlesbrough *p315* 01642 230700
Tyler, G T (Cripps Harries Hall LLP) *Q O Zq Zj A3 J1*
Tunbridge Wells *p415* 01892 515121
Tyler, Miss H A G (Brutton & Co) *E L S1 A1 W C1 F1 P R1 K1 Zd Ze*
Fareham *p223*. 01329 236171
Tyler, Ms J (Macfarlanes) *C1*
London EC4 *p56*. 020 7831 9222
Tyler, M L (CMS Cameron McKenna LLP)
London EC3 *p17*. 020 7367 3000
Tyler, Miss M L (Flint Bishop Solicitors) *N*
Nottingham *p337*. 0115 964 4450
Tyler, N M (Information Commisioner)
Wilmslow *p476*. 01625 545700
Tyler, R C (Hogan Lovells International LLP)
London EC1 *p42*. 020 7296 2000
Tyler, R H (CMS Cameron McKenna LLP)
London EC3 *p17*. 020 7367 3000
Tym, R (Hogan Lovells International LLP)
London EC1 *p42*. 020 7296 2000
Tyman, Miss S L (Morgan & Lamplugh) *N L K1 F1 V*
Hastings *p243* 01424 721821
Tymanowski, C (Peter Lynn & Partners) *C1 C2 E R2 S1 S2*
Morriston *p319*. 01792 310731
Tymkiw, R P (Kidd Rapinet) *C1 K1 J1 M1 G F1 Zc Ze Zf O Zq*
London WC2 *p49* 020 7205 2115
Tynan, Miss K (Donaldson Dunstall) *S1 S2 E*
Bexhill *p131* 01424 216329
Tynan, Ms N (Luton Borough Council)
Luton *p464* 01582 546000
Tyndall, Miss G (Rodgers & Burton) *K3 K1*
London SW13 *p73*. 020 8939 6300
London SW13 *p84*. 020 8876 8811
Tyrell, Mrs V M (Edwards Angell Palmer & Dodge)
London EC2 *p28*. 020 7583 4055
Tyreman, M J (Reed Smith LLP) *B1*
London EC2 *p71*. 020 3116 3000
Tyrer, A P (National Grid PLC)
Warwick *p471* 01926 653000
Tyrer, D R G (Cousins Tyrer) *G H*
Leeds *p272* 0113 247 0400
Tyrer, Ms L A (ASB Law) *K1 D1 G*
Maidstone *p298* 01622 656500
Tyrrell, Mrs D G (Rugby Borough Council)
Rugby *p470* 01788 533533
Tyrrell, G (Harbottle & Lewis LLP) *O Q Zf Ze Zv*
London W1 *p38* 020 7667 5000
Tyrrell, Ms H M (North Kensington Law Centre)
London W10 *p108* 020 8969 7473
Tyrrell, Mrs L M (Tollers LLP) *K4 W*
Northampton *p332*. 01604 258558
Tysall, Miss D L (Alfred Newton & Co) *K1 K3 W S1 D1*
Stockport *p396*. 0161 430 8831
Tysh, I M (Berry & Berry) *Q L J1 O N X J2 F1 Ze Zq Zp*
Tunbridge Wells *p414* 01892 526344
Tyson, D R (Keoghs LLP) *N Zj O Q*
Bolton *p149* 01204 677000
Tyson, J (Coodes)
Newquay *p329*. 01637 878111
Tyson, Ms L J (Keoghs LLP) *N Zj O Q*
Bolton *p149* 01204 677000
Tyson, Mrs M A (Charles Russell LLP) *K1*
Guildford *p235*. 01483 252525
Tyson, P V (Thompson Leatherdale) *E C1 L R1 S1*
Reading *p361* 0118 959 1773
Tyson, R (J A Kemp & Co)
London WC1 *p48* 020 7405 3292
Tyson, Miss S (Hempsons) *N Zr Zq Zm*
Manchester *p305* 0161 228 0011
Stoke-on-Trent *p398*. 01782 406200
Tyson, Miss V M (Corbett & Co International Construction Lawyers Ltd) *O M2 A3 Zc*
Teddington *p409*. 020 8614 6200
Tyson, Mrs W J (Cockshott Peck Lewis) *K1 J1 F1 S1 W K4*
Southport *p388* 01704 211649
Southport *p388* 01704 534034

U

Ubbey, Ms M K (Maxwell Winward LLP) *E S2 L R2*
London EC4 *p59*. 020 7651 0000
Ubhi, Miss N (Dass Solicitors) *B2 G H L Zi N Zg*
Birmingham *p137* 0121 248 4000
Ucar, Miss S (Sal & Co)
London N18 *p76*. 020 8807 5888
Uche, Miss E (Letchers) *J1 Q O C1 F1 N G*
Ringwood *p364* 01425 471424
Uddin, M (Martin Murray & Associates) *G H B2*
Slough *p382*. 01753 551313
Uddin, N (Charles Simmons)
Ilford *p261*. 020 8514 0000

6

Uddin, Ms R (Clegg Manuel) *S1 L*
Islington *p20* 020 7847 5600

Ude, A (Armitage Sykes LLP) *O Q N*
Huddersfield *p255* 01484 538121

Ufland, R M (Hogan Lovells International LLP) *C1*
London EC1 *p42* 020 7296 2000

Uglow, Ms S (Shell International Ltd)
London SE1 *p109* 020 7934 1234

Uhrynuk, M (Mayer Brown International LLP)
London EC2 *p59* 020 3130 3000

Ullah, M A (Applebys) *K1 N Q D1 G H L J1 B1 W Zj Zd Zf Zc Zo*
Bradford *p153* 01274 728838

Ullock, J E R (Holden Son & Ullock) *S1 W K3 L S2*
Thornton Cleveleys *p411* . . .01253 852613 / 862606

Ulm, A M J (Reynolds Porter Chamberlain LLP) *O Zj Q Zq*
London E1 *p71* 020 3060 6000

Umasuthan, Mrs M (Sri Kanth & Co) *S1 L V Q J1 K1 G N Zi Zh*
Wembley *p426* 020 8795 0648

Umenyilora, Miss E (Henscott Solicitors) *G H*
London E17 *p40* 0870 880 0007

Umer, T L (Schofield Sweeney) *J1 N Q O*
Bradford *p154* 01274 306000

Unarkat, Mrs S R (George Green LLP) *E*
Cradley Heath *p201* 01384 410410
Leicester *p280* 0116 254 5454

Underhill, Ms A R (Wards Solicitors) *N Zr*
Staple Hill *p394* 0117 943 4800
Bristol *p165* 0117 929 2811

Underhill, K L H (Reynolds Porter Chamberlain LLP) *A3 O Q Zj Zq*
London E1 *p71* 020 3060 6000

Underhill, M D (IBB Solicitors) *N*
Uxbridge *p417* 0845 638 1381

Underhill, Ms S (Reed Smith LLP) *Za*
London EC2 *p71* 020 3116 3000

Underhill, S D (Shentons) *N Q O J1 Zr Zq*
Winchester *p434* 01962 844544

Underhill, T C (Symes Robinson & Lee) *S1*
Exeter *p222* 01392 270867

Underhill, T C (Ford Simey LLP) *S1*
Exeter *p221* 01392 274126

Underwood, Mrs A G (Thursfields) *L S1 W*
Stourport-on-Severn *p399* . . 01299 827517

Underwood, Mrs A M (Birmingham City Council Legal & Democratic Services)
Birmingham *p449* 0121 303 2066

Underwood, A R (Keoghs LLP) *N Zj O Q*
Bolton *p149* 01204 677000

Underwood, C (HCB Solicitors) *Zl J1 X*
Walsall *p420* 01922 720000

Underwood, I M (Last Cawthra Feather LLP) *K1 D1 S1 E W C1 A1 L C2 D2 Zc*
Bradford *p154* 01274 848800

Underwood, Ms N (Challinors)
Birmingham *p136* 0121 212 9393

Underwood, Ms R L (Fox Williams) *J1*
London EC2 *p33* 020 7628 2000

Underwood, R L (Penningtons)
Basingstoke *p127* 01256 407100

Underwood, S G (Barlow Robbins LLP) *Zr N*
Woking *p436* 01483 748500

Underwood, S J (Butcher Andrews) *W*
Fakenham *p223* 01328 863131

Unger, Ms H (Simmons & Simmons)
London EC2 *p79* 020 7628 2020

Unnisa, Mrs F (The Watson Ramsbottom Partnership) *K1*
Blackburn *p146* 01254 672222
Darwen *p207* 01254 701111

Unsworth, A K (Norton & Co) *B1 Zc C1 S2 E F1 J1 K2 L Q N S1 V W*
Prescot *p356* 0151 426 7001

Unsworth, Ms E L (Bryan Cave) *C1 C2*
London EC2 *p19* 020 7207 1100

Unsworth, I T (Renders) *S1 G H W*
Cardiff *p180* 029 2054 4900

Unsworth, M B (Maxwell Hodge Solicitors) *F1 C1 O Q F2 Zq N*
Liverpool *p289* 0151 227 4545

Unsworth, P M (Unsworth Rose) *S1 E R1*
Camden *p89* 020 7483 4411

Unsworth, Miss S J (Scott Bailey)
Lymington *p296* 01590 676933

Unuefa, G (S Ali & Company Solicitors)
Haringey *p5* 020 8340 5544

Unwin, M S (Mundays LLP) *E S1 L*
Cobham *p196* 01932 590500

Unwin, Miss P C (Girlings) *K1*
Ashford *p119* 01233 647377

Unwin, S J (Hough Halton & Soal) *J1*
Carlisle *p182* 01228 524379

Unwin, S J T (Andrew Jackson) *E*
Hull *p257* 01482 325242

Unwin, W R C (Battens) *A1 J1 L*
Yeovil *p443* 01935 846000

Upadhyaya, M (Markand & Co) *E S1 W G R1 L Zi Zl*
London E7 *p58* 020 8470 1422

Upfield, C M (Coffin Mew & Clover) *D1 K1 V*
Fareham *p223* 01329 825617

Upfold, Mrs A K (Hine Downing Solicitors) *S1 E L A1 S2 C1*
Falmouth *p223* 01326 316655

Upfold, M (Shoosmiths) *N*
Northampton *p332* . . 0370 086 3000 / 01604 543000

Uphill, L (Bishop & Sewell LLP) *L*
London WC1 *p13* 020 7631 4141

Upil, J (Prospect Solicitors) *S1*
London W4 *p69* 020 8899 6063

Uppal, C S (Squire Sanders (UK) LLP)
Leeds *p277* 0113 284 7000

Uppal, Mrs K (Thompsons (formerly Robin/Brian Thompson & Partners)) *N Zr*
Stoke-on-Trent *p398* 01782 406200

Uppal, R (Parker Bird Gardner) *D2 D1 K3 K1 Zi*
Huddersfield *p256* 01484 825200

Uppal, Ms S (Thomas Andrew & Daodu Solicitors) *J1 K1 N Q L S1 H F2 D1 J2 Zp Zi*
Westminster *p87* 020 7224 9522

Uppal, Ms S S (Chambers Solicitors)
Slough *p381* 01753 522204

Uprichard, A (Irwin Mitchell LLP) *C1 C2 Zd Zu Zs Zw*
Sheffield *p376* 0870 150 0100
Leeds *p277* 0113 283 2500

Upson, S N (Stewarts Law LLP) *O Q A3*
London EC4 *p83* 020 7822 8000

Upton, J (McDonalds Restaurants Ltd)
London N2 *p107* 0870 241 3300

Upton, J A (Hill Dickinson LLP) *J1*
Manchester *p305* 0161 817 7200

Upton, Mrs J A (W F Smith LLP) *G H S1*
Watton *p424* 01953 880800
Dereham *p209* 01362 852900

Upton, N A (SJ Berwin LLP)
London EC4 *p75* 020 7111 2222

Upton, Ms S (Lyons Davidson)
Bristol *p163* 0117 904 6000

Upton, S C (Hodge Jones & Allen LLP) *D2 D1 K1 K2 K3*
London NW1 *p41* 020 7874 8300

Ure, J (Alun James & Co) *C1 E S1*
Uxbridge *p417* 01895 811511

Uren, Mrs S H (Harding Evans LLP) *Zr*
Newport *p328* 01633 244233

Urpeth, D J (Irwin Mitchell LLP) *N*
Sheffield *p376* 0870 150 0100

Ursell, Mrs L E (Wannop Fox Staffurth & Bray) *D1 K1*
Worthing *p442* 01903 228200

Urwin, A (Ince & Co Services Ltd)
London E1 *p44* 020 7481 0010

Urwin, Ms J L (Pannone LLP) *N Zr*
Manchester *p308* 0161 909 3000

Urwin, N D (Lee Bolton Monier-Williams) *C1 Ze Zf I*
Westminster *p52* 020 7222 5381

Urwin, P B (E D C Lord & Co) *S1 E L N P K1 H W C1*
Ealing *p55* 020 8579 9292
Hayes *p245* 020 8848 9988

Usden, W S (Nicholls Henstock & Stevenson)
Altrincham *p117* 0161 980 6099

Usewicz, Ms A (Hodge Jones & Allen LLP)
London NW1 *p41* 020 7874 8300

Usher, Mrs A C (The International Family Law Group) *K1 M2 K3 D1 D2 K2*
London WC2 *p45* 020 3178 5668
London E1 *p71* 020 3060 6000

Usher, Mrs C F (DLA Piper UK LLP)
London EC2 *p24* 0870 011 1111

Usher, Miss C J (Hindle Campbell) *D1 K1 D2*
North Shields *p330* 0191 296 1777

Usher, G (Field Fisher Waterhouse LLP)
London EC3 *p31* 020 7861 4000

Usher, V (R A W Clark & Co) *G H L M1 S1*
Morpeth *p319* 01670 512391

Usher-Warren, Mrs E C R (Trobridges) *K1 K3 D1*
Plymouth *p350* 01752 664022

Usiskin, N S (Usiskin & Co) *C1 O N Q Ze*
Oxford *p344* 01865 322160

Usman, G (Cartwright King) *Zi*
Nottingham *p336* 0115 958 7444

Utting, Mrs E (Godloves) *S1 E W C1 L*
Leeds *p273* 0113 225 8811
Leeds *p273* 0113 286 8822

Uttridge, Ms L S J (Max Barford & Co) *Q O*
Tunbridge Wells *p414* 01892 539379

Uwaifo, Mrs E A (Sidley Austin Brown & Wood) *Zb*
London EC2 *p78* 020 7360 3600

Uwins, J T (CMS Cameron McKenna LLP)
London EC3 *p17* 020 7367 3000

V

Vaccaro, Ms H M (Cheshire County Council)
Chester *p454* 01244 602382

Vachino, Ms C (The Royal Borough of Kensington & Chelsea)
London W8 *p109* 020 7361 2741

Vadgama, A (Hayman Solicitors)
Guildford *p236* 01483 600900

Vadher, B N D (Jay Vadher & Co) *C1 D1 E F1 G H J1 K1 Q S1 Zi Zl Zc*
London E15 *p89* 020 8519 3000

Vadher, R B (Jay Vadher & Co) *S1 S2 R2 K1 E W Zl*
London E15 *p89* 020 8519 3000

Vagjiani, Ms G (The Law Partnership) *K1 Q K3 L W N Zq F1 B1*
Harrow *p242* 020 8416 7004

Vaitilingam, J (Hughes Fowler Carruthers) *K1 K3*
London WC2 *p43* 020 7421 8383

Vala, R K (Jeffrey Green Russell) *E R1 Zb Zs Zc*
London W1 *p46* 020 7339 7000

Valcin, Mrs L M (Colemans - CTTS) *J1 O Q Zi Zp*
Kingston upon Thames *p267*. 020 8296 9966

Vale, Mrs B C (Luton Borough Council)
Luton *p464* 01582 546000

Vale, Miss C (Lanyon Bowdler LLP) *N O Q F1 Zp*
Shrewsbury *p379* 01743 280280

Vale, Miss C F (BLB Solicitors)
Swindon *p406* 01793 615011

Vale, R W (Stevenage Borough Council)
Stevenage *p472* 01438 242242

Valente, N H (Curry Popeck) *S1 W S2*
Kenton *p264* . . .020 8907 2000 / 8907 8896

Valente, Ms S (Canter Levin & Berg) *L*
Liverpool *p287* 0151 239 1000

Valentine, Mrs A V (Black Rock)
London EC4 *p104* 020 7743 3000

Valentine, D S (Hadfields Butt & Bowyer) *S1 E W L Zv*
Farnham *p225* 01252 716101

Valentine, K (Pinsent Masons LLP) *A3 Zc O*
London EC2 *p67* 020 7418 7000

Valentine, Miss R E (Buckinghamshire County Council)
Aylesbury *p448* 01296 383653

Valenzuela, Miss T L (Aspinall & Co)
Bolton *p148* 01204 388200

Valero, A (Nockolds) *M1 Zw M2 O Q*
Bishop's Stortford *p144* . . . 01279 755777

Valimahomed, A (Amphlett Lissimore) *Q S1 S2*
Croydon *p6* 020 8771 5254

Vallance, L Z (Caunters) *Q N K1 Zl O L K3*
Liskeard *p285* . . . .01579 343165 / 343484

Vallance, R A (Charles Russell LLP) *N Q*
London EC4 *p19* 020 7203 5000

Vallely, Mrs C (Vallelys) *K1 D1 J1 V F1*
Letchworth *p283* 01462 483800

Vallgren, Mrs M E (Hansells) *W T2*
Norwich *p334* 01603 615731

Vallings, R R (Radcliffes Le Brasseur) *T2 W*
Westminster *p70* 020 7222 7040

Vallis, H A (Bailey & Cogger) *W T2 K4*
Tonbridge *p412* 01732 353305

Vallow, M P (Turners) *S1 S2 W*
Cross Hills *p204* 01535 634149

Valmond, Ms C (Salans) *E R1 L S1*
London EC4 *p76* 020 7429 6000

Vamplew, T J C (John Barkers) *G H*
Louth *p294* 01507 604773
Mablethorpe *p297* 01507 477673

Van, G (Tickle Hall Cross)
St Helens *p391* 0800 854379

Van Baskerville, G S (Ramsbottom & Co Solicitors Limited) *W Zl*
Hayling Island *p245* 023 9246 5931

Van De Weyer, Mrs M (Newbold & Co) *K1 N S1 Q J1 L D1 F1 J2 W*
Cwmbran *p206* 01633 874715

Van Den Berg, Miss A M (Cadbury Schweppes PLC (Legal Dept))
Birmingham *p449* 0121 625 7000

Van Den Berg, Ms S (Gowmans) *K3 K1*
Paignton *p345* 01803 546100

Van der Borgh, N (CVS Solicitors)
London W1 *p17* 020 7493 2903

Van Der Breggen, C (Reynolds Porter Chamberlain LLP)
London E1 *p71* 020 3060 6000

Van der Feijst, Mrs C G (Lincolnshire County Council Resources - Legal Services)
Lincoln *p463* 01522 552222

van der Klugt, Ms D E (The College of Law Guildford)
Guildford *p459* 01483 460200

Van Der Meer, A W (Streathers Solicitors LLP) *O N B1 C1 Ze Zf Zl*
London W1 *p84* 020 7034 4200

Van der Velde, Mrs E (Geoffrey Forrester & Co) *D1 F1 G H K1 N Q S1 V W Zb Zh*
South Shields *p383* 0191 456 2255

Van Der Weit, Mrs E (Hameed & Co) *V Q K1 J1 L W M1 K2 D1 F1 O*
London NW10 *p38* 020 8830 1335

Van der Zyl, Mrs M S (Davenport Lyons)
London W1 *p25* 020 7468 2600

Van Kesteren, Ms M (Linklaters LLP)
London EC2 *p54* 020 7456 2000

Van Reesh, P (Coca-Cola Enterprises Ltd)
Uxbridge *p474* 01895 231313

Van Schoote, Ms C (Simmons & Simmons)
London EC2 *p79* 020 7628 2020

Van Til Leedham, Mrs S J D (Chubb Insurance Company of Europe S.A.)
London EC3 *p105* 020 7956 5000

Van Vessem, Ms M (Barcan Woodward) *N Zr*
Bristol *p161* 0117 925 8080

van Wely, Ms A M (Sansbury Douglas) *G H*
Knowle *p269* 0117 963 5044
Bristol *p164* 0117 955 2663

Van Zyl, J (Short Richardson & Forth LLP) *J1*
Newcastle upon Tyne *p326* . 0191 232 0283

Vance, M C L (Bunzl PLC) *C2 U2 Zb*
London W1 *p104* 020 7725 5000

Vance, S P S (Vance Harris) *S1 S2*
Crowborough *p204* 01892 653434

Vandaele, M (R N Williams & Co Limited) *K1 K3 Q S1 W*
Wolverhampton *p438* 01902 429051

Vandale, Ms F (Langleys) *A1 C1 E S1*
Lincoln *p284* 01522 888555

Vander Cruyssen, Ms D K D (Reynolds Porter Chamberlain LLP) *C1 C2 C3 I Ze*
London E1 *p71* 020 3060 6000

Vandermark, S N (Nelsons) *O Q Ze B1*
Nottingham *p338* 0115 958 6262

Vandersteen, Mrs S E (Field Seymour Parkes) *C1 T1 J1 Ze I Zd X*
Reading *p360* 0118 951 6200

Vandervlies, Ms J (The College of Law)
London WC1 *p105* 0800 289997

Vandrewala, Z (KJD)
Stoke-on-Trent *p398* 01782 202020

Vangeen, Mrs M (Solomon Taylor & Shaw) *J1 Zi*
London NW3 *p80* 020 7431 1912

Vanheems, Miss J G D A (Bower & Bailey) *S1 S2 E W*
Banbury *p122* 01295 265566

Vanhees, A R I (Sydney G Thomas & Co) *S1 A1 K1 L W T1*
Builth Wells *p168* 01982 553289

Vania, N A (Alsters Kelley) *G*
Nuneaton *p339* 0844 561 0100

Vann Jones, A D G (3M Health Care Ltd)
Loughborough *p463* 01509 611611

Vannelli, Ms E (Barlow Lyde & Gilbert LLP)
London EC3 *p10* 020 7247 2277

Van't Goor, Ms M C (Marina C Van't Goor) *D1 K1 H G V L J1 W N*
Milford Haven *p316* 01646 697700

Vantyghem, J E (FDR Ltd)
Basildon *p448* 01268 296431

Vaqueiro, Mrs E J (Lodders Solicitors LLP) *K4 W*
Stratford-upon-Avon *p400* . . 01789 293259

Varachhia, A R (Lin & Co Solicitors) *Zi K1 K3 S2 L S1*
Sutton Coldfield *p403* 0121 244 2300

Varaitch, K (IBB Solicitors)
Uxbridge *p417* 0845 638 1381

Varco, Ms P (Fishburns) *Zj O Q Zu A3 Zc*
London EC3 *p32* 020 7280 8888

Varcoe, Ms P (Fishburns) *Zc Zj O Q*
London EC3 *p32* 020 7280 8888

Varcoe-Cocks, M D (Wyeth)
Maidenhead *p464* 01628 604377

Vareis-Tharmaraj, Mrs D (British Telecommunications PLC)
London EC1 *p104* 020 7356 6181

Varholy, J (Troutman Sanders LLP)
London EC2 *p88* 020 7038 6650

Varia, M (Travers Smith LLP) *T1*
London EC1 *p87* 020 7295 3000

Varley, A S (VHS Fletchers Solicitors) *G H*
Nottingham *p339* 0115 959 9550

Varley, C J (Walker Foster) *S1 J1 E S2*
Skipton *p381* 01756 700200

Varley, J (Salans) *B1*
London EC4 *p76* 020 7429 6000

Varley, M P (Thomson Snell & Passmore) *C1 C2 C3 F1*
Tunbridge Wells *p415* 01892 510000

Varma, Miss N (Arnold Fooks Chadwick LLP) *N Zr*
London W1 *p7* 020 7499 3007

Varma, S (Clifford Harris & Co)
London W1 *p21* 020 7486 0031

Varoujian, R (Field Fisher Waterhouse LLP)
London EC3 *p31* 020 7861 4000

Vartoukian, Miss R (Field Fisher Waterhouse LLP)
London EC3 *p31* 020 7861 4000

Varuna Sanjaya, S (Taylor Wessing)
London EC4 *p86* 020 7300 7000

Vary, Ms T (Keoghs LLP) *B2*
Bolton *p149* 01204 677000

Vashisht, Ms A (The Bank of Tokyo Mitsubishi UFJ Ltd)
London EC2 *p104* 020 7330 5000

Vasisht, Ms A (Wilson & Co) *Zi*
London N17 *p92* 020 8808 7535

Vasishta, T (Paragon Law) *X K4 J1 Q Zu Zm Zi*
Nottingham *p338* 0115 964 4123

Vasmer, Mrs R M (Walker Smith Way) *Zr N*
Wrexham *p443* 0844 346 3100

Vassall, Miss C E (Chamberlain Martin Solicitors) *D1 K1 V*
Bognor Regis *p148* 01243 825211

Vassallo, Miss J M (TWM Solicitors LLP) *O Q*
London SW19 *p85* 020 8946 6454

Vassell, R (Simmons & Simmons) *J1 O X Zo*
London EC2 *p79* 020 7628 2020

Vassie, Ms H (TV Edwards LLP)
London SE8 *p85* 020 7790 7000

Vassou, V M (Charles Ross Solicitors)
Barnet *p124* 020 8216 2300

Vaswani, Ms M B A (Allen & Overy LLP)
London E1 *p5* 020 3088 0000

Vaughan, A (Hodge Jones & Allen LLP) *D2 D1 K1 K2 K3*
London NW1 *p41* 020 7874 8300

Vaughan, Ms A E (Campbell Hooper & Co LLP) *S1 W*
Sunningdale *p402* 01344 622141

Vaughan, A T W (British Telecommunications PLC)
London EC1 *p104* 020 7356 6181

Vaughan, C (Swayne Johnson Solicitors)
Denbigh *p208* 01745 812835

Vaughan, C J (The Notaries Society) *S1 E W A1 C1*
Woodbridge *p477* 01394 380436
Northampton *p331* 01604 750506

Vaughan, D J (Gabb & Co) *E A1 S1 R1 C1 T1 W*
Abergavenny *p113* 01873 852432

Vaughan, E G (Glovers Solicitors LLP) *Zq O*
London W1 *p36* 020 7935 8882

Vaughan, J A S (Fladgate LLP) *C1 C2 W*
London WC2 *p32* 020 3036 7000

Vaughan, J G (South Gloucestershire Council) *R1*
Thornbury *p474* 01454 868686

 See p634 for the Key to Work Categories

Vaughan, K J (Bird Wilford & Sale) *C1 C2 E U2 S2 T1*
Loughborough *p293* 01509 232611

Vaughan, N J (Paris Smith LLP) *E L Zd R2 S2 Zb*
Southampton *p386*. 023 8048 2482

Vaughan, P J H (Simmons & Simmons) *O M1 Q*
London EC2 *p79*. 020 7628 2020

Vaughan, Miss R (Herrington & Carmichael LLP) *C1 F1 C3 I Ze B1 C2 U2 Zza Zb F2 Zw*
Wokingham *p437* 0118 977 4045

Vaughan, R H (Rhys Vaughan) *G H K1 D1*
Manchester *p311* 0161 224 1439

Vaughan, R J (Battens) *E*
Yeovil *p443* 01935 846000

Vaughan, T R (Scott Fowler) *O N Q K1 J1 C1 H G Zl Ze Zk K3 Zq*
Northampton *p331*. 01604 750506

Vaughan, W N P (Powys County Council)
Llandrindod Wells *p463* . . . 01597 826000

Vaughan-Birch, D (Cleggs) *F1 F2 Ze J1 L O I C1*
Nottingham *p336*. 0115 977 5877

Vaughan-Brown, Miss J N G (Peters & Peters) *B2*
London EC4 *p67*. 020 7629 7991

Vause, C M (Maclay Murray & Spens LLP)
London EC2 *p57*. 020 7002 8500

Vautier, D D A (Brown & Vautier) *D1 K1 J1 K3 S1 S2 E C1 K4 O Q N W*
Frome *p227* 01373 465222

Vautier, Mrs H (London Borough of Greenwich Legal Services)
London SE18 *p106* 020 8921 5123

Vaux, C G (Punch Robson) *E J1 C1 S1 A1 Zi C2*
Middlesbrough *p315*. 01642 230700

Vaux, K (Freers) *C1 R1 E S1 G H J1 K1 L W Zl*
Middlesbrough *p315*. 01642 244666

Vaux, R (Freers) *G H N Q V*
Middlesbrough *p315*. 01642 244666

Vayro, D A (Squire Sanders (UK) LLP)
Manchester *p310* 0161 830 5000

Veakins, S P D (Place Blair & Hatch) *N Q K1 G S1 F1 J1*
Northallerton *p331*. 01609 780101

Veale, J (Kangs Solicitors) *G H B2 S1*
Birmingham *p139* 0121 449 9888

Veale, P J (Clerical Medical Investment Group)
London EC2 *p105* 020 7321 1425

Veall, Miss M D (Sweeney Miller) *W K4*
Sunderland *p402*. 0191 568 2050

Veasey, Ms E (Barratt Goff & Tomlinson) *N Zr*
Nottingham *p335*. 0115 931 5171

Veasey, J P (Mossop & Bowser) *K1 D1 O Q Zq*
Holbeach *p251*. 01406 422651

Vecerova, V (CKFT) *E S1*
London NW3 *p17* 020 7431 7262

Ved, V (Frank Forney & Partners LLP) *E G K1 N P H L W S1 B1 Zi*
Haringey *p33* . . .020 8889 1971 / 8888 5481
London NW10 *p89*. 020 8459 8686

Vedy, Miss H A (Alsters Kelley) *M1 P K1 W*
Leamington Spa *p270* 0844 561 0100

Veevers, Mrs S E (Maxwell Hodge Solicitors) *J1 O Q N Zq*
Liverpool *p289*. 0151 227 4545

Veiga, Ms G (Plexus Law (A Trading Name of Parabis Law LLP)) *N Q T2*
London EC3 *p68*. 0844 245 4000

Veitch, A M (Guy Clapham & Co) *N Q J1 S1 L B1 W*
London W1 *p20* 020 7935 1095

Veitch, C J (David Gray Solicitors) *S1 W S2 K4 Zd Zl*
Newcastle upon Tyne *p324* . 0191 232 9547

Veitch, M H (Maxwell Winward LLP) *Zc*
London EC4 *p59*. 020 7651 0000

Veja, R (Veja & Co Solicitors) *G H*
Hayes *p245* 020 8581 1502

Venables, Miss A E (Forshaws Davies Ridgway LLP) *S1 K1 W G L P J1*
Warrington *p422*. 01925 230000

Venables, H (DWF)
Manchester *p303* 0161 603 5000

Venables, H V (Sylvester Mackett) *E*
Trowbridge *p414*. 01225 755621

Venables, Ms L (Department for Business, Enterprise and Regulatory Reform)
London SW1 *p105*. 020 7215 0105

Venables, P (Enoch Evans LLP) *K1 V W*
Walsall *p420*. 01922 720333

Venables, R C (Bircham Dyson Bell)
Westminster *p13*. 020 7227 7000

Venables, Miss S J (Ward & Rider Limited) *J1*
Coventry *p201*. 024 7655 5400

Vengadesan, J (Penningtons) *Ze*
Basingstoke *p127* 01256 407100

Venters, Ms J M (Venters Solicitors) *D1 D2 G H K1 K2 W*
London SE5 *p89*. 020 7277 0110
Reigate *p363* 01737 229610

Vercoe, Miss S C (Anthony Collins Solicitors LLP) *E L Zh*
Birmingham *p137* 0121 200 3242

Verdi, Mrs S (Palmers) *K1 K3*
Basildon *p126*. 01268 240000

Verdin, M J (Nyland & Beattie) *Q N*
Widnes *p432*. 0151 424 5656

Verdu De Haro, A (HC Solicitors LLP) *O Q T2*
Peterborough *p347* 01733 882800

Vergette, N (Nabarro LLP)
London WC1 *p63* 020 7524 6000

Verhagen, Ms A (Goad & Butcher) *A1 E K4 S1 W*
Settle *p374* 01729 823500

Verity, D A (Foys Solicitors) *D1 K1 G H Zl B2*
Worksop *p441*. 01909 473560

Verity, Miss L (Hornby & Levy) *D1 D2 K1 X*
London SW9 *p43* 020 7737 0909

Verity, M D (Davitt Jones Bould) *E*
Taunton *p408* 01823 279279

Verity, S A (Last Cawthra Feather LLP) *E L S1 W*
Bradford *p154*. 01274 848800

Verlander, P (Carpenter & Co) *B1 C1 J1 L Zk Zl O Q N Zq Zp*
Wallington *p419* 020 8669 5145

Verma, A (McGrath Litigation Partnership) *N*
Birmingham *p140* 0121 643 4828

Verma, P (Verma & Co) *E L S1 W Zi Zl*
Wembley *p427*. 020 8903 0309

Verma, P (Field Seymour Parkes) *S2 E S1*
Reading *p360* 0118 951 6200

Verma, V K (Barker Gillette) *G B2*
London W1 *p9*. 020 7636 0555

Vermeulen, Ms L (Matthew & Matthew Limited) *E S1*
Southbourne *p387* 01202 431943

Vernall, Mrs L K (Kemp Little LLP) *C1 C2 U1 U2 I Zb*
London EC2 *p48*. 020 7600 8080

Vernalls, Ms P (Brown & Vautier) *N Q O W L K4 J1 J2 B1*
Frome *p227* 01373 465222

Vernede, D (Darbys Solicitors LLP) *W T2 K4*
Oxford *p343*. 01865 811700

Vernell, M L (Watson Farley & Williams)
London EC2 *p90*. 020 7814 8000

Verney, Mrs M C (Charles Lucas & Marshall) *W K4*
Newbury *p322*. 01635 521212

Vernick, V N (Bude Nathan Iwanier) *E L O S1 Zc Zb*
London NW11 *p16*. 020 8458 5656

Vernon, A C (FBC Manby Bowdler LLP) *T2 W Zo*
Wolverhampton *p437* 01902 578000

Vernon, Miss B J M (Flintshire County Council)
Mold *p466*. 01352 702411

Vernon, C (Girlings) *W*
Canterbury *p177*. 01227 768374

Vernon, Miss C A (Kennedys)
London EC3 *p49*. 020 7667 9667

Vernon, Miss C F (Hunters) *Zd C1 J1 O*
London WC2 *p44* 020 7412 0050

Vernon, C S (Buller Jeffries) *S2 E S1 W R2 L*
Birmingham *p136* 0121 212 2620

Vernon, Mrs H (Hill Dickinson LLP) *E S1 L*
London EC3 *p41*. 020 7283 9033

Vernon, Miss J L (FBC Manby Bowdler LLP) *K1*
Wolverhampton *p437* 01902 578000

Vernon, J P (Beale and Company Solicitors LLP) *Zq O Zc Zj*
London WC2 *p11* 020 7240 3474

Vernon, P (Merseyside Police)
Liverpool *p463*. 0151 777 8080

Vernon, P W (Ashurst LLP)
London EC2 *p7* 020 7638 1111

Vernon, Ms R (Thomson Snell & Passmore) *C1*
Tunbridge Wells *p415* 01892 510000

Vernon, R (Buckles Solicitors LLP) *E Ze K4 K1 Q W*
Peterborough *p346* 01733 888888

Vernon, R D (Ashurst LLP) *B1 E*
London EC2 *p7* 020 7638 1111

Vernon-Hunt, J M (Brighton & Hove Council - Legal Services)
Hove *p461*. 01273 290000

Vernor-Miles, J C (Hunters) *S1 S2 Zd*
London WC2 *p44* 020 7412 0050

Vernor-Miles, J C (Hunters) *W T2 Zd*
London WC2 *p44* 020 7412 0050

Vernor-Miles, W E (Hunters) *W T2 Zd*
London WC2 *p44* 020 7412 0050

Verrill, J R (LG Lawyers) *B1 C1 Zg Zn*
London SE1 *p50*. 020 7379 0000

Verrinder, K (Roach Pittis) *G H*
Newport *p328* 01983 524431

Vertigan, J M O (Purdys) *S1 E W C1 A1 L*
Reepham *p363* 01603 870606

Vertigen, J (Simmons & Simmons)
London EC2 *p79*. 020 7628 2020

Vervitsioti, Ms K (Watson Farley & Williams)
London EC2 *p90*. 020 7814 8000

Vervoorts, Mrs A A (Bhatia Best) *G H*
Nottingham *p336*. 0115 950 3231

Vesely, M W (Hellewell Pasley & Brewer) *C1 S1 W L O S2 E Zc Zl Zk Zv*
Dewsbury *p210* 01924 455515

Vesely, Mrs S F (Hellewell Pasley & Brewer) *K1 D1 S1 W Zl Zm Zv V K2*
Dewsbury *p210* 01924 455515

Vesey, Ms M E (Shacklocks) *J1 Zp O*
Mansfield *p312* 01623 626141

Vexter, Ms D A (London Fire & Emergency Planning Authority)
London SE1 *p107* 020 8555 1200

Veysey, G (Field Fisher Waterhouse LLP)
London EC3 *p31*. 020 7861 4000

Veysey, P E (Dolmans) *N*
Cardiff *p178* 029 2034 5531

Veysey, Ms S A (Atherton Godfrey) *Zr N*
Doncaster *p211* 01302 320621

Veysey, S J (Mogers) *M1 P N F1 J1 L Zl Zc Ze O*
Bath *p127*. 01225 750000

Vialls, P R M (Wilkinson & Butler) *G N H J1 Q O F1*
St Neots *p392*. 01480 219229

Vicary, I S (Weightmans LLP) *C1 C2 C3 F1 J1 T1 Zb Ze Zv*
Liverpool *p291*. 0151 227 2601

Vick, L N (Michelmores LLP) *Zr N*
Exeter *p221* 01392 688688

Vickerman, Miss C A (Glaisyers Solicitors LLP) *K1 K2*
Manchester *p304* 0161 224 3311

Vickerman, J R (Fox Williams) *C1*
London EC2 *p33*. 020 7628 2000

Vickers, A (O'Garra's) *G H K1 K2 K3*
Leeds *p276* 0113 247 1477

Vickers, A J T (Burton Copeland LLP) *G H*
Manchester *p302* 0161 827 9500

Vickers, C (Canter Levin & Berg)
Liverpool *p287*. 0151 239 1000

Vickers, Ms C H (Shacklocks) *C1 I U2 Zj X*
Belper *p131* 01773 822333

Vickers, Miss C J (Pinsent Masons LLP) *E L*
Bristol *p164* 0117 924 5678

Vickers, J H (Swayne Johnson Solicitors) *S1 W S2 E*
Llandudno *p291* 01492 876271

Vickers, Mrs L E (Vickers & Co) *K1 S1 W T1 B1 C1 D1 G P Zh*
Ealing *p89*. . .020 8579 2559 / 8840 3999

Vickers, M H (Ashurst LLP) *C1 Zb*
London EC2 *p7* 020 7638 1111

Vickers, N E (SNR Denton) *C2*
London EC4 *p75*. 020 7242 1212

Vickers, Mrs N M (Kennedys) *O*
London EC3 *p49*. 020 7667 9667

Vickers, P (Paul Robinson Solicitors) *G H*
Westcliff-on-Sea *p428* 01702 338338

Vickers, P D (Stockdale & Reid Ltd) *S2 E C1 W S1 L*
Monkseaton *p318* 0191 251 9494

Vickers, P G (HSR Law (Hayes, Son & Richmond)) *S1 E W A1 L Zc*
Gainsborough *p228* 01427 613831
Doncaster *p211* 01302 347800

Vickers, S G (Middlesbrough Council) *M1 P N G H B1 C1 W F1 K1 Zl Zc Zj*
Middlesbrough *p465* 01642 245432

Vickers, Mrs S M (Wilkin Chapman Grange Solicitors) *W*
Louth *p294* 01507 606161

Vickers, T (Vickers Chisman & Wishlade) *K1 G M1 H P S1 D1 C1 W L Zc Zl*
Stockton-on-Tees *p397* . . . 01642 615439

Vickers, T R (Aviva PLC)
London EC3 *p103* . . 020 7283 7500 / 01603 687905
Norwich *p467* 01603 622200

Vickery, A B (Trowers & Hamlins) *Zc*
London EC3 *p88*. 020 7423 8000

Vickery, Ms C M J (Capsticks Solicitors LLP) *C1 Zd I Ze M1*
London SW19 *p18*. 020 8780 2211

Vickery, C R L (Whatley Weston & Fox) *E R2 S1*
Worcester *p440* 01905 731731

Vickery, D (Sheehans Solicitors) *D1 N Q W Zq*
Neath *p320* 01639 630844
Port Talbot *p353* 01639 883237

Vickery, J (DLA Piper UK LLP)
Liverpool *p287*. 0870 011 1111

Vickery, Mrs M (Devon County Council)
Exeter *p458* 01392 382000

Vickery, R A (Humphrys & Co) *G H K1 N D1 Q F1 J1 L S1 Zq Zl Zp*
Rhyl *p363* 01745 343158

Vickery, Mrs S J (Lancashire County Council) *K1 N L*
Preston *p469* 01772 254868
Stafford *p472* 01785 223121

Vickery, Miss V P (The College of Law) *K1 D1*
London WC1 *p105*. 0800 289997

Vidal, R (Squire Sanders (UK) LLP)
London EC2 *p81*. 020 7655 1000

Videon, Ms A (DLA Piper UK LLP)
London EC2 *p24*. 0870 011 1111

Vidgen, A D (Harvey Son & Filby) *W S1 K4 S2*
Ipswich *p262*. 01473 712962

Vidnes, E S K (Burningham & Brown) *W*
Bath *p127* 01225 320090

Vienot, Miss J A (Kendall & Davies) *W S1*
Burford *p168*. 01993 822025

Vietri, U (AWB Charlesworth LLP) *C1 C2 F1 I J1 Zb Zd Ze Zw*
Keighley *p263* 01535 613678

Vig, Miss R J K (Watson Farley & Williams) *E*
London EC2 *p90*. 020 7814 8000

Vigneswaran, A (Waran & Co) *E W*
London SW4 *p90* 020 7498 3328

Vigrass, C (Ashurst LLP) *O Q B1 Zc Zb Zj*
London EC2 *p7* 020 7638 1111

Vijayapalan, M V (Vijayapalans) *S1 W Q Zi*
Hounslow *p254* 020 8755 3239

Vijayapalan, Mrs Y (Vijayapalans) *S1 E W L Q V Zi Zl*
Hounslow *p254* 020 8755 3239

Village, G A (hlw Keeble Hawson LLP) *E S2*
Sheffield *p376* 0114 276 5555

Vilvaraj, Mrs S (Nag & Co Solicitors)
London SW9 *p63* 020 7737 1211

Vinall-Morgan, Mrs K A M (Neale Turk Rochfort) *S1 R1*
Farnborough *p224*. 01252 515155

Vince, P R (PR Vince Solicitors) *S1 E C1 W O N Q A1 L*
Forest Row *p227* 01342 822112

Vincent, Miss A (Gabbs LLP) *K1 K3 Q N Zq S1 J1*
Leominster *p282*. 01568 616333

Vincent, C A (Girlings) *J1*
Ashford *p119* 01233 664711

Vincent, G W (Bircham Dyson Bell)
Westminster *p13*. 020 7227 7000

Vincent, Mrs H (Jasper & Vincent) *N Zq Zr*
Southampton *p386*. 01489 885788

Vincent, Mrs K (Nuffield Hospitals)
Surbiton *p473* 020 8390 1200

Vincent, K G (Wilson & Co) *G H B2*
London N17 *p92*. 020 8808 7535

Vincent, K J (Prettys) *C1 C2*
Ipswich *p262*. 01473 232121

Vincent, M (Weightmans LLP) *C1*
Manchester *p311* 0161 233 7330

Vincent, Ms M P (Harold Benjamin) *K1 Q O N W J1 C1 B1 Zl*
Harrow *p241*. 020 8422 5678

Vincent, M T (Jasper & Vincent) *B1 C1 G H N*
Southampton *p386*. 01489 885788

Vincent, P H (Wrigley Claydon) *A1 C1 E J1 L M1 P R1 S1 T1 Zc Ze Zh*
Oldham *p341* 0161 624 6811

Vincent, Ms S (Rollingsons) *N*
London EC1 *p73*. 020 7611 4848

Vincent, Mrs S G (Northamptonshire Magistrates Courts)
Northampton *p467*. 01604 497000

Vine, C M (Winckworth Sherwood LLP)
London SE1 *p92*. 020 7593 5000

Vine, Mrs G (Farleys Solicitors LLP) *Zg Q*
Manchester *p304* 0161 660 4254

Vine, R H W (Middleton & Upsall LLP) *S1 A1 R1 W L E*
Warminster *p421*. 01985 214444

Vine, R S (Gardner Croft LLP) *E C1 L R1 S1 S2*
Canterbury *p176*. 01227 813400

Viner, C G (Millichips) *S1 E L C1 W R1*
West Bromwich *p427* 0121 500 6363

Viner, P T (Thomson Snell & Passmore) *E A1 P*
Tunbridge Wells *p415* 01892 510000

Viney, R F (DAC Beachcroft) *O Q M1 P Zj*
London EC4 *p24*. 020 7936 2222

Vingoe, A G (Vingoe Lloyd Solicitors) *D1 K1 K3*
Hayle *p245* 01736 754075

Vingoe, P G (Goughs) *S1 E W C1 L M1 R1 F1 K1*
Trowbridge *p414*. 01225 762683

Vining, R L (Crown Prosecution Service Avon & Somerset)
Bristol *p451* 0117 930 2800

Vinsen, Miss J (Fox Williams)
London EC2 *p33*. 020 7628 2000

Vinter, G D (Allen & Overy LLP)
London E1 *p5* 020 3088 0000

Vinti, M (Sydney Mitchell) *K1*
Birmingham *p142* 0121 698 2200 / 0808 166 8827

Vintner, B S (Worsdell & Vintner) *C1 E S2 S1*
Harefield *p239*. 01895 824713
Ickenham *p259* 01895 672631

Vipan, M R A (DLA Piper UK LLP) *C1 C2*
Leeds *p272* 0870 011 1111

Vipan, R F M (Chattertons Solicitors) *C1 E A1 S1 W P B1 J1 L M1 Zc Zj Zl Zt*
Stamford *p393*. 01780 764145

Vipas, K E (G Cartwright & Co) *Q O W J1 K1*
Chatteris *p185*. 01354 692607

Virani-Bland, Mrs N (Brethertons LLP) *W T1 A1 Zd*
Rugby *p368* 01788 579579
Rugby *p368* 01788 579579

Virdee, Mrs G K (The Paragon Group of Companies PLC)
Solihull *p471*. 0121 711 3333

Virdee, M (Reemans Solicitors) *E S2 C1 K3 K1 L Zi*
Hounslow *p254* 020 8622 3638

Virdee, S (Simon Crosfield & Co)
Ripon *p365* 01765 692277

Virgin, Z A (Mills & Reeve) *C1 C2 Zb Zw U2 Ze C3 F1*
Norwich *p335* 01603 660155

Virginia, F (South Cambridgeshire District Council)
Cambridge *p453* 0845 045 0500

Visick, W A (Hedley Visick & Co) *S1 W C1 E L R1 B1*
Eastleigh *p216*. 023 8061 1133

Visintin, A O (Squire Sanders (UK) LLP) *B1 C1 E N P Zb*
London EC2 *p81*. 020 7655 1000

Viskovich, D G (ABN Amro UK Services Ltd)
London EC2 *p103* 020 7392 3500

Vitagliano, T B (Henriques Griffiths) *S1*
Winterbourne *p435*. 01454 854000

Vitta, I (Thomas Cooper) *O Za A3*
London EC3 *p22*. 020 7481 8851

Vittachi, A (Rossides Caine) *Q N K1 L F1 C1 B1 J1 S1 Zq W*
London N13 *p74*. 020 8882 9292

Vitty, S F (Courtyard Solicitors LLP) *F1 J1 L O Q*
London SW19 *p23*. 020 8946 9466

Vivian, J M (SJ Berwin LLP)
London EC4 *p75*. 020 7111 2222

Vlahos, D (Lee Bolton Monier-Williams)
Westminster *p52*. 020 7222 5381

Vnuk, S C (Fisher Meredith) *Zi Zg*
Lambeth *p32*. 020 7091 2700
Wembley *p426*. 020 8733 7200

6

For a range of specialised Legal Services please refer to Section 20

Voakes, Miss V M (Miller Parris) *E C1 S1 W Zj S2* Worthing *p442*. 01903 205771

Voce, Mrs H K (Bowcock & Pursaill) *E O Q* Hanley *p239*. 01782 200000

Vogel, D N (Dechert) *C1 C2* London EC4 *p26*. 020 7184 7000

Vogel, Ms S M (Carvers (Part of the Wilkes Partnership LLP)) *O K1 D1* Birmingham *p136* 0121 784 8484

Voisey, P G (Clifford Chance) London E14 *p20*. 020 7006 1000

Voisin, Mrs M E (Barcan Woodward) *Zr N Zq Q* Bristol *p161* 0117 925 8080

Voisin, M R M (Linklaters LLP) London EC2 *p54*. 020 7456 2000

Voke, R (Lyons Davidson) Bristol *p163* 0117 904 6000

Volikas, M (Ince & Co Services Ltd) London E1 *p44* 020 7481 0010

Voller, E (Warner Goodman LLP) *N* Southampton *p387*. 023 8063 9311

Voller, P M G (Bircham Dyson Bell) *C1 Zb Zd* Westminster *p13*. 020 7227 7000

Volokhova, Ms A (Salans) *Zb* London EC4 *p76*. 020 7429 6000

von Finckenhagen, Mrs L M M (McGuire Woods London LLP) *F2 M1 K1 N W* London EC4 *p57*. 020 7632 1600

von Hagen, D (Taylor Walton LLP) Luton *p295* 01582 731161

Von Peltz, S P (Radcliffes Le Brasseur) *E C1 L S1 R1 T1 N Zb Zc* Westminster *p70*. 020 7222 7040

Von Sauckon, D (Ashurst LLP) London EC2 *p7* 020 7638 1111

von Schmidt, Ms S (Farrer & Co LLP) London WC2 *p31* 020 3375 7000

Von Schmieder, C (Bristows) *Ze C1 U2* London EC4 *p15*. 020 7400 8000

Vooght, J (Wansbroughs) Devizes *p210* 01380 733300

Vooght, R D (Sharples & Co) *W T2 K4* Bristol *p165* 0117 942 8214

Vora, Ms B (IBB Solicitors) Uxbridge *p417*. 0845 638 1381

Vos, M S (Cripps Harries Hall LLP) *E C1 A1 C2* Tunbridge Wells *p415* 01892 515121

Vos, T R (Macfarlanes) *T1 W Zi* London EC4 *p56*. 020 7831 9222

Vosper, Mrs A P (Goldstones) *S1 R1 W* Swansea *p405*. 01792 643021

Voss, Ms M E O (Thompsons (formerly Robin/ Brian Thompson & Partners)) *N* Birmingham *p143* 0121 262 1200

Votsis, M C (YVA Solicitors) *E C2 S1 S2* London N12 *p93*. 020 8445 9898

Vouvoussiras, Ms K (Thomas Cooper) *C1 M2 Zb Zo* London EC3 *p22*. 020 7481 8851

Vowles, Miss L (PCB Solicitors LLP) *G* Shrewsbury *p379* 01743 248148

Voyce, Mrs A J (Taylor Walton LLP) *W* Luton *p295* 01582 731161

Voyle, L (Red Kite Law) *D1 K1 L N Q V* Carmarthen *p183* 01267 239000

Voznick, Ms M (London Borough of Haringey) London N22 *p106* 020 8489 0000

Vroobel, R D (Vroobel Kaye) *S1 E* Harrow *p242*. 020 8427 5006

Vyas, A (Vyman Solicitors) *O S2 C1 Zq E B1 Zb J1 B2 Ze W Zk C2 U2* Gravesend *p233*. . . . . . . 01474 537270 Harrow *p242*. 020 8427 9080

Vyas, A R (Matwala Vyas LLP) Ilford *p260*. 020 8597 5097

W

Wacher, C B (Furley Page LLP) *C2 A1 E T1 C1 R1 Zd* Canterbury *p176*. 01227 763939

Wachtel, D M P (Wachtel Fox & Co) *E S1 W B1 L R1 C1 F1* Rickmansworth *p364*. 01923 775651

Wachtel, M (Dorman Joseph Wachtel) *C1 C2 J1 Zb* London EC3 *p27*. 020 7680 6300

Wacks, D A (Wolfson & Co) *C1 E F1 G N J1 Zm Zq L O Q S1 S2 W U2* Manchester *p311* 0161 873 8999

Waddell, C Q O (Hannays Solicitors and Advocates) *G H* South Shields *p383* . . 0191 456 7893 / 455 5361

Waddell, Ms E C (Glaisyers Solicitors LLP) *D1 K1* Manchester *p304* 0161 224 3311

Waddell, H C K (CMS Cameron McKenna LLP) London EC3 *p17*. 020 7367 3000

Waddell, J C J (TLT Solicitors) *C1 I T1 J1 Zb Ze* Bristol *p165* 0117 917 7777

Waddingham, G J (Birchall Blackburn LLP) *W S1 A1 E L R1 C1 T1 Zc Zl Zo* Preston *p356* 01772 561663

Waddingham, K (Cartwright King) *G H* Derby *p208* 01332 346111

Waddington, Ms J (Brabners Chaffe Street) *S1 S2 Zh* Liverpool *p286*. 0151 600 3000

Waddington, Miss K (Stephensons Solicitors LLP) *C1* Wigan *p432* 01942 777777

Waddington, M N G (Harrison Clark LLP) *K1* Cheltenham *p188* . . . . . . 01242 269198 Worcester *p439* . . . . 01905 612001 Worcester *p439* 01905 612001

Waddington, Miss S (Collins Long) *Zf Ze* Southwark *p21*. . . . . 020 7401 9800 London WC1 *p79* 020 7874 5600

Waddington, Ms S K I (Mills & Reeve) Birmingham *p140* 0121 454 4000

Wade, A G (LG Lawyers) *E* London SE1 *p50*. 020 7379 0000

Wade, A L (F Arthur Jones & Co) *C1 E G K1 L M1 N P S1 W Zl* Exmouth *p222*. 01395 265668

Wade, B A (Chebsey & Co) *W K4 Zm* Beaconsfield *p128*. 01494 670440

Wade, C A R (Bevan Brittan LLP) *C1 Zc M1 R2* Bristol *p161* 0870 194 1000

Wade, D P (Eric Bowes & Co) *K1 K3 Q* Solihull *p382*. 0121 744 3691

Wade, Mrs E P (Oxfordshire County Council) *K1 D1 W* Oxford *p468* 01865 792422

Wade, J (Terry Jones Solicitors & Advocates) *G H B2* Telford *p409*. 01952 297979

Wade, Miss J S (Platt & Fishwick) *K3 D1 D2 K1* Wigan *p432* 01942 243281

Wade, Miss K L (Roebucks) *D1 K1* Blackburn *p145* 01254 274000

Wade, P R (Wayman & Long) *W S1 K1 S2 L E K3 T2* Sudbury *p401* 01787 277375

Wade, R J (Leeds City Council) *R1 S1 J1 Zl* Leeds *p462* 0113 224 3513

Wade, R S M (Blake Lapthorn) Oxford *p342*. 01865 248607

Wade, S (Wright Son & Pepper LLP) *Q O B1 Zc* Camden *p93*. 020 7242 5473

Wade, S J (Brockington Carroll) *E J1 K1 L S1 T2 W* Godalming *p231*. 01252 703770

Wade, T W (Emmerson Brown & Brown) *S1 W C1 R1 T1* Dover *p212* 01304 211766

Wadeson, R T (Wadesons Solicitors) *J1 Q Zp* London SW6 *p90* 020 7384 3333

Wadham, J J W (Edmondson Hall) *C1 O Q Zw* Newmarket *p327*. 01638 560556

Wadham-Smith, C J (Nockolds) *C1 S2 E* Bishop's Stortford *p144* 01279 755777

Wadhawa, Miss A (Stephen Burdon Solicitors) *G H* Nottingham *p336*. 0115 950 0054

Wadkin, R C F (Shulmans) *O Q Zt Zk Zc B1 Zb Zq* Leeds *p276* 0113 245 2833

Wadlow, C M (Simmons & Simmons) London EC2 *p79*. 020 7628 2020

Wadsworth, Mrs E L (S V Wadsworth & Co) *J1 Zr Q* Solihull *p383*. 0121 745 8550

Wadsworth, J (S V Wadsworth & Co) *J1 K1 N Q T2 Zr* Solihull *p383*. 0121 745 8550

Wadsworth, Mrs J M (Stapleton Gardner & Co) *W K4* Morley *p319* 0113 253 8111

Wadsworth, Ms K (Needhams) *K4 S1 T2 W* Bradford *p154* 01274 371088

Wadsworth, Ms M (Faegre & Benson LLP) *C1 C2* London EC4 *p30*. 020 7450 4500

Wadsworth, R (Darbys Solicitors LLP) *W* Oxford *p343* 01865 811700

Wadsworth, S V (S V Wadsworth & Co) *W S1 E* Solihull *p383*. 0121 745 8550

Wadsworth, Miss V (Roebucks) *Zm* Blackburn *p145* 01254 274000

Wadsworth-Jones, Mrs C (The College of Law) *W T1* London WC1 *p105*. 0800 289997

Wafer, Mrs L (North Tyneside Council) *K3 K1* Newcastle upon Tyne *p466* . 0191 643 5000

Wafer, M (Wafer-Phillips) *D1 F1 G H K1 L M1 P S1 V Zw* Liverpool *p290*. 0151 256 7898

Wagland, N C (Marriott Davies Yapp) *O Zc* Sutton *p402* 020 8643 9794

Wagner, A W (Lopian Wagner) *N B1 M1 P J1 F1 C1 K1 D1 G Ze Zb Zi* Manchester *p307* 0161 834 2324

Wagner, E R (Anglo-Spanish Law) *M2 W G* Hathersage *p244* 01433 631508

Wagner, S P (Martin-Kaye LLP) *S1 S2 W* Telford *p409*. 01952 272222

Wagstaff, Miss A H (Gordon Dadds) *K1 K3* London W1 *p25* 020 7493 6151

Wagstaff, T R D (Mills & Reeve) *J1* Norwich *p335* 01603 660155

Wagstaffe, Miss G K (Gates & Moloney) *K1 K3* Lancing *p270* 01903 766046

Wagstaffe, Mrs V (Plexus Law (A Trading Name of Parabis Law LLP)) *N Q* Evesham *p220*. 01386 769160

Waheed, T (Hempsons) *M1 P Zr* Manchester *p305* 0161 228 0011

Wahlberg, Miss C J (Alsters Kelley) Leamington Spa *p270* 0844 561 0100

Wahlhaus, Ms N K (Kenneth Elliott & Rowe) *S1 E L S2* Romford *p366* 01708 757575

Wailoo, Miss H (Darbys Solicitors LLP) *W T2 K4* Oxford *p343* 01865 811700

Wain, T (Taylor Wessing) *N Zj* London EC4 *p86*. 020 7300 7000

Waine, I M (Prettys) *B1 C1 C2* Ipswich *p262*. 01473 232121

Waine, Miss J N (Stevens & Bolton) *B1 D1 F1 J1 K1 L M1 N P Zc Zj* Guildford *p237*. 01483 302264

Waine, P G (Merriman Waine & Co) *S1 S2 E W L* Pewsey *p348* 01672 563666

Waine, T (Trobridges) *B1 J1 N O Q V Zq G H* Plymouth *p350*. 01752 664022

Wain-Heapy, Ms S (Marks & Spencer PLC) London W2 *p107* 020 7935 4422

Wainman, Mrs K E (Wrigleys Solicitors LLP) *W T2* Leeds *p278* 0113 244 6100

Wainman, R J (Baily Gibson) *K1 D1 L Q N* High Wycombe *p249*. 01494 442661

Wainman, T (Wrigleys Solicitors LLP) *W T2* Leeds *p278* 0113 244 6100

Wainman, W N (Hancocks) *K1 M1 N F1 L D1 J1 W Zl J2 O Q Zr Zq* Banbury *p122* 01295 253211

Wainwright, A J (Wainwright & Cummins) *G H J1 M1 K1 L P S1 Zm Zi Zp* Lambeth *p90*. 020 7737 9330

Wainwright, J B (Muckle LLP) *E S2 C2* Newcastle upon Tyne *p325* . 0191 211 7777

Wainwright, Mrs L M (Lynn M Wainwright) *K4 T2 V W* Willenhall *p433* 01902 609842

Wainwright, Ms N (Leigh Day & Co) *Zr* London EC1 *p52*. 020 7650 1200

Wainwright, P A (GLP Solicitors) *B1 C1 F1 J1 K1 L N O Q* Manchester *p304* 0161 834 6721

Waistell, M K (Colemans) *J1 S1 W C1 T1 L Q N F1 Zl* Haywards Heath *p245* 01444 459555

Wait, S J (Stephenson Harwood) *O Zc* London EC2 *p82*. 020 7329 4422

Waite, D H (Edward Hayes LLP) *E K4 S1 T2 W S2 L* Bognor Regis *p148* 01243 822655

Waite, G A (G A Waite Solicitor) *H* Crowborough *p204*. 01892 652800

Waite, Mrs J M (Oxfordshire County Council) Oxford *p468* 01865 792422

Waite, M D (Matthew Waite & Co) *K3 S2 C1 F1 J1 K1 L O Q N S1 W* Tring *p413*. 01442 890111

Waite, R (Freeth Cartwright LLP) *R1* Nottingham *p337*. 0115 936 9369

Waite, Mrs S C (Thompsons (formerly Robin/Brian Thompson & Partners)) *N J1 V* Bristol *p165* 0117 304 2400

Waite, V (Ince & Co Services Ltd) London E1 *p44* 020 7481 0010

Waites, Miss H (V G Waugh) *N Q V G H* Peterlee *p348* 0191 527 2727

Waitt, Ms K L (Waitt & Co Solicitors) *G H* Canterbury *p177*. 01227 470600

Waitt, T (Anthony Gold) *L Zg* London SE17 *p6*. 020 7940 4000

Wake, A (SBW Lawyers) *Zj N* St Helens *p391* 01744 762070

Wake, C (Herbert Smith LLP) London EC2 *p40*. 020 7374 8000

Wake, S (The Endeavour Partnership LLP) Stockton-on-Tees *p397* . . . 01642 610300

Wake, Miss V (Burt Brill & Cardens) *S1* Brighton *p159* 01273 604123

Wakefield, Mrs A J (East Staffordshire Borough Council) Burton-on-Trent *p452* 01283 508000

Wakefield, G J (Mossop & Bowser) *S1 A1* Holbeach *p251*. 01406 422651

Wakefield, J C W (Wartnabys) *S1 S2 Zl E* Market Harborough *p312*. . . . 01858 463322

Wakefield, Ms L (Peter Peter & Wright) *W T2 Zd K4* Holsworthy *p251*. 01409 253262

Wakefield, R J (Bhatia Best) *M1 P F1 J1 N L* Nottingham *p336*. 0115 950 3231

Wakeford, Mrs C A (Cripps Harries Hall LLP) *O E B1 P R1 Q A3* Tunbridge Wells *p415* 01892 515121

Wakeham, J (Withers LLP) *A1* London EC4 *p92*. 020 7597 6000

Wakeling, M J (Lodders Solicitors LLP) *J1 M1 N F1 Q O* Stratford-upon-Avon *p400* . . 01789 293259

Wakeman, A E (Talbots Legal Advice Centre) *Q N G H J1* Stourbridge *p399* . .01384 445850 / 447777

Wakeman, Mrs L J (Bridgeman Kettle) *E S1 W S2* Bletchley *p147*. 01908 376321

Wakeman, M D (Mills & Reeve) *S2 R2 E* Cambridge *p175*. 01223 364422

Wakerley, Ms S E (Nottinghamshire County Council Legal Services Division) West Bridgford *p475*. 0115 977 3478

Walace, Miss S (Irwin Mitchell LLP) *B2* London EC1 *p45*. 0870 150 0100

Walcot, Ms A (Welsh Health Legal Services) Cardiff *p453* 029 2031 5500

Wald, M C (Stephens & Scown) *B1 Zb C1* Exeter *p222* 01392 210700

Walden, Mrs C L (Cambridge City Council) Cambridge *p452*. 01223 457000

Walden, J (Herbert Smith LLP) *E* London EC2 *p40*. 020 7374 8000

Walden, J (Bury & Walkers LLP) *S1 W L E C1* Wombwell *p438* 01226 753433

Waldman, Mrs B M (Salford City Council) Swinton *p473* 0161 794 4711

Waldman, Ms N (CKFT) *W T2 K4* London NW3 *p17* 020 7431 7262

Waldon, J P (A K Gulati & Co) *K3 K1 D1* Sutton *p402* 020 8770 7979

Waldron, A J (Lodders Solicitors LLP) Stratford-upon-Avon *p400* . . 01789 293259

Waldron, J F (Waldron & Schofield) Heywood *p249*. 01706 624029

Waldron, J R N (Eddowes Waldron) *C1 E R1 T1 J1 L Q O F1 Zi Zl Zt* Derby *p208* 01332 348484

Waldron, Mrs N (Eddowes Waldron) *A1 T2 W* Derby *p208* 01332 348484

Waldron, P W (Waldrons) *C1 C2 C3 E Ze* Brierley Hill *p158*. 01384 811811

Wale, Miss S E (Corby Borough Council) Corby *p456* 01536 402551

Wales, M E F (LD Law) *C1 E L A1 R1 S1 S2 W Zc* Norwich *p334* . . . .

Wales, Mrs S E (Brethertons LLP) *W* Banbury *p122* 01295 270999

Walford, C M H (Watson Farley & Williams) *C1 M1* London EC2 *p90*. 020 7814 8000

Walford, Mrs J (Greenland Houchen Pomeroy) *S2 E Zh L R2 S1* Norwich *p334* 01603 660744

Walford, L (Ellis Jones) *J1* Bournemouth *p151*. 01202 525333

Walford, R S (Gilbert Stephens) *W T2 Zd* Exeter *p221* 01392 424242

Walia, Mrs K (Daniel and Harris) *S1 S2 W* Camden *p25*. 020 7625 0202

Walia, Ms S (HSR Solicitors) *Zi* London E1 *p37* 020 7791 1111

Walji, B R (F W Meggitt & Co) *W Zi K3 K1 Q B1 B2 T2 T1 B3* Sheffield *p376* 0114 272 7955

Walkden, W I (Baxter Caulfield) *E S1 C1 L* Huddersfield *p255* 01484 519519

Walker, A (Farrer & Co LLP) London WC2 *p31* 020 3375 7000

Walker, A (Martin Murray & Associates) *G H* Slough *p382*. 01753 551313

Walker, Miss A (Russell-Cooke LLP) *N Zr* London SW15 *p74*. 020 8789 9111

Walker, A (Irwin Mitchell LLP) *B1 O Zb* Sheffield *p376* 0870 150 0100

Walker, A J (Hogan Lovells International LLP) London EC1 *p42*. 020 7296 2000

Walker, A K (Sintons LLP) *S1 W E L K1 D1 C1 F1 J1 G Zl Zd S2 R2* Newcastle upon Tyne *p326* . 0191 226 7878

Walker, Ms A L (Nottingham City Council (City Sec Dept)) Nottingham *p467*. 0115 915 5555

Walker, A L (CMS Cameron McKenna LLP) *L O R1* London EC3 *p17*. 020 7367 3000

Walker, Mrs A M (Chesterfield Borough Council) Chesterfield *p455* 01246 345345

Walker, A P (Lincolnshire County Council Resources - Legal Services) Lincoln *p463*. 01522 552222

Walker, A P (Grahame Stowe Bateson) *K1 M1 F1 W P D1* Leeds *p274* 0113 276 0044

Walker, A P (Walker & Co) *A1 B1 C1 D1 E F1 G H J1 K1 Zl Zm* Rotherham *p367*. 01709 817112

Walker, B (Cumbria County Council) Carlisle *p453*. . . . .01228 607374 / 607351

Walker, Ms B E M (Leeds Metropolitan University) *K1 S1 T1 W A1 P L M1 G* Leeds *p463* 0113 812 9028

Walker, B M (Walker & Walker) *E S1 C1 S2* Sevenoaks *p374*. 01732 450699

Walker, C (Ince & Co Services Ltd) London E1 *p44* 020 7481 0010

Walker, Miss C (Sheridans) *J1* London WC1 *p78* 020 7079 0100

Walker, Miss C (O'Keeffe Solicitors) *G* Brent *p64* 020 7644 8800

Walker, C (Hill Dickinson LLP) *Zb B1 C1 O E* Liverpool *p288*. 0151 600 8000

Walker, Mrs C A (Shakespeares) *N K1* Stratford-upon-Avon *p400* . . 0845 630 8833

Walker, Ms C E (LG Lawyers) London SE1 *p50*. 020 7379 0000

Walker, C G (Goodman Derrick LLP) *N P M1 Zf Zk* London EC4 *p36*. 020 7404 0606

Walker, C J (Allen & Overy LLP) London E1 *p5* 020 3088 0000

Walker, C J R (Adams & Remers) *W S1 T2 Zd* Lewes *p283* 01273 480616

Walker, Prof C P (Clive Walker) *Zg* Leeds *p277* 0113 268 4660

Walker, C R (Stanley Hays) *S1 S2 W K4* Heckmondwike *p246*. 01924 403809

Walker, C R (Walker Tomaszewski Solicitors) *C1 O F2 I Ze Zf* Camden *p90*. 020 7722 7740

Walker, Mrs D (Armitage Sykes LLP) *S1 R1* Huddersfield *p255* 01484 538121

Walker, Mrs D A (Hewitts) Bishop Auckland *p144* 01388 604691

See p634 for the Key to Work Categories

Walker, Mrs D A (Brabners Chaffe Street) *C1 C2* Liverpool *p286* . . . 0151 600 3000

Walker, D C (Logica PLC) London NW1 *p107* . . . 020 7637 9111

Walker, D C (Memery Crystal) *C1 C2 F1 U2 Ze* London WC2 *p60* . . . 020 7242 5905

Walker, D C (Treasury Solicitors Department) London WC2 *p110* . . . 020 7210 3000

Walker, D J (Clifford Chance) London E14 *p20* . . . 020 7006 1000

Walker, D K B (The Royal Borough of Kensington & Chelsea) *E S1 R1 C1 L W Zd* London W8 *p109* . . . 020 7361 2741

Walker, D M (Talbot Walker LLP) *G H L R1 S1 W Zl Zt* Andover *p118* . . . 01264 363354

Walker, D R (Dale R Walker Solicitor) *B1 C1 E F1 G H J1 K1 L* Sevenoaks *p374* . . . 020 8466 0967

Walker, D W (Patterson Glenton & Stracey) *K1 D1 G H P F1 L M1 V W* South Shields *p384* . . . 0800 011 6487

Walker, Miss E (Powell & Young) *K1 K3* Pocklington *p351* . . . 01759 302113

Walker, E G (Gallaher Ltd) Weybridge *p476* . . . 01932 859777

Walker, Mrs F M (Southern Stewart & Walker) *D1 K1 G H N* South Shields *p384* . . . 0191 427 0770

Walker, G J (Grenville J Walker) *A1 F1 G J1 K1 L Q S1 T1 W Zl Zv* Blandford Forum *p147* . . . 01258 459911

Walker, G R J (Nash & Co Solicitors LLP) *N O Q P Zj Za Zk Zq* Plymouth *p350* . . . 01752 664444

Walker, G S (Ward & Rider Limited) *N J2* Coventry *p201* . . . 024 7655 5400

Walker, I F (Thompsons (formerly Robin/Brian Thompson & Partners)) *Q Zo* London WC1 *p87* . . . 020 7290 0000

Walker, I J (Smith Llewelyn Partnership) *S1 W K4 S2 E* Swansea *p405* . . . 01792 464444

Walker, I S (Tozers) *K1 D1* Exeter *p222* . . . 01392 207020

Walker, Miss J (Universal Pictures International Ltd) London WC1 *p110* . . . 020 7079 6000

Walker, Mrs J (Stanley Tee LLP) *T2 W* Cambridge *p175* . . . 01223 311141

Walker, Ms J (Higgs & Sons) Brierley Hill *p158* . . . 0845 111 5050

Walker, Ms J (Freeth Cartwright LLP) Birmingham *p138* . . . 0845 634 2575

Walker, J A (DFA Law LLP) *O Q N* Northampton *p331* . . . 01604 609560

Walker, J A (Guest Walker & Co) *A1 C1 E S1 W L K1 M1 J1* York *p444* . . . 01904 624903

Walker, Mrs J C (Michelmores LLP) *E S2 R2 X Zx* Exeter *p221* . . . 01392 688688

Walker, Ms J D (The Thrasher Walker Partnership) *N O Q V S1 S2 W X B1 J1* Stockport *p396* . . . 0161 442 6240

Walker, Mrs J K (BHR Law) Exeter *p220* . . . 01392 496100

Walker, Mrs J L (Talbot Walker LLP) *W K4 T2* Andover *p118* . . . 01264 363354

Walker, J M O H (Morrisons Solicitors LLP) *W* Woking *p437* . . . 01483 726146

Walker, J P (Challinors) *G H* Birmingham *p136* . . . 0121 212 9393

Walker, Ms K (Nelsons) Nottingham *p338* . . . 0115 958 6262

Walker, Ms K (Pinsent Masons LLP) London EC2 *p67* . . . 020 7418 7000

Walker, Ms K A (Newcastle Upon Tyne City Council) Newcastle upon Tyne *p466* . 0191 232 8520

Walker, K G (Arnison & Co Solicitors Limited) *G H J1 C1 R1 Zl Zd* Penrith *p346* . . . 01768 862007

Walker, Ms K G A (TWM Solicitors LLP) *D1 K1 K2* Guildford *p237* . . . 01483 752700

Walker, K M A (Jackson Brierley Hudson Stoney) *W E C1 J1 S2* Rochdale *p365* . . . 01706 644187 / 649214

Walker, Mrs L (Butcher & Barlow LLP) *S1* Sandbach *p372* . . . 01270 762521

Walker, Mrs L (Hunters) *G H* London WC2 *p44* . . . 020 7412 0050

Walker, Miss L (Keoghs LLP) Bolton *p149* . . . 01204 677000

Walker, Ms L (Osborne Clarke) *Zb* Bristol *p164* . . . 0117 917 3000

Walker, Mrs L C (Irwin Mitchell LLP) *D1 D2 K1* Leeds *p274* . . . 0870 150 0100

Walker, Miss L M (Everys) *J1 Q* Exeter *p221* . . . 01392 477983

Walker, Mrs L M (Durham County Council) Durham *p457* . . . 0191 383 3513

Walker, Mrs L V (Hamnett Osborne Tisshaw) *G H B2* Haywards Heath *p245* . . . 01444 443030

Walker, M (Mayer Brown International LLP) London EC2 *p59* . . . 020 3130 3000

Walker, M (Squire Sanders (UK) LLP) *E* Birmingham *p142* . . . 0121 222 3000

Walker, Mrs M (Gosschalks) *J1* Hull *p256* . . . 01482 324252

Walker, M B A (London Borough of Wandsworth) London SW18 *p110* . . . 020 8871 6000

Walker, M F J (Kennedys) London EC3 *p49* . . . 020 7667 9667

Walker, M I (Crown Prosecution Service Durham) Durham *p457* . . . 0191 383 5800

Walker, M J M (Bury & Walkers LLP) *E C1 S1 T1 W* Barnsley *p124* . . . 01226 733533

Walker, M R H (Gillings and Walker) *A1 C1 E L S1 T1 W* York *p444* . . . 01904 655755

Walker, M S J (Allen & Overy LLP) London E1 *p5* . . . 020 3088 0000

Walker, Mrs M V F (Walker & Walker) *K1 W K3* Sevenoaks *p374* . . . 01732 450699

Walker, Miss N (Latimer Hinks) *W K4 Zm* Darlington *p206* . . . 01325 341500

Walker, Mrs N (Norton & Co) *D2 D1 K1 L Q N S1 V K3* Prescot *p356* . . . 0151 426 7001

Walker, N E (Norris & Miles) *O E N K1 J1 L R1 F1 A1 Zc Zt Zy S2* Tenbury Wells *p409* . . . 01584 810575

Walker, N F C (ConocoPhillips (UK) Ltd) London W1 *p105* . . . 020 7408 6000

Walker, P C (Walker Foster) *S1 W S2* Barnoldswick *p124* . . . 01282 812340

Walker, P F W (Punch Robson) *E S1 W T2 Zd* Middlesbrough *p315* . . . 01642 230700

Walker, P L (Walker Morris) *E L R1 S1 A1 Zc* Leeds *p277* . . . 0113 283 2500

Walker, P M (JMW Solicitors) *E J1 Zp S2* Manchester *p306* . . . 0845 872 6666

Walker, Ms R (DFA Law LLP) *K4 K1 S1 T2 W* Northampton *p331* . . . 01604 609560

Walker, Ms R (Plexus Law (A Trading Name of Parabis Law LLP)) *N Q* Evesham *p220* . . . 01386 769160

Walker, Miss R (Armitage Sykes LLP) *E S1 S2 W* Brighouse *p158* . . . 01484 714431

Walker, Mrs R E (Redrow PLC) Flint *p458* . . . 01244 520044

Walker, R E S (Bolton Magistrates Court) Bolton *p450* . . . 01204 558200

Walker, Ms R J (Eaton Smith LLP) *K1* Huddersfield *p255* . . . 01484 821300

Walker, R L (Kenwright Walker Wyllie) *G K1 M1 N H D1 C1 P W S1 S2* East Molesey *p215* . . . 020 8979 1131

Walker, Ms R M (Salans) *C1 C2 C3 M2* London EC4 *p76* . . . 020 7429 6000

Walker, Mrs S (Rio Tinto PLC) London W2 *p109* . . . 020 7781 2000

Walker, S (Taylor Wessing) *C1 C2* London EC4 *p86* . . . 020 7300 7000

Walker, S (Gosschalks) *S1 W* Hull *p256* . . . 01482 324252

Walker, S (Livingstons) *J1 G H* Ulverston *p416* . . . 01229 585555

Walker, Mrs S C (Shipton Hallewell & Co) *K1 D2* Chesterfield *p192* . . . 01246 232140

Walker, S E (Appleby Hope & Matthews) *K1 N Q G H S1 D1 J1 W* Middlesbrough *p314* . . . 01642 440444

Walker, S J (PricewaterhouseCoopers Legal LLP) London SE1 *p69* . . . 020 7212 1616

Walker, S J (Ashfords LLP) *N Q O* Tiverton *p412* . . . 01884 203000

Walker, S J G (Walker Lahive) *G H* Plymouth *p350* . . . 01752 551722

Walker, Ms S L (Howells LLP) *D1 D2 K1* Barnsley *p124* . . . 01226 805190

Walker, S M (Bevans) *A3 B1 C1 C2 J1 O Q Zj Zq* London WC2 *p12* . . . 020 7353 9995

Walker, S R (Winston Solicitors LLP) *N Zr* Leeds *p278* . . . 0113 320 5000

Walker, Miss S T (Bermans LLP) *S1 R1 L* Liverpool *p286* . . . 0151 224 0500

Walker, S T (Stone King LLP) *D1 K1* Bath *p128* . . . 01225 337599

Walker, S T Q (Talbot Walker LLP) *A1 C1 C2 B1 E F1 J1 L N O Q S1 S2 W Zc F2 Zr* Andover *p118* . . . 01264 363354

Walker, T (Clarke Willmott) *E R2 S2* Taunton *p408*0845 209 1000 / 0117 305 6000

Walker, T E (Henmans LLP) *C1 C2 F1 U2* Oxford *p343* . . . 01865 781000 Newbury *p322* . . . 01635 521212

Walker, Miss T J (Bartons) *K1 K2 L D1 Q K3* Totnes *p413* . . . 01803 864705

Walker, Miss V H (Arnold Thomson Limited) *Q* Towcester *p413* . . . 01327 350266

Walker, Miss V M (Hurlow & Partners) *D1 K1 D2* Cardiff *p179* . . . 029 2039 6087 Cardiff *p180* . . . 029 2072 9888

Walkey, J R C (Bird & Bird LLP) *C1 Zw* London EC4 *p13* . . . 020 7415 6000

Walkingshaw, Miss F M A (Treasury Solicitors Department) London WC2 *p110* . . . 020 7210 3000

Walkington, J T P W (Pengillys LLP) *K1 N Q G H S1 F1 D1 W* Weymouth *p430* . . . 01305 768888

Walkington, Ms L (Linklaters LLP) London EC2 *p54* . . . 020 7456 2000

Walkington, M (Batchelors Solicitors) *Zc O A3 Zq L Q E S2 R2 J1* Bromley *p166* . . . 020 8768 7000

Walkington, M D (Reed Smith LLP) *Za* London EC2 *p71* . . . 020 3116 3000

Walkinshaw, Miss B S (Pickworths) *O C1 Q N* Hemel Hempstead *p247* . . . 01442 261731

Walkinshaw, D (Keoghs LLP) *N Zj O Q B2* Bolton *p149* . . . 01204 677000

Walkinshaw, Ms F (Reynolds Porter Chamberlain LLP) London E1 *p71* . . . 020 3060 6000

Walkling, A K (Simmons & Simmons) London EC2 *p79* . . . 020 7628 2020

Wall, Mrs A (Merrony Wall) *K1 K2 W D1* Twickenham *p416* . . . 020 8898 4700

Wall, J (Bond Pearce LLP) Southampton *p385* . . . 0845 415 0000

Wall, Mrs L (Charles Coleman LLP) *S2 E Zl* Windsor *p434* . . . 01753 861115

Wall, Mrs L J (Hellewell Pasley & Brewer) *S2 E T2 B1* Batley *p128* . . . 01924 472596

Wall, Ms T (The Smith Partnership) *W* Derby *p209* . . . 01332 225225

Wallace, A (3i PLC) *C2 C1* London SW1 *p103* . . . 020 7928 3131

Wallace, Ms A M (Steptoe & Johnson) *O J1 C1 Q Zj* London EC2 *p83* . . . 020 7367 8000

Wallace, C (Plexus Law (A Trading Name of Parabis Law LLP)) *Zj N* Manchester *p309* . . . 0161 214 7933

Wallace, Miss C A L (Pinsent Masons LLP) Leeds *p276* . . . 0113 244 5000

Wallace, Ms E N A (Wallace McNally) *G H* Coventry *p201* . . . 024 7622 0300

Wallace, F N (Rix & Kay Solicitors LLP) *L R1 M1 B1 O* Uckfield *p416* . . . 01825 700177

Wallace, Mrs G E (Furley Page LLP) *W T2 S1 Zd* Canterbury *p176* . . . 01227 763939

Wallace, Ms H (Rundlewalker) *G H* Exeter *p222* . . . 01392 209209

Wallace, J (Lees Solicitors LLP) *W* Heswall *p249* . . . 0151 342 6273

Wallace, Miss J L (Granville-West) *K1 Q N W* Pontypool *p352* . . . 01495 751111

Wallace, K (Reed Smith LLP) *Zo* London EC2 *p71* . . . 020 3116 3000

Wallace, K E W (Lee Bolton Monier-Williams) *E R1 R2* Westminster *p52* . . . 020 7222 5381

Wallace, Mrs K M (Stafford Young Jones) *K3 K1 K2 Q J1 O* London EC4 *p82* . . . 020 7623 9490

Wallace, Ms L H (CMS Cameron McKenna LLP) *C2 C1* Bristol *p162* . . . 0117 930 0200 London EC3 *p17* . . . 020 7367 3000

Wallace, Miss M A (Forbes) *N Zr* Preston *p356* . . . 01772 220022

Wallace, Mrs P (MacLaren Britton) *J1* Nottingham *p338* . . . 0115 941 1469

Wallace, P (Anthony Gold) *Q S1 E L W O* London SW16 *p6* . . . 020 7940 4000

Wallace, R I (Tomlinson & Dickinson) *S1 W S2* Sudbury *p401* . . . 01787 375189 / 376820

Wallace, Ms S (DLA Piper UK LLP) Birmingham *p137* . . . 0870 011 1111

Wallace-Cook, A D M (Whitemans) *C1 S2 J1 L R2 S1 T2* Gloucester *p231* . . . 01452 411601

Wallbank, A (DAC Beachcroft) Manchester *p303* . . . 0161 934 3000

Wallbank, M C (Pickering & Butters) *N F1 O Q* Rugeley *p368* . . . 01889 803080

Wallen, Miss C (Swale Borough Council) *G H* Sittingbourne *p471* . . . 01795 417324

Waller, A F (Graham & Rosen) *E C1* Hull *p257* . . . 01482 323123

Waller, Ms C (R Bell & Son) *D1 K1 L Q* Hartlepool *p242* . . . 01429 273165

Waller, Ms C (Watson Burton LLP) *C1 C3 I F1 Ze* Newcastle upon Tyne *p327* . 0845 901 2100

Waller, C (Blandfords) *Q J1 O K1 F1 L Zi Zp* London W1 *p14* . . . 020 7935 7373 London W1 *p16* .020 7935 7235 / 7935 7270

Waller, C R d W (Waller Needham & Green) *S1 C1 E F1 L P N T1 W Ze* Peterborough *p347* . . . 01733 311422

Waller, G A (Waller Pollins) *C1 E S1 L W* Edgware *p217* . . . 020 8238 5858

Waller, Mrs H J (Glovers Solicitors LLP) *Zl Zq* London W1 *p36* . . . 020 7935 8882

Waller, Miss I (D C Kaye & Co) *K1 D1 K3* Great Missenden *p234* . . . 01494 864650 / 862226

Waller, J (Michael Conn Goldsobel) *B1 J1 K1 L O Q N* London W1 *p60* . . . 020 7580 8902

Waller, J (Waller Pollins) *C1 E S1 L Zd W T1* Edgware *p217* . . . 020 8238 5858

Waller, Mrs J (Blandfords) *Q J1 O K1 F1 L Zi Zp* London W1 *p14* . . . 020 7935 7373 London W1 *p16* .020 7935 7235 / 7935 7270

Waller, Ms M (Morrisons Solicitors LLP) *E L R1 S1* Redhill *p362* . . . 01737 854500

Waller, M (Corries Solicitors) *N* York *p444* . . . 0845 241 5566

Waller, M G (Earle & Waller) *E S2 C1 S1 O J1 C2 Zl* London N13 *p28* . . . 020 8888 7866

Waller, Ms R (Pierre Thomas & Partners) *N Zj O Q* London W6 *p67* . . . 020 7602 0305

Waller, R (Rotherham Metropolitan Borough Council) Rotherham *p470* . . . 01709 382121

Waller, R G L (TLT Solicitors) *O Q S1* Bristol *p165* . . . 0117 917 7777

Walley, A (Hibberts LLP) *A1 K4 K1 T2 V W* Nantwich *p320* . . . 01270 624225

Walley, K S (Tarmac Ltd) *S1 W Q L K1 J1 B1 F1 Ze* Wolverhampton *p477* . . . 01902 353522

Walling, Mrs H L (Jobling & Knape) *K1 Q N* Lancaster *p269* . . . 01524 598300

Wallington, G (Ellisons) *J1 Q O L F1 B1 R1 Zo* Colchester *p197* . . . 01206 764477

Wallington, Miss H L (Bennetts Solicitors Attorneys & Notaries) *B3 J1 M2 O Q Zd* Wrington *p443* . . . 01934 862786

Wallis, A R (Staffordshire County Council) Stafford *p472* . . . 01785 223121

Wallis, Mrs C A (Boyes Turner) *W T1* Reading *p360* . . . 0118 959 7711 Winchester *p433* . . . 01962 844333

Wallis, D (Gill Akaster) *S1* Plymouth *p349* . . . 01752 203500 Wadebridge *p418* . . . 01208 812277 Newquay *p329* . . . 01637 872218

Wallis, Ms D (The College of Law) London WC1 *p105* . . . 0800 289997

Wallis, D G (Dechert) London EC4 *p26* . . . 020 7184 7000

Wallis, Mrs E M (Cockertons) *S2 E S1 A1* Bakewell *p121* . . . 01629 812613

Wallis, G (Browne Jacobson LLP) *E S1 R1 A1* Nottingham *p336* . . . 0115 976 6000

Wallis, G S J (DWF) *E R2 S1 S2* Liverpool *p287* . . . 0151 907 3000

Wallis, Mrs L C (Horsey Lightly) *K1 D1 D2* Newbury *p322* . . . 01635 580858

Wallis, P H (GCA Solicitors (Giffen Couch & Archer)) *N Q L J1 D1 F1 O V* Luton *p295* . . . 01582 410041

Wallis, R (Simmons & Simmons) London EC2 *p79* . . . 020 7628 2020

Wallis, R H (Hill Dickinson LLP) *N Za Zj* London EC3 *p41* . . . 020 7283 9033

Wallis, R T (Symes Bains Broomer) *A1 S1 W T1 E F1 Zc Zl C1 C2 S2* Scunthorpe *p373* . . . 01724 281616

Wallis, S W (Michael Cullen & Partners) *E C1 L A1 R1 S1* Billericay *p133* . . . 01277 623132

Walls, D (London Borough of Lewisham) London SE6 *p107* . . . 020 8695 6000

Walls, Mrs D M (Arnold Greenwood) *C1 S2 E S1* Kendal *p264* . . . 01539 720049

Walls, Ms M A (Nelsons) *N* Nottingham *p338* . . . 0115 958 6262

Walls, Ms S (Morgan Cole) *O Q* Oxford *p344* . . . 01865 262600

Walls, S M (Quality Solicitors Hill & Abbott) *N* Chelmsford *p187* . . . 01245 258892

Walls, W A (Linklaters LLP) London EC2 *p54* . . . 020 7456 2000

Wallsgrove, J S (Blake Lapthorn) *Zi* Chandlers Ford *p184* . . . 023 8090 8090

Wallwork, E (Hargreaves Gilman) *S1* Manchester *p305* . . . 0161 443 1711

Wallwork, Mrs J (Treasury Solicitors Department) London WC2 *p110* . . . 020 7210 3000

Wallwork, Mrs L (Land Registry - Lancashire Office) Preston *p469* . . . 01772 836700

Wallwork, S J (Pannone LLP) *C1 C2 I U2* Manchester *p308* . . . 0161 909 3000

Wallworth, C M (Ferguson Bricknell) *W T2 C1 I E S1* Oxford *p343* . . . 01865 241814

Walmsley, D (Farnworth Shaw) *E S1 L W* Nelson *p321* . . . 01282 699996

Walmsley, J B (Blake Lapthorn) *B1 C1 C2* London EC1 *p13* . . . 020 7405 2000

Walmsley, Mrs J N Y (Hatchers Solicitors LLP) *S1 K1* Shrewsbury *p379* . . . 01743 248545

Walmsley, K (Keith Walmsley) *C1* Carshalton *p183* . . . 020 8669 3643

Walmsley, Mrs L J (Farleys Solicitors LLP) *G H B2* Blackburn *p145* . . . 01254 367855

Walmsley, N R (Greene & Greene) *C1 I C2 J1 C3 F1 T1 Ze* Bury St Edmunds *p171* . . . 01284 762211

Walmsley, P (Barlow Lyde & Gilbert LLP) *N Zq* Manchester *p301* . . . 0161 829 6400

Walmsley, R (Lancaster City Council) Lancaster *p462* . . . 01524 582000

Walmsley, S (Broudie Jackson Canter) *Zg* Liverpool *p286* . . . 0151 227 1429

Walne, Ms V (Anthony Gold) *N Zr* London SE1 *p6* . . . 020 7940 4000

Walser, N M (Gateley LLP) *O C1 Za Zj A3* London EC4 *p35* . . . 020 7653 1600

Walsh, A (Farleys Solicitors LLP) Blackburn *p145* . . . 01254 367856

Walsh, Ms A (Blake Lapthorn) *O* Oxford *p342* . . . 01865 248607

Walsh, A G (Speechly Bircham LLP) *Zc C1 Zu Zn Zb* London EC4 *p81* . . . 020 7427 6400

Walsh, A R (Nexus Solicitors) *S2 S1* Manchester *p308* . . . 0161 819 4900

Walsh, B T (Osborne Clarke) *C1* Reading *p361* . . . 0118 925 2000

Walsh, Ms C (Reynolds Porter Chamberlain LLP)
London E1 *p71* 020 3060 6000
Walsh, C (Ince & Co Services Ltd)
London E1 *p44* 020 7481 0010
Walsh, Mrs C P (DWF) *Zj Q N*
Liverpool *p287* 0151 907 3000
Walsh, Ms C V (Barlow Lyde & Gilbert LLP) *A3 Zj O*
London EC3 *p10* 020 7247 2277
Walsh, D (Kingsley Napley) *C1 E T1 Zb*
London EC1 *p50* 020 7814 1200
Walsh, D A (Holroyd & Co) *Zo Zv W*
Huddersfield *p256* 01484 645464
Walsh, D M (National Grid PLC)
Warwick *p471* 01926 653000
Walsh, Ms E (Martello Professional Risks Limited) *O Q P Zj Zq*
London EC3 *p108* 020 7337 7500
Walsh, Miss E C (Harcus Sinclair) *W T2*
London WC2 *p38* 020 7242 9700
Walsh, Miss F J (Frances J Walsh) *S1*
Stroud *p401* 01453 755092
Walsh, Ms G H (HCB Solicitors) *S1 W K1 L J1 E F1*
Solihull *p382* 0121 705 2255
Walsh, I (Cottrill Stone Lawless)
Manchester *p302* 0161 835 3681
Walsh, J (Anthony Collins Solicitors LLP) *C1 Zb*
Birmingham *p137* 0121 200 3242
Manchester *p303* 0161 603 5000
Walsh, Ms J (Trowers & Hamlins)
London EC3 *p88* 020 7423 8000
Walsh, J G M (Stephenson Harwood) *K1*
London EC2 *p82* 020 7329 4422
Walsh, J J (Wolferstans) *N*
Plymouth *p351* 01752 663295
Walsh, J M (Travers Smith LLP) *B1 Zb*
London EC1 *p87* 020 7295 3000
Walsh, J P (Dewes LLP) *G H M1 P K1 J1 Zl*
Tamworth *p407* 01827 58391
Walsh, J P J (Sutton-Mattocks & Co LLP) *C1 E L S1 S2*
London SW13 *p84* 020 8876 8811
Walsh, K J (Machins Solicitors LLP) *S1 S2 E*
Luton *p295* 01582 514000
Walsh, K M (Vale of Glamorgan Council)
Barry *p448* 01446 700111
Walsh, Mrs L M (DAC Beachcroft)
London EC4 *p24* 020 7936 2222
Walsh, M (Berwins Solicitors Limited) *J1*
Harrogate *p240* 01423 509000
Walsh, Mrs M (Lichfield Reynolds) *K1*
Stoke-on-Trent *p398* 01782 313212
Walsh, M (Lyons Davidson)
Solihull *p382* 0121 683 8310
Walsh, M (Sidley Austin Brown & Wood) *C1 C2 Zb Zn M2 U2*
London EC2 *p78* 020 7360 3600
Walsh, M (Sills & Betteridge LLP)
Lincoln *p285* 01522 542211
Walsh, M (Henry Hyams) *G H*
Leeds *p274* 0113 243 2288
Walsh, Ms M B (Winckworth Sherwood LLP) *J1 O Q*
London SE1 *p92* 020 7593 5000
Walsh, Ms N (IBB Solicitors) *E*
Uxbridge *p417* 0845 638 1381
Walsh, Ms N (Swain & Co) *L Q K1*
Southampton *p386* 023 8063 1111
Walsh, N A P (Blaker Son & Young) *S1 W E L Q O F1*
Lewes *p283* 01273 480234
Walsh, N F (Weightmans LLP) *J1 N Q*
Leicester *p281* 0116 253 9747
Walsh, N J (VHS Fletchers Solicitors) *G H B2*
Nottingham *p339* 0115 959 9550
Walsh, P (Boyes Turner) *C1 Zd J1 F1 C2*
Reading *p360* 0118 959 7711
Walsh, P A (Bristows) *O Ze Zf C1 C3 I M1 M2*
London EC4 *p15* 020 7400 8000
Walsh, Ms P J (Hartley Thomas & Wright) *K3 K1 D1*
Rochdale *p365* 01706 644118
Walsh, Ms P M (Osborne Clarke) *J1*
London EC2 *p65* 020 7105 7000
Walsh, P M (Clifford Johnston & Co) *L Zg Q N Zq*
Manchester *p302* 0161 975 1900
Walsh, P R (Kent County Council)
Maidstone *p464* 01622 694320
Walsh, R (North East Lincolnshire Borough Council)
Cleethorpes *p455* 01472 324001
Walsh, Miss R C (Russell & Russell) *G H*
Bolton *p149* 01204 399299
Walsh, S (Global Aerospace Underwriting Managers Ltd)
London EC3 *p106* 020 7369 2244
Walsh, S (South Cheshire Magistrates Court)
Crewe *p456* 0870 162 6261
Walsh, S J (Mayer Brown International LLP) *J1 F1 B1 Zb Zj Zf C2 R2*
London EC2 *p59* 020 3130 3000
Walsh, S J (McGrigors LLP)
London EC4 *p56* 020 7054 2500
Walsh, T (Walsh & Company) *N O Zq Q B1 K1 J1 F1 C1 L S1 Zh W F2 E*
Truro *p414* 01872 870923
Walsh, W T A (Rawlison Butler LLP)
Crawley *p202* 01293 527744
Walsham, Miss Y (Bassetlaw District Council)
Worksop *p477* 01909 533533
Walshaw, T C (Barlow Lyde & Gilbert LLP) *N Q*
London EC3 *p10* 020 7247 2277
Walshe, K P (DWF) *N Zq Q*
Manchester *p303* 0161 603 5000
Walshe, N G (Foys Solicitors) *Zr Q N*
Doncaster *p211* 01302 327136
Walshe, P A (Moore Blatch Solicitors) *L*
Southampton *p386* 023 8071 8000
Walshe, T A (William Sturges & Co) *O J1 N C1 B1 L Zq Q Zp Zk*
Westminster *p84* 020 7873 1000
Walter, Mrs A H (Russell-Cooke LLP) *W*
London SW15 *p74* 020 8789 9111
Walter, J (Clifford Chance)
London E14 *p20* 020 7006 1000
Walter, J C (Simmons & Simmons)
London EC2 *p79* 020 7628 2020
Walter, M (Herbert Smith LLP) *C2 C1*
London EC2 *p40* 020 7374 8000
Walter, S F (Jones Day) *E*
London EC4 *p46* 020 7039 5959
Walter-Browne, Miss O S J (Tendring District Council) *J1 X P Q Zp Zy*
Clacton-on-Sea *p455* 01255 686567
Walters, A (MLM Cartwright) *C1 Ze Zf C2 U2 I*
Cardiff *p179* 029 2046 2562
Walters, A (Anthony Walters & Co) *S1 L W K1 C1 E F1 R1 P T1*
Bishop Auckland *p144* 01388 662222
Walters, Ms A M (A M Walters & Co)
Ilford *p261* 020 8551 5894
Walters, Miss B (Quality Solicitors Burroughs Day) *Q O Zq*
Bristol *p164* 0117 929 0333
Walters, C M (Gough Clinton & Broom) *D1 F1 G H J1 K1 S1 V*
Welling *p424* 020 8301 9000
Walters, G M (Dechert) *C1 C2*
London EC4 *p26* 020 7184 7000
Walters, Mrs G M (Bonallack & Bishop) *S2 E S1 C1*
Salisbury *p371* 01722 422300
Walters, G R (Irwin Mitchell LLP) *Zj*
Birmingham *p139* 0870 150 0100
Walters, J (Ramsdens Solicitors) *S1*
Huddersfield *p256* 01484 821500
Walters, J (TBI Solicitors) *C1 E M1 N P S1 T1 J1*
Hartlepool *p243* 0800 052 6824 / 01429 264101
Walters, Mrs L N (Streathers Solicitors LLP) *E S1 P N K1 C1 B1 W M1 L Ze Zk Zi*
London W1 *p84* 020 7034 4200
Walters, M J (North East Lincolnshire Borough Council)
Grimsby *p459* 01472 313131
Cleethorpes *p455* 01472 324001
Walters, Miss M R (Ormerods) *D1 D2 K1*
Croydon *p205* 020 8686 5000
Walters, M W S (Moxons) *K1 D1 N S1 W K2*
Pontefract *p351* 01977 703215
Walters, P G (Astle Paterson Ltd) *K1 D1 K2 K3*
Burton-on-Trent *p170* 01283 531366
Walters, R (Grahame Stowe Bateson) *K1 N Q D1 D2 J1 V W F1*
Leeds *p274* 0113 255 8666
Walters, Ms S (Wills Group Ltd)
London EC3 *p110* 020 7488 8111
Walters, S (Simmons & Simmons)
London EC2 *p79* 020 7628 2020
Walters, T B (Serious Law LLP - The Serious Law Practice) *N O*
Bolton *p150* 0800 616 681
Walton Williams, Mrs B V G (Brooke Williams) *K1 D1 N Q W*
York *p444* 01904 677888
Walton, A (Bond Pearce LLP) *E S2 R2 S1*
Southampton *p385* 0845 415 0000
Walton, A R (Chubb Bulleid) *K1 W P S1 L J1 R1 A1 Zl*
Somerton *p383* 01749 836100
Walton, B (Jones Day) *O*
London EC4 *p46* 020 7039 5959
Walton, B (Field Fisher Waterhouse LLP)
London EC3 *p31* 020 7861 4000
Walton, Miss C A (Downs) *S1 E L*
Dorking *p212* 01306 880110
Walton, C M (Dass Solicitors) *B2 G H*
Birmingham *p137* 0121 248 4000
Walton, D C (Salehs LLP) *S2 E S1 R2*
Manchester *p309* 0161 434 9991
Walton, D J (Davidson Large LLP) *O*
Harrogate *p240* 01423 727272
Walton, D M (Keoghs LLP) *O Zj N Q*
Bolton *p149* 01204 677000
Walton, Mrs D R (Anthony Collins Solicitors LLP) *O Q*
Birmingham *p137* 0121 200 3242
Walton, G (John Lewis plc)
London SW1 *p107* 020 7828 1000
Walton, G A (Wilson Bullough Walton & Knowles) *S1 W N K1 C1 L E S2*
Newton-le-Willows *p330* 01925 224569 / 224560
Walton, L (Walton Mills & Co) *Zq O Zt Zy*
Southampton *p387* 023 8047 7221
Walton, M H (Allen & Overy LLP)
London E1 *p5* 020 3088 0000
Walton, P (Davis Blank Furniss) *F1 J1 M1 N P Zc Zj Zx Zk O Q Zq Zp*
Manchester *p303* 0161 832 3304
Liverpool *p288* 0151 600 8000
Walton, P (Mundays LLP) *C2 C1*
Cobham *p196* 01932 590500
Walton, P W (McKeag & Co) *N Q J1*
Gosforth *p231* 0191 213 1010
Walton, S (Frisby & Co) *B2 G H*
Stafford *p392* 01785 244114
Walton, Mrs S P (Wycombe & Beaconsfield Magistrates Court)
High Wycombe *p461* 01494 651035
Walton, Miss S V L (Weightmans LLP) *C1 C2 Zb*
Manchester *p311* 0161 233 7330
Walton, Ms V (Mills & Reeve) *C1*
Cambridge *p175* 01223 364422
Walton Williams, Mrs B V G (Brooke Williams) *K1 D1 N Q W*
Hull *p256* 01482 610886
Walton-Jones, N P (Myer Wolff) *K3 K1 D2 D1 K2*
Hull *p257* 01482 223693
Wan, Ms E (Ford & Warren) *N*
Leeds *p273* 0113 243 6601
Wan, Ms L (Carillion PLC)
Wolverhampton *p477* 01902 422431
Wan, Miss M M Y (Burton Burton & Ho LLP) *S2 O Q Zq*
Leeds *p272* 0113 297 8787
Wan, Miss O (Oldham Marsh Page Flavell)
Melton Mowbray *p314* 01664 563162
Wanambwa, E (Bryan Cave) *Zi*
London EC2 *p19* 020 7207 1100
London SW15 *p74* 020 8789 9111
Wand, Miss J S (Nockolds) *W K4 Zm*
Bishop's Stortford *p144* 01279 755777
Wander, C D (Fladgate LLP) *C1 T1 E J1 Zb Zj*
London WC2 *p32* 020 3036 7000
Wandless, M (Holman Fenwick Willan)
London EC3 *p42* 020 7264 8000
Wanford, M (Goodman Derrick LLP)
London EC4 *p36* 020 7404 0606
Wangermann, M A (Ashton KCJ) *N M1*
Bury St Edmunds *p171* 01284 762331
Wankling, Ms S J (Parker Bullen) *W T2 Zd*
Salisbury *p371* 01722 412000
Wann, Ms T J R (Irwin Mitchell LLP) *N*
Birmingham *p139* 0870 150 0100
Wansbrough, R D (Bedfordshire County Council)
Bedford *p448* 01234 363222
Wanstall, I R (Parrott & Coales LLP) *W T2*
Aylesbury *p121* 01296 318500
Want, J (Tinsdills) *O*
Hanley *p239* 01782 262031
Want, Mrs M J (Vanderpump & Sykes) *W E D1*
Enfield *p219* 020 8367 3999
Warbey, J M (Horwood & James LLP) *W J1*
Aylesbury *p121* 01296 487361
Warboys, K R (Copleys) *G H K1 J1 M1 P S1 D1 V W*
Huntingdon *p258* 01480 456191
Warburton, D (Squire Sanders (UK) LLP) *C1 C2*
Manchester *p310* 0161 830 5000
Warburton, F W (Bankside Commercial Solicitors) *B1 C1 E L M1 N P R1 S1 W Ze Zf Zk*
Southwark *p9* 020 7654 0200
Warburton, Ms L M (McGrigors LLP)
London EC4 *p56* 020 7054 2500
Warburton, N R (Jones Knowles Warburton) *G H*
Stockport *p395* 0161 474 1992
Warburton, Mrs P M (Thorp Parker LLP) *W S1*
Stokesley *p398* 01642 711354
Warburton, S (Shakespeares) *N Zu Zj*
Birmingham *p142* 0121 237 3000
Warchester, Ms A S (Donns)
Manchester *p303* 0161 834 3311
Ward, Ms A (Shell International Ltd)
London SE1 *p109* 020 7934 1234
Ward, Mrs A (Cripps Harries Hall LLP) *O Zq*
Tunbridge Wells *p415* 01892 515121
Ward, A (Hamers Solicitors) *K4 K1 S1 W*
Hull *p257* 01482 326666
Ward, A (Simmons & Simmons)
London EC2 *p79* 020 7628 2020
Ward, A D (T Vincent Howells & Co) *S1 W L K1 M1 J1 F1 C1 P*
Harrow *p241* 020 8863 6655
Ward, Ms A H (Cartwright King) *Zm*
Nottingham *p336* 0115 958 7444
Derby *p209* 01332 225225
Ward, A J (Shearman & Sterling LLP) *Zb*
London EC2 *p78* 020 7655 5000
Ward, A R (Eastleigh Borough Council)
Eastleigh *p457* 023 8068 8068
Ward, Mrs A R (Addison O'Hare) *K1 O Q N*
Walsall *p419* 01922 725515
Ward, B (Jones Day) *E*
London EC4 *p46* 020 7039 5959
Ward, B M (Herbert Smith LLP) *C1 C2*
London EC2 *p40* 020 7374 8000
Ward, C (Donnelly McArdle Adamson) *K1 Q N*
Hartlepool *p243* 01429 274732
Ward, C (Penningtons)
Godalming *p231* 01483 791800
Ward, Ms C (Tollers LLP) *E*
Kettering *p265* 01536 520111
Ward, C (Greenland Houchen Pomeroy)
Norwich *p334* 01603 660744
Ward, C D (Hogan Lovells International LLP)
London EC1 *p42* 020 7296 2000
Ward, Miss C L (The Generics Group AG) *C1*
Cambridge *p453* 01223 875200
Ward, Ms C M (Danbank Development Ltd)
Market Drayton *p465* 01630 658282
Ward, C M H (T A Capron & Co) *B1 C1 E J1 L R1 S1 T1 W Zi*
Grays *p233* 01375 378331
Ward, D (Keoghs LLP) *B2 N O Q*
Bolton *p149* 01204 677000
Ward, D (Atkinson Ritson) *S1 E W A1 G C1 L N B1 T1 Zd Zl*
Carlisle *p181* 01228 525221
Ward, D (DW Solicitors) *E S2 S1 O Q L C1 J1 W*
Northampton *p331* 01604 624222
Ward, Ms D (O'Neill Morgan Solicitors Limited) *N K1*
Stockport *p396* 0161 429 8383
Ward, Mrs D J (Davies Johnson & Co (Shipping & Commercial Solicitors)) *N Q O Za M2 A3 Zq*
Plymouth *p349* 01752 226020
Ward, D J (Andrew Jackson) *Za*
Hull *p257* 01482 325242
Ward, D J (Gisby Harrison) *E*
Cheshunt *p189* 01707 878300
Ward, D J M (Speechly Bircham LLP) *Zo T2 W*
London EC4 *p81* 020 7427 6400
Ward, Ms D S (Squire Sanders (UK) LLP)
Birmingham *p142* 0121 222 3000
Ward, Ms E M (hlw Keeble Hawson LLP)
Leeds *p274* 0113 244 3121
Ward, Mrs F T (Jobling & Knape) *K4 K1 W*
Lancaster *p269* 01524 598300
Ward, G C (Ashurst LLP)
London EC2 *p7* 020 7638 1111
Ward, G D (Healys LLP) *E S2 R2 S1*
London EC4 *p39* 020 7822 4000
Ward, G M (North East Lincolnshire Borough Council) *N O K1 D1 F1 V B1 J1 Zq*
Cleethorpes *p455* 01472 324001
Ward, Lady H M (Manches LLP) *K1*
London WC2 *p58* 020 7404 4433
Ward, I (Dickinson Dees) *E*
Newcastle upon Tyne *p324* 0191 279 9000
Ward, J (Lee Bolton Monier-Williams) *T2 W*
Westminster *p52* 020 7222 5381
Ward, Ms J C (Barlow Lyde & Gilbert LLP) *O Zj Za A3*
London EC3 *p10* 020 7247 2277
Ward, J F (Brindley Twist Tafft & James) *Q*
Coventry *p200* 024 7653 1532
Ward, J G (Sheffield City Council)
Sheffield *p471* 0114 273 4019
Ward, J J (Beale and Company Solicitors LLP) *O C1 P M1 Zc Zj Zq A3 M2*
London WC2 *p11* 020 7240 3474
Ward, J J (Napthens LLP) *W*
Preston *p357* 01772 888444
Ward, J O (Osman Ward & Sons) *S1 W K4*
Hove *p255* 01273 778787 / 778788
Ward, J P (Stephenson Harwood)
London EC2 *p82* 020 7329 4422
Ward, Miss K J (Brooke-Taylors) *W K3 S2 D1 E G H J1 K1 L Q S1*
Buxton *p172* 01298 22741
Ward, Mrs L (Greenland Houchen Pomeroy)
Norwich *p334* 01603 660744
Ward, Mrs L N (Stewarts Law LLP) *O*
London EC4 *p83* 020 7822 8000
Ward, M (Robinsons) *K1 D1*
Ilkeston *p261* 0115 932 4101
Ward, M (Blake Lapthorn) *E*
Oxford *p342* 01865 248607
Ward, M A (Hibberts LLP) *A1 E Q S1 W*
Nantwich *p320* 01270 624225
Ward, Ms M A (Carter Bells LLP) *S1 E*
Kingston upon Thames *p267* 020 8939 4000
Ward, M J (Saunders Goodin Riddleston Solicitors) *K1 D1 K2*
Ipswich *p263* 01473 225600
Ward, M J (Gateley LLP) *C1 Zb Zo*
Birmingham *p138* 0121 234 0000
Ward, Miss M M J (Macrory Ward) *B1 C1 S2 E K1 L Zl R2 Zv S1 T2 W*
Barnet *p124* 020 8440 3258
Ward, M R (Taylor & Emmet LLP) *S1*
Sheffield *p377* 0114 218 4000
Ward, M R (Michael Ward) *S1 E K1 G N D1 W P F1 J1*
Sheffield *p377* 0114 233 6198
Ward, M V (Gregsons) *S1*
London SW19 *p37* 020 8946 1173
Ward, Miss N (Thursfields) *K1*
Stourport-on-Severn *p399* 01299 827517
Ward, N G (Eric Wright Group Ltd) *E*
Bamber Bridge *p448* 01772 698822
Ward, N H (Read Dunn Connell) *Zd S2 E W S1*
Ilkley *p261* 01943 601173
Bradford *p154* 01274 723858
Ward, N T (Ashurst LLP) *C1 B1 Zb*
London EC2 *p7* 020 7638 1111
Ward, P C (Trowers & Hamlins) *E*
London EC3 *p88* 020 7423 8000
Ward, P J (James & Co)
Brighton *p159* 01273 665470
Ward, P J (Turner Atkinson & Ward) *S1 G K1 C1 E P M1 W J1 H Zb Zf Zh*
Mansfield *p312* 01623 823450
Worksop *p441* 01909 473489
Ward, P J (Chronnell Hibbert) *K1 D1 G H*
Hyde *p259* 0161 368 3434
Ward, P L (Rich & Carr Freer Bouskell) *W A1 S1 T1 Zd Zi*
Leicester *p281* 0116 253 8021
Ward, R (Kidd & Spoor) *K3 K1*
Whitley Bay *p431* 0191 297 0011
Ward, R G (Hodders) *D1 D2 K1*
London NW10 *p41* 020 8838 1537
Ward, R J (Bird & Bird LLP) *T1*
London EC4 *p13* 020 7415 6000
Ward, Mrs R J (Wilkins) *W S1 E L T1*
Aylesbury *p121* 01296 424681

See p634 for the Key to Work Categories

Ward, Miss S (Stanley Tee) *K1 W D1*
Braintree *p155* 01376 552277

Ward, S (Akermans) *C1 F1 J1 L O F2 S2*
Worthing *p441* 01903 820413

Ward, Miss S (Environment Agency (Anglian Region))
Peterborough *p468* 01733 371811

Ward, S (hlw Keeble Hawson LLP) *F1 O Q*
Sheffield *p375* 0114 272 2061

Ward, Miss S (Hampshire County Council)
Winchester *p476* 01962 841841

Ward, S D (Wigan Borough Council) *N K1 L Q*
Wigan *p476* 01942 244991

Ward, S D (Derrick Bridges & Co) *S1 L W G H Q K1 J1 V D1 Zi Zm*
Barnet *p123* 020 8449 7326

Ward, S J (George Ide LLP)
Chichester *p192* 01243 786668

Ward, Miss S L (Baxter Caulfield) *O Q N Zl*
Huddersfield *p255* 01484 519519

Ward, S P P (H F T Gough & Co) *G H K1 F1 F2 Q N L J1 J2 B1 Zl*
Whitehaven *p431* 01946 692461

Ward, T (BPE Solicitors LLP) *C2 C1*
Cheltenham *p187* 01242 224433

Ward, T (Linder Myers Solicitors)
Manchester *p306* 0844 984 6000

Ward, T J (Radcliffes Le Brasseur) *Zl Zf O*
Leeds *p276* 0113 234 1220

Ward, Miss T L (Meaby & Co Trading as Hart Scales & Hodges)
Dorking *p212* 01306 884432

Ward, Ms V A (Atteys)
Doncaster *p211* 01302 340400

Ward, W A (Patterson Glenton & Stracey) *D1 G H K1 M1 S1 W*
South Shields *p384* 0800 011 6487

Ward-Jones, R (Rentokil Initial PLC)
London SW1 *p108* 020 7592 2700

Ward-Lowery, Dr N J L (Heptonstalls LLP) *Zr*
Scunthorpe *p373* 01724 289959

Ward-Smith, Miss C (Fishburns) *Zj O Q Zo A3 Zc*
London EC3 *p32* 020 7280 8888

Warden, Miss E L (TV Edwards LLP) *G H B2*
London EC3 *p85* 020 7790 7000

Warden, J S (Rosalind Watchorn) *S2 E S1 W*
Sheffield *p377* 0114 229 0160

Warder, D J (Watson Farley & Williams)
London EC2 *p90* 020 7814 8000

Wardle, J A (Newcastle Upon Tyne City Council)
Newcastle upon Tyne *p466* 0191 232 8520

Wardle, J D (Watson Farley & Williams)
London EC2 *p90* 020 7814 8000

Wardle, Miss J J (British Telecommunications PLC)
London EC1 *p104* 020 7356 6181

Wardley, J F (Pictons Solicitors LLP)
Luton *p295* 01582 870870

Wardley, M R (Straw & Pearce) *G H*
Loughborough *p293* 01509 268931

Wardley-Tipple, Mrs K (Alsters Kelley) *E*
Leamington Spa *p270* 0844 561 0100

Wardrop, M C (Pictons Solicitors LLP) *N Q*
Milton Keynes *p317* 01908 663511

Wardrope, Mrs E (Rawlison Butler LLP)
Horsham *p253* 01403 252492

Wardropper, Miss S L (Gotelee) *K1*
Ipswich *p262* 01473 211121
Milton Keynes *p317* 01908 696002

Ware, A L (Cowling Swift & Kitchin)
York *p444* 01904 625678 / 625679
Boroughbridge *p150* 01423 322312

Ware, Mrs A M (Aviva PLC)
London EC3 *p103* 020 7283 7500 / 01603 687905
Norwich *p467* 01603 622200

Ware, Mrs D J (Stephens & Scown) *S1*
St Austell *p391* 01726 74433

Ware, D W B (Wake Smith & Tofields) *C2 C1 M2 P M1 C3 T1 J2 X Zb Ze*
Sheffield *p377* 0114 266 6660

Ware, R R H (Morecrofts Solicitors LLP)
Liverpool *p290* 0151 236 8871

Ware, T G (Shell International Ltd)
London SE1 *p109* 020 7934 1234

Ware, W R R (Warner Goodman LLP) *N W*
Fareham *p224* 01329 288121

Wareham, A J (Gregg Latchams LLP) *W K4 T2*
Bristol *p162* 0117 906 9400

Wareham, S J (Bonnetts Solicitors LLP) *S1 E*
Hounslow *p253* 020 8570 5286

Wareing, A D (Wilkin Chapman LLP) *K2 K1 D1 V*
Grimsby *p235* 01472 262626

Wareing, D (Hill Dickinson LLP)
Manchester *p305* 0161 817 7200

Wareing, I D (Higgins & Co) *B2 G*
Birkenhead *p134* 0151 653 5222

Warfield, R G (Knowles Benning) *G H D1 R1 Zl Zp Zm*
Luton *p295* 01582 798000

Wargent, N (K&L Gates LLP) *C1 C2*
London EC4 *p47* 020 7648 9000

Waring, Mrs A D E (CGM) *S1 S2 E*
Southampton *p385* 023 8063 2733
Southampton *p386* 023 8084 2765

Waring, C J (Warings Solicitors) *S1 W B1 E K1 M1 P C1 F1 L*
Blackpool *p147* 01253 293106

Waring, D R (DWF) *N*
Liverpool *p287* 0151 907 3000

Waring, Miss J A (Morecrofts Solicitors LLP) *K1 D1*
Liverpool *p290* 0151 236 8871

Waring, J P (CGM) *K1 S2*
Southampton *p385* 023 8063 2733

Waring, M (The College of Law Chester)
Chester *p454* 0800 289997

Waring, Ms V (Squire Sanders (UK) LLP)
Leeds *p277* 0113 284 7000

Warlow, A P (Wolferstans) *N*
Plymouth *p351* 01752 663295

Warman, Ms F (Williamson & Soden) *G H B2*
Solihull *p383* 0121 733 8000

Warman, H (Principality Building Society)
Cardiff *p453* 029 2038 2000

Warman, P J (Leathes Prior) *C1 U2 C2*
Norwich *p334* 01603 610911

Warman, Ms V C (Kimbells LLP) *S2 E*
Milton Keynes *p317* 01908 668555

Warmingham, G J (The College of Law Guildford)
Guildford *p459* 01483 460200

Warn, T J (The Environment Agency (North West Region [HQ]))
Warrington *p475* 01925 653999

Warnapala, H U (Warnapala & Co Ltd) *N Zh Zi*
Southall *p385* 020 8571 1823

Warnapala, N K (Warnapala & Co Ltd) *V Zi*
Southall *p385* 020 8571 1823

Warnapala, S (Polpitiya & Co) *Zi V*
Southall *p384* 020 8813 9282

Warne, B J (hlw Keeble Hawson LLP) *J1*
Sheffield *p376* 0114 276 5555

Warne, D G (Reed Smith LLP) *N B1*
London EC2 *p71* 020 3116 3000

Warne, Ms I (Gilbert Stephens) *W*
Exeter *p221* 01392 424242

Warne, J D (Nabarro LLP)
London WC1 *p63* 020 7524 6000

Warne, Mrs S P (CMS Cameron McKenna LLP) *C1 E S1*
London EC3 *p17* 020 7367 3000

Warne, T M (Peters Langsford Davies) *N Q O K1 L F1 J1 B1 Zl Zc Zp Zq D1*
Launceston *p270* 01566 772451

Warner, A R (Hadgkiss Hughes & Beale) *S1 W S2 E*
Birmingham *p138* 0121 449 5050

Warner, C (Waddington & Son) *K1 D1*
Burnley *p169* 01282 426666

Warner, C J (Warners Solicitors) *C1 T2 W Zd Zw*
Tonbridge *p412* 01732 770660

Warner, Mrs D P W (Julia Frimond Solicitors) *S1 W*
Guildford *p236* 01483 452224

Warner, E (Langleys)
York *p445* 01904 610886

Warner, Miss K R (James Mason Tucker) *A2 S1 S2 E*
Newton Abbot *p329* 01626 204060

Warner, Mrs M V L (Wycombe & Beaconsfield Magistrates Court)
High Wycombe *p461* 01494 651035

Warner, R L A (Bray & Dilks) *S1 G H L E A1 Zl S2*
Truro *p414* 01872 271717

Warner, S J (Maclaren Warner) *C1 E L R1 S1*
Beeston *p130* 0115 943 6696
Stapleford *p394* 0115 939 5252

Warner, T D (Geoffrey Leaver Solicitors LLP) *K1 G Q Zl*
Milton Keynes *p317* 01908 692769

Warner, Miss T M (T M Warner & Co) *S1 S2 W*
Kidlington *p266* 01865 379311

Warner, V (Anderson & Company) *C1 L J1 E Ze*
Shillingford *p378* 01865 858878

Warner, Mrs V S (Wallace Robinson & Morgan) *W*
Solihull *p383* 0121 705 7571

Warner-Smith, Ms E A (Magnox Electric PLC)
Berkeley *p449* 01452 652222 / 01453 813484

Warnock-Smith, A (Morgan Lewis & Bockius) *C1 C2 M1 F1 Ze Zy*
London EC4 *p61* 020 3201 5000

Warran-Smith, Mrs F (Thomson Snell & Passmore) *E L Zc*
Tunbridge Wells *p415* 01892 510000

Warren, A N H (Burges Salmon)
Bristol *p161* 0117 939 2000

Warren, Miss H M (Pritchard Joyce & Hinds) *D1 K3 K1*
Beckenham *p129* 020 8658 3922

Warren, Mrs J M (Taylor Vinters) *E S1 L*
Cambridge *p176* 01223 423444

Warren, L (Ross Coates) *Zc E L S1*
Ipswich *p263* 01473 695400

Warren, Ms L C (Downs) *B1*
Dorking *p212* 01306 880110

Warren, Mrs L S (Linda S Warren) *S1 S2 W*
Northwood *p333* 01923 821213

Warren, M M (Bristows) *C1 C3 Ze M1 I*
London EC4 *p15* 020 7400 8000

Warren, M R (BTMK Solicitors LLP) *G H*
Southend-on-Sea *p387* 01702 339222

Warren, Miss R (Michelmores LLP) *O Q Ze A3 F2 Zk Zq*
Exeter *p221* 01392 688688

Warren, R C (Woodford Robinson) *D1 G H K1*
Northampton *p333* 01604 624926

Warren, R S R (Rodney Warren & Co) *G H B2 Zl*
Eastbourne *p216* 01323 430430

Warren, Mrs S (Burt Brill & Cardens) *S1*
Brighton *p159* 01273 604123

Warren, Ms S C L (Hugh James) *N*
Cardiff *p179* 029 2022 4871

Warren, Mrs S T (The Stokes Partnership) *E S1*
Crewkerne *p203* 01460 279279

Warren, T B (Pothecary Witham Weld) *Zd Zx E C1*
Westminster *p69* 020 7821 8211

Warren-Dickens, C (Trowers & Hamlins)
London EC3 *p88* 020 7423 8000

Warren-Jones, M P (Squire Sanders (UK) LLP)
Manchester *p310* 0161 830 5000

Warrilow, Miss S (MFG Solicitors) *K1*
Kidderminster *p265* 01562 820181

Warriner, G (Ison Harrison) *N*
Leeds *p274* 0113 284 5000

Warriner, N (Herbert Smith LLP) *C1 T1 C2*
London EC2 *p40* 020 7374 8000

Warrington, G (Pinsent Masons LLP) *C3*
Birmingham *p141* 0121 200 1050

Warrington, Mrs R (Kendall & Davies)
Moreton-in-Marsh *p319* 01608 650312

Warry, J R (James Warry & Co) *S1 S2 K3 W*
Coleford *p198* 01594 833184

Warsop, Mrs R J (Maurice Smiths) *R1 R2 S1 S2 W*
Castleford *p183* 01977 557171
Pontefract *p351* 01977 794395

Warwick, Ms E (Wilkin Chapman LLP) *B1 N Q*
Grimsby *p235* 01472 262626

Warwick, Miss K (Hough Halton & Soal) *N*
Carlisle *p182* 01228 524379

Warwick, N K (Dickinson Dees) *C1 C3*
Newcastle upon Tyne *p324* 0191 279 9000

Warwick, Ms S L (Kundert & Co) *K1 D1*
Coventry *p200* 024 7668 4928

Wasem, R E (Bates NVH) *S1 W E*
Fleet *p226* 01252 629292

Washington, J (Grindeys LLP) *B1 J1 Q*
Stoke-on-Trent *p397* 01782 846441

Washington, Ms K (Grindeys LLP) *A1 Zb Zc Zd E P L R1 S1*
Stoke-on-Trent *p397* 01782 846441

Washington, P R (Newcastle Under Lyme Borough Council)
Newcastle Under Lyme *p466* 01782 717717

Waskett, J D (Keppe & Partners Solicitors) *G H X*
Twickenham *p416* 020 8891 4488

Wasling, Mrs S L (Myer Wolff) *K3 K1*
Hull *p257* 01482 223693

Wason, S (Wason & Co) *E S1 C1 S2 L W Zl*
Potters Bar *p355* 01707 664888

Wass, W B S (Warners Solicitors) *E L R2 S2*
Tonbridge *p412* 01732 770660

Wassall, R G (Coffin Mew & Clover) *P L B1 F1 O Q Zh Zq Zg*
Fareham *p223* 01329 825617

Wasserberg, V L (Goodman Ray) *K1 D1 D2*
Hackney *p36* 020 7608 1227

Wastie, W (Addleshaw Goddard)
London EC1 *p4* 020 7606 8855

Watchorn, Ms R A (Rosalind Watchorn) *W T2 K4*
Sheffield *p377* 0114 229 0160

Waterfield, P (Universal Pictures International Ltd)
London WC1 *p110* 020 7079 6000

Waterfield, S I (Nelsons)
Nottingham *p338* 0115 958 6262

Waterfield, Ms S J (Waldrons) *D1 D2 K1*
Brierley Hill *p158* 01384 811811

Waterhouse, A J H (Turner & Wall) *D1 V*
Keighley *p264* 01535 607831

Waterhouse, J P (J P Waterhouse & Co) *F1 G H J1 K1 L M1 S1 V*
Banbury *p122* 01295 267555

Waterhouse, Ms L (Derbyshire County Council) *D1 X K4 J1 Zu Zm*
Matlock *p465* 01629 580000

Waterman, H J (Sidley Austin Brown & Wood) *Zb*
London EC2 *p78* 020 7360 3600

Watermeyer, Mrs V (Dolmans) *N*
Cardiff *p178* 029 2034 5531

Waters, Mrs A (CKFT)
London NW3 *p17* 020 7431 7262

Waters, B (Harding Evans LLP) *G H*
Newport *p328* 01633 244233

Waters, Miss C (Fisher Scoggins Waters LLP) *Q J2*
London EC4 *p32* 020 7489 2035

Waters, C J (Mortimers)
Bridgnorth *p157* 01746 761000

Waters, Ms E J (Birkett Long LLP) *W*
Chelmsford *p186* 01245 453800

Waters, Miss F (Curtis Davis Garrard) *A3 O Za*
Uxbridge *p417* 020 8734 2800

Waters, J (Stephen Rimmer LLP) *L O Q N*
Eastbourne *p216* 01323 644222

Waters, J S (Hay & Kilner) *E C1 S2*
Newcastle upon Tyne *p325* 0191 232 8345

Waters, Miss K L (Clarion Solicitors LLP) *J1 Zp*
Leeds *p272* 0113 246 0622

Waters, M J (Barlow Lyde & Gilbert LLP)
London EC3 *p10* 020 7247 2277

Waters, P (Ayres Waters) *K1 D1*
Stockport *p395* 0161 480 5229

Waters, P J (Aplin Stockton Fairfax) *O W K4*
Banbury *p122* 01295 251234

Waters, R (GHP Legal) *F1 F2 Zza Q*
Wrexham *p442* 01978 291456

Waters, Ms T C (Waters & Co) *W F1 J1 Q S1*
Birmingham *p143* 01675 463855

Waters, V L B (Waters & Co) *B1 C1 E F1 L N P S1*
Birmingham *p143* 01675 463855

Waters, Miss V N (Nottingham City Council (City Sec Dept))
Nottingham *p467* 0115 915 5555

Waterson, Miss J E (John Pickering & Partners LLP) *N W*
Halifax *p238* 0808 144 0959

Wathan, Miss N (Barcan Woodward) *K1 D1*
Bristol *p160* 0117 963 5237

Wathen, Ms M (Harrison Clark LLP) *E*
Cheltenham *p188* 01242 269198
Worcester *p439* 01905 612001
Worcester *p439* 01905 612001

Watkin, L J (Steele Raymond) *E R2 P S2 Zc*
Bournemouth *p152* 01202 294566

Watkin, N E A (Watkin & Co) *E S2 R2 S1 O K3 L W Q*
Sutton Coldfield *p404* 0121 321 2200

Watkin, R M (Brabners Chaffe Street) *A1 O Q E L Zq R2*
Liverpool *p286* 0151 600 3000

Watkin, R O (Ceredigion County Council)
Aberaeron *p447* 01545 570881

Watkins, Mrs D (Gordon Jones & Co) *S1 S2 E W C1*
Birmingham *p139* 0121 453 8151

Watkins, D E (Wilkinson & Butler) *W S1 T2 Zm*
St Neots *p392* 01480 219229

Watkins, D L (Wilson Browne) *D1 D2 K1*
Kettering *p265* 01536 410041

Watkins, D M (Benson Watkins) *E J1 S1 T1 W*
Swansea *p404* 01792 704320

Watkins, D T (David Watkins) *S1 W L N K1*
Pontypridd *p352* 01443 409401

Watkins, D W (Linklaters LLP)
London EC2 *p54* 020 7456 2000

Watkins, E M (Brabners Chaffe Street) *Zw Q*
Manchester *p301* 0161 836 8800

Watkins, Ms G (Gail Watkins & Co)
Birmingham *p143* 0121 427 9583

Watkins, G (Nabarro LLP)
Sheffield *p376* 0114 279 4000

Watkins, Ms H (Davies & Partners) *N Zr*
Birmingham *p137* 0121 616 4450

Watkins, J (DLA Piper UK LLP)
Manchester *p303* 0870 011 1111

Watkins, J K G (RG Legal Solicitors) *O E S2 Q S1*
Cardiff *p180* 029 2049 0047

Watkins, Ms L (Harding Evans LLP) *Zr*
Newport *p328* 01633 244233

Watkins, Ms L A (Spicketts Battrick Law Practice) *D1 K1*
Pontypridd *p352* 01443 407221

Watkins, Miss M C (Hugh James) *L O Q B1 Zh*
Cardiff *p179* 029 2022 4871

Watkins, N G (Hill Hofstetter LLP) *E R2*
Solihull *p382* 0121 210 6000

Watkins, N P (Bolitho Way) *C1 S1 T1 W N E Ze Zc Zo*
Portsmouth *p354* 023 9282 0747

Watkins, P (Neath Port Talbot County Borough Council)
Port Talbot *p469* 01639 763333

Watkins, P (Beviss & Beckingsale)
Seaton *p373* 01297 626950
Helston *p246* 01326 555800

Watkins, Mrs R (McGrigors LLP)
London EC4 *p56* 020 7054 2500

Watkins, R A (Martyn Prowel) *G H P B2 J2*
Cardiff *p180* 029 2047 0909

Watkins, R A J (Thursfields) *S1 E W L B1 C1 C2 T2*
Worcester *p440* 01905 730450

Watkins, Mrs R C (Eastgate Assistance Ltd) *D1 F1 K1 N Q S1 W X Zj*
Colchester *p455* 0870 523 4500

Watkins, Miss R J (Squire Sanders (UK) LLP) *J1 J2 C1*
Leeds *p277* 0113 284 7000

Watkins, T (Clarke Willmott) *A3 Q Zw*
Bristol *p162* 0845 209 1000 / 0117 305 6000

Watkins, T J (Lewis Silkin LLP)
London EC4 *p53* 020 7074 8000

Watkinson, B K (Sheltons) *E S1 W L S2 Zl*
Nottingham *p339* 0115 955 3444

Watkinson, Mrs J C (Wrigleys Solicitors LLP) *S1 R2 Zc*
Sheffield *p377* 0114 267 5588

Watkinson, Mrs J M (Hillyer McKeown LLP) *J1*
Chester *p190* 01244 318131

Watkinson, R (Pinsent Masons LLP) *C1 U2*
Leeds *p276* 0113 244 5000

Watkinson, Ms S (Ashurst LLP)
London EC2 *p7* 020 7638 1111

Watkis, J B H (Alletsons) *K1 S1 E*
Burnham-on-Sea *p169* 01278 780151

Watkiss, Miss N J (O H Parsons & Partners) *N J1*
London WC2 *p66* 020 7379 7277

Watler, Mrs S M J (Rootes & Alliott) *V D1 Zm D2 J2 N*
Folkestone *p227* 01303 851100

Watling, S J (Walker Smith Way) *N*
Wrexham *p443* 0844 346 3100

Watmore, S C (Wiseman Lee LLP) *C1 Q O L*
Redbridge *p92* 020 8215 1000

Watmough, J P (Reynolds Porter Chamberlain LLP) *C1 C2*
London E1 *p71* 020 3060 6000

Watmough, Miss M (Penningtons) *Zb*
London EC2 *p66* 020 7457 3000

Watney, A J (Pinsent Masons LLP)
London EC2 *p67* 020 7418 7000

Watsham, R J (Field Seymour Parkes) *W S1 E T1 Zl Zd*
Reading *p360* 0118 951 6200

6

Watson, Mrs A (South Somerset District Council)
Yeovil *p477* . . . 01935 462462

Watson, A A (McDermott Will & Emery UK LLP)
London EC2 *p56* . . . 020 7577 6900

Watson, A D (Girlings) *O Q L A3*
Ashford *p119* . . . 01233 664711

Watson, A J (Squire Sanders (UK) LLP) *C1 C2 Zb Ze*
London EC2 *p81* . . . 020 7655 1000

Watson, A J P (Alasdair Watson & Co) *G H K1 S1 W D1 V*
Newcastle upon Tyne *p327* . 0191 488 4521

Watson, Miss A M (Pinsent Masons LLP) *O A3*
Manchester *p308* . . . 0161 234 8234

Watson, A S (Thomson Snell & Passmore) *N Zr*
Tunbridge Wells *p415* . . . 01892 510000

Watson, Miss B C (Cozens-Hardy LLP) *K1 K3 D1 D2*
Norwich *p334* . . . 01603 625231

Watson, C (O'Garra's) *G H*
Leeds *p276* . . . 0113 247 1477

Watson, Miss C J (George Ide LLP) *N M1 K1 P S1 L D1*
Chichester *p192* . . . 01243 786668

Watson, C K (Cockshott Peck Lewis) *S1 W E A1 R1 Zm Zd Zh C1 T2*
Southport *p388* . . . 01704 534034

Watson, Ms C L (Linklaters LLP)
London EC2 *p54* . . . 020 7456 2000

Watson, D (Norton Peskett)
Lowestoft *p294* . . . 01502 533000

Watson, D (Lazard & Co Ltd)
London W1 *p107* . . . 020 7187 2000

Watson, D A (Geldards LLP) *E S2*
Derby *p208* . . . 01332 331631

Watson, D G (Browns)
Princes Risborough *p358* . . 01844 344123

Watson, D J (Luton Borough Council)
Luton *p464* . . . 01582 546000

Watson, Ms E S (LG Lawyers)
London SE1 *p50* . . . 020 7379 0000

Watson, G (Ashurst LLP) *E Ze*
London EC2 *p7* . . . 020 7638 1111

Watson, G (Thomson Webb & Corfield) *S1*
Cambridge *p176* . . . 01223 518317

Watson, G (Brooke North LLP)
Leeds *p272* . . . 0113 283 2100

Watson, Mrs G C (Kennedys) *Zc Zj Zq*
London EC3 *p49* . . . 020 7667 9667

Watson, G J (Edward Hayes LLP) *S1 W*
Chichester *p192* . . . 01243 672124

Watson, Mrs H A (Aaron & Partners LLP Solicitors) *J1 J2 Q*
Chester *p190* . . . 01244 405555

Watson, Mrs H A (The College of Law Guildford)
Guildford *p459* . . . 01483 460200

Watson, H J (Herbert Smith LLP) *N*
London EC2 *p40* . . . 020 7374 8000

Watson, Ms J (Blanchards Bailey LLP) *S1*
Shaftesbury *p374* . . . 01747 440447

Watson, J (Watson Woodhouse)
Stockton-on-Tees *p397* . . . 01642 247656

Watson, Ms J (Simmons & Simmons)
London EC2 *p79* . . . 020 7628 2020

Watson, J (Tuckers) *N*
Manchester *p310* . . . 0161 233 4321

Watson, J (Taylor Wessing) *C2 C1*
London EC4 *p86* . . . 020 7300 7000

Watson, Ms J (Worthing Borough Council)
Worthing *p477* . . . 01903 239999

Watson, Mrs J E (Roebucks) *K1 D1 D2*
Blackburn *p145* . . . 01254 274000

Watson, J G (Ashurst LLP) *T1 Zo*
London EC2 *p7* . . . 020 7638 1111

Watson, Mrs J L (Wilkinson & Butler) *K1 G V N H D1*
St Neots *p392* . . . 01480 219229

Watson, Mrs J R (P B & W Solicitors LLP t/a Pooley Bendall & Watson) *S1 W*
Ely *p218* . . . 01353 666075

Watson, Ms K (London Borough of Greenwich Legal Services)
London SE18 *p106* . . . 020 8921 5123

Watson, Miss K (Kingsley Brookes) *G H*
Huddersfield *p256* . . . 01484 302800

Watson, Mrs L (The Watson Ramsbottom Partnership) *K1*
Blackburn *p146* . . . 01254 672222

Watson, Miss L (North Tyneside Council)
Newcastle upon Tyne *p466* . 0191 643 5000

Watson, L A F (Mowbray Woodwards Solicitors) *O Q J1 Zq N B1*
Bath *p128* . . . 01225 485700

Watson, Ms L H (Heaney Watson) *K1 K2 K3 D1 D2*
Liverpool *p288* . . . 0151 282 5555

Watson, Mrs L J (Watson Nevill) *E L S1 W C1 S2*
Maidstone *p299* . . . 01622 661177

Watson, Miss M (Bradbury Roberts & Raby) *N J1 Q Zr Zp*
Scunthorpe *p373* . . . 01724 854000

Watson, M A (Fox Williams) *J1 Zo Zi*
London EC2 *p33* . . . 020 7628 2000

Watson, M A (Watson Farley & Williams)
London EC2 *p90* . . . 020 7814 8000

Watson, M J (Portmans Solicitors)
Esher *p220* . . . 01372 464488

Watson, M R (Crombie Wilkinson) *F1 G H M1 N P*
York *p444* . . . 01904 624185

Watson, M R (Shulmans) *E O U1 A1 A3 Zc L R1*
Leeds *p276* . . . 0113 245 2833

Watson, M W (Trethowans LLP) *C2 C1 I Ze U2 F1*
Southampton *p387* . . . 023 8032 1000

Watson, N (Ince & Co Services Ltd)
London E1 *p44* . . . 020 7481 0010

Watson, N F (Travers Smith LLP) *C1 C2*
London EC1 *p87* . . . 020 7295 3000

Watson, Mrs N J (The Environment Agency (North West Region [HQ]))
Warrington *p475* . . . 01925 653999

Watson, N S J (Stone King LLP) *B1 J1 O Zc Ze*
Bath *p128* . . . 01225 337599

Watson, P G (Lattey & Dawe) *S1 S2 W*
London EC2 *p51* . . . 020 7623 2345

Watson, P J (AST Hampsons) *K1 N Q O B1 D1 F1 V J1*
Rochdale *p365* . . . 01706 522311

Watson, P J (Paul J Watson) *K1 M1 S1 G D1 H L V W F1 Zc Zj Zl*
Middlesbrough *p315* . . . 01642 293427

Watson, P M (Allen & Overy LLP)
London E1 *p5* . . . 020 3088 0000

Watson, P R (Simpson Millar LLP) *N*
Leeds *p276* . . . 0844 858 3200

Watson, R (Department for Business, Enterprise and Regulatory Reform)
London SW1 *p105* . . . 020 7215 0105

Watson, R A (Lattey & Dawe) *S1 S2 R2*
London EC2 *p51* . . . 020 7623 2345

Watson, R A V (Fitzhugh Gates) *W T1*
Brighton *p159* . . . 01273 686811

Watson, R C (Hill Dickinson LLP) *N Zr Q*
Liverpool *p288* . . . 0151 600 8000

Watson, R G (Brignalls Balderston Warren) *Q K1 O L J1 N F1*
Stevenage *p394* . . . 01438 359311

Watson, R G (Donald Galbraith & Co) *D1 K1*
London N12 *p34* . . . 020 8492 2700

Watson, Miss S (Edmondson Hall) *S1 S2*
Newmarket *p327* . . . 01638 560556

Watson, S J (Simmons & Simmons)
London EC2 *p79* . . . 020 7628 2020

Watson, Mrs S L (AST Hampsons) *M1 P K1 F1 W G B1 D1 L N*
Rochdale *p365* . . . 01706 522311

Watson, S M (CMS Cameron McKenna LLP)
London EC3 *p17* . . . 020 7367 3000

Watson, Ms T M (Jacobs & Reeves) *G H B2*
Poole *p353* . . . 01202 731849

Watson, Mrs U (Carr Hepburn Solicitors Ltd) *D1 K1*
Hemel Hempstead *p246* . . . 01442 241466

Watson, Mrs V A (McKinnells) *K1 K3 D1*
Lincoln *p284* . . . 01522 541181

Watson, Mrs V R (Burnetts) *Zr*
Carlisle *p181* . . . 01228 552222
Carlisle *p182* . . . 01228 552222

Watson, Miss W A (DLA Piper UK LLP) *B1 Zb*
London EC2 *p24* . . . 0870 011 1111

Watson, W A (Pinders) *K1 D1*
Derby *p209* . . . 01332 364751

Watson-Cook, Miss E L (RSPCA) *E*
Horsham *p461* . . . 0870 010 1181

Watson-Lee, Mrs A P (Williams Thompson) *W*
Christchurch *p194* . . . 01202 484242

Watson-Lee, P J (Williams Thompson) *K3 K1 W K4*
Christchurch *p194* . . . 01202 484242

Watson-Weinberg, A (The Johnson Partnership) *B2*
Nottingham *p337* . . . 0115 941 9141

Watt, Mrs A (HM Land Registry - Hull)
Hull *p461* . . . 01482 223244

Watt, A (Manches LLP) *C1 Zf O Ze Zl Zza*
London WC2 *p58* . . . 020 7404 4433

Watt, D J (EMW) *O Q F1*
Milton Keynes *p316* . . . 0845 070 6000
Milton Keynes *p317* . . . 01908 660966

Watt, L J (Charles Russell LLP) *O Q M2*
London EC4 *p19* . . . 020 7203 5000

Watt, Ms L U (George Ide LLP) *S1 E C1 L W T1 R1 K1 J1*
Chichester *p192* . . . 01243 786668

Watt, Ms S J (Welsh Health Legal Services) *N Zr*
Cardiff *p453* . . . 029 2031 5500

Watters, J A D (Watson Farley & Williams)
London EC2 *p90* . . . 020 7814 8000

Watters, J P (Okell & Stewart) *A1 W S1 E C1 C3 O N L*
Ross-on-Wye *p367* . . . 01989 762009

Watters, P J (J W Hughes & Co) *N Q L J1 F1 K1 W S1 G V*
Llandudno *p291* . . . 01492 874774

Watterson, M (Pepperells) *G H*
Scunthorpe *p373* . . . 01724 871999

Watts, A (Alsters Kelley) *E*
Leamington Spa *p270* . . . 0844 561 0100

Watts, Miss A J (Nockolds) *S1 W A1*
Bishop's Stortford *p144* . . . 01279 755777

Watts, A T (Herbert Smith LLP) *O Zf Zw A3*
London EC2 *p40* . . . 020 7374 8000

Watts, Mrs C (Hart Brown Solicitors) *E*
Guildford *p236* . . . 0800 068 8177

Watts, Mrs C A (Oxfordshire County Council)
Oxford *p468* . . . 01865 792422

Watts, C R (Osborne Clarke) *C1*
Bristol *p164* . . . 0117 917 3000

Watts, D (Nelsons) *G H*
Leicester *p280* . . . 0116 222 6666

Watts, Mrs E C E (Wansbroughs) *N Q*
Devizes *p210* . . . 01380 733300

Watts, Mrs G M (Rowe Radcliffe) *W*
South Croydon *p383* . . . 020 8680 2070

Watts, H (Bedwell Watts & Co) *S1 W L A1 K1 F1 G N T1*
Scarborough *p372* . 01723 373356 / 363553

Watts, Ms H L (The National Trust)
Swindon *p475* . . . 01793 817400

Watts, J (Forrester & Forrester) *A1 E S1*
Chippenham *p193* . . . 01249 444300

Watts, Ms J (Wheltons) *K1 K3*
Guildford *p237* . . . 01483 537633

Watts, Mrs J A (Bracknell Forest Borough Council)
Bracknell *p450* . . . 01344 424642

Watts, Dr J J S (Bristows) *O I M1 T1 Ze Zd*
London EC4 *p15* . . . 020 7400 8000

Watts, J M (W J Williams & Davies)
Cardigan *p181* . . . 01239 612262

Watts, Mrs J R (Tallents Solicitors) *W S1 E S2 Zd A1*
Southwell *p389* . . . 01636 813411

Watts, J R (M J Payton & Co) *D2 K1*
Malvern *p300* . . . 01684 563318

Watts, Ms K (Hogan Lovells International LLP) *E S2 R2*
London EC1 *p42* . . . 020 7296 2000
London EC2 *p58* . . . 020 7600 3800

Watts, Miss L (Wendy Hopkins Family Law Practice LLP) *K1 D1 K3*
Cardiff *p178* . . . 029 2034 2233

Watts, Mrs L (Plexus Law (A Trading Name of Parabis Law LLP)) *A3 J2 N Zj*
Leeds *p276* . . . 0844 245 4100

Watts, Mrs L M (Loughridge Bowler) *K4 W V T2*
Coventry *p200* . . . 024 7663 1632

Watts, Ms M L (Diageo PLC)
London W1 *p105* . . . 020 7927 5300

Watts, Miss N (Radcliffes Le Brasseur) *E*
Leeds *p276* . . . 0113 234 1220

Watts, N A (John Fowlers LLP Solicitors)
Colchester *p197* . . . 01206 576151

Watts, P (Northumberland County Council)
Morpeth *p466* . . . 01670 533000

Watts, P D (Hogan Lovells International LLP)
London EC1 *p42* . . . 020 7296 2000

Watts, R J (Ratcliffe Duce & Gammer LLP) *S2 S1 C1*
Reading *p361* . . . 0118 957 4291

Watts, Ms S B (Allen & Overy LLP)
London E1 *p5* . . . 020 3088 0000

Watts, Mrs S J (Birmingham City Council Legal & Democratic Services)
Birmingham *p449* . . . 0121 303 2066

Watts, S P (Dickinson Dees) *C1 C2*
Newcastle upon Tyne *p324* . 0191 279 9000

Watts, T E (Reed Smith LLP) *C1 C2*
London EC2 *p71* . . . 020 3116 3000

Watts, Mrs V L (Cambridge City Council)
Cambridge *p452* . . . 01223 457000

Waudby, Miss C E (Bolton Metropolitan Borough Council) *R1 P*
Bolton *p450* . . . 01204 333333

Waugh, Ms E (City of Sunderland)
Sunderland *p473* . . . 0191 520 5555

Waugh, Ms S L (SAS Daniels LLP) *K4 W*
Stockport *p396* . . . 0161 475 7676

Waugh, Ms V G (V G Waugh) *G K1 N S1 H D1*
Peterlee *p348* . . . 0191 527 2727

Wawiye, L (Clarke Kiernan)
Tonbridge *p412* . . . 01732 360999

Wax, Ms S J (Finers Stephens Innocent LLP) *C1 C2*
London W1 *p32* . . . 020 7323 4000

Waxler, Ms R (Citi Financial Europe PLC)
London E14 *p469*

Waxman, S (Sills & Betteridge LLP) *G*
Boston *p151* . . . 01205 364615

Way, A P (Latimer Hinks)
Darlington *p206* . . . 01325 341500

Way, Mrs J A (Radcliffes Le Brasseur) *Zr N Zq*
Westminster *p70* . . . 020 7222 7040

Way, J D (Pope & Co) *K1 N Q W L J1 S2 F1 K4 K3*
Sittingbourne *p380* . . . 01795 474004

Waygood, M J (Cardiff Magistrates Court)
Cardiff *p453* . . . 029 2046 3040

Wayman, T J (The Beavis Partnership) *S2 E C1 K1 J1 L S1 W*
Chelmsford *p186* . . . 01245 264748
Witham *p435* . . . 01376 500255

Wayne, H N (Wayne Leighton) *E S1 R2 S2 C1*
Edgware *p217* . . . 020 8951 2988

Wayne, R (Medlicott Snows) *C1 E L Q S1 W S2 A1*
Bishops Castle *p145* . . . 01588 638425

Wayt, J L (Lancasters) *S1 W J1 S2*
Epsom *p219* . . . 01372 724931

Wayte, P B (DLA Piper UK LLP)
London EC2 *p24* . . . 0870 011 1111

Weakley, Ms J (Field Fisher Waterhouse LLP)
London EC3 *p31* . . . 020 7861 4000

Weale, Miss S E (Cardiff County Council)
Cardiff *p453* . . . 029 2087 2000

Wealleans, Miss S J (Attwaters) *Zr N*
Harlow *p239* . . . 01279 638888

Weare, J (Jones Day) *O*
London EC4 *p46* . . . 020 7039 5959

Weare, R (Kitsons LLP) *L Q*
Torquay *p413* . . . 01803 202020

Wearing, J H (Anthony Collins Solicitors LLP) *C1 C2 T1 Zd Ze*
Birmingham *p137* . . . 0121 200 3242

Wearing, J L M (Berry & Berry) *N*
Eccles *p216* . . . 0161 789 7414
Leeds *p274* . . . 0113 284 5000

Weate, J A (Roberts Moore Nicholas Jones) *G H*
Birkenhead *p134* . . . 0151 647 0000

Weatherby, Ms A C (Emerson Developments (Holdings) Ltd)
Alderley Edge *p447* . . . 01625 588420

Weatherby, M (Pattinson & Brewer) *N Q L*
London WC1 *p66* . . . 020 7400 5100

Weatherill, B N A (Wedlake Bell LLP) *C1 Zw*
London WC1 *p91* . . . 020 7395 3000

Weatherill, Ms L M (Battens) *K1*
Yeovil *p443* . . . 01935 846000

Weatherley-Wright, Mrs C (Hethertons LLP) *S1*
York *p445* . . . 01904 528200

Weatherly, Ms J (Weightmans LLP)
Liverpool *p291* . . . 0151 227 2601

Weaver, A P (Inghams) *N Q*
Fleetwood *p226* . . . 01253 873481

Weaver, F A (Kingsley Napley) *A1 B1 C1 E L R1 S1*
London EC1 *p50* . . . 020 7814 1200

Weaver, Ms J (Walker Morris) *E*
Leeds *p277* . . . 0113 283 2500

Weaver, J A (Edward Pilling & Co) *K1 Q W N F1 L S1*
Oxford *p344* . . . 01865 741122

Weaver, J G (Woodford Robinson) *G S1 H P J1 W*
Northampton *p333* . . . 01604 624926

Weaver, Mrs J M (Graham M Riley & Co) *N Q*
Southport *p388* . . . 01704 532229

Weaver, J P (Walker Smith Way) *Zc F1 Zk O Q Zq*
Chester *p191* . . . 0844 346 3100

Weaver, K (Lanyon Bowdler LLP) *N*
Shrewsbury *p379* . . . 01743 280280

Weaver, M S (Burstalls) *J1 Q O N I*
Hull *p256* . . . 01482 621800

Weaver, P (Pitmans LLP) *C1 C2 Ze I*
Reading *p361* . . . 0118 958 0224

Weaver, Miss P A (Flint Bishop Solicitors) *W S1 A1 L T2*
Ashbourne *p118* . . . 01335 342208
Derby *p208* . . . 01332 340211

Weaver, Mrs R A (F B Jevons Riley & Pope) *W*
Edenbridge *p216* . . . 01732 864411

Weavill, Ms H (Alison Fielden & Co) *K1 K3 D1*
Cirencester *p195* . . . 01285 653261

Webb, A (J A Kemp & Co)
London WC1 *p48* . . . 020 7405 3292

Webb, A (Andrew Webb) *H Zm*
Bristol *p165* . . . 0117 953 8408

Webb, Mrs A D (Hopkins) *N*
Mansfield *p311* . . . 01623 468468

Webb, Miss A J (Kenneth Bush) *D1 K1 K3*
King's Lynn *p266* . . . 01553 692737

Webb, A L (Dutton Gregory) *D1 K1 F1 H V Zm Zl*
Winchester *p433* . . . 01962 844333

Webb, A L (Anthony Leonard Associates) *T2 W N S1 Q O F1 K1 E*
Croydon *p205* . . . 020 8288 3548

Webb, B L (Angel Trains Ltd)
London SW1 *p103* . . . 020 7592 0500

Webb, Mrs C (Verisona Solicitors) *K1 G L D1 Q*
Waterlooville *p423* . . . 023 9226 5251

Webb, Ms C A (Howard Pollok & Webb) *S1 E C1 C2 W L A1 F1 R1 V*
Norwich *p334* . . . 01603 660051
Great Yarmouth *p234* . . . 01493 853725

Webb, D (Desor & Co) *D2 D1 K3 K1 Q N Zq S1 W O L F1 S2*
Hayes *p245* . . . 020 8569 0708

Webb, D A (David Webb & Co) *F1 N O Q E S2 K3*
Westcliff-on-Sea *p428* . . . 01702 392939

Webb, D J (D J Webb & Co) *Zi*
London E1 *p90* . . . 020 7480 5999

Webb, D J (Dennis J Webb) *S1 E C1 S2*
Worthing *p442* . . . 01903 236006

Webb, D M (Mander Hadley & Co) *T1 W T2*
Coventry *p200* . . . 024 7663 1212

Webb, D R (Matthew & Matthew Limited) *W S1 S2*
Southbourne *p387* . . . 01202 431943

Webb, E (HC Solicitors LLP) *G H Zm*
Peterborough *p347* . . . 01733 882800

Webb, Ms E A (Kerseys) *K1 K3 D1*
Ipswich *p262* . . . 01473 213311

Webb, Mrs F (Biscoes) *K1 K3*
Waterlooville *p423* . . . 023 9225 1257

Webb, Ms H L (McGrigors LLP)
London EC4 *p56* . . . 020 7054 2500

Webb, Mrs H M (Kirklands) *W*
Romsey *p366* . . . 01794 513466

Webb, Miss H M (Field Seymour Parkes) *W*
Reading *p360* . . . 0118 951 6200

Webb, Mrs I J (Eastleys) *K1 D1*
Paignton *p345* . . . 01803 559257

Webb, Miss J (Thompsons (formerly Robin/Brian Thompson & Partners)) *N Zr*
Birmingham *p143* . . . 0121 262 1200

Webb, J (Holman Fenwick Willan)
London EC3 *p42* . . . 020 7264 8000

Webb, Ms J R (Pictons Solicitors LLP) *J1*
Luton *p295* . . . 01582 870870

Webb, J R G (Davitt Jones Bould) *E S2*
Taunton *p408* . . . 01823 279279

Webb, J R R (Layton & Co) *G H K1 W Zl Q D1*
Haverfordwest *p244* . . . 01437 766671

Webb, Mrs K L (Coffin Mew & Clover)
Fareham *p223* . . . 01329 825617

Webb, K R (Shakespeares) *E L S1 S2*
Stratford-upon-Avon *p400* . . 0845 630 8833

Webb, Miss L (George Davies Solicitors LLP) *O Q*
Manchester *p303* . . . 0161 236 8992

See p634 for the Key to Work Categories

Webb, M F (Eaton Smith LLP) *N P K1 J1 G F1 D1 H W*
Huddersfield *p255* . . . 01484 821300

Webb, M J (Wolverhampton City Council)
Wolverhampton *p477* . . . 01902 556556

Webb, N A (The Environment Agency (North West Region [HQ]))
Warrington *p475* . . . 01925 653999

Webb, Mrs N M (Gabbs LLP) *W T2 K4 X*
Leominster *p282* . . . 01568 616333

Webb, P D R (Goodman Derrick LLP) *C1 J1 B1 T1 Zb Zi Ze*
London EC4 *p36* . . . 020 7404 0606

Webb, Ms S (Crane & Staples) *W*
Welwyn Garden City *p425* . . . 01707 329333

Webb, Mrs S (Anthony Collins Solicitors LLP) *Ze C1 A3 U2 Zk*
Birmingham *p137* . . . 0121 200 3242

Webb, S J (Thompson Smith & Puxon) *N Q O*
Colchester *p198* . . . 01206 574431

Webb, Mrs S L (Russell Jones & Walker)
London WC2 *p74* . . . 020 7657 1555

Webb, Miss S L (Broxbourne Borough Council)
Cheshunt *p454* . . . 01992 785555

Webb, Mrs V (Evans + Webb) *S1 W*
Malvern *p300* . . . 01684 562526

Webb, W J (Sherwood Wheatley) *G M1 K1 H F1 L P J1 D1 S1 Zl Zk*
Kingston upon Thames *p267*. 020 8546 0144

Webb-Jenkins, C (Browne Jacobson LLP)
Nottingham *p336* . . . 0115 976 6000

Webbe, Mrs E R (Trethowans LLP) *W T2*
Salisbury *p371* . . . 01722 412512

Webber, A (TV Edwards LLP) *K1*
London SE8 *p85* . . . 020 7790 7000

Webber, Mrs D (Curry Popeck) *J1 G H B2 Zw*
London W1 *p24* . . . 020 7224 6633

Webber, Ms F (Welsh Health Legal Services)
Cardiff *p453* . . . 029 2031 5500

Webber, J M (Russell Jones & Walker)
London WC2 *p74* . . . 020 7657 1555

Webber, L (Public Interest Lawyers)
Birmingham *p141* . . . 0121 515 5069

Webber, M F (National Australia Bank)
London EC2 *p108* . . . 020 7710 2100
Bexleyheath *p449* . . . 020 8298 5000

Webber, N L (SNR Denton)
London EC4 *p75* . . . 020 7242 1212

Webber, Miss R (West Sussex County Council)
Chichester *p455* . . . 01243 777100

Webber, R P (Field Fisher Waterhouse LLP)
London EC3 *p31* . . . 020 7861 4000

Webber, S J (Hugh James) *N Q Zw Zu Zq*
Cardiff *p179* . . . 029 2022 4871

Webber-Brown, C (Michelmores LLP) *Zr N*
Exeter *p221* . . . 01392 688688

Weber, A W (Coles Miller Solicitors LLP)
Poole *p352* . . . 01202 673011

Weber, C A L (Wedlake Bell LLP) *T1 Zo*
London WC1 *p91* . . . 020 7395 3000

Weber, Mrs J A (Simmonds Grant) *S1 R2*
Oakham *p340* . . . 01572 756866

Weber, K (Charles Russell LLP) *Zo*
London EC4 *p19* . . . 020 7203 5000

Webley, Miss L C (Hallmark Hulme)
Worcester *p439* . . . 01905 726600

Webster, Miss C (Quality Solicitors Jackson & Canter) *W*
Liverpool *p290* . . . 0151 282 1700

Webster, Mrs C S (North Yorkshire Law) *K1 D1*
Scarborough *p372* . . . 01723 360001

Webster, D (Russell-Cooke LLP) *C1*
London WC1 *p74* . . . 020 7405 6566

Webster, D M (National Institutions of the Church of England, Legal Office)
London SW1 *p108* . . . 020 7898 1000

Webster, Mrs E C (Humphries Kirk) *S1 S2*
Poole *p352* . . . 01202 725400

Webster, Ms H (Keoghs LLP) *N Zj O Q*
Bolton *p149* . . . 01204 677000

Webster, Miss H F (Clough & Willis) *W K4*
Bury *p170* . . . 0161 764 5266

Webster, I L U (Garner Canning)
Tamworth *p407* . . . 01827 314004

Webster, J (Veale Wasbrough Vizards) *N Zr*
Bristol *p165* . . . 0117 925 2020

Webster, J D (Webster O'Brien LLP)
Stockport *p396* . . . 0161 283 3750

Webster, J D (Woodfines LLP) *S1 W L E*
Bedford *p130* . . . 01234 270600

Webster, J E A (Fieldings Porter)
Bolton *p149* . . . 01204 540900

Webster, J M (Kenyon Son & Craddock) *K1*
Goole *p231* . . . 01405 720850

Webster, J N (Memery Crystal) *T1*
London WC2 *p60* . . . 020 7242 5905

Webster, J S (Leach Rawlence & Hart) *W T2*
Croydon *p205* . . . 020 8680 5850

Webster, K S (Andrew Jackson) *T1 W Zd*
Hull *p257* . . . 01482 325242

Webster, L (Scott Duff & Co) *D1 K1 K4 S1 T2 V W*
Keswick *p265* . . . 01768 774321

Webster, Ms L (Tollers LLP) *K4 T2 W*
Kettering *p265* . . . 01536 520111

Webster, L M (Mayo Wynne Baxter LLP) *S1 W E K1 L D1 V A1 Zl*
Brighton *p160* . . . 01273 775533

Webster, M (Pinsent Masons LLP) *C1 C2 T1 I*
London EC2 *p67* . . . 020 7418 7000

Webster, M (Webster Dixon LLP) *C1 J1 O S2 Zo Zp Zg Ze*
London EC1 *p90* . . . 020 7353 8300

Webster, Miss M L (The Paul Rooney Partnership)
Liverpool *p290* . . . 0151 227 2851

Webster, R (Jeffrey Green Russell) *Q L N O Zl*
London W1 *p46* . . . 020 7339 7000

Webster, Mrs R A H (Dodd Lewis Solicitors) *O Q J1 Zq L B1*
London SE3 *p27* . . . 020 8852 1255

Webster, R B (Richard Webster & Co) *S1 E W R1 Zd*
Eastleigh *p216* . . . 023 8061 4583

Webster, Ms S (Trowers & Hamlins)
London EC3 *p88* . . . 020 7423 8000

Webster, Miss S (Horne Engall & Freeman LLP)
Egham *p217* . . . 01784 432292
Sunbury-on-Thames *p401* . . . 01932 765741

Webster-Martin, Ms L (Wessex Solicitors Chambers Ltd) *G H*
Portsmouth *p355* . . . 023 9238 1114

Wedderburn-Day, A R (Allen & Overy LLP)
London E1 *p5* . . . 020 3088 0000

Wedgwood, D E (Anthony Gold) *O Q Zq N J1 Zf J2 L Zw Zz Ze C1 B1*
London SE1 *p6* . . . 020 7940 4000

Wedlinscky, Ms L (Lester Morrill) *K1 N W*
Leeds *p275* . . . 0113 245 8549

Weed, D R (Burton Copeland LLP) *G H*
Sale *p370* . . . 0161 905 8530

Weeden, Ms A (Boyes Turner) *J1*
Reading *p360* . . . 0118 959 7711

Weeden, Mrs S M (Susan Weeden & Company) *S1 W K1 L S2*
Keighley *p264* . . . 01535 658488

Weekes, R J (Squire Sanders (UK) LLP) *B1 B2 O Q Ze Zk*
London EC2 *p81* . . . 020 7655 1000

Weeks, Miss A (Andrew Markham & Co) *S1 Q G H*
Carmarthen *p182* . . 01267 221550 / 236199

Weeks, Mrs A D (TLT Solicitors) *J1 O Q*
Bristol *p165* . . . 0117 917 7777

Weeks, E J S (Cripps Harries Hall LLP) *O Q Zb Ze Zj Zc*
Tunbridge Wells *p415* . . . 01892 515121

Weeks, J R (Ford & Warren) *O Q Zl*
Leeds *p273* . . . 0113 243 6601

Weeks, M I (Wilson & Berry) *G H J1 K1 L N Q*
Bracknell *p153* . . . 01344 420555

Weeks, M J (Clark & Weeks) *S1 K1 W*
Plymouth *p349* . . . 01752 345311

Weeks, Mrs M J E (Whiteside & Knowles Ltd) *K4 W K1 K3 D1*
Morecambe *p319* . . . 01524 416315

Weeks, R (Allen & Overy LLP)
London E1 *p5* . . . 020 3088 0000

Weeks, Miss R (Peter Peter & Wright) *Q N L O F1 C2 C1*
Bude *p168* . . . 01288 352101

Weeks, S (Keoghs LLP) *Q N*
Bolton *p149* . . . 01204 677000

Weelen, R A (Bartlett Gooding & Weelen) *G H S1 L K1 M1 Q W N*
Castle Cary *p183* . . . 01963 350888
Shepton Mallet *p378* . . . 01749 343091

Weerakoon, T (Weerakoon Solicitors) *Zi Q L J1 K3 S1 W Zp Zj F2 F1 C1 Zb*
Hounslow *p254* . . . 020 8814 1883

Weetch, Ms T (Thompsons (formerly Robin/Brian Thompson & Partners))
London SW19 *p87* . . . 020 8947 4163

Wegenek, R (Squire Sanders (UK) LLP)
London EC2 *p81* . . . 020 7655 1000

Wegg-Prosser, S B (WGS Solicitors) *C1 S2 E L Zl S1 W*
Westminster *p90* . . . 020 7723 1656

Wegorzewski, E (Runhams) *N Q F1 Zl*
Bradford *p154* . . . 01274 532233

Wehrle, R (Briffa) *O U2 Q Ze Zf*
Islington *p15* . . . 020 7288 6003

Weider, J M (Howard Kennedy LLP) *L Q O K1 B1 Zc Zb Zi Zj Zk*
London W1 *p48* . . . 020 7636 1616

Weidner, C O (Hathaways) *S1 G K1 P W E H R1 F1 L Zm*
Gateshead *p228* . . . 0191 477 2288

Weighell, S N (Stephen Weighell & Co) *Zi G H N L J1 C1 F1 R1 W Zc Ze*
Swindon *p406* . . . 01793 600724

Weightman, Ms A (DLA Piper UK LLP) *E R1 L A1 B1 Zc*
Manchester *p303* . . . 0870 011 1111

Weightman, A S (DLA Piper UK LLP) *E R1 L A1 B1 Zc*
Manchester *p303* . . . 0870 011 1111

Weights, I (Jones Robertson)
Runcorn *p369* . . . 01928 711119

Weil, Ms N J (LG Lawyers)
London SE1 *p50* . . . 020 7379 0000

Weil, S P (Bircham Dyson Bell)
Westminster *p13* . . . 020 7227 7000

Weinberg, A V (Austin Weinberg)
London N2 *p91* . . . 020 8815 0720

Weinberg, J C O (Julian Young & Co) *G H B2*
London W1 *p93* . . . 020 7724 8414

Weiniger, M (Herbert Smith LLP) *O*
London EC2 *p40* . . . 020 7374 8000

Weinstock, Ms D (Sykes Anderson LLP) *E*
London EC2 *p85* . . . 020 3178 3770

Weir, A F (Landau Zeffertt Weir) *E S1 S2 T2 W*
London SE1 *p51* . . . 020 7357 9494

Weir, A H M (Ince & Co Services Ltd)
London E1 *p44* . . . 020 7481 0010

Weir, C J (Waring & Co) *N*
Barnet *p124* . . . 0870 444 2782

Weir, D (Watmores) *N Q O J2 Zj Zm Zr*
London WC2 *p90* . . . 020 7430 1512

Weir, D J (Bevan Brittan LLP) *A3 O*
Bristol *p161* . . . 0870 194 1000

Weir, D P (Farnfield & Nicholls) *W K4 T2*
Warminster *p421* . . . 01985 214661

Weir, Miss E A (Pillsbury Winthrop Shaw Pittman LLP) *I U1 U2 Ze*
London EC2 *p67* . . . 020 7847 9500

Weir, F P (Louth Town Council)
Louth *p464* . . . 01507 617305

Weir, I T (Farrell Matthews & Weir) *S1 E*
London W6 *p30* . . . 020 8746 3771

Weir, Ms K (Leeds City Council)
Leeds *p462* . . . 0113 224 3513

Weiss, O A R (Ince & Co Services Ltd)
London E1 *p44* . . . 020 7481 0010

Weiss, P (Davenport Lyons) *C1 Zf M1 C2 Zz Zw R2 Zo*
London W1 *p25* . . . 020 7468 2600

Welbourn, A C (Hogan Lovells International LLP)
London EC1 *p42* . . . 020 7296 2000

Welbourn, Mrs N L (Dale & Co Solicitors Lincoln) *S2 E C1 S1*
Lincoln *p284* . . . 01522 513399

Welburn, J (The Ringrose Law Group) *Zr Q N*
Lincoln *p285* . . . 01522 561020

Welburn, P (Welburn & Co) *E U2 C1 M2*
Southampton *p387* . . . 023 8023 0500

Welch, A (Stephensons Solicitors LLP) *N*
St Helens *p391* . . . 01942 777777

Welch, A R (Stafford Borough Council)
Stafford *p472* . . . 01785 619000

Welch, C J (Sintons LLP) *J1 C1 C2 J2*
Newcastle upon Tyne *p326* . 0191 226 7878

Welch, D R (Knowles Benning) *K1*
Luton *p295* . . . 01582 798000

Welch, Miss H (Manches LLP) *E*
London WC2 *p58* . . . 020 7404 4433

Welch, H B (Muckle LLP) *C1 C2 C3 M1*
Newcastle upon Tyne *p325* . 0191 211 7777

Welch, J W (Muckle LLP) *J1*
Newcastle upon Tyne *p325* . 0191 211 7777

Welch, Mrs L J (John Fowlers LLP Solicitors) *W K4 K1 K3 Zm*
Colchester *p197* . . . 01206 576151

Welch, M J (Morton Pugh Welch) *B1 F1 G L N O Q Zc Zl Zq*
London EC2 *p62* . . . 020 7374 4141

Welch, Mrs M L (Welch & Co) *D1 K1 W K3*
Cardigan *p181* . . . 01239 614070

Welch, M R (Fisher Jones Greenwood LLP) *G H J1 N W Zl Zj*
Colchester *p197* . . . 01206 578282

Welch, N F (Duffield Stunt) *C1 S1 S2 W K4 E*
Chelmsford *p186* . . . 01245 262351

Welch, N S (Wilkin Chapman Epton Blades) *E S1 L S2*
Lincoln *p285* . . . 01522 512345

Welch, P J (Chivers Walsh Smith and Irvine & Co) *G H D1*
Bradford *p153* . . . 01274 740077

Welch, S A H (Welch & Co) *H S1 G L A1 W Zl*
Cardigan *p181* . . . 01239 614070

Welchew, T (Trowers & Hamlins)
London EC3 *p88* . . . 020 7423 8000

Welchman, Ms C E (Osborne Clarke) *T1*
Bristol *p164* . . . 0117 917 3000

Welcomme, S J (Metcalfe Copeman & Pettefar) *K1*
Wisbech *p435* . . . 01945 464331

Weldhen, R L (Derrick Bridges & Co) *C1 Q G L S1 W T1 Zl Zt*
Barnet *p123* . . . 020 8449 7326

Weldon, A P (Lambert Taylor & Gregory) *K1 L N O Q S1 W Zq S2 E*
Gateshead *p228* . . . 0191 477 0616

Weldon, Mrs C R (Morgan Cole) *N Zj*
Bristol *p164* . . . 0117 916 7220

Weldon, Mrs N M (Blocks) *W K4*
Felixstowe *p225* . . . 01394 283241

Weldrake, Miss R (Tayntons LLP Solicitors) *K1*
Gloucester *p230* . . . 01452 522047

Welfare, Miss C (B A A PLC)
London UB3 *p103* . . . 0870 000 0123

Welfare, R (Hogan Lovells International LLP)
London EC1 *p42* . . . 020 7296 2000

Welfare, S B (Royds LLP) *N*
London EC4 *p74* . . . 020 7583 2222

Welford, A R H (Stephens & Scown) *C1 C2 C3 E*
Truro *p414* . . . 01872 265100

Welham, D S (Thompson Smith & Puxon) *W T2*
Colchester *p198* . . . 01206 574431

Welham, R J (Brewer Harding & Rowe) *W T1 S1*
Barnstaple *p125* . . . 01271 342271

Welham, S P C (Thompson Smith & Puxon) *J1 G Zl*
Clacton-on-Sea *p195* . . . 01255 221919

Welivitigodage, Mrs N R (Nandy & Co) *L Zg Zi Q V*
Newham *p63* . . . 020 8536 1800

Weller, C G (Reed Smith LLP) *A3 Za*
London EC2 *p71* . . . 020 3116 3000

Weller, N J (Nigel Weller & Co) *G H*
Lewes *p283* . . . 01273 487123

Weller, W A (Thatcher & Hallam) *N*
Midsomer Norton *p316* . . . 01761 414646

Wellham, G S (Richard Reed) *W S1*
Sunderland *p402* . . . 0191 567 0465

Wellicome, Miss S L (Neil Myerson LLP) *O Q*
Altrincham *p117* . . . 0161 941 4000

Wellington, Mrs M (Parlett Kent) *Zr N Zq*
London EC1 *p66* . . . 020 7430 0712

Wellington, R J (Shakespeares) *S1 R2*
Moreton-in-Marsh *p319* . . . 0845 630 8833

Wellman, D M (Chattertons Solicitors) *Zx S1 Zd S2 L A1 W*
Lincoln *p284* . . . 01522 814600

Wellman, R H (DWF) *E S2 Zc*
Manchester *p303* . . . 0161 603 5000

Wells, A J W (Surrey County Council)
Kingston upon Thames *p462*. 020 8541 9088

Wells, B S (Allen & Overy LLP)
London E1 *p5* . . . 020 3088 0000

Wells, C (Skadden Arps Slate Meagher & Flom (UK) LLP)
London E14 *p80* . . . 020 7519 7000

Wells, C (Ellis Jones) *S1 S2*
Bournemouth *p151* . . . 01202 525333
Swanage *p404* . . . 01929 422233

Wells, Ms D (Woolwich PLC) *C1 C2*
Bexleyheath *p449* . . . 020 8298 5000

Wells, D A (Bailey Smailes) *W T2 S1 K4*
Huddersfield *p255* . . . 01484 435543

Wells, D P C (DAC Beachcroft) *E S2 Zb*
London EC4 *p24* . . . 020 7242 1011

Wells, D R (Ellis-Fermor & Negus)
Beeston *p130* . . . 0115 922 1591

Wells, D W (The Wells Law Partnership) *S1 E W M1 C1 T1*
Bolton *p150* . . . 01204 709959

Wells, E C J (Hogan Lovells International LLP)
London EC1 *p42* . . . 020 7296 2000

Wells, Mrs H A (Mills & Reeve) *O Zb Zc*
Norwich *p335* . . . 01603 660155

Wells, Miss J A (Taylor Vinters) *K1 K2*
Cambridge *p176* . . . 01223 423444

Wells, J C (Sprake & Kingsley) *S1 S2*
Beccles *p129* . . . 01502 713214

Wells, Mrs J E (The Wells Law Partnership) *D1 M1 P K1*
Bolton *p150* . . . 01204 709959

Wells, Miss J I (Cripps Harries Hall LLP) *B1 O Q Zq*
Tunbridge Wells *p415* . . . 01892 515121

Wells, Miss K A (Surrey Heath Borough Council)
Camberley *p452* . . . 01276 707100

Wells, Ms K E (E Edwards Son & Noice) *K1*
Billericay *p133* . . . 01277 658551

Wells, Ms M (East Sussex County Council) *E R1*
Lewes *p463* . . . 01273 481000

Wells, M D (Spicketts Battrick Law Practice) *K1 K3 D1 J1 B1*
Cardiff *p181* . . . 029 2046 1480

Wells, M J (Kennedys)
London EC3 *p49* . . . 020 7667 9667

Wells, M J (Malcolm Wilson & Cobby) *W Zd Zm Zo T2 V S1*
Worthing *p442* . . . 01903 237581

Wells, M P (Callaghans) *C1 C2 C3 T1 Ze*
Farnham *p224* . . . 01252 723477
London WC1 *p78* . . . 020 7079 0100

Wells, Ms N J (Withers LLP) *Zd*
London EC4 *p92* . . . 020 7597 6000

Wells, Mrs P E (Clive G Wood & Co) *S2 W S1*
Stockport *p396* . . . 0161 480 1000

Wells, Ms S (Elizabeth Muirhead Solicitors) *K3 K1*
London WC2 *p62* . . . 020 7936 4445

Wells, S J (Co-operative Insurance Society Ltd)
Manchester *p464* . . . 0161 832 8686

Wells, T (Linklaters LLP)
London EC2 *p54* . . . 020 7456 2000

Wells, T W T (Wells Connor & Co) *P N K1 J1 M1 B1 C1 G H*
Horsforth *p253* . . . 0113 239 0088

Wells, Miss V (Daniel & Edwards) *K1 D1*
Ramsgate *p359* . . . 01843 594651

Wells, Ms V L D (City of London Corporation)
London EC2 *p107* . . . 020 7606 3030

Welsby, G A (Dixon & Templeton) *W E S1*
Ringwood *p364* . . . 01425 476231

Welsh, Ms A J (Heseltine Bray & Welsh) *K1 D1*
Barnsley *p124* . . . 01226 210777

Welsh, C J (Linklaters LLP)
London EC2 *p54* . . . 020 7456 2000

Welsh, Miss K E (Meikles) *K1 D1 W*
Spennymoor *p389* . . . 01388 814336

Welsh, Miss N J (O H Parsons & Partners) *N Q O K1 F1 J1 L F2 G D1 Zh Zi Zr Zq Zl*
London WC2 *p66* . . . 020 7379 7277

Welsh, R (Beswicks) *G N*
Hanley *p239* . . . 01782 205000

Welsh, Ms R J (Environment Agency (South West Region))
Exeter *p458* . . . 0870 850 6506

Welsh, Ms R M (Trinity Mirror PLC) *Zk O Zf Q Ze*
London E14 *p110* . . . 020 7293 3934

Welsh, W G (Michael Hill Partnership) *M1 P G H K1 S1 W J1 F1 Zc Zk Zp*
Leicester *p280* . . . 0116 254 1609

Welton, B (Foot Anstey) *E S1*
Plymouth *p349* . . . 01752 675000

Welton, J C (Chafes) *S1 W G L T1 C1 P H M1 E Zb Zc Ze*
Wilmslow *p433* . . . 01625 531676

Welton, Mrs M (Peterborough City Council)
Peterborough *p468* . . . 01733 747474

Welton, T (Welton Harrison) *E L S1 S2 R2 W*
Hessle *p249* . . . 01482 627711

Wemyss, D M (Douglas Wemyss Solicitors) *C1 E J1 K1 O Q S1 W* Leicester *p281* . . . 0116 299 9199

Wemyss, J A (Stephensons Solicitors LLP) *G H K1 Zk Zl Zt* Leigh *p282* . . . 01942 777777

Wendon, A (Brewer Harding & Rowe) *N* Barnstaple *p125* . . . 01271 342271

Wendon, A (Dunn & Baker) *N Q* Exeter *p221* . . . 01392 285000

Wengraf, Miss L M (Buckinghamshire County Council) Aylesbury *p448* . . . 01296 383653

Wenham, Mrs H (Stafford Young Jones) *S1 O* London EC4 *p82* . . . 020 7623 9490

Wensley-Stock, Mrs A (Wansbroughs) *T1 T2 W Zd* Devizes *p210* . . . 01380 733300

Went, J M (Manches LLP) *C1* Oxford *p343* . . . 01865 722106

Went, Ms K E (Bower & Bailey) *K1 S1 W* Swindon *p406* . . . 01793 610466

Wentworth, Ms C (Edwards Duthie) *L V* London E6 *p29* . . . 020 8514 9000

Wentworth, S (Plymouth City Council) Plymouth *p468* . . . 01752 668000

Werenowski, L S (Werenowski Solicitors) *O Q J1 Zj* Colchester *p198* . . . 01206 367907

Wereszczynski, B S (Belvederes) London WC2 *p120* 020 7404 5262 / 7405 0046

Werlen, T (Allen & Overy LLP) London E1 *p5* . . . 020 3088 0000

Werry, Miss L J (Jerman Simpson Pearson & Samuels) *N G H* Southend-on-Sea *p387* . . . 01702 610071

Wershof, A R (Wiseman Lee LLP) *O N T1 Zj Q J1* Newham *p92* . . . 020 8215 1000

Wershof, D L (Wiseman Lee LLP) *C1 C2 E S1 W* Redbridge *p92* . . . 020 8215 1000

Wershof, P A (Wiseman Lee LLP) *O N Q* Newham *p92* . . . 020 8215 1000

Werth, P S (Wise Geary) *O Q B1 Zq* Banbury *p122* . . . 01295 278500

Wesley, A D (VHS Fletchers Solicitors) *G H B2* Nottingham *p339* . . . 0115 959 9550

Wesley-Jones, Mrs K M (Hewitsons) *E S2* Northampton *p332* . . . 01604 233233

Wessel, Ms J (Crowell & Moring) *M2 O A3* London EC4 *p23* . . . 020 7413 0011

Wessels, W I (Tassells) *K4 W* Faversham *p225* . . . 01795 533337

Wesson, A M (South Bedfordshire Magistrates Courts) Luton *p464* . . . 01582 524200

Wesson, P N (Bhatia Best) *G H* Nottingham *p336* . . . 0115 950 3231

West, A (Clarke Willmott) *Zj N* Southampton *p385* 0845 209 1000 / 0117 305 6000

West, A D (UK Coal PLC) *C1 E A1 S1 T1 R1 L B1 Zn* Doncaster *p457* . . . 01302 751751

West, A J (Andrew Jackson) *S2 E* Hull *p257* . . . 01482 325242

West, Ms A L (Isle of Wight Council) Newport *p466* . . . 01983 823207

West, A M (Squire Sanders (UK) LLP) Manchester *p310* . . . 0161 830 5000

West, B P (London Borough of Bexley) Bexleyheath *p449* . . . 020 8303 7777

West, Mrs C M (Edwin Coe LLP) *R2 R1 S1 E* London WC2 *p29* . . . 020 7691 4000

West, Ms C V (Martyn Prowel) *F1 M1 I K1 R1* Cardiff *p180* . . . 029 2047 0909

West, D E (Freeth Cartwright LLP) *C1 C2* Leicester *p279* . . . 0116 248 1100 Nottingham *p337* . . . 0115 936 9369

West, Mrs E A (Austen Whetham & Guest) *S1 S2 W* Bridport *p158* . . . 01308 422236

West, Mrs G (Jackson West) *D1 K1 S1 K3* Stratford-upon-Avon *p400* . . . 01789 204020

West, Ms H (Thomson Snell & Passmore) *W Zm K4* Tunbridge Wells *p415* . . . 01892 510000

West, Miss H (Huggins & Lewis Foskett) *K1 D1 K3* Redbridge *p43* . . . 020 8989 3000

West, I R (Carter Lemon Camerons) *E S1 L R1 W* London EC1 *p18* . . . 020 7406 1000

West, J (Stokes Solicitors) *O K1 Q* Portsmouth *p355* . . . 023 9282 8131

West, J (Pearce West Solicitors) *O Q N L J1 F1 Zk* Oxford *p344* . . . 01865 812020

West, J (Wilkin Chapman LLP) *Q J1 F1 Zl O A3* Grimsby *p235* . . . 01472 262626

West, Mrs J (Julie West Solicitor) *E R2 S1 W K4 R1* Leatherhead *p271* . . . 01372 383273

West, J F (Graysons) *N* Sheffield *p375* . . . 0114 272 9184

West, Ms K (Jones Day) *E* London EC4 *p46* . . . 020 7039 5959

West, K L (Kennedys) *N J1 O P Q Zj* Chelmsford *p186* . . . 0845 838 4800

West, L (Hanne & Co) London SW11 *p38* . . . 020 7228 0017

West, Mrs M (Canter Levin & Berg) *N* St Helens *p391* . . . 01744 634141

West, M J (Laderman & Co) *W Q S1* Redbridge *p51* . . . 020 8530 7319

West, Ms N B H (SNR Denton) *E* London EC4 *p75* . . . 020 7242 1212

West, N G C (Radcliffes Le Brasseur) Westminster *p70* . . . 020 7222 7040

West, N W (DLA Piper UK LLP) *Zf* London EC2 *p24* . . . 0870 011 1111

West, P (The Watson Ramsbottom Partnership) Blackburn *p146* . . . 01254 672222

West, P F C (Kennedys) *J2 Q N Zj Zc* London EC3 *p49* . . . 020 7667 9667

West, R (Young & Co) *K1* Stoke-on-Trent *p398* . . . 01782 339200

West, R A (Gotelee) *J1* Ipswich *p262* . . . 01473 211121

West, R P (Kennedys) *N Zj* Chelmsford *p186* . . . 0845 838 4800

West, R W (Gilbert Turner Coomber) *S1* Waltham Forest *p35* . . . 020 8520 5886

West, S C (DB Law) *N Q K1 D1 L G H* Camborne *p173* . . . 01209 712428

West, S J (Anderson Longmore & Higham) *S1 S2 E* Petworth *p348* . . . 01798 342391

West, T J (Trevor West Property Lawyer) Crowborough *p204* . . . 01892 853135

Westbrook, Ms A (Cripps Harries Hall LLP) *E Zj* Tunbridge Wells *p415* . . . 01892 515121

Westbrook, Mrs A G (Gullands) *Zd* Maidstone *p299* . . . 01622 678341

Westbrook, Mrs G (Ellisons) *W K4 S1 Q* Colchester *p197* . . . 01206 764477

Westbrook, Mrs J E (Attwaters) *N* Harlow *p239* . . . 01279 638888

Westbrook, M J (Romain Coleman & Co) *S1 W E Zd L* Waltham Forest *p73* . . . 020 8520 3322

Westbrook, P (Attwaters) *S1 S2* Harlow *p239* . . . 01279 638888

Westbury, R J M (Skanska UK PLC) *N* Rickmansworth *p470* . . . 01923 776666

Westcott Rudd, M (Land Registry) London WC2 *p107* . . . 020 7917 8888

Westcott, P (Last Cawthra Feather LLP) *N K1 F1 O* Bradford *p154* . . . 01274 848800

Westcott, P (Oxford Law Group) *K1 Zm S1* Oxford *p344* . . . 01865 297300

Westcott, P G (Burton & Dyson) *C1* Gainsborough *p228* . . . 01427 610761

Westcott, Ms R (Crown Prosecution Service Avon & Somerset) Bristol *p451* . . . 0117 930 2800

Westcott, W J (Lightfoot O'Brien Westcott) *S2 E C1* Woodbridge *p438* . . . 01394 386336

Westell, A (Galbraith Branley) London N12 *p34* . . . 020 8446 8474

Westell, Ms S (Bevan Brittan LLP) London EC4 *p12* . . . 0870 194 1000 London EC4 *p86* . . . 020 7300 7000

Westerman, Miss E (Berry Smith LLP) Cardiff *p177* . . . 029 2034 5511

Westhead, Miss V (Windsor & Maidenhead Borough Council) Maidenhead *p464* . . . 01628 798888

Westlake, C J (Wards Solicitors) *C2 E R1 S1 W Zc Zd Zl* Nailsea *p320* . . . 01275 858515

Westlake, C P (Clayton Mott) *S1 W E* Nottingham *p336* . . . 0115 941 7422

Westlake, Mrs J (Lyons Rounsfell) *E K4 Q N S1* Westbury-on-Trym *p428* . . . 0117 950 6506

Westlake, Ms L A (Thompsons (formerly Robin/Brian Thompson & Partners)) *N* Cardiff *p181* . . . 029 2044 5300

Westlake, T N J (Thatcher & Hallam) *S2 E A1 S1 R2 Zl* Midsomer Norton *p316* . . . 01761 414646

Westley, R J (Fawcett & Pattni) *K1 Q* Walsall *p420* . . . 01922 640424

Westmacott, Miss K H (Wolferstans) *K1 D1 V Zm* Plymouth *p351* . . . 01752 663295

Westmacott, P G (Bristows) *C3 I M1 O Ze* London EC4 *p15* . . . 020 7400 8000

Westoby, Ms R (Taylor Wessing) London EC4 *p86* . . . 020 7300 7000

Weston, Ms A L (Denison Till) *C1 U2 Ze* York *p444* . . . 01904 611411

Weston, Ms D E (Woolley Beardsleys & Bosworth) *S1 W* Loughborough *p293* . . . 01509 212266

Weston, D J (Mercers) *W A1 K1 Zd Zo T2* Henley-on-Thames *p247* . . . 01491 572138

Weston, D J (CMS Cameron McKenna LLP) London EC3 *p17* . . . 020 7367 3000

Weston, Miss J (Kennedys) London EC3 *p49* . . . 020 7667 9667

Weston, Mrs J (AXA UK PLC) London E22 *p103* . . . 020 7920 5900

Weston, Miss J (Simmons & Simmons) London EC2 *p79* . . . 020 7628 2020

Weston, J A (Virgin Atlantic Airways Ltd) Crawley *p456* . . . 01293 562345

Weston, Miss K S (Mills & Reeve) *E* Cambridge *p175* . . . 01223 364422

Weston, Miss L J (Cardiff County Council) Cardiff *p453* . . . 029 2087 2000

Weston, M (Matthew Arnold & Baldwin LLP) *U2 I Ze O Q C1 G M1* Watford *p423* . . . 01923 202020

Weston, Ms M A (TV Edwards LLP) *K1* London SE8 *p85* . . . 020 7790 7000

Weston, M R (Birketts LLP (Wollastons LLP)) *O B1 Q* Chelmsford *p186* . . . 01245 211211

Weston, M S (Chambers Fletcher LLP) *S1 E A1 W C1* Northwich *p333* . . . 01606 780400

Weston, N J (John Weston & Co) *O M2 N Q M1 P Za Zj Zt* Felixstowe *p225* . . . 01394 282527

Weston, R (Watson Farley & Williams) *Zb* London EC2 *p90* . . . 020 7814 8000

Weston, Miss R A (Harvey Ingram LLP) *C1* Leicester *p280* . . . 0116 254 5454

Weston, W R J (Burges Salmon) *C2 C3 C1* Bristol *p161* . . . 0117 939 2000

Westwell, J P (Foot Anstey) *O Q L E* Plymouth *p349* . . . 01752 675000

Westwell, P S (Bromleys Solicitors LLP) *E S2 C1 L J1* Ashton-under-Lyne *p120* . . . 0161 330 6821

Westwood, C J (Olswang LLP) *C1 I Ze* London WC1 *p64* . . . 020 7067 3000

Westwood, Mrs S (Buckles Solicitors LLP) Peterborough *p346* . . . 01733 888888

Westwood, Mrs S (Morgan Jones & Pett) *Zr K1* Norwich *p335* . . . 01603 877000

Wetherall, J (DBL Talbots LLP) *E W S1 S2 G L D1 H K1 M1 P Zl Zh* Dudley *p213* . . . 01384 459551 Codsall *p197* . . . 01902 843427 Wolverhampton *p437* . . . 01902 427561

Wetherall, P (Bond Pearce LLP) *Q O L* Bristol *p161* . . . 0845 415 0000

Wethered, S R (Charles Russell LLP) *B1 Zd* London EC4 *p19* . . . 020 7203 5000

Wetherell, I S (Blaser Mills) *E C1 S1 A1 L S2* Chesham *p189* . . . 01494 782291

Wetherfield, Ms A C (McDermott Will & Emery UK LLP) *J1 Zp* London EC2 *p56* . . . 020 7577 6900

Wettern, A H (Watson Farley & Williams) London EC2 *p90* . . . 020 7814 8000

Wetton, Ms I J (Thompsons (formerly Robin/Brian Thompson & Partners)) *N* Manchester *p310* . . . 0161 819 3500

Wexler, R (Ford & Warren) *C1 C2 T1 T2* Leeds *p273* . . . 0113 243 6601

Whale, Miss A (Burges Salmon) Bristol *p161* . . . 0117 939 2000

Whale, Mrs E J (Bookers & Bolton) *E S2* Alton *p116* . . . 01420 82881 / 88903

Whale, F R (Harvey Ingram LLP) *B1 F1 Zl Q* Leicester *p280* . . . 0116 254 5454

Whalebone, Ms J L (St Helens Borough Council) St Helens *p472* . . . 01744 456000

Whaley, Miss A N (Greenwoods Solicitors LLP) *O Zk* Peterborough *p347* . . . 01733 887700

Whaley, M J (Belmont & Lowe) *B1 C1 E I P Zb Zc Ze* London EC1 *p11* . . . 020 7608 4600

Whalley, A G (Squire Sanders (UK) LLP) London EC2 *p81* . . . 020 7655 1000

Whalley, Ms H (Russell-Cooke LLP) *O* London SW15 *p74* . . . 020 8789 9111

Whalley, M A (Keoghs LLP) *N Zj O Q* Bolton *p149* . . . 01204 677000

Whalley, M D (Minter Ellison) *C1 T1 J1 I C2 Zz T2 Ze* London EC2 *p61* . . . 020 7448 4800

Whalley, R (Brabners Chaffe Street) *J1 C1* Manchester *p301* . . . 0161 836 8800

Whalley, Miss S (Butcher & Barlow LLP) *Q Zr L W* Leigh *p281* . . . 01942 674144

Wharmby, J C (Wollen Michelmore Solicitors) *E C1 S2* Newton Abbot *p330* . . . 01626 332266

Wharmby, S G (Howe & Spender) *S1 K1 W D1 K2 K3 D2* Neath *p320* . . . 01639 881571 Port Talbot *p353* . . . 01639 881571

Wharmby, Miss S M (Max Gold Law) *S2 E S1* Hull *p257* . . . 01482 224900

Wharry, Mrs N (Charles Lucas & Marshall) *W T2 K4* Newbury *p322* . . . 01635 521212

Wharry, Mrs N (Quality Solicitors Clarke & Son) *K4 W* Basingstoke *p127* . . . 01256 320555

Wharton, Ms A (Morgan Cole) *Zr* Oxford *p344* . . . 01865 262600

Wharton, H (Walker Morris) *I U2 C1 Zza Ze* Leeds *p277* . . . 0113 283 2500

Wharton, I T (Morrish Solicitors LLP) *N B1* Leeds *p276* . . . 0113 245 0733

Wharton, Miss J (Ramsdens Solicitors) *N* Huddersfield *p256* . . . 01484 821500

Wharton, K C (Wharton & Wharton) *Zo* Westminster *p91* . . . 020 7038 3577

Wharton, Ms S (DAC Beachcroft) *T2 W Zj* Leeds *p272* . . . 0113 251 4700

Wharton, T A F (FDR Ltd) Basildon *p448* . . . 01268 296431

Whatham, M (David Phillips & Partners) *S1 S2* Liverpool *p290* . . . 0151 236 3331

Whatley, M (Mills & Reeve) *E R2 S2* Cambridge *p175* . . . 01223 364422

Whatley, M C (Whatley Lane) *B1 C1 S2 E F1 G H L O Q N S1 W* Newmarket *p327* . . . 01638 561133

Whatling, Ms C (Babergh District Council) Hadleigh *p459* . . . 01473 822801

Whaymand, Mrs C (Essex County Council) Chelmsford *p454* . . . 0845 743 0430

Wheadon, Mrs A M (Eddowes Perry & Osbourne) *S1 W* Sutton Coldfield *p403* . . . 0121 686 9444

Wheadon, Mrs S (Blake Lapthorn) *J2 Q G F2* Chandlers Ford *p184* . . . 023 8090 8090 Southampton *p386* . . . 023 8048 2482

Wheadon, T R E (Simmons & Simmons) *C1 M1 B1 Zf Ze* London EC2 *p79* . . . 020 7628 2020

Wheal, Ms E (Reynolds Porter Chamberlain LLP) London E1 *p71* . . . 020 3060 6000

Wheatcroft, R F J (Woodroffes) Westminster *p93* . . . 020 7730 0001

Wheater, Mrs C J (City of Lincoln Council) Lincoln *p463* . . . 01522 881188

Wheater, P T (Forbes Hall LLP) *B1 C1 F1 J1 M1 C2* London EC2 *p33* . . . 020 7729 9111 Woodford Green *p439* . . . 020 8498 0080

Wheatley, A (Alan Wheatley) *J1 Q N F1 S1 S2 Zr K3 W* Worthing *p442* . . . 01903 216116

Wheatley, J G (Mills & Reeve) *B1 O* Cambridge *p175* . . . 01223 364422

Wheatley, Ms K (Bindmans LLP) *N G H* London WC1 *p12* . . . 020 7833 4433

Wheatley, Ms M F (Bevan Kidwell) *J1 O Q Zp* London EC1 *p12* . . . 020 7843 1820

Wheatley, P J (Kingsmead Parks Ltd) Camberley *p452* . . . 01252 512324

Wheatley, T N P (Wace Morgan) *E S1 C1* Shrewsbury *p379* . . . 01743 280100

Wheatley, V A (CMS Cameron McKenna LLP) *Zj* London EC3 *p17* . . . 020 7367 3000

Wheaton, A D (Ford Simey LLP) *S1 E A1 W L R1 C1 F1* Sidmouth *p380* . . 01395 577061 / 0800 169 3741

Wheelan, D (South Ribble Borough Council) Preston *p469* . . . 01772 421491

Wheeldon, Ms K (Banner Jones) *T2 W* Sheffield *p375* . . . 0114 275 5266

Wheeldon, Ms L (Hugh James) *W* Cardiff *p179* . . . 029 2022 4871

Wheeldon, R A (Addleshaw Goddard) Manchester *p300* . . . 0161 934 6000

Wheeler, A L (Stephens Wheeler Cooke & Sons) Luton *p295* . . . 01582 720175

Wheeler, Miss C M A (Andrew & Co LLP) *C1 C2 E J1* Lincoln *p284* . . . 01522 512123

Wheeler, D (Curtis Turner & Drukker Ltd) London EC4 *p24* . . . 020 7353 1770

Wheeler, G A (Taylor Vinters) *U2 C1 C3 F1 F2 I U1 Ze* Cambridge *p176* . . . 01223 423444

Wheeler, G R (Camerons Jones) *C1 E B1 M1 O Q* Harrow *p241* . . . 020 8423 6666

Wheeler, J (Morrison & Foerster (UK) LLP) *O Q* London EC2 *p62* . . . 020 7920 4000 London EC4 *p92* . . . 020 7597 6000

Wheeler, J C (Neale Turk) Basingstoke *p127* . . . 01256 473013

Wheeler, Ms J E (Forsters LLP) *J1* Westminster *p33* . . . 020 7863 8333

Wheeler, Ms J M L (Atkins Bassett) *K1 D1 O S1 K3 Zm W* Hinckley *p250* . . . 01455 632685

Wheeler, J P (Crowell & Moring) *C1 C2 Zj T1 Zo J1 M1 C3* London EC4 *p23* . . . 020 7413 0011

Wheeler, J R (Bolt Burdon) *N* Islington *p14* . . . 020 7288 4700

Wheeler, J R C (Neale Turk) *O Ze L Zk* Fleet *p226* . . . 01252 811070 Leicester *p281* . . . 0116 262 4225

Wheeler, J S C (Cadbury Schweppes PLC (Legal Dept)) Birmingham *p449* . . . 0121 625 7000

Wheeler, Miss K J (Atkinson Ritson) *K1 D1 G* Carlisle *p181* . . . 01228 525221

Wheeler, Mrs L L (Blake Lapthorn) *N* Portsmouth *p354* . . . 023 9222 1122

Wheeler, N (Brabners Chaffe Street) *Zu S1 E* Liverpool *p286* . . . 0151 600 3000

Wheeler, P J (Collyer Bristow LLP) *Ze Zf* London WC1 *p22* . . . 020 7242 7363

Wheeler, Miss S (J Keith Park & Co) *G J1* St Helens *p391* . . . 01744 636000

Wheeler, S J K (National Power PLC) Swindon *p473* . . . 01793 877777

Wheelhouse, Ms H (Howard & Co) *D1 K1* Barnsley *p124* . . . 01226 215215

Wheen, E C L (Moorhead James LLP) *J1 Zp O Q B1* London EC4 *p61* . . . 020 7831 8888

Whelan, D T (Barlow Lyde & Gilbert LLP) *Zj* London EC3 *p10* . . . 020 7247 2277

Whelan, Mrs F (Anne Jarvis & Co) *K1 D1 G H Zm V* Harrogate *p240* . . . 01423 858582

Whelan, Mrs K A (Spelthorne Borough Council) Staines *p472* . . . 01784 451499 Camberley *p452* . . . 01276 707100

Whelan, Miss K A (HM Revenue & Customs) Salford *p470* . . . 0870 785 8545

Whelan, Ms P (Shakespeares) Birmingham *p142* . . . 0121 237 3000

Whelan, T A (Hogan Lovells International LLP) London EC1 *p42* . . . 020 7296 2000

Wheldon, A J (Black Graf & Co) *N O Q* London NW3 *p13* . . . 020 7586 1141

See p634 for the Key to Work Categories

Wheldon, S J E (Browne Jacobson LLP) E
Nottingham p336. . . . . . . 0115 976 6000

Whelpton, A (Stephen Rimmer LLP) E K1 L Q N S1
Eastbourne p216. . . . . . . 01323 644222

Wherity, Ms N (Clifford Chance)
London E14 p20. . . . . . . 020 7006 1000

Whetham, Miss A C (Pinsent Masons LLP) C1 E O B1 T1 J1 F1 P S1 W Zb Ze Zo
London EC2 p67. . . . . . . 020 7418 7000

Whetnall, S (Winchester City Council)
Winchester p476. . . . . . . 01962 840222

Whetter, J M W (Whetter Duckworth Fowler) A1 C1 E G H L R1 S1 T1
Kidlington p266 . . . . 01865 842100

Whetter, P W (Henmans LLP) A1 S2 E S1
Oxford p343. . . . . 01865 781000

Whibley, J (Fishburns) Zc Zj O Q
London EC3 p32. . . . . 020 7280 8888

Whichcord, A M (Batchelors Solicitors) S2 R2 E S1 Zc
Bromley p166 . . . . 020 8768 7000

Whicher, P G (Berry Redmond & Robinson) E L S1 W S2
Weston-super-Mare p429 . . 01934 513963

Whiddett, D S J (Brignalls Balderston Warren) W S1 J1
Biggleswade p133. . . . . . 01767 313813

Whiddington, C R (Field Fisher Waterhouse LLP) M1 C1 Zb Ze
London EC3 p31. . . . . . . 020 7861 4000

Whigham, J F (Hood Vores & Allwood) W K4 T2 Zd
Aylsham p121 . . . . 01263 732123
Dereham p209. . . . . 01362 692424

Whight, P (Law Hurst & Taylor)
Westcliff-on-Sea p428 . . . . 01702 337864

Whiles, Ms A J (Henriques Griffiths) K1 N D1 Q
Bristol p163 . . . . 0117 909 4000

Whiley, Mrs A M (Withers LLP) E
London EC4 p92. . . . . . . 020 7597 6000

Whimster, P W (Whimsters Solicitors)
London SE3 p91. . . . . . . 020 8269 2444

Whincup, D H (Squire Sanders (UK) LLP) J1 Zp Zi
London EC2 p81. . . . . . . 020 7655 1000

Whipp, D E (Rowley Dickinson) N
Manchester p309 . . . . . . 0161 834 4215

Whipp, W S (Cozens-Hardy LLP) C1
Norwich p334 . . . . 01603 625231

Whipps, A J (Alistair J Whipps) B1
Southend-on-Sea p388 . . . 01702 616516

Whipps, D W G (Holmes & Hills LLP) R1 Q J1 P Zh Zu
Braintree p155. . . . . 01376 320456

Whiston, S P (Pitt & Cooksey) S1 W
Bridgnorth p157 . . .01746 763101 / 763642

Whitaker, Ms C J (Memery Crystal) O Zv
London WC2 p60 . . . . . . 020 7242 5905

Whitaker, Ms C L E (Field Seymour Parkes) W
Reading p360 . . . . 0118 951 6200

Whitaker, Ms C M (Warner Goodman LLP) C1
Southampton p387. . . . . . 023 8063 9311

Whitaker, D M (Lupton Fawcett) A1 E S2
Leeds p275 . . . . 0113 280 2000

Whitaker, Miss E (Raworths LLP) S1
Harrogate p240 . . . . 01423 566666

Whitaker, G G (Gard & Co) N Q O
Plymouth p349. . . . . 01752 668246

Whitaker, Ms I R (Pinsent Masons LLP) Zo
London EC2 p67. . . . . . . 020 7418 7000

Whitaker, J G (Butcher & Barlow LLP) S1 S2 C1 W
Runcorn p369 . . . . 01928 572268

Whitaker, M D (Wilkins & Thompson) K3 K1 N W S1
Uttoxeter p417. . . . . 01889 562875

Whitaker, N C (Pinsent Masons LLP) B1 C1 E S1
Leeds p276 . . . . 0113 244 5000

Whitaker, P R A (Moore Blatch Solicitors)
Southampton p386. . . . . . 023 8071 8000

Whitaker, R J (Stanley Tee) J1 Q N
Bishop's Stortford p144 . . . 01279 755200

Whitaker, R M (Hellewell Pasley & Brewer) N O Q F1 J1 Zv J2
Dewsbury p210 . . . . 01924 455515

Whitaker, S R (Anthony Gold) E S1 R1 Zc Zl
London SW16 p6 . . . . . . 020 7940 4000

Whitbread, J R (Harrison Clark LLP)
Cheltenham p188 . . . . . . 01242 269198
Worcester p439 . . . . 01905 612001
Worcester p439 . . . . 01905 612001

Whitby, Mrs J L (Wright Hassall LLP) E S2 R2
Leamington Spa p270 . . . . 01926 886688

Whitby, Mrs S L (The Child Law Partnership) K1 V D1
Guildford p236. . . . . 01483 543790

White, Mrs A (Malcolm C Foy & Co) W K4
Doncaster p211 . . . . 01302 340005

White, A G (Mayer Brown International LLP) Zo Zj
London EC2 p59. . . . . . . 020 3130 3000

White, A H (P B & W Solicitors LLP t/a Pooley Bendall & Watson) S1 K3 W
Ely p218. . . . . 01638 780170

White, A H (P B & W Solicitors LLP t/a Pooley Bendall & Watson) S1 W
Ely p218. . . . . 01353 666075
Ely p218. . . . . 01353 688228

White, A J (Davis Blank Furniss) W C1
Manchester p303 . . . . . . 0161 832 3304

White, A L (Bramsdon & Childs) F1 C1 K1 L N Zc Zk Zq
Southsea p388. . . . . 023 9282 1251

White, Ms A R N (Plexus Law (A Trading Name of Parabis Law LLP)) Zj O Q N Zr
Leeds p276 . . . . 0844 245 4100

White, Mrs A V C (Blackpool Borough Council)
Blackpool p450 . . . . 01253 477450

White, A V S (Henmans LLP) E S2 R2 R1 P
Oxford p343. . . . . 01865 781000

White, B A (Morrish Solicitors LLP) K1 S1
Leeds p276 . . . . 0113 245 0733

White, B B (Linklaters LLP)
London EC2 p54. . . . . . . 020 7456 2000

White, Mrs C (Shammah Nicholls LLP) O Q
Manchester p309 . . . . . . 0161 832 9272

White, Miss C (HCB Solicitors)
Solihull p382. . . . . 0121 705 2255

White, C J G (Milne & Lyall) E S1 C1 R1 A1 W T1 O G Zh
Bridport p158 . . . . 01308 422362

White, C J H (Edwin Coe LLP) U1 I U2 C1 O Zza M1 Ze F1 C3
London WC2 p29 . . . . . . 020 7691 4000

White, C P (London Borough of Wandsworth)
London SW18 p110 . . . . . 020 8871 6000

White, Mrs D (Hertfordshire County Council)
Hertford p460 . . . . 01992 555555

White, D (Morecrofts Solicitors LLP)
Birkenhead p134. . . . . . . 0151 666 2210

White, Mrs D A (Coole & Haddock) H G P V
Horsham p253. . . . . 01403 210200

White, D I (Suffolk County Council)
Ipswich p462. . . . . 01473 583000

White, D I (Avery Naylor) S1 W E Q N Zm Zl Zi
Swansea p404. . . . . 01792 463276

White, D J (McGrigors LLP) C1 C2
London EC4 p56. . . . . . . 020 7054 2500

White, D J J (Pickering & Butters) C1 C2 C3 R1
Stafford p393 . . . . 01785 603060

White, D L (Bernard Pearce & Co) D1 F1 G K1 N O Q
Enfield p219. . . . . 020 8804 5271

White, D P (Ashfords LLP) N
Exeter p220 . . . . 01392 337000

White, D W (HC Solicitors LLP) K1 K2 D1 D2 X
Peterborough p347 . . . . . 01733 882800

White, E (Batchelors Solicitors) W K4 T2 Zm
Bromley p166 . . . . 020 8768 7000

White, Ms E J (Forsters LLP) W T2
Westminster p33. . . . . . . 020 7863 8333

White, Ms F (Robert Kyle & Co) S1 S2 W
Marlow p313. . . . . 01628 475751

White, Miss F M (Beecham Fisher Ridley) S1 W E C1 K4 T1 T2
Southend-on-Sea p387 . . . 01702 348384

White, G (Flint Bishop Solicitors) C1 C2
Nottingham p337. . . . . . . 0115 964 4450

White, G B (Dixon Ward) W T2 K4
Richmond upon Thames p364 020 8940 4051

White, Mrs G H (White & Co) S1 S2 L W E
London NW1 p91 . . . . . . 020 7258 0206

White, G J (Shrewsbury and Atcham Borough Council)
Shrewsbury p471 . . . . . . 01743 281000

White, G M (Clifford Chance)
London E14 p20. . . . . . . 020 7006 1000

White, Mrs H M (Morrisons Solicitors LLP) E
Woking p437. . . . . 01483 726146

White, I C (Knights Solicitors LLP) E L R1 X
Newcastle under Lyme p323. 01782 619225

White, I D (Cozens-Hardy LLP) K1 D1
Norwich p334 . . . . 01603 625231

White, I J (McCarthy & White)
Thornbury p411 . . . . 01454 413696

White, J (Pinsent Masons LLP) C2
London EC2 p67. . . . . . . 020 7418 7000

White, Miss J (Susan Hall & Co) K1
Hitchin p251. . . . . 01462 433800

White, J (Kidd Rapinet) E S1
Aylesbury p121 . . . . 0845 017 9616

White, J A (Hewitsons) W
Northampton p332. . . . . . 01604 233233

White, J A (MLS Solicitors LLP) E C2 C1 S2
Stockport p396. . . . . 0161 968 7037

White, Dr J C (Irwin Mitchell LLP) N
Birmingham p139 . . . . . . 0870 150 0100

White, J C S (Crosse Wyatt Verney & Ayre) W S1 L S2 T2 C1
South Molton p383. . . . . . 01769 572157

White, J D R (Leo Abse & Cohen) M1 N P
Cardiff p179 . . .029 2038 3252 / 2034 5421

White, Miss J E (Kendall & Davies) S1 S2 W E L
Stow-on-the-Wold p399 . . . 01451 830295

White, Miss J M (Marsons Solicitors LLP) O Zq J1
Bromley p166 . . . . 020 8313 1300

White, J R C (F Barnes & Son) S2 E S1 L
Romford p366 . . . . 01708 745183

White, J W (Harvey Ingram LLP) N
Leicester p280. . . . . 0116 254 5454

White, Mrs K (Newark & Sherwood District Council)
Newark p466 . . . . 01636 650000

White, Miss K D (Cambridgeshire County Council)
Cambridge p453. . . . . . . 01223 717111

White, Mrs K M (North Hertfordshire District Council)
Letchworth p463 . . . . 01462 474000

White, Ms L M (Debridge Solicitors)
Hackney p26. . . . . 020 8986 2581

White, M (WBW Solicitors) N Zr
Exeter p222 . . . . 01392 202404

White, M (Prettys)
Chelmsford p187. . . . . . . 01245 295295

White, Miss M (Hansells) K3 K1
Norwich p334 . . . . 01603 615731

White, M A (E J Moyle) G S1 W E Zl S2
Rustington p369 . . . . 01903 784447

White, M A (Penningtons) E
London EC2 p66. . . . . . . 020 7457 3000

White, Miss M G (Hugh Jones & Co) S2 S1 O Q L
London N3 p43 . . . . 020 8346 2236

White, M J (Pinsent Masons LLP)
Birmingham p141 . . . . . . 0121 200 1050

White, M J (TBI Solicitors) S1 K1 G H D1 M1 W J1 Zl Zn
Barnard Castle p123. . . . . 01833 638326

White, M R (Peter Browne) W M2 K3 Zm
Bristol p161 . . . . 0117 944 1966

White, Miss N (Sternberg Reed) G H
Barking p123 . . . . 020 8591 3366

White, N (Howes Percival LLP)
Norwich p334 . . . . 01603 762103

White, N (Harrowells)
York p444 . . . . 01904 558600

White, N (Brabners Chaffe Street)
Liverpool p286. . . . . 0151 600 3000

White, N G (Taylor Wessing) N E L Ze Zc Zk
London EC4 p86. . . . . . . 020 7300 7000

White, N J (Rawlins Davy PLC) S2 S1 R2 E
Bournemouth p152. . . . . . 01202 558844

White, N J (Eccles Heddon) S2 C1 E
Ripon p365 . . . . 01765 601717

White, Mrs N J (South Wales Police)
Bridgend p451. . . . . 01656 869476

White, N J (Mayer Brown International LLP) Zb
London EC2 p59. . . . . . . 020 3130 3000

White, N W (Trowers & Hamlins) O Q
London EC3 p88. . . . . . . 020 7423 8000

White, P F V (Lee-Barber Goodrich & Co) N K1 L G F1 O S1 J1 B1 Q Zl Za Zk
Torquay p413 . . . . 01803 295535

White, P J L (Challinors) G H P
Halesowen p237. . . . . . . 0121 550 0481

White, R J (Walker Morris) C1 Zu
Leeds p277 . . . . 0113 283 2500

White, Mrs R K (Henriques Griffiths) K2 K1 K3
Bristol p163 . . . . 0117 909 4000

White, R W H (Pitman Blackstock White)
Lydney p296. . . . . 01594 842475

White, Ms S (Stone King LLP) Zd X
Bath p128 . . . . 01225 337599

White, S (Courtyard Solicitors LLP) S1 K3 S2 E Zi W C1 K4 K1 O Q
London SW19 p23. . . . . . 020 8946 9466

White, Ms S (Stephenson Harwood) C1 C2
London EC2 p82. . . . . . . 020 7329 4422

White, Miss S (Bretherton Law) K1 Zh D1
St Albans p389 . . . . 01727 869293

White, S (Leigh Day & Co) Zr
London EC1 p52. . . . . . . 020 7650 1200

White, Mrs S A (London Borough of Greenwich Legal Services) R1
London SE18 p106 . . . . . 020 8921 5123

White, Ms S C (Pennon Group PLC)
Exeter p458 . . . . 01392 446677

White, Miss S C (Goodman Derrick LLP) N P L
London EC4 p36. . . . . . . 020 7404 0606

White, S G (Hextalls) J1 O Zc Ze Zj
London EC2 p41. . . . . . . 020 7382 0700
London E1 p71 . . . . 020 3060 6000

White, S R (Turners Solicitors LLP) C1 E R1 S1 Zc S2
Bournemouth p153. . . . . . 01202 291291

White, Mrs S V (Bedwell Watts & Co) K1 D1 Q
Scarborough p372. .01723 373356 / 363553

White, T D (White & Co) S1 W Q E S2
Gloucester p231 . . . . . . 01452 413222
London NW1 p91 . . . . . . 020 7258 0206

White, T H (Barlow Lyde & Gilbert LLP)
London EC3 p10. . . . . . . 020 7247 2277

White, Ms V E (V E White & Co)
Strood p400 . . . . 01634 739195

White, Miss W (Nuneaton and Bedworth Borough Council)
Nuneaton p468 . . . . 024 7637 6376

White, W H (Pinniger Finch & Co) K1 Q G N L B1 J1 Zm
Westbury p428. . . . . 01373 823791

White, W J (Crown Prosecution Service Thames Valley)
Abingdon p447. . . . . 01235 551900

Whiteaker, Mrs V C (Lamb Brooks LLP) E S2
Basingstoke p126 . . . . . . 01256 844888

Whitefoot, Miss P M (South Gloucestershire Council)
Thornbury p474 . . . . 01454 868686

Whiteford, Miss L (Blake Lapthorn) O
Oxford p342. . . . . 01865 248607

Whitehall, I R (Burges Salmon) C1 C2 M1 B1 Zb
Bristol p161 . . . . 0117 939 2000

Whitehall, S E (Eaton Ryan & Taylor) N Q Zj J2 O A3 F2
Birmingham p138 . . . . . . 0121 236 1999

Whitehead, A (HC Solicitors LLP) E C2
Peterborough p347 . . . . . 01733 882800

Whitehead, A F (Russell Jones & Walker) J1 J2 N Zq
London WC2 p74 . . . . . . 020 7657 1555

Whitehead, A J (Nestle UK Ltd)
Croydon p456 . . . . 020 8667 5260

Whitehead, A R (SGH Martineau LLP) C1
Birmingham p142 . . . . . . 0870 763 2000

Whitehead, Miss C (Simmons & Simmons)
London EC2 p79. . . . . . . 020 7628 2020

Whitehead, Ms C H (Darlington Borough Council)
Darlington p456 . . . . 01325 388055

Whitehead, Miss D (Darlington Borough Council)
Darlington p456 . . . . 01325 388055

Whitehead, Miss D (Watson Burton LLP) E
Leeds p278 . . . . 0845 901 2100

Whitehead, Ms D (Olswang LLP) C1 C3 Zf Ze
London WC1 p64 . . . . . . 020 7067 3000

Whitehead, Miss F (Backhouse Jones Ltd) N Q Zj
Clitheroe p196. . . . . 01254 828300

Whitehead, F (Whitehead Woodward & Co) S1 W L J1
Wrexham p443 . . . . 01978 855478

Whitehead, J (Whitehead & Low)
Blyth p148. . . . . 01670 541531

Whitehead, Miss J (AXA UK PLC)
London E22 p103 . . . . . . 020 7920 5900

Whitehead, Miss J M (Inesons) D2 K1 Q W L
Cleckheaton p195 . . . . . . 01274 872202

Whitehead, J W (Speechly Bircham LLP) B1 E L O Q Zb Ze Zf
London EC4 p81. . . . . . . 020 7427 6400

Whitehead, K (Alker & Ball) P B1 O Q
Wigan p432 . . . . 01942 246241

Whitehead, Ms K (Reuters Group PLC)
London E14 p109 . . . . . . 020 7250 1122

Whitehead, Ms L J (Hansells)
Norwich p334 . . . . 01603 615731

Whitehead, Miss L J (Harvey Ingram LLP) R1
Leicester p280. . . . . 0116 254 5454

Whitehead, M (Couchmans LLP)
London WC1 p23 . . . . . . 020 7611 9660

Whitehead, M (Watson Burton LLP)
Newcastle upon Tyne p327 . 0845 901 2100

Whitehead, M A (Squire Sanders (UK) LLP) Zw C1
London EC2 p81. . . . . . . 020 7655 1000

Whitehead, M R (Andrew Jackson) C1 J1 A1 W R1 T1 Ze
Hull p257 . . . . 01482 325242

Whitehead, M V (Foot Anstey) J1
Exeter p221 . . . . 01392 411221

Whitehead, P (Whiteheads Solicitors Limited)
Chorley p194 . . . . 01257 266008

Whitehead, R L (Shulmans) O Q Zq Zb Zj
Leeds p276 . . . . 0113 245 2833

Whitehead, Mrs R M (Horsey Lightly) K1 D1 D2
Newbury p322. . . . . 01635 580858

Whitehead, Ms S (Russell & Russell) N
Bury p171 . . . . 0161 762 2888

Whitehead, S (Brabners Chaffe Street) J1 O
Manchester p301 . . . . . . 0161 836 8800
Altrincham p117 . . . . 0161 926 9969

Whitehead, Miss S (Ferguson Bricknell) S1 E C1 W Zl
Oxford p343 . . . . 01865 241814

Whitehorn, K (Whitehorns)
Edgware p217. . . . . 020 8440 9900

Whitehouse, Mrs B E (Tarmac Ltd)
Wolverhampton p477 . . . . 01902 353522

Whitehouse, Ms C A (Stoke-on-Trent City Council)
Stoke-on-Trent p472. . . . . 01782 234567

Whitehouse, Ms E F C (British Medical Association)
London WC1 p104. . . . . . 020 7387 4499

Whitehouse, G (Pengillys LLP) J1 J2 Q
Weymouth p430. . . . . . . 01305 768888

Whitehouse, L (Penningtons) W
London EC2 p66. . . . . . . 020 7457 3000

Whitehouse, M R (Knights Solicitors LLP) A1 J1 O
Newcastle under Lyme p323. 01782 619225

Whitehouse, N H (Waldrons) C1 E F1 J1 K1 L R1 T1 S1 W Zc Zi Zl
Walsall p420. . . . . 01384 811811

Whitehouse, P I (Irwin Mitchell LLP) S1 S2
Sheffield p376 . . . . 0870 150 0100

Whitehouse, R J (Tinsdills) O Q N
Hanley p239. . . . . 01782 262031

Whitehouse, Miss S L (Fentons)
Failsworth p223 . . . . 0161 682 7101

Whitehurst, Mrs H (The Paul Rooney Partnership)
Liverpool p290. . . . . 0151 227 2851

Whitehurst, P F O (Treasury Solicitors Department)
London WC2 p110. . . . . . 020 7210 3000

Whitehurst, P R (DWF) C1 C2 M1 Zd
Liverpool p287. . . . . 0151 907 3000

Whitelam, Mrs L J (Burton & Dyson) C1 O Q S1 S2 J1 L Zm
Gainsborough p228 . . . . . 01427 610761

Whitelaw, R (Linskills Solicitors) N
Liverpool p289. . . . . 0151 236 2224
Liverpool p290. . . . . 0151 282 1700

Whitelegge, Miss S (Russell & Russell) K1
Atherton p120 . . . . 01942 884469

Whiteley, A (M&A Solicitors LLP) C1
Cardiff p179 . . . . 029 2048 2288

Whiteley, C (Ashurst LLP)
London EC2 p7 . . . . 020 7638 1111

Whiteley, C L (Trethowans LLP) Zr N Zq
Salisbury p371. . . . . 01722 412512

Whiteley, D L (Slee Blackwell) T1 T2 W Zd
Barnstaple p125 . . . . 01271 372128

Whiteley, Miss H (Debenhams Ottaway)
St Albans p390 . . . . 01727 837161
Watford p424 . . . .01923 225212 / 239566

Whiteley, J M (Curry Popeck) S1 S2 E L W
London W1 p24 . . . . 020 7224 6633

Whiteley, Miss K (Corries Solicitors) N
York p444 . . . . 0845 241 5566

Whiteley, Ms N (Squire Sanders (UK) LLP)
London EC2 p81. . . . . . . 020 7655 1000

6

Whiteley, N A (Irwin Mitchell LLP) *N* Sheffield *p376* 0870 150 0100
Whiteley, R B (Ellis-Fermor & Negus) *S1* Belper *p131* 01773 821665
Whiteley, W (Clarke Willmott) Bristol *p162* 0845 209 1000 / 0117 305 6000
Whiteman, Miss C L (Dean Wilson Laing) *L Q N O Zh* Brighton *p159* 01273 327241
Whiteman, D F (Cooper Whiteman) *C1 D1 E J1 K1 L M1 N P S1 Zj Zk* London WC1 *p22* 020 7831 5222
Whiteman, M B (RHW Solicitors LLP) *E S2 Zc A3 C2 J1* Guildford *p237*. 01483 302000
Whitemore, Ms S J (Warner Goodman LLP) *J1* Southampton *p387*. 023 8063 9311
Whiter, J P (Blake Lapthorn) *J1* Oxford *p342*. 01865 248607
Whitern, C R (Baron Grey) *E S1 W R1 S2* Twickenham *p416* 020 8891 4311
Whiteside, J D (Land Registry - Gloucester Office) *E* Gloucester *p459*. 01452 511111
Whitewright, Miss L L (Hogan Lovells International LLP) London EC1 *p42*. 020 7296 2000
Whitfield, A C (Billson & Sharp) *K1 L N Q O F1* Leicester *p279*. 0116 255 9911
Whitfield, Ms A E (Macfarlanes) London EC4 *p56*. 020 7831 9222
Whitfield, Miss A F (Eaton Smith LLP) *Zr N* Huddersfield *p255* 01484 821300
Whitfield, B (Whitfields) *B1 C1 E F1 G H N O Q* Formby *p227* 01704 878501
Whitfield, J (Michelmores LLP) *C2 C1 M2* London W1 *p60* . . . . 020 7659 7660; Exeter *p221* 01392 688688
Whitfield, Mrs J C (Hay & Kilner) *K1* Newcastle upon Tyne *p325* . 0191 232 8345; Newcastle upon Tyne *p326* . 0191 226 7878
Whitfield, Miss J D (Wellers Law Group LLP) *Zd K4 W T2* Bromley *p167* 020 8464 4242
Whitfield, J D (Taylor Wessing) *E S1* London EC4 *p86*. 020 7300 7000
Whitfield, Miss K (Teacher Stern LLP) *C1 J1 C2* London WC1 *p86* 020 7242 3191
Whitfield, Mrs L E (Payne Marsh Stillwell) *N Zr Zq* Southampton *p386*. 023 8022 3957
Whitfield, P M (Plexus Law (A Trading Name of Parabis Law LLP)) *N Q J1* Leeds *p276* . . . . 0844 245 4100; Huddersfield *p256* 01484 821500
Whitfield, S J M (Bevan Brittan LLP) *C1 C2 I Zz Ze Zb* Bristol *p161* 0870 194 1000
Whitfield, T R (Crutes) *Q N O I Zq* Newcastle upon Tyne *p324* . 0191 233 9700
Whitfield-Jones, C (Jeffrey Green Russell) *E R1 Zc Zs* London W1 *p46* 020 7339 7000
Whitford, Miss K A (Kathryn Whitford Solicitor) *F1 N Q B1 Zb* Truro *p414*. 01872 275300
Whiting, C W (Charles Whiting) *S1 S2 E K3 K1 Q O W B1 C1 R2 Zl L Zq* Chelmsford *p187*. 01245 496911
Whiting, D N (Whiting & Purches) *J2 Zy F2 P G H Zl* Solihull *p383*. 0121 605 5050
Whiting, Mrs G M (BRB (Residuary) Ltd) London N1 *p104*. 020 7904 5087
Whiting, Ms J E (Baker Macdonald) *S1 E W F1* Sevenoaks *p374*. 01732 457978
Whiting, J R (Irwin Mitchell LLP) *Zj* Birmingham *p139* 0870 150 0100
Whiting, L M (Andrew Jackson) *J1 Zp* Hull *p257* 01482 325242
Whiting, Miss R (Nicol Denvir & Purnell) *D1* Cardiff *p180*. 029 2079 6311
Whiting, R J (John Whiting & Co) *S1 G P K1 L W J1 D1 R1 H Zl* Launceston *p270* 01566 777677
Whiting, R S (R G Frisby & Small) *E L C1 C2 S1 W Zh* Leicester *p279*. . . . . 0116 233 5522; Leicester *p279*. 01455 282832
Whiting, Mrs V (Chester City Council) Chester *p454* 01244 324324
Whitington, D (Collins Long) *Zf C1 Ze* Southwark *p21*. 020 7401 9800
Whitlam, R C (hlw Keeble Hawson LLP) *O B1 Q* Sheffield *p376*. 0114 276 5555
Whitley, Miss P R (GHP Legal) *C1 W S1 E L N A1 O J1 Q Zc Zd S2* Wrexham *p442* 01978 291456
Whitlock, K R (Turners Solicitors LLP) *K1 N C1 A3 F1 B1 Zh L O Q* Bournemouth *p153*. 01202 291291
Whitmore, A E (Clyde Chappell & Botham) *S1 L S2* Stoke-on-Trent *p397*. 01782 599577
Whitmore, A T (Fraser Brown) *Zb B1 Zc F1 Zj Q* Nottingham *p337*. 0115 988 8777
Whitmore, M S (Roythornes LLP) *S2 E R2* Spalding *p389* 01775 842500
Whitney, Mrs E K (Nuneaton and Bedworth Borough Council) Nuneaton *p468* 024 7637 6376
Whitney, H J S (Kundert & Co) *S1 W H G L C1 A1 B1 E* Coventry *p200*. 024 7622 7741
Whitney, T (Barlow Robbins LLP) *K1* Guildford *p235*. 01483 543200
Whitston, M G (Whitstons) London SE3 *p91*. 020 8853 5226
Whittaker, A (Gordon Dadds) *C1 C2 Zn* London W1 *p25* 020 7493 6151
Whittaker, A D (Russell & Russell) *G H Zl* Bolton *p149* 01204 399299
Whittaker, A M (Financial Services Authority) London E14 *p106* 020 7066 1000
Whittaker, Miss A R (Stone King LLP) *Zd* Bath *p128* 01225 337599
Whittaker, Ms B (Stevens & Bolton) Guildford *p237*. 01483 302264
Whittaker, B G (Thomson Wilson Pattinson) *W S1 S2 E* Windermere *p434* 01539 442233
Whittaker, Mrs C L (Foreman Laws) *E P R1 W L* Hitchin *p251* 01462 458711
Whittaker, Mrs C S (Gordon Lutton) *D1 K1 N Q* Hereford *p248* 01432 355345
Whittaker, D N (Jacklyn Dawson) *S1 S2 E Zl R2 W L* Newport *p328* 01633 262952
Whittaker, Mrs E M (Clough & Willis) *K1 K3 V* Bury *p170* 0161 764 5266
Whittaker, I (Department for Business, Enterprise and Regulatory Reform) London SW1 *p105*. 020 7215 0105
Whittaker, J M (SAS Daniels LLP) *J1* Stockport *p396*. 0161 475 7676
Whittaker, Mrs L C (Yorklaw Ltd (t/a Burn & Company)) *E S2* York *p445* 01904 655442
Whittaker, Miss L K (Bosley & Co) *G H K1 D1* Brighton *p159* 01273 608181
Whittaker, Mrs M A (The Watson Ramsbottom Partnership) *K1 K3 D1* Blackburn *p146* 01254 672222
Whittaker, M S (Hugh James) *N B1 Zj Zq* Cardiff *p179* 029 2022 4871
Whittaker, Q J (Addleshaw Goddard) Manchester *p300* 0161 934 6000
Whittaker, R (Lanyon Bowdler LLP) *A1 C1 E R1 S1* Shrewsbury *p379* 01743 280280
Whittaker, R (DLA Piper UK LLP) London EC2 *p24*. 0870 011 1111
Whittaker, Miss R J (Macfarlanes) *C1* London EC4 *p56*. 020 7831 9222
Whittaker, R J (Rollits LLP) *W* Hull *p258* 01482 323239
Whittaker, Miss S (Bennetts Solicitors Attorneys & Notaries) *W* Wrington *p443*. 01934 862786
Whittaker, S J (Druces LLP) *S1 S2* London EC2 *p27*. 020 7638 9271
Whittaker, S J (Simmons & Simmons) London EC2 *p79*. 020 7628 2020
Whittall, Miss M A (Pannone LLP) *N* Manchester *p308* 0161 909 3000
Whittall, Ms S (Carvers (Part of the Wilkes Partnership LLP)) *D1 K1* Birmingham *p136* 0121 784 8484
Whittall, Mrs S C (Gabbs LLP) *E S2 R2* Hereford *p248* 01432 353481
Whitten, Miss S K (Charles Russell LLP) *K1* London EC4 *p19*. 020 7203 5000
Whitter, Ms K L (Clark Holt) *S2 R1 E* Swindon *p406* 01793 617444
Whitters, Miss B M (The College of Law Guildford) Guildford *p459*. 01483 460200
Whitting, M H (Capsticks Solicitors LLP) *O Q B2* London SW19 *p18*. 020 8780 2211
Whittingdale, M R (Whittingdales) *C1 C2 E J1 R1 S1 T1 T2 W* London WC2 *p91* 020 7831 5591
Whittingham, Mrs M O (Nottinghamshire County Council Legal Services Division) West Bridgford *p475*. 0115 977 3478
Whittingham, P S (Ashton KCJ) *C1 C2 Ze* Ipswich *p262*. 01473 232425
Whittingham, Miss R M (Farleys Solicitors LLP) *K1* Blackburn *p145* . . . . 01254 367854; Manchester *p304* 0161 660 4254
Whittingham-Jones, A F (Guy Williams Layton) *W S1 K1 D1 J1 E C1 L M1 G Zl* Liverpool *p288*. 0151 236 7171
Whittingslow, J R (Napthens LLP) *N O Q* Preston *p357* 01772 888444
Whittington, C M (Thomson Snell & Passmore) *Zc* Tunbridge Wells *p415* 01892 510000
Whittington, Mrs L (Larken & Co) Newark *p322* 01636 703333
Whittle, A C (Greens) *Q J1 K3 O S1 L N* Ludlow *p294*. . . . . 01584 873918; Birmingham *p143* 0121 633 3233
Whittle, A J (Jeromes) *A1 E L R2 S1 S2 W* Sandown *p372*. 01983 402026
Whittle, C (Tyne & Wear Passenger Transport Executive) *P M1 K1 F1 S1 W G L D1* Newcastle upon Tyne *p466* . 0191 203 3333
Whittle, C D (Coles Miller Solicitors LLP) *N Q* Bournemouth *p151*. 01202 511512
Whittle, Miss D L (Smith Roddam) Crook *p203* 01388 762564
Whittle, Ms D L (TBI Solicitors) *K1* Hartlepool *p243* . . . 0800 052 6824 / 01429 264101
Whittle, J W (Keoghs LLP) *K1 D1 M1 N G P* Bolton *p149*. 01204 677000
Whittle, J W (Keoghs LLP) *N Zj O Q A3* Coventry *p200*. 024 7665 8200
Whittle, M (Bournemouth Borough Council) *S1 L S2 W A1* Bournemouth *p450*. 01202 451178
Whittle, Miss M J (Graysons) *Zr Zq N* Sheffield *p375* 0114 272 9184
Whittle, Mrs M P R (Oliver D'Sa Solicitors) *G H* Leicester *p279*. 0116 275 5549
Whittle, S (Goodman Derrick LLP) London EC4 *p36*. 020 7404 0606
Whittle, S J (Weightmans LLP) *Q* Liverpool *p291*. 0151 227 2601
Whittles, Miss C A (Bowcock & Pursaill) *A2 E R1 S2 Zl S1* Leek *p278* 01538 399199
Whittles, D R (Hardman & Whittles) Heywood *p249*. 01706 369027
Whittock, Mrs S L (Davies & Partners) *J1 C1* Almondsbury *p115* 01454 619619
Whitton, Ms A (Pinsent Masons LLP) London EC2 *p67*. 020 7418 7000
Whitton, M (Edwin Coe LLP) *O Q N Zj* London WC2 *p29* 020 7691 4000
Whitton, Mrs S M (Freeth Cartwright LLP) *E L S1 Zh S2 R2* Manchester *p304* 0845 634 2540
Whitwam, Ms J (The College of Law) London WC1 *p105*. 0800 289997
Whitwell, A R (Penningtons) Godalming *p231* 01483 791800
Whitworth, Ms A (Gloucester Law Centre) Gloucester *p459* 01452 423492
Whitworth, B J (Wigan Borough Council) Wigan *p476* 01942 244991
Whitworth, B J (Maddocks Clarke) *C1 D1 E F1 G H K1 L M1* Altrincham *p117* 0844 805 5170
Whitworth, Miss D I (Northumbrian Water Ltd) Durham *p457* 0870 608 4820
Whitworth, D L (Mowbray Woodwards Solicitors) Bath *p128* 01225 485700
Whitworth, G (Cozens Moxon & Harts) *S1 S2 E K4 Q Zd C1* Teddington *p409* . 020 8977 8486 / 8977 4424
Whitworth, Ms J (Kemps Solicitors) *G H B2* Oldham *p340* 0161 633 0555
Whitworth, M O (Gotelee) *E R2 S2 L R1 S1* Ipswich *p262*. 01473 211121
Whitworth, M R (Grayson Willis Bennett) *G H B2* Sheffield *p375* . . . . 0114 290 9500; Sheffield *p376* 0870 150 0100
Whitworth, N J (Maddocks Clarke) *S1* Altrincham *p117* 0844 805 5170
Whitworth, Mrs S F (Malletts Solicitors) *K1 K3* King's Lynn *p266* 01553 777744
Wholley, R D (Wholley Goodings LLP) *S1 E C1 N O S2 D1 G J1 Q* Bedlington *p130* . . . . 01670 824080; Morpeth *p319* 01670 519714
Whomes, I (Clerk to the Justices) Lowestoft *p464* 01502 501060
Whur, P (Walker Morris) Leeds *p277* 0113 283 2500
Whybrew, R (Plexus Law (A Trading Name of Parabis Law LLP)) *Zj E* Colchester *p198* 0844 245 4950
Whybrow, J (Howells LLP) *D1 D2 K1* Sheffield *p376* 0114 249 6666
Whybrow, Mrs J A (Birketts LLP) *B1 C1 F1 J1 T1 Zb Zo* Ipswich *p262*. 01473 232300
Whybrow, S K (CMS Cameron McKenna LLP) London EC3 *p17*. 020 7367 3000
Whyld, Miss J M (Barlow Lyde & Gilbert LLP) *Q O Zj Zq* London EC3 *p10*. 020 7247 2277
Whyley, Mrs F L (Gedling Borough Council) Nottingham *p467*. 0115 901 3901
Whyley, J (Bhatia Best) *G H* Nottingham *p336*. 0115 950 3231
Whyman, K R (Field Seymour Parkes) *A1 E S2* Reading *p360* 0118 951 6200
Whyman, Miss S E (Barker Gotelee Solicitors) *K4 T2 W* Ipswich *p262*. 01473 611211
Whymant, Ms H (Dickinson Dees) *W* Newcastle upon Tyne *p324* . 0191 279 9000
Whysall, Ms J V F (Irwin Mitchell LLP) *N* Leeds *p274* 0870 150 0100
Whyte, A A F (Land Law LLP) *E S2* Altrincham *p116* 0161 928 8383
Whyte, A J (Coodes) *E S1 K1* Truro *p414*. 01872 246200
Whyte, G F (Sedgwick Kelly LLP) Watford *p424* 01923 228311
Whyte, J (Addison O'Hare) *Q L J1* Walsall *p419*. 01922 725515
Wibley, C T (Edward Harte LLP) *K1 L F1 N D1 Q O Zq* Brighton *p159* 01273 662750
Wiblin, J R (Longmores) *O Q J1* Hertford *p248* 01992 300333
Wick, N (Holman Fenwick Willan) London EC3 *p42*. 020 7264 8000
Wickenden, J (Herbert Smith LLP) *C1 C2* London EC2 *p40*. 020 7374 8000
Wickett, J R C (Pardoes) *Zr N Zq* Taunton *p408* 01823 446200
Wickham, G S (CLS Holdings PLC) *E* London SE1 *p104* 020 7582 7766
Wickramasingha, Ms T (Greenwich Community Law Centre) London SE10 *p106* 020 8305 3350
Wicks, Ms C (ASB Law) *O* Crawley *p202* 01293 603600
Wicks, Mrs C E (Mills & Reeve) *T1* Cambridge *p175*. 01223 364422
Wicks, D P (Wilson Browne) *C1 S1 K1 E L W M1 N J1* Higham Ferrers *p250* 01933 410000
Wicks, G (Plexus Law (A Trading Name of Parabis Law LLP)) London EC3 *p68*. 0844 245 4000
Wicks, Miss J A R (Blick & Co) *D1 E K1 L N O Q S1 K2* London EC3 *p14*. 020 7247 9696
Wicks, Miss K M (Thompson Smith & Puxon) *W* Colchester *p198* 01206 574431
Wicks, R F (GLRS Phoenix LLP) *A1 C1 S1 W K4* Stroud *p400* 01453 763433
Wicks, R R (Gadsby Wicks) *N Zr* Chelmsford *p186*. 01245 494929
Wickstead, J (Quantum Solicitors) *Zj B1 C1 D1 F1 G H J1 K1 L N O Q* Worcester *p440* 01905 673311
Wickwar, P F (Hart Brown Solicitors) *W* Guildford *p236*. 0800 068 8177
Widdall, Ms H (Hayes & Storr) *W K4* Sheringham *p378* 01263 825959
Widdison, Ms P (Quality Solicitors Jackson & Canter) *K1 D1 K3* Liverpool *p290*. 0151 282 1700
Widdowson, D G (Bevan Brittan LLP) *J1 O* London EC4 *p12*. 0870 194 1000
Widdowson, D T D (Bruce Lance & Co) *S1 C1 E W K1 M1 L T1 N R1 Zb Zh Zo* Poole *p353* 01202 679379
Widdowson, Ms R (Hallmark Hulme) Worcester *p439* 01905 726600
Widdrington, P E T (Crowdy & Rose) *A1 C1 C2 E J1 R1 S1 T1 T2 W* Faringdon *p224* 01367 240285
Widgery, Ms R L P (Hanne & Co) *S1 S2 E* London SW11 *p38*. 020 7228 0017
Widley, Miss L (Foot Anstey) Exeter *p221* . . . . 01392 411221; Plymouth *p349*. 01752 675000
Wieck, M R (Pinniger Finch & Co) *S1 E H G V Zl L* Westbury *p428*. 01373 823791
Wieder, R (Bryan Cave) *C1 C2* London EC2 *p19*. 020 7207 1100
Wiegand, Mrs L (Aaron & Partners LLP Solicitors) *C1 C2 Zl* Chester *p190* 01244 405555
Wieliczko, M M (Maxwell Winward LLP) *Zc A3 Zq O* London EC4 *p59*. 020 7651 0000
Wienand, P (Farrer & Co LLP) London WC2 *p31* 020 3375 7000
Wiener, Mrs C A M (The College of Law Guildford) Guildford *p459*. 01483 460200
Wiese, J P (Rochman Landau LLP) *S2 E R2* London W1 *p72* . . . . 020 7544 2424; London EC2 *p79*. 020 7628 2020
Wifa, S (O'Melveny & Myers LLP) London EC4 *p64*. 020 7088 0000
Wigan, P (Welch & Co) *V N H F1 L* Cardigan *p181*. 01239 614070
Wigan, Ms Z (DAC Beachcroft) London EC4 *p24*. 020 7242 1011
Wigfall, A (Nabarro LLP) London WC1 *p63* 020 7524 6000
Wigg, D C (Chandler Ray) *S1 B1 E C1 L O Q J1 F1 N Zq* Buckingham *p167* 01280 814040
Wigg, P (Forsters LLP) *C1* Westminster *p33*. 020 7863 8333
Wiggans, R N (Hellewell Pasley & Brewer) *G S1 C1 P N W D1 H M1 K1* Batley *p128* 01924 472596
Wiggert, K (Morrison & Foerster (UK) LLP) *C1 C2 U2 M2* London EC2 *p62*. 020 7920 4000
Wiggett, C (Phillips Osbourne) *N* Slough *p382*. 01628 663344
Wiggins, C L (Jeromes) *N Q O G B1 M1 W E C1 F1 Zj Zc Zb* Newport *p328* 01983 522664
Wiggins, Miss E (Hart Brown Solicitors) *W* Godalming *p231*. 0800 068 8177
Wiggins, J D L (Mary Ward Legal Centre) London WC1 *p110*. 020 7831 7079
Wiggins, Ms S M (Linklaters LLP) London EC2 *p54*. 020 7456 2000
Wigginton, J T (T G Baynes) *D2 D1 K3 K1* Orpington *p341* . . .01689 886000 / 886042
Wiggs, H S (Winckworth Sherwood LLP) London SE1 *p92*. 020 7593 5000
Wigham, Ms C (Boodle Hatfield) Westminster *p14*. 020 7629 7411
Wigham, Mrs K (Punch Robson) *Zd K4 K1 S1 T2 W* Middlesbrough *p315* 01642 230700
Wigham, Miss K F E (Blandy & Blandy) Reading *p360* 0118 951 6800
Wigham, P (Watson Burton LLP) *Zb C3* Newcastle upon Tyne *p327* . 0845 901 2100
Wight, Ms J (Society of Lloyd's) London EC3 *p107* 020 7327 1000

 See p634 for the Key to Work Categories

Wightman, D J (Wrigleys Solicitors LLP) *A1 E L T1 W R1 C1 Zc Zn*
Leeds *p278* 0113 244 6100

Wightman, Ms S (Hill Dickinson LLP) *C1 C2*
Chester *p190* 01244 896600

Wigley, I T (Peacock Group Ltd) *S2 S1 E*
Cardiff *p453* 029 2027 0228

Wigley, K B (Brewer Harding & Rowe) *B1 C1 D1 P S1 H J1 K1 L M1 Zp Zc Zl*
Barnstaple *p125* 01271 342271

Wigley, T (Trowers & Hamlins)
London EC3 *p88*. 020 7423 8000

Wigmore, C M (Monro Fisher Wasbrough LLP) *E*
London WC1 *p61* 020 7404 7001

Wigmore, G (Guy Wigmore Solicitor)
Southport *p388* 01704 222277

Wignall, D J (Douglas Wignall & Co) *C1 S1 E L Zv*
London WC2 *p91* 020 7583 1362

Wignall, P J (Shepway District Council)
Folkestone *p458*. 01303 852248

Wigner, S E (Croudace Ltd)
Caterham *p454* 01883 346464

Wigul, S (Milner Elledge)
Dagenham *p206*. 020 8984 0940

Wilberforce, Mrs J C L (Kirklees Metropolitan Borough Council)
Huddersfield *p461* 01484 221421

Wilbourn, S D (Batchelors Solicitors) *E R2 S1 S2*
Bromley *p166* 020 8768 7000

Wilby, Miss H J T (Olswang LLP) *C1 J1 T1 B1 Zb Ze*
London WC1 *p64* 020 7067 3000

Wilby, J J (Band Hatton LLP) *N O F1 Q Ze Zl Zq*
Coventry *p200*. 024 7663 2121

Wilby, Miss N (HBOS PLC)
Halifax *p460*. 0870 600 5000

Wilcock, C (MKB Solicitors LLP)
Barnsley *p124*. 01226 210000

Wilcock, D (Burnley Borough Council)
Burnley *p452* 01282 425011

Wilcock, G P (Salisbury Magistrates Court)
Salisbury *p470*. 01722 333225

Wilcock, R K (R K Wilcock) *C1 S2 E R2 S1 W*
Manchester *p311* 0161 602 3395

Wilcockson, L M (BTMK Solicitors LLP) *G H*
Southend-on-Sea *p387* . . . 01702 339222

Wilcockson, Mrs V (North Lincolnshire Council)
Scunthorpe *p470*. 01724 296296

Wilcox, Miss E (Taylor Wessing)
London EC4 *p86*. 020 7300 7000

Wilcox, R (Alan Simons & Co) *J1 K1 L N Q S1 S2 W*
Penarth *p345* 029 2070 3991

Wilcox-Jones, P T (Dilwyns)
Llandrindod Wells *p291* . . . 01597 822707

Wild, Ms A L (DWF) *J1 Zp*
Manchester *p303* 0161 603 5000

Wild, B D (Bourne Jaffa) *S1 W E*
Birmingham *p135* 0121 443 3486 / 444 8440

Wild, Ms C M (Marsden Duncan) *K3 K1*
Ramsgate *p359* 01843 584500

Wild, Ms E (Barlow Lyde & Gilbert LLP)
London EC3 *p10*. 020 7247 2277

Wild, Miss E J (Derbyshire County Council)
Matlock *p465* 01629 580000

Wild, G D (Kent County Council)
Maidstone *p464* 01622 694320

Wild, Mrs J (Hegarty LLP) *W K4*
Stamford *p393*. 01780 752066
Peterborough *p347* 01733 346333

Wild, J N (Rollits LLP)
Hull *p258* 01482 323239

Wild, Miss K (Aviva PLC)
London EC3 *p103* . . 020 7283 7500 / 01603 687905
Eastleigh *p458*. 023 8037 2270

Wild, Ms K (Aitken Associates) *D1 K1 K3*
Islington *p4* 020 7700 6006

Wild, Ms N (Blake Lapthorn) *S1 W*
Oxford *p342*. 01865 248607

Wild, P R (Kidd Rapinet) *C1 J1 B1 Ze C2 U2 I*
London WC2 *p49* 020 7205 2115

Wild, P S (Barrett & Co Solicitors LLP) *K3 K2*
Reading *p359* 0118 958 9711
Cambridge *p174*. 01223 461155

Wild, S P (Bird & Co) *G H*
Grantham *p232* 01476 591711

Wild, T R (Pluck Andrew & Co) *G H*
Hyde *p259*. 0161 368 6311

Wildbridge, B C (Vickers Chisman & Wishlade) *D1 G H K1 N Q*
Stockton-on-Tees *p397* . . . 01642 615439

Wilde, Ms A (Coley & Tilley) *N Zr Zq Q*
Birmingham *p136* 0121 643 5531

Wilde, Ms C (Hugh James) *N*
Cardiff *p179* 029 2022 4871

Wilde, D (Harding Evans LLP) *J1*
Newport *p328* 01633 244233

Wilde, D M (Chilcotts) *Q K3 N J1 K1 O F1 L S2 S1 Zl*
Tavistock *p408*. . . .01822 612535 / 614242

Wilde, Miss E M L (Lanyon Bowdler LLP) *A1 A2 C1 S2 E*
Oswestry *p342*. 01691 652241

Wilde, P M (The College of Law Chester)
Chester *p454* 0800 289997

Wilde, S P R (Wilde & Co) *O E W T1 C1 K1 N Q T2 Ze Zj Zc Zf Zk*
Neston *p321*. 0151 353 1899

Wilder, Ms K S (Lewis Silkin LLP) *E*
London EC4 *p53*. 020 7074 8000

Wilder, Ms V (Blake Lapthorn) *M1*
Chandlers Ford *p184* 023 8090 8090

Wilders, J C (Dickinson Dees) *Q*
Newcastle upon Tyne *p324* . 0191 279 9000

Wilders-Pratt, Miss E (Parker Bullen) *K3 K1 D1*
Andover *p118* 01264 400500

Wildig, G A T (Quality Solicitors Copley Clark) *W T2*
Sutton *p403* 020 8643 7221

Wilding, Miss E A (Yates Ardern) *G H B2*
Ashton-under-Lyne *p120*. . . 0161 330 3332

Wilding, Mrs J H (Dixon Coles & Gill) *S1 K1 W N*
Wakefield *p418* 01924 373467

Wilding, J J E (Gabbs LLP) *N Q L Zq Zr*
Hereford *p248* 01432 353481

Wilding, P D (Wildings)
Birmingham *p143* 0121 786 2555

Wildish, N D (Field Fisher Waterhouse LLP)
London EC3 *p31*. 020 7861 4000

Wilds, Miss A R (Harbottle & Lewis LLP)
London W1 *p38* 020 7667 5000

Wiles, Ms A (Rawlison Butler LLP) *E S1*
Crawley *p202* 01293 527744

Wiles, A O (Chancellors Lea Brewer) *G N K1 A2 Zl Zk Q*
Bexleyheath *p132* 020 8303 0077

Wiles, B J (Bristol City Council) *C1 A1 E S1 O W B1 C2 Q Zl Zc Ze Zv Zf*
Bristol *p451* 0117 922 2000

Wiles, Ms C (Birkett Long LLP) *N Q*
Chelmsford *p186*. 01245 453800

Wiles, Ms C (Hanne & Co) *L*
London SW11 *p38* 020 7228 0017

Wiles, Mrs E K (Public and Commercial Services Union)
London SW11 *p108* 020 7924 2727

Wiles, Miss R J (Walters & Barbary) *K1 D1 L N Q*
Camborne *p173* 01209 712454

Wiley, D M (Max Wiley & Co) *W T2 S1 Zd E S2*
Holt *p251* 01263 711771

Wilford, J (The Johnson Partnership) *F2 J2 G*
Chesterfield *p192* 01246 520930

Wilford, Mrs M (Snowball Worthy Lowe) *W S1 S2 K4*
Sunderland *p402*. 0191 565 3221

Wilford, Miss P (Bristol City Council) *O Q Zc*
Bristol *p451* 0117 922 2000

Wilford, R L (Bird Wilford & Sale) *E C1 R1 S1 A1 L W J1*
Loughborough *p293* 01509 232611

Wilford, S F (Wilford Smith Solicitors) *L S1 W R1 E C1 N V F1 K1 Zc Zp Zl*
Rotherham *p367*. 01709 828044

Wilkes, B J (Davitt Jones Bould) *S2 E Zh*
Taunton *p408* 01823 279279

Wilkes, C J (DAC Beachcroft) *E C1 I Zf*
London EC3 *p24*. 020 7208 6800

Wilkes, D (Davisons) *S1*
Birmingham *p137* 0121 685 1234

Wilkes, Miss D J (Kirklees Metropolitan Borough Council)
Huddersfield *p461* 01484 221421

Wilkes, Mrs H T (Hacking Ashton LLP) *R1*
Newcastle under Lyme *p323*. 01782 715555

Wilkes, J D (Pigotts) *Q L O S1 Zd Zl W*
Dover *p213* . . . . . .01304 210614 / 212206

Wilkes, Mrs J L (Trafford Metropolitan Borough Council)
Stretford *p473* 0161 912 1212

Wilkes, Ms L (FBC Manby Bowdler LLP) *N*
Wolverhampton *p437* 01902 578000

Wilkes, Mrs L S (Brain Sinnott & Co) *N P L B1 C1 F1 M1 K1*
Kingswood *p268*. 0117 960 6880

Wilkes, M F (Christine Lee & Co (Solicitors) Ltd)
Birmingham *p140* 0121 666 6228
London W1 *p52* 020 7287 6233

Wilkes, Dr N A J (Hay & Kilner) *N Zr*
Newcastle upon Tyne *p325* . 0191 232 8345

Wilkes, R A (Hansell Wilkes & Co) *W E L S1 C1*
Dartmouth *p207* 01803 833993

Wilkes, R J (Hallmark Hulme) *G H N Q*
Worcester *p439* 01905 726600

Wilkes, S (Morrisons Solicitors LLP) *S1*
Redhill *p362*. 01737 854500

Wilkes, S I (Wilson & Berry) *F1 J1 K1 L N O Q V*
Bracknell *p153*. 01344 420555

Wilkes, Miss T (Lewis & Lines) *G H S1 W Q V N L D1 K1*
Abertillery *p113* 01495 212286

Wilkes, Ms V H (Clarke Willmott)
Birmingham *p136* 0845 209 1000 / 0117 305 6000

Wilkey, B G (Thomas Boyd Whyte) *S1 W*
Bexleyheath *p132* 020 8303 7755

Wilkey, J P (Gwyn James Solicitors) *E C1 W T1 S1 L Zv Zl*
Cinderford *p195* 01594 822277

Wilkie, A B (Gosschalks) *N P J1*
Hull *p256* 01482 324252

Wilkie, C D (Housemans) *W S1 E A1 C1 L K1 T1 G M1 Zl Zi Zm*
Newcastle upon Tyne *p325* . 0191 232 1307

Wilkie, Miss T L (Harris Cartier LLP) *N Zr*
London WC2 *p39* 020 7405 7100

Wilkie-Smith, C E (Michael Anderson & Co) *S1 W L N K1 E*
Whickham *p430* 0191 488 1221
Newcastle upon Tyne *p324* . 0191 232 8058

Wilkin, A J (Boyes Turner) *T2 W*
Reading *p360* 0118 959 7711

Wilkin, J (Punch Robson) *N Q B1 O L Zk J1 X Zq*
Middlesbrough *p315* 01642 230700

Wilkin, J A (Borlase & Company) *Q N K1 J1 B1 O Za Zd Zi Zl*
Helston *p246* 01326 574988

Wilkin, Ms L G (Weightmans LLP)
Liverpool *p291*. 0151 227 2601

Wilkin, R P (Logica PLC)
London NW1 *p107*. 020 7637 9111

Wilkins, Mrs B D (Pannone LLP) *K1*
Manchester *p308* 0161 909 3000

Wilkins, D C N (Sanders & Co) *G H D1 K1 N L J1 F1 K3*
Stourbridge *p399* . .01384 375437 / 378991

Wilkins, D M (Freeth Cartwright LLP) *E*
Nottingham *p337*. 0115 936 9369

Wilkins, Ms E L (Veale Wasbrough Vizards) *A3 J1 K1 K2 L N Q Zk Zm Zp Zq Zr*
London EC4 *p89*. 020 7405 1234

Wilkins, Miss E T (Davies Parsons Allchurch) *K1 J1 V W*
Llanelli *p292*. 01554 749144

Wilkins, G J (Hall Ward & Fox) *S1 W E C1 L A1 Zc*
Weston-super-Mare *p429* . .01934 626656 / 626657

Wilkins, J J D (The Grech Gooden Partnership LLP) *G H*
Cardiff *p178* 029 2022 2255

Wilkins, Mrs L (Wilkins & Co)
Dagenham *p206*. . . . .

Wilkins, M A (Davies Sully Wilkins) *D2 D1 K1*
Caerphilly *p172* 029 2088 7828

Wilkins, P M (Hudgell & Partners) *D1 K1 L*
Greenwich *p43*. 020 8854 1331

Wilkins, R (Simmons & Simmons)
London EC2 *p79*. 020 7628 2020

Wilkins, Miss S D (Lamb Brooks LLP) *E S2 R2*
Basingstoke *p126* 01256 844888

Wilkins, W (Stephens & Scown) *K1 D1*
Exeter *p222* 01392 210700

Wilkinson, A C (John Donkin & Co) *G H K1*
Gateshead *p228*. 0191 495 2896 / 477 1781
Gosforth *p231* 0191 213 1010

Wilkinson, A J (Wilkinsons) *S1 E S2*
London E11 *p91* 020 8532 9270

Wilkinson, Miss A J (Wace Morgan) *K4 D1 Zm*
Shrewsbury *p379* 01743 280100

Wilkinson, C (George Davies Solicitors LLP) *C1*
Manchester *p303* 0161 236 8992

Wilkinson, C (Simmons & Simmons)
London EC2 *p79*. 020 7628 2020

Wilkinson, C (Squire Sanders (UK) LLP)
Leeds *p277* 0113 284 7000

Wilkinson, Miss C (Short Richardson & Forth LLP) *J1 E S2 S1*
Newcastle upon Tyne *p326* . 0191 232 0283

Wilkinson, C J (Maples Teesdale LLP) *R2 S2 E L R1*
London EC2 *p58*. 020 7600 3800

Wilkinson, D (Crown Prosecution Service Durham)
Durham *p457* 0191 383 5800

Wilkinson, D (The Penhale Practice) *W*
Morecambe *p319* 01524 401010

Wilkinson, Mrs D (Hewitsons) *E A1 Zd*
Cambridge *p174*. 01223 461155

Wilkinson, D (Kimbells LLP) *U2 C1 I*
Milton Keynes *p317* 01908 668555

Wilkinson, D C (Bristows) *C3 I J1 O Ze Zf Zk*
London EC4 *p15*. 020 7400 8000

Wilkinson, D L (Field Fisher Waterhouse LLP) *C1*
London EC3 *p31*. 020 7861 4000

Wilkinson, D S (Terence St J Millett) *E S1*
London SW7 *p82* 020 7581 7500

Wilkinson, Mrs G A (Ware & Kay LLP) *J1 O*
Wetherby *p429* 01937 583210

Wilkinson, G A R (Taylor & Emmet LLP) *C1 Zd E Ze U2 Zw*
Sheffield *p377*. 0114 218 4000

Wilkinson, G M J (Cumbria County Council)
Carlisle *p453*. . . .01228 607374 / 607351

Wilkinson, G T N (Ashfords LLP) *C1 C2 Zo*
Plymouth *p349*. 01752 521500

Wilkinson, I A (The Castle Partnership) *G H Zl*
Guildford *p235*. 01483 300905

Wilkinson, I J (Barlow Lyde & Gilbert LLP)
London EC3 *p10*. 020 7247 2277

Wilkinson, I R (Osborne Clarke) *E*
Bristol *p164* 0117 917 3000

Wilkinson, Ms J (Breens Solicitors) *W K4*
Liverpool *p286*. 0151 928 6544

Wilkinson, J (Bird & Bird LLP) *Ze*
London EC4 *p13*. 020 7415 6000

Wilkinson, Mrs J A (Badhams Law (A Trading Name of Parabis Law LLP)) *Q Zj Zq*
Croydon *p204* 0844 245 4000

Wilkinson, Miss J C (David Gray Solicitors) *K1 K3 D1*
Newcastle upon Tyne *p324* . 0191 232 9547

Wilkinson, J P d G (Bury & Walkers LLP) *K4 K1 N W*
Wombwell *p438* 01226 753433

Wilkinson, J R (JWP Solicitors) *G H*
Wakefield *p418* 01924 387171

Wilkinson, Ms J V (Jane V Wilkinson)
Blandford Forum *p147*. . . . 01258 817719

Wilkinson, K J (Shulmans) *S2 E R2 L S1*
Leeds *p276* 0113 245 2833

Wilkinson, Ms K M (LG Lawyers)
London SE1 *p50*. 020 7379 0000

Wilkinson, Ms L (British Medical Association)
London WC1 *p104*. 020 7387 4499

Wilkinson, Miss L A (AMD Solicitors) *S1*
Bristol *p160* 0117 962 1460

Wilkinson, L N (Williamson Hill) *Zl W S1 L S2*
Middlesbrough *p315* 01642 217961

Wilkinson, Miss L R (East Riding of Yorkshire Council)
Beverley *p449*. 01482 887700

Wilkinson, M (Ablitts) *S1 S2 W*
Bromley *p3* 020 8776 8783

Wilkinson, M B (Matthew Wilkinson Solicitors Ltd) *Zq N K1 O Q W S1 S2*
Middlesbrough *p315* 01642 218888

Wilkinson, P (Ford & Warren) *L O Q*
Leeds *p273* 0113 243 6601

Wilkinson, P (Charles Lucas & Marshall) *E S2*
Newbury *p322*. 01635 521212

Wilkinson, P (Smith Sutcliffe) *E L S1 S2 W X*
Burnley *p169* 01282 426251
Padiham *p344*. 01282 778434

Wilkinson, P (Thorneycroft Solicitors Ltd) *S1 W K1*
Macclesfield *p297* 01625 503444

Wilkinson, P D (B P Collins LLP) *W T2 Zd Zm*
Gerrards Cross *p229*. 01753 889995

Wilkinson, Ms P D (Cherwell District Council)
Banbury *p448* 01295 252535

Wilkinson, P D (Chambers Fletcher LLP) *D1 D2 K1 N O Q Zq Zr*
Northwich *p333* 01606 780400

Wilkinson, P J (Warings Solicitors) *N*
Blackpool *p147* 01253 293106

Wilkinson, P R (Bradleys) *N O Q L Zq*
Dover *p212* 01304 204080

Wilkinson, P T (Holt & Longworth) *S1 W E F1 K1 R1*
Rossendale *p367* . .01706 213251 / 229131

Wilkinson, R (DLA Piper UK LLP)
London EC2 *p24*. 0870 011 1111

Wilkinson, Ms R A (CIBA Specialty Chemicals PLC) *C1 J1*
Macclesfield *p464* 01625 421933

Wilkinson, R A (R A Wilkinson & Co) *O Q C1 E B1 J1 F1 C2 C3 S1*
Birkenhead *p135*. 0151 647 6259

Wilkinson, R C (Bedfordshire County Council)
Bedford *p448* 01234 363222

Wilkinson, R J (Global Aerospace Underwriting Managers Ltd)
London EC3 *p106* 020 7369 2244

Wilkinson, R J (Reynolds Porter Chamberlain LLP) *E*
London E1 *p71* 020 3060 6000

Wilkinson, Mrs S (Cocks Lloyd) *D1 K1 D2*
Nuneaton *p339* 024 7664 1642

Wilkinson, S (Royds LLP) *O Q B1 Zb*
London EC4 *p74*. 020 7583 2222

Wilkinson, S C (Herbert Smith LLP) *C1 C2*
London EC2 *p40*. 020 7374 8000

Wilkinson, Mrs S C (Gamlins) *N*
Rhyl *p363* 01745 343500

Wilkinson, Ms T (Stone King LLP) *J1*
Bath *p128*. 01225 337599

Wilkinson, T (Argyles) *C1 N O Zc J1 Q*
Tamworth *p407* 01827 56276

Wilkinson, T (Bracher Rawlins LLP) *E S2 P R2 S1*
London WC1 *p15* 020 7404 9400

Wilkinson, T J (Burr Sugden) *S1 W B1 N C1 Q G*
Keighley *p263* 01535 605407

Wilkinson, T P (Sharp & Partners) *G H R1 Zl*
Nottingham *p339*. 0115 959 0055

Wilkinson, Mrs V P (Sharp & Partners) *S1 E L W R1 K1 C1*
Nottingham *p339*. 0115 965 4881
Nottingham *p339*. 0115 959 0055

Wilks, Miss A (Royds LLP) *K1 K2 K3 D1*
London EC4 *p74*. 020 7583 2222

Wilks, C (SA Law) *E C1 C2*
St Albans *p390* 01727 798000

Wilks, N (Penningtons)
London EC2 *p66*. 020 7457 3000

Wilks, Ms W (Maclay Murray & Spens LLP)
London EC2 *p57*. 020 7002 8500

Will, D P J (Aviva PLC)
London EC3 *p103* . . 020 7283 7500 / 01603 687905
Norwich *p467* 01603 622200

Willan, P N D C (Linder Myers Solicitors)
Manchester *p306* 0844 984 6000

Willans, P J (Willans & Co Limited) *A3 Zc D1 C1 E J1 K1 L Zl O Q N Zp S1 W*
St Albans *p390* 01727 840549

Willatt, D P C (Waller Needham & Green)
Peterborough *p347* 01733 311422

Willcocks, A G (Kirby Sheppard) *N*
Bristol *p163* 0845 840 0045

Willcox, M D (Willcox Lewis LLP) *T1*
Norwich *p335* 01508 480100

Willcox, O (Harlow District Council)
Harlow *p460*. 01279 446611

Willcox, R F (The Ringrose Law Group - Richard Harwood) *K1*
Lincoln *p285*. 01522 814700

Willcox, T N V (Gilbert Stephens) *G H Zm*
Exeter *p221* 01392 424242

Willden, W (Kitsons LLP)
Plymouth *p350*. 01752 603040

Willets, Mrs K (R N Williams & Co Limited) *K3 K1 S1 W G Q*
Wolverhampton *p438* 01902 429051

Willett, C N (Willett & Co) *C1 W A1 E T1 B1 N S1 L R1 Zb Zn Zo*
Bury St Edmunds *p171* . . . 01284 701323

Willett, M A (Howard de Walden Estates Ltd)
London W1 *p105* 020 7580 3163

6

Willetts, G (Shoosmiths) Nottingham *p339*. 0370 086 5000 / 0115 906 5000

Willetts, Ms M R L (Blake Lapthorn) *E* Chandlers Ford *p184* . . . 023 8090 8090

Willetts, N (Passmore Lewis & Jacobs) *C1 D1 E K1 L M1 P R1 S1* Barry *p126*. . . . 01446 721000

Willetts, N P (Sanders & Co) *G H* Stourbridge *p399* . .01384 375437 / 378991

Willetts, P G (Chilcotts) *S1 W L E C1 A1 T1 R1 V F1 Zv Zd Zj* Tavistock *p408*. . . .01822 612535 / 614242

Willey, L (Bannister Preston) *C1 E K1 M1* Sale *p370* 0161 973 2434

Willey, M C (Jobling & Knape) *G H K1 K2 K3 Q Zm V* Lancaster *p269* 01524 598300

Willey, S E J (Ford & Warren) *J1* Leeds *p273* 0113 243 6601

Willey, Miss S M (Jobling & Knape) *K3 K1 K2* Lancaster *p269* 01524 598300

William, M (McMillan Williams) *S1* Coulsdon *p199*. . . . 020 8668 4131

Williams, A (Forbes) *G H B2* Preston *p356* 01772 220022

Williams, A (British Telecommunications PLC) London EC1 *p104* 020 7356 6181

Williams, A (Gwent Constabulary) Cwmbran *p456* . . . .

Williams, A (Michelmores LLP) *Q Zc* Exeter *p221* 01392 688688

Williams, Miss A (T R Harris Arnold & Co) *K1 D1 D2* Gorseinon *p231* . .01792 892166 / 891331

Williams, Ms A (Trowers & Hamlins) London EC3 *p88*. . . . 020 7423 8000

Williams, A (Fox Williams) *O Q* London EC2 *p33*. . . . 020 7628 2000

Williams, A (Andrew Williams Solicitors) *X K1 L Zi T1 T2* Leeds *p278* 0113 244 1911

Williams, Ms A (Angela Williams) *G H* Oxted *p344* 01883 714618

Williams, Ms A (Michelmores LLP) *E R2 S1 S2* Exeter *p221* 01392 688688

Williams, Ms A (Institute of Chartered Accountants in England & Wales) *D1 K1* Milton Keynes *p466* 01908 248100

Williams, A (Vine Orchards) *K1 D1 G H N Q O L J1 F1 Zl* Exmouth *p223*. . . .01395 273035 / 264646

Williams, A C (Hay & Kilner) *M1 P G N F1 K1 Zj Zt* Newcastle upon Tyne *p325* . 0191 232 8345

Williams, A D (JNP Legal) *G H* Merthyr Tydfil *p314* 01685 350421

Williams, Ms A J (J Keith Park & Co) *S1* St Helens *p391* 01744 636000

Williams, Mrs A J (Wolferstans) *N Zr* Plymouth *p351*. . . . 01752 663295

Williams, A J (Hill Dickinson LLP) *E L* Liverpool *p288*. . . . 0151 600 8000

Williams, A J (Kenneth Bush) *S1 C1 E L A1 W Zc Zd Ze* King's Lynn *p266* 01553 692233

Williams, A J (Daltons) *E S1 L W C1 T1 R1 B1 Zh* Stamford *p393*. . . . 01780 762526

Williams, A M (Gullands) *S1* Maidstone *p299* 01622 678341

Williams, A R (Rubin Lewis O'Brien) *G H M1 P S1 V K1 L F1 Zl Zm Zt* Cwmbran *p206* 01633 867000

Williams, A R (Lillywhite Williams & Co) Dagenham *p206*. . . . 020 8593 7471

Williams, A V (GHP Legal) *G H* Wrexham *p442* 01978 291456

Williams, A W (Cheyney Goulding) *C1 J1 Zd U2* Guildford *p236*. . . . 01483 567676

Williams, B (Weightmans LLP) *N O Q* Dartford *p207* . . . . 020 7822 1900 London EC4 *p91*. . . . 020 7822 1900

Williams, Mrs B H A (Infields) *W* Kingston upon Thames *p267* 020 8977 7633 / 8977 1149

Williams, B H L (Nelsons) *M1 P* Nottingham *p338*. . . . 0115 958 6262

Williams, B J (Family Law in Partnership LLP) *K1 K2 D1* London WC2 *p30* 020 7420 5000

Williams, Mrs B M (Western Division Service Magistrates Court) Caernarfon *p452*. . . . 01286 675200

Williams, B M (Hill Dickinson LLP) *S2 E R2 S1* Chester *p190* 01244 896600

Williams, Ms C (GLP Solicitors) Prestwich *p357* 0161 773 8626

Williams, Mrs C (Northern Foods PLC) Leeds *p461* 0113 390 0110

Williams, Ms C (Fox Williams) *J1* London EC2 *p33*. . . . 020 7628 2000

Williams, C (Shakespeares) Birmingham *p142* 0121 237 3000

Williams, C (Fanshaw Porter & Hazlehurst) *N Zm* Birkenhead *p134*. . . . 0151 647 4051

Williams, Mrs C A (Hawley & Rodgers) *W T2* Nottingham *p337*. . . . 0115 955 9000 Loughborough *p293* 01509 230333

Williams, C C (Arnold Davies Vincent Evans) *S1 A1 W S2 K4 L R1* Lampeter *p269*. . . . 01570 422233 Lampeter *p269*. . . . 01570 423300

Williams, Ms C E (Squire Sanders (UK) LLP) *A3 B1 B2 O Q Zq* London EC2 *p81*. . . . 020 7655 1000

Williams, Miss C E (Druces LLP) *S2 E S1 R2 L* London EC2 *p27*. . . . 020 7638 9271

Williams, C G (Goldsmith Williams) *S1 S2 W* Liverpool *p288* 0845 373 3737

Williams, Mrs C J (Fox Williams) *C1 C2 Zb* London EC2 *p33*. . . . 020 7628 2000

Williams, C J (DWF) *C2 C1 F1 U2* Manchester *p303* 0161 603 5000

Williams, C J (B P Collins LLP) *Q O Zq* Gerrards Cross *p229*. . . . 01753 889995

Williams, C J C (CMS Cameron McKenna LLP) London EC3 *p17*. . . . 020 7367 3000

Williams, Miss C J E (Radcliffes Le Brasseur) Leeds *p276* 0113 234 1220

Williams, C M (WBW Solicitors) *K1 D1 D2* Torquay *p413* 0870 701 4321

Williams, Miss C M (Quastel Midgen LLP) *O Q B1 K1 J1 N L Zl Zr Zq* London W1 *p70* 020 7908 2525

Williams, Ms C R (Conwy County Borough Council) Conwy *p455*. . . . 01492 576108

Williams, C R (FWD Law Associates) *C1 Ze J1 O Q N* Newport *p328* 01633 660440

Williams, C R G (Thomas Cooper) *Zb Za* London EC3 *p22*. . . . 020 7481 8851

Williams, Miss C S (Hallinan Blackburn Gittings & Nott) *G H* Westminster *p38*. . . . 020 7233 3999

Williams, Miss C S (Davis Blank Furniss) *E S2* Manchester *p303* 0161 832 3304

Williams, D (Keelys LLP) Lichfield *p284* 01543 420000

Williams, D (Kemp Little LLP) *J1* London EC2 *p48*. . . . 020 7600 8080

Williams, D (Nicholson Portnell) *Q N L F1 S1 K3 J1 G* Hexham *p249* 01434 603656

Williams, Mrs D (Mortimers) Bridgnorth *p157* 01746 761000

Williams, D A (Philip Ross & Co) *S2 E R2 S1* London W1 *p73* 020 7636 6969

Williams, D A G (Llewellyn Jones & Co) *S1 W R2 Zl L F1 Zj* Mold *p318*. . . . 01352 755305

Williams, D C H (Field Seymour Parkes) *R1 E* Reading *p360* 0118 951 6200

Williams, D E (Williams & Co) *S1 W L A1 E T2 S2* Bridgnorth *p157* . . .01746 762157 / 765603

Williams, D G (Rees Wood Terry) *S2 E S1* Cardiff *p180* 029 2040 8800

Williams, D G (Chronnell Hibbert) *S1 W E L S2* Hyde *p259*. . . . 0161 368 3434 Stockport *p395*. . . . 0161 494 6085

Williams, D G (Ellis Jones) *K1* Bournemouth *p151*. . . . 01202 525333

Williams, Miss D G (Llewellyn Jones & Co) *K3 K1 W V S1 S2* Ruthin *p369* 01824 704495

Williams, D H (Watkins & Gunn) *G H J1 K1 W N Q* Pontypool *p352* 01495 762244

Williams, D H (Alletsons) *S1 E L W* Burnham-on-Sea *p169*. . . . 01278 780151

Williams, D H (Geldards LLP) *E S2* Derby *p208* 01332 331631

Williams, D H W (Harrisons Solicitors LLP) *P S1 G M1 K1 H J1 N W V Zr* Welshpool *p425* 01938 552545

Williams, D I (Red Kite Law) *G H Zl* Carmarthen *p183* 01267 239000

Williams, D J (Squire Sanders (UK) LLP) *P O* Leeds *p277* 0113 284 7000

Williams, D J (R R Williams & Son) *S1 W K1 P C1 L M1 E R1* Sutton Coldfield *p404* 0121 354 7870

Williams, D J G (Wykes O'Donnell Williams) *K1 G S1 B2 H W D1 N Q V* Ilkeston *p261* 0115 932 8776

Williams, D J G (National Grid PLC) *M1 N P* Warwick *p471* 01926 653000

Williams, D L (Sintons LLP) *L S1* Newcastle upon Tyne *p326* . 0191 226 7878

Williams, D L (Allen & Overy LLP) London E1 *p5* 020 3088 0000

Williams, D M (Chivers Easton Brown) *S1* Surbiton *p402* 020 8390 6155

Williams, Mrs D M (East Hampshire District Council) Petersfield *p468* 01730 266551

Williams, D M (Freeman Johnson) *N J1 Q F1 Zr Zp Zq O L* Durham *p214* . . 0191 386 4843 / 386 9619

Williams, D M G (Lodders Solicitors LLP) *C1* Stratford-upon-Avon *p400* . . 01789 293259

Williams, D R (Swayne Johnson Solicitors) *N K1 G Q Zr* Llandudno *p291* 01492 876271

Williams, D R (British American Tobacco) London WC2 *p104*. . . . 020 7845 1000

Williams, D R (Ford Simey LLP) *N* Exeter *p221* 01392 274126

Williams, D R (Carlyon & Son) *E S2 S1 O C1 C2 L W* Truro *p414*. . . . 01872 278641

Williams, D S (Latimer Hinks) *T2 W K4* Darlington *p206* 01325 341500

Williams, D T (Geoffrey T Smith & Co) *G H K1 L S1 S2 V W Zi Zl Zo Zv* Wolverhampton *p438* 01902 426961

Williams, Ms E (Hugh James) *J1* Cardiff *p179* 029 2022 4871

Williams, Miss E A (Wendy Hopkins Family Law Practice LLP) *K1 K3 D1 D2* Cardiff *p178* 029 2034 2233

Williams, Ms E A (LG Lawyers) London SE1 *p50*. . . . 020 7379 0000

Williams, E B (Weightmans LLP) *J1 O Q Zp* Liverpool *p291*. . . . 0151 227 2601

Williams, E G (Speakman & Co) *S1 W L E* Crewe *p203* 01270 214237

Williams, E J (Eirian J Williams a'i Gwmni) *A1 L S1 W M2 X K4* Llandysul *p292*. . . . 01559 363244

Williams, E L (R Gordon Roberts Laurie & Co) *C1 D1 F1 G H J1 K1 L M1* Llangefni *p292*. . . .01248 722215 / 723312

Williams, Miss E M (Welsh Health Legal Services) Cardiff *p453* 029 2031 5500

Williams, Miss E M (Burnetts) *W K4* Carlisle *p182*. . . . 01228 552222

Williams, Mrs E M (Field Seymour Parkes) *S2 E R2 S1 Zh L* Reading *p360* 0118 951 6200

Williams, E W (Cobleys LLP) *D1 E F1 G H J1 K1 M1 P W* Liverpool *p287*. . . . 0151 242 9000

Williams, Mrs F (Cleggs) *N Q O* Nottingham *p336*. . . . 0115 977 5877

Williams, Miss F (Wrexham County Borough Council) Wrexham *p477* 01978 292000

Williams, F C (Maxwell Hodge Solicitors) *C1 E L S1 W S2* Formby *p227* 01704 872156

Williams, Ms F G B (Knocker & Foskett) *L D1 E F1 J1 K1 M1 S1* Sevenoaks *p374*. . . . 01732 459931

Williams, Miss F W (Larby Williams with Gwyn & Gwyn) *K1 D1 K3* Cowbridge *p201* 01446 775535

Williams, Mrs G (Hay & Kilner) *K1 W S1 K2* Newcastle upon Tyne *p325* . 0191 232 8345

Williams, G (Keoghs LLP) *N Zj O Q A3 Zw Zq* Bolton *p149* 01204 677000

Williams, G (Bartletts Solicitors) *J1 J2 L N Q S1 Zj Zr* Liverpool *p286*. . . . 0151 521 7333

Williams, Mrs G (J A Hughes) *K1* Barry *p126*. . . . 01446 411000

Williams, G (Geoffrey Williams & Christopher Green) *G Zq Zt* Cardiff *p181* 029 2034 3377

Williams, G (Rhondda Cynon Taff County Borough Council) Pentre *p468* 01443 424300

Williams, G B (Royds LLP) *E S2 R2 Zu* London EC4 *p74*. . . . 020 7583 2222

Williams, G C (Northern Rock PLC) Gosforth *p459* 0191 285 7191

Williams, G I (Wiseman Lee LLP) *S1 E C1 M1* Redbridge *p92*. . . . 020 8215 1000

Williams, G J (Hugh James) *N B1 F1 Zj O Zw* Cardiff *p179* 029 2022 4871

Williams, Ms G L (Goodman Ray) *D1 K1 D2* Hackney *p36*. . . . 020 7608 1227

Williams, G M (Charles Newton & Co) *K1 D1 K3 J1 Q* Eastwood *p216* 01773 535535

Williams, Mrs G M (Blake Lapthorn) *P J2 Zy* Chandlers Ford *p184* 023 8090 8090

Williams, G R (HCB Solicitors) Solihull *p382*. . . . 0121 705 2255

Williams, G R (The John W Davies Partnership) Newport *p329* 01633 841773

Williams, G R (Richard Williams) *T1* London W11 *p92*. . . . 020 7221 1188

Williams, Mrs G W (Caerphilly County Borough Council) Hengoed *p460*. . . . 01443 815588

Williams, G W (The Specter Partnership) *N O Q* Birkenhead *p135*. . . . 0151 647 3000

Williams, H (Lewis Lewis & Company Ltd) *S1 W E A1 L* St Clears *p391*. . . . 01994 231044 Tenby *p410* 01834 844844

Williams, Miss H E (Bournemouth Borough Council) *S1* Bournemouth *p450*. . . . 01202 451178

Williams, H G (Stephenson Harwood) London EC2 *p82*. . . . 020 7329 4422

Williams, H R C (Geldards LLP) *R2* Cardiff *p178* 029 2023 8239

Williams, Ms H S (Thompsons (formerly Robin/ Brian Thompson & Partners)) *N* Bristol *p165* 0117 304 2400

Williams, I G (Geldards LLP) Nottingham *p337*. . . . 0115 983 3650

Williams, I M (Robertsons) *D1 G H K1* Cardiff *p180* 029 2023 7777

Williams, Mrs J (Collard & Co) *K1 Q S1 V W* Highworth *p250* 01793 765327

Williams, Miss J (Freeth Cartwright LLP) *N Zr* Leicester *p279*. . . . 0116 248 1100 Nottingham *p337*. . . . 0115 936 9369

Williams, Mrs J (Martin Tolhurst Partnership LLP) *E S1 K1 S2* Longfield *p293*. . . . 01474 706168

Williams, Ms J (Sharpe & Perl) *K1 S1 W* Dartford *p207* . . . .01474 872576 / 873359

Williams, J (Hewitsons) *C1 C2* Cambridge *p174*. . . . 01223 461155

Williams, J (Bankside Law Ltd) *Q G B2 Zq* London SE1 *p9* 0844 745 4000

Williams, Ms J (Backhouse Jones Ltd) *Q N* Clitheroe *p196*. . . . 01254 828300

Williams, Mrs J (Andrew Markham & Co) *K1 D1 S1 S2 W Zm L* Carmarthen *p182* . .01267 221550 / 236199

Williams, J A G (Archon Solicitors) *J1* London EC4 *p7* . . . . 020 7397 9650 London EC2 *p81*. . . . 020 7655 1000

Williams, J A J (MacQuillan & Co) Ebbw Vale *p216* . . . . 01495 304382 Tredegar *p413*. . . . 01495 725031

Williams, J B (Breese-Gwyndaf) *S1 W G M1 J1 L E R1 A1 Zj Zk Zl Zt T1 T2* Harlech *p239* . . . . 01766 780334 Porthmadog *p353* . .01766 512253 / 514227

Williams, J B A (DAC Beachcroft) Bristol *p162* 0117 918 2000

Williams, Ms J C (Sidley Austin Brown & Wood) *Zb* London EC2 *p78*. . . . 020 7360 3600

Williams, Mrs J C (West Lancashire District Council) Ormskirk *p468*. . . . 01695 577177

Williams, J F (Chafes) *K1 M1 P S1 W F1 J1 G C1 L* Wilmslow *p433*. . . . 01625 531676

Williams, J G (Bell & Co) *C1 E K1 S1* Cheam *p185*. . . . 020 8642 6099

Williams, J G G (Taylor Wessing) London EC4 *p86*. . . . 020 7300 7000

Williams, Mrs J H (Legal Services Commission Wales Office) Cardiff *p453* 0845 608 7070

Williams, J K (Southend-on-Sea Borough Council) Southend-on-Sea *p472* 01702 215000

Williams, Miss J L (Fishburns) *N Zj A3 Zc Zk O Q* London EC3 *p32*. . . . 020 7280 8888

Williams, J M (Cooper Sons Hartley & Williams) *S1 W T1 E A1 C1 R1 L F1 B1 Zc Zd Zf* Chapel-en-le-Frith *p184* 01298 812138

Williams, J M (Roythornes LLP) *S1 E W L Zn Zd* Peterborough *p347* 01733 558585

Williams, J M L (Calvert Smith & Sutcliffe) *D1 F1 J1 K1 L M1 P* Richmond upon Thames *p364* 020 8940 0017

Williams, J P N (DWF) *N Zj* Preston *p356* 01772 556677

Williams, J R L (Buller Jeffries) *S2 S1 W L C1* Birmingham *p136* 0121 212 2620

Williams, J T (H Jenkins & Hughes) *S1 K1 P M1 L G W F1 C1 D1 Zc Zk Zj* Holyhead *p251*. . . . 01407 762301

Williams, Ms J W (Newcastle Building Society) Newcastle upon Tyne *p466* . 0191 244 2000

Williams, Miss J W (Wollen Michelmore Solicitors) *Zl S2 E S1* Newton Abbot *p330* 01626 332266

Williams, Miss K (Colemans Solicitors LLP) *Q O* Maidenhead *p298* 01628 631051

Williams, Miss K (Coodes) *S1* Holsworthy *p251*. . . . 01409 253425

Williams, Ms K (Radcliffes Le Brasseur) Westminster *p70*. . . . 020 7222 7040

Williams, Miss K (Quality Solicitors D'Angibau) *L K1 D1* Boscombe *p151* 01202 393506

Williams, K A (Greenwoods Solicitors LLP) *J1 Zp* Peterborough *p347* 01733 887700

Williams, K N (South Hams District Council) Totnes *p474* 01803 861234

Williams, Ms L (Field Seymour Parkes) *O Q* Reading *p360* 0118 951 6200

Williams, L (Hallmark Hulme) *Zr F1 J1 K1 Q* Worcester *p439* 01905 726600

Williams, Miss L (Williams & Co) *W D1 K1* Edgware *p217*. . . . 020 8952 8882

Williams, Ms L (Shoosmiths) Milton Keynes *p317* . 0370 086 8300 / 01908 488300

Williams, L (Patchell Davies (Trading Name of PD Law Ltd)) *D1 F1 G H J1 K1 N* Blackwood *p147*. . . . 01495 227128

Williams, L (Painters) *N* Kidderminster *p266* 01562 822295

Williams, Miss L C P (Hutchinson Thomas) *W* Neath *p320* 01639 645061

Williams, Ms L C S (Page Gulliford & Gregory Limited) *W K3 L K1 J1 Q S1* Southampton *p386*. . . . 023 8022 5821

Williams, L H W (Larby Williams with Gwyn & Gwyn) *A1 E S1 T2 W* Cowbridge *p201* 01446 775535

Williams, Miss L J (Ward & Rider Limited) *N K1 J1 S1 W Q* Coventry *p201*. . . . 024 7655 5400

Williams, L M (Barlow Lyde & Gilbert LLP) London EC3 *p10*. . . . 020 7247 2277

Williams, Ms L P (East Cornwall Magistrates Courts) Bodmin *p450* 01208 262700

Williams, Miss L S (W H Darbyshire & Son) *K1 N Q K3 D1* Blackpool *p146* 01253 346646

Williams, Ms M (Western Division Service Magistrates Court) Caernarfon *p452*. . . . 01286 675200

Williams, Ms M (John Poyser Solicitors) *K3 K4 K1 L S1 W* Manchester *p309* 0161 860 7354

See p634 for the Key to Work Categories

Williams, Miss M (Hodge Jones & Allen LLP) *Q N Zq*
London NW1 *p41* 020 7874 8300

Williams, M A (Burchell Williams Limited) *G H*
Brighton *p159* 01273 606555

Williams, M E (Gaby Hardwicke) *C1 C2*
Eastbourne *p215*. 01323 435900

Williams, M H (Gillhams Solicitors LLP)
London NW10 *p35*. 020 8965 4266

Williams, M H (Southerns) *G H*
Burnley *p169* 01282 438446

Williams, M H (Robertsons) *S1 E C1*
Cardiff *p180* 029 2023 7777

Williams, M I (W Davies) *O Q Zc Zq B1 Ze*
Woking *p436*. 01483 744900

Williams, M J (Fearon & Co) *O Q K3*
Guildford *p236*. 01483 540840

Williams, M J (Martin J Williams & Co) *C1 O E S1 Q K1 B1 W Zc Zf Ze*
Wandsworth *p92*. 020 8875 9833

Williams, M J (Bond Pearce LLP) *O T1*
Plymouth *p349*. 0845 415 0000

Williams, M K (Cleggs) *S1 W E C1 N M1*
Nottingham *p336*. 0115 977 5877

Williams, M N (WBW Solicitors) *G H*
Torquay *p413* 0870 701 4321

Williams, M O (CVS Solicitors) *E S2 R2 S1*
London W1 *p17* 020 7493 2903

Williams, Ms M R (Charles Russell LLP) *E L*
London EC4 *p19*. 020 7203 5000

Williams, M R (East Devon District Council)
Sidmouth *p471*. 01395 516551

Williams, M R (Paynes) *W S1 S2*
Bedworth *p130*. 024 7631 9820

Williams, M S (Rose Williams & Partners) *G H B2*
Wolverhampton *p438* 01902 710822

Williams, Ms M Z (Squire Sanders (UK) LLP) *E*
Birmingham *p142* 0121 222 3000

Williams, N (Trowers & Hamlins)
London EC3 *p88*. 020 7423 8000

Williams, Ms N (Saunders Law Partnership LLP) *N Q J1*
London WC2 *p76* 020 7632 4300

Williams, N (Allen & Overy LLP)
London E1 *p5* 020 3088 0000

Williams, N (Edwin Coe LLP)
London WC2 *p29* 020 7691 4000
London EC2 *p81*. 020 7655 1000

Williams, N C (Jacklyn Dawson) *Zd Zx*
Newport *p328* 01633 262952

Williams, N D (Kennedys)
London EC3 *p49*. 020 7667 9667

Williams, N J (Hammon Oakley) *Q O N L S1*
Coventry *p200*. 024 7644 8585

Williams, N J (Brabners Chaffe Street) *E S2 R2 C1*
Liverpool *p286*. 0151 600 3000

Williams, N R (George Green LLP) *O Q B1 I Zq*
Cradley Heath *p201* 01384 410410

Williams, N T (Dickinson Dees) *C1*
Newcastle upon Tyne *p324* . 0191 279 9000

Williams, O L E (Stephensons Solicitors LLP) *W*
Leigh *p282*. 01942 777777

Williams, O T G (Lewis Silkin LLP) *O I Ze*
London EC4 *p53*. 020 7074 8000

Williams, P (Veale Wasbrough Vizards) *Q*
Bristol *p165* 0117 925 2020

Williams, P (Paul Crowley & Co) *G H N*
Liverpool *p287*. 0151 264 7363

Williams, Ms P (Withers LLP) *T2 W*
London EC4 *p92*. 020 7597 6000

Williams, P (Field Fisher Waterhouse LLP)
London EC3 *p31*. 020 7861 4000

Williams, P B (Grays) *W T2 K4 Zm*
York *p444* 01904 634771

Williams, P D (Treasury Solicitors Department)
London WC2 *p110*. 020 7210 3000

Williams, P G (Bracher Rawlins LLP) *O Q N C1 J1 B1 Zza Zp*
London WC1 *p15* 020 7404 9400

Williams, P G (Milne Moser) *G S1 H J1 Zr E S2 C1 L Q O N*
Kendal *p264*. . . . .01539 729786 / 725582

Williams, P J (Williams & Co Solicitors) *S1 E J1 C1 S2*
Cleckheaton *p195* 01274 851608

Williams, P J B (Wollen Michelmore Solicitors) *S1 A1 E L Zc*
Newton Abbot *p330* 01626 332266

Williams, P L (Bobbetts Mackan) *S1 S2 E*
Bristol *p161* 0117 929 9001

Williams, P M (Marchant Harries & Co) *N Zr Q*
Aberdare *p113*. 01685 885500

Williams, P R (Burges Salmon) *A1*
Bristol *p161* 0117 939 2000

Williams, Miss R (Caversham Solicitors Ltd) *K3 K1 D1 D2*
Reading *p360* 0118 947 8638

Williams, Ms R (Hutchinson Thomas) *W K4 T2*
Neath *p320* 01639 645061

Williams, R (British American Tobacco)
London WC2 *p104*. 020 7845 1000

Williams, R (Richard Griffiths & Co)
Salisbury *p371*. 01722 329966

Williams, R (Charles Hart Solicitors)
Cheddar *p186* 01934 742315

Williams, R (Ince & Co Services Ltd)
London E1 *p44* 020 7481 0010

Williams, R (Rosling King) *O N Q J1*
London EC4 *p73*. 020 7353 2353

Williams, R (Tudur Owen Roberts Glynne & Co) *G S1 H K1 M1 D1 E V N P*
Caernarfon *p172*. . .01286 672207 / 672851

Williams, R (Nabarro LLP)
Sheffield *p376* 0114 279 4000

Williams, R A (Hugh James) *N*
Cardiff *p179* 029 2022 4871

Williams, R A (Cornwall County Council)
Truro *p474*. 01872 322197

Williams, R D (Pinsent Masons LLP) *B1 C1*
London EC2 *p67*. 020 7418 7000

Williams, R D (GHP Legal) *L J1 O Q N E S1 Zp Zl Ze*
Wrexham *p442* 01978 291456

Williams, R G (Charles Hart Solicitors)
Cheddar *p186* 01934 742315

Williams, R G (Flintshire County Council)
Mold *p466*. 01352 702411

Williams, R G (Leo Abse & Cohen) *N J1 F1 Zo Zk*
Cardiff *p179* . . .029 2038 3252 / 2034 5421

Williams, R H (Alletsons) *S1 Q W*
Burnham-on-Sea *p169*. . . . 01278 780151

Williams, R H (Gales) *S1 E L W S2*
Bournemouth *p152*. .01202 512227 / 512446

Williams, R H (Gamlins)
Llandudno *p291* 01492 860420

Williams, R H (Robin Williams) *S1 W T2*
Tunbridge Wells *p415* 01892 863057

Williams, R H P (Hutchinson Thomas) *G N P K1 M1 L F1 S1 W C1 Zl Zt Zc*
Neath *p320* 01639 645061

Williams, Ms R J (Warwickshire County Council) *Q O*
Warwick *p475* 01926 410410

Williams, R J (Walker Smith Way) *A1 W E*
Chester *p191* 0844 346 3100

Williams, R J (R R Williams & Son) *S1 W K1 P C1 L M1 E R1*
Sutton Coldfield *p404* 0121 354 7870

Williams, R J T (Simmons & Simmons) *O*
London EC2 *p79*. 020 7628 2020

Williams, R L (Weightmans LLP) *N G J1 Zl Zq*
Liverpool *p291*. 0151 227 2601

Williams, R M (Dawson & Burgess with Bell Dallman & Co) *S1 S2 E A1 W C1 L R1 R2 Zd*
Doncaster *p211* 01302 349463

Williams, R M L (Dunn & Baker) *A1 E L R1 S1*
Exeter *p221* 01392 285000

Williams, R N (R N Williams & Co Limited) *G H N S1 K1 W F1 B1 C1 S2 E K3 Q Zq T1*
Wolverhampton *p438* 01902 429051

Williams, R O (Tudur Owen Roberts Glynne & Co) *G H S1 W K4 S2 K1 D1 Q K3*
Blaenau Ffestiniog *p147* . . . 01766 830206

Williams, R P (Biscoes) *S1 S2 W*
Portsmouth *p354*. 023 9266 0261

Williams, R Q (The BOC Group PLC)
Guildford *p476*. 01483 579857

Williams, Mrs S (Cyril Jones & Co) *S1 W S2 E K3 K1 K4 L J1 D1 A1*
Wrexham *p443* 01978 367830

Williams, Ms S (Russell-Cooke LLP) *D1*
Kingston upon Thames *p267*. 020 8546 6111

Williams, Miss S (Hatten Wyatt) *G H*
Gravesend *p232*. 01474 351199

Williams, S (Boodle Hatfield)
Westminster *p14*. 020 7629 7411

Williams, S (Christopher Green McCarrahers) *K1 Q*
Southampton *p386*. 023 8084 2765

Williams, Mrs S (Maidments) *G H L S1*
Sale *p370* 0870 403 4000

Williams, S (Britannia Building Society)
Leek *p463*. 01538 399399

Williams, Miss S (Debenhams Ottaway) *W*
St Albans *p390* 01727 837161

Williams, Ms S (Chloride Group PLC)
London SW1 *p105*. 020 7881 1440

Williams, Ms S A (Neil Myerson LLP) *C1 C2*
Altrincham *p117* 0161 941 4000

Williams, Miss S E (Davies & Partners) *N Q Zr*
Almondsbury *p115*. 01454 619619

Williams, S G (Unilever PLC)
London EC4 *p110*. 020 7822 5252

Williams, Mrs S H (Partridge & Wilson) *B1 D1 F1 J1 K1 L N O Q Ze Zc*
Bury St Edmunds *p171* . . . 01284 762281

Williams, S H K (Mayer Brown International LLP) *E R2 S2*
London EC2 *p59*. 020 3130 3000

Williams, S I (Anthony Holden Crofts & Co) *C1 E S1 W S2*
Brentford *p156*. 020 8568 7768

Williams, S J (Edwards Angell Palmer & Dodge) *C1 C2 Zj*
London EC2 *p28*. 020 7583 4055

Williams, S J (Jolliffe & Co) *C1 C2 U2 Ze F1 F2 Zza J1 Zp*
Chester *p190* 01244 310022

Williams, S K (British Standards Institution)
London W4 *p104* 020 8996 7010

Williams, Miss S K V (Gabb & Co)
Abergavenny *p113*. 01873 852432

Williams, Miss S L (Blake Lapthorn) *J1*
Chandlers Ford *p184* 023 8090 8090

Williams, Ms S L (DP Law Ltd t/a David Prosser & Co) *S1 S2 W*
Bridgend *p157*. 01656 645921

Williams, Mrs S L (Vincent Sykes & Higham LLP) *W K4 T2 Zd*
Thrapston *p411* 01832 732161

Williams, Ms S L (Geldards LLP) *W*
Cardiff *p178* 029 2023 8239

Williams, S L (Ashton KCJ)
Ipswich *p262*. 01473 232425

Williams, Ms S L (Reed Smith LLP) *O Zc*
London EC2 *p71*. 020 3116 3000

Williams, Miss S M (Kirby Sheppard) *N J2 L Q*
Bristol *p163* 0845 840 0045

Williams, Mrs S M (Gartsides)
Abergavenny *p113*. 01873 857555

Williams, S N (Tilbury Goddard) *S1 S2 E*
Thornton Heath *p411*. 020 8684 5581

Williams, S R (Cripps Harries Hall LLP) *C1 Zl Zb C3 F1*
Tunbridge Wells *p415* 01892 515121

Williams, T (Williams Gorman LLP)
Haringey *p91* . . . .

Williams, T (Criminal Defence Solicitors) *H*
Westminster *p23*. 020 7353 7000

Williams, T (Tudor Williams & Co) *G H J1 M1 P R1 V Zd Zg Zm*
Wrexham *p443* 01978 362006

Williams, T A S (Bank Of Ireland UK Financial Services)
Bristol *p451* 0117 979 2222

Williams, T G (Lee & Priestley LLP) *C1 C2 Zb Zd Ze Zz*
Leeds *p275* 0845 129 2300

Williams, Ms T J (Kidd Rapinet) *S1 W K4*
Slough *p382*. 0845 017 9638

Williams, T R (Weightmans LLP) *A1 E R1 R2 Zc*
Manchester *p311* 0161 233 7330

Williams, Miss U D M (Cullimore Dutton) *K3 J1 K1 O Q N Zq*
Chester *p190* 01244 356789

Williams, Mrs V (Rochman Landau LLP) *C1 U2 C2*
London W1 *p72* 020 7544 2424

Williams, V R (Howe & Spender) *G H K1*
Port Talbot *p353* 01639 881571

Williams, W (Harding Evans LLP) *S1*
Newport *p328* 01633 244233

Williams, W J (TLT Solicitors) *A1 C1 D1 K1 L R1 S1*
Bristol *p165* 0117 917 7777

Williams, W R (T R Evans Hughes & Co) *A1 C1 D1 F1 G H J1 K1 L N S1*
Amlwch *p117* 01407 830400
Holyhead *p251*. 01407 762204

Williams, W S G (Taylor Woodrow Construction Legal Department)
Watford *p475* 01923 478442

Williams-Jauvel, Mrs K (Morrisons Solicitors LLP) *Q*
London SW19 *p62*. 020 8971 1020

Williams-White, C J D (Lancashire County Council)
Preston *p469* 01772 254868

Williamson, A (Stephens & Scown) *W T2*
Exeter *p222* 01392 210700

Williamson, A (Aughton Ainsworth)
Salford *p370*. 0161 877 8555

Williamson, Miss A (Global Aerospace Underwriting Managers Ltd) *Zq O*
London EC3 *p106* 020 7369 2244

Williamson, A J (Walker Morris) *R1 E Zn*
Leeds *p277* 0113 283 2500

Williamson, A R (Pannone LLP) *A3 Zc*
Manchester *p308* 0161 909 3000

Williamson, C A (Crown Prosecution Service Durham) *L E A1 R1 S1 W C1 J1 F1 B1 Zc Zl*
Durham *p457* 0191 383 5800

Williamson, D (Freeth Cartwright LLP)
Birmingham *p138* 0845 634 2575

Williamson, D J (David Clark & Co) *K1 D1 W*
London NW3 *p20* 020 7433 1562

Williamson, Mrs D M (Hewitsons) *E*
Cambridge *p174*. 01223 461155

Williamson, D S (Soulsby Williamson) *S1 E K1 N Q W J1 C1 F1 R1 Zl*
Ruislip *p369* 01895 636999

Williamson, Miss G (A H Brooks & Co) *K1 S1 W V D1 F1 Zi*
Cheadle *p185* 01538 754253
Leek *p278*. 01538 383201

Williamson, Miss H (Worcestershire County Council)
Worcester *p477* 01905 766335

Williamson, H E (Gosschalks) *E S1 A1 W L Zd*
Hull *p256* 01482 324252

Williamson, Dr I B (Wards Solicitors) *O B1 F1 Zb*
Bristol *p165* 0117 929 2811

Williamson, I P (Williamson & Soden) *S1 W E C1 R2 R1*
Solihull *p383*. 0121 733 8000

Williamson, Ms J (Susan Howarth & Co) *D1 D2*
Northwich *p333* 01606 48777

Williamson, Mrs J M (Cook & Talbot) *W T2*
Southport *p388* 01704 535216

Williamson, J M (Darbys Solicitors LLP) *C2 C1*
Oxford *p343*. 01865 811700

Williamson, J R (John Williamson Solicitor) *E S1 C1 L W*
Wandsworth *p92*. 020 8673 7508

Williamson, Mrs L E G (Forsters LLP) *E*
Westminster *p33*. 020 7863 8333

Williamson, M A H M (Malcolm A H M Williamson) *P R1 E S2*
Farnham *p225*. 0845 230 1022

Williamson, M D (Wills Group Ltd)
London EC3 *p110* 020 7488 8111

Williamson, M R (The Stokes Partnership) *O N J1 B1 F1 J2 Q U2 Ze Zk Zq*
Crewkerne *p203*. 01460 279279

Williamson, N C (Ashurst LLP) *C1 Zb*
London EC2 *p7* 020 7638 1111

Williamson, N H T (Marriott Davies Yapp) *C1 M1 I M2 Ze*
Sutton *p402* 020 8643 9794

Williamson, N J (Williams Thompson) *K3 K1*
Christchurch *p194* 01202 484242

Williamson, Ms P (Trafford Metropolitan Borough Council)
Stretford *p473* 0161 912 1212

Williamson, P S (Paul S Williamson) *C1 E F1 K1 N O Q S1 W*
Berkhamsted *p131*. 01442 862475

Williamson, R E F (K&L Gates LLP) *R2 C2 Zb*
London EC4 *p47*. 020 7648 9000

Williamson, R G (Cuttle & Co) *G H K1*
Manchester *p302* 0161 835 2050

Williamson, Ms S (Boyes Turner) *C1*
Reading *p360* 0118 959 7711

Williamson, S (Park Woodfine Heald Mellows LLP) *S1*
Bedford *p130* 01234 400000

Williamson, Miss S A (Browne Jacobson LLP) *C1 C2*
Nottingham *p336*. 0115 976 6000

Williamson, Ms S D (DWF) *O Zb B1*
Manchester *p303* 0161 603 5000

Williamson, S J (Punch Robson) *S2 E S1 C2*
Middlesbrough *p315* 01642 230700

Williamson, T D (Harris Cartier LLP) *O Q*
London WC2 *p39* 020 7405 7100

Williamson, Mrs V L (Blakestons) *W N T1 A1 O L E K4*
Driffield *p213* 01377 253476

Williets, S L (William Wright & Son) *K1 D1 G H Q Zl*
Dudley *p213*. 01384 255344

Willimott, P J (Birmingham City Council Legal & Democratic Services) *G H J1 N O V F1*
Birmingham *p449* 0121 303 2066

Willis Stewart, Ms M (Birnberg Peirce & Partners) *Zg*
Camden *p13*. 020 7911 0166

Willis, Ms A (Watford Borough Council)
Watford *p475* 01923 226400

Willis, B (Veale Wasbrough Vizards) *E L S2 Zd*
Bristol *p165* 0117 925 2020

Willis, B G (LG Lawyers)
London SE1 *p50*. 020 7379 0000

Willis, D A (Herbert Smith LLP) *Zb C2*
London EC2 *p40*. 020 7374 8000

Willis, D I (Mundays LLP) *S1 S2 E*
Cobham *p196* 01932 590500

Willis, F M (DAC Beachcroft) *Q N O P Zk*
Leeds *p272* 0113 251 4700

Willis, G P W (EMW) *E S2 R2*
Milton Keynes *p316* 0845 070 6000

Willis, J (Clark Willis) *Q Zm Zq Zr*
Darlington *p206* 01325 281111

Willis, J M (Thomson Snell & Passmore) *J1 Zp*
Tunbridge Wells *p415* 01892 510000

Willis, Ms K J (Metcalfe Copeman & Pettefar) *K1*
King's Lynn *p266* 01553 778102

Willis, K R (Aviva PLC)
London EC3 *p103* . . 020 7283 7500 / 01603 687905
Norwich *p467* 01603 622200
York *p477* 01904 452210

Willis, Mrs L (Torfaen Borough Council)
Pontypool *p469* 01495 766373

Willis, M G (Grayson Willis Bennett) *G H J2 B2*
Sheffield *p375* 0114 290 9500

Willis, N P (PricewaterhouseCoopers Legal LLP) *J1*
London SE1 *p69*. 020 7212 1616

Willis, P (Taylor Wessing)
London EC4 *p86*. 020 7300 7000

Willis, R (MLM Cartwright) *O Q F2 Za Zc A3 Zq Ze J2*
Cardiff *p179* 029 2046 2562

Willis, R (Thomson Snell & Passmore) *E A1 R1 P S1 Zc*
Tunbridge Wells *p415* 01892 510000

Willis, R E (Geoffrey Leaver Solicitors LLP) *E C1 S1 L R1 W Zh Ze Zc*
Milton Keynes *p317* 01908 692769

Willis, Mrs S F C (Solihull Metropolitan Borough Council)
Solihull *p471*. 0121 704 6000

Willison, C A (Squire Sanders (UK) LLP) *O J1 C1 Q E Ze*
London EC2 *p81*. 020 7655 1000

Willits, Mrs J (Sintons LLP) *N J2*
Newcastle upon Tyne *p326* . 0191 226 7878

Willman, Mrs G M (Cumbria County Council) *N Q F1 G Zl*
Carlisle *p453*. . . . .01228 607374 / 607351

Willmott, B (Thomson Training & Simulation Ltd)
Crawley *p456* 01293 562822

Willmott, Mrs E R (Maples Teesdale LLP) *E*
London EC2 *p58*. 020 7600 3800

Willmott, Mrs S A (Gateshead Metropolitan Borough Council)
Gateshead *p458*. 0191 433 3000

Willmott, Miss S J (John Lewis plc)
London SW1 *p107*. 020 7828 1000

Willmott, S J (Hereford Magistrates Court)
Hereford *p460*. 01562 514000

Willott, Ms E J (Bevirs) *K1 K3*
Calne *p173* 01249 814536

Willoughby, A (Rouse Legal (Formerly Willoughby & Partners)) *Ze A3*
London E14 *p74*. 020 7536 4100

Willoughby, Miss G (Argyles) *W T2*
Tamworth *p407* 01827 56276

Willoughby, P M (Foot Anstey) *K1 D1 G Q*
Exeter *p221* 01392 411221

Willoughby, R (Brignalls Balderston Warren) *W*
Biggleswade *p133*. 01767 313813

Willoughby, R (Smith Jones Solicitors) *N Zq Q*
Kenilworth *p264* 01926 859933
Burnley *p169* 01282 855400

Willoughby, R G (C W Booth & Co) *G H K1 N Q S1*
Bishop Auckland *p144* 01388 606660

Willoughby-Foster, Ms N (Linder Myers Solicitors) *E L B3*
Manchester *p307* 0844 984 6400

Willows, Miss A J (Wolferstans) *K1 D1 V*
Plymouth *p351*. 01752 663295

Wills, A N (AW Law) *C1 L O S1 S2*
Esher *p219* 01372 469100

Wills, D (Speechly Bircham LLP) *C1 K1 O Zf*
London EC4 *p81*. 020 7427 6400

Wills, Miss F (Reynolds Porter Chamberlain LLP) *C1*
London E1 *p71* 020 3060 6000

Wills, I (East Cornwall Magistrates Courts)
Bodmin *p450* 01208 262700

Wills, Miss J H (Torbay Council)
Torquay *p474* 01803 201201

Wills, M (Park Woodfine Heald Mellows LLP) *S2 E*
Bedford *p130* 01234 400000

Wills, P (BHP Law) *Q L Zy*
Durham *p214* 0191 384 0840

Wills, T (Watson Burton LLP)
Newcastle upon Tyne *p327* . 0845 901 2100

Willsher, J (William Heath & Co) *W Q K3*
London SW11 *p40*. 020 7350 1068

Willson, N S (TLT Solicitors)
London EC2 *p85*. 020 3465 4000

Willson, R W (Willson Hawley & Co) *S1 R1 Q O L J1 F1 C1 B1 A1*
Nuneaton *p339* 024 7638 7821

Willson, Ms S (Eastleys) *K1*
Paignton *p345* 01803 559257

Willson, S P (CB Legal) *J1 C1 W T1 T2*
Camden *p17*. 020 7323 9192

Willson, S P (SJ Berwin LLP)
London EC4 *p75*. 020 7111 2222

Wilman, Ms J J (Aviva PLC) *B1 C1 E Zj Zo*
London EC3 *p103* . . 020 7283 7500 / 01603 687905

Wilman, Mrs J J (Norwich Union Insurance Group)
Norwich *p467* 01603 622200

Wilman, Ms J J (Norwich Union Life) *B1 C1 E Zj Zo*
York *p477* 01904 452210

Wilmot, G (Russell-Cooke LLP) *C1*
London SW15 *p74*. 020 8789 9111

Wilmot, S J (Mayo Wynne Baxter LLP) *D1 D2 J1 J2 K1 N V Zq*
East Grinstead *p215* 01342 310600

Wilmot, S J (J R Brown & Co) *S1 W*
Clevedon *p195*. 01275 879292

Wilmot-Smith, A (Boodle Hatfield)
Westminster *p14*. 020 7629 7411

Wilner, Miss L E (Harold Benjamin) *E S2*
Harrow *p241*. 020 8422 5678

Wilsdon, T J (Tilly Bailey & Irvine LLP) *N*
Stockton-on-Tees *p397* . . . 01642 673797

Wilsher, Miss C A (Behr & Co) *K1 K3 D1*
Brynmawr *p167* 01495 310581

Wilsher, Ms K (Charles Russell LLP)
Guildford *p235*. 01483 252525

Wilsher, Ms K (Charles Russell LLP) *K1*
Guildford *p235*. 01483 252525

Wilsher, K R (Ellisons) *E S1 A1*
Colchester *p197* 01206 764477

Wilson, A (Bristows) *O*
London EC4 *p15*. 020 7400 8000

Wilson, Mrs A (Kirby & Co) *K1 K3*
London SW19 *p50*. 020 8545 7171

Wilson, A (Travers Smith LLP) *B1*
London EC1 *p87*. 020 7295 3000

Wilson, A (Allen & Overy LLP)
London E1 *p5* 020 3088 0000

Wilson, A (Fishburns) *Zj O Q Zo A3 Zc*
London EC3 *p32*. 020 7280 8888

Wilson, Mrs A (Jobling & Knape) *N K4*
Lancaster *p269* 01524 598300

Wilson, A A (Thompsons (formerly Robin/Brian Thompson & Partners))
Manchester *p310* 0161 819 3500

Wilson, A C (Russell Jones & Walker) *N J1 Zw*
Birmingham *p141* 0121 233 8300

Wilson, A C (Gordons Solicitors LLP) *N Q O*
Marlow *p313*. 01628 487487

Wilson, Mrs A E (Kirby Sheppard) *K3 K1*
Kingswood *p268*. 0845 840 0045

Wilson, Miss A E (Sills & Betteridge LLP) *O Q*
Lincoln *p285*. 01522 542211

Wilson, A E (Hill Dickinson LLP) *N O Q P K1 M1 Zj*
Liverpool *p288*. 0151 600 8000

Wilson, A H G (Brachers) *Q O Zc Zj Zq*
Maidstone *p299* 01622 690691

Wilson, Mrs A J (Menneer Shuttleworth) *K3 K1 W*
St Leonards-on-Sea *p392* . . 01424 720044

Wilson, A J (Martins) *O E W Zl*
Eccles *p216* 0161 707 3660

Wilson, A J D (Bristows) *Ze I Zy*
London EC4 *p15*. 020 7400 8000

Wilson, Mrs A M (Burstalls) *W T2*
Hull *p256* 01482 621800

Wilson, A R (Serious Fraud Office) *J1 Zp*
London WC1 *p109*. 020 7239 7272

Wilson, C (Trowers & Hamlins)
London EC3 *p88*. 020 7423 8000

Wilson, C (Coodes) *S2 Zl*
Truro *p414*. 01872 246200

Wilson, C (McMillan Williams) *K1*
Wallington *p419* 020 8669 4962

Wilson, Miss C A (Herbert Smith LLP) *C1*
London EC2 *p40*. 020 7374 8000

Wilson, C B (Bates & Mountain) *S1 W E A1 L R1 C1 T1 Zc Zs S2 T2*
Grimsby *p235* 01472 357291

Wilson, C D N (Hatchers Solicitors LLP) *G H K1 J1 Q A1 D1 Zl Zt Zp*
Shrewsbury *p379* 01743 248545

Wilson, C H (Lovetts PLC) *O*
Guildford *p236*. 01483 457500

Wilson, C H (Whiteside & Knowles Ltd) *K1 S1 S2 W Zl K3 E*
Morecambe *p319* 01524 416315

Wilson, Mrs C J (Philip Ross & Co) *K1 D1*
London W1 *p73* 020 7636 6969

Wilson, C J (Hereward & Foster)
London E16 *p41*. 020 7476 6600

Wilson, C J (DLA Piper UK LLP) *C1 C2 C3 O*
London EC2 *p24*. 0870 011 1111

Wilson, Miss C M (Healys LLP) *O Q Zq B2 Zk*
London EC4 *p39*. 020 7822 4000

Wilson, Mrs C S (Southampton City Council)
Southampton *p472*. 023 8022 3855

Wilson, C T (Westminster City Council)
London SW1 *p110*. 020 7641 6000

Wilson, Miss D (Creighton & Partners) *K1*
London WC1 *p23* 020 7976 2233

Wilson, D (Reynolds Porter Chamberlain LLP)
London E1 *p71* 020 3060 6000

Wilson, Ms D (Worcestershire County Council)
Worcester *p477* 01905 766335

Wilson, Ms D (Anthony Gold) *L Zg*
London SW16 *p6* 020 7940 4000

Wilson, D A (Peachey & Co)
London WC2 *p66* 020 7316 5200

Wilson, D F (Wilson Barca LLP) *C1 E J1 K1 M1*
London W1 *p92* 020 7272 2072

Wilson, D I (Sema Group UK Ltd)
London NW1 *p109*. 020 7830 4213

Wilson, D J (W H Matthews & Co) *W K4 S1 E S2 L*
Sutton *p402* 020 8642 6677

Wilson, D J M (BHP Law) *C1*
Newcastle upon Tyne *p323* . 0191 221 0898

Wilson, D L (Bird & Bird LLP) *C1 Ze*
London EC4 *p13*. 020 7415 6000

Wilson, D L (Squire Sanders (UK) LLP) *C1 C2*
Leeds *p277* 0113 284 7000

Wilson, D M (Cumbria County Council)
Carlisle *p453*. . . . .01228 607374 / 607351

Wilson, D M (Addleshaw Goddard) *Zb*
London EC1 *p4* 020 7606 8855

Wilson, D R (MKB Solicitors LLP)
Barnsley *p124*. 01226 210000

Wilson, D S (Warners Solicitors) *J1 K1 N O Q Zq*
Tonbridge *p412* 01732 770660

Wilson, D W (Parfitt Cresswell) *C1 S2 J1 O R1 R2 E T1 L*
London SW6 *p65* 020 7381 8311

Wilson, Mrs E (Wrigleys Solicitors LLP) *E S2 Zx Zd*
Leeds *p278* 0113 244 6100

Wilson, Miss E (Bolt Burdon) *N*
Islington *p14*. 020 7288 4700

Wilson, Mrs E (Michelmores LLP) *R1 O E*
Exeter *p221* 01392 688688

Wilson, Miss E C (Hindle Campbell)
North Shields *p330* 0191 296 1777

Wilson, Miss E J (Macfarlanes) *S1 S2*
London EC4 *p56*. 020 7831 9222

Wilson, Mrs E V (Brignalls Balderston Warren) *K1 D1 D2 K3*
Letchworth *p283*. 01462 482248

Wilson, Miss F (Hempsons) *T2 W Zd*
Westminster *p40*. 020 7839 0278

Wilson, F A J (Pictons Solicitors LLP)
Luton *p295* 01582 870870

Wilson, Mrs F J (Cocks Lloyd) *K1 V*
Nuneaton *p339* 024 7664 1642

Wilson, Ms F M (Castle Point Borough Council)
Benfleet *p449* 01268 882200

Wilson, Miss F S R (Parkinson Wright LLP) *W*
Worcester *p440* 01905 726789

Wilson, G (Barlow Robbins LLP) *S2 E R2 S1*
Woking *p436*. 01483 748500

Wilson, G O (Gareth Wilson)
Monmouth *p318* 01600 772500

Wilson, G R (M&A Solicitors LLP) *E S2 L R2 S1*
Cardiff *p179* 029 2048 2288

Wilson, G S (JMW Solicitors) *S1 K1 M1 P W L E D1 H*
Manchester *p306* 0845 872 6666

Wilson, Miss H (Doncaster Metropolitan Borough Council) *W S1 T2*
Doncaster *p457* 01302 734651
Gosport *p232* 023 9250 5500

Wilson, Miss H (John Pickering & Partners LLP)
Halifax *p238* 0808 144 0959

Wilson, Ms H (Shoosmiths)
Birmingham *p142* 0370 086 4000 / 0121 335 4440

Wilson, H A (Stephenson Harwood) *T2 W Zd*
London EC2 *p82*. 020 7329 4422

Wilson, H J (Wilsons Solicitors) *K1 S1 N G H E F1 W C1 D1 Zl*
Oxford *p344* 01865 874497

Wilson, Miss H P (Newcastle Upon Tyne City Council) *E L*
Newcastle upon Tyne *p466* . 0191 232 8520

Wilson, I C (Lyons Wilson) *N M1 K1 F1 J1 C1 P G B1 D1*
Manchester *p307* 0161 830 7777

Wilson, I D (Russell Jones & Walker) *G H D1 Zl*
Bristol *p164* 0117 374 2222

Wilson, I K R (Dean Wilson Laing) *J1 C1 Zl Zc Zp*
Brighton *p159* 01273 327241

Wilson, I R (Hacking Ashton LLP) *E S2 S1 R2 L A1 R1*
Newcastle under Lyme *p323* . 01782 715555

Wilson, J (Reed Smith LLP) *C1*
London EC2 *p71*. 020 3116 3000

Wilson, J (Ridley & Hall) *X V*
Huddersfield *p256* 01484 538421

Wilson, Miss J (Biscoes) *K3 K1 W*
Petersfield *p348* 01730 264799

Wilson, J (Wilsons)
Leeds *p278* 0113 264 3444

Wilson, J C R (Richard J Knaggs & Co) *K1 S1 F1 D1 W Zk*
Redcar *p362*. 01642 487011

Wilson, J G (Thompson Smith & Puxon) *N O L*
Colchester *p198* 01206 574431

Wilson, J H C (Kaim Todner Ltd) *Zm*
London SE17 *p47* 020 7701 4747

Wilson, Miss J L (Bannister Preston) *D2 J1 K1 N*
Sale *p370* 0161 973 2434

Wilson, Mrs J L (Heptonstalls LLP) *S1 W S2 K1 A3*
Howden *p255* 01430 430209

Wilson, J M (J M Wilson Solicitors) *G H Zi S1*
Birmingham *p143* 0121 356 4556

Wilson, Ms J M (Fisher Jones Greenwood LLP) *K1 D1 G M1 W P S1*
Colchester *p197* 01206 578282

Wilson, Mrs J P (Hartley Thomas & Wright) *D1 K1 K3 D2*
Rochdale *p365*. 01706 644118

Wilson, J R K (Ince & Co Services Ltd)
London E1 *p44* 020 7481 0010

Wilson, J S R (Baines Wilson LLP) *C1 C2 C3 I Ze*
Carlisle *p181*. 01228 552600

Wilson, Mrs K (Brown & Corbishley) *D1 K1 V*
Newcastle under Lyme *p323* . 01782 717888

Wilson, Mrs K (Barlow Lyde & Gilbert LLP) *Zj*
London EC3 *p10*. 020 7247 2277

Wilson, K (Redcar and Cleveland Borough Council)
Redcar *p465*. 01642 466201

Wilson, K G H (Jeffrey Green Russell) *E S1*
London W1 *p46* 020 7339 7000

Wilson, K J (Marsden Rawsthorn LLP) *O Q N B1 Zq Zr I*
Preston *p357* 01772 799600

Wilson, Mrs K J (Hempsons) *N Q D1 Zm Zr*
Harrogate *p240* 01423 522331

Wilson, Mrs K L (West Sussex County Council) *K1 D1*
Chichester *p455* 01243 777100

Wilson, Miss L (Dawson Hart) *N*
Uckfield *p416* 01825 762281

Wilson, L (Wilsons Solicitors)
Oxford *p344* 01865 874497

Wilson, Miss L (Redcar and Cleveland Borough Council)
Redcar *p465*. 01642 466201

Wilson, Miss L (Pannone LLP) *N*
Manchester *p308* 0161 909 3000

Wilson, Ms L I (Allen & Overy LLP)
London E1 *p5* 020 3088 0000

Wilson, Mrs L J (Wards Solicitors) *S1*
Bristol *p165* 01454 204880

Wilson, Ms L M (Barlow Lyde & Gilbert LLP)
London EC3 *p10*. 020 7247 2277

Wilson, Ms L M (Marathon Oil UK Ltd)
London NW1 *p107*. 020 7298 2500

Wilson, M (Christies International PLC)
London SW1 *p105*. 020 7839 9060

Wilson, M (Muckle LLP) *S2 E R2 S1*
Newcastle upon Tyne *p325* . 0191 211 7777

Wilson, M (Clarke Willmott) *J1 O Zp*
Southampton *p385*0845 209 1000 / 0117 305 6000

Wilson, M A (Stokes Solicitors)
Portsmouth *p355*. 023 9282 8131

Wilson, Mrs M C (Wilson Browne) *K1 D1 V L*
Northampton *p333*. 01604 876697

Wilson, M G (Thompson Smith & Puxon) *E K1 W A1 R1 S1*
Colchester *p198* 01206 574431

Wilson, M G (Meikles) *G H Zm*
Stockton-on-Tees *p397* . . . 01740 620255

Wilson, M G W (Lincoln Financial Group) *C1 Zj Zo*
Gloucester *p459*. 0845 678 8888

Wilson, M G W (Prudential PLC)
London EC4 *p108* 020 7220 7588

Wilson, M J (Salans) *B1 C1 F1 Zb*
London EC4 *p76*. 020 7429 6000

Wilson, M J (Hine Downing Solicitors) *D2 A3 K3 K2 K1*
Falmouth *p223*. 01326 316655

Wilson, M J F T (Stephenson Harwood) *Q*
London EC2 *p82*. 020 7329 4422

Wilson, M R (North East Lincolnshire Borough Council)
Cleethorpes *p455* 01472 324001

Wilson, M S (Panel Agency Ltd) *C1 S1 L E*
Dartford *p456* 01474 872578

Wilson, M S (Cartwright King) *P B2 F2 J2*
Nottingham *p336*. 0115 958 7444

Wilson, Mrs M T (Birketts LLP (Wollastons LLP)) *D1 K1 K2*
Chelmsford *p186*. 01245 211211

Wilson, M V (Graham & Rosen) *C1 E S1 R1 A1 B1 J1 M1 N W Zb Ze Zl*
Hull *p257* 01482 323123

Wilson, Miss N (Rosling King) *O N Q*
London EC4 *p73*. 020 7353 2353

Wilson, N C B (Maxwell Winward LLP) *E L R2 S2*
London EC4 *p59*. 020 7651 0000

Wilson, N D (Hugh James) *S1 L Zh S2*
Cardiff *p179* 029 2022 4871

Wilson, Mrs N E (Astle Paterson Ltd) *E S2 W S1 C1*
Burton-on-Trent *p170* 01283 531366

Wilson, Ms N J (Fentons)
Manchester *p304* 0161 786 8320

Wilson, Mrs N J (SAS Daniels LLP) *N Zr*
Macclesfield *p297* 01625 442100

Wilson, Ms N K (Wilson Browne) *A1 B1 C1 C2 E F1 S2 Ze*
Kettering *p265*. 01536 410041

Wilson, N M (Irwin Mitchell LLP) *K1 D1 Zl L*
Leeds *p274* 0870 150 0100

Wilson, N R (N R Wilson) *S1 K1 G F1 W E L*
Kenilworth *p264* 01926 857631

Wilson, N S R (Bentleys Stokes & Lowless)
London EC3 *p12*. 020 7782 0990

Wilson, O (Nigel Davis Solicitors) *O Q A1 A2 R1 P Ze F1 J1*
Belper *p131* 01335 372889

Wilson, P (Avery Naylor) *G H J1 K1 N Zl*
Swansea *p404*. 01792 463276

Wilson, P (Wilson & Co Solicitors) *L N Q K1 O V*
Middlesbrough *p315* 01642 222292

Wilson, P (Wilson Devonald Ltd)
Swansea *p406*. 01792 484566

Wilson, P (Bolton Metropolitan Borough Council) *N Q G*
Bolton *p450* 01204 333333

Wilson, P C (Blake Lapthorn) *B2 I O Zl*
London EC1 *p13*. 020 7405 2000
London WC2 *p60* 020 7242 5905

Wilson, P H (Wake Smith & Tofields) *C1 C2*
Sheffield *p377* 0114 266 6660

Wilson, Mrs P J (Marsh & Co) *J1 K1 S1 K3 K2 W*
Lancaster *p269* 01524 68102

Wilson, P J (HCB Solicitors) *C1 A1 E S2 R1 R2*
Walsall *p420*. 01922 720000

Wilson, P J (Wilson Browne) *B1 E W T1 A1*
Kettering *p265*. 01536 410041

Wilson, P M (Town & Country Lawyers) *E S1 S2*
Cheltenham *p188* 01242 587900

Wilson, Mrs R (Debenhams Ottaway) *W*
St Albans *p390* 01727 837161

Wilson, R (Capsticks Solicitors LLP) *Zr N*
London SW19 *p18*. 020 8780 2211

Wilson, R (Holman Fenwick Willan)
London EC3 *p42*. 020 7264 8000

Wilson, R (VHS Fletchers Solicitors) *G H*
Nottingham *p339*. 0115 959 9550

Wilson, R C (hlw Keeble Hawson LLP) *C1 G*
Sheffield *p376* 0114 276 5555

Wilson, R C (Peachey & Co)
London WC2 *p66* 020 7316 5200

Wilson, R E (Robert Wilson Solicitors) *S1 K1 W C1 A1 E*
Okehampton *p340*. 01837 55880

Wilson, R G (Royal Mail Group)
London EC4 *p109* 020 7250 2468

Wilson, Ms R H (Barlow Lyde & Gilbert LLP)
London EC3 *p10*. 020 7247 2277

Wilson, R J (Cottrill Stone Lawless)
Manchester *p302* 0161 835 3681

Wilson, Miss R L (Act Family Law)
Plymouth *p349*. 01752 226224

Wilson, R M (Dickinson Dees) *W*
Newcastle upon Tyne *p324* . 0191 279 9000

Wilson, Ms R M S (City of Bradford Metropolitan District Council)
Bradford *p451* 01274 752236

Wilson, R N (Graham Withers & Co) *S1 S2*
Market Drayton *p312*. 01630 657222

Wilson, R S (Saunders Roberts) *B1 C1 D1 F1 G H J1 M1*
Evesham *p220*. 01386 442558

Wilson, R T H (TLT Solicitors)
London EC2 *p85*. 020 3465 4000

Wilson, Ms S (Kaim Todner Ltd)
London SE17 *p47* 020 7701 4747

Wilson, Ms S (Walker Morris)
Leeds *p277* 0113 283 2500

Wilson, Ms S (Watson Burton LLP)
Newcastle upon Tyne *p327* . 0845 901 2100

Wilson, Miss S (Hill Dickinson LLP) *Zm N D1 Zr Q*
Liverpool *p288*. 0151 600 8000

Wilson, S C (Osborne Clarke) *R2 C2*
Reading *p361* 0118 925 2000

Wilson, S D (Ward Gethin) *C1 S2 E S1*
King's Lynn *p266* 01553 660033

Wilson, Ms S E (LG Lawyers)
London SE1 *p50*. 020 7379 0000

Wilson, S G (Morrish Solicitors LLP) *N Q*
Leeds *p276* 0113 245 0733

Wilson, Miss S I (Thompsons (formerly Robin/Brian Thompson & Partners)) *Q N Zq*
Leeds *p277* 0113 205 6300

Wilson, Mrs S J (Hall Smith Whittingham LLP) *K1 K3*
Crewe *p203* 01270 212000
Nantwich *p320*. 01270 610300

 See p634 for the Key to Work Categories

Wilson, Ms S L (Wycombe District Council)
High Wycombe *p461* 01494 461002

Wilson, S M (Gateley LLP) *Zb B1 O*
Birmingham *p138* 0121 234 0000

Wilson, S R (Sills & Betteridge LLP) *N Zq J2*
Lincoln *p285* 01522 542211

Wilson, T (The Hughes Parry Partnership) *N Q F1 K1 Zq K3*
Holywell *p252* 01352 712422

Wilson, T (Ashley Wilson)
London SW1 *p92* 020 7802 4802

Wilson, T C (Batchelors Solicitors) *Zh L*
Bromley *p166* 020 8768 7000

Wilson, T J (Kennedys)
London EC3 *p49* 020 7667 9667

Wilson, T J (Payne & Payne) *K1 D1 G*
Hull *p257* 01482 326446

Wilson, T J R (Lily Driver Investments)
Silsden *p471* 01535 653959

Wilson, Miss V C (GHP Legal) *W*
Oswestry *p342* 01691 659194

Wilson, W F (Dickinson Dees) *S1*
Newcastle upon Tyne *p324* 0191 279 9000

Wilson, W R (Bankside Law Ltd) *G B2 Zq*
London SE1 *p9* 0844 745 4000

Wilson-McMahon, Mrs S J (Symons & Gay) *G H K1 M1 P*
Romford *p366* 01708 744211

Wilson-Smith, Ms J (Boodle Hatfield)
Westminster *p14* 020 7629 7411

Wilton, Ms C (Heald Solicitors) *E Zc S2 Zb P R2 J2*
Milton Keynes *p317* 01908 662277

Wilton, C (Hartley & Worstenholme) *S1 E A1 W L C1 R1 T1 Zd Zm*
Pontefract *p351* 01977 732222

Wilton, C S (Bank of Scotland) *N P F1*
Chester *p454* 01244 690000

Wilton, D R (Addison O'Hare) *E S1 S2*
Walsall *p419* 01922 725515

Wilton, Miss L (Russell-Cooke LLP) *N*
London SW15 *p74* 020 8789 9111

Wilton, P (Park Woodfine Heald Mellows LLP) *W*
Northampton *p332* 01604 233200

Wilton, R C (Chambers Rutland & Crauford) *S1 W E*
London N12 *p19* 020 8446 2777

Wiltshear, R G (Haywards) *W*
Stowmarket *p399* 01449 613631

Wiltshire, H E C (HKB Wiltshires) *C1 S1 E L W T1*
Great Yarmouth *p234* 01493 855676

Wiltshire, Mrs J M (Clarke Willmott) *T1 W Zd*
Southampton *p385* 0845 209 1000 / 0117 305 6000

Wiltshire, P R (CMS Cameron McKenna LLP) *B1 Zb*
London EC3 *p17* 020 7367 3000

Wiltshire, R C (BAE Systems PLC) *Zb B1*
London SW1 *p104* 01252 373232

Wiltshire, S A (Shoosmiths) *E S1 R1 L*
Northampton *p332* 0370 086 3000 / 01604 543000

Winarskie, L (Tyndallwoods)
Birmingham *p143* 0121 624 1111

Winayak, Ms S S (S Winayak) *E S1 S2*
Leatherhead *p271* 020 8941 6022

Winchester, Miss C L (Metcalfe Copeman & Pettefar) *G*
King's Lynn *p266* 01553 778102

Winckler, B (Kennedys) *Q Zj Zq N*
London EC3 *p49* 020 7667 9667

Winder, W M G (Clarkson Hirst)
Lancaster *p269* 01524 39760

Windle, J M B (Napthens LLP) *W*
Blackburn *p145* 01254 667733

Windmill, J A (Glaisyers) *S1 S2 W*
Birmingham *p138* 0121 233 2971

Windows, A R (Henriques Griffiths) *S1 E W*
Bristol *p163* 0117 965 9444

Windsor, Mrs E Y M (Ellen Yee-Man Windsor) *M2 O B1 F1 Zb Zi*
Coventry *p201* 024 7641 4984

Windsor, J (Linklaters LLP)
London EC2 *p54* 020 7456 2000

Windsor, Ms J Y (Penman Johnson) *E L S1 T2 W X Zd*
Watford *p424* 01923 225212 / 239566

Wineman, V (DWFM Beckman) *B1 C1 E S1 T1 W*
Westminster *p25* 020 7872 0023

Winfield, A (EMW) *S1 W R1 P L J1 F1 E Zm*
Milton Keynes *p316* 0845 070 6000

Winfield, A C (TBI Solicitors) *K1 D1*
Hartlepool *p243* 0800 052 6824 / 01429 264101

Winfield, Mrs J (Wortley Byers) *S2*
Brentwood *p156* 01277 268368

Winfield, R H (Butcher Burns LLP) *Q O E S1 W Zd*
London WC1 *p16* 020 7713 7100

Winfield, Mrs R J (RWP Solicitors) *W*
Pangbourne *p345* 0118 984 2266

Wing, M J D (Barlow Lyde & Gilbert LLP) *A3 Zj O Q*
London EC3 *p10* 020 7247 2277

Wing, Mrs R (Hertfordshire County Council)
Hertford *p460* 01992 555555

Wingate-Saul, M A (Letchers) *W*
Ringwood *p364* 01425 471424

Wingfield, A N B (Simmons & Simmons) *C1 T1 J1*
London EC2 *p79* 020 7628 2020

Wingfield, C (Woodfines LLP) *S1 W*
Bedford *p130* 01234 270600

Wingfield, Mrs H M (Scott Fowler) *W*
Northampton *p331* 01604 750506
Bury St Edmunds *p171* 01284 762211

Wingfield, J R (LG Lawyers)
London SE1 *p50* 020 7379 0000

Wingfield, Miss K (Penningtons)
London EC2 *p66* 020 7457 3000

Wingfield, Miss S (Goodall Barnett James)
St Leonards-on-Sea *p392* 01424 444475

Wingrove, Mrs R M (Reading Borough Council)
Reading *p469* 0118 939 0900

Winkley, G (Boodle Hatfield) *C1 T1 T2 E*
Westminster *p14* 020 7629 7411

Winkworth, Miss C (Blake Lapthorn) *C1*
Chandlers Ford *p184* 023 8090 8090

Winn, Ms J D (Morrish Solicitors LLP) *N O Q Zi Zr*
Leeds *p276* 0113 245 0733

Winn, J P (Birketts LLP) *C1 M1 I Ze*
Ipswich *p262* 01473 232300

Winnard, Mrs K D (Doncaster Metropolitan Borough Council)
Doncaster *p457* 01302 734651

Winnard, Miss L (Churchill Insurance Group)
London EC1 *p105* 020 7656 6838

Winnard, Miss P J (Penelope J Winnard) *C1 T1 W K1 M1 E B1 A1 D1 N Zo Zw*
Holywell *p252* 01352 780229

Winnett, Ms B A (Warners Solicitors) *E S2 R1 R2*
Tonbridge *p412* 01732 770660

Winnett, D W (Hopkins) *K3 K1 K2*
Nottingham *p337* 0115 910 5555

Winrow, Ms J (Trowers & Hamlins)
London EC3 *p88* 020 7423 8000

Winrow, Ms J A (Trowers & Hamlins) *L E Zh*
Manchester *p310* 0161 211 0000

Winship, Mrs J C (Royal Mail Group)
London EC4 *p109* 020 7250 2468

Winship, K A (Ryedale District Council) *E L R1 S1 H*
Malton *p464* 01653 600666

Winship-Lee, Mrs M (Hewitts) *K1 D1*
Bishop Auckland *p144* 01388 604691

Winskell, Miss F H (Stone Milward Rapers) *W*
Chichester *p193* 01243 780211

Winskell, Ms L (Sintons LLP) *Zl*
Newcastle upon Tyne *p326* 0191 226 7878

Winskill, J P (Carrick District Council)
Truro *p474* 01872 224400

Winslade, G R T (Blake Lapthorn) *S1*
Portsmouth *p354* 023 9222 1122

Winslade, P J (Warner Goodman LLP) *E S1*
Portsmouth *p355* 023 9275 3575

Winslow, D (Healys LLP) *L O*
London EC4 *p39* 020 7822 4000

Winstanley, J M (Stoke-on-Trent City Council)
Stoke-on-Trent *p472* 01782 234567

Winstanley, Mrs T (Heaney Watson) *K1 D1 D2 K3*
Liverpool *p288* 0151 256 7777

Winston, D R (Waring & Co)
Barnet *p124* 0870 444 2782

Winston, J (Winston Solicitors LLP) *J1 N Zp*
Leeds *p278* 0113 320 5000

Winston, L M (Squire Sanders (UK) LLP) *O B2 Q*
London EC2 *p81* 020 7655 1000

Winter Morris, Mrs E A (A H Brooks & Co) *K1 D1 S1 W*
Leek *p278* 01538 383201

Winter, C (South Tyneside Metropolitan Borough Council)
South Shields *p471* 0191 427 1717

Winter, D (Nockolds) *O Q*
Bishop's Stortford *p144* 01279 755777

Winter, D (Mortons) *K1 D1 K2 D2 K3*
Sunderland *p401* 0191 514 4323

Winter, Ms D (Linklaters LLP)
London EC2 *p54* 020 7456 2000

Winter, Ms E S (Lightfoots LLP) *K3 K1*
Thame *p410* 01844 212305

Winter, G (Sintons LLP) *E Q*
Newcastle upon Tyne *p326* 0191 226 7878

Winter, G (Shepherd + Wedderburn LLP)
London EC4 *p78* 020 7429 4900

Winter, Ms H (Fox Williams) *C1 C2*
London EC2 *p33* 020 7628 2000

Winter, Mrs H (Walsall Metropolitan Borough Council)
Walsall *p475* 01922 650000

Winter, Miss K (Stephen Burdon Solicitors) *G H*
Nottingham *p336* 0115 950 0054

Winter, M A S (Taylor Wessing) *C1*
London EC4 *p86* 020 7300 7000

Winter, N C (Rawlison Butler LLP)
Horsham *p253* 01403 252492
Crawley *p202* 01293 527744

Winter, N J (Stitt & Co) *R2 S1 E L*
London EC4 *p83* 020 7832 0840

Winter, R A (Samuel Phillips Law Firm) *O L Q*
Newcastle upon Tyne *p326* 0191 232 8451

Winter, Mrs R E (Coffin Mew & Clover) *N*
Fareham *p223* 01329 825617

Winter, R J (City of Bradford Metropolitan District Council)
Bradford *p451* 01274 752236

Winterbone, I M (Ashton KCJ) *K1 N D1 Q O G F1 L V H Zl Zh Zt*
Bury St Edmunds *p171* 01284 762331

Winterborne, P H (Clarke Willmott) *B1 O*
Bristol *p162* 0845 209 1000 / 0117 305 6000

Winterbotham, H (Stones Solicitors LLP)
Exeter *p222* 01392 666777

Winterbottom, Ms R (DAC Beachcroft)
Leeds *p272* 0113 251 4700

Winterbourne, N (CMS Cameron McKenna LLP) *Zj O Q*
London EC3 *p17* 020 7367 3000

Winter-Evans, Mrs J E (Vale of Glamorgan Council)
Barry *p448* 01446 700111

Winters, R E (Winters & Co) *S1 E R1 W M1 J1 P C1 B1 T1 Zg Ze Zj*
Ware *p421* 01920 466696

Winters, Mrs S M (Winters & Co)
Ware *p421* 01920 466696

Winterton, A D (Stephenson Harwood) *Zo Zb C1 M2 U2 O Zj C2 M1 Ze F1 I R2 T1 T2*
London EC2 *p82* 020 7329 4422

Winterton, Miss K C (Fox Williams) *C2 C1*
London EC2 *p33* 020 7628 2000

Winterton, S J (Barlow Lyde & Gilbert LLP) *N Q*
London EC3 *p10* 020 7247 2277

Winthrop, M D (Short Richardson & Forth LLP) *J1 Zp*
Newcastle upon Tyne *p326* 0191 232 0283

Winton, Ms A (Pinsent Masons LLP)
London EC2 *p67* 020 7418 7000

Winton, A P (Osborne Clarke) *C1 C3 I F1 Ze Zf*
London EC2 *p65* 020 7105 7000

Winton, G E (Treasury Solicitors Department)
London WC2 *p110* 020 7210 3000

Winton, J K (Gross & Curjel) *S1 W E C1 K1 L A1 K3*
Woodbridge *p438* 01394 383436

Winton, P J (Winton Raynes & Co) *S1 E W J1 C2 Zl Zv S2 C1 L*
Swindon *p406* 01793 522688

Winyard, Ms A H (Leigh Day & Co) *Zr*
London EC1 *p52* 020 7650 1200

Wiper, C R (Close Thornton) *Q O C1 I B1 P X J1 N*
Darlington *p206* 01325 466461

Wiper, R (Matthew Arnold & Baldwin LLP) *B1 E S1*
Watford *p423* 01923 202020

Wippell, M A (Allen & Overy LLP)
London E1 *p5* 020 3088 0000

Wirth, Ms C (George Davies Solicitors LLP)
Manchester *p303* 0161 236 8992

Wirth, H P (Swindon Borough Council) *F1 G J1 N O P Q X C1 W Ze Zl Zp Zy*
Swindon *p473* 01793 463000

Wirz, N (Gateshead Metropolitan Borough Council)
Gateshead *p458* 0191 433 3000

Wisbey, D J (Birkett Long LLP) *C3 Zu T1*
Chelmsford *p186* 01245 453800

Wisbey, Mrs J L (Squire Sanders (UK) LLP) *O P Q Zy*
London EC2 *p81* 020 7655 1000

Wisdom, G (Hugh James)
Cardiff *p179* 029 2022 4871

Wise, C J D (Anderson Longmore & Higham) *E C1 W S1 T2 S2*
Storrington *p399* 01903 745666

Wise, D (Cottrill Stone Lawless) *Zc E F1 J1 Q S1*
Manchester *p302* 0161 835 3681

Wise, Miss D J (Walker Smith Way) *W T2 K4*
Chester *p191* 0844 346 3100

Wise, Miss D L (Gateshead Metropolitan Borough Council)
Gateshead *p458* 0191 433 3000

Wise, G (M23LAW Solicitors (Hedley-Saunders & Co)) *N*
Crawley *p202* 0844 264 0999

Wise, Ms J (The College of Law)
London WC1 *p105* 0800 289997

Wise, Ms L (Squire Sanders (UK) LLP) *Ze Zf*
London EC2 *p81* 020 7655 1000

Wise, Ms L C (Irwin Mitchell LLP) *Zr*
Manchester *p306* 0870 150 0100

Wise, Miss M C (Hadfields Butt & Bowyer) *W T2 K4*
Farnham *p225* 01252 716101

Wise, N M (Dale & Co Solicitors Lincoln) *G H*
Lincoln *p284* 01522 513399

Wise, P R (Hillyer McKeown LLP) *E C1 S2 T1 T2 W*
Bebington *p129* 0151 645 4255

Wise, P R (Hillyer McKeown LLP) *W T2 T1 E C1 S2 C2*
Chester *p190* 01244 318131

Wise, Ms S E (Gallaher Ltd)
Weybridge *p476* 01932 859777

Wise, S J S (Wise Geary) *E R2 S1 Zb*
Banbury *p122* 01295 278500

Wiseman, A (Sternberg Reed) *Zr*
Barking *p123* 020 8591 3366

Wiseman, Miss A C (Stewarts Law LLP) *N*
London EC4 *p83* 020 7822 8000

Wiseman, A D (Trowers & Hamlins) *J2 P R1 M1 Zu*
London EC3 *p88* 020 7423 8000

Wiseman, Ms C J (Williamson & Soden) *K3 K1*
Solihull *p383* 0121 733 8000

Wiseman, Ms E (Brown & Corbishley) *G H*
Newcastle under Lyme *p323* 01782 717888

Wiseman, Mrs J M (The Mitchell Plampin Partnership) *E C1 S1 L S2*
Maldon *p299* 01621 852566

Wiseman, R M (Shell International Ltd)
London SE1 *p109* 020 7934 1234

Wisener, Mrs T (Doyle Clayton Solicitors Limited) *J1 Zp*
Reading *p360* 0118 959 6839

Wish, I (Shammah Nicholls LLP) *S2 E G L Zl C1 M1 R1 W S1*
Manchester *p309* 0161 832 9272

Wishart, Mrs H L (Jeremy Wood & Co) *S1 K1 L N Q W F1 T1 V*
Yeovil *p444* 01935 426047

Wishart, Miss K M (Silverman Livermore) *D1 K1 D2*
Runcorn *p369* 01928 714121

Wishlade, P (Vickers Chisman & Wishlade) *G H*
Stockton-on-Tees *p397* 01642 615439

Wisking, S (Herbert Smith LLP) *C1 M1 C2*
London EC2 *p40* 020 7374 8000

Wismayer, C R (Wismayers) *L O N J1 C1 E B1 Q W F1 Zc*
Great Bookham *p233* 01372 451114

Wisnia, R A (Levi Solicitors LLP) *S2 E S1*
Leeds *p275* 0113 244 9931

Wisniewski, A C (Scutt Beaumont Solicitors Ltd) *D1 K1*
Leicester *p281* 0116 254 4200

Wisniewski, A D (Andrew & Andrew Solicitors) *N Q*
Portsmouth *p354* 023 9266 1381

Wistow, M J (Clifford Chance)
London E14 *p20* 020 7006 1000

Wistrich, Ms H (Birnberg Peirce & Partners)
Camden *p13* 020 7911 0166

Witehead, Mrs J C (Gateshead Metropolitan Borough Council)
Gateshead *p458* 0191 433 3000

Witek, Mrs J M (Hughes Paddison) *S1 E*
Cheltenham *p188* 01242 574244

Witham, Ms C (Rochdale Metropolitan Borough Council)
Rochdale *p470* 01706 647474

Withams, Mrs J C (Cunningtons) *S1*
Braintree *p155* 01376 326868

Withecombe, B J R (Beecham Fisher Ridley) *A3 B1 F1 F2 J1 J2 K1 N O Q Zb Zj Zl Zq Zr*
Southend-on-Sea *p387* 01702 348384

Witherall, C J (Alsters Kelley) *C1 C2 J1 E*
Leamington Spa *p270* 0844 561 0100

Witherall, J B (Jones Day) *C1*
London EC4 *p46* 020 7039 5959

Witheridge, Miss S M (WBW Solicitors) *W T2 S1 L J1 A1*
Exeter *p222* 01392 202404

Withers, C (Arthur & Co) *W S1 K1 N O*
Pinner *p348* 020 8866 8282

Withers, D (Wilford Smith Solicitors) *G H Zy B2 J2*
Rotherham *p367* 01709 828044

Withers, M (Paris Smith LLP) *E R2 P S2*
Southampton *p386* 023 8048 2482

Withers, Ms S (Edwards Duthie) *K1*
London E6 *p29* 020 8514 9000

Withers, S P (EEF West Midlands Association) *E J1 W S1 C1*
Birmingham *p449* 0121 456 2222

Witherspoon, M (Massers) *W Zm*
Nottingham *p338* 0115 851 1666

Witherspoon, M J (Sharp & Partners) *Zm T2 W*
Nottingham *p339* 0115 959 0055

Witherspoon, P C (Sanders Witherspoon LLP) *C1 D1 E G N L S1 W Zm*
Brentwood *p156* 01277 221010

Withey, G (Collyer Bristow LLP)
London WC1 *p22* 020 7242 7363

Withinshaw, J (Brabners Chaffe Street) *Zn E S2 C1 A1 R1 O S1*
Liverpool *p286* 0151 600 3000

Withnell, Miss C (KBL Solicitors) *S2 E*
Bolton *p149* 01204 527777

Withnell, M H (Land Registry - Lytham Office) *E S1 W A1 L Zl C1*
Lytham *p464* 01253 849849 / 840012

Withyman, T A (LG Lawyers) *C1*
London SE1 *p50* 020 7379 0000

Witkover, A M (Freedman Sharman & Co) *N J1 F1 L*
Borehamwood *p150* 020 8953 9111

Witkowski, Mrs J C (Information Commisioner)
Wilmslow *p476* 01625 545700

Witney, S R (SJ Berwin LLP) *C1 C2*
London EC4 *p75* 020 7111 2222

Witt, A (Waldrons) *N*
Brierley Hill *p158* 01384 811811

Witt, D W (IBM United Kingdom Ltd) *C1 I C3 M1 M2 Ze*
London SE1 *p107* 020 7202 3000

Witt, J N E (Capsticks Solicitors LLP) *O A3 B2 Q*
London SW19 *p18* 020 8780 2211

Witt, J S (Maxwell Winward LLP) *E S2 L R2*
London EC4 *p59* 020 7651 0000

Witter, K (Davis Blank Furniss) *K1*
Manchester *p303* 0161 832 3304

Witts, A (LG Lawyers)
London SE1 *p50* 020 7379 0000

Wodzianski, J (IBB Solicitors)
Uxbridge *p417* 0845 638 1381

Woffenden, J P (Parker Rhodes Hickmotts) *S1 W*
Rotherham *p367* 01709 511100

Woffenden, K J (Simmons & Simmons)
London EC2 *p79* 020 7628 2020

Woffenden, Ms S J (Bevan Brittan LLP) *J1 Zp*
Birmingham *p135* 0870 194 1000

Wojciechowski, E (Shoosmiths)
Reading *p361* 0370 086 8800 / 0118 965 8765

Wolf, A C (Patterson Wolf & Co) *B1 C1 D1 F1 G H K1 M1 P*
Ryton *p370* 0191 488 7777
Wolf, Miss S (Russell Jones & Walker)
London WC2 *p74* 020 7657 1555
Wolfarth, G E (Reynolds Porter Chamberlain LLP) *E L*
London E1 *p71* 020 3060 6000
Wolfe, Miss H L (Willson Hawley & Co) *D1 K1 V W G H S1 N O*
Nuneaton *p339* 024 7638 7821
Wolfe, S E A (Furley Page LLP) *K1 F1 Q*
Canterbury *p176*. 01227 763939
Wolfenden, M J (Tyrer Roxburgh & Co) *K1 D1*
Haringey *p89* 020 8889 3319
Wolferstan, Miss N (Hempsons) *Zr*
Westminster *p40*. 020 7839 0278
Wolfgang, P (Michelmores LLP) *A1 W*
Exeter *p221* 01392 688688
Wolfle, C J (Reading Borough Council)
Reading *p469* 0118 939 0900
Wolfson, D (Bullivant & Partners)
London EC4 *p16*. 020 7332 8250
Wolfson, L (Wolfson & Co) *N J1 Zm Zq O Q S1 S2 E W F1 L C1 U2 G*
Manchester *p311* 0161 873 8999
Wolinsky, J (Allen & Overy LLP)
London E1 *p5* 020 3088 0000
Woliter, R C (Borough of Telford & Wrekin)
Telford *p473*. 01952 380000
Wollacott, R B (Fraser Brown) *S2 E S1*
Bingham *p133*. 01949 830812
Wollaston, Mrs C F (Birketts LLP (Wollastons LLP)) *W T2*
Chelmsford *p186*. 01245 211211
Wollaston, R H (Birketts LLP (Wollastons LLP)) *C1 C2 M1 Zo F1 U2 C3*
Chelmsford *p186*. 01245 211211
Wollenberg, A (Salans)
London EC4 *p76*. 020 7429 6000
Wolley, T J (Bowcock & Pursaill) *Q O A3 Zq L B1 Ze F1 J1*
Leek *p278*. 01538 399199
Wolman, S (Lloyd Platt & Co) *K3 K1 Q*
London N3 *p55* 020 8343 2998
Wolny, R M (Birkett Long LLP) *E*
Chelmsford *p186*. 01245 453800
Woloshak, M O O (Eastleys) *N P M1 L J1 Zb Q Zh Zq F1*
Paignton *p345*. 01803 559257
London SW13 *p73*. 020 8939 6300
Wolstenholme, Ms J (Speechly Bircham LLP) *Zo J1 C2 T2 T1 Zp*
London EC4 *p81*. 020 7427 6400
Wolstenholme, Mrs J (Wedlake Bell LLP)
London WC1 *p91* 020 7395 3000
Wolton, A P (Edwards Duthie) *C1 E L R1 S1 W Zc Zl Zv*
Ilford *p260*. 020 8514 9000
Wolton, Ms K M (Wolton & Co) *Zm*
Deal *p207* 01304 389789
Womersley, M R A (Osborne Clarke) *J1 Zo*
Bristol *p164* 0117 917 3000
Wones, Miss E C (Treasury Solicitors Department) *E S1*
London WC2 *p110*. 020 7210 3000
Wong, A (Fruhman Davies Livingstones)
Manchester *p304* 0161 833 0578
Wong, C Z (Grayson Willis Bennett) *G H B2*
Sheffield *p375*. 0114 290 9500
Sheffield *p376*. 0870 150 0100
Wong, E K W (Clifford Chance)
London E14 *p20*. 020 7006 1000
Wong, Ms E S Y (Elizabeth Wong & Company) *C1 E K1 L Q S1 W Zi Zl*
London WC2 *p93* 020 7766 5228
Wong, F (Pictons Solicitors LLP) *Q*
Milton Keynes *p317* 01908 663511
Wong, H (Simmons & Simmons)
London EC2 *p79*. 020 7628 2020
Wong, Miss J B (SAS Daniels LLP) *W*
Stockport *p396*. 0161 475 7676
Wong, K H E (Lin & Co Solicitors) *S2 K3 K1 Zi S1 W E*
Birmingham *p140* 0121 244 2300
Wong, Ms N S P (Nadine Wong & Co) *Zg Zi S1*
London W2 *p93* 020 7243 8888
Wong, Miss O (Coffin Mew & Clover) *K1 K2*
Fareham *p223*. 01329 825617
Wong, Ms T (Glazer Delmar) *L Zh*
London SE22 *p35* 020 8299 0021
Wong, Miss T Y M (Parrott & Coales LLP) *W*
Aylesbury *p121* 01296 318500
Wong-Robinson, Mrs B W S (Pooley Dale & Co) *D1 K1 Zi*
Swindon *p406* 01793 488848
Wonnacott, C (Penningtons)
Basingstoke *p127* 01256 407100
Wontner, A G I (Wontner & Sons) *G H J1 M1*
London WC2 *p93* 020 7936 2414
Wontner-Smith, A H (Simpson Millar LLP) *N Zq*
London EC1 *p80*. 0844 858 3400
Woo, A T H (Brewer Harding & Rowe) *K1 D1 K3 D2 V*
Bideford *p132* 01237 472666
Woo, N (Reed Smith LLP) *Za*
London EC2 *p71*. 020 3116 3000
Wood, A (BHP Law) *S2 A1*
Darlington *p206* 01325 466794
Wood, A (Hogan Lovells International LLP)
London EC1 *p42*. 020 7296 2000
Wood, Ms A (Stone King LLP) *E Q S1*
Bath *p128* 01225 337599
Wood, Ms A (Morgan Cole) *O Q B1 L Zq Zk*
Oxford *p344* 01865 262600
Wood, Ms A (Rubin Lewis O'Brien)
Cardiff *p180* 029 2077 9988
Wood, Miss A (Thackray Williams)
Bromley *p167* 020 8290 0440
Wood, A (Mills & Reeve) *E*
Cambridge *p175*. 01223 364422
Wood, A (Hardman Wood) *D1 D2 K1 K2 K3*
Blackburn *p145* 01254 295540
Wood, A (Tozers) *K1 D1*
Newton Abbot *p329* 01626 207020
Wood, A J (Clarkson Wright & Jakes Ltd) *N Zr*
Orpington *p341* 01689 887887
Wood, A K (Pinsent Masons LLP) *C2*
Birmingham *p141* 0121 200 1050
Wood, A M (hlw Keeble Hawson LLP) *O B1 Q*
Sheffield *p376* 0114 276 5555
Wood, Miss A N (Rolls-Royce PLC) *E L C1 R1*
Derby *p456* 01332 242424
Wood, Ms B (Potter & Co) *K1 K4 Q S1 T2 W*
Matlock *p313* 01629 582308
Wood, Ms B E (Blake Lapthorn) *C1 J1 C2 C3*
London EC1 *p13*. 020 7405 2000
Wood, C G (Clive G Wood & Co) *K1 D1 S1 S2 E*
Stockport *p396*. 0161 480 1000
Wood, C J (Jeremy Wood & Co) *E K1 Q B1 A1 C1 C2 C3 D1 W N J1 Zl Zk*
Yeovil *p444* 01935 426047
Wood, Mrs C M (Sintons LLP) *O Q Zb*
Newcastle upon Tyne *p326* . 0191 226 7878
Wood, C W C (SNR Denton)
London EC4 *p75*. 020 7242 1212
Wood, D (Langleys) *A1 K4 K1 Zo T1 T2 W*
Lincoln *p284*. 01522 888555
York *p445* 01904 610886
Wood, D E (Tickle Hall Cross) *M1 P K1 N B1 F1 C1 G L*
St Helens *p391* 0800 854379
Wood, D J (United Utilities)
Warrington *p475*. 01925 237000
Wood, D L (DWF) *O Zb*
Manchester *p303* 0161 603 5000
Wood, D L (Everys) *A1 C1 E L R1 S1 T1 T2 W Zc Zs Zv*
Honiton *p252* 01404 43431
Wood, Ms E (Thompsons (formerly Robin/Brian Thompson & Partners)) *F1 F2 K1 L*
Sheffield *p377* 0114 270 3300
Wood, Ms E (Walker Morris) *Zu C1 Zd Zh*
Leeds *p277* 0113 283 2500
Wood, Ms E J (Russell & Russell) *K1 Q N T2 V W K4*
Bolton *p150* 01204 707926
Wood, Ms F (Pannone LLP)
Manchester *p308* 0161 909 3000
Wood, F (Ashurst LLP)
London EC2 *p7* 020 7638 1111
Wood, F (Rochdale Middleton & Heywood Magistrates Court)
Rochdale *p470*. 01706 514800
Wood, Miss F C (Ashfords LLP) *N Q*
Tiverton *p412* 01884 203000
Wood, G (Appleby Hope & Matthews) *G H Zm*
Middlesbrough *p314* 01642 440444
Wood, G A (Solicitors First LLP) *N G S1 O C2 C1 H Q E F1 Zc Zv*
Wandsworth *p80*. 0870 770 7016
Wood, G I (Coley & Tilley) *S1 K1 W E L V D1 Zl*
Birmingham *p136* 0121 643 5531
Wood, Mrs H (BHP Law)
Stockton-on-Tees *p396* . . . 01642 672770
Stockton-on-Tees *p396* . . . 01642 672770
Wood, I C (Mayer Brown International LLP) *Ze*
London EC2 *p59*. 020 3130 3000
Wood, J (The Smith Partnership) *S1 E J1 T1*
Derby *p209* 01332 225225
Wood, J (Belmont & Lowe)
London EC1 *p11*. 020 7608 4600
Wood, Miss J (Thompsons (formerly Robin/Brian Thompson & Partners)) *M1*
Plymouth *p350*. 01752 675810
Wood, J C (JWP Solicitors) *D1 G H*
Wakefield *p418* 01924 387171
Wood, Mrs J E (Alker & Ball) *K1 D1 D2 K3 K2*
Wigan *p432* 01942 246241
Wood, J G (Rutters) *N Q K1 K3 Zl J1*
Shaftesbury *p374* 01747 852377
Wood, J G (John G Wood) *C1 E M2 S1 S2*
London W1 *p93* 020 7580 2277
Wood, J G (DAC Beachcroft) *C1 E S1*
London EC4 *p24*. 020 7936 2222
Wood, J G K (John G K Wood) *P N M1 C1 G J1*
Westminster *p93*. 020 7439 1122
Wood, J G W (Atteys)
Doncaster *p211* 01302 340400
Wood, J L (BHP Law) *F1 K1 M1 P S1 E L N W*
Durham *p214* 0191 384 0840
Wood, J M (Wood Sherwood & Co) *W A1 C1 S2 E K4 L Zl C2 S1*
Pocklington *p351* 01759 302791
Wood, Mrs J M (Nicholls Christie & Crocker) *S1*
Harrow *p242*. 020 8863 6366
Wood, Miss J S (Lake District National Park Authority) *Q J1 F1 W*
Kendal *p462*. 01539 724555
Wood, Miss K A (Shulmans) *E S2 S1*
Leeds *p276* 0113 245 2833
Wood, Ms K F (Dickinson Wood) *K1 D1 P J1 V W*
Doncaster *p211* 01302 329504
Wood, K J (Lewis Nedas & Co) *G H*
Camden *p53*. 020 7387 2032
Wood, K J (Bobbetts Mackan) *F1 J1 N Q Zp*
Bristol *p161* 0117 929 9001
Wood, Mrs L J (Rothera Dowson) *Zt*
Nottingham *p338*. 0115 910 0600
Wood, Mrs L R (Elliot Mather LLP) *D1 K1 L N S1*
Chesterfield *p192* 01246 231288
Wood, M (Dickinson Dees) *E*
Newcastle upon Tyne *p324* . 0191 279 9000
Wood, Mrs M (Staffordshire County Council)
Stafford *p472* 01785 223121
Wood, M (HSR Law (Hayes, Son & Richmond)) *G H B2*
Doncaster *p211* 01302 347800
Gainsborough *p228* 01427 613831
Wood, M (Martello Professional Risks Limited) *O Q Zj Zc*
London EC3 *p108* 020 7337 7500
Wood, M (North Lincolnshire Council)
Scunthorpe *p470*. 01724 296296
Wood, M (Boodle Hatfield)
Westminster *p14*. 020 7629 7411
Wood, M B (AWB Charlesworth LLP) *S2 E S1*
Keighley *p263* 01535 613678
Wood, M D (Bircham Dyson Bell)
Westminster *p13*. 020 7227 7000
Wood, M J (Rupert Wood & Son) *S1 E C1 W F1 M1 P N Zl Zm*
Ashton-under-Lyne *p120*. . . 0161 330 9121
Wood, M W R (Ellen Court Partnership Solicitors) *F1 G H J1 K1 L M1 P S1 W Zc Zl Zp*
Preston *p356* 01772 882888
Wood, Ms N (Morrisons Solicitors LLP) *C1 I Ze J2 N*
Redhill *p362*. 01737 854500
Wood, N (Nabarro LLP) *Q O N Zq J1*
London WC1 *p63* 020 7524 6000
Wood, N (Atherton Godfrey) *Zr N*
Doncaster *p211* 01302 320621
Wood, N R (The Wilkes Partnership LLP) *B1 O Ze*
Birmingham *p143* 0121 233 4333
Wood, P (Pinsent Masons LLP)
London EC2 *p67*. 020 7418 7000
Wood, P (Withers LLP) *O M2*
London EC4 *p92*. 020 7597 6000
Wood, P A (Graham & Rosen) *K1 D1*
Hull *p257* 01482 323123
Wood, Ms P A (The Smith Partnership) *G H*
Derby *p209* 01332 225225
Wood, P C (Davis Wood) *M1 P K1 L F1 J1 D1 G H*
Bristol *p162* 0117 965 3504
Wood, Mrs P J (North Somerset District Council) *G H K1 V Q*
Weston-super-Mare *p476* . . 01934 888888
Wood, P J (Kirwans) *G H*
Birkenhead *p134*. 0151 608 9078
Wood, P R (Fraser Brown) *E S2 S1 R2*
Nottingham *p337*. 0115 988 8777
Wood, P S (Kidd Rapinet) *K1 S1 W E S2 K4*
Farnham *p225*. 0845 017 9609
Wood, R (Kimbells LLP) *C1 C2*
Milton Keynes *p317* 01908 668555
Wood, R A (Thompsons (formerly Robin/Brian Thompson & Partners)) *N*
Plymouth *p350*. 01752 675810
Wood, Mrs R A (Mellor & Jackson) *W K4*
Oldham *p340* 0161 624 7081
Wood, Ms R A (Brooke-Taylors) *K1 D1 N J1 F1 L Q W B1 O Zg K3*
Buxton *p172*. 01298 22741
Wood, R C (Harrowells) *N*
York *p444* 01904 558600
Wood, R C (Humphries Kirk) *Q O N*
Poole *p352* 01202 725400
Wood, Miss R J (Harold Stock & Co) *S1 S2 Q O E R1*
Ashton-under-Lyne *p120*. . . 01457 838136
Wood, R R (Double & Megson) *G K1 Q F1 D1 B1 H J1 N F2*
Bourne *p151*. 01778 423376
Wood, S (Stephen Wood) *O N K1 Zr*
Norwich *p335* 01603 766539
Wood, Mrs S (Davis Blank Furniss) *S1 W L R1 E*
Glossop *p230* 01457 860606
Wood, Ms S A (Gloucestershire County Council - Legal & Democratic Services)
Gloucester *p459*. 01452 425203
Wood, S C (BAE Systems PLC)
London SW1 *p104*. 01252 373232
Wood, Mrs S C (MSAS Cargo International Ltd)
Bracknell *p451*. 01344 52222
Wood, S J (Clegg Manuel) *E*
Islington *p20*. 020 7847 5600
Wood, Ms S M (Fishburns) *Zq N Q O M2 Zj B2 Zc A3*
London EC3 *p32*. 020 7280 8888
Wood, S M (O H Parsons & Partners) *J1 N*
London WC2 *p66* 020 7379 7277
Wood, Mrs S N (Richard Sedgley & Co)
Bournemouth *p152*. 01202 556222
Wood, S P (Thompsons (formerly Robin/Brian Thompson & Partners)) *N*
Sheffield *p377* 0114 270 3300
Wood, S P (Hoben Johnson) *J1 O Q N J2 Zc F1*
Rushden *p369*. 01933 411375
Wood, Miss T A (Costain Engineering & Construction Ltd)
Maidenhead *p464* 01628 842444
Wood, T J (Bradshaws Hamer Park & Haworth) *S1 W E L S2*
Lytham *p296*. . . . .01253 724251 / 728451
Wood, T J (Brains) *Q O J1 N E S2 K3 K1 B1 L Zh J2 Zq F2 F1*
St Austell *p391* 01726 68111
Wood, T W (Treasury Solicitors Department)
London WC2 *p110*. 020 7210 3000
Wood, Ms V (Mowbray Woodwards Solicitors) *W T2*
Bath *p128* 01225 485700
Wood, V (Penningtons)
Godalming *p231* 01483 791800
Wood-Robertson, J (Walker Morris) *C1 Zu*
Leeds *p277* 0113 283 2500
Wood-Smith, I M (Field Seymour Parkes) *C1 Zc Zw C2*
Reading *p360* 0118 951 6200
Wood-Williams, M A (Swinburne & Jackson LLP) *C1 S2 E Zl C2*
Gateshead *p229*. 0191 477 2531 / 477 3222
Woodall, Ms L A (Allen & Overy LLP)
London E1 *p5* 020 3088 0000
Woodall, M C (Horwich Cohen Coghlan) *N*
Manchester *p305* 0161 830 4600
Woodall, S (Forshaws Davies Ridgway LLP) *S1 G H F1 W K1 J1 E C1*
Warrington *p422*. 01925 230000
Woodall, S (Hunt & Wrigley) *A1 C1 S1 W T1*
Northallerton *p331*. 01609 772502
Woodall, Mrs S D (OMW Solicitors) *S1 W E S2 Zl R1 A1 B1*
Burton-on-Trent *p170*01283 563401 / 530333
Woodbridge, Miss V C (Department for Business, Enterprise and Regulatory Reform)
London SW1 *p105*. 020 7215 0105
Woodburn, U A (Henriques Griffiths) *O N J1 F1 P Q*
Bristol *p163* 0117 909 4000
Winterbourne *p435*. 01454 854000
Woodcock, Ms A E (Anne Woodcock & Co) *G H N*
St Albans *p390* 01727 861212
Woodcock, A J J (Stephenson Harwood) *G O*
London EC2 *p82*. 020 7329 4422
Woodcock, Ms B H (Rowley Dickinson) *N O Q B1 F1 J1 L*
Manchester *p309* 0161 834 4215
Woodcock, Mrs D (Harold G Walker) *J1*
Bournemouth *p152*. 01202 203200
Woodcock, D J (Birchall Blackburn LLP) *S2 E*
Manchester *p301* 0161 236 0662
Woodcock, P (West Wiltshire District Council)
Trowbridge *p474*. 01225 770396
Woodcraft, J (Jeffrey Green Russell) *Zi*
London W1 *p46* 020 7339 7000
Woodcroft, Ms P U (Cadwalader Wickersham & Taft)
London WC2 *p17* 020 7170 8700
Woodend, Ms H (Chebsey & Co) *S1 W Zl*
Beaconsfield *p128* 01494 670440
Wooderson, R J T (Lambe Corner) *K3 F1 D1 L P Q K1 N O S1 V Zl G J1 J2 Zq*
Hereford *p248* 01432 355301
Woodfield, B (Cartwright King) *G*
Sheffield *p375*. 0114 321 1000
Woodfield, P J (CMS Cameron McKenna LLP) *O Zb*
Bristol *p162* 0117 930 0200
Woodford, Mrs H K (Everys) *S1 W*
Budleigh Salterton *p168* . . . 01395 442223
Woodford, J P (Bailey & Cogger) *F1 J1 K1 L N O Q*
Tonbridge *p412* 01732 353305
Woodford, P (Sintons LLP) *N*
Newcastle upon Tyne *p326* . 0191 226 7878
Woodgate, A J (Simmons & Simmons) *C1 M1 E*
London EC2 *p79*. 020 7628 2020
Woodgate, Ms C M (Howard Kennedy LLP) *E R2 S2*
London W1 *p48* 020 7636 1616
Woodgates, Mrs J A (WBW Solicitors) *W T2*
Exeter *p222* 01392 202404
Woodhall, J D (Sidley Austin Brown & Wood) *Zb*
London EC2 *p78*. 020 7360 3600
Woodham, L S (Quality Solicitors Burroughs Day) *J2 N*
Bristol *p164* 0117 929 0333
Woodhams, B D (E Rex Makin & Co) *G H Zl*
Liverpool *p289*. 0151 709 4491
Woodhead, C F (Plessey Network & Office Systems)
Beeston *p449* 0115 943 0300
Woodhead, Miss D A (Cooper Sons Hartley & Williams) *K3 D1 K1*
Buxton *p172*. 01298 77511
Woodhead, D C (Smith Jones Solicitors) *N K1*
Kenilworth *p264* 01926 859933
Burnley *p169* 01282 855400
Woodhead, E (Wallace Robinson & Morgan) *E C1 S1 W*
Solihull *p383*. 0121 705 7571
Woodhead, G J (Penningtons) *E*
London EC2 *p66*. 020 7457 3000
Woodhead, J G (HBOS PLC)
Halifax *p460*. 0870 600 5000
Woodhead, R (BRM Solicitors) *W*
Chesterfield *p191* 01246 555111
Woodhead, Miss R (Lanyon Bowdler LLP) *W*
Shrewsbury *p379* 01743 280280
Woodhead, R A C (Woodhead & Hoole) *S1 W E L N R1 F1 Zl*
Chesterfield *p192* . .01246 233149 / 209001
Woodhead, Ms S (Grahame Stowe Bateson) *D1 K1 L*
Leeds *p274* 0113 246 8163

See p634 for the Key to Work Categories

Woodhorse, J G I (Dunn & Baker) *S1 S2*
Exeter *p221* 01392 285000

Woodhouse, Miss A E (Reed Smith LLP) *A1*
London EC2 *p71* 020 3116 3000

Woodhouse, A J (Woodhouse & Company) *S1 E P W K1 C1 A1 B1 D1*
Wolverhampton *p438* 01902 773616

Woodhouse, A J (Edwards Angell Palmer & Dodge) *O Zj Zq*
London EC2 *p28* 020 7583 4055

Woodhouse, Ms A L (Aviva PLC)
London EC3 *p103* 020 7283 7500 / 01603 687905
Norwich *p467* 01603 622200

Woodhouse, Miss C E S (Glanvilles) *D1 K1 N Q*
Havant *p244* 023 9249 2300

Woodhouse, G (Penningtons) *J1*
Basingstoke *p127* 01256 407100

Woodhouse, G (GLP Solicitors)
Manchester *p304* 0161 703 8677

Woodhouse, J G I (Foot Anstey) *S1 C1 E A1 L*
Exeter *p221* 01392 411221

Woodhouse, Ms J H (Varley Hibbs LLP) *J1 Q Zl*
Coventry *p201* 024 7663 1000

Woodhouse, Mrs K E (Hampshire County Council)
Winchester *p476* 01962 841841

Woodhouse, N J (Cook Taylor Woodhouse) *S1 E L W C1*
London SE9 *p22* 020 8859 0936

Woodhouse, N J M (Watson Woodhouse)
Stockton-on-Tees *p397* 01642 247656

Woodhouse, P M (Stone King LLP) *J1 G Zp*
Bath *p128* 01225 337599

Woodhouse, Mrs S J (B A A PLC)
London UB3 *p103* 0870 000 0123

Woodhouse, Ms S J (Blake Lapthorn) *N O Q B1 Za*
Chandlers Ford *p184* 023 8090 8090

Woodhouse, T R (Field Seymour Parkes) *O Q B1*
Reading *p360* 0118 951 6200

Woodhouse, Miss V (Graysons) *E*
Sheffield *p375* 0114 272 9184

Woodier, K D (Pennon Group PLC)
Exeter *p458* 01392 446677

Wooding, A C (Kerseys) *Q O L*
Ipswich *p262* 01473 213311

Woodings, S (Beswicks) *C1 E A1 J1 M1 B1 S1 W L*
Stoke-on-Trent *p397* 01782 205000

Woodison, Miss K L (Reynolds Parry-Jones) *W K4*
High Wycombe *p250* 01494 525941

Woodland, Mrs J (Freeman Johnson) *E R2 S1 S2 A1*
Darlington *p206* 01325 466221

Woodland, Ms K (Kennedys) *Zj*
London EC3 *p49* 020 7667 9667

Woodley, Miss C A (OBW Perera) *G H N Q*
Colchester *p197* 01206 541111

Woodley, D (Lawson Lewis & Co) *S2 C1 E*
Peacehaven *p345* 01273 582680
Eastbourne *p215* 01323 720142

Woodley, Ms E J (Brighton & Hove Council - Legal Services)
Hove *p461* 01273 290000

Woodley, Mrs R J (Fraser Dawbarns) *K1*
Downham Market *p213* 01366 383171

Woodman, Mrs D (John Hodge Solicitors) *S2 A1*
Weston-super-Mare *p429* 01934 623511

Woodman, D J (Brain Sinnott & Co) *G H J1 Q Zl*
Kingswood *p268* 0117 960 6880

Woodman, J J (West Midlands Police Authority)
Birmingham *p450* 0121 626 5143

Woodman, P R (Anthony Collins Solicitors LLP) *C1 S2 E F1 Ze*
Birmingham *p137* 0121 200 3242

Woodman, R A (Richard A Woodman) *S1 W*
Harpenden *p239* 01582 768222

Woodman, R M (Royds LLP) *N J1 P B1 F1 Ze Zj Zk*
London EC4 *p74* 020 7583 2222

Woodnead, Mrs F (Sheffield City Council)
Sheffield *p471* 0114 273 4019

Woodroffe, J F (Ashley Wilson) *E S1 F1*
London SW1 *p92* 020 7802 4802

Woodroffe, P W H (Borough of Poole)
Poole *p469* 01202 262808

Woodrow, R D (Aviva PLC)
London EC3 *p103* 020 7283 7500 / 01603 687905
Norwich *p467* 01603 622200

Woodrow, W M (F B Jevons Riley & Pope) *S1 W S2 E*
Edenbridge *p216* 01732 864411

Woodruff, Mrs A (Moore & Tibbits) *K1 S1 W*
Warwick *p422* 01926 491181

Woodruff, C L (Maclay Murray & Spens LLP) *O Q*
London EC2 *p57* 020 7002 8500

Woodruff, E (Ince & Co Services Ltd)
London E1 *p44* 020 7481 0010

Woodruff, Mrs S J (Thomson Webb & Corfield) *W*
Cambridge *p176* 01223 578068

Woods, Miss A (Frodshams) *W K4*
St Helens *p391* 01744 626600

Woods, A (Walker Morris)
Leeds *p277* 0113 283 2500

Woods, Mrs A (Walker Smith Way) *K1 D1 K2 K3*
Chester *p191* 0844 346 3100

Woods, A A (Spratt Endicott) *E W*
Banbury *p122* 01295 204000

Woods, A C (Sills & Betteridge LLP) *K1*
Gainsborough *p228* 01427 616816
Lincoln *p285* 01522 542211

Woods, A J (Department for Business, Enterprise and Regulatory Reform)
London SW1 *p105* 020 7215 0105

Woods, A J (Gosschalks) *Zl*
Hull *p256* 01482 324252

Woods, A S (Barwells)
Seaford *p373* 01323 899331

Woods, A S C d F (Aidan Woods & Co) *G H B2 Zm*
Bristol *p165* 0117 952 2006

Woods, B (Cousins Tyrer) *G*
Leeds *p272* 0113 247 0400

Woods, Miss C (Bramsdon & Childs) *Q N C1 L*
Southsea *p388* 023 9282 1251

Woods, Miss D (The College of Law Chester) *W*
Chester *p454* 0800 289997

Woods, D V (Greenwoods Solicitors LLP) *C1 I U2 C2 Ze U1*
Peterborough *p347* 01733 887700

Woods, G (Bennett Griffin) *W V T2 K4*
Rustington *p369* 01903 777690

Woods, G M (North Yorkshire County Council)
Northallerton *p467* 01609 780780

Woods, Mrs J (Bracknell Forest Borough Council)
Bracknell *p450* 01344 424642

Woods, Ms J M (Barlow Lyde & Gilbert LLP)
London EC3 *p10* 020 7247 2277

Woods, J V (Nigel Glassey Solicitor)
Stockport *p395* 0161 443 1395

Woods, Ms J Y (Jackman Woods) *S1 W E*
Winchcombe *p433* 01242 602378

Woods, Ms K M (Russell & Russell) *S1 W*
Chester *p191* 01244 405700

Woods, P D (Hill Dickinson LLP) *I Ze*
Manchester *p305* 0161 817 7200

Woods, P L (Wolferstans) *K1 D1*
Plymouth *p351* 01752 663295

Woods, P M (Ormerods) *W*
Croydon *p205* 020 8686 5000

Woods, S P (Burtonwoods) *E S1 W Zf*
London WC1 *p16* 020 7636 2448

Woodside, Ms K J (Squire Sanders (UK) LLP)
Manchester *p310* 0161 830 5000

Woodside, S F (Matthews Lewis & Co) *G K1 N Q J1 K3*
Chester *p191* 01244 327750

Woodthorpe, C (Walker Morris) *E S2*
Leeds *p277* 0113 283 2500

Woodward, A M T (Bevan Brittan LLP)
Bristol *p161* 0870 194 1000

Woodward, D (hlw Keeble Hawson LLP)
Sheffield *p375* 0114 272 2061

Woodward, Mrs D (Cullimore Dutton) *K3 K1 K2*
Chester *p190* 01244 356789

Woodward, D A (Caversham Solicitors Ltd) *S1*
Reading *p360* 0118 947 8638

Woodward, D W (TLT Solicitors) *K1 K2*
Bristol *p165* 0117 917 7777

Woodward, Mrs E J (Neves Solicitors) *K3 K1 K2 A3 D1*
Milton Keynes *p317* 01908 304560

Woodward, Ms E M (H L F Berry & Co) *S1*
Failsworth *p223* 0161 681 4005

Woodward, G (Barcan Woodward) *S1 W*
Bristol *p161* 0117 923 2141

Woodward, Ms G A (Network Rail)
London NW1 *p108* 020 7557 8000

Woodward, Ms H (Bristol City Council)
Bristol *p451* 0117 922 2000

Woodward, Miss H J (Gloucester City Council)
Gloucester *p459* 01452 522232

Woodward, Mrs H K (Brighton & Hove Council - Legal Services)
Hove *p461* 01273 290000

Woodward, J (Armitage Sykes LLP) *K1 D1*
Huddersfield *p255* 01484 344140

Woodward, Mrs J A (Crown Prosecution Service Dorset) *K1 S1 P M1 W J1 C1 B1 D1 F1*
Bournemouth *p450* 01202 498700

Woodward, Ms J S (Stephenson Harwood) *C1 Zb*
London EC2 *p82* 020 7329 4422

Woodward, J W (Nash & Co Solicitors LLP) *S1 L E P A1*
Plymouth *p350* 01752 664444

Woodward, K (Mowlem PLC)
Isleworth *p462* 020 8568 9111

Woodward, M (Osborne Clarke) *Zd R1 W*
Bristol *p164* 0117 917 3000

Woodward, M H (Crampton Pym & Lewis)
Oswestry *p342* 01691 653301

Woodward, Mrs M J (Gloucestershire County Council - Legal & Democratic Services)
Gloucester *p459* 01452 425203

Woodward, M P (Blackhams Solicitors) *S2 S1 W*
Birmingham *p135* 0121 233 6900

Woodward, N (CMS Cameron McKenna LLP) *N O Q Zj Zw*
London EC3 *p17* 020 7367 3000

Woodward, N (Woodwards) *S1 S2*
Biggleswade *p133* 01767 601111

Woodward, N A D (Freemans Solicitors) *E S1 S2*
London W1 *p34* 020 7935 3522

Woodward, P D (Keene & Kelly) *D1 K1 Q N O*
Mold *p318* 01352 753882

Woodward, R (Aaron & Partners LLP Solicitors) *O Q*
Chester *p190* 01244 405555

Woodward, S (K&L Gates LLP)
London EC4 *p47* 020 7648 9000

Woodward, T (Bond Pearce LLP) *C1 Zb Zo*
Bristol *p161* 0845 415 0000

Woodwark, Ms S A (Radcliffes Le Brasseur) *J2 N Q Zr Zm Zi*
Leeds *p276* 0113 234 1220

Woodyard, Ms J (Hand Morgan & Owen) *Zq*
Stafford *p393* 01785 211411

Woodyard, S R (Essex County Council)
Chelmsford *p454* 0845 743 0430

Wookey, N (Sharratts (London) LLP) *L R1 E S1 S2*
Westerham *p429* 01959 568000

Woolacott, G J (Woolacott & Co) *S1 E W L S2*
Lancing *p270* 01903 763011 / 764334

Woolacott, Mrs M A (Woolacott & Co) *K1 Q G N J1 V D1 H*
Lancing *p270* 01903 763011 / 764334

Woolaghan, M J (Brockbank Curwen Cain & Hall) *N S1 G P K1 D1 Q W*
Workington *p440* 01900 603563

Woolcock, B (DLA Piper UK LLP) *Zb R2*
Birmingham *p137* 0870 011 1111

Woolcott, A J (Savage Crangle)
Otley *p342* 01943 465050

Wooldridge, M G (Michael G Wooldridge) *G H F1 K1 P S1*
Birmingham *p143* 0121 706 2259

Wooler, P G (Gordons LLP) *W T1*
Leeds *p273* 0113 227 0100

Woolf, A (Howard Kennedy LLP) *C1*
London W1 *p48* 020 7636 1616

Woolf, Mrs C F (CMS Cameron McKenna LLP)
London EC3 *p17* 020 7367 3000

Woolf, G S (SJ Berwin LLP) *B1 F1 Zb Zd*
London EC4 *p75* 020 7111 2222

Woolf, Ms J (Linklaters LLP)
London EC2 *p54* 020 7456 2000

Woolf, M (Fellowes Solicitors) *G H B2*
London E17 *p31* 020 8520 7392

Woolf, N P (Woolf Simmonds) *C1 E N S1 K1 B1 W Zi Zl*
Westminster *p93* 020 7262 1266

Woolf, P G (Berg Legal) *M1 N P K1 C1 J1 F1 B1 E Zc Ze Zk*
Manchester *p301* 0161 833 9211

Woolfall, A (Backhouse Jones Ltd) *Zt G Q*
Clitheroe *p196* 01254 828300

Woolfe, I R (Collyer Bristow LLP) *E C1 A1 S1 L W Zc*
London WC1 *p22* 020 7242 7363

Woolfe, M A (Close Thornton) *E S2 S1 C1 L A1*
Darlington *p206* 01325 466461

Woolfe, S H (Harvey Ingram LLP) *J1 T2 W E Zo*
Leicester *p280* 0116 254 5454

Woolford, A L (Brett Holt Solicitors) *K1 M1 N O Q S1 W J1*
Worcester Park *p440* 020 8337 0174

Woolfson, Mrs D B (Pannone LLP) *N Zq*
Manchester *p308* 0161 909 3000

Woolgar, Miss K J (DWF) *Zb R2 C1 E F1*
Liverpool *p287* 0151 907 3000

Woolgar, N D (Lawcomm Solicitors) *C1 E S1 N O Q D1 F1 G*
Fareham *p224* 01489 864100

Woolhouse, C (Herrington & Carmichael LLP) *K4 K1 T2 W*
Wokingham *p437* 0118 977 4045

Woolhouse, Mrs C A (OGR Stock Denton) *S1 J1 K1 L M1 W*
London N3 *p64* 020 8349 0321

Woolhouse, G E (Radcliffes Le Brasseur) *O Ze Zf Zk*
Westminster *p70* 020 7222 7040

Woolhouse, Miss H E (Laytons) *W T2*
London EC4 *p52* 020 7842 8000

Woolhouse, N T (Addleshaw Goddard)
Leeds *p271* 0113 209 2000
Manchester *p300* 0161 934 6000

Woolhouse, Ms T (Bates Wells & Braithwaite London LLP) *Zi*
London EC4 *p11* 020 7551 7777

Woolich, A (Holman Fenwick Willan) *C1 Zg*
London EC3 *p42* 020 7264 8000

Woolich, R (DLA Piper UK LLP) *T1*
London EC2 *p24* 0870 011 1111

Woollam, E V (CMS Cameron McKenna LLP)
London EC3 *p17* 020 7367 3000

Woollams, Miss L J (Wolferstans) *N*
Plymouth *p351* 01752 663295

Woollard, Mrs E V (Gotelee) *W*
Ipswich *p262* 01473 211121

Woollard, M D (Squire Sanders (UK) LLP) *B1 C1 M2*
Leeds *p277* 0113 284 7000

Woollaston, Mrs F I (Woollastons) *K1 N S1 W G J1 L Q F1 Zv*
Sutton Coldfield *p404* 0121 355 5516

Woollett, Mrs J E (Aviva PLC) *S2*
London EC3 *p103* 020 7283 7500 / 01603 687905
Norwich *p467* 01603 622200

Woollett, M C (Aviva PLC) *C1 C2*
London EC3 *p103* 020 7283 7500 / 01603 687905
Norwich *p467* 01603 622200
Norwich *p335* 01603 660155

Woolley, A (Squire Sanders (UK) LLP)
London EC2 *p81* 020 7655 1000

Woolley, D P K (Addleshaw Goddard) *C1*
Manchester *p300* 0161 934 6000

Woolley, J C (J C Woolley) *S1 W S2*
Holbeach *p251* 01406 423777

Woolley, Mrs K L (Storrar Cowdry) *N Q K3 K1*
Chester *p191* 01244 400567

Woolley, Ms L (Kingsley Napley) *N G B2*
London EC1 *p50* 020 7814 1200

Woolley, M D (Hill Dickinson LLP) *N P M1*
Manchester *p305* 0161 817 7200

Woolley, P (Blandy & Blandy) *B1*
Reading *p360* 0118 951 6800

Woolley, R D (Thompsons (formerly Robin/Brian Thompson & Partners)) *N J1*
Plymouth *p350* 01752 675810

Woolley, R D (Lester Aldridge LLP) *R1 E Zc*
Bournemouth *p152* 01202 786161

Woolley, S J D (Robinsons) *Q N O J1 L F1 V C1 M1 Zl Ze Zc*
Derby *p209* 01332 291431

Woolliams, M E (Fynmores) *S1 W C1 S2*
Bexhill *p132* 01424 732333

Woolliscroft, C R (Hacking Ashton LLP) *J1*
Newcastle under Lyme *p323* 01782 715555

Woolnough, Mrs S L (Bevirs) *L G N H Q Zl*
Wootton Bassett *p439* 01793 848900

Woolsey, Mrs C J (Peter Peter & Wright) *W K4*
Holsworthy *p251* 01409 253262

Woolsey, M (Mid Bedfordshire District Council)
Shefford *p471* 0845 230 4040

Woolsey-Brown, G W (Overburys & Raymond Thompson) *W S1 T2 K4*
Norwich *p335* 01603 610481

Woosnam, J M (Napthens LLP) *Q O N*
Preston *p357* 01772 888444

Wootten, Miss N L (Hampshire County Council)
Winchester *p476* 01962 841841

Wootton, D H (Allen & Overy LLP)
London E1 *p5* 020 3088 0000

Wootton, R I M (Large & Gibson) *E S1 C2 W L Zd*
Southsea *p388* 023 9229 6296

Worby, Ms J P (Brachers) *Q N*
Maidstone *p299* 01622 690691

Worcester, Mrs J A (Blackhurst Swainson Goodier LLP) *K1 D1 D2*
Preston *p356* 01772 253841

Worden, Ms N (MBNA Europe Bank Ltd)
Chester *p454* 01244 672002

Wordley, P (Holman Fenwick Willan)
London EC3 *p42* 020 7264 8000

Wordsworth, G M C (Mackesys) *D1 G H S1*
London SE14 *p57* 020 7639 0888

Worgan, Mrs R K (Sherwood Wheatley) *K1 D1 D2*
Kingston upon Thames *p267* 020 8546 0144

Worger, A D (Worger Howcroft) *O Q N F1 J1 L Zq S1 B1 Zi*
Bingley *p133* 01274 511246

Worger, Mrs A L (Morrish Solicitors LLP) *K1 K3 D1*
Leeds *p276* 0113 245 0733
Skipton *p381* 01756 799000

Workman, A T (Wheelers) *Zl*
Aldershot *p115* 01252 316316

Workman, Ms C (Pinsent Masons LLP) *C1*
London EC2 *p67* 020 7418 7000

Workman, J K (BPE Solicitors LLP) *C1 C2 C3 Ze*
Cheltenham *p187* 01242 224433

Workman, J R A (Crombie Wilkinson) *N Q*
York *p444* 01904 624185

Workman, Mrs L J (Dorset County Council)
Dorchester *p457* 01305 251000

Wormald, A (Clarkson Wright & Jakes Ltd) *N Zr J2 Q Zq*
Orpington *p341* 01689 887887

Wormald, P L (Richard Reed) *S2 E S1*
Sunderland *p402* 0191 567 0465

Wormald, S (Sheffield City Council)
Sheffield *p471* 0114 273 4019

Wormald, Miss V (Carr & Co) *D1 K1 D2 K2*
Gosforth *p231* 0191 284 0363
Blyth *p147* 01670 351251

Worrall, D J (Pickering & Butters) *S1 E L W A1 R1*
Stafford *p393* 01785 603060

Worrall, E (Jordans) *W*
Castleford *p183* 01977 518778

Worrall, Mrs G M (Worralls Solicitors)
Preston *p357* 01772 612494

Worrall, J N (White & Case LLP) *Zb*
London EC2 *p91* 020 7532 1000

Worrall, Mrs M S (Walker Foster with Kennedy Thompson) *K4 W T2*
Ilkley *p261* 01943 609969

Worrall, P (Worralls Solicitors) *S2 S1 R2 W C2 J1 Zv*
Preston *p357* 01772 612494

Worrall, P D (George Davies Solicitors LLP) *S1*
Manchester *p303* 0161 236 8992

Worrall, S (Chambers Fletcher LLP) *E S2 A1 S1*
Northwich *p333* 01606 780400

Worsley, F P (Bolitho Way) *P K1 S1 W M1 T1 F1*
Portsmouth *p354* 023 9282 0747

Wort, Ms J (Charles Russell LLP) *J1 O Q*
London EC4 *p19* 020 7203 5000

Wort, M (Anthony Collins Solicitors LLP) *J1*
Birmingham *p137* 0121 200 3242

Worth, Ms A L (Capsticks Solicitors LLP) *N Zr*
London SW19 *p18* 020 8780 2211

Worth, Mrs B E (Russell Worth) *N*
Plympton *p351* 01752 334100

Worth, Mrs H R (Fiona Bruce & Co LLP) *W K4*
Warrington *p421* 01925 263273

Worth, Miss S (Robinson Allfree)
Cliftonville *p196* 01843 228635

Worthing, R M (Rawlison Butler LLP) *K1 K2 K3 N*
Crawley *p202* 01293 527744
Horsham *p253* 01403 252492

Worthington, C (Lansbury Worthington) *N G H Zq J1 B2*
London W6 *p51* 020 8563 9797

Worthington, D (Veale Wasbrough Vizards) *C1 C2 M1 M2 Zb C3 Ze*
Bristol *p165* 0117 925 2020

Worthington, Ms G A (Wright Hassall LLP) *E S2 R2*
Leamington Spa *p270* 01926 886688

Worthington, Miss G L (Hibberts LLP) *W K4 J1*
Nantwich *p320* 01270 624225

Worthington, Mrs H C R (Winder Taylor Fallows) *D1 K1 S1 Q W*
Bolton *p150* 01204 389908 / 522888

Worthington, J J (Fairchild Dobbs) *S1 E L S2 W Zd*
Gerrards Cross *p229* 01753 883127

Worthington, J M (Andrew Jackson) *A1 E*
Hull *p257* 01482 325242

Worthington, K J (Lavin Copitch) *K3 K1 D1 Q*
Manchester *p306* 0161 223 5484
Macclesfield *p297* 01625 429511

Worthington, Ms T K (FBC Manby Bowdler LLP) *J1*
Wolverhampton *p437* 01902 578000

Worthy, C J (Beardsells) *N P Zj Zt*
Cheadle *p185* 0161 477 2288

Worthy, D P (Peter Dunn & Co) *S1 S2 W*
Sunderland *p401* 0191 568 9000

Worthy, E M (Gepp & Sons) *A1 S2 E R2 S1*
Chelmsford *p186* 01245 493939
Colchester *p197* 01206 369889

Worthy, J N (SNR Denton) *I Ze*
London EC4 *p75* 020 7242 1212

Worthy, P J (Hamers Solicitors) *E C2 S2*
Hull *p257* 01482 326666

Wortley, R J F (Willcox Lewis LLP) *W A1 T2 Zd*
Norwich *p335* 01508 480100

Wortley, S S (Pinsent Masons LLP) *N O Q F1 L*
Leeds *p276* 0113 244 5000

Worton, C (MKB Solicitors LLP)
Barnsley *p124* 01226 210000

Worwood, Mrs A V (Manches LLP) *K1*
London WC2 *p58* 020 7404 4433

Worwood, Miss L (Browne Jacobson LLP) *T2 W*
Nottingham *p336* 0115 976 6000

Wosskow, M (Wosskow Brown) *C1 C2 B1 J1 R1 E O Zf Zl Zt*
Sheffield *p377* 0114 256 1560

Wotherspoon, D J H (Whatley Weston & Fox) *B1 C1 L Zl*
Worcester *p440* 01905 731731

Wotherspoon, J (City of Sunderland)
Sunderland *p473* 0191 520 5555

Wotherspoon, R (Kennedys)
London EC3 *p49* 020 7667 9667

Wotherspoon, Mrs S (Tewkesbury Borough Council)
Tewkesbury *p474* 01684 272012

Wotton, J P (Allen & Overy LLP)
London E1 *p5* 020 3088 0000

Wotton, Miss P A (Field Fisher Waterhouse LLP) *K1 T2 W*
London EC3 *p31* 020 7861 4000

Wou, T T (Blaser Mills) *N Q O*
Staines *p393* 01784 462511

Wragg, B M (Pricketts) *C1 E O Ze Zl*
Buxton *p172* 01298 22874

Wragg, Mrs G L (Wragg Mark-Bell Solicitors) *A1 A2 Zb Zd C1 S2 E C3 F1 F2 Ze J1 L Zl R1 S1 K4 W*
Carlisle *p182* 01228 711728

Wragg, M J (Lightfoots LLP) *S1*
Thame *p410* 01844 212305

Wragg, Miss Y (The Johnson Partnership) *G H*
Mansfield *p311* 01623 427575

Wray, Mrs C A L (Gloucestershire County Council - Legal & Democratic Services)
Gloucester *p459* 01452 425203

Wray, E (Hodge Jones & Allen LLP)
London NW1 *p41* 020 7874 8300

Wray, Miss F J (Thorpe & Co) *O Q N W K4*
Scarborough *p372* 01723 364321

Wray, Miss H E (Wrigleys Solicitors LLP) *T2 W*
Leeds *p278* 0113 244 6100

Wray, M (Aitken Associates) *K1 K2 D1 S1 D2 W*
Islington *p4* 020 7700 6006

Wray, N (Nicholas Wray Solicitor) *G H K1 W Zd*
Haverhill *p244* 01440 704467

Wray, Mrs S L (Field Seymour Parkes) *S1*
Reading *p360* 0118 951 6200

Wreford, Mrs E D (Ellis-Fermor & Negus)
Long Eaton *p293* 0115 972 5222

Wrennall, Mrs B S (Quality Solicitors C Turner) *K1*
Blackburn *p145* 01254 688400

Wrigglesworth, P A (Paul Bullen & Co) *W*
Doncaster *p211* 01302 819000

Wright, Ms A (TV Edwards LLP) *G H*
London N15 *p85* 020 7790 7000

Wright, Mrs A (Denbighshire County Council)
Ruthin *p470* 01824 706000

Wright, Ms A (Gateley LLP)
Birmingham *p138* 0121 234 0000

Wright, A (Stuckey Carr & Co) *S1 W E A1 L C1 R1*
Storrington *p399* 01903 743201

Wright, Miss A (Nabarro LLP)
London WC1 *p63* 020 7524 6000

Wright, Miss A (Rosalind Watchorn) *W K4*
Sheffield *p377* 0114 229 0160

Wright, A C (Clarkson Wright & Jakes Ltd) *C1 U2 C2*
Orpington *p341* 01689 887887

Wright, Ms A E (Lawrence Stephens)
London EC1 *p82* 020 7935 1211

Wright, A G M (Wright & Wright) *S2 S1 Q O W E C1 J1*
Guildford *p237* 01483 531264

Wright, A G P (Dickinson Dees) *C1*
Newcastle upon Tyne *p324* 0191 279 9000

Wright, Mrs A J (Scaiff LLP) *D1 W*
Worcester *p440* 01905 727700

Wright, A J (Tate & Lyle PLC)
London EC3 *p109* 020 7626 6525

Wright, Mrs A M (Wright & Wright) *S2 S1 Q O W E C1 J1*
Guildford *p237* 01483 531264

Wright, A M (Aspinall Wright) *S1 W L E C1 B1 A1 S2 K4*
Glossop *p230* 01457 854645

Wright, A R (EDC Lord & Co) *E S1 W Zl*
Hayes *p245* 020 8848 9988

Wright, A S (Stanley Tee) *S1 S2*
Bishop's Stortford *p144* 01279 755200

Wright, A W (More Fisher Brown) *O Za*
London EC4 *p61* 020 7330 8000

Wright, B (Edwards Duthie) *N Zw*
Ilford *p260* 020 8514 9000

Wright, Mrs B J (Thomson Snell & Passmore) *K1 D1 K3*
Tunbridge Wells *p415* 01892 510000

Wright, Ms B M (Barlow Robbins LLP) *K1 K2*
Woking *p436* 01483 748500

Wright, Ms C (Boodle Hatfield) *K1*
Westminster *p14* 020 7629 7411

Wright, Mrs C (Stephenson Harwood) *T1 T2*
London EC2 *p82* 020 7329 4422

Wright, Ms C (Harbottle & Lewis LLP)
London W1 *p38* 020 7667 5000

Wright, C (Morris Orman Hearle) *N G*
Cheltenham *p188* 01242 257188

Wright, C B (Ashfords LLP) *E*
Exeter *p220* 01392 337000

Wright, C D (Greenland Houchen Pomeroy) *S1 W E A1 T1 C1 R1 G H K1 Zd Zc Zo*
Attleborough *p120* 01953 453143

Wright, Mrs C E (Hugh James) *W Zd*
Cardiff *p179* 029 2022 4871

Wright, C G (Rooks Rider) *W T1 S1 Zd A1 L*
London EC1 *p73* 020 7689 7000

Wright, C J (Thursfields) *Zc C1 S2 E F1 C2*
Worcester *p440* 01905 730450

Wright, C J A (Storrar Cowdry) *S1 S2 E*
Chester *p191* 01244 400567

Wright, Ms C M (Squire Sanders (UK) LLP)
Leeds *p277* 0113 284 7000

Wright, C P (Hopkins) *Q L N V*
Mansfield *p311* 01623 460460

Wright, C R (Royds LLP) *W*
London EC4 *p74* 020 7583 2222

Wright, D (Osborne Clarke) *R2*
Bristol *p164* 0117 917 3000

Wright, D (DLA Piper UK LLP) *C1 Zo Zd*
Liverpool *p287* 0870 011 1111

Wright, D A (MKB Solicitors LLP) *S1 E A1 C1 L R1 T1 W Zc Ze Zm*
Barnsley *p124* 01226 210000

Wright, D A (Osborne Clarke) *O*
London EC2 *p65* 020 7105 7000

Wright, Ms D A (Irwin Mitchell LLP) *J1 Zp*
Leeds *p274* 0870 150 0100

Wright, Ms D C (Milton Keynes Council)
Milton Keynes *p466* 01908 691691

Wright, D G (The Worcester Family Law Practice) *K1 D1 D2*
Worcester *p440* 01905 730900

Wright, Ms D L (Pritchard Englefield) *O Zb*
London EC2 *p69* 020 7972 9720

Wright, D M J (Hillyer McKeown LLP) *S1 S2 E*
Chester *p190* 01244 318131

Wright, E (Draycott Browne Solicitors)
Manchester *p303* 0161 228 2244

Wright, E A (Leslie Harris Solicitors & Advocates) *S1 E W S2*
Lytham *p297* 01253 724974

Wright, Ms E J (Irwin Mitchell LLP) *N*
Sheffield *p376* 0870 150 0100

Wright, Mrs F E (Wright & McMillan Bennett) *G H D1 K1 D2*
Telford *p409* 01952 291100

Wright, Mrs G (Smith & Graham) *K1 D1*
Peterlee *p348* 0191 517 3393

Wright, Ms G (R G Frisby & Small) *D1 K1*
Leicester *p279* 0116 233 5522
Leicester *p279* 01455 282832

Wright, G E (Shakespeares) *Zza C1 C3 F1 F2 I M1 M2 M3 U1 U2 Ze Zw Zz*
Nottingham *p339* 0115 945 3700

Wright, Ms G G (Lightfoots LLP) *K1 K3*
Thame *p410* 01844 212305

Wright, G J (Wright & Co) *F1 J1 K1 L M1 N V W*
Pontefract *p351* 01977 878130

Wright, G P (Wright & Co)
Harpenden *p239* 01582 767686

Wright, G T (Russell Worth) *N*
Plympton *p351* 01752 334100

Wright, Miss H (Blaker Son & Young) *W S1*
Lewes *p283* 01273 480234
Cheam *p185* 020 8641 2771

Wright, Ms H C (Cullimore Dutton) *J1 Q*
Chester *p190* 01244 356789

Wright, Miss H E (Payne Marsh Stillwell) *S2 E S1 L*
Southampton *p386* 023 8022 3957

Wright, Ms H K (Cumberland Ellis Peirs) *D1 G K1 L O Q Zi N*
London WC1 *p23* 020 7242 0422

Wright, I L (Gregsons) *K1 G D1 V H F1 N Zp Zi*
Liverpool *p288* 0151 703 2550

Wright, Ms J (Merrony Wall) *K3 K1 K2*
Twickenham *p416* 020 8898 4700
Richmond upon Thames *p364* 020 8940 2525

Wright, J (Roythornes LLP) *T2 W A1 T1 K4 Zo*
Spalding *p389* 01775 842500

Wright, J (J Wright) *J1 N Q O*
Lytham *p297* 01253 727875

Wright, J (Reed Smith LLP) *A3 O Q*
London EC2 *p71* 020 3116 3000

Wright, J (Hodge Jones & Allen LLP) *G H*
London NW1 *p41* 020 7874 8300

Wright, Ms J (Forbes)
Preston *p356* 01772 220022

Wright, J (Saunders Law Partnership LLP)
London WC2 *p76* 020 7632 4300

Wright, J (Metropolitan Police Directorate of Legal Services) *N*
London SW1 *p108* 020 7230 7210

Wright, J C (Wright & Co) *C1 E G L N Q S1 W Zc Ze Zw*
London SW3 *p93* 020 7584 7557

Wright, Ms J E Y (Cartmell Shepherd) *W M1 T2*
Penrith *p346* 01768 862326

Wright, J H (Last Cawthra Feather LLP) *S1 E L*
Shipley *p378* 01274 585459

Wright, J N (Wilson Browne) *P N M1 D1 J1 K1 F1 B1 H*
Kettering *p265* 01536 410041

Wright, J P M (Marsh & McLennan Companies, Inc) *O Zj*
London EC3 *p108* 020 7357 1000

Wright, K (Stephens & Scown) *S2 E Zh R2 S1 L A1*
Truro *p414* 01872 265100

Wright, Miss K (Sherrards) *J1*
St Albans *p390* 01727 832830

Wright, Ms K (Anthony Gold) *N Zr*
London SE1 *p6* 020 7940 4000

Wright, Miss K A (Scott Duff & Co) *K1 D1 K2 N L*
Carlisle *p182* 01228 531054

Wright, K A (Moore & Tibbits) *S1 S2 E K1 W K4 G K3 L Q*
Warwick *p422* 01926 491181

Wright, Miss K L (Lloyds TSB Group PLC) *O Q Zb Ze Zj*
Bristol *p452* 0117 905 5500

Wright, Miss K V (Hunters) *S1 A1*
London WC2 *p44* 020 7412 0050

Wright, Miss L (Coles Miller Solicitors LLP)
Poole *p352* 01202 673011

Wright, Miss L J (Ford Simey LLP) *N K1 L V*
Exmouth *p222* 01395 272241 / 0800 169 3741

Wright, M (John Hodge Solicitors) *S1*
Weston-super-Mare *p429* 01934 623511

Wright, M (Speechly Bircham LLP) *C1 C2 T1*
London EC4 *p81* 020 7427 6400

Wright, M (Wright & Morton) *G N S1 D1 F1 W J1*
Sunderland *p402* 0191 567 4289

Wright, Ms M (London Borough of Southwark)
London SE1 *p109* 020 7525 5000

Wright, Mrs M A (Dootsons LLP) *D1 K1 K3*
Leigh *p282* 01942 673431

Wright, M B (Rix & Kay Solicitors LLP) *W T2 Zd Zm*
Hove *p255* 01273 329797

Wright, M C E (Ashurst LLP) *E B1 R1 L*
London EC2 *p7* 020 7638 1111

Wright, M J (Holmes & Hills LLP) *E S1 S2*
Braintree *p155* 01376 320456

Wright, M J (Heald Nickinson) *S2 E L R1 S1 R2*
Camberley *p173* 01276 680000

Wright, Mrs M P (Beaty & Co) *W S1 L K4 Q T2*
Wigton *p432* 01697 342121

Wright, N (GHP Legal) *K1 D1 Zm*
Wrexham *p442* 01978 291456

Wright, N (Coldham Shield & Mace) *S1 P K1 G M1 F1 J1 V W*
London E4 *p21* 020 8524 6323

Wright, N A (Mayer Brown International LLP)
London EC2 *p59* 020 3130 3000

Wright, N E (Middlesbrough Council)
Middlesbrough *p465* 01642 245432

Wright, N J (Wright Son & Pepper LLP) *C1 Zb Zq*
Camden *p93* 020 7242 5473

Wright, Miss N J (Hague Lambert) *J1 O*
Manchester *p305* 0161 834 6066

Wright, N J G (Darbys Solicitors LLP) *Q L Zq*
Oxford *p343* 01865 811700

Wright, N K (HM Land Registry - Birkenhead (Rosebrae)) *K1 S1 M1 G W H F1 C1 B1 L Zk*
Birkenhead *p449* 0151 472 6666

Wright, N V (Pinders) *D1 G H K1 V*
Derby *p209* 01332 364751

Wright, O T I (Forsters LLP) *R1*
Westminster *p33* 020 7863 8333

Wright, P (Cartwright King)
Nottingham *p336* 0115 958 7444
Nottingham *p338* 0115 958 6262

Wright, P (Napthens LLP) *E*
Preston *p357* 01772 888444

Wright, P (Simmons & Simmons)
London EC2 *p79* 020 7628 2020

Wright, P A (Brown Turner Ross) *D1 G H K1 L N Q V S1 S2*
Southport *p388* 01704 542002

Wright, Miss P C (Hopkins) *N Q L O*
Nottingham *p337* 0115 910 5555

Wright, P D (Bell Wright & Co) *S1 K1 W P M1 G E C1 H A1 Ze Zi K4*
Gainsborough *p228* 01427 611722

Wright, P H (Mark Gilbert Morse) *S2 B1 C1 E F1 K4 L Zl W*
Newcastle upon Tyne *p325* 0191 261 0096

Wright, P S K (Taylor Nelson Sofres PLC)
London W5 *p109* 020 8967 4348

Wright, Ms R (Lewis Silkin LLP)
London EC4 *p53* 020 7074 8000

Wright, Ms R (Franklins LLP) *K1 K4 Q S1 W*
Northampton *p332* 01604 828282

Wright, R (Furley Page LLP) *C1 C2 E S2 Zn*
Canterbury *p176* 01227 763939

Wright, R C (The Stokes Partnership) *S2 E A1 Zc*
Crewkerne *p203* 01460 279279

Wright, R E (Freeth Cartwright LLP) *E R1 L S1*
Nottingham *p337* 0115 936 9369

Wright, R J (T G Pollard & Co) *K1 G J1 F1 Q V D1 N H*
Wells *p425* 01749 674722

Wright, R J (Gotelee) *Q*
Ipswich *p262* 01473 211121

Wright, R M (Fraser Brown) *C1 S2 E R2 Ze S1*
Nottingham *p337* 0115 988 8777

Wright, Ms R S (Gamlins) *M1 P F1 J1 W*
Llandudno *p291* 01492 860420

Wright, R W (May May & Merrimans) *W T2*
London WC1 *p59* 020 7405 8932

Wright, S (Shoosmiths)
Fareham *p224* 0370 086 6800 / 01489 616800

Wright, S (J A Kemp & Co)
London WC1 *p48* 020 7405 3292

Wright, S (Sandwell Metropolitan Borough Council)
Oldbury *p468* 0121 569 2200

Wright, S C (Blake Lapthorn) *E S1 R1 L C1 A1 Zc Zh*
Chandlers Ford *p184* 023 8090 8090

Wright, Ms S E (PCB Solicitors LLP) *K1 K3 V*
Telford *p409* 01952 403000

Wright, Ms S J (Brindley Twist Tafft & James) *C1*
Coventry *p200* 024 7653 1532

Wright, S J (John Lewis plc)
London SW1 *p107* 020 7828 1000

Wright, S J P (Newman & Bond) *S1 E S2*
Barnsley *p125* 01226 213434

Wright, S N (Wright & Lord) *N O Q J1 E S1 L K1 C1 F1 Zl S2 Zw*
Morecambe *p319* 01524 402050

Wright, S P (Banner Jones) *N O*
Chesterfield *p191* 01246 209773

Wright, T (Penningtons) *Zr N*
Basingstoke *p127* 01256 407100

Wright, Mrs T (Nash & Co Solicitors LLP) *N Q W*
Plymouth *p350* 01752 664444

Wright, T (Keelys LLP)
Lichfield *p284* 01543 420000

Wright, T M (Pillsbury Winthrop Shaw Pittman LLP) *I U2 U1 Ze*
London EC2 *p67* 020 7847 9500

Wright, T W (Parfitt Cresswell) *K1 S1 W J1 L S2*
London SW6 *p65* 020 7381 8311

Wright, Ms V (Darbys Solicitors LLP) *Q O Zd Zk*
Oxford *p343* 01865 811700

Wright, Mrs V (Otten Penna Ltd) *K1 K3*
Northenden *p333* 0161 945 1431

Wright, Miss V (Swain & Co) *Q N X*
Havant *p244* 023 9248 3322

Wright, Miss V J (Swain & Co) *N Q X*
Southampton *p386* 023 8063 1111

Wrighton, R (Ward Hadaway)
Newcastle upon Tyne *p327* 0191 204 4000

Wrightson, Miss A (Sternberg Reed) *G H*
Romford *p366* 01708 766155

Wrightson, G R (Squire Sanders (UK) LLP) *Zo*
London EC2 *p81* 020 7655 1000

Wrightson, Ms M (TWM Solicitors LLP) *J1 K1*
Reigate *p363* 01737 221212

Wrightson, M P M (Burnetts) *S1 W A1*
Carlisle *p181* 01228 552222
Carlisle *p182* 01228 552222

Wriglesworth, A D (Wrigleys Solicitors LLP) *W*
Leeds *p278* 0113 244 6100

Wrigley, H C (Freeman Johnson) *S1 W A1 C1 T1 E Zc*
Northallerton *p331* 01609 772160
Durham *p214* 0191 386 4843 / 386 9619

Wrigley, Ms P (Thompsons (formerly Robin/Brian Thompson & Partners)) *N*
Liverpool *p290* 0151 224 1600

Wrigley, R (SGH Martineau LLP) *C1 Zb C2*
Birmingham *p142* 0870 763 2000

Wrigley, R B (Norrie Waite & Slater) *N P B1 C1 G*
Sheffield *p377* 0114 276 6166

Wrigley, S J (Thomas Solicitors) *C1 E F1 G J1 K1 L M1 N P Zc*
Loughborough *p293* 01509 611061

Wrigley, T (Wrigleys Solicitors LLP) *Zd E*
Leeds *p278* 0113 244 6100

Wrigley, W M (Wrigleys Solicitors LLP) *T2 W X A2 Zd*
Leeds *p278* 0113 244 6100

Wrinch, M P J (Birkett Long LLP) *Q A1 B1 O*
Colchester *p197* 01206 217300

Wroblewski, J J (Alker & Ball) *Q J1 O J2 F2*
Wigan *p432* 01942 246241

See p634 for the Key to Work Categories

Wroe, J C (J C Wroe & Co) *G S1 H E N W C1 M1 K1 P Zm*
Reading *p362* 0118 959 1496

Wu, M L (Radcliffes Le Brasseur)
Westminster *p70*. 020 7222 7040

Wyatt, C (Baldwin Wyatt Solicitors) *G H S1 S2 W Zi T2 Zl*
Burnley *p169* 01282 429999

Wyatt, D (Underwood Solicitors LLP) *E I Q Ze*
Westminster *p89*. 020 7526 6000

Wyatt, Ms D (Howard de Walden Estates Ltd)
London W1 *p105* 020 7580 3163

Wyatt, Ms E J (Anthony Collins Solicitors LLP) *D1 Zm K1*
Birmingham *p137* 0121 200 3242

Wyatt, Mrs E L (Penmans) *W S1 T2 K4*
Kenilworth *p264* 01926 858222

Wyatt, Ms H J (Goodman Derrick LLP) *O Q B1 L*
London EC4 *p36*. 020 7404 0606

Wyatt, J (Hamers Solicitors) *N*
Hull *p257* 01482 326666

Wyatt, J G (Nash & Co Solicitors LLP) *N Q Zl*
Plymouth *p350*. 01752 664444

Wyatt, Ms S C (Cheltenham & Gloucester PLC)
Gloucester *p459*. 01452 372372

Wyatt, S J (Dixon & Templeton) *W T2 Zd Zm*
Fordingbridge *p227* 01425 652194
Ringwood *p364* 01425 476231

Wyatt, Ms V (Capsticks Solicitors LLP) *Zr N*
London SW19 *p18*. 020 8780 2211

Wybar, D K (Birkett Long LLP) *E A1 A2 T2 S1 W T1 S2*
Colchester *p197* 01206 217300

Wyborn, Mrs E (The Johnson Partnership) *G H*
Nottingham *p337*. 0115 941 9141

Wybrew, P H (Christos Wybrew Kenneth Shaw & Co) *B1 J1 M1 N P Ze Zf Zh*
Enfield *p218*. . .020 8366 1345 / 8367 0840

Wyburn, Miss S E (Wendy Hopkins Family Law Practice LLP)
Cardiff *p178* 029 2034 2233

Wydra, M N (Michael Wydra & Co) *A1 Zb B1 Zc C1 S2 E C3 I K4 J1 B2 L Zj O Q N C2 Zz Zq R2 Zv S1 T1 T2 W*
Westminster *p93*. 020 7437 3640

Wyer, S J (George Green LLP) *C1 Ze U2 Zza F1 F2 I C3*
Cradley Heath *p201* 01384 410410

Wyers, W A (Serjeant & Son) *S1 W A1 C1 E L T2 Zd*
Ramsey *p359* 01487 812325

Wykeham, N P (Wykeham & Co) *E S1 W*
Chippenham *p193* 01249 721010

Wykeham-Hurford, The Hon J L A B (Wykeham Hurford Sheppard & Son LLP) *E L W S1 Zd*
Chislehurst *p193*.020 8297 0393 / 8467 8307
Battle *p128* 01424 775088

Wykes, Mrs N (Caversham Solicitors Ltd) *S2 L E*
Reading *p360* 0118 947 8638

Wyld, C J C (Burges Salmon) *T2 W A1 Zd*
Bristol *p161* 0117 939 2000

Wylde, A (AEW Litigation) *N Q*
Sutton Coldfield *p403* 0121 354 8640
Birmingham *p139* 0870 150 0100

Wylde, J R A (Financial Services Authority)
London E14 *p106* 020 7066 1000

Wylde, P R (Irwin Mitchell LLP) *O C1 B1 P Q*
London EC1 *p45*. 0870 150 0100

Wyles, Miss A E (Loveday & Keighley) *K4 W Zm V*
Matlock *p313* . . . . 01629 583142 / 56660

Wyles, Mrs B M (Royal Mail Group)
London EC4 *p109* 020 7250 2468

Wyles, D A (Herbert Smith LLP) *C1 M2 Zb*
London EC2 *p40*. 020 7374 8000

Wyles, Mrs J (Linder Myers Solicitors) *K1 N S1 E*
Manchester *p307* 0844 984 6400

Wyles, J J A (Reynolds Porter Chamberlain LLP) *O Q Zc Zj Zq*
London E1 *p71* 020 3060 6000

Wylie, Ms D A (Cooper Nimmo) *K1*
Blackpool *p146* 01253 626793

Wylie, Mrs J (Penningtons)
Godalming *p231*. 01483 791800

Wylie, Mrs J A (JW Law)
Wimborne *p433* 01202 690658

Wylie, Ms L (Ratcliffe Duce & Gammer LLP) *B1 F1 J1 O Q Zp*
Reading *p361* 0118 957 4291

Wylie, Ms S L (Simons Muirhead & Burton) *K1 K3*
London W1 *p79* 020 7734 4499

Wyllie, E J (Russells) *Zf Ze*
London W1 *p75* 020 7439 8692

Wyllie, M J S (Kenwright Walker Wyllie) *S1 E W A1 S2*
East Molesey *p215* 020 8979 1131

Wylly, Miss J L (Mills & Reeve) *Zu Zh*
Birmingham *p140* 0121 454 4000

Wyman, C J (Clifford Chance)
London E14 *p20*. 020 7006 1000

Wyman, Ms J (Tyrer Roxburgh & Co) *K1*
Haringey *p89* 020 8889 3319

Wyman, M J (Simmons & Simmons)
London EC2 *p79*. 020 7628 2020

Wyn Davies, Mrs C (Pinsent Masons LLP)
Birmingham *p141* 0121 200 1050

Wyn Thomas, Ms S (Wrexham County Borough Council)
Wrexham *p477* 01978 292000

Wynds, Miss L (IBB Solicitors) *G H*
Uxbridge *p417*. 0845 638 1381

Wynn Green, Mrs G (Rootes & Alliott) *E F1 L P V W Zh*
Folkestone *p227*. 01303 851100

Wynn, D C (Denis Wynn & Co) *K1 L S1 W*
Chipping Norton *p193* 01608 643036

Wynn, D M (Keoghs LLP) *N Zj O Q*
Bolton *p149* 01204 677000

Wynn, J W (Birmingham City Council Legal & Democratic Services)
Birmingham *p449* 0121 303 2066

Wynn-Evans, C A (Dechert) *J1 Zp*
London EC4 *p26*. 020 7184 7000

Wynn-Evans, J R (National Grid PLC)
Warwick *p471* 01926 653000

Wynn-Jones, Ms R (Walker Smith Way) *K1 K3 D1*
Wrexham *p443* 0844 346 3100

Wynn-Williams, N S (Rees Page) *D1 K1 W*
Wolverhampton *p438* 01902 577777

Wynne Thomas, G (More Group PLC) *C1 C2 C3 E J1 R1 O M1 M2 Zb Zc Ze Zk Zo*
London W1 *p108* 020 7287 6100

Wynne, A (FBC Manby Bowdler LLP) *E C1*
Wolverhampton *p437* 01902 578000

Wynne, G (SNR Denton) *C2 Zb*
London EC4 *p75*. 020 7242 1212

Wynne, S (Linder Myers Solicitors) *N*
Manchester *p306* 0844 984 6000

Wynne, Ms S L (Willans LLP) *S2 Zc E*
Cheltenham *p189* 01242 514000

Wynne, T M (J Charles Hughes & Co) *S1 W A1 R1 L C1 G T1 N*
Dolgellau *p211*. 01341 422464

Wynne, Ms V L (D P Roberts Hughes & Denye) *N O Q Zr*
Birkenhead *p134*. 0151 647 6000

Wynter Bee, P F (ZincOx Resources PLC) *P N M1 L S1 J1 W C1 Zi Zc Zs*
Bagshot *p448* 01276 450100

Wynter, A (Wainwright & Cummins)
Lambeth *p90*. 020 7326 7460

Wynter, Mrs G (Avery Naylor) *K1 Zq*
Swansea *p404*. 01792 463276

Wynter, Miss N (Sheffield City Council)
Sheffield *p471* 0114 273 4019

Wyresdale, Miss J (EEF West Midlands Association)
Birmingham *p449* 0121 456 2222

Wyvill, R M (Harvey Ingram LLP) *S1 Q E*
Leicester *p280*. 0116 254 5454

Wyvill, R M (Spearing Waite LLP) *E S2 R2 Zc A1*
Leicester *p281*. 0116 262 4225

X

Xanthopol, Ms N (Linklaters LLP)
London EC2 *p54*. 020 7456 2000

Xavier, L A (Bevans) *J1 O Q N*
London WC2 *p12* 020 7353 9995

Xavier-Phillips, Mrs A (GE Money Home Finance Limited)
Harrow *p460*. 020 8861 1313

Xitsas, C (Maples Teesdale LLP)
London EC2 *p58*. 020 7600 3800

Y

Yacoubou, Miss C J (Norwich Union Insurance Group)
Norwich *p467* 01603 622200
York *p477* 01904 452210

Yafai, Mrs F (Birmingham City Council Legal & Democratic Services)
Birmingham *p449* 0121 303 2066

Yakoob, A (Himayah Solicitors) *S1 S2 Zi K3*
Birmingham *p139* 0121 356 5007

Yakub, M A (Environment Agency (Wales))
Cardiff *p453* 0870 850 6506

Yam, P (SJ Berwin LLP)
London EC4 *p75*. 020 7111 2222

Yamin, M (Dollman & Pritchard) *K1 K3*
Caterham *p183* 01883 347823

Yamin, S (Hodge Jones & Allen LLP)
London NW1 *p41* 020 7874 8300

Yandle, Miss I L H (Gill Akaster) *W T2*
Plymouth *p349*. 01752 203500

Yao, Ms S A (Hopkin Murray Beskine) *K1 D1 L*
London N4 *p42* 020 7272 1234

Yap, Miss J M K (Pickworths) *W*
Hemel Hempstead *p247*. . . 01442 261731

Yapp, T (Marriott Davies Yapp) *C1 I C2 J1 P O M2 M1 C3 T1 Zb Zd Ze Zf*
Sutton *p402* 020 8643 9794

Yaqoob, A (Shuttari Paul & Co)
Southall *p384* 020 8574 7151

Yaqub, Ms R S (Edwards Duthie) *N Zr J2*
Ilford *p260*. 020 8514 9000

Yaqub, S (Martin Murray & Associates) *G H*
West Drayton *p427* 01895 431332

Yard, Mrs S (Shirley May Yard) *E F1 J1 K1 L N S1 W*
Sidmouth *p380*. 01395 577199

Yardley, Ms M (Memery Crystal) *C1 C2 Zn*
London WC2 *p60* 020 7242 5905

Yardley, M D (Weightmans LLP) *F1 C1 B1 J1 T1 Zb*
Manchester *p311* 0161 233 7330

Yardley, P D (Atkinson Ritson) *K1 M1 S1 J1 E L G H P W Zl*
Carlisle *p181*. 01228 525221

Yardy, J S (Oslers Solicitors) *G H*
Stowmarket *p400* 01449 774670

Yarnold, H W (Humphries Kirk) *L E S1 R1 A1 S2*
Dorchester *p212*. 01305 251007

Yasmin, Mrs M (Robinsons) *S2 E S1*
Derby *p209* 01332 291431

Yasser, M (Gregorys Solicitors)
Stockport *p395*. 0161 456 8125

Yasutake, Ms N (Howard Kennedy LLP) *T2 C1*
London W1 *p48* 020 7636 1616

Yates, A (Brignalls Balderston Warren) *E*
Letchworth *p283*. 01462 482248

Yates, A (Elliot Mather LLP) *S1 S2 E*
Chesterfield *p192* 01246 231288

Yates, A E (Yates Barnes) *N M1 P C1 K1 E J1*
Chorley *p194* 01257 267014

Yates, A J (Trowers & Hamlins) *O Zc*
London EC3 *p88*. 020 7423 8000

Yates, A M (Parkes Wilshire Johnson)
Barnet *p124* 020 8364 9955

Yates, A P (Pinsent Masons LLP) *E*
Birmingham *p141* 0121 200 1050

Yates, B I (Howlett Clarke Crowther Wood)
Brighton *p159* . . . .01273 327272 / 326341

Yates, C (George Davies Solicitors LLP) *C1 C2 B1 F1*
Manchester *p303* 0161 236 8992

Yates, Ms C (Radcliffes Le Brasseur)
Westminster *p70*. 020 7222 7040

Yates, D (Bassetlaw District Council)
Worksop *p477* 01909 533533

Yates, Ms D M (Thompsons (formerly Robin/Brian Thompson & Partners)) *N J2*
Manchester *p310* 0161 819 3500

Yates, D R (Forbes) *N Q G Zj*
Blackburn *p145* 01254 662831

Yates, G (Watson Burton LLP)
London EC3 *p90*. 0845 901 2100

Yates, G (Addison Legal) *Zb C1 F1 Zj Q N*
Stockport *p395*. 0161 660 9232

Yates, Ms J (Biscoes) *W S1*
Portsmouth *p354*. 023 9266 0261

Yates, J D (Kennedys) *N*
Chelmsford *p186*. 0845 838 4800

Yates, J I (Inghams) *O N Q J1 Zc*
Blackpool *p146* 01253 626642

Yates, J T (Green Wright Chalton Annis) *S1 E W T1 C1 K1 F1 L J1*
Rustington *p369* 01903 774131
Worthing *p441*. 01903 234064

Yates, Mrs K (Elliot Mather LLP) *W S1*
Chesterfield *p192* 01246 231288

Yates, K A (Lumsdons Solicitors LLP) *E K4 K1 S1 T2 W*
Stourport-on-Severn *p399* . . 01299 827766

Yates, L (Beswicks) *G H*
Hanley *p239*. 01782 205000

Yates, Ms M (Heckford Norton) *S1*
Stevenage *p395* 01438 312211

Yates, Miss M (Birkett Long LLP) *E*
Colchester *p197*. 01206 217300

Yates, M J (DWF) *J1*
Manchester *p303* 0161 603 5000

Yates, M J (Hunters) *W T2*
London WC2 *p44* 020 7412 0050

Yates, M J (Maxwell Hodge Solicitors) *S1 W C1 E K4*
Formby *p227* 01704 872156

Yates, N J (Stephensons Solicitors LLP) *C1 S2*
Wigan *p432*. 01942 777777

Yates, N J (Horwich Farrelly) *Q G N*
Manchester *p305* 0161 834 3585

Yates, N P R (Plexus Law (A Trading Name of Parabis Law LLP)) *N G O Q*
Evesham *p220*. 01386 769160

Yates, P J (Ian N Gunby & Co) *K1 K2*
Milnthorpe *p316* 01539 562044
Barrow-in-Furness *p125* . . . 01229 811811

Yates, Ms R (Platt Halpern) *G H*
Manchester *p308* 0161 224 2555

Yates, R L (Vincent Laverys) *S1 E W*
Preston *p357* 01772 555176

Yates, Mrs R M (Maples Teesdale LLP) *S2 E*
London EC2 *p58*. 020 7600 3800

Yates, R M (Winckworth Sherwood LLP) *E S1 S2 Zh*
London SE1 *p92*. 020 7593 5000

Yates, S L (Andrew Jackson)
Hull *p257* 01482 325242

Yates, S R (Simmons & Simmons)
London EC2 *p79*. 020 7628 2020
London EC1 *p87*. 020 7295 3000

Yau, Mrs F M (STA International Ltd T/A STA Graydon)
Maidstone *p464* 01622 600900

Yau, R (G T Stewart Solicitors) *G H B2 J2*
London SE22 *p83* 020 8299 6000

Yaxley, C W (Security Investments (Industrial) Ltd)
Shrewsbury *p471* 01743 454455

Yazbeck, Mrs G (Cadbury Schweppes Europe, Middle East & Africa)
Rickmansworth *p470*. 01923 483483

Yeadon, N J (Aplin Stockton Fairfax) *W T1 Zv K4*
Banbury *p122* 01295 251234

Yeaman, A G (Weightmans LLP)
Birmingham *p143* 0121 632 6100

Yeates, D (Karslakes Solicitors Limited)
Guildford *p236*. 01483 454242

Yeates, Mrs D J (Reynolds Parry-Jones) *K1 D1*
High Wycombe *p250*. 01494 525941

Yeates, Mrs J (Hethertons LLP) *J1*
York *p445* 01904 528200

Yeend, Mrs V H J (Claremont Richards) *E Zu R1 S2 R2*
London EC4 *p20*. 020 7353 3030

Yeldham, G R (Wortley Redmayne Kershaw) *C1 E B1 J1*
Chelmsford *p187*. 01245 491122

Yell, E (Carter-Ruck) *Zk O Zq Q*
London EC4 *p18*. 020 7353 5005

Yelland, C J (Association of Train Operating Companies)
London WC1 *p103*. 020 7841 8000

Yelland, Mrs P E (Stafford Young Jones) *Zh L S2*
London EC4 *p82*. 020 7623 9490

Yemm, C A M (Fisher Jones Greenwood LLP) *N K1 O Q Zq Zc Zr*
Colchester *p197* 01206 578282

Yendole, A (Ashfords LLP) *J1*
Exeter *p220* 01392 337000

Yeo, Miss B (Black Graf & Co) *S1*
London NW3 *p13* 020 7586 1141

Yeo, N J (Ash Clifford) *S1 W L E G H A1 T1 C1 P*
Bridgwater *p157* 01278 451327

Yeoman, G E (Dickinson Manser) *S1 S2 W E*
Broadstone *p166*. .01202 692308 / 694490
Poole *p352* 01202 673071

Yeoman, Mrs S A (Cardiff County Council) *K1*
Cardiff *p453* 029 2087 2000

Yeomans, Miss L C (Orme & Slade Ltd) *S1 S2 W L*
Ledbury *p271* 01531 632226

Yeomans, Miss M (Nexus Solicitors) *C1 C2 Zb*
Manchester *p308* 0161 819 4900

Yeomans, R (Addleshaw Goddard)
London EC1 *p4* 020 7606 8855

Yeowart, G B B (Hogan Lovells International LLP)
London EC1 *p42*. 020 7296 2000

Yeowart, S (Hodders) *Zh L Q O F1 J1*
London NW10 *p41*. 020 8838 1537

Yerburgh, T W (Collyer Bristow LLP) *K1*
London WC1 *p22* 020 7242 7363

Yerbury, P D (Fasken Martineau LLP) *T1 T2 W*
London W1 *p31* 020 7917 8500

Yeshin, Ms A J (Kennards Wells) *D1 K3 K1 K2 L O Q*
London E11 *p48* 020 8539 8338

Yeshua, Mrs N (Williams & Co) *K1 L K3 D1 F1 V W B1 J1*
Edgware *p217*. 020 8952 8882

Yetman, P J (Coffin Mew & Clover) *E C1 L S1 R1 Zs*
Portsmouth *p354*. 023 9238 8021

Yeung, P H (P H Yeung)
London W1 *p93* 020 7287 1882

Yew, J (Penningtons) *J1*
London EC2 *p66*. 020 7457 3000

Yiannakas, A M (YVA Solicitors) *F1 L R1 S1*
London N12 *p93*. 020 8445 9898

Yiannakas, C (YVA Solicitors) *F1 G H J1 K1 L M1 P S1*
London N12 *p93*. 020 8445 9898

Yianni, A S (Clifford Chance)
London E14 *p20*. 020 7006 1000

Yogadeva, Miss A (Boyes Turner) *N Zr*
Reading *p360* 0118 959 7711

Yonge, W J G R (McDermott Will & Emery UK LLP)
London EC2 *p56*. 020 7577 6900

York, D J (Field Seymour Parkes) *E R2*
Reading *p360* 0118 951 6200

York, Mrs H E (Smith Chamberlain) *K1 D1 D2*
Wellingborough *p425* 01933 224971

York, Mrs K M (Dzimitrowicz York) *K1 N Q D1*
Croydon *p205* 020 8667 0340

York, P C D (P C D York & Co) *G H S2 K1 K3 B2 Zi W N*
London W6 *p93* 020 8741 4512

York, S (National Institutions of the Church of England, Legal Office)
London SW1 *p108*. 020 7898 1000

Yorke, Miss C (Lanyon Bowdler LLP) *K1 V K3*
Oswestry *p342*. 01691 652241

Yorke, J (Barlow Lyde & Gilbert LLP)
London EC3 *p10*. 020 7247 2277
London EC2 *p71*. 020 3116 3000

Youdale, S (Herbert Smith LLP) *C1*
London EC2 *p40*. 020 7374 8000

Youdan, Miss C (Tennant & Knight) *D1 K1 D2*
Brighton *p160* 01273 202050

Youdell, J C (Treasury Solicitors Department) *N P K1 G B1 D1 L V Zc Zj Zl*
London WC2 *p110*. 020 7210 3000

Youldon, Ms C A (Browne Jacobson LLP) *Q Zq Zj*
Nottingham *p336*. 0115 976 6000

Youle, R (Linklaters LLP)
London EC2 *p54*. 020 7456 2000

Youles, Mrs C L (South Kesteven District Council)
Grantham *p459* 01476 406080

Younas, S (Platt Halpern)
Manchester *p308* 0161 224 2555

Young, A (The Johnson Partnership) *G H*
Nottingham *p337*. 0115 941 9141

Young, A (Mundays LLP) *C2 C1*
Cobham *p196* 01932 590500

Young, Miss A (Pillsbury Winthrop Shaw Pittman LLP) *C1 U1 U2*
London EC2 *p67*. 020 7847 9500

Young, A (Pannone LLP) *N Zq*
Manchester *p308* 0161 909 3000

Young, A (Bevan Brittan LLP)
Bristol *p161* 0870 194 1000

Young, A H (LG Lawyers) *T2*
London SE1 *p50*. 020 7379 0000

Young, Mrs C E (Wilmot & Co Solicitors LLP) *W T2*
Cirencester *p195*. 01285 650551
Young, Miss C J (Pannone LLP) *K1 K2*
Manchester *p308* 0161 909 3000
Young, C J (Boodle Hatfield) *Q O*
Westminster *p14*. 020 7629 7411
Young, C M (Gibson Young) *B1 C1 E F1 K1 L M1 P S1 W Zc Ze Zk*
London SW11 *p35*. . .020 7228 2211 / 7228 2213
Young, C S (Young & Co) *E L S1 W*
Bedford *p130* . . . .01234 346411 / 344211
Young, D (Young Swistak Solicitors) *G H*
Melton Mowbray *p314*. . . . 01664 501801
Young, D (Hibberts LLP) *A1 E R1 S1 T2 W X Zd Zn Zv*
Nantwich *p320*. 01270 624225
Young, D A (DWF) *N*
Liverpool *p287*. 0151 907 3000
Young, D B S (Arnold Fooks Chadwick LLP) *E S1 C1 F1 L I Ze Zza J1*
London W1 *p7*. 020 7499 3007
Young, D G (Gaby Hardwicke) *D1 X K1 Q N Zu S1 W*
Hastings *p243*. 01424 438011
Young, D G (HKB Wiltshires)
Great Yarmouth *p234* 01493 855676
Young, D R (Amory Glass & Co) *S1 S2 W L E*
Wembley *p426*. 020 8904 8236
Young, E (Bolt Burdon) *W*
Islington *p14*. 020 7288 4700
Young, E (Thompsons (formerly Robin/Brian Thompson & Partners)) *N*
London SW19 *p87*. 020 8947 4163
Young, E (Sutton-Mattocks & Co LLP)
London W4 *p84* 020 8994 7344
Young, E G (PCB Lawyers LLP) *E S1 Zk*
London W1 *p65* 020 7486 2566
Young, Mrs E J (Clifford Chance)
London E14 *p20*. 020 7006 1000
Young, F C (Fieldings Porter) *F1 G H N Q*
Bolton *p149* 01204 540900
Young, Miss F S (Reynolds Porter Chamberlain LLP) *O Zj*
London E1 *p71* 020 3060 6000
Young, Miss G (Nottingham Magistrates Court)
Nottingham *p467*. 0115 955 8111
Young, G R (Cheyney Goulding) *O Q A3 J1 B1*
Guildford *p236*. 01483 567676
Young, H (C R Burton & Co) *G H K1 D1 W K3*
London SE20 *p16* . . 020 8778 4455 / 8659 5775
Horley *p252* 01293 772424
Young, Miss H (Debenhams Ottaway)
St Albans *p390* 01727 837161
Young, H A (Hugh Young) *K1*
Nottingham *p339*. 0115 988 6050
Young, Mrs H M A (Gepp & Sons) *S1*
Chelmsford *p186*. 01245 493939
Colchester *p197* 01206 369889
Young, Ms H T S (Blake Lapthorn) *Zr Zq*
Chandlers Ford *p184* 023 8090 8090
Young, I (Stephenson Harwood) *C1*
London EC2 *p82*. 020 7329 4422
Young, I (Lancashire County Council)
Preston *p469* 01772 254868
Young, Mrs I M (Goughs) *Q N O*
Chippenham *p193* 01249 444499
Young, I R (Young & Lee) *D1 E R2 S2*
Birmingham *p143* 0121 633 3233
Young, Ms J (Russell Jones & Walker)
London WC2 *p74* 020 7657 1555
Young, Ms J A (Taylor Walton LLP) *J1 K1 D1 N O B1 Q*
Luton *p295* 01582 731161
Young, J A (Pinders) *G Zl*
Derby *p209* 01332 364751
Young, Ms J C (Youngs Criminal Defence Services Limited) *G H*
Sheffield *p377* 0114 249 5444
Young, J D (Julian Young & Co) *G H Zi B2*
London W1 *p93* 020 7724 8414
Young, Ms J K (Wills Group Ltd) *O Q Zj*
London EC3 *p110* 020 7488 8111
Young, J N (Baily Gibson) *Q J1 C1 F1 O*
High Wycombe *p249*. 01494 442661
Young, J R (Youngs) *K1 N S1 W R1 F1 V Zu Zy*
Cardiff *p181* 029 2076 3211
Young, J T (Hogan Lovells International LLP)
London EC1 *p42*. 020 7296 2000
Young, K (Keoghs LLP) *N Zj O Q A3*
Bolton *p149* 01204 677000
Coventry *p200*. 024 7665 8200
Young, Ms K A (EMW) *O Q F1*
Milton Keynes *p316* 0845 070 6000
Young, L (Clarke Willmott)
Southampton *p385*0845 209 1000 / 0117 305 6000
Young, L (Cripps Harries Hall LLP) *W T2*
Tunbridge Wells *p415* 01892 515121
Young, L (Frettens Solicitors) *W T2 K4*
Christchurch *p194* 01202 491777
Young, Miss L (Norwich Union Life)
York *p477*. 01904 452210
Leeds *p273* 0113 227 0100
Young, Mrs L (GLRS Phoenix LLP) *K1 D1 V*
Dursley *p214* 01453 547221
Young, Ms M (Parlett Kent) *N Zq Zr*
Exeter *p222*. 01392 494455
Young, M (Mark Young & Co) *K1 E N Zq S1 W*
Ipswich *p263*. 01473 226630
Young, Mrs M A (Clifton Ingram LLP) *K1 D1 D2*
Wokingham *p437* 0118 978 0099
Young, M E (Hibberts LLP) *W T1 S1 A1*
Nantwich *p320*. 01270 624225
Young, M J G (Reed Smith LLP) *C1 C2*
London EC2 *p71*. 020 3116 3000
Young, N M (DAC Beachcroft) *M2 O Q B1 F1 L N Zh Zj Zk Zo*
London EC4 *p24*. 020 7936 2222
Young, Ms P (Pinsent Masons LLP) *E R1 L*
London EC2 *p67*. 020 7418 7000
Young, Mrs P (Young & Co) *K1*
Bedford *p130* . . . .01234 346411 / 344211
Young, P (Levy & Co Solicitors LLP)
Witham *p436* 01376 511819
Young, P S (Gordons LLP)
Leeds *p273* 0113 227 0100
Young, R (Jolliffe & Co) *C1 S2 E S1*
Chester *p190* 01244 310022
Young, Ms S (Hegarty LLP) *G H*
Peterborough *p347* 01733 346333
Young, Ms S (Douglas Solicitors) *N K1 Q*
Redhill *p362*. 01737 780295
Young, S (McCormicks) *O Q Ze*
Harrogate *p240* 01423 530630
Young, Ms S (Blake Lapthorn) *Q*
Oxford *p342*. 01865 248607
Young, S D (Eden District Council)
Penrith *p468*. 01768 817817
Young, S D (Squire Sanders (UK) LLP) *O Q*
Leeds *p277* 0113 284 7000
Young, S D (S D Young) *K1 N L K3*
St Neots *p392*. 01480 470411
Young, Miss S E (Glaisyers Solicitors LLP) *J1*
Manchester *p304* 0161 832 4666
Young, Ms S E (Ridley & Hall) *N Zr*
Huddersfield *p256* 01484 538421
Young, Miss S J (Salusburys Harding & Barnett) *L S1 T1 W S2*
Leicester *p281*. . 0116 262 9033 / 262 6052
Young, S L (Steven Young & Co) *M1 D1 P R1 S1 L J1 F1 Zc Zs*
Cheltenham *p188* 01242 257269
Gloucester *p230*. 01452 332882
Young, Ms S M (Jefferies Essex LLP) *D1 K1 K2 D2*
Westcliff-on-Sea *p428* . . . 01702 332311
Young, Mrs V (Blocks) *J1*
Ipswich *p262*. 01473 230033
Younghusband, Ms V M (LG Lawyers)
London SE1 *p50*. 020 7379 0000
Youngs, Mrs J (Redcar and Cleveland Borough Council)
Redcar *p465*. 01642 466201
Youngs, Miss R K (stevensdrake) *B1*
Crawley *p202* 01293 596900
Youngson, Ms J G (BBC)
London W12 *p103* 020 8752 5734
Younis, H (Ford & Warren) *C1 C2 F1*
Leeds *p273* 0113 243 6601
Younis, I (Amal Solicitors) *H Zi*
Huddersfield *p255* 01484 431999
Younson, F R (McDermott Will & Emery UK LLP) *J1 Zp Zg*
London EC2 *p56*. 020 7577 6900
Younus, M M (Appleby Shaw) *E Zi S1*
Windsor *p434* 01753 860606
Yousaf, Miss N (Edwards Duthie) *S1*
London E6 *p29* 020 8514 9000
Youssouf, H (Bowling & Co) *S1 S2 E R2*
London E15 *p15*. 020 8221 8000
Yousuf, S (Gawor & Co) *S1 E S2*
London E1 *p35* 020 7481 8888
Yu, Ms J S (Kerman & Co LLP) *C2*
London WC2 *p49* 020 7539 7272
Yuen, S F (Reed Executive PLC)
London WC2 *p108*. 020 7421 1640
Yugin, M L (Yugin & Partners)
Stanmore *p394* 020 8954 2410
Yuill, Mrs S E (DAC Beachcroft) *F1 K1 M1 N*
Bristol *p162* 0117 918 2000
Yule, C J (Crown Prosecution Service Suffolk)
Ipswich *p461*. 01473 282100
Yule, M E (Powell Spencer & Partners) *G H N*
London NW6 *p69* 020 7604 5600
Yussuf, A (A-Z Law Solicitors) *Zg Zi*
Wandsworth *p3* 020 8355 0830
Yusuf, Ms S (Bircham Dyson Bell) *E S1 C1 W R1 T2*
Westminster *p13*. 020 7227 7000

Z

Zachary, A A (B P Collins LLP) *C1 C2 I U2*
Gerrards Cross *p229*. 01753 889995
Zafer, Ms L (Hogan Lovells International LLP)
London EC1 *p42*. 020 7296 2000
Zafir, M (Equity Solicitors) *S2 E L Zl S1*
Birmingham *p138* 0121 554 7470
Zagel, Mrs D (Gallaher Ltd)
Weybridge *p476* 01932 859777
Zahara, M C (WBW Solicitors) *G H*
Newton Abbot *p329* 01626 202404
Zahn, Miss L (Jones Day) *C3*
London EC4 *p46*. 020 7039 5959
Zahoor, A (Mian & Co)
Birmingham *p140* 0121 684 8000
Zaidi, A (Edwin Coe LLP) *O B1 F1 Zq*
London WC2 *p29* 020 7691 4000
Zailer, I (Herbert Smith LLP) *C1*
London EC2 *p40*. 020 7374 8000
Zainab, C (Crowell & Moring) *Zj*
London EC4 *p23*. 020 7413 0011
Zaiwalla, S R (Zaiwalla & Co) *B1 M1 Za Zb Zp O Q*
London WC2 *p93* 020 7312 1000
Zakharova, Ms K (M P Jones & Co) *J1 N*
Plymouth *p350*. 01752 269007
Zaki, Miss N (Anthony Collins Solicitors LLP) *K1*
Birmingham *p137* 0121 200 3242
Zakir, Mrs R (Underwood Solicitors LLP)
Westminster *p89*. 020 7526 6000
Zakis, D M (Wallace Robinson & Morgan) *O Q J1*
Solihull *p383*. 0121 705 7571
Zala, P (Varley Hibbs LLP) *F1 F2 L Zj Zk O Q Zq*
Coventry *p201*. 024 7663 1000
Zaleski, A E P (A E P Zaleski) *S2 L S1 W*
London SW18 *p93*. 020 8875 1791
Zanellato, Miss N (Palmer Capital Partners)
London W1 *p108* 020 7409 5500
Zant-Boer, I L (EMW) *C1 C2 C3 Zb*
Milton Keynes *p316* 0845 070 6000
Zar, N (Herbert Smith LLP) *O*
London EC2 *p40*. 020 7374 8000
Zarif, A (Baxter Caulfield) *O Q A3 J1*
Huddersfield *p255* 01484 519519
Zatman, A B (Zatman & Co) *B1 C1 E S1 T1*
Manchester *p311* 0161 832 2500
Zatman, B (Zatman & Co) *Zb S2 E*
Manchester *p311* 0161 832 2500
Zavos, Ms A (Speechly Bircham LLP) *W Q Zd B2 Zm Zq*
London EC4 *p81*. 020 7427 6400
Zavos, C S (Barlow Lyde & Gilbert LLP) *O P Q Za Zj*
London EC3 *p10*. 020 7247 2277
Zavros, S (Philippou & Co) *K1 J1 E S2 C1 D1 L O Q W*
London N13 *p67*. 020 8882 4222
Zeb, U (J D Spicer & Co) *G H B2 Zi K1 Zh W S2 E*
London NW6 *p81* 020 7625 5590
Zeffertt, A D M (Landau Zeffertt Weir) *B1 C1 E J1 N Q S1 T2 W Zc Ze Zi Zl*
London SE1 *p51*. 020 7357 9494
Zeffman, D C (Olswang LLP) *C1 C3 M1 Ze Zf*
London WC1 *p64* 020 7067 3000
Zeiss, Mrs S J (Dorset County Council)
Dorchester *p457*. 01305 251000
Zelnik, Dr P R (Peter Zelnik & Co) *C1 D1 F1 K1 O Q L S2 E S1 W K3 K4*
Biggin Hill *p133* 01959 570730
Zentner, H (Hopkin Murray Beskine)
London N4 *p42* 020 7272 1234
Zermansky, V D (Zermansky & Partners) *C1 K1 P B1 F1*
Leeds *p278* 0113 245 9766
Zervos, N A E (CMS Cameron McKenna LLP)
London EC3 *p17*. 020 7367 3000
Zhu-Cruickshank, Dr X (Cruickshanks Solicitors) *Ze Zb C1 S1 E Zi W O*
London W1 *p23* 020 7487 4468
Zietman, C H (Manches LLP) *Q O*
London WC2 *p58* 020 7404 4433
London EC4 *p83*. 020 7822 8000
Ziff, J M (Clifford Chance) *C1 Zb M1*
London E14 *p20*. 020 7006 1000
Zikking, Ms K (Quality Solicitors Burroughs Day) *D1 K1*
Bristol *p164* 0117 929 0333
Zilic-Munic, Mrs B (Nockolds) *S2 E*
Bishop's Stortford *p144* . . . 01279 755777
Ziman, N J (Fasken Martineau LLP) *C1 C2 Zz Ze*
London W1 *p31* 020 7917 8500
Ziman, P D (Ellicotts) *C1 S2 E W*
London N20 *p29*.020 8445 5257 / 8445 2880
Edgware *p217*. 020 8951 2988
Zimand, Miss Z A (Crown Prosecution Service Derbyshire)
Derby *p456* 01332 614000
Zimareva-Locke, Ms N (Shepherd Harris & Co) *G H*
Enfield *p219*. 020 8363 8341
Zimmer, G H (Zimmers)
London NW11 *p94*. 0870 770 0171
Zimmerman, F (Plexus Law (A Trading Name of Parabis Law LLP))
London EC3 *p68*. 0844 245 4000
Ziskind, D (Fruhman Davies Livingstones)
Manchester *p304* 0161 833 0578
Zuberi, F (Lighthouse Solicitors) *Zi V N Q*
Harrow *p242*. . .020 3170 7588 / 3170 7589
Zuberi, Mrs S R (Wessex Housing Partnership Ltd)
Basingstoke *p448* 01256 844506
Zuckerman, M A (Benson Mazure LLP) *C1 N P Zl Zi Zc*
Westminster *p12*. 020 7486 8091
Zulfiqar, Ms N (Birmingham City Council Legal & Democratic Services)
Birmingham *p449* 0121 303 2066
Zulfiqar, Miss S (Cotterhill Hitchman LLP) *C1 J1 S2 W S1 E Zl*
Sutton Coldfield *p403* 0121 323 1860
Zurbrugg, M R W (Irwin Mitchell LLP) *N M1 M2*
London EC1 *p45*. 0870 150 0100
Zysblat, M (LSG Solicitors) *P K1 S1 N M1 G D1 E B1 W Ze Zi Zj*
London W1 *p51* 020 7851 0100

SECTION 7

SOLICITORS

NORTHERN IRELAND

CONTENTS

7

FIRMS, NORTHERN IRELAND – BY TOWN

ANTRIM

David G Bell
6 Fountain Street Antrim Co Antrim BT41 4BB
Tel: 028 9446 6444

Conway Todd & Co
Mirtna Building 22 Market Square Antrim Co Antrim BT41 4DT
Tel: 028 9446 3477 *Fax:* 028 9446 5378 *Dx:* 3450NR ANTRIM

Holmes & Swann
16 High Street Antrim Co Antrim BT41 4AN
Tel: 028 9442 9112 *Fax:* 028 9446 3063

G A H Lockhart
32 Church Street Antrim Co Antrim BT41 4BA
Tel: 028 9446 2636 *Fax:* 028 9446 6822 *Dx:* 3455NR ANTRIM 1
E-mail: post@gahlockhart.com

David A Martin
18a Church Street Antrim Co Antrim BT41 4BA
Tel: 028 9446 1509 *Dx:* 3451NR ANTRIM

O'Rorke McDonald & Tweed
37-39 Church Street Antrim Co Antrim BT41 4BD
Tel: 028 9446 3108 *Dx:* 3453NR ANTRIM

Sheridan & Leonard
25 Fountain Street Antrim Co Antrim BT41 4BG
Tel: 028 9442 8271

Small & Marken
31 Church Street Antrim Co Antrim BT41 4BE
Tel: 028 9446 8000 *Fax:* 028 9446 5000 *Dx:* 3457NR ANTRIM

ARMAGH

Blair & Hanna
2 Seven Houses English Street Armagh Co Armagh BT61 7LA
Tel: 028 3752 6426 *Dx:* 2797NR ARMAGH

Campbell Francis
7 College Street Armagh Co Armagh BT61 9BT
Tel: 028 3752 4690

Francis Curley
2 Ogle Street Armagh Co Armagh BT61 7EN
Tel: 028 3752 5244 *Dx:* 2793NR ARMAGH
E-mail: patrick@franciscurley.plus.com

Ian Dawson & Co
13-15 Market Street Armagh Co Armagh BT61 7QS
Tel: 028 3752 5566 *Fax:* 028 3752 6651
E-mail: i.dawson@btconnect.com

D & E Fisher
Main Street Market Hill Armagh Co Armagh BT60 1PH

Jerome J Haughey
19 College Street Armagh Co Armagh BT61 9BT
Tel: 028 3752 3493

Sharon Keeley
5 College Street Armagh Co Armagh BT61 9BT
Tel: 028 3751 1622 *Dx:* 2792NR ARMAGH
E-mail: sharon@sharonkeeley.co.uk

Maurice Kempton
23 College Street Armagh Co Armagh BT61 9BT
Tel: 028 3752 3875 *Fax:* 028 3751 0555
E-mail: maurice.kempton@btconnect.com

Lennon Toner & O'Neill
54 English Street Armagh Co Armagh BT61 7DU
Tel: 028 3752 2527 *Dx:* 2796NR ARMAGH
E-mail: conall.corrigan@lton.co.uk

John McStravick
3 Greenpark Terrace Lower Irish Street Armagh Co Armagh BT61 7ER
Tel: 028 3752 7999 *Fax:* 028 3752 6333
E-mail: info@jmcslaw.com

L J Mallon & Co
9 English Street Armagh Co Armagh BT61 7BH
Tel: 028 3752 2512 *Dx:* 2804NR ARMAGH

K J Morgan
21 Market Street Armagh Co Armagh BT61 7BU
Tel: 028 3752 4790

John J Rice & Co
33 Cathedral Road Armagh Co Armagh BT61 7QX
Tel: 028 3752 7402 *Dx:* 2795NR ARMAGH
E-mail: pauldougan@johnjricesolicitors.com

Gordon Wallace & Co
17 College Street Armagh Co Armagh BT61 9BT
Tel: 028 3752 3676 *Fax:* 028 3752 5577 *Dx:* 2790NR ARMAGH
E-mail: gordonwallace@btconnect.com

AUGHNACLOY

C T McAlpine & Son
126 Moore Street Aughnacloy Co Tyrone BT69 6AR
Tel: 028 8555 7951

BALLYCASTLE

Berkeley White
7 The Diamond Ballycastle Co Antrim BT54 6AW
Tel: 028 2076 8090 *Fax:* 028 2076 8828 *Dx:* 3258NR BALLYMONEY (BALLYCASTLE)
E-mail: office@berkeleywhite.com

Campbell McKee
82 Castle Street Ballycastle Co Antrim BT54 6AR
Tel: 028 2076 2236

James O'Brien & Co
2b The Diamond Ballycastle Co Antrim BT54 6AW
Tel: 028 2076 9797

BALLYCLARE

Gray Magee
13 The Square Ballyclare Co Antrim BT39 9BB
Tel: 028 9334 2666

James J W McNinch & Son
5 The Square Ballyclare Co Antrim BT39 9BB
Tel: 028 9332 2217 *Fax:* 028 9335 2518 *Dx:* 2400NR BALLYCLARE
E-mail: law@jwmcninch.co.uk

Reid Black & Co
59 Main Street Ballyclare Co Antrim BT39 9AA
Tel: 028 9335 2221 *Dx:* 2402NR BALLYCLARE
E-mail: info@reidblack.com

BALLYMENA

Anderson Agnew & Co
14 Mill Street Ballymena Co Antrim BT43 5AE
Tel: 028 2564 2118

James Ballentine & Son
Bank Buildings The Pentagon Ballymena Co Antrim BT43 5LL
Tel: 028 2565 6161 *Dx:* 3216NR BALLYMENA
E-mail: kmc@james-ballentine-andsons.com

Boal Anderson & Co
56 High Street Ballymena Co Antrim BT43 6UH
Tel: 028 2565 6464 *Dx:* 3203NR BALLYMENA

Breslin Thomas
64 William Street Ballymena Co Antrim BT43 6AW
Tel: 028 2564 8479 *Fax:* 028 2564 8507

Caruth & Bamber
80 Broughshane Street Ballymena Co Antrim BT43 6ED
Tel: 028 2565 2758

Lyle Cubitt & Co
1 Broadway Avenue Ballymena Co Antrim BT43 7AA
Tel: 028 2565 2125

Samuel Cumming & Son
39 Linenhall Street Ballymena Co Antrim BT43 5AJ
Tel: 028 2564 6026 *Dx:* 3200NR BALLYMENA
E-mail: law@samuelcumming.co.uk

Liam Donnelly & Co
18 Greenvale Street Ballymena Co Antrim BT43 6AR
Tel: 028 2564 7967

T S McAllister & Son
32-36 Mill Street Ballymena Co Antrim BT43 5AE
Tel: 028 2565 2469 *Fax:* 028 2564 4979 *Dx:* 3207NR BALLYMENA
E-mail: bmaguire@ballymenalegal.co.uk

Jack McCann & Son
20 Ballymoney Road Ballymena Co Antrim BT43 5BY
Tel: 028 2564 2388 *Dx:* 3217NR BALLYMENA
E-mail: emma.mccann@jackmccann.com

Old School House Mill Street Cushendall Ballymena Co Antrim BT44 0RR

McConaghie Lynch
28 Ballymoney Road Ballymena Co Antrim BT43 5BY
Tel: 028 2565 4226

C H McElhenny LLB
66 High Street Ballymena Co Antrim BT43 6DT
Tel: 028 2564 6007 *Dx:* 3208NR BALLYMENA

Gordon F W McIlrath & Co
4 Ballymoney Road Ballymena Co Antrim BT43 5BY
Tel: 028 2564 3036

James L Russell & Son
55 High Street Ballymena Co Antrim BT43 6DT
Tel: 028 2565 2154 *Fax:* 028 2564 1400 *Dx:* 3209NR BALLYMENA
E-mail: law@jameslrussell.com

Stewarts Solicitors
25 Ballymoney Road Ballymena Co Antrim BT43 5DD
Tel: 028 2565 1414 *Dx:* 3218NR BALLYMENA
E-mail: ballymena@stewartsolicitors.com

BALLYMONEY

Campbell McKee
5 Victoria Street Ballymoney Co Antrim BT53 6DW
Tel: 028 2766 6698 *Fax:* 028 2766 7111

Doherty Brennan & Co
15 Victoria Street Ballymoney Co Antrim BT53 6DW
Tel: 028 2766 2753

Ferguson & Logue
14 Charlotte Street Ballymoney Co Antrim BT53 6AY
Tel: 028 2766 3033 *Dx:* 3255NR BALLYMONEY
E-mail: fergusonlogue@btconnect.com

Greer Hamilton & Gailey
27 The High Street Ballymoney Co Antrim BT53 6AJ
Tel: 028 2766 2104 *Fax:* 028 2766 5856 *Dx:* 3256NR BALLYMONEY

Hastings & Co
6a Charlotte Street Ballymoney Co Antrim BT53 6AY
Tel: 028 2766 2277 *Fax:* 028 2766 7733
E-mail: swrhastings@aol.com

Murphy Carey
27 High Street Ballymoney Co Antrim BT53 6AJ
Tel: 028 2766 2132 *Fax:* 028 2766 8682
Dx: 3256NR BALLYMONEY
E-mail: law@ghandg.co.uk

John W Pinkerton & Son
5 Linenhall Street Ballymoney Co Antrim BT53 6DP
Tel: 028 2766 2133 *Fax:* 028 2766 5036
Dx: 3250NR BALLYMONEY
E-mail: solicitors@pinkerton-law.com

T Taggart & Sons
27 Church Street Ballymoney Co Antrim BT53 6HS
Tel: 028 2766 2118 *Dx:* 3254NR BALLYMONEY

BALLYNAHINCH

Donard King & Co
27 High Street Ballynahinch Co Down BT24 8AB
Tel: 028 9756 5525 *Fax:* 028 9756 1867
Dx: 3002NR BALLYNAHINCH
E-mail: info@donardkingsolicitors.com

Alan Gilliland
83 Cahard Road Ballynahinch Co Down BT24 8YD
Tel: 028 9751 0827

Hamilton & Millar
5-9 Church Street Ballynahinch Co Down BT24 8AF
Tel: 028 9756 2534

Paul McMullan
2-4 Church Street Ballynahinch Co Down BT24 8AF
Tel: 028 9756 2357

John McRobert & Co
1 Church Street Ballynahinch Co Down BT24 8AF
Tel: 028 9756 2209

W G Maginess & Son
7 Lisburn Street Ballynahinch Co Down BT24 8BD
Tel: 028 9756 3982

J G Rice & Co
33 Church Street Ballynahinch Co Down BT24 8AF
Tel: 028 9756 2726 *Dx:* 3000NR BALLYNAHINCH
E-mail: legal@jamestrice.co.uk

BANBRIDGE

Byrne & Herbert
Avonmore House 15 Church Square Banbridge Co Down BT32 4AP
Tel: 028 4066 2251 *Dx:* 3327NR BANBRIDGE

Arthur J Downey & Co
Tyrella House 5 Church Street Banbridge Co Down BT32 4AA
Tel: 028 4066 2123

Paul Ferris
2 Newry Road Banbridge Co Down BT32 3HE
Tel: 028 4062 8828 *Dx:* 3328NR BANBRIDGE
E-mail: admin@paulferris.com

Michael Gillen
3 Old Kenlis Street Banbridge Co Down BT32 3BD
Tel: 028 4062 6639 *Dx:* 3325NR BANBRIDGE
E-mail: michael@michaelgillen.co.uk

Heron & Dobson
6 Bridge Street Banbridge Co Down BT32 3JS
Tel: 028 4066 2672 *Fax:* 028 4066 2158 *Dx:* 3320NR BANBRIDGE

Emmet J Kelly
21 Rathfriland Street Banbridge Co Down BT32 3LA
Tel: 028 4062 9397 *Fax:* 028 4062 9397

Paul J Kennedy
9 Church Street Banbridge Co Down BT32 4AA
Tel: 028 4062 4757 *Dx:* 3324NR BANBRIDGE
E-mail: pjkennedysolicitors@utvinternet.com

McBurney & Co
5 Church Square Banbridge Co Down BT32 4AS
Tel: 028 4066 2226

F A Edward Orr
9a Church Square Banbridge Co Down BT32 4AS
Tel: 028 4066 2609 *Fax:* 028 4066 2171 *Dx:* 3326NR BANBRIDGE
E-mail: ed.orr@solicit-orr.co.uk

Adrian Travers
82a Newry Street Banbridge Co Down BT32 3HA
Tel: 028 4062 9990

BANGOR

Bigger & Strahan
40 Hamilton Road Bangor Co Down BT20 4LE
Tel: 028 9127 0313 *Dx:* 2500NR BANGOR

Bryan Law
111 Main Street Bangor Co Down BT20 4AG
Tel: 028 9145 6666 *Dx:* 2503NR BANGOR 1

Carnson Morrow Graham
3a Market Street Bangor Co Down BT20 4SP
Tel: 028 9145 7911 *Fax:* 028 9145 0679

Peter Dornan & Co
14 Hamilton Road Bangor Co Down BT20 4LE
Tel: 028 9127 3054 *Fax:* 028 9147 0114
E-mail: law@peterdornan.com

Denis D Humphrey
10 Donaghadee Road Bangor Co Down BT20 5RU
Tel: 028 9127 3131 *Fax:* 028 9147 2486 *Dx:* 2510NR BANGOR
E-mail: denis.humphrey@btconnect.com

McConnell Kelly & Co
45 Main Street Bangor Co Down BT20 5AF
Tel: 028 9147 9900 *Fax:* 028 9147 9222
E-mail: bangor@mcconnellkelly.com

McCoubrey-Hinds
61 Main Street Bangor Co Down BT20 5AF
Tel: 028 9127 1916 *Fax:* 028 9127 1315 *Dx:* 2505NR BANGOR
E-mail: info@mccoubrey-mcclelland.co.uk

McFadden Perry
4 Balloo Court Balloo Drive Bangor Co Down BT19 7AT
Tel: 028 9147 9494 *Fax:* 028 9147 9595 *Dx:* 2515NR BANGOR 1
E-mail: lmcfadden@mcfaddenperry.com

McQueenie Boyle
1 Grays Hill Bangor Co Down BT20 3BB
Tel: 028 9147 0030 *Fax:* 028 9127 2222 *Dx:* 2527NR BANGOR 1
E-mail: reception@mcqueenieboyle.com

Minnis & Braden
123-125 Main Street Bangor Co Down BT20 4AE
Tel: 028 9127 2334 *Dx:* 2516NR BANGOR

Murray McCourt Kelly
1-3 Dufferin Avenue Bangor Co Down BT20 3AL
Tel: 028 9127 0000 *Dx:* 2550NR BANGOR 2
E-mail: murraymccourtkelly@mmksolicitors.com

Patterson Donnelly
26 Balloo Avenue Bangor Co Down BT19 7QT
Tel: 028 9127 4644 *Fax:* 028 9127 7300 *Dx:* 2524NR BANGOR

David Russell & Co
66 Abbey Street Bangor Co Down BT20 4JB
Tel: 028 9127 4022 *Dx:* 2554NR BANGOR
E-mail: david@davidrussellsolicitors.co.uk

Worthingtons
74 High Street Bangor Co Down BT20 5AZ
Tel: 028 9147 5929 *Fax:* 028 9147 5928
E-mail: info@worthingtonslaw.co.uk

BELFAST

ALB Solicitors
Windsor Gardens 34-36 Alfred Street Belfast BT2 8EP
Tel: 028 9026 8490 *Fax:* 028 9023 7197

Agnew Andress Higgins
2nd Floor 92 High Street Belfast BT1 2DG
Tel: 028 9024 3040 *Dx:* 436NR BELFAST

Archer Heaney & Magee
2nd Floor 18-22 Hill Street Belfast BT1 2LA
Tel: 028 9033 0000 *Fax:* 028 9033 1000 *Dx:* 423NR BELFAST 1

Thomas Armstrong
51-53 Upper Arthur Street Belfast BT1 4GJ
Tel: 028 9032 1399 *Dx:* 486NR BELFAST 1

Bigger & Strahan
89 Royal Avenue Belfast BT1 1EX
Tel: 028 9032 5229 *Dx:* 412NR BELFAST

C & J Black
Linenhall House 13 Linenhall Street Belfast BT2 8AA
Tel: 028 9032 1441 *Fax:* 028 9023 4125 *Dx:* 431NR BELFAST
E-mail: mail@cjblack.co.uk

J Blair Employment Law
106 Malone Avenue Belfast BT9 6ES
Tel: 028 9066 2211 *Fax:* 028 9066 4455
E-mail: info@blairemployment.com

James Boston & Sullivan
1-3 Lombard Street Belfast BT1 1RB
Tel: 028 9032 0603 *Fax:* 028 9033 2770 *Dx:* 407NR BELFAST
E-mail: paul.carson@bostonsullivan.com

24 Cregagh Road Belfast BT6 9EQ
Tel: 028 9045 6601 *Dx:* 407NR BELFAST

John Boston & Co
565 Upper Newtownards Road Belfast BT4 3LP
Tel: 028 9048 0460 *Fax:* 028 9048 9563
E-mail: solicitors@john-boston.co.uk

Patrick J G Bradley
Washington House 14-16 High Street Belfast BT1 2BD
Tel: 028 9032 1765

Brangam Bagnall & Co
Hildon House 30/34 Hill Street Belfast BT1 2LB
Tel: 028 9032 6060 *Dx:* 485NR BELFAST

Martin Brennan
1 Fitzwilliam Street Belfast BT9 6AW
Tel: 028 9023 3477 *Fax:* 028 9032 1783 *Dx:* 2822NR UNIVERSITY
E-mail: martinbrennan@dnet.co.uk

Alan M Brown
288 Newtownards Road Belfast BT4 1HF
Tel: 028 9045 9687 *Fax:* 028 9045 3695
Dx: 3024NR HOLYWOOD ARCHES
E-mail: judithbrownsolicitor@hotmail.com

Caldwell Warner
Floral Buildings 4 East Bridge Street Belfast BT1 3NX
Tel: 028 9059 5300 *Fax:* 028 9059 5301 *Dx:* 417NR BELFAST
E-mail: john@caldwellwarner.co.uk

Bernard Campbell & Co
91-93 Victoria Street Belfast BT1 4PB
Tel: 028 9023 2008 *Fax:* 028 9023 6126 *Dx:* 398NR BELFAST

Campbell Fitzpatrick
51 Adelaide Street Belfast BT2 8FE
Tel: 028 9032 7388 *Dx:* 483NR BELFAST

Campbell Stafford
41 Fitzwilliam Street Belfast BT9 6AW
Tel: 028 9023 0808 *Fax:* 028 9031 0774 *Dx:* 533NR BELFAST 1
E-mail: info@campbellstafford.com

Carnson Morrow Graham
20 May Street Belfast BT1 4NL
Tel: 028 9023 4606 *Fax:* 028 9032 6578 *Dx:* 404NR BELFAST

Carson & McDowell
Murray House 4/5 Murray Street Belfast BT1 6DN
Tel: 028 9024 4951 *Fax:* 028 9024 5768
E-mail: law@carson-mcdowell.com

Chesney & Co
479 Upper Newtownards Road Belfast BT4 3LJ
Tel: 028 9065 9777

Comerton & Hill
14 Great Victoria Street Belfast BT2 7BA
Tel: 028 9023 4629 *Fax:* 028 9023 3908 *Dx:* 415NR BELFAST
E-mail: solicitors@comerton.co.uk

T H Conlan
28 College Gardens Belfast BT9 6BT
Tel: 028 9068 2228
E-mail: thconlan@btinternet.com

Cousins & Gilmore
121 Andersonstown Road Belfast BT11 9BT
Tel: 028 9030 1360 *Dx:* 2942NR ANDERSONSTOWN

Arthur Cox Northern Ireland
Stokes House 17-25 College Square East Belfast BT1 6DE
Tel: 028 9023 0007 *Fax:* 028 9023 3464 *Dx:* 2012NR BELFAST 1
E-mail: belfast@arthurcox.com

Crawford & Lockhart
7-11 Linenhall Street Belfast BT2 8AH
Tel: 028 9032 2204 *Fax:* 028 9032 4177 *Dx:* 505NR BELFAST

R P Crawford & Co
517 Antrim Road Belfast BT15 3BS
Tel: 028 9078 1187

17 Stranmills Road Belfast BT9 5AF
Tel: 028 9038 1024

Creighton & Co
122 Bloomfield Avenue Belfast BT5 5AE
Tel: 028 9073 2461

Francis Crilly
24 Antrim Road Belfast BT15 2AA
Tel: 028 9075 5722

Culbert & Martin
7 Donegal Square West Belfast BT1 6JB
Tel: 028 9032 5508 *Dx:* 498NR BELFAST 1
E-mail: law@culbert-martin.co.uk

Cunningham & Dickey
68 Upper Church Lane Belfast BT1 4LG
Tel: 028 9024 5896 *Fax:* 028 9032 7657 *Dx:* 438NR BELFAST 1
E-mail: adm@cdlegal.co.uk
Web: www.cdlegal.co.uk
Particular areas of work include: Commercial and Company Law, Commercial Property, Housing, Landlord and Tenant, Litigation, Accidents and Injury Claims, Debt Recovery, Transportation Law.

Delaney & Co
54 Andersonstown Road Belfast BT11 9AN
Tel: 028 9030 1334

Diamond Heron
Diamond House 7-19 Royal Avenue Belfast BT1 1FB
Tel: 028 9024 3726 *Fax:* 028 9023 0651 *Dx:* 506NR BELFAST 1
E-mail: info@diamondheron.com

Donaghy Carey
45-47 Rosemary Street Belfast BT1 1QB
Tel: 028 9023 8222 *Fax:* 028 9023 1782 *Dx:* 375NR BELFAST 1
E-mail: mail@donaghycarey.com

Patrick C Donaghy Solicitors
587a Lisburn Road Belfast BT9 7GS
Tel: 028 9066 9636 *Fax:* 028 9066 9636
E-mail: enquiries@pcdonaghysolicitors.co.uk

Donnelly & Kinder
4th Floor Premier Business 22 Adelaide Street Belfast BT2 8GD
Tel: 028 9024 4999 *Fax:* 028 9024 1222 *Dx:* 418NR BELFAST 1
E-mail: info@donnellykinder.com

Donnelly & Wall
Cathedral Terrace 19-27 Church Street Lower North Street Belfast BT1 1PG
Tel: 028 9023 3157 *Fax:* 028 9032 9743
E-mail: mail@donnellyandwall.co.uk

Joseph Donnelly & Co
6 Callender Street Belfast BT1 5HX
Tel: 028 9024 2061 / 9032 5043 *Fax:* 028 9023 9118
Dx: 388NR BELFAST
E-mail: peterconlon@btconnect.com

James G Doran & Co
Holbeck House 19 Cornmarket Belfast BT1 4DB
Tel: 028 9024 0440 *Dx:* 386NR BELFAST

Peter Dornan & Co
Metropole House 2-10 York Street Belfast BT15 1AQ
Tel: 028 9023 4559
E-mail: law@peterdornan.com

P Drinan
Conway Street Belfast BT13 2DE
Tel: 028 9032 2071

P A Duffy & Co
183 Victoria Street Belfast BT1 4PE
Tel: 028 9023 0688 *Dx:* 425NR BELFAST

Edwards & Co
28 Hill Street Belfast BT1 2LA
Tel: 028 9032 1863 *Fax:* 028 9033 2723 *Dx:* 410NR BELFAST
E-mail: admin@edwardsandcompany.co.uk

Elliott Duffy Garrett
2nd Floor Royston House 34 Upper Queen Street Belfast BT1 6FD
Tel: 028 9024 5034 *Fax:* 028 9024 1337 *Dx:* 400NR BELFAST
E-mail: edg@edglegal.com

Fearon & McCoy
135 Cromac Street Belfast BT2 8JE
Tel: 028 9024 0214 *Fax:* 028 9024 7619

J G Ferguson
Scottish Amicable House 11 Donegall Square South Belfast BT1 5JE
Tel: 028 9032 2998 *Dx:* 448NR BELFAST

Michael Ferguson
249 Lisburn Road Belfast BT9 7EN
Tel: 028 9038 2030 *Dx:* 4221NR BELFAST
E-mail: info@mfergusonsolicitors.com

James F Fitzpatrick & Co
Carlton House 28 Fountain Street Belfast BT1 5ED
Tel: 028 9024 6741 *Dx:* 479NR BELFAST

Michael Flanigan
207 Falls Road Belfast BT12 6FB
Tel: 028 9023 3309 *Dx:* 4002NR BELFAST 17
E-mail: info@michaelflanigan.com

Flynn & McGettrick
1st Floor 9 Clarence Street Belfast BT2 8DX
Tel: 028 9002 6500 *Fax:* 028 9023 6490 *Dx:* 463NR BELFAST
E-mail: flynn.mcgettrick@btconnect.com

Fox & Associates
Insurance Chambers 403 Lisburn Road Belfast BT9 7EW
Tel: 028 9038 2788 *Fax:* 028 9038 2787 *Dx:* 4217NR BELFAST 24

Franklin Solicitors
Franklin House 10-12 Brunswick Street Belfast BT2 7GE
Tel: 028 9050 4300 *Fax:* 028 9050 4301 *Dx:* 2025NR BELFAST 2
E-mail: pkearney@franklinsolicitors.com

Gaffney Solicitors
332 Lisburn Road Belfast BT9 6GH
Tel: 028 9050 0760

Philip Gallen & Co
195 Lisburn Road Belfast BT9 7EJ
Tel: 028 9066 3364 *Dx:* 4216NR BELFAST 24

Gaston Graham
73 Holywood Road Belfast BT4 3BA
Tel: 028 9047 1869 *Fax:* 028 9047 1359
Dx: 3023NR HOLYWOOD ARCHES

John F Gibbons & Co
40 Church Lane Belfast BT1 4FR
Tel: 028 9023 9990 *Fax:* 028 9023 9998 *Dx:* 493NR BELFAST 1
E-mail: john@jfgibbons.co.uk

Basil Glass & Co
21 University Street Belfast BT7 1FY
Tel: 028 9032 2061 *Fax:* 028 9033 1302 *Dx:* 2823NR UNIVERSITY

97 Saintfield Road Belfast BT8 4HN
Tel: 028 9040 1463 *Fax:* 028 9033 1302 *Dx:* 513NR BELFAST
E-mail: basilglassandcompany@utvinternet.com

A & L Goodbody
42-46 Fountain Street Belfast BT1 5EF
Tel: 028 9031 4466 *Fax:* 028 9031 4477 *Dx:* 2016NR BELFAST 2
E-mail: belfast@algoodbody.com

Nigel Greeves
Sinclair House 89 Royal Avenue Belfast BT1 1FE
Tel: 028 9024 2371 *Dx:* 3705NR BELFAST 8
E-mail: nigelgreeves@freenetname.co.uk

Francis Hanna & Co
32-36 May Street Belfast BT1 4NZ
Tel: 028 9024 3901 *Fax:* 028 9024 4215 *Dx:* 473NR BELFAST 1
E-mail: info@fhanna.co.uk

Harrisons Solicitors
15-17 Chichester Street Belfast BT1 4JB
Tel: 028 9032 3843 *Fax:* 028 9033 2644 *Dx:* 401NR BELFAST
E-mail: law@harrisonsni.com

Hart & Co
4th Floor Causeway Tower 9 James Street South Belfast BT2 8DN
Tel: 028 9032 3545 *Fax:* 028 9024 5005 *Dx:* 446NR BELFAST
E-mail: mail@hartandcosolicitors.com

Stephen R Haslett
517 Antrim Road Belfast BT15 3BW
Tel: 028 9037 0213

J G Haughey & Co
1st Floor TSB House 134a Upper Lisburn Road Belfast BT10 0BE
Tel: 028 9043 1222

Haugheys
138 Upper Lisburn Road Belfast BT10 0BE
Tel: 028 9060 0088 *Dx:* 3475NR FINAGHY
E-mail: info@haugheys.com

Gerald P Henvey
37 Glen Road Anderson Belfast BT11 8BB
Tel: 028 9061 0372 *Fax:* 028 9030 0162
Dx: 2943NR ANDERSONSTOWN

Hewitt & Gilpin
Thomas House 14-16 James Street South Belfast BT2 7GA
Tel: 028 9057 3573 *Dx:* 2000NR BELFAST

Higgins Hollywood Deazley
523 Antrim Road Belfast BT15 3TF
Tel: 028 9077 0770 *Fax:* 028 9074 9988 *Dx:* 4500NR BELFAST 15
E-mail: enquiries@hhdsolicitors.com

296 Cliftonville Road Belfast BT14 6LE
Tel: 028 9077 0770
E-mail: enquiries@hhdsolicitors.com

Hoffman & Co
27-29 Gordon Street Belfast BT1 2LG
Tel: 028 9031 2020

Holmes & Moffitt
289 Shankill Road Belfast BT13 1FT
Tel: 028 9023 0836 *Fax:* 028 9033 2530
E-mail: shankill@holmof.co.uk

John M Hughes & Co
47 University Street Belfast BT7 1FY
Tel: 028 9032 0831 *Dx:* 2820NR UNIVERSITY
E-mail: law@jmhughes.com

Francis J Irvine & Co
42 Dublin Road Belfast BT2 7HN
Tel: 028 9024 6451 *Fax:* 028 9033 1735 *Dx:* 437NR BELFAST
E-mail: info@fjisolicitors.co.uk

C & H Jefferson
Norwich Union House 7 Fountain Street Belfast BT1 5EA
Tel: 028 9032 9545 *Dx:* 439NR BELFAST

Johns Elliot
40 Linenhall Street Belfast BT2 8BA
Tel: 028 9032 6881 *Fax:* 028 9024 8236 *Dx:* 419NR BELFAST
E-mail: info@johnselliot.com

Johnsons Solicitors
Johnson House 50-56 Wellington Place Belfast BT1 6GF
Tel: 028 9024 0183 *Fax:* 028 9023 3266 *Dx:* 405NR BELFAST

James T Johnston & Co
138 Donegall Street Belfast BT1 2HX
Tel: 028 9024 6091 *Dx:* 3704NR BELFAST 8
E-mail: info@johnstonsolicitors.com

Jones & Co
4th Floor The Potthouse 1 Hill Street Belfast BT1 2LB
Tel: 028 9024 5471 *Dx:* 537NR BELFAST 1
E-mail: info@tjonessolicitors.co.uk

Jones Cassidy Jones Solicitors
220 Ormeau Road Belfast BT7 2FY
Tel: 028 9064 2290 *Fax:* 028 9064 2297
E-mail: info@jcjsolicitors.co.uk

Kearney Sefton
Franklin House 10-12 Brunswick Street Belfast BT2 7GE
Tel: 028 9023 2940 *Fax:* 028 9033 2865 *Dx:* 2025NR BELFAST 2
E-mail: pkearney@kearneysefton.co.uk

Francis Keenan
Unit A Lyndon Court Queen Street Belfast BT1 6EF
Tel: 028 9032 1409 *Fax:* 028 9043 9252 *Dx:* 390NR BELFAST 1

796 Springfield Road Belfast BT12 7JD
Tel: 028 9032 9011

Keenan Solicitors
54 Knockbreda Road Belfast BT6 0JB
Tel: 028 9049 3349

Brian Kelly
299 Ormeau Road Belfast BT7 3GG
Tel: 028 9059 3030 *Dx:* 4162NR BELFAST 21

E&L Kennedy
72 High Street Belfast BT1 2BE
Tel: 028 9023 2352 *Fax:* 028 9023 3118 *Dx:* 508NR BELFAST 1
E-mail: enquiries@eandlkennedy.co.uk

Kennedys
5th Floor Lesley Buildings 61-65 Fountain Street Belfast BT1 5EX
Tel: 028 9024 0067 *Fax:* 028 9031 5557 *Dx:* 490NR BELFAST
E-mail: s.craig@kennedys-law.com

Keown Solicitors
Lynden House 19 Cregagh Road Belfast BT6 8PX
Tel: 028 9045 6042 *Fax:* 028 9045 6405 *Dx:* 491NR BELFAST
E-mail: info@keownsolicitors.co.uk

King & Gowdy
298 Upper Newtownards Road Belfast BT4 3EJ
Tel: 028 9065 9511 *Fax:* 028 9067 1550
Dx: 2150NR BALLYHACKAMORE
E-mail: ah@king-gowdy.co.uk

Pauline Knight & Co
10 Wellington Park Belfast BT9 6DJ
Tel: 028 9050 9666

Brian Leeson Solicitors
425 Woodstock Road Belfast BT6 8PW
Tel: 028 9022 0400 *Fax:* 028 9022 0400

Anthony G Lundy & Co
430 Antrim Road Belfast BT15 5GB
Tel: 028 9037 0930

5 Stranmillis Road Belfast BT9 5AF
Tel: 028 9066 3995
E-mail: lundy@globalnet.co.uk

C M McAlister
25 Lismoyne Park Belfast BT15 5HE
Tel: 028 9077 1939

McAteer & Co
97 Bloomfield Road Belfast BT5 5LN
Tel: 028 9047 1480 *Fax:* 028 9065 0124
Dx: 2152NR BALLYHACKAMORE
E-mail: o@lexlink-mcateer.co.uk

Macaulay & Ritchie
Cathedral Chambers 11 Talbot Street Belfast BT1 2LD
Tel: 028 9032 9696 *Fax:* 028 9033 1305 *Dx:* 427NR BELFAST
E-mail: law@mac-rit.com

Ciaran J McCaffrey & Co
137b Upper Lisburn Road Belfast BT10 0LH
Tel: 028 9060 0666 *Fax:* 028 9030 0666 *Dx:* 3473NR FINAGHY
E-mail: ciaranjmccaffrey@btconnect.com

McCann & Greyston
Canston House 38 Church Lane Belfast BT1 4QH
Tel: 028 9024 6098 *Dx:* 511NR BELFAST 1
E-mail: email@mccann-greyston.co.uk

McCann & McCann
19 Church Street Belfast BT1 1PG
Tel: 028 9029 9999 *Fax:* 028 9028 2810 *Dx:* 374NR BELFAST 1

135 Newtownards Road Belfast BT4 1AB
Tel: 028 9022 2298 *Fax:* 028 9028 2888 *Dx:* 372NR BELFAST 1

Ashton Centre 5 Churchill Street Belfast BT15 2BP
Tel: 028 9029 8880 *Fax:* 028 9029 1888

McCartan Turkington Breen
88 Victoria Street Belfast BT1 3GN
Tel: 028 9032 9801 *Dx:* 408NR BELFAST
E-mail: legal@mtb-law.co.uk

McCloskeys
Rochester Building 28 Adelaide Street Belfast BT2 8GD
Tel: 028 9024 0310 *Dx:* 495NR BELFAST 1
E-mail: mccloskeys@mccloskeys.co.uk

Gerard McClure & Co
Unit 7 190 Saintfield Road Belfast BT8 4HG
Tel: 028 9070 9348

McCollum & Co
60-64 May Street Belfast BT1 4NP
Tel: 028 9032 5852 *Fax:* 028 9043 8371 *Dx:* 397NR BELFAST

McConnell Kelly & Co
217 Upper Newtownards Road Belfast BT4 3JD
Tel: 028 9065 5511 *Fax:* 028 9065 9570
Dx: 2151NR BALLYHACKAMORE
E-mail: ballyhack@mcconnellkelly.com

D G McCormick & Co
149 Andersonstown Road Belfast BT11 9BW
Tel: 028 9062 2738

MacElhatton & Co
58 Andersonstown Road Belfast BT11 9AN
Tel: 028 9060 2828 *Dx:* 2940NR ANDERSONSTOWN

131-133 North Street Belfast BT1 1NE
Tel: 028 9032 1776 *Dx:* 482NR BELFAST

McEvoy Sheridan Solicitors
344 Ormeau Road Belfast BT7 2HL
Tel: 028 9069 4444

James E McGovern & Co
Elmwood House 44-46 Elmwood Avenue Belfast BT9 6AZ
Tel: 028 9068 1850 *Fax:* 028 9068 7439
E-mail: jamesmcgovern@btconnect.com

D G McGowan
469 Falls Road Belfast BT12 6DD
Tel: 028 9023 1792

McGrigors LLP
2 Donegall Square East Belfast BT1 5HB
Tel: 028 9027 8800 *Fax:* 028 9027 8881 *Dx:* 539NR BELFAST 1

P J McGrory & Co
Mountain View 52 Andersonstown Road Belfast BT11 9AN
Tel: 028 9060 2986 *Fax:* 028 9062 1201
Dx: 2945NR ANDERSONSTOWN
E-mail: mail@pjmcgrory.com

McIldowies
2nd Floor 65-67 Chichester Street Belfast BT1 4GD
Tel: 028 9032 6411 *Dx:* 474NR BELFAST
E-mail: mail@mcildowies.com

McIlveen Solicitors
80 Donegal Pass Belfast BT7 1BX
Tel: 028 9032 2335

McIvor Farrell
129 Springfield Road Belfast BT12 7AE
Tel: 028 9032 4565

McIvor Magill
Bradley House 25 Howard Street Belfast BT1 6NB
Tel: 028 9024 4299 *Dx:* 2006NR BELFAST 2
E-mail: mgm@magillmcivor.co.uk

John McKee & Son
32-38 Linen Hall Street Belfast BT2 8BG
Tel: 028 9023 2303 *Fax:* 028 9023 0081 *Dx:* 470NR BELFAST 1
E-mail: info@jmckee.co.uk

Kenneth McKee
309-311 Donegal Road Belfast BT12 6FQ
Tel: 028 9031 3233

McKenna Boyd
337 Woodstock Road Belfast BT6 8PT
Tel: 028 9073 9979 *Fax:* 028 9073 9949

MacKenzie & Dorman
94-96 Holywood Road Belfast BT4 1NN
Tel: 028 9067 3211 *Fax:* 028 9067 1751
Dx: 3021NR HOLYWOOD ARCHES
E-mail: info@mackenzieanddorman.co.uk

Harry McKibben & Co
18 Myrtlefield Park Belfast BT9 6NE
Tel: 028 9066 5651

McKinty & Wright
5-7 Upper Queen Street Belfast BT1 6FS
Tel: 028 9024 6751 *Fax:* 028 9023 1432 *Dx:* 510NR BELFAST 1
E-mail: post@mckinty-wright.co.uk

George L MacLaine & Co
13 Lombard Street Belfast BT1 1RH
Tel: 028 9024 3126 *Fax:* 028 9024 8124 *Dx:* 411NR BELFAST

McLaughlin & Co
1st Floor 218/220 Woodstock Road Belfast BT6 9DL
Tel: 028 9080 7000

John G McLaughlin
The Rectory 2 St Judes Avenue Belfast BT7 2GZ
Tel: 028 9049 1133

McManus & Kearney
2-12 Montgomery Street Belfast BT1 4NX
Tel: 028 9024 3658 *Fax:* 028 9033 2151 *Dx:* 497NR BELFAST
E-mail: law@mcmk.co.uk

Madden & Finucane
88 Castle Street Belfast BT1 1HE
Tel: 028 9023 8007 *Fax:* 028 9043 9276 *Dx:* 434NR BELFAST
E-mail: enquiries@madden-finucane.com

Charles Maunsell
4 Greenview Park Belfast BT9 6TZ
Tel: 028 9061 3788 *Fax:* 028 9061 3788

Millar McCall Wylie
Imperial House 4-10 Donegal Square East Belfast BT1 5HD
Tel: 028 9020 0050 *Fax:* 028 9020 0051 *Dx:* 465NR BELFAST
E-mail: mmw@mmwlegal.com

Eastleigh House 396 Upper Newtownards Road Belfast BT4 3EY
Tel: 028 9020 0050 *Fax:* 028 9047 4999
E-mail: mmw@mmwlegal.com

Mills Selig
21 Arthur Street Belfast BT1 4GA
Tel: 028 9024 3878 *Fax:* 028 9023 1956 *Dx:* 459NR BELFAST

Minnis & Braden
76 Shore Road Belfast BT15 3PG
Tel: 028 9077 6422

Richard Monteith
258 Shankhill Road Belfast BT13 2BL
Tel: 028 9031 1550 *Fax:* 028 9031 1550

Morgan & Murphy
Second Floor Sturgen Building 9-15 Queen Street Belfast BT1 6EA
Tel: 028 9024 4545 *Dx:* 391NR BELFAST
E-mail: info@morganandmurphysolicitors.co.uk

Morrison & Broderick
Merrion Business Centre 58 Howard Street Belfast BT1 6PJ
Tel: 028 9032 8822

Morrow & Wells
57 Upper Arthur Street Belfast BT1 4GJ
Tel: 028 9023 3866 *Dx:* 441NR BELFAST

Murphy & O'Rawe
Scottish Provident Building 7 Donegall Square West Belfast BT1 6JF
Tel: 028 9032 6636 *Dx:* 4031NR BELFAST 18

Murtagh Breen & Co
458 Oldpark Road Belfast BT14 6QT
Tel: 028 9074 4594

Alameda Terrace 266 Falls Road Belfast BT11 6AL
Tel: 028 9043 4550

Napier & Sons
1-9 Castle Arcade High Street Belfast BT1 5DF
Tel: 028 9024 4602 *Fax:* 028 9033 0330
E-mail: jg@napiers.com

Nesbitt
167 Upper Newtonards Road Belfast BT4 3HZ
Tel: 028 9047 1851
E-mail: nesbittsolicitors@btconnect.com

Nesbitt Solicitors
109 Cregagh Road Belfast BT6 8PZ
Tel: 028 9045 4005

Nixon & Co
2-4a Kilcoole Park Belfast BT14 8LB
Tel: 028 9071 9703

Paul K Nolan & Co
135 Upper Lisburn Road Belfast BT10 0LH
Tel: 028 9030 1113 *Fax:* 028 9060 1784 *Dx:* 3472NR FINAGHY
E-mail: law@pkn.co.uk

J G O'Hare & Co
37-41 High Street Belfast BT1 2AB
Tel: 028 9023 4800

Paschal J O'Hare
Donegal House 98-102 Donegall Street Belfast BT1 2GW
Tel: 028 9031 3613 *Fax:* 028 9031 3713 *Dx:* 3708NR BELFAST 8

O'Reilly Stewart
O'Reilly Stewart House 114-116 Royal Avenue Belfast BT1 1DL
Tel: 028 9032 1000 *Fax:* 028 9032 3003 *Dx:* 3700NR BELFAST 8
E-mail: oreillystewart@dnet.co.uk

O'Toole & MacRandal
162 Lisburn Road Belfast BT9 6AL
Tel: 028 9020 3000 *Dx:* 4224NR BELFAST 24
E-mail: solicitors@otooleandmacrandal.co.uk

Orr & Co
14 Montgomery Street Belfast BT1 4QT
Tel: 028 9023 0101 *Dx:* 458NR BELFAST
E-mail: orrandco@btconnect.com

Patterson Taylor & Co
72 High Street Belfast BT1 2BE
Tel: 028 9023 5987 *Fax:* 028 9023 5842 *Dx:* 3703NR BELFAST 8
E-mail: patterson.taylor@btconnect.com

Peden & Reid
22 Callender Street Belfast BT1 5BU
Tel: 028 9032 5617 *Fax:* 028 9024 7343 *Dx:* 389NR BELFAST
E-mail: law@pedenreid.com

J C W Rea & Co
32-36 May Street Belfast BT1 4NZ
Tel: 028 9024 7121 *Dx:* 473NR BELFAST 1
E-mail: info@jcwrea.com

John J Rice & Co
Law Society House 94 Victoria Street Belfast BT1 5HB
Tel: 028 9028 8688 *Dx:* 489NR BELFAST 1

9-11 Crumlin Road Belfast BT14 6AA
Tel: 028 9035 1510

Rodgers & Co
2nd Floor The Bedeck Building 463-469 Lisburn Road Belfast BT9 7GZ
Tel: 028 9038 6464

Savage & Co
11 Arthur Street Belfast BT1 4GA
Tel: 028 9024 9969 *Fax:* 028 9032 6432
E-mail: savageandco@btconnect.com

Norman Shannon & Co
3-5 Union Street Belfast BT1 2JF
Tel: 028 9023 1179 *Fax:* 028 9023 4879 *Dx:* 409NR BELFAST
E-mail: info@norman-shannon-solicitors.co.uk

Shean Dickson Merrick
Washington House 14-16 High Street Belfast BT1 2BS
Tel: 028 9032 6878 *Dx:* 460NR BELFAST
E-mail: law@shean-dickson-merrick.com

Sheldon & Stewart
70 Donegal Pass Belfast BT7 1BU
Tel: 028 9032 7691 *Dx:* 4314NR BELFAST
E-mail: solicitor@sheldon-stewart.co.uk

Sheridan & Leonard
19-21 High Street Belfast BT1 2AA
Tel: 028 9043 8833 *Dx:* 523NR BELFAST 1

Robert G Sinclair & Co
23 Bedford Street Belfast BT2 7EJ
Tel: 028 9023 1770 *Dx:* 420NR BELFAST 1
E-mail: info@rgsinclair.co.uk

Skelton & Co
3-5 Commercial Court Donegall Street Belfast BT1 6NB
Tel: 028 9024 1661 *Dx:* 379NR BELFAST
E-mail: skeltonlegal@aol.com

Philip J Smith & Co
1a Lisburn Avenue Belfast BT9 7FX
Tel: 028 9066 1116 *Dx:* 4219NR BELFAST 24
E-mail: philipjsmith@btconnect.com

Trevor Smyth & Co
Chester House 13 Chichester Street Belfast BT1 4JB
Tel: 028 9032 0360 *Dx:* 430NR BELFAST
E-mail: noel@trevorsmyth.com

The Gate Lodge 260 Antrim Road Belfast BT15 2AT
Tel: 028 9074 4994

Ciaran P Steele
177 Victoria Street Belfast BT1 4PE
Tel: 028 9043 5345

Stewarts Solicitors
Tedford House 3-4 Donegall Quay Belfast BT1 3EA
Tel: 028 9031 2777 *Fax:* 028 9043 4404
E-mail: belfast@stewartsolicitors.com

Sullivans
Fortwilliam Chambers 531 Antrim Road Belfast BT15 3BS
Tel: 028 9071 7222
E-mail: psullivan@sullivanslaw.co.uk

Thompson Crooks
325 Shankill Road Belfast BT13 1FX
Tel: 028 9059 5551 *Fax:* 028 9059 5553 *Dx:* 3800NR BELFAST 10
E-mail: info@tclegal.co.uk

Thompsons (formerly Robin/Brian Thompson & Partners)
171-175 Victoria Street Belfast BT1 4HS
Tel: 028 9089 0400 *Fax:* 028 9032 6020 *Dx:* 428NR BELFAST

Murty M Toolan & Co
174-184 Ormeau Road Belfast BT7 2ED
Tel: 028 9024 1840

Tughans
Marlborough House 30 Victoria Street Belfast BT1 3GG
Tel: 028 9055 3300 *Fax:* 028 9055 0096 *Dx:* 433NR BELFAST
E-mail: law@tughans.com

Stephen Tumelty
224b Stewartstown Road Belfast BT17 0LB
Tel: 028 9061 8877

Liam Vallely & Co
85 Andersonstown Road Belfast BT11 9AH
Tel: 028 9062 4442 *Fax:* 028 9062 6226

Wallace Harris & Robb
16 Donegall Square South Belfast BT1 5JF
Tel: 028 9032 7970

John G H Wilson & Co
Spencer House 71 Royal Avenue Belfast BT1 1EY
Tel: 028 9032 2301

Wilson Nesbitt
Citylink Business Park Albert Street Belfast BT12 4HB
Tel: 028 9032 3864 *Fax:* 028 9033 3707 *Dx:* 484NR BELFAST 1
E-mail: info@wilson-nesbitt.com

Kevin R Winters & Co
46 Castle Street Belfast BT1 1HB
Tel: 028 9024 1888 *Fax:* 028 9024 4804

Worthingtons
21 Oxford Street Belfast BT1 3LA
Tel: 028 9043 4015 *Fax:* 028 9043 4016 *Dx:* 416NR BELFAST 1
E-mail: info@worthingtonslaw.co.uk

CARRICKFERGUS

Bernard Campbell & Co
17 High Street Carrickfergus Co Antrim BT38 7AN
Tel: 028 9336 9033

Glover & King
8 Joymount Carrickfergus Co Antrim BT38 7DN
Tel: 028 9336 7025 *Fax:* 028 9336 0320
Dx: 2882NR CARRICKFERGUS

Nigel Greeves
3-5 Market Place Carrickfergus Co Antrim BT38 7AW

James J Macaulay
4 Joymount Carrickfergus Co Antrim BT38 7DN
Tel: 028 9336 8568 *Fax:* 028 9335 1745
Dx: 2880NR CARRICKFERGUS

James J W McNinch & Son
19 Joymont Carrickfergus Co Antrim BT38 7DN
Tel: 028 9336 8238 *Fax:* 028 9336 9194
Dx: 2881NR CARRICKFERGUS
E-mail: law@jwmcninch-carrick.co.uk

Paschal J O'Hare & Co
31 High Street Carrickfergus Co Antrim BT38 7AN
Tel: 028 9336 1184
E-mail: patrick@pjohare.com

Skelton & Co
4 High Street Carrickfergus Co Antrim BT38 7AF

CARRYDUFF

James Murland & Co
33 Church Road Carryduff Co Down BT8 8DT
Tel: 028 9081 4344

CASTLEDERG

Thomas Elliott & Son
61a Main Street Castlederg Co Tyrone BT81 7AN
Tel: 028 8167 1013 *Dx:* 3612NR OMAGH 1

Porter & McCanny
77 Main Street Castlederg Co Tyrone BT81 7AN
Tel: 028 8167 1234

CASTLEREAGH

Holmes & Moffitt
218 Knock Road Castlereagh Belfast BT5 6QD
Tel: 028 9079 9597

Wylie & Co
37 Glen Road Castlereagh Belfast BT5 7LT
Tel: 028 9070 9129

CASTLEWELLAN

Donard King & Co
66 Main Street Castlewellan Co Down BT31 9DL
Tel: 028 4377 0555 *Dx:* 3002NR BALLYNAHINCH
E-mail: info@donardkingsolicitors.com

Eamonn P King
2 Castle Avenue Castlewellan Co Down BT31 9DX
Tel: 028 4477 1049

COALISLAND

P A Duffy & Co
21 The Square Coalisland Co Tyrone BT71 4LN
Tel: 028 8774 7159
E-mail: coalisland@paduffy.com

Francis J Madden
23 The Square Coalisland Co Tyrone BT71 4LN
Tel: 028 8774 8840 *Fax:* 028 8774 9846

Carmel O'Meara & Co
12 Dungannon Road Coalisland Co Tyrone BT71 4HP
Tel: 028 8774 7919

COLERAINE

Anderson & Co
17 New Row Coleraine Co Londonderry BT52 1AD
Tel: 028 7034 3180 *Dx:* 3973NR COLERAINE 2

Babington & Croasdaile
23 New Row Coleraine Co Londonderry BT52 1AD
Tel: 028 7034 2007 *Fax:* 028 7034 4277
Dx: 3976NR COLERAINE 2
E-mail: noel.donalop@babington-croasdaile.co.uk

Doherty Brennan & Co
33 New Row Coleraine Co Londonderry BT52 1AE
Tel: 028 7035 3444 *Fax:* 028 7034 3215
Dx: 3978NR COLERAINE 2
E-mail: doherty.brennan@virgin.net

Gillan Barr
41 New Row Coleraine Co Londonderry BT52 1AE
Tel: 028 7034 3491 *Fax:* 028 7034 2377 *Dx:* 3417NR COLERAINE
E-mail: gillan.barr@btinternet.com

John F Hickey
Dunmore Chambers 2/4 Dunmore Street Coleraine Co Londonderry BT52 1EL
Tel: 028 7034 3244 *Fax:* 028 7032 0338 *Dx:* 3424NR COLERAINE
E-mail: hickeylaw@tiscali.co.uk

David Hunter
8 Hillside Crescent Ballycairn Road Coleraine Co Londonderry BT51 3AP
Tel: 028 7034 2121

Hazel K E Kennedy
111 Dunboe Road Macosquin Coleraine Co Londonderry BT51 4JS
Tel: 028 7035 6346 *Fax:* 028 7035 6346

Macaulay Wray
35 New Row Coleraine Co Londonderry BT52 1AH
Tel: 028 7035 2421 *Fax:* 028 7035 2425
Dx: 3972NR COLERAINE 2
E-mail: info@macaulaywray.com

McCallum O'Kane
8 Blindgate Street Coleraine Co Londonderry BT52 1EZ
Tel: 028 7032 7112 *Fax:* 028 7032 7113
Dx: 3984NR COLERAINE 2
E-mail: info@mccallumokane.com

Lara McIlroy Solicitors
18 Long Commons Coleraine Co Londonderry BT52 1LH
Tel: 028 7032 7755 *Fax:* 028 7032 7766
Dx: 3981NR COLERAINE 2
E-mail: office@laramcilroy.co.uk

Fergus McIntosh
5 Upper Abbey Street Coleraine Co Londonderry BT52 1EZ
Tel: 028 7035 1248 *Fax:* 028 7035 7788 *Dx:* 33410NR COLERAINE
E-mail: law@fmcintosh.co.uk

Daniel A McKenna & Co
29 New Row Coleraine Co Londonderry BT52 1AD
Tel: 028 7035 3800 *Fax:* 028 7035 8703
Dx: 3970NR COLERAINE 2
E-mail: brendan@danielmckenna.com

Rafferty & Boyle
3 Castlerock Road Coleraine Co Londonderry BT51 3HP
Tel: 028 7034 3483 *Fax:* 028 7035 4097
Dx: 3422NR COLERAINE 1
E-mail: rafferty-boyle@btconnect.com

COMBER

Campbell Bates & Co
10 The Square Comber Co Down BT23 5DT
Tel: 028 9187 2037 *Fax:* 028 9187 4515 *Dx:* 2301NR COMBER
E-mail: campbellbates@btconnect.com

COOKSTOWN

Corr & Sally
1-3 Molesworth Street Cookstown Co Tyrone BT80 8NX
Tel: 028 8676 2226

Doris & MacMahon
63 James Street Cookstown Co Tyrone BT80 8AE
Tel: 028 8676 2484 *Dx:* 3273NR COOKSTOWN

P A Duffy & Co
14 Molesworth Street Cookstown Co Tyrone BT80 8NX
Tel: 028 8676 3406 *Fax:* 028 8676 3176
Dx: 3270NR COOKSTOWN
E-mail: cookstown@paduffy.com

Anne Kelly & Co Solicitors
5 Loy Street Cookstown Co Tyrone BT80 8PZ
Tel: 028 8676 9141 *Dx:* 3278NR COOKSTOWN

Millar Shearer & Black
40 Molesworth Street Cookstown Co Tyrone BT80 8PH
Tel: 028 8676 2346 *Fax:* 028 8676 6761 *Dx:* 3272NR COOKSTOWN

Gerard P Mooney
44 Union Street Cookstown Co Tyrone BT80 8NN
Tel: 028 8676 9100 *Fax:* 028 8676 9010 *Dx:* 3279NR COOKSTOWN

Toal & Heron
10 Loy Street Cookstown Co Tyrone BT80 8PE
Tel: 028 8676 2395 *Fax:* 028 8676 6552 *Dx:* 3281NR COOKSTOWN

J B & R H Twigg
26 Fairhill Road Cookstown Co Tyrone BT80 8LZ
Tel: 028 8676 2225 *Dx:* 3276NR COOKSTOWN
E-mail: info@twigg-solicitors.com

CRAIGAVON

John P Hagan
Unit 8 Legahorey Shopping Centre Craigavon Belfast BT65 5BE
Tel: 028 3834 9370
E-mail: law@jphagan.com

CROSSGAR

Holmes & Moffitt
60 Downpatrick Street Crossgar Co Down BT30 9EA
Tel: 028 4481 8283

CROSSMAGLEN

S C Connolly & Co
19 North Street Crossmaglen Co Down BT35 9AB
Tel: 028 3086 8539
E-mail: mail@scconnolly.com

Tiernans
2 North Street Crossmaglen Co Down BT35 9AB
Tel: 028 3086 1066

DERRYLIN

Morris & Co
136 Main Street Derrylin Co Fermanagh BT92 9LA
Tel: 028 6774 8265

DONAGHADEE

Carnson Morrow Graham
41 High Street Donaghadee Co Down BT21 0AQ
Tel: 028 9188 3770

Fisher & Fisher
1 The Market House New Street Donaghadee Co Down BT21 0AG
Tel: 028 9188 8388

DOWNPATRICK

King & Boyd
37 St Patrick's Avenue Downpatrick Co Down BT30 6DW
Tel: 028 4461 2035 *Fax:* 028 4461 5215 *Dx:* 2973NR DOWNPATRICK

McGrady Collins
48 St Patrick's Avenue Downpatrick Co Down BT30 6DW
Tel: 028 4461 6411 *Dx:* 2972NR DOWNPATRICK
E-mail: info@mcgradylegal.com

James Murland & Co
15 English Street Downpatrick Co Down BT30 6AP
Tel: 028 4461 9980 *Fax:* 028 4461 3527
Dx: 2970NR DOWNPATRICK
E-mail: law@murlands.co.uk

Kieran O'Toole & Co
24 English Street Downpatrick Co Down BT30 6AB
Tel: 028 4461 5153 *Fax:* 028 4461 5345
Dx: 2974NR DOWNPATRICK
E-mail: kieranotoole@btconnect.com

Sheridan & Co
29 St Patricks Avenue Downpatrick Co Down BT30 6DW
Tel: 028 4483 9944

Kevin R Winters & Co
11 English Street Downpatrick Co Down BT30 6AB
Tel: 028 4483 9111 *Fax:* 028 4461 7904

DROMORE

W J Baxter & Co
27 Church Street Dromore Co Down BT25 1AA
Tel: 028 9269 2277

Arthur J Downey & Co
2 Princes Street Dromore Co Down BT25 1AY
Tel: 028 9269 3444

Nelson-Singleton
21 Gallows Street Dromore Co Down BT25 1BG
Tel: 028 9269 3475 *Fax:* 028 9269 9560 *Dx:* 6020NR DROMORE
E-mail: nelson.singleton@btconnect.com

Norman Shannon & Co
Gunning Office 5 Church Street Dromore Co Down BT25 1AA
Tel: 028 9269 9103 *Fax:* 028 9269 9203 *Dx:* 6023NR DROMORE
E-mail: teresa@norman-shannon-solicitors.co.uk

DUNDONALD

Michael Andress & Co
961 Upper Newtownards Road Dundonald Belfast BT16 IRL
Tel: 028 9048 4188 *Fax:* 028 9048 4370 *Dx:* 6204NR DUNDONALD 3

Brangam Bagnall & Co
Commercial Mews 69/71 Comber Road Dundonald Belfast BT16 0AE
Tel: 028 9048 8800

Robert Kennedy
1005 Upper Newtownards Road Dundonald Belfast BT16 1RN
Tel: 028 9041 8962 *Fax:* 028 9048 7545 *Dx:* 6202NR DUNDONALD 3

McConnell Kelly & Co
49 Comber Road Dundonald Belfast BT16 0AA
Tel: 028 9048 9816 *Fax:* 028 9041 0301
Dx: 2151NR BALLYHACKAMORE
E-mail: dundonald@mcconnellkelly.com

McCullough & Co
Unit 4 St Johns Court 734 Upper Newtownwards Road Dundonald Belfast BT16 1RJ
Tel: 028 9048 2800

DUNGANNON

P A Duffy & Co
5-7 Irish Street Dungannon Co Tyrone BT70 1JW
Tel: 028 8772 2102 *Fax:* 028 8772 6159 *Dx:* 2900NR DUNGANNON
E-mail: dungannon@paduffy.com

Faloon & Co
27 Thomas Street Dungannon Co Tyrone BT70 1HN
Tel: 028 8775 2099 *Fax:* 028 8775 3874 *Dx:* 2916NR DUNGANNON 1

P Haughey & Co
21 William Street Dungannon Co Tyrone BT70 1DX
Tel: 028 8775 2433 *Fax:* 028 8775 2414
Dx: 4122NR DUNGANNON 2
E-mail: paul@phaughey.co.uk

W J Irwin & Son
37 Market Square Dungannon Co Tyrone BT70 1JH
Tel: 028 8772 2746 *Fax:* 028 8772 2746 *Dx:* 2905NR DUNGANNON
E-mail: irwinsolicitor@aol.com

Kennedy Hughes & Co
Northland Mews 1 Northland Place Dungannon Co Tyrone BT71 6AN
Tel: 028 8772 5554

C T McAlpine & Son
12 Northland Row Dungannon Co Tyrone BT71 6AT
Tel: 028 8772 2718 *Fax:* 028 8772 3226

Mallon & Anderson
84 Lower Scotch Street Dungannon Co Tyrone BT70 1BJ
Tel: 028 8722 2680

Mallon & Mallon
46 Irish Street Dungannon Co Tyrone BT70 1DB
Tel: 028 8775 2959 *Fax:* 028 8775 3192 *Dx:* 2906NR DUNGANNON
E-mail: christopher@mallonandmallon.com

Millar Shearer & Black
2 Georges Street Dungannon Co Tyrone BT70 1BP
Tel: 028 8775 3111 *Dx:* 4123NR DUNGANNON 2

Carmel O'Meara & Co
32 Irish Street Dungannon Co Tyrone BT70 1DB
Tel: 028 8775 2455 *Fax:* 028 8772 2386 *Dx:* 2912NR DUNGANNON
E-mail: carmelomeara@btconnect.com

Fergus G Patton
14 Thomas Street Dungannon Co Tyrone BT70 1HN
Tel: 028 8772 4333 *Fax:* 028 8772 7313 *Dx:* 2902NR DUNGANNON
E-mail: fgp@fgpatton.co.uk

Aidan Quinn
18 Thomas Street Dungannon Co Tyrone BT70 1HW
Tel: 028 8775 2088 *Fax:* 028 8775 3265 *Dx:* 2908NR DUNGANNON
E-mail: office@aidanquinnsolicitor.com

Rafferty & Donaghy
2 Donaghmore Road Dungannon Co Tyrone BT70 1EZ
Tel: 028 8772 7055 *Fax:* 028 8775 2085 *Dx:* 2909NR DUNGANNON

Simmons Meglaughlin & Orr
20 Northland Row Dungannon Co Tyrone BT71 6BL
Tel: 028 8772 2016 *Fax:* 028 8772 3398
Dx: 3050NR DUNGANNON 3
E-mail: oliver.ross@smosolicitors.co.uk

DUNMURRY

P C Donaghy Meehan Murphy
218-220 Kingsway Dunmurry Belfast BT17 9AE
Tel: 028 9061 2144 *Fax:* 028 9061 8351

ENNISKILLEN

J C Brady & Son
10 Belmore Street Enniskillen Co Fermanagh BT74 6AA
Tel: 028 6632 2112

Cooper Wilkinson
Imperial Buildings 38-40 Queen Elizabeth Road Enniskillen Co Fermanagh BT74 7BY
Tel: 028 6632 2615 *Fax:* 028 6632 4033 *Dx:* 3550NR ENNISKILLEN
E-mail: info@cwsolicitors.co.uk

Fahy Corrigan & Co
1 Water Street Enniskillen Co Fermanagh BT74 7DY
Tel: 028 6632 0066

Falls & Hanna
24 East Bridge Street Enniskillen Co Fermanagh BT74 7BT
Tel: 028 6632 2009 *Fax:* 028 6632 4875 *Dx:* 3552NR ENNISKILLEN

Fergusons
18-20 Bellmore Street Enniskillen Co Fermanagh BT74 6AA
Tel: 028 6632 2234 *Fax:* 028 6632 3088 *Dx:* 3556NR ENNISKILLEN

P J Flanagan & Co
5 Church Street Enniskillen Co Fermanagh BT74 7DW
Tel: 028 6632 4521 *Fax:* 028 6632 5072 *Dx:* 3551NR ENNISKILLEN
E-mail: sol@pjflanagan.com

Sean McHugh
33 East Bridge Street Enniskillen Co Fermanagh BT74 7BW
Tel: 028 6632 4611

Maguire & Corrigan
20 East Bridge Street Enniskillen Co Fermanagh BT74 7BT
Tel: 028 6632 4724 / 6632 4110 *Fax:* 028 6632 5900
Dx: 3562NR ENNISKILLEN
E-mail: maguire.corrigan@btconnect.com

Thomas T Montague
42 Forthill Street Enniskillen Co Fermanagh BT74 6AJ
Tel: 028 6632 4233

Murnaghan & Fee
Boston Chambers Queen Elizabeth Road Enniskillen Co Fermanagh BT74 7JA
Tel: 028 6632 2819 *Fax:* 028 6632 3073 *Dx:* 3557NR ENNISKILLEN
E-mail: law@murnaghanfee.com

Murphy & McManus
19 East Bridge Street Enniskillen Co Fermanagh BT74 7BW
Tel: 028 6632 2933 *Fax:* 028 6632 5501
E-mail: solicitors@murphy-mcmanus.com

John Quinn
14 Belmore Street Enniskillen Co Fermanagh BT74 6AA
Tel: 028 6632 6008 *Fax:* 028 6632 2592
E-mail: johnquinn@utv.internet.com

FINTONA

Thomas T Montague
Tattymoyle Street Fintona Co Tyrone BT78 2AA
Tel: 028 8284 1251

FIVEMILETOWN

Falls & Hanna
125 Main Street Fivemiletown Co Tyrone BT75 0PG
Tel: 028 8952 1234 *Fax:* 028 8952 1989 *Dx:* 3552NR ENNISKILLEN
E-mail: fallsandhanna@btconnect.com

Murnaghan & Fee
118 Main Street Fivemiletown Co Tyrone BT75 0PW
Tel: 028 6652 1409

GLENGORMLEY

D M Kane & Co
Abbey Chambers 7 Farmley Road Glengormley Co Antrim BT36 7TY
Tel: 028 9083 7586 *Fax:* 028 9084 1460
Dx: 2704NR GLENGORMLEY

E J Lavery & Co
1 Hightown Road Glengormley Co Antrim BT36 7TZ
Tel: 028 9084 3436 *Fax:* 028 9083 7927
Dx: 2700NR GLENGORMLEY

Michael D Loughrey
9 Portland Avenue Glengormley Co Antrim BT36 5EY
Tel: 028 9084 8116

James J W McNinch & Son
16 Portland Avenue Glengormley Co Antrim BT36 5EY
Tel: 028 9083 6480 *Fax:* 028 9084 2662
Dx: 2713NR GLENGORMLEY
E-mail: law@jwmcninch-gg.co.uk

Noel Wilson & Co
5 Farmley Road Glengormley Co Antrim BT36 7TY
Tel: 028 9083 6682 *Dx:* 2710NR GLENGORMLEY
E-mail: noelwilson@btconnect.com

HILLSBOROUGH

Thompson Mitchell
Trevor House 9 The Square Hillsborough Co Down BT26 6AG
Tel: 028 9268 9666 *Fax:* 028 9268 9886 *Dx:* 2753NR PORTADOWN
E-mail: reception@thompsonmitchell.co.uk

HILLTOWN

Emmet J Kelly
36 Main Street Hilltown Co Down BT34 5UJ
Tel: 028 6790 1636

J G O'Hare & Co
36 Main Street Hilltown Co Down BT34 5UH
Tel: 028 4063 8858

HOLYWOOD

Hewitt & Gilpin
34 Shore Road Holywood Co Down BT18 9HX
Tel: 028 9042 8828 *Fax:* 028 9042 8829 *Dx:* 2000NR BELFAST 2

Hunt & Company
77 High Street Holywood Co Down BT18 9AQ
Tel: 028 9042 8600 *Fax:* 028 9042 8144 *Dx:* 3720NR HOLYWOOD
E-mail: info@huntsolicitors.com

George L MacLaine & Co
131 High Street Holywood Co Down BT18 9LG
Tel: 028 9039 7977

Murphys Solicitors
Suite 1 45 High Street Holywood Co Down BT18 9AB
Tel: 028 9039 7771

Stephen Perrott & Co
49c High Street Holywood Co Down BT18 9AB
Tel: 028 9042 8330 *Dx:* 3725NR HOLYWOOD
E-mail: info@stephenperrott.co.uk

116 High Street Holywood Co Down BT18 9HW
Tel: 028 9042 2505

Tully & Co
74a High Street Holywood Co Down BT18 9AE
Tel: 028 9042 2556 *Fax:* 028 9042 3636 *Dx:* 3722NR HOLYWOOD
E-mail: info@talktotully.com

IRVINESTOWN

Thomas T Montague
Ulster Bank Buildings 50-52 Main Street Irvinestown Co Fermanagh BT94 1GL
Tel: 028 6772 1274

KILKEEL

S C Connolly & Co
44 Greencastle Street Kilkeel Co Down BT34 4BH
Tel: 028 3026 5311
E-mail: mail@scconnolly.com

M Diane M Coulter Solicitors
127a Harbour Road Kilkeel Co Down BT34 4AU
Tel: 028 4176 9772 *Fax:* 028 4176 9773

Fisher & Fisher
Greencastle Street Kilkeel Co Down BT34 4BH
Tel: 028 4176 5083

D & E Fisher
The Square Kilkeel Co Down BT34 4BH
Tel: 028 7146 4509

McBurney & Co
1 Greencastle Street Kilkeel Co Down BT34 4BH
Tel: 028 4176 3906

McCartan Turkington Breen
15 Newry Street Kilkeel Co Down BT34 4DN
Tel: 028 4176 3333

McShane & Co
17a The Square Kilkeel Co Down BT34 4AA
Tel: 028 4176 2445 *Fax:* 028 4176 5101 *Dx:* 2050NR NEWRY
E-mail: rmcs@mcshaneandco.com

C Murnion & Co
7 Greencastle Street Kilkeel Co Down BT34 4BH
Tel: 028 4176 9088 *Fax:* 028 4176 9148
E-mail: c.murnion@talk21.com

KIRCUBBIN

Stewarts Solicitors
65a Main Street Kircubbin Co Down BT22 2SR
Tel: 028 4273 8999
E-mail: admin@stewartsolicitors.com

LARNE

MacAllister Keenan & Co
20 High Street Larne Co Antrim BT40 1JN
Tel: 028 2827 8844 *Dx:* 2200NR LARNE
E-mail: advice@macallisterkeenan.co.uk

Macaulay & Ritchie
1 St John's Place Larne Co Antrim BT40 1TB
Tel: 028 2827 2038 *Fax:* 028 2826 0378 *Dx:* 2201NR LARNE
E-mail: karen.burke@mac-rit.com

George L MacLaine & Co
55 Main Street Larne Co Antrim BT40 1JE
Tel: 028 2827 3937

James J W McNinch & Son
2 Cross Street Larne Co Antrim BT40 1JP
Tel: 028 2827 2010 *Fax:* 028 2826 0173 *Dx:* 2204NR LARNE
E-mail: law@jwmcninch-larne.co.uk

Neal McAllister
13 Agnew Street Larne Co Antrim BT40 1RF
Tel: 028 2827 7550 *Dx:* 4199NR LARNE

O'Rorke McDonald & Tweed
29 The Roddens Larne Co Antrim BT40 1HX
Tel: 028 2827 2291 *Dx:* 2203NR LARNE

LIMAVADY

D R Brewster
Court Chambers 19 Main Street Limavady Co Londonderry BT49 0EP
Tel: 028 7776 8700 *Fax:* 028 7776 8811 *Dx:* 3500NR LIMAVADY
E-mail: drbrewster@btconnect.com

R G Connell & Son
13 Main Street Limavady Co Londonderry BT49 0EP
Tel: 028 7772 2617 *Fax:* 028 7772 2447 *Dx:* 3501NR LIMAVADY
E-mail: law@rgconnell.co.uk

Michael Kilfeather
Regency House 18-20 Main Street Limavady Co Londonderry BT49 0EU
Tel: 028 7772 2996

Martin King French & Ingram
52 Catherine Street Limavady Co Londonderry BT49 9DB
Tel: 028 7776 2307 *Dx:* 3503NR LIMAVADY

T P Rafferty LLB
47a Catherine Street Limavady Co Londonderry BT49 9DA
Tel: 028 7772 2214 *Fax:* 028 7772 2057 *Dx:* 3508NR LIMAVADY
E-mail: tprllb@btconnect.com

M S Sandhu & Company
1 Main Street Limavady Co Londonderry BT49 0EP
Tel: 028 7772 2594

Stelfox Solicitors
14 Main Street Limavady Co Londonderry BT49 0EU
Tel: 028 7134 8855 *Fax:* 028 7134 8817 *Dx:* 3509NR LIMAVADY
E-mail: limavady@stelfoxsolicitors.com

W B Thompson & Co
36 Catherine Street Limavady Co Londonderry BT49 9DB
Tel: 028 7772 2400 *Fax:* 028 7776 6055 *Dx:* 3502NR LIMAVADY
E-mail: wbt@wbthompson.co.uk

LISBURN

Archer Heaney & Magee
2nd Floor 39a Market Square South Lisburn Co Antrim BT28 1AD
Tel: 028 9263 4445 *Fax:* 028 9263 4443 *Dx:* 423NR BELFAST

Mildred Breakey Solicitors
52 Bachelors Walk Lisburn Co Antrim BT28 1XN
Tel: 028 9266 9566 *Fax:* 028 9266 9566 *Dx:* 3392NR LISBURN
E-mail: mildredbreakeysolicitors@yahoo.co.uk

Conn & Fenton
39 Bow Street Lisburn Co Antrim BT28 1BJ
Tel: 028 9267 4321 *Dx:* 3381NR LISBURN

Donaldson McConnell & Co
Castle Chambers 1 Castle Street Lisburn Co Antrim BT27 4SR
Tel: 028 9260 1421 *Fax:* 028 9267 5705 *Dx:* 3384NR LISBURN
E-mail: info@donaldson-mcconnell.com

R J Eastwood
Linenhall Chambers 27 Linenhall Street Lisburn Co Antrim BT28 1FG
Tel: 028 9266 2727 *Fax:* 028 9260 1011 *Dx:* 3391NR LISBURN
E-mail: rjeastwood@btconnect.com

Green & Malpas
138 Longstone Street Lisburn Co Antrim BT28 1TR
Tel: 028 9267 5140 *Fax:* 028 9266 0963 *Dx:* 3386NR LISBURN
E-mail: greenmalpas@btconnect.com

John R Kirk
7 Sepon Park Lisburn Co Antrim BT28 3BQ
Tel: 028 9269 3336

Joseph Lockhart & Son
24 Bachelors Walk Lisburn Co Antrim BT20 1XJ
Tel: 028 9266 3225 *Dx:* 3388NR LISBURN
E-mail: law@joseph-lockart.co.uk

E F McAllister & Co
1 Cormac Road Ballinderry Upper Lisburn Co Antrim BT28 2HL
Tel: 028 9265 2799

MacCorkell Legal & Commercial
Garvey Studios 8-10 Longstone Street Lisburn Co Antrim BT28 1TP
Tel: 028 9266 9555 *Fax:* 028 9266 9777 *Dx:* 3396NR LISBURN
E-mail: mail@mlclegal.org

Terence McCourt
19 Bachelors Walk Lisburn Co Antrim BT28 1XJ
Tel: 028 9267 8122 *Dx:* 3395NR LISBURN

McFarland Graham McCombe
41-43 Bachelors Walk Lisburn Co Antrim BT28 1XN
Tel: 028 9267 4447 *Fax:* 028 9260 7472 *Dx:* 3389NR LISBURN
E-mail: mgm@nilaw.co.uk

Kenneth McKee
18 Railway Street Lisburn Co Antrim BT28 1XG
Tel: 028 9260 5525 *Dx:* 3401NR LISBURN

Harry McPartland & Sons
Niagara Buildings Tonagh Drive Lisburn Co Antrim BT28 1TY
Tel: 028 9267 0325

W G Maginess & Son
68 Bow Street Lisburn Co Antrim BT28 1AL
Tel: 028 9267 2161 *Dx:* 3380NR LISBURN
E-mail: law@wgmaginess.com

Reid & Co
48 Bachelors Walk Lisburn Co Antrim BT28 1XN
Tel: 028 9266 3310 *Dx:* 3390NR LISBURN

John P Slevin
144b-c Longstone Street Lisburn Co Antrim BT28 1TR
Tel: 028 9266 8700

LISNASKEA

W Neil Ferguson
102 Main Street Lisnaskea Co Fermanagh BT92 0JD
Tel: 028 6772 2086

T R Gibson & Co
2 Bloomfield Terrace Lisnaskea Co Fermanagh BT92 0JE
Tel: 028 6772 1541 *Fax:* 028 6772 2224
E-mail: tgibson@btconnect.com

Murphy & McManus
Bank of Ireland Building 143 Main Street Lisnaskea Co Fermanagh BT92 0JE
Tel: 028 6772 1012 *Fax:* 028 6772 2357
E-mail: solicitors@murphy-mcmanus.com

LONDONDERRY

Babington & Croasdaile
9 Limavady Road Waterside Londonderry Co Londonderry BT47 6JU
Tel: 028 7131 0600 *Fax:* 028 7134 5785
Dx: 3060NR LONDONDERRY
E-mail: law@babington-croasdaile.com

Barr & Co
57 Clarendon Street Londonderry Co Londonderry BT48 7ER
Tel: 028 7126 4230 *Fax:* 028 7126 4231 *Dx:* 3116NR DERRY 2
E-mail: info@barrandco.com

Caldwell & Robinson
Artillery Chambers 10-12 Artillery Street Londonderry Co Londonderry BT48 6RG
Tel: 028 7126 1334 *Fax:* 028 7137 1659
Dx: 4101NR LONDONDERRY 4
E-mail: enquiries@caldwellrobinson.com

Campbell Fitzpatrick
6 Castle Street Londonderry Co Londonderry BT48 6HQ
Tel: 028 7137 2660 *Fax:* 028 7126 7766
Dx: 3153NR LONDONDERRY 3
E-mail: derry@cfs-law.com

Casey & Co
8 Shipquay Street Londonderry Co Londonderry BT48 6DN
Tel: 028 7136 8982

Deery & Conway
1 Castle Gate Londonderry Co Londonderry BT48 6HG
Tel: 028 7126 5864 *Fax:* 028 7137 2632

Desmond J Doherty & Co
7 Clarendon Street Londonderry Co Londonderry BT48 7EP
Tel: 028 7128 8870 *Fax:* 028 7128 8871 *Dx:* 3100NR DERRY 2
E-mail: desmond.doherty@talk21.com

Gibson & Quigley
4 Queen Street Londonderry Co Londonderry BT48 7EF
Tel: 028 7137 4420 *Dx:* 3103NR LONDONDERRY 2

Hasson & Co
39-41 Clarendon Street Londonderry Co Londonderry BT48 7ER
Tel: 028 7126 6818 *Fax:* 028 7126 7780
Dx: 3101NR LONDONDERRY
E-mail: hasson@telinco.co.uk

Hegarty & McFeely
10 Queen Street Londonderry Co Londonderry BT48 7EG
Tel: 028 7126 7072

Brendan Kearney & Co
4 Clarendon Street Londonderry Co Londonderry BT48 7ES
Tel: 028 7136 6612 *Fax:* 028 7137 1845
Dx: 3106NR LONDONDERRY 2
E-mail: info@brendankearney.com

John G Logue & Co
PO Box 214 114 Strand Road Londonderry Co Londonderry BT48 7YS
Tel: 028 7137 1656 *Fax:* 028 7137 4083
E-mail: logue@derry68.freeserve.co.uk

McCartney & Casey
3-4 Castle Gate Londonderry Co Londonderry BT48 6HG
Tel: 028 7128 8888 *Dx:* 3150NR LONDONDERRY 3
E-mail: property@mccartneycasey.com

MacDermott & McGurk
12 Clarendon Street Londonderry Co Londonderry BT48 7ET
Tel: 028 7126 4415 *Dx:* 3108NR LONDONDERRY 2
E-mail: office@mmpsolicitors.com

McElhinney McDaid & Hegarty
48 Clarendon Street Londonderry Co Londonderry BT48 7ET
Tel: 028 7137 3365 / 7137 3496 *Fax:* 028 7126 9946
Dx: 3104NR LONDONDERRY 2
E-mail: info@mcelhinneymcdaid.co.uk

McGuinness & Canavan
42 Great James Street Londonderry Co Londonderry BT48 7DW
Tel: 028 7126 3562 *Fax:* 028 7137 2373 *Dx:* 3102NR DERRY 2

McKeone & Co
1 Carlisle Terrace Londonderry Co Londonderry BT48 6JX
Tel: 028 7126 5566

Denis E Mullan
1 Shipquay Street Londonderry Co Londonderry BT48 6DH
Tel: 028 7136 8292

David J Nagra & Co
45 Carlisle Road Londonderry Co Londonderry BT48 6JJ
Tel: 028 7126 6877

Tughans
10 Northland Road Londonderry Co Londonderry BT48 7JD
Tel: 028 7127 8111 *Fax:* 028 7127 8110
E-mail: law@tughans.com

Dermot Walker & Co
6 Queen Street Londonderry Co Londonderry BT48 7FF
Tel: 028 7126 3082 *Dx:* 3107NR LONDONDERRY 2
E-mail: dwalkerandcosols@btconnect.com

LOUGHGALL

T D Gibson & Co
18 Main Street Loughgall Co Armagh BT61 8HZ
Tel: 028 3889 1356

LURGAN

Campbell & Haughey
85 William Street Lurgan Co Armagh BT66 6JB
Tel: 028 3832 5335 *Fax:* 028 3832 1894 *Dx:* 2101NR LURGAN

Gallery & Campbell
Cinema Buildings 48a Church Place Lurgan Co Armagh BT66 6HD
Tel: 028 3832 4112 *Fax:* 028 3832 1758 *Dx:* 2100NR LURGAN
E-mail: law@galleryandcampbell.com

Eamonn McEvoy & Co
22 Church Place Lurgan Co Armagh BT66 6EY
Tel: 028 3832 7734 *Dx:* 2104NR LURGAN
E-mail: law@e-mcevoy.co.uk

John F McEvoy & Co
8 Church Place Lurgan Co Armagh BT66 6EY
Tel: 028 3832 6977

Patrick McMahon
74 Edward Street Lurgan Co Armagh BT66 6DB
Tel: 028 3834 1330 *Fax:* 028 3834 1165 *Dx:* 2118NR LURGAN
E-mail: patmcmahonlurgan@btconnect.com

Harry McPartland & Sons
11 Market Street Lurgan Co Armagh BT66 6AR
Tel: 028 3832 2452 *Dx:* 2108NR LURGAN
E-mail: info@mcpartland.com

T G Menary & Co
19 Windsor Avenue Lurgan Co Armagh BT67 9BG
Tel: 028 3832 7811 *Dx:* 2110NR LURGAN

Peter Murphy LLM
28 Church Place Lurgan Co Armagh BT66 6EU
Tel: 028 3834 8150 *Dx:* 2105NR LURGAN
E-mail: peter.murphy@petermurphysolicitors.co.uk

O'Connor & Moriarty
Bank of Ireland Chambers 13a Market Street Lurgan Co Armagh BT66 6AR
Tel: 028 3834 3611 *Fax:* 028 3834 2753 *Dx:* 2102NR LURGAN
E-mail: law@oconnormoriarty.co.uk

Con O'Hagan
13 Church Place Lurgan Co Armagh BT66 6EY
Tel: 028 3832 4511

Patrick Park
17a Market Street Lurgan Co Armagh BT66 6AR
Tel: 028 3832 7436 *Dx:* 2117NR LURGAN
E-mail: p.park@pparksolicitors.co.uk

Richard M Redman
13 High Street Lurgan Co Armagh BT66 8BS
Tel: 028 3832 7531 *Dx:* 2130NR LURGAN 2
E-mail: richardmredman@hotmail.com

Watson & Neill
23 High Street Lurgan Co Armagh BT66 8AQ
Tel: 028 3832 5111 *Fax:* 028 3832 7319
E-mail: watsonandneill@aol.com

MAGHERA

Burnside & Logue
43-49 Main Street Maghera Co Londonderry BT46 5AA
Tel: 028 7964 2224 *Fax:* 028 7964 4433 *Dx:* 3652NR MAGHERA
E-mail: mail@burnside-logue.co.uk

Cullen McAleer
Unit 1-2 The Cornstore Market Yard Maghera Co Londonderry BT45 7PE
Tel: 028 8674 7320

Patrick J J McGuckin
57 Hall Street Maghera Co Londonderry BT46 5DA
Tel: 028 7964 4199 *Fax:* 028 7964 4488 *Dx:* 3653NR MAGHERA

Mallon McCormick
69 Main Street Maghera Co Londonderry BT46 5AB
Tel: 028 7964 2670 *Dx:* 3650NR MAGHERA
E-mail: info@mallonmccormick.co.uk

MAGHERAFELT

Blaney & Diamond
15 Kirk Avenue Magherafelt Co Londonderry BT45 6BT
Tel: 028 7930 0660 *Fax:* 028 7930 0662
E-mail: tracey@blaney-diamond.com

Richard Doherty
15a Broad Street Magherafelt Co Londonderry BT45 6EB
Tel: 028 7963 2375

P A Duffy & Co
27 Broad Street Magherafelt Co Londonderry BT45 6EB
Tel: 028 7963 3433 *Fax:* 028 7930 1658
Dx: 3303NR MAGHERAFELT
E-mail: magherafelt@paduffy.com

7

McLernon & McCann
15 Meeting Street Magherafelt Co Londonderry BT45 6BN
Tel: 028 7963 2533 *Fax:* 028 7930 1201
Dx: 3300NR MAGHERAFELT
E-mail: mclaw@dnet.co.uk

John J McNally & Co
2 Moneymore Road Magherafelt Co Londonderry BT45 6AD
Tel: 028 7963 1537 *Fax:* 028 7963 3715
Dx: 3308NR MAGHERAFELT

Bernadette Mulholland
37 King Street Magherafelt Co Londonderry BT45 6AR
Tel: 028 7963 2030 *Fax:* 028 7963 3633
Dx: 3305NR MAGHERAFELT
E-mail: info@bernadettemulholland.com

James O'Brien & Co
15 Broad Street Magherafelt Co Londonderry BT45 6EB
Tel: 028 7930 0577 *Dx:* 3307NR MAGHERAFELT
E-mail: obrien-magherafelt@talk21.com

MARKETHILL

Nelson-Singleton
107 Main Street Markethill Co Armagh BT60 1PH
Tel: 028 3755 2199

MOIRA

Watson & Neill
43 Main Street Moira Co Down BT67 0LQ
Tel: 028 9261 1900
E-mail: watsonandneill@aol.com

NEWCASTLE

Buckley & Co
10 Marguerite Close Newcastle Co Down BT33 0RZ
Tel: 028 4372 2903 *Fax:* 028 4372 6314
E-mail: info@buckleysol.com

Michael F Curran
29 Central Promenade Newcastle Co Down BT33 0AA
Tel: 028 4372 2970 *Fax:* 028 4372 5115
E-mail: info@curran-solicitors.com

Fisher & Fisher
57a Main Street Newcastle Co Down BT33 0LU
Tel: 028 4372 3059

Colman R Hanna & Co
11 Causeway Road Newcastle Co Down BT33 0DL
Tel: 028 4372 3232 *Fax:* 028 4372 3352 *Dx:* 4350NR NEWCASTLE
E-mail: rosalin.grant@colmanhanna.co.uk

McBurney & Co
27 Causeway Road Newcastle Co Down BT33 0DL
Tel: 028 4372 5066

Dominic McInerney
123a Main Street Newcastle Co Down BT33 0AE
Tel: 028 4372 5238 *Fax:* 028 4372 5297 *Dx:* 4351NR NEWCASTLE
E-mail: law@d-mcinerney.fsnet.co.uk

NEWRY

Stephen Begley & Co
Regina House 9 Merchants Quay Newry Co Down BT35 6AL
Tel: 028 3026 7538 *Fax:* 028 3026 7538 *Dx:* 2603NR NEWRY
E-mail: sbegleyco@aol.com

Gordon Bell & Son
9-11 Newry Street Newry Co Down BT34 5PY
Tel: 028 4176 4857

Campbell & Grant
17 Sugar Island Newry Co Down BT35 6HT
Tel: 028 3026 6660 *Dx:* 2065NR NEWRY
E-mail: margaret@campbellandgrant.com

Casey & Casey
Legal House 25-27 Catherine Street Newry Co Down BT35 6BE
Tel: 028 3026 6214 *Fax:* 028 3026 0909 *Dx:* 2071NR NEWRY
E-mail: info@caseysolicitors.co.uk

S C Connolly & Co
Bank Buildings 39 Hill Street Newry Co Down BT34 1AG
Tel: 028 3026 5311 *Fax:* 028 3026 2096 *Dx:* 2070NR NEWRY
E-mail: mail@scconnolly.com

Luke Curran & Co
6 Marcus Square Newry Co Down BT34 1AY
Tel: 028 3026 7134 *Fax:* 028 3026 5726 *Dx:* 2078NR NEWRY
E-mail: law@lukecurran.co.uk

Donnelly Neary & Donnelly
1 Downshire Road Newry Co Down BT34 1EE
Tel: 028 3026 4611 *Fax:* 028 3026 7000 *Dx:* 2056NR NEWRY
E-mail: kevinneary@dndlaw.com

Fisher & Fisher
9 John Mitchell Place Newry Co Down BT34 2BS
Tel: 028 3026 1811 *Fax:* 028 3026 6695 *Dx:* 2072NR NEWRY
E-mail: mg@fisherandfisher.co.uk

D & E Fisher
8 Trevor Hill Newry Co Down BT34 1DN
Tel: 028 3026 1616 *Fax:* 028 3026 7712 *Dx:* 2052NR NEWRY
E-mail: norville@dandefisher.com

52 Downshire Road Newry Co Down BT34 1EE

McGuigan Solicitors
5 Lower Catherine Street Newry Co Down BT35 6BE
Tel: 028 3026 7939 *Fax:* 028 3025 0747 *Dx:* 2057NR NEWRY
E-mail: info@mcguigansolicitors.com

Patrick McMahon
23 Canal Street Newry Co Down BT35 6JB
Tel: 028 3083 5885 *Fax:* 028 3083 5886
E-mail: patrickmcmahon@btconnect.com

McShane & Co
34 Hill Street Newry Co Down BT34 1AR
Tel: 028 3026 6611 *Fax:* 028 3026 9492 *Dx:* 2050NR NEWRY
E-mail: info@mcshaneandco.com

Robert A Mullan & Son
9 Trevor Hill Newry Co Down BT34 1DN
Tel: 028 3026 1611 *Fax:* 028 3026 8125 *Dx:* 2051NR NEWRY

Raffertys Solicitors
83 Hill Street Newry Co Down BT34 1DG
Tel: 028 3026 1102

Tiernans
7 St Colman's Park Newry Co Down BT34 2BX
Tel: 028 3026 3222 *Dx:* 2075NR NEWRY

Elliott Trainor Partnership Solicitors
3 Downshire Road Newry Co Down BT34 1EE
Tel: 028 3026 8116 *Dx:* 2053NR NEWRY
E-mail: info@etpsolicitors.com

Tara Walsh
5-6 Sandys Street Newry Co Down BT34 1EN
Tel: 028 3025 0920 *Dx:* 2060NR NEWRY
E-mail: t.w@tarawalshsolicitors.co.uk

M L White
43-45 Monaghan Street Newry Co Down BT35 6AY
Tel: 028 3026 8144 *Dx:* 2073NR NEWRY
E-mail: lawyers@mlwhitesolicitors.com

NEWTOWNABBEY

Armstrong Solicitors
1 Monkstown Village Centre Newtownabbey Co Antrim BT37 0HS
Tel: 028 9085 5955
E-mail: admin@armstrongsolicitors.com

T Bergin
30a The Diamond Rathcoole Newtownabbey Co Antrim BT37 9BJ
Tel: 028 9036 5883
E-mail: tony@tonybergin.co.uk

Edward Dougan & Co
14 The Diamond Rathcoole Newtownabbey Co Antrim BT37 9BJ
Tel: 028 9086 2800 *Fax:* 028 9085 3000

Gray Magee
22 Hillview Avenue Newtownabbey Co Antrim BT36 6AE
Tel: 028 9036 5955

James Macauley
22 Carmmoney Road Glengormley Newtownabbey Co Antrim BT36 6HW
Tel: 028 9084 4926 *Fax:* 028 9084 4978
Dx: 2716NR GLENGORMLEY
E-mail: jjmcr@btconnect.com

Magennis & Creighton
572 Shore Road Newtownabbey Co Antrim BT37 0SL
Tel: 028 9036 5777 *Fax:* 028 9036 5999 *Dx:* 6000NR WHITEABBEY

S G Murphy & Co
Unit 2 858/886 Shore Road Greencastle Newtownabbey Co Antrim BT36 7DQ
Tel: 028 9036 5595

Reevey & Co Solicitors
22 The Diamond Rathcoole Newtownabbey Co Antrim BT37 9BJ
Tel: 028 9086 0335 *Fax:* 028 9036 5124 *Dx:* 6002NR WHITEABBEY

E M Walker & Co
5a Carnmoney Road Newtownabbey Co Antrim BT36 6HL
Tel: 028 9034 2568 *Fax:* 028 9034 2630
Dx: 2702NR GLENGORMLEY

NEWTOWNARDS

Boyd Rice & Co
6 Mill Street Newtownards Co Down BT23 4LU
Tel: 028 9181 7715 *Fax:* 028 9181 2374
Dx: 2604NR NEWTOWNARDS
E-mail: info@boydricelegal.com

Carnson Morrow Graham
44b High Street Newtownards Co Down BT23 7HZ
Tel: 028 9181 3145 *Fax:* 028 9181 6024
Dx: 2601NR NEWTOWNARDS
E-mail: michael.body@cmgsolicitors.co.uk

Alana Jones Solicitors
40b Frances Street Newtownards Co Down BT23 7DN
Tel: 028 9182 0040 *Fax:* 028 9182 8488

Joseph F McCollum & Co
52 Regent Street Newtownards Co Down BT23 4LP
Tel: 028 9181 3142 *Fax:* 028 9181 2499
Dx: 2614NR NEWTOWNARDS

Patterson Donnelly
4 North Street Newtownards Co Down BT23 4DE
Tel: 028 9181 1411 *Fax:* 028 9182 2744
Dx: 2609NR NEWTOWNARDS
E-mail: colin@pdslaw.co.uk

John J Rice & Co
39 Movilla Street Newtownards Co Down BT23 7JQ
Tel: 028 9182 2323 *Fax:* 028 9181 3606
Dx: 2612NR NEWTOWNARDS
E-mail: newtownards@johnjricesolicitors.com

John Ross & Son
30 Frances Street Newtownards Co Down BT23 7DN
Tel: 028 9181 3173 *Fax:* 028 9181 9797
Dx: 2606NR NEWTOWNARDS
E-mail: office@john-ross.co.uk

Russells
11 Lower Mary Street Newtownards Co Down BT23 7JJ
Tel: 028 9181 4444 *Fax:* 028 9181 2782
Dx: 2603NR NEWTOWNARDS
E-mail: info@russells-sol.com

Stephen Scott & Co
45 Court Street Newtownards Co Down BT23 7NX
Tel: 028 9182 1700 *Fax:* 028 9182 1332
Dx: 2618NR NEWTOWNARDS
E-mail: info@stephenscottsolicitors.com

Trevor Smyth & Co
136 Francis Street Newtownards Co Down BT23 4AB
Tel: 028 9181 3113 *Fax:* 028 9181 0750
Dx: 2616NR NEWTOWNARDS

Stewarts Solicitors
3 Regent Street Newtownards Co Down BT23 4AB
Tel: 028 9182 6444 *Fax:* 028 9182 6333
Dx: 2600NR NEWTOWNARDS
E-mail: ards@stewartsolicitors.com

Thompsons
39 Frances Street Newtownards Co Down BT23 7DW
Tel: 028 9181 1652 *Fax:* 028 9181 9645
Dx: 2262NR NEWTOWNARDS
E-mail: enquiries@thompsons-solicitors.co.uk

Elizabeth R Warden
Seaview Farm 92 Bowtown Road Newtownards Co Down BT23 8SL
Tel: 028 9181 1644

Worthingtons
2 Court Street Newtownards Co Down BT23 3NX
Tel: 028 9181 1538 *Fax:* 028 9181 0532
Dx: 5010NR NEWTOWNARDS
E-mail: info@worthingtonslaw.co.uk

NEWTOWNSTEWART

J J Roche
9 Castle Brae Newtownstewart Co Tyrone BT78 4AS
Tel: 028 8166 1254

OMAGH

Andrew T Armstrong & Co
19 High Street Omagh Co Tyrone BT78 1BA
Tel: 028 8224 1222

A F Colhoun & Co
21 Market Street Omagh Co Tyrone BT78 1EE
Tel: 028 8223 2136

Patrick Fahy & Co
4 John Street Omagh Co Tyrone BT78 1DW
Tel: 028 8224 3447 *Dx:* 3607NR OMAGH

Patrick Laverty & Co
10-12 George's Street Omagh Co Tyrone BT78 1DE
Tel: 028 8224 6048 *Dx:* 3605NR OMAGH

Logan & Corry
20 High Street Omagh Co Tyrone BT78 1BQ
Tel: 028 8225 0400 *Fax:* 028 8225 0401 *Dx:* 3608NR OMAGH
E-mail: info@loganandcorry.com

Oliver M Loughran
9 Holmview Terrace Campsie Road Omagh Co Tyrone BT79 0AH
Tel: 028 8224 1530 *Fax:* 028 8225 7897 *Dx:* 33741NR OMAGH 2
E-mail: info@oliverloughran.com

John McCaffrey & Company
8-10 Church Hill Omagh Co Tyrone BT78 1DQ
Tel: 028 8224 3902 *Fax:* 028 8224 9220 *Dx:* 3600NR OMAGH
E-mail: frontoffice@johnmcaffrey.co.uk

McConnell & Fyffe
The Old Rectory 21 Church Street Omagh Co Tyrone BT78 1DG
Tel: 028 8224 2099 *Fax:* 028 8224 9217 *Dx:* 3609NR OMAGH
E-mail: law@mcconnellfyffe.co.uk

MJT McCullagh
TIC Unit 10 Omagh Business Complex Great Northern Road Omagh Co Tyrone BT78 5LU
Tel: 028 8224 9494 ext: 242
E-mail: mary@mjtmccullagh.com

John McGale Kelly & Co
26 John Street Omagh Co Tyrone BT78 1DN
Tel: 028 8223 3621 *Dx:* 3610NR OMAGH

James McNulty & Co
25-27 Georges Street Omagh Co Tyrone BT78 1DE
Tel: 028 8224 5695

Meyler McGuigan
40 John Street Omagh Co Tyrone BT78 1DN
Tel: 028 8225 7777

Murnaghan Colton
3 John Street Omagh Co Tyrone BT78 1DW
Tel: 028 8224 2744 *Dx:* 3611NR OMAGH
E-mail: law@murnaghancolton.co.uk

M T O'Neill
5 Dergmoney Lane Omagh Co Tyrone BT78 1AE
Tel: 028 8224 5025 *Fax:* 028 8224 1638
E-mail: mtoneill@fsmail.net

Orr & Rountree
13 High Street Omagh Co Tyrone BT78 1BA
Tel: 028 8224 3151 *Fax:* 028 8224 9481 *Dx:* 3612NR OMAGH 1

PORTADOWN

Francis A Campbell
13 Church Street Portadown Co Armagh BT62 3LN
Tel: 028 3833 1834

Gus Campbell
44-48 Carlton Street Portadown Co Armagh BT62 3EP
Tel: 028 3833 4801

Paul Connolly
32 Carleton Street Portadown Co Armagh BT62 3EP
Tel: 028 3839 1218 *Fax:* 028 3836 2126
E-mail: pconnolly@rapiddial.co.uk

R M Cullen & Son
16-22 Edward Street Portadown Co Armagh BT62 3NA
Tel: 028 3833 3241 *Fax:* 028 3833 0895 *Dx:* 2751NR PORTADOWN
E-mail: enquiries@rmcullenandson.co.uk

T D Gibson & Co
Morrison House 107 Church Street Portadown Co Armagh BT62 3DD
Tel: 028 3833 2176 *Fax:* 028 3833 0834 *Dx:* 2756NR ARMAGH
E-mail: tdg@caslaw.freeserve.co.uk

Hagan & McConville
34 Edward Street Portadown Co Armagh BT62 3NE
Tel: 028 3839 0930 *Fax:* 028 3833 0931 *Dx:* 2754NR PORTADOWN
E-mail: mail@hagan-mcconville.com

John P Hagan
17-21 Church Street Portadown Co Armagh BT62 3LN
Tel: 028 3833 3333 *Fax:* 028 3835 0011 *Dx:* 2752NR PORTADOWN
E-mail: law@jphagan.com

John Hare & Co
Darragh House 18 Carleton Street Portadown Co Armagh BT62 3EN
Tel: 028 3833 4021

G R Ingram & Co
16 Church Street Portadown Co Armagh BT62 3LQ
Tel: 028 3839 2909

McElhone & Co
1b High Street Portadown Co Armagh BT62 1HZ
Tel: 028 3835 0464 *Fax:* 028 3835 1119 *Dx:* 2755NR PORTADOWN
E-mail: info@mcelhone-solicitors.co.uk

John McGrane & Company
46a Meadow Lane Portadown Co Armagh BT62 3LN
Tel: 028 3839 1787

Gerard Maguire
4a Carleton Street Portadown Co Armagh BT62 3EN
Tel: 028 3839 3488 *Fax:* 028 3839 3489

Hugh B Marley
8 Edward Street Portadown Co Armagh BT62 3LX
Tel: 028 3833 5418 *Fax:* 028 3835 0081 *Dx:* 2757NR PORTADOWN

Timothy Mayes LLB
24a High Street Portadown Co Armagh BT62 1HJ
Tel: 028 3835 0949 *Fax:* 028 3839 4577 *Dx:* 2760NR PORTADOWN
E-mail: info@tmayes.co.uk

Richard Monteith
32-34 Portmore Street Portadown Co Armagh BT62 3NG
Tel: 028 3833 0780 *Dx:* 2768NR PORTADOWN

James H Rodgers
15 Church Street Portadown Co Armagh BT62 3LN
Tel: 028 3833 7211 *Fax:* 028 3835 0980
E-mail: info@jameshrodgers.com

Thompson Mitchell
12-14 Mandeville Street Portadown Co Armagh BT62 3NZ
Tel: 028 3833 7172 *Fax:* 028 3835 0950 *Dx:* 2753NR PORTADOWN
E-mail: reception@thompsonmitchell.co.uk

Walker McDonald
2-6 Edward Street Portadown Co Armagh BT62 3LX
Tel: 028 3833 1086 *Fax:* 028 3833 0873 *Dx:* 2750NR PORTADOWN
E-mail: lawyers@walkermcdonald.co.uk

PORTSTEWART

Greer Hamilton & Gailey
22 The Diamond Portstewart Co Londonderry BT54 7JN
Tel: 028 7083 2518 *Dx:* 3256NR BALLYMONEY

Macaulay Wray
4 The Diamond Portstewart Co Londonderry BT55 7AF
Tel: 028 7083 2564

RANDALSTOWN

Diamond & Co
29 New Street Randalstown Co Antrim BT41 3AF
Tel: 028 9447 9696

Deirdre Doran
35b Main Street Randalstown Co Antrim BT41 3AB
Tel: 028 9447 3732

RATHFRILAND

Arthur J Downey & Co
15 Church Square Rathfriland Co Down BT34 5PT

Fisher & Fisher
1 Newry Street Rathfriland Co Down BT34 5PY
Tel: 028 4063 0217

SAINTFIELD

McMillan & Ervine
Campbell House 31 Main Street Saintfield Co Down BT24 7AB
Tel: 028 9751 9082 *Fax:* 028 9751 9084
E-mail: mcmillan-ervine@btconnect.com

STRABANE

Barry Brady
2 Church Street Strabane Co Tyrone BT82 8BS
Tel: 028 7138 2380 *Fax:* 028 7138 3200
E-mail: info@wmurnaghan.com

Copeland McCaffrey
PO Box 9 29 Patrick Street Strabane Co Tyrone BT82 8DQ
Tel: 028 7188 2262 *Fax:* 028 7138 2770 *Dx:* 3311NR STRABANE

Crawford Scally & Co
45 Bowling Green Strabane Co Tyrone BT82 8BW
Tel: 028 7188 3591 *Fax:* 028 7138 2298 *Dx:* 3316NR STRABANE
E-mail: crawford.scally@btinternet.com

John Fahy & Co
8 Bowling Green Strabane Co Tyrone BT82 8BW
Tel: 028 7138 2391 *Fax:* 028 7138 2180 *Dx:* 3315NR STRABANE
E-mail: enquiry@jfahy.demon.co.uk

McCanny & Keohane
38 Railway Road Strabane Co Tyrone BT82 8EH
Tel: 028 7188 3374

Oliver Roche
5 Butcher Street Strabane Co Tyrone BT82 8BJ
Tel: 028 7188 3377 *Dx:* 3310NR STRABANE
E-mail: info@oliverroche.com

Wilson & Simms
35-37 Bowling Green Strabane Co Tyrone BT82 8BW
Tel: 028 7188 2208

WARRENPOINT

Siobhan Armstrong
29 Church Street Warrenpoint Co Down BT34 3HN
Tel: 028 4175 2978
E-mail: info@lawyersni.net

Patrick J Cole
12 Duke Street Warrenpoint Co Down BT34 3JY
Tel: 028 4177 2021
E-mail: patrick@colelaw.fsnet.co.uk

Rosemary Connolly
2 The Square Warrenpoint Co Down BT34 3JT
Tel: 028 4175 3121 *Dx:* 2079NR NEWRY
E-mail: rosemaryconnolly@solicitorsni.net

WATERSIDE

Hilary Carmichael
6 Ebrington Street Waterside Co Londonderry BT47 6JS
Tel: 028 7131 8288 *Dx:* 4146NR LONDONDERRY 5
E-mail: hcarmichael@btclick.com

Dickson & McNulty
50 Spencer Road Waterside Co Londonderry BT47 6AA
Tel: 028 7134 1864 *Dx:* 4140NR LONDONDERRY 5
E-mail: info@dickson-mcnulty.co.uk

A D McClay & Co
1 Limavady Road Waterside Co Londonderry BT47 6JU
Tel: 028 7134 5666 *Fax:* 028 7131 1198
Dx: 3061NR LONDONDERRY 1

FIRMS, NORTHERN IRELAND – A-Z

7

A

ALB Solicitors
Belfast *p877* 028 9026 8490

Agnew Andress Higgins
Belfast *p877* 028 9024 3040

Anderson Agnew & Co
Ballymena *p876* 028 2564 2118

Anderson & Co
Coleraine *p879* 028 7034 3180

Michael Andress & Co
Dundonald *p880* 028 9048 4188

Archer Heaney & Magee
Belfast *p877* 028 9033 0000
Lisburn *p881* 028 9263 4445

Andrew T Armstrong & Co
Omagh *p882* 028 8224 1222

Siobhan Armstrong
Warrenpoint *p883* 028 4175 2978

Armstrong Solicitors
Newtownabbey *p882* 028 9085 5955

Thomas Armstrong
Belfast *p877* 028 9032 1399

B

Babington & Croasdaile
Coleraine *p879* 028 7034 2007
Londonderry *p881* 028 7131 0600

James Ballentine & Son
Ballymena *p876* 028 2565 6161

Barr & Co
Londonderry *p881* 028 7126 4230

W J Baxter & Co
Dromore *p880* 028 9269 2277

Stephen Begley & Co
Newry *p882* 028 3026 7538

David G Bell
Antrim *p876* 028 9446 6444

Gordon Bell & Son
Newry *p882* 028 4176 4857

T Bergin
Newtownabbey *p882* 028 9036 5883

Berkeley White
Ballycastle *p876* 028 2076 8090

Bigger & Strahan
Bangor *p877* 028 9127 0313
Belfast *p877* 028 9032 5229

C & J Black
Belfast *p877* 028 9032 1441

Blair & Hanna
Armagh *p876* 028 3752 6426

J Blair Employment Law
Belfast *p877* 028 9066 2211

Blaney & Diamond
Magherafelt *p881* 028 7930 0660

Boal Anderson & Co
Ballymena *p876* 028 2565 6464

James Boston & Sullivan
Belfast *p877* 028 9032 0603
p877 .... 028 9045 6601

John Boston & Co
Belfast *p877* 028 9048 0460

Boyd Rice & Co
Newtownards *p882* 028 9181 7715

Patrick J G Bradley
Belfast *p877* 028 9032 1765

Barry Brady
Strabane *p883* 028 7138 2380

J C Brady & Son
Enniskillen *p880* 028 6632 2112

Brangam Bagnall & Co
Belfast *p877* 028 9032 6060
Dundonald *p880* 028 9048 8800

Mildred Breakey Solicitors
Lisburn *p881* 028 9266 9566

Martin Brennan
Belfast *p877* 028 9023 3477

Breslin Thomas
Ballymena *p876* 028 2564 8479

D R Brewster
Limavady *p881* 028 7776 8700

Alan M Brown
Belfast *p877* 028 9045 9687

Bryan Law
Bangor *p877* 028 9145 6666

Buckley & Co
Newcastle *p882* 028 4372 2903

Burnside & Logue
Maghera *p881* 028 7964 2224

Byrne & Herbert
Banbridge *p876* 028 4066 2251

C

Caldwell & Robinson
Londonderry *p881* 028 7126 1334

Caldwell Warner
Belfast *p877* 028 9059 5300

Campbell & Grant
Newry *p882* 028 3026 6660

Campbell & Haughey
Lurgan *p881* 028 3832 5335

Campbell Bates & Co
Comber *p879* 028 9187 2037

Bernard Campbell & Co
Belfast *p877* 028 9023 2008
Carrickfergus *p879* 028 9336 9033

Campbell Fitzpatrick
Belfast *p877* 028 9032 7388
Londonderry *p881* 028 7137 2660

Campbell Francis
Armagh *p876* 028 3752 4690

Francis A Campbell
Portadown *p882* 028 3833 1834

Gus Campbell
Portadown *p882* 028 3833 4801

Campbell McKee
Ballycastle *p876* 028 2076 2236
Ballymoney *p876* 028 2766 6698

Campbell Stafford
Belfast *p877* 028 9023 0808

Hilary Carmichael
Waterside *p883* 028 7131 8288

Carnson Morrow Graham
Bangor *p877* 028 9145 7911
Belfast *p877* 028 9023 4606
Donaghadee *p879* 028 9188 3770
Newtownards *p882* 028 9181 3145

Carson & McDowell
Belfast *p877* 028 9024 4951

Caruth & Bamber
Ballymena *p876* 028 2565 2758

Casey & Casey
Newry *p882* 028 3026 6214

Casey & Co
Londonderry *p881* 028 7136 8982

Chesney & Co
Belfast *p877* 028 9065 9777

Patrick J Cole
Warrenpoint *p883* 028 4177 2021

A F Colhoun & Co
Omagh *p882* 028 8223 2136

Comerton & Hill
Belfast *p877* 028 9023 4629

T H Conlan
Belfast *p877* 028 9068 2228

Conn & Fenton
Lisburn *p881* 028 9267 4321

R G Connell & Son
Limavady *p881* 028 7772 2617

Paul Connolly
Portadown *p882* 028 3839 1218

Rosemary Connolly
Warrenpoint *p883* 028 4175 3121

S C Connolly & Co
Crossmaglen *p879* 028 3086 8539
Kilkeel *p880* 028 3026 5311
Newry *p882* 028 3026 5311

Conway Todd & Co
Antrim *p876* 028 9446 3477

Cooper Wilkinson
Enniskillen *p880* 028 6632 2615

Copeland McCaffrey
Strabane *p883* 028 7188 2262

Corr & Sally
Cookstown *p879* 028 8676 2226

M Diane M Coulter Solicitors
Kilkeel *p880* 028 4176 9772

Cousins & Gilmore
Belfast *p877* 028 9030 1360

Arthur Cox Northern Ireland
Belfast *p877* 028 9023 0007

Crawford & Lockhart
Belfast *p877* 028 9032 2204

R P Crawford & Co
Belfast *p877* 028 9038 1024
p877 .... 028 9078 1187

Crawford Scally & Co
Strabane *p883* 028 7188 3591

Creighton & Co
Belfast *p877* 028 9073 2461

Francis Crilly
Belfast *p877* 028 9075 5722

Lyle Cubitt & Co
Ballymena *p876* 028 2565 2125

Culbert & Martin
Belfast *p877* 028 9032 5508

Cullen McAleer
Maghera *p881* 028 8674 7320

R M Cullen & Son
Portadown *p882* 028 3833 3241

Samuel Cumming & Son
Ballymena *p876* 028 2564 6026

Cunningham & Dickey
Belfast *p877* 028 9024 5896

Francis Curley
Armagh *p876* 028 3752 5244

Luke Curran & Co
Newry *p882* 028 3026 7134

Michael F Curran
Newcastle *p882* 028 4372 2970

D

Ian Dawson & Co
Armagh *p876* 028 3752 5566

Deery & Conway
Londonderry *p881* 028 7126 5864

Delaney & Co
Belfast *p877* 028 9030 1334

Diamond & Co
Randalstown *p883* 028 9447 9696

Diamond Heron
Belfast *p877* 028 9024 3726

Dickson & McNulty
Waterside *p883* 028 7134 1864

Doherty Brennan & Co
Ballymoney *p876* 028 2766 2753
Coleraine *p879* 028 7035 3444

Desmond J Doherty & Co
Londonderry *p881* 028 7128 8870

Richard Doherty
Magherafelt *p881* 028 7963 2375

Donaghy Carey
Belfast *p877* 028 9023 8222

Patrick C Donaghy Solicitors
Belfast *p877* 028 9066 9636

Donaldson McConnell & Co
Lisburn *p881* 028 9260 1421

Donard King & Co
Ballynahinch *p876* 028 9756 5525
Castlewellan *p879* 028 4377 0555

Donnelly & Kinder
Belfast *p877* 028 9024 4999

Donnelly & Wall
Belfast *p877* 028 9023 3157

Joseph Donnelly & Co
Belfast *p877* .... 028 9024 2061 / 9032 5043

Liam Donnelly & Co
Ballymena *p876* 028 2564 7967

Donnelly Neary & Donnelly
Newry *p882* 028 3026 4611

Deirdre Doran
Randalstown *p883* 028 9447 3732

James G Doran & Co
Belfast *p877* 028 9024 0440

Doris & MacMahon
Cookstown *p879* 028 8676 2484

Peter Dornan & Co
Bangor *p877* 028 9127 3054
Belfast *p877* 028 9023 4559

Edward Dougan & Co
Newtownabbey *p882* 028 9086 2800

Arthur J Downey & Co
Banbridge *p876* 028 4066 2123
Dromore *p880* 028 9269 3444
Rathfriland *p883* 028 4063 0217

P Drinan
Belfast *p877* 028 9032 2071

P A Duffy & Co
Belfast *p877* 028 9023 0688
Coalisland *p879* 028 8774 7159
Cookstown *p879* 028 8676 3406
Dungannon *p880* 028 8772 2102
Magherafelt *p881* 028 7963 3433

E

R J Eastwood
Lisburn *p881* 028 9266 2727

Edwards & Co
Belfast *p877* 028 9032 1863

Elliott Duffy Garrett
Belfast *p877* 028 9024 5034

Thomas Elliott & Son
Castlederg *p879* 028 8167 1013

F

Fahy Corrigan & Co
Enniskillen *p880* 028 6632 0066

John Fahy & Co
Strabane *p883* 028 7138 2391

Patrick Fahy & Co
Omagh *p882* 028 8224 3447

Falls & Hanna
Enniskillen *p880* 028 6632 2009
Fivemiletown *p880* 028 8952 1234

Faloon & Co
Dungannon *p880* 028 8775 2099

Fearon & McCoy
Belfast *p877* 028 9024 0214

Ferguson & Logue
Ballymoney *p876* 028 2766 3033

J G Ferguson
Belfast *p877* 028 9032 2998

Michael Ferguson
Belfast *p877* 028 9038 2030

W Neil Ferguson
Lisnaskea *p881* 028 6772 2086

Fergusons
Enniskillen *p880* 028 6632 2234

Paul Ferris
Banbridge *p876* 028 4062 8828

Fisher & Fisher
Donaghadee *p879* 028 9188 8388
Kilkeel *p880* 028 4176 5083
Newcastle *p882* 028 4372 3059
Newry *p882* 028 3026 1811
Rathfriland *p883* 028 4063 0217

D & E Fisher
- Armagh *p876* ... 028 3752 3493
- Kilkeel *p880* ... 028 7146 4509
- Newry *p882* ... 028 3026 1616
- *p882* ... 028 3026 7939

James F Fitzpatrick & Co
- Belfast *p877* ... 028 9024 6741

P J Flanagan & Co
- Enniskillen *p880* ... 028 6632 4521

Michael Flanigan
- Belfast *p877* ... 028 9023 3309

Flynn & McGettrick
- Belfast *p877* ... 028 9002 6500

Fox & Associates
- Belfast *p877* ... 028 9038 2788

Franklin Solicitors
- Belfast *p877* ... 028 9050 4300

G

Gaffney Solicitors
- Belfast *p877* ... 028 9050 0760

Philip Gallen & Co
- Belfast *p877* ... 028 9066 3364

Gallery & Campbell
- Lurgan *p881* ... 028 3832 4112

Gaston Graham
- Belfast *p877* ... 028 9047 1869

John F Gibbons & Co
- Belfast *p877* ... 028 9023 9990

Gibson & Quigley
- Londonderry *p881* ... 028 7137 4420

T D Gibson & Co
- Loughgall *p881* ... 028 3889 1356
- Portadown *p882* ... 028 3833 2176

T R Gibson & Co
- Lisnaskea *p881* ... 028 6772 1541

Gillan Barr
- Coleraine *p879* ... 028 7034 3491

Michael Gillen
- Banbridge *p877* ... 028 4062 6639

Alan Gilliland
- Ballynahinch *p876* ... 028 9751 0827

Basil Glass & Co
- Belfast *p877* ... 028 9032 2061
- *p877* ... 028 9040 1463

Glover & King
- Carrickfergus *p879* ... 028 9336 7025

A & L Goodbody
- Belfast *p877* ... 028 9031 4466

Gray Magee
- Ballyclare *p876* ... 028 9334 2666
- Newtownabbey *p882* ... 028 9036 5955

Green & Malpas
- Lisburn *p881* ... 028 9267 5140

Greer Hamilton & Gailey
- Ballymoney *p876* ... 028 2766 2104
- Portstewart *p883* ... 028 7083 2518

Nigel Greeves
- Belfast *p877* ... 028 9024 2371
- Carrickfergus *p879* ... 028 9336 8568

H

Hagan & McConville
- Portadown *p882* ... 028 3839 0930

John P Hagan
- Craigavon *p879* ... 028 3834 9370
- Portadown *p882* ... 028 3833 3333

Hamilton & Millar
- Ballynahinch *p876* ... 028 9756 2534

Colman R Hanna & Co
- Newcastle *p882* ... 028 4372 3232

Francis Hanna & Co
- Belfast *p877* ... 028 9024 3901

John Hare & Co
- Portadown *p882* ... 028 3833 4021

Harrisons Solicitors
- Belfast *p877* ... 028 9032 3843

Hart & Co
- Belfast *p877* ... 028 9032 3545

Stephen R Haslett
- Belfast *p878* ... 028 9037 0213

Hasson & Co
- Londonderry *p881* ... 028 7126 6818

Hastings & Co
- Ballymoney *p876* ... 028 2766 2277

J G Haughey & Co
- Belfast *p878* ... 028 9043 1222

Jerome J Haughey
- Armagh *p876* ... 028 3752 3493

P Haughey & Co
- Dungannon *p880* ... 028 8775 2433

Haugheys
- Belfast *p878* ... 028 9060 0088

Hegarty & McFeely
- Londonderry *p881* ... 028 7126 7072

Gerald P Henvey
- Belfast *p878* ... 028 9061 0372

Heron & Dobson
- Banbridge *p877* ... 028 4066 2672

Hewitt & Gilpin
- Belfast *p878* ... 028 9057 3573
- Holywood *p880* ... 028 9042 8828

John F Hickey
- Coleraine *p879* ... 028 7034 3244

Higgins Hollywood Deazley
- Belfast *p878* ... 028 9077 0770

Hoffman & Co
- Belfast *p878* ... 028 9031 2020

Holmes & Moffitt
- Belfast *p878* ... 028 9023 0836
- Castlereagh *p879* ... 028 9079 9597
- Crossgar *p879* ... 028 4481 8283

Holmes & Swann
- Antrim *p876* ... 028 9442 9112

John M Hughes & Co
- Belfast *p878* ... 028 9032 0831

Denis D Humphrey
- Bangor *p877* ... 028 9127 3131

Hunt & Company
- Holywood *p880* ... 028 9042 8600

David Hunter
- Coleraine *p879* ... 028 7034 2121

I

G R Ingram & Co
- Portadown *p882* ... 028 3839 2909

Francis J Irvine & Co
- Belfast *p878* ... 028 9024 6451

W J Irwin & Son
- Dungannon *p880* ... 028 8772 2746

J

C & H Jefferson
- Belfast *p878* ... 028 9032 9545

Johns Elliot
- Belfast *p878* ... 028 9032 6881

Johnsons Solicitors
- Belfast *p878* ... 028 9024 0183

James T Johnston & Co
- Belfast *p878* ... 028 9024 6091

Jones & Co
- Belfast *p878* ... 028 9024 5471

Alana Jones Solicitors
- Newtownards *p882* ... 028 9182 0040

Jones Cassidy Jones Solicitors
- Belfast *p878* ... 028 9064 2290

K

D M Kane & Co
- Glengormley *p880* ... 028 9083 7586

Brendan Kearney & Co
- Londonderry *p881* ... 028 7136 6612

Kearney Sefton
- Belfast *p878* ... 028 9023 2940

Sharon Keeley
- Armagh *p876* ... 028 3751 1622

Francis Keenan
- Belfast *p878* ... 028 9032 1409
- *p878* ... 028 9032 9011

Keenan Solicitors
- Belfast *p878* ... 028 9049 3349

Anne Kelly & Co Solicitors
- Cookstown *p879* ... 028 8676 9141

Brian Kelly
- Belfast *p878* ... 028 9059 3030

Emmet J Kelly
- Banbridge *p877* ... 028 4062 9397
- Hilltown *p880* ... 028 6790 1636

Maurice Kempton
- Armagh *p876* ... 028 3752 3875

E&L Kennedy
- Belfast *p878* ... 028 9023 2352

Hazel K E Kennedy
- Coleraine *p879* ... 028 7035 6346

Kennedy Hughes & Co
- Dungannon *p880* ... 028 8772 5554

Paul J Kennedy
- Banbridge *p877* ... 028 4062 4757

Robert Kennedy
- Dundonald *p880* ... 028 9041 8962

Kennedys
- Belfast *p878* ... 028 9024 0067

Keown Solicitors
- Belfast *p878* ... 028 9045 6042

Michael Kilfeather
- Limavady *p881* ... 028 7772 2996

King & Boyd
- Downpatrick *p880* ... 028 4461 2035

King & Gowdy
- Belfast *p878* ... 028 9065 9511

Eamonn P King
- Castlewellan *p879* ... 028 4477 1049

John R Kirk
- Lisburn *p881* ... 028 9269 3336

Pauline Knight & Co
- Belfast *p878* ... 028 9050 9666

L

Patrick Laverty & Co
- Omagh *p882* ... 028 8224 6048

E J Lavery & Co
- Glengormley *p880* ... 028 9084 3436

Brian Leeson Solicitors
- Belfast *p878* ... 028 9022 0400

Lennon Toner & O'Neill
- Armagh *p876* ... 028 3752 2527

G A H Lockhart
- Antrim *p876* ... 028 9446 2636

Joseph Lockhart & Son
- Lisburn *p881* ... 028 9266 3225

Logan & Corry
- Omagh *p882* ... 028 8225 0400

John G Logue & Co
- Londonderry *p881* ... 028 7137 1656

Oliver M Loughran
- Omagh *p882* ... 028 8224 1530

Michael D Loughrey
- Glengormley *p880* ... 028 9084 8116

Anthony G Lundy & Co
- Belfast *p878* ... 028 9037 0930
- *p878* ... 028 9066 3995

M

C M McAlister
- Belfast *p878* ... 028 9077 1939

E F McAllister & Co
- Lisburn *p881* ... 028 9265 2799

MacAllister Keenan & Co
- Larne *p880* ... 028 2827 8844

T S McAllister & Son
- Ballymena *p876* ... 028 2565 2469

C T McAlpine & Son
- Aughnacloy *p876* ... 028 8555 7951
- Dungannon *p880* ... 028 8772 2718

McAteer & Co
- Belfast *p878* ... 028 9047 1480

Macaulay & Ritchie
- Belfast *p878* ... 028 9032 9696
- Larne *p880* ... 028 2827 2038

James J Macaulay
- Carrickfergus *p879* ... 028 9336 8568

Macaulay Wray
- Coleraine *p879* ... 028 7035 2421
- Portstewart *p883* ... 028 7083 2564

James Macauley
- Newtownabbey *p882* ... 028 9084 4926

McBurney & Co
- Banbridge *p877* ... 028 4066 2226
- Kilkeel *p880* ... 028 4176 3906
- Newcastle *p882* ... 028 4372 5066

Ciaran J McCaffrey & Co
- Belfast *p878* ... 028 9060 0666

John McCaffrey & Company
- Omagh *p882* ... 028 8224 3902

McCallum O'Kane
- Coleraine *p879* ... 028 7032 7112

McCann & Greyston
- Belfast *p878* ... 028 9024 6098

McCann & McCann
- Belfast *p878* ... 028 9022 2298
- *p878* ... 028 9029 8880
- *p878* ... 028 9029 9999

Jack McCann & Son
- Ballymena *p876* ... 028 2564 2388
- *p876* ... 028 2565 4226

McCanny & Keohane
- Strabane *p883* ... 028 7188 3374

McCartan Turkington Breen
- Belfast *p878* ... 028 9032 9801
- Kilkeel *p880* ... 028 4176 3333

McCartney & Casey
- Londonderry *p881* ... 028 7128 8888

A D McClay & Co
- Waterside *p883* ... 028 7134 5666

McCloskeys
- Belfast *p878* ... 028 9024 0310

Gerard McClure & Co
- Belfast *p878* ... 028 9070 9348

McCollum & Co
- Belfast *p878* ... 028 9032 5852

Joseph F McCollum & Co
- Newtownards *p882* ... 028 9181 3142

McConaghie Lynch
- Ballymena *p876* ... 028 2565 4226

McConnell & Fyffe
- Omagh *p882* ... 028 8224 2099

McConnell Kelly & Co
- Bangor *p877* ... 028 9147 9900
- Belfast *p878* ... 028 9065 5511
- Dundonald *p880* ... 028 9048 9816

MacCorkell Legal & Commercial
- Lisburn *p881* ... 028 9266 9555

D G McCormick & Co
- Belfast *p878* ... 028 9062 2738

McCoubrey-Hinds
- Bangor *p877* ... 028 9127 1916

Terence McCourt
- Lisburn *p881* ... 028 9267 8122

MJT McCullagh
- Omagh, 028 8224 9494 ext: 242 *p882*

McCullough & Co
- Dundonald *p880* ... 028 9048 2800

MacDermott & McGurk
- Londonderry *p881* ... 028 7126 4415

MacElhatton & Co
- Belfast *p878* ... 028 9032 1776
- *p878* ... 028 9060 2828

C H McElhenny LLB
- Ballymena *p876* ... 028 2564 6007

McElhinney McDaid & Hegarty
- Londonderry *p881* ... 028 7137 3365 / 7137 3496

McElhone & Co
- Portadown *p883* ... 028 3835 0464

Eamonn McEvoy & Co
- Lurgan *p881* ... 028 3832 7734

John F McEvoy & Co
- Lurgan *p881* ... 028 3832 6977

McEvoy Sheridan Solicitors
- Belfast *p878* ... 028 9069 4444

McFadden Perry
- Bangor *p877* ... 028 9147 9494

McFarland Graham McCombe
- Lisburn *p881* ... 028 9267 4447

John McGale Kelly & Co
- Omagh *p882* ... 028 8223 3621

James E McGovern & Co
- Belfast *p878* ... 028 9068 1850

D G McGowan
- Belfast *p878* ... 028 9023 1792

McGrady Collins
- Downpatrick *p880* ... 028 4461 6411

John McGrane & Company
- Portadown *p883* ... 028 3839 1787

McGrigors LLP
- Belfast *p878* ... 028 9027 8800

P J McGrory & Co
- Belfast *p878* ... 028 9060 2986

Patrick J J McGuckin
- Maghera *p881* ... 028 7964 4199

McGuigan Solicitors
- Newry *p882* ... 028 3026 7939

McGuinness & Canavan
- Londonderry *p881* ... 028 7126 3562

Sean McHugh
- Enniskillen *p880* ... 028 6632 4611

McIldowies
- Belfast *p878* ... 028 9032 6411

Gordon F W McIlrath & Co
- Ballymena *p876* ... 028 2564 3036

Lara McIlroy Solicitors
- Coleraine *p879* ... 028 7032 7755

McIlveen Solicitors
- Belfast *p878* ... 028 9032 2335

Dominic McInerney
- Newcastle *p882* ... 028 4372 5238

Fergus McIntosh
- Coleraine *p879* ... 028 7035 1248

McIvor Farrell
- Belfast *p878* ... 028 9032 4565

McIvor Magill
- Belfast *p878* ... 028 9024 4299

John McKee & Son
- Belfast *p878* ... 028 9023 2303

Kenneth McKee
- Belfast *p878* ... 028 9031 3233
- Lisburn *p881* ... 028 9260 5525

McKenna Boyd
- Belfast *p878* ... 028 9073 9979

Daniel A McKenna & Co
- Coleraine *p879* ... 028 7035 3800

MacKenzie & Dorman
- Belfast *p878* ... 028 9067 3211

McKeone & Co
- Londonderry *p881* ... 028 7126 5566

Harry McKibben & Co
- Belfast *p878* ... 028 9066 5651

McKinty & Wright
- Belfast *p878* ... 028 9024 6751

George L MacLaine & Co
- Belfast *p878* ... 028 9024 3126
- Holywood *p880* ... 028 9039 7977
- Larne *p880* ... 028 2827 3937

McLaughlin & Co
- Belfast *p878* ... 028 9080 7000

John G McLaughlin
- Belfast *p878* ... 028 9049 1133

McLernon & McCann
- Magherafelt *p881* ... 028 7963 2533

Patrick McMahon
- Lurgan *p881* ... 028 3834 1330
- Newry *p882* ... 028 3083 5885

McManus & Kearney
- Belfast *p878* ... 028 9024 3658

McMillan & Ervine
- Saintfield *p883* ... 028 9751 9082

Paul McMullan
- Ballynahinch *p876* ... 028 9756 2357

John J McNally & Co
Magherafelt *p881* 028 7963 1537

James J W McNinch & Son
Ballyclare *p876* 028 9332 2217
Carrickfergus *p879* 028 9336 8238
Larne *p880* 028 2827 2010

James J W McNinch & Son
Glengormley *p880* 028 9083 6480

James McNulty & Co
Omagh *p882* 028 8224 5695

Harry McPartland & Sons
Lisburn *p881* 028 9267 0325
Lurgan *p881* 028 3832 2452

McQueenie Boyle
Bangor *p877* 028 9147 0030

John McRobert & Co
Ballynahinch *p876* 028 9756 2209

McShane & Co
Kilkeel *p880* 028 4176 2445
Newry *p882* 028 3026 6611

John McStravick
Armagh *p876* 028 3752 7999

Madden & Finucane
Belfast *p878* 028 9023 8007

Francis J Madden
Coalisland *p879* 028 8774 8840

Magennis & Creighton
Newtownabbey *p882* 028 9036 5777

W G Maginess & Son
Ballynahinch *p876* 028 9756 3982
Lisburn *p881* 028 9267 2161

Maguire & Corrigan
Enniskillen *p880* 028 6632 4724 / 6632 4110

Gerard Maguire
Portadown *p883* 028 3839 3488

Mallon & Anderson
Dungannon *p880* 028 8722 2680

Mallon & Mallon
Dungannon *p880* 028 8775 2959

L J Mallon & Co
Armagh *p876* 028 3752 2512

Mallon McCormick
Maghera *p881* 028 7964 2670

Hugh B Marley
Portadown *p883* 028 3833 5418

David A Martin
Antrim *p876* 028 9446 1509

Martin King French & Ingram
Limavady *p881* 028 7776 2307

Charles Maunsell
Belfast *p878* 028 9061 3788

Timothy Mayes LLB
Portadown *p883* 028 3835 0949

T G Menary & Co
Lurgan *p881* 028 3832 7811

Meyler McGuigan
Omagh *p882* 028 8225 7777

Millar McCall Wylie
Belfast *p878* 028 9020 0050

Millar Shearer & Black
Cookstown *p879* 028 8676 2346
Dungannon *p880* 028 8775 3111

Mills Selig
Belfast *p878* 028 9024 3878

Minnis & Braden
Bangor *p877* 028 9127 2334
Belfast *p878* 028 9077 6422

Thomas T Montague
Enniskillen *p880* 028 6632 4233
Fintona *p880* 028 8284 1251
Irvinestown *p880* 028 6772 1274

Richard Monteith
Belfast *p878* 028 9031 1550
Portadown *p883* 028 3833 0780

Gerard P Mooney
Cookstown *p879* 028 8676 9100

Morgan & Murphy
Belfast *p878* 028 9024 4545

K J Morgan
Armagh *p876* 028 3752 4790

Morris & Co
Derrylin *p879* 028 6774 8265

Morrison & Broderick
Belfast *p878* 028 9032 8822

Morrow & Wells
Belfast *p878* 028 9023 3866

Bernadette Mulholland
Magherafelt *p881* 028 7963 2030

Denis E Mullan
Londonderry *p881* 028 7136 8292

Robert A Mullan & Son
Newry *p882* 028 3026 1611

James Murland & Co
Carryduff *p879* 028 9081 4344
Downpatrick *p880* 028 4461 9980

Murnaghan & Fee
Enniskillen *p880* 028 6632 2819
Fivemiletown *p880* 028 6652 1409

Murnaghan Colton
Omagh *p882* 028 8224 2744

C Murnion & Co
Kilkeel *p880* 028 4176 9088

Murphy & McManus
Enniskillen *p880* 028 6632 2933
Lisnaskea *p881* 028 6772 1012

Murphy & O'Rawe
Belfast *p878* 028 9032 6636

Murphy Carey
Ballymoney *p876* 028 2766 2132

Peter Murphy LLM
Lurgan *p881* 028 3834 8150

S G Murphy & Co
Newtownabbey *p882* 028 9036 5595

Murphys Solicitors
Holywood *p880* 028 9039 7771

Murray McCourt Kelly
Bangor *p877* 028 9127 0000

Murtagh Breen & Co
Belfast *p878* 028 9043 4550
p878 028 9074 4594

N

David J Nagra & Co
Londonderry *p881* 028 7126 6877

Napier & Sons
Belfast *p878* 028 9024 4602

Neal McAllister
Larne *p881* 028 2827 7550

Nelson-Singleton
Dromore *p880* 028 9269 3475
Markethill *p882* 028 3755 2199

Nesbitt
Belfast *p878* 028 9047 1851

Nesbitt Solicitors
Belfast *p878* 028 9045 4005

Nixon & Co
Belfast *p878* 028 9071 9703

Paul K Nolan & Co
Belfast *p878* 028 9030 1113

O

James O'Brien & Co
Ballycastle *p876* 028 2076 9797
Magherafelt *p881* 028 7930 0577

O'Connor & Moriarty
Lurgan *p881* 028 3834 3611

Con O'Hagan
Lurgan *p881* 028 3832 4511

J G O'Hare & Co
Belfast *p878* 028 9023 4800
Hilltown *p880* 028 4063 8858

Paschal J O'Hare
Belfast *p878* 028 9031 3613
Carrickfergus *p879* 028 9336 1184

Carmel O'Meara & Co
Coalisland *p879* 028 8774 7919
Dungannon *p880* 028 8775 2455

M T O'Neill
Omagh *p882* 028 8224 5025

O'Reilly Stewart
Belfast *p878* 028 9032 1000

O'Rorke McDonald & Tweed
Antrim *p876* 028 9446 3108
Larne *p881* 028 2827 2291

O'Toole & MacRandal
Belfast *p878* 028 9020 3000

Kieran O'Toole & Co
Downpatrick *p880* 028 4461 5153

Orr & Co
Belfast *p878* 028 9023 0101

Orr & Rountree
Omagh *p882* 028 8224 3151

F A Edward Orr
Banbridge *p877* 028 4066 2609

P

P C Donaghy Meehan Murphy
Dunmurry *p880* 028 9061 2144

Patrick Park
Lurgan *p881* 028 3832 7436

Patterson Donnelly
Bangor *p877* 028 9127 4644
Newtownards *p882* 028 9181 1411

Patterson Taylor & Co
Belfast *p879* 028 9023 5987

Fergus G Patton
Dungannon *p880* 028 8772 4333

Peden & Reid
Belfast *p879* 028 9032 5617

Stephen Perrott & Co
Holywood *p880* 028 9042 2505
p880 028 9042 8330

John W Pinkerton & Son
Ballymoney *p876* 028 2766 2133

Porter & McCanny
Castlederg *p879* 028 8167 1234

Q

Aidan Quinn
Dungannon *p880* 028 8775 2088

John Quinn
Enniskillen *p880* 028 6632 6008

R

Rafferty & Boyle
Coleraine *p879* 028 7034 3483

Rafferty & Donaghy
Dungannon *p880* 028 8772 7055

T P Rafferty LLB
Limavady *p881* 028 7772 2214

Raffertys Solicitors
Newry *p882* 028 3026 1102

J C W Rea & Co
Belfast *p879* 028 9024 7121

Richard M Redman
Lurgan *p881* 028 3832 7531

Reevey & Co Solicitors
Newtownabbey *p882* 028 9086 0335

Reid & Co
Lisburn *p881* 028 9266 3310

Reid Black & Co
Ballyclare *p876* 028 9335 2221

J G Rice & Co
Ballynahinch *p876* 028 9756 2726

John J Rice & Co
Armagh *p876* 028 3752 7402
Belfast *p879* 028 9028 8688
p879 028 9035 1510
Newtownards *p882* 028 9182 2323

J J Roche
Newtownstewart *p882* 028 8166 1254

Oliver Roche
Strabane *p883* 028 7188 3377

Rodgers & Co
Belfast *p879* 028 9038 6464

James H Rodgers
Portadown *p883* 028 3833 7211

John Ross & Son
Newtownards *p882* 028 9181 3173

David Russell & Co
Bangor *p877* 028 9127 4022

James L Russell & Son
Ballymena *p876* 028 2565 2154

Russells
Newtownards *p882* 028 9181 4444

S

M S Sandhu & Company
Limavady *p881* 028 7772 2594

Savage & Co
Belfast *p879* 028 9024 9969

Stephen Scott & Co
Newtownards *p882* 028 9182 1700

Norman Shannon & Co
Belfast *p879* 028 9023 1179
Dromore *p880* 028 9269 9103

Shean Dickson Merrick
Belfast *p879* 028 9032 6878

Sheldon & Stewart
Belfast *p879* 028 9032 7691

Sheridan & Co
Downpatrick *p880* 028 4483 9944

Sheridan & Leonard
Antrim *p876* 028 9442 8271
Belfast *p879* 028 9043 8833

Simmons Meglaughlin & Orr
Dungannon *p880* 028 8772 2016

Robert G Sinclair & Co
Belfast *p879* 028 9023 1770

Skelton & Co
Belfast *p879* 028 9024 1661
Carrickfergus *p879* 028 9081 4344

John P Slevin
Lisburn *p881* 028 9266 8700

Small & Marken
Antrim *p876* 028 9446 8000

Philip J Smith & Co
Belfast *p879* 028 9066 1116

Trevor Smyth & Co
Belfast *p879* 028 9032 0360
p879 028 9074 4994
Newtownards *p882* 028 9181 3113

Ciaran P Steele
Belfast *p879* 028 9043 5345

Stelfox Solicitors
Limavady *p881* 028 7134 8855

Stewarts Solicitors
Ballymena *p876* 028 2565 1414
Belfast *p879* 028 9031 2777
Kircubbin *p880* 028 4273 8999
Newtownards *p882* 028 9182 6444

Sullivans
Belfast *p879* 028 9071 7222

T

T Taggart & Sons
Ballymoney *p876* 028 2766 2118

Thompson Crooks
Belfast *p879* 028 9059 5551

Thompson Mitchell
Hillsborough *p880* 028 9268 9666
Portadown *p883* 028 3833 7172

W B Thompson & Co
Limavady *p881* 028 7772 2400

Thompsons
Newtownards *p882* 028 9181 1652

Thompsons (formerly Robin/Brian Thompson & Partners)
Belfast *p879* 028 9089 0400

Tiernans
Crossmaglen *p879* 028 3086 1066
Newry *p882* 028 3026 3222

Toal & Heron
Cookstown *p879* 028 8676 2395

Murty M Toolan & Co
Belfast *p879* 028 9024 1840

Elliott Trainor Partnership Solicitors
Newry *p882* 028 3026 8116

Adrian Travers
Banbridge *p877* 028 4062 9990

Tughans
Belfast *p879* 028 9055 3300
Londonderry *p881* 028 7127 8111

Tully & Co
Holywood *p880* 028 9042 2556

Stephen Tumelty
Belfast *p879* 028 9061 8877

J B & R H Twigg
Cookstown *p879* 028 8676 2225

V

Liam Vallely & Co
Belfast *p879* 028 9062 4442

W

Dermot Walker & Co
Londonderry *p881* 028 7126 3082

E M Walker & Co
Newtownabbey *p882* 028 9034 2568

Walker McDonald
Portadown *p883* 028 3833 1086

Gordon Wallace & Co
Armagh *p876* 028 3752 3676

Wallace Harris & Robb
Belfast *p879* 028 9032 7970

Tara Walsh
Newry *p882* 028 3025 0920

Elizabeth R Warden
Newtownards *p882* 028 9181 1644

Watson & Neill
Lurgan *p881* 028 3832 5111
Moira *p882* 028 9261 1900

M L White
Newry *p882* 028 3026 8144

Wilson & Simms
Strabane *p883* 028 7188 2208

John G H Wilson & Co
Belfast *p879* 028 9032 2301

Wilson Nesbitt
Belfast *p879* 028 9032 3864

Noel Wilson & Co
Glengormley *p880* 028 9083 6682

Kevin R Winters & Co
Belfast *p879* 028 9024 1888
Downpatrick *p880* 028 4483 9111

Worthingtons
Bangor *p877* 028 9147 5929
Belfast *p879* 028 9043 4015
Newtownards *p882* 028 9181 1538

Wylie & Co
Castlereagh *p879* 028 9070 9129

SECTION 8

SOLICITORS

SCOTLAND

CONTENTS

FIRMS, SCOTLAND – BY TOWN

ABERDEEN

ABERDEIN CONSIDINE & CO
7-9 Bon-Accord Crescent Aberdeen AB11 6DN
Tel: 01224 589700 *Fax:* 01224 572575 *Dx:* AB46 ABERDEEN
E-mail: mail@acandco.com

413 & 415 Union Street Aberdeen AB11 6DA
Tel: 01224 589589 *Fax:* 01224 589456 *Dx:* AB46 ABERDEEN
E-mail: propshop@acandco.com

MICHAEL S ALLAN
9 Byron Square Northfield Aberdeen AB16 7LL
Tel: 01224 696968 *Fax:* 01224 696363
E-mail: michaelsallancdl@hotmail.com

GAVIN BAIN & COMPANY
432 Union Street Aberdeen AB10 1TR
Tel: 01224 623040 *Fax:* 01224 623050 *Dx:* AB40 ABERDEEN
E-mail: info@gavin-bain.co.uk

BURN & MCGREGOR
48a Union Street Aberdeen AB10 1BB
Tel: 01224 639660 *Fax:* 01224 635525
E-mail: enquiries@burnandmcgregor.com

BURNETT & COMPANY
6 Kings Gate Aberdeen AB15 4EJ
Tel: 01224 648797 *Fax:* 01224 647175
E-mail: burnettco@hotmail.com

BURNETT & REID
15 Golden Square Aberdeen AB10 1WF
Tel: 01224 644333 *Fax:* 01224 632173 *Dx:* AB19 ABERDEEN
E-mail: mail@burnett-reid.co.uk

CMS CAMERON MCKENNA
6 Queens Road Aberdeen AB15 4ZT
Tel: 01224 622002 *Fax:* 01224 622066 *Dx:* AB64 ABERDEEN

CAMPBELL CONNON
36 Albyn Place Aberdeen AB10 1YF
Tel: 01224 585585 *Fax:* 01224 580766 *Dx:* AB14 ABERDEEN
E-mail: info@campbellconnon.co.uk

ADAM COCHRAN
6 Bon-Accord Square Aberdeen AB11 6XU
Tel: 01224 588913 *Fax:* 01224 581149 *Dx:* AB1 ABERDEEN
E-mail: adamco@btinternet.com

MATTHEW COHEN & ASSOCIATES
269 Holburn Street Aberdeen AB10 7FL
Tel: 01224 433301 *Fax:* 01224 433302

JAMES & GEORGE COLLIE
1 East Craibstone Street Aberdeen AB11 6YQ
Tel: 01224 581581 *Fax:* 01224 580119 *Dx:* AB43 ABERDEEN

CRAIGENS
13 Bon-Accord Crescent Aberdeen AB11 6NN
Tel: 01224 588295 *Fax:* 01224 575400
E-mail: info@craigens.com

DUTHIE WARD
42 Carden Place Aberdeen AB10 1UP
Tel: 01224 621622 *Fax:* 01224 621623
E-mail: info@duthieward.co.uk

ESSLEMONT CAMERON GAULD
18 Carden Place Aberdeen AB10 1UQ
Tel: 01224 632244 *Fax:* 01224 631729 *Dx:* AB9 ABERDEEN
E-mail: mail@ecglaw.co.uk

FRASER & MULLIGAN
1 Carden Place Aberdeen AB10 1UT
Tel: 01224 646428 *Fax:* 01224 643773 *Dx:* AB23 ABERDEEN
E-mail: mail@fraser-mulligan.co.uk

GAIL GOODFELLOW & CO
52 Victoria Road Torry Aberdeen AB11 9DR
Tel: 01224 878417 *Fax:* 01224 896535
E-mail: info@gailgoodfellow.com

GRAY & CONNOCHIE
Suite 1 Braehead Way Bridge of Don Aberdeen AB22 8RR
Tel: 01224 823282 *Fax:* 01224 826394 *Dx:* AB21 ABERDEEN
E-mail: info@graycon.co.uk

6 Alford Place Aberdeen AB10 1YD
Tel: 01224 649101 *Fax:* 01224 649102 *Dx:* AB21 ABERDEEN
E-mail: info@graycon.co.uk

ALASTAIR HART & CO
11 The Green Berrymuir Road Portlethen Aberdeen AB12 4UN
Tel: 01224 784855 *Fax:* 01224 784856
E-mail: portlethen@alastairhart.co.uk

76a Counteswells Road Seafield Shopping Centre Aberdeen AB15 7YJ
Tel: 01224 310600 *Fax:* 01224 310604
E-mail: info@alastairhart.co.uk

MICHAEL HORSMAN & CO
11 Back Wynd Aberdeen AB10 1JN
Tel: 01224 633333 *Fax:* 01224 620099

HOUGHTON MELVIN SMITH & CO
15a Victoria Street Aberdeen AB10 1XB
Tel: 01224 641555 *Fax:* 01224 639517 *Dx:* AB65 ABERDEEN
E-mail: info@houghtonmelvinsmith.co.uk

ALEX HUTCHEON & CO
248 Union Street Aberdeen AB10 1TN
Tel: 01224 623400 *Fax:* 01224 623401

BRYAN KEENAN & CO
38 Chapel Street Aberdeen AB10 1SP
Tel: 01224 648080 *Fax:* 01224 620863 *Dx:* AB56 ABERDEEN
E-mail: property@bryankeenan.co.uk

23 Rubislaw Terrace Aberdeen AB10 1XE
Tel: 01224 638996 *Fax:* 01224 647099 *Dx:* AB56 ABERDEEN
E-mail: rubislaw@bryankeenan.co.uk

LAURIE & CO
17 Victoria Street Aberdeen AB10 1PU
Tel: 01224 645085 *Fax:* 01224 645114 *Dx:* AB16 ABERDEEN
E-mail: info@laurieandco.co.uk

LEDINGHAM CHALMERS
Johnstone House 52-54 Rose Street Aberdeen AB10 1HA
Tel: 01224 408408 *Fax:* 01224 408400 *Dx:* AB15 ABERDEEN
E-mail: mail@ledinghamchalmers.com

LEFEVRE LITIGATION
70 Carden Place Queen's Cross Aberdeen AB10 1UL
Tel: 01224 657657 *Fax:* 01224 626917 *Dx:* AB79 ABERDEEN
E-mail: gjk@lefevre-litigation.com

BRUCE MACDONALD & CO
6 Albert Place Aberdeen AB25 1RG
Tel: 01224 643332 *Fax:* 01224 643334

MCDOUGALL & CO
21 Carden Place Aberdeen AB10 1UQ
Tel: 01224 632663 *Fax:* 01224 638913
E-mail: enquiries@mcdougallandco.co.uk

MCINTOSH MCTAGGART
52-54 Albert Street Aberdeen AB25 1XS
Tel: 01224 593100 *Fax:* 01224 593200
E-mail: info@mcintoshmctaggart.com

MACKIE & DEWAR
18 Bon-Accord Square Aberdeen AB11 6YP
Tel: 01224 596341 *Fax:* 01224 574327 *Dx:* AB11 ABERDEEN 1
E-mail: info@mackieanddewar.co.uk

MACKINNONS
14 Carden Place Aberdeen AB10 1UR
Tel: 01224 632464 *Fax:* 01224 632184 *Dx:* AB34 ABERDEEN
E-mail: admin@mackinnons.com

379 North Deeside Road Cults Aberdeen AB15 9SX
Tel: 01224 868687 *Fax:* 01224 861012 *Dx:* AB34 ABERDEEN
E-mail: admin@mackinnons.com

MACLAY MURRAY & SPENS
66 Queens Road Aberdeen AB15 4YE
Tel: 01224 356130 *Fax:* 01224 356131 *Dx:* AB17 ABERDEEN

MASTERS LEGAL SERVICES
85 Rosemount Viaduct Aberdeen AB25 1NS
Tel: 01224 652352 *Fax:* 01224 652356
E-mail: info@linmasters.co.uk

GEORGE MATHERS & CO
23 Adelphi Aberdeen AB11 5BL
Tel: 01224 588599 *Fax:* 01224 584147
E-mail: georgemathers@aol.com

A C MORRISON & RICHARDS
18 Bon-Accord Crescent Aberdeen AB11 6XY
Tel: 01224 573321 *Fax:* 01224 576115 *Dx:* AB50 ABERDEEN
E-mail: info@acmr.co.uk

GRAEME MURRAY & CO
17 Menzies Road Torry Aberdeen AB11 9AX
Tel: 01224 897766 *Fax:* 01224 874147

PATIENCE & BUCHAN
10 Golden Square Aberdeen AB10 1RB
Tel: 01224 648222 *Fax:* 01224 648848
E-mail: iain@patienceandbuchan.com

PAULL & WILLIAMSONS
Union Plaza 1 Union Wynd Aberdeen AB10 1DQ
Tel: 01224 621621 *Fax:* 01224 627437 *Dx:* AB35 ABERDEEN
E-mail: info@paull-williamsons.co.uk

PETERKINS
100 Union Street Aberdeen AB10 1QR
Tel: 01224 428000 *Fax:* 01224 626123 *Dx:* AB3 ABERDEEN
E-mail: propcen@peterkins.com

PLENDERLEATH RUNCIE
Anderson House 24 Rose Street Aberdeen AB10 1UA
Tel: 01224 640666 *Fax:* 01224 639658 *Dx:* AB125 ABERDEEN
E-mail: mail@plenrun.com

PROACTIVE EMPLOYMENT LAWYERS
7 Queens Gardens Aberdeen AB15 4YD
Tel: 01224 619208

RAEBURN CHRISTIE CLARK & WALLACE
12-16 Albyn Place Aberdeen AB10 1PS
Tel: 01224 332400 *Fax:* 01224 332401 *Dx:* AB2 ABERDEEN
E-mail: info@raeburns.co.uk

SIMPSON & MARWICK
4 Carden Terrace Aberdeen AB10 1US
Tel: 01224 624924 *Fax:* 01224 626590 *Dx:* AB6 ABERDEEN
E-mail: email@simpmar.com

PAT SINCLAIR & CO
39 Albert Street Aberdeen AB25 1XU
Tel: 01224 626070 *Fax:* 01224 626050 *Dx:* AB106 ABERDEEN
E-mail: info@patsinclair.com

GRANT SMITH LAW PRACTICE
Amicable House 252 Union Street Aberdeen AB10 1TN
Tel: 01224 621620 *Fax:* 01224 622621 *Dx:* AB529443 ABERDEEN 6

IAIN SMITH & CO
18 Queen's Road Aberdeen AB15 4ZT
Tel: 01224 626250 *Fax:* 01224 626912 *Dx:* AB4 ABERDEEN 1
E-mail: dorothy@iainsmith.com

SOLICITORS DIRECT
4 Golden Square Aberdeen AB10 1RD
Tel: 01224 643000 *Fax:* 01224 643101 *Dx:* AB29 ABERDEEN

STORIE CRUDEN & SIMPSON
2 Bon-Accord Crescent Aberdeen AB11 6DH
Tel: 01224 587261 *Fax:* 01224 580850 *Dx:* AB12 ABERDEEN
E-mail: info@storiecs.co.uk

STRONACHS
34 Albyn Place Aberdeen AB10 1FW
Tel: 01224 845845 *Fax:* 01224 845800 *Dx:* AB41 ABERDEEN
E-mail: info@stronachs.com

TAGGART MEIL MATHERS
20 Bon-Accord Square Aberdeen AB11 6DJ
Tel: 01224 588020 *Fax:* 01224 588030 *Dx:* AB93 ABERDEEN
E-mail: info@tmmsolicitors.co.uk

JONATHAN TAIT & CO
9 Crown Street Aberdeen AB11 6HA
Tel: 01224 582211 *Fax:* 01224 584343 *Dx:* AB51 ABERDEEN
E-mail: info@jonathantait.co.uk

WILSONE & DUFFUS
1 Watson Street Aberdeen AB25 2QB
Tel: 01224 625032 *Fax:* 01224 625205 *Dx:* AB24 ABERDEEN
E-mail: info@key-moves.co.uk

7 Golden Square Aberdeen AB10 1EP
Tel: 01224 651700 *Fax:* 01224 647329 *Dx:* AB24 ABERDEEN
E-mail: info@key-moves.co.uk

ABOYNE

CAMPBELL CONNON
The Hall Charleston Road Aboyne Aberdeenshire AB34 5EJ
Tel: 01339 886732 *Fax:* 01339 887303 *Dx:* AB14 ABERDEEN
E-mail: aboyne@campbellconnon.co.uk

AIRDRIE

BELL RUSSELL & CO
111 Graham Street Airdrie North Lanarkshire ML6 6DE
Tel: 01236 764781 *Fax:* 01236 764009 *Dx:* 570410 AIRDRIE

BONNAR & CO
61a Stirling Street Airdrie North Lanarkshire ML6 0AS
Tel: 0800 163978 *Fax:* 01236 761899 *Dx:* 570411 AIRDRIE

CARTY'S
10a Anderson Street Airdrie North Lanarkshire ML6 0AA
Tel: 01236 761127 *Fax:* 01236 753858
E-mail: airdrie@cartylaw.co.uk

HAMILTON ROSS
18 Anderson Street Airdrie North Lanarkshire ML6 0AA
Tel: 01236 627627 *Fax:* 01236 627628 *Dx:* 570426 AIRDRIE

MFY PARTNERSHIP
71 South Bridge Street Airdrie North Lanarkshire ML6 6JH
Tel: 01236 607180 *Fax:* 01236 607181
E-mail: office@themfypartnership.co.uk

MCAFEE
81 Graham Street Airdrie North Lanarkshire ML6 6DE
Tel: 01236 755339 *Fax:* 01236 755339 *Dx:* 570422 AIRDRIE

MCCARRON & CO
Bank House 17 East High Street Airdrie North Lanarkshire ML6 6LF
Tel: 01236 762012 *Fax:* 01236 748459

MCWHINNEY RICHARDS
8a Bank Street Airdrie North Lanarkshire ML6 6AF
Tel: 01236 754571 *Fax:* 01236 765339
E-mail: general@mcwhinneyrichards.com

MALCOLM & HUTCHISON
34-36 Alexandra Street Airdrie North Lanarkshire ML6 0BA
Tel: 01236 755050 *Fax:* 01236 747470
E-mail: ann@malcolmandhutchison.co.uk

NICOLSON O'BRIEN
12 Stirling Street Airdrie North Lanarkshire ML6 0AH
Tel: 01236 751224 *Fax:* 01236 748205 *Dx:* 570415 AIRDRIE
E-mail: maildesk@nicolsonobrien.co.uk

ALEXANDRIA

CAIRNS BROWN
112 Main Street Alexandria West Dunbartonshire G83 0NZ
Tel: 01389 756979 *Fax:* 01389 754281
E-mail: mail@cairnsbrown.co.uk

MY LAWYERS
134 Main Street Alexandria West Dunbartonshire G83 0NZ
Tel: 01389 755235 *Fax:* 01389 755282 *Dx:* 501102 ALEXANDRIA
E-mail: mail@mylawyers.co.uk

STIRLING & GILMOUR
24 Gilmour Street Alexandria West Dunbartonshire G83 0DB
Tel: 01389 752641 *Fax:* 01389 758258 *Dx:* 501103 ALEXANDRIA

ALFORD

JOHN DAVIE & COMPANY
Archballoch Business Centre Alford Aberdeenshire AB33 8HP
Tel: 01224 656356 *Fax:* 01975 563813
E-mail: mail@johndavieandco.com

PETERKINS
39 Main Street Alford Aberdeenshire AB33 8PX
Tel: 01975 562939 *Fax:* 01975 563361
E-mail: maildesk@peterkins.com

ALLOA

CAESAR & HOWIE (IN ASSOC WITH WILSON & JARVIS)
27 Mar Street Alloa Clackmannanshire FK10 1HX
Tel: 01506 815900 *Fax:* 01259 724036 *Dx:* 560434 ALLOA
E-mail: enquiries@caesar-howie.co.uk

HIGGINS MORLEDGE & LITTERICK
2 Candleriggs Alloa Clackmannanshire FK10 1EA
Tel: 01259 725922 *Fax:* 01259 725923

JARDINE DONALDSON
18-22 Bank Street Alloa Clackmannanshire FK10 1HP
Tel: 01259 724411 *Fax:* 01259 213064
E-mail: stirling@jardinedonaldson.co.uk

MAILERS
70 Drysdale Street Alloa Clackmannanshire FK10 1JA
Tel: 01259 217009 *Fax:* 01259 219346
E-mail: mail@mailers.co.uk

RUSSEL & AITKEN
8 Shillinghill Alloa Clackmannanshire FK10 1JT
Tel: 01259 723201 *Fax:* 01259 219398 *Dx:* 560432 ALLOA
E-mail: info@russel-aitken.co.uk

ALNESS

MACMILLAN & CO
89 High Street Alness Highland IV17 0SH
Tel: 01349 883338 *Fax:* 01349 883338
E-mail: macmillanandco@btconnect.com

MIDDLETON ROSS & ARNOT
76 High Street Alness Highland IV17 0SG
Tel: 01349 882870
E-mail: lisa@middletonross.co.uk

ALYTH

A & R ROBERTSON & BLACK WS
11 Airlie Street Alyth Perth & Kinross PH11 8AH
Tel: 01828 632116
E-mail: admin@robertson-black.co.uk

ANNAN

HANN & CO
1 Bridgend High Street Annan Dumfries & Galloway DG12 6AD
Tel: 01461 203836 *Fax:* 01461 205634
E-mail: hannandco@gmail.com

HARPER ROBERTSON & SHANNON
100 High Street Annan Dumfries & Galloway DG12 6EH
Tel: 01461 203418 *Fax:* 01461 205057 *Dx:* 580400 ANNAN
E-mail: office@hrands.co.uk

MURRAY LITTLE & KNOX
27 Bank Street Annan Dumfries & Galloway DG12 6AU
Tel: 01461 202866 *Fax:* 01461 205995 *Dx:* 580402 ANNAN
E-mail: mlandk@mlandk.co.uk

JOHN RODDICK & SON
Royal Bank Buildings 52 High Street Annan Dumfries & Galloway DG12 6AL
Tel: 01461 202822 *Fax:* 01461 201822 *Dx:* 580403 ANNAN
E-mail: office@roddicks.co.uk

ANSTRUTHER

MURRAY DONALD DRUMMOND COOK
1 St Andrews Road Anstruther Fife KY10 3HA
Tel: 01333 310481 *Fax:* 01333 312279 *Dx:* 560996 ST ANDREWS
E-mail: mail@mddc.co.uk

PAGAN OSBORNE
5a Shore Street Anstruther Fife KY10 3EA
Tel: 01333 310703 *Fax:* 01333 311918 *Dx:* 561132 ANSTRUTHER
E-mail: webenquiry@pagan.co.uk

ARBROATH

BLACKADDERS
37 Commerce Street Arbroath Angus DD11 1NA
Tel: 01241 872087 *Fax:* 01241 872018
E-mail: arbroath@blackadders.co.uk

R BRUCE & CO
89-91 High Street Arbroath Angus DD11 1DP
Tel: 01241 430660 *Fax:* 01241 430144 *Dx:* 530450 ARBROATH
E-mail: info@bruce-co.co.uk

CONNELLY & YEOMAN
78 High Street Arbroath Angus DD11 1HL
Tel: 01241 434200 *Fax:* 01241 434100 *Dx:* 530449 ARBROATH
E-mail: enquiries@connellyyeoman.com

MARJORY MACDONALD
Bankhead Arbirlot Arbroath Angus DD11 2NS
Tel: 01241 874898 *Fax:* 01241 873501
E-mail: legal@marjorymacdonald.co.uk

SHIELD & KYD
207 High Street Arbroath Angus DD11 1DZ
Tel: 01241 870739 *Fax:* 01241 873593 *Dx:* 530447 ARBROATH
E-mail: arbroath@shieldandkyd.co.uk

THORNTONS WS
Brothockbank House Arbroath Angus DD11 1NE
Tel: 01241 872683 *Fax:* 01241 871541
E-mail: arbroath@thorntons-law.co.uk

ARDROSSAN

JAS CAMPBELL & CO WS
76 Princes Street Ardrossan North Ayrshire KA22 8DF
Tel: 01294 464131
E-mail: mail@jascampbell.co.uk

ARMADALE

SNEDDON & SON SSC
47-49 West Main Street Armadale West Lothian EH48 3PZ
Tel: 01501 733200 *Fax:* 01501 733155
E-mail: armadale@sneddonandson.com

AUCHINLECK

G TIERNEY & CO
189 Main Street Auchinleck East Ayrshire KA18 2BA
Tel: 01290 423311 *Fax:* 01290 423355

AUCHTERARDER

JAMESON & MACKAY
71 High Street Auchterarder Perth & Kinross PH3 1BN
Tel: 01764 663830 *Fax:* 01764 663135
E-mail: admin@jamesonmackay.co.uk

AYR

BLACK HAY & CO
5 Wellington Square Ayr South Ayrshire KA7 1EN
Tel: 01292 268988 *Fax:* 01292 610353

J & A B BOYD
33 Newmark Street Ayr South Ayrshire KA7 1LL
Tel: 01292 265073 *Fax:* 01292 610240 *Dx:* AY13 AYR
E-mail: jmjlaw@btconnect.com

R B CAMPBELL & CO
7 Wellington Square Ayr South Ayrshire KA7 1EN
Tel: 01292 261125 *Fax:* 01292 283755
E-mail: rbcampbellandco@tiscali.co.uk

D & J DUNLOP
2 Barns Street Ayr South Ayrshire KA7 1XD
Tel: 01292 264091 *Fax:* 01292 289856 *Dx:* AY3 AYR
E-mail: ayrlawhay@btinternet.com

FRAZER COOGANS
46 Dalblair Road Ayr South Ayrshire KA7 1UQ
Tel: 01292 280499 *Fax:* 01292 611645 / 01292 272601
Dx: AY29 AYR
E-mail: law@frazercoogans.co.uk

Dalblair House 46 Dalblair Road Ayr South Ayrshire KA7 1UQ
Tel: 01292 280499 *Fax:* 01292 611645 *Dx:* AY29 AYR
E-mail: law@frazercoogans.co.uk

J IAN GILLIES
Wellington Chambers 64-70 Fort Street Ayr South Ayrshire KA7 1EH
Tel: 01292 288860 *Fax:* 01292 282887 *Dx:* AY5 AYR
E-mail: jig@iangillies.com

KILPATRICK & WALKER
4 Wellington Square Ayr South Ayrshire KA7 1EN
Tel: 01292 618585 *Fax:* 01292 885678 *Dx:* AY45 AYR
E-mail: info@k-and-w.com

LAMBERT & CO
12 Cathcart Street Ayr South Ayrshire KA7 1BJ
Tel: 01292 282811 *Fax:* 01292 288028 *Dx:* AY38 AYR
E-mail: lambert.co@btconnect.com

LAMONTS
Miller Chambers 16 Miller Road Ayr South Ayrshire KA7 2AY
Tel: 01292 262266 *Fax:* 01292 610210 *Dx:* AY23 AYR
E-mail: mail@lamontslaw.co.uk

GEORGE S LOCKHART
9 Castle Walk Ayr South Ayrshire KA7 4HH
Tel: 01292 441127 *Fax:* 01292 445534
E-mail: gslockhart@tiscali.co.uk

LOCKHARTS
12 Bareford Terrace Ayr South Ayrshire KA7 2EG
Tel: 01292 265045
E-mail: info@lockhartslaw.com

THE MCKINSTRY COMPANY
25 Barns Street Ayr South Ayrshire KA7 1XB
Tel: 01292 281711 *Fax:* 01292 611636 *Dx:* AY25 AYR

Queen's Court House 39 Sandgate Ayr South Ayrshire KA7 1BE
Tel: 01292 281711 *Fax:* 01292 610206 *Dx:* AY8 AYR

MCLENNAN ADAM DAVIS
13 Alloway Place Ayr South Ayrshire KA7 2AA
Tel: 01292 289584 *Fax:* 01292 611034
E-mail: administrator@mad-law.co.uk

MCMILLAN KILPATRICK SSC
12 Alloway Place Ayr South Ayrshire KA7 2AG
Tel: 01292 264696 *Fax:* 01292 610647
E-mail: generalenq@mcmillankilpatrick.co.uk

MCNEILS
26 Wellington Square Ayr South Ayrshire KA7 1HH
Tel: 01292 886600 *Fax:* 01292 886611 *Dx:* AY40 AYR
E-mail: mail@mcneils.co.uk

MARTIN & COMPANY
2 Wellington Square Ayr South Ayrshire KA7 1EN
Tel: 01292 265024 *Fax:* 01292 610192 *Dx:* AY14 AYR
E-mail: martinandcompany@btinternet.com

MATHIE-MORTON BLACK & BUCHANAN
4 Alloway Place Ayr South Ayrshire KA7 2AD
Tel: 01292 263549 *Fax:* 01292 264944
E-mail: mailbox@mathie-morton.co.uk

D W SHAW
34a Sandgate Ayr South Ayrshire KA7 1BW
Tel: 01292 265033 *Fax:* 01292 284906 *Dx:* AY9 AYR
E-mail: enquiries@dwshaw.co.uk

8

SPRANG TERRAS
64 Kyle Street Ayr South Ayrshire KA7 1RZ
Tel: 01292 288300 *Fax:* 01292 288400
E-mail: mail@sprangterras.co.uk

WALLACE HODGE & CO
6 Killoch Place Ayr South Ayrshire KA7 2EA
Tel: 01292 611177 *Fax:* 01292 611977 *Dx:* AY49 AYR 1
E-mail: john.hodge@wallace-hodge.co.uk

ELIZABETH WELSH FAMILY LAW PRACTICE
26 Miller Road Ayr South Ayrshire KA7 2AY
Tel: 01292 284786 *Fax:* 01292 283739
E-mail: lizw@familylawpractice.co.uk

A C WHITE
23 Wellington Square Ayr South Ayrshire KA7 1HG
Tel: 01292 266900 *Fax:* 01292 610152 *Dx:* AY10 AYR
E-mail: mail@acwhiteayr.co.uk

AYTON

DOUGHTYS WS
High Street Ayton Scottish Borders TD14 5QH
Tel: 01890 781209 *Fax:* 01890 781601
E-mail: info@doughtys.co.uk

BALIVANICH

ANDERSON BANKS
6 Uachdar Balivanich Western Isles HS7 5LY
Tel: 01870 602061 *Fax:* 01870 602878
E-mail: info@andersonbanks.co.uk

BANCHORY

ABERDEIN CONSIDINE & CO
8 Dee Street Banchory Aberdeenshire AB31 5ST
Tel: 01330 824646 / 824647 *Fax:* 01330 824854
Dx: AB46 ABERDEEN
E-mail: ban@acandco.com

RAEBURN CHRISTIE CLARK & WALLACE
75 High Street Banchory Aberdeenshire AB31 5TJ
Tel: 01330 822931 *Fax:* 01330 824799
E-mail: banchory@raeburns.co.uk

BANFF

ALEXANDER GEORGE & CO
25 High Street Banff Aberdeenshire AB45 1AN
Tel: 01261 815678 *Fax:* 01261 818825
E-mail: banff@alexander-george.com

A & E A BRODIE
Royal Bank Buildings 40 High Street Banff Aberdeenshire AB45 1AL
Tel: 01261 812681 *Fax:* 01261 815594
E-mail: lesley@brodiebanff.co.uk

STEWART & WATSON
1 Catherine Street Banff Aberdeenshire AB45 1HU
Tel: 01261 815493 *Fax:* 01261 815082
E-mail: info@stewartwatson.co.uk

WILSON DEFENCE
17 Low Street Banff Aberdeenshire AB45 1AU
Tel: 01261 819831 *Fax:* 01261 819835
E-mail: info@wilsondefence.com

BARRHEAD

MACKINLAY & SUTTIE
The Centre 48 Cross Arthurlie Street Barrhead East Renfrewshire G78 1QU
Tel: 0141 881 1572 *Fax:* 0141 881 8269
E-mail: m.lynch@mackinlay-suttie.co.uk

TURNBULL & WARD
54 Main Street Barrhead East Renfrewshire G78 1RB
Tel: 0141 881 2357 *Fax:* 0141 881 8461 *Dx:* 501317 BARRHEAD

BATHGATE

CAESAR & HOWIE (IN ASSOC WITH WILSON & JARVIS)
64 George Street Bathgate West Lothian EH48 1PD
Tel: 01506 815900 *Fax:* 01506 815930 *Dx:* 540460 BATHGATE
E-mail: enquiries@caesar-howie.co.uk

DRUMMOND MILLER WS
64 South Bridge Street Bathgate West Lothian EH48 1TL
Tel: 01506 656645 *Fax:* 01506 652347 *Dx:* 540462 BATHGATE

KW LAW
12 Whitburn Road Bathgate West Lothian EH48 1HH
Tel: 01506 635533 *Fax:* 01506 635456
E-mail: bathgate@kwlaw.co.uk

RITCHIE NEILL
48 North Bridge Street Bathgate West Lothian EH48 4PP
Tel: 01506 635590 *Fax:* 01506 630027
E-mail: enquiries@rnsolicitors.com

BEARSDEN

IAIN G GOW
18 Cairnhill Road Bearsden East Dunbartonshire G61 1AU
Tel: 0141 943 0536
E-mail: iain@iaingow.com

PATERSON HOLMS
4 Roman Road Bearsden East Dunbartonshire G61 2SW
Tel: 0141 942 8825 *Fax:* 0141 942 4457
E-mail: scott@patersonholms.co.uk

BEITH

STEWART & OSBORNE
37 Eglinton Street Beith North Ayrshire KA15 1AE
Tel: 01505 503345 *Fax:* 01505 503345

BELLSHILL

BELL SOLICITORS
17 Hamilton Road Bellshill North Lanarkshire ML4 1AF
Tel: 01698 749977 *Fax:* 01698 748847

T G BRADSHAW & CO
The Old Library Bellshill North Lanarkshire ML4 1AB
Tel: 01698 747171 *Fax:* 01698 749733

MURRAY HAMILTON & CHALMERS
66 Hamilton Road Bellshill North Lanarkshire ML4 1AG
Tel: 01698 327488 *Fax:* 01698 327491
E-mail: mhc@mhcsol.co.uk

BIGGAR

SMAIL & EWART
79 High Street Biggar South Lanarkshire ML12 6DE
Tel: 01899 220058 *Fax:* 01899 221269 *Dx:* 571300 BIGGAR
E-mail: enquiry@smail-ewart.co.uk

BISHOPBRIGGS

S P FLANAGAN
6 Boclair Road Bishopbriggs East Dunbartonshire G64 2NA
Tel: 0141 563 0553 *Fax:* 0141 563 0553

HENNESSY BOWIE & CO
2 Kenmure Lane Bishopbriggs East Dunbartonshire G64 2RA
Tel: 0141 762 4040 *Fax:* 0141 762 0742
E-mail: mail@hennessybowie.co.uk

MACFARLANE & CO
4 Kenmure Avenue Bishopbriggs East Dunbartonshire G64 2RE
Tel: 0141 772 6063 *Fax:* 0141 772 7228
E-mail: jmk@macfarlane-law.co.uk

PACITTI JONES
175 Kirkintilloch Road Bishopbriggs East Dunbartonshire G64 2LS
Tel: 0141 772 2211 *Fax:* 0141 563 2221
E-mail: bishopbriggs@pjglasgow.co.uk

BLACKBURN

SNEDDON MORRISON
17 The Mill Centre Blackburn West Lothian EH47 7LG
Tel: 01506 636550 *Fax:* 01501 745440
E-mail: law@sneddons-ssc.co.uk

BLAIRGOWRIE

ELLIOT & CO WS
1 High Street Blairgowrie Perth & Kinross PH10 6ET
Tel: 01250 870840 *Fax:* 01250 875608
E-mail: jbaxter@elliotsperth.co.uk

HODGE SOLICITORS
28 Wellmeadow Blairgowrie Perth & Kinross PH10 6AX
Tel: 01250 874441 *Fax:* 01250 873998
E-mail: info@hodgesolicitors.co.uk

MILLER GERRARD
The Studio 13 High Street Blairgowrie Perth & Kinross PH10 6ET
Tel: 01250 873468 *Fax:* 01250 875257

A & R ROBERTSON & BLACK WS
Bank Street Blairgowrie Perth & Kinross PH10 6DE
Tel: 01250 872043 *Fax:* 01250 875485 *Dx:* 531150 BLAIRGOWRIE
E-mail: admin@robertson-black.co.uk

Property Department 38 Allan Street Blairgowrie Perth & Kinross PH10 6AD
Tel: 01250 875050
E-mail: admin@robertson-black.co.uk

BLANTYRE

GILLIAN BAKER FAMILY LAW
16 Clyde View Centre Blantyre South Lanarkshire G72 0QD
Tel: 01698 820700
E-mail: enquiries@gillianbaker.co.uk

CARTY'S
9 Clydeview Centre Glasgow Road Blantyre South Lanarkshire G72 0QD
Tel: 01698 820896 *Fax:* 01698 823866
E-mail: blantyre@cartylaw.co.uk

CRAWFORD MASON & CO
261 Glasgow Road Blantyre South Lanarkshire G72 0YS
Tel: 01698 821999 *Fax:* 01698 822319
E-mail: crawford.mason@btconnect.com

BO'NESS

LIDDLE & ANDERSON
2 Market Street Bo'ness Falkirk EH51 9AD
Tel: 01506 822727 *Fax:* 01506 828066 *Dx:* 541180 BO'NESS

SNEDDON & SON SSC
1-3 South Street Bo'ness Falkirk EH51 0EA
Tel: 01506 826232 *Fax:* 01506 824810
E-mail: boness@sneddonandson.com

P H YOUNG & CO
54 South Street Bo'ness Falkirk EH51 9HA
Tel: 01506 826166 *Fax:* 01506 823019
E-mail: anne@phyoung.co.uk

BONNYRIGG

STUART & STUART WS
7 High Street Bonnyrigg Midlothian EH19 2DA
Tel: 0131 663 7135 *Fax:* 0131 654 2580 *Dx:* 551350 BONNYRIGG
E-mail: info@stuartandstuart.co.uk

BRECHIN

FERGUSON & WILL
28 Clerk Street Brechin Angus DD9 6AY
Tel: 01356 622289 *Fax:* 01356 623343
E-mail: mail@fergusonandwill.com

NEIL C HUNTER
Enterprise Business Centre West Road Brechin Angus DD9 6RJ
Tel: 0845 108 4484 *Fax:* 0872 115 2391
E-mail: nch@neilchunter.com

SHIELLS SOLICITORS
31a St David Street Brechin Angus DD9 6EG
Tel: 01356 622171 *Fax:* 01356 625232
E-mail: mail@shiells-law.co.uk

BRIDGE OF ALLAN

MAILERS
88 Henderson Street Bridge of Allan Stirling FK9 4HA
Tel: 01786 832314 *Fax:* 01786 834114
E-mail: mail@mailers.co.uk

BRIDGE OF WEIR

1 MOVE
Kilmacolm Road Bridge of Weir Renfrewshire PA11 3PU
Tel: 01505 690033 *Fax:* 01505 614892
E-mail: headoffice@1move4u.co.uk

COCKBURN & CO
Burngill Place Main Street Bridge of Weir Renfrewshire PA11 3PF
Tel: 01505 690500 *Fax:* 01505 690235
E-mail: cockburnandco77@googlemail.com

CRAXTON & GRANT
1 Station Road Bridge of Weir Renfrewshire PA11 3LH
Tel: 01505 610612 *Fax:* 01505 610613 *Dx:* 591753 JOHNSTONE
E-mail: mail@craxtonandgrant.com

BRODICK

JAS CAMPBELL & CO WS
Invercloy House Brodick North Ayrshire KA27 8AJ
Tel: 01770 302027
E-mail: mail@jascampbell.co.uk

BROXBURN

THE CONVEYANCING PRACTICE
33 East Main Street Broxburn West Lothian EH52 5AB
Tel: 01506 863949 *Fax:* 01506 857816

RITCHIE NEILL
88-90 East Main Street Broxburn West Lothian EH52 5EG
Tel: 01506 858856 *Fax:* 01506 854733
E-mail: enquiries@rnsolicitors.com

WHITTEN & COMPANY
50 East Main Street Broxburn West Lothian EH52 5AE
Tel: 01506 855777 *Fax:* 01506 856694 *Dx:* 541120 BROXBURN
E-mail: contact@whittensolicitors.co.uk

BUCKIE

ALEXANDER GEORGE & CO
16 East Church Street Buckie Moray AB56 1AE
Tel: 01542 831307 *Fax:* 01542 833856
E-mail: buckie@alexander-george.com

ANTONS
14 East Church Street Buckie Moray AB56 1AE
Tel: 01542 832148 *Fax:* 01542 834307
E-mail: stephen@antons-bck.co.uk

STEWART & WATSON
42-44 East Church Street Buckie Moray AB56 1AB
Tel: 01542 833255 *Fax:* 01542 834611
E-mail: buckie.property@stewartwatson.co.uk

BURNTISLAND

BROWN & GILMOUR
112 High Street Burntisland Fife KY3 9AR
Tel: 01592 873389 *Fax:* 01592 873050
E-mail: browngilmour@msn.com

W & A S BRUCE
6 Kirkgate Burntisland Fife KY3 9DB
Tel: 01592 873501 *Fax:* 01592 873618
E-mail: info@wasbruce.co.uk

CALLANDER

DONALD MCLAREN & CO
Royal Bank Buildings 55 Main Street Callander Stirling FK17 8DZ
Tel: 01877 330033 *Fax:* 01877 331248
E-mail: donaldmclaren@btconnect.com

MCLEAN & STEWART
95 Main Street Callander Stirling FK17 8BQ
Tel: 01877 330014
E-mail: mail@mcleanandstewart.co.uk

CAMBUSLANG

CARR & CO
124 Main Street Cambuslang South Lanarkshire G72 7EL
Tel: 0141 641 2912 / 8346 *Fax:* 0141 643 3780
Dx: 501280 RUTHERGLEN

DUFFY TOSHNER & CO
23 Main Street Cambuslang South Lanarkshire G72 7EX
Tel: 0141 641 8081 *Fax:* 0141 641 0091 *Dx:* 501281 RUTHERGLEN
E-mail: enquiries@duffytoshner.co.uk

HEPWORTH & CO
235 Hamilton Road Halfway Cambuslang South Lanarkshire G72 7PH
Tel: 0141 641 0089 *Fax:* 0141 641 9538
E-mail: admin@hepworthsolicitors.co.uk

CAMPBELTOWN

C & D MACTAGGART
Castlehill Campbeltown Argyll & Bute PA28 6AR
Tel: 01586 552317 *Fax:* 01586 554719
E-mail: mail@cdm-law.co.uk

STEWART BALFOUR & SUTHERLAND
24-26 Longrow South Campbeltown Argyll & Bute PA28 6AH
Tel: 01586 553737 *Fax:* 01586 554228
E-mail: sales@sbsproperty.co.uk

CARLUKE

FORREST CAMPBELL & ANDERSON
23 Kirkton Street Carluke South Lanarkshire ML8 4AB
Tel: 01555 771383 *Fax:* 01555 773421 *Dx:* 570472 CARLUKE
E-mail: enquiries@fcasolicitors.co.uk

MORISON & SMITH
37 High Street Carluke South Lanarkshire ML8 4AL
Tel: 01555 751916 *Fax:* 01555 751701

CASTLE DOUGLAS

GILLESPIE GIFFORD & BROWN
133 King Street Castle Douglas Dumfries & Galloway DG7 1NA
Tel: 01556 503744 *Fax:* 01556 503094
E-mail: mail@ggblaw.co.uk

HEWATS
63 King Street Castle Douglas Dumfries & Galloway DG7 1AG
Tel: 01556 502391 *Fax:* 01556 504171
E-mail: info@hewats.co.uk

CLYDEBANK

BLAIR & BRYDEN
23 Kilbowie Road Clydebank West Dunbartonshire G81 1TL
Tel: 0141 952 3322 *Fax:* 0141 952 3232 *Dx:* 500499 CLYDEBANK

CLYDE DEFENCE LAWYERS
30 Alexander Street Clydebank West Dunbartonshire G81 1RZ
Tel: 0141 951 2211 *Fax:* 0141 951 2233
E-mail: plafferty@clydedefencelawyers.com

JAMES A MCCANN & CO
499 Kilbowie Road Clydebank West Dunbartonshire G81 2AX
Tel: 01389 879791 *Fax:* 01389 879005 *Dx:* 500493 CLYDEBANK
E-mail: marion-jamccannfirm@btconnect.com

THE PRG PARTNERSHIP
1 Kilbowie Road Clydebank West Dunbartonshire G81 1TL
Tel: 0141 952 0019 *Fax:* 0141 952 4957 *Dx:* 500491 CLYDEBANK

PHILPOTT PLATT NIBLETT & WIGHT
4 Miller Street Clydebank West Dunbartonshire G81 1UQ
Tel: 0141 952 9545 *Fax:* 0141 952 8333
E-mail: clydebank@ppnw.co.uk

STIRLING & GILMOUR
45 Kilbowie Road Clydebank West Dunbartonshire G81 1BL
Tel: 0141 952 2669 *Fax:* 0141 951 2088 *Dx:* 500492 CLYDEBANK

COATBRIDGE

FRIELS
5 Bank Street Coatbridge North Lanarkshire ML5 1AN
Tel: 01236 421136 *Fax:* 01236 429890

A J LINDEN & CO
315 Muiriehall Street Coatbridge North Lanarkshire ML5 3RY
Tel: 01236 449921 *Fax:* 01236 449686
E-mail: lindenandco@btconnect.com

MCAFEE
83d Main Street Coatbridge North Lanarkshire ML5 3EH
Tel: 01236 423437 *Fax:* 01236 440507 *Dx:* 570506 COATBRIDGE

TAYLOR & KELLY
3 Main Street Coatbridge North Lanarkshire ML5 3AJ
Tel: 01236 710999 *Fax:* 01236 429080
E-mail: tony@taylorkelly.co.uk

TRAINOR ALSTON
18 Academy Street Coatbridge North Lanarkshire ML5 3AU
Tel: 01236 600600 *Fax:* 01236 600666 *Dx:* 570500 COATBRIDGE

WOODS & COMPANY
97 Main Street Coatbridge North Lanarkshire ML5 3EL
Tel: 01236 428237 *Fax:* 01236 428223

COUPAR ANGUS

A & R ROBERTSON & BLACK WS
14 George Street Coupar Angus Perth & Kinross PH13 9DH
Tel: 01828 627542
E-mail: admin@robertson-black.co.uk

WATSON & LYALL BOWIE
Union Bank Buildings Colpan Street Coupar Angus Perth & Kinross PH13 9AJ
Tel: 01828 628395 *Fax:* 01828 627147
E-mail: legalservices@wandlb.co.uk

COWDENBEATH

BSW SOLICITORS LLP
450 High Street Cowdenbeath Fife KY4 8LR
Tel: 01383 515020 *Fax:* 01383 610249
E-mail: info@bswsolicitors.co.uk

CRIEFF

GRAHAM & FINLAYSON WS
29 Comrie Street Crieff Perth & Kinross PH7 4BD
Tel: 01764 652224 *Fax:* 01764 653999
E-mail: mail@grahamandfinlayson.co.uk

IRVING GEDDES
25 West High Street Crieff Perth & Kinross PH7 4AU
Tel: 01764 653771 *Fax:* 01764 654654
E-mail: enquiries@irvinggeddes.co.uk

MILLER HENDRY
14 Comrie Street Crieff Perth & Kinross PH7 4AZ
Tel: 01764 655151 *Fax:* 01764 652903
E-mail: info@miller-hendry.co.uk

CUMBERNAULD

BARROWMANS
30 Ettrick Walk Cumbernauld North Lanarkshire G67 1NE
Tel: 01236 731911 *Fax:* 01236 730038 *Dx:* 500520 CUMBERNAULD

BARTON & HENDRY
4th Floor Tryst Road Cumbernauld North Lanarkshire G67 1JW
Tel: 01236 735466 *Fax:* 01236 735451
E-mail: info@bartonandhendry.co.uk

BERRY POGGI & CO
PO Box 3248 Cumbernauld North Lanarkshire G68 9YE
Tel: 0870 243 0665 *Fax:* 0141 429 7453
E-mail: berrypoggidefence@gmail.com

DUNIPACE BROWN
Clyde Chambers 6 Clyde Walk Town Centre Cumbernauld North Lanarkshire G67 1BH
Tel: 01236 453004 *Fax:* 01236 458989
E-mail: dunipacebrown@hotmail.com

MOORE & PARTNERS
Lennox House Lennox Road Cumbernauld North Lanarkshire G67 1LL
Tel: 01236 727715 *Fax:* 01236 730570
Dx: 500523 CUMBERNAULD
E-mail: info@moorepartners.com

ANTHONY QUINN
3 Glen Fannox Grove Cumbernauld North Lanarkshire G68 0GH
Tel: 07968 951741
E-mail: anthonyquinn141@btinternet.com

IAN S SMART & CO
3 Annan House Town Centre Cumbernauld North Lanarkshire G67 1DP
Tel: 01236 731027 *Fax:* 01236 457841

CUMNOCK

R D HUNTER & CO
1 The Square Cumnock East Ayrshire KA18 1BQ
Tel: 01290 421185 *Fax:* 01290 420840
E-mail: rdhunter@btconnect.com

R A LOGAN & CO
1 Ayr Road Cumnock East Ayrshire KA18 1DT
Tel: 01290 424566 *Fax:* 01290 426263
E-mail: robertlogan7@yahoo.co.uk

D W SHAW
Royal Bank Buildings Glaisnock Street Cumnock East Ayrshire KA18 1BT
Tel: 01290 421484 *Fax:* 01290 425537
E-mail: enquiries@dwshaw.co.uk

CUPAR

BAIRD & CO
7 St Catherine Street Cupar Fife KY15 4LS
Tel: 01334 656644 *Fax:* 01334 655333 *Dx:* 560546 CUPAR
E-mail: creception@bairdco.co.uk

MCQUITTYS
97 Bonnygate Cupar Fife KY15 4LG
Tel: 01334 655207 *Fax:* 01334 656683 *Dx:* 560542 CUPAR
E-mail: mcquitty@mcquittys.co.uk

MURRAY DONALD DRUMMOND COOK
35 Bonnygate Cupar Fife KY15 4BU
Tel: 01334 652331 *Fax:* 01334 653582 *Dx:* 560996 ST ANDREWS
E-mail: mail@mddc.co.uk

PAGAN OSBORNE
12 St Catherine Street Cupar Fife KY15 4HH
Tel: 01334 653777 *Fax:* 01334 655063 *Dx:* 560543 CUPAR
E-mail: webenquiry@pagan.co.uk

PATERSON BELL
22 St Catherine Street Cupar Fife KY15 4HH
Tel: 01334 657310 *Fax:* 01334 656066
E-mail: crime@patersonbell.co.uk

ROLLO DAVIDSON & MCFARLANE
67 Crossgate Cupar Fife KY15 5AS
Tel: 01334 654081 *Fax:* 01334 656350 *Dx:* 560544 CUPAR
E-mail: cupar@rollos.co.uk

STEEL ELDRIDGE STEWART
18 Crossgate Cupar Fife KY15 5HH
Tel: 01334 652285 *Fax:* 01334 656331 *Dx:* 560541 CUPAR
E-mail: enquiries@ses-solicitors.co.uk

WILLIAMS MCRAE
Law House Ferguson Square Cupar Fife KY15 5JU
Tel: 01334 658222 *Fax:* 01334 657771 *Dx:* 560539 CUPAR
E-mail: enquiries@williams-mcrae.com

DALBEATTIE

AUSTINS
52 High Street Dalbeattie Dumfries & Galloway DG5 4AB
Tel: 01556 610259 *Fax:* 01556 610259
E-mail: property@austins-solicitors.co.uk

GILLESPIE GIFFORD & BROWN
33 High Street Dalbeattie Dumfries & Galloway DG5 4AD
Tel: 01556 611247 *Fax:* 01556 611626
E-mail: mail@ggblaw.co.uk

DALKEITH

ALLAN MCDOUGALL
93 High Street Dalkeith Midlothian EH22 1JA
Tel: 0131 663 7261 *Fax:* 0131 663 5483 *Dx:* 540573 DALKEITH
E-mail: dalkeith@allanmcdougall.co.uk

DRUMMOND MILLER WS
11 White Hart Street Dalkeith Midlothian EH22 1AE
Tel: 0131 663 9568 *Fax:* 0131 654 2676 *Dx:* 570 DALKEITH

ANDREW T GILBERTSON
112 High Street Dalkeith Midlothian EH22 1HZ
Tel: 0131 660 9888 *Fax:* 0131 660 9888
E-mail: gilbertsonsols@hotmail.com

DALRY

BLACKWOOD CRATE & COMPANY
16 New Street Dalry North Ayrshire KA24 5AG
Tel: 01294 832108 *Fax:* 01294 833051

J & J MCCOSH
Clydesdale Bank Chambers The Cross Dalry North Ayrshire KA24 5AB
Tel: 01294 832112 *Fax:* 01294 833350
E-mail: info@jjmccosh.co.uk

JAMES PATRICK & MUIR
44 New Street Dalry North Ayrshire KA24 5AE
Tel: 01294 832442 *Fax:* 01294 833415

DENNY

RUSSEL & AITKEN
22 & 24 Stirling Street Denny Falkirk FK6 6AZ
Tel: 01324 822194 *Fax:* 01324 824560 *Dx:* 561171 DENNY
E-mail: mail@radenny.co.uk

DINGWALL

J C BARTLETT & CO
6 McGregor Court Dingwall Highland IV15 9HS
Tel: 01349 867100 *Fax:* 01349 867849

T S H BURNS & SON
PO Box 1 Park Street Dingwall Highland IV15 9JJ
Tel: 01349 863222 *Fax:* 01349 869839 *Dx:* 520580 DINGWALL
E-mail: property@tshburns.co.uk

FOGGO MACINNES HINGSTON
1 Castle Street Dingwall Highland IV15 9HU
Tel: 01349 867200 *Fax:* 01349 862987
E-mail: info@foggomacinnes.co.uk

GEORGE STREET LAW
4 George Street Dingwall Highland IV15 9SA
Tel: 01349 866777 *Fax:* 01349 866888 *Dx:* 520590 DINGWALL
E-mail: legal@georgestreetlaw.co.uk

MIDDLETON ROSS & ARNOT
Mansefield House 7 High Street Dingwall Highland IV15 9HJ
Tel: 01349 862214 *Fax:* 01349 863819 *Dx:* 520582 DINGWALL
E-mail: lisa@middletonross.co.uk

DOLLAR

ALASTAIR J GORDON WS
Pitfar Lodge Dollar Clackmannanshire FK14 7NS
Tel: 01259 740007 *Fax:* 01259 740007
E-mail: mail@alastairjgordon.ws

DORNOCH

ARTHUR & CARMICHAEL
Cathedral Square Dornoch Highland IV25 3SW
Tel: 01862 810202 *Fax:* 01862 810166
E-mail: properties@arthur-carmichael.co.uk

EWAN HARRIS & CO
The West Deanery Castle Street Dornoch Highland IV25 3SN
Tel: 01862 810686 *Fax:* 01862 811020
E-mail: legal@ewan-harris.co.uk

DUFFTOWN

STEPHEN & ROBB
Royal Bank Buildings Fife Street Dufftown Moray AB55 4AL
Tel: 01340 820101 *Fax:* 01340 820857 *Dx:* 520781 KEITH
E-mail: dufftown@stephenrobb.co.uk

DUMBARTON

ADAIRS
3 Castle Street Dumbarton West Dunbartonshire G82 1QS
Tel: 01389 767625 *Fax:* 01389 730606
Dx: 500591 DUMBARTON 1
E-mail: mail@adairssolicitors.com

CAIRNS BROWN
45 High Street Dumbarton West Dunbartonshire G82 1LS
Tel: 01389 742777 *Fax:* 01389 742888
E-mail: mail@cairnsbrown.co.uk

CLYDE DEFENCE LAWYERS
21 Station Road Dumbarton West Dunbartonshire G82 1NR
Tel: 01389 730666 *Fax:* 01389 761567
E-mail: plafferty@clydedefencelawyers.com

MCARTHUR STANTON
35 High Street Dumbarton West Dunbartonshire G82 1LS
Tel: 01389 762266 *Fax:* 01389 742282 *Dx:* 500590 DUMBARTON 1

MACINTOSH HUMBLE
21 High Street Dumbarton West Dunbartonshire G82 1LT
Tel: 01389 763491 *Fax:* 01389 742240 *Dx:* 500596 DUMBARTON

A C O'NEILL & CO
32 High Street Dumbarton West Dunbartonshire G82 1LL
Tel: 01389 762997 *Fax:* 01389 739006
E-mail: enquiries@aconeill.com

PHILPOTT PLATT NIBLETT & WIGHT
103/105 Glasgow Road Dumbarton West Dunbartonshire G82 1RE
Tel: 01389 733777 *Fax:* 01389 734363
E-mail: dumbarton@ppnw.co.uk

DUMFRIES

BRAIDWOODS
1 Charlotte Street Dumfries Dumfries & Galloway DG1 2AG
Tel: 01387 257272 *Fax:* 01387 257282 *Dx:* 580626 DUMFRIES
E-mail: info@braidwoods.com

8

BRAZENALL & ORR
104 Irish Street Dumfries Dumfries & Galloway DG1 2PB
Tel: 01387 255695 *Fax:* 01387 252036
E-mail: info@brazenallandorr.co.uk

GILLESPIE GIFFORD & BROWN
135 Irish Street Dumfries Dumfries & Galloway DG1 2NT
Tel: 01387 255351 *Fax:* 01387 257306
E-mail: mail@ggblaw.co.uk

GRIEVE GRIERSON MOODIE & WALKER
14 Castle Street Dumfries Dumfries & Galloway DG1 1DR
Tel: 01387 266250 *Fax:* 01387 257950
E-mail: hilary.grieve@ggmw.co.uk

JOHN HENDERSON & SONS
8 Bank Street Dumfries Dumfries & Galloway DG1 2NS
Tel: 01387 739000 *Fax:* 01387 251320 *Dx:* 580612 DUMFRIES
E-mail: enquiries@jhslaw.co.uk

LATHAM & CO
197 High Street Dumfries Dumfries & Galloway DG1 2QT
Tel: 01387 252888 *Fax:* 01387 257747 *Dx:* 580629 DUMFRIES

LINDSAY
33 Buccleuch Street Dumfries Dumfries & Galloway DG1 2AB
Tel: 01387 259236 *Fax:* 01387 267747 *Dx:* 580639 DUMFRIES
E-mail: info@lindsaysolicitors.co.uk

A B & A MATTHEWS
The Old Bank Buccleuch Street Bridge Dumfries Dumfries & Galloway DG2 7TJ
Tel: 01387 257300 *Fax:* 01387 257333 *Dx:* 580637 DUMFRIES
E-mail: dumfriesoffice@abamatthews.com

OAG & CO
77 Buccleuch Street Dumfries Dumfries & Galloway DG1 2AB
Tel: 01387 263857

POLLOCK & MCLEAN
10 Buccleuch Street Dumfries Dumfries & Galloway DG1 2AH
Tel: 01387 255666 *Fax:* 01387 248777

PRIMROSE & GORDON
1 Newall Terrace Dumfries Dumfries & Galloway DG1 1LN
Tel: 01387 267316 *Fax:* 01387 269747 *Dx:* 580616 DUMFRIES
E-mail: enquiries@primroseandgordon.co.uk

WALKER & SHARPE
37 George Street Dumfries Dumfries & Galloway DG1 1EB
Tel: 01387 267222 *Fax:* 01387 254775 *Dx:* 580619 DUMFRIES
E-mail: law@walker-sharpe.co.uk

WHITELAW EDGAR & BALDWIN
19 Bank Street Dumfries Dumfries & Galloway DG1 2NZ
Tel: 01387 255414 *Fax:* 01387 251115 *Dx:* 580620 DUMFRIES
E-mail: enquiries@whitelawedgarbaldwin.co.uk

DUNBAR

BROOKE & BROWN WS
116 High Street Dunbar East Lothian EH42 1JJ
Tel: 01368 862746 *Fax:* 01368 864150 *Dx:* 541196 DUNBAR
E-mail: email@brookeandbrown.co.uk

GARDEN STIRLING BURNET
39 High Street Dunbar East Lothian EH42 1EW
Tel: 01368 862376 *Fax:* 01368 864748 *Dx:* 541197 DUNBAR
E-mail: dunbar@gsbsolicitors.co.uk

DUNBLANE

THO & J W BARTY
61 High Street Dunblane Stirling FK15 0EH
Tel: 01786 822296 *Fax:* 01786 824249 *Dx:* 560630 DUNBLANE
E-mail: bartys@bartys.co.uk

MCLEAN & STEWART
51-53 High Street Dunblane Stirling FK15 0EG
Tel: 01786 823217 *Fax:* 01786 822575 *Dx:* 560631 DUNBLANE
E-mail: mail@mcleanandstewart.co.uk

DUNDEE

ALLARDICE & CREEGAN
6 Panmure Street Dundee DD1 2BW
Tel: 01382 527777 *Fax:* 01382 527778

BAILLIES
37 Union Street Dundee DD1 4BS
Tel: 01382 202444 *Fax:* 01382 202208
E-mail: enquiries@baillies-law.co.uk

KIM BARCLAY
9 South Tay Street Dundee DD1 1NU
Tel: 01382 228722 *Fax:* 01382 224248
E-mail: law@kimbarclay.co.uk

BLACKADDERS
30 & 34 Reform Street Dundee DD1 1RJ
Tel: 01382 229222 *Fax:* 01382 342220
E-mail: enquiries@blackadders.co.uk

BOWMAN SCOTTISH LAWYERS
27 Bank Street Dundee DD1 1RP
Tel: 01382 322267 *Fax:* 01382 225000
E-mail: property@bowmansolicitors.co.uk

BOYLE'S
15 Albert Square Dundee DD1 1DJ
Tel: 01382 221214
E-mail: enquiries@wgboyle.co.uk

JACK BROWN & COMPANY
7 Ward Road Dundee DD1 1LP
Tel: 01382 200411 *Fax:* 01382 203033

MICHAEL A BROWN
17 South Tay Street Dundee DD1 1NR
Tel: 01382 204242 *Fax:* 01382 204911

CAIRD & VAUGHAN
1 Bank Street Dundee DD1 1RL
Tel: 01382 229399 *Fax:* 01382 322003
E-mail: cairdvaughan@btconnect.com

CALDERS
10 Whitehall Street Dundee DD1 4AQ
Tel: 01382 224391 *Fax:* 01382 202924
E-mail: admin@calders.com

CAMPBELL BOATH
Bank House 1 Stirling Street Dundee DD3 6PJ
Tel: 01382 200110 *Fax:* 01382 201078 *Dx:* DD18 DUNDEE
E-mail: enquiries@campbellboath.com

THE CHAMBER PRACTICE
11-13 Crichton Street Dundee DD1 3AP
Tel: 01382 203000 *Fax:* 01382 203011
E-mail: enquiries@thechamberpractice.co.uk

DIGBY BROWN
Panmure Street Dundee DD1 1DU
Tel: 0845 273 2323 *Fax:* 01382 205915 *Dx:* DD26 DUNDEE
E-mail: maildesk@digbybrown.co.uk

FINLAY MACRAE
84 Commercial Street Dundee DD1 2AP
Tel: 01382 228288 *Fax:* 01382 205757
E-mail: enquiries@finlaymacraesolicitors.co.uk

FLYNN & CO
1 West Bell Street Dundee DD1 1EX
Tel: 01382 223145 *Fax:* 01382 322019
E-mail: flynnuk00@aol.com

ANIKA JETHWA & CO
7 West Bell Street Dundee DD1 1EX
Tel: 01382 223399 *Fax:* 01382 228833

LAWSON COULL & DUNCAN
136/138 Nethergate Dundee DD1 4PA
Tel: 01382 227555 *Fax:* 01382 200978

MACKENZIE & MACKENZIE
24 Abercorn Street Dundee DD4 7FA
Tel: 01382 455263

ANDREW G MANDERSON & CO
51 Reform Street Dundee DD1 1SL
Tel: 01382 200840 *Fax:* 01382 200486 *Dx:* DD95 DUNDEE
E-mail: andrewgmanderson@btconnect.com

MILLER HENDRY
13 Ward Road Dundee DD1 1LU
Tel: 01382 200000 *Fax:* 01382 200098
E-mail: info@miller-hendry.co.uk

MUIR MYLES LAVERTY
Meadow Place Buildings Bell Street Dundee DD1 1EJ
Tel: 01382 206000 *Fax:* 01382 206012
E-mail: enquiries@muirmyleslaverty.co.uk

J MYLES & CO
7-9 South Tay Street Dundee DD1 1NU
Tel: 01382 204625 *Fax:* 01382 227972

RSB MACDONALD
4 Whitehall Street Dundee DD1 4AF
Tel: 01382 202025 *Fax:* 01382 202233
E-mail: law@rsbmacdonald.co.uk

17 Crichton Street Dundee DD1 3AR
Tel: 01382 202025 *Fax:* 01382 203201
E-mail: law@rsbmacdonald.co.uk

RICHMOND & CO
26 Commercial Street Dundee DD1 3EJ
Tel: 01382 201964 *Fax:* 01382 224214 *Dx:* DD53 DUNDEE
E-mail: richmondco@btconnect.com

ROBERTSON SMITH
31 Hawkhill Dundee DD1 5DH
Tel: 01382 226602 *Fax:* 01382 322884

SHEPHERDS
21 Dock Street Dundee DD1 3DP
Tel: 01382 322781 *Fax:* 01382 202394
E-mail: reception@shepherds-solicitor.co.uk

SHIELD & KYD
5 Bank Street Dundee DD1 1RL
Tel: 01382 224112 *Fax:* 01382 200109 *Dx:* DD17 DUNDEE
E-mail: dundee@shieldandkyd.co.uk

BRUCE SHORT & CO
3 Rattery Street Dundee DD1 1NA
Tel: 01382 223400 *Fax:* 01382 224550

SIMPSON & MARWICK
1 Courthouse Square Dundee DD1 1NH
Tel: 01382 200373 *Fax:* 01382 200370 *Dx:* DD52 DUNDEE
E-mail: email@simpmar.com

ROSS STRACHAN & CO
2 India Buildings 86 Bell Street Dundee DD1 1JQ
Tel: 01382 201010 *Fax:* 01382 202368
E-mail: mail@ross-strachan.co.uk

THORNTONS WS
Whitehall House 33 Yeamen Shore Dundee DD1 4BJ
Tel: 01382 229111 *Fax:* 01382 202288
E-mail: dundee@thorntons-law.co.uk

DUNFERMLINE

THOMAS BLAIR & SON
35 East Port Dunfermline Fife KY12 7JE
Tel: 01383 724015 *Fax:* 01383 620804
E-mail: property@tblairandson.co.uk

BONNAR & CO
8 New Row Dunfermline Fife KY12 7ES
Tel: 0800 694 0209 *Fax:* 01383 604113 *Dx:* DF20 DUNFERMLINE

W & A S BRUCE
15-17 Chalmers Street Dunfermline Fife KY12 8AT
Tel: 01383 738000 *Fax:* 01383 729105
E-mail: info@wasbruce.co.uk

CCW LLP
Crescent House Carnegie Campus Dunfermline Fife KY11 8GR
Tel: 0845 223 3001 *Fax:* 01383 626111 *Dx:* DF48 DUNFERMLINE
E-mail: info@ccwlegal.co.uk

DRUMMOND MILLER WS
5 East Port Dunfermline Fife KY12 7JG
Tel: 01383 624244 *Fax:* 01383 625599 *Dx:* DF32 DUNFERMLINE 1

GORRIE & DAVIDSON
26 Viewfield Terrace Dunfermline Fife KY12 7LB
Tel: 01383 723618 *Fax:* 01383 620367
E-mail: info@gorriedavidson.co.uk

HUNTER BURNS & OGG
Office 11 Albany Business Centre Gardeners Street Dunfermline Fife KY12 0RN
Tel: 01383 725906 *Fax:* 01383 723450
E-mail: hunterburns@tiscali.co.uk

MACBETH CURRIE
Barnet House 38 High Street Dunfermline Fife KY12 7DD
Tel: 01383 731011 *Fax:* 01383 737059 *Dx:* DF7 DUNFERMLINE

MCILROY HIPWELL & DINGWALL
24 Chalmers Street Dunfermline Fife KY12 8DF
Tel: 01383 808198 *Fax:* 01383 729429
E-mail: mail@mhdsolicitors.com

MALCOLM JACK & MATHESON
Walmer House Walmer Drive East Port Dunfermline Fife KY12 7LH
Tel: 01383 723444 *Fax:* 01383 730672 *Dx:* DF8 DUNFERMLINE
E-mail: enquiries@malcolmjack.co.uk

MARTIN JOHNSTON & SOCHA
11 Maygate Dunfermline Fife KY12 7NE
Tel: 01383 730466 *Fax:* 01383 621440
E-mail: dunfermline1@btconnect.com

MORGANS
33 East Port Dunfermline Fife KY12 7JE
Tel: 01383 620222 *Fax:* 01383 621213
E-mail: info@morganlaw.co.uk

THOMAS QUEEN
Office 4 Dunfermline Business Centre Izatt Avenue Dunfermline Fife KY11 3BZ
Tel: 0800 169 4046
E-mail: tom@tomqueen.co.uk

PAUL W RALPH
25 Adia Road The Meadows Torryburn Dunfermline Fife KY12 8LB
Tel: 07986 431730 *Fax:* 01383 881095

ROSS & CONNEL
18 Viewfield Terrace Dunfermline Fife KY12 7JH
Tel: 01383 721156 *Fax:* 01383 721150
E-mail: enquiries@ross.connel.co.uk

STENHOUSE HUSBAND & IRVINE
3 East Port Dunfermline Fife KY12 7JG
Tel: 01383 724949 *Fax:* 01383 620643

STEVENSON & MARSHALL
41 East Port Dunfermline Fife KY12 7LG
Tel: 01383 721141 *Fax:* 01383 723779
E-mail: maildesk@stevenson-marshall.co.uk

STEWARTS
27 Canmore Street Dunfermline Fife KY12 7NU
Tel: 01383 620101 *Fax:* 01383 621452 *Dx:* DF3 DUNFERMLINE 1

STIRLING EUNSON & FERGUSON LEGAL SERVICES
90 High Street Dunfermline Fife KY12 7DP
Tel: 01383 748900 *Fax:* 01383 731619
E-mail: law@sef.co.uk

YOUNG & PARTNERS
1 George Square Castle Brae Dunfermline Fife KY11 8QF
Tel: 01383 721621 *Fax:* 01383 722080
E-mail: enquiries@businesslaw.co.uk

YOUR CONVEYANCER
87 High Street Dunfermline Fife KY12 7DR
Tel: 0844 576 7777 *Fax:* 0844 576 7700
Dx: DF550420 DUNFERMLINE 4
E-mail: enquiries@yourconveyancer.co.uk

DUNOON

BLAIR & BRYDEN
11 Hillfoot Street Dunoon Argyll & Bute PA23 7DR
Tel: 01369 704037 *Fax:* 01369 706677

CORRIGALL BLACK
20 John Street Dunoon Argyll & Bute PA23 8BN
Tel: 01369 702941 *Fax:* 01369 704304 *Dx:* 591651 DUNOON
E-mail: info@corrigallblack.com

STEWART & BENNETT
82 Argyll Street Dunoon Argyll & Bute PA23 7NJ
Tel: 01369 702885 *Fax:* 01369 706695 *Dx:* 591650 DUNOON
E-mail: property@stewartbennett.com

DUNS

J D CLARK & ALLAN
Tolbooth House Market Square Duns Scottish Borders TD11 3DR
Tel: 01361 882501 *Fax:* 01361 883130
E-mail: property@jdca.co.uk

MELROSE & PORTEOUS
47 Market Square Duns Scottish Borders TD11 3BX
Tel: 01361 882752 *Fax:* 01361 883136
E-mail: info@melroseporteous.co.uk

IAIN SMITH & PARTNERS WS
11-13 Murray Street Duns Scottish Borders TD11 3DF
Tel: 01361 882733 *Fax:* 01361 883517
E-mail: duns@iainsmith.co.uk

DYCE

ABERDEIN CONSIDINE & CO
115 Victoria Street Dyce Aberdeen AB21 7AX
Tel: 01224 723737 *Fax:* 01224 724867 *Dx:* 551960 DYCE
E-mail: dyce@acandco.com

WILSONE & DUFFUS
75 Victoria Street Dyce Aberdeen AB2 0AX
Tel: 01224 797979 *Fax:* 01224 797978 *Dx:* AB24 ABERDEEN
E-mail: info@key-moves.co.uk

EAST KILBRIDE

BONNAR LAW
216 Edinburgh House Righead Gate East Kilbride South Lanarkshire G74 1LS
Tel: 01355 268866 *Fax:* 01355 268868
E-mail: brianbonnar@bonnarlaw.com

BUCHANAN BURTON
2 Strathmore House Princes Square East Kilbride South Lanarkshire G74 1LQ
Tel: 01355 249228 *Fax:* 01355 265535 *Dx:* 500648 EAST KILBRIDE

GOLDSMITH & HUGHES
51 Strathmore House Princes Square East Kilbride South Lanarkshire G74 1LF
Tel: 01355 260602 *Fax:* 01355 260603
Dx: 500685 EAST KILBRIDE
E-mail: info@goldsmithhughes.com

GUARINO & THOMSON
E209 Edinburgh House Town Centre East Kilbride South Lanarkshire G74 1LJ
Tel: 01355 263848 *Fax:* 01355 237029
Dx: 500647 EAST KILBRIDE
E-mail: admin@guarinothomson.co.uk

AUSTIN LAFFERTY LAW
213 Edinburgh House Princes Square East Kilbride South Lanarkshire G74 1LJ
Tel: 01355 263777 *Fax:* 01355 263886
E-mail: jroberts@laffertylaw.com

MACALLANS
Brouster Gate East Kilbride South Lanarkshire G74 1LE
Tel: 01355 261361 *Fax:* 01355 261453
Dx: 500688 EAST KILBRIDE
E-mail: mail@macallans.co.uk

MACDONALDS
22 Cornwall Way East Kilbride South Lanarkshire G74 1JY
Tel: 01355 588900 *Fax:* 01355 220686
E-mail: info@maclaw.co.uk

GERARD MCGUIRE & CO
115 Strathmore House Town Centre East Kilbride South Lanarkshire G74 1LF
Tel: 01355 225322 *Fax:* 01355 279350
E-mail: gerard-mcguire@btconnect.com

E & W MAINS
55 Strathmore House East Kilbride South Lanarkshire G74 1LS
Tel: 01355 225111 *Fax:* 01355 225964
E-mail: admin@mains-sols.co.uk

ROSS HARPER
2 Main Street The Village East Kilbride South Lanarkshire G74 4JH
Tel: 0141 649 9511 *Fax:* 0141 632 5680
E-mail: info@rossharper.com

EDINBURGH

ADAMS WHYTE
20 Leith Walk Edinburgh EH6 5AA
Tel: 0131 225 8813 *Fax:* 0131 555 7021
Dx: ED550864 EDINBURGH
E-mail: edinburgh@adamswhyte.com

AIKMAN RUSSELL & DUNLOP WS
13 South Charlotte Street Edinburgh EH2 4BH
Tel: 0131 226 5121 *Fax:* 0131 225 9418 *Dx:* ED281 EDINBURGH
E-mail: andrewa@aikmanrusselldunlop.co.uk

AITKEN NAIRN WS
7 Abercromby Place Edinburgh EH3 6LA
Tel: 0131 556 6644 *Fax:* 0131 556 6509 *Dx:* ED18 EDINBURGH 1
E-mail: reception@aitkennairn.co.uk

ALLAN MCDOUGALL
3 Coates Crescent Edinburgh EH3 7AL
Tel: 0131 225 2121 *Fax:* 0131 225 8659 *Dx:* ED32 EDINBURGH
E-mail: edinburgh@allanmcdougall.co.uk

ALLINGHAM & CO
134 Marchmont Road Edinburgh EH9 1AQ
Tel: 0131 447 9341 *Fax:* 0131 452 9383
E-mail: mail@allingham.co.uk

9-15 Bridge Road Colinton Edinburgh EH13 0LH
Tel: 0131 447 9341 *Fax:* 0131 441 4517
E-mail: info@allingham.co.uk

4a Buckstone Terrace Edinburgh EH10 6PZ
Tel: 0131 447 9341 *Fax:* 0131 445 5551
E-mail: info@allingham.co.uk

ANDERSON STRATHERN LLP
163 Lanark Road West Currie Edinburgh EH14 5NZ
Tel: 0131 449 2833 *Fax:* 0131 449 6725 *Dx:* ED3 EDINBURGH 1
E-mail: info@andersonstrathern.co.uk

1 Rutland Court Edinburgh EH3 8EY
Tel: 0131 270 7700 *Fax:* 0131 270 7788 *Dx:* ED3 EDINBURGH 1
E-mail: info@andersonstrathern.co.uk

ANDERSONS LLP
24 Dublin Street Edinburgh EH1 3PP
Tel: 0131 524 7790 *Fax:* 0131 524 7791
Dx: ED551112 EDINBURGH 7
E-mail: mailbox@andersonsllp.co.uk

ARBUTHNOTT & MCCLANACHAN
77 Main Street Davidsons Mains Edinburgh EH4 5AD
Tel: 0131 312 7276 *Fax:* 0131 312 6029
E-mail: enquiries@amsolicitors.com

ARCHIBALD CAMPBELL & HARLEY WS
37 Queen Street Edinburgh EH2 1JX
Tel: 0131 220 3000 *Fax:* 0131 220 2288
E-mail: enquiries@achws.co.uk

BCKM
53 George IV Bridge Edinburgh EH1 1YH
Tel: 0131 225 3456 *Fax:* 0131 225 6543

BALFOUR & MANSON
54-66 Fredrick Street Edinburgh EH2 1LS
Tel: 0131 200 1200 *Fax:* 0131 200 1300 *Dx:* ED4 EDINBURGH
E-mail: emma.mccall@balfour-manson.co.uk

NIGEL BEAUMONT & CO
31 Albany Street Edinburgh EH1 3QN
Tel: 0131 557 3565 *Fax:* 0131 556 4273
E-mail: office@nigelbeaumont.co.uk

BELMONTE & CO
9 Craigmillar Castle Road Edinburgh EH16 4BY
Tel: 0131 661 9779 *Dx:* ED52 EDINBURGH
E-mail: mail@belmonte.uk.com

7 Rutland Square Edinburgh EH1 2AS
Tel: 0131 229 5323 *Dx:* ED52 EDINBURGH
E-mail: mail@belmonte.uk.com

ADAM BEVAN & CO
177b Great Junction Street Edinburgh EH6 5LQ
Tel: 0131 467 6767 *Fax:* 0131 467 6776
E-mail: bevans385@btinternet.com

BEVERIDGE & KELLAS
52 Leith Walk Leith Edinburgh EH6 5HW
Tel: 0131 554 6321 *Fax:* 0131 553 5319 *Dx:* 550850 LEITH
E-mail: mail@beveridgekellas.com

BEVERIDGE PHILP & ROSS
22 Bernard Street Leith Edinburgh EH6 6PS
Tel: 0131 554 6244 *Fax:* 0131 553 2988 *Dx:* 550851 LEITH
E-mail: mail@bprsolicitors.co.uk

BIGGART BAILLIE
2 Lochrin Square 96 Fountain Bridge Edinburgh EH3 9QA
Tel: 0131 226 5541 *Fax:* 0131 226 2278 *Dx:* ED15 EDINBURGH
E-mail: info@biggartbaillie.co.uk

BLACKLOCKS
89 Constitution Street Edinburgh EH6 7AS
Tel: 0131 555 7500 *Fax:* 0131 555 5535 *Dx:* 550863 LEITH
E-mail: info@blacklocks.co.uk

COLIN BLAIKIE & CO
62 Broughton Street Edinburgh EH1 3SA
Tel: 0131 557 1867 *Fax:* 0131 557 6712
Dx: ED550483 EDINBURGH 45
E-mail: colin@colinblaikie.co.uk

BLAIR CADELL SOLICITORS
Property Sales Centre 1 Harrison Gardens Edinburgh EH11 1SJ
Tel: 0131 337 1800 *Fax:* 0131 337 1118 *Dx:* ED92 EDINBURGH
E-mail: office@blaircadell.com

The Bond House 5 Breadalbane Street Edinburgh EH6 5JH
Tel: 0131 555 5800 *Fax:* 0131 555 1022 *Dx:* ED92 EDINBURGH
E-mail: office@blaircadell.com

BONAR MACKENZIE WS
9 Hill Street Edinburgh EH2 3JT
Tel: 0131 225 8371 *Fax:* 0131 225 2048 *Dx:* ED7 EDINBURGH
E-mail: law@bonarmac.co.uk

BONNAR & CO
27 Alva Street Edinburgh EH2 4PS
Tel: 0800 073 0065 *Fax:* 0131 225 7252 *Dx:* ED121 EDINBURGH

BRECHIN TINDAL OATTS
One Edinburgh Quay 133 Fountainbridge Edinburgh EH3 9QG
Tel: 0131 222 2939 *Fax:* 0131 222 2949 *Dx:* ED77 EDINBURGH
E-mail: lawyers@bto.co.uk

BRODIES LLP
15 Atholl Crescent Edinburgh EH3 8HA
Tel: 0131 228 3777 *Fax:* 0131 228 3878 *Dx:* ED10 EDINBURGH 1
E-mail: mailbox@brodies.co.uk

FRASER BROOKS & CO WS
45 Frederick Street Edinburgh EH2 1ES
Tel: 0131 225 6226 *Fax:* 0131 220 0651 *Dx:* ED111 EDINBURGH
E-mail: fraserbrooks@btconnect.com

BROWN & CO
c/o Legal Services Agency Princes House 5 Shandwick Place Edinburgh EH2 4RG
Tel: 0131 228 9993 *Fax:* 0131 228 9994
Dx: ED231 EDINBURGH 1
E-mail: lsaedin@lsa.org.uk

KENNETH F BROWN
23b Dundas Street Edinburgh EH3 6QQ
Tel: 0131 556 7525 *Fax:* 0131 556 3924
E-mail: info@kennethfbrown.co.uk

M J BROWN SON & CO
Dean Bank Lodge 10 Dean Bank Lane Edinburgh EH3 5BS
Tel: 0131 332 1200 *Fax:* 0131 332 4600 *Dx:* ED122 EDINBURGH
E-mail: jmat985725@aol.com

BURNESS
50 Lothian Road Festival Square Edinburgh EH3 9WJ
Tel: 0131 473 6000 *Fax:* 0131 473 6006

C & N DEFENCE
5 York Place Edinburgh EH1 3EB
Tel: 0131 202 9233

CCW LLP
40 Charlotte Square Edinburgh EH2 4HQ
Tel: 0845 223 3001 *Fax:* 0131 220 7609 *Dx:* ED45 EDINBURGH
E-mail: info@ccwlegal.co.uk

CMS CAMERON MCKENNA
2nd Floor 7 Castle Street Edinburgh EH2 3AH
Tel: 0131 220 7676 *Fax:* 0131 220 7670 *Dx:* ED194 EDINBURGH

CAMPBELL SMITH WS (INC GRAY MUIRHEAD WS)
21 York Place Edinburgh EH1 3EN
Tel: 0131 556 3737 *Fax:* 0131 473 7700 *Dx:* ED51 EDINBURGH
E-mail: mailbox@camsmith.co.uk

CAMPBELLS
49 London Road Edinburgh EH7 5SP
Tel: 0131 661 7236 *Fax:* 0131 661 7408
Dx: ED551151 EDINBURGH 8
E-mail: campbellslaw@aol.com

P H CLANCY & CO
15 Roseburn Terrace Edinburgh EH12 5NG
Tel: 0131 337 7771 *Fax:* 0131 346 2057 *Dx:* ED432 EDINBURGH
E-mail: phclancyco@btconnect.com

RORY COLLINS
17 Drummond Place Edinburgh EH3 6PL
Tel: 0131 557 0691

CONNELL & CONNELL WS
10 Dublin Street Edinburgh EH1 3PR
Tel: 0131 556 2993 *Fax:* 0131 557 5542 *Dx:* ED184 EDINBURGH
E-mail: property@connellws.co.uk

CONNOR MALCOLM
1 Inverleith Terrace Edinburgh EH3 5NS
Tel: 0131 557 3188 *Fax:* 0131 557 6561 *Dx:* ED188 EDINBURGH
E-mail: mailroom@connormalcolm.com

CORNILLON CRAIG & CO
28 Drumsheugh Gardens Edinburgh EH3 7RN
Tel: 0131 225 4356 *Fax:* 0131 226 4123 *Dx:* ED17 EDINBURGH
E-mail: cornillons@btconnect.com

CURRIE GILMOUR & CO
41-43 Warrender Park Road Edinburgh EH9 1EU
Tel: 0131 229 2077 *Dx:* ED150 EDINBURGH
E-mail: enquiries@curriegilmour.co.uk

DLA PIPER SCOTLAND LLP
Rutland Square Edinburgh EH1 2AA
Tel: 0870 011 1111 *Fax:* 0131 242 5555 *Dx:* ED271 EDINBURGH 1
E-mail: info@dlapiper.com

DMD LAW
22 St John's Road Corstorphine Edinburgh EH12 6NZ
Tel: 0131 316 4666 *Fax:* 0131 539 7035
Dx: ED440550 EDINBURGH 44

DAVIDSON CHALMERS LLP
12 Hope Street Edinburgh EH2 4DB
Tel: 0131 625 9191 *Fax:* 0131 625 9192
Dx: ED408 EDINBURGH 2
E-mail: mailbox@davidsonchalmers.com

DAVIDSONS SOLICITORS WS
35 Albany Street Edinburgh EH1 3QN
Tel: 0131 558 9999 *Fax:* 0131 557 3139
Dx: ED51061 EDINBURGH 6
E-mail: iainhaigh@davidsons-solicitors.co.uk

LESLIE DEANS & CO
3 St Patrick Street Edinburgh EH8 9ES
Tel: 0131 667 1900 *Dx:* ED82 EDINBURGH

DICKSON MINTO WS
16 Charlotte Square Edinburgh EH2 4DF
Tel: 0131 225 4455 *Fax:* 0131 225 2712 *Dx:* ED199 EDINBURGH

DIGBY BROWN
Causewayside House 160 Causewayside Edinburgh EH9 1PR
Tel: 0845 273 2323 *Fax:* 0131 319 8111 *Dx:* ED182 EDINBURGH
E-mail: maildesk@digbybrown.co.uk

DOYLE & CO
24 Haddington Place Edinburgh EH7 4AF
Tel: 0131 557 2333 *Fax:* 0131 556 7147

DRUMMOND MILLER WS
32 Moray Place Edinburgh EH3 6BZ
Tel: 0131 226 5151 *Fax:* 0131 225 2608 *Dx:* ED104 EDINBURGH

DUNCAN & WALLACE SSC
131 Newhaven Road Edinburgh EH6 4NP
Tel: 0131 467 7550 *Fax:* 0131 467 7553 *Dx:* 550852 LEITH
E-mail: mail@solicitoredinburgh.co.uk

DUNDAS & WILSON CS
Saltire Court 20 Castle Terrace Edinburgh EH1 2EN
Tel: 0131 228 8000 *Fax:* 0131 228 8888 *Dx:* 553001 EDINBURGH 6

EDINBURGH LAW
Barrie's Close 1 Parliament Square Edinburgh EH1 1RB
Tel: 0131 220 6600 *Fax:* 0131 225 3444
E-mail: info@edinburghlaw.info

FAIRBAIRNS
2 Young Street Lane South Edinburgh EH2 4JF
Tel: 0131 226 5955 *Fax:* 0131 220 3155
E-mail: fairbairns@fsmail.net

FORRESTER OGILVIE & CO
10 Polwarth Terrace Edinburgh EH11 1ND
Tel: 0131 228 2303 *Fax:* 0131 229 4787 *Dx:* ED233 EDINBURGH
E-mail: mo263@msn.com

FRANKS MACADAM BROWN
9-10 St Andrew's Square Edinburgh EH2 2AF
Tel: 0131 718 6060 *Fax:* 0131 718 6104
E-mail: clivef@franksmb.co.uk

FYFE IRELAND WS
32 Charlotte Square Edinburgh EH2 4ET
Tel: 0131 220 5100 *Fax:* 0131 220 5101 *Dx:* ED23 EDINBURGH
E-mail: mail@fyfeireland.com

GATELEY LLP
Exchange Tower 19 Canning Street Edinburgh EH3 8EH
Tel: 0131 228 2400 *Fax:* 0131 222 9800 *Dx:* ED27 EDINBURGH
E-mail: info@gateleyuk.com

GIBSON KERR & CO
46 India Street Edinburgh EH3 6HJ
Tel: 0131 225 7558 *Fax:* 0131 225 1108
Dx: ED551100 EDINBURGH 7
E-mail: info@gibsonkerr.co.uk

GILDEAS
30 Melville Street Edinburgh EH3 7HA
Tel: 0845 051 0810

GILFEDDER & MCINNES
101 Leith Walk Edinburgh EH6 8NP
Tel: 0131 554 3550 *Fax:* 0131 554 2718
E-mail: gilfedder@btconnect.com

8

GILLESPIE MACANDREW
5 Atholl Crescent Edinburgh EH3 8EJ
Tel: 0131 225 1677 *Fax:* 0131 225 4519 *Dx:* ED1131 EDINBURGH

LESLEY A GRAY
Purvesholm Sandy Loan Gullane Edinburgh EH31 2BH
Tel: 01620 843872 *Fax:* 01620 842232
E-mail: lesley@lagray.co.uk

GRIGOR HALES
135 Gorgie Road Edinburgh EH11 1TH
Tel: 0131 313 5556
E-mail: mail@grigorhales.co.uk

GUILD & GUILD WS
51 Castle Street Edinburgh EH2 3LJ
Tel: 0131 225 9155 *Fax:* 0131 225 9040 *Dx:* ED202 EDINBURGH
E-mail: info@guildandguild.co.uk

HBM SAYERS
18 Hanover Street Edinburgh EH2 2EN
Tel: 0131 225 9855 *Fax:* 0131 226 7677 *Dx:* ED76 EDINBURGH
E-mail: enqedin@hbmsayers.com

HADDEN RANKIN
40 Howe Street Edinburgh EH3 6TH
Tel: 0131 220 5241 *Fax:* 0131 220 5242
Dx: ED551113 EDINBURGH 7

DUNCAN HAMILTON & CO WS
45 Frederick Street Edinburgh EH2 1ES
Tel: 0131 226 3199 *Fax:* 0131 225 4781

HARLEY & CO SSC
12 South Charlotte Street Edinburgh EH2 4AX
Tel: 0131 624 9839 *Fax:* 0131 225 5191
E-mail: roymharley@harleyandco.co.uk

HARPER MACLEOD
8 Melville Street Edinburgh EH3 7NS
Tel: 0131 247 2500 *Fax:* 0131 247 2501 *Dx:* ED167 EDINBURGH
E-mail: info@harpermacleod.co.uk

HENDERSON & CO
4a New March Road Edinburgh EH14 1RL
Tel: 0131 477 3511 *Fax:* 0131 477 3512 *Dx:* ED276 EDINBURGH
E-mail: henderson.solicitors@virgin.net

HUNTERS RESIDENTIAL
76-80 Morningside Road Edinburgh EH10 4BY
Tel: 0131 447 4747

DAVID JOHNSON & CO
14 Stafford Street Edinburgh EH3 7AU
Tel: 0131 622 9222 *Fax:* 0131 622 7922 *Dx:* ED401 EDINBURGH
E-mail: sales@davidjohnson.co.uk

LAWFORD KIDD
12 Hill Street Edinburgh EH2 3LB
Tel: 0800 027 1480 *Fax:* 0131 226 2069 *Dx:* ED159 EDINBURGH
E-mail: enquiries@lawfordkidd.co.uk

LEDINGHAM CHALMERS
Crichton House 4 Crichton's Close Holyrood Edinburgh EH8 8DT
Tel: 0131 200 1000 *Fax:* 0131 200 1060 *Dx:* ED275 EDINBURGH
E-mail: mail@ledinghamchalmers.com

LINDSAY DUNCAN & BLACK
16 Queen Street Edinburgh EH2 1JW
Tel: 0131 225 2354 *Fax:* 0131 220 2388 *Dx:* ED30 EDINBURGH
E-mail: info@ldbproperty.com

LINDSAYS
Caledonian Exchange 19a Canning Street Edinburgh EH3 8HE
Tel: 0131 229 1212 *Fax:* 0131 229 5611 *Dx:* ED25 EDINBURGH
E-mail: mail@lindsays.co.uk

THE LINTS PARTNERSHIP
8-9 Crighton Place Leith Walk Edinburgh EH7 4NZ
Tel: 0131 555 4100 *Fax:* 0131 555 5656 *Dx:* ED289 EDINBURGH
E-mail: legal@lints.co.uk

MACBETH CURRIE
8 Manor Place Edinburgh EH3 7DD
Tel: 0131 226 5066 *Fax:* 0131 220 0004 *Dx:* ED189 EDINBURGH

MCCLURE NAISMITH
3 Ponton Street Edinburgh EH3 9QQ
Tel: 0131 228 4994 *Fax:* 0131 228 4260 *Dx:* ED135 EDINBURGH
E-mail: edinburgh@mcclurenaismith.com

FRANCIS M MCCONNELL SSC
12 Drumsheugh Gardens Edinburgh EH3 7QG
Tel: 0131 477 8902 *Fax:* 0131 225 7216 *Dx:* ED210 EDINBURGH
E-mail: fmmcconnell@hotmail.com

9b Melville Crescent Edinburgh EH3 7LZ
Tel: 0131 477 8902 *Fax:* 0131 477 8992 *Dx:* ED155 EDINBURGH
E-mail: fmmcconnell@hotmail.com

MCGRIGORS LLP
Princes Exchange 1 Earl Grey Street Edinburgh EH3 9AQ
Tel: 0131 777 7000 *Fax:* 0131 777 7003
Dx: ED723301 EDINBURGH 43
E-mail: enquiries@mcgrigors.com

MCINTYRE LEWIS
158 Portobello High Street Edinburgh EH15 1AH
Tel: 0131 669 7218 *Fax:* 0131 669 8352

MCKAY & NORWELL WS
5 Rutland Square Edinburgh EH1 2AX
Tel: 0131 222 8000 *Fax:* 0131 222 8008
Dx: ED138 EDINBURGH 1
E-mail: enquiries@mckaynorwell.co.uk

MACKAY SINCLAIR
11-15 Easter Road Edinburgh EH7 5PJ
Tel: 0131 652 1166 *Fax:* 0131 652 1199

MACLACHLAN & MACKENZIE
10 Walker Street Edinburgh EH3 7LA
Tel: 0131 220 2226 *Fax:* 0131 220 1183 *Dx:* ED33 EDINBURGH
E-mail: mail@macmac.com

MACLAY MURRAY & SPENS
Quartermile One 15 Lauriston Place Edinburgh EH3 9EP
Tel: 0131 228 7000 *Fax:* 0131 228 7001 *Dx:* ED137 EDINBURGH

ANGUS MCLENNON & COMPANY SOLICITORS
Unit 6 Sighthill Shopping Centre Edinburgh EH11 4AN
Tel: 0131 442 2244 *Fax:* 0131 442 3344

MARY R MCQUEEN
2b New Mart Road Edinburgh EH14 1RL
Tel: 0131 445 3208 *Fax:* 0131 477 7052

MACRAE FLETT & RENNIE
2 Randolph Place Edinburgh EH3 7TQ
Tel: 0131 225 5985 *Fax:* 0131 225 2470 *Dx:* ED34 EDINBURGH
E-mail: mail@macraeflett.com

MCSPORRANS
2 East London Street Edinburgh EH7 4BH
Tel: 0131 557 9151
E-mail: enquiries@mcsporrans.com

MCWILLIAM WS
3 Hartington Place Edinburgh EH10 4LF
Tel: 0131 229 3612 *Fax:* 0131 228 6534

MARWICKS
40 Dundas Street Edinburgh EH3 6JN
Tel: 0131 556 5938 *Fax:* 0131 556 9429
E-mail: mike.marwick@marwicks.co.uk

MEGSON & CO SSC
1 Grindlay Street Court Edinburgh EH3 9AR
Tel: 0131 228 2501 *Fax:* 0131 228 5554 *Dx:* ED256 EDINBURGH
E-mail: megson@blueyonder.co.uk

ALEXANDER MOFFAT & CO WS
13a Alva Street Edinburgh EH2 4PH
Tel: 0131 225 6200 *Fax:* 0131 220 1324 *Dx:* ED170 EDINBURGH
E-mail: enquiries@moffat.ws

GEORGE MORE & CO
19 Dublin Street Edinburgh EH1 3PG
Tel: 0131 557 1110 *Fax:* 0131 557 8882

MORGAN CUNNINGHAM
10a Castle Terrace Edinburgh EH1 2DP
Tel: 0131 623 9323 *Fax:* 0131 623 9322 *Dx:* ED446 EDINBURGH

MORISONS
Erskine House 68 Queen Street Edinburgh EH2 4NN
Tel: 0131 226 6541 *Fax:* 0131 226 3156 *Dx:* ED38 EDINBURGH
E-mail: enquiries@morisonsllp.com

MORTON FRASER
Quartermile Two 2 Lister Square Edinburgh EH3 9GL
Tel: 0131 247 1000 *Fax:* 0131 247 1007 *Dx:* ED119 EDINBURGH
E-mail: infodesk@morton-fraser.com

MOWAT HALL DICK
45 Queen Charlotte Street Leith Edinburgh EH6 7HT
Tel: 0131 555 0616 *Fax:* 0131 553 1523 *Dx:* 550856 LEITH
E-mail: edinburgh@mhdlaw.co.uk

A G MUIR WS
89 Ravenscroft Street Edinburgh EH17 8QS
Tel: 0131 664 3320 *Fax:* 0131 621 7006

MUIRS WS
31 Palmerston Place Edinburgh EH12 5AP
Tel: 0131 226 3058 *Fax:* 0131 220 2565 *Dx:* ED186 EDINBURGH
E-mail: muirsws@btconnect.com

MURRAY BEITH MURRAY WS
3 Glenfinlas Street Edinburgh EH3 6AQ
Tel: 0131 225 1200 *Fax:* 0131 225 4412 *Dx:* ED40 EDINBURGH
E-mail: mbm@murraybeith.co.uk

MURRAYS WS
40 North Castle Street Edinburgh EH2 3BN
Tel: 0131 625 6625 *Fax:* 0131 625 6626 *Dx:* ED203 EDINBURGH
E-mail: mail@murraysnell.co.uk

NEILSONS
138 St John's Road Edinburgh EH12 8AY
Tel: 0131 316 4444 *Fax:* 0131 334 8003
Dx: ED550441 EDINBURGH 44
E-mail: mail@neilsons.co.uk

2a Picardy Place Edinburgh EH1 3JT
Tel: 0131 556 5522 *Fax:* 0131 556 3666
Dx: ED551051 EDINBURGH 6
E-mail: mail@neilsons.co.uk

ANN OGG
27-13 West Bryson Road Edinburgh EH11 1BN
Tel: 0131 337 0912 *Fax:* 0131 346 0588
E-mail: an.og@btinternet.com

PAULL & WILLIAMSONS
Thistle House 21-23 Thistle Street Edinburgh EH2 1DF
Tel: 0131 226 6180 *Fax:* 0131 226 6797 *Dx:* ED261 EDINBURGH
E-mail: info@paull-williamsons.co.uk

PINSENT MASONS LLP
3rd Floor Quay 2 139 Fountainbridge Edinburgh EH3 9QG
Tel: 0131 225 0000 *Fax:* 0131 225 0099

JOHN PRYDE SSC
53 George IV Bridge Edinburgh EH1 1EJ
Tel: 0131 220 2160 *Fax:* 0131 220 2170

PURDIE & CO
69 Haymarket Terrace Edinburgh EH12 5HD
Tel: 0131 346 7240 *Fax:* 0131 346 7707
E-mail: info@purdiesolicitors.co.uk

PATRICIA S QUIGLEY WS
1 Lauriston Gardens Edinburgh EH3 9HH
Tel: 0131 228 1165 *Fax:* 0131 510 1165

RAE REID & STEPHEN WS
The Cottage 235 Corstorphine Road Edinburgh EH12 7AR
Tel: 0131 334 8977 *Fax:* 0131 334 5518
E-mail: mail@raereidstephen.co.uk

RITCHIE NEILL
12 Brougham Street Edinburgh EH3 9JH
Tel: 0131 222 4860 *Fax:* 0131 222 4861
E-mail: enquiries@rnsolicitors.com

GRAEME RUNCIE & CO
1 Grindley Street Court Edinburgh EH3 9AR
Tel: 0131 228 8999 *Fax:* 0131 228 8999

RUSSEL & AITKEN
27 Rutland Square Edinburgh EH1 2BU
Tel: 0131 228 5500 *Fax:* 0131 229 0644 *Dx:* ED47 EDINBURGH
E-mail: enquiries@russelaitken.com

RUSSELL JONES & WALKER
1st Floor Centrum House 108-114 Dundas Street Edinburgh EH3 5DQ
Tel: 0131 718 4150 *Fax:* 0131 220 3386 *Dx:* ED70 EDINBURGH
E-mail: enquiries@rjw.co.uk

SEMPLE FRASER WS
80 George Street Edinburgh EH2 3BU
Tel: 0131 273 3771 *Fax:* 0131 273 3776 *Dx:* ED447 EDINBURGH
E-mail: info@semplefraser.co.uk

SHEPHERD + WEDDERBURN LLP
1 Exchange Crescent Conference Square Edinburgh EH3 8UL
Tel: 0131 228 9900 *Fax:* 0131 228 1222
Dx: ED551970 EDINBURGH 53
E-mail: info@shepwedd.co.uk

SHIELD & KYD
15 Rutland Street Edinburgh EH1 2AN
Tel: 0131 228 2381 *Fax:* 0131 229 2710 *Dx:* ED124 EDINBURGH
E-mail: rutland@shieldandkyd.co.uk

100 Easter Road Edinburgh EH7 5RH
Tel: 0131 661 5358 *Fax:* 0131 652 2082
Dx: ED551152 EDINBURGH 8
E-mail: easter@shieldandkyd.co.uk

SIMPSON & MARWICK
Albany House 58 Albany Street Edinburgh EH1 3QR
Tel: 0131 557 1545 *Fax:* 0131 525 8651
Dx: ED550480 EDINBURGH 45
E-mail: email@simpmar.com

SOMERVILLE & RUSSELL
22 Manor Place Edinburgh EH3 7DS
Tel: 0131 220 3503 *Fax:* 0131 220 3506 *Dx:* ED20 EDINBURGH

THOMAS H G STEWART
41 Barclay Place Bruntsfield Edinburgh EH10 4HW
Tel: 0131 229 4939 *Fax:* 0131 656 0689 *Dx:* ED434 EDINBURGH
E-mail: enquiries@thomashgstewart.co.uk

STUART & STUART WS
25 Rutland Street Edinburgh EH1 2RN
Tel: 0131 228 6449 *Fax:* 0131 229 6987 *Dx:* ED54 EDINBURGH
E-mail: info@stuartandstuart.co.uk

STURROCK ARMSTRONG & THOMSON
7a Dundas Street Edinburgh EH3 6QG
Tel: 0131 556 0159 *Fax:* 0131 556 2079 *Dx:* ED109 EDINBURGH
E-mail: property@satsolicitors.co.uk

THOMPSONS
16-20 Castle Street Edinburgh EH2 3AT
Tel: 0131 225 4297 *Fax:* 0131 225 9591 *Dx:* ED101 EDINBURGH
E-mail: edinburgh@thompsons-compensation-claims.co.uk

TODS MURRAY WS
Edinburgh Quay 133 Fountainbridge Edinburgh EH3 9AG
Tel: 0131 656 2000 *Fax:* 0131 656 2020 *Dx:* ED58 EDINBURGH
E-mail: maildesk@todsmurray.com

TURCAN CONNELL
Princes Exchange 1 Earl Grey Street Edinburgh EH3 9EE
Tel: 0131 228 8111 *Fax:* 0131 228 8118
Dx: ED723300 EDINBURGH 43
E-mail: enquiries@turcanconnell.com

A & W M URQUHART
16 Heriot Row Edinburgh EH3 6HR
Tel: 0131 556 2896 *Fax:* 0131 556 0046 *Dx:* ED206 EDINBURGH
E-mail: enquiries@urquharts.co.uk

VALENTE MCCOMBIE & HUNTER
10 South Clerk Street Newington Edinburgh EH8 9JE
Tel: 0131 622 2626 *Fax:* 0131 622 2627 *Dx:* ED12 EDINBURGH
E-mail: accounts@vmh.co.uk

43-45 Easter Road Edinburgh EH7 5PL
Tel: 0131 661 5911 *Fax:* 0131 661 0193
Dx: ED551153 EDINBURGH 8
E-mail: accounts@vmh.co.uk

WARDLAW STEPHENSON ALLAN
28a Albany Street Edinburgh EH1 3QH
Tel: 0131 557 8020 *Fax:* 0131 557 9622
E-mail: admin@wsalawyers.com

WARNERS
247b St John's Road Corstorphine Edinburgh EH12 7XD
Tel: 0131 662 4747 *Fax:* 0131 334 0099 *Dx:* ED168 EDINBURGH
E-mail: mail@warnersllp.com

22 St Patrick Square Edinburgh EH8 9EY
Tel: 0131 662 4747 *Fax:* 0131 662 4117 *Dx:* ED168 EDINBURGH
E-mail: mail@warnersllp.com

176 Portobello High Street Edinburgh EH15 1EX
Tel: 0131 662 4747 *Fax:* 0131 669 5252 *Dx:* ED168 EDINBURGH
E-mail: mail@warnersllp.com

STEWART WATT & CO
171 Dalry Road Edinburgh EH11 2EB
Tel: 0131 337 9692 *Fax:* 0131 313 2848 *Dx:* ED166 EDINBURGH
E-mail: law@stewartwatt.co.uk

PATRICK WHEATLEY
34 Leith Walk Edinburgh EH6 5AA
Tel: 07765 244030

WILSON MCLEOD
3 Boroughloch Square Edinburgh EH8 9NJ
Tel: 0131 668 3299 *Fax:* 0131 668 1988
E-mail: wilsonmcleod@btconnect.com

WILSON TERRIS & CO SSC
2 Alcorn Rigg Edinburgh EH14 3BF
Tel: 0131 442 1444 *Fax:* 0131 458 5572
E-mail: mail@wilsonterris.co.uk

WRIGHT & CO
5e Giles Street Leith Edinburgh EH6 6DJ
Tel: 0131 467 5566 *Fax:* 0131 467 3344 *Dx:* 550861 LEITH
E-mail: info@propertywright.com

WRIGHT JOHNSTON & MACKENZIE
18 Charlotte Square Edinburgh EH2 4DF
Tel: 0131 225 5660 *Fax:* 0131 225 8713 *Dx:* ED26 EDINBURGH
E-mail: enquiries@wjm.co.uk

T C YOUNG
Melrose House 69a George Street Edinburgh EH2 2JG
Tel: 0131 220 7660 *Fax:* 0131 220 7661 *Dx:* ED112 EDINBURGH
E-mail: mail@tcyoung.co.uk

ELGIN

ALLAN BLACK & MCCASKIE
151 High Street Elgin Moray IV30 1DX
Tel: 01343 543355 *Fax:* 01343 549667 *Dx:* 520650 ELGIN
E-mail: mail@abmsols.co.uk

COCKBURNS
82 High Street Elgin Moray IV30 1BL
Tel: 01343 542684 *Fax:* 01343 540024 *Dx:* 520651 ELGIN
E-mail: elgin@cockburns-solicitors.com

THE CRUICKSHANK LAW PRACTICE
7 Mayne Road Elgin Moray IV30 1NY
Tel: 01343 544466 *Fax:* 01343 541999
E-mail: cruickshanks@btconnect.com

GRIGOR & YOUNG
1 North Street Elgin Moray IV30 1UA
Tel: 01343 544077 *Fax:* 01343 548523
E-mail: mail@grigor-young.co.uk

JAMES MCKAY
17 High Street Elgin Moray IV30 1EQ
Tel: 01343 556500 *Fax:* 01343 556501
E-mail: info@jamesmckay.eu

PATRICIA L MENNIE
Innesmill Urquhart Elgin Moray IV30 8NH
Tel: 01343 842643 *Fax:* 01343 842643

STEWART & MCISAAC
141 High Street Elgin Moray IV30 1DS
Tel: 01343 544971 *Fax:* 01343 541205
E-mail: office@lexelgin.com

WINK & MACKENZIE
The Old Station Maisondieu Road Elgin Moray IV30 1RH
Tel: 01343 542623 *Fax:* 01343 540775 *Dx:* 551380 ELGIN 2
E-mail: ann@wink.co.uk

ELLON

ABERDEIN CONSIDINE & CO
57 Bridge Street Ellon Aberdeenshire AB41 9AA
Tel: 01358 721893 *Fax:* 01358 724104 *Dx:* AB46 ABERDEEN
E-mail: eln@acandco.com

GRAY & GRAY
69 Station Road Ellon Aberdeenshire AB41 9AR
Tel: 01358 724455 *Fax:* 01358 722506
E-mail: property@graygraylaw.com

RAEBURN CHRISTIE CLARK & WALLACE
The Square Ellon Aberdeenshire AB41 9JB
Tel: 01358 720777 *Fax:* 01358 724401
E-mail: ellon@raeburns.co.uk

WINCHESTERS
57 Station Road Ellon Aberdeenshire AB41 9AR
Tel: 01358 724252 *Fax:* 01358 722125
E-mail: info@winchesters-law.co.uk

EYEMOUTH

MELROSE & PORTEOUS
1 Manse Road Eyemouth Scottish Borders TD14 5JE
Tel: 01620 892307 *Fax:* 01620 895106
E-mail: info@melroseporteous.co.uk

FALKIRK

A & J C ALLAN & CO
North Bank Chambers 36 Newmarket Street Falkirk FK1 1JG
Tel: 01324 621263 *Fax:* 01324 612657

BLACKADDER & MCMONAGLE
41 High Street Falkirk FK1 1EN
Tel: 01324 612999 *Fax:* 01324 612026 *Dx:* FA4 FALKIRK
E-mail: maildesk@blackandmac.com

BROPHY & COMPANY
13 Cockburn Street Falkirk FK1 1DJ
Tel: 01324 635035
E-mail: gb@brophyandcompany.freeserve.co.uk

CAESAR & HOWIE (IN ASSOC WITH WILSON & JARVIS)
29 Upper New Market Street Falkirk FK1 1JH
Tel: 01324 628332 *Fax:* 01324 632621 *Dx:* FA24 FALKIRK
E-mail: enquiries@caesar-howie.co.uk

GAIR & GIBSON (INC K J DOUGLAS & CO)
7/9 Newmarket Street Falkirk FK1 1JY
Tel: 01324 623928 *Fax:* 01324 611697 *Dx:* FA7 FALKIRK
E-mail: mail@gairgibson.co.uk

GIBSON & KENNEDY
Benview Wellside Place Falkirk FK1 5RP
Tel: 01324 622741 *Fax:* 01324 611559 *Dx:* FA8 FALKIRK
E-mail: mail@gibsonkennedy.co.uk

HUTCHISON MCLEAN
Ground Floor 5 Manse Place Falkirk FK1 1JN
Tel: 01324 633000 *Fax:* 01324 633005 *Dx:* FA37 FALKIRK
E-mail: hutchisonlaw@hotmail.co.uk

MTM DEFENCE LAWYERS
1 Cockburn Street Falkirk FK1 1DJ
Tel: 01324 633221 *Fax:* 01324 611694 *Dx:* FA20 FALKIRK
E-mail: enquiries@mtmdefence.co.uk

MARSHALL WILSON
2 High Street Falkirk FK1 1EZ
Tel: 01324 612569 *Fax:* 01324 623512 *Dx:* FA10 FALKIRK
E-mail: falkirk@marshallwilson.com

NELSONS
326 Main Street Camelon Falkirk FK1 4EG
Tel: 01324 613316 *Fax:* 01324 613317
E-mail: mail@nelsonslawyers.co.uk

RUSSEL & AITKEN
Kings Court High Street Falkirk FK1 1PQ
Tel: 01324 622888 *Fax:* 01324 620994 *Dx:* FA12 FALKIRK
E-mail: info@russel-aitken.co.uk

SANDEMANS
34 Union Road Camelon Falkirk FK1 4PG
Tel: 01324 633222 *Fax:* 01324 630322
E-mail: office@sandemans.co.uk

STIRLING & CO
122 High Street Falkirk FK1 1NW
Tel: 01324 636181 *Fax:* 01324 622595
E-mail: stirling.co@btconnect.com

FORFAR

BLACKADDERS
128 Castle Street Forfar Angus DD8 3HS
Tel: 01307 461234 *Fax:* 01307 466573
E-mail: forfar@blackadders.co.uk

BOWMAN SCOTTISH LAWYERS
37 East High Street Forfar Angus DD8 2EL
Tel: 01307 464088 *Fax:* 01307 468868
E-mail: forfar@bowmansolicitors.co.uk

BOYLE'S
77 Castle Street Forfar Angus DD8 3AG
Tel: 01307 475320
E-mail: mail@boylesforfar.co.uk

R BRUCE & CO
24 West High Street Forfar Angus DD8 1BA
Tel: 01307 460666 *Fax:* 01307 460682 *Dx:* 530684 FORFAR
E-mail: info@bruce-co.co.uk

W & J S GORDON
Albion House 52 East High Street Forfar Angus DD8 2EG
Tel: 01307 462188 *Fax:* 01307 467571 *Dx:* 50676 FORFAR
E-mail: info@wjsgordon.co.uk

MACHARDY ALEXANDER & WHYTE WS
71 Castle Street Forfar Angus DD8 3AG
Tel: 01307 463593 *Fax:* 01307 468507
E-mail: forfar@machardy.co.uk

MACLEAN & LOWSON
94 East High Street Forfar Angus DD8 2ET
Tel: 01307 462103 *Fax:* 01307 467001
E-mail: enquiries@macleanandlowson.co.uk

THORNTONS WS
53 East High Street Forfar Angus DD8 2EL
Tel: 01307 466886 *Fax:* 01307 464643
E-mail: forfar@thorntons-law.co.uk

FORRES

MACKENZIE & GRANT
100 High Street Forres Moray IV36 1PD
Tel: 01309 672126 *Fax:* 01309 676384

R & R URQUHART
117-121 High Street Forres Moray IV36 1AB
Tel: 01309 672216 *Fax:* 01309 673161 *Dx:* 520690 FORRES
E-mail: info.forres@r-r-urquhart.com

FORT WILLIAM

MACARTHUR STEWART
87 High Street Fort William Highland PH33 6DG
Tel: 01397 702455 *Fax:* 01397 705949
Dx: 531402 FORT WILLIAM
E-mail: fortwilliam@macarthurstewart.co.uk

MCINTYRE & CO
38 High Street Fort William Highland PH33 6AT
Tel: 01397 703231 *Fax:* 01397 705070
Dx: 531403 FORT WILLIAM
E-mail: law@solicitors-scotland.com

MACPHEE & PARTNERS
Airds House An Aird Fort William Highland PH33 6BL
Tel: 01397 701000 *Fax:* 01397 701777
Dx: 531408 FORT WILLIAM
E-mail: law@macphee.co.uk

FRASERBURGH

BROWN & MCRAE
9-11 Frithside Street Fraserburgh Aberdeenshire AB43 9AB
Tel: 01346 515797 *Fax:* 01346 519168
E-mail: property@brown-mcrae.co.uk

MACRAE STEPHEN & CO
40 Broad Street Fraserburgh Aberdeenshire AB43 9AH
Tel: 01346 514545 *Fax:* 01346 510147
E-mail: info@macraestephen.co.uk

MASSON & GLENNIE
83 Broad Street Fraserburgh Aberdeenshire AB43 9AX
Tel: 01346 513338 *Fax:* 01346 513114
Dx: 521361 FRASERBURGH
E-mail: mail@masson-glennie.co.uk

STEWART & WATSON
38 Broad Street Fraserburgh Aberdeenshire AB43 9AH
Tel: 01346 514443 *Fax:* 01346 514449
E-mail: fraserburgh.property@stewartwatson.co.uk

GALASHIELS

BANNERMAN BURKE
72 Bank Street Galashiels Scottish Borders TD1 1EL
Tel: 01896 750350 *Fax:* 01896 750360 *Dx:* 580711 GALASHIELS

COLLIE & CO
70 High Street Galashiels Scottish Borders TD1 1SQ
Tel: 01896 755466 *Fax:* 01896 661036
E-mail: info@collieandco.com

CULLEN KILSHAW
27 Market Street Galashiels Scottish Borders TD1 3AF
Tel: 01896 758311 *Fax:* 01896 758112 *Dx:* 580700 GALASHIELS

EDINGTON & COMPANY
88 High Street Galashiels Scottish Borders TD1 1SQ
Tel: 01896 756161 *Fax:* 01896 751919 *Dx:* 580710 GALASHIELS
E-mail: info@edingtonlaw.co.uk

PIKE & CHAPMAN
36 Bank Street Galashiels Scottish Borders TD1 1ER
Tel: 01896 752379 *Fax:* 01896 754439 *Dx:* 580701 GALASHIELS
E-mail: mail@pikeandchapman.co.uk

IAIN SMITH & PARTNERS WS
Bank Close Galashiels Scottish Borders TD1 1BG
Tel: 01896 752231 *Fax:* 01896 754469
E-mail: gala@iainsmith.co.uk

WARDLAW STEPHENSON ALLAN
The Lodge 53 Market Street Galashiels Scottish Borders TD1 3AF
Tel: 01896 668669 *Fax:* 01896 756900
E-mail: admin@wsalawyers.com

GALSTON

MCSHERRY HALLIDAY DALE & MARSHALL
18 Wallace Street Galston East Ayrshire KA4 8HP
Tel: 01563 820216 *Fax:* 01563 822188
E-mail: rural@daleandmarshall.co.uk

GIFFNOCK

CAMPBELL RIDDELL BREEZE PATERSON
229 Fenwick Road Giffnock East Renfrewshire G46 6JQ
Tel: 0141 638 7405 *Fax:* 0141 638 2512 *Dx:* 501607 GIFFNOCK
E-mail: law@crbp.co.uk

AUSTIN LAFFERTY LAW
213 Fenwick Road Giffnock East Renfrewshire G46 6JD
Tel: 0141 621 2212 *Fax:* 0141 621 1342
E-mail: jroberts@laffertylaw.com

GIRVAN

LAMBERT & CO
1 Hamilton Street Girvan South Ayrshire KA26 9EY
Tel: 01465 715434 *Fax:* 01465 715005 *Dx:* AY38 AYR
E-mail: lambert.co@btconnect.com

MURRAY & TAIT
146 Dalrymple Street Girvan South Ayrshire KA26 9BQ
Tel: 01465 713118 *Fax:* 01465 715085
E-mail: murray-tait@tiscali.co.uk

GLASGOW

ADIE HUNTER
15 Newton Terrace Glasgow G3 7PJ
Tel: 0141 248 3828 *Fax:* 0141 221 2384
E-mail: enquiries@adiehunter.co.uk

JEFFREY AITKEN
Fortune House 74 Waterloo Street Glasgow G2 7DA
Tel: 0141 221 5983 *Fax:* 0141 225 5750
E-mail: maildesk@jeffrey-aitken.co.uk

ALEXANDER JUBB & TAYLOR
5 Annfield Place Duke Street Glasgow G31 2XQ
Tel: 0141 554 1016 *Fax:* 0141 554 7659
E-mail: info@alexjt.co.uk

ANDERSON FYFE
140 West George Street Glasgow G2 2HG
Tel: 0141 353 0035 *Fax:* 0141 353 7777
E-mail: mail@andersonfyfe.co.uk

ANDERSON STRATHERN LLP
24 Blythswood Square Glasgow G2 4BG
Tel: 0141 242 6060 *Fax:* 0141 221 4733 *Dx:* GW157 GLASGOW
E-mail: info@andersonstrathern.co.uk

6th Floor Lomond House 9 George Square Glasgow G2 1DY
Tel: 0141 285 3800 *Fax:* 0141 221 7974 *Dx:* GW102 GLASGOW

ANDERSONS LLP
125 West Regent Street Glasgow G2 2SA
Tel: 0141 248 6688 *Fax:* 0141 248 9697
Dx: 512403 GLASGOW BATH STREET
E-mail: mailbox@andersonsllp.co.uk

BMK WILSON
90 St Vincent's Street Glasgow G2 5UB
Tel: 0141 221 8004 *Fax:* 0141 221 8088 *Dx:* GW55 GLASGOW
E-mail: bmkw@bmkwilson.co.uk

BAILLIE & REID
175 Saltmarket Glasgow G1 5LG
Tel: 0141 429 1100 *Fax:* 0141 429 1100
E-mail: law@galletly.eclipse.co.uk

BAILLIE SPOWART
16 Alexander Street Clydebank Glasgow G81 1RZ
Tel: 0141 585 2300 *Fax:* 0141 585 2500
E-mail: baillie.spowart@ntlbusiness.com

BANNATYNE KIRKWOOD FRANCE & CO
16 Royal Exchange Square Glasgow G1 3AG
Tel: 0141 221 6020 *Fax:* 0141 221 5120 *Dx:* GW7 GLASGOW

BARCLAY & CO
1174 Maryhill Road Glasgow G20 9TA
Tel: 0141 946 3555 *Fax:* 0141 948 0002
E-mail: barclayco@tiscali.co.uk

BELTRAMI & CO
83 Carlton Place Glasgow G5 9TD
Tel: 0141 429 2262 *Fax:* 0141 429 2526
E-mail: enquiries@beltramiandcompany.co.uk

8

BIGGART BAILLIE
Dalmore House 310 St Vincent Street Glasgow G2 5QR
Tel: 0141 228 8000 *Fax:* 0141 228 8310 *Dx:* GW9 GLASGOW
E-mail: info@biggartbaillie.co.uk

BILKUS & BOYLE
2175 Paisley Road West Cardonald Glasgow G52 3SJ
Tel: 0141 882 3221 *Fax:* 0141 883 4848 *Dx:* 500300 CARDONALD

2236 Paisley Road West Cardonald Glasgow G52 3SJ
Tel: 0141 882 1667 *Fax:* 0141 882 6314 *Dx:* 500301 CARDONALD

BIRD SEMPLE
Private Client Solicitors 21 Blythswood Square Glasgow G2 4BL
Tel: 0141 304 3434 *Fax:* 0141 304 0004
Dx: GW561476 GLASGOW 15
E-mail: enquiries@bsemple.com

BLANEY CARNAN
Festival House 177-179 West George Street Glasgow G2 2LB
Tel: 0141 248 8111 *Fax:* 0141 221 8420
E-mail: mail@blaneycarnan.com

BOYLE SHAUGHNESSY
Standard Buildings 94 Hope Street Glasgow G2 6QB
Tel: 0141 248 1888 *Fax:* 0141 248 2030
E-mail: mail@boyleshaughnessy.com

216 Kilmarnock Road Shawlands Glasgow G43 1TY
Tel: 0141 636 5115 *Fax:* 0141 636 5673
E-mail: mail@boyleshaughnessy.com

BREADY & CO
255 Dumbarton Road Partick Glasgow G11 6AB
Tel: 0141 334 2265 *Fax:* 0141 334 3284

BRECHIN TINDAL OATTS
48 St Vincent Street Glasgow G2 5HS
Tel: 0141 221 8012 *Fax:* 0141 221 7803 *Dx:* GW96 GLASGOW
E-mail: lawyers@bto.co.uk

BROWN & CO
c/o Legal Services Agency 3rd Floor Fleming House Glasgow G3 6ST
Tel: 0141 353 3354 *Fax:* 0141 353 0354 *Dx:* GW12 GLASGOW
E-mail: lsa@btconnect.com

BROWN'S
48 Shandwick Square Easterhouse Glasgow G34 9DT
Tel: 0141 781 0000 *Fax:* 0141 781 1708

BRUNTON MILLER
Herbert House 22 Herbert Street Glasgow G20 6NB
Tel: 0141 337 1199 *Fax:* 0141 337 3300 *Dx:* GW21 GLASGOW
E-mail: info@bruntonmiller.com

BUCHANAN CAMPBELL
11 Bothwell Street Glasgow G2 6LY
Tel: 0141 572 0770 *Fax:* 0141 572 0771 *Dx:* GW289 GLASGOW
E-mail: mail@bcsols.com

BUCHANAN MACLEOD
180 West Regent Street Glasgow G2 4RW
Tel: 0141 221 4440 *Fax:* 0141 221 2343 *Dx:* GW62 GLASGOW
E-mail: mail@buchananmacleod.co.uk

BURNESS
120 Bothwell Street Glasgow G2 7JL
Tel: 0141 248 4933 *Fax:* 0141 204 1601 *Dx:* GW154 GLASGOW

HECTOR CAMERON
2 Lancaster Crescent Glasgow G12 0RR
Tel: 0141 337 6363 *Fax:* 0141 337 6618
E-mail: mail@hectorcameron.com

J K CAMERON
St George's Buildings 5 St Vincent Place Glasgow G1 2DH
Tel: 0141 221 4787 *Fax:* 0141 221 0701 *Dx:* GW261 GLASGOW
E-mail: info@jkcameron.co.uk

CAMPBELL & CO
93 Hope Street Glasgow G2 6LD
Tel: 0141 221 5992 *Fax:* 0141 204 4201
E-mail: georgecampbell@yahoo.com

CAMPBELL & MEECHAN
19 Waterloo Street Glasgow G2 6AY
Tel: 0141 248 8898 *Fax:* 0141 248 7022
E-mail: campbell.meechan@btopenworld.com

CAMPBELL D JOSS
Unit 4 1987 Maryhill Road Glasgow G20 0BT
Tel: 0141 945 5533 *Fax:* 0141 945 5577
E-mail: cdjoss@tiscali.co.uk

PATRICK CAMPBELL & CO
430 Victoria Road Glasgow G42 8YU
Tel: 0141 423 2222 *Fax:* 0141 423 2424
E-mail: reception@patrickcampbellsolicitors.co.uk

CAMPBELL RIDDELL BREEZE PATERSON
80 St Vincents Street Glasgow G2 5UB
Tel: 0141 204 2040 *Fax:* 0141 204 2300 *Dx:* GW18 GLASGOW
E-mail: law@crbp.co.uk

CAMPBELL SIEVEWRIGHT & CO
357 Victoria Road Glasgow G42 8YZ
Tel: 0141 422 2642 *Fax:* 0141 423 6726
E-mail: pdunlop@cs-homes.co.uk

CANNONS
11 Somerset Square Glasgow G3 7JT
Tel: 0141 204 5115 *Fax:* 0141 226 2221 *Dx:* GW370 GLASGOW
E-mail: margaret@cannonslaw.com

JAMES M CARMICHAEL
1 Duke Street Glasgow G4 0UL
Tel: 0141 553 1717 *Fax:* 0141 553 1166 *Dx:* GW297 GLASGOW
E-mail: ellen@jamesmcarmichael.co.uk

CARR & CO
556 Broomfield Road Barmulloch Glasgow G21 3HN
Tel: 0141 558 0234 *Fax:* 0141 558 7805

81 Main Street Baillieston Glasgow G69 6AD
Tel: 0141 773 2145 *Fax:* 0141 771 7246 *Dx:* 500100 BAILLIESTON

534 St Vincent Street Glasgow G3 8XZ
Tel: 0141 248 2999 *Fax:* 0141 248 7373

JOHN CARROLL & CO
40 Carlton Place Glasgow G5 9TS
Tel: 0141 429 0666 *Fax:* 0141 429 6680
E-mail: johncarroll2000@aol.com

CARRUTHERS GEMMILL (INC J C MUIR & BARR)
81 Bath Street Glasgow G2 2EH
Tel: 0141 333 0033 *Fax:* 0141 332 1072
E-mail: twg@carruthersgemmill.co.uk

CASSELS BOYLE
34 West George Street Glasgow G2 1DE
Tel: 0141 332 1856 *Fax:* 0141 332 0881 *Dx:* GW267 GLASGOW

CLAPHAMS
1b & 1c Helena House Busby Road Clarkston Toll Glasgow G76 7RA
Tel: 0141 620 0800 *Fax:* 0141 620 0089 *Dx:* 501602 GIFFNOCK
E-mail: lawagents@davidcclapham.co.uk

CLARK BOYLE & CO
33a Gordon Street Glasgow G1 3PF
Tel: 0141 227 2200 *Fax:* 0141 227 2222 *Dx:* GW227 GLASGOW
E-mail: dwb@clarkboyle.co.uk

CONROY MCINNES
51 Gartcraig Road Glasgow G33 2NW
Tel: 0141 770 8777 *Fax:* 0141 770 8400 *Dx:* 501171 SHAWLANDS
E-mail: mail@conroymcinnes.co.uk

268 Kilmarnock Road Shawlands Glasgow G43 2XS
Tel: 0141 616 6622 *Fax:* 0141 616 6633 *Dx:* 501171 SHAWLANDS
E-mail: mail@conroymcinnes.co.uk

CONVEYANCING DIRECT
The Salmond Chambers 53 Morrison Street Glasgow G5 8LB
Tel: 0141 420 5040 *Fax:* 0141 429 8904
E-mail: info@conveyancingdirect.co.uk

CORRIES (SCOTLAND)
Pentagon House Washington Street Glasgow G3 8AZ
Tel: 0845 612 4488 *Fax:* 0141 249 3401 *Dx:* GW410 GLASGOW
E-mail: enquiries@corries-g.co.uk

COWAN & CO
81 Berkeley Street Glasgow G3 7DX
Tel: 0141 221 1803 *Fax:* 0141 204 1650
E-mail: mail@cowanandco.co.uk

DLA PIPER SCOTLAND LLP
249 West George Street Glasgow G2 4RB
Tel: 0870 011 1111 *Fax:* 0141 204 1902
Dx: GW561481 GLASGOW 16
E-mail: info@dlapiper.com

MIKE DAILLY
Orkney Street Enterprise Centre Unit 4 & Unit 6 18-20 Orkney Street Glasgow G51 2BZ
Tel: 0141 440 2503 *Fax:* 0141 445 3934
E-mail: m@govanlc.com

DALLAS MCMILLAN
Regent Court 70 West Regent Street Glasgow G2 2QZ
Tel: 0141 333 6750 *Fax:* 0141 333 6777

ALFRED W H DALLMAN
22 Thomson Drive Bearsden Glasgow G61 3NU
Tel: 0141 942 8537 *Fax:* 0141 942 8537
E-mail: alfred.dallman@tiscali.co.uk

DICKSONS
19 Waterloo Street Glasgow G2 6BG
Tel: 0141 248 4448 *Fax:* 0141 221 8484
E-mail: mail@dicksons-law.co.uk

DIGBY BROWN
2 West Regent Street Glasgow G2 1RW
Tel: 0845 273 2323 *Fax:* 0141 566 9500 *Dx:* GW17 GLASGOW
E-mail: maildesk@digbybrown.co.uk

DONALDSON ALEXANDER RUSSELL & HADDOW
Rothesay House 134 Douglas Street Glasgow G2 4HF
Tel: 0141 331 1333 *Fax:* 0141 331 1577
Dx: GW512408 GLASGOW BATH STREET

DOONAN MCCAIG & CO
151 Stockwell Street Glasgow G1 4LR
Tel: 0141 552 6600 *Fax:* 0141 552 6230 *Dx:* GW296 GLASGOW
E-mail: david.mccaig@btconnect.com

JACQUELINE DOYLE & CO
Ladywell Unit 6 94 Duke Street Glasgow G4 0UW
Tel: 0141 548 1000 *Fax:* 0141 552 9909
E-mail: barbara.doyle@jdsolicitors.co.uk

DRUMCHAPEL LAW AND MONEY ADVICE CENTRE
Unit 10 42 Dalsetter Avenue Drumchapel Glasgow G15 8TE
Tel: 0141 944 0507 *Fax:* 0141 944 5504

DRUMMOND MILLER WS
65 Bath Street Glasgow G2 2DD
Tel: 0141 332 0086 *Fax:* 0141 332 8295
Dx: GW512813 GLASGOW BATH STREET

DUNDAS & WILSON CS
191 West George Street Glasgow G2 2LD
Tel: 0141 222 2200 *Fax:* 0141 222 2201
Dx: GW561475 GLASGOW 16

DUNLOP ALLEN & CO
177 Saltmarket Glasgow G1 5LG
Tel: 0141 552 1726 *Fax:* 0141 552 6077
E-mail: dunlopallen@btconnect.com

DYKES GLASS & CO
65 Bath Street Glasgow G2 2BX
Tel: 0141 332 2794 *Dx:* GW512053 GLASGOW CENTRAL
E-mail: dykesglass@btclick.com

PETER G FARRELL
70 Royston Road Glasgow G21 2NT
Tel: 0141 552 0033 *Fax:* 0141 552 0333
E-mail: paton.farrell@btconnect.com

1594 Dumbarton Road Glasgow G14 9DB
Tel: 0141 950 2961 *Fax:* 0141 950 6708
E-mail: paton.farrell@btconnect.com

FIELDING MCLEAN & CO
1986 Great Western Road Knightswood Cross Glasgow G13 2SW
Tel: 0141 959 1674 *Fax:* 0141 954 0113
E-mail: douglas.fielding@fieldingmclean.co.uk

FINLAYSON WISE
1148-1152 Shettleston Road Glasgow G32 7PQ
Tel: 0141 763 1337 *Fax:* 0141 763 1015
E-mail: enquiries@finlaysonwise.co.uk

1 Tollcross Road Parkhead Glasgow G31 4UG
Tel: 0141 556 6651 *Fax:* 0141 554 1110
E-mail: enquiries@finlaysonwise.co.uk

FITZPATRICK & CO
875-877 Govan Road Glasgow G51 3DL
Tel: 0141 445 3355 *Fax:* 0141 445 5341
E-mail: mail.govan@fitzpatrickandco.co.uk

FLEMING & REID
180 Hope Street Glasgow G2 2UE
Tel: 0141 331 1144 *Fax:* 0141 331 1800
E-mail: mail@flemingandreid.co.uk

FRANCHI FINNIESTON
24 St Enoch Square Glasgow G1 4DB
Tel: 0141 226 3000 *Fax:* 0141 204 1199 *Dx:* GW146 GLASGOW
E-mail: lawyers@franchifinnieston.co.uk

FREDERICK & CO
19 Sandyford Place Sauchiehall Street Glasgow G3 7NQ
Tel: 0141 221 5575 *Fax:* 0141 221 1161
Dx: 512204 SANDYFORD PLACE
E-mail: info@frederickandco.co.uk

JIM FRIEL & CO
44 Carlton Place Glasgow G5 9TW
Tel: 0141 420 1234 *Fax:* 0141 420 3966
E-mail: jim.friel@jimfriel.co.uk

GALLEN & CO
40 Carlton Place Glasgow G5 9TW
Tel: 0141 420 8250 *Fax:* 0141 420 8258 *Dx:* GW204 GLASGOW
E-mail: mail@gallenandco.com

879 Govan Road Glasgow G51 3DL
Tel: 0141 445 2949 *Fax:* 0141 440 2990 *Dx:* GW204 GLASGOW
E-mail: mail@gallenandco.com

419 Nitshill Road Glasgow G53 7BN
Tel: 0141 880 7148 *Fax:* 0141 880 6435 *Dx:* GW204 GLASGOW
E-mail: mail@gallenandco.com

GILDEAS
97 & 99 West Regent Street Glasgow G2 2BA
Tel: 0845 051 0810

GRADY & CO
2nd Floor 24 St Enoch Square Glasgow G1 4DB
Tel: 0141 221 5000 *Fax:* 0141 221 3000

GRANT & WYLIE
90 Mitchell Street Glasgow G1 3LY
Tel: 0141 221 1035 *Fax:* 0141 204 1917 *Dx:* GW130 GLASGOW
E-mail: law@grantwylie.com

GRANT BROWN LINDSAY
180 West Regent Street Glasgow G2 4RW
Tel: 0141 572 1910 *Fax:* 0141 572 1909
E-mail: maildesk@grantbrownlindsay.com

GRAY & CO
16 Bilsland Drive Glasgow G20 9TH
Tel: 0141 946 7777 *Fax:* 0141 946 9402
E-mail: grayandcompany@btconnect.com

LLOYD GREEN & CO
2nd Floor Suite 49 Bath Street Glasgow G2 2DL
Tel: 0141 353 8700 *Fax:* 0141 353 8701
Dx: 512059 GLASGOW CENTRAL
E-mail: mail@lloyd-green-scotland.com

HBM SAYERS
13 Bath Street Glasgow G2 1HY
Tel: 0141 353 2121 *Fax:* 0141 353 2181 *Dx:* GW47 GLASGOW
E-mail: enqbath@hbmsayers.com

1087 Cathcart Road Mount Florida Glasgow G42 9XR
Tel: 0141 632 2248 *Fax:* 0141 649 0301
E-mail: enqcath@hbmsayers.com

4 Howie Buildings Mearns Road Clarkston Glasgow G76 7ET
Tel: 0141 621 1816 *Fax:* 0141 621 1820
E-mail: enqclark@hbmsayers.com

192 Kilmarnock Road Shawlands Glasgow G41 3PG
Tel: 0141 649 2020 *Fax:* 0141 649 9676
E-mail: enqshaw@hbmsayers.com

HALL & HAUGHEY
87 Carlton Place Glasgow G5 9TD
Tel: 0141 418 0505 *Fax:* 0141 429 3131
E-mail: margaret@hall-haughey.co.uk

HAMILTON BURNS & COMPANY
63 Carlton Place Glasgow G5 9TW
Tel: 0141 429 0600 *Fax:* 0141 429 0650
E-mail: enquiries@hamiltonburns.com

HANNAY FRASER & CO
95 Douglas Street Glasgow G2 4EU
Tel: 0141 221 1381 *Fax:* 0141 204 0277

HARDING & CO
79 Saltmarket Glasgow G1 5LE
Tel: 0141 552 8880

HARDY MACPHAIL
2nd Floor 78 St Vincent Street Glasgow G2 5UB
Tel: 0141 204 0841 *Fax:* 0141 221 4216 *Dx:* GW84 GLASGOW
E-mail: mail@hardymacphail.com

HARPER MACLEOD
14-18 Cadogan Street Glasgow G2 6QN
Tel: 0845 878 4504 *Fax:* 0141 308 4347
E-mail: info@harpermacleod.co.uk

The Ca'd'oro 45 Gordon Street Glasgow G1 3PE
Tel: 0141 221 8888 *Fax:* 0141 226 4198 *Dx:* GW86 GLASGOW
E-mail: info@harpermacleod.co.uk

HART SMITH & CO
43 Crow Road Glasgow G11 7SH
Tel: 0141 339 5252 *Fax:* 0141 339 4617 *Dx:* 500903 PARTICK
E-mail: jhart@hartsmith.co.uk

HARTER & CO
4 Midlock Street Ibrox Glasgow G51 1SL
Tel: 0141 427 0901 *Fax:* 0141 427 7446
E-mail: hartersolicitors@tiscali.co.uk

HASTIES
19 Lynedoch Crescent Glasgow G3 6EQ
Tel: 0141 332 1454 *Fax:* 0141 332 4652
Dx: 512217 SANDYFORD PLACE
E-mail: pbrodie@hasties.co.uk

CHARLES HENNESSY & CO
182 Bath Street Glasgow G2 4AE
Tel: 0141 332 6442 *Fax:* 0141 332 9442
E-mail: mail@charleshennessy.com

R & J M HILL BROWN & CO
3 Newton Place Glasgow G3 7PU
Tel: 0141 332 3265 *Fax:* 0141 332 0414
Dx: 512207 SANDYFORD PLACE
E-mail: info@hillbrown.co.uk

HISLOP NOTARIES
234 West George Street Glasgow G2 4QY
Tel: 0141 221 5955 *Fax:* 0141 221 5955

HOLMES MACKILLOP
109 Douglas Street Blythswood Square Glasgow G2 4HB
Tel: 0141 226 4942 *Fax:* 0141 204 0136
E-mail: general@homack.co.uk

HUGHES DOWDALL
20 Renfield Street Glasgow G2 5AP
Tel: 0141 240 7020 *Fax:* 0141 240 7058 *Dx:* GW51 GLASGOW

J C HUGHES & CO
1028 Tollcross Road Glasgow G32 8UW
Tel: 0141 778 2468 *Fax:* 0141 778 8883

55a Main Street Rutherglen Glasgow G73 2JH
Tel: 0141 647 0700 *Fax:* 0141 647 9800

721 Springfield Road Parkhead Glasgow G31 4JU
Tel: 0141 550 8080 *Fax:* 0141 550 8585

1007 Tollcross Road Administration Office Glasgow G32 8UW
Tel: 0141 778 5585 *Fax:* 0141 778 2611

HUNTER & CO
243-245 Crow Road Broomhill Glasgow G11 7BE
Tel: 0141 334 4759 *Fax:* 0141 357 4987
E-mail: gghlaw@btconnect.com

INKSTERS
Baltic Chambers 50 Wellington Street Glasgow G2 6HJ
Tel: 0141 229 0880 *Fax:* 0141 229 0550 *Dx:* GW28 GLASGOW
E-mail: info@inksters.com

INTERNATIONAL & DOMESTIC LAW PRACTICE
2 Roman Road Glasgow G61 2SW
Tel: 0141 942 4455 *Fax:* 0141 942 5522
E-mail: law@idlp.co.uk

A & S IRELAND
18 Waterloo Street Glasgow G2 6DB
Tel: 0141 227 8200 *Fax:* 0141 227 8219

FRANK IRVINE
69 Aberdalgie Road Easterhouse Glasgow G34 9HJ
Tel: 0141 773 2111 *Fax:* 0141 773 4111
E-mail: fji@frankirvine.com

IRWIN MITCHELL LLP
Stewart House 123 Elderslie Street Glasgow G3 7AR
Tel: 0141 300 4300 *Fax:* 0141 300 4350

JAIN NEIL & RUDDY
The Town House 12 Sandyford Place Sauchiehall Street Glasgow G3 7NB
Tel: 0141 221 8778 *Fax:* 0141 221 8338
Dx: GW512214 GLASGOW SANDYFORD PLACE
E-mail: info@jnrsolicitors.com

HAROLD W JOSEPH
54 Carlton Place Glasgow G5 9TW
Tel: 0141 420 1896
E-mail: harold@haroldwjoseph.com

KELLY & CO
184 Abercromby Street Bridgeton Glasgow G40 2RZ
Tel: 0141 554 4141 *Fax:* 0141 554 2288

KERR BARRIE
250 West George Street Glasgow G2 4QY
Tel: 0141 221 6844 *Fax:* 0141 221 6024
Dx: GW561489 GLASGOW 16
E-mail: law@kerrbarrie.com

DAVID KINLOCH & CO
211 Saracen Street Glasgow G22 5JN
Tel: 0141 336 3000 *Fax:* 0141 336 2005

LAMBIE LAW PARTNERSHIP
2345 Dumbarton Road Yoker Glasgow G14 0NN
Tel: 0141 959 7000 *Fax:* 0141 950 1441

377 Tormusk Road Castlemilk Glasgow G45 0HF
Tel: 0141 631 2412 *Fax:* 0141 631 2420

B J LANIGAN & CO
14 Drumchapel Road Glasgow G15 6QE
Tel: 0141 944 0671 *Fax:* 0141 944 5037
E-mail: brian.lanigan@btinternet.com

LANIGAN MEECHAN & CO
2 Hillkirk Street Lane Springburn Glasgow G21 1TE
Tel: 0141 557 0111 *Fax:* 0141 557 5544
E-mail: laniganmeechan@live.co.uk

LAVERY SMITH & CO
49 Main Street Thornliebank Glasgow G46 7SF
Tel: 0141 638 2141 *Fax:* 0141 620 3827 *Dx:* 501168 SHAWLANDS

12 Westray Circus Milton Glasgow G22 7BE
Tel: 0141 336 4446 *Fax:* 0141 336 6766

LAWRIE JACKSON
13 Granville Street Glasgow G3 7EE
Tel: 0141 248 1111 *Fax:* 0141 564 2993
Dx: 512208 SANDYFORD PLACE
E-mail: mail@lawriejackson.co.uk

LEVY & MCRAE
266 St Vincent Street Glasgow G2 5RL
Tel: 0141 307 2311 *Fax:* 0141 307 6857 *Dx:* GW149 GLASGOW
E-mail: info@lemac.co.uk

LINDSAYS
1 Royal Bank Place Buchanan Street Glasgow G1 3AA
Tel: 0141 221 6551 *Fax:* 0141 204 0507
E-mail: mail@lindsays.co.uk

LIVINGSTONE BROWN
775 Shettleston Road Glasgow G32 7NN
Tel: 0141 778 9657 *Fax:* 0141 778 4331
E-mail: sh@livbrown.co.uk

84 Carlton Place Glasgow G5 9TD
Tel: 0141 429 8166 *Fax:* 0141 420 1337
E-mail: gb@livbrown.co.uk

RICHARD J LOBJOIE & CO
93 Hope Street Glasgow G2 6LD
Tel: 0141 221 7584 *Fax:* 0141 204 3149
E-mail: rjlobjoie@aol.com

LOW BEATON RICHMOND
326 Dumbarton Road Partick Glasgow G11 6TF
Tel: 0141 339 8442 *Fax:* 0141 339 6851
E-mail: scot@lbr-west.demon.co.uk

Sterling House 20 Renfield Street Glasgow G2 5AP
Tel: 0141 221 8931 *Fax:* 0141 248 4411 *Dx:* GW83 GLASGOW
E-mail: murdoch@lbr-city.demon.co.uk

LYNCH & CO
15-17 Carmunnock Road Mount Florida Glasgow G44 4TZ
Tel: 0141 649 9552 *Fax:* 0141 632 4682 *Dx:* 501142 SHAWLANDS
E-mail: lynch_g@btconnect.com

5 North Gower Street Ibrox Glasgow G51 1PW
Tel: 0141 427 6162 *Fax:* 0141 427 1888 *Dx:* 500605 GOVAN
E-mail: lynch_g@btconnect.com

MSM SOLICITORS
2 Bridgeton Cross Bridgeton Glasgow G40 1BW
Tel: 0141 554 8111 *Fax:* 0141 554 6566
E-mail: mail@msmlaw.co.uk

MCARDLE
116 Levernside Road Pollok Glasgow G53 5NH
Tel: 0141 810 1001 *Fax:* 0141 891 5390
E-mail: mcardle.solicitors@hotmail.co.uk

MCAULEY MCCARTHY & CO
417 Paisley Road West Glasgow G51 1LS
Tel: 0141 427 7150 *Fax:* 0141 427 1794

ALEXANDER MCBURNEY
338 Dumbarton Road Partick Glasgow G11 6TG
Tel: 0141 576 4808

IAN MCCARRY
157 Maryhill Road Glasgow G20 7XL
Tel: 0141 332 7345 *Fax:* 0141 331 2634
E-mail: mail@ianmccarry.co.uk

4 St Andrews Street Glasgow G1 5PB
Tel: 0141 552 0486 *Fax:* 0141 553 1600
E-mail: mail@ianmccarry.co.uk

1980-1984 Maryhill Road Glasgow G20 0EF
Tel: 0141 945 1911 *Fax:* 0141 946 4705
E-mail: mail@ianmccarry.co.uk

IAN C MCCARTHY
905 Shettleston Road Glasgow G32 7NU
Tel: 0141 763 1366 *Fax:* 0141 778 0675
E-mail: info@iancmccarthy.co.uk

306 Dumbarton Road Partick Glasgow G11 6TD
Tel: 0141 339 2929 *Fax:* 0141 339 1440
E-mail: info@iancmccarthy.co.uk

MCCLAY & CO
944 Govan Road Glasgow G51 3AF
Tel: 0141 445 2130 *Fax:* 0141 445 2550

MCCLURE & PARTNERS
2nd Floor Troon House 199 St Vincent Street Glasgow G2 5QD
Tel: 0141 204 0445 *Fax:* 0141 204 6181 *Dx:* GW65 GLASGOW
E-mail: michael@mcclurepartners.co.uk

MCCLURE COLLINS
139 Allison Street Glasgow G42 8RY
Tel: 0141 423 7181 *Fax:* 0141 423 7022
E-mail: reception@mcclurecollins.co.uk

MCCLURE NAISMITH
292 St Vincent Street Glasgow G2 5TQ
Tel: 0141 204 2700 *Fax:* 0141 248 3998 *Dx:* GW64 GLASGOW
E-mail: glasgow@mcclurenaismith.com

W W & J MCCLURE
7th Floor 90 St Vincents Street Glasgow G2 5UB
Tel: 0141 221 0045 *Fax:* 0141 204 4457 *Dx:* GW240 GLASGOW
E-mail: enquiries@mcclure-solicitors.co.uk

R T MCCORMACK
54 Gordon Street Glasgow G1 3PU
Tel: 0141 221 9491 *Fax:* 0141 226 4617 *Dx:* GW210 GLASGOW

MCCUSKER COCHRANE & GUNN
1242 Shettleston Road Glasgow G32 7PG
Tel: 0141 778 2222 *Fax:* 0141 763 1948

MCDAID FARRELL
20 Croftfoot Road Glasgow G44 5JT
Tel: 0808 120 1628
E-mail: mcdaidfarrell@btconnect.com

MACDONALD-HENDERSON
Standard Buildings 94 Hope Street Glasgow G2 6PH
Tel: 0141 248 4957 *Fax:* 0141 248 8455 *Dx:* GW255 GLASGOW
E-mail: info@macdonaldhenderson.co.uk

THOMAS J MCDONALD
35 Duncan Avenue Glasgow G14 9HS
Tel: 0141 954 1440

MACDONALDS
St Stephen's House 279 Bath Street Glasgow G2 4JL
Tel: 0141 303 7100 *Fax:* 0141 303 7150 *Dx:* GW142 GLASGOW
E-mail: info@macdonaldslaw.co.uk

MACFARLANE & CO
142 St Vincent Street Glasgow G2 5LA
Tel: 0141 248 3307 *Fax:* 0141 221 2713 *Dx:* GW66 GLASGOW
E-mail: city@macfarlane-law.co.uk

IAN A MCFARLANE & CO
256 Castlemilk Road King's Park Glasgow G44 4LB
Tel: 0141 649 9772 *Fax:* 0141 632 0777 *Dx:* 501175 SHAWLANDS
E-mail: ian@ianmcfarlanesolicitors.co.uk

MCGINN SOLICITORS
4 Woodside Place Glasgow G3 7QF
Tel: 0141 353 5355 *Fax:* 0141 353 5356
E-mail: admin@mcginnsolicitors.co.uk

MCGRIGORS LLP
141 Bothwell Street Glasgow G2 7EQ
Tel: 0141 567 8400 *Fax:* 0141 567 8401 *Dx:* GW135 GLASGOW
E-mail: enquiries@mcgrigors.com

RAYMOND MCILWHAM & CO
63 Carlton Place Glasgow G5 9TW
Tel: 0141 429 7677
E-mail: advice@mcilwhamsolicitors.com

MCINTOSH & MACLACHLAN
3 Carment Drive Shawlands Glasgow G41 3PP
Tel: 0141 632 4022 *Fax:* 0141 632 4318 *Dx:* 501164 SHAWLANDS
E-mail: mcinandmacl@msn.com

ANGUS MCINTOSH & SIMON HODGE
Castlemilk Law & Money Advice Centre 155 Castlemilk Drive Glasgow G45 9UG
Tel: 0141 634 0313 *Fax:* 0141 634 1944
E-mail: mail@castlemilklawcentre.co.uk

D DOUGLAS MACKIE
29 Park Circus Glasgow G3 6AP
Tel: 0141 331 2882 *Fax:* 0141 331 1873
E-mail: ddouglasmackie@msn.com

MACKINLAY & SUTTIE
365 Paisley Road West Glasgow G51 1LX
Tel: 0141 427 6023 *Fax:* 0141 427 4577
E-mail: m.lynch@mackinlay-suttie.co.uk

MACLAY MURRAY & SPENS
1 George Square Glasgow G2 1AL
Tel: 0141 248 5011 *Fax:* 0141 248 5819 *Dx:* GW67 GLASGOW

MCLEISH CARSWELL
6th Floor Atlantic House 5 Hope Street Glasgow G2 6AE
Tel: 0141 429 7662 *Fax:* 0141 237 9224
E-mail: mail@mclc-law.co.uk

7 Admiral Street Glasgow G41 1HP
Tel: 0141 429 7662 *Fax:* 0141 429 8037
E-mail: mail@mclc-law.co.uk

ALASTAIR C MACMILLAN
143 West Regent Street Glasgow G2 2SG
Tel: 0141 204 3385 *Fax:* 0141 248 2729 *Dx:* GW283 GLASGOW
E-mail: a-macmillan@btconnect.com

MACMILLANS
328 Tollcross Road Glasgow G31 4XR
Tel: 0141 551 8669 *Fax:* 0141 550 1006
E-mail: maildesk@macmillans-solicitors.com

MACNAIRS
662 Alexandra Parade Glasgow G31 3BU
Tel: 0141 551 8185 *Fax:* 0141 554 6235 *Dx:* 500402 DENNISTOUN
E-mail: law@macnairs.co.uk

MACPHERSON MAGUIRE COOK
19 Waterloo Street Glasgow G2 6BP
Tel: 0141 221 6913 *Fax:* 0141 221 9659
E-mail: mail@mgmc.co.uk

MACROBERTS LLP
Capella 60 York Street Glasgow G2 8JX
Tel: 0141 303 1100 *Fax:* 0141 332 8886 *Dx:* GW70 GLASGOW

MCSPARRAN MCCORMICK
Waterloo Chambers 19 Waterloo Street Glasgow G2 6AH
Tel: 0141 248 7962 *Fax:* 0141 204 2232
E-mail: mail@mcsparranmccormick.co.uk

663 Clarkston Road Netherlee Glasgow G44 3SE
Tel: 0141 633 1557 *Fax:* 0141 633 0061
E-mail: mail@mcsparranmccormick.co.uk

MCVEY & MURRICANE
13 Bath Street Glasgow G2 1BW
Tel: 0141 333 9688 *Fax:* 0845 058 2541 *Dx:* GW71 GLASGOW
E-mail: mail@mcvey-murricane.com

ANTHONY MAHON & CO
10 Rozelle Avenue Glasgow G15 7QR
Tel: 0141 944 1001 *Fax:* 0141 944 1001
E-mail: amahon@btinternet.com

48 West George Street Glasgow G2 1BP
Tel: 0141 332 1587 *Fax:* 0141 332 1585
E-mail: amahon@btinternet.com

MANN & CO
4th Floor 63 Carlton Place Glasgow G5 9TW
Tel: 0141 420 7407 *Fax:* 0141 429 3110
E-mail: info@mannsolicitors.co.uk

J E MARR & CO
82 Mitchell Street Glasgow G1 3NA
Tel: 0141 248 5737 *Fax:* 0141 204 2227 *Dx:* GW182 GLASGOW
E-mail: jemco@jemarr.co.uk

MARTIN RAMSAY MCINNES
5 Drumby Crescent Williamwood Glasgow G76 7HN
Tel: 0141 571 6387 *Fax:* 0141 571 6387

R & R S MEARNS
2 Carment Drive Shawlands Glasgow G41 3PR
Tel: 0141 632 6162 *Fax:* 0141 632 2490

MELLICKS
160 Hope Street Glasgow G2 2TL
Tel: 0141 332 0902 *Fax:* 0141 333 9125 *Dx:* GW23 GLASGOW
E-mail: mail@mellicks.co.uk

MILLER & CO
6 St Ninian Terrace Crown Street Glasgow G5 0RJ
Tel: 0141 429 3270 *Fax:* 0141 429 3709

MILLER BECKETT & JACKSON
190 St Vincent Street Glasgow G2 5SP
Tel: 0141 204 2833 *Fax:* 0141 248 7185 *Dx:* GW20 GLASGOW

MILLER SAMUEL LLP
RWF House 5 Renfield Street Glasgow G2 5EZ
Tel: 0141 221 1919 *Fax:* 0141 221 3796 *Dx:* GW161 GLASGOW
E-mail: enquiries@millersamuel.co.uk

MILLER STEWART
1252 Shettleston Road Glasgow G32 7YR
Tel: 0141 778 7070 *Fax:* 0141 778 7227
E-mail: property@millerstewart.com

MINGLYE LEE
9 Royal Crescent Glasgow G3 7SL
Tel: 0141 333 1777 *Fax:* 0141 333 1777
E-mail: mleelaw@lineone.net

MITCHELLS ROBERTON
George House 36 North Hanover Street Glasgow G1 2AD
Tel: 0141 552 3422 *Fax:* 0141 552 2935 *Dx:* GW77 GLASGOW
E-mail: info@mitchells-roberton.co.uk

MORAN & CO
1/1 102 Lancefield Quay Glasgow G3 8HF
Tel: 0141 221 7479 *Fax:* 0141 221 7479

MORISONS
53 Bothwell Street Glasgow G2 6TS
Tel: 0141 332 5666 *Fax:* 0141 332 6757 *Dx:* GW95 GLASGOW
E-mail: enquiries@morisonsllp.com

MOWAT HALL DICK
63 Carlton Place Glasgow G5 9TW
Tel: 0141 420 2430 *Fax:* 0141 420 2431
E-mail: glasgow@mhdlaw.co.uk

MURPHY & CO
10 Newton Place Glasgow G3 7PR
Tel: 0141 332 2804 *Fax:* 0141 332 8765

STEWART MURRAY & CO
3 Oakfield Avenue Hillhead Glasgow G12 8JF
Tel: 0141 357 5151 *Fax:* 0141 357 3573

NAFTALIN DUNCAN & CO
534 Sauchiehall Street Glasgow G2 3LX
Tel: 0141 332 0979 *Fax:* 0141 332 0760
E-mail: reception@naftalinduncan.co.uk

O'DONNELL & COMPANY
79 Kinfauns Drive Drumchapel Glasgow G15 7TG
Tel: 0141 944 1441 *Fax:* 0141 944 6631

LIAM O'DONNELL & CO
4th Floor Carlton Buildings 63 Carlton Place Glasgow G5 9TW
Tel: 0141 429 3100 *Fax:* 0141 429 3110
E-mail: info@liamodonnell.co.uk

OPTIMA LEGAL
RWF House 5 Renfield Street Glasgow G2 5EZ
Tel: 0844 571 5200
E-mail: info@optimalegal.co.uk

8

THE PRG PARTNERSHIP
12 Royal Crescent Glasgow G3 7SL
Tel: 0141 353 0550 *Fax:* 0141 331 2231
Dx: 512215 SANDYFORD PLACE

208 Saracen Street Glasgow G22 5EP
Tel: 0141 336 3241 *Fax:* 0141 336 2627 *Dx:* 501703 MUIRHEAD

PACITTI JONES
6 Havelock Street (off Byres Road) Glasgow G11 5JA
Tel: 0141 334 6444 *Fax:* 0141 576 0101
E-mail: westend@pjglasgow.co.uk

218 Stonelaw Road Burnside Glasgow G73 3SA
Tel: 0141 647 3322 *Fax:* 0141 569 4445
E-mail: burnside@pjglasgow.co.uk

STEPHEN PATERSON & CO
895 Govan Road Glasgow G51 3DN
Tel: 0141 445 1150 *Fax:* 0141 445 4252

PATTISON & SIM
117 Byres Road Glasgow G12 8TT
Tel: 0141 334 7706 *Fax:* 0141 357 2871
E-mail: info@pattisonsim.co.uk

PEACOCK JOHNSTON
Ashfield House 402 Sauchiehall Street Glasgow G2 3JD
Tel: 0141 333 9505 *Fax:* 0141 331 2823 *Dx:* GW165 GLASGOW
E-mail: enquiries@peacockjohnston.co.uk

PEDEN & PATRICK LTD
Albert Chambers 13 Bath Street Glasgow G2 1HY
Tel: 0141 333 0175 *Fax:* 0141 333 0334
E-mail: info@peden-patrick.co.uk

PENMANS
201 Saracen Street Glasgow G22 5JN
Tel: 0141 336 6646 *Fax:* 0141 336 6345
E-mail: jean@penmanslawyers.co.uk

187 Shawbridge Street Glasgow G43 1QN
Tel: 0141 632 7001 *Fax:* 0141 632 7002
E-mail: jean@penmanslawyers.co.uk

KATE PHILLIPS SOLICITORS
4th Floor Carlton Buildings 63 Carlton Place Glasgow G5 9TW
Tel: 0141 420 6120 *Fax:* 0141 429 3110

PHINN & CO
Second Floor 87 Carlton Place Glasgow G5 9TD
Tel: 0141 221 4664 *Fax:* 0141 638 9161

PIERI GRAHAM
James Miller House 98 West George Street Glasgow G2 1PJ
Tel: 0141 332 2525 *Fax:* 0141 331 2858 *Dx:* GW218 GLASGOW

PINSENT MASONS LLP
123 St Vincent Street Glasgow G2 5EA
Tel: 0141 248 4858 *Fax:* 0141 248 6655 *Dx:* GW74 GLASGOW

QUINN MARTIN & LANGAN
87 Carlton Place Glasgow G5 9TD
Tel: 0141 429 4354 *Fax:* 0141 429 6826
E-mail: qml1@btconnect.com

68 Maryhill Road St George's Cross Glasgow G20 7QB
Tel: 0141 332 3702 *Fax:* 0141 353 3364
E-mail: qml1@btconnect.com

RAFFERTY WOOD & CO
33 Castlemilk Arcade Castlemilk Glasgow G45 9AA
Tel: 0141 634 0485 *Fax:* 0141 631 1121
E-mail: raffertywood@aol.com

JEFFREY RANKIN & CO
2a Dunkenny Square Drumchapel Glasgow G15 8NB
Tel: 0141 944 0660 *Fax:* 0141 944 0660

REID COOPER SOLICITORS
78 Carlton Place Glasgow G5 9TH
Tel: 0141 429 4656 *Fax:* 0141 429 1494 *Dx:* GW94 GLASGOW
E-mail: info@reidcooper.co.uk

REILLY CASSIDY & CO
40 Carlton Place Glasgow G5 9TW
Tel: 0141 420 6007 *Fax:* 0141 429 7670

RICHMOND EVANS & CO
4 Somerset Place Glasgow G3 7JT
Tel: 0141 332 9218 *Fax:* 0141 353 0964

EUAN ROBERTSON
498 Cathcart Road Govanhill Glasgow G42 7BX
Tel: 0141 423 7389 *Fax:* 0141 423 8041
E-mail: euanrobertsonsolicitors@gmail.com

LIAM ROBERTSON & CO
46 Carlton Place Glasgow G5 9TW
Tel: 0141 429 7979
E-mail: liam@liamrobertsonsolicitors.co.uk

PHILIP ROONEY & CO
320 Langside Drive Glasgow G42 8XW
Tel: 0141 423 0000 *Fax:* 0141 423 0300

ROSS & FOX
44 Carlton Place Glasgow G5 9TW
Tel: 0141 429 1230 *Fax:* 0141 420 3441
E-mail: rossfoxsolicitors@yahoo.co.uk

ROSS HARPER
Sun House 58 West Regent Street Glasgow G2 2QZ
Tel: 0141 333 6334 *Fax:* 0141 333 6336
E-mail: info@rossharper.com

269 Kilmarnock Road Shawlands Glasgow G43 1TX
Tel: 0141 649 9511 *Fax:* 0141 632 5680
E-mail: info@rossharper.com

2 Dixon Street Glasgow G1 4AR
Tel: 0141 248 5777 *Fax:* 0141 223 6799
E-mail: info@rossharper.com

RUSSELLS GIBSON MCCAFFREY
13 Bath Street Glasgow G2 1HY
Tel: 0141 271 1000 *Fax:* 0141 332 7908 *Dx:* GW24 GLASGOW
E-mail: info@russellsgm.co.uk

1020a Govan Road Glasgow G51 3DU
Tel: 0141 445 3110 *Fax:* 0141 445 5533 *Dx:* GW24 GLASGOW
E-mail: info@russellsgm.co.uk

RUTHVEN KEENAN POLLOCK & CO
832 Crow Road Anniesland Glasgow G13 1HB
Tel: 0141 954 2901 *Fax:* 0141 954 7296 *Dx:* 501422 ANNIESLAND
E-mail: mail@rkpsolicitors.co.uk

371 Victoria Road Queen's Park Glasgow G42 8YY
Tel: 0141 423 8951 *Fax:* 0141 424 1955
Dx: 502000 QUEENS PARK
E-mail: mail@rkpsolicitors.co.uk

CLARE RYAN
2 Douglas Gardens Bearsden Glasgow G61 2SJ
Tel: 0141 931 5254

ARCHIBALD SHARP & SON
270 Dumbarton Road Partick Glasgow G11 6TX
Tel: 0141 339 3036 *Fax:* 0141 341 6317 *Dx:* 500904 PARTICK
E-mail: info@archibaldsharp.co.uk

SHEPHERD + WEDDERBURN LLP
191 West George Street Glasgow G2 2LB
Tel: 0141 566 9900 *Fax:* 0141 565 1222 *Dx:* GW409 GLASGOW
E-mail: info@shepwedd.co.uk

SHERIDANS
166 Buchanan Street Glasgow G1 2LW
Tel: 0141 332 3536 *Fax:* 0141 353 3819 *Dx:* GW266 GLASGOW
E-mail: info@sheridanssolicitors.co.uk

SIMPSON & MARWICK
144 West George Street Glasgow G2 2HG
Tel: 0141 248 2666 *Fax:* 0141 248 9590 *Dx:* GW377 GLASGOW
E-mail: email@simpmar.com

ROSIE SORRELL
Ethnic Minorities Law Centre 41 St Vincent's Place Glasgow G1 2ER
Tel: 0141 204 2888 *Fax:* 0141 204 2006
E-mail: admin@emlc.org.uk

STEWARTS & MURDOCHS
8 Gordon Street Glasgow G1 3PL
Tel: 0141 248 8810 *Fax:* 0141 248 8116 *Dx:* GW211 GLASGOW

G SWEENEY & CO
2nd Floor 87 Carlton Place Glasgow G5 9TD
Tel: 0141 429 0677 *Fax:* 0141 429 0677

THOMAS CARLIN & PENDER
1490 Paisley Road West Glasgow G52 1SP
Tel: 0141 883 6227 *Fax:* 0141 810 5346
E-mail: carlin.pender@btconnect.com

THOMPSONS
Berkeley House 285 Bath Street Glasgow G2 4HQ
Tel: 0141 221 8840 *Fax:* 0141 226 5738 *Dx:* GW162 GLASGOW
E-mail: glasgow@thompsons-compensation-claims.co.uk

TODS MURRAY WS
33 Bothwell Street Glasgow G2 6NL
Tel: 0141 275 4771 *Fax:* 0141 275 4781
Dx: GW512815 GLASGOW CENTRAL
E-mail: maildesk@todsmurray.com

KEITH J TUCK
254 Saracen Street Possilpark Glasgow G22 5LF
Tel: 0141 336 2020 *Fax:* 0141 347 1000

TURNBULL MCCARRON
478 Dumbarton Road Partick Glasgow G11 6SE
Tel: 0141 339 8887 *Fax:* 0141 339 8030 *Dx:* GW293 GLASGOW

457 Duke Street Dennistoun Glasgow G31 1RD
Tel: 0141 554 3535 *Fax:* 0141 554 5846 *Dx:* GW293 GLASGOW

124 Westmuir Street Parkhead Glasgow G31 5BW
Tel: 0141 551 0096 *Fax:* 0141 550 4821 *Dx:* GW293 GLASGOW

VALLANCE KLINER & ASSOCIATES
Cambridge House 8 Cambridge Street Glasgow G2 3DZ
Tel: 0141 332 5332 *Fax:* 0141 332 3273
E-mail: mail@vallancekliner.co.uk

R S VAUGHAN & CO
114 Union Street Glasgow G1 3QQ
Tel: 0141 221 5482 *Fax:* 0141 221 7066 *Dx:* GW198 GLASGOW
E-mail: rvaughan@rsvaughan.co.uk

GRAHAM WALKER
1584 Maryhill Road Maryhill Glasgow G20 0HL
Tel: 0141 946 0111 *Fax:* 0141 945 6298
E-mail: is@thedefencelawyers.com

22 Balmore Road Possilpark Glasgow G22 6RN
Tel: 0141 336 6603 *Fax:* 0141 336 2500
E-mail: is@thedefencelawyers.com

28 St Andrew's Street Glasgow G1 5PD
Tel: 0141 552 2234 *Fax:* 0141 552 8124
E-mail: is@thedefencelawyers.com

JAMES R WALLACE
312 Kilmarnock Road Newlands Glasgow G43 2DG
Tel: 0141 649 9717
E-mail: james.robertson@wallace.ms

WALLACE QUINN & CO
21a Barrachnie Road Baillieston Glasgow G69 6HB
Tel: 0141 771 3911 *Fax:* 0141 771 4545 *Dx:* 500101 BAILLIESTON
E-mail: law@wallacequinn.co.uk

WEST ANDERSON & CO
92 Bath Street Glasgow G2 2EJ
Tel: 0141 332 6671 *Fax:* 0141 332 6842
E-mail: westanderson@freeuk.com

DERICK WILLIAMSON & CO
17b Castlemilk Arcade Dougrie Drive Castlemilk Glasgow G45 9AA
Tel: 0141 634 3200 *Fax:* 0141 634 3200
E-mail: derickwilliamsonandco@btconnect.com

WILSON GREEN & MORRISON
17 Minard Road Shawlands Glasgow G41 2HR
Tel: 0141 616 6655 *Fax:* 0141 616 6611
E-mail: mail@wgmlegal.co.uk

LESLIE WOLFSON & CO
Waterloo Chambers 19 Waterloo Street Glasgow G2 6BQ
Tel: 0141 226 4499 *Fax:* 0141 221 6070 *Dx:* GW106 GLASGOW
E-mail: enquiries@lesliewolfson.co.uk

PETER J WOOLFSON & CO
1980 Maryhill Road Glasgow G20 0EF
Tel: 0141 946 6666 *Fax:* 0141 946 6666

WRIGHT JOHNSTON & MACKENZIE
302 St Vincent Street Glasgow G2 5RZ
Tel: 0141 248 3434 *Fax:* 0141 221 1226 *Dx:* GW129 GLASGOW
E-mail: enquiries@wjm.co.uk

T C YOUNG
7 West George Street Glasgow G2 1BA
Tel: 0141 221 5562 *Fax:* 0141 221 5024 *Dx:* GW78 GLASGOW
E-mail: mail@tcyoung.co.uk

YUILL & KYLE
79 West Regent Street Glasgow G2 2AR
Tel: 0141 331 2332 *Fax:* 0141 332 4223 *Dx:* GW186 GLASGOW
E-mail: info@debtscotland.com

GLENROTHES

BAIRD & CO
North House North Street Glenrothes Fife KY7 5NA
Tel: 01592 759555 *Fax:* 01592 610414 *Dx:* 560715 GLENROTHES
E-mail: greception@bairdco.co.uk

BEVERIDGE HERD & SANDILANDS WS
3 Acorn Court Glenrothes Fife KY7 5LZ
Tel: 01592 752080 *Fax:* 01592 750936 *Dx:* 560716 GLENROTHES
E-mail: mail@bhssolicitors.co.uk

BRADY LEGAL
Unit 5 Lomond Business Park Baltimore Road Glenrothes Fife KY6 2SU
Tel: 01592 623980 *Fax:* 01592 775812 *Dx:* 560727 GLENROTHES
E-mail: info@bradylegal.co.uk

DIGBY BROWN
14 Hanover Court North Street Glenrothes Fife KY7 5SB
Tel: 0845 273 2323 *Fax:* 01592 610398 *Dx:* 560732 GLENROTHES
E-mail: maildesk@digbybrown.co.uk

JOHN W GILBERTSON
3 Hanover Court Glenrothes Fife KY7 5SD
Tel: 01592 759557 *Fax:* 01592 759416 *Dx:* 560710 GLENROTHES
E-mail: jwg@jwgsolicitor.co.uk

GLEESON MCCAFFERTY
4 Acorn Court Glenrothes Fife KY7 5LZ
Tel: 01592 611660 *Fax:* 01592 611810
E-mail: gleesonmccafferty@hotmail.co.uk

INNES JOHNSTON & CO
32 North Street Glenrothes Fife KY7 5NA
Tel: 01592 757114 *Fax:* 01592 765607 *Dx:* 560711 GLENROTHES

MCKENNAS
10 Acorn Court Glenrothes Fife KY7 5LZ
Tel: 01592 756449 *Fax:* 01592 756460

MCKINNON & CO
13 Postgate Glenrothes Fife KY7 5LH
Tel: 01592 750309 *Fax:* 01592 754949 *Dx:* 560718 GLENROTHES
E-mail: mckinnond@aol.com

ROLLO DAVIDSON & MCFARLANE
12 Lyon Way Glenrothes Fife KY7 5NW
Tel: 01592 759414 *Fax:* 01592 754530 *Dx:* 560713 GLENROTHES
E-mail: glenrothes@rollos.co.uk

GOREBRIDGE

MARTIN GRAY & CO
26 Main Street Gorebridge Midlothian EH23 4BY
Tel: 01875 821960 *Fax:* 01875 822827 *Dx:* 540572 DALKEITH

GOUROCK

MCCONNACHIE & CO
13 Glen Avenue Gourock Inverclyde PA19 1XL
Tel: 01475 638248

GRANGEMOUTH

RGM
9 La Porte Precinct Grangemouth Falkirk FK3 8AZ
Tel: 01324 482197 *Fax:* 01324 482098
E-mail: legal@rgmsolicitors.co.uk

TAIT & MACKENZIE
Royal Bank Chambers 4 La Porte Precinct Grangemouth Falkirk FK3 8AT
Tel: 01324 471121 *Fax:* 01324 484275
Dx: 560722 GRANGEMOUTH
E-mail: law@taitandmackenzie.co.uk

GRANTOWN-ON-SPEY

MASSON CAIRNS
Strathspey House Grantown-On-Spey Highland PH26 3EQ
Tel: 01479 874800 *Fax:* 01479 874806
E-mail: property@lawscot.com

GREENOCK

BLAIR & BRYDEN
27 Union Street Greenock Inverclyde PA16 8DD
Tel: 01475 888777 *Fax:* 01475 731815

BRADLEY CAMPBELL & CO
8 Brougham Street Greenock Inverclyde PA16 8AA
Tel: 01475 726363 *Fax:* 01475 724936
E-mail: office@bradleycampbell.co.uk

COOK STEVENSON & CO
56 West Blackhall Street Greenock Inverclyde PA15 1UY
Tel: 01475 722100 *Fax:* 01475 806669
E-mail: mail@cookstevenson.co.uk

FYFE & MURRAY
132 Cathcart Street Greenock Inverclyde PA15 1BQ
Tel: 01475 721251 *Fax:* 01475 721937
E-mail: mail@fyfemurray.sol.co.uk

G KEENAN & CO
2 Argyle Street Greenock Inverclyde PA15 1XA
Tel: 01475 732122 *Fax:* 01475 732123 *Dx:* GR32 GREENOCK
E-mail: gklaw2@aol.com

KENNEDY & CO
11 Union Street Greenock Inverclyde PA16 8JL
Tel: 01475 888830 *Fax:* 01475 888874
E-mail: kennedycolaw@aol.com

W W & J MCCLURE
35 Nicolson Street Greenock Inverclyde PA15 1UL
Tel: 01475 888222 *Fax:* 01475 725222 *Dx:* GR19 GREENOCK 1
E-mail: enquiries@mcclure-solicitors.co.uk

MACPHERSON & DISSELDUFF
Clydesdale Bank Buildings 132 Cathcart Street Greenock Inverclyde PA15 1BQ
Tel: 01369 702071 *Fax:* 01475 721937
E-mail: general@fyfemurray.sol.co.uk

MAITLANDS
6 Brougham Street Greenock Inverclyde PA16 8AA
Tel: 01475 892131 *Fax:* 01475 720713 *Dx:* GR15 GREENOCK
E-mail: maitlands@btconnect.com

NEILL CLERK & MURRAY
3 Ardgowan Square Greenock Inverclyde PA16 8NW
Tel: 01475 724522 *Fax:* 01475 784339 *Dx:* GR7 GREENOCK
E-mail: info@neillclerkmurray.co.uk

PATTEN & PRENTICE
2 Ardgowan Square Greenock Inverclyde PA16 8PP
Tel: 01475 720306 *Fax:* 01475 888127
E-mail: mail@patten.co.uk

HADDINGTON

ANDERSON STRATHERN LLP
14 Court Street Haddington East Lothian EH41 3JA
Tel: 01620 822127 *Fax:* 01620 825839 *Dx:* 540736 HADDINGTON
E-mail: info@andersonstrathern.co.uk

GARDEN STIRLING BURNET
22 Hardgate Haddington East Lothian EH41 3JS
Tel: 01620 824996 *Fax:* 01620 828901
E-mail: hardgate@gsbsolicitors.co.uk

M M TAIT & CO
49 Market Street Haddington East Lothian EH41 3JE
Tel: 01620 823280 *Fax:* 01620 823280 *Dx:* 540737 HADDINGTON
E-mail: mmtait@tiscali.co.uk

HAMILTON

JOHN A BRYAN & CO
27 Bothwell Road Hamilton South Lanarkshire ML3 0AS
Tel: 01698 281535 *Fax:* 01698 284699
E-mail: johnabryan@btconnect.com

CAMPBELL SIEVEWRIGHT & CO
12 Campbell Street Hamilton South Lanarkshire ML3 6AS
Tel: 01698 284994 *Fax:* 01698 284242
E-mail: pdunlop@cs-homes.co.uk

CARTY'S
3 Cadzow Street Hamilton South Lanarkshire ML3 6EE
Tel: 01698 285432 *Fax:* 01698 327285
E-mail: hamilton@cartylaw.co.uk

T J & W A DYKES
5 Church Street Hamilton South Lanarkshire ML3 6BA
Tel: 01698 282726 *Fax:* 01698 425892 *Dx:* HA4 HAMILTON
E-mail: dykes@dykeslaw.co.uk

CHARLES FERGUSON & CO
43 Quarry Street Hamilton South Lanarkshire ML3 7AH
Tel: 01698 285885 *Fax:* 01698 422886
E-mail: charles.ferguson@btconnect.com

RAYMOND FERGUSON & CO
27 Bothwell Road Hamilton South Lanarkshire ML3 0AS
Tel: 01698 891623 *Fax:* 01698 891623

ROBERT FERGUSON & SONS
7 Gateside Street Hamilton South Lanarkshire ML3 7HT
Tel: 01698 282551 *Fax:* 01698 286438 *Dx:* HA5 HAMILTON
E-mail: general@robert-ferguson-solicitors.co.uk

LINDA GEORGE FAMILY LAW
Mediacorp House 2 Caird Park Hamilton South Lanarkshire ML3 0EU
Tel: 01698 768857 *Fax:* 01698 459215 *Dx:* HA15 HAMILTON
E-mail: info@lgfamilylaw.co.uk

HAY CASSELS
Almada Chambers 95 Almada Street Hamilton South Lanarkshire ML3 0EY
Tel: 01698 284844 *Fax:* 01698 891146 *Dx:* HA22 HAMILTON

JOHN JACKSON & DICK
48 Cadzow Street Hamilton South Lanarkshire ML3 6DT
Tel: 01698 281747 *Fax:* 01698 891419 *Dx:* HA18 HAMILTON

LEONARDS
133 Cadzow Street Hamilton South Lanarkshire ML3 6JG
Tel: 01698 457313 *Fax:* 01698 425931 *Dx:* HA6 HAMILTON
E-mail: info@leonardslaw.com

MCQUILLAN GLASSER & WAUGHMAN
53 Quarry Street Hamilton South Lanarkshire ML3 7AH
Tel: 01698 200006 *Fax:* 01698 200159

D A MILLIGAN & CO
104 Quarry Street Hamilton South Lanarkshire ML3 7AX
Tel: 01698 219001 *Fax:* 01698 457733
E-mail: damilliganandco@btconnect.com

NELSON GIBB & LANDA
62 Burnbank Road Hamilton South Lanarkshire ML3 9AQ
Tel: 01698 207050 *Fax:* 01698 283979
E-mail: mail@ngllaw.net

POMPHREYS
79 Quarry Street Hamilton South Lanarkshire ML3 7AG
Tel: 01698 891616 *Fax:* 01698 891617

JOHN Y ROBERTSON
28 Gateside Street Hamilton South Lanarkshire ML3 7JG
Tel: 01698 282900 *Fax:* 01698 283740 *Dx:* HA32 HAMILTON
E-mail: enquiries@johnyrobertson.co.uk

SCULLION LAW
105 Cadzow Street Hamilton South Lanarkshire ML3 6HJ
Tel: 01698 283265 *Fax:* 01698 281155 *Dx:* HA17 HAMILTON
E-mail: info@scullionlaw.com

STIRLING DUNLOP
36 Cadzow Street Hamilton South Lanarkshire ML3 6DG
Tel: 01698 307170 *Fax:* 01698 307177
E-mail: enquiries@stirlingdunlop.co.uk

STODARTS
Almada Chambers 95 Almada Street Hamilton South Lanarkshire ML3 0EY
Tel: 01698 200302 *Fax:* 01698 891144
E-mail: mail@stodarts.co.uk

STREFFORD TULIPS
118 Cadzow Street Hamilton South Lanarkshire ML3 6HP
Tel: 01698 429428 *Fax:* 01698 303020
E-mail: enquiries@strefford-tulips.co.uk

WATSON SCOTT
McAdam House 1 Cadzow Lane Hamilton South Lanarkshire ML3 6AY
Tel: 01698 282370 *Fax:* 01698 282616
E-mail: info@watsonscott.co.uk

HAWICK

BANNERMAN BURKE
28 High Street Hawick Scottish Borders TD9 9BY
Tel: 01450 372750 *Fax:* 01450 378525 *Dx:* 580741 HAWICK

HADDON & TURNBULL
55 High Street Hawick Scottish Borders TD9 9BP
Tel: 01450 372336 *Fax:* 01450 377463
E-mail: solicitors@htws.co.uk

ANDREW HADDON & CROWE WS
3 Oliver Place Hawick Scottish Borders TD9 9BG
Tel: 01450 372738 *Fax:* 01450 372786
E-mail: info@ahcsolicitors.co.uk

GEORGE & JAMES OLIVER WS
13 High Street Hawick Scottish Borders TD9 9DH
Tel: 01450 372791 *Fax:* 01450 377654 *Dx:* 580744 HAWICK
E-mail: solicitors@gandjoliver.co.uk

HELENSBURGH

BRUNTON MILLER
7 & 9 Colquhoun Street Helensburgh Argyll & Bute G84 8AN
Tel: 01436 675454 *Fax:* 01436 678434
Dx: 500750 HELENSBURGH
E-mail: info@bruntonmiller.com

MCARTHUR STANTON
22-24 Colquhoun Square Helensburgh Argyll & Bute G84 8AG
Tel: 01436 672212 *Fax:* 01436 674411 *Dx:* 500752 HELENSBURGH

RAEBURN HOPE
77 Sinclair Street Helensburgh Argyll & Bute G84 8TG
Tel: 01436 671221 *Fax:* 01436 675888 *Dx:* 500751 HELENSBURGH

STIRLING & GILMOUR
13 West Princess Street Helensburgh Argyll & Bute G84 8TF
Tel: 01436 678185 *Fax:* 01436 671539 *Dx:* 500753 HELENSBURGH

HUNTLY

MURDOCH MCMATH & MITCHELL
27-29 Duke Street Huntly Aberdeenshire AB54 8DP
Tel: 01466 792291 *Fax:* 01466 794280 *Dx:* 520760 HUNTLY
E-mail: info@murdoch-mcmath-mitchell.com

PETERKINS
3 The Square Huntly Aberdeenshire AB54 8AE
Tel: 01466 792101 *Fax:* 01466 792241 *Dx:* 520761 HUNTLY
E-mail: huntlypropshop@peterkins.com

INVERGORDON

WILSONS
107 High Street Invergordon Highland IV18 0AB
Tel: 01349 852131 *Fax:* 01349 853715
E-mail: enquiries@wilsons-lawyers.co.uk

INVERNESS

ALLEN & SHAW
23 Academy Street Inverness Highland IV1 1JN
Tel: 01463 225555 *Fax:* 01463 235107
E-mail: enquiries@allenandshaw.co.uk

ANDERSON SHAW & GILBERT
York House 20 Church Street Inverness Highland IV1 1ED
Tel: 01463 236123
E-mail: email@solicitorsinverness.com

ALEX BROWN & CO
Kintail House Beechwood Business Park Inverness Highland IV2 3BW
Tel: 01463 243450
E-mail: mail@alexbrownandco.com

CROWN LAW PRACTICE
3 Crown Circus Inverness Highland IV2 3NH
Tel: 01463 667850 *Fax:* 01463 667855
E-mail: joan.merchant@crownlawpractice.com

DAVIDSON SCOTT & CO
11 Queensgate Inverness Highland IV1 1DF
Tel: 01463 231066 *Fax:* 01463 712596 *Dx:* IN2 INVERNESS
E-mail: davscott@btconnect.com

FERGUSON & WILSON
Market Arcade 24 Union Street Inverness Highland IV1 1PL
Tel: 01463 212986

FLEETWOOD & ROBB
11 Queensgate Inverness Highland IV1 1DF
Tel: 01463 226232 *Fax:* 01463 713447
E-mail: mail@fleetwoodandrobb.co.uk

FRASER & CO
106 Church Street Inverness Highland IV1 1EP
Tel: 01463 229917 *Fax:* 01463 243111
E-mail: info@afrasersolicitors.com

JACK GOWANS & MARC DICKSON
46 Church Street Inverness Highland IV1 1EH
Tel: 01463 710677 *Fax:* 01463 729251
E-mail: enquiries@gowandickson.co.uk

HARPER MACLEOD
Alder House Cradlehall Business Park Inverness Highland IV2 5GH
Tel: 01463 798777 *Fax:* 01463 798787
Dx: IN521005 INVERNESS 3
E-mail: info@harpermacleod.co.uk

INNES & MACKAY
Kintail House Beechwood Business Park Inverness Highland IV2 3BW
Tel: 01463 232273 *Fax:* 01463 243091
Dx: IN521008 INVERNESS 3
E-mail: reception@innesmackay.com

INVERNESS LEGAL SERVICES FOR CRIMINAL ADVOCACY
33 Bellfield Park Inverness Highland IV2 4TA
Tel: 01463 229981
E-mail: info@inverness-legal.co.uk

LEDINGHAM CHALMERS
Kintail House Beechwood Business Park Inverness Highland IV2 3BW
Tel: 01463 667400 *Fax:* 01463 713755
Dx: IN521009 INVERNESS 3
E-mail: mail@ledinghamchalmers.com

MACANDREW & JENKINS WS
5 Drummond Street Inverness Highland IV1 1QF
Tel: 01463 723500 *Fax:* 01463 230743 *Dx:* IN8 INVERNESS
E-mail: e-mail@macandrewjenkins.co.uk

MACARTHUR & CO
7 Ardross Street Inverness Highland IV3 5PL
Tel: 01463 234445 *Fax:* 01463 224995 *Dx:* IN9 INVERNESS
E-mail: property@macarthur.co.uk

THE MACKENZIE LAW PRACTICE
2nd Floor Highland Rail House Station Square Inverness Highland IV1 1LE
Tel: 01463 713718 *Fax:* 01463 713718
E-mail: dmm@mackenzie-law.co.uk

MACLEOD & MACCALLUM
28 Queensgate Inverness Highland IV1 1YN
Tel: 01463 239393 *Fax:* 01463 222879 *Dx:* IN12 INVERNESS
E-mail: mail@macandmac.co.uk

MACNEILL & CRITCHLEY
9 Ardross Street Inverness Highland IV3 5NP
Tel: 01463 232081 *Fax:* 01463 225080 *Dx:* IN13 INVERNESS
E-mail: mail@macneillcritchley.co.uk

MUNRO & NOBLE
26 Church Street Inverness Highland IV1 1HX
Tel: 01463 221727 *Fax:* 01463 225165 *Dx:* IN15 INVERNESS
E-mail: legal@munronoble.com

MURCHISON LAW
5 Ardross Terrace Inverness Highland IV3 5NQ
Tel: 01463 709992 *Fax:* 01463 713722
E-mail: email@murchisonlaw.co.uk

LORNA MURRAY
45 Culduthel Road Inverness Highland IV2 4HQ
Tel: 01463 717719 *Fax:* 01463 717720
E-mail: lorna.murray@btconnect.com

SOUTH FORREST
8 Ardross Terrace Inverness Highland IV3 5NW
Tel: 01463 237171 *Fax:* 01463 243548 *Dx:* IN16 INVERNESS
E-mail: email@southforrest.co.uk

STRONACHS
Camas House Pavilion 3 Fairways Business Park Inverness Highland IV2 6AA
Tel: 01463 713225 *Fax:* 01463 238177
Dx: IN521002 INVERNESS 3
E-mail: info.inverness@stronachs.com

R & R URQUHART
2 Ardross Street Inverness Highland IV3 5NN
Tel: 01463 714477 *Fax:* 01463 718867 *Dx:* IN22 INVERNESS
E-mail: info.inverness@r-r-urquhart.com

ROGER WEBB
2 Curduphel Lane Inverness Highland IV2 6RD
Tel: 01463 234036

CRAIG WOOD
16 Union Street Inverness Highland IV1 1PL
Tel: 01463 225544 *Fax:* 01463 235244
E-mail: nicola@craigwood.co.uk

INVERURIE

ABERDEIN CONSIDINE & CO
43 West High Street Inverurie Aberdeenshire AB51 3QQ
Tel: 01467 621263 *Fax:* 01467 625195
E-mail: inv@acandco.com

MICHAEL S ALLAN
Tillycairn Sauchen Inverurie Aberdeenshire AB51 7RX
Tel: 01330 833224 *Fax:* 01330 833429
E-mail: michaelsallancdl@hotmail.com

THE KELLAS PARTNERSHIP
2-6 High Street Inverurie Aberdeenshire AB51 3XQ
Tel: 01467 627300 *Fax:* 01467 622030 *Dx:* 520771 INVERURIE
E-mail: info@kellas.biz

MORTGAGE SAVINGS AND LOAN
1 Inver House Inverurie Aberdeenshire AB51 3SN
Tel: 01467 672820 *Fax:* 01467 672825

PETERKINS
60 Market Place Inverurie Aberdeenshire AB51 3XN
Tel: 01467 672800 *Fax:* 01467 672819 *Dx:* 520772 INVERURIE
E-mail: invprop@peterkins.com

RAEBURN CHRISTIE CLARK & WALLACE
6 North Street Inverurie Aberdeenshire AB51 4QR
Tel: 01467 629300 *Fax:* 01467 629001
E-mail: inverurie@raeburns.co.uk

IRVINE

MATTHEW BROWN
Eglinton House 22 Eglinton Street Irvine North Ayrshire KA12 8AS
Tel: 01294 273721 *Fax:* 01294 312199
E-mail: mail@matthewbrownsolicitors.co.uk

ADAM CURRIE
Galt House 31 Bank Street Irvine North Ayrshire KA12 0LL
Tel: 01294 273735 *Fax:* 01294 272749 *Dx:* IR1 IRVINE

JAMES IRVINE
57 High Street Irvine North Ayrshire KA12 0AL
Tel: 01294 276116 *Fax:* 01294 312493

AUSTIN KELLY & CO
29 Bridgegate Irvine North Ayrshire KA12 8BJ
Tel: 01294 275215 *Fax:* 01294 272215 *Dx:* IR6 IRVINE
E-mail: mail@austinkelly.net

MCKINNON HEWITT
65 East Road Irvine North Ayrshire KA12 0AA
Tel: 01294 312801 *Fax:* 01294 312851
E-mail: solicitors@mckinnonhewitt.co.uk

MCSHERRY HALLIDAY DALE & MARSHALL
Galt House 78 East Road Irvine North Ayrshire KA12 0AA
Tel: 01294 274097 *Fax:* 01294 279692
E-mail: irvine@mcsherryhalliday.co.uk

ALEX MUIR SOLICITORS
PO Box 8289 148 High Street Irvine North Ayrshire KA12 8AH
Tel: 01294 442949

R B RICHARDSON & CO
10 Eglinton Street Irvine North Ayrshire KA12 8AS
Tel: 01294 273888 *Fax:* 01294 273295

TAYLOR & HENDERSON
65 High Street Irvine North Ayrshire KA12 0AL
Tel: 01294 278306 *Fax:* 01294 272886
E-mail: mail@taylorandhenderson.co.uk

ISLE OF ARRAN

REID BLAIR
Creag An Iar Corriecravie Isle of Arran North Ayrshire KA27 8PD
Tel: 01770 870370 *Fax:* 01770 870370
E-mail: elizabeth.blair910@btinternet.com

JEDBURGH

CHARLES & R B ANDERSON WS
Royal Bank Buildings 38 High Street Jedburgh Scottish Borders TD8 6DF
Tel: 01835 863202 *Fax:* 01835 864016 *Dx:* 581220 JEDBURGH
E-mail: enquiries@crba.co.uk

LINDSAYS
26 High Street Jedburgh Scottish Borders TD8 6AE
Tel: 01835 862391 *Fax:* 01835 862017 *Dx:* 581223 JEDBURGH
E-mail: jedburgh@lindsays.co.uk

JOHNSTONE

HOLMES MACKILLOP
35 William Street Johnstone Renfrewshire PA5 8DR
Tel: 01505 328271 *Fax:* 01505 331907
E-mail: general@homack.co.uk

MCCUSKER MCELROY & COMPANY
61 High Street Johnstone Renfrewshire PA5 8QG
Tel: 01505 322299 *Fax:* 01505 337887 *Dx:* 591756 JOHNSTONE
E-mail: mccuskerlaw@btinternet.com

STIRLING & MAIR
28 High Street Johnstone Renfrewshire PA5 8AH
Tel: 01505 329373 *Fax:* 01505 331842 *Dx:* 591750 JOHNSTONE
E-mail: info@stirlingmair.com

KEITH

PETERKINS
145 Mid Street Keith Moray AB55 5BJ
Tel: 01542 882537 *Fax:* 01542 886176 *Dx:* 520782 KEITH
E-mail: keithoffice@peterkins.com

STEPHEN & ROBB
Clydesdale Bank Buildings 163 Mid Street Keith Moray AB55 5BL
Tel: 01542 886267 *Fax:* 01542 886015 *Dx:* 520781 KEITH
E-mail: keith@stephenrobb.co.uk

KELSO

BANNERMAN BURKE
24 Woodmarket Kelso Scottish Borders TD5 7AT
Tel: 01573 229760 *Fax:* 01573 229767

HASTINGS & CO
15 The Square Kelso Scottish Borders TD5 7HH
Tel: 01573 226999 *Fax:* 01573 229219
E-mail: enq@hastingslegal.co.uk

STORMONTH DARLING WS
Bank of Scotland Buildings The Square Kelso Scottish Borders TD5 7HQ
Tel: 01573 224143 *Fax:* 01573 225706
E-mail: info@stormonthdarling.co.uk

TAITS
10 The Square Kelso Scottish Borders TD5 7HJ
Tel: 01573 224311 *Fax:* 01573 225858
E-mail: info@taitskelso.co.uk

KILBARCHAN

D P B KANE & CO
39 Dalhousie Road Kilbarchan Renfrewshire PA10 2AT
Tel: 01505 704986 *Fax:* 01505 704986
E-mail: davidkane89@yahoo.co.uk

KILBIRNIE

CARRICK ROBB
71 Main Street Kilbirnie North Ayrshire KA25 7AB
Tel: 01505 682408 *Fax:* 01505 682060
E-mail: carrickrobb@btconnect.com

KILCONQUHAR

DOUGLAS MCVEAN
33 Main Street Kilconquhar Fife KY9 1LG
Tel: 01333 340868
E-mail: dmacvee@aol.com

KILMACOLM

KINGSLEY WOOD & CO
Burnside Chambers Kilmacolm Inverclyde PA13 4ET
Tel: 01505 874114 *Fax:* 01505 874009 *Dx:* 500350 KILMACOLM

KILMARNOCK

BARNETTS
7-9 Grange Place Kilmarnock East Ayrshire KA1 2BH
Tel: 01563 522137 *Fax:* 01563 571382
E-mail: info@barnettslaw.co.uk

BELL & CO
12 Grange Place Kilmarnock East Ayrshire KA1 2AB
Tel: 01563 535545 *Fax:* 01563 535505

BLACKWOOD & CO
44 Main Street Dunlop Kilmarnock East Ayrshire KA3 4AN
Tel: 0844 811 4150 *Fax:* 0844 811 4151
E-mail: blackwoodlegal@btconnect.com

CARRUTHERS CURDIE STURROCK & CO
1 Howard Street Kilmarnock East Ayrshire KA1 2BW
Tel: 01563 572727 *Fax:* 01563 527901
E-mail: mail@carrutherscurdiesturrock.co.uk

MARTIN DUFFY
67 Mure Avenue Kilmarnock East Ayrshire KA3 1TT
Tel: 01563 528580

JAMES GUTHRIE & CO
3 Portland Road Kilmarnock East Ayrshire KA1 2AN
Tel: 01563 525155 *Fax:* 01563 530898
E-mail: info@jamesguthrie.co.uk

ALLAN KERR
13 Grange Place Kilmarnock East Ayrshire KA1 2AB
Tel: 01563 571571 *Fax:* 01563 571571

N S LOCKHART
71 King Street Kilmarnock East Ayrshire KA1 1PT
Tel: 01563 531424 *Fax:* 01563 544769
E-mail: nslockhart@onetel.com

MCCLUSKEY BROWNE
7 Portland Road Kilmarnock East Ayrshire KA1 2BT
Tel: 01563 544545 *Fax:* 01563 537672 *Dx:* KK11 KILMARNOCK
E-mail: enquiries@mccluskeybrowne.co.uk

MACKINTOSH & WYLIE
PO Box 31 23 The Foregate Kilmarnock East Ayrshire KA1 1LE
Tel: 01563 525104 *Fax:* 01563 537100
E-mail: enquiries@mackwylie.com

DUNCAN MCLEAN & CO
81 John Finnie Street Kilmarnock East Ayrshire KA1 1BG
Tel: 01563 524222 *Fax:* 01563 525597 *Dx:* KK9 KILMARNOCK

NEIL F MCPHERSON
63 Titchfield Street Kilmarnock East Ayrshire KA1 1QS
Tel: 01563 535363 *Fax:* 01563 542998
E-mail: n.mcpherson@btconnect.com

MCSHERRY HALLIDAY DALE & MARSHALL
Bank Chambers 42 Bank Street Kilmarnock East Ayrshire KA1 1HA
Tel: 01563 533121 *Fax:* 01563 522762 / 570840
E-mail: kilmarnock@mcsherryhalliday.co.uk

DOUGLAS WRIGHT
78 John Finnie Street Kilmarnock East Ayrshire KA1 1BS
Tel: 01563 532177 *Fax:* 01563 571393

KILSYTH

MATHIE LENNOX & CO
Market Chambers Market Square Kilsyth North Lanarkshire G65 0AZ
Tel: 01236 823139 *Fax:* 01236 825991
E-mail: jgibson@mathielennox.co.uk

KILWINNING

RUTH ANDERSON & CO
PO Box 3 180a Main Street Kilwinning North Ayrshire KA13 6EE
Tel: 01294 551551 *Fax:* 01294 556572

KINGSWELLS

ABERDEIN CONSIDINE & CO
3 Village Centre Kingswells Aberdeen AB15 8TG
Tel: 01224 741411 *Fax:* 01224 741747 *Dx:* AB46 ABERDEEN
E-mail: kin@acandco.com

KINROSS

MACBETH CURRIE
62 High Street Kinross Perth & Kinross KY13 8AN
Tel: 01577 863424 *Fax:* 01577 864464

J & G WILSON
18 High Street Kinross Perth & Kinross KY13 8AN
Tel: 01577 862302 *Fax:* 01577 864591

KIRKCALDY

BAIRD & CO
2 Park Place Kirkcaldy Fife KY1 1XL
Tel: 01592 268608 *Fax:* 01592 203369 *Dx:* KY9 KIRKCALDY
E-mail: breception@bairdco.co.uk

BEVERIDGE HERD & SANDILANDS WS
1 East Fergus Place Kirkcaldy Fife KY1 1XT
Tel: 01592 261616 *Fax:* 01592 642153 *Dx:* KY1 KIRKCALDY
E-mail: mail@bhssolicitors.co.uk

BLACK & GUILD
38 Hunter Street Kirkcaldy Fife KY1 1ED
Tel: 01592 261624 *Fax:* 01592 642307

W & A S BRUCE
8 Hunter Street Kirkcaldy Fife KY1 1ED
Tel: 01592 204774 *Fax:* 01592 262011
E-mail: info@wasbruce.co.uk

FORDS
15 Tolbooth Street Kirkcaldy Fife KY1 1RW
Tel: 01592 640630 *Fax:* 01592 640622 *Dx:* KY24 KIRKCALDY
E-mail: info@fords-solicitors.co.uk

GIBSON & SPEARS DOW & SON
9 East Fergus Place Kirkcaldy Fife KY1 1XU
Tel: 01592 264782 *Fax:* 01592 641059 *Dx:* KY3 KIRKCALDY
E-mail: gibsonspears@btconnect.com

JAS S GROSSET
2 Brodick Road Kirkcaldy Fife KY2 6EY
Tel: 01592 205816

INNES JOHNSTON & CO
197 High Street Kirkcaldy Fife KY1 1JE
Tel: 01592 263455 *Fax:* 01592 200069 *Dx:* KY4 KIRKCALDY

MACGREGOR
28 Links Street Kirkcaldy Fife KY1 1QE
Tel: 01592 644477 *Fax:* 01592 640022

MCKENZIES
26 East Fergus Place Kirkcaldy Fife KY1 1XT
Tel: 01592 206605 *Fax:* 01592 268803 *Dx:* KY21 KIRKCALDY
E-mail: enquiries@mckenzies-sols.co.uk

MARTIN JOHNSTON & SOCHA
47 Whytescauseway Kirkcaldy Fife KY1 1XD
Tel: 01592 640680 *Fax:* 01592 640687

PATERSON BELL
45a High Street Kirkcaldy Fife KY1 1LL
Tel: 01592 646600 *Fax:* 01592 646800
E-mail: crime@patersonbell.co.uk

ANDREW K PRICE
18 Whytescauseway Kirkcaldy Fife KY1 1XF
Tel: 01592 205151 *Fax:* 01592 640848 *Dx:* KY5 KIRKCALDY
E-mail: andrew@andrewkprice.co.uk

JAMES THOMSON & SON
51a High Street Kirkcaldy Fife KY1 1LJ
Tel: 01592 268575 *Fax:* 01592 642082 *Dx:* KY10 KIRKCALDY
E-mail: jamesthomson.son@btinternet.com

CHARLES WOOD & SON
37 Kirk Wynd Kirkcaldy Fife KY1 1EN
Tel: 01592 261621 *Fax:* 01592 200663 *Dx:* KY7 KIRKCALDY
E-mail: charleswood@btconnect.com

KIRKCUDBRIGHT

GILLESPIE GIFFORD & BROWN
27 St Cuthbert Street Kirkcudbright Dumfries & Galloway DG6 4DJ
Tel: 01557 330539 *Fax:* 01557 331059
E-mail: mail@ggblaw.co.uk

WILLIAMSON & HENRY
13 St Mary Street Kirkcudbright Dumfries & Galloway DG6 4AA
Tel: 01557 330692 *Fax:* 01557 331540 *Dx:* 580813 KIRKCUDBRIGHT

KIRKINTILLOCH

ALDER HOGG & CO
45a Townhead Kirkintilloch East Dunbartonshire G66 1NG
Tel: 0141 776 3350 *Fax:* 0141 776 0946 *Dx:* 500820 KIRKINTILLOCH

GALLACHER & CO
106 Cowgate Kirkintilloch East Dunbartonshire G66 1JU
Tel: 0141 776 1111 *Fax:* 0141 777 7875 *Dx:* 828 KIRKINTILLOCH

HUGHES DOWDALL
119 Cowgate Kirkintilloch East Dunbartonshire G66 1JD
Tel: 0141 776 7104 *Fax:* 0141 777 8140 *Dx:* 821 KIRKINTILLOCH

NOLAN MACLEOD
Donaldson House 39 Donaldson Street Kirkintilloch East Dunbartonshire G66 1XE
Tel: 0141 777 6366 *Fax:* 0141 777 8639
Dx: 500822 KIRKINTILLOCH
E-mail: nolmac@dial.pipex.com

THE PRG PARTNERSHIP
111 Cowgate Kirkintilloch East Dunbartonshire G66 1JD
Tel: 0141 776 2298 *Fax:* 0141 776 6974 *Dx:* 500823 KIRKINTILLOCH

PACITTI JONES
64 Townhead Kirkintilloch East Dunbartonshire G66 1NZ
Tel: 0141 777 8899 *Fax:* 0141 578 0081
E-mail: kirkintilloch@pjglasgow.co.uk

KIRKWALL

DREVER & HEDDLE
56a Albert Street Kirkwall Orkney KW15 1HQ
Tel: 01856 872216 *Fax:* 01856 872483

LOWS ORKNEY
5 Broad Street Kirkwall Orkney KW15 1DH
Tel: 01856 873151

KIRRIEMUIR

MACLEAN & LOWSON
7 Schoolwynd Kirriemuir Angus DD8 4BQ
Tel: 01575 575255 *Fax:* 01575 575300
E-mail: enquiries@macleanandlowson.co.uk

WILKIE & DUNDAS WS
28 Marywell Brae Kirriemuir Angus DD8 4BP
Tel: 01575 572608 *Fax:* 01575 574529
E-mail: wd@wdws.co.uk

KYLE OF LOCHALSH

FERGUSON MACSWEEN & STEWART
Main Street Kyle of Lochalsh Highland IV40 8AB
Tel: 01599 534500 *Fax:* 01599 534480
E-mail: law@fmskyle.co.uk

LANARK

CAMPBELL SIEVEWRIGHT & CO
64 Thornton Road Kirkmuirhill Lanark South Lanarkshire ML11 9QE
Tel: 01555 895123 *Fax:* 01555 895095
E-mail: pdunlop@cs-homes.co.uk

CRIGGIES
30 Broomgate Lanark South Lanarkshire ML11 9EE
Tel: 01555 662674 *Fax:* 01555 662388 *Dx:* 570833 LANARK
E-mail: info@criggies.com

DAVIDSON & SHIRLEY
11 Hope Street Lanark South Lanarkshire ML11 7ND
Tel: 01555 662576 *Fax:* 01555 661904 *Dx:* 570830 LANARK
E-mail: reception@davidsonandshirley.co.uk

MORISON & SMITH
61 High Street Lanark South Lanarkshire ML11 7LN
Tel: 01555 661435 *Fax:* 01555 664048 *Dx:* 570831 LANARK

20 Hope Street Lanark South Lanarkshire ML11 7NG
Tel: 01555 662488 *Fax:* 01555 664048 *Dx:* 570831 LANARK

SMAIL & EWART
68-70 High Street Lanark South Lanarkshire ML11 7ES
Tel: 01555 666111 *Fax:* 01555 665989 *Dx:* 570838 LANARK
E-mail: enquiry@smail-ewart.co.uk

LANGHOLM

STEVENSON & JOHNSTONE
38 High Street Langholm Dumfries & Galloway DG13 0JH
Tel: 01387 380428 *Fax:* 01387 381144
E-mail: office@sandjlangholm.co.uk

LARBERT

J S B GILLESPIE & CO
158 Main Street Stenhousemuir Larbert Falkirk FK5 3JP
Tel: 01324 553207 *Fax:* 01324 551281
E-mail: legal@jsbgillespie.co.uk

JAMES TURNBULL & CO
Carron House 27a King Street Stenhousemuir Larbert Falkirk FK5 4HD
Tel: 01324 552456 *Fax:* 01324 562394
E-mail: info@jamesturnbullandco.co.uk

LARGS

COLVIN HOUSTON & COMPANY LLP
PO Box 3 1 Bellman's Close Largs North Ayrshire KA30 8AP
Tel: 01475 672003 *Fax:* 01475 687332

ROBERT F DUFF & CO
PO Box 2 30 Main Street Largs North Ayrshire KA30 8AB
Tel: 01475 673663 *Fax:* 01475 674798
E-mail: rfduff.law@dsl.pipex.com

LOW BEATON RICHMOND
4a Frazer Street Largs North Ayrshire KA30 9HP
Tel: 01475 674576 *Fax:* 01475 672024
E-mail: yvonne@lbr-largs.demon.co.uk

DOROTHY MCGHIE
16 Scott Street Largs North Ayrshire KA30 9NU
Tel: 01475 674970
E-mail: mail@dorothymcghie.com

MACTAGGART & CO
72/74 Main Street Largs North Ayrshire KA30 8AL
Tel: 01475 674646 *Fax:* 01475 672650 *Dx:* 590840 LARGS
E-mail: law@mactaggarts.co.uk

LARKHALL

CARTY'S
14 Montgomery Street Larkhall South Lanarkshire ML9 2AA
Tel: 01698 885888 *Fax:* 01698 885909
E-mail: larkhall@cartylaw.co.uk

KENNETH M GREENER
1 New Street The Cross Stonehouse Larkhall South Lanarkshire ML9 3LT
Tel: 01698 793366
E-mail: kenneth@kmglaw.co.uk

LAURENCEKIRK

BANSKI & CO
Royal Bank Buildings Laurencekirk Aberdeenshire AB30 1AF
Tel: 01561 377245 *Fax:* 01561 378020
Dx: 521090 LAURENCEKIRK
E-mail: reception@banski.co.uk

LEITH

WATERMANS SOLICITORS
The Oval Office 83 The Shore Leith Edinburgh EH6 6RG
Tel: 0131 555 7055 *Fax:* 0131 561 1492 *Dx:* 550855 LEITH
E-mail: admin@watermans.ws

LENZIE

MILLER BECKETT & JACKSON
1 Alexandra Avenue Lenzie East Dunbartonshire G66 5BE
Tel: 0141 776 7761 *Fax:* 0141 776 0792
E-mail: mail@millerbj.co.uk

MIKE SMITH & CO
6 Ingleside Lenzie East Dunbartonshire G66 4GN
Tel: 0141 776 2621 *Fax:* 0141 776 4344
E-mail: law@mike-smith.co.uk

LERWICK

ALLANS
Nordhus North Ness Lerwick Shetland Islands ZE1 0LZ
Tel: 01595 690749 *Fax:* 01595 690749
E-mail: allans1@btinternet.com

ANDERSON & GOODLAD
52 Commercial Street Lerwick Shetland Islands ZE1 0BD
Tel: 01595 692297 *Fax:* 01595 692247
E-mail: solicitors@anderson-goodlad.co.uk

DOWLE SMITH & RUTHERFORD
St Olaf's Hall Lerwick Shetland Islands ZE1 0FD
Tel: 01595 695583 *Fax:* 01595 695310
E-mail: solicitors@d-s-r.co.uk

MICHAEL INKSTER & CO
159 Commercial Street Lerwick Shetland Islands ZE1 0EX
Tel: 01595 696901 *Fax:* 01595 696904
E-mail: michaelinksterandco@lineone.net

NEIL RISK
Nordhus North Ness Business Park Lerwick Shetland Islands ZE1 0LZ
Tel: 01595 695262 *Fax:* 01595 695331
E-mail: mail@neilrisk.com

TAIT & PETERSON
Bank of Scotland Buildings Commercial Street Lerwick Shetland Islands ZE1 0EB
Tel: 01595 693010 *Fax:* 01595 695999
E-mail: info@tait-peterson.co.uk

LEVEN

DEWAR SPENCE
260 High Street Lower Methil Leven Fife KY8 3EQ
Tel: 01333 425200 *Fax:* 01333 421811

JAS S GROSSET
Royal Bank House High Street Leven Fife KY8 4PX
Tel: 01333 426023 *Fax:* 01333 428910

LYNN HERBERT & CO
82 High Street Leven Fife KY8 4NB
Tel: 01333 429007 *Fax:* 01333 424800 *Dx:* 560879 LEVEN
E-mail: enquiries@lynnherbert.co.uk

INNES JOHNSTON & CO
5-7 Commercial Road Leven Fife KY8 4LE
Tel: 01333 429320 *Fax:* 01333 424973 *Dx:* 560874 LEVEN

JACKSON & COMPANY SSC
39 High Street Leven Fife KY8 4NE
Tel: 01333 422330 *Fax:* 01333 422339 *Dx:* 560868 LEVEN
E-mail: info@jacksonsolicitors.co.uk

SMITH & GRANT
Rathellan High Street Leven Fife KY8 4PR
Tel: 01333 423441 *Fax:* 01333 427342
E-mail: mail@smithandgrant.com

F T & D C WALLACE
Forth House Forth Street Leven Fife KY8 4PW
Tel: 01333 423804 *Fax:* 01333 428360 *Dx:* 560873 LEVEN
E-mail: email@ft-dc-wallace.co.uk

LINLITHGOW

PETERKIN & KIDD
8 High Street Linlithgow West Lothian EH49 7AF
Tel: 01506 845191 *Fax:* 01506 845444 *Dx:* 540880 LINLITHGOW

RGM
19-21 High Street Linlithgow West Lothian EH49 7AB
Tel: 01506 847070 *Fax:* 01506 847090
E-mail: legal@rgmsolicitors.co.uk

THOMAS S VEITCH & SON
12 High Street Linlithgow West Lothian EH49 7AG
Tel: 01506 842100 *Fax:* 01506 670470 *Dx:* 540882 LINLITHGOW

LIVINGSTON

ADAMS WHYTE
9 Grampian Court Dedridge Livingston West Lothian EH54 6QF
Tel: 01506 401999 *Fax:* 01506 462909 *Dx:* 540890 LIVINGSTON
E-mail: livingston@adamswhyte.com

AITKENS THE FAMILY LAW SOLICITORS
17 Grampian Court Beveridge Square Livingston West Lothian EH54 6QF
Tel: 01506 417737 *Fax:* 01506 460613

ALLCOURT
1 Carmondean Centre Carmondean Livingston West Lothian EH54 8PT
Tel: 01506 443999 *Fax:* 01506 443909

CAESAR & HOWIE (IN ASSOC WITH WILSON & JARVIS)
107 Almondvale South Almondvale Centre Livingston West Lothian EH54 6QT
Tel: 01506 435306 *Fax:* 01506 448301 *Dx:* 540891 LIVINGSTON
E-mail: enquiries@caesar-howie.co.uk

CENTRAL CRIMINAL LAWYERS
15 Grampian Court Livingston West Lothian EH54 6QF
Tel: 01506 416999 *Fax:* 01506 414000 *Dx:* 554003 LIVINGSTON 8
E-mail: centralcriminallaw@gmail.com

CURRIE JOHNSTON & CO
18 Grampian Court Beveridge Square Livingston West Lothian EH54 6QF
Tel: 01506 412377 *Fax:* 01506 412315 *Dx:* 540909 LIVINGSTON
E-mail: admin@currie-johnston.com

KW LAW
Torridon House Almondvale Boulevard Livingston West Lothian EH54 6QY
Tel: 01506 415333 *Fax:* 01506 416116
E-mail: livingston@kwlaw.co.uk

P C MCFARLANE & CO
Law House Fairbairn Place Livingston West Lothian EH54 6TN
Tel: 01506 497160 *Fax:* 01506 497177
E-mail: pmcf@pcmcfarlane.co.uk

LOCHGILPHEAD

MACARTHUR STEWART
18 Argyll Street Lochgilphead Argyll & Bute PA31 8NE
Tel: 01546 602424 *Fax:* 01546 603949
Dx: 599702 LOCHGILPHEAD
E-mail: lochgilphead@macarthurstewart.co.uk

JANE MACLEOD
Achnaba House Lochgilphead Argyll & Bute PA31 8RY
Tel: 01546 606666 *Fax:* 01546 600166
Dx: 599705 LOCHGILPHEAD
E-mail: jane@janemacleod.co.uk

C & D MACTAGGART
57 Lochnell Street Lochgilphead Argyll & Bute PA31 8JN
Tel: 01546 602581
E-mail: mail@cdm-law.co.uk

RUBENS
77 Argyll Street Lochgilphead Argyll & Bute PA31 8NE
Tel: 01546 602084 *Dx:* 599703 LOCHGILPHEAD
E-mail: ruben.murdanaigum@live.uk

STEWART BALFOUR & SUTHERLAND
Colchester Square Lochgilphead Argyll & Bute PA31 8LH
Tel: 01546 602903 *Fax:* 01546 603716
E-mail: sales@sbsproperty.co.uk

LOCKERBIE

HENDERSON & MACKAY
Victoria Square Lockerbie Dumfries & Galloway DG11 2JP
Tel: 01576 202137 *Fax:* 01576 203090
E-mail: info@lockerbielaw.co.uk

MACDUFF

WALTER GERRARD & CO
31 Duff Street Macduff Aberdeenshire AB44 1QL
Tel: 01261 832491 *Fax:* 01261 833444
E-mail: macduff@waltergerrard.co.uk

8

MAUCHLINE

HOWAT ASSOCIATES
5 Kilmarnock Road Mauchline East Ayrshire KA5 5DB
Tel: 01290 553055 *Fax:* 01290 553046
E-mail: andrew.smith@howats.co.uk

D W SHAW
9 Earl Grey Street Mauchline East Ayrshire KA5 5AB
Tel: 01290 550249 *Fax:* 01290 550972
E-mail: enquiries@dwshaw.co.uk

MELROSE

CULLEN KILSHAW
Property Department 7 Market Square Melrose Scottish Borders TD6 9PQ
Tel: 01896 822796 *Fax:* 01896 823465 *Dx:* 581240 MELROSE

Royal Bank Chambers High Street Melrose Scottish Borders TD6 9PE
Tel: 01896 822177 *Fax:* 01896 824488 *Dx:* 581240 MELROSE

METHIL

PATERSON BELL
343 Methilhaven Road Methil Fife KY8 3HR
Tel: 01333 427999 *Fax:* 01333 439399
E-mail: crime@patersonbell.co.uk

MID CALDER

PETERKIN & KIDD
1/3 Market Street Mid Calder West Lothian EH53 0AP
Tel: 01506 880548 *Fax:* 01506 884495 *Dx:* 540880 LINLITHGOW

MILNGAVIE

CAMPBELL RIDDELL BREEZE PATERSON
21 Park Road Milngavie East Dunbartonshire G62 6PJ
Tel: 0141 956 5454 *Fax:* 0141 956 6594 *Dx:* 581600 MILNGAVIE
E-mail: law@crbp.co.uk

MACGREGOR & CO
11 Stewart Street Milngavie East Dunbartonshire G62 6BW
Tel: 0141 956 4263 *Fax:* 0141 956 2696

RUTHVEN KEENAN POLLOCK & CO
18 Main Street Milngavie East Dunbartonshire G62 6BL
Tel: 0141 956 4647 *Fax:* 0141 956 1055 *Dx:* 581602 MILNGAVIE
E-mail: mail@rkpsolicitors.co.uk

MONTROSE

SCOTT ALEXANDER
46 High Street Montrose Angus DD10 8JF
Tel: 01674 671477 *Fax:* 01674 671445
E-mail: info@scottalexander.org.uk

R BRUCE & CO
184 High Street Montrose Angus DD10 8PH
Tel: 01674 675534 *Fax:* 01674 675534
E-mail: info@bruce-co.co.uk

T DUNCAN & CO
192 High Street Montrose Angus DD10 8NA
Tel: 01674 672533 *Fax:* 01674 673812 *Dx:* 530911 MONTROSE
E-mail: info@tduncan.com

ALAN K SMITH
2 Lowerhall Street Montrose Angus DD10 8JW
Tel: 01674 662155 *Fax:* 01674 662151 *Dx:* 530913 MONTROSE
E-mail: aks@alanksmith-solicitors.net

WATTS
55 High Street Montrose Angus DD10 8LR
Tel: 01674 673444 *Fax:* 01674 673948
E-mail: info@wattssolicitors.com

MOTHERWELL

BALLANTYNE & COPLAND
The Old Bank Chambers 44 Civic Square Motherwell North Lanarkshire ML1 1TP
Tel: 01698 266200 *Fax:* 01698 269387

FREELANDS
36 Muir Street Motherwell North Lanarkshire ML1 1BW
Tel: 01698 352600 *Fax:* 01698 266240

JACK GRANT & CO
14 Hamilton Road Motherwell North Lanarkshire ML1 1BB
Tel: 01698 254636 *Fax:* 01698 275121 *Dx:* 570926 MOTHERWELL
E-mail: enquiries@jackgrantsolicitors.co.uk

MICHAEL LOTT
1 Merry Street Motherwell North Lanarkshire ML1 1JJ
Tel: 01698 252331 *Fax:* 01698 252984
E-mail: michaellott@btconnect.com

BRUCE MCCORMACK
2nd Floor 1 Merry Street Motherwell North Lanarkshire ML1 1JJ
Tel: 01698 260033 *Fax:* 01698 250101
E-mail: brucemccormackltd@hotmail.co.uk

MARSHALL ROSS & MUNRO
106 Hamilton Road Motherwell North Lanarkshire ML1 3DG
Tel: 01698 263522 *Fax:* 01698 275484 *Dx:* 570923 MOTHERWELL
E-mail: mail@marshallrossmunro.co.uk

MOORE MACDONALD
2 Scott Street Motherwell North Lanarkshire ML1 1PN
Tel: 01698 262111 *Fax:* 01698 260123

MUNRO LIDDELL
Top Floor 15 Merry Street Motherwell North Lanarkshire ML1 1JJ
Tel: 01698 276255 *Fax:* 01698 230998
E-mail: admin@munroliddell.co.uk

NESS GALLAGHER & CO
358 Brandon Street Motherwell North Lanarkshire ML1 1XA
Tel: 01698 254644 *Fax:* 01698 262012
E-mail: mail@nessgallagher.co.uk

BRIAN D SELBY & CO
30 Windmillhill Street Motherwell North Lanarkshire ML1 1TA
Tel: 01698 230032 *Fax:* 01698 230033
E-mail: bdselby@btinternet.com

WATTERS STEVEN & CO
291-293 Brandon Street Motherwell North Lanarkshire ML1 1RS
Tel: 01698 276550 *Fax:* 01698 269211

WRIGHTS
70 Brandon Parade East Merry Street Motherwell North Lanarkshire ML1 1LY
Tel: 01698 267361 *Fax:* 01698 264224 *Dx:* 570924 MOTHERWELL

MUIRHEAD

CALLAN & CO
157 Cumbernauld Road Muirhead North Lanarkshire G69 9AF
Tel: 0141 779 2114 *Fax:* 0141 779 1470 *Dx:* 501700 MUIRHEAD
E-mail: guycallan@aol.com

CARR & CO
100 Cumbernauld Road Muirhead North Lanarkshire G69 9AB
Tel: 0141 779 4466 *Fax:* 0141 779 2683 *Dx:* 501701 MUIRHEAD

MUSSELBURGH

DRUMMOND MILLER WS
151 High Street Musselburgh East Lothian EH21 7DD
Tel: 0131 665 7393 *Fax:* 0131 653 6192 *Dx:* 940 MUSSELBURGH

ALEX MITCHELL & SONS
21 Eskside West Musselburgh East Lothian EH21 6PW
Tel: 0131 665 2468 *Fax:* 0131 653 2003
Dx: 540942 MUSSELBURGH
E-mail: mail@amslegal.com

SOMERVILLE & RUSSELL
39 Bridge Street Musselburgh East Lothian EH21 6AA
Tel: 0131 665 9041 *Fax:* 0131 665 1951

NAIRN

DONALDSON & HENDERSON
75-77 High Street Nairn Highland IV12 4BW
Tel: 01667 453395 *Fax:* 01667 452178 *Dx:* 520953 NAIRN
E-mail: donhen@btinternet.com

R & R URQUHART
Royal Bank Buildings 20 High Street Nairn Highland IV12 4AX
Tel: 01667 453278 *Fax:* 01667 453499 *Dx:* 520950 NAIRN
E-mail: info.nairn@r-r-urquhart.com

NEWMILNS

MAIR MATHESON
53 Main Street Newmilns East Ayrshire KA16 9DA
Tel: 01560 321225 *Fax:* 01560 322109 *Dx:* KK22 KILMARNOCK
E-mail: reception@mairmatheson.co.uk

NEWTON MEARNS

A & S IRELAND
138 Ayr Road Newton Mearns East Renfrewshire G77 6EG
Tel: 0141 639 2277 *Fax:* 0141 616 2412

NEWTON STEWART

MCCORMICK & NICHOLSON
66 Victoria Street Newton Stewart Dumfries & Galloway DG8 6DD
Tel: 01671 402813 *Fax:* 01671 403763
E-mail: mail@mccormicknicholson.co.uk

A B & A MATTHEWS
37 Albert Street Newton Stewart Dumfries & Galloway DG8 6EG
Tel: 01671 404100 *Fax:* 01671 404140
Dx: 580962 NEWTON STEWART
E-mail: enquiries@abamatthews.com

IAN MILLIGAN
2 Albert Street Newton Stewart Dumfries & Galloway DG8 6EJ
Tel: 01671 403036 *Fax:* 01671 403046

NORTH BERWICK

ISABEL J ANDERSON WS
PO Box 13706 North Berwick East Lothian EH39 4ZD
Tel: 01620 895855 *Fax:* 01620 895865
Dx: 541248 NORTH BERWICK
E-mail: isabel@anderson-ws.co.uk

LINDSAYS
33 Westgate North Berwick East Lothian EH39 4AG
Tel: 01620 893481 *Fax:* 01620 894442
Dx: 541245 NORTH BERWICK
E-mail: northberwick@lindsays.co.uk

PARIS STEELE & CO WS
35 Westgate North Berwick East Lothian EH39 4AG
Tel: 01620 892138 *Fax:* 01620 895162
Dx: 541246 NORTH BERWICK

WALLACE & MENZIES
21 Westgate North Berwick East Lothian EH39 4AE
Tel: 01620 892307 *Fax:* 01620 895106
E-mail: north.berwick@melroseporteous.co.uk

OBAN

ANDERSON BANKS
22 Argyll Square Oban Argyll & Bute PA34 4AT
Tel: 01631 563158 *Fax:* 01631 565459 *Dx:* OB1 OBAN
E-mail: info@andersonbanks.co.uk

MACARTHUR STEWART
Boswell House Argyll Square Oban Argyll & Bute PA34 4BD
Tel: 01631 562215 *Fax:* 01631 565490 *Dx:* OB3 OBAN
E-mail: carol@macarthurstewart.co.uk

D M MACKINNON WS
Bank of Scotland Buildings Station Road Oban Argyll & Bute PA34 4LN
Tel: 01631 563014 *Fax:* 01631 566463 *Dx:* OB4 OBAN
E-mail: mail@dmmackinnon-law.co.uk

MACPHEE & PARTNERS
8 George Street Oban Argyll & Bute PA34 5SB
Tel: 01631 562308 *Fax:* 01631 564983 *Dx:* OB10 OBAN
E-mail: law@macphee.co.uk

STEVENSON KENNEDY
Linndhu House 19 Stevenson Street Oban Argyll & Bute PA34 5NA
Tel: 01631 562317 *Fax:* 01631 566288 *Dx:* OB6 OBAN
E-mail: mail@stevensonkennedy.co.uk

E THORNTON & CO
17-19 Lochfide Street Oban Argyll & Bute PA34 4HP
Tel: 01631 566771 *Fax:* 01631 564011 *Dx:* OB12 OBAN
E-mail: info@ethornton.co.uk

OLDMELDRUM

STEWART & WATSON
21 Market Square Oldmeldrum Aberdeenshire AB51 0AA
Tel: 01651 872314 *Fax:* 01651 872885
E-mail: oldmeldrum.property@stewartwatson.co.uk

PAISLEY

1 MOVE
33 Causeyside Street Paisley Renfrewshire PA1 1UL
Tel: 0141 889 8899 *Fax:* 0141 889 8799
E-mail: headoffice@1move4u.co.uk

BANKS DEVLIN & CO
78 Causeyside Street Paisley Renfrewshire PA1 1YP
Tel: 0141 889 4949 *Fax:* 0141 848 0273
E-mail: banksdevlin@aol.com

BILKUS & BOYLE
21 Wellmeadow Street Paisley Renfrewshire PA1 2EF
Tel: 0141 889 1500 *Fax:* 0141 848 9465

BUCHANAN DICKSON FRAME
Studio 301 The Old Embroidery Mill Abbey Mill Business Centre Paisley Renfrewshire PA1 1TJ
Tel: 0141 848 0303 *Fax:* 0141 848 6818
E-mail: info@bdflaw.co.uk

CAMERON PINKERTON & CO
21 Gauze Street Paisley Renfrewshire PA1 1ES
Tel: 0141 887 5211 *Fax:* 0141 889 3926 *Dx:* PA46 PAISLEY

HUNTER & ROBERTSON
35 High Street Paisley Renfrewshire PA1 2AG
Tel: 0141 889 3196
E-mail: mail@hunter-robertson.co.uk

THE ROBERT KERR PARTNERSHIP
12a Moss Street Paisley Renfrewshire PA1 1BL
Tel: 0141 889 6458 *Fax:* 0141 889 8758 *Dx:* PA43 PAISLEY
E-mail: info@therobertkerrpartnership.com

MSM SOLICITORS
51 Moss Street Paisley Renfrewshire PA1 1DR
Tel: 0141 889 6244 *Fax:* 0141 887 0964
E-mail: mail@msmlaw.co.uk

MCALLISTER & MCKECHNIE
6 Moss Street Paisley Renfrewshire PA1 1BL
Tel: 0141 887 8961 *Fax:* 0141 887 2999

MCAULEY MCCARTHY & CO
29 Moss Street Paisley Renfrewshire PA1 1DL
Tel: 0141 561 7779 *Fax:* 0141 561 7797

MCCUSKER COCHRANE & GUNN
1 Orr Square High Street Paisley Renfrewshire PA1 2DL
Tel: 0845 832 3228 *Fax:* 0141 887 5324

MCCUSKER MCELROY & COMPANY
9 St James Street Paisley Renfrewshire PA3 2HL
Tel: 0141 561 9999 *Fax:* 0141 561 9996 *Dx:* PA58 PAISLEY
E-mail: mccuskerlaw@btinternet.com

MACFARLANE YOUNG & CO
26 New Street Paisley Renfrewshire PA1 1YB
Tel: 0141 889 3257 *Fax:* 0141 889 0695
E-mail: mail@macfarlaneyoung.com

MACKIE THOMPSON & CO
53 Moss Street Paisley Renfrewshire PA1 1DR
Tel: 0141 848 6000 *Fax:* 0141 848 6111

MACNAIRS
15 Glasgow Road Paisley Renfrewshire PA1 3QS
Tel: 0141 887 5181 *Fax:* 0141 887 9527
E-mail: law@macnairs.co.uk

KENNETH PATERSON
31 Wellmeadow Street Paisley Renfrewshire PA1 2EH
Tel: 0141 561 2215 *Fax:* 0141 561 2215

PATTISON & SIM
19 Glasgow Road Paisley Renfrewshire PA1 3QX
Tel: 0141 889 3296 *Fax:* 0141 887 0316
E-mail: info@pattisonsim.co.uk

T F REID & DONALDSON
48 Causeyside Street Paisley Renfrewshire PA1 1YH
Tel: 0141 889 7531 *Fax:* 0141 887 3380 *Dx:* PA22 PAISLEY
E-mail: mail@reidlaw.co.uk

ROBERTSON & ROSS
7 Causeyside Street Paisley Renfrewshire PA1 1UW
Tel: 0141 887 7971 *Fax:* 0141 887 5561
E-mail: robertson_ross@btconnect.com

STIRLING & MAIR
12a Moss Street Paisley Renfrewshire PA1 1BE
Tel: 0141 889 6458 *Fax:* 0141 889 8758 *Dx:* PA43 PAISLEY
E-mail: info@stirlingmair.com

TOD & MITCHELL
Terrace Buildings The Cross Paisley Renfrewshire PA1 2YA
Tel: 0141 889 1444 *Fax:* 0141 889 1555 *Dx:* PA35 PAISLEY
E-mail: enquiries@todandmitchell.co.uk

WALKER LAIRD
9 Gilmour Street Paisley Renfrewshire PA1 1DG
Tel: 0141 887 5271 *Fax:* 0141 889 3268 *Dx:* PA32 PAISLEY
E-mail: info@walkerlaird.co.uk

WRIGHT & CRAWFORD
11 Glasgow Road Paisley Renfrewshire PA1 3QS
Tel: 0141 887 6211 *Fax:* 0141 887 1122
E-mail: info@wright-crawford.co.uk

PEEBLES

BLACKWOOD & SMITH WS
39 High Street Peebles Scottish Borders EH45 8AH
Tel: 01721 720131 *Fax:* 01721 729804

CULLEN KILSHAW
23 Northgate Peebles Scottish Borders EH45 8RX
Tel: 01721 723999 *Fax:* 01721 723888 *Dx:* 540979 PEEBLES

PENICUIK

ALLAN MCDOUGALL
20 High Street Penicuik Midlothian EH26 8HR
Tel: 01968 675694 *Fax:* 01968 676546 *Dx:* 541111 PENICUIK
E-mail: penicuik@allanmcdougall.co.uk

STUART & STUART WS
12 John Street Penicuik Midlothian EH26 8AD
Tel: 01968 677294 *Fax:* 01968 678935 *Dx:* 541114 PENICUIK
E-mail: info@stuartandstuart.co.uk

PERTH

ANDERSON BEATON LAMOND
Bordeaux House 31 Kinnoull Street Perth Perth & Kinross PH1 5EN
Tel: 01738 639999 *Fax:* 01738 630063 *Dx:* PE5 PERTH
E-mail: info@abl-law.co.uk

CONDIES
2 Tay Street Perth Perth & Kinross PH1 5LJ
Tel: 01738 440088 *Fax:* 01738 441131 *Dx:* PE25 PERTH
E-mail: enquiries@condies.co.uk

CULLEY & MCALPINE
40-42 South Street Perth Perth & Kinross PH2 8PD
Tel: 01738 502704 *Fax:* 01738 625511
E-mail: enquiries@culleymcalpine.co.uk

ELLIOT & CO WS
8 Charlotte Street Perth Perth & Kinross PH1 5LL
Tel: 01738 638246 *Fax:* 01738 630527 *Dx:* PE27 PERTH
E-mail: elliots@elliotsperth.co.uk

JAMESON & MACKAY
1 Charlotte Street Perth Perth & Kinross PH1 5LP
Tel: 01738 631666 *Fax:* 01738 643430
E-mail: admin@jamesonmackay.co.uk

KIPPEN CAMPBELL WS
48 Tay Street Perth Perth & Kinross PH1 5TR
Tel: 01738 635353 *Fax:* 01738 643773

KIRKLANDS
7 King Street Perth Perth & Kinross PH2 8HR
Tel: 01738 442299 *Fax:* 01738 443999
E-mail: info@kirklands-law.co.uk

MCCASH & HUNTER
25 South Methven Street Perth Perth & Kinross PH1 5ES
Tel: 01738 620451 *Fax:* 01738 631155 *Dx:* PE4 PERTH
E-mail: admin@mccash.co.uk

MACNABS
10 Barossa Place Perth Perth & Kinross PH1 5JX
Tel: 01738 623432 *Fax:* 01738 638594
E-mail: mail@macnabs-law.com

A C MILLER & MACKAY
63 Scott Street Perth Perth & Kinross PH2 8JN
Tel: 01738 620087 *Fax:* 01738 444239 *Dx:* PE15 PERTH
E-mail: acmillermackay@btconnect.com

MILLER HENDRY
10 Blackfriars Street Perth Perth & Kinross PH1 5NS
Tel: 01738 637311 *Fax:* 01738 638685
E-mail: info@miller-hendry.co.uk

THORNTONS WS
17-21 George Street Perth Perth & Kinross PH1 5JY
Tel: 01738 621212 *Fax:* 01738 444766
E-mail: perth@thorntons-law.co.uk

NEIL WHITTET
25 Barossa Street Perth Perth & Kinross PH1 5NR
Tel: 01738 628900
E-mail: info@neilwhittet.co.uk

WYLLIE & HENDERSON
Market Chambers Caledonian Road Perth Perth & Kinross PH1 5NJ
Tel: 01738 638465 *Fax:* 01738 635499
E-mail: email@wyllie-henderson.co.uk

PETERHEAD

ABERDEIN CONSIDINE & CO
40 & 42 Queen Street Peterhead Aberdeenshire AB42 1TQ
Tel: 01779 475365 *Fax:* 01779 478780 *Dx:* 521370 PETERHEAD
E-mail: ph@acandco.com

GRAY & GRAY
8-10 Queen Street Peterhead Aberdeenshire AB42 1TS
Tel: 01779 480222 *Fax:* 01779 470741
E-mail: property@graygraylaw.com

JOHN MACRITCHIE & CO SSC
Townhouse Broad Street Peterhead Aberdeenshire AB42 1BY
Tel: 01779 478877 *Fax:* 01779 481133

MASSON & GLENNIE
Broad House Broad Street Peterhead Aberdeenshire AB42 1HY
Tel: 01779 474271 *Fax:* 01779 476037 *Dx:* 521371 PETERHEAD
E-mail: mail@masson-glennie.co.uk

STEWART & WATSON
35 Queen Street Peterhead Aberdeenshire AB42 1TP
Tel: 01779 476351 *Fax:* 01779 478792
E-mail: peterhead.property@stewartwatson.co.uk

4 North Street Mintlaw Peterhead Aberdeenshire AB42 5HH
Tel: 01771 622338 *Fax:* 01771 623332
E-mail: mintlaw.property@stewartwatson.co.uk

PITLOCHRY

MACNABS
21 Atholl Road Pitlochry Perth & Kinross PH16 5BX
Tel: 01796 472409
E-mail: mail@macnabs-law.com

J & H MITCHELL WS
51 Atholl Road Pitlochry Perth & Kinross PH16 5BU
Tel: 01796 472606 *Fax:* 01796 473198 *Dx:* 552040 PITLOCHRY
E-mail: j@hmitchell.co.uk

PORT GLASGOW

BLAIR & BRYDEN
39 Princes Street Port Glasgow Inverclyde PA14 5JH
Tel: 01475 745117 *Fax:* 01475 744170 *Dx:* 591460 PORT GLASGOW

KENNEDY & CO
24 John Wood Street Port Glasgow Inverclyde PA14 5HU
Tel: 01475 741188 *Fax:* 01475 744140
E-mail: kennedycolaw@aol.com

PORTREE

ANDERSON MACARTHUR & CO
MacDonald House Somerled Square Portree Highland IV51 9EH
Tel: 01478 612197 *Fax:* 01478 612451
E-mail: legal@amac.co.uk

FERGUSON MACSWEEN & STEWART
Bridge Road Portree Highland IV51 9ER
Tel: 01478 612991 *Fax:* 01478 612709
E-mail: admin@fmslaw.co.uk

PRESTONPANS

MCKINNON FORBES
131 High Street Prestonpans East Lothian EH32 9AX
Tel: 01875 813219 *Fax:* 01875 819229
E-mail: info@mckinnonforbes.co.uk

PRESTWICK

BLACK HAY & CO
45 Main Street Prestwick South Ayrshire KA9 1AF
Tel: 01292 477235 *Fax:* 01292 671310

LAWSON RUSSELL & CO
163 Main Street Prestwick South Ayrshire KA9 1LB
Tel: 01292 478487 *Fax:* 01292 671386

RENFREW

MCAULEY MCCARTHY & CO
58-60 High Street Renfrew Renfrewshire PA4 8PQ
Tel: 0141 561 4449 *Fax:* 0141 561 4494

MCCARTNEY STEWART
1b Paisley Road Renfrew Renfrewshire PA4 8JH
Tel: 0141 885 1858 *Fax:* 0141 886 5425
E-mail: law@mccartneystewart.co.uk

WALKER LAIRD
7 Canal Street Renfrew Renfrewshire PA4 8QF
Tel: 0141 886 2152 *Fax:* 0141 885 0296 *Dx:* 590753 RENFREW
E-mail: info@walkerlaird.co.uk

15 Hairst Street Renfrew Renfrewshire PA4 8QU
Tel: 0141 886 5678 *Dx:* 590753 RENFREW
E-mail: info@walkerlaird.co.uk

ROTHESAY

HANNAY FRASER & CO
34 Castle Street Rothesay Argyll & Bute PA20 9HD
Tel: 01700 503112 *Fax:* 01700 504875

WILLIAM SKELTON & CO
Castle Chambers 49 High Street Rothesay Argyll & Bute PA20 9DB
Tel: 01700 502881 *Fax:* 01700 505270 *Dx:* 590651 ROTHESAY

RUTHERGLEN

CARR BERMAN CRICHTON
90 Main Street Rutherglen South Lanarkshire G73 2HZ
Tel: 0141 647 9851 *Fax:* 0141 643 2171
E-mail: enquiries@cbcsolicitors.co.uk

MACALLANS
236 Stonelaw Road Burnside Rutherglen South Lanarkshire G73 3SA
Tel: 0141 613 1787 *Fax:* 0141 613 1431
Dx: 500250 RUTHERGLEN 2
E-mail: mail@macallans.co.uk

PACITTI JONES
85 Main Street Rutherglen South Lanarkshire G73 2JQ
Tel: 0141 647 4444 *Fax:* 0141 569 4442
E-mail: rutherglen@pjglasgow.co.uk

ROBERTS & CO
81 Main Street Rutherglen South Lanarkshire G73 2JQ
Tel: 0141 613 3344 *Fax:* 0141 613 3626

ROSS ROGERS & CO
221 Main Street Rutherglen South Lanarkshire G73 2HH
Tel: 0141 647 9771 *Fax:* 0141 647 9310
E-mail: louise@rossrogers.co.uk

SALTCOATS

JAS CAMPBELL & CO WS
Bank of Scotland Buildings 57 Dockhead Street Saltcoats North Ayrshire KA21 5EH
Tel: 01294 464301 *Fax:* 01294 603023 *Dx:* 591001 SALTCOATS
E-mail: mail@jascampbell.co.uk

NELLANY & CO
35 Chapelwell Street Saltcoats North Ayrshire KA21 5EB
Tel: 01294 464175 *Fax:* 01294 603431
E-mail: mail@nellanysols.co.uk

TAYLOR & HENDERSON
51 Hamilton Street Saltcoats North Ayrshire KA21 5DX
Tel: 01294 464341 *Fax:* 01294 464827
E-mail: mail@taylorandhenderson.co.uk

DERRICK TRAINER
5 Dockhead Street Saltcoats North Ayrshire KA21 5EF
Tel: 01294 469994 *Fax:* 01294 469994

DOUGLAS WRIGHT
20 Chapelwell Street Saltcoats North Ayrshire KA21 5EA
Tel: 01294 466990 *Fax:* 01294 466990

SANQUHAR

POLLOCK & MCLEAN
61 High Street Sanquhar Dumfries & Galloway DG4 6DT
Tel: 01659 50241 *Fax:* 01659 50443

ROBERT WILSON & SON
47 High Street Sanquhar Dumfries & Galloway DG4 6DJ
Tel: 01659 50251 *Fax:* 01659 50939
E-mail: sanquhar@robertwilsonandson.co.uk

SELKIRK

COLLIE & CO
26 High Street Selkirk Scottish Borders TD7 4DD
Tel: 01750 23868 *Fax:* 01750 23866
E-mail: info@collieandco.com

DOUGLAS GILMOUR & SON
20 Market Place Selkirk Scottish Borders TD7 4BL
Tel: 01750 20271 *Fax:* 01750 22686 *Dx:* 581010 SELKIRK
E-mail: mainoffice@douglasgilmour.co.uk

SHOTTS

SNEDDON MORRISON
156 Station Road Shotts North Lanarkshire ML7 4AW
Tel: 01501 823923 *Fax:* 01501 745440
E-mail: law@sneddons-ssc.co.uk

SOUTH QUEENSFERRY

LESLIE DEANS & CO
31a High Street South Queensferry Edinburgh EH30 9PP
Tel: 0131 331 3560 *Dx:* ED551441 EDINBURGH 52

ST ANDREWS

MCILROY HIPWELL & DINGWALL
147 Market Street St Andrews Fife KY16 9PF
E-mail: mail@mhdsolicitors.com

MURRAY DONALD DRUMMOND COOK
Kinburn Castle St Andrews Fife KY16 9DR
Tel: 01334 477107 *Fax:* 01334 476862 *Dx:* 560996 ST ANDREWS
E-mail: mail@mddc.co.uk

PAGAN OSBORNE
106 South Street St Andrews Fife KY16 9QD
Tel: 01334 475001 *Fax:* 01334 476322 *Dx:* 560992 ST ANDREWS
E-mail: webenquiry@pagan.co.uk

ROLLO DAVIDSON & MCFARLANE
6 Bell Street St Andrews Fife KY16 9UX
Tel: 01334 477700 *Fax:* 01334 478282 *Dx:* 560991 ST ANDREWS
E-mail: standrews@rollos.co.uk

STEVENSTON

J D BANNATYNE & CAMPBELL
35 Boglemart Street Stevenston North Ayrshire KA20 3EL
Tel: 01294 463382 *Fax:* 01294 464229 *Dx:* 591008 SALTCOATS
E-mail: info@bannatynejdandcampbell.co.uk

STEWARTON

MAIR MATHESON
46 High Street Stewarton East Ayrshire KA3 5DB
Tel: 01560 482666 *Fax:* 01560 484666 *Dx:* KK22 KILMARNOCK
E-mail: reception@mairmatheson.co.uk

STIRLING

BARTON & HENDRY
28 & 39 Murray Place Stirling FK8 2DD
Tel: 01786 445441 *Fax:* 01786 445502
E-mail: info@bartonandhendry.co.uk

BELL & CRAIG
Albert House 4 Albert Place Dumbarton Road Stirling FK8 2QL
Tel: 01786 470444 *Fax:* 01786 447175

BLACKWOOD & CO
1 Melville Terrace Stirling FK8 2ND
Tel: 01786 464119 *Fax:* 01786 474225
E-mail: blackwoodlegal@btconnect.com

COMRIE POLLOCK LAW PARTNERSHIP
Viewfield House 8 Viewfield Place Stirling FK8 1NQ
Tel: 01786 461900 *Fax:* 01786 462550

VIRGIL M CRAWFORD
20 Viewfield Street Stirling FK8 1UA
Tel: 01786 464055 *Fax:* 01786 464052

DALLING
83 Barnton Street Stirling FK8 1HJ
Tel: 01786 448111 *Fax:* 01786 448222

HILL & ROBB
3 Pitt Terrace Stirling FK8 2EY
Tel: 01786 450985
E-mail: info@hillandrobb.co.uk

JARDINE DONALDSON
80 Port Street Stirling FK8 2LR
Tel: 01786 450366 *Fax:* 01786 450543
E-mail: stirling@jardinedonaldson.co.uk

KERR STIRLING LLP
10 Albert Place Stirling FK8 2QL
Tel: 01786 463414 *Fax:* 01786 451395 *Dx:* ST9 STIRLING
E-mail: enquiries@kerrstirling.co.uk

MAILERS
2a King Street Stirling FK8 1BA
Tel: 01786 450555 *Fax:* 01786 451353
E-mail: mail@mailers.co.uk

MATHIE MACLUCKIE
Wellington House Dumbarton Road Stirling FK8 2RW
Tel: 01786 475112 *Fax:* 01786 450451 *Dx:* ST11 STIRLING
E-mail: mail@mathiemacluckie.co.uk

MUIRHEAD BUCHANAN
8 Allan Park Stirling FK8 2QE
Tel: 01786 450944 *Fax:* 01786 450229
E-mail: info@muirbuch.co.uk

G W T MURPHY & CO
6 Viewfield Place Stirling FK8 1NQ
Tel: 01786 470060 *Fax:* 01786 450680
E-mail: gordon@gwtmurphy.co.uk

POLLOCK SOMERVILLE & CO
18b Maxwell Place Stirling FK8 1JU
Tel: 01786 449933 *Fax:* 01786 449777
E-mail: info@pollocksomerville.co.uk

STONEHAVEN

ABERDEIN CONSIDINE & CO
40 Allardice Street Stonehaven Aberdeenshire AB39 2BU
Tel: 01569 766166 *Fax:* 01569 766110 *Dx:* 521027 STONEHAVEN
E-mail: st@acandco.com

JAMES & GEORGE COLLIE
20 Ann Street Stonehaven Aberdeenshire AB39 2EN
Tel: 01569 763555 *Fax:* 01569 766548 *Dx:* AB43 ABERDEEN

CONNONS OF STONEHAVEN
50 Allardice Street Stonehaven Aberdeenshire AB39 2RA
Tel: 01569 762971 *Fax:* 01569 764125 *Dx:* 521020 STONEHAVEN
E-mail: info@connons.co.uk

RAEBURN CHRISTIE CLARK & WALLACE
1 Market Buildings Stonehaven Aberdeenshire AB39 2BY
Tel: 01569 762947 *Fax:* 01569 766702
E-mail: stonehaven@raeburns.co.uk

IAIN SMITH & CO
9 Market Square Stonehaven Aberdeenshire AB39 2BT
Tel: 01569 767778 *Fax:* 01569 766540
E-mail: ronald@iainsmith.com

STORNOWAY

ANDERSON MACARTHUR & CO
Old Bank of Scotland Buildings Stornoway Western Isles HS1 2BG
Tel: 01851 703356 *Fax:* 01851 702766
E-mail: legal@amac.co.uk

KEN MACDONALD & CO
9 Kenneth Street Stornoway Western Isles HS1 2DP
Tel: 01851 704040 *Fax:* 01851 705083
E-mail: enquiries@kenmacdonaldlawyers.co.uk

MACDONALD MACIVER & CO
20 Francis Street Stornoway Western Isles HS1 2NB
Tel: 01851 704343 *Fax:* 01851 706923
E-mail: macdmac@aol.com

STRANRAER

FERGUSON & CO
Clydesdale Bank Buildings 91 Hanover Street Stranraer Dumfries & Galloway DG9 7RS
Tel: 01776 702561 *Fax:* 01776 706272
E-mail: mailbox@ferguson-company.co.uk

HUNTER & MURRAY
25 Lewis Street Stranraer Dumfries & Galloway DG9 7LA
Tel: 01776 702581 *Fax:* 01776 702524 *Dx:* 581256 STRANRAER
E-mail: huntermurray@abamatthews.com

MCANDREW & CO
44 Hanover Street Stranraer Dumfries & Galloway DG9 7RP
Tel: 01776 704324 *Fax:* 01776 704329
E-mail: mcandrewandco@btconnect.com

NICOL HARVEY & PIERCE
31 Lewis Street Stranraer Dumfries & Galloway DG9 7AB
Tel: 01776 707111 *Fax:* 01776 706111
E-mail: info@nhpsolicitors.co.uk

RANKIN & AITKEN
4/6 South Strand Street Stranraer Dumfries & Galloway DG9 7JE
Tel: 01776 702336 *Fax:* 01776 706800 *Dx:* 581260 STRANRAER
E-mail: enq@rankinaitken.co.uk

STRATHAVEN

GEBBIE & WILSON
18 Common Green Strathaven South Lanarkshire ML10 6AG
Tel: 01357 520082 *Fax:* 01357 529477 *Dx:* 570200 STRATHAVEN
E-mail: mail@gebbiewilson.co.uk

JOHN JACKSON & DICK
3 Bridge Street Strathaven South Lanarkshire ML10 6AN
Tel: 01357 522959 *Fax:* 01357 522881 *Dx:* 570201 STRATHAVEN

STROMNESS

J E P ROBERTSON & SON
26 Victoria Street Stromness Orkney KW16 3AA
Tel: 01856 850232 *Fax:* 01856 851085
E-mail: enquiries@jeprobertson.co.uk

TAIN

MACKENZIE & CORMACK
20 Tower Street Tain Highland IV19 1DZ
Tel: 01862 892046 *Fax:* 01862 892715
E-mail: mail@tainlaw.co.uk

THORNHILL

POLLOCK & MCLEAN
1 West Morton Street Thornhill Dumfries & Galloway DG3 5NE
Tel: 01848 330207 *Fax:* 01848 331600

ROBERT WILSON & SON
109 Drumlanrig Street Thornhill Dumfries & Galloway DG3 5LX
Tel: 01848 330251 *Fax:* 01848 331633
E-mail: thornhill@robertwilsonandson.co.uk

THURSO

GEORGESONS
19 Traill Street Thurso Highland KW14 8EG
Tel: 01847 892225 *Fax:* 01847 892235

YOUNG ROBERTSON & CO
29 Traill Street Thurso Highland KW14 8EG
Tel: 01847 893247 *Fax:* 01847 896358
E-mail: property@youngrob.co.uk

TILLICOULTRY

WATERSRULE SOLICITORS
76-78 High Street Tillicoultry Clackmannanshire FK13 6AB
Tel: 01259 753330 *Fax:* 01259 753331
E-mail: info@watersrule.co.uk

TRANENT

GARDEN STIRLING BURNET
121 High Street Tranent East Lothian EH33 1LW
Tel: 01875 611616 *Fax:* 01875 612089 *Dx:* 541033 TRANENT
E-mail: tranent@gsbsolicitors.co.uk

ALEX LAFFERTY & CO
93 High Street Tranent East Lothian EH33 1LT
Tel: 01875 614059 *Fax:* 01875 611977
E-mail: laffertyalex@googlemail.com

MCKINNON FORBES
54 High Street Tranent East Lothian EH33 1HH
Tel: 01875 611211 *Fax:* 01875 612565 *Dx:* 541030 TRANENT
E-mail: info@mckinnonforbes.co.uk

TROON

MCSHERRY HALLIDAY DALE & MARSHALL
8 Academy Street Troon South Ayrshire KA10 6HS
Tel: 01292 313737 *Fax:* 01292 317856
E-mail: troon@mcsherryhalliday.co.uk

D W SHAW
20 West Portland Street Troon South Ayrshire KA10 6AB
Tel: 01292 312577 *Fax:* 01292 314186
E-mail: enquiries@dwshaw.co.uk

WADDELL & MACKINTOSH
29 Ayr Street Troon South Ayrshire KA10 6EB
Tel: 01292 314922 *Fax:* 01292 317422

36 West Portland Street Troon South Ayrshire KA10 6AB
Tel: 01292 312222 *Fax:* 01292 318090

TURRIFF

BROWN & MCRAE
10 High Street Turriff Aberdeenshire AB53 4DS
Tel: 01888 568950 *Fax:* 01888 563031
E-mail: property@brown-mcrae.co.uk

GRANT SMITH LAW PRACTICE
The Old Bank Buildings Balmellie Street Turriff Aberdeenshire AB53 4DW
Tel: 01888 562245 *Fax:* 01888 563590 *Dx:* 521395 TURRIFF

STEWART & WATSON
57-59 High Street Turriff Aberdeenshire AB53 4EL
Tel: 01888 563773 *Fax:* 01888 563227
E-mail: info@stewartwatson.co.uk

UDDINGSTON

D J FALLS & CO
16 Main Street Uddingston South Lanarkshire G71 7LS
Tel: 01698 810102 *Fax:* 01698 813725 *Dx:* 501051 UDDINGSTON
E-mail: dj.falls@blueyonder.co.uk

FRIELS
The Cross Main Street Uddingston South Lanarkshire G71 7ES
Tel: 01698 815114 *Fax:* 01698 810325

ULLAPOOL

MACLEOD & CO
26 Argyle Street Ullapool Highland IV26 2UB
Tel: 01854 612555 *Fax:* 01854 612210

WEST CALDER

STEWART WATT & CO
50 Main Street West Calder West Lothian EH55 8DR
Tel: 01506 872911 *Fax:* 01506 871630
E-mail: law@stewartwatt.co.uk

WEST KILBRIDE

JAS CAMPBELL & CO WS
85 Main Street West Kilbride North Ayrshire KA23 9AP
Tel: 01294 829599
E-mail: mail@jascampbell.co.uk

TAYLOR & HENDERSON
27 Ritchie Street West Kilbride North Ayrshire KA23 9AL
Tel: 01294 823888 *Fax:* 01294 823903
E-mail: mail@taylorandhenderson.co.uk

WESTHILL

ABERDEIN CONSIDINE & CO
14 Westhill Shopping Centre Westhill Aberdeenshire AB32 6RL
Tel: 01224 749444 *Fax:* 01224 749222 *Dx:* AB46 ABERDEEN
E-mail: wl@acandco.com

STORIE CRUDEN & SIMPSON
Unit 10 Westhill Shopping Centre Westhill Aberdeenshire AB32 6RL
Tel: 01224 740718 *Fax:* 01224 743986 *Dx:* AB12 ABERDEEN
E-mail: info@storiecs.co.uk

WHITBURN

CAESAR & HOWIE (IN ASSOC WITH WILSON & JARVIS)
32 West Main Street Whitburn West Lothian EH47 0QZ
Tel: 01506 741161 *Fax:* 01501 742001 *Dx:* 541061 WHITBURN
E-mail: enquiries@caesar-howie.co.uk

SNEDDON MORRISON
16 East Main Street Whitburn West Lothian EH47 0RB
Tel: 01501 740345 *Fax:* 01501 745440 *Dx:* 541062 WHITBURN
E-mail: law@sneddons-ssc.co.uk

WICK

GEORGESONS
22 Bridge Street Wick Highland KW1 4NG
Tel: 01955 606060 *Fax:* 01955 603016

YOUNG ROBERTSON & CO
21 Bridge Street Wick Highland KW1 4AJ
Tel: 01955 605151 *Fax:* 01955 602200
E-mail: wick@youngrob.co.uk

WISHAW

DOUGLAS BARR & CO
17 Main Street Wishaw North Lanarkshire ML2 7AF
Tel: 01698 350350 *Fax:* 01698 356742
E-mail: dbarrlaw@btinternet.com

FREELANDS
139 Main Street Wishaw North Lanarkshire ML2 7AU
Tel: 01698 355936 *Fax:* 01698 354100

LAVERTY & CO
15 Kirk Road Wishaw North Lanarkshire ML2 7BL
Tel: 01698 373731 *Fax:* 01698 373733

STEPHEN J MACBRIDE & CO
17 Main Street Wishaw North Lanarkshire ML2 7AF
Tel: 01698 350310 *Fax:* 01698 350288
E-mail: sandra@sjmacbride.co.uk

MCCAFFERTY & CO
118 Shieldmuir Street Craigneuk Wishaw North Lanarkshire ML2 7TH
Tel: 01698 355577 *Fax:* 01698 327241

MCGOVERN & CO
23 Caledonian Road Wishaw North Lanarkshire ML2 8AP
Tel: 01698 359550 *Fax:* 01698 376360

NESS GALLAGHER & CO
95 Stewarton Street Wishaw North Lanarkshire ML2 8AG
Tel: 01698 355525 *Fax:* 01698 357029
E-mail: mail@nessgallagher.co.uk

H K PAUL & CO
4 Hill Street Wishaw North Lanarkshire ML2 7AT
Tel: 01698 357225 *Fax:* 01698 351486

POMPHREYS
1 Kenilworth Avenue Town Centre Wishaw North Lanarkshire ML2 7LP
Tel: 01698 373365 *Fax:* 01698 356409

FIRMS, SCOTLAND – A-Z

1

1 MOVE
Bridge of Weir *p892* 01505 690033
Paisley *p904* 0141 889 8899

A

ABERDEIN CONSIDINE & CO
Aberdeen *p890* 01224 589589
p890 .... 01224 589700
Banchory *p891* ..... 01330 824646 / 824647
Dyce *p894* 01224 723737
Ellon *p896* 01358 721893
Inverurie *p901* 01467 621263
Kingswells *p902* 01224 741411
Peterhead *p905* 01779 475365
Stonehaven *p905* 01569 766166
Westhill *p906* 01224 749444

ADAIRS
Dumbarton *p893* 01389 767625

ADAMS WHYTE
Edinburgh *p894* 0131 225 8813
Livingston *p903* 01506 401999

ADIE HUNTER
Glasgow *p897* 0141 248 3828

AIKMAN RUSSELL & DUNLOP WS
Edinburgh *p894* 0131 226 5121

JEFFREY AITKEN
Glasgow *p897* 0141 221 5983

AITKEN NAIRN WS
Edinburgh *p894* 0131 556 6644

AITKENS THE FAMILY LAW SOLICITORS
Livingston *p903* 01506 417737

ALDER HOGG & CO
Kirkintilloch *p902* 0141 776 3350

ALEXANDER GEORGE & CO
Banff *p891* 01261 815678
Buckie *p892* 01542 831307

ALEXANDER JUBB & TAYLOR
Glasgow *p897* 0141 554 1016

SCOTT ALEXANDER
Montrose *p903* 01674 671477

A & J C ALLAN & CO
Falkirk *p897* 01324 621263

ALLAN BLACK & MCCASKIE
Elgin *p896* 01343 543355

ALLAN MCDOUGALL
Dalkeith *p893* 0131 663 7261
Edinburgh *p895* 0131 225 2121
Penicuik *p904* 01968 675694

MICHAEL S ALLAN
Aberdeen *p890* 01224 696968
Inverurie *p901* 01330 833224

ALLANS
Lerwick *p903* 01595 690749

ALLARDICE & CREEGAN
Dundee *p894* 01382 527777

ALLCOURT
Livingston *p903* 01506 443999

ALLEN & SHAW
Inverness *p901* 01463 225555

ALLINGHAM & CO
Edinburgh *p895* 0131 447 9341

ANDERSON & GOODLAD
Lerwick *p903* 01595 692297

ANDERSON BANKS
Balivanich *p891* 01870 602061
Oban *p904* 01631 563158

ANDERSON BEATON LAMOND
Perth *p904* 01738 639999

CHARLES & R B ANDERSON WS
Jedburgh *p902* 01835 863202

ANDERSON FYFE
Glasgow *p897* 0141 353 0035

ISABEL J ANDERSON WS
North Berwick *p904* 01620 895855

ANDERSON MACARTHUR & CO
Portree *p905* 01478 612197
Stornoway *p905* 01851 703356

RUTH ANDERSON & CO
Kilwinning *p902* 01294 551551

ANDERSON SHAW & GILBERT
Inverness *p901* 01463 236123

ANDERSON STRATHERN LLP
Edinburgh *p895* 0131 270 7700
p895 .... 0131 449 2833
Glasgow *p897* 0141 242 6060
Glasgow *p897* 0141 285 3800
Haddington *p901* 01620 822127

ANDERSONS LLP
Edinburgh *p895* 0131 524 7790
Glasgow *p897* 0141 248 6688

ANTONS
Buckie *p892* 01542 832148

ARBUTHNOTT & MCCLANACHAN
Edinburgh *p895* 0131 312 7276

ARCHIBALD CAMPBELL & HARLEY WS
Edinburgh *p895* 0131 220 3000

ARTHUR & CARMICHAEL
Dornoch *p893* 01862 810202

AUSTINS
Dalbeattie *p893* 01556 610259

B

BCKM
Edinburgh *p895* 0131 225 3456

BMK WILSON
Glasgow *p897* 0141 221 8004

BSW SOLICITORS LLP
Cowdenbeath *p893* 01383 515020

BAILLIE & REID
Glasgow *p897* 0141 429 1100

BAILLIE SPOWART
Glasgow *p897* 0141 585 2300

BAILLIES
Dundee *p894* 01382 202444

GAVIN BAIN & COMPANY
Aberdeen *p890* 01224 623040

BAIRD & CO
Cupar *p893* 01334 656644
Glenrothes *p900* 01592 759555
Kirkcaldy *p902* 01592 268608

GILLIAN BAKER FAMILY LAW
Blantyre *p892* 01698 820700

BALFOUR & MANSON
Edinburgh *p895* 0131 200 1200

BALLANTYNE & COPLAND
Motherwell *p904* 01698 266200

BANKS DEVLIN & CO
Paisley *p904* 0141 889 4949

J D BANNATYNE & CAMPBELL
Stevenston *p905* 01294 463382

BANNATYNE KIRKWOOD FRANCE & CO
Glasgow *p897* 0141 221 6020

BANNERMAN BURKE
Galashiels *p897* 01896 750350
Hawick *p901* 01450 372750
Kelso *p902* 01573 229760

BANSKI & CO
Laurencekirk *p903* 01561 377245

BARCLAY & CO
Glasgow *p897* 0141 946 3555

KIM BARCLAY
Dundee *p894* 01382 228722

BARNETTS
Kilmarnock *p902* 01563 522137

DOUGLAS BARR & CO
Wishaw *p906* 01698 350350

BARROWMANS
Cumbernauld *p893* 01236 731911

J C BARTLETT & CO
Dingwall *p893* 01349 867100

BARTON & HENDRY
Cumbernauld *p893* 01236 735466
Stirling *p905* 01786 445441

THO & J W BARTY
Dunblane *p893* 01786 822296

NIGEL BEAUMONT & CO
Edinburgh *p895* 0131 557 3565

BELL & CO
Kilmarnock *p902* 01563 535545

BELL & CRAIG
Stirling *p905* 01786 470444

BELL RUSSELL & CO
Airdrie *p890* 01236 764781

BELL SOLICITORS
Bellshill *p892* 01698 749977

BELMONTE & CO
Edinburgh *p895* 0131 229 5323
p895 .... 0131 661 9779

BELTRAMI & CO
Glasgow *p897* 0141 429 2262

BERRY POGGI & CO
Cumbernauld *p893* 0870 243 0665

ADAM BEVAN & CO
Edinburgh *p895* 0131 467 6767

BEVERIDGE & KELLAS
Edinburgh *p895* 0131 554 6321

BEVERIDGE HERD & SANDILANDS WS
Glenrothes *p900* 01592 752080
Kirkcaldy *p902* 01592 261616

BEVERIDGE PHILP & ROSS
Edinburgh *p895* 0131 554 6244

BIGGART BAILLIE
Edinburgh *p895* 0131 226 5541
Glasgow *p897* 0141 228 8000

BILKUS & BOYLE
Glasgow *p897* 0141 882 1667
p897 .... 0141 882 3221
Paisley *p904* 0141 889 1500

BIRD SEMPLE
Glasgow *p897* 0141 304 3434

BLACK & GUILD
Kirkcaldy *p902* 01592 261624

BLACK HAY & CO
Ayr *p891* 01292 268988
Prestwick *p905* 01292 477235

BLACKADDER & MCMONAGLE
Falkirk *p897* 01324 612999

BLACKADDERS
Arbroath *p891* 01241 872087
Dundee *p894* 01382 229222
Forfar *p897* 01307 461234

BLACKLOCKS
Edinburgh *p895* 0131 555 7500

BLACKWOOD & CO
Kilmarnock *p902* 0844 811 4150
Stirling *p905* 01786 464119

BLACKWOOD & SMITH WS
Peebles *p904* 01721 720131

BLACKWOOD CRATE & COMPANY
Dalry *p893* 01294 832108

COLIN BLAIKIE & CO
Edinburgh *p895* 0131 557 1867

BLAIR & BRYDEN
Clydebank *p892* 0141 952 3322
Dunoon *p894* 01369 704037
Greenock *p900* 01475 888777
Port Glasgow *p905* 01475 745117

BLAIR CADELL SOLICITORS
Edinburgh *p895* 0131 337 1800
p895 .... 0131 555 5800

THOMAS BLAIR & SON
Dunfermline *p894* 01383 724015

BLANEY CARNAN
Glasgow *p897* 0141 248 8111

BONAR MACKENZIE WS
Edinburgh *p895* 0131 225 8371

BONNAR & CO
Airdrie *p890* 0800 163978
Dunfermline *p894* 0800 694 0209
Edinburgh *p895* 0800 073 0065

BONNAR LAW
East Kilbride *p894* 01355 268866

BOWMAN SCOTTISH LAWYERS
Dundee *p894* 01382 322267
Forfar *p897* 01307 464088

J & A B BOYD
Ayr *p891* 01292 265073

BOYLE SHAUGHNESSY
Glasgow *p897* 0141 248 1888
p897 .... 0141 636 5115

BOYLE'S
Dundee *p894* 01382 221214
Forfar *p897* 01307 475320

T G BRADSHAW & CO
Bellshill *p892* 01698 747171

BRADY LEGAL
Glenrothes *p900* 01592 623980

BRAIDWOODS
Dumfries *p893* 01387 257272

BRAZENALL & ORR
Dumfries *p893* 01387 255695

BREADY & CO
Glasgow *p897* 0141 334 2265

BRECHIN TINDAL OATTS
Edinburgh *p895* 0131 222 2939
Glasgow *p897* 0141 221 8012

A & E A BRODIE
Banff *p891* 01261 812681

BRODIES LLP
Edinburgh *p895* 0131 228 3777

BROOKE & BROWN WS
Dunbar *p893* 01368 862746

FRASER BROOKS & CO WS
Edinburgh *p895* 0131 225 6226

BROPHY & COMPANY
Falkirk *p897* 01324 635035

BROWN & CO
Edinburgh *p895* 0131 228 9993
Glasgow *p897* 0141 353 3354

ALEX BROWN & CO
Inverness *p901* 01463 243450

8

BROWN & GILMOUR
Burntisland p892 01592 873389

BROWN & MCRAE
Fraserburgh p897 01346 515797
Turriff p906 01888 568950

JACK BROWN & COMPANY
Dundee p894 01382 200411

KENNETH F BROWN
Edinburgh p895 0131 556 7525

M J BROWN SON & CO
Edinburgh p895 0131 332 1200

MATTHEW BROWN
Irvine p902 01294 273721

MICHAEL A BROWN
Dundee p894 01382 204242

BROWN'S
Glasgow p897 0141 781 0000

R BRUCE & CO
Arbroath p891 01241 430660
Forfar p897 01307 460666
Montrose p903 01674 675534

W & A S BRUCE
Burntisland p892 01592 873501
Dunfermline p894 01383 738000
Kirkcaldy p902 01592 204774

BRUNTON MILLER
Glasgow p897 0141 337 1199
Helensburgh p901 01436 675454

JOHN A BRYAN & CO
Hamilton p901 01698 281535

BUCHANAN BURTON
East Kilbride p894 01355 249228

BUCHANAN CAMPBELL
Glasgow p897 0141 572 0770

BUCHANAN DICKSON FRAME
Paisley p904 0141 848 0303

BUCHANAN MACLEOD
Glasgow p897 0141 221 4440

BURN & MCGREGOR
Aberdeen p890 01224 639660

BURNESS
Edinburgh p895 0131 473 6000
Glasgow p897 0141 248 4933

BURNETT & COMPANY
Aberdeen p890 01224 648797

BURNETT & REID
Aberdeen p890 01224 644333

T S H BURNS & SON
Dingwall p893 01349 863222

C

C & N DEFENCE
Edinburgh p895 0131 202 9233

CCW LLP
Dunfermline p894 0845 223 3001
Edinburgh p895 0845 223 3001

CMS CAMERON MCKENNA
Aberdeen p890 01224 622002
Edinburgh p895 0131 220 7676

CAESAR & HOWIE (IN ASSOC WITH WILSON & JARVIS)
Alloa p891 01506 815900
Bathgate p892 01506 815900
Falkirk p897 01324 628332
Livingston p903 01506 435306
Whitburn p906 01506 741161

CAIRD & VAUGHAN
Dundee p894 01382 229399

CAIRNS BROWN
Alexandria p891 01389 756979
Dumbarton p893 01389 742777

CALDERS
Dundee p894 01382 224391

CALLAN & CO
Muirhead p904 0141 779 2114

HECTOR CAMERON
Glasgow p897 0141 337 6363

J K CAMERON
Glasgow p897 0141 221 4787

CAMERON PINKERTON & CO
Paisley p904 0141 887 5211

CAMPBELL & CO
Glasgow p897 0141 221 5992

CAMPBELL & MEECHAN
Glasgow p898 0141 248 8898

CAMPBELL BOATH
Dundee p894 01382 200110

BRADLEY CAMPBELL & CO
Greenock p900 01475 726363

CAMPBELL CONNON
Aberdeen p890 01224 585585
Aboyne p890 01339 886732

CAMPBELL D JOSS
Glasgow p898 0141 945 5533

JAS CAMPBELL & CO WS
Ardrossan p891 01294 464131
Brodick p892 01770 302027
Saltcoats p905 01294 464301
West Kilbride p906 01294 829599

PATRICK CAMPBELL & CO
Glasgow p898 0141 423 2222

R B CAMPBELL & CO
Ayr p891 01292 261125

CAMPBELL RIDDELL BREEZE PATERSON
Giffnock p897 0141 638 7405
Glasgow p898 0141 204 2040
Milngavie p903 0141 956 5454

CAMPBELL SIEVEWRIGHT & CO
Glasgow p898 0141 422 2642
Hamilton p901 01698 284994
Lanark p903 01555 895123

CAMPBELL SMITH WS (INC GRAY MUIRHEAD WS)
Edinburgh p895 0131 556 3737

CAMPBELLS
Edinburgh p895 0131 661 7236

CANNONS
Glasgow p898 0141 204 5115

JAMES M CARMICHAEL
Glasgow p898 0141 553 1717

CARR & CO
Cambuslang p892 0141 641 2912 / 8346
Glasgow p898 0141 248 2999
p898 0141 558 0234
p898 0141 773 2145
Muirhead p904 0141 779 4466

CARR BERMAN CRICHTON
Rutherglen p905 0141 647 9851

CARRICK ROBB
Kilbirnie p902 01505 682408

JOHN CARROLL & CO
Glasgow p898 0141 429 0666

CARRUTHERS CURDIE STURROCK & CO
Kilmarnock p902 01563 572727

CARRUTHERS GEMMILL (INC J C MUIR & BARR)
Glasgow p898 0141 333 0033

CARTY'S
Airdrie p890 01236 761127
Blantyre p892 01698 820896
Hamilton p901 01698 285432
Larkhall p903 01698 885888

CASSELS BOYLE
Glasgow p898 0141 332 1856

CENTRAL CRIMINAL LAWYERS
Livingston p903 01506 416999

THE CHAMBER PRACTICE
Dundee p894 01382 203000

P H CLANCY & CO
Edinburgh p895 0131 337 7771

CLAPHAMS
Glasgow p898 0141 620 0800

CLARK BOYLE & CO
Glasgow p898 0141 227 2200

J D CLARK & ALLAN
Duns p894 01361 882501

CLYDE DEFENCE LAWYERS
Clydebank p892 0141 951 2211
Dumbarton p893 01389 730666

ADAM COCHRAN
Aberdeen p890 01224 588913

COCKBURN & CO
Bridge of Weir p892 01505 690500

COCKBURNS
Elgin p896 01343 542684

MATTHEW COHEN & ASSOCIATES
Aberdeen p890 01224 433301

COLLIE & CO
Galashiels p897 01896 755466
Selkirk p905 01750 23868

JAMES & GEORGE COLLIE
Aberdeen p890 01224 581581
Stonehaven p905 01569 763555

RORY COLLINS
Edinburgh p895 0131 557 0691

COLVIN HOUSTON & COMPANY LLP
Largs p903 01475 672003

COMRIE POLLOCK LAW PARTNERSHIP
Stirling p905 01786 461900

CONDIES
Perth p904 01738 440088

CONNELL & CONNELL WS
Edinburgh p895 0131 556 2993

CONNELLY & YEOMAN
Arbroath p891 01241 434200

CONNONS OF STONEHAVEN
Stonehaven p905 01569 762971

CONNOR MALCOLM
Edinburgh p895 0131 557 3188

CONROY MCINNES
Glasgow p898 0141 616 6622
p898 0141 770 8777

CONVEYANCING DIRECT
Glasgow p898 0141 420 5040

THE CONVEYANCING PRACTICE
Broxburn p892 01506 863949

COOK STEVENSON & CO
Greenock p900 01475 722100

CORNILLON CRAIG & CO
Edinburgh p895 0131 225 4356

CORRIES (SCOTLAND)
Glasgow p898 0845 612 4488

CORRIGALL BLACK
Dunoon p894 01369 702941

COWAN & CO
Glasgow p898 0141 221 1803

CRAIGENS
Aberdeen p890 01224 588295

CRAWFORD MASON & CO
Blantyre p892 01698 821999

VIRGIL M CRAWFORD
Stirling p905 01786 464055

CRAXTON & GRANT
Bridge of Weir p892 01505 610612

CRIGGIES
Lanark p903 01555 662674

CROWN LAW PRACTICE
Inverness p901 01463 667850

THE CRUICKSHANK LAW PRACTICE
Elgin p896 01343 544466

CULLEN KILSHAW
Galashiels p897 01896 758311
Melrose p903 01896 822177
p903 01896 822796
Peebles p904 01721 723999

CULLEY & MCALPINE
Perth p904 01738 502704

ADAM CURRIE
Irvine p902 01294 273735

CURRIE GILMOUR & CO
Edinburgh p895 0131 229 2077

CURRIE JOHNSTON & CO
Livingston p903 01506 412377

D

DLA PIPER SCOTLAND LLP
Edinburgh p895 0870 011 1111
Glasgow p898 0870 011 1111

DMD LAW
Edinburgh p895 0131 316 4666

MIKE DAILLY
Glasgow p898 0141 440 2503

DALLAS MCMILLAN
Glasgow p898 0141 333 6750

DALLING
Stirling p905 01786 448111

ALFRED W H DALLMAN
Glasgow p898 0141 942 8537

DAVIDSON & SHIRLEY
Lanark p903 01555 662576

DAVIDSON CHALMERS LLP
Edinburgh p895 0131 625 9191

DAVIDSON SCOTT & CO
Inverness p901 01463 231066

DAVIDSONS SOLICITORS WS
Edinburgh p895 0131 558 9999

JOHN DAVIE & COMPANY
Alford p891 01224 656356

LESLIE DEANS & CO
Edinburgh p895 0131 667 1900
South Queensferry p905 0131 331 3560

DEWAR SPENCE
Leven p903 01333 425200

DICKSON MINTO WS
Edinburgh p895 0131 225 4455

DICKSONS
Glasgow p898 0141 248 4448

DIGBY BROWN
Dundee p894 0845 273 2323
Edinburgh p895 0845 273 2323
Glasgow p898 0845 273 2323
Glenrothes p900 0845 273 2323

DONALDSON & HENDERSON
Nairn p904 01667 453395

DONALDSON ALEXANDER RUSSELL & HADDOW
Glasgow p898 0141 331 1333

DOONAN MCCAIG & CO
Glasgow p898 0141 552 6600

DOUGHTYS WS
Ayton p891 01890 781209

DOWLE SMITH & RUTHERFORD
Lerwick p903 01595 695583

DOYLE & CO
Edinburgh p895 0131 557 2333

JACQUELINE DOYLE & CO
Glasgow p898 0141 548 1000

DREVER & HEDDLE
Kirkwall p902 01856 872216

DRUMCHAPEL LAW AND MONEY ADVICE CENTRE
Glasgow p898 0141 944 0507

DRUMMOND MILLER WS
Bathgate p892 01506 656645
Dalkeith p893 0131 663 9568
Dunfermline p894 01383 624244
Edinburgh p895 0131 226 5151
Glasgow p898 0141 332 0086
Musselburgh p904 0131 665 7393

ROBERT F DUFF & CO
Largs p903 01475 673663

MARTIN DUFFY
Kilmarnock p902 01563 528580

DUFFY TOSHNER & CO
Cambuslang p892 0141 641 8081

DUNCAN & WALLACE SSC
Edinburgh p895 0131 467 7550

T DUNCAN & CO
Montrose p903 01674 672533

DUNDAS & WILSON CS
Edinburgh p895 0131 228 8000
Glasgow p898 0141 222 2200

DUNIPACE BROWN
Cumbernauld p893 01236 453004

DUNLOP ALLEN & CO
Glasgow p898 0141 552 1726

D & J DUNLOP
Ayr p891 01292 264091

DUTHIE WARD
Aberdeen p890 01224 621622

DYKES GLASS & CO
Glasgow p898 0141 332 2794

T J & W A DYKES
Hamilton p901 01698 282726

E

EDINBURGH LAW
Edinburgh p895 0131 220 6600

EDINGTON & COMPANY
Galashiels p897 01896 756161

ELLIOT & CO WS
Blairgowrie p892 01250 870840
Perth p904 01738 638246

ESSLEMONT CAMERON GAULD
Aberdeen p890 01224 632244

F

FAIRBAIRNS
Edinburgh p895 0131 226 5955

D J FALLS & CO
Uddingston p906 01698 810102

PETER G FARRELL
Glasgow p898 0141 552 0033
p898 0141 950 2961

FERGUSON & CO
Stranraer p906 01776 702561

FERGUSON & WILL
Brechin p892 01356 622289

FERGUSON & WILSON
Inverness p901 01463 212986

CHARLES FERGUSON & CO
Hamilton p901 01698 285885

FERGUSON MACSWEEN & STEWART
Kyle of Lochalsh p903 01599 534500
Portree p905 01478 612991

RAYMOND FERGUSON & CO
Hamilton *p901* 01698 891623

ROBERT FERGUSON & SONS
Hamilton *p901* 01698 282551

FIELDING MCLEAN & CO
Glasgow *p898* 0141 959 1674

FINLAY MACRAE
Dundee *p894* 01382 228288

FINLAYSON WISE
Glasgow *p898* 0141 556 6651
p898 .... 0141 763 1337

FITZPATRICK & CO
Glasgow *p898* 0141 445 3355

S P FLANAGAN
Bishopbriggs *p892* 0141 563 0553

FLEETWOOD & ROBB
Inverness *p901* 01463 226232

FLEMING & REID
Glasgow *p898* 0141 331 1144

FLYNN & CO
Dundee *p894* 01382 223145

FOGGO MACINNES HINGSTON
Dingwall *p893* 01349 867200

FORDS
Kirkcaldy *p902* 01592 640630

FORREST CAMPBELL & ANDERSON
Carluke *p892* 01555 771383

FORRESTER OGILVIE & CO
Edinburgh *p895* 0131 228 2303

FRANCHI FINNIESTON
Glasgow *p898* 0141 226 3000

FRANKS MACADAM BROWN
Edinburgh *p895* 0131 718 6060

FRASER & CO
Inverness *p901* 01463 229917

FRASER & MULLIGAN
Aberdeen *p890* 01224 646428

FRAZER COOGANS
Ayr *p891* 01292 280499

FREDERICK & CO
Glasgow *p898* 0141 221 5575

FREELANDS
Motherwell *p904* 01698 352600
Wishaw *p906* 01698 355936

JIM FRIEL & CO
Glasgow *p898* 0141 420 1234

FRIELS
Coatbridge *p892* 01236 421136
Uddingston *p906* 01698 815114

FYFE & MURRAY
Greenock *p900* 01475 721251

FYFE IRELAND WS
Edinburgh *p895* 0131 220 5100

G

GAIR & GIBSON (INC K J DOUGLAS & CO)
Falkirk *p897* 01324 623928

GALLACHER & CO
Kirkintilloch *p902* 0141 776 1111

GALLEN & CO
Glasgow *p898* 0141 420 8250
p898 .... 0141 445 2949
p898 .... 0141 880 7148

GARDEN STIRLING BURNET
Dunbar *p893* 01368 862376
Haddington *p901* 01620 824996
Tranent *p906* 01875 611616

GATELEY LLP
Edinburgh *p895* 0131 228 2400

GEBBIE & WILSON
Strathaven *p906* 01357 520082

LINDA GEORGE FAMILY LAW
Hamilton *p901* 01698 768857

GEORGE STREET LAW
Dingwall *p893* 01349 866777

GEORGESONS
Thurso *p906* 01847 892225
Wick *p906* 01955 606060

WALTER GERRARD & CO
Macduff *p903* 01261 832491

GIBSON & KENNEDY
Falkirk *p897* 01324 622741

GIBSON & SPEARS DOW & SON
Kirkcaldy *p902* 01592 264782

GIBSON KERR & CO
Edinburgh *p895* 0131 225 7558

ANDREW T GILBERTSON
Dalkeith *p893* 0131 660 9888

JOHN W GILBERTSON
Glenrothes *p900* 01592 759557

GILDEAS
Edinburgh *p895* 0845 051 0810
Glasgow *p898* 0845 051 0810

GILFEDDER & MCINNES
Edinburgh *p895* 0131 554 3550

GILLESPIE GIFFORD & BROWN
Castle Douglas *p892* 01556 503744
Dalbeattie *p893* 01556 611247
Dumfries *p893* 01387 255351
Kirkcudbright *p902* 01557 330539

J S B GILLESPIE & CO
Larbert *p903* 01324 553207

GILLESPIE MACANDREW
Edinburgh *p895* 0131 225 1677

J IAN GILLIES
Ayr *p891* 01292 288860

DOUGLAS GILMOUR & SON
Selkirk *p905* 01750 20271

GLEESON MCCAFFERTY
Glenrothes *p900* 01592 611660

GOLDSMITH & HUGHES
East Kilbride *p894* 01355 260602

GAIL GOODFELLOW & CO
Aberdeen *p890* 01224 878417

ALASTAIR J GORDON WS
Dollar *p893* 01259 740007

W & J S GORDON
Forfar *p897* 01307 462188

GORRIE & DAVIDSON
Dunfermline *p894* 01383 723618

IAIN G GOW
Bearsden *p892* 0141 943 0536

JACK GOWANS & MARC DICKSON
Inverness *p901* 01463 710677

GRADY & CO
Glasgow *p898* 0141 221 5000

GRAHAM & FINLAYSON WS
Crieff *p893* 01764 652224

GRANT & WYLIE
Glasgow *p898* 0141 221 1035

GRANT BROWN LINDSAY
Glasgow *p898* 0141 572 1910

JACK GRANT & CO
Motherwell *p904* 01698 254636

GRAY & CO
Glasgow *p898* 0141 946 7777

GRAY & CONNOCHIE
Aberdeen *p890* 01224 649101
p890 .... 01224 823282

GRAY & GRAY
Ellon *p896* 01358 724455
Peterhead *p905* 01779 480222

LESLEY A GRAY
Edinburgh *p895* 01620 843872

MARTIN GRAY & CO
Gorebridge *p900* 01875 821960

LLOYD GREEN & CO
Glasgow *p898* 0141 353 8700

KENNETH M GREENER
Larkhall *p903* 01698 793366

GRIEVE GRIERSON MOODIE & WALKER
Dumfries *p893* 01387 266250

GRIGOR & YOUNG
Elgin *p896* 01343 544077

GRIGOR HALES
Edinburgh *p895* 0131 313 5556

JAS S GROSSET
Kirkcaldy *p902* 01592 205816
Leven *p903* 01333 426023

GUARINO & THOMSON
East Kilbride *p894* 01355 263848

GUILD & GUILD WS
Edinburgh *p895* 0131 225 9155

JAMES GUTHRIE & CO
Kilmarnock *p902* 01563 525155

H

HBM SAYERS
Edinburgh *p895* 0131 225 9855
Glasgow *p898* 0141 353 2121
p898 .... 0141 621 1816
p898 .... 0141 632 2248
p898 .... 0141 649 2020

HADDEN RANKIN
Edinburgh *p895* 0131 220 5241

HADDON & TURNBULL
Hawick *p901* 01450 372336

ANDREW HADDON & CROWE WS
Hawick *p901* 01450 372738

HALL & HAUGHEY
Glasgow *p898* 0141 418 0505

HAMILTON BURNS & COMPANY
Glasgow *p898* 0141 429 0600

DUNCAN HAMILTON & CO WS
Edinburgh *p895* 0131 226 3199

HAMILTON ROSS
Airdrie *p890* 01236 627627

HANN & CO
Annan *p891* 01461 203836

HANNAY FRASER & CO
Glasgow *p898* 0141 221 1381
Rothesay *p905* 01700 503112

HARDING & CO
Glasgow *p898* 0141 552 8880

HARDY MACPHAIL
Glasgow *p898* 0141 204 0841

HARLEY & CO SSC
Edinburgh *p895* 0131 624 9839

HARPER MACLEOD
Edinburgh *p895* 0131 247 2500
Glasgow *p898* 0141 221 8888
p898 .... 0845 878 4504
Inverness *p901* 01463 798777

HARPER ROBERTSON & SHANNON
Annan *p891* 01461 203418

EWAN HARRIS & CO
Dornoch *p893* 01862 810686

ALASTAIR HART & CO
Aberdeen *p890* 01224 310600
p890 .... 01224 784855

HART SMITH & CO
Glasgow *p898* 0141 339 5252

HARTER & CO
Glasgow *p898* 0141 427 0901

HASTIES
Glasgow *p898* 0141 332 1454

HASTINGS & CO
Kelso *p902* 01573 226999

HAY CASSELS
Hamilton *p901* 01698 284844

HENDERSON & CO
Edinburgh *p895* 0131 477 3511

HENDERSON & MACKAY
Lockerbie *p903* 01576 202137

JOHN HENDERSON & SONS
Dumfries *p893* 01387 739000

HENNESSY BOWIE & CO
Bishopbriggs *p892* 0141 762 4040

CHARLES HENNESSY & CO
Glasgow *p898* 0141 332 6442

HEPWORTH & CO
Cambuslang *p892* 0141 641 0089

LYNN HERBERT & CO
Leven *p903* 01333 429007

HEWATS
Castle Douglas *p892* 01556 502391

HIGGINS MORLEDGE & LITTERICK
Alloa *p891* 01259 725922

HILL & ROBB
Stirling *p905* 01786 450985

R & J M HILL BROWN & CO
Glasgow *p898* 0141 332 3265

HISLOP NOTARIES
Glasgow *p898* 0141 221 5955

HODGE SOLICITORS
Blairgowrie *p892* 01250 874441

HOLMES MACKILLOP
Glasgow *p898* 0141 226 4942
Johnstone *p902* 01505 328271

MICHAEL HORSMAN & CO
Aberdeen *p890* 01224 633333

HOUGHTON MELVIN SMITH & CO
Aberdeen *p890* 01224 641555

HOWAT ASSOCIATES
Mauchline *p903* 01290 553055

HUGHES DOWDALL
Glasgow *p898* 0141 240 7020
Kirkintilloch *p902* 0141 776 7104

J C HUGHES & CO
Glasgow *p898* 0141 550 8080
p898 .... 0141 647 0700
p898 .... 0141 778 2468
p898 .... 0141 778 5585

HUNTER & CO
Glasgow *p898* 0141 334 4759

HUNTER & MURRAY
Stranraer *p906* 01776 702581

HUNTER & ROBERTSON
Paisley *p904* 0141 889 3196

HUNTER BURNS & OGG
Dunfermline *p894* 01383 725906

NEIL C HUNTER
Brechin *p892* 0845 108 4484

R D HUNTER & CO
Cumnock *p893* 01290 421185

HUNTERS RESIDENTIAL
Edinburgh *p895* 0131 447 4747

ALEX HUTCHEON & CO
Aberdeen *p890* 01224 623400

HUTCHISON MCLEAN
Falkirk *p897* 01324 633000

I

MICHAEL INKSTER & CO
Lerwick *p903* 01595 696901

INKSTERS
Glasgow *p898* 0141 229 0880

INNES & MACKAY
Inverness *p901* 01463 232273

INNES JOHNSTON & CO
Glenrothes *p900* 01592 757114
Kirkcaldy *p902* 01592 263455
Leven *p903* 01333 429320

INTERNATIONAL & DOMESTIC LAW PRACTICE
Glasgow *p898* 0141 942 4455

INVERNESS LEGAL SERVICES FOR CRIMINAL ADVOCACY
Inverness *p901* 01463 229981

A & S IRELAND
Glasgow *p898* 0141 227 8200
Newton Mearns *p904* 0141 639 2277

FRANK IRVINE
Glasgow *p898* 0141 773 2111

JAMES IRVINE
Irvine *p902* 01294 276116

IRVING GEDDES
Crieff *p893* 01764 653771

IRWIN MITCHELL LLP
Glasgow *p898* 0141 300 4300

J

JACKSON & COMPANY SSC
Leven *p903* 01333 422330

JAIN NEIL & RUDDY
Glasgow *p899* 0141 221 8778

JAMESON & MACKAY
Auchterarder *p891* 01764 663830
Perth *p904* 01738 631666

JARDINE DONALDSON
Alloa *p891* 01259 724411
Stirling *p905* 01786 450366

ANIKA JETHWA & CO
Dundee *p894* 01382 223399

JOHN JACKSON & DICK
Hamilton *p901* 01698 281747
Strathaven *p906* 01357 522959

DAVID JOHNSON & CO
Edinburgh *p895* 0131 622 9222

HAROLD W JOSEPH
Glasgow *p899* 0141 420 1896

K

KW LAW
Bathgate *p892* 01506 635533
Livingston *p903* 01506 415333

D P B KANE & CO
Kilbarchan *p902* 01505 704986

BRYAN KEENAN & CO
Aberdeen *p890* 01224 638996
p890 .... 01224 648080

G KEENAN & CO
Greenock *p901* 01475 732122

THE KELLAS PARTNERSHIP
Inverurie *p901* 01467 627300

KELLY & CO
Glasgow *p899* 0141 554 4141

AUSTIN KELLY & CO
Irvine *p902* 01294 275215

KENNEDY & CO
Greenock *p901* 01475 888830
Port Glasgow *p905* 01475 741188

For information regarding Charities please consult Section 17

ALLAN KERR
Kilmarnock p902 .... 01563 571571

KERR BARRIE
Glasgow p899 .... 0141 221 6844

THE ROBERT KERR PARTNERSHIP
Paisley p904 .... 0141 889 6458

KERR STIRLING LLP
Stirling p905 .... 01786 463414

KILPATRICK & WALKER
Ayr p891 .... 01292 618585

DAVID KINLOCH & CO
Glasgow p899 .... 0141 336 3000

KIPPEN CAMPBELL WS
Perth p904 .... 01738 635353

KIRKLANDS
Perth p904 .... 01738 442299

L

ALEX LAFFERTY & CO
Tranent p906 .... 01875 614059

AUSTIN LAFFERTY LAW
East Kilbride p894 .... 01355 263777
Giffnock p897 .... 0141 621 2212

LAMBERT & CO
Ayr p891 .... 01292 282811
Girvan p897 .... 01465 715434

LAMBIE LAW PARTNERSHIP
Glasgow p899 .... 0141 631 2412
p899 .... 0141 959 7000

LAMONTS
Ayr p891 .... 01292 262266

B J LANIGAN & CO
Glasgow p899 .... 0141 944 0671

LANIGAN MEECHAN & CO
Glasgow p899 .... 0141 557 0111

LATHAM & CO
Dumfries p893 .... 01387 252888

LAURIE & CO
Aberdeen p890 .... 01224 645085

LAVERTY & CO
Wishaw p906 .... 01698 373731

LAVERY SMITH & CO
Glasgow p899 .... 0141 336 4446
p899 .... 0141 638 2141

LAWFORD KIDD
Edinburgh p895 .... 0800 027 1480

LAWRIE JACKSON
Glasgow p899 .... 0141 248 1111

LAWSON COULL & DUNCAN
Dundee p894 .... 01382 227555

LAWSON RUSSELL & CO
Prestwick p905 .... 01292 478487

LEDINGHAM CHALMERS
Aberdeen p890 .... 01224 408408
Edinburgh p895 .... 0131 200 1000
Inverness p901 .... 01463 667400

LEFEVRE LITIGATION
Aberdeen p890 .... 01224 657657

LEONARDS
Hamilton p901 .... 01698 457313

LEVY & MCRAE
Glasgow p899 .... 0141 307 2311

LIDDLE & ANDERSON
Bo'ness p892 .... 01506 822727

A J LINDEN & CO
Coatbridge p892 .... 01236 449921

LINDSAY
Dumfries p893 .... 01387 259236

LINDSAY DUNCAN & BLACK
Edinburgh p895 .... 0131 225 2354

LINDSAYS
Edinburgh p895 .... 0131 229 1212
Glasgow p899 .... 0141 221 6551
Jedburgh p902 .... 01835 862391
North Berwick p904 .... 01620 893481

THE LINTS PARTNERSHIP
Edinburgh p895 .... 0131 555 4100

LIVINGSTONE BROWN
Glasgow p899 .... 0141 429 8166
p899 .... 0141 778 9657

RICHARD J LOBJOIE & CO
Glasgow p899 .... 0141 221 7584

GEORGE S LOCKHART
Ayr p891 .... 01292 441127

N S LOCKHART
Kilmarnock p902 .... 01563 531424

LOCKHARTS
Ayr p891 .... 01292 265045

R A LOGAN & CO
Cumnock p893 .... 01290 424566

MICHAEL LOTT
Motherwell p904 .... 01698 252331

LOW BEATON RICHMOND
Glasgow p899 .... 0141 221 8931
p899 .... 0141 339 8442
Largs p903 .... 01475 674576

LOWS ORKNEY
Kirkwall p902 .... 01856 873151

LYNCH & CO
Glasgow p899 .... 0141 427 6162
p899 .... 0141 649 9552

M

MFY PARTNERSHIP
Airdrie p891 .... 01236 607180

MSM SOLICITORS
Glasgow p899 .... 0141 554 8111
Paisley p904 .... 0141 889 6244

MTM DEFENCE LAWYERS
Falkirk p897 .... 01324 633221

MY LAWYERS
Alexandria p891 .... 01389 755235

MCAFEE
Airdrie p891 .... 01236 755339
Coatbridge p892 .... 01236 423437

MACALLANS
East Kilbride p894 .... 01355 261361
Rutherglen p905 .... 0141 613 1787

MCALLISTER & MCKECHNIE
Paisley p904 .... 0141 887 8961

MCANDREW & CO
Stranraer p906 .... 01776 704324

MACANDREW & JENKINS WS
Inverness p901 .... 01463 723500

MCARDLE
Glasgow p899 .... 0141 810 1001

MACARTHUR & CO
Inverness p901 .... 01463 234445

MCARTHUR STANTON
Dumbarton p893 .... 01389 762266
Helensburgh p901 .... 01436 672212

MACARTHUR STEWART
Fort William p897 .... 01397 702455
Lochgilphead p903 .... 01546 602424
Oban p904 .... 01631 562215

MCAULEY MCCARTHY & CO
Glasgow p899 .... 0141 427 7150
Paisley p904 .... 0141 561 7779
Renfrew p905 .... 0141 561 4449

MACBETH CURRIE
Dunfermline p894 .... 01383 731011
Edinburgh p895 .... 0131 226 5066
Kinross p902 .... 01577 863424

STEPHEN J MACBRIDE & CO
Wishaw p906 .... 01698 350310

ALEXANDER MCBURNEY
Glasgow p899 .... 0141 576 4808

MCCAFFERTY & CO
Wishaw p906 .... 01698 355577

JAMES A MCCANN & CO
Clydebank p892 .... 01389 879791

MCCARRON & CO
Airdrie p891 .... 01236 762012

IAN MCCARRY
Glasgow p899 .... 0141 332 7345
p899 .... 0141 552 0486
p899 .... 0141 945 1911

IAN C MCCARTHY
Glasgow p899 .... 0141 339 2929
p899 .... 0141 763 1366

MCCARTNEY STEWART
Renfrew p905 .... 0141 885 1858

MCCASH & HUNTER
Perth p904 .... 01738 620451

MCCLAY & CO
Glasgow p899 .... 0141 445 2130

MCCLURE & PARTNERS
Glasgow p899 .... 0141 204 0445

MCCLURE COLLINS
Glasgow p899 .... 0141 423 7181

MCCLURE NAISMITH
Edinburgh p896 .... 0131 228 4994
Glasgow p899 .... 0141 204 2700

W W & J MCCLURE
Glasgow p899 .... 0141 221 0045
Greenock p901 .... 01475 888222

MCCLUSKEY BROWNE
Kilmarnock p902 .... 01563 544545

MCCONNACHIE & CO
Gourock p900 .... 01475 638248

FRANCIS M MCCONNELL SSC
Edinburgh p896 .... 0131 477 8902

BRUCE MCCORMACK
Motherwell p904 .... 01698 260033

R T MCCORMACK
Glasgow p899 .... 0141 221 9491

MCCORMICK & NICHOLSON
Newton Stewart p904 ...... 01671 402813

J & J MCCOSH
Dalry p893 .... 01294 832112

MCCUSKER COCHRANE & GUNN
Glasgow p899 .... 0141 778 2222
Paisley p904 .... 0845 832 3228

MCCUSKER MCELROY & COMPANY
Johnstone p902 .... 01505 322299
Paisley p904 .... 0141 561 9999

MCDAID FARRELL
Glasgow p899 .... 0808 120 1628

BRUCE MACDONALD & CO
Aberdeen p890 .... 01224 643332

MACDONALD-HENDERSON
Glasgow p899 .... 0141 248 4957

KEN MACDONALD & CO
Stornoway p905 .... 01851 704040

MACDONALD MACIVER & CO
Stornoway p905 .... 01851 704343

MARJORY MACDONALD
Arbroath p891 .... 01241 874898

THOMAS J MCDONALD
Glasgow p899 .... 0141 954 1440

MACDONALDS
East Kilbride p894 .... 01355 588900
Glasgow p899 .... 0141 303 7100

MCDOUGALL & CO
Aberdeen p890 .... 01224 632663

MACFARLANE & CO
Bishopbriggs p892 .... 0141 772 6063
Glasgow p899 .... 0141 248 3307

IAN A MCFARLANE & CO
Glasgow p899 .... 0141 649 9772

P C MCFARLANE & CO
Livingston p903 .... 01506 497160

MACFARLANE YOUNG & CO
Paisley p904 .... 0141 889 3257

DOROTHY MCGHIE
Largs p903 .... 01475 674970

MCGINN SOLICITORS
Glasgow p899 .... 0141 353 5355

MCGOVERN & CO
Wishaw p906 .... 01698 359550

MACGREGOR
Kirkcaldy p902 .... 01592 644477

MACGREGOR & CO
Milngavie p903 .... 0141 956 4263

MCGRIGORS LLP
Edinburgh p896 .... 0131 777 7000
Glasgow p899 .... 0141 567 8400

GERARD MCGUIRE & CO
East Kilbride p894 .... 01355 225322

MACHARDY ALEXANDER & WHYTE WS
Forfar p897 .... 01307 463593

MCILROY HIPWELL & DINGWALL
Dunfermline p894 .... 01383 808198
St Andrews p905 .... 01334 477107

RAYMOND MCILWHAM & CO
Glasgow p899 .... 0141 429 7677

MCINTOSH & MACLACHLAN
Glasgow p899 .... 0141 632 4022

ANGUS MCINTOSH & SIMON HODGE
Glasgow p899 .... 0141 634 0313

MACINTOSH HUMBLE
Dumbarton p893 .... 01389 763491

MCINTOSH MCTAGGART
Aberdeen p890 .... 01224 593100

MCINTYRE & CO
Fort William p897 .... 01397 703231

MCINTYRE LEWIS
Edinburgh p896 .... 0131 669 7218

MCKAY & NORWELL WS
Edinburgh p896 .... 0131 222 8000

JAMES MCKAY
Elgin p896 .... 01343 556500

MACKAY SINCLAIR
Edinburgh p896 .... 0131 652 1166

MCKENNAS
Glenrothes p900 .... 01592 756449

MACKENZIE & CORMACK
Tain p906 .... 01862 892046

MACKENZIE & GRANT
Forres p897 .... 01309 672126

MACKENZIE & MACKENZIE
Dundee p894 .... 01382 455263

THE MACKENZIE LAW PRACTICE
Inverness p901 .... 01463 713718

MCKENZIES
Kirkcaldy p902 .... 01592 206605

MACKIE & DEWAR
Aberdeen p890 .... 01224 596341

D DOUGLAS MACKIE
Glasgow p899 .... 0141 331 2882

MACKIE THOMPSON & CO
Paisley p904 .... 0141 848 6000

MACKINLAY & SUTTIE
Barrhead p891 .... 0141 881 1572
Glasgow p899 .... 0141 427 6023

MCKINNON & CO
Glenrothes p900 .... 01592 750309

D M MACKINNON WS
Oban p904 .... 01631 563014

MCKINNON FORBES
Prestonpans p905 .... 01875 813219
Tranent p906 .... 01875 611211

MCKINNON HEWITT
Irvine p902 .... 01294 312801

MACKINNONS
Aberdeen p890 .... 01224 632464
p890 .... 01224 868687

THE MCKINSTRY COMPANY
Ayr p891 .... 01292 281711

MACKINTOSH & WYLIE
Kilmarnock p902 .... 01563 525104

MACLACHLAN & MACKENZIE
Edinburgh p896 .... 0131 220 2226

DONALD MCLAREN & CO
Callander p892 .... 01877 330033

MACLAY MURRAY & SPENS
Aberdeen p890 .... 01224 356130
Edinburgh p896 .... 0131 228 7000
Glasgow p899 .... 0141 248 5011

MACLEAN & LOWSON
Forfar p897 .... 01307 462103
Kirriemuir p902 .... 01575 575255

MCLEAN & STEWART
Callander p892 .... 01877 330014
Dunblane p893 .... 01786 823217

DUNCAN MCLEAN & CO
Kilmarnock p902 .... 01563 524222

MCLEISH CARSWELL
Glasgow p899 .... 0141 429 7662

MCLENNAN ADAM DAVIS
Ayr p891 .... 01292 289584

ANGUS MCLENNON & COMPANY SOLICITORS
Edinburgh p896 .... 0131 442 2244

MACLEOD & CO
Ullapool p906 .... 01854 612555

MACLEOD & MACCALLUM
Inverness p901 .... 01463 239393

JANE MACLEOD
Lochgilphead p903 .... 01546 606666

MACMILLAN & CO
Alness p891 .... 01349 883338

ALASTAIR C MACMILLAN
Glasgow p899 .... 0141 204 3385

MCMILLAN KILPATRICK SSC
Ayr p891 .... 01292 264696

MACMILLANS
Glasgow p899 .... 0141 551 8669

MACNABS
Perth p904 .... 01738 623432
Pitlochry p905 .... 01796 472409

MACNAIRS
Glasgow p899 .... 0141 551 8185
Paisley p904 .... 0141 887 5181

MACNEILL & CRITCHLEY
Inverness p901 .... 01463 232081

MCNEILS
Ayr p891 .... 01292 886600

MACPHEE & PARTNERS
Fort William p897 .... 01397 701000
Oban p904 .... 01631 562308

MACPHERSON & DISSELDUFF
Greenock p901 .... 01369 702071

MACPHERSON MAGUIRE COOK
Glasgow p899 .... 0141 221 6913

NEIL F MCPHERSON
Kilmarnock *p902* 01563 535363

MARY R MCQUEEN
Edinburgh *p896* 0131 445 3208

MCQUILLAN GLASSER & WAUGHMAN
Hamilton *p901* 01698 200006

MCQUITTYS
Cupar *p893* 01334 655207

MACRAE FLETT & RENNIE
Edinburgh *p896* 0131 225 5985

MACRAE STEPHEN & CO
Fraserburgh *p897* 01346 514545

JOHN MACRITCHIE & CO SSC
Peterhead *p905* 01779 478877

MACROBERTS LLP
Glasgow *p899* 0141 303 1100

MCSHERRY HALLIDAY DALE & MARSHALL
Galston *p897* 01563 820216
Irvine *p902* 01294 274097
Kilmarnock *p902* 01563 533121
Troon *p906* 01292 313737

MCSPARRAN MCCORMICK
Glasgow *p899* 0141 248 7962
p899 .... 0141 633 1557

MCSPORRANS
Edinburgh *p896* 0131 557 9151

MACTAGGART & CO
Largs *p903* 01475 674646

C & D MACTAGGART
Campbeltown *p892* 01586 552317
Lochgilphead *p903* 01546 602581

DOUGLAS MCVEAN
Kilconquhar *p902* 01333 340868

MCVEY & MURRICANE
Glasgow *p899* 0141 333 9688

MCWHINNEY RICHARDS
Airdrie *p891* 01236 754571

MCWILLIAM WS
Edinburgh *p896* 0131 229 3612

ANTHONY MAHON & CO
Glasgow *p899* 0141 332 1587
p899 .... 0141 944 1001

MAILERS
Alloa *p891* 01259 217009
Bridge of Allan *p892* 01786 832314
Stirling *p905* 01786 450555

E & W MAINS
East Kilbride *p894* 01355 225111

MAIR MATHESON
Newmilns *p904* 01560 321225
Stewarton *p905* 01560 482666

MAITLANDS
Greenock *p901* 01475 892131

MALCOLM & HUTCHISON
Airdrie *p891* 01236 755050

MALCOLM JACK & MATHESON
Dunfermline *p894* 01383 723444

ANDREW G MANDERSON & CO
Dundee *p894* 01382 200840

MANN & CO
Glasgow *p899* 0141 420 7407

J E MARR & CO
Glasgow *p899* 0141 248 5737

MARSHALL ROSS & MUNRO
Motherwell *p904* 01698 263522

MARSHALL WILSON
Falkirk *p897* 01324 612569

MARTIN & COMPANY
Ayr *p891* 01292 265024

MARTIN JOHNSTON & SOCHA
Dunfermline *p894* 01383 730466
Kirkcaldy *p902* 01592 640680

MARTIN RAMSAY MCINNES
Glasgow *p899* 0141 571 6387

MARWICKS
Edinburgh *p896* 0131 556 5938

MASSON & GLENNIE
Fraserburgh *p897* 01346 513338
Peterhead *p905* 01779 474271

MASSON CAIRNS
Grantown-On-Spey *p900* 01479 874800

MASTERS LEGAL SERVICES
Aberdeen *p890* 01224 652352

GEORGE MATHERS & CO
Aberdeen *p890* 01224 588599

MATHIE LENNOX & CO
Kilsyth *p902* 01236 823139

MATHIE MACLUCKIE
Stirling *p905* 01786 475112

MATHIE-MORTON BLACK & BUCHANAN
Ayr *p891* 01292 263549

A B & A MATTHEWS
Dumfries *p893* 01387 257300
Newton Stewart *p904* 01671 404100

R & R S MEARNS
Glasgow *p899* 0141 632 6162

MEGSON & CO SSC
Edinburgh *p896* 0131 228 2501

MELLICKS
Glasgow *p899* 0141 332 0902

MELROSE & PORTEOUS
Duns *p894* 01361 882752
Eyemouth *p897* 01620 892307

PATRICIA L MENNIE
Elgin *p896* 01343 842643

MIDDLETON ROSS & ARNOT
Alness *p891* 01349 882870
Dingwall *p893* 01349 862214

MILLER & CO
Glasgow *p899* 0141 429 3270

A C MILLER & MACKAY
Perth *p904* 01738 620087

MILLER BECKETT & JACKSON
Glasgow *p899* 0141 204 2833
Lenzie *p903* 0141 776 7761

MILLER GERRARD
Blairgowrie *p892* 01250 873468

MILLER HENDRY
Crieff *p893* 01764 655151
Dundee *p894* 01382 200000
Perth *p905* 01738 637311

MILLER SAMUEL LLP
Glasgow *p899* 0141 221 1919

MILLER STEWART
Glasgow *p899* 0141 778 7070

D A MILLIGAN & CO
Hamilton *p901* 01698 219001

IAN MILLIGAN
Newton Stewart *p904* 01671 403036

MINGLYE LEE
Glasgow *p899* 0141 333 1777

ALEX MITCHELL & SONS
Musselburgh *p904* 0131 665 2468

J & H MITCHELL WS
Pitlochry *p905* 01796 472606

MITCHELLS ROBERTON
Glasgow *p899* 0141 552 3422

ALEXANDER MOFFAT & CO WS
Edinburgh *p896* 0131 225 6200

MOORE & PARTNERS
Cumbernauld *p893* 01236 727715

MOORE MACDONALD
Motherwell *p904* 01698 262111

MORAN & CO
Glasgow *p899* 0141 221 7479

GEORGE MORE & CO
Edinburgh *p896* 0131 557 1110

MORGAN CUNNINGHAM
Edinburgh *p896* 0131 623 9323

MORGANS
Dunfermline *p894* 01383 620222

MORISON & SMITH
Carluke *p892* 01555 751916
Lanark *p903* 01555 661435
p903 .... 01555 662488

MORISONS
Edinburgh *p896* 0131 226 6541
Glasgow *p899* 0141 332 5666

A C MORRISON & RICHARDS
Aberdeen *p890* 01224 573321

MORTGAGE SAVINGS AND LOAN
Inverurie *p901* 01467 672820

MORTON FRASER
Edinburgh *p896* 0131 247 1000

MOWAT HALL DICK
Edinburgh *p896* 0131 555 0616
Glasgow *p899* 0141 420 2430

A G MUIR WS
Edinburgh *p896* 0131 664 3320

ALEX MUIR SOLICITORS
Irvine *p902* 01294 442949

MUIR MYLES LAVERTY
Dundee *p894* 01382 206000

MUIRHEAD BUCHANAN
Stirling *p905* 01786 450944

MUIRS WS
Edinburgh *p896* 0131 226 3058

MUNRO & NOBLE
Inverness *p901* 01463 221727

MUNRO LIDDELL
Motherwell *p904* 01698 276255

MURCHISON LAW
Inverness *p901* 01463 709992

MURDOCH MCMATH & MITCHELL
Huntly *p901* 01466 792291

MURPHY & CO
Glasgow *p899* 0141 332 2804

G W T MURPHY & CO
Stirling *p905* 01786 470060

MURRAY & TAIT
Girvan *p897* 01465 713118

MURRAY BEITH MURRAY WS
Edinburgh *p896* 0131 225 1200

MURRAY DONALD DRUMMOND COOK
Anstruther *p891* 01333 310481
Cupar *p893* 01334 652331
St Andrews *p905* 01334 477107

GRAEME MURRAY & CO
Aberdeen *p890* 01224 897766

MURRAY HAMILTON & CHALMERS
Bellshill *p892* 01698 327488

MURRAY LITTLE & KNOX
Annan *p891* 01461 202866

LORNA MURRAY
Inverness *p901* 01463 717719

STEWART MURRAY & CO
Glasgow *p899* 0141 357 5151

MURRAYS WS
Edinburgh *p896* 0131 625 6625

J MYLES & CO
Dundee *p894* 01382 204625

N

NAFTALIN DUNCAN & CO
Glasgow *p899* 0141 332 0979

NEILL CLERK & MURRAY
Greenock *p901* 01475 724522

NEILSONS
Edinburgh *p896* 0131 316 4444
p896 .... 0131 556 5522

NELLANY & CO
Saltcoats *p905* 01294 464175

NELSON GIBB & LANDA
Hamilton *p901* 01698 207050

NELSONS
Falkirk *p897* 01324 613316

NESS GALLAGHER & CO
Motherwell *p904* 01698 254644
Wishaw *p906* 01698 355525

NICOL HARVEY & PIERCE
Stranraer *p906* 01776 707111

NICOLSON O'BRIEN
Airdrie *p891* 01236 751224

NOLAN MACLEOD
Kirkintilloch *p902* 0141 777 6366

O

O'DONNELL & COMPANY
Glasgow *p899* 0141 944 1441

LIAM O'DONNELL & CO
Glasgow *p899* 0141 429 3100

A C O'NEILL & CO
Dumbarton *p893* 01389 762997

OAG & CO
Dumfries *p893* 01387 263857

ANN OGG
Edinburgh *p896* 0131 337 0912

GEORGE & JAMES OLIVER WS
Hawick *p901* 01450 372791

OPTIMA LEGAL
Glasgow *p899* 0844 571 5200

P

THE PRG PARTNERSHIP
Clydebank *p892* 0141 952 0019
Glasgow *p900* 0141 336 3241
p900 .... 0141 353 0550
Kirkintilloch *p902* 0141 776 2298

PACITTI JONES
Bishopbriggs *p892* 0141 772 2211
Glasgow *p900* 0141 334 6444
p900 .... 0141 647 3322
Kirkintilloch *p902* 0141 777 8899
Rutherglen *p905* 0141 647 4444

PAGAN OSBORNE
Anstruther *p891* 01333 310703
Cupar *p893* 01334 653777
St Andrews *p905* 01334 475001

PARIS STEELE & CO WS
North Berwick *p904* 01620 892138

PATERSON BELL
Cupar *p893* 01334 657310
Kirkcaldy *p902* 01592 646600
Methil *p903* 01333 427999

PATERSON HOLMS
Bearsden *p892* 0141 942 8825

KENNETH PATERSON
Paisley *p904* 0141 561 2215

STEPHEN PATERSON & CO
Glasgow *p900* 0141 445 1150

PATIENCE & BUCHAN
Aberdeen *p890* 01224 648222

JAMES PATRICK & MUIR
Dalry *p893* 01294 832442

PATTEN & PRENTICE
Greenock *p901* 01475 720306

PATTISON & SIM
Glasgow *p900* 0141 334 7706
Paisley *p904* 0141 889 3296

H K PAUL & CO
Wishaw *p906* 01698 357225

PAULL & WILLIAMSONS
Aberdeen *p890* 01224 621621
Edinburgh *p896* 0131 226 6180

PEACOCK JOHNSTON
Glasgow *p900* 0141 333 9505

8

PEDEN & PATRICK LTD
Glasgow *p900* 0141 333 0175

PENMANS
Glasgow *p900* 0141 336 6646
p900 .... 0141 632 7001

PETERKIN & KIDD
Linlithgow *p903* 01506 845191
Mid Calder *p903* 01506 880548

PETERKINS
Aberdeen *p890* 01224 428000
Alford *p891* 01975 562939
Huntly *p901* 01466 792101
Inverurie *p901* 01467 672800
Keith *p902* 01542 882537

KATE PHILLIPS SOLICITORS
Glasgow *p900* 0141 420 6120

PHILPOTT PLATT NIBLETT & WIGHT
Clydebank *p892* 0141 952 9545
Dumbarton *p893* 01389 733777

PHINN & CO
Glasgow *p900* 0141 221 4664

PIERI GRAHAM
Glasgow *p900* 0141 332 2525

PIKE & CHAPMAN
Galashiels *p897* 01896 752379

PINSENT MASONS LLP
Edinburgh *p896* 0131 225 0000
Glasgow *p900* 0141 248 4858

PLENDERLEATH RUNCIE
Aberdeen *p890* 01224 640666

POLLOCK & MCLEAN
Dumfries *p893* 01387 255666
Sanquhar *p905* 01659 50241
Thornhill *p906* 01848 330207

POLLOCK SOMERVILLE & CO
Stirling *p905* 01786 449933

POMPHREYS
Hamilton *p901* 01698 891616
Wishaw *p906* 01698 373365

ANDREW K PRICE
Kirkcaldy *p902* 01592 205151

PRIMROSE & GORDON
Dumfries *p893* 01387 267316

PROACTIVE EMPLOYMENT LAWYERS
Aberdeen *p890* 01224 619208

JOHN PRYDE SSC
Edinburgh *p896* 0131 220 2160

PURDIE & CO
Edinburgh *p896* 0131 346 7240

Q

THOMAS QUEEN
Dunfermline *p894* 0800 169 4046

PATRICIA S QUIGLEY WS
Edinburgh *p896* 0131 228 1165

ANTHONY QUINN
Cumbernauld *p893* 07968 951741

QUINN MARTIN & LANGAN
Glasgow *p900* 0141 332 3702
p900 .... 0141 429 4354

R

RGM
Grangemouth *p900* 01324 482197
Linlithgow *p903* 01506 847070

RSB MACDONALD
Dundee *p894* 01382 202025

RAE REID & STEPHEN WS
Edinburgh *p896* 0131 334 8977

RAEBURN CHRISTIE CLARK & WALLACE
Aberdeen *p890* 01224 332400
Banchory *p891* 01330 822931
Ellon *p896* 01358 720777
Inverurie *p902* 01467 629300
Stonehaven *p905* 01569 762947

RAEBURN HOPE
Helensburgh *p901* 01436 671221

RAFFERTY WOOD & CO
Glasgow *p900* 0141 634 0485

PAUL W RALPH
Dunfermline *p894* 07986 431730

RANKIN & AITKEN
Stranraer *p906* 01776 702336

JEFFREY RANKIN & CO
Glasgow *p900* 0141 944 0660

REID BLAIR
Isle of Arran *p902* 01770 870370

REID COOPER SOLICITORS
Glasgow *p900* 0141 429 4656

T F REID & DONALDSON
Paisley *p904* 0141 889 7531

REILLY CASSIDY & CO
Glasgow *p900* 0141 420 6007

R B RICHARDSON & CO
Irvine *p902* 01294 273888

RICHMOND & CO
Dundee *p894* 01382 201964

RICHMOND EVANS & CO
Glasgow *p900* 0141 332 9218

NEIL RISK
Lerwick *p903* 01595 695262

RITCHIE NEILL
Bathgate *p892* 01506 635590
Broxburn *p892* 01506 858856
Edinburgh *p896* 0131 222 4860

ROBERTS & CO
Rutherglen *p905* 0141 613 3344

A & R ROBERTSON & BLACK WS
Alyth *p891* 01828 632116
Blairgowrie *p892* 01250 872043
p892 .... 01250 875050
Coupar Angus *p893* 01828 627542

ROBERTSON & ROSS
Paisley *p904* 0141 887 7971

EUAN ROBERTSON
Glasgow *p900* 0141 423 7389

J E P ROBERTSON & SON
Stromness *p906* 01856 850232

JOHN Y ROBERTSON
Hamilton *p901* 01698 282900

LIAM ROBERTSON & CO
Glasgow *p900* 0141 429 7979

ROBERTSON SMITH
Dundee *p894* 01382 226602

JOHN RODDICK & SON
Annan *p891* 01461 202822

ROSS ROGERS & CO
Rutherglen *p905* 0141 647 9771

ROLLO DAVIDSON & MCFARLANE
Cupar *p893* 01334 654081
Glenrothes *p900* 01592 759414
St Andrews *p905* 01334 477700

PHILIP ROONEY & CO
Glasgow *p900* 0141 423 0000

ROSS & CONNEL
Dunfermline *p894* 01383 721156

ROSS & FOX
Glasgow *p900* 0141 429 1230

ROSS HARPER
East Kilbride *p894* 0141 649 9511
Glasgow *p900* 0141 248 5777
p900 .... 0141 333 6334
p900 .... 0141 649 9511

RUBENS
Lochgilphead *p903* 01546 602084

GRAEME RUNCIE & CO
Edinburgh *p896* 0131 228 8999

RUSSEL & AITKEN
Alloa *p891* 01259 723201
Denny *p893* 01324 822194
Edinburgh *p896* 0131 228 5500
Falkirk *p897* 01324 622888

RUSSELL JONES & WALKER
Edinburgh *p896* 0131 718 4150

RUSSELLS GIBSON MCCAFFREY
Glasgow *p900* 0141 271 1000
p900 .... 0141 445 3110

RUTHVEN KEENAN POLLOCK & CO
Glasgow *p900* 0141 423 8951
p900 .... 0141 954 2901
Milngavie *p903* 0141 956 4647

CLARE RYAN
Glasgow *p900* 0141 931 5254

S

SANDEMANS
Falkirk *p897* 01324 633222

SCULLION LAW
Hamilton *p901* 01698 283265

BRIAN D SELBY & CO
Motherwell *p904* 01698 230032

SEMPLE FRASER WS
Edinburgh *p896* 0131 273 3771

ARCHIBALD SHARP & SON
Glasgow *p900* 0141 339 3036

D W SHAW
Ayr *p891* 01292 265033
Cumnock *p893* 01290 421484
Mauchline *p903* 01290 550249
Troon *p906* 01292 312577

SHEPHERD + WEDDERBURN LLP
Edinburgh *p896* 0131 228 9900
Glasgow *p900* 0141 566 9900

SHEPHERDS
Dundee *p894* 01382 322781

SHERIDANS
Glasgow *p900* 0141 332 3536

SHIELD & KYD
Arbroath *p891* 01241 870739
Dundee *p894* 01382 224112
Edinburgh *p896* 0131 228 2381
p896 .... 0131 661 5358

SHIELLS SOLICITORS
Brechin *p892* 01356 622171

BRUCE SHORT & CO
Dundee *p894* 01382 223400

SIMPSON & MARWICK
Aberdeen *p890* 01224 624924
Dundee *p894* 01382 200373
Edinburgh *p896* 0131 557 1545
Glasgow *p900* 0141 248 2666

PAT SINCLAIR & CO
Aberdeen *p890* 01224 626070

WILLIAM SKELTON & CO
Rothesay *p905* 01700 502881

SMAIL & EWART
Biggar *p892* 01899 220058
Lanark *p903* 01555 666111

IAN S SMART & CO
Cumbernauld *p893* 01236 731027

SMITH & GRANT
Leven *p903* 01333 423441

ALAN K SMITH
Montrose *p903* 01674 662155

GRANT SMITH LAW PRACTICE
Aberdeen *p890* 01224 621620
Turriff *p906* 01888 562245

IAIN SMITH & CO
Aberdeen *p890* 01224 626250
Stonehaven *p905* 01569 767778

IAIN SMITH & PARTNERS WS
Duns *p894* 01361 882733
Galashiels *p897* 01896 752231

MIKE SMITH & CO
Lenzie *p903* 0141 776 2621

SNEDDON & SON SSC
Armadale *p891* 01501 733200
Bo'ness *p892* 01506 826232

SNEDDON MORRISON
Blackburn *p892* 01506 636550
Shotts *p905* 01501 823923
Whitburn *p906* 01501 740345

SOLICITORS DIRECT
Aberdeen *p890* 01224 643000

SOMERVILLE & RUSSELL
Edinburgh *p896* 0131 220 3503
Musselburgh *p904* 0131 665 9041

ROSIE SORRELL
Glasgow *p900* 0141 204 2888

SOUTH FORREST
Inverness *p901* 01463 237171

SPRANG TERRAS
Ayr *p891* 01292 288300

STEEL ELDRIDGE STEWART
Cupar *p893* 01334 652285

STENHOUSE HUSBAND & IRVINE
Dunfermline *p894* 01383 724949

STEPHEN & ROBB
Dufftown *p893* 01340 820101
Keith *p902* 01542 886267

STEVENSON & JOHNSTONE
Langholm *p903* 01387 380428

STEVENSON & MARSHALL
Dunfermline *p894* 01383 721141

STEVENSON KENNEDY
Oban *p904* 01631 562317

STEWART & BENNETT
Dunoon *p894* 01369 702885

STEWART & MCISAAC
Elgin *p896* 01343 544971

STEWART & OSBORNE
Beith *p892* 01505 503345

STEWART & WATSON
Banff *p891* 01261 815493
Buckie *p892* 01542 833255
Fraserburgh *p897* 01346 514443
Oldmeldrum *p904* 01651 872314
Peterhead *p905* 01771 622338
p905 .... 01779 476351
Turriff *p906* 01888 563773

STEWART BALFOUR & SUTHERLAND
Campbeltown *p892* 01586 553737
Lochgilphead *p903* 01546 602903

THOMAS H G STEWART
Edinburgh *p896* 0131 229 4939

STEWARTS
Dunfermline *p894* 01383 620101

STEWARTS & MURDOCHS
Glasgow *p900* 0141 248 8810

STIRLING & CO
Falkirk *p897* 01324 636181

STIRLING & GILMOUR
Alexandria *p891* 01389 752641
Clydebank *p892* 0141 952 2669
Helensburgh *p901* 01436 678185

STIRLING & MAIR
Johnstone *p902* 01505 329373
Paisley *p904* 0141 889 6458

STIRLING DUNLOP
Hamilton *p901* 01698 307170

STIRLING EUNSON & FERGUSON LEGAL SERVICES
Dunfermline *p894* 01383 748900

STODARTS
Hamilton *p901* 01698 200302

STORIE CRUDEN & SIMPSON
Aberdeen *p890* 01224 587261
Westhill *p906* 01224 740718

STORMONTH DARLING WS
Kelso *p902* 01573 224143

ROSS STRACHAN & CO
Dundee *p894* 01382 201010

STREFFORD TULIPS
Hamilton *p901* 01698 429428

STRONACHS
Aberdeen *p890* 01224 845845
Inverness *p901* 01463 713225

STUART & STUART WS
Bonnyrigg *p892* 0131 663 7135
Edinburgh *p896* 0131 228 6449
Penicuik *p904* 01968 677294

STURROCK ARMSTRONG & THOMSON
Edinburgh *p896* 0131 556 0159

G SWEENEY & CO
Glasgow *p900* 0141 429 0677

T

TAGGART MEIL MATHERS
Aberdeen *p890* 01224 588020

TAIT & MACKENZIE
Grangemouth *p900* 01324 471121

TAIT & PETERSON
Lerwick *p903* 01595 693010

JONATHAN TAIT & CO
Aberdeen *p890* 01224 582211

M M TAIT & CO
Haddington *p901* 01620 823280

TAITS
Kelso *p902* 01573 224311

TAYLOR & HENDERSON
Irvine *p902* 01294 278306
Saltcoats *p905* 01294 464341
West Kilbride *p906* 01294 823888

TAYLOR & KELLY
Coatbridge *p892* 01236 710999

THOMAS CARLIN & PENDER
Glasgow *p900* 0141 883 6227

THOMPSONS
Edinburgh *p896* 0131 225 4297
Glasgow *p900* 0141 221 8840

JAMES THOMSON & SON
Kirkcaldy *p902* 01592 268575

E THORNTON & CO
Oban *p904* 01631 566771

THORNTONS WS
Arbroath *p891* 01241 872683
Dundee *p894* 01382 229111
Forfar *p897* 01307 466886
Perth *p905* 01738 621212

G TIERNEY & CO
Auchinleck *p891* 01290 423311

TOD & MITCHELL
Paisley *p904* 0141 889 1444

TODS MURRAY WS
Edinburgh *p896* 0131 656 2000
Glasgow *p900* 0141 275 4771

DERRICK TRAINER
Saltcoats *p905* 01294 469994

TRAINOR ALSTON
Coatbridge *p893* 01236 600600

KEITH J TUCK
Glasgow *p900* 0141 336 2020

TURCAN CONNELL
Edinburgh *p896* 0131 228 8111

TURNBULL & WARD
Barrhead *p892* 0141 881 2357

JAMES TURNBULL & CO
Larbert *p903* 01324 552456

TURNBULL MCCARRON
Glasgow *p900* 0141 339 8887
p900 .... 0141 551 0096
p900 .... 0141 554 3535

U

A & W M URQUHART
Edinburgh *p896* 0131 556 2896

R & R URQUHART
Forres *p897* 01309 672216
Inverness *p901* 01463 714477
Nairn *p904* 01667 453278

V

VALENTE MCCOMBIE & HUNTER
Edinburgh *p896* 0131 622 2626
p896 .... 0131 661 5911

VALLANCE KLINER & ASSOCIATES
Glasgow *p900* 0141 332 5332

R S VAUGHAN & CO
Glasgow *p900* 0141 221 5482

THOMAS S VEITCH & SON
Linlithgow *p903* 01506 842100

W

WADDELL & MACKINTOSH
Troon *p906* 01292 312222
p906 .... 01292 314922

WALKER & SHARPE
Dumfries *p893* 01387 267222

GRAHAM WALKER
Glasgow *p900* 0141 336 6603
p900 .... 0141 552 2234
p900 .... 0141 946 0111

WALKER LAIRD
Paisley *p904* 0141 887 5271
Renfrew *p905* 0141 886 2152
p905 .... 0141 886 5678

WALLACE & MENZIES
North Berwick *p904* 01620 892307

F T & D C WALLACE
Leven *p903* 01333 423804

WALLACE HODGE & CO
Ayr *p891* 01292 611177

JAMES R WALLACE
Glasgow *p900* 0141 649 9717

WALLACE QUINN & CO
Glasgow *p900* 0141 771 3911

WARDLAW STEPHENSON ALLAN
Edinburgh *p896* 0131 557 8020
Galashiels *p897* 01896 668669

WARNERS
Edinburgh *p896* 0131 662 4747

WATERMANS SOLICITORS
Leith *p903* 0131 555 7055

WATERSRULE SOLICITORS
Tillicoultry *p906* 01259 753330

WATSON & LYALL BOWIE
Coupar Angus *p893* 01828 628395

WATSON SCOTT
Hamilton *p901* 01698 282370

STEWART WATT & CO
Edinburgh *p896* 0131 337 9692
West Calder *p906* 01506 872911

WATTERS STEVEN & CO
Motherwell *p904* 01698 276550

WATTS
Montrose *p903* 01674 673444

ROGER WEBB
Inverness *p901* 01463 234036

ELIZABETH WELSH FAMILY LAW PRACTICE
Ayr *p891* 01292 284786

WEST ANDERSON & CO
Glasgow *p900* 0141 332 6671

PATRICK WHEATLEY
Edinburgh *p896* 07765 244030

A C WHITE
Ayr *p891* 01292 266900

WHITELAW EDGAR & BALDWIN
Dumfries *p893* 01387 255414

WHITTEN & COMPANY
Broxburn *p892* 01506 855777

NEIL WHITTET
Perth *p905* 01738 628900

WILKIE & DUNDAS WS
Kirriemuir *p902* 01575 572608

WILLIAMS MCRAE
Cupar *p893* 01334 658222

WILLIAMSON & HENRY
Kirkcudbright *p902* 01557 330692

DERICK WILLIAMSON & CO
Glasgow *p900* 0141 634 3200

WILSON DEFENCE
Banff *p891* 01261 819831

WILSON GREEN & MORRISON
Glasgow *p900* 0141 616 6655

J & G WILSON
Kinross *p902* 01577 862302

WILSON MCLEOD
Edinburgh *p896* 0131 668 3299

ROBERT WILSON & SON
Sanquhar *p905* 01659 50251
Thornhill *p906* 01848 330251

WILSON TERRIS & CO SSC
Edinburgh *p896* 0131 442 1444

WILSONE & DUFFUS
Aberdeen *p890* 01224 625032
p890 . . . . . 01224 651700
Dyce *p894* 01224 797979

WILSONS
Invergordon *p901* 01349 852131

WINCHESTERS
Ellon *p896* 01358 724252

WINK & MACKENZIE
Elgin *p896* 01343 542623

LESLIE WOLFSON & CO
Glasgow *p900* 0141 226 4499

CHARLES WOOD & SON
Kirkcaldy *p902* 01592 261621

CRAIG WOOD
Inverness *p901* 01463 225544

KINGSLEY WOOD & CO
Kilmacolm *p902* 01505 874114

WOODS & COMPANY
Coatbridge *p893* 01236 428237

PETER J WOOLFSON & CO
Glasgow *p900* 0141 946 6666

WRIGHT & CO
Edinburgh *p896* 0131 467 5566

WRIGHT & CRAWFORD
Paisley *p904* 0141 887 6211

DOUGLAS WRIGHT
Kilmarnock *p902* 01563 532177
Saltcoats *p905* 01294 466990

WRIGHT JOHNSTON & MACKENZIE
Edinburgh *p896* 0131 225 5660
Glasgow *p900* 0141 248 3434

WRIGHTS
Motherwell *p904* 01698 267361

WYLLIE & HENDERSON
Perth *p905* 01738 638465

Y

YOUNG & PARTNERS
Dunfermline *p894* 01383 721621

P H YOUNG & CO
Bo'ness *p892* 01506 826166

YOUNG ROBERTSON & CO
Thurso *p906* 01847 893247
Wick *p906* 01955 605151

T C YOUNG
Edinburgh *p896* 0131 220 7660
Glasgow *p900* 0141 221 5562

YOUR CONVEYANCER
Dunfermline *p894* 0844 576 7777

YUILL & KYLE
Glasgow *p900* 0141 331 2332

8

SECTION 9

AGENCY COMMISSIONS

CONTENTS

9

AGENCY COMMISSIONS

AGENCY COMMISSIONS

APPLEBY (CUMBRIA)

Heelis Solicitors 7 Boroughgate, Appleby, Cumbria, CA16 6XF. Tel: 01768 351591. Fax: 01768 352057. Email: bobearnshaw@heelis.co.uk. We are happy to undertake all categories of Agency work in the High Court, County Court and Magistrates' Court. For further information please contact us at the above address.

AYLESBURY (BUCKINGHAMSHIRE)

Horwood & James LLP 7 Temple Square, Aylesbury, Buckinghamshire, HP20 2QB. Tel: 01296 487361. Fax: 01296 427155. DX: 4102 AYLESBURY. Email: enquiries@horwoodjames.co.uk. Undertake all categories of agency work in the Aylesbury County Court.

BARNSLEY (SOUTH YORKSHIRE)

Bury & Walkers LLP Britannic House, Regent Street, Barnsley, South Yorkshire, S70 2EQ. Tel: 01226 733533. Fax: 01226 207610 / 283611. DX: 12251 BARNSLEY. Email: info@burywalkers.com. We are happy to undertake all categories of Agency work in the High Court, County Court and Magistrates' Court. For further information please contact us at the above address.

BEESTON (NOTTINGHAMSHIRE)

Ellis-Fermor & Negus 2 Devonshire Avenue, Beeston, Nottinghamshire, NG9 1BS. Tel: 0115 922 1591. Fax: 0115 925 9341. DX: 11652 BEESTON. Email: beeston@ellis-fermor.co.uk. We are happy to undertake all categories of Agency work in the High Court, County Court and Magistrates' Court. For further information please contact us at the above address.

BELFAST

CUNNINGHAM & DICKEY

SOLICITORS

68 UPPER CHURCH LANE, BELFAST, NORTHERN IRELAND, BT1 4LG

Cunningham & Dickey 68 Upper Church Lane, Belfast, BT1 4LG. Tel: 028 9024 5896. Fax: 028 9032 7657. DX: 438NR BELFAST 1. Email: adm@cdlegal.co.uk. We are happy to undertake all categories of Agency work in the High Court, County Court and Magistrates' Court. For further information please contact us at the above address.

BIRMINGHAM (WEST MIDLANDS)

Coley & Tilley Neville House, 14 Waterloo Street, Birmingham, West Midlands, B2 5UF. Tel: 0121 643 5531. Fax: 0121 643 5711. DX: 13065 BIRMINGHAM. Email: cls@coleyandtilley.co.uk. We are happy to undertake all categories of Agency work in the High Court, County Court and Magistrates' Court. For further information please contact us at the above address.

Garner Canning 301-303 Chester Road, Castle Bromwich, Birmingham, West Midlands, B36 0JG. Tel: 0121 749 5577. Fax: 0121 749 2765. DX: 23251 CASTLE BROMWICH. Email: enquiries@garnercanning.co.uk. We are happy to undertake all categories of Agency work in the High Court, County Court and Magistrates' Court. For further information please contact us at the above address.

Purcell Parker 204-206 Corporation Street, Birmingham, West Midlands, B4 6QB. Tel: 0121 236 9781. Fax: 0121 236 8243. DX: 23508 BIRMINGHAM 3. Email: info@purcellparker.co.uk. We are happy to undertake all categories of Agency work in the High Court, County Court and Magistrates' Court. For further information please contact us on the above numbers.

BLACKPOOL

Roland Robinsons & Fentons LLP 85-89 Adelaide Street, Blackpool, FY1 4LX. Tel: 01253 621432. Fax: 01253 751161. DX: 17039 BLACKPOOL 1. Email: caj@rrfsolicitors.com. We are happy to undertake all categories of Agency work in the High Court, County Court and Magistrates' Court. For further information please contact us at the above address.

BODMIN (CORNWALL)

C Nicholls 71 Fore Street, Bodmin, Cornwall, PL31 2JB. Tel: 01208 76969. Fax: 01208 73796. DX: 81851 BODMIN. Email: cnicholls@cnicholls.co.uk. We are happy to undertake all categories of Agency work in the High Court, County Court, Crown Court and Magistrates' Court. By experienced solicitors.

BOURNEMOUTH

Preston Redman Hinton House, Hinton Road, Bournemouth, BH1 2EN. Tel: 01202 292424. Fax: 01202 552758. DX: 7611 BOURNEMOUTH. Email: office@prestonredman.co.uk. We are happy to undertake all categories of Agency Work in the High Court, County Court and Magistrates' Court. For further information please contact John Bridger or Mark Hensleigh on the above number.

BRIGHTON (BRIGHTON & HOVE)

Healys LLP 8 & 9 Old Steine, Brighton, Brighton & Hove, BN1 1EJ. Tel: 01273 685888. Fax: 01273 685454. DX: 2702 BRIGHTON 1. We are happy to undertake all categories of Agency work in the High Court, County Court and Magistrates' Court. For further information please contact us at the above address.

BURTON-ON-TRENT (STAFFORDSHIRE)

Advance Legal
Suites 3-9
Imex Business Park
Shobnall Road
Burton upon Trent
Staffordshire
DE14 2AZ

We cover all agency work for the Burton upon Trent County Court

Please contact us by:
Telephone 01283 544492
Facsimile 01283 493192
E-mail: help@advancelegal.co.uk

Advance Legal Suites 3-9, Imex Business Park, Shobnall Road, Burton-on-Trent, Staffordshire, DE14 2AZ. Tel: 01283 544492. Fax: 01283 545584. Email: help@advancelegal.co.uk. Website: www.advancelegal.co.uk. We are happy to undertake all categories of Agency work in the High Court/ County Court. For further information please contact us at the above address.

9

BURY (GREATER MANCHESTER)

Clough & Willis 2 Manchester Road, Bury, Greater Manchester, BL9 0DT. Tel: 0161 764 5266. Fax: 0161 797 6157. DX: 20508 BURY 1. Email: info@clough-willis.co.uk. All categories of legal work undertaken including agency work in Bury County Court / Magistrates' Court.

CAMBRIDGE (CAMBRIDGESHIRE)

Thomson Webb & Corfield 94 Regent Street, Cambridge, Cambridgeshire, CB2 1DP. Tel: 01223 578068. Fax: 01223 477639. DX: 5840 CAMBRIDGE. Email: enquiries@twclaw.co.uk. We are happy to undertake all categories of Agency work in the High Court, County Court and Magistrates' Court. For further information please contact us at the above address.

Thomson Webb & Corfield 16 Union Road, Cambridge, Cambridgeshire, CB2 1HE. Tel: 01223 578070. Fax: 01223 578050. DX: 5840 CAMBRIDGE. Email: enquiries@twclaw.co.uk. We are happy to undertake all categories of Agency work in the High Court, County Court and Magistrates' Court. For further information please contact us at the above address.

CATTERICK GARRISON (NORTH YORKSHIRE)

Clark Willis 18 Richmond Road, Catterick Garrison, North Yorkshire, DL9 3JA. Tel: 01748 830000. Fax: 01748 830850. Email: enquiries@clarkwillis.co.uk. We are happy to undertake all categories of Agency work in the High Court, County Court and Magistrates' Court. For further information please contact us at the above address.

CHORLEY (LANCASHIRE)

Marsden Rawsthorn LLP 43 St Thomas's Road, Chorley, Lancashire, PR7 1JE. Tel: 01257 279511. Fax: 01257 271022. DX: 18401 CHORLEY. Email: info@marsdenrawsthorn.com. We are happy to undertake all categories of Agency work in the High Court, County Court and Magistrates' Court. For further information please contact us at the above address.

COCKERMOUTH (CUMBRIA)

COLCHESTER (ESSEX)

John Fowlers LLP Solicitors Town Hall Chambers, St Runwald Street, Colchester, Essex, CO1 1DS. Tel: 01206 576151. Fax: 01206 761916. DX: 3605 COLCHESTER. Email: info@johnfowlers.co.uk. We are happy to undertake all categories of Agency work in the High Court, County Court and Magistrates' Court. For further information please contact us at the above address.

CREWE (CHESHIRE)

Hall Smith Whittingham LLP 172-174 Nantwich Road, Crewe, Cheshire, CW2 6BW. Tel: 01270 212000. Fax: 01270 259727. DX: 708512 CREWE 5. Email: law@hswsolicitors.co.uk. We undertake all agency work. Contact refs: Childcare (KL) Family (KM). Legal Aid franchise, Accident line, Childcare Panel.

EASTBOURNE (EAST SUSSEX)

FALMOUTH (CORNWALL)

Hine Downing Solicitors 8-14 Berkeley Vale, Falmouth, Cornwall, TR11 3PA. Tel: 01326 316655. Fax: 01326 313448. DX: 81150 FALMOUTH. Email: general@hinedowning.com. We gladly undertake all categories of Agency work.

GRAYS (THURROCK)

T A Capron & Co Milton House, 68 Orsett Road, Grays, Thurrock, RM17 5EJ. Tel: 01375 378331. Fax: 01375 390153. DX: 54002 GRAYS. Email: tacapron@plus.com. We are happy to undertake all categories of Agency work in the High Court, County Court and Magistrates' Court. For further information please contact us at the above address.

GUILDFORD (SURREY)

Barlow Robbins LLP The Oriel, Sydenham Road, Guildford, Surrey, GU1 3SR. Tel: 01483 562901. Fax: 01483 464260. DX: 2407 GUILDFORD. Email: enquiries@barlowrobbins.com. Daily attendances at Guildford County Court and Guildford District Registry. Ref: David Foster

HITCHIN (HERTFORDSHIRE)

Chamberlins 14-15 High Street, Hitchin, Hertfordshire, SG5 1AT. Tel: 01462 623456. Fax: 01462 453413. DX: 7103 HITCHIN. Email: chamberlins@btconnect.com. We undertake all categories of Agency work in the County and Magistrates' Courts.

HORLEY (SURREY)

Goodall Barnett James 7a High Street, Horley, Surrey, RH6 7BE. Tel: 01293 414448. Fax: 01293 414449. DX: 2004 HORLEY 10. Email: horley@gbj-crime.co.uk. We are happy to undertake all categories of Agency work in the High Court, County Court and Magistrates' Court. For further information please contact us at the above address.

HULL (KINGSTON UPON HULL)

Myer Wolff King William House, Lowgate, Hull, Kingston upon Hull, HU1 1YE. Tel: 01482 223693. Fax: 01482 225089. DX: 11904 HULL 1. Email: info@myer-wolff.co.uk. Undertake all categories of Agency work in the High Court, County Court and Magistrates' Court. For further information please contact us at the above address.

HYDE (GREATER MANCHESTER)

Pluck Andrew & Co 6-16a Norfolk Street, Hyde, Greater Manchester, SK14 1NB. Tel: 0161 368 6311. Fax: 0161 368 9494. DX: 25907 HYDE. Email: reception@pluckandrew.com. We are happy to undertake all categories of Agency work in the High Court, County Court and Magistrates' Court. For further information please contact us at the above address.

KINGSTON UPON THAMES (SURREY)

PALMERS
Solicitors

Palmers Solicitors 89-91 Clarence Street, Kingston upon Thames, Surrey, KT1 1QY. Tel: 020 8549 7444. Fax: 020 8547 2117. DX: 31524 KINGSTON UPON THAMES. Email: enquiries@palmerssolicitors.co.uk. Solicitor. Lisa K Day.

LANCASTER (LANCASHIRE)

Oglethorpe Sturton & Gillibrand 16 Castle Park, Lancaster, Lancashire, LA1 1YG. Tel: 01524 846846. Fax: 01524 382247. DX: 63500 LANCASTER. Email: office@osg.co.uk. We are happy to undertake all categories of Agency work in the High Court and County Court.

LEEDS (WEST YORKSHIRE)

Bury & Walkers LLP 4 Butts Court, Leeds, West Yorkshire, LS1 5JS. Tel: 0113 244 4227. Fax: 0113 246 5965. DX: 12048 LEEDS 1. Email: leeds@burywalkers.com. Contact S.G. Nuttall member of Eurolink.

Ford & Warren Westgate Point, Westgate, Leeds, West Yorkshire, LS1 2AX. Tel: 0113 243 6601. Fax: 0113 242 0905. DX: 706968 LEEDS PARK SQUARE. Email: clientmail@forwarn.com. Website: www.forwarn.com. We are happy to undertake all categories of Agency work in the High Court, County Court and Magistrates' Court. For further information please contact us at the above address.

Shulmans 120 Wellington Street, Leeds, West Yorkshire, LS1 4LT. Tel: 0113 245 2833. Fax: 0113 246 7326. DX: 729700 LEEDS 69. Email: mail@shulmans.co.uk. We undertake all categories of work in all Courts.

LEWES (EAST SUSSEX)

Blaker Son & Young 211 High Street, Lewes, East Sussex, BN7 2NL. Tel: 01273 480234. Fax: 01273 485111. DX: 3103 LEWES 1. Email: legal@bs-y.co.uk. Website: www.bs-y.co.uk. We are happy to undertake all categories of Agency work in the High Court, County Court and Magistrates' Court. For further information please contact us at the above address.

LINCOLN (LINCOLNSHIRE)

Sills & Betteridge
Solicitors | Together We Can

Sills & Betteridge LLP 46 Silver Street, Lincoln, Lincolnshire, LN2 1ED. Tel: 01522 542211. Fax: 01522 510463. DX: 11025 LINCOLN 1. Email: info@sillslegal.co.uk. Website: www.sillsonline.co.uk. Agency work, family, civil and criminal undertaken. Contact: Gareth Woodhouse.

LIVERPOOL (MERSEYSIDE)

Bermans LLP 2nd Floor, Lancaster House, Mercury Court, Tithebarn Street, Liverpool, Merseyside, L2 2QP. Tel: 0151 224 0500. Fax: 0151 236 2107. DX: 14116 LIVERPOOL. Email: info@bermans.co.uk. Agency instructions taken at all levels. Fixed fees agreed in advance for most matters. Reduced charges for repeat instructions. Guaranteed same day reporting on the outcome of all matters.

LONDON - E

Garcha & Co 88a Whitechapel High Street, Tower Hamlets, London, E1 7QX. Tel: 020 7375 1888. Fax: 020 7375 1999. We are happy to undertake all categories of Agency work in the High Court, County Court and Magistrates' Court. For further information please contact us at the above address.

LONDON - NW

Hodge Jones & Allen LLP 180 North Gower Street, London, NW1 2NB. Tel: 020 7874 8300. Fax: 020 7388 2106. DX: 2101 EUSTON. Email: hja@hja.net. We are happy to undertake all categories of Agency work in the High Court, County Court and Magistrates' Court. For further information please contact us at the above address.

LONDON - SE

Anthony Gold The Counting House, 53 Tooley Street, London Bridge City, London, SE1 2QN. Tel: 020 7940 4000. Fax: 020 7378 8025. DX: 39915 LONDON BRIDGE SOUTH. Email: mail@anthonygold.co.uk. We are happy to undertake all categories of Agency work in the High Court and County Court. For further information please contact us at the above address.

LONDON - SW

Anthony Gold Lloyds Bank Chambers, 186 Streatham High Road, London, SW16 1BG. Tel: 020 7940 4000. Fax: 020 8664 6484. DX: 58604 STREATHAM. Email: mail@anthonygold.co.uk. Website: www.anthonygold.co.uk. We are happy to undertake all categories of Agency work in the High Court and County Court. For further information please contact us at the above address.

Pothecary Witham Weld 70 St George's Square, Westminster, London, SW1V 3RD. Tel: 020 7821 8211. Fax: 020 7630 6484. DX: 86164 VICTORIA 2. Email: info@pwwsolicitors.co.uk. We are happy to undertake all categories of Agency work in the High Court, County Court and Magistrates' Court. For further information please contact us at the above address.

LONDON - W

Alan Edwards & Co Campden Hill House, 192-196 Campden Hill Road, Kensington & Chelsea, London, W8 7TH. Tel: 020 7221 7644. Fax: 020 7243 1076. DX: 94205 NOTTING HILL GATE. Email: admin@aewardssolicitors.co.uk. Website: www.aelaw.co.uk. We are happy to undertake all categories of Agency work in the High Court, County Court and Magistrates' Court. For further information please contact us at the above address.

LONDON - WC

Bishop & Sewell LLP 59-60 Russell Square, London, WC1B 4HP. Tel: 020 7631 4141. Fax: 020 7636 5369. DX: 278 LONDON/CHANCERY LN. Email: info@bishopandsewell.co.uk. Website: www.bishopandsewell.co.uk. Contact Mr M Gillman. All civil litigation undertaken (e.g. commercial, insolvency, matrimonial). Close to Courts. Solicitor Advocate (all proceedings). Family Law Panel. Urgent Instructions accepted.

Fenwick Elliott
The construction & energy law specialists

Fenwick Elliott Aldwych House, 71-91 Aldwych, London, WC2B 4HN. Tel: 020 7421 1986. Fax: 020 7421 1987. DX: 178 LONDON/CHANCERY LN. Email: nelliot@fenwickelliott.com. We are construction and energy law specialists. We are happy to undertake all categories of agency work in the High Court, County Court and Magistrates' Court. For further information please contact us at the above address.

Gregory Rowcliffe Milners 1 Bedford Row, London, WC1R 4BZ. Tel: 020 7242 0631. Fax: 020 7242 6652. DX: 95 LONDON/CHANCERY LN. Email: law@grm.co.uk. Website: www.grm.co.uk. Agency work undertaken in all High Court matters and appeals, including Supreme Court and Privy Council; also selected London County Courts and Principal Registry. Ref: Agency Department.

HUNTERS

Hunters 9 New Square, Lincoln's Inn, London, WC2A 3QN. Tel: 020 7412 0050. Fax: 020 7412 0049. DX: 61 LONDON/CHANCERY LN. Email: info@hunters-solicitors.co.uk. We are happy to undertake all categories of Agency work in the High Court, County Court and Magistrates' Court. For further information please contact us at the above address.

Reynolds Dawson 34 John Adam Street, Charing Cross, London, WC2N 6HW. Tel: 020 7839 2373 / 07659 130481. Fax: 020 7839 2344. DX: 40040 COVENT GARDEN. We are happy to undertake all categories of Agency work in the Crown Court and Magistrates' Court. For further information please contact us at the above address.
Est: 1982

MANCHESTER (GREATER MANCHESTER)

Glaisyers Solicitors LLP One St James's Square, Manchester, Greater Manchester, M2 6DN. Tel: 0161 832 4666. Fax: 0161 832 1981. DX: 14364 MANCHESTER 1. Email: info@glaisyers.com. We are happy to undertake all categories of Agency work in the High Court, County Court and Magistrates' Court. For further information please contact us at the above address.

MIDDLESBROUGH

Appleby Hope & Matthews 35 High Street, Normanby, Middlesbrough, TS6 0LE. Tel: 01642 440444. Fax: 01642 440342. DX: 60040 NORMANBY. Email: info@ahmsolicitors.co.uk. Website: www.ahmsolicitors.co.uk. We are happy to undertake all categories of Agency work.

Community Legal Service

Brown Beer Nixon Mallon 24 Cleveland Street, Redcar, Redcar & Cleveland, TS10 1AP. Tel: 01642 490202. Fax: 01642 489187. DX: 60029 REDCAR. Email: enquiries@bbnm.co.uk. Daily attendance at Teesside (Middlesbrough) Magistrates' and Crown/County/ High Courts. Also attending Guisborough and Northallerton. All Family and Criminal work undertaken.

NELSON (LANCASHIRE)

Steele Ford & Newton 13-15 Carr Road, Nelson, Lancashire, BB9 7JY. Tel: 01282 692531. Fax: 01282 617640. DX: 14657 NELSON. Email: reception@steelefordnewton.com. We are happy to undertake all categories of Agency work in the High Court, County Court and Magistrates' Court. For further information please contact us at the above address. Accident Advice Helpline: 0800 480 1998.

NEWTOWN (POWYS)

Hanratty & Co The Eagles, Shortbridge Street, Newtown, Powys, SY16 2LW. Tel: 01686 626239. Fax: 01686 624052. DX: 29235 NEWTOWN (POWYS). Email: enquiries@hanrattylaw.com. We are happy to undertake all categories of Agency work in the Welshpool County Court and Magistrates' Court.

NORTHAMPTON (NORTHAMPTONSHIRE)

Carter Slater & Co 41 Harborough Road, Kingsthorpe, Northampton, Northamptonshire, NN2 7SH. Tel: 01604 717505. Fax: 01604 721165. DX: 16051 KINGSTHORPE. Email: info@carterslaterandco.co.uk. We are happy to undertake all categories of Agency work in the High Court, County Court and Magistrates' Court. For more information please contact us at the above address.

NORWICH (NORFOLK)

Belmores 40 Crown Road, Norwich, Norfolk, NR1 3DX. Tel: 01603 499999. Fax: 01603 499998. DX: 5232 NORWICH. Email: info@belmores.co.uk. Website: www.belmores.co.uk. We are happy to undertake all categories of Agency work in the High Court, County Court and Magistrates' Court. For further information please contact us at the above address.

NOTTINGHAM

The Johnson Partnership Cannon Courtyard, Long Row, Nottingham, NG1 6JE. Tel: 0115 941 9141. Fax: 0115 947 0178. DX: 10082 NOTTINGHAM. Email: mail@thejohnsonpartnership.co.uk. Website: www.thejohnsonpartnership.co.uk. All areas of Criminal law conducted. Agencies accepted at short notice. In-house counsel. Member of Serious Fraud Panel. Higher Rights Advocates. Prison Law Specialists. Youth Court Specialists. Taxi Licensing
Est: 1988

PETERBOROUGH

Terrells LLP 61 Lincoln Road, Peterborough, PE1 2SE. Tel: 01733 896789. Fax: 01733 890709. DX: 16852 PETERBOROUGH 2. Email: enquiries@terrells.co.uk. We are happy to undertake all categories of Agency Work in the District Registry & County Court.

9

PORT TALBOT (NEATH PORT TALBOT)

Cameron Jones Hussell & Howe Solicitors

In brief, we are a dynamic and innovative law firm based in Port Talbot. We believe in combining the traditional client friendly values of a high street practice with the efficiency and working practices of a City firm.

As you might expect, we offer a wide range of legal services. However, what we believe distinguishes us from other firms is Client focus. Put simply, we make it our business to understand all we can about our clients, their goals and the challenges and opportunities they face.

1 – 3 Grove Place, Port Talbot
Neath Port CB, SA13 1HX

Tel: 01639 885261
reception@cjhh.com
www.cjhh.com

READING

Field Seymour Parkes 1 London Street, Reading, RG1 4QW. Tel: 0118 951 6200. Fax: 0118 950 2704. DX: 4001 READING 1. Email: enquiry@fsp-law.com. Our agency dept. undertakes all types of High Court, County Court and Licensing work

REDHILL (SURREY)

Goodhand and Forsyth Quality Solicitors 76 Station Road, Redhill, Surrey, RH1 1PL. Tel: 01737 773533. Fax 01737 761222. DX: 100206 REDHILL. Email: reception@goodhandandforsyth.co.uk. Website: www.goodhandandforsyth.co.uk. Undertake agencies in County and Magistrates Court

Morrisons Solicitors LLP Clarendon House, Clarendon Road, Redhill, Surrey, RH1 1FB. Tel: 01737 854500. Fax: 01737 854596. DX: 100201 REDHILL. Email: info@morrlaw.com. We are happy to undertake all categories of Agency work in the High Court, County Court and Magistrates' Court. For further information please contact us at the above address.

SCUNTHORPE (NORTH LINCOLNSHIRE)

QualitySolicitors
Bradbury Roberts & Raby

Bradbury Roberts & Raby Wadsworth House, Laneham Street, Scunthorpe, North Lincolnshire, DN15 6PB. Tel: 01724 854000. Fax: 01724 856213. DX: 14704 SCUNTHORPE. Email: reception@brrlaw.co.uk. Website: www.brrlaw.co.uk. Adjacent to Magistrates' and County Courts. Legal Aid Franchise. Agency work for civil and domestic matters.

Symes Bains Broomer 2 Park Square, Laneham Street, Scunthorpe, North Lincolnshire, DN15 6JH. Tel: 01724 281616. Fax: 01724 280678. DX: 14701 SCUNTHORPE. Email: info@sbblaw.com. We are happy to undertake all categories of Agency work in the High Court, County Court and Magistrate's Court. For further information please contact us at the above address.

SHEFFIELD (SOUTH YORKSHIRE)

Norrie Waite & Slater 9-12 East Parade, Sheffield, South Yorkshire, S1 2ET. Tel: 0114 276 6166. Fax: 0114 273 9311. DX: 10559 SHEFFIELD. Email: info@norrie-waite.com. We are happy to undertake all categories of Agency work in the High Court, County Court and Magistrates' Court. For further information please contact us at the above address.

SHEPTON MALLET (SOMERSET)

Dyne Drewett Solicitors Ltd 65 High Street, Shepton Mallet, Somerset, BA4 5AH. Tel: 01749 342323. Fax: 01749 345016. DX: 43003 SHEPTON MALLET. Email: info@dynedrewett.com. We are happy to undertake all categories of Agency work in the High Court, County Court and Magistrates' Court. For further information please contact us at the above address.

SOUTHEND-ON-SEA

Drysdales Cumberland House, 24-28 Baxter Avenue, Southend-on-Sea, SS2 6HZ. Tel: 01702 423400. Fax: 01702 423408. DX: 2808 SOUTHEND. Email: a.murrell@drysdales.net.

ST LEONARDS-ON-SEA (EAST SUSSEX)

Goodall Barnett James 59 London Road, St Leonards-on-Sea, East Sussex, TN37 6AY. Tel: 01424 444475. Fax: 01424 444080. DX: 33113 ST LEONARDS-ON-SEA. Email: hastings@gbj-crime.co.uk. We are happy to undertake all categories of Agency work in the High Court, County Court and Magistrates' Court. For further information please contact us at the above address.

STAFFORD (STAFFORDSHIRE)

Frisby & Co 26-28 Eastgate Street, Stafford, Staffordshire, ST16 2LZ. Tel: 01785 244114. Fax: 01785 251508. DX: 14564 STAFFORD. Email: enquiries@frisbysolicitors.co.uk. We are happy to undertake all categories of Agency work in the High Court, County Court and Magistrates' Court. For further information please contact us at the above address.

SUNDERLAND (TYNE & WEAR)

Richard Reed 3-6 Frederick Street, Sunderland, Tyne & Wear, SR1 1NA. Tel: 0191 567 0465. Fax: 0191 510 9013. DX: 60726 SUNDERLAND. Email: ar@richardreed.co.uk. Website: www.richardreed.co.uk. We are happy to undertake all categories of Agency work in the High Court, County Court and Magistrates' Court. For further information please contact us at the above address.

TELFORD (SHROPSHIRE)

Martin-Kaye LLP The Foundry, Euston Way, Telford, Shropshire, TF3 4LY. Tel: 01952 272222. Fax: 01952 272223. DX: 725100 TELFORD 10. Email: law@martinkaye.co.uk. Website: www.martinkaye.co.uk. We are happy to undertake all categories of Agency work.

TUNBRIDGE WELLS (KENT)

CooperBurnett Napier House, 14-16 Mount Ephraim Road, Tunbridge Wells, Kent, TN1 1EE. Tel: 01892 515022. Fax: 01892 515088. DX: 3905 TUNBRIDGE WELLS. Email: jmo@cooperburnett.com. Website: www.cooperburnett.com. We are happy to undertake all categories of Agency work in the High Court, County Court and Magistrates' Court. For further information please contact us at the above address.

WALSALL (WEST MIDLANDS)

Enoch Evans LLP St Pauls Chambers, 6-9 Hatherton Road, Walsall, West Midlands, WS1 1XS. Tel: 01922 720333. Fax: 01922 720623. DX: 12125 WALSALL. Email: ee@enoch-evans.co.uk. We are happy to undertake all categories of Agency work in the High Court, County Court and Magistrates' Court. For further information please contact us at the above address.

Fawcett & Pattni 150 Lichfield Street, Walsall, West Midlands, WS1 1SE. Tel: 01922 640424. Fax: 01922 721661. Email: agency@fp-law.com. Website: www.fp-law.com. Family Law agency. All Courts. Birmingham, Wolverhampton, Walsall.
Est: **1983**

WELSHPOOL (POWYS)

Harrisons Solicitors LLP 11 Berriew Street, Welshpool, Powys, SY21 7SL. Tel: 01938 552545. Fax: 01938 552970. DX: 29215 WELSHPOOL. Email: enquiries@harrisonsllp.com. LSC Franchise. Crime/Civil/Family Law Advanced acc

WESTCLIFF-ON-SEA (SOUTHEND-ON-SEA)

David Webb & Co 492 London Road, Westcliff-on-Sea, Southend-on-Sea, SS0 9LD. Tel: 01702 392939. Fax: 01702 349770. DX: 100822 WESTCLIFF 1. Email: david@davidwebb.co.uk. We are happy to undertake categories of Agency Work in the High Court and County Court. For further information please contact us at the above address.

WITHAM (ESSEX)

Bawtrees LLP 65 Newland Street, Witham, Essex, CM8 1AB. Tel: 01376 513491. Fax: 01376 510713. DX: 33400 WITHAM. Email: mail@bawtrees.co.uk.

WORTHING (WEST SUSSEX)

Green Wright Chalton Annis 13-14 Liverpool Terrace, Worthing, West Sussex, BN11 1TQ. Tel: 01903 234064. Fax: 01903 200743. DX: 3722 WORTHING. Email: enquiries@gwca.co.uk. Website: www.gwca.co.uk. Agency work undertaken in Worthing County Court & District Registry & Worthing Family Courts. Same day Fax report on case if required.

SECTION 10

BARRISTERS

LONDON

CONTENTS

COUNSEL'S CHAMBERS – LONDON

Key Facts

See Notice, Data Protections Act 1984, p. iv

The wording after each name shows the Inn of Court and the month and year of Call: Where

G = Gray's Inn I = Inner Temple L = Lincoln's Inn M = Middle Temple

ADR CHAMBERS (UK) LTD,
CITY POINT, 1 ROPEMAKER STREET, LONDON EC2Y 9HT
Tel: 0845 072 0111 ***Fax:*** 0845 072 0112
E-mail: duggan@adrchambers.co.uk
Clerk: Ian Duggan.

Chambers of Marion Lonsdale

ACADEMY CHAMBERS,
63 BRIM HILL, LONDON N2 0HA
Tel: 07979 265321 ***Fax:*** 0870 705 2837
Dx: 120 LONDON/CHANCERY LANE
E-mail: clerks@academychambers.com
Chambers Director: Marion Lonsdale
Head of Chambers:
Lonsdale, Miss Marion . . . . G. . . . Jul 1984

Turner, Mr Alan Joseph . . . . G. . . . Oct 1984
Lau, Sarah . . . . L. . . . Oct 1998
Reeds, Gareth . . . . L. . . . Oct 2001

Chambers of Mobin Uddin Ahmed

CHAMBERS OF MOBIN U AHMED,
36 CHASE ROAD, LONDON N14 4EU
Tel: 020 8886 2015 ***Fax:*** 020 8886 2015
E-mail: mobinuahmed@hotmail.co.uk
Clerk: T Ahmed.
Head of Chambers:
Ahmed, Mobin Uddin . . . . L. . . . Nov 1969

ALEXANDER CHAMBERS,
13 HALSTEAD ROAD, LONDON E11 2AY
Tel: 0845 652 0451 ***Fax:*** 0845 652 0499
Dx: 52554 WANSTEAD
E-mail: clerks@alexanderchambers.co.uk

CHAMBERS OF ANWOBO AMIHERE,
20 SEWARDSTONE GARDENS, CHINGFORD, LONDON E4 7QE
Tel: 020 8524 3054 ***Fax:*** 020 8524 3054

Chambers of Gamini Bertram Angammana

CHAMBERS OF GAMINI ANGAMMANA,
'WOODCROFT', 13 WOODEND , UPPER NORWOOD, LONDON SE19 3NU
Tel: 020 8771 5205
Head of Chambers:
Angammana, Mr Gamini Bertram . . . . L. . . . Nov 1983

Chambers of John Tackaberry QC

ARBITRATION CHAMBERS,
22 WILLES ROAD, LONDON NW5 3DS
Tel: 020 7267 2137 ***Fax:*** 020 7482 1018
E-mail: john.tackaberry@39essex.com
Clerk: Sarah Rangeley.
Head of Chambers:
Tackaberry, Mr John (Q.C.) . . . . G. . . . Jul 1967

Chambers of Andrew Arden QC

ARDEN CHAMBERS,
2 JOHN STREET, LONDON WC1N 2ES
Tel: 020 7242 4244 ***Fax:*** 020 7242 3224
Dx: 29 LONDON/CHANCERY LANE
E-mail: clerks@ardenchambers.com
Clerk: Danny O'Brien; Mike Alexander; Neil Goodwright; Danielle Osmond.
Administrator: Anita Heartfield
Head of Chambers:
Arden, Mr Andrew (Q.C.) . . . . G. . . . Feb 1974

Carter, Mr David John . . . . G. . . . Nov 1971
Robson, Mr John Malcolm; Part-time Chairman Appeals Service . . . . I . . . . Jul 1974
Gallivan, Mr Terence . . . . I . . . . Jul 1981
Baker, Mr Christopher Michael . . . . M. . . . Jul 1984
Balogh, Mr Christopher T . . . . M. . . . Nov 1984
Roberts, Miss Clare . . . . M. . . . Nov 1988
Manning, Mr Jonathan David Grant . . . . I . . . . Jul 1989
Colville, Mr Iain David; Legal Advisor . . . . I . . . . Jul 1989
Okoya, Mr William Ebikise . . . . G. . . . Nov 1989
Dymond, Mr Andrew Mark . . . . M. . . . Nov 1991
Cafferkey, Ms Annette M . . . . I . . . . Nov 1994
Armstrong, Mr Stuart . . . . G. . . . Nov 1995
Vanhegan, Mr Toby . . . . M. . . . Oct 1996
McKeown, Ms Sarah . . . . M. . . . Nov 1998
McCafferty, Mr John A . . . . G. . . . Jul 2000
Hodgson, Mrs Jane L . . . . L . . . . Oct 2000
Sadiq, Mr Faisel . . . . I . . . . Oct 2000
Loveland, Mr Ian . . . . I . . . . Mar 2001
Ackland-Vincent, Ms Gillian . . . . M. . . . Jul 2001
Osler, Miss Victoria Louise . . . . M. . . . Nov 2001
Sandham, Mr James Andrew . . . . L . . . . Mar 2002
Conlan, Ms Tina . . . . G. . . . Jul 2002
Seifert, Ms Victoria . . . . M. . . . Oct 2002
Bates, Mr Justin . . . . G. . . . Jan 2003
Orme, Miss Emily . . . . L . . . . Jul 2003
Blackmore, Miss Sally Anne . . . . L . . . . Nov 2003
Smith, Miss Stephanie . . . . L . . . . Nov 2004
Cowan, Mr David . . . . M. . . . Nov 2006
West, Ms Laura . . . . G. . . . Nov 2006
Chan, Miss Rebecca . . . . M. . . . Nov 2006
Salmon, Miss Sarah . . . . L . . . . Jun 2007
Babington, Ms Vanessa . . . . G. . . . Jul 2008
Madge-Wyld, Mr Sam . . . . M. . . . Oct 2008
Brown, Mr Robert . . . . L . . . . Oct 2008
Hayton, Mrs Linda* . . . . L . . . . Nov 1975
McGrath, Miss Siobhan Evelyn* . . . . M. . . . Jul 1982
Partington, Prof Thomas; Professor of Law University of Bristol* . . . . M. . . . Nov 1984
Hunter, Miss Caroline Margaret; Law Lecturer* . . . . M. . . . Nov 1985
Halloran, Ms Ceilidh Ann* . . . . L . . . . Nov 1992
Saunders, Ms Emma* . . . . G. . . . Nov 1994
Pengelly, Ms Sarah* . . . . I . . . . Oct 1996

This Chamber with 42 Barristers is based in London and led by Andrew Arden QC. You may contact any of our clerks at any time by sending a message to clerks@ardenchambers.com.

Chambers of Harendra De Silva QC

ARGENT CHAMBERS,
5 BELL YARD, LONDON WC2A 2JR
Tel: 020 7556 5500 ***Fax:*** 020 7556 5565
Dx: 494 LONDON/CHANCERY LANE
E-mail: briefsin@argentchambers.co.uk
Clerk: Seniors: Michael Martin; Billy Harris. Lynn Pilkington; Will Taborn; Liam Kitcher; Alex King; Stephen Jones (Business Development Manager).
Administrator: Hannah Sparkes (Reception/Administration)
Practice Manager: John Holland (Chambers Manager)
Head of Chambers:
De Silva, Harendra (Q.C.); Recorder . . . . M. . . . Jul 1970

De Silva, Sir Desmond (Q.C.) . . . . M. . . . Jul 1964
Newman, Mr Alan (Q.C.); Recorder; Attorney at Law State Bar of California, USA . . . . M. . . . Nov 1968
Bishop, Mr Malcolm (Q.C.); Recorder; Deputy High Court Judge . . . . I . . . . Jul 1968
Hackett, Mr Philip (Q.C.) . . . . I . . . . Oct 1978
Nathan, Mr David (Q.C.) . . . . M. . . . Oct 1971
Johnson, Mr Roderick (Q.C.) . . . . L . . . . Nov 1975
Lett, Mr Brian (Q.C.); Recorder . . . . I . . . . Nov 1971
Benson, Mr Charles (Q.C.) . . . . M. . . . Feb 1990
Zorbas, Mr Panos C . . . . L . . . . Jun 1964
Mullen, Mr Patrick A . . . . G. . . . Jul 1967
Wheatley, Mr Robin Pearse; Recorder . . . . I . . . . Jul 1971
Sutton-Mattocks, Mr Christopher . . . . M. . . . Jul 1975
Hoon, Notu . . . . I . . . . Nov 1975
Hayes, Mr Jerry . . . . M. . . . Nov 1977
Blower, Mr Graham . . . . G. . . . Nov 1980
Bolton, Mrs Frances . . . . I . . . . Jul 1981
Horgan, Mr Tim . . . . I . . . . Jul 1982
Ward, Mr Simon K . . . . M. . . . Nov 1984
Ong, Miss Grace Y; Pupil Supervisor . . . . L . . . . Jul 1985
Metzer, Mr Anthony; Recorder . . . . M. . . . Jan 1987
Lawrence, Miss Rachel C . . . . I . . . . Nov 1992
Gersch, Mr Adam . . . . L . . . . Oct 1993
D'Souza, Mr Dominic . . . . I . . . . Nov 1993
Mylvaganam, Mr Paul . . . . M. . . . Nov 1993
Gatley, Mr Mark . . . . G. . . . Oct 1993
Wayne, Mr Nicholas . . . . M. . . . Jul 1994
Cox, Mr Dominic . . . . L . . . . Oct 1994
Milsom, Ms Catherine M . . . . I . . . . Nov 1994
Bentwood, Mr Richard . . . . I . . . . Nov 1994
Harrison, Mr Gordon . . . . I . . . . Jan 1996
Morgan, Mr Adam . . . . G. . . . Jan 1996
Fielding, Mr Janick . . . . I . . . . Oct 1997
Carrasco, Mr Glenn . . . . I . . . . Oct 1997
Wright, Mr Alex . . . . I . . . . Nov 1997
Baker, Mr Simon . . . . I . . . . Oct 1998
Gregory, Mr Rupert . . . . L . . . . Jul 1998
Turner, Mr Jonathan . . . . I . . . . Nov 1999
Page, Ms Philippa . . . . G. . . . Nov 1999
Lowe, Miss Elizabeth . . . . M. . . . Nov 1999
Paul, Mr Matthew . . . . I . . . . Oct 2000
Goudie, Mr Alex . . . . I . . . . Nov 2000
James, Mr Nicholas . . . . M. . . . Jul 2001
O'Kane, Miss Sarah . . . . M. . . . Oct 2001
Duyvenbode, Mr Damian . . . . M. . . . Nov 2001
Jones, Mr Daniel . . . . G. . . . Mar 2002
Marney, Mr Nicholas . . . . M. . . . Jul 2002
Williams, Mr Meyrick . . . . I . . . . Jan 2003
Nartey, Miss Elizabeth . . . . M. . . . Jan 2003
Holmes, Miss Jessica . . . . I . . . . Oct 2003
Carpenter, Naomi . . . . I . . . . Jan 2004
Collins, Miss Louisa . . . . L . . . . Nov 2004
Willmer, Mr Stephen . . . . M. . . . Nov 2004
Culver, Mr Edward . . . . I . . . . Jan 2005
Booker, Miss Szilvia . . . . I . . . . Nov 2005
Hale, Miss Victoria . . . . M. . . . Jul 2006
Edge, Mr Alan . . . . L . . . . Jul 2006
Forbes, Victoria . . . . I . . . . Jan 2007
Marsh, Miss Nancy . . . . I . . . . Jul 2008
McCoy, Mr Gerard (Q.C.)* . . . . M. . . . Nov 1986
Hinchcliffe, Prof Doreen* . . . . G. . . . Nov 1953
Berrick, Mr Steven* . . . . M. . . . Jun 1986
Baxter, Mrs Sharon* . . . . I . . . . Jul 1987
Brotherton, Mr Matthew* . . . . L . . . . Jan 1995
Hikmet, Miss Berin* . . . . M. . . . Oct 2000

10

Chambers of Michael Arnheim

CHAMBERS OF DR MICHAEL ARNHEIM,
101 QUEEN ALEXANDRA MANSIONS, JUDD STREET, LONDON WC1H 9DP
Tel: 020 7833 5093
Head of Chambers:
Arnheim, Dr Michael . . . . L . . . . Jul 1988

Chambers of Andrew White QC

ATKIN CHAMBERS,
1 ATKIN BUILDING, GRAY'S INN, LONDON WC1R 5AT
Tel: 020 7404 0102 ***Fax:*** 020 7405 7456
Dx: 1033 LONDON/CHANCERY LANE
E-mail: clerks@atkinchambers.com
Clerk: Seniors: Simon Slattery; Justin Wilson.
Head of Chambers:
White, Mr Andrew (Q.C.) . . . . L . . . . Jul 1980

Forbes, Sir Thayne (Q.C.) KB . . . . I . . . . Jan 1966
Dennys, Mr Nicholas (Q.C.); Recorder . . . . M. . . . Nov 1975
Acton Davis, Mr Jonathan (Q.C.); Recorder . . . . I . . . . Jul 1977
Baatz, Mr Nicholas (Q.C.) . . . . G. . . . Nov 1978
Bowdery, Mr Martin (Q.C.); Recorder . . . . I . . . . Jul 1980
Dennison, Mr Stephen (Q.C.) . . . . M. . . . Nov 1985
Streatfeild-James, Mr David (Q.C.) . . . . I . . . . Jul 1986
Raeside, Mr Mark (Q.C.) . . . . M. . . . Nov 1982
Goddard, Mr Andrew (Q.C.) . . . . M. . . . Nov 1985
Lofthouse, Mr Simon (Q.C.); Recorder . . . . G. . . . Jul 1988
Barwise, Ms Stephanie (Q.C.) . . . . M. . . . Jul 1988
Doerries, Ms Chantal-Aimee (Q.C.) . . . . M. . . . Oct 1992
Fraser, Mr Peter D (Q.C.); Recorder . . . . M. . . . Nov 1989
McMullan, Mr Manus (Q.C.) . . . . M. . . . Nov 1994
Parkin, Ms Fiona Jane (Q.C.) . . . . I . . . . Oct 1993
Royce, Mr Darryl . . . . G. . . . Nov 1976
Burr, Mr Andrew . . . . I . . . . Nov 1981
Clay, Mr Robert . . . . I . . . . Jul 1989
Rawley, Miss Dominique . . . . M. . . . Oct 1991
Walker, Mr Steven John . . . . M. . . . Oct 1993
Howells, Mr James . . . . M. . . . Nov 1995
Collings, Mr Nicholas . . . . G. . . . Nov 1997
Clarke, Mr Patrick J . . . . G. . . . Oct 1997
Lewis, Mr Christopher David . . . . M. . . . Nov 1998
Cheng, Miss Serena . . . . L . . . . Oct 2000
Hussain, Mr Riaz . . . . G. . . . Oct 2002
Slow, Miss Camille . . . . M. . . . Jul 2002
Chennells, Mr Mark . . . . G. . . . Oct 2002
Jones, Miss Jennifer . . . . L . . . . Oct 2003
Briggs, Miss Lucie . . . . L . . . . Oct 2004
Crawshaw, Mr Simon . . . . L . . . . Jul 2005
Lixenberg, Mr Marc . . . . G. . . . Jul 2005
Hanna, Mr Ronan . . . . I . . . . Oct 2006
Fenn, Mr Andrew . . . . G. . . . Mar 2007
Khayum, Mr Zulfikar . . . . G. . . . Oct 2006
Land, Mr Peter . . . . M. . . . Oct 2007
Neuberger, Mr Edmund . . . . L . . . . Jul 2008
Eljadi, Mr Omar . . . . M. . . . Jan 2009
Butcher, Mr Anthony J (Q.C.)* . . . . G. . . . Jan 1947

Lloyd, His Honour Humphrey (Q.C.)* . . . I . . . Jul 1963
Blackburn, Mr John (Q.C.)* . . . M. . . . Jul 1969
Reese, Mr Colin (Q.C.); Recorder* . . . G. . . . Jul 1973
Reid, Mr James Gordon (Q.C.)* . . . I . . . Jan 1980
Valentine, Mr Donald* . . . L. . . . Jun 1956
Dumaresq, Ms Delia* . . . I . . . Jul 1984

Chambers of Nicholas Jeremy Atkinson QC

ATKINSON BEVAN CHAMBERS,
1ST FLOOR, 2 HARCOURT BUILDINGS, MIDDLE TEMPLE LANE, LONDON EC4Y 9DB
Tel: 020 7353 2112 ***Fax:*** 020 7353 8339
Dx: 489 LONDON/CHANCERY LANE
E-mail: clerks@2hb.co.uk
Clerk: Senior: Simon Butler.
Administrator: Vicky Beasley
Head of Chambers:
Atkinson, Mr Nicholas Jeremy (Q.C.); Recorder . . . I . . . Nov 1971

Shorrock, Mr Michael (Q.C.); Recorder . . . I . . . Oct 1966
Jafferjee, Mr Aftab Asger (Q.C.) . . . I . . . Nov 1980
Howes, Miss Sally Margaret (Q.C.) . . . M. . . . Nov 1983
Etherton, Miss Gillian Felicity Amanda (Q.C.) . . . M. . . . Jul 1988
Clayton, Mr Stephen Charles . . . I . . . May 1973
Williams, Mr John Robert Selwyn; Recorder . . . M. . . . Nov 1973
Smyth, Mr Stephen Mark James A; Recorder . . . I . . . Jul 1974
Paltenghi, Mr Mark . . . M. . . . Jul 1979
Gadsden, Mr Mark Jeremy . . . I . . . Jul 1980
Carpenter, Miss Jane . . . I . . . Oct 1984
Farmer, Mr Matthew . . . I . . . Jun 1987
Clement, Mr Peter Guy . . . I . . . Nov 1988
Bleaney, Mr Nicholas . . . I . . . Nov 1988
Fitzgerald, Mr Toby Jonathan . . . L. . . . Oct 1993
Wilkins, Mr Thomas A. . . . M. . . . Nov 1993
Dawes, Mr James Christopher . . . I . . . Nov 1993
Halkerston, Miss Sally . . . M. . . . Oct 1994
Thompson, Miss Sally . . . M. . . . Oct 1994
Kelleher, Mr Benedict Peter John . . . I . . . Nov 1994
Cavin, Mr Paul . . . G. . . . Nov 1995
Thompson, Miss Lindsey C . . . M. . . . Nov 1995
Knight, Ms Jennifer . . . G. . . . Oct 1996
Alexander, Mr Nicholas . . . I . . . Nov 1996
Hunter, Mr Timothy . . . I . . . Oct 1998
Stimpson, Mr Christopher . . . M. . . . Jan 1999
Blumgart, Miss Kate . . . M. . . . Jan 1999
Giddens, Miss Sarah . . . L. . . . Oct 1999
Brown, Mr James Richard Charles . . . I . . . Oct 1999
Osborne, Miss Jane . . . L. . . . Apr 2000
Banerjee, Mr Subhankar . . . I . . . Nov 2000
Nicholson, Mr Thomas Edward Cyril . . . G. . . . Jul 2001
Stangoe, Miss Heather Elizabeth . . . I . . . Oct 2001
Duncan, Miss Hannah Gillian Isobella . . . I . . . Oct 2002
Gordon, Mr James Cosmo Alexander . . . M. . . . Oct 2004
French, Mr Hugh . . . I . . . Oct 2004
Brown, Mr Sam Clement . . . I . . . Nov 2004
Franklin, Mr Edward Thomas Robert . . . G. . . . Jul 2006
Fleck, Miss Nicola . . . M. . . . Nov 2006
Kent, Mr Rupert Haworth Harcourt . . . M. . . . Nov 2006
Seelig, Mr Leo . . . L. . . . Nov 2007
Burgess, Dr Jenny Claire . . . M. . . . Jul 2008
Fitzherbert, Mr Francis Brian Royds . . . L. . . . Oct 2008
Cooke, Mr Duncan Matthew . . . I . . . Mar 2010

AVONDALE CHAMBERS,
1 ETCHINGHAM COURT, ETCHINGHAM PARK ROAD, LONDON N3 2EA
Tel: 020 8346 1126

BALHAM CHAMBERS,
BASEMENT, 82 BALHAM HIGH ROAD, LONDON SW12 9AG
Tel: 020 8675 4609 ***Fax:*** 020 8675 3415
Dx: 34002 TOOTING NORTH

Chambers of Abdul-Saleem Qureshi

BARCLAY CHAMBERS,
GROUND FLOOR, 2A BARCLAY ROAD, LEYTONSTONE, LONDON E11 3DG
Tel: 020 8558 2289 / 8558 3849 ***Fax:*** 020 8558 3849
E-mail: arifqureshi786@hotmail.com
Clerk: Shamin Suleman.
Administrator: Shamin Suleman
Head of Chambers:
Qureshi, Mr Abdul-Saleem . . . M. . . . Jul 1972

17A BARCLAY ROAD,
WALTHAMSTOW, LONDON E17 9JH
Tel: 020 8521 3112 ***Fax:*** 020 8521 3112

Chambers of Muhammad A Rahman

BARRISTERS' COMMON LAW CHAMBER,
57 WHITECHAPEL ROAD, ALDGATE, LONDON E1 1DU
Tel: 020 7375 3012 ***Fax:*** 020 7375 3068

Chambers of William Clegg QC

2 BEDFORD ROW,
LONDON WC1R 4BU
Tel: 020 7440 8888 ***Fax:*** 020 7242 1738
Dx: 17 LONDON/CHANCERY LANE
E-mail: clerks@2bedfordrow.co.uk
Clerk: Senior: John Grimmer.
Administrator: Marion Ohlson
Head of Chambers:
Clegg, Mr William (Q.C.); Recorder . . . G. . . . Jul 1972

Morris of Aberavon KG, Rt Hon Lord (Q.C.) MP; Recorder . . . G. . . . Feb 1954
Godfrey, Mr Howard (Q.C.); Recorder . . . M. . . . Nov 1970
Griffiths, Mr J Peter (Q.C.); Recorder . . . G. . . . Oct 1970
Jenkins, Mr Alun (Q.C.) . . . L. . . . May 1972
Munday, Mr Andrew (Q.C.); Recorder . . . M. . . . Nov 1973
Thomas, Dr David Arthur (Q.C.)* . . . L. . . . Feb 1992
Lithman, Mr Nigel (Q.C.); Recorder . . . I . . . Nov 1976
Wolkind, Mr Michael (Q.C.) . . . M. . . . Nov 1976
McGowan, Miss Maura (Q.C.); Recorder . . . M. . . . Nov 1980
Lodder, Mr Peter (Q.C.); Recorder . . . M. . . . Jul 1981
Sturman, Mr Jim (Q.C.) . . . G. . . . Jul 1982
Dodd, Mr John (Q.C.); Recorder . . . G. . . . Nov 1979
Ayling, Miss Tracy Jane (Q.C.) . . . I . . . Jul 1983
Milliken-Smith, Mr Mark (Q.C.); Recorder . . . G. . . . Nov 1986
Kearl, Mr Guy A (Q.C.); Recorder 1999* . . . M. . . . Sep 1982
Flach, Mr Robert . . . M. . . . Jan 1950
Conway, Mr Charles . . . M. . . . Jul 1969
Champion, Ms Deborah; Recorder . . . G. . . . Jul 1970
Ingram, Mr Nigel . . . I . . . Jul 1972
Halsey, Mr Mark . . . I . . . Feb 1974
Neill, Mr Robert . . . M. . . . Jul 1975
Caudle, Mr John; Recorder . . . M. . . . Nov 1976
Abell, Mr Anthony; Recorder . . . G. . . . Jul 1977
Gilbert, Mr Barry . . . G. . . . Jul 1978
Haynes, Mr Michael John . . . G. . . . Jul 1979
Dodd, Ms Margaret; Deputy Secretary* . . . M. . . . Jul 1979
Levy, Mr Michael . . . G. . . . Nov 1979
Barnett, Mr Jeremy V; Recorder 2000* . . . G. . . . Jul 1980
Livingston, Mr John . . . G. . . . Jul 1980
Altman, Mr Brian; Senior Treasury Counsel at CCC; Recorder . . . M. . . . Jul 1981
Donnelly, Mr John Patrick . . . I . . . Nov 1983
King, Mr Gelaga; Recorder . . . G. . . . Jul 1985
Kendal, Mr Timothy . . . G. . . . Oct 1985
Matthews, Mr Richard . . . I . . . Feb 1989
Adebayo, Mr Ibitayo Alade . . . I . . . Nov 1989
Rush, Mr Craig . . . I . . . Nov 1989
Ageros, Mr James . . . I . . . May 1990
Charbit, Miss Valerie . . . M. . . . Oct 1992
Budworth, Mr Adam J D . . . I . . . Nov 1992
Agnew, Miss Christine . . . I . . . Oct 1992
Epstein, Mr Michael . . . M. . . . Nov 1992
Hurlock, Mr John . . . G. . . . Oct 1993
Pople, Miss Alison . . . M. . . . Nov 1993
Compton, Mr Allan . . . I . . . Nov 1994
Vullo, Mr Stephen . . . M. . . . Oct 1996
Galvin, Mr Kieran . . . M. . . . Nov 1996
Dineen, Miss Maria . . . I . . . Oct 1997
Daruwalla, Miss Navaz . . . M. . . . Oct 1997
Hodivala, Mr Jamas . . . L. . . . Oct 1998
McGee, Mr Andrew . . . M. . . . Jul 1999
Langley, Mr Charles . . . M. . . . Oct 1999
King, Miss Emma . . . I . . . Nov 1999
Carey, Miss Jacqueline . . . L. . . . Oct 1999
Hunt, Mr Quentin John . . . G. . . . Oct 2000
Ritchie, Miss Shauna . . . L. . . . Nov 2000
Oakley, Miss Louise . . . M. . . . Jul 2001
Bathurst Norman, Miss Harriet Anstice . . . I . . . Oct 2001
Wyatt, Mr Anthony . . . M. . . . Mar 2002
George, Mr Dean . . . G. . . . Jul 2002
Harrison, Mr James . . . L. . . . Nov 2002
Toomey, Mr Kevin . . . G. . . . Jul 2004
Singh, Mr Sandesh . . . I . . . Oct 2004
Sanderson, Miss Eleanor . . . I . . . Jul 2005

Chambers of Kathryn Mary Thirlwall QC

7 BEDFORD ROW,
LONDON WC1R 4BS
Tel: 020 7242 3555 ***Fax:*** 020 7242 2511
Dx: 347 LONDON/CHANCERY LANE
E-mail: clerks@7br.co.uk
Clerk: Wayne King; Paul Eeles; John Gillespie.
Head of Chambers:
Thirlwall, Ms Kathryn Mary (Q.C.); Recorder . . . L. . . . Jul 1982

Ahmed, Mr Farooq T; Recorder . . . I . . . Nov 1983
Andrews, Mr Peter (Q.C.); Recorder (1990)* . . . L. . . . Jul 1970
Allwood, Mrs Gina Louisa . . . G. . . . Jul 2002
Aspden, Mr Gordon . . . M. . . . Nov 1988
Baker, Ms Maureen Anne (Q.C.); Recorder . . . G. . . . Jul 1984
Baker, Mr Richard . . . M. . . . Nov 2000
Banton, Miss Elaine Rose . . . M. . . . Oct 1986
Barnes, Mr Timothy Paul (Q.C.); Recorder . . . L. . . . Jul 1968
Bertram, Mr Jonathan . . . I . . . Oct 2003
Bishop, Mr Daniel . . . I . . . Oct 2007
Blackburn, Mr Luke . . . M. . . . Nov 1994
Bowden, Mr Timothy John . . . M. . . . Jan 2003
Carr, Mr Craig . . . M. . . . Oct 2006
Carter-Manning, Ms Jenny . . . M. . . . Oct 1999
Chapman, Mr William . . . G. . . . Jul 2003
Christie, Mr David H . . . I . . . Jul 1973
Clemens, Mr Adam . . . L. . . . Dec 1985
Coe, Miss Rosalind (Q.C.); Recorder . . . M. . . . Jan 1983
Coen, Ms Yvonne Anne (Q.C.); Recorder . . . M. . . . Nov 1982
Coker, Mr William John (Q.C.); Recorder . . . I . . . Jul 1973
Connolly, Ms Barbara Winifred . . . M. . . . Jul 1986
Coward, Mr John Stephen (Q.C.); Recorder* . . . I . . . Apr 1964
Cropp, Mr Nicholas . . . G. . . . Nov 1999
Dawes, Ms Laura . . . L. . . . Oct 2001
Dean, Mr Nicholas (Q.C.); Recorder . . . L. . . . Nov 1982
Dufficy, Mr Conor . . . M. . . . Jul 2004
Ellis, Dr Peter; Mediator; Assistant Deputy Coroner . M. . . . Nov 1997
Elmer, Mr Thomas . . . M. . . . Jul 2001
Farrer, Mr David John (Q.C.); Recorder . . . M. . . . Apr 1967
Ford, Mr Steven . . . M. . . . Nov 1992
Godsmark, Mr Nigel Graham (Q.C.); Recorder . . . M. . . . Nov 1979
Gray, Mr Steven . . . L. . . . Nov 2000
Harland, Mr Rob . . . M. . . . Oct 2006
Holt, Mr Craig . . . G. . . . Jan 2002
Huston, Mr Graham . . . I . . . Feb 1991
Johnson, Ms Susannah . . . M. . . . Nov 1996
Jowitt, Mr Matthew* . . . M. . . . Nov 1994
Jupp, Mr Jeffrey . . . M. . . . Nov 1994
Kaur, Miss Harinder . . . I . . . Jan 1995
Keegan, Mr Leslie . . . M. . . . Nov 1989
King, Mr Simon Paul; Recorder . . . I . . . Nov 1987
Korn, Mr Richard Adam . . . I . . . Nov 1992
Langdale, Mr Adrian Mark . . . G. . . . Mar 1996
Langdale, Miss Rachel (Q.C.) . . . M. . . . Oct 1990
Latham, Mr Richard Brunton (Q.C.); Recorder . . . I . . . Jul 1971
Leonard, Ms Patricia . . . L. . . . Jan 2007
Lindfield, Miss Gemma . . . I . . . Oct 2002
Lumbers, Miss Kate . . . I . . . Oct 1999
Lyons, Miss Christina . . . L. . . . Jul 2004
Mansell, Mr Jason . . . I . . . Jan 1991
Marshall, Ms Vanessa . . . G. . . . Nov 1994
Maskrey, Mr Simeon Andrew (Q.C.); Recorder, Deputy High Court Judge . . . I . . . Jul 1977
Matthew, Mr Alfred David Hugh . . . G. . . . Nov 1987
Matthews, Mr Julian David; Recorder . . . G. . . . Jul 1979
Nashashibi, Mr Anwar David . . . M. . . . Nov 1995
O'Mahony, Mr David . . . I . . . Oct 2000
Patel, Miss Hanisha . . . L. . . . Oct 2002
Pendlebury, Mr Jeremy . . . I . . . Jul 1980
Perkins, Miss Victoria . . . L. . . . Nov 2002
Pini, Mr John (Q.C.); Recorder . . . G. . . . Jul 1981
Povoas, Mr Nigel . . . L. . . . Oct 1998
Preston, Mr Hugh . . . M. . . . Oct 1994
Rafter, Miss Lauren . . . I . . . Oct 2007
Rawat, Mr Bilal . . . M. . . . Oct 1995
Redgrave, Mr William Alexander* . . . I . . . Oct 1995
Reed, Ms Susan Catherine . . . I . . . Jul 1984
Roche, Mr Brendan . . . G. . . . Jul 1989
Rumfitt, Mr Nigel John (Q.C.); Recorder . . . G. . . . Jul 1974
Scotland, Ms Maria Lyn . . . G. . . . Oct 1995
Shears, Mr Philip Peter (Q.C.); Recorder . . . I . . . Nov 1972
Slater, Mr Justin . . . I . . . Jul 1999
Soor, Smair Singh . . . G. . . . Jul 1988
Spencer, Mr Timothy John (Q.C.); Recorder . . . M. . . . Jul 1982
Sweeting, Mr Derek Anthony (Q.C.); Recorder . . . G. . . . Jul 1983
Syed, Miss Maryam . . . L. . . . Oct 1993
Thomas, Mr Simon . . . I . . . Oct 1995
Thompson, Mr Collingwood Forster James (Q.C.); Recorder . . . M. . . . Jul 1975
Varty, Ms Louise Jane* . . . G. . . . Nov 1986
Walker, Mr Timothy John . . . I . . . Jul 1984
Weetman, Mr Gareth . . . G. . . . Oct 1999
Weitzman, Mr Adam . . . M. . . . Nov 1993
Weston, Mr James Paul Radovic . . . L. . . . Jan 2007
Wheatley, Mr Simon D J; Deputy Judge Advocate Courts Martial . . . M. . . . Jul 1979
Wheeler, Mr Andrew . . . M. . . . Jul 1988
Will, Mr Gerhardt* . . . M. . . . Jun 2001
Wilson, Mr Martin (Q.C.); Recorder* . . . M. . . . Nov 1963
Wood, Miss Sarah . . . I . . . Jan 1996
Young, Mr Andrew Charles Alexander . . . L. . . . Nov 2008

Chambers of Anthony C Berry QC

NINE BEDFORD ROW,
LONDON WC1R 4AZ
Tel: 020 7489 2727 ***Fax:*** 020 7489 2828
Dx: 453 LONDON/CHANCERY LANE
E-mail: clerks@9bedfordrow.co.uk
Clerk: Senior: Michael Eves. Juniors: Paul Outen; Trevor Austin.
Administrator: Julian Bradley
Head of Chambers:
Berry, Mr Anthony C (Q.C.); Recorder . . . G. . . . Jul 1976

Garside, Mr Charles (Q.C.); Recorder . . . G. . . . Nov 1971
Kay, Mr Steven (Q.C.) . . . I . . . Nov 1977
Marsh, Miss Elizabeth A (Q.C.) . . . G. . . . Nov 1979
Carey-Hughes, Mr Richard J (Q.C.); Recorder . . . G. . . . Jul 1977
Watson, Mr Paul (Q.C.); Recorder . . . G. . . . Nov 1978
Chinn, Mr Antony (Q.C.); Recorder . . . M. . . . Nov 1972
Fortune, Mr Robert A (Q.C.) . . . M. . . . Feb 1976
Lakha, Abbas (Q.C.) . . . I . . . Nov 1984
May, Mrs Patricia R; Recorder . . . G. . . . Jul 1965
Germain, Mr Richard . . . I . . . Jul 1968
Carne, Mr Roger E . . . I . . . Nov 1969
Lockyer, Miss Jane . . . G. . . . Jul 1970
Sheridan, Mr Shane P B . . . I . . . Feb 1973
Williams, Mr Owen J . . . M. . . . Jul 1974
Zeitlin, Mr Derek J . . . L. . . . Jul 1974
Mirwitch, Miss Jane D . . . M. . . . Nov 1974
Burgess, Mr David Clifford . . . L. . . . Jan 1975
Traversi, Mr John S D A . . . G. . . . Jul 1977
French, Mr Louis . . . I . . . Nov 1979
Hughes, Mr David . . . I . . . Jul 1980
Kennedy, Mr Matthew A . . . G. . . . Nov 1981
Rouse, Mr Justin; Recorder . . . L. . . . Jul 1982
King, Mr John . . . I . . . Jan 1983
Amer, Mr Adrian . . . G. . . . Nov 1984
Karu, Mr Lee . . . L. . . . Jan 1985
Cleaver, Mr Wayne . . . L. . . . Jul 1986
Whittaker, Mr David; Recorder . . . M. . . . Nov 1986
Young, Mr David . . . M. . . . Jul 1986
Cammegh, Mr John . . . I . . . Nov 1987
D'Arcy, Miss Louise . . . I . . . Nov 1988
Stirling, Mr Simon . . . G. . . . Nov 1989
Bickerstaff, Ms Jane D . . . I . . . Nov 1989
Squirrell, Mr Benjamin . . . I . . . Oct 1990
Glenser, Mr Peter . . . I . . . Oct 1993
Akinsanya, Mr Stephen O . . . I . . . Nov 1993
Akinsanya, Mr Jonathan . . . I . . . Nov 1993
Vickers, Mr Edmund . . . M. . . . Nov 1993
Arora, Miss Anita . . . L. . . . Nov 1994
Cohen, Miss Samantha . . . I . . . Nov 1995
Faul, Mrs Anne . . . M. . . . Oct 1996
Higgins, Miss Gillian . . . G. . . . Nov 1997
Selby, Mr Lawrence . . . G. . . . Oct 1997
Chandarana, Yogain . . . L. . . . Jan 1997
Banham, Mr Matthew Ian . . . I . . . Oct 1999
O'Connor, Miss Charlotte . . . I . . . Oct 1999
De Silva, Miss Camilla . . . G. . . . Oct 1999
Noble, Mr Will . . . G. . . . Jul 2000
Hakme, Mr Mustapha . . . M. . . . Aug 2000
Darling, Miss Polly . . . I . . . Nov 2000
Jessop, Mr Stuart . . . G. . . . Jul 2002
Khan, Miss Aisha . . . L. . . . Oct 2002
Higgins, Mr Daniel Malcolm Buhlea . . . I . . . Jan 2003
Benlamkadem, Ms Fayza . . . I . . . Jan 2003
Jones, Miss Ruth . . . I . . . Jan 2004
Hardy, Mr Max . . . I . . . Jan 2004
Paton-Philip, Mr Richard . . . G. . . . Jan 2004
Sullivan, Mr Sean . . . I . . . Jun 2004
Lyle, Miss Helen . . . I . . . Jul 2006
Shorey, Miss Carrie . . . M. . . . Jul 2006
Bentley, Mr Harry . . . G. . . . Jan 2007
Charnley, Miss Bethan . . . L. . . . Oct 2007

Williams, Mr David B (Q.C.); Recorder*	M.	Nov 1972
Hughes, Mr Ignatius (Q.C.)*	M.	Apr 1986
Mackeson, Miss Antoinette*	L.	Oct 1993
Welsh, Mr James Anthony Kirkman*	M.	Nov 1994
Maher, Mr Michael*	G.	Nov 1995
Goldstein, Miss Heather*	M.	Nov 1998

Chambers of George Carter-Stephenson QC and Paul Mendelle QC

25 BEDFORD ROW,
LONDON WC1R 4HD
Tel: 020 7067 1500 ***Fax:*** 020 7067 1507
Dx: 1043 LONDON/CHANCERY LANE
E-mail: clerks@25bedfordrow.com
Web: www.25bedfordrow.com
Clerk: Senior: Guy Williams. Emma Makepeace; John Carson.
Administrator: Jacky Chase
Head of Chambers:

Carter-Stephenson, Mr George (Q.C.)	I	Jul 1975
Mendelle, Mr Paul (Q.C.)	L	Jul 1981
Tansey, Rock B (Q.C.)	L	Jul 1966
Salmon, Mr Charles Nathan (Q.C.)	I	Nov 1972
Sangster, Mr Nigel H (Q.C.)	M.	Nov 1976
Ellis, Miss Diana (Q.C.)	I	Jul 1978
Doyle, Mr Peter (Q.C.)	M.	Jan 1975
Hollis, Mrs Kim (Q.C.)	G.	Jul 1979
Dein, Mr Jeremy (Q.C.)	M.	Nov 1982
Keleher, Mr Paul (Q.C.)	G.	Jul 1980
Hooper, Mr David (Q.C.)	M.	Feb 1971
Fortson, Mr Rudi (Q.C.)	M.	Nov 1976
Cooper, Mr John (Q.C.)	M.	Jul 1983
Price, Mr Thomas (Q.C.)	I	Nov 1985
Hynes, Mr Paul (Q.C.)	L	Nov 1987
Allan, Mr Colin	I	Jul 1971
Jaffa, Mr Ronald	G.	Jul 1974
Mitchell, Mr Jonathan	M.	Nov 1974
Offenbach, Mr Roger	I	Jun 1978
Beyts, Chester	I	Nov 1978
Pentol, Mr Simon	M.	Nov 1982
Maley, Mr William	G.	Jul 1982
Redhead, Mr Leroy	L	Nov 1982
Henry, Miss Annette	G.	Jul 1984
Wells, Mr Colin	I	Nov 1987
Mann, Mr Jonathan	I	Nov 1989
Valley, Ms Helen	M.	Oct 1990
Piercy, Ms Arlette	L	Nov 1990
Akuwudike, Ms Emma	I	May 1992
Potter, Mr Harry	G.	Oct 1993
Sidhu, Navjot	L	Nov 1993
Furlong, Mr Richard	L	Jul 1994
Smith, Mr Tyrone	G.	May 1994
Byrnes, Ms Aisling	G.	May 1994
Osman, Mr Osman	I	Feb 1995
Howard, Ms Nicola	M.	Jul 1995
Guiloff, Ms Carolina	I	Oct 1996
Riggs, Ms Samantha	G.	Oct 1996
Rudolf, Mr Nathaniel	M.	Nov 1996
Gardiner, Mr Sebastian	I	Oct 1997
Keating, Mr Dermot	I	Nov 1997
Simpson, Ms Melanie	G.	Jan 1998
Evans, Ms Joanne	M.	Oct 1998
O'Reilly, Miss Beth	L	Oct 2000
Smitten, Mr Ben	M.	Jan 1999
Braun, Minka	I	Jul 2000
Payne, Mr Geoff	I	Nov 2000
Qureshi, Mr Tanveer	L	Jan 2000
Sherborn, Miss Natalie	G.	Nov 2000
Cook, Miss Emily	L	Jan 2002
Gomulka, Mr Michael	I	Jan 2002
Patel, Mr Yasin	G.	Jul 2002
Baki, Mr Neil	M.	Jul 2003
Stevenson, Ms Monica	M.	Jan 2004
Radstone, Mr Matthew	M.	Jan 2005
Randall, Ms Rebecca	G.	Jul 2005
Breger, Mr Daniel	G.	Nov 2005
Ledgister, Mr Roy	I	Nov 2005
Chadwick, Mr Daniel	M.	Oct 2006
Blom-Cooper, Mr Samuel	M.	Oct 2006
Malhotra, Priya	I	Jan 2007
Shaw, Mr Robert	M.	Jan 2008

This set of Chambers with 59 Barristers is based in London and led by Paul Mendelle QC and George Carter-Stephenson QC. For further details please see our internet site www.25bedfordrow.com. You may contact any of our clerks at any time by sending a message to clerks@25bedfordrow.com

29
BEDFORD ROW
CHAMBERS

Chambers of Nicholas Francis QC

29 BEDFORD ROW,
LONDON WC1R 4HE
Tel: 020 7404 1044 ***Fax:*** 020 7831 0626
Dx: 1044 LONDON/CHANCERY LANE
E-mail: clerks@29br.co.uk
Web: www.29br.co.uk
Clerk: Senior: James Shortall.
Administrator: Nicola Kessell
Head of Chambers:

Francis, Mr Nicholas (Q.C.); Assistant Recorder	M.	Jul 1981
Scott, Mr Timothy John Whittaker (Q.C.)	G.	Nov 1975
Storey, Mr Paul (Q.C.)	L	Nov 1982
Cayford, Mr Philip (Q.C.)	M.	Jul 1975
Peel, Mr Robert (Q.C.)	M.	Nov 1990
Chamberlayne, Mr Patrick (Q.C.)	I	Nov 1992
Shaw, Mr John Howard (Q.C.)	I	Jul 1973
Wagstaffe, Mr Christopher David (Q.C.)	I	Nov 1992
Duckworth, Mr Peter Arthur	M.	Nov 1971
Renton, The Hon Clare	L	Nov 1972
Swift, Mr Jonathan Peter; Member Western Circuit; Bar European Group; FLBA	I	Nov 1977
Ramsahoye, Miss Indira	L	Nov 1980
Wehrle, Ms Jacqueline	L	Nov 1984
Walden-Smith, Mr David	L	Jul 1985
Emanuel, Mr Mark	I	Nov 1985
Reynolds, Mr Stephen Alan	I	Nov 1987
Story-Rea, Mrs Alexa	M.	Feb 1990
Chapman, Mr Nicholas	I	Oct 1990
Wentworth, Miss Annabel	I	Oct 1990
Arnot, Mr Lee A.	L	Nov 1990
Campbell, Miss Alexis	I	Nov 1990
Tod, Mr Jonathan Alan	I	Nov 1990
Bates, Mr Richard	M.	Oct 1992
Southgate, Mr Jonathan Blake	M.	Nov 1992
Butler, Miss Judith	I	Oct 1993
Domenge, Mrs Victoria Jane	M.	Nov 1993
Molyneux, Mr Brent	L	Feb 1994
Allen, Mr Nicholas	M.	Oct 1995
Mitchell, Mr Peter	I	Oct 1996
Collins, Mr Ken G W	I	Oct 1996
Amaouche, Miss Sassa-Ann	I	Oct 1996
Griffiths, Mr Dafydd	G.	Mar 1997
Owens, Mrs Lucy	M.	Oct 1997
Heaton, Miss Laura Jane	M.	Nov 1998
Calhaem, Mr Simon	L	Jan 1999
Black, Miss Georgina	M.	Oct 1999
Willins, Mr Andrew Jan	G.	Jul 2000
Hudd, Miss Anne	G.	Oct 2000
Geadah, Mr Anthony	G.	Oct 2000
Francis, Miss Victoria	M.	Oct 2001
Fearnley, Mr Ben	M.	Nov 2001
Lewis, Mr Max	G.	Jan 2002
Butterfield, Mr Christopher	M.	Nov 2004
Cade Davies, Miss Lynsey	I	Jul 2005
Teacher, Miss Petra	I	Jan 2006
Williams, Miss Helen	M.	Jan 2007
Briant, Miss Sophie	I	Oct 2007
Sheridan, Miss Amber	M.	Jan 2008
Eriera, Mr Anton	L	Jan 2010

Practice is conducted from spacious accommodation near to Gray's Inn. Chambers specialise in all aspects of Family Law work. Members of Chambers also have their own individual areas of expertise about which the Clerks are able to offer advice.

Chambers of David Barnard

33 BEDFORD ROW,
LONDON WC1R 4JH
Tel: 020 7242 6476 ***Fax:*** 020 7831 6065
Dx: 75 LONDON/CHANCERY LANE
E-mail: clerks@33bedfordrow.co.uk
Clerk: Helen D'Agostino; Paul Sams.
Practice Manager: Michael Lieberman
Head of Chambers:

Barnard, Mr David	G.	Jul 1967
Whippman, Mrs Constance	G.	Nov 1978
Bendall, Mr Richard	L	Jul 1979
Carrow, Mr Robert; Member of California & New York Bar*	M.	Nov 1981
Galberg, Mr Marc	M.	Jul 1982
Burke, Mr Michael	G.	Nov 1985
Castle, Miss Susan Elizabeth	M.	Jul 1986
Spratt, Mr Christopher David	G.	Nov 1986
Thorne, Mr Timothy	G.	Nov 1987
Oxlade, Miss Joanne	M.	Jul 1988
Lonsdale, Mr David	I	Nov 1988
Sinclair, Mr Jean-Paul	M.	Feb 1989
Jones, Mr Rhys	M.	May 1990
Brown, Mr Phillip Steven	L	Oct 1991
Otwal, Mr Mukhtiar	L	Nov 1991
Cleeve, Mr Thomas	L	Feb 1993

Armstrong, Mr Stuart	G.	Nov 1995
Law, Mr John	L	Oct 1996
Stanger, Mr Mark Fullerton	M.	Jan 1998
Edmonds, Mr Michael	I	Aug 2000
Revere, Miss Carla	I	Jan 2001
Sharpe, Mr Richard	M.	Jan 2002
Nartey, Miss Elizabeth	M.	Jan 2003

Chambers of Frances Oldham QC

36 BEDFORD ROW,
LONDON WC1R 4JH
Tel: 020 7421 8000 ***Fax:*** 020 7421 8080
Dx: 360 LONDON/CHANCERY LANE
E-mail: chambers@36bedfordrow.co.uk
Clerk: Senior: David Green.
Administrator: Gemma Chapman; Grace Obidipe
Chambers Director: Louise West
Head of Chambers:

Oldham, Mrs Frances (Q.C.); Recorder	G.	Jul 1977
Muller, Mr Franz Joseph (Q.C.)	G.	Feb 1961
Farrell, Mr David (Q.C.); Recorder	I	Jul 1978
Wilson, Mr Richard C (Q.C.)	L	Nov 1981
Harbage, Mr William J H (Q.C.)	M.	Jul 1983
Tayton, Miss Lynn M (Q.C.)	G.	Jul 1981
Donnellan, Mr Christopher J (Q.C.)	I	Jul 1981
Urquhart, Mr Andrew	M.	Nov 1963
Altaras, Mr David; Recorder	L	Nov 1969
Lee, Mr David C	G.	Jul 1973
De Burgos, Mr Jamie M A	I	Jul 1973
Mainds, Mr Sam A G; Recorder	I	Feb 1977
Gargan, Miss Catherine J.	M.	Jul 1978
Temple-Bone, Miss Gillian	G.	Nov 1978
Akman, Miss Mercy L.	G.	Nov 1982
Matthews-Stroud, Miss Jacqueline	G.	Nov 1984
Ecob, Miss Joanne A F	I	Jul 1985
Underwood, Mr Robert A	L	Jul 1986
Malik, Mr Amjad R	L	Nov 1987
Dean, Mr Peter T	M.	Nov 1987
O'Dair, Mr Richard	G.	Nov 1987
Pryce, Mr Gregory H	G.	Jul 1988
Howarth, Mr Andrew	L	Nov 1988
Cave, Miss Patricia	M.	Jan 1989
Lucking, Mrs Adrienne	M.	Jan 1989
Johnson, Miss Amanda	M.	Nov 1990
Gibson, Mr John	I	Nov 1991
Lowe, Mr Matthew	L	Nov 1991
Gaunt, Miss Sarah	L	Oct 1992
Alford, Mr Stuart	M.	Oct 1992
Dean, Miss Rosa M.	G.	Oct 1993
Lloyd-Jones, Mr John B.	I	Nov 1993
Gerry, Miss Felicity	M.	Jan 1994
Abbott, Mrs Mary	G.	Oct 1994
Bojarski, Mr Andrzej	G.	Oct 1995
Spicer, Mr Jonathan	I	Oct 1995
Kirk, Mr Jonathan (Q.C.)	L	Nov 1995
Daniels, Miss Philipa	I	Dec 1995
Tyler, Mr William J	I	Jan 1996
Connolly, Mr Oliver	M.	Jul 1997
Evans, Mr Steven	M.	Oct 1997
Blake, Mr Nick	G.	Nov 1997
Rushton, Mr Jonathon	I	Nov 1997
Barry, Mr Kevin	L	Nov 1997
Markham, Miss Hannah Megan	L	Jul 1998
Crane, Miss Rebecca	G.	Oct 1998
Harding, Mr Simon	M.	Oct 1998
Sjolin, Miss Catarina	G.	Nov 1998
Ash, Mr Simon	G.	Mar 1999
Wood, Mrs Penelope	L	Apr 1999
Kingerley, Mr Martin	L	Jul 1999
Bacon, Ms Jane	M.	Oct 1999
Norton-Taylor, Mr Hugo	I	Oct 2000
Pearson, Mr Adam	M.	Oct 2000
Summers, Miss Allison	L	Oct 2000
Meredith, Miss Clare	L	Oct 2000
Carrion Benitez, Ms Miriam	G.	Jul 2001
McDowell, Mr Daniel Robin	G.	Oct 2001
Silver, Ms Nadia	M.	Nov 2001
Carr, Mr Christopher	I	Nov 2002
Rudd, Mr Michael	I	Jan 2002
Crowe, Mr Cameron	I	Oct 2002
Tompkins, Miss Kate	L	Jul 2003
O'Connell, Miss Joanna	G.	Oct 2003
Howell, Miss Claire	I	Nov 2003
Lorne, Miss Victoria	L	Jan 2005
Howarth, Miss Kathryn	L	Nov 2005
Grieve, Miss Kate Makepeace	L	Jul 2006
Pottle, Miss Emilie	L	Jan 2008
Von Berg, Mr Piers	G.	Jan 2009

Chambers of Frank T Feehan QC

42 BEDFORD ROW,
LONDON WC1R 4LL
Tel: 020 7831 0222 ***Fax:*** 020 7831 2239
Dx: 201 LONDON/CHANCERY LANE
E-mail: clerks@42br.com
Clerk: Senior: Alan Brewer. Maxine Rogers; Steve Sheridan.
Administrator: Tony Charlick
Head of Chambers:

Feehan, Mr Frank T (Q.C.)	L	Jul 1988
Hytner, Mr Benet (Q.C.)	M.	Feb 1952
Machell, Mr Raymond D (Q.C.); Recorder	G.	Jul 1973
Tattersall, Mr Geoffrey Frank (Q.C.); Recorder; Judge of Appeal(Isle Of Man)	L	Jul 1970
Dodson, Joanna (Q.C.)	M.	Nov 1971
Allan, Mr David (Q.C.); Recorder	G.	Jul 1974
Hunter, Mr Winston Ronald (Q.C.); Recorder	L	Jul 1985
Melton, Mr Christopher (Q.C.)	G.	Jul 1982
Myerson, Mr Simon (Q.C.)	M.	Jan 1986
Rowley, Mr James (Q.C.)	L	Jul 1987
Heaton, Mr David (Q.C.)	M.	Jul 1983
Hamlin, Mr Patrick Lindop	G.	Nov 1970
Batchelor, Mr Mark Alfred Lowe	I	Nov 1971
Daiches, Mr Michael Salis	M.	Jul 1977

10

Newman, Mr Philip	G	Nov 1977
Utley, Mr Charles	M	Nov 1979
Treasure, Mr Francis	G	Feb 1980
Lederman, Mr Howard	G	Jul 1982
Azim, Miss Rehna	M	Jul 1984
Dabbs, Mr David	L	Jul 1984
Bennett, Mr Jonathan Charles Lyddon	G	Jul 1985
Rosenblatt, Mr Jeremy	G	Jul 1985
King, Miss Fawzia	M	Nov 1985
Pearce, Mr Richard	M	Jul 1985
Braithwaite, Mr Garfield Z.	G	Feb 1987
Cook, Ms Tina Gail	M	Jul 1988
Taylor, Miss Gemma Mary	I	Feb 1988
Phile-Ebosie, Miss Shelia	G	Nov 1988
Hatfield, Miss Sally	I	Nov 1988
Coster, Mr Ronald	L	Jul 1989
Jerman, Mr Anthony	M	Nov 1989
Haukeland, Mr Martin	M	Feb 1989
Kilcoyne, Mr Desmond	I	May 1990
Furniss, Mr Richard	M	Oct 1991
Lazarus, Ms Mary Helen	M	Oct 1991
Todman, Ms Deborah	G	Oct 1991
Shield, Miss Deborah	I	Nov 1991
Murch, Mr Stephen	L	Oct 1991
Uduje, Mr Benjamin Elliot	M	Nov 1992
Hutchings, Mr Matthew	I	Nov 1993
Ruck, Miss Mary Ida	G	Oct 1993
Hawkes, Ms Naomi	M	Oct 1994
McKenna, Miss Anna	M	Nov 1994
McCormack, Mr Philip Alexander	G	Oct 1994
Woodward-Carlton, Mr Damian	I	Oct 1995
Choudhury, Mrs Fareha	G	Oct 1995
Feldman, Mr Matthew	I	Oct 1995
Allen, Mr Darryl	L	Oct 1995
Matthewson, Mr Scott	I	Oct 1996
Shepherd, Miss Jude	L	Oct 1996
Ahmad, Ms Aysha	M	Oct 1996
Whyte, Miss Monica	I	Oct 1996
Gardner, Miss Eilidh	M	Oct 1997
Petts, Mr Peter Simon Tinsley	I	Oct 1998
Horseley, Mr Nicholas	M	Oct 1998
Thomas, Miss Rebecca	I	Nov 1999
Naughton, Mr Sebastian	G	Nov 1999
Beddoe, Mr Richard	G	Oct 1999
Gregory, Mr Richard	M	Oct 2000
Datta, Mr Shomik	G	Nov 2000
Little, Mr Richard John	I	Jul 2000
Titmuss, Mr Jonathan	L	Nov 2001
Ormond-Walshe, Ms Sarah	M	Nov 2001
Ganteaume, Ms Natalie	M	Nov 2001
Wood, Mr Thomas	L	Oct 2002
Phillips, Miss Katie	L	Jul 2002
Cameron, Mr Robert	L	Mar 2003
Walker, Ms Maria-Amalia	I	Oct 2003
Tharoo, Safia	I	Jul 2004
Holloway, Mr Orlando	I	Oct 2004
Adkin, Mr Tim	L	Nov 2004
Allison, Mr Simon	L	Oct 2005
Robertson, Mary	L	Jun 2005
Webber, Ms Ruth	L	Jul 2006
Singer, Mr Nicholas	G	Jul 2006
Longmore, Mrs Beatrice	I	Jul 2006
Oganah, Ms Janet	M	Jul 2007
Clark, Mr Neil	I	Jul 2007
Barnes, Mr Christopher	G	Oct 2008

Chambers of Roderick Charles I'Anson Banks

48 BEDFORD ROW,
LONDON WC1R 4LR
Tel: 020 7430 2005 ***Fax:*** 020 7831 4885
Dx: 284 LONDON/CHANCERY LANE
E-mail: tyroon@partnershipcounsel.co.uk
Practice Manager: Tyroon Win
Head of Chambers:

Banks, Mr Roderick Charles I'Anson	L	Jul 1974
Jelf, Mr Simon E	G	Oct 1996

7 BELL YARD,
LONDON WC2A 2JR
Tel: 020 7831 0636 ***Fax:*** 020 7831 0719
Dx: 98 LONDON/CHANCERY LANE

Community Legal Service

Criminal Defence Service

Chambers of Philip Katz QC

9-12 BELL YARD CHAMBERS,
LONDON WC2A 2JR
Tel: 020 7400 1800 ***Fax:*** 020 7404 1405
Dx: 390 LONDON/CHANCERY LANE
E-mail: clerks@9-12bellyard.com
Web: www.9-12bellyard.com
Clerk: Senior: Angela May.
Administrator: Keith Secker
Head of Chambers:

Katz, Mr Philip (Q.C.); Recorder	M	Nov 1976
Carlile of Berriew, Lord (Q.C.); Recorder; Deputy High Court Judge	G	Jul 1970
Birnbaum, Mr Michael Ian (Q.C.); Recorder	M	Nov 1969
McGuinness, Mr John (Q.C.); Recorder	L	Jul 1980
Chawla, Mr Mukul (Q.C.)	G	Jul 1983
Egan, Mr Michael (Q.C.); Recorder	G	Nov 1981
Holland, Mr Michael Frederick Richard (Q.C.)	I	Nov 1984
Kerrigan, Mr Herbert (Q.C.)	M	Jul 1990
Kaul, Miss Kalyani (Q.C.)	M	Jul 1983
Healy, Miss Alexandra (Q.C.)	G	Oct 1992
Merz, Mr Richard; Recorder	I	Jul 1972
Barker, Miss Alison	M	Jul 1973
Heaton-Armstrong, Mr Anthony	G	Jul 1973
Wild, Mr Simon Peter	I	Jul 1977
Orsulik, Mr Michael	M	Nov 1978
Chan, Miss Abberlaine Dianne Pao Che	G	Jul 1979
Davies, Mr Jonathan Norval	I	Jul 1981
Smith, Mr Alisdair	G	Jul 1981
Briscoe, Miss Constance; Recorder	I	Nov 1983
Waddington, Mr James; Recorder	G	Jul 1983
Burton, Mr Charles	I	Nov 1983
Harounoff, Mr David	M	Nov 1984
Bryant-Heron, Mr Mark	M	Nov 1986
Elliott, Miss Tracey	G	Jul 1986
Hadley, Mr Steven Frank	I	Jul 1987
Smith, Mr David	M	Jul 1988
Ellis, Miss Sarah	G	Nov 1989
Hughes, Mr William	G	Nov 1989
Scutt, Mr David	M	Nov 1989
Chaplin, Mr Adrian	G	Oct 1990
Henderson, Mr Lawrence	M	Nov 1990
Seymour, Mr Mark William	M	Oct 1992
Jory, Mr Richard Norman	M	Nov 1993
Poku, Miss Mary Laureen	L	Nov 1993
Tatford, Mr Warwick Henry Patrick	L	Nov 1993
Hall, Mr Jonathan	G	Jul 1994
Kinnear, Mr Jonathan S.	G	Oct 1994
Shaw, Mr Michael John	M	Jan 1994
Smaller, Miss Elizabeth	G	Oct 1995
Sugarman, Mr Jason	I	Jul 1995
Amarasinha, Revantha	M	Oct 1996
Griffin, Mr Neil Patrick Luke	G	Oct 1996
Bahra, Miss Narita	L	Oct 1997
Brown, Mr Cameron	I	Oct 1998
Selby, Miss Sarah	G	Oct 1998
Biggs, Mr Stuart	M	Nov 1999
Dunham, Mr Nicholas	M	Oct 1999
Paget, Miss Henrietta	I	Oct 1999
Huntley, Miss Clare Helen Patricia	G	Jul 2000
Sharkey, Mr Paul	M	Nov 2000
Ward, Miss Alexandra	L	Jul 2000
Chapman, Mr Nicholas	M	Nov 2001
Dodd, Miss Stephanie	G	Jul 2001
Smith, Mr Alastair	I	Oct 2001
Stevenson, Mr Daniel	L	Oct 2002
Mannion, Ms Amy	I	Oct 2003
Watson, Mr Hal	M	Nov 2002
Newbold, Mr Michael	I	Jul 2004
Sternberg, Mr Daniel	G	Oct 2006
Watkinson, Mr Howard	L	Oct 2006
Hindmarsh, Mr Luke	M	Mar 2007
Sayer, Mr Sebastian	L	Jul 2007
Sareen, Mr Ellis	M	Oct 2008
Hoskins, Mr Thomas	L	Jan 2009
Mackinnon, Laura	I	Jan 2009
Tyler, Katherine	I	Jan 2009
Barnes, Ms Natasha	G	Jul 2010
Martin, Mr William	G	Nov 2010

Chambers of Philip Sutton

BELL YARD CHAMBERS,
4TH FLOOR, 116-118 CHANCERY LANE,
LONDON WC2A 1PP
Tel: 020 7306 9292 / 7404 5138 ***Fax:*** 020 7404 5143
Dx: 0075 LONDON/CHANCERY LANE
E-mail: byclerks@bellyardchambers.co.uk
Clerk: Karen Bardens.
Head of Chambers:

Sutton, Mr Philip	I	Nov 1971
Gibson-Lee, Mr David	L	Jul 1970
Roebuck, Mr Roy*	G	Nov 1974
Mitchell, Mr Brenton OBE*	I	Jul 1973
Kerner, Ms Angela*	I	Jul 1965
Fridd, Mr Nicholas*	I	Nov 1975
Hussain, Mr Rafaquat Mahmood*	M	Jan 1996
Weeden, Mr Ross	M	Oct 1996
Abbasi, Miss Nylah Naz	L	Mar 2001
Dick, Mr James Anthony	M	Jan 2003
Heybroek, Miss Jane Myrna	I	Jan 2003
Mardner, Miss Sharn	I	Jan 2003
Bowen, Miss Nicola	G	Nov 2003

Chambers of Viveca Cecile Cameron

BELMARSH CHAMBERS,
20 WARLAND ROAD, LONDON SE18 2EU
Tel: 020 8316 7322 ***Fax:*** 020 8316 7322
Clerk: Viveca Cecile Cameron.
Head of Chambers:

Cameron, Ms Viveca Cecile	M	Feb 1987

Chambers of Christian Moll

BLACKFRIARS CHAMBERS,
79-83 TEMPLE CHAMBERS, 3-7 TEMPLE AVENUE,
LONDON EC4Y 0HP
Tel: 020 7353 7400 ***Fax:*** 020 7353 7100
Dx: 260 LONDON/CHANCERY LANE
E-mail: templechambers55@aol.com
Clerk: Senior: Donna Parham.
Head of Chambers:

Moll, Mr Christian	M	Jul 1986

Chambers of J Blackmore

BLACKMORE CHAMBERS,
39 LLOYD BAKER STREET, ISLINGTON,
LONDON WC1X 9AB
Tel: 020 7566 8244
Head of Chambers:

Blackmore, Mr J	I	Aug 2002

Chambers of Thomas Beazley QC and Ian Mill QC

BLACKSTONE CHAMBERS,
BLACKSTONE HOUSE, TEMPLE, LONDON
EC4Y 9BW
Tel: 020 7583 1770 ***Fax:*** 020 7822 7350
Dx: 281 LONDON/CHANCERY LANE
E-mail: clerks@blackstonechambers.com
Clerk: Senior: Gary Oliver.
Chambers Director: Julia Hornor
Head of Chambers:

Beazley, Mr Thomas (Q.C.)	M	Jul 1979
Mill, Mr Ian (Q.C.)	M	Jul 1981
Ross-Munro, Mr Colin W G (Q.C.)	M	Jun 1951
Edward, Sir David (Q.C.)	G	Jan 1962
Brodie, Mr Stanley E (Q.C.)	I	Feb 1954
Lester of Herne Hill, Lord Anthony (Q.C.)	L	Feb 1963
Beloff, Mr Michael J (Q.C.)	G	Nov 1967
Donaldson, Mr David (Q.C.)	G	Nov 1968
Englehart, Mr Robert (Q.C.)	M	Nov 1969
Hunt, Mr David (Q.C.)	G	Jul 1969
Dohmann, Miss Barbara (Q.C.)	G	Nov 1971
Mendelson, Mr Maurice (Q.C.)	L	Nov 1965
Harvie, Mr Jonathan (Q.C.)	M	Jul 1973
Pannick, Lord David (Q.C.)	G	Jul 1979
Jowell, Mr Jeffrey (Q.C.)	M	Feb 1965
Nathan, Mr Stephen (Q.C.)	M	Nov 1969
Howell, Mr John (Q.C.)	M	Feb 1979
Keen, Mr Richard (Q.C.); Dean of Faculty 2007	M	Jan 1980
Flint, Mr Charles (Q.C.)	M	Jul 1975
Lang, Miss Beverley (Q.C.)	I	Nov 1978
Goulding, Mr Paul (Q.C.)	M	Jul 1984
Carss-Frisk, Miss Monica (Q.C.)	G	Jul 1985
Page, Mr Hugo (Q.C.)	I	Nov 1977
Shaw, Mr Mark (Q.C.)	I	Jul 1987
Anderson, Mr Robert E (Q.C.)	M	Nov 1986
Rose, Miss Dinah (Q.C.)	G	Jul 1989
Fordham, Mr Michael (Q.C.)	G	Feb 1990
Otty, Mr Timothy John (Q.C.)	L	Oct 1990
Eadie, Mr James (Q.C.)	M	Jul 1984
Howe, Mr Robert (Q.C.)	M	Nov 1988
Saini, Mr Pushpinder (Q.C.)	G	Oct 1991
Peto, Mr Anthony (Q.C.)	M	Feb 1985
Lewis, Mr Adam (Q.C.)	G	Jul 1985
Green, Mr Andrew (Q.C.)	I	Nov 1988
Herberg, Mr Javan (Q.C.)	L	Oct 1992
Woolf, Lord Harry	I	Oct 1955
Goodwin-Gill, Mr Guy	I	Sep 1971
Clarke, Mr Gerard J P	M	Jul 1986
Whittaker, Prof Simon	L	Jan 1987
Briggs, Mr Adrian	M	Apr 1989
Croxford, Mr Thomas	M	Oct 1992
Gledhill, Mr Andreas	M	Nov 1992
Pollard, Miss Joanna	G	Nov 1993
Hunter, Mr Andrew	M	Nov 1993
Dixon, Ms Emma	G	Jan 1994
White, Miss Gemma	I	Nov 1994
Collier, Miss Jane	M	Nov 1994
de la Mare, Mr Thomas O.	M	Oct 1995
Weisselberg, Mr Tom	I	Oct 1995
Mulcahy, Miss Jane S.	M	Oct 1995
Beal, Mr Kieron	I	Oct 1995
McCrudden, Prof Christopher	G	Oct 1995
George, Mr Andrew	G	Oct 1997
Gallafent, Miss Kate	G	Oct 1997
Weir, Miss Claire	M	Sep 1998
Jaffey, Mr Ben	M	Sep 1999
Kennelly, Mr Brian	M	Sep 1999
Callaghan, Ms Catherine	I	Sep 1999
Powell, Ms Leona	M	Jul 2000
Palmer, Dr Stephanie	M	Sep 2000
Sen Gupta, Ms Diya	I	Oct 2000
De Marco, Mr Nick	M	Jul 2001
Pievsky, Mr David	I	Jul 2001
Fatima, Miss Shaheed	G	Oct 2001
Windle, Miss Victoria	I	Nov 2001
Hare, Mr Ivan	G	Oct 1991
Vinall, Mr Mark	I	Jul 2002
Wilkinson, Miss Sarah	G	Jul 2003
Weekes, Mr Robert	M	Oct 2003
Hickman, Mr Tom	L	Oct 2003
Donnelly, Miss Catherine	G	Nov 2003
Segan, Mr James	I	Nov 2004
Steele, Mr Iain	I	Oct 2005
Patel, Miss Naina	I	Oct 2005
Richards, Mr Tom	G	Jan 2006
Jones, Mr Tristan	G	Jan 2006
Mussa, Mr Hanif	I	Jul 2007
Potter, Mr Charlie	G	Jul 2007
Pritchard, Mr Simon	L	Jul 2007
Boyd, Miss Jessica	I	Nov 2007
Neill, Ms Emily	I	Jan 2008
Lowe, Mr David	G	Nov 2008

Cleaver, Mr Tom . . . L . . . Jan 2009
Mountford, Mr Tom . . . L . . . Jan 2009
Luckhurst, Mr Paul . . . L . . . Jan 2009

Chambers of Nicholas P Valios QC and Stuart Trimmer QC

4 BREAMS BUILDINGS,
CHANCERY LANE, LONDON EC4A 1HP
Tel: 020 7092 1900 ***Fax:*** 020 7092 1999
Dx: 441 LONDON/CHANCERY LANE
E-mail: clerks@4bb.co.uk
Clerk: Paul Martin.
Head of Chambers:
Valios, Mr Nicholas P (Q.C.) . . . I . . . Jun 1964
Trimmer, Mr Stuart (Q.C.) . . . G . . . Jul 1977

Waylen, Mr Barnaby J . . . I . . . Jul 1968
Stage, Mr Peter James . . . L . . . Jul 1971
Mandel, Mr Richard . . . G . . . Jul 1972
Lewis, Mr Edward T G; Prosecuting Counsel to DHSS . . . G . . . Jul 1972
Davis, Miss Sheilagh . . . M . . . Feb 1974
Landsbury, Mr Alan . . . G . . . Jun 1975
Colover, Mr Robert Mark . . . M . . . Nov 1975
Miric, Mr Robin . . . G . . . Jul 1978
Heimler, Mr George . . . I . . . Jul 1978
Burns, Miss Rosemary . . . I . . . Nov 1978
Woodcock, Mr Jonathan . . . M . . . Nov 1981
Robertson, Jollyon . . . M . . . Feb 1983
Jones, Mr Richard H F . . . G . . . Jul 1984
Goh, Mr Allan Lee Guan . . . G . . . Jul 1984
Misner, Mr Philip . . . M . . . Jul 1984
Delamere, Ms Isabel S . . . M . . . Nov 1985
Lewis, Mr Andrew . . . M . . . Nov 1986
Lee, Mr Michael . . . M . . . Jul 1987
Trigg, Mr Miles Haddon . . . I . . . Jul 1987
Lobbenberg, Mr Nicholas . . . G . . . Nov 1987
Daniel, Mr Nigel . . . I . . . Nov 1988
Minihan, Mr Sean . . . G . . . Nov 1988
English, Miss Caroline . . . I . . . Nov 1989
Bailey, Mr Stephen . . . G . . . Oct 1991
Pottinger, Mr Gavin . . . I . . . Oct 1991
Marshall, Mr Peter D . . . L . . . Nov 1991
Hayne, Ms Janette . . . I . . . Nov 1991
O'Connor, Mr Gerard . . . L . . . Nov 1993
McLoughlin, Mr Ian . . . L . . . Nov 1993
Hasslacher, Mr James . . . M . . . Nov 1993
Piyadasa, Miss Susan . . . L . . . Jan 1994
Wilshire, Mr Simon . . . G . . . Jul 1994
Harris, Mr Glenn . . . L . . . Oct 1994
Thompson, Mr Lyall . . . I . . . Jan 1995
Underhill, Mr Gareth . . . L . . . Oct 1995
Krikler, Mr Alexander Richard . . . M . . . Nov 1995
Stanford, Mr Tony . . . L . . . Nov 1996
Surtees-Jones, Mr Christopher . . . I . . . Oct 1997
Blackband, Ms Laura . . . I . . . Nov 1997
Stradling, Mr Michael Donat . . . G . . . Nov 1998
Walls, Mr Kevin Andrew . . . G . . . Jan 1999
Patel, Jai . . . G . . . Oct 1999
Penny, Miss Abigail . . . M . . . Oct 1999
Crane, Miss Denece Elizabeth . . . L . . . Oct 1999
Banham, Mr Colin . . . L . . . Oct 1999
Fenner, Mr Edward . . . M . . . Jul 2000
Drury, Miss Claire . . . L . . . Oct 2000
Nwosu, Miss Sheryl . . . M . . . Nov 2000
McCarroll, Ms Isobel . . . G . . . Nov 2001
Walsh, Mr Kevin . . . L . . . Mar 2003
Dannatt, Ms Lucinda . . . L . . . Oct 2003
Mootien, Ms Davina . . . G . . . Jan 2004
Draycott, Mr Christopher . . . I . . . Jan 2005
Sakr, Ms Farida . . . M . . . Jan 2005
Haines, Mr Alex . . . L . . . Jan 2007
Okewale, Mr Tunde . . . I . . . Jan 2007
Robinson, Mr Nick . . . L . . . Jan 2007
Jameson, Mr Rodney Mellor Maples (Q.C.)* . . . I . . . Jul 1976

Chambers of Andrew H Caldecott QC

ONE BRICK COURT,
1 BRICK COURT, TEMPLE, LONDON EC4Y 9BY
Tel: 020 7353 8845 ***Fax:*** 020 7583 9144
Dx: 468 LONDON/CHANCERY LANE
E-mail: clerks@onebrickcourt.com
Web: www.onebrickcourt.com
Clerk: Senior: David Mace. Melvin Warner.
Administrator: Emma Billimore
Head of Chambers:
Caldecott, Mr Andrew H (Q.C.) . . . I . . . Jul 1975

Rampton, Mr Richard (Q.C.) . . . I . . . Nov 1965
Hartley, Mr Richard L C (Q.C.)* . . . G . . . Jun 1956
Garnier, Mr Edward H (Q.C.)* . . . M . . . Jul 1976
Barca, Mr Manuel D (Q.C.) . . . L . . . Nov 1986
Starte, Mr Harvey N A . . . G . . . Nov 1985
Atkinson, Mr Timothy G B . . . I . . . Jul 1988
Phillips, Miss Jane R . . . I . . . Jul 1989
Addy, Ms Caroline . . . I . . . Nov 1991
Evans, Miss Catrin . . . I . . . Nov 1994
Palin, Miss Sarah . . . M . . . Nov 1999
Glen, Mr David . . . M . . . Mar 2002
Eardley, Mr Aidan . . . L . . . Nov 2002
Helme, Mr Ian . . . M . . . Jul 2005
Wilson, Ms Kate . . . I . . . Nov 2005
Kissin, Miss Clare . . . M . . . Oct 2009
Scherbel-Ball, Mr Jonathan . . . M . . . Oct 2010
Ready, Miss Hannah . . . L . . . Oct 2010

Chambers offers a wealth of experience and expertise in defamation, privacy, breach of confidence, contempt of court, malicious falsehood, media reporting restrictions (in criminal and civil proceedings), data protection, freedom of information, passing off and all claims involving a tension between rights to reputation and privacy and freedom of expression; all other related human rights law, including in judicial review applications, for further information please view the chambers website or contact David Mace.

Chambers of Jonathan Sumption QC and Jonathan Hirst QC

BRICK COURT CHAMBERS,
7-8 ESSEX STREET, LONDON WC2R 3LD
Tel: 020 7379 3550 ***Fax:*** 020 7379 3558
Dx: 302 LONDON/CHANCERY LANE
E-mail: clerks@brickcourt.co.uk
Clerk: Julian Hawes; Ian Moyler.
Administrator: Nancy Lockwood
Head of Chambers:
Sumption, Mr Jonathan (Q.C.) . . . I . . . Jul 1975
Hirst, Mr Jonathan (Q.C.) . . . I . . . Jul 1975

Kentridge, Sir Sydney (Q.C.) . . . L . . . Jul 1977
Vaughan, Mr David (Q.C.) CBE . . . I . . . Nov 1963
Heilbron, Miss Hilary (Q.C.) . . . G . . . Jul 1971
Cran, Mr Mark (Q.C.) . . . G . . . Jul 1973
Barling, Mr Gerald (Q.C.) . . . M . . . Nov 1972
Wyatt, Mr Derrick (Q.C.) . . . L . . . Jul 1972
Charlton, Mr Timothy (Q.C.) . . . I . . . Nov 1974
Gordon, Mr Richard (Q.C.) . . . M . . . Jul 1972
Hapgood, Mr Mark (Q.C.) . . . G . . . Feb 1979
Howard, Mr Mark (Q.C.) . . . G . . . Jul 1980
Ruttle, Mr Stephen (Q.C.) . . . G . . . Nov 1976
Popplewell, Mr Andrew (Q.C.) . . . I . . . Nov 1981
Wood, Mr William (Q.C.) . . . M . . . Nov 1980
Leggatt, Mr George (Q.C.) . . . M . . . Jul 1983
Green, Dr Nicholas (Q.C.) . . . I . . . Jul 1986
Hollander, Mr Charles (Q.C.) . . . G . . . Jul 1978
Anderson, Mr David (Q.C.) . . . M . . . Jul 1985
Otton-Goulder, Miss Catharine (Q.C.) . . . L . . . Nov 1983
Lord, Mr Richard (Q.C.) . . . I . . . Nov 1981
Brealey, Mr Mark (Q.C.) . . . M . . . Jul 1984
Swainston, Mr Michael (Q.C.) . . . L . . . Nov 1985
Flynn, Mr James (Q.C.) . . . M . . . Jul 1978
Lydiard, Mr Andrew (Q.C.) . . . I . . . Jul 1980
Quigley, Mr Conor (Q.C.) . . . G . . . Nov 1985
Irvin, Mr Peter . . . G . . . Jul 1972
Brunner, Mr Peter . . . M . . . Jul 1971
Randolph, Mr Fergus . . . M . . . Jul 1985
Garland, Mr David . . . M . . . Nov 1986
Calver, Mr Neil Richard . . . M . . . Nov 1987
Slade, Mr Richard . . . L . . . Nov 1987
Matovu, Mr Harry . . . I . . . Jul 1988
Wright, Mr Paul . . . I . . . Nov 1990
Lee, Miss Sarah . . . M . . . Nov 1990
Davies, Miss Helen . . . I . . . Nov 1991
Adam, Mr Thomas . . . I . . . Nov 1991
Hoskins, Mr Mark George . . . G . . . Nov 1991
Roxburgh, Mr Alan . . . G . . . Oct 1992
Lord, Mr Timothy M . . . I . . . Nov 1992
Maclean, Mr Alan . . . G . . . Nov 1993
Stratford, Miss Jemima . . . M . . . Oct 1993
Haydon, Mr Alec G . . . G . . . Oct 1993
Bools, Mr Michael David . . . M . . . Oct 1991
Masefield, Mr Roger . . . M . . . Jan 1994
Robertson, Mr Aidan . . . M . . . Jul 1995
Salzedo, Mr Simon . . . L . . . Jan 1995
Jowell, Mr Daniel . . . M . . . Nov 1995
Demetriou, Ms Marie-Eleni . . . M . . . Nov 1995
Dhillon, Mr Jasbir . . . G . . . Oct 1996
Thomas, Mr Andrew . . . I . . . May 1996
Chamberlain, Mr Martin . . . G . . . Oct 1997
Gray, Miss Margaret . . . G . . . Feb 1998
Birt, Mr Simon . . . G . . . Jan 1998
Bacon, Miss Kelyn . . . I . . . Feb 1998
West, Mr Colin . . . I . . . Oct 1999
Henshaw, Mr Andrew . . . I . . . Oct 2000
Lester, Miss Maya . . . L . . . Nov 2000
Pilbrow, Mr Fionn . . . I . . . Jan 2001
Midwinter, Mr Stephen . . . M . . . Jul 2002
Stevens, Miss Sarah Louise . . . L . . . Nov 2002
Scannell, Mr David . . . I . . . Jan 2003
Wakefield, Ms Victoria . . . G . . . Jan 2003
Willis, Mr Tony . . . L . . . Jan 2004

Chambers of Janet Vivien Mitchell

4 BRICK COURT CHAMBERS,
4 BRICK COURT, TEMPLE, LONDON EC4Y 9AD
Est: 1977
Tel: 020 7832 3200 ***Fax:*** 020 7797 8929
Dx: 491 LONDON/CHANCERY LANE
E-mail: clerks@4bc.co.uk
Clerk: Clive Barrett.
Head of Chambers:
Mitchell, Miss Janet Vivien . . . M . . . Feb 1978

Hildyard, Miss Marianna (Q.C.) . . . M . . . Nov 1977
Medhurst, Mr David Charles . . . G . . . Nov 1969
Chatterjee, Miss Mira . . . M . . . Nov 1973
Whelan, Miss Roma . . . G . . . May 1981
Quinn, Miss Susan . . . G . . . Jun 1983
Roberts, Mr Marc . . . I . . . Nov 1984
Lynch, Mr Peter . . . L . . . Jul 1985
Moore, Mrs Finola . . . L . . . Jul 1988
Harrill, Ms Jayne . . . M . . . Oct 1990
Azhar, Ms Marina . . . L . . . Nov 1990
Watson, Miss Isabelle . . . M . . . Nov 1991
Gilliatt, Ms Jacqueline . . . M . . . Feb 1992
Pavlou, Mr Paul . . . L . . . Nov 1993
Morton, Miss Rachel Joanna Eaden . . . L . . . Feb 1995
Lams, Mr Barnabus . . . G . . . Oct 1995
Rawcliffe, Mr Mark . . . M . . . Jan 1996
Tyler, Mr Thomas . . . L . . . Oct 1996
Griffin, Mr Ian . . . M . . . Nov 1997
Bayley, Miss Laura . . . G . . . Jan 1999
Adler, Mr Johnathan . . . I . . . Jan 1999
Hopkinson, Miss Joy . . . M . . . Jan 1999
Jamil, Miss Yasmin . . . L . . . Nov 1998
Bhachu, Miss Sharan . . . L . . . Mar 1999
Purss, Mr C Nairn . . . I . . . Oct 1999
Pepper, Miss Judith Leah . . . L . . . Oct 1999
Cogin, Mr Leo . . . M . . . Oct 2000
Cassidy, Mr Francis . . . M . . . Nov 2000
Maclynn, Miss Louise . . . G . . . Jan 2001
Rahman, Miss Tahmina . . . L . . . Jan 2001
Knott, Ms Helen . . . M . . . Jul 2002
Butler, Mr George . . . I . . . May 2003
Pearman, Mr Lee Charles . . . M . . . Jul 2003
Mustafa, Miss Hala . . . M . . . Jun 2004
Davies, Mr Gregory . . . M . . . Jan 2005
Potter, Mr Timothy . . . L . . . Jan 2005
Fuller, Mr Stuart Kenneth . . . I . . . Mar 2007

Chambers of Peter M Hayward

30 BROOKSBY STREET,
LONDON N1 1HA
Tel: 020 7607 3854 ***Fax:*** 020 7607 3854
E-mail: peter.hayward@orange.net
Clerk: Peter M Hayward.
Head of Chambers:
Hayward, Mr Peter M . . . G . . . Jul 1974

BRUNSWICK CHAMBERS,
2 MIDDLE TEMPLE LANE, TEMPLE, LONDON EC4Y 7AA
Tel: 020 7353 1987 / 7353 2818 ***Fax:*** 020 7583 1558

CHAMBERS OF MARTIN BURR,
FIRST FLOOR, TEMPLE CHAMBERS, TEMPLE AVENUE, LONDON EC4Y 0DA
Tel: 020 7353 4636 ***Fax:*** 020 7353 4637
Dx: 146 LONDON/CHANCERY LANE

Chambers of Kris Gledhill

CAMBERWELL CHAMBERS,
66 GROVE PARK, LONDON SE5 8LF
Tel: 020 7274 0830 ***Fax:*** 020 7274 0830
E-mail: krisgledhill@aol.com
Clerk: Kris Gledhill.
Head of Chambers:
Gledhill, Kris . . . I . . . Jul 1989

CARMELITE CHAMBERS,
9 CARMELITE STREET, LONDON EC4Y 0DR
Tel: 020 7936 6300 ***Fax:*** 020 7936 6301
Dx: 226 LDE
E-mail: clerks@carmelitechambers.co.uk
Web: www.carmelitechambers.co.uk
Clerk: Senior: Marc King. Deputy Senior Clerk: Matthew Butchard; Clerks: Christopher Mitchell; Dean Allen; Thomas Barnes; Ryan Fahey; Sophie Walsh; Fees Clerk: Norman Brooks; Sian Marshall; Reception: Lois Hayes.
Administrator: Orla O'Sullivan
Lambert, Mr Nigel R W (Q.C.); Recorder . . . G . . . Nov 1974
Bott, Mr Charles Adrian (Q.C.) . . . G . . . Nov 1979
Marshall-Andrews, Mr Robert Graham (Q.C.) MP; Recorder . . . G . . . Feb 1967
Lederman, Mr David (Q.C.) . . . I . . . Jan 1966
Hogg, The Hon Douglas Martin (Q.C.) MP . . . L . . . Jul 1968
Hussain, Mukhtar (Q.C.) . . . M . . . Jul 1971
Taylor, Mr William (Q.C.) . . . M . . . Jul 1990
Wood, Mr Michael (Q.C.) . . . M . . . Jul 1976
Jones, Mr John Richard (Q.C.) . . . M . . . Jul 1981
Smith, Mr Leonard (Q.C.) . . . G . . . Jan 1986
Orchard, Mr Anthony (Q.C.) . . . M . . . Oct 1991
Corrigan, Mr Peter A . . . M . . . Jul 1973
Cousens, Mr Michael P . . . L . . . Feb 1973
Kogan, Mr Barry . . . I . . . Jul 1973
Brickman, Miss Laura . . . I . . . Jul 1976
Shields, Miss Sonja M . . . G . . . Jul 1977
Turton, Mr Andrew Philip . . . M . . . Jul 1977
Gillard, Miss Isabelle . . . M . . . Jul 1980
Woodall, Mr Peter . . . M . . . Jul 1983
Molyneux, Mr Simon Rowley . . . I . . . Apr 1986
Taylor, Mr Martin . . . M . . . Jul 1988
Clark, Mr Peter Lestor . . . M . . . Nov 1988
Kayne, Mr Adrian . . . I . . . Jul 1989
James, Mr Grahame . . . G . . . Apr 1989
Henley, Mr Christopher M . . . G . . . Jul 1989
Aylott, Mr Colin . . . I . . . Nov 1989
Fitzgibbon, Mr Neil . . . L . . . Nov 1989
Hargreaves, Mr Benjamin . . . L . . . Nov 1989
Liddiard, Mr Martin . . . I . . . Jan 1989
Sherry, Mr Eamonn . . . G . . . Nov 1990
Miah, Mr Zacharias . . . I . . . Nov 1990
Modgil, Sangita . . . G . . . Oct 1990
Johnston, Miss Annie . . . I . . . Nov 1990
Ventham, Mr Tony . . . M . . . Apr 1991
England, Mr William . . . I . . . Nov 1991
Jones, Mr Howard . . . G . . . Oct 1992
Gruchy, Mr Simon . . . M . . . May 1993
Kane, Mr Adam . . . G . . . Nov 1993

Button, Mr Richard James . . . G. . . . Oct 1993
Qazi, Mr Ayaz . . . G. . . . Jan 1993
Sweet, Ms Louise . . . G. . . . Jun 1994
Walker, Mr James . . . L. . . . Oct 1994
Sherratt, Mr Mathew . . . I . . . . Oct 1994
Lawson, Mr Matthew . . . G. . . . Oct 1995
Bell, Alphege . . . I . . . . Nov 1995
Harries, Mr Mark . . . L. . . . Oct 1995
Panayi, Mr Pavlos . . . G. . . . Oct 1995
Zoest, Miss Jacqueline . . . G. . . . Nov 1995
Haeems, Mr David . . . I . . . . Mar 1996
Page, Mr Jonathan R T . . . M. . . . Oct 1996
Tilbury, Mr James . . . G. . . . Jan 1996
Morrell, Miss Roxanne T . . . M. . . . Jun 1996
Fosuhene, Miss Amelia . . . M. . . . Nov 1996
Stapleton, Miss Elaine . . . I . . . . Nov 1997
Johnson, Mr Gregory . . . I . . . . Dec 1998
Buckland, Mr Matthew . . . L. . . . Jan 1998
Halliday-Davis, Miss Lee . . . I . . . . Jul 1999
Lawrence, Miss Soraya . . . I . . . . Jan 1999
Hillman, Mr Gerard . . . G. . . . Jan 1999
Spenwyn, Miss Marie . . . G. . . . Jan 1999
Mahmood, Miss Saleema . . . G. . . . Nov 1999
Muir-Wilson, Miss Louise . . . M. . . . Jan 1999
Power, Miss Laurie-Anne . . . M. . . . Oct 2000
Rawat, Miss Houzla . . . M. . . . Oct 2001
Hallworth, Mr Andrew . . . G. . . . Mar 2002
King-Underwood, Mr Gregory . . . M. . . . Oct 2002
Leake, Mr Stephen . . . M. . . . Jan 2002
Webster, Miss Shelley . . . L. . . . Jan 2002
Titus, Miss Francesca . . . M. . . . Jul 2003
Page, Mr Douglas . . . L. . . . Jan 2003
O'Donoghue, Mr Hugh . . . M. . . . Oct 2004
Rollin, Mr Aron . . . M. . . . Jan 2004
Hendron, Mr Ashley . . . L. . . . Jan 2005
Hocknell, Miss Laura . . . I . . . . Jan 2005
Sheppard-Jones, Miss Victoria . . . G. . . . Jan 2005
Spears, Miss Katharine . . . M. . . . Jan 2005
McGowan, Miss Laura . . . G. . . . Jan 2006
Hingston, Mr Joe . . . L. . . . Jan 2007
Oborne, Miss Jennifer . . . I . . . . Jan 2007
MacManus, Miss Sabha . . . L. . . . Jan 2008

This is one of the largest and most established sets in England specialising in criminal law. Notable expertise is provided in serious fraud, money laundering, terrorism, murder, espionage, court martials and miscarriages of justice. Advocates at Chambers are at the forefront of UK and international practice and are regularly instructed in high profile cases. Chambers premises have been fully refurbished in order to offer an innovative working environment that includes the latest technology and conference facilities. Members have an unparalleled reputation for offering fearless advocacy.

Chambers of Paul Kishore

CHANCERY CHAMBERS,
3RD FLOOR, 74 CHANCERY LANE, HOLBORN, LONDON WC2A 1AD
Tel: 020 7405 6879 ***Fax:*** 020 7403 0502
Dx: 161 LONDON/CHANCERY LANE
Clerk: Danny Currie.
Head of Chambers:
Kishore, Mr Paul . . . L. . . . Nov 1982

Grayson, Mr Edward . . . L. . . . Jan 1948
Ramlogan, Mr Oudit . . . L. . . . Jan 1960
Butler, Miss Magueda . . . L. . . . Jul 1966
Unigwe, Mr Sylvester Emefiena . . . L. . . . Jan 1972
Jibowu, Mr Olumuyiwa A O . . . I . . . . Jan 1994
Deighan, Mr Patricia . . . I . . . . Jan 1996
Pocock, Mr Louis John . . . G. . . . Jan 1997
Bhatoo, Mr Khauck . . . L. . . . Jan 1999
Khan, Mr Muhammed Babar . . . I . . . . Jan 1999
Onipede, Dr Victor . . . L. . . . Jan 2000

Chambers of John G Ross QC

1 CHANCERY LANE,
LONDON WC2A 1LF
Tel: 0845 634 6666 ***Fax:*** 0845 634 6667
Dx: 364 LONDON/CHANCERY LANE
E-mail: clerks@1chancerylane.com
Clerk: Senior: Clark Chessis.
Administrator: Jenny Fensham
Practice Manager: Genevieve Quierin
Head of Chambers:
Ross, Mr John G (Q.C.) . . . I . . . . Jul 1971

Faulks, Mr Edward (Q.C.) . . . M. . . . Nov 1973
Readhead, Mr Simon (Q.C.) . . . M. . . . Jul 1979
Bishop, Mr Edward (Q.C.) . . . M. . . . Nov 1983
Hunter, Mr William . . . I . . . . Jul 1972
Walmsley, Mr Keith . . . I . . . . Jul 1973
Bryant, Mr John Malcolm C . . . I . . . . Nov 1976
Goodman, Mr Andrew . . . L. . . . Jul 1978
Yell, Mr Nicholas . . . M. . . . Jul 1979
Norman, Mr John . . . L. . . . Nov 1979
Hammerton, Mr Alastair . . . I . . . . Jul 1983
Waters, Mr Julian P . . . M. . . . Nov 1986
Rivalland, Mr Marc-Edouard . . . M. . . . Jul 1987
Althaus, Mr Justin . . . I . . . . Jul 1988
Weddell, Mr Geoffrey D A . . . I . . . . Jan 1989
Shuman, Miss Karen Ann Elizabeth . . . L. . . . Jan 1991
Piper, Mr Angus . . . L. . . . Nov 1991
Warnock, Mr Andrew . . . I . . . . Nov 1993
Chapman, Mr Matthew . . . G. . . . Oct 1994
Stagg, Mr Paul . . . G. . . . Nov 1994
Thomson, Dr David . . . L. . . . Nov 1994
Collett, Mr Ivor . . . M. . . . Nov 1995
Bredemear, Mr Zachary . . . I . . . . Oct 1996
Mortimer, Ms Sophie . . . L. . . . Nov 1996
Jackson, Ms Samantha . . . M. . . . Nov 1996
Waite, Mr Kiril . . . G. . . . Jan 1997
Prager, Miss Sarah . . . L. . . . Oct 1997
Miller, Mr Ian . . . G. . . . Oct 1999
Murray, Mr Simon . . . I . . . . Oct 2000
Trigger, Mr Simon . . . M. . . . Nov 2000
Khalid, Mr Saleem . . . L. . . . May 2001
Hicks, Mr Ben . . . I . . . . Jul 2001
Johnson, Miss Laura . . . G. . . . Nov 2001
Harding, Mr Jack . . . M. . . . Jan 2004
Spencer, Mr Andrew . . . G. . . . Jan 2004
Clarke, Mr Ian . . . I . . . . Jan 2005
Dobie, Miss Lisa . . . I . . . . Jan 2006
Abbott, Mr Roderick . . . M. . . . Jan 2006
Grant, Miss Rebecca . . . I . . . . Jan 2008
McClenaghan, Miss Frances . . . L. . . . Jan 2009
Crockett, Mr Thomas . . . G. . . . Jan 2009

Chambers of Andrew Mitchell QC

33 CHANCERY LANE,
LONDON WC2A 1EN
Tel: 020 7440 9950 ***Fax:*** 020 7430 2818
Dx: 33 CHANCERY LANE
Administrator: Clara Colvin
Chambers Director: Martin Adams (Practice Director); Sophie Collier (Deputy Practice Director); David Cox (Deputy Practice Director)
Head of Chambers:
Mitchell, Mr Andrew (Q.C.) . . . G. . . . Jul 1976

Evans, Mr David (Q.C.) . . . M. . . . Jul 1972
Webster, Mr Alistair S (Q.C.) . . . M. . . . Jul 1976
Marks, Mr Richard (Q.C.) . . . G. . . . Jul 1975
Rainsford, Mr Mark David (Q.C.) . . . L. . . . Nov 1985
Mitchell, Mr Keith A . . . I . . . . Nov 1981
Talbot, Mr Kennedy . . . G. . . . Nov 1984
Saunt, Ms Linda P . . . I . . . . Nov 1986
Hellman, Mr Stephen G . . . I . . . . Jul 1988
Brodie, Mr Graham . . . M. . . . Jul 1989
Evans, Mr Martin . . . M. . . . Nov 1989
Small, Ms Penelope . . . I . . . . Oct 1992
Taylor, Mr Simon . . . I . . . . Oct 1993
Pearce, Mr Ivan . . . G. . . . Oct 1994
Convey, Mr Christopher . . . L. . . . Nov 1994
Coghill-Smith, Ms Abigail . . . G. . . . Nov 1997
Jackson, Miss Fiona . . . I . . . . Nov 1998
Osman, Mr Faisal . . . L. . . . Mar 2002
Torode, Miss Joanna Dorothea . . . M. . . . Nov 2006

Chambers of Stephen Solley QC

CHARTER CHAMBERS,
33 JOHN STREET, LONDON WC1N 2AT
Tel: 020 7618 4400
E-mail: clerks@charterchambers.com
Clerk: Senior: P Duane. K Crawley; R McGurk; A Baum; M Martin; C Blake.
Administrator: John Brewster
Head of Chambers:
Solley, Mr Stephen (Q.C.) . . . I . . . . Nov 1969

Bishop, Mr Malcolm (Q.C.); Recorder; Deputy High Court Judge . . . I . . . . Jul 1968
Forster, Mr Brian Clive (Q.C.) . . . L. . . . Jan 1977
Bayliss, Mr Roderic A; Recorder . . . I . . . . Jul 1966
Gould, Mr Dennis . . . M. . . . Nov 1969
Fogg, Mr Anthony G . . . G. . . . Nov 1970
Davies, Mr Graham J . . . I . . . . Nov 1971
Bruce, Mr Richard Henderson; Recorder . . . G. . . . Jul 1974
Batcup, Mr David . . . G. . . . Jul 1974
Wurtzel, Mr David I . . . M. . . . Nov 1974
Higginson, Mr Peter . . . I . . . . Jul 1975
Sherman, Mr Robert . . . G. . . . Jul 1977
Wheatly, Mr Ian . . . I . . . . Nov 1977
Davey, Mr Roger Lawrence . . . I . . . . Feb 1978
Armstrong, Mr Grant B . . . L. . . . Jul 1978
Williams, Ms Susan . . . M. . . . Nov 1978
Mejzner, Mr Stephen . . . M. . . . Nov 1978
Rhodes, Mr Nicholas . . . L. . . . Jul 1981
Barnes, Mr David Jonathan . . . G. . . . Nov 1981
Tomassi, Mr Mark David . . . M. . . . Nov 1981
Oon, Miss Pamela Beng Sue . . . I . . . . Jul 1982
Buxton, Mr Thomas . . . G. . . . Jul 1983
Belger, Mr Tyrone . . . I . . . . Jul 1984
Tetlow, Mr Bernard . . . M. . . . Nov 1984
Marsh, Miss Carolyn . . . I . . . . Jul 1985
Khamisa, Mr Mohammed J (Q.C.) . . . M. . . . Nov 1985
Taylor, Mr David . . . G. . . . Jul 1986
Rose, Mr Jonathon . . . M. . . . Nov 1986
Buck, Mr John . . . G. . . . Nov 1987
Hamilton-Shield, Ms Anna . . . M. . . . Nov 1989
Hawes, Mr Neil . . . I . . . . Nov 1989
Wade, Ms Clare . . . I . . . . Jul 1990
Fraser, Mr Alan . . . G. . . . Sep 1990
Hastings, Miss Frances M . . . I . . . . Oct 1990
Lavers, Mr Michael . . . M. . . . Oct 1990
Phillips, Mr Paul Stuart . . . G. . . . Feb 1991
Robinson, Ms Claire . . . G. . . . Oct 1991
Deignan, Ms Mary-Teresa . . . M. . . . Oct 1991
Edwards, Miss Jennifer . . . G. . . . Oct 1992
Benzynie, Mr Robert . . . G. . . . Nov 1992
Flanagan, Ms Julia . . . L. . . . Oct 1993
Grey, Ms Siobhan . . . G. . . . Oct 1994
McCalla, Mr Tarquin . . . L. . . . Oct 1994
Jones, Mr Daniel . . . G. . . . Oct 1994
Raudnitz, Mr Paul . . . I . . . . Nov 1994
Goudie, Mr W Martin P . . . I . . . . Oct 1996
Morgan, Mr Adam . . . G. . . . Jan 1996
Slater, Miss Alison . . . M. . . . Nov 1996
Murray, Miss Lucy . . . L. . . . May 1997
Bowyer, Miss Juliet . . . L. . . . Oct 1997
Thomas, Mr Dominic . . . G. . . . Sep 1998
Shah, Ms Roshnee . . . M. . . . Oct 1998
James, Mr Roddy . . . L. . . . Mar 1999

CLAPHAM LAW CHAMBERS,
85 LANDOR ROAD, CLAPHAM NORTH, LONDON SW1 9RT
Tel: 020 7978 8482 / 7642 5777 ***Fax:*** 020 7642 5888
Dx: 53263 CLAPHAM COMMON
E-mail: danny@claphamlawchambers.co.uk
Clerk: Barry Leach.
Practice Manager: Danny Barnes
Shamim, Mr Mohammed . . . L. . . . Jan 1975
Reid, Mr Errol . . . G. . . . Feb 1978
Hamid, Mrs Beebee Nass . . . L. . . . Jul 1980
Rana, Mr M Akram . . . L. . . . Jan 1995
Hyde, Mr David . . . L. . . . Nov 1997
Marshall-Bain, Miss Lydia . . . G. . . . Jan 1998
Ahmed, Mr Sharaz . . . L. . . . Jan 2000
Louis, Miss Angela . . . L. . . . Jan 2002
Edwards, Mr Charles Edwin . . . M. . . . Jan 2002
Malik, Mr Ahmed . . . G. . . . Jan 2008

Chambers of Ben Beaumont

CLARENDON CHAMBERS,
1 PLOWDEN BUILDINGS, TEMPLE, LONDON EC4Y 9BU
Tel: 020 7353 0003 ***Fax:*** 020 7353 9213
Dx: 0022 LONDON/CHANCERY LANE

CLERKSROOM,
3RD FLOOR, 218 STRAND, LONDON WC2R 1AT
Tel: 0845 083 3000 ***Fax:*** 0845 083 3001
Dx: 232 LONDON/CHANCERY LANE

Chambers of Robin Allen QC and Brian Langstaff QC

CLOISTERS,
1ST FLOOR, 1 PUMP COURT, TEMPLE, LONDON EC4Y 7AA
Tel: 020 7827 4000 ***Fax:*** 020 7827 4100
Dx: 452 LONDON/CHANCERY LANE
E-mail: clerks@cloisters.com
Clerk: Glenn Hudson.
Administrator: Louise Newton
Practice Manager: Jagdip Jagpal
Chambers Director: Jagdip Jagpal
Head of Chambers:
Allen, Mr Robin (Q.C.) . . . M. . . . Nov 1974
Langstaff, Mr Brian (Q.C.) . . . M. . . . Jul 1971

Davidson, Mr Arthur (Q.C.) . . . M. . . . Nov 1953
Taylor, Dr Simon W (Q.C.) . . . M. . . . Jul 1984
Crystal, Mr Jonathan . . . M. . . . Jul 1972
Seaward, Mr Martin V . . . G. . . . Nov 1978
Engelman, Mr Philip . . . G. . . . Jul 1979
Romney, Miss Daphne . . . I . . . . Nov 1979
Algazy, Mr Jacques . . . G. . . . Nov 1980
Buchan, Mr Andrew . . . G. . . . Jul 1981
Hendy, Ms Pauline . . . L. . . . Nov 1985
Dyer, Mr Simon C . . . L. . . . Jul 1987
O'Dempsey, Mr Declan John . . . M. . . . Nov 1987
Hitchcock, Ms Patricia . . . I . . . . Nov 1988
Epstein, Mr Paul . . . I . . . . Nov 1988
Spencer, Mr Paul Anthony . . . M. . . . Nov 1988
Bradley, Mr Anthony . . . I . . . . Apr 1989
Brodie, Mr Graham . . . M. . . . Jul 1989
Donovan, Scott . . . L. . . . Jul 1975
Genn, Ms Yvette . . . I . . . . Oct 1991
Galbraith-Marten, Mr Jason . . . I . . . . Oct 1991
Michell, Mr Paul . . . M. . . . Nov 1991
Quinn, Mr Chris . . . M. . . . Oct 1992
Glyn, Mr Caspar . . . I . . . . Nov 1992
Horan, Mr John . . . I . . . . Feb 1993
McCarthy, Mr Damian . . . M. . . . May 1994
Crasnow, Ms Rachel . . . M. . . . Nov 1994
Latimer-Sayer, Mr William Laurence . . . G. . . . Oct 1995
Robertson, Ms Sally . . . I . . . . Nov 1995
Coghlin, Mr Thomas . . . I . . . . Jan 1998
Solomon, Mr Adam Jonathan . . . G. . . . Oct 1998
Cohen, Mr Jonathan Michael . . . G. . . . Oct 1999
Jolly, Miss Schona . . . G. . . . Oct 1999
Massarella, Mr David . . . M. . . . Nov 1999
Reindorf, Miss Akua . . . M. . . . Nov 1999
Jacobs, Ms Linda . . . M. . . . Jan 2000
McCann, Ms Claire . . . I . . . . Oct 2000
Brown, Mr Thomas . . . M. . . . Nov 2000
Beale, Ms Anna . . . G. . . . Nov 2001
Ohringer, Mr Adam . . . M. . . . Jan 2001
Godfrey, Ms Hannah . . . L. . . . Jan 2004
Chambers, Ms Rachel . . . M. . . . Jan 2002
Palmer, Mr Martin . . . I . . . . Jul 2003

CLOTH FAIR CHAMBERS,
39-40 CLOTH FAIR, LONDON EC1A 7NT
Tel: 020 7710 6444 ***Fax:*** 020 7710 6446
Dx: 321 LONDON/CHANCERY LANE
Purnell, Mr Nicholas (Q.C.) . . . M. . . . Jul 1968
Kelsey-Fry, Mr John (Q.C.) . . . G. . . . Nov 1978
Langdale, Mr Timothy (Q.C.) . . . L. . . . Jul 1966
Winter, Mr Ian . . . I . . . . Jul 1988
Barnard, Mr Jonathan . . . I . . . . Oct 1997
Sibson, Ms Clare . . . M. . . . Oct 1997

CHAMBERS OF MR ANTHONY CLOVER,
GROVE HOUSE, 432 UPPER RICHMOND ROAD, LONDON SW15 5RQ
Tel: 020 8876 5795 ***Fax:*** 020 8392 9426

Chambers of Martha Cover

CORAM CHAMBERS,
9-11 FULWOOD PLACE, LONDON EC1V 6HG
Tel: 020 7092 3700 ***Fax:*** 020 7092 3777
Dx: 404 LONDON/CHANCERY LANE
E-mail: mail@coramchambers.co.uk
Clerk: Senior: Paul Sampson.
Practice Manager: Chris Bean
Head of Chambers:
Cover, Ms Martha . . . G . . . Nov 1979

McCarthy, Mr Roger J (Q.C.) . . . G . . . Jul 1975
Drew, Ms Jane . . . M . . . Jul 1976
Boyd, Mr David . . . M . . . Feb 1977
Nicholes, Ms Catherine . . . I . . . May 1977
Sen, Mr Aditya Kumar . . . L . . . Jul 1977
Sheldrake, Miss Christine; Deputy District Judge . . . M . . . Jul 1977
Spratling, Ms Anne . . . L . . . Jul 1980
Hudson, Miss Kate . . . M . . . Jul 1981
Gill, Ms Meena . . . M . . . Jul 1982
Gibb, Miss Fiona M; Barrister . . . M . . . Jul 1983
Morris, Ms Christina . . . G . . . Nov 1983
Marks, Ms Jacqueline; Deputy District Judge (Principal Registry) . . . M . . . Jul 1984
Warner, Miss Pamela . . . G . . . Feb 1985
O'Brien, Mr Nicholas . . . M . . . Nov 1985
Bhatia, Miss Divya; Barrister . . . M . . . Jul 1986
Purkiss, Miss Kate . . . L . . . Jul 1988
LeCointe, Ms Elpha . . . L . . . Nov 1988
Inglis, Mr Alan . . . M . . . Jul 1989
Orchover, Ms Frances . . . M . . . Jul 1989
Mitropoulos, Miss Georgia . . . G . . . Jul 1989
Bullock, Mr Neil . . . M . . . Nov 1989
George, Ms Susan . . . G . . . Nov 1990
Sapnara, Ms Khatun . . . M . . . Nov 1990
Twomey, Mr Mark James . . . I . . . Nov 1990
Fry, Mr Neil . . . I . . . Feb 1992
Vavrecka, Mr David . . . M . . . Oct 1992
Kothari, Miss Sima . . . G . . . Oct 1992
Hyde, Ms Marcia . . . I . . . Oct 1992
Sawyerr, Miss Sharon . . . I . . . Nov 1992
Chaudhry, Miss Sabuhi . . . L . . . Oct 1993
Horton, Mr Michael John Edward . . . G . . . Nov 1993
Langridge, Ms Niki . . . I . . . Nov 1993
Gore, Mrs Susan Diana . . . M . . . Nov 1993
Easton, Miss Alison . . . I . . . Nov 1994
Casey, Mr Dermot Fintan . . . M . . . Nov 1994
Marley, Miss Sarah . . . L . . . Oct 1995
Kelly, Ms Siobhan Frances . . . M . . . Oct 1995
Lewis, Miss Danielle Soraya . . . L . . . Nov 1995
Fitzpatrick, Mr Jerry . . . M . . . Mar 1996
Ferris, Ms Caitlin Tara . . . I . . . Mar 1996
Freeston, Miss Lynn . . . G . . . Oct 1996
Stamford, Ms Susan Deborah . . . M . . . Oct 1997
Horsley, Mr Nicholas . . . M . . . Oct 1998
Hughes, Ms Daisy . . . M . . . Oct 1999
Beddoe, Mr Richard . . . G . . . Oct 1999
Glover, Miss Anne-Marie . . . M . . . Oct 2000
de Souza, Mr Mark . . . G . . . Oct 2000
Branson, Ms Sarah Louise . . . M . . . Jul 2001
Fottrell, Ms Deirdre May . . . M . . . Oct 2001
Taylor, Ms Mary-Jane . . . I . . . Oct 2003
Brown, Miss Tamzin . . . G . . . Oct 2003
McMullan, Ms Laura Christina . . . I . . . Nov 2004
Schofield, Mr James John . . . G . . . Jul 2004
Aman, Ms Rosina . . . G . . . Jul 2005
Akhavan-Tabib, Ms Maryam . . . I . . . Oct 2005
Andrews, Miss Katherine . . . G . . . Jul 2006
Yorke, Mr Richard . . . I . . . Oct 2006
Wicks, Lucinda . . . M . . . Nov 2006
Rushworth, Miss Georgina . . . L . . . Oct 2007
Handa, Radhika . . . I . . . Jul 2008
Shah, Mr Neil . . . M . . . Jul 2008
Chapman, Ms Tracy . . . M . . . Jul 2009
Tyler, Ms Sarah . . . I . . . Oct 2009
Rensten, Ms Katy . . . I . . . Jul 2010
Honeyman, Ms Gillian . . . G . . . Jul 2011

Chambers of Mary Cook and James Findlay QC

CORNERSTONE BARRISTERS,
2-3 GRAY'S INN SQUARE, LONDON WC1R 5JH
Tel: 020 7242 4986 ***Fax:*** 020 7405 1166
Dx: 316 LONDON/CHANCERY LANE
E-mail: clerks@cornerstonebarristers.com
Clerk: Martin Hart; Stuart Pullum; Frances Kaliszewska; Jason Savage; Paul Cray; Greg Goodman; Alex Hill.
Administrator: Rose Vance
Chambers Director: Lynne Orsborn
Head of Chambers:
Cook, Ms Mary . . . G . . . Jul 1982
Findlay, Mr James (Q.C.) . . . M . . . Nov 1984

Porten, Mr Anthony (Q.C.) . . . I . . . Jul 1969
Dinkin, Mr Anthony (Q.C.) . . . L . . . Nov 1968
Sauvain, Mr Stephen (Q.C.) . . . L . . . Jul 1977
Lowe, Mr Mark (Q.C.) . . . G . . . Jul 1972
Fraser, Mr Vincent (Q.C.) . . . G . . . Jul 1981
Matthias, Mr David H (Q.C.) . . . I . . . Jul 1980
Ellis, Ms Morag (Q.C.) . . . I . . . Jul 1984
Gasztowicz, Mr Steven (Q.C.)* . . . G . . . Jul 1981
Kolvin, Mr Philip (Q.C.) . . . I . . . Jul 1988
Bird, Mr Simon (Q.C.) . . . M . . . Jul 1987
McGuire, Mr Bryan Nicholas (Q.C.) . . . M . . . Jul 1983
Forlin, Mr Gerard (Q.C.) . . . G . . . Jun 1984
Stephenson, Mr Geoffrey . . . G . . . Nov 1971
Lamming, Mr David . . . G . . . Nov 1972
Alesbury, Mr Alun . . . I . . . Jul 1974
Trevelyan Thomas, Mr Adrian . . . G . . . Jul 1974
Nardecchia, Mr Nicholas . . . M . . . Nov 1974
Stoker, Mr Graham . . . M . . . Nov 1977
Albutt, Mr Ian . . . G . . . Jul 1981
Shadarevian, Mr Paul . . . G . . . Jul 1984
Bedford, Mr Michael . . . G . . . Jul 1985
Druce, Mr Michael . . . I . . . Jul 1988
Bhose, Mr Ranjit . . . G . . . Jul 1989
Rutledge, Mr Kelvin Albert . . . M . . . Jul 1989
Clay, Mr Jonathan . . . L . . . Oct 1990
Holbrook, Mr Jon . . . I . . . Nov 1991
Green, Mr Robin . . . I . . . Oct 1992
Townsend, Mrs Harriet . . . M . . . Nov 1992
Miller, Mr Peter . . . L . . . Oct 1993
Cosgrove, Mr Thomas James . . . I . . . Oct 1994
Ground, Mr Richard William . . . I . . . Oct 1994
Beglan, Mr Wayne . . . L . . . Oct 1996
Clarke, Mr Rory . . . I . . . Oct 1996
Lintott, Mr David J . . . G . . . Oct 1996
Bhogal, Ms Kuljit . . . L . . . Oct 1999
Davies, Miss Sian . . . G . . . Oct 1999
Murphy, Miss Melissa Rosalind Gillian . . . M . . . Nov 2001
Etiebet, Ms Peggy . . . G . . . Oct 2001
Ranatunga, Mr Asitha Nandika . . . I . . . Oct 2001
Welfare, Mr Damien Francis John . . . I . . . Jul 2001
Cannon, Mr Josef David . . . L . . . Jul 2002
Parry, Ms Clare . . . M . . . Jan 2005
Weller, Ms Sophie . . . G . . . Jan 2005
Oscroft, Jennifer . . . M . . . Jan 2006
Dring, Emma . . . L . . . Jan 2009
Davies, Mr Karl . . . I . . . Nov 1999
Skerrett, Ms Katy; Tenant . . . M . . . Oct 1999

Chambers of Terence William de Lury

COURT YARD CHAMBERS,
ELTHAM PALACE, PO BOX 370, LONDON SE9 2RP
Tel: 020 7936 2710
Dx: 32508 ELTHAM
Clerk: Wanda Bogucka.
Head of Chambers:
de Lury, Mr Terence William . . . G . . . Jul 1985

Ferguson, Mr Christopher Mark* . . . M . . . May 1979

Chambers of Ishmael Job Kumi

CROMWELL-AYEH-KUMI CHAMBERS,
25 TAYLORS GREEN, LONDON W3 7PF
Tel: 020 8740 6982 ***Fax:*** 020 8740 6982
E-mail: ismaelkumi@gmail.com
Head of Chambers:
Kumi, Mr Ishmael Job . . . G . . . Nov 1977

Chambers of Andrew V B Bartlett QC

CROWN OFFICE CHAMBERS,
2 CROWN OFFICE ROW, TEMPLE, LONDON EC4Y 7HJ
Tel: 020 7797 8100 ***Fax:*** 020 7797 8101
Dx: 80 LONDON/CHANCERY LANE
E-mail: mail@crownofficechambers.com
Web: www.crownofficechambers.com
Clerk: Senior: Andy Flanagan.
Head of Chambers:
Bartlett, Mr Andrew V B (Q.C.) . . . M . . . Jul 1974

Harvey, Mr Michael (Q.C.); Recorder . . . G . . . Jul 1966
Spencer, Mr Michael (Q.C.) . . . I . . . Jul 1970
Purchas, Mr Christopher Patrick Brooks (Q.C.); Recorder . . . I . . . Jul 1966
ter Haar, Mr Roger (Q.C.) . . . I . . . Jul 1974
Stevenson, Mr William (Q.C.); Recorder . . . L . . . Nov 1968
Lynagh, Mr Richard (Q.C.); Recorder . . . G . . . Jul 1975
Kent, Mr Michael (Q.C.); Recorder . . . M . . . Jul 1975
Turner, Mr Mark G (Q.C.); Recorder . . . G . . . Jul 1981
Waite, Mr Jonathan (Q.C.) . . . I . . . Jul 1978
Smith, Mr Andrew (Q.C.) . . . G . . . Jan 1988
Bickford-Smith, Mrs Margaret Osbourne (Q.C.) . . . I . . . Jul 1973
Curtis, Mr Michael (Q.C.) . . . M . . . Jan 1982
Rigney, Mr Andrew (Q.C.) . . . G . . . Oct 1992
Platt, Mr David W (Q.C.) . . . M . . . Jul 1987
Berkin, Mr Martyn . . . M . . . Jul 1966
Chern, Dr Cyril . . . G . . . Jan 1972
Nixon, Mr Colin . . . L . . . Jul 1973
Matthews, Mr Dennis . . . M . . . Jul 1973
Davies, Mr Nicholas . . . M . . . Jul 1975
Stevenson, Mr John Melford . . . I . . . Nov 1975
Phillips, Mr Andrew . . . M . . . Jul 1978
Greenbourne, Mr John . . . G . . . Jul 1978
Catford, Mr Gordon B . . . L . . . Jul 1980
Field, Mr Julian . . . G . . . Nov 1980
Dean, Mr Paul . . . I . . . Jul 1982
Jones, Ms Charlotte . . . M . . . Jul 1982
Williams, Mr A John . . . L . . . Jul 1983
Coles, Mr Steven . . . M . . . Jul 1983
Franklin, Miss Kim . . . M . . . Nov 1984
Cooper, Mr John . . . I . . . Jul 1985
Medd, Mr James . . . M . . . Jul 1985
Ferris, Mr Shaun . . . G . . . Nov 1985
Foster, Ms Catherine . . . I . . . Jan 1986
Vandyck, Mr William . . . L . . . Jul 1988
Wright, Mr Ian F G . . . I . . . Jul 1989
Morton, Mr Peter . . . M . . . Oct 1988
Woolgar, Mr Dermot . . . I . . . Jul 1988
Brown, Mr Simon J . . . G . . . Jan 1988
Snowden, Mr Steven . . . I . . . Jul 1989
Power, Miss Erica . . . L . . . Oct 1990
Evans-Tovey, Mr Jason R . . . G . . . Oct 1990
Gee, Mr Toby . . . I . . . Oct 1992
Hitching, Ms Isabel . . . M . . . Nov 1992
Antelme, Mr Alexander . . . G . . . Oct 1993
Blakesley, Mr Patrick . . . I . . . Nov 1993
Tyrell, Mr Richard . . . G . . . Oct 1993
Toogood, Miss Claire Victoria . . . M . . . Oct 1995
Stokell, Mr Robert . . . L . . . Oct 1995
Chalmers, Ms Suzanne . . . G . . . Oct 1995
Antrobus, Mr Simon . . . I . . . Oct 1995
Balysz, Mr Mark A . . . G . . . Oct 1995
Maxwell-Scott, Mr James H . . . G . . . Nov 1995
Davis, Mr Andrew . . . G . . . Oct 1996
Broome, Mr Edward . . . I . . . Oct 1996
Haque, Mr Muhammed L . . . L . . . Sep 1997
Kay, Mr Dominic . . . G . . . Oct 1997
Lindsey, Miss Susan . . . I . . . Nov 1997
Quiney, Mr Ben . . . G . . . Mar 1998
Ferro, Mr Jack . . . I . . . Sep 1998
Horne, Mr Julian . . . M . . . Sep 1998
Woodbridge, Miss Victoria . . . L . . . Oct 1998
Laney, Miss Anna . . . L . . . Oct 1998
Shapiro, Mr Daniel . . . I . . . Oct 1999
Mauladad, Miss Farrah . . . M . . . Oct 1999
Armitage, Mr Mark . . . M . . . Oct 1999
Boyle, Mr Matthew . . . G . . . Jul 2000
Macpherson, Mr Alexander . . . M . . . Nov 2000
Taylor, Miss Rebecca . . . G . . . Oct 2001
Pimlott, Mr Charles; Junior Tenant . . . M . . . Nov 2001
De Gregorio, Mr Michele . . . I . . . Jul 2003
Winser, Mr Crispin . . . I . . . Oct 2003
Vann, Mr Harry . . . M . . . Oct 2003
Davis, Mr Justin . . . L . . . Oct 2003
Hellebronth, Miss Rosanna . . . M . . . Oct 2004
Houghton, Mr Peter . . . L . . . Oct 2005
Kendrick, Miss Julia; Junior Tenant . . . M . . . Oct 2005
Boon, Miss Elizabeth . . . I . . . Jul 2006
Atkins, Mr Michael . . . M . . . Oct 2006
Sage, Mr Richard . . . L . . . Nov 2006
Myhill, Mr David . . . L . . . Nov 2006
Lambertson, Ms Siobhan . . . M . . . Nov 2007
Whittaker, Miss Nadia . . . I . . . Jul 2007
Pagett, Helen . . . I . . . Jul 2008
Macaulay, Mr Jack . . . L . . . Oct 2009
Holmes, Mr Rory . . . M . . . Nov 2009
Taczalski, Mr Carlo . . . M . . . Jan 2010
McColgan, Ms Caroline . . . M . . . Jan 2010

Alternative Dispute Resolution (ADR), Arbitration including International Trade, Building, Chancery - General, Clinical Negligence, Commercial Law, Common Law - General, Company Law, Consumer Law - Agreements/Credit/Licensing/Sale of Goods, Consumer Protection - Advertising/Trade Descriptions/Trading Standards/Product Liability, Criminal Work - Criminal Procedures, Environment, Health & Safety at Work, Insurance, Licensing, Mediation, Personal Injury, Planning & Rating, Professional Negligence.

Chambers of Philip Havers QC

1 CROWN OFFICE ROW,
TEMPLE, LONDON EC4Y 7HH
Tel: 020 7797 7500 ***Fax:*** 020 7797 7550
Dx: 1020 LDE
E-mail: mail@1cor.com
Web: www.1cor.com
Clerk: Senior: Matthew Phipps.
Chambers Director: Bob Wilson
Head of Chambers:
Havers, The Hon Philip (Q.C.) . . . I . . . Jul 1974

Seabrook, Mr Robert (Q.C.); Recorder . . . M . . . Jun 1964
Badenoch, Mr James (Q.C.); Recorder . . . L . . . Nov 1968
Miller, Mr Stephen (Q.C.); Recorder . . . M . . . Jul 1971
Coonan, Mr Kieran (Q.C.); Recorder of the Crown Court (1996) . . . G . . . Jul 1971
Coghlan, Mr Terence (Q.C.); Recorder . . . I . . . Dec 1968
Mansfield, Hon Guy (Q.C.); Recorder . . . M . . . Nov 1972
Smith, Ms Sally (Q.C.) . . . I . . . Nov 1977
Gumbel, Ms Elizabeth Anne (Q.C.) . . . M . . . Nov 1974
Rees, Mr Paul (Q.C.) . . . G . . . Nov 1980
Bowron, Ms Margaret (Q.C.); Recorder . . . I . . . Nov 1978
Garnham, Mr Neil (Q.C.); Recorder . . . M . . . Jul 1982
Balcombe, Mr David (Q.C.); Recorder . . . L . . . Nov 1980
Glynn, Ms Joanna (Q.C.) . . . M . . . Nov 1983
Hart, Mr David (Q.C.) . . . M . . . Jul 1982
Forde, Mr Martin (Q.C.) . . . M . . . Feb 1984
Edis, Mr William (Q.C.) . . . L . . . Jul 1985
Lambert, Ms Christina (Q.C.) . . . I . . . Jan 1988
Outhwaite, Ms Wendy (Q.C.) . . . L . . . May 1990
McCullough, Mr Angus (Q.C.) . . . M . . . Oct 1990
Whipple, Ms Philippa (Q.C.) . . . M . . . Nov 1994
Whitting, Mr John (Q.C.) . . . M . . . Oct 1991
Gimlette, Mr John . . . I . . . Nov 1986

Wheeler, Ms Marina . . . G . . . Nov 1987
Evans, Mr David . . . M . . . Jul 1988
Witcomb, Mr Henry . . . L . . . Apr 1989
Kennedy, Mr Andrew . . . M . . . Jan 1989
Downs, Mr Martin . . . I . . . Nov 1990
Booth, Mr Richard . . . M . . . Oct 1993
Colin, Mr Giles . . . I . . . Feb 1994
Chawatama, Mr Sydney . . . M . . . Oct 1994
Lambert, Ms Sarah . . . G . . . Oct 1994
Levinson, Mr Justin . . . M . . . Oct 1994
Thomas, Mr Owain . . . I . . . Oct 1995
Hyam, Mr Jeremy . . . G . . . Nov 1995
Sanders, Mr Oliver . . . I . . . Jul 1995
Collins, Mr Ben . . . M . . . Nov 1996
Rahman, Ms Shaheen . . . G . . . Nov 1996
Skelton, Mr Peter . . . M . . . Oct 1997
Taylor, Ms Zoe . . . G . . . Oct 1998
Sheldon, Mr Neil . . . G . . . Nov 1998
Neenan, Ms Caroline . . . G . . . Oct 1998
Smith, Mr Richard . . . I . . . Oct 1999
Mellor, Mr Christopher . . . M . . . Nov 1999
Kellar, Mr Robert . . . G . . . Jan 1999
Barnes, Mr Matthew . . . M . . . Nov 2000
O'Donnell, Mr Iain . . . L . . . Jul 2000
Singh, Mr Sarabjit . . . L . . . Oct 2001
Manknell, Mr David . . . M . . . Nov 2001
Lambert, Ms Suzanne . . . L . . . Oct 2002
Rogerson, Ms Judith . . . L . . . Jul 2003
Lindsay Strugo, Ms Andrea . . . I . . . Jan 2003
Wastell, Mr Robert . . . L . . . Jul 2004
Mumford, Mr Richard . . . L . . . Nov 2004
Jolliffe, Mr John . . . I . . . Jan 2005
Marcus, Ms Rachel . . . I . . . Jan 2005
Rathod, Mr Pritesh . . . M . . . Jan 2006
Cross, Ms Caroline . . . G . . . Jan 2006
Donmall, Mr Matthew . . . L . . . Jan 2006
Beattie, Ms Kate . . . I . . . Jan 2007
Wagner, Mr Adam . . . I . . . Jan 2007
McArdle, Ms Isabel . . . L . . . Jul 2008
Hill, Mr Matthew . . . I . . . Jan 2009
Henderson, Mr Alasdair . . . I . . . Jan 2009
Flinn, Mr Matthew . . . I . . . Jan 2010
Roche, Maria . . . I . . . Jan 2010

Recognised as a leading civil set, in particular for clinical negligence, personal injury, professional disciplinary, public law, human rights, environmental law, tax, professional negligence, employment and costs.

Chambers of Elizabeth Ann Ayodele Joseph

66 DAUBENEY ROAD,
LONDON E5 0EF
Tel: 020 8985 3030 ***Fax:*** 020 8985 3030
Head of Chambers:
Joseph, Ms Elizabeth Ann Ayodele . . . G . . . Jul 1983

DEAL CHAMBERS,
60 MOORDOWN, SHOOTERS HILL, LONDON SE18 3NG
Tel: 020 8856 8738 ***Fax:*** 0871 433 4376

DESIGN CHAMBERS,
24 ARTERBURY ROAD, WIMBLEDON, LONDON SW20 8AH
Tel: 020 7353 0747 ***Fax:*** 020 7353 0772

Chambers of Colin Edelman QC

DEVEREUX CHAMBERS,
DEVEREUX COURT, LONDON WC2R 3JH
Tel: 020 7353 7534 ***Fax:*** 020 7583 5150
Dx: 349 LONDON/CHANCERY LANE
E-mail: clerks@devchambers.co.uk
Clerk: Vince Plant (Head of Clerking Services).
Chambers Director: Beverly Landais (Chief Executive Officer)
Head of Chambers:
Edelman, Mr Colin (Q.C.) . . . M . . . Jul 1977

Cotton, Miss Diana (Q.C.) . . . M . . . Jun 1964
Glancy, Mr Robert (Q.C.) . . . M . . . Jul 1972
Brennan, Mr Timothy (Q.C.) . . . G . . . Nov 1981
Fisher, Mr Jonathan (Q.C.) . . . G . . . Jul 1980
Read, Mr Graham Stephen (Q.C.) . . . G . . . Jul 1981
Killalea, Mr Stephen (Q.C.) . . . M . . . Jul 1981
Wynter, Mr Colin (Q.C.) . . . I . . . Nov 1984
Simler, Miss Ingrid (Q.C.) . . . I . . . Jul 1987
Carr, Mr Bruce (Q.C.) . . . I . . . Nov 1986
Weir, Mr Robert (Q.C.) . . . M . . . Nov 1992
Lee, Mr Ian . . . G . . . Jul 1973
Bard, Mr Nicholas . . . G . . . Jul 1979
Silvester, Mr Bruce Ross . . . I . . . Jul 1983
Mendoza, Mr Colin . . . I . . . Nov 1983
Hyams, Mr Oliver; Part Time Employment Tribunal Chairman . . . M . . . Jan 1989
Randall, Mr Nicholas . . . M . . . Oct 1990
Harrison, Mr Richard . . . L . . . Nov 1991
Mckie, Ms Suzanne . . . L . . . Nov 1991
Edwards, Mr Peter . . . I . . . Oct 1992
Padfield, Miss Alison Mary . . . L . . . Oct 1992
Sadiq, Mr Tariq . . . G . . . Jul 1993
Burns, Mr Andrew . . . M . . . Oct 1993
Cartwright, Mr Richard . . . I . . . Jan 1994
Thomas, Ms Anna . . . I . . . Nov 1995
Sethi, Mr Mohinderpal . . . M . . . Jan 1996
Frith, Mr Timothy . . . M . . . Nov 1996
Nawbatt, Mr Akash . . . G . . . Jun 1999
Catherwood, Shaen . . . G . . . Jul 2000
Hunter, Mr Robert Neil . . . G . . . Oct 2000
Belgrove, Ms Sophie . . . M . . . Sep 2001
Lynch, Mr Ben . . . M . . . Oct 2001
Mayhew, Ms Alice . . . I . . . Dec 2001
Watson, Miss Sarah . . . L . . . Jan 2002
Avery, Miss Rachel . . . L . . . Jan 2003
Butlers, Mr Jonathan . . . M . . . Jan 2003
Harris, Miss Lucinda . . . M . . . Jan 2004
Bell, Miss Laura . . . L . . . Jul 2004
Vonberg, Mr Thomas . . . M . . . Nov 2004
Cordrey, Mr Thomas . . . L . . . Jul 2006
Nicholls, Mr Samuel David . . . I . . . Nov 2006
Stone, Mr Christopher Mark . . . L . . . Oct 2007
Barsam, Ms Talia . . . I . . . Nov 2007
McNair-Wilson, Ms Laura . . . G . . . Nov 2007
Hirsch, Ms Georgina . . . G . . . Jan 2009

Chambers of Gazi Mosta Gawsal Haque

DOLLIS HILL CHAMBERS,
197 ELLESMERE ROAD, LONDON NW10 1LG
Tel: 020 8208 1663 ***Fax:*** 020 8208 1663
E-mail: gmghaque@yahoo.co.uk
Clerk: S N Haque.
Head of Chambers:
Haque, Gazi Mosta Gawsal . . . I . . . Jul 1970

Chambers of Geoffrey Robertson QC and Edward Fitzgerald QC

DOUGHTY STREET CHAMBERS,
53-54 DOUGHTY STREET, LONDON WC1N 2LS
Est: 1990
Tel: 020 7404 1313 ***Fax:*** 020 7404 2283 / 7404 2284
Dx: 223 LONDON/CHANCERY LANE
E-mail: enquiries@doughtystreet.co.uk
Clerk: Senior Civil: Paul Friend; Senior Crime: Graham Briggs; Crime: Richard Goodman; Chris Errity; Civil: Richard Bayliss; Mark Byrne; Paul Read; Arsineh Gaspariance; Junior: Eresha Reid; Fiona Mckenzie.
Practice Manager: Martin Griffiths
Chambers Director: Robin Jackson
Head of Chambers:
Robertson, Mr Geoffrey (Q.C.); Recorder, Joint Head of Chambers . . . M . . . Jul 1973
Fitzgerald, Mr Edward (Q.C.); Recorder . . . I . . . Nov 1978

Kennedy, Ms Helena (Q.C.) . . . G . . . Jul 1972
O'Connor, Mr Patrick M J (Q.C.) . . . I . . . Nov 1970
Sallon, Mr Christopher (Q.C.); Recorder . . . G . . . Jul 1973
Gibson, Mr Christopher (Q.C.); Recorder . . . M . . . Oct 1976
Rees, Mr Edward (Q.C.) . . . G . . . Feb 1973
Grieve, Mr Michael (Q.C.); Recorder . . . M . . . Nov 1975
Wood, Mr James (Q.C.); Recorder . . . M . . . Nov 1975
Millar, Mr Gavin (Q.C.) . . . L . . . Jul 1981
Hall, Mr Andrew (Q.C.) . . . G . . . Feb 1991
Rogers, Miss Heather (Q.C.) . . . M . . . Jul 1983
Williams, Ms Heather (Q.C.) . . . G . . . Jul 1985
Oppenheim, Mr Robin (Q.C.) . . . M . . . Nov 1988
Otty, Mr Timothy John (Q.C.) . . . L . . . Oct 1990
Bowen, Mr Nicholas (Q.C.) . . . L . . . Jan 1984
Hermer, Mr Richard (Q.C.) . . . M . . . Oct 1993
Latham, Mr Robert . . . M . . . Jul 1976
Hislop, Mr David . . . G . . . Feb 1989
Evans, Ms Jill . . . G . . . Jul 1986
Markus, Ms Kate . . . G . . . Nov 1981
Hough, Mr Christopher . . . M . . . Jul 1981
Forshall, Ms Isabella . . . G . . . Feb 1982
Mackie, Ms Jeannie . . . I . . . Jul 1995
Bentley, Mr David . . . G . . . Feb 1984
Bloom, Ms Tracey . . . G . . . Jul 1984
Westgate, Mr Martin . . . M . . . Nov 1985
Weereratne, Ms Aswini . . . G . . . Jul 1986
Samuel, Mr Gerwyn . . . G . . . Jul 1986
Fitzgibbon, Mr Francis . . . M . . . Jan 1986
Hatfield, Miss Sally* . . . I . . . Nov 1988
Maidment, Mr Kieran . . . G . . . Nov 1989
Taylor, Mr Paul . . . M . . . Nov 1989
Brown, Mr Nicholas . . . L . . . Jan 1989
Stone, Mr Joseph . . . L . . . Jan 1989
Kaufmann, Ms Phillippa . . . G . . . Oct 1991
Whitaker, Ms Quincy . . . M . . . Oct 1991
Reeder, Mr Stephen . . . M . . . Oct 1991
Brimelow, Ms Kirsty . . . G . . . Oct 1991
Wise, Mr Ian . . . G . . . Nov 1992
Cox, Mr Simon F . . . I . . . Nov 1992
Cooper, Mr Jonathan OBE . . . G . . . Oct 1992
Jones, Mr John R W D . . . I . . . Jan 1992
Farbey, Miss Judith . . . M . . . Oct 1992
Bowen, Mr Paul . . . I . . . Nov 1993
Walsh, Mr John L . . . I . . . Nov 1993
Pullen, Mr Timothy . . . M . . . Nov 1993
Henderson, Mr Mark . . . G . . . Oct 1994
Sparks, Ms Paula . . . G . . . Oct 1994
Fisher, Mr Richard . . . L . . . Nov 1994
Draycott, Mr Paul . . . G . . . Nov 1994
Brown, Ms Althea . . . L . . . Feb 1995
Trowler, Ms Rebecca . . . G . . . Oct 1995
Jordash, Mr Wayne . . . M . . . Oct 1995
Preston, Mr Dominic . . . I . . . Feb 1995
Hudson, Mr Anthony . . . I . . . Nov 1996
Cragg, Mr Stephen J . . . M . . . Nov 1996
Toms, Mr Nicholas . . . M . . . Nov 1996
Elliott, Miss Sarah . . . G . . . Nov 1996
Mukherjee, Mr Tublu . . . I . . . Jan 1996
Middleton, Mr Joseph . . . I . . . Nov 1997
Durance, Mr Alex . . . G . . . Nov 1997
Burnham, Ms Ulele . . . I . . . Feb 1997
Hill, Ms Henrietta . . . I . . . Jan 1997
Powles, Mr Stephen . . . I . . . Oct 1997
Johnson, Mr Lindsay . . . I . . . Oct 1997
Stanage, Mr Nick . . . I . . . Jan 1997
Lownds, Mr Peter . . . G . . . Nov 1998
Shepherd, Mr Jim . . . M . . . Oct 1998
Arshad, Miss Farrhat . . . I . . . Nov 1998
Burton, Mr Jamie . . . I . . . Jan 1999
Narain, Mr Benjamin . . . M . . . Jan 1999
Cooper, Mr Ben . . . M . . . Jan 1999
Kilroy, Ms Charlotte . . . I . . . Jan 1999
Hobson, Mr John . . . L . . . Oct 1999
Mushtaq, Erimnaz . . . I . . . Jan 2000
Bennett, Mr Daniel . . . G . . . Jan 2000
Morris, Mr Peter . . . I . . . Oct 2000
Vassall-Adams, Mr Guy . . . M . . . Nov 2000
Haywood, Mr Phil . . . M . . . Mar 2001
Brander, Ms Ruth . . . M . . . Oct 2001
Hart, Ms Amanda . . . M . . . Jul 2001
Marquis, Mr Piers . . . G . . . Jul 2001
Sleeman, Ms Susan . . . I . . . Oct 2001
Gallagher, Ms Caoilfhionn . . . L . . . Oct 2006
Farazi, Ms Seema . . . L . . . Jul 2001
Corrin, Ms Lucy . . . M . . . Oct 2001
Dubinsky, Ms Laura . . . M . . . Oct 2002
Power, Ms Eloise . . . G . . . Jan 2002
Rhodes, Mr David . . . M . . . Jul 2002
Thomas, Mr Richard . . . I . . . Oct 2002
Gerry, Ms Alison . . . I . . . Jan 2003
Mackenzie, Mr Alasdair . . . G . . . Jan 2004
Suterwalla, Mr Azeem . . . I . . . Jan 2004
Newton, Mr Benjamin . . . L . . . Jan 2004
Hobcraft, Ms Gemma . . . L . . . Jan 2006
Annand, Ms Kate . . . M . . . Jan 2007
Pickup, Ms Alison . . . M . . . Jan 2007
Gask, Mr Alex . . . M . . . Jan 2008
Broach, Mr Steve . . . M . . . Jan 2008

Chambers of Robin Griffiths

2 DR JOHNSON'S BUILDINGS,
TEMPLE, LONDON EC4Y 7AY
Tel: 020 7936 2613 ***Fax:*** 020 7353 9439
Dx: 210 LONDON/CHANCERY LANE
Clerk: Marc Newson; Joanne Thomas.
Head of Chambers:
Griffiths, Mr Robin . . . M . . . Nov 1970

Love, Mr Dudley Mark; Director . . . G . . . Nov 1979
Dennison, Mr James . . . I . . . Jul 1986
Sapsard, Jamal . . . L . . . Jul 1987
Comfort, Miss Polly-Anne . . . L . . . Feb 1988
Stern, Mr Mark Richard Alexander . . . L . . . Feb 1988
Talbot-Bagnall, Mr John . . . I . . . Nov 1988
Stone, Mr Joseph . . . I . . . Jan 1989
Dent, Mr Kevin . . . G . . . Nov 1991
Pathak, Pankaj . . . L . . . Oct 1992
Petersen, Mr Lewis Neil . . . M . . . Jul 1993
Syed, Miss Maryam . . . L . . . Oct 1993
Tolkien, Mr Simon . . . M . . . Jul 1994
Baker, Ms Fay . . . G . . . Oct 1994
Dahlsen, Mr Peter . . . G . . . Oct 1996

Chambers of Andrei Michael Szerard

3 DR JOHNSON'S BUILDINGS,
GROUND FLOOR, TEMPLE, LONDON EC4Y 7BA
Tel: 020 7353 4854 ***Fax:*** 020 7583 8784
Dx: 1009 LONDON/CHANCERY LANE
E-mail: clerks@3djb.co.uk
Clerk: John E Hubbard.
Head of Chambers:
Szerard, Mr Andrei Michael . . . I . . . Apr 1986

Miskin, Miss Claire M; Recorder . . . M . . . Nov 1970
Hay, Mr Malcolm . . . G . . . Nov 1972
Allston, Mr Anthony Stanley . . . G . . . Jul 1975
Harris, Miss Annemarie . . . M . . . Jul 1975
Limbrey, Mr Bernard Martin . . . M . . . Nov 1980
Hasan, Miss Ayesha . . . G . . . Jul 1987
Maxwell, Miss Judith Mary Angela . . . L . . . Jul 1988
Moss, Mr Norman William . . . I . . . Oct 1990
Teggin, Miss Victoria . . . I . . . Nov 1990
Glanville, Miss Susan Elizabeth . . . I . . . Oct 1991
Hellens, Mr Matthew . . . M . . . Oct 1992
Peacock, Miss Lisa Jayne . . . L . . . Oct 1992
Cronshaw, Mr Michael . . . M . . . Oct 1993
Carter, Miss Holly . . . I . . . Oct 1993
Redford, Miss Jessica K . . . I . . . Nov 1994
Steadman, Mr Russell Charles . . . I . . . Nov 1995
Barnes, Mr Luke C . . . G . . . Nov 1996
Jones, Mr Mark Simeon . . . M . . . Jul 1997
Davies, Mr Adrian Michael . . . L . . . Jul 1998
Artesi, Miss Desiree A A . . . I . . . Oct 1998
Mayhew, Miss Judith . . . M . . . Jul 2000
Lashbrook, Miss Kellie . . . I . . . Jul 2001
Kerr, Mr Neil . . . I . . . Oct 2001
Ellis, Miss Catherine S . . . M . . . Jan 2003
Piskolti, Miss Catherine . . . L . . . Jul 2003
Beer, Miss Emily . . . M . . . Jan 2004
Islam, Mr Saiful . . . L . . . Jan 2005
Palmer, Miss Briony Madelaine . . . I . . . Jul 2009

Chambers of Beverley J Gutteridge

36 DUNMORE ROAD,
WIMBLEDON, LONDON SW20 8TN
Tel: 07710 326130
Head of Chambers:
Gutteridge, Miss Beverley J . . . M . . . Jul 1987

DYERS CHAMBERS,
35 BEDFORD ROW, LONDON WC1R 4JH
Tel: 020 7404 1881 ***Fax:*** 020 7404 1991
Dx: 175 LONDON/CHANCERY LANE
E-mail: dave.scothern@dyerschambers.com

EASTERN CHAMBERS,
25 EASTERN ROAD, EAST FINCHLEY, LONDON N2 9LB
Paul, Mr John . . . I . . . Apr 1972

Chambers of Jane Walker

43 EGLANTINE ROAD,
LONDON SW18 2DE
Tel: 020 8874 3469
Head of Chambers:
Walker, Miss Jane . . . M . . . Nov 1974

ELY PLACE CHAMBERS,
30 ELY PLACE, LONDON EC1N 6TD
Tel: 020 7400 9600 ***Fax:*** 020 7400 9630
Dx: 291 LONDON/CHANCERY LANE
Clerk: Senior: Christopher Drury. Richard Sheehan; Kevin Morrow; David Lovitt.
Administrator: Carol Ann Belford
Practice Manager: Christopher Drury; Richard Sheehan
Chambers Director: Christopher Drury

Thwaites, Mr Ronald (Q.C.) . . . G . . . Nov 1970
Stewart, Mr Nicholas (Q.C.) . . . I . . . Jul 1971
McCormick, Mr William (Q.C.) . . . G . . . Jul 1985
Willer, Mr Robert . . . G . . . Jan 1970
Evans, Mr William . . . G . . . Jan 1977
Charalamides, Mr Leo . . . I . . . Jul 1988
Stone, Mr Russell . . . I . . . Jan 1992
Daniels, Mr Ian . . . L . . . Jan 1992
Preston, Mr David . . . L . . . Jan 1992
Barlow, Mr Craig Martin . . . G . . . Nov 1992
Butler, Mr Simon . . . I . . . Jan 1996
Sinai, Mr Ali Reza . . . G . . . Jan 1997
Payne, Mr Johnathan . . . G . . . Jan 1997
Perhar, Mr Simon . . . G . . . Oct 1997
Crew, Ms Gillian . . . G . . . Jan 1998
Pearman, Mr Scott . . . M . . . Jan 1999
Salter, Mr Michael . . . G . . . Oct 1999
Newman, Mr James . . . G . . . Jul 2000
Samson, Mr John . . . I . . . Jan 2001
Ahmed, Bushra . . . M . . . Jan 2001
Mitchell, Mr David . . . I . . . Jan 2004
Price, Mr Jonathan . . . M . . . Oct 2004
Stroud, Miss Amy . . . I . . . Nov 2004
Ryan, Mr Liam Michael . . . I . . . Jan 2007
Briggs, Mr Aidan . . . I . . . Jun 2009
Powlesland, Mr Paul . . . M . . . Oct 2009
Urqhart, Miss Catherine . . . M . . . Oct 2010

Chambers of Bernard Weatherill QC

ENTERPRISE CHAMBERS,
9 OLD SQUARE, LINCOLN'S INN, LONDON WC2A 3SR
Tel: 020 7405 9471 ***Fax:*** 020 7242 1447
Dx: 301 LONDON/CHANCERY LANE
E-mail: london@enterprisechambers.com
Web: www.enterprisechambers.com
Clerk: Senior: Antony Armstrong. Juniors: Mark Belford; Michael Ireland; Charlotte Temple; Luke Daws.
Head of Chambers:
Weatherill, Mr Bernard (Q.C.); Recorder; Mediator . M . . . Jul 1974

Arden, Mr Peter (Q.C.) . . . G . . . Jul 1983
Bhaloo, Miss Zia (Q.C.) . . . M . . . Nov 1990
Morgan, Mr Charles; Junior Counsel to the Crown (Regional) . . . M . . . Jul 1978
Hutton, Miss Caroline; Mediator (CEDR) . . . M . . . Nov 1979
James, Mr Michael; Mediator . . . L . . . Feb 1976
Ife, Ms Linden . . . M . . . Nov 1982
Zelin, Mr Geoffrey . . . M . . . Jul 1984
Barker, Mr James . . . G . . . Jul 1984
Jack, Mr Adrian; Recorder . . . M . . . Nov 1986
Groves, Mr Hugo . . . G . . . Oct 1980
Jarron, Miss Stephanie . . . L . . . May 1990
Pickering, Mr James . . . M . . . Oct 1991
Jory, Mr Hugh . . . L . . . Oct 1992
Noble, Mr Andrew; Mediator . . . L . . . Nov 1992
Duddridge, Mr Robert . . . L . . . Feb 1992
Williamson, Miss Bridget . . . L . . . Feb 1993
Klein, Mr Jonathan; Junior Counsel to the Crown (Regional) . . . L . . . Oct 1992
Francis, Mr Edward . . . I . . . Nov 1995
Mauger, Miss Shanti . . . I . . . Oct 1996
Ilyas, Mr Shaiba . . . L . . . Mar 1998
Calland, Mr Timothy . . . L . . . Nov 1999
Rodger, Mr Jonathan . . . M . . . Nov 1999
McCulloch, Mr Niall . . . L . . . Oct 2000
Johnson, Mr Simon . . . M . . . Oct 2000
Murphy, Mr Damian . . . M . . . Jul 2001
Page, Miss Rebecca . . . G . . . Nov 2001
Jackson, Ms Claire . . . L . . . Mar 2002
West, Mr Matthew . . . M . . . Nov 2000
Kalfon, Mr Olivier . . . I . . . Oct 2003
Gunaratna, Mr Kavan . . . L . . . Nov 2004
Toman, Miss Cristin . . . L . . . Jan 2004
Griffin, Miss Margaret . . . G . . . Jul 2004
Beswetherick, Mr Anthony . . . L . . . Mar 2003
Markandya, Miss Susannah . . . I . . . Oct 2005
Bond, Miss Kelly . . . M . . . Jul 2007
Heath, Mr Duncan . . . L . . . Nov 2007
Meech, Miss Jennifer . . . M . . . Oct 2008
Burslem, Miss Sarah . . . G . . . Oct 2008
Gale, Mr Phillip . . . L . . . Oct 2008
Davies, Mr James . . . L . . . Jul 2009
Maddison, Mr Matthew . . . M . . . Jul 2010
Child, Mr Jeremy* . . . L . . . Mar 2003

A leading commercial chancery set based in London, Leeds and Newcastle, specialising in: banking, insolvency, building and construction, company and commercial law (other than shipping), contract, employment, equitable remedies, environmental law, insurance, intellectual property, international disputes, judicial review, landlord & tenant, partnership law, pensions, probate, professional negligence (except medical negligence) property & trusts. Fluent French and Italian speakers. Cutchi, German, Swahili and Dutch also spoken.

Chambers of Michael Todd QC

ERSKINE CHAMBERS,
33 CHANCERY LANE, LONDON WC2A 1EN
Tel: 020 7242 5532 ***Fax:*** 020 7831 0125
Dx: 308 LONDON/CHANCERY LANE
E-mail: clerks@erskinechambers.com
Web: www.erskinechambers.com
Clerk: Mike Hannibal.
Administrator: Monika Graczykowska
Head of Chambers:
Todd, Mr Michael (Q.C.) . . . L . . . Jul 1977

Mabb, Mr David (Q.C.) . . . L . . . Jul 1979
Moore, Mr Martin (Q.C.) . . . L . . . Jul 1982
Chivers, Mr David (Q.C.) . . . L . . . Jul 1983
Snowden, Mr Richard (Q.C.) . . . L . . . Jun 1986
Cone, Mr John . . . M . . . Jul 1975
Prentice, Prof Dan . . . L . . . Nov 1982
Bryant, Ms Ceri . . . L . . . Jul 1984
Roberts, Miss Catherine . . . L . . . Nov 1986
Gillyon, Mr Philip . . . M . . . Jul 1988
Stokes, Ms Mary . . . L . . . Jul 1989
Thompson, Mr Andrew . . . I . . . Nov 1991
Dougherty, Mr Nigel . . . G . . . Oct 1993
Potts, Mr James . . . G . . . Oct 1994
Thornton, Mr Andrew James . . . L . . . Nov 1994
Davies, Mr Edward . . . I . . . Jan 1998
Horan, Mr Stephen . . . L . . . Nov 2002
Shaw, Mr Benjamin . . . L . . . Nov 2002
Griffiths, Mr Ben . . . M . . . Oct 2004
Barden, Mr Alex . . . I . . . Oct 2005
Parfitt, Mr Matthew . . . L . . . Nov 2005
Harty, Mr Patrick . . . L . . . Jan 2008
Nolan, Mr Richard* . . . M . . . Jul 1999

Erskine Chambers has a long established reputation in company law and provides specialists at all levels of experience in the fields of English and Commonwealth company law, corporate insolvency, financial services and related commercial and professional negligence matters.

Chambers of Lord Grabiner QC

ONE ESSEX COURT,
GROUND FLOOR, TEMPLE, LONDON EC4Y 9AR
Tel: 020 7583 2000 ***Fax:*** 020 7583 0118
Dx: 430 LONDON/CHANCERY LANE
E-mail: clerks@oeclaw.co.uk
Clerk: Senior: Darren Burrows.
Administrator: Joanne Huxley
Head of Chambers:
Grabiner, Lord (Q.C.) . . . L . . . Nov 1968

Strauss, Mr Nicholas (Q.C.) . . . M . . . Nov 1965
Leaver, Mr Peter (Q.C.) . . . L . . . Jul 1967
Glick, Mr Ian (Q.C.) . . . I . . . Nov 1970
Hobbs, Mr Geoffrey (Q.C.) . . . I . . . Jul 1977
Sharpe, Mr Thomas (Q.C.) . . . L . . . May 1976
Onions, Mr Jeffery (Q.C.) . . . M . . . Jul 1981
FitzGerald, Ms Susanna (Q.C.) . . . I . . . Jul 1973
Davies, Mr Rhodri (Q.C.) . . . M . . . Jul 1979
Auld, Mr Stephen (Q.C.) . . . G . . . Jul 1979
MacLean, Mr Kenneth (Q.C.) . . . G . . . May 1985
Rabinowitz, Mr Laurence (Q.C.) . . . M . . . Nov 1987
Gammie, Mr Malcolm (Q.C.) . . . M . . . Oct 1997
McCaughran, Mr John (Q.C.) . . . G . . . Jul 1982
Graham, Mr Charles (Q.C.) . . . M . . . Nov 1986
Gillis, Mr Richard (Q.C.) . . . L . . . Nov 1982
Lenon, Mr Andrew (Q.C.) . . . L . . . Nov 1982
de Garr Robinson, Mr Anthony (Q.C.) . . . L . . . Jul 1987
Sullivan, Mr Michael (Q.C.) . . . L . . . Jul 1983
Kitchener, Mr Neil (Q.C.) . . . M . . . Nov 1991
Choo Choy, Mr Alain (Q.C.) . . . I . . . Nov 1991
Wolfson, Mr David (Q.C.) . . . I . . . Nov 1992
Toledano, Mr Daniel (Q.C.) . . . I . . . Oct 1993
Cavender, Mr David (Q.C.) . . . M . . . Jul 1993
Boulton, Mr Richard (Q.C.) . . . G . . . Jul 2003
Redfern, Mr Alan . . . M . . . May 1995
Foyle, Mr Andrew . . . L . . . Jan 2006
Malone, Mr Michael . . . G . . . Nov 1975
Grainger, Mr Ian . . . I . . . Jul 1978
Griffiths, Mr Alan . . . G . . . Feb 1981
Reffin, Ms Clare . . . M . . . Jul 1981
Brown, Miss Hannah . . . I . . . Oct 1992
O'Sullivan, Ms Zoe . . . M . . . Oct 1993
Himsworth, Ms Emma . . . G . . . Oct 1993
Nourse, Mr Edmund . . . L . . . Nov 1994
Hossain, Sa'ad . . . G . . . Nov 1995
Bingham, Ms Camilla . . . I . . . Oct 1996
Roberts, Mr Philip . . . I . . . Oct 1996
Fealy, Mr Michael . . . M . . . May 1997
Gledhill, Mr Orlando . . . I . . . Oct 1998
Colton, Mr Simon . . . I . . . Nov 1999
Cook, Mr Matthew . . . M . . . Nov 1999
Elliott, Mr Steven . . . L . . . Jul 2001
Hollingworth, Mr Guy . . . L . . . Oct 2001
Strong, Mr Ben . . . M . . . Nov 2001
Spitz, Mr Derek . . . L . . . Nov 2001
Boase, Miss Anna . . . M . . . Oct 2002
Goldsmith, Mr James . . . G . . . Oct 2002
Nadin, Mr James . . . L . . . Oct 2002
Hubbard, Mr Daniel . . . L . . . Jul 2003
Menashy, Miss Michelle . . . G . . . Oct 2003
Patton, Mr Conall . . . G . . . Jan 2004
Emmett, Mr Laurence . . . L . . . Jan 2004
Forbes Smith, Mr Henry . . . M . . . Jan 2004
Polley, Mr Alexander . . . I . . . Jan 2005
Isaac, Mr Sebastian . . . L . . . Jan 2005
Dracos, Mr Marcos . . . M . . . Jan 2005
Campbell, Miss Eleanor . . . L . . . Jan 2005
Clark, Mr Michael . . . L . . . Jan 2005
Mott, Mr Richard . . . M . . . Jan 2006
Caplan, Mr David . . . I . . . Jan 2006
Oakeshott, Miss Rachel . . . I . . . Jan 2006
Lemer, Mr Saul . . . G . . . Jan 2007
Sloboda, Mr Nicholas . . . L . . . Jan 2007
O'Leary, Mr Samuel . . . L . . . Jan 2007
Edelman, Mr James . . . L . . . Mar 2008
Bompas, Miss Abra . . . L . . . Jul 2008
d'Arcy, Mr Michael . . . I . . . Jul 2008
Shah, Miss Nehali . . . M . . . Oct 2008
Brown, Mr Alexander . . . L . . . Jul 2009
Baiou, Mr Mehdi . . . M . . . Jul 2009
Paine, Mr Douglas . . . L . . . Oct 2009
Watkins, Mr Michael . . . L . . . Oct 2009
Petkovic, Mr James . . . L . . . Jul 2009
Jones, Miss Emma . . . I . . . Jul 2010
Butler, Mr Oliver . . . I . . . Oct 2010
Rushworth, Mr Adam . . . L . . . Nov 2010

Chambers of Tony Baldry MP

ONE ESSEX COURT,
1ST FLOOR, TEMPLE, LONDON EC4Y 9AR
Tel: 020 7936 3030 ***Fax:*** 020 7583 1606
Dx: 371 LONDON/CHANCERY LANE
E-mail: ihogg@1ec.co.uk
Clerk: Senior: Ian Hogg. First Junior: Lloyd Parkes; Junior: Billy Gander.
Head of Chambers:
Baldry MP, Mr Tony . . . M . . . Jan 1975

Wilson, Miss Elizabeth . . . G . . . Nov 1989
Joshi, Mr Pramod Kumar . . . I . . . Nov 1992
Campbell-Brown, Louise . . . M . . . Jan 1993
Macpherson, Mr Duncan . . . M . . . May 1994
Hatch, Miss Lisa Sharmila . . . M . . . May 1995
Chesner, Mr Howard . . . G . . . Jul 1995
Oakley, Mr Paul . . . G . . . Nov 1995
Halstead, Mr Robin Bernard . . . I . . . Oct 1996
Hutchin, Mr Edward . . . M . . . Oct 1996
Mackenzie, Mr Robert . . . G . . . Jan 1996
Sidhu, Sukhwant . . . L . . . Oct 1996
Miller, Mr Jonathan . . . M . . . Nov 1996
Miles, Mr Richard Iain . . . G . . . Nov 1997
Sonaike, Kola . . . I . . . Jan 1998
Grunberg, Angela . . . I . . . Jan 1999
Sampson, Dr Timothy . . . L . . . Jan 2000
Shaw, Miss Joanna . . . M . . . Jan 2000
Kirk, Mr Graeme . . . I . . . Jun 2001
Hyde, Mr Sarah-Jane . . . I . . . Jan 2002
Freedman, Miss Michelle . . . L . . . Jan 2002
Degun, Mr Jasvir . . . M . . . Jan 2003
Parke, Genevieve . . . M . . . Jan 2006

10

5 ESSEX COURT,
TEMPLE, LONDON EC4Y 9AH
Tel: 020 7410 2000 ***Fax:*** 020 7410 2010 / 7410 2011
Dx: 1048 LONDON/CHANCERY LANE

Chambers of Gordon Pollock QC

ESSEX COURT CHAMBERS,
24 LINCOLN'S INN FIELDS, LONDON WC2A 3EG
Tel: 020 7813 8000 ***Fax:*** 020 7813 8080
Dx: 320 LONDON/CHANCERY LANE
E-mail: clerksroom@essexcourt.net
Clerk: David Grief; Joe Ferrigno; Sam Biggerstaff; Ben Perry.
Administrator: Lisa Young
Head of Chambers:
Pollock, Mr Gordon (Q.C.); Recorder . . . G . . . Nov 1968

Thomas, Mr Michael D (Q.C.) CMG . . . M . . . Nov 1955
Hunter, Mr Ian G A (Q.C.); Recorder and a Member of Gibraltar Bar . . . I . . . Nov 1967
Boyd, Mr Stewart C (Q.C.) CBE; Recorder . . . M . . . Jul 1967
Veeder, Mr Van V (Q.C.) . . . I . . . Nov 1971
Siberry, Mr W Richard (Q.C.) . . . M . . . Jul 1974
Gilman, Mr Jonathan C B (Q.C.) . . . M . . . Feb 1965
Berman, Sir Franklin (Q.C.) KCMG . . . M . . . Nov 1966
Cordara, Mr Roderick C (Q.C.); Counsel to the Department of Trade; SC (Australia) . . . M . . . Jul 1975
Crookenden, Mr Simon R (Q.C.); Recorder . . . G . . . Nov 1975
Gruder, Mr Jeffrey (Q.C.) . . . M . . . Jul 1977
Hochhauser, Mr Andrew R (Q.C.) . . . M . . . Jul 1977
Jacobs, Mr Richard D (Q.C.) . . . M . . . Nov 1979
Mildon, Mr David W (Q.C.) . . . M . . . Jul 1980
Andrews, Miss Geraldine M (Q.C.) . . . G . . . Nov 1981
Dunning, Mr Graham (Q.C.) . . . L . . . Jul 1982
Berry, Mr Steven J (Q.C.) . . . M . . . Nov 1984
Shaw, Prof Malcolm N (Q.C.) . . . G . . . Jul 1988
Templeman, Mr Mark J (Q.C.) . . . M . . . Nov 1981
Joseph, Mr David P (Q.C.) . . . M . . . Nov 1984
Millett, Mr Richard L (Q.C.) . . . L . . . Jul 1985
Smouha, Mr Joe (Q.C.) . . . M . . . Jul 1986
Davies, Mr E Huw (Q.C.) . . . G . . . Nov 1985
Griffiths, Mr Martin (Q.C.) . . . I . . . Nov 1986
Lockey, Mr John C G (Q.C.) . . . M . . . Jun 1987
Bryan, Mr Simon J (Q.C.) . . . L . . . Jul 1988
Foxton, Mr David A (Q.C.) . . . G . . . Feb 1989
Mercer, Mr Hugh (Q.C.) . . . M . . . Jul 1985
Flynn, Mr Vernon J H (Q.C.) . . . L . . . Oct 1991
Lowe, Prof Vaughan (Q.C.) . . . G . . . Oct 1993
Landau, Mr Toby (Q.C.) . . . M . . . Oct 1993
Dicks, Mr Anthony (Q.C.) . . . I . . . Nov 1961
Doyle, Mr Shane . . . L . . . Jan 2001
Smith, Mr Christopher (Q.C.) . . . I . . . Jul 1989
Blanchard, Ms Claire (Q.C.) . . . G . . . Oct 1992
Stanley, Mr Paul (Q.C.) . . . M . . . Oct 1993
Cockerill, Miss Sara E (Q.C.) . . . L . . . Oct 1990
Eicke, Mr Tim (Q.C.) . . . M . . . Oct 1993
McGrath, Mr Paul A (Q.C.) . . . I . . . Nov 1994
Boyle, Mr Alan . . . M . . . Jan 1977
Smith, Mr Mark V . . . L . . . Jul 1981
Watson, Ms Philippa . . . M . . . Jul 1988
Snider, Mr John . . . M . . . Jul 1982
Dye, Mr Brian W . . . M . . . Oct 1991
Eaton, Mr Nigel T . . . G . . . Nov 1991

Ciumei, Mr Charles Gregg	M.	Oct 1991
Hunter, Mr Martin	L.	Nov 1994
Hopkins, Ms Phillipa M	M.	Oct 1994
Collins, Mr James	G.	Feb 1995
Houseman, Mr Stephen	I	Nov 1995
Key, Mr Paul	I	Jan 1997
Lau, Mr Martin	M.	Jan 1996
Scorey, Mr David	L.	Jun 1997
Wordsworth, Mr Samuel	L.	Jan 1997
Pillow, Mr Nathan	G.	Jan 1997
Craig, Mr David	I	Oct 1997
Moollan, Mr Salim	M.	Jan 1998
Diwan, Mr Ricky	L.	Jan 1998
Hart, Mr Neil	G.	Jan 1998
King, Mr Edmund	I	Nov 1999
Quirk, Mr Iain	L.	Oct 2002
Ng, Mr Jern-Fei	L.	Jan 2002
Davies, Mr David	G.	Jan 2004
Brown, Mr Edward	L.	Jan 2002
Brier, Mr Jeremy	M.	Jan 2004
Wells, Mrs Jessica	L.	Jan 2004
Sarooshi, Mr Dan	M.	Jan 2005
Walker, Mr Damien	L.	Jan 2006
Dhar, Siddharth	M.	Jan 2005
Willan, Mr James	G.	Jan 2006
Wood, Ms Emily	M.	Jan 2006
Sander, Ms Amy	M.	Jan 2006
Ford, Mr Tom	G.	Jan 2008
Dudnikov, Mr Anton	G.	Jul 2008

ESSEX HOUSE CHAMBERS,
122-126 KILBURN HIGH ROAD, KILBURN,
LONDON NW6 4HY
Tel: 020 7692 0677

Chambers of Iain Milligan QC

20 ESSEX STREET,
LONDON WC2R 3AL
Tel: 020 7842 1200 *Fax:* 020 7482 1270
Dx: 0009 LONDON/CHANCERY LANE
E-mail: clerks@20essexst.com
Clerk: Neil Palmer; Brian Lee; Mathew Kesbey; Arron Zitver; Christopher Theobald.
Administrator: Daniel Clark
Head of Chambers:

Milligan, Mr Iain (Q.C.)	I	Jul 1973
Lauterpacht, Sir Elihu (Q.C.) CBE	G.	Nov 1950
Pickering, Mr Murray A (Q.C.)	L.	Nov 1963
North, Sir Peter (Q.C.)	I	May 1992
Layton, Mr Alexander William (Q.C.)	M.	Jul 1976
Young, Mr Timothy (Q.C.)	G.	Jul 1977
Males, Mr Stephen M (Q.C.)	M.	Jul 1978
Hancock, Mr Christopher P (Q.C.)	M.	Jul 1983
Morris, Mr Stephen N (Q.C.)	L.	Jul 1981
Matthews, Mr Duncan H R (Q.C.)	G.	Nov 1986
Bethlehem, Sir Daniel (Q.C.) KCMG	M.	Nov 1988
Tselentis, Mr Michael (Q.C.)	G.	Oct 1995
Owen, Mr David C (Q.C.)	M.	Nov 1983
Baker, Mr Andrew (Q.C.)	L.	Jul 1988
Morpuss, Mr Guy (Q.C.)	L.	Oct 1991
Coburn, Mr Michael (Q.C.)	I	Nov 1990
Edey, Mr Philip David (Q.C.)	G.	Nov 1994
Kimmins, Mr Charles Dominic (Q.C.)	I	Nov 1994
Ashcroft, Mr Michael (Q.C.)	G.	Sep 1997
Wood, Sir Michael	M.	Jan 1968
Broadbent, Mr Edmund J	G.	Jul 1980
Akka, Mr Lawrence	L.	Nov 1991
Ambrose, Miss Clare	G.	Nov 1992
Charkham, Mr Graham	I	Oct 1993
Masters, Ms Sara Alayna	I	Oct 1993
Anderson, Miss Julie	G.	Nov 1993
Collett, Mr Michael	G.	Oct 1995
Swaroop, Sudhanshu	I	Oct 1997
Kenny, Mr Julian	G.	Nov 1997
Jarvis, Mr Malcolm	I	Oct 1998
Lewis, Mr David	M.	Nov 1999
Jones, Miss Susannah	G.	Nov 1999
Raphael, Mr Thomas	M.	Nov 1999
Snook, Mr Sean	L.	Jan 2000
Byam-Cook, Mr Henry	I	Jan 2000
Papadopoulos, Mr Socrates	I	Jan 2001
Parry, Miss Angharad	G.	Oct 2002
Thompson, Mr Antony	M.	Oct 2002
Hanley, Miss Colleen	I	Jan 2003
Olbourne, Mr Ben	I	Nov 2003
Bovensiepen, Mr Daniel	M.	Jul 2004
Milnes, Mr Simon	G.	Oct 2005
Verdirame, Dr Guglielmo	I	Mar 2006
Davies, Miss Josephine	L.	Oct 2006
Talmon, Prof Stefan	L.	Jul 2007
Edwards, Patricia	I	Oct 2007
Pearce, Mr Luke	L.	Nov 2007
Tan, Charlotte	M.	Jul 2008
Tresman, Miss Sarah	M.	Oct 2008
Ho, Mr Edward	M.	Jul 2009
Nevill, Miss Penelope	M.	Jul 2010
Bentham, Prof Richard*	G.	Nov 1955
Allott, Mr Philip James*	G.	Feb 1960
Collier, Mr John Greenwood*	G.	Nov 1961
Plant, Dr Glen*	I	Jul 1985

Chambers of Simon Russell Flint QC

23 ESSEX STREET,
LONDON WC2R 3AA
Tel: 020 7413 0353 *Fax:* 020 7413 0374
Dx: 148 LONDON/CHANCERY LANE
E-mail: clerks@23es.com
Web: www.23es.com
Clerk: Senior: Richard Fowler. Sean Gould; Robert Mayes; Jamie Clack; Adam Chapman; Joe Wheeler.
Administrator: Tracey McCormack
Practice Manager: Richard Fowler
Head of Chambers:

Russell Flint, Mr Simon (Q.C.); Recorder	I	Nov 1980
Austin-Smith, Mr Michael (Q.C.); Recorder	I	Jul 1969
Miskin, Mr Charles (Q.C.); Recorder	G.	Jul 1975
Kinch, Mr Christopher (Q.C.); Recorder	L.	Jul 1976
Weekes, Miss Anesta (Q.C.); Recorder	G.	Jul 1981
Janner, Mr Daniel (Q.C.)	M.	Jul 1980
Rees, Mr Gareth (Q.C.)	G.	Jul 1981
Shant, Ms Nirmal Kanta (Q.C.); Recorder; Master Grays Inn Chair of The Midlands Society of Asian Lawyers	G.	Jul 1984
Enoch, Mr Dafydd (Q.C.); Recorder	G.	Nov 1985
Price, Mr John (Q.C.); Recorder	I	Jul 1982
Kent, Mr Alan (Q.C.)	I	Nov 1986
Morley, Mr Iain Charles (Q.C.)	I	Jul 1988
Richardson, Mr James (Q.C.)*	G.	Jul 1975
Nelson, Mr Cairns (Q.C.); Recorder	G.	Jan 1987
Bogan, Mr Paul (Q.C.)	L.	Jul 1983
Causer, Mr John C	I	Jul 1979
Harrison, Mr Michael	I	Jan 1979
Del Fabbro, Mr Oscar; Recorder	G.	Jul 1982
Brown, Mr Roy; Deputy District Judge (Magistrates)	G.	Jul 1983
Claxton, Mr Elroy G; Recorder	I	Jul 1983
Riley, Mr John	M.	Nov 1983
Pardoe, Mr Rupert	I	Jul 1984
Summers, Mr Gary	G.	Nov 1985
Bradley, Ms Caroline	M.	Jul 1985
Cranston-Morris, Mr Wayne	L.	Jul 1986
Moore, Mr Neil	G.	Jul 1986
Ozin, Mr Paul David	M.	Nov 1987
Holt, Miss Karen Jane; Recorder	L.	Nov 1987
Forgan, Mr Hugh	L.	Jan 1989
Easteal, Mr Andrew; Recorder	L.	Jul 1990
Davis, Mr Simon*	M.	Oct 1990
Ascherson, Miss Isobel	G.	Feb 1991
Griffin, Miss Lynn	G.	Oct 1991
Acheson, Mr Ian	G.	Feb 1992
Fenhalls, Mr Mark	G.	Oct 1992
Milne, Mr Richard	M.	Oct 1992
Curtis-Raleigh, Mr Giles; Recorder	M.	Oct 1992
Hurst, Mr Andrew; Recorder	I	Nov 1992
Trafford, Mr Mark	I	May 1992
Clark, Mr Tim; Recorder	I	Feb 1993
Lumsdon, Miss Kate	M.	Oct 1993
O'Connor, Mr Ged	L.	Sep 1993
Marshall, Miss Eloise M K S	G.	Oct 1994
Stilgoe, Mr Rufus	I	Nov 1994
Sellers, Mr Robin St John	I	Nov 1994
Ali, Zafar	M.	Oct 1994
McDonagh, Mr Matthew; Recorder	M.	Oct 1994
Platt, Mr Stephen*	M.	Jan 1994
Durran, Miss Alexia; Recorder	M.	Sep 1995
McGrath, Mr Frank	M.	Oct 1995
Casella, Mr Bartholamu	L.	Nov 1995
Raynor, Mr Keith; Recorder	L.	Oct 1995
Branston, Mr Gareth; Deputy District Judge	G.	Oct 1996
Hope, Mr Ian S	I	Nov 1996
Aiolfi, Mr Laurence	I	Oct 1996
Hossain, Mr Ahmed	G.	Nov 1996
Lennon, Mr Jonathan	L.	Mar 1997
Campbell, Miss Sarah	L.	Oct 1997
Hunter, Miss Katherine	G.	Oct 1997
Allan, Mr David	I	Jan 1998
Turkson, Tetteh	G.	Oct 1998
Sandys, Mr Neil	I	Oct 1998
Salako, Miss Toyin	M.	Nov 1998
Scamardella, Mr Rossano	G.	Nov 1998
Austin-Smith, Mr James*	I	Jul 1999
Dunkin, Mr Oliver	G.	Oct 1999
Fugallo, Mr Daniel	M.	Oct 1999
Bates, Miss Lesley	I	Nov 1999
Khan, Mr Ashraf	M.	Jan 1999
Smith, Mr Graham	I	Oct 1999
Van Der Bosch, Miss Zoe	M.	Jan 1999
Povall, Mr David	L.	Jul 2000
Husbands, Miss Abigail	M.	Nov 2000
Hatt, Miss Samantha	M.	Nov 2000
Singh, Mr Dapinderpaul	M.	Jul 2000
Eaglestone, Mr William	M.	Nov 2001
Harris, Mr Adrian	I	Oct 2001
Lees, Miss Elisabeth*	L.	Oct 2002
Badger, Mr Christopher	M.	Nov 2002
Saul, Ms Sonya	G.	Jan 2002
Sharpe, Mr Richard	M.	Jan 2002
Common, Mr Hamish	L.	Jul 2003
Paley, Miss Ruth	G.	Oct 2003
Godfrey, Mr Thomas	I	Jul 2003
Rimmer, Mr Nicholas	L.	Jul 2004
Mills, Mr Alexander	G.	Jul 2004
Upton, Mr Alexander	L.	Jan 2004
Mohammed, Mr Rashad	L.	Jul 2004
Culleton, Miss Louise	M.	Jan 2005
Templeton, Mr Joseph	M.	Jan 2006
Kinch, Miss Hannah	M.	Jan 2006
Webb, Miss Holly	L.	Nov 2006
Vanstone, Miss Rebecca	I	Jan 2006
Harris, Miss Sarah	G.	Jan 2007
Pulle, Miss Roshani	M.	Jan 2007
Rasiah, Mr Nathan	I	Jan 2007
Duffy, Mr Patrick	M.	Jul 2007
Elia, Miss Elena	M.	Oct 2009
Devlin, Mr Thomas	L.	Jul 2009
Lister, Mr Daniel	I	Jan 2009

This Chamber with 100 Barristers is based in London and led by Simon Russell Flint QC and specialises in Criminal Work - General, Tribunals and Inquiries, Fraud. Although the majority are based in London, our Barristers work out of all 3 annexes. You may contact any of our clerks at any time by sending an email to clerks@23es.com.

ThirtyNine
ESSEX STREET

Chambers of Robert M Jay QC and Stephen Tromans QC

THIRTY NINE ESSEX STREET,
LONDON WC2R 3AT
Tel: 020 7832 1111 *Fax:* 020 7353 3978
Dx: 298 LONDON/CHANCERY LANE
E-mail: clerks@39essex.com
Web: www.39essex.com
Clerk: David Barnes (Chief Executive and Director of Clerking); Alastair Davidson (Senior Clerk); Sheraton Doyle; Andrew Poyser; Ben Sundborg; Owen Lawrence; Graham Smith; Peter Campbell; Niki Merison; Luke Diebelius; Gemma Goodwin.
Chambers Director: David Barnes
Head of Chambers:

Jay, Mr Robert M (Q.C.)	M.	Jun 1981
Tromans, Mr Stephen (Q.C.)	I	Jul 1999
Goldblatt, Mr Simon (Q.C.)	G.	Jun 1953
Tackaberry, Mr John (Q.C.)	G.	Jul 1967
Glasgow, Mr Edwin (Q.C.)	G.	Nov 1969
Horton, Mr Matthew (Q.C.)	M.	Jul 1969
Pleming, Mr Nigel (Q.C.)	I	Feb 1971
Ullstein, Mr Augustus Rupert Patrick Anthony (Q.C.)	I	Jul 1970
Wilmot-Smith, Mr Richard (Q.C.)	M.	Jul 1978
Norris, Mr William (Q.C.)	M.	Jul 1974
Kelly, Mr Matthias (Q.C.); Recorder	G.	Feb 1979
Nelson, Mr Vincent (Q.C.)	I	Nov 1980
Melville, Mr Richard David (Q.C.)	I	Jul 1975
Block, Mr Neil Selwyn (Q.C.)	G.	Jul 1980
Treverton-Jones, Mr Gregory (Q.C.); Recorder	I	Nov 1977
Rodway, Miss Susan (Q.C.)	M.	Jul 1981
Foster, Miss Alison L C (Q.C.)	I	Jul 1984
Catchpole, Mr Stuart P (Q.C.)	I	Jul 1987
Morgan, Mr Jeremy (Q.C.)	M.	Apr 1989
McCaul, Mr Colin (Q.C.)	G.	Jul 1978
Cory-Wright, Mr Charles A. (Q.C.)	M.	Feb 1984
Hughes, Mr Adrian (Q.C.)	M.	Jul 1984
Manzoni, Mr Charles (Q.C.)	M.	Jul 1988
Nardell, Mr Gordon (Q.C.)	I	Nov 1995
Kovats, Mr Steven (Q.C.)	M.	Jul 1989
Wilken, Mr Sean (Q.C.)	M.	Nov 1991
Grey, Ms Eleanor (Q.C.)	G.	Oct 1990
Giovannetti, Miss Lisa (Q.C.)	G.	Oct 1990
Richards, Ms Jennifer (Q.C.)	M.	Oct 1991
Pershad, Mr Rohan Anthony (Q.C.)	L.	Oct 1991
Brodie, Mr Bruce	I	May 1993
Tonna, Mr John	G.	Jul 1974
Noble, Mr Roderick G.	G.	Nov 1977
Pugh-Smith, Mr John	G.	Jul 1977
Edwards, Mr Simon	M.	Nov 1978
Brown, Mr Geoffrey B.	I	Jul 1981
Smith, Miss Marion	G.	Jul 1981
Edwards, Mr Martin Richard	I	Nov 1995
Du Cann, Mr Christian D L	G.	Jun 1982
Gough, Ms Karen Louise	I	Jul 1983
Mayhew, Mr David	I	Nov 2011
Bellamy, Mr Jonathan M	L.	Nov 1986
Bradly, Mr David	M.	Jul 1987
O'Sullivan, Mr Derek	L.	Jan 1990
Morris, Ms Fenella	M.	Oct 1990
Doherty, Mr Bernard	M.	Nov 1990
Todd, Mr James	G.	Nov 1990
Rees, Mr Hefin	I	Nov 1992
Harwood, Mr Richard	M.	Nov 1993
Formby, Ms Emily	M.	Nov 1993
Brynmor Thomas, Mr David	M.	Jan 2011
Thornton, Ms Justine	L.	Feb 1994
Marven, Mr Robert	M.	Oct 1994
Williams, Mr Benjamin	L.	Nov 1994
Robb, Mr Adam	I	Nov 1995
Patel, Mr Parishil	M.	Nov 1996
Sinclair, Mr Duncan	L.	Sep 1996
Zwart, Mr Christiaan	I	Oct 1997
Wald, Mr Richard	G.	Nov 1997
Denis-Smith, Mr John	G.	Jan 1998
Ayling, Ms Judith A	M.	Oct 1998
Grange, Ms Kate	L.	Nov 1998
Truscott, Ms Caroline	L.	Nov 1998
Sachdeva, Mr Vikram	I	Oct 1998
Church, Ms Camilla	M.	Nov 1998
Greaney, Ms Nicola	M.	Nov 1999
Thomann, Mr Colin	I	Jul 1999
Scott, Ms Katharine	M.	Jun 2000
Allen, Mr Neil	M.	Oct 1999
Connors, Ms Jess	G.	Apr 2000
Ghaly, Mr Karim	I	Jul 2001
Burton, Mr James	G.	Oct 2001
Ruck Keene, Mr Alexander	L.	Oct 2002
Dunlop, Mr Rory	L.	Nov 2002
Staker, Mr Christopher	M.	Oct 2003
Bodnar, Ms Alexandra	L.	Jul 2004
Crapper, Ms Sadie	G.	Nov 2004
Lazarus, Mr Robert	I	Oct 2004
Allen, Miss Caroline	L.	Oct 2005
Butler-Cole, Miss Victoria	M.	Jul 2005

Name	Inn	Call
Hearnden, Miss Alexis	I	Oct 2005
Deakin, Mr Andrew	L	Jan 2006
Mant, Mr Peter	I	Jan 2006
O'Hagan, Ms Rachael	I	Oct 2006
Fraser, Mr Quintin	M	Nov 2006
Drake, Ms Rebecca	L	Jul 2007
Wiles, Ms Ellen	I	Oct 2007
Holborn, Mr Jack	L	Jun 2008
Norris, Ms Josephine	G	Jul 2008
Dobson, Ms Catherine	I	Jan 2009
Simons, Mr Zack	I	Jan 2009
Rainey, Miss Angela	I	Nov 2009
Hennessey, Mr Patrick	M	Jul 2010
Brown, Mr Anthony	L	Nov 2010
Grogan, Miss Rose	L	Jul 2010
Lane, Mr Patrick; Senior Counsel - South Africa 1993*	G	Oct 1997
Stern, Ms Kristina*	I	Nov 1996
Findlay, Mr Archibald*	G	Jan 1999
Hayes, Mr Paul*	L	Mar 2005

Thirty Nine Essex Street is a set of 95 barristers, including 30 QCs, offering the full range of legal services in almost every aspect of commercial, common, construction, costs, public, environmental & planning, energy and regulatory & disciplinary law. Members of Chambers have extensive experience in all courts and tribunals in England and Wales and the EU, and many have participated in recent high-profile public inquiries. Instructions are frequently received in or from overseas jurisdictions and several members are qualified domestic and international arbitrators and/or fully trained mediators.

Chambers of Jonathan Gaunt QC and Guy Fetherstonhaugh QC

FALCON CHAMBERS,

FALCON COURT, TEMPLE, LONDON EC4Y 1AA

Tel: 020 7353 2484 ***Fax:*** 020 7353 1261
Dx: 408 LONDON/CHANCERY LANE
E-mail: clerks@falcon-chambers.com
Web: www.falcon-chambers.com
Clerk: Steven Francis.
Administrator: Geraldine Owen
Chambers Director: Edith A Robertson
Head of Chambers:

Name	Inn	Call
Gaunt, Mr Jonathan (Q.C.)	L	Jul 1972
Fetherstonhaugh, Mr Guy (Q.C.)	I	Jul 1983

Name	Inn	Call
Wood, Mr Derek (Q.C.) CBE	M	Feb 1964
Reynolds, Mr Kirk (Q.C.)	M	Jul 1974
Dowding, Mr Nicholas (Q.C.)	I	Jul 1979
Fancourt, Mr Timothy (Q.C.)	L	Nov 1987
Rodger, Mr Martin (Q.C.)	M	Jul 1986
Small, Mr Jonathan (Q.C.)	L	Oct 1990
Jourdan, Mr Stephen (Q.C.)	G	Nov 1989
Moss, Ms Joanne R.	I	Jul 1976
Radevsky, Mr Anthony	I	Jul 1978
Cole, Mr Edward	G	Jul 1980
Clark, Mr Wayne	M	Jul 1982
Denyer-Green, Mr Barry	M	Nov 1972
Cowen, Mr Gary	I	Oct 1990
Bignell, Miss Janet	L	Oct 1992
Dray, Mr Martin	G	Oct 1992
Tanney, Mr Anthony	L	Nov 1994
Shea, Ms Caroline	M	Nov 1994
Taskis, Miss Catherine	I	Oct 1995
Windsor, Miss Emily	I	Oct 1995
Sefton, Mr Mark	M	Nov 1996
Tozer, Miss Stephanie	L	Oct 1996
Cope, Siri	I	Nov 1997
Peters, Mr Edward	M	Nov 1998
Rosenthal, Mr Adam	G	Oct 1999
Harpum, Dr Charles	L	Jul 1976
Fitzgerald, Ms Elizabeth	M	Jan 2001
Healey, Mr Greville	I	Oct 2002
Duckworth, Mr Nathaniel	L	Oct 2002
Radley-Gardner, Mr Oliver	G	Jan 2003
Summers, Mr John Emrys	L	Oct 2004
Cox, Miss Tamsin Victoria Elizabeth	L	Oct 2005
Sissons, Mr Philip	I	Nov 2005
Ollech, Mr Joseph	L	Oct 2007
Robinson, Mr Daniel	L	Jan 2008
Lees, Mr Kester	I	Jan 2010
Sutherland, Mr Jamie	L	Jan 2010

Work Description: Real Property (including conveyancing, easements, mortgages), Landlord and Tenant, Commercial Property, Agricultural Holdings, Rent Review, Professional Negligence, Planning and Compulsory Purchase, Building, Housing and General Chancery (including insolvency).

Chambers of Patrick Harrington QC

FARRAR'S BUILDING,

TEMPLE, LONDON EC4Y 7BD

Tel: 020 7583 9241 ***Fax:*** 020 7583 0090
Dx: 406 LONDON/CHANCERY LANE
E-mail: chambers@farrarsbuilding.co.uk
Web: www.farrarsbuilding.co.uk
Clerk: Senior: Alan Kilbey MBE.
Administrator: Janet Eades
Head of Chambers:

Name	Inn	Call
Harrington, Mr Patrick (Q.C.); Recorder	G	Nov 1973

Name	Inn	Call
Elias, Mr Gerard (Q.C.); Dep.High Court Judge; Recorder	I	Jul 1968
Leighton Williams, Mr John (Q.C.); Dep. High Court Judge; Recorder	G	Apr 1964
Day, Mr Douglas (Q.C.); Dep.High Court Judge; Recorder	L	Jul 1967
Murphy, Mr Ian (Q.C.); Recorder	M	Jul 1972
Jeffreys, Mr Alan (Q.C.); Recorder	G	Jul 1970
Lewis, Mr Paul Keith (Q.C.)	G	Feb 1981
Chambers, Mr Michael (Q.C.)	L	Jan 1980
Murphy, Mr Peter (Q.C.); Recorder	G	Nov 1980
Watt-Pringle, Mr Jonathan (Q.C.)	M	Jul 1987
Nussey, Mr Richard; Dep.Q.B.Manter	L	Nov 1971
Ridd, Mr Ian	M	Jul 1975
Keene, Mrs Gillian Margaret	G	Nov 1980
Ley, Mr N Spencer	M	Jul 1985
Peebles, Mr Andrew	I	Nov 1987
Meredith-Hardy, Mr John	I	Jun 1989
Lakha, Mr Shabbir	L	Jul 1989
Hobhouse, Ms Helen	I	Oct 1990
Freeman, Mr Peter	M	Oct 1992
Jones, Miss Rhiannon	I	Nov 1993
Evans, Mr Lee J	G	Nov 1996
Davies, Mr Huw P.	G	Nov 1998
Pretsell, Mr James	G	Nov 1998
Tozzi, Miss Sarah	I	Oct 1998
Wille, Mr Andrew	L	Oct 1998
Cohen, Mr Howard	G	Oct 1999
Rodger, Miss Senay	L	Oct 1999
Watkins, Mr Guy Thomas	L	Oct 1999
Cox, Mr Carwyn	L	Oct 2002
Kerruish-Jones, Mr Matthew	L	Nov 2003
Plant, Mr James Richard	M	Nov 2004
Hodson, Mr Matthew	L	Nov 2004
Thomas, Mr Clive	G	Jul 2005
Bourne-Arton, Mr Tom	I	Oct 2005
Roderick, Mr David	M	Oct 2005
Sole, Miss Emma	L	Oct 2005
Goodlad, Mr Grant	L	Nov 2006
Found, Mr Tim	L	Jul 2006
Read, Mr Daniel	G	Oct 2006
Townsend, Mr Edmund	M	Mar 2006
Khan, Mr Changez	L	Jul 2008
Erinle, Miss Bonike	L	Oct 2008
Saxena, Miss Hannah	M	Mar 2010

Administrative & Public Law, Contract & Commercial, Criminal Law, Disciplinary Tribunals, Employment, Health & Safety, Insurance Litigation, Landlord & Tenant, Licensing, Medical Law, Personal Injury, Police Actions & Civil Liberties, Product Liability, Public Enquiries & Tribunals, Professional Negligence. Solicitors' Costs & Taxation and Sports & Competition Law. Languages: French, German, Welsh.

Chambers of Paul Oliver Purnell QC

FARRINGDON CHAMBERS,

180 BERMONDSEY STREET, LONDON SE1 3TQ

Tel: 020 7089 5700 ***Fax:*** 020 7089 5701
Dx: 80707 BERMONDSEY
E-mail: info@farringdon-law.co.uk
Clerk: Lloyd Richards; Michael Bazeley; Laura Martin; Zoe Preston.
Head of Chambers:

Name	Inn	Call
Purnell, Mr Paul Oliver (Q.C.)	I	Nov 1962

Chambers of Lucy Morgan Theis QC

FIELD COURT CHAMBERS,

5 FIELD COURT, GRAY'S INN, LONDON WC1R 5EF

Est: 1975
Tel: 020 7405 6114 ***Fax:*** 020 7831 6112 / 7831 0061
Dx: 457 LONDON/CHANCERY LANE
E-mail: clerks@fieldcourt.co.uk
Clerk: Senior: Ian Boardman.
Chambers Director: Delia Lees-Buckley
Head of Chambers:

Name	Inn	Call
Theis, Miss Lucy Morgan (Q.C.)	G	Jul 1982

Name	Inn	Call
Gill, Ms Jane	G	Jul 1973
Jones, Miss Kay Mary	G	Jul 1974
Bowring, Prof William Schuyler Beakbane	M	Nov 1974
Sharpe, Mr Dennis	I	Jul 1976
Russell, Mr Martin Howard	I	Nov 1977
Harrop Griffiths, Mr Hilton	I	Jul 1978
Reza, Mr Hashim	M	Jul 1981
Evans, Mr Franklin St Clair Melville	G	Nov 1981
Tapson, Miss Lesley	G	Nov 1982
Cowen, Mr Jonathan	M	Nov 1983
Carlisle, Mr Timothy St John Ogilvie	G	Nov 1984
Church, Mr John	L	Nov 1984
Critchley, Mr John	G	Jul 1985
Swirsky, Mr Joshua Max Bradbury	M	Nov 1987
Croally, Mr Miles	M	Nov 1987
Hamilton, Mr John C	G	Nov 1988
Date, Mr Julian	M	Nov 1988
Youll, Miss Joanna Isabel	G	Nov 1989
Champion, Ms Rowena	M	Feb 1990
McLinden, Mr John	I	Apr 1975
Lo, Mr Bernard	I	Nov 1991
Alderson, Miss Philippa Elizabeth Loveday	M	Jan 1993
Stirling, Mr Christopher W.	I	Oct 1993
Godfrey, Miss Emma	L	Nov 1995
Thorowgood, Mr Max	L	Nov 1995
Crosfill, Mr John	M	Nov 1995
Rahman, Mr Sami	L	Oct 1996
Davis, Mr Adrian	G	Oct 1996
Joy, Mr Michael	M	Nov 1997
Screeche-Powell, Ms Genevieve	G	Oct 1997
Cabeza, Miss Ruth	M	Mar 1998
Matharoo, Miss Reena	L	Aug 1998
Burt, Ms Joanna	G	Oct 1998
Pennington Legh, Mr Jonathan	I	Oct 2000
Diaz, Ms Paula	M	Oct 2000
Wilkinson, Mr Francis	M	Oct 2001
Baumohl, Mr Mark	M	Oct 2001
Norman, Mr Jared	M	Nov 2001
Braier, Mr Jason	I	Jul 2002
Shalom, Miss Miriam	M	Jul 2003
Kinnear, Miss Elise	G	Oct 2003
Bartholomew, Miss Ami	L	Nov 2003
Fowler, Mr David	L	Oct 2004
Kennedy, Miss Fleur Jennifer	L	Oct 2005
Stott, Mr Matthew	M	Oct 2005
Cooper, Miss Christine	I	Jul 2006
Bhutta, Miss Ayeesha	M	Oct 2006
Hadden, Mr Rhys Thomas	M	Nov 2006
Fuller, Mr Steven	M	Jul 2008

Fleet Street

Community Legal Service

Criminal Defence Service

Chambers of Andrew Trollope QC

187 FLEET STREET,

LONDON EC4A 2AT

Tel: 020 7430 7430 ***Fax:*** 020 7430 7431
Dx: 464 LONDON/CHANCERY LANE
E-mail: chambers@187fleetstreet.com
Web: www.187fleetstreet.com
Clerk: John Pyne.
Administrator: Emma Gluckstein
Head of Chambers:

Name	Inn	Call
Trollope, Mr Andrew (Q.C.)	I	Nov 1971

Name	Inn	Call
Radford, Mrs Nadine (Q.C.)	L	Jan 1974
Borrelli, Mr Michael (Q.C.)	M	Nov 1977
King, Mr Philip (Q.C.)	I	Nov 1974
Fuller, Mr Jonathan (Q.C.)	L	Oct 1977
Mayo, Mr Simon (Q.C.)	I	Nov 1985
Davies, Mr Jonathan	M	Nov 1971
Price, Mr Roderick	I	Jan 1971
Argyle, Mr Brian	G	Jul 1972
Reece, Mr Brian	M	Jul 1974
Guest, Mr Peter	I	Jan 1971
Sheikh, Mr Irshad	L	Mar 1983
Rimmer, Mr Anthony	G	Jul 1983
Amor, Mr Christopher	G	May 1984
Lachkovic, Mr James	G	Nov 1987
Evans, Mr Bill	M	Nov 1988
Vanstone, Mr Grant	M	Jan 1988
Newton, Mr Andrew	I	Nov 1991
Woods, Mr Terence	M	Nov 1989
Chaudhuri, Mr Avirup	M	Feb 1990
Barraclough, Mr Nicholas	I	Nov 1990
Bright, Miss Rachel Zelda	L	Oct 1991
Graffius, Mr Mark	M	Nov 1990
Wong, Miss Natasha Pui-Wai	M	Nov 1993
Aleeson, Mr Warwick	G	Nov 1994
Bartfeld, Mr Jason	M	Jan 1995
Frymann, Mr Andrew P	I	Nov 1995
Cammerman, Mr Gideon	I	Nov 1996
Fishwick, Mr Gregory David Philip Kyle	G	Oct 1996
Madden, Mr John Andrew	I	Aug 1997
Butler, Mr Adam	L	Jan 1997
Kazantzis, Mr Philip	I	Mar 1998
Kazakos, Mr Leon	I	Oct 1999
Kurzner, Miss Emma	M	Feb 1999
Rouse, Mr James	G	Jul 2000
Sharma, Miss Neelam	L	Jun 2000
Punjani, Miss Yasmin	L	Jan 2000
Hopper, Mr Stephen	M	Jan 2001
Hossain, Mr Mozammel	I	Jan 2001
Baird, Mr David Anthony	M	Jun 2003
Eadie, Miss Charlotte	L	Oct 2003
Hughes, Mr Henry	I	Oct 2003
Lee, Miss Rebecca	I	Oct 2005
Ellis, Miss Rachel	L	Oct 2004
Fleck, Miss Helen	L	Oct 2005
Weaver, Miss Victoria	G	Jul 2006
Sharma, Mr Jamie	I	Jan 2005
Bewley, Mr James	L	Jan 2007

For a range of specialised Legal Services please refer to Section 20

Woods, Mr Alex.	L	Jan 2007
Keighley, Miss Anna	M	Jan 2006
Unwin, Mr Greg.	M	Jan 2008
Osman, Mr Nabeel	M	Jan 2008
Korda, Mr Anthony*	I	Jan 1988

The chambers of Andrew Trollope QC is a specialist criminal set, conducting defence and prosecution work. Full details can be found at our website.

FLEET STREET CHAMBERS,
4TH FLOOR, FALCON COURT, 30-32 FLEET STREET, LONDON EC4Y 1AA
Tel: 020 7353 9412
E-mail: clerks@fleetstreetchambers.co.uk

Chambers of Wilfred Forster-Jones

CHAMBERS OF WILFRED FORSTER-JONES,
79 GRAYS INN ROAD, LONDON WC1X 8TT
Tel: 020 7831 0037 ***Fax:*** 020 7404 9707
Dx: 0008 LONDON/CHANCERY LANE
E-mail: chambers_79graysinnroad@yahoo.co.uk
Head of Chambers:

Forster-Jones, Mr Wilfred	M	Nov 1976
Gratwicke, Miss Susan Aileen	G	Nov 1976
Wordsworth, Mr Filo Jones	M	Jan 1986

Chambers of Victoria Nassar

FORTIS GREEN CHAMBERS,
69 FORTIS GREEN, FORTIS GREEN, LONDON N2 9JD
Tel: 020 8883 8117
Head of Chambers:

Nassar, Ms Victoria	G	Feb 1994

Chambers of Timothy Dutton QC

FOUNTAIN COURT CHAMBERS,
TEMPLE, LONDON EC4Y 9DH
Tel: 020 7583 3335 ***Fax:*** 020 7353 0329
Dx: 5 LDE
E-mail: chambers@fountaincourt.co.uk
Clerk: Director of Clerking: Alex Taylor; Senior Clerk: Mark Watson.
Administrator: Prue Woodbridge
Head of Chambers:

Dutton, Mr Timothy (Q.C.)	M	Nov 1979
Dehn, Mr Conrad Francis (Q.C.)	G	Jul 1952
Jacobs, Sir Francis Geoffrey (Q.C.)	M	Jan 1964
Boswood, Mr Anthony Richard (Q.C.)	M	Nov 1970
Brindle, Mr Michael (Q.C.)	L	Nov 1975
Lerego, Mr Michael (Q.C.)*	I	Jul 1972
Crane, Mr Michael (Q.C.)	M	Nov 1975
Railton, Mr David (Q.C.)	G	Jul 1979
Browne-Wilkinson, Mr Simon (Q.C.)	L	Nov 1981
Moriarty, Mr Stephen (Q.C.)	M	Nov 1986
Doctor, Mr Brian (Q.C.)	L	Jul 1991
Rubin, Mr Stephen Charles (Q.C.)	M	Jul 1977
McLaren, The Hon Michael Duncan (Q.C.)	M	Nov 1981
Brook Smith, Mr Philip Andrew (Q.C.)	M	Jul 1982
Cox, Mr Raymond Edwin (Q.C.)	G	Jul 1982
Philipps, Mr Guy Wogan (Q.C.)	I	Jul 1986
Burrows, Mr Andrew (Q.C.)*	M	Apr 1985
Béar, Mr Charles (Q.C.)	L	Jul 1986
Thanki, Bankim (Q.C.)	M	Jul 1988
Orr, Mr Craig Wyndham (Q.C.)	M	Jul 1986
Robertson, Ms Patricia (Q.C.)	I	Nov 1988
Howe, Mr Timothy Jean-Paul (Q.C.)	M	Nov 1987
Simpson, Mr Mark (Q.C.)	M	Oct 1992
Green, Mr Michael (Q.C.)	L	Jul 1987
Handyside, Mr Richard Neil (Q.C.)	L	Oct 1993
Wormington, Mr Timothy Michael*	M	Nov 1977
Lucas, Miss Bridget A.	I	Nov 1989
Chapman, Mr Jeffrey (Q.C.)	M	Nov 1989
Shah, Akhil (Q.C.)	I	Nov 1990
Dale, Mr Derrick (Q.C.)	M	Dec 1990
Buehrlen, Miss Veronique Eira (Q.C.)	M	Oct 1991
Gott, Mr Paul Andrew	L	Oct 1991
Smith, Mr Marcus Alexander (Q.C.)	L	Oct 1991
Mitchell, Mr Andrew Edward	M	Nov 1992
Taylor, Mr John Charles	M	Oct 1993
Coleman, Mr Richard J L	L	Feb 1994
Tolley, Mr Adam Richard	L	Oct 1994
Merrett, Ms Louise Ann*	G	Nov 1995
Hamilton, Ms Philippa*	L	Oct 1996
Sinclair, Mr Paul	M	Jan 1997
Goodall, Mr Patrick	I	Mar 1998
Wheeler, Mr Giles	M	Oct 1998
Nambisan, Mr Deepak	G	Oct 1998
Phelps, Ms Rosalind J	L	Nov 1998
King, Mr Henry	I	Nov 1998
Levey, Mr Edward	I	Nov 1999
Stopps, Miss Natalie	G	Jul 2000
Cutress, Mr James	L	Oct 2000
Yeo, Mr Nik	M	Nov 2000
Zellick, Mr Adam	L	Oct 2000
Carpenter, Miss Chloe	L	Oct 2001
Casey, Mr Paul	I	Oct 2002
Watt, Miss Katherine Anna Mary	M	Oct 2002
Oppenheimer, Miss Tamara Helen	I	Oct 2002
Butler, Ms Marianne Jane	L	Jul 2003
McClelland, Mr James	L	Jul 2004
Murray, Mr David John	L	Jul 2004
Said, Mr Sebastian William St.John	L	Nov 2004
Atrill, Mr Simon	I	Jul 2005
Allen, Mr Rupert Alexander Dendy	L	Jul 2005
Duffy, Mr James	L	Oct 2005
Milner, Mr Alexander Nathan	L	Oct 2006
Jones-Fenleigh, Miss Harriet	L	Jul 2007
Sher, Mr Adam	L	Oct 2007
Power, Mr Richard	L	Oct 2007
Ulyatt, Mr Craig Owen	L	Jul 2008
Bennett, Miss Natasha	L	Oct 2009

Chambers of Robin Purchas QC

FRANCIS TAYLOR BUILDING,
INNER TEMPLE, LONDON EC4Y 7BY
Tel: 020 7353 8415 ***Fax:*** 020 7353 7622
Dx: 402 LONDON/CHANCERY LANE
E-mail: clerks@ftb.eu.com
Clerk: Senior: Paul Coveney. Principle: Andrew Briton; James Kemp.
Chambers Director: Vicki Cousins (Chambers Manager)
Head of Chambers:

Purchas, Mr Robin (Q.C.)	I	Nov 1968
Roots, Mr Guy (Q.C.)	M	Jul 1969
Phillips, Mr Richard (Q.C.)	I	Nov 1970
George, Mr Charles (Q.C.)	I	Jul 1974
Newberry, Mr Clive (Q.C.)	I	Jul 1978
Mehigan, Mr Simon (Q.C.)	L	Jul 1980
De Haan, Mr Kevin (Q.C.)	I	Jul 1976
McCracken, Mr Robert (Q.C.)	I	Jul 1973
Tait, Mr Andrew (Q.C.)	I	Jul 1981
Humphries, Mr Michael (Q.C.)	I	Jul 1982
Gouriet, Mr Gerald William (Q.C.)	I	Jul 1974
Humphreys, Mr Richard (Q.C.)	I	Jul 1986
Howell Williams, Mr Craig (Q.C.)	G	Jul 1983
Glover, Mr Richard (Q.C.)	I	Jul 1984
Phillips, Mr Simon Benjamin (Q.C.)	I	Jul 1985
Newcombe, Mr Andrew (Q.C.)	M	Jul 1987
Edwards, Mr Douglas (Q.C.)	L	Nov 1992
Fookes, Mr Robert	L	Jul 1975
Petchey, Mr Philip	M	Jul 1976
Milner, Mr Jonathan	I	Jul 1977
Comyn, Mr Timothy	I	Jul 1980
Rankin, Mr James	I	Jul 1983
Ornsby, Miss Suzanne	M	Nov 1986
Lewis, Mr Meyric	G	Nov 1986
Mynors, Dr Charles	M	Nov 1988
Jones, Mr Gregory	L	Nov 1991
Pereira, Mr James	M	Oct 1996
Phillpot, Mr Hereward	G	Nov 1997
Booth, Mr Alexander	M	Feb 2000
Sheikh, Ms Saira Kabir	I	Nov 2000
Pike, Mr Jeremy	M	Jul 2001
Lopez, Mr Juan	L	Oct 2002
Edwards, Mr Denis	M	Oct 2002
Honey, Mr Richard	I	Jul 2003
Phillips, Mr Jeremy	I	Oct 2004
Westmoreland Smith, Mr Mark	L	Jan 2006
Eleftheriadis, Dr Pavlos	L	Jan 2006
Ormondroyd, Mr Cain	L	Jan 2007
Graham Paul, Annabel	M	Jan 2008
Sackman, Sarah	I	Jan 2008
Clutten, Rebecca	I	Jan 2008
Westaway, Mr Ned	L	Jan 2009

Chambers of Oliver Blunt QC and Sally O'Neill QC

FURNIVAL CHAMBERS,
32 FURNIVAL STREET, LONDON EC4A 1JQ
Tel: 020 7405 3232 ***Fax:*** 020 7405 3322
Dx: 72 LONDON/CHANCERY LANE
E-mail: clerks@furnivallaw.co.uk
Web: www.furnivallaw.co.uk
Clerk: Stephen Ball; Joel Mason; Darin Marsh; Lewis Duffy; Adrian Steel; Alfie Lee.
Head of Chambers:

Blunt, Mr Oliver (Q.C.)	M	Nov 1974
O'Neill, Miss Sally (Q.C.)	G	Nov 1976
Evans, Mr Anthony (Q.C.)	G	Jan 1965
Lodge, Mr Anton James Corduff (Q.C.)	G	Nov 1966
Rees, Mr John Charles (Q.C.)	L	Jul 1972
Leslie, Mr Stephen W (Q.C.)	L	Feb 1971
Carter-Manning, Mr Jeremy (Q.C.)	M	Apr 1975
Woodley, Miss Sonia (Q.C.)	G	Jul 1968
Garlick, Mr Paul (Q.C.)	M	Jan 1973
Menary, Mr Andrew (Q.C.)	I	Nov 1982
Cole, Mr Gordon (Q.C.)	I	Jan 1974
McAtasney, Ms Philippa (Q.C.)	L	Nov 1985
Rafferty, Mr Stuart (Q.C.)	G	Jul 1975
Lewis, Mr Raymond	M	Jul 1971
Baur, Mr Christopher	M	Jul 1972
Griffiths, Mr Hugh	I	Nov 1972
May, Mr Nigel	I	Jul 1974
Connor, Mr Gino	G	Nov 1974
Matthews, Miss Lisa	G	Nov 1974
Winberg, Mr Stephen A	I	Nov 1974
Latham, Mr Michael	G	Nov 1975
Hadrill, Mr Keith	L	Jan 1977
Bendall, Mr Richard	L	Jul 1979
Romans, Mr Philip*	G	Nov 1982
Headlan, Mr Roy	G	Nov 1983
Merrick, Miss Nicola	G	Nov 1983
Swain, Mr Jon	L	Nov 1983
Brock, Mr David J.	M	Nov 1984
Devlin, Mr Timothy R	L	Jul 1985
Hunter, Miss Allison	L	Jul 1986
Hirst, Miss Kathryn	I	Nov 1986
Sherrard, Mr Charles	M	Nov 1986
Boulter, Mr Terence	L	Jul 1986
Wilson, Mr Graeme	I	Feb 1987
Gregory, Mr Barry	G	Nov 1987
Evans, Mr Charles	M	Nov 1988
Meredith, Mr Christopher	I	Jul 1988
English, Ms Caroline	I	Jul 1989
Forster, Mr Timothy	M	Oct 1990
Rutherford, Mr Martin	L	Oct 1990
Henley, Mr Andrew	M	Oct 1992
Power, Ms Alexia	G	Oct 1992
Fawcett, Miss Michelle	I	Nov 1993
Smith, Miss Emma	M	Oct 1994
Kearney, Mr John	M	Nov 1994
Carberry, Miss Caroline	G	Oct 1995
Hussain, Miss Frida Khanam	I	Oct 1995
Hamilton, Miss Amanda	L	Jan 1995
Winship, Mr Julian	G	Oct 1995
Cockings, Mr Giles F S	M	Oct 1996
Durose, Mr David W	L	Oct 1996
Leake, Laban	M	Oct 1996
Moses, Mr Stephen	G	Nov 1997
Meek, Ms Susan	G	Nov 1997
Chinner, Miss Fer	I	Oct 1998
Hearnden, Mr Richard	G	Mar 1998
Mather, Mr Nicholas I S	M	Oct 1998
Miller, Mr David	I	Oct 1998
Fudge, Miss Sally	L	Nov 1998
Yarrow, Miss Charlotte	L	Oct 1999
Haughey, Ms Caroline	M	Nov 1999
Norrman, Ms Edith	I	Nov 2000
Omideyi, Ms Anu	L	Jul 2001
Cohen, Mr Ross	I	Nov 2001
Smith, Mr Joel	I	Jul 2002
Fapohunda, Kemi	G	Jul 2002
Spreadborough, Mr Paul	G	Oct 2002
Ganesan, Muthupandi	L	Oct 2003
Jameson, Mr Daniel	M	Nov 2004
Fordham, Ms Chloe	I	Jul 2005
Powell, Ms Charlotte	I	Jul 2005
Freeman, Ms Lisa	L	Oct 2005
Gordon, Mr Ben	I	Nov 2005
Brown, Ms Catherine	M	Jan 2005
Harris, Mr Craig	M	Jul 2006
Hearn, Mr Nicholas	M	Jan 2007
Jordan, Mr Andrew	I	Jan 2008
Wilson, Lisa	I	Jan 2008
Ibekwe, Ms Frances	M	Mar 2008
Chidley, Mr Matthew	M	Jan 2008
Draper, Mr Guy	M	Mar 2008
Boulton, Ms Clementine	L	Jan 2009
Graham, Ms Amina	I	Jan 2010
Ganner, Mr Joseph M*	I	Jul 1983
Coughlin, Ms Elizabeth*	M	Nov 1989
Garson, Mr Robert*	M	Nov 1999

Work Description: Crime; all aspects from Murder to Rape and Fraud. Specialisations: Commercial Fraud, Confiscation proceedings Crown Court and High Court. Languages: French, Spanish, Italian.

Chambers of Stephen William Scott Cobb QC and Janet Clare Bazley QC

1 GARDEN COURT,
FAMILY LAW CHAMBERS, TEMPLE, LONDON EC4Y 9BJ
Tel: 020 7797 7900 ***Fax:*** 020 7797 7929
Dx: 1034 LONDON/CHANCERY LANE
E-mail: clerks@1gc.com
Web: www.1gc.com
Clerk: Senior: Howard Rayner.
Chambers Director: Shona Kelly
Head of Chambers:

Cobb, Mr Stephen William Scott (Q.C.)	I	Jul 1985
Bazley, Miss Janet Clare (Q.C.)	L	Jul 1980
Platt, Miss Eleanor Frances (Q.C.)	G	Feb 1960
Ball, Miss Alison (Q.C.)	M	Nov 1972
Crowley, Mrs Jane (Q.C.); Recorder; Deputy High Court Judge	G	Jul 1976
Rowe, Miss Judith May (Q.C.)	G	Jul 1979
Geekie, Mr Charles (Q.C.)	I	Jul 1985
Russell, Ms Alison (Q.C.)	G	Jul 1983
Morgan, Miss Sarah Mary (Q.C.)	G	Nov 1988
Wilbourne, Miss Caroline	I	Nov 1970
Coleman, Mr Bruce Robert	I	Jul 1972
Shenton, Miss Suzanne	M	Jul 1973
Szwed, Miss Elizabeth	M	Jul 1974
Horrocks, Mr Peter Leslie	M	Nov 1977
Halkyard, Miss Kay	G	Jul 1980
Burles, Mr David	M	Nov 1985
McIlwain, Mr Sylvester	L	Jul 1985
Stocker, Mr John Crispin	I	Nov 1985
Pyle, Miss Susan	G	Nov 1985
Crawley, Mr Gary Thomas	M	Feb 1988
Daniels, Mr Nicholas	I	Feb 1988
Gillman, Miss Rachel	G	Jul 1988
Giz, Ms Alev	G	Oct 1988
Bagchi, Mr Andrew Kumar	M	Jul 1989
Liebrecht, Mr Michael	I	Nov 1989
Chisholm, Mr Malcolm	I	Nov 1989
Nichols, Mr Stuart	L	Nov 1989
Mather, Miss Kate	G	Oct 1990
Jenkins, Miss Catherine Phillida	M	Nov 1990
Heppenstall, Miss Claire	I	Nov 1990
Sugar, Mr Simon	M	Dec 1990
Robbins, Mr Ian Geoffrey	M	Feb 1991
Krish, Miss Doushka	M	Jun 1991
Norton, Mr Andrew David	I	Oct 1992
Auld, Ms Rohan	G	Nov 1992
Bugg, Mr Ian Stephen	M	Oct 1992
Howe, Mr Darren Francis	G	Oct 1992
Hurworth, Miss Jillian	I	Oct 1993
Downham, Miss Gillian	M	Nov 1993
Moore, Miss Alison	M	Nov 1994
Stone, Ms Sally	I	Nov 1994
Hudson, Ms Emma	L	Feb 1995
Chandler, Mr Alexander	M	Oct 1995
Momtaz, Mr Sam	L	Nov 1995
Foster, Mr Julien	M	Oct 1995
Wiley, Miss Francesca	G	May 1996
Fox, Miss Nicola S	M	Oct 1996
McEleavy, Mr Peter	G	Jan 1999
Segal, Miss Sharon	I	Oct 2000
Mitchell, Miss Rebecca	G	Oct 2000
Stanley, Mrs Gillian	M	Jul 2001
Middleton, Ms Caroline	I	Oct 2002
Flood, Mr Edward A	M	Oct 2002
Perrins, Mr Philip	M	Jan 2002
Jones, Mr Richard Gwyn	I	Oct 2003
Procter, Mr Alfred George Haydn	M	Jul 2005

Jarmain, Mr Stephen Robert . . . M . . . Jul 2005
Tambling, Mr Richard . . . M . . . Oct 2005
MacLeod, Ms Elena . . . L . . . Jul 2007
Cole, Ms Georgina . . . L . . . Jul 2007
Clapham, Miss Penelope . . . I . . . Jan 2008
Sprinz, Miss Lucy . . . I . . . Jan 2008
Dudley, Mr Thomas . . . I . . . Jan 2008
O'Donoghue, Miss Lisa . . . G . . . Jan 2008
Jones, Miss Eleri . . . M . . . Jan 2009

This Chamber with 65 Barristers is based in London and led by Stephen Cobb QC and Janet Bazley QC and specialises in Public and Private, Children, Family Law and Family Financial Provision. You may contact any of our clerks at any time by sending a message to clerks@1gc.com.

Chambers of Owen Handel Davies QC and Courtenay Griffiths QC

GARDEN COURT CHAMBERS,
57-60 LINCOLNS INN FIELDS, LONDON WC2A 3LJ
Tel: 020 7993 7600 ***Fax:*** 020 7993 7700
Dx: 34 LONDON/CHANCERY LANE

Chambers of Ferdous Shah

1 GARFIELD ROAD,
BATTERSEA, LONDON SW11 5PL
Tel: 020 7228 1137 ***Fax:*** 020 7228 1137
Clerk: Farhat Shah.
Head of Chambers:
Shah, Ferdous . . . L . . . Jul 1969

Chambers of Martin Thomas of Gresford QC

GOLDSMITH CHAMBERS,
GOLDSMITH BUILDING, TEMPLE, LONDON EC4Y 7BL
Tel: 020 7353 6802 ***Fax:*** 020 7583 5255
Dx: 376 LDN
E-mail: clerks@goldsmithchambers.com
Clerk: John Francis.
Practice Manager: Simon Milton
Head of Chambers:
Thomas of Gresford, Lord Martin (Q.C.) MBE; Recorder. . . . G . . . Nov 1967

Riza, Mr Alper (Q.C.); Recorder . . . G . . . Nov 1973
Sapsford, Mr Philip (Q.C.) . . . I . . . Nov 1974
Sullivan, Miss Linda Elizabeth (Q.C.); Recorder . . . M . . . Jul 1973
Mason, Mr James . . . G . . . Jul 1967
Meikle, Mr Robert . . . G . . . Jul 1970
Britton, Mr Robert; Recorder . . . I . . . Jul 1973
Harkus, Mr George . . . I . . . Nov 1975
Sabido, Mr John . . . L . . . Jul 1976
Dean, Mr James P . . . L . . . Nov 1977
Routley, Mr Patrick . . . I . . . Jul 1979
Jenkins, Mr Alun . . . G . . . May 1981
Clark, Mr Dingle . . . M . . . Jul 1981
Hulme, Mr John . . . M . . . Nov 1983
Norris, Mr James . . . I . . . May 1984
Morris, Mr Michael . . . G . . . Jun 1984
Wernham, Mr Stewart . . . M . . . Jul 1984
Khatoon, Ms Najma . . . I . . . Nov 1986
Day, Mr Dorian . . . M . . . Jul 1987
Mailer, Mr Clifford . . . M . . . Jul 1987
Whitehouse, Mr Stuart . . . M . . . Jul 1987
Maynard, Mr Christopher . . . G . . . Jul 1988
Gill, Miss Pamila . . . L . . . Apr 1989
Livingstone, Mr Douglas . . . I . . . Nov 1989
George, Mr Michael Robert . . . G . . . Dec 1990
Rogers, Mr Don H . . . M . . . Nov 1991
Siddle, Mr Trevor Brian . . . G . . . Oct 1991
Fane, Miss Angela . . . M . . . Nov 1992
Hope, Miss Heather . . . G . . . Oct 1993
Smart, Miss Julia . . . G . . . Oct 1993
McLevy, Miss Tracey . . . L . . . Nov 1993
Pollock, Miss Hilary . . . I . . . Nov 1993
Jubb, Mr David . . . I . . . Oct 2002
Brennan, Mr Christopher Patrick . . . G . . . Feb 1995
Allen, Mr Douglas . . . L . . . Oct 1995
Foster, Mr Julien . . . M . . . Oct 1995
Thompson, Mr Lyall . . . I . . . Jan 1995
Lucas, Mr John . . . M . . . Oct 1995
Nott, Miss Emma . . . G . . . Nov 1995
Okine, Miss Julie . . . L . . . Oct 1996
Cadman, Mr David J . . . L . . . Nov 1996
Royle, Mr Charles . . . L . . . Oct 1997
Smith, Mr Benjamin . . . I . . . Oct 1997
Blake-James, Mr Hugh D . . . M . . . Mar 1998
Sheriff, Mr Simon . . . I . . . Nov 1999
Hunter, Mr Peter Michael . . . L . . . Jun 2000
Harris, Mr Jake . . . M . . . Jul 2000
Elliott, Mr Edward . . . G . . . Oct 2000
Wells, Mr Casper John Mowlem . . . M . . . Oct 2000
McCune, Mr Rodney James . . . L . . . Nov 2000
Dodd, Miss Stephanie . . . G . . . Jul 2001
Wilson, Miss Victoria . . . G . . . Jul 2002
Dye, Mr John . . . I . . . Nov 2002
Petersen, Mr Thomas . . . L . . . Jul 2004
Barrie, Miss Laura . . . L . . . Jul 2005
Gilmore, Miss Alexandra . . . L . . . Jul 2005
Brooks, Mr Matthew . . . I . . . Oct 2005
Bishop, Mr Stephen . . . I . . . Jul 2006
Horne-Roberts, Mrs Jennifer* . . . M . . . Nov 1976

Chambers of Grahame Aldous QC

9 GOUGH SQUARE,
LONDON EC4A 3DG
Tel: 020 7832 0500 ***Fax:*** 020 7353 1344
Dx: 439 LONDON/CHANCERY LANE
E-mail: clerks@9goughsquare.co.uk
Clerk: Garry Farrow; Michael Goodridge; Tom Robinson.
Practice Manager: John Kerr
Head of Chambers:
Aldous, Mr Grahame (Q.C.); Recorder . . . I . . . Jul 1979

Roberston, Mr Andrew (Q.C.) . . . M . . . Jul 1975
Foy, Mr John Leonard (Q.C.); Recorder . . . G . . . Jul 1969
Baillie, Mr Andrew Bruce (Q.C.); Recorder . . . I . . . Nov 1970
Goddard, Mr Christopher . . . M . . . Jul 1973
Eyre, Mr Giles . . . G . . . Jul 1974
Davies, Mr Trevor Glyn . . . G . . . Jul 1978
Ferguson, Mr Frederick Morris Gifford . . . M . . . Jul 1978
Henry, Mr Philip Ivan . . . G . . . Oct 1979
Macleod, Mr Duncan . . . M . . . Jul 1980
Wilson, Mr Christopher; Recorder . . . G . . . Jul 1980
Pinfold, Mr Martin . . . M . . . Jan 1981
Hillier, Mr Nicholas Peter . . . I . . . Jul 1982
Hiorns, Mr Roger Martin Fairchild . . . M . . . Jul 1983
Carr, Mr Simon; Recorder . . . I . . . Nov 1984
Ritchie, Mr Andrew . . . I . . . Jan 1985
Naik, Gaurang Ramamlal . . . G . . . Jul 1985
Williams, Mr Vincent . . . M . . . Jul 1985
Levy, Mr Jacob . . . I . . . Jul 1986
Loades, Mr Jonathan C . . . M . . . Nov 1986
Buckett, Mr Edwin . . . I . . . Jul 1988
Cottage, Miss Rosina . . . I . . . Nov 1988
Whalan, Mr Mark . . . M . . . Nov 1988
Holmes-Milner, Mr James . . . M . . . Jul 1989
Belgrave, Ms Susan Loraine . . . I . . . Jul 1989
Glynn, Mr Stephen . . . M . . . Oct 1990
Jones, Mr Philip A . . . M . . . Nov 1990
Crowther, Mr Jeremy Gage . . . M . . . Oct 1991
Padley, Miss Clare . . . I . . . Oct 1991
Lucas, Mr Edward . . . M . . . Oct 1991
Downey, Miss Aileen Patricia . . . L . . . Nov 1991
Begley, Miss Laura Anne . . . L . . . Nov 1993
Stephenson, Mr Christopher . . . L . . . Nov 1994
Lawson, Mr Daniel . . . I . . . Oct 1994
Shetty, Rajeev . . . I . . . Jan 1996
Elfield, Miss Laura . . . G . . . Sep 1996
Winter, Ms Melanie . . . M . . . Nov 1996
Ford, Mr Jeremy . . . L . . . Oct 1996
Vindis, Ms Tara . . . L . . . Nov 1996
Little, Mr Tom . . . M . . . Oct 1997
Godfrey, Mr Timothy . . . M . . . Oct 1997
McKechnie, Mr Stuart . . . I . . . Oct 1997
Brindle, Mr Simon . . . G . . . Jul 1998
Gibbons, Mr Perrin . . . M . . . Oct 1998
Mooney, Mr Giles . . . G . . . Nov 1998
Sharghy, Mr Shahram . . . L . . . Jul 2000
Nelson, Miss Linda . . . G . . . Jul 2000
Dawson, Mr Adam . . . M . . . Oct 2000
Harden, Miss Claire . . . M . . . Nov 2000
Munday, Mr Gareth . . . M . . . Nov 2000
Mawrey, Ms Eleanor . . . G . . . Jul 2001
Mahood, Miss Emma-Jane . . . G . . . Jul 2001
Thacker, Mr James . . . G . . . Nov 2001
McAllister, Mr Robert . . . I . . . Oct 2002
Millington, Mr Oliver . . . G . . . Jul 2003
Pounder, Ms Esther . . . I . . . Jul 2003
Radcliffe, Ms Emily . . . G . . . Oct 2003
Maclachlan, Ms Esther . . . M . . . Jul 2005
Hogarth, Mr Alistair . . . G . . . Oct 2005
Scott, Ms Jennifer . . . I . . . Jul 2006
Lamb, Mr Edward . . . L . . . Oct 2006
Atkinson, Ms Catherine . . . L . . . Oct 2006
Rodgers, Mr Benedict . . . I . . . Nov 2007

Chambers of Claire Andrews

GOUGH SQUARE CHAMBERS,
6-7 GOUGH SQUARE, LONDON EC4A 3DE
Tel: 020 7353 0924 ***Fax:*** 020 7353 2221
Dx: 476 LONDON/CHANCERY LANE
E-mail: gsc@goughsq.co.uk
Web: www.goughsq.co.uk
Clerk: Senior: Bob Weekes.
Head of Chambers:
Andrews, Miss Claire . . . G . . . Nov 1979

Kirk, Mr Jonathan (Q.C.) . . . L . . . Nov 1995
Philpott, Mr Fred . . . G . . . Jul 1974
Sayer, Mr Peter . . . M . . . Jul 1975
Hayes, Miss Josephine . . . L . . . Jul 1980
Goulding, Mr Jonathan . . . I . . . Jul 1984
Neville, Mr Stephen . . . M . . . Nov 1986
Gun Cuninghame, Mr Julian . . . L . . . Nov 1989
Say, Mr Bradley John . . . I . . . Nov 1993
Macdonald, Mr Iain . . . M . . . Jul 1996
Popplewell, Mr Simon . . . G . . . Oct 2000
Urell, Miss Kate . . . M . . . Nov 2002
Howells, Mr Geraint . . . G . . . Nov 2002
Ross, Mr James . . . L . . . Jan 2006
Bala, Miss Ruth . . . L . . . Jun 2006
Samuels, Mr Thomas David . . . L . . . Jan 2009

Consumer Credit, Food, Trade Descriptions, Pricing, Consumer Banking / Finance, Mortgages, Timeshare, Trading Schemes, Health & Safety, Environmental Pollution, Package Holidays, Consumer Contracts, Sale of Goods, Land, Landlord and Tenant, Company / Partnership, Insolvency, Criminal Fraud, Professional Negligence, Tourism & Travel, Licensing and Gaming.

Chambers of Joy Okoye

GRAY'S INN CHAMBERS,
2ND FLOOR, SUITE 1, LONDON WC1R 5JA
Tel: 07976 426871
Administrator: Alan Beddall
Head of Chambers:
Okoye, Ms Joy . . . G . . . Jul 1981

Ocan, Ms Akidi; Barrister . . . M . . . Jul 1982

Chambers of Shiraz Musa Bhanji

1 GRAY'S INN SQUARE,
LONDON WC1R 5EU
Tel: 020 7405 0001 ***Fax:*** 020 7405 1617
E-mail: bhanji@regencyhotelwestend.co.uk
Clerk: Justin Dyer; Daniel Gatt.
Administrator: Bill Harris
Practice Manager: Bill Harris
Chambers Director: Reg Harris
Head of Chambers:
Bhanji, Shiraz Musa . . . G . . . Jul 1979

Chambers of Angus Gloag

1 GRAY'S INN SQUARE,
GROUND FLOOR, LONDON WC1R 5AA
Tel: 020 7405 8946 ***Fax:*** 020 7405 1617
Dx: 1013 LONDON/CHANCERY LANE
E-mail: clerks@1gis.law.co.uk
Clerk: Lloyd Richards; Justin Dyer; Reg Harris; Daniel Gatt; Bob Bywaters; Louisa Wheeler.
Administrator: Myrna Legon
Practice Manager: Rohit Pandya
Head of Chambers:
Gloag, Mr Angus . . . I . . . Jan 1992

Weisman, Mr Malcolm OBE . . . M . . . Jun 1961
Cruickshank, Miss Cynthia . . . L . . . Nov 1968
Johnson, Mr Alan . . . M . . . Jul 1971
Sofaer, Miss Moira . . . M . . . Jul 1975
Charlton, Mr Hugo . . . G . . . Jan 1978
D'Aigremont, Maitre Gilles . . . L . . . Jul 1978
Campbell, Mr Colin W . . . G . . . Jul 1979
Bhanji, Shiraz Musa . . . G . . . Jul 1979
Gelbart, Mr Geoffrey Alan . . . L . . . Nov 1982
Agbaje, Mr Edward . . . M . . . Nov 1984
Mehta, Mr Sailesh . . . L . . . Jul 1986
Coates, Mr John . . . M . . . Nov 1988
Giles, Mr David W . . . L . . . Nov 1988
Neubert, Mr Jolyon . . . M . . . Jul 1989
Wells, Mr Nicholas . . . L . . . Nov 1990
Hunter, Mr John . . . L . . . Feb 1991
Attridge, Mr Steven . . . I . . . Nov 1991
Wayne, Mr Nicholas . . . M . . . Jul 1994
Coleman, Mr Daniel . . . G . . . Nov 1994
Cole-Wilson, Ms Lois . . . I . . . Nov 1995
Amarasinha, Revantha . . . M . . . Oct 1996
Moonan, Miss Caroline . . . L . . . Mar 1997
Malone, Mr David John . . . G . . . Oct 1998
Mitchell, Mr Jonathon . . . G . . . Mar 1998
Davison, Mr Guy . . . L . . . Oct 1998
Cooper, Mr Nicholas . . . I . . . Nov 1998
Mackworth, Ms Julia . . . I . . . Jul 1999
Burrett, Mr Alex . . . I . . . Aug 1999

Chambers of Timothy Straker QC and W Robert Griffiths QC

4-5 GRAY'S INN SQUARE,
GRAY'S INN, LONDON WC1R 5AH
Tel: 020 7404 5252 ***Fax:*** 020 7242 7803
Dx: 1029 LONDON/CHANCERY LANE
E-mail: clerks@4-5.co.uk
Clerk: Senior: Michael Kaplan.
Practice Manager: Tracey Jones
Head of Chambers:
Straker, Mr Timothy (Q.C.) . . . G . . . Jul 1977
Griffiths, Mr W Robert (Q.C.) . . . M . . . Nov 1974

Ash, Mr Brian (Q.C.) . . . G . . . Nov 1975
Steel, Mr John (Q.C.) . . . G . . . Jul 1978
Spearman, Mr Richard (Q.C.) . . . M . . . Nov 1977
McManus, Mr J Richard (Q.C.) . . . I . . . Jul 1982
Malek, Mr Hodge M (Q.C.) . . . G . . . Jul 1983
Hobson, Mr John (Q.C.) . . . I . . . Jul 1980
Clayton, Mr Richard (Q.C.); Recorder . . . M . . . Nov 1977
Corner, Mr Timothy Frank (Q.C.) . . . G . . . Nov 1981
Village, Mr Peter (Q.C.) . . . I . . . Jul 1983
Lyons, Mr Timothy (Q.C.) . . . I . . . Jul 1980
Hill, Mr Thomas (Q.C.) . . . I . . . Jul 1988
Brown, Mr Paul (Q.C.) . . . I . . . Nov 1991
Coppel, Mr Philip (Q.C.) . . . L . . . Nov 1994

Stinchcombe, Mr Paul (Q.C.)	L	Jul 1985
Campbell, Mr John (Q.C.)	L	Jun 2009
Davey, Mr Toby	G	Jul 1977
Carnes, Mr Andrew	L	Jul 1984
Byrne, Mr Garrett Thomas	G	Nov 1986
Ramsden, Mr James	M	Nov 1987
Marshall, Mr Paul	I	Jan 1991
Bourne, Mr Charles	M	Jul 1991
Tabachnik, Mr Andrew	I	Nov 1991
O'Riordan, Mr Thomas	I	Jan 1993
Fraser-Urquhart, Mr Andrew	M	Oct 1993
White, Mr Robert Douglas	I	Nov 1993
Falkowski, Mr Damian	G	Oct 1994
Davies, Ms Sarah Jane	I	Oct 1996
Moffett, Mr Jonathan	I	Oct 1996
Sharland, Mr Andrew	G	Oct 1996
Strachan, Mr James	M	Oct 1996
Bolton, Ms Caroline	M	Jan 1998
Dearing, Mr Anthony John	M	Nov 1998
Greatorex, Mr Paul	L	Nov 1999
Auburn, Mr Jonathan Walter	M	Oct 1999
Busch, Ms Lisa	I	Sep 2000
Whale, Mr Stephen	G	Oct 1999
Hanif, Ms Saima	L	Jan 2002
Hannett, Ms Sarah	L	Jan 2003
Goodman, Mr Alex	L	Jan 2003
Bicarregui, Miss Anna	L	Jul 2004
Buttler, Mr Christopher	I	Jan 2004
Wenban-Smith, Mr Mungo	L	Jan 2004
Bedenham, Mr David	G	Jun 2005
Pratley, Miss Michelle	L	Jan 2006
Anderson, Mr Jack	I	Jan 2006
Dehon, Ms Estelle	I	Jul 2005
Amraoui, Mr Thomas	G	Nov 2007
Loveday, Mr David	I	Nov 2007
Helme, Mr Ned	L	Oct 2006
Thelen, Ms Jennifer	I	Nov 2007
Jackson, Ms Philippa	L	Oct 2008
Emmerson, Heather	L	Oct 2009
Tankel, Mr Benjamin	M	Nov 2009
Lee, Annabel	M	Jan 2010

Chambers of Sarah Forster

14 GRAY'S INN SQUARE,
GRAY'S INN, LONDON WC1R 5JP
Tel: 020 7242 0858 ***Fax:*** 020 7242 5434
Dx: 399 LONDON/CHANCERY LANE
E-mail: clerks@14graysinnsquare.co.uk
Clerk: Senior: Geoffrey Carr.
Head of Chambers:

Forster, Miss Sarah	M	Nov 1976
Hall, Ms Joanna Mary	I	Nov 1973
McNab, Miss Mhairi	M	Jul 1974
Slomnicka, Miss Barbara Irene	G	Nov 1976
Kingsley, Mr Richard	I	Jul 1977
Morris, Miss Brenda	M	Jul 1978
Ford, Miss Monica	M	Jul 1984
McIlwain, Mr Sylvester	L	Jul 1985
Spooner, Miss Judith	M	Jul 1987
Habboo, Miss Camille	L	Jul 1987
Roberts, Ms Patricia	G	Nov 1987
Evans, Mr Dylan	G	Apr 1989
Alomo, Mr Richard	I	Nov 1990
Pearson, Miss Carolyn	G	Nov 1990
De Zonie, Miss Jane	M	Nov 1993
Moore, Miss Alison	M	Nov 1994
O'Donovan, Mr Ronan Daniel James	L	Oct 1995
Whittam, Miss Samantha	M	Nov 1995
Glaser, Mr Michael Samson	M	Oct 1998
Savage, Miss Mai-Ling Carmen Pilar	I	Oct 1998
Miller, Mr Christopher	L	Oct 1998
Bhari, Miss Poonam	L	Jan 1999
Mitchell, Miss Rebecca	G	Oct 2000
Turner, Mr James Paul	I	Jul 2001
Cameron, Mr Gillon	I	Jan 2002
Lamb, Mr Henry	I	Jan 2004
Spencer, Miss Anna	G	Jan 2004
Gore, Miss Sally	I	Jul 2006
Pope, Ms Sarah	L	Jul 2006
Walker-McKevitt, Miss Emma	G	Jul 2006

Chambers of Milton Grundy

GRAY'S INN TAX CHAMBERS,
3RD FLOOR, GRAY'S INN CHAMBERS, GRAY'S INN, LONDON WC1R 5JA
Tel: 020 7242 2642 ***Fax:*** 020 7831 9017
Dx: 352 LONDON/CHANCERY LANE
E-mail: clerks@taxbar.com
Clerk: Chris Broom; Paul Connor.
Head of Chambers:

Grundy, Mr Milton	I	Nov 1954
Flesch, Mr Michael Charles (Q.C.)	G	May 1963
Goldberg, Mr David Gerard (Q.C.)	L	Jul 1971
Goy, Mr David John Lister (Q.C.)	M	May 1973
Walters, Mr John Latimer (Q.C.)	M	Jul 1977
Baker, Mr Philip Woolf (Q.C.)	G	Jul 1979
Cullen, Mrs Felicity Ann (Q.C.)	L	Jul 1985
Soares, Mr Patrick C	L	Nov 1983
Akin, Mr Barrie	M	Jul 1976
Way, Mr Patrick	L	Nov 1994
Mehta, Mr Nikhil	L	Jan 1976
Nathan, Miss Aparna	M	Nov 1994
McDonnell, Mr Conrad	L	Oct 1994
Shaw, Ms Nicola	I	Nov 1995
Thomas, Mr Michael	G	Mar 2000
Lemos, Ms Marika	M	Oct 2002
McCarthy, Miss Hui Ling	I	Jul 2005
Jones, Mr Michael	L	Jan 2006
Sykes, Mr Laurent	G	Jan 2007
Afzal, Mr Imran	L	Jan 2008

GREAT JAMES STREET CHAMBERS,
37 GREAT JAMES STREET, LONDON WC1N 3HB
Tel: 020 7440 4949 ***Fax:*** 020 7440 4950
Dx: 440 CHANCERY LANE
E-mail: chambers@greatjames.co.uk

Chambers of Martin Benedict Spencer QC

HAILSHAM CHAMBERS,
GROUND FLOOR, 4 PAPER BUILDINGS, TEMPLE, LONDON EC4Y 7EX
Tel: 020 7643 5000 ***Fax:*** 020 7353 5778
Dx: 1036 LONDON/CHANCERY LANE
E-mail: clerks@hailshamchambers.com
Clerk: Senior: Stephen Smith. Michael Kilbey.
Head of Chambers:

Spencer, Mr Martin Benedict (Q.C.)	I	Jul 1979
McGregor, Mr Harvey (Q.C.)	I	Feb 1955
Pooles, Mr Michael (Q.C.)	I	Jul 1978
West-Knights, Mr Laurence James (Q.C.)	G	Nov 1977
Pittaway, Mr David (Q.C.)	I	Jul 1977
de Freitas, Mr Anthony Peter Stanley	I	Jul 1971
Tracy Forster, Ms Jane	I	Jul 1975
Mishcon, Ms Jane Malca	G	Jul 1979
Holwill, Mr Derek Paul Winsor	G	Jul 1982
Campbell, Mr Glenn	L	Jul 1985
Jackson, Mr Matthew David Everard	M	Jul 1986
Picton, Mr Julian Mark	M	Feb 1988
Bacon, Mr Francis	G	Jul 1988
Flenley, Mr William	M	Nov 1988
Price, Ms Clare	M	Jul 1988
Post, Mr Andrew	M	Jul 1988
Mangat, Dr Tejina	M	Oct 1990
Peacock, Mr Nicholas	G	Oct 1992
Hutton, Mr Alexander	G	Oct 1992
Wilton, Mr Simon	G	Oct 1993
Christie-Brown, Ms Sarah	M	Oct 1994
Charlwood, Mr Spike Llewellyn	M	Nov 1994
Ewins, Ms Catherine	G	Nov 1995
Sawyer, Ms Katrine	M	Jul 1996
Ferguson, Ms Eva	M	Nov 1999
Mitchell, Mr Paul	L	Oct 1999
Carpenter, Mr Jamie	I	Jul 2000
Munro, Mr Joshua Neil	G	Jul 2001
Stacey, Mr Dan	G	Oct 1996
Gilberthorpe, Mr James	M	Jan 2002
MacKinnon, Ms Lucy	L	Jul 2003
Heap, Dr Emma	I	Nov 2004
Benson, Mr Imran	M	Jan 2005
Bennett, Mr David	M	Jan 2005
Simpson, Ms Jacqueline	I	Jan 2006
Nash, Miss Alice	I	Jan 2006
Bankes-Jones, Mr Henry	L	Nov 2004
O'Reilly, Miss Niamh	M	Jan 2007
McMahon, Heather	M	Jan 1999
Bailey, Stephen	I	Jan 2006

Chambers of Frances Judd QC

HARCOURT CHAMBERS,
2 HARCOURT BUILDINGS, TEMPLE, LONDON EC4Y 9DB
Tel: 0844 561 7135 ***Fax:*** 020 7353 6968
Dx: 373 LONDON/CHANCERY LANE
E-mail: clerks@harcourtchambers.law.co.uk
Practice Manager: Judith Partington
Chambers Director: Simon Boutwood
Head of Chambers:

Judd, Ms Frances (Q.C.)	M	Jul 1984
Pressdee, Mr Piers (Q.C.)	M	Oct 1991
Evans, Mr Roger	M	Nov 1970
Rodgers, Ms June	M	Nov 1971
Sefi, Mr Benedict	I	Jul 1972
Collinson, Ms Alicia	M	Jul 1982
Brett, Mr Matthew	M	Nov 1987
Gibbons, Ms Sarah	M	Nov 1987
Hay, Ms Fiona Ruth	I	Nov 1989
Granshaw, Ms Sara	L	Oct 1991
Max, Ms Sally	L	Oct 1991
Garrido, Mr Damian	M	Nov 1993
Potter, Ms Louise	I	Nov 1993
Vater, Mr John	G	Feb 1995
Goodwin, Mr Nicholas	I	Oct 1995
Vine, Mr Aidan	M	Oct 1995
Miller, Mr Simon	L	Oct 1996
Sampson, Mr Jonathan R	M	Oct 1997
Barrett, Miss Cecilia M	I	Jul 1998
Wraight, Mr Oliver	M	Oct 1998
Leong, Mr Andrew	M	Oct 1998
Little, Ms Helen	L	Oct 1999
Kirkwood, Mr Edward	L	Nov 1999
Styles, Ms Margaret	M	Oct 2000
Turner, Mr James Paul	I	Jul 2001
Devereux, Mr Edward	M	Oct 2001
Green, Mr Jason	G	Oct 2001
Brightman, Ms Justina	L	Oct 2003
Forbes, Mr Alex	L	Oct 2003
Tomlinson, Miss Elizabeth	L	Jul 2004
Williams, Miss Alison	G	Oct 2004
Higgins, Mr Mark	I	Jan 2005
Harris, Miss Frances	L	Jan 2005
Wilkins, Miss Chloe	G	Jan 2006
Wilkinson, Miss Helen	M	Jul 2007
Hylton, Miss Nasstassia	I	Jul 2007
Kelly, Miss Gemma	I	Nov 2007
Cox, Miss Sian	M	Jul 2008
Crispin, Mr Stephen	L	Nov 2008
Rayner, Miss Emily	M	Jul 2009
Sharp, Mr Christopher (Q.C.)*	I	Jul 1975
Jacklin, Miss Susan (Q.C.)*	I	Nov 1980

Chambers of Nigel Jones QC and Paul Reed QC

HARDWICKE,
HARDWICKE BUILDING, NEW SQUARE, LINCOLN'S INN, LONDON WC2A 3SB
Tel: 020 7242 2523 ***Fax:*** 020 7691 1234
Dx: 393 LONDON/CHANCERY LANE
E-mail: enquiries@hardwicke.co.uk
Administrator: Lisa Pick
Practice Manager: Ann Buxton
Chambers Director: Amanda Illing
Head of Chambers:

Jones, Mr Nigel (Q.C.)	G	Jul 1976
Reed, Mr Paul (Q.C.)	I	Jul 1988
Akhtar, Miss Shazia	M	Nov 2001
Allison, Mr Simon	L	Oct 2005
Azam, Mr Ajmal	G	Jul 2006
Bagot, Mr Charles	I	Oct 1997
Baker, Mr Nicholas	G	Jul 1980
Bastin, Mr Alexander	M	Oct 1995
Bell, Mr Thomas	L	Oct 2006
Benbow, Miss Sara	M	Nov 1990
Betts, Ms Emily	M	Jul 2009
Bloom, Dr Margaret	L	Oct 1994
Bretherton, Miss Kerry Louise	L	Oct 1992
Buckhaven, Mr Simon	G	Jul 1970
Buswell, Mr Richard	M	Jul 1985
Calvert, Mr Charles	M	Jul 1975
Camp, Mr Christopher	I	Jan 1996
Campbell, Mr Alexander	G	Jul 2010
Clarke, Mr Jamie	G	Nov 1995
Creer, Miss Andy	L	Sep 2006
Cummerson, Miss Romilly	M	Oct 1998
Cunningham, Mr Graham T	G	Jul 1976
de Waal, Mr John	M	Oct 1992
Dhar, Mr Zeeshan	L	Jan 1999
Engelman, Mr Mark	G	Nov 1987
Fagborun-Bennett, Ms Morayo	I	Jul 2004
Fellows, Mr Philip	L	Jan 2007
Friel, Mr John	G	Jul 1974
Gallagher, Mr John	G	Nov 1974
Gatty, Mr Daniel	M	Aug 1990
Goold, Mr Alexander	L	Oct 1994
Hale, Mr Simon	G	Jan 2006
Harris, Miss Philippa	G	Jan 2005
Hay, Miss Deborah	M	Apr 1991
Heal, Ms Madeleine	L	Jan 1996
Hewson, Miss Barbara	M	Nov 1985
Higgins, Mr Rupert	I	Oct 1991
Jacobs, Mr Robin	M	Jan 2006
Johal, Miss Suki	M	Nov 1991
King, Mr Karl	G	Nov 1985
Kirby, Mr Peter	I	Jul 1989
Lane, Mr Andrew	L	Oct 1999
Lawson, Mr David A	M	Jul 2000
Lennard, Mr Stephen	G	Jul 1976
Leonard, Mr Robert	I	Jul 1976
Lewis, Mr David	L	Jan 1997
Malik, Miss Sarah	L	Nov 1999
McBrinn, Ms Diane	G	Jul 2002
McCann, Miss Sarah	L	Jan 2001
Meacher, Miss Alison	L	Nov 1998
Moore, Mr Arthur James	G	Oct 1992
Morwood, Mr Boyd	M	Jan 1996
Mosteshar, Dr Sa'id*	L	Jul 1975
Muir, Miss Nicola	I	Nov 1998
Mullee, Mr Brendan	M	Oct 1996
Murphy, Ms Jasmine	G	Jul 2002
Nugent, Mr Colm	I	Oct 1992
Oguntayo, Tosin	M	Nov 2001
Parker, Miss Wendy	M	Jul 1978
Petts, Mr Peter Simon Tinsley	I	Oct 1998
Pliener, Mr David	M	Nov 1996
Pulman, Mr George F (Q.C.)	M	Jul 1972
Raffin, Mr Charles	M	Jan 2005
Rawlings, Mr Clive	I	Oct 1994
Redpath-Stevens, Mr Alastair Y	M	Jan 1998
Richardson, Miss Rebecca	M	Oct 2003
Rowntree, Mr Edward	L	Apr 1996
Ryan, Mr Richard	G	Oct 2004
Scolding, Ms Fiona	G	Jan 1996
Silcock, Mr Ian	M	Oct 1997
Skelly, Mr Andrew	I	Oct 1994
Slack, Mr Henry	L	Oct 1999
Stevens-Hoare, Ms Michelle	M	Jul 1986
Titmuss, Mr Jonathan	L	Nov 2001
Tkaczynska, Ms Anna	M	Jul 2008
Tweedy, Miss Laura	L	Jan 2007
Underwood, Mr Dean	M	Oct 2002
Venn, Ms Sarah	G	Jul 2002
Walker, Miss Amelia	I	Jan 2007
Watthey, Mr James	G	Nov 2000
Weddle, Mr Steven	G	Nov 1977
Wheater, Mr Michael	L	Oct 2003
White, Ms Helena	M	Jan 2007
Witherington, Ms Gemma	I	Jan 2008
Woolf, Mr Steven	I	Jul 1989
Zaman, Mr Mohammed Khalil (Q.C.)	G	Jul 1985

Chambers of Philip D Moor QC

1 HARE COURT,
TEMPLE, LONDON EC4Y 7BE
Tel: 020 7797 7070 ***Fax:*** 020 7797 7435
Dx: 342 LONDON/CHANCERY LANE
E-mail: clerks@1hc.com
Clerk: Senior: Steve McCrone. Junior: Michael Lay.
Administrator: Sarah Hardwicke
Head of Chambers:

Moor, Mr Philip D (Q.C.)	I	Jul 1982
Blair, Mr Bruce (Q.C.)	M	Jul 1969
Pointer, Mr Martin J (Q.C.)	G	Jul 1976
LeGrice, Mr Valentine (Q.C.)	M	Jan 1977
Nicholls, Mr Michael John Gadsby (Q.C.)	M	Nov 1975
Bangay, Miss Deborah (Q.C.)	G	Feb 1981

Dyer, Mr Nigel I G (Q.C.)	I	Feb 1982
Irving, Miss Gillian (Q.C.); P/T Chairman of Registered Homes Tribunal; Mental Health Review Tribunal*	I	Jul 1984
Cusworth, Mr Nicholas N C (Q.C.)	L	Nov 1986
Todd, Mr Richard F (Q.C.)	M	Jul 1988
Leong, Ms Jacqueline; QC (Hong Kong)*	I	Jul 1970
Pope, Ms Heather	I	Jul 1977
Carden, Mr Nicholas	G	Jul 1981
Hussey, Miss Ann Elizabeth	M	May 1981
Wilson, Mr John	I	Jan 1981
Smith, Mr Roger Gavin A	M	Oct 1981
Wood, Mr Christopher M	M	Feb 1986
Davidson, Ms Katharine M	L	Nov 1987
Smithburn, Prof John Eric*	M	Nov 1989
Todd, Mrs Elisabeth Helen Margaret	M	Oct 1990
Gray, Miss Nichola Jayne	L	Jul 1991
Bishop, Mr Timothy	I	Nov 1991
Kingscote, Mr Geoffrey	I	Nov 1993
Trowell, Mr Stephen	M	Oct 1995
Warshaw, Mr Justin	G	Nov 1995
Yates, Mr Nicholas	I	Oct 1996
Webster, Mr Simon	I	Jan 1997
Bradley, Mr Michael James	G	Mar 1999
Carew-Pole, Mrs Rebecca J	I	Jun 1999
Sumner, Miss Emma Jane	I	Oct 1999
Bailey-Harris, Prof Rebecca	I	Jul 2000
Harris, Miss Eleanor	M	Jan 2000
Carter, Mr Tom	G	Jan 2001
Spicer, Miss Rachel	M	Jan 2002
Kenny, Mr Christian	I	Jan 2003
Allen, Jude	I	Jan 2004
Sear, Mr Richard	M	Jan 2005
Harris, Ms Amelia	M	Jan 2006
Wilkinson, Mr Nicholas	M	Jan 2006
Cook, Miss Katherine	L	Jul 2007
Brunsdon-Tully, Mr Matthew	L	Oct 2007
Kabra, Miss Madhavi	M	Jul 2008

Chambers of Orlando Pownall QC

2 HARE COURT,
TEMPLE, LONDON EC4Y 7BH
Tel: 020 7353 5324 ***Fax:*** 020 7353 0667
Dx: 444 LONDON/CHANCERY LANE
E-mail: clerks@2harecourt.com
Clerk: Senior: Nathan Lee-Walsh.
Administrator: Stephen Wall
Chambers Director: Barbara-Ann Tweedie
Head of Chambers:

Pownall, Mr Orlando (Q.C.); Recorder	M	Jul 1975
Green, Sir Allan (Q.C.) KCB; KCB	I	Jun 1959
Heslop, Mr Martin Sydney (Q.C.); Recorder	L	Jul 1972
Waters, Mr David (Q.C.); Recorder	M	May 1973
Radcliffe, Mr Andrew Allen (Q.C.); Recorder	M	Nov 1975
Wright, Mr Peter D (Q.C.)	I	Jul 1981
Pickup, Mr James K (Q.C.); Recorder	G	Jul 1976
Benson, Mr Jeremy Keith (Q.C.); Recorder	M	Jul 1978
Howker, Mr David Thomas (Q.C.)	I	Jul 1982
Hicks, Mr Martin Leslie Arthur (Q.C.)	I	May 1977
Bennett-Jenkins, Miss Sallie Ann (Q.C.); Recorder; Junior Treasury Counsel	G	Jul 1984
Holland, Mr Michael Frederick Richard (Q.C.); Recorder	I	Nov 1984
Laidlaw, Mr Jonathan James (Q.C.); Recorder; Senior Treasury Counsel	I	Jul 1982
Kelly, Mr Brendan Damien (Q.C.); Recorder	G	Jul 1988
Samuel, Miss Jacqueline Eleanor	G	Jul 1971
Jones, Mr William John; Recorder	I	Nov 1972
Kamill, Miss Louise Naima Rachel; Recorder	I	Jul 1974
Lloyd-Eley, Mr Andrew	M	Nov 1979
Colman, Mr Andrew	L	Jul 1980
Leist, Mr Ian	I	Jul 1981
Dawson, Mr James; Recorder	M	Jul 1984
Belger, Mr Tyrone	I	Jul 1984
Armstrong, Mr Dean	G	Jul 1985
Mehta, Mr Sailesh	L	Jul 1986
Rees, Mr Jonathan; Junior Treasury Council	G	Jan 1987
O'Neill, Mr Brian P; Recorder; Secretary of Criminal Bar Association	G	Nov 1987
Logsdon, Mr Michael Anthony	I	Feb 1988
Millett, Mr Kenneth James	I	Jul 1988
Cheema, Miss Parmjit-Kaur; Junior Treasury Council	G	Jul 1989
Lambis, Mr Marios P; Recorder	M	Nov 1989
Lewis, Miss Alex	M	Nov 1990
Ferguson, Mr Stephen Michael	I	Nov 1991
Ferguson, Mr Craig Charles	M	Feb 1992
Khan, Mr Karim A A (Q.C.)*	L	Oct 1992
Bex, Miss Kate	M	Nov 1992
Foulkes, Mr Christopher D	L	Oct 1994
Brassington, Mr Stephen D	I	Nov 1994
Ahmad, Mr Zubair	L	Oct 1995
Glasgow, Mr Oliver	M	Nov 1995
Karmy-Jones, Miss Riel	L	Nov 1995
Lowe, Miss Emma; Non-Practising Door Tenant	G	Oct 1996
Coltart, Mr Christopher	I	Nov 1998
Hawkins, Mr Quinn	L	Jan 1999
Barclay, Mr Robin	M	Jul 1999
Bunyan, Mr Angus Guy	L	Oct 1999
Robinson, Ms Karen	L	Sep 2000
Bevan, Miss Miranda Jane	I	Oct 2000
Stevens, Miss Hanne	M	Jul 2002
Hummerstone, Miss Rebekah	G	Jul 2002
Kolhatkar, Mr Ishan	M	Oct 2002
Faure Waliter, Miss Julia	L	Jan 2004
Tanchel, Ms Vivienne	M	Jan 2005
Bedenham, Mr David	G	Jul 2005
Przybylska, Miss Sarah	M	Oct 2006
Dummett, Miss Emily	M	Nov 2006

Chambers of James M Dingemans QC

3 HARE COURT,
TEMPLE, LONDON EC4Y 7BJ
Tel: 020 7415 7800 ***Fax:*** 020 7415 7811
Dx: 212 LONDON/CHANCERY LANE
E-mail: clerks@3harecourt.com
Web: www.3harecourt.com
Clerk: Senior: James Donovan.
Administrator: Michael Oliver
Head of Chambers:

Dingemans, Mr James M (Q.C.)	I	Jul 1987
Strachan, Mr Mark (Q.C.)	I	Jul 1969
Guthrie, Mr James D (Q.C.)	I	Jul 1975
Knox, Mr Simon C Peter (Q.C.)	M	Nov 1983
Davenport, Mr Simon (Q.C.)	I	Nov 1987
McLeod, Mr Iain	I	Jul 1969
Neville-Clarke, Mr Sebastian A B	I	Nov 1973
Young, Mr Andrew G	L	Jul 1977
Janusz, Mr Pierre P	M	Jul 1979
Godwin, Mr William George Henry	M	Nov 1986
Letman, Mr Paul	M	Jul 1987
Butler, Mr Rupert James	M	Jul 1988
Juss, Prof Satvinder Singh	G	Nov 1989
Stevens, Mr Howard	M	Oct 1990
Casey, Mr Aidan P	G	Nov 1992
Dignum, Mr Marcus B	M	Oct 1994
Roe, Mr Thomas	M	Nov 1995
Samuel, Mr Richard G G	M	Jan 1996
Deal, Ms Katherine Alison Frances	M	Oct 1997
Crowther, Miss Sarah Helen	M	Oct 1999
Saxby, Mr Daniel James	M	Nov 2000
Poole, Mr Tom	I	Jan 2001
Atwal, Navjot	L	Jan 2002
Strang, Mr Robert	I	Jan 2003
Hawkins, Mr James	M	Jan 2003
Lewis, Mr Daniel	M	Jan 2003
Clarke, Mr J Daniel	G	Jul 2005
Johnson, Miss Clara	I	Nov 2005
Tivadar, Mr Daniel	M	Nov 2005
Ibrahim, Miss Sara Elise Lewis	L	Oct 2006
Masood, Miss Hafsah	M	Oct 2006
Pugh, Miss Helen Elizabeth	L	Oct 2008
Wijeyaratne, Mr Asela Lochana Neville	L	Nov 2008
Ajmone-Marsan, Mr Cosimo Marco	L	Jul 2009

This Chamber with 34 Barristers is based in London and led by James Dingemans QC. You may contact any of our clerks at any time by sending a message to clerks@3harecourt.com.

Chambers of Charles Gibson QC

HENDERSON CHAMBERS,
2 HARCOURT BUILDINGS, TEMPLE, LONDON EC4Y 9DB
Tel: 020 7583 9020 ***Fax:*** 020 7583 2686
Dx: 1039 LONDON/CHANCERY LANE
E-mail: clerks@hendersonchambers.co.uk
Clerk: Senior: John White.
Head of Chambers:

Gibson, Mr Charles (Q.C.); Recorder	I	Jul 1984
Mawrey, Mr Richard (Q.C.); Recorder; Deputy High Court Judge	G	Feb 1964
Brunner, Mr Adrian (Q.C.); Recorder	I	Jul 1968
Susman, Mr Peter Joseph (Q.C.); Recorder, Deputy Technology Court Judge	I	Nov 1966
West, Mr Lawrence (Q.C.); Recorder	G	May 1979
Popat, Prashant (Q.C.)	G	Feb 1992
Dashwood, Prof Alan (Q.C.) CBE	I	Nov 1969
Williams, Mr Rhodri (Q.C.)	G	Jul 1987
O'Sullivan, Mr Bernard	I	Jul 1971
Harvey, Mr Jonathan	I	Jul 1974
Hamer, Mr Kenneth M H; Recorder	I	Apr 1975
Palmer, Mr James	M	Nov 1983
Steinert, Mr Jonathan	M	Feb 1986
Brook, Mr David L	I	Jul 1988
Davies, Mr Andrew	I	Jul 1988
Goldman, Mrs Linda	I	Oct 1990
Green, Mr Patrick	M	Nov 1990
Campbell, Mr Oliver	M	Oct 1992
Sheehan, Mr Malcolm	L	Oct 1993
Webb, Mr Geraint	I	Oct 1995
Riley-Smith, Mr Toby	M	Nov 1995
Withington, Mr Angus Richard	G	Nov 1995
Kinnier, Mr Andrew	M	Oct 1996
Heppinstall, Mr Adam	M	Oct 1999
Dilworth, Mr Noel	I	Jul 2001
Sethi, Miss Natasha	M	Jan 2001
Burne, Miss Anna	I	Oct 2002
Chowdury, Mr Nazeer A	I	Jun 2002
Purnell, Mr James	M	Oct 2002
Bradley, Mr Matthew	I	Jan 2004
Donnelly, Miss Kathleen	L	Jan 2005
Cohen, Miss Abigail	L	Jan 2005
Wilson, Miss Hannah	L	Jan 2005
Roberts, Mr Richard	L	Jan 2006
Richardson, Mr Matthew	G	Oct 2006
Robertson, Nicole	L	Jan 2007
Lewis, Mr Jonathan	M	Jan 2007
Evans, Mr Thomas	L	Jan 2008
Rosenthal, Mr Dennis	G	Nov 2009
Humphreys, Elizabeth	M	Jan 2009
Griffiths, Mr Conrad (Q.C.)*	G	Nov 1986
Ashworth, Mr Lance D P (Q.C.)*	M	Nov 1987
Schoneveld, Mr Frank*	I	Jul 1992
Mitchell, Miss Julianna*	L	Oct 1994
Fenston, Ms Felicia*	M	Nov 1994

Chambers of Muhammad Abu Sayeed

10 HIGHLEVER ROAD,
NORTH KENSINGTON, LONDON W10 6PS
Tel: 020 8969 8514 ***Fax:*** 020 8969 8514
Clerk: Zahirun Neesa Sayeed.
Head of Chambers:

Sayeed, Mr Muhammad Abu	I	Jul 1973

Chambers of Alastair Wilson QC and Roger Wyand QC

HOGARTH CHAMBERS,
5 NEW SQUARE, LINCOLN'S INN, LONDON WC2A 3RJ
Tel: 020 7404 0404 ***Fax:*** 020 7404 0505
Dx: 16 LONDON/CHANCERY LANE
E-mail: barristers@hogarthchambers.com
Clerk: Senior: Sue Harding. Clive Nicholls; Andy Clayton; Adam Homes; John Davies.
Administrator: Catherine Hanley
Head of Chambers:

Wilson, Mr Alastair (Q.C.)	M	Jul 1968
Wyand, Mr Roger (Q.C.); Recorder, Deputy High Court Judge	M	May 1973
Morcom, Mr Christopher (Q.C.)	M	Jul 1963
Rayner James, Mr Jonathan E (Q.C.); Recorder	L	Nov 1971
Davies, Dr Gillian DL	L	Nov 1961
Stewart, Mr Alexander J	G	Jul 1975
Hicks, Mr Michael C	I	Nov 1976
Bragiel, Mr Edward	M	Jul 1977
Michaels, Ms Amanda L	G	Jul 1981
Clark, Ms Julia E	G	Jul 1984
Caddick, Mr Nicholas; Junior Counsel to the Crown	M	Nov 1986
Tritton, Mr Guy H	I	Jul 1987
Harbottle, Gwilym Thomas	L	Nov 1987
Colley, Dr Peter McLean	G	Jul 1989
Roughton, Mr Ashley Wentworth	I	Oct 1992
Davis, Mr Richard	G	Oct 1992
Norris, Mr Andrew James	M	Nov 1995
Reed, Mr Jeremy	M	Oct 1997
St Quintin, Mr Thomas Christopher	I	Jan 2006
Longstaff, Mr Benjamin	G	Jan 2009

Chambers of Stuart S Stevens

HOLBORN CHAMBERS,
6 GATE STREET, LINCOLN'S INN FIELDS, LONDON WC2A 3HP
Tel: 020 7242 6060 ***Fax:*** 020 7242 2777
Dx: 159 LONDON/CHANCERY LANE
Clerk: Senior: Anthony Martin Halls. Juniors: Winston Nugara; Nicola Kitching.
Head of Chambers:

Stevens, Mr Stuart S	G	Jul 1970
Mahmood, Mr Imran	M	Jan 1992
Sutton, Mr Paul E	M	Jul 1973
Bell, Miss Anne OBE	G	Jan 1975
Farrell, Ms Patricia	I	Jul 1976
Radcliffe, Miss Pamela Joan C	G	Jul 1979
Herrity, Mr Peter	L	Jul 1982
Living, Mr Marc Stephen	M	Oct 1983
Harris, Miss Alexandra	G	Jul 1989
Rhodes, Ms Amanda	L	May 1990
O'Malley, Ms Helen	L	Oct 1991
McKinley, Mr Gregor Charles	G	Oct 1992
Murphy, Ms Sheila	M	Oct 1992
Levene, Mr Anthony*	M	Jul 1993
Walsh, Ms Annie	I	Oct 1993
Osborne, Ms Katie	M	Nov 1993
Qadri, Khalid	M	Nov 1993
Lallane, Mr Bernard*	I	Jul 1994
Boodia, Ms Anuradha	G	Oct 1994
Cartwright, Ms Suzanne Jane	L	Oct 1994
Cotter, Mr Mark	M	Nov 1994
Naik, Mr Timothy	G	Nov 1994
Johal, Miss Davinder	G	Oct 1995
Singh, Ms Ranjana	M	Oct 1995
Milner, Mr Nicolas	G	Mar 1996

Chambers of John V Fitzgerald

INGENUITY IP CHAMBERS,
3 FLEET STREET, LONDON EC4Y 1DP
Tel: 020 7936 4474 ***Fax:*** 020 7936 4473
Dx: 398 LONDON/CHANCERY LANE
E-mail: clerks@ingenuityip.co.uk
Clerk: Senior: Lee Parkes.
Head of Chambers:

Fitzgerald, Mr John V	M	Jul 1971
Firth, Miss Alison	I	Nov 1980
Kime, Mr Matthew	G	Jul 1988
Rogers, Miss Christy	M	Nov 1999

Chambers of Steven Frank Hadley

1 INNER TEMPLE LANE,
TEMPLE, LONDON EC4Y 1AF
Tel: 020 7427 4400 ***Fax:*** 020 7427 4427
Dx: 286 LONDON/CHANCERY LANE
E-mail: clerks@1itl.com
Clerk: Mark Auger; Jo Lewis.
Head of Chambers:

Hadley, Mr Steven Frank	I	Jul 1987
Adonis, Mr George	L	Jul 1973
Blake, Mr Richard	G	Nov 1982
Johnson, Mr Christopher	M	Jul 1983
Manley, Miss Lesley	M	Nov 1983
Gedge, Mr Simon	I	Nov 1984
Smullen, Mrs Marion	G	Mar 1985
Brain, Miss Pamela	I	Nov 1985
Etherton, Miss Gillian Felicity Amanda (Q.C.)	M	Jul 1988
Lindop, Ms Sarah	G	Nov 1989

10

Le Foe, Ms Sarah	M	Nov 1989
Anders, Mr Jonathan James	I	Feb 1990
Fuad, Mr Kerim	I	Nov 1992
Tedore, Ms Amanda	M	Oct 1992
Clark, Mr Tim	I	Feb 1993
Hart, Ms Jenny	M	Oct 1993
McDonagh, Mr Matthew	M	Oct 1994
McGrath, Mr Frank	M	Oct 1995
Smaller, Miss Elizabeth	G	Oct 1995
Connell, Mr Edward	M	Oct 1996
Inyundo, Mr Richard Kwame Swaka	G	Mar 1997
Ahmed, Mr Gulam	G	Sep 1997
Wolfe, Ms Madeline Louise	I	Oct 1998
Anoom, Mr Joseph Kwesi	M	Jul 1998
Stevens, Mr Mark	I	Jul 1998
Blackman, Mr Edmund Arthur William	M	Jul 1999
Wilson, Mr Steven	I	Jul 1999
Molloy, Mr Kevin Anthony Joseph	M	Mar 1999
Stringer, Ms Jacinta Maria Rockingham	G	Nov 1999
Weetch, Mr Oliver	M	Jul 2000
Hutchings, Mr Richard	G	Jul 2001
Cornwall, Miss Virginia*	M	Oct 1990
Baker, Mr William D*	I	Oct 1992
Whaites, Miss Louise*	G	Nov 1994

Chambers of Sami D El-Falahi

INTERNATIONAL LAW CHAMBERS,
ILC HOUSE, 77 CHEPSTOW ROAD,
BAYSWATER, LONDON W2 5QR
Tel: 020 7221 5685 / 7352 6649 ***Fax:*** 020 7221 5685
E-mail: ilcuk@aol.com
Clerk: Teresa Kennedy.
Head of Chambers:

El-Falahi, Sami D	I	Jul 1972
Barratt, Mr Robin Alexander (Q.C.)	M	Nov 1970
Farrell, Mr Edmund G.	G	Jul 1981
Lambis, Mr Marios P	M	Nov 1989

Chambers of Lawrence Power

4 KBW,
4 KING'S BENCH WALK, TEMPLE, LONDON
EC4Y 7DL
Tel: 020 7822 8822 ***Fax:*** 020 7822 8844
Dx: 422 LONDON/CHANCERY LANE
E-mail: sp@4kbw.net
Clerk: Senior: Spencer Payne.
Administrator: Anita Bhowmick
Practice Manager: Sallie Berrif
Chambers Director: Lawrence Power
Head of Chambers:

Power, Mr Lawrence	M	Oct 1995
Beckman, Mr Michael (Q.C.)	L	May 1954
Toogood, Mr John QPM	G	Jul 1957
Jarman, Mr Samuel	I	Jul 1989
Rudeloff, Walter	M	Jan 1990
Fairclough, Sara	M	Jan 1992
Murphy, Nicola	G	Oct 1995
Toogood, Katherine	G	Jan 1998
Comerton, Julie-Anne	G	Jan 2003
Follon, Daniel	M	Jul 2003
McKinney, Nicola	G	Jan 2004
Zoubir, Adam	L	Jan 2005
Tunley, James	L	Jan 2007
Wacek, Kim Marie	M	Nov 2003
Dann, Mr Jared	M	Jan 2007
Ditchburn, Mr John	M	Jan 2007

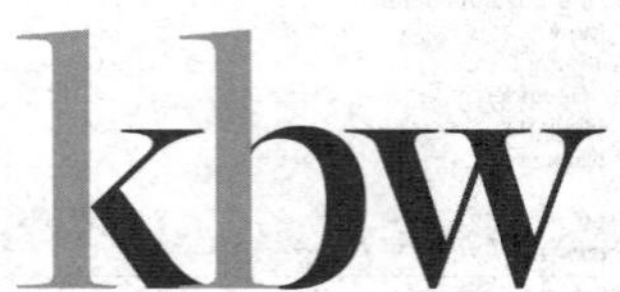

Chambers of James Goudie QC

11KBW,
11 KING'S BENCH WALK, TEMPLE, LONDON
EC4Y 7EQ
Tel: 020 7632 8500 ***Fax:*** 020 7583 9123
Dx: 368 LONDON/CHANCERY LANE
E-mail: clerksteam@11kbw.com
Web: www.11kbw.com
Clerk: Seniors: Lucy Barbet; (Joint) Philip Monham. Juniors: Mark Dann; Darren Bacon; John Davitt. Michael Smith.
Administrator: Claire Halas
Head of Chambers:

Goudie, Mr James (Q.C.); Recorder; Deputy High Court Judge; President of National Security Panel of the Information Tribunal	I	Jul 1970
McGregor, Mr Alistair J (Q.C.)	M	Jul 1974
Jeans, Mr Christopher (Q.C.); P/T Chairman of Employment Tribunal	G	Jul 1980
Lynch, Mr Adrian (Q.C.); Recorder	G	Nov 1983
Kerr, Mr Tim (Q.C.); P/T Chairman of Employment Tribunal	G	Nov 1983
Cavanagh, Mr John (Q.C.); Recorder	G	Nov 1985
Hillier, Mr Andrew (Q.C.)	G	Jul 1972
Giffin, Mr Nigel (Q.C.)	I	Nov 1986
Lewis, Mr Clive (Q.C.); Recorder; First junior counsel to the national assembly of Wales	M	Nov 1987
Laing, Miss Elisabeth (Q.C.); Recorder	M	Jul 1980
Wallington, Mr Peter (Q.C.); P/T Chairman of employment tribunal	G	Jul 1987
Devonshire, Mr Simon (Q.C.)	G	Feb 1988
Swift, Mr Jonathan M (Q.C.); First Treasury Council	I	Jul 1989
Pitt-Payne, Mr Timothy (Q.C.)	I	Nov 1989
Oldham, Mr Peter (Q.C.)	G	Oct 1990
Stilitz, Mr Daniel (Q.C.)	L	Oct 1992
Oudkerk, Mr Daniel Richard (Q.C.)	I	Nov 1992
Sheldon, Mr Clive (Q.C.)	I	Nov 1991
Oldham, Mrs Jane	M	Jul 1985
Moore, Miss Sarah; Part-Time Chairman of Employment Tribunal	M	Nov 1990
Jones, Mr Sean	I	Oct 1991
Choudhury, Mr Akhlaq	I	Oct 1992
Nicholls, Mr Paul	I	Oct 1992
Wilson, Mr Julian	I	Oct 1997
Coppel, Mr Jason	I	Nov 1994
Porter, Mr Nigel	M	Nov 1994
Ivimy, Miss Cecilia	M	Nov 1995
Steyn, Miss Karen	M	Nov 1995
Leiper, Mr Richard	G	Oct 1996
Proops, Miss Anya	I	Oct 1998
Rhee, Miss Deok Joo	G	Oct 1998
McCafferty, Miss Jane	M	Nov 1998
Iyengar, Ms Harini	I	Oct 1999
Milford, Mr Julian Robert	M	Jul 2000
Blake, Mr Andrew Mark	L	Oct 2000
Hooper, Mr Benjamin Richard	I	Oct 2000
Cornwell, Mr James Matthew	M	Jan 2002
Clement, Miss Joanne	G	Jan 2002
Stout, Miss Holly	L	Jul 2003
Edge, Mr Andrew	I	Oct 2003
Stone, Miss Judith	I	Jan 2003
Forshaw, Mr Simon	G	Mar 2004
Halliday, Mr Patrick	G	Jan 2005
Kamm, Miss Rachel	L	Oct 2006
Shahbahrami, Miss Tara	L	Oct 2006
Rogers, Miss Amy	L	Jan 2007
Cross, Mr Tom	L	Jan 2007
Hopkins, Mr Robin	L	Jul 2008
Knight, Mr Christopher	I	Jan 2008
Lee, Mr Michael	L	Jan 2009
Capewell, Mr Edward	I	Jan 2009
Eddy, Ms Katherine	L	Jan 2009
Moore, Mr George*	I	Jan 1970

11KBW has 52 Barristers including 18 QCs operating in almost every aspect of Employment, Public and Business Law. We act in some of the most high profile and technically challenging cases for UK and overseas clients, regularly appearing in the House of Lords, Court of Appeal, ECJ and ECHR.

Chambers of John Marrin QC

KEATING CHAMBERS,
15 ESSEX STREET, LONDON WC2R 3AA
Tel: 020 7544 2600 ***Fax:*** 020 7544 2700
Dx: 1045 LONDON/CHANCERY LANE
E-mail: jmunton@keatingchambers.com
Clerk: Barry Bridgman; John Munton; Nick Child; Simon Wigley; Robert Bryant; Chris Sunderland.
Administrator: Nicola Humphreys
Head of Chambers:

Marrin, Mr John (Q.C.); Recorder & Deputy High Court Judge, TCC	I	Nov 1974
Uff, Mr John F (Q.C.); Recorder; Deputy Judge, TCC	G	Jul 1970
Fernyhough, Mr Richard (Q.C.); Recorder 1986	M	Nov 1970
Thomas, Mr Christopher S (Q.C.); Recorder	L	Jul 1973
Furst, Mr Stephen A (Q.C.); Recorder	M	Jul 1975
Elliott, Mr Timothy S (Q.C.)	M	Jul 1975
Gaitskell, Dr Robert (Q.C.); Recorder	G	Jul 1978
Boulding, Mr Philip V (Q.C.)	G	Nov 1979
Darling, Mr Paul A (Q.C.)	M	Jul 1983
Taverner, Mr Marcus L (Q.C.)	G	Jul 1981
O'Farrell, Ms Finola M (Q.C.)	I	Jul 1983
Williamson, Mr Adrian J G H (Q.C.)	M	Nov 1983
Thomas, Mr William David (Q.C.)	M	Jul 1982
Pennicott, Mr Ian (Q.C.); Member of Hong Kong Bar	M	Jul 1982
Jackson, Ms Rosemary E (Q.C.)	M	Jul 1981
Nissen, Mr Alexander D (Q.C.)	M	Jul 1985
Jefford, Ms Nerys A (Q.C.)	G	Nov 1986
Hannaford, Ms Sarah J (Q.C.)	M	Jul 1989
Steynor, Mr Alan C; Recorder	G	Jul 1975
Randall, Mr Louise E	M	Jul 1988
Evans, Mr Robert J	G	Jul 1989
Rowlands, Mr Mark	G	Nov 1990
Hargreaves, Mr Simon J	I	Oct 1991
Moran, Mr Vincent	G	Oct 1991
McCredie, Ms Fionnula	M	Oct 1992
Harding, Mr Richard A	M	Oct 1992
Lemon, Ms Jane Katherine	I	Nov 1993
Stansfield, Mr Piers A	I	Nov 1993
Lee, Mr Jonathan James Wilton	G	Oct 1993
Mort, Mr Justin	M	Nov 1994
Hughes, Mr Simon David	G	May 1995
Jinadu, Mr Abdul-Lateef	M	May 1995
Constable, Mr Adam	I	Jan 1995
Buckingham, Mr Paul	M	Nov 1995
Lee, Miss Krista	L	Nov 1996
Coplin, Mr Richard	M	Oct 1997
Chambers, Ms Gaynor	G	Oct 1998
Townend, Mr Samuel	L	Oct 1999
Scott Holland, Mr Gideon	L	Jul 1999
Selby, Mr Jonathan	G	Nov 1999
Stephens, Miss Jessica	L	Jan 2001
Holt, Mr Matthew	G	Oct 2001
Garrett, Miss Lucy	G	Oct 2001
Repper, Miss Elizabeth	I	Jan 2002
Lamont, Mr Calum	I	Jan 2004
Webb, Mr William	L	Jul 2005
Thompson, Mr James	M	Jul 2005
Lazur, Mr Thomas	I	Nov 2005
Brogden, Mr Peter	I	Jan 2008
Bowsher, Mr Peter (Q.C.)	M	Jan 1959
Furmston, Prof Philip Michael*	G	Oct 1960
Ellis, Ms Charlotte*	M	Oct 2001

KENSINGTON CHAMBERS,
5A PHILBEACH GARDENS, LONDON SW5 9DY
Tel: 020 7373 2217 ***Fax:*** 020 7373 2217

CHAMBERS OF DR NEVILLE KESSELMAN,
3 VINCENT COURT , BELL LANE, LONDON
NW4 2AN
Tel: 020 8203 4711 ***Fax:*** 020 8203 4711
E-mail: nissanbeneli@googlemail.com
Administrator: Jacquelina Pamela Kesselman

Kesselman, Dr Neville; Head of Chambers	G	Jul 1970

Chambers of Richard Anelay QC

1 KING'S BENCH WALK,
TEMPLE, LONDON EC4Y 7DB
Tel: 020 7936 1500 ***Fax:*** 020 7936 1590
Dx: 20 LONDON/CHANCERY LANE
E-mail: clerks@1kbw.co.uk
Web: www.1kbw.co.uk
Clerk: Senior: David Dear.
Chambers Director: Sue Gray
Head of Chambers:

Anelay, Mr Richard (Q.C.)	M	Jul 1970
Singleton, Mr Barry (Q.C.)	G	Jul 1968
Pratt, Mr Richard Camden (Q.C.)	G	Jul 1970
Scriven, Miss Pamela (Q.C.)	I	Nov 1970
Bellamy, Mr Stephen (Q.C.)	L	Jan 1974
Turner, Mr James (Q.C.)	I	Jul 1976
Howard, Mr Charles (Q.C.)	I	Jul 1975
Kirk, Mr Anthony (Q.C.)	G	Jan 1981
Newton, Mr Clive (Q.C.)	M	Nov 1968
Eaton, Miss Deborah A (Q.C.)	I	Jul 1985
Pocock, Mr Christopher (Q.C.)	I	Jul 1984
Warren, Mr Michael	M	Nov 1971
Reddish, Mr John	M	Jan 1973
Budden, Miss Caroline	M	Jan 1977
Harding, Ms Cherry	G	Nov 1978
Hornsby, Mr Walton Francis Petre	L	Jul 1980
Lister, Miss Caroline	M	Nov 1980
Woodbridge, Mr Julian	M	Nov 1981
Cudby, Ms Markanza	M	Oct 1983
Shay, Mr Stephen	M	Nov 1984
Cellan-Jones, Mr Deiniol	M	Oct 1988
Marshall, Mr Philip	G	Jul 1989
Selman, Miss Elizabeth	I	Nov 1989
Barton, Mr Richard	L	Oct 1990
Fletcher, Mr Marcus Alexander	M	Oct 1990
Roberts, Mr James	G	Oct 1993
Harrison, Mr Richard Tristan	I	Nov 1993
McCourt, Mr Christopher	I	Nov 1993
Cook, Mr Ian Reginald Blacklin	I	Nov 1994
Baughan, Mr Andrew	M	Oct 1994
Green, Ms Victoria	G	Oct 1994
Crosthwaite, Mr Graham	I	Nov 1995
Brazil, Mr Dominic	M	Nov 1995
Hamilton, Ms Carolyn	G	Jul 1996
Thain, Miss Ashley	I	Oct 1996
Gardner, Mr Alan	M	Jan 1997
Hall, Mr Robert	G	Oct 1997
Anderson, Mr Nicholas	G	Jan 1995
Castle, Mr Richard	G	Oct 1998
Rogers, Miss Shona	I	Oct 1998
Oliver, Mr Harry	G	Nov 1999
Reardon, Miss Madeleine	M	Nov 2001
Nagpal, Mr Deepak	L	Oct 2002
Kelsey, Miss Katherine	L	Jul 2003
Holmes, Ms Martha Felicity	I	Jul 2003
Wilkins, Miss Susan	L	Jul 2004
Harris, Miss Caroline	I	Nov 2004
Perrins, Miss Jennifer	I	Jul 2004
Newman, Mr Peter	I	Jul 2005
Watts, Miss Andrea	L	Oct 2006
Tatton-Bennett, Mr Alex	G	Oct 2007
Ozwell, Miss Kate	L	Nov 2007
McHugh, Mr Kelan	I	Oct 2007
Moys, Miss Laura	G	Jul 2008
Ridley, Ms Samantha	I	Jul 2009
Hartley, Miss Charlotte	G	Jul 2009
Grice, Miss Joanna*	M	Oct 1991

At 1kbw we specialise in family law and criminal law. Consistently among the top ranked sets in the leading law directories we have a long and distinguished history appearing in many groundbreaking cases in the House of Lords. We have 56 members of whom 11 are distinguished QCs complemented by an excellent team of junior barristers encompassing a range of call to suit all requirements. 1kbw are committed to excellence.

Chambers of Timothy T Mousley QC

2 KING'S BENCH WALK,
GROUND FLOOR, TEMPLE, LONDON EC4Y 7DE
Tel: 020 7353 1746 ***Fax:*** 020 7583 2051
Dx: 1032 LONDON/CHANCERY LANE
E-mail: clerks@2kbw.com
Clerk: James Whiffin.
Administrator: Joan Garforth
Practice Manager: James Whiffin
Head of Chambers:
Mousley, Mr Timothy T (Q.C.); Recorder . . . M . . . Jul 1979

Donne, Mr Anthony M (Q.C.); Recorder . . . M . . . Apr 1973
Selfe, Mr Michael R; Recorder . . . M . . . Nov 1965
Parish, Mr Stephen A B; Recorder . . . I . . . Jul 1966
Jenkins, Mr David Crofton . . . I . . . Nov 1967
Wright, Mr Jeremy J; Recorder . . . I . . . Jul 1970
Bailey, Mr Anthony R . . . I . . . Nov 1972
Stopa, Mr Christopher . . . M . . . Nov 1976
Shapiro, Mr Selwyn . . . I . . . Jul 1979
Lofthouse, Mr John C . . . M . . . Nov 1979
Foster, Mr Simon . . . M . . . Jul 1982
Mousley, Mr William . . . M . . . Jul 1986
Bolton, Mr Robert . . . G . . . Jul 1987
Clarke, Miss Michelle . . . I . . . Jul 1988
Dugdale, Mr Paul . . . G . . . Oct 1990
Amis, Mr Christopher J . . . G . . . Nov 1991
Fleming, Mr Adrian . . . M . . . Nov 1991
Pyne, Mr Russell . . . I . . . Nov 1991
Trafford, Mr Mark . . . L . . . Nov 1992
Lumsdon, Miss Kate . . . M . . . Oct 1993
Feest, Mr Adam . . . I . . . Feb 1994
Russell, Miss Fern . . . M . . . Oct 1994
McAvock, Miss Gabrielle . . . L . . . Oct 1996
Britton, Mr James . . . I . . . Nov 1996
Jones, Miss Sarah . . . L . . . Nov 1996
Venturi, Mr Gary . . . M . . . Oct 1996
Bussey-Jones, Miss Elisabeth . . . I . . . Oct 1997
Taylor, Mr Rufus . . . M . . . Oct 1998
Pattinson, Miss Catherine . . . G . . . Jan 2000
Elton, Mr Edward S O . . . M . . . Nov 2000
Wood, Miss Natalie . . . M . . . Jul 2001
Wright, Mr Thomas . . . I . . . Jul 2001
Austin, Miss Rebecca . . . M . . . Oct 2002
McElduff, Mr Barry . . . L . . . Jan 2003
Lane, Miss Rachel Caroline . . . L . . . Nov 2002
Freemantle, Miss Kate . . . L . . . Jan 2003
Sharman, Mr Brian . . . G . . . Jan 2004
Dhadda, Miss Sukwinder . . . L . . . Jan 2004
Bennett, Miss Emma . . . L . . . Jan 2004
Fortescue, Miss Kate . . . M . . . Jan 2004
Williams, Mr Micheal . . . I . . . Jan 2005
Barton, Mr Jeremy . . . M . . . Jan 2004
Wellings, Mr Oliver . . . I . . . Jan 2001
Sproson, Miss Eileen . . . G . . . Jan 2005
Long, Mr Benjamin . . . M . . . Jan 2006
Davies, Unime . . . M . . . Jan 2006
Forrest, Mr Robert . . . L . . . Jan 2007
Jones, Miss Ximena . . . M . . . Jan 2007
Fleurie, Mr Jean-Francois . . . M . . . Jan 2003

Chambers of Alun Evans

2 KING'S BENCH WALK,
1ST FLOOR, TEMPLE, LONDON EC4Y 7DE
Tel: 020 7353 9276 ***Fax:*** 020 7353 9949
Dx: 477 LONDON/CHANCERY LANE

Chambers of Michael Hartman

TWO KING'S BENCH WALK,
2ND FLOOR, INNER TEMPLE, LONDON EC4Y 7DE
Tel: 020 7353 7202 / 7353 3909 ***Fax:*** 020 7583 2030
Dx: 472 LONDON/CHANCERY LANE
E-mail: clerks@2kingsbenchwalk.com
Clerk: Lee Parkes.
Head of Chambers:
Hartman, Mr Michael . . . L . . . Nov 1975

Yasnik, Mr Ram . . . I . . . Nov 1965
Popat, Mr Surendra . . . L . . . Jul 1969
Gribble, Mr Peter J . . . G . . . Jul 1972
Mendes Da Costa, Mr David . . . I . . . Nov 1976
Greenslade, Mr Henry Michael; Parking Adjudicator; Commissioner for Oaths . . . G . . . Nov 1982
Hamilton, Miss Caroline . . . M . . . Jul 1989
Amin, Miss Farah . . . L . . . Jul 1991
Fama, Mrs Gudrun . . . G . . . Oct 1991
Obuka, Miss Obi . . . I . . . Oct 1993
Yong, Miss Pearl . . . L . . . Nov 1993
Harris, Mr Lee . . . M . . . Oct 1996
Mustakim, Mr Al . . . L . . . May 1997
Kelly, Mr Eamonn . . . I . . . Oct 1997
Stedman, Mr Aryan . . . M . . . Nov 1997
Record, Miss Celia . . . M . . . Mar 1998
Hawkin, Mr Benjamin . . . M . . . Oct 1998
Maka, Mr Isaac . . . L . . . Nov 1998
Iqbal, Miss Samina . . . L . . . Oct 1999
Vernon, Mr Elliot . . . L . . . Oct 2001

Chambers of Timothy Raggatt QC

4 KING'S BENCH WALK,
2ND FLOOR, TEMPLE, LONDON EC4Y 7DL
Est: 1972
Tel: 020 7822 7000 ***Fax:*** 0871 288 5693
Dx: 1050 LONDON/CHANCERY LANE
E-mail: clerks@4kbw.co.uk
Web: www.4kbw.co.uk
Clerk: Lee Cook.
Head of Chambers:
Raggatt, Mr Timothy (Q.C.); Recorder . . . I . . . Jan 1972

Thomas, Mr Roger (Q.C.); Recorder . . . G . . . Jul 1969
Leighton, Peter . . . I . . . Jan 1966
Hillman, Mr Basil . . . G . . . Nov 1968
Spencer Bernard, Mr Robert; Recorder of the Crown Court . . . I . . . Nov 1969
Knight, Keith . . . G . . . Jan 1969
Perry, Mrs Naomi Melanie . . . M . . . Jul 1974
Mallison, Miss Kate . . . M . . . Nov 1974
Deschampsneufs, Miss Alice . . . I . . . Jul 1976
Fortune, Peter . . . I . . . Jan 1978
McConnell, Mr Christopher . . . L . . . Jul 1979
Purdie, Mr Robert . . . M . . . Jul 1979
Doherty, Mr Nicholas . . . L . . . Jul 1983
Arkhurst, Mr Reginald . . . M . . . Jul 1984
Price-Rowlands, Mr Gwynn . . . I . . . May 1985
Bhakar, Surinder . . . G . . . Jan 1986
Granville Stafford, Mr Andrew . . . G . . . Jul 1987
Jacobs, Miss Claire . . . G . . . Jul 1989
Preston, Miss Kim . . . I . . . Nov 1991
Burnett, Mr Iain . . . L . . . Oct 1993
Lal, Mr Sanjay . . . L . . . Oct 1993
Davis, Mr Brendan . . . G . . . Oct 1994
Bond, Ms Jackie . . . M . . . Oct 1994
Ojuitku, Mrs Kemi . . . L . . . Jan 1994
McGee, Miss Tamala . . . L . . . Oct 1995
Palmer, Ms Suzanne . . . M . . . Nov 1995
Chbat, Miss Nadia . . . M . . . Nov 1996
Lycourgou, Miss Olive . . . G . . . Jan 1997
Martin, Mr Piers . . . I . . . Oct 1997
Roberts, Miss Beverly . . . M . . . Jan 1998
Upton, Mr John . . . G . . . Jan 1998
Harris, Mr Lee . . . M . . . Jan 1999
Holme, Mr Gavin James . . . I . . . Jan 1999
Salis, Robert . . . M . . . Jan 1999
Khan, Ms Sabina . . . M . . . Feb 1999
Roques, Mr Michael . . . G . . . Nov 2000
Turner, Mr Justyn . . . I . . . Jan 2001
Davidge, Miss Justine . . . G . . . Jul 2001
Griffiths, Ms Alison . . . I . . . Oct 2001
Silva, Mr Jerome . . . I . . . Oct 2001
Tregidgo, Mr Marc . . . M . . . Jul 2002
Bryden, Mr Christopher . . . I . . . Jan 2003
Bailey, Tom . . . M . . . Jan 2005
Sawtell, Mr David . . . L . . . Jan 2005
Moss, Richard . . . M . . . Jan 2005
Durber, Joanna . . . L . . . Jan 2005
Brown, John . . . I . . . Jan 2005
Williams, Mr Greg . . . L . . . Jan 2006
Webster, Keith . . . G . . . Jul 2006
Vooght, Miss Abbey . . . I . . . Jan 2006
Wright, Miss Lisa . . . I . . . Jan 2007
Costello, Mr Brian . . . M . . . Jan 2007
Chaplin, Ms Sophie . . . M . . . Jan 2007
Bonavero, Philippe . . . M . . . Jan 2008
Dobby, Miss Helen . . . M . . . Jan 2008

Child Care and Wardship, Clinical Negligence, Common Law General, Criminal Work, Employment Law, Family Law, Human Rights and Civil Liberties, Immigration, Personal Injury, Professional negligence, Armed Forces, Fraud, Licensing, Alternative Dispute Resolution, Arbitration, Arbitration including International Trade

Chambers of Sarah Forshaw QC and Mark Heywood QC

5 KING'S BENCH WALK,
GROUND FLOOR, 5 KING'S BENCH WALK, TEMPLE, LONDON EC4Y 7DN
Tel: 020 7353 5638 ***Fax:*** 020 7353 6166
Dx: 367 LONDON/CHANCERY LANE
E-mail: clerks@5kbw.co.uk
Clerk: Lee Hughes Gage; Matt Harper; Katy Peat; Lorine Parkinson; Jim Jeffs; Zach May.
Practice Manager: Simon Cleveland MBE
Head of Chambers:
Forshaw, Miss Sarah (Q.C.) . . . M . . . Nov 1987
Heywood, Mr Mark (Q.C.); Senior Treasury Counsel; Recorder . . . G . . . Jul 1985

Glen, Mr Ian (Q.C.) . . . G . . . Nov 1973
Bayliss, Mr Tom (Q.C.); Recorder* . . . M . . . Jan 1977
Higgs, Mr Jonathan (Q.C.) . . . M . . . Nov 1987
Sones, Mr Richard . . . I . . . Nov 1969
Ford, Mr Graeme . . . I . . . Jul 1972
Fairhead, Mr John . . . M . . . Nov 1978
Sandford, Mr Simon . . . G . . . Nov 1979
Hofford, Mr Peter . . . G . . . Nov 1979
O'Toole, Mr Bartholomew . . . M . . . Nov 1980
Dias, Miss Sappho . . . G . . . Nov 1982
Doyle, Mr James . . . M . . . Jul 1985
Dacey, Mr Mark . . . M . . . Nov 1985
Webber, Mr Dominic Denzil Fernandez . . . G . . . Nov 1985
Briegel, Mr Pieter . . . M . . . Nov 1986
Canavan, Miss Sandy; Recorder . . . L . . . Jul 1987
Collings, Mr Andrew . . . G . . . Nov 1987
Chippeck, Mr Stephen . . . L . . . Jul 1988
Hooper, Mr Martin C . . . M . . . Jul 1988
Rodham, Miss Susan Anne . . . G . . . Nov 1989
Blake, Mr Christopher . . . I . . . Nov 1990
Walmsley, Mr Alan . . . I . . . Nov 1991
Fowler, Mr Edmund . . . G . . . Oct 1992
Walker, Mr Paul . . . L . . . Oct 1993
Robinson, Mr Daniel M . . . L . . . Nov 1993
Newell, Miss Charlotte . . . G . . . Oct 1994
Ellison, Mr Robert . . . M . . . Oct 1996
Temple, Mr Benjamin . . . I . . . Oct 1997
Thompson, Ms Pauline . . . M . . . Jul 1998
Stavrou, Miss Xenia . . . M . . . Nov 1998
Dear, Mr Ian . . . L . . . Jul 1999
Farrelly, Miss Catherine . . . M . . . Nov 1999
Israel, Mr Jeffrey Antony . . . M . . . Oct 2000
Daly, Miss Orla Marie . . . G . . . Nov 2000
Polnay, Mr Jonathan . . . M . . . Nov 2000
Dilliway-Parry, Mr Guy . . . G . . . Jul 2002
Jackson, Mr Paul . . . I . . . Jul 2002
Carse, Mr Gordon . . . I . . . Oct 2002
Martin, Mr James . . . L . . . Mar 2003
Swift, Miss Valeria . . . L . . . Oct 2003
Wilkes, Miss Alison . . . M . . . Oct 2005
Reid, Mr Dickon . . . I . . . Nov 2005
Nathwani, Mr Rishi . . . M . . . Jul 2006
Holt, Mr Ben . . . I . . . Oct 2006
Kong, Mr Senghin . . . M . . . Jul 2008
Soule, Miss Natalie . . . L . . . Oct 2008
Ryan, Miss Fiona . . . G . . . Mar 2009

Chambers of Roy Amlot QC

6 KING'S BENCH WALK,
GROUND FLOOR, TEMPLE, LONDON EC4Y 7DR
Tel: 020 7583 0410 ***Fax:*** 020 7353 8791
Dx: 26 LONDON/CHANCERY LANE
E-mail: clerks@6kbw.com
Clerk: Senior: Andrew Barnes.
Administrator: Christine Brown
Head of Chambers:
Amlot, Mr Roy (Q.C.) . . . L . . . Nov 1963

Worsley, Mr Michael (Q.C.) . . . I . . . Jun 1955
Curnow, Miss Ann (Q.C.) . . . G . . . Feb 1957
Mallalieu, Baroness Ann (Q.C.) . . . I . . . Jul 1970
Curtis, Mr James (Q.C.) . . . I . . . Jul 1970
Lovell-Pank, Mr Dorian (Q.C.) . . . I . . . Jul 1971
Temple, Mr Victor (Q.C.) . . . I . . . Jul 1971
Korner, Ms Joanna (Q.C.) CMG . . . I . . . Nov 1974
Houlder, Mr Bruce (Q.C.) . . . G . . . Jul 1969
Spens, Mr David (Q.C.) . . . I . . . Jan 1973
Fisher, Mr David (Q.C.) . . . G . . . Jul 1973
Joseph, Miss Wendy (Q.C.) . . . G . . . Nov 1975
Leonard, Mr Anthony (Q.C.) . . . I . . . Jul 1978
Sweeney, Mr Nigel (Q.C.) . . . M . . . Jul 1976
Ryder, Mr John (Q.C.) . . . I . . . Nov 1980
Wass, Miss Sasha (Q.C.) . . . G . . . Nov 1981
Turner, Mr Jonathan (Q.C.) . . . G . . . Jul 1974
Dennis, Mr Mark; Senior Treasury Counsel . . . M . . . Jul 1977
Jessel, Mrs Philippa . . . I . . . Jul 1978
Marks Moore, Mr Douglas . . . G . . . Nov 1979
Perry, Mr David; Standing Counsel to DTI; Senior Treasury Counsel . . . L . . . Jul 1980
Hilliard, Mr Nicholas; Senior Treasury Counsel . . . M . . . Jul 1981
Bowyer, Mr Martyn . . . I . . . Nov 1984
Denison, Mr Simon; Junior Treasury Counsel . . . L . . . Nov 1984
Cray, Mr Timothy . . . I . . . Nov 1989
Grieves-Smith, Mr Peter . . . M . . . Nov 1989
Dunn-Shaw, Mr Jason . . . L . . . Oct 1992
Penny, Mr Duncan . . . M . . . Oct 1992
Dakyns, Miss Isabel . . . L . . . Nov 1992
Whitehouse, Miss Sarah . . . L . . . Oct 1993
Darlow, Miss Annabel . . . M . . . Oct 1993
Patterson, Mr Gareth . . . G . . . Jul 1995
Pilling, Miss Annabel . . . M . . . Oct 1995
Atkinson, Mr Duncan . . . G . . . Oct 1995
Hallam, Mr Jacob W . . . G . . . Oct 1996
Badenoch, Mr Tony . . . M . . . Nov 1996
Ezekiel, Miss Adina . . . L . . . Apr 1997
Mably, Mr Louis . . . L . . . Apr 1997
Wilkinson, Miss Kate . . . M . . . Oct 1998
Hill, Miss Miranda . . . M . . . Oct 1999
Weekes, Mr Mark . . . L . . . Nov 1999
McCoubrey, Mr Robin . . . I . . . Jul 2000
Schutzer-Weissman, Ms Esther . . . M . . . Oct 2000
Morgan, Miss Alison . . . M . . . Nov 2000
Ray, Mr Simon . . . G . . . Nov 2001
Rosefield, Ms Laura . . . M . . . Jul 2003
Ratliff, Mr Peter . . . L . . . Oct 2003
Greaney, Mr Paul Richard (Q.C.)* . . . I . . . Oct 1993
Oldland, Mr Andrew (Q.C.)* . . . I . . . Nov 1990
Laws, Mr Simon (Q.C.)* . . . I . . . Oct 1991
Anderson, Mr Clive* . . . M . . . Nov 1976
Ray-Crosby, Miss Irena* . . . M . . . Nov 1990
Cumberland, Miss Melanie* . . . L . . . Oct 2001

Chambers of Sibghat Kadri QC

6 KING'S BENCH WALK,
GROUND FLOOR SOUTH, 3RD & 4TH FLOOR, TEMPLE, LONDON EC4Y 7DR
Tel: 020 7583 0695 / 7353 4931 ***Fax:*** 020 7353 1726
Dx: 471 LONDON/CHANCERY LANE
E-mail: admin@6kbw.co.uk
Clerk: Gary Jeffery.
Head of Chambers:
Kadri, Sibghat (Q.C.) . . . I . . . Nov 1969

de Mello, Ramby . . . L . . . Feb 1983
Cogan, Mr Michael . . . M . . . Feb 1986
Neathey, Ms Rona . . . I . . . Nov 1990
Halligan, Mr Brendan . . . M . . . Jan 1998

McCulloch-James, Ms Melissa . . . I . . . Oct 1999
Rogers, Mr Ken. . . . I . . . Nov 1999
Bellara, Mr Susheel. . . . I . . . Nov 2000
Whittaker, Miss Isobel. . . . I . . . Oct 2002
Ahmed, Rashid . . . L . . . Jan 2003
Henley, Mr Martin. . . . I . . . Oct 2004
Samuel, Mr Tim. . . . M . . . Jan 2005
Mohsin, Miss Andlub . . . L . . . Jan 2006
Grant, Miss Karen . . . I . . . Jan 2004
Abashiekh, Mr Omar . . . G . . . Jul 2006
Bhatt, Unnati . . . M . . . Oct 2007
Virk, Sundeep . . . G . . . Nov 2004

Chambers of Gavin Sean Kealey QC

7 KING'S BENCH WALK,
TEMPLE, LONDON EC4Y 7DS
Tel: 020 7910 8300 ***Fax:*** 020 7910 8400
Dx: 239 LONDON/CHANCERY LANE
E-mail: clerks@7kbw.co.uk
Clerk: Seniors: Bernie Hyatt; Greg Leyden. Eddie Johns; Gary Rose; Dean Cunniff.
Administrator: Susan Luxford
Chambers Director: Lawrence Williams
Head of Chambers:
Kealey, Mr Gavin Sean (Q.C.). . . . I . . . Feb 1977

Saloman, Mr Timothy P D (Q.C.) . . . M . . . Nov 1975
Reynolds, Prof Francis (Q.C.). . . . I . . . Feb 1961
Gaisman, Mr Jonathan N C (Q.C.) . . . I . . . Nov 1979
Kendrick, Mr Dominic John (Q.C.). . . . M . . . Jul 1981
Brenton, Mr Timothy (Q.C.) . . . M . . . Jul 1981
Schaff, Mr Alistair Graham (Q.C.) . . . I . . . Jul 1983
Hofmeyr, Mr Stephen Murray (Q.C.). . . . G . . . Jul 1982
Butcher, Mr Christopher John (Q.C.)* . . . G . . . Jul 1986
Fenton, Mr Adam (Q.C.) . . . I . . . Jul 1984
Kenny, Mr Stephen Charles Wilfred (Q.C.) . . . I . . . Jul 1987
Southern, Mr Richard Michael (Q.C.) . . . M . . . Nov 1987
Bright, Mr Robert Graham (Q.C.) . . . G . . . Nov 1987
Bailey, Mr David John (Q.C.) . . . G . . . Jul 1989
Edwards, Mr David Leslie (Q.C.) . . . L . . . Jul 1989
Picken, Mr Simon Derek (Q.C.)* . . . M . . . Jul 1989
Dias, Miss Julia Amanda (Q.C.). . . . I . . . Jul 1982
Allen, Mr Michael David (Q.C.) . . . G . . . Jul 1990
Phillips, Stephen J (Q.C.). . . . L . . . Oct 1993
Healy, Ms Sioban (Q.C.) . . . I . . . Jul 1993
Drake, Mr James (Q.C.) . . . L . . . Jan 1998
MacDonald Eggers, Mr Peter (Q.C.) . . . M . . . Jul 1999
Priday, Mr Charles N B . . . M . . . Nov 1982
Geary, Mr Gavin . . . G . . . Feb 1989
Wales, Mr Andrew . . . G . . . Nov 1992
Sabben-Clare, Ms Rebecca. . . . G . . . Oct 1993
Khurshid, Mr Jawdat . . . L . . . Oct 1994
Waller, Mr Richard B . . . G . . . Oct 1994
Kenefick, Mr Timothy . . . G . . . Oct 1996
Bignall, Mr John . . . L . . . Nov 1996
Holroyd, Mr Charles. . . . G . . . Jan 1997
Kerr, Mr Simon . . . L . . . Jan 1997
Brocklebank, Mr James. . . . M . . . Oct 1999
Holmes, Mr Michael. . . . M . . . Oct 1999
Parker, Mr Benjamin . . . M . . . Jan 2000
Gotts, Miss Anna . . . L . . . Jan 2001
Macdonald, Mr Alexander. . . . L . . . Jan 2001
Higgs, Miss Josephine Amy. . . . M . . . Nov 2000
Sutherland, Miss Jessica . . . M . . . Oct 2003
Mander, Mr Marcus. . . . M . . . Jan 2005
Casey, Mr Noel G. . . . L . . . Oct 1995
Sarll, Mr Richard . . . M . . . Oct 2005
Hilliard, Miss Emma. . . . L . . . Jul 2006
Cowey, Miss Sarah. . . . L . . . Oct 2006
Ananda, Miss Sushma . . . L . . . Nov 2007
Martin, Miss Sarah . . . I . . . Mar 2008
Turner, Mr Adam . . . L . . . Oct 2008
Lindesay, Ms Elizabeth . . . G . . . Jan 2009
Jenns, Mr Tim . . . I . . . Jan 2009
Gale, Jocelin . . . I . . . Jan 2009
Howie, Mr Keir . . . M . . . Jan 2010

Chambers of Ali Mohammad Azhar

9 KING'S BENCH WALK,
LOWER GROUND SOUTH, TEMPLE, LONDON EC4Y 7DX
Tel: 020 7353 9564 ***Fax:*** 020 7353 7943
Dx: 118 LONDON/CHANCERY LANE

Chambers of Claudius J Algar

10 KING'S BENCH WALK,
GROUND FLOOR, TEMPLE, LONDON EC4Y 7EB
Tel: 020 7353 7742 ***Fax:*** 020 7583 0579
Dx: 24 LDE
E-mail: chambers@10kingsbenchwalk.co.uk
Web: www.10kingsbenchwalk.co.uk
Clerk: Senior: Bernard Hayward. William Ingleton; Sheila Doyle; Kerry Player; Stephen Herbert.
Head of Chambers:
Algar, Mr Claudius J . . . I . . . Nov 1972

de Moller, Mr Andre. . . . I . . . Nov 1965
Hart, Mr Colin. . . . M . . . Nov 1966
Cartwright, Mr James D'Arcy Cayley . . . G . . . Feb 1968
Christensen, Mr Carlton. . . . I . . . Jul 1977
Forward, Mr Barry Miles . . . G . . . Jul 1981
Gibbons, Mr Orlando . . . G . . . Nov 1982
Wise, Leslie M . . . M . . . Nov 1985
Talacchi, Mr Carlo . . . L . . . Jul 1986
Murphy, Mr Michael. . . . I . . . Jan 1990
Bogle, Mr James . . . I . . . Oct 1991
Harris, Mr Micheal . . . M . . . Oct 1993
Martin, Mr Jonathan . . . M . . . Nov 1994
Bailey, Miss Rosanna. . . . G . . . Oct 1994
Heller, Mrs Anne . . . M . . . Nov 1995
Panton, Mr Alastair H. . . . I . . . Oct 1996
Nabijou, Miss Sherry . . . I . . . Oct 1996
Gill, Ms Baljinder . . . I . . . Oct 1996
O'Brien, Mr Nicholas . . . M . . . Nov 1996
Taylor, Ms Susan . . . L . . . Oct 1996

Turner, Mr Paul. . . . I . . . Nov 1998
Seehra, Ms Amarjit . . . G . . . Oct 1999
Palmer, Mr Ian Franlyn . . . M . . . Nov 1999
Schama, Mr Lee . . . M . . . Nov 2003
McFarlane, Ms Cynthia . . . M . . . Nov 2003
Steinfeld, Ms Charlotte . . . L . . . Oct 2004
Spurling, Mr Rudolph . . . I . . . Jan 2007
Shibli, Faraz . . . I . . . Nov 2007
Wass, Krystelle . . . I . . . Mar 2007
Anzani, Sara . . . I . . . Jul 2008
Arumugam, Mr Raj . . . L . . . Oct 2008
McKenzie Smith, Catherine* . . . I . . . Nov 1960
Onuaguluchi, Jones* . . . I . . . Feb 1971
Hedworth, Mr Leonard* . . . L . . . Jul 1979
Cohen, Mr Michael*. . . . G . . . Oct 1992

Chambers of Andrew Hogarth QC

12 KING'S BENCH WALK,
TEMPLE, LONDON EC4Y 7EL
Tel: 020 7583 0811 ***Fax:*** 020 7583 7228
Dx: 1037 LONDON/CHANCERY LANE
E-mail: chambers@12kbw.co.uk
Web: www.12kbw.co.uk
Clerk: Graham Johnson; John Cooper.
Practice Manager: Kevin McCourt; Lexie Adams; Laura Wells; Tristan Whigham; Philip Austin
Chambers Director: Jason Rowley
Head of Chambers:
Hogarth, Mr Andrew (Q.C.) . . . L . . . Jul 1974

Walker, Mr Ronald (Q.C.); Recorder. . . . G . . . Jul 1962
Methuen, Mr Richard (Q.C.); Recorder . . . L . . . Nov 1972
Burton, Mr Frank (Q.C.); Recorder . . . G . . . Jul 1982
Martin, Mr Gerard James (Q.C.); Recorder . . . M . . . Jul 1978
Worthington, Mr Stephen (Q.C.); Recorder . . . G . . . Nov 1976
Heathcote Williams, Mr Nicholas (Q.C.); Recorder. . . . I . . . Nov 1976
Featherby, Mr William (Q.C.); Recorder . . . M . . . Nov 1978
Rawlinson, Mr Michael (Q.C.). . . . I . . . Dec 1991
Russell, Mr Paul (Q.C.) . . . M . . . Jul 1984
Spencer-Lewis, Mr Neville . . . I . . . Jul 1970
King, Mr John. . . . I . . . Nov 1973
Gallagher, Mr Brian. . . . I . . . Jul 1975
Tudor-Evans, Mr Quintin . . . L . . . Jul 1977
Levene, Mr Simon; Recorder . . . M . . . Jul 1977
Crawford, Mr Lincoln OBE; Recorder . . . G . . . Nov 1977
Davison, Mr Richard Harold; Recorder . . . G . . . Jul 1982
Sanderson, Mr David F . . . I . . . Nov 1985
Lewers, Mr Nigel . . . G . . . Nov 1986
Newbery, Ms Freya; Recorder. . . . M . . . Nov 1986
Charles, Mr Henry . . . I . . . Nov 1987
Pickering, Andrew. . . . L . . . Nov 1987
Hamill, Mr Hugh . . . I . . . Jul 1988
Chambers, Mr Adam; Deputy District Judge. . . . M . . . Jul 1989
Brown, Ms Catherine; Recorder. . . . M . . . Oct 1990
Chandler, Ms Kate . . . I . . . Oct 1990
Candlin, Mr James Richard . . . L . . . Oct 1991
Thornett, Mr Gary; Deputy District Judge; Former Solicitor . . . M . . . Oct 1991
Spears, Ms Portia. . . . G . . . Jan 1992
Vincent, Mr Patrick . . . M . . . Oct 1992
Audland, Mr William. . . . G . . . Nov 1992
Jackson, Ms Stephanie L . . . I . . . Oct 1992
Katyar, Mr Arun. . . . L . . . Nov 1993
Kendall, Mr Joel . . . M . . . Oct 1993
Viney, Mr Richard; Deputy District Judge . . . M . . . Feb 1994
D'Souza, Ms Carolyn . . . M . . . Oct 1994
Tobin, Mr Daniel . . . M . . . Oct 1994
Peck, Ms Catherine. . . . G . . . Nov 1995
Petts, Mr Timothy; Recorder . . . I . . . Oct 1996
Thomson, Miss Louise . . . L . . . Nov 1996
Steinberg, Mr Harry. . . . G . . . Nov 1997
Leech, Mr Benedict . . . I . . . Jan 1997
Madan, Mr Pankaj; Deputy District Judge . . . M . . . Jan 1997
Callow, Mr David; Deputy District Judge. . . . M . . . Nov 1998
Awadalla, Miss Katherine. . . . M . . . Oct 1998
Vincent, Ms Joanna; Deputy District Judge . . . M . . . Oct 1998
Aggrey-Orleans, Kweku. . . . I . . . Jan 1998
Sharpe, Dr David. . . . I . . . Nov 2004
White, Mr David. . . . L . . . Oct 1999
Stephenson, Ms Lisa . . . L . . . Oct 1999
Rankin, Ms Jane . . . L . . . Jan 2000
Frost, Miss Angela . . . G . . . Jan 2001
Reynolds, Miss Charlotte . . . M . . . Oct 2001
Roy, Mr Andrew. . . . L . . . Jul 2002
Greenwood, Miss Ruth . . . G . . . Oct 2003
Newnham, Ms Mary. . . . L . . . Nov 2003
Kemp, Mr Edward William. . . . I . . . Jan 2005
Scott, Miss Gemma. . . . L . . . Jan 2005
Sullivan, Mr James William . . . I . . . Oct 2005
Kerr, Mr Patrick. . . . G . . . Oct 2006
Beslee, Ms Sarah. . . . M . . . Oct 2006
Carington, Mr Alex . . . L . . . Oct 2006
Crawford, Miss Georgina Aynsley. . . . I . . . Oct 2006
Consolo, Dr Henrietta Katherine . . . M . . . Nov 2006
Gordon Walker, Miss Emily Clare . . . M . . . Jul 2007
Read, Miss Emily. . . . M . . . Jul 2007
Robertshaw, Mr Charles . . . M . . . Nov 2007
Holland, Mr Russell. . . . L . . . Jan 2008
Maclean, Mr Niall. . . . I . . . Jul 2008
Wilson, Miss Thea . . . I . . . Jul 2008
Aldred, Miss Lois . . . I . . . Jul 2008
Pacey, Mr Thomas . . . G . . . Nov 2008
Rudd, Mr Oliver. . . . L . . . Jan 2009
Boyle, Ms Lucy. . . . M . . . Jan 2009
Cashman, Ms Vanessa . . . L . . . Jul 2009

Work description: civil and commercial law specialising in personal injury, professional and clinical negligence, insurance, construction, employment, contract, landlord and tenant, public and environment law.

Chambers of Nicholas Syfret QC

13 KING'S BENCH WALK,
TEMPLE, LONDON EC4Y 7EN
Tel: 020 7353 7204 ***Fax:*** 020 7583 0252
Dx: 359 LONDON/CHANCERY LANE
E-mail: clerks@13kbw.co.uk
Clerk: Senior: Kevin Kelly.
Administrator: Penny McFall
Head of Chambers:
Syfret, Mr Nicholas (Q.C.). . . . M . . . Oct 1979

Baughan, Mr Julian James (Q.C.). . . . I . . . Jul 1967
Ellis, Mr Roger John (Q.C.). . . . G . . . Jul 1962
Dawson, Mr Alexander William . . . M . . . Jul 1969
McGeorge, Mr Anthony William . . . I . . . Nov 1969
Lamb, Mr Robert Glasson. . . . M . . . Jul 1973
Goodwin, Ms Deirdre Evelyn . . . G . . . Jul 1974
Bright, Mr David Reginald. . . . L . . . Jun 1976
Higgins, Mr Anthony . . . G . . . Nov 1978
Daly, Mr Nigel. . . . G . . . Jul 1979
Scott, Mr Charles. . . . M . . . Jul 1980
Pote, Mr Andrew Thomas. . . . G . . . Nov 1983
Coode, Mr Jonathan . . . M . . . Jul 1984
Vickery, Mr Neil. . . . G . . . Jul 1985
Maitland-Jones, Mr Mark . . . M . . . Nov 1986
Blake, Mr Arthur . . . I . . . Feb 1988
Cramsie, Mr Sinclair James Beresford . . . I . . . Nov 1988
Higgins, Mr Adrian . . . L . . . Oct 1990
Wallace, Ms Nicola . . . I . . . Oct 2006
Walters, Mr Edmund . . . M . . . Nov 1991
Williams, Mr Hugh . . . G . . . Jul 1992
Edwards, Miss Jennifer. . . . G . . . Oct 1992
Buttimore, Mr Gabriel. . . . G . . . Feb 1993
Coombe, Mr Peter . . . M . . . Nov 1993
Chan, Miss Susan . . . G . . . Oct 1994
Clargo, Mr John. . . . M . . . Oct 1994
Nicol, Mr Stuart. . . . L . . . Nov 1994
Duncan, Ms Nikki. . . . G . . . Nov 1994
Drake, Miss Rachel Alexia . . . M . . . Nov 1995
Robertson, Miss Alice. . . . G . . . Oct 1996
Woodhouse, Mr Nigel. . . . G . . . Nov 1997
Harrington, Ms Clare . . . L . . . Oct 1998
Hobbs, Mr Daniel S. . . . L . . . Oct 1998
Mann, Mr Christopher. . . . L . . . Oct 1998
Grainger, Mr Alistair. . . . L . . . Nov 1998
James, Mr Henry . . . G . . . Nov 1999
Lippold, Mrs Sarah . . . I . . . Nov 1999
Owen-Thomas, Mr Richard . . . M . . . Nov 2000
Van der Leij, Ms Martina . . . I . . . Jul 2001
Brady, Ms Jane. . . . M . . . Oct 2001
Grant, Mr Murray . . . I . . . Oct 2003
Sear, Miss Joanne . . . G . . . Jul 2004
Gurnham, Mr Paul . . . L . . . Jul 2004
Bennion-Pedley, Mr Edward. . . . M . . . Nov 2004
Boswell, Mr Timothy . . . G . . . Nov 2004
Brown, Mr Timothy . . . I . . . Mar 2005
Malcolm, Miss Jane. . . . M . . . Jul 2005
Corrie, Mr Matthew . . . M . . . Jun 2006
Yeatman, Ms Trudi . . . I . . . Jan 2006
Ashton, Mr David Sambrook; Chartered Arbitrator* . . . G . . . Jul 1962
Reid, Mr Paul William* . . . I . . . Jul 1975

Chambers of Lanre Oke

KINGSWAY CHAMBERS,
HAMILTON HOUSE, 1 TEMPLE AVENUE, LONDON EC4Y 0HA
Tel: 020 7404 2357 ***Fax:*** 020 7404 2357
Dx: 205 LONDON/CHANCERY LANE
Clerk: Lanre Oke.
Head of Chambers:
Oke, Lanre . . . L . . . Jun 1979

Sharma, Rakhee . . . G . . . Jan 1995

Chambers of Ami Feder

LAMB BUILDING,
TEMPLE, LONDON EC4Y 7AS
Tel: 020 7797 7788 ***Fax:*** 020 7353 0535
Dx: 1038 LONDON/CHANCERY LANE
E-mail: clerks@lambbuilding.co.uk
Clerk: Gary Goodger; David Corne; Paul Hammond; David O'Sullivan; Harry Butcher; Luke Clark.
Administrator: Maxine Smith
Head of Chambers:
Feder, Mr Ami . . . I . . . Jul 1965

Worrall, Ms Anna (Q.C.) . . . M . . . Nov 1959
Richmond, Mr Bernard Grant (Q.C.); Recorder . . . M . . . Jul 1988
Power, Mr Lewis (Q.C.). . . . G . . . Oct 1990
Krolick, Mr Ivan. . . . G . . . Nov 1966
Guy, Mr Richard Perran. . . . I . . . Nov 1970
Fox, Mr John Harvey . . . I . . . Jul 1973
Gordon, Mr Jeremy* . . . I . . . Jul 1974
Barton, Mr Alan. . . . M . . . Nov 1975
Sherman, Mr Robert . . . G . . . Jul 1977
Phillips, Mr Michael Charles. . . . M . . . Feb 1980
Brennan, Miss Janice. . . . M . . . Jul 1980
O'Malley, Miss Julie. . . . G . . . Nov 1983
Toch, Miss Joanna . . . M . . . Oct 1988
Wainwright, Mr Jeremy . . . G . . . Oct 1990
McCullough, Miss Louise Clare . . . M . . . Oct 1991
Gray, Jennifer. . . . M . . . Jan 1992
Kearney, Mr Seamus . . . G . . . Feb 1992
Crampin, Mr Paul. . . . M . . . Oct 1992
Dykers, Miss C Joy. . . . G . . . Oct 1995
Peterson, Miss Geri. . . . M . . . Oct 1997
Pretzell, Mr Andreas . . . M . . . Oct 1997
Shannon, Ms Nicola . . . M . . . Oct 1997
Selby, Andrew . . . G . . . Nov 1997
Rhone-Adrien, Miss Paula . . . I . . . Oct 1998
Alexander, Mr Andrew . . . L . . . Jan 1999
Newport, Mr Michael . . . M . . . Jul 1999
Pease, Ms Alexandra. . . . M . . . Nov 1999
Kelleher, Ms Katherine . . . M . . . Jul 2000
Powell, Miss Michelle. . . . I . . . Jul 2001
Leslie, Miss Clare. . . . M . . . Jan 2002

James, Rhodri	I	Jul 2002
Harrison, Mr Jon	L	Mar 2003
Loke, Miss Siew	G	Jul 2003
Reeve, Miss Veronica	I	Jun 2004
Merrigan, Mr David	L	Jul 2004
Rawal, Anita	M	Jan 2004
Darnborough, Mr Daniel	M	Jan 2006
Mobbs, Mr Richard	L	Jan 2007
Abzarian, Arash	L	Mar 2007
Ul Haq, Miss Yasmeen	I	Jan 2008
Di Francesco, Alex	M	Jul 2008
Chapman, Miss Juliet	L	Jan 2009
Stevens, Miss Heather	M	Jan 2009
Hodkinson, Mr Gary	M	Jan 2010

LAMB CHAMBERS,

LAMB BUILDING, TEMPLE, LONDON EC4Y 7AS

Tel: 020 7797 8300 ***Fax:*** 020 7797 8308
Dx: 418 LONDON/CHANCERY LANE
E-mail: info@lambchambers.co.uk
Clerk: John Kelly.

Cherry, Mr John M (Q.C.)	G	Nov 1961
Winchester, Mr Leonard Clive Allyn	L	Jul 2002
Hay, Mr Robin	I	Nov 1964
Challenger, Mr Colin Westcott	I	Nov 1970
West, Mr Mark R; Recorder; Mediator	I	May 1973
Maxwell Lewis, Mr Cameron	M	Jul 1974
Connerty, Anthony	I	Jul 1974
Stewart, Mr Paul	G	Jul 1975
Brilliant, Mr Simon Howard	M	Jul 1976
Briden, Mr Timothy	I	Jul 1976
Caun, Mr Lawrence	L	Nov 1977
Mayall, Mr David	G	Jul 1979
Power, Mr Richard	M	Nov 1983
Emerson, Mr Paul Michael	M	Jul 1984
Colbey, Mr Richard	I	Jul 1984
Blackwood, Mr Clive	I	Nov 1986
Miles, Mr Edward Napier Tremayne	I	Feb 1989
Swirsky, Mr Adam	M	Nov 1989
Stuart, Mr James	G	Oct 1990
Menzies, Mr Richard	M	Nov 1993
Slaughter, Mr Andrew MP	M	Oct 1993
Sefton-Smith, Mr Lloyd	L	Oct 1993
Haggerty, Miss Elizabeth Frances	L	Nov 1994
Kerr, Mr Derek William	M	Oct 1994
Browne, Mr James William	M	Oct 1994
Hayes, Mr Richard	L	Oct 1995
Richards, Dr Jonathan Nicholas	M	Nov 1995
Prand, Dr Annette B	I	Nov 1995
Pearson, Mr Christopher	I	Oct 1995
King, Mr Charles	M	Nov 1995
Dippenaar, Mr Daniel Jacobus	M	Jan 2007
Stagi, Miss Alexandra F V	L	Nov 1997
Daley, Mr Howard M	G	Oct 1997
King, Mr Mark	I	Oct 1997
O'Brien, Miss Niamh Katrina	M	Nov 1998
Topal, Mr Erol	M	Jul 1998
Coleman, Mr Guy	I	Nov 1998
Walker, Mr Adam Nigel	L	Jul 2000
Wright, Ms Abigail Mary Barbara	M	Oct 2000
Davies, Miss Emily Sparham	M	Jan 2000
Clifton, Ms Jane	M	Oct 2001
Kerr, Dr Joanna	G	Oct 2001
Winn-Smith, Mr Matthew	L	Mar 2003
Willink, Mr David Christopher	M	Nov 2004
Turnbull, Miss Helen	I	Jan 2004
Gist, Mr Robin	G	Jul 2004
John, Mr Morgan	G	Jan 2004
Pressman, Mr Bernard	M	Nov 2004
Jacob, Mr Winston	M	Jul 2005
Dwomoh, Miss Elizabeth	M	Oct 2005
Kinghorn, Miss Helen	M	Jul 2006
Varma, Mr Rahul	I	Nov 2007
Seal, Ms Philippa	L	Nov 2008
Mathew, Mr Oscar	M	Jul 2009

29A LAMBS CONDUIT STREET,

HOLBORN, LONDON WC1N 3NG

Tel: 020 7831 9907 ***Fax:*** 020 7831 9907

Chambers of Neil King QC

LANDMARK CHAMBERS,

180 FLEET STREET, LONDON EC4A 2HG

Tel: 020 7430 1221 ***Fax:*** 020 7421 6060
Dx: 1042 LONDON/CHANCERY LANE
E-mail: clerks@landmarkchambers.co.uk
Web: www.landmarkchambers.co.uk
Clerk: Senior: Jay Fullilove.
Head of Chambers:

King, Mr Neil (Q.C.)	I	Jul 1980
Woolley, Mr David Rorie (Q.C.)	M	Jul 1962
Lockhart-Mummery, Mr Christopher (Q.C.)	I	Jul 1971
Martin, Mr Roy (Q.C.)	L	Jul 1990
Clarkson, Mr Patrick Robert James (Q.C.)	L	Jul 1972
Harper, Mr Joseph (Q.C.)	G	Jul 1970
Drabble, Mr Richard (Q.C.)	I	Nov 1975
Hicks, Mr William David Anthony (Q.C.)	L	Jul 1975
Holgate, Mr David (Q.C.)	M	Jul 1978
Katkowski, Mr Christopher (Q.C.)	G	Feb 1982
Male, Mr John (Q.C.)	L	Jul 1976
Elvin, Mr David (Q.C.)	M	Nov 1983
Price Lewis, Mr Rhodri (Q.C.)	M	Jul 1975
Underwood, Mr Ashley Grenville (Q.C.)	G	Jul 1976
Harris, Mr Russell James (Q.C.)	G	Nov 1986
Mould, Mr Timothy (Q.C.)	G	Jul 1987
Lieven, Ms Nathalie (Q.C.)	G	Jul 1989
Cameron, Mr Neil St Clair (Q.C.)	G	Jul 1982
Holland, Ms Katharine Jane (Q.C.)	M	Jul 1989
Litton, Mr John (Q.C.)	M	Jul 1989
Holland, Mr David Moore (Q.C.)	I	Jul 1986
Morshead, Mr Timothy (Q.C.)	L	Feb 1995
Bickford-Smith, Mr Stephen	I	Jul 1972
Caws, Mr Eian	I	Nov 1974
Lewsley, Mr Christopher	L	Jul 1976
Pickles, Mr Simon Robert	I	Jul 1978
Smith, Mr David	I	Nov 1980
Jefferies, Mr Thomas	M	Nov 1981
Morgan, Mr Stephen Francis	G	Nov 1983
Langham, Mr Richard Geoffrey	L	Nov 1986
Taylor, Mr Reuben	G	Oct 1990
Taggart, Mr Nicholas	M	Oct 1991
White, Mr Sasha	I	Oct 1991
Forsdick, Mr David John	G	Oct 1993
Warren, Mr Rupert	G	Oct 1994
Boyle, Mr Christopher	L	Nov 1994
Keen, Mr Graeme	M	Mar 1995
Weekes, Mr Thomas Charles	I	Oct 1995
Lamont, Miss Camilla	M	Nov 1995
Reed, Mr Matthew	M	Nov 1995
Lyness, Mr Scott Edward	L	Oct 1996
Oakes, Ms Alison Denise	I	Nov 1996
Maurici, Mr James Patrick	I	Nov 1996
Watkin, Mr Toby Paul	I	Oct 1996
Broadfoot, Ms Samatha	M	Nov 1997
Kolinsky, Mr Daniel	I	Oct 1998
Stacey, Ms Myriam	I	Oct 1998
Walton, Mr Robert	L	Jan 1999
Olley, Ms Katherine	I	Oct 1999
Patry Hoskins, Ms Carine	I	Jul 1999
Ward, Miss Galina	G	Mar 2000
Williams, Mr Guy	I	Jul 2000
Buley, Mr Tim	L	Jul 2000
Blundell, Mr David Anthony	I	Oct 2001
Walder, Mr Aaron	I	Jan 2002
Banner, Mr Charles	L	Jan 2004
Moules, Mr Richard	M	Jan 2005
Blackmore, Ms Sasha	L	Jan 2005
Lewis, Mr Gwion	G	Apr 2005
Yates, Ms Katrina	L	Oct 2006
Wills, Mr Jonathan Stuart	L	Jan 2006
Lean, Ms Jacqueline	G	Jul 2007
Turney, Mr Richard	G	Jan 2007
Fisher, Mr Toby	L	Jan 2008
Harling-Phillips, Emma	G	Jan 2009
Helmore, Katie	L	Jan 2009
Parkinson, Mr Andrew	L	Jan 2010
Byass, Mr Andrew	L	Jan 2010

Chambers of Ernest John Wollner

21 LAUDERDALE TOWER,

BARBICAN, LONDON EC2Y 8BY

Tel: 020 7920 9308
E-mail: wollner@talk21.com
Clerk: Iidiko Koltai.
Head of Chambers:

Wollner, Mr Ernest John	I	Nov 1988
Stotesbury, Mr David Charles	G	Feb 1980

Chambers of Andrew Clarke QC and Clive Freedman QC

LITTLETON CHAMBERS,

3 KING'S BENCH WALK NORTH, TEMPLE, LONDON EC4Y 7HR

Tel: 020 7797 8600 ***Fax:*** 020 7797 8699
Dx: 1047 LONDON/CHANCERY LANE
E-mail: clerks@littletonchambers.co.uk
Web: www.littletonchambers.com
Clerk: Alistair Coyne; Tim Tarring; Jason Drakeford; Tracy Thomson; Andrew Sargeant.
Administrator: Paula Fox
Chambers Director: Nigel Alistair McEwen
Head of Chambers:

Clarke, Mr Andrew (Q.C.)	M	Jul 1980
Freedman, Mr Clive (Q.C.); Recorder	G	Jul 1978
Mayes, Mr Ian (Q.C.); Recorder	M	Jul 1974
Price, Mr Richard M (Q.C.) OBE	G	Nov 1969
Bowers, Mr John Simon (Q.C.)	M	Nov 1979
Stafford, Mr Andrew (Q.C.)	M	Jul 1980
Bloch, Mr Selwyn (Q.C.)	M	Jul 1982
Bartle, Mr Philip M (Q.C.)	M	Jul 1976
Reade, Mr David J (Q.C.)	M	Jul 1983
Harry Thomas, Miss Caroline Jane (Q.C.); Recorder	M	Feb 1981
Samek, Mr Charles (Q.C.)	M	Nov 1989
Ellenbogen, Ms Naomi (Q.C.)	G	Oct 1992
Perkoff, Mr Richard Michael	M	Jul 1971
Higginson, Mr Timothy Nicholas B	I	Nov 1977
Bothroyd, Miss Shirley	M	Jul 1982
Fodder, Mr Martin	I	Jul 1983
Sendall, Mr Antony	L	Jul 1984
Duggan, Mr Michael	G	Jul 1984
Trepte, Mr Peter-Armin	G	Jul 1987
Downey, Mr B Raoul D	I	Jul 1988
Neaman, Mr Sam L	I	Jul 1988
Barklem, Mr Martyn; Recorder	L	Jul 1989
Bacon, Mr Jeffrey	M	Nov 1989
Brown, Mr Damian	I	Feb 1989
D'Cruz, Mr Rupert	L	Nov 1989
Lewis, Mr Jeremy	L	May 1992
Mansfield, Mr Gavin	M	Nov 1992
Quinn, Mr Chris	M	Oct 1992
Tatton-Brown, Mr Daniel N; Treasury Counsel	M	Oct 1994
Ritchie, Mr Stuart	M	Oct 1995
Davis, Miss Carol	M	Oct 1996
Martin, Mr Dale	I	Oct 1997
De Silva, Mr Niran	L	Oct 1997
Solomon, Mr Adam Jonathan	G	Oct 1998
Bone, Ms Lucy	M	Oct 1999
Cohen, Mr Jonathan Michael	G	Oct 1999
Sheridan, Mr Matthew	G	Jul 2000
Misra, Miss Eleena	M	Jul 2001
White, Mr Oliver	I	Jul 2001
Sefton, Ms Joanne	I	Jul 2002
Wynne, Mr James	M	Jul 2002
Lascelles, Mr David	L	Nov 2003
Newman, Mr Christopher	I	Jan 2003
Palmer, Mr Martin	I	Jul 2003
Mehrzad, Mr John	I	Oct 2005
Lacy, Mr Brian	L	Nov 2006
Apps, Miss Katherine	G	Jul 2006
Robson, Mr Alexander	M	Jul 2006
Davies, Miss Charlotte	L	Oct 2006
Carter, Miss Lydia	M	Nov 2007
Hawkins, Miss Charlene	M	Jul 2008
Bickford Smith, Mr James	L	Oct 2008
Goodfellow, Mr Nicholas	L	Jul 2009
Rajgopaul, Mr Craig	I	Nov 2010

Work Description: Employment Law, Commercial Law (excluding shipping), Professional Negligence, Clinical Negligence, Sports Law, Mediation and Arbitration.

114 LIVERPOOL ROAD,

LONDON N1 0RE

Tel: 020 7226 9863 ***Fax:*** 020 7704 1111
E-mail: mark.eldridge3@btopenworld.com

Eldridge, Mr Mark	G	Jul 1982

CHAMBERS OF L LLOYD,

3 ARCHERY FIELDS HOUSE , WHARTON STREET, LONDON WC1X 9PN

Tel: 020 7837 4727

24 LOCHMORE HOUSE,

CUNDY STREET, LONDON SW1W 9JX

Tel: 020 7730 3299 ***Fax:*** 020 7730 3299

LOMBARD CHAMBERS,

1 SEKFORDE STREET, CLERKENWELL, LONDON EC1R 0BE

Tel: 020 7107 2100 ***Fax:*** 020 7107 2101
Dx: 53332 CLERKENWELL
Web: www.lombardchambers.com
Clerk: Ian Lee.

Davis, Mr Greville	L	Jul 1976
Bull, Mr Gregory (Q.C.)	I	Jul 1976
Stuart, Mr Bruce	G	Nov 1977
Stafford-Michael, Mr Simon	G	Nov 1982
McGuire, Mr Donal Patrick	G	Jul 1983
Butcher, Mr Richard	G	Nov 1985
Sharma, Pavan	M	Jan 1993
Alfred, Mr Stephan	I	Jan 1996
Zaffuto, Ms Rosa	M	Jan 2000
Thomas, Mr Timothy	L	Jan 2002
Mohindru, Mr Anurag	M	Jan 2003
Panesar, Mr Rashvinder	G	Jan 2004
Cole, Mr Gordon (Q.C.)*	I	Jun 1979
Pratt, Mr Richard J (Q.C.)*	G	Jul 1980
Jarman, Mr Samuel*	I	Jul 1989

Work Description: Commercial Fraud, Insurance Reinsurance, Family Law, Criminal, Common Law / Landlord & Tenant, Licensing, Employment, Chancery, Immigration, Companies, Banking, Tribunals & Inquiries.

LONDON CHAMBERS,

3RD FLOOR, 218 STRAND, LONDON WC2R 1AT

Tel: 0845 083 3000 ***Fax:*** 0870 166 0547
Dx: 232 LONDON/CHANCERY LANE
E-mail: dacosta@clerksroom.com
Clerk: Greg Speller.
Administrator: Tim Dingle
Practice Manager: Martin Davies
Chambers Director: Stephen Ward

MFL CHAMBERS,

27 LEICESTER ROAD, EAST FINCHLEY, LONDON N2 9DY

Fisher, Ms Mel	L	Jun 1985

Chambers of Michael Driscoll QC

MAITLAND CHAMBERS,

7 STONE BUILDINGS, LINCOLN'S INN, LONDON WC2A 3SZ

Tel: 020 7406 1200 ***Fax:*** 020 7406 1300
Dx: 326 LONDON/CHANCERY LANE
E-mail: clerks@maitlandchambers.com
Clerk: Seniors: Lee Cutler; John Wiggs. Colin Dawson; Danny Wilkinson; Rob Penson; Daniel Woodbridge; Danielle Jerome; Sam Dempsey.
Administrator: Valerie Piper
Chambers Director: Robert Graham-Campbell
Head of Chambers:

Driscoll, Mr Michael (Q.C.)	M	Jul 1970
McCall, Mr Christopher H (Q.C.)	L	Nov 1966
Jackson, Ms Judith (Q.C.)	I	Nov 1975
Newman, Miss Catherine Mary (Q.C.); Recorder; Lt. Bailiff in the Royal Courts of Guernsey; Deputy High Court Judge; Accredited Mediator	M	Jul 1979
Pymont, Mr Christopher Howard (Q.C.); Recorder; Deputy High Court Judge	G	Jul 1979
Trace, Mr Anthony John (Q.C.)	L	Jul 1981
Cunningham, Mr Mark (Q.C.); Accredited Mediator	I	Nov 1980
Newey, Mr Guy (Q.C.); Deputy High Court Judge, Acting Deemster IoM	M	Jul 1982
Girolami, Mr Paul Julian (Q.C.); Deputy High Court Judge; Accredited Mediator	M	Nov 1983
McGhee, Mr John Alexander (Q.C.)	L	Jul 1984
Collings, Mr Matthew G B (Q.C.)	L	Jul 1985
Nicholls, Mr John Peter (Q.C.)	L	Jul 1986
Johnson, Mr Edwin Geoffrey (Q.C.)	L	Nov 1987
Parker, Mr Christopher R (Q.C.)	L	Dec 1984
Chambers, Mr Dominic (Q.C.)	G	Nov 1987
Peacock, Mr Nicholas (Q.C.)	M	Nov 1989
Russen, Mr Jonathan (Q.C.)	L	Jul 1986
Leech, Mr Thomas Alexander Crispin (Q.C.); Accredited Mediator	M	Nov 1988

Morgan, Mr Richard (Q.C.) . . . G . . . Nov 1988
Tipples, Miss Amanda J (Q.C.); Recorder, Junior Counsel to Crown A Panel . . . G . . . Oct 1991
Gibbon, Mr Michael (Q.C.); Junior Counsel to Crown A Panel . . . G . . . Nov 1993
Thomas, Mr Nigel Matthew; Recorder; Accredited Mediator . . . L . . . Jul 1976
Walton, Mr Alastair H . . . L . . . Jul 1977
Evans, Mr Timothy . . . L . . . Jul 1979
Dagnall, Mr John Marshall Anthony; Accredited Mediator . . . L . . . Nov 1983
Harry, Mr Timothy Hawkins; Accredited Mediator . . . L . . . Jul 1983
Clifford, Mr James . . . L . . . Nov 1984
Harrison, Ms Philomena . . . M . . . Nov 1985
Dutton, Mr Timothy Christopher . . . L . . . Jul 1985
Walton, Miss Carolyn Margery; Accredited Mediator . G . . . Jul 1980
Banner, Mr Gregory S . . . G . . . Jul 1989
Wonnacott, Mr Mark A . . . L . . . Jul 1989
Cullen, Mr Edmund . . . L . . . Oct 1990
Pryor, Mr Michael . . . I . . . Oct 1992
Stubbs, Miss Rebecca . . . M . . . Oct 1994
Aldridge, Mr James . . . L . . . Oct 1994
Westwood, Mr Andrew; Junior Counsel to the Crown B Panel . . . I . . . Nov 1994
Johns, Mr Alan Grant . . . G . . . Oct 1994
Atkins, Siward . . . M . . . Oct 1995
Margolin, Mr Daniel; Junior Counsel to Crown B Panel . . . G . . . Nov 1995
Ayres, Mr Andrew . . . G . . . Oct 1996
Clarke, Mr Paul Sebastian . . . G . . . Jan 1997
Addy, Ms Catherine; Junior Counsel to Crown B Panel . . . M . . . Nov 1998
Hutton, Miss Louise . . . I . . . Nov 1998
Mumford, Mr David . . . L . . . Oct 2000
Smith, Mr Matthew; Junior Counsel to Crown C Panel . . . I . . . Jan 2001
Smith, Mr Adam . . . G . . . Nov 2001
Higgins, Miss Gabrielle . . . L . . . Jul 2002
John, Mr Benjamin . . . L . . . Jan 2002
Smith, Mr Charles . . . L . . . Jan 2002
Fowler, Mr Richard . . . I . . . Jan 2003
Winter, Mr Alexander . . . M . . . Jul 2003
Keller, Mr Ciaran . . . L . . . Jul 2004
McCluskey, Mr Alec . . . L . . . Oct 2005
Dewar, Miss Fiona . . . L . . . Nov 2005
Munby, Mr Thomas . . . I . . . Oct 2006
Allcock, Mr Jonathan . . . M . . . Jan 2007
Foskett, Miss Rosanna . . . L . . . Jul 2008
Scher, Mr Laurie . . . M . . . Jul 2008
Sheehan, Mr James . . . M . . . Oct 2008
Phillips, Mr Oliver . . . M . . . Jul 2009
Ballance, Mr James Conrad . . . G . . . Jul 2009
Alberga, Mr Ramon (Q.C.)* . . . M . . . Sep 1951
Lyndon-Stanford, Mr Michael Andrew Flemying (Q.C.); Deputy High Court Judge* . . . I . . . Feb 1962
Randall, Mr John (Q.C.); Recorder; Deputy HC Judge* . . . L . . . Jul 1978
Hopkins, Mr John* . . . M . . . Apr 1963
Shankardass, Vijay* . . . L . . . May 1972
Stewart, Miss Lindsey* . . . I . . . Nov 1983
Courtenay, Mr Charles P* . . . I . . . Jan 1999
Fox, Mr David* . . . L . . . Jul 2005

MALINS CHAMBERS,
115 TEMPLE CHAMBERS, TEMPLE AVENUE, LONDON EC4Y 0DA
Tel: 020 7353 8868
E-mail: info@malinschambers.com

INVESTOR IN PEOPLE

MATRIX CHAMBERS,
GRIFFIN BUILDING, GRAY'S INN, LONDON WC1R 5LN
Est: 2000
Tel: 020 7404 3447 ***Fax:*** 020 7404 3448
Dx: 400 LONDON/CHANCERY LANE
E-mail: matrix@matrixlaw.co.uk
Web: www.matrixlaw.co.uk
Administrator: Kevin Hooper
Chambers Director: Lindsay Scott
Afeeva, Mr Mark . . . I . . . Oct 1997
Armstrong, Dr Nicholas . . . M . . . Jul 2001
Bailin, Mr Alex (Q.C.) . . . L . . . Nov 1995
Bodnar, Mr Andrew . . . L . . . Jan 1995
Booth, Ms Cherie (Q.C.); Recorder(1999); Bencher(1999) . . . L . . . Jul 1976
Brennan, Lord Daniel (Q.C.); Deputy High Court Judge . . . G . . . Jul 1967
Brown, Mr Christopher Martin . . . M . . . Nov 2002
Butler, Miss Michelle . . . I . . . Jun 2007
Chinkin, Professor Christine . . . L . . . Mar 2003
Choo, Professor Andrew . . . I . . . Jul 2002
Cook, Ms Kate . . . M . . . Nov 1990
Craven, Mr Edward . . . L . . . Jan 2007
Crawford, Professor James . . . G . . . Jun 1999
Darwin, Ms Claire Louise . . . I . . . Oct 2005
Desai, Mr Raj . . . L . . . Jan 2010
Douglas, Mr Zachary . . . G . . . Mar 2006
Emmerson, Mr Ben (Q.C.) . . . M . . . Nov 1986
Friedman, Mr Daniel . . . I . . . Oct 1996
Gearty, Professor Conor . . . M . . . Jan 1995
Gibson, Mr Nicholas; Former Solicitor . . . L . . . Jan 2009
Glasson, Mr Jonathan; Former Solicitor . . . M . . . Feb 1996
Grodzinski, Mr Sam (Q.C.) . . . M . . . Mar 1996
Hetherington, Ms Tessa . . . L . . . Jul 2004
Husain, Mr Raza (Q.C.) . . . M . . . Oct 1993
Kentridge, Ms Janet . . . L . . . Jul 1999
Kibling, Mr Thomas . . . M . . . Nov 1990
Knights, Ms Samantha . . . L . . . Nov 1996
Knowles, Mr Julian (Q.C.) . . . I . . . Nov 1994
Laddie, Mr James . . . M . . . Nov 1995
Law, Ms Helen . . . G . . . Oct 2005
Linden, Mr Thomas (Q.C.) . . . G . . . Nov 1989
Logan, Ms Rachel . . . I . . . Jan 2008
Macdonald, Lord Ken (Q.C.) KB . . . I . . . Jul 1978
Macdonald, Ms Alison . . . G . . . Jan 2000
Mansoori, Ms Sara . . . L . . . Nov 1997
Marks, Mr Jonathan H . . . I . . . Oct 1992
McColgan, Professor Aileen . . . L . . . Jan 2001
McNair-Wilson, Ms Laura . . . G . . . Nov 2007
Mitrophanous, Miss Eleni . . . I . . . Oct 1999
Monaghan, Ms Karon (Q.C.) . . . I . . . Jul 1989
Montgomery, Miss Clare P (Q.C.); Recorder(2000); Deputy High Court Judge(2003); Judge Court of Appeal Guernsey and Jersey (2008) . . . G . . . Nov 1980
Morris, Professor Gillian . . . L . . . Jan 1997
Mountfield, Ms Helen (Q.C.) . . . G . . . Jul 1991
Ni Ghralaigh, Ms Blinne . . . L . . . Nov 2005
O'Flaherty, Mr John . . . M . . . Oct 2001
O'Neill, Mr Aidan (Q.C.) . . . I . . . Jul 1996
Owen, Mr Tim (Q.C.); Recorder of the Crown Court (2006); Deputy High Court Judge (2010) . . . M . . . Jul 1983
Prince, Miss Laura . . . L . . . Jun 2003
Prochaska, Miss Elizabeth . . . I . . . Jan 2007
Purchase, Mr Mathew . . . L . . . Jan 2002
Ryder, Mr Matthew (Q.C.) . . . G . . . Oct 1992
Sandell, Mr Adam . . . L . . . Jul 2008
Sands, Professor Philippe (Q.C.) . . . M . . . Nov 1985
Sheridan, Mr Maurice . . . M . . . Jul 1984
Simor, Miss Jessica . . . M . . . Nov 1992
Skinner, Miss Lorna . . . M . . . Nov 1997
Smith, Mr Andrew . . . L . . . Oct 2008
Squires, Mr Daniel . . . M . . . Nov 1998
Summers, Mr Mark . . . I . . . Nov 1996
Temple, Ms Booan . . . M . . . Jan 2001
Thompson, Mr Rhodri (Q.C.) . . . M . . . Jul 1989
Tomlinson, Mr Hugh (Q.C.) . . . G . . . Nov 1983
Tridimas, Professor Takis . . . M . . . Jan 2000
White, Mr Antony (Q.C.) . . . M . . . Nov 1983
Wolfe, Mr David . . . M . . . Nov 1992

This Chamber with 70 members is based in London. Contact any of our Practice Team at any time by sending an email to matrix@matrixlaw.co.uk or telephoning +44(0)20 7404 3447.

Chambers of Robert Turrall-Clarke

MAYFAIR CHAMBERS,
EMPIRE HOUSE, 175 PICCADILLY, MAYFAIR, LONDON W1V 9DB
Tel: 01428 681666
E-mail: email@robert-turrall-clarke.co.uk
Clerk: Veronica Ashby.
Head of Chambers:
Turrall-Clarke, Mr Robert . . . M . . . Jun 1971

Chambers of Anthony Gifford QC

1 MITRE COURT BUILDINGS,
TEMPLE, LONDON EC4Y 7BS
Tel: 020 7452 8900 ***Fax:*** 020 7452 8999
Dx: 195 LONDON/CHANCERY LANE
E-mail: clerks@1mcb.com
Clerk: Senior: Marc Foss.
Head of Chambers:
Gifford, Lord Anthony (Q.C.) . . . M . . . Jul 1962

Hart-Leverton, Mr Colin (Q.C.) . . . G . . . May 1957
Gibbs, Mrs Jocelyn . . . L . . . Nov 1972
Gassman, Miss Caroline . . . I . . . Jul 1974
Daniells-Smith, Mr Roger . . . M . . . Nov 1974
Yearwood, Mr Jeffrey . . . I . . . Nov 1975
Sofaer, Miss Moira . . . M . . . Jul 1975
Wynne Jones, Mr Martin . . . I . . . Nov 1977
Mullen, Mr Peter . . . L . . . Jul 1977
Fessal, Mr Ignatius . . . I . . . Nov 1981
MacKinnon, Mr Thomas . . . M . . . Jul 1982
Allen, Ms Sylvia Delores . . . G . . . Jul 1983
McIntosh, Ms Jacqueline . . . I . . . Apr 1987
Murray-Smith, Mr James . . . M . . . May 1990
Kivdeh, Mr Sean . . . M . . . Oct 1992
Owosu-Yianoma, Mr David . . . I . . . Sep 1992
Ivens, Miss Jemma . . . L . . . Feb 1994
Sultan, Ms Neelim . . . G . . . Apr 1993
Chipperfield, Mr Jeremy . . . I . . . Jan 1995
Ali, Mr Raymond A . . . G . . . Nov 1995
Mansoor, Ms Parveen . . . I . . . Nov 1996
Penn, Mr Jon . . . I . . . Mar 1996
Richmond, Mr Paul . . . I . . . Oct 1998
Rustom, Mr Shiraz . . . M . . . Oct 1998
Stephens, Mr Mark . . . M . . . Nov 1998
Lule, Ms Jacqueline . . . M . . . Oct 1999
O'Sullivan, Mr Richard . . . I . . . May 1999
Roscoe, Mr Mark . . . L . . . Oct 1999
Canter, Mr Simon . . . I . . . Oct 2000
Howell, Mr Jacques . . . L . . . Oct 2000
Edwards, Mr Iain . . . M . . . Apr 2000
Levinson, Miss Jemma . . . G . . . Oct 2001
Judge, Ms Parveen . . . L . . . Mar 2001
Jones, Ms Anika . . . G . . . Mar 2002
Bains, Mr Satnam . . . M . . . Apr 2002
Jones, Ms Jacinta . . . G . . . Jul 2002
Crinion, Mr Charles . . . M . . . Jan 2002
Silver, Ms Tamsin . . . G . . . Nov 2002
Russell-Mitra, Ms Jessica . . . M . . . Jan 2003
Shah Begum, Ms Monwara . . . L . . . Mar 2004
Munro, Mr Campell . . . M . . . Jul 2006
Delany, Ms Francesca . . . M . . . Oct 2006
Waterson, Ms Anna . . . I . . . Jan 2007
Moran, Mr Christopher . . . M . . . Jan 2007
Bart, Mr Delano* . . . L . . . Jun 1977
Williams, Ms Nicola* . . . L . . . Nov 1985
Boateng, Mr Paul MP* . . . G . . . Nov 1989
Kerr, Mr Stuart* . . . I . . . Nov 1995

Chambers of Francis P Gilbert

MITRE HOUSE CHAMBERS,
9 GOWER STREET, LONDON WC1E 6HA
Tel: 020 7307 7100 ***Fax:*** 020 7307 7139
Dx: 35709 BLOOMSBURY
E-mail: clerks@mitrehouse.co.uk
Web: www.mitrehouse.co.uk
Clerk: Senior: Ian Kitchen. Junior: Philip Silverman. Tom Tracy.
Administrator: Paula Burt
Head of Chambers:
Gilbert, Mr Francis P . . . L . . . Jul 1980

Ahluwalia, Ms Paramjit* . . . G . . . Mar 2002
Akinbolu, Ms Sandra . . . L . . . Oct 2002
Asanovic, Ms Bojana . . . M . . . Jul 2000
Briddock, Mr Alan . . . I . . . Mar 2000
Caldwell, Mr Andrew . . . M . . . Jan 1984
Cansick, Mr Allen . . . I . . . Jan 2004
Chapman, Ms Dawn . . . L . . . Jan 2001
Collins, Ms Deirdre . . . I . . . Nov 1999
Daykin, Emma . . . I . . . Jan 2005
Fisher, Miss Justine . . . I . . . Nov 1994
Fripp, Mr Eric William Burtin . . . G . . . Oct 1994
Hulse, Ms Cecilia . . . M . . . Nov 1998
Hyde, Mr Michael Thomas . . . I . . . Nov 2006
Jesurum, Raphael . . . G . . . Jan 2007
Laughton, Ms Victoria . . . L . . . Apr 1998
Lee, Gordon . . . M . . . Jan 1998
McCarthy, Keelin . . . G . . . Jan 2007
McKeown, Mr Paul Michael Gerard* . . . G . . . Nov 1998
Meredith, Ms Catherine Amy . . . G . . . Jan 2008
Motz, Stephanie* . . . G . . . Jan 2007
Radford, Ms Althea Jane . . . L . . . Jan 2009
Rogers, Mr Michael . . . G . . . Jul 2002
Sahu, Mr Mark . . . M . . . Nov 1995
Samimi, Ms Maryam . . . M . . . Jul 1994
Short, Harriet . . . G . . . Jan 2007
Syed, Safora . . . L . . . Jan 2000
Wilford, Ellis . . . G . . . Jan 2006

Chambers of Paul Lasok QC

MONCKTON CHAMBERS,
1 & 2 RAYMOND BUILDINGS, GRAY'S INN, LONDON WC1R 5NR
Tel: 020 7405 7211 ***Fax:*** 020 7405 2084
Dx: 257 LONDON/CHANCERY LANE
E-mail: chambers@monckton.com
Clerk: Senior: David Hockney.
Chambers Director: Ann Langford
Head of Chambers:
Lasok, Mr Paul (Q.C.) . . . M . . . Jul 1977

Lever, Sir Jeremy (Q.C.) . . . G . . . Nov 1957
Swift, Mr John (Q.C.) . . . I . . . Nov 1965
Currie, Mr Heriot (Q.C.) . . . G . . . Jan 1979
Collins, Mr Michael . . . L . . . Jan 1987
Paines, Mr Nicholas (Q.C.) . . . G . . . Apr 1978
Vajda, Mr Christopher (Q.C.) . . . G . . . Jul 1979
Unterhalter, Mr David SC . . . G . . . Jan 2009
Hall, Mrs Melanie (Q.C.) . . . I . . . Nov 1982
Bowsher, Mr Michael F T (Q.C.) . . . M . . . Nov 1985
Turner, Mr Jonathan (Q.C.) . . . M . . . Nov 1988
Harris, Mr Paul (Q.C.) . . . G . . . Oct 1994
Ward, Mr Tim (Q.C.) . . . G . . . Oct 1994
Beard, Mr Daniel (Q.C.) . . . L . . . Jul 1996
Fitzgerald, Mr Michael Edward . . . L . . . May 1979
Macnab, Mr Andrew . . . M . . . Jul 1986
Mantle, Mr Peter . . . I . . . Jul 1989
Peretz, Mr George . . . M . . . Sep 1990
Skilbeck, Ms Jennifer . . . L . . . Oct 1991
Hill, Mr Raymond . . . L . . . Oct 1992
Moser, Mr Philip Curt Harold . . . I . . . Oct 1992
Lindsay, Mr Alistair David . . . I . . . Nov 1993
Haynes, Miss Rebecca . . . I . . . Nov 1994
Smith, Ms Kassie . . . I . . . Nov 1995
Rogers, Mr Ian Paul . . . G . . . Nov 1995
Rayment, Mr Benedick M . . . I . . . Jun 1996
Holmes, Mr Josh . . . I . . . Jan 1997
Palmer, Mr Robert H . . . G . . . Oct 1998
Kreisberger, Miss Ronit . . . G . . . Jan 1999
Pickford, Mr Meredith . . . I . . . Oct 1999
Williams, Mr Robert Brychan James . . . M . . . Jan 2000
Gardner, Mr Piers . . . G . . . Mar 2000
Sloane, Miss Valentina . . . G . . . Oct 2000
Angiolini, Mr Mario . . . M . . . Oct 2000
Gregory, Mr Julian . . . I . . . Nov 2000
Facenna, Mr Gerry . . . L . . . Nov 2001
Howard, Ms Anneli . . . G . . . Jan 2002
Bates, Mr Alan . . . M . . . Oct 2003
Holmes, Miss Elisa . . . I . . . Nov 2003
Lask, Mr Benjamin Bela David . . . M . . . Nov 2003
Woolfe, Mr Philip John . . . I . . . Oct 2004
McBride, Mr Jeremy . . . I . . . Nov 2004
Holiner, Mr Drew . . . L . . . Jul 2005
Knibbe, Mr Jorren . . . M . . . Oct 2005
West, Mr Ewan . . . L . . . Jan 2006
Banks, Miss Fiona . . . I . . . Oct 2006

Blackwood, Ms Anneliese Rose. . . . . M. . . . Jul 2007
John, Miss Laura Elizabeth . . . . I . . . . Oct 2007
Draper, Mr Owain. . . . . L. . . . Jan 2008
Osepciu, Miss Ligia. . . . . L. . . . Jan 2008
Mitchell, Mr Frank. . . . . G. . . . Jan 2010
Lall, Mr Tarlochan. . . . . M. . . . Jan 2010

EC Law, Competition, Intellectual Property, Dumping, Trade, Social Security and Agriculture. Competition Law and Trade Regulation, Human Rights, Mergers, Monopolies and Restrictive Trade Practices, Air Transport Licensing, Judicial Review, Disciplinary Proceedings and Consumer Credit. Media and Entertainment Law. Commercial Litigation and Arbitration concerning Commercial Contracts, Construction and Civil Engineering, and Professional Negligence. Languages : French, German & Russian.

Chambers of Timothy Deal

60 MOORDOWN,
SHOOTERS HILL, LONDON SE18 3NG
Tel: 020 8856 8738 ***Fax:*** 0871 433 4376
E-mail: timothy.deal@btinternet.com
Head of Chambers:
Deal, Mr Timothy . . . . G. . . . . Jul 1988

Chambers of Patrick Charles Upward QC

15 NEW BRIDGE STREET CHAMBERS,
15 NEW BRIDGE STREET, LONDON EC4V 6AU
Est: 2004
Tel: 020 7842 1900 ***Fax:*** 020 7842 1901
Dx: 162 LONDON/CHANCERY LANE
E-mail: clerks@15nbs.com
Clerk: Senior: John Gillespie.
Head of Chambers:
Upward, Mr Patrick Charles (Q.C.) . . . . I . . . . . Jul 1972

Nolan, Mr Benjamin (Q.C.) . . . . M. . . . . Jul 1971
Burton, Mr John Malcolm (Q.C.) . . . . I . . . . . Jul 1979
Aaronberg, Mr David (Q.C.). . . . . I . . . . . Jul 1981
Mulholland, Mr James (Q.C.) . . . . I . . . . . Jul 1986
Aylett, Mr Kenneth George . . . . I . . . . . Jul 1972
Oliver, Mr Michael R . . . . I . . . . . Jul 1977
Walsh, Mr Peter Anthony Joseph . . . . M. . . . Nov 1978
Amakye, Miss Grace Tina. . . . . G. . . . Nov 1983
Banks, Mr Timothy . . . . I . . . . Nov 1983
Greenan, Mr John . . . . G. . . . . Jul 1984
Hugheston-Roberts, Mr Justin. . . . . M. . . . Jan 1986
McCormack, Ms Helen . . . . M. . . . Feb 1986
Nicholson Pratt, Mr Tom . . . . L. . . . Nov 1986
Lloyd, Mr Francis . . . . I . . . . . Jul 1987
Forsyth, Mr Andrew. . . . . I . . . . Nov 1989
Mulligan, Ms Ann . . . . G. . . . . Jul 1989
Argyropoulos, Mr Kyriakos . . . . I . . . . Nov 1991
Bertham, Mr Christopher . . . . L. . . . . Oct 1993
St Louis, Mr Brian. . . . . M. . . . . Oct 1994
Maggs, Mr Patrick . . . . I . . . . . Oct 1996
Beharrylal, Mr Anand . . . . L. . . . . Oct 1997
Hardyman, Mr Matthew. . . . . L. . . . Jan 1997
Moran, Mr Patrick. . . . . I . . . . . Oct 1997
Logan, Mr Graeme . . . . M. . . . . Oct 1998
Shotton, Miss Sophie . . . . I . . . . . Oct 1999
Edmonds, Mr Michael. . . . . I . . . . Aug 2000
Hussain, Miss Fara . . . . M. . . . Jan 2000
Edenborough, Mr James Scott . . . . M. . . . Nov 2001
Rollinson, Mr Darryn . . . . L. . . . . Jul 2001
Benthall, Mr Dominic . . . . M. . . . Nov 2002
Dashani, Ms Sonal . . . . L. . . . Nov 2002
Morrison, Mr Giles . . . . M. . . . Jan 2002
Boyes, Mr Ian. L. . . . Nov 2003
Brook, Mr Dale . . . . I . . . . Jan 2003
Turner, Mr Mathew . . . . G. . . . . Oct 2003
Collis, Mr Michael. . . . . I . . . . Nov 2004
Zentler-Munro, Ms Ruth. . . . . I . . . . Nov 2004
Higgins, Ms Nichola. . . . . L. . . . . Jul 2005
Crocker, Ms Beth . . . . M. . . . Nov 2006
Ross, Mr Neil. G. . . . . Oct 2006
Hitchcock, Jodie-Jane. . . . . M. . . . Jan 2006
Callinan, Ms Clodaghmuire . . . . M. . . . Jan 2007
Hobbs, Mrs Ruth . . . . L. . . . . Jul 2007
Ridout, Frances. . . . . M. . . . Jan 2007
Ward, Mr Robert . . . . L. . . . Jan 2007
Grout, Mr Christopher. . . . . I . . . . Jan 2007
Hartley, Louise . . . . M. . . . Jan 2008

Chambers of Giuseppe Cala

NEW COURT CHAMBERS,
NEW COURT TEMPLE, LONDON EC4Y 9BE
Tel: 020 7583 5123 ***Fax:*** 020 7353 3383
Dx: 0018 LONDON/CHANCERY LANE
E-mail: clerks@newcourtchambers.net
Clerk: Paul Bloomfield.
Head of Chambers:
Cala, Mr Giuseppe . . . . I . . . . Jan 1971

Chambers of Simon Joe Thorley QC

3 NEW SQUARE,
1ST FLOOR, LINCOLN'S INN, LONDON WC2A 3RS
Est: 1940
Tel: 020 7405 1111 ***Fax:*** 020 7405 7800
Dx: 454 LONDON/CHANCERY LANE
E-mail: clerks@3newsquare.co.uk
Web: www.3newsquare.co.uk
Clerk: Senior: Ian Bowie. Juniors: Tim Fairburn; David Court.
Administrator: Zena Dodd
Head of Chambers:
Thorley, Mr Simon Joe (Q.C.). . . . . I . . . . . Jul 1972

Watson, Mr Antony Edward Douglas (Q.C.) . . . . . I . . . . Nov 1968
Miller, Mr Richard Hugh (Q.C.) . . . . M. . . . . Jul 1976
Waugh, Mr Andrew Peter (Q.C.) . . . . G. . . . . Jul 1982
Burkill, Mr Guy Alexander (Q.C.) . . . . M. . . . Feb 1981
Turner, Dr Justin John (Q.C.) . . . . M. . . . Nov 1992
McFarland, Miss Denise . . . . I . . . . . Jul 1987
Campbell, Mr Douglas James; Recorder . . . . . . I . . . . . Oct 1993
Mitcheson, Mr Thomas George . . . . I . . . . Nov 1996
Hinchliffe, Mr Thomas. . . . . M. . . . . Oct 1997
Malynicz, Mr Simon. . . . . I . . . . . Oct 1997
Pritchard, Mr Geoffrey . . . . M. . . . Nov 1998
Hughes, Dr Dominic Wyndham . . . . G. . . . . Jul 2001
Copeland, Mr Miles J S. . . . . L. . . . . Oct 2004
Delaney, Mr Joe . . . . M. . . . . Oct 2006
Heald, Mr Jeremy. . . . . M. . . . Jan 2010
Howard, Ms Katrina* . . . . G. . . . Jan 2009

Patents, Copyright, Design, Intellectual Property. Trade Marks, Passing Off, Computer Law, Product Licences Licensing, Confidential Information & Arbitration related European Economic Community Law, Professional Negligence, Mediation.

Chambers of Jeremy Hugh Stuart-Smith QC

FOUR NEW SQUARE,
LINCOLN'S INN, LONDON WC2A 3RJ
Tel: 020 7822 2000 ***Fax:*** 020 7822 2001
Dx: 1041 LONDON/CHANCERY LANE
E-mail: barristers@4newsquare.com
Clerk: Lizzy Wiseman.
Head of Chambers:
Stuart-Smith, Mr Jeremy Hugh (Q.C.) . . . . G. . . . . Jul 1978

Powell, Mr John Lewis (Q.C.) . . . . M. . . . . Jul 1974
Davidson, Mr Nicholas Ranking (Q.C.) . . . . I . . . . . Jul 1974
Fenwick, Mr Justin (Q.C.). . . . . I . . . . Nov 1980
Stewart, Mr Roger (Q.C.) . . . . I . . . . . Jul 1986
Soole, Mr Michael (Q.C.) . . . . I . . . . . Jul 1977
Eklund, Mr Graham (Q.C.) . . . . I . . . . May 1984
Lawrence, Mr Patrick John Tristram (Q.C.) . . . . . I . . . . Feb 1985
Monty, Mr Simon (Q.C.). . . . . I . . . . . Jul 1982
Carr, Miss Sue (Q.C.). . . . . M. . . . . Jul 1982
Sears, Mr David (Q.C.) . . . . M. . . . Nov 1984
Halpern, Mr David (Q.C.) . . . . G. . . . . Jul 1978
Cannon, Mr Mark (Q.C.) . . . . M. . . . . Jul 1985
McPherson, Mr Graeme (Q.C.) . . . . G. . . . Nov 1993
Hubble, Mr Ben (Q.C.) . . . . M. . . . Nov 1992
Turner, Mr David (Q.C.). . . . . G. . . . Nov 1992
Mulcahy, Miss Leigh-Ann Maria (Q.C.) . . . . I . . . . . Oct 1993
Patten, Mr Benedict Joseph (Q.C.) . . . . M. . . . . Jul 1986
Asif, Mr Jalil (Q.C.) . . . . L. . . . Nov 1988
Bacon, Mr Nicholas M (Q.C.) . . . . I . . . . . Oct 1992
Lomnicka, Miss Eva . . . . M. . . . . Jul 1974
Douthwaite, Mr Charles. . . . . G. . . . . Jul 1977
Tyrell, Mr Glen . . . . I . . . . . Jul 1977
Mew, Mr Graeme . . . . I . . . . . Jul 1982
Parker, Mr Paul . . . . M. . . . . Jul 1986
Evans, Mr Hugh . . . . M. . . . Nov 1987
Sinclair, Miss Fiona . . . . I . . . . . Jul 1989
Burroughs, Mr Nigel . . . . M. . . . . Apr 1991
Nicol, Mr Andrew R . . . . I . . . . Nov 1991
Phipps, Mr Charles . . . . M. . . . Nov 1992
Sutherland, Mr Paul. . . . . M. . . . Nov 1992
Bijlani, Dr Aisha. . . . . M. . . . Nov 1993
Shaldon, Miss Nicola . . . . M. . . . . Oct 1994
Sandells, Miss Nicole . . . . I . . . . Nov 1994
Smith, Mr Jamie . . . . L. . . . . Oct 1995
Hext, Mr Neil . . . . G. . . . . Oct 1995
Day, Miss Anneliese . . . . I . . . . . Oct 1996
Elkington, Mr Ben. . . . . G. . . . . Oct 1996
Gilmore, Miss Seanin. . . . . G. . . . Nov 1996
Hall Taylor, Mr Alex . . . . I . . . . . Oct 1996
Mirchandani, Ms Sian. . . . . I . . . . . Oct 1997
Bowmer, Mr Michael . . . . M. . . . . Oct 1997
Hough, Mr Jonathan . . . . M. . . . . Oct 1997
Chapman, Mr Graham . . . . I . . . . . Oct 1998
Mallalieu, Mr Roger. . . . . M. . . . Nov 1998
Liddell, Mr Richard . . . . M. . . . Nov 1999
Savage, Ms Amanda . . . . M. . . . Nov 1999
Innes, Mr Stephen . . . . G. . . . . Oct 2000
Allen, Mr Scott . . . . I . . . . Nov 2000
Feldschreiber, Dr Peter . . . . I . . . . Aug 2000
Evans, Miss Helen . . . . M. . . . Aug 2001
Troman, Mr Carl . . . . L. . . . . Jul 2001
Shaw, Miss Annabel . . . . G. . . . . Jul 2002
Dixon, Miss Claire Elizabeth . . . . G. . . . Nov 2002
Harris, Mr Miles. . . . . G. . . . . Oct 2003
Chelmick, Mr Timothy. . . . . L. . . . Jan 2004
Spalton, Mr George. . . . . L. . . . Jan 2004

McGurk, Dr Brendan . . . . M. . . . Jan 2004
Jones, Ms Emilie . . . . M. . . . Jan 2005
Wood, Mr Benjamin. . . . . L. . . . Jan 2005
O'Brien, Mr Richard. . . . . L. . . . Jan 2005
Powell, Ms Katie . . . . M. . . . Jan 2005
Patel, Shail . . . . I . . . . Jan 2006
McDonald, Mr George . . . . L. . . . Jan 2007
Asquith, Mr Tom . . . . L. . . . Jan 2007
Yeginsu, Can . . . . I . . . . Jan 2007
Saoul, Mr Daniel . . . . L. . . . Jan 2008
Colter, Lucy. . . . . L. . . . Jan 2008
Martin, Josephine. . . . . L. . . . Jan 2008
Ogden, Mr Thomas. . . . . L. . . . Jan 2008

Chambers of Mark Platts Mills QC

8 NEW SQUARE,
LINCOLN'S INN, LONDON WC2A 3QP
Tel: 020 7405 4321 ***Fax:*** 020 7405 9955
Dx: 379 LONDON/CHANCERY LANE
E-mail: clerks@8newsquare.co.uk
Clerk: John Call (Senior); Tony Liddon (Deputy); Nicholas Wise (Practice Manager); Martin Williams (Practice Manager); Ben Newham; Paul Worrall; Sean Manley.
Administrator: Furhana Mallick (Business Development Manager)
Head of Chambers:
Platts Mills, Mr Mark (Q.C.) . . . . I . . . . . Jul 1974

Prescott, Mr Peter R K (Q.C.). . . . . L. . . . Nov 1970
Baldwin, Dr John (Q.C.). . . . . G. . . . . Jul 1977
Howe, Mr Martin (Q.C.) . . . . M. . . . . Jul 1978
Alexander, Mr Daniel (Q.C.). . . . . M. . . . . Jul 1988
Mellor, Mr James (Q.C.) . . . . M. . . . . Jul 1986
Meade, Mr Richard (Q.C.) . . . . L. . . . Nov 1991
Tappin, Dr Michael (Q.C.). . . . . M. . . . . Oct 1991
Hamer, Mr George . . . . G. . . . Nov 1974
Clark, Miss Fiona . . . . M. . . . . Jul 1982
Onslow, Mr Robert . . . . L. . . . . Oct 1991
Speck, Mr Adrian . . . . G. . . . . Oct 1993
Lykiarpoulos, Mr Andrew . . . . M. . . . . Oct 2004
St Ville, Mr James . . . . G. . . . . Oct 1995
May, Miss Charlotte. . . . . I . . . . Nov 1995
Moody-Stuart, Mr Thomas . . . . M. . . . Nov 1995
Lane, Ms Lindsay. . . . . M. . . . . Oct 1996
Abrahams, Mr James. . . . . G. . . . . Oct 1997
Chacksfield, Mr Mark Andrew. . . . . M. . . . . Oct 1999
Berkeley, Miss Iona Sarah . . . . M. . . . . Oct 1999
Hill, Mr Jonathon Bron . . . . L. . . . . Oct 2000
Ward, Mr Henry. . . . . M. . . . Nov 2000
Bowhill, Miss Jessie. . . . . G. . . . . Oct 2003
Whyte, Mr James. . . . . L. . . . . Oct 2005
Jamal, Isabel . . . . L. . . . Jan 2008

Chambers of John R Gardiner QC

11 NEW SQUARE,
LINCOLN'S INN, LONDON WC2A 3QB
Tel: 020 7242 4017 ***Fax:*** 020 7831 2391
Dx: 315 LONDON/CHANCERY LANE
E-mail: clerks@11newsquare.com
Web: www.11newsquare.com
Clerk: Senior: John Moore. Junior: John Casey.
Practice Manager: John Moore
Head of Chambers:
Gardiner, Mr John R (Q.C.) . . . . M. . . . Nov 1968

Peacock, Mr Jonathan David (Q.C.). . . . . M. . . . . Jul 1987
Fitzpatrick, Mr Francis . . . . I . . . . Nov 1990
Maugham, Jolyon. . . . . M. . . . Mar 1997
Walford, Mr Philip. . . . . L. . . . Jan 2003
Brinsmead-Stockham, Mr John . . . . M. . . . . Oct 2005
Ripley, Mr Michael . . . . L. . . . Jan 2008

This Chambers specialises exclusively in revenue law and duties offering tax planning advice, resolution of tax disputes and advocacy from Tribunal level to the Supreme Court.

Chambers of Robin Hollington QC

NEW SQUARE CHAMBERS,
12 NEW SQUARE, LINCOLN'S INN, LONDON WC2A 3SW
Tel: 020 7419 8000 ***Fax:*** 020 7419 8050
Dx: 1056 LONDON/CHANCERY LANE
E-mail: clerks@newsquarechambers.co.uk
Web: www.newsquarechambers.co.uk
Clerk: Senior: Clive Petchey. Juniors: Neil Garrett; Phil Reeves. Michelle Greene; Daniel Westerman.
Practice Manager: Kerry McLean
Head of Chambers:
Hollington, Mr Robin (Q.C.) . . . . L. . . . . Jul 1979

Macdonald, Mr John (Q.C.). . . . . L. . . . Jun 1955
Laurence, Mr George F (Q.C.) . . . . M. . . . Nov 1972
Mathew, Mr Robin (Q.C.) . . . . L. . . . Nov 1974
Smith, Mr Stephen (Q.C.). . . . . M. . . . . Jul 1983
Cawson, Mr Mark (Q.C.); Recorder* . . . . L. . . . . Jul 1982
Thom, Mr James (Q.C.); Recorder . . . . L. . . . Nov 1974
Le Poidevin, Mr Nicholas (Q.C.). . . . . M. . . . Nov 1975
Levy, Mr Robert (Q.C.) . . . . M. . . . Nov 1988
Stewart Smith, Mr Rodney W . . . . M. . . . Jun 1964
Kennedy, Mr Michael . . . . M. . . . . Jul 1967
Ross Martyn, Mr John Greaves . . . . M. . . . . Oct 1969
Buckley, Prof Richard* . . . . I . . . . . Oct 1969
Sterling, Robert* . . . . G. . . . . Jul 1970
Tucker, Mr Lynton A . . . . L. . . . Feb 1971
Braham, Mr Colin. . . . . M. . . . Nov 1971
Munro, Mr Kenneth S. . . . . I . . . . Nov 1973
Bennett, Mr Gordon. . . . . G. . . . Feb 1974
Chapple, Mr Malcolm Dundas. . . . . G. . . . Nov 1975

Name	Inn	Called
Semken, Mr Christopher	L	Jul 1977
Hill-Smith, Mr Alexander George Levander; Immigration adjudicator	G	Oct 1978
Birch, Mr Roger*	G	Nov 1979
Jones, Mr Clive Hugh	M	Jul 1981
Sagar, Mr Leigh	L	Jul 1983
Eaton Turner, Mr David	L	Jul 1984
Staddon, Ms Claire	M	Jul 1985
Graham, Mr Thomas	M	Nov 1985
Selwyn Sharpe, Mr Richard*	L	Nov 1985
Fisher, Mr David	L	Nov 1985
Crail, Miss Ross	L	Jul 1986
Holbech, Mr Charles Edward	L	Jul 1988
Schaw Miller, Mr Stephen	I	Nov 1988
Peacock, Mr Ian	G	Oct 1990
Van Tonder, Mr Gerard	M	Nov 1990
Simpson, Mr Edwin	L	Nov 1990
Adamyk, Mr Simon	L	Nov 1991
Hubbard, Mr Mark Iain	M	Nov 1991
Eidinow, Mr John Samuel	M	Nov 1992
Evans-Gordon, Ms Jane	I	Nov 1992
Hood, Mr Nigel Anthony	I	Oct 1993
Prentis, Mr Sebastian	M	Oct 1996
Pryce, Mr Gary D	L	Oct 1997
Bailey, Mr James; Barrister	G	Mar 1999
Pay, Mr Adrian	M	Nov 1999
Learmonth, Mr Alexander Robert Magnus	L	Oct 2000
Brightwell, Mr James	L	Nov 2000
Allsop, Ms Nicola	L	Jul 2002
White, Ms Shelley*	M	Oct 2003
Akkouh, Mr Tim	L	Jul 2004
Pringle, Mr Watson	I	Jul 2005
Gillet, Ms Emily	L	Oct 2005
Ford, Miss Charlotte Jennifer	L	Oct 2007
Littler, Miss Anna	L	Jan 2008
Wright, Mr Caley Denis Alastair	L	Jul 2008

NO 3 FLEET STREET CHAMBERS,
LONDON EC4Y 1DP

Tel: 020 7936 4474 ***Fax:*** 020 7936 4473
Dx: 398 LONDON/CHANCERY LANE
Clerk: Senior: Lee Parkes. Dean Fenlon (1st Junior).

Name	Inn	Called
Kelly, Mr Eamonn	I	Oct 1997
Mustakim, Mr Al	L	May 1997
Fitzgerald, Mr John V	M	Jul 1971
Kime, Mr Matthew	G	Jul 1988
Harris, Mr Lee	I	Jan 1997
Rogers, Miss Christy	M	Nov 1999
Rahman, Miss Khadiua	I	Jan 2000
Itari Wills, Miss Alexandra	I	Jan 2000
Vernon, Mr Elliot	L	Oct 2001
Gibbon, Miss Zoe	I	Jan 2009
Mohammad, Mr Nazar	G	Jan 2008

Chambers of Paul Bleasdale QC

NO5 CHAMBERS,
76 SHOE LANE, LONDON EC4A 3JB

Tel: 0845 210 5555 ***Fax:*** 020 7240 9458
Dx: 449 LONDON/CHANCERY LANE
E-mail: info@no5.com
Practice Manager: P Hawkins; R Woods; G Smith; A Trotter; M Hulbert; J Parks; A Hafeez; J Luckman; Z Owen; A Bisbey
Chambers Director: Tony McDaid
Head of Chambers:

Name	Inn	Called
Bleasdale, Mr Paul (Q.C.); Recorder	I	Jul 1978
Tedd, Mr Rex (Q.C.); Deputy High Court Judge; Recorder	I	Feb 1970
Dove, Mr Ian (Q.C.); Deputy High Court Judge; Recorder	I	Jul 1986
Tucker, Sir Richard (Q.C.)*	L	Jan 1954
Smith, Mr Antony (Q.C.)	I	Jan 1958
Wolton, Mr Harry (Q.C.)*	G	Dec 1969
Barker, Mr Anthony (Q.C.); Recorder	M	Dec 1966
Kingston, Mr Martin (Q.C.)	M	Apr 1972
Hotten, Mr Christopher (Q.C.); Recorder	I	Nov 1972
Evans, Mr Gareth R W (Q.C.); Recorder	G	Nov 1973
Jones, Mr Richard Henry (Q.C.); Recorder	I	Nov 1972
Gill, Mr Manjit (Q.C.)	G	Jul 1982
Cahill, Mr Jeremy (Q.C.)	M	Jul 1975
Hunjan, Satinder P S (Q.C.); Deputy High Court Judge; Recorder	G	Jul 1984
Howker, Mr David Thomas (Q.C.)	I	Jul 1982
Armstrong, Mr Douglas (Q.C.)*	I	Jan 1999
Meyer, Miss Lorna (Q.C.)	I	Jul 1986
Crean, Mr Anthony (Q.C.)	G	Jul 1987
Humphreys, Mr Richard (Q.C.)	I	Jul 1986
Burrows, Mr Michael (Q.C.); Recorder	I	Nov 1979
Bright, Mr Christopher (Q.C.); Recorder	G	Nov 1985
Anderson, Mr Mark (Q.C.); Recorder	M	Jul 1983
Mason, Mr David (Q.C.); Recorder	I	Jul 1986
Lock, Mr David (Q.C.)	G	Nov 1985
Drew, Mr Simon (Q.C.)	I	Nov 1987
Duck, Mr Michael (Q.C.)	G	Nov 1988
Keeling, Mr Adrian (Q.C.)	I	Oct 1990
West, Mr John R	M	Dec 1965
Bermingham, Mr Gerald	G	Feb 1967
Smith, Mr Roger H T	G	Nov 1968
Harvey, Mr John Gilbert; Recorder	G	Jan 1973
Whitaker, Mr Stephen	L	Nov 1970
Dooley, Mr Allan; Recorder; Deputy District Judge	L	Apr 1970
Arnold, Mr Peter	L	Jul 1972
Cliff, Mr Graham Hilton; Recorder	I	Jul 1973
Jones, Mr Timothy	I	Jul 1975
Worlock, Mr Simon	M	Jul 1975
Giles, Mr Roger S	G	Jul 1976
Bealby, Mr Walter	M	Jul 1976
Henson, Mr Graham	G	Jul 1976
Smallwood, Ms Anne E	M	Nov 1977
Iles, Mr David	I	Jul 1977
James, Mr Christopher	G	Nov 1977
Rowland, Mr Robin Frank; Recorder	M	Nov 1977
Pusey, Mr William James	I	Nov 1977
O'Donovan, Mr Kevin	M	Jul 1978
Michael, Mr Simon	M	Nov 1978
Morgan, Ms Adrienne	G	Nov 1978
Korn, Mr Anthony	G	Nov 1978
Keogh, Mr Andrew	I	Nov 1978
Brough, Mr Alasdair	G	Jul 1979
Cairnes, Mr Paul	G	Oct 1980
Newman, Mr Timothy	G	Jul 1981
Brown, Miss Stephanie	L	Jul 1982
Thompson, Mr Howard Neil	L	Jul 1982
Campbell, Mr Stephen; Recorder	M	Jul 1982
McGrath, Mr Andrew J	G	Jul 1983
Maccabe, Mr Irvine	G	Nov 1983
de Mello, Ramby	L	Feb 1983
Sharif, Ms Nadia J	L	Nov 1985
Moat, Mr Richard	L	Jul 1985
Kelly, Mr Mark	G	Nov 1985
Bell, Mr Anthony	I	Jan 1985
Bailey, Mr Russell	I	Nov 1985
Barrett, Mr Kevin	M	Jan 1985
Thorogood, Mr Bernard; Recorder	G	Jul 1986
Heywood, Mr Mark	G	Jul 1986
Leigh, Mr Kevin	L	Nov 1986
Wignall, Mr Gordon; Part Time Employment Tribunal Chairman	G	Oct 1987
O'Brien, Mr Michael	M	Jan 1987
Hickey, Mr Eugene	L	Jul 1988
Baker, Mrs Caroline; Deputy District Judge	G	Jul 1988
Chadwick, Miss Joanna	M	Nov 1988
Tiwana, Mr Ekwall Singh	M	Jan 1988
Bridge, Mr Ian	I	Nov 1988
Wallace, Mr Andrew	G	Nov 1988
Birk, Miss Dewinder	L	Jul 1988
Duthie, Mr Malcolm	I	Jul 1989
Bedford, Mr Becket	M	Nov 1989
Bell, Mr Gary	I	Feb 1989
Liddiard, Mr Martin	I	Nov 1989
Murray, Miss Carole*	M	Nov 1989
Hanson, Mr Timothy*	I	Jan 1989
Attwood, Mr John	G	Nov 1989
Phillips, Ms Moira	G	Jan 1989
Anning, Mr Michael	I	Nov 1990
Wynne, Ashley	G	Nov 1990
Baker, Mr Andrew	M	Oct 1990
Mann, Mr Jasvir	M	Jan 1990
Boora, Mr Jinder	G	Oct 1990
McDonald, Mrs Melanie	G	Jan 1990
Radburn, Mr Mark Charles Crispin	L	Oct 1991
Friel, Miss Michele E	L	Jul 1991
Buckingham, Miss Sarah J	I	Oct 1991
Grant, Mr Edward*	I	Nov 1991
Al-Rashid, Mr Mahmud	G	Jul 1991
Park, Mr David	L	Jul 1992
Goatley, Mr Peter	I	Jul 1992
Xydias, Mr Nicholas	L	Oct 1992
Wilkinson, Mr Marc	L	Oct 1992
Preston, Ms Nicola	L	Jul 1992
Richards, Mr Hugh	I	Nov 1992
Hansen, Mr William; Deputy Adjudicator to HM Land Registry	L	Nov 1992
Brockley, Mr Nigel	L	Nov 1992
Farrer, Mr Adam	G	Sep 1992
Bailey, Mr Steven	M	Oct 1992
Joseph, Mr Paul	I	Oct 1992
Mahmood, Mr Abid	I	Oct 1992
Ismail, Miss Nazmun	L	May 1992
Mallick, Miss Nabila	G	Oct 1992
Bazini, Mr Danny	G	Nov 1992
Taylor, Mr David; Deputy Adjudicator to HM Land Registry	L	Nov 1993
Clover, Ms Sarah	L	Nov 1993
Sumeray, Ms Caroline	M	Jan 1993
Bradley, Mr Phillip	L	Nov 1993
Bains, Ms Param Kaur	I	Oct 1993
Dutta, Miss Nandini	M	Feb 1993
Rothwell, Miss Joanne	I	Oct 1993
Nicholson, Mr Edward	M	Nov 1993
Edhem, Miss Emma	G	Oct 1993
Price, Miss Rachael	I	Nov 1994
Smallwood, Mr Robert	I	Nov 1994
Cotter, Miss Rachel	M	Nov 1994
Potter, Mr Anthony	G	Jul 1994
Collie, Mr Peter	M	Nov 1994
Choongh, Dr Satnam*	L	Apr 1994
Jones, Mr Jonathan	L	Oct 1994
Fox, Dr Simon	I	Jan 1994
Khalique, Miss Nageena	G	Oct 1994
Tyack, Mr David	M	Nov 1994
Renouf, Mr Mark*	I	Oct 1994
Dean, Mr Brian	G	Nov 1994
Stoll, Mr James	I	Nov 1994
Diamond, Miss Anna	G	Nov 1995
Mitchell, Mr David	L	Oct 1995
Sheppard, Mr Tim	I	Nov 1995
Hignett, Mr Richard	I	Nov 1995
Kershaw, Mr Dean	L	Oct 1995
Butterfield, Mr John Arthur	I	Oct 1995
Monaghan, Ms Susan	I	Oct 1995
Wright, Mr Jeremy*	I	Oct 1996
Hogan, Miss Emma	L	Oct 1996
Hancox, Ms Sally	L	Nov 1996
Jones, Mrs Cheryl S; Deputy District Judge	G	Oct 1996
Pitchers, Mr Henry	I	Nov 1996
Power, Ms Elizabeth	I	Jan 1996
Case, Mr Richard	M	Oct 1996
Holloway, Mr David	G	Jul 1996
Davidson, Ms Laura	L	Oct 1996
Bagral, Miss Ravinder	L	Oct 1996
Knotts, Miss Carol	L	Nov 1996
Hirst, Mr Karl	I	Oct 1997
Young, Mr Christopher	M	Oct 1997
Hadley, Mr Richard	G	Oct 1997
Lally, Mr Harbinder Singh	L	Jan 1997
Brunning, Mr Matthew	M	Nov 1997
Chatterjee, Miss Adreeja Julia	G	Nov 1997
Compton, Mr Gareth	M	Mar 1997
Rowley, Miss Rachel	M	Nov 1997
Singh, Mr Talbir	G	Jan 1997
Stein, Mr Alexander	G	Jul 1998
Kimblin, Mr Richard	M	Jul 1998
Derrington, Mr Jonathan	I	Oct 1998
Brown, Miss Kristina	G	Oct 1998
Gamble, Mr Jamie	M	Nov 1999
Denning, Ms Louisa	G	Nov 1999
Hargreaves, Ms Teresa	L	Nov 1999
Crow, Mr Charles	L	Nov 1999
Coughlan, Mr John	M	Nov 1999
Price, Mr Charles	M	Nov 1999
Barney, Miss Helen	L	Jan 1999
Butt, Miss Nassera	M	Jul 1999
Afzal, Dr Fayyaz OBE; Doctorate	L	Jan 1999
Chelvan, S	I	Oct 1999
Willets, Mr Glenn	M	Nov 2000
Chawla, Mr Neil	I	Jan 2000
Wigley, Miss Jenny	M	Nov 2000
Ensaff, Mr Omar Sherif	G	Oct 2000
Abberley, Mr Stephen	M	Nov 2000
Evans, Mr Paul	I	Jan 2001
Heeley, Ms Michelle	G	Jan 2001
Beloff, Mr Rupert	G	Jan 2001
Forster, Ms Bridget	I	Jan 2001
Brown, Ms Emma	I	Jan 2001
Wingrave, Mr Michael	M	Jul 2001
Pole, Mr Tim	M	Jul 2001
Schofield, Mr Thomas	L	Oct 2001
Chaffin-Laird, Miss Olivia	G	Jul 2001
Adkinson, Mr Richard	M	Jul 2001
Dixon, Mr James	L	Jan 2001
Mantle, Mr Philip	L	Jan 2002
Clifford, Miss Victoria	G	Jul 2002
Bradshaw, Mr Mark	G	Jul 2002
Kurji, Miss Fatim*	I	Jan 2003
Arthur, Mrs Helen	M	Oct 2003
Oscroft, Mr Daniel	M	Nov 2003
Pinnock, Mr Earl	M	Nov 2003
Owen, Miss Denise	G	Oct 2003
van Overdijk, Mrs Claire	L	Jan 2003
Cobill, Mr Nicholas	M	Jan 2003
Deacon, Ms Jennifer*	I	Jul 2004
Davies, Mr Rhys	G	Oct 2004
Gupta, Miss Mamta	L	Oct 2004
Leslie, Mr James	M	Jan 2004
Williams, Mr Philip	I	Apr 2005
Allen, Miss Sarah	G	Nov 2005
Punt, Dr Jonathan	I	Jul 2005
Cooke, Mr Richard	I	Jul 2005
Grant, Miss Orla	I	Jul 2005
Sandhu, Mr Harpreet Singh	G	Jul 2005
Reed, Mr Steven	I	Jul 2005
Fernandes, Ms Suella	M	Oct 2005
Allen, Miss Juliet	G	Nov 2005
Taylor, Miss Kathryn	I	Jul 2005
Feeney, Miss Katie	I	Jul 2005
Yasseri, Miss Yasmin	I	Jul 2005
Tyers-Smith, Mr Peter	L	Nov 2005
Feeny, Mr Jack	I	Jan 2005
Roberts, Miss Gemma	G	Oct 2006
Enonchong, Prof Nelson	I	Jan 2006
Yates, Miss Victoria	M	Nov 2006
Gallacher, Kirsty	G	Nov 2006
Hunka, Mr Simon	M	Jul 2007
Smyth, Mr Jack	M	Oct 2007
Oakes, Mr Richard	M	Oct 2007
Meager, Ms Rowena	L	Jul 2007
Pye, Mr Derek	L	Jul 2008
Corfield, Miss Louise	I	Oct 2008
Williams, Hermione	M	Jan 2008
Osmund-Smith, Miss Thea	I	Jan 2010

OLD BAILEY CHAMBERS,
15 OLD BAILEY, LONDON EC4M 7EF

Tel: 020 3008 6404 / 07787 543659 ***Fax:*** 020 3008 6405
Dx: 157380 OLD BAILEY 3
E-mail: clerks@15oldbaileychambers.com

Chambers of Martin Mann QC and Alan Steinfeld QC

XXIV OLD BUILDINGS,
GROUND FLOOR, 24 OLD BUILDINGS,
LINCOLN'S INN, LONDON WC2A 3UP

Tel: 020 7691 2424 ***Fax:*** 0870 460 2178
Dx: 307 LONDON/CHANCERY LANE
E-mail: clerks@xxiv.co.uk
Clerk: Paul Matthews; Daniel Wilson; Martyn Nicholls; James Ladbrook.
Administrator: Kathryn Williams
Practice Manager: Nicholas Luckman (Practice Director)
Head of Chambers:

Name	Inn	Called
Mann, Mr Martin (Q.C.)	G	Jul 1968
Steinfeld, Mr Alan (Q.C.)	L	Nov 1968
Black, Mr Michael (Q.C.)	M	Feb 1978
Moverley Smith, Mr Stephen (Q.C.)	M	Feb 1985
Shepherd, Mr Philip (Q.C.)	G	Nov 1975
Tregear, Mr Francis (Q.C.)	M	Jul 1980
Brownbill, Mr David John (Q.C.)	I	Jul 1989
Talbot Rice, Mrs Elspeth (Q.C.)	L	Oct 1990
King, Mr Michael	G	Jul 1971
Stephens, Mr John Lewis	M	Jul 1975
Ritchie, Mr Richard	M	Jul 1978
Gadd, Mr Michael	L	Jul 1981
Weaver, Miss Elizabeth	L	Jul 1982
Galley, Mrs Helen	G	Jul 1987
Harington, Miss Amanda	L	Jul 1989
Meakin, Mr Ian	G	Nov 1991
Ghaffar, Mr Arshad	M	Oct 1991
Staff, Mr Marcus	I	Oct 1994
Adair, Mr Stuart Anthony	I	Oct 1995
Pelling, Mr Alexander	M	Oct 1995
Shah, Mr Bajul	L	Oct 1996
Thompson, Mr Steven	I	Oct 1996
Hughes, Mrs Jessica	L	Jan 1997
Langlois, Mrs Nicole	L	May 2008
de Mestre, Ms Lyndsey	L	Nov 1999
Knight, Mr Edward	L	Nov 1999
Herbert, Mr David	M	Jan 2000
Montagu-Smith, Mr Tom	L	Oct 2001

Bayliss, Miss Sarah . . . M . . . Oct 2002
McLarnon, Mr Neil . . . L . . . Jan 2004
Cloherty, Mr Adam . . . L . . . Jan 2005
Cumming, Mr Edward . . . L . . . Jan 2006
Hitchens, Miss Erin . . . L . . . Jan 2006
Holden, Mr Andrew . . . I . . . Nov 2007
Murphy, Heather . . . L . . . Jan 2009
Sharpe, Mr Harry . . . M . . . Jan 2010
Curry, Owen . . . L . . . Oct 2010
Warrents, Daniel . . . L . . . Oct 2010

Chambers of Leolin Price QC

TEN OLD SQUARE,
LINCOLN'S INN, LONDON WC2A 3SU
Tel: 020 7405 0758 ***Fax:*** 020 7831 8237
Dx: 306 LONDON/CHANCERY LANE
E-mail: clerks@tenoldsquare.com
Web: www.tenoldsquare.com
Clerk: Senior: Keith Plowman.
Head of Chambers:
Price, Mr Leolin (Q.C.) CBE . . . M . . . Nov 1949

Taube, Mr Simon (Q.C.) . . . M . . . Jul 1980
Barlow, Mr Francis (Q.C.) . . . I . . . Feb 1965
Rajah, Mr Eason (Q.C.) . . . G . . . Jul 1989
Ainger, Mr David . . . L . . . Jun 1961
Hill, Mr Gregory . . . L . . . Jul 1972
Wallington, Mr Richard . . . M . . . Jul 1972
Schmitz, Mr David Reuben; Mediator . . . L . . . Nov 1976
Stafford, Dr Paul . . . G . . . Nov 1987
Meadway, Miss Susannah . . . M . . . Jul 1988
Callman, Mr Jeremy . . . M . . . Oct 1991
Gavaghan, Mr Jonathan . . . L . . . Nov 1992
Laughton, Mr Samuel . . . M . . . Feb 1992
Farrelly, Mr Kevin . . . M . . . May 1993
Waterworth, Mr Michael Christopher . . . L . . . Oct 1994
Arnfield, Mr Robert . . . I . . . Oct 1996
Price, Mr Evan . . . M . . . Oct 1997
Dew, Mr Richard J . . . I . . . Oct 1999
Bedworth, Miss Georgia Selina . . . M . . . Jul 2001
Beer, Ms Julia . . . G . . . Jul 2003
Boutle, Mr Toby . . . L . . . Jul 2004
Winston, Miss Naomi . . . M . . . Jan 2006
Roseman, Mr Gideon . . . I . . . Jul 2007
Pickering, Mr Leon . . . L . . . Jul 2010
Mello, Mr Michael J (Q.C.)* . . . G . . . Jul 1972
Burton, Mrs Frances* . . . I . . . Nov 1972
Arbuthnot, Rt Hon James MP* . . . L . . . Jul 1975
Walker, Mr Andrew Greenfield; Mediator* . . . L . . . Jul 1975
Montgomery, Prof John Warwick* . . . M . . . Oct 1984
Roberts, Dr Julian* . . . L . . . Jul 1987

Work Description: Specialist Chancery chambers dealing with a wide range of trust, tax, property, partnership and commercial matters.

Chambers of Charlotte Boaitey

12 OLD SQUARE,
1ST FLOOR & GROUND FLOOR, LINCOLN'S INN, LONDON WC2A 3TX
Tel: 020 7404 0875 ***Fax:*** 020 7404 8377
Dx: 130 LONDON/CHANCERY LANE
E-mail: stevenrussell@btconnect.com
Clerk: Steven Russell.
Head of Chambers:
Boaitey, Mrs Charlotte . . . I . . . Nov 1976

Malhotra, Miss Mehtab . . . L . . . Oct 1996
Offeh, Mr John . . . I . . . Nov 1969
Waithe, Mr John . . . I . . . Jul 1972
Ume, Mr Cyril Obiora . . . L . . . Jul 1972
Ndlovu, Mr Lazarus . . . I . . . Jul 1979
Abebrese, Mr Owusu* . . . I . . . Jul 1985
Akwagyiram, Mr Samuel . . . I . . . Nov 1985
Rahman, Mr Anis . . . I . . . Nov 1990
Edwards, Miss Nicola . . . I . . . Nov 1991
Okai, Mr Anthony . . . I . . . Jul 1973
Oke, Lanre . . . L . . . Jun 1979
Adams, Mr Derek; Attorney(New York Bar) . . . M . . . Nov 1988
Solomon, Mr Reuben . . . L . . . Jan 1992
Layne, Mr Ronald . . . L . . . Jan 1992
Desouza, Mrs Josephine Claudia . . . L . . . Nov 1992
Kodagoda, Fritz . . . L . . . Nov 1993
Allen, Frances . . . I . . . Oct 1995
Waheed, Erum . . . L . . . Jan 1995
Jaisri, Shashi . . . L . . . Jan 1995
Brissett, Miss Nicola Luana . . . M . . . Feb 1995
Sher, Miss Shamim . . . L . . . Jun 1995
Ghaffar, Mr Rasib . . . L . . . Jun 1995
Gandhi, Miss Paulene . . . I . . . Oct 1995
Heller, Mrs Anne . . . M . . . Nov 1995
Taylor, Ms Susan . . . L . . . Oct 1996
Love, Miss Sharon Anne . . . G . . . Jan 1997
Muquit, Mr Mohammed Shuyeb . . . I . . . Jan 1998
Morgan, Mr David John . . . M . . . Nov 1998
Dulay, Miss Ranjeet . . . I . . . Jan 1999
Anyene, Eleazar . . . L . . . Oct 1999
Bonsu, Miss Michaela . . . L . . . Jan 2000
Manyarara, Miss Natsai . . . G . . . Jul 2001
Jones, Ms Anika . . . G . . . Mar 2002

Chambers of George Rex Bretten QC

15 OLD SQUARE,
LINCOLN'S INN, LONDON WC2A 3UE
Tel: 020 7242 2744 ***Fax:*** 020 7831 8095
Dx: 386 LONDON/CHANCERY LANE
E-mail: taxchambers@15oldsquare.co.uk
Clerk: Anthony Hall.
Head of Chambers:
Bretten, Mr George Rex (Q.C.) . . . L . . . May 1965

Venables, Mr Robert (Q.C.) . . . M . . . Jul 1973
Brandon, Mr Stephen David (Q.C.) . . . G . . . Jul 1978
Lyons, Mr Timothy (Q.C.) . . . I . . . Jul 1980
Kessler, Mr James R (Q.C.) . . . L . . . Jul 1984
Argles, Mr Guy Robert Ainsworth . . . M . . . Nov 1965
Nock, Mr Reginald Stanley . . . L . . . Nov 1968
Sokol, Mr Christopher John Francis . . . L . . . Jul 1975
Hardy, Mrs Amanda . . . M . . . Nov 1993
Mullan, Mr Rory . . . G . . . Jul 2000
Cannon, Mr Patrick . . . G . . . Dec 2003

Chambers of Nigel Cooksley QC and Jane McNeill QC

OLD SQUARE CHAMBERS,
10-11 BEDFORD ROW, LONDON WC1R 4BU
Tel: 020 7269 0300 ***Fax:*** 020 7405 1387
Dx: 1046 LONDON/CHANCERY LANE
E-mail: clerks@oldsquare.co.uk
Clerk: Senior: William Meade. Clerks: Oliver Parkhouse; James Wilkinson; Laurence Willicombe.
Chambers Director: Felicity Schneider (Chambers Manager)
Head of Chambers:
Cooksley, Mr Nigel (Q.C.); Chairman of BAR Council CFA Panel . . . I . . . Jul 1975
McNeill, Ms Jane (Q.C.); Part-Time Employment Tribunal Chair . . . L . . . Nov 1982

Reynold, Mr Frederic (Q.C.); Bencher, Gray's Inn . . . G . . . Jul 1960
Hendy, Mr John (Q.C.); Bencher, Gray's Inn . . . G . . . Jul 1971
Truscott, Mr Ian (Q.C.) . . . G . . . Nov 1995
Wilby, Mr David C (Q.C.); Recorder . . . I . . . Jul 1974
Rose, Mr Paul (Q.C.) . . . G . . . Nov 1981
Gilroy, Mr Paul (Q.C.) . . . G . . . Jul 1985
Eady, Ms Jennifer (Q.C.); Part-Time Employment Tribunal Chair . . . I . . . Jul 1989
Sutton, Mr Mark (Q.C.); Employment Tribunal: Part-time Chairman . . . M . . . Jul 1982
Gorton, Simon (Q.C.) . . . I . . . Jul 1988
Segal, Mr Oliver (Q.C.) . . . M . . . Oct 1992
Upex, Prof Robert . . . M . . . Jul 1973
Bates, Mr John H . . . M . . . Jul 1973
Makey, Mr Christopher . . . M . . . Jul 1975
Pugh, Mr Charles . . . G . . . Jan 1975
Kempster, Mr Toby . . . I . . . Jul 1980
Smith, Mr Alan Arthur . . . M . . . Jul 1981
Chudleigh, Ms Louise; Part-Time Employment Tribunal Chair . . . L . . . Jul 1987
Omambala, Ijeoma . . . G . . . Apr 1989
Mead, Mr Philip . . . L . . . Jul 1989
Gill, Ms Tess; Part-Time Employment Tribunal Chair . . . L . . . Feb 1990
Clarke, Mr Jonathan . . . M . . . Oct 1990
Walker, Mr Christopher D B . . . M . . . Nov 1990
Powell, Mr Giles . . . G . . . Jan 1990
Scott, Mr Ian . . . L . . . Oct 1991
Cheetham, Mr Simon . . . M . . . Nov 1991
Lewis, Prof Roy; Employment Tribunal Part-Time Chairman . . . L . . . May 1992
Ford, Mr Michael . . . M . . . Jul 1992
Cummins, Mr Brian Dominic . . . M . . . Nov 1992
Gower, Ms Helen . . . M . . . Oct 1992
Galloway, Mr Malcolm . . . I . . . Oct 1992
Panesar, Mr Deshpal Singh . . . I . . . Jan 1993
Nicholson, Mr Michael . . . M . . . Jan 1993
Melville, Miss Elizabeth E J . . . G . . . Oct 1994
Howells, Miss Katherine . . . G . . . Oct 1994
Whitcombe, Mr Mark D . . . M . . . Nov 1994
Tether, Ms Melanie . . . G . . . Nov 1995
Smith, Miss Emma . . . L . . . Oct 1995
Pirani, Mr Rohan C . . . M . . . Oct 1995
White, Mr Robin . . . G . . . Oct 1995
Woodhouse, Mr Charles . . . M . . . Oct 1997
Tuck, Miss Rebecca L . . . G . . . Oct 1998
Winstone, Ms Hilary . . . G . . . Oct 1998
Brittenden, Mr Stuart . . . G . . . Jan 1999
Newton, Miss Katharine . . . M . . . Oct 1999
Palmer, Ms Anya . . . I . . . Jan 1999
McDonald, Mr Brent . . . G . . . Oct 2000
Morris, Miss Bella . . . G . . . Oct 2000
Cooper, Mr Ben . . . L . . . Nov 2000
Moretto, Mr Robert Salvatore . . . I . . . Oct 2000
Midgley, Mr Andrew . . . G . . . Oct 2000
Fredman, Prof Sandra . . . G . . . Jan 2002
Rivers, Mr David . . . G . . . Jan 2002
Pilgerstorfer, Mr Marcus . . . M . . . Jan 2002
Criddle, Miss Betsan . . . M . . . Oct 2002
Davies, Mr Jonathan Huw . . . L . . . Jan 2003
Samuel, Mr Adam . . . I . . . Jul 2003
Motraghi, Miss Nadia . . . G . . . Jul 2004
Freman (nee Sampson), Miss Hannah . . . L . . . Jul 2004
Risoli, Mr Andreá . . . G . . . Jan 2005
Cunnington, Mr David . . . L . . . Jan 2005
Edwards, Mr Christopher . . . G . . . Jan 2006
Sparling, Mr Charlie . . . I . . . Jan 2006
Loraine, Miss Kara . . . M . . . Jan 2006
Bowsher-Murray, Miss Claire . . . G . . . Jan 2007
Fudakowski, Katherine . . . L . . . Jan 2008
Newbegin, Miss Nicola . . . M . . . Jan 2009
Webb, Victoria . . . M . . . Jan 2009
Harris, Mr Lance . . . L . . . Jan 2011
Bennett, Hannah . . . M . . . Jan 2011
Cotter, Mr Barry (Q.C.)* . . . L . . . Jul 1985
Carling, Mr Christopher* . . . L . . . Nov 1969
Moor, Ms Sarah* . . . M . . . Oct 1991
Ferguson, Miss Corina* . . . L . . . Jul 2003

Chambers of John McDonnell QC

13 OLD SQUARE CHAMBERS,
13-14 OLD SQUARE, LINCOLN'S INN, LONDON WC2A 3UE
Tel: 020 7831 4445 ***Fax:*** 020 7841 5825
Dx: 52 LONDON/CHANCERY LANE
E-mail: warren@13oldsquare.com
Clerk: Senior: Justin Brown.
Administrator: Warren Lee
Head of Chambers:
McDonnell, Mr John (Q.C.) . . . L . . . Jul 1968

Lowe, Mr David (Q.C.) . . . L . . . Jul 1965
Oliver, The Hon David (Q.C.) . . . L . . . Jul 1972
Bartley Jones, Mr Edward (Q.C.) . . . L . . . Jan 1975
Booth, Mr Michael (Q.C.) . . . L . . . Nov 1981
Castle, Mr Peter . . . M . . . Jan 1970
Lloyd, Mr Stephen . . . M . . . Jul 1971
Jefferis, Mr Michael . . . M . . . Jan 1976
Jarman, Mr Christopher . . . I . . . Jan 1976
Detter, Ms Ingrid; Judge Stockholm High Court; Swedish Immigration Appeal Tribunal . . . G . . . Jul 1978
Bourne, Mr Robert . . . G . . . Jul 1978
Turner, Mr Jonathan . . . G . . . Feb 1982
Vaughan-Williams, Mr Laurence . . . L . . . Oct 1988
Watson-Gandy, Prof Mark . . . I . . . Oct 1990
Maynard-Connor, Mr Giles . . . I . . . Nov 1992
Peat, Mr Richard . . . G . . . Jan 1993
Ludbrook, Mr Timothy . . . I . . . Oct 1996
Perkins, Ms Marianne . . . G . . . Jan 1997
Joseph, Ms Sandradee . . . I . . . Jan 1998
Devereux-Cooke, Mr Richard . . . M . . . Oct 1999
Mohyuddin, Mr David Niaz . . . L . . . Oct 1999
Couser, Mr James . . . L . . . May 2000
Chichester-Clark, Mr Adam . . . M . . . Oct 2000
Olleson, Mr Simon . . . L . . . Jan 2002
Henderson, Mr Duncan . . . L . . . Jan 2003
Sjostrand, Ekaterina . . . I . . . Jan 2003
Lowe, Mr Mungo . . . M . . . Jan 2003
Kokelaar, Mr Sebastian . . . L . . . Jul 2004
Hallett, Ms Katherine . . . L . . . Jul 2006
Burkitt, Mr Daniel . . . G . . . Jan 2008
Knight, Emma . . . L . . . Jul 2008
Smith, Mr Michael . . . I . . . Nov 2008
Miall, Mr Hugh . . . L . . . Jul 2009
Fairpo, Ms Anne . . . G . . . Nov 2009
Hunter, Mr Simon . . . G . . . Nov 2009

Chambers of Philip Charles Mott QC

OUTER TEMPLE CHAMBERS,
THE OUTER TEMPLE, 222 STRAND, LONDON WC2R 1BA
Tel: 020 7353 6381 ***Fax:*** 020 7583 1786
Dx: 351 LONDON/CHANCERY LANE
E-mail: clerks@outertemple.com
Clerk: Derek Jenkins.
Chambers Director: Christine Kings
Head of Chambers:
Mott, Mr Philip Charles (Q.C.) . . . I . . . Jul 1970

Rawley, Mr Alan David (Q.C.) . . . M . . . Jun 1958
Inglis Jones, Mr Nigel John (Q.C.) . . . I . . . Nov 1954
Wilson-Smith, Mr Christopher (Q.C.) . . . G . . . Nov 1965
Rhodes, Mr Robert Elliott (Q.C.) . . . I . . . Jul 1968
Lissack, Mr Richard A (Q.C.) . . . I . . . Nov 1978
McDermott, Mr Gerard Francis (Q.C.) . . . M . . . Jul 1978
Tolson, Mr Robin Stewart (Q.C.) . . . I . . . Nov 1980
Bowes, Mr Michael (Q.C.) . . . M . . . Jul 1980
Bebb, Mr Gordon M (Q.C.) . . . M . . . Nov 1975
Finucane, Mr Brendan Godfrey Eamonn (Q.C.); Recorder . . . M . . . Jul 1976
Westcott, Mr David Guy (Q.C.) . . . M . . . Nov 1982
Spink, Mr Andrew Murray (Q.C.); Recorder . . . M . . . Nov 1985
Short, Mr Andrew (Q.C.) . . . G . . . Nov 1990
Compton, Mr Benjamin (Q.C.); Recorder . . . L . . . Nov 1979
Stallworthy, Mr Nicolas (Q.C.) . . . M . . . Oct 1993
Jenkins, Mr Hywel Iestyn . . . I . . . Jul 1974
Morris, Mr David . . . I . . . Oct 1976
Mawhinney, Mr Richard Martin . . . M . . . Nov 1977
Climie, Mr Stephen . . . L . . . Jul 1982
Haycroft, Mr Anthony Mark . . . M . . . Nov 1982
Jenkins, Mr Alan . . . M . . . Feb 1984
Counsell, Mr James H . . . I . . . Jul 1984
Kemp, Mr Christopher Mark; Recorder . . . M . . . Nov 1984
Sadd, Mr Patrick . . . M . . . Nov 1984
Trusted, Mr Harry . . . I . . . Jul 1985
Aldridge, Mr James . . . I . . . Nov 1987
Mullins, Mr Mark . . . L . . . Nov 1988
Foster, Mr Charles A; Recorder . . . I . . . Oct 1988
McCormick, Ms Alison Claire . . . M . . . Nov 1988
Freeborn, Ms Susan Christine . . . G . . . Jul 1989
Rogers, Mr Paul* . . . I . . . Nov 1989
Hitchcock, Mr Richard Guy . . . M . . . Nov 1989
Leonard, Mr James . . . I . . . Jan 1989
Hand, Mr Jonathan E S . . . I . . . Nov 1990
Hallissey, Ms Caroline . . . I . . . Feb 1990
Leeper, Mr Thomas R G . . . M . . . Nov 1991
Brown, Ms Jillian . . . M . . . Nov 1991
Bryant, Mr Keith . . . M . . . Oct 1991
Nesbitt, Mr Timothy . . . M . . . Feb 1991
Tavares, Mr Nathan W . . . M . . . Oct 1992
Joffe, Ms Natasha . . . G . . . Oct 1992
Vickers, Miss Rachel . . . I . . . Nov 1992
Phillips, Mr Matthew . . . L . . . Nov 1993
Woolf, Mr Eliot C A . . . I . . . Oct 1993
Barnett, Mr Daniel Alexander . . . L . . . Oct 1993
Cunningham, Ms Naomi . . . G . . . Jan 1994
Mukherjee, Abhijeet . . . M . . . Feb 1995
Allen, Mr Andrew . . . I . . . Oct 1995
Burgher, Mr Benjamin . . . G . . . Nov 1995
Jan-Temmink, Mr Robert . . . M . . . Oct 1996
Seymour, Ms Lydia . . . I . . . Oct 1997
Medcroft, Mr Nicholas . . . L . . . Sep 1998
Jerram, Ms Harriet A . . . G . . . Oct 1998
Grant, Mr David E . . . I . . . Mar 1999
McKendrick, Mr John; Part-time Tribunal Judge . . . I . . . Nov 1999
Guthrie, Ms Cara . . . I . . . Jan 2000

10

Presland, Ms Samantha . . . M . . . Jan 2000
Ling, Ms Naomi . . . M . . . Mar 2002
Rickards, Mr James . . . I . . . Mar 2002
Assersohn, Mr Oliver . . . I . . . Jul 2003
Almihdar, Mr Ali . . . M . . . Nov 2003
Davison, Miss Eleanor . . . L . . . Nov 2003
Uberoi, Mr Michael . . . M . . . Jun 2004
Margo, Mr Saul . . . L . . . Oct 2005
Khan, Mr Farhaz . . . M . . . Oct 2005
Edwards, Mrs Kate . . . M . . . Oct 2006
Bradley, Mr Benjamin . . . I . . . Oct 2007
Baker, Ms Clare . . . M . . . Jan 2007
Dickason, Mr Robert James . . . L . . . Jan 2007
Gore, Miss Keira . . . M . . . Jan 2008
Farara, Mr Gerard St Claire* . . . G . . . Jul 1977
Kerins, Mr Charles* . . . M . . . Oct 1984
Moore, Mr Roderick A* . . . I . . . Nov 1993

Chambers of David Hood

90 OVERSTRAND MANSIONS,
PRINCE OF WALES DRIVE, LONDON SW11 4EU
Tel: 020 7622 7415 ***Fax:*** 020 7622 6929
Head of Chambers:
Hood, Mr David . . . I . . . Nov 1980

3PB,
3 PAPER BUILDINGS, TEMPLE, LONDON EC4Y 7EU
Tel: 020 7583 8055 ***Fax:*** 020 7353 6271
Dx: 1024 LDE
E-mail: clerks.all@3paper.co.uk
Clerk: David Phillips (Senior Clerk); Paul Adams; Craig Brown; Simon Lyons; Sam Watson; Jay Carter.
Administrator: Neil Monro (Head of Business Administration and Finance)
Practice Manager: Stephen Evers (Practice Development Clerk)
Chambers Director: Stephen Clark (Head of Clerking); Charles Charlick (Consultant Clerk)
Parroy, Mr Michael (Q.C.); Recorder . . . M . . . Nov 1969
Farley, Mr Roger (Q.C.) . . . M . . . May 1974
Vere-Hodge, Mr Michael (Q.C.); Recorder . . . G . . . Nov 1970
Jones, Mr Stewart E (Q.C.); Recorder . . . G . . . Nov 1972
Braslavsky, Mr Nicholas (Q.C.); Recorder . . . I . . . Jul 1983
Bromley-Davenport, Mr John (Q.C.) . . . G . . . Feb 1972
Wood, Mr Graham (Q.C.)* . . . M . . . Jul 1979
Lawrie, Mr Ian (Q.C.); Recorder . . . G . . . Nov 1985
Parrish, Mr Samuel . . . I . . . Feb 1962
Solomon, Miss Susan . . . M . . . Jul 1967
Aylwin, Mr Christopher . . . I . . . Nov 1970
Jennings, Mr Peter N . . . M . . . Jul 1972
Stephenson, Mr Benedict . . . L . . . Jul 1973
Leviseur, Mr Nicholas T . . . G . . . Nov 1979
Partridge, Mr Ian; Deputy Master . . . I . . . Jul 1979
Hamilton, Mr Gavin . . . G . . . Jul 1979
Edge, Mr Ian . . . M . . . Feb 1981
Marshall, Mr David . . . L . . . Jan 1981
Sampson, Mr Graeme William . . . G . . . Nov 1981
Stancombe, Mr Barry . . . G . . . Jul 1983
Palfrey, Mr Montague . . . M . . . Nov 1985
Whittle-Martin, Miss Lucia . . . M . . . Jan 1985
Opperman, Mr Guy T* . . . M . . . Nov 1989
Aeberli, Mr Peter . . . M . . . Oct 1990
Katrak, Mr Cyrus Pesi . . . G . . . Oct 1991
Bingham, Mr Anthony William . . . L . . . Nov 1992
Musgrave, Ms Kerry . . . M . . . Nov 1992
McIlroy, Mr David . . . I . . . Nov 1995
Wilson, Mr Lachlan . . . I . . . Oct 1996
Davison, Mr James . . . G . . . Jan 1996
Kennedy, Mr Stuart . . . L . . . Oct 1999
Hadfield, Miss Charlotte . . . I . . . Jan 1999
Helmi, Hala* . . . M . . . Jan 2000
Isaacs, Mr Oliver . . . M . . . Jan 2000
Jones, Mr Rupert . . . M . . . Oct 2000
O'Doherty, Mr Paul . . . M . . . Jan 2000
Nicholas, Mr Garvin* . . . I . . . Jan 2001
Cassidy, Miss Sheena . . . I . . . Jan 2001
Chaudary, Ms Ambereen . . . L . . . Jan 2002
Moss, Miss Karen . . . M . . . Jan 2002
Norris, Mr Adam . . . I . . . Jan 2002
Gullick, Mr Mathew . . . G . . . Jan 2003
Demachkie, Mr Jamal . . . I . . . Jan 2004
Stone, Caroline . . . M . . . Jan 2005
MacWhannell, Mr Iain . . . M . . . Jan 2006
Powell, Mr Oliver . . . G . . . Jan 2006
Green, Mr Mark . . . L . . . Jan 2006
Brewin, Mr Carl . . . M . . . Jan 2006
Perfect, Mr Andrew . . . I . . . Jan 2007
O'Donohoe, Mr Thomas . . . L . . . Jan 2007
Paulin, Mr Michael . . . I . . . Jan 2007
Oram, Mr Seb . . . L . . . Jan 2007
Edwards, Mr Christopher . . . L . . . Jan 2008
Chegwidden, Mr James . . . L . . . Jan 2008
Alleyne, Ms Ebony . . . I . . . Jan 2009
Sanghera, Ms Sharan . . . M . . . Jan 2009
Line, Alex . . . G . . . Jan 2009

Chambers of Nicholas Grundy

FIVE PAPER,
GROUND FLOOR, 5 PAPER BUILDINGS, TEMPLE, LONDON EC4Y 7HB
Tel: 020 7815 3200 ***Fax:*** 020 7815 3201
Dx: 415 LONDON/CHANCERY LANE
E-mail: clerks@fivepaper.com
Web: www.fivepaper.com
Clerk: Alan Stammers.
Head of Chambers:
Grundy, Mr Nicholas . . . G . . . Nov 1993

Norris, Mr Paul H . . . M . . . Nov 1963
Walsh, Mr Steven James Franklin . . . L . . . Feb 1965
Wood, Mr Nicholas A . . . I . . . Jul 1970
Platford, Mr Graham . . . G . . . Nov 1970
Broatch, Mr Michael Donald . . . M . . . May 1971
Percival, Mr Robert Eldon . . . I . . . Nov 1971
Bull, Mr Roger D . . . M . . . Jul 1974
King, Mr Richard . . . I . . . Jul 1978
Lyne, Mr Mark . . . I . . . Jul 1981
Wright, Mr Ian . . . M . . . Nov 1983
Jacobson, Mr Lawrence . . . G . . . Nov 1985
Rich, Mr Jonathan . . . M . . . Dec 1989
John, Mr Peter C . . . I . . . Nov 1989
Henderson, Miss Josephine . . . I . . . Oct 1990
Evans, Mr Stephen . . . M . . . Oct 1992
Rushton, Ms Nicola Jane . . . G . . . Oct 1993
Mills, Mr Simon . . . L . . . Nov 1994
Adjei, Mr Cyril John . . . I . . . Oct 1995
Sleeman, Miss Rachel . . . G . . . Nov 1996
Davies, Mr Jake . . . I . . . Oct 1997
Harrap, Mr Robert . . . I . . . Oct 1997
Brownhill, Miss Joanna . . . G . . . Oct 1997
Rai, Miss Sonia . . . G . . . Oct 1998
Maltz, Mr Ben . . . L . . . Nov 1998
Jack, Mrs Angela . . . I . . . Jan 1999
Beecham, Miss Sara . . . M . . . Nov 1999
Hall, Miss Angela . . . G . . . Jul 2000
Leivesley, Miss Julie . . . L . . . Nov 2000
Holland, Mr Guy . . . M . . . Mar 2001
Glass, Miss Mary . . . M . . . Oct 2001
Macro, Miss Morwenna . . . I . . . Jul 2002
Christopher-Chambers, Gillian . . . M . . . Jul 2003
Rogers, Mr Christopher Thomas . . . M . . . Jul 2004
Reid, Miss Helen . . . L . . . Jul 2005
Ter Haar, Miss Camilla . . . I . . . Jul 2005
LeGallais, Mr James . . . M . . . Oct 2005
Moate, Jennifer . . . M . . . Jul 2006
Preston, Lewis . . . M . . . Jul 2007
Williams, Mr Rhys . . . M . . . Nov 2007
Adams, Brynmor . . . L . . . Jul 2008
Britton, Mr Byron; Former Solicitor . . . M . . . Oct 2008

Five Paper, led by Nicholas Grundy, has 42 Barristers and is based in London. Please contact our clerks by telephone or e-mail, clerks@fivepaper.com, with any enquiries.

Chambers of Michael J Hubbard QC

1 PAPER BUILDINGS,
1ST FLOOR, TEMPLE, LONDON EC4Y 7EP
Tel: 020 7353 3728 ***Fax:*** 020 7353 2911
Dx: 332 LONDON/CHANCERY LANE
E-mail: clerks@onepaper.co.uk
Clerk: Senior: Mark Cornell.
Head of Chambers:
Hubbard, Mr Michael J (Q.C.); Recorder . . . G . . . May 1972

Malcolm, Mr Alistair (Q.C.); Recorder . . . I . . . Feb 1971
Davies, Mr Anthony (Q.C.); Recorder . . . G . . . Jul 1971
Khalil, Karim (Q.C.); Recorder . . . L . . . Jul 1984
Harrison, Mr Roger; Recorder . . . G . . . Feb 1970
Farmer, Mr John . . . G . . . Nov 1970
Kellett, Mr Charles . . . M . . . Nov 1971
Privett, Mr Simon; Recorder . . . M . . . Jul 1976
Spence, Mr Stephen . . . G . . . Jul 1983
Vass, Mr Hugh . . . G . . . Nov 1983
Cox, Mr Lindsay . . . M . . . Jun 1984
Lamb, Ms Maria Jane; Recorder . . . G . . . Nov 1984
Wing, Mr Christopher J . . . G . . . Jul 1985
Seely, Mr Jonathan . . . I . . . Jan 1987
Morgan, Mr Christopher . . . M . . . Oct 1987
Carter, Mr William . . . G . . . Jul 1989
Jewell, Mr Matthew . . . L . . . Nov 1989
Hobson, Miss Sally . . . I . . . Apr 1991
O'Donnell, Mr Duncan . . . G . . . Oct 1992
Bryan, Mr Robert . . . M . . . Oct 1992
Myatt, Mr Charles . . . G . . . Oct 1993
Rafferty, Miss Angela . . . L . . . Feb 1995
Shaw, Mr Samuel Benjamin Barnaby . . . M . . . Nov 1996
Perrins, Mr Gregory . . . I . . . Oct 1997
Eley, Miss Joanne Mary . . . M . . . Oct 1997
Shaw, Mr Andrew . . . L . . . Mar 1998
Matthews, Miss Claire . . . I . . . Nov 1998
Cotter, Mr Nicholas . . . L . . . Oct 1999
Gibbs, Ms Georgina . . . G . . . Jan 2000
Brown, Miss Azza . . . M . . . Jan 2000
Ball, Ms Ruth . . . L . . . Jan 2002
Bagley, Miss Louisa . . . M . . . Oct 2002
Devas, Ms Nicola . . . G . . . Jan 2003
Archer, Miss Audrey . . . M . . . Oct 2004
Newcomb, Mr Quinton . . . M . . . Jul 2005
Hone, Mr Barnaby . . . M . . . Jan 2006
Edwards, Mr Jacob . . . L . . . Jan 2007
Waine, Lydia . . . L . . . Jan 2007
Talbot, Miss Nicola . . . L . . . Oct 2007
Mustafa, Mr Jehad . . . M . . . Nov 2007

Chambers of Jonathan Cohen QC

4 PAPER BUILDINGS,
1ST FLOOR, TEMPLE, LONDON EC4Y 7EX
Est: 1953
Tel: 020 7583 0816 ***Fax:*** 020 7353 4979
Dx: 1035 LDE
E-mail: clerks@4pb.com
Clerk: Senior: Michael Reeves.
Practice Manager: Clare Bello
Head of Chambers:
Cohen, Mr Jonathan (Q.C.) . . . L . . . Jul 1974

Scotland, Baroness (Q.C.) . . . M . . . Oct 1977
Setright, Mr Henry John (Q.C.) . . . M . . . Nov 1979
Scott-Manderson, Mr Marcus C W (Q.C.) . . . L . . . Jul 1980
Branigan, Miss Kate (Q.C.) . . . I . . . Jul 1984
Delahunty, Ms Johanne Erica (Q.C.) . . . M . . . Oct 1986
Verdan, Mr Alex (Q.C.) . . . I . . . Jan 1987
Sternberg, Mr Michael V (Q.C.) . . . G . . . Jul 1975
Wood, Miss Catherine (Q.C.) . . . M . . . Jul 1985
Howling, Mr Rex (Q.C.) . . . M . . . Jan 1991
Turcan, Mr Henry W . . . I . . . Jul 1965
Barrington-Smyth, Miss Amanda R . . . M . . . Nov 1972
Barda, Mr Robin J B . . . G . . . Jul 1975
Rayson, Miss Jane . . . G . . . Jul 1982
Johnstone, Mr Mark . . . I . . . Jul 1984
Coleman, Miss Elizabeth J . . . I . . . Jul 1985
Perkins, Mr Alistair G . . . M . . . Jul 1986
Hames, Mr Christopher . . . I . . . Jul 1987
Lyon, Mr Stephen . . . I . . . Jul 1987
Probyn, Miss Jane; Recorder (SE) 2003 . . . M . . . Feb 1988
Shaw, Mr James . . . I . . . Jan 1988
Jarman, Mr Mark Christopher . . . I . . . Nov 1989
Bradley, Ms Sally . . . I . . . Nov 1989
Brown, Ms Rebecca . . . I . . . Jul 1989
Mills, Miss Barbara . . . I . . . Oct 1990
Williams, Mr David B . . . I . . . Oct 1990
Grief, Ms Alison . . . I . . . Oct 1990
King, Miss Samantha . . . M . . . Nov 1990
Brown, Miss Joanne . . . I . . . Nov 1990
Gupta, Mr Teertha . . . I . . . Nov 1990
Brereton, Miss Joy . . . G . . . Nov 1990
Bedingfield, Mr David . . . G . . . Nov 1991
Tughan, Mr John . . . I . . . Nov 1991
Larizadeh, Mr Cyrus . . . I . . . Nov 1992
Hale, Mr Charles . . . M . . . Oct 1992
Simon, Mr Michael . . . I . . . Nov 1992
Ageros, Mr Justin . . . I . . . Nov 1993
Littlewood, Mr Robert . . . I . . . Oct 1993
Hepher, Mr Paul Arthur Richard . . . G . . . Jan 1994
Kirby, Miss Ruth . . . M . . . Oct 1994
Murray, Ms Judith . . . M . . . Oct 1994
Papazian, Miss Cliona . . . I . . . Nov 1994
Nuvoloni, Mr Stefano . . . I . . . Nov 1994
Lewis, Miss Sarah Louise . . . M . . . Nov 1995
Copley, Mr James . . . I . . . Oct 1997
Johnston, Ms Justine . . . M . . . Oct 1997
Jones, Mr Oliver . . . I . . . Nov 1998
Cheetham, Miss Lucy . . . G . . . Oct 1999
Khan, Mr Hassan . . . L . . . Nov 1999
Perry, Miss Cleo . . . G . . . Oct 2000
Gates, Mr Harry . . . L . . . Nov 2001
Foulkes, Miss Rebecca . . . L . . . Jul 2001
Wood, Ms Katie . . . I . . . Jul 2001
Lloyd, Miss Rhiannon . . . I . . . Oct 2002
Van Rol, Miss Katherine . . . L . . . Jul 2002
White, Ms Ceri . . . G . . . Jan 2002
Couch, Miss Elizabeth . . . I . . . Jul 2003
Turner, Miss Annabel . . . I . . . Jul 2003
Persson, Mr Matthew . . . I . . . Nov 2003
Gartland, Ms Dorothea . . . I . . . Jan 2004
Woodham, Ms Samantha . . . I . . . Jan 2006
Morley, Miss Laura . . . M . . . Jul 2006
Wallace, Ms Nicola . . . I . . . Oct 2006
Renton, Miss Jacqueline . . . M . . . Jul 2007
Gration, Mr Michael . . . I . . . Nov 2007
Powell, Mr Andrew . . . G . . . Nov 2008
Clayton, Mr Henry . . . M . . . Jan 2007
Baird-Murray, Mr Jasper . . . M . . . Jan 2008
Connors, Mrs Sophie . . . M . . . Oct 2009
Edwards, Mr Michael . . . I . . . Jul 2010
Nosworthy, Mr Harry . . . M . . . Oct 2010
Baldock, Ms Susan* . . . L . . . Jul 1988

Chambers of Jonathan Caplan QC and Michael Brompton QC

5 PAPER BUILDINGS,
1ST FLOOR, TEMPLE, LONDON EC4Y 7HB
Tel: 020 7583 6117 ***Fax:*** 020 7353 0075
Dx: 365 LONDON/CHANCERY LANE
E-mail: clerks@5pb.co.uk
Clerk: Dale Jones.
Head of Chambers:
Caplan, Mr Jonathan (Q.C.) . . . G . . . Nov 1973
Brompton, Mr Michael (Q.C.) . . . M . . . Nov 1973

Corkery, Mr Michael (Q.C.) . . . L . . . Nov 1949
Cassel, Mr Timothy (Q.C.) . . . L . . . Jul 1965
Carey, Mr Godfrey (Q.C.) . . . I . . . Jul 1969
Sells, Mr Oliver (Q.C.) . . . I . . . Jul 1972
Jenkins, Mr Edward (Q.C.) . . . M . . . Jul 1977
Trembath, Mr Graham (Q.C.) . . . M . . . Jul 1978
Moore, Mr Miranda J (Q.C.) . . . L . . . Jul 1983
Pinto, Miss Amanda (Q.C.) . . . M . . . Nov 1983
Wyeth, Mr Mark Charles (Q.C.) . . . I . . . Jul 1983
Wade, Mr Ian . . . G . . . Nov 1977
Fooks, Mr Nicholas . . . I . . . Jan 1978
Rector, Ms Penelope . . . G . . . Nov 1980
Judge, Mr Charles . . . I . . . Jul 1981
Aston, Mr Maurice . . . I . . . Jul 1982
Bennett, Mr Miles . . . I . . . Nov 1986
O'Sullivan, Mr Robert . . . L . . . Jul 1988
Christopher, Mr Julian . . . G . . . Nov 1988
Dhir, Miss Anuja . . . G . . . Nov 1989
McCartney, Mr Kevin . . . M . . . Nov 1991
Cole, Mr Justin . . . I . . . May 1992
Griffin, Mr Nicholas . . . I . . . Oct 1992
Deacon, Ms Emma . . . I . . . Nov 1993
Heer, Miss Deanna . . . G . . . Jan 1994
Allen, Mr Tom . . . M . . . Feb 1994
Weeks, Miss Janet . . . I . . . Nov 1994
Hick, Mr Michael . . . G . . . Oct 1995
Barry, Mr Denis . . . I . . . Jan 1996
Quinton, Mr Thomas . . . I . . . Oct 1997
Douglas-Jones, Mr Benjamin . . . G . . . Nov 1998
Purnell, Ms Catherine . . . I . . . Oct 1999
Lewis, Mr Dominic . . . I . . . Jul 2000
Rees, Mr Jonathan . . . I . . . Oct 2000
Norman, Mr James . . . M . . . Nov 2000
Hay, Miss Teresa . . . M . . . Jul 2001
Keene, Mr Rory . . . M . . . Dec 2001
Rabaiotti, Miss Catherine . . . I . . . Mar 2002
Sumnall, Miss Charlene . . . L . . . Jan 2003
Mackay, Mr Archie . . . M . . . Jan 2003
Dalling, Mr Robert . . . M . . . Jan 2003
Richards, Mr Alan . . . I . . . Oct 2004
Oakes, Miss Victoria . . . I . . . Jan 2005
Garn, Miss Jennifer . . . I . . . Jan 2006
Odell, Mr Alex . . . L . . . Oct 2007

Chambers of David Raymond Harris

PRINCE HENRY'S CHAMBERS,
2 TAMAR HOUSE, 12 TAVISTOCK PLACE, BLOOMSBURY, LONDON WC1H 9RD
Est: 1992
Tel: 020 7837 1645 ***Fax:*** 020 7713 0377
E-mail: d.harris4@btconnect.com
Head of Chambers:

Harris, Mr David Raymond; Head of Chambers	L	Nov 1973
Young, Mr Andrew Paul	L	Jan 1992
Wicks, Mr Raymond	I	Oct 1997

1 PUMP COURT,
ELM COURT, TEMPLE, LONDON EC4Y 7AH
Est: 1978
Tel: 020 7842 7070 ***Fax:*** 020 7842 7088
Dx: 109 LONDON/CHANCERY LANE
E-mail: clerks@1pumpcourt.co.uk
Clerk: Senior: Ian Burrow. Clerks: Mycal Thomas; Scott Haley; Kevin McCarthy; John Collins; Sian Wilkins; Claire Sabido; Sam Windle; Family Fees: Brian Mitchell; Civil/Criminal Fees: Sarah Bowyer; Assistant Fees: Lucy Adams; Mayani Weeraman.
Administrator: Jeannine Lewis

Adams, Ms Lindsay	M	Nov 1987
Adedeji, Ms Yinka	I	Nov 1997
Adler, Mr Johnathan	I	Jan 1999
Ahmad, Ms Tayyiba	L	Jul 1998
Archer, Ms Lorna	G	Nov 1986
Barker, Miss Jennifer	I	Jan 2000
Barnett, Miss Adrienne	M	Jul 1981
Bartlet-Jones, Mr Stephen	I	Jan 2004
Bevan, Mr Stephen	I	Nov 1986
Blum, Mr Doron	M	Sep 1998
Breese-Laughran, Ms Delphine	L	Oct 1991
Cecil, Ms Joanne	I	Jan 2005
Chandran, Miss Parosha	L	Oct 1997
Carrott, Mr Sylvester Emanuel	G	Jul 1980
Chirico, Mr David	L	Jan 2002
Cohen, Ms Marisa	I	Jan 2010
Compton, Ms Justine	M	Jan 2005
Davies, Ms Sarah Jeannette	G	Feb 1984
Dean, Ms Christine	L	Jan 2007
Del Mese, Miss Francesca M	M	Jan 1998
Denholm, Mr Graham	M	Jul 2001
Dent, Ms Sally	L	Jul 1989
Dingiswayo, Zani	I	Jan 2001
Dixon, Ms Annie	M	Nov 1991
Dubin, Mr Joshua	M	Nov 1997
Eldergill, Mr Edmund	I	Nov 1991
English, Mr Robert	I	Oct 1996
Field, Mr Stephen A	G	Nov 1993
Gannon, Mr Kevin	I	May 1993
Garwood, Mr Joshua	M	Jan 1992
Gillan, Shauna	L	Jan 2006
Gordon, Ms Clare	G	Jan 1995
Hall, Toby	L	Jan 2008
Harris, Ms Michelle	M	Jul 2000
Hayden, Mr Anthony (Q.C.)	M	Nov 1987
Hemerey, Ms Philippa	G	Jan 2009
Hilken, Ms Alice Mary	M	Nov 1994
Hodgson, Mr Martin	M	Jan 1980
Holloway, Ms Sharon	I	Oct 1994
Hoyal, Ms Jane	M	Nov 1976
Huda, Miss Abida Alia Jehan	M	Nov 1989
Hughes, Ms Mary	I	Jan 1994
Hussein, Mr Tim	I	Jan 1993
Hutchison, Eleanor	M	Jan 2007
Johnson, Ms Melanie	M	Oct 1996
Kaler, Ms Manjeet	M	Feb 1993
Kaza, Miss Ajanta	L	Nov 1998
Khubber, Mr Ranjiv	M	Nov 1994
Kiai, Gilda	G	Jan 2004
Kingsley, Mr Daniel	L	Oct 1994
Kotak, Mr Raggi	I	Mar 2000
Ladak, Miss Tahera	G	Nov 1986
Lamb, Mr John	M	May 1990
Littlewood, Ms Rebecca M	I	Nov 1988
Loughran, Ms Gemma	I	Nov 2008
McCrindell, Mr James	M	Oct 1993
McDonald, Mr Mark	I	Jan 1997
Mahmud, Saamir	G	Jan 1996
Martin, Ms Rebecca	L	Jan 2002
Masters, Mr Alan B R	M	Jul 1979
Monah, Ms Helen Anne	L	Nov 1996
Nabi, Mr Zia U	M	Nov 1991
Nicol, Mr Nicholas K	I	Nov 1986
O'Ceallaigh, Greg	I	Jan 2006
O'Leary, Miss Michele	G	Nov 1983
Parham, Sam	M	Jan 2000
Peat, Mr Charlie	G	Jan 2003
Pedro, Mr Terry Adebisi	M	Oct 1996
Pettit, Mr Sean	I	Oct 1997
Phillips, Ms Emma	M	Nov 2001
Polson, Mr Alistair	M	Nov 1989
Presland, Mr Frederick James Adrian	G	Jul 1985
Ramdas-Harsia, Mr Rohan	M	Nov 1999
Ross, Mr Tony	G	Jan 1991
Rubens, Miss Jacqueline	I	Nov 1989
Sammy, Ms Natasha	L	Jan 2006
Sayed, Miss Ruby	I	Mar 1999
Scott, Mr Stuart	I	Jan 1998
Sinclair, Ms Caroline	I	Jan 2005
Singleton, Ms Sarah (Q.C.)	M	Jul 1983
Teji, Miss Usha	L	Jul 1981
Tueje, Ms Patricia	I	Jan 1999
Waldron, Ms Lorraine	G	Jan 2004
Wibberley, Lucie	G	Jan 2005
Wilkinson, Mr Peter	G	Jul 2003
Wood, Ms Joanna	M	Jan 1996
Barry, Mr Simon*	M	Jan 1997
Brazier, Prof Margaret*	G	Jan 2001
Bryan, Ms Deborah*	L	Jul 1987
Butcher, Ms Helen*	M	Nov 1999
Calvert, Ms Barbara*	L	Jan 1997
Chesters, Ms Colette L*	M	Mar 1996
Fisher, Mr Martin*	G	Jan 1999
Jahangir, Asma*	G	Jan 2000
Kempe, Ms Dianna*	M	Jan 2001
Khanzada, Ms Najma*	I	Nov 1992
Lawson, Ms Elizabeth A (Q.C.)*	I	Jul 1969
Mtetwa, Ms Beatrice*	L	Jan 2002
Muhammad, Ms Tamara*	M	Jul 1998
Roberts, Mr Simon*	G	Jan 1975
Rowlands, Mr Mark*	G	Nov 1990
Rudston, Mr Neville*	M	Jan 2000
Sprack, Mr John*	M	Jul 1984
Tracey, Ms Helen*	L	Jan 2001
Vine, Ms Catriona*	M	Jul 2002

Chambers of Richard Christie QC

2 PUMP COURT,
1ST FLOOR, TEMPLE, LONDON EC4Y 7AH
Est: 1973
Tel: 020 7353 5597 ***Fax:*** 020 7583 2122
Dx: 290 LONDON/CHANCERY LANE
E-mail: clerks@2pumpcourt.co.uk
Clerk: Senior: Andrew Newey. Criminal: Jo Haigh; Fees: Martin Filby; Rachel Shepherd.
Head of Chambers:

Christie, Mr Richard (Q.C.)	I	Jul 1986
Singer, Mr Philip (Q.C.)	I	Feb 1964
Renouf, Mr Gerard	I	Jul 1977
Barrett, Mr Robert Scott	G	Jul 1978
Pigot, Miss Diana	I	Nov 1978
Dooley, Ms Christine	L	Jul 1980
Hughes, Mr Gareth	G	Nov 1985
Lyons, Mr David	M	May 1987
Kerr, Mr Christopher	M	Nov 1988
Davey, Miss Kate	I	May 1988
Burrington, Mr Richard J H	I	Nov 1993
Volz, Mr Karl	M	Nov 1993
Bagnall, Mr Matthew	M	Oct 1993
Roochove, Mr Mark	G	Oct 1994
Vine, Ms Sarah	I	Jan 1997
Husain, Miss Laureen	L	Mar 1997
Bradshaw, Miss Catherine	M	Jul 1998
Mostafa, Miss Margia	L	Oct 1999
Clark, Mr Peter	I	Oct 2000
Nash, Miss Emma	I	Oct 2001
Coles-Harrington, Miss Frances	L	Jan 2001
Evans, Mr Paul	G	Jan 2001
Brown, Mr Marc	L	Mar 2001
Price-Marmion, Miss Alexandra	M	Oct 2002
Bailey, Miss Sasha	L	Jul 2002
Akudolu, Nneka	M	Oct 2002
Hayhurst, Mr Benjamin David	G	Nov 2004
Morgan, Mr Matt	L	Jan 2004
Onalaja, Mr James	L	Jan 2004
Fitzpatrick, Mr Stephen	L	Jan 2004
Abadoo, Mr Joseph	M	Jan 2005
Walsh, Mr Jack	L	Jan 2006
Chapman, Helen	M	Jan 2006
Wainwright, Mr Scott	M	Oct 2006
Grime, Mr Stephen (Q.C.)*	M	Jan 1978
Giovene, Mr Laurence*	L	Jul 1962
Leigh, Prof Leonard*	I	May 1993
Tarr, Miss Beverly*	M	Oct 1995
Burrows, Mr Ross*	L	Jan 2009

Chambers of Jeremy Storey QC and Nigel Tozzi QC

4 PUMP COURT,
TEMPLE, LONDON EC4Y 7AN
Tel: 020 7842 5555 ***Fax:*** 020 7583 2036
Dx: 303 LDE
E-mail: clerks@4pumpcourt.com
Clerk: Carl Wall; Stewart Gibbs; Jon Robinson; Mark Winrow; Billy Griffiths.
Practice Manager: Carolyn McCombe
Head of Chambers:

Storey, Mr Jeremy (Q.C.); Recorder	I	Jul 1974
Tozzi, Mr Nigel (Q.C.)	G	Jul 1980
Temple, Mr Anthony (Q.C.); Recorder; Dep High Court judge	I	Jul 1968
Friedman, Mr David (Q.C.)	I	Jul 1968
Blunt, Mr David (Q.C.); Recorder	M	Nov 1967
Moger, Mr Christopher (Q.C.); Recorder	I	Jul 1972
Speaight, Mr Anthony (Q.C.)	M	Jul 1973
Marks, Mr Jonathan (Q.C.)	I	Jul 1975
Douglas, Mr Michael (Q.C.); Recorder	G	Nov 1974
Nicholson, Mr Jeremy (Q.C.)	M	Jul 1977
Cross, Mr James (Q.C.)	G	Jul 1985
Vineall, Mr Nicholas (Q.C.)	M	Nov 1988
Charlton, Mr Alexander (Q.C.)	M	Jul 1983
McCall, Mr Duncan (Q.C.)	G	Feb 1988
Christie, Mr Aidan (Q.C.); Recorder	M	Jul 1988
Neish, Mr Andrew (Q.C.)	L	Jul 1988
Brannigan, Mr Sean (Q.C.)	G	Oct 1994
Davie, Mr Michael (Q.C.)	M	Nov 1993
Hamilton, Mr Peter	I	Feb 1968
Dyer, Mr Allen	I	Jul 1976
Ticciati, Mr Oliver	I	Jul 1979
Bergin, Mr Terence Edward	I	Nov 1985
Henderson, Mr Simon	I	Oct 1993
Gunning, Mr Alexander	I	Mar 1994
Vaughan-Neil, Ms Kate	I	Oct 1994
Hickey, Mr Alexander Frederick	L	Jul 1995
Ansell, Ms Rachel	M	Oct 1995
Lewis, Mr Jonathan M	I	Mar 1996
Packman, Miss Claire	I	Oct 1996
Taylor, Mr Michael	M	Nov 1996
McCafferty, Ms Lynne	M	Oct 1997
Purchas, Mr James	I	Oct 1997
O'Sullivan, Mr Sean	I	Nov 1997
Pilling, Mr Benjamin	I	Nov 1997
Potter, Ms Alison	M	Feb 1987
Leabeater, Mr James	L	Oct 1999
Bowling, Mr James	M	Nov 1999
Gillies, Miss Jennie	M	Nov 2000
Livesey, Ms Kate	M	Nov 2001
Oliver, Mr Peter	L	Jul 2002
Crangle, Mr Thomas	G	Jul 2002
Woods, Mr George	M	Mar 2003
Hatt, Mr James	L	Oct 2003
Chatterjee, Mr Rangan	L	Jul 2004
Lavy, Mr Matthew	L	Jul 2004
Goldstone, Mr Simon	M	Jul 2004
Wygas, Mr Luke	M	Nov 2004
Crowley, Miss Laura	I	Jul 2005
Osborne, Mr Richard	I	Nov 2005
Wright, Mr Alexander	M	Jul 2007
Owens, Miss Elspeth	M	Oct 2007
Stevens, Mr Andrew	L	Jan 2007
Temple, Mr Adam	M	Jul 2008
Goodkin, Mr Daniel	L	Oct 2008
Munro, Mr Iain	L	Jan 2009
Naylor, Mr Martyn	I	Jul 2009

Chambers of Michael Collard

5 PUMP COURT,
TEMPLE, LONDON EC4Y 7AP
Tel: 020 7353 2532 / 7583 7133 ***Fax:*** 020 7353 5321
Dx: 497 LONDON/CHANCERY LANE
E-mail: clerks@5pumpcourt.com
Clerk: Tim Markham.
Head of Chambers:

Collard, Mr Michael	M	Jul 1986
Primost, Mr Norman	M	Jul 1954
Hunter, Mr Anthony	I	Nov 1963
Hopkins, Mr Simeon	I	Nov 1968
Dow, Mr Kenneth	L	Nov 1970
Clarke, Mr Ivan George Robert	G	Nov 1973
Evison, Mr John	L	Jul 1974
Keith, Mr Alistair	M	Nov 1974
Cartwright, Mr Crispian; Recorder	M	Nov 1976
Chaize, Mr Tristan	I	Nov 1977
Corben, Mr Paul	G	Jul 1979
Ratcliffe, Miss Anne	I	Feb 1981
Gray, Mr Roger	L	Jul 1984
O'Toole, Mr Simon Gerard	I	Jul 1984
Nicholls, Mr Jack	I	Nov 1991
Mahmood, Mr Imran	M	Jan 1992
Maddan, Mr Archie	G	Nov 1993
Taylor, Miss Maureen J	I	Nov 1993
Smith, Miss Emma	M	Oct 1994
Mitropoulos, Chris	L	Mar 1997
Hearnden, Mr Richard	G	Mar 1998
Newman, Mr James	G	Jul 2000
Ryle, Ms Kate	I	Aug 2002

10

Chambers of Stephen Hockman QC

6 PUMP COURT,
1ST FLOOR, TEMPLE, LONDON EC4Y 7AR
Tel: 020 7797 8400 ***Fax:*** 020 7797 8401
Dx: 293 LONDON/CHANCERY LANE
E-mail: clerks@6pumpcourt.co.uk
Clerk: Senior: Richard Constable.
Administrator: Arlene Outen
Head of Chambers:

Hockman, Mr Stephen (Q.C.)	M	Jul 1970
Willard, Mr Neville	G	Jul 1976
Armstrong, Mr Grant B	L	Jul 1978
Barraclough, Mr Richard	I	Nov 1980
Travers, Mr David	M	Jul 1981
Baldock, Mr Nicholas	L	Nov 1983
Topping, Miss Caroline	M	Oct 1984
Gower, Mr Peter	L	Jul 1985
Walden-Smith, Mr David	L	Jul 1985
Leigh, Mr Kevin	L	Nov 1986
Harrison, Mr Peter	I	Jul 1987
Laws, Miss Eleanor (Q.C.)	I	Oct 1990
Forbes, Mr Peter	I	Oct 1990
Upton, Mr William	I	Nov 1990
Saxby, Mr Oliver	I	Nov 1992
Watson, Mr Mark	G	Jul 1994
Grant, Mr Edward	I	Nov 1994
Ellin, Miss Nina	I	Nov 1994
Alcock, Mr Peter	G	Oct 1995
Wright, Miss Clare	I	Oct 1995
Beard, Mr Mark	G	Oct 1996
Charles, Miss Deborah	L	Oct 1996
Robinson, Miss Tanya	I	Nov 1997
Menzies, Mr Gordon	I	Oct 1998
Banwell, Mr Richard	L	Oct 1998
Bennett, Mr Lee	M	Nov 1998
Knowles, Miss Linsey	L	Jul 2000
Fox, Miss Katie	I	Oct 2001
Wood, Mr Simon	M	Oct 2001

Community Legal Service

Criminal Defence Service

Chambers of Oba E Nsugbe QC

PUMP COURT CHAMBERS,
UPPER GROUND FLOOR, 3 PUMP COURT, TEMPLE, LONDON EC4Y 7AJ
Tel: 020 7353 0711 ***Fax:*** 0845 259 3241
Dx: 362 LONDON/CHANCERY LANE
E-mail: clerks@3pumpcourt.com
Web: www.3pumpcourt.com
Clerk: David Barber; Tony Atkins; Jonathan Cue; Charlotte Horn; Tim Dockrill; Sam Coarse.
Administrator: Andrea Cheshire
Head of Chambers:

Nsugbe, Mr Oba E (Q.C.); Recorder	G	Jul 1985
Pascoe, Mr Nigel (Q.C.); Recorder	I	Jul 1966
Donne, Mr Anthony M (Q.C.)	M	Apr 1973
Campbell, Miss Susan Claire (Q.C.)	M	Nov 1986

Hill, Mr Mark (Q.C.); Recorder	M	Jul 1987
Samuels, Ms Leslie (Q.C.); Deputy District Judge	G	Jul 1989
Patterson, Mr Stewart; Recorder	M	Nov 1967
Pearson, Mr Thomas Adam Spencer	M	Nov 1969
Harrap, Mr Giles Thresher; Recorder	I	Nov 1971
Abbott, Mr Frank; Recorder	L	Nov 1972
Parry, Mr Charles	M	Nov 1973
Ker-Reid, Mr John	I	Nov 1974
Butt, Mr Michael	M	Nov 1974
Gabb, Mr Charles H	M	Feb 1975
Mackenzie, Miss Julie	L	Nov 1978
Jones, Mr Stephen	I	Nov 1978
Allardice, Miss Miranda	L	Jul 1982
Blount, Mr Martin J	G	Nov 1982
Scott, Mr Matthew	I	Nov 1985
Bloom-Davis, Mr Desmond; Deputy District Judge	I	Jul 1986
Travers, Mr Hugh; Employment Tribunal Chairman	M	Nov 1988
Gau, Mr Justin	I	Jul 1989
Wicks, Mr David	M	Jul 1989
Boydell, Mr Edward Patrick Stirrup; Recorder	M	Nov 1989
Houston, Mr Andrew	I	Nov 1989
Breslin, Miss Catherine	I	Jan 1990
Khan, Miss Helen M G	M	Nov 1990
Lorenzo, Ms Claudia	I	Apr 1991
Howe, Miss Penny	I	Nov 1991
Kelly, Mr Geoffrey	M	Feb 1992
Newton-Price, Mr James	M	Oct 1992
Ruffell, Mr Mark	M	Nov 1992
Tregilgas-Davey, Mr Marcus	G	Feb 1993
Morton, Mr Gary	G	May 1993
Russell, Ms Alison	M	Oct 1993
Peirson, Mr Oliver	L	Oct 1993
Gunther, Miss Elizabeth	L	Oct 1993
Ashley, Mr Mark R E	L	Nov 1993
Smith, Miss Leonorah	I	Nov 1993
Moore, Mr Roderick A	I	Nov 1993
Pawson, Mr Robert Edward	I	Nov 1994
Hall, Mr Richard Andrew	I	Nov 1995
Hall, Mr Michael Richard	I	Oct 1996
Asteris, Mr Peter	L	Jun 1996
Dubbery, Mr Mark	M	Oct 1996
Jones, Miss Sarah	L	Nov 1996
Ephgrave, Ms Amy	G	Oct 1997
Arlow, Ms Ruth	I	Oct 1997
Grime, Mr Andrew	I	Oct 1997
Ward, Ms Anne	G	Nov 1997
Gallagher, Miss Maria	I	Nov 1997
Allan, Ms Kirsten	M	Jul 1998
Keen, Mr Spencer	M	Jan 1998
Dracass, Mr Timothy	I	Oct 1998
Bond, Mr Andrew	I	Jan 1999
De Rozarieux, Ms Louise	L	Oct 1999
Spearing, Miss Rachel M	L	Nov 1999
Tutt, Mr Richard	M	Jul 2000
Brown, Miss Anne	M	Jul 2000
Ramadhan, Miss Lubeya	M	Jul 2000
Islam, Miss Naznin	G	Oct 2000
Hartley, Miss Caroline	M	Aug 2002
Burge, Miss Alison Jayne	G	Jul 2002
Platt, Miss Heather	L	Oct 2002
Shravat, Mr Neelo	M	Nov 2002
Chapman, Mr John	L	Jul 2003
Street, Miss Charlotte	G	Jul 2003
Davis, Miss Lucy	G	Nov 2003
Berry, Miss Amy	L	Jan 2003
Gadd, Mr Adam	G	Jan 2004
Leach, Mr Stuart	G	Jun 2004
Trotter, Miss Helen	G	Oct 2004
Lyons, Miss Tara	M	Oct 2005
Troup, Miss Rachel	L	Nov 2005
Long, Mr Benjamin	M	Jan 2006
Iten, Miss Corinne	I	Oct 2006
O'Driscoll, Ms Patricia	M	Oct 2006
Lee, Ms Jennifer	L	Jan 2007
Gilbert, Daniella	I	Mar 2007
Connors, Hannah	I	Jan 2008
Bruce, Ms Eleanor	M	Jan 2008
Purkis, Mr Simon	I	Oct 2008
Williamson, Nicholas	M	Mar 2009
Birt, Mr Robin	M	Oct 2009
Cohen, Mr Jonathan (Q.C.)*	L	Jul 1974
Bradley, Mrs Sally (Q.C.)*	L	Nov 1978
Fielding, Mr Stephen*	I	Jan 1974

Specialist teams cover a wide range of Common Law and Criminal work, including Family & Matrimonial; Employment; Environment; Inheritance; Landlord & Tenant; Personal Injury; Customs & Excise; Serious Fraud; Extradition; Ecclesiastical; Professional & Medical Negligence; Courts Martial.

PUMP COURT
TAX CHAMBERS

Chambers of Andrew Robert Thornhill QC

PUMP COURT TAX CHAMBERS,
16 BEDFORD ROW, LONDON WC1R 4EF
Tel: 020 7414 8080 ***Fax:*** 020 7414 8099
Dx: 312 LONDON/CHANCERY LANE
E-mail: clerks@pumptax.com
Web: www.pumptax.com
Clerk: Senior: Nigel Jones.
Administrator: Pia Giles
Head of Chambers:

Thornhill, Mr Andrew Robert (Q.C.)	M	Jul 1969

Aaronson, Mr Graham (Q.C.)	M	Nov 1966
Milne, Mr David C (Q.C.)	L	Jul 1970
Massey, Mr William (Q.C.)	M	Jul 1977
Prosser, Mr Kevin (Q.C.)	L	Jul 1982
Tallon, Mr John (Q.C.)	M	Jul 1975
Goodfellow, Mr Giles (Q.C.)	M	Jul 1983
Ewart, Mr David (Q.C.)	G	Nov 1987
Ghosh, Mr Julian (Q.C.)	L	Jul 1993
Baldry, Mr Rupert (Q.C.)	M	Nov 1987
Richards, Mr Ian	L	Nov 1971
Matthews, Janek P	G	Jul 1972
Thomas, Mr Roger C	L	Jul 1979
Hamilton, Mrs Penelope Ann	G	Jul 1972
White, Mr Jeremy	G	Jun 1976
Woolf, The Hon Jeremy	I	Jul 1986
Hitchmough, Mr Andrew	I	Oct 1991
Shipwright, Mr Adrian	M	Feb 1993
Wilson, Miss Elizabeth	M	Oct 1995
Vallat, Mr Richard	G	Oct 1997
Henderson, Mr James	G	Nov 1997
Dunn, Miss Sarah	L	Oct 1998
Choudhury, Ms Sadiya	L	May 2002
Conolly, Mr Oliver	L	Oct 2003
Rivett, Mr James	L	Nov 2004
Bremner, Mr Jonathan	I	Oct 2005
Yates, Mr David	L	Jan 2004
Poots, Ms Laura	M	Jan 2007
Chacko, Mr Thomas	I	Oct 2007
Yang, Miss Zizhen	L	Jan 2009
Bradley, Mr Charles	L	Jan 2010

As the largest specialist chambers concentrating on tax, we are able to offer advice and full litigation services in all areas of revenue law, both direct and indirect, corporate and personal. Please contact the senior clerk for further information.

Chambers of Rebecca Poulet QC and Peter Whiteman QC

QEB HOLLIS WHITEMAN,
1-2 LAURENCE POUNTNEY HILL, LONDON
EC4R 0EU
Tel: 020 7933 8855 ***Fax:*** 020 7929 3732
Dx: 858 LONDON CITY
E-mail: barristers@qebholliswhiteman.co.uk
Clerk: Martin Secrett.
Administrator: Sarah Finlayson
Head of Chambers:

Poulet, Ms Rebecca (Q.C.)	L	Nov 1975
Whiteman, Mr Peter (Q.C.)	L	Sep 1967

Grey, Mr Robin (Q.C.)	G	Feb 1957
Glass, Mr Anthony (Q.C.)	I	Jul 1965
Hilton, Mr John (Q.C.)	M	Nov 1964
Evans, Mr David (Q.C.)	M	Jul 1972
Kyte, Mr Peter (Q.C.)	L	Jul 1970
Boyce, Mr William (Q.C.)	G	Jul 1976
Donne, Mr Jeremy (Q.C.)	M	Nov 1978
Jeremy, Mr David Hugh Thomas (Q.C.)	M	Jul 1977
Ellison, Mr Mark (Q.C.)	G	Nov 1979
Brown, Mr Edward (Q.C.)	G	Jul 1983
Finnigan, Mr Peter (Q.C.)	L	Jul 1979
Wilcken, Mr Anthony	M	Nov 1966
Strudwick, Ms Linda	L	Jul 1973
Paton, Mr Ian	M	Apr 1975
Kark, Mr Tom	I	Jul 1982
Bennetts, Mr Phillip	L	Jul 1986
Larkin, Mr Sean	I	Jul 1987
Groome, Mr David	M	Nov 1987
Plaschkes, Ms Sarah	I	Jul 1988
Henry, Mr Edward	L	Nov 1988
Norton, Miss Heather	M	Nov 1988
Smart, Mr Roger	I	Jul 1989
Johnson, Ms Zoe	I	Oct 1990
Wakerley, Mr Paul	G	Nov 1990
Barnfather, Ms Lydia	I	Oct 1992
Ramasamy, Selva	I	Nov 1992
Darbishire, Mr Adrian	L	Nov 1993
Maguire, Mr Benn	I	Nov 1994
Raudnitz, Mr Paul	I	Nov 1994
Evans, Mr Philip	L	Oct 1995
Aldred, Mr Mark	M	Mar 1996
Evans, Mr Julian	M	Oct 1997
Harris, Ms Rebecca	M	Oct 1997
Tahta, Ms Natasha	I	Jan 1998
Ledward, Ms Jocelyn	M	Jan 1999
Felix, Miss Alexandra	M	Oct 1999
FitzGerald, Mr Benedict	L	Oct 2000
Kennedy, Miss Lucy	M	Oct 2000
Petherbridge, Ms Bridget	G	Oct 2002
Alibhai, Mr Ari	G	Jan 2003
McGhee, Mr Philip	G	Jan 2003
Stott, Mr Philip	M	Jan 2004
Warwick, Ms Joanna	L	Jan 2004
Baker, Mr Tom	M	Jan 2004
Coxhill, Mr Fraser	L	Jan 2004
King, Mr Adam	I	Jan 2005
Daly, Ms Caoimhe	I	Jan 2005
Rooney, Mr Paul	I	Jan 2007
Wormington, Mr Jim	G	Jan 2007
Broomfield, Mr Tom	L	Jan 2007
Lynch, Mr John	G	Jan 2008

Chambers of Lionel Edward Persey QC and Simon Rainey QC

QUADRANT CHAMBERS,
QUADRANT HOUSE, 10 FLEET STREET,
LONDON EC4Y 1AU
Tel: 020 7583 4444 ***Fax:*** 020 7583 4455
Dx: 292 LONDON/CHANCERY LANE
E-mail: info@quadrantchambers.com
Clerk: Senior: Gary Ventura.
Administrator: Natalie Wallis
Practice Manager: Pauline Roberts; John Walker; Jason Roukin; Tony Stephenson
Chambers Director: Tim Gerrard (Chief Executive)
Head of Chambers:

Persey, Mr Lionel Edward (Q.C.)	G	Jul 1981
Rainey, Mr Simon (Q.C.)	L	Jul 1982

Howard, Michael N (Q.C.)	G	May 1971
Russell, Mr Jeremy (Q.C.)	M	Nov 1975
Haddon-Cave, Mr Charles (Q.C.)	G	Jul 1978
Kverndal, Mr Simon (Q.C.)	M	Nov 1982
Parsons, Mr Luke (Q.C.)	I	Jul 1985
Jacobs, Mr Nigel (Q.C.)	M	Nov 1983
Goldstone, Mr David Julian (Q.C.); Treasury A Panel Counsel(Admiralty Junior)	M	May 1986
Croall, Mr Simon (Q.C.)	M	Nov 1986
Lawson, Mr Robert (Q.C.)	I	Nov 1989
O'Donovan, Mr Hugh	G	Jan 1975
Nolan, Mr Michael	M	Jul 1981
McParland, Mr Michael	I	Jul 1983
Cogley, Mr Stephen William	G	Nov 1984
Cooper, Mr Nigel	L	Jul 1987
Reeve, Mr Matthew	L	Nov 1987
Karia, Mr Chirag	L	Nov 1988
Melwani, Miss Poonam	I	Nov 1989
Turner, Mr James M	I	Jul 1990
Davey, Mr Michael	G	Nov 1990
Phillips, Mr Nevil David	G	Oct 1992
Thomas, Mr Robert	L	Nov 1992
Russell, Mr John	M	Oct 1993
Macey-Dare, Mr Thomas	M	Feb 1994
Kimbell, Mr John Ashley	I	Nov 1995
Chambers, Mr Jonathan	I	Oct 1996
Buckingham, Mr Stewart	L	Oct 1996
Blackwood, Mr Guy	I	Oct 1997
Kulkarni, Mr Yash	L	Jan 1998
Ferrer, Mr Peter A	I	Mar 1998
Smith, Mr Christopher M	I	Oct 1999
Marland, Mr Timothy	I	Jul 2002
Hosking, Ms Ruth	L	Nov 2002
Pounds, Miss Caroline	L	Jan 2003
Toms, Mr Paul	G	Jan 2003
Coldrick, Mr Emmet	G	Jan 2004
Henton, Mr Paul	I	Jan 2004
Paruk, Miss Saira	L	Jan 2004
Stone, Mr Turlough	I	Nov 2004
Morgan, Miss Gemma	M	Jan 2006
Moore, Miss Natalie	L	Jan 2007
Walsh, Mr David	I	Jan 2007
Bucknall, Miss Belinda (Q.C.)*	M	Nov 1974
Boswell, Ms Lindsay (Q.C.)*	G	Jan 1982
Gault, Mr Simon*	G	Nov 1970
Warrender, Ms Nichola Mary*	I	Nov 1995
Tamblyn, Mr Nathan*	G	Nov 1999

Chambers of Lewis Marks QC

QUEEN ELIZABETH BUILDINGS,
TEMPLE, LONDON EC4Y 9BS
Tel: 020 7797 7837 ***Fax:*** 020 7353 5422
Dx: 339 LONDON/CHANCERY LANE
E-mail: clerks@qeb.co.uk
Web: www.qeb.co.uk
Clerk: Ivor Treherne.
Head of Chambers:

Marks, Mr Lewis (Q.C.)	M	Jul 1984

Stone, Miss Lucy (Q.C.)	M	Jul 1983
Hyde, Mr Charles Gordon (Q.C.); Recorder	M	Jul 1988
Amos, Mr Timothy (Q.C.)	L	Jul 1987
Roberts, Mrs Jennifer (Q.C.)	I	Jul 1988
Leech, Mr Stewart (Q.C.)	L	Oct 1992
Hosford-Tanner, Mr J Michael	L	Nov 1974
Tidbury, Mr Andrew	I	Jul 1976
Brudenell, Mr Thomas	I	Nov 1977
Wise, Mr Oliver	L	Jul 1981
Edwards, Miss Sarah	I	Nov 1990
Firth, Mr Mathew	G	Jul 1991
Clarke, Miss Elizabeth	G	Nov 1991
Thorpe, Mr Alexander	L	Nov 1995
Cowton, Miss Catherine	M	Nov 1995
Ewins, Mr James	M	Jul 1996
Phipps, Miss Sarah Elizabeth	L	Nov 1997
Lazarides, Mr Marcus	M	Nov 1999
Brooks, Mr Duncan	G	Oct 2000
Bentham, Mr Daniel	M	Jan 2000
Cadbury, Miss Justine	M	Jan 2001
Harvey, Mr Tristan	M	Jan 2002
Sirikanda, Morgan	M	Jan 2002
Budden, Ms Rosemary	L	Jan 2003
Batt, Miss Charanjit	L	Oct 2004
Singer, Ms Samantha	G	Jul 2004
Westley, Mr Nicholas	L	Oct 2005
Baker, Ms Hannah	M	Nov 2005
Faggionato, Miss Marina	L	Jan 2006
Tyzack, Mr William	M	Jan 2007
Younis, Miss Saima	I	Nov 2008
Kisser, Miss Amy	I	Jul 2009

This Chamber with 32 Barristers is based in London and led by Lewis Marks QC. You may contact any of our clerks at any time by sending a message to clerks@qeb.co.uk.

Chambers of Adrienne Page QC and Desmond Browne QC

5RB,
5 RAYMOND BUILDINGS, GRAY'S INN,
LONDON WC1R 5BP
Tel: 020 7242 2902 ***Fax:*** 020 7831 2686
Dx: 1054 LDE
E-mail: clerks@5rb.com
Clerk: Senior: Kim Janes. Junior: John Sizer.
Administrator: Ella Barraclough
Head of Chambers:

Page, Miss Adrienne (Q.C.)	M	Jul 1974
Browne, Mr Desmond (Q.C.)	G	Nov 1969

Milmo, Mr Patrick Helenus (Q.C.)	M	Jul 1962
Price, Mr James (Q.C.)	I	Jul 1974
Warby, Mr Mark (Q.C.)	G	Nov 1981
Bishop, Mr Gordon	M	Nov 1968
Bate, Mr Stephen	M	Jul 1981
Monson, The Hon Andrew	M	Sep 1983
Christie, Mr Iain	I	Jul 1989
Marzec, Ms Alexandra	M	Nov 1990
Smith, Prof Anthony	M	May 1992
Sherborne, Mr David Alexander	G	Oct 1992
Rushbrooke, Mr Justin	M	Jul 1992
Nicklin, Mr Matthew	M	Nov 1993
Busuttil, Mr Godwin	L	Oct 1994

Bennett, Mr William . . . I . . . Oct 1994
Michalos, Miss Christina Antigone Diana . . . G . . . Nov 1994
Wolanski, Mr Adam . . . L . . . Feb 1995
Dean, Mr Jacob . . . I . . . Oct 1995
Coppola, Miss Anna Francesca . . . L . . . Nov 1996
Barnes, Mr Jonathan . . . L . . . Jun 1999
Speker, Mr Adam . . . M . . . Oct 1999
Munden, Mr Richard . . . L . . . Oct 2003
Hirst, Mr David . . . G . . . Oct 2003
Shore, Miss Victoria Louise . . . L . . . Nov 2005
Jolliffe, Ms Victoria . . . L . . . Nov 2005
Takatsuki, Miss Yuli . . . L . . . Jan 2007

Chambers of Malcolm Waters QC and Hedley Marten

RADCLIFFE CHAMBERS,
11 NEW SQUARE, LINCOLN'S INN, LONDON WC2A 3QB
Tel: 020 7831 0081 *Fax:* 020 7405 2560
Dx: 319 LDE
E-mail: clerks@radcliffechambers.com
Clerk: Senior: John Clark. Keith Nagle; Robert Barrow; Justin Allen.
Administrator: Isobel Gurrie
Chambers Director: Catherine Calder
Head of Chambers:
Waters, Mr Malcolm (Q.C.) . . . L . . . Jul 1977
Marten, Mr Hedley . . . L . . . Nov 1966

Crampin, Mr Peter (Q.C.) . . . M . . . Nov 1976
Rowley, Mr Keith (Q.C.) . . . G . . . Jul 1979
Pearce, Mr Robert E (Q.C.) . . . M . . . Jul 1977
Quint, Mrs Francesca . . . G . . . Jul 1970
di Mambro, Mr David . . . M . . . Nov 1973
Nurse, Mr Gordon . . . M . . . Nov 1973
Crawford, Mr Grant . . . M . . . Jul 1974
Heywood, Mr Michael Edmondson . . . I . . . Jul 1975
Lewis, Mr Robert . . . G . . . Nov 1996
Acton, Mr Stephen . . . I . . . Jul 1977
Ovey, Ms Elizabeth . . . M . . . Jul 1978
Hargreaves, Miss Sara . . . M . . . Jul 1979
Dumont, Mr Thomas . . . G . . . Nov 1979
Staunton, Mr Ulick . . . M . . . Jul 1984
Williams, Mr Simon . . . M . . . Jan 1984
Feltham, Mr Piers . . . G . . . Jul 1985
Smith, Mr Howard . . . I . . . Jul 1986
West, Mr Mark . . . M . . . Jul 1987
Mullis, Mr Roger . . . L . . . Nov 1987
Moys, Mr Clive . . . L . . . Jul 1998
McQuail, Ms Katherine . . . M . . . Nov 1989
Dodge, Mr Peter . . . L . . . Oct 1992
Majumdar, Mr Shantanu . . . M . . . Nov 1992
Smith, Dr Peter . . . L . . . Jun 1993
Bleasdale, Ms Marie-Claire . . . L . . . Oct 1993
Holmes, Mr Justin . . . I . . . Jan 1994
Ohrenstein, Mr Dov . . . G . . . Oct 1995
Selway, Ms Kate; Junior Counsel to the Crown . . . I . . . Nov 1995
Moffett, Mr William . . . G . . . Sep 2000
Wells, Mr Nathan . . . L . . . Oct 2000
Mullen, Mr Mark . . . L . . . Jul 2001
Winfield, Mr Joshua . . . I . . . Oct 2001
Flavin, Mr Marcus Benedict Sean . . . L . . . Nov 2001
Ratcliffe, Ms Frances . . . L . . . Jan 2002
Buckley, Mr Christopher . . . L . . . Jul 2004
Fell, Mr Mark . . . L . . . Jan 2004
Hicks, Mr Edward . . . M . . . Jan 2004
Lewison, Mr Josh . . . L . . . Jan 2005
Christie, Mr Robert . . . M . . . Jan 2006
Bor, Dr Harris . . . I . . . Jan 2006
Mathers, Ms Wendy . . . I . . . Jan 2005
Thomson, Mr Mark . . . L . . . Jan 2006
Doran, Ms Catherine . . . I . . . Jan 2008
Brown, Ms Natalie . . . G . . . Jan 2009

CHAMBERS OF MR M H RAHMAN,
11 REGAL CLOSE, OLD MONTAGUE STREET, LONDON E1 5JB
Tel: 020 7377 5803

Chambers of Julius Damien Seal

189 RANDOLPH AVENUE,
LONDON W9 1DJ
Tel: 020 7328 0158
Head of Chambers:
Seal, Mr Julius Damien . . . L . . . Nov 1967

Chhotu, Jasvant . . . G . . . Jun 1979
Patel, Jayantilal . . . I . . . Nov 1999

Chambers of Clive Victor Nicholls QC

3 RAYMOND BUILDINGS,
GRAY'S INN, LONDON WC1R 5BH
Tel: 020 7400 6400 *Fax:* 020 7400 6464
Dx: 237 LONDON/CHANCERY LANE

Chambers of David Etherington QC

18 RED LION COURT,
LONDON EC4A 3EB
Tel: 020 7520 6000 *Fax:* 020 7520 6248
Dx: 478 LONDON/CHANCERY LANE
E-mail: chambers@18rlc.co.uk
Web: www.18rlc.co.uk
Practice Manager: Mark Bennett (Practice Director)
Chambers Director: Elliot Perry
Head of Chambers:
Etherington, Mr David (Q.C.); Recorder . . . M . . . Nov 1979

Spencer, Sir Derek Harold (Q.C.) . . . G . . . Feb 1961
Arlidge, Mr Anthony (Q.C.) . . . M . . . Feb 1962
Cocks, Mr David (Q.C.) . . . L . . . Jun 1961
Parkins, Mr Graham (Q.C.); Recorder . . . I . . . Jul 1972
Sutton, Mr Richard (Q.C.); Recorder . . . M . . . Jul 1969
Shaw, Mr Antony (Q.C.); Recorder . . . M . . . Jul 1975
Carter, Mr Peter (Q.C.) . . . G . . . Jul 1974
Horwood-Smart, Miss Rosamund (Q.C.); Recorder . . . I . . . Jul 1974
Peters, Mr Nigel (Q.C.); Recorder . . . L . . . Jul 1976
Black, Mr John (Q.C.) . . . I . . . Jul 1975
Lynch, Miss Patricia (Q.C.); Recorder . . . I . . . Nov 1979
Benson, Mr Jeremy (Q.C.) . . . I . . . Jul 1978
Johnston, Ms Carey (Q.C.) . . . M . . . Jul 1977
Coughlin, Mr Vincent (Q.C.) . . . M . . . Jul 1980
Harvey, Mr Stephen (Q.C.) . . . G . . . Jul 1979
Lucraft, Mr Mark (Q.C.) . . . I . . . Jul 1984
Lucas, Mr Noel (Q.C.); Recorder . . . M . . . Jul 1979
Hill, Mr Max (Q.C.) . . . M . . . Nov 1987
Spence, Mr Simon (Q.C.) . . . I . . . Jul 1985
Milne, Mr Alexander (Q.C.) . . . G . . . Nov 1981
Bewsey, Miss Jane (Q.C.) . . . I . . . Jul 1986
Levett, Mr Martyn . . . M . . . Nov 1978
Pounder, Mr Gerard . . . L . . . Jul 1980
Jenkins, Miss Kim . . . G . . . Jul 1982
Tucker, Ms Lorraine . . . M . . . Nov 1982
Sheff, Miss Janine . . . M . . . Jan 1983
Shroff, Mr Cyrus . . . G . . . Jul 1983
Joshi, Mr Raj . . . I . . . Jul 1983
Morris, Mr Brendan . . . M . . . Jul 1985
Du Preez, Mr Robin . . . I . . . Nov 1985
Lyons, Mr John . . . M . . . Jul 1986
Marshall, Mr Andrew; Recorder . . . I . . . Jul 1986
Mehta, Mr Sailesh . . . L . . . Jul 1986
Dyble, Mr Steven . . . M . . . Nov 1986
Farrimond, Miss Stephanie . . . M . . . Jul 1987
Walbank, Mr David . . . I . . . Nov 1987
Collery, Mr Shane . . . L . . . Jul 1988
Hales, Ms Sally-Anne . . . G . . . Jul 1988
Beynon, Mr Richard J L . . . I . . . Jul 1990
Lawson, Miss Sara . . . I . . . Oct 1990
Holborn, Mr David . . . I . . . Oct 1991
Thompson, Mr Andrew . . . G . . . Oct 1991
Skelley, Mr Michael . . . I . . . Oct 1991
Gursoy, Mr Ramiz A . . . M . . . Nov 1991
Paxton, Mr Christopher . . . G . . . Nov 1991
Potts, Mr Richard . . . I . . . Nov 1991
Clare, Ms Allison . . . G . . . Oct 1992
Gowen, Mr Matthew . . . L . . . Oct 1992
McNiff, Mr Matthew . . . G . . . Oct 1992
Dempster, Miss Jennifer . . . L . . . Apr 1993
D'Cruz, Mr Rufus . . . L . . . Oct 1993
Forster, Mr Thomas . . . I . . . Nov 1993
May, Miss Nicola . . . G . . . Nov 1993
Jameson, Mr Barnaby . . . M . . . Nov 1993
Nelson, Miss Michelle . . . M . . . Nov 1994
Hall, Miss Jacqueline . . . L . . . Nov 1994
Wiseman, Mr Adam . . . I . . . Nov 1994
Fell, Mr Alistair . . . M . . . Nov 1994
Leigh, Ms Samantha . . . I . . . Nov 1995
Casey, Mr Noel G . . . L . . . Oct 1995
Rose, Mr Stephen . . . G . . . Nov 1995
Karmy-Jones, Miss Riel . . . L . . . Nov 1995
Jones, Ms Gillian . . . I . . . Oct 1996
Wilson, Mr David . . . G . . . Oct 1996
Pickersgill, Mr David . . . M . . . Nov 1996
Requena, Mr Stephen . . . I . . . Oct 1997
Payne, Mr Tom . . . M . . . Oct 1998
Moll, Mr Louis-Peter . . . M . . . Oct 1998
Atkins, Ms Victoria . . . M . . . Nov 1998
Chalkley, Ms Rebecca . . . M . . . Jan 1999
Rickard, Mr Marcus . . . I . . . Jul 2000
Willcocks, Miss Hannah . . . M . . . Jul 2001
Khanna, Ms Priyadarshani . . . I . . . Oct 2001
Dance, Mr Mathew . . . L . . . Jul 2001
Owen, Miss Carys . . . L . . . Oct 2002
Hamid, Ms Ruby . . . L . . . Nov 2002
Islam, Mr Mohammad . . . M . . . Oct 2002
Sawyer, Mr Jamie . . . I . . . Oct 2003
Gargitter, Ms Emma . . . L . . . Nov 2003
Eales, Miss Hannah . . . M . . . Nov 2003
Orr, Mr Matthew . . . L . . . Oct 2004
Oldfield, Ms Jane . . . M . . . Oct 2004
Baines, Mr Max . . . L . . . Mar 2005
Archer, Mr Trevor . . . I . . . Jul 2005
Mahmutaj, Miss Klentiana . . . M . . . Jul 2005
Lewis, Miss Sarah . . . M . . . Jul 2006
Chibafa, Mr Jonathan . . . M . . . Nov 2006
Parsons, Miss Naomi . . . I . . . Oct 2008
Claxton, Mr David . . . M . . . Oct 2008
Dite, Mr Alexis . . . I . . . Nov 2008
Kingswell, Miss Gemma . . . I . . . Jul 2008
Hennessy, Ms Clare . . . G . . . Jul 2009
Kenyon, Ms Laura . . . I . . . Nov 2009
Robinson, Mr Daniel . . . G . . . Jul 2010

Chambers of Ashitey Kwame Nii-Amaa Ollennu

REDEMPTION CHAMBERS,
121 THE VALE, GOLDERS GREEN, LONDON NW11 8TL
Tel: 020 8458 5486 / 07929 511917
E-mail: home@ollennu92.freeserve.co.uk
Administrator: Sylviana Ollennu
Head of Chambers:
Ollennu, Ashitey Kwame Nii-Amaa . . . L . . . Jul 1981

Davies, Mr Harold Rodney Olonindieh . . . L . . . Jan 1978
Goh, Ms Sue . . . G . . . Mar 1997
Glass, Ms Mary Patricia . . . G . . . Nov 2000

renaissance chambers

Chambers of Brian Patrick Jubb

RENAISSANCE CHAMBERS,
5TH FLOOR, GRAY'S INN CHAMBERS, GRAY'S INN, LONDON WC1R 5JA
Tel: 020 7404 1111 *Fax:* 020 7430 1522
Dx: 0074 LONDON/CHANCERY LANE
E-mail: clerks@renaissancechambers.co.uk
Web: www.renaissancechambers.co.uk
Clerk: Mark Venables.
Chambers Director: Elaine Cheeseman
Head of Chambers:
Jubb, Brian Patrick . . . G . . . Nov 1971

Dodson, Joanna (Q.C.) . . . M . . . Nov 1971
Weiniger, Noah; Former Solicitor admitted 1969 . . . G . . . Nov 1984
Clough, Richard William Butler . . . I . . . Nov 1971
Haywood, Janette . . . M . . . Nov 1977
Main Thompson, Dermot . . . G . . . Jul 1977
Wingert, Rachel Thomas . . . M . . . Jul 1980
Plange, Janet . . . G . . . Jul 1981
More O'Ferrall, Geraldine . . . M . . . Jul 1983
Posner, Gabrielle; Recorder . . . I . . . Jul 1984
Nazareth, Melanie Bernadette . . . I . . . Jul 1984
Cox, Nigel John . . . I . . . Nov 1986
Boye-Anawomah, Margo . . . I . . . Nov 1989
Calway, Mark . . . I . . . Feb 1989
Cregan, John-Paul . . . M . . . Nov 1990
Thompson, Polly . . . M . . . Nov 1990
Ancliffe, Shiva . . . L . . . Nov 1991
Seitler, Deborah . . . I . . . Nov 1991
Gilling, Denise . . . L . . . Oct 1992
Jegarajah, Shivani . . . M . . . Jul 1993
Phelan, Margaret; Former Solicitor . . . I . . . Oct 1993
Amiraftabi, Roshanak . . . G . . . Feb 1993
Fisher, Sandra . . . I . . . Nov 1993
Yong, Miss Pearl . . . L . . . Nov 1993
Parr, Judith . . . I . . . Feb 1994
Ahmed, Amina . . . M . . . Feb 1995
Metaxa, William . . . M . . . Nov 1995
Bayati, Charlotte . . . G . . . Nov 1995
Allen, Frances . . . I . . . Oct 1995
Gandhi, Miss Paulene . . . I . . . Oct 1995
Archer, Christopher . . . G . . . Nov 1996
Barran, Tabitha . . . I . . . Oct 1998
Coyle, Stephen . . . M . . . Oct 1998
Gasparro, Julia . . . L . . . Jul 1999
Iqbal, Miss Samina . . . L . . . Oct 1999
Paramjorthy, Mr Nishan . . . L . . . Nov 1999
Palmer, Mr Iain . . . M . . . Nov 1999
Saifolahi, Ms Sanaz . . . L . . . Jul 2000
White, Helen . . . M . . . Oct 2001
Benneh Prempeh, Adelaide . . . L . . . Oct 2001
Yeo, Colin . . . M . . . Mar 2002
Fletcher, Matthew . . . L . . . Mar 2003
Akther, Ms Ripon . . . L . . . Jul 2003
Chokowry, Katy; Former Solicitor . . . M . . . Oct 2003
Fox, Claire . . . M . . . Oct 2003
Physsas, Claire . . . L . . . Oct 2004
Train, Sophie . . . M . . . Jul 2005
Chaudhry, Mehvish . . . L . . . Oct 2008
Pinder, Sarah; Former Solicitor . . . M . . . Oct 2006
Tobin, Kezia . . . M . . . Oct 2010
Swan, Jennifer . . . M . . . Oct 2009
Hinchcliffe, Prof Doreen* . . . G . . . Nov 1953
Lillington, Mr Simon* . . . M . . . Nov 1980
Compton, Timothy* . . . I . . . Nov 1984

Chambers specialises in all aspects of family law, including public and private child law, adoption, wardship, child abduction, forced marriage, domestic violence and financial/ancillary relief. Chambers also specialises in immigration law, including asylum, judicial review and entry clearance/deportation proceedings.

Chambers of Chaim David Hirsch Wolchover

RIDGEWAY CHAMBERS,
6 THE RIDGEWAY, GOLDERS GREEN, LONDON NW11 8TB
Tel: 020 8455 2939
E-mail: davidwolchover@ukonline.co.uk
Head of Chambers:
Wolchover, Mr Chaim David Hirsch . . . G . . . Jul 1971

Chambers of Phillip Proghoulis

ROEHAMPTON CHAMBERS,
30 STOUGHTON CLOSE, ROEHAMPTON, LONDON SW15 4LS
Tel: 020 8788 1238 *Fax:* 020 8788 1238
Head of Chambers:
Proghoulis, Mr Phillip* . . . I . . . Nov 1963

10

SELBORNE CHAMBERS,
10 ESSEX STREET, LONDON WC2R 3AA
Tel: 020 7420 9500 ***Fax:*** 020 7420 9555
Dx: 185 LONDON/CHANCERY LANE
E-mail: clerks@selbornechambers.co.uk
Clerk: Greg Piner.
Administrator: Angela Wiggett

Chambers of James Watson QC and John Beggs QC

3 SERJEANTS' INN,
LONDON EC4Y 1BQ
Est: 1973
Tel: 020 7427 5000 ***Fax:*** 020 7353 0425
Dx: 421 LONDON/CHANCERY LANE
E-mail: clerks@3serjeantsinn.com
Clerk: Nick Salt; Lee Johnson.
Practice Manager: Martin Dyke
Head of Chambers:
Watson, Mr James (Q.C.) . . . M. . . Nov 1979
Beggs, Mr John (Q.C.) . . . G. . . Nov 1989

Francis, Mr Robert Anthony (Q.C.) . . . I . . . Jul 1973
Hopkins, Mr Adrian Mark (Q.C.) . . . L. . . Nov 1984
Moon, Mr Philip Charles Angus (Q.C.) . . . M. . . Nov 1986
O'Rourke, Miss Mary Bernadette (Q.C.) . . . G. . . Nov 1981
Hugh-Jones, Mr George (Q.C.) . . . M. . . Nov 1983
Johnston, Mr Christopher (Q.C.) . . . G. . . Nov 1990
Naughton, Mr Philip Anthony (Q.C.)* . . . G. . . Apr 1970
Gaisford, Mr Philip David . . . G. . . Nov 1969
Fortune, Mr Malcolm Donald Porter; Recorder (1994) . . . M. . . Jul 1972
Neale, Miss Fiona Rosalind . . . M. . . Jul 1981
Hockton, Mr Andrew Ian Callinhan . . . M. . . Nov 1984
Mylonas, Mr Michael John . . . G. . . Jul 1988
Spencer, Mr Paul Anthony . . . M. . . Nov 1988
Holl-Allen, Mr Jonathan . . . I . . . Nov 1990
Mullany, Mr Nicholas . . . I . . . Oct 2007
Horne, Mr Michael . . . G. . . Oct 1992
Boyle, Mr Gerard . . . G. . . Nov 1992
Gollop, Katie . . . G. . . Jan 1993
Partridge, Dr Richard Charles . . . L. . . Nov 1994
Ley-Morgan, Mr Mark John . . . G. . . Nov 1994
Clarke, Ms Sarah . . . I . . . Oct 1994
Powell, Ms Debra . . . G. . . Oct 1995
de Bono, Mr John . . . G. . . Oct 1995
Thomas, Mr George L . . . G. . . Oct 1995
Bradley, Ms Clodagh Maria . . . L. . . Oct 1996
Morley, Mr Stephen . . . I . . . Oct 1996
Davidson, Dr Ranald . . . I . . . Nov 1996
Dolan, Ms Bridget . . . M. . . Oct 1997
Green, Mr Samuel . . . L. . . Oct 1998
Cridland, Mr Simon James . . . M. . . Mar 1999
Davy, Mr Neil Geoffrey . . . M. . . Oct 2000
Ballard, Ms Briony Elizabeth . . . M. . . Nov 2000
Watson, Miss Claire Elizabeth . . . M. . . Jan 2001
Simcock, Miss Sarah Louise . . . I . . . Jan 2001
Knight, Heidi . . . L. . . Jan 2001
Street, Miss Amy Caroline . . . I . . . Oct 2002
Paterson, Miss Fiona . . . M. . . Mar 2003
Hallin, Mr Conrad . . . I . . . Jul 2004
Woods, Ms Leanne . . . I . . . Oct 2005
Pleeth, Mr Edward . . . I . . . Jul 2005
Berry, Mr James Michael . . . L. . . Jun 2006
Williamson, Mr Oliver Jack . . . M. . . Jul 2008
Rickard, Ms Susanna . . . M. . . Jul 2009
Fernando, Mr Pravin . . . I . . . Oct 2009
Jackson, Mr Anthony Warren* . . . I . . . Oct 1995
Goodrich, Ms Siobhan* . . . G. . . Nov 1980

Chambers of Alan Boyle QC

SERLE COURT,
6 NEW SQUARE, LINCOLN'S INN, LONDON WC2A 3QS
Tel: 020 7242 6105 ***Fax:*** 020 7405 4004
Dx: 1025 LONDON/CHANCERY LANE
E-mail: clerks@serlecourt.co.uk
Clerk: Seniors: Steve Whitaker (Head Clerk); Nick Hockney; Paul Reece.
Practice Manager: Nicola Sawford
Chambers Director: Nicola Sawford
Head of Chambers:
Boyle, Mr Alan (Q.C.) . . . L. . . Nov 1972

Talbot, Mr Patrick (Q.C.); Recorder . . . L. . . Jul 1969
Hinks, Mr Frank (Q.C.) . . . L. . . Jul 1973
Corbett, James (Q.C.) . . . I . . . Jul 1975
Singh, Mr Kuldip (Q.C.) . . . M. . . Jul 1975
Joffe, Mr Victor (Q.C.) . . . M. . . Nov 1975
McMaster, Mr Peter (Q.C.) . . . M. . . Jul 1981
Dowley, Mr Dominic (Q.C.) . . . G. . . Jul 1983
Jones, Ms Elizabeth (Q.C.) . . . M. . . Nov 1984
Jones, Mr Philip (Q.C.) . . . L. . . Jul 1985
Marshall, Mr Philip (Q.C.) . . . L. . . Jun 1987
Lavender, Mr Nicholas (Q.C.) . . . I . . . Jul 1989
Qureshi, Mr Khawar (Q.C.) . . . M. . . Jul 1990
Asprey, Mr Nicholas . . . I . . . Jul 1969
Ballantyne, Prof William . . . I . . . Nov 1977
Francis, Mr Andrew . . . L. . . Nov 1977
Rogers, Ms Beverly-Ann . . . M. . . Jul 1978
Henderson, Mr William H . . . I . . . Jul 1978
Behrens, James . . . M. . . Jul 1979
Walford, Mr Richard . . . M. . . Jul 1984
Harrison, Mr Nicholas . . . L. . . Jul 1988
Clark, Miss Geraldine . . . G. . . Jul 1988
Moran, Mr Andrew . . . M. . . Feb 1989
Hoffmann, Ms Clare . . . G. . . Oct 1990
Stoner, Mr Christopher P . . . L. . . Oct 1991
Close, Mr Douglas . . . L. . . Nov 1991
Blayney, Mr David . . . L. . . Oct 1992
Bruce, Mr Andrew . . . M. . . Oct 1992
Machell, Mr John . . . I . . . Oct 1993
Drake, Mr David . . . I . . . Nov 1994
Higgo, Mr Justin . . . G. . . Feb 1995
Lightman, Mr Daniel . . . L. . . Oct 1995
Norbury, Mr Hugh . . . L. . . Nov 1995
Collingwood, Mr Timothy . . . G. . . Oct 1996
Adkin, Mr Jonathan . . . G. . . Nov 1997
Richardson, Mr Giles . . . I . . . Oct 1997
Braithwaite, Mr Thomas J . . . L. . . Oct 1998
Hattan, Mr Simon . . . M. . . Jan 1999
Haywood, Jennifer . . . L. . . Jul 2001
Jordan, Ms Ruth; Junior Counsel to the Crown (C Panel) . . . I . . . Oct 2001
Holtham, Ms Ruth . . . M. . . Jan 2001
Hagen, Mr Dakis . . . L. . . Oct 2002
Fowles, Mr Jonathan . . . G. . . Jul 2004
Morrison, Mr Matthew John . . . L. . . Jan 2004
Rathmell, Mr Robin . . . I . . . Oct 2006
Mather, Mr James David . . . L. . . Oct 2006
Fritz, Mr Dan McCourt . . . L. . . Jan 2007
Tilley, Mr Gareth . . . L. . . Jan 2007

SETTLEMENT COUNSEL,
24 CYRIL MANSIONS, PRINCE OF WALES DRIVE, LONDON SW11 4HP
Tel: 07976 706128
E-mail: dstern@settlementcounsel.com

Chambers of Anwobo Amihere

20 SEWARDSTONE GARDENS,
LONDON E4 7QE
Tel: 020 8524 3054
Head of Chambers:
Amihere, Mr Anwobo . . . M. . . Nov 1970

Chambers of N Smith

NICK SMITH BARRISTER,
FLAT 2, HART HOUSE, 4 LILFORD ROAD, LONDON SE5 9HJ
Tel: 020 7566 8244
Head of Chambers:
Smith, Mr Nick . . . L. . . Jan 1988

SNARESBROOK CHAMBERS,
45 EMPRESS AVENUE, LONDON E12 5ET
Tel: 07966 194001 ***Fax:*** 020 8989 7765
E-mail: info@snaresbrookchambers.com

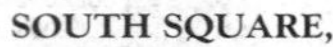

SOUTH SQUARE,
3-4 SOUTH SQUARE, GRAY'S INN, LONDON WC1R 5HP
Tel: 020 7696 9900 ***Fax:*** 020 7696 9911
Dx: 338 LONDON/CHANCERY LANE
E-mail: practicemanagers@southsquare.com
Web: www.southsquare.com
Practice Manager: Michael Killick; Jim Costa; Dylan Playfoot; Marco Malatesta
Crystal, Mr Michael (Q.C.) . . . M. . . Nov 1970
Brougham, Mr Christopher J (Q.C.) . . . I . . . Nov 1969
Moss, Mr Gabriel (Q.C.) . . . L. . . Jul 1974
Mortimore, Mr Simon (Q.C.) . . . I . . . Jul 1972
Adkins, Mr Richard (Q.C.) . . . M. . . Jul 1982
Sheldon, Mr Richard M (Q.C.) . . . G. . . Jul 1979
Hacker, Mr Richard D (Q.C.) . . . L. . . Nov 1977
Knowles, Mr Robin St J (Q.C.) CBE . . . M. . . Jul 1982
Phillips, Mr Mark (Q.C.) . . . I . . . Jul 1984
Dicker, Mr Robin (Q.C.) . . . M. . . Apr 1986
Trower, Mr William S P (Q.C.) . . . L. . . Jul 1983
Pascoe, Mr Martin (Q.C.) . . . L. . . Jul 1977
Oditah, Mr Fidelis (Q.C.) . . . L. . . Nov 1992
Alexander, Mr David R J (Q.C.) . . . M. . . Nov 1987
Zacaroli, Mr Antony (Q.C.) . . . M. . . Nov 1987
Atherton, Mr Stephen N (Q.C.) . . . M. . . Jul 1989
Marks, Mr David M (Q.C.) . . . G. . . Nov 1974
Davis, Mr Glen (Q.C.) . . . M. . . Oct 1992
Isaacs, Mr Barry (Q.C.) . . . I . . . Oct 1994
Toube, Ms Felicity (Q.C.) . . . I . . . Nov 1995
DeKoven, Mr Ronald . . . L. . . Jan 2009
Briggs, Mr John B . . . G. . . Jul 1973
Shandro, Mr Sandy . . . L. . . Jan 2008
Arnold, Mr Mark . . . M. . . Jul 1988
Goodison, Mr Adam . . . M. . . Oct 1990
Stonefrost, Ms Hilary . . . M. . . Nov 1991
Tamlyn, Mr Lloyd . . . G. . . Nov 1991
Valentin, Mr Ben . . . I . . . Nov 1995
Goldring, Mr Jeremy . . . L. . . Oct 1996
Frazer, Ms Lucy . . . M. . . Oct 1996
Allison, Mr David . . . M. . . Nov 1998
Bayfield, Mr Daniel . . . I . . . Oct 1998
Smith, Mr Tom . . . M. . . Oct 1999
Fisher, Mr Richard . . . I . . . Oct 2000
Leahy, Miss Blair . . . I . . . Jun 2001
Robins, Mr Stephen . . . L. . . Nov 2001
Perkins, Joanna . . . M. . . Jan 2001
Haywood, Mr Marcus . . . L. . . Nov 2002
Thornley, Miss Hannah . . . L. . . Oct 2003
Willson, Mr William . . . L. . . Oct 2006
Peters, Ms Georgina . . . L. . . Jul 2005
Al-Attar, Mr Adam . . . L. . . Nov 2007
Phillips, Mr Henry . . . L. . . Jan 2008
Cooke, Miss Charlotte . . . M. . . Jan 2008
Fletcher, Prof Ian F . . . L. . . Nov 1971
Worthington, Prof Sarah (Q.C.) . . . M. . . Mar 2005
Mokal, Prof Riz . . . G. . . Nov 1997
Mortimer, Mr Barry (Q.C.)* . . . M. . . Oct 1956
Bristoll, Ms Sandra* . . . M. . . Jan 1989
Ismail, Ms Roxanne* . . . L. . . Nov 1993
Bamford, Mr Colin* . . . M. . . May 2002
Heinz, Mr Volker* . . . I . . . Jan 1989
Fuller, Mr Simon; Associate Member . . . L. . . Oct 2003

All aspects of business, financial and commercial law, in particular Corporate and International insolvency, personal insolvency, company law, partnership disputes, banking, commercial litigation, financial services, stock exchange and commodities, trust law, domestic and international arbitration, insurance/reinsurance, European Union Law, professional negligence and disciplinary matters.

Chambers of Michael Silverleaf QC

11 SOUTH SQUARE,
GRAY'S INN, LONDON WC1R 5EY
Tel: 020 7405 1222 ***Fax:*** 020 7242 4282
Dx: 433 LONDON/CHANCERY LANE
E-mail: clerks@11southsquare.com
Clerk: Senior: Ashley Carr. Ben Connor.
Head of Chambers:
Silverleaf, Mr Michael (Q.C.) . . . G. . . May 1980

Carr, Mr Henry (Q.C.) . . . G. . . May 1982
Purvis, Mr Iain (Q.C.) . . . G. . . Jul 1986
Vanhegan, Mr Mark (Q.C.) . . . L. . . Nov 1990
Acland, Dr Piers (Q.C.) . . . L. . . Nov 1993
Whittle, Dr Henry . . . G. . . Jul 1975
Hacon, Mr Richard . . . G. . . Nov 1979
Lawrence, Dr Heather B . . . M. . . Oct 1990
Reid, Miss Jacqueline . . . M. . . Oct 1992
Cuddigan, Mr Hugo Jonathan . . . M. . . Nov 1995
Fernando, Mr Giles Rudyard . . . G. . . Mar 1998
Brandreth, Mr Benet Xan . . . M. . . Nov 1999
Nicholson, Dr Brian . . . L. . . Jul 2000
Edwards-Stuart, Miss Anna . . . L. . . Oct 2003
Pickard, Miss Kathryn . . . I . . . Oct 2002
Alkin, Mr Tom . . . M. . . Jan 2007
Bently, Prof Lionel* . . . I . . . Jan 2009

Chambers of Simon Draycott QC

5 ST ANDREW'S HILL,
LONDON EC4V 5BZ
Tel: 020 7332 5400 ***Fax:*** 020 7489 7847
Dx: 417 LONDON
E-mail: clerks@5sah.co.uk
Clerk: William Lavell; Gary Norton.
Head of Chambers:
Draycott, Mr Simon (Q.C.) . . . M. . . Jul 1977

Bartlett, Mr Roger J L . . . M. . . Jul 1968
Ross, Mr David . . . M. . . Nov 1974
Bennett, Mr Charles H . . . I . . . Jul 1972
Harris, Mr James . . . G. . . Nov 1975
Birch, Mr Roger . . . G. . . Nov 1979
Devlin, Mr Bernard . . . G. . . Nov 1980
May, Mr Christopher . . . M. . . Nov 1983
Ingram, Mr Jonathan . . . I . . . Jul 1984
Prosser, Mr Anthony . . . I . . . Jul 1985
Foinette, Mr Ian . . . M. . . Nov 1986
Knight, Miss Caroline . . . I . . . Jul 1985
Rupasinha, Mr Sunil . . . I . . . Nov 1983
Bird, Mr Andrew J . . . I . . . Jul 1987
Munir, Dr A Edward . . . G. . . Jun 1956
Connolly, Mr Dominic . . . M. . . Feb 1989
Walker, Mr Allister David . . . I . . . Nov 1990
Hewitt, Mr David . . . M. . . Jul 1991
Walters, Miss Vivian . . . M. . . Nov 1991
Wright, Mr Trevor . . . M. . . Nov 1992
Cotter, Mr Mark . . . M. . . Nov 1994
Goldring, Miss Jenny . . . M. . . Nov 1993
Galway-Copper, Mr Philip . . . I . . . Jan 1993
Valder, Mr Paul . . . I . . . Nov 1994
Mullins, Mr Mark . . . I . . . Nov 1995
Pons, Mr Gary . . . G. . . Jan 1995
Connell, Mr Edward . . . M. . . Oct 1996
Burge, Mr Edmund . . . L. . . Oct 1997
Scott, Mr Richard Michael . . . M. . . Jul 1997
Levett, Miss Francesca . . . L. . . Oct 1997
Ramble, Mr Don . . . M. . . Nov 1998
Turner, Mr Jonathan . . . I . . . Nov 1999
Hewitt, Miss Wendy . . . M. . . Nov 1999
Warrington, Mr John . . . L. . . Jul 2000
Fletcher, Mr James . . . M. . . Jan 2000
Heylin, Mr Alexander . . . M. . . Jan 2000
White, Miss Abigail Claire . . . L. . . Jan 2000
Rooke, Mr Alex . . . L. . . Jan 2001
Todd, Miss Bridget . . . G. . . Jan 2001
Gates, Miss Serena . . . M. . . Jan 2001
Butt, Miss Nasra . . . G. . . Oct 2002
Udom, Miss Ini . . . L. . . Jan 2002
McNeill, Mr David . . . I . . . Jan 2003
Keal, Mr John . . . L. . . Jan 2004
Cooper, Miss Claire . . . L. . . Jan 2002
Draycott, Miss Natasha . . . M. . . Jan 2005
Nejranowski, Miss Tessa . . . M. . . Jan 2005
Keith, Mr Ben . . . L. . . Jan 2004

Chambers of Veronica Mary Ramsden

STAPLE INN CHAMBERS,
1ST FLOOR, 9-10 STAPLE INN, HOLBORN BARS, LONDON WC1V 7QH
Tel: 020 7242 5240 ***Fax:*** 020 7405 9495
Dx: 132 LONDON/CHANCERY LANE
E-mail: clerks@stapleinn.co.uk
Clerk: Senior: Yvonne Simmons. Cameron Clements; Stuart Davis.
Head of Chambers:
Ramsden, Miss Veronica Mary . . . G . . . Jul 1979

Llewellyn, Mr Charles . . . G . . . Jul 1978
Tresman, Mr Lewis Robert Simon . . . G . . . Nov 1980
Jones, Mr Paul Alan . . . I . . . Jul 1981
Aslam, Q Mahmud . . . G . . . Jul 1983
Trumpington, Mr John Henry . . . M . . . Feb 1985
Brooks, Miss Alison Louise . . . I . . . Jul 1989
McCormack, Mr Alan . . . L . . . Oct 1990
Brown, Miss Andrea . . . L . . . Nov 1991
Vakil, Mr Jimmy . . . M . . . Oct 1993
Panagiotopoulou, Miss Tania . . . M . . . Oct 1994
Clarke, Miss Lisa . . . G . . . Oct 1995
Panagiotopoulou, Miss Sophie . . . M . . . Nov 1995
Frame, Mr Stuart . . . G . . . May 1997
Kelly, Mr Shaw M . . . M . . . Oct 1997
Marks, Ms Katherine . . . M . . . Oct 1998
D'Aguilar, Mr Hugh . . . L . . . Nov 1998
Evans, Mr Nicholas . . . I . . . Jan 2001
Eaton, Mr Tobias . . . I . . . Nov 2001
Matthews, Miss Nicola . . . M . . . Jan 2002
Glaister-Young, Ms Shelly . . . I . . . Jan 2004
Chan, Miss Rachel Siv Yee . . . I . . . Jul 2004
Webster, Miss Sarah . . . M . . . Jul 2006
Talbot, Miss Ann-Marie . . . M . . . Oct 2006
Henry, Miss Winsome H* . . . M . . . Nov 1979
Woodhouse, Mr Alaric* . . . L . . . Jul 2003

Chambers of Jamal Jamil Nasir

2 STONE BUILDINGS,
1ST FLOOR, LINCOLN'S INN, LONDON WC2A 3RH
Tel: 020 7405 3818 ***Fax:*** 020 7831 1971
E-mail: nasirja@btconnect.com
Clerk: E J Morris.
Head of Chambers:
Nasir, Dr Jamal Jamil . . . L . . . Jan 1948

Chambers of Sarah Jane Asplin QC

3 STONE BUILDINGS,
LINCOLN'S INN, LONDON WC2A 3XL
Tel: 020 7242 4937 ***Fax:*** 020 7405 3896
Dx: 317 LONDON/CHANCERY LANE
E-mail: clerks@3sb.law.co.uk
Clerk: Senior: Andrew Palmer. Gary Bateman; Adie Palmer; Bill Rice; Rory Harrison.
Head of Chambers:
Asplin, Miss Sarah Jane (Q.C.) . . . G . . . Jul 1984

De Lacy, Mr Richard (Q.C.) . . . M . . . Jul 1976
Chaisty, Mr Paul (Q.C.) . . . L . . . Jul 1982
Cooper, Mr Gilead P (Q.C.) . . . M . . . Nov 1983
Lord, Mr David William (Q.C.) . . . M . . . Jul 1987
Palmer, Prof Norman Ernest (Q.C.) . . . G . . . Jul 1973
Topham, Mr Geoffrey John . . . L . . . Jun 1964
Cosedge, Mr Andrew John . . . I . . . Jul 1972
Gibbons, Mr James Francis . . . G . . . Jul 1974
Tunkel, Mr Alan Michael . . . M . . . Jul 1976
da Silva, Mr David . . . M . . . Nov 1978
Hantusch, Mr Robert Anthony . . . I . . . Jul 1982
Peacocke, Mrs Teresa Rosen . . . L . . . Nov 1982
Collaco Moraes, Francis . . . L . . . Jan 1985
Watson, Mr Ian David . . . L . . . Jul 2005
Twigger, Mr Andrew Mark . . . I . . . Nov 1994
Carney, Mr Joseph . . . L . . . Nov 2004
Moeran, Mr Fenner Orlando . . . L . . . Nov 1996
Wilson, Mr Richard . . . M . . . Nov 1996
Child, Mr Andrew J . . . L . . . Nov 1997
Burton, Mr Paul . . . L . . . Oct 1998
Bornman, Miss Kerry . . . M . . . Nov 1999
Downes, Ms Charlotte . . . L . . . May 1997
McDonnell, Miss Constance . . . L . . . Jul 2000
Dilnot, Miss Anna . . . L . . . Mar 2008
Harris, Mr Luke . . . I . . . Jul 2001
Hilton, Mr Oliver James . . . L . . . Jul 2002
Slater, Mr Matthew James; Treasury Counsel . . . M . . . Nov 2005
Edge, Miss Charlotte Louise . . . L . . . Oct 2006
Weale, Mr James . . . I . . . Jan 2007
Seaman, Miss Jennifer . . . L . . . Jan 2007

Chambers of George Bompas QC

4 STONE BUILDINGS,
GROUND FLOOR, LINCOLN'S INN, LONDON WC2A 3XT
Tel: 020 7242 5524 ***Fax:*** 020 7831 7907
Dx: 385 LONDON/CHANCERY LANE
E-mail: clerks@4stonebuildings.com
Web: www.4stonebuildings.com
Clerk: Senior: David Goddard.
Head of Chambers:
Bompas, Mr George (Q.C.) . . . M . . . Jul 1975

Brisby, Mr John C S M (Q.C.) . . . L . . . Jul 1978
Davis-White, Mr Malcolm (Q.C.) . . . M . . . Jul 1984
Miles, Mr Robert J (Q.C.) . . . L . . . Nov 1987
Crow, Mr Jonathan R (Q.C.); First Treasury Counsel to the Crown . . . L . . . Jul 1981
Hunt, Mr Stephen . . . L . . . Jul 1968
Griffiths, Mr Peter R . . . I . . . Jul 1977
Nicholson, Miss Rosalind V; Tenant . . . G . . . Jul 1987
Marquand, Mr Charles . . . I . . . Nov 1987
Harman, Miss Sarah Jane; Junior Counsel to the Crown (A) . . . L . . . Nov 1987
Harrison, Mr Christopher . . . G . . . Nov 1988
Brettler, Mr Jonathan Samuel . . . L . . . Nov 1988
Greenwood, Mr Paul Jerome . . . L . . . Nov 1991
Clutterbuck, Mr Andrew . . . M . . . Oct 1992
Cox, Mr Nicholas; Junior Counsel to the Crown (A) . M . . . Oct 1992
Hill, Mr Richard Geoffrey; Junior Counsel to the Crown (A) . . . G . . . Oct 1993
Fraser, Mr Orlando . . . I . . . Nov 1994
Markham, Miss Anna . . . L . . . Oct 1996
Boeddinghaus, Mr Hermann . . . L . . . Nov 1996
de Mestre, Mr Andrew . . . M . . . Mar 1998
Denton-Cox, Mr Gregory; Junior Counsel to the Crown (C) . . . L . . . Jul 2000
Shivji, Mr Sharif . . . L . . . Jul 2001
Neressian, Mr Tiran; Junior Counsel to the Crown (C) . . . L . . . Nov 2002
Tomson, Mr Alastair . . . L . . . Jan 2004
Holliman, Mr Adam . . . L . . . Jan 2005
Gentleman, Mr Tom . . . L . . . Jan 2005
Lilly, Mr Donald . . . M . . . Jan 2006
Cook, Mr Alexander . . . L . . . Oct 2008
Timmins, Miss Nicola . . . G . . . Oct 2008
Knott, Mr James . . . I . . . Jan 2008
Holland, Mrs Eleanor . . . L . . . Jan 2010
Wigley, Mr Joseph . . . M . . . Jan 2010

Work Description: Company Law, Insolvency, Regulatory, Financial Service Law and related Commercial and Business Law.

Chambers of Henry Harrod

5 STONE BUILDINGS,
LINCOLN'S INN, LONDON WC2A 3XT
Tel: 020 7242 6201 ***Fax:*** 020 7831 8102
Dx: 304 LONDON/CHANCERY LANE
E-mail: clerks@5sblaw.com
Clerk: Senior: Paul Jennings.
Administrator: Annie Girling
Head of Chambers:
Harrod, Mr Henry . . . L . . . Jul 1963

Herbert, Mr Mark (Q.C.) . . . L . . . Jul 1974
Simmonds, Mr Andrew John (Q.C.) . . . M . . . Nov 1980
Warnock-Smith, Mrs Shan (Q.C.) . . . G . . . Jul 1971
Tidmarsh, Mr Christopher Ralph Francis (Q.C.) . . . L . . . Nov 1985
Reed, Miss Penelope (Q.C.) . . . I . . . Jul 1983
Whitehouse, Mr Christopher J . . . L . . . Feb 1972
Blackett-Ord, Mr Mark . . . L . . . Jul 1974
Farber, Mr Martin . . . G . . . Jul 1976
O'Sullivan, Mr Michael Morton . . . L . . . Jul 1986
Rolfe, Mr Patrick . . . M . . . Nov 1987
Rich, Miss A Barbara . . . G . . . Oct 1990
Angus, Ms Tracey A . . . I . . . Nov 1991
Legge, Mr Henry . . . M . . . Nov 1993
Rees, Mr David Benjamin . . . L . . . Oct 1994
Clarke, Miss Anna Victoria . . . I . . . Nov 1994
Sartin, Mr Leon . . . M . . . Nov 1997
Haren, Ms Sarah . . . M . . . Jan 1999
Entwistle, Mr Thomas . . . G . . . Nov 2001
Goldsmith, Mr Joseph . . . L . . . Nov 2003
Baxter, Mr Mark . . . L . . . Jul 2006
Kenny, Ms Caroline . . . I . . . Oct 2006
Hughes, Ms Ruth . . . L . . . Jan 2007
East, Mr William . . . L . . . Jan 2008
Holland, Mr Jordan . . . M . . . Oct 2009

Chambers of Edward Cohen

11 STONE BUILDINGS,
LINCOLN'S INN, LONDON WC2A 3TG
Tel: 020 7831 6381 ***Fax:*** 020 7831 2575
Dx: 1022 LONDON/CHANCERY LANE
E-mail: clerks@11sb.com
Clerk: Matthew Curness; Gary Collins; Richard Powell; Lee Wright; Chris Chiles; Justin Yoong; Ben Opoku; Harrison Killick.
Administrator: Nilam Shah
Chambers Director: Michael Couling
Head of Chambers:
Cohen, Mr Edward . . . M . . . Jul 1972

Beckman, Mr Michael (Q.C.) . . . L . . . May 1954
Cousins, Mr Jeremy (Q.C.); Deputy High Court Judge . . . M . . . Jul 1977
Giret, Ms Jane (Q.C.) . . . I . . . Jul 1981
Gourgey, Mr Alan (Q.C.) . . . L . . . Jul 1984
Agnello, Ms Raquel (Q.C.) . . . I . . . Nov 1986
Hilliard, Miss Alexandra (Q.C.) . . . M . . . Nov 1987
Salter, Mr Adrian . . . M . . . Jul 1973
Bishop, Mr Alan . . . M . . . Jul 1973
McCue, Mr Donald . . . L . . . Jul 1974
Meares, Mr Nigel . . . M . . . Nov 1975
Deacon, Mr Robert . . . G . . . Jul 1976
Arkush, Mr Jonathan . . . M . . . Nov 1977
Ross, Mr Sidney . . . M . . . Jul 1983
Kyriakides, Ms Tina . . . L . . . Jul 1984
Shekerdemian, Ms Marcia . . . M . . . Jul 1987
Penny, Mr Tim . . . I . . . Jul 1988
Stern, Mr David; Associate Member* . . . L . . . Jul 1989
Kennedy-McGregor, Ms Marilyn . . . G . . . Jul 1989
Deacock, Mr Adam Jason . . . M . . . Nov 1991
Eilledge, Miss Amanda . . . L . . . Nov 1991
Meyer, Miss Birgitta . . . M . . . Nov 1992
Mallin, Mr Max . . . I . . . Oct 1993
Barnard, Mr James . . . M . . . Oct 1993
Cowen, Mr Timothy . . . I . . . Oct 1993
Pettican, Mr Kevin . . . I . . . Jan 1994
Lopian, Dr Jonathan B . . . M . . . Nov 1994
Boardman, Mr Christopher . . . L . . . Oct 1995
Riley, Mr Jamie . . . L . . . Nov 1995
Keel, Mr Douglas; Associate Member* . . . L . . . Oct 1997
Watson, Mr Alaric . . . M . . . Oct 1997
Pester, Mr Iain . . . L . . . Nov 1999
Ouwehand, Mr Martin . . . L . . . Oct 2002
Comiskey, Mr Reuben . . . L . . . Nov 2002
Nicholls, Mr David . . . L . . . Dec 2002
Robinson, Mr Thomas . . . L . . . Jan 2003
Peters, Mr David . . . M . . . Jan 2005
McCambley, Ms Dawn . . . L . . . Oct 2005
Hinks, Mr Philip Martyn . . . L . . . Oct 2008
Shepherd, Mr Thomas Paul . . . L . . . Oct 2008
Head, Mr Peter James . . . L . . . Oct 2008
Newton, Miss Laura . . . M . . . Oct 2009

Chambers of Christopher Cant

9 STONE BUILDINGS BARRISTERS CHAMBERS,
LINCOLN'S INN, LONDON WC2A 3NN
Tel: 020 7404 5055 ***Fax:*** 020 7405 1551
Dx: 314 LONDON/CHANCERY LANE
E-mail: clerks@9stonebuildings.com
Clerk: Senior: Alan Austin.
Head of Chambers:
Cant, Mr Christopher . . . L . . . Jul 1973

Chapman, Mr Vivian (Q.C.); Recorder . . . L . . . Jul 1970
Ashe, Mr Michael (Q.C.) . . . M . . . Jul 1971
Jacob, Mr Isaac; Recorder/Assistant Parliamentary Boundary Commissioner . . . L . . . Jul 1963
Rowell, Mr David Stewart . . . G . . . Jul 1972
Denehan, Mr Edward B A . . . L . . . Jul 1981
Young, Mr Martin . . . M . . . Nov 1984
Counsell, Miss Lynne M . . . I . . . Jul 1986
Spratt, Mr Christopher David . . . G . . . Nov 1986
Foley, Miss Sheila . . . I . . . Nov 1988
Sisley, Mr Timothy Julian Crispin . . . M . . . Jul 1989
Smart, Mr John Andrew C . . . M . . . Nov 1989
Flower, Mr Philip . . . I . . . Nov 1979
Brown, Mr Phillip Steven . . . L . . . Oct 1991
Richman, Mrs Helene Pines . . . M . . . Jul 1992
Wood, Miss Lana Claire . . . G . . . Oct 1993
Shaw, Mr Peter M . . . M . . . Nov 1995
Bromilow, Mr Daniel . . . G . . . Nov 1996
Palser, Miss Elaine Jaqueline . . . M . . . Oct 2002
O'Mahony, Mr Jonathan Solomon . . . I . . . Nov 2000
Curl, Mr Joseph . . . L . . . Jan 2007
Hewitt, Mr Edward . . . I . . . Jan 2007
MacEvilly, Mr Conn . . . I . . . Jan 1997
Brown, Mr Rory Steven . . . I . . . Jan 2009
Deb, Miss Shuvra . . . I . . . Nov 2007

Chambers of Gary Fern

7 STONE BUILDINGS INTELLECTUAL PROPERTY,
FIRST FLOOR, 7 STONE BUILDINGS, LINCOLN'S INN, LONDON WC2A 3SZ
Tel: 020 7242 8848 ***Fax:*** 020 7242 8849
E-mail: 7stonebuildings@btconnect.com
Head of Chambers:
Fern, Mr Gary . . . L . . . Oct 1992

Ehiribe, Ike . . . L . . . Nov 1996
Aston, Eva . . . L . . . Jan 2003

10

Chambers of Steven M Gee QC

STONE CHAMBERS,
4 FIELD COURT, GRAY'S INN, LONDON WC1R 5EA
Tel: 020 7440 6900 ***Fax:*** 020 7242 0197
Dx: 483 LONDON/CHANCERY LANE
E-mail: clerks@stonechambers.com
Clerk: Senior: Jean-Pierre Schulz.
Head of Chambers:
Gee, Mr Steven M (Q.C.) . . . M . . . Jul 1975

Reeder, Mr John (Q.C.) . . . G . . . Jul 1971
Blackburn, Mrs Elizabeth (Q.C.) . . . M . . . Jul 1978
Selvaratnam, Miss Vasanti (Q.C.) . . . M . . . Jul 1983
Hill, Mr Timothy (Q.C.) . . . M . . . Oct 1990
Martin-Clark, Mr David . . . G . . . Jun 1961
Miller, Miss Sarah Elizabeth Barbara . . . G . . . Nov 1971
Benny, Mr Dato' Jude; Associate Member . . . M . . . Jan 1982
Wright, Mr Colin . . . M . . . Jul 1987
Happe, Mr Dominic . . . G . . . Nov 1993
Toney, Miss Rachel . . . L . . . Nov 1998
Gibbons, Miss Mary . . . L . . . Mar 1999
Ahmed, Mr Ishfaq . . . L . . . Oct 1999
Aswani, Ravi . . . L . . . Jul 2000
Jones, Mr Mark . . . L . . . Nov 2000
Riches, Mr Philip . . . I . . . Nov 2001
Whitehead, Mr Tom . . . I . . . Oct 2002
Shirley, Mr James . . . M . . . Nov 2002
Debattista, Professor Charles . . . M . . . Jul 2004
Henderson, Mr Neil . . . I . . . Oct 2004
Howells, Mr Stephen . . . M . . . Jul 2006
Lightfoot, Mr Jeremy . . . L . . . Jul 2006
Whitehouse-Vaux, Mr William Edward* . . . I . . . Nov 1977
Healy, Miss Sandra Ita . . . M . . . Jul 2007
Ellis, Mr Henry . . . L . . . Jan 2008
Stevenson, Mr Peter . . . I . . . Jan 2008

Chambers of Gavin B Purves

SWAN HOUSE,
PO BOX 8749, LONDON W13 8ZX
Tel: 020 8998 3035 ***Fax:*** 020 8998 3055
E-mail: swanchambers@yahoo.co.uk
Clerk: Julie Harmer; Andrew Hutchin.
Head of Chambers:
Purves, Mr Gavin B . . . G . . . Jul 1979

Chambers of Geraint Jones QC

TANFIELD CHAMBERS,
2-5 WARWICK COURT, LONDON WC1R 5DJ
Tel: 020 7421 5300 ***Fax:*** 020 7421 5333
Dx: 46 LONDON/CHANCERY LANE
E-mail: clerks@tanfieldchambers.co.uk
Web: www.tanfieldchambers.co.uk

Clerk: Senior: Kevin Moore.
Administrator: Eamonn Kelly
Head of Chambers:
Jones, Mr Geraint (Q.C.) . . . M . . . Jul 1976

Berkley, Mr David (Q.C.) . . . M . . . May 1979
Rainey, Mr Philip (Q.C.) . . . M . . . Oct 1990
Raw, Mr Edward . . . I . . . Jul 1963
Merrylees, Mr Gavin . . . G . . . Nov 1964
Thompson, Mr Andrew . . . I . . . Nov 1969
Shuttleworth, Mr Timothy William . . . G . . . Jul 1971
Guy, Mr David . . . G . . . Jul 1972
Conrath, Mr Philip . . . G . . . Jul 1972
Monkcom, Mr Stephen Philip . . . M . . . Nov 1974
Pears, Derrick A . . . I . . . Jul 1975
Staddon, Mr Paul . . . I . . . Jul 1976
Nowinski, Mr Richard . . . M . . . Jun 1977
Dencer, Mr Mark . . . L . . . Apr 1978
Boyd, Miss Kerstin . . . G . . . Jul 1979
Daly, Mr David . . . M . . . Jul 1979
Coney, Mr Christopher Ronald Ramsden . . . I . . . Jul 1979
Cheves, Mr Simon T . . . I . . . Jul 1980
Joseph, Mr Charles Henry . . . L . . . Jul 1980
Holland, Mr William . . . G . . . Jul 1982
Reid, Mr Sebastian . . . G . . . Jul 1982
Loveday, Mr Mark Allen . . . I . . . Jul 1986
Sharp, Mr David . . . M . . . Nov 1986
Bailey, Mr Michael . . . G . . . Nov 1986
Bamford, Mr Christopher . . . I . . . Nov 1987
Buck, Mr John . . . G . . . Nov 1987
Maynard, Mr Christopher . . . G . . . Jan 1988
Buckpitt, Mr Michael . . . G . . . Feb 1988
Wilson, Mr Gerald . . . G . . . Nov 1989
Aliker, Mr Phillip . . . I . . . Oct 1990
Heath, Mr Stephen . . . L . . . Feb 1992
MacLaren, Miss Catriona . . . I . . . Oct 1993
Isaac, Mr Nicholas . . . G . . . Oct 1993
Butler, Mr Andrew . . . M . . . Nov 1993
Powell, Mr Robin . . . I . . . Nov 1993
Gallagher, Mr Stanley Harold . . . L . . . Feb 1994
Linstead, Mr Peter James . . . G . . . Oct 1994
Marnham, Miss Michelle J . . . I . . . Nov 1994
Heather, Mr Christopher . . . M . . . Oct 1995
Polli, Mr Timothy . . . M . . . Jan 1997
Dovar, Mr Daniel . . . G . . . Jan 1997
Harrison, Mr Piers . . . L . . . Mar 1997
Fieldsend, Mr James . . . L . . . Oct 1997
Murphy, Miss Martina . . . G . . . Jan 1998
Hormaeche, Miss Alejandra . . . L . . . Jan 1998
Glover, Mr Marc . . . G . . . Jan 1999
Stanzel, Ms Sarah Astrid . . . I . . . Jul 1999
Gibbons, Miss Ellodie . . . I . . . Oct 1999
Cattermole, Ms Rebecca . . . M . . . Oct 1999
Jewell, Miss Charlotte . . . M . . . Nov 1999
Carr, Mr Adrian . . . I . . . Nov 1999
Walker, Mr Steven Peter . . . M . . . Mar 2008
Murphy, Miss Olivia . . . M . . . Mar 2001
Scott, Ms Laura . . . L . . . Jul 2001
Fain, Mr Carl Ian . . . I . . . Oct 2001
Robinson, Ms Laura . . . I . . . Oct 2001
Carpenter-Leitch, Mr Tom Gordon . . . L . . . Mar 2002
Hammond, Mr Tim Mark . . . L . . . Mar 2003
Short, Ms Mandy . . . M . . . Jul 2003
Upton, Mr Jonathan . . . G . . . Jan 2004
Gourlay, Miss Amanda Kirsten . . . G . . . Jul 2004
Sheftel, Mr Andrew Lawson Baylies . . . I . . . Nov 2004
Mankau, Mrs Louise . . . L . . . Jan 2005
Watts, Mr Darren . . . M . . . Oct 2005
Jepson, Mrs Amanda . . . G . . . Oct 2005
Walsh, Mr Michael . . . M . . . Jan 2006
de Cordova, Miss Gemma . . . I . . . Jan 2006
Lear, Miss Estelle Christine . . . L . . . Jul 2006
Stevenson, Mr Paul Anthony . . . M . . . Oct 2006
Lewis, Sara . . . I . . . Jan 2007
Evans, Mr Gwynfor Owen . . . G . . . Jul 2007
Crampin, Miss Cecily Mary . . . M . . . Oct 2008
Modha, Mr Niraj . . . L . . . Jan 2010

TEMPLE COURT CHAMBERS,
2 DR JOHNSON'S BUILDINGS, LONDON EC4Y 7AY
Tel: 020 7353 7888 ***Fax:*** 020 7353 7885
Dx: 425 LONDON/CHANCERY LANE

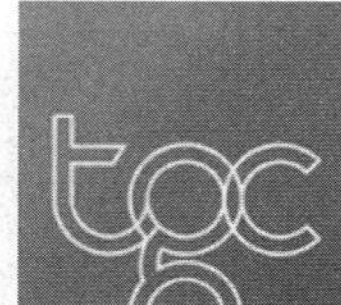

Chambers of Nigel Wilkinson QC

TEMPLE GARDEN CHAMBERS,
1 HARCOURT BUILDINGS, TEMPLE, LONDON EC4Y 9DA
Tel: 020 7583 1315 ***Fax:*** 020 7353 3969
E-mail: clerks@tgchambers.com
Web: www.tgchambers.com
Head of Chambers:
Wilkinson, Mr Nigel (Q.C.); Recorder . . . M . . . Jul 1972

Nice, Sir Geoffrey (Q.C.); Recorder . . . I . . . Jul 1971
Prynne, Mr Andrew (Q.C.) . . . M . . . Jul 1975
Jackson, Mr Simon Malcolm Dermot (Q.C.) . . . G . . . Nov 1982
Tam, Mr Robin B K (Q.C.) . . . M . . . Jul 1986
Grieve, Mr Dominic C R (Q.C.) . . . M . . . Nov 1980
MacLeod, Mr Murdo (Q.C.) . . . I . . . Jul 1994
Browne, Mr Simon Peter Buchanan (Q.C.) . . . M . . . Nov 1982
Morton, Mr Keith (Q.C.) . . . L . . . Oct 1990
Khan, Mr Karim A A (Q.C.) . . . L . . . Oct 1992
Bate-Williams, Mr John R A; Recorder . . . I . . . Nov 1976
Holdsworth, Mr James . . . M . . . Feb 1977
Ashford-Thom, Mr Ian . . . G . . . Jul 1977
Macpherson, Mr Angus . . . I . . . Jul 1977
McLoughlin, Mr Kevin . . . M . . . May 2007
Hoskins, Mr William G . . . M . . . Nov 1980
Alliott, Mr George . . . I . . . Jul 1981
Hewitt, Miss Alison B . . . M . . . Jul 1984
McFarlane, Mr Alastair D J . . . M . . . Jul 1985
Kilcoyne, Mr Paul A J . . . L . . . Nov 1985
Bell, Mr James . . . M . . . Nov 1987
James, Mr Mark . . . M . . . Nov 1987
Astor, Mr Philip D P . . . I . . . Nov 1989
McGahey, Ms Cathryn . . . I . . . Nov 1990
Laughland, Mr James . . . I . . . Nov 1991
Curtis, Mr Charles . . . L . . . Oct 1992
Wilkinson, Mr Richard . . . L . . . Oct 1992
Arney, Mr James . . . L . . . Oct 1992
Grant, Mr Marcus . . . L . . . Oct 1993
Barr, Mr David . . . G . . . Nov 1993
Issa, Ms Alexandra . . . L . . . Nov 1993
Glassbrook, Mr Alexander . . . M . . . Oct 1995
Moss, Mr Nicholas . . . M . . . Nov 1995
O'Connor, Mr Andrew . . . G . . . Oct 1996
Hobbs, Ms Emma-Jane . . . G . . . Oct 1996
Hutchin, Mr Edward . . . M . . . Oct 1996
McGrath, Mr Paul . . . G . . . Oct 1997
Adamson, Mr Dominic . . . L . . . Oct 1997
Kotzeva, Miss Anna . . . M . . . Oct 1998
Ackland, Miss Sacha . . . I . . . Sep 1998
Cottrell, Mr Stephen . . . I . . . Oct 1998
Davies, Mr George . . . L . . . Nov 1998
Kapoor, Mr Shaman . . . L . . . Oct 1999
Dixon, Mr Rodney . . . I . . . Mar 2000
Casey, Mr Benjamin . . . I . . . Oct 2000
Dardis, Mrs Heather . . . L . . . Nov 2000
Canby, Miss Fiona . . . M . . . Jul 2001
Rapp, Mr Michael . . . I . . . Jul 2002
Sharpe, Mr Timothy . . . L . . . Oct 2002
Sweeney, Miss Lydia . . . I . . . Oct 2002
Hay, Mr Benjamin . . . M . . . Jul 2004
Jones, Miss Louise . . . M . . . Jul 2004
Ellis, Mr Aidan . . . M . . . Jul 2005
Stride, Mr Lionel . . . L . . . Oct 2005
Johnson, Mr Anthony . . . M . . . Nov 2006
Hughes, Miss Joanna Elizabeth . . . M . . . Jul 2007
Price, Miss Emma Charlotte Louisa . . . G . . . Oct 2007
Reeves, Miss Sian . . . G . . . Jul 2006
White, Mr David . . . I . . . Jul 2009

Chambers of Benjamin James Browne QC

2 TEMPLE GARDENS,
TEMPLE, LONDON EC4Y 9AY
Est: 1946
Tel: 020 7822 1200 ***Fax:*** 020 7822 1300
Dx: 134 LONDON/CHANCERY LANE
E-mail: clerks@2tg.co.uk
Clerk: Senior: Lee Tyler.
Chambers Director: Sarah Webbe
Head of Chambers:
Browne, Mr Benjamin James (Q.C.) . . . I . . . Jul 1976

De Navarro, Mr Michael Anthony (Q.C.) . . . I . . . Jul 1968
Moxon Browne, Mr Robert William (Q.C.) . . . G . . . Jul 1969
Palmer, Mr Howard William Arthur (Q.C.) . . . I . . . Jul 1977
Perry, Miss Jacqueline (Q.C.) . . . G . . . May 1975
Porter, Mr Martin Hugh (Q.C.) . . . I . . . Jul 1986
Vaughan Jones, Ms Sarah J (Q.C.) . . . M . . . Jul 1983
Moody, Mr Neil (Q.C.) . . . G . . . Nov 1989
Downes, Mr Paul (Q.C.) . . . G . . . Oct 1991
Foster, Miss Rosalind Mary . . . M . . . Nov 1969
Green, Ms Alison . . . M . . . Jul 1974
Archer, Mr Stephen . . . I . . . Nov 1979
McDonald, Mr John William . . . M . . . Nov 1981
Russell, Mr Christopher John . . . G . . . Nov 1982
Matovu, Mr Daniel . . . I . . . Nov 1985
Harrison, Ms Caroline Marie Alice . . . L . . . Jul 1986
Miller, Mr Andrew . . . I . . . Jul 1989
de Rohan, Mr Jonathan Stewart . . . M . . . Jul 1989
Martin, Mr Bradley . . . L . . . Oct 1990
Crowley, Mr Daniel . . . G . . . Oct 1990
Lundie, Mr Christopher . . . I . . . Nov 1991
Kinsler, Ms Marie-Louise . . . I . . . Jan 1992
Brown, Miss Clare . . . M . . . Oct 1993
Green, Mr Dore . . . L . . . May 1994
Gardiner, Mr Bruce . . . M . . . Nov 1994
Wyles, Miss Lucy . . . L . . . Oct 1994
Goolamali, Ms Nina . . . M . . . Oct 1995
Harris, Mr Roger C J . . . I . . . Oct 1996
Dougherty, Mr Charles . . . M . . . Oct 1997
Fetto, Mr Niazi . . . I . . . Oct 1999
Karseras, Miss Anastasia . . . G . . . Oct 2000
Shiu, Miss Ming Yee . . . M . . . Oct 2000
Unthank, Miss Nina . . . M . . . Jul 2001
Bell, Miss Helen Louise . . . M . . . Jul 2002
Wolstenholme, Ms Helen . . . L . . . Nov 2002
Nolten, Miss Sonia Jayne . . . I . . . Nov 2002
Benzie, Mr Stuart . . . G . . . Nov 2002
Azib, Miss Rehana . . . I . . . Nov 2003
McTague, Miss Meghann Rose . . . I . . . Oct 2004
Saunderson, Miss Emily . . . G . . . Jul 2005
Chirnside, Mr Stewart Murray . . . I . . . Jul 2005
Hughes, Miss Anna . . . M . . . Jul 2008
McLorinan, Miss Hayley . . . I . . . Jul 2008
Morton Jack, Mr Henry . . . L . . . Jul 2009
Wraight, Mr William . . . L . . . Jul 2009
Thomas, Mr David C . . . L . . . Oct 2009
O'Brien, Mr Dermod Patrick (Q.C.)* . . . I . . . Jul 1962
Anyadike-Danes, Ms Monya N M* . . . G . . . Jul 1980
Pepperall, Mr Edward Brian* . . . L . . . Jul 1989
Snell, Mr John* . . . L . . . Oct 1991
Reece, Mr Rupert* . . . L . . . Oct 1992
Eales, Mr Darren* . . . G . . . Jan 2000
Wale, Elizabeth* . . . I . . . Jul 2004

Chambers of John Coffey QC

3 TEMPLE GARDENS,
GROUND FLOOR, TEMPLE, LONDON EC4Y 9AU
Est: 1969
Tel: 020 7353 3102 ***Fax:*** 020 7353 0960
Dx: 485 LONDON/CHANCERY LANE
E-mail: clerks@3tg.co.uk
Clerk: Senior: Kevin Aldridge.
Head of Chambers:
Coffey, Mr John (Q.C.); Recorder . . . M . . . Nov 1970

Rouch, Mr Peter Christopher (Q.C.) . . . G . . . Jul 1972
Davey, Mr Neil (Q.C.) . . . M . . . Jul 1978
Laing, Ms Christine (Q.C.); Recorder . . . L . . . Jan 1984
Brady, Mr Scott . . . M . . . Jul 1987
Birch, Mr Geoffrey . . . L . . . Feb 1972
Crabtree, Mr Richard . . . G . . . Jul 1974
Reed, Mr Piers Knowle Moorehouse . . . L . . . Nov 1974
Whittaker, Mr Robert . . . M . . . Jul 1977
Saunders, Mr William Anthony . . . G . . . Nov 1980
Connolly, Mr Simon . . . M . . . Jul 1981
Smith, Mr Simon . . . G . . . Nov 1981
Stork, Mr Brian Raymond . . . I . . . Jul 1981
Barnes, Mr David Jonathan . . . G . . . Nov 1981
Woodcock, Mr Jonathan . . . M . . . Nov 1981
Knight, Miss Adrienne . . . G . . . Jan 1981
Lahiffe, Mr Martin Patrick Joseph . . . M . . . Nov 1984
Ryan, Mr David Patrick . . . G . . . Nov 1985
Femi-Ola, Mr John . . . G . . . Nov 1985
Ross, Mr Gordon MacRae . . . I . . . Jul 1986
Perian, Mr Steven . . . L . . . Nov 1987
McKeever, Miss Frances . . . G . . . Jul 1988
Hayhow, Mrs Lyndsay . . . I . . . Nov 1990
Salter, Miss Sibby . . . M . . . Oct 1991
Corsellis, Mr Nicholas . . . L . . . Jul 1992
Ossack, Mrs Tanya Rachelle Elise . . . G . . . Oct 1993
Hallowes, Mr Rupert J M . . . I . . . Oct 1995
Williams, Mr Alexander . . . M . . . Nov 1995
Dempsey, Ms Karen . . . L . . . Jan 1996
Crinnion, Miss Neena . . . G . . . Oct 1997
Joseph, Mr Henry . . . M . . . Nov 1998
Shannon, Mr Simon . . . I . . . Mar 1999
Elliott, Mr Richard . . . M . . . Oct 2001
Dowse, Ms Clare . . . I . . . Jul 2002
Wing, Mr James . . . L . . . Oct 2002
Wellfare, Miss Aimee Mia . . . L . . . Oct 2004
Whawell, Miss Leesha . . . L . . . Jul 2005
Kenyon, Miss Flavia . . . L . . . Oct 2005
Storey, Mr Richard . . . L . . . Nov 2005
Cooke, Mr Stephen . . . G . . . Jan 2006
Chidgey, Miss Kate . . . I . . . Jun 2006
Durrant, Mr Charles . . . I . . . Jul 2006
Dean, Miss Elizabeth . . . I . . . Jul 2006
Dave, Miss Priya . . . L . . . Oct 2006
Harte, Mr Patrick . . . L . . . Oct 2006
Herman, Mr Saul . . . I . . . Jul 2007

Chambers of Richard Mervyn Bramwell QC

TEMPLE TAX CHAMBERS,
1ST FLOOR, 3 TEMPLE GARDENS, TEMPLE, LONDON EC4Y 9AU
Tel: 020 7353 7884 / 7353 8982 ***Fax:*** 020 7583 2044
E-mail: clerks@templetax.com
Clerk: Junior: Claire James. Anne M De Rose; Lucy Campbell.
Head of Chambers:
Bramwell, Mr Richard Mervyn (Q.C.) . . . M . . . Jul 1967

Conlon, Mr Michael (Q.C.) . . . I . . . Jul 1974
Barlow, Mr Richard L . . . M . . . Jan 1970
Sherry, Mr Michael Gabriel . . . G . . . Nov 1978
Southern, Mr David Boardman . . . L . . . Jan 1982
James, Mr Alun Edward . . . M . . . Nov 1986
Ridgway, Mr Philip . . . M . . . Nov 1986
McNicholas, Mr Eamon . . . L . . . Oct 1994
Redpath, Mr Scott . . . M . . . Jan 1996
Schwarz, Mr Jonathan S . . . M . . . Mar 1998
Rippon, Louise Jane . . . M . . . Jun 2000
Collins, Mr Michael . . . L . . . Jan 2001
Murray, Miss Rebecca . . . L . . . Jan 2001
Brown, Mr Timothy . . . I . . . Jul 2001
Arthur, Mr Stephen Joseph . . . M . . . Nov 2002
Redston, Ms Anne . . . M . . . Jan 2009

TEMPLIS CHAMBERS,
3RD FLOOR SOUTH, 1A MIDDLE TEMPLE LANE, LONDON EC4Y 9AA
Tel: 020 7649 9808 ***Fax:*** 020 7649 9432
Dx: 236 LONDON/CHANCERY LANE

Chambers of Geoffrey Cox QC

THOMAS MORE CHAMBERS,
7 LINCOLNS INN FIELDS, LINCOLN'S INN, LONDON WC2A 3BP
Tel: 020 7404 7000 ***Fax:*** 020 7831 4606
Dx: 90 LONDON/CHANCERY LANE
Clerk: Senior: Christopher James Hallett. Stuart Sellen; Nick Bryant.
Head of Chambers:
Cox, Mr Geoffrey (Q.C.) . . . M . . . Jul 1982

Baker, Mr Jeremy R (Q.C.); Recorder . . . M . . . May 1979
Noble, Mr Philip R . . . I . . . Jul 1978
Ray, Mr Jonathan Richard . . . G . . . Jul 1980
Gottlieb, Mr David . . . I . . . Nov 1988
Aylott, Mr Colin . . . I . . . Nov 1989
Livingstone, Mr Simon . . . I . . . Oct 1990
Farmer, Miss Sarah . . . L . . . Nov 1991
Egan, Mr Manus . . . M . . . Nov 1991
Harding, Mr Christopher . . . I . . . Nov 1992

Cross, Mr Richard ... L ... Oct 1993
Cooper, Miss Sarah Lucy ... I ... Nov 1993
Baruah, Mrs Rima ... I ... Feb 1994
Sherratt, Mr Mathew ... I ... Oct 1994
Quinn, Miss Victoria K ... L ... Oct 1995
Jackson, Mr Myles ... L ... Oct 1995
Rowe, Ms Freya E B ... I ... Oct 1996
Collingnon, Ms Laura ... L ... Jan 1998
Edington, Mrs Fiona A R ... M ... Oct 1998
Harding, Mr Simon ... M ... Oct 1998
Porter, Ms Alexandra ... M ... Jan 2002
Walker-Nolan, Mr Ben ... M ... Mar 2002
Palmer, Ms Claire ... M ... Jan 2003
Saifee, Mr Faisal ... M ... Jan 2003
Rai, Miss Puneet ... L ... Jan 2004
Morgan, Miss Victoria ... I ... Jan 2005

TOLLGATE MEWS CHAMBERS,
28 TATE ROAD, ROYAL DOCKS, LONDON E16 2HJ
Tel: 020 7511 1838 *Fax:* 020 7511 1838

Chambers of Michael Mansfield QC and Patrick Roche

TOOKS CHAMBERS,
81 FARRINGDON STREET, LONDON EC4A 4BL
Tel: 020 7842 7575 *Fax:* 020 7842 7576
Dx: 68 LONDON/CHANCERY LANE
E-mail: clerks@tooks.co.uk
Clerk: Senior: Martin Parker.
Head of Chambers:
Mansfield, Mr Michael (Q.C.) ... G ... Nov 1967
Roche, Mr Patrick; Recorder ... M ... Jul 1977

Aspinall, Mr John M (Q.C.) ... I ... Nov 1971
Massih, Mr Michel (Q.C.) ... M ... Nov 1979
Topolski, Mr Michael (Q.C.); Recorder ... I ... Apr 1986
Kamlish, Mr Stephen (Q.C.) ... G ... Jul 1979
Bennathan, Mr Joel (Q.C.); Recorder ... M ... Nov 1985
Waterman, Mr Adrian (Q.C.); Recorder ... I ... Jun 1988
Moloney, Mr Tim (Q.C.) ... M ... Nov 1993
Southey, Mr David Hugh (Q.C.); Recorder ... I ... Nov 1996
Magarian, Mr Michael (Q.C.) ... G ... Jul 1988
Montrose, Mr Stuart ... I ... May 1972
Woodcraft, Ms Elizabeth ... M ... Jul 1980
Boswell, Miss Jenny ... M ... Jul 1982
McNulty, Mr Lawrence ... M ... Nov 1985
Farnon, Ms Patricia R G ... I ... Nov 1986
Williams, Mr Christopher P ... I ... Feb 1988
Wilcock, Mr Peter ... I ... Jul 1988
Dick, Ms Julia ... M ... Nov 1988
Gingell, Ms Melanie ... M ... Jan 1988
Huseyin, Mr Martin ... I ... Nov 1988
Rayner, Ms Catherine ... G ... Oct 1989
Mostyn, Mr Piers ... M ... Nov 1989
Hawley, Ms Carol ... G ... Oct 1990
Chapman, Miss Rebecca ... I ... Nov 1990
Braganza, Ms Nicola ... M ... Oct 1992
Munroe, Ms Allison ... M ... Oct 1992
Drew, Ms Sandhya ... G ... Nov 1993
Thorne, Ms Katy ... I ... Nov 1994
Brown, Ms Grace ... I ... Oct 1995
Chute, Ms Andrea ... M ... Oct 1995
Weston, Ms Amanda ... I ... Oct 1995
Hodgetts, Mr Glen ... I ... Nov 1995
Bourke, Ms Sarah ... G ... Oct 1996
Wrack, Mr Nick ... I ... Mar 1997
Vallejo, Miss Jacqueline ... M ... Apr 1997
Middleton, Ms Di ... I ... Oct 1997
Troop, Mr Paul Benjamin ... L ... Aug 1998
Wilson, Ms Rebekah ... M ... Nov 1998
Rought-Brooks, Ms Hannah ... M ... Mar 1999
Cooper, Ms Danielle ... L ... Oct 1999
Green, Mr Garry ... I ... Nov 1999
Slatter, Ms Alexis ... I ... Nov 1999
Haymerle, Mr Friedrich ... I ... Oct 2000
Sethi, Ms Rita ... I ... Nov 2000
Williams, Felicity ... L ... Nov 2000
Choudhry, Kamran ... L ... Oct 2001
Mian, Mr Naeem ... I ... Oct 2002
Robinson, Mr Sam ... M ... Nov 2002
Harris, Ms Stella ... G ... Nov 2002
Smith, Ms Abigail ... L ... Oct 2003
Harrison, Mr Anthony ... L ... Jul 2004
Straw, Mr Adam ... G ... Oct 2004
Russell, Ms Jane ... G ... Nov 2004
Tautz, Mr William ... G ... Nov 2004
Tafadar, Ms Sultana ... L ... Mar 2005
Bunting, Mr Jude ... G ... Jul 2006
Hirst, Ms Leonie ... I ... Oct 2006
Ali, Khadija ... L ... Nov 2006
Newell, Mr Giles ... M ... Mar 2007
Nereshraaj, Mr Srikantharajah ... G ... Jun 2007
Eatwell, Tatyana ... I ... Jul 2007
Reynolds, Mr Richard ... M ... Jul 2007
Ekeledo, Ms Peggy ... L ... Nov 2007
Obi-Ezekpazu, Ms Maureen ... G ... Jan 2008
Mehigan, Mr James ... M ... Nov 2008
Jones, Bronwen ... M ... Jul 2009
Redley, Clive ... I ... Nov 2010
Kershen, Mr Lawrence (Q.C.)* ... M ... Jul 1967
Baird, Ms Vera (Q.C.)* ... G ... Nov 1975
Bovey, Mungo (Q.C.)* ... I ... Nov 2000
Yeboah, Yaa* ... G ... Nov 1977
Herbert, Mr Donald Peter OBE* ... G ... Nov 1982
Shamash, Miss Anne* ... G ... Nov 1986
Kirby, Mr James* ... G ... Oct 1994
Heraghty, Mr David* ... I ... Oct 1995
Halloran, Miss Cathy* ... L ... Oct 1997

Chambers of Kutub Shikder MBE

TOWER HAMLETS BARRISTERS CHAMBERS,
178 WHITECHAPEL ROAD, LONDON E1 1BJ
Tel: 020 7377 8090 *Fax:* 020 7377 6322
Clerk: Abdul Kayum.
Head of Chambers:
Shikder, Kutub MBE ... L ... Nov 1990

TURLEY CHAMBERS,
NO 5 BARRIER POINT ROAD, LONDON E16 2SB
Dx: 122030 FINSBURY 3
E-mail: cc.dann@btinternet.com

45 ULLSWATER CRESCENT,
KINGSTON VALE, LONDON SW15 3RG
Tel: 020 8546 9284

Chambers of Ali Malek QC

3 VERULAM BUILDINGS,
GRAY'S INN, LONDON WC1R 5NT
Tel: 020 7831 8441 *Fax:* 020 7831 8479
Dx: 331 LONDON/CHANCERY LANE
E-mail: chambers@3vb.com
Web: www.3vb.com
Administrator: R Merry-Price
Practice Manager: Nicholas Hill
Head of Chambers:
Malek, Mr Ali (Q.C.) ... G ... Jul 1980

Jarvis, Mr John (Q.C.) ... L ... Jul 1970
Symons, Mr Christopher (Q.C.) ... M ... Jul 1972
Geering, Mr Ian (Q.C.); Associate Member ... I ... Nov 1974
Elliott, Mr Nicholas (Q.C.) ... G ... Jul 1972
Salter, Mr Richard (Q.C.) ... I ... Jul 1975
Blair, Mr Michael Campbell (Q.C.) Honoris Causa ... M ... Jul 1965
Mitchell, Mr Gregory (Q.C.) ... G ... Jul 1979
Sutcliffe, Mr Andrew (Q.C.) ... I ... Nov 1983
Onslow, Mr Andrew (Q.C.) ... M ... Jul 1982
Phillips, Mr Stephen (Q.C.) ... G ... Jul 1984
Phillips, Mr Rory (Q.C.) ... I ... Jul 1984
Weitzman, Mr Thomas (Q.C.) ... G ... Jul 1984
McQuater, Mr Ewan (Q.C.) ... M ... Jul 1985
Fletcher, Mr Andrew (Q.C.) ... I ... Nov 1980
Nash, Mr Jonathan (Q.C.) ... G ... Nov 1986
Beltrami, Mr Adrian (Q.C.) ... L ... Jul 1989
Lowenstein, Mr Paul (Q.C.) ... M ... Nov 1988
Kinsky, Mr Cyril (Q.C.) ... M ... Nov 1988
Tolaney, Ms Sonia (Q.C.) ... M ... Oct 1995
Freedman, Mr S Clive ... G ... Jul 1975
Birch, Miss Elizabeth B ... G ... Jul 1978
Cranfield, Mr Peter Anthony ... G ... Jul 1982
Lazarus, Mr Michael ... M ... Nov 1987
Start, Miss Angharad ... L ... Nov 1988
Odgers, Mr John ... G ... Oct 1990
Phillips, Mr Jonathan Mark ... I ... Nov 1991
Evans, Mr James ... G ... Nov 1991
Quest, Mr David ... G ... Oct 1993
Edwards, Mr Richard ... M ... Oct 1993
Davies-Jones, Mr Jonathan ... M ... Nov 1994
Hardwick, Mr Matthew ... G ... Oct 1994
Brent, Mr Richard ... M ... Jul 1995
Wilson, Mr Ian ... M ... Oct 1995
Gibaud, Miss Catherine ... G ... Oct 1996
Parker, Mr Matthew ... M ... Oct 1997
Head, Mr David ... M ... Nov 1997
McKendrick, Mr Ewan ... M ... Mar 1998
Ratcliffe, Mr Peter ... M ... Oct 1998
Craig, Mr Nicholas ... I ... Oct 1998
de Verneuil Smith, Mr Peter ... L ... Jan 1998
Mallinckrodt, Ms Sophie ... L ... Jul 1999
Knox, Mr Henry ... G ... Jan 2000
John, Miss Laura ... G ... Jan 2001
Edwards, Mr William ... M ... Jan 2002
Harris, Mr Christopher ... L ... Jan 2002
Pillai, Mr Rajesh ... M ... Jan 2002
McPherson, Mr George ... I ... Jan 2003
Simpson, Mr David ... G ... Jan 2003
Lacob, Ms Lisa ... G ... Jan 2004
Eborall, Ms Charlotte ... M ... Jan 2004
Kramer, Mr Adam ... G ... Jan 2004
MacDonald, Mr James ... I ... Jan 2005
Hobson, Mr Fred ... L ... Jan 2005
Hanke, Mr Richard ... L ... Jan 2006
Maher, Ms Felicity ... I ... Jan 2006
Purves, Mr Robert ... M ... Jan 2007
Knight, Ms Alexia ... M ... Jan 2007
Bond, Mr Christopher ... I ... Jan 2008
Jeavons, Ms Anne ... M ... Jan 2008
Phipps, Mr Sandy ... L ... Jan 2008
Holderness, Kate ... G ... Jan 2008
De Vecchi, Mr Tom ... I ... Jan 2009
van Sante, Mr Theodor ... I ... Jan 2009
Onabajo, Teniola ... M ... Jan 2010
Choon Kiat Wee, Mr Paul ... L ... Jan 2010
Burdin, Mr Christopher ... M ... Jan 2010

Work Description / Specialisations: Domestic & International Banking; Financial Services, Financial Regulation (Domestic & E.C.); Insurance, Reinsurance, Sale of Goods, International Trade, Entertainment, Employment, Construction, IT and Telecommunications, Building and Engineering, Professional Negligence, Product Liability, Insolvency, Company, Commercial Fraud, Copyright and Passing Off, Commercial Arbitrations, E.C. and International, Shipping, Dispute Resolution and ADR. Languages: French, German, Italian, Portuguese, Russian, Spanish, Welsh and Arabic.

CHAMBERS OF MR PETER WARD,
88 KINGSWAY, LONDON WC2A 6AA
Tel: 020 3402 2152 *Fax:* 020 7841 1001
E-mail: whurr@yahoo.com
Ward, Mr Peter ... I ... Oct 1996

Chambers of Paul Terence Philip Warrick

LAW OFFICE OF PAUL WARRICK,
7 HOBURY STREET, LONDON SW10 0JD
Tel: 020 7795 1122 *Fax:* 020 7795 0123
E-mail: paulwarrick@pwlawyer.com
Head of Chambers:
Warrick, Mr Paul Terence Philip ... I ... Jul 1972

Chambers of Christopher Thomas Drew and Cheryl Drew

WARWICK HOUSE CHAMBERS,
8 WARWICK COURT, GRAY'S INN, LONDON WC1R 5DJ
Tel: 020 7430 2323 *Fax:* 020 7430 9171
Dx: 1001 LONDON/CHANCERY LANE
E-mail: clerks@warwickhousechambers.com
Clerk: Gemma Louise Hanson.
Head of Chambers:
Drew, Mr Christopher Thomas ... G ... Nov 1969
Drew, Mrs Cheryl ... G ... Nov 1972

Roberts, Dr John (Q.C.)* ... G ... Nov 1969
Fox, Mr Martin George ... M ... Jul 1981
Sharma, Mrs Suman ... M ... Jan 1994
Bagral, Miss Ravinder ... I ... Oct 1996
McDonnell, Mr Martin ... M ... Jan 1997
de Pourbaix, Mr Roman ... L ... Jan 2001
Garrod, Mr Neil ... I ... Jan 2000
Hayhoe, The Honourable Crispin ... L ... Jan 2004
Rathour, Miss Delvinder Kaur ... G ... Nov 2005

10

Chambers of Claire Holder

243 WESTBOURNE GROVE,
LONDON W11 2SE
Tel: 020 7229 3819 *Fax:* 020 7243 5906
E-mail: claireholden@aol.com
Clerk: D Holder.
Head of Chambers:
Holder, Miss Claire OBE ... L ... Jul 1978

Chambers of John Martin QC

WILBERFORCE CHAMBERS,
8 NEW SQUARE, LINCOLN'S INN, LONDON WC2A 3QP
Tel: 020 7306 0102 *Fax:* 020 7306 0095
Dx: 311 LONDON/CHANCERY LANE
E-mail: chambers@wilberforce.co.uk
Web: www.wilberforce.co.uk
Clerk: Senior: Declan Redmond. Danny Smillie; Tanya Tong.
Administrator: John Treacy
Head of Chambers:
Martin, Mr John (Q.C.) ... L ... Jul 1972

Nugee, Mr Edward (Q.C.) TD ... I ... Jun 1955
Barnes, Mr Michael (Q.C.); Recorder ... M ... Jul 1965
Croxford, Mr Ian (Q.C.) ... G ... Jul 1976
Ham, Mr Robert (Q.C.) ... M ... Nov 1973
Furber, Mr John (Q.C.) ... I ... Jul 1973
Mowschenson, Mr Terence (Q.C.); Recorder ... M ... Jul 1977
Philips, Mr David (Q.C.); Deputy High Court Judge, Recorder, Bencher of Gray's Inn; Director of Disability Law Service ... G ... Nov 1976
Green, Mr Brian (Q.C.) ... M ... Nov 1980
Bloch, Mr Michael (Q.C.) ... L ... Jul 1979
Nugee, Mr Christopher (Q.C.); Recorder ... I ... Jul 1983
Furness, Mr Michael (Q.C.) ... L ... Jul 1982
Wardell, Mr John (Q.C.) ... G ... Jul 1979
Seitler, Mr Jonathan (Q.C.) ... I ... Nov 1985
Tennet, Mr Michael (Q.C.) ... I ... Jul 1985
Lowe, Mr Thomas (Q.C.) ... I ... Nov 1985
Karas, Mr Jonathan (Q.C.) ... M ... Jul 1986
Ayliffe, Mr James (Q.C.) ... L ... Nov 1987
Smith, Ms Joanna (Q.C.) ... L ... Nov 1990
Newman, Mr Paul (Q.C.) ... L ... Oct 1991
Wicks, Ms Joanne (Q.C.) ... L ... Nov 1990
Child, Mr John ... L ... Nov 1966
Seymour, Mr Thomas ... I ... Jul 1975
Studer, Mr Mark ... L ... Jul 1976
Hughes, Miss Gabriel ... L ... Apr 1978
Hochberg, Mr Daniel Alan ... L ... Jul 1982
Hutchings, Mr Martin ... M ... Feb 1986
Bryant, Miss Judith ... L ... Jul 1987
Fadipe, Mr Gabriel ... I ... Nov 1991
Evans, Mr Johnathan ... M ... Nov 1994
Campbell, Miss Emily ... L ... Nov 1995
Reed, Mr Rupert ... L ... May 1996

Greenhill, Mr Julian . . . . I . . . . Feb 1997
Scott, Ms Tiffany . . . . M. . . . . Jul 1998
Singla, Nikki . . . . M. . . . Jul 2000
Sawyer, Mr Edward . . . . M. . . . Oct 2001
Davey, Mr Jonathan . . . . L . . . . Oct 2003
Hilliard, Mr Jonathan . . . . L . . . . Oct 2003
Mold, Mr Andrew . . . . L . . . . Oct 2003
Bryson, Mr Alan . . . . I . . . . Feb 2004
McKechnie, Miss Emily . . . . L . . . . Jan 2005
Black, Ms Charlotte . . . . M. . . . Oct 2006
Allen, Mr Sebastian . . . . L . . . . Oct 2006
Walmsley, Mr James . . . . L . . . . Jan 2008
Faulkner, Mr Benjamin . . . . L . . . . Jan 2008
Murphy, Miss Emer . . . . I . . . . Jan 2009
McCreath, Mr James . . . . I . . . . Jul 2009
Furze, Miss Caroline* . . . . L . . . . Oct 1992

Chambers of George Syril

WILLESDEN CHAMBERS,
108 HARLESDEN GARDENS, LONDON NW10 4HA
Tel: 020 8965 8856 ***Fax:*** 020 8838 3603
Clerk: Gloria Syril.
Head of Chambers:
Syril, Mr George . . . . L . . . . Jul 1980

39 WINDSOR ROAD,
LONDON N3 3SN
Tel: 020 8349 9194 ***Fax:*** 020 8346 8506
E-mail: lindacohen@cobeck.clara.co.uk
Clerk: F Becket.
Cohen, Ms Linda . . . . M. . . . Jul 1985

Chambers of Martin Haldane Ahmad Thomson

WYNNE CHAMBERS,
5 KIMBERLEY ROAD, LONDON NW6 7SG
Tel: 020 3239 6964 ***Fax:*** 020 3014 8839
E-mail: ahmadthomson@wynnechambers.co.uk
Head of Chambers:
Thomson, Mr Martin Haldane Ahmad . . . . G. . . . . Jul 1979

CHAMBERS OF MR ISMAIL YUSUF,
2 WARGRAVE AVENUE, LONDON N15 6UD
Tel: 020 8880 2871

THE INNS OF COURT

GRAY'S INN

TREASURER'S OFFICE

8 South Square, Gray's Inn, London WC1R 5ET
Tel: 020 7458 7800
Hours: 10am to 4pm
Closed: Saturdays and Sundays.

Under Treasurer

Faith, Brigadier Anthony, C.B.E.

Director of Finance

McAleenan, Mr Michael, F.C.A.

Director of Education

Clarke, Miss Quinn

Director of Estates

Harbour, Mrs Helen

Administration and Events Officer

Clark, Mrs Michelle

LIBRARY

Hours: Monday-Friday, 9am to 8pm. Vacation hours will be screened. Closed: Saturdays and Sundays. Closed same as Treasury unless otherwise screened.

Librarian

Thom, Mrs Theresa, M.A., A.L.A.
Tel: 020 7458 7800

Deputy Librarian

Jones, Mark

Benchers

H.R.H. The Prince of Wales, K.G., K.T., G.C.B.
H.R.H. The Duke of Gloucester, K.G., G.C.V.O.
H.R.H. Grand Duke Jean of Luxembourg (Honorary)
Ahmed, Justice Shahabuddin, Formerly President of the People's Republic of Bangladesh (Honorary)
Alpa, Professor Dr. Guido, Professor of Civil Law, La Sapienza University, Rome; President of Italian Bar Council (Honorary)
Andrews, Geraldine Mary, Q.C., Deputy High Court Judge & Recorder
Andrews, Professor John, C.B.E., J.P., Emeritus Professor of Law, University of Wales, Aberystwyth
Arbour, The Hon. Louise, President & C.E.O., International Crisis Group (Honorary)
Archer of Sandwell, The Right Hon Lord, Q.C., Formerly Solicitor General; Chairman of Enemy Property Compensation Panel; Formerly Chairman, Council on Tribunals
Arfon-Jones, Elisabeth, D.L.
Asplin, Sarah Jane, Q.C., Deputy High Court Judge
Astwood, Sir James K.T., K.B.E., Retired Chief Justice of Bermuda; Retired President of the Court of Appeal of Bermuda (Honorary)
Auld, The Right Hon Sir Robin Ernest, Formerly a Lord Justice of Appeal
Baker, Philip Woolf, O.B.E, Q.C.
Baldwin, John Paul, Q.C., Deputy High Court Judge; Recorder
Banda, R.A., S.C., Chief Justice of Swaziland (Honorary)
von Bar, Professor Dr. Christian, Dr.Iur.h.c.(Leuven, Uppsala,Tartu, Helsinki), F.B.A., Director of the European Legal Studies Institute, University of Osnabrück (Honorary)
Barker, Brian John, Q.C., A Senior Circuit Judge & The Common Serjeant of London
Barnard, David Nowell, Recorder
Barnes, Adrian Francis Patrick, C.V.O., D.L., Formerly The Remembrancer of the City of London; A Deputy Lieutenant
Barnes, Timothy Paul, Q.C., Recorder
Beinisch, President Dorit, President of the Supreme Court of Israel (Honorary)
Beloff, The Hon Michael Jacob, Q.C., Senior Ordinary Judge of the Court of Appeal, Jersey & Guernsey; Former President, Trinity College, Oxford; Member of the Court of Arbitration for Sport; Judge of the Upper Tribunal (Admin Appeals Chamber), Ethics Commissioner to The London 2012 Olympic Bid; Treasurer-2008
Berry, Anthony Charles, Q.C.
Bevan, (Edward) Julian, Q.C.
Birtles, His Honour Judge William, A Circuit Judge; Resident Judge At The Mayor's And City of London Court; Judge of the Employment Appeal Tribunal; Deputy High Court Judge
Birts, His Honour Judge Peter William, Q.C., A Circuit Judge
Blackett, His Honour Judge Jeffrey, Judge Advocate General of Her Majesty's Armed Forces
Block, Neil, Q.C.
Boal, His Honour (John) Graham, Q.C., Formerly A Circuit Judge
Bok, President Derek, President Emeritus of Harvard University (Honorary)
Boswell, Lindsay, Q.C.
Boulding, Philip Vincent, Q.C.
Boyce, William, Q.C., Recorder
Boyd, (David) John, Q.C.
Brennan, Timothy Roger, Q.C., Recorder, Deputy High Court Judge
Brennan of Bibury, Lord, Q.C.
Brewer, Sir David, C.M.G., Formerly Lord Mayor of London; The Lord Lieutenant of Greater London (Honorary)
Brooke, His Honour Michael Eccles Macklin, Q.C., Formerly a Circuit Judge
Brown, Sir Douglas Dunlop, Formerly A Justice of the High Court
Browne, Desmond John Michael, Q.C.
Burton, Dr Frank Patrick, Q.C., Recorder
Burton, The Hon Sir Michael John, A Justice of the High Court; Vice-Treasurer, 2011
Butcher, Anthony John, Q.C., Master of Silver; Treasurer-2003
Butcher, Christopher John, Q.C.
Butcher, Michael Joseph Edward
Campbell, The Right Hon Sir Anthony (Honorary)
Canivet, Guy, President Honoraire, Cour De Cassation; Membre Du Conseil Constitutionnel (Honorary)
Caplan, Jonathan Michael, Q.C., Recorder
Carey-Hughes, Richard, Q.C., Recorder
Carlile of Berriew, The Lord (Alex), Q.C., Master of the House
Carr, Henry James, Q.C.
Carss-Frisk, Monica Gunnel Constance, Q.C.
Carswell, The Right Hon Lord, Formerly A Lord of Appeal In Ordinary (Honorary)
Carter, Peter, Q.C.
Cartwright, The Hon Silvia Rose, P.C.N.Z.M., D.B.E., Q.S.O., Formerly Govenor-General of New Zealand; Judge, Trial Chamber, Khmer Rouge Tribunal, Cambodia (Honorary)
Chambers, His Honour Judge Nicholas Mordaunt, Q.C., A Circuit Judge; Chairman of the Council of Law Reporting
Chapple, His Honour Judge Roger, A Senior Circuit Judge
Chawla, Mukul, Q.C.
Cherryman, John Richard, Q.C., Formerly Deputy High Court Judge And Recorder
Clark, His Honour Judge Christopher Harvey, Q.C., A Circuit Judge; Chancellor of the Dioceses of Portsmouth & Winchester
Clarke, Sir Ellis, T.C., G.C.B., G.C.M.G., Formerly President of Trinidad & Tobago (Honorary)
Clarke, The Right Hon Kenneth, Q.C., M.P., Secretary of State for Justice & Lord Chancellor
Clegg, William, Q.C., Recorder; Master of Events
Clitheroe, John, Solicitor (Honorary)
Coghlin, The Right Hon Lord Justice Patrick, Lord Justice of Appeal, Northern Ireland (Honorary)
Collier, John Greenwood, M.A., Ll.B
Collins, (John) Martin, Q.C., Formerly A Judge of the Courts of Appeal, Jersey & Guernsey; Formerly Commissioner, Jersey; Treasurer-1999
Collins, Michael Geoffrey, Q.C.
Collyear, Sir John, F.R.Eng. (Honorary)
Colman, The Hon Sir Anthony David, Formerly A Justice of the High Court Judge of The DIFC Court, Dubai
Cook, (Jeremy) David, Master of the Queen's Bench Division
Coonan, Kieran Benet, Q.C., Recorder
Cooper, Beryl Phyllis, Q.C., Former Deputy High Court Judge
Corner, Timothy, Q.C., Recorder, Deputy High Court Judge
Cornish, Professor William Rodolph, Q.C.(Hon), LL.D., F.B.A.
Coulson, The Hon Sir Peter, A Justice of the High Court
Cowen, The Right Hon Sir Zelman, A.K., G.C.M.G., G.C.V.O., Q.C., D.C.L., Formerly Governor-General of Australia (Honorary)
Cox, Philip Joseph, D.S.C., Q.C., Hon. Recorder of Northampton; Formerly A Deputy High Court Judge And Recorder; Treasurer-1991
Cox, Raymond, Q.C.
Craig, Professor Paul, M.A., B.C.L., F.B.A., Q.C.(Hon) (Honorary)
Cran, Mark, Q.C.
Crane, Sir Peter Francis, Formerly Justice of the High Court
Cranston, The Hon Sir Ross Frederick, F.B.A., Formerly Solicitor-General; A Justice of the High Court
Crawford, Professor James, Whewell Professor of International Law, University of Cambridge (Honorary)
Crennan, The Hon Justice Susan Maree, A.C., High Court Judge of Australia (Honorary)
Cresswell, Sir Peter John, Formerly A Justice of the High Court; Master of Pictures
Crookenden, Simon Robert, Q.C., Recorder
Cross, James Edward Michael, Q.C.
Crowley, Jane Elizabeth Rosser, Q.C., Deputy High Court Judge & Recorder
Croxford, Ian Lionel, Q.C.
Curran, His Honour Judge Patrick David, Q.C., A Circuit Judge
Dandrieux Lisfranc, Katherine, Avocat À La Cour D'appel De Paris, Directrice Du Département Des Langues Et Des Droits Étrangers De L'efb. (Honorary)
Davidson, Edward Alan, Q.C.
Davies, The Hon Dame Nicola Velfor, D.B.E., A Justice of the High Court; Master of Admin & Modern Records
Davies, Professor Paul Lyndon, Q.C., F.B.A., Allen & Overy Professor of Corporate Law, Oxford (Honorary)
Davies, His Honour Sir Rhys Everson, Q.C., Formerly A Senior Circuit Judge And Honorary Recorder of Manchester
Davies, (Robert) Leighton, Q.C., Recorder
Davies, Stephen Rees, Q.C.
Dear, The Rt Hon The Lord (Geoffrey), Q.P.M. (Honorary)
Dehn, Conrad Francis, Q.C., Formerly Deputy High Court Judge , Recorder & Chairman of General Tax Commissioner for The Inn; Treasurer-1996
De La Bastide, The Rt Hon Michael Anthony, Q.C., T.C., M.A.(Oxon), B.C.L., Formerly Chief Justice of Trinidad & Tobago; Privy Councillor & President of the Caribbean Court of Justice (Honorary)
De Villepin, Dominique, Prime Minister of France (Honorary)
Denny, William Eric, C.B.E., Q.C.
Dhir, Anuja Ravindra (Lavender), Q.C., Recorder
Diamond, His Honour Anthony Edward John, Q.C., Formerly A Circuit Judge
Dickinson, Gregory David, Q.C., Recorder
Dobbs, The Hon Dame Linda, D.B.E., A Justice of the High Court
Dohmann, Barbara, Q.C.
Donaldson, David Torrance, Q.C.
Eastman, Roger, Master of the Queen's Bench Division
Edward, The Right Hon Sir David Alexander Ogilvy, K.C.M.G., Ll.D., Dr.H.C., D.Univ., F.R.S.E., Formerly Judge of the Court of Justice of the European Communities (Honorary)
Edwards, His Honour Judge (David) Elgan (Hugh), D.L., A Senior Circuit Judge And Honorary Recorder of Chester
Edwards-Stuart, The Hon Sir Antony James Cobham, A Justice of the High Court
Ehlermann, Professor Dr. Claus-Dieter, Dr.H.C., Formerly Chairman of the Appellate Body of the World Trade Organisation (Honorary)
Elliott, Nicholas Blethyn, Q.C.
Engelman, Mark
Etherton, The Right Hon Sir Terence Michael Elkan Barnet, A Lord Justice of Appeal
Evans, The Right Hon Sir Anthony Howell Meurig, Formerly A Lord Justice of Appeal Chief Justice of DIFC Courts, Dubai; Treasurer-2000
Evans, (David) Anthony, Q.C.
Evans, The Hon Sir (David) Roderick, A Justice of The High Court
Evans, Elwen, Q.C., Recorder
Evans, James, C.B.E.
Evans, Gareth, Q.C., Recorder; Leader of the Midland Circuit
Ewbank, Sir Anthony Bruce, Formerly A Justice of the High Court
Falkowski, Damian
Field, Patrick John, Q.C.
Fisher, David Paul, Q.C., Recorder
Flesch, Michael Charles, Q.C.
Fluker, (Christine) Louise
Focke, His Honour Paul Everard Justus, Q.C., Formerly A Senior Circuit Judge
Fordham, Michael John, Q.C., Recorder
Foskett, The Hon Sir David Robert, A Justice of the High Court
Foster, His Honour Judge Jonathan, Q.C., A Circuit Judge
Foxton, David, Q.C.
Foy, John, Q.C., Recorder
Freedland, Professor Mark, F.B.A., Professor of Employment Law, University of Oxford
Freeland, His Honour Judge Simon Dennis Marsden, Q.C., A Circuit Judge
French, The Hon Robert, A.C., Chief Justice High Court of Australia (Honorary)
Frossard, Sir Charles, K.B.E., Formerly Bailiff of Guernsey And President of the Court of Appeal of Guernsey (Honorary)
Furmston, Professor Michael Philip, T.D., Dean, School of Law, SMU
Gaitskell, Robert, Q.C., Recorder
Genn, Professor Dame Hazel, D.B.E., Q.C.(Hon) (Honorary)
Gill, Manjit Singh, Q.C.
Gillen, The Hon Sir John, A Justice of the High Court (Honorary)
Girvan, The Right Hon Lord Justice, Lord Justice of Appeal, Supreme Court of Judicature, Northern Ireland (Honorary)
Glasgow, Edwin John, C.B.E., Q.C., Master of the Library
Glen, Ian Douglas, Q.C., Recorder
Glidewell, The Right Hon Sir Iain Derek Laing, Formerly A Lord Justice of Appeal; Formerly President of the Court of Appeal for Gibraltar; Treasurer-1995
Goldblatt, Simon, Q.C.
Goldsack, His Honour Judge Alan Raymond, Q.C., D.L., A Senior Circuit Judge & Honorary Recorder of Sheffield
Goldsmith, The Right Hon The Lord, Q.C., Formerly H.M. Attorney General
Gompertz, (Arthur John) Jeremy, Q.C.
Graham, Sir Peter, K.C.B., Q.C.

10

Greenberg, Joanna Elishever Gabrielle, Q.C., Recorder
Griffith Williams, The Hon Sir John, A Justice of the High Court Chancellor of the Diocese of Llandaff
Griffiths, Courtenay Delsdue Mcvay, Q.C., Recorder
Grigson, The Hon Sir Geoffrey, Formerly A Justice of the High Court
Gross, The Rt Hon Sir Peter Henry, A Lord Justice of Appeal
Grunwald, Henry Cyril, O.B.E., Q.C.
Guest, Anthony Gordon, C.B.E., Q.C., F.B.A., Emeritus Professor of King's College London
Guy, (John) David Colin
Haddon-Cave, Charles Anthony, Q.C., Recorder
Hale of Richmond, The Right Hon The Baroness, D.B.E., Justice of the Supreme Court
Hall, Andrew Joseph, Q.C.
Hall, His Honour Judge Julian, Formerly A Circuit Judge; Honorary Recorder of Oxford
Halpern, David, Q.C.
Hamer, George Clemens
Hamilton, Penelope
Hand, His Hon Judge John Lester, Q.C., A Circuit Judge
Hapgood, Mark Bernard, Q.C.
Hardie Boys, The Right Hon Sir Michael, G.N.Z.M., G.C.M.G., Q.S.O., Formerly Governor-General of New Zealand (Honorary)
Hardy, His Hon Judge (Christopher) Robert Hurst, A Circuit Judge
Hargrove, His Honour Bernard, O.B.C., Q.C., Formerly A Circuit Judge
Harman, The Right Hon Harriet, Q.C., M.P., Leader of The House of Commons, Lord Privy Seal, Minster for Women & Equality And Deputy Leader of The Labour Party (Honorary)
Harman, Robert Donald, Q.C., Formerly A Judge of the Courts of Appeal, Jersey & Guernsey
Harper, Joseph Charles, Q.C.
Harrington, Patrick John, Q.C., Recorder
Harris, Russell, Q.C.
Harrison, Sir Michael Guy Vicat, Formerly A Justice of the High Court
Harrison, (Robert) Michael, Q.C.
Hartley, Richard Leslie Clifford, Q.C.
Harvey, Michael Llewellyn Tucker, Q.C., Recorder & Deputy High Court Judge
Hascher, Judge Dominique, Presiding Judge, Court of Appeal, Reims, Champagne (Honorary)
Hatton, David William, Q.C.
Hawkesworth, His Honour Judge (Thomas) Simon Ashwell, Q.C., A Circuit Judge
Hawkins, His Honour Judge Richard, Q.C., A Circuit Judge
Hedley, The Hon Sir Mark, A Justice of the High Court; Master of Moots
Heilbron, Hilary, Q.C.
Hemming, Martin John, C.B.
Hendy, John, Q.C.
Hepple, Professor Sir Bob, Q.C.(Hon), F.B.A., Ll.D., Emeritus Master of Clare College & Emeritus Professor of Law, University of Cambridge
Herzog, Herr Bundespräsident Roman, Formerly President of the Federal Republic of Germany (Honorary)
Hewitt, Penelope Ann, C.B.E., Formerly Senior District Judge At Bow Street Magistrates' Court
Heydon, The Hon John Dyson, A.C., A Justice of the High Court of Australia (Honorary)
Higgs, Brian James, Q.C.
Hillier, Andrew Charles, Q.C.
Hoffmann of Chedworth, The Right Hon The Lord, Formerly Lord of Appeal In Ordinary
Hollander, Charles, Q.C.
Hollis, Kim, Q.C.
Hooson, The Lord, Q.C., Treasurer-1986
Hope of Craighead, The Right Hon The Lord, K.T., F.R.S.E., Deputy President of the Supreme Court of the United Kingdom (Honorary)
Horwell, Richard, Q.C.
Houlder, Bruce Fiddes, Q.C., Recorder, Director of Service Prosecutions
Howard, Mark Steven, Q.C.
Howard, Michael Newman, Q.C., Recorder
Howard, Robin Ivan, Master of Finance
Howse, Patricia, C.B.E.
Hudson-Phillips, Karl T., Q.C., Formerly A Justice of the International Criminal Court
Huebner, Michael Denis, C.B.
Hughes, His Hon Judge Peter Thomas, Q.C., A Circuit Judge
Hunt, David Roderic Notley, Q.C., Recorder; Master of Education
Hurst, Peter, Ll.B., M.Phil., Senior Costs Judge (Honorary)
Hutchison, The Right Hon Sir Michael, Formerly A Lord Justice of Appeal
Ibbeteson, Professor David John, Ph.D., D.Phil., F.B.A., Deputy Head of Faculty, Corpus Chisti College, Cambridge (Honorary)
Inglese, Anthony Michael Christopher, C.B., General Counsel & Solicitor, Her Majesty's Revenue & Customs
Irvin, Peter
Irwin, The Hon Sir Stephen John, A Justice of the High Court
Jacob, The Right Hon Professor Sir Robin, Formerly A Lord Justice of Appeal; Treasurer-2007
James, The Revd Canon Eric, D.D., F.K.C., Canon of St Albans (Emeritus); Extra Chaplain to Her Majesty The Queen (Honorary)
Jarman, His Hon Judge (John) Milwyn, Q.C., A Circuit Judge
Jeans, Christopher, Q.C., Recorder
Jefford, Nerys, Q.C., Recorder
Jeffreys, David Alfred, Q.C.
Jeffreys, Rosemary Anne
Jeffs, Julian, Q.C., Encomienda De La Orden De Isabel La Católica
Jenkins, Major General David John Malcolm, C.B., C.B.E. (Honorary)
Johnson, Sir Robert Lionel, Formerly A Justice of the High Court
Jolowicz, (John) Anthony, Q.C., Emeritus Professor of Comparative Law, University of Cambridge
Jones, Stewart Elgan, Q.C., Recorder
Joseph, Her Honour Judge Wendy Rose, Q.C., A Circuit Judge
Junkin, (William) Roy, C.B., Formerly Deputy Director of Public Prosecutions
Kabbah, President Ahmad Tejan (Honorary)
Kallipetis, Michel Louis, Q.C., C.I.Arb., Recorder; Deputy High Court Judge; Chartered Arbitrator
Katkowski, Christopher, Q.C.
Kay, The Right Hon Sir Maurice Ralph, A Lord Justice of Appeal
Kelly, Matthias John, Q.C.
Kennedy, The Right Hon Sir Paul Joseph Morrow, Formerly A Lord Justice of Appeal Interception of Communications Commissioner; Treasurer-2002
Kennedy of the Shaws, Baroness Helena, Q.C., Chairman of the Governing Council of Justice
Kerr of Tonaghmore, The Right Hon The Lord, Justice of the Supreme Court (Honorary)
Kirk, Anthony James Nigel, Q.C.
Kitchin, The Hon Sir David James Tyson, A Justice of the High Court
Kramer, His Honour Judge Stephen Ernest, Q.C., A Senior Circuit Judge
Kriegler, Judge Johann, Formerly A Justice of the Constitutional Court of South Africa (Honorary)
Lamb, His Hon Judge (Timothy), Q.C., A Circuit Judge
Lambert, Nigel Robert Woolf, Q.C., Recorder
Latham, Richard, Q.C., Recorder
Lauterpacht, Sir Elihu, C.B.E., Q.C.
Lawson, Elizabeth Ann, Q.C.
Leighton Williams, John, Q.C., Deputy High Court Judge And Recorder, Treasurer-2010
Lenoir, Mme. Noelle, Formerly Minister for European Affairs; President of European Institute of Hec; President of The Cercle De Européens (Honorary)
Lever, Sir Jeremy Frederick, K.C.M.G., Q.C.
Lewer, Michael Edward, C.B.E., Q.C.
Lewis, James, Q.C., Recorder
Lickley, Nigel James Dominic, Q.C.
Lieven, Nathalie, Q.C.
Limbach, Professor Dr.,H.C. Jutta, President, Goethe-Institut, Germany (Honorary)
Lindblom, The Hon Sir Keith John, A Justice of the High Court
Litton, The Hon Henry, C.B.E., Non-Permanent Judge of the Court of Final Appeal, Hong Kong (Honorary)
Lodge, Anton James Corduff, Q.C., Recorder
Lofthouse, Simon Timothy, Q.C., Recorder
Lowe, Professor (Alan) Vaughan, Q.C.
Lowe, (Nicholas) Mark, Q.C., Recorder
Lowry, Her Honour Nina, Formerly A Circuit Judge
Lynagh, Richard Dudley, Q.C.
Ma, The Hon Geoffrey Tao-Li, Chief Justice of Hong Kong; Special Administrative Region (Honorary)
Macdonald, Alistair Neil, Q.C.
Machell, Raymond, Q.C.
Machin, David (Honorary)
Macrory, Richard
Malek, Ali, Q.C., Recorder
Malek, (Mehdi) Hodge, Q.C., Recorder
Mann, Paul, Q.C., Recorder
Manning, Colin, Recorder; Master of the Walks
Mansfield, Michael, Q.C.
Markesinis, Sir Basil, Q.C.(Hon), D.Iur(Athen), Ph.D., LL.D.(Cantab), D.C.L.(Oxon), D.Iur.H.C.(Ghent, Paris I, Munich), F.B.A.
Marks, Richard, Q.C.
Marriott, Arthur Leslie, Q.C., Solicitor (Honorary)
Marsh, Elizabeth Ann, Q.C.
Marshall-Andrews, Robert, Q.C., Recorder
Matthews, Duncan Henry Rowland, Q.C.
Mawrey, Richard Brooks, Q.C., Recorder
McCaughran, John, Q.C.
McCaul, Colin, Q.C., Master of Advocacy
McClean, (John) David, C.B.E., Q.C.(Hon), D.C.L. (Oxon), F.B.A., Emeritus Professor of Law, University of Sheffield
McCollum, The Right Hon Sir Liam, Formerly A Lord Justice of Appeal; Surveillance Commissioner (Honorary)
McFarlane, The Hon Sir Andrew Ewart, A Justice of the High Court
McKendrick, Professor Ewan
McLachlin, The Right Hon Beverley, P.C., Chief Justice of Canada (Honorary)
McLaren, Ian Alban Bryant, Q.C., Dr.Jur.hc.
McLaughlin, The Hon Sir Richard, A Justice of the High Court (Honorary)
Miskin, Charles James Monckton, Q.C., Recorder
Mitchell, Andrew Robert, Q.C., Recorder
Mitchell, Gregory Charles Mathew, Q.C., Recorder
Mitting, The Hon Sir John Edward, A Justice of the High Court Master of Debates
Montgomery, Clare, Q.C., Deputy High Court Judge Court of Appeal Jersey & Guernsey
Moran, Andrew Gerard, Q.C., Deputy High Court Judge
Morison, The Hon Sir Thomas Richard Atkin, A Justice of the High Court
Morris, His Honour Judge Anthony Paul, Q.C., A Senior Circuit Judge
Morris of Aberavon, The Right Hon The Lord, K.G., Q.C., Formerly Attorney General
Morrison, His Excellency Judge Howard Andrew Clive, C.B.E.
Moss, His Honour Judge Christopher, Q.C., A Senior Circuit Judge
Muller, Franz Joseph, Q.C.
Mummery, The Right Hon Sir John Frank, A Lord Justice of Appeal; Treasurer-2005
Murray, The Right Hon Sir Donald, Formerly A Lord Justice of Appeal (Honorary)
Mustill, The Right Hon The Lord, Ll.D., F.B.A., Formerly A Lord of Appeal
Muttukumaru, Christopher Peter Jayantha C.B., General Counsel, Dept for Transport
Napier, (Thomas) Michael, C.B.E., Q.C.(Hon), Ll.B., Ll.D. (Hon), Solicitor (Honorary)
Naughton, Philip Anthony, Q.C.
Neill of Bladen, The Lord, Q.C., Chairman, Senate of The Inns of Court & The Bar 1974-75; Judge of the Courts of Appeal Jersey & Guernsey 1977-94; Warden of All Souls College, Oxford 1977-95; Vice Chancellor, University of Oxford, 1985-89; Chairman, Committee on Standards In Public Life 1997-2001; Treasurer-1990
Nelson, Paula
Ngulube, Matthew, M.S.W., Formerly Chief Justice of Zambia (Honorary)
Nicholls, Clive, Q.C.
Nicholls, Colin, Q.C.
Nicholson, The Right Hon Alastair, A.O., R.F.D., Q.C., Formerly Chief Justice of the Family Court of Australia; Honorary Professorial Fellow, University of Melbourne (Honorary)
Nicholson, The Right Hon Sir James Michael Anthony, Formerly A Lord Justice of Appeal (Honorary)
Nsugbe, Eric, Q.C.
O'Connor, The Hon Justice Sandra Day, Associate Justice of the Supreme Court of the United States (Ret) (Honorary)
O'Neill, Sally Jane, Q.C., Recorder
O'Neill of Bengarve, The Baroness, C.B.E., F.B.A., Hon.F.R.S., F.Med.Sci. (Honorary)
Ognall, Sir Harry Henry, Formerly A Justice of the High Court
Oldham, Frances Mary Theresa, Q.C., Recorder And Deputy High Court Judge (Family Division);
Osborne, Clive
Otton, The Right Hon Sir Philip Howard, Formerly A Lord Justice of Appeal
Oulton, Sir (Antony) Derek Maxwell, G.C.B., Q.C., Fellow Magdalene College, Cambridge; Formerly Clerk of the Crown In Chancery And Permanent Secretary to The Lord Chancellor
Ouseley, The Hon Sir Duncan Brian Walter, A Justice of the High Court
Owen, His Hon Judge Robert Frank, Q.C., Circuit Judge
Pannick, The Lord (David), Q.C.
Parker, Christopher
Parker, The Hon Sir Kenneth Blades, A Justice of the High Court
Parkes, His Hon Judge Richard, Q.C., A Circuit Judge
Patten of Barnes, Right Hon Lord, C.H. (Honorary)
Paulsson, Jan (Honorary)
Pearl, His Honour Judge David, Ph.D., A Circuit Judge; Tribunal Member of the Judicial Appointments Commission
Peppitt, His Honour John Raymond, Q.C., Formerly A Circuit Judge
Perry, Jacqueline Anne, Q.C.
Phillips, David John, Q.C., Deputy High Court Judge & Recorder
Phillips, His Honour Judge John, C.B.E., A Circuit Judge
Phillips, Stephen Edmund, Q.C., Deputy High Court Judge And Recorder
Phillips of Worth Matravers, The Right Hon The Lord (Honorary)
Pill, The Right Hon Sir Malcolm Thomas, A Lord Justice of Appeal
Pinson, Barry, Q.C.
Plume, John Trevor
Pollock, Alan Gordon Seton, Q.C.
Posnansky, Jeremy Ross Leon, Q.C., Deputy High Court Judge
Potter, The Right Hon Sir Mark Howard, Treasurer-2004; Master of the Cellar
Pratt, (Richard) Camden, Q.C., Recorder; Deputy High Court Judge
Pratt, Richard James, Q.C.
Price, His Honour Judge John Charles
Price, His Honour Judge Nicholas Peter Lees, Q.C., A Circuit Judge
Price, Richard Mervyn, OBE., Q.C., Recorder; Master of the Library
Pringle, Ian Derek, Q.C., Recorder
Prosser, His Honour (Elvet) John, Q.C., Formerly A Circuit Judge
Quirk, The Right Hon Lord, C.B.E., D.Litt., Ll.D., F.B.A., Past President of the British Academy; Formerly Vice-Chancellor of the University of London (Honorary)
Radford, His Honour Judge David Wyn Radford
Rafferty, The Hon Dame Anne, D.B.E., A Justice of the High Court; Formerly Presiding Judge of the South Eastern Circuit

Railton, David, Q.C., Recorder
Ramphal, The Hon Sir Shridath Surendranath, O.E., G.C.M.G., O.M., Oc.C., Q.C. (Honorary)
Ramsbotham, General The Lord David John, G.C.B., C.B.E., Formerly HM Chief Inspector of Prisons for England And Wales (Honorary)
Read, Lionel Frank, Q.C., Formerly Deputy High Court Judge And Recorder; Treasurer-2001
Reese, Colin Edward, Q.C., Recorder; Chairman Tecbar 2000-03
Reynold, Frederic, Q.C.
Richards, The Right Hon Sir Stephen Price, A Lord Justice of Appeal
Ritchie, Jean H., Q.C., Formerly Recorder
Roberts, Dr John Anthony, C.B.E, Q.C., D.C.L., F.C.I.Arb., Recorder; Formerly A Justice of the Supreme Courts of the British Virgin Islands And Anguilla, B.W.I.
Roberts, Timothy David Roberts, Q.C., Recorder
Roch, The Right Hon Sir John Ormond, Formerly A Lord Justice of Appeal
Roddick, (George) Winston, C.B., Q.C., Recorder
Rodrîguez Iglesias, Gil Carlos, Formerly President of the EU Court of Justice; Professor, Universidad Complutense De Madrid (Honorary)
Rogers, His Honour Judge John Michael Thomas, Q.C., A Circuit Judge
Rokison, Kenneth Stuart, Q.C.
Rook, His Honour Judge Peter Francis Grosvenor, Q.C., A Senior Circuit Judge
Rose, Dinah Gwen Lison, Q.C.
Rowe, Miss Judith May, Q.C.
Rowland, Sir Geoffrey, The Bailiff of Guernsey; President of the Guernsey Court of Appeal; Judge of the Jersey Court of Appeal (Honorary)
Royce, The Hon Sir (Roger) John, A Justice of the High Court
Rozenberg, Joshua Rufus (Honorary)
Russell, Christopher John
Ruttle, (Henry) Stephen Mayo, Q.C.
Ryder, The Hon Sir Ernest Nigel, T.D., A Justice of the High Court
Sallon, Christopher Robert Anthony, Q.C., Recorder
Saunders, The Hon Sir John Henry Boulton, A Justice of the High Court; Formerly Senior Circuit Judge At Birmingham Crown Court; Honorary Recorder of Birmingham
Sawyer, The Right Hon Dame Joan A, D.B.E., P.C., President of the Court of Appeal of the Bahamas (Honorary)
Schmidt, Benno C., Jr., Chairman, Schools Edison Project (Honorary)
Schwebel, Judge Stephen M., Formerly President, International Court of Justice (Honorary)
Scott, Professor Ian, Ph.D., Professor of Law (Honorary)
Seagroatt, The Hon Conrad, Q.C., Formerly A Judge of the High Court of Hong Kong
Sentamu, John Tucker Mugabi, Most Revd & Right Hon, Archbishop of York (Honorary)
Seymour, David, C.B., Legal Adviser to the Home Office
Seys Llewellyn, His Hon Judge Anthony John, Q.C., Senior Circuit Judge And Designated Civil Judge (Wales)
Shant, Nirmal, Q.C.
Shaw, Martin (Honorary)
Sheil, The Right Hon Sir John, Formerly A Lord Justice of Appeal (Honorary)
Sheldon, Richard, Q.C.
Silber, The Hon Sir Stephen Robert, A Justice of the High Court
Silverleaf, (Alexander) Michael, Q.C.
Smellie, The Hon Justice Anthony, Q.C., J.P., Chief Justice, Cayman Islands (Honorary)
Smith, The Hon Lady (Anne), Senator of the College of Justice, Court of Session, Scotland (Honorary)
Sotomayor, Justice Sonia, Associate Justice of the United States Supreme Court (Honorary)
Souter, The Hon David H., Associate Justice of the United States Supreme Court
Spence, Malcolm Hugh, Q.C.
Spencer, Sir Derek Harold, Q.C., Formerly Solicitor General
Spencer, The Hon Mr Justice Robin Godfrey, A Justice of the High Court
Spokes, John Arthur Clayton, Q.C.
Stapleton, Professor Jane (Honorary)
Steel, Dame Heather, D.B.E., Formerly A Justice of the High Court Judge of the Court of Appeal, Jersey & Guernsey
Steel, John Brychan, Q.C., Recorder; Master of the Estate
Stephen, The Righ Hon Sir Ninian, K.G., A.K., G.C.M.G., G.C.V.O., K.B.E., Formerly Justice of the Supreme Court of Victoria And Justice of the High Court of Australia; Formerly A Judge of the International Criminal Tribunal for the Former Yugoslavia; Formerly Governor-General of the Commonwealth of Australia (Honorary)
Stevens, Professor Robert (Bocking), D.C.L., Ll.D. (Hon), D.Litt. (Hon), Formerly Master of Pembroke College, Oxford
Stockwell, Peter Lewis, Fciarb, Solicitor, Partner, Payne Hicks Beach (Honorary)
Stow, His Honour Judge Timothy Montague Fenwick, Q.C., A Circuit Judge
Straker, Timothy Derrick, Q.C., Deputy High Court Judge & Recorder
Stuart-Smith, Jeremy Hugh, Q.C., Recorder
Stuart-Smith, The Right Hon Sir Murray, Formerly A Lord Justice of Appeal Treasurer-1998
Stubbs, William Frederick, Q.C.
Sturman, James Anthony Sturman, Q.C.
Swift, Malcolm Robin Farquhar, Q.C.
Taverner, Marcus, Q.C.
Tejan-Jalloh, The Hon Justice Uma Hawa, Chief Justice of Sierra Leone (Honorary)
Thatcher of Kesteven, The Right Hon The Baroness, L.G., O.M., F.R.S., Formerly Prime Minister And First Lord of the Treasury (Honorary)
Theis, The Hon Mrs Justice Lucy, A Justice of the High Court
Thomas, Clarence, Associate Justice of the Supreme Court of the United States (Honorary)
Thomas, Professor Sir John Meurig, Ll.D., F.R.S., Hon. F.R. Eng., Hon. Professor, University of Cambridge; Formerly Master of Peterhouse, Cambridge 1993-2002; Formerly Director of the Royal Institution of Great Britain (Honorary)
Thomas, His Hon Judge Patrick Anthony, Q.C., A Circuit Judge
Thomas, His Hon Judge Paul (Huw), Q.C., A Circuit Judge
Thomas, The Right Hon Sir (Roger) John Laugharne, Vice-President of the Queen's Bench Division; A Lord Justice of Appeal
Thomas of Gresford, Lord, O.B.E., Q.C.
Tomlinson, Hugh, Q.C.
Treitel, Sir Guenter Heinz, Q.C., D.C.L., F.B.A., Formerly Vinerian Professor of English Law; Emeritus Fellow of All Souls & Magdalen Colleges, Oxford (Honorary)
Tselentis, Michael, Q.C.
Turner, David, Q.C., Recorder
Turner, Mark George, Q.C.
Turner, Robert Lockley, Formerly the Senior Master And Queen's Remembrancer
Tyrrell, Alan Rupert, Q.C.
Turvill, Sarah
Uff, John Francis, C.B.E, Q.C., Emeritus Professor of Engineering Law, King's College, London; Treasurer-2011
Underhill, The Hon Sir Nicholas Edward, A Justice of the High Court
Underwood, Ashley Grenville, Q.C.
Vajda, Christopher Stephen, Q.C.
Vandermeer, (Arnold) Roy, O.B.E., Q.C., Formerly Deputy High Court Judge And Recorder
Van Gerven, Professor Baron Walter (Honorary)
Venne, Roger André, Q.C., Registrar of Criminal Appeals And Master of the Crown Office, Administrative Court
Vere-Hodge, Michael John Davy, Q.C., Recorder
Waddington, The Right Hon The Lord, G.C.V.O., Q.C.
Waite, The Right Hon Sir John Douglas, Formerly A Lord Justice of Appeal
Walker, The Hon Sir Paul James, A Justice of the High Court
Walker, Ronald Jack, Q.C., Recorder
Wall, The Right Hon Sir Nicholas Peter Rathbone, A Lord Justice of Appeal; President of the Family Division
Waller, The Right Hon Sir Mark, Formerly A Lord Justice of Appeal, Vice President of the Civil Division, Treasurer-2009
Wallop, The Hon Mrs Nicholas, M.B.E. (Honorary)
Warby, Mark, Q.C., Recorder
Ward, The Right Hon Sir Alan, A Lord Justice of Appeal; Treasurer-2006
Warnock of Weeke, Baroness, D.B.E., Formerly Mistress of Girton College, Cambridge (Honorary)
Wass, Sasha, Q.C., Recorder
Weatherup, The Hon Sir Ronald Eccles, A Justice of the High Court (Honorary)
Weekes, Anesta Glendora, Q.C., Recorder
Weinberg, Sir Mark, B.Com., Ll.M. (Honorary)
Weitzman, Peter, Q.C.
Weitzman, Thomas Edward Benjamin, Q.C.
West-Knights, Laurence James, Q.C., Recorder
Wheldon, Dame Juliet Louise, D.C.B., Q.C.(Hon)
White, His Honour Sir Frank, Formerly A Senior Circuit Judge
Whitehead, (Edwin Francis) Romilly
Wilson, His Honour Harold, A.E., Formerly A Deputy High Court Judge; A Judge of the Employment Appeal Tribunal; Formerly A Circuit Judge and Honorary Recorder of Oxford
Wilson-Smith, Christopher, Q.C.
Workman, Timothy Henry, C.B.E., Senior District Judge & Chief Magistrate of London (Honorary)
Wood, Sir Michael Charles, K.C.M.G., Member, UN International Law Commission; Formerly Legal Adviser, Foreign and Commonwealth Office
Woodley, Sonia, Q.C., Recorder
Wooler, Stephen, C.B.
Woolf, The Right Hon The Lord, Formerly the Lord Chief Justice of England And Wales (Honorary)
Worthington, Stephen, Q.C.
Yaakob, The Hon Tan Sri Dato' Seri Siti Norma, P.S.M., S.P.T.J., D.S.N.S., J.S.M., Judge of the DIFC Courts, Dubai; Formerly Chief Judge, Malaya (Honorary)
Yang, The Hon Sir Ti Liang Yang, Formerly Chief Justice of Hong Kong (Honorary)
Young, Timothy Nicholas, Q.C.

INNER TEMPLE

TREASURY OFFICE

Inner Temple EC4Y 7HL
Tel: 020 7797 8250
Fax: 020 7797 8178
Email: information@innertemple.org.uk
Hours: 10am to 4pm (10am to 3pm in Long Vacation)

Sub-Treasurer

Maddams, Patrick

LIBRARY

Inner Temple, London EC4Y 7DA
Tel: 020 7797 8217
Fax: 020 7797 8224
Emali: library@innertemple.org.uk

Term-time: Monday to Thursday - 9am to 8pm,
Friday - 9am to 7pm.
Outside term-time: Monday to Friday - 9am to 7pm
Long Vacation: closed last two weeks in August, otherwise
Monday to Friday - 9am to 5.30pm.
Long Vacation: closed last two weeks in August.
Closed on Bank Holidays.

Librarian and Keeper of Manuscripts

Clay, Miss Margaret
Tel: 020 7797 8215

MASTERS OF THE BENCH

H.R.H. The Princess Royal
Hallett, The Rt Hon Lady Justice, D.B.E.
H.R.H. Prince Philip, Duke of Edinburgh, K.G., K.T., O.M., G.B.E.
Hirst, Jonathan, Esq, Q.C.
Monier-Williams, His Honour E F (Senior)
Le Quesne, Sir Godfray, Q.C. (Senior)
Griffiths, The Rt Hon The Lord, M.C. (Senior)
Brown, The Rt Hon Sir Stephen, G.B.E. (Senior)
Hirst, The Rt Hon Sir David (Supernumerary)
Nugee, Edward, Esq, T.D., Q.C. (Senior)
Staughton, The Rt Hon Sir Christopher (Supernumerary)
Baroness Butler-Sloss of Marsh Green, The Rt Hon The, G.B.E. (Senior)
Lloyd of Berwick, The Rt Hon The Lord, D.L. (Senior)
Brodie, Stanley, Esq, Q.C. (Senior)
Thomas, The Rt Hon Sir Swinton (Senior)
Southwell, Richard, Esq, Q.C. (Senior)
Schiemann, The Rt Hon Sir Konrad (Senior)
Chadwick, The Rt Hon Sir John
Rix, The Rt Hon Lord Justice
Keene, The Rt Hon Sir David
Williamson, Stephen, Esq, Q.C. (Senior)
May, The Rt Hon Sir Anthony (Senior)
Robinson, Vivian, Esq, Q.C.
Laws, The Rt Hon Lord Justice
Dunn, The Rt Hon Sir Robin, M.C. (Supernumerary)
Campbell of Alloway, The Rt Hon The Lord, Q.C. (Supernumerary)
Widdicombe, David, Esq, Q.C. (Supernumerary)
Goff of Chieveley, The Rt Hon The Lord (Senior)
Willmer, John, Esq, Q.C. (Senior)
Woolf of Barnes, The Rt Hon The Lord (Senior)
Neill, The Rt Hon Sir Brian (Senior)
Leggatt, The Rt Hon Sir Andrew (Senior)
Dobry, His Honour George, C.B.E., Q.C. (Supernumerary)
Glover, William, Esq, Q.C. (Supernumerary)
Beldam, The Rt Hon Sir Roy (Senior)
Popplewell, Sir Oliver (Senior)
Macpherson of Cluny, Sir William, T.D. (Supernumerary)
Morrison, The Hon Sir Charles, Q.C. (Supernumerary)
Mackay of Clashfern, The Rt Hon The Lord, K.T. (Honorary)
Reynolds, Professor Francis, D.C.L., F.B.A., Q.C. (Honorary)
Morland, Sir Michael (Senior)
Drinkwater, Sir John, Q.C. (Senior)
Worsley, Michael, Esq, Q.C. (Supernumerary)
Alliott, Sir John (Supernumerary)
Turner, Sir Michael (Senior)
Inglis-Jones, Nigel, Esq, Q.C. (Supernumerary)
Scott of Foscote, The Rt Hon The Lord (Senior)
Graham-Dixon, Anthony, Esq, Q.C. (Supernumerary)
Kingsdown, The Rt Hon The Lord, KG (Honorary)
Brittan of Spennithorne, The Rt Hon The Lord, Q.C. (Senior)
Sullivan, David, Esq, Q.C. (Supernumerary)
Legg, Sir Thomas, K.C.B., Q.C. (Senior)
Tennant, Mark, Esq (Senior)
Barker, David, Esq, Q.C. (Senior)
McGregor, Harvey, Esq, Q.C. (Senior)
Curtis, Sir Richard (Supernumerary)
Green, Sir Allan, KCB, Q.C. (Supernumerary)
Aldous, Sir William (Supernumerary)
Hidden, Sir Anthony (Senior)
Thomas, Neville, Esq, Q.C. (Supernumerary)
Richard of Ammanford, The Rt Hon The Lord, Q.C. (Supernumerary)
Williams, The Hon Melville, Q.C. (Senior)
Smith, Anthony, Esq, Q.C. (Supernumerary)
Holland, Sir Christopher (Senior)
Evans-Lombe, Sir Edward (Senior)
Irvine of Lairg, The Rt Hon The Lord (Senior)
Stone, Evan, Esq, Q.C. (Senior)
Anwyl, Her Honour Shirley, Q.C. (Senior)
Hamilton, Eben, Esq, Q.C. (Senior)
Previte, His Honour John, Q.C. (Supernumerary)
Sainsbury of Preston Candover, The Rt Hon The Lord, K.G. (Honorary)
Clegg, Richard, Esq, Q.C. (Supernumerary)
Lyndon-Stanford, Michael, Esq, Q.C. (Supernumerary)
Parker, The Rt Hon Sir Jonathan (Senior)
Beveridge, John, Esq, Q.C. (Supernumerary)
Lloyd, His Honour Humphrey, Q.C. (Senior)
Cazalet, Sir Edward (Senior)
Thorpe, The Rt Hon Lord Justice (Senior)
Crowther, William, Esq, Q.C. (Supernumerary)
Henderson, Roger, Esq, Q.C.
Deby, John, Esq, Q.C. (Senior)
Thompson, His Honour Anthony, Q.C. (Senior)
Armstrong of Ilminster, The Rt Hon The Lord, G.C.B., C.V.O. (Honorary)
Scalia, The Honourable Justice Antonin (Honorary)
Hunter, Ian, Esq, Q.C.
Brooke, Sir Henry (Senior)
North, Sir Peter, C.B.E., D.C.L., F.B.A., Q.C. (Honorary)
Jacomb, Sir Martin (Honorary)
Ground, Patrick, Esq, Q.C. (Senior)
Connell, Sir Michael (Senior)
Vaughan, David, Esq, C.B.E., Q.C. (Senior)
Baker, Professor Sir John, LL.D., F.B.A., Q.C. (Honorary)
Hutton, The Rt Hon The Lord (Honorary)
Robson, David, Esq, Q.C. (Senior)
Wadsworth, His Honour James, Q.C. (Senior)
Sher, Jules, Esq, Q.C.
Tabachnik, Eldred, Esq, Q.C. (Supernumerary)
Tugendhat, The Hon Mr Justice
Crowley, John, Esq, Q.C. (Senior)
Sedley, The Rt Hon Sir Stephen (Senior)
Higgins, Dame Rosalyn, D.B.E., J.S.D., F.B.A., Q.C. (Senior)
Elfer, His Honour David, Q.C.
Potter, Raymond, Esq, C.B. (Senior)
Hamilton, Nigel, Esq, Q.C. (Senior)
Lipworth, Sir Sydney, Q.C. (Honorary)
Sumption, Jonathan, Esq, O.B.E., Q.C.
Woodley, Leonard, Esq, Q.C. (Supernumerary)
Tomlinson, The Rt Hon Lord Justice
Wood, Nicholas, Esq
Slade, The Hon Mrs Justice
Verney, His Honour Sir Lawrence (Supernumerary)
Knorpel, Henry, Esq, C.B., Q.C. (Senior)
Topley, Keith, Esq (Supernumerary)
Carey of Clifton, The Rt Rev and Rt Hon Lord, P.C. (Honorary)
Feldman, Judge Martin (Honorary)
Lawrence, Sir Ivan, Q.C. (Senior)
Goudie, James, Esq, Q.C.
Lockhart-Mummery, Christopher, Esq, Q.C.
Prince, Edwin, Esq (Supernumerary)
Salter, Richard, Esq, Q.C.
Steel, The Hon Mr Justice David
Kaplan, Neil, Esq, C.B.E., Q.C., SC (HK)
Gage, The Rt Hon Sir William (Senior)
Purnell, Paul, Esq, Q.C. (Supernumerary)
Playford, His Honour Jonathan, Q.C. (Senior)
Forbes, Sir John Thayne (Senior)
Jenkins, Sir Brian, G.B.E. (Honorary)
Pickering, Murray, Esq, Q.C. (Senior)
Moore-Bick, The Rt Hon Lord Justice
Baroness Mallalieu, The, Q.C. (Supernumerary)
Gloster, The Hon Mrs Justice, D.B.E.
Cryan, His Honour Judge
Anderson, Anthony, Esq, Q.C. (Supernumerary)
Turcan, Harry, Esq
Angel, Gerald, Esq (Senior)
Buxton, The Rt Hon Sir Richard (Senior)
Goode, Professor Sir Royston, C.B.E., F.B.A., Q.C. (Honorary)
Viscount Runciman of Doxford, The Rt Hon, C.B.E., FBA (Honorary)
Swift, John, Esq, Q.C. (Supernumerary)
Stewart, His Honour Judge James, Q.C.
Howard of Lympne, The Rt Hon The Lord, C.H., Q.C.
Roberts, His Honour Jeremy, Q.C.
Clarke, Sir David
Butterfield, The Hon Mr Justice
Singer, Sir Peter
Lawson, His Honour Judge, Q.C.
ter Haar, The Reverend Roger, Q.C.
Bickford-Smith, Stephen, Esq
Bickford-Smith, Mrs Margaret, Q.C.
Sullivan, The Rt Hon Lord Justice
Penry-Davey, Sir David
Wilson of Culworth, The Rt Hon Lord
Kirkwood, Sir Andrew
Sheldon, Mark, Esq, C.B.E. (Honorary)
Wingate-Saul, Giles, Esq, Q.C.
Elias, Gerard, Esq, Q.C.
Fuad, The Hon Mr Justice Kutlu, C.B.E. (Honorary)
Beatson, The Hon Mr Justice, F.B.A.
Tiley, Professor John, C.B.E., LL.D., Q.C.
Hacking, Anthony, Esq, Q.C.
Bennett, Sir Hugh
O'Brien, Dermod, Esq, Q.C. (Senior)
Hooper, The Rt Hon Lord Justice (Senior)
Mauleverer, Bruce, Esq, Q.C.
Butter, His Honour Neil, C.B.E., Q.C. (Senior)
Matheson, His Honour Duncan, Q.C.
Bevington, Her Honour Christian (Senior)
Willbourne, Miss Caroline
Hughes, Her Honour Judge, Q.C.
Sayers, Michael, Esq, Q.C. (Supernumerary)
Henriques, The Hon Mr Justice
Sumner, Sir Christopher (Senior)
Bowley, Martin, Esq, Q.C. (Senior)
Breyer, The Honourable Justice Stephen (Honorary)
Kennedy, The Honourable Justice Anthony (Honorary)
Gower, His Honour John, Q.C. (Senior)
Toulson, The Rt Hon Lord Justice
Shields, Tom, Esq, Q.C.
Havelock-Allan, His Honour Judge, Q.C.
Brown, His Honour Judge Simon, Q.C.
Acton-Davis, Jonathan, Esq, Q.C.
Temple, Anthony, Esq, Q.C.
Rampton, Richard, Esq, Q.C.
Owen, The Hon Mr Justice
Flather, Gary, Esq, O.B.E., Q.C. (Senior)
Purchas, Christopher, Esq, Q.C.
Scriven, Miss Pamela, Q.C.
Padfield, Nicholas, Esq, Q.C.
Elias, The Rt Hon Lord Justice
Smith, Sir Andrew Hugh (Honorary)
Glass, Anthony, Esq, Q.C. (Senior)
Shorrock, Michael, Esq, Q.C.
Langley, Sir Gordon
Pitchers, Sir Christopher
Pascoe, Nigel, Esq, Q.C.
Korner, Miss Joanna, C.M.G., Q.C.
Sells, Oliver, Esq, Q.C.
Aylett, Kenneth, Esq
Tidbury, Andrew, Esq
Walker, Sir Timothy
Merriman, Nicholas, Esq, Q.C.
de Wilde, Robin, Esq, Q.C.
Birkett, Peter, Esq, Q.C.
Williams, Graeme, Esq, Q.C. (Senior)
Purchas, Robin, Esq, Q.C.
Nice, Sir Geoffrey, Q.C.
Crawford, Sir Frederick, D.L., FR.Eng. (Honorary)
Baroness Deech of Cumnor, The, D.B.E.
Kennedy, Professor Sir Ian, F.B.A. (Honorary)
Keith, The Hon Mr Justice
Weeks, His Honour John, Q.C. (Supernumerary)
Spencer, Michael, Esq, Q.C.
Denyer, His Honour Judge, Q.C.
Temple, Victor, Esq, Q.C.
Plender, Sir Richard
Akenhead, The Hon Mr Justice
Swift, The Hon Mrs Justice
Fenwick, Justin, Esq, Q.C.
Baxendale, Thomas, Esq (Senior)
de Haan, Kevin, Esq, Q.C.
Burke, His Honour Judge Jeffrey, Q.C.
Glick, Ian, Esq, Q.C.
Falconer of Thoroton, The Rt Hon The Lord
Straw, The Rt Hon Jack, M.P.
Yong, Chief Justice Pung How (Honorary)
Posner, Judge Richard (Honorary)
Ashworth, Professor Andrew, Ph.D., D.C.L., F.B.A.
Hughes, The Rt Hon Lord Justice
Adams, His Honour John (Senior)
Kadri, Sibghatullah, Esq, Q.C. (Senior)
Webb, Robert, Esq, Q.C., FRAeS
Davidson, Nicholas, Esq, Q.C.
Horwood-Smart, Miss Rosamund, Q.C.
Brown, Stuart, Esq, Q.C.
Everall, His Honour Judge, Q.C.
Pittaway, David, Esq, Q.C.
Dyer, His Honour Mark (Senior)
Milford, His Honour Judge, Q.C.
Solley, Stephen, Esq, Q.C.
Lovell-Pank, Dorian, Esq, Q.C.
Field, The Hon Mr Justice
Phillips, Sir Hayden, G.C.B., D.L. (Honorary)
Orde, His Honour Denis (Senior)
MacDermott, The Rt Hon Sir John (Honorary)
Anand, The Hon Dr Justice Adarsh (Honorary)
Bowman, Sir Jeffery, F.C.A. (Honorary)
Goldstone, Justice Richard (Honorary)
Fysh, His Honour Michael, Q.C. (Senior)
Friedman, David, Esq, Q.C.
Stewart, Nicholas, Esq, Q.C.
Thorley, Simon, Esq, Q.C.
Raggatt, Timothy, Esq, Q.C.
Cox, The Hon Mrs Justice, D.B.E.
Black, The Rt Hon Lady Justice, D.B.E.
Habgood of Calverton, The Rt Rev and Rt Hon Lord (Honorary)
Gibbs, Sir Richard (Supernumerary)
Collins of Mapesbury, The Rt Hon The Lord
Baroness Clark of Calton, Q.C.
Murphy-O'Connor, His Eminence Cardinal Cormac (Honorary)
Staple, George, Esq, C.B., Q.C. (Honorary)

de Navarro, Michael, Esq, Q.C.
Carey, Godfrey, Esq, Q.C.
Tedd, Rex, Esq, Q.C.
Veeder, Johnny, Esq, Q.C.
Hooper, His Honour Judge, Q.C.
Guthrie, James, Esq, Q.C.
Jack, Sir Raymond
Hodson, His Honour Thomas
McGregor-Johnson, His Honour Judge
Gyllenhammar, Dr Pehr (Honorary)
Wilkie, The Hon Mr Justice
Joyce, Peter, Esq, Q.C.
Moger, Christopher, Esq, Q.C.
Havers, The Hon Philip, Q.C.
Hughes, His Honour Judge Iain, Q.C.
Charlton, Tim, Esq, Q.C.
Floyd, The Hon Mr Justice
Chan, The Hon Mr Justice Patrick (Honorary)
McGrath, The Honourable Justice (Honorary)
Sacks of Aldgate, The Chief Rabbi Lord (Honorary)
Dashwood, Professor Alan, C.B.E., Q.C.
Pleming, Nigel, Esq, Q.C.
Davies, Owen, Esq, Q.C.
George, Charles, Esq, Q.C.
Cullen of Whitekirk, The Rt Hon The Lord, K.T. (Honorary)
Costa, M Jean-Paul (Honorary)
Wildhaber, M Luzius (Honorary)
Coward, Stephen, Esq, Q.C. (Supernumerary)
Austin-Smith, Michael, Esq, Q.C.
Collier, His Honour Judge Peter, Q.C.
Redfern, Michael, Esq, Q.C.
Smith, Robert, Esq, Q.C.
Trollope, Andrew, Esq, Q.C.
Milligan, Iain, Esq, Q.C.
Francis, Robert, Esq, Q.C.
Gumbel, Miss Elizabeth-Anne, Q.C.
Marrin, John, Esq, Q.C.
Drabble, Richard, Esq, Q.C.
Kealey, Gavin, Esq, Q.C.
Burrell, His Honour Judge, Q.C.
Flaux, The Hon Mr Justice
Fitzgerald, Edward, Esq, C.B.E., Q.C.
Inman, His Honour Judge Melbourne, Q.C.
Green, Dr Nicholas, Q.C.
Lipton, Sir Stuart (Honorary)
Porten, Anthony, Esq, Q.C.
Browne, His Honour Judge Nicholas, Q.C.
Pegden, His Honour Judge, Q.C.
Wilby, David, Esq, Q.C.
Goss, His Honour Judge, Q.C.
Leonard, His Honour Judge, Q.C.
Foster, Miss Alison, Q.C.
Stewart, Roger, Esq, Q.C.
Ribeiro, The Hon Mr Justice (Honorary)
Forsyth, Professor Christopher
Gardner, Professor John
Andenas, Dr Mads, Ph.D., M.A., D.Phil.
Spencer, Professor John, Q.C.
Williams, The Most Rev and Rt Hon Rowan (Honorary)
Bishop, Malcolm, Esq, Q.C.
Martin, Mrs Gay
Sapsford, Philip, Esq, Q.C.
Bourne-Arton, Simon, Esq, Q.C.
Nugee, Christopher, Esq, Q.C.
Gault, The Rt Hon Justice, D.C.N.Z.M. (Honorary)
Schwarze, Professor Dr Jürgen (Honorary)
Paget, His Honour Judge, Q.C.
Fisher, Her Honour Judge
Openshaw, The Hon Mr Justice
Critchlow, His Honour Judge
Macdonald of River Glaven, The Rt Hon The Lord, Q.C.

Byron, The Rt Hon Sir Dennis
Coghlan, Terence, Esq, Q.C.
Caldecott, Andrew, Esq, Q.C.
Gaisman, Jonathan, Esq, Q.C.
Popplewell, Andrew, Esq, Q.C.
Moor, Philip, Esq, Q.C.
Allan, Alexander, Esq (Honorary)
Caldwell, Sir Edward, K.C.B., Q.C.(Hon) (Honorary)
Laing, Ian, Esq, C.B.E., D.L. (Honorary)
McKellen, Sir Ian, C.H., C.B.E. (Honorary)
Spens, David, Esq, Q.C.
Ford, His Honour Judge, Q.C.
Hammerton, Alastair, Esq
Crowther, His Honour Thomas, Q.C. (Senior)
Maddison, The Hon Mr Justice
Coleman, His Honour Judge
Little, Brigadier Peter, C.B.E. (Honorary)
Williamson, Sir Brian, C.B.E. (Honorary)
Cretney, Dr Stephen
Hamilton, The Rt Hon Lord (Honorary)
Kirby, The Hon Justice Michael, A.C., C.M.G. (Honorary)
Mott, Philip, Esq, Q.C.
Seymour, Thomas, Esq
Stadlen, The Hon Mr Justice
Streatfeild-James, David, Esq, Q.C.
Dingemans, James, Esq, Q.C.
Carr, Miss Sue, Q.C.
Malecka, Dr Mary
Master of the Temple Church (Honorary)
Brunner, Adrian, Esq, Q.C.
Asprey, Nicholas, Esq
Ilstein, Augustus, Esq, Q.C.
Ross, John, Esq, Q.C.
Lerego, Professor Michael, Q.C.
Storey, Jeremy, Esq, Q.C.
Turner, James, Esq, Q.C.
Lang, Miss Beverley, Q.C.
Belgore, The Hon Justice Salihu Moddibo Alfa
Davis, His Honour Judge
Arbuthnot, District Judge
Keith, His Excellency Judge Kenneth, O.N.Z., K.B.E. (Honorary)
Williams, The Hon Mr Justice Wyn
Moylan, The Hon Mr Justice
Roberts, His Honour Mervyn
Rhodes, Robert, Esq, Q.C.
Tyzack, His Honour Judge, Q.C.
Upward, Patrick, Esq, Q.C.
Melville, David, Esq, Q.C.
Smith, Miss Sally, Q.C.
Hyland, Graham, Esq, Q.C.
Richardson, His Honour Judge Jeremy, Q.C.
Giffin, Nigel, Esq, Q.C.
Swift, Jonathan, Esq, Q.C.
Brougham, Christopher, Esq, Q.C.
Atkinson, Nicholas, Esq, Q.C.
FitzGerald, Miss Susanna, Q.C.
Pownall, Orlando, Esq, Q.C.
Eder, The Hon Mr Justice
Davis, His Honour Judge William, Q.C.
Lissack, Richard, Esq, Q.C.
Lakha, Abbas, Esq, Q.C.
Kirkham, Her Honour Judge Frances, C.B.E. (Honorary)
King, The Hon Mrs Justice Eleanor
Soole, Michael, Esq, Q.C.
Grainger, His Honour Judge
Bowron, Miss Margaret, Q.C.
Seed, His Honour Judge, Q.C.
Gibson, Charles, Esq, Q.C.
Simler, Miss Ingrid, Q.C.
Catchpole, Stuart, Esq, Q.C.

Christie, Iain, Esq
Forrester, His Honour Judge (Senior)
McCreath, His Honour Judge
Stone, His Honour Judge, Q.C.
O'Connor, Patrick, Esq, Q.C.
Corbett, James, Esq, Q.C.
Bayliss, Thomas, Esq, Q.C.
Kay, Steven, Esq, Q.C.
Green, David, Esq, Q.C.
Wright, Peter, Esq, Q.C.
Eaton, Miss Deborah, Q.C.
Lavender, Nicholas, Esq, Q.C.
Harris, His Honour Judge Charles, Q.C.
Brown, His Honour Judge Mark
Sharp, The Hon Mrs Justice
Yuen, The Honourable Tan Sri Dato' James Foong Cheng
Beringer, Guy, Esq, Q.C. (Honorary)
Yale, David, Esq, F.B.A., Q.C.
Baroness James of Holland Park, O.B.E. (Honorary)
Lithman, Nigel, Esq, Q.C.
Hildyard, Miss Marianna, Q.C.
Goodman, Andrew, Esq
Aldous, Grahame, Esq, Q.C.
Fetherstonhaugh, Guy, Esq, Q.C.
Reeve, Matthew, Esq
Coleman, Russell, Esq, SC
Nichols, The Most Reverend Vincent, M.A., M.Ed., S.T.L. (Honorary)
Taylor, Her Honour Judge Deborah
Humphries, Michael, Esq, Q.C.
Harrison, Peter, Esq, Q.C.
Levitt, Miss Alison, Q.C.
Oliver-Jones, His Honour Judge, Q.C.
Wide, His Honour Judge, Q.C.
Woodcock, Thomas, Esq, L.V.O., F.S.A., D.L.
Rider, Professor Barry
May, Her Honour Judge, Q.C.
Walsh, Professor Robert
Baragwanath, The Honourable Justice, K.N.Z.M., Q.C.
Jackson, The Hon Mr Justice Peter
Ayling, Miss Tracy, Q.C.
Dove, Ian, Esq, Q.C.
Morley, Iain, Esq, Q.C.
Ong, Dr Colin
Davies, Miss Helen, Q.C.
Bonomy, The Rt Hon Lord Iain, LL.D. (Honorary)
Lenaerts, Judge Koen (Honorary)
Tonking, His Honour Judge
Bleasdale, Paul, Esq, Q.C.
Tait, Andrew, Esq, Q.C.
O'Toole, Simon, Esq
Cobb, Stephen, Esq, Q.C.
Caruana, The Hon Peter, Q.C.
Ramgoolam, Dr The Hon Prime Minister Navinchandra
Wangchuck of Bhutan, His Majesty The King Jigme Khesar Namgyel (Honorary)
Wait, His Honour Judge
Waller, Senior District Judge, C.B.E.
Maude, The Rt Hon Francis, M.P.
Pooles, Michael, Esq, Q.C.
Spencer, Martin, Esq, Q.C.
Lynch, Miss Patricia, Q.C.
Jacklin, Miss Susan, Q.C.
Jafferjee, Aftab, Esq, Q.C.
Barraclough, Richard, Esq, Q.C.
Village, Peter, Esq, Q.C.
Stern, Ian, Esq, Q.C.
Agnello, Miss Raquel, Q.C.
Hill, Professor the Worshipful Mark, Q.C.
Robertson, Miss Patricia, Q.C.
Stein, Sam, Esq, Q.C.

LINCOLN'S INN

TREASURY OFFICE

Lincoln's Inn, London WC2A 3TL *under the library at the north end of the Hall*
Tel: 020 7405 1393
Fax: 020 7831 1839
Email: mail@lincolnsinn.org.uk

Under Treasurer

Hills, Colonel D H, M.B.E.

Assistant Under Treasurer

Campbell, M

Director of Finance

Barnett, Mrs L

Director of Estates

Spooner, P

LIBRARY

Lincoln's Inn Library, London WC2A 3TN
Hours: 9am to 8pm in term, except August and September which is 9.30am to 6pm, *Closed on Saturdays*

Librarian

Holborn, G F
Tel: 020 7242 4371

Deputy Librarian

McArdle, Mrs C

Benchers

His Royal Highness The Duke of Kent, K.G., G.C.M.G., G.C.V.O.
Eveleigh, The Rt Hon Sir Edward, E.R.D.
Corkery, Michael, Esq, Q.C.
Slade, The Rt Hon Sir Christopher
Gibson, The Rt Hon Sir Peter
Drake, Sir (Frederick) Maurice, D.F.C.
Harman, Sir Jeremiah
Nourse, The Rt Hon Sir Martin
Tucker, Sir Richard
Wright, Sir Michael
Millett, The Rt Hon Lord
Morritt, The Rt Hon Sir Andrew, C.V.O.
Rattee, Sir Donald
Amlot, Roy, Esq, Q.C.
Lightman, Sir Gavin
Appleby, Miss Elizabeth, Q.C.
Walker of Gestingthorpe, The Rt Hon Lord
Warren, Ian, Esq
Milsom, Professor S F C, Q.C., F.B.A. (Honorary)
Tudor-Evans, Sir Haydn
Mathew, John, Esq, Q.C.
Honore, Professor Antony, Q.C., D.C.L., F.B.A. (Honorary)
Davies, Sir Mervyn, M.C., T.D.
Jones, Professor Gareth, Q.C., LL.D., F.B.A. (Honorary)
Baroness Thatcher of Kesteven, The Rt Hon, L.G., O.M. (Honorary)
Gratwick, Stephen, Esq, Q.C.
Taylor, (Peter) William E, Esq, Q.C.
Knox, Sir John
Browne-Wilkinson, The Rt Hon Lord
Wood, Sir John Kember, M.C.
Roberts, The Hon Sir Denys, K.B.E., Q.C. (Honorary)
Potts, Sir (Francis) Humphrey
Baker, His Honour Paul, Q.C.
Davison, The Rt Hon Sir Ronald, G.B.E., C.M.G. (Honorary)
Hamilton, Adrian, Esq, Q.C.
Burn, Professor Edward (Honorary)
Machin, (Edward) Anthony, Esq, Q.C.
Roth, Martin, Esq
Romer, Ian, Esq
Moriarty, Gerald, Esq, Q.C.
Mowbray, (William) John, Esq, Q.C.
Engle, Sir George, K.C.B., Q.C.
Kerry, Sir Michael, K.C.B., Q.C.
Cameron of Lochbroom, The Rt Hon Lord (Honorary)
Lester of Herne Hill, The Lord, Q.C.
Crawford, His Honour Peter, Q.C.
Heath, Christopher G, Esq
Steyn, The Rt Hon Lord
Escott Cox, Brian, Esq, Q.C.
Scrivener, Anthony, Esq, Q.C.
Freeland, Sir John, K.C.M.G., Q.C.
Blackett-Ord, His Honour Andrew, C.V.O.
Macdonald, John, Esq, Q.C.
Whiteman, Peter, Esq, Q.C.
Shah, His Royal Highness Azlan (Honorary)
Park, Sir Andrew
Goodhart, The Lord, Q.C.
Kentridge, Sir Sydney, K.C.M.G., Q.C.
Heim, Paul, Esq, C.M.G.
Ferris, Sir Francis
Mason, The Rt Hon Sir Anthony, K.B.E. (Honorary)
Brookes, John, Esq
McKinnon, Sir Stuart
Hague, His Honour Nigel, Q.C.
Koopmans, The Hon Thijmen (Honorary)
Reid, His Honour Judge (James) Robert, Q.C.
Young, David, Esq, Q.C.
Fraser of Carmyllie, The Rt Hon Lord, P.C., Q.C. (Honorary)
Bretten, (George) Rex, Esq, Q.C.
de Waal, Sir Henry, K.C.B., Q.C.
Levy, Ben K, Esq
Henty, Jonathan, Esq
Tuckey, The Rt Hon Sir Simon
Grabiner, The Lord, Q.C.
Fox, Lady, C.M.G., Q.C.
Charles, The Hon Mr Justice William (Bill)
Eichelbaum, The Rt Hon Sir Thomas, G.B.E. (Honorary)
Dunn, His Honour Judge Hubert, Q.C.
Samuels, His Honour John, Q.C.
Blofeld, Sir John
Cocks, David, Esq, Q.C.
Mann, Martin, Esq, Q.C.
Harrod, Henry, Esq
Jaques, Geoffrey W, Esq
Gray, The Hon Mr Justice Charles
Blackburne, The Hon Mr Justice William (Bill)
Milmo, His Honour Judge John, Q.C.
Bello, The Hon Mr Justice Muhammed (Honorary)
Rodger of Earlsferry, The Rt Hon Lord (Honorary)
Smith, The Rt Hon Dame Janet, D.B.E.
Arden, The Rt Hon Lady Justice, D.B.E.
McDonnell, John, Esq, Q.C.
McWilliams, Sir Francis, G.B.E.
Aldous, Charles, Esq, Q.C.
Baroness Elles, The (Honorary)
McCall, Christopher, Esq, Q.C.
Neuberger, The Rt Hon Lord
Bratza, The Hon Mr Justice Nicholas
Ainger, David, Esq
Denison, His Honour Neil, Q.C.
Oliver, David, Esq, Q.C.
Rayner James, Jonathan, Esq, Q.C.
Stockdale, Sir Thomas, B.t.
Cooke, His Honour Judge Roger
Mandela, President Nelson (Honorary)
Koroma, His Excellency Abdul (Honorary)
Page, Howard, Esq, Q.C.
Barlow, Francis, Esq, Q.C.
Rimer, The Rt Hon Lord Justice
Blair, The Rt Hon Tony, M.P. (Honorary)
Lindsay, His Honour Crawford, Q.C.
Cassel, Sir Timothy, B.t., Q.C.
Rahman, The Hon Muhammed (Honorary)
Shah, The Hon Mr Justice Sajjad Ali (Honorary)
Brennan, The Hon Sir Gerard, A.C., K.B.E. (Honorary)
Leaver, Peter, Esq, Q.C.
Hogg, The Hon Mrs Justice Mary, D.B.E.
Cooke, Judge John Donal (Honorary)
Goldring, The Rt Hon Lord Justice
Milne, David, Esq, Q.C.
Day, Douglas, Esq, Q.C.
Steinfeld, Alan, Esq, Q.C.
McCombe, The Hon Mr Justice Richard
Talbot, Patrick, Esq, Q.C.
Proudman, The Hon Mrs Justice Sonia, D.B.E.
Buckley, Martin, Esq
Thomas, Dr David Arthur, Q.C. (Honorary)
Patten, The Rt Hon Lord Justice
Kaye, His Honour Judge Roger, T.D., Q.C.
Horowitz, His Honour Judge Michael, Q.C.
Manohar, The Hon Mrs Sujata V (Honorary)
Goldberg, David, Esq, Q.C.
Spencer, His Honour Judge Shaun, Q.C.
Jarvis, John, Esq, Q.C.
Tattersall, Geoffrey, Esq, Q.C.
Carver, Captain P Malcolm, R.N. (Honorary)
Gubbay, The Hon Mr Justice Anthony (Honorary)
Hardie, The Rt Hon Lord, Q.C. (Honorary)
Pardoe, His Honour Judge Alan, Q.C.
Alexander, His Honour Judge Ian, Q.C.
Berry, Simon, Esq, Q.C.
Gaunt, Jonathan, Esq, Q.C.
King, Michael, Esq
Easterman, Nicholas, Esq
Moss, Gabriel, Esq, Q.C.
Bannister, Edward, Esq, Q.C.
Lewison, The Hon Mr Justice Kim
Powers, Dr Michael, Q.C.
Cousins, Edward, Esq
Crow, Jonathan, Esq, Q.C.
Eames, The Most Revd Dr Robin (Robert) (Honorary)
Beale, Professor Hugh, Q.C. (Honorary)
Kruger, Dr Hans Christian (Honorary)
Leigh, His Honour Christopher, Q.C.
Viscount Hailsham, The Rt Hon, Q.C.
Livesey, Bernard, Esq, Q.C.
Andrews, Peter, Esq, Q.C.
Martin, John Vandeleur, Esq, Q.C.
Booth, Miss Cherie, Q.C.
Craig, Kenneth, Esq
Kenny, Sir Anthony, F.B.A. (Honorary)
Malcolm, The Hon David K, A.C., Q.C. (Honorary)
Ibbs, Sir Robin, K.B.E. (Honorary)
Elias, The Rt Hon Dame Sian (Honorary)
Marr-Johnson, His Honour Frederick
Morris, His Honour Judge David
Isaacs, Stuart, Esq, Q.C.
Baxendale, Miss Presiley, Q.C.
Linehan, Stephen, Esq, Q.C.
Radford, Mrs Nadine, Q.C.
Ross Martyn, John Greaves, Esq
Jefferis, Michael, Esq
Battersby, Professor Graham
McLachlin, The Rt Hon Beverley (Honorary)
Brazier, Professor Rodney
Mendelson, Professor Maurice, Q.C.
Daintith, Professor Terence
Ajibola, His Excellency Judge Bola, K.B.E. (Honorary)
Winegarten, Master Jonathan Isaac
Keane, The Hon Mr Justice Ronan (Honorary)
Badenoch, James, Esq, Q.C.
Collender, His Honour Judge Andrew, Q.C.
King, The Hon Mr Justice Timothy R
Driscoll, Michael, Esq, Q.C.
Gilbert, His Honour Judge Francis H, Q.C.
Richards, The Hon Mr Justice David
Davis, The Hon Mr Justice Nigel A
Lee, Martin C M, Esq (Honorary)
Brodrick, His Honour Michael J L
Collins, His Honour Judge Paul H
Garnett, Kevin M, Esq, Q.C.
Trevett, Peter, Esq, Q.C.
Smith, The Hon Mr Justice Peter Winston
Vos, Geoffrey C, Esq, Q.C.
Hodge, His Honour Judge David R, Q.C.
Marten, (Richard) Hedley W, Esq
Beaumont, His Honour Judge Peter, Q.C.
Ockelton, Mark, Esq
Harpum, Dr Charles, LL.D.
Prescott, Peter Richard Kyle, Esq, Q.C.
Leslie, Stephen Windsor, Esq, Q.C.
Bompas, (Anthony) George, Esq, Q.C.
Jackson, Miss Judith Mary, Q.C.
Poulet, Mrs Rebecca Maria, Q.C.
Stevenson, (Arthur) William, Esq, Q.C.
Chapman, Vivian Robert, Esq, Q.C.
Turnquest, Sir Orville, G.C.M.G., Q.C. (Honorary)
Pillay, The Hon Mr Justice Ariranga Govindasamy (Honorary)
Cooke, The Hon Mr Justice Jeremy Lionel
Morgan, The Hon Mr Justice Paul Hyacinth
Briggs, The Hon Mr Justice Michael Townley Featherstone
Gill, The Rt Hon Lord (Honorary)
Singh, His Honour Sir Mota, Q.C.
Pearlman, Her Honour Valerie, C.B.E.
Watson, Anthony, Esq
Sokol, Christopher John Francis, Esq, Q.C.
Bowman, Sir Geoffrey, K.C.B., Q.C.
Mann, The Hon Mr Justice Anthony
Brindle, Michael, Esq, Q.C.
Sales, The Hon Mr Justice Philip
MacDuff, The Hon Mr Justice Alastair
O'Brien, His Honour Judge Patrick
Dinkin, Anthony David, Esq, Q.C.
Blair, The Hon Mr Justice William James Lynton
White, Andrew, Esq, Q.C.
Fookes, Robert Lawrence, Esq
Simpkiss, His Honour Judge (Richard) Jonathan
Feldman, Professor David (Honorary)
Stevens, Justice John Paul (Honorary)
Ginsburg, Justice Ruth Bader (Honorary)
Boyle, Alan Gordon, Esq, Q.C.
Randall, John Yeoman, Esq, Q.C.
Clarke, His Honour Judge Peter William, Q.C.
Dabbs, David Leslie, Esq
Fletcher, Professor Ian
George, His Honour Judge William
Batty, His Honour Judge Paul Daniel, Q.C.
Holland, The Hon Justice Randy (Honorary)
Purle, His Honour Judge Charles, Q.C.
Herbert, Mark, Esq, Q.C.
Henderson, The Hon Mr Justice Launcelot
Cohen, Jonathan, Esq, Q.C.
Vitoria, Dr Mary, Q.C.
Giret, Mrs Jane, Q.C.
Castle, Peter, Esq
Perry, David, Esq, Q.C.
Hayton, Professor David
Jaeger, Judge Renate (Honorary)
Stock, The Hon Mr Justice Frank, J.A. (Honorary)
Handley, The Hon Mr Justice Kenneth (Honorary)
Tansey, Rock, Esq, Q.C.
Teare, The Hon Mr Justice Nigel
Rosen, Murray, Esq, Q.C.
Sharpe, Thomas, Esq, Q.C.
Blackett-Ord, Mark, Esq
Sri Ram, Mr Justice Gopal (Honorary)
Norris, The Hon Mr Justice Alastair
Cutler, His Honour Judge Keith, C.B.E.
Hildyard, Robert, Esq, Q.C.
Kay, (Robert) Jervis, Esq, Q.C.
Brisby, John, Esq, Q.C.
Macur, The Hon Mrs Justice Julia, D.B.E.
Warnock-Smith, Mrs Shan, Q.C.
Gibbons, James, Esq
Kolbert, His Honour Dr Colin
Le Pichon, The Hon Mrs Justice Doreen

Prosser, Kevin, Esq, Q.C.
Wallington, Richard, Esq
Le Poidevin, Nicholas, Esq, Q.C.
Mensah, Her Honour Judge Barbara
Kufuor, His Excellency Mr John Agyekum (Honorary)
Platts-Mills, Mark, Esq, Q.C.
Bellamy, Stephen, Esq, Q.C.
Trace, Anthony, Esq, Q.C.
Simmons, The Hon Sir David, K.A., B.C.H. (Honorary)
Wolfe, The Hon Lensley, O.J. (Honorary)
Norman, The Rev Canon William (Honorary)
Peters, Nigel, Esq, Q.C.
Todd, Michael, Esq, Q.C.
Hunt, Stephen, Esq
Spigelman, The Honourable James J, Q.C. (Honorary)
Diehl, His Honour John, Q.C.
Glennie, The Hon Lord
Smyth, The Hon Thomas C
Jones, Edward Bartley, Esq, Q.C.
Kinch, Christopher, Esq, Q.C.
Hollington, Robin, Esq, Q.C.
Jones, Ms Elizabeth, Q.C.
Hargreaves, Ms Sara
Saggerson, His Honour Judge Alan
Balakrishnan, The Hon Mr Justice Konakuppakatil (Honorary)
Forster, His Honour Judge Brian, Q.C.
McNeill, Miss Jane, Q.C.
Miles, Robert, Esq, Q.C.

Reed, Piers, Esq
Studer, Mark, Esq
O'Leary, Miss Michele
O'Regan, The Hon Justice Kate (Honorary)
Sachs, The Hon Justice Albie (Honorary)
Brett-Holt, Ms Alexis
Browne-Wilkinson, Simon, Esq, Q.C.
Booth, Michael, Esq, Q.C.
Hinks, Frank, Esq, Q.C.
Taube, Simon, Esq, Q.C.
Coen, Miss Yvonne, Q.C.
Lynch, Jerome, Esq, Q.C.
Rowley, Keith, Esq, Q.C.
Swainston, Michael, Esq, Q.C.
Virgo, Professor Graham
Munday, Dr Roderick
Chan, The Hon Sek Keong (Honorary)
Bidder, His Honour Judge Neil, Q.C.
Jenkins, Alun, Esq, Q.C.
Lowe, William, Esq, Q.C.
Mehigan, Simon, Esq, Q.C.
Quint, Miss Francesca
French, The Hon Robert S (Honorary)
Hamblen, The Hon Mr Justice Nicholas
Doctor, Brian, Esq, Q.C.
Furness, Michael, Esq, Q.C.
Dunning, Graham, Esq, Q.C.
Trower, William, Esq, Q.C.
Goose, Julian, Esq, Q.C.

Singh, Rabinder, Esq, Q.C.
Makey, Christopher, Esq
Brown, Graham S, Esq (Honorary)
Hague, The Rt Hon William, Esq, M.P. (Honorary)
Yeung Sik Yuen, The Hon Y K J, G.O.S.K. (Honorary)
Faber, Her Honour Judge Diana
Waksman, His Honour Judge David, Q.C.
Burbidge, James, Esq, Q.C.
Davis-White, Malcolm, Esq, Q.C.
Oditah, Fidelis, Esq, Q.C.
Hill, Gregory, Esq
Francis, Andrew, Esq
Azmi, The Rt Hon Mr Justice Zaki (Honorary)
McKinnon, His Honour Judge Warwick
Cawson, Mark, Esq, Q.C.
Tregear, Francis, Esq, Q.C.
Snowden, Richard, Esq, Q.C.
Evans, Timothy, Esq
Southern, David, Esq
Michell, Michael, Esq
Dight, His Honour Judge Marc
Moore, Martin, Esq, Q.C.
Hochberg, Daniel, Esq
Myjer, Judge Egbert
Hunter, Winston, Esq, Q.C.
Pascoe, Martin, Esq, Q.C.
Marshall, Philip, Esq, Q.C.
Asif, Jalil, Esq, Q.C.
Collier, Stephen J, Esq

MIDDLE TEMPLE

TREASURY OFFICE
2 Plowden Buildings, Temple, London EC4Y 9AT
Tel: 020 7427 4800
Hours: 10am to 4pm. Long Vacation: 10am to 3pm. Short Vacations (limited days only): 10am to 3pm. *Closed on Saturdays.*

Under Treasurer
Quinn, Ms Catherine

Deputy Under Treasurer (Education)
Richmond, Mrs Christa

LIBRARY
Middle Temple Lane, London EC4Y 9BT
Tel: 020 7427 3832

Termtime Hours:
Mon to Thu - 9.00 am to 8.00 pm
Fri - 9.00 am to 7.00 pm
1 Sat in 4 - 10.00 am to 5.00 pm

Vacation Hours:
Mon to Fri - 9.00 am to 5.30 pm

Librarian and Keeper of the Records
Hayward, Miss Vanessa

Benchers

Aaronson, Graham Raphael, Esq, Q.C.
Abraham, Tan Sri Cecil Wilbert Mohanaraj
Ackner, Her Honour Judge Claudia Madeleine
Ahmadi, The Honourable Mr Justice Aziz Mushabber (Honorary)
Aikens, The Rt Hon Lord Justice Richard John Pearson
Allen, Robin Geoffrey Bruere, Esq, Q.C.
Allison, (Samuel) Austin, Esq
Allsop, The Hon Justice James (Honorary)
Altman, Brian, Esq, Q.C.
Anderson, David William Kinloch, Esq, Q.C.
Anderson, Miss Lesley Jane, Q.C.
Andrews, Professor Neil Howard
Anelay, Richard Alfred, Esq, Q.C.
Appleby, His Honour Brian John, Q.C. (Senior)
Arlidge, Anthony John, Esq, Q.C. (Senior)
Arnold, The Hon Mr Justice Richard David
Arnold, The Right Rev John Stanley Kenneth
Arthur, His Honour Judge Sir Gavyn Farr
Ashe, (Thomas) Michael, Esq, Q.C.
Astill, Sir Michael John, K.T. (Senior)
Aubrey, David John Morgan, Esq, Q.C.
Aylen, Walter Stafford, Esq, Q.C. (Senior)
Bailhache, Sir Philip Martin (Honorary)
Baker, Nigel Robert James, Esq, Q.C.
Baker, The Hon Mr Justice Jonathan Leslie
Ball, Miss Alison, Q.C.
Barak, Professor Aharon (Honorary)
Barker, Anthony, Esq, Q.C.
Barling, The Honourable Mr Justice Gerald Edward
Barnes, (David) Michael William, Esq, Q.C.
Baron, The Hon Mrs Justice Florence Jaqueline, D.B.E.
Bartle, Philip Martyn, Esq, Q.C.
Bartlett, Andrew Vincent Bramwell, Esq, Q.C.
Bartlett, George Robert, Esq, Q.C.
Barwise, Miss Stephanie Nicola, Q.C.
Batten, Stephen Duval, Esq, Q.C.
Beale, Simon Russell, C.B.E. (Honorary)
Bean, The Hon Mr Justice David Michael
Bell, Sir Rodger, (Senior)
Bellamy, Sir Christopher William, Q.C.
Benson, Sir Christopher John, F.R.I.C.S., J.P., D.L. (Honorary)
Benson, Jeremy Keith, Esq, Q.C.
Berlins, Marcel, Esq (Honorary)
Berman, Sir Franklin Delow, K.C.M.G., Q.C. (Honorary)
Bethlehem, Sir Daniel Lincoln, K.C.M.G., Q.C.
Bevan, His Honour Judge John Penry Vaughan, Q.C.
Birch, Dr John Anthony, F.R.C.M., F.R.C.O.(C.H.M.), L.R.A.M. (Honorary)
Bird, Mrs Ruth (Honorary)
Birss, His Honour Judge Colin Ian, Q.C.
Birt, Michael Cameron St John, Esq, Q.C.
Black, Michael Jonathan, Esq, Q.C.
Blackburn, John, Esq, Q.C.
Blackburn, Mrs Elizabeth, Q.C.
Blair, Bruce Graeme Donald, Esq, Q.C.
Blair, Michael Campbell, Esq, Q.C.
Blake, The Hon Mr Justice Nicholas John Gorrod
Blom-Cooper, Sir Louis Jacques, Q.C.
Blunt, David John, Esq, Q.C.
Blunt, Oliver Simon Peter, Esq, Q.C.
Bodey, The Hon Mr Justice David Roderic Lessiter
Bogdanor, Professor Vernon, C.B.E. (Honorary)
Bokhary, The Hon Mr Justice Syed Kemal Shah, P.J. (Honorary)
Boney, His Honour Judge Guy Thomas Knowles, Q.C.
Booth, Dame Margaret Myfanwy Wood, D.B.E. (Senior)
Borrie, Lord, Q.C. (Senior)
Boswood, Anthony Richard, Esq, Q.C.
Bowers, John Simon, Esq, Q.C.
Bowes, Michael Anthony, Esq, Q.C.
Bowsher, His Honour Peter Charles, Q.C. (Senior)
Boyd, Stewart Crauford, C.B.E., Q.C.
Braham, David Gerald Henry, Esq, Q.C. (Senior)
Brendel, Dr Alfred, K.B.E. (Honorary)
Brennan, Miss Janice Lesley
Bridge, Mr Stuart Nigel
Brown of Eaton-Under-Heywood, The Rt Hon The Lord, (Senior)
Buckley, Sir Roger John (Senior)
Bucknall, Miss Belinda, Q.C.
Bueno, Antonio De Padua Jose Maria, Esq, Q.C.
Burke, His Honour John Kenneth, Q.C. (Senior)
Burnett, The Hon Mr Justice Ian Duncan
Burnton, The Rt Hon Lord Justice Stanley Jeffrey
Burrows, Professor Andrew Stephen, Q.C., F.B.A. (Honorary)
Butler of Brockwell, The Rt Hon Lord, K.G., G.C.B., C.V.O. (Honorary)
Calvert, Mrs Barbara Adamson, Q.C.
Calvert-Smith, The Hon Mr Justice David
Cameron, The Rt Hon David William Donald, M.P., Prime Minister (Honorary)
Cameron, Mr Justice Edwin (Honorary)
Cameron, Miss Sheila Morag Clark, C.B.E., Q.C. (Senior)
Campbell, Andrew Neville, Esq, Q.C.
Carlisle, Hugh Bernard Harwood, Esq, Q.C. (Senior)
Carnwath, The Rt Hon Lord Justice Robert
Carrington, The Rt Hon The Lord (Honorary)
Carter-Manning, Jeremy James, Esq, Q.C.
Catto, Jr, Ambassador Henry E (Honorary)
Chakrabarti, Sir Sumantra, K.C.B. (Honorary)
Chakrabarti, Sharmishta, C.B.E.
Chartres, The Rt Rev & Rt Hon Richard John Carew, P.C. (Honorary)
Clarke, Andrew Terence, Esq
Clarke, The Hon Mr Justice Christopher Simon Courtenay
Clarke of Stone-Cum-Ebony, The Rt Hon The Lord
Clayton, Richard Anthony, Esq, Q.C.
Clifton, His Honour Judge Gerald Michael
Coleridge, The Hon Mr Justice Paul James Duke
Coles, His Honour (Norman) Bruce Cameron, Q.C. (Senior)
Collins, The Hon Mr Justice Andrew David
Colyer, His Honour John Stuart, Q.C. (Senior)
Compston, His Honour Judge Christopher Dean
Cone, John Crawford, Esq
Connor, His Honour Jeremy George
Cooke, His Honour Judge Nicholas Orton, Q.C.
Cooper-Rousseau, Mrs Bertha Mae
Cordara, Roderick Charles, Esq, Q.C.
Cotton, Miss Diana Rosemary, Q.C.
Cowell, His Honour Judge Peter Reginald
Crane, Michael John, Esq, Q.C.
Crystal, Michael, Esq, Q.C.
Cumaraswamy, Dato' Param (Honorary)
Darling, Paul Antony, Esq, Q.C.
Davey, Neil Martin, Esq, Q.C.
Davies, William Rhodri, Esq, Q.C.
Davies, Her Honour Judge Jacqueline
Davies, Miss Sheilagh Elizabeth
de Lacy, Richard Michael, Esq, Q.C.
de Silva, Harendra Aneurin Domingo, Esq, Q.C.
de Silva, Sir (George) Desmond Lorenz, Q.C.
de Speville, Bertrand Edouard Doger, Esq
Deeny, The Hon Mr Justice Donnell Justin Patrick
Denham, Chief Justice Susan (Honorary)
Dennys, Nicholas Charles Jonathan, Esq, Q.C.
Dillon, His Honour Thomas Michael, Q.C. (Senior)
Dodson, Miss Joanna, Q.C.
Doerries, Miss Chantal-Aimee Renee Aemelia, Q.C.
Donne, Anthony Maurice, Esq, Q.C. (Senior)
Duke of Cambridge, His Royal Highness The (Honorary)
Dutton, Timothy James, Esq, Q.C.
Dworkin, Professor Ronald Myles, Q.C., F.B.A. (Honorary)
Dyson, The Rt Hon The Lord
Eadie, James Raymond, Esq, Q.C.
Eady, The Hon Mr Justice David
Eccles, His Honour Judge Hugh William Patrick, Q.C.
Edelman, Colin Neil, Esq, Q.C.
Edis, Andrew Jeremy Coulter, Esq, Q.C.
Edwards, Patricia Anne
Emmerson, Michael Benedict, Esq, Q.C.
Englehart, Robert Michael, Esq, Q.C.
Essayan, Michael, Esq, Q.C. (Senior)
Etherington, David Charles Lynch, Esq, Q.C.
Evans, David Howard, Esq, Q.C.
Farish III, Ambassador William Stamps (Honorary)
Farley, Roger Boyd, Esq, Q.C.
Farrer, David John, Esq, Q.C.
Faulks, Lord, Q.C.
Fennelly, Mr Justice Nial
Fernyhough, Richard, Esq, Q.C.
Finlay, The Honourable Thomas Aloysius (Honorary)
Finnegan, Mr Justice Joseph Gerald
Finucane, Brendan Godfrey Eamonn, Esq, Q.C.
Fitzgerald, Michael Frederick Clive, O.B.E., Q.C. (Senior)
Flint, Charles John Raffles, Esq, Q.C.
Ford, Ms Anna (Honorary)
Forde, Martin Andrew, Esq, Q.C.
Forwood, The Hon Judge Nicholas James
Foster, Miss Rosalind Mary
Freedman, (Benjamin) Clive, Esq, Q.C.
Fulford, The Hon Mr Justice Adrian Bruce
Furst, Stephen Andrew, Esq, Q.C.
Gale, Michael, Esq, Q.C. (Senior)
Gammie, Malcolm James, C.B.E., Q.C.
Gardiner, John Ralph, Esq, Q.C.
Garland, Sir Patrick Neville (Senior)
Garlick, Paul Richard, Esq, Q.C.
Garnham, Neil Stephen, Esq, Q.C.
Garnier, Edward Henry, Q.C., M.P., Solicitor General
Gauntlett, Jeremy John, S.C.
Geoghegan, Mr Justice Hugh (Senior)
Gibson, Christopher Allen Wood, Esq, Q.C.
Gilbart, His Honour Judge Andrew James, Q.C.
Gilbert, Professor Geoffrey Scott
Glancy, Robert Peter, Esq, Q.C.
Gledhill, His Honour Judge Michael Geoffrey James, Q.C.
Gleeson, The Honourable (Anthony) Murray, A.C. (Honorary)
Globe, His Honour Judge Henry Brian, Q.C.
Glover, Sir Victor Joseph Patrick, K.T., G.O.S.K. (Honorary)
Glynn, Joanna Elizabeth, Q.C.
Godfrey, Howard Anthony, Esq, Q.C.
Goldstone, His Honour Judge Leonard Clement, Q.C.
Gordon, Richard John Francis, Esq, Q.C.
Gordon, His Honour Judge (Cosmo) Gerald Maitland
Goulding, Paul Anthony, Esq, Q.C.
Goy, David John Lister, Esq, Q.C.
Graffy, Professor Colleen Patricia
Grant, Professor Malcolm John, C.B.E.
Greenwood, Sir Christopher John, C.M.G., Q.C.
Grenfell, (Jeremy) Gibson, Esq, Q.C.
Grieve, Michael Robertson Crichton, Esq, Q.C.
Grieve, The Rt Hon Dominic Charles Roberts, Q.C., M.P., Attorney General
Griffith-Jones, The Reverend Robin (Honorary)
Griffiths, John Calvert, C.M.G., Q.C., S.C. (Senior)
Griffiths, (William) Robert, Q.C., S.C.
Grime, Mark Stephen Eastburn, Esq, Q.C.
Gruder, Jeffrey Nigel, Esq, Q.C.
Guthrie of Craigiebank, General The Lord (Honorary)
Hallgarten, His Honour Anthony Bernard Richard, Q.C. (Senior)
Ham, Robert Wallace, Esq, Q.C.
Hancock, Christopher Patrick, Q.C.
Hardiman, Mr Justice Adrian Patrick
Hare, Miss Rosina Selena Alice, Q.C. (Senior)
Harlow, Professor Carol Rhian, Q.C., F.B.A.
Harris, His Honour (John) Percival, D.S.C., Q.C. (Senior)
Harris, His Honour Judge David Michael, Q.C.
Harris, His Honour Judge Sir Michael Frank
Harry Thomas, Miss Caroline Jane, Q.C.
Harvie, Jonathan Alexander, Esq, Q.C.
Havery, His Honour Richard Orbill, Q.C.
Hickinbottom, The Hon Mr Justice Gary
Higgins, The Rt Hon Lord Justice Malachy Joseph (Honorary)
Hill, Rear Admiral (John) Richard (Honorary)
Hilliard, Nicholas Richard Maybury, Esq, Q.C.
Hitching, His Honour Alan Norman
Hochhauser, Andrew Romain, Esq, Q.C.
Hockman, Stephen Alexander, Esq, Q.C.
Holgate, David John, Esq, Q.C.
Hollis, Daniel Ayrton, Esq, Q.C. (Senior)
Hollis, Mrs Stella, (Senior)
Holman, The Hon Mr Justice Edward James
Holroyde, Timothy Victor, Esq, Q.C.
Hone, His Honour Judge Richard Michael, Q.C.
Hope, The Rt Rev & Rt Hon David Michael, K.C.V.O. (Honorary)
Hopkins, Mr John Allen (Honorary)
Horlock, Timothy John, Esq, Q.C.
Horsfield, Peter Muir Francis, Esq, Q.C. (Senior)
Howard, The Honourable John Winston, A.C. (Honorary)
Howe of Aberavon, The Rt Hon Lord, C.H., Q.C. (Senior)
Howell, John, Esq, Q.C.
Hugill, John, Esq, Q.C. (Senior)
Hull, His Honour John Grove, Q.C. (Senior)
Husbands, His Excellency Sir Clifford Straughn, G.C.M.G., K.A. (Senior)
Hussain, Mukhtar, Esq, Q.C.
Hutchinson of Lullington, Lord, Q.C. (Senior)
Hytner, Sir Nicholas Robert (Honorary)
Hytner, Benet Alan, Esq, Q.C. (Senior)
Jackson, The Rt Hon Lord Justice Rupert Matthew
Jacobs, The Rt Hon Sir Francis Geoffrey, K.C.M.G., Q.C. (Senior)
Jacobs, Richard David, Esq, Q.C.
James, Mrs Anita Mary
Janner, The Hon Daniel Joseph Mitchell, Q.C.
Jay, Robert Maurice, Esq, Q.C.
Jenkins, Paul Christopher, Esq, Q.C.
Jennings, Peter Nigel, Esq
Johnston, Carey Ann, Q.C.
Jones, Jonathan Guy, Esq
Joseph, Leslie, Esq, Q.C. (Senior)
Jowell, Professor Jeffrey Lionel, K.C.M.G., Q.C. (Honorary)
Jowitt, Sir Edwin Frank (Senior)
Judge, The Rt Hon Lord Chief Justice
Katz, Philip Alec, Esq, Q.C.
Kearns, Mr Justice Nicholas James
Keen, Richard Sanderson, Esq, Q.C.
Kempe, Dianna Penelope, Q.C., J.P.
Kennedy, Sir Ian Alexander (Senior)
Khamisa, Mohammed Jaffer, Esq, Q.C.
Kingston, William Martin, Esq, Q.C.

Knowles, Robin St John, C.B.E., Q.C.
Kosmin, Leslie Gordon, Esq, Q.C.
Lader, Ambassador Philip (Honorary)
Langdale, Miss Rachel Ann, Q.C.
Langstaff, The Hon Mr Justice Brian Frederick James
Lasok, Dr (Karol) Paul (Edward), Esq, Q.C.
Latham, Sir David Nicholas Ramsay
Laurence, George Frederick, Esq, Q.C.
Laws, Sir Stephen Charles, K.C.B., Q.C.
Layton, Mr Stephen David, F.R.C.O. (Honorary)
Layton, Alexander William, Esq, Q.C.
Le Sueur, Professor Andrew Philip
Leary, Brian Leonard, Esq, Q.C. (Senior)
Leggatt, George Andrew Midsomer, Esq, Q.C.
Lemons, The Hon Justice Donald W (Honorary)
Leslie, Master (Harman) John
Leveson, The Rt Hon Lord Justice Brian Henry
Lewis, (Alun) Kynric, Esq, Q.C. (Senior)
Lewis, Clive Buckland, Esq, Q.C.
Li, The Honourable Andrew Kwok Nang, C.B.E. (Honorary)
Lindsay, Sir John Edmund Fredric (Senior)
Littman, Mark, Esq, Q.C. (Senior)
Lloyd, Stephen James George, Esq
Lloyd, The Rt Hon Lord Justice Timothy Andrew Wigram
Lloyd Jones, The Hon Mr Justice David
Lodder, Peter Norman, Esq, Q.C.
Longmore, The Rt Hon Lord Justice Andrew Centlivres
Lowe, David Alexander, Esq, Q.C.
Luba, Jan Michael Andrew, Esq, Q.C.
Lyons, His Honour Judge Shaun, C.B.E.
Macdonald, Ian Alexander, Esq, Q.C.
Mackay, The Hon Mr Justice Colin Crichton
Macken, Dr Justice Fidelman
Major, The Rt Hon Sir John, K.G., C.H. (Honorary)
Males, Stephen Martin, Esq, Q.C.
Malins, Julian Henry, Esq, Q.C.
Malleson, Professor Kate (Honorary)
Mance, The Rt Hon The Lord
Mansfield, Guy Rhys John, Esq, Q.C.
Margrethe II of Denmark, Her Majesty Queen (Honorary)
Martin, Roy (Robert Logan), Esq, Q.C.
Masire-Mwamba, Mrs Mmasekgoa (Honorary)
Massey, William Greville Sale, Esq, Q.C.
Mayes, Ian, Esq, Q.C.
Mayhew of Twysden, The Rt Hon Lord, Q.C. (Senior)
McCredie, Miss Fionnuala Mary Constance, Q.C.
McCullough, Sir (Iain) Charles (Robert)
McDermott, Gerard Francis, Esq, Q.C.
McGowan, Ms Maura Patricia, Q.C.
McKenzie, Michael, C.B., Q.C. (Senior)
McLachlin, The Rt Hon Beverley, P.C. (Honorary)
McMullen, His Honour Judge Jeremy John, Q.C.
Mildon, His Honour Arthur Leonard, Q.C. (Senior)
Mill, Ian Alexander, Esq, Q.C.
Miller, Richard Hugh, Esq, Q.C.
Miller, Stephen Mackenzie, Esq, Q.C.
Milmo, Patrick Helenus, Esq, Q.C.
Miskin, Miss Claire Marianne
Mitchell, The Hon Sir Stephen George
Moloney, His Honour Judge Patrick Martin Joseph, Q.C.
Monty, Simon Trevor, Esq, Q.C.
Morcom, Christopher, Esq, Q.C.
Morgan, Mrs Marilynne Ann, C.B.
Moriarty, Stephen, Esq, Q.C.
Morris, The Honourable Frederick Reginald (Honorary)
Mortimer, The Hon John Barry, G.B.S., Q.C. (Senior)
Moses, The Rt Hon Lord Justice Alan George
Mostyn, The Hon Mr Justice Nicholas Anthony Joseph
Mowschenson, Terence Rennie, Esq, Q.C.
Munby, The Rt Hon Lord Justice James Lawrence
Murphy, Ian Patrick, Esq, Q.C.
Mylne, Nigel James, Esq, Q.C. (Senior)
Nathan, Stephen Andrew, Esq, Q.C.
Nelson, Sir Robert Franklin
Newbery, Miss Freya Patricia
Newey, The Hon Mr Justice Guy Richard
Newman, Alan Ronald Harvey, Esq, Q.C.
Newman, Catherine Mary, Q.C.
Newman, Sir George Michael
Nicholls of Birkenhead, The Rt Hon The Lord (Senior)
Nicol, The Hon Mr Justice Andrew George Lindsay
Noble, Mr Adrian Keith (Honorary)
Nolan, Benjamin, Esq, Q.C.
Norris, William John, Esq, Q.C.
Nursaw, Sir James, K.C.B., Q.C. (Senior)
Nutting, Sir John Grenfell, B.T., Q.C. (Senior)
O'Brien, Miss Patricia
Oliver, Sir Stephen John Lindsay, Q.C. (Senior)
Oliver, Professor (Ann) Dawn Harrison, F.B.A.
Onions, Jeffery Peter, Esq, Q.C.
Ormerod, Professor David Christopher
Owen, Timothy Wynn, Esq, Q.C.
Padfield, Mrs Nicola Margaret
Page, Miss Adrienne May, Q.C.
Palmer, Adrian Oliver, Esq, Q.C.
Papadimitriou, Anthony, Esq (Honorary)
Parker, The Hon Ms Justice Judith Mary Frances, D.B.E.
Parroy, Michael Picton, Esq, Q.C.
Partington, Professor (Thomas) Martin, C.B.E., Q.C.
Patterson, Frances Silvia, Q.C.
Pauffley, The Hon Mrs Justice Anna Evelyn, D.BE.
Paul, Mr William George (Honorary)
Pearce-Higgins, His Honour Judge Daniel John, Q.C.
Peart, Icah Delano Everard, Esq, Q.C.
Pelling, His Honour Judge Philip Mark, Q.C.
Phillips of Worth Matravers, The Rt Hon The Lord
Pigott, Mrs Margaret Louise, C.B.E.
Pillay, His Honour Judge Thavarajoo Deva
Pitchford, The Rt Hon Sir Christopher John
Plumstead, Her Honour Judge Isobel Mary
Pontius, His Honour Judge Timothy Gordon
Powell, John Lewis, Esq, Q.C.
Price, Arthur Leolin, C.B.E., Q.C.
Price II, Ambassador Charles Harry (Honorary)
Pulman, George Frederick, Esq, Q.C.
Purnell, Nicholas Robert, Esq, Q.C.
Rabinowitz, Laurence Anton, Esq, Q.C.
Ramsey, The Hon Mr Justice Vivian Arthur
Randolph, Fergus Mark Harry, Esq, Q.C.
Rawley, Alan David, Esq, Q.C. (Senior)
Rawlings, Professor Richard William (Honorary)
Reade, David Jarrett, Esq, Q.C.
Reynolds, James Kirk, Esq, Q.C.
Rich, His Honour Michael Samuel, Q.C. (Senior)
Richmond, Bernard Grant, Esq, Q.C.
Rivlin, His Honour Judge Geoffrey, Q.C.
Roberts, Jr, The Honorable John Glover (Honorary)
Robertson, Geoffrey Ronald, Esq, Q.C.
Robinson, Mrs Mary Terese Winifred (Honorary)
Rodway, Miss Susan Caroline, Q.C.
Rogers, Heather, Q.C.
Roots, Guy Robert Godfrey, Esq, Q.C.
Rose, The Rt Hon Sir Christopher Dudley Roger (Senior)
Ross-Munro, Colin William Gordon, Esq, Q.C. (Senior)
Roth, The Honourable Mr Justice Peter Marcel
Rowe, John Jermyn, Esq, Q.C. (Senior)
Rumfitt, Nigel John, Esq, Q.C.
Russell, His Honour Judge Anthony Patrick, Q.C.
Rutter, John Milford, C.B.E. (Honorary)
Ryan, Gerard Charles, Esq, Q.C. (Senior)
Rylance, Mr Mark (Honorary)
Saloman, Timothy Peter, Esq, Q.C.
Sands, Professor Philippe Joseph, Esq, Q.C.
Sangster, Nigel Hiralal, Esq, Q.C.
Sauve, Jean-Marc (Honorary)
Saville of Newdigate, The Rt Hon The Lord (Senior)
Scotland of Asthal, The Rt Hon The Baroness, Q.C.
Scott, Peter Denys John, Esq, Q.C. (Senior)
Scott Baker, The Rt Hon Sir Thomas Gillespie, (Senior)
Seabrook, Robert John, Esq, Q.C.
Seitz, The Honourable Raymond George Hardenbergh (Honorary)
Selvaratnam, Miss Vasanti Emily Indrami, Q.C.
Sepulveda-Amor, Judge Bernardo (Honorary)
Shahabuddeen, The Honourable Mohamed (Honorary)
Sharp, Alastair Richard Francis, Esq
Sharpston, Advocate General Eleanor Veronica, Q.C.
Shaw, Antony Michael Ninian, Esq, Q.C.
Sheil, The Rt Hon Sir John Joseph (Honorary)
Sheinwald, Sir Nigel Elton, G.C.M.G.(Honorary)
Sherrard, Michael David, C.B.E., Q.C. (Senior)
Shorrock, His Honour Judge Philip Geoffrey
Siberry, William Richard, Esq, Q.C.
Simon, The Hon Mr Justice Peregrine Charles Hugh
Simpson, Robin Muschamp Garry, Esq, Q.C. (Senior)
Sinclair, Sir Ian, K.C.M.G., Q.C. (Senior)
Singh, Kuldip, Esq, Q.C.
Singleton, Miss Sarah Louise, Q.C.
Smith, Professor Anthony Terry Hanmer, LL.D. (Honorary)
Smith, The Hon Mr Justice Andrew Charles
Smouha, Joseph, Esq, Q.C.
Speaight, Anthony Hugh, Esq, Q.C.
Spearman, Richard, Esq, Q.C.
Spencer, Paul Anthony, Esq
Spink, Andrew John Murray, Esq, Q.C.
Stable, His Honour Rondle Owen Charles, Q.C. (Senior)
Stafford, Andrew Bruce, Esq, Q.C.
Stafford Smith, Clive, O.B.E. (Honorary)
Starmer, Keir Rodney, Esq, Q.C., D.P.P.
Steer, David, Esq, Q.C.
Stephens, Michael Allen, Esq
Stephens, His Honour Judge (Stephen) Martin, Q.C.
Stewart, Robin Milton, Esq, Q.C. (Senior)
Stewart Smith, William Rodney, Esq
Stockdale, His Honour Eric, (Senior)
Stockdale, His Honour Judge David Andrew, Q.C.
Stone, Miss Lucille Madeline, Q.C.
Suckling, Alan Blair, Esq, Q.C. (Senior)
Sullivan, Her Honour Judge Linda Elizabeth, Q.C.
Supperstone, The Hon Mr Justice Michael Alan
Susman, Ambassador Louis B (Honorary)
Susman, Peter Joseph, Esq, Q.C.
Sutherland, Peter Denis William, Esq, Q.C.
Sutton, Mark, Esq, Q.C.
Sutton, Richard Patrick, Esq, Q.C.
Sweeney, The Hon Mr Justice Nigel Hamilton
Swindells, Her Honour Judge Heather Hughson, Q.C.
Symons, Christopher John Maurice, Esq, Q.C.
Tapping, Her Honour Judge Susan Amanda Mary
Temkin, Professor Jennifer
Templeman, The Rt Hon Lord, M.B.E. (Senior)
Thanki, Bankim, Esq, Q.C.
Thirlwall, The Hon Mrs Justice Kathryn Mary, D.B.E.
Thomas, Professor Dame Jean, D.B.E. (Honorary)
Thomas, Michael David, C.M.G., Q.C. (Senior)
Thorn, His Honour Judge Roger Eric, Q.C.
Thornhill, Andrew Robert, Esq, Q.C.
Thornton, His Honour Judge Anthony Christopher Lawrence, Q.C.
Thornton, His Honour Judge Peter Ribblesdale, Q.C.
Thrower, James Simeon, Esq
Toulmin, His Honour John Kelvin, C.M.G., Q.C.
Townend, James Barrie Stanley, Esq, Q.C. (Senior)
Treacy, The Hon Mr Justice Colman Maurice
Turner-Samuels, David Jessel, Esq, Q.C. (Senior)
Turner-Warwick, Prof Dame Margaret, D.B.E. (Honorary)
Tuttle, Ambassador Robert Holmes (Honorary)
Van Doosselaere, Batonnier Michel (Honorary)
Venables, Robert, Esq, Q.C.
Warren, The Hon Mr Justice Nicholas Roger
Waters, David Ebsworth Benjamin, Esq, Q.C.
Weatherill, Bernard Richard, Esq, Q.C.
Webster, Alistair Stevenson, Esq, Q.C.
Wedderburn of Charlton, Prof Lord, Q.C., F.B.A. (Senior)
Whitaker, Steven Dixon, Senior Master & Queen's Remembrancer
Whitfield, Adrian, Esq, Q.C.
Wilkinson, Nigel Vivian Marshall, Esq, Q.C.
Wilmot-Smith, Richard James Crosbie, Esq, Q.C.
Wilson of Dinton, The Lord, G.C.B. (Honorary)
Wong, The Honourable Yan Lung, S.C., J.P.
Wood, Derek Alexander, C.B.E., Q.C. (Senior)
Wood, Graham Nash, Esq, Q.C.
Wood, William James, Esq, Q.C.
Wood, The Hon Mr Justice Roderic Lionel James
Woolley, David Rorie, Esq, Q.C. (Senior)
Worrall, Miss Anna Maureen, Q.C.
Worsley, His Honour Judge Paul Frederick, Q.C.
Worthington, Professor Sarah Elizabeth, Q.C., F.B.A.
Wright, Brigadier Charles Thomas Johnstone (Honorary)
Wright, Mrs Rosalind, C.B., Q.C.
Wright, His Honour Judge Peter Malcolm, Q.C.
Wurtzel, David Ira, Esq
Wyand, Roger Nicholas Lewes, Esq, Q.C.
Yeung Sik Yuen, His Lordship The Chief Justice (Honorary)
Yew, The Hon Lee Kuan, C.H. (Honorary)
Young, The Hon Justice William Gillow Gibbes Austen (Honorary)
Zacca, The Rt Hon Edward, O.J., P.C. (Honorary)
Zellick, Professor Graham John, C.B.E., Q.C.

SECTION 11

BARRISTERS

PROVINCIAL

CONTENTS

11

PROVINCIAL CHAMBERS – BY TOWN

Key Facts

See Notice, Data Protections Act 1984, p. iv

The wording after each name shows the Inn of Court and the month and year of Call: Where

G = Gray's Inn I = Inner Temple L = Lincoln's Inn M = Middle Temple

ALTRINCHAM, Greater Manchester

Chambers of Maura Logan

ST JOHN'S CHAMBERS,
ONE HIGH ELM DRIVE, HALE BARNS, ALTRINCHAM, GREATER MANCHESTER WA15 0JD
Tel: 0161 980 7379 ***Fax:*** 0161 980 7379
E-mail: maura.logan@fsmail.net
Head of Chambers:
Logan, Ms Maura . . . I . . . Jul 1971

ASHFORD, Kent

199 KINGSWORTH ROAD,
ASHFORD, KENT TN23 6NB
Tel: 01233 645805 ***Fax:*** 01233 645805
Hogben, Mr Paul . . . G . . . Nov 1993

AYLESBURY, Buckinghamshire

Chambers of Royln Jean-Paul Seeboruth

CHAMBERS OF ROYLN SEEBORUTH,
4 ABBOTTS CLOSE, AYLESBURY, BUCKINGHAMSHIRE HP20 1HZ
Tel: 01296 393329 ***Fax:*** 01296 393329
E-mail: rseeboruth@homecall.co.uk
Clerk: C Seeboruth.
Head of Chambers:
Seeboruth, Mr Royln Jean-Paul . . . M . . . Oct 1986

BARNET, Hertfordshire

Chambers of M Petrou

PETROU CHAMBERS,
214 CHURCH HILL ROAD, EAST BARNET, BARNET, HERTFORDSHIRE EN4 8PP
Tel: 020 7566 8244
Head of Chambers:
Petrou, Ms Mandy . . . G . . . Aug 2006

BEDFORD, Bedfordshire

ERIMUS CHAMBERS,
PO BOX 1440, BEDFORD, BEDFORDSHIRE MK43 6AJ
Tel: 01234 720952
E-mail: clerks@erimuschambers.com
Clerk: James Caswell.

Chambers of Peter-John White and Tanya White

CHAMBERS OF TANYA AND PETER-JOHN WHITE,
BRIDGE COTTAGE, 88 GREEN END ROAD, GREAT BARFORD, BEDFORD, BEDFORDSHIRE MK44 3HD
Tel: 01234 870004 ***Fax:*** 01234 870009
E-mail: peter_johnwhite@hotmail.com
Head of Chambers:
White, Mr Peter-John . . . I . . . Jul 1977
White, Mrs Tanya . . . M . . . Feb 1983

BIRMINGHAM, West Midlands

Chambers of Andrew Fisher QC

CITADEL CHAMBERS,
CITADEL, 190 CORPORATION STREET, BIRMINGHAM, WEST MIDLANDS B4 6QD
Tel: 0121 233 8500 ***Fax:*** 0121 233 8501
Dx: 23503 BIRMINGHAM 3
Web: www.citadelchambers.com
Clerk: Rodney Neeld; David Dobson; Michael Powell; Richard Cornes.
Administrator: R Ellison
Practice Manager: Bill Maynard
Head of Chambers:
Fisher, Mr Andrew (Q.C.) . . . G . . . Jul 1980

Andreae-Jones, Mr William P (Q.C.) . . . I . . . Nov 1965
Redgrave, Mr Adrian (Q.C.); Recorder* . . . I . . . Oct 1968
Benson, Mr Richard (Q.C.) . . . I . . . Jul 1974
Brand, Ms Rachel (Q.C.) . . . G . . . Jul 1981
Syfret, Mr Nicholas (Q.C.); Recorder* . . . M . . . Oct 1979
Wall, Mr Mark (Q.C.) . . . L . . . Nov 1985
Draycott, Mr Simon (Q.C.)* . . . M . . . Jul 1977
Redmond, Mr Stephen . . . G . . . Jul 1975
Grey, Mr Michael Henry John . . . M . . . Nov 1975
Nicholls, Mr Benjamin . . . G . . . Jan 1978
Warner, Mr Anthony Charles Broughton . . . G . . . Jul 1979
Harris, Mr Julian Gilbert . . . M . . . Oct 1982
Khan, Mr Mohammed Asif . . . L . . . Nov 1983
Masters, Mr Lee . . . M . . . Nov 1984
Powis, Miss Samantha . . . L . . . Nov 1984
Butterworth, Mr Martin Frank . . . L . . . Jul 1985
Aspinall, Mr Michael . . . G . . . Nov 1986
Stelling, Mr Nigel Roy . . . I . . . Jul 1987
Bond, Mr Richard Ian Winsor . . . M . . . Jul 1988
Forsyth, Ms Samantha . . . I . . . Jul 1988
Watts, Mr Lawrence . . . I . . . Jul 1988
Quirke, Mr Gerard . . . M . . . Nov 1988
Kenning, Mr Thomas . . . L . . . Feb 1989
Muller, Antonie . . . M . . . Jul 1990
Nixon, Miss Abigail; Recorder . . . I . . . Oct 1991
Sidhu-Brar, Mr Sean . . . G . . . Oct 1991
Campbell, Ms Rhona . . . I . . . Feb 1993
Parker, Mr Alan P . . . G . . . May 1995
Hannam, Mr Timothy . . . G . . . Oct 1995
Loram, Miss Mary . . . I . . . Nov 1995
Tatlow, Mr Nicholas . . . G . . . May 1996
Crabb, Ms Samantha . . . I . . . Nov 1996
Rippon, Mr Simon John . . . G . . . Nov 1996
Western, Mr Adam . . . G . . . Oct 1997
Harrington, Mr Timothy M . . . G . . . Mar 1997
Garcha, Mr Gurdeep Singh . . . L . . . Nov 1997
Aris, Mr Jason . . . I . . . Jan 1998
Orchard, Miss Cathlyn . . . L . . . Jan 1999
Henry, Mr Delroy . . . I . . . Oct 1999
Meegan, Mr Trevor . . . L . . . Jan 2000
Grego, Mr Kevin C . . . G . . . Nov 2001
Miller, Ms Wendy . . . M . . . Jan 2001
McClement, Ms Lynette . . . I . . . Jan 2002
Davidson, Mr Andrew Edward . . . G . . . Oct 2003
White, Mr Daniel . . . G . . . Oct 2003
Bhatti, Miss Balvinder . . . L . . . Oct 2003
Hobson, Miss Laura . . . G . . . Jan 2003
Challinor, Mr Thomas . . . G . . . Jan 2004
Berry, Mr Nicholas Charles . . . L . . . Jan 2004
Russell, Mr Graham . . . I . . . Nov 2004
Collins, Miss Siobhan . . . I . . . Jan 2005
Culley, Miss Laura . . . L . . . Oct 2006
Lomas, Miss Sophie Victoria . . . I . . . Oct 2006
Hamer, Mr Charles; Former Solicitor . . . M . . . Jan 2007
Close, Mr Ben . . . L . . . Jan 2009

COMMONWEALTH CHAMBERS,
354 MOSELEY ROAD, BIRMINGHAM, WEST MIDLANDS B12 9AZ
Tel: 0121 446 5732
E-mail: mirzarashid786@hotmail.com
Rashid, Mr Mirza Abdul . . . L . . . Nov 1981

Chambers of Roger D H Smith QC

CORNWALL STREET CHAMBERS,
85-87 CORNWALL STREET, BIRMINGHAM, WEST MIDLANDS B3 3BY
Tel: 0121 233 7500 ***Fax:*** 0121 233 7501
Dx: 741120 BIRMINGHAM 70
E-mail: clerks@cornwallstreet.co.uk
Web: www.cornwallstreet.co.uk
Clerk: Clive S Ridley.
Chambers Director: Nigel Ledger
Head of Chambers:
Smith, Mr Roger D H (Q.C.) . . . G . . . Feb 1972

Mason, Mr John J . . . I . . . Nov 1971
Seddon, Miss Dorothy . . . M . . . Jul 1974
Desmond, Mr Denis . . . M . . . Nov 1974
Rickarby, Mr William . . . G . . . Nov 1975
Lowe, Mr Anthony Marshall . . . M . . . Jul 1976
Pitt-Lewis, Mrs Janet . . . M . . . Jul 1976
Tucker, Mr Andrew R S . . . M . . . Jul 1977
Somerville, Mr Bryce E . . . M . . . Jul 1980
Pittaway, Miss Amanda M . . . G . . . Jul 1980
Davis, Mr Jonathan; Head of Civil & Employment Team . . . M . . . Dec 1983
Cooke, Mr Peter . . . L . . . Jul 1985
O'Gorman, Mr Christopher . . . G . . . Jan 1987
Tarbitt, Mr Nicholas E H . . . I . . . Jul 1988
Slater, Miss Julie . . . L . . . Jul 1988
Hearne, Miss Juliet . . . G . . . Jan 1989
Shakoor, Mr Tariq Bin . . . I . . . Feb 1992
Clarke, Mr Timothy J . . . M . . . Oct 1992
Drummond, Mr Bruce . . . G . . . Oct 1992
Ball, Mr Ian . . . M . . . Oct 1992
Cadwaladr, Mr Stephen . . . M . . . Nov 1992
Egan, Miss Caroline . . . G . . . Nov 1993
Brotherton, Mr John . . . L . . . Jan 1994
Fairburn, Mr George . . . L . . . Mar 1995
Wilkins, Mr Andrew . . . L . . . Oct 1995
Swinnerton, Mr David . . . L . . . Nov 1995
Faux, Mr Andrew John . . . L . . . Nov 1995
Woolhouse, Mr Oliver . . . I . . . Nov 1996
Sapwell, Mr Timothy . . . L . . . Jan 1997
Hussain, Mr Basharat . . . G . . . Jan 1997
Bugeja, Miss Evelyn . . . M . . . Oct 1997
McCracken, Mr Jamie . . . M . . . Nov 1998
Challinor, Mr Jonathan . . . I . . . Nov 1998
Brook, Mr Matthew . . . G . . . Jan 1999
Hall, Mr James Edward . . . L . . . Oct 2000
Kasasian, Miss Laura . . . M . . . Jan 2002
Plunkett, Mr Raymond . . . G . . . Jan 2004
Sharman, Mr Mark . . . L . . . Jan 2004
Veasey-Pugh, Mr Jonathan . . . L . . . Jul 2005
Giles, Miss Molly . . . G . . . Jul 2005
Lenehan, Miss Emma . . . G . . . Jan 2006
Shoker, Mr Chanvir . . . M . . . Jan 2006
Ballard, Miss Appa . . . L . . . Jul 2006
Hancox, Miss Lisa . . . I . . . Nov 2006
Langdon, Ms Katie Jane . . . M . . . Jan 2007
Jacques, Mr Timothy . . . M . . . Jan 2008
Dyal, Miss Mandeep . . . I . . . Jan 2008
Wood, Mr James M* . . . L . . . Jan 1989
Hall, Mr Nigel* . . . I . . . Jul 2001

Principally common law, crime and family with specialists in Commercial, Insolvency, Licensing, Personal Injury, Employment and Landlord and Tenant.

11

Chambers of Balbir Singh

EQUITY CHAMBERS,
3RD FLOOR, 153A CORPORATION STREET,
BIRMINGHAM, WEST MIDLANDS B4 6PH
Tel: 0121 233 2100 ***Fax:*** 0121 233 2102
Dx: 23531 BIRMINGHAM 3
E-mail: clerks@equitychambers.org.uk
Clerk: Senior: Resham Toora.
Head of Chambers:
Singh, Balbir . . . L . . . Jul 1984

Thomas, Mr Roger (Q.C.); Recorder* . . . G . . . Jul 1969
Sandhu, Sunit . . . M . . . Feb 1990
Daneshyar, Mr Osama . . . I . . . Mar 1996
Lallie, Ranjit Singh . . . L . . . Jan 1997

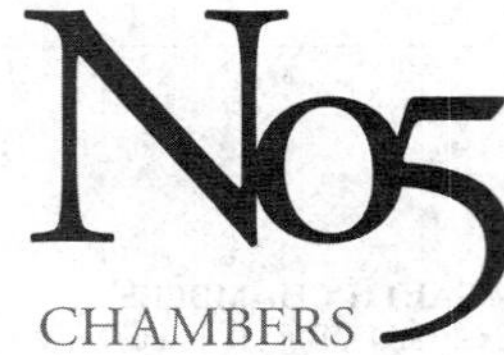

Chambers of Paul Bleasdale QC

NO5 CHAMBERS,
FOUNTAIN COURT, STEELHOUSE LANE,
BIRMINGHAM, WEST MIDLANDS B4 6DR
Tel: 0845 210 5555 ***Fax:*** 0121 606 1501
Dx: 16075 BIRMINGHAM FOUNTAIN COURT
E-mail: info@no5.com
Web: www.no5.com
Practice Manager: J Luckman; P Hawkins; G Smith; A Trotter; J Parks; A Hafeez; M Hulbert; Z Owen; R Woods; A Bisbey
Chambers Director: Tony McDaid
Head of Chambers:
Bleasdale, Mr Paul (Q.C.); Recorder . . . I . . . Jul 1978

Tedd, Mr Rex (Q.C.); Deputy High Court Judge; Recorder. . . . I . . . Feb 1970
Dove, Mr Ian (Q.C.); Deputy High Court Judge; Recorder. . . . I . . . Jul 1986
Tucker, Sir Richard (Q.C.)* . . . L . . . Jan 1954
Smith, Mr Antony (Q.C.) . . . L . . . Jan 1958
Wolton, Mr Harry (Q.C.)* . . . G . . . Dec 1969
Barker, Mr Anthony (Q.C.); Recorder . . . M . . . Dec 1966
Kingston, Mr Martin (Q.C.) . . . M . . . Apr 1972
Hotten, Mr Christopher (Q.C.); Recorder . . . I . . . Nov 1972
Evans, Mr Gareth R W (Q.C.); Recorder . . . G . . . Nov 1973
Jones, Mr Richard Henry (Q.C.); Recorder . . . I . . . Nov 1972
Gill, Mr Manjit (Q.C.) . . . G . . . Jul 1982
Cahill, Mr Jeremy (Q.C.) . . . M . . . Jul 1975
Hunjan, Satinder P S (Q.C.); Deputy High Court Judge; Recorder. . . . G . . . Jul 1984
Howker, Mr David Thomas (Q.C.). . . . I . . . Jul 1982
Armstrong, Mr Douglas (Q.C.)* . . . I . . . Jan 1999
Meyer, Miss Lorna (Q.C.) . . . I . . . Jul 1986
Crean, Mr Anthony (Q.C.). . . . G . . . Jul 1987
Humphreys, Mr Richard (Q.C.) . . . I . . . Jul 1986
Burrows, Mr Michael (Q.C.); Recorder. . . . I . . . Nov 1979
Bright, Mr Christopher (Q.C.); Recorder. . . . G . . . Nov 1985
Anderson, Mr Mark (Q.C.); Recorder . . . M . . . Jul 1983
Mason, Mr David (Q.C.); Recorder . . . I . . . Jul 1986
Lock, Mr David (Q.C.). . . . G . . . Nov 1985
Drew, Mr Simon (Q.C.) . . . L . . . Nov 1987
Duck, Mr Michael (Q.C.) . . . I . . . Nov 1988
Keeling, Mr Adrian (Q.C.). . . . I . . . Oct 1990
West, Mr John R . . . M . . . Dec 1965
Bermingham, Mr Gerald . . . G . . . Feb 1967
Smith, Mr Roger H T . . . G . . . Nov 1968
Harvey, Mr John Gilbert; Recorder . . . G . . . Jan 1973
Whitaker, Mr Stephen. . . . L . . . Nov 1970
Dooley, Mr Allan; Recorder; Deputy District Judge. . . . L . . . Apr 1970
Arnold, Mr Peter . . . L . . . Jul 1972
Cliff, Mr Graham Hilton; Recorder. . . . M . . . Jul 1973
Jones, Mr Timothy . . . I . . . Jul 1975
Worlock, Mr Simon . . . M . . . Jul 1975
Giles, Mr Roger S. . . . G . . . Jul 1976
Bealby, Mr Walter. . . . M . . . Jul 1976
Henson, Mr Graham . . . G . . . Jul 1976
Smallwood, Ms Anne E. . . . M . . . Nov 1977
Iles, Mr David. . . . I . . . Jul 1977
James, Mr Christopher . . . G . . . Nov 1977
Rowland, Mr Robin Frank; Recorder . . . M . . . Nov 1977
Pusey, Mr William James . . . I . . . Nov 1977
O'Donovan, Mr Kevin. . . . M . . . Jul 1978
Michael, Mr Simon . . . M . . . Nov 1978
Morgan, Ms Adrienne. . . . G . . . Nov 1978
Korn, Mr Anthony. . . . G . . . Nov 1978
Keogh, Mr Andrew . . . I . . . Nov 1978
Brough, Mr Alasdair. . . . G . . . Jul 1979
Cairnes, Mr Paul . . . G . . . Oct 1980
Newman, Mr Timothy. . . . G . . . Jul 1981
Brown, Miss Stephanie . . . L . . . Jul 1982
Thompson, Mr Howard Neil. . . . L . . . Jul 1982
Campbell, Mr Stephen; Recorder . . . M . . . Jul 1982
McGrath, Mr Andrew J . . . G . . . Jul 1983
Maccabe, Mr Irvine . . . G . . . Nov 1983
de Mello, Ramby . . . L . . . Feb 1983
Sharif, Ms Nadia J . . . L . . . Nov 1985
Moat, Mr Richard . . . L . . . Jul 1985
Kelly, Mr Mark . . . G . . . Nov 1985
Bell, Mr Anthony . . . I . . . Jan 1985
Bailey, Mr Russell. . . . I . . . Nov 1985
Barrett, Mr Kevin . . . M . . . Jan 1985
Thorogood, Mr Bernard; Recorder. . . . G . . . Jul 1986
Heywood, Mr Mark . . . G . . . Jul 1986
Leigh, Mr Kevin. . . . L . . . Nov 1986
Wignall, Mr Gordon; Part Time Employment Tribunal Chairman . . . G . . . Oct 1987
O'Brien, Mr Michael. . . . M . . . Jan 1987
Hickey, Mr Eugene . . . L . . . Jul 1988
Baker, Mrs Caroline; Deputy District Judge . . . G . . . Jul 1988
Chadwick, Miss Joanna. . . . M . . . Nov 1988
Tiwana, Mr Ekwall Singh . . . M . . . Jan 1988
Bridge, Mr Ian . . . I . . . Nov 1988
Wallace, Mr Andrew. . . . G . . . Nov 1988
Birk, Miss Dewinder. . . . L . . . Jul 1988
Duthie, Mr Malcolm. . . . I . . . Jul 1989
Bedford, Mr Becket . . . M . . . Nov 1989
Bell, Mr Gary . . . I . . . Feb 1989
Liddiard, Mr Martin . . . I . . . Nov 1989
Murray, Miss Carole* . . . M . . . Nov 1989
Hanson, Mr Timothy* . . . I . . . Jan 1989
Attwood, Mr John. . . . G . . . Nov 1989
Phillips, Ms Moira. . . . G . . . Jan 1989
Anning, Mr Michael . . . I . . . Nov 1990
Wynne, Ashley . . . G . . . Nov 1990
Baker, Mr Andrew. . . . M . . . Oct 1990
Mann, Mr Jasvir. . . . M . . . Jan 1990
Boora, Mr Jinder . . . G . . . Oct 1990
McDonald, Mrs Melanie. . . . G . . . Jan 1990
Radburn, Mr Mark Charles Crispin . . . L . . . Oct 1991
Friel, Miss Michele E . . . L . . . Jul 1991
Buckingham, Miss Sarah J . . . I . . . Oct 1991
Grant, Mr Edward* . . . I . . . Nov 1991
Al-Rashid, Mr Mahmud . . . G . . . Jul 1991
Park, Mr David . . . L . . . Jul 1992
Goatley, Mr Peter. . . . I . . . Jul 1992
Xydias, Mr Nicholas. . . . L . . . Oct 1992
Wilkinson, Mr Marc . . . L . . . Oct 1992
Preston, Ms Nicola . . . L . . . Jul 1992
Richards, Mr Hugh . . . I . . . Nov 1992
Hansen, Mr William; Deputy Adjudicator to HM Land Registry . . . L . . . Nov 1992
Brockley, Mr Nigel . . . L . . . Nov 1992
Farrer, Mr Adam . . . G . . . Sep 1992
Bailey, Mr Steven. . . . M . . . Oct 1992
Joseph, Mr Paul . . . I . . . Oct 1992
Mahmood, Mr Abid . . . I . . . Oct 1992
Ismail, Miss Nazmun . . . L . . . May 1992
Mallick, Miss Nabila. . . . G . . . Oct 1992
Bazini, Mr Danny . . . G . . . Nov 1992
Taylor, Mr David; Deputy Adjudicator to HM Land Registry . . . L . . . Nov 1993
Clover, Ms Sarah . . . L . . . Nov 1993
Sumeray, Ms Caroline . . . M . . . Jan 1993
Bradley, Mr Phillip. . . . L . . . Nov 1993
Bains, Ms Param Kaur . . . I . . . Oct 1993
Dutta, Miss Nandini. . . . M . . . Feb 1993
Rothwell, Miss Joanne . . . I . . . Oct 1993
Nicholson, Mr Edward . . . M . . . Nov 1993
Edhem, Miss Emma . . . G . . . Oct 1993
Price, Miss Rachael. . . . I . . . Nov 1994
Smallwood, Mr Robert . . . L . . . Nov 1994
Cotter, Miss Rachel. . . . M . . . Nov 1994
Potter, Mr Anthony . . . G . . . Jul 1994
Collie, Mr Peter. . . . M . . . Nov 1994
Choongh, Dr Satnam* . . . L . . . Apr 1994
Jones, Mr Jonathan. . . . L . . . Oct 1994
Fox, Dr Simon . . . I . . . Jan 1994
Khalique, Miss Nageena . . . G . . . Oct 1994
Tyack, Mr David . . . M . . . Nov 1994
Renouf, Mr Mark*. . . . M . . . Oct 1994
Dean, Mr Brian . . . G . . . Nov 1994
Stoll, Mr James. . . . L . . . Nov 1994
Diamond, Miss Anna . . . G . . . Nov 1995
Mitchell, Mr David. . . . L . . . Oct 1995
Sheppard, Mr Tim. . . . I . . . Nov 1995
Hignett, Mr Richard . . . I . . . Nov 1995
Kershaw, Mr Dean . . . L . . . Oct 1995
Butterfield, Mr John Arthur . . . L . . . Oct 1995
Monaghan, Ms Susan. . . . L . . . Oct 1995
Wright, Mr Jeremy* . . . I . . . Oct 1996
Hogan, Miss Emma. . . . L . . . Oct 1996
Hancox, Ms Sally. . . . L . . . Nov 1996
Jones, Mrs Cheryl S; Deputy District Judge . . . G . . . Oct 1996
Pitchers, Mr Henry . . . L . . . Nov 1996
Power, Ms Elizabeth . . . I . . . Jan 1996
Case, Mr Richard. . . . M . . . Oct 1996
Holloway, Mr David . . . G . . . Jul 1996
Davidson, Ms Laura. . . . L . . . Oct 1996
Bagral, Miss Ravinder. . . . I . . . Oct 1996
Knotts, Miss Carol . . . I . . . Nov 1996
Hirst, Mr Karl . . . I . . . Oct 1997
Young, Mr Christopher . . . M . . . Oct 1997
Hadley, Mr Richard . . . G . . . Oct 1997
Lally, Mr Harbinder Singh . . . L . . . Jan 1997
Brunning, Mr Matthew. . . . M . . . Nov 1997
Chatterjee, Miss Adreeja Julia. . . . G . . . Nov 1997
Compton, Mr Gareth . . . M . . . Mar 1997
Rowley, Miss Rachel . . . M . . . Nov 1997
Singh, Mr Talbir. . . . G . . . Jan 1997
Stein, Mr Alexander. . . . G . . . Jul 1998
Kimblin, Mr Richard. . . . M . . . Jul 1998
Derrington, Mr Jonathan . . . I . . . Oct 1998
Brown, Miss Kristina . . . G . . . Oct 1998
Gamble, Mr Jamie . . . M . . . Nov 1999
Denning, Ms Louisa. . . . G . . . Nov 1999
Hargreaves, Ms Teresa. . . . L . . . Nov 1999
Crow, Mr Charles. . . . L . . . Nov 1999
Coughlan, Mr John . . . M . . . Nov 1999
Price, Mr Charles. . . . M . . . Nov 1999
Barney, Miss Helen. . . . L . . . Jan 1999
Butt, Miss Nassera . . . M . . . Jul 1999
Afzal, Dr Fayyaz OBE; Doctorate . . . L . . . Jan 1999
Chelvan, S . . . I . . . Oct 1999
Willets, Mr Glenn . . . M . . . Nov 2000
Chawla, Mr Neil. . . . I . . . Jan 2000
Wigley, Miss Jenny . . . M . . . Nov 2000
Ensaff, Mr Omar Sherif . . . G . . . Oct 2000
Abberley, Mr Stephen. . . . M . . . Nov 2000
Evans, Mr Paul . . . I . . . Jan 2001
Heeley, Ms Michelle. . . . G . . . Jan 2001
Beloff, Mr Rupert . . . G . . . Jan 2001
Forster, Ms Bridget . . . I . . . Jan 2001
Brown, Ms Emma. . . . I . . . Jan 2001
Wingrave, Mr Michael. . . . M . . . Jul 2001
Pole, Mr Tim . . . M . . . Jul 2001
Schofield, Mr Thomas. . . . L . . . Oct 2001
Chaffin-Laird, Miss Olivia . . . G . . . Jul 2001
Adkinson, Mr Richard. . . . M . . . Jul 2001
Dixon, Mr James . . . L . . . Jan 2001
Mantle, Mr Philip . . . L . . . Jan 2002
Clifford, Miss Victoria . . . G . . . Jul 2002
Bradshaw, Mr Mark. . . . G . . . Jul 2002
Kurji, Miss Fatim*. . . . I . . . Jan 2003
Arthur, Mrs Helen. . . . M . . . Oct 2003
Oscroft, Mr Daniel . . . M . . . Nov 2003
Pinnock, Mr Earl . . . M . . . Nov 2003
Owen, Miss Denise. . . . G . . . Oct 2003
van Overdijk, Mrs Claire . . . L . . . Jan 2003
Cobill, Mr Nicholas . . . M . . . Jan 2003
Deacon, Ms Jennifer*. . . . I . . . Jul 2004
Davies, Mr Rhys . . . G . . . Oct 2004
Gupta, Miss Mamta. . . . L . . . Oct 2004
Leslie, Mr James . . . M . . . Jan 2004
Williams, Mr Philip . . . I . . . Apr 2005
Allen, Miss Sarah. . . . G . . . Nov 2005
Punt, Dr Jonathan . . . I . . . Jul 2005
Cooke, Mr Richard . . . I . . . Jul 2005
Grant, Miss Orla . . . L . . . Jul 2005
Sandhu, Mr Harpreet Singh. . . . G . . . Jul 2005
Reed, Mr Steven . . . I . . . Jul 2005
Fernandes, Ms Suella. . . . M . . . Oct 2005
Allen, Miss Juliet . . . G . . . Nov 2005
Taylor, Miss Kathryn . . . L . . . Jul 2005
Feeney, Miss Katie . . . I . . . Jul 2005
Yasseri, Miss Yasmin . . . I . . . Jul 2005
Tyers-Smith, Mr Peter. . . . L . . . Nov 2005
Feeny, Mr Jack . . . I . . . Jan 2005
Roberts, Miss Gemma . . . G . . . Oct 2006
Enonchong, Prof Nelson . . . I . . . Jan 2006
Yates, Miss Victoria. . . . M . . . Nov 2006
Gallacher, Kirsty . . . G . . . Nov 2006
Hunka, Mr Simon. . . . M . . . Jul 2007
Smyth, Mr Jack. . . . M . . . Oct 2007
Oakes, Mr Richard . . . M . . . Oct 2007
Meager, Ms Rowena . . . L . . . Jul 2007
Pye, Mr Derek . . . L . . . Jul 2008
Corfield, Miss Louise . . . I . . . Oct 2008
Williams, Hermione . . . M . . . Jan 2008
Osmund-Smith, Miss Thea . . . I . . . Jan 2010

No5 Chambers (Chambers of Paul Bleasdale QC) has over 200 Barristers and are based in Birmingham, London & Bristol. For more information visit our website at www.no5.com

Chambers of Mark Jackson

NO 8 CHAMBERS,
STEELHOUSE LANE, BIRMINGHAM, WEST MIDLANDS B4 6DR
Tel: 0121 236 5514 ***Fax:*** 0121 236 8225
Dx: 16078 BIRMINGHAM FOUNTAIN COURT
E-mail: clerks@no8chambers.co.uk
Clerk: Christine Maloney; Rosemarie Maloney.
Head of Chambers:
Jackson, Mr Mark. . . . L . . . Jan 1997

White, Miss Amanda . . . G . . . Nov 1976
James, Mrs Venice I . . . L . . . Jul 1983
Vokes, Mr Stephen . . . L . . . Jan 1989
Cook, Mr Gary . . . I . . . Jan 1989
Dhaliwal, Miss Davinder. . . . M . . . Nov 1990
Scott-Jones, Miss Alison . . . M . . . Feb 1991
Hartley, Mr Anthony. . . . G . . . Feb 1991
Brunt, Mr Philip. . . . L . . . Nov 1991
Cowley, Mr Robert . . . L . . . Oct 1992
Chaggar, Mrs Maninder. . . . I . . . Jul 1992
Hobbs, Miss Naomi . . . G . . . Oct 1993
Manning, Miss Ruth. . . . G . . . Oct 1993
Thomas, Miss Kate . . . G . . . Nov 1994
Mondair, Mr Rashpal . . . M . . . Jun 1995
Alakija, Mr Dele* . . . G . . . Oct 1996
Azmi, Mr Mohammad. . . . M . . . Mar 1998
Williams, Miss June. . . . I . . . Jan 1999
Pipe, Mr Adam . . . M . . . Oct 1999
Masih, Mrs Harleen. . . . M . . . Jul 1999
O'Shea, Miss Joanne . . . M . . . Nov 2000
De Oliveira, Mrs Liz. . . . L . . . Oct 2000
Lane, Mr Christopher Paul . . . L . . . Nov 2002
Rutherford, Miss Emma. . . . M . . . Nov 2002
Strongman, Mrs Carol . . . L . . . Sep 2003
Payne, Mr David . . . G . . . Jun 2003
Cairns, Mrs Sally . . . G . . . Jul 2006
Barnfield, Mr Alexander. . . . M . . . Jul 2007
Thomas, Lord Martin (Q.C.) OBE* . . . G . . . Jan 1970
Valios, Mr Nicholas (Q.C.)* . . . I . . . Jan 1964
Hevingham, Mr Paul* . . . G . . . Jan 2006

Chambers of Wilbert A. Harris

4 ROWCHESTER COURT,
WHITTALL STREET, BIRMINGHAM, WEST MIDLANDS B4 6DH
Tel: 0121 233 2327 ***Fax:*** 0121 236 7645
Dx: 16080 BIRMINGHAM FOUNTAIN COURT
Clerk: Steve Wilson.
Head of Chambers:
Harris, Mr Wilbert A.; Head of Chambers . . . I . . . Nov 1973

Crane, Ms Suzanne. . . . L . . . Nov 1995
Hopkins, Mr Rowland. . . . I . . . Nov 1970
Mead, Mr Larry* . . . M . . . Jan 1977
Gibbons, Mr Christopher C . . . G . . . Jul 1977
Norman, Miss Elizabeth. . . . M . . . Oct 1977
Guishard, Mr David E K. . . . M . . . Feb 1978
Martin, Mr Richard H B . . . I . . . Nov 1978
Gill, Gurnam . . . M . . . Nov 1978
Wiggans, Miss Amanda J. . . . M . . . Nov 1986
Vokes, Mr Stephen . . . L . . . Jul 1989
Brunt, Mr Philip. . . . L . . . Nov 1991
Kershaw, Mr Dean*. . . . L . . . Oct 1995
Vencatachellum, Ms Glenda Roxande. . . . M . . . Oct 1996
Maynard, Miss Sandra . . . I . . . Oct 1998
Harris, Miss Claire . . . L . . . Oct 1998

Chambers of Michael Keehan QC

ST IVES CHAMBERS,
WHITTALL STREET, BIRMINGHAM, WEST MIDLANDS B4 6DH
Tel: 0121 236 0863 ***Fax:*** 0121 236 6961
Dx: 16072 BIRMINGHAM FOUNTAIN COURT
E-mail: clerks@stiveschambers.co.uk
Clerk: Craig Jeavons.
Administrator: Lyndsey Jeavons
Head of Chambers:

Keehan, Mr Michael (Q.C.)	M	Jul 1982
Chavasse, Miss Ann	G	May 1971
Hodgson, Miss Margaret Julia	L	Jul 1975
Coke, Mr Edward	I	Jul 1976
Anthony, Mr Peter	G	Jul 1981
Lopez, Mr Paul Anthony	M	Jul 1982
Stephens, Mr Michael	I	Jul 1983
Price Rowlands, Mr Gwynn	I	May 1985
Jackson, Mr David	G	Jul 1986
Singleton, Mr Michael	M	Jul 1987
Clarkson, Mr Stuart	G	Nov 1987
Preen, Miss Catherine	M	Nov 1988
Mullen, Miss Jayne	G	Jul 1989
Starks, Mr Nicholas	I	Aug 1989
Weston, Mr Jeremy	I	Nov 1991
Haynes, Mr Matthew T B	L	Nov 1991
Chapman, Ms Claire	M	Nov 1991
Lattimer, Miss Justine	I	Apr 1992
Brown, Ms Michelle	I	Feb 1992
Dewsbery, Mr Richard	I	Oct 1992
Rogers, Mr Gregory Charles	G	Nov 1992
Cole, Mr Nicholas	L	Oct 1993
Lakin, Ms Tracy	I	Oct 1993
Pritchard, Miss Sarah	G	Oct 1993
Nuvoloni, Mr Stefano	I	Nov 1994
Hawkins, Miss Lucy	L	Nov 1994
Simpson, Mr Graeme	M	Jan 1994
Cooper, Mr Peter John	G	Nov 1996
Jacobs, Mr Alexander Marc	G	Oct 1997
Watkin, Mr Tony	M	Oct 1998
Brown, Miss Kristina	G	Oct 1998
Isaacs, Miss Elizabeth	L	Jan 1998
Coughtrie, Mr Scott	L	Jan 2000
Howell-Jones, Mr Nicholas	G	Jul 2000
Jones, Mr Mark	M	Oct 2000
Singh, Mr Karamjit	L	Mar 2000
Bache, Miss Nina	I	Jan 2001
Thomas, Mr Roger	I	Jul 2001
Bowe, Mr Timothy	I	Jan 2003
Day, Mr Andrew	I	Oct 2003
Saunders, Mr Kevin	G	Jan 2003
Molloy, Mr Andrew	G	Jan 2004
Picken, Mr James	G	Oct 2004
Caney, Miss Michelle	M	Jan 2004
Lohmus, Mr Michael	G	Jan 2005
Jacobs, Miss Amy	M	Jan 2005
Briggs, Miss Claire	M	Jan 2005
Cheetham, Mr Gareth	L	Jan 2005
Edge, Miss Romilly	M	Jan 2005
Mian, Miss Najma	G	Jan 2006
Fawcett, Mr Neil	L	Jan 2006
Newman, Miss Anya	I	Jan 2007

Chambers of Kevin Hegarty QC

ST PHILIPS CHAMBERS,
55 TEMPLE ROW, BIRMINGHAM, WEST MIDLANDS B2 5LS
Tel: 0121 246 7000 ***Fax:*** 0121 246 7001
Dx: 723240 BIRMINGHAM
E-mail: jwilson@st-philips.com
Web: www.st-philips.com
Clerk: Joe Wilson (Chief Clerk).
Administrator: Julie Tromans (Director of Administration & Finance)
Chambers Director: Chris Owen (Chief Executive)
Head of Chambers:

Hegarty, Mr Kevin (Q.C.); Recorder	M	Nov 1982
Crigman, Mr David (Q.C.); Recorder	G	Jul 1969
Linehan, Mr Stephen (Q.C.); Recorder	L	Jan 1970
Raggatt, Mr Timothy (Q.C.); Recorder	I	Jan 1972
Randall, Mr John (Q.C.); Recorder; Deputy HC Judge	L	Jul 1978
Millington, Mr Christopher John (Q.C.); Recorder	G	Jul 1976
Khangure, Mr Avtar (Q.C.); Recorder	G	Nov 1985
Ashworth, Mr Lance D P (Q.C.); Recorder	M	Nov 1987
Haynes, Mr Peter (Q.C.)	G	Jul 1983
Zaman, Mr Mohammed Khalil (Q.C.)	G	Jul 1985
Lockhart, Mr Andrew (Q.C.); Recorder	L	Oct 1991
Laird, Mr Francis (Q.C.); Recorder	G	Jan 1986
Atkins, Mr Richard (Q.C.); Recorder	G	Jul 1989
MacDonald, Mr Alistair (Q.C.); Recorder	I	Nov 1995
Garrett, Mr Michael Owen	G	Jul 1967
Morse, Mr Malcolm George McEwan; Recorder	I	Jul 1967
Hodgkinson, Mr Robert	I	Nov 1968
Readings, Mr Douglas George; Recorder	M	Jul 1972
Dillon, Miss Clare	M	Jan 1974
Quirke, Mr James K	G	Nov 1974
Spollon, Mr Guy	G	Nov 1976
Neaves, Mr Andrew	G	Jul 1977
Harrison-Hall, Mr Giles Arthur	G	Jul 1977
Darby, Mr Patrick	M	Jan 1978
Linnemann, Mr Bernard	G	Jan 1980
Clegg, Mr Simon	L	Jul 1980
Kushner, Miss Martine; Recorder	M	Jul 1980
Thomas, Mr Stephen Edward Owen; Recorder	G	Jul 1980
Shoker, Mr Makhan Singh	I	May 1981
Berlin, Mr Barry; Recorder	G	Jul 1981
Eyre, Mr Stephen John Arthur; Recorder	I	Jul 1981
Mathew, Miss Nergis-Anne	I	Nov 1981
Mytton, Mr Paul	L	Jul 1982
Evans, Mr John Wainwright	I	Jan 1983
Edwards, Mr John David; Recorder	I	Jul 1983
Messling, Mr Lawrence David	M	Jul 1983
Starcevic, Petar	I	Jul 1983
Rochford, Mr Thomas Nicholas Beverley; Recorder	I	Jul 1984
Williams, Mr Neal Moreton	L	Nov 1984
Stockill, Mr David	L	Jul 1985
Latif, Mr Mohammed	L	Jul 1985
Jackson, Mr Andrew	L	Jan 1986
Adams, Mr Christopher Alan; Recorder	L	Jul 1986
Cartwright, Mr Nicolas F; Deputy District Judge; Recorder	M	Jul 1986
Ward, Mr Simon John; Recorder	L	Jul 1986
Craig, Mr Aubrey J	I	Nov 1987
Thompson, Miss Blondel Marguerite	M	Jul 1987
McGrath, Ms Elizabeth	I	Nov 1987
Salmon, Mr Jonathan Carl; Deputy District Judge	I	Nov 1987
Rumney, Mr Conrad	I	Feb 1988
Buxton, Sarah Ruth	I	Jul 1988
Maguire, Mr Andrew	I	Nov 1988
Bristoll, Ms Sandra; Recorder	M	Jan 1989
Cook, Miss Alison	G	Feb 1989
Pepperall, Mr Edward Brian; Recorder	L	Jul 1989
Rai, Amarjit Singh	M	Jul 1989
Puzey, Mr James	I	Jul 1990
Garner, Ms Sophie	M	Oct 1990
Beever, Mr Edmund	L	Oct 1990
Davis, Mr Simon	M	Oct 1990
Meachin, Miss Vanessa; Recorder	I	Oct 1990
Gidney, Mr Jonathan	I	Jun 1991
Todd, Ms Susan	G	Oct 1991
Samuel, Mr Glyn	L	Oct 1991
George, Miss Sarah; Part-time Employment Tribunal Judge	M	Oct 1991
Lewis, Mr Robin Arwel	I	Nov 1991
Barnes, Mr Matthew	M	Jan 1992
Baker, Mr William D.	I	Oct 1992
Moseley, Ms Julie	I	Oct 1992
Montgomery, Miss Kristina; Recorder	M	Jan 1993
Marklew, Mr Lee	G	Jan 1993
Kubik, Ms Heidi	L	Jan 1993
Garside, Mr Mark	L	Feb 1993
Sadiq, Mr Tariq	G	Jul 1993
Verduyn, Mr Anthony; Recorder	L	Oct 1993
Kolodynski, Mr Stefan	L	Oct 1993
Johnston, Mr Anthony	M	Nov 1993
Hankin, Mr Jonas K.	M	Jan 1994
Maxwell, Mr David; Part-time Employment Tribunal Judge	I	Feb 1994
Smith, Mr Nicholas	G	Oct 1994
Burden, Mr Angus	L	Oct 1994
Wainwright, Mr Patrick	L	Oct 1994
Pigott, Ms Frances	G	Oct 1994
Walker, Mrs Elizabeth	G	Oct 1994
Carter, Miss Rosalyn	L	Nov 1994
Charman, Mr Andrew	L	Nov 1994
Dunstan, Mr James P.	G	Jan 1995
Jones, Miss Carolyn	L	Oct 1995
Whitehead, Mr Darron	I	Nov 1995
Brennan, Mr John	L	Jan 1996
Gilchrist, Ms Naomi	L	Jan 1996
Green, Mr Timothy	G	Jan 1996
McCabe, Miss Louise; Assistant Deputy Coroner	I	Oct 1996
Morgan, Mr James; Recorder	L	Oct 1996
Phillips, Mr Simon David	I	Oct 1996
Crawford, Mr Shane	L	Oct 1996
Warner, Mr David	G	Oct 1996
Jones, Mr Huw	L	Jan 1997
Mandalia, Mr Vinesh	I	Jan 1997
Ali, Miss Huma	G	Mar 1997
Smith, Mr Andrew Duncan; Recorder	M	Oct 1997
Kelly, Ms Emma; Deputy District Judge	L	Oct 1997
Hussain, Zira	L	Oct 1998
Hodgetts, Miss Elizabeth	M	Nov 1998
Allen, Ms Lucianne	M	Nov 1998
Punia, Raj	L	Jan 1999
Caulfield, Ms Barbara	I	Jun 1999
Najib, Mr Shakil Mohammed	L	Oct 1999
Adams, Mr Richard	G	Oct 1999
Bond, Ms Leisha	G	Oct 1999
Williams, Miss Heledd Llwyd	G	Oct 1999
Iliffe, Ms Kate	L	Jan 2000
Evans, Mr Andrew	L	Jan 2000
Sarginson, Ms Jane	M	Mar 2000
Afzal, Zaheer	G	Jun 2000
Josephs, Ms Jennifer	M	Jul 2000
Bahia, Miss Sharon	G	Oct 2000
Speed, Mr Ian	G	Oct 2000
Mills, Mr Ben	I	Oct 2000
Nosworthy, Mr Jonathan	M	Nov 2000
Walkling, Mr Tom	L	Jan 2001
Gamble, Ms Esther	M	Jul 2001
Franklin, Ms Rebecca	L	Jul 2001
O'Brien, Mr Sean	L	Oct 2001
Griffiths, Mr David	I	Oct 2001
Richards, Ms Elizabeth	M	Oct 2001
Munro, Mr David	G	Nov 2001
Dean, Mr Paul J	I	Nov 2001
Pemberton, Ms Yolanda	L	Mar 2002
Tindal, Mr Jim; Deputy District Judge; Part-time Employment Tribunal Judge	L	Nov 2002
McCormack, Miss Theresa	I	Jul 2002
Weaver, Mr Matthew	L	Nov 2002
Watson, Mr Christopher	I	Jul 2003
Bagshaw, Mr Duncan	I	Jul 2003
Baran, Mr Colin	M	Oct 2003
Candlin, Ms Naomi	L	Oct 2003
Riley, Miss Davinia	I	Jan 2004
Parathalingam, Miss Amrisha	L	Jan 2004
Edmonds, Ms Victoria	G	Jul 2004
Brown, Mr Marc	G	Jul 2004
Coleclough, Ms Suzanne	I	Mar 2005
Brown, Mr Nick	L	Jul 2005
Dickinson, Miss Rosa	I	Jan 2006
Meichen, Mr Jonathan	I	Jan 2006
Williams, Mr Ben	L	Jan 2006
Barker, Mr Jonathan	M	Jan 2006
Winstanley, Miss Alice	L	Jan 2006
Gupta, Mr Amit	G	Jul 2006
Pemberton, Miss Lydia	L	Jul 2006
Tabari, Mr Ali-Reza	I	Nov 2006
Collins, Miss Deborah	G	Jan 2007
Bush, Miss Hannah	M	Jan 2007
Mohammed, Mr Iqbal	M	Jan 2007
Garvie, Mr Carl	L	Mar 2008
French, Miss Lucie	I	Jul 2008
Mundy, Mr Robert	M	Jul 2008
Redmond, Mr Jack	G	Jan 2009
Millington, Mr Joseph	I	Jan 2009
Vernon-Asimeng, Miss Kathryn	M	Jan 2009
Rogers, Miss Kate	I	Jan 2009

BOURNEMOUTH

KING'S BENCH CHAMBERS,
WELLINGTON HOUSE, 175 HOLDENHURST ROAD, BOURNEMOUTH BH8 8DQ
Tel: 01202 250025 ***Fax:*** 01202 250026
Dx: 145960 BOURNEMOUTH 19

3PB,
30 CHRISTCHURCH ROAD, BOURNEMOUTH BH1 3PD
Tel: 01202 292102 ***Fax:*** 01202 298498
Dx: 7612 BOURNEMOUTH
E-mail: clerks.all@3paper.co.uk
Clerk: Robert Leonard; Katie Sidaway; Sian Constant.
Administrator: Neil Monro (Head of Business Administration and Finance)
Practice Manager: Stephen Evers (Practice Development Clerk)
Chambers Director: Stephen Clark (Head of Clerking); Charles Charlick (Consultant Clerk)

Norman, Mr Michael; Recorder	G	Feb 1971
Bartlett, Mr David A; Recorder	G	Jul 1975
Mitchell, Mr Nigel C.	L	Feb 1978
Leach, Mr Robin Anthony Langley	L	Jul 1979
Grey, Mr Robert W	G	Jul 1979
Coombes, Mr Timothy J.	I	Jul 1980
Hendry, Mrs Lucy	I	Jan 1988
Bradbury, Mr Timothy	I	Jun 1989
Hester, Mr Paul	M	Jul 1989
Knapp, Ms Sophie	G	Feb 1990
Griffiths, Mrs Hayley	I	Oct 1990
Dunlop, Mr Hamish	M	Nov 1991
Ross, Mr Iain	I	Nov 1991
Earle, Miss Judy	M	Oct 1994
Jameson, Miss Antonia	M	Nov 1999
Goodall, Miss Rachael	G	Jul 2000
Ludlow, Mr Craig	L	Jan 2002
Pearce, Ms Nicola	M	Jan 2002
Tomlinson, Mr Michael	M	Jan 2002
Hepworth, Miss Elizabeth	G	Mar 2004
Horder, Mr Tom	M	Jul 2004
Robinson, Mr Nicholas	I	Jan 2006
Sharma, Ms Sunyana	I	Jan 2006
da Costa, Ms Francisca	M	Jan 2006
Elliott, Mr Mark	L	Oct 2007
Ashkar, Ms Natalie	I	Jan 2009
Howard, Mr Steven	I	Jan 2009
Borrett, Mr Richard	L	Jan 2009

11

BRADFORD, West Yorkshire

Chambers of J Graham Keith Hyland QC

BROADWAY HOUSE CHAMBERS,
3RD FLOOR, 9 BANK STREET, BRADFORD, WEST YORKSHIRE BD1 1TW
Tel: 01274 722560 ***Fax:*** 01274 370708
Dx: 729860 BRADFORD 22
E-mail: clerks@broadwayhouse.co.uk
Clerk: Crime: David Rhodes; Civil & Family: Robin Slade.
Administrator: Helen Craven
Head of Chambers:

Hyland, Mr J Graham Keith (Q.C.); Recorder	I	Jul 1978
Colborne, Miss Michelle Diane (Q.C.)	G	May 1993
Khan, Mr Tahir Zaffar (Q.C.)	L	Jul 1986
Wood, Mr Martin John	I	Jul 1973
Topham, Mr John David	G	Jul 1970
Isaacs, Mr Paul; Recorder	M	Feb 1974
Kershaw, Mr Andrew; Recorder	M	Jul 1975
Newbon, Mr Ian	M	Feb 1977
Cohen, Mr Raphael	L	Jul 1981
Shelton, Mr Gordon Edward; Recorder	I	Nov 1981
McGonigal, Mr David Ambrose	G	Jul 1982
Jones, Mr David Nicholas	G	Jul 1985
Howard, Mr Ian	L	Nov 1987
Myers, Mr Simon	M	Nov 1987
Askins, Mr Nicholas Peter	G	Nov 1989
Wilson, Mr Paul	L	Jan 1989
Drake, Miss Sophie Helena	G	Oct 1990
Cole, Mr Robert	M	Jan 1991
Wood, Mr Stephen	I	Nov 1991
Crosland, Mr James Benjamin	G	Feb 1993
Hendron, Mr Gerald James	L	Oct 1992
Barlow, Miss Sarah H.	G	Oct 1993
Walker-Kane, Mr Jonathan	G	Jul 1994
Rudd, Mr Matthew	I	Nov 1994
Beckett, Mrs Jayne Louise	M	Nov 1995
Peers, Miss Nicola Jane	I	Oct 1996
Morland, Miss Camille	G	Nov 1996
Hussain, Tasaddat	L	Nov 1998
Miller, Mr Ian	L	Nov 1999
Williams, Miss Helen	I	Jul 2000
Bridge, Mr Giles	M	Jan 2000
Green, Mr Kenneth C	L	Jul 2001

Downing, Miss Emma . . . M . . . Jan 2002
Shaikh, Miss Semaab . . . L . . . Nov 2002
Hampton, Mr Peter J G . . . G . . . Jan 2003
Brown, Mr Chris I . . . M . . . Jan 2001
Modgill, Mr Alexander Jeffrey . . . L . . . Feb 2002
Power, Mr Nicholas . . . L . . . Jul 2004
Azmi, Mrs Louise Jacqueline . . . L . . . Jul 2004
Samra, Miss Sharn . . . L . . . Nov 2002
Hamilton, Mr Nigel James . . . I . . . Oct 2004
Mellor, Miss Rachel . . . L . . . Jan 2004
Larton, Miss Claire . . . L . . . Jan 2005
Langford, Miss Abigail . . . L . . . Nov 2005
Walsh, Miss Kathryn . . . M . . . Nov 2008
Durham Hall, Mr Christian . . . G . . . Jul 2009
Benson, Miss Clare . . . L . . . Jul 2009
Smith, Mr Paul . . . G . . . Nov 2008
Carlin, Mr Niall . . . I . . . Jul 2009
Hill, Mr James M (Q.C.); Recorder* . . . I . . . Jul 1984
Cannan, Mr Jonathan* . . . G . . . Nov 1989
Jamil, Miss Aisha* . . . L . . . Nov 1995
Stott, Mr Matthew* . . . M . . . Oct 2005

BRENTFORD, Middlesex

Chambers of Emily Rose Driver

BOSTON MANOR CHAMBERS,
BOSTON HOUSE, 69-75 BOSTON MANOR ROAD, BRENTFORD, MIDDLESEX TW8 9JJ
Tel: 07980 328753 *Fax:* 020 8810 0781
Dx: 153663 EALING 5
E-mail: bostonmanorchambers@gmail.com
Head of Chambers:
Driver, Miss Emily Rose . . . I . . . Oct 1988

Chambers of Lesley Mitchell

STAPLETON LODGE,
71 HAMILTON ROAD, BRENTFORD, MIDDLESEX TW8 0QJ
Tel: 020 8568 2164 *Fax:* 020 8560 2798
E-mail: lesley@mitchellsegal.co.uk
Head of Chambers:
Mitchell, Ms Lesley . . . I . . . Nov 1987

BRIDGNORTH, Shropshire

Chambers of Alistair Mitchell

49 CHAMBERS,
PO BOX 3956, BRIDGNORTH, SHROPSHIRE WV16 4NA
Tel: 01746 761545 *Fax:* 01746 708053
Dx: 23205 BRIDGNORTH
E-mail: 49chambers@googlemail.com
Clerk: Alexandra Preston.
Head of Chambers:
Mitchell, Mr Alistair . . . M . . . Oct 1997

BRIGHTON, Brighton & Hove

Chambers of Philip Havers QC

CROWN OFFICE ROW CHAMBERS,
119 CHURCH STREET, BRIGHTON, BRIGHTON & HOVE BN1 1UD
Tel: 01273 625625 *Fax:* 01273 698888
Dx: 36670 BRIGHTON 2
E-mail: clerks@1cor.com
Clerk: Senior: David Bingham.
Chambers Director: Bob Wilson
Head of Chambers:
Havers, The Hon Philip (Q.C.) . . . I . . . Jul 1974

King-Smith, Mr James . . . M . . . Nov 1980
Ashwell, Mr Paul . . . I . . . Oct 1977
Booth, Mr Roger TD . . . G . . . Oct 1966
Morris-Coole, Mr Christopher; Recorder . . . I . . . Jul 1974
McLaughlin, Miss Karen . . . M . . . Jul 1982
Stevenson-Watt, Mr Neville William . . . M . . . Nov 1985
Smith, Mr Adam . . . I . . . Jul 1987
Bergin, Mr Timothy . . . M . . . Jul 1987
Le Prevost, Mrs Aviva . . . I . . . Nov 1990
Rice, Mr Christopher . . . M . . . Jul 1991
Grant, Miss Jules . . . M . . . Oct 1991
Cave, Mr Jeremy . . . M . . . Oct 1992
Bateman, Ms Christine . . . L . . . Oct 1992
Sinnatt, Mr Simon . . . I . . . Oct 1993
Taylor, Mr Nigel . . . I . . . Jul 1993
Morelli, Miss Luisa T . . . M . . . Nov 1993
Jenkins, Mr Rowan . . . L . . . Jul 1994
Henson, Miss Christine . . . M . . . Oct 1994
Healey, Ms Susan . . . M . . . Jul 1995
Claridge, Miss Rachael . . . I . . . Oct 1996
Roach, Miss Jacqueline Alison . . . M . . . Oct 1996
Sharghy, Ms Pegah . . . I . . . Jan 1998
Wells, Miss Camilla . . . I . . . Nov 1998
Hussain, Mr Ghulam . . . I . . . Oct 1998
Peckham, Ms Jane . . . I . . . Jan 1999
Wright, Mr Stuart . . . I . . . Jul 2000
Cogin, Mr Leo . . . M . . . Oct 2000
Lewington, Miss Francesca . . . I . . . Jan 2001
Mehta, Miss Anita . . . L . . . Oct 2002
Howe, Mr Gavin . . . G . . . Nov 2003
Ager, Mr Richard . . . M . . . Jan 2004
Battie, Miss Eleanor . . . L . . . Jan 2004
Mustafa, Miss Hala . . . M . . . Jun 2004
Miller, Mr Daniel . . . L . . . Jan 2005
Knott, Ms Samantha . . . L . . . Jan 2005
Godfrey, Mr Lauren . . . I . . . Jan 2007
John, Miss Charlotte . . . M . . . Jan 2008
Willcock, Miss Rachel . . . I . . . Jan 2008
Saunders, Denise . . . I . . . Jan 2008
Walker, Mr Michael . . . M . . . Jan 2008
Tregoning, Mr Bruce . . . M . . . Jan 2009
Ciborowska, Clare . . . I . . . Jan 2009

Chambers of Ami Feder

LAMB BUILDING,
22 SHIP STREET, BRIGHTON, BRIGHTON & HOVE BN1 1AD
Tel: 01273 820490 *Fax:* 01273 827536
Dx: 2731 BRIGHTON
E-mail: clerks@lambbuilding.co.uk
Clerk: Gary Goodger; David Corne; Paul Hammond; David O'Sullivan; Harry Butcher; Luke Clark.
Administrator: Maxine Smith
Head of Chambers:
Feder, Mr Ami . . . I . . . Jul 1965

Worrall, Ms Anna (Q.C.) . . . M . . . Nov 1959
Richmond, Mr Bernard Grant (Q.C.); Recorder . . . M . . . Jul 1988
Power, Mr Lewis (Q.C.) . . . G . . . Oct 1990
Krolick, Mr Ivan . . . G . . . Nov 1966
Guy, Mr Richard Perran . . . I . . . Nov 1970
Fox, Mr John Harvey . . . I . . . Jul 1973
Gordon, Mr Jeremy* . . . I . . . Jul 1974
Barton, Mr Alan . . . M . . . Nov 1975
Sherman, Mr Robert . . . G . . . Jul 1977
Phillips, Mr Michael Charles . . . M . . . Feb 1980
Brennan, Miss Janice . . . M . . . Jul 1980
O'Malley, Miss Julie . . . G . . . Nov 1983
Toch, Miss Joanna . . . M . . . Oct 1988
Wainwright, Mr Jeremy . . . G . . . Oct 1990
McCullough, Miss Louise Clare . . . M . . . Oct 1991
Gray, Jennifer . . . M . . . Jan 1992
Kearney, Mr Seamus . . . G . . . Feb 1992
Crampin, Mr Paul . . . M . . . Oct 1992
Dykers, Miss C Joy . . . G . . . Oct 1995
Peterson, Miss Geri . . . M . . . Oct 1997
Pretzell, Mr Andreas . . . M . . . Oct 1997
Shannon, Ms Nicola . . . M . . . Oct 1997
Selby, Andrew . . . G . . . Nov 1997
Rhone-Adrien, Miss Paula . . . I . . . Oct 1998
Alexander, Mr Andrew . . . L . . . Jan 1999
Newport, Mr Michael . . . M . . . Jul 1999
Pease, Ms Alexandra . . . M . . . Nov 1999
Kelleher, Ms Katherine . . . L . . . Jul 2000
Powell, Miss Michelle . . . I . . . Jul 2001
Leslie, Miss Clare . . . M . . . Jan 2002
James, Rhodri . . . I . . . Jul 2002
Harrison, Mr Jon . . . L . . . Mar 2003
Loke, Miss Siew . . . G . . . Jul 2003
Reeve, Miss Veronica . . . I . . . Jun 2004
Merrigan, Mr David . . . L . . . Jul 2004
Rawal, Anita . . . M . . . Jan 2004
Darnborough, Mr Daniel . . . M . . . Jan 2006
Mobbs, Mr Richard . . . L . . . Jan 2007
Abzarian, Arash . . . L . . . Mar 2007
Ul Haq, Miss Yasmeen . . . I . . . Jan 2008
Di Francesco, Alex . . . M . . . Jul 2008
Chapman, Miss Juliet . . . L . . . Jan 2009
Stevens, Miss Heather . . . M . . . Jan 2009
Hodkinson, Mr Gary . . . M . . . Jan 2010

BRISTOL

Chambers of Michael David Guy Fitton QC

ALBION CHAMBERS,
BROAD STREET, BRISTOL BS1 1DR
Tel: 0117 927 2144 *Fax:* 0117 926 2569
Dx: 7822 BRISTOL
E-mail: clerks@albionchambers.co.uk
Clerk: B Colbeck; M Harding; N Jeanes; J Hathway; Theresa Lyne.
Chambers Director: Paul Fletcher
Head of Chambers:
Fitton, Mr Michael David Guy (Q.C.) . . . G . . . Nov 1991

Hughes, Mr Ignatius (Q.C.) . . . M . . . Apr 1986
Vaitilingam, Mr Adam (Q.C.) . . . M . . . Nov 1987
Ekaney, NKumbe (Q.C.) . . . G . . . Oct 1990
Jervis, Mr Christopher Robert . . . I . . . Jul 1966
Hills, Mr Timothy James . . . L . . . Jul 1968
O'Brien, Mr Bernard Nicholas . . . M . . . Jul 1968
Price, Mrs Louise . . . M . . . Nov 1972
Grumbar, Mr Paul . . . M . . . Nov 1974
Fridd, Mr Nicholas . . . I . . . Nov 1975
Steen, Mr Martin Gamper . . . I . . . Jul 1976
Duval, Mr Robert . . . G . . . Nov 1979
Norris, Mr J Geraint . . . L . . . Jul 1980
Tait, Mr Don . . . I . . . Feb 1987
Mooney, Mr Stephen John . . . I . . . Nov 1987
Wills Goldingham, Ms Claire L M . . . I . . . Jul 1988
Elder, Miss Fiona Ann Morag . . . G . . . Jul 1988
Dinan-Hayward, Miss Deborah . . . I . . . Jul 1988
Cornwall, Miss Virginia . . . M . . . Oct 1990
Livesey, Mr John W A . . . L . . . Nov 1990
Rowsell, Miss Claire . . . M . . . Feb 1991
Burns, Mr Simon H . . . I . . . Oct 1992
Cook, Mr Paul . . . M . . . Nov 1992
Sproull, Mr Nicholas . . . G . . . Nov 1992
Fuller, Mr Alan Peter . . . G . . . Oct 1993
Stanniland, Mr Jonathan . . . I . . . Nov 1993
Burgess, Mr Edward . . . I . . . Nov 1993
Nelson, Mr Giles . . . I . . . Feb 1995
Taylor, Mr Jason . . . M . . . Dec 1995
Cunningham, Miss Elizabeth . . . M . . . Oct 1995
Leafe, Mr Daniel . . . G . . . Jul 1996
Posta, Mr Adrian . . . M . . . Oct 1996
Real, Miss Kirsty . . . I . . . Oct 1996
Siva, Mr Kannan . . . G . . . Nov 1996
Brunner, Miss Kate . . . I . . . Oct 1997
Wiltshire, Mrs Hannah . . . G . . . Oct 1998
Pitts, Miss Charlotte . . . I . . . Oct 1999
Leslie, Miss Marie . . . I . . . Jan 2000
Chidgey, Mr David . . . M . . . Oct 2000
Regan, Mrs Sarah . . . L . . . Oct 2000
Shepherd, Mr Richard . . . M . . . Jan 2001
Cotterell, Mr David . . . L . . . Jan 2001
Cranfield, Mr James . . . I . . . Jan 2002
Goldie, Miss Kate . . . I . . . Oct 2004
Jenkins, Mr Benjamin . . . G . . . Jan 2004
Borkowski, Miss Gemma . . . I . . . Oct 2005
Midgley, Miss Anna . . . M . . . Oct 2005
Khandker, Miss Monisha . . . I . . . Jul 2005
Heckscher, Mr William H . . . M . . . Oct 2006
Emslie, Mr Simon . . . I . . . Jul 2007
Fuller, Mr Stuart Kenneth . . . I . . . Mar 2007
Baggley, Mr Philip . . . G . . . Jul 2009
Brazenall, Miss Emily . . . I . . . Jul 2009

ASSIZE COURT CHAMBERS,
14 SMALL STREET, BRISTOL BS1 1DE
Tel: 0117 926 4587 *Fax:* 0117 922 6835
Dx: 78134 BRISTOL
E-mail: chambers@assize.co.uk
Clerk: Carly Ash-Lucas; Jarrad Young.

Chambers of Peter Blair QC

GUILDHALL CHAMBERS,
23 BROAD STREET, BRISTOL BS1 2HG
Tel: 0117 930 9000 *Fax:* 0117 930 3800
Dx: 7823 BRISTOL
E-mail: info@guildhallchambers.co.uk
Web: www.guildhallchambers.co.uk
Clerk: Justin Emmett; Alastair Campbell; Lucy Northeast; Grant Bidwell; Charlie Ellis; Maggie Pearce; Heather Bidwell; Elena Cherry; Dan Cuthbertson.
Chambers Director: Jeremy Sweetland
Head of Chambers:
Blair, Mr Peter (Q.C.) . . . I . . . Jul 1983

Palmer, Mr Adrian (Q.C.) . . . M . . . Jul 1972
Davies, Mr Stephen (Q.C.) . . . M . . . Jul 1983
Smith, Mr Richard (Q.C.) . . . M . . . Jul 1986
Pringle, Mr Ian (Q.C.) . . . G . . . Jul 1979
Langdon, Mr Andrew (Q.C.) . . . M . . . Jul 1986
Quinlan, Mr Christopher John (Q.C.) . . . I . . . Nov 1992
Barker, Mr Kerry . . . G . . . Jul 1972
Newsom, Mr George . . . L . . . Nov 1973
Chippindall, Mr Adam . . . G . . . Jul 1975
Fenny, Mr Ian . . . G . . . Jul 1978
Warner, Mr Malcolm . . . L . . . Jul 1979
Townsend, Mr James . . . I . . . Jul 1980
Batstone, Mr William . . . M . . . Nov 1982
Virgo, Mr John . . . I . . . Jul 1983
Dixey, Mr Ian . . . I . . . Jan 1984
Brockman, Mr Christopher . . . M . . . Nov 1985
Levy, Mr Neil . . . L . . . Nov 1986
Sahonte, Rajinder Kumar . . . L . . . Nov 1986
Tully, Mr Ray . . . I . . . Nov 1987
Gerasimidis, Mr Nicolas . . . I . . . Nov 1988
French, Mr Paul . . . I . . . Nov 1989
Bamford, Mr Jeremy . . . L . . . Nov 1989
Thomas, Mr Charles . . . M . . . Oct 1990
Dent, Mr Stephen . . . G . . . Nov 1991
Plowden, Ms Selena . . . I . . . Oct 1991
Benson, Mr Julian C W . . . M . . . Oct 1991
Reddiford, Mr Anthony . . . I . . . Nov 1991
Snell, Mr John . . . L . . . Oct 1991
Moorhouse, Mr Brendon . . . M . . . Nov 1992
Wales, Mr Matthew . . . I . . . Oct 1993
McMeel, Mr Gerard . . . I . . . Nov 1993
Garner, Mr Stephen . . . G . . . Oct 1994
Briggs, Mr Nicholas . . . L . . . Oct 1994
Worsley, Mr Mark . . . I . . . Nov 1994
Farmer, Mr Gabriel . . . G . . . Nov 1994
Ascroft, Mr Richard G . . . L . . . Nov 1995
Collins, Ms Rosaleen . . . I . . . Nov 1996
Pakrooh, Ramin . . . L . . . Oct 1996
Paton, Mr Ewan W . . . I . . . Oct 1996
Vigars, Ms Anna L . . . G . . . Nov 1996
Lowe, Mr Rupert . . . I . . . Nov 1998
Sims, Mr Hugh . . . L . . . Oct 1999
Gibb, Ms Katherine Anne . . . G . . . Oct 1999
Porter-Bryant, Mr Matthew Seymour . . . M . . . Nov 1999
Sowersby, Mr Robert . . . G . . . Jan 2000
Tallentire, Ms Jennifer . . . L . . . Jul 2000
Walsh, Mr Timothy Edmund . . . I . . . Oct 2000
Wolfe, Ms Tara . . . I . . . Nov 2000
Lanchester, Mr Martin . . . M . . . Jan 2001
Stevens, Mr Henry . . . I . . . Oct 2002
Ramel, Stefan . . . I . . . Oct 2002
Bennett, Mr James . . . I . . . Oct 2002
Fentem, Mr Ross . . . L . . . Nov 2003
Cavender, Ms Susan . . . G . . . Oct 2004
Stamp, Ms Abigail . . . G . . . Oct 2004
Haskell, Mr James . . . I . . . Nov 2004
Moore, Mr Oliver . . . G . . . Mar 2005
Brown, Ms Daisy . . . L . . . Nov 2006
Cowe, Ms Mary . . . I . . . Nov 2006
Selway, Mr Michael . . . M . . . Nov 2007
Walker, Ms Lucy . . . M . . . Jan 2008
Jones, Mr Samuel . . . G . . . Jan 2008
Doyle, Miss Holly . . . L . . . Jan 2008
Neill, Mr Daniel . . . L . . . Nov 2008
Holme, Ms Sophie . . . G . . . Jan 2009
Passfield, Mr Simon . . . G . . . Jul 2009

Guildhall Chambers is a modern, forward thinking set who practice within five specialist teams covering Commercial, Crime, Insolvency, Personal Injury & Clinical Negligence, and Property Law. We

also have various sub-specialities covering Sports Law, Alternative Dispute Resolution, Church Law, Equine Law and Licensing. Chambers work is not limited to the South West and members frequently appear in London and elsewhere. We offer a prompt, efficient and considerate service to solicitors and lay clients.

Chambers of Paul Bleasdale QC

NO5 CHAMBERS,
38 QUEEN SQUARE, BRISTOL BS1 4QS
Tel: 0845 210 5555 ***Fax:*** 0117 917 8501
Dx: 7838 BRISTOL
E-mail: info@no5.com
Practice Manager: P Hawkins; A Trotter; M Hulbert; J Parks; A Hafeez; J Luckman; Z Owen; G Smith; R Woods; A Bisbey
Chambers Director: Tony McDaid
Head of Chambers:

Name	Inn	Date
Bleasdale, Mr Paul (Q.C.); Recorder	I	Jul 1978
Tedd, Mr Rex (Q.C.); Deputy High Court Judge; Recorder	I	Feb 1970
Dove, Mr Ian (Q.C.); Deputy High Court Judge; Recorder	I	Jul 1986
Tucker, Sir Richard (Q.C.)*	L	Jan 1954
Smith, Mr Antony (Q.C.)	I	Jan 1958
Wolton, Mr Harry (Q.C.)*	G	Dec 1969
Barker, Mr Anthony (Q.C.); Recorder	M	Dec 1966
Kingston, Mr Martin (Q.C.)	M	Apr 1972
Hotten, Mr Christopher (Q.C.); Recorder	I	Nov 1972
Evans, Mr Gareth R W (Q.C.); Recorder	G	Nov 1973
Jones, Mr Richard Henry (Q.C.); Recorder	I	Nov 1972
Gill, Mr Manjit (Q.C.)	G	Jul 1982
Cahill, Mr Jeremy (Q.C.)	M	Jul 1975
Hunjan, Satinder P S (Q.C.); Deputy High Court Judge; Recorder	G	Jul 1984
Howker, Mr David Thomas (Q.C.)	I	Jul 1982
Armstrong, Mr Douglas (Q.C.)*	I	Jan 1999
Meyer, Miss Lorna (Q.C.)	I	Jul 1986
Crean, Mr Anthony (Q.C.)	G	Jul 1987
Humphreys, Mr Richard (Q.C.)	I	Jul 1986
Burrows, Mr Michael (Q.C.); Recorder	I	Nov 1979
Bright, Mr Christopher (Q.C.); Recorder	G	Nov 1985
Anderson, Mr Mark (Q.C.); Recorder	M	Jul 1983
Mason, Mr David (Q.C.); Recorder	I	Jul 1986
Lock, Mr David (Q.C.)	G	Nov 1985
Drew, Mr Simon (Q.C.)	L	Nov 1987
Duck, Mr Michael (Q.C.)	G	Nov 1988
Keeling, Mr Adrian (Q.C.)	I	Oct 1990
West, Mr John R	M	Dec 1965
Bermingham, Mr Gerald	G	Feb 1967
Smith, Mr Roger H T	G	Nov 1968
Harvey, Mr John Gilbert; Recorder	G	Jan 1973
Whitaker, Mr Stephen	L	Nov 1970
Dooley, Mr Allan; Recorder; Deputy District Judge	L	Apr 1970
Arnold, Mr Peter	L	Jul 1972
Cliff, Mr Graham Hilton; Recorder	L	Jul 1973
Jones, Mr Timothy	I	Jul 1975
Worlock, Mr Simon	M	Jul 1975
Giles, Mr Roger S	G	Jul 1976
Bealby, Mr Walter	M	Jul 1976
Henson, Mr Graham	G	Jul 1976
Smallwood, Ms Anne E	M	Nov 1977
Iles, Mr David	I	Jul 1977
James, Mr Christopher	G	Nov 1977
Rowland, Mr Robin Frank; Recorder	M	Nov 1977
Pusey, Mr William James	I	Nov 1977
O'Donovan, Mr Kevin	M	Jul 1978
Michael, Mr Simon	M	Nov 1978
Morgan, Ms Adrienne	G	Nov 1978
Korn, Mr Anthony	G	Nov 1978
Keogh, Mr Andrew	I	Nov 1978
Brough, Mr Alasdair	G	Jul 1979
Cairnes, Mr Paul	G	Oct 1980
Newman, Mr Timothy	G	Jul 1981
Brown, Miss Stephanie	L	Jul 1982
Thompson, Mr Howard Neil	L	Jul 1982
Campbell, Mr Stephen; Recorder	M	Jul 1982
McGrath, Mr Andrew J	G	Jul 1983
Maccabe, Mr Irvine	G	Nov 1983
de Mello, Ramby	L	Feb 1983
Sharif, Ms Nadia J	L	Nov 1985
Moat, Mr Richard	L	Jul 1985
Kelly, Mr Mark	G	Nov 1985
Bell, Mr Anthony	I	Jan 1985
Bailey, Mr Russell	I	Nov 1985
Barrett, Mr Kevin	M	Jan 1985
Thorogood, Mr Bernard; Recorder	G	Jul 1986
Heywood, Mr Mark	G	Jul 1986
Leigh, Mr Kevin	L	Nov 1986
Wignall, Mr Gordon; Part Time Employment Tribunal Chairman	G	Oct 1987
O'Brien, Mr Michael	M	Jan 1987
Hickey, Mr Eugene	L	Jul 1988
Baker, Mrs Caroline; Deputy District Judge	G	Jul 1988
Chadwick, Miss Joanna	M	Nov 1988
Tiwana, Mr Ekwall Singh	M	Jan 1988
Bridge, Mr Ian	I	Nov 1988
Wallace, Mr Andrew	G	Nov 1988
Birk, Miss Dewinder	L	Jul 1988
Duthie, Mr Malcolm	I	Jul 1989
Bedford, Mr Becket	M	Nov 1989
Bell, Mr Gary	I	Feb 1989
Liddiard, Mr Martin	I	Nov 1989
Murray, Miss Carole*	M	Nov 1989
Hanson, Mr Timothy*	I	Jan 1989
Attwood, Mr John	G	Nov 1989
Phillips, Ms Moira	G	Jan 1989
Anning, Mr Michael	I	Nov 1990
Wynne, Ashley	G	Nov 1990
Baker, Mr Andrew	M	Oct 1990
Mann, Mr Jasvir	M	Jan 1990
Boora, Mr Jinder	G	Oct 1990
McDonald, Mrs Melanie	G	Jan 1990
Radburn, Mr Mark Charles Crispin	L	Oct 1991
Friel, Miss Michele E	L	Jul 1991
Buckingham, Miss Sarah J	I	Oct 1991
Grant, Mr Edward*	I	Nov 1991
Al-Rashid, Mr Mahmud	G	Jul 1991
Park, Mr David	L	Jul 1992
Goatley, Mr Peter	I	Jul 1992
Xydias, Mr Nicholas	L	Oct 1992
Wilkinson, Mr Marc	L	Oct 1992
Preston, Ms Nicola	L	Jul 1992
Richards, Mr Hugh	I	Nov 1992
Hansen, Mr William; Deputy Adjudicator to HM Land Registry	L	Nov 1992
Brockley, Mr Nigel	L	Nov 1992
Farrer, Mr Adam	G	Sep 1992
Bailey, Mr Steven	M	Oct 1992
Joseph, Mr Paul	I	Oct 1992
Mahmood, Mr Abid	I	Oct 1992
Ismail, Miss Nazmun	L	May 1992
Mallick, Miss Nabila	G	Oct 1992
Bazini, Mr Danny	G	Nov 1992
Taylor, Mr David; Deputy Adjudicator to HM Land Registry	L	Nov 1993
Clover, Ms Sarah	L	Nov 1993
Sumeray, Ms Caroline	M	Jan 1993
Bradley, Mr Phillip	L	Nov 1993
Bains, Ms Param Kaur	I	Oct 1993
Dutta, Miss Nandini	M	Feb 1993
Rothwell, Miss Joanne	I	Oct 1993
Nicholson, Mr Edward	M	Nov 1993
Edhem, Miss Emma	G	Oct 1993
Price, Miss Rachael	I	Nov 1994
Smallwood, Mr Robert	L	Nov 1994
Cotter, Miss Rachel	M	Nov 1994
Potter, Mr Anthony	G	Jul 1994
Collie, Mr Peter	M	Nov 1994
Choongh, Dr Satnam*	L	Apr 1994
Jones, Mr Jonathan	L	Oct 1994
Fox, Dr Simon	I	Jan 1994
Khalique, Miss Nageena	G	Oct 1994
Tyack, Mr David	M	Nov 1994
Renouf, Mr Mark*	M	Oct 1994
Dean, Mr Brian	G	Nov 1994
Stoll, Mr James	I	Nov 1994
Diamond, Miss Anna	G	Nov 1995
Mitchell, Mr David	L	Oct 1995
Sheppard, Mr Tim	I	Nov 1995
Hignett, Mr Richard	I	Nov 1995
Kershaw, Mr Dean	L	Oct 1995
Butterfield, Mr John Arthur	L	Oct 1995
Monaghan, Ms Susan	I	Oct 1995
Wright, Mr Jeremy*	I	Oct 1996
Hogan, Miss Emma	L	Oct 1996
Hancox, Ms Sally	L	Nov 1996
Jones, Mrs Cheryl S; Deputy District Judge	G	Oct 1996
Pitchers, Mr Henry	I	Nov 1996
Power, Ms Elizabeth	I	Jan 1996
Case, Mr Richard	M	Oct 1996
Holloway, Mr David	G	Jul 1996
Davidson, Ms Laura	L	Oct 1996
Bagral, Miss Ravinder	L	Oct 1996
Knotts, Miss Carol	I	Nov 1996
Hirst, Mr Karl	I	Oct 1997
Young, Mr Christopher	M	Oct 1997
Hadley, Mr Richard	G	Oct 1997
Lally, Mr Harbinder Singh	L	Jan 1997
Brunning, Mr Matthew	M	Nov 1997
Chatterjee, Miss Adreeja Julia	G	Nov 1997
Compton, Mr Gareth	M	Mar 1997
Rowley, Miss Rachel	M	Nov 1997
Singh, Mr Talbir	G	Jan 1997
Stein, Mr Alexander	L	Jul 1998
Kimblin, Mr Richard	M	Jul 1998
Derrington, Mr Jonathan	I	Oct 1998
Brown, Miss Kristina	G	Oct 1998
Gamble, Mr Jamie	M	Nov 1999
Denning, Ms Louisa	G	Nov 1999
Hargreaves, Ms Teresa	L	Nov 1999
Crow, Mr Charles	L	Nov 1999
Coughlan, Mr John	M	Nov 1999
Price, Mr Charles	M	Nov 1999
Barney, Miss Helen	L	Jan 1999
Butt, Miss Nassera	M	Jul 1999
Afzal, Dr Fayyaz OBE; Doctorate	L	Jan 1999
Chelvan, S	I	Oct 1999
Willets, Mr Glenn	M	Nov 2000
Chawla, Mr Neil	I	Jan 2000
Wigley, Miss Jenny	M	Nov 2000
Ensaff, Mr Omar Sherif	G	Oct 2000
Abberley, Mr Stephen	M	Nov 2000
Evans, Mr Paul	I	Jan 2001
Heeley, Ms Michelle	G	Jan 2001
Beloff, Mr Rupert	G	Jan 2001
Forster, Ms Bridget	I	Jan 2001
Brown, Ms Emma	I	Jan 2001
Wingrave, Mr Michael	M	Jul 2001
Pole, Mr Tim	M	Jul 2001
Schofield, Mr Thomas	L	Oct 2001
Chaffin-Laird, Miss Olivia	G	Jul 2001
Adkinson, Mr Richard	M	Jul 2001
Dixon, Mr James	L	Jan 2001
Mantle, Mr Philip	L	Jan 2002
Clifford, Miss Victoria	G	Jul 2002
Bradshaw, Mr Mark	G	Jul 2002
Kurji, Miss Fatim*	I	Jan 2003
Arthur, Mrs Helen	M	Oct 2003
Oscroft, Mr Daniel	M	Nov 2003
Pinnock, Mr Earl	M	Nov 2003
Owen, Miss Denise	G	Oct 2003
van Overdijk, Mrs Claire	L	Jan 2003
Cobill, Mr Nicholas	M	Jan 2003
Deacon, Ms Jennifer*	I	Jul 2004
Davies, Mr Rhys	G	Oct 2004
Gupta, Miss Mamta	L	Oct 2004
Leslie, Mr James	M	Jan 2004
Williams, Mr Philip	I	Apr 2005
Allen, Miss Sarah	G	Nov 2005
Punt, Dr Jonathan	I	Jul 2005
Cooke, Mr Richard	I	Jul 2005
Grant, Miss Orla	L	Jul 2005
Sandhu, Mr Harpreet Singh	G	Jul 2005
Reed, Mr Steven	I	Jul 2005
Fernandes, Ms Suella	M	Oct 2005
Allen, Miss Juliet	G	Nov 2005
Taylor, Miss Kathryn	L	Jul 2005
Feeney, Miss Katie	I	Jul 2005
Yasseri, Miss Yasmin	I	Jul 2005
Tyers-Smith, Mr Peter	L	Nov 2005
Feeny, Mr Jack	I	Jan 2005
Roberts, Miss Gemma	G	Oct 2006
Enonchong, Prof Nelson	I	Jan 2006
Yates, Miss Victoria	M	Nov 2006
Gallacher, Kirsty	G	Nov 2006
Hunka, Mr Simon	M	Jul 2007
Smyth, Mr Jack	M	Oct 2007
Oakes, Mr Richard	M	Oct 2007
Meager, Ms Rowena	L	Jul 2007
Pye, Mr Derek	L	Jul 2008
Corfield, Miss Louise	I	Oct 2008
Williams, Hermione	M	Jan 2008
Osmund-Smith, Miss Thea	I	Jan 2010

Chambers of John Hendy QC

OLD SQUARE CHAMBERS,
3 ORCHARD COURT, ST AUGUSTINES YARD, BRISTOL BS1 5DP
Tel: 0117 930 5100 ***Fax:*** 0117 927 3478
Dx: 78229 BRISTOL 1
E-mail: clerks@oldsquare.co.uk
Clerk: Senior: William Meade. Clerks: Oliver Parkhouse; James Wilkinson; Laurence Willicombe.
Head of Chambers:

Name	Inn	Date
Hendy, Mr John (Q.C.); Bencher, Gray's Inn	G	Jul 1971
Reynold, Mr Frederic (Q.C.); Bencher, Gray's Inn	G	Jul 1960
Hand, Mr John (Q.C.); Recorder; Bencher,Gray's Inn	G	Jul 1972
Truscott, Mr Ian (Q.C.)	G	Nov 1995
Wilby, Mr David C (Q.C.); Recorder	I	Jul 1974
Cooksley, Mr Nigel (Q.C.); Chairman of BAR Council CFA Panel	I	Jul 1975
Rose, Mr Paul (Q.C.)	G	Nov 1981
McNeill, Ms Jane (Q.C.); Part-Time Employment Tribunal Chair	L	Nov 1982
Gilroy, Mr Paul (Q.C.)	G	Jul 1985
Eady, Ms Jennifer (Q.C.); Part-Time Employment Tribunal Chair	I	Jul 1989
Sutton, Mr Mark (Q.C.); Employment Tribunal: Part-time Chairman	M	Jul 1982
Gorton, Simon (Q.C.)	I	Jul 1988
Segal, Mr Oliver (Q.C.)	M	Oct 1992
Upex, Prof Robert	M	Jul 1973
Brahams, Ms Diana	M	Jul 1972
Bates, Mr John H	M	Jul 1973
Makey, Mr Christopher	M	Jul 1975
Pugh, Mr Charles	G	Jan 1975
Kempster, Mr Toby	I	Jul 1980
Smith, Mr Alan Arthur	M	Jul 1981
Chudleigh, Ms Louise; Part-Time Employment Tribunal Chair	L	Jul 1987
Omambala, Ijeoma	G	Apr 1989
Mead, Mr Philip	L	Jul 1989
Gill, Ms Tess; Part-Time Employment Tribunal Chair	L	Feb 1990
Clarke, Mr Jonathan	M	Oct 1990
Walker, Mr Christopher D B	M	Nov 1990
Scott, Mr Ian	L	Oct 1991
Booth, Mr Nicholas	M	Sep 1991
Cheetham, Mr Simon	M	Nov 1991
Lewis, Prof Roy; Employment Tribunal Part-Time Chairman	L	May 1992
Ford, Mr Michael	M	Jul 1992
Cummins, Mr Brian Dominic	M	Nov 1992
Gower, Ms Helen	M	Oct 1992
Galloway, Mr Malcolm	I	Oct 1992
Panesar, Mr Deshpal Singh	I	Jan 1993
Nicholson, Mr Michael	M	Jan 1993
Howells, Miss Katherine	G	Oct 1994
Melville, Miss Elizabeth E J	G	Oct 1994
Whitcombe, Mr Mark D	M	Nov 1994
Tether, Ms Melanie	G	Nov 1995
Pirani, Mr Rohan C	M	Oct 1995
Smith, Miss Emma	L	Oct 1995
Woodhouse, Mr Charles	M	Oct 1997
Tuck, Miss Rebecca L	G	Oct 1998
Winstone, Ms Hilary	G	Oct 1998
Newton, Miss Katharine	M	Oct 1999
Brittenden, Mr Stuart	G	Jan 1999
Palmer, Ms Anya	I	Jan 1999
McDonald, Mr Brent	G	Oct 2000
Morris, Miss Bella	M	Oct 2000
Cooper, Mr Ben	L	Nov 2000
Moretto, Mr Robert Salvatore	I	Oct 2000
Midgley, Mr Andrew	G	Oct 2000
Rivers, Mr David	G	Jan 2002
Pilgerstorfer, Mr Marcus	M	Jan 2002
Criddle, Miss Betsan	M	Oct 2002
Davies, Mr Jonathan Huw	L	Jan 2003
Samuel, Mr Adam	I	Jul 2003
Motraghi, Miss Nadia	G	Jul 2004
Freman (nee Sampson), Miss Hannah	L	Jul 2004
Risoli, Mr Andreá	G	Jan 2005
Edwards, Mr Christopher	G	Jan 2006
Fudakowski, Katherine	L	Jan 2008
Webb, Victoria	M	Jan 2009
Harris, Mr Lance	L	Jan 2011
Bennett, Hannah	M	Jan 2011
Cotter, Mr Barry (Q.C.)*	L	Jul 1985
Carling, Mr Christopher*	L	Nov 1969
Moor, Ms Sarah*	M	Oct 1991
Ferguson, Miss Corina*	L	Jul 2003

Chambers of Richard Tyson

3PB,
ROYAL TALBOT HOUSE, 2 VICTORIA STREET, BRISTOL BS1 6BN
Tel: 0117 928 1520 ***Fax:*** 0117 928 1525
Dx: 7836 BRISTOL
E-mail: clerks.all@3paper.co.uk
Clerk: Mark Heath (Senior Clerk); Tom Cox; Philippa Caine.
Administrator: Neil Monro (Head of Business Administration and Finance)
Practice Manager: Stephen Evers (Practice Development Clerk)
Chambers Director: Stephen Clark (Head of Clerking); Charles Charlick (Consultant Clerk)
Head of Chambers:

Name	Inn	Date
Tyson, Mr Richard	I	Nov 1975
Newman, Mr Paul	G	Jan 1982
Zabihi, Mrs Tanya	G	Jun 1988
Jones, Miss Victoria	L	Oct 2003
Anderson, Ms Katherine	I	Jan 2005

11

Clarke, Ms Sarah ... I ... Jan 2005
Cannings, Mr Matthew ... M ... Jan 2006
Frost, Ms Nicola ... I ... Jan 2009

Chambers of Christopher Taylor

QUEEN SQUARE CHAMBERS,
56 QUEEN SQUARE, BRISTOL BS1 4PR
Tel: 0117 921 1966 ***Fax:*** 0117 927 6493
Dx: 7870 BRISTOL
E-mail: civil@qs-c.co.uk
Clerk: Senior: Steve Freeman.
Practice Manager: Steve Freeman
Head of Chambers:
Taylor, Mr Christopher ... G ... Nov 1982

Jenkins, Mr T Alun (Q.C.); Recorder ... L ... Jul 1972
Levy, Mr Robert (Q.C.) ... M ... Jan 2003
Martin, Mr David ... I ... Oct 1969
Threlfall, Mr George ... G ... Jan 1972
Darian, Mrs Ann ... M ... Jul 1974
Halden, Mr Angus Robert ... M ... Oct 1999
Rea, Ms Karen; Deputy District Judge; Legal Chairman FHSAA ... G ... Jul 1980
Roberts, Mr Stephen ... L ... Jan 2002
Butterfield, Ms Kay ... G ... Jan 1980
Warren, Mr Philip ... G ... May 1988
Smyth, Mr Christopher ... G ... Jan 2006
Goodall, Mr Charles ... I ... Jul 1986
Matthews, Ms Lynne ... I ... Nov 1987
Halliday, Mr Ian Nicolas ... L ... Nov 1989
Smith, Mr Nicholas ... L ... Oct 1990
Barlow, Miss Melissa E B ... M ... Oct 1991
Carron, Mr Richard ... M ... Oct 1992
Shellard, Mr Robin ... I ... Nov 1992
Maunder, Mr David ... M ... Dec 1993
Richards, Mr Stephan ... M ... May 1993
Row, Mr Charles ... L ... Oct 1993
Dennis, Ms Rebecca ... I ... Nov 1993
Goodman, Mr Simon ... G ... Nov 1996
Grennan, Ms Debbie ... G ... Oct 1997
Walsh, Mr Darren ... I ... Oct 1997
Williams, Mr Mark ... G ... Oct 1998
Allsop, Mr Julian E ... L ... Oct 1999
Frazer, Miss Alison ... G ... Oct 1999
Fryer, Mr Nigel ... M ... Nov 1999
Gohil, Ms Pushpanjali ... M ... Jul 2000
Armstrong, Miss Ruth Elizabeth ... I ... Nov 2001
Willmott, Mr Oliver ... M ... Jan 2002
Elford, Ms Caroline ... I ... Jan 2002
Farquhar, Ms Fiona ... I ... Jan 2002
McBeam, Mr Hamish ... L ... Jan 2002
Leach, Mr Douglas ... I ... Jan 2003
Lucas, Ms Joanna ... G ... Jan 2004
Lewis, Ms Joanna ... M ... Jan 2004
Heard, Mr Jonathan ... M ... Jan 2004
Tucker, Mr James ... G ... Oct 2004
Roberts, Mr Allan ... M ... Jan 2004
Walsh, Ms Rosie ... M ... Jan 2006
Byrne, Mr James ... L ... Jan 2006
Graham, Mr Gareth ... M ... Jan 2006
Tibbitts, Mr Simon ... I ... Jan 2006
Gardiner, Ms Kerry ... M ... Jan 2006
Darian, Ms Alice ... M ... Jan 2006
Lay, Ms Georgia ... L ... Jan 2007
Jennings, Ms Sarah ... L ... Jan 2009
Pascoe, Mr Nigel (Q.C.)* ... I ... Jul 1966
Donne, Mr Anthony M (Q.C.); Recorder* ... M ... Apr 1973
Keehan, Mr Michael (Q.C.)* ... M ... Jul 1982
Johnston, Ms Carey (Q.C.)* ... M ... Jul 1977

Chambers of Richard Stead

ST JOHN'S CHAMBERS,
101 VICTORIA STREET, BRISTOL BS1 6PU
Tel: 0117 921 3456 ***Fax:*** 0117 929 4821
Dx: 743350 BRISTOL 36
E-mail: clerks@stjohnschambers.co.uk
Administrator: Client Development Manager: Sarah Tune
Practice Manager: Annette Bushell; Robert Bocock; Luke Hodgson
Chambers Director: Derek Jenkins
Head of Chambers:
Stead, Mr Richard ... M ... Jul 1979

Sharp, Mr Christopher (Q.C.) ... I ... Jul 1975
Tolson, Mr Robin Stewart (Q.C.) ... I ... Nov 1980
Jacklin, Miss Susan (Q.C.) ... I ... Nov 1980
Blohm, Mr Leslie (Q.C.) ... L ... Jul 1982
Fletcher, Mr David H ... G ... Jul 1971
Bullock, Mr Ian ... I ... Nov 1975
Grice, Mr Timothy James ... M ... Jul 1975
Corfield, Miss Sheelagh ... M ... Jul 1975
Blackmore, Mr John ... I ... May 1983
Neill, Mr Robin ... G ... Jul 1979
Auld, Mr Charles ... M ... Dec 1980
Wadsley, Mr Peter ... M ... Jun 1984
Duthie, Miss Catriona ... I ... Jul 1981
Hunter, Miss Susan ... I ... Jul 1985
Miller, Mr Nicholas ... I ... Jul 1994
Maher, Mrs Martha ... I ... Jan 1987
Edwards, Mr Glyn ... I ... Jul 1987
Morgan, Mr Simon ... G ... Nov 1988
O'Neill, Ms Louise ... G ... Feb 1989
Adams, Mr Guy ... M ... Jul 1989
Marsden, Mr Andrew ... L ... May 1994
Das, Miss Kamala ... M ... Nov 1975
Sharples, Mr John ... M ... Nov 1992
Kearney, Mr Andrew ... I ... Jan 2007
Leeper, Mr Thomas R G ... M ... Nov 1991
Martin, Ms Dianne ... G ... Jun 1992
Light, Prof Roy ... G ... Oct 1992
Skellorn, Ms Kathryn ... G ... Nov 1993
McLaughlin, Mr Andrew ... M ... Nov 1993
Maxwell, Mr Adrian Robert ... M ... Jan 1993
Humphreys, Miss Jacqueline ... L ... Oct 1994
Phillimore, Ms Sarah ... L ... Oct 1994
Regan, Mr David ... I ... Nov 1994
Pearce-Smith, Mr James ... I ... Jan 2002
Dickinson, Mr John ... M ... Oct 1995
Evans, Ms Judi ... M ... Nov 1996
White, Mr Matthew J ... G ... Oct 1997
Moradifar, Mr Kambiz ... G ... Nov 1998
Zeb, Miss Emma ... I ... Jul 1998
Horne, Mr Julian ... M ... Nov 1998
Troup, Mr Alex ... G ... Nov 1998
Bond, Ms Abigail Rachel ... M ... Oct 1999
Thornton, Mrs Delia ... L ... Oct 1999
Mashembo, Mrs Carol ... L ... Oct 1999
McKinlay, Miss Vanessa Jane ... M ... Oct 2000
Hussain, Mr Zahid ... L ... Jan 2001
Russell, Ms Rachel ... G ... Oct 2001
Symington, Ms Anna ... I ... Oct 2002
Cope, Ms Stephanie ... L ... Jan 2008
Reed, Mrs Lucy ... L ... Oct 2002
Belyavin, Ms Julia ... G ... Mar 2003
Saunders, Miss Zoe ... G ... Oct 2003
Taylor, Miss Rebecca ... L ... Nov 2003
Jenkins, Mr Philip ... M ... Jan 2003
Jones, Mr Christopher ... G ... Jul 2004
Lewis, Mr Darren Eurwyn ... I ... Oct 2004
Commins, Mr Andrew ... M ... Oct 2004
Rowell, Mr George ... L ... Jan 2004
Atkinson, Mr Jody Roy ... I ... Jul 2005
Gold, Mr Richard ... I ... Nov 2006
Knapton, Ms Sarah ... M ... Jun 2007
Lewis, Paul ... M ... Jul 2007
West, Mr Patrick ... L ... Jan 2007
Coventry, Mr Charles ... G ... Jan 2007
Dunkerton, Mrs Katie ... L ... Jul 2008
Clarke, Mr Michael ... L ... Jan 2009
Norman, Mr Richard ... G ... Jan 2009
Leonard, Miss Claire ... I ... Jan 2009
Wooding, Mr Oliver ... M ... Jan 2009

Chambers of John Isherwood

UNITY STREET CHAMBERS,
5 UNITY STREET, COLLEGE GREEN, BRISTOL BS1 5HH
Tel: 0117 906 9789 ***Fax:*** 0117 906 9799
Dx: 7868 BRISTOL
Clerk: Clair Wadden.
Head of Chambers:
Isherwood, Mr John ... G ... Jul 1978

Tackaberry, Mr John (Q.C.); Recorder ... G ... Jul 1967
Vere-Hodge, Mr Michael (Q.C.); Recorder ... G ... Nov 1970
Ferguson, Mr Christopher Mark ... M ... May 1979
Curwen, Mr David ... G ... Jul 1982
Wightwick, Mr Iain ... I ... Nov 1985
Langlois, Mr Peter John ... L ... Oct 1991
Halliwell, Mr Toby ... M ... Nov 1992
Dawson, Miss Judy ... G ... Oct 1993
Stanniland, Mr Jonathan ... I ... Nov 1993
Currie, Mr Fergus ... G ... Mar 1997
Boyd, Miss Sarah ... G ... Oct 1998
Huggins, Mr Toby ... M ... Oct 1998
Cameron-Mowatt, Mrs Rosalind ... M ... Jul 2000
Hurrion, Miss Sarah-Jane ... G ... Jul 2000

BROMLEY, Kent

Chambers of N McMurray

MCMURRAY CHAMBERS,
274 FOOTSCRAY ROAD, NEW ELTHAM, BROMLEY, KENT SE9 2EJ
Tel: 020 7566 8244
Head of Chambers:
McMurray, Ms N ... M ... Jun 2001

SUNDRIDGE CHAMBERS,
10 SUNDRIDGE HOUSE, BURNT ASH LANE, BROMLEY, KENT BR1 5AE
Tel: 020 8464 9772 ***Fax:*** 020 8460 3603
E-mail: clerksroom@sundridgechambers.com
Clerk: Tony Greenwood.

BURY, Greater Manchester

Chambers of Farooq Ahmad Chaudhry

10 SPRINGWATER AVENUE,
HOLCONBE BROOK, BURY, GREATER MANCHESTER BL0 9RH
Tel: 01204 886883 ***Fax:*** 01204 886738
E-mail: chaudhry_7a@yahoo.co.uk
Clerk: Rubina Farook.
Head of Chambers:
Chaudhry, Dr Farooq Ahmad ... L ... Jul 1970

CAMBRIDGE, Cambridgeshire

Chambers of Martin Collier

FENNERS CHAMBERS,
3 MADINGLEY ROAD, CAMBRIDGE, CAMBRIDGESHIRE CB3 0EE
Tel: 01223 368761 ***Fax:*** 01223 313007
Dx: 5809 CAMBRIDGE
E-mail: clerks@fennerschambers.com
Clerk: Paul Green.
Administrator: Sharon Bannerman
Head of Chambers:
Collier, Mr Martin ... G ... Jul 1982

Jones, Mr Geraint Martyn; Chairman Rent Assessment Committee ... G ... Nov 1972
Gore, Mr Andrew Roger; Deputy Chairman Agricultural Lands Tribunal ... M ... Nov 1973
Davies, Miss Lindsay Jane; Assistant Recorder ... G ... Jul 1975
Espley, Miss Susan ... G ... Jul 1976
Tattersall, Mr Simon Mark Rogers; Deputy District Judge ... M ... Nov 1977
Brown, Tim C E ... G ... Nov 1980
Bennington, Ms Jane ... G ... Jul 1981
Hollow, Mr Paul John; Deputy District Judge ... G ... Nov 1981
Gold, Ms Debra ... M ... Jul 1985
Taylor, Miss Araba Arba Kurankyiwa ... M ... Jul 1985
Howard, Mr Robin William John ... M ... Jan 1986
Willis, Miss Pearl ... I ... Jul 1986
Sutton, Mr Clive ... I ... Jul 1987
Hughes, Miss Meryl Elizabeth ... G ... Nov 1987
Wilson, Mr Alasdair John ... G ... Nov 1988
Pithers, Mr Clive Robert ... G ... Feb 1989
Deegan, Mr Jeffrey ... I ... Jul 1989
Saunders, Mr Nicholas Joseph ... M ... Jul 1989
Monnington, Mr Bruce ... I ... Sep 1989
Procter, Mr Michael ... G ... Nov 1993
Ferguson, Mrs Katharine ... I ... Feb 1995
Pitt, Mr Daniel C ... I ... Oct 1995
Vaughan, Mr Terence Paul ... M ... Oct 1996
Earle, Mr James Christopher ... G ... Oct 1996
Spinks, Mr Roderick ... I ... Jan 1997
Magee, Mr Mike ... I ... Oct 1997
Benedict, Mr Peers ... M ... Mar 1998
Owen, Mr Daniel R S ... I ... Oct 1999
Sims, Mr Guy ... I ... Jul 2000
Bruce, Mr Lawrence ... L ... Nov 2000
Gribbin, Mr Liam ... I ... Jul 2001
Allison, Miss Caroline ... L ... Jul 2002
Williams, Mr Timothy ... M ... Nov 2003
Mussa, Miss Azreen ... M ... Oct 2003
Grewcock, Miss Penelope ... M ... Oct 2004
Snelling, Mr Charles William ... M ... Oct 2005
Bain, Mr Iain ... M ... Jan 2007
Urwin, Mr Tom ... M ... Jan 2007
Coccaro, Mr Carlo Eduardo ... L ... Jul 2007
Davies, Mr Nicholas ... L ... Jul 2007
Cooper, Ms Samantha ... G ... Oct 2007
Pilkington, Miss Abigail Jane ... I ... Jul 2008
Masters, Mr Jonathan ... M ... Jan 2009

CANTERBURY, Kent

BECKET CHAMBERS,
17 NEW DOVER ROAD, CANTERBURY, KENT CT1 3AS
Tel: 01227 786331 ***Fax:*** 01227 786329
Dx: 5330 CANTERBURY
E-mail: clerks@becket-chambers.co.uk
Clerk: Senior: Paul Eaton.
Kee, Mr Peter William ... M ... Jul 1983
Newton, Mr Philip ... M ... Jul 1984
Edginton, Mr Horace Ronald ... G ... Nov 1984
Jackson, Mr Kevin ... M ... Nov 1984
Wall, Mr Christopher ... L ... Nov 1987
Mills, Corey ... M ... Nov 1987
Hall, Mr Jeremy J ... G ... Feb 1988
Styles, Mr Clive R ... G ... Oct 1990
Tapsell, Mr Paul ... M ... Oct 1991
Adamson, Ms Lilias L ... G ... Nov 1994
Fairbank, Mr Nicholas ... L ... Nov 1996
McIntosh, Miss Melanie ... L ... Sep 2002
Murkin, Ms Sandria ... I ... Oct 2004
Andrews, Miss Melanie Alexandra ... M ... Jan 2005
Coates, Miss Holly ... L ... Oct 2008
Kenny, Mr Edward ... M ... Jan 2009
Thistle, Mr Dean Terence ... L ... Dec 2010
Bartlett, Mr Andrew V B (Q.C.)* ... M ... Jul 1974

Chambers of Sita Cox

STOUR CHAMBERS,
MILL STUDIO, 17A STOUR STREET, CANTERBURY, KENT CT1 2NR
Tel: 01227 764899 ***Fax:*** 01227 764941
Dx: 5342 CANTERBURY
E-mail: clerks@stourchambers.co.uk
Clerk: Senior: Marc Goddard. 1st Junior: Jennifer Rees; Junior: John Parkinson.
Head of Chambers:
Cox, Miss Sita ... M ... Nov 1987

Hendry, Mrs Sandra ... G ... Nov 1985
Johnson, Mr Simon ... G ... Jul 1987
Batey, Mr Michael; Deputy District Judge ... G ... Jul 1989
Pearson, Miss Carolyn ... G ... Nov 1990
Buckley, Miss Gerardine Maria ... G ... Nov 1991
Farrington, Ms Gemma ... G ... Oct 1994
Clegg, Mr Adam ... G ... Nov 1994
Monday, Ms Martha ... M ... Oct 1998
Bragge, Mr Thomas Herewad ... I ... Jul 2000
Beach, Mrs Fiona ... L ... Oct 2001
Thornton, Mr John Robert ... G ... Jun 2002
Hutchings, Mr Mark ... G ... Jan 2005
Spence, Ms Elizabeth ... G ... Jul 2006
Slee, Lydia ... M ... Jan 2007
Kochnari, Kate ... I ... Jan 2008
Porter, Ms Joanne Emily ... I ... Nov 2010
Pulman, Mr George F (Q.C.)* ... M ... Jul 1972
Thompson, Polly* ... M ... Nov 1990
Pines Richman, Ms Helene* ... M ... Jul 1992
Weir, Mr Darren* ... M ... Oct 1998
Charleton, Miss Laura* ... G ... Jul 2002

CARDIFF

APEX CHAMBERS,
33- 35 CATHEDRAL ROAD, CARDIFF CF11 9HB
Tel: 029 2023 2032 ***Fax:*** 029 2023 3636

CIVITAS LAW,
GLOBAL REACH, CELTIC GATEWAY, CARDIFF CF11 0SN
Tel: 0845 071 3007 ***Fax:*** 0845 071 3008
E-mail: clerks@civitaslaw.com
Thomas, Mr Bryan ... G ... Jul 1978
Walters, Mr Jonathan ... I ... Jul 1984
Huckle, Mr Theodore ... L ... Jul 1985
Walters, Mr Graham ... G ... Apr 1986
Jones, Mr Nicholas David ... G ... Nov 1987
Coombes Davies, Mrs Mair ... L ... Jun 1988
O'Leary, Mr Robert Michael ... I ... Oct 1990
Brace, Mr Michael Wesley ... L ... Apr 1991
Jones, Mr Gareth ... L ... Jan 1991
Vines, Mr Anthony ... G ... Nov 1993
Arentsen, Mr Andrew ... G ... Oct 1995
John, Mr Simon ... L ... Jul 1996
Williams, Ms Joanne ... I ... Oct 1999

Cole, Mr Richard	G	Oct 2000
Hughes, Mr Simon Ieuan	G	Oct 2003
Thomas-Symonds, Mr Nicklaus	L	Oct 2004
Bayoumi, Miss Mona	M	Nov 2004
Hillier, Miss Victoria Jane	G	Jul 2005
Mansell, Miss Rebecca Lily	G	Jul 2005
Amesbury, Mr Ryan	G	Jan 2007
Grubb, Miss Cathrine	M	Jan 2007

Chambers of Gregg Taylor QC

9 PARK PLACE,
9 & 10 PARK PLACE, CARDIFF CF10 3DP
Tel: 029 2038 2731 ***Fax:*** 029 2022 2542
Dx: 50751 CARDIFF 2
E-mail: clerks@9parkplace.co.uk
Clerk: James Williams; Nigel East; Lesley Haikney; Adam Marchant.
Administrator: John Sayce
Head of Chambers:

Taylor, Mr Gregg (Q.C.)	M	Jul 1974
Roddick, Mr Winston (Q.C.) CB; Recorder	G	Nov 1968
Keyser, Mr Andrew (Q.C.); Recorder	M	Nov 1986
Kelly, Mr Martyn	I	Nov 1972
Littman, Mr Jeffrey James	M	Jul 1974
Francis, Mr Richard	G	Nov 1974
Essex Williams, Mr David	M	Jul 1975
Twomlow, Mr Richard; Recorder	G	Jul 1976
Ieuan, Mr Morris	G	Jul 1979
Williams, Mr Karl	M	Jul 1982
McDonald, Ms Janet	G	Jul 1984
Lewis, Mr Owen P	M	Jul 1985
Ferrier, Ms Susan	G	Jul 1985
Brooks, Mr Peter	G	Jul 1986
Hopkins, Mr Paul A	G	Jul 1989
Bennett, Mr Ieuan	M	Jul 1989
Davies, Ms Emily J	G	Nov 1989
Withers, Ms Michelle J M	I	Jul 1991
Reed, Mr Julian	I	Nov 1991
Donoghue, Mr Steven M	M	Oct 1992
Thomas, Mr Gareth	I	Oct 1993
Wallace, Mr Hugh	G	Nov 1993
Parry, Miss Sian Rachel	G	Oct 1994
Thomas, Mr Owen	G	Oct 1994
Roberts, Mr Matthew J P	G	Oct 1994
Kember, Mr Richard	M	Oct 1993
Ace, Mr Richard	L	Oct 1993
Elias, Mr David	I	Nov 1994
Hughes, Mr Y Gwydion	G	Nov 1994
Davies, Mr Peter	L	Oct 1996
Edwards, Mr Heath	G	Nov 1996
Felstead, Mr Christopher	L	Oct 1998
Thomas, Ms Lisa	M	Oct 1998
Cobbe, Mr Matthew	G	Oct 1998
Gobir, Nuhu	M	Oct 1998
Jones, Mr Emyr	G	Oct 1999
Pearson, Ms Elizabeth Anne	I	Oct 1999
Williams, Mr Owen	G	Sep 2000
Hammett, Mr Michael	G	Nov 2001
Barry, Mr Matthew	G	Oct 2002
Vernon, Mr Robert	L	Nov 2002
Morris, Mr Phillip	G	Jul 2003
Broadhurst, Miss Katherine	G	Jul 2003
Roddick, Miss Helen	G	Jul 2004
Tuttiett, Miss Emily	G	Oct 2004
Amos, Mr Justin Edward	G	Mar 2005
Moelwyn-Williams, Miss Anna Charlotte	G	Jul 2006
Horsham, Miss Irene Ansa-Asare	L	Jul 2004
Seagrim, Mr William	G	Jul 2007
Williams, Miss Carys Ellen	G	Oct 2007
Evans, Mr David Gareth Evan	G	Jul 2008
Murphy, Mr Ian (Q.C.); Recorder; Bencher*	M	Jul 1972
Thomas, Mr Roger (Q.C.); Recorder*	G	Jul 1969

Chambers of Jonathan Furness QC

THIRTY PARK PLACE,
CARDIFF CF10 3BS
Tel: 029 2039 8421 ***Fax:*** 029 2039 8725
Dx: 50756 CARDIFF 2
E-mail: clerks@30parkplace.co.uk
Clerk: Senior: Phil Griffiths.
Administrator: Hugh Wakins
Head of Chambers:

Furness, Mr Jonathan (Q.C.); Recorder	G	Jun 1979
Bishop, Mr Malcolm (Q.C.); Deputy High Court Judge; Recorder	I	Jul 1968
Griffiths, Mr J Peter (Q.C.); Recorder	G	Oct 1970
Crowley, Mrs Jane (Q.C.); Recorder; Deputy High Court Judge	G	Jul 1976
Lewis, Mr Paul Keith (Q.C.); Recorder	G	Feb 1981
Tillyard, Mr James H H (Q.C.); Recorder	M	Jun 1978
Murphy, Mr Peter John (Q.C.); Recorder	G	May 1980
Williams, Mr Lloyd (Q.C.); Recorder	I	Jul 1981
Henke, Ms Ruth Sara Margaret (Q.C.)	I	Nov 1987
Williams, Mr Rhodri (Q.C.)	G	Jul 1987
Parry-Evans, Ms Mary	I	Jun 1953
Parsley, Mr Charles Ronald	I	Jul 1973
Green, Mr Andrew	G	Jul 1974
Treharne, Miss Jennet	M	Oct 1975
Hartley-Davies, Mr Paul Kevil; Recorder	G	Jul 1977
Lewis, Miss Marian	M	Nov 1977
Mather-Lees, Mr Michael Anthony	I	Feb 1981
Allen, Mr Mark Graham	M	Jul 1981
Taylor, Mr Andrew	G	Jan 1984
Evans, Mr Huw David	I	Jul 1985
Harrison, Mr Robert John McIntosh	L	Feb 1988
Lloyd-Nesling, Miss Tracey	M	Jul 1988
Philpotts, Mr Robert John; Recorder	G	Oct 1990
Jonathan-Jones, Mr Gareth	I	Jan 1991
Withers, Ms Michelle J M	I	Jul 1991
Heyworth, Ms Catherine Louise	I	Nov 1991
John, Miss Emma Catrin	G	Jun 1992
Hughes, Miss Kathryn Ann	I	Nov 1992
Egan, Mr Eugene	I	Oct 1993
McGahey, Ms Elizabeth	I	Oct 1994
Rees, Ms Caroline	G	Oct 1994
Hughes, Mr Hywel	G	Nov 1995
Jones, Mr Andrew	I	Oct 1996
Harrison, Mr Carl	G	Nov 1997
Hughes, Mr David Gordon	M	Jan 1997
Edmondson, Miss Harriet	G	Nov 1997
Davies, Mr Benjamin Guy	L	Oct 1999
Waters, Ms Sarah	M	Oct 1999
Holmes, Mr Jon A	G	Oct 1999
Morse, Mr Andrew Philip Richard	G	Jul 2000
Sandercock, Ms Natalie	M	Sep 2000
Davies, Miss Angharad	L	Oct 2000
Kirby, Miss Rhian Faith	L	Oct 2000
Morgan, Miss Katie	I	Aug 2002
Jones, Mr Jeffrey	G	Jul 2003
Harrington, Miss Rebecca	G	Jan 2004
Joseph, Mr Andrew	G	Jan 2004
Williams, Miss Claire	G	Jan 2004
Garrett, Mr Luke	G	Jul 2005
Manley, Mr Oliver	G	Jul 2005
Sutton, Ms Emma	G	Jan 2006
Puar, Mr Mikhael	G	Jan 2006
Howells, Mr Christian James	I	Jul 2007
Stickler, Miss Rebecca	M	Oct 2007
Al-Khayat, Mr Joe	I	Jan 2008
Pike, Olivia	M	Jan 2008
Jones, Mr Nathan Richard	L	Jul 2008
Jones, Miss Rhian	G	Jul 2008
Evans, Mr Rhys	G	Jan 2010
Duncan, Mr Gareth	L	Jan 2010

Chambers of Hilary Roberts

TEMPLE CHAMBERS,
32 PARK PLACE, CARDIFF CF10 3BA
Tel: 029 2039 7364 ***Fax:*** 029 2023 8423
Dx: 50769 CARDIFF 2
E-mail: dbrinning@temple-chambers.co.uk
Clerk: Seniors: David Brinning; Family: Helen Dench; Nicola Morgan; Claire Bater. Criminal & Civil: Tony Naylon; Emma King.
Administrator: John Garlick
Head of Chambers:

Roberts, Mr Hilary	G	Nov 1978
Aubrey, Mr David J M (Q.C.); Recorder	M	Jul 1976
Davies, Mr J Meirion	G	Jul 1975
McKay, Mr Christopher; Deputy District Judge (Civil)	G	Nov 1976
Griffiths, Mr Roger V	G	Jul 1983
Morgan, Ms Lynne; Recorder (Family Law)	M	Jul 1984
Jeary, Mr Stephen	I	Jul 1987
Rowley, Miss Jane	G	Jul 1988
Hughes, Leighton; Part-Time Chairman SSAT	I	Jul 1989
Miller, Mr Richard James	G	Oct 1991
Powell, Mr Bernard Hilson	G	Oct 1991
Thomas, Mr Steven	G	Feb 1993
Webster, Mr David; Deputy District Judge (Criminal)	G	Nov 1993
Foulser-McFarlane, Ms Jane; Lead Counsel to Welsh Assembly Govt on IP	G	Jan 1994
Thomas, Ms Christina	I	Feb 1994
Gibbon, Ms Juliet; Legal Advisor to Care Counsel for Wales; And NMC	L	Jan 1994
Owen, Ms Sara	I	Oct 1995
Taylor, Mr Rhys; Part-Time Chairman of Residential Property Tribunal	I	Nov 1996
Jones, Mr Laurence	G	Oct 1997
Jones, Mr Steffan R	G	Nov 1997
Seal, Mr Kevin	G	Jan 1998
Douglas, Mr Colin	L	Oct 1998
Hawkins, Mr Robert	L	Jan 1998
Abbott, Ms Christine	M	Oct 1999
Lucas, Ms Felicie	M	Oct 1999
Jowett, Mr Christian	G	Oct 1999
Pickthall, Ms Claire	G	Nov 1999
Williams, Mr Eifion	G	Oct 2000
Barcello, Mr Andrew	L	Mar 2001
Evans, Mr James	L	Jul 2002
Broadstock, Mr Byron	G	Nov 2002
Nixon, Ms Elaine	L	Jul 2003
Radcliffe, Ms Sheila Mary	M	Jul 2003
Bennett, Miss Marianne	I	Oct 2003
North, Ms Claire	I	Oct 2003
Salmman, Mr Hashim	L	Jan 2005
Davies, Mr Max	M	Oct 2005
Moore, Mr Guy	G	Jul 2006
Dieu, Mr Hoa	G	Jan 2006
Daniel, Ms Hayley	I	Jan 2007
Pinnell, Mr David	G	Mar 2008
Underhill, Mr Jonathan	I	Jan 2008
Ahmadi, Ms Hannah	G	Jan 2009
Fear, Ms Claire	M	Jan 2010

CARMARTHEN, Carmarthenshire

VICTORY CHAMBERS,
DAN-Y-COED, NEW MILL, ST CLEARS, CARMARTHEN, CARMARTHENSHIRE SA33 4HS
Tel: 01994 231704 ***Fax:*** 01994 231689
E-mail: legaleyes@btinternet.com
Clerk: Marian Folland.

Folland, Mr David	L	Jan 1976

CARSHALTON, Surrey

146 CARSHALTON PARK ROAD,
CARSHALTON, SURREY SM5 3SG
Tel: 020 8773 0531 ***Fax:*** 020 8773 0531

CHELMSFORD, Essex

EAST ANGLIAN CHAMBERS,
140 NEW LONDON ROAD, CHELMSFORD, ESSEX CM2 0AW
Tel: 01245 215660 ***Fax:*** 01245 215661
Dx: 89714 CHELMSFORD 2
E-mail: chelmsford@ealaw.co.uk
Clerk: Fraser McLaren; Deputy Senior: Alison Scanes.
Administrator: Carol Bull (Head of Administration)

Akast, Mr John F; Recorder	I	Nov 1968
Wardlow, Mr John; Recorder	G	Jul 1971
Bryan, Mr Rex; Recorder	L	Nov 1971
Waters, Mr John Clough; Pupil Supervisor	L	May 1974
Marsden, Mr Andrew; Recorder; Pupil Supervisor	M	Jul 1975
Bryant, Ms Caroline; Pupil Supervisor	M	Jul 1976
Sinclair, Mr Graham; Part time Chairman LVTRAC	G	Jul 1979
Hamey, Mr John	I	Jul 1979
Brooke-Smith, Mr John; Recorder; Pupil Supervisor	G	Jul 1981
Redmayne, Mr Simon	I	Jul 1982
Lane, Mr Michael	M	Jul 1983
Bettle, Ms Janet; Pupil Supervisor	I	Jul 1985
Elcombe, Mr Nicholas; Pupil Supervisor	I	Jul 1987
Capon, Mr Philip; Pupil Supervisor	I	Oct 1990
Watson, Ms Claire; Pupil Supervisor	L	Nov 1991
Butcher, Mr Russell Henry	M	Oct 1992
Parry-Jones, Ms Carole Ann	M	Nov 1992
Barratt, Mr Dominic Anthony Richard; Pupil Supervisor	G	Nov 1992
Walsh, Ms Patricia C	L	Nov 1993
Kelly, Mr Richard	G	Oct 1994
Wheetman, Mr Alan	M	Oct 1995
Freeman, Ms Sally Jane; Pupil Supervisor	L	Nov 1995
Wood, Mr Richard	G	Nov 1995
Underhill, Ms Allison	G	Oct 1997
Goodfellow, Mr Stephen	M	Nov 1997
Ashley, Mr Neil	L	Mar 1999
Korniej, Ms Rebekah	M	Oct 1999
Bradbury, Ms Joanna	M	Nov 1999
Harvey, Miss Shona	M	Nov 1999
Hayes, Ms Christine	M	Nov 1999
Pigram, Mr Christopher Stuart; Pupil Supervisor	G	Jul 2000
O'Sullivan, Mr Richard; Pupil Supervisor	I	Jul 2000
Brown, Mr Luke Henry William	M	Oct 2000
Parnell, Ms Cherie	M	Nov 2000
Stevens, Ms Hazel	L	Jul 2001
Shirley, Ms Lynne	M	Jul 2002
Donovan, Miss Juliet	M	Jul 2002
Plant, Ms April	L	Oct 2002
Wastall, Mrs Rebecca	L	Oct 2002
Voelcker, Ms Harriet	G	Jul 2003
Michael, Mr Nicholas	M	Jul 2003
Croskell, Mr Marcus	L	Jul 2003
Miller, Miss Kate	G	Jul 2003
Wahiwala, Mr Amrik	M	Jul 2003
Martin, Miss Jade	L	Oct 2003
Dyer, Miss Shereen	L	Oct 2003
Williams, Miss Micaila	I	Jul 2004
Cattermull, Ms Emma	L	Oct 2004
Strelitz, Mr Paul	L	Nov 2005
Edwards, Mr Matthew	G	Jul 2006
White, Miss Elizabeth	L	Jul 2006
Connell, Miss Amy	M	Oct 2006
Bewley, Miss Suhayla	L	Jul 2007
Spence, Miss Gemma-Louise	L	Jul 2007
Pine, Miss Mika	M	Nov 2007
Myers, Mr Rupert	I	Nov 2008
Newton, Miss Alice	I	Jul 2009
Slaughter, Miss Jessica	M	Jul 2009
Sorel-Cameron, Mr Matthew	M	Oct 2009
Smith, Miss Fiona	G	Nov 2009
Duxbury, Sarah	M	Mar 2010
Nicklin, Mr Andrew	M	Jul 2010
Sheehan, Mr Michael	M	Oct 2010

Chambers of David Etherington QC

18 RED LION COURT (ANNEXE),
102 NEW LONDON ROAD, CHELMSFORD, ESSEX CM2 0RG
Tel: 01245 280880 ***Fax:*** 01245 280882
Dx: 139165 CHELMSFORD 11
E-mail: chelmsford@18rlc.co.uk
Web: www.18rlc.co.uk
Practice Manager: Mark Bennett (Practice Director)
Chambers Director: Elliot Perry
Head of Chambers:

Etherington, Mr David (Q.C.); Recorder	M	Nov 1979
Spencer, Sir Derek Harold (Q.C.)	G	Feb 1961
Arlidge, Mr Anthony (Q.C.)	M	Feb 1962
Cocks, Mr David (Q.C.)	L	Jun 1961
Parkins, Mr Graham (Q.C.); Recorder	I	Jul 1972
Sutton, Mr Richard (Q.C.); Recorder	M	Jul 1969
Shaw, Mr Antony (Q.C.); Recorder	M	Jul 1975
Carter, Mr Peter (Q.C.)	G	Jul 1974
Horwood-Smart, Miss Rosamund (Q.C.); Recorder	I	Jul 1974
Peters, Mr Nigel (Q.C.); Recorder	L	Jul 1976
Black, Mr John (Q.C.)	I	Jul 1975
Lynch, Miss Patricia (Q.C.); Recorder	L	Nov 1979
Benson, Mr Jeremy (Q.C.)	I	Jul 1978
Johnston, Ms Carey (Q.C.)	M	Jul 1977
Coughlin, Mr Vincent (Q.C.)	I	Jul 1980
Harvey, Mr Stephen (Q.C.)	G	Jul 1979
Lucraft, Mr Mark (Q.C.)	L	Jul 1984
Lucas, Mr Noel (Q.C.); Recorder	M	Jul 1979
Hill, Mr Max (Q.C.)	M	Nov 1987
Spence, Mr Simon (Q.C.)	I	Jul 1985
Milne, Mr Alexander (Q.C.)	G	Nov 1981
Bewsey, Miss Jane (Q.C.)	L	Jul 1986
Levett, Mr Martyn	M	Nov 1978
Pounder, Mr Gerard	L	Jul 1980
Jenkins, Miss Kim	G	Jul 1982
Tucker, Ms Lorraine	M	Nov 1982
Sheff, Miss Janine	M	Jan 1983
Shroff, Mr Cyrus	G	Jul 1983
Joshi, Mr Raj	I	Jul 1983
Morris, Mr Brendan	M	Jul 1985
Du Preez, Mr Robin	I	Nov 1985
Lyons, Mr John	M	Jul 1986
Marshall, Mr Andrew; Recorder	I	Jul 1986
Mehta, Mr Sailesh	I	Jul 1986
Dyble, Mr Steven	M	Nov 1986
Farrimond, Miss Stephanie	M	Jul 1987
Walbank, Mr David	I	Nov 1987
Collery, Mr Shane	L	Jul 1988
Hales, Ms Sally-Anne	G	Jul 1988
Beynon, Mr Richard J L	I	Jul 1990
Lawson, Miss Sara	G	Oct 1990
Holborn, Mr David	I	Oct 1991
Thompson, Mr Andrew	G	Oct 1991
Skelley, Mr Michael	I	Oct 1991
Gursoy, Mr Ramiz A	M	Nov 1991
Paxton, Mr Christopher	G	Nov 1991
Potts, Mr Richard	I	Nov 1991
Clare, Ms Allison	G	Oct 1992
Gowen, Mr Matthew	L	Oct 1992
McNiff, Mr Matthew	G	Oct 1992
Dempster, Miss Jennifer	L	Apr 1993

D'Cruz, Mr Rufus . . . L . . . Oct 1993
Forster, Mr Thomas . . . I . . . Nov 1993
May, Miss Nicola . . . G . . . Nov 1993
Jameson, Mr Barnaby . . . M . . . Nov 1993
Nelson, Miss Michelle . . . M . . . Nov 1994
Hall, Miss Jacqueline . . . L . . . Nov 1994
Wiseman, Mr Adam . . . I . . . Nov 1994
Fell, Mr Alistair . . . M . . . Nov 1994
Leigh, Ms Samantha . . . I . . . Nov 1995
Casey, Mr Noel G . . . L . . . Oct 1995
Rose, Mr Stephen . . . G . . . Nov 1995
Karmy-Jones, Miss Riel . . . L . . . Nov 1995
Jones, Ms Gillian . . . L . . . Oct 1996
Wilson, Mr David . . . G . . . Oct 1996
Pickersgill, Mr David . . . M . . . Nov 1996
Requena, Mr Stephen . . . I . . . Oct 1997
Payne, Mr Tom . . . M . . . Oct 1998
Moll, Mr Louis-Peter . . . M . . . Oct 1998
Atkins, Ms Victoria . . . M . . . Nov 1998
Chalkley, Ms Rebecca . . . M . . . Jan 1999
Rickard, Mr Marcus . . . I . . . Jul 2000
Willcocks, Miss Hannah . . . M . . . Jul 2001
Khanna, Ms Priyadarshani . . . I . . . Oct 2001
Dance, Mr Mathew . . . L . . . Jul 2001
Owen, Miss Carys . . . L . . . Oct 2002
Hamid, Ms Ruby . . . L . . . Nov 2002
Islam, Mr Mohammad . . . M . . . Oct 2002
Sawyer, Mr Jamie . . . I . . . Oct 2003
Gargitter, Ms Emma . . . L . . . Nov 2003
Eales, Miss Hannah . . . M . . . Nov 2003
Orr, Mr Matthew . . . L . . . Oct 2004
Oldfield, Ms Jane . . . M . . . Oct 2004
Baines, Mr Max . . . L . . . Mar 2005
Archer, Mr Trevor . . . I . . . Jul 2005
Mahmutaj, Miss Klentiana . . . M . . . Jul 2005
Lewis, Miss Sarah . . . M . . . Jul 2006
Chibafa, Mr Jonathan . . . M . . . Nov 2006
Parsons, Miss Naomi . . . I . . . Oct 2008
Claxton, Mr David . . . M . . . Oct 2008
Dite, Mr Alexis . . . I . . . Nov 2008
Kingswell, Miss Gemma . . . I . . . Jul 2008
Hennessy, Ms Clare . . . G . . . Jul 2009
Kenyon, Ms Laura . . . I . . . Nov 2009
Robinson, Mr Daniel . . . G . . . Jul 2010

Chambers of Lorraine Webb

ROXWELL CHAMBERS,
DUKES MANOR, THE STREET, ROXWELL, CHELMSFORD, ESSEX CM1 4PE
Tel: 01245 248341
E-mail: lorrainewebbbarrister@yahoo.co.uk
Head of Chambers:
Webb, Miss Lorraine . . . M . . . Jul 1980

Chambers of Tina Amanda Harrington

TRINITY CHAMBERS,
HIGHFIELD HOUSE, MOULSHAM STREET, CHELMSFORD, ESSEX CM2 9AH
Tel: 01245 605040 ***Fax:*** 01245 605041
Dx: 89725 CHELMSFORD 2
E-mail: clerks@trinitychambers.law.co.uk
Web: www.trinitychambers.com
Clerk: Keith Patrick Willmore; Tony Sleigh.
Head of Chambers:
Harrington, Miss Tina Amanda . . . M . . . Oct 1985

Harper, Mr Joseph (Q.C.)* . . . G . . . Jul 1970
Dagg, Mr John D . . . M . . . Jul 1980
Twydell, Ms Cherry . . . M . . . Jun 1985
Williams, Miss Anna . . . G . . . Nov 1990
Bailey, Mr Andrew . . . L . . . Oct 1993
Spratt-Dawson, Ms Josephine . . . G . . . Oct 1993
Simison, Mr Jeremy Charles . . . I . . . Oct 1993
Wickins, Miss Stefanie . . . L . . . Nov 1994
O'Brien, Mr David . . . M . . . Nov 1994
Cade, Mrs Diana . . . I . . . Nov 1994
Green, Mr William* . . . M . . . Jul 1998
Attridge, Mr Daniel . . . M . . . Nov 2000
Richardson, Mr Grahame . . . M . . . Jul 2001
Wilkinson, Miss Tiffany . . . I . . . Nov 2003
Lambert, Mrs Alison . . . M . . . Jul 2005
Lucey, Miss Anne-Marie . . . M . . . Nov 2005
Yule, Miss Stephanie . . . L . . . Oct 2005
Ahern, Mr Eugene . . . M . . . Jul 2007
Vickers, Mr Craig . . . I . . . Jul 2008
Sullivan, Mr Liam . . . L . . . Jul 2009
Catton-Newell, Miss Sally . . . G . . . Jul 2009
Taylor, Mr Mark . . . M . . . Jul 2010

CHESTER, Cheshire

Chambers of Anthony O'Toole and Wyn Lloyd Jones

LINENHALL CHAMBERS,
1 STANLEY PLACE CHAMBERS, CHESTER, CHESHIRE CH1 2LU
Tel: 01244 348282 ***Fax:*** 01244 342336
Dx: 19984 CHESTER

Chambers of Michael Howard Redfern QC

ST JOHNS BUILDINGS,
21 WHITE FRIARS, CHESTER, CHESHIRE CH1 1NZ
Tel: 01244 323070 ***Fax:*** 01244 342930
Dx: 19979 CHESTER
E-mail: mary.berry@stjohnsbuildings.co.uk
Head of Chambers:
Redfern, Mr Michael Howard (Q.C.) . . . I . . . Jul 1970

Bentham, Mr Howard (Q.C.) . . . G . . . Nov 1970
Shorrock, Mr Michael (Q.C.) . . . I . . . Jul 1966
Berkley, Mr David (Q.C.) . . . M . . . May 1979
Marks, Mr Richard (Q.C.) . . . G . . . Jul 1975
Hayden, Mr Anthony (Q.C.) . . . M . . . Nov 1987
Singleton, Ms Sarah (Q.C.) . . . M . . . Jul 1983
O'Byrne, Mr Andrew (Q.C.) . . . G . . . Jul 1978
Samuels, Mr Jeffrey K (Q.C.) . . . M . . . Jul 1988
Harrison, Miss Sally (Q.C.) . . . G . . . Oct 1992
Wolff, Mr Michael . . . G . . . Jun 1964
Cattan, Mr Philip David . . . G . . . Nov 1970
Lamberty, Mr Mark . . . I . . . Nov 1970
Herman, Mr Ray . . . I . . . Feb 1972
Green, Mr Roger . . . L . . . Jul 1972
Hedgecoe, Mr John Philip . . . I . . . Nov 1972
Bedford, Mr Stephen . . . G . . . Jul 1972
McNeill, Mr John Seddon . . . G . . . Jul 1974
Shannon, Mr Eric . . . M . . . Nov 1974
Lowe, Mr Geoffrey . . . G . . . Jul 1975
Longworth, Mr Antony Stephen . . . M . . . Jul 1978
Andrews, Mr Philip . . . I . . . Feb 1977
Feeny, Mr Charles . . . I . . . Nov 1977
Grundy, Mr Philip Michael David . . . M . . . Jul 1980
Owen, Miss Gail . . . G . . . Nov 1980
Mercer, Mr David . . . L . . . Jul 1980
Uff, Mr David C . . . G . . . Jul 1981
Long, Mr Andrew . . . I . . . Jul 1981
Holt, Mr Julian . . . M . . . Jan 1982
Gal, Miss Sonia . . . I . . . Nov 1982
Greene, Mr Maurice A . . . I . . . Nov 1982
Garside, Mr David . . . G . . . Nov 1982
Bruce, Mr David . . . M . . . Jul 1982
Harrison, Mr Peter John . . . M . . . Jul 1983
Khawar, Aftab . . . G . . . Jul 1983
McKee, Mr Hugh A . . . M . . . Nov 1983
Goodman, Miss Bernadette . . . I . . . Nov 1983
McKenna, Mr Brian . . . M . . . Jun 1983
Harrison, Mr J Keith . . . L . . . Nov 1983
Shaw, Mr Julian . . . G . . . Sep 1984
Pickup, Mr David . . . I . . . Jul 1984
Kennedy, Mr Michael . . . M . . . May 1985
Lloyd, Mr Julian . . . G . . . Jul 1985
Gray, Mr Richard . . . M . . . Nov 1986
Kloss, Mrs Diana Mary . . . G . . . Jul 1986
Oates, Mr John Richard . . . G . . . Jul 1987
Taylor, Mr Julian . . . M . . . Jul 1986
Dickinson, Mr Jonathan . . . I . . . Nov 1986
Walker, Miss Jane . . . M . . . Jul 1987
Brennand, Mr Timothy W . . . G . . . Nov 1987
Dagnall, Ms Jane . . . I . . . Jan 1987
Batra, Bunty Lalit . . . G . . . Feb 1987
Eastwood, Mr Charles Peter . . . L . . . Jul 1988
Crabtree, Mr Simon J G . . . L . . . Nov 1988
Davitt, Ms Paula . . . G . . . Oct 1988
Sanders, Mr Damian . . . M . . . Nov 1988
Britcliffe, Ms Anne E . . . I . . . Apr 1989
Grundy, Ms Clare . . . G . . . Jul 1989
Partington, Miss Lisa . . . I . . . Jul 1989
Holder, Mr Simon . . . I . . . Jul 1989
Blakey, Mr Michael . . . M . . . Nov 1989
Carter, Mr Richard . . . I . . . Nov 1990
Thompson, Mr Patrick . . . G . . . Oct 1990
Watson, Mr David W . . . M . . . Oct 1990
Thompson, Mr Jonathan Richard . . . I . . . Oct 1990
Wright, Mr Alastair . . . L . . . Dec 1991
Mawdsley, Mr Matthew . . . I . . . Nov 1991
Roberts, Mr Mark Vaughan . . . I . . . Sep 1991
Chaudhry, Ms Zia . . . I . . . Nov 1991
Pratt, Mrs Patricia . . . L . . . Oct 1991
Taylor, Mr Jonathan . . . M . . . Nov 1991
Case, Magdalen . . . M . . . Nov 1992
Green, Mr Andrew . . . G . . . Oct 1992
Norton, Mr Richard . . . L . . . Nov 1992
Ashmole, Mr Timothy . . . I . . . Oct 1992
McNerney, Mr Kevin . . . I . . . Jan 1992
Lloyd, Ms Gaynor Elizabeth . . . L . . . Oct 1992
Jones, Mr Benjamin . . . M . . . Feb 1993
Flood, Mr David . . . M . . . Nov 1993
Kloss, Mr Alexander . . . G . . . Oct 1993
Mathieson, Mr Guy . . . M . . . Oct 1993
Wilson, Mr Myles . . . L . . . Oct 1993
Searle, Mr Jason Ario Xavier . . . M . . . Oct 1993
Gibson, Mr John Arthur . . . L . . . Nov 1993
Fitzharris, Miss Ginnette . . . L . . . Nov 1993
Blackshaw, Mr Henry . . . M . . . Oct 1993
Orme, Mr Richard . . . L . . . Oct 1993
Rodikis, Miss Joanna . . . M . . . Oct 1993
Harrison, Miss Leona . . . M . . . Nov 1993
Polglase, Mr David S . . . M . . . Oct 1993
Connor, Mr Mark . . . I . . . May 1994
Frieze, Mr Daniel . . . G . . . Oct 1994
Gumbs, Miss Annette . . . G . . . Oct 1994
Wild, Mr Steven . . . G . . . Oct 1994
Douglas, Mr Stephen John . . . I . . . Nov 1994
Reynolds, Mr Gary William . . . L . . . Nov 1994
McGinty, Mr Robert Fraser . . . I . . . Nov 1994
Rowley, Mr Karl John . . . M . . . Nov 1994
Houghton, Ms Lisa . . . G . . . May 1994
Booth, Mr Nigel Robert . . . G . . . Oct 1994
Mann, Miss Sara . . . M . . . Nov 1994
Chukwuemeka, Mr John O . . . L . . . Nov 1994
Hargan, Mr Carl . . . L . . . Nov 1995
Lawson, Mr Andrew . . . I . . . Jan 1995
Mchugh, Miss Pauline Mary . . . G . . . Nov 1995
Parry, Mr Philip . . . L . . . Jan 1995
Crangle, Miss Charlotte . . . G . . . Jan 1995
Simkin, Mr Iain . . . I . . . Feb 1995
Dixon, Mr John . . . G . . . Nov 1995
Aslett, Pepin . . . L . . . Nov 1996
Crilley, Mr Darrel . . . I . . . Feb 1996
Roussak, Mr Jeremy Brian . . . M . . . Oct 1996
Leene, Miss Sharon . . . G . . . Oct 1996
Sastry, Mr Bob . . . I . . . Oct 1996
Mahmood, Ghazan . . . I . . . Sep 1997
Mintz, Mr Simon . . . I . . . Nov 1996
Zentar, Dr Remy . . . G . . . Jul 1997
Spear, Miss Sarah . . . I . . . Oct 1997
Williams, Ms Zillah . . . L . . . Nov 1997
Mensah, Miss Lorraine S L . . . G . . . Oct 1997
Denton, Mr Douglas . . . L . . . Nov 1997
Parry, Mr Simon . . . I . . . Nov 1997
Tyler, Mr Paul . . . M . . . Jan 1997
Evans, Mr Simeon . . . L . . . Jun 1997
Buckley, Mr Patrick James . . . G . . . Jul 1998
Bentley, Mr David Paul . . . L . . . Oct 1998
Muth, Ms Susanne . . . I . . . Jul 1998
Simmonds, Ms Alexandra . . . G . . . Oct 1998
Taylor, Mr David Christopher . . . L . . . Oct 1998
Murdin, Mr Liam . . . L . . . Jul 1998
James, Mr David . . . I . . . Oct 1998
Burnell, Miss Kate . . . M . . . Oct 1998
Stockwell, Mr Matthew . . . G . . . Oct 1998
Edwards, Miss Susan . . . L . . . Nov 1998
Deas, Ms Susan Margaret . . . G . . . Jul 1999
Astbury, Mr Philip . . . G . . . Oct 1999
Holsgrove, Lara . . . M . . . Jan 1999
Ratledge, Mr John . . . L . . . Jun 1999
Sweeney, Ms Linda Mary . . . M . . . Nov 1999
Cavanagh, Ms Lorraine . . . G . . . Jan 2000
Leach, Ms Natasha . . . L . . . Jan 2000
Bridgman, Mr Andrew . . . G . . . Jan 2000
Porter-Phillips, Mrs Clare . . . L . . . Mar 2001
Ahmed, Siraj Issap . . . M . . . Apr 2001
King, Mr Oliver . . . G . . . Jul 2001
Vir Singh, Miss Sylvia . . . M . . . Jul 2001
Van Der Haer, Ms Audrey . . . G . . . Oct 2001
Blewitt, Miss Jennifer . . . M . . . Jul 2001
Pojur, Mr David . . . M . . . Nov 2001
Farley, Mr David . . . M . . . Jan 2001
Montaldo, Mr Neil . . . L . . . Mar 2002
Hodgkinson, Mr Paul George . . . L . . . Jul 2002
Owen, Wendy Jane . . . M . . . Jan 2002
Senior, Mr Mark . . . G . . . Jul 2002
Smith, Mr Paul . . . G . . . Oct 2002
Moss, Mr Christopher . . . L . . . Oct 2002
Malam, Mr James . . . G . . . Jan 2002
Menzies, Mr Jennifer . . . L . . . Oct 2002
Stringer, Ms Rosie . . . M . . . Jan 2002
McCloskey, Miss Louise . . . G . . . Oct 2002
Smith, Ms Rebecca Ellen . . . L . . . Jan 2002
Lawrence, Mr Benjamin . . . L . . . Jan 2003
Ali, Kashif . . . L . . . Jan 2003
Hudson, Ms Abigail . . . G . . . Jan 2003
Quigley, Ms Louise . . . I . . . Jan 2003
Newstead, Ms Jennifer Elizabeth . . . G . . . Nov 2003
Akers, Mr Robert . . . I . . . Nov 2003
Maguire, Clodagh . . . I . . . Jan 2003
Connolly, Mr Timothy . . . I . . . Mar 2004
Poole, Mr William . . . M . . . Jan 2004
Waddell, Ms Philippa . . . L . . . Jan 2004
Watkins, Mr Adam . . . G . . . Jul 2004
Murphy, Mr Paul . . . G . . . Jul 2004
Greenhalgh, Miss Jane . . . L . . . Nov 2004
Rimmer, Miss Catherine . . . G . . . Jul 2004
Harrison, Miss Petra . . . I . . . Jul 2004
Samuel, Ms Ana . . . I . . . Jul 2004
Wilson, Ms Helen . . . G . . . Oct 2004
Cooper, Mr Douglas . . . I . . . Jan 2004
Sutton, Rebecca . . . I . . . Jan 2004
Abraham, Ms Joanne Jade . . . G . . . Nov 2004
Spencer, Mr Shaun . . . L . . . Jan 2005
Marshall, Lucy . . . M . . . Jan 2005
White, Mrs Debra . . . G . . . Oct 2005
Christian, Mr Neil . . . M . . . Oct 2005
Thompson, Mr Gareth . . . G . . . Jan 2005
McGarry, Mr Steven . . . L . . . Mar 2005
De Navarro, Frances . . . I . . . Jan 2005
Pare, Mr Christopher . . . M . . . Jan 2006
Scully, Ms Jennifer . . . M . . . Jul 2006
Wilkinson, Mr Timothy . . . I . . . Jan 2006
Kelly, Mr Ben . . . L . . . Jan 2006
Flynn, Mr Steven . . . G . . . Jan 2006
Scott, Louise . . . M . . . Jan 2006
Haggis, Mr Andrew . . . M . . . Mar 2007
Wood, Hannah . . . L . . . Jan 2007
Vanderpump, Henry . . . I . . . Jan 2007
Owen-Easey, Neil . . . G . . . Jan 2007
Goode, Julian . . . L . . . Jan 2006
Allen, Mr Fegal . . . L . . . Oct 2007
Murray, Simon . . . I . . . Jan 2008
Cooper, Elisabeth . . . M . . . Jan 2008
Gomer, Mr Elis . . . G . . . Jan 2008
Williams, Miss Cerys . . . G . . . Jul 2008
Maddison, Mr Simon . . . I . . . Jan 2008
Edwards, Mr Huw . . . G . . . Jan 2009
England, Laura . . . M . . . Jan 2008
Roberts, Elliw . . . G . . . Jan 2009
Nash, Laura . . . L . . . Jan 2009

CHICHESTER, West Sussex

Chambers of Lucinda Davis

PALLANT CHAMBERS,
12 NORTH PALLANT, CHICHESTER, WEST SUSSEX PO19 1TQ
Est: 1977
Tel: 01243 784538 ***Fax:*** 01243 780861
Dx: 30303 CHICHESTER
E-mail: clerks@pallantchambers.co.uk
Web: www.pallantchambers.co.uk
Clerk: Senior: Alister Williams. Civil: Danny Hazell; Family: Sarah Sweatman; Junior: Ashley Clark; Credit Control: Michael Lawrence.
Head of Chambers:
Davis, Miss Lucinda . . . G . . . Jul 1981

Taylor, Mr Charles . . . M . . . Jul 1974
Rowlinson, Miss Wendy . . . G . . . Jul 1981
Egleton, Mr Richard . . . G . . . Jul 1981
Haven, Mr Kevin . . . G . . . Jul 1982
Living, Mr Marc Stephen . . . M . . . Oct 1983
Darton, Mr Clifford . . . M . . . Jul 1988
Morgan, Mr Colin . . . M . . . Nov 1989
Loosemoore, Mrs Mary . . . I . . . May 1992
Geser, Miss Anita . . . G . . . Jul 1992
Emerson, Mr William . . . M . . . Nov 1992
Wilkins, Mr Christopher . . . L . . . May 1993
Pain, Mr Kevin . . . G . . . Jan 1994
Magee, Miss Rosein . . . G . . . Oct 1994
Woodward, Mr Jeremy . . . I . . . Nov 1996
Moys, Mr Clive . . . L . . . Jul 1998
Earley, Ms Sarah Jane . . . I . . . Oct 1998
Ward, Miss Kelly . . . M . . . Jan 2001
Maton, Mr Neil Foster . . . M . . . Nov 2001
Tai, Miss Farzana . . . M . . . Jul 2003
Turnill, Mr Evan . . . G . . . Sep 2003
Anstey, Mrs Eve . . . M . . . Nov 2005

Cooke, Mr Tom	G	Mar 2006
Worthen, Mr Thomas	G	Jul 2007
Hoile, Miss Elinor	L	Mar 2008
Dewhurst, Ms Eleanor	M	Nov 2008
Brookes, Mr Christopher	L	Jan 2010
Tawfik, Miss Nicola	M	Jan 2010
Beckman, Mr Michael (Q.C.)*	L	May 1954
Weatherill, Mr Bernard (Q.C.)*	G	Nov 1974
Gibbons, Mr Orlando*	G	Nov 1982
Mullis, Mr Roger*	L	Nov 1987
Deacock, Mr Adam Jason*	M	Nov 1991
Rowlands, Miss Sara*	G	Jan 2001

Pallant Chambers continues to expand its provision of specialist advocates to the South of England in its core areas of Family and Civil Litigation.

CLIFTON, Bristol

FREDERICK PLACE CHAMBERS,
9 FREDERICK PLACE, CLIFTON, BRISTOL BS8 1AS
Tel: 0117 946 7059
E-mail: rsp4593558@aol.com

COLCHESTER, Essex

EAST ANGLIAN CHAMBERS,
53 NORTH HILL, COLCHESTER, ESSEX CO1 1PY
Tel: 01206 572756 ***Fax:*** 01206 245800
Dx: 3611 COLCHESTER
E-mail: colchester@ealaw.co.uk
Clerk: Fraser McLaren; Deputy Senior: Alison Scanes.
Administrator: Carol Bull (Head of Administration)

Akast, Mr John F; Recorder	I	Nov 1968
Wardlow, Mr John; Recorder	G	Jul 1971
Bryan, Mr Rex; Recorder	L	Nov 1971
Waters, Mr John Clough; Pupil Supervisor	L	May 1974
Marsden, Mr Andrew; Recorder; Pupil Supervisor	M	Jul 1975
Bryant, Ms Caroline; Pupil Supervisor	M	Jul 1976
Sinclair, Mr Graham; Part time Chairman LVTRAC	G	Jul 1979
Hamey, Mr John	I	Jul 1979
Brooke-Smith, Mr John; Recorder; Pupil Supervisor	G	Jul 1981
Redmayne, Mr Simon	I	Jul 1982
Lane, Mr Michael	M	Jul 1983
Bettle, Ms Janet; Pupil Supervisor	I	Jul 1985
Elcombe, Mr Nicholas; Pupil Supervisor	I	Jul 1987
Capon, Mr Philip; Pupil Supervisor	I	Oct 1990
Watson, Ms Claire; Pupil Supervisor	L	Nov 1991
Butcher, Mr Russell Henry	M	Oct 1992
Parry-Jones, Ms Carole Ann	M	Nov 1992
Barratt, Mr Dominic Anthony Richard; Pupil Supervisor	G	Nov 1992
Walsh, Ms Patricia C	L	Nov 1993
Kelly, Mr Richard	G	Oct 1994
Wheetman, Mr Alan	M	Oct 1995
Freeman, Ms Sally Jane; Pupil Supervisor	L	Nov 1995
Wood, Mr Richard	G	Nov 1995
Underhill, Ms Allison	G	Oct 1997
Goodfellow, Mr Stephen	M	Nov 1997
Ashley, Mr Neil	L	Mar 1999
Korniej, Ms Rebekah	M	Oct 1999
Bradbury, Ms Joanna	M	Nov 1999
Harvey, Miss Shona	M	Nov 1999
Hayes, Ms Christine	M	Nov 1999
Pigram, Mr Christopher Stuart; Pupil Supervisor	G	Jul 2000
O'Sullivan, Mr Richard; Pupil Supervisor	I	Jul 2000
Brown, Mr Luke Henry William	M	Oct 2000
Parnell, Ms Cherie	M	Nov 2000
Stevens, Ms Hazel	L	Jul 2001
Shirley, Ms Lynne	M	Jul 2002
Donovan, Miss Juliet	M	Jul 2002
Plant, Ms April	L	Oct 2002
Wastall, Mrs Rebecca	L	Oct 2002
Voelcker, Ms Harriet	G	Jul 2003
Michael, Mr Nicholas	M	Jul 2003
Croskell, Mr Marcus	L	Jul 2003
Miller, Miss Kate	G	Jul 2003
Wahiwala, Mr Amrik	M	Jul 2003
Martin, Miss Jade	M	Oct 2003
Dyer, Miss Shereen	L	Oct 2003
Williams, Miss Micaila	I	Jul 2004
Cattermull, Ms Emma	L	Oct 2004
Strelitz, Mr Paul	L	Nov 2005
Edwards, Mr Matthew	G	Jul 2006
White, Miss Elizabeth	I	Jul 2006
Connell, Miss Amy	M	Oct 2006
Bewley, Miss Suhayla	L	Jul 2007
Spence, Miss Gemma-Louise	L	Jul 2007
Pine, Miss Mika	M	Nov 2007
Myers, Mr Rupert	I	Nov 2008
Newton, Miss Alice	I	Jul 2009
Slaughter, Miss Jessica	M	Jul 2009
Sorel-Cameron, Mr Matthew	M	Oct 2009
Smith, Miss Fiona	G	Nov 2009
Duxbury, Sarah	M	Mar 2010
Nicklin, Mr Andrew	M	Jul 2010
Sheehan, Mr Michael	M	Oct 2010

CROYDON, Surrey

ADVOLEX CHAMBERS,
70 COULSDON ROAD, COULSDON, CROYDON, SURREY CR5 2LB
Tel: 0871 717 7321 ***Fax:*** 0871 781 1201
E-mail: advolex.chambers@yipple.com

Leech, Mr Geoffrey Anthony	L	Nov 1992

DAGENHAM, Essex

ELLERTON CHAMBERS,
34 ELLERTON GARDENS, DAGENHAM, ESSEX RM9 4HT

Wilkins, Mrs Liz	L	Mar 1985

EASTBOURNE, East Sussex

Chambers of Julian Dale

EASTBOURNE CHAMBERS,
5 CHISWICK PLACE, EASTBOURNE, EAST SUSSEX BN21 4NH
Tel: 01323 642102 ***Fax:*** 01323 641402
Dx: 6925 EASTBOURNE
E-mail: clerks@eastbournechambers.co.uk
Clerk: Senior: Teresa Shehu. Junior: Lucy Morrison.
Practice Manager: Teresa Shehu
Head of Chambers:

Dale, Mr Julian	M	Nov 1991
Tully, Ms Anne Margaret	G	Nov 1989
Crawford, Miss Marie	L	Oct 1992
Valks, Mr Michael	G	Oct 1994
Collins, Miss Jennifer	G	Oct 1994
Morris, Mr Arthur Rowland	G	Jan 1997
Upton, Miss Rebecca	G	Jul 1999
German, Miss Kelly	L	Jul 2000
Scott-Beckett, Miss Alissa	L	Jul 2000
Potter, Mr Ian Edward James	I	Nov 2001
Arnone, Miss Anna	M	Jul 2002
Frier, Mr Daniel	G	Oct 2005
Weedon, Mr Rupert Stuart	M	Jan 2006
Heywood, Mr Matthew	M	Jul 2006
Celikoz, Miss Tara	M	Jan 2007
Talbott, Mr Ross	M	Jan 2008
Platt, Miss Eleanor Frances (Q.C.)*	G	Feb 1960
Russell Flint, Mr Simon (Q.C.)*	I	Nov 1980

CHAMBERS OF ERNLE MONEY,
FURNESS GRANGE, FURNESS ROAD, EASTBOURNE, EAST SUSSEX BN21 4EX
Tel: 01323 723609 ***Fax:*** 01323 639900

EDGWARE, Middlesex

CLAVENES CHAMBERS,
46 STAG LANE, EDGWARE, MIDDLESEX HA8 5JY
Tel: 020 8931 2648 ***Fax:*** 020 8931 2648

Bankole-Jones, Mr John Edward	M	Oct 1963

ETCHINGHAM, East Sussex

Chambers of Robert Banks

RYE GREEN CHAMBERS,
RYE GREEN FARM, BURWASH, ETCHINGHAM, EAST SUSSEX TN19 7HP
Tel: 01435 882577 ***Fax:*** 01435 882545
E-mail: law@banksr.com
Clerk: Shane McMechan.
Head of Chambers:

Banks, Mr Robert	I	Jul 1978

EXETER, Devon

Chambers of R Martin J Meeke QC

COLLETON CHAMBERS,
COLLETON CRESCENT, EXETER, DEVON EX2 4DG
Tel: 01392 274898 ***Fax:*** 01392 412368
Dx: 8330 EXETER
E-mail: clerks@colletonchambers.co.uk
Web: www.colletonchambers.co.uk
Clerk: Senior: Philip Alden.
Head of Chambers:

Meeke, Mr R Martin J (Q.C.)	G	Jul 1973
Crabb, Mr Richard Blechyndem	M	Nov 1975
Horton, Mr Mark V	M	Jul 1981
Whitehall, Mr Mark	I	Jul 1983
Holder, Mr Terence	G	Jul 1984
Hayward, Mr James	M	Jan 1985
Farquharson, Mr Jonathan	I	Jul 1988
Ingham, Miss Elizabeth	M	Nov 1989
Sapiecha, Mr David J	M	Oct 1990
Galloway, Mr Malcolm	M	Oct 1992
Godfrey, Mr Christopher Nicholas	L	Jan 1992
Macfarlane, Mr Andrew Lennox	I	May 1995
Evans, Mr T Gareth	M	Oct 1996
Watson, Mr Graham	L	Oct 1996
Bradnock, Mr Thomas	G	Oct 1997
Barraclough, Miss Lisa	L	Jan 1999
Pitts, Miss Emily	I	Jan 2000
Vahib, Miss Ayse	M	Jan 2003
Wraith, Mr Nigel	M	Jul 2004
Taghdissian, Mr James	G	Oct 2005
Brunton, Mr Sean	M	Nov 1990

Chambers with specialist teams in the fields of Crime & Regulatory, Family & Child Care and Employment Law.

Chambers of Michael Berkley

ROUGEMONT CHAMBERS,
VICTORY HOUSE, DEAN CLARKE GARDENS, SOUTHERNHAY EAST, EXETER, DEVON EX2 4AA
Tel: 01392 208484 ***Fax:*** 01392 208204
Dx: 8396 EXETER
E-mail: clerks@rougemontchambers.co.uk
Clerk: Lisa Glithero; Sam Morgan; Harry Turner.
Head of Chambers:

Berkley, Mr Michael; Civil Recorder	M	Jul 1989
Bell, Miss Anne OBE	G	Jan 1975
Richardson, Mr Garth	M	Jul 1975
Felton, Mr Timothy J F; Associate Member*	M	Jul 1977
Berry, Mr Nicholas Michael	I	Nov 1988
Lloyd, Mr John Nesbitt	I	Nov 1988
Haughty, Mr Jeremy Nicholas	L	Nov 1989
Gloag, Mr Angus	I	Jan 1992
Collett, Mr Gavin Charles	I	Oct 1993
Bryan, Miss Carmel	M	Nov 1993
Ball, Mr Steven	I	Oct 1995
Devine, Mr Michael*	G	Oct 1995
Chute, Ms Andrea*	M	Oct 1995
Hatton, Miss Theresa*	L	Mar 1998
Bax, Mr James	L	Oct 1999
Hopkin, Mr William	I	Aug 2000
Brady, Dr Ann; Associate Member*	M	Mar 2001
Lane, Mr Simon Charles	I	Jul 2002
Thomas, Dr David Keith	I	Jan 2003
Worthley, Mr Andrew	L	Oct 2004
Murray, Mr Charles	I	Mar 2005
Hornblower, Mrs Sarah	G	Jul 2005
Ferrari, Mr Nicholas*	G	Nov 2005
Rozier, Mr James Ian*	M	Jan 2007
Boyden, Mr Matthew	M	Jan 2007
O'Neill, Mr Jonathan	I	Jan 2007
Herbert, Miss Jane	G	Jan 2008

Chambers of Christopher Naish and Susan Claire Campbell QC

SOUTHERNHAY CHAMBERS,
33 SOUTHERNHAY EAST, EXETER, DEVON EX1 1NX
Tel: 01392 255777 ***Fax:*** 01392 412021
Dx: 8353 EXETER
E-mail: clerks@southernhaychambers.co.uk
Clerk: Senior: Joy Daniell.
Head of Chambers:

Naish, Mr Christopher	I	Jul 1980
Campbell, Miss Susan Claire (Q.C.)	M	Nov 1986
Tolson, Mr Robin (Q.C.); Recorder	M	Oct 1994
Ahmed, Miss Jacqueline	I	Jul 1988
Ogle, Miss Rebecca	I	Jan 1989
Powell, Mr Richard	M	Jul 1989
Archer, Miss Deborah; Deputy Coroner	I	Nov 1989
Rees, Mr James	G	Oct 1994
Mann, Miss Daya Lucienne	L	Feb 1995
Trumper, Miss Sarah	L	Nov 1996
Williams, Miss Juliet	I	Nov 1998
Sheridan, Mr Robert	L	Nov 2001
Blackwood, Ms Rebecca	I	Nov 2001
Willsteed, Miss Elizabeth	L	Nov 2004
Evans, Miss Sarah	I	Nov 2004
Gape, Mr Christian	M	Jul 2005
Lidbury, Mr David	L	Oct 2006
Smith, Mrs Jane	I	Jan 2007
McKechnie, Mrs Gail	G	Jul 2007
Storey, Mr Paul (Q.C.); Recorder*	L	Nov 1982
Telford, Mr Peter*	L	Jul 1985
Akther, Miss Tahina*	L	Oct 2003

Chambers of Geoffrey Mercer QC

WALNUT HOUSE CHAMBERS,
63 ST DAVID'S HILL, EXETER, DEVON EX4 4DW
Tel: 01392 279751 ***Fax:*** 01392 412080
Dx: 115582 EXETER
E-mail: clerks@walnuthouse.co.uk
Clerk: Chris Doe.
Head of Chambers:

Mercer, Mr Geoffrey (Q.C.); Recorder	I	Nov 1975
Dunkels, Mr Paul (Q.C.); Recorder	I	May 1972
Oldland, Mr Andrew (Q.C.); Recorder	I	Nov 1990
Laws, Mr Simon (Q.C.)	I	Oct 1991
Barnes, Mr H Jonathan; Recorder	G	Jul 1970
Searle, Miss Corinne; Recorder	G	Jul 1982
Melville-Shreeve, Mr Michael; Deputy District Judge	G	Jul 1986
Treneer, Mr Mark	I	Jul 1987
Eaton-Hart, Mr Andrew	G	Jul 1989
Matuk, Miss Helen	G	Jun 1990
McCarthy, Miss Mary	M	Oct 1994
Evans, Mr David	G	Mar 1996
Kenny, Mr Martin	I	Jan 1997
Spencer, Miss Lara	I	Jul 2000
Bremridge, Mr Lee	G	Jan 2003
White, Mr Barry	G	Jan 2004
Bray, Ms Helen	M	Jul 2004
Cassel, Miss Bathsheba	I	Jul 2005
Ticehurst, Mr Joss	I	Jan 2006
Asprey, Miss Louise	L	Oct 2007

11

GREENFORD, Middlesex

MIDDLESEX CHAMBERS,
150 BILTON ROAD, GREENFORD, MIDDLESEX UB6 7HW
Tel: 020 8931 1493 ***Fax:*** 020 8810 5518

GUILDFORD, Surrey

Chambers of George Alexander Nigel Coates

GUILDFORD CHAMBERS,
STOKE HOUSE, LEAPALE LANE, GUILDFORD, SURREY GU1 4LY
Tel: 01483 539131 ***Fax:*** 01483 300542
Dx: 97863 GUILDFORD 5
E-mail: clerks@guildfordchambers.co.uk
Clerk: Senior: Simon Morris. Junior: Gavin Street.
Head of Chambers:

Coates, Mr George Alexander Nigel	M	Nov 1990
Jones, Mr Michael Adrian Lyster	I	Jul 1972
Templeman, The Hon Michael Richard	L	Nov 1973
Shrimpton, Miss Claire Alison	I	Jul 1983
Pascall, Mr Matthew Stephen	M	Jul 1984
Haywood, Miss Janet	I	Jul 1985
Smithers, Dr Roger Howard	I	Nov 1990
Julien, Miss Christine	I	Nov 1991
Ward, Mr Martin	L	Oct 1992
Moulder, Mr Paul J	L	Oct 1997
Gillan, Ms Dominique	G	Oct 1998
Tee, Mr Greg	I	Jul 1999
Hirst (nee Clapham), Miss Catherine Victoria	I	Jul 1999
Long, Mr Ben	I	Nov 2000
Appiah, Miss Linda	M	Jan 2001

Mitchell, Mr Christian . . . M . . . Jul 2001
Griffin, Miss Fiona E . . . G . . . Jul 2003
Morton, Miss Rowan . . . L . . . Jan 2004
McLaughlin, Victoria . . . G . . . Jan 2004
Cannon, Miss Lauren . . . M . . . Jan 2004
Smout, Mr Will . . . L . . . Jan 2005
Jagutpal, Mr Previn . . . M . . . Oct 2005
Woodhead, Mr George Byron . . . L . . . Nov 2009
Minto, Miss Amanada . . . M . . . Nov 2009
McSorley, Miss Hannah . . . I . . . Nov 2009
Clements, Miss Paula Kate* . . . I . . . Jul 1985
Widdup, Mr Stanley Jeffrey; Recorder* . . . G . . . Nov 1973
Dancer, Miss Helen* . . . M . . . Jul 2001
Malcolm, Miss Rosalind* . . . M . . . Jul 1977

HALESOWEN, West Midlands

CHAMBERS OF ALANA GRAHAM,
CHEMIX BUILDINGS, MAYPOLE FIELDS, CRADLEY, HALESOWEN, WEST MIDLANDS B63 2QB
Tel: 01384 894560
Clerk: Jeff Collins.
Graham, Mrs Alana . . . L . . . Jan 1993

HANLEY, Staffordshire

Chambers of Barry George Cliff

REGENT CHAMBERS,
REGENT HOUSE, 3 PALL MALL, HANLEY, STAFFORDSHIRE ST1 1HP
Tel: 01782 286666 ***Fax:*** 01782 201866
Dx: 20720 HANLEY
E-mail: clerks@regentchambers.co.uk
Clerk: Senior: Nicola Dobson.
Head of Chambers:
Cliff, Mr Barry George . . . L . . . Jul 1988

Jay, Mr Grenville R* . . . I . . . Dec 1975
McCartney, Mr Peter . . . I . . . Nov 1983
Cliff, Mr Paul Richard . . . G . . . Oct 1992
Johnson, Mr John Richard Henesey . . . M . . . Nov 1993
Moore, Miss Kirstie Elizabeth . . . M . . . Oct 1994
O'Hagan, Miss Sophie Maria . . . M . . . Jan 1996
Ali, Mr Anis . . . L . . . Mar 1997
Wallbanks, Miss Joanne . . . M . . . May 1997
O'Reilly, Miss Catherine Mary . . . G . . . Oct 1998
Powell, Mr Frederick Mansell . . . I . . . Nov 1999
Palmer, Mr Edward James . . . L . . . Jul 2000
Fisher, Mr Craig . . . M . . . May 2004

HARROW, Middlesex

Chambers of Mark Fenton Kimsey

CASTLE CHAMBERS,
THE OLD FIRE STATION, 90 HIGH STREET, HARROW, MIDDLESEX HA1 3LP
Tel: 020 8423 6579 ***Fax:*** 020 8423 2926
Dx: 4211 HARROW
Clerk: Senior: Paul J Staplehurst.
Administrator: Marion Wallbridge
Practice Manager: Ann Kenyon
Head of Chambers:
Kimsey, Mr Mark Fenton . . . I . . . Oct 1990

Dowden, Mr Andrew Philip . . . L . . . Jan 1991
Bearman, Mr Justin Ian . . . I . . . Nov 1992
Whitley, Mr Jonathan Denton . . . I . . . Nov 1993
Wilkins, Mr Andrew . . . L . . . Oct 1995
Steele, Miss Laura C . . . I . . . Oct 1996
Crinnion, Miss Neena . . . G . . . Oct 1997
Staley, Miss Helen . . . L . . . Mar 1997
Wright, Mr Jonathan Nicholas . . . M . . . Oct 1997
Reilly, Miss Ffyon . . . I . . . Sep 1999
Fanshawe, Ms Lynn H C . . . M . . . Oct 1999

Chambers of Ryan W Clement

CONFERENCE CHAMBERS,
PO BOX 626, HARROW, MIDDLESEX HA2 2DZ
Tel: 07958 421595 ***Fax:*** 0800 242 5323
Dx: 35162 EASTCOTE
E-mail: carole@conferencechambers.com
Clerk: Senior: Carole Paterson.
Practice Manager: Carole Paterson
Head of Chambers:
Clement, Mr Ryan W . . . M . . . Oct 1996

Shah, Mr Jilan* . . . M . . . Jan 2001

Chambers of Nasiruddin Alsolaimani

10 KINGSFIELD AVENUE,
HARROW, MIDDLESEX HA2 6AH
Tel: 020 8427 8709 ***Fax:*** 020 8427 8709
Head of Chambers:
Alsolaimani, Mr Nasiruddin . . . L . . . Nov 1971

Chambers of Donald E J George

LEONE CHAMBERS,
218A KINGS ROAD, HARROW, MIDDLESEX HA2 9JR
Tel: 020 8868 2736 ***Fax:*** 020 8868 2736
Clerk: Vincent Nicholas.
Practice Manager: Danny Currie
Head of Chambers:
George, Mr Donald E J . . . G . . . Jul 1973

Tucker, Dr Peter Louis . . . G . . . Nov 1970
Bash-Taqi, Mrs Shahineh . . . I . . . Nov 1972

10 MAXTED PARK,
HARROW-ON-THE-HILL, HARROW, MIDDLESEX HA1 3BB
Tel: 020 8537 8674 ***Fax:*** 020 8537 8674

HAYES, Middlesex

Chambers of Benoit Esprit

23 HARRIES ROAD,
HAYES, MIDDLESEX UB4 9DD
Tel: 020 8841 8236
Head of Chambers:
Esprit, Mr Benoit . . . I . . . Nov 1982

HENLEY-ON-THAMES, Oxfordshire

Chambers of Jennifer Kavanagh

HENLEY CHAMBERS,
12A FRIDAY STREET, HENLEY-ON-THAMES, OXFORDSHIRE RG9 1AH
Tel: 01491 636000 ***Fax:*** 01491 572653
Dx: 80510 HENLEY-ON-THAMES
E-mail: clerks@henleychambers.co.uk
Clerk: June Elizabeth Lamacraft.
Head of Chambers:
Kavanagh, Mrs Jennifer . . . L . . . Oct 1993

Chambers of Gail Caroline Carrodus

HUNTERCOMBE CHAMBERS,
TIMBERS FARMHOUSE, TIMBERS LANE, NUFFIELD, HENLEY-ON-THAMES, OXFORDSHIRE RG9 5SY
Tel: 01491 641934 ***Fax:*** 01491 683766
Dx: 80516 HENLEY-ON-THAMES
E-mail: chambers@carrodus.co.uk
Clerk: Gail Caroline Carrodus.
Head of Chambers:
Carrodus, Miss Gail Caroline . . . G . . . Nov 1978

HULL, Kingston upon Hull

Community Legal Service

Criminal Defence Service

Chambers of Anil P Murray

WILBERFORCE CHAMBERS,
7 BISHOP LANE, HULL, KINGSTON UPON HULL HU1 1PA
Tel: 01482 323264 ***Fax:*** 01482 325533
Dx: 11940 HULL 1
E-mail: clerks@hullbar.co.uk
Web: www.wilberforcechambershull.co.uk
Practice Manager: Phillip James Paxton
Head of Chambers:
Murray, Mr Anil P . . . M . . . Jul 1989

Swift, Mr Malcolm Robin (Q.C.) . . . G . . . Jul 1970
Gateshill, Mr J Bernard; Recorder . . . L . . . Jul 1972
Miller, Mr Paul W; Recorder . . . L . . . Jul 1974
Genney, Mr Paul W . . . M . . . May 1976
Godfrey, Mr John P . . . G . . . May 1985
Garth, Mr Steven David . . . G . . . Nov 1983
Cameron, Mr Neil A; Recorder . . . G . . . Jul 1984
Bury, Mr Mark; Recorder . . . I . . . Jul 1986
Comaish, Mr Andrew J C . . . M . . . Nov 1989
Trimmer, Miss Carol Jane . . . G . . . Nov 1993
Hirst, Mr Simon David; Recorder . . . L . . . Oct 1993
Thackray, Mr John R . . . L . . . Oct 1994
Pickering, Mr Simon T . . . I . . . Oct 1996
Clive, Mr Nigel Philip Trevor . . . G . . . Nov 1998
Robinson, Mr Stephen M . . . G . . . Nov 1999
Fearon, Miss Sarah Louise . . . M . . . Nov 2000
Baines, Miss Charlotte Louise . . . L . . . Oct 2000
Scott, Miss January . . . G . . . Jul 2000
Collins, Mrs Sally . . . M . . . Oct 2002
Thompson, Mr Richard Anthony . . . M . . . Jul 2007
Wilson, Mr Andrew James . . . M . . . Jun 2005
Foster, Miss Wendy . . . I . . . Oct 2005
Carnie, Mr Alan . . . L . . . Jul 2006
Baggs, Miss Julia C . . . I . . . Mar 2008
Reed, Mrs Claire . . . G . . . Oct 2009
Ledden, Mr Thomas . . . G . . . Nov 2009
Jenkins, Miss Joanne Frances . . . M . . . Jul 2009
Bevan, Prof Hugh K* . . . M . . . Jun 1959

This well established set with 28 barristers led by John Godfrey is based in Hull and has dedicated criminal, civil and family teams.

Waterlow endeavours to provide the most accurate information for the Legal Profession. Help us keep your details up to date by informing us of any changes to your Chambers.

ILFORD, Essex

LLOYDS BANK CHAMBERS,
2ND FLOOR, 45 CRANBROOK ROAD, ILFORD, ESSEX IG1 4DP
Tel: 020 8514 0000
E-mail: cssolicitors@aol.com

IPSWICH, Suffolk

EAST ANGLIAN CHAMBERS,
GRESHAM HOUSE, 5 MUSEUM STREET, IPSWICH, SUFFOLK IP1 1HQ
Tel: 01473 214481 ***Fax:*** 01473 231388
Dx: 3227 IPSWICH
E-mail: ipswich@ealaw.co.uk
Clerk: Fraser McLaren; Deputy Senior: Alison Scanes.
Administrator: Carol Bull (Head of Administration)
Akast, Mr John F; Recorder . . . I . . . Nov 1968
Wardlow, Mr John . . . G . . . Jul 1971
Bryan, Mr Rex; Recorder . . . L . . . Nov 1971
Waters, Mr John Clough; Pupil Supervisor . . . L . . . May 1974
Marsden, Mr Andrew; Recorder; Pupil Supervisor . . . M . . . Jul 1975
Bryant, Ms Caroline; Pupil Supervisor . . . M . . . Jul 1976
Sinclair, Mr Graham; Part time Chairman LVTRAC . . . G . . . Jul 1979
Hamey, Mr John . . . I . . . Jul 1979
Brooke-Smith, Mr John; Recorder; Pupil Supervisor . . . G . . . Jul 1981
Redmayne, Mr Simon . . . I . . . Jul 1982
Lane, Mr Michael . . . M . . . Jul 1983
Bettle, Ms Janet; Pupil Supervisor . . . I . . . Jul 1985
Elcombe, Mr Nicholas; Pupil Supervisor . . . I . . . Jul 1987
Capon, Mr Philip; Pupil Supervisor . . . I . . . Oct 1990
Watson, Ms Claire; Pupil Supervisor . . . L . . . Nov 1991
Butcher, Mr Russell Henry . . . M . . . Oct 1992
Parry-Jones, Ms Carole Ann . . . M . . . Nov 1992
Barratt, Mr Dominic Anthony Richard; Pupil Supervisor . . . G . . . Nov 1992
Walsh, Ms Patricia C . . . L . . . Nov 1993
Kelly, Mr Richard . . . G . . . Oct 1994
Wheetman, Mr Alan . . . M . . . Oct 1995
Freeman, Ms Sally Jane; Pupil Supervisor . . . L . . . Nov 1995
Wood, Mr Richard . . . G . . . Nov 1995
Underhill, Ms Allison . . . G . . . Oct 1997
Goodfellow, Mr Stephen . . . M . . . Nov 1997
Ashley, Mr Neil . . . L . . . Mar 1999
Korniej, Ms Rebekah . . . M . . . Oct 1999
Bradbury, Ms Joanna . . . M . . . Nov 1999
Harvey, Miss Shona . . . M . . . Nov 1999
Hayes, Ms Christine . . . M . . . Nov 1999
Pigram, Mr Christopher Stuart; Pupil Supervisor . . . G . . . Jul 2000
O'Sullivan, Mr Richard; Pupil Supervisor . . . I . . . Jul 2000
Brown, Mr Luke Henry William . . . M . . . Oct 2000
Parnell, Ms Cherie . . . M . . . Nov 2000
Stevens, Ms Hazel . . . L . . . Jul 2001
Shirley, Ms Lynne . . . M . . . Jul 2002
Donovan, Miss Juliet . . . M . . . Jul 2002
Plant, Ms April . . . L . . . Oct 2002
Wastall, Mrs Rebecca . . . L . . . Oct 2002
Voelcker, Ms Harriet . . . G . . . Jul 2003
Michael, Mr Nicholas . . . L . . . Jul 2003
Croskell, Mr Marcus . . . L . . . Jul 2003
Miller, Miss Kate . . . G . . . Jul 2003
Wahiwala, Mr Amrik . . . M . . . Jul 2003
Martin, Miss Jade . . . M . . . Oct 2003
Dyer, Miss Shereen . . . L . . . Oct 2003
Williams, Miss Micaila . . . I . . . Jul 2004
Cattermull, Ms Emma . . . L . . . Oct 2004
Strelitz, Mr Paul . . . L . . . Nov 2005
Edwards, Mr Matthew . . . G . . . Jul 2006
White, Miss Elizabeth . . . I . . . Jul 2006
Connell, Miss Amy . . . M . . . Oct 2006
Bewley, Miss Suhayla . . . L . . . Jul 2007
Spence, Miss Gemma-Louise . . . L . . . Jul 2007
Pine, Miss Mika . . . M . . . Nov 2007
Myers, Mr Rupert . . . I . . . Nov 2008
Newton, Miss Alice . . . I . . . Jul 2009
Slaughter, Miss Jessica . . . M . . . Jul 2009
Sorel-Cameron, Mr Matthew . . . M . . . Oct 2009
Smith, Miss Fiona . . . G . . . Nov 2009
Duxbury, Sarah . . . M . . . Mar 2010
Nicklin, Mr Andrew . . . M . . . Jul 2010
Sheehan, Mr Michael . . . M . . . Oct 2010

KEW, Surrey

Chambers of Steve Fisher

KEW CHAMBERS,
354 KEW ROAD, KEW, SURREY TW9 3DU
Tel: 0844 809 9991 ***Fax:*** 020 8332 7152
Dx: 90354 BRENTFORD
E-mail: admin@kewchambers.co.uk
Practice Manager: Caroline Prior
Head of Chambers:
Fisher, Mr Steve . . . G . . . Jan 2000

Graham, Mr Roger . . . M . . . Oct 1973
Kwiatkowski, Mr Feliks Jerzy . . . M . . . Jul 1977
Brooke, Mr Johan . . . L . . . Jan 1997
Adamson, Mr Alan . . . I . . . Jan 1997
Worrall, Mr Philip . . . G . . . Jan 2001
Whittock, Mr Robert . . . L . . . Oct 2006

KIDDERMINSTER, Worcestershire

Chambers of Alistair Mitchell

FOREGATE CHAMBERS,
29 YELLOWHAMMER COURT, KIDDERMINSTER, WORCESTERSHIRE DY10 4RP
Tel: 07760 766152 ***Fax:*** 01562 634417
Dx: 16302 KIDDERMINSTER
E-mail: clerk@foregatechambers.co.uk
Clerk: Senior: Julia Vaughan.
Head of Chambers:
Mitchell, Mr Alistair . . . M . . . Oct 1997

Busby, Mr Thomas Andrew* . . . L . . . Jul 1975

Price-Rowlands, Mr Gwynn . . . I . . . May 1985
Worrall, Mr Philip* . . . G . . . Jan 2001
Marsh, Mr Graham Ian . . . L . . . Oct 2004

KINGSTON UPON THAMES, Surrey

CHAMBERS OF MR S A KHAN,
1 WOLVERTON AVENUE, KINGSTON UPON THAMES, SURREY KT2 7QF
Tel: 020 8541 3875 ***Fax:*** 020 8541 3875
E-mail: saukatatchambers@googlemail.com
Khan, Mr Shaukat . . . L . . . May 1971

LANGPORT, Somerset

Chambers of James Harry Laird Leckie

WESTLEIGH CHAMBERS,
4 VICKERY CLOSE, CURRY RIVEL, LANGPORT, SOMERSET TA10 0PY
Tel: 01458 251261
E-mail: jhlleckie@aol.com
Head of Chambers:
Leckie, Mr James Harry Laird . . . G . . . Jul 1964

LEAMINGTON SPA, Warwickshire

Chambers of Clifford Payton

ALPHA COURT CHAMBERS,
STUART HOUSE, 23 KENILWORTH ROAD, LEAMINGTON SPA, WARWICKSHIRE CV32 6JD
Tel: 0800 634 9650 / 01926 886412 ***Fax:*** 01926 671221
E-mail: cp@payton.uk.net
Head of Chambers:
Payton, Mr Clifford . . . I . . . Jul 1972

McDonald, Miss Rachael . . . L . . . Nov 2000
Payton, Mr Alexander . . . L . . . Nov 1998
Robson, Mrs Sarah . . . I . . . Jul 2002

LEEDS, West Yorkshire

Chambers of J Graham Keith Hyland QC

BROADWAY HOUSE CHAMBERS,
25 PARK SQUARE WEST, LEEDS, WEST YORKSHIRE LS1 2PW
Tel: 0113 246 2600 ***Fax:*** 0113 246 2609
Dx: 26403 LEEDS PARK SQUARE
E-mail: clerks@broadwayhouse.co.uk
Clerk: Crime: David Rhodes; Civil & Family: Robin Slade.
Administrator: Helen Craven
Head of Chambers:
Hyland, Mr J Graham Keith (Q.C.); Recorder . . . I . . . Jul 1978

Colborne, Miss Michelle Diane (Q.C.) . . . G . . . May 1993
Khan, Mr Tahir Zaffar (Q.C.) . . . L . . . Jul 1986
Wood, Mr Martin John . . . I . . . Jul 1973
Topham, Mr John David . . . G . . . Jul 1970
Isaacs, Mr Paul; Recorder . . . M . . . Feb 1974
Kershaw, Mr Andrew; Recorder . . . M . . . Jan 1975
Newbon, Mr Ian . . . M . . . Feb 1977
Cohen, Mr Raphael . . . L . . . Jul 1981
Shelton, Mr Gordon Edward; Recorder . . . I . . . Nov 1981
McGonigal, Mr David Ambrose . . . G . . . Jul 1982
Jones, Mr David Nicholas . . . G . . . Jul 1985
Howard, Mr Ian . . . L . . . Nov 1987
Myers, Mr Simon . . . M . . . Nov 1987
Askins, Mr Nicholas Peter . . . G . . . Nov 1989
Wilson, Mr Paul . . . L . . . Jan 1989
Drake, Miss Sophie Helena . . . G . . . Oct 1990
Cole, Mr Robert . . . M . . . Jan 1991
Wood, Mr Stephen . . . I . . . Nov 1991
Crosland, Mr James Benjamin . . . G . . . Feb 1993
Hendron, Mr Gerald James . . . L . . . Oct 1992
Barlow, Miss Sarah H . . . G . . . Oct 1993
Walker-Kane, Mr Jonathan . . . G . . . Jul 1994
Rudd, Mr Matthew . . . I . . . Nov 1994
Beckett, Mrs Jayne Louise . . . M . . . Nov 1995
Peers, Miss Nicola Jane . . . I . . . Oct 1996
Morland, Miss Camille . . . G . . . Nov 1996
Hussain, Tasaddat . . . L . . . Nov 1998
Miller, Mr Ian . . . L . . . Nov 1999
Williams, Miss Helen . . . I . . . Jul 2000
Bridge, Mr Giles . . . M . . . Jan 2000
Green, Mr Kenneth C . . . L . . . Jul 2001
Downing, Miss Emma . . . M . . . Jan 2002
Shaikh, Miss Semaab . . . L . . . Nov 2002
Hampton, Mr Peter J G . . . G . . . Jan 2003
Brown, Mr Chris I . . . M . . . Jan 2001
Modgill, Mr Alexander Jeffrey . . . L . . . Feb 2002
Power, Mr Nicholas . . . L . . . Jul 2004
Azmi, Mrs Louise Jacqueline . . . L . . . Jul 2004
Samra, Miss Sharn . . . L . . . Nov 2002
Hamilton, Mr Nigel James . . . I . . . Oct 2004
Mellor, Miss Rachel . . . L . . . Jan 2004
Larton, Miss Claire . . . L . . . Jan 2005
Langford, Miss Abigail . . . L . . . Nov 2005
Walsh, Miss Kathryn . . . M . . . Nov 2008
Durham Hall, Mr Christian . . . G . . . Jul 2009
Benson, Miss Clare . . . L . . . Jul 2009
Smith, Mr Paul . . . G . . . Nov 2008
Carlin, Mr Niall . . . I . . . Jul 2009
Hill, Mr James M (Q.C.)* . . . I . . . Jul 1984
Cannan, Mr Jonathan* . . . G . . . Nov 1989
Jamil, Miss Aisha* . . . L . . . Jan 1995
Stott, Mr Matthew* . . . M . . . Oct 2005

Chambers of Gregory Pipe

CHANCERY HOUSE CHAMBERS,
7 LISBON SQUARE, LEEDS, WEST YORKSHIRE LS1 4LY
Tel: 0113 244 6691 ***Fax:*** 0113 244 6766
Dx: 26421 LEEDS
E-mail: clerks@chanceryhouse.co.uk
Web: www.chanceryhouse.co.uk
Clerk: Colin G Hedley.
Head of Chambers:
Pipe, Mr Gregory . . . L . . . Oct 1995

Walker, Mr Mark J . . . M . . . Nov 1986
Craig, Mr Aubrey J* . . . I . . . Nov 1987
Roberts, Mr Stuart . . . M . . . Nov 1994
Brennan, Mr John . . . L . . . Jan 1996
Edwards, Mr Anthony . . . M . . . Nov 1999
Buck, Mr William . . . L . . . Jul 2001
Cherry, Mr Peter . . . L . . . Mar 2003
Crossley, Mr Dominic . . . G . . . Oct 2006
Gardiner, Miss Helen . . . G . . . Oct 2007
Gale, Mr Jonathan . . . G . . . Oct 2009

Chambers of Bernard Weatherill QC

ENTERPRISE CHAMBERS,
43 PARK SQUARE, LEEDS, WEST YORKSHIRE LS1 2NP
Tel: 0113 246 0391 ***Fax:*** 0113 242 4802
Dx: 26448 LEEDS PARK SQUARE
E-mail: leeds@enterprisechambers.com
Web: www.enterprisechambers.com
Clerk: Senior: Antony Armstrong. Junior: Joanne Caunt. Ellen Cockcroft.
Head of Chambers:
Weatherill, Mr Bernard (Q.C.); Recorder; Mediator . M . . . Jul 1974

Arden, Mr Peter (Q.C.) . . . G . . . Jul 1983
Bhaloo, Miss Zia (Q.C.) . . . M . . . Nov 1990
Morgan, Mr Charles; Junior Counsel to the Crown (Regional) . . . M . . . Jul 1978
Hutton, Miss Caroline; Mediator (CEDR) . . . M . . . Nov 1979
James, Mr Michael; Mediator . . . L . . . Feb 1976
Ife, Ms Linden . . . M . . . Nov 1982
Zelin, Mr Geoffrey . . . M . . . Jul 1984
Barker, Mr James . . . G . . . Jul 1984
Jack, Mr Adrian; Recorder . . . M . . . Nov 1986
Groves, Mr Hugo . . . G . . . Oct 1980
Jarron, Miss Stephanie . . . L . . . May 1990
Pickering, Mr James . . . M . . . Oct 1991
Jory, Mr Hugh . . . L . . . Oct 1992
Noble, Mr Andrew; Mediator . . . L . . . Nov 1992
Duddridge, Mr Robert . . . L . . . Feb 1992
Williamson, Miss Bridget . . . L . . . Feb 1993
Klein, Mr Jonathan; Junior Counsel to the Crown (Regional) . . . L . . . Oct 1992
Francis, Mr Edward . . . L . . . Nov 1995
Mauger, Miss Shanti . . . I . . . Oct 1996
Ilyas, Mr Shaiba . . . L . . . Mar 1998
Calland, Mr Timothy . . . L . . . Nov 1999
Rodger, Mr Jonathan . . . M . . . Nov 1999
McCulloch, Mr Niall . . . L . . . Oct 2000
Johnson, Mr Simon . . . M . . . Oct 2000
Murphy, Mr Damian . . . M . . . Jul 2001
Page, Miss Rebecca . . . G . . . Nov 2001
Jackson, Ms Claire . . . L . . . Mar 2002
West, Mr Matthew; Attorney - New York State . . . M . . . Nov 2000
Kalfon, Mr Olivier . . . I . . . Oct 2003
Gunaratna, Mr Kavan . . . L . . . Nov 2004
Toman, Miss Cristin . . . L . . . Jan 2004
Griffin, Miss Margaret . . . G . . . Jul 2004
Beswetherick, Mr Anthony . . . L . . . Mar 2003
Markandya, Miss Susannah . . . I . . . Oct 2005
Bond, Miss Kelly . . . M . . . Jul 2007
Heath, Mr Duncan . . . L . . . Nov 2007
Meech, Miss Jennifer . . . M . . . Oct 2008
Burslem, Miss Sarah . . . G . . . Oct 2008
Gale, Mr Phillip . . . L . . . Oct 2008
Davies, Mr James . . . L . . . Jul 2009
Maddison, Mr Matthew . . . M . . . Jul 2010
Child, Mr Jeremy* . . . L . . . Mar 2003

A leading commercial chancery set based in London, Leeds and Newcastle.

Chambers of Bill Braithwaite QC

EXCHANGE CHAMBERS,
OXFORD HOUSE, OXFORD ROW, LEEDS, WEST YORKSHIRE LS1 3BE
Tel: 0113 203 1970 ***Fax:*** 0113 345 3326
Dx: 26406 LEEDS PARK SQUARE
E-mail: info@exchangechambers.co.uk
Clerk: Seniors: Nick Buckley; Ian Spencer. Denise Sheen; Dave Haley; Leigh Daniels; Lynn Salter; Rachel Williams; Stuart Cofield; Suzanne Dutch; Kate Masher; Joe Ashcroft.
Administrator: Sally Smylie
Practice Manager: Roy Finney
Chambers Director: Tom Handley
Head of Chambers:
Braithwaite, Mr Bill (Q.C.) . . . G . . . Nov 1970

Elleray, Mr Anthony (Q.C.) . . . I . . . Jan 1977
Jones, Mr Edward Bartley (Q.C.) . . . L . . . Jul 1975
Martin, Mr Gerard James (Q.C.) . . . M . . . Jul 1978
Cawson, Mr Mark (Q.C.); Junior Counsel to the Crown(Provincial Panel); Recorder* . . . L . . . Jul 1982
Jones, Mr John Richard (Q.C.); Recorder . . . M . . . Jul 1981
Cole, Mr Gordon (Q.C.) . . . I . . . Jun 1979
Griffiths, Miss Tania (Q.C.); Recorder . . . G . . . Jul 1982
Waldron, Mr William F (Q.C.); Recorder(2000) . . . G . . . Nov 1986
Cummings, Mr Brian (Q.C.); Recorder(2005) . . . L . . . Nov 1988
Meadowcroft, Mr Stephen (Q.C.) . . . G . . . Jan 1973
Yip, Mrs Amanda (Q.C.); Recorder . . . G . . . Dec 1991
Nance, Mr Francis . . . G . . . Nov 1970
Scholes, Mr Michael . . . I . . . Jan 1996
Goode, Miss Rowena Margaret; Recorder . . . G . . . Jul 1974
Earlam, Mr Simon; Recorder . . . G . . . Feb 1975
Lamb, Mr Eric; Recorder . . . L . . . Jul 1975
Fordham, Mrs Judith; Deputy District Judge . . . I . . . Jul 1991
Jess, Dr Digby C . . . G . . . Jul 1978
Goff, Mr Anthony Thomas . . . M . . . Jul 1978
Troy, Ms Karen . . . L . . . Jan 1981
Harris, Mr Ian . . . I . . . Oct 1990
Kirtley, Mr Paul G . . . M . . . Jul 1982
Gregory, Miss Karen . . . M . . . Jul 1985
Hillman, Mr Roger; Deputy District Judge . . . G . . . Jul 1983
Cadwallader, Mr Neil; Chancery Recorder 2009 . . . I . . . Jul 1984
Taylor, Mr Paul . . . G . . . Jan 1985
Clark, Mr Paul Robert . . . M . . . May 1994
Hanbury, Mr William; P/T Immigration Judge/Deputy Judge of Upper Tribunal (Immigration & Asylum Chamber) . . . I . . . Nov 1985
Berkson, Mr Simon . . . G . . . Jul 1986
Vickers, Mr Guy . . . M . . . Nov 1986
Knifton, Mr David Alan; Recorder . . . I . . . Jul 1986
Dodd, Miss Sara . . . L . . . Jul 1987
Mulrooney, Mr Mark; P/T President of Mental Health Review Tribunal . . . M . . . Jul 1988
McCarroll, Mr John Johnston . . . I . . . Nov 1988
Browne, Mr Louis; Recorder . . . L . . . Nov 1988
Foster, Mr Ian . . . L . . . Jul 1988
Landale, Miss Tina Jeanette; Recorder . . . M . . . Jul 1988
Clark, Miss Rebecca . . . I . . . Jul 1989
Howells, Miss Catherine; Recorder . . . G . . . Jul 1989
Wood, Mr Michael . . . L . . . Nov 1989
Vaughan, Mr Simon P . . . G . . . Nov 1989
Cannan, Mr Jonathan* . . . G . . . Nov 1989
Rhind, Mr Mark A . . . M . . . May 1989
Stables, Mr Christopher . . . G . . . Oct 1990
Case, Miss Julie . . . M . . . Oct 1990
Cook, Mr Christopher . . . I . . . Oct 1990
Lavery, Mr Michael . . . G . . . Feb 1990
Potter, Mr David . . . L . . . Oct 1990
MacAdam, Mr Jason . . . L . . . Nov 1990
Golinski, Mr Robert . . . M . . . Oct 1990
Toal, Mr David . . . G . . . Feb 1990
Evans, Mr Paul Timothy . . . G . . . Oct 1992
Maynard-Connor, Mr Giles . . . I . . . Nov 1992
Woods, Ms Rachel Helen . . . G . . . Oct 1992
Ainsworth, Mr Mark; Recorder . . . L . . . Oct 1992
Naylor, Dr Kevin . . . L . . . Oct 1992
Hoare, Mr Gregory Blake . . . G . . . Nov 1992
Jarvis, Mr Oliver . . . I . . . Nov 1992
Johnson, Miss Amanda . . . G . . . Oct 1992
Kenny, Miss Charlotte . . . G . . . Nov 1993
Dudley, Mr Robert Michael . . . G . . . Oct 1993
Wyn Jones, Mr Robert . . . L . . . Jan 1993
Connolly, Mr Stephen . . . I . . . Jan 2003
Graham-Wells, Miss Alison . . . I . . . Jul 1992
Jebb, Mr Andrew John; Deputy District Judge (Mags) . . . G . . . Nov 1993
Bassano, Mr Alaric . . . G . . . Nov 1993
Garside, Mr Mark . . . I . . . Feb 1993
Pennifer, Ms Kelly . . . M . . . Nov 1994
Johnson, Mr Nicholas J . . . I . . . Nov 1994
Whittlestone, Ms Kim . . . M . . . Oct 1994
Whaites, Ms Louise . . . G . . . Jan 1994
Nolan, Mr Damian Francis Hardwicke Scholar . . . L . . . Nov 1994
Littler, Mr Richard . . . G . . . May 1994
Walker, Mr Bruce . . . G . . . Nov 1994
Myers, Mr Benjamin . . . I . . . Nov 1994
Maher, Mr Michael . . . G . . . Nov 1995
Linklater, Ms Lisa . . . I . . . Oct 1995
Gourley, Miss Claire . . . M . . . Oct 1996
Redpath, Mr Scott . . . M . . . Jan 1996
Acton, Miss Jayne . . . L . . . Mar 1996
Guirguis, Miss Sheren . . . I . . . Jan 1996
Smith, Mr Andrew William . . . L . . . Oct 1996
Dawar, Mrs Archna . . . L . . . Oct 1996
Slack, Mr Kevin John . . . G . . . Oct 1997
Farrow, Mr Adrian John . . . M . . . Jul 1997
Metcalf, Miss Louise . . . I . . . Oct 1997
Stephenson, Mr Mark . . . G . . . Nov 1997
French, Mr Jonathan . . . L . . . Nov 1997
Close, Mr Jon . . . L . . . Oct 1997
Burns, Mr Paul . . . L . . . Oct 1998
O'Brien, Ms Sarah . . . I . . . Jul 1998
Titchmarsh, Miss Katharine . . . L . . . Nov 1998
Walker, Mr Nicholas . . . L . . . Oct 1998
Jones, Miss Sian Scott; Assistant Deputy Coroner . L . . . Oct 1998
Smart, Mr Neil; Assistant Deputy Coroner . . . L . . . May 1998
Edwards, Mr Nigel D H . . . L . . . Jan 1999
Travers, Mr Daniel . . . L . . . Oct 1999
Clarke, Mr Jonathan . . . I . . . Oct 1999
Mohyuddin, Mr David Niaz . . . L . . . Oct 1999
Barnes, Mr Christopher . . . G . . . Jun 2000
Snowdon, Miss Martine . . . L . . . Oct 2000
Rogers, Mr Jonathan . . . M . . . Oct 2000
Vinson, Mr Andrew . . . M . . . Jul 2000
Ward, Mr Andrew John . . . M . . . Jul 2000
Daley, Miss Nicola . . . G . . . Jul 2000
Gooding, Miss Laura . . . L . . . Jan 2001
Shields, Mr Josh . . . M . . . Mar 2000
Temkin, Mr David . . . I . . . Jul 2000
Grattage, Mr Stephen . . . L . . . Nov 2000
Gee, Ms Caroline . . . G . . . Jan 2003
Atherton, Ms Charlotte . . . G . . . Jul 2003
Taylor, Mr Christian . . . L . . . Jan 2003
McNally, Mr Stephen . . . G . . . Nov 2003
Sutherland, Miss Sara . . . L . . . Oct 2004
Johnston, Miss Sarah . . . G . . . Jul 2004
Petterson, Mr Andrew . . . M . . . Oct 2004
Lin, Miss Esther . . . M . . . Jan 2002
Bennett, Miss Emma . . . L . . . Jan 2004
Rohrer, Mr Kerron . . . I . . . Oct 2005
Moss, Mr Edward . . . I . . . Jan 2005
Sandbach, Miss Carly . . . L . . . Jul 2006
Gutteridge, Mr Christopher . . . I . . . Oct 2006
Tetlow, Mr Richard . . . M . . . Jul 2006

11

Birrell, Mr David	I	Nov 2006
Weiss, Mr Alfred	L	Oct 2006
Cornwall, Miss Natalia	M	Jul 2007
Shires, Mr Gareth Richard	L	Jul 2007
Lowe, Mr Jonathan	L	Mar 2008
Durston, Mr Jeremy	I	Jan 2008
Whitfield, Mr Simon	L	Jul 2009
Royle, Mr Chris	L	Jul 2009
Speakman, Mr Lee	M	Jul 2009
Tucker, Mr Ian	M	Jul 2010
Rees, Mr John Charles (Q.C.)*	L	Jul 1972
Janner, Mr Daniel (Q.C.)*	M	Jan 1980
Bartle, Mr Philip M (Q.C.)*	M	Jul 1976
Turner, Mr Jonathan (Q.C.)*	G	Jul 1974
Enoch, Mr Dafydd (Q.C.)*	G	Nov 1985
Nelson, Mr Cairns (Q.C.)*	G	Jan 1987
Laws, Miss Eleanor (Q.C.)*	I	Oct 1990
Medland, Mr Simon (Q.C.)*	M	Oct 1991
James, Mr Alun Edward*	M	Nov 1986
Fox, Dr Simon*	I	Oct 1994
Maguire, Mr Andrew*	I	Nov 1988
Tyack, Mr David*	M	Nov 1994
Eyers, Mr Anthony*	I	Nov 1994
Dooher, Ms Nancy Helen*	L	Nov 1997
Chichester-Clark, Mr Adam*	M	Oct 2000

Chambers of Franz Joseph Muller QC

11 KING'S BENCH WALK,
3 PARK COURT, LEEDS, WEST YORKSHIRE LS1 2QH
Tel: 0113 297 1200 ***Fax:*** 0113 297 1201
Dx: 26433 LEEDS PARK SQUARE
E-mail: clerks@11kbw.co.uk
Clerk: Senior: Jo Pickersgill. Juniors: Jayne Turner; J McDonald; D Pain. Deborah Sykes; Lee Baines.
Administrator: Amanda Kershaw
Head of Chambers:

Muller, Mr Franz Joseph (Q.C.); Recorder	G	Feb 1961
Robertson, Mr Andrew James (Q.C.); Recorder	M	Jul 1975
Campbell, Mr Nicholas Charles Wilson (Q.C.); Recorder	I	Jul 1978
Richardson, Mr Jeremy William (Q.C.); Recorder	I	Jul 1980
Radcliffe, Mr Francis Charles Joseph	G	Nov 1962
Caswell, Mr Matthew	M	May 1968
Attwooll, Mr Christopher Benjamin; Recorder	M	Jul 1980
Wynn, Mr Toby	G	Jul 1982
Caswell, Miss Rebecca Mary	M	Jan 1983
Mallett, Mr Simon Jeremy	I	Jul 1986
Waterman, Mr Adrian (Q.C.)	I	Jun 1988
Mallett, Miss Sarah Victoria	I	Nov 1988
Brooke, Mr David Michael Graham	I	Nov 1990
Toone, Mr Robert	I	Oct 1993
Skelt, Mr Ian	L	Jul 1994
Margree, Miss Sarah	I	Oct 1996
Doswell, Mr Rupert	I	Oct 1996
Dempster, Ms Tina	G	Nov 1997
Bean, Mr Matthew	M	Nov 1997
Connolly, Miss Martina	L	Nov 1999
Farnsworth, Miss Emma	L	Nov 2000
Strong, Mr Adrian	G	Jul 2001
Spencer, Mr Joseph	G	Jul 2001

Chambers of Nicholas Braslavsky QC

KINGS CHAMBERS,
5 PARK SQUARE EAST, LEEDS, WEST YORKSHIRE LS1 2NE
Tel: 0113 242 1123 ***Fax:*** 0113 242 1124
Dx: 713113 LEEDS PARK SQUARE
E-mail: clerks@kingschambers.com
Clerk: Seniors: William Brown; Colin Griffin. Andrew Reeves; Paul Clarke; Stephen Loxton; Gary Young; Mark Ronson; Harry Young.
Administrator: Alison Brereton
Chambers Director: Debra Andres
Head of Chambers:

Braslavsky, Mr Nicholas (Q.C.)	I	Jul 1983
Sauvain, Mr Stephen (Q.C.); Assistant Boundary Commissioner	L	Jul 1977
Booth, Mr Michael (Q.C.)	L	Nov 1981
Fraser, Mr Vincent (Q.C.); Recorder	G	Jul 1981
Chaisty, Mr Paul (Q.C.); Recorder	L	Jul 1982
Manley, Mr David (Q.C.); Recorder	I	Jul 1981
Anderson, Ms Lesley (Q.C.); CEDR Accredited Mediator	M	Nov 1989
Casement, Mr David (Q.C.)	M	Oct 1992
Rawlinson, Mr Michael (Q.C.)	I	Dec 1991
Tucker, Mr Paul (Q.C.)	G	Nov 1990
Owen, Mr Eric	G	Nov 1969
Terry, Mr Jeffrey	L	Jul 1976
Lancaster, Mr Roger	M	Nov 2002
Khan, Shokat	M	Nov 1979
Barrett, Mr John; Recorder	G	May 1982
Berragan, Mr Howard Neil	G	Jul 1982
Evans, Mr Alan	L	Jul 1978
Halliwell, Mr Mark; Recorder	L	Jun 1985
Hilton, Mr Simon; Recorder	G	Nov 1987
Clayton, Mr Nigel; Recorder	I	Jul 1987
Stockley, Miss Ruth	L	Jul 1988
Ashworth, Miss Fiona	L	Jul 1988
Pass, Mr Geoffrey	M	Jul 1975
Pritchett, Mr Stephen	L	Jun 1989
Poole, Mr Nigel	M	Nov 1989
Singer, Mr Andrew; Panel of TEBAR Adjudicators	G	Nov 1990
Johnson, Mr Paul	G	Nov 2006
Burrows, Mr Simon	I	Nov 1990
Smith, Mr Matthew	L	Oct 1991
Grantham, Mr Andrew Timothy	M	Oct 1991
Carter, Mr Martin	M	Nov 1992
Horne, Mr Wilson	I	Oct 1992
Powis, Miss Lucy	G	Oct 1992
Harper, Mr Mark	I	Oct 1993
Pritchard, Miss Sarah	G	Oct 1993
Lander, Mr Richard	L	Oct 1993
Ponter, Mr Ian	M	Oct 1993
Boyd, Mr James	I	Nov 1994
Latimer, Mr Andrew	G	Nov 1995
Fullwood, Mr Adam	G	Mar 1996
McBride, Mr Gavin	M	Sep 1996
Doyle, Mr Louis G	L	Nov 1996
Easton, Mr Jonathan	G	Nov 1996
Plimmer, Ms Melanie	G	Mar 1996
Siddall, Mr Nicholas	M	Oct 1997
Young, Mr Simon	I	Nov 1998
Plaut, Mr Simon M	L	Oct 1997
Bourne, Mr Colin	G	Oct 1997
Friston, Dr Mark	M	Nov 1997
Cooper, Mr Mark	M	Mar 1998
Maguire, Mr Stephen	M	Mar 2007
Cannock, Mr Giles	L	Oct 1998
McGee, Mr Andrew	L	Nov 1998
Hall, Mr Matthew	M	Mar 1999
Mulholland, Miss Helen M	M	Oct 1999
Budworth, Mr Martin	I	Nov 1999
Brown, Miss Catherine	I	Nov 1999
Ranales-Cotos, Ms Tina	L	Oct 1999
Temple, Miss Eleanor	I	Jul 2000
Griffiths, Mr Brian J	G	Nov 1999
Walmisley, Mrs Lisa	M	Jul 2000
Lakin, Mr Paul	M	Jul 2000
Hughes, Mr Paul	M	Oct 2001
Williams, Mr Ben D	M	Jan 2001
Wheatley, Mr Geraint	G	Sep 2001
Steward, Miss Claire	L	Nov 2002
Ralph, Mr Craig	M	Jan 2002
Hunter, Mr John	L	Nov 2002
Karim, Mr Sam	G	Nov 2002
Duckworth, Miss Emily	I	Jul 2003
Mayoh, Ms Michelle	L	Jul 2003
Reid, Miss Sarah	L	Sep 2004
Gardner, Miss Francesca	L	Oct 2004
Galloway, Miss Rachel	G	Oct 2004
Allan, Miss Sophie	L	Oct 2004
Gorasia, Mr Paras	I	Oct 2005
Law, Miss Charlotte	M	Oct 2005
Harding, Mr Ben	I	Oct 2005
Dainty, Miss Cheryl	I	Jul 2006
Livingston, Mr Richard	M	Oct 2006
Ward, Mr Johnny	L	Jan 2007
Smith, Dr Nathan	L	Jan 2007
Lieberman, Gemma	M	Jan 2007
Latham, Mr Kevin	M	Oct 2007
McNamara, Mr Stephen	G	Jul 2008
d'Arcy, Miss Eleanor	L	Oct 2008
Gill, Mr Anthony	L	Jan 2008
Keay, Prof Andrew; Associate Member	L	Mar 2010
Taylor, Miss Ruth	M	Jul 2010
Gilliland, His Hon David (Q.C.)	G	Nov 1964
Freedman, Mr Clive (Q.C.)	G	Jul 1978
Crawford, Mr Colin	M	Jul 1997
Henderson, Mr James	G	Nov 1997

Chambers of Rodney Mellor Maples Jameson QC

NO 6 BARRISTERS CHAMBERS,
6 PARK SQUARE EAST, LEEDS, WEST YORKSHIRE LS1 2LW
Tel: 0113 245 9763 ***Fax:*** 0113 242 4395
Dx: 26402 LEEDS PARK SQUARE
E-mail: helen@no6.co.uk
Clerk: Kate Heald; Richard Sadler; Liz Johnson; Andrew Thornton; Carrie Hoyles; Alannah Craig.
Practice Manager: Tim Collins
Head of Chambers:

Jameson, Mr Rodney Mellor Maples (Q.C.); Recorder	I	Jul 1976
Allen, Mr James H (Q.C.); Recorder	G	Nov 1973
Mansell, Mr Richard Austin (Q.C.)	G	Nov 1991
Rose, Mr David Leslie	M	Jul 1977
Dallas, Mr Andrew T A; Recorder	G	Nov 1978
Stead, Mr Timothy Harold; Recorder	G	Nov 1979
Smith, Mr Michael Anthony; Recorder	I	Jul 1980
Caswell, Miss Rebecca Mary	M	Jan 1983
Gargan, Mr Mark Patrick; Recorder	M	Jul 1983
Hill-Baker, Mr Jeremy Robert; Recorder	I	Jul 1983
Frieze, Mr Robin Bennett	L	Jul 1985
Hunt, Ms Alison J	G	Jul 1986
Troy, Mrs Jill Mary	M	Jul 1986
Capstick, Mr Timothy	G	Jul 1986
Clews, Mr Richard Anthony	G	Jul 1986
Clark, Mr Neil Andrew	I	Jul 1987
Hatton, Mr Andrew	I	Nov 1987
Williamson, Miss Melanie J	I	Oct 1990
Smales, Mrs Suzanne	I	Nov 1990
Mitchell, Mr Andrew Jonathan Mills	L	Nov 1991
Moulson, Mr Peter	G	Jul 1992
Kelbrick, Mr Anthony M; Recorder	G	Jul 1992
Taylor, Miss Kitty	M	Oct 1992
Gioserano, Mr Richard Stephen	G	Nov 1992
Sukhbir, Singh Bassra	M	May 1993
Hill, Mr Nicholas Ian	L	Oct 1993
Caswell, Mr Benjamin Cecil	M	Oct 1993
Al'Hassan, Khadim	I	Nov 1993
Iqbal, Mr Abdul S	G	Jan 1994
Wilson, Mr Adam	I	Nov 1994
Barker, Mr Nicholas	G	Dec 1994
Valli, Yunis	L	Jul 1995
Batiste, Mr Simon Anthony	L	Nov 1995
Melly, Miss Kama	M	Jan 1997
Megyery, Ayshea Khatune	M	Oct 1997
Collins, Mr Michael	M	Jan 1998
Wright, Mr Richard	G	Oct 1998
Griffiths, Mr Brian J	G	Nov 1999
Holmes, Ms Helen	I	Jul 2000
Robinson, Miss Katherine	G	Jul 2002
Worsley, Ms Charlotte H G	M	Oct 2002
Saunders, Mr Mark	I	Oct 2002
Semple, Mr Gordon	G	Oct 2003
Korobowicz, Ms Natalia W	I	Oct 2004
Renvoize, Mr Edward	L	Oct 2004
Coade, Ms Georgina	G	Jul 2005
Prest, Mr Charles	I	Nov 2005
Broughton, Miss Kerrie	I	Mar 2006
Switalski, Mr Stephen	I	Mar 2006
Hollins, Miss Catherine	L	Jul 2007
Bissett, Miss Kate	L	Jul 2009

Chambers of Robert Steen Smith QC

PARK COURT CHAMBERS,
16 PARK PLACE, LEEDS, WEST YORKSHIRE LS1 2SJ
Tel: 0113 243 3277 ***Fax:*** 0113 242 1285
Dx: 26401 LEEDS PARK SQUARE
E-mail: clerks@parkcourtchambers.co.uk
Administrator: Karen Wade
Chambers Director: Michael Meeson (Chief Executive)
Head of Chambers:

Smith, Mr Robert Steen (Q.C.)	I	Jul 1971
Lodge, Mr Anton James Corduff (Q.C.)	G	Nov 1966
Bourne-Arton, Mr Simon Nicholas (Q.C.)	I	Nov 1975
Hatton, Mr David William (Q.C.)	G	Jul 1976
MacDonald, Mr Alistair Neil (Q.C.)	G	Jul 1983
Bayliss, Mr Thomas William Maxwell (Q.C.)	I	Jul 1977
Jackson, Mr Simon Malcolm Dermot (Q.C.)	G	Nov 1982
Cox, Mr Bryan R (Q.C.)	M	Oct 1979
Phillips, Mr Simon Benjamin (Q.C.)	I	Jul 1985
Greaney, Mr Paul Richard (Q.C.)	I	Oct 1993
Hartley, Mr Timothy Guy	G	Jul 1970
Reid, Mr Paul William	I	Jul 1975
Sterling, Miss Valerie	G	Jul 1981
Brook, Mr Ian	L	Jan 1983
Mason, Mr Nicholas	G	Jul 1984
Wigin, Miss Caroline Rosemary	I	Jul 1984
Uttley, Mr Stephen	I	Apr 1986
Beattie, Miss Sharon Michelle	I	Nov 1986
Taylor, Mr Alan Jeremy	L	Nov 1986
Bashir, Nadim	M	Nov 1988
Sharpe, Mr Martin Laurence	M	Nov 1989
Turner, Mrs Taryn Jones	G	Feb 1990
Tucker, Mr Ashley Russell	M	Nov 1990
Tehrani, Mr Christopher I	I	Nov 1990
Patel, Elyas Mohammed	G	Nov 1991
Cross, Ms Joanna	L	Oct 1992
Lumley, Mr Nicholas	L	Oct 1992
Williams, Mr Paul	I	Jan 1994
Pitter, Mr Jason	G	Jun 1994
Widdett, Miss Ceri L	G	Nov 1994
Terris, Ms Sally	M	Nov 1997
Anderson, Mr Simon P B	L	Nov 1997
White, Mr Steven	I	Jan 1998
Green, Mr Samuel	L	Oct 1998
Offer, Mr Alex	M	Oct 1998
Parsons, Mr Glen	L	Jan 1999
Skittrell, Miss Elaine	M	Jan 1999
Zakers, Mr Franklyn R	L	Nov 1999
Batts, Ms Gillian	L	Nov 1999
Hussain, Mr Gul Nawaz	G	Jan 2000
Taylor, Mr Alex	I	Oct 2000
Cranidge, Miss Ruth	L	Oct 2001
Sherwood, Miss Hannah	M	Jul 2002
Escoriza, Miss Natalia	M	Nov 2002
Hudson, Miss Chloe	L	Apr 2003
de la Poer, Mr Nicholas	G	Jul 2003
Knowles, Miss Catherine	M	Jul 2004
Fairley, Miss Chloe	G	Oct 2004
Normington, Mr James	L	Jan 2005
Kitzing, Miss Susanna	M	Jan 2005
Nadeem, Mr Afshan	L	Jan 2005
Beattie, Ms Annabel	I	Jul 2005
Wastall, Mr Andrew	G	Oct 2005
Mercer, Miss Kirsten	I	Jan 2006
Birkby, Mr Adam	M	Sep 2006
Fry, Miss Eleanor	M	Nov 2007
Aspinall, Mr Chris	M	Jan 2008
Campbell, Mr Benjamin	M	Jan 2008
Alistari, Nicoleta	M	Jan 2009
Dodson, Joanna (Q.C.)*	M	Nov 1971
Carter, Mr Peter (Q.C.)*	G	Jul 1974
Price, Mr Richard M (Q.C.) OBE*	G	Nov 1969
Young, Mr David*	M	Jul 1986
Singh, Mr Dapinderpaul*	M	Jul 2000

Chambers of Neil Davey QC

39 PARK SQUARE,
LEEDS, WEST YORKSHIRE LS1 2NU
Tel: 0113 245 6633 ***Fax:*** 0113 242 1567
Dx: 26407 LEEDS PARK SQUARE
E-mail: seniorclerk@39parksquarechambers.co.uk
Clerk: Mark Heald.
Head of Chambers:

Davey, Mr Neil (Q.C.)	M	Jul 1978
Bubb, Mr Timothy	G	Jul 1970
Robertshaw, Mr Martin	M	Nov 1977
Moore, Mr Anthony	L	Jul 1984
Armbrister, Mr Allan	I	Jan 1984
Reevell, Mr Simon	L	Oct 1990
Andrews, Mr Samuel J	G	Nov 1991
Young, Miss Rebecca Leah	I	Nov 1993
Reevell, Miss Louise	L	Oct 2001
Williams, Miss Cassie	M	Jan 2002
Harding, Mr Mathew	L	Oct 2002
Skyner, Mr Robert	M	Mar 2003
Ward, Mr David	L	Jul 2004
Stuckey, Miss Kathryn	I	Oct 2004
Canning, Mr Richard	L	Nov 2004
Moran, Mr Christopher	M	Jan 2007
Morris, Mr Philip	M	Jul 2011
Dent, Mr Adrian*	L	Jul 1974
Hurst, Mr Brian*	M	Jul 1983

Chambers of Rodney E Ferm and Stephen J Glover

37 PARK SQUARE CHAMBERS,
LEEDS, WEST YORKSHIRE LS1 2NY
Tel: 0113 243 9422 ***Fax:*** 0113 242 4229
Dx: 26405 LEEDS
E-mail: chambers@no37.co.uk
Clerk: Ian Spencer.
Administrator: Linda Parker
Head of Chambers:

Ferm, Mr Rodney E	M	Jul 1972
Glover, Mr Stephen J	M	Jul 1978
Hogg, The Hon Douglas Martin (Q.C.) MP*	L	Jul 1968
Oldham, Mrs Frances (Q.C.)*	G	Jul 1977

Dunning, Mr John . . . I . . . Jul 1973
Sleightholme, Mr John T . . . G . . . Nov 1982
Fleming, Mr Paul S . . . G . . . Nov 1983
Ginsburg, Mrs Amanda . . . L . . . Jul 1985
Apfel, Mr Freddy . . . M . . . Jul 1986
Lindsay, Mr Jeremy M H . . . G . . . Jul 1986
Hill, Mr Piers . . . I . . . Jul 1987
Cains, Miss Linda H . . . M . . . Oct 1990
Lee, Miss Taryn J . . . I . . . Jul 1992
Frith, Mr Nicholas John . . . G . . . Oct 1992
Ford, Miss Caroline E . . . G . . . Oct 1993
Blackmore, Miss Sarah . . . I . . . Oct 1993
Burdon, Mr Michael Stewart . . . L . . . Nov 1993
Gore, Mr Mark . . . M . . . Oct 1994
Taylor, Mr David . . . I . . . Jan 1995
Pye, Miss Jayne M . . . M . . . May 1995
Josling, Mr William . . . L . . . Nov 1995
Shaw, Miss Elizabeth . . . M . . . Nov 1996
Thompson, Miss Clare . . . M . . . Oct 1998
Thomas, Miss Jacqueline L . . . L . . . Oct 2000
Chippendale, Miss Emma L . . . M . . . Jul 2002
Butters, Mr Richard J . . . M . . . Oct 2001
Edwards, Mr Paul . . . L . . . Mar 2002
Andrews, Miss Natasha E . . . L . . . Nov 2002
Madderson, Miss Naomi M . . . G . . . Oct 2003
Eastwood, Miss Charlotte . . . M . . . Nov 2003
Wilson, Mr Jonathan . . . L . . . Mar 2005
Zaman, Miss Shazma . . . M . . . Nov 2003
Couch, Mr Stephen . . . I . . . Mar 2005

Chambers of Stuart C Brown QC

PARKLANE PLOWDEN,
19 WESTGATE, LEEDS, WEST YORKSHIRE
LS1 2RD
Tel: 0113 228 5000 ***Fax:*** 0113 228 1500
Dx: 26404 LEEDS

Chambers of Guy A Kearl QC

ST PAULS CHAMBERS,
5TH FLOOR, ST PAULS HOUSE, 23 PARK SQUARE SOUTH, LEEDS, WEST YORKSHIRE
LS1 2ND
Tel: 0113 245 5866 ***Fax:*** 0113 245 5807
Dx: 26410 LEEDS PARK SQUARE
E-mail: clerks@stpaulschambers.com
Clerk: Senior: Jayne Drake.
Administrator: Vine Pemberton Joss
Head of Chambers:
Kearl, Mr Guy A (Q.C.); Recorder . . . M . . . Sep 1982

Bethel, Mr Martin (Q.C.); Deputy High Court Judge . I . . . Nov 1965
Nolan, Mr Benjamin (Q.C.); Deputy High Court Judge . . . M . . . Jul 1971
Sangster, Mr Nigel H (Q.C.); Recorder . . . M . . . Nov 1976
Myerson, Mr Simon (Q.C.); Recorder . . . M . . . Jan 1986
Stubbs, Mr Andrew J (Q.C.); Recorder . . . M . . . Jul 1988
Devlin, Mr Jonathan Nicholas Ponton . . . I . . . Nov 1978
Barnett, Mr Jeremy V; Recorder . . . G . . . Jul 1980
Standfast, Mr Philip Arthur . . . I . . . Jul 1980
Mason, Mr Stephen* . . . M . . . Jan 1988
MacAdam, Mr Jason* . . . L . . . Nov 1990
Duffy, Mr Derek J . . . G . . . Mar 1997
Bickler, Mr Simon Lloyd . . . I . . . Nov 1988
Haslam, Mr Andrew P; Recorder . . . G . . . Oct 1991
Mairs, Mr Robin . . . G . . . Oct 1992
Sandiford, Mr Jonathan; Recorder . . . G . . . Oct 1992
Crossley, Mr Steven R . . . I . . . Nov 1992
Saxton, Ms Nicola Helen . . . I . . . Nov 1992
Wilson, Mr Scott* . . . L . . . Nov 1993
Harrison, Mr John Foster . . . L . . . Oct 1994
Crossley, Miss Joanne . . . M . . . Jan 1994
Bates, Mr Alexander A . . . G . . . Oct 1994
Gregory, Miss Ann-Marie . . . M . . . Nov 1994
Smith, Mr Robert . . . L . . . Jul 1995
Watson, Ms Kirstie A . . . M . . . Oct 1995
Edwards, Mr Nigel Royston . . . L . . . Nov 1995
Dry, Mr Nicholas D . . . L . . . Nov 1996
Hussain, Miss Rukshanda . . . G . . . Sep 1998
Campbell, Mr Alasdair . . . L . . . Jan 1999
Breen-Lawton, Miss Denise . . . G . . . Jan 2000
Stranex, Mr Andrew . . . G . . . Jul 2000
Bourne-Arton, Mr James . . . I . . . Jan 2001
Butt, Miss Nasra* . . . G . . . Oct 2002
Jones, Mr Alun J . . . L . . . Jul 2003
Graham, Ms Danielle . . . G . . . Oct 2003
Lake, Mr James . . . I . . . Oct 2005
Murray, Miss Joanne . . . M . . . Mar 2006
Nixon, Mr Andrew . . . G . . . Jun 2006
Dobkin, Mr Matthew . . . G . . . Jan 2007
Welch, Mr Voldi . . . M . . . Oct 2008
Beaumont, Mr Adam . . . L . . . Jul 2009

Chambers of Julian N Goose QC

ZENITH CHAMBERS,
10 PARK SQUARE, LEEDS, WEST YORKSHIRE
LS1 2LH
Tel: 0113 245 5438 ***Fax:*** 0113 242 3515
Dx: 26412 LEEDS PARK SQUARE
E-mail: clerks@zenithchambers.co.uk
Clerk: Elizabeth Gage; Clive Taylor.
Practice Manager: Andrew Argyle (Chief Executive)
Head of Chambers:
Goose, Julian N (Q.C.); Recorder . . . L . . . Jul 1984

Campbell, Andrew (Q.C.); Recorder . . . M . . . Nov 1972
Nathan, David (Q.C.); Associate Tenant . . . M . . . Nov 1971
Corbett, James (Q.C.); Recorder; Associate Tenant . I . . . Jul 1975
Lyons, Mr Timothy (Q.C.); Associate Tenant . . . I . . . Jul 1980
Heaton, Clive (Q.C.); Recorder . . . G . . . Jul 1992
Collins, John M . . . M . . . Jul 1956
Sterling, Robert; Associate Tenant . . . G . . . Jul 1970
Connerty, Anthony; Associate Tenant . . . I . . . Jul 1974
Bradshaw, David; Recorder . . . L . . . Jul 1975
Behrens, James; Associate Tenant . . . M . . . Jul 1979
Hall, David P . . . G . . . Jul 1980
Worrall, John R G . . . G . . . Jul 1984
Hajimitsis, Anthony . . . I . . . Nov 1984
Bickerdike, Roger . . . L . . . Nov 1986
Newman, Austin . . . I . . . Jan 1987
Greenan, Sarah . . . G . . . Jul 1987
Wilson-Barnes, Lucy; Associate Tenant . . . I . . . Jul 1989
Read, Simon . . . I . . . Nov 1989
Howd, Stephen . . . M . . . Jul 1989
Holroyd, John J . . . G . . . Nov 1989
Hookway, Aelred . . . G . . . Nov 1990
Kealey, Simon . . . I . . . Apr 1991
Exall, Gordon . . . L . . . Jul 1991
Barber, Philip . . . G . . . Nov 1991
Boumphrey, John . . . I . . . Jan 1992
Hayes, John . . . L . . . Nov 1992
Storey, Tom . . . G . . . Feb 1993
Crossley, Justin . . . I . . . Nov 1993
Bindloss, Edward; Recorder . . . G . . . Nov 1993
Pema, Anesh . . . M . . . Nov 1994
Henley, Mark . . . L . . . Oct 1994
Carroll, Jonathan; Recorder; Deputy Judge Advocate (Courts Martial Judge) . . . G . . . Nov 1994
Potts, Warren; Associate Tenant . . . M . . . Jul 1995
Wordsworth, Philippa . . . G . . . Oct 1995
Wilson, Andrew . . . G . . . Nov 1995
Tyson, Thomas David . . . G . . . Oct 1995
Browne, Gerald Robert . . . I . . . Nov 1995
Kelly, Geraldine . . . M . . . Mar 1996
Smith, Chris . . . L . . . Jan 1997
Madan, Pankaj . . . M . . . Sep 1997
Greatorex, Helen . . . I . . . Mar 1997
Branchflower, George . . . L . . . Mar 1997
Worsley, Nicholas . . . M . . . Oct 1998
Allman, Miss Marisa . . . L . . . Oct 1998
Shaw, Howard James . . . M . . . Oct 1999
Ross, Simon . . . L . . . Nov 1999
Phillipson, Nicola . . . L . . . Jun 1999
Darlington, Elizabeth . . . M . . . Oct 1998
Perkins, Simon . . . G . . . Nov 1999
McCallum, Louise . . . G . . . May 1999
Rippon, Louise Jane; Associate Tenant . . . M . . . Jun 2000
Exall, Rosemary . . . M . . . Dec 2000
Bell, Jillian . . . I . . . Aug 2000
Stuart-Lofthouse, Michelle . . . L . . . Nov 2001
McKinlay, Kate . . . M . . . Oct 2001
Haywood, Jennifer; Associate Tenant . . . L . . . Jul 2001
Hartshorn, Sabrina . . . M . . . Nov 2001
Vodanovic, Vilma . . . G . . . Oct 2002
Abengowe, Mr Julian . . . I . . . Nov 2002
Strange, Miss Jessica . . . I . . . Jun 2003
Jamieson, Stuart Owen . . . G . . . Oct 2003
Duffy, Catherine . . . L . . . Oct 2003
Lawrenson, Ms Sarah . . . M . . . Oct 2003
Coyle, Mr Anthony . . . L . . . Nov 2003
Donkin, Matthew . . . I . . . Jul 2004
Marcus, Mr Peter . . . M . . . Jul 2004
Garner, Mr Stephen . . . G . . . Oct 2004
Garnham, Clare . . . G . . . Jan 2005
Khan, Ruwena . . . I . . . Jul 2005
Hartley, Bronia . . . G . . . Jan 2006
Swoboda, John-Paul . . . G . . . Jul 2006
Sowden, Ms Lucy . . . I . . . Jul 2006
Weiss, Mr Alfred . . . L . . . Oct 2006
Pratt, Mr Ashley . . . G . . . Oct 2006
Hudson, Mr John . . . I . . . Nov 2006
Lawley, Frances . . . L . . . Jan 2007
Myers, John . . . I . . . Mar 2007
Ahmed, Miss Sobia . . . L . . . Oct 2007
Shaw, Jonathan . . . I . . . Jan 2008
Donnelley, Mr Lewis . . . M . . . Jul 2008
Pye, Mr Derek . . . L . . . Jul 2008
Clappison, James* . . . G . . . Nov 1981

LEICESTER

Chambers of Faizul Aqtab Siddiqi

JUSTICE COURT CHAMBERS,
23 WYKIN ROAD, HINCKLEY, LEICESTER
LE10 0HU
Tel: 024 7632 5859
E-mail: siddiqi@justicecourtchambers.com
Clerk: Fareed Chedie.
Practice Manager: Rizwan Ali
Head of Chambers:
Siddiqi, Mr Faizul Aqtab . . . L . . . Jul 1990

Chambers of Stephen Lowne

KCH GARDEN SQUARE CHAMBERS,
96A NEW WALK, LEICESTER LE1 7EA
Tel: 0115 941 8851 ***Fax:*** 0116 298 7501
Dx: 17003 LEICESTER 2
E-mail: clerks@kchgardensquare.co.uk
Head of Chambers:
Lowne, Mr Stephen . . . I . . . Jul 1981

Philo, Mr Noel P . . . G . . . Feb 1975
Howlett, Mr James Anthony . . . M . . . Jul 1980
Gallagher, Mr Patrick . . . G . . . Jul 1984
Dhadli, Mrs Perminder . . . M . . . Nov 1984
Cranny, Miss Amanda . . . L . . . Nov 1984
Bradley, Ms Caroline . . . M . . . Jul 1985
Cranmer-Brown, Mr Michael Timothy . . . M . . . Nov 1986
Eley, Mr Jonathan . . . M . . . Jun 1987
Van Der Zwart, Mr Mark Andrew . . . M . . . Feb 1988
Way, Mr Ian . . . I . . . Nov 1988
Munt, Mr Alastair . . . G . . . Jul 1989
Dee, Mr Jonathan . . . I . . . Nov 1989
Taylor, Mr Andrew Peter . . . G . . . Nov 1989
Knowles, Mr Mark . . . M . . . Nov 1989
Lody, Mr Stuart T . . . G . . . Nov 1991
Gibbs, Mr Philip . . . I . . . Oct 1991
Leonard, Mrs Edna . . . G . . . Oct 1992
Straw, Mr Jonathan . . . M . . . Oct 1992
Janes, Mr Jeremy . . . L . . . Nov 1992
Macdonald, Miss Sheila . . . M . . . Feb 1993
Warburton, Ms Julie . . . M . . . Oct 1993
Cartwright, Mr Ivan . . . G . . . Nov 1993
Moore, Nicola . . . L . . . Jan 1993
Ahya, Miss Sonal . . . L . . . Sep 1995
Stobart, Mrs Tracey . . . M . . . Jan 1995
Soubry, Ms Anna . . . I . . . Nov 1995
Wylie, Mr Neil . . . G . . . Nov 1996
Ewing, Mr Hal . . . G . . . Nov 1997
Hale, Mrs Grace . . . G . . . Mar 1998
Beaumont, Mr Andrew . . . L . . . Jul 1999
Watson, Mr Mark . . . G . . . Jul 1999
Briden, Miss Sarah . . . I . . . Jul 1999
Thomas, Mr James . . . M . . . Jan 1999
Robson, Mr Jeremy . . . M . . . Oct 1999
Bowe, Mr Patrick . . . L . . . Jan 2000
James-Moore, Siward . . . L . . . Jul 2000
George, Mr Timothy David . . . I . . . Oct 2000
Lowe, Mr Christopher . . . M . . . Jul 2001
Kabweru-Namulemu, Miss Karen . . . L . . . Jul 2001
Harrison, Esther . . . I . . . Jan 2002
Cleary, Mr James . . . M . . . Nov 2003
Russell, Mr Tom . . . I . . . Jan 2004
Sapstead, Miss Louise . . . L . . . Jul 2004
Williams, Ms Anne . . . M . . . Mar 2005
Mansfield, Mr Ben . . . I . . . Jan 2005
Cox, Mr Jonathan . . . L . . . Jan 2005
Mellor, Faye . . . M . . . Jan 2005
Mansfield, Ms Nadia . . . I . . . Nov 2006
Holt, Mrs Jane . . . M . . . Oct 2006
Gunstone, Mr Giles . . . M . . . Jul 2007
Veitch, Mr Steven . . . L . . . Nov 2007
Wells, Mr Chris . . . I . . . Jan 2007

Chambers of Nancy Hillier

KING STREET CHAMBERS,
65-67 KING STREET CHAMBERS, LEICESTER
LE1 6RP
Tel: 0116 254 7710 ***Fax:*** 0116 247 0145
Dx: 10873 LEICESTER 1

Chambers of Mark Wyatt

2 NEW STREET,
LEICESTER LE1 5NA
Tel: 0116 262 5906 ***Fax:*** 0116 251 2023
Dx: 10849 LEICESTER
E-mail: clerks@2newstreet.co.uk
Clerk: Senior: Paul Burtenshaw.
Practice Manager: Dorothy Stoneley
Head of Chambers:
Wyatt, Mr Mark . . . M . . . Jul 1976

Spencer, Mr Paul . . . I . . . Nov 1965
Clark, Mr Timothy . . . M . . . Jul 1974
Allen, Mr David . . . M . . . Jul 1975
Neal, Prof Alan . . . G . . . Jul 1975
Scott, Miss Alexandra . . . G . . . Jul 1983
Barr, Mr Edward . . . I . . . Oct 1983
Barnett, Miss Sally . . . M . . . Nov 1987
Monk, Mr David . . . M . . . Jul 1991
Peet, Mr Andrew . . . I . . . Oct 1991
McCandless, Mr Paul . . . L . . . Nov 1991
Herbert, Mr David . . . G . . . Oct 1992
Herbert, Mrs Rebecca . . . I . . . Oct 1993
Gerry, Miss Felicity . . . M . . . Jan 1994
Allingham-Nicholson, Mrs Elizabeth . . . L . . . Oct 1995
Davies, Miss Carol E . . . M . . . Oct 1995

Chambers of John Snell

NEW WALK CHAMBERS,
27 NEW WALK, LEICESTER LE1 6TE
Tel: 0871 200 1298 ***Fax:*** 0871 200 1288
Dx: 723940 LEICESTER 22
E-mail: clerks@newwalkchambers.co.uk
Head of Chambers:
Snell, Mr John; Pupil Master . . . I . . . Jul 1973

Jones, Mr Geraint (Q.C.)* . . . M . . . Jul 1976
Bown, Mr Philip Clive* . . . M . . . Nov 1974
Rees, Mr Robert Charles David; Pupil Master . . . M . . . Feb 1978
Bates, Mr Peter S . . . L . . . Jul 1978
Fitton-Brown, Ms Rebeca; Pupil Master . . . I . . . Apr 1981
George, Mr Nicholas . . . I . . . Jul 1983
Lawrence, Mr Nalla; Deputy District Judge; Immigrations Adjudicator & Special Adjudicator (Part Time); Pupil Master . . . M . . . May 1987
Monk, Mr David . . . M . . . Jul 1991
Willetts, Mr Andrew . . . M . . . Jan 1997
Maginn, Miss Olivia . . . L . . . Jan 1998
Reed, Mr Simon; Pupil Master . . . G . . . Mar 1998
Danton, Ms Kirstie . . . L . . . Jul 1999
Steele, Ms Jennifer . . . M . . . Jul 2002
Allen, Mr Christopher . . . G . . . Jul 2002
Eveleigh-Winstone, Ms Adelle . . . G . . . Oct 2003
Bull, Ms Nathalie . . . I . . . Jul 2004
Dasani, Kajal . . . M . . . Oct 2004
David, Mr Alastair Robert Oulpe . . . L . . . Jul 2005
Hasson, Mr James . . . I . . . Nov 2006
Walker, Pauline . . . M . . . Jul 2008
Brankovic, Victoria . . . I . . . Jul 2008
Winter, Louise . . . L . . . Jul 2009

4 OVERDALE ROAD,
KNIGHTON, LEICESTER LE2 3YH
Tel: 0116 288 3930 ***Fax:*** 0116 288 3930

Chambers of James T Nisbett

7 WESTMEATH AVENUE,
EVINGTON, LEICESTER LE5 6SS
Tel: 0116 212 8497 ***Fax:*** 0116 212 4527
Clerk: Agnes Nisbett.
Head of Chambers:
Nisbett, Mr James T . . . L . . . Jun 1973

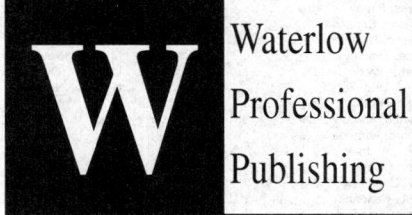

11

LEWES, East Sussex

1 KBW CHAMBERS,
174 HIGH STREET, LEWES, EAST SUSSEX
BN7 1YE
Tel: 01273 402600 ***Fax:*** 01273 402609
Dx: 97398 LEWES 4
Administrator: Sal Robarts
Chambers Director: Sue Gray

Chambers of John Collins and Jeremy Gold QC

WESTGATE CHAMBERS,
64 HIGH STREET, LEWES, EAST SUSSEX
BN7 1XG
Tel: 01273 480510 ***Fax:*** 01273 483179
Dx: 50250 LEWES 4
E-mail: clerks@westgate-chambers.co.uk
Clerk: Seniors: Sumaya Gilmore; Jason Britcher.
Head of Chambers:
Collins, Mr John ... M ... Jul 1967
Gold, Mr Jeremy (Q.C.); Recorder ... M ... Jul 1977

Urquhart, Miss Doris ... M ... Apr 1968
Hall, Mr Nicholas ... G ... Jul 1973
Argent, Mr Gavin ... M ... Jul 1978
Campbell, Mr Graham ... G ... Jul 1979
Meredith, Mr Philip Granville ... I ... Jul 1979
Rowling, Miss Fiona ... I ... Jan 1980
Hamblin, Mr Nicholas ... L ... Nov 1981
Russell, Mr Guy ... G ... Nov 1985
Judge, Mr Andrew John ... M ... Jul 1986
Jakens, Miss Claire; Recorder ... M ... Jul 1988
Marsden-Lynch, Mr John Francis ... M ... Nov 1988
Lindop, Ms Sarah ... G ... Nov 1989
Wainwright, Mr Jeremy ... G ... Oct 1990
Ray-Crosby, Miss Irena ... M ... Nov 1990
Le Prevost, Mrs Aviva ... I ... Nov 1990
Lamb, Mr Jeffrey ... M ... Oct 1992
Gray, Miss Jennifer ... M ... Oct 1992
Frith, Miss Alexandra ... L ... Feb 1993
Howe, Miss Sara ... L ... Oct 1993
Edwards, Mr Jonathan ... L ... Nov 1994
Hancock, Ms Maria ... G ... Nov 1995
Thorne, Miss Sarah Louise ... M ... Nov 1995
Davies, Miss Rebecca ... L ... Nov 1996
McMillan, Ms Carol ... M ... Jan 1996
Cherrill, Mrs Beverley ... M ... Nov 1996
Hossain, Mr Ahmed ... G ... Nov 1996
Watson, Mr Duncan ... I ... Oct 1997
Selby, Andrew ... G ... Nov 1997
Clarke, Miss Amanda ... M ... Jul 1998
Taylor, Miss Linda ... I ... Oct 1998
Down, Miss Barbara ... L ... Nov 1999
Walsh, Miss Martha ... M ... Nov 2000
Palmer (nee Biggs), Miss Nicola ... M ... Jul 2001
Rhodri, Mr James ... I ... Jul 2002
Mehta, Miss Anita ... L ... Oct 2002
Wilson, Miss Charmaine ... I ... Jul 2003
Winslett, Mr Frank ... M ... Mar 2004
Sadler, Miss Rhiannon ... M ... Jul 2004
Stephens, Mr Andrew ... L ... Jul 2004
Loeb, Miss Dinah ... M ... Nov 2004
Knight, Mr Peter ... M ... Nov 2005

LIVERPOOL, Merseyside

Chambers of Scott Donovan

ATLANTIC CHAMBERS,
4-6 COOK STREET, LIVERPOOL, MERSEYSIDE
L2 9QU
Tel: 0151 236 4421 ***Fax:*** 0151 236 1559
Dx: 14176 LIVERPOOL 1
E-mail: clerks@atlanticchambers.co.uk
Web: www.atlanticchambers.co.uk
Clerk: Head Clerk: Lee Cadwallader; Deputy Head Clerk: Gary Quinn.
Administrator: Julie Evans
Head of Chambers:
Donovan, Scott ... L ... Jul 1975

Benson, John (Q.C.) ... M ... Jul 1978
Driver, Stuart (Q.C.) ... G ... Nov 1988
Edis, Andrew (Q.C.) ... M ... Jul 1980
Whyte, Anne (Q.C.) ... G ... Feb 1993
Gorton, Simon (Q.C.) ... I ... Jul 1988
Knowles, Gwynneth (Q.C.) ... G ... Nov 1993
Haselhurst, Ian ... G ... Jul 1976
Ginniff, Nigel ... I ... Nov 1978
Sellars, Michael ... I ... Jul 1980
Thomas, Gareth ... G ... Jul 1977
Howe, Ruth ... L ... Oct 1983
Corless, John ... M ... Nov 1984
Woolfenden, Ivan ... M ... Jul 1986
Ryan, Nicholas ... G ... Jan 1984
Booth, Simon ... L ... Jan 1985
Pickering, Andrew ... L ... Nov 1987
Lund, Celia ... L ... Nov 1988
Sharpe, Malcolm ... L ... Jul 1989
Beattie, Ann ... M ... Jul 1989
Sellers, Graham ... M ... Oct 1990
Dawes, Simon ... I ... Oct 1990
Johnson, Christine ... I ... Nov 1991
Jackson, Nicholas ... I ... Nov 1992
Grace, Timothy ... M ... Nov 1993
Green, David ... L ... Oct 1993
Davey, Michelle ... L ... Nov 1993
Banks, Rachael ... L ... Nov 1993
Williams, Andrew ... G ... Nov 1994
Howard, Amanda ... I ... Nov 1994
Banks, Andrew ... G ... Jul 1995
Grundy, Liam ... I ... Jul 1995
Prior, Charles ... L ... Oct 1995
Horne, Kenderik ... L ... Mar 1996
Hillas, Samantha ... I ... Oct 1996
Delaney, Kenneth ... I ... Oct 1996
McDonald, Lawrence ... I ... Oct 1996
Downey, Neil ... M ... Mar 1997
Bennett, Ms Abigail ... M ... Nov 1998
Smith, Sophie ... L ... Oct 1999
Gorton, Carl ... I ... Nov 1999
Valentine, Justin ... M ... Oct 1999
Bonner, Lee ... L ... Nov 2000
Livesley, Rhian ... G ... Jul 2000
Sigee, Peter ... M ... Nov 2002
Hughes-Deane, Charlotte ... L ... Nov 2002
Chester, Mark ... L ... Oct 2002
Armstrong, Michael ... I ... Oct 2002
Cline, Robert ... G ... Oct 2002
Fraser, Donald ... I ... Jul 2003
Sumner, Daian ... G ... Jan 2004
Tinkler, David ... L ... Oct 2004
Derbyshire, Hugh ... G ... Jan 2004
Wale, Elizabeth ... I ... Jul 2004
Mensah, Martin ... I ... Oct 2004
Cuddy, Natalie ... I ... Jan 2004
Cox, Olivia ... M ... Nov 2007
Patience, James ... M ... Jan 2007
Eastwood, Shannon ... I ... Oct 2007
Bar, Monika ... L ... Oct 2008
McCann, Katie ... L ... Oct 2009

This Chamber with over 60 Barristers is based in Liverpool and led by Scott Donovan. You may contact any of our clerks at any time by sending a message to clerks@atlanticchambers.co.uk.

CASTLE STREET CHAMBERS,
2ND FLOOR, 42 CASTLE STREET, LIVERPOOL, MERSEYSIDE L2 7LD
Tel: 0151 242 0500 ***Fax:*** 0151 242 0505
Dx: 14169 LIVERPOOL

Chambers of John Raymond McDermott QC

CHAVASSE COURT CHAMBERS,
18 QUEEN AVENUE, LIVERPOOL, MERSEYSIDE
L2 4TX
Tel: 0151 229 2030 ***Fax:*** 0151 229 2039
Dx: 14223 LIVERPOOL
E-mail: clerks@chavassechambers.co.uk
Web: www.chavassechambers.co.uk
Clerk: Senior: Colin Derek Cubley. Sandra McConnell; Alan Harvey; Christopher Jones; Mark Shannon.
Head of Chambers:
McDermott, Mr John Raymond (Q.C.) ... G ... Nov 1976

Baxter, Mr Gerald Pearson ... L ... Jul 1971
Pepper, Miss Theresa; Recorder ... G ... Nov 1973
Pickavance, Mr Graham ... G ... Nov 1973
Cliff, Miss Elizabeth Dunbar ... M ... Jul 1975
Rose, Mr Anthony Kenneth ... M ... Nov 1978
Barraclough, Mr Anthony Roger ... I ... Nov 1978
Forsyth, Miss Julie Patricia ... G ... Jul 1983
O'Donohoe, Mr Anthony Francis; Recorder ... M ... Jul 1983
Bagley, Mr Michael Wallace Welsby ... G ... Nov 1984
Christie, Mr Simon ... M ... Feb 1988
Haygarth, Mr Edmund Bruce ... G ... Nov 1988
Williams, Mr David Henry; Recorder ... G ... Feb 1990
Watson, Mr Tom ... I ... Oct 1990
Becker, Mr Paul A ... L ... Nov 1990
Greenwood, Miss Celestine ... L ... Oct 1991
Sherman, Ms Susan Elizabeth ... M ... Nov 1993
Lander, Mr Charles Gideon ... L ... Nov 1993
Gatenby, Mr James ... M ... Oct 1994
Bannon, Miss Tammi ... L ... Nov 1994
Morris, Mr Ben ... M ... Oct 1996
Povoas, Mr Simon ... L ... Oct 1996
Biswas, Miss Nisha ... L ... Oct 1996
Deans, Miss Jacqueline ... L ... Dec 1998
Morgan, Mr Lloyd John ... M ... Mar 1999
Machin, Ms Susan ... I ... Jul 1999
Jones, Miss Claire ... L ... Jan 1999
Phelan, Miss Sarah Jane ... L ... Nov 1999
Mercer, Mr Ian ... L ... Oct 2001
Steward, Mr Mark ... I ... Oct 2002
Hughes, Mrs Kathryn ... M ... Mar 2003
Robinson, Miss Kirsty ... G ... Oct 2003
Hawks, Mr James Philip ... G ... Nov 2003
Gosling, Miss Deborah ... L ... Mar 2004
Cook, Mr Oliver James Alexander ... G ... Oct 2004
Wilde, Miss Carmel ... I ... Oct 2004
Morley, Miss Kate ... L ... Oct 2004
Temple, Miss Rachel ... G ... Nov 2004
Beardmore, Mr William E ... G ... Jul 2005
Wint, Mr Peter ... G ... Mar 2007
Noble, Mr Arthur; Recorder* ... I ... Jul 1965
Vollenweider, Amiot* ... G ... Oct 2000

This set of Chambers with 42 Barristers is based in Liverpool and specialises in Criminal Work, Child Care and Family Law.

Chambers of Bill Braithwaite QC

EXCHANGE CHAMBERS,
ONE DERBY SQUARE, LIVERPOOL, MERSEYSIDE
L2 9XX
Tel: 0151 236 7747 ***Fax:*** 0151 236 3433
Dx: 14207 LIVERPOOL
E-mail: info@exchangechambers.co.uk
Clerk: Seniors: Nick Buckley; Ian Spencer. Lynn Salter; Rachel Williams; Suzanne Dutch; Kate Masher; Denise Sheen; Dave Haley; Sarah Rotherham; Leigh Daniels; Stuart Cofield; Joe Ashcroft.
Administrator: Sally Smylie
Practice Manager: Roy Finney
Chambers Director: Tom Handley
Head of Chambers:
Braithwaite, Mr Bill (Q.C.) ... G ... Nov 1970

Elleray, Mr Anthony (Q.C.) ... I ... Jan 1977
Jones, Mr Edward Bartley (Q.C.) ... L ... Jul 1975
Martin, Mr Gerard James (Q.C.) ... M ... Jul 1978
Cawson, Mr Mark (Q.C.); Junior Counsel to the Crown(Provincial Panel); Recorder ... L ... Jul 1982
Jones, Mr John Richard (Q.C.); Recorder ... M ... Jul 1981
Cole, Mr Gordon (Q.C.) ... I ... Jun 1979
Griffiths, Miss Tania (Q.C.); Recorder ... G ... Jul 1982
Waldron, Mr William F (Q.C.); Recorder(2000) ... G ... Nov 1986
Cummings, Mr Brian (Q.C.); Recorder(2005) ... L ... Nov 1988
Meadowcroft, Mr Stephen (Q.C.) ... G ... Jan 1973
Yip, Mrs Amanda (Q.C.); Recorder ... G ... Dec 1991
Nance, Mr Francis ... G ... Nov 1970
Scholes, Mr Michael ... L ... Jan 1996
Goode, Miss Rowena Margaret; Recorder ... G ... Jul 1974
Earlam, Mr Simon; Recorder ... G ... Feb 1975
Lamb, Mr Eric; Recorder ... L ... Jul 1975
Fordham, Mrs Judith; Deputy District Judge ... I ... Jul 1991
Jess, Dr Digby C ... G ... Jul 1978
Goff, Mr Anthony Thomas ... M ... Jul 1978
Troy, Ms Karen ... L ... Jan 1981
Harris, Mr Ian ... I ... Oct 1990
Kirtley, Mr Paul G ... M ... Jul 1982
Gregory, Miss Karen ... M ... Jul 1985
Hillman, Mr Roger; Deputy District Judge ... G ... Jul 1983
Cadwallader, Mr Neil; Chancery Recorder 2009 ... I ... Jul 1984
Taylor, Mr Paul ... G ... Jan 1985
Clark, Mr Paul Robert ... M ... May 1994
Hanbury, Mr William; P/T Immigration Judge/Deputy Judge of Upper Tribunal (Immigration & Asylum Chamber) ... I ... Nov 1985
Berkson, Mr Simon ... G ... Jul 1986
Vickers, Mr Guy ... M ... Nov 1986
Knifton, Mr David Alan; Recorder ... I ... Jul 1986
Dodd, Miss Sara ... L ... Jul 1987
Mulrooney, Mr Mark; P/T President of Mental Health Review Tribunal ... M ... Jul 1988
McCarroll, Mr John Johnston ... I ... Nov 1988
Browne, Mr Louis; Recorder ... L ... Nov 1988
Foster, Mr Ian ... L ... Jul 1988
Landale, Miss Tina Jeanette; Recorder ... M ... Jul 1988
Clark, Miss Rebecca ... I ... Jul 1989
Howells, Miss Catherine; Recorder ... G ... Jul 1989
Wood, Mr Michael ... L ... Nov 1989
Vaughan, Mr Simon P ... G ... Nov 1989
Cannan, Mr Jonathan ... G ... Nov 1989
Rhind, Mr Mark A ... M ... May 1989
Stables, Mr Christopher ... G ... Oct 1990
Case, Miss Julie ... M ... Oct 1990
Cook, Mr Christopher ... I ... Oct 1990
Lavery, Mr Michael ... G ... Feb 1990
Potter, Mr David ... L ... Oct 1990
MacAdam, Mr Jason ... L ... Nov 1990
Golinski, Mr Robert ... M ... Oct 1990
Toal, Mr David ... G ... Feb 1990
Evans, Mr Paul Timothy ... G ... Oct 1992
Maynard-Connor, Mr Giles ... I ... Nov 1992
Woods, Ms Rachel Helen ... G ... Oct 1992
Ainsworth, Mr Mark; Recorder ... L ... Oct 1992
Naylor, Dr Kevin ... L ... Oct 1992
Hoare, Mr Gregory Blake ... G ... Nov 1992
Jarvis, Mr Oliver ... I ... Nov 1992
Johnson, Miss Amanda ... G ... Oct 1992
Kenny, Miss Charlotte ... G ... Nov 1993
Dudley, Mr Robert Michael ... G ... Oct 1993
Wyn Jones, Mr Robert ... L ... Jan 1993
Connolly, Mr Stephen ... L ... Jan 2003
Graham-Wells, Miss Alison ... I ... Jul 1992
Jebb, Mr Andrew John; Deputy District Judge (Mags) ... G ... Nov 1993
Bassano, Mr Alaric ... G ... Nov 1993
Garside, Mr Mark ... I ... Feb 1993
Pennifer, Ms Kelly ... M ... Nov 1994
Johnson, Mr Nicholas J ... I ... Nov 1994
Whittlestone, Ms Kim ... M ... Oct 1994
Whaites, Ms Louise ... G ... Jan 1994
Nolan, Mr Damian Francis Hardwicke Scholar ... L ... Nov 1994
Littler, Mr Richard ... G ... May 1994
Walker, Mr Bruce ... G ... Nov 1994
Myers, Mr Benjamin ... I ... Nov 1994
Maher, Mr Michael ... G ... Nov 1995
Linklater, Ms Lisa ... I ... Oct 1995
Gourley, Miss Claire ... M ... Oct 1996
Redpath, Mr Scott ... M ... Jan 1996
Acton, Miss Jayne ... L ... Mar 1996
Guirguis, Miss Sheren ... I ... Jan 1996
Smith, Mr Andrew William ... L ... Oct 1996
Dawar, Mrs Archna ... L ... Oct 1996
Slack, Mr Kevin John ... G ... Oct 1997
Farrow, Mr Adrian John ... M ... Jul 1997
Metcalf, Miss Louise ... I ... Oct 1997
Stephenson, Mr Mark ... G ... Nov 1997
French, Mr Jonathan ... L ... Nov 1997
Close, Mr Jon ... L ... Oct 1997
Burns, Mr Paul ... L ... Oct 1998
O'Brien, Ms Sarah ... I ... Jul 1998
Titchmarsh, Miss Katharine ... L ... Nov 1998
Walker, Mr Nicholas ... L ... Oct 1998
Jones, Miss Sian Scott; Assistant Deputy Coroner ... L ... Oct 1998
Smart, Mr Neil; Assistant Deputy Coroner ... L ... May 1998
Edwards, Mr Nigel D H ... L ... Jan 1999
Travers, Mr Daniel ... L ... Oct 1999
Clarke, Mr Jonathan ... I ... Oct 1999
Mohyuddin, Mr David Niaz ... I ... Oct 1999
Barnes, Mr Christopher ... G ... Jun 2000
Snowdon, Miss Martine ... L ... Oct 2000
Rogers, Mr Jonathan ... M ... Oct 2000
Vinson, Mr Andrew ... M ... Jul 2000
Ward, Mr Andrew John ... M ... Jul 2000
Daley, Miss Nicola ... G ... Jul 2000
Gooding, Miss Laura ... L ... Jan 2001
Shields, Mr Josh ... M ... Mar 2000
Temkin, Mr David ... I ... Jul 2000
Grattage, Mr Stephen ... L ... Nov 2000
Gee, Ms Caroline ... G ... Jan 2003
Atherton, Ms Charlotte ... G ... Jul 2003
Taylor, Mr Christian ... L ... Jan 2003
McNally, Mr Stephen ... G ... Nov 2003
Sutherland, Miss Sara ... L ... Oct 2004
Johnston, Miss Sarah ... G ... Jul 2004
Petterson, Mr Andrew ... M ... Oct 2004
Lin, Miss Esther ... M ... Jan 2002
Bennett, Miss Emma ... L ... Jan 2004
Rohrer, Mr Kerron ... I ... Oct 2005
Moss, Mr Edward ... I ... Jan 2005
Sandbach, Miss Carly ... I ... Jul 2006
Gutteridge, Mr Christopher ... I ... Oct 2006
Tetlow, Mr Richard ... M ... Jul 2006
Birrell, Mr David ... I ... Nov 2006
Weiss, Mr Alfred ... L ... Oct 2006

Cornwall, Miss Natalia	M	Jul 2007
Shires, Mr Gareth Richard	L	Jul 2007
Lowe, Mr Jonathan	L	Mar 2008
Durston, Mr Jeremy	I	Jan 2008
Whitfield, Mr Simon	L	Jul 2009
Royle, Mr Chris	L	Jul 2009
Speakman, Mr Lee	M	Jul 2009
Tucker, Mr Ian	M	Jul 2010
Rees, Mr John Charles (Q.C.)*	L	Jul 1972
Janner, Mr Daniel (Q.C.)*	M	Jan 1980
Bartle, Mr Philip M (Q.C.)*	M	Jul 1976
Turner, Mr Jonathan (Q.C.)*	G	Jul 1974
Enoch, Mr Dafydd (Q.C.)*	G	Nov 1985
Nelson, Mr Cairns (Q.C.)*	G	Jan 1987
Laws, Miss Eleanor (Q.C.)*	I	Oct 1990
Medland, Mr Simon (Q.C.)*	M	Oct 1991
James, Mr Alun Edward*	M	Nov 1986
Fox, Dr Simon*	I	Oct 1994
Maguire, Mr Andrew*	I	Nov 1988
Tyack, Mr David*	M	Nov 1994
Eyers, Mr Anthony*	I	Nov 1994
Dooher, Ms Nancy Helen*	L	Nov 1997
Chichester-Clark, Mr Adam*	M	Oct 2000

Chambers of David Steer QC

7 HARRINGTON STREET CHAMBERS,
7 HARRINGTON STREET, LIVERPOOL,
MERSEYSIDE L2 9YH
Tel: 0151 242 0707 ***Fax:*** 0151 236 1120 / 236 2800
Dx: 14221 LIVERPOOL
E-mail: clerks@7hs.co.uk
Web: www.7hs.co.uk
Clerk: Senior: John Kilgallon.
Administrator: Pauline Haines
Chambers Director: John Kilgallon
Head of Chambers:

Steer, Mr David (Q.C.); Recorder; Leader of The Northern Circuit 2002-2004	I	Nov 1974
Goldrein, Mr Iain S (Q.C.); Recorder	I	Jul 1975
Riordan, Mr Stephen (Q.C.)	I	Jul 1972
Lawson-Rogers, Mr Stuart (Q.C.)	G	Jul 1969
Moran, Mr Andrew (Q.C.)	G	Nov 1976
Flewitt, Mr Neil (Q.C.); Recorder	M	Jul 1981
Menary, Mr Andrew (Q.C.); Recorder	I	Nov 1982
Pratt, Mr Richard J (Q.C.); Recorder; Leader of the Northern Circuit 2011	G	Jul 1980
Johnson, Mr Nicholas Robert (Q.C.)	I	Jul 1987
Unsworth, Mr Ian (Q.C.)	L	Oct 1992
Power, Mr Nigel John (Q.C.)	I	Nov 1992
Geey, Mr David S; Recorder	I	Jul 1970
McDonald, Mr Andrew	G	Jul 1971
Bellis, Mr W Gordon	I	Jul 1972
Halligan, Mr Rodney	G	Jul 1972
Compton-Rickett, Miss Mary	G	Nov 1972
Pickavance, Mr Michael J	M	Jul 1974
Biddle, Mr Neville Leslie	G	Nov 1974
Rae, Mr James	I	Jul 1976
Grice, Mr A Kevin; Recorder	G	Jul 1977
Davies, Mr Michael	M	Jul 1979
Gibson, Mr Arthur George	L	Jul 1980
Carville, Mr Brendan Owen	I	Jul 1980
Riding, Mr Henry	M	Jul 1981
Lazarus, Mr Grant P	G	Nov 1981
Owen, Mr David	G	Jul 1981
Gregory, Mr Peter; Recorder	G	Jul 1982
McKeon, Mr James	L	Nov 1982
Loveridge, Mr Andrew R; Recorder	L	Jul 1983
Chatterton, Mr Mark	G	Jul 1983
McGuire, Miss Deirdre	I	Nov 1983
Byrne, Mr James	G	Jul 1983
Reade, Mr Kevin	G	Jul 1983
Killeen, Mr Simon; Recorder	I	Jul 1984
Khan, Mr B Jamil	L	Jul 1986
Knapp, Mr Stephen	G	Jul 1986
Davies, Mr Peter; Recorder	G	Jul 1986
Lennon, Mr Desmond Joseph	G	Nov 1986
Kidd, Mr Peter	L	Jul 1987
Reaney, Miss Janet E	M	Jul 1987
Parker, Mr Steven N; Deputy District Judge	G	Nov 1987
Kenward, Mr Tim David	G	Nov 1987
Sutton, Mr Keith A	G	Nov 1988
Lawrence, Mr Nigel	L	Jul 1988
Flood, Mr Diarmuid	L	Apr 1989
Smith, Mr Jason	M	Jul 1989
Symms, Miss Kate	G	Mar 1990
Downie, Mr Andrew	G	Nov 1990
Bispham, Miss Christine	L	Oct 1991
Seed, Mr Stephen Nicholas	G	Oct 1991
Grover, Mr Timothy	I	Nov 1991
Driver, Mr Simon Gregory	I	Nov 1991
Parry-Jones, Mr John Trevor	G	Feb 1992
Alty, Mr Andrew	I	Feb 1992
Whitehurst, Mr Ian	I	Nov 1994
Wrenn, Ms Helen	I	Nov 1994
Loftus, Miss Teresa Anne Martine	L	Mar 1995
Jones, Mr Gerald William	G	Jul 1995
Baker, Mr Clive A	G	Oct 1995
Carney, Mr Andrew	I	Oct 1995
Greenfield, Mr Jeremy	I	Oct 1995
Burke, Mr Brendan	I	Oct 1995
Turner, Miss Nicola	G	Nov 1995
Mallon, Miss Joanna	L	Oct 1996
Ball, Mr Steven	I	Oct 1996
McLachlan, Mr David Robert	I	Oct 1996
Ford, Mr Andrew	M	Oct 1997
Rogers, Mr Daniel	I	Oct 1997
Grant, Mr Kenneth John	I	Mar 1998
Swain, Miss Jacqueline	L	Oct 1998
Brennan, Miss Elizabeth Gail	L	Nov 1998
Bisarya, Mr Neil	L	Nov 1998
Jones, Mr Michael Wyn	G	Mar 1999
Thorne, Miss Zoe	L	Jul 1999
Miles, Miss Nicola	L	Oct 1999
Naughton, Miss Lianne Eve	I	Oct 1999
Holt, Miss Sarah Louise	M	Oct 1999
Wood, Mr Daniel	L	Jul 2000
Ralston, Mr William	I	Oct 2000
Tully, Mr Philip	M	Oct 2000
Whalley, Miss Alison	L	Nov 2000
Jenkinson, Mr Lee	G	Mar 2001
Roberts, Mr Mark	G	Mar 2001
Langley, Miss Sarah	L	Nov 2001
Hertzog, Miss Frances Dawn	G	Nov 2001
Edmunds, Miss Lisa	I	Oct 2002
Freeman, Miss Emma	I	Oct 2002
Duffy, Mr Jonathan Bernard	G	Oct 2002
Wright, Mr Paul	I	Oct 2003
Reid, Mr Martin	L	Nov 2003
Webster, Miss Barbara	L	Oct 2005
Knagg, Mr Christopher	G	Nov 2005
Dunne, Mr David	M	Jul 2005
Lindsay, Mr Fraser	M	Jul 2006
O'Donohue, Miss Katherine	G	Jul 2006
Birkett, Miss Lianne	I	Jul 2006
Treadwell, Mr Brian	L	Oct 2006
Woerner, Mr Steven	M	Nov 2006
Ashley, Mrs Julie	L	Mar 2007
Paton, Miss Danielle	I	Jul 2007
Watters, Miss Sarah Louise	L	Oct 2007
Harthan, Mr Peter James	I	Oct 2007
Emery, Mr Philip Anthony	M	Mar 2008
Handy, Mr Benjamin	L	Oct 2008
O'Leary, Mr John	M	Jul 2010
Berry, Mr Anthony C (Q.C.)*	G	Jul 1976
Nutter, Mr Julian*	G	Jan 1979
Dutchman-Smith, Mr Malcolm*	G	Feb 1995

7 Harrington Street is one of the largest sets of chambers in the country. We have a policy of excellence, innovation and expansion with expertise in all aspects of law. We have earned our reputation through continued professional excellence and a commitment to working to the highest ethical standards.
Currently there are 108 barristers, including 11 QCs. They are supported by a large and dedicated team of clerking and administrative staff who consistently provide clients with a high level of service.
As holders of the Legal Services Quality Mark we offer quality assured services to members of the public who need legal information, advice and assistance. Chambers is firmly committed to equal opportunities, and we accept instructions from anyone regardless of background or circumstances.
We are located in the heart of the commercial and legal centre of Liverpool, only a short walk from the QE II Combined Courts centre and the Liverpool Civil and Family Courts. 7 Harrington Street has extensive state of the art conference and seminar facilities, including a video conferencing suite.
Practice Manager/Senior Clerk:- John Kilgallon. Assistant Practice Manager/Civil Clerk:- Nick Roberts. Assistant Practice Manager/Senior Criminal Clerk:- Rachel Kehoe. Criminal Clerks:- Claire Smith, Amy Chadwick. Senior Family Clerk:- Carolyn Cregreen. Family Clerks:- Jenny Mogan, Hannah Gilligan, Civil Clerks:- Sarah Gleaves, Faye Woods.

Chambers of Keith Thomas

NEW BAILEY CHAMBERS,
4TH FLOOR, THE CORN EXCHANGE, FENWICK STREET, LIVERPOOL, MERSEYSIDE L2 7SX
Tel: 0151 236 9402 ***Fax:*** 0151 231 1296
Dx: 14193 LIVERPOOL
Head of Chambers:

Thomas, Mr Keith	G	Jul 1969
Bailey, Miss Patricia*	M	Nov 1969
Askey, Mr Robert	L	Oct 1998

Chambers of Richard Bradley

ORIEL CHAMBERS,
14 WATER STREET, LIVERPOOL, MERSEYSIDE
L2 8TD
Est: 1965
Tel: 0151 236 7191 / 236 4321 ***Fax:*** 0151 227 5909 / 236 3332
Dx: 14106 LIVERPOOL
E-mail: clerks@orielchambers.co.uk
Web: www.orielchambers.co.uk
Clerk: Andrew Hampton; John Newsham; Paul Gotham; Sarah Stephenson; Tom Craig.
Practice Manager: Paul Thompson
Chambers Director: Sarah Cavanagh
Head of Chambers:

Bradley, Mr Richard	M	Jul 1978
Bennett, Mr Martyn	G	Jul 1969
Alldis, Mr Christopher; Recorder	G	Nov 1970
Hind, Mr Kenneth CBE	G	Jul 1973
Murray, Ashley C; Recorder	M	Jul 1974
Cowan, Mr Peter S M; Recorder	M	Jul 1980
Wells, Mr Graham; Recorder	M	Jul 1982
Bundred, Ms Gillian S	G	Jul 1982
O'Keeffe, Mr Darren	I	Jul 1984
Evans, Ms Suzanne Marie	M	Nov 1985
Fox, Ms Anna Katherine Helen	M	Jul 1986
Goodbody, Mr Peter James	L	Jul 1986
Ellis, Ms Catherine	L	Jul 1987
Baldwin, Mr John G	G	Oct 1990
Rahman, Yaqub; Recorder	G	Oct 1991
Holloway, Mr Timothy	I	Nov 1991
Gruffydd, Mr John	G	Feb 1992
Belbin, Ms Heather P	L	Oct 1992
Mills, Mr Stuart	M	Oct 1992
Foster, Mr Peter	M	Nov 1992
Brant, Mr Paul David	L	Nov 1993
Brandon, Ms Helen Elizabeth	M	Nov 1993
Rankin, Mr William K	G	Oct 1994
Hughes, Ms Rachel	G	Nov 1995
Benson, Mr James	G	Nov 1995
Cottrell, Mr Matthew R	G	Oct 1996
Frodsham, Mr Alexander	L	Oct 1996
Clarke, Ms Susan	M	Oct 1996
Hennessy, Ms Shirley	L	Oct 1997
Stanger, Mr Mark Fullerton	M	Jan 1998
Clarke, Lindsay	G	Jul 1999
Berry, Mr Karl	M	Nov 1999
Huyton, Ms Katherine	M	Nov 1999
Purcell, Miss Deirdre Marie	L	Nov 2000
Burns, Ms Judith	M	Jan 2001
Gray, Mr John	L	Oct 2001
Williams, Mr Graham	M	Jan 2002
Middleton, Mr Christopher	I	Jan 2002
Howe, Mr Andrew	L	Jan 2002
Gruffydd, Miss Sarah	G	Jul 2003
McMurtrie, Mr Christopher	G	Jul 2003
Bartlett, Mrs Catherine	I	Jan 2004
Williams, Mr Alexander	M	Jan 2004
Gosling, Mr Tom Adam	L	Nov 2004
Cooper, Mr Mark	L	Jan 2005
Champion, Miss Karina	I	Jan 2005
Wolfenden, Mr Peter	M	Jul 2007
Parr, Miss Margaret	L	Mar 2008
Fazackerley, Mr Tom Brian	G	Oct 2010
Cummings, Miss Stephanie Anne	M	Nov 2010
Garden, Mr Ian*	L	Jul 1989
Nicholls, Ms Jane*	I	Nov 1989
Lewthwaite, Ms Joanne*	I	Oct 1990
Dawson, Mr James*	I	Nov 1994
Sholicar, Ms Ann*	L	Nov 2000

Civil, commercial, family, crime, employment, clinical negligence, professional negligence, environmental law, general common law.

Chambers of John Pugh

JOHN PUGH'S CHAMBERS,
707 THE CORN EXCHANGE, FENWICK STREET, LIVERPOOL, MERSEYSIDE L2 7RB
Tel: 0151 236 5415 ***Fax:*** 0151 227 5468
Dx: 14182 LIVERPOOL
E-mail: eileen@johnpughschambers.co.uk
Administrator: Suzanne Thomas
Practice Manager: Eileen Ashton
Head of Chambers:

Pugh, Mr John	L	Jul 1972

Chambers of Michael Howard Redfern QC

ST JOHNS BUILDINGS,
8TH FLOOR, INDIA BUILDINGS, WATER STREET, LIVERPOOL, MERSEYSIDE L2 0XG
Tel: 0151 243 6000 ***Fax:*** 0151 243 6040
Dx: 14227 LIVERPOOL
E-mail: clerks@indiabuildings.co.uk
Head of Chambers:
Redfern, Mr Michael Howard (Q.C.) . . . I . . . Jul 1970

Bentham, Mr Howard (Q.C.)	G	Nov 1970
Shorrock, Mr Michael (Q.C.)	I	Jul 1966
Berkley, Mr David (Q.C.)	M	May 1979
Marks, Mr Richard (Q.C.)	G	Jul 1975
Hayden, Mr Anthony (Q.C.)	M	Nov 1987
Singleton, Ms Sarah (Q.C.)	M	Jul 1983
O'Byrne, Mr Andrew (Q.C.)	G	Jul 1978
Samuels, Mr Jeffrey K (Q.C.)	M	Jul 1988
Harrison, Miss Sally (Q.C.)	G	Oct 1992
Wolff, Mr Michael	G	Jun 1964
Cattan, Mr Philip David	G	Nov 1970
Lamberty, Mr Mark	I	Nov 1970
Herman, Mr Ray	I	Feb 1972
Green, Mr Roger	L	Jul 1972
Hedgecoe, Mr John Philip	I	Nov 1972
Bedford, Mr Stephen	G	Jul 1972
McNeill, Mr John Seddon	G	Jul 1974
Shannon, Mr Eric	M	Nov 1974
Lowe, Mr Geoffrey	G	Jul 1975
Longworth, Mr Antony Stephen	M	Jul 1978
Andrews, Mr Philip	I	Feb 1977
Feeny, Mr Charles	I	Nov 1977
Grundy, Mr Philip Michael David	M	Jul 1980
Owen, Miss Gail	G	Nov 1980
Mercer, Mr David	L	Jul 1980
Uff, Mr David C	G	Jul 1981
Long, Mr Andrew	I	Jul 1981
Holt, Mr Julian	M	Jan 1982
Gal, Miss Sonia	I	Nov 1982
Greene, Mr Maurice A	I	Nov 1982
Garside, Mr David	G	Nov 1982
Bruce, Mr David	M	Jul 1982
Harrison, Mr Peter John	M	Jul 1983
Khawar, Aftab	G	Jul 1983
McKee, Mr Hugh A	M	Nov 1983
Goodman, Miss Bernadette	I	Nov 1983
McKenna, Mr Brian	M	Jun 1983
Harrison, Mr J Keith	L	Nov 1983
Shaw, Mr Julian	G	Sep 1984
Pickup, Mr David	I	Jul 1984
Kennedy, Mr Michael	M	May 1985
Lloyd, Mr Julian	G	Jul 1985
Gray, Mr Richard	M	Nov 1986
Kloss, Mrs Diana Mary	G	Jul 1986
Oates, Mr John Richard	G	Jul 1987
Taylor, Mr Julian	M	Jul 1986
Dickinson, Mr Jonathan	I	Nov 1986
Walker, Miss Jane	M	Jul 1987
Brennand, Mr Timothy W	G	Nov 1987
Dagnall, Ms Jane	I	Jan 1987
Batra, Bunty Lalit	G	Feb 1987
Eastwood, Mr Charles Peter	L	Jul 1988
Crabtree, Mr Simon J G	L	Nov 1988
Davitt, Ms Paula	G	Oct 1988
Sanders, Mr Damian	M	Nov 1988
Britcliffe, Ms Anne E	I	Apr 1989
Grundy, Ms Clare	G	Jul 1989
Partington, Miss Lisa	I	Jul 1989
Holder, Mr Simon	I	Jul 1989
Blakey, Mr Michael	M	Nov 1989
Carter, Mr Richard	I	Nov 1990
Thompson, Mr Patrick	G	Oct 1990
Watson, Mr David W	M	Oct 1990
Thompson, Mr Jonathan Richard	I	Oct 1990
Wright, Mr Alastair	L	Dec 1991
Mawdsley, Mr Matthew	I	Nov 1991
Roberts, Mr Mark Vaughan	I	Sep 1991
Chaudhry, Ms Zia	I	Nov 1991
Pratt, Mrs Patricia	L	Oct 1991
Taylor, Mr Jonathan	M	Nov 1991
Case, Magdalen	M	Nov 1992
Green, Mr Andrew	G	Oct 1992
Norton, Mr Richard	L	Nov 1992
Ashmole, Mr Timothy	I	Oct 1992
McNerney, Mr Kevin	I	Jan 1992
Lloyd, Ms Gaynor Elizabeth	L	Oct 1992
Jones, Mr Benjamin	M	Feb 1993
Flood, Mr David	M	Nov 1993
Kloss, Mr Alexander	G	Oct 1993
Mathieson, Mr Guy	M	Oct 1993
Wilson, Mr Myles	L	Oct 1993
Searle, Mr Jason Ario Xavier	I	Oct 1993
Gibson, Mr John Arthur	L	Nov 1993
Fitzharris, Miss Ginnette	L	Nov 1993
Blackshaw, Mr Henry	M	Oct 1993
Orme, Mr Richard	L	Oct 1993
Rodikis, Miss Joanna	M	Oct 1993
Harrison, Miss Leona	M	Nov 1993
Polglase, Mr David S	M	Oct 1993
Connor, Mr Mark	I	May 1994
Frieze, Mr Daniel	G	Oct 1994
Gumbs, Miss Annette	G	Oct 1994
Wild, Mr Steven	G	Oct 1994
Douglas, Mr Stephen John	I	Nov 1994
Reynolds, Mr Gary William	L	Nov 1994
McGinty, Mr Robert Fraser	I	Nov 1994
Rowley, Mr Karl John	M	Nov 1994
Houghton, Ms Lisa	G	May 1994
Booth, Mr Nigel Robert	G	Oct 1994
Mann, Miss Sara	M	Nov 1994
Chukwuemeka, Mr John O	L	Nov 1994
Hargan, Mr Carl	L	Nov 1995
Lawson, Mr Andrew	I	Jan 1995
Mchugh, Miss Pauline Mary	G	Nov 1995
Parry, Mr Philip	L	Jan 1995
Crangle, Miss Charlotte	G	Jan 1995
Simkin, Mr Iain	I	Feb 1995
Dixon, Mr John	G	Nov 1995
Aslett, Pepin	I	Nov 1996
Crilley, Mr Darrel	I	Feb 1996
Roussak, Mr Jeremy Brian	M	Oct 1996
Leene, Miss Sharon	G	Oct 1996
Sastry, Mr Bob	I	Oct 1996
Mahmood, Ghazan	I	Sep 1997
Mintz, Mr Simon	I	Nov 1996
Zentar, Dr Remy	G	Jul 1997
Spear, Miss Sarah	I	Oct 1997
Williams, Ms Zillah	L	Nov 1997
Mensah, Miss Lorraine S L	G	Oct 1997
Denton, Mr Douglas	L	Nov 1997
Parry, Mr Simon	I	Nov 1997
Tyler, Mr Paul	M	Jan 1997
Evans, Mr Simeon	L	Jun 1997
Buckley, Mr Patrick James	G	Jul 1998
Bentley, Mr David Paul	L	Jul 1998
Muth, Ms Susanne	I	Jul 1998
Simmonds, Ms Alexandra	G	Oct 1998
Taylor, Mr David Christopher; Junior of the Northern Circuit	L	Oct 1998
Murdin, Mr Liam	L	Jul 1998
James, Mr David	I	Oct 1998
Burnell, Miss Kate	M	Oct 1998
Stockwell, Mr Matthew	G	Oct 1998
Edwards, Miss Susan	L	Nov 1998
Deas, Ms Susan Margaret	G	Jul 1999
Astbury, Mr Philip	G	Oct 1999
Holsgrove, Lara	M	Jan 1999
Ratledge, Mr John	L	Jun 1999
Sweeney, Ms Linda Mary	M	Nov 1999
Cavanagh, Ms Lorraine	G	Jan 2000
Leach, Ms Natasha	L	Jan 2000
Bridgman, Mr Andrew	G	Jan 2000
Porter-Phillips, Mrs Clare	L	Mar 2001
Ahmed, Siraj Issap	M	Apr 2001
King, Mr Oliver	G	Jul 2001
Vir Singh, Miss Sylvia	M	Jul 2001
Van Der Haer, Ms Audrey	G	Oct 2001
Blewitt, Miss Jennifer	M	Jul 2001
Pojur, Mr David	M	Nov 2001
Farley, Mr David	M	Jan 2001
Montaldo, Mr Neil	L	Mar 2002
Hodgkinson, Mr Paul George	L	Jul 2002
Owen, Wendy Jane	M	Jan 2002
Senior, Mr Mark	G	Jul 2002
Smith, Mr Paul	G	Oct 2002
Moss, Mr Christopher	L	Oct 2002
Malam, Mr James	G	Jan 2002
Menzies, Mr Jennifer	L	Oct 2002
Stringer, Ms Rosie	M	Jan 2002
McCloskey, Miss Louise	G	Oct 2002
Smith, Ms Rebecca Ellen	L	Jan 2002
Lawrence, Mr Benjamin	L	Jan 2003
Ali, Kashif	L	Jan 2003
Hudson, Ms Abigail	G	Jan 2003
Quigley, Ms Louise	I	Jan 2003
Newstead, Ms Jennifer Elizabeth	G	Nov 2003
Akers, Mr Robert	I	Nov 2003
Maguire, Clodagh	I	Jan 2003
Connolly, Mr Timothy	I	Mar 2004
Poole, Mr William	M	Jan 2004
Waddell, Ms Philippa	L	Jan 2004
Watkins, Mr Adam	G	Jul 2004
Murphy, Mr Paul	G	Jul 2004
Greenhalgh, Miss Jane	L	Nov 2004
Rimmer, Miss Catherine	G	Jul 2004
Harrison, Miss Petra	I	Jul 2004
Samuel, Ms Ana	I	Jul 2004
Wilson, Ms Helen	G	Oct 2004
Cooper, Mr Douglas	I	Jan 2004
Sutton, Rebecca	I	Jan 2004
Abraham, Ms Joanne Jade	G	Nov 2004
Spencer, Mr Shaun	L	Jan 2005
Marshall, Lucy	M	Jan 2005
White, Mrs Debra	G	Oct 2005
Christian, Mr Neil	M	Oct 2005
Thompson, Mr Gareth	G	Jan 2005
McGarry, Mr Steven	L	Mar 2005
De Navarro, Frances	I	Jan 2005
Pare, Mr Christopher	L	Jan 2006
Scully, Ms Jennifer	M	Jul 2006
Wilkinson, Mr Timothy	I	Jan 2006
Kelly, Mr Ben	L	Jan 2006
Flynn, Mr Steven	G	Jan 2006
Scott, Louise	L	Jan 2006
Haggis, Mr Andrew	M	Mar 2007
Wood, Hannah	L	Jan 2007
Vanderpump, Henry	I	Jan 2007
Owen-Easey, Neil	G	Jan 2007
Goode, Julian	L	Jan 2006
Allen, Mr Fegal	L	Oct 2007
Murray, Simon	I	Jan 2008
Cooper, Elisabeth	M	Jan 2008
Gomer, Mr Elis	G	Jan 2008
Williams, Miss Cerys	G	Jul 2008
Maddison, Mr Simon	I	Jan 2008
Edwards, Mr Huw	G	Jan 2009
England, Laura	M	Jan 2008
Roberts, Elliw	G	Jan 2009
Nash, Laura	L	Jan 2009

LUTON

Chambers of Mahmood Shafi Khan

LUTON CHAMBERS,
103 WEXHAM CLOSE, LUTON, LUTON LU3 3TX
Tel: 01582 598394 ***Fax:*** 01582 618335
E-mail: mshafikhan@hotmail.com
Clerk: Syed Rizvi.
Chambers Director: Mahmood Shafi Khan
Head of Chambers:
Khan, Mr Mahmood Shafi . . . L . . . Feb 1994

MAIDSTONE, Kent

BECKET CHAMBERS,
KENT HOUSE, ROMNEY PLACE, MAIDSTONE, KENT ME15 6LH
Tel: 01622 230957 ***Fax:*** 0844 443 2686
Dx: 4803 MAIDSTONE
E-mail: clerks@becket-chambers.co.uk
Clerk: Paul Eaton.

Kee, Mr Peter William	M	Jul 1983
Newton, Mr Philip	M	Jul 1984
Edginton, Mr Horace Ronald	G	Nov 1984
Jackson, Mr Kevin	M	Nov 1984
Wall, Mr Christopher	L	Nov 1987
Mills, Corey	M	Nov 1987
Hall, Mr Jeremy J	G	Feb 1988
Styles, Mr Clive R	G	Oct 1990
Tapsell, Mr Paul	M	Oct 1991
Adamson, Ms Lilias L	G	Nov 1994
Fairbank, Mr Nicholas	L	Nov 1996
McIntosh, Miss Melanie	L	Sep 2002
Murkin, Ms Sandria	I	Oct 2004
Andrews, Miss Melanie Alexandra	M	Jan 2005
Coates, Miss Holly	L	Oct 2008
Kenny, Mr Edward	M	Jan 2009
Thistle, Mr Dean Terence	L	Dec 2010
Bartlett, Mr Andrew V B (Q.C.)*	M	Jul 1974

Chambers of Philip Sinclair

MAIDSTONE CHAMBERS,
33 EARL STREET, MAIDSTONE, KENT ME14 1PF
Tel: 01622 688592 ***Fax:*** 01622 683305
Dx: 51982 MAIDSTONE 2
E-mail: admin@maidstonechambers.co.uk
Clerk: Senior: Danielle Dixon. Junior: Kay Burford.
Head of Chambers:
Sinclair, Mr Philip . . . G . . . Nov 1995

Jacobson, Miss Mary Inge	M	Oct 1992
Wright, Mr Trevor	M	Nov 1992
Zimbler, Miss Alexia	L	Oct 1993
Greene, Mr Paul	M	Oct 1994
Stern, Mr Thomas	G	Nov 1995
Allen, Mr Thomas	I	Nov 1995
Wickens, Mr Simon	L	Oct 1998
Fitzgerald, Mr John	L	Oct 1998
Dunn, Mr Tom	L	Jan 1998
Burt, Ms Joanna	G	Oct 1998
De Banzie, Mr Robert	G	Jan 2000
Ross, Mr James	G	Nov 2001
Farley, Anna	I	Jan 2002
King, Miss Judith	M	Jul 2002
Restell, Mr Piers	M	Jul 2002
Calder, Lynette	L	Jan 2003
Brand, Kieran	M	Jan 2007
Lewis, Katherine	I	Jan 2009

Chambers of Stephen Hockman QC

6-8 MILL STREET,
MAIDSTONE, KENT ME15 6XH
Tel: 01622 688094 / 688095 ***Fax:*** 01622 688096
Dx: 51967 MAIDSTONE 2
E-mail: annexe@6pumpcourt.co.uk
Clerk: Senior: Richard Constable.
Administrator: Arlene Outen
Head of Chambers:
Hockman, Mr Stephen (Q.C.) . . . M . . . Jul 1970

Willard, Mr Neville	G	Jul 1976
Armstrong, Mr Grant B	L	Jul 1978
Barraclough, Mr Richard	I	Nov 1980
Travers, Mr David	M	Jul 1981
Baldock, Mr Nicholas	L	Nov 1983
Topping, Miss Caroline	M	Oct 1984
Gower, Mr Peter	L	Jul 1985
Walden-Smith, Mr David	L	Jul 1985
Leigh, Mr Kevin	L	Nov 1986
Harrison, Mr Peter	I	Jul 1987
Laws, Miss Eleanor (Q.C.)	I	Oct 1990
Forbes, Mr Peter	I	Oct 1990
Upton, Mr William	I	Nov 1990
Saxby, Mr Oliver	I	Nov 1992
Watson, Mr Mark	G	Jul 1994
Grant, Mr Edward	I	Nov 1994
Ellin, Miss Nina	I	Nov 1994
Wright, Miss Clare	I	Oct 1995
Alcock, Mr Peter	G	Oct 1995
Beard, Mr Mark	G	Oct 1996
Charles, Miss Deborah	L	Oct 1996
Robinson, Miss Tanya	I	Nov 1997
Banwell, Mr Richard	I	Oct 1998
Menzies, Mr Gordon	I	Oct 1998
Bennett, Mr Lee	M	Nov 1998
Knowles, Miss Linsey	L	Jul 2000
Fox, Miss Katie	I	Oct 2001
Wood, Mr Simon	M	Oct 2001

MALVERN, Worcestershire

RESOLUTION CHAMBERS,
THE OLD SCHOOL HOUSE, WALWYN ROAD, UPPER COLWALL, MALVERN, WORCESTERSHIRE WR13 6PL
Tel: 01684 541008 ***Fax:*** 01684 541008
E-mail: mmilne@milne-arbitration.co.uk
Clerk: Penny Milne.

Milne, Mr Michael . . . L . . . Jul 1987

MANCHESTER, Greater Manchester

Chambers of Raymond D Machell QC

BYROM STREET CHAMBERS,
12 BYROM STREET, MANCHESTER, GREATER MANCHESTER M3 4PP
Tel: 0161 829 2100 ***Fax:*** 0161 829 2101
Dx: 718156 MANCHESTER 3
E-mail: clerks@byromstreet.com
Web: www.byromstreet.com
Clerk: Senior: Terry Creathorn. Deputy Senior: Steve Price.
Head of Chambers:

Machell, Mr Raymond D (Q.C.); Deputy High Court Hudge	G	Jul 1973

Tattersall, Mr Geoffrey Frank (Q.C.); Recorder; Judge of Appeal(Isle Of Man)	L	Jul 1970
Allan, Mr David (Q.C.); Recorder; Deputy High Court Judge	G	Jul 1974
Hunter, Mr Winston Ronald (Q.C.); Recorder; Deputy High Court Hudge	L	Jul 1985
Melton, Mr Christopher (Q.C.); Recorder	G	Jul 1982
Myerson, Mr Simon (Q.C.)	M	Jan 1986
Rowley, Mr James (Q.C.); Recorder / Regional Treasury Counsel	L	Jul 1987
Heaton, Mr David (Q.C.); Recorder	M	Jul 1983
Lewis, Mr Andrew (Q.C.); Recorder	L	Jul 1985
Pearce, Mr Richard; Recorder	M	Jul 1985
Hatfield, Miss Sally; Recorder	I	Nov 1988
Ruck, Miss Mary Ida	G	Oct 1993
Burns, Mr Peter R	G	Oct 1993
Allen, Mr Darryl	L	Oct 1995

CENTRAL CHAMBERS,
89 PRINCESS STREET, MANCHESTER, GREATER MANCHESTER M1 4HT
Tel: 0161 236 1133 ***Fax:*** 0161 236 1177
Dx: 14467 MANCHESTER 2
E-mail: clerks@centralchambers.co.uk
Clerk: Senior: Neil Vickers. Brooke Clarke; Jayne Lever.

Massey, Miss Stella M	M	Feb 1990
Karnik, Mr Mikhil	G	Jan 2006

CLERKSROOM,
3RD FLOOR, 64 BRIDGE STREET, MANCHESTER, GREATER MANCHESTER M3 3BN
Tel: 0845 083 3000 ***Fax:*** 0845 083 3001
Dx: 14349 MANCHESTER

Chambers of Roger Farley QC

COBDEN HOUSE CHAMBERS,
19 QUAY STREET, MANCHESTER, GREATER MANCHESTER M3 3HN
Tel: 0161 833 6000 ***Fax:*** 0161 833 6001
Dx: 14327 MANCHESTER
E-mail: clerks@cobden.co.uk
Clerk: Seniors: Neil McHugh; David Hewitt; Daniel Monaghan; Martin Leech.
Administrator: Jackie Morton
Head of Chambers:

Farley, Mr Roger (Q.C.); Recorder	M	May 1974

Goldberg, Mr Jonathan (Q.C.)*	M	Feb 1971
Blackwell, Miss Louise M (Q.C.)	L	Jul 1985
Hartley, Mr Richard A (Q.C.); Recorder	M	Jul 1985
Bowes, Mr Michael (Q.C.)*	M	Jul 1980
Leslie, Mr Stephen W (Q.C.)*	L	Feb 1971
Narayan, Mr Harry; Recorder	L	Nov 1970
Buckley, Mr Peter Evered	G	Jul 1972
Broadley, Mr John	M	Jul 1973
Johnson, Mrs Carolyn	G	Nov 1974
Goldwater, Mr Michael	M	Jul 1977
Neale, Mr Stuart*	M	Jul 1976
Oughton, Mr Richard Donald; Member of the Irish Bar	L	Jul 1978
White, Mr Timothy	M	Jul 1978
Brereton, Mrs Fiorella	G	Nov 1979
Fallows, Miss Paula	L	Jul 1981
Farrell, Mr Edmund G	G	Jul 1981
Green, Mr Colin Richard	L	Jul 1982
Kenny, Mr David J	M	Nov 1982
Sheridan, Mr Paul	L	Jul 1984
Leigh, Miss Sarah	I	Jan 1984
Metcalfe, Mr Ian	M	Nov 1985
Oultram, Mr Jonathan	M	Nov 1988
Hymanson, Miss Deanna S	M	Feb 1988
Willitts, Mr Timothy L	G	Nov 1989
Littler, Mr Martin	G	Nov 1989
Parr, Mr John E	M	Nov 1989
Willems, Mr Marc P; Recorder	L	Nov 1990
Wright, Mrs Yasmin	I	Nov 1990
Musaheb, Mr Kevin	M	Jan 1990
Kilpatrick, Miss Alyson	M	Jul 1991
Dalal, Mr Rajen C J	L	Sep 1991
Hodgson, Mr Timothy P	I	Nov 1991
Gilmour, Miss Susan	L	Nov 1994
Nichol, Mr Simon B	L	May 1994
Maddison, Mr David	G	Oct 1995
Sandiford, Mr David	G	Oct 1995
Orr, Mr Julian	L	Oct 1995
Oakes, Mr Christopher N	L	Oct 1996
Mazzag, Mr Anthony	L	Nov 1996
Nowland, Mr Lee	L	Jan 1997
Callery, Mr Martin	M	Mar 1997
Georgiou, Ms Angela	I	Oct 1997
Jones, Mr Michael	L	Oct 1998
Del Priore, Miss Assunta	M	Oct 1998
Goddard, Mr Richard A	I	Mar 1999
MacGregor, Mr Craig	L	Jan 1997
Pearson, Miss Rebecca	G	Oct 1999
Hirst, Miss Rebecca	G	Nov 1999
Stringer, Ms Jacinta Maria Rockingham	G	Nov 1999
Milne, Mrs Arlene	M	Jan 1999
Knowles, Mr Michael	M	Oct 2000
Piears, Miss Angela	M	Oct 2001
Riley, Miss Geraldine	L	Jan 2002
Whatley, Mr Paul	L	Oct 2002
Gregg, Miss Rebecca	G	Jan 2003
Parmar, Miss Chetna	L	Jan 2003
Marriott, Mr Jamie	G	Jul 2003
Akther, Miss Tahina	L	Oct 2003
Flanagan, Mr Nicholas	L	Jul 2004
Mirza, Mr Mussadak	M	Jan 2004
Openshaw, Miss Samantha	L	Jan 2005
Keeling-Roberts, Mr Sam	I	Jul 2005
Ferber, Miss Iris	I	Jan 2005
Boyle, Mr Jonathan	M	Jan 2005
Kumeta, Miss Jennifer*	M	Oct 2005
Walthall, Mr Arron	I	Jan 2005
Stephens, Mr Richard	L	Jan 2008

Chambers of Mark G Turner QC

DEANS COURT CHAMBERS,
4A ST JOHN STREET, MANCHESTER, GREATER MANCHESTER M3 4DF
Tel: 0161 214 6000 ***Fax:*** 0161 214 6001
Dx: 718155 MANCHESTER 3

23 ESSEX STREET,
82 KING STREET, MANCHESTER, GREATER MANCHESTER M2 4WQ
Tel: 0161 870 9969
E-mail: clerks@23es.com
Web: www.23es.com
Clerk: Senior: Richard Fowler. Sean Gould; Robert Mayes; Jamie Clack; Adam Chapman; Joe Wheeler.
Administrator: Tracey McCormack
Practice Manager: Richard Fowler

This Chamber with 100 Barristers is based in London and led by Simon Russell Flint QC and specialises in Criminal Work - General, Tribunals and Inquiries, Fraud. Although the majority are based in London, our Barristers work out of all 3 annexes. You may contact any of our clerks at any time by sending an email to clerks@23es.com.

THIRTY NINE ESSEX STREET,
82 KING STREET, MANCHESTER, GREATER MANCHESTER M2 4WQ
Tel: 0161 870 0333 ***Fax:*** 020 7353 3978

Chambers of Bill Braithwaite QC

EXCHANGE CHAMBERS,
7 RALLI COURTS, WEST RIVERSIDE, MANCHESTER, GREATER MANCHESTER M3 5FT
Tel: 0161 833 2722 ***Fax:*** 0161 833 2789
Dx: 14330 MANCHESTER
E-mail: info@exchangechambers.co.uk
Clerk: Senior: Nick Buckley. Ian Spencer; Denise Sheen; Dave Haley; Sarah Rotherham; Leigh Daniels; Lynn Salter; Rachel Williams; Stuart Cofield; Suzanne Dutch; Kate Masher; Joe Ashcroft.
Administrator: Sally Smylie
Practice Manager: Roy Finney
Chambers Director: Tom Handley
Head of Chambers:

Braithwaite, Mr Bill (Q.C.)	G	Nov 1970

Elleray, Mr Anthony (Q.C.)	I	Jan 1977
Jones, Mr Edward Bartley (Q.C.)	L	Jul 1975
Martin, Mr Gerard James (Q.C.)	M	Jul 1978
Cawson, Mr Mark (Q.C.); Junior Counsel to the Crown(Provincial Panel); Recorder*	L	Jul 1982
Jones, Mr John Richard (Q.C.); Recorder	M	Jul 1981
Cole, Mr Gordon (Q.C.)	I	Jun 1979
Griffiths, Miss Tania (Q.C.); Recorder	G	Jul 1982
Waldron, Mr William F (Q.C.); Recorder(2000)	G	Nov 1986
Cummings, Mr Brian (Q.C.); Recorder(2005)	L	Nov 1988
Meadowcroft, Mr Stephen (Q.C.)	G	Jan 1973
Yip, Mrs Amanda (Q.C.); Recorder	G	Dec 1991
Nance, Mr Francis	G	Nov 1970
Scholes, Mr Michael	I	Jan 1996
Goode, Miss Rowena Margaret; Recorder	G	Jul 1974
Earlam, Mr Simon; Recorder	G	Feb 1975
Lamb, Mr Eric; Recorder	L	Jul 1975
Fordham, Mrs Judith; Deputy District Judge	L	Jul 1991
Jess, Dr Digby C	G	Jul 1978
Goff, Mr Anthony Thomas	M	Jul 1978
Troy, Ms Karen	L	Jan 1981
Harris, Mr Ian	I	Oct 1990
Kirtley, Mr Paul G	M	Jul 1982
Gregory, Miss Karen	M	Jul 1985
Hillman, Mr Roger; Deputy District Judge	G	Jul 1983
Cadwallader, Mr Neil; Chancery Recorder 2009	I	Jul 1984
Taylor, Mr Paul	G	Jan 1985
Clark, Mr Paul Robert	M	May 1994
Hanbury, Mr William; P/T Immigration Judge/Deputy Judge of Upper Tribunal (Immigration & Asylum Chamber)	I	Nov 1985
Berkson, Mr Simon	G	Jul 1986
Vickers, Mr Guy	M	Nov 1986
Knifton, Mr David Alan; Recorder	I	Jul 1986
Dodd, Miss Sara	L	Jul 1987
Mulrooney, Mr Mark; P/T President of Mental Health Review Tribunal	M	Jul 1988
McCarroll, Mr John Johnston	I	Nov 1988
Browne, Mr Louis; Recorder	I	Nov 1988
Foster, Mr Ian	L	Jul 1988
Landale, Miss Tina Jeanette; Recorder	L	Jul 1988
Clark, Miss Rebecca	I	Jul 1989
Howells, Miss Catherine; Recorder	G	Jul 1989
Wood, Mr Michael	L	Nov 1989
Vaughan, Mr Simon P	G	Nov 1989
Cannan, Mr Jonathan*	G	Nov 1989
Rhind, Mr Mark A	M	May 1989
Stables, Mr Christopher	G	Oct 1990
Case, Miss Julie	M	Oct 1990
Cook, Mr Christopher	I	Oct 1990
Lavery, Mr Michael	G	Feb 1990
Potter, Mr David	L	Oct 1990
MacAdam, Mr Jason	L	Nov 1990
Golinski, Mr Robert	M	Oct 1990
Toal, Mr David	G	Feb 1990
Evans, Mr Paul Timothy	G	Oct 1992
Maynard-Connor, Mr Giles	I	Nov 1992
Woods, Ms Rachel Helen	G	Oct 1992
Ainsworth, Mr Mark; Recorder	L	Oct 1992
Naylor, Dr Kevin	L	Oct 1992
Hoare, Mr Gregory Blake	G	Nov 1992
Jarvis, Mr Oliver	I	Nov 1992
Johnson, Miss Amanda	G	Oct 1992
Kenny, Miss Charlotte	G	Nov 1993
Dudley, Mr Robert Michael	G	Oct 1993
Wyn Jones, Mr Robert	L	Jan 1993
Connolly, Mr Stephen	L	Jan 2003
Graham-Wells, Miss Alison	I	Jul 1992
Jebb, Mr Andrew John; Deputy District Judge (Mags)	G	Nov 1993
Bassano, Mr Alaric	G	Nov 1993
Garside, Mr Mark	I	Feb 1993
Pennifer, Ms Kelly	M	Nov 1994
Johnson, Mr Nicholas J	I	Nov 1994
Whittlestone, Ms Kim	M	Oct 1994
Whaites, Ms Louise	G	Jan 1994
Nolan, Mr Damian Francis Hardwicke Scholar	L	Nov 1994
Littler, Mr Richard	G	May 1994
Walker, Mr Bruce	G	Nov 1994
Myers, Mr Benjamin	I	Nov 1994
Maher, Mr Michael	G	Nov 1995
Linklater, Ms Lisa	I	Oct 1995
Gourley, Miss Claire	M	Oct 1996
Redpath, Mr Scott	M	Jan 1996
Acton, Miss Jayne	L	Mar 1996
Guirguis, Miss Sheren	I	Jan 1996
Smith, Mr Andrew William	L	Oct 1996
Dawar, Mrs Archna	L	Oct 1996
Slack, Mr Kevin John	G	Oct 1997
Farrow, Mr Adrian John	M	Jul 1997
Metcalf, Miss Louise	I	Oct 1997
Stephenson, Mr Mark	G	Nov 1997
French, Mr Jonathan	L	Nov 1997
Close, Mr Jon	L	Oct 1997
Burns, Mr Paul	L	Oct 1998
O'Brien, Ms Sarah	I	Jul 1998
Titchmarsh, Miss Katharine	L	Nov 1998
Walker, Mr Nicholas	L	Oct 1998
Jones, Miss Sian Scott; Assistant Deputy Coroner	L	Oct 1998
Smart, Mr Neil; Assistant Deputy Coroner	L	May 1998
Edwards, Mr Nigel D H	L	Jan 1999
Travers, Mr Daniel	L	Oct 1999
Clarke, Mr Jonathan	I	Oct 1999
Mohyuddin, Mr David Niaz	L	Oct 1999
Barnes, Mr Christopher	G	Jun 2000
Snowdon, Miss Martine	L	Oct 2000
Rogers, Mr Jonathan	M	Oct 2000
Vinson, Mr Andrew	M	Jul 2000
Ward, Mr Andrew John	M	Jul 2000
Daley, Miss Nicola	G	Jul 2000
Gooding, Miss Laura	L	Jan 2001
Shields, Mr Josh	M	Mar 2000
Temkin, Mr David	I	Jul 2000
Grattage, Mr Stephen	L	Nov 2000
Gee, Ms Caroline	G	Jan 2003
Atherton, Ms Charlotte	G	Jul 2003
Taylor, Mr Christian	L	Jan 2003
McNally, Mr Stephen	G	Nov 2003
Sutherland, Miss Sara	L	Oct 2004
Johnston, Miss Sarah	G	Jul 2004
Petterson, Mr Andrew	M	Oct 2004
Lin, Miss Esther	M	Jan 2002
Bennett, Miss Emma	L	Jan 2004
Rohrer, Mr Kerron	I	Oct 2005
Moss, Mr Edward	I	Jan 2005
Sandbach, Miss Carly	L	Jul 2006
Gutteridge, Mr Christopher	I	Oct 2006
Tetlow, Mr Richard	M	Jul 2006
Birrell, Mr David	L	Nov 2006
Weiss, Mr Alfred	L	Oct 2006
Cornwall, Miss Natalia	M	Jul 2007
Shires, Mr Gareth Richard	L	Jul 2007
Lowe, Mr Jonathan	L	Mar 2008
Durston, Mr Jeremy	I	Jan 2008
Whitfield, Mr Simon	L	Jul 2009
Royle, Mr Chris	L	Jul 2009
Speakman, Mr Lee	M	Jul 2009
Tucker, Mr Ian	M	Jul 2010
Rees, Mr John Charles (Q.C.)*	L	Jul 1972
Janner, Mr Daniel (Q.C.)*	M	Jan 1980
Bartle, Mr Philip M (Q.C.)*	M	Jul 1976
Turner, Mr Jonathan (Q.C.)*	G	Jul 1974
Enoch, Mr Dafydd (Q.C.)*	G	Nov 1985
Nelson, Mr Cairns (Q.C.)*	G	Jan 1987
Laws, Miss Eleanor (Q.C.)*	I	Oct 1990
Medland, Mr Simon (Q.C.)*	M	Oct 1991
James, Mr Alun Edward*	M	Nov 1986
Fox, Dr Simon*	I	Oct 1994
Maguire, Mr Andrew*	I	Nov 1988
Tyack, Mr David*	M	Nov 1994
Eyers, Mr Anthony*	I	Nov 1994
Dooher, Ms Nancy Helen*	L	Nov 1997
Chichester-Clark, Mr Adam*	M	Oct 2000

Chambers of Ian Alexander Macdonald QC

GARDEN COURT NORTH CHAMBERS,
22 OXFORD COURT, MANCHESTER, GREATER MANCHESTER M2 3WQ
Tel: 0161 236 1840 ***Fax:*** 0161 236 0929
Dx: 715637 MANCHESTER 2
E-mail: clerks@gcnchambers.co.uk
Clerk: Senior: Sarah Wright. Juniors: Annmarie Nightingale; Nicola Carroll.
Head of Chambers:

Macdonald, Mr Ian Alexander (Q.C.)	M	Feb 1963

Baillie, Ms Brigid	I	Jul 2007
Barlow, Mr Mark	M	Oct 1992
Birdee, Ms Sonia	M	Jan 2004
Byles, Mr Andrew	L	Jan 2003
Cawsey, Ms Laura	L	Nov 2004
Daley, Miss Sarah	L	Jan 2007
Firth, Ms Georgina	M	Oct 1995
Fitzpatrick, Mr Andrew	G	Jan 2003
George, Mr Mark (Q.C.)	I	Nov 1976
Grahame, Miss Nina	M	Nov 1993
Hodson, Mr Peter	I	Nov 1994

Jagadesham, Mr Vijay . . . I . . . Jan 2004
McCormack, Mr Ben . . . G . . . Nov 2005
McKeone, Ms Mary . . . G . . . Feb 1986
O'Ryan, Mr Rory . . . M . . . Mar 2000
Poynor, Miss Bryony . . . L . . . Jan 2009
Smith, Ms Kerry Ann . . . L . . . Jul 2002
Stanbury, Mr Matthew . . . G . . . Jan 2004
Stark, Mr James . . . M . . . Jan 1998
Stone, Ms Kate . . . I . . . Oct 2004
Warren, Miss Camille . . . I . . . Jan 2008
Weatherby, Mr Peter . . . G . . . Nov 1992

Chambers of Francis J Burns

KENWORTHY'S CHAMBERS,
ARLINGTON HOUSE, BLOOM STREET, MANCHESTER, GREATER MANCHESTER M3 6AJ
Tel: 0161 832 4036 ***Fax:*** 0161 832 0370
Dx: 718200 MANCHESTER 3
E-mail: maria@kenworthysbarristers.co.uk
Clerk: Senior Criminal Clerk: Paul Mander; Junior Criminal Clerk:Thomas Harrington; Civil Clerk: Rachel Campbell; Immigration Clerk: Courtney Soden.
Administrator: Sue Barlow
Practice Manager: Maria Rushworth
Head of Chambers:
Burns, Mr Francis J. . . . G . . . May 1971

Nolan, Mr Benjamin (Q.C.); Recorder; Deputy High Court Judge (QBD)* . . . M . . . Jul 1971
Woodcock, Mr Robert (Q.C.)* . . . I . . . Feb 1978
Brown, Mr Roger . . . I . . . Nov 1976
Grennan, Mr Barry E . . . L . . . Jul 1977
Marsh, Mr John . . . G . . . Jul 1977
Donnelly, Mr William . . . G . . . Nov 1981
Cassidy, Mr Patrick . . . L . . . Jul 1982
Morris, Mr Anthony . . . G . . . Nov 1986
Patel, Miss Gita . . . I . . . Jul 1988
Edusei, Mr Francis . . . I . . . Jul 1989
Wolstenholme, Mr Alan . . . L . . . Jul 1989
Williamson, Mr Patrick . . . I . . . Nov 1989
Flattery, Miss Amanda . . . L . . . Oct 1993
Timson, Mr Corin . . . I . . . Nov 1994
Marrs, Mr Andrew . . . I . . . Nov 1995
Whelan, Mr Geoff . . . G . . . Mar 1996
Mather, Ms Alison . . . L . . . Oct 1997
Harwood-Gray, Mr Barry . . . L . . . Nov 1998
Asquith, Mr Marc . . . M . . . Oct 1999
Morton, Mr David . . . I . . . Nov 1999
Khan, Miss Shazia . . . L . . . Jul 2000
FitzPatrick, Miss Denise . . . M . . . Jul 2000
Penni, Miss Sally . . . G . . . Oct 2000
White, Ms Rachel . . . M . . . Nov 2000
Haque, Ms Sara . . . M . . . Nov 2000
McDonald, Ms Margaret . . . I . . . Nov 2000
Schwenk, Mr Mark . . . L . . . Jul 2001
Emmanuel, Ms Joy . . . M . . . Oct 2001
Johnson, Sarah . . . L . . . Oct 2001
Smith, Mr Michael . . . L . . . Oct 2001
Buckle, Mr Colin . . . M . . . Mar 2002
Brown, Mr George . . . M . . . Jul 2002
Habib, Ms Shysta . . . L . . . Jul 2002
Mottram, Miss Cheryl . . . L . . . Oct 2002
Grant, Chudi . . . L . . . Nov 2002
Nicholson, Mr John . . . G . . . Jul 2004
Niaz, Miss Anisa . . . M . . . Oct 2004
Cragg, Miss Janet . . . L . . . Jul 2005
Chawdhery, Miss Yasmin . . . L . . . Oct 2005
Lugsdin, Mr Martin . . . M . . . Nov 2005
Wilson, Mr Alan . . . I . . . Nov 2005
Luck, Ms Julie-Anne . . . L . . . Jul 2006
Pickering, Miss Rebecca . . . I . . . Jul 2007
Micah, Carol . . . L . . . Jan 2009
Varle, Miss Stephanie . . . L . . . Jul 2009
Tettey, Mr Stephen . . . G . . . Mar 2010
Quegan, Mr Peter . . . I . . . Jul 2010
Blakebrough, Mr Simon . . . L . . . Mar 2011

A progressive and modern set based in Salford, Manchester, Kenworthy's Chambers specialises in crime, civil, employment, costs, PI, family and immigration. Contact us on maria@kenworthysbarristers.co.uk

Chambers of Nicholas Braslavsky QC

KINGS CHAMBERS,
36 YOUNG STREET, MANCHESTER, GREATER MANCHESTER M3 3FT
Tel: 0161 832 9082 ***Fax:*** 0161 835 2139
Dx: 718188 MANCHESTER 3
E-mail: clerks@kingschambers.com
Clerk: Seniors: William Brown; Colin Griffin. Paul Clarke; Gary Young; Stephen Loxton; Andrew Reeves; Mark Ronson; Harry Young.
Administrator: Debra Andres
Chambers Director: Debra Andres
Head of Chambers:
Braslavsky, Mr Nicholas (Q.C.); Recorder . . . I . . . Jul 1983

Sauvain, Mr Stephen (Q.C.); Assistant Boundary Commissioner . . . L . . . Jul 1977
Booth, Mr Michael (Q.C.)* . . . L . . . Nov 1981
Fraser, Mr Vincent (Q.C.); Recorder . . . G . . . Jul 1981
Chaisty, Mr Paul (Q.C.); Recorder . . . L . . . Jul 1982
Manley, Mr David (Q.C.); Recorder . . . I . . . Jul 1981
Anderson, Ms Lesley (Q.C.); CEDR Accredited Mediator . . . M . . . Nov 1989
Casement, Mr David (Q.C.) . . . M . . . Oct 1992
Rawlinson, Mr Michael (Q.C.) . . . I . . . Dec 1991
Tucker, Mr Paul (Q.C.) . . . G . . . Nov 1990
Owen, Mr Eric . . . G . . . Nov 1969
Terry, Mr Jeffrey . . . L . . . Jul 1976
Lancaster, Mr Roger . . . M . . . Nov 2002
Khan, Shokat . . . M . . . Nov 1979
Barrett, Mr John; Recorder . . . G . . . May 1982
Berragan, Mr Howard Neil . . . G . . . Jul 1982
Evans, Mr Alan . . . L . . . Jul 1978
Halliwell, Mr Mark; Recorder . . . L . . . Jun 1985
Hilton, Mr Simon; Recorder . . . G . . . Nov 1987
Clayton, Mr Nigel . . . I . . . Jul 1987
Stockley, Miss Ruth . . . L . . . Jul 1988
Ashworth, Miss Fiona . . . L . . . Jul 1988
Pass, Mr Geoffrey . . . M . . . Jul 1975
Pritchett, Mr Stephen . . . L . . . Jun 1989
Poole, Mr Nigel . . . M . . . Nov 1989
Singer, Mr Andrew; Panel of TEBAR Adjudicators . . . G . . . Nov 1990
Johnson, Mr Paul . . . G . . . Nov 2006
Burrows, Mr Simon . . . I . . . Nov 1990
Smith, Mr Matthew . . . L . . . Oct 1991
Grantham, Mr Andrew Timothy . . . M . . . Nov 1991
Carter, Mr Martin . . . M . . . Nov 1992
Horne, Mr Wilson . . . L . . . Oct 1992
Powis, Miss Lucy . . . G . . . Oct 1992
Harper, Mr Mark . . . L . . . Oct 1993
Pritchard, Miss Sarah . . . G . . . Oct 1993
Lander, Mr Richard . . . L . . . Oct 1993
Ponter, Mr Ian . . . M . . . Oct 1993
Boyd, Mr James . . . I . . . Nov 1994
Latimer, Mr Andrew . . . G . . . Nov 1995
Fullwood, Mr Adam . . . G . . . Mar 1996
McBride, Mr Gavin . . . M . . . Sep 1996
Doyle, Mr Louis G . . . L . . . Nov 1996
Easton, Mr Jonathan . . . L . . . Nov 1996
Plimmer, Ms Melanie . . . G . . . Mar 1996
Siddall, Mr Nicholas . . . M . . . Oct 1997
Young, Mr Simon . . . I . . . Nov 1998
Plaut, Mr Simon M . . . L . . . Oct 1997
Bourne, Mr Colin . . . G . . . Oct 1997
Friston, Dr Mark . . . M . . . Nov 1997
Cooper, Mr Ian Mark . . . M . . . Mar 1998
Maguire, Mr Stephen . . . M . . . Mar 2007
Cannock, Mr Giles . . . L . . . Oct 1998
McGee, Mr Andrew . . . L . . . Nov 1998
Hall, Mr Matthew . . . M . . . Mar 1999
Mulholland, Miss Helen M . . . M . . . Oct 1999
Budworth, Mr Martin . . . I . . . Nov 1999
Brown, Miss Catherine . . . I . . . Nov 1999
Ranales-Cotos, Ms Tina . . . L . . . Oct 1999
Temple, Miss Eleanor . . . I . . . Jul 2000
Griffiths, Mr Brian J . . . G . . . Nov 1999
Walmisley, Mrs Lisa . . . M . . . Jul 2000
Lakin, Mr Paul . . . M . . . Jul 2000
Hughes, Mr Paul . . . M . . . Oct 2001
Williams, Mr Ben D . . . M . . . Jan 2001
Wheatley, Mr Geraint . . . G . . . Sep 2001
Steward, Miss Claire . . . L . . . Nov 2002
Ralph, Mr Craig . . . M . . . Jan 2002
Hunter, Mr John . . . L . . . Nov 2002
Karim, Mr Sam . . . G . . . Nov 2002
Duckworth, Miss Emily . . . I . . . Jul 2003
Mayoh, Ms Michelle . . . L . . . Jul 2003
Reid, Miss Sarah . . . L . . . Sep 2004
Gardner, Miss Francesca . . . L . . . Oct 2004
Galloway, Miss Rachel . . . G . . . Oct 2004
Allan, Miss Sophie . . . L . . . Oct 2004
Gorasia, Mr Paras . . . I . . . Oct 2005
Law, Miss Charlotte . . . M . . . Oct 2005
Harding, Mr Ben . . . I . . . Oct 2005
Dainty, Miss Cheryl . . . I . . . Jul 2006
Livingston, Mr Richard . . . M . . . Oct 2006
Ward, Mr Johnny . . . L . . . Jan 2007
Smith, Dr Nathan . . . L . . . Jan 2007
Lieberman, Gemma . . . M . . . Jan 2007
Latham, Mr Kevin . . . M . . . Oct 2007
McNamara, Mr Stephen . . . G . . . Jul 2008
d'Arcy, Miss Eleanor . . . L . . . Oct 2008
Gill, Mr Anthony . . . L . . . Jan 2008
Keay, Prof Andrew; Associate Member . . . L . . . Mar 2010
Taylor, Miss Ruth . . . M . . . Jul 2010
Gilliland, His Hon David (Q.C.) . . . G . . . Nov 1964
Freedman, Mr Clive (Q.C.) . . . G . . . Jul 1978
Crawford, Mr Colin . . . M . . . Jul 1997
Henderson, Mr James; Associate Member . . . G . . . Nov 1997

Chambers of Mukhtar Hussain QC

LINCOLN HOUSE CHAMBERS,
5TH FLOOR , LINCOLN HOUSE, 1 BRAZENNOSE STREET, MANCHESTER, GREATER MANCHESTER M2 5EL
Tel: 0161 832 5701 ***Fax:*** 0161 832 0839
Dx: 14338 MANCHESTER 1
E-mail: info@lincolnhousechambers.com
Clerk: Senior: David Wright.
Head of Chambers:
Hussain, Mukhtar (Q.C.); Recorder . . . M . . . Jul 1971

Webster, Mr Alistair S (Q.C.); Recorder . . . M . . . Jul 1976
Gozem, Mr Guy (Q.C.); Recorder . . . M . . . Jul 1972
Conrad, Mr Alan (Q.C.); Recorder . . . M . . . Jul 1976
Wright, Mr Peter D (Q.C.); Recorder . . . I . . . Jul 1981
Pickup, Mr James K (Q.C.); Recorder . . . G . . . Jul 1976
Reid, Mr Paul C (Q.C.); Recorder . . . G . . . Jul 1973
Cross, Mr Anthony (Q.C.) . . . G . . . Jan 1982
Goddard, Ms Suzanne (Q.C.); Recorder . . . G . . . Nov 1987
Thomas, Mr Andrew (Q.C.) . . . G . . . Jul 1989
Watson, Mr Dennis (Q.C.); Recorder . . . I . . . Jul 1985
Gregory, Mr James Hans . . . G . . . Jul 1970
Platts, Mr Robert; Recorder . . . L . . . Jul 1973
Lasker, Mr Jeremy S . . . I . . . Jul 1976
Nuttall, Mr Andrew P . . . L . . . Nov 1978
Curran, Mr Phillip C; Recorder . . . L . . . May 1979
Elias, Mr Robert W . . . M . . . Jul 1979
Nicholls, Ms Elizabeth J; Recorder . . . I . . . Jul 1984
Bloomer, Mr Charles H . . . L . . . Jul 1985
Butcher, Mr Richard . . . G . . . Nov 1985
Stuart, Mr Douglas Mark . . . G . . . Nov 1985
McMeekin, Mr Ian . . . M . . . Jan 1987
Baxter, Miss Bernadette; Recorder . . . M . . . Jul 1987
Lawton, Mr Paul; Recorder . . . L . . . Nov 1987
Johnson, Ms Kathryn Margaret . . . G . . . Jul 1989
Fryman, Mr Neil . . . M . . . Jul 1989
Barton, Mr Hugh . . . M . . . Nov 1989
Smith, Ms Rachel . . . L . . . Oct 1990
Bowley, Mr Ivan R . . . M . . . Nov 1990
Simons, Mr Richard G . . . G . . . Feb 1991
Donnelly, Mr Kevin G . . . L . . . Oct 1991
Blackwell, Ms Katherine . . . L . . . Nov 1992
Holt, Ms Abigail . . . L . . . Sep 1993
Roberts, Ms Lisa . . . L . . . Oct 1993
Usher, Mr Neil . . . M . . . Oct 1993
Warne, Mr Peter . . . I . . . Oct 1993
Storrie, Mr Timothy . . . M . . . Oct 1993
Boyd, Mr Joseph P G . . . G . . . Nov 1993
Doran, Mr Gerard . . . G . . . Nov 1993
Holden, Mr Philip . . . L . . . Oct 1994
Holland, Mr Rick . . . G . . . Nov 1994
Hackett, Mr Martin John . . . M . . . Jan 1995
Nawaz, Mr Mohammed . . . L . . . Nov 1995
Holland, Ms Charlotte Kate . . . L . . . Oct 1996
Priestley, Mr Roderick . . . G . . . Nov 1996
Kearney, Mr Robert . . . I . . . Nov 1996
Nield, Ms Zoe . . . G . . . Oct 1998
Pierpoint, Ms Katherine . . . L . . . Oct 1998
Kitchin, Miss Louise . . . M . . . Oct 1998
Nicholson, Ms Amy . . . L . . . Dec 1999
Leach, Mr Alexander . . . I . . . Dec 2001
Jones, Mr Gareth . . . M . . . Oct 2002
English, Mr Richard . . . I . . . Mar 2003
Jones, Miss Katie Laura . . . G . . . Oct 2003
Prokofiev, Mr Sergey . . . L . . . Jul 2004
Thomas, Mr Daniel James . . . M . . . Jul 2005
Gurney, Mr Simon . . . I . . . Jul 2006
Barbour, Ms Laura . . . G . . . Oct 2006

St.James's
CHAMBERS

Chambers of Robert Sterling

ST JAMES'S CHAMBERS,
68 QUAY STREET, MANCHESTER, GREATER MANCHESTER M3 3EJ
Tel: 0161 834 7000 ***Fax:*** 0161 834 2341
Dx: 14350 MANCHESTER 1
E-mail: clerks@stjameschambers.com
Clerk: Paul S Morecroft.
Head of Chambers:
Sterling, Robert . . . G . . . Jul 1970

Lyons, Mr Timothy (Q.C.)* . . . I . . . Jul 1980
Wood, Mr Percy . . . G . . . Feb 1961
Machin, Mr Charles Kim . . . L . . . Nov 1973
Searle, Mr Barrie; Recorder; Legal Assessor . . . M . . . Jul 1975
Porter, Mr David . . . L . . . Jul 1980
Mulholland, Mr Michael . . . G . . . Sep 1976
Binns, Mr David . . . M . . . Jul 1983
Selwyn Sharpe, Mr Richard . . . L . . . Nov 1985
Wilson-Barnes, Lucy; Junior Counsel to the Crown(Provincial Panel) . . . I . . . Jul 1989
Harrison, Ms Sarah . . . L . . . Nov 1989
Wheeldon, Miss Sarah Helen . . . G . . . Oct 1990
Stephenson, Mr Paul . . . M . . . Oct 1990
Kelly, Mr Sean . . . G . . . Jan 1990
Smith, Mr Jonathan . . . G . . . Jan 1992
Hurd, Mr James . . . G . . . Oct 1994
Calvert, Mr David . . . I . . . Nov 1995
Potts, Warren . . . M . . . Jul 1995
Taft, Mr Christopher . . . M . . . Nov 1997
Short, Miss Anna . . . G . . . Nov 1997
Hammond, Mr Fayaz . . . G . . . Oct 1999
Moore, Mr Richard . . . L . . . Oct 1992
Tindall, Mr Paul R . . . G . . . Oct 1999
Bilsland, Miss Alisan . . . L . . . Oct 2000
Rashid, Mr Haroon . . . L . . . Mar 1999
Taskeen, Mr Wasim . . . L . . . Jan 1998
Boyle, Miss Karen . . . L . . . Jan 2000
Mulderig, Mr Joseph . . . L . . . Jan 2002
Banks, Mr Nathan . . . L . . . Oct 2003
Hammond, Ms Claire . . . L . . . Jul 2003
Lawrenson, Ms Sarah . . . M . . . Oct 2003
Pomfret, Mr Brad . . . L . . . Jan 2004
Kamal, Setu* . . . L . . . Jan 2004
Youshani, Elahe . . . L . . . Jan 2005
Bunbury, Ms Claire . . . M . . . Jan 2006
Hogg, Mr James . . . I . . . Jan 2006
O'Neill, Mr Michael . . . I . . . Jan 2006
Green, Miss Louise . . . G . . . Jul 2009
Rivers Mansfield, Mrs Suzanne . . . M . . . Jul 2010

This Chamber with 39 Barristers is based in Manchester and led by Robert Sterling. You may contact any of our clerks at any time by sending a message to clerks@stjameschambers.com.

NINESTJOHNSTREET

Community Legal Service

Criminal Defence Service

Chambers of Charles Garside QC

9 ST JOHN STREET CHAMBERS,
9 ST JOHN STREET, MANCHESTER, GREATER MANCHESTER M3 4DN
Tel: 0161 955 9000 ***Fax:*** 0161 955 9001
Dx: 14326 MANCHESTER
E-mail: clerks@9sjs.com
Web: www.9sjs.com

Clerk: Tony Morrissey; Chris Swann.
Practice Manager: Ruth Ann Bailey
Head of Chambers:

Garside, Mr Charles (Q.C.); Recorder	G	Nov 1971
Carus, Mr Roderick (Q.C.); Recorder	G	Nov 1971
Hill, Mr Mark (Q.C.)	M	Jul 1987
Hinchliffe, Mr Nicholas (Q.C.); Recorder	M	Nov 1980
Jones, Mr Geraint (Q.C.)*	M	Jul 1976
Jackson, Mr Simon (Q.C.); Recorder*	G	Jan 1982
Clarke, Mr Nicholas (Q.C.)	M	Jan 1981
McDermott, Mr Gerard Francis (Q.C.); Recorder	M	Jul 1978
Irving, Miss Gillian (Q.C.); P/T Chairman of Registered Homes Tribunal; Mental Health Review Tribunal	I	Jul 1984
Gilroy, Mr Paul (Q.C.)	G	Jul 1985
Kennedy, Mr Christopher (Q.C.)	G	Jul 1989
Rigby, Mr Terence; Recorder	G	May 1971
Cadwallader, Mr Peter	G	Jul 1973
Riley, Miss Christine	G	Jul 1974
McDonald, Mr Paul	L	Jul 1975
Grundy, Mr Nigel	M	Jul 1983
Bower, Mr Alistair	I	Jul 1986
Leeming, Mr Michael; Recorder	I	Jul 1983
Breen, Mr Carlo	M	Nov 1987
Gilchrist, Mr David Somerled	I	Nov 1987
Monaghan, Mr Mark	L	Jul 1987
Gatto, Ms Nicola	M	Nov 1987
Fitzpatrick, Mr Thomas A	L	Nov 1988
Little, Mr Ian	M	Feb 1989
Morgan, Mr Edward	L	Jul 1989
Barnett, Ms Joanne	M	Nov 1989
Woodward, Miss Joanne	G	Nov 1989
Preston, Mr Darren	G	Oct 1991
Howard, Mr Anthony	I	Oct 1992
Connolly, Miss Joanne	M	Oct 1992
Sabry, Karim S	I	Oct 1992
Bailey, Mr Graham R	I	Feb 1993
Wedderspoon, Miss Rachel	M	Oct 1993
Barry, Miss Kirsten	L	Nov 1993
Hamilton, Mr Jaime	G	Nov 1993
Fryer-Spedding, Mr James	G	Feb 1994
Lemmy, Mr Michael	M	Jan 1994
Clark, Mr Andrew R	I	Oct 1994
Darbyshire, Mr Robert	L	Nov 1995
McCluggage, Mr Brian	M	Oct 1995
Brochwicz-Lewinski, Mr Stefan	G	Oct 1995
Nowell, Ms Katie	L	Nov 1996
Lewis, Miss Sara	L	Jan 1996
Woodhall, Mr Gary	G	Oct 1997
Heppenstall, Miss Rachael	M	Aug 1997
Hollyoak, Ms Kate	G	Nov 1997
Thomson, Vanessa	L	Dec 1997
Del Priore, Miss Assunta	M	Oct 1998
Mallory, Miss Kathrine	I	Jan 1998
Mabon, Mrs Jane	G	Jul 1998
Redmond, Miss Helen	G	Jan 1999
Leeming, Miss Lucinda	M	Jan 1999
Thompson, Mrs Zoe	M	Jan 1999
Haisley, Mr Matthew	L	Oct 1999
Rigby, Miss Victoria	M	Jan 2000
Eeley, Miss Rebecca	M	Mar 2001
Heyworth, Miss Alison	I	Mar 2001
Snarr, Mr Matthew	I	Jan 2001
Thomas, Miss Dawn Marie	L	Oct 2001
McKinlay, Miss Kirsty	L	Mar 2001
Dickinson, Mr Russell	L	Jul 2002
Savage, Mr Jonathan	G	Jan 2003
Brandon, Miss Louise	M	Jan 2003
Gilbart, Mr Tom	M	Jan 2003
Vicary, Miss Joanna	M	Jan 2003
Curry, Miss Caroline	M	Nov 2003
Denham, Mr Ian	M	Jul 2003
Northall, Mr Daniel	L	Jan 2004
Morris, Mr Benjamin Francis Joseph	L	Jan 2004
Haines, Miss Hannah	L	Feb 2005
Hardy, Dr Stephen	L	Oct 2005
Smith, Mr Robert	G	Oct 2005
D'Cruz, Miss Laura	I	Nov 2006
Levene, Miss Rachael	G	Oct 2006
Lewis, Ms Rachael	M	Nov 2006
Amartey, Miss Lena	M	Oct 2008
Samuel, Mr Zimran	M	Nov 2008
Hamilton, Mr William	M	Nov 2008
Robinson, Mr Graham	M	Jul 2009
Price, Mr Richard	L	Mar 2011
Greenhalgh, Emma	M	Jan 2010
Langhorn, Mr Alex	M	Jan 2010
Cundy, Catherine	M	Jan 2011

These Chambers were established in Manchester approximately one hundred years ago. The last decade has brought rapid and radical change and 9 St John Street now comprises 11 Silks and 72 Junior Counsel supported by dedicated Clerking and Administration Teams determined to meet the requirements and expectations of our clients. We are committed to providing a modern, accessible and efficient service whilst maintaining our reputation for excellence and integrity. Our premises provide up-to-date, well equipped and comfortable accommodation conveniently located in the centre of Manchester, together with state of the art video-conferencing facilities. In order to meet the increasing demands for specialisation, Members of Chambers have formed themselves into the following special interest groups: Insurance Fraud, Commercial, Crime, Employment, Family and Personal Injury. Special Interest Group brochures are available on request as is a full Curriculum Vitae for each member of Chambers. The Clerking Team will be only too pleased to supply more information about the experience and practice of individual members of Chambers so as to ensure that we provide the service to match your specific requirements.

Chambers of Peter Birkett QC

18 ST JOHN STREET CHAMBERS,
MANCHESTER, GREATER MANCHESTER
M3 4EA
Tel: 0161 278 1800 ***Fax:*** 0161 278 8220
Dx: 728854 MANCHESTER 4
E-mail: clerks@18sjs.com
Clerk: John Hammond.
Administrator: Cat Nash
Practice Manager: Rachel Swift
Head of Chambers:

Birkett, Mr Peter (Q.C.)	I	Feb 1972
Wigglesworth, Mr Raymond (Q.C.)	G	Jul 1974
Forrest, Mr Alastair	G	Jul 1972
Rylands, Ms Elizabeth	M	Jan 1973
Dockery, Mr Paul	G	Jul 1973
O'Brien, Mr Paul	G	Nov 1974
Limb, Mr Christopher	G	Jul 1975
Diamond, Mr Christopher	G	Nov 1975
Fewtrell, Mr Nicholas Austin	I	Nov 1977
Laprell, Mr Mark	G	Nov 1979
Huffer, Mr Ian	G	Dec 1979
Wills, Ms Janice	L	Oct 1991
Stansby, Ms Alexandra	M	Nov 1985
Vardon, Mr Richard	G	Nov 1985
Murray, Mr Stephen John	I	Aug 1986
Healing, Ms Yvonne	I	Jan 1987
Sasse, Mr Toby	M	Jul 1988
Birtles, Ms Samantha	L	Jul 1989
Holloran, Miss Fiona	G	Nov 1989
Tythcott, Ms Elisabeth	I	Nov 1989
Simpson, Ms Raquel	I	Oct 1990
Dale, Mr Jonathan Paul	G	Jan 1991
Brady, Mr Michael	G	Oct 1992
Booth, Miss Joy	G	Oct 1992
Harrison, Miss Susan Kathryn	M	Oct 1993
Daw, Mr Christopher	G	Nov 1993
Shenton, Miss Rachel	M	Nov 1993
Kilvington, Mr Simon Charles	L	Nov 1995
Manasse, Dr Paul	G	Nov 1995
Moore, Mr Andrew David	I	Oct 1996
Lodge, Mr Adam	G	Oct 1996
Brody, Mr Saul Amos	I	Nov 1996
Hoffman, Mr David A	L	Oct 1997
Faux, Ms Rachel	I	Oct 1997
Mackley, Mr David	L	Oct 1997
Maqsood, Ms Kalsoom	M	Oct 1998
Chapman, Mr Richard	G	Oct 1998
Goldstein, Mr Wayne	L	Jan 1999
Kilvington, Miss Sarah	M	Oct 1999
Bramall, Miss Kate L	G	Oct 1999
Grierson, Mr Jonathan	M	Nov 1999
Norman, Mr Ben	G	Jan 2000
Markham, Miss Andrea	G	Jan 2000
Kaur, Lukhvinder	I	Nov 2000
Kajue, Miss Soria	M	Jan 2001
Caplan, Mrs Leonie	I	Mar 2001
Clarke, Mr Nicholas	L	Oct 2001
Thomas, Mrs Laura	L	Jan 2003
Donaldson, Ms Sarah	I	Jul 2003
Denham, Mr Ian	M	Jul 2003
Begum, Miss Rehana	L	Jul 2003
De Berry, Mr Philip	L	Oct 2003
Charles, Mr Simon	L	Jun 2004
McNall, Dr Christopher	M	Jan 2005
Lau, Miss Vanessa	M	Mar 2005
Henthorn, Miss Kate	M	Mar 2005
Chaudhry, Miss Saiqa	I	Jul 2005
Thomas, Mr Arron	L	Oct 2005
Murray, Miss Elizabeth	I	Oct 2005
Wilkinson, Mr Michael	I	Jan 2006
Firbank, Mr Kit	L	Oct 2005
Chan, Evonnie	M	Jan 2006
Ameen, Mr Danish	L	Jan 2006
Evans, Mr Andrew	M	Jan 2007
Wells, Mr Jason	L	Jan 2007
Davies, Mr Rupert	G	Jan 2007
Simons, Mr Kane	L	Oct 2007
Martin, Mr Stuart	L	Oct 2007
O'Leary, Mr Brendan	M	Oct 2007
Scott, Mr Andrew	M	Nov 2000

Chambers of Michael Howard Redfern QC

ST JOHNS BUILDINGS,
24A-28 ST JOHN STREET, MANCHESTER,
GREATER MANCHESTER M3 4DJ
Tel: 0161 214 1500 ***Fax:*** 0161 835 3929
Dx: 728861 MANCHESTER 4
E-mail: mary.berry@stjohnsbuildings.co.uk
Head of Chambers:

Redfern, Mr Michael Howard (Q.C.)	I	Jul 1970
Bentham, Mr Howard (Q.C.)	G	Nov 1970
Shorrock, Mr Michael (Q.C.)	I	Jul 1966
Berkley, Mr David (Q.C.)	M	May 1979
Marks, Mr Richard (Q.C.)	G	Jul 1975
Hayden, Mr Anthony (Q.C.)	M	Nov 1987
Singleton, Ms Sarah (Q.C.)	M	Jul 1983
O'Byrne, Mr Andrew (Q.C.)	G	Jul 1978
Samuels, Mr Jeffrey K (Q.C.)	M	Jul 1988
Harrison, Miss Sally (Q.C.)	G	Oct 1992
Wolff, Mr Michael	G	Jun 1964
Cattan, Mr Philip David	G	Nov 1970
Lamberty, Mr Mark	I	Nov 1970
Herman, Mr Ray	I	Feb 1972
Green, Mr Roger	L	Jul 1972
Hedgecoe, Mr John Philip	I	Nov 1972
Bedford, Mr Stephen	G	Jul 1972
McNeill, Mr John Seddon	L	Jul 1974
Shannon, Mr Eric	M	Nov 1974
Lowe, Mr Geoffrey	G	Jul 1975
Longworth, Mr Antony Stephen	M	Jul 1978
Andrews, Mr Philip	I	Feb 1977
Feeny, Mr Charles	I	Nov 1977
Grundy, Mr Philip Michael David	M	Jul 1980
Owen, Miss Gail	G	Nov 1980
Mercer, Mr David	L	Jul 1980
Uff, Mr David C	G	Jul 1981
Long, Mr Andrew	L	Jul 1981
Holt, Mr Julian	M	Jan 1982
Gal, Miss Sonia	I	Nov 1982
Greene, Mr Maurice A	I	Nov 1982
Garside, Mr David	G	Nov 1982
Bruce, Mr David	M	Jul 1982
Harrison, Mr Peter John	M	Jul 1983
Khawar, Aftab	G	Jul 1983
McKee, Mr Hugh A	M	Nov 1983
Goodman, Miss Bernadette	I	Nov 1983
McKenna, Mr Brian	M	Jun 1983
Harrison, Mr J Keith	L	Nov 1983
Shaw, Mr Julian	G	Sep 1984
Pickup, Mr David	I	Jul 1984
Kennedy, Mr Michael	M	May 1985
Lloyd, Mr Julian	G	Jul 1985
Gray, Mr Richard	I	Nov 1986
Kloss, Mrs Diana Mary	G	Jul 1986
Oates, Mr John Richard	G	Jul 1987
Taylor, Mr Julian	M	Jul 1986
Dickinson, Mr Jonathan	I	Nov 1986
Walker, Miss Jane	M	Jul 1987
Brennand, Mr Timothy W	G	Nov 1987
Dagnall, Ms Jane	I	Jan 1987
Batra, Bunty Lalit	G	Feb 1987
Eastwood, Mr Charles Peter	L	Jul 1988
Crabtree, Mr Simon J G	L	Nov 1988
Davitt, Ms Paula	G	Oct 1988
Sanders, Mr Damian	M	Nov 1988
Britcliffe, Ms Anne E	I	Apr 1989
Grundy, Ms Clare	G	Jul 1989
Partington, Miss Lisa	I	Jul 1989
Holder, Mr Simon	I	Jul 1989
Blakey, Mr Michael	M	Nov 1989
Carter, Mr Richard	I	Nov 1990
Thompson, Mr Patrick	G	Oct 1990
Watson, Mr David W	M	Oct 1990
Thompson, Mr Jonathan Richard	I	Oct 1990
Wright, Mr Alastair	L	Dec 1991
Mawdsley, Mr Matthew	I	Nov 1991
Roberts, Mr Mark Vaughan	I	Sep 1991
Chaudhry, Ms Zia	I	Nov 1991
Pratt, Mrs Patricia	L	Oct 1991
Taylor, Mr Jonathan	M	Nov 1991
Case, Magdalen	M	Nov 1992
Green, Mr Andrew	G	Oct 1992
Norton, Mr Richard	L	Nov 1992
Ashmole, Mr Timothy	L	Oct 1992
McNerney, Mr Kevin	I	Jan 1992
Lloyd, Ms Gaynor Elizabeth	L	Oct 1992
Jones, Mr Benjamin	M	Feb 1993
Flood, Mr David	M	Nov 1993
Kloss, Mr Alexander	G	Oct 1993
Mathieson, Mr Guy	M	Oct 1993
Wilson, Mr Myles	L	Oct 1993
Searle, Mr Jason Ario Xavier	M	Oct 1993
Gibson, Mr John Arthur	L	Nov 1993
Fitzharris, Miss Ginnette	L	Nov 1993
Blackshaw, Mr Henry	M	Oct 1993
Orme, Mr Richard	L	Oct 1993
Rodikis, Miss Joanna	M	Oct 1993
Harrison, Miss Leona	M	Nov 1993
Polglase, Mr David S	M	Oct 1993
Connor, Mr Mark	I	May 1994
Frieze, Mr Daniel	G	Oct 1994
Gumbs, Miss Annette	G	Oct 1994
Wild, Mr Steven	G	Oct 1994
Douglas, Mr Stephen John	I	Nov 1994
Reynolds, Mr Gary William	L	Nov 1994
McGinty, Mr Robert Fraser	I	Nov 1994
Rowley, Mr Karl John	M	Nov 1994
Houghton, Ms Lisa	G	May 1994
Booth, Mr Nigel Robert	G	Oct 1994
Mann, Miss Sara	M	Nov 1994
Chukwuemeka, Mr John O	L	Nov 1994
Hargan, Mr Carl	L	Nov 1995
Lawson, Mr Andrew	L	Jan 1995
Mchugh, Miss Pauline Mary	G	Nov 1995
Parry, Mr Philip	L	Jan 1995
Crangle, Miss Charlotte	G	Jan 1995
Simkin, Mr Iain	I	Feb 1995
Dixon, Mr John	G	Nov 1995
Aslett, Pepin	I	Nov 1996
Crilley, Mr Darrel	I	Feb 1996
Roussak, Mr Jeremy Brian	M	Oct 1996
Leene, Miss Sharon	G	Oct 1996
Sastry, Mr Bob	I	Oct 1996
Mahmood, Ghazan	I	Sep 1997
Mintz, Mr Simon	I	Nov 1996
Zentar, Dr Remy	G	Jul 1997
Spear, Miss Sarah	I	Oct 1997
Williams, Ms Zillah	L	Nov 1997
Mensah, Miss Lorraine S L	G	Oct 1997
Denton, Mr Douglas	L	Nov 1997
Parry, Mr Simon	I	Nov 1997
Tyler, Mr Paul	M	Jan 1997
Evans, Mr Simeon	L	Jun 1997
Buckley, Mr Patrick James	G	Jul 1998
Bentley, Mr David Paul	L	Oct 1998
Muth, Ms Susanne	I	Jul 1998
Simmonds, Ms Alexandra	G	Oct 1998
Taylor, Mr David Christopher	L	Oct 1998
Murdin, Mr Liam	L	Jul 1998
James, Mr David	I	Oct 1998
Burnell, Miss Kate	M	Oct 1998
Stockwell, Mr Matthew	G	Oct 1998
Edwards, Miss Susan	L	Nov 1998
Deas, Ms Susan Margaret	G	Jul 1999
Astbury, Mr Philip	G	Oct 1999
Holsgrove, Lara	M	Jan 1999
Ratledge, Mr John	L	Jun 1999
Sweeney, Ms Linda Mary	M	Nov 1999
Cavanagh, Ms Lorraine	G	Jan 2000
Leach, Ms Natasha	L	Jan 2000
Bridgman, Mr Andrew	G	Jan 2000
Porter-Phillips, Mrs Clare	L	Mar 2001
Ahmed, Siraj Issap	M	Apr 2001
King, Mr Oliver	G	Jul 2001
Vir Singh, Miss Sylvia	M	Jul 2001
Van Der Haer, Ms Audrey	G	Oct 2001
Blewitt, Miss Jennifer	M	Jul 2001
Pojur, Mr David	M	Nov 2001
Farley, Mr David	M	Jan 2001
Montaldo, Mr Neil	L	Mar 2002
Hodgkinson, Mr Paul George	L	Jul 2002

11

Owen, Wendy Jane	M	Jan 2002
Senior, Mr Mark	I	Jul 2002
Smith, Mr Paul	G	Oct 2002
Moss, Mr Christopher	L	Oct 2002
Malam, Mr James	G	Jan 2002
Menzies, Mr Jennifer	L	Oct 2002
Stringer, Ms Rosie	M	Jan 2002
McCloskey, Miss Louise	G	Oct 2002
Smith, Ms Rebecca Ellen	L	Jan 2002
Lawrence, Mr Benjamin	L	Jan 2003
Ali, Kashif	L	Jan 2003
Hudson, Ms Abigail	G	Jan 2003
Quigley, Ms Louise	I	Jan 2003
Newstead, Ms Jennifer Elizabeth	G	Nov 2003
Akers, Mr Robert	I	Nov 2003
Maguire, Clodagh	I	Jan 2003
Connolly, Mr Timothy	I	Mar 2004
Poole, Mr William	M	Jan 2004
Waddell, Ms Philippa	L	Jan 2004
Watkins, Mr Adam	G	Jul 2004
Murphy, Mr Paul	G	Jul 2004
Greenhalgh, Miss Jane	L	Nov 2004
Rimmer, Miss Catherine	G	Jul 2004
Harrison, Miss Petra	I	Jul 2004
Samuel, Ms Ana	I	Jul 2004
Wilson, Ms Helen	G	Oct 2004
Cooper, Mr Douglas	I	Jan 2004
Sutton, Rebecca	I	Jan 2004
Abraham, Ms Joanne Jade	G	Nov 2004
Spencer, Mr Shaun	L	Jan 2005
Marshall, Lucy	M	Jan 2005
White, Mrs Debra	G	Oct 2005
Christian, Mr Neil	M	Oct 2005
Thompson, Mr Gareth	G	Jan 2005
McGarry, Mr Steven	L	Mar 2005
De Navarro, Frances	I	Jan 2005
Pare, Mr Christopher	M	Jan 2006
Scully, Ms Jennifer	M	Jul 2006
Wilkinson, Mr Timothy	I	Jan 2006
Kelly, Mr Ben	L	Jan 2006
Flynn, Mr Steven	G	Jan 2006
Scott, Louise	M	Jan 2006
Haggis, Mr Andrew	M	Mar 2007
Wood, Hannah	L	Jan 2007
Vanderpump, Henry	I	Jan 2007
Owen-Easey, Neil	G	Jan 2007
Goode, Julian	L	Jan 2006
Allen, Mr Fegal	L	Oct 2007
Murray, Simon	I	Jan 2008
Cooper, Elisabeth	M	Jan 2008
Gomer, Mr Elis	G	Jan 2008
Williams, Miss Cerys	G	Jul 2008
Maddison, Mr Simon	I	Jan 2008
Edwards, Mr Huw	G	Jan 2009
England, Laura	M	Jan 2008
Roberts, Elliw	G	Jan 2009
Nash, Laura	L	Jan 2009

MELKSHAM, Wiltshire

BATH CHAMBERS,
PO BOX 2046, MELKSHAM, WILTSHIRE SN12 6WE
Tel: 01225 702347 ***Fax:*** 01225 702320
Dx: 43920 MELKSHAM
E-mail: barrister@bristolbar.freeserve.co.uk

MIDDLESBROUGH

AMICUS CHAMBERS,
QUEENS COURT, NEWPORT ROAD, MIDDLESBROUGH TS1 5EH
Tel: 01642 876334 / 876335 ***Fax:*** 01642 881300
Dx: 60540 MIDDLESBROUGH
E-mail: enquiries@amicuschambers.co.uk
Clerk: Cheryl McGee.
Chambers Director: Derek Hall

Brissenden, Ms Claire Judith	I	Nov 2004

Chambers of James M Hill QC

FOUNTAIN CHAMBERS,
CLEVELAND BUSINESS CENTRE, 1 WATSON STREET, MIDDLESBROUGH TS1 2RQ
Tel: 01642 804040 ***Fax:*** 01642 804060
Dx: 711700 MIDDLESBROUGH 11
E-mail: clerks@fountainchambers.co.uk
Clerk: Senior: Russell Ayles.
Head of Chambers:

Hill, Mr James M (Q.C.)	I	Jul 1984

Bethel, Mr Martin (Q.C.)	I	Nov 1965
Hatton, Mr David William (Q.C.); Recorder	G	Jul 1976
Roberts, Mr Timothy (Q.C.)	G	Jul 1978
Miller, Mr Keith	G	Jan 1973
Dent, Mr Adrian	L	Jul 1974
Pinkney, Mr Giles	G	Nov 1978
Sherwin, Miss Deborah	I	Jul 1979
Hunt, Mr Roderick	M	Jul 1981
West, Mr Ian	I	Jan 1985
Gilbert, Mr Robert	M	Jul 1986
Burke, Miss Patricia	G	Oct 1990
Gaston, Mr Graeme	L	Jul 1991
Kidd, Miss Joanne	L	Oct 1995
Mitchell, Mr Tom	L	Oct 1995
Bennett, Mr Richard A	I	Oct 1996
Turton, Robin	I	Jan 1996
Haugstaud, Annelise	L	Jan 1996
Towers, Mr Martin	G	Oct 1996
Walker, Mr Jonathan	L	Jan 1997
Price, Miss Collette	G	Nov 1997
Faulks, Mr Samuel	I	Oct 1997
Gamble, Helen	I	Jan 1998
Dodds, Kate	G	Jan 2000
Allison, Mr Stuart	M	Jan 2002
Kane, Gillian	G	Jan 2002
Smith, Mr Scott	G	Jan 2003
Murray, Mr Harvey	M	Jan 2004
Rainey, Mr Kieran	G	Jan 2004
Boucher-Giles, Mr Benjamin	L	Jan 2004
Taylor, Teresa	G	Jan 1994
Hogben, Helen	G	Jan 2006
Brown, Rebecca	L	Jan 2007

This Chamber with 33 Barristers is based in Middlesbrough and led by James M Hill QC and specialises in Children, Common Law, General, Criminal Work. You may contact any of our clerks at any time by sending a message to clerks@fountainchambers.co.uk.

104 GYPSY LANE,
NUNTHORPE, MIDDLESBROUGH TS7 0DR
Tel: 01642 316018

Chambers of Nigel Soppitt and Stephen Constantine

OLD COURT CHAMBERS,
NEWHAM HOUSE, 96-98 BOROUGH ROAD, MIDDLESBROUGH TS1 2HJ
Tel: 01642 232523 ***Fax:*** 01642 232896
Dx: 60591 MIDDLESBROUGH
E-mail: clerks@oldcourtchambers.com
Clerk: Daniel Folger; Barbara Hudson.
Administrator: Claire Gibson
Head of Chambers:

Soppitt, Mr Nigel	G	Jan 1996
Constantine, Mr Stephen	M	Jan 1992

Constable, Mr John Martyn Chester	G	Feb 1972
Baker, Mr Christopher Michael	M	Jul 1984
Ford, Mr Gerard	I	Jul 1986
Morrison, Mr Christopher Quentin	I	Nov 1986
Grier, Mr Warren	I	Nov 1989
Dodds, Mr Shaun	G	Jul 1990
Gillette, Mr John	M	Jul 1990
Newcombe, Mr Paul	I	Feb 1991
Bradshaw, Mr Ian Charles	M	Jan 1992
Sabiston, Mr Peter	G	Feb 1992
Fagan, Ms Catherine	G	Jan 1993
Dryden, Mr Shaun	L	Jan 1994
Lamballe, Miss Victoria Jane	M	Jul 2002
Abrahams, Mr Paul	G	Nov 2002
Borgen, Miss Inga	I	Oct 2004
O'Brien, Mr Liam	M	Jan 2007

Chambers of Alan Toby Hedworth QC

TRINITY (TEESSIDE) CHAMBERS,
MULTI MEDIA EXCHANGE, 72-80 CORPORATION ROAD, MIDDLESBROUGH TS1 2RF
Tel: 01642 247569 ***Fax:*** 01624 249897
Dx: 60357 MIDDLESBROUGH
E-mail: info@trinitychambers.co.uk
Web: www.trinitychambers.co.uk
Clerk: Senior: Alison Dickason. Silks & Criminal Clerk: Chris Gibbin; Civil & Family Clerks: Rebecca Dixon; Richard Embley; Kirsty Hart; Ken McLafferty; Criminal Clerks: Peter Finkill; David Knight; Tracie Rutter.
Administrator: Fiona Bullock (Teesside Co-ordinator)
Chambers Director: Simon M P Stewart (Practice Director); Chris Lucarelli (Business Development Manager)
Head of Chambers:

Hedworth, Mr Alan Toby (Q.C.); Recorder 1991	I	Jul 1975

Bradley, Sally (Q.C.); Recorder 1999; Deputy High Court Judge 2001	L	Jan 1977
Cobb, Mr Stephen William Scott (Q.C.)*	L	Jul 1985
Elliott, Mr Eric A (Q.C.); Recorder	G	Jul 1974
Duffield, Mr Stephen Michael	G	Jul 1969
Knox, Mr Christopher John; Recorder	I	Jul 1974
Hawks, Mr Anthony Joseph Vincent; Recorder	M	Nov 1975
Vane, Mr Christopher John Fletcher	I	Nov 1976
Callan, Mr David	M	Jul 1979
Wilkinson, Mr Michael John	G	Jul 1979
Engelman, Mr Philip	G	Jul 1979
Smart, Miss Jacqueline Ann	M	Nov 1981
Walsh, Mr Peter P	G	May 1982
Richardson, Mr James David	G	Nov 1982
McKenzie, Miss Lesley Sharon	L	Jan 1983
Spain, Mr Timothy Harrisson	G	Jul 1983
O'Sullivan, Mr John	M	Jul 1984
McCrae, Miss Fiona	G	Jul 1986
Taylor, Miss Susan; Recorder	M	Jan 1987
Goodwin, Miss Caroline Tracy; Recorder	I	Nov 1988
Routledge, Mr Shaun	G	Nov 1988
Gumsley, Mr Carl John; Recorder	I	Nov 1989
Rutter, Mr Andrew M	M	Jul 1990
Gittins, Mr Timothy James; Recorder	M	Oct 1990
Smith, Ms Rachel	M	Feb 1992
Temple, Miss Michelle J; Deputy District Judge 2010	L	Oct 1992
Shaw, Mrs Nicola; Deputy District Judge 2010	L	Oct 1992
Adams, Mr Robert George Seton; Recorder (Crime)	I	Oct 1993
Dunn, Ms Katherine L	L	Oct 1993
Scott Bell, Mrs Rosalind Sara; General Medical Council Legal Assessor	M	Oct 1993
Stonor, Mr Nicholas William	M	Oct 1993
Gray, Mr Justin H W	I	Nov 1993
Callan, Mrs Jane	M	Jan 1995
Sweeting, Ms Margaret	L	Jan 1996
Crawley, Mr Kevin	G	Jul 1998
Walker, Mrs Fiona	I	Jul 1998
Mills, Mr Kristian	M	Oct 1998
Taylor, Mrs Yvonne M	I	Jul 1998
Kitching, Mrs Kossar	I	Jan 1999
Allan, Miss Nicola	G	Jan 1999
Kemp, Mr James	I	Jan 1999
Graham, Mr Michael J G	L	Mar 1999
Goldberg, Mr Simon Ian	M	Jul 1999
Hedworth, Miss Rachel	I	Jul 1999
Mendoza, Miss Elizabeth Kagaba	I	Jul 1999
Craddock, Miss Xanthe	M	Oct 2000
Currer, Mr Paul J	M	Oct 2000
Giovannini, Mrs Angela	G	Nov 2000
Rasoul, Ms Miriam	L	Jul 2001
Phillips, Miss Ruth	M	Jul 2001
Mitford, Mr Christopher	M	Nov 2001
Foley, Miss Jane	G	Jan 2002
Mather, Mr Brian	G	Jul 2002
Wood, Miss Katherine	M	Jul 2002
Smith, Miss Joan	M	Oct 2002
Spragg, Mr Robert	M	Jan 2003
Hill, Mr Michael	G	Jun 2004
Anderson, Mr Jamie Henrie	L	Jul 2004
Tinnion, Mr Antoine	L	Nov 2004
Stubbs, Mr Richard	L	Jul 2005
Comb, Mr David	L	Oct 2005
Byrne, Mr William	G	Jan 2006
Morgan, Mr Jamie	I	Aug 2006
Darby, Miss Johanna Louise	M	Oct 2007
Crammond, Mr Andrew	L	Jan 2008
Marwick, Mr James	L	Jan 2008
Stafford, Mr Andrew (Q.C.)*	M	Jul 1980

Trinity has experienced practice teams for Administrative and Public Law, Agriculture, Business, Chancery, Crime, Employment, Family, Immigration, Mental Health, PI and Clinical Negligence, Planning, Regulatory and Disciplinary Laws.

MILTON KEYNES

MK FAMILY LAW CHAMBERS,
PO BOX 6017, MILTON KEYNES MK1 9AP
Tel: 0845 123 1234 ***Fax:*** 0845 430 4321

MINEHEAD, Somerset

CHAMBERS OF MISS S COTTER,
HIGHER COMBE, HAWKCOMBE, MINEHEAD, SOMERSET TA24 8LP
Tel: 01643 862722 ***Fax:*** 01643 862871

MITCHAM, Surrey

Chambers of Mohammad Ali Syed

PARK AVENUE CHAMBERS,
39 PARK AVENUE, MITCHAM, SURREY CR4 2ER
Tel: 020 8648 1684 ***Fax:*** 020 8715 6615
Head of Chambers:

Syed, Mr Mohammad Ali MBE	L	Jul 1970

NEW MALDEN, Surrey

5 BARNSBURY CLOSE,
NEW MALDEN, SURREY KT3 5BP
Tel: 020 8949 7748 ***Fax:*** 020 8949 7748

Yakubu, Mr Emmanuel Mahama	M	Jul 1970

NEWCASTLE UPON TYNE, Tyne & Wear

Chambers of Benjamin Nolan QC

BROAD CHARE CHAMBERS,
33 BROAD CHARE, NEWCASTLE UPON TYNE, TYNE & WEAR NE1 3DQ
Tel: 0191 232 0541 ***Fax:*** 0191 261 0043
Dx: 61001 NEWCASTLE UPON TYNE
E-mail: clerks@broadcharechambers.co.uk
Clerk: Brian Bell.
Chambers Director: Simon Coatsworth
Head of Chambers:

Nolan, Mr Benjamin (Q.C.)	M	Jul 1971

Cosgrove, Mr Patrick J (Q.C.)	G	Jul 1976
Woodcock, Mr Robert (Q.C.)	I	Feb 1978
Duff, Mr Euan C	I	Jul 1973
Harmer, Miss Christine	M	Jul 1973
Horner, Mr Robin	L	Jul 1975
Dorman-O'Gowan, Mr Christopher P D	L	Nov 1979
Finch, Mr Thomas Michael	L	Nov 1981
Armstrong, Kester I S	L	Nov 1982
Moulder, Miss Pauline M	L	Jul 1983
Mason, Mr David Hugh Rothwell	M	Feb 1984
Richardson, Miss Anne L	I	Jul 1986
Davis, Mr Anthony	G	Nov 1986
Fletcher, Mr Stephen Jeffery	M	Nov 1987
Rowlands, Mr David P	M	Nov 1988
Styles, Mr Mark Patrick	I	Jul 1988
Brown, Mr James	L	Nov 1990
Carr, Mr Jonathon	M	Oct 1990
Choudhury, Nafeesa	I	Jan 1990
Middleton, Miss Claire	L	Oct 1991
Clemitson, Miss Julie	I	Nov 1991
Shaw, Mrs Nicola	L	Oct 1992
Rippon, Mrs Amanda Jayne	G	Oct 1993
Zimbler, Miss Alexia	L	Oct 1993
Elliott, Mr Jason	I	Oct 1993

Lugg, Ms Elizabeth Claire	G	Oct 1994
Holland, Mr Charles Christopher	I	Nov 1994
Wadge, Mr Richard	G	Mar 1997
MacFaul, Mr Donald William	I	Mar 1998
Walker, Mr Andrew	I	Oct 1998
Robinson-Young, Mr David	L	Jul 1999
Mustard, Ms Lorraine	L	Oct 1999
Holmes, Mr Andrew Christopher	L	Jul 2000
Gray, Miss Ruth Elizabeth	L	Jul 2000
Giovannini, Mrs Angela	G	Nov 2000
Wilkinson, Mr Paul	G	Jul 2001
Ainsley, Mr Stephen Paul	M	Jul 2001
Senior, Mr Anthony James	L	Jul 2002
McCain, Mr Charles Stuart	M	Oct 2002
Henley, Miss Carly	L	Jul 2003
Smith, Miss Caroline	I	Jul 2003
Donnelly, Mr Timothy	L	Jan 2004
Mcdermott, Mr Frazer	I	Mar 2004
Gibson, Miss Claire Michelle	L	Oct 2004
Miller, Miss Amanda	L	Jul 2005
Dawson, Miss Beatrice Grace	L	Jan 2006
Nolan, Miss Georgina	M	Jul 2006
Rook, Mr Stuart Alan	G	Oct 2006
Wigglesworth, Mr Timothy Robin	M	Jul 2007
Blair, Mr Bruce (Q.C.)*	M	Jul 1969
Scriven, Miss Pamela (Q.C.)*	I	Jan 1970
Upward, Mr Patrick Charles (Q.C.)*	I	Jul 1972
Hyland, Mr Graham (Q.C.)*	I	Jul 1978
Nicholls, Mr Michael John Gadsby (Q.C.)*	M	Nov 1975
Blackwell, Miss Louise M (Q.C.)*	L	Jul 1985
Harte, Mr John David*	G	Jul 1967
O'Brien, Mr Joseph*	I	Jan 1989

CATHEDRAL CHAMBERS,
17 QUEEN STREET, NEWCASTLE UPON TYNE, TYNE & WEAR NE1 3UG
Tel: 0191 232 1311 ***Fax:*** 0191 232 1422
Dx: 61277 NEWCASTLE 1
E-mail: mail@cathedralchambers.com
Clerk: Dawn Kipling.

Chambers of Bernard Weatherill QC

ENTERPRISE CHAMBERS,
65 QUAYSIDE, NEWCASTLE UPON TYNE, TYNE & WEAR NE1 3DE
Tel: 0191 222 3344 ***Fax:*** 0191 222 3340
Dx: 61134 NEWCASTLE UPON TYNE
E-mail: newcastle@enterprisechambers.com
Web: www.enterprisechambers.com
Clerk: Senior: Antony Armstrong. Junior: Stephen Walker.
Head of Chambers:
Weatherill, Mr Bernard (Q.C.); Recorder; Mediator . M . Jul 1974

Arden, Mr Peter (Q.C.)	G	Jul 1983
Bhaloo, Miss Zia (Q.C.)	M	Nov 1990
Morgan, Mr Charles; Junior Counsel to the Crown (Regional)	M	Jul 1978
Hutton, Miss Caroline; Mediator (CEDR)	M	Nov 1979
James, Mr Michael; Mediator	L	Feb 1976
Ife, Ms Linden	M	Nov 1982
Zelin, Mr Geoffrey	L	Jul 1984
Barker, Mr James	G	Jul 1984
Jack, Mr Adrian; Recorder	M	Nov 1986
Groves, Mr Hugo	G	Oct 1980
Jarron, Miss Stephanie	L	May 1990
Pickering, Mr James	M	Oct 1991
Jory, Mr Hugh	L	Oct 1992
Noble, Mr Andrew; Mediator	L	Nov 1992
Duddridge, Mr Robert	L	Feb 1992
Williamson, Miss Bridget	L	Feb 1993
Klein, Mr Jonathan; Junior Counsel to the Crown (Regional)	L	Oct 1992
Francis, Mr Edward	I	Nov 1995
Mauger, Miss Shanti	I	Oct 1996
Ilyas, Mr Shaiba	L	Mar 1998
Calland, Mr Timothy	L	Nov 1999
Rodger, Mr Jonathan	M	Nov 1999
McCulloch, Mr Niall	L	Oct 2000
Johnson, Mr Simon	M	Oct 2000
Murphy, Mr Damian	M	Jul 2001
Page, Miss Rebecca	G	Nov 2001
Jackson, Ms Claire	L	Mar 2002
West, Mr Matthew; Attorney - New York State	M	Nov 2000
Kalfon, Mr Olivier	I	Oct 2003
Gunaratna, Mr Kavan	L	Nov 2004
Toman, Miss Cristin	L	Jan 2004
Griffin, Miss Margaret	G	Jul 2004
Beswetherick, Mr Anthony	L	Mar 2003
Markandya, Miss Susannah	I	Oct 2005
Bond, Miss Kelly	M	Jul 2007
Heath, Mr Duncan	L	Nov 2007
Meech, Miss Jennifer	M	Oct 2008
Burslem, Miss Sarah	G	Oct 2008
Gale, Mr Phillip	L	Oct 2008
Davies, Mr James	L	Jul 2009
Maddison, Mr Matthew	M	Jul 2010
Child, Mr Jeremy*	L	Mar 2003

A leading commercial chancery set based in London, Leeds and Newcastle.

Chambers of John Roy Falkenstein

CHAMBERS OF JOHN ROY FALKENSTEIN,
204 JESMOND DENE ROAD, JESMOND, NEWCASTLE UPON TYNE, TYNE & WEAR NE2 2NL
Tel: 07973 776801 ***Fax:*** 0191 281 0735
Dx: 62560 JESMOND
E-mail: johnfalkenstein204@googlemail.com
Head of Chambers:
Falkenstein, Mr John Roy . L . Aug 1996

Chambers of Roger A Moore

NEW COURT CHAMBERS,
1ST FLOOR, 3 BROAD CHARE, QUAYSIDE, NEWCASTLE UPON TYNE, TYNE & WEAR NE1 3DQ
Tel: 0191 232 1980 ***Fax:*** 0191 232 3730
Dx: 61012 NEWCASTLE UPON TYNE
E-mail: bd@newcourt-chambers.co.uk
Clerk: Frank Hughes; Andrea Eccleston; A Herron; S Robson.
Practice Manager: Bryan Dickson
Head of Chambers:
Moore, Mr Roger A . L . Jul 1969

Robson, Mr David Ernest Henry (Q.C.)	I	Feb 1965
Parkin, Mr Timothy C	I	Nov 1971
Gatland, Mr Glenn	G	Nov 1972
Mitchell, Mr Ronald	I	Jan 1973
Hodson, Mr Michael	M	Feb 1977
Woodcock, Mr Robert (Q.C.)	I	Feb 1978
Adams, Mr James Robert	G	Jul 1978
Cross, Mr Paul	G	Jul 1981
Schofield, Mr Peter	G	Nov 1982
Patton, Mr Robin	I	Jul 1983
Bloomfield, Mr Richard W	G	Jul 1984
Moreland, Miss Penelope Jane	G	Jul 1986
Burns, Mr Alexander Laurence	I	Jul 1988
Gumsley, Mr Carl John	I	Nov 1989
Cartmell, Mr Nicholas	I	Oct 1990
Smith, Mr Julian	I	Nov 1991
Adkin, Mr James	L	Oct 1992
Waugh, Miss Jane	I	Nov 1992
Doig, Mr Gavin A	L	Nov 1995
Graham, Mr Stuart	L	Jan 1996
Moran, Mr Thomas	G	Oct 1996
Wadge, Mr Richard	G	Mar 1997
Ward, Mr Vincent	M	Jan 1998
Wortley, Ms Natalie	G	Jan 1999
Rose, Mr Christopher	L	Jan 1999
MacDonald, Ms Ailsa	M	Jan 2000
Piasecki, Ms Emma	G	Jan 2001
Hirst, Ms Susan	M	Jan 2001
Fish, Mr Lee	L	Jan 2003
Cordery, Mr Philip	G	Jan 2003
Robson, Mr Barry James	G	Jul 2004
McClory, Ms Elizabeth	I	Jan 2005

Chambers of Jeremy Freedman

PARKLANE PLOWDEN,
LOMBARD HOUSE, 4/8 LOMBARD STREET, NEWCASTLE UPON TYNE, TYNE & WEAR NE1 3AE
Tel: 0191 221 2121 ***Fax:*** 0191 221 2122
Dx: 61062 NEWCASTLE UPON TYNE

Chambers of Alan Toby Hedworth QC

TRINITY (NEWCASTLE) CHAMBERS,
THE CUSTOM HOUSE, QUAYSIDE, NEWCASTLE UPON TYNE, TYNE & WEAR NE1 3DE
Tel: 0191 232 1927 ***Fax:*** 0191 232 7975
Dx: 61185 NEWCASTLE UPON TYNE
E-mail: info@trinitychambers.co.uk
Web: www.trinitychambers.co.uk
Clerk: Senior: Alison Dickason. Silks & Criminal Clerk: Chris Gibbin; Civil & Family Clerks: Rebecca Dixon; Richard Embley; Kirsty Hart; Criminal Clerks: Peter Finkill; David Knight; Tracie Rutter.
Administrator: Fiona Bullock (Teesside Co-ordinator)
Chambers Director: Simon M P Stewart (Practice Director); Chris Lucarelli (Business Development Manager)
Head of Chambers:
Hedworth, Mr Alan Toby (Q.C.); Recorder . I . Jul 1975

Bradley, Sally (Q.C.); Recorder; Deputy High Court Judge 2001	L	Jan 1977
Cobb, Mr Stephen William Scott (Q.C.)*	I	Jul 1985
Elliott, Mr Eric A (Q.C.); Recorder	G	Jul 1974
Duffield, Mr Stephen Michael	G	Jul 1969
Knox, Mr Christopher John; Recorder	G	Jul 1974
Hawks, Mr Anthony Joseph Vincent; Recorder	M	Nov 1975
Vane, Mr Christopher John Fletcher	I	Nov 1976
Callan, Mr David	M	Jul 1979
Wilkinson, Mr Michael John	G	Jul 1979
Engelman, Mr Philip	G	Jul 1979
Smart, Miss Jacqueline Ann	M	Nov 1981
Walsh, Mr Peter P	G	May 1982
Richardson, Mr James David	G	Nov 1982
McKenzie, Miss Lesley Sharon	L	Jan 1983
Spain, Mr Timothy Harrisson	G	Jul 1983
O'Sullivan, Mr John	M	Jul 1984
McCrae, Miss Fiona	G	Jul 1986
Taylor, Miss Susan; Recorder	M	Jan 1987
Goodwin, Miss Caroline Tracy; Recorder	I	Nov 1988
Routledge, Mr Shaun	G	Nov 1988
Gumsley, Mr Carl John; Recorder	I	Nov 1989
Rutter, Mr Andrew M	M	Jul 1990
Gittins, Mr Timothy James; Recorder	M	Oct 1990
Smith, Ms Rachel	M	Feb 1992
Temple, Miss Michelle J	L	Oct 1992
Shaw, Mrs Nicola	L	Oct 1992
Adams, Mr Robert George Seton; Recorder	I	Oct 1993
Dunn, Ms Katherine L	L	Oct 1993
Scott Bell, Mrs Rosalind Sara; GMC Legal Assessor	M	Oct 1993
Stonor, Mr Nicholas William	M	Oct 1993
Gray, Mr Justin H W	I	Nov 1993
Callan, Mrs Jane	M	Jan 1995
Sweeting, Ms Margaret	L	Jan 1996
Crawley, Mr Kevin	G	Jul 1998
Walker, Mrs Fiona	I	Jul 1998
Mills, Mr Kristian	M	Oct 1998
Taylor, Mrs Yvonne M	I	Jul 1998
Kitching, Mrs Kossar	I	Jan 1999
Allan, Miss Nicola	G	Jan 1999
Kemp, Mr James	I	Jan 1999
Graham, Mr Michael J G	L	Mar 1999
Goldberg, Mr Simon Ian	M	Jul 1999
Hedworth, Miss Rachel	I	Jul 1999
Mendoza, Miss Elizabeth Kagaba	I	Jul 1999
Craddock, Miss Xanthe	M	Oct 2000
Currer, Mr Paul J	M	Oct 2000
Giovannini, Mrs Angela	G	Nov 2000
Rasoul, Ms Miriam	L	Jul 2001
Phillips, Miss Ruth	M	Jul 2001
Mitford, Mr Christopher	M	Nov 2001
Foley, Miss Jane	G	Jan 2002
Mather, Mr Brian	G	Jul 2002
Wood, Miss Katherine	M	Jul 2002
Smith, Miss Joan	M	Oct 2002
Spragg, Mr Robert	M	Jan 2003
Hill, Mr Michael	G	Jun 2004
Anderson, Mr Jamie Henrie	L	Jul 2004
Tinnion, Mr Antoine	L	Nov 2004
Stubbs, Mr Richard	I	Jul 2005
Comb, Mr David	I	Oct 2005
Byrne, Mr William	G	Jan 2006
Morgan, Mr Jamie	I	Aug 2006
Darby, Miss Johanna Louise	M	Oct 2007
Crammond, Mr Andrew	L	Jan 2008
Marwick, Mr James	L	Jan 2008
Stafford, Mr Andrew (Q.C.)*	M	Jul 1980

Trinity has experienced practice teams for Administrative and Public Law, Agriculture, Business, Chancery, Crime, Employment, Family, Immigration, Mental Health, PI and Clinical Negligence, Planning, Regulatory and Disciplinary Laws.

Chambers of Gilbert Gray QC

YORK CHAMBERS,
ROTTERDAM HOUSE, 116 THE QUAYSIDE, NEWCASTLE UPON TYNE, TYNE & WEAR NE1 3DY
Tel: 0191 206 4677 ***Fax:*** 0191 206 4172
Dx: 716754 NEWCASTLE 20
E-mail: clerks@yorkchambers.co.uk
Clerk: Senior: Kevin Beaumont.
Head of Chambers:
Gray, Mr Gilbert (Q.C.) . G . Nov 1953

Lowe, Mr William (Q.C.)*	I	Jul 1972
Elvidge, Mr John (Q.C.)	G	Nov 1988
Palmer, Prof Norman Ernest (Q.C.)	G	Jul 1973
Denny, Mr Robin H A	I	May 1969
Chamberlain, Mr Kevin	G	Aug 1965
Harvey, Mr Colin	G	Jan 1973
Twist, Mr Stephen	M	Jul 1979
Hunter, Mr Geoffrey	G	Feb 1979
O'Neill, Mr Michael	I	Jul 1979
Smith, Mr Duncan	I	Jul 1979
Bosomworth, Mr Michael	M	Jul 1979
Proops, Miss Helen	M	Jul 1986
Johnson, Mr Peter	I	Jul 1986
Morris, Mr Paul H	L	Nov 1986
Price, Mr Nicholas	G	Nov 1987
Lee, Ms Rosslyn	G	Nov 1987
Lamb, Mr David S	M	Nov 1987
Makepeace, Mr Peter	L	Jul 1988
Boothroyd, Miss Susan	M	Oct 1990
Cordey, Mr Dan	G	Nov 1990
Oliver, Mr Crispin Arthur	M	Nov 1990
Todd, Mr Martin	I	Nov 1991
Robinson, Mr James	M	Oct 1992
Edwards, Mr Daniel	L	Oct 1993
Wadoodi, Miss Aisha	M	May 1994
Woolrich, Miss Sarah	M	Nov 1994
Campbell, Ms Diane	G	Nov 1995
Randhawa, Miss Ravinder	L	Nov 1995
Legard, Mr Edward	G	Oct 1996
Callaghan, Ms Elizabeth	L	Jul 1998
Withyman, Mr Jim	M	Jun 1999
Healy, Mr Sam	G	Jul 1999
Holmes-Willis, Mrs Sarah	M	Jul 1999
Buckley, Miss Sophie	M	Nov 1999
Smoult-Hawtree, Ms Karen	G	Jun 2000
Morrison, Ms Andrea	I	Jun 2000
Smith, Ms Jennie	I	Jan 2002
Lennon, Miss Karen	I	Jan 2003
Thornton, Mr Stephen	G	Jan 2003
Trory, Mr Henry	I	Jan 2003
Adcock, Ms Deborah	G	Jan 2005
Adams, Mr Nathan	M	Jan 2004
Herrmann, Mr Richard	G	Jan 2004
Gough, Ms Emma	I	Jan 2005
Willoughby, Mr James	M	Jan 2005

Frew, Mr Bruce . . . L . . . Jan 2005
Addicott, Miss Elizabeth . . . I . . . Jul 2006
Davies, Miss Angharad . . . M . . . Jan 2006
Mugliston, Mr Adam . . . L . . . Oct 2008
Lippiatt, Mr Huw . . . G . . . Mar 2010
Raitt, Miss Kate . . . L . . . Jul 2009

NEWPORT, Isle of Wight

Chambers of Hilary Roberts

TEMPLE CHAMBERS,
12 CLYTHA PARK ROAD, NEWPORT NP20 4PB
Tel: 01633 267403 / 255855 ***Fax:*** 01633 253441
Dx: 33208 NEWPORT (GWENT)
Clerk: Seniors: David Brinning; Family: Helen Dench; Nicola Morgan; Claire Bater. Criminal & Civil: Tony Naylon; Emma King.
Administrator: John Garlick
Head of Chambers:
Roberts, Mr Hilary . . . G . . . Nov 1978

Aubrey, Mr David J M (Q.C.); Recorder . . . M . . . Jul 1976
Davies, Mr J Meirion . . . G . . . Jul 1975
McKay, Mr Christopher; Deputy District Judge (Civil) . G . . . Nov 1976
Griffiths, Mr Roger V . . . G . . . Jul 1983
Morgan, Ms Lynne; Recorder (Family Law) . . . M . . . Jul 1984
Jeary, Mr Stephen . . . I . . . Jul 1987
Rowley, Miss Jane . . . G . . . Jul 1988
Hughes, Leighton; Part-Time Chairman SSAT . . . I . . . Jul 1989
Miller, Mr Richard James . . . G . . . Oct 1991
Powell, Mr Bernard Hilson . . . G . . . Oct 1991
Thomas, Mr Steven . . . G . . . Feb 1993
Webster, Mr David; Deputy District Judge (Criminal) . G . . . Nov 1993
Foulser-McFarlane, Ms Jane; Lead Counsel to Welsh Assembly Govt on IP . . . G . . . Jan 1994
Thomas, Ms Christina . . . I . . . Feb 1994
Gibbon, Ms Juliet; Legal Advisor to Care Counsel for Wales; And NMC . . . L . . . Jan 1994
Owen, Ms Sara . . . I . . . Oct 1995
Taylor, Mr Rhys; Part-Time Chairman of Residential Property Tribunal . . . I . . . Nov 1996
Jones, Mr Laurence . . . G . . . Oct 1997
Jones, Mr Steffan R . . . G . . . Nov 1997
Seal, Mr Kevin . . . G . . . Jan 1998
Douglas, Mr Colin . . . L . . . Oct 1998
Hawkins, Mr Robert . . . L . . . Jan 1998
Abbott, Ms Christine . . . M . . . Oct 1999
Lucas, Ms Felicie . . . M . . . Oct 1999
Jowett, Mr Christian . . . G . . . Oct 1999
Pickthall, Ms Claire . . . G . . . Nov 1999
Williams, Mr Eifion . . . G . . . Oct 2000
Barcello, Mr Andrew . . . L . . . Mar 2001
Evans, Mr James . . . L . . . Jul 2002
Broadstock, Mr Byron . . . G . . . Nov 2002
Nixon, Ms Elaine . . . L . . . Jul 2003
Radcliffe, Ms Sheila Mary . . . M . . . Jul 2003
Bennett, Miss Marianne . . . I . . . Oct 2003
North, Ms Claire . . . I . . . Oct 2003
Salmman, Mr Hashim . . . I . . . Jan 2005
Davies, Mr Max . . . M . . . Oct 2005
Moore, Mr Guy . . . G . . . Jul 2006
Dieu, Mr Hoa . . . G . . . Jan 2006
Daniel, Ms Hayley . . . I . . . Jan 2007
Pinnell, Mr David . . . G . . . Mar 2008
Underhill, Mr Jonathan . . . I . . . Jan 2008
Ahmadi, Ms Hannah . . . G . . . Jan 2009
Fear, Ms Claire . . . M . . . Jan 2010

Chambers of Julian David Samiloff

WIGHT CHAMBERS,
6 MEDINA AVENUE, NEWPORT, ISLE OF WIGHT PO30 1EJ
Tel: 01983 522828 / 07976 512823
E-mail: medinachambers@onwight.net
Practice Manager: Eugenie Samiloff
Head of Chambers:
Samiloff, Mr Julian David . . . I . . . May 1988

NORTHAMPTON, Northamptonshire

Chambers of Jane Page and Joy Pinkham

CHARTLANDS CHAMBERS,
3 ST GILES TERRACE, NORTHAMPTON, NORTHAMPTONSHIRE NN1 2BN
Tel: 01604 603322 ***Fax:*** 01604 603388
Dx: 12408 NORTHAMPTON
E-mail: enquiries@chartlands-chambers.co.uk
Clerk: Senior: Andrew Davies.
Head of Chambers:
Page, Mrs Jane . . . I . . . Jul 1982
Pinkham, Mrs Joy . . . G . . . Jan 1993

Cowen, Mr Jonathan . . . M . . . Nov 1983
Van Besouw, Mr Eufron . . . M . . . Nov 1988
Tapper, Mr Paul . . . M . . . Jan 1991
Robinson, Mr Matthew . . . I . . . Jan 1994
Maycock, Miss Elizabeth . . . I . . . Jan 1996
Ali, Mr Ishtiyaq . . . L . . . Oct 1996
Watkins, Miss Rachel . . . M . . . Oct 1998
Vissian, Mrs Hena . . . L . . . Oct 2002
Rashid, Mr Waqas . . . L . . . Jan 2006
Dawson, Miss Rachael . . . M . . . Jul 2007
Lince, Miss Elizabeth . . . M . . . Jul 2007

Chambers of Ben Beaumont

CLARENDON CHAMBERS,
5 ST GILES TERRACE, NORTHAMPTON, NORTHAMPTONSHIRE NN1 2BN
Tel: 01604 637245 ***Fax:*** 01604 633167
Dx: 12404 NORTHAMPTON

Chambers of Maria Savvides

NORTHAMPTON CHAMBERS,
22 ALBION PLACE, NORTHAMPTON, NORTHAMPTONSHIRE NN1 1UD
Tel: 01604 636271 ***Fax:*** 01604 232931
Dx: 12464 NORTHAMPTON
E-mail: clerks@northampton-chambers.co.uk
Clerk: Senior: Stuart Hall.
Head of Chambers:
Savvides, Miss Maria . . . M . . . Jul 1986

Brookes-Baker, Mr Matthew . . . L . . . Jul 1998
Christie, Miss Michelle . . . M . . . Sep 1999
Yeung, Mr Stuart . . . I . . . Nov 1999
Walsh, Miss Moira . . . M . . . Jul 2000
Gooderham, Miss Elizabeth . . . I . . . Jul 2001
Pettitt, Mr Robert . . . M . . . Jul 2002
Maynard, Mr Matthew . . . I . . . Nov 2003
Wade, Miss Rebecca . . . G . . . Nov 2003
Fairclough, Miss Lucy . . . G . . . Oct 2005
Mettam, Miss Hannah . . . I . . . Nov 2006
Lyon, Mr Gavin . . . M . . . Jan 2006
Turner, Miss Abigail . . . M . . . Jan 2006
Keyes, Mr Grant . . . G . . . Jul 2007
Rose, Mr Neil . . . G . . . Jan 2007
McLernon, Mr James . . . M . . . Jan 2007
O'Malley, Miss Laura . . . L . . . Jan 2007

NORWICH, Norfolk

EAST ANGLIAN CHAMBERS,
15 THE CLOSE, NORWICH, NORFOLK NR1 4DZ
Tel: 01603 617351 ***Fax:*** 01603 751400
Dx: 5213 NORWICH
E-mail: norwich@ealaw.co.uk
Clerk: Senior: Fraser McLaren. Deputy Senior: Alison Scanes.
Administrator: Carol Bull (Head of Administration)
Akast, Mr John F; Recorder . . . I . . . Nov 1968
Wardlow, Mr John . . . G . . . Jul 1971
Bryan, Mr Rex; Recorder . . . L . . . Nov 1971
Waters, Mr John Clough; Pupil Supervisor . . . L . . . May 1974
Marsden, Mr Andrew; Recorder; Pupil Supervisor . . M . . . Jul 1975
Bryant, Ms Caroline; Pupil Supervisor . . . M . . . Jul 1976
Sinclair, Mr Graham; Part time Chairman LVTRAC . G . . . Jul 1979
Hamey, Mr John . . . I . . . Jul 1979
Brooke-Smith, Mr John; Recorder; Pupil Supervisor . G . . . Jul 1981
Redmayne, Mr Simon . . . I . . . Jul 1982
Lane, Mr Michael . . . M . . . Jul 1983
Bettle, Ms Janet; Pupil Supervisor . . . I . . . Jul 1985
Elcombe, Mr Nicholas; Pupil Supervisor . . . I . . . Jul 1987
Capon, Mr Philip; Pupil Supervisor . . . I . . . Oct 1990
Watson, Ms Claire . . . I . . . Nov 1991
Butcher, Mr Russell Henry . . . M . . . Oct 1992
Parry-Jones, Ms Carole Ann . . . M . . . Nov 1992
Barratt, Mr Dominic Anthony Richard; Pupil Supervisor . . . G . . . Nov 1992
Walsh, Ms Patricia C . . . L . . . Nov 1993
Kelly, Mr Richard . . . G . . . Oct 1994
Wheetman, Mr Alan . . . M . . . Oct 1995
Freeman, Ms Sally Jane; Pupil Supervisor . . . L . . . Nov 1995
Wood, Mr Richard . . . G . . . Nov 1995
Underhill, Ms Allison . . . G . . . Oct 1997
Goodfellow, Mr Stephen . . . M . . . Nov 1997
Ashley, Mr Neil . . . L . . . Mar 1999
Korniej, Ms Rebekah . . . M . . . Oct 1999
Bradbury, Ms Joanna . . . M . . . Nov 1999
Harvey, Miss Shona . . . M . . . Nov 1999
Hayes, Ms Christine . . . M . . . Nov 1999
Pigram, Mr Christopher Stuart; Pupil Supervisor . . G . . . Jul 2000
O'Sullivan, Mr Richard; Pupil Supervisor . . . I . . . Jul 2000
Brown, Mr Luke Henry William . . . M . . . Oct 2000
Parnell, Ms Cherie . . . M . . . Nov 2000
Stevens, Ms Hazel . . . L . . . Jul 2001
Shirley, Ms Lynne . . . M . . . Jul 2002
Donovan, Miss Juliet . . . M . . . Jul 2002
Plant, Ms April . . . L . . . Oct 2002
Wastall, Mrs Rebecca . . . L . . . Oct 2002
Voelcker, Ms Harriet . . . G . . . Jul 2003
Michael, Mr Nicholas . . . M . . . Jul 2003
Croskell, Mr Marcus . . . L . . . Jul 2003
Miller, Miss Kate . . . G . . . Jul 2003
Wahiwala, Mr Amrik . . . M . . . Jul 2003
Martin, Miss Jade . . . M . . . Oct 2003
Dyer, Miss Shereen . . . L . . . Oct 2003
Williams, Miss Micaila . . . I . . . Jul 2004
Cattermull, Ms Emma . . . L . . . Oct 2004
Strelitz, Mr Paul . . . L . . . Nov 2005
Edwards, Mr Matthew . . . G . . . Jul 2006
White, Miss Elizabeth . . . I . . . Jul 2006
Connell, Miss Amy . . . M . . . Oct 2006
Bewley, Miss Suhayla . . . L . . . Jul 2007
Spence, Miss Gemma-Louise . . . L . . . Jul 2007
Pine, Miss Mika . . . M . . . Nov 2007
Myers, Mr Rupert . . . I . . . Nov 2008
Newton, Miss Alice . . . I . . . Jul 2009
Slaughter, Miss Jessica . . . M . . . Jul 2009
Sorel-Cameron, Mr Matthew . . . M . . . Oct 2009
Smith, Miss Fiona . . . G . . . Nov 2009
Duxbury, Sarah . . . M . . . Mar 2010
Nicklin, Mr Andrew . . . M . . . Jul 2010
Sheehan, Mr Michael . . . M . . . Oct 2010

Chambers of Christopher Michael Fletcher

OCTAGON HOUSE,
19 COLEGATE, NORWICH, NORFOLK NR3 1AT
Tel: 01603 623186 ***Fax:*** 01603 760519
Dx: 5249 NORWICH 1
E-mail: clerks@octagonhouse.co.uk
Clerk: Senior: Stephen Unsworth. Daniel Twite.
Head of Chambers:
Fletcher, Mr Christopher Michael . . . I . . . Nov 1984

Lindqvist, Mr Andrew . . . M . . . Nov 1968
Ayers, Mr Guy; Recorder . . . I . . . Jul 1979
Shackleford, Miss Susan . . . I . . . Oct 1980
Kefford, Mr Anthony . . . M . . . Nov 1980
James, Mr Ian . . . G . . . Jul 1981
Butterworth, Mr Paul . . . M . . . Jul 1982
Aldous, Mr Robert . . . I . . . Jun 1985
Clare, Mr Michael . . . G . . . Nov 1986
Bundell, Ms Katharine Michelle . . . M . . . Oct 1991
Bell, Marika Pamela . . . G . . . Nov 1991
Dugdale, Mr Jeremy . . . I . . . Oct 1992
Prinn, Miss Helen . . . M . . . Oct 1993
Oliver, Mr Andrew . . . L . . . Nov 1993
Gilbertson, Ms Helen . . . M . . . Nov 1993
Moore, Miss Katharine Elizabeth; Recorder . . . M . . . Oct 1995
Durr, Jude . . . I . . . Nov 1995
Morgans, Mr John Morgan . . . M . . . Nov 1996
Baruah, Miss Fiona . . . I . . . Oct 1996
Jones, Miss Susannah . . . M . . . Jan 1997
Goodman, Mr Jonathan . . . I . . . Nov 1999
Jack, Mr Nicholas . . . L . . . Jan 2003
Grey, Miss Sharon . . . I . . . Jan 2003
Harris, Miss Katie . . . I . . . Nov 2005

This Chamber with 24 Barristers is based in Norwich and led by Christopher Michael Fletcher and specialises in Common Law, General, Family Law, Criminal Work - Criminal Procedures. You may contact any of our clerks at any time by sending a message to clerks@octagonhouse.co.uk.

NOTTINGHAM

70 CHARLECOTT DRIVE,
NOTTINGHAM NG8 2SB
Tel: 0115 928 8901 ***Fax:*** 0115 928 8901

23 ESSEX STREET,
CITY GATE EAST, TOLL HOUSE HILL, NOTTINGHAM NG1 5FS
Tel: 0115 935 2233
E-mail: clerks@23es.com
Web: www.23es.com
Clerk: Senior: Richard Fowler. Sean Gould; Robert Mayes; Jamie Clack; Adam Chapman; Joe Wheeler.
Administrator: Tracey McCormack
Practice Manager: Richard Fowler

This Chamber with 100 Barristers is based in London and led by Simon Russell Flint QC and specialises in Criminal Work - General, Tribunals and Inquiries, Fraud. Although the majority are based in London, our Barristers work out of all 3 annexes. You may contact any of our clerks at any time by sending an email to clerks@23es.com.

Chambers of Gregory D M Dickinson QC and Shaun M Smith QC

1 HIGH PAVEMENT,
SPECIALIST CRIMINAL CHAMBERS, NOTTINGHAM NG1 1HF
Tel: 0115 941 8218 ***Fax:*** 0115 941 8240
Dx: 10168 NOTTINGHAM
E-mail: clerks@1highpavement.co.uk
Web: www.1highpavement.co.uk
Clerk: David Duric.
Head of Chambers:
Dickinson, Mr Gregory D M (Q.C.) . . . G . . . Jul 1981
Smith, Mr Shaun M (Q.C.) . . . G . . . Jul 1981

Joyce, Mr Peter Stuart Langford (Q.C.) . . . I . . . Jul 1968
Mann, Mr Paul (Q.C.) . . . G . . . Nov 1980
Rafferty, Mr Stuart (Q.C.) . . . G . . . Jul 1975
Wigoder, Hon Justin . . . G . . . Jul 1977
Napthine, Mr David Robert Guy . . . I . . . Nov 1979
Elwick, Mr Bryan Martin . . . M . . . Jul 1981
Bhatia, Mr Balraj S . . . I . . . Jul 1982
Palmer, Mr Timothy N J . . . M . . . Jul 1982
Reynolds, Mr Adrian L; Recorder . . . G . . . Nov 1982
Ballentyne, Mr Errol Stanley . . . G . . . Nov 1983
Hurst, Mr Martin . . . M . . . Jul 1985
Egbuna, Mr Robert Obiora . . . G . . . Nov 1988
Stockwell, Mr Graham Clive . . . I . . . Nov 1988
Evans, Mr Michael Ritho . . . M . . . Nov 1988
Thatcher, Mr Richard . . . I . . . Jul 1989
Geeson, Mr Christopher . . . G . . . Nov 1989
McNamara, Mr James . . . I . . . May 1990
Mukherjee, Mr Avik . . . G . . . Jul 1990
Munro, Ms Sarah . . . M . . . Oct 1990
Auty, Mr Michael . . . I . . . Nov 1990
Coupland, Mr Steven . . . L . . . Nov 1993
Kemp, Mr Stephen Richard . . . L . . . Oct 1995
Achurch, Mr Mark . . . M . . . Jan 1996
Eckersley, Mr Simon . . . L . . . May 1996
Knight, Ms Sarah . . . M . . . Jul 1996
Purcell, Mr Gregor . . . L . . . Oct 1997
King, Ms Julia . . . I . . . Jul 1998
Joyce, Ms Abigail . . . I . . . Oct 1998
Pitman, Ms Laura . . . L . . . Oct 2000
Shelley, Mr Dominic . . . G . . . Jul 2003
Chasemore, Ms Catherine . . . L . . . Jan 2004
Outterside, Mr David . . . I . . . Jul 2004
Lloyd, Ms Sarah . . . M . . . Jul 2005
Wilson, Katrina . . . L . . . Jul 2007
Gabbitas, Mr Christopher . . . L . . . Dec 2009
Hardy, Mrs Lisa Marie . . . L . . . Jan 2011

Chambers has 39 Tenants including 5 QC's and is based in Nottingham. We prosecute and defend criminal cases all over the Midlands. For specialisms of individuals please contact us at clerks@1highpavement.co.uk

Chambers of Stephen Lowne

KCH GARDEN SQUARE CHAMBERS,
1 OXFORD STREET, NOTTINGHAM NG1 5BH
Tel: 0115 941 8851 ***Fax:*** 0115 941 4169
Dx: 10042 NOTTINGHAM
E-mail: clerks@kchgardensquare.co.uk
Clerk: Russell Hobbs.
Administrator: Ellen Thompson
Head of Chambers:

Name		Date
Lowne, Mr Stephen	I	Jul 1981
Philo, Mr Noel P.	G	Feb 1975
Howlett, Mr James Anthony	M	Jul 1980
Gallagher, Mr Patrick	G	Jul 1984
Dhadli, Mrs Perminder	M	Nov 1984
Cranny, Miss Amanda	L	Nov 1984
Bradley, Ms Caroline	M	Jul 1985
Cranmer-Brown, Mr Michael Timothy	M	Nov 1986
Eley, Mr Jonathan	M	Jun 1987
Van Der Zwart, Mr Mark Andrew	M	Feb 1988
Way, Mr Ian	I	Nov 1988
Munt, Mr Alastair	G	Jul 1989
Dee, Mr Jonathan	I	Nov 1989
Taylor, Mr Andrew Peter	G	Nov 1989
Knowles, Mr Mark	M	Nov 1989
Lody, Mr Stuart T	G	Nov 1991
Gibbs, Mr Philip	I	Oct 1991
Leonard, Mrs Edna	G	Oct 1992
Straw, Mr Jonathan	M	Oct 1992
Janes, Mr Jeremy	L	Nov 1992
Macdonald, Miss Sheila	M	Feb 1993
Warburton, Ms Julie	M	Oct 1993
Cartwright, Mr Ivan	G	Nov 1993
Moore, Nicola	L	Jan 1993
Ahya, Miss Sonal	L	Sep 1995
Stobart, Mrs Tracey	M	Jan 1995
Soubry, Ms Anna	I	Nov 1995
Wylie, Mr Neil	G	Nov 1996
Ewing, Mr Hal	G	Nov 1997
Hale, Mrs Grace	G	Mar 1998
Beaumont, Mr Andrew	L	Jul 1999
Watson, Mr Mark	G	Jul 1999
Briden, Miss Sarah	I	Jul 1999
Thomas, Mr James	M	Jan 1999
Robson, Mr Jeremy	M	Oct 1999
Bowe, Mr Patrick	L	Jan 2000
James-Moore, Siward	L	Jul 2000
George, Mr Timothy David	I	Oct 2000
Lowe, Mr Christopher	M	Jul 2001
Kabweru-Namulemu, Miss Karen	L	Jul 2001
Harrison, Esther	I	Jan 2002
Cleary, Mr James	M	Nov 2003
Russell, Mr Tom	I	Jan 2004
Sapstead, Miss Louise	L	Jul 2004
Williams, Ms Anne	M	Mar 2005
Mansfield, Mr Ben	I	Jan 2005
Cox, Mr Jonathan	L	Jan 2005
Mellor, Faye	M	Jan 2005
Mansfield, Ms Nadia	I	Nov 2006
Holt, Mrs Jane	M	Oct 2006
Gunstone, Mr Giles	M	Jul 2007
Veitch, Mr Steven	L	Nov 2007
Wells, Mr Chris	I	Jan 2007

Chambers of Dominic Nolan QC

ROPEWALK CHAMBERS,
24 THE ROPEWALK, NOTTINGHAM NG1 5EF
Tel: 0115 947 2581 ***Fax:*** 0115 947 6532
Dx: 10060 NOTTINGHAM 17
E-mail: clerks@ropewalk.co.uk
Web: www.ropewalk.co.uk
Clerk: Senior: Tony Hill.
Head of Chambers:

Name		Date
Nolan, Mr Dominic (Q.C.)	L	Jul 1985
Limb, Mr Patrick (Q.C.)	M	Jul 1987
Machin, Mr Graham Edward	G	Jul 1965
Burns, Mr Richard; Recorder	M	Nov 1967
Herbert, Mr Douglas C; Recorder	M	Jul 1972
Beresford, Mr Stephen	G	Jun 1976
Gash, Mr Simon	G	Jul 1977
Beard, Mr Simon	G	Nov 1980
Adams, Miss Jayne Margaret	G	Jul 1982
Hedley, Mr Richard P; Recorder	M	Nov 1983
Din, Soofi P I	L	Nov 1984
Prestwich, Mr Andrew	G	Nov 1986
Seabrook, Mr Richard M	I	Jul 1987
Turton, Mr Philip	G	Nov 1989
Stewart, Mr Toby	M	Jul 1989
Mitchell, Mr Jonathan	G	Nov 1992
Cox, Mr Jason	G	Oct 1992
McNamara, Mr Andrew	I	Nov 1992
Davies, Ms Deborah	G	Nov 1993
Gregory, Mr Richard	M	Oct 1993
Hogan, Mr Andrew	I	Oct 1996
Diggle, Mr Mark	I	Oct 1996
Shah, Ms Shilpa	L	Jul 1998
Haddon, Ms Clare	G	Jan 1999
Panton, Mr Tom	L	Jul 2002
Lyons, Mr Andrew	I	Jul 2002
James, Mr Edward	I	Oct 2002
Owen, Mr Jonathan	I	Jan 2004
Herbert, Miss Kate	G	Jan 2004
Rong, Miss Rochelle	L	Jan 2005
Jaspal, Mr Kam	L	Jan 2005
Young, Miss Rachel	I	Jan 2006
Cursham, Mrs Georgina	G	Jan 2007
Robinson, Mr Nicholas	L	Jan 2007
Buss, Mr Simon	L	Jan 2007
Wood, Mr Daniel	L	Jan 2008
Wibberley, Mr James	L	Jan 2009

Chambers of Nigel B Page

ST MARY'S CHAMBERS,
26-28 HIGH PAVEMENT, LACE MARKET, NOTTINGHAM NG1 1HN
Tel: 0115 950 3503 ***Fax:*** 0115 958 3060
Dx: 10036 NOTTINGHAM
E-mail: clerks@stmarysflc.co.uk
Web: www.stmarysflc.co.uk
Clerk: Senior: Scott Baldwin.
Head of Chambers:

Name		Date
Page, Mr Nigel B	G	Jul 1976
Anderson, Mr Colin	G	Nov 1973
Hodges, Miss Victoria	G	Jul 1980
Buchanan, Mrs Vivien	I	Oct 1981
Salmon, Mr Kevin	G	Oct 1984
Gilead, Miss Beryl L	I	Feb 1989
Mulrennan, Miss Maria H A	I	Nov 1990
Claxton, Miss Judith	M	Oct 1990
Beese, Miss Nicola	M	Mar 1998
Snelus, Mr James	I	Oct 1999
Reece, Mr Jason	G	Nov 2000
Simpson, Miss Hannah	M	Oct 2000
McCluskey, Mr Mark	G	Jul 2001
Gillespie, Miss Jane	I	Oct 2001
Arshad, Ms Raffia	M	Oct 2002
Covington, Miss Rebecca	M	Mar 2006
Wren, Mr Andrew John	M	Jul 2005
Davey, Miss Helen	L	Jan 2008
Bewley, Miss Amanda	I	Jan 2005
Farrington, Mrs Gail	G	Jul 2011
O'Grady, Mr Matthew	G	Aug 2010
Mannering, Mr Stephen	L	Nov 2011
Geekie, Mr Charles (Q.C.); Recorder*	I	Jul 1985
Casey, Miss Mairin*	I	Nov 1989
Lee, Miss Jessica*	M	Oct 2000
Cockayne, Miss Kerry*	L	Jul 2002
Clarke, Miss Laura*	M	Jan 2003

OADBY, Leicestershire

Chambers of Mohammad Tayab Khan

MELBURY HOUSE,
55 MANOR ROAD, OADBY, LEICESTERSHIRE LE2 2LL
E-mail: melburyhousechambers@yahoo.co.uk
Clerk: Senior: Y Khan. Junior: T Khan. Assistant: S Gill.
Administrator: M Yusuf Khan
Practice Manager: S Imran Khan; S Khan
Head of Chambers:

Name		Date
Khan, Mr Mohammad Tayab	L	Feb 1972

OXFORD, Oxfordshire

Chambers of Frances Judd QC

HARCOURT CHAMBERS,
CHURCHILL HOUSE, 3 ST ALDATES COURTYARD, 38 ST ALDATES, OXFORD, OXFORDSHIRE OX1 1BN
Tel: 0844 561 7135 ***Fax:*** 01865 791585
Dx: 96453 OXFORD 4
E-mail: clerks@harcourtchambers.law.co.uk
Practice Manager: Judith Partington
Chambers Director: Simon Boutwood
Head of Chambers:

Name		Date
Judd, Ms Frances (Q.C.)	M	Jul 1984
Pressdee, Mr Piers (Q.C.)	M	Oct 1991
Evans, Mr Roger	M	Nov 1970
Rodgers, Ms June	M	Nov 1971
Sefi, Mr Benedict	I	Jul 1972
Collinson, Ms Alicia	M	Jul 1982
Brett, Mr Matthew	M	Nov 1987
Gibbons, Ms Sarah	M	Nov 1987
Hay, Ms Fiona Ruth	I	Nov 1989
Granshaw, Ms Sara	L	Oct 1991
Max, Ms Sally	L	Oct 1991
Garrido, Mr Damian	M	Nov 1993
Potter, Ms Louise	I	Nov 1993
Vater, Mr John	G	Feb 1995
Goodwin, Mr Nicholas	L	Oct 1995
Vine, Mr Aidan	M	Oct 1995
Miller, Mr Simon	L	Oct 1996
Sampson, Mr Jonathan R	M	Oct 1997
Barrett, Miss Cecilia M	I	Jul 1998
Wraight, Mr Oliver	M	Oct 1998
Leong, Mr Andrew	M	Oct 1998
Little, Ms Helen	L	Oct 1999
Kirkwood, Mr Edward	I	Nov 1999
Styles, Ms Margaret	M	Oct 2000
Turner, Mr James Paul	I	Jul 2001
Devereux, Mr Edward	M	Oct 2001
Green, Mr Jason	G	Oct 2001
Brightman, Ms Justina	L	Oct 2003
Forbes, Mr Alex	L	Oct 2003
Tomlinson, Miss Elizabeth	I	Jul 2004
Williams, Miss Alison	G	Oct 2004
Higgins, Mr Mark	I	Jan 2005
Harris, Miss Frances	L	Jan 2005
Wilkins, Miss Chloe	G	Jan 2006
Wilkinson, Miss Helen	M	Jul 2007
Hylton, Miss Nasstassia	I	Jul 2007
Kelly, Miss Gemma	I	Nov 2007
Cox, Miss Sian	M	Jul 2008
Crispin, Mr Stephen	L	Nov 2008
Rayner, Miss Emily	M	Jul 2009
Sharp, Mr Christopher (Q.C.)*	I	Jul 1975
Jacklin, Miss Susan (Q.C.)*	I	Nov 1980

Chambers of Julian James Baughan QC

KING'S BENCH CHAMBERS,
32 BEAUMONT STREET, OXFORD, OXFORDSHIRE OX1 2NP
Tel: 01865 311066 ***Fax:*** 01865 311077
Dx: 145842 OXFORD 6
E-mail: clerks@13kbw.co.uk
Clerk: Senior: K Kelly.
Administrator: Penny McFall
Head of Chambers:

Name		Date
Baughan, Mr Julian James (Q.C.)	I	Jul 1967
Ellis, Mr Roger John (Q.C.)	G	Jul 1962
Syfret, Mr Nicholas (Q.C.)	M	Oct 1979
Ashton, Mr David Sambrook; Chartered Arbitrator	G	Jul 1962
Dawson, Mr Alexander William	M	Jul 1969
McGeorge, Mr Anthony William	I	Nov 1969
Lamb, Mr Robert Glasson	M	Jul 1973
Goodwin, Ms Deirdre Evelyn	G	Jul 1974
Bright, Mr David Reginald	L	Jun 1976
Higgins, Mr Anthony	G	Nov 1978
Daly, Mr Nigel	G	Jul 1979
Glennie, Mr Andrew	M	Jul 1982
Pote, Mr Andrew Thomas	G	Nov 1983
Coode, Mr Jonathan	M	Jul 1984
Vickery, Mr Neil	G	Jul 1985
Moore, Mr Neil	G	Jul 1986
Maitland-Jones, Mr Mark	M	Nov 1986
Blake, Mr Arthur	I	Feb 1988
Cramsie, Mr Sinclair James Beresford	I	Nov 1988
Higgins, Mr Adrian	L	Oct 1990
Wallace, Ms Nicola	I	Oct 2006
Walters, Mr Edmund	M	Nov 1991
Williams, Mr Hugh	G	Jul 1992
Edwards, Miss Jennifer	G	Oct 1992
Buttimore, Mr Gabriel	G	Feb 1993
Coombe, Mr Peter	M	Nov 1993
Clargo, Mr John	M	Oct 1994
Chan, Miss Susan	G	Oct 1994
Nicol, Mr Stuart	L	Nov 1994
Duncan, Ms Nikki	G	Nov 1994
Drake, Miss Rachel Alexia	M	Nov 1995
Robertson, Miss Alice	G	Oct 1996
Woodhouse, Mr Nigel	G	Nov 1997
Mann, Mr Christopher	L	Oct 1998
Harrington, Ms Clare	L	Oct 1998
Grainger, Mr Alistair	I	Nov 1998
Hopkins, Ms Julie	I	Jul 1999
James, Mr Henry	G	Nov 1999
Lippold, Mrs Sarah	I	Nov 1999
Mann, Mr Ian	L	Oct 2000
Owen-Thomas, Mr Richard	M	Nov 2000
Van der Leij, Ms Martina	L	Jul 2001
Brady, Ms Jane	M	Oct 2001
Tapper, Miss Lucy	M	Nov 2002
Grant, Mr Murray	I	Oct 2003
Sear, Miss Joanne	G	Jul 2004
Gurnham, Mr Paul	L	Jul 2004
Boswell, Mr Timothy	G	Nov 2004
Bennion-Pedley, Mr Edward	M	Nov 2004
Brown, Mr Timothy	I	Mar 2005
Malcolm, Miss Jane	M	Jul 2005
Corrie, Mr Matthew	M	Jun 2006
Williams, Mr Graeme (Q.C.)*	I	Jun 1959
Reid, Mr Paul William*	I	Jul 1975

3PB,
23 BEAUMONT STREET, OXFORD, OXFORDSHIRE OX1 2NP
Tel: 01865 793736 ***Fax:*** 01865 790760
Dx: 4302 OXFORD
E-mail: clerks.all@3paper.co.uk
Clerk: Russell Porter (Senior Clerk); David Snook; James Newman; Sophie Bruce.
Administrator: Neil Monro (Head of Business Administration and Finance)
Practice Manager: Stephen Evers (Practice Development Clerk)
Chambers Director: Stephen Clark (Head of Clerking); Charles Charlick (Consultant Clerk)

Name		Date
Curran, Mr Leo	G	Jul 1972
Kent, Mr Peter	G	Nov 1978
Strutt, Mr Martin	I	Nov 1981
Martin, Mrs Nicola	I	Jan 1982
Buckley-Clarke, Mrs Amanda	L	Oct 1991
Sweeney, Mr Christian	G	Oct 1992
Clargo, Mr John	M	Oct 1994
Mitchell, Mr Jack	I	Oct 1994
Strachan, Miss Elaine	M	Nov 1995
Griffiths, Miss Emma	G	Oct 1998
Maqsood, Ms Kalsoom*	M	Oct 1998
Horner, Mr Robert	I	Nov 1999
Worton, Ms Louise	I	Jan 2000
Sheriff, Mr Andrew	M	Jan 2000
Whelan, Mr Christopher	M	Jan 2001
Shillingford, Ms Julia	M	Jan 2002
Courts, Mr Robert	L	Jan 2003
Davies, Mr James	L	Oct 2004
Musgrave, Ms Anarkali	I	Jan 2005
Davies, Mr Nick	G	Jan 2006
MacPhail, Mr Andrew	M	Jan 2007
Dunseath, Katherine	G	Jan 2008
Bowes, Ms Gemma	M	Jan 2009

11

PENCADER, Carmarthenshire

PORTAL CHAMBERS,
GLANDULAIS, LLANLWNI, PENCADER, CARMARTHENSHIRE SA39 9DS
Tel: 01559 395292 ***Fax:*** 01559 395292
Dx: 200254 LLANDYSUL
E-mail: clerk@portalchambers.co.uk
Clerk: Rosemary Harrison.

PERIVALE, Middlesex

Chambers of Saleem Ahmed

PERIVALE CHAMBERS,
15 COLWYN AVENUE, PERIVALE, MIDDLESEX UB6 8JX
Tel: 020 8998 1935 / 8991 1823
Clerk: Hoora Ahmed.
Head of Chambers:
- Ahmed, Mr Saleem . . . I . . . Feb 1971

PETERBOROUGH

Chambers of Ian Martignetti

REGENCY CHAMBERS,
45 PRIESTGATE, PETERBOROUGH PE1 1LB
Tel: 01733 315215 ***Fax:*** 01733 565967
Dx: 12349 PETERBOROUGH 1
E-mail: clerks@regencychambers.law.co.uk
Clerk: Senior: Paul Wright.
Administrator: Tina Clayton
Head of Chambers:
- Martignetti, Mr Ian . . . I . . . Nov 1990

- Hockman, Mr Stephen (Q.C.)* . . . M . . . Jul 1970
- Storey, Mr Paul (Q.C.)* . . . L . . . Nov 1982
- Powell, Mr William . . . L . . . Nov 1971
- Thind, Miss Anita . . . L . . . Nov 1988
- Elliott, Miss Margot . . . G . . . Nov 1989
- Buckle, Mr Jonathan . . . L . . . Nov 1990
- Bennet, Miss Pauline . . . L . . . Oct 1991
- Fender, Mr Carl . . . L . . . Feb 1994
- Bramwell, Mr Christopher . . . G . . . Nov 1996
- Sleight, Mr Nigel . . . L . . . Oct 1998
- Hunt, Miss Alison . . . M . . . Nov 2001
- Lindsey, Miss Amy . . . M . . . Jan 2001
- Walji, Miss Shabnam . . . G . . . Jul 2001
- Chapman, Ms Gemma . . . M . . . Jan 2002
- Jacques, Mr Gareth Edward . . . I . . . Jan 2007
- Dunlop, Mrs Patricia . . . M . . . Jan 2009
- Thomas, Mrs Paula Angelique . . . L . . . Jan 2009

PINNER, Middlesex

Chambers of Khandakar Abdul Quddus

19 CHESTNUT DRIVE,
PINNER, MIDDLESEX HA5 1LX
Tel: 020 8866 7603 ***Fax:*** 020 8866 7603
E-mail: sara.tania@googlemail.com
Clerk: Tania Sara Quddus.
Head of Chambers:
- Quddus, Khandakar Abdul . . . I . . . Jul 1968

PLYMOUTH

Chambers of Gina Small and Colin Elliott

KING'S BENCH GODOLPHIN CHAMBERS,
115 NORTH HILL, PLYMOUTH PL4 8JY
Tel: 0845 308 1551 ***Fax:*** 01752 664379
Dx: 8237 PLYMOUTH
E-mail: clerks@kbgchambers.co.uk
Clerk: Senior: Colin Palmer. Beverley Williams; Lizzie Jenkinson; Jamie Kyte; Anthony Chapman; Yvonne Simmons.
Administrator: Sally Finan
Head of Chambers:
- Small, Miss Gina . . . L . . . Oct 1991
- Elliott, Mr Colin . . . G . . . Jul 1987

- Meredith, Mr George . . . G . . . Jul 1969
- Maitland, Mr Andrew H R . . . L . . . Jul 1970
- Guy, Mr Richard Perran . . . I . . . Nov 1970
- Sellick, Mr Llewelyn . . . M . . . Jul 1973
- Lyon, Mrs Shane . . . M . . . Nov 1976
- Wallace, Miss Ann . . . I . . . Jul 1979
- Wilson, Miss Jennifer Mary Pentreath . . . G . . . Jul 1979
- Down, Miss Susan . . . M . . . Nov 1984
- Crozier, Rawdon R C . . . M . . . Nov 1984
- Beechey, Miss Hilary . . . M . . . Nov 1987
- Lewin, Mr Nicholas . . . G . . . Jul 1989
- Peers, Miss Heather . . . G . . . Oct 1991
- Antell, Mr John Jason . . . M . . . Oct 1992
- MacKean, Miss Sarah . . . I . . . Nov 1992
- Rafati, Mr Ali . . . G . . . Nov 1993
- Pullen, Mr Timothy . . . M . . . Nov 1993
- Clarke, Mr Malcolm . . . G . . . Oct 1994
- Holland, Mrs Annie . . . M . . . Nov 1994
- Richards, Dr Jonathan Nicholas . . . M . . . Nov 1995
- Mathews, Mr Deni . . . G . . . Jul 1996
- Willetts, Mr Andrew . . . M . . . Jan 1997
- Birt, Miss Emma . . . I . . . Oct 2000
- Bosanko, Mr Jonathan . . . M . . . Jul 2001
- Hall, Mr Nigel . . . I . . . Jul 2001
- Sutherland, Miss Yvonne . . . I . . . Jul 2001
- Higginson, Mr William . . . L . . . Oct 2001
- Appleby, Miss Claire . . . L . . . Oct 2002
- Rawlings, Carrie-Ann . . . I . . . Oct 2005
- Kumeta, Miss Jennifer . . . M . . . Oct 2005
- Pearce, Miss Emma . . . L . . . Jul 2006
- Challacombe, Mr Thomas . . . G . . . Jul 2006
- Rose, Mr Will . . . L . . . Jul 2007
- Dyson, Mr Daniel Bryn William . . . G . . . Nov 2007
- Donne, Mr Anthony M (Q.C.)* . . . M . . . Apr 1973
- Vere-Hodge, Mr Michael (Q.C.)* . . . G . . . Nov 1970
- Jones, Mr Stewart E (Q.C.)* . . . G . . . Nov 1972
- Wright, Mr Jeremy J . . . I . . . Jul 1970
- Climie, Mr Stephen* . . . L . . . Jul 1982

PONTYCLUN, Rhondda Cynon Taff

Chambers of Roger Everest

TWINFIRS,
PO BOX 32, TALYGARN, PONTYCLUN, RHONDDA CYNON TAFF CF72 9BY
Tel: 01443 229850 ***Fax:*** 01443 222252
Head of Chambers:
- Everest, Mr Roger . . . G . . . Nov 1968

PORTSMOUTH

Chambers of Lee Young

GUILDHALL CHAMBERS,
PRUDENTIAL BUILDING, 16 GUILDHALL WALK, PORTSMOUTH PO1 2DE
Tel: 023 9275 2400 ***Fax:*** 023 9275 3100
Dx: 2225 PORTSMOUTH 1
E-mail: gcpclerks@fsmail.net
Clerk: Senior: Tristan Thwaites. Junior: Sarah Mayer.
Administrator: Stephanie Mezulis
Head of Chambers:
- Young, Mr Lee . . . M . . . Oct 1991

- Day, Miss Robyn* . . . I . . . May 1997
- Parker, Ms Karen . . . I . . . Jul 2001
- Jenking-Rees, Ms Laura . . . L . . . Mar 2002
- Fortune, Mr Peter . . . I . . . Jul 1978
- Colbey, Mr Richard . . . I . . . Jul 1984
- Lynch, Mr Patrick . . . I . . . Jul 1988
- England, Mrs Lisa . . . G . . . Jan 1992
- Brookes, Mr Lincoln Paul . . . I . . . Nov 1992
- Hall, Mrs Yasmin . . . I . . . Jan 1993
- Concannon, Mr Timothy . . . I . . . Jul 1993
- Withey, Mr Richard . . . I . . . Jan 1996
- Bullen, Ms Mary . . . I . . . Mar 2005

Chambers of Paul McCormick

HAMPSHIRE CHAMBERS,
MALTON HOUSE, 24 HAMPSHIRE TERRACE, PORTSMOUTH PO1 2QF
Tel: 023 9282 6636 / 9229 7144 ***Fax:*** 023 9229 7101
Dx: 2270 PORTSMOUTH
Clerk: Joanna Gutteridge.
Head of Chambers:
- McCormick, Dr Paul . . . M . . . Jul 1983

Chambers of Andrew James Parsons

PORTSMOUTH BARRISTERS CHAMBERS,
VICTORY HOUSE, 7 BELLEVUE TERRACE, PORTSMOUTH PO5 3AT
Est: 1989
Tel: 023 9283 1292 ***Fax:*** 023 9229 1262
Dx: 2239 PORTSMOUTH
E-mail: clerks@portsmouthbar.com
Clerk: Jackie Morrison.
Head of Chambers:
- Parsons, Mr Andrew James . . . I . . . Jul 1985

PRESTON, Lancashire

Chambers of Mark G Turner QC

DEANS COURT CHAMBERS,
101 WALKER STREET, PRESTON, LANCASHIRE PR1 2RR
Tel: 01772 565600 ***Fax:*** 01772 565601
Dx: 710057 PRESTON 10

NEW BAILEY CHAMBERS,
FIRST FLOOR, LIGHT BUILDING, 99 WALKER STREET, PRESTON, LANCASHIRE PR1 2RR
Tel: 01772 258087 ***Fax:*** 01772 880100
Dx: 710050 PRESTON 10
E-mail: clerks@newbailey.co.uk
Clerk: Laura Armstrong; Chris Kushner; Rob Armstrong; John Stewart.
- Wood, Mr Graeme . . . M . . . Jul 1968
- Thomas, Mr Keith . . . G . . . Jul 1969
- Simpson, Mr Paul Richard . . . L . . . Jul 1980
- Beeson, Mr Nigel A L . . . M . . . Oct 1983
- Clarke, Mr Jeremy . . . I . . . Jul 1985
- Barnes, Ashley J . . . I . . . Nov 1990
- Sinker, Mr Andrew . . . L . . . Oct 1991
- Dacre, Mr Ian . . . M . . . Nov 1991
- Ackerley, Mr David . . . I . . . Oct 1992
- Gow, Mr Henry McCallion . . . G . . . Oct 1995
- Gray, Mr Mark J . . . G . . . Nov 1996
- Pritchard, Miss Cecilia . . . M . . . Jan 1998
- Bradbury, Miss Sara . . . G . . . Jan 1998
- Thomas, Miss Claire . . . I . . . Oct 1998
- Omran-Baber, Mr Waheed . . . G . . . Nov 1999
- Leong, Mr Simon . . . M . . . Jan 2001
- Santmera, Miss Louise . . . G . . . Oct 2002
- Campbell, Miss Bernice . . . M . . . Jan 2004
- Ackerley, Miss Rebecca . . . L . . . Jan 2004

Chambers of Richard Bradley

ORIEL CHAMBERS,
18 RIBBLESDALE PLACE, PRESTON, LANCASHIRE PR1 3NA
Est: 1965
Tel: 01772 254764 ***Fax:*** 01772 554910
Dx: 714583 PRESTON 14
E-mail: clerks@orielchambers.co.uk
Web: www.orielchambers.co.uk
Clerk: Julie Hall.
Practice Manager: Paul Thompson
Chambers Director: Sarah Cavanagh
Head of Chambers:
- Bradley, Mr Richard . . . M . . . Jul 1978

- Bennett, Mr Martyn . . . G . . . Jul 1969
- Alldis, Mr Christopher; Recorder . . . G . . . Nov 1970
- Hind, Mr Kenneth CBE . . . G . . . Jul 1973
- Murray, Ashley C; Recorder . . . M . . . Jul 1974
- Cowan, Mr Peter S M; Recorder . . . M . . . Jul 1980
- Wells, Mr Graham; Recorder . . . M . . . Jul 1982
- Bundred, Ms Gillian S . . . G . . . Jul 1982
- O'Keeffe, Mr Darren . . . I . . . Jul 1984
- Evans, Ms Suzanne Marie . . . M . . . Nov 1985
- Fox, Ms Anna Katherine Helen . . . M . . . Jul 1986
- Goodbody, Mr Peter James . . . L . . . Jul 1986
- Ellis, Ms Catherine . . . L . . . Jul 1987
- Baldwin, Mr John G . . . G . . . Oct 1990
- Rahman, Yaqub; Recorder . . . G . . . Oct 1991
- Holloway, Mr Timothy . . . I . . . Nov 1991
- Gruffydd, Mr John . . . G . . . Feb 1992
- Belbin, Ms Heather P . . . L . . . Oct 1992
- Mills, Mr Stuart . . . M . . . Oct 1992
- Foster, Mr Peter . . . M . . . Nov 1992
- Brant, Mr Paul David . . . L . . . Nov 1993
- Brandon, Ms Helen Elizabeth . . . M . . . Nov 1993
- Rankin, Mr William K . . . G . . . Oct 1994
- Hughes, Ms Rachel . . . G . . . Nov 1995
- Benson, Mr James . . . G . . . Nov 1995
- Cottrell, Mr Matthew R . . . G . . . Oct 1996
- Frodsham, Mr Alexander . . . L . . . Oct 1996
- Clarke, Ms Susan . . . M . . . Oct 1996
- Hennessy, Ms Shirley . . . L . . . Oct 1997
- Stanger, Mr Mark Fullerton . . . M . . . Jan 1998
- Clarke, Lindsay . . . G . . . Jul 1999
- Berry, Mr Karl . . . M . . . Nov 1999
- Huyton, Ms Katherine . . . M . . . Nov 1999
- Purcell, Miss Deirdre Marie . . . L . . . Nov 2000
- Burns, Ms Judith . . . M . . . Jan 2001
- Gray, Mr John . . . L . . . Oct 2001
- Williams, Mr Graham . . . M . . . Jan 2002
- Middleton, Mr Christopher . . . I . . . Jan 2002
- Howe, Mr Andrew . . . L . . . Jan 2002
- Gruffydd, Miss Sarah . . . G . . . Jul 2003
- McMurtrie, Mr Christopher . . . G . . . Jul 2003
- Bartlett, Mrs Catherine . . . I . . . Jan 2004
- Williams, Mr Alexander . . . M . . . Jan 2004
- Gosling, Mr Tom Adam . . . L . . . Nov 2004
- Cooper, Mr Mark . . . L . . . Jan 2005
- Champion, Miss Karina . . . I . . . Jan 2005
- Wolfenden, Mr Peter . . . M . . . Jul 2007
- Parr, Miss Margaret . . . L . . . Mar 2008
- Fazackerley, Mr Tom Brian . . . G . . . Oct 2010
- Cummings, Miss Stephanie Anne . . . M . . . Nov 2010
- Garden, Mr Ian* . . . L . . . Jul 1989
- Nicholls, Ms Jane* . . . I . . . Nov 1989
- Lewthwaite, Ms Joanne* . . . I . . . Oct 1990
- Dawson, Mr James* . . . I . . . Nov 1994
- Sholicar, Ms Ann* . . . L . . . Nov 2000

This Chambers with 55 Barristers is based in Preston and led by Richard Bradley.

Chambers of Michael Howard Redfern QC

ST JOHNS BUILDINGS,
16 WINCKLEY SQUARE, PRESTON, LANCASHIRE PR1 3JJ
Tel: 01772 256100 ***Fax:*** 01772 256101
Dx: 714582 PRESTON 14
E-mail: mary.berry@stjohnsbuildings.co.uk
Head of Chambers:
- Redfern, Mr Michael Howard (Q.C.) . . . I . . . Jul 1970

- Bentham, Mr Howard (Q.C.) . . . G . . . Nov 1970
- Shorrock, Mr Michael (Q.C.) . . . I . . . Jul 1966
- Berkley, Mr David (Q.C.) . . . M . . . May 1979
- Marks, Mr Richard (Q.C.) . . . G . . . Jul 1975
- Hayden, Mr Anthony (Q.C.) . . . M . . . Nov 1987
- Singleton, Ms Sarah (Q.C.) . . . M . . . Jul 1983
- O'Byrne, Mr Andrew (Q.C.) . . . G . . . Jul 1978
- Samuels, Mr Jeffrey K (Q.C.) . . . M . . . Jul 1988
- Harrison, Miss Sally (Q.C.) . . . G . . . Oct 1992
- Wolff, Mr Michael . . . G . . . Jun 1964
- Cattan, Mr Philip David . . . G . . . Nov 1970
- Lamberty, Mr Mark . . . I . . . Nov 1970
- Herman, Mr Ray . . . I . . . Feb 1972
- Green, Mr Roger . . . L . . . Jul 1972
- Hedgecoe, Mr John Philip . . . I . . . Nov 1972
- Bedford, Mr Stephen . . . G . . . Jul 1972

McNeill, Mr John Seddon . . . G . . . Jul 1974
Shannon, Mr Eric . . . M . . . Nov 1974
Lowe, Mr Geoffrey . . . G . . . Jul 1975
Longworth, Mr Antony Stephen . . . M . . . Jul 1978
Andrews, Mr Philip . . . I . . . Feb 1977
Feeny, Mr Charles . . . I . . . Nov 1977
Grundy, Mr Philip Michael David . . . M . . . Jul 1980
Owen, Miss Gail . . . G . . . Nov 1980
Mercer, Mr David . . . L . . . Jul 1980
Uff, Mr David C . . . G . . . Jul 1981
Long, Mr Andrew . . . I . . . Jul 1981
Holt, Mr Julian . . . M . . . Jan 1982
Gal, Miss Sonia . . . I . . . Nov 1982
Greene, Mr Maurice A . . . I . . . Nov 1982
Garside, Mr David . . . G . . . Nov 1982
Bruce, Mr David . . . M . . . Jul 1982
Harrison, Mr Peter John . . . M . . . Jul 1983
Khawar, Aftab . . . G . . . Jul 1983
McKee, Mr Hugh A . . . M . . . Nov 1983
Goodman, Miss Bernadette . . . I . . . Nov 1983
McKenna, Mr Brian . . . M . . . Jun 1983
Harrison, Mr J Keith . . . L . . . Nov 1983
Shaw, Mr Julian . . . G . . . Sep 1984
Pickup, Mr David . . . I . . . Jul 1984
Kennedy, Mr Michael . . . M . . . May 1985
Lloyd, Mr Julian . . . G . . . Jul 1985
Gray, Mr Richard . . . M . . . Nov 1986
Kloss, Mrs Diana Mary . . . G . . . Jul 1986
Oates, Mr John Richard . . . G . . . Jul 1987
Taylor, Mr Julian . . . M . . . Jul 1986
Dickinson, Mr Jonathan . . . I . . . Nov 1986
Walker, Miss Jane . . . M . . . Jul 1987
Brennand, Mr Timothy W . . . G . . . Nov 1987
Dagnall, Ms Jane . . . I . . . Jan 1987
Batra, Bunty Lalit . . . G . . . Feb 1987
Eastwood, Mr Charles Peter . . . L . . . Jul 1988
Crabtree, Mr Simon J G . . . L . . . Nov 1988
Davitt, Ms Paula . . . G . . . Oct 1988
Sanders, Mr Damian . . . M . . . Nov 1988
Britcliffe, Ms Anne E . . . I . . . Apr 1989
Grundy, Ms Clare . . . G . . . Jul 1989
Partington, Miss Lisa . . . I . . . Jul 1989
Holder, Mr Simon . . . I . . . Jul 1989
Blakey, Mr Michael . . . M . . . Nov 1989
Carter, Mr Richard . . . I . . . Nov 1990
Thompson, Mr Patrick . . . G . . . Oct 1990
Watson, Mr David W . . . M . . . Oct 1990
Thompson, Mr Jonathan Richard . . . I . . . Oct 1990
Wright, Mr Alastair . . . L . . . Dec 1991
Mawdsley, Mr Matthew . . . I . . . Nov 1991
Roberts, Mr Mark Vaughan . . . I . . . Sep 1991
Chaudhry, Ms Zia . . . I . . . Nov 1991
Pratt, Mrs Patricia . . . L . . . Oct 1991
Taylor, Mr Jonathan . . . M . . . Nov 1991
Case, Magdalen . . . M . . . Nov 1992
Green, Mr Andrew . . . G . . . Oct 1992
Norton, Mr Richard . . . L . . . Nov 1992
Ashmole, Mr Timothy . . . I . . . Oct 1992
McNerney, Mr Kevin . . . I . . . Jan 1992
Lloyd, Ms Gaynor Elizabeth . . . L . . . Oct 1992
Jones, Mr Benjamin . . . M . . . Feb 1993
Flood, Mr David . . . M . . . Nov 1993
Kloss, Mr Alexander . . . G . . . Oct 1993
Mathieson, Mr Guy . . . M . . . Oct 1993
Wilson, Mr Myles . . . L . . . Oct 1993
Searle, Mr Jason Ario Xavier . . . M . . . Oct 1993
Gibson, Mr John Arthur . . . L . . . Nov 1993
Fitzharris, Miss Ginnette . . . L . . . Nov 1993
Blackshaw, Mr Henry . . . M . . . Oct 1993
Orme, Mr Richard . . . L . . . Oct 1993
Rodikis, Miss Joanna . . . M . . . Oct 1993
Harrison, Miss Leona . . . M . . . Nov 1993
Polglase, Mr David S . . . M . . . Oct 1993
Connor, Mr Mark . . . I . . . May 1994
Frieze, Mr Daniel . . . G . . . Oct 1994
Gumbs, Miss Annette . . . G . . . Oct 1994
Wild, Mr Steven . . . G . . . Oct 1994
Douglas, Mr Stephen John . . . I . . . Nov 1994
Reynolds, Mr Gary William . . . L . . . Nov 1994
McGinty, Mr Robert Fraser . . . L . . . Nov 1994
Rowley, Mr Karl John . . . M . . . Nov 1994
Houghton, Ms Lisa . . . G . . . May 1994
Booth, Mr Nigel Robert . . . G . . . Oct 1994
Mann, Miss Sara . . . M . . . Nov 1994
Chukwuemeka, Mr John O . . . L . . . Nov 1994
Hargan, Mr Carl . . . L . . . Nov 1995
Lawson, Mr Andrew . . . I . . . Jan 1995
Mchugh, Miss Pauline Mary . . . G . . . Nov 1995
Parry, Mr Philip . . . L . . . Jan 1995
Crangle, Miss Charlotte . . . G . . . Jan 1995
Simkin, Mr Iain . . . I . . . Feb 1995
Dixon, Mr John . . . G . . . Nov 1995
Aslett, Pepin . . . I . . . Nov 1996
Crilley, Mr Darrel . . . I . . . Feb 1996
Roussak, Mr Jeremy Brian . . . M . . . Oct 1996
Leene, Miss Sharon . . . G . . . Oct 1996
Sastry, Mr Bob . . . I . . . Oct 1996
Mahmood, Ghazan . . . I . . . Sep 1997
Mintz, Mr Simon . . . I . . . Nov 1996
Zentar, Dr Remy . . . G . . . Jul 1997
Spear, Miss Sarah . . . I . . . Oct 1997
Williams, Ms Zillah . . . L . . . Nov 1997
Mensah, Miss Lorraine S L . . . G . . . Oct 1997
Denton, Mr Douglas . . . L . . . Nov 1997
Parry, Mr Simon . . . I . . . Nov 1997
Tyler, Mr Paul . . . M . . . Jan 1997
Evans, Mr Simeon . . . L . . . Jun 1997
Buckley, Mr Patrick James . . . G . . . Jul 1998
Bentley, Mr David Paul . . . I . . . Oct 1998
Muth, Ms Susanne . . . I . . . Jul 1998
Simmonds, Ms Alexandra . . . G . . . Oct 1998
Taylor, Mr David Christopher . . . L . . . Oct 1998
Murdin, Mr Liam . . . L . . . Jul 1998
James, Mr David . . . I . . . Oct 1998
Burnell, Miss Kate . . . M . . . Oct 1998
Stockwell, Mr Matthew . . . G . . . Oct 1998
Edwards, Miss Susan . . . L . . . Nov 1998
Deas, Ms Susan Margaret . . . G . . . Jul 1999
Astbury, Mr Philip . . . G . . . Oct 1999
Holsgrove, Lara . . . M . . . Jan 1999
Ratledge, Mr John . . . L . . . Jun 1999
Sweeney, Ms Linda Mary . . . M . . . Nov 1999
Cavanagh, Ms Lorraine . . . G . . . Jan 2000

Leach, Ms Natasha . . . L . . . Jan 2000
Bridgman, Mr Andrew . . . G . . . Jan 2000
Porter-Phillips, Mrs Clare . . . L . . . Mar 2001
Ahmed, Siraj Issap . . . M . . . Apr 2001
King, Mr Oliver . . . G . . . Jul 2001
Vir Singh, Miss Sylvia . . . M . . . Jul 2001
Van Der Haer, Ms Audrey . . . G . . . Oct 2001
Blewitt, Miss Jennifer . . . M . . . Jul 2001
Pojur, Mr David . . . M . . . Nov 2001
Farley, Mr David . . . M . . . Jan 2001
Montaldo, Mr Neil . . . L . . . Mar 2002
Hodgkinson, Mr Paul George . . . L . . . Jul 2002
Owen, Wendy Jane . . . M . . . Jan 2002
Senior, Mr Mark . . . G . . . Jul 2002
Smith, Mr Paul . . . G . . . Oct 2002
Moss, Mr Christopher . . . L . . . Oct 2002
Malam, Mr James . . . G . . . Jan 2002
Menzies, Mr Jennifer . . . L . . . Oct 2002
Stringer, Ms Rosie . . . M . . . Jan 2002
McCloskey, Miss Louise . . . G . . . Oct 2002
Smith, Ms Rebecca Ellen . . . L . . . Jan 2002
Lawrence, Mr Benjamin . . . L . . . Jan 2003
Ali, Kashif . . . L . . . Jan 2003
Hudson, Ms Abigail . . . G . . . Jan 2003
Quigley, Ms Louise . . . I . . . Jan 2003
Newstead, Ms Jennifer Elizabeth . . . G . . . Nov 2003
Akers, Mr Robert . . . I . . . Nov 2003
Maguire, Clodagh . . . I . . . Jan 2003
Connolly, Mr Timothy . . . I . . . Mar 2004
Poole, Mr William . . . M . . . Jan 2004
Waddell, Ms Philippa . . . L . . . Jan 2004
Watkins, Mr Adam . . . G . . . Jul 2004
Murphy, Mr Paul . . . G . . . Jul 2004
Greenhalgh, Miss Jane . . . L . . . Nov 2004
Rimmer, Miss Catherine . . . G . . . Jul 2004
Harrison, Miss Petra . . . I . . . Jul 2004
Samuel, Ms Ana . . . I . . . Jul 2004
Wilson, Ms Helen . . . G . . . Oct 2004
Cooper, Mr Douglas . . . I . . . Jan 2004
Sutton, Rebecca . . . I . . . Jan 2004
Abraham, Ms Joanne Jade . . . G . . . Nov 2004
Spencer, Mr Shaun . . . L . . . Jan 2005
Marshall, Lucy . . . M . . . Jan 2005
White, Mrs Debra . . . G . . . Oct 2005
Christian, Mr Neil . . . M . . . Oct 2005
Thompson, Mr Gareth . . . G . . . Jan 2005
McGarry, Mr Steven . . . L . . . Mar 2005
De Navarro, Frances . . . I . . . Jan 2005
Pare, Mr Christopher . . . M . . . Jan 2006
Scully, Ms Jennifer . . . M . . . Jul 2006
Wilkinson, Mr Timothy . . . I . . . Jan 2006
Kelly, Mr Ben . . . L . . . Jan 2006
Flynn, Mr Steven . . . G . . . Jan 2006
Scott, Louise . . . M . . . Jan 2006
Haggis, Mr Andrew . . . M . . . Mar 2007
Wood, Hannah . . . L . . . Jan 2007
Vanderpump, Henry . . . I . . . Jan 2007
Owen-Easey, Neil . . . G . . . Jan 2007
Goode, Julian . . . L . . . Jan 2006
Allen, Mr Fegal . . . L . . . Oct 2007
Murray, Simon . . . I . . . Jan 2008
Cooper, Elisabeth . . . M . . . Jan 2008
Gomer, Mr Elis . . . G . . . Jan 2008
Williams, Miss Cerys . . . G . . . Jul 2008
Maddison, Mr Simon . . . I . . . Jan 2008
Edwards, Mr Huw . . . G . . . Jan 2009
England, Laura . . . M . . . Jan 2008
Roberts, Elliw . . . G . . . Jan 2009
Nash, Laura . . . L . . . Jan 2009

Chambers of P Nicholas D Kennedy

15 WINCKLEY SQUARE,
PRESTON, LANCASHIRE PR1 3JJ
Tel: 01772 252828 ***Fax:*** 01772 258520
Dx: 17110 PRESTON
E-mail: clerks@15winckleysq.co.uk
Clerk: Jonathan Borrow.
Administrator: John Schofield
Chambers Director: Elaine Wallis
Head of Chambers:
Kennedy, Mr P Nicholas D . . . L . . . Jul 1977

Baldwin, Mr Roger M . . . G . . . Jul 1969
Haworth, Mr Richard A . . . I . . . Nov 1978
Hart, Mr Paul . . . G . . . Jul 1982
Woodward, Mr John . . . L . . . Nov 1984
Hunt, Mr Richard M . . . L . . . Jul 1985
Bennett, Mr Richard John . . . M . . . Jul 1986
Wall, Miss Jacqueline . . . G . . . Jul 1986
Anderson, Mr Peter . . . I . . . Jul 1988
Bowcock, Miss Samantha J . . . M . . . Oct 1990
Tankel, Mrs Ruth . . . M . . . Jul 1990
Harvey, Ms Louise . . . L . . . Oct 1991
Whyatt, Mr Michael . . . G . . . Feb 1992
Taylor, Miss Julie . . . I . . . Nov 1992
Buchan, Mr Jonathan . . . M . . . Oct 1994
Akerman, Miss Kate . . . M . . . Oct 1994
Watson, Miss Sharon . . . M . . . Nov 1994
Blakey, Mr Lee . . . L . . . Oct 1995
Dyer, Mr Jacob Jackson . . . L . . . Nov 1995
Korol, Ms Kathryn . . . M . . . Mar 1996
Gillott, Mr Paul Alan Anthony . . . M . . . Oct 1996
Stringer, Mr Leon . . . L . . . Oct 1996
Maqsood, Miss Zabeda . . . G . . . Nov 1996
Barron-Eaves, Mrs Emma . . . L . . . Jul 1998
Bhat, Ms Saima . . . M . . . Jul 1999
Dixon, Mr Huw . . . L . . . Jan 1999
Carleton, Ms Erica . . . M . . . Mar 2000
Beever, Ms Prudence M . . . M . . . Jul 2000
Probert, Miss Sarah . . . M . . . Nov 2000
Traynor, Mr David . . . L . . . Oct 2002
Lee, Miss Sarah Jane . . . L . . . Jan 2002
Patterson, Miss Anna Louise . . . L . . . Oct 2004
Newton, Mrs Alexandra . . . L . . . Mar 2007
Archer, Mr Richard . . . M . . . Jul 2007
Perplus, Miss Stephanie . . . L . . . Oct 2008
Woods, Miss Danielle . . . M . . . Oct 2009
Clark, Mrs Patricia Jane . . . L . . . Nov 2009
Irving, Miss Gillian (Q.C.)* . . . I . . . Jul 1984
Talbot, Mr Kevin* . . . M . . . Jul 1970

Crawford, Mr Robert; Recorder* . . . L . . . Jul 1976
Hague, Mr Paul* . . . L . . . Jul 1983
Smith, Mr Matthew* . . . L . . . Oct 1991
Shaw, Mrs Nicola* . . . L . . . Oct 1992

RADLETT, Hertfordshire

SHERIDAN CHAMBERS,
KNARESBROOK, KING EDWARD ROAD,
SHENLEY, RADLETT, HERTFORDSHIRE WD7 9BY
Tel: 01923 856345
E-mail: norman.sheridan@gmail.com
Sheridan, Mr Norman . . . M . . . Oct 1990

RICHMOND UPON THAMES, Surrey

Chambers of Richard Henderson Bruce

CHAMBERS OF RICHARD HENDERSON BRUCE,
PO BOX 748, RICHMOND UPON THAMES,
SURREY TW9 2WU
Tel: 020 8940 5895 ***Fax:*** 020 8255 4170
Dx: 100253 RICHMOND 2
Head of Chambers:
Bruce, Mr Richard Henderson; Recorder . . . G . . . Jul 1974

RICHMOND GREEN CHAMBERS,
5 CONNAUGHT ROAD, RICHMOND UPON
THAMES, SURREY TW10 6DW
Tel: 020 8948 4801
E-mail: richmondchambers@btconnect.com
Clerk: Elizabeth Robson Taylor.
Practice Manager: Elizabeth Robson Taylor
Taylor, Mr Phillip Brian MBE* . . . L . . . Nov 1991

ROTHERHAM, South Yorkshire

Chambers of Robert Clive Smith

RCS CHAMBERS,
PENNY HILL, HOLME HILL LANE, STAINTON,
ROTHERHAM, SOUTH YORKSHIRE S66 7RD
Tel: 01709 814147 ***Fax:*** 01709 818793
E-mail: robert@rcschambers.com
Head of Chambers:
Smith, Mr Robert Clive . . . M . . . Jul 1974

ROYSTON, Hertfordshire

CHAMBERS OF MR KEITH PITTS,
TUSSOCKS, THE CAUSEWAY, THERFIELD,
ROYSTON, HERTFORDSHIRE SG8 9PP
Tel: 01763 287760 ***Fax:*** 01763 287434
E-mail: keithpitts@keithpitts.f2s.com
Pitts, Mr Keith . . . M . . . Oct 1997

11

SALFORD, Greater Manchester

A M ROSEMARINE'S INTERNATIONAL LAW CHAMBERS (EUROPEAN HQ),
INTERNATIONAL LAW CHAMBERS, 78
CAVENDISH ROAD, SALFORD, GREATER
MANCHESTER M7 4WA
Tel: 0161 740 3861 ***Fax:*** 0161 740 3861

SEDGEMOOR, Somerset

CHAMBERS OF RICHARD HICKMET,
THE CHANTRY, RHODE, NORTH PETHERTON,
SEDGEMOOR, SOMERSET TA5 2AD
Tel: 01278 663388 ***Fax:*** 01278 663981
Dx: 32131 TAUNTON

SHEFFIELD, South Yorkshire

Chambers of James Stevenson Baird

BANK HOUSE CHAMBERS,
OLD BANK HOUSE, 3 HARTSHEAD, SHEFFIELD,
SOUTH YORKSHIRE S1 2EL
Tel: 0114 275 1223 ***Fax:*** 0114 276 8439
Dx: 10522 SHEFFIELD
E-mail: w.digby@bankhousechambers.co.uk
Web: www.bankhousechambers.co.uk
Clerk: David Harrison; Wayne Digby.
Administrator: Karen Davis
Practice Manager: Wayne Digby
Head of Chambers:
Baird, Mr James Stevenson; Recorder . . . M . . . Nov 1977

Carus, Mr Roderick (Q.C.)* . . . G . . . Nov 1971
Garside, Mr Charles (Q.C.)* . . . G . . . Nov 1971
Clarke, Mr Nicholas (Q.C.)* . . . M . . . Jan 1981
Smith, Mr Shaun M (Q.C.)* . . . G . . . Jul 1981
Cranfield, Mr Tony . . . M . . . Nov 1975
Mason, Mr David John . . . G . . . Jul 1979
Hillis, Mr John . . . G . . . Jul 1982
Syed, Gulzar . . . G . . . Jul 1983
Sheldon, Mr Richard Neil . . . L . . . Jul 1984
Goddard, Ms Katherine Lesley . . . I . . . Nov 1987

Tonge, Mr Christopher ... I ... Jan 1988
O'Shea, Mr Paul Andrew ... I ... Jun 1989
Singh, Gurdial ... L ... Jan 1989
Pimm, Mr Peter J; Recorder ... G ... Apr 1991
Smith, Mr Andrew D MBE; TD ... M ... Oct 1991
Hawkins, Mr David J ... G ... Oct 1991
Walker, Mrs Fiona L ... I ... Feb 1992
Dorrell, Miss Alison G. ... G ... Feb 1992
Upson, Mr Michael James ... L ... Oct 1993
Cole, Miss Justine Amanda ... I ... Nov 1994
Weir, Miss Olivia ... I ... Nov 1995
West, Mr Ian Herbert ... M ... Nov 1996
Gould, Mr James ... G ... Jan 1997
Cane-Soothill, Mr Michael ... L ... Jan 1997
Webster, Mr David ... M ... Jan 1998
Alam, Miss Zaiban ... G ... Jan 1998
Cotton, Ms Heidi E ... L ... Jan 1998
Wrottesley, Miss Angela ... I ... Jan 1999
Sandford, Mr Robert ... M ... Jan 1999
Clark, Mr Robert ... M ... Jan 2002
Pallo, Mr Simon ... G ... Jan 2003
Jones, Mr Kevin ... M ... Jan 2003
Horne, Mr James ... M ... Jan 2004
Stanbury, Mrs Louise ... L ... Jan 2004
Huggins, Mrs Bianca ... G ... Jul 2004
Bhatty, Farah ... L ... Jan 2005
Morley, Miss Kate ... L ... Jan 2006
Wheatley, Ms Jane ... G ... Jan 2007
Dodgson, Mr Lance ... M ... Jan 2007
Chu, Miss Josephine ... L ... Oct 2007
Horne, Mr David ... G ... Jul 2009
Holsgrove, Mr Jonathan ... G ... Jan 2011

Chambers of Francis Paul Watson QC

PARADISE CHAMBERS,
26 PARADISE SQUARE, SHEFFIELD, SOUTH YORKSHIRE S1 2DE
Tel: 0114 273 8951 ***Fax:*** 0114 276 0848
Dx: 10565 SHEFFIELD
E-mail: clerks@paradisechambers.co.uk
Clerk: Senior: Andrew Timothy Booth.
Head of Chambers:
Watson, Mr Francis Paul (Q.C.) ... G ... Nov 1978

Lowe, Mr William (Q.C.) ... I ... Jul 1972
Brown, Mr Stuart C (Q.C.)* ... I ... Jul 1974
Phillips, Mr William Bernard ... I ... Jul 1970
Neale, Mr Nicholas L ... G ... Jul 1972
Slater, Mr Michael N ... I ... Jul 1983
Wright, Miss Sarah ... G ... Oct 1984
O'Brien, Mr Joseph P A P ... I ... Nov 1989
Jackson, Mr Adrian ... I ... Oct 1990
Groom, Mr Ian ... M ... Nov 1990
Rosario, Mr Desmond D L ... I ... Nov 1990
Edwards, Miss Ann Mererid ... G ... Sep 1991
Hughes, Mr Dermot Francis ... G ... Nov 1993
Savage, Mr Timothy ... I ... Nov 1991
Harrison, Miss Rachel ... I ... Nov 1993
Nijabat, Sharma B ... M ... Nov 1993
Newton, Mr Stuart R J ... M ... Nov 1993
Ford, Miss Caroline E. ... G ... Oct 1993
Rhys, Miss Megan J ... I ... Nov 1994
Lowe, Mr Craig ... I ... Oct 1994
Robinson, Miss Sara J ... I ... Nov 1994
Stables, Mr Gordon ... L ... Oct 1995
Kelly, Miss Siobhan ... G ... Oct 1995
Goldsack, Mr Ian ... G ... May 1997
Bailey, Mr Andrew ... L ... Oct 1997
Stanistreet, Miss Penelope ... L ... Oct 1993
Lord, Mr Andrew ... G ... Oct 1999
Rawlinson, Mr Michael John ... I ... Jan 2002
Quinney, Miss Nicola T ... G ... Jan 2001
Marshall, Miss Laura J ... M ... Jul 2001
Thyne, Mr Richard M ... L ... Jan 2002
Hickinbottom, Miss Abigail ... I ... Nov 2004
Hayes, Mrs Kathryn E ... M ... Jan 2000
Erlen, Miss Nicole G ... I ... Jan 2007
Pemberton, Miss Jessica L ... I ... Jan 2007
Rook, Miss Rachel ... L ... Jan 2006
Bower, Miss Laurinda ... L ... Jan 2006
Garcha, Mr Sukdev ... M ... Jan 2008
Bellamy, Mr Jonathan C ... I ... Jan 2008

SHEPPERTON, Surrey

Chambers of Arthur Ronald Alfred James

ABBEY CHAMBERS,
PO BOX 47, SHEPPERTON, SURREY TW17 0LD
Tel: 01932 560913 ***Fax:*** 01932 567764
E-mail: arthurjames27@btinternet.co.uk
Administrator: Ann James
Head of Chambers:
James, Mr Arthur Ronald Alfred ... M ... Nov 1975

Aslangul, Mr Michel L J* ... M ... Nov 1978
Pandey, Mr Reuben* ... L ... Jan 1996
Brooke, Mr Johan* ... L ... Jan 1997
Burdis-Smith, Mr Alan* ... I ... Jan 1998
Carolan, Ms Candia* ... M ... Jan 1999
Hay, Mrs Georgia S* ... I ... Oct 1999
Taylor, Mr Phillip MBE* ... L ... Jan 2001

SLOUGH

Chambers of Ardhendu Bhattacharya

SLOUGH BARRISTERS CHAMBER,
11 ST BERNARDS ROAD, SLOUGH SL3 7NT
Tel: 01753 553806 / 817989 ***Fax:*** 01753 553806
E-mail: arden@cp-computers.com
Clerk: S P Chadha.
Head of Chambers:
Bhattacharya, Mr Ardhendu ... I ... Nov 1974

SOLIHULL, West Midlands

AVON CHAMBERS,
72 WYCHWOOD AVENUE, KNOWLE, SOLIHULL, WEST MIDLANDS B93 9DQ
Tel: 01564 775959 ***Fax:*** 01564 774484

SOUTHAMPTON

Chambers of Martin J Blount

EIGHTEEN CARLTON CRESCENT,
18 CARLTON CRESCENT, SOUTHAMPTON SO15 2ET
Tel: 023 8063 9001 ***Fax:*** 023 8033 9625
Dx: 96877 SOUTHAMPTON 10

Chambers of Robin Belben

COLLEGE CHAMBERS,
19 CARLTON CRESCENT, SOUTHAMPTON SO15 2ET
Est: 1989
Tel: 023 8023 0338 ***Fax:*** 023 8023 0376
Dx: 38533 SOUTHAMPTON 3
E-mail: clerks@college-chambers.co.uk
Clerk: Senior: Wayne Effeny. First Junior: Mark Windebank; Junior Clerks: Natalie Alani; Sophie Lanzoni; Sofala Stokes.
Administrator: Claire Evans
Head of Chambers:
Belben, Mr Robin; Recorder ... L ... Nov 1969

Marshall, Mr Derek ... I ... Jun 1980
Taylor, Mr Douglas; Deputy District Judge/Judge of Mental Health Tribunal ... M ... Jan 1981
Lillington, Mr Simon ... M ... Nov 1980
Hand, Mr Anthony ... L ... Jul 1989
Self, Mr Gary; Part-time Employment Judge ... L ... Oct 1991
Nother, Mr Daniel ... I ... Nov 1994
Davies, Miss Carol E ... M ... Oct 1995
Bath, Miss Baljinder ... L ... Oct 1996
Cotton, Mr Stephen David ... L ... Mar 1998
Gillett, Miss Amanda Josephine ... G ... Oct 1998
Ballingall, Ms Joanne ... I ... Nov 1999
McGhee, Mr Stuart ... L ... Mar 2000
Harvey, Miss Louise ... M ... Jul 2000
Skinner, Mr Andrew ... L ... Jul 2000
Newport, Mr Ian ... G ... Oct 2000
Nickless, Mr Jason ... G ... Oct 2001
Josty, Mr David ... G ... Jul 2002
Rudd, Miss Zoe ... G ... Jul 2003
Gough, Mrs Sian ... G ... Nov 2003
Gayford, Ms Justine ... M ... Oct 2005
Henstock-Turner, Ms Sarah ... M ... Oct 2004
Bower, Ms Gemma ... M ... Jul 2006
Harby, Mr David ... M ... Jul 2006
Carroll, Mr Grant ... M ... Jul 2005
Grasso, Ms Antonietta ... M ... Nov 2004
Curtis, Mr Matthew ... M ... Jul 2006
Langrish, Mr Adam ... I ... Jul 2006
Davidson, Ms Sally ... I ... Jul 2006
Hughes, Mr Jason ... I ... Jul 2009
Pugh, Mr David ... M ... Oct 2008

Chambers of Nicholas S Haggan QC

12 COLLEGE PLACE,
FAUVELLE BUILDINGS, SOUTHAMPTON SO15 2FE
Tel: 023 8032 0320 ***Fax:*** 023 8032 0321
Dx: 96875 SOUTHAMPTON 10
E-mail: clerks@12cp.co.uk
Clerk: Mark Harrison; Lucy Darby; Hollie Grubb; Ashley Goddard; Chloe Phillips (Marketing).
Administrator: Rosemary Tilt
Practice Manager: Mark Harrison
Head of Chambers:
Haggan, Mr Nicholas S (Q.C.); Recorder ... M ... Jul 1977

Webster, Mr William H ... M ... Jul 1975
Towler, Mr Peter J H; Recorder ... M ... Jul 1974
Merry, Mr Hugh G ... I ... Jul 1979
Spink, Mr Peter John William ... G ... Jul 1979
Gibney, Mr Malcom T P; Recorder ... I ... Jul 1981
Pine-Coffin, Miss Margaret A ... I ... Jul 1981
Glen, Mr Philip A; Deputy District Judge ... M ... Jul 1983
Forster, Mr Michael W ... G ... Feb 1984
Compton, Timothy ... I ... Nov 1984
Grant, Mr Gary A ... M ... Nov 1985
Morgan, Mr Dylan R ... G ... Jul 1986
Moores, Mr Timothy K ... L ... Jul 1987
Doughty, Mr Peter ... L ... Jul 1988
Griffiths, Mr Robert Norton ... M ... May 1988
Holland, Mrs Roberta ... L ... Nov 1989
Malik, Mr Omar L ... I ... Nov 1990
Blain, Mr Roderick ... M ... Oct 1991
Ward, Mr Trevor ... M ... Apr 1991
Habel, Mrs Jessica Jennet ... M ... Jul 1991
Burrett, Mrs Catherine ... M ... Oct 1992
Tucker, Mr Nicholas J ... I ... Oct 1993
Savill, Mr Peter John ... I ... Nov 1995
Burns, Mr Jeremy Stuart; Deputy Employment Judge ... L ... Nov 1996
Norie-Miller, Mr Jeffery ... I ... Jul 1996
Harrison, Dr Graeme ... I ... Jan 1997
Aspinall-Miles, Mrs Mary ... L ... Nov 1999
Kelly, Mrs Amy Louise ... M ... Nov 2000
Stemp, Mr Scott ... I ... Oct 2000
Elton, Mr Edward ... G ... Jan 2000
Crorie, Mr Ethu ... M ... Aug 2000
Lees, Miss Charlotte ... L ... Nov 2001
Agnihotri, Mr Naveen ... G ... Jul 2001
Hennessey, Miss Tracey ... L ... Jul 2001
Chaloner, Mr Mark ... M ... Jul 2002
Kinloch-Jones, Miss Caroline ... L ... Nov 2002
Keniston, Miss Zosia ... L ... Jul 2004
Mittell, Miss Jodie ... L ... Jul 2004
Rebane, Ms Lena Marie ... L ... Mar 2006
Southern, Miss Emma Catherine ... L ... Jan 2006
Kirk, Mr Thomas ... L ... Jul 2007
Wilmshurst, Mr Paul ... M ... Jan 2007
Milne, Mr Duncan ... L ... Oct 2007

Chambers of Peter Renfree

HARBOUR COURT CHAMBERS,
140 WARSASH ROAD, WARSASH, SOUTHAMPTON SO31 9JD
Tel: 01489 557999 ***Fax:*** 023 8000 1809
Dx: 45255 PARK GATE
E-mail: peter_renfree@harbourcourt.co.uk
Clerk: Mandy Young.
Head of Chambers:
Renfree, Mr Peter ... M ... Jan 1992

ST ALBANS, Hertfordshire

LAUREL CHAMBERS,
1 LAUREL EDGE, AVENUE ROAD, ST ALBANS, HERTFORDSHIRE AL1 3NZ
Tel: 01727 830704 ***Fax:*** 01727 830704

ST ALBANS CHAMBERS,
2-4 ST PETER'S STREET, ST ALBANS, HERTFORDSHIRE AL1 3LF
Tel: 01727 843383 ***Fax:*** 01727 842820
Dx: 6116 ST ALBANS
E-mail: clerks@stalbanschambers.com
Administrator: Andrea Loveless
Practice Manager: Alex Carter-Gaunt
Reeves-Croft, Mr Christopher ... M ... Nov 1992
Stanton, Miss Lisa ... I ... Oct 1993
Carvahlo-Gomes, Ms Ana ... M ... Jan 1996
Rasul, Ms Lubna ... M ... Jan 1997
Harris, Mr David ... L ... Jan 1997
Nall-Cain, Mr Richard ... I ... Jan 1997
George, Miss Eve ... I ... Oct 1997
Wigley, Miss Rachel ... G ... Nov 1997
Hadgill, Mr Clinton ... M ... Jan 1998
Ricks, Mr Richard ... L ... Oct 1999
McCombie, Mr Fergus ... G ... Oct 1999
Darlington-Pearce, Ms Susan ... L ... Nov 1999
Khan, Mr Imran ... L ... Nov 2001
Krishnan, Ms Davina ... L ... Jul 2004
Redmond, Mr David ... M ... Oct 2006
Snook, Mr Harry ... I ... Nov 2006

SUDBURY, Suffolk

Chambers of Susan Aileen Gratwicke

LAVENHAM CHAMBERS,
ROOKERY FARM, NEAR LAVENHAM, SUDBURY, SUFFOLK CO10 0BJ
Tel: 01787 248247 ***Fax:*** 01787 247846
Dx: 41311 SUDBURY
E-mail: susangratwicke@yahoo.co.uk
Head of Chambers:
Gratwicke, Miss Susan Aileen ... G ... Nov 1976

SUTTON, Surrey

61 ELM GROVE,
SUTTON, SURREY SM1 4EX
Tel: 020 8643 9714 ***Fax:*** 020 8643 9714
Dsane, Miss Victoria T ... M ... Nov 1971

SWANSEA

Chambers of Geraint W Walters

ANGEL CHAMBERS,
ETHOS BUILDING, KINGS ROAD, SWANSEA SA1 8AS
Tel: 01792 464623 ***Fax:*** 01792 648501
Dx: 743460 SWANSEA 21
E-mail: clerks@angelchambers.co.uk
Clerk: Michael Dean; Clare Dollard; Jennifer Davies; Michael Carey; Robin Whinnett.
Administrator: Jamie Dun
Head of Chambers:
Walters, Mr Geraint W; Recorder ... G ... Nov 1981

Davis, Mr Jim; Deputy District Judge (MC) ... G ... Jul 1997
Clee, Mr Christopher (Q.C.); Recorder ... G ... Jul 1983
Rees, Mr Ieuan ... G ... Nov 1982
Campbell, Susan (Q.C.) ... M ... Nov 1996
Clemes, Mr Andrew ... G ... Nov 1984
Donovan, Ms Alison ... M ... Nov 1987
Wood, Miss Joanna ... I ... Nov 1989
Harris-Jenkins, Mr Philip; Recorder ... G ... Nov 1990
Boothroyd, Mr Dominic ... I ... Nov 2010
Blake, Mr David ... L ... Feb 1992
Thomas, Mr Dyfed L L ... M ... Oct 1992
Harris, Ms Elizabeth ... I ... Feb 1992
Pulling, Mr Dean ... M ... Nov 1993
James, Ms Sharon Ann Sarah ... G ... Oct 1995
Rees, Mr Matthew ... G ... Oct 1996
James, Mr Christopher ... G ... Nov 1977
Chinnock, Mrs Christina Frances ... M ... Nov 1998
Jenkins, Susan ... G ... Oct 1998
Jones, Mr Rhys ... G ... Nov 1998
Richards, Mr Cennydd ... G ... Oct 1999
Khan, Ms Sabina ... M ... Feb 1999
Gedrych, Miss Janet ... G ... Oct 2000
Steer, Mr Richard ... G ... Jan 2001
Owen, Miss Glenda Caroline ... G ... Jul 2002
Monaghan, Mr Mark ... L ... Oct 2002
Leader, Miss Lucy ... L ... Oct 2002
Hughes, Miss Anna Carina ... M ... Oct 2003
Pratt, Mr Jake ... L ... Oct 2004
Templeman, Miss Clare ... I ... Nov 2004
Stephenson, Mr Simon ... I ... Jul 2005
Leavesley, Miss Laura Mariel ... I ... Jul 2005
Smith, Miss Kate ... G ... Jan 2008
Dewi, Miss Cadi ... G ... Jan 2008

Chambers of Elwen Mair Evans QC and Paul Huw Thomas QC

ISCOED CHAMBERS,
86 ST HELENS ROAD, SWANSEA SA1 4BQ
Tel: 01792 652988 ***Fax:*** 01792 458089
Dx: 39554 SWANSEA
E-mail: clerks@iscoedchambers.co.uk
Clerk: Jeff Evans; Julie Snary; Donna Williams.
Chambers Director: Avril Llewellyn
Head of Chambers:
Evans, Miss Elwen Mair (Q.C.) . . . G . . . Jul 1980
Thomas, Mr Paul Huw (Q.C.) . . . G . . . Jul 1979

Rouch, Mr Peter Christopher (Q.C.); Recorder* . . . G . . . Jul 1972
Phillips, Mr Frank . . . L . . . Nov 1972
Griffiths, Mr Patrick . . . G . . . Nov 1972
Riordan, Mr Kevin . . . G . . . Nov 1972
Jenkins, Mr James John . . . G . . . Nov 1974
Marshall, Mr Philip Derek . . . M . . . Nov 1975
Rees, Mr Stephen Robert Tristram . . . G . . . Nov 1979
Craven, Mr Robert Michael . . . G . . . Nov 1979
Jones, Mr Francis . . . I . . . Jul 1980
Sandbrook-Hughes, Mr Stewert . . . L . . . Nov 1980
Roblin, Laraine A . . . L . . . Jul 1981
Rees, Mr Owen Huw . . . G . . . Jul 1983
Spackman, Mr Mark A . . . L . . . Nov 1986
Hipkin, Mr John Leslie . . . G . . . Nov 1989
Harris, Mr David A . . . G . . . Oct 1990
Pulling, Mr Dean . . . M . . . Nov 1993
Wright, Mr Ian Bernard . . . M . . . Nov 1994
Davies, Mr Iwan Rhun . . . G . . . Feb 1995
Marshall, Mrs Elizabeth Suzanne . . . I . . . Oct 1995
Rouch, Mr Robin . . . G . . . Nov 1999
Richards, Ms Catherine . . . L . . . Nov 2000
Anthony, Mrs Rachel Jane . . . M . . . Nov 2000
Collins, Mrs Catherine . . . M . . . Nov 2000
Ashworth, Miss Phillipa . . . G . . . Dec 2000
Rowlands, Miss Sara . . . G . . . Jan 2001
Hobson, Mr Paul . . . G . . . Jul 2001
Jones, Mr Craig . . . I . . . Nov 2003
Gill, Mr Ned . . . M . . . Jul 2004
Blakemore, Mr Benjamin . . . G . . . Jul 2004
Flynn, Mr Steven . . . G . . . Jan 2006
Preece, Miss Nicola . . . G . . . Jan 2006

Chambers of Sara Rudman

PENDRAGON CHAMBERS,
111 WALTER ROAD, SWANSEA SA1 5QQ
Tel: 01792 411188 ***Fax:*** 01792 411189
Dx: 39572 SWANSEA
E-mail: clerks@pendragonchambers.com
Clerk: Senior: Nolan Goodman. Ann Patron.
Practice Manager: Martin Bowen
Head of Chambers:
Rudman, Ms Sara . . . I . . . Nov 1992

Griffiths, Mr Richard Stephen . . . G . . . Nov 1983
Frith, Miss Heather Vivien . . . M . . . Jul 1989
Brooks, Mr John Dylan; Fee Paid Judge First Tier Tax Chamber . . . G . . . Feb 1990
Mann, Miss Rebecca . . . G . . . Jan 1995
Hill, Mr Jonathan . . . M . . . Oct 1997
Thompson, Mr Philip Nigel . . . G . . . Jul 2000
Hale, Miss Rachel Paula* . . . L . . . Mar 2003
Sykes, Caroline Jayne . . . G . . . Jan 2004
Sefton, Mr Nicholas Edward* . . . G . . . Jul 2004
David, Mr Alastair Robert Oulpe* . . . G . . . Jul 2005
Indulska, Naomi Lydia . . . G . . . Jan 2006

RIVER CHAMBERS,
34 CLOS YR HESG, SWANSEA SA7 0NA
Tel: 07833 766055
E-mail: nick@riverchambers.com

Chambers of Julie Ann Vallack

ST DAVID'S CHAMBERS,
10 CALVERT TERRACE, SWANSEA SA1 6AR
Tel: 01792 644466 ***Fax:*** 01792 644321
Dx: 52956 SWANSEA
Head of Chambers:
Vallack, Miss Julie Ann . . . G . . . Oct 1993

Folland, Mr David; Justices Clerk . . . L . . . Jan 1976
Lloyd, Mr David G B . . . G . . . Jan 1998

SWINDON

Chambers of Oba E Nsugbe QC

PUMP COURT CHAMBERS,
5 TEMPLE CHAMBERS, TEMPLE STREET, SWINDON SN1 1SQ
Tel: 01793 539899 ***Fax:*** 0845 259 3242
Dx: 38639 SWINDON 2
E-mail: clerks@3pumpcourt.com
Web: www.3pumpcourt.com
Clerk: David Barber; Holly Bell.
Administrator: Andrea Cheshire
Head of Chambers:
Nsugbe, Mr Oba E (Q.C.); Recorder . . . G . . . Jul 1985

Pascoe, Mr Nigel (Q.C.); Recorder . . . I . . . Jul 1966
Donne, Mr Anthony M (Q.C.) . . . M . . . Apr 1973
Campbell, Miss Susan Claire (Q.C.) . . . M . . . Nov 1986
Hill, Mr Mark (Q.C.); Recorder . . . M . . . Jul 1987
Samuels, Ms Leslie (Q.C.); Deputy District Judge . . . G . . . Jul 1989
Patterson, Mr Stewart; Recorder . . . M . . . Nov 1967
Pearson, Mr Thomas Adam Spencer . . . M . . . Nov 1969
Harrap, Mr Giles Thresher; Recorder . . . I . . . Nov 1971
Abbott, Mr Frank; Recorder . . . L . . . Nov 1972
Parry, Mr Charles . . . M . . . Nov 1973
Ker-Reid, Mr John . . . I . . . Nov 1974
Butt, Mr Michael . . . M . . . Nov 1974
Gabb, Mr Charles H . . . M . . . Feb 1975
Mackenzie, Miss Julie . . . L . . . Nov 1978
Jones, Mr Stephen . . . I . . . Nov 1978
Allardice, Miss Miranda . . . L . . . Jul 1982
Blount, Mr Martin J . . . G . . . Nov 1982
Scott, Mr Matthew . . . I . . . Nov 1985
Bloom-Davis, Mr Desmond; Deputy District Judge . . . I . . . Jul 1986
Travers, Mr Hugh; Employment Tribunal Chairman . . . M . . . Nov 1988
Gau, Mr Justin . . . M . . . Jul 1989
Wicks, Mr David . . . M . . . Jul 1989
Boydell, Mr Edward Patrick Stirrup; Recorder . . . M . . . Nov 1989
Houston, Mr Andrew . . . I . . . Nov 1989
Breslin, Miss Catherine . . . I . . . Jan 1990
Khan, Miss Helen M G . . . M . . . Nov 1990
Lorenzo, Ms Claudia . . . I . . . Apr 1991
Howe, Miss Penny . . . I . . . Nov 1991
Kelly, Mr Geoffrey . . . M . . . Feb 1992
Newton-Price, Mr James . . . M . . . Oct 1992
Ruffell, Mr Mark . . . M . . . Nov 1992
Tregilgas-Davey, Mr Marcus . . . G . . . Feb 1993
Morton, Mr Gary . . . G . . . May 1993
Russell, Ms Alison . . . M . . . Oct 1993
Peirson, Mr Oliver . . . L . . . Oct 1993
Gunther, Miss Elizabeth . . . L . . . Oct 1993
Ashley, Mr Mark R E . . . L . . . Nov 1993
Smith, Miss Leonorah . . . I . . . Nov 1993
Moore, Mr Roderick A . . . I . . . Nov 1993
Pawson, Mr Robert Edward . . . I . . . Nov 1994
Hall, Mr Richard Andrew . . . I . . . Nov 1995
Hall, Mr Michael Richard . . . I . . . Oct 1996
Asteris, Mr Peter . . . L . . . Jun 1996
Dubbery, Mr Mark . . . M . . . Oct 1996
Jones, Miss Sarah . . . L . . . Nov 1996
Ephgrave, Ms Amy . . . G . . . Oct 1997
Arlow, Ms Ruth . . . I . . . Oct 1997
Grime, Mr Andrew . . . L . . . Oct 1997
Ward, Ms Anne . . . G . . . Nov 1997
Gallagher, Miss Maria . . . I . . . Nov 1997
Allan, Ms Kirsten . . . M . . . Jul 1998
Keen, Mr Spencer . . . M . . . Jan 1998
Dracass, Mr Timothy . . . I . . . Oct 1998
Bond, Mr Andrew . . . I . . . Jan 1999
De Rozarieux, Ms Louise . . . L . . . Oct 1999
Spearing, Miss Rachel M . . . I . . . Nov 1999
Tutt, Mr Richard . . . M . . . Jul 2000
Brown, Miss Anne . . . M . . . Jul 2000
Ramadhan, Miss Lubeya . . . M . . . Jul 2000
Islam, Miss Naznin . . . G . . . Oct 2000
Hartley, Miss Caroline . . . M . . . Aug 2002
Burge, Miss Alison Jayne . . . G . . . Jul 2002
Platt, Miss Heather . . . L . . . Oct 2002
Shravat, Mr Neelo . . . M . . . Nov 2002
Chapman, Mr John . . . L . . . Jul 2003
Street, Miss Charlotte . . . G . . . Jul 2003
Davis, Miss Lucy . . . G . . . Nov 2003
Berry, Miss Amy . . . L . . . Jan 2003
Gadd, Mr Adam . . . G . . . Jan 2004
Leach, Mr Stuart . . . G . . . Jun 2004
Trotter, Miss Helen . . . G . . . Oct 2004
Lyons, Miss Tara . . . M . . . Oct 2005
Troup, Miss Rachel . . . L . . . Nov 2005
Long, Mr Benjamin . . . M . . . Jan 2006
Iten, Miss Corinne . . . I . . . Oct 2006
O'Driscoll, Ms Patricia . . . G . . . Oct 2006
Lee, Ms Jennifer . . . L . . . Jan 2007
Gilbert, Daniella . . . I . . . Mar 2007
Connors, Hannah . . . I . . . Jan 2008
Bruce, Ms Eleanor . . . M . . . Jan 2008
Purkis, Mr Simon . . . I . . . Oct 2008
Williamson, Nicholas . . . M . . . Mar 2009
Birt, Mr Robin . . . M . . . Oct 2009
Cohen, Mr Jonathan (Q.C.)* . . . L . . . Jul 1974
Bradley, Mrs Sally (Q.C.)* . . . L . . . Nov 1978
Fielding, Mr Stephen* . . . I . . . Jan 1974

Specialist teams cover a wide range of Common Law and Criminal work, including Family & Matrimonial; Employment; Environment; Inheritance; Landlord & Tenant; Personal Injury; Customs & Excise; Serious Fraud; Extradition; Ecclesiastical; Professional & Medical Negligence; Courts Martial.

TAUNTON, Somerset

CLERKSROOM - ADMINISTRATION CENTRE,
EQUITY HOUSE, BLACKBROOK PARK AVENUE, TAUNTON, SOMERSET TA1 2PX
Tel: 0845 083 3000 ***Fax:*** 0845 083 3001
Dx: 97188 TAUNTON BLACKBROOK
E-mail: mail@clerksroom.com
Clerk: Senior: Gregory Speller. Juniors: Jenny Richards; Sophie Brightman.
Administrator: Hazel Altria
Practice Manager: Stephen Ward (Managing Director)
Chambers Director: Martin Davies
Bueno, Antonio (Q.C.) . . . M . . . Jun 1964
de Wilde, Robin (Q.C.) . . . I . . . Jan 1971
Powers, Dr Michael J (Q.C.) . . . L . . . Jul 1979
Dumbill, Eric Alexander . . . G . . . Nov 1971
Havenhand, Barry . . . M . . . Oct 1976
Robinson, Ali . . . L . . . Jul 1978
Infield, Paul . . . I . . . Jul 1980
Dixon, Ralph . . . M . . . Nov 1980
Dugdale, Nicholas . . . M . . . Feb 1982
Mott, Geoffrey Edward . . . G . . . Jul 1982
Hodgkin, Harry John . . . G . . . Jul 1983
Tompkinson, Deborah A . . . M . . . Nov 1984
Coulter, Barry . . . I . . . Nov 1985
Heap, Gerard . . . G . . . Jan 1985
Preston, Nicholas . . . G . . . Jul 1986
Dingle, Jonathan . . . M . . . Jul 1986
Dable, Jeremy . . . G . . . Nov 1987
Austins, Christopher . . . G . . . Jul 1988
Hinds, Oriel G . . . I . . . Jul 1988
Davey, Charles . . . M . . . Feb 1989
Killen, Geoffrey . . . I . . . Oct 1990
Trevis, Robert . . . I . . . Apr 1990
Da Costa, Elissa . . . M . . . Oct 1990
Taurah, Sheila . . . L . . . Oct 1991
Hodgkin, Rebecca . . . L . . . Nov 1991
Becker, Timothy . . . M . . . Jul 1992
Leader, Mr Timothy James . . . M . . . Oct 1994
Darroch, Fiona . . . I . . . Oct 1994
McHugh, David . . . L . . . Oct 1994
Villarosa, Tina . . . M . . . Jul 1995
Last, Peter . . . L . . . Oct 1995
ffitch, Nigel . . . G . . . Oct 1996
Parkinson, William H . . . L . . . Oct 1997
Simpson, Ian . . . L . . . Oct 1997
Small, Arlene Ann-Marie . . . M . . . Oct 1997
Sajid, Ahmer . . . L . . . Nov 1998
James, Winston . . . M . . . Oct 1999
Barnes, Andrea . . . L . . . Nov 1999
Bennett, Jane . . . M . . . Jan 2000
Cawsey, Barry . . . I . . . Jul 2001
Mainwaring, Henry . . . L . . . Jan 2001
Skeate, Ian . . . L . . . Jan 2002
Barham, Mr Jonathan . . . L . . . Jan 2002
Fanneran, Michelle . . . G . . . Jul 2003
McNair, Duncan . . . M . . . Jul 2003
Quinn, Michelle . . . I . . . Jan 2005
Hodder, Philip . . . L . . . Mar 2005
Rahman, Zia . . . L . . . Jan 2006
Jones, Philip Walter . . . G . . . Jan 2007
Pangraz, Theo . . . M . . . Jan 2007
Cutler, Mr Anthony . . . G . . . Jan 2007
Dales, Mr Colin . . . L . . . Jan 2007
Sallar, Tara . . . M . . . Jan 2007
Goodhead, Mr Thomas . . . L . . . Jan 2010
Turner, Andrew . . . L . . . Nov 2010
Leckie, James Harry Laird* . . . G . . . Jan 1964
Harris, Mr Peter* . . . M . . . Jul 1980
Howard, Mr Graham* . . . L . . . Nov 1987
Millin, Ms Leslie M* . . . G . . . Nov 1988
Saunders, Mr Nicholas Joseph* . . . M . . . Jul 1989
Smithers, Dr Roger Howard* . . . I . . . Nov 1990
Allerhand, Mr Ludwik* . . . I . . . Nov 2001
Wacek, Kim Marie* . . . M . . . Jan 2003
Stenning, Mr James* . . . L . . . Jan 2006
Whittock, Mr Robert* . . . L . . . Oct 2006

Chambers of Rebecca Bradberry

OCTAGON CHAMBERS,
29 PARK STREET, TAUNTON, SOMERSET TA1 4DG
Tel: 01823 331919 ***Fax:*** 01823 330553
Dx: 32146 TAUNTON
E-mail: clerks@octagonchambers.co.uk
Clerk: Joanna Cload.
Head of Chambers:
Bradberry, Ms Rebecca . . . L . . . Oct 1996

Askham, Mr Nigel H . . . I . . . Feb 1973
McVay, Ms Bridget . . . I . . . Feb 1990
Wilcox, Mr Lawrence . . . L . . . Sep 1996
Mason, Mr Patrick . . . L . . . Oct 1997
Ahuja, Mr Harry . . . L . . . Oct 2001
Martin, Mrs Emma . . . L . . . Jan 2002
Perry, Mr Derek . . . G . . . Jan 2006
Smith, Mr Richard (Q.C.)* . . . M . . . Jul 1986

Work Description: Crime (prosecution and defence, all levels), Court Martial defence specialists. Personal Injury. Small Claims. Family. Tribunals, Enquiries and Immigration.

11

TENBY, Pembrokeshire

Chambers of Davina Gammon

STONES THROW,
JAMESON, TENBY, PEMBROKESHIRE SA70 8QD
Tel: 01834 870174 ***Fax:*** 01834 870174
Head of Chambers:
Gammon, Mrs Davina; Head of Chambers* . . . M . . . Jul 1979

THORNTON CLEVELEYS, Lancashire

Chambers of Roy A Burgess

2 SOUTH AVENUE,
THORNTON CLEVELEYS, LANCASHIRE FY5 1JY
Tel: 01253 825463
Clerk: Roy A Burgess.
Head of Chambers:
Burgess, Mr Roy A . . . L . . . Nov 1970

TILEHURST, Reading

BROOKSBY CHAMBERS,
88 BROOKSBY ROAD, TILEHURST, READING
RG13 6LY
Tel: 0118 962 5832

TRURO, Cornwall

Chambers of Gina Small and Colin Elliott

KING'S BENCH GODOLPHIN CHAMBERS,
23 FRANCES STREET, TRURO, CORNWALL
TR1 3DP
Tel: 0845 308 1551 ***Fax:*** 01872 271920
Dx: 81233 TRURO
E-mail: clerks@kbgchambers.co.uk
Clerk: Senior: Colin Palmer. Beverley Williams; Lizzie Jenkinson; Jamie Kyte; Anthony Chapman; Yvonne Simmons.
Administrator: Sally Finan
Head of Chambers:
Small, Miss Gina . . . . L . . . . Oct 1991
Elliott, Mr Colin . . . . G . . . . Jul 1987

Meredith, Mr George . . . . G . . . . Jul 1969
Maitland, Mr Andrew H R . . . . L . . . . Jul 1970
Guy, Mr Richard Perran . . . . I . . . . Nov 1970
Sellick, Mr Llewelyn . . . . M . . . . Jul 1973
Lyon, Mrs Shane . . . . M . . . . Nov 1976
Wallace, Miss Ann . . . . I . . . . Jul 1979
Wilson, Miss Jennifer Mary Pentreath . . . . G . . . . Jul 1979
Down, Miss Susan . . . . M . . . . Nov 1984
Crozier, Rawdon R C . . . . M . . . . Nov 1984
Beechey, Miss Hilary . . . . M . . . . Nov 1987
Lewin, Mr Nicholas . . . . G . . . . Jul 1989
Peers, Miss Heather . . . . G . . . . Oct 1991
Antell, Mr John Jason . . . . M . . . . Oct 1992
MacKean, Miss Sarah . . . . I . . . . Nov 1992
Rafati, Mr Ali . . . . G . . . . Nov 1993
Pullen, Mr Timothy . . . . G . . . . Nov 1993
Clarke, Mr Malcolm . . . . G . . . . Oct 1994
Holland, Mrs Annie . . . . M . . . . Nov 1994
Richards, Dr Jonathan Nicholas . . . . M . . . . Nov 1995
Mathews, Mr Deni . . . . G . . . . Jul 1996
Willetts, Mr Andrew . . . . M . . . . Jan 1997
Birt, Miss Emma . . . . I . . . . Oct 2000
Bosanko, Mr Jonathan . . . . M . . . . Jul 2001
Hall, Mr Nigel . . . . I . . . . Jul 2001
Sutherland, Miss Yvonne . . . . I . . . . Jul 2001
Higginson, Mr William . . . . L . . . . Oct 2001
Appleby, Miss Claire . . . . L . . . . Oct 2002
Rawlings, Carrie-Ann . . . . I . . . . Oct 2005
Kumeta, Miss Jennifer . . . . M . . . . Oct 2005
Pearce, Miss Emma . . . . L . . . . Jul 2006
Challacombe, Mr Thomas . . . . G . . . . Jul 2006
Rose, Mr Will . . . . I . . . . Jul 2007
Dyson, Mr Daniel Bryn William . . . . G . . . . Nov 2007
Donne, Mr Anthony M (Q.C.)* . . . . M . . . . Apr 1973
Vere-Hodge, Mr Michael (Q.C.)* . . . . G . . . . Nov 1970
Jones, Mr Stewart E (Q.C.)* . . . . G . . . . Nov 1972
Wright, Mr Jeremy J* . . . . I . . . . Jul 1970
Climie, Mr Stephen* . . . . L . . . . Jul 1982

WARRINGTON

Chambers of Jonathan Daniel Rule

PALMYRA CHAMBERS,
1ST FLOOR, ROYAL HOUSE, 46 LEGH STREET,
WARRINGTON WA1 1UJ
Tel: 01925 444919 ***Fax:*** 01925 444949
Dx: 17774 WARRINGTON
E-mail: clerk@palmyrachambers.com
Clerk: Senior: Mike Jones.
Head of Chambers:
Rule, Mr Jonathan Daniel . . . . G . . . . Oct 1993

WEMBLEY, Middlesex

CHAMBERS OF ZAHUR-UD-DIN BUTT,
54 NATHANS ROAD, WEMBLEY, MIDDLESEX
HA0 3RX
Tel: 020 8904 7357

CHAMBERS OF SHAUN A WALLACE,
124 MONKS PARK, WEMBLEY, MIDDLESEX
HA9 6JH
Tel: 020 8903 2360

WIDNES, Cheshire

Chambers of Joseph Gerard Lawler

CHAMBERS OF J G LAWLER,
9 MEADWAY, HOUGH GREEN, WIDNES,
CHESHIRE WA8 8XT
Tel: 0151 424 3246 ***Fax:*** 0151 495 3806
E-mail: j.g.lawler@btinternet.com
Head of Chambers:
Lawler, Mr Joseph Gerard . . . . M . . . . Nov 1978

WINCHESTER, Hampshire

3PB,
4 ST PETER STREET, WINCHESTER, HAMPSHIRE
SO23 8BW
Tel: 01962 868884 ***Fax:*** 01962 868644
Dx: 2507 WINCHESTER
E-mail: clerks.all@3paper.co.uk
Clerk: Stuart Pringle (Senior Clerk); Lee Giles; Stephen Arnold; Michael Corrigan (Credit Controller); Tom Wood.
Administrator: Neil Monro (Head of Business Administration and Finance)
Practice Manager: Stephen Evers (Practice Development Clerk)
Chambers Director: Stephen Clark (Head of Clerking); Charles Charlick (Consultant Clerk)
Lickley, Mr Nigel J D (Q.C.); Recorder; Leader of Western Circuit (2010) . . . . G . . . . Jul 1983
Parker, Mr Christopher (Q.C.); Recorder . . . . G . . . . Jul 1986
Swinstead, Mr David L . . . . L . . . . Jul 1970
Coleman, Mr Anthony J S; Recorder . . . . M . . . . Jul 1973
Onslow, Mr Richard; Recorder . . . . I . . . . Jul 1982
Lomas, Mr Mark S . . . . M . . . . Jul 1983
O'Hara, Miss Sarah . . . . M . . . . Jul 1984
Clark, Ms Tonia Anne; Deputy District Judge . . . . M . . . . Jul 1986
Hudson, Miss Elisabeth . . . . G . . . . Nov 1987
Rowland, Mr Nicholas . . . . I . . . . Jun 1988
Hiddleston, Mr Adam . . . . I . . . . Oct 1990
Robins, Miss Imogen . . . . I . . . . Nov 1991
Topliss, Miss Megan . . . . G . . . . Nov 1994
Dawson, Mr James . . . . I . . . . Nov 1994
Reid, Mr David . . . . G . . . . Nov 1994
Weston, Mr Louis . . . . L . . . . Nov 1994
McDevitt, Mr Colin John . . . . I . . . . Oct 1995
De Freitas, Miss Melanie . . . . M . . . . Nov 1995
Lorie, Mr Andrew . . . . M . . . . Oct 1996
Purdy, Miss Catherine . . . . I . . . . Jan 1997
Sullivan, Mr Mark . . . . M . . . . Jan 1997
Dooher, Ms Nancy Helen . . . . L . . . . Nov 1997
Campbell, Miss Gillian . . . . G . . . . Jan 2002
Wheeler, Mr Richard . . . . I . . . . Jul 2004
Archer, Miss Audrey . . . . M . . . . Oct 2004
Langford, Ms Sarah . . . . G . . . . Jan 2005
Rees, Ms Naomi . . . . M . . . . Jan 2006
Wyeth, Mr Stephen . . . . I . . . . Jan 2010

Criminal Defence Service

Chambers of Oba E Nsugbe QC

PUMP COURT CHAMBERS,
31 SOUTHGATE STREET, WINCHESTER,
HAMPSHIRE SO23 9EB
Tel: 01962 868161 ***Fax:*** 0845 259 3240
Dx: 2514 WINCHESTER
E-mail: clerks@3pumpcourt.com
Web: www.3pumpcourt.com
Clerk: David Barber; Tony George; Ben Harfield; John Chapman; Hugh McGuire.
Administrator: Andrea Cheshire
Head of Chambers:
Nsugbe, Mr Oba E (Q.C.); Recorder . . . . G . . . . Jul 1985

Pascoe, Mr Nigel (Q.C.); Recorder . . . . I . . . . Jul 1966
Donne, Mr Anthony M (Q.C.) . . . . M . . . . Apr 1973
Campbell, Miss Susan Claire (Q.C.) . . . . M . . . . Nov 1986
Hill, Mr Mark (Q.C.); Recorder . . . . M . . . . Jul 1987
Samuels, Ms Leslie (Q.C.); Deputy District Judge . . . . G . . . . Jul 1989
Patterson, Mr Stewart; Recorder . . . . M . . . . Nov 1967
Pearson, Mr Thomas Adam Spencer . . . . M . . . . Nov 1969
Harrap, Mr Giles Thresher; Recorder . . . . I . . . . Nov 1971
Abbott, Mr Frank; Recorder . . . . L . . . . Nov 1972
Parry, Mr Charles . . . . M . . . . Nov 1973
Ker-Reid, Mr John . . . . I . . . . Nov 1974
Butt, Mr Michael . . . . M . . . . Nov 1974
Gabb, Mr Charles H . . . . M . . . . Feb 1975
Mackenzie, Miss Julie . . . . L . . . . Nov 1978
Jones, Mr Stephen . . . . I . . . . Nov 1978
Allardice, Miss Miranda . . . . L . . . . Jul 1982
Blount, Mr Martin J . . . . G . . . . Nov 1982
Scott, Mr Matthew . . . . I . . . . Nov 1985
Bloom-Davis, Mr Desmond; Deputy District Judge . . . . I . . . . Jul 1986
Travers, Mr Hugh; Employment Tribunal Chairman . . . . M . . . . Nov 1988
Gau, Mr Justin . . . . I . . . . Jul 1989
Wicks, Mr David . . . . M . . . . Jul 1989
Boydell, Mr Edward Patrick Stirrup; Recorder . . . . M . . . . Nov 1989
Houston, Mr Andrew . . . . I . . . . Nov 1989
Breslin, Miss Catherine . . . . I . . . . Jan 1990
Khan, Miss Helen M G . . . . M . . . . Nov 1990
Lorenzo, Ms Claudia . . . . I . . . . Apr 1991
Howe, Miss Penny . . . . I . . . . Nov 1991
Kelly, Mr Geoffrey . . . . M . . . . Feb 1992
Newton-Price, Mr James . . . . M . . . . Oct 1992
Ruffell, Mr Mark . . . . M . . . . Nov 1992
Tregilgas-Davey, Mr Marcus . . . . G . . . . Feb 1993
Morton, Mr Gary . . . . G . . . . May 1993
Russell, Ms Alison . . . . M . . . . Oct 1993
Peirson, Mr Oliver . . . . L . . . . Oct 1993
Gunther, Miss Elizabeth . . . . L . . . . Oct 1993
Ashley, Mr Mark R E . . . . I . . . . Nov 1993
Smith, Miss Leonorah . . . . I . . . . Nov 1993
Moore, Mr Roderick A . . . . I . . . . Nov 1993
Pawson, Mr Robert Edward . . . . I . . . . Nov 1994
Hall, Mr Richard Andrew . . . . I . . . . Nov 1995
Hall, Mr Michael Richard . . . . I . . . . Oct 1996
Asteris, Mr Peter . . . . L . . . . Jun 1996
Dubbery, Mr Mark . . . . M . . . . Oct 1996
Jones, Miss Sarah . . . . L . . . . Nov 1996
Ephgrave, Ms Amy . . . . G . . . . Oct 1997
Arlow, Ms Ruth . . . . I . . . . Oct 1997
Grime, Mr Andrew . . . . L . . . . Oct 1997
Ward, Ms Anne . . . . G . . . . Nov 1997
Gallagher, Miss Maria . . . . I . . . . Nov 1997
Allan, Ms Kirsten . . . . M . . . . Jul 1998
Keen, Mr Spencer . . . . M . . . . Jan 1998
Dracass, Mr Timothy . . . . I . . . . Oct 1998
Bond, Mr Andrew . . . . I . . . . Jan 1999
De Rozarieux, Ms Louise . . . . L . . . . Oct 1999
Spearing, Miss Rachel M . . . . I . . . . Nov 1999
Tutt, Mr Richard . . . . M . . . . Jul 2000
Brown, Miss Anne . . . . M . . . . Jul 2000
Ramadhan, Miss Lubeya . . . . M . . . . Jul 2000
Islam, Miss Naznin . . . . G . . . . Oct 2000
Hartley, Miss Caroline . . . . M . . . . Aug 2002
Burge, Miss Alison Jayne . . . . G . . . . Jul 2002
Platt, Miss Heather . . . . L . . . . Oct 2002
Shravat, Mr Neelo . . . . M . . . . Nov 2002
Chapman, Mr John . . . . L . . . . Jul 2003
Street, Miss Charlotte . . . . G . . . . Jul 2003
Davis, Miss Lucy . . . . G . . . . Nov 2003
Berry, Miss Amy . . . . L . . . . Jan 2003
Gadd, Mr Adam . . . . G . . . . Jan 2004
Leach, Mr Stuart . . . . G . . . . Jun 2004
Trotter, Miss Helen . . . . G . . . . Oct 2004
Lyons, Miss Tara . . . . M . . . . Oct 2005
Troup, Miss Rachel . . . . L . . . . Nov 2005
Long, Mr Benjamin . . . . M . . . . Jan 2006
Iten, Miss Corinne . . . . I . . . . Oct 2006
O'Driscoll, Ms Patricia . . . . M . . . . Oct 2006
Lee, Ms Jennifer . . . . L . . . . Jan 2007
Gilbert, Daniella . . . . I . . . . Mar 2007
Connors, Hannah . . . . I . . . . Jan 2008
Bruce, Ms Eleanor . . . . M . . . . Jan 2008
Purkis, Mr Simon . . . . I . . . . Oct 2008
Williamson, Nicholas . . . . M . . . . Mar 2009
Birt, Mr Robin . . . . M . . . . Oct 2009
Cohen, Mr Jonathan (Q.C.)* . . . . L . . . . Jul 1974
Bradley, Mrs Sally (Q.C.)* . . . . L . . . . Nov 1978
Fielding, Mr Stephen* . . . . I . . . . Jan 1974

Specialist teams cover a wide range of Common Law and Criminal work, including Family & Matrimonial; Employment; Environment; Inheritance; Landlord & Tenant; Personal Injury; Customs & Excise; Serious Fraud; Extradition; Ecclesiastical; Professional & Medical Negligence; Employment; Courts Martial.

WINDSOR, Windsor & Maidenhead

WINDSOR BARRISTERS CHAMBERS,
CASTLE HILL HOUSE, 12 CASTLE HILL,
WINDSOR, WINDSOR & MAIDENHEAD SL4 1PD
Tel: 01753 839321 ***Fax:*** 01344 621545
E-mail: admin@windsorchambers.com
Clerk: Wendy Marks.

WINKLEIGH, Devon

BARNSTAPLE CHAMBERS,
GLEBE COTTAGE, BROADWOODKELLY,
WINKLEIGH, DEVON EX19 8ED
Tel: 01837 83763 ***Fax:*** 01837 83763

WOLVERHAMPTON, West Midlands

Chambers of Ajmer Singh Garcha

1 ARGYLE ROAD,
WOLVERHAMPTON, WEST MIDLANDS
WV2 4NY
Tel: 01902 561047 ***Fax:*** 01902 561047
Head of Chambers:
Garcha, Ajmer Singh . . . . L . . . . Nov 1980

CLOCK CHAMBERS,
18 WATERLOO ROAD, WOLVERHAMPTON,
WEST MIDLANDS WV1 4BL
Tel: 01902 313444 ***Fax:*** 01902 421110

WOODCOTE, Oxfordshire

Chambers of Cathy Gordon

3 WAYSIDE GREEN,
WOODCOTE, OXFORDSHIRE RG8 0PR
Tel: 01491 680722 ***Fax:*** 01491 681878
E-mail: cathy@cathygordon.co.uk
Head of Chambers:
Gordon, Miss Cathy . . . . M . . . . Jul 1989

YARM, Stockton-on-Tees

Chambers of Stuart Lightwing

COUNSELS CHAMBERS,
8 THIRSK ROAD, YARM, STOCKTON-ON-TEES
TS15 9HE
Tel: 01642 650550 ***Fax:*** 01642 650550
Dx: 60524 MIDDLESBROUGH
E-mail: stuartlightwing@yahoo.co.uk
Clerk: Laura Bateman.
Head of Chambers:
Lightwing, Mr Stuart . . . . M . . . . Jul 1972

YORK

Chambers of Gilbert Gray QC

YORK CHAMBERS,
14 TOFT GREEN, YORK YO1 6JT
Tel: 01904 620048 ***Fax:*** 01904 610056
Dx: 65517 YORK 7
E-mail: clerks@yorkchambers.co.uk
Clerk: Kevin Beaumont.
Head of Chambers:
Gray, Mr Gilbert (Q.C.) . . . . G. . . . Nov 1953

Lowe, Mr William (Q.C.)* . . . . I . . . . Jul 1972
Elvidge, Mr John (Q.C.). . . . . G. . . . Nov 1988
Palmer, Prof Norman Ernest (Q.C.) . . . . G. . . . Jul 1973
Denny, Mr Robin H A . . . . I . . . . May 1969
Chamberlain, Mr Kevin . . . . G. . . . Aug 1965
Harvey, Mr Colin . . . . G. . . . Jan 1973
Twist, Mr Stephen . . . . M. . . . Jul 1979
Hunter, Mr Geoffrey. . . . . G. . . . Feb 1979
O'Neill, Mr Michael . . . . I . . . . Jul 1979
Smith, Mr Duncan . . . . I . . . . Jul 1979
Bosomworth, Mr Michael . . . . M. . . . Jul 1979
Proops, Miss Helen. . . . . M. . . . Jul 1986
Johnson, Mr Peter . . . . I . . . . Jul 1986
Morris, Mr Paul H. . . . . L . . . . Nov 1986
Price, Mr Nicholas . . . . G. . . . Nov 1987
Lee, Ms Rosslyn . . . . G. . . . Nov 1987
Lamb, Mr David S . . . . M. . . . Nov 1987
Makepeace, Mr Peter. . . . . L . . . . Jul 1988
Boothroyd, Miss Susan . . . . M. . . . Oct 1990
Cordey, Mr Dan. . . . . G. . . . Nov 1990
Oliver, Mr Crispin Arthur. . . . . M. . . . Nov 1990
Todd, Mr Martin. . . . . I . . . . Nov 1991
Robinson, Mr James . . . . M. . . . Oct 1992
Edwards, Mr Daniel. . . . . L . . . . Oct 1993
Wadoodi, Miss Aisha . . . . M. . . . May 1994
Woolrich, Miss Sarah . . . . M. . . . Nov 1994
Campbell, Ms Diane . . . . G. . . . Nov 1995
Randhawa, Miss Ravinder . . . . L . . . . Nov 1995
Legard, Mr Edward . . . . G. . . . Oct 1996
Callaghan, Ms Elizabeth . . . . L . . . . Jul 1998
Withyman, Mr Jim . . . . M. . . . Jun 1999
Healy, Mr Sam . . . . G. . . . Jul 1999
Holmes-Willis, Mrs Sarah . . . . M. . . . Jul 1999
Buckley, Miss Sophie . . . . M. . . . Nov 1999
Smoult-Hawtree, Ms Karen . . . . G. . . . Jun 2000
Morrison, Ms Andrea . . . . I . . . . Jun 2000
Smith, Ms Jennie . . . . I . . . . Jan 2002
Lennon, Miss Karen. . . . . I . . . . Jan 2003
Thornton, Mr Stephen. . . . . G. . . . Jan 2003
Trory, Mr Henry. . . . . I . . . . Jan 2003
Adcock, Ms Deborah . . . . G. . . . Jan 2005
Adams, Mr Nathan . . . . M. . . . Jan 2004
Herrmann, Mr Richard . . . . G. . . . Jan 2004
Gough, Ms Emma . . . . I . . . . Jan 2005
Willoughby, Mr James. . . . . M. . . . Jan 2005
Frew, Mr Bruce . . . . L . . . . Jan 2005
Addicott, Miss Elizabeth. . . . . I . . . . Jul 2006
Davies, Miss Angharad . . . . M. . . . Jan 2006
Mugliston, Mr Adam . . . . L . . . . Oct 2008
Lippiatt, Mr Huw . . . . G. . . . Mar 2010
Raitt, Miss Kate. . . . . L . . . . Jul 2009

11

SECTION 12

BARRISTERS

CONTENTS

12

Chambers Specialisations

Administrative Law, Constitutional Law and Public Law
Alternative Dispute Resolution (ADR)
Arbitration
Arbitration including International Trade
Aviation
Banking
Bankruptcy
Building
Chancery, General
Charities
Children
Clinical Negligence
Commercial Law
Common Law, General
Communications and Telecommunications
Company Law
Competition Law
Construction
Consumer Law – Agreements, Credit, Licensing, Sale of Goods
Consumer Protection – Advertising, Trade Descriptions, Trading Standards, Product Liability
Contract Law
Coroner
Corporate Finance
Court of Protection
Criminal Work - Criminal Procedures
Criminal Work - General
Criminal Work - International
Criminal Work - Police & Prisons
Data Protection
Defamation and Slander
Discrimination
Ecclesiastical Courts
Education
Employment Law
Energy
Entertainment, Artists and Performers
Environment
European Community Law
Evidence
Family Law
Farming and Agriculture
Financial Services
Firearms
Food and Drugs Law
Fraud
Gaming and Lotteries
Health and Safety at Work
Healthcare Law
Housing and Social Welfare
Human Rights and Civil Liberties
Immigration
Information Technology
Insolvency
Insurance
Intellectual Property
International Law
Islamic Law
Landlord & Tenant
Licensing
Litigation
Local Government and Public Sector
Media
Mediation
Medical Law
Mental Health
Military Law
Military Law & Courts Martial
Mines and Minerals
Offshore
Parliamentary Law
Partnerships and Business Arrangements
Pensions
Personal Injury
Planning & Rating
Private Client
Probate
Professional Negligence
Property
Public International Law
Revenue
Road Traffic Law
Shipping and Admiralty
Sports Law
Taxation – Business
Taxation – Personal
Terrorism
Tourism and Travel
Transport
Tribunals and Inquiries
Utilities - Electric, Gas, Water
Wills & Trusts

COUNSEL'S CHAMBERS SPECIALISATION INDEX

12

NO5 CHAMBERS
Birmingham *p968* 0845 210 5555

TEN OLD SQUARE
London WC2 *p945* 020 7405 0758

ORIEL CHAMBERS
Liverpool *p981* 0151 236 7191 / 236 4321

ORIEL CHAMBERS
Preston *p990* 01772 254764

SOUTH SQUARE
London WC1 *p950* 020 7696 9900

ST JAMES'S CHAMBERS
Manchester *p984* 0161 834 7000

9 ST JOHN STREET CHAMBERS
Manchester *p984* 0161 955 9000

ST PHILIPS CHAMBERS
Birmingham *p969* 0121 246 7000

4 STONE BUILDINGS
London WC2 *p951* 020 7242 5524

11 Stone Buildings
London WC2 *p951* 020 7831 6381

9 Stone Buildings Barristers Chambers
London WC2 *p951* 020 7404 5055

Zenith Chambers
Leeds *p979* 0113 245 5438

BUILDING

Arbitration Chambers
London NW5 *p923* 020 7267 2137

Atkin Chambers
London WC1 *p923* 020 7404 0102

Cobden House Chambers
Manchester *p983* 0161 833 6000

CROWN OFFICE CHAMBERS
London EC4 *p929* 020 7797 8100

Devereux Chambers
London WC2 *p930* 020 7353 7534

One Essex Court
London EC4 *p931* 020 7936 3030

THIRTY NINE ESSEX STREET
London WC2 *p932* 020 7832 1111

Field Court Chambers
London WC1 *p933* 020 7405 6114

Henderson Chambers
London EC4 *p937* 020 7583 9020

Keating Chambers
London WC2 *p938* 020 7544 2600

2 King's Bench Walk
London EC4 *p939* 020 7353 1746

New Walk Chambers
Leicester *p979* 0871 200 1298

TEN OLD SQUARE
London WC2 *p945* 020 7405 0758

ORIEL CHAMBERS
Liverpool *p981* 0151 236 7191 / 236 4321

ORIEL CHAMBERS
Preston *p990* 01772 254764

PUMP COURT CHAMBERS
Swindon *p993* 01793 539899

PUMP COURT CHAMBERS
Winchester *p994* 01962 868161

Resolution Chambers
Malvern *p982* 01684 541008

2 Temple Gardens
London EC4 *p952* 020 7822 1200

CHANCERY, GENERAL

ATLANTIC CHAMBERS
Liverpool *p980* 0151 236 4421

Castle Chambers
Harrow *p976* 020 8423 6579

CHANCERY HOUSE CHAMBERS
Leeds *p977* 0113 244 6691

1 Chancery Lane
London WC2 *p928* 0845 634 6666

Conference Chambers
Harrow *p976* 07958 421595

CROWN OFFICE CHAMBERS
London EC4 *p929* 020 7797 8100

3 Dr Johnson's Buildings
London EC4 *p930* 020 7353 4854

ENTERPRISE CHAMBERS
Leeds *p977* 0113 246 0391

ENTERPRISE CHAMBERS
London WC2 *p931* 020 7405 9471

ENTERPRISE CHAMBERS
Newcastle upon Tyne *p987* 0191 222 3344

One Essex Court
London EC4 *p931* 020 7583 2000

One Essex Court
London EC4 *p931* 020 7936 3030

Exchange Chambers
Liverpool *p980* 0151 236 7747

Exchange Chambers
Manchester *p983* 0161 833 2722

FARRAR'S BUILDING
London EC4 *p933* 020 7583 9241

Goldsmith Chambers
London EC4 *p935* 020 7353 6802

GUILDHALL CHAMBERS
Bristol *p970* 0117 930 9000

3 HARE COURT
London EC4 *p937* 020 7415 7800

Hogarth Chambers
London WC2 *p937* 020 7404 0404

2 King's Bench Walk
London EC4 *p939* 020 7353 1746

Two King's Bench Walk
London EC4 *p939*
. . . . .020 7353 7202 / 7353 3909

Lamb Building
London EC4 *p940* 020 7797 7788

NEW SQUARE CHAMBERS
London WC2 *p943* 020 7419 8000

New Walk Chambers
Leicester *p979* 0871 200 1298

NO5 CHAMBERS
Birmingham *p968* 0845 210 5555

No 6 Barristers Chambers
Leeds *p978* 0113 245 9763

XXIV Old Buildings
London WC2 *p944* 020 7691 2424

TEN OLD SQUARE
London WC2 *p945* 020 7405 0758

13 Old Square Chambers
London WC2 *p945* 020 7831 4445

ORIEL CHAMBERS
Liverpool *p981* 0151 236 7191 / 236 4321

ORIEL CHAMBERS
Preston *p990* 01772 254764

PALLANT CHAMBERS
Chichester *p974* 01243 784538

PUMP COURT CHAMBERS
Swindon *p993* 01793 539899

189 Randolph Avenue
London W9 *p949* 020 7328 0158

Serle Court
London WC2 *p950* 020 7242 6105

SOUTH SQUARE
London WC1 *p950* 020 7696 9900

Southernhay Chambers
Exeter *p975* 01392 255777

St Ives Chambers
Birmingham *p969* 0121 236 0863

ST JAMES'S CHAMBERS
Manchester *p984* 0161 834 7000

St John's Chambers
Bristol *p972* 0117 921 3456

18 St John Street Chambers
Manchester *p985* 0161 278 1800

ST PHILIPS CHAMBERS
Birmingham *p969* 0121 246 7000

5 Stone Buildings
London WC2 *p951* 020 7242 6201

11 Stone Buildings
London WC2 *p951* 020 7831 6381

9 Stone Buildings Barristers Chambers
London WC2 *p951* 020 7404 5055

Swan House
London W13 *p951* 020 8998 3035

TRINITY (NEWCASTLE) CHAMBERS
Newcastle upon Tyne *p987* 0191 232 1927

TRINITY (TEESSIDE) CHAMBERS
Middlesbrough *p986* . . . 01642 247569

WILBERFORCE CHAMBERS
London WC2 *p953* 020 7306 0102

Zenith Chambers
Leeds *p979* 0113 245 5438

CHARITIES

Goldsmith Chambers
London EC4 *p935* 020 7353 6802

Justice Court Chambers
Leicester *p979* 024 7632 5859

TEN OLD SQUARE
London WC2 *p945* 020 7405 0758

CHILDREN

7 Bedford Row
London WC1 *p924* 020 7242 3555

29 BEDFORD ROW
London WC1 *p925* 020 7404 1044

4 Brick Court Chambers
London EC4 *p927* 020 7832 3200

CHAVASSE COURT CHAMBERS
Liverpool *p980* 0151 229 2030

COLLETON CHAMBERS
Exeter *p975* 01392 274898

Coram Chambers
London EC1 *p929* 020 7092 3700

CORNWALL STREET CHAMBERS
Birmingham *p967* 0121 233 7500

Crown Office Row Chambers
Brighton *p970* 01273 625625

3 Dr Johnson's Buildings
London EC4 *p930* 020 7353 4854

FOUNTAIN CHAMBERS
Middlesbrough *p986* . . . 01642 804040

1 GARDEN COURT
London EC4 *p934* 020 7797 7900

9 Gough Square
London EC4 *p935* 020 7832 0500

Guildford Chambers
Guildford *p975* 01483 539131

Harcourt Chambers
London EC4 *p936* 0844 561 7135

Harcourt Chambers
Oxford *p989* 0844 561 7135

1 Hare Court
London EC4 *p936* 020 7797 7070

Henley Chambers
Henley-on-Thames *p976* . 01491 636000

1 KBW Chambers
Lewes *p980* 01273 402600

KCH Garden Square Chambers
Nottingham *p989* 0115 941 8851

King's Bench Godolphin Chambers
Truro *p994* 0845 308 1551

1 KING'S BENCH WALK
London EC4 *p938* 020 7936 1500

4 KING'S BENCH WALK
London EC4 *p939* 020 7822 7000

5 King's Bench Walk
London EC4 *p939* 020 7353 5638

1 Mitre Court Buildings
London EC4 *p942* 020 7452 8900

MITRE HOUSE CHAMBERS
London WC1 *p942* 020 7307 7100

2 New Street
Leicester *p979* 0116 262 5906

New Walk Chambers
Leicester *p979* 0871 200 1298

NO5 CHAMBERS
Birmingham *p968* 0845 210 5555

Northampton Chambers
Northampton *p988* 01604 636271

4 Paper Buildings
London EC4 *p946* 020 7583 0816

37 Park Square Chambers
Leeds *p978* 0113 243 9422

PUMP COURT CHAMBERS
Swindon *p993* 01793 539899

PUMP COURT CHAMBERS
Winchester *p994* 01962 868161

PUMP COURT CHAMBERS
London EC4 *p947* 020 7353 0711

QUEEN ELIZABETH BUILDINGS
London EC4 *p948* 020 7797 7837

RENAISSANCE CHAMBERS
London WC1 *p949* 020 7404 1111

Southernhay Chambers
Exeter *p975* 01392 255777

St Ives Chambers
Birmingham *p969* 0121 236 0863

St John's Chambers
Altrincham *p967* 0161 980 7379

ST MARY'S CHAMBERS
Nottingham *p989* 0115 950 3503

ST PHILIPS CHAMBERS
Birmingham *p969* 0121 246 7000

Temple Chambers
Cardiff *p973* 029 2039 7364

TRINITY CHAMBERS
Chelmsford *p974* 01245 605040

TRINITY (NEWCASTLE) CHAMBERS
Newcastle upon Tyne *p987* 0191 232 1927

TRINITY (TEESSIDE) CHAMBERS
Middlesbrough *p986* . . . 01642 247569

Walnut House Chambers
Exeter *p975* 01392 279751

Westgate Chambers
Lewes *p980* 01273 480510

Wight Chambers
Newport *p988*
. . . . 01983 522828 / 07976 512823

WILBERFORCE CHAMBERS
Hull *p976* 01482 323264

Zenith Chambers
Leeds *p979* 0113 245 5438

CLINICAL NEGLIGENCE

ATLANTIC CHAMBERS
Liverpool *p980* 0151 236 4421

BYROM STREET CHAMBERS
Manchester *p983* 0161 829 2100

1 Chancery Lane
London WC2 *p928* 0845 634 6666

Counsels Chambers
Yarm *p994* 01642 650550

CROWN OFFICE CHAMBERS
London EC4 *p929* 020 7797 8100

1 CROWN OFFICE ROW
London EC4 *p929* 020 7797 7500

THIRTY NINE ESSEX STREET
London WC2 *p932* 020 7832 1111

FARRAR'S BUILDING
London EC4 *p933* 020 7583 9241

GUILDHALL CHAMBERS
Bristol *p970* 0117 930 9000

Hailsham Chambers
London EC4 *p936* 020 7643 5000

1 KBW Chambers
Lewes *p980* 01273 402600

Kew Chambers
Kew *p976* 0844 809 9991

1 KING'S BENCH WALK
London EC4 *p938* 020 7936 1500

4 KING'S BENCH WALK
London EC4 *p939* 020 7822 7000

12 KING'S BENCH WALK
London EC4 *p940* 020 7583 0811

NO5 CHAMBERS
Birmingham *p968* 0845 210 5555

Old Square Chambers
Bristol *p971* 0117 930 5100

ORIEL CHAMBERS
Liverpool *p981* 0151 236 7191 / 236 4321

ORIEL CHAMBERS
Preston *p990* 01772 254764

PUMP COURT CHAMBERS
Swindon *p993* 01793 539899

PUMP COURT CHAMBERS
Winchester *p994* 01962 868161

PUMP COURT CHAMBERS
London EC4 *p947* 020 7353 0711

St John's Chambers
Bristol *p972* 0117 921 3456

ST PHILIPS CHAMBERS
Birmingham *p969* 0121 246 7000

COMMERCIAL LAW

Arbitration Chambers
London NW5 *p923* 020 7267 2137

Argent Chambers
London WC2 *p923* 020 7556 5500

7 Bedford Row
London WC1 *p924* 020 7242 3555

Blackstone Chambers
London EC4 *p926* 020 7583 1770

Brick Court Chambers
London WC2 *p927* 020 7379 3550

Cloisters
London EC4 *p928* 020 7827 4000

CROWN OFFICE CHAMBERS
London EC4 *p929* 020 7797 8100

ENTERPRISE CHAMBERS
Leeds *p977* 0113 246 0391

ENTERPRISE CHAMBERS
London WC2 *p931* 020 7405 9471

ENTERPRISE CHAMBERS
Newcastle upon Tyne *p987* 0191 222 3344

ERSKINE CHAMBERS
London WC2 *p931* 020 7242 5532

One Essex Court
London EC4 *p931* 020 7583 2000

THIRTY NINE ESSEX STREET
London WC2 *p932* 020 7832 1111

Exchange Chambers
Liverpool *p980* 0151 236 7747

Exchange Chambers
Manchester *p983* 0161 833 2722

4-5 GRAY'S INN SQUARE
London WC1 *p935* 020 7404 5252

3 HARE COURT
London EC4 *p937* 020 7415 7800

Henderson Chambers
London EC4 *p937* 020 7583 9020

Hogarth Chambers
London WC2 *p937* 020 7404 0404

Justice Court Chambers
Leicester *p979* 024 7632 5859

11KBW
London EC4 *p938* 020 7632 8500

KCH Garden Square Chambers
Nottingham *p989* 0115 941 8851

7 King's Bench Walk
London EC4 *p940* 020 7910 8300

Lamb Chambers
London EC4 *p941* 020 7797 8300

Maitland Chambers
London WC2 *p941* 020 7406 1200

Malins Chambers
London EC4 *p942* 020 7353 8868

MITRE HOUSE CHAMBERS
London WC1 *p942* 020 7307 7100

NEW SQUARE CHAMBERS
London WC2 *p943* 020 7419 8000

2 New Street
Leicester *p979* 0116 262 5906

NO5 CHAMBERS
Birmingham *p968* 0845 210 5555

XXIV Old Buildings
London WC2 *p944* 020 7691 2424

TEN OLD SQUARE
London WC2 *p945* 020 7405 0758

See p998 for the Firms Specialisations

13 Old Square Chambers
London WC2 *p945* 020 7831 4445

ORIEL CHAMBERS
Liverpool *p981* 0151 236 7191 / 236 4321

ORIEL CHAMBERS
Preston *p990* 01772 254764

Outer Temple Chambers
London WC2 *p945* 020 7353 6381

FIVE PAPER
London EC4 *p946* 020 7815 3200

Park Court Chambers
Leeds *p978* 0113 243 3277

Portsmouth Barristers Chambers
Portsmouth *p990* 023 9283 1292

John Pugh's Chambers
Liverpool *p981* 0151 236 5415

4 Pump Court
London EC4 *p947* 020 7842 5555

5 Pump Court
London EC4 *p947*
. . . . .020 7353 2532 / 7583 7133

PUMP COURT CHAMBERS
Swindon *p993* 01793 539899

PUMP COURT CHAMBERS
Winchester *p994* 01962 868161

PUMP COURT CHAMBERS
London EC4 *p947* 020 7353 0711

Quadrant Chambers
London EC4 *p948* 020 7583 4444

5RB
London WC1 *p948* 020 7242 2902

ROPEWALK CHAMBERS
Nottingham *p989* 0115 947 2581

Rougemont Chambers
Exeter *p975* 01392 208484

Serle Court
London WC2 *p950* 020 7242 6105

SOUTH SQUARE
London WC1 *p950* 020 7696 9900

Southernhay Chambers
Exeter *p975* 01392 255777

St Ives Chambers
Birmingham *p969* 0121 236 0863

ST JAMES'S CHAMBERS
Manchester *p984* 0161 834 7000

St John's Chambers
Bristol *p972* 0117 921 3456

ST PHILIPS CHAMBERS
Birmingham *p969* 0121 246 7000

4 STONE BUILDINGS
London WC2 *p951* 020 7242 5524

11 Stone Buildings
London WC2 *p951* 020 7831 6381

Stone Chambers
London WC1 *p951* 020 7440 6900

TANFIELD CHAMBERS
London WC1 *p951* 020 7421 5300

TRINITY (NEWCASTLE) CHAMBERS
Newcastle upon Tyne *p987* 0191 232 1927

TRINITY (TEESSIDE) CHAMBERS
Middlesbrough *p986* . . . 01642 247569

Walnut House Chambers
Exeter *p975* 01392 279751

Law Office of Paul Warrick
London SW10 *p953* . . . 020 7795 1122

WILBERFORCE CHAMBERS
London WC2 *p953* 020 7306 0102

Windsor Barristers Chambers
Windsor *p994* 01753 839321

COMMON LAW, GENERAL

Abbey Chambers
Shepperton *p992* 01932 560913

Advolex Chambers
Croydon *p975* 0871 717 7321

Argent Chambers
London WC2 *p923* 020 7556 5500

BANK HOUSE CHAMBERS
Sheffield *p991* 0114 275 1223

Bath Chambers
Melksham *p986* 01225 702347

Becket Chambers
Canterbury *p972* 01227 786331

33 Bedford Row
London WC1 *p925* 020 7242 6476

36 Bedford Row
London WC1 *p925* 020 7421 8000

42 Bedford Row
London WC1 *p925* 020 7831 0222

Broad Chare Chambers
Newcastle upon Tyne *p986* 0191 232 0541

BYROM STREET CHAMBERS
Manchester *p983* 0161 829 2100

Castle Chambers
Harrow *p976* 020 8423 6579

49 Chambers
Bridgnorth *p970* 01746 761545

1 Chancery Lane
London WC2 *p928* 0845 634 6666

Chartlands Chambers
Northampton *p988* 01604 603322

College Chambers
Southampton *p992* 023 8023 0338

Cornerstone Barristers
London WC1 *p929* 020 7242 4986

CROWN OFFICE CHAMBERS
London EC4 *p929* 020 7797 8100

1 CROWN OFFICE ROW
London EC4 *p929* 020 7797 7500

Crown Office Row Chambers
Brighton *p970* 01273 625625

2 Dr Johnson's Buildings
London EC4 *p930* 020 7936 2613

3 Dr Johnson's Buildings
London EC4 *p930* 020 7353 4854

East Anglian Chambers
Chelmsford *p973* 01245 215660

East Anglian Chambers
Colchester *p975* 01206 572756

East Anglian Chambers
Ipswich *p976* 01473 214481

East Anglian Chambers
Norwich *p988* 01603 617351

Eastbourne Chambers
Eastbourne *p975* 01323 642102

THIRTY NINE ESSEX STREET
London WC2 *p932* 020 7832 1111

FARRAR'S BUILDING
London EC4 *p933* 020 7583 9241

FOUNTAIN CHAMBERS
Middlesbrough *p986* . . . 01642 804040

1 Garfield Road
London SW11 *p935* . . . 020 7228 1137

9 Gough Square
London EC4 *p935* 020 7832 0500

1 Gray's Inn Square
London WC1 *p935* 020 7405 8946

Guildford Chambers
Guildford *p975* 01483 539131

Harbour Court Chambers
Southampton *p992* 01489 557999

Harcourt Chambers
London EC4 *p936* 0844 561 7135

Harcourt Chambers
Oxford *p989* 0844 561 7135

King's Bench Chambers
Oxford *p989* 01865 311066

1 KING'S BENCH WALK
London EC4 *p938* 020 7936 1500

4 KING'S BENCH WALK
London EC4 *p939* 020 7822 7000

10 KING'S BENCH WALK
London EC4 *p940* 020 7353 7742

13 King's Bench Walk
London EC4 *p940* 020 7353 7204

Lamb Chambers
London EC4 *p941* 020 7797 8300

114 Liverpool Road
London N1 *p941* 020 7226 9863

LOMBARD CHAMBERS
London EC1 *p941* 020 7107 2100

Malins Chambers
London EC4 *p942* 020 7353 8868

6-8 Mill Street
Maidstone *p982* . .01622 688094 / 688095

MITRE HOUSE CHAMBERS
London WC1 *p942* 020 7307 7100

Four New Square
London WC2 *p943* 020 7822 2000

2 New Street
Leicester *p979* 0116 262 5906

NO5 CHAMBERS
Birmingham *p968* 0845 210 5555

OCTAGON HOUSE
Norwich *p988* 01603 623186

Old Court Chambers
Middlesbrough *p986* . . . 01642 232523

ORIEL CHAMBERS
Liverpool *p981* 0151 236 7191 / 236 4321

ORIEL CHAMBERS
Preston *p990* 01772 254764

Paradise Chambers
Sheffield *p992* 0114 273 8951

9 Park Place
Cardiff *p973* 029 2038 2731

Thirty Park Place
Cardiff *p973* 029 2039 8421

39 Park Square
Leeds *p978* 0113 245 6633

Portal Chambers
Pencader *p990* 01559 395292

John Pugh's Chambers
Liverpool *p981* 0151 236 5415

2 Pump Court
London EC4 *p947* 020 7353 5597

6 Pump Court
London EC4 *p947* 020 7797 8400

PUMP COURT CHAMBERS
Swindon *p993* 01793 539899

PUMP COURT CHAMBERS
Winchester *p994* 01962 868161

PUMP COURT CHAMBERS
London EC4 *p947* 020 7353 0711

189 Randolph Avenue
London W9 *p949* 020 7328 0158

ROPEWALK CHAMBERS
Nottingham *p989* 0115 947 2581

Chambers of Royln Seeboruth
Aylesbury *p967* 01296 393329

3 Serjeants' Inn
London EC4 *p950* 020 7427 5000

Slough Barristers Chamber
Slough *p992* . . .01753 553806 / 817989

5 St Andrew's Hill
London EC4 *p950* 020 7332 5400

ST JAMES'S CHAMBERS
Manchester *p984* 0161 834 7000

St John's Chambers
Altrincham *p967* 0161 980 7379

18 St John Street Chambers
Manchester *p985* 0161 278 1800

St Johns Buildings
Manchester *p985* 0161 214 1500

ST PHILIPS CHAMBERS
Birmingham *p969* 0121 246 7000

Stour Chambers
Canterbury *p972* 01227 764899

Swan House
London W13 *p951* 020 8998 3035

Temple Chambers
Newport *p988* . . .01633 267403 / 255855

TRINITY CHAMBERS
Chelmsford *p974* 01245 605040

TRINITY (NEWCASTLE) CHAMBERS
Newcastle upon Tyne *p987* 0191 232 1927

TRINITY (TEESSIDE) CHAMBERS
Middlesbrough *p986* . . . 01642 247569

Walnut House Chambers
Exeter *p975* 01392 279751

Chambers of Tanya and Peter-John White
Bedford *p967* 01234 870004

COMMUNICATIONS AND TELECOMMUNICATIONS

Atkin Chambers
London WC1 *p923* 020 7404 0102

CROWN OFFICE CHAMBERS
London EC4 *p929* 020 7797 8100

THIRTY NINE ESSEX STREET
London WC2 *p932* 020 7832 1111

1 Paper Buildings
London EC4 *p946* 020 7353 3728

COMPANY LAW

CROWN OFFICE CHAMBERS
London EC4 *p929* 020 7797 8100

ENTERPRISE CHAMBERS
Leeds *p977* 0113 246 0391

ENTERPRISE CHAMBERS
London WC2 *p931* 020 7405 9471

ENTERPRISE CHAMBERS
Newcastle upon Tyne *p987* 0191 222 3344

ERSKINE CHAMBERS
London WC2 *p931* 020 7242 5532

THIRTY NINE ESSEX STREET
London WC2 *p932* 020 7832 1111

Chambers of Alana Graham
Halesowen *p976* 01384 894560

MITRE HOUSE CHAMBERS
London WC1 *p942* 020 7307 7100

NEW SQUARE CHAMBERS
London WC2 *p943* 020 7419 8000

NO5 CHAMBERS
Birmingham *p968* 0845 210 5555

TEN OLD SQUARE
London WC2 *p945* 020 7405 0758

13 Old Square Chambers
London WC2 *p945* 020 7831 4445

ORIEL CHAMBERS
Liverpool *p981* 0151 236 7191 / 236 4321

ORIEL CHAMBERS
Preston *p990* 01772 254764

PUMP COURT CHAMBERS
Swindon *p993* 01793 539899

PUMP COURT CHAMBERS
Winchester *p994* 01962 868161

PUMP COURT CHAMBERS
London EC4 *p947* 020 7353 0711

Serle Court
London WC2 *p950* 020 7242 6105

SOUTH SQUARE
London WC1 *p950* 020 7696 9900

ST JAMES'S CHAMBERS
Manchester *p984* 0161 834 7000

ST PHILIPS CHAMBERS
Birmingham *p969* 0121 246 7000

4 STONE BUILDINGS
London WC2 *p951* 020 7242 5524

TRINITY (NEWCASTLE) CHAMBERS
Newcastle upon Tyne *p987* 0191 232 1927

TRINITY (TEESSIDE) CHAMBERS
Middlesbrough *p986* . . . 01642 247569

COMPETITION LAW

THIRTY NINE ESSEX STREET
London WC2 *p932* 020 7832 1111

MONCKTON CHAMBERS
London WC1 *p942* 020 7405 7211

3 NEW SQUARE
London WC2 *p943* 020 7405 1111

NO5 CHAMBERS
Birmingham *p968* 0845 210 5555

CONSTRUCTION

Atkin Chambers
London WC1 *p923* 020 7404 0102

CROWN OFFICE CHAMBERS
London EC4 *p929* 020 7797 8100

THIRTY NINE ESSEX STREET
London WC2 *p932* 020 7832 1111

NO5 CHAMBERS
Birmingham *p968* 0845 210 5555

4 Pump Court
London EC4 *p947* 020 7842 5555

ST PHILIPS CHAMBERS
Birmingham *p969* 0121 246 7000

CONSUMER LAW - AGREEMENTS, CREDIT, LICENSING, SALE OF GOODS

CROWN OFFICE CHAMBERS
London EC4 *p929* 020 7797 8100

THIRTY NINE ESSEX STREET
London WC2 *p932* 020 7832 1111

GOUGH SQUARE CHAMBERS
London EC4 *p935* 020 7353 0924

Henley Chambers
Henley-on-Thames *p976* . 01491 636000

MITRE HOUSE CHAMBERS
London WC1 *p942* 020 7307 7100

NO5 CHAMBERS
Birmingham *p968* 0845 210 5555

TEN OLD SQUARE
London WC2 *p945* 020 7405 0758

ORIEL CHAMBERS
Liverpool *p981* 0151 236 7191 / 236 4321

ORIEL CHAMBERS
Preston *p990* 01772 254764

John Pugh's Chambers
Liverpool *p981* 0151 236 5415

ST PHILIPS CHAMBERS
Birmingham *p969* 0121 246 7000

TRINITY (NEWCASTLE) CHAMBERS
Newcastle upon Tyne *p987* 0191 232 1927

TRINITY (TEESSIDE) CHAMBERS
Middlesbrough *p986* . . . 01642 247569

Law Office of Paul Warrick
London SW10 *p953* . . . 020 7795 1122

CONSUMER PROTECTION - ADVERTISING, TRADES DESCRIPTION, TRADING STANDARDS, PRODUCT LIABILITY

CROWN OFFICE CHAMBERS
London EC4 *p929* 020 7797 8100

Crown Office Row Chambers
Brighton *p970* 01273 625625

THIRTY NINE ESSEX STREET
London WC2 *p932* 020 7832 1111

GOUGH SQUARE CHAMBERS
London EC4 *p935* 020 7353 0924

MITRE HOUSE CHAMBERS
London WC1 *p942* 020 7307 7100

3 NEW SQUARE
London WC2 *p943* 020 7405 1111

NO5 CHAMBERS
Birmingham *p968* 0845 210 5555

ST PHILIPS CHAMBERS
Birmingham *p969* 0121 246 7000

CONTRACT LAW

THIRTY NINE ESSEX STREET
London WC2 *p932* 020 7832 1111

FARRAR'S BUILDING
London EC4 *p933* 020 7583 9241

MITRE HOUSE CHAMBERS
London WC1 p942 . . . . 020 7307 7100
ORIEL CHAMBERS
Liverpool p981 0151 236 7191 / 236 4321
ORIEL CHAMBERS
Preston p990 . . . . 01772 254764
PUMP COURT CHAMBERS
Swindon p993 . . . . . . 01793 539899
PUMP COURT CHAMBERS
Winchester p994 . . . . . 01962 868161
PUMP COURT CHAMBERS
London EC4 p947 . . . . 020 7353 0711
TRINITY (NEWCASTLE) CHAMBERS
Newcastle upon Tyne p987 0191 232 1927
TRINITY (TEESSIDE) CHAMBERS
Middlesbrough p986 . . . 01642 247569

CORONER

1 Chancery Lane
London WC2 p928 . . . . 0845 634 6666
COLLETON CHAMBERS
Exeter p975 . . . . 01392 274898
1 CROWN OFFICE ROW
London EC4 p929 . . . . 020 7797 7500
15 New Bridge Street Chambers
London EC4 p943 . . . . 020 7842 1900

CORPORATE FINANCE

ERSKINE CHAMBERS
London WC2 p931 . . . . 020 7242 5532
THIRTY NINE ESSEX STREET
London WC2 p932 . . . . 020 7832 1111
15 New Bridge Street Chambers
London EC4 p943 . . . . 020 7842 1900

COURT OF PROTECTION

4 Brick Court Chambers
London EC4 p927 . . . . 020 7832 3200
THIRTY NINE ESSEX STREET
London WC2 p932 . . . . 020 7832 1111
1 KBW Chambers
Lewes p980 . . . . 01273 402600
NEW SQUARE CHAMBERS
London WC2 p943 . . . . 020 7419 8000
NO5 CHAMBERS
Birmingham p968 . . . . 0845 210 5555
TEN OLD SQUARE
London WC2 p945 . . . . 020 7405 0758
4 Paper Buildings
London EC4 p946 . . . . 020 7583 0816
5 Stone Buildings
London WC2 p951 . . . . 020 7242 6201

CRIMINAL WORK - CRIMINAL PROCEDURES

Nine Bedford Row
London WC1 p924 . . . . 020 7489 2727
CROWN OFFICE CHAMBERS
London EC4 p929 . . . . 020 7797 8100
East Anglian Chambers
Chelmsford p973 . . . . 01245 215660
East Anglian Chambers
Colchester p975 . . . . 01206 572756
East Anglian Chambers
Ipswich p976 . . . . . . 01473 214481
East Anglian Chambers
Norwich p988 . . . . . . 01603 617351
23 ESSEX STREET
London WC2 p932 . . . . 020 7413 0353
23 ESSEX STREET
Manchester p983 . . . . 0161 870 9969
23 ESSEX STREET
Nottingham p988 . . . . 0115 935 2233
187 FLEET STREET
London EC4 p933 . . . . 020 7430 7430
1 KBW Chambers
Lewes p980 . . . . 01273 402600
1 KING'S BENCH WALK
London EC4 p938 . . . . 020 7936 1500
MITRE HOUSE CHAMBERS
London WC1 p942 . . . . 020 7307 7100
15 New Bridge Street Chambers
London EC4 p943 . . . . 020 7842 1900
OCTAGON HOUSE
Norwich p988 . . . . . . 01603 623186
PUMP COURT CHAMBERS
Swindon p993 . . . . . . 01793 539899
PUMP COURT CHAMBERS
Winchester p994 . . . . . 01962 868161
PUMP COURT CHAMBERS
London EC4 p947 . . . . 020 7353 0711

CRIMINAL WORK – GENERAL

Abbey Chambers
Shepperton p992 . . . . . 01932 560913
Albion Chambers
Bristol p970 . . . . 0117 927 2144
Angel Chambers
Swansea p992 . . . . . . 01792 464623
Argent Chambers
London WC2 p923 . . . . 020 7556 5500
Atkinson Bevan Chambers
London EC4 p924 . . . . 020 7353 2112
ATLANTIC CHAMBERS
Liverpool p980 . . . . . . 0151 236 4421
BANK HOUSE CHAMBERS
Sheffield p991 . . . . . . 0114 275 1223
Barnstaple Chambers
Winkleigh p994 . . . . 01837 83763
2 Bedford Row
London WC1 p924 . . . . 020 7440 8888
7 Bedford Row
London WC1 p924 . . . . 020 7242 3555
Nine Bedford Row
London WC1 p924 . . . . 020 7489 2727
25 BEDFORD ROW
London WC1 p925 . . . . 020 7067 1500
33 Bedford Row
London WC1 p925 . . . . 020 7242 6476
36 Bedford Row
London WC1 p925 . . . . 020 7421 8000
Bell Yard Chambers
London WC2 p926
. . . . .020 7306 9292 / 7404 5138
9-12 BELL YARD CHAMBERS
London WC2 p926 . . . . 020 7400 1800
Broad Chare Chambers
Newcastle upon Tyne p986 0191 232 0541
Broadway House Chambers
Leeds p977 . . . . 0113 246 2600
Broadway House Chambers
Bradford p969 . . . . . . 01274 722560
CARMELITE CHAMBERS
London EC4 p927 . . . . 020 7936 6300
Cathedral Chambers
Newcastle upon Tyne p987 0191 232 1311
CHAVASSE COURT CHAMBERS
Liverpool p980 . . . . . . 0151 229 2030
CITADEL CHAMBERS
Birmingham p967 . . . . . 0121 233 8500
12 College Place
Southampton p992 . . . . 023 8032 0320
COLLETON CHAMBERS
Exeter p975 . . . . 01392 274898
Commonwealth Chambers
Birmingham p967 . . . . . 0121 446 5732
Cornerstone Barristers
London WC1 p929 . . . . 020 7242 4986
CORNWALL STREET CHAMBERS
Birmingham p967 . . . . . 0121 233 7500
Crown Office Row Chambers
Brighton p970 . . . . 01273 625625
Doughty Street Chambers
London WC1 p930 . . . . 020 7404 1313
2 Dr Johnson's Buildings
London EC4 p930 . . . . 020 7936 2613
Eastbourne Chambers
Eastbourne p975 . . . . . 01323 642102
23 ESSEX STREET
London WC2 p932 . . . . 020 7413 0353
23 ESSEX STREET
Manchester p983 . . . . . 0161 870 9969
23 ESSEX STREET
Nottingham p988 . . . . . 0115 935 2233
Exchange Chambers
Liverpool p980 . . . . . . 0151 236 7747
Exchange Chambers
Manchester p983 . . . . . 0161 833 2722
FARRAR'S BUILDING
London EC4 p933 . . . . 020 7583 9241
187 FLEET STREET
London EC4 p933 . . . . 020 7430 7430
FOUNTAIN CHAMBERS
Middlesbrough p986 . . . 01642 804040
FURNIVAL CHAMBERS
London EC4 p934 . . . . 020 7405 3232
9 Gough Square
London EC4 p935 . . . . 020 7832 0500
1 Gray's Inn Square
London WC1 p935 . . . . 020 7405 0001
1 Gray's Inn Square
London WC1 p935 . . . . 020 7405 8946
Guildford Chambers
Guildford p975 . . . . . . 01483 539131
GUILDHALL CHAMBERS
Bristol p970 . . . . 0117 930 9000
2 Hare Court
London EC4 p937 . . . . 020 7353 5324
7 HARRINGTON STREET CHAMBERS
Liverpool p981 . . . . . . 0151 242 0707
1 HIGH PAVEMENT
Nottingham p988 . . . . . 0115 941 8218
Iscoed Chambers
Swansea p993 . . . . . . 01792 652988
1 KBW Chambers
Lewes p980 . . . . 01273 402600
KCH Garden Square Chambers
Nottingham p989 . . . . . 0115 941 8851
KENWORTHY'S CHAMBERS
Manchester p984 . . . . . 0161 832 4036
Chambers of Dr Neville Kesselman
London NW4 p938 . . . . 020 8203 4711
Chambers of Mr S A Khan
Kingston upon Thames p977
. . . . 020 8541 3875
King's Bench Chambers
Oxford p989 . . . . 01865 311066
1 KING'S BENCH WALK
London EC4 p938 . . . . 020 7936 1500
4 KING'S BENCH WALK
London EC4 p939 . . . . 020 7822 7000
5 King's Bench Walk
London EC4 p939 . . . . 020 7353 5638
6 King's Bench Walk
London EC4 p939
. . . . .020 7583 0695 / 7353 4931
6 King's Bench Walk
London EC4 p939 . . . . 020 7583 0410
10 KING'S BENCH WALK
London EC4 p940 . . . . 020 7353 7742
13 King's Bench Walk
London EC4 p940 . . . . 020 7353 7204
21 Lauderdale Tower
London EC2 p941 . . . . 020 7920 9308
Lincoln House Chambers
Manchester p984 . . . . . 0161 832 5701
114 Liverpool Road
London N1 p941 . . . . . 020 7226 9863
LOMBARD CHAMBERS
London EC1 p941 . . . . 020 7107 2100
MAIDSTONE CHAMBERS
Maidstone p982 . . . . . 01622 688592
Malins Chambers
London EC4 p942 . . . . 020 7353 8868
6-8 Mill Street
Maidstone p982 .01622 688094 / 688095
1 Mitre Court Buildings
London EC4 p942 . . . . 020 7452 8900
MITRE HOUSE CHAMBERS
London WC1 p942 . . . . 020 7307 7100
15 New Bridge Street Chambers
London EC4 p943 . . . . 020 7842 1900
New Court Chambers
Newcastle upon Tyne p987 0191 232 1980
NO5 CHAMBERS
Birmingham p968 . . . . . 0845 210 5555
No 6 Barristers Chambers
Leeds p978 . . . . 0113 245 9763
No 8 Chambers
Birmingham p968 . . . . . 0121 236 5514
Northampton Chambers
Northampton p988 . . . . 01604 636271
OCTAGON CHAMBERS
Taunton p993 . . . . 01823 331919
Old Court Chambers
Middlesbrough p986 . . . 01642 232523
12 Old Square
London WC2 p945 . . . . 020 7404 0875
ORIEL CHAMBERS
Liverpool p981 0151 236 7191 / 236 4321
ORIEL CHAMBERS
Preston p990 . . . . 01772 254764
3PB
Bristol p971 . . . . 0117 928 1520
PALLANT CHAMBERS
Chichester p974 . . . . . 01243 784538
1 Paper Buildings
London EC4 p946 . . . . 020 7353 3728
5 Paper Buildings
London EC4 p946 . . . . 020 7583 6117
Paradise Chambers
Sheffield p992 . . . . . . 0114 273 8951
Park Court Chambers
Leeds p978 . . . . 0113 243 3277
9 Park Place
Cardiff p973 . . . . 029 2038 2731
Thirty Park Place
Cardiff p973 . . . . 029 2039 8421
39 Park Square
Leeds p978 . . . . 0113 245 6633
37 Park Square Chambers
Leeds p978 . . . . 0113 243 9422
Portal Chambers
Pencader p990 . . . . . . 01559 395292
1 Pump Court
London EC4 p947 . . . . 020 7842 7070
2 Pump Court
London EC4 p947 . . . . 020 7353 5597
5 Pump Court
London EC4 p947
. . . . .020 7353 2532 / 7583 7133
6 Pump Court
London EC4 p947 . . . . 020 7797 8400
PUMP COURT CHAMBERS
Swindon p993 . . . . . . 01793 539899
PUMP COURT CHAMBERS
Winchester p994 . . . . . 01962 868161
PUMP COURT CHAMBERS
London EC4 p947 . . . . 020 7353 0711
QEB Hollis Whiteman
London EC4 p948 . . . . 020 7933 8855
18 RED LION COURT
London EC4 p949 . . . . 020 7520 6000
18 RED LION COURT (ANNEXE)
Chelmsford p973 . . . . . 01245 280880
Regent Chambers
Hanley p976 . . . . 01782 286666
Ridgeway Chambers
London NW11 p949 . . . 020 8455 2939
Roxwell Chambers
Chelmsford p974 . . . . . 01245 248341
Rye Green Chambers
Etchingham p975 . . . . . 01435 882577
Chambers of Royln Seeboruth
Aylesbury p967 . . . . . . 01296 393329
St Albans Chambers
St Albans p992 . . . . . . 01727 843383
5 St Andrew's Hill
London EC4 p950 . . . . 020 7332 5400
St John's Chambers
Altrincham p967 . . . . . 0161 980 7379
St John's Chambers
Bristol p972 . . . . 0117 921 3456
18 St John Street Chambers
Manchester p985 . . . . . 0161 278 1800
St Pauls Chambers
Leeds p979 . . . . 0113 245 5866
ST PHILIPS CHAMBERS
Birmingham p969 . . . . . 0121 246 7000
Temple Chambers
Cardiff p973 . . . . 029 2039 7364
Temple Chambers
Newport p988 . .01633 267403 / 255855
3 Temple Gardens
London EC4 p952 . . . . 020 7353 3102
Thomas More Chambers
London WC2 p952 . . . . 020 7404 7000
Tooks Chambers
London EC4 p953 . . . . 020 7842 7575
Tower Hamlets Barristers Chambers
London E1 p953 . . . . . 020 7377 8090
TRINITY (NEWCASTLE) CHAMBERS
Newcastle upon Tyne p987 0191 232 1927
TRINITY (TEESSIDE) CHAMBERS
Middlesbrough p986 . . . 01642 247569
Unity Street Chambers
Bristol p972 . . . . 0117 906 9789
Warwick House Chambers
London WC1 p953 . . . . 020 7430 2323
Westgate Chambers
Lewes p980 . . . . 01273 480510
Wight Chambers
Newport p988
. . . . .01983 522828 / 07976 512823
WILBERFORCE CHAMBERS
Hull p976 . . . . 01482 323264
15 Winckley Square
Preston p991 . . . . 01772 252828

CRIMINAL WORK - INTERNATIONAL

Nine Bedford Row
London WC1 p924 . . . . 020 7489 2727
1 KBW Chambers
Lewes p980 . . . . 01273 402600
MITRE HOUSE CHAMBERS
London WC1 p942 . . . . 020 7307 7100
15 New Bridge Street Chambers
London EC4 p943 . . . . 020 7842 1900
PUMP COURT CHAMBERS
Swindon p993 . . . . . . 01793 539899

CRIMINAL WORK - POLICE & PRISONS

Barnstaple Chambers
Winkleigh p994 . . . . 01837 83763
COLLETON CHAMBERS
Exeter p975 . . . . 01392 274898
1 KBW Chambers
Lewes p980 . . . . 01273 402600
1 KING'S BENCH WALK
London EC4 p938 . . . . 020 7936 1500
MITRE HOUSE CHAMBERS
London WC1 p942 . . . . 020 7307 7100
15 New Bridge Street Chambers
London EC4 p943 . . . . 020 7842 1900
ORIEL CHAMBERS
Liverpool p981 0151 236 7191 / 236 4321
ORIEL CHAMBERS
Preston p990 . . . . 01772 254764

See p998 for the Firms Specialisations

DATA PROTECTION

DEFAMATION AND SLANDER

DISCRIMINATION

ECCLESIASTICAL COURTS

EDUCATION

EMPLOYMENT LAW

ENERGY

ENTERTAINMENT, ARTISTS AND PERFORMERS

ENVIRONMENT

EUROPEAN COMMUNITY LAW

EVIDENCE

FAMILY LAW

12

New Court Chambers
Newcastle upon Tyne *p987* 0191 232 1980

NO5 CHAMBERS
Birmingham *p968* 0845 210 5555

No 6 Barristers Chambers
Leeds *p978* 0113 245 9763

No 8 Chambers
Birmingham *p968* 0121 236 5514

Northampton Chambers
Northampton *p988* 01604 636271

OCTAGON CHAMBERS
Taunton *p993* 01823 331919

OCTAGON HOUSE
Norwich *p988* 01603 623186

Old Court Chambers
Middlesbrough *p986* . . . 01642 232523

12 Old Square
London WC2 *p945* 020 7404 0875

ORIEL CHAMBERS
Liverpool *p981* 0151 236 7191 / 236 4321

ORIEL CHAMBERS
Preston *p990* 01772 254764

3PB
Bristol *p971* 0117 928 1520

PALLANT CHAMBERS
Chichester *p974* 01243 784538

FIVE PAPER
London EC4 *p946* 020 7815 3200

4 Paper Buildings
London EC4 *p946* 020 7583 0816

9 Park Place
Cardiff *p973* 029 2038 2731

Thirty Park Place
Cardiff *p973* 029 2039 8421

39 Park Square
Leeds *p978* 0113 245 6633

Pendragon Chambers
Swansea *p993* 01792 411188

Portsmouth Barristers Chambers
Portsmouth *p990* 023 9283 1292

1 Pump Court
London EC4 *p947* 020 7842 7070

2 Pump Court
London EC4 *p947* 020 7353 5597

5 Pump Court
London EC4 *p947*
. . . . 020 7353 2532 / 7583 7133

PUMP COURT CHAMBERS
Swindon *p993* 01793 539899

PUMP COURT CHAMBERS
Winchester *p994* 01962 868161

PUMP COURT CHAMBERS
London EC4 *p947* 020 7353 0711

QUEEN ELIZABETH BUILDINGS
London EC4 *p948* 020 7797 7837

Regent Chambers
Hanley *p976* 01782 286666

RENAISSANCE CHAMBERS
London WC1 *p949* 020 7404 1111

Rougemont Chambers
Exeter *p975* 01392 208484

Slough Barristers Chamber
Slough *p992* . . . 01753 553806 / 817989

St Albans Chambers
St Albans *p992* 01727 843383

ST JAMES'S CHAMBERS
Manchester *p984* 0161 834 7000

St John's Chambers
Bristol *p972* 0117 921 3456

18 St John Street Chambers
Manchester *p985* 0161 278 1800

ST MARY'S CHAMBERS
Nottingham *p989* 0115 950 3503

ST PHILIPS CHAMBERS
Birmingham *p969* 0121 246 7000

Stapleton Lodge
Brentford *p970* 020 8568 2164

Stour Chambers
Canterbury *p972* 01227 764899

TANFIELD CHAMBERS
London WC1 *p951* 020 7421 5300

Temple Chambers
Cardiff *p973* 029 2039 7364

Temple Chambers
Newport *p988* . . . 01633 267403 / 255855

Thomas More Chambers
London WC2 *p952* 020 7404 7000

Tooks Chambers
London EC4 *p953* 020 7842 7575

TRINITY CHAMBERS
Chelmsford *p974* 01245 605040

TRINITY (NEWCASTLE) CHAMBERS
Newcastle upon Tyne *p987* 0191 232 1927

TRINITY (TEESSIDE) CHAMBERS
Middlesbrough *p986* . . . 01642 247569

Westgate Chambers
Lewes *p980* 01273 480510

Chambers of Tanya and Peter-John White
Bedford *p967* 01234 870004

15 Winckley Square
Preston *p991* 01772 252828

FARMING AND AGRICULTURE

FALCON CHAMBERS
London EC4 *p933* 020 7353 2484

Fenners Chambers
Cambridge *p972* 01223 368761

NEW SQUARE CHAMBERS
London WC2 *p943* 020 7419 8000

NO5 CHAMBERS
Birmingham *p968* 0845 210 5555

Radcliffe Chambers
London WC2 *p949* 020 7831 0081

3 Stone Buildings
London WC2 *p951* 020 7242 4937

TRINITY (NEWCASTLE) CHAMBERS
Newcastle upon Tyne *p987* 0191 232 1927

TRINITY (TEESSIDE) CHAMBERS
Middlesbrough *p986* . . . 01642 247569

FINANCIAL SERVICES

ERSKINE CHAMBERS
London WC2 *p931* 020 7242 5532

THIRTY NINE ESSEX STREET
London WC2 *p932* 020 7832 1111

NO5 CHAMBERS
Birmingham *p968* 0845 210 5555

TEN OLD SQUARE
London WC2 *p945* 020 7405 0758

SOUTH SQUARE
London WC1 *p950* 020 7696 9900

4 STONE BUILDINGS
London WC2 *p951* 020 7242 5524

FIREARMS

15 New Bridge Street Chambers
London EC4 *p943* 020 7842 1900

FOOD AND DRUGS LAW

GOUGH SQUARE CHAMBERS
London EC4 *p935* 020 7353 0924

NO5 CHAMBERS
Birmingham *p968* 0845 210 5555

FRAUD

Argent Chambers
London WC2 *p923* 020 7556 5500

Atkinson Bevan Chambers
London EC4 *p924* 020 7353 2112

25 BEDFORD ROW
London WC1 *p925* 020 7067 1500

9-12 BELL YARD CHAMBERS
London WC2 *p926* 020 7400 1800

CARMELITE CHAMBERS
London EC4 *p927* 020 7936 6300

CITADEL CHAMBERS
Birmingham *p967* 0121 233 8500

23 ESSEX STREET
London WC2 *p932* 020 7413 0353

23 ESSEX STREET
Manchester *p983* 0161 870 9969

23 ESSEX STREET
Nottingham *p988* 0115 935 2233

THIRTY NINE ESSEX STREET
London WC2 *p932* 020 7832 1111

FARRAR'S BUILDING
London EC4 *p933* 020 7583 9241

187 FLEET STREET
London EC4 *p933* 020 7430 7430

FURNIVAL CHAMBERS
London EC4 *p934* 020 7405 3232

GUILDHALL CHAMBERS
Bristol *p970* 0117 930 9000

1 KBW Chambers
Lewes *p980* 01273 402600

1 KING'S BENCH WALK
London EC4 *p938* 020 7936 1500

4 KING'S BENCH WALK
London EC4 *p939* 020 7822 7000

Lincoln House Chambers
Manchester *p984* 0161 832 5701

LOMBARD CHAMBERS
London EC1 *p941* 020 7107 2100

MITRE HOUSE CHAMBERS
London WC1 *p942* 020 7307 7100

15 New Bridge Street Chambers
London EC4 *p943* 020 7842 1900

NEW SQUARE CHAMBERS
London WC2 *p943* 020 7419 8000

NO5 CHAMBERS
Birmingham *p968* 0845 210 5555

ORIEL CHAMBERS
Liverpool *p981* 0151 236 7191 / 236 4321

ORIEL CHAMBERS
Preston *p990* 01772 254764

PUMP COURT CHAMBERS
Swindon *p993* 01793 539899

PUMP COURT CHAMBERS
Winchester *p994* 01962 868161

PUMP COURT CHAMBERS
London EC4 *p947* 020 7353 0711

18 RED LION COURT
London EC4 *p949* 020 7520 6000

18 RED LION COURT (ANNEXE)
Chelmsford *p973* 01245 280880

Roxwell Chambers
Chelmsford *p974* 01245 248341

SOUTH SQUARE
London WC1 *p950* 020 7696 9900

St Pauls Chambers
Leeds *p979* 0113 245 5866

ST PHILIPS CHAMBERS
Birmingham *p969* 0121 246 7000

4 STONE BUILDINGS
London WC2 *p951* 020 7242 5524

3 Temple Gardens
London EC4 *p952* 020 7353 3102

TRINITY (NEWCASTLE) CHAMBERS
Newcastle upon Tyne *p987* 0191 232 1927

TRINITY (TEESSIDE) CHAMBERS
Middlesbrough *p986* . . . 01642 247569

GAMING & LOTTERIES

TANFIELD CHAMBERS
London WC1 *p951* 020 7421 5300

HEALTH & SAFETY AT WORK

Argent Chambers
London WC2 *p923* 020 7556 5500

CROWN OFFICE CHAMBERS
London EC4 *p929* 020 7797 8100

THIRTY NINE ESSEX STREET
London WC2 *p932* 020 7832 1111

FARRAR'S BUILDING
London EC4 *p933* 020 7583 9241

GUILDHALL CHAMBERS
Bristol *p970* 0117 930 9000

15 New Bridge Street Chambers
London EC4 *p943* 020 7842 1900

NO5 CHAMBERS
Birmingham *p968* 0845 210 5555

PUMP COURT CHAMBERS
Swindon *p993* 01793 539899

PUMP COURT CHAMBERS
Winchester *p994* 01962 868161

PUMP COURT CHAMBERS
London EC4 *p947* 020 7353 0711

ST PHILIPS CHAMBERS
Birmingham *p969* 0121 246 7000

TRINITY (NEWCASTLE) CHAMBERS
Newcastle upon Tyne *p987* 0191 232 1927

TRINITY (TEESSIDE) CHAMBERS
Middlesbrough *p986* . . . 01642 247569

HEALTHCARE LAW

THIRTY NINE ESSEX STREET
London WC2 *p932* 020 7832 1111

HOUSING AND SOCIAL WELFARE

ARDEN CHAMBERS
London WC1 *p923* 020 7242 4244

Court Yard Chambers
London SE9 *p929* 020 7936 2710

Crown Office Row Chambers
Brighton *p970* 01273 625625

ENTERPRISE CHAMBERS
Leeds *p977* 0113 246 0391

ENTERPRISE CHAMBERS
London WC2 *p931* 020 7405 9471

ENTERPRISE CHAMBERS
Newcastle upon Tyne *p987* 0191 222 3344

MITRE HOUSE CHAMBERS
London WC1 *p942* 020 7307 7100

NO5 CHAMBERS
Birmingham *p968* 0845 210 5555

TEN OLD SQUARE
London WC2 *p945* 020 7405 0758

ORIEL CHAMBERS
Liverpool *p981* 0151 236 7191 / 236 4321

ORIEL CHAMBERS
Preston *p990* 01772 254764

Prince Henry's Chambers
London WC1 *p947* 020 7837 1645

1 Pump Court
London EC4 *p947* 020 7842 7070

PUMP COURT CHAMBERS
Swindon *p993* 01793 539899

PUMP COURT CHAMBERS
Winchester *p994* 01962 868161

PUMP COURT CHAMBERS
London EC4 *p947* 020 7353 0711

189 Randolph Avenue
London W9 *p949* 020 7328 0158

ST PHILIPS CHAMBERS
Birmingham *p969* 0121 246 7000

TRINITY (NEWCASTLE) CHAMBERS
Newcastle upon Tyne *p987* 0191 232 1927

TRINITY (TEESSIDE) CHAMBERS
Middlesbrough *p986* . . . 01642 247569

Warwick House Chambers
London WC1 *p953* 020 7430 2323

Chambers of Tanya and Peter-John White
Bedford *p967* 01234 870004

HUMAN RIGHTS AND CIVIL LIBERTIES

Argent Chambers
London WC2 *p923* 020 7556 5500

Camberwell Chambers
London SE5 *p927* 020 7274 0830

1 Chancery Lane
London WC2 *p928* 0845 634 6666

Coram Chambers
London EC1 *p929* 020 7092 3700

Cromwell-Ayeh-Kumi Chambers
London W3 *p929* 020 8740 6982

1 CROWN OFFICE ROW
London EC4 *p929* 020 7797 7500

Doughty Street Chambers
London WC1 *p930* 020 7404 1313

THIRTY NINE ESSEX STREET
London WC2 *p932* 020 7832 1111

FARRAR'S BUILDING
London EC4 *p933* 020 7583 9241

1 GARDEN COURT
London EC4 *p934* 020 7797 7900

Garden Court North Chambers
Manchester *p983* 0161 236 1840

4-5 GRAY'S INN SQUARE
London WC1 *p935* 020 7404 5252

Chambers of Dr Neville Kesselman
London NW4 *p938* 020 8203 4711

1 KING'S BENCH WALK
London EC4 *p938* 020 7936 1500

4 KING'S BENCH WALK
London EC4 *p939* 020 7822 7000

6 King's Bench Walk
London EC4 *p939* 020 7583 0410

MATRIX CHAMBERS
London WC1 *p942* 020 7404 3447

MITRE HOUSE CHAMBERS
London WC1 *p942* 020 7307 7100

15 New Bridge Street Chambers
London EC4 *p943* 020 7842 1900

NO5 CHAMBERS
Birmingham *p968* 0845 210 5555

ORIEL CHAMBERS
Liverpool *p981* 0151 236 7191 / 236 4321

ORIEL CHAMBERS
Preston *p990* 01772 254764

PUMP COURT CHAMBERS
Swindon *p993* 01793 539899

PUMP COURT CHAMBERS
Winchester *p994* 01962 868161

PUMP COURT CHAMBERS
London EC4 *p947* 020 7353 0711

RENAISSANCE CHAMBERS
London WC1 *p949* 020 7404 1111

ST PHILIPS CHAMBERS
Birmingham *p969* 0121 246 7000

Chambers of Mr Peter Ward
London WC2 *p953* 020 3402 2152

IMMIGRATION

Chambers of Mobin U Ahmed
London N14 *p923* 020 8886 2015

ARDEN CHAMBERS
London WC1 *p923* 020 7242 4244

Argent Chambers
London WC2 *p923* 020 7556 5500

Bell Yard Chambers
London WC2 *p926*
. . . . 020 7306 9292 / 7404 5138

Cathedral Chambers
Newcastle upon Tyne *p987* 0191 232 1311

Chartlands Chambers
Northampton *p988* 01604 603322

Court Yard Chambers
London SE9 *p929* 020 7936 2710

Cromwell-Ayeh-Kumi Chambers
London W3 *p929* 020 8740 6982

THIRTY NINE ESSEX STREET
London WC2 *p932* 020 7832 1111

FURNIVAL CHAMBERS
London EC4 *p934* 020 7405 3232

1 Garfield Road
London SW11 *p935* 020 7228 1137

See p998 for the Firms Specialisations

INFORMATION TECHNOLOGY

INSOLVENCY

INSURANCE

INTELLECTUAL PROPERTY

INTERNATIONAL LAW

ISLAMIC LAW

LANDLORD & TENANT

LICENSING

LITIGATION

LOCAL GOVERNMENT AND PUBLIC SECTOR

12

MEDIA

MEDIATION

MEDICAL LAW

1 KING'S BENCH WALK
London EC4 *p938* 020 7936 1500
15 New Bridge Street Chambers
London EC4 *p943* 020 7842 1900
NO5 CHAMBERS
Birmingham *p968* 0845 210 5555

MENTAL HEALTH

1 CROWN OFFICE ROW
London EC4 *p929* 020 7797 7500
THIRTY NINE ESSEX STREET
London WC2 *p932* 020 7832 1111
1 KING'S BENCH WALK
London EC4 *p938* 020 7936 1500
MITRE HOUSE CHAMBERS
London WC1 *p942* 020 7307 7100
15 New Bridge Street Chambers
London EC4 *p943* 020 7842 1900
NO5 CHAMBERS
Birmingham *p968* 0845 210 5555
PUMP COURT CHAMBERS
Swindon *p993* 01793 539899
PUMP COURT CHAMBERS
Winchester *p994* 01962 868161
PUMP COURT CHAMBERS
London EC4 *p947* 020 7353 0711
Chambers of Royln Seeboruth
Aylesbury *p967* 01296 393329
St Johns Buildings
Liverpool *p982* 0151 243 6000
ST PHILIPS CHAMBERS
Birmingham *p969* 0121 246 7000
TRINITY (NEWCASTLE) CHAMBERS
Newcastle upon Tyne *p987* 0191 232 1927
TRINITY (TEESSIDE) CHAMBERS
Middlesbrough *p986* . . . 01642 247569
3 Wayside Green
Woodcote *p994* 01491 680722

MILITARY LAW

Argent Chambers
London WC2 *p923* 020 7556 5500
1 KING'S BENCH WALK
London EC4 *p938* 020 7936 1500
4 KING'S BENCH WALK
London EC4 *p939* 020 7822 7000
15 New Bridge Street Chambers
London EC4 *p943* 020 7842 1900
ST PHILIPS CHAMBERS
Birmingham *p969* 0121 246 7000

MILITARY LAW & COURTS MARTIAL

Argent Chambers
London WC2 *p923* 020 7556 5500
Atkinson Bevan Chambers
London EC4 *p924* 020 7353 2112
CARMELITE CHAMBERS
London EC4 *p927* 020 7936 6300
15 New Bridge Street Chambers
London EC4 *p943* 020 7842 1900
OCTAGON CHAMBERS
Taunton *p993* 01823 331919
PUMP COURT CHAMBERS
Swindon *p993* 01793 539899
PUMP COURT CHAMBERS
Winchester *p994* 01962 868161
PUMP COURT CHAMBERS
London EC4 *p947* 020 7353 0711
TRINITY (NEWCASTLE) CHAMBERS
Newcastle upon Tyne *p987* 0191 232 1927
TRINITY (TEESSIDE) CHAMBERS
Middlesbrough *p986* . . . 01642 247569

MINES AND MINERALS

THIRTY NINE ESSEX STREET
London WC2 *p932* 020 7832 1111
NO5 CHAMBERS
Birmingham *p968* 0845 210 5555

OFFSHORE

Atkin Chambers
London WC1 *p923* 020 7404 0102
NEW SQUARE CHAMBERS
London WC2 *p943* 020 7419 8000
4 STONE BUILDINGS
London WC2 *p951* 020 7242 5524

PARLIAMENTARY LAW

THIRTY NINE ESSEX STREET
London WC2 *p932* 020 7832 1111
LANDMARK CHAMBERS
London EC4 *p941* 020 7430 1221
TEN OLD SQUARE
London WC2 *p945* 020 7405 0758

PARTNERSHIPS AND BUSINESS ARRANGEMENTS

48 Bedford Row
London WC1 *p926* 020 7430 2005
ERSKINE CHAMBERS
London WC2 *p931* 020 7242 5532
GUILDHALL CHAMBERS
Bristol *p970* 0117 930 9000
NEW SQUARE CHAMBERS
London WC2 *p943* 020 7419 8000
NO5 CHAMBERS
Birmingham *p968* 0845 210 5555
TEN OLD SQUARE
London WC2 *p945* 020 7405 0758
ORIEL CHAMBERS
Liverpool *p981* 0151 236 7191 / 236 4321
ORIEL CHAMBERS
Preston *p990* 01772 254764
SOUTH SQUARE
London WC1 *p950* 020 7696 9900
ST JAMES'S CHAMBERS
Manchester *p984* 0161 834 7000
ST PHILIPS CHAMBERS
Birmingham *p969* 0121 246 7000
4 STONE BUILDINGS
London WC2 *p951* 020 7242 5524

PENSIONS

WILBERFORCE CHAMBERS
London WC2 *p953* 020 7306 0102

PERSONAL INJURY

ATLANTIC CHAMBERS
Liverpool *p980* 0151 236 4421
Bath Chambers
Melksham *p986* 01225 702347
Broadway House Chambers
Bradford *p969* 01274 722560
BYROM STREET CHAMBERS
Manchester *p983* 0161 829 2100
1 Chancery Lane
London WC2 *p928* 0845 634 6666
Counsels Chambers
Yarm *p994* 01642 650550
CROWN OFFICE CHAMBERS
London EC4 *p929* 020 7797 8100
1 CROWN OFFICE ROW
London EC4 *p929* 020 7797 7500
Crown Office Row Chambers
Brighton *p970* 01273 625625
THIRTY NINE ESSEX STREET
London WC2 *p932* 020 7832 1111
FARRAR'S BUILDING
London EC4 *p933* 020 7583 9241
GUILDHALL CHAMBERS
Bristol *p970* 0117 930 9000
Hailsham Chambers
London EC4 *p936* 020 7643 5000
Harbour Court Chambers
Southampton *p992* 01489 557999
7 HARRINGTON STREET CHAMBERS
Liverpool *p981* 0151 242 0707
Iscoed Chambers
Swansea *p993* 01792 652988
KENWORTHY'S CHAMBERS
Manchester *p984* 0161 832 4036
Kew Chambers
Kew *p976* 0844 809 9991
King's Bench Godolphin Chambers
Truro *p994* 0845 308 1551
1 KING'S BENCH WALK
London EC4 *p938* 020 7936 1500
4 KING'S BENCH WALK
London EC4 *p939* 020 7822 7000
12 KING'S BENCH WALK
London EC4 *p940* 020 7583 0811
Lincoln House Chambers
Manchester *p984* 0161 832 5701
MITRE HOUSE CHAMBERS
London WC1 *p942* 020 7307 7100
New Court Chambers
Newcastle upon Tyne *p987* 0191 232 1980
NO5 CHAMBERS
Birmingham *p968* 0845 210 5555
Old Square Chambers
Bristol *p971* 0117 930 5100
Old Square Chambers
London WC1 *p945* 020 7269 0300
ORIEL CHAMBERS
Liverpool *p981* 0151 236 7191 / 236 4321
ORIEL CHAMBERS
Preston *p990* 01772 254764
Outer Temple Chambers
London WC2 *p945* 020 7353 6381
PALLANT CHAMBERS
Chichester *p974* 01243 784538
Pendragon Chambers
Swansea *p993* 01792 411188
PUMP COURT CHAMBERS
Swindon *p993* 01793 539899
PUMP COURT CHAMBERS
Winchester *p994* 01962 868161
PUMP COURT CHAMBERS
London EC4 *p947* 020 7353 0711
Regent Chambers
Hanley *p976* 01782 286666
ROPEWALK CHAMBERS
Nottingham *p989* 0115 947 2581
ST JAMES'S CHAMBERS
Manchester *p984* 0161 834 7000
St John's Chambers
Bristol *p972* 0117 921 3456
ST PHILIPS CHAMBERS
Birmingham *p969* 0121 246 7000
TANFIELD CHAMBERS
London WC1 *p951* 020 7421 5300
TRINITY CHAMBERS
Chelmsford *p974* 01245 605040
TRINITY (NEWCASTLE) CHAMBERS
Newcastle upon Tyne *p987* 0191 232 1927
TRINITY (TEESSIDE) CHAMBERS
Middlesbrough *p986* . . . 01642 247569
Unity Street Chambers
Bristol *p972* 0117 906 9789
WILBERFORCE CHAMBERS
Hull *p976* 01482 323264
15 Winckley Square
Preston *p991* 01772 252828

PLANNING AND RATING

CROWN OFFICE CHAMBERS
London EC4 *p929* 020 7797 8100
Crown Office Row Chambers
Brighton *p970* 01273 625625
THIRTY NINE ESSEX STREET
London WC2 *p932* 020 7832 1111
Francis Taylor Building
London EC4 *p934* 020 7353 8415
4-5 GRAY'S INN SQUARE
London WC1 *p935* 020 7404 5252
LANDMARK CHAMBERS
London EC4 *p941* 020 7430 1221
MITRE HOUSE CHAMBERS
London WC1 *p942* 020 7307 7100
NO5 CHAMBERS
Birmingham *p968* 0845 210 5555
TEN OLD SQUARE
London WC2 *p945* 020 7405 0758
Portal Chambers
Pencader *p990* 01559 395292
ST PHILIPS CHAMBERS
Birmingham *p969* 0121 246 7000
TRINITY CHAMBERS
Chelmsford *p974* 01245 605040
TRINITY (NEWCASTLE) CHAMBERS
Newcastle upon Tyne *p987* 0191 232 1927
TRINITY (TEESSIDE) CHAMBERS
Middlesbrough *p986* . . . 01642 247569

PRIVATE CLIENT

15 New Bridge Street Chambers
London EC4 *p943* 020 7842 1900
TEN OLD SQUARE
London WC2 *p945* 020 7405 0758
PUMP COURT TAX CHAMBERS
London WC1 *p948* 020 7414 8080

PROBATE

MITRE HOUSE CHAMBERS
London WC1 *p942* 020 7307 7100
NEW SQUARE CHAMBERS
London WC2 *p943* 020 7419 8000
NO5 CHAMBERS
Birmingham *p968* 0845 210 5555
TEN OLD SQUARE
London WC2 *p945* 020 7405 0758
PUMP COURT CHAMBERS
Swindon *p993* 01793 539899
PUMP COURT CHAMBERS
Winchester *p994* 01962 868161
PUMP COURT CHAMBERS
London EC4 *p947* 020 7353 0711
ST JAMES'S CHAMBERS
Manchester *p984* 0161 834 7000
St John's Chambers
Bristol *p972* 0117 921 3456
ST PHILIPS CHAMBERS
Birmingham *p969* 0121 246 7000
TRINITY (NEWCASTLE) CHAMBERS
Newcastle upon Tyne *p987* 0191 232 1927
TRINITY (TEESSIDE) CHAMBERS
Middlesbrough *p986* . . . 01642 247569

PROFESSIONAL NEGLIGENCE

Advolex Chambers
Croydon *p975* 0871 717 7321
Atkin Chambers
London WC1 *p923* 020 7404 0102
1 Chancery Lane
London WC2 *p928* 0845 634 6666
CROWN OFFICE CHAMBERS
London EC4 *p929* 020 7797 8100
1 CROWN OFFICE ROW
London EC4 *p929* 020 7797 7500
ENTERPRISE CHAMBERS
Leeds *p977* 0113 246 0391
ENTERPRISE CHAMBERS
London WC2 *p931* 020 7405 9471
ENTERPRISE CHAMBERS
Newcastle upon Tyne *p987* 0191 222 3344
ERSKINE CHAMBERS
London WC2 *p931* 020 7242 5532
THIRTY NINE ESSEX STREET
London WC2 *p932* 020 7832 1111
FARRAR'S BUILDING
London EC4 *p933* 020 7583 9241
Fountain Court Chambers
London EC4 *p934* 020 7583 3335
GUILDHALL CHAMBERS
Bristol *p970* 0117 930 9000
Hailsham Chambers
London EC4 *p936* 020 7643 5000
Keating Chambers
London WC2 *p938* 020 7544 2600
1 KING'S BENCH WALK
London EC4 *p938* 020 7936 1500
4 KING'S BENCH WALK
London EC4 *p939* 020 7822 7000
MITRE HOUSE CHAMBERS
London WC1 *p942* 020 7307 7100
Four New Square
London WC2 *p943* 020 7822 2000
NO5 CHAMBERS
Birmingham *p968* 0845 210 5555
TEN OLD SQUARE
London WC2 *p945* 020 7405 0758
ORIEL CHAMBERS
Liverpool *p981* 0151 236 7191 / 236 4321
ORIEL CHAMBERS
Preston *p990* 01772 254764
Prince Henry's Chambers
London WC1 *p947* 020 7837 1645
PUMP COURT CHAMBERS
Swindon *p993* 01793 539899
PUMP COURT CHAMBERS
Winchester *p994* 01962 868161
PUMP COURT CHAMBERS
London EC4 *p947* 020 7353 0711
PUMP COURT TAX CHAMBERS
London WC1 *p948* 020 7414 8080
QUEEN ELIZABETH BUILDINGS
London EC4 *p948* 020 7797 7837
5 St Andrew's Hill
London EC4 *p950* 020 7332 5400
ST JAMES'S CHAMBERS
Manchester *p984* 0161 834 7000
ST PHILIPS CHAMBERS
Birmingham *p969* 0121 246 7000
TRINITY (NEWCASTLE) CHAMBERS
Newcastle upon Tyne *p987* 0191 232 1927
TRINITY (TEESSIDE) CHAMBERS
Middlesbrough *p986* . . . 01642 247569

PROPERTY

ARDEN CHAMBERS
London WC1 *p923* 020 7242 4244
1 Chancery Lane
London WC2 *p928* 0845 634 6666
ENTERPRISE CHAMBERS
Leeds *p977* 0113 246 0391
ENTERPRISE CHAMBERS
London WC2 *p931* 020 7405 9471
ENTERPRISE CHAMBERS
Newcastle upon Tyne *p987* 0191 222 3344
THIRTY NINE ESSEX STREET
London WC2 *p932* 020 7832 1111
FALCON CHAMBERS
London EC4 *p933* 020 7353 2484
GUILDHALL CHAMBERS
Bristol *p970* 0117 930 9000
Two King's Bench Walk
London EC4 *p939*
. . . . 020 7353 7202 / 7353 3909
LANDMARK CHAMBERS
London EC4 *p941* 020 7430 1221
Maitland Chambers
London WC2 *p941* 020 7406 1200
NEW SQUARE CHAMBERS
London WC2 *p943* 020 7419 8000

See p998 for the Firms Specialisations

PUBLIC INTERNATIONAL LAW

REVENUE

ROAD TRAFFIC LAW

SHIPPING AND ADMIRALTY

SPORTS LAW

TAXATION – BUSINESS

TAXATION – PERSONAL

TERRORISM

TOURISM AND TRAVEL

TRANSPORT

TRIBUNALS AND INQUIRIES

UTILITIES - ELECTRICITY, GAS, WATER

WILLS AND TRUSTS

SECTION 13

BARRISTERS

CONTENTS

13

Work Categories for Barristers

1 Administrative Law, Constitutional Law and Public Law
2 Farming and Agriculture
3 Arbitration including International Trade
4 Aviation
5 Banking
6 Bankruptcy
7 Building
8 Chancery, General
9 Charities
10 Children
11 Commercial Law
12 Common Law, General
13 Intellectual Property
14 Court of Protection
15 Criminal Work – General
16 Defamation and Slander
17 Ecclesiastical Courts
18 Employment Law
19 European Community Law
20 Family Law
21 International Law
22 Housing and Social Welfare
23 Immigration
24 Insurance
25 Licensing
26 Local Government and Public Sector
27 Medical Law
28 Parliamentary Law
29 Partnerships and Business Arrangements
30 Personal Injury
31 Planning & Rating
32 Probate
33 Public International Law
34 Revenue
35 Shipping and Admiralty
36 Tribunals and Inquiries
37 Wills & Trusts
38 Insolvency
39 Food and Drugs Law
40 Professional Negligence
41 Arbitration
42 Military Law
43 Communications and Telecommunications
44 Competition Law
45 Information Technology
46 Environment
47 Consumer Law – Agreements, Credit, Licensing, Sale of Goods
48 Consumer Protection – Advertising, Trade Descriptions, Trading Standards, Product Liability
49 Alternative Dispute Resolution (ADR)
50 Entertainment, Artists and Performers
51 Human Rights and Civil Liberties
52 Media
53 Clinical Negligence
54 Mines and Minerals
55 Discrimination
56 Sports Law
57 Taxation – Business
58 Taxation – Personal
59 Tourism and Travel
60 Transport
61 Utilities – Electric, Gas, Water
62 Fraud
63 Mental Health
64 Islamic Law
65 Accountancy
66 Agency
67 Contract Law
68 Coroner
69 Corporate Finance
70 Criminal Work – Police & Prisons
71 Criminal Work – International
72 Criminal Work – Criminal Procedures
73 Data Protection
74 Construction
75 E-Commerce
76 Education
77 Elder Law & Elder Care
78 Energy
79 Offshore
80 Evidence
81 Financial Services
82 Firearms
83 Gaming & Lotteries
84 Health & Safety at Work
85 Healthcare Law
86 Private Client
87 Internet Law
88 Landlord & Tenant
89 Litigation
91 Military Law & Courts Martial
92 Pensions
93 Property
94 Road Traffic Law
95 Terrorism
96 Mediation
97 Company Law

Key Facts

See Notice, Data Protection Act 1984, p. iv

The wording after each name shows the Inn of Court and the month and year of Call: where

G = Gray's Inn I = Inner Temple L = Lincoln's Inn M = Middle Temple

INDIVIDUAL BARRISTERS, ENGLAND & WALES – A-Z

Italic figures after names refer to the Work Categories for Barristers

Aaronberg, Mr David I *Jul 1981*
(Q.C.) *15, 62*
15 New Bridge Street Chambers, London EC4
p943 . . . . 020 7842 1900

AARONSON, Mr Graham M *Nov 1966*
(Q.C.) *34, 57, 58*
Pump Court Tax Chambers, London WC1
p948 . . . . 020 7414 8080

Abadoo, Mr Joseph M *Jan 2005*
2 Pump Court, London EC4
p947 . . . . 020 7353 5597

Abashiekh, Mr Omar G *Jul 2006*
6 King's Bench Walk, London EC4
p939 . . . . 020 7583 0695 / 7353 4931

Abbasi, Miss Nylah Naz BA L *Mar 2001*
15, 23, 20, 18, 10, 88, 94
Bell Yard Chambers, London WC2
p926 . . . . 020 7306 9292 / 7404 5138

Abberley, Mr Stephen M *Nov 2000*
20, 10
No5 Chambers, Bristol
p971 . . . . 0845 210 5555
No5 Chambers, London EC4
p944 . . . . 0845 210 5555
No5 Chambers, Birmingham
p968 . . . . 0845 210 5555

ABBOTT, Ms Christine LLB M *Oct 1999*
20, 10
Temple Chambers, Newport
p988 . . . . 01633 267403 / 255855
Temple Chambers, Cardiff
p973 . . . . 029 2039 7364

ABBOTT, Mr Frank BA(Oxon); LLB(Cantab); Recorder L *Nov 1972*
12, 15, 20, 49
Pump Court Chambers, Swindon
p993 . . . . 01793 539899
Pump Court Chambers, Winchester
p994 . . . . 01962 868161
Pump Court Chambers, London EC4
p947 . . . . 020 7353 0711

Abbott, Mrs Mary G *Oct 1994*
20, 10
36 Bedford Row, London WC1
p925 . . . . 020 7421 8000

Abbott, Mr Roderick M *Jan 2006*
53, 12, 22, 88, 26, 30, 40
1 Chancery Lane, London WC2
p928 . . . . 0845 634 6666

Abebrese, Mr Owusu LLB; LLM(Lond) I *Jul 1985*
11, 12
12 Old Square, London WC2
p945 . . . . 020 7404 0875

Abell, Mr Anthony LLB(Hons); Recorder G *Jul 1977*
15, 62
2 Bedford Row, London WC1
p924 . . . . 020 7440 8888

Abengowe, Mr Julian LLB I *Nov 2002*
Zenith Chambers, Leeds
p979 . . . . 0113 245 5438

Abraham, Ms Joanne Jade G *Nov 2004*
10, 20
St Johns Buildings, Preston
p990 . . . . 01772 256100
St Johns Buildings, Chester
p974 . . . . 01244 323070
St Johns Buildings, Manchester
p985 . . . . 0161 214 1500
St Johns Buildings, Liverpool
p982 . . . . 0151 243 6000

Abrahams, Mr James BA(Oxon) G *Oct 1997*
13, 50, 45, 56
8 New Square, London WC2
p943 . . . . 020 7405 4321

Abrahams, Mr Paul LLB(Sheff) G *Nov 2002*
25, 30, 22, 61, 36, 26, 15, 72, 70
Old Court Chambers, Middlesbrough
p986 . . . . 01642 232523

Abzarian, Arash L *Mar 2007*
15, 1, 94
Lamb Building, Brighton
p970 . . . . 01273 820490
Lamb Building, London EC4
p940 . . . . 020 7797 7788

Ace, Mr Richard BSc(Hons); DipLaw(Lond) L *Oct 1993*
15
9 Park Place, Cardiff
p973 . . . . 029 2038 2731

ACHESON, Mr Ian BA(Oxon) G *Feb 1992*
15, 62
23 Essex Street, London WC2
p932 . . . . 020 7413 0353

ACHURCH, Mr Mark M *Jan 1996*
15
1 High Pavement, Nottingham
p988 . . . . 0115 941 8218

Ackerley, Mr David I *Oct 1992*
12, 15, 51
New Bailey Chambers, Preston
p990 . . . . 01772 258087

Ackerley, Miss Rebecca L *Jan 2004*
15
New Bailey Chambers, Preston
p990 . . . . 01772 258087

ACKLAND, Miss Sacha BA(Lond) I *Sep 1998*
Temple Garden Chambers, London EC4
p952 . . . . 020 7583 1315

ACKLAND-VINCENT, Ms Gillian M *Jul 2001*
1, 22, 26, 88, 93
Arden Chambers, London WC1
p923 . . . . 020 7242 4244

Acland, Dr Piers BSc; PhD L *Nov 1993*
(Q.C.) *73, 50, 19, 45, 13, 52, 96, 41*
11 South Square, London WC1
p950 . . . . 020 7405 1222

Acton, Miss Jayne LLB L *Mar 1996*
10, 20
Exchange Chambers, Manchester
p983 . . . . 0161 833 2722
Exchange Chambers, Liverpool
p980 . . . . 0151 236 7747
Exchange Chambers, Leeds
p977 . . . . 0113 203 1970

Acton, Mr Stephen MA(Cantab) I *Jul 1977*
5, 6, 8, 11, 22, 29, 32, 37, 40
Radcliffe Chambers, London WC2
p949 . . . . 020 7831 0081

Acton Davis, Mr Jonathan LLB(Lond); Recorder I *Jul 1977*
(Q.C.) *3, 7, 11, 31, 40, 41, 43, 45, 49, 54, 61, 78, 74*
Atkin Chambers, London WC1
p923 . . . . 020 7404 0102

Adair, Mr Stuart Anthony LLB(Exon) I *Oct 1995*
6, 8, 11, 29, 32, 37, 40, 5, 36, 41, 49, 62
XXIV Old Buildings, London WC2
p944 . . . . 020 7691 2424

Adam, Mr Thomas MA(Cantab) I *Nov 1991*
11, 5, 40, 24, 35
Brick Court Chambers, London WC2
p927 . . . . 020 7379 3550

ADAMS, Brynmor BA(Oxon) L *Jul 2008*
8, 93, 18, 88, 22
Five Paper, London EC4
p946 . . . . 020 7815 3200

ADAMS, Mr Christopher Alan LLB(Lond); Recorder L *Jul 1986*
20
St Philips Chambers, Birmingham
p969 . . . . 0121 246 7000

Adams, Mr Derek LLM; BA; DipLaw; Attorney(New York Bar) M *Nov 1988*
23, 18
12 Old Square, London WC2
p945 . . . . 020 7404 0875

Adams, Mr Guy MA(Cantab) M *Jul 1989*
1, 5, 6, 8, 11, 29, 32, 37, 88
St John's Chambers, Bristol
p972 . . . . 0117 921 3456

Adams, Mr James Robert LLB; BL G *Jul 1978*
15
New Court Chambers, Newcastle upon Tyne
p987 . . . . 0191 232 1980

ADAMS, Miss Jayne Margaret LLB G *Jul 1982*
30, 53, 40
Ropewalk Chambers, Nottingham
p989 . . . . 0115 947 2581

Adams, Ms Lindsay LLB M *Nov 1987*
15, 10, 20
1 Pump Court, London EC4
p947 . . . . 020 7842 7070

Adams, Mr Nathan M *Jan 2004*
York Chambers, York
p995 . . . . 01904 620048
York Chambers, Newcastle upon Tyne
p987 . . . . 0191 206 4677

ADAMS, Mr Richard G *Oct 1999*
11, 12
St Philips Chambers, Birmingham
p969 . . . . 0121 246 7000

ADAMS, Mr Robert George Seton MA(Cantab); Recorder (Crime) I *Oct 1993*
15, 25, 2, 91
Trinity (Teesside) Chambers, Middlesbrough
p986 . . . . 01642 247569
Trinity (Newcastle) Chambers, Newcastle upon Tyne
p987 . . . . 0191 232 1927

Adamson, Mr Alan I *Jan 1997*
30, 68
Kew Chambers, Kew
p976 . . . . 0844 809 9991

ADAMSON, Mr Dominic LLB(Newc) L *Oct 1997*
Temple Garden Chambers, London EC4
p952 . . . . 020 7583 1315

Adamson, Ms Lilias L BA(Hons) G *Nov 1994*
10, 20
Becket Chambers, Canterbury
p972 . . . . 01227 786331
Becket Chambers, Maidstone
p982 . . . . 01622 230957

ADAMYK, Mr Simon BA(Cantab); LLM(Harv) L *Nov 1991*
6, 8, 11, 22, 40, 62
New Square Chambers, London WC2
p943 . . . . 020 7419 8000

Adcock, Ms Deborah G *Jan 2005*
York Chambers, York
p995 . . . . 01904 620048
York Chambers, Newcastle upon Tyne
p987 . . . . 0191 206 4677

Addicott, Miss Elizabeth I *Jul 2006*
York Chambers, York
p995 . . . . 01904 620048
York Chambers, Newcastle upon Tyne
p987 . . . . 0191 206 4677

ADDY, Ms Caroline LLB(Hons) I *Nov 1991*
16, 52, 73
One Brick Court, London EC4
p927 . . . . 020 7353 8845

Addy, Ms Catherine MA; LLM; Junior Counsel to Crown B Panel M *Nov 1998*
Maitland Chambers, London WC2
p941 . . . . 020 7406 1200

Adebayo, Mr Ibitayo Alade BA(Hons); DipLaw(Bris) I *Nov 1989*
15, 62
2 Bedford Row, London WC1
p924 . . . . 020 7440 8888

Adedeji, Ms Yinka MA(Hons); LLB(Hons) L *Nov 1997*
1 Pump Court, London EC4
p947 . . . . 020 7842 7070

ADJEI, Mr Cyril John LLB(LSE); LLM(Cantab); PhD(EUI Florence) I *Oct 1995*
18
Five Paper, London EC4
p946 . . . . 020 7815 3200

Adkin, Mr James LLB(Hons) L *Oct 1992*
12, 15, 18, 20, 30
New Court Chambers, Newcastle upon Tyne
p987 . . . . 0191 232 1980

Adkin, Mr Jonathan MA(Oxon) G *Nov 1997*
11, 62, 8, 89, 37
Serle Court, London WC2
p950 . . . . 020 7242 6105

Adkin, Mr Tim BSc(Hons)(Bris) L *Nov 2004*
42 Bedford Row, London WC1
p925 . . . . 020 7831 0222

ADKINS, Mr Richard MA(Oxon) M *Jul 1982*
(Q.C.) *5, 6, 8, 11, 12, 24, 29, 38*
South Square, London WC1
p950 . . . . 020 7696 9900

Adkinson, Mr Richard MEng(Hons); PG DipLaw M *Jul 2001*
8, 11, 67, 55, 18, 88, 93, 37
No5 Chambers, Bristol
p971 . . . . 0845 210 5555
No5 Chambers, London EC4
p944 . . . . 0845 210 5555
No5 Chambers, Birmingham
p968 . . . . 0845 210 5555

Adler, Mr Johnathan BA I *Jan 1999*
23, 15, 10, 20
4 Brick Court Chambers, London EC4
p927 . . . . 020 7832 3200
1 Pump Court, London EC4
p947 . . . . 020 7842 7070

13

Adonis, Mr George L *Jul 1973*
15, 25, 20, 12
1 Inner Temple Lane, London EC4
p937 . . . 020 7427 4400

Aeberli, Mr Peter MA(Edin); BA(Oxon); RIBA; RIAS; FCIArb M *Oct 1990*
41
3PB, London EC4
p946 . . . 020 7583 8055

AFEEVA, Mr Mark LLB(Lond); LLM(Lond) I *Oct 1997*
16, 49, 18, 55, 56, 50, 12
Matrix Chambers, London WC1
p942 . . . 020 7404 3447

Afzal, Dr Fayyaz LLB L *Jan 1999* OBE; Doctorate
1, 10, 12, 72, 15, 20, 62, 23, 30, 64
No5 Chambers, Bristol
p971 . . . 0845 210 5555
No5 Chambers, London EC4
p944 . . . 0845 210 5555
No5 Chambers, Birmingham
p968 . . . 0845 210 5555

Afzal, Mr Imran BA; MBCL L *Jan 2008*
34, 57, 58
Gray's Inn Tax Chambers, London WC1
p936 . . . 020 7242 2642

AFZAL, Zaheer G *Jun 2000*
15, 62
St Philips Chambers, Birmingham
p969 . . . 0121 246 7000

Agbaje, Mr Edward BA M *Nov 1984*
15, 23
1 Gray's Inn Square, London WC1
p935 . . . 020 7405 8946

Ager, Mr Richard M *Jan 2004*
10, 20
Crown Office Row Chambers, Brighton
p970 . . . 01273 625625

Ageros, Mr James BA I *May 1990*
15, 62
2 Bedford Row, London WC1
p924 . . . 020 7440 8888

Ageros, Mr Justin BA(Cantab) I *Nov 1993*
10, 20
4 Paper Buildings, London EC4
p946 . . . 020 7583 0816

AGGREY-ORLEANS, Kweku LLB(Lond) I *Jan 1998*
12, 18, 24, 30, 67
12 King's Bench Walk, London EC4
p940 . . . 020 7583 0811

Agnello, Ms Raquel BA(Sussex) I *Nov 1986*
(Q.C.) *5, 6, 11, 38*
11 Stone Buildings, London WC2
p951 . . . 020 7831 6381

Agnew, Miss Christine LLB(Hons) I *Oct 1992*
15, 62
2 Bedford Row, London WC1
p924 . . . 020 7440 8888

Agnihotri, Mr Naveen LLB(Hons)(LSE) G *Jul 2001*
15, 18, 12, 31, 22, 30, 23
12 College Place, Southampton
p992 . . . 023 8032 0320

AHERN, Mr Eugene M *Jul 2007*
20, 10
Trinity Chambers, Chelmsford
p974 . . . 01245 605040

AHLUWALIA, Ms Paramjit G *Mar 2002*
15, 70
Mitre House Chambers, London WC1
p942 . . . 020 7307 7100

Ahmad, Ms Aysha BA(Hons)(Lond); LLM(Lond) M *Oct 1996*
18, 40, 12, 10, 20, 55
42 Bedford Row, London WC1
p925 . . . 020 7831 0222

Ahmad, Ms Tayyiba L *Jul 1998*
23, 10, 20
1 Pump Court, London EC4
p947 . . . 020 7842 7070

Ahmad, Mr Zubair LLB(Hons)(Lond) L *Oct 1995*
15, 42
2 Hare Court, London EC4
p937 . . . 020 7353 5324

Ahmadi, Ms Hannah LLB G *Jan 2009*
12, 15, 20, 23
Temple Chambers, Newport
p988 . . . 01633 267403 / 255855
Temple Chambers, Cardiff
p973 . . . 029 2039 7364

AHMED, Amina BSc(Hons)(Lond); CPE(Lond) M *Feb 1995*
10, 20
Renaissance Chambers, London WC1
p949 . . . 020 7404 1111

Ahmed, Bushra M *Jan 2001*
18, 11, 12
Ely Place Chambers, London EC1
p931 . . . 020 7400 9600

Ahmed, Mr Farooq T LLB(Hons); Recorder I *Nov 1983*
1, 20, 10, 26
7 Bedford Row, London WC1
p924 . . . 020 7242 3555

Ahmed, Mr Gulam G *Sep 1997*
15, 23
1 Inner Temple Lane, London EC4
p937 . . . 020 7427 4400

Ahmed, Mr Ishfaq LLB(Hons)(Bris) L *Oct 1999*
3, 11, 12, 18, 21, 24, 35, 41, 55
Stone Chambers, London WC1
p951 . . . 020 7440 6900

Ahmed, Miss Jacqueline LLB I *Jul 1988*
10, 20
Southernhay Chambers, Exeter
p975 . . . 01392 255777

Ahmed, Mobin Uddin BCom(Hons) L *Nov 1969*
10, 53, 12, 15, 71, 18, 20, 22, 51, 23, 64, 88, 25
Chambers of Mobin U Ahmed, London N14
p923 . . . 020 8886 2015

Ahmed, Rashid L *Jan 2003*
6 King's Bench Walk, London EC4
p939 . . . 020 7583 0695 / 7353 4931

Ahmed, Mr Saleem BA I *Feb 1971*
15, 23, 20
Perivale Chambers, Perivale
p990 . . . 020 8998 1935 / 8991 1823

Ahmed, Mr Sharaz L *Jan 2000*
Clapham Law Chambers, London SW1
p928 . . . 020 7978 8482 / 7642 5777

Ahmed, Siraj Issap LLB(Hons)(Bris) M *Apr 2001*
10, 30, 23, 20
St Johns Buildings, Preston
p990 . . . 01772 256100
St Johns Buildings, Chester
p974 . . . 01244 323070
St Johns Buildings, Manchester
p985 . . . 0161 214 1500
St Johns Buildings, Liverpool
p982 . . . 0151 243 6000

Ahmed, Miss Sobia LLB(Hons) L *Oct 2007*
Zenith Chambers, Leeds
p979 . . . 0113 245 5438

AHUJA, Mr Harry I *Oct 2001*
15, 10, 12, 20
Octagon Chambers, Taunton
p993 . . . 01823 331919

Ahya, Miss Sonal L *Sep 1995*
15
KCH Garden Square Chambers, Nottingham
p989 . . . 0115 941 8851
KCH Garden Square Chambers, Leicester
p979 . . . 0115 941 8851

AINGER, Mr David MA(Oxon) L *Jun 1961*
2, 3, 5, 6, 8, 9, 11, 12, 14, 17, 22, 24, 26, 28, 29, 32, 36, 37
Ten Old Square, London WC2
p945 . . . 020 7405 0758

Ainsley, Mr Stephen Paul M *Jul 2001*
15, 20
Broad Chare Chambers, Newcastle upon Tyne
p986 . . . 0191 232 0541

Ainsworth, Mr Mark Recorder L *Oct 1992*
15, 36, 64, 84
Exchange Chambers, Manchester
p983 . . . 0161 833 2722
Exchange Chambers, Liverpool
p980 . . . 0151 236 7747
Exchange Chambers, Leeds
p977 . . . 0113 203 1970

AIOLFI, Mr Laurence LLB I *Oct 1996*
15
23 Essex Street, London WC2
p932 . . . 020 7413 0353

AJMONE-MARSAN, Mr Cosimo Marco L *Jul 2009*
11, 12, 18, 30, 40, 51
3 Hare Court, London EC4
p937 . . . 020 7415 7800

Akast, Mr John F LLB; Recorder I *Nov 1968*
15, 12, 30, 32, 10
East Anglian Chambers, Norwich
p988 . . . 01603 617351
East Anglian Chambers, Colchester
p975 . . . 01206 572756
East Anglian Chambers, Chelmsford
p973 . . . 01245 215660
East Anglian Chambers, Ipswich
p976 . . . 01473 214481

Akerman, Miss Kate LLB(Hons) M *Oct 1994*
20
15 Winckley Square, Preston
p991 . . . 01772 252828

Akers, Mr Robert I *Nov 2003*
15
St Johns Buildings, Preston
p990 . . . 01772 256100
St Johns Buildings, Chester
p974 . . . 01244 323070
St Johns Buildings, Manchester
p985 . . . 0161 214 1500
St Johns Buildings, Liverpool
p982 . . . 0151 243 6000

Akhavan-Tabib, Ms Maryam LLB; LLM(KCL) I *Oct 2005*
10, 20
Coram Chambers, London EC1
p929 . . . 020 7092 3700

Akhtar, Miss Shazia BSocSc M *Nov 2001*
19, 51, 26, 49, 1
Hardwicke, London WC2
p936 . . . 020 7242 2523

Akin, Mr Barrie LLB(Sheff); FCA M *Jul 1976*
34, 57, 58
Gray's Inn Tax Chambers, London WC1
p936 . . . 020 7242 2642

AKINBOLU, Ms Sandra L *Oct 2002*
15, 23
Mitre House Chambers, London WC1
p942 . . . 020 7307 7100

Akinsanya, Mr Jonathan I *Nov 1993*
15, 51, 62, 63
Nine Bedford Row, London WC1
p924 . . . 020 7489 2727

Akinsanya, Mr Stephen O LLB(Hons) I *Nov 1993*
15, 51, 63, 42
Nine Bedford Row, London WC1
p924 . . . 020 7489 2727

Akka, Mr Lawrence BA(Oxon) L *Nov 1991*
3, 11, 12, 24, 35, 41
20 Essex Street, London WC2
p932 . . . 020 7842 1200

AKKOUH, Mr Tim LLB(Lond); LLM(Lond) L *Jul 2004*
6, 8, 11, 37, 29
New Square Chambers, London WC2
p943 . . . 020 7419 8000

Akman, Miss Mercy L LLB(Hons)(Wales) G *Nov 1982*
20, 10, 23, 41, 14, 18
36 Bedford Row, London WC1
p925 . . . 020 7421 8000

AKTHER, Ms Ripon L *Jul 2003*
23, 57
Renaissance Chambers, London WC1
p949 . . . 020 7404 1111

Akther, Miss Tahina LLB L *Oct 2003*
8
Cobden House Chambers, Manchester
p983 . . . 0161 833 6000
Southernhay Chambers, Exeter
p975 . . . 01392 255777

Akudolu, Nneka LLB(Hons) M *Oct 2002*
2 Pump Court, London EC4
p947 . . . 020 7353 5597

AKUWUDIKE, Ms Emma I *May 1992*
15
25 Bedford Row, London WC1
p925 . . . 020 7067 1500

Akwagyiram, Mr Samuel BA(Hons) I *Nov 1985*
15, 20, 22, 23
12 Old Square, London WC2
p945 . . . 020 7404 0875

AL-ATTAR, Mr Adam BA; BCL(Oxon) L *Nov 2007*
8, 5, 6, 11, 97, 38
South Square, London WC1
p950 . . . 020 7696 9900

Al'Hassan, Khadim LLB I *Nov 1993*
15, 30, 23
No 6 Barristers Chambers, Leeds
p978 . . . 0113 245 9763

Al-Khayat, Mr Joe I *Jan 2008*
30, 8, 11, 12, 47, 48, 49
Thirty Park Place, Cardiff
p973 . . . 029 2039 8421

Al-Rashid, Mr Mahmud G *Jul 1991*
1, 71, 51, 23, 33
No5 Chambers, Bristol
p971 . . . 0845 210 5555
No5 Chambers, London EC4
p944 . . . 0845 210 5555
No5 Chambers, Birmingham
p968 . . . 0845 210 5555

ALAKIJA, Mr Dele LLB(Hons) G *Oct 1996*
12, 15
No 8 Chambers, Birmingham
p968 . . . 0121 236 5514

ALAM, Miss Zaiban G *Jan 1998*
Bank House Chambers, Sheffield
p991 . . . 0114 275 1223

Alberga, Mr Ramon M *Sep 1951*
(Q.C.)
Maitland Chambers, London WC2
p941 . . . 020 7406 1200

Albutt, Mr Ian LLB(Lond) G *Jul 1981*
1, 12, 22, 26, 31, 8, 18, 25, 36, 29
Cornerstone Barristers, London WC1
p929 . . . 020 7242 4986

Alcock, Mr Peter BA(Hons) G *Oct 1995*
15, 51
6-8 Mill Street, Maidstone
p982 . . . 01622 688094 / 688095
6 Pump Court, London EC4
p947 . . . 020 7797 8400

Alderson, Miss Philippa Elizabeth Loveday M *Jan 1993*
Field Court Chambers, London WC1
p933 . . . 020 7405 6114

Aldous, Mr Grahame LLB(Exon); Recorder I *Jul 1979*
(Q.C.) *53, 30, 40, 18, 96*
9 Gough Square, London EC4
p935 . . . 020 7832 0500

ALDOUS, Mr Robert MA; MSc I *Jun 1985*
20, 10, 30, 2, 3, 6, 8, 12, 22, 26, 31, 36, 18
Octagon House, Norwich
p988 . . . 01603 623186

ALDRED, Miss Lois LLB(UEA) I *Jul 2008*
12 King's Bench Walk, London EC4
p940 . . . 020 7583 0811

Aldred, Mr Mark M *Mar 1996*
15, 25, 36
QEB Hollis Whiteman, London EC4
p948 . . . 020 7933 8855

Aldridge, Mr James I *Nov 1987*
53, 30
Outer Temple Chambers, London WC2
p945 . . . 020 7353 6381
Maitland Chambers, London WC2
p941 . . . 020 7406 1200

ALEESON, Mr Warwick G *Nov 1994*
15, 62, 95
187 Fleet Street, London EC4
p933 . . . 020 7430 7430

Alesbury, Mr Alun MA(Cantab) I *Jul 1974*
1, 2, 26, 28, 31, 36
Cornerstone Barristers, London WC1
p929 . . . 020 7242 4986

Alexander, Mr Andrew BA L *Jan 1999*
23, 10, 20
Lamb Building, Brighton
p970 . . . 01273 820490
Lamb Building, London EC4
p940 . . . 020 7797 7788

Alexander, Mr Daniel BA(Oxon); LLM(Harv) M *Jul 1988*
(Q.C.) *13, 45, 50, 43, 56, 44, 41*
8 New Square, London WC2
p943 . . . 020 7405 4321

ALEXANDER, Mr David R J MA(Cantab) M *Nov 1987*
(Q.C.) *5, 6, 8, 11, 12, 24, 29, 37, 40, 38*
South Square, London WC1
p950 . . . 020 7696 9900

See p1010 for the Key to Work Categories

Alexander, Mr Nicholas M *Nov 1996*
15, 63
Atkinson Bevan Chambers, London EC4
p924 . . . . . 020 7353 2112

Alford, Mr Stuart BSc(Reading) M *Oct 1992*
12, 15, 20, 30, 21, 86
36 Bedford Row, London WC1
p925 . . . . . 020 7421 8000

ALFRED, Mr Stephan I *Jan 1996*
Lombard Chambers, London EC1
p941 . . . . . 020 7107 2100

ALGAR, Mr Claudius J I *Nov 1972*
12, 15
10 King's Bench Walk, London EC4
p940 . . . . . 020 7353 7742

Algazy, Mr Jacques G *Nov 1980*
11, 43, 56, 55, 18, 19, 51, 33, 1, 50
Cloisters, London EC4
p928 . . . . . 020 7827 4000

Ali, Mr Anis LLB L *Mar 1997*
15, 23, 20
Regent Chambers, Hanley
p976 . . . . . 01782 286666

ALI, Miss Huma LLB(Hons) G *Mar 1997*
20
St Philips Chambers, Birmingham
p969 . . . . . 0121 246 7000

Ali, Mr Ishtiyaq L *Oct 1996*
23, 30
Chartlands Chambers, Northampton
p988 . . . . . 01604 603322

Ali, Kashif L *Jan 2003*
St Johns Buildings, Preston
p990 . . . . . 01772 256100
St Johns Buildings, Chester
p974 . . . . . 01244 323070
St Johns Buildings, Manchester
p985 . . . . . 0161 214 1500
St Johns Buildings, Liverpool
p982 . . . . . 0151 243 6000

Ali, Khadija L *Nov 2006*
20, 33, 18
Tooks Chambers, London EC4
p953 . . . . . 020 7842 7575

Ali, Mr Raymond A LLM G *Nov 1995*
1 Mitre Court Buildings, London EC4
p942 . . . . . 020 7452 8900

ALI, Zafar BA(Hons) M *Oct 1994*
15, 62
23 Essex Street, London WC2
p932 . . . . . 020 7413 0353

Alibhai, Mr Ari G *Jan 2003*
15
QEB Hollis Whiteman, London EC4
p948 . . . . . 020 7933 8855

ALIKER, Mr Phillip BA; LLB(Hons); DipICA; MCIArb I *Oct 1990*
22, 8, 56, 40, 11
Tanfield Chambers, London WC1
p951 . . . . . 020 7421 5300

Alistari, Nicoleta M *Jan 2009*
Park Court Chambers, Leeds
p978 . . . . . 0113 243 3277

Alkin, Mr Tom BA(Natural Sciences) M *Jan 2007*
73, 50, 19, 45, 13, 52, 96, 41
11 South Square, London WC1
p950 . . . . . 020 7405 1222

ALLAN, Mr Colin I *Jul 1971*
15
25 Bedford Row, London WC1
p925 . . . . . 020 7067 1500

ALLAN, Mr David MA(Law) L *Jan 1998*
15, 62, 13
23 Essex Street, London WC2
p932 . . . . . 020 7413 0353
Byrom Street Chambers, Manchester
p983 . . . . . 0161 829 2100
42 Bedford Row, London WC1
p925 . . . . . 020 7831 0222

ALLAN, Ms Kirsten BA(Hons); DipLaw; CPE M *Jul 1998*
10, 20, 23, 30
Pump Court Chambers, Swindon
p993 . . . . . 01793 539899
Pump Court Chambers, Winchester
p994 . . . . . 01962 868161
Pump Court Chambers, London EC4
p947 . . . . . 020 7353 0711

ALLAN, Miss Nicola BA(Hons)(Newc)(Town & County Planning) G *Jan 1999*
31, 1, 38, 2, 8
Trinity (Newcastle) Chambers, Newcastle upon Tyne
p987 . . . . . 0191 232 1927
Trinity (Teesside) Chambers, Middlesbrough
p986 . . . . . 01642 247569

Allan, Miss Sophie BA L *Oct 2004*
30, 12, 27
Kings Chambers, Leeds
p978 . . . . . 0113 242 1123
Kings Chambers, Manchester
p984 . . . . . 0161 832 9082

ALLARDICE, Miss Miranda BA L *Jul 1982*
8, 10, 12, 20, 32
Pump Court Chambers, Swindon
p993 . . . . . 01793 539899
Pump Court Chambers, Winchester
p994 . . . . . 01962 868161
Pump Court Chambers, London EC4
p947 . . . . . 020 7353 0711

Allcock, Mr Jonathan BA(Hons) M *Jan 2007*
Maitland Chambers, London WC2
p941 . . . . . 020 7406 1200

ALLDIS, Mr Christopher MA; LLB(Cantab); Recorder G *Nov 1970*
27, 30, 12, 40
Oriel Chambers, Liverpool
p981 . . . . . 0151 236 7191 / 236 4321
Oriel Chambers, Preston
p990 . . . . . 01772 254764

Allen, Mr Andrew MA(Cantab); LLM I *Oct 1995*
18, 22, 30, 23, 1, 63
Outer Temple Chambers, London WC2
p945 . . . . . 020 7353 6381

ALLEN, Miss Caroline BA; GDpL L *Oct 2005*
30, 11, 1
Thirty Nine Essex Street, London WC2
p932 . . . . . 020 7832 1111

Allen, Mr Christopher G *Jul 2002*
New Walk Chambers, Leicester
p979 . . . . . 0871 200 1298

Allen, Mr Darryl LLB(Hons)(Leeds) L *Oct 1995*
30, 53, 27, 40, 56
42 Bedford Row, London WC1
p925 . . . . . 020 7831 0222
Byrom Street Chambers, Manchester
p983 . . . . . 0161 829 2100

Allen, Mr David BA; MPhil M *Jul 1975*
2 New Street, Leicester
p979 . . . . . 0116 262 5906

Allen, Mr Douglas BA(Hons) L *Oct 1995*
Goldsmith Chambers, London EC4
p935 . . . . . 020 7353 6802

Allen, Mr Fegal L *Oct 2007*
15, 10, 20, 30
St Johns Buildings, Preston
p990 . . . . . 01772 256100
St Johns Buildings, Chester
p974 . . . . . 01244 323070
St Johns Buildings, Manchester
p985 . . . . . 0161 214 1500
St Johns Buildings, Liverpool
p982 . . . . . 0151 243 6000

Allen, Frances I *Oct 1995*
23
12 Old Square, London WC2
p945 . . . . . 020 7404 0875
Renaissance Chambers, London WC1
p949 . . . . . 020 7404 1111

ALLEN, Mr James H Recorder G *Nov 1973*
(Q.C.) *8, 11*
No 6 Barristers Chambers, Leeds
p978 . . . . . 0113 245 9763

Allen, Jude I *Jan 2004*
1 Hare Court, London EC4
p936 . . . . . 020 7797 7070

Allen, Miss Juliet LLB G *Nov 2005*
20, 10
No5 Chambers, Bristol
p971 . . . . . 0845 210 5555
No5 Chambers, London EC4
p944 . . . . . 0845 210 5555
No5 Chambers, Birmingham
p968 . . . . . 0845 210 5555

ALLEN, Ms Lucianne M *Nov 1998*
15
St Philips Chambers, Birmingham
p969 . . . . . 0121 246 7000

Allen, Mr Mark Graham LLB M *Jul 1981*
20, 22, 10
Thirty Park Place, Cardiff
p973 . . . . . 029 2039 8421

Allen, Mr Michael David BSc; LLB; MRICS; ACIArb G *Jul 1990*
(Q.C.) *35, 11, 7, 3, 40, 24*
7 King's Bench Walk, London EC4
p940 . . . . . 020 7910 8300

ALLEN, Mr Neil LLB(Hons) M *Oct 1999*
1, 4, 26
Thirty Nine Essex Street, London WC2
p932 . . . . . 020 7832 1111

ALLEN, Mr Nicholas MA(Cantab); LLM(Cantab) M *Oct 1995*
20
29 Bedford Row, London WC1
p925 . . . . . 020 7404 1044

Allen, Mr Robin M *Nov 1974*
(Q.C.) *18, 19, 51, 26, 1, 55*
Cloisters, London EC4
p928 . . . . . 020 7827 4000

Allen, Mr Rupert Alexander Dendy MA(Law); BCL; BVC L *Jul 2005*
Fountain Court Chambers, London EC4
p934 . . . . . 020 7583 3335

Allen, Miss Sarah G *Nov 2005*
15, 62, 25, 46, 18, 55
No5 Chambers, Bristol
p971 . . . . . 0845 210 5555
No5 Chambers, London EC4
p944 . . . . . 0845 210 5555
No5 Chambers, Birmingham
p968 . . . . . 0845 210 5555

ALLEN, Mr Scott I *Nov 2000*
8, 12, 24, 40
Four New Square, London WC2
p943 . . . . . 020 7822 2000

ALLEN, Mr Sebastian L *Oct 2006*
Wilberforce Chambers, London WC2
p953 . . . . . 020 7306 0102

Allen, Ms Sylvia Delores LLB G *Jul 1983*
1 Mitre Court Buildings, London EC4
p942 . . . . . 020 7452 8900

ALLEN, Mr Thomas I *Nov 1995*
Maidstone Chambers, Maidstone
p982 . . . . . 01622 688592

Allen, Mr Tom BA(Hons) M *Feb 1994*
62, 15, 48, 13, 25
5 Paper Buildings, London EC4
p946 . . . . . 020 7583 6117

Allerhand, Mr Ludwik I *Nov 2001*
Clerksroom - Administration Centre, Taunton
p993 . . . . . 0845 083 3000

Alleyne, Ms Ebony I *Jan 2009*
3PB, London EC4
p946 . . . . . 020 7583 8055

Allingham-Nicholson, Mrs Elizabeth LLB L *Oct 1995*
12
2 New Street, Leicester
p979 . . . . . 0116 262 5906

ALLIOTT, Mr George LLB(Warw) I *Jul 1981*
Temple Garden Chambers, London EC4
p952 . . . . . 020 7583 1315

Allison, Miss Caroline LLB(Leics) L *Jul 2002*
15, 20, 12
Fenners Chambers, Cambridge
p972 . . . . . 01223 368761

ALLISON, Mr David MA(Cantab) M *Nov 1998*
5, 6, 8, 11, 24, 29, 40, 97, 38
South Square, London WC1
p950 . . . . . 020 7696 9900

Allison, Mr Simon LLB(Hons)(Lond) L *Oct 2005*
93, 22, 11, 40, 38
42 Bedford Row, London WC1
p925 . . . . . 020 7831 0222
Hardwicke, London WC2
p936 . . . . . 020 7242 2523

ALLISON, Mr Stuart M *Jan 2002*
15, 25
Fountain Chambers, Middlesbrough
p986 . . . . . 01642 804040

Allman, Miss Marisa LLB L *Oct 1998*
10, 20
Zenith Chambers, Leeds
p979 . . . . . 0113 245 5438

Allott, Mr Philip James MA; LLB(Cantab) G *Feb 1960*
20 Essex Street, London WC2
p932 . . . . . 020 7842 1200

Allsop, Mr Julian E LLB; LLM L *Oct 1999*
7, 8, 11, 47, 40, 41, 49, 96, 74, 73, 12, 55, 18, 89, 36
Queen Square Chambers, Bristol
p972 . . . . . 0117 921 1966

ALLSOP, Ms Nicola LLB L *Jul 2002*
8, 11, 38
New Square Chambers, London WC2
p943 . . . . . 020 7419 8000

Allston, Mr Anthony Stanley BA G *Jul 1975*
6, 8, 9, 67, 38, 88, 96, 30, 32, 40, 93, 37
3 Dr Johnson's Buildings, London EC4
p930 . . . . . 020 7353 4854

Allwood, Mrs Gina Louisa LLB(Hons); BVC G *Jul 2002*
1, 10, 12, 15, 70, 76, 18, 19, 20, 22, 51, 21, 23, 56
7 Bedford Row, London WC1
p924 . . . . . 020 7242 3555

Almihdar, Mr Ali LLB; MA M *Nov 2003*
41, 11, 12, 47, 67, 78, 64, 89, 54, 29
Outer Temple Chambers, London WC2
p945 . . . . . 020 7353 6381

Alomo, Mr Richard LLB I *Nov 1990*
14 Gray's Inn Square, London WC1
p936 . . . . . 020 7242 0858

Alsolaimani, Mr Nasiruddin BA; MA L *Nov 1971*
15, 20, 23, 36
10 Kingsfield Avenue, Harrow
p976 . . . . . 020 8427 8709

Altaras, Mr David BA; MA(TCD); Dip Crim(Cantab); Recorder L *Nov 1969*
7, 12, 13, 22, 26, 30, 31, 40
36 Bedford Row, London WC1
p925 . . . . . 020 7421 8000

Althaus, Mr Justin BA(Oxon) I *Jul 1988*
22, 30, 40, 93, 62
1 Chancery Lane, London WC2
p928 . . . . . 0845 634 6666

Altman, Mr Brian LLB(Hons); Dip Eur Int(Amsterdam); Senior Treasury Counsel at CCC; Recorder M *Jul 1981*
15
2 Bedford Row, London WC1
p924 . . . . . 020 7440 8888

ALTY, Mr Andrew LLB(Leics) I *Feb 1992*
15, 62
7 Harrington Street Chambers, Liverpool
p981 . . . . . 0151 242 0707

Amakye, Miss Grace Tina G *Nov 1983*
15 New Bridge Street Chambers, London EC4
p943 . . . . . 020 7842 1900

Aman, Ms Rosina BA(Lond) G *Jul 2005*
10, 20
Coram Chambers, London EC1
p929 . . . . . 020 7092 3700

AMAOUCHE, Miss Sassa-Ann LLB(KCL) I *Oct 1996*
20
29 Bedford Row, London WC1
p925 . . . . . 020 7404 1044

AMARASINHA, Revantha M *Oct 1996*
15, 20
9-12 Bell Yard Chambers, London WC2
p926 . . . . . 020 7400 1800
1 Gray's Inn Square, London WC1
p935 . . . . . 020 7405 8946

AMARTEY, Miss Lena M *Oct 2008*
9 St John Street Chambers, Manchester
p984 . . . . . 0161 955 9000

Ambrose, Miss Clare BA(Oxon); LLM(Cantab) G *Nov 1992*
3, 11, 12, 24, 35, 41
20 Essex Street, London WC2
p932 . . . . . 020 7842 1200

Ameen, Mr Danish LLB(Hons) L *Jan 2006*
20
18 St John Street Chambers, Manchester
p985 . . . . . 0161 278 1800

Amer, Mr Adrian LLB(Hons) G *Nov 1984*
15, 51
Nine Bedford Row, London WC1
p924 . . . . . 020 7489 2727

Amesbury, Mr Ryan G *Jan 2007*
Civitas Law, Cardiff
p972 . . . . . 0845 071 3007

13

Amihere, Mr Anwobo M *Nov 1970*
20 Sewardstone Gardens, London E4
p950 . . . . . 020 8524 3054

Amin, Miss Farah LLB(Hons)(Lond) L *Jul 1991*
3, 6, 8, 11, 12, 37, 24, 10, 20, 22, 29, 32, 40, 63, 50
Two King's Bench Walk, London EC4
p939 . . . . . 020 7353 7202 / 7353 3909

AMIRAFTABI, Roshanak G *Feb 1993*
10, 20
Renaissance Chambers, London WC1
p949 . . . . . 020 7404 1111

Amis, Mr Christopher J LLB(Lond) G *Nov 1991*
2 King's Bench Walk, London EC4
p939 . . . . . 020 7353 1746

Amlot, Mr Roy L *Nov 1963*
(Q.C.) *15, 62, 36*
6 King's Bench Walk, London EC4
p939 . . . . . 020 7583 0410

AMOR, Mr Christopher MA(Oxon) G *May 1984*
15, 62, 95
187 Fleet Street, London EC4
p933 . . . . . 020 7430 7430

Amos, Mr Justin Edward BA; PGDL G *Mar 2005*
12, 15, 18, 30
9 Park Place, Cardiff
p973 . . . . . 029 2038 2731

AMOS, Mr Timothy MA(Oxon) L *Jul 1987*
(Q.C.) *20*
Queen Elizabeth Buildings, London EC4
p948 . . . . . 020 7797 7837

AMRAOUI, Mr Thomas BVC; DipLaw; BA(Oxon) G *Nov 2007*
18, 1, 31, 63
4-5 Gray's Inn Square, London WC1
p935 . . . . . 020 7404 5252

Ananda, Miss Sushma L *Nov 2007*
41, 24, 35, 61
7 King's Bench Walk, London EC4
p940 . . . . . 020 7910 8300

ANCLIFFE, Shiva LLB L *Nov 1991*
10, 12, 20, 23, 30
Renaissance Chambers, London WC1
p949 . . . . . 020 7404 1111

Anders, Mr Jonathan James I *Feb 1990*
15
1 Inner Temple Lane, London EC4
p937 . . . . . 020 7427 4400

Anderson, Mr Clive MA M *Nov 1976*
6 King's Bench Walk, London EC4
p939 . . . . . 020 7583 0410

ANDERSON, Mr Colin MA(Cantab) G *Nov 1973*
10, 12, 20, 30, 53
St Mary's Chambers, Nottingham
p989 . . . . . 0115 950 3503

Anderson, Mr David MA(Oxon); BA(Cantab) M *Jul 1985*
(Q.C.) *1, 51, 19, 44*
Brick Court Chambers, London WC2
p927 . . . . . 020 7379 3550

ANDERSON, Mr Jack BVC; BCL; BA(Law) I *Jan 2006*
1, 31, 18
4-5 Gray's Inn Square, London WC1
p935 . . . . . 020 7404 5252

ANDERSON, Mr Jamie Henrie LLB(Hons); LLM(Bris) L *Jul 2004*
18
Trinity (Newcastle) Chambers, Newcastle upon Tyne
p987 . . . . . 0191 232 1927
Trinity (Teesside) Chambers, Middlesbrough
p986 . . . . . 01642 247569

Anderson, Miss Julie G *Nov 1993*
1, 11, 41, 19, 23, 55, 36
20 Essex Street, London WC2
p932 . . . . . 020 7842 1200

Anderson, Ms Katherine LLB(Cambs) I *Jan 2005*
96, 18, 30, 53, 76
3PB, Bristol
p971 . . . . . 0117 928 1520

Anderson, Ms Lesley LLB; CEDR Accredited Mediator M *Nov 1989*
(Q.C.) *5, 6, 7, 8, 11, 22, 29, 40, 41, 45, 49*
Kings Chambers, Leeds
p978 . . . . . 0113 242 1123
Kings Chambers, Manchester
p984 . . . . . 0161 832 9082

Anderson, Mr Mark BA(Oxon); Recorder M *Jul 1983*
(Q.C.) *11, 30, 40, 53, 5, 12, 8, 18, 29, 38, 67, 68, 80, 89, 97, 96, 93, 86, 81, 41*
No5 Chambers, Bristol
p971 . . . . . 0845 210 5555
No5 Chambers, London EC4
p944 . . . . . 0845 210 5555
No5 Chambers, Birmingham
p968 . . . . . 0845 210 5555

ANDERSON, Mr Nicholas LLB(Newc) G *Jan 1995*
10, 20, 49, 96
1 King's Bench Walk, London EC4
p938 . . . . . 020 7936 1500

Anderson, Mr Peter BA I *Jul 1988*
12, 20, 30
15 Winckley Square, Preston
p991 . . . . . 01772 252828

Anderson, Mr Robert E BA(Cantab) M *Nov 1986*
(Q.C.) *8, 11, 24, 29, 40, 41, 50, 56, 52, 62, 89*
Blackstone Chambers, London EC4
p926 . . . . . 020 7583 1770

Anderson, Mr Simon P B LLB(Hons) L *Nov 1997*
Park Court Chambers, Leeds
p978 . . . . . 0113 243 3277

ANDREAE-JONES, Mr William P MA(Cantab) I *Nov 1965*
(Q.C.)
Citadel Chambers, Birmingham
p967 . . . . . 0121 233 8500

ANDREWS, Miss Claire LLB(Manc) G *Nov 1979*
22, 39, 47, 48
Gough Square Chambers, London EC4
p935 . . . . . 020 7353 0924

Andrews, Miss Geraldine M LLB; LLM(Lond) G *Nov 1981*
(Q.C.)
Essex Court Chambers, London WC2
p931 . . . . . 020 7813 8000

Andrews, Miss Katherine BA(Leeds) G *Jul 2006*
10, 20
Coram Chambers, London EC1
p929 . . . . . 020 7092 3700

Andrews, Miss Melanie Alexandra M *Jan 2005*
10, 12, 20, 30, 26, 88, 67
Becket Chambers, Canterbury
p972 . . . . . 01227 786331
Becket Chambers, Maidstone
p982 . . . . . 01622 230957

Andrews, Miss Natasha E LLB(Hons) L *Nov 2002*
15, 20, 22, 30
37 Park Square Chambers, Leeds
p978 . . . . . 0113 243 9422

Andrews, Mr Peter LLB(Bris); D Crime(Cantab); Recorder (1990) L *Jul 1970*
(Q.C.) *53, 30, 27*
7 Bedford Row, London WC1
p924 . . . . . 020 7242 3555

Andrews, Mr Philip LLB(Hons) I *Feb 1977*
15, 72, 71, 70
St Johns Buildings, Preston
p990 . . . . . 01772 256100
St Johns Buildings, Chester
p974 . . . . . 01244 323070
St Johns Buildings, Manchester
p985 . . . . . 0161 214 1500
St Johns Buildings, Liverpool
p982 . . . . . 0151 243 6000

Andrews, Mr Samuel J G *Nov 1991*
39 Park Square, Leeds
p978 . . . . . 0113 245 6633

ANELAY, Mr Richard BA(Bris) M *Jul 1970*
(Q.C.) *10, 12, 15, 20, 30, 49, 96*
1 King's Bench Walk, London EC4
p938 . . . . . 020 7936 1500

Angammana, Mr Gamini Bertram LLB(Hons)(Lond); LLM; PGCE L *Nov 1983*
Chambers of Gamini Angammana, London SE19
p923 . . . . . 020 8771 5205

ANGIOLINI, Mr Mario LLB M *Oct 2000*
11, 44, 19, 57
Monckton Chambers, London WC1
p942 . . . . . 020 7405 7211

Angus, Ms Tracey A MA(Edin) I *Nov 1991*
8, 32, 14, 37, 40
5 Stone Buildings, London WC2
p951 . . . . . 020 7242 6201

Annand, Ms Kate LLB; MA M *Jan 2007*
70, 15, 18, 55, 51, 21
Doughty Street Chambers, London WC1
p930 . . . . . 020 7404 1313

Anning, Mr Michael I *Nov 1990*
15, 25, 62, 72
No5 Chambers, Bristol
p971 . . . . . 0845 210 5555
No5 Chambers, London EC4
p944 . . . . . 0845 210 5555
No5 Chambers, Birmingham
p968 . . . . . 0845 210 5555

ANOOM, Mr Joseph Kwesi M *Jul 1998*
15
1 Inner Temple Lane, London EC4
p937 . . . . . 020 7427 4400

Ansell, Ms Rachel BA(Cantab) M *Oct 1995*
7, 40, 11, 78, 24
4 Pump Court, London EC4
p947 . . . . . 020 7842 5555

ANSTEY, Mrs Eve M *Nov 2005*
15
Pallant Chambers, Chichester
p974 . . . . . 01243 784538

Antell, Mr John Jason LLB(Hons); MBCS; CEng M *Oct 1992*
66, 41, 7, 8, 11, 12, 43, 74, 47, 67, 73, 55, 75, 18, 45, 24, 88, 30
King's Bench Godolphin Chambers, Truro
p994 . . . . . 0845 308 1551
King's Bench Godolphin Chambers, Plymouth
p990 . . . . . 0845 308 1551

ANTELME, Mr Alexander G *Oct 1993*
53, 40, 11, 12, 24, 30, 3
Crown Office Chambers, London EC4
p929 . . . . . 020 7797 8100

Anthony, Mr Peter LLB G *Jul 1981*
10, 15, 20, 30
St Ives Chambers, Birmingham
p969 . . . . . 0121 236 0863

Anthony, Mrs Rachel Jane M *Nov 2000*
Iscoed Chambers, Swansea
p993 . . . . . 01792 652988

ANTROBUS, Mr Simon LLB I *Oct 1995*
84, 47, 46
Crown Office Chambers, London EC4
p929 . . . . . 020 7797 8100

Anyadike-Danes, Ms Monya N M BA(Cantab) G *Jul 1980*
6, 5, 11, 8, 29, 24, 37, 40
2 Temple Gardens, London EC4
p952 . . . . . 020 7822 1200

Anyene, Eleazar L *Oct 1999*
15
12 Old Square, London WC2
p945 . . . . . 020 7404 0875

ANZANI, Sara I *Jul 2008*
15, 23, 51
10 King's Bench Walk, London EC4
p940 . . . . . 020 7353 7742

Apfel, Mr Freddy LLM M *Jul 1986*
15
37 Park Square Chambers, Leeds
p978 . . . . . 0113 243 9422

Appiah, Miss Linda M *Jan 2001*
Guildford Chambers, Guildford
p975 . . . . . 01483 539131

Appleby, Miss Claire L *Oct 2002*
12, 15, 20
King's Bench Godolphin Chambers, Truro
p994 . . . . . 0845 308 1551
King's Bench Godolphin Chambers, Plymouth
p990 . . . . . 0845 308 1551

APPS, Miss Katherine MA(Law)(Cantab); LLM(Harv) G *Jul 2006*
18, 11, 56
Littleton Chambers, London EC4
p941 . . . . . 020 7797 8600

ARBUTHNOT, Rt Hon James MA(Cantab) L *Jul 1975* MP
Ten Old Square, London WC2
p945 . . . . . 020 7405 0758

Archer, Miss Audrey LLB; LLM M *Oct 2004*
15
3PB, Winchester
p994 . . . . . 01962 868884
1 Paper Buildings, London EC4
p946 . . . . . 020 7353 3728

ARCHER, Christopher G *Nov 1996*
10, 20
Renaissance Chambers, London WC1
p949 . . . . . 020 7404 1111

Archer, Miss Deborah LLB; Deputy Coroner I *Nov 1989*
10, 20
Southernhay Chambers, Exeter
p975 . . . . . 01392 255777

Archer, Ms Lorna G *Nov 1986*
20
1 Pump Court, London EC4
p947 . . . . . 020 7842 7070

Archer, Mr Richard LLB M *Jul 2007*
15
15 Winckley Square, Preston
p991 . . . . . 01772 252828

Archer, Mr Stephen MA(Oxon) I *Nov 1979*
30
2 Temple Gardens, London EC4
p952 . . . . . 020 7822 1200

ARCHER, Mr Trevor I *Jul 2005*
15, 62, 68, 84, 94
18 Red Lion Court, London EC4
p949 . . . . . 020 7520 6000
18 Red Lion Court (Annexe), Chelmsford
p973 . . . . . 01245 280880

ARDEN, Mr Andrew LLB(Lond) G *Feb 1974*
(Q.C.) *1, 51, 44, 22, 9, 31, 8, 12, 23, 26*
Arden Chambers, London WC1
p923 . . . . . 020 7242 4244

ARDEN, Mr Peter LLB(Lond); LLM(Cantab) G *Jul 1983*
(Q.C.) *5, 6, 8, 11, 29, 40, 49, 38*
Enterprise Chambers, London WC2
p931 . . . . . 020 7405 9471
Enterprise Chambers, Leeds
p977 . . . . . 0113 246 0391
Enterprise Chambers, Newcastle upon Tyne
p987 . . . . . 0191 222 3344

Arentsen, Mr Andrew G *Oct 1995*
1, 12, 15, 22, 30
Civitas Law, Cardiff
p972 . . . . . 0845 071 3007

Argent, Mr Gavin BA M *Jul 1978*
12, 15, 30, 27, 22, 20
Westgate Chambers, Lewes
p980 . . . . . 01273 480510

Argles, Mr Guy Robert Ainsworth BA(Oxon) M *Nov 1965*
34, 37, 36, 29, 8, 9
15 Old Square, London WC2
p945 . . . . . 020 7242 2744

ARGYLE, Mr Brian G *Jul 1972*
15, 62, 95
187 Fleet Street, London EC4
p933 . . . . . 020 7430 7430

Argyropoulos, Mr Kyriakos BA(Hons); DipLaw I *Nov 1991*
15, 62, 70, 72
15 New Bridge Street Chambers, London EC4
p943 . . . . . 020 7842 1900

ARIS, Mr Jason I *Jan 1998*
Citadel Chambers, Birmingham
p967 . . . . . 0121 233 8500

ARKHURST, Mr Reginald BA(Hons) M *Jul 1984*
15, 12, 23
4 King's Bench Walk, London EC4
p939 . . . . . 020 7822 7000

Arkush, Mr Jonathan MA(Oxon) M *Nov 1977*
5, 6, 8, 11, 13, 29, 32, 37
11 Stone Buildings, London WC2
p951 . . . . . 020 7831 6381

ARLIDGE, Mr Anthony M *Feb 1962*
(Q.C.) *15, 36, 62, 95*
18 Red Lion Court, London EC4
p949 . . . . . 020 7520 6000
18 Red Lion Court (Annexe), Chelmsford
p973 . . . . . 01245 280880

ARLOW, Ms Ruth MA; LLM I *Oct 1997*
10, 20, 18, 12
Pump Court Chambers, Swindon
p993 . . . . . 01793 539899
Pump Court Chambers, Winchester
p994 . . . . . 01962 868161
Pump Court Chambers, London EC4
p947 . . . . . 020 7353 0711

Armbrister, Mr Allan I *Jan 1984*
39 Park Square, Leeds
p978 . . . . . 0113 245 6633

ARMITAGE, Mr Mark BA(Hons)(Law) M *Oct 1999*
30, 11, 46, 68
Crown Office Chambers, London EC4
p929 . . . . . 020 7797 8100

See p1010 for the Key to Work Categories

Armstrong, Mr Dean G *Jul 1985*
15, 62, 36
2 Hare Court, London EC4
p937 . . . . . 020 7353 5324

Armstrong, Mr Douglas I *Jan 1999*
(Q.C.) *31, 46*
No5 Chambers, Bristol
p971 . . . . . 0845 210 5555
No5 Chambers, London EC4
p944 . . . . . 0845 210 5555
No5 Chambers, Birmingham
p968 . . . . . 0845 210 5555

ARMSTRONG, Mr Grant B LLB(Lond) L *Jul 1978*
8, 10, 11, 12, 15, 20, 22, 29, 30, 37, 40, 51
Charter Chambers, London WC1
p928 . . . . . 020 7618 4400
6-8 Mill Street, Maidstone
p982 . . . . . 01622 688094 / 688095
6 Pump Court, London EC4
p947 . . . . . 020 7797 8400

Armstrong, Kester I S I *Nov 1982*
10, 20
Broad Chare Chambers, Newcastle upon Tyne
p986 . . . . . 0191 232 0541

ARMSTRONG, Michael LLB(Hons) I *Oct 2002*
30
Atlantic Chambers, Liverpool
p980 . . . . . 0151 236 4421

ARMSTRONG, Dr Nicholas I *Jul 2001*
1, 22, 23, 26, 51, 55, 63, 68, 70, 76, 85
Matrix Chambers, London WC1
p942 . . . . . 020 7404 3447

Armstrong, Miss Ruth Elizabeth I *Nov 2001*
15, 39, 84, 94
Queen Square Chambers, Bristol
p972 . . . . . 0117 921 1966

ARMSTRONG, Mr Stuart LLB; LLM G *Nov 1995*
8, 47, 88, 93
Arden Chambers, London WC1
p923 . . . . . 020 7242 4244
33 Bedford Row, London WC1
p925 . . . . . 020 7242 6476

ARNEY, Mr James LLB(Bris) L *Oct 1992*
10, 11, 12, 20, 22
Temple Garden Chambers, London EC4
p952 . . . . . 020 7583 1315

ARNFIELD, Mr Robert BA(Oxon) I *Oct 1996*
32, 34, 37
Ten Old Square, London WC2
p945 . . . . . 020 7405 0758

Arnheim, Dr Michael BA; MA; LLB(Lond); PhD(Cantab) L *Jul 1988*
7, 11, 12, 15, 16, 18, 19, 29, 30
Chambers of Dr Michael Arnheim, London WC1
p923 . . . . . 020 7833 5093

ARNOLD, Mr Mark MA(Cantab) M *Jul 1988*
5, 6, 11, 24, 29, 40, 38
South Square, London WC1
p950 . . . . . 020 7696 9900

Arnold, Mr Peter LLB L *Jul 1972*
No5 Chambers, Bristol
p971 . . . . . 0845 210 5555
No5 Chambers, London EC4
p944 . . . . . 0845 210 5555
No5 Chambers, Birmingham
p968 . . . . . 0845 210 5555

Arnone, Miss Anna LLB; BA M *Jul 2002*
15, 22, 94
Eastbourne Chambers, Eastbourne
p975 . . . . . 01323 642102

ARNOT, Mr Lee A MA(Hons)(Cantab) L *Nov 1990*
10, 20
29 Bedford Row, London WC1
p925 . . . . . 020 7404 1044

Arora, Miss Anita L *Nov 1994*
15, 51
Nine Bedford Row, London WC1
p924 . . . . . 020 7489 2727

Arshad, Miss Farrhat I *Nov 1998*
1, 91, 15
Doughty Street Chambers, London WC1
p930 . . . . . 020 7404 1313

ARSHAD, Ms Raffia M *Oct 2002*
10, 20, 64
St Mary's Chambers, Nottingham
p989 . . . . . 0115 950 3503

Artesi, Miss Desiree A A BSc; LLB(Hons) I *Oct 1998*
8, 11, 18, 22, 36, 38
3 Dr Johnson's Buildings, London EC4
p930 . . . . . 020 7353 4854

Arthur, Mrs Helen LLB M *Oct 2003*
10, 20, 63
No5 Chambers, Bristol
p971 . . . . . 0845 210 5555
No5 Chambers, London EC4
p944 . . . . . 0845 210 5555
No5 Chambers, Birmingham
p968 . . . . . 0845 210 5555

Arthur, Mr Stephen Joseph LLB; CTA; TEP M *Nov 2002*
34, 57, 58, 37, 29, 8, 97, 92, 96
Temple Tax Chambers, London EC4
p952 . . . . . 020 7353 7884 / 7353 8982

ARUMUGAM, Mr Raj L *Oct 2008*
6, 7, 8, 11, 67, 88, 93, 21, 30, 53
10 King's Bench Walk, London EC4
p940 . . . . . 020 7353 7742

ASANOVIC, Ms Bojana M *Jul 2000*
15, 23
Mitre House Chambers, London WC1
p942 . . . . . 020 7307 7100

ASCHERSON, Miss Isobel LLB G *Feb 1991*
12, 15, 25, 36
23 Essex Street, London WC2
p932 . . . . . 020 7413 0353

ASCROFT, Mr Richard G LLB(Hons)(Otago) NZ; BCL(Oxon) L *Nov 1995*
5, 6, 8, 11, 97, 38
Guildhall Chambers, Bristol
p970 . . . . . 0117 930 9000

ASH, Mr Brian BA(Oxon) G *Nov 1975*
(Q.C.) *1, 26, 31, 22, 46, 40, 43*
4-5 Gray's Inn Square, London WC1
p935 . . . . . 020 7404 5252

Ash, Mr Simon BA(Oxon) G *Mar 1999*
12, 15, 95, 62, 34, 63
36 Bedford Row, London WC1
p925 . . . . . 020 7421 8000

Ashcroft, Mr Michael BA; BCL(Oxon) G *Sep 1997*
(Q.C.) *3, 11, 12, 24, 35, 41*
20 Essex Street, London WC2
p932 . . . . . 020 7842 1200

Ashe, Mr Michael Member Irish Bar; QC N Ireland 1998; SC Ireland 2000 M *Jul 1971*
(Q.C.) *1, 8, 11, 21, 34, 51, 29, 37, 62, 38*
9 Stone Buildings Barristers Chambers, London WC2
p951 . . . . . 020 7404 5055

ASHFORD-THOM, Mr Ian LLB(Exon) G *Jul 1977*
Temple Garden Chambers, London EC4
p952 . . . . . 020 7583 1315

Ashkar, Ms Natalie I *Jan 2009*
3PB, Bournemouth
p969 . . . . . 01202 292102

ASHLEY, Mrs Julie L *Mar 2007*
20, 10
7 Harrington Street Chambers, Liverpool
p981 . . . . . 0151 242 0707

ASHLEY, Mr Mark R E LLB(Hons) L *Nov 1993*
12, 15, 30, 42, 91
Pump Court Chambers, Swindon
p993 . . . . . 01793 539899
Pump Court Chambers, Winchester
p994 . . . . . 01962 868161
Pump Court Chambers, London EC4
p947 . . . . . 020 7353 0711

Ashley, Mr Neil LLB(Hons) L *Mar 1999*
18, 27, 40, 30
East Anglian Chambers, Norwich
p988 . . . . . 01603 617351
East Anglian Chambers, Colchester
p975 . . . . . 01206 572756
East Anglian Chambers, Chelmsford
p973 . . . . . 01245 215660
East Anglian Chambers, Ipswich
p976 . . . . . 01473 214481

Ashmole, Mr Timothy LLB I *Oct 1992*
15, 30, 12
St Johns Buildings, Preston
p990 . . . . . 01772 256100
St Johns Buildings, Chester
p974 . . . . . 01244 323070
St Johns Buildings, Manchester
p985 . . . . . 0161 214 1500
St Johns Buildings, Liverpool
p982 . . . . . 0151 243 6000

Ashton, Mr David Sambrook MA(Oxon); Chartered Arbitrator G *Jul 1962*
King's Bench Chambers, Oxford
p989 . . . . . 01865 311066
13 King's Bench Walk, London EC4
p940 . . . . . 020 7353 7204

Ashwell, Mr Paul BA I *Oct 1977*
1, 6, 8, 11, 22, 26, 29, 32, 40, 37
Crown Office Row Chambers, Brighton
p970 . . . . . 01273 625625

Ashworth, Miss Fiona LLB L *Jul 1988*
10, 12, 20, 30, 53
Kings Chambers, Leeds
p978 . . . . . 0113 242 1123
Kings Chambers, Manchester
p984 . . . . . 0161 832 9082

Ashworth, Mr Lance D P MA(Cantab) M *Nov 1987*
(Q.C.) *6, 8, 11, 30, 38*
Henderson Chambers, London EC4
p937 . . . . . 020 7583 9020
St Philips Chambers, Birmingham
p969 . . . . . 0121 246 7000

Ashworth, Miss Phillipa G *Dec 2000*
Iscoed Chambers, Swansea
p993 . . . . . 01792 652988

Asif, Mr Jalil MA L *Nov 1988*
(Q.C.) *8, 12, 24, 40, 48, 53*
Four New Square, London WC2
p943 . . . . . 020 7822 2000

Askey, Mr Robert LLB(Hons) L *Oct 1998*
8, 11, 15, 22, 30, 50, 52
New Bailey Chambers, Liverpool
p981 . . . . . 0151 236 9402

ASKHAM, Mr Nigel H LLB I *Feb 1973*
72, 15, 70, 42
Octagon Chambers, Taunton
p993 . . . . . 01823 331919

Askins, Mr Nicholas Peter LLB(Lond) G *Nov 1989*
12, 15, 25, 30
Broadway House Chambers, Leeds
p977 . . . . . 0113 246 2600
Broadway House Chambers, Bradford
p969 . . . . . 01274 722560

Aslam, Q Mahmud BA G *Jul 1983*
15, 22, 23, 30, 20
Staple Inn Chambers, London WC1
p951 . . . . . 020 7242 5240

Aslangul, Mr Michel L J BA; MA(Business Law) M *Nov 1978*
1, 3, 6, 8, 11, 12, 13, 15, 18, 19, 20, 21, 22, 23, 29
Abbey Chambers, Shepperton
p992 . . . . . 01932 560913

Aslett, Pepin LLB(Hons) L *Nov 1996*
12, 30, 40, 6, 18, 22
St Johns Buildings, Preston
p990 . . . . . 01772 256100
St Johns Buildings, Chester
p974 . . . . . 01244 323070
St Johns Buildings, Manchester
p985 . . . . . 0161 214 1500
St Johns Buildings, Liverpool
p982 . . . . . 0151 243 6000

Aspden, Mr Gordon LLB(Hull) M *Nov 1988*
12, 15, 62
7 Bedford Row, London WC1
p924 . . . . . 020 7242 3555

Aspinall, Mr Chris M *Jan 2008*
Park Court Chambers, Leeds
p978 . . . . . 0113 243 3277

Aspinall, Mr John M LLB I *Nov 1971*
(Q.C.) *15*
Tooks Chambers, London EC4
p953 . . . . . 020 7842 7575

ASPINALL, Mr Michael G *Nov 1986*
Citadel Chambers, Birmingham
p967 . . . . . 0121 233 8500

Aspinall-Miles, Mrs Mary MA(Oxon) L *Nov 1999*
15, 48, 25, 70
12 College Place, Southampton
p992 . . . . . 023 8032 0320

Asplin, Miss Sarah Jane MA(Cantab); BCL(Oxon) G *Jul 1984*
(Q.C.) *8, 9, 32, 37, 40*
3 Stone Buildings, London WC2
p951 . . . . . 020 7242 4937

Asprey, Miss Louise L *Oct 2007*
30, 67, 12, 93, 15
Walnut House Chambers, Exeter
p975 . . . . . 01392 279751

Asprey, Mr Nicholas LLB(Edin) I *Jul 1969*
8, 9, 11, 28, 29, 32, 37, 93
Serle Court, London WC2
p950 . . . . . 020 7242 6105

ASQUITH, Mr Marc M *Oct 1999*
30, 4, 12, 47, 67, 68, 24, 56, 89
Kenworthy's Chambers, Manchester
p984 . . . . . 0161 832 4036

Asquith, Mr Tom L *Jan 2007*
Four New Square, London WC2
p943 . . . . . 020 7822 2000

Assersohn, Mr Oliver BA I *Jul 2003*
18, 62, 81, 11
Outer Temple Chambers, London WC2
p945 . . . . . 020 7353 6381

Astbury, Mr Philip LLB(Hons) G *Oct 1999*
15, 30, 12
St Johns Buildings, Preston
p990 . . . . . 01772 256100
St Johns Buildings, Chester
p974 . . . . . 01244 323070
St Johns Buildings, Manchester
p985 . . . . . 0161 214 1500
St Johns Buildings, Liverpool
p982 . . . . . 0151 243 6000

ASTERIS, Mr Peter L *Jun 1996*
18, 15
Pump Court Chambers, Swindon
p993 . . . . . 01793 539899
Pump Court Chambers, Winchester
p994 . . . . . 01962 868161
Pump Court Chambers, London EC4
p947 . . . . . 020 7353 0711

ASTON, Eva BA; MA L *Jan 2003*
7 Stone Buildings Intellectual Property, London WC2
p951 . . . . . 020 7242 8848

Aston, Mr Maurice LLB I *Jul 1982*
15, 62
5 Paper Buildings, London EC4
p946 . . . . . 020 7583 6117

ASTOR, Mr Philip D P MA(Oxon) I *Nov 1989*
Temple Garden Chambers, London EC4
p952 . . . . . 020 7583 1315

Aswani, Ravi LLB(Lond) L *Jul 2000*
11, 5, 41, 44, 30, 35, 60
Stone Chambers, London WC1
p951 . . . . . 020 7440 6900

Atherton, Ms Charlotte G *Jul 2003*
15, 30, 12
Exchange Chambers, Manchester
p983 . . . . . 0161 833 2722
Exchange Chambers, Liverpool
p980 . . . . . 0151 236 7747
Exchange Chambers, Leeds
p977 . . . . . 0113 203 1970

ATHERTON, Mr Stephen N LLB(Lancs); LLM(Cantab) M *Jul 1989*
(Q.C.) *5, 6, 8, 11, 12, 24, 29, 38*
South Square, London WC1
p950 . . . . . 020 7696 9900

ATKINS, Mr Michael M *Oct 2006*
84, 46, 68, 11, 74, 24, 30
Crown Office Chambers, London EC4
p929 . . . . . 020 7797 8100

ATKINS, Mr Richard MA(Oxon); Recorder G *Jul 1989*
(Q.C.) *15, 62, 84, 25*
St Philips Chambers, Birmingham
p969 . . . . . 0121 246 7000

Atkins, Siward MA(Edin); PhD(Cantab) M *Oct 1995*
Maitland Chambers, London WC2
p941 . . . . . 020 7406 1200

ATKINS, Ms Victoria BA M *Nov 1998*
36, 15, 62, 84, 46
18 Red Lion Court, London EC4
p949 . . . . . 020 7520 6000
18 Red Lion Court (Annexe), Chelmsford
p973 . . . . . 01245 280880

Atkinson, Ms Catherine L *Oct 2006*
20, 15, 30
9 Gough Square, London EC4
p935 . . . . . 020 7832 0500

Atkinson, Mr Duncan G *Oct 1995*
15, 62, 16
6 King's Bench Walk, London EC4
p939 . . . . . 020 7583 0410

Atkinson, Mr Jody Roy Grad DipLaw; MA; BA(Hons) I *Jul 2005*
20, 10, 18
St John's Chambers, Bristol
p972 . . . . . 0117 921 3456

Atkinson, Mr Nicholas Jeremy Recorder I *Nov 1971*
(Q.C.) *15, 62*
Atkinson Bevan Chambers, London EC4
p924 . . . . . 020 7353 2112

ATKINSON, Mr Timothy G B BA(Oxon) I *Jul 1988*
16, 52, 73
One Brick Court, London EC4
p927 . . . . . 020 7353 8845

Atrill, Mr Simon I *Jul 2005*
Fountain Court Chambers, London EC4
p934 . . . . . 020 7583 3335

ATTRIDGE, Mr Daniel M *Nov 2000*
8, 10, 11, 12, 32, 47, 15, 18, 20, 22, 25, 40, 37, 89
Trinity Chambers, Chelmsford
p974 . . . . . 01245 605040

Attridge, Mr Steven LLB(Hons) I *Nov 1991*
12, 15, 18, 20, 25
1 Gray's Inn Square, London WC1
p935 . . . . . 020 7405 8946

Attwood, Mr John LLB(Hons) G *Nov 1989*
95, 15, 70, 72, 84, 62, 39, 82, 71
No5 Chambers, Bristol
p971 . . . . . 0845 210 5555
No5 Chambers, London EC4
p944 . . . . . 0845 210 5555
No5 Chambers, Birmingham
p968 . . . . . 0845 210 5555

Attwooll, Mr Christopher Benjamin BA(Keele); Recorder M *Jul 1980*
15, 30, 40, 12
11 King's Bench Walk, Leeds
p978 . . . . . 0113 297 1200

ATWAL, Navjot LLB; LLM L *Jan 2002*
30, 11, 12, 59, 20
3 Hare Court, London EC4
p937 . . . . . 020 7415 7800

Aubrey, Mr David J M LLB(Wales); Recorder M *Jul 1976*
(Q.C.) *15, 30, 36*
Temple Chambers, Newport
p988 . . . . . 01633 267403 / 255855
Temple Chambers, Cardiff
p973 . . . . . 029 2039 7364

AUBURN, Mr Jonathan Walter LLB(Hons)(W Aust); BCL; D Phil(Oxon) M *Oct 1999*
1, 11, 26, 51, 55
4-5 Gray's Inn Square, London WC1
p935 . . . . . 020 7404 5252

AUDLAND, Mr William BA(Oxon) G *Nov 1992*
11, 24, 30, 40
12 King's Bench Walk, London EC4
p940 . . . . . 020 7583 0811

Auld, Mr Charles BA(Dunelm) M *Dec 1980*
8, 16, 17, 29, 32, 37, 88
St John's Chambers, Bristol
p972 . . . . . 0117 921 3456

AULD, Ms Rohan MA(Cantab) G *Nov 1992*
1 Garden Court, London EC4
p934 . . . . . 020 7797 7900

Auld, Mr Stephen G *Jul 1979*
(Q.C.)
One Essex Court, London EC4
p931 . . . . . 020 7583 2000

Austin, Miss Rebecca M *Oct 2002*
2 King's Bench Walk, London EC4
p939 . . . . . 020 7353 1746

AUSTIN-SMITH, Mr James I *Jul 1999*
15, 72
23 Essex Street, London WC2
p932 . . . . . 020 7413 0353

AUSTIN-SMITH, Mr Michael LLB; Recorder I *Jul 1969*
(Q.C.) *25, 15, 18, 36, 12*
23 Essex Street, London WC2
p932 . . . . . 020 7413 0353

Austins, Christopher LLB G *Jul 1988*
Clerksroom - Administration Centre, Taunton
p993 . . . . . 0845 083 3000

AUTY, Mr Michael BA I *Nov 1990*
15
1 High Pavement, Nottingham
p988 . . . . . 0115 941 8218

Avery, Miss Rachel L *Jan 2003*
24, 18, 55, 51, 11, 12
Devereux Chambers, London WC2
p930 . . . . . 020 7353 7534

AWADALLA, Miss Katherine M *Oct 1998*
18, 30
12 King's Bench Walk, London EC4
p940 . . . . . 020 7583 0811

AYERS, Mr Guy LLB; Recorder I *Jul 1979*
15, 25, 36
Octagon House, Norwich
p988 . . . . . 01603 623186

Aylett, Mr Kenneth George BA; BL(Dublin) I *Jul 1972*
15, 19, 25, 54, 36, 39, 42, 51, 57, 58, 62, 63, 70, 71, 80, 81, 82, 83, 84, 91, 94, 95
15 New Bridge Street Chambers, London EC4
p943 . . . . . 020 7842 1900

AYLIFFE, Mr James BA(Oxon) L *Nov 1987*
(Q.C.) *3, 5, 6, 8, 11, 29, 40*
Wilberforce Chambers, London WC2
p953 . . . . . 020 7306 0102

AYLING, Ms Judith A MA(Cantab); DipLaw M *Oct 1998*
1, 11, 30, 53, 24
Thirty Nine Essex Street, London WC2
p932 . . . . . 020 7832 1111

Ayling, Miss Tracy Jane BA(Dunelm) I *Jul 1983*
(Q.C.) *15, 62*
2 Bedford Row, London WC1
p924 . . . . . 020 7440 8888

AYLOTT, Mr Colin LLB I *Nov 1989*
Carmelite Chambers, London EC4
p927 . . . . . 020 7936 6300
Thomas More Chambers, London WC2
p952 . . . . . 020 7404 7000

Aylwin, Mr Christopher MA(Cantab) I *Nov 1970*
3PB, London EC4
p946 . . . . . 020 7583 8055

Ayres, Mr Andrew MA(Hons)(Oxon) G *Oct 1996*
Maitland Chambers, London WC2
p941 . . . . . 020 7406 1200

Azam, Mr Ajmal LLB G *Jul 2006*
20, 40, 1, 37
Hardwicke, London WC2
p936 . . . . . 020 7242 2523

Azhar, Ms Marina LLB(Hons) L *Nov 1990*
10, 20
4 Brick Court Chambers, London EC4
p927 . . . . . 020 7832 3200

Azib, Miss Rehana I *Nov 2003*
12, 24, 30, 53, 11, 48, 18, 50, 40
2 Temple Gardens, London EC4
p952 . . . . . 020 7822 1200

Azim, Miss Rehna LLB M *Jul 1984*
10, 20
42 Bedford Row, London WC1
p925 . . . . . 020 7831 0222

Azmi, Mrs Louise Jacqueline L *Jul 2004*
15
Broadway House Chambers, Leeds
p977 . . . . . 0113 246 2600
Broadway House Chambers, Bradford
p969 . . . . . 01274 722560

Azmi, Mr Mohammad LLB M *Mar 1998*
20, 15, 12
No 8 Chambers, Birmingham
p968 . . . . . 0121 236 5514

Baatz, Mr Nicholas MA; BCL(Oxon) G *Nov 1978*
(Q.C.) *3, 7, 11, 31, 40, 41, 43, 45, 49, 54, 61, 78, 74*
Atkin Chambers, London WC1
p923 . . . . . 020 7404 0102

BABINGTON, Ms Vanessa G *Jul 2008*
Arden Chambers, London WC1
p923 . . . . . 020 7242 4244

Bache, Miss Nina I *Jan 2001*
St Ives Chambers, Birmingham
p969 . . . . . 0121 236 0863

Bacon, Mr Francis BA; MSc G *Jul 1988*
40, 11, 24
Hailsham Chambers, London EC4
p936 . . . . . 020 7643 5000

Bacon, Ms Jane M *Oct 1999*
20, 10
36 Bedford Row, London WC1
p925 . . . . . 020 7421 8000

BACON, Mr Jeffrey BA; Dip M *Nov 1989*
6, 8, 11, 12, 18, 19, 7, 29
Littleton Chambers, London EC4
p941 . . . . . 020 7797 8600

Bacon, Miss Kelyn MA(Oxon); LLM(E U Florence) I *Feb 1998*
11, 19, 1, 44
Brick Court Chambers, London WC2
p927 . . . . . 020 7379 3550

Bacon, Mr Nicholas M LLB(Essex) I *Oct 1992*
(Q.C.) *12*
Four New Square, London WC2
p943 . . . . . 020 7822 2000

BADENOCH, Mr James MA(Oxon); Recorder L *Nov 1968*
(Q.C.) *12, 27, 30, 36, 40, 53, 56*
1 Crown Office Row, London EC4
p929 . . . . . 020 7797 7500

Badenoch, Mr Tony M *Nov 1996*
15, 25, 62
6 King's Bench Walk, London EC4
p939 . . . . . 020 7583 0410

BADGER, Mr Christopher M *Nov 2002*
15, 56, 46, 62, 27, 36
23 Essex Street, London WC2
p932 . . . . . 020 7413 0353

BAGCHI, Mr Andrew Kumar LLB(Lond) M *Jul 1989*
10, 20
1 Garden Court, London EC4
p934 . . . . . 020 7797 7900

Baggley, Mr Philip BA(Hons)(Oxon) G *Jul 2009*
15, 18, 20
Albion Chambers, Bristol
p970 . . . . . 0117 927 2144

BAGGS, Miss Julia C BA(Hons)(Durham) I *Mar 2008*
15, 12, 10
Wilberforce Chambers, Hull
p976 . . . . . 01482 323264

Bagley, Miss Louisa M *Oct 2002*
15, 84, 91
1 Paper Buildings, London EC4
p946 . . . . . 020 7353 3728

BAGLEY, Mr Michael Wallace Welsby BSc G *Nov 1984*
7, 12, 15, 18, 25, 30, 31, 36
Chavasse Court Chambers, Liverpool
p980 . . . . . 0151 229 2030

Bagnall, Mr Matthew LLB M *Oct 1993*
12, 15, 20, 25, 30, 18
2 Pump Court, London EC4
p947 . . . . . 020 7353 5597

Bagot, Mr Charles I *Oct 1997*
30, 40, 53
Hardwicke, London WC2
p936 . . . . . 020 7242 2523

Bagral, Miss Ravinder I *Oct 1996*
1, 51, 23
No5 Chambers, Bristol
p971 . . . . . 0845 210 5555
No5 Chambers, London EC4
p944 . . . . . 0845 210 5555
No5 Chambers, Birmingham
p968 . . . . . 0845 210 5555
Warwick House Chambers, London WC1
p953 . . . . . 020 7430 2323

BAGSHAW, Mr Duncan L *Jul 2003*
11, 38, 93, 67, 8, 30
St Philips Chambers, Birmingham
p969 . . . . . 0121 246 7000

BAHIA, Miss Sharon G *Oct 2000*
15
St Philips Chambers, Birmingham
p969 . . . . . 0121 246 7000

BAHRA, Miss Narita L *Oct 1997*
15
9-12 Bell Yard Chambers, London WC2
p926 . . . . . 020 7400 1800

BAILEY, Mr Andrew BA; LLB L *Oct 1993*
10, 12, 18, 20, 22, 30, 40, 89
Trinity Chambers, Chelmsford
p974 . . . . . 01245 605040
Paradise Chambers, Sheffield
p992 . . . . . 0114 273 8951

Bailey, Mr Anthony R I *Nov 1972*
2 King's Bench Walk, London EC4
p939 . . . . . 020 7353 1746

Bailey, Mr David John BA(Oxon); LLM(Uni of LA) G *Jul 1989*
(Q.C.) *3, 11, 35, 21, 24, 5, 40*
7 King's Bench Walk, London EC4
p940 . . . . . 020 7910 8300

BAILEY, Mr Graham R LLB(Hons) I *Feb 1993*
30, 20, 10
9 St John Street Chambers, Manchester
p984 . . . . . 0161 955 9000

BAILEY, Mr James BA(Oxon); BCL; Barrister G *Mar 1999*
8, 11
New Square Chambers, London WC2
p943 . . . . . 020 7419 8000

BAILEY, Mr Michael LLM G *Nov 1986*
8, 10, 11, 18, 20, 25, 14, 29
Tanfield Chambers, London WC1
p951 . . . . . 020 7421 5300

Bailey, Miss Patricia LLB; Dip Adv Stud Econ M *Nov 1969*
10, 20, 30
New Bailey Chambers, Liverpool
p981 . . . . . 0151 236 9402

BAILEY, Miss Rosanna LLB G *Oct 1994*
20, 51
10 King's Bench Walk, London EC4
p940 . . . . . 020 7353 7742

Bailey, Mr Russell LLB(Lond) I *Nov 1985*
11, 3, 12, 41, 49, 55, 66, 67, 18, 97
No5 Chambers, Bristol
p971 . . . . . 0845 210 5555
No5 Chambers, London EC4
p944 . . . . . 0845 210 5555
No5 Chambers, Birmingham
p968 . . . . . 0845 210 5555

Bailey, Miss Sasha L *Jul 2002*
2 Pump Court, London EC4
p947 . . . . . 020 7353 5597

Bailey, Mr Stephen LLB(Hons) G *Oct 1991*
15
4 Breams Buildings, London EC4
p927 . . . . . 020 7092 1900

Bailey, Stephen I *Jan 2006*
40, 27, 30, 11
Hailsham Chambers, London EC4
p936 . . . . . 020 7643 5000

Bailey, Mr Steven BA; MPhil M *Oct 1992*
15, 62, 72
No5 Chambers, Bristol
p971 . . . . . 0845 210 5555
No5 Chambers, London EC4
p944 . . . . . 0845 210 5555
No5 Chambers, Birmingham
p968 . . . . . 0845 210 5555

BAILEY, Tom M *Jan 2005*
4 King's Bench Walk, London EC4
p939 . . . . . 020 7822 7000

Bailey-Harris, Prof Rebecca I *Jul 2000*
1 Hare Court, London EC4
p936 . . . . . 020 7797 7070

BAILIN, Mr Alex MA(Hons)(Cantab) L *Nov 1995*
(Q.C.) *51, 15, 1, 11, 62, 52, 81, 33, 71*
Matrix Chambers, London WC1
p942 . . . . . 020 7404 3447

Baillie, Mr Andrew Bruce BA; Recorder I *Nov 1970*
(Q.C.) *62, 15, 96, 65, 81, 39, 38, 84*
9 Gough Square, London EC4
p935 . . . . . 020 7832 0500

Baillie, Ms Brigid I *Jul 2007*
Garden Court North Chambers, Manchester
p983 . . . . . 0161 236 1840

Bain, Mr Iain BA(UAE) M *Jan 2007*
Fenners Chambers, Cambridge
p972 . . . . . 01223 368761

BAINES, Miss Charlotte Louise LLB(Hons) L *Oct 2000*
15
Wilberforce Chambers, Hull
p976 . . . . . 01482 323264

BAINES, Mr Max L *Mar 2005*
15, 62, 25, 36, 91, 34
18 Red Lion Court, London EC4
p949 . . . . . 020 7520 6000
18 Red Lion Court (Annexe), Chelmsford
p973 . . . . . 01245 280880

See p1010 for the Key to Work Categories

BAINS, Ms Param Kaur I *Oct 1993*
20, 10, 64
No5 Chambers, Bristol
p971 . . . . . 0845 210 5555
No5 Chambers, London EC4
p944 . . . . . 0845 210 5555
No5 Chambers, Birmingham
p968 . . . . . 0845 210 5555

BAINS, Mr Satnam M *Apr 2002*
1 Mitre Court Buildings, London EC4
p942 . . . . . 020 7452 8900

Baiou, Mr Mehdi M *Jul 2009*
One Essex Court, London EC4
p931 . . . . . 020 7583 2000

BAIRD, Mr David Anthony M *Jun 2003*
15, 62, 95
187 Fleet Street, London EC4
p933 . . . . . 020 7430 7430

BAIRD, Mr James Stevenson LLB; Recorder M *Nov 1977*
15, 20
Bank House Chambers, Sheffield
p991 . . . . . 0114 275 1223

Baird, Ms Vera LLB G *Nov 1975*
(Q.C.) *15*
Tooks Chambers, London EC4
p953 . . . . . 020 7842 7575

Baird-Murray, Mr Jasper M *Jan 2008*
20, 10
4 Paper Buildings, London EC4
p946 . . . . . 020 7583 0816

Baker, Mr Andrew MA(Oxon) L *Jul 1988*
(Q.C.) *3, 11, 12, 24, 35, 41, 61*
20 Essex Street, London WC2
p932 . . . . . 020 7842 1200
No5 Chambers, Bristol
p971 . . . . . 0845 210 5555
No5 Chambers, London EC4
p944 . . . . . 0845 210 5555
No5 Chambers, Birmingham
p968 . . . . . 0845 210 5555

Baker, Mrs Caroline BA; MSc; Deputy District Judge G *Jul 1988*
10, 20
No5 Chambers, Bristol
p971 . . . . . 0845 210 5555
No5 Chambers, London EC4
p944 . . . . . 0845 210 5555
No5 Chambers, Birmingham
p968 . . . . . 0845 210 5555

BAKER, Mr Christopher Michael MA(Cantab); LLM M *Jul 1984*
1, 12, 22, 26, 36, 51, 54, 46, 15, 72
Arden Chambers, London WC1
p923 . . . . . 020 7242 4244
Old Court Chambers, Middlesbrough
p986 . . . . . 01642 232523

Baker, Ms Clare MA(Cantab) M *Jan 2007*
81, 18
Outer Temple Chambers, London WC2
p945 . . . . . 020 7353 6381

BAKER, Mr Clive A LLB(Hons) G *Oct 1995*
20, 10
7 Harrington Street Chambers, Liverpool
p981 . . . . . 0151 242 0707

Baker, Ms Fay BSc G *Oct 1994*
2 Dr Johnson's Buildings, London EC4
p930 . . . . . 020 7936 2613

BAKER, Ms Hannah MA(Cantab) M *Nov 2005*
20, 12, 10
Queen Elizabeth Buildings, London EC4
p948 . . . . . 020 7797 7837

Baker, Mr Jeremy R Recorder M *May 1979*
(Q.C.) *15, 12, 30, 18, 84*
Thomas More Chambers, London WC2
p952 . . . . . 020 7404 7000

Baker, Ms Maureen Anne BA; Recorder G *Jul 1984*
(Q.C.) *15, 27*
7 Bedford Row, London WC1
p924 . . . . . 020 7242 3555

Baker, Mr Nicholas G *Jul 1980*
20
Hardwicke, London WC2
p936 . . . . . 020 7242 2523

Baker, Mr Philip Woolf BA; BCL; LLM; PhD G *Jul 1979*
(Q.C.) *34, 57, 58*
Gray's Inn Tax Chambers, London WC1
p936 . . . . . 020 7242 2642

Baker, Mr Richard LLB M *Nov 2000*
53, 30
7 Bedford Row, London WC1
p924 . . . . . 020 7242 3555

Baker, Mr Simon BA(Oxon) I *Oct 1998*
15, 25, 84, 62, 46, 28
Argent Chambers, London WC2
p923 . . . . . 020 7556 5500

Baker, Mr Tom M *Jan 2004*
15
QEB Hollis Whiteman, London EC4
p948 . . . . . 020 7933 8855

Baker, Mr William D LLB I *Oct 1992*
20
1 Inner Temple Lane, London EC4
p937 . . . . . 020 7427 4400
St Philips Chambers, Birmingham
p969 . . . . . 0121 246 7000

BAKI, Mr Neil M *Jul 2003*
15, 62, 72
25 Bedford Row, London WC1
p925 . . . . . 020 7067 1500

BALA, Miss Ruth L *Jun 2006*
Gough Square Chambers, London EC4
p935 . . . . . 020 7353 0924

BALCOMBE, Mr David BA(Kent); Recorder L *Nov 1980*
(Q.C.) *12, 20, 27, 30, 40, 53*
1 Crown Office Row, London EC4
p929 . . . . . 020 7797 7500

Baldock, Mr Nicholas MA(Cantab) L *Nov 1983*
12, 15, 22, 30, 46, 51, 56
6-8 Mill Street, Maidstone
p982 . . . . . 01622 688094 / 688095
6 Pump Court, London EC4
p947 . . . . . 020 7797 8400

Baldock, Ms Susan BA; DipLaw L *Jul 1988*
20, 10
4 Paper Buildings, London EC4
p946 . . . . . 020 7583 0816

BALDRY, Mr Rupert BA M *Nov 1987*
(Q.C.) *34, 57, 58*
Pump Court Tax Chambers, London WC1
p948 . . . . . 020 7414 8080

Baldry MP, Mr Tony M *Jan 1975*
One Essex Court, London EC4
p931 . . . . . 020 7936 3030

Baldwin, Dr John BSc; DPhil(Oxon) G *Jul 1977*
(Q.C.) *13, 45, 50, 56*
8 New Square, London WC2
p943 . . . . . 020 7405 4321

BALDWIN, Mr John G BA(Cantab) G *Oct 1990*
7, 11, 12, 30
Oriel Chambers, Liverpool
p981 . . . . . 0151 236 7191 / 236 4321
Oriel Chambers, Preston
p990 . . . . . 01772 254764

Baldwin, Mr Roger M LLB G *Jul 1969*
15
15 Winckley Square, Preston
p991 . . . . . 01772 252828

BALL, Miss Alison LLB(Lond) M *Nov 1972*
(Q.C.) *10, 20*
1 Garden Court, London EC4
p934 . . . . . 020 7797 7900

BALL, Mr Ian M *Oct 1992*
15, 46
Cornwall Street Chambers, Birmingham
p967 . . . . . 0121 233 7500

Ball, Ms Ruth L *Jan 2002*
15
1 Paper Buildings, London EC4
p946 . . . . . 020 7353 3728

Ball, Mr Steven BSc(Hons); LLB(Hons) I *Oct 1995*
11, 12, 30, 40, 1, 7, 47, 48, 22, 26, 29, 36
Rougemont Chambers, Exeter
p975 . . . . . 01392 208484
7 Harrington Street Chambers, Liverpool
p981 . . . . . 0151 242 0707

BALLANCE, Mr James Conrad BA(Jurisprudence); BCL; MPhil; DPhil G *Jul 2009*
Maitland Chambers, London WC2
p941 . . . . . 020 7406 1200

Ballantyne, Prof William MA(Cantab); Former Solicitor I *Nov 1977*
3, 21, 11, 64, 67
Serle Court, London WC2
p950 . . . . . 020 7242 6105

BALLARD, Miss Appa MA(Hons)(Edin); LLB; LLM L *Jul 2006*
12, 10, 20, 93, 49, 8, 92
Cornwall Street Chambers, Birmingham
p967 . . . . . 0121 233 7500

Ballard, Ms Briony Elizabeth BSc(Hons)(B'ham) M *Nov 2000*
12, 30, 27, 40, 53, 68, 85, 36
3 Serjeants' Inn, London EC4
p950 . . . . . 020 7427 5000

BALLENTYNE, Mr Errol Stanley BA G *Nov 1983*
15
1 High Pavement, Nottingham
p988 . . . . . 0115 941 8218

Ballingall, Ms Joanne LLB(Hons) I *Nov 1999*
10, 12, 20
College Chambers, Southampton
p992 . . . . . 023 8023 0338

BALOGH, Mr Christopher T MA(Cantab); MSc(Econ); DipLaw M *Nov 1984*
1, 12, 15, 22, 26, 25, 31
Arden Chambers, London WC1
p923 . . . . . 020 7242 4244

BALYSZ, Mr Mark A G *Oct 1995*
84, 68, 30, 25
Crown Office Chambers, London EC4
p929 . . . . . 020 7797 8100

BAMFORD, Mr Christopher LLB(Hull) I *Nov 1987*
11, 12, 45, 18, 21, 30, 25
Tanfield Chambers, London WC1
p951 . . . . . 020 7421 5300

BAMFORD, Mr Colin MA(Cantab) M *May 2002*
5, 41, 11, 47, 40
South Square, London WC1
p950 . . . . . 020 7696 9900

BAMFORD, Mr Jeremy BA(Oxon) L *Nov 1989*
6, 8, 11, 29, 38, 97
Guildhall Chambers, Bristol
p970 . . . . . 0117 930 9000

Banerjee, Mr Subhankar I *Nov 2000*
15
Atkinson Bevan Chambers, London EC4
p924 . . . . . 020 7353 2112

Bangay, Miss Deborah LLB(Hons) G *Feb 1981*
(Q.C.) *10, 20*
1 Hare Court, London EC4
p936 . . . . . 020 7797 7070

Banham, Mr Colin LLB(Hons) L *Oct 1999*
15, 36
4 Breams Buildings, London EC4
p927 . . . . . 020 7092 1900

Banham, Mr Matthew Ian LLB I *Oct 1999*
15, 51
Nine Bedford Row, London WC1
p924 . . . . . 020 7489 2727

Bankes-Jones, Mr Henry L *Nov 2004*
27, 40, 30
Hailsham Chambers, London EC4
p936 . . . . . 020 7643 5000

Bankole-Jones, Mr John Edward M *Oct 1963*
Clavenes Chambers, Edgware
p975 . . . . . 020 8931 2648

BANKS, Andrew BA(Hons) G *Jul 1995*
10, 20
Atlantic Chambers, Liverpool
p980 . . . . . 0151 236 4421

BANKS, Miss Fiona MA(Cantab) I *Oct 2006*
11, 44, 1, 46, 19, 36, 56, 51, 26
Monckton Chambers, London WC1
p942 . . . . . 020 7405 7211

BANKS, Mr Nathan LLB(Hons) L *Oct 2003*
41, 6, 7, 8, 11, 47, 22, 25, 29, 31, 32, 34, 58, 37
St James's Chambers, Manchester
p984 . . . . . 0161 834 7000

BANKS, Rachael LLB I *Nov 1993*
20
Atlantic Chambers, Liverpool
p980 . . . . . 0151 236 4421

Banks, Mr Robert BSc(Econ) I *Jul 1978*
15, 62
Rye Green Chambers, Etchingham
p975 . . . . . 01435 882577

Banks, Mr Roderick Charles I'Anson LLB(Lond) L *Jul 1974*
29
48 Bedford Row, London WC1
p926 . . . . . 020 7430 2005

Banks, Mr Timothy BA(Hons)(Law) I *Nov 1983*
6, 7, 8, 15, 42, 51, 62, 91
15 New Bridge Street Chambers, London EC4
p943 . . . . . 020 7842 1900

BANNER, Mr Charles L *Jan 2004*
1, 46, 51, 23, 31, 36
Landmark Chambers, London EC4
p941 . . . . . 020 7430 1221

Banner, Mr Gregory S MA(Cantab) G *Jul 1989*
3, 6, 8, 11, 13, 19, 22, 29, 32, 37
Maitland Chambers, London WC2
p941 . . . . . 020 7406 1200

BANNON, Miss Tammi LLB(Hons) L *Nov 1994*
10, 20
Chavasse Court Chambers, Liverpool
p980 . . . . . 0151 229 2030

Banton, Miss Elaine Rose M *Oct 1986*
18, 55
7 Bedford Row, London WC1
p924 . . . . . 020 7242 3555

Banwell, Mr Richard LLB(Hons); LLM L *Oct 1998*
1, 2, 6, 12, 15, 22, 26, 29, 30, 31, 46, 51
6-8 Mill Street, Maidstone
p982 . . . . . 01622 688094 / 688095
6 Pump Court, London EC4
p947 . . . . . 020 7797 8400

BAR, Monika LLB; BA(History) I *Oct 2008*
8
Atlantic Chambers, Liverpool
p980 . . . . . 0151 236 4421

BARAN, Mr Colin M *Oct 2003*
30, 18, 8, 47
St Philips Chambers, Birmingham
p969 . . . . . 0121 246 7000

Barber, Philip LLB G *Nov 1991*
1, 47, 22, 51, 88, 89, 63, 93
Zenith Chambers, Leeds
p979 . . . . . 0113 245 5438

Barbour, Ms Laura G *Oct 2006*
Lincoln House Chambers, Manchester
p984 . . . . . 0161 832 5701

BARCA, Mr Manuel D BA(Cantab) L *Nov 1986*
(Q.C.) *16, 52, 73*
One Brick Court, London EC4
p927 . . . . . 020 7353 8845

Barcello, Mr Andrew LLB L *Mar 2001*
20
Temple Chambers, Newport
p988 . . . . . 01633 267403 / 255855
Temple Chambers, Cardiff
p973 . . . . . 029 2039 7364

Barclay, Mr Robin BA(Hons); DipLaw M *Jul 1999*
15, 62, 36
2 Hare Court, London EC4
p937 . . . . . 020 7353 5324

Bard, Mr Nicholas MA(Oxon) G *Jul 1979*
1, 11, 12, 7, 16, 24, 27, 36, 29, 40
Devereux Chambers, London WC2
p930 . . . . . 020 7353 7534

Barda, Mr Robin J B BA(Oxon) G *Jul 1975*
10, 20, 12, 15
4 Paper Buildings, London EC4
p946 . . . . . 020 7583 0816

BARDEN, Mr Alex MA(Cantab); LLM(Pem) I *Oct 2005*
11, 38, 97
Erskine Chambers, London WC2
p931 . . . . . 020 7242 5532

Barham, Mr Jonathan L *Jan 2002*
Clerksroom - Administration Centre, Taunton
p993 . . . . . 0845 083 3000

BARKER, Miss Alison LLB(Hons) M *Jul 1973*
15
9-12 Bell Yard Chambers, London WC2
p926 . . . . . 020 7400 1800

Barker, Mr Anthony Recorder M *Dec 1966*
(Q.C.) *15, 30, 39, 56, 84, 46, 62, 95, 70, 72, 91, 42*
No5 Chambers, Bristol
p971 . . . . . 0845 210 5555
No5 Chambers, London EC4
p944 . . . . . 0845 210 5555
No5 Chambers, Birmingham
p968 . . . . . 0845 210 5555

BARKER, Mr James LLB(B'ham) G *Jul 1984*
5, 6, 8, 11, 22, 32, 37, 40, 49, 38, 88
Enterprise Chambers, London WC2
p931 . . . . . 020 7405 9471
Enterprise Chambers, Leeds
p977 . . . . . 0113 246 0391

Enterprise Chambers, Newcastle upon Tyne
p987 . . . . . . 0191 222 3344

Barker, Miss Jennifer I *Jan 2000*
1 Pump Court, London EC4
p947 . . . . . . 020 7842 7070

BARKER, Mr Jonathan M *Jan 2006*
12, 30
St Philips Chambers, Birmingham
p969 . . . . . . 0121 246 7000

BARKER, Mr Kerry LLB(Hons) G *Jul 1972*
15, 25, 46, 84
Guildhall Chambers, Bristol
p970 . . . . . . 0117 930 9000

Barker, Mr Nicholas G *Dec 1994*
15, 20, 10
No 6 Barristers Chambers, Leeds
p978 . . . . . . 0113 245 9763

BARKLEM, Mr Martyn LLB; Accredited Mediator; Recorder M *Jul 1989*
1, 18, 4, 11, 6, 36, 5, 3, 49
Littleton Chambers, London EC4
p941 . . . . . . 020 7797 8600

Barling, Mr Gerald MA(Oxon) M *Nov 1972*
(Q.C.) *19, 1*
Brick Court Chambers, London WC2
p927 . . . . . . 020 7379 3550

Barlow, Mr Craig Martin LLB G *Nov 1992*
1, 11, 12, 18, 22, 23, 26
Ely Place Chambers, London EC1
p931 . . . . . . 020 7400 9600

BARLOW, Mr Francis MA(Oxon) I *Feb 1965*
(Q.C.) *6, 8, 9, 14, 22, 29, 32, 34, 37*
Ten Old Square, London WC2
p945 . . . . . . 020 7405 0758

Barlow, Mr Mark LLB M *Oct 1992*
15, 12, 91, 51, 82
Garden Court North Chambers, Manchester
p983 . . . . . . 0161 236 1840

Barlow, Miss Melissa E B BA M *Oct 1991*
10, 20
Queen Square Chambers, Bristol
p972 . . . . . . 0117 921 1966

Barlow, Mr Richard L M *Jan 1970*
57, 58
Temple Tax Chambers, London EC4
p952 . . . . . . 020 7353 7884 / 7353 8982

Barlow, Miss Sarah H LLB(Hons) G *Oct 1993*
12, 30, 22, 15, 27
Broadway House Chambers, Leeds
p977 . . . . . . 0113 246 2600
Broadway House Chambers, Bradford
p969 . . . . . . 01274 722560

Barnard, Mr David BA(Cantab) G *Jul 1967*
11, 15, 30, 1
33 Bedford Row, London WC1
p925 . . . . . . 020 7242 6476

Barnard, Mr James BA(Bris) M *Oct 1993*
5, 24, 29, 18, 19, 62
11 Stone Buildings, London WC2
p951 . . . . . . 020 7831 6381

Barnard, Mr Jonathan M *Oct 1997*
Cloth Fair Chambers, London EC1
p928 . . . . . . 020 7710 6444

Barnes, Andrea L *Nov 1999*
30
Clerksroom - Administration Centre, Taunton
p993 . . . . . . 0845 083 3000

Barnes, Ashley J LLB(Hons) I *Nov 1990*
15
New Bailey Chambers, Preston
p990 . . . . . . 01772 258087

Barnes, Mr Christopher G *Jun 2000*
30, 53
Exchange Chambers, Manchester
p983 . . . . . . 0161 833 2722
Exchange Chambers, Liverpool
p980 . . . . . . 0151 236 7747
Exchange Chambers, Leeds
p977 . . . . . . 0113 203 1970
42 Bedford Row, London WC1
p925 . . . . . . 020 7831 0222

Barnes, Mr David Jonathan BSc G *Nov 1981*
15, 62
Charter Chambers, London WC1
p928 . . . . . . 020 7618 4400
3 Temple Gardens, London EC4
p952 . . . . . . 020 7353 3102

Barnes, Mr H Jonathan LLB(Soton); Recorder G *Jul 1970*
30, 12, 7, 8, 11, 22, 24, 27, 29, 31, 36, 15
Walnut House Chambers, Exeter
p975 . . . . . . 01392 279751

Barnes, Mr Jonathan BA(Hons)(Oxon) L *Jun 1999*
11, 12, 13, 16, 18, 50, 51
5RB, London WC1
p948 . . . . . . 020 7242 2902

Barnes, Mr Luke C BA(Oxon) G *Nov 1996*
20, 12, 22, 30, 25
3 Dr Johnson's Buildings, London EC4
p930 . . . . . . 020 7353 4854

BARNES, Mr Matthew MA(Cantab) M *Jan 1992*
15, 62
St Philips Chambers, Birmingham
p969 . . . . . . 0121 246 7000
1 Crown Office Row, London EC4
p929 . . . . . . 020 7797 7500

BARNES, Mr Michael BA(Oxon); Recorder M *Jul 1965*
(Q.C.) *22, 31*
Wilberforce Chambers, London WC2
p953 . . . . . . 020 7306 0102

BARNES, Ms Natasha G *Jul 2010*
15
9-12 Bell Yard Chambers, London WC2
p926 . . . . . . 020 7400 1800

Barnes, Mr Timothy Paul MA(Cantab); Recorder L *Jul 1968*
(Q.C.) *15, 62*
7 Bedford Row, London WC1
p924 . . . . . . 020 7242 3555

Barnett, Miss Adrienne BA(Cape Town) M *Jul 1981*
20, 10
1 Pump Court, London EC4
p947 . . . . . . 020 7842 7070

Barnett, Mr Daniel Alexander LLB L *Oct 1993*
18, 55
Outer Temple Chambers, London WC2
p945 . . . . . . 020 7353 6381

Barnett, Mr Jeremy V LLB(Hons); Recorder 2000 G *Jul 1980*
15, 62, 12, 81, 84, 48, 36, 69, 27
2 Bedford Row, London WC1
p924 . . . . . . 020 7440 8888
St Pauls Chambers, Leeds
p979 . . . . . . 0113 245 5866

BARNETT, Ms Joanne LLB(Wales) M *Nov 1989*
20
9 St John Street Chambers, Manchester
p984 . . . . . . 0161 955 9000

Barnett, Miss Sally M *Nov 1987*
2 New Street, Leicester
p979 . . . . . . 0116 262 5906

Barney, Miss Helen L *Jan 1999*
18, 55
No5 Chambers, Bristol
p971 . . . . . . 0845 210 5555
No5 Chambers, London EC4
p944 . . . . . . 0845 210 5555
No5 Chambers, Birmingham
p968 . . . . . . 0845 210 5555

BARNFATHER, Ms Lydia I *Oct 1992*
15, 25, 36
QEB Hollis Whiteman, London EC4
p948 . . . . . . 020 7933 8855

Barnfield, Mr Alexander M *Jul 2007*
15, 12, 23
No 8 Chambers, Birmingham
p968 . . . . . . 0121 236 5514

BARR, Mr David MA(Cantab) G *Nov 1993*
Temple Garden Chambers, London EC4
p952 . . . . . . 020 7583 1315

Barr, Mr Edward LLB(Hons) I *Oct 1983*
15
2 New Street, Leicester
p979 . . . . . . 0116 262 5906

BARRACLOUGH, Mr Anthony Roger BA(Dunelm); BL I *Nov 1978*
15
Chavasse Court Chambers, Liverpool
p980 . . . . . . 0151 229 2030

BARRACLOUGH, Miss Lisa L *Jan 1999*
10, 20
Colleton Chambers, Exeter
p975 . . . . . . 01392 274898

BARRACLOUGH, Mr Nicholas LLB I *Nov 1990*
15, 62, 95
187 Fleet Street, London EC4
p933 . . . . . . 020 7430 7430

Barraclough, Mr Richard MA(Oxon) I *Nov 1980*
7, 8, 12, 15, 18, 20, 22, 27, 30, 31, 32, 37, 40, 47, 51, 53
6-8 Mill Street, Maidstone
p982 . . . . . . 01622 688094 / 688095
6 Pump Court, London EC4
p947 . . . . . . 020 7797 8400

BARRAN, Tabitha I *Oct 1998*
10, 20
Renaissance Chambers, London WC1
p949 . . . . . . 020 7404 1111

Barratt, Mr Dominic Anthony Richard BA(Hons)(Leeds); Pupil Supervisor G *Nov 1992*
10, 12, 20, 25, 18
East Anglian Chambers, Norwich
p988 . . . . . . 01603 617351
East Anglian Chambers, Colchester
p975 . . . . . . 01206 572756
East Anglian Chambers, Chelmsford
p973 . . . . . . 01245 215660
East Anglian Chambers, Ipswich
p976 . . . . . . 01473 214481

Barratt, Mr Robin Alexander MA(Oxon) M *Nov 1970*
(Q.C.) *31, 19*
International Law Chambers, London W2
p938 . . . . . . 020 7221 5685 / 7352 6649

Barrett, Miss Cecilia M LLB(Hons)(Warw) I *Jul 1998*
20, 10
Harcourt Chambers, London EC4
p936 . . . . . . 0844 561 7135
Harcourt Chambers, Oxford
p989 . . . . . . 0844 561 7135

Barrett, Mr John BA; Recorder G *May 1982*
1, 26, 31, 46, 54
Kings Chambers, Leeds
p978 . . . . . . 0113 242 1123
Kings Chambers, Manchester
p984 . . . . . . 0161 832 9082

Barrett, Mr Kevin M *Jan 1985*
7, 40, 41, 49, 96, 74, 3
No5 Chambers, Bristol
p971 . . . . . . 0845 210 5555
No5 Chambers, London EC4
p944 . . . . . . 0845 210 5555
No5 Chambers, Birmingham
p968 . . . . . . 0845 210 5555

BARRETT, Mr Robert Scott MA(Cantab) G *Jul 1978*
15, 12
2 Pump Court, London EC4
p947 . . . . . . 020 7353 5597

Barrie, Miss Laura L *Jul 2005*
Goldsmith Chambers, London EC4
p935 . . . . . . 020 7353 6802

Barrington-Smyth, Miss Amanda R LLB(Lond) M *Nov 1972*
10, 20
4 Paper Buildings, London EC4
p946 . . . . . . 020 7583 0816

Barron-Eaves, Mrs Emma LLB(Hons) L *Jul 1998*
10, 20
15 Winckley Square, Preston
p991 . . . . . . 01772 252828

Barry, Mr Denis I *Jan 1996*
15, 62, 48, 13, 25
5 Paper Buildings, London EC4
p946 . . . . . . 020 7583 6117

Barry, Mr Kevin LLB(Hons)(B'ham) L *Nov 1997*
12, 15, 62, 70
36 Bedford Row, London WC1
p925 . . . . . . 020 7421 8000

BARRY, Miss Kirsten LLB(Hons) L *Nov 1993*
12, 18, 30, 55, 22
9 St John Street Chambers, Manchester
p984 . . . . . . 0161 955 9000

Barry, Mr Matthew BA(Cantab) G *Oct 2002*
12, 30, 15, 18, 20
9 Park Place, Cardiff
p973 . . . . . . 029 2038 2731

Barry, Mr Simon BA(Hons) M *Jan 1997*
15
1 Pump Court, London EC4
p947 . . . . . . 020 7842 7070

Barsam, Ms Talia BA; LLM I *Nov 2007*
24, 30, 18, 55, 11, 12
Devereux Chambers, London WC2
p930 . . . . . . 020 7353 7534

Bart, Mr Delano LLB L *Jun 1977*
1 Mitre Court Buildings, London EC4
p942 . . . . . . 020 7452 8900

BARTFELD, Mr Jason M *Jan 1995*
15, 62, 95
187 Fleet Street, London EC4
p933 . . . . . . 020 7430 7430

Bartholomew, Miss Ami L *Nov 2003*
Field Court Chambers, London WC1
p933 . . . . . . 020 7405 6114

Bartle, Mr Philip M MA; BCL(Oxon); Accredited Mediator M *Jul 1976*
(Q.C.) *3, 5, 7, 8, 11, 12, 18, 24, 27, 29, 30, 36, 49*
Exchange Chambers, Manchester
p983 . . . . . . 0161 833 2722
Exchange Chambers, Liverpool
p980 . . . . . . 0151 236 7747
Exchange Chambers, Leeds
p977 . . . . . . 0113 203 1970
Littleton Chambers, London EC4
p941 . . . . . . 020 7797 8600

Bartlet-Jones, Mr Stephen I *Jan 2004*
20
1 Pump Court, London EC4
p947 . . . . . . 020 7842 7070

Bartlett, Mr Andrew V B BA(Oxon); FCIArb M *Jul 1974*
(Q.C.) *74, 24, 7, 40, 41, 3, 11*
Becket Chambers, Canterbury
p972 . . . . . . 01227 786331
Becket Chambers, Maidstone
p982 . . . . . . 01622 230957
Crown Office Chambers, London EC4
p929 . . . . . . 020 7797 8100

BARTLETT, Mrs Catherine LLB I *Jan 2004*
11, 12, 18, 30, 76
Oriel Chambers, Liverpool
p981 . . . . . . 0151 236 7191 / 236 4321
Oriel Chambers, Preston
p990 . . . . . . 01772 254764

Bartlett, Mr David A BA(Oxon); Recorder G *Jul 1975*
15, 72
3PB, Bournemouth
p969 . . . . . . 01202 292102

Bartlett, Mr Roger J L BA(Oxon) M *Jul 1968*
11, 12, 30, 37
5 St Andrew's Hill, London EC4
p950 . . . . . . 020 7332 5400

Bartley Jones, Mr Edward L *Jan 1975*
(Q.C.)
13 Old Square Chambers, London WC2
p945 . . . . . . 020 7831 4445

Barton, Mr Alan LLM M *Nov 1975*
8, 20, 30, 40, 22
Lamb Building, Brighton
p970 . . . . . . 01273 820490
Lamb Building, London EC4
p940 . . . . . . 020 7797 7788

Barton, Mr Hugh BA; DipLaw M *Nov 1989*
15, 51
Lincoln House Chambers, Manchester
p984 . . . . . . 0161 832 5701

Barton, Mr Jeremy M *Jan 2004*
2 King's Bench Walk, London EC4
p939 . . . . . . 020 7353 1746

BARTON, Mr Richard BA(Oxon); BCL(Oxon) L *Oct 1990*
10, 12, 15, 18, 20, 22, 30, 36, 72, 70
1 King's Bench Walk, London EC4
p938 . . . . . . 020 7936 1500

BARUAH, Miss Fiona LLB(Hons) I *Oct 1996*
12, 20, 30
Octagon House, Norwich
p988 . . . . . . 01603 623186

Baruah, Mrs Rima BSc; CPE I *Feb 1994*
Thomas More Chambers, London WC2
p952 . . . . . . 020 7404 7000

Barwise, Ms Stephanie MA; LLM(Cantab) M *Jul 1988*
(Q.C.) *3, 7, 11, 31, 40, 41, 43, 45, 49, 54, 61, 78, 74*
Atkin Chambers, London WC1
p923 . . . . . . 020 7404 0102

Bash-Taqi, Mrs Shahineh BA(Dunelm) I *Nov 1972*
15, 20, 18, 12, 22, 23
Leone Chambers, Harrow
p976 . . . . . . 020 8868 2736

 See p1010 for the Key to Work Categories

Bashir, Nadim LLB M *Nov 1988*
Park Court Chambers, Leeds
p978 . . . . . 0113 243 3277

Bassano, Mr Alaric BA(Oxon) G *Nov 1993*
15, 72
Exchange Chambers, Manchester
p983 . . . . . 0161 833 2722
Exchange Chambers, Liverpool
p980 . . . . . 0151 236 7747
Exchange Chambers, Leeds
p977 . . . . . 0113 203 1970

Bastin, Mr Alexander LLB(Hons); BA(Hons) M *Oct 1995*
22, 6, 8, 37, 40, 88, 93
Hardwicke, London WC2
p936 . . . . . 020 7242 2523

Batchelor, Mr Mark Alfred Lowe I *Nov 1971*
1, 12, 26, 10
42 Bedford Row, London WC1
p925 . . . . . 020 7831 0222

Batcup, Mr David LLB(Lond) G *Jul 1974*
10, 15, 12, 20, 30, 22
Charter Chambers, London WC1
p928 . . . . . 020 7618 4400

Bate, Mr Stephen MA(Cantab); DipLaw M *Jul 1981*
8, 13, 16, 43, 36, 50, 51, 56
5RB, London WC1
p948 . . . . . 020 7242 2902

BATE-WILLIAMS, Mr John R A LLB(Wales); Recorder I *Nov 1976*
Temple Garden Chambers, London EC4
p952 . . . . . 020 7583 1315

Bateman, Ms Christine LLB(Nott'm) L *Oct 1992*
22, 40, 10, 20
Crown Office Row Chambers, Brighton
p970 . . . . . 01273 625625

BATES, Mr Alan BA; LLM M *Oct 2003*
1, 43, 44, 46, 48, 18, 19, 51, 26, 63, 33, 36, 61, 38, 25
Monckton Chambers, London WC1
p942 . . . . . 020 7405 7211

Bates, Mr Alexander A BA(Hons)(Cantab) G *Oct 1994*
51
St Pauls Chambers, Leeds
p979 . . . . . 0113 245 5866

Bates, Mr John H M *Jul 1973*
26, 28, 31, 46, 61
Old Square Chambers, Bristol
p971 . . . . . 0117 930 5100
Old Square Chambers, London WC1
p945 . . . . . 020 7269 0300

BATES, Mr Justin MA(Oxon); LLM(Toronto) G *Jan 2003*
1, 22, 12
Arden Chambers, London WC1
p923 . . . . . 020 7242 4244

BATES, Miss Lesley I *Nov 1999*
15, 27, 48, 13, 36
23 Essex Street, London WC2
p932 . . . . . 020 7413 0353

Bates, Mr Peter S BA L *Jul 1978*
30, 8
New Walk Chambers, Leicester
p979 . . . . . 0871 200 1298

BATES, Mr Richard BA(Hons) M *Oct 1992*
20, 10
29 Bedford Row, London WC1
p925 . . . . . 020 7404 1044

Batey, Mr Michael BA(Keele); Deputy District Judge G *Jul 1989*
10, 12, 20, 22, 30, 38
Stour Chambers, Canterbury
p972 . . . . . 01227 764899

Bath, Miss Baljinder LLB(Hons) L *Oct 1996*
6, 8, 10, 53, 11, 12, 67, 14, 20, 22, 88, 30
College Chambers, Southampton
p992 . . . . . 023 8023 0338

Bathurst Norman, Miss Harriet Anstice BA(Hons); PGDL I *Oct 2001*
15, 62
2 Bedford Row, London WC1
p924 . . . . . 020 7440 8888

Batiste, Mr Simon Anthony LLB L *Nov 1995*
15
No 6 Barristers Chambers, Leeds
p978 . . . . . 0113 245 9763

Batra, Bunty Lalit LLB G *Feb 1987*
10, 12, 15, 20, 30, 18
St Johns Buildings, Preston
p990 . . . . . 01772 256100
St Johns Buildings, Chester
p974 . . . . . 01244 323070
St Johns Buildings, Manchester
p985 . . . . . 0161 214 1500
St Johns Buildings, Liverpool
p982 . . . . . 0151 243 6000

BATSTONE, Mr William BA(York) M *Nov 1982*
2, 93
Guildhall Chambers, Bristol
p970 . . . . . 0117 930 9000

BATT, Miss Charanjit L *Oct 2004*
20, 10, 12
Queen Elizabeth Buildings, London EC4
p948 . . . . . 020 7797 7837

Battie, Miss Eleanor BA(Hons) L *Jan 2004*
12, 15, 20, 30, 10
Crown Office Row Chambers, Brighton
p970 . . . . . 01273 625625

Batts, Ms Gillian LLB(Hons) L *Nov 1999*
Park Court Chambers, Leeds
p978 . . . . . 0113 243 3277

BAUGHAN, Mr Andrew M *Oct 1994*
15, 70, 72, 91
1 King's Bench Walk, London EC4
p938 . . . . . 020 7936 1500

Baughan, Mr Julian James BA(Oxon) I *Jul 1967*
(Q.C.)
King's Bench Chambers, Oxford
p989 . . . . . 01865 311066
13 King's Bench Walk, London EC4
p940 . . . . . 020 7353 7204

Baumohl, Mr Mark M *Oct 2001*
Field Court Chambers, London WC1
p933 . . . . . 020 7405 6114

BAUR, Mr Christopher M *Jul 1972*
15
Furnival Chambers, London EC4
p934 . . . . . 020 7405 3232

Bax, Mr James LLB(Hons) L *Oct 1999*
12, 30, 47, 48, 18, 36, 55, 67, 68
Rougemont Chambers, Exeter
p975 . . . . . 01392 208484

Baxter, Miss Bernadette LLB; Recorder M *Jul 1987*
12, 15, 20, 30
Lincoln House Chambers, Manchester
p984 . . . . . 0161 832 5701

BAXTER, Mr Gerald Pearson LLB(Sheff); LLM L *Jul 1971*
15
Chavasse Court Chambers, Liverpool
p980 . . . . . 0151 229 2030

Baxter, Mr Mark L *Jul 2006*
8, 32, 37, 14
5 Stone Buildings, London WC2
p951 . . . . . 020 7242 6201

Baxter, Mrs Sharon I *Jul 1987*
10, 15, 20
Argent Chambers, London WC2
p923 . . . . . 020 7556 5500

BAYATI, Charlotte LLB G *Nov 1995*
23
Renaissance Chambers, London WC1
p949 . . . . . 020 7404 1111

BAYFIELD, Mr Daniel MA(Cantab) I *Oct 1998*
6, 11, 40, 50, 56, 97, 38
South Square, London WC1
p950 . . . . . 020 7696 9900

Bayley, Miss Laura G *Jan 1999*
20, 10
4 Brick Court Chambers, London EC4
p927 . . . . . 020 7832 3200

Bayliss, Mr Roderic A Recorder I *Jul 1966*
10, 12, 15, 20, 30
Charter Chambers, London WC1
p928 . . . . . 020 7618 4400

Bayliss, Miss Sarah M *Oct 2002*
6, 8, 11, 24, 29, 40, 37, 32, 5, 49, 62
XXIV Old Buildings, London WC2
p944 . . . . . 020 7691 2424

Bayliss, Mr Thomas William Maxwell LLB I *Jul 1977*
(Q.C.) *15, 62*
Park Court Chambers, Leeds
p978 . . . . . 0113 243 3277

Bayliss, Mr Tom Recorder M *Jan 1977*
(Q.C.)
5 King's Bench Walk, London EC4
p939 . . . . . 020 7353 5638

Bayoumi, Miss Mona M *Nov 2004*
12, 20, 30, 67
Civitas Law, Cardiff
p972 . . . . . 0845 071 3007

Bazini, Mr Danny G *Nov 1992*
1, 51, 23
No5 Chambers, Bristol
p971 . . . . . 0845 210 5555
No5 Chambers, London EC4
p944 . . . . . 0845 210 5555
No5 Chambers, Birmingham
p968 . . . . . 0845 210 5555

BAZLEY, Miss Janet Clare LLB(Bris) L *Jul 1980*
(Q.C.) *10, 20*
1 Garden Court, London EC4
p934 . . . . . 020 7797 7900

Beach, Mrs Fiona BA(Hons) L *Oct 2001*
10, 20, 23, 76
Stour Chambers, Canterbury
p972 . . . . . 01227 764899

Beal, Mr Kieron BA(Hons)(Cantab)(Law); LLM(Harvard) I *Oct 1995*
11, 19, 33, 44, 51
Blackstone Chambers, London EC4
p926 . . . . . 020 7583 1770

Bealby, Mr Walter BA M *Jul 1976*
15, 72
No5 Chambers, Bristol
p971 . . . . . 0845 210 5555
No5 Chambers, London EC4
p944 . . . . . 0845 210 5555
No5 Chambers, Birmingham
p968 . . . . . 0845 210 5555

Beale, Ms Anna BA(Jurisprudence) G *Nov 2001*
18, 55, 30, 23
Cloisters, London EC4
p928 . . . . . 020 7827 4000

Bean, Mr Matthew BA(Dunelm) M *Nov 1997*
15, 12, 23
11 King's Bench Walk, Leeds
p978 . . . . . 0113 297 1200

Béar, Mr Charles BA(Oxon) L *Jul 1986*
(Q.C.)
Fountain Court Chambers, London EC4
p934 . . . . . 020 7583 3335

BEARD, Mr Daniel MA(Cantab); BCL M *Jul 1996*
(Q.C.) *1, 18, 19, 23, 40, 44, 51, 61, 57*
Monckton Chambers, London WC1
p942 . . . . . 020 7405 7211

Beard, Mr Mark LLB(Hons)(Lond) G *Oct 1996*
12, 15, 22, 26, 30, 31, 46, 51
6-8 Mill Street, Maidstone
p982 . . . . . 01622 688094 / 688095
6 Pump Court, London EC4
p947 . . . . . 020 7797 8400

BEARD, Mr Simon BA(Oxon) G *Nov 1980*
30, 53, 40
Ropewalk Chambers, Nottingham
p989 . . . . . 0115 947 2581

BEARDMORE, Mr William E G *Jul 2005*
15
Chavasse Court Chambers, Liverpool
p980 . . . . . 0151 229 2030

Bearman, Mr Justin Ian LLB I *Nov 1992*
15
Castle Chambers, Harrow
p976 . . . . . 020 8423 6579

BEATTIE, Ann BSc; Dip M *Jul 1989*
20
Atlantic Chambers, Liverpool
p980 . . . . . 0151 236 4421

Beattie, Ms Annabel BA(Hons) I *Jul 2005*
Park Court Chambers, Leeds
p978 . . . . . 0113 243 3277

BEATTIE, Ms Kate BA(Sydney) L *Jan 2007*
51, 68, 40, 53, 30, 18, 46, 26, 67, 57, 58
1 Crown Office Row, London EC4
p929 . . . . . 020 7797 7500

Beattie, Miss Sharon Michelle LLB I *Nov 1986*
Park Court Chambers, Leeds
p978 . . . . . 0113 243 3277

Beaumont, Mr Adam L *Jul 2009*
15, 48, 47, 62, 25, 85, 46
St Pauls Chambers, Leeds
p979 . . . . . 0113 245 5866

Beaumont, Mr Andrew BSc L *Jul 1999*
6, 7, 8, 11, 18, 22, 45, 13, 40, 36, 37
KCH Garden Square Chambers, Nottingham
p989 . . . . . 0115 941 8851
KCH Garden Square Chambers, Leicester
p979 . . . . . 0115 941 8851

Beazley, Mr Thomas BA(Cantab); LLB M *Jul 1979*
(Q.C.) *3, 5, 8, 11, 12, 24, 29, 36, 41, 62, 44, 19, 89*
Blackstone Chambers, London EC4
p926 . . . . . 020 7583 1770

Bebb, Mr Gordon M M *Nov 1975*
(Q.C.) *53, 84, 30, 85, 36*
Outer Temple Chambers, London WC2
p945 . . . . . 020 7353 6381

BECKER, Mr Paul A LLB(Hons) L *Nov 1990*
15
Chavasse Court Chambers, Liverpool
p980 . . . . . 0151 229 2030

Becker, Timothy BA(Lond); DipLaw; AKC M *Jul 1992*
Clerksroom - Administration Centre, Taunton
p993 . . . . . 0845 083 3000

Beckett, Mrs Jayne Louise MA(Hons)(Cantab) M *Nov 1995*
15, 12, 30
Broadway House Chambers, Leeds
p977 . . . . . 0113 246 2600
Broadway House Chambers, Bradford
p969 . . . . . 01274 722560

Beckman, Mr Michael LLB(Lond) L *May 1954*
(Q.C.) *62*
4 KBW, London EC4
p938 . . . . . 020 7822 8822
Pallant Chambers, Chichester
p974 . . . . . 01243 784538
11 Stone Buildings, London WC2
p951 . . . . . 020 7831 6381

Beddoe, Mr Richard BA(Hons)(Law & Politics)(Wales) G *Oct 1999*
42 Bedford Row, London WC1
p925 . . . . . 020 7831 0222
Coram Chambers, London EC1
p929 . . . . . 020 7092 3700

BEDENHAM, Mr David LLB(Hons); LLM(Lond) G *Jun 2005*
1, 22, 72
4-5 Gray's Inn Square, London WC1
p935 . . . . . 020 7404 5252
2 Hare Court, London EC4
p937 . . . . . 020 7353 5324

Bedford, Mr Becket LLB(Cardiff) M *Nov 1989*
18, 55, 5, 6, 7, 8, 29, 47, 49, 67, 89, 93, 97
No5 Chambers, Bristol
p971 . . . . . 0845 210 5555
No5 Chambers, London EC4
p944 . . . . . 0845 210 5555
No5 Chambers, Birmingham
p968 . . . . . 0845 210 5555

Bedford, Mr Michael LLB(Lond) G *Jul 1985*
1, 12, 22, 26, 31
Cornerstone Barristers, London WC1
p929 . . . . . 020 7242 4986

Bedford, Mr Stephen BA G *Jul 1972*
10, 20
St Johns Buildings, Preston
p990 . . . . . 01772 256100
St Johns Buildings, Chester
p974 . . . . . 01244 323070
St Johns Buildings, Manchester
p985 . . . . . 0161 214 1500
St Johns Buildings, Liverpool
p982 . . . . . 0151 243 6000

Bedingfield, Mr David BA G *Nov 1991*
20, 10
4 Paper Buildings, London EC4
p946 . . . . . 020 7583 0816

BEDWORTH, Miss Georgia Selina BA; BCL(Oxon) M *Jul 2001*
8
Ten Old Square, London WC2
p945 . . . . . 020 7405 0758

BEECHAM, Miss Sara BA(Oxon) M *Nov 1999*
18, 22
Five Paper, London EC4
p946 . . . . . 020 7815 3200

Beechey, Miss Hilary BA; DipLaw(City) M *Nov 1987*
10, 20
King's Bench Godolphin Chambers, Truro
p994 . . . . . 0845 308 1551

13

King's Bench Godolphin Chambers, Plymouth
p990 . . . . . 0845 308 1551

Beer, Miss Emily BA(Hons)(Warw); PGDL M *Jan 2004*
20, 10
3 Dr Johnson's Buildings, London EC4
p930 . . . . . 020 7353 4854

BEER, Ms Julia G *Jul 2003*
20, 8, 37, 40, 93, 32, 88, 14, 11, 6
Ten Old Square, London WC2
p945 . . . . . 020 7405 0758

BEESE, Miss Nicola M *Mar 1998*
10, 20
St Mary's Chambers, Nottingham
p989 . . . . . 0115 950 3503

Beeson, Mr Nigel A L LLB(Hons) M *Oct 1983*
15
New Bailey Chambers, Preston
p990 . . . . . 01772 258087

BEEVER, Mr Edmund BA(Oxon) L *Oct 1990*
12, 30, 18, 55, 11, 38
St Philips Chambers, Birmingham
p969 . . . . . 0121 246 7000

Beever, Ms Prudence M LLB(Hons) M *Jul 2000*
10, 20
15 Winckley Square, Preston
p991 . . . . . 01772 252828

Beggs, Mr John LLB(Brunel) G *Nov 1989*
(Q.C.) *12, 18, 27, 30, 40, 1, 36*
3 Serjeants' Inn, London EC4
p950 . . . . . 020 7427 5000

Beglan, Mr Wayne BA L *Oct 1996*
1, 12, 15, 18, 22, 26, 31, 36
Cornerstone Barristers, London WC1
p929 . . . . . 020 7242 4986

Begley, Miss Laura Anne LLB(Hons)(Leeds) L *Nov 1993*
53, 30
9 Gough Square, London EC4
p935 . . . . . 020 7832 0500

Begum, Miss Rehana BA(Hons) L *Jul 2003*
20
18 St John Street Chambers, Manchester
p985 . . . . . 0161 278 1800

Beharrylal, Mr Anand LLB(Hons); LLM; London attorney at law (Trinidad & Tobago) L *Oct 1997*
15, 62
15 New Bridge Street Chambers, London EC4
p943 . . . . . 020 7842 1900

Behrens, James MA(Cantab); LLM; PhD M *Jul 1979*
6, 8, 9, 11, 29, 32, 37, 17, 41, 96
Serle Court, London WC2
p950 . . . . . 020 7242 6105
Zenith Chambers, Leeds
p979 . . . . . 0113 245 5438

Belben, Mr Robin LLB(Lond); Recorder L *Nov 1969*
10, 12, 20, 88, 31
College Chambers, Southampton
p992 . . . . . 023 8023 0338

BELBIN, Ms Heather P LLB(Hons) L *Oct 1992*
30, 62
Oriel Chambers, Liverpool
p981 . . . . . 0151 236 7191 / 236 4321
Oriel Chambers, Preston
p990 . . . . . 01772 254764

Belger, Mr Tyrone LLB(LSE) I *Jul 1984*
15, 62
Charter Chambers, London WC1
p928 . . . . . 020 7618 4400
2 Hare Court, London EC4
p937 . . . . . 020 7353 5324

Belgrave, Ms Susan Loraine BA(Hons); MSc(Econ)(LSE); LLB(Hons); LLM(Brussels) I *Jul 1989*
1, 18, 19, 22, 23, 26, 36, 38, 93
9 Gough Square, London EC4
p935 . . . . . 020 7832 0500

Belgrove, Ms Sophie M *Sep 2001*
24, 18, 55, 51, 11, 12
Devereux Chambers, London WC2
p930 . . . . . 020 7353 7534

BELL, Alphege I *Nov 1995*
Carmelite Chambers, London EC4
p927 . . . . . 020 7936 6300

Bell, Miss Anne BA G *Jan 1975* OBE
10, 20
Holborn Chambers, London WC2
p937 . . . . . 020 7242 6060
Rougemont Chambers, Exeter
p975 . . . . . 01392 208484

Bell, Mr Anthony I *Jan 1985*
15, 62, 36, 70, 72
No5 Chambers, Bristol
p971 . . . . . 0845 210 5555
No5 Chambers, London EC4
p944 . . . . . 0845 210 5555
No5 Chambers, Birmingham
p968 . . . . . 0845 210 5555

BELL, Mr Gary LLB I *Feb 1989*
15, 62, 72
No5 Chambers, Bristol
p971 . . . . . 0845 210 5555
No5 Chambers, London EC4
p944 . . . . . 0845 210 5555
No5 Chambers, Birmingham
p968 . . . . . 0845 210 5555

Bell, Miss Helen Louise BA(Oxon) M *Jul 2002*
18, 30, 12
2 Temple Gardens, London EC4
p952 . . . . . 020 7822 1200

BELL, Mr James LLB(Wales) M *Nov 1987*
Temple Garden Chambers, London EC4
p952 . . . . . 020 7583 1315

Bell, Jillian I *Aug 2000*
20, 10
Zenith Chambers, Leeds
p979 . . . . . 0113 245 5438

Bell, Miss Laura L *Jul 2004*
30, 18, 11, 12, 55, 24
Devereux Chambers, London WC2
p930 . . . . . 020 7353 7534

BELL, Marika Pamela LLB(B'ham) G *Nov 1991*
10, 20
Octagon House, Norwich
p988 . . . . . 01603 623186

Bell, Mr Thomas BA(Hons) L *Oct 2006*
5, 11, 40, 24, 74
Hardwicke, London WC2
p936 . . . . . 020 7242 2523

Bellamy, Mr Jonathan C I *Jan 2008*
Paradise Chambers, Sheffield
p992 . . . . . 0114 273 8951

BELLAMY, Mr Jonathan M L *Nov 1986*
40, 24, 11, 30, 12, 41, 56, 96, 52
Thirty Nine Essex Street, London WC2
p932 . . . . . 020 7832 1111

BELLAMY, Mr Stephen MA(Cantab) L *Jan 1974*
(Q.C.) *10, 20, 49, 96*
1 King's Bench Walk, London EC4
p938 . . . . . 020 7936 1500

Bellara, Mr Susheel I *Nov 2000*
6 King's Bench Walk, London EC4
p939 . . . . . 020 7583 0695 / 7353 4931

BELLIS, Mr W Gordon MA(Cantab) I *Jul 1972*
10, 12, 20, 26, 30, 18, 53, 67, 1, 62
7 Harrington Street Chambers, Liverpool
p981 . . . . . 0151 242 0707

Beloff, Mr Michael J MA(Oxon); FRSA; FICPD G *Nov 1967*
(Q.C.) *1, 3, 4, 5, 11, 44, 16, 18, 19, 50, 51, 26, 56, 89, 41, 12*
Blackstone Chambers, London EC4
p926 . . . . . 020 7583 1770

Beloff, Mr Rupert G *Jan 2001*
1, 6, 8, 11, 19, 22, 51, 56, 30, 68, 94
No5 Chambers, Bristol
p971 . . . . . 0845 210 5555
No5 Chambers, London EC4
p944 . . . . . 0845 210 5555
No5 Chambers, Birmingham
p968 . . . . . 0845 210 5555

BELTRAMI, Mr Adrian MA(Cantab); LLM L *Jul 1989*
(Q.C.) *5, 6, 11, 40*
3 Verulam Buildings, London WC1
p953 . . . . . 020 7831 8441

Belyavin, Ms Julia BA(Cantab) G *Mar 2003*
20, 10
St John's Chambers, Bristol
p972 . . . . . 0117 921 3456

Benbow, Miss Sara LLB M *Nov 1990*
22, 18, 49, 5, 11, 62, 38, 31, 93, 37
Hardwicke, London WC2
p936 . . . . . 020 7242 2523

Bendall, Mr Richard L *Jul 1979*
33 Bedford Row, London WC1
p925 . . . . . 020 7242 6476
Furnival Chambers, London EC4
p934 . . . . . 020 7405 3232

BENEDICT, Mr Peers MA(Oxon); DipLaw(City) M *Mar 1998*
Fenners Chambers, Cambridge
p972 . . . . . 01223 368761

Benlamkadem, Ms Fayza LLB(Hons) I *Jan 2003*
15
Nine Bedford Row, London WC1
p924 . . . . . 020 7489 2727

Bennathan, Mr Joel LLB(Lond); Recorder M *Nov 1985*
(Q.C.) *15*
Tooks Chambers, London EC4
p953 . . . . . 020 7842 7575

BENNEH PREMPEH, Adelaide L *Oct 2001*
10, 20, 23
Renaissance Chambers, London WC1
p949 . . . . . 020 7404 1111

Bennet, Miss Pauline L *Oct 1991*
20, 12, 76, 10
Regency Chambers, Peterborough
p990 . . . . . 01733 315215

BENNETT, Ms Abigail M *Nov 1998*
10, 20
Atlantic Chambers, Liverpool
p980 . . . . . 0151 236 4421

Bennett, Mr Charles H BA(Oxon) I *Jul 1972*
11, 12, 30, 37
5 St Andrew's Hill, London EC4
p950 . . . . . 020 7332 5400

Bennett, Mr Daniel BA; LLM G *Jan 2000*
27, 30, 48, 53
Doughty Street Chambers, London WC1
p930 . . . . . 020 7404 1313

Bennett, Mr David M *Jan 2005*
53, 30
Hailsham Chambers, London EC4
p936 . . . . . 020 7643 5000

Bennett, Miss Emma LLB; LLM L *Jan 2004*
62, 15, 27, 30, 53, 67
Exchange Chambers, Manchester
p983 . . . . . 0161 833 2722
Exchange Chambers, Liverpool
p980 . . . . . 0151 236 7747
Exchange Chambers, Leeds
p977 . . . . . 0113 203 1970
2 King's Bench Walk, London EC4
p939 . . . . . 020 7353 1746

BENNETT, Mr Gordon LLB(Edin) G *Feb 1974*
New Square Chambers, London WC2
p943 . . . . . 020 7419 8000

Bennett, Hannah M *Jan 2011*
Old Square Chambers, Bristol
p971 . . . . . 0117 930 5100
Old Square Chambers, London WC1
p945 . . . . . 020 7269 0300

Bennett, Mr Ieuan LLB; MA M *Jul 1989*
15
9 Park Place, Cardiff
p973 . . . . . 029 2038 2731

BENNETT, Mr James LLB(Hons) I *Oct 2002*
15, 46, 84
Guildhall Chambers, Bristol
p970 . . . . . 0117 930 9000

Bennett, Jane M *Jan 2000*
Clerksroom - Administration Centre, Taunton
p993 . . . . . 0845 083 3000

Bennett, Mr Jonathan Charles Lyddon MA(Cantab) G *Jul 1985*
10, 12, 20
42 Bedford Row, London WC1
p925 . . . . . 020 7831 0222

Bennett, Mr Lee LLB(Hons); LLM(Cantab) M *Nov 1998*
1, 12, 15, 19, 22, 26, 27, 30, 31, 47, 51
6-8 Mill Street, Maidstone
p982 . . . . . 01622 688094 / 688095
6 Pump Court, London EC4
p947 . . . . . 020 7797 8400

Bennett, Miss Marianne LLB I *Oct 2003*
15, 20
Temple Chambers, Newport
p988 . . . . . 01633 267403 / 255855
Temple Chambers, Cardiff
p973 . . . . . 029 2039 7364

BENNETT, Mr Martyn LLB(Hons) G *Jul 1969*
10, 12, 20, 36, 40
Oriel Chambers, Liverpool
p981 . . . . . 0151 236 7191 / 236 4321
Oriel Chambers, Preston
p990 . . . . . 01772 254764

Bennett, Mr Miles LLB(Hull) I *Nov 1986*
13, 62, 48, 15
5 Paper Buildings, London EC4
p946 . . . . . 020 7583 6117

Bennett, Miss Natasha L *Oct 2009*
Fountain Court Chambers, London EC4
p934 . . . . . 020 7583 3335

BENNETT, Mr Richard A BSc; CPE I *Oct 1996*
12, 15
Fountain Chambers, Middlesbrough
p986 . . . . . 01642 804040

Bennett, Mr Richard John LLB(Hons) M *Jul 1986*
15, 42
15 Winckley Square, Preston
p991 . . . . . 01772 252828

Bennett, Mr William BA(L'pool) I *Oct 1994*
13, 16, 50, 51
5RB, London WC1
p948 . . . . . 020 7242 2902

Bennett-Jenkins, Miss Sallie Ann LLB; Recorder; Junior Treasury Counsel G *Jul 1984*
(Q.C.) *15, 62, 95*
2 Hare Court, London EC4
p937 . . . . . 020 7353 5324

Bennetts, Mr Phillip L *Jul 1986*
15, 25, 36
QEB Hollis Whiteman, London EC4
p948 . . . . . 020 7933 8855

Bennington, Ms Jane BA(Hons) G *Jul 1981*
10, 20
Fenners Chambers, Cambridge
p972 . . . . . 01223 368761

Bennion-Pedley, Mr Edward BSc(Hons)(Lond); DipLaw M *Nov 2004*
King's Bench Chambers, Oxford
p989 . . . . . 01865 311066
13 King's Bench Walk, London EC4
p940 . . . . . 020 7353 7204

Benny, Mr Dato' Jude Associate Member M *Jan 1982*
Stone Chambers, London WC1
p951 . . . . . 020 7440 6900

Benson, Mr Charles MA; LLM; BAdmin(Hons) M *Feb 1990*
(Q.C.) *62, 15*
Argent Chambers, London WC2
p923 . . . . . 020 7556 5500

Benson, Miss Clare BA(Hons)(Cantab) L *Jul 2009*
15
Broadway House Chambers, Leeds
p977 . . . . . 0113 246 2600
Broadway House Chambers, Bradford
p969 . . . . . 01274 722560

Benson, Mr Imran BPP; BVC M *Jan 2005*
30, 40, 53, 22, 24, 18, 27
Hailsham Chambers, London EC4
p936 . . . . . 020 7643 5000

BENSON, Mr James BA(Hons)(Oxon) G *Nov 1995*
12, 30, 40, 62, 68
Oriel Chambers, Liverpool
p981 . . . . . 0151 236 7191 / 236 4321
Oriel Chambers, Preston
p990 . . . . . 01772 254764

BENSON, Mr Jeremy I *Jul 1978*
(Q.C.) *72, 15, 62, 34, 36*
18 Red Lion Court, London EC4
p949 . . . . . 020 7520 6000
18 Red Lion Court (Annexe), Chelmsford
p973 . . . . . 01245 280880

BENSON, Mr Jeremy Keith BA; Recorder M *Jul 1978*
(Q.C.) *15, 62, 36*
2 Hare Court, London EC4
p937 . . . . . 020 7353 5324

BENSON, John LLB(Hons)(L'pool) M *Jul 1978*
(Q.C.) *15, 18, 25, 30, 53, 62, 84*
Atlantic Chambers, Liverpool
p980 . . . . . 0151 236 4421

BENSON, Mr Julian C W BA(Hons)(Dunelm); MA(Cantab); LLM(Cantab) M *Oct 1991*
30, 40
Guildhall Chambers, Bristol
p970 . . . . . 0117 930 9000

See p1010 for the Key to Work Categories

BENSON, Mr Richard I *Jul 1974*
(Q.C.)
Citadel Chambers, Birmingham
p967 . . . . . 0121 233 8500

Benthall, Mr Dominic MA(Hons) M *Nov 2002*
15, 62
15 New Bridge Street Chambers, London EC4
p943 . . . . . 020 7842 1900

BENTHAM, Mr Daniel BA M *Jan 2000*
20, 10
Queen Elizabeth Buildings, London EC4
p948 . . . . . 020 7797 7837

Bentham, Mr Howard G *Nov 1970*
(Q.C.) *15*
St Johns Buildings, Preston
p990 . . . . . 01772 256100
St Johns Buildings, Chester
p974 . . . . . 01244 323070
St Johns Buildings, Manchester
p985 . . . . . 0161 214 1500
St Johns Buildings, Liverpool
p982 . . . . . 0151 243 6000

Bentham, Prof Richard G *Nov 1955*
20 Essex Street, London WC2
p932 . . . . . 020 7842 1200

Bentley, Mr David LLB G *Feb 1984*
15, 51, 91
Doughty Street Chambers, London WC1
p930 . . . . . 020 7404 1313

Bentley, Mr David Paul LLB L *Oct 1998*
15
St Johns Buildings, Preston
p990 . . . . . 01772 256100
St Johns Buildings, Chester
p974 . . . . . 01244 323070
St Johns Buildings, Manchester
p985 . . . . . 0161 214 1500
St Johns Buildings, Liverpool
p982 . . . . . 0151 243 6000

Bentley, Mr Harry G *Jan 2007*
Nine Bedford Row, London WC1
p924 . . . . . 020 7489 2727

Bently, Prof Lionel BA(Law) I *Jan 2009*
13
11 South Square, London WC1
p950 . . . . . 020 7405 1222

Bentwood, Mr Richard LLB(Nott'm) I *Nov 1994*
15, 62, 84, 82
Argent Chambers, London WC2
p923 . . . . . 020 7556 5500

Benzie, Mr Stuart LLB(Hons) G *Nov 2002*
5, 6, 11, 62, 24, 40, 29, 12
2 Temple Gardens, London EC4
p952 . . . . . 020 7822 1200

Benzynie, Mr Robert LLB G *Nov 1992*
Charter Chambers, London WC1
p928 . . . . . 020 7618 4400

BERESFORD, Mr Stephen G *Jun 1976*
40, 7, 11, 26, 1, 29, 31
Ropewalk Chambers, Nottingham
p989 . . . . . 0115 947 2581

Bergin, Mr Terence Edward BA(Cantab) I *Nov 1985*
45, 11, 40
4 Pump Court, London EC4
p947 . . . . . 020 7842 5555

Bergin, Mr Timothy LLB; MA M *Jul 1987*
15, 20, 62, 10
Crown Office Row Chambers, Brighton
p970 . . . . . 01273 625625

Berkeley, Miss Iona Sarah MA(Oxon) M *Oct 1999*
13, 50
8 New Square, London WC2
p943 . . . . . 020 7405 4321

BERKIN, Mr Martyn MA(Cantab) I *Jul 1966*
74, 1, 6, 7, 8, 11, 12, 18, 20, 22, 24, 30, 32, 37, 36, 40
Crown Office Chambers, London EC4
p929 . . . . . 020 7797 8100

Berkley, Mr David LLB(Hons)(Manc) M *May 1979*
(Q.C.) *5, 6, 11, 18, 29, 40, 8*
St Johns Buildings, Preston
p990 . . . . . 01772 256100
St Johns Buildings, Chester
p974 . . . . . 01244 323070
St Johns Buildings, Manchester
p985 . . . . . 0161 214 1500
St Johns Buildings, Liverpool
p982 . . . . . 0151 243 6000
Tanfield Chambers, London WC1
p951 . . . . . 020 7421 5300

Berkley, Mr Michael LLB(Business Law); Civil Recorder M *Jul 1989*
11, 12, 22, 29, 40, 47, 32, 7
Rougemont Chambers, Exeter
p975 . . . . . 01392 208484

Berkson, Mr Simon LLB G *Jul 1986*
15, 30, 51, 62, 82, 70, 72, 84, 94
Exchange Chambers, Manchester
p983 . . . . . 0161 833 2722
Exchange Chambers, Liverpool
p980 . . . . . 0151 236 7747
Exchange Chambers, Leeds
p977 . . . . . 0113 203 1970

BERLIN, Mr Barry BSc; Recorder G *Jul 1981*
1, 15, 26, 25, 46, 48, 84
St Philips Chambers, Birmingham
p969 . . . . . 0121 246 7000

Berman, Sir Franklin M *Nov 1966*
(Q.C.) KCMG
Essex Court Chambers, London WC2
p931 . . . . . 020 7813 8000

Bermingham, Mr Gerald LLB(Hons) G *Feb 1967*
15, 62, 70, 72
No5 Chambers, Bristol
p971 . . . . . 0845 210 5555
No5 Chambers, London EC4
p944 . . . . . 0845 210 5555
No5 Chambers, Birmingham
p968 . . . . . 0845 210 5555

Berragan, Mr Howard Neil LLB G *Jul 1982*
5, 6, 7, 8, 11, 24, 40, 41
Kings Chambers, Leeds
p978 . . . . . 0113 242 1123
Kings Chambers, Manchester
p984 . . . . . 0161 832 9082

Berrick, Mr Steven LLB M *Jun 1986*
15, 29, 50, 56
Argent Chambers, London WC2
p923 . . . . . 020 7556 5500

BERRY, Miss Amy L *Jan 2003*
Pump Court Chambers, Swindon
p993 . . . . . 01793 539899
Pump Court Chambers, Winchester
p994 . . . . . 01962 868161
Pump Court Chambers, London EC4
p947 . . . . . 020 7353 0711

BERRY, Mr Anthony C G *Jul 1976*
(Q.C.) *15, 51*
7 Harrington Street Chambers, Liverpool
p981 . . . . . 0151 242 0707
Nine Bedford Row, London WC1
p924 . . . . . 020 7489 2727

Berry, Mr James Michael LLM(Harv); LLB(UCL) L *Jun 2006*
18, 27, 53, 68, 85, 30, 40, 36
3 Serjeants' Inn, London EC4
p950 . . . . . 020 7427 5000

BERRY, Mr Karl BA M *Nov 1999*
15, 20, 30
Oriel Chambers, Liverpool
p981 . . . . . 0151 236 7191 / 236 4321
Oriel Chambers, Preston
p990 . . . . . 01772 254764

BERRY, Mr Nicholas Charles L *Jan 2004*
Citadel Chambers, Birmingham
p967 . . . . . 0121 233 8500

Berry, Mr Nicholas Michael BA(Hons) I *Nov 1988*
11, 29, 31, 40, 12, 8, 9, 37, 47, 32, 48, 46, 7, 13
Rougemont Chambers, Exeter
p975 . . . . . 01392 208484

Berry, Mr Steven J BA; BCL(Oxon) M *Nov 1984*
(Q.C.)
Essex Court Chambers, London WC2
p931 . . . . . 020 7813 8000

Bertham, Mr Christopher L *Oct 1993*
15 New Bridge Street Chambers, London EC4
p943 . . . . . 020 7842 1900

Bertram, Mr Jonathan I *Oct 2003*
15, 62, 12, 30, 18, 27, 53, 67, 11
7 Bedford Row, London WC1
p924 . . . . . 020 7242 3555

BESLEE, Ms Sarah M *Oct 2006*
30, 12, 53, 47, 67
12 King's Bench Walk, London EC4
p940 . . . . . 020 7583 0811

BESWETHERICK, Mr Anthony BA(Oxon) L *Mar 2003*
5, 6, 8, 11, 22, 29, 40, 38, 88
Enterprise Chambers, London WC2
p931 . . . . . 020 7405 9471
Enterprise Chambers, Leeds
p977 . . . . . 0113 246 0391
Enterprise Chambers, Newcastle upon Tyne
p987 . . . . . 0191 222 3344

BETHEL, Mr Martin MA; LLM I *Nov 1965*
(Q.C.) *12, 15, 62, 70*
Fountain Chambers, Middlesbrough
p986 . . . . . 01642 804040
St Pauls Chambers, Leeds
p979 . . . . . 0113 245 5866

Bethlehem, Sir Daniel BA(Wits); LLB(Bris); LLM(Cantab) M *Nov 1988*
(Q.C.) KCMG*33, 21, 3, 19, 41, 12*
20 Essex Street, London WC2
p932 . . . . . 020 7842 1200

Bettle, Ms Janet LLB; Pupil Supervisor I *Jul 1985*
20, 10, 51
East Anglian Chambers, Norwich
p988 . . . . . 01603 617351
East Anglian Chambers, Colchester
p975 . . . . . 01206 572756
East Anglian Chambers, Chelmsford
p973 . . . . . 01245 215660
East Anglian Chambers, Ipswich
p976 . . . . . 01473 214481

Betts, Ms Emily M *Jul 2009*
11, 5, 18, 86, 93
Hardwicke, London WC2
p936 . . . . . 020 7242 2523

BEVAN, Prof Hugh K M *Jun 1959*
8
Wilberforce Chambers, Hull
p976 . . . . . 01482 323264

Bevan, Miss Miranda Jane BA(Oxon) I *Oct 2000*
15, 62
2 Hare Court, London EC4
p937 . . . . . 020 7353 5324

Bevan, Mr Stephen BA I *Nov 1986*
15
1 Pump Court, London EC4
p947 . . . . . 020 7842 7070

BEWLEY, Miss Amanda I *Jan 2005*
10, 20
St Mary's Chambers, Nottingham
p989 . . . . . 0115 950 3503

BEWLEY, Mr James L *Jan 2007*
15, 62, 95
187 Fleet Street, London EC4
p933 . . . . . 020 7430 7430

Bewley, Miss Suhayla LLB(Hons) L *Jul 2007*
11
East Anglian Chambers, Norwich
p988 . . . . . 01603 617351
East Anglian Chambers, Colchester
p975 . . . . . 01206 572756
East Anglian Chambers, Chelmsford
p973 . . . . . 01245 215660
East Anglian Chambers, Ipswich
p976 . . . . . 01473 214481

BEWSEY, Miss Jane I *Jul 1986*
(Q.C.) *15, 36, 62*
18 Red Lion Court, London EC4
p949 . . . . . 020 7520 6000
18 Red Lion Court (Annexe), Chelmsford
p973 . . . . . 01245 280880

BEX, Miss Kate BA M *Nov 1992*
15, 62
2 Hare Court, London EC4
p937 . . . . . 020 7353 5324

BEYNON, Mr Richard J L I *Jul 1990*
15, 62, 84
18 Red Lion Court, London EC4
p949 . . . . . 020 7520 6000
18 Red Lion Court (Annexe), Chelmsford
p973 . . . . . 01245 280880

BEYTS, Chester BA I *Nov 1978*
15, 46
25 Bedford Row, London WC1
p925 . . . . . 020 7067 1500

Bhachu, Miss Sharan L *Mar 1999*
20, 10
4 Brick Court Chambers, London EC4
p927 . . . . . 020 7832 3200

BHAKAR, Surinder G *Jan 1986*
4 King's Bench Walk, London EC4
p939 . . . . . 020 7822 7000

BHALOO, Miss Zia LLB; LLM(Lond) M *Nov 1990*
(Q.C.) *6, 8, 22, 49, 88*
Enterprise Chambers, London WC2
p931 . . . . . 020 7405 9471
Enterprise Chambers, Leeds
p977 . . . . . 0113 246 0391
Enterprise Chambers, Newcastle upon Tyne
p987 . . . . . 0191 222 3344

Bhanji, Shiraz Musa BSc(Wales) G *Jul 1979*
23, 18, 20, 15
1 Gray's Inn Square, London WC1
p935 . . . . . 020 7405 0001
1 Gray's Inn Square, London WC1
p935 . . . . . 020 7405 8946

Bhari, Miss Poonam L *Jan 1999*
14 Gray's Inn Square, London WC1
p936 . . . . . 020 7242 0858

Bhat, Ms Saima LLB(Hons); LLM(Bris) M *Jul 1999*
15, 20
15 Winckley Square, Preston
p991 . . . . . 01772 252828

BHATIA, Mr Balraj S I *Jul 1982*
15
1 High Pavement, Nottingham
p988 . . . . . 0115 941 8218

Bhatia, Miss Divya BA(Oxon); Barrister M *Jul 1986*
10, 20
Coram Chambers, London EC1
p929 . . . . . 020 7092 3700

Bhatoo, Mr Khauck BA; LLB(Hons); MPhil G *Jan 1999*
Chancery Chambers, London WC2
p928 . . . . . 020 7405 6879

Bhatt, Unnati M *Oct 2007*
6 King's Bench Walk, London EC4
p939 . . . . . 020 7583 0695 / 7353 4931

Bhattacharya, Mr Ardhendu BA; DipCl; FCIS; FCMI; MCIArb; Barrister I *Nov 1974*
66, 12, 18, 20, 26, 96, 30, 31
Slough Barristers Chamber, Slough
p992 . . . . . 01753 553806 / 817989

BHATTI, Miss Balvinder L *Oct 2003*
Citadel Chambers, Birmingham
p967 . . . . . 0121 233 8500

BHATTY, Farah L *Jan 2005*
20
Bank House Chambers, Sheffield
p991 . . . . . 0114 275 1223

Bhogal, Ms Kuljit LLB(Hons) L *Oct 1999*
18, 22, 55, 26
Cornerstone Barristers, London WC1
p929 . . . . . 020 7242 4986

Bhose, Mr Ranjit BA(Oxon) G *Jul 1989*
1, 8, 11, 12, 18, 22, 26, 36
Cornerstone Barristers, London WC1
p929 . . . . . 020 7242 4986

Bhutta, Miss Ayeesha M *Oct 2006*
20
Field Court Chambers, London WC1
p933 . . . . . 020 7405 6114

BICARREGUI, Miss Anna BA(Oxon); CPE; BVC L *Jul 2004*
1, 18, 26, 31
4-5 Gray's Inn Square, London WC1
p935 . . . . . 020 7404 5252

Bickerdike, Roger LLB L *Nov 1986*
20, 10
Zenith Chambers, Leeds
p979 . . . . . 0113 245 5438

Bickerstaff, Ms Jane D I *Nov 1989*
15, 51, 1
Nine Bedford Row, London WC1
p924 . . . . . 020 7489 2727

BICKFORD SMITH, Mr James BA(Oxon); MSt(Oxon); DPhil(Oxon); DGL(City) L *Oct 2008*
18, 11, 12, 55, 6, 56
Littleton Chambers, London EC4
p941 . . . . . 020 7797 8600

BICKFORD-SMITH, Mrs Margaret Osbourne BA(Oxon) I *Jul 1973*
(Q.C.) *96, 53, 30, 46, 27, 24, 12*
Crown Office Chambers, London EC4
p929 . . . . . 020 7797 8100

13

BICKFORD-SMITH, Mr Stephen BA(Oxon); FCIArb I *Jul 1972*
93
Landmark Chambers, London EC4
p941 . . . 020 7430 1221

Bickler, Mr Simon Lloyd BA(Sheff) I *Nov 1988*
10, 12, 15, 70, 62, 14, 84, 86, 94
St Pauls Chambers, Leeds
p979 . . . 0113 245 5866

BIDDLE, Mr Neville Leslie BSc(Econ)(Aberystwyth) G *Nov 1974*
62, 15, 23
7 Harrington Street Chambers, Liverpool
p981 . . . 0151 242 0707

BIGGS, Mr Stuart MA(Hons)(Cantab) M *Nov 1999*
12, 15
9-12 Bell Yard Chambers, London WC2
p926 . . . 020 7400 1800

Bignall, Mr John MA(Cantab); CPE(City) L *Nov 1996*
3, 11, 24, 35, 40
7 King's Bench Walk, London EC4
p940 . . . 020 7910 8300

BIGNELL, Miss Janet MA(Cantab); BCL(Oxon) L *Oct 1992*
Falcon Chambers, London EC4
p933 . . . 020 7353 2484

Bijlani, Dr Aisha MB; BS M *Nov 1993*
8, 12, 24, 40, 53
Four New Square, London WC2
p943 . . . 020 7822 2000

BILSLAND, Miss Alisan BA(Hons) L *Oct 2000*
12, 18, 20, 30
St James's Chambers, Manchester
p984 . . . 0161 834 7000

Bindloss, Edward BA; Recorder G *Nov 1993*
15, 25, 36, 62, 68, 70, 72, 80, 91, 94, 95
Zenith Chambers, Leeds
p979 . . . 0113 245 5438

Bingham, Mr Anthony William LLB(Hons) L *Nov 1992*
7, 3
3PB, London EC4
p946 . . . 020 7583 8055

Bingham, Ms Camilla I *Oct 1996*
One Essex Court, London EC4
p931 . . . 020 7583 2000

BINNS, Mr David LLB(L'pool) M *Jul 1983*
7, 10, 12, 18, 20, 30, 40
St James's Chambers, Manchester
p984 . . . 0161 834 7000

BIRCH, Miss Elizabeth B LLB(Lond); FCIArb; QDR G *Jul 1978*
3, 5, 11, 24, 35
3 Verulam Buildings, London WC1
p953 . . . 020 7831 8441

Birch, Mr Geoffrey MA(Lond) L *Feb 1972*
15, 62, 42, 25, 94
3 Temple Gardens, London EC4
p952 . . . 020 7353 3102

BIRCH, Mr Roger BA(Cantab) G *Nov 1979*
New Square Chambers, London WC2
p943 . . . 020 7419 8000
5 St Andrew's Hill, London EC4
p950 . . . 020 7332 5400

Bird, Mr Andrew J MA(Cantab) I *Jul 1987*
12, 15, 22, 37, 18
5 St Andrew's Hill, London EC4
p950 . . . 020 7332 5400

Bird, Mr Simon LLB(Reading) M *Jul 1987*
(Q.C.) *1, 26, 30, 31, 22, 28*
Cornerstone Barristers, London WC1
p929 . . . 020 7242 4986

Birdee, Ms Sonia BVC; BA(Jurisprudence) M *Jan 2004*
72, 15, 70, 22, 88, 51
Garden Court North Chambers, Manchester
p983 . . . 0161 236 1840

Birk, Miss Dewinder L *Jul 1988*
63, 64, 10, 20
No5 Chambers, Bristol
p971 . . . 0845 210 5555
No5 Chambers, London EC4
p944 . . . 0845 210 5555
No5 Chambers, Birmingham
p968 . . . 0845 210 5555

BIRKBY, Mr Adam M *Sep 2006*
Park Court Chambers, Leeds
p978 . . . 0113 243 3277

BIRKETT, Miss Lianne LLB I *Jul 2006*
15
7 Harrington Street Chambers, Liverpool
p981 . . . 0151 242 0707

Birkett, Mr Peter I *Feb 1972*
(Q.C.) *15, 62, 34, 11*
18 St John Street Chambers, Manchester
p985 . . . 0161 278 1800

BIRNBAUM, Mr Michael Ian BA(Oxon); Recorder M *Nov 1969*
(Q.C.) *1, 51, 15, 33*
9-12 Bell Yard Chambers, London WC2
p926 . . . 020 7400 1800

Birrell, Mr David I *Nov 2006*
72, 70, 15
Exchange Chambers, Manchester
p983 . . . 0161 833 2722
Exchange Chambers, Liverpool
p980 . . . 0151 236 7747
Exchange Chambers, Leeds
p977 . . . 0113 203 1970

Birt, Miss Emma I *Oct 2000*
15, 20, 30, 12
King's Bench Godolphin Chambers, Truro
p994 . . . 0845 308 1551
King's Bench Godolphin Chambers, Plymouth
p990 . . . 0845 308 1551

BIRT, Mr Robin M *Oct 2009*
10, 12, 72, 18, 20, 91, 42, 30, 32, 36
Pump Court Chambers, Swindon
p993 . . . 01793 539899
Pump Court Chambers, Winchester
p994 . . . 01962 868161
Pump Court Chambers, London EC4
p947 . . . 020 7353 0711

BIRT, Mr Simon BA; BCL(Oxon) G *Jan 1998*
11, 35, 24, 5, 40
Brick Court Chambers, London WC2
p927 . . . 020 7379 3550

Birtles, Ms Samantha LLB(B'ham) L *Jul 1989*
15, 20, 30, 12
18 St John Street Chambers, Manchester
p985 . . . 0161 278 1800

BISARYA, Mr Neil MA(Hons)(Cantab) L *Nov 1998*
15, 51, 12, 20
7 Harrington Street Chambers, Liverpool
p981 . . . 0151 242 0707

Bishop, Mr Alan LLB(Lond); ACII M *Jul 1973*
1, 8, 11, 18, 24, 26
11 Stone Buildings, London WC2
p951 . . . 020 7831 6381

Bishop, Mr Daniel BA(Oxon) I *Oct 2007*
15, 30
7 Bedford Row, London WC1
p924 . . . 020 7242 3555

Bishop, Mr Edward MA(Cantab); DipLaw M *Nov 1983*
(Q.C.) *30, 40, 53, 63, 27, 26, 85, 51*
1 Chancery Lane, London WC2
p928 . . . 0845 634 6666

Bishop, Mr Gordon MA(Cantab) M *Nov 1968*
11, 12, 13, 16, 50, 51, 36
5RB, London WC1
p948 . . . 020 7242 2902

Bishop, Mr Malcolm MA(Oxon); Deputy High Court Judge; Recorder I *Jul 1968*
(Q.C.) *15, 95, 71, 1, 10, 20, 8, 11, 62*
Thirty Park Place, Cardiff
p973 . . . 029 2039 8421
Argent Chambers, London WC2
p923 . . . 020 7556 5500
Charter Chambers, London WC1
p928 . . . 020 7618 4400

Bishop, Mr Stephen I *Jul 2006*
Goldsmith Chambers, London EC4
p935 . . . 020 7353 6802

Bishop, Mr Timothy BA(Cantab) I *Nov 1991*
10, 20
1 Hare Court, London EC4
p936 . . . 020 7797 7070

BISPHAM, Miss Christine LLB L *Oct 1991*
12, 20, 15, 10, 30
7 Harrington Street Chambers, Liverpool
p981 . . . 0151 242 0707

Bissett, Miss Kate L *Jul 2009*
15
No 6 Barristers Chambers, Leeds
p978 . . . 0113 245 9763

BISWAS, Miss Nisha LLB(Hons) L *Oct 1996*
10, 12, 15, 20, 22, 30
Chavasse Court Chambers, Liverpool
p980 . . . 0151 229 2030

BLACK, Ms Charlotte M *Oct 2006*
Wilberforce Chambers, London WC2
p953 . . . 020 7306 0102

BLACK, Miss Georgina BA(Hons); LLB(Hons) M *Oct 1999*
20
29 Bedford Row, London WC1
p925 . . . 020 7404 1044

BLACK, Mr John I *Jul 1975*
(Q.C.) *15, 62, 34*
18 Red Lion Court, London EC4
p949 . . . 020 7520 6000
18 Red Lion Court (Annexe), Chelmsford
p973 . . . 01245 280880

BLACK, Mr Michael LLB(Lond); FCIArb M *Feb 1978*
(Q.C.) *66, 49, 41, 3, 5, 6, 7, 8, 11, 43, 97, 67, 69, 78, 81, 62, 38, 24, 21, 89, 29, 96, 40, 61*
XXIV Old Buildings, London WC2
p944 . . . 020 7691 2424

Blackband, Ms Laura I *Nov 1997*
15
4 Breams Buildings, London EC4
p927 . . . 020 7092 1900

Blackburn, Mrs Elizabeth BA(Manc) M *Jul 1978*
(Q.C.) *3, 11, 35, 41*
Stone Chambers, London WC1
p951 . . . 020 7440 6900

Blackburn, Mr John BA(Oxon) M *Jul 1969*
(Q.C.) *3, 7, 11, 31, 40, 41, 43, 45, 49, 54, 61, 78, 74*
Atkin Chambers, London WC1
p923 . . . 020 7404 0102

Blackburn, Mr Luke M *Nov 1994*
15, 62, 84
7 Bedford Row, London WC1
p924 . . . 020 7242 3555

Blackett-Ord, Mr Mark MA(Oxon) L *Jul 1974*
8, 29, 37, 40, 41
5 Stone Buildings, London WC2
p951 . . . 020 7242 6201

Blackman, Mr Edmund Arthur William M *Jul 1999*
15
1 Inner Temple Lane, London EC4
p937 . . . 020 7427 4400

Blackmore, Mr J I *Aug 2002*
Blackmore Chambers, London WC1
p926 . . . 020 7566 8244

Blackmore, Mr John LLB(Lond) I *May 1983*
8, 11, 13, 29, 40
St John's Chambers, Bristol
p972 . . . 0117 921 3456

BLACKMORE, Miss Sally Anne BA; MA L *Nov 2003*
22, 1, 26
Arden Chambers, London WC1
p923 . . . 020 7242 4244

Blackmore, Miss Sarah I *Oct 1993*
37 Park Square Chambers, Leeds
p978 . . . 0113 243 9422

BLACKMORE, Ms Sasha L *Jan 2005*
1, 46, 31, 36
Landmark Chambers, London EC4
p941 . . . 020 7430 1221

Blackshaw, Mr Henry M *Oct 1993*
15
St Johns Buildings, Preston
p990 . . . 01772 256100
St Johns Buildings, Chester
p974 . . . 01244 323070
St Johns Buildings, Manchester
p985 . . . 0161 214 1500
St Johns Buildings, Liverpool
p982 . . . 0151 243 6000

Blackwell, Ms Katherine L *Nov 1992*
Lincoln House Chambers, Manchester
p984 . . . 0161 832 5701

Blackwell, Miss Louise M LLB(Hons) L *Jul 1985*
(Q.C.) *15, 62, 84, 94, 95*
Broad Chare Chambers, Newcastle upon Tyne
p986 . . . 0191 232 0541
Cobden House Chambers, Manchester
p983 . . . 0161 833 6000

BLACKWOOD, Ms Anneliese Rose LLB; BCL M *Jul 2007*
1, 44, 19, 51, 57
Monckton Chambers, London WC1
p942 . . . 020 7405 7211

Blackwood, Mr Clive BA(Cantab) I *Nov 1986*
11, 18, 24, 29, 47, 5, 6
Lamb Chambers, London EC4
p941 . . . 020 7797 8300

Blackwood, Mr Guy LLB(Hons)(Lond) I *Oct 1997*
3, 5, 11, 24, 35, 36, 41, 54
Quadrant Chambers, London EC4
p948 . . . 020 7583 4444

Blackwood, Ms Rebecca L *Nov 2001*
10, 20, 23
Southernhay Chambers, Exeter
p975 . . . 01392 255777

Blain, Mr Roderick BA M *Oct 1991*
15, 42
12 College Place, Southampton
p992 . . . 023 8032 0320

Blair, Mr Bruce MA(Cantab) M *Jul 1969*
(Q.C.) *20, 10*
Broad Chare Chambers, Newcastle upon Tyne
p986 . . . 0191 232 0541
1 Hare Court, London EC4
p936 . . . 020 7797 7070

BLAIR, Mr Michael Campbell MA; LLM(Cantab); MA(Yale) M *Jul 1965*
(Q.C.) Honoris Causa*5, 8, 11*
3 Verulam Buildings, London WC1
p953 . . . 020 7831 8441

BLAIR, Mr Peter MA(Oxon) I *Jul 1983*
(Q.C.) *12, 15, 26, 84, 46*
Guildhall Chambers, Bristol
p970 . . . 0117 930 9000

BLAKE, Mr Andrew Mark BA; LLM L *Oct 2000*
1, 18, 26, 51, 55
11KBW, London EC4
p938 . . . 020 7632 8500

Blake, Mr Arthur LLB I *Feb 1988*
King's Bench Chambers, Oxford
p989 . . . 01865 311066
13 King's Bench Walk, London EC4
p940 . . . 020 7353 7204

Blake, Mr Christopher I *Nov 1990*
15, 91
5 King's Bench Walk, London EC4
p939 . . . 020 7353 5638

Blake, Mr David BA(Cantab); LLM(Cantab) L *Feb 1992*
15, 20, 23, 1, 10, 70, 71, 72, 76, 51, 91, 26, 63, 31, 56, 36
Angel Chambers, Swansea
p992 . . . 01792 464623

Blake, Mr Nick G *Nov 1997*
12, 46, 31, 30, 86, 18, 94, 93
36 Bedford Row, London WC1
p925 . . . 020 7421 8000

Blake, Mr Richard LLB G *Nov 1982*
13, 15, 25
1 Inner Temple Lane, London EC4
p937 . . . 020 7427 4400

Blake-James, Mr Hugh D M *Mar 1998*
Goldsmith Chambers, London EC4
p935 . . . 020 7353 6802

BLAKEBROUGH, Mr Simon L *Mar 2011*
15, 62, 70
Kenworthy's Chambers, Manchester
p984 . . . 0161 832 4036

Blakemore, Mr Benjamin G *Jul 2004*
Iscoed Chambers, Swansea
p993 . . . 01792 652988

BLAKESLEY, Mr Patrick BA(Oxon) I *Nov 1993*
30, 24, 12, 11, 40
Crown Office Chambers, London EC4
p929 . . . 020 7797 8100

Blakey, Mr Lee LLB(Hons) L *Oct 1995*
12, 30
15 Winckley Square, Preston
p991 . . . 01772 252828

Blakey, Mr Michael LLB(Hons) M *Nov 1989*
15, 72, 71, 70
St Johns Buildings, Preston
p990 . . . 01772 256100
St Johns Buildings, Chester
p974 . . . 01244 323070
St Johns Buildings, Manchester
p985 . . . 0161 214 1500
St Johns Buildings, Liverpool
p982 . . . 0151 243 6000

See p1010 for the Key to Work Categories

Blanchard, Ms Claire LLB(L'pool) G *Oct 1992*
(Q.C.)
Essex Court Chambers, London WC2
p931 . . . . . 020 7813 8000

Blayney, Mr David BA(Oxon) L *Oct 1992*
6, 8, 9, 11, 29, 37, 40, 5
Serle Court, London WC2
p950 . . . . . 020 7242 6105

Bleaney, Mr Nicholas LLB(Nott'm) L *Nov 1988*
15
Atkinson Bevan Chambers, London EC4
p924 . . . . . 020 7353 2112

Bleasdale, Ms Marie-Claire MA(Cantab) L *Oct 1993*
6, 8, 9, 11, 14, 22, 29, 32, 37, 40
Radcliffe Chambers, London WC2
p949 . . . . . 020 7831 0081

Bleasdale, Mr Paul Recorder I *Jul 1978*
(Q.C.) *30, 53, 40, 94, 56, 36, 31, 46*
No5 Chambers, Bristol
p971 . . . . . 0845 210 5555
No5 Chambers, London EC4
p944 . . . . . 0845 210 5555
No5 Chambers, Birmingham
p968 . . . . . 0845 210 5555

Blewitt, Miss Jennifer M *Jul 2001*
12, 15, 30
St Johns Buildings, Preston
p990 . . . . . 01772 256100
St Johns Buildings, Chester
p974 . . . . . 01244 323070
St Johns Buildings, Manchester
p985 . . . . . 0161 214 1500
St Johns Buildings, Liverpool
p982 . . . . . 0151 243 6000

BLOCH, Mr Michael L *Jul 1979*
(Q.C.) *13, 11, 48, 49, 50, 41*
Wilberforce Chambers, London WC2
p953 . . . . . 020 7306 0102

BLOCH, Mr Selwyn BA; LLB M *Jul 1982*
(Q.C.) *5, 8, 11, 12, 13, 18, 29, 36, 49, 55*
Littleton Chambers, London EC4
p941 . . . . . 020 7797 8600

BLOCK, Mr Neil Selwyn G *Jul 1980*
(Q.C.) *30, 40, 24, 12, 27, 11, 53, 84, 48*
Thirty Nine Essex Street, London WC2
p932 . . . . . 020 7832 1111

Blohm, Mr Leslie MA(Oxon) L *Jul 1982*
(Q.C.) *6, 8, 29, 22, 9, 1, 46, 31, 32, 37, 93, 86, 2, 88*
St John's Chambers, Bristol
p972 . . . . . 0117 921 3456

BLOM-COOPER, Mr Samuel M *Oct 2006*
15
25 Bedford Row, London WC1
p925 . . . . . 020 7067 1500

Bloom, Dr Margaret B Med Sci; BMBS L *Oct 1994*
30, 53
Hardwicke, London WC2
p936 . . . . . 020 7242 2523

Bloom, Ms Tracey BA(Cantab) G *Jul 1984*
1, 22, 51
Doughty Street Chambers, London WC1
p930 . . . . . 020 7404 1313

BLOOM-DAVIS, Mr Desmond BA(Lond); Deputy District Judge I *Jul 1986*
10, 12, 20, 30, 27, 7
Pump Court Chambers, Swindon
p993 . . . . . 01793 539899
Pump Court Chambers, Winchester
p994 . . . . . 01962 868161
Pump Court Chambers, London EC4
p947 . . . . . 020 7353 0711

Bloomer, Mr Charles H LLB L *Jul 1985*
Lincoln House Chambers, Manchester
p984 . . . . . 0161 832 5701

Bloomfield, Mr Richard W BA G *Jul 1984*
New Court Chambers, Newcastle upon Tyne
p987 . . . . . 0191 232 1980

BLOUNT, Mr Martin J LLB G *Nov 1982*
10, 20
Pump Court Chambers, Swindon
p993 . . . . . 01793 539899
Pump Court Chambers, Winchester
p994 . . . . . 01962 868161
Pump Court Chambers, London EC4
p947 . . . . . 020 7353 0711

Blower, Mr Graham G *Nov 1980*
15, 62
Argent Chambers, London WC2
p923 . . . . . 020 7556 5500

Blum, Mr Doron BA(Hons)(Lond) M *Sep 1998*
15, 23
1 Pump Court, London EC4
p947 . . . . . 020 7842 7070

Blumgart, Miss Kate M *Jan 1999*
15
Atkinson Bevan Chambers, London EC4
p924 . . . . . 020 7353 2112

BLUNDELL, Mr David Anthony BA(Cantab); MPhil(Oxon); CPCE I *Oct 2001*
Landmark Chambers, London EC4
p941 . . . . . 020 7430 1221

Blunt, Mr David MA(Cantab); Recorder M *Nov 1967*
(Q.C.) *3, 7, 11, 12, 30, 24*
4 Pump Court, London EC4
p947 . . . . . 020 7842 5555

BLUNT, Mr Oliver LLB M *Nov 1974*
(Q.C.)
Furnival Chambers, London EC4
p934 . . . . . 020 7405 3232

Boaitey, Mrs Charlotte LLB(Lond); M Phil I *Nov 1976*
13, 20, 23, 15
12 Old Square, London WC2
p945 . . . . . 020 7404 0875

Boardman, Mr Christopher LLB(Lond) L *Oct 1995*
5, 6, 8, 11, 29, 38, 62
11 Stone Buildings, London WC2
p951 . . . . . 020 7831 6381

Boase, Miss Anna M *Oct 2002*
One Essex Court, London EC4
p931 . . . . . 020 7583 2000

Boateng, Mr Paul LLB G *Nov 1989* MP
1 Mitre Court Buildings, London EC4
p942 . . . . . 020 7452 8900

BODNAR, Ms Alexandra I *Jul 2004*
49, 41, 3, 7, 11, 12, 74, 48, 67, 78, 24, 21, 89, 96, 40, 61
Thirty Nine Essex Street, London WC2
p932 . . . . . 020 7832 1111

BODNAR, Mr Andrew L *Jan 1995*
72, 15, 62, 1, 5, 6, 11, 34, 38, 71, 79, 81, 89
Matrix Chambers, London WC1
p942 . . . . . 020 7404 3447

BOEDDINGHAUS, Mr Hermann BSc(Cape Town); BCL; MA(Oxon) L *Nov 1996*
5, 6, 11, 29
4 Stone Buildings, London WC2
p951 . . . . . 020 7242 5524

BOGAN, Mr Paul BA(Business Law) G *Jul 1983*
(Q.C.) *72, 15, 62*
23 Essex Street, London WC2
p932 . . . . . 020 7413 0353

BOGLE, Mr James M *Oct 1991*
20, 30, 31, 1, 41, 6, 53, 11, 12, 47, 97, 51, 21, 88, 28, 29, 40
10 King's Bench Walk, London EC4
p940 . . . . . 020 7353 7742

Bojarski, Mr Andrzej LLB G *Oct 1995*
6, 11, 12, 18, 20, 22, 30
36 Bedford Row, London WC1
p925 . . . . . 020 7421 8000

BOLTON, Ms Caroline M *Jan 1998*
11, 26, 5, 24, 40, 35, 56
4-5 Gray's Inn Square, London WC1
p935 . . . . . 020 7404 5252

Bolton, Mrs Frances LLB(Hons) M *Jul 1981*
15, 62
Argent Chambers, London WC2
p923 . . . . . 020 7556 5500

Bolton, Mr Robert G *Jul 1987*
2 King's Bench Walk, London EC4
p939 . . . . . 020 7353 1746

Bompas, Miss Abra L *Jul 2008*
One Essex Court, London EC4
p931 . . . . . 020 7583 2000

BOMPAS, Mr George BA(Oxon) M *Jul 1975*
(Q.C.) *6, 11, 29*
4 Stone Buildings, London WC2
p951 . . . . . 020 7242 5524

BONAVERO, Philippe M *Jan 2008*
4 King's Bench Walk, London EC4
p939 . . . . . 020 7822 7000

Bond, Ms Abigail Rachel BA(Oxon); LLM(East Anglia) M *Oct 1999*
20, 10
St John's Chambers, Bristol
p972 . . . . . 0117 921 3456

BOND, Mr Andrew I *Jan 1999*
10, 20
Pump Court Chambers, Swindon
p993 . . . . . 01793 539899
Pump Court Chambers, Winchester
p994 . . . . . 01962 868161
Pump Court Chambers, London EC4
p947 . . . . . 020 7353 0711

BOND, Mr Christopher I *Jan 2008*
5, 81, 24, 62, 40, 38, 37, 97
3 Verulam Buildings, London WC1
p953 . . . . . 020 7831 8441

BOND, Ms Jackie LLB M *Oct 1994*
1, 12, 23
4 King's Bench Walk, London EC4
p939 . . . . . 020 7822 7000

BOND, Miss Kelly MA(Cantab) M *Jul 2007*
5, 6, 8, 11, 22, 29, 40, 38, 47, 67, 88, 89, 93
Enterprise Chambers, London WC2
p931 . . . . . 020 7405 9471
Enterprise Chambers, Leeds
p977 . . . . . 0113 246 0391
Enterprise Chambers, Newcastle upon Tyne
p987 . . . . . 0191 222 3344

BOND, Ms Leisha M *Oct 1999*
20
St Philips Chambers, Birmingham
p969 . . . . . 0121 246 7000

BOND, Mr Richard Ian Winsor M *Jul 1988*
15, 51
Citadel Chambers, Birmingham
p967 . . . . . 0121 233 8500

BONE, Ms Lucy LLB; LLM(Lond) M *Oct 1999*
6, 11, 12, 18, 40
Littleton Chambers, London EC4
p941 . . . . . 020 7797 8600

BONNER, Lee LLB L *Nov 2000*
15, 30
Atlantic Chambers, Liverpool
p980 . . . . . 0151 236 4421

Bonsu, Miss Michaela L *Jan 2000*
15, 20, 18, 23
12 Old Square, London WC2
p945 . . . . . 020 7404 0875

Boodia, Ms Anuradha G *Oct 1994*
Holborn Chambers, London WC2
p937 . . . . . 020 7242 6060

Booker, Miss Szilvia I *Nov 2005*
15, 94, 84
Argent Chambers, London WC2
p923 . . . . . 020 7556 5500

Bools, Mr Michael David LLB(East Anglia); D Phil(Oxon) M *Oct 1991*
11, 35
Brick Court Chambers, London WC2
p927 . . . . . 020 7379 3550

BOON, Miss Elizabeth BA(Oxon) I *Jul 2006*
11, 24, 74, 7, 30, 40
Crown Office Chambers, London EC4
p929 . . . . . 020 7797 8100

Boora, Mr Jinder G *Oct 1990*
No5 Chambers, Bristol
p971 . . . . . 0845 210 5555
No5 Chambers, London EC4
p944 . . . . . 0845 210 5555
No5 Chambers, Birmingham
p968 . . . . . 0845 210 5555

BOOTH, Mr Alexander LLB M *Feb 2000*
1, 12, 46, 25, 26, 54, 31, 36
Francis Taylor Building, London EC4
p934 . . . . . 020 7353 8415

BOOTH, Ms Cherie LLB(Lond); FRSA; FJMU; Recorder(1999); Bencher(1999) L *Jul 1976*
(Q.C.) *1, 9, 11, 19, 18, 26, 40, 43, 10, 21, 51, 23, 56, 36, 27, 55, 12*
Matrix Chambers, London WC1
p942 . . . . . 020 7404 3447

Booth, Miss Joy LLB(Sheff) G *Oct 1992*
20
18 St John Street Chambers, Manchester
p985 . . . . . 0161 278 1800

Booth, Mr Michael MA(Cantab) L *Nov 1981*
(Q.C.)
Kings Chambers, Leeds
p978 . . . . . 0113 242 1123
Kings Chambers, Manchester
p984 . . . . . 0161 832 9082
13 Old Square Chambers, London WC2
p945 . . . . . 020 7831 4445

Booth, Mr Nicholas BA(Oxon); MA(Cantab) M *Sep 1991*
16, 18, 30, 55, 36, 51, 1
Old Square Chambers, Bristol
p971 . . . . . 0117 930 5100

Booth, Mr Nigel Robert G *Oct 1994*
15
St Johns Buildings, Preston
p990 . . . . . 01772 256100
St Johns Buildings, Chester
p974 . . . . . 01244 323070
St Johns Buildings, Manchester
p985 . . . . . 0161 214 1500
St Johns Buildings, Liverpool
p982 . . . . . 0151 243 6000

BOOTH, Mr Richard MA(Cantab); LSDE(Brussels) M *Oct 1993*
1, 12, 18, 27, 30, 36, 39, 46, 56
1 Crown Office Row, London EC4
p929 . . . . . 020 7797 7500

Booth, Mr Roger LLB; TD; FRPSL G *Oct 1966* TD
13, 15, 62
Crown Office Row Chambers, Brighton
p970 . . . . . 01273 625625

BOOTH, Simon LLB(L'pool) L *Jan 1985*
8, 6, 9, 11, 22, 32, 37, 29, 31
Atlantic Chambers, Liverpool
p980 . . . . . 0151 236 4421

Boothroyd, Mr Dominic I *Nov 2010*
20, 22, 51, 2
Angel Chambers, Swansea
p992 . . . . . 01792 464623

Boothroyd, Miss Susan LLB M *Oct 1990*
10, 12, 15, 20, 30
York Chambers, York
p995 . . . . . 01904 620048
York Chambers, Newcastle upon Tyne
p987 . . . . . 0191 206 4677

Bor, Dr Harris I *Jan 2006*
5, 81, 11, 97, 47, 38, 40, 37
Radcliffe Chambers, London WC2
p949 . . . . . 020 7831 0081

Borgen, Miss Inga I *Oct 2004*
20
Old Court Chambers, Middlesbrough
p986 . . . . . 01642 232523

Borkowski, Miss Gemma LLB(Hons) I *Oct 2005*
10, 12, 15, 18, 20, 30
Albion Chambers, Bristol
p970 . . . . . 0117 927 2144

Bornman, Miss Kerry LLB(Reading) M *Nov 1999*
8, 11, 14, 29, 32, 40, 34, 37
3 Stone Buildings, London WC2
p951 . . . . . 020 7242 4937

BORRELLI, Mr Michael M *Nov 1977*
(Q.C.) *15, 62, 95*
187 Fleet Street, London EC4
p933 . . . . . 020 7430 7430

Borrett, Mr Richard L *Jan 2009*
15, 89
3PB, Bournemouth
p969 . . . . . 01202 292102

Bosanko, Mr Jonathan LLB(Hons) M *Jul 2001*
King's Bench Godolphin Chambers, Truro
p994 . . . . . 0845 308 1551
King's Bench Godolphin Chambers, Plymouth
p990 . . . . . 0845 308 1551

Bosomworth, Mr Michael M *Jul 1979*
York Chambers, York
p995 . . . . . 01904 620048
York Chambers, Newcastle upon Tyne
p987 . . . . . 0191 206 4677

Boswell, Miss Jenny BA M *Jul 1982*
20
Tooks Chambers, London EC4
p953 . . . . . 020 7842 7575

Boswell, Ms Lindsay BSc(Hons)(Econ) G *Jan 1982*
(Q.C.) *4, 41*
Quadrant Chambers, London EC4
p948 . . . . . 020 7583 4444

13

Boswell, Mr Timothy BA(Oxon) G *Nov 2004*
King's Bench Chambers, Oxford
p989 . . . . . 01865 311066
13 King's Bench Walk, London EC4
p940 . . . . . 020 7353 7204

Boswood, Mr Anthony Richard BA; BCL(Oxon) M *Nov 1970*
(Q.C.)
Fountain Court Chambers, London EC4
p934 . . . . . 020 7583 3335

BOTHROYD, Miss Shirley BA M *Jul 1982*
5, 6, 11, 12, 18, 29, 34, 36
Littleton Chambers, London EC4
p941 . . . . . 020 7797 8600

BOTT, Mr Charles Adrian MA(Cantab) G *Nov 1979*
(Q.C.) *15*
Carmelite Chambers, London EC4
p927 . . . . . 020 7936 6300

BOUCHER-GILES, Mr Benjamin L *Jan 2004*
Fountain Chambers, Middlesbrough
p986 . . . . . 01642 804040

Boulding, Mr Philip V MA; LLB(Cantab) G *Nov 1979*
(Q.C.) *3, 7, 11, 22, 24, 40*
Keating Chambers, London WC2
p938 . . . . . 020 7544 2600

BOULTER, Mr Terence LLB(Coventry) L *Jul 1986*
Furnival Chambers, London EC4
p934 . . . . . 020 7405 3232

BOULTON, Ms Clementine L *Jan 2009*
Furnival Chambers, London EC4
p934 . . . . . 020 7405 3232

Boulton, Mr Richard G *Jul 2003*
(Q.C.)
One Essex Court, London EC4
p931 . . . . . 020 7583 2000

Boumphrey, John I *Jan 1992*
15, 36, 39, 48
Zenith Chambers, Leeds
p979 . . . . . 0113 245 5438

Bourke, Ms Sarah G *Oct 1996*
18, 22, 55
Tooks Chambers, London EC4
p953 . . . . . 020 7842 7575

BOURNE, Mr Charles MA(Cantab); DipLaw M *Jul 1991*
1, 11, 18
4-5 Gray's Inn Square, London WC1
p935 . . . . . 020 7404 5252

Bourne, Mr Colin G *Oct 1997*
18, 96
Kings Chambers, Leeds
p978 . . . . . 0113 242 1123
Kings Chambers, Manchester
p984 . . . . . 0161 832 9082

Bourne, Mr Robert BA(Oxon)(Modern History) G *Jul 1978*
13 Old Square Chambers, London WC2
p945 . . . . . 020 7831 4445

Bourne-Arton, Mr James I *Jan 2001*
30, 53, 15, 72, 70, 68, 31
St Pauls Chambers, Leeds
p979 . . . . . 0113 245 5866

Bourne-Arton, Mr Simon Nicholas LLB I *Nov 1975*
(Q.C.)
Park Court Chambers, Leeds
p978 . . . . . 0113 243 3277

BOURNE-ARTON, Mr Tom MA(Edin) I *Oct 2005*
30, 12
Farrar's Building, London EC4
p933 . . . . . 020 7583 9241

BOUTLE, Mr Toby BA(Hons)(Oxon) L *Jul 2004*
8
Ten Old Square, London WC2
p945 . . . . . 020 7405 0758

Bovensiepen, Mr Daniel MA; LLM M *Jul 2004*
49, 41, 3, 5, 11, 43, 47, 78, 24, 54, 35
20 Essex Street, London WC2
p932 . . . . . 020 7842 1200

Bovey, Mungo I *Nov 2000*
(Q.C.) *23*
Tooks Chambers, London EC4
p953 . . . . . 020 7842 7575

Bowcock, Miss Samantha J LLB M *Oct 1990*
10, 20
15 Winckley Square, Preston
p991 . . . . . 01772 252828

Bowden, Mr Timothy John LLB M *Jan 2003*
15, 70, 72, 62, 94
7 Bedford Row, London WC1
p924 . . . . . 020 7242 3555

Bowdery, Mr Martin BA(Oxon); Recorder I *Jul 1980*
(Q.C.) *3, 7, 11, 31, 40, 41, 43, 45, 49, 54, 61, 78, 74*
Atkin Chambers, London WC1
p923 . . . . . 020 7404 0102

Bowe, Mr Patrick LLB L *Jan 2000*
KCH Garden Square Chambers, Nottingham
p989 . . . . . 0115 941 8851
KCH Garden Square Chambers, Leicester
p979 . . . . . 0115 941 8851

Bowe, Mr Timothy I *Jan 2003*
St Ives Chambers, Birmingham
p969 . . . . . 0121 236 0863

Bowen, Mr Nicholas L *Jan 1984*
(Q.C.) *1, 51, 26, 8, 10, 12, 14, 63*
Doughty Street Chambers, London WC1
p930 . . . . . 020 7404 1313

Bowen, Miss Nicola LLB G *Nov 2003*
15, 23, 20, 18, 10, 88, 94
Bell Yard Chambers, London WC2
p926 . . . . . 020 7306 9292 / 7404 5138

Bowen, Mr Paul LLB I *Nov 1993*
1, 12, 15, 26, 38, 51
Doughty Street Chambers, London WC1
p930 . . . . . 020 7404 1313

BOWER, Mr Alistair LLB(Leeds) I *Jul 1986*
12, 18, 24, 22, 30, 59, 26, 48
9 St John Street Chambers, Manchester
p984 . . . . . 0161 955 9000

Bower, Ms Gemma LLB(Hons) M *Jul 2006*
10, 12, 15, 18, 20, 25, 30
College Chambers, Southampton
p992 . . . . . 023 8023 0338

Bower, Miss Laurinda L *Jan 2006*
15, 20, 12
Paradise Chambers, Sheffield
p992 . . . . . 0114 273 8951

BOWERS, Mr John Simon MA(Oxon); BCL; Accredited Mediator M *Nov 1979*
(Q.C.) *18, 1, 11, 19, 30, 38, 26, 36, 29, 3, 49, 55*
Littleton Chambers, London EC4
p941 . . . . . 020 7797 8600

Bowes, Ms Gemma LLB(Hons); MSc(Oxon) M *Jan 2009*
11, 97, 20, 10, 30, 53, 93, 8, 71
3PB, Oxford
p989 . . . . . 01865 793736

Bowes, Mr Michael LLB M *Jul 1980*
(Q.C.) *15, 81, 62*
Cobden House Chambers, Manchester
p983 . . . . . 0161 833 6000
Outer Temple Chambers, London WC2
p945 . . . . . 020 7353 6381

Bowhill, Miss Jessie LLB G *Oct 2003*
13, 50
8 New Square, London WC2
p943 . . . . . 020 7405 4321

Bowley, Mr Ivan R BSc(Hons) M *Nov 1990*
Lincoln House Chambers, Manchester
p984 . . . . . 0161 832 5701

Bowling, Mr James BA(Hons)(Oxon); DipLaw M *Nov 1999*
12, 40, 5, 6, 7, 8, 11, 62
4 Pump Court, London EC4
p947 . . . . . 020 7842 5555

Bowmer, Mr Michael LLB(Lond) M *Oct 1997*
Four New Square, London WC2
p943 . . . . . 020 7822 2000

Bown, Mr Philip Clive LLB(Lond); FCIArb M *Nov 1974*
New Walk Chambers, Leicester
p979 . . . . . 0871 200 1298

Bowring, Prof William Schuyler Beakbane BA(Kent) M *Nov 1974*
Field Court Chambers, London WC1
p933 . . . . . 020 7405 6114

BOWRON, Ms Margaret LLB(Lond); Recorder I *Nov 1978*
(Q.C.) *12, 20, 27, 30*
1 Crown Office Row, London EC4
p929 . . . . . 020 7797 7500

BOWSHER, Mr Michael F T BA(Oxon); FCIArb M *Nov 1985*
(Q.C.) *3, 7, 19, 26, 40, 44, 49, 61*
Monckton Chambers, London WC1
p942 . . . . . 020 7405 7211

Bowsher, Mr Peter MA(Oxon) M *Jan 1959*
(Q.C.)
Keating Chambers, London WC2
p938 . . . . . 020 7544 2600

Bowsher-Murray, Miss Claire G *Jan 2007*
26, 51, 36, 46, 18, 55, 48, 49, 53
Old Square Chambers, London WC1
p945 . . . . . 020 7269 0300

Bowyer, Miss Juliet L *Oct 1997*
Charter Chambers, London WC1
p928 . . . . . 020 7618 4400

Bowyer, Mr Martyn BA(Cantab) I *Nov 1984*
15, 62
6 King's Bench Walk, London EC4
p939 . . . . . 020 7583 0410

Boyce, Mr William G *Jul 1976*
(Q.C.) *15, 25, 36*
QEB Hollis Whiteman, London EC4
p948 . . . . . 020 7933 8855

Boyd, Mr David LLB(B'ham) M *Feb 1977*
20, 10
Coram Chambers, London EC1
p929 . . . . . 020 7092 3700

Boyd, Mr James I *Nov 1994*
18, 8, 11, 56
Kings Chambers, Leeds
p978 . . . . . 0113 242 1123
Kings Chambers, Manchester
p984 . . . . . 0161 832 9082

Boyd, Miss Jessica PhD(Princeton); DipLaw I *Nov 2007*
1, 11, 18, 51, 50, 52, 56, 89
Blackstone Chambers, London EC4
p926 . . . . . 020 7583 1770

Boyd, Mr Joseph P G MA G *Nov 1993*
Lincoln House Chambers, Manchester
p984 . . . . . 0161 832 5701

BOYD, Miss Kerstin BA(Cantab) G *Jul 1979*
20, 30, 53
Tanfield Chambers, London WC1
p951 . . . . . 020 7421 5300

Boyd, Miss Sarah MA(Cantab) G *Oct 1998*
15, 30, 53
Unity Street Chambers, Bristol
p972 . . . . . 0117 906 9789

Boyd, Mr Stewart C MA(Cantab); Recorder M *Jul 1967*
(Q.C.) CBE
Essex Court Chambers, London WC2
p931 . . . . . 020 7813 8000

BOYDELL, Mr Edward Patrick Stirrup BEd(Hons)(Cantab); Recorder M *Nov 1989*
10, 12, 7, 20, 30, 31, 27
Pump Court Chambers, Swindon
p993 . . . . . 01793 539899
Pump Court Chambers, Winchester
p994 . . . . . 01962 868161
Pump Court Chambers, London EC4
p947 . . . . . 020 7353 0711

Boyden, Mr Matthew M *Jan 2007*
65, 5, 8, 12, 47, 69, 15, 38
Rougemont Chambers, Exeter
p975 . . . . . 01392 208484

BOYE-ANAWOMAH, Margo I *Nov 1989*
10, 20
Renaissance Chambers, London WC1
p949 . . . . . 020 7404 1111

Boyes, Mr Ian LLM(Hons)(Intl & European Business Law) L *Nov 2003*
72, 15, 80, 82, 94, 91
15 New Bridge Street Chambers, London EC4
p943 . . . . . 020 7842 1900

Boyle, Mr Alan MA(Oxon) L *Nov 1972*
(Q.C.) *8, 11, 62, 32, 37, 81, 96, 89*
Serle Court, London WC2
p950 . . . . . 020 7242 6105
Essex Court Chambers, London WC2
p931 . . . . . 020 7813 8000

BOYLE, Mr Christopher BA(Oxon) L *Nov 1994*
Landmark Chambers, London EC4
p941 . . . . . 020 7430 1221

Boyle, Mr Gerard BA(Cantab) G *Nov 1992*
12, 18, 27, 30, 40, 53, 68, 85, 1
3 Serjeants' Inn, London EC4
p950 . . . . . 020 7427 5000

Boyle, Mr Jonathan BSc(Hons); PG DipLaw M *Jan 2005*
12, 24, 30, 36, 40, 53, 56
Cobden House Chambers, Manchester
p983 . . . . . 0161 833 6000

BOYLE, Miss Karen L *Jan 2000*
30, 18, 12
St James's Chambers, Manchester
p984 . . . . . 0161 834 7000

BOYLE, Ms Lucy LLB(Hons)(Law); MA(Medical Law) M *Jan 2009*
12 King's Bench Walk, London EC4
p940 . . . . . 020 7583 0811

BOYLE, Mr Matthew BA(Oxon) G *Jul 2000*
30, 40, 12
Crown Office Chambers, London EC4
p929 . . . . . 020 7797 8100

Brace, Mr Michael Wesley LLB(Hons)(Lond) L *Apr 1991*
30
Civitas Law, Cardiff
p972 . . . . . 0845 071 3007

BRADBERRY, Ms Rebecca L *Oct 1996*
15, 36, 20, 10
Octagon Chambers, Taunton
p993 . . . . . 01823 331919

Bradbury, Ms Joanna BA(Hons) M *Nov 1999*
12, 1, 41, 6, 18, 30
East Anglian Chambers, Norwich
p988 . . . . . 01603 617351
East Anglian Chambers, Colchester
p975 . . . . . 01206 572756
East Anglian Chambers, Chelmsford
p973 . . . . . 01245 215660
East Anglian Chambers, Ipswich
p976 . . . . . 01473 214481

Bradbury, Miss Sara G *Jan 1998*
20, 67, 6, 10
New Bailey Chambers, Preston
p990 . . . . . 01772 258087

Bradbury, Mr Timothy LLB I *Jun 1989*
11, 15, 20, 30
3PB, Bournemouth
p969 . . . . . 01202 292102

Bradley, Mr Anthony I *Apr 1989*
1, 28, 51
Cloisters, London EC4
p928 . . . . . 020 7827 4000

Bradley, Mr Benjamin BA(Hons)(Oxon) I *Oct 2007*
30, 18, 53
Outer Temple Chambers, London WC2
p945 . . . . . 020 7353 6381

BRADLEY, Ms Caroline BA M *Jul 1985*
23 Essex Street, London WC2
p932 . . . . . 020 7413 0353
KCH Garden Square Chambers, Nottingham
p989 . . . . . 0115 941 8851
KCH Garden Square Chambers, Leicester
p979 . . . . . 0115 941 8851

BRADLEY, Mr Charles BA(Cantab); MPhil L *Jan 2010*
Pump Court Tax Chambers, London WC1
p948 . . . . . 020 7414 8080

Bradley, Ms Clodagh Maria MA(Hons)(Cantab) M *Oct 1996*
12, 27, 30, 40, 53, 68, 85, 36
3 Serjeants' Inn, London EC4
p950 . . . . . 020 7427 5000

Bradley, Mr Matthew MA(Hons)(Oxon) I *Jan 2004*
Henderson Chambers, London EC4
p937 . . . . . 020 7583 9020

Bradley, Mr Michael James G *Mar 1999*
20, 10
1 Hare Court, London EC4
p936 . . . . . 020 7797 7070

Bradley, Mr Phillip BA L *Nov 1993*
15, 62, 72, 70
No5 Chambers, Bristol
p971 . . . . . 0845 210 5555
No5 Chambers, London EC4
p944 . . . . . 0845 210 5555
No5 Chambers, Birmingham
p968 . . . . . 0845 210 5555

BRADLEY, Mr Richard LLB(Hons) M *Jul 1978*
7, 11, 12, 18, 22, 29, 30, 36, 40, 46, 5, 61
Oriel Chambers, Liverpool
p981 . . . . . 0151 236 7191 / 236 4321
Oriel Chambers, Preston
p990 . . . . . 01772 254764

BRADLEY, Mrs Sally LLB L *Nov 1978*
(Q.C.) *20, 10*
Pump Court Chambers, Swindon
p993 . . . . . 01793 539899

See p1010 for the Key to Work Categories

Pump Court Chambers, Winchester
p994 . . . . . 01962 868161
Pump Court Chambers, London EC4
p947 . . . . . 020 7353 0711

Bradley, Ms Sally BA I *Nov 1989*
20, 10
4 Paper Buildings, London EC4
p946 . . . . . 020 7583 0816

BRADLEY, Sally Recorder 1999; Deputy High Court Judge 2001 L *Jan 1977*
(Q.C.) *20*
Trinity (Teesside) Chambers, Middlesbrough
p986 . . . . . 01642 247569
Trinity (Newcastle) Chambers, Newcastle upon Tyne
p987 . . . . . 0191 232 1927

BRADLY, Mr David LLB M *Jul 1987*
30, 40, 53, 36
Thirty Nine Essex Street, London WC2
p932 . . . . . 020 7832 1111

BRADNOCK, Mr Thomas G *Oct 1997*
15, 30, 12
Colleton Chambers, Exeter
p975 . . . . . 01392 274898

Bradshaw, Miss Catherine M *Jul 1998*
15
2 Pump Court, London EC4
p947 . . . . . 020 7353 5597

Bradshaw, David Recorder I *Jul 1975*
15, 70, 72
Zenith Chambers, Leeds
p979 . . . . . 0113 245 5438

Bradshaw, Mr Ian Charles M *Jan 1992*
15, 20, 26, 36, 12
Old Court Chambers, Middlesbrough
p986 . . . . . 01642 232523

Bradshaw, Mr Mark G *Jul 2002*
No5 Chambers, Bristol
p971 . . . . . 0845 210 5555
No5 Chambers, London EC4
p944 . . . . . 0845 210 5555
No5 Chambers, Birmingham
p968 . . . . . 0845 210 5555

BRADY, Dr Ann PhD; Associate Member M *Mar 2001*
49, 96
Rougemont Chambers, Exeter
p975 . . . . . 01392 208484

Brady, Ms Jane MA(Cantab) M *Oct 2001*
King's Bench Chambers, Oxford
p989 . . . . . 01865 311066
13 King's Bench Walk, London EC4
p940 . . . . . 020 7353 7204

Brady, Mr Michael LLB(Hons) G *Oct 1992*
15
18 St John Street Chambers, Manchester
p985 . . . . . 0161 278 1800

Brady, Mr Scott QC(Scotland) M *Jul 1987*
15, 62, 25
3 Temple Gardens, London EC4
p952 . . . . . 020 7353 3102

Braganza, Ms Nicola LLB(Hons)(Reading) M *Oct 1992*
18, 23
Tooks Chambers, London EC4
p953 . . . . . 020 7842 7575

Bragge, Mr Thomas Herewad BA; MA I *Jul 2000*
88, 37, 30, 18, 11
Stour Chambers, Canterbury
p972 . . . . . 01227 764899

Bragiel, Mr Edward MA(Cantab) M *Jul 1977*
6, 8, 9, 11, 13, 22, 29, 32, 36, 37
Hogarth Chambers, London WC2
p937 . . . . . 020 7404 0404

BRAHAM, Mr Colin MA(Cantab); MSc M *Nov 1971*
1, 8, 51, 26, 63, 32, 37
New Square Chambers, London WC2
p943 . . . . . 020 7419 8000

Brahams, Ms Diana M *Jul 1972*
27, 30, 53
Old Square Chambers, Bristol
p971 . . . . . 0117 930 5100

Braier, Mr Jason LLB; LLM I *Jul 2002*
Field Court Chambers, London WC1
p933 . . . . . 020 7405 6114

Brain, Miss Pamela I *Nov 1985*
15
1 Inner Temple Lane, London EC4
p937 . . . . . 020 7427 4400

Braithwaite, Mr Bill LLB(L'pool) G *Nov 1970*
(Q.C.) *30, 53*
Exchange Chambers, Manchester
p983 . . . . . 0161 833 2722
Exchange Chambers, Liverpool
p980 . . . . . 0151 236 7747
Exchange Chambers, Leeds
p977 . . . . . 0113 203 1970

Braithwaite, Mr Garfield Z LLB(Hons) G *Feb 1987*
10, 20
42 Bedford Row, London WC1
p925 . . . . . 020 7831 0222

Braithwaite, Mr Thomas J MA(Cantab) L *Oct 1998*
8, 11, 43, 93, 38, 6, 88, 37
Serle Court, London WC2
p950 . . . . . 020 7242 6105

Bramall, Miss Kate L G *Oct 1999*
20
18 St John Street Chambers, Manchester
p985 . . . . . 0161 278 1800

Bramwell, Mr Christopher G *Nov 1996*
12, 20, 10, 15
Regency Chambers, Peterborough
p990 . . . . . 01733 315215

Bramwell, Mr Richard Mervyn LLM(Lond) M *Jul 1967*
(Q.C.) *34*
Temple Tax Chambers, London EC4
p952 . . . . . 020 7353 7884 / 7353 8982

Branchflower, George L *Mar 1997*
8, 11, 18, 30
Zenith Chambers, Leeds
p979 . . . . . 0113 245 5438

BRAND, Kieran M *Jan 2007*
Maidstone Chambers, Maidstone
p982 . . . . . 01622 688592

BRAND, Ms Rachel G *Jul 1981*
(Q.C.) *15, 51*
Citadel Chambers, Birmingham
p967 . . . . . 0121 233 8500

Brander, Ms Ruth M *Oct 2001*
15, 51, 63, 1, 33
Doughty Street Chambers, London WC1
p930 . . . . . 020 7404 1313

BRANDON, Ms Helen Elizabeth LLB(Lancs) M *Nov 1993*
10, 20, 30
Oriel Chambers, Liverpool
p981 . . . . . 0151 236 7191 / 236 4321
Oriel Chambers, Preston
p990 . . . . . 01772 254764

BRANDON, Miss Louise BA(Hons) M *Jan 2003*
15
9 St John Street Chambers, Manchester
p984 . . . . . 0161 955 9000

Brandon, Mr Stephen David MA; BA; LLM G *Jul 1978*
(Q.C.) *34, 37, 36, 29, 8, 9*
15 Old Square, London WC2
p945 . . . . . 020 7242 2744

Brandreth, Mr Benet Xan BA(Hons)(Cantab) M *Nov 1999*
73, 50, 19, 45, 13, 52, 96, 41
11 South Square, London WC1
p950 . . . . . 020 7405 1222

Branigan, Miss Kate BA(Soton) I *Jul 1984*
(Q.C.) *10, 12, 15, 20, 22, 30*
4 Paper Buildings, London EC4
p946 . . . . . 020 7583 0816

Brankovic, Victoria I *Jul 2008*
New Walk Chambers, Leicester
p979 . . . . . 0871 200 1298

Brannigan, Mr Sean BA(Oxon) G *Oct 1994*
(Q.C.) *7, 11, 12, 18, 40, 78, 24*
4 Pump Court, London EC4
p947 . . . . . 020 7842 5555

Branson, Ms Sarah Louise BA(Hons) M *Jul 2001*
10, 20
Coram Chambers, London EC1
p929 . . . . . 020 7092 3700

BRANSTON, Mr Gareth Deputy District Judge G *Oct 1996*
15, 25, 62, 27, 13, 36
23 Essex Street, London WC2
p932 . . . . . 020 7413 0353

BRANT, Mr Paul David LLB(Hons)(L'pool) L *Nov 1993*
11, 12, 22, 30, 47, 18, 5, 6, 88
Oriel Chambers, Liverpool
p981 . . . . . 0151 236 7191 / 236 4321
Oriel Chambers, Preston
p990 . . . . . 01772 254764

Braslavsky, Mr Nicholas LLB; PhD I *Jul 1983*
(Q.C.) *12, 27, 30, 36, 49, 50, 56*
Kings Chambers, Leeds
p978 . . . . . 0113 242 1123
Kings Chambers, Manchester
p984 . . . . . 0161 832 9082
3PB, London EC4
p946 . . . . . 020 7583 8055

Brassington, Mr Stephen D BSc(Hons) I *Nov 1994*
15, 62
2 Hare Court, London EC4
p937 . . . . . 020 7353 5324

BRAUN, Minka I *Jul 2000*
15
25 Bedford Row, London WC1
p925 . . . . . 020 7067 1500

Bray, Ms Helen M *Jul 2004*
20, 30, 12
Walnut House Chambers, Exeter
p975 . . . . . 01392 279751

Brazenall, Miss Emily I *Jul 2009*
15, 18, 20
Albion Chambers, Bristol
p970 . . . . . 0117 927 2144

Brazier, Prof Margaret G *Jan 2001*
1 Pump Court, London EC4
p947 . . . . . 020 7842 7070

BRAZIL, Mr Dominic BA(Oxon) M *Nov 1995*
10, 20
1 King's Bench Walk, London EC4
p938 . . . . . 020 7936 1500

Brealey, Mr Mark LLB; LLM; DEA M *Jul 1984*
(Q.C.) *44, 19*
Brick Court Chambers, London WC2
p927 . . . . . 020 7379 3550

Bredemear, Mr Zachary LLB; LLM(Reading) I *Oct 1996*
22, 8, 93, 88, 40
1 Chancery Lane, London WC2
p928 . . . . . 0845 634 6666

BREEN, Mr Carlo M *Nov 1987*
12, 15, 18, 30
9 St John Street Chambers, Manchester
p984 . . . . . 0161 955 9000

Breen-Lawton, Miss Denise G *Jan 2000*
84, 62, 70, 68, 15, 12, 10, 20, 81, 36, 86
St Pauls Chambers, Leeds
p979 . . . . . 0113 245 5866

Breese-Laughran, Ms Delphine MA(Hons)(Cantab) L *Oct 1991*
10, 20
1 Pump Court, London EC4
p947 . . . . . 020 7842 7070

BREGER, Mr Daniel G *Nov 2005*
15
25 Bedford Row, London WC1
p925 . . . . . 020 7067 1500

BREMNER, Mr Jonathan BA(Oxon); BCL; BA(French Law) I *Oct 2005*
37, 57, 58, 34
Pump Court Tax Chambers, London WC1
p948 . . . . . 020 7414 8080

Bremridge, Mr Lee G *Jan 2003*
15
Walnut House Chambers, Exeter
p975 . . . . . 01392 279751

Brennan, Mr Christopher Patrick G *Feb 1995*
Goldsmith Chambers, London EC4
p935 . . . . . 020 7353 6802

BRENNAN, Lord Daniel LLB(Manc); Deputy High Court Judge G *Jul 1967*
(Q.C.) *30, 40, 27, 1, 3, 8, 53, 51, 36, 46, 33, 41*
Matrix Chambers, London WC1
p942 . . . . . 020 7404 3447

BRENNAN, Miss Elizabeth Gail LLB(Hons) L *Nov 1998*
15, 25, 39, 20
7 Harrington Street Chambers, Liverpool
p981 . . . . . 0151 242 0707

Brennan, Miss Janice LLB M *Jul 1980*
15, 62
Lamb Building, Brighton
p970 . . . . . 01273 820490
Lamb Building, London EC4
p940 . . . . . 020 7797 7788

BRENNAN, Mr John L *Jan 1996*
Chancery House Chambers, Leeds
p977 . . . . . 0113 244 6691
St Philips Chambers, Birmingham
p969 . . . . . 0121 246 7000

Brennan, Mr Timothy BCL; MA(Oxon) G *Nov 1981*
(Q.C.) *11, 12, 18, 1, 24, 34, 36, 26, 40, 55, 57, 58*
Devereux Chambers, London WC2
p930 . . . . . 020 7353 7534

Brennand, Mr Timothy W LLB(Hons) G *Nov 1987*
15, 18
St Johns Buildings, Preston
p990 . . . . . 01772 256100
St Johns Buildings, Chester
p974 . . . . . 01244 323070
St Johns Buildings, Manchester
p985 . . . . . 0161 214 1500
St Johns Buildings, Liverpool
p982 . . . . . 0151 243 6000

BRENT, Mr Richard MA(Cantab); D Phil(Oxon) M *Jul 1995*
5, 11, 19, 40
3 Verulam Buildings, London WC1
p953 . . . . . 020 7831 8441

Brenton, Mr Timothy LLB(Bris) M *Jul 1981*
(Q.C.) *3, 24, 35, 41, 11*
7 King's Bench Walk, London EC4
p940 . . . . . 020 7910 8300

Brereton, Mrs Fiorella G *Nov 1979*
10, 12, 15, 20
Cobden House Chambers, Manchester
p983 . . . . . 0161 833 6000

Brereton, Miss Joy LLB(Cardiff); LLM(Bris) G *Nov 1990*
10, 20, 27, 37
4 Paper Buildings, London EC4
p946 . . . . . 020 7583 0816

BRESLIN, Miss Catherine I *Jan 1990*
10, 20, 30
Pump Court Chambers, Swindon
p993 . . . . . 01793 539899
Pump Court Chambers, Winchester
p994 . . . . . 01962 868161
Pump Court Chambers, London EC4
p947 . . . . . 020 7353 0711

BRETHERTON, Miss Kerry Louise BA(Hons); CPE(B'ham) L *Oct 1992*
22, 31, 93, 1, 88
Hardwicke, London WC2
p936 . . . . . 020 7242 2523

Brett, Mr Matthew BA(Oxon) M *Nov 1987*
20, 88, 93
Harcourt Chambers, London EC4
p936 . . . . . 0844 561 7135
Harcourt Chambers, Oxford
p989 . . . . . 0844 561 7135

Bretten, Mr George Rex MA; LLM(Cantab) L *May 1965*
(Q.C.) *34, 37, 36, 29, 8, 9*
15 Old Square, London WC2
p945 . . . . . 020 7242 2744

BRETTLER, Mr Jonathan Samuel LLB(LSE); BCL(Oxon) L *Nov 1988*
1, 6, 8, 11, 22, 32, 29
4 Stone Buildings, London WC2
p951 . . . . . 020 7242 5524

Brewin, Mr Carl BSc(Hons)(LSE) M *Jan 2006*
96, 8, 93, 74
3PB, London EC4
p946 . . . . . 020 7583 8055

BRIANT, Miss Sophie BA(Hons)(Oxon); MA(Brown) I *Oct 2007*
10, 20
29 Bedford Row, London WC1
p925 . . . . . 020 7404 1044

BRICKMAN, Miss Laura I *Jul 1976*
15
Carmelite Chambers, London EC4
p927 . . . . . 020 7936 6300

BRIDDOCK, Mr Alan I *Mar 2000*
23
Mitre House Chambers, London WC1
p942 . . . . . 020 7307 7100

Briden, Miss Sarah LLB(Hons) I *Jul 1999*
KCH Garden Square Chambers, Nottingham
p989 . . . . . 0115 941 8851
KCH Garden Square Chambers, Leicester
p979 . . . . . 0115 941 8851

Briden, Mr Timothy MA; LLB(Cantab) I *Jul 1976*
53, 17, 30, 24
Lamb Chambers, London EC4
p941 . . . . . 020 7797 8300

13

Bridge, Mr Giles BA(Hons); PGCE M *Jan 2000*
15, 20, 23, 10
Broadway House Chambers, Leeds
p977 . . . . . 0113 246 2600
Broadway House Chambers, Bradford
p969 . . . . . 01274 722560

Bridge, Mr Ian LLB(Sheff) I *Nov 1988*
15, 30, 25, 27, 36, 39, 46, 50, 56, 57, 62, 68, 70, 72, 91, 94, 42
No5 Chambers, Bristol
p971 . . . . . 0845 210 5555
No5 Chambers, London EC4
p944 . . . . . 0845 210 5555
No5 Chambers, Birmingham
p968 . . . . . 0845 210 5555

Bridgman, Mr Andrew G *Jan 2000*
St Johns Buildings, Preston
p990 . . . . . 01772 256100
St Johns Buildings, Chester
p974 . . . . . 01244 323070
St Johns Buildings, Manchester
p985 . . . . . 0161 214 1500
St Johns Buildings, Liverpool
p982 . . . . . 0151 243 6000

Briegel, Mr Pieter M *Nov 1986*
15
5 King's Bench Walk, London EC4
p939 . . . . . 020 7353 5638

Brier, Mr Jeremy BA M *Jan 2004*
Essex Court Chambers, London WC2
p931 . . . . . 020 7813 8000

Briggs, Mr Adrian MA(Oxon); BCL(Oxon) M *Apr 1989*
3, 21
Blackstone Chambers, London EC4
p926 . . . . . 020 7583 1770

Briggs, Mr Aidan I *Jun 2009*
Ely Place Chambers, London EC1
p931 . . . . . 020 7400 9600

Briggs, Miss Claire M *Jan 2005*
St Ives Chambers, Birmingham
p969 . . . . . 0121 236 0863

BRIGGS, Mr John B LLB(Lond) G *Jul 1973*
5, 6, 8, 11, 12, 24, 29, 38
South Square, London WC1
p950 . . . . . 020 7696 9900

Briggs, Miss Lucie BSc; PgDL(Lond); BVC(Lond) L *Oct 2004*
3, 7, 11, 31, 40, 41, 43, 45, 49, 54, 61, 78, 74
Atkin Chambers, London WC1
p923 . . . . . 020 7404 0102

BRIGGS, Mr Nicholas LLM L *Oct 1994*
6, 38
Guildhall Chambers, Bristol
p970 . . . . . 0117 930 9000

Bright, Mr Christopher BA(Dunelm); Recorder G *Nov 1985*
(Q.C.) *30, 53, 40, 94, 56, 36*
No5 Chambers, Bristol
p971 . . . . . 0845 210 5555
No5 Chambers, London EC4
p944 . . . . . 0845 210 5555
No5 Chambers, Birmingham
p968 . . . . . 0845 210 5555

Bright, Mr David Reginald L *Jun 1976*
King's Bench Chambers, Oxford
p989 . . . . . 01865 311066
13 King's Bench Walk, London EC4
p940 . . . . . 020 7353 7204

BRIGHT, Miss Rachel Zelda LLB(Manc) L *Oct 1991*
15, 62, 95
187 Fleet Street, London EC4
p933 . . . . . 020 7430 7430

Bright, Mr Robert Graham BA; BCL(Oxon) G *Nov 1987*
(Q.C.) *3, 35, 19, 33, 24, 5, 11, 40*
7 King's Bench Walk, London EC4
p940 . . . . . 020 7910 8300

Brightman, Ms Justina LLB L *Oct 2003*
20, 10
Harcourt Chambers, London EC4
p936 . . . . . 0844 561 7135
Harcourt Chambers, Oxford
p989 . . . . . 0844 561 7135

BRIGHTWELL, Mr James BA; LLM(Cantab) L *Nov 2000*
8, 22, 37
New Square Chambers, London WC2
p943 . . . . . 020 7419 8000

Brilliant, Mr Simon Howard LLB; BCL M *Jul 1976*
22, 30, 11, 40, 53
Lamb Chambers, London EC4
p941 . . . . . 020 7797 8300

Brimelow, Ms Kirsty LLB G *Oct 1991*
15, 21, 51
Doughty Street Chambers, London WC1
p930 . . . . . 020 7404 1313

Brindle, Mr Michael BA(Oxon); LLB(Manc) L *Nov 1975*
(Q.C.)
Fountain Court Chambers, London EC4
p934 . . . . . 020 7583 3335

Brindle, Mr Simon LLB(Reading) G *Jul 1998*
40, 18, 30, 60, 53
9 Gough Square, London EC4
p935 . . . . . 020 7832 0500

BRINSMEAD-STOCKHAM, Mr John M *Oct 2005*
34, 57, 58
11 New Square, London WC2
p943 . . . . . 020 7242 4017

BRISBY, Mr John C S M MA(Oxon) L *Jul 1978*
(Q.C.) *6, 11, 29*
4 Stone Buildings, London WC2
p951 . . . . . 020 7242 5524

BRISCOE, Miss Constance LLB(Newc); Recorder I *Nov 1983*
15, 16
9-12 Bell Yard Chambers, London WC2
p926 . . . . . 020 7400 1800

Brissenden, Ms Claire Judith I *Nov 2004*
Amicus Chambers, Middlesbrough
p986 . . . . . 01642 876334 / 876335

Brissett, Miss Nicola Luana BA M *Feb 1995*
15, 20, 23
12 Old Square, London WC2
p945 . . . . . 020 7404 0875

BRISTOLL, Ms Sandra M *Jan 1989*
11, 38, 67, 29
South Square, London WC1
p950 . . . . . 020 7696 9900
St Philips Chambers, Birmingham
p969 . . . . . 0121 246 7000

Britcliffe, Ms Anne E LLB(Bris) I *Apr 1989*
10, 15, 20, 30
St Johns Buildings, Preston
p990 . . . . . 01772 256100
St Johns Buildings, Chester
p974 . . . . . 01244 323070
St Johns Buildings, Manchester
p985 . . . . . 0161 214 1500
St Johns Buildings, Liverpool
p982 . . . . . 0151 243 6000

Brittenden, Mr Stuart LLB; LLM G *Jan 1999*
18, 30, 36, 55
Old Square Chambers, Bristol
p971 . . . . . 0117 930 5100
Old Square Chambers, London WC1
p945 . . . . . 020 7269 0300

BRITTON, Mr Byron Former Solicitor M *Oct 2008*
1, 8, 22, 51, 88, 89, 26, 93
Five Paper, London EC4
p946 . . . . . 020 7815 3200

Britton, Mr James I *Nov 1996*
2 King's Bench Walk, London EC4
p939 . . . . . 020 7353 1746

Britton, Mr Robert Recorder I *Jul 1973*
Goldsmith Chambers, London EC4
p935 . . . . . 020 7353 6802

Broach, Mr Steve MA(Hons)(Edin); DipLaw M *Jan 2008*
15, 22, 21, 23, 63, 70, 1, 51
Doughty Street Chambers, London WC1
p930 . . . . . 020 7404 1313

Broadbent, Mr Edmund J MA; LLB(Cantab) G *Jul 1980*
3, 11, 12, 24, 35, 41, 54
20 Essex Street, London WC2
p932 . . . . . 020 7842 1200

BROADFOOT, Ms Samatha M *Nov 1997*
Landmark Chambers, London EC4
p941 . . . . . 020 7430 1221

Broadhurst, Miss Katherine BA(Oxon) G *Jul 2003*
12, 15, 20, 30
9 Park Place, Cardiff
p973 . . . . . 029 2038 2731

Broadley, Mr John LLB(Hons) M *Jul 1973*
15, 25, 62
Cobden House Chambers, Manchester
p983 . . . . . 0161 833 6000

Broadstock, Mr Byron LLB G *Nov 2002*
15, 12
Temple Chambers, Newport
p988 . . . . . 01633 267403 / 255855
Temple Chambers, Cardiff
p973 . . . . . 029 2039 7364

BROATCH, Mr Michael Donald LLB; LLM(Lond) M *May 1971*
1, 18, 51, 26, 55, 36
Five Paper, London EC4
p946 . . . . . 020 7815 3200

BROCHWICZ-LEWINSKI, Mr Stefan LLB(Hons) G *Oct 1995*
5, 6, 8, 11, 18, 29, 40
9 St John Street Chambers, Manchester
p984 . . . . . 0161 955 9000

BROCK, Mr David J BHum M *Nov 1984*
12, 15, 18
Furnival Chambers, London EC4
p934 . . . . . 020 7405 3232

Brocklebank, Mr James M *Oct 1999*
3, 5, 35, 40, 24, 11
7 King's Bench Walk, London EC4
p940 . . . . . 020 7910 8300

Brockley, Mr Nigel BA(Hons); CPE L *Nov 1992*
1, 5, 8, 11, 12, 18, 22, 24, 30, 40, 53, 55
No5 Chambers, Bristol
p971 . . . . . 0845 210 5555
No5 Chambers, London EC4
p944 . . . . . 0845 210 5555
No5 Chambers, Birmingham
p968 . . . . . 0845 210 5555

BROCKMAN, Mr Christopher LLB M *Nov 1985*
6, 38, 97
Guildhall Chambers, Bristol
p970 . . . . . 0117 930 9000

BRODIE, Mr Bruce Chartered Arbitrator; CEDR Mediator I *May 1993*
3, 11, 12, 40, 41, 49, 50, 30, 24, 96, 56
Thirty Nine Essex Street, London WC2
p932 . . . . . 020 7832 1111

Brodie, Mr Graham LLB(Lond) M *Jul 1989*
11
33 Chancery Lane, London WC2
p928 . . . . . 020 7440 9950
Cloisters, London EC4
p928 . . . . . 020 7827 4000

Brodie, Mr Stanley E MA(Oxon) I *Feb 1954*
(Q.C.) *5, 11, 12, 24, 8, 29, 3, 41, 1, 50, 52, 51, 89*
Blackstone Chambers, London EC4
p926 . . . . . 020 7583 1770

Brody, Mr Saul Amos LLB(Leeds) I *Nov 1996*
15, 20, 30
18 St John Street Chambers, Manchester
p985 . . . . . 0161 278 1800

Brogden, Mr Peter LLB; BCL I *Jan 2008*
Keating Chambers, London WC2
p938 . . . . . 020 7544 2600

Bromilow, Mr Daniel BA(Cantab) G *Nov 1996*
8, 6, 37, 93, 88, 38
9 Stone Buildings Barristers Chambers, London WC2
p951 . . . . . 020 7404 5055

Bromley-Davenport, Mr John G *Feb 1972*
(Q.C.) *15*
3PB, London EC4
p946 . . . . . 020 7583 8055

Brompton, Mr Michael BA(Sussex) M *Nov 1973*
(Q.C.) *15, 62*
5 Paper Buildings, London EC4
p946 . . . . . 020 7583 6117

Brook, Mr Dale I *Jan 2003*
15 New Bridge Street Chambers, London EC4
p943 . . . . . 020 7842 1900

Brook, Mr David L BA(Hons)(Lond); DipLaw(City) I *Jul 1988*
18
Henderson Chambers, London EC4
p937 . . . . . 020 7583 9020

Brook, Mr Ian L *Jan 1983*
Park Court Chambers, Leeds
p978 . . . . . 0113 243 3277

BROOK, Mr Matthew G *Jan 1999*
15
Cornwall Street Chambers, Birmingham
p967 . . . . . 0121 233 7500

Brook Smith, Mr Philip Andrew BSc; MSc M *Jul 1982*
(Q.C.)
Fountain Court Chambers, London EC4
p934 . . . . . 020 7583 3335

Brooke, Mr David Michael Graham BA(Durham); DipLaw(City) I *Nov 1990*
15
11 King's Bench Walk, Leeds
p978 . . . . . 0113 297 1200

Brooke, Mr Johan L *Jan 1997*
30
Abbey Chambers, Shepperton
p992 . . . . . 01932 560913
Kew Chambers, Kew
p976 . . . . . 0844 809 9991

Brooke-Smith, Mr John LLB(Oxon); Recorder; Pupil Supervisor G *Jul 1981*
12, 30, 20, 35, 10
East Anglian Chambers, Norwich
p988 . . . . . 01603 617351
East Anglian Chambers, Colchester
p975 . . . . . 01206 572756
East Anglian Chambers, Chelmsford
p973 . . . . . 01245 215660
East Anglian Chambers, Ipswich
p976 . . . . . 01473 214481

BROOKES, Mr Christopher BA(Oxon) L *Jan 2010*
Pallant Chambers, Chichester
p974 . . . . . 01243 784538

Brookes, Mr Lincoln Paul BA(Hons)(Lond) I *Nov 1992*
10, 12, 15, 18, 20, 22, 30
Guildhall Chambers, Portsmouth
p990 . . . . . 023 9275 2400

Brookes-Baker, Mr Matthew LLB(Hons) L *Jul 1998*
12, 15, 20, 30
Northampton Chambers, Northampton
p988 . . . . . 01604 636271

Brooks, Miss Alison Louise LLB I *Jul 1989*
10, 12, 15, 20, 22, 25, 30, 32, 36, 37
Staple Inn Chambers, London WC1
p951 . . . . . 020 7242 5240

BROOKS, Mr Duncan LLB(Hons) G *Oct 2000*
20, 10, 12
Queen Elizabeth Buildings, London EC4
p948 . . . . . 020 7797 7837

Brooks, Mr John Dylan LLB; Fee Paid Judge First Tier Tax Chamber G *Feb 1990*
34, 57, 58, 37, 32, 31
Pendragon Chambers, Swansea
p993 . . . . . 01792 411188

Brooks, Mr Matthew I *Oct 2005*
Goldsmith Chambers, London EC4
p935 . . . . . 020 7353 6802

Brooks, Mr Peter LLB(L'pool) G *Jul 1986*
10, 20, 30, 36, 53
9 Park Place, Cardiff
p973 . . . . . 029 2038 2731

BROOME, Mr Edward BA(Oxon) I *Oct 1996*
30, 84, 40, 11, 56
Crown Office Chambers, London EC4
p929 . . . . . 020 7797 8100

Broomfield, Mr Tom MA; BA L *Jan 2007*
15
QEB Hollis Whiteman, London EC4
p948 . . . . . 020 7933 8855

BROTHERTON, Mr John BA(Hons) L *Jan 1994*
12, 15
Cornwall Street Chambers, Birmingham
p967 . . . . . 0121 233 7500

Brotherton, Mr Matthew L *Jan 1995*
Argent Chambers, London WC2
p923 . . . . . 020 7556 5500

Brough, Mr Alasdair MA(Cantab) G *Jul 1979*
30, 94, 56, 40
No5 Chambers, Bristol
p971 . . . . . 0845 210 5555
No5 Chambers, London EC4
p944 . . . . . 0845 210 5555
No5 Chambers, Birmingham
p968 . . . . . 0845 210 5555

BROUGHAM, Mr Christopher J BA(Oxon) I *Nov 1969*
(Q.C.) *5, 6, 11, 24, 29, 40, 38*
South Square, London WC1
p950 . . . . . 020 7696 9900

Broughton, Miss Kerrie I *Mar 2006*
20, 10
No 6 Barristers Chambers, Leeds
p978 . . . . . 0113 245 9763

Brown, Mr Alexander L *Jul 2009*
One Essex Court, London EC4
p931 . . . . . 020 7583 2000

See p1010 for the Key to Work Categories

Brown, Ms Althea L *Feb 1995*
1, 12, 15, 18, 22, 30, 51
Doughty Street Chambers, London WC1
p930 . . . . . 020 7404 1313

Brown, Miss Andrea LLB L *Nov 1991*
10, 12, 15, 18, 20, 22, 23, 25, 30, 36, 38
Staple Inn Chambers, London WC1
p951 . . . . . 020 7242 5240

BROWN, Miss Anne M *Jul 2000*
15, 62, 91
Pump Court Chambers, Swindon
p993 . . . . . 01793 539899
Pump Court Chambers, Winchester
p994 . . . . . 01962 868161
Pump Court Chambers, London EC4
p947 . . . . . 020 7353 0711

BROWN, Mr Anthony L *Nov 2010*
95, 94, 78, 76, 74, 53, 51, 46, 40, 36, 33, 31, 30, 26, 12, 11, 1, 63
Thirty Nine Essex Street, London WC2
p932 . . . . . 020 7832 1111

Brown, Miss Azza M *Jan 2000*
15
1 Paper Buildings, London EC4
p946 . . . . . 020 7353 3728

BROWN, Mr Cameron I *Oct 1998*
15
9-12 Bell Yard Chambers, London WC2
p926 . . . . . 020 7400 1800

Brown, Miss Catherine LLB I *Nov 1999*
12, 30, 53
Kings Chambers, Leeds
p978 . . . . . 0113 242 1123
Kings Chambers, Manchester
p984 . . . . . 0161 832 9082

BROWN, Ms Catherine M *Jan 2005*
Furnival Chambers, London EC4
p934 . . . . . 020 7405 3232
12 King's Bench Walk, London EC4
p940 . . . . . 020 7583 0811

Brown, Mr Chris I LLB(Hons) M *Jan 2001*
10, 12, 20, 22, 30
Broadway House Chambers, Leeds
p977 . . . . . 0113 246 2600
Broadway House Chambers, Bradford
p969 . . . . . 01274 722560

BROWN, Mr Christopher Martin LLB(Lond); LLM(Bruges) M *Nov 2002*
1, 11, 19, 43, 44, 56, 57, 51
Matrix Chambers, London WC1
p942 . . . . . 020 7404 3447

Brown, Miss Clare MA(Cantab); BCL(Oxon) M *Oct 1993*
12, 23, 27, 30, 51, 40
2 Temple Gardens, London EC4
p952 . . . . . 020 7822 1200

BROWN, Ms Daisy L *Nov 2006*
11, 93, 38, 5, 88
Guildhall Chambers, Bristol
p970 . . . . . 0117 930 9000

BROWN, Mr Damian I *Feb 1989*
18, 55, 56, 1
Littleton Chambers, London EC4
p941 . . . . . 020 7797 8600

Brown, Mr Edward G *Jul 1983*
(Q.C.) *15, 25, 36*
QEB Hollis Whiteman, London EC4
p948 . . . . . 020 7933 8855
Essex Court Chambers, London WC2
p931 . . . . . 020 7813 8000

Brown, Ms Emma I *Jan 2001*
30, 53, 27, 68, 94
No5 Chambers, Bristol
p971 . . . . . 0845 210 5555
No5 Chambers, London EC4
p944 . . . . . 0845 210 5555
No5 Chambers, Birmingham
p968 . . . . . 0845 210 5555

BROWN, Mr Geoffrey B I *Jul 1981*
30, 40, 24, 12, 11, 84
Thirty Nine Essex Street, London WC2
p932 . . . . . 020 7832 1111

BROWN, Mr George M *Jul 2002*
23, 1, 51
Kenworthy's Chambers, Manchester
p984 . . . . . 0161 832 4036

Brown, Ms Grace BA(Hons)(Lond); CPE(City) I *Oct 1995*
23
Tooks Chambers, London EC4
p953 . . . . . 020 7842 7575

Brown, Miss Hannah BA(Cantab) I *Oct 1992*
5, 11, 12, 24
One Essex Court, London EC4
p931 . . . . . 020 7583 2000

Brown, Mr James L *Nov 1990*
10, 12, 15, 20
Broad Chare Chambers, Newcastle upon Tyne
p986 . . . . . 0191 232 0541

Brown, Mr James Richard Charles L *Oct 1999*
15, 62
Atkinson Bevan Chambers, London EC4
p924 . . . . . 020 7353 2112

Brown, Ms Jillian BA(Hons)(Oxon) M *Nov 1991*
12, 18, 20, 22, 23, 30
Outer Temple Chambers, London WC2
p945 . . . . . 020 7353 6381

Brown, Miss Joanne LLB(Hons) I *Nov 1990*
20, 10
4 Paper Buildings, London EC4
p946 . . . . . 020 7583 0816

BROWN, John I *Jan 2005*
4 King's Bench Walk, London EC4
p939 . . . . . 020 7822 7000

Brown, Miss Kristina LLB(Hons) G *Oct 1998*
20, 10
No5 Chambers, Bristol
p971 . . . . . 0845 210 5555
No5 Chambers, London EC4
p944 . . . . . 0845 210 5555
No5 Chambers, Birmingham
p968 . . . . . 0845 210 5555
St Ives Chambers, Birmingham
p969 . . . . . 0121 236 0863

Brown, Mr Luke Henry William BA(Hons) M *Oct 2000*
18, 30, 40, 12
East Anglian Chambers, Norwich
p988 . . . . . 01603 617351
East Anglian Chambers, Colchester
p975 . . . . . 01206 572756
East Anglian Chambers, Chelmsford
p973 . . . . . 01245 215660
East Anglian Chambers, Ipswich
p976 . . . . . 01473 214481

BROWN, Mr Marc G *Jul 2004*
11, 38, 97, 67, 18
St Philips Chambers, Birmingham
p969 . . . . . 0121 246 7000
2 Pump Court, London EC4
p947 . . . . . 020 7353 5597

Brown, Ms Michelle LLB(Hons) I *Feb 1992*
12, 15, 20, 22
St Ives Chambers, Birmingham
p969 . . . . . 0121 236 0863

Brown, Ms Natalie G *Jan 2009*
97, 11, 47, 38, 40, 93, 37
Radcliffe Chambers, London WC2
p949 . . . . . 020 7831 0081

Brown, Mr Nicholas MA L *Jan 1989*
53, 51, 27, 30
Doughty Street Chambers, London WC1
p930 . . . . . 020 7404 1313

BROWN, Mr Nick L *Jul 2005*
20
St Philips Chambers, Birmingham
p969 . . . . . 0121 246 7000

BROWN, Mr Paul LLB(Hons); PhD(Cantab) I *Nov 1991*
(Q.C.) *1, 51, 11, 55, 18, 23, 26, 31*
4-5 Gray's Inn Square, London WC1
p935 . . . . . 020 7404 5252

Brown, Mr Phillip Steven LLB(Hons)(Leeds) L *Oct 1991*
8, 11, 29, 38, 37, 6, 93, 88
33 Bedford Row, London WC1
p925 . . . . . 020 7242 6476
9 Stone Buildings Barristers Chambers, London WC2
p951 . . . . . 020 7404 5055

Brown, Ms Rebecca BA; DipLaw I *Jul 1989*
20, 10
4 Paper Buildings, London EC4
p946 . . . . . 020 7583 0816

BROWN, Rebecca L *Jan 2007*
Fountain Chambers, Middlesbrough
p986 . . . . . 01642 804040

BROWN, Mr Robert L *Oct 2008*
Arden Chambers, London WC1
p923 . . . . . 020 7242 4244

BROWN, Mr Roger I *Nov 1976*
72, 71, 25, 56, 15
Kenworthy's Chambers, Manchester
p984 . . . . . 0161 832 4036

Brown, Mr Rory Steven MA; MRes; BVC; PhD I *Jan 2009*
8, 6, 88, 93, 37, 38
9 Stone Buildings Barristers Chambers, London WC2
p951 . . . . . 020 7404 5055

BROWN, Mr Roy LLB; Deputy District Judge (Magistrates) G *Jul 1983*
15
23 Essex Street, London WC2
p932 . . . . . 020 7413 0353

Brown, Mr Sam Clement I *Nov 2004*
15
Atkinson Bevan Chambers, London EC4
p924 . . . . . 020 7353 2112

BROWN, Mr Simon J G *Jan 1988*
12, 40, 18, 30, 47, 11
Crown Office Chambers, London EC4
p929 . . . . . 020 7797 8100

Brown, Miss Stephanie LLB(Exon) L *Jul 1982*
20
No5 Chambers, Bristol
p971 . . . . . 0845 210 5555
No5 Chambers, London EC4
p944 . . . . . 0845 210 5555
No5 Chambers, Birmingham
p968 . . . . . 0845 210 5555

Brown, Mr Stuart C I *Jul 1974*
(Q.C.) *30, 53, 63*
Paradise Chambers, Sheffield
p992 . . . . . 0114 273 8951

Brown, Miss Tamzin LLB(Hons)(B'ham) G *Oct 2003*
10, 20
Coram Chambers, London EC1
p929 . . . . . 020 7092 3700

Brown, Mr Thomas M *Nov 2000*
55, 18, 19, 1
Cloisters, London EC4
p928 . . . . . 020 7827 4000

Brown, Tim C E MA(Cantab) G *Nov 1980*
12, 15, 20, 51
Fenners Chambers, Cambridge
p972 . . . . . 01223 368761

Brown, Mr Timothy MA(Hons)(Edin) I *Mar 2005*
King's Bench Chambers, Oxford
p989 . . . . . 01865 311066
13 King's Bench Walk, London EC4
p940 . . . . . 020 7353 7204
Temple Tax Chambers, London EC4
p952 . . . . . 020 7353 7884 / 7353 8982

Brownbill, Mr David John LLB(Nott'm) G *Jul 1989*
(Q.C.) *8, 37, 38, 29, 49, 62, 32*
XXIV Old Buildings, London WC2
p944 . . . . . 020 7691 2424

Browne, Mr Benjamin James MA(Oxon) I *Jul 1976*
(Q.C.) *2, 11, 24, 27, 30, 36, 40*
2 Temple Gardens, London EC4
p952 . . . . . 020 7822 1200

Browne, Mr Desmond BA(Oxon) G *Nov 1969*
(Q.C.) *16, 13, 50, 51*
5RB, London WC1
p948 . . . . . 020 7242 2902

Browne, Gerald Robert MB; ChB I *Nov 1995*
20, 10
Zenith Chambers, Leeds
p979 . . . . . 0113 245 5438

Browne, Mr James William BA; MSt M *Oct 1994*
8, 22, 67, 88, 93
Lamb Chambers, London EC4
p941 . . . . . 020 7797 8300

Browne, Mr Louis LLB; BCL; Recorder L *Nov 1988*
8, 11, 22, 29, 30, 40, 53, 1, 51, 41, 7, 26, 27, 36
Exchange Chambers, Manchester
p983 . . . . . 0161 833 2722
Exchange Chambers, Liverpool
p980 . . . . . 0151 236 7747
Exchange Chambers, Leeds
p977 . . . . . 0113 203 1970

BROWNE, Mr Simon Peter Buchanan LLB M *Nov 1982*
(Q.C.)
Temple Garden Chambers, London EC4
p952 . . . . . 020 7583 1315

Browne-Wilkinson, Mr Simon BA(Oxon) L *Nov 1981*
(Q.C.)
Fountain Court Chambers, London EC4
p934 . . . . . 020 7583 3335

BROWNHILL, Miss Joanna G *Oct 1997*
22, 26
Five Paper, London EC4
p946 . . . . . 020 7815 3200

Bruce, Mr Andrew MA(Oxon) M *Oct 1992*
8, 22, 40, 11
Serle Court, London WC2
p950 . . . . . 020 7242 6105

Bruce, Mr David LLB(Hons) M *Jul 1982*
15, 12
St Johns Buildings, Preston
p990 . . . . . 01772 256100
St Johns Buildings, Chester
p974 . . . . . 01244 323070
St Johns Buildings, Manchester
p985 . . . . . 0161 214 1500
St Johns Buildings, Liverpool
p982 . . . . . 0151 243 6000

BRUCE, Ms Eleanor M *Jan 2008*
10, 12, 72, 18, 20, 91, 42, 30, 32, 36
Pump Court Chambers, Swindon
p993 . . . . . 01793 539899
Pump Court Chambers, Winchester
p994 . . . . . 01962 868161
Pump Court Chambers, London EC4
p947 . . . . . 020 7353 0711

BRUCE, Mr Lawrence LLB(Hons) L *Nov 2000*
15, 30
Fenners Chambers, Cambridge
p972 . . . . . 01223 368761

Bruce, Mr Richard Henderson LLB; LLM; FCIArb; Recorder G *Jul 1974*
Chambers of Richard Henderson Bruce, Richmond upon Thames
p991 . . . . . 020 8940 5895
Charter Chambers, London WC1
p928 . . . . . 020 7618 4400

BRUDENELL, Mr Thomas I *Nov 1977*
10, 12, 20
Queen Elizabeth Buildings, London EC4
p948 . . . . . 020 7797 7837

Brunner, Mr Adrian Recorder I *Jul 1968*
(Q.C.) *1, 7, 11, 12, 24, 26, 27, 28, 29, 30, 36, 40, 48*
Henderson Chambers, London EC4
p937 . . . . . 020 7583 9020

Brunner, Miss Kate MA(Hons); DipLaw(Edin, City) I *Oct 1997*
15, 62
Albion Chambers, Bristol
p970 . . . . . 0117 927 2144

Brunner, Mr Peter BA; LLB(Cantab) M *Jul 1971*
11, 24, 5, 35
Brick Court Chambers, London WC2
p927 . . . . . 020 7379 3550

Brunning, Mr Matthew M *Nov 1997*
30, 40, 53, 97, 68, 63
No5 Chambers, Bristol
p971 . . . . . 0845 210 5555
No5 Chambers, London EC4
p944 . . . . . 0845 210 5555
No5 Chambers, Birmingham
p968 . . . . . 0845 210 5555

BRUNSDON-TULLY, Mr Matthew L *Oct 2007*
1 Hare Court, London EC4
p936 . . . . . 020 7797 7070

Brunt, Mr Philip L *Nov 1991*
15, 12
No 8 Chambers, Birmingham
p968 . . . . . 0121 236 5514
4 Rowchester Court, Birmingham
p968 . . . . . 0121 233 2327

BRUNTON, Mr Sean M *Nov 1990*
15
Colleton Chambers, Exeter
p975 . . . . . 01392 274898

Bryan, Miss Carmel LLB(Hons) M *Nov 1993*
20, 10, 18
Rougemont Chambers, Exeter
p975 . . . . . 01392 208484

Bryan, Ms Deborah LLB L *Jul 1987*
10, 20
1 Pump Court, London EC4
p947 . . . . . 020 7842 7070

Bryan, Mr Rex MA(Oxon); Recorder L *Nov 1971*
15
East Anglian Chambers, Norwich
p988 . . . . . 01603 617351
East Anglian Chambers, Colchester
p975 . . . . . 01206 572756
East Anglian Chambers, Chelmsford
p973 . . . . . 01245 215660
East Anglian Chambers, Ipswich
p976 . . . . . 01473 214481

Bryan, Mr Robert M *Oct 1992*
15, 91
1 Paper Buildings, London EC4
p946 . . . . . 020 7353 3728

Bryan, Mr Simon J MA(Hons)(Cantab) L *Jul 1988*
(Q.C.)
Essex Court Chambers, London WC2
p931 . . . . . 020 7813 8000

Bryant, Ms Caroline LLB; Pupil Supervisor M *Jul 1976*
10, 12, 20, 25, 30, 15
East Anglian Chambers, Norwich
p988 . . . . . 01603 617351
East Anglian Chambers, Colchester
p975 . . . . . 01206 572756
East Anglian Chambers, Chelmsford
p973 . . . . . 01245 215660
East Anglian Chambers, Ipswich
p976 . . . . . 01473 214481

BRYANT, Ms Ceri MA; LLM(Cantab) L *Jul 1984*
11, 38, 97
Erskine Chambers, London WC2
p931 . . . . . 020 7242 5532

Bryant, Mr John Malcolm C MA(Cantab) I *Nov 1976*
11, 12, 22, 30, 40, 93
1 Chancery Lane, London WC2
p928 . . . . . 0845 634 6666

BRYANT, Miss Judith MA; LLM(Cantab) L *Jul 1987*
8, 9, 14, 32, 34, 37, 40
Wilberforce Chambers, London WC2
p953 . . . . . 020 7306 0102

Bryant, Mr Keith MA(Cantab); Dip Comp Sci(Cantab) M *Oct 1991*
1, 18, 26, 40, 55, 92
Outer Temple Chambers, London WC2
p945 . . . . . 020 7353 6381

BRYANT-HERON, Mr Mark MA(Cantab) M *Nov 1986*
15
9-12 Bell Yard Chambers, London WC2
p926 . . . . . 020 7400 1800

BRYDEN, Mr Christopher BA; LLM I *Jan 2003*
30, 20, 12, 18, 22, 55
4 King's Bench Walk, London EC4
p939 . . . . . 020 7822 7000

BRYNMOR THOMAS, Mr David MBChB(Edin) M *Jan 2011*
49, 41, 21, 96
Thirty Nine Essex Street, London WC2
p932 . . . . . 020 7832 1111

BRYSON, Mr Alan BA(Oxon) I *Feb 2004*
13, 45, 48, 49, 50, 52, 44
Wilberforce Chambers, London WC2
p953 . . . . . 020 7306 0102

Bubb, Mr Timothy G *Jul 1970*
12, 15, 25
39 Park Square, Leeds
p978 . . . . . 0113 245 6633

Buchan, Mr Andrew LLB G *Jul 1981*
1, 12, 18, 27, 29, 30, 36, 53, 55
Cloisters, London EC4
p928 . . . . . 020 7827 4000

Buchan, Mr Jonathan MA(Cantab) M *Oct 1994*
10, 20, 18
15 Winckley Square, Preston
p991 . . . . . 01772 252828

BUCHANAN, Mrs Vivien LLB I *Oct 1981*
10, 20, 12
St Mary's Chambers, Nottingham
p989 . . . . . 0115 950 3503

Buck, Mr John BA; MA G *Nov 1987*
6, 12, 20, 22, 30
Charter Chambers, London WC1
p928 . . . . . 020 7618 4400
Tanfield Chambers, London WC1
p951 . . . . . 020 7421 5300

BUCK, Mr William L *Jul 2001*
8, 11, 12, 47, 24, 29, 40, 35, 60
Chancery House Chambers, Leeds
p977 . . . . . 0113 244 6691

Buckett, Mr Edwin I *Jul 1988*
30, 93, 70
9 Gough Square, London EC4
p935 . . . . . 020 7832 0500

Buckhaven, Mr Simon G *Jul 1970*
20
Hardwicke, London WC2
p936 . . . . . 020 7242 2523

Buckingham, Mr Paul BSc M *Nov 1995*
3, 7, 24, 40, 61
Keating Chambers, London WC2
p938 . . . . . 020 7544 2600

Buckingham, Miss Sarah J LLB I *Oct 1991*
15, 62, 36, 94, 72
No5 Chambers, Bristol
p971 . . . . . 0845 210 5555
No5 Chambers, London EC4
p944 . . . . . 0845 210 5555
No5 Chambers, Birmingham
p968 . . . . . 0845 210 5555

Buckingham, Mr Stewart BA; BCL(Oxon) L *Oct 1996*
11, 35, 24, 5
Quadrant Chambers, London EC4
p948 . . . . . 020 7583 4444

BUCKLAND, Mr Matthew L *Jan 1998*
Carmelite Chambers, London EC4
p927 . . . . . 020 7936 6300

BUCKLE, Mr Colin M *Mar 2002*
15, 62, 63, 70
Kenworthy's Chambers, Manchester
p984 . . . . . 0161 832 4036

Buckle, Mr Jonathan BA; DipLaw L *Nov 1990*
10, 12, 18, 20, 22, 25, 30
Regency Chambers, Peterborough
p990 . . . . . 01733 315215

Buckley, Mr Christopher BA(Hons)(Cantab)(Law) L *Jul 2004*
6, 8, 11, 22, 29, 32, 40, 37
Radcliffe Chambers, London WC2
p949 . . . . . 020 7831 0081

Buckley, Miss Gerardine Maria BA(Kent) G *Nov 1991*
10, 20, 38
Stour Chambers, Canterbury
p972 . . . . . 01227 764899

Buckley, Mr Patrick James BA(Hons); G DipLaw G *Jul 1998*
15
St Johns Buildings, Preston
p990 . . . . . 01772 256100
St Johns Buildings, Chester
p974 . . . . . 01244 323070
St Johns Buildings, Manchester
p985 . . . . . 0161 214 1500
St Johns Buildings, Liverpool
p982 . . . . . 0151 243 6000

Buckley, Mr Peter Evered BA(Oxon) G *Jul 1972*
10, 15, 16, 20, 30
Cobden House Chambers, Manchester
p983 . . . . . 0161 833 6000

BUCKLEY, Prof Richard MA; D Phil(Oxon) I *Oct 1969*
New Square Chambers, London WC2
p943 . . . . . 020 7419 8000

Buckley, Miss Sophie M *Nov 1999*
York Chambers, York
p995 . . . . . 01904 620048
York Chambers, Newcastle upon Tyne
p987 . . . . . 0191 206 4677

Buckley-Clarke, Mrs Amanda BA(Oxon) L *Oct 1991*
15, 20, 30
3PB, Oxford
p989 . . . . . 01865 793736

Bucknall, Miss Belinda MA(Oxon) M *Nov 1974*
(Q.C.) *35, 24, 30, 11*
Quadrant Chambers, London EC4
p948 . . . . . 020 7583 4444

BUCKPITT, Mr Michael LLB G *Feb 1988*
88, 93
Tanfield Chambers, London WC1
p951 . . . . . 020 7421 5300

BUDDEN, Miss Caroline LLB(Bris) M *Jan 1977*
10, 20
1 King's Bench Walk, London EC4
p938 . . . . . 020 7936 1500

BUDDEN, Ms Rosemary BA L *Jan 2003*
20, 12, 10
Queen Elizabeth Buildings, London EC4
p948 . . . . . 020 7797 7837

Budworth, Mr Adam J D BA(Hons) I *Nov 1992*
15, 62
2 Bedford Row, London WC1
p924 . . . . . 020 7440 8888

Budworth, Mr Martin LLB(Hons) I *Nov 1999*
5, 8, 11, 18, 50, 24, 40, 48, 56
Kings Chambers, Leeds
p978 . . . . . 0113 242 1123
Kings Chambers, Manchester
p984 . . . . . 0161 832 9082

Buehrlen, Miss Veronique Eira MA; DipLaw M *Oct 1991*
(Q.C.)
Fountain Court Chambers, London EC4
p934 . . . . . 020 7583 3335

Bueno, Antonio M *Jun 1964*
(Q.C.) *5*
Clerksroom - Administration Centre, Taunton
p993 . . . . . 0845 083 3000

BUGEJA, Miss Evelyn LLB M *Oct 1997*
10, 20
Cornwall Street Chambers, Birmingham
p967 . . . . . 0121 233 7500

BUGG, Mr Ian Stephen LLB(Hons) M *Oct 1992*
20, 10
1 Garden Court, London EC4
p934 . . . . . 020 7797 7900

BULEY, Mr Tim L *Jul 2000*
Landmark Chambers, London EC4
p941 . . . . . 020 7430 1221

BULL, Mr Gregory I *Jul 1976*
(Q.C.)
Lombard Chambers, London EC1
p941 . . . . . 020 7107 2100

Bull, Ms Nathalie I *Jul 2004*
New Walk Chambers, Leicester
p979 . . . . . 0871 200 1298

BULL, Mr Roger D LLB M *Jul 1974*
20
Five Paper, London EC4
p946 . . . . . 020 7815 3200

Bullen, Ms Mary BA(Hons); PGDL I *Mar 2005*
53, 12, 15, 51, 30, 40, 20
Guildhall Chambers, Portsmouth
p990 . . . . . 023 9275 2400

Bullock, Mr Ian LLB(Bris) I *Nov 1975*
12, 30, 53
St John's Chambers, Bristol
p972 . . . . . 0117 921 3456

Bullock, Mr Neil BA(Hons) M *Nov 1989*
10, 20
Coram Chambers, London EC1
p929 . . . . . 020 7092 3700

BUNBURY, Ms Claire M *Jan 2006*
St James's Chambers, Manchester
p984 . . . . . 0161 834 7000

BUNDELL, Ms Katharine Michelle BA(Hons)(Cantab) M *Oct 1991*
10, 20
Octagon House, Norwich
p988 . . . . . 01603 623186

BUNDRED, Ms Gillian S LLB(Hons) G *Jul 1982*
10, 20
Oriel Chambers, Liverpool
p981 . . . . . 0151 236 7191 / 236 4321
Oriel Chambers, Preston
p990 . . . . . 01772 254764

Bunting, Mr Jude G *Jul 2006*
1, 70, 18, 51
Tooks Chambers, London EC4
p953 . . . . . 020 7842 7575

Bunyan, Mr Angus Guy BA; MA L *Oct 1999*
15, 62, 36
2 Hare Court, London EC4
p937 . . . . . 020 7353 5324

BURDEN, Mr Angus BA(Hons)(Exon) L *Oct 1994*
11, 37, 88, 93
St Philips Chambers, Birmingham
p969 . . . . . 0121 246 7000

BURDIN, Mr Christopher M *Jan 2010*
5, 81, 24, 47, 40, 38, 97, 62, 41
3 Verulam Buildings, London WC1
p953 . . . . . 020 7831 8441

Burdis-Smith, Mr Alan BSc; DipLaw I *Jan 1998*
15, 6, 42
Abbey Chambers, Shepperton
p992 . . . . . 01932 560913

Burdon, Mr Michael Stewart LLB(Hons)(Leeds) L *Nov 1993*
20, 10
37 Park Square Chambers, Leeds
p978 . . . . . 0113 243 9422

BURGE, Miss Alison Jayne LLM; LLB(Hons) G *Jul 2002*
12, 18, 22, 30
Pump Court Chambers, Swindon
p993 . . . . . 01793 539899
Pump Court Chambers, Winchester
p994 . . . . . 01962 868161
Pump Court Chambers, London EC4
p947 . . . . . 020 7353 0711

Burge, Mr Edmund BA L *Oct 1997*
15
5 St Andrew's Hill, London EC4
p950 . . . . . 020 7332 5400

Burgess, Mr David Clifford LLB(Hons) L *Jan 1975*
15, 51, 62
Nine Bedford Row, London WC1
p924 . . . . . 020 7489 2727

Burgess, Mr Edward MA(Oxon) I *Nov 1993*
72, 15, 70
Albion Chambers, Bristol
p970 . . . . . 0117 927 2144

Burgess, Dr Jenny Claire M *Jul 2008*
15
Atkinson Bevan Chambers, London EC4
p924 . . . . . 020 7353 2112

Burgess, Mr Roy A LLB; M Phil L *Nov 1970*
5, 11, 15, 29, 30, 40, 53
2 South Avenue, Thornton Cleveleys
p993 . . . . . 01253 825463

Burgher, Mr Benjamin LLB(Hons) G *Nov 1995*
11, 12, 16, 18, 21, 55
Outer Temple Chambers, London WC2
p945 . . . . . 020 7353 6381

BURKE, Mr Brendan MA(Cantab); DipLaw I *Oct 1995*
12, 15, 18, 20, 22, 24, 30, 40
7 Harrington Street Chambers, Liverpool
p981 . . . . . 0151 242 0707

Burke, Mr Michael LLB(L'pool) G *Nov 1985*
15
33 Bedford Row, London WC1
p925 . . . . . 020 7242 6476

BURKE, Miss Patricia LLB(Newc) G *Oct 1990*
10, 12, 15, 20, 30
Fountain Chambers, Middlesbrough
p986 . . . . . 01642 804040

BURKILL, Mr Guy Alexander MA(Cantab) M *Feb 1981*
(Q.C.) *13, 3, 44, 45*
3 New Square, London WC2
p943 . . . . . 020 7405 1111

Burkitt, Mr Daniel MPhil(Law)(Oxon) G *Jan 2008*
13 Old Square Chambers, London WC2
p945 . . . . . 020 7831 4445

BURLES, Mr David LLB(Bris) M *Nov 1985*
20, 10
1 Garden Court, London EC4
p934 . . . . . 020 7797 7900

Burne, Miss Anna BA(Cantab) M *Oct 2002*
12, 22, 24, 30
Henderson Chambers, London EC4
p937 . . . . . 020 7583 9020

Burnell, Miss Kate LLB(Hons) M *Oct 1998*
20, 12, 15
St Johns Buildings, Preston
p990 . . . . . 01772 256100
St Johns Buildings, Chester
p974 . . . . . 01244 323070
St Johns Buildings, Manchester
p985 . . . . . 0161 214 1500
St Johns Buildings, Liverpool
p982 . . . . . 0151 243 6000

BURNETT, Mr Iain LLB L *Oct 1993*
23, 15, 25
4 King's Bench Walk, London EC4
p939 . . . . . 020 7822 7000

Burnham, Ms Ulele BA(Hons); MPhil(Cantab) I *Feb 1997*
51, 1, 18, 33
Doughty Street Chambers, London WC1
p930 . . . . . 020 7404 1313

See p1010 for the Key to Work Categories

Burns, Mr Alexander Laurence LLB I *Jul 1988*
15
New Court Chambers, Newcastle upon Tyne
p987 . . . . . 0191 232 1980

Burns, Mr Andrew BA(Cantab) M *Oct 1993*
1, 11, 12, 18, 36, 24, 26, 27, 40, 55
Devereux Chambers, London WC2
p930 . . . . . 020 7353 7534

BURNS, Mr Francis J G *May 1971*
10, 20
Kenworthy's Chambers, Manchester
p984 . . . . . 0161 832 4036

Burns, Mr Jeremy Stuart BA; LLB; LLM(Cantab); Former Solicitor; Deputy Employment Judge L *Nov 1996*
8, 12, 22, 31, 40, 18, 93
12 College Place, Southampton
p992 . . . . . 023 8032 0320

BURNS, Ms Judith LLB(Hons) M *Jan 2001*
30, 12, 11, 96, 18, 62
Oriel Chambers, Liverpool
p981 . . . . . 0151 236 7191 / 236 4321
Oriel Chambers, Preston
p990 . . . . . 01772 254764

Burns, Mr Paul LLB(L'pool) L *Oct 1998*
30, 12, 22, 26, 1, 88, 51
Exchange Chambers, Manchester
p983 . . . . . 0161 833 2722
Exchange Chambers, Liverpool
p980 . . . . . 0151 236 7747
Exchange Chambers, Leeds
p977 . . . . . 0113 203 1970

BURNS, Mr Peter R BA(Oxon) G *Oct 1993*
Byrom Street Chambers, Manchester
p983 . . . . . 0161 829 2100

BURNS, Mr Richard Recorder M *Nov 1967*
30, 40, 53, 2, 18
Ropewalk Chambers, Nottingham
p989 . . . . . 0115 947 2581

Burns, Miss Rosemary I *Nov 1978*
15, 12, 30, 20
4 Breams Buildings, London EC4
p927 . . . . . 020 7092 1900

Burns, Mr Simon H LLB M *Oct 1992*
15, 62
Albion Chambers, Bristol
p970 . . . . . 0117 927 2144

Burr, Mr Andrew MA(Cantab); ACIArb I *Nov 1981*
3, 7, 11, 31, 40, 41, 43, 45, 49, 54, 61, 78, 74
Atkin Chambers, London WC1
p923 . . . . . 020 7404 0102

Burrett, Mr Alex I *Aug 1999*
1 Gray's Inn Square, London WC1
p935 . . . . . 020 7405 8946

Burrett, Mrs Catherine LLB(Lond) M *Oct 1992*
20, 10, 63
12 College Place, Southampton
p992 . . . . . 023 8032 0320

Burrington, Mr Richard J H BA(Hons)(Soton) I *Nov 1993*
15
2 Pump Court, London EC4
p947 . . . . . 020 7353 5597

Burroughs, Mr Nigel BA(Lond) M *Apr 1991*
6, 8, 9, 11, 29
Four New Square, London WC2
p943 . . . . . 020 7822 2000

Burrows, Mr Andrew MA(Oxon) M *Apr 1985*
(Q.C.)
Fountain Court Chambers, London EC4
p934 . . . . . 020 7583 3335

Burrows, Mr Michael BA; Recorder I *Nov 1979*
(Q.C.) *15, 62, 84, 95, 70, 72*
No5 Chambers, Bristol
p971 . . . . . 0845 210 5555
No5 Chambers, London EC4
p944 . . . . . 0845 210 5555
No5 Chambers, Birmingham
p968 . . . . . 0845 210 5555

Burrows, Mr Ross L *Jan 2009*
2 Pump Court, London EC4
p947 . . . . . 020 7353 5597

Burrows, Mr Simon BA(Durham) I *Nov 1990*
18, 30, 63
Kings Chambers, Leeds
p978 . . . . . 0113 242 1123
Kings Chambers, Manchester
p984 . . . . . 0161 832 9082

BURSLEM, Miss Sarah LLB(Hons); BCL; BVC G *Oct 2008*
6, 8, 11, 46, 38, 88, 93
Enterprise Chambers, London WC2
p931 . . . . . 020 7405 9471
Enterprise Chambers, Leeds
p977 . . . . . 0113 246 0391
Enterprise Chambers, Newcastle upon Tyne
p987 . . . . . 0191 222 3344

Burt, Ms Joanna LLB G *Oct 1998*
Field Court Chambers, London WC1
p933 . . . . . 020 7405 6114
Maidstone Chambers, Maidstone
p982 . . . . . 01622 688592

BURTON, Mr Charles I *Nov 1983*
15
9-12 Bell Yard Chambers, London WC2
p926 . . . . . 020 7400 1800

BURTON, Mrs Frances LLB(Lond); LLM(Leics) I *Nov 1972*
18, 20
Ten Old Square, London WC2
p945 . . . . . 020 7405 0758

BURTON, Mr Frank BA(Kent); PhD(LSE); Recorder G *Jul 1982*
(Q.C.) *12, 24, 53, 30, 40*
12 King's Bench Walk, London EC4
p940 . . . . . 020 7583 0811

BURTON, Mr James G *Oct 2001*
1, 12, 18, 51, 26, 30, 55, 31, 46
Thirty Nine Essex Street, London WC2
p932 . . . . . 020 7832 1111

Burton, Mr Jamie LLB(Hons)(Euro) I *Jan 1999*
1, 22, 51, 18
Doughty Street Chambers, London WC1
p930 . . . . . 020 7404 1313

Burton, Mr John Malcolm LLB(Hons) I *Jul 1979*
(Q.C.) *15, 62, 70, 95*
15 New Bridge Street Chambers, London EC4
p943 . . . . . 020 7842 1900

Burton, Mr Paul L *Oct 1998*
11, 37, 6, 38, 93, 97
3 Stone Buildings, London WC2
p951 . . . . . 020 7242 4937

BURY, Mr Mark LLB; Recorder I *Jul 1986*
15
Wilberforce Chambers, Hull
p976 . . . . . 01482 323264

Busby, Mr Thomas Andrew LLB(Hons) L *Jul 1975*
15
Foregate Chambers, Kidderminster
p976 . . . . . 07760 766152

BUSCH, Ms Lisa BA; LLB; BPhil I *Sep 2000*
1, 26, 11, 12, 51, 31, 18, 19
4-5 Gray's Inn Square, London WC1
p935 . . . . . 020 7404 5252

BUSH, Miss Hannah M *Jan 2007*
15, 20
St Philips Chambers, Birmingham
p969 . . . . . 0121 246 7000

BUSS, Mr Simon L *Jan 2007*
12, 30, 11, 40, 53, 22, 29
Ropewalk Chambers, Nottingham
p989 . . . . . 0115 947 2581

Bussey-Jones, Miss Elisabeth I *Oct 1997*
2 King's Bench Walk, London EC4
p939 . . . . . 020 7353 1746

Busuttil, Mr Godwin MA; M Phil(Cantab) L *Oct 1994*
13, 16, 36, 50, 51, 56
5RB, London WC1
p948 . . . . . 020 7242 2902

Buswell, Mr Richard LLB M *Jul 1985*
49, 20, 40, 37
Hardwicke, London WC2
p936 . . . . . 020 7242 2523

Butcher, Mr Anthony J MA(Cantab); LLB G *Jan 1947*
(Q.C.) *3, 7, 11, 31, 40, 41, 43, 45, 49, 54, 61, 78, 74*
Atkin Chambers, London WC1
p923 . . . . . 020 7404 0102

Butcher, Mr Christopher John MA(Oxon) G *Jul 1986*
(Q.C.) *3, 35, 19, 33, 24, 1, 5, 11*
7 King's Bench Walk, London EC4
p940 . . . . . 020 7910 8300

Butcher, Ms Helen BA(Hons)(Oxon) M *Nov 1999*
15
1 Pump Court, London EC4
p947 . . . . . 020 7842 7070

Butcher, Mr Richard LLB(Cardiff) G *Nov 1985*
15
Lincoln House Chambers, Manchester
p984 . . . . . 0161 832 5701
Lombard Chambers, London EC1
p941 . . . . . 020 7107 2100

Butcher, Mr Russell Henry BA(Hons); DipLaw M *Oct 1992*
15, 30, 22, 18, 11, 6, 8, 12, 47, 62, 35, 36
East Anglian Chambers, Norwich
p988 . . . . . 01603 617351
East Anglian Chambers, Colchester
p975 . . . . . 01206 572756
East Anglian Chambers, Chelmsford
p973 . . . . . 01245 215660
East Anglian Chambers, Ipswich
p976 . . . . . 01473 214481

BUTLER, Mr Adam L *Jan 1997*
15, 62, 95
187 Fleet Street, London EC4
p933 . . . . . 020 7430 7430

BUTLER, Mr Andrew MA(Oxon) M *Nov 1993*
22, 18, 47, 8
Tanfield Chambers, London WC1
p951 . . . . . 020 7421 5300

Butler, Mr George MA(Hons) I *May 2003*
10, 20, 77, 15
4 Brick Court Chambers, London EC4
p927 . . . . . 020 7832 3200

BUTLER, Miss Judith BA(Hons)(History) I *Oct 1993*
10, 20
29 Bedford Row, London WC1
p925 . . . . . 020 7404 1044

Butler, Miss Magueda L *Jul 1966*
Chancery Chambers, London WC2
p928 . . . . . 020 7405 6879

Butler, Ms Marianne Jane BA(Hons)(Oxon); DipLaw(BPP) L *Jul 2003*
Fountain Court Chambers, London EC4
p934 . . . . . 020 7583 3335

BUTLER, Miss Michelle BA; LLB(Hons)(Queensland); LLM(Cantab) I *Jun 2007*
1, 3, 71, 70, 95, 33, 21, 23
Matrix Chambers, London WC1
p942 . . . . . 020 7404 3447

Butler, Mr Oliver I *Oct 2010*
One Essex Court, London EC4
p931 . . . . . 020 7583 2000

BUTLER, Mr Rupert James LLB(Republic of Ireland; Barrister 1998) M *Jul 1988*
6, 11, 12, 18, 20, 22, 30, 59
3 Hare Court, London EC4
p937 . . . . . 020 7415 7800

Butler, Mr Simon I *Jan 1996*
30, 53, 26, 22, 31
Ely Place Chambers, London EC1
p931 . . . . . 020 7400 9600

BUTLER-COLE, Miss Victoria MA M *Jul 2005*
1, 18, 53, 30, 63, 85, 14
Thirty Nine Essex Street, London WC2
p932 . . . . . 020 7832 1111

Butlers, Mr Jonathan BA(Hons) M *Jan 2003*
30, 53
Devereux Chambers, London WC2
p930 . . . . . 020 7353 7534

BUTT, Mr Michael LLB(Lond) M *Nov 1974*
15, 31, 42, 91
Pump Court Chambers, Swindon
p993 . . . . . 01793 539899
Pump Court Chambers, Winchester
p994 . . . . . 01962 868161
Pump Court Chambers, London EC4
p947 . . . . . 020 7353 0711

Butt, Miss Nasra LLB(Hons) G *Oct 2002*
10, 20, 15, 72
5 St Andrew's Hill, London EC4
p950 . . . . . 020 7332 5400
St Pauls Chambers, Leeds
p979 . . . . . 0113 245 5866

Butt, Miss Nassera M *Jul 1999*
10, 20
No5 Chambers, Bristol
p971 . . . . . 0845 210 5555
No5 Chambers, London EC4
p944 . . . . . 0845 210 5555
No5 Chambers, Birmingham
p968 . . . . . 0845 210 5555

BUTTERFIELD, Mr Christopher LLM; MA(Cantab) M *Nov 2004*
20, 10
29 Bedford Row, London WC1
p925 . . . . . 020 7404 1044

Butterfield, Mr John Arthur LLB L *Oct 1995*
15, 62, 36, 84, 89, 82, 68
No5 Chambers, Bristol
p971 . . . . . 0845 210 5555
No5 Chambers, London EC4
p944 . . . . . 0845 210 5555
No5 Chambers, Birmingham
p968 . . . . . 0845 210 5555

Butterfield, Ms Kay G *Jan 1980*
20
Queen Square Chambers, Bristol
p972 . . . . . 0117 921 1966

Butters, Mr Richard J LLB(Hons) M *Oct 2001*
15, 62
37 Park Square Chambers, Leeds
p978 . . . . . 0113 243 9422

BUTTERWORTH, Mr Martin Frank L *Jul 1985*
15, 51
Citadel Chambers, Birmingham
p967 . . . . . 0121 233 8500

BUTTERWORTH, Mr Paul M *Jul 1982*
8, 10, 12, 22, 20, 18
Octagon House, Norwich
p988 . . . . . 01603 623186

Buttimore, Mr Gabriel G *Feb 1993*
29
King's Bench Chambers, Oxford
p989 . . . . . 01865 311066
13 King's Bench Walk, London EC4
p940 . . . . . 020 7353 7204

BUTTLER, Mr Christopher I *Jan 2004*
1, 63, 31, 20
4-5 Gray's Inn Square, London WC1
p935 . . . . . 020 7404 5252

BUTTON, Mr Richard James LLB(Hons) G *Oct 1993*
12, 15
Carmelite Chambers, London EC4
p927 . . . . . 020 7936 6300

BUXTON, Sarah Ruth LLB(Hons) I *Jul 1988*
20, 10
St Philips Chambers, Birmingham
p969 . . . . . 0121 246 7000

Buxton, Mr Thomas LLB G *Jul 1983*
15, 20, 10, 12, 30
Charter Chambers, London WC1
p928 . . . . . 020 7618 4400

Byam-Cook, Mr Henry BA I *Jan 2000*
41, 3, 5, 11, 43, 47, 49, 24, 54, 35, 61, 45
20 Essex Street, London WC2
p932 . . . . . 020 7842 1200

BYASS, Mr Andrew LLB; LLM L *Jan 2010*
Landmark Chambers, London EC4
p941 . . . . . 020 7430 1221

Byles, Mr Andrew BVC; PgDL L *Jan 2003*
15, 55, 18, 22, 51, 88, 30, 96
Garden Court North Chambers, Manchester
p983 . . . . . 0161 236 1840

BYRNE, Mr Garrett Thomas LLM G *Nov 1986*
11, 36, 46
4-5 Gray's Inn Square, London WC1
p935 . . . . . 020 7404 5252

BYRNE, Mr James MA(Oxon) G *Jul 1983*
12, 30, 40, 21
7 Harrington Street Chambers, Liverpool
p981 . . . . . 0151 242 0707
Queen Square Chambers, Bristol
p972 . . . . . 0117 921 1966

BYRNE, Mr William G *Jan 2006*
15, 30, 12, 94
Trinity (Newcastle) Chambers, Newcastle upon Tyne
p987 . . . . . 0191 232 1927
Trinity (Teesside) Chambers, Middlesbrough
p986 . . . . . 01642 247569

BYRNES, Ms Aisling G *May 1994*
15
25 Bedford Row, London WC1
p925 . . . . . 020 7067 1500

Cabeza, Miss Ruth M *Mar 1998*
Field Court Chambers, London WC1
p933 . . . . . 020 7405 6114

13

CADBURY, Miss Justine M *Jan 2001*
20, 12, 10
Queen Elizabeth Buildings, London EC4
p948 . . . . . 020 7797 7837

Caddick, Mr Nicholas MA; BCL(Oxon); Junior Counsel to the Crown M *Nov 1986*
5, 6, 8, 11, 13, 22, 29, 32, 37, 38
Hogarth Chambers, London WC2
p937 . . . . . 020 7404 0404

CADE, Mrs Diana LLB(Hons); LLM I *Nov 1994*
10, 20, 41, 89, 26
Trinity Chambers, Chelmsford
p974 . . . . . 01245 605040

CADE DAVIES, Miss Lynsey I *Jul 2005*
10, 20
29 Bedford Row, London WC1
p925 . . . . . 020 7404 1044

Cadman, Mr David J BA(Dunelm) L *Nov 1996*
Goldsmith Chambers, London EC4
p935 . . . . . 020 7353 6802

CADWALADR, Mr Stephen LLB M *Nov 1992*
15, 46, 48, 31
Cornwall Street Chambers, Birmingham
p967 . . . . . 0121 233 7500

Cadwallader, Mr Neil MA(Cantab); DipLaw; Chancery Recorder 2009 I *Jul 1984*
49, 41, 97, 8, 11, 88, 89, 96, 29, 40, 93
Exchange Chambers, Manchester
p983 . . . . . 0161 833 2722
Exchange Chambers, Liverpool
p980 . . . . . 0151 236 7747
Exchange Chambers, Leeds
p977 . . . . . 0113 203 1970

CADWALLADER, Mr Peter LLB(Cantab) G *Jul 1973*
12, 15
9 St John Street Chambers, Manchester
p984 . . . . . 0161 955 9000

CAFFERKEY, Ms Annette M LLB(Hons) I *Nov 1994*
8, 12, 22, 6
Arden Chambers, London WC1
p923 . . . . . 020 7242 4244

Cahill, Mr Jeremy M *Jul 1975*
(Q.C.) *31, 46, 54, 43, 60, 61, 78*
No5 Chambers, Bristol
p971 . . . . . 0845 210 5555
No5 Chambers, London EC4
p944 . . . . . 0845 210 5555
No5 Chambers, Birmingham
p968 . . . . . 0845 210 5555

CAINS, Miss Linda H BA M *Oct 1990*
10, 14, 20
37 Park Square Chambers, Leeds
p978 . . . . . 0113 243 9422

Cairnes, Mr Paul G *Oct 1980*
8, 11, 30, 31, 96, 1, 49, 2, 89, 26, 32, 40, 93, 37, 46, 51, 67, 25
No5 Chambers, Bristol
p971 . . . . . 0845 210 5555
No5 Chambers, London EC4
p944 . . . . . 0845 210 5555
No5 Chambers, Birmingham
p968 . . . . . 0845 210 5555

CAIRNS, Mrs Sally G *Jul 2006*
15, 10, 20
No 8 Chambers, Birmingham
p968 . . . . . 0121 236 5514

Cala, Mr Giuseppe I *Jan 1971*
New Court Chambers, London EC4
p943 . . . . . 020 7583 5123

CALDECOTT, Mr Andrew H BA(Oxon) I *Jul 1975*
(Q.C.) *16, 52, 73*
One Brick Court, London EC4
p927 . . . . . 020 7353 8845

CALDER, Lynette L *Jan 2003*
Maidstone Chambers, Maidstone
p982 . . . . . 01622 688592

CALDWELL, Mr Andrew M *Jan 1984*
70, 15, 25, 12
Mitre House Chambers, London WC1
p942 . . . . . 020 7307 7100

CALHAEM, Mr Simon MA; DipLaw L *Jan 1999*
20
29 Bedford Row, London WC1
p925 . . . . . 020 7404 1044

Callaghan, Ms Catherine BA; LLB(Hons)(Vuw); LLM(Cantab) I *Sep 1999*
1, 18, 81, 51, 5, 56, 76, 89
Blackstone Chambers, London EC4
p926 . . . . . 020 7583 1770

Callaghan, Ms Elizabeth L *Jul 1998*
York Chambers, York
p995 . . . . . 01904 620048
York Chambers, Newcastle upon Tyne
p987 . . . . . 0191 206 4677

CALLAN, Mr David MA M *Jul 1979*
15, 30, 53, 1
Trinity (Newcastle) Chambers, Newcastle upon Tyne
p987 . . . . . 0191 232 1927
Trinity (Teesside) Chambers, Middlesbrough
p986 . . . . . 01642 247569

CALLAN, Mrs Jane M *Jan 1995*
18, 1
Trinity (Newcastle) Chambers, Newcastle upon Tyne
p987 . . . . . 0191 232 1927
Trinity (Teesside) Chambers, Middlesbrough
p986 . . . . . 01642 247569

CALLAND, Mr Timothy BA(Lond) L *Nov 1999*
6, 8, 11, 22, 40, 38, 88, 97
Enterprise Chambers, London WC2
p931 . . . . . 020 7405 9471
Enterprise Chambers, Leeds
p977 . . . . . 0113 246 0391
Enterprise Chambers, Newcastle upon Tyne
p987 . . . . . 0191 222 3344

Callery, Mr Martin LLB(Hons) M *Mar 1997*
15, 62, 94
Cobden House Chambers, Manchester
p983 . . . . . 0161 833 6000

Callinan, Ms Clodaghmuire M *Jan 2007*
15 New Bridge Street Chambers, London EC4
p943 . . . . . 020 7842 1900

CALLMAN, Mr Jeremy MA(Cantab) M *Oct 1991*
1, 5, 6, 7, 8, 9, 11, 14, 19, 22, 24, 29, 32, 34, 37
Ten Old Square, London WC2
p945 . . . . . 020 7405 0758

CALLOW, Mr David LLB(Cardiff); Deputy District Judge M *Nov 1998*
30, 18, 26
12 King's Bench Walk, London EC4
p940 . . . . . 020 7583 0811

Calver, Mr Neil Richard MA(Cantab) G *Nov 1987*
11, 24, 1, 19, 56, 41
Brick Court Chambers, London WC2
p927 . . . . . 020 7379 3550

Calvert, Ms Barbara L *Jan 1997*
1 Pump Court, London EC4
p947 . . . . . 020 7842 7070

Calvert, Mr Charles BA M *Jul 1975*
11, 31
Hardwicke, London WC2
p936 . . . . . 020 7242 2523

CALVERT, Mr David BA I *Nov 1995*
12, 30, 18, 47, 53
St James's Chambers, Manchester
p984 . . . . . 0161 834 7000

CALWAY, Mark I *Feb 1989*
10, 20
Renaissance Chambers, London WC1
p949 . . . . . 020 7404 1111

Cameron, Mr Gillon BA L *Jan 2002*
14 Gray's Inn Square, London WC1
p936 . . . . . 020 7242 0858

CAMERON, Mr Neil A LLB; Recorder G *Jul 1984*
31, 26, 18, 88
Wilberforce Chambers, Hull
p976 . . . . . 01482 323264

CAMERON, Mr Neil St Clair BA(Dunelm) G *Jul 1982*
(Q.C.) *31, 36, 46*
Landmark Chambers, London EC4
p941 . . . . . 020 7430 1221

Cameron, Mr Robert LLB(Durham); BA(Cantab) L *Mar 2003*
42 Bedford Row, London WC1
p925 . . . . . 020 7831 0222

Cameron, Ms Viveca Cecile M *Feb 1987*
15, 20
Belmarsh Chambers, London SE18
p926 . . . . . 020 8316 7322

Cameron-Mowatt, Mrs Rosalind MA(York); DipLaw M *Jul 2000*
15, 12, 30
Unity Street Chambers, Bristol
p972 . . . . . 0117 906 9789

Cammegh, Mr John LLB(Hons) I *Nov 1987*
15, 51
Nine Bedford Row, London WC1
p924 . . . . . 020 7489 2727

CAMMERMAN, Mr Gideon M *Nov 1996*
15, 62, 95
187 Fleet Street, London EC4
p933 . . . . . 020 7430 7430

Camp, Mr Christopher I *Jan 1996*
49, 11, 74, 18, 24, 40
Hardwicke, London WC2
p936 . . . . . 020 7242 2523

Campbell, Mr Alasdair LLB L *Jan 1999*
70, 62, 48, 68, 84, 36, 72
St Pauls Chambers, Leeds
p979 . . . . . 0113 245 5866

Campbell, Mr Alexander G *Jul 2010*
14, 76, 1, 18, 40, 30, 94
Hardwicke, London WC2
p936 . . . . . 020 7242 2523

CAMPBELL, Miss Alexis LLB(Leeds) I *Nov 1990*
20, 10
29 Bedford Row, London WC1
p925 . . . . . 020 7404 1044

Campbell, Andrew Recorder M *Nov 1972*
(Q.C.) *15, 62, 70, 72*
Zenith Chambers, Leeds
p979 . . . . . 0113 245 5438

Campbell, Mr Benjamin MA(Hons) M *Jan 2008*
Park Court Chambers, Leeds
p978 . . . . . 0113 243 3277

Campbell, Miss Bernice M *Jan 2004*
15
New Bailey Chambers, Preston
p990 . . . . . 01772 258087

Campbell, Mr Colin W BA(Kent) G *Jul 1979*
15
1 Gray's Inn Square, London WC1
p935 . . . . . 020 7405 8946

Campbell, Ms Diane G *Nov 1995*
York Chambers, York
p995 . . . . . 01904 620048
York Chambers, Newcastle upon Tyne
p987 . . . . . 0191 206 4677

CAMPBELL, Mr Douglas James MA(Oxon); DipLaw; Recorder I *Oct 1993*
13, 45, 48
3 New Square, London WC2
p943 . . . . . 020 7405 1111

Campbell, Miss Eleanor L *Jan 2005*
One Essex Court, London EC4
p931 . . . . . 020 7583 2000

CAMPBELL, Miss Emily BA; BCL(Oxon) L *Nov 1995*
8, 9, 32, 34, 37
Wilberforce Chambers, London WC2
p953 . . . . . 020 7306 0102

Campbell, Miss Gillian G *Jan 2002*
3PB, Winchester
p994 . . . . . 01962 868884

Campbell, Mr Glenn L *Jul 1985*
40, 11, 24
Hailsham Chambers, London EC4
p936 . . . . . 020 7643 5000

Campbell, Mr Graham G *Jul 1979*
20, 10, 8, 12, 18, 22, 30
Westgate Chambers, Lewes
p980 . . . . . 01273 480510

CAMPBELL, Mr John LLM(Lond) G *Jun 2009*
(Q.C.) *1, 44, 52*
4-5 Gray's Inn Square, London WC1
p935 . . . . . 020 7404 5252

Campbell, Mr Nicholas Charles Wilson BA(Cantab); Recorder I *Jul 1978*
(Q.C.) *15*
11 King's Bench Walk, Leeds
p978 . . . . . 0113 297 1200

Campbell, Mr Oliver BA(Oxon) M *Oct 1992*
8, 12, 18, 20, 22, 30, 40, 47, 48, 51
Henderson Chambers, London EC4
p937 . . . . . 020 7583 9020

CAMPBELL, Ms Rhona BA(Hons) I *Feb 1993*
Citadel Chambers, Birmingham
p967 . . . . . 0121 233 8500

CAMPBELL, Miss Sarah BA(Hons) I *Oct 1997*
15, 4, 62, 36, 27
23 Essex Street, London WC2
p932 . . . . . 020 7413 0353

Campbell, Mr Stephen LLB; Recorder M *Jul 1982*
30, 40, 53, 94, 68
No5 Chambers, Bristol
p971 . . . . . 0845 210 5555
No5 Chambers, London EC4
p944 . . . . . 0845 210 5555
No5 Chambers, Birmingham
p968 . . . . . 0845 210 5555

Campbell, Susan M *Nov 1996*
(Q.C.)
Angel Chambers, Swansea
p992 . . . . . 01792 464623

CAMPBELL, Miss Susan Claire MA(Cantab) M *Nov 1986*
(Q.C.)
Pump Court Chambers, Swindon
p993 . . . . . 01793 539899
Pump Court Chambers, Winchester
p994 . . . . . 01962 868161
Pump Court Chambers, London EC4
p947 . . . . . 020 7353 0711
Southernhay Chambers, Exeter
p975 . . . . . 01392 255777

Campbell-Brown, Louise M *Jan 1993*
One Essex Court, London EC4
p931 . . . . . 020 7936 3030

Canavan, Miss Sandy LLB; Recorder L *Jul 1987*
15
5 King's Bench Walk, London EC4
p939 . . . . . 020 7353 5638

CANBY, Miss Fiona LLB(Manc) M *Jul 2001*
Temple Garden Chambers, London EC4
p952 . . . . . 020 7583 1315

CANDLIN, Mr James Richard BSc(Hons); DipLaw L *Oct 1991*
30, 53, 40, 12, 27
12 King's Bench Walk, London EC4
p940 . . . . . 020 7583 0811

CANDLIN, Ms Naomi L *Oct 2003*
11, 93, 31
St Philips Chambers, Birmingham
p969 . . . . . 0121 246 7000

CANE-SOOTHILL, Mr Michael LLB(Hons) L *Jan 1997*
12, 15
Bank House Chambers, Sheffield
p991 . . . . . 0114 275 1223

Caney, Miss Michelle M *Jan 2004*
St Ives Chambers, Birmingham
p969 . . . . . 0121 236 0863

Cannan, Mr Jonathan LLB(Lond); ACA; ATII G *Nov 1989*
32, 40, 57, 58, 37
Broadway House Chambers, Leeds
p977 . . . . . 0113 246 2600
Broadway House Chambers, Bradford
p969 . . . . . 01274 722560
Exchange Chambers, Manchester
p983 . . . . . 0161 833 2722
Exchange Chambers, Liverpool
p980 . . . . . 0151 236 7747
Exchange Chambers, Leeds
p977 . . . . . 0113 203 1970

Canning, Mr Richard L *Nov 2004*
39 Park Square, Leeds
p978 . . . . . 0113 245 6633

Cannings, Mr Matthew LLB(Hons)(KCL) M *Jan 2006*
11, 97, 8, 93, 71
3PB, Bristol
p971 . . . . . 0117 928 1520

Cannock, Mr Giles BA(Cantab) L *Oct 1998*
12, 30, 31, 53, 26
Kings Chambers, Leeds
p978 . . . . . 0113 242 1123
Kings Chambers, Manchester
p984 . . . . . 0161 832 9082

Cannon, Mr Josef David LLB(Hons) L *Jul 2002*
22, 26, 18, 23, 12, 31, 25, 15
Cornerstone Barristers, London WC1
p929 . . . . . 020 7242 4986

Cannon, Miss Lauren M *Jan 2004*
Guildford Chambers, Guildford
p975 . . . . . 01483 539131

Cannon, Mr Mark BA M *Jul 1985*
(Q.C.) *8, 12, 24, 40, 11, 54*
Four New Square, London WC2
p943 . . . . . 020 7822 2000

See p1010 for the Key to Work Categories

Cannon, Mr Patrick G *Dec 2003*
34, 57, 58, 37, 9
15 Old Square, London WC2
p945 . . . 020 7242 2744

CANSICK, Mr Allen I *Jan 2004*
15
Mitre House Chambers, London WC1
p942 . . . 020 7307 7100

Cant, Mr Christopher MA(Cantab) L *Jul 1973*
8, 9, 11, 29, 32, 34, 37, 40, 93
9 Stone Buildings Barristers Chambers, London WC2
p951 . . . 020 7404 5055

Canter, Mr Simon I *Oct 2000*
1 Mitre Court Buildings, London EC4
p942 . . . 020 7452 8900

CAPEWELL, Mr Edward L *Jan 2009*
1, 18, 76, 51
11KBW, London EC4
p938 . . . 020 7632 8500

Caplan, Mr David I *Jan 2006*
One Essex Court, London EC4
p931 . . . 020 7583 2000

Caplan, Mr Jonathan MA(Cantab) G *Nov 1973*
(Q.C.) *15, 62, 16*
5 Paper Buildings, London EC4
p946 . . . 020 7583 6117

Caplan, Mrs Leonie I *Mar 2001*
20
18 St John Street Chambers, Manchester
p985 . . . 0161 278 1800

Capon, Mr Philip LLB; Pupil Supervisor I *Oct 1990*
8, 6, 11, 67, 38, 40
East Anglian Chambers, Norwich
p988 . . . 01603 617351
East Anglian Chambers, Colchester
p975 . . . 01206 572756
East Anglian Chambers, Chelmsford
p973 . . . 01245 215660
East Anglian Chambers, Ipswich
p976 . . . 01473 214481

Capstick, Mr Timothy BA G *Jul 1986*
15, 30
No 6 Barristers Chambers, Leeds
p978 . . . 0113 245 9763

CARBERRY, Miss Caroline G *Oct 1995*
Furnival Chambers, London EC4
p934 . . . 020 7405 3232

Carden, Mr Nicholas LLB G *Jul 1981*
20, 10
1 Hare Court, London EC4
p936 . . . 020 7797 7070

Carew-Pole, Mrs Rebecca J LLB I *Jun 1999*
10, 20
1 Hare Court, London EC4
p936 . . . 020 7797 7070

Carey, Mr Godfrey I *Jul 1969*
(Q.C.) *15, 62*
5 Paper Buildings, London EC4
p946 . . . 020 7583 6117

Carey, Miss Jacqueline LLB(Hons) L *Oct 1999*
15, 62
2 Bedford Row, London WC1
p924 . . . 020 7440 8888

Carey-Hughes, Mr Richard J Recorder G *Jul 1977*
(Q.C.) *15, 51, 62*
Nine Bedford Row, London WC1
p924 . . . 020 7489 2727

CARINGTON, Mr Alex L *Oct 2006*
30, 53, 12, 94, 84, 85
12 King's Bench Walk, London EC4
p940 . . . 020 7583 0811

Carleton, Ms Erica LLB(Hons) M *Mar 2000*
20, 10
15 Winckley Square, Preston
p991 . . . 01772 252828

CARLILE OF BERRIEW, Lord LLB; Recorder; Deputy High Court Judge G *Jul 1970*
(Q.C.) *15, 25, 26, 27, 1, 51, 12*
9-12 Bell Yard Chambers, London WC2
p926 . . . 020 7400 1800

Carlin, Mr Niall I *Jul 2009*
72, 15
Broadway House Chambers, Leeds
p977 . . . 0113 246 2600
Broadway House Chambers, Bradford
p969 . . . 01274 722560

Carling, Mr Christopher MA(Cantab) L *Nov 1969*
27, 30, 36, 53, 56
Old Square Chambers, Bristol
p971 . . . 0117 930 5100
Old Square Chambers, London WC1
p945 . . . 020 7269 0300

Carlisle, Mr Timothy St John Ogilvie DipLaw G *Nov 1984*
12, 47, 53
Field Court Chambers, London WC1
p933 . . . 020 7405 6114

Carne, Mr Roger E I *Nov 1969*
15, 51, 62
Nine Bedford Row, London WC1
p924 . . . 020 7489 2727

CARNES, Mr Andrew LLB(Leics) L *Jul 1984*
36, 15, 11
4-5 Gray's Inn Square, London WC1
p935 . . . 020 7404 5252

CARNEY, Mr Andrew BA; MSc I *Oct 1995*
15, 20, 30, 22, 12
7 Harrington Street Chambers, Liverpool
p981 . . . 0151 242 0707

Carney, Mr Joseph LLB; BEc(Adelaide) L *Nov 2004*
5, 6, 8, 11, 24, 29, 41, 40, 37
3 Stone Buildings, London WC2
p951 . . . 020 7242 4937

CARNIE, Mr Alan LLB(Hons)(Hull) L *Jul 2006*
20, 10
Wilberforce Chambers, Hull
p976 . . . 01482 323264

Carolan, Ms Candia BA(Hons); MA M *Jan 1999*
12, 20, 6, 9
Abbey Chambers, Shepperton
p992 . . . 01932 560913

Carpenter, Miss Chloe LLB(KCL); BCL(Oxon) L *Oct 2001*
Fountain Court Chambers, London EC4
p934 . . . 020 7583 3335

Carpenter, Mr Jamie BA; CPE I *Jul 2000*
40, 53, 30, 27
Hailsham Chambers, London EC4
p936 . . . 020 7643 5000

Carpenter, Miss Jane BSc I *Oct 1984*
15
Atkinson Bevan Chambers, London EC4
p924 . . . 020 7353 2112

Carpenter, Naomi I *Jan 2004*
15, 20, 10, 67
Argent Chambers, London WC2
p923 . . . 020 7556 5500

CARPENTER-LEITCH, Mr Tom Gordon MA(Cantab); ACA L *Mar 2002*
6, 8, 11, 12, 45, 47, 20, 62, 22, 29
Tanfield Chambers, London WC1
p951 . . . 020 7421 5300

CARR, Mr Adrian BA(Dunelm); DipLaw I *Nov 1999*
11, 22, 37, 6, 8
Tanfield Chambers, London WC1
p951 . . . 020 7421 5300

Carr, Mr Bruce BSc(Econ) I *Nov 1986*
(Q.C.) *11, 12, 18, 27, 36, 26, 1, 55*
Devereux Chambers, London WC2
p930 . . . 020 7353 7534

Carr, Mr Christopher BA(Hons) I *Nov 2002*
2, 11, 18, 20, 30, 56
36 Bedford Row, London WC1
p925 . . . 020 7421 8000

Carr, Mr Craig M *Oct 2006*
53, 11, 12, 18, 55, 85, 27, 30, 40
7 Bedford Row, London WC1
p924 . . . 020 7242 3555

Carr, Mr Henry BA; LLM G *May 1982*
(Q.C.) *73, 50, 19, 45, 13, 52, 96, 41*
11 South Square, London WC1
p950 . . . 020 7405 1222

Carr, Mr Jonathon M *Oct 1990*
12, 30
Broad Chare Chambers, Newcastle upon Tyne
p986 . . . 0191 232 0541

Carr, Mr Simon LLB(Soton); Recorder I *Nov 1984*
12, 15, 18, 53, 40, 30, 70
9 Gough Square, London EC4
p935 . . . 020 7832 0500

Carr, Miss Sue MA(Cantab) M *Jul 1982*
(Q.C.) *8, 12, 24, 40, 11, 48, 18*
Four New Square, London WC2
p943 . . . 020 7822 2000

Carrasco, Mr Glenn BA; MSc I *Oct 1997*
15, 62, 84, 96
Argent Chambers, London WC2
p923 . . . 020 7556 5500

Carrion Benitez, Ms Miriam G *Jul 2001*
20, 10, 12, 51, 18, 23, 76
36 Bedford Row, London WC1
p925 . . . 020 7421 8000

Carrodus, Miss Gail Caroline G *Nov 1978*
20
Huntercombe Chambers, Henley-on-Thames
p976 . . . 01491 641934

Carroll, Mr Grant BSc(Hons); DipLaw M *Jul 2005*
6, 7, 8, 10, 11, 12, 47, 67, 15, 20, 22, 88, 30
College Chambers, Southampton
p992 . . . 023 8023 0338

Carroll, Jonathan BA; AKC; Recorder; Deputy Judge Advocate (Courts Martial Judge) G *Nov 1994*
15, 42, 62, 70, 71, 72, 80, 82, 84, 91
Zenith Chambers, Leeds
p979 . . . 0113 245 5438

Carron, Mr Richard M *Oct 1992*
10, 20
Queen Square Chambers, Bristol
p972 . . . 0117 921 1966

Carrott, Mr Sylvester Emanuel LLB G *Jul 1980*
1 Pump Court, London EC4
p947 . . . 020 7842 7070

Carrow, Mr Robert BA; Member of California & New York Bar M *Nov 1981*
33 Bedford Row, London WC1
p925 . . . 020 7242 6476

Carse, Mr Gordon I *Oct 2002*
15
5 King's Bench Walk, London EC4
p939 . . . 020 7353 5638

Carss-Frisk, Miss Monica LLB(Lond); BCL(Oxon) G *Jul 1985*
(Q.C.) *1, 8, 11, 12, 19, 29, 51, 55, 89, 44, 18, 43*
Blackstone Chambers, London EC4
p926 . . . 020 7583 1770

CARTER, Mr David John LLB(Hons) G *Nov 1971*
22, 26, 18, 1, 9, 23, 51, 55, 63, 12
Arden Chambers, London WC1
p923 . . . 020 7242 4244

Carter, Miss Holly BA(Manc) I *Oct 1993*
10, 20
3 Dr Johnson's Buildings, London EC4
p930 . . . 020 7353 4854

CARTER, Miss Lydia BA(Cantab) M *Nov 2007*
18, 11, 12, 55, 6, 56
Littleton Chambers, London EC4
p941 . . . 020 7797 8600

Carter, Mr Martin MA(Oxon) M *Nov 1992*
1, 26, 31, 46, 54
Kings Chambers, Leeds
p978 . . . 0113 242 1123
Kings Chambers, Manchester
p984 . . . 0161 832 9082

Carter, Mr Peter LLB(Lond) G *Jul 1974*
(Q.C.) *15, 62, 51, 95*
Park Court Chambers, Leeds
p978 . . . 0113 243 3277
18 Red Lion Court, London EC4
p949 . . . 020 7520 6000
18 Red Lion Court (Annexe), Chelmsford
p973 . . . 01245 280880

Carter, Mr Richard LLB I *Nov 1990*
6, 7, 8, 11, 18, 22, 40
St Johns Buildings, Preston
p990 . . . 01772 256100
St Johns Buildings, Chester
p974 . . . 01244 323070
St Johns Buildings, Manchester
p985 . . . 0161 214 1500
St Johns Buildings, Liverpool
p982 . . . 0151 243 6000

CARTER, Miss Rosalyn LLB(Hons) L *Nov 1994*
20
St Philips Chambers, Birmingham
p969 . . . 0121 246 7000

Carter, Mr Tom BA G *Jan 2001*
1 Hare Court, London EC4
p936 . . . 020 7797 7070

Carter, Mr William BA(Oxon) G *Jul 1989*
15, 84
1 Paper Buildings, London EC4
p946 . . . 020 7353 3728

Carter-Manning, Ms Jenny M *Oct 1999*
15, 20, 62
7 Bedford Row, London WC1
p924 . . . 020 7242 3555

CARTER-MANNING, Mr Jeremy M *Apr 1975*
(Q.C.)
Furnival Chambers, London EC4
p934 . . . 020 7405 3232

CARTER-STEPHENSON, Mr George LLB I *Jul 1975*
(Q.C.) *15, 62, 36, 95*
25 Bedford Row, London WC1
p925 . . . 020 7067 1500

Cartmell, Mr Nicholas LLB I *Oct 1990*
10, 12, 15, 18, 19, 20, 25, 27, 30, 36, 38
New Court Chambers, Newcastle upon Tyne
p987 . . . 0191 232 1980

Cartwright, Mr Crispian MA(Oxon); Recorder M *Nov 1976*
5 Pump Court, London EC4
p947 . . . 020 7353 2532 / 7583 7133

Cartwright, Mr Ivan G *Nov 1993*
12, 15, 30, 18, 62, 40
KCH Garden Square Chambers, Nottingham
p989 . . . 0115 941 8851
KCH Garden Square Chambers, Leicester
p979 . . . 0115 941 8851

CARTWRIGHT, Mr James D'Arcy Cayley G *Feb 1968*
15, 63
10 King's Bench Walk, London EC4
p940 . . . 020 7353 7742

CARTWRIGHT, Mr Nicolas F LLB; Deputy District Judge; Recorder M *Jul 1986*
15, 62
St Philips Chambers, Birmingham
p969 . . . 0121 246 7000

Cartwright, Mr Richard BA(Hons) I *Jan 1994*
30, 53
Devereux Chambers, London WC2
p930 . . . 020 7353 7534

Cartwright, Ms Suzanne Jane L *Oct 1994*
Holborn Chambers, London WC2
p937 . . . 020 7242 6060

CARUS, Mr Roderick BA(Oxon) G *Nov 1971*
(Q.C.) *15, 12*
Bank House Chambers, Sheffield
p991 . . . 0114 275 1223
9 St John Street Chambers, Manchester
p984 . . . 0161 955 9000

Carvahlo-Gomes, Ms Ana LLB(Hons); MA M *Jan 1996*
10, 20, 15
St Albans Chambers, St Albans
p992 . . . 01727 843383

CARVILLE, Mr Brendan Owen BA I *Jul 1980*
15
7 Harrington Street Chambers, Liverpool
p981 . . . 0151 242 0707

Case, Miss Julie LLB(Leics) M *Oct 1990*
8, 11, 32, 37, 22, 29, 6, 38, 40, 88, 93, 97
Exchange Chambers, Manchester
p983 . . . 0161 833 2722
Exchange Chambers, Liverpool
p980 . . . 0151 236 7747
Exchange Chambers, Leeds
p977 . . . 0113 203 1970

Case, Magdalen BA(Oxon); DipLaw M *Nov 1992*
St Johns Buildings, Preston
p990 . . . 01772 256100
St Johns Buildings, Chester
p974 . . . 01244 323070
St Johns Buildings, Manchester
p985 . . . 0161 214 1500
St Johns Buildings, Liverpool
p982 . . . 0151 243 6000

Case, Mr Richard M *Oct 1996*
18, 30, 55, 46, 68, 94
No5 Chambers, Bristol
p971 . . . 0845 210 5555
No5 Chambers, London EC4
p944 . . . 0845 210 5555
No5 Chambers, Birmingham
p968 . . . 0845 210 5555

13

CASELLA, Mr Bartholamu L *Nov 1995*
72, 15, 62
23 Essex Street, London WC2
p932 . . . . 020 7413 0353

Casement, Mr David M *Oct 1992*
(Q.C.) *41, 6, 74, 47, 67, 81, 62, 24, 29, 8, 11, 97, 38, 56, 89, 5, 40*
Kings Chambers, Leeds
p978 . . . . 0113 242 1123
Kings Chambers, Manchester
p984 . . . . 0161 832 9082

CASEY, Mr Aidan P G *Nov 1992*
11, 12, 47, 5, 6, 18
3 Hare Court, London EC4
p937 . . . . 020 7415 7800

CASEY, Mr Benjamin BA(York) I *Oct 2000*
Temple Garden Chambers, London EC4
p952 . . . . 020 7583 1315

Casey, Mr Dermot Fintan BA(Hons); DipLaw(City); MSc(Lond) M *Nov 1994*
10, 20, 63
Coram Chambers, London EC1
p929 . . . . 020 7092 3700

CASEY, Miss Mairin BA; LLB I *Nov 1989*
10, 20
St Mary's Chambers, Nottingham
p989 . . . . 0115 950 3503

CASEY, Mr Noel G L *Oct 1995*
15, 71
18 Red Lion Court, London EC4
p949 . . . . 020 7520 6000
18 Red Lion Court (Annexe), Chelmsford
p973 . . . . 01245 280880
7 King's Bench Walk, London EC4
p940 . . . . 020 7910 8300

CASEY, Mr Paul BA I *Oct 2002*
Fountain Court Chambers, London EC4
p934 . . . . 020 7583 3335

CASHMAN, Ms Vanessa BA(Hons); GDL; BVC L *Jul 2009*
30, 53, 18
12 King's Bench Walk, London EC4
p940 . . . . 020 7583 0811

Cassel, Miss Bathsheba BA I *Jul 2005*
15, 72, 81
Walnut House Chambers, Exeter
p975 . . . . 01392 279751

Cassel, Mr Timothy L *Jul 1965*
(Q.C.) *15, 62, 25*
5 Paper Buildings, London EC4
p946 . . . . 020 7583 6117

Cassidy, Mr Francis LLB M *Nov 2000*
20, 30
4 Brick Court Chambers, London EC4
p927 . . . . 020 7832 3200

CASSIDY, Mr Patrick L *Jul 1982*
15, 76
Kenworthy's Chambers, Manchester
p984 . . . . 0161 832 4036

Cassidy, Miss Sheena I *Jan 2001*
57, 58, 23, 20, 10
3PB, London EC4
p946 . . . . 020 7583 8055

Castle, Mr Peter M *Jan 1970*
13 Old Square Chambers, London WC2
p945 . . . . 020 7831 4445

CASTLE, Mr Richard LLB(Bris) G *Oct 1998*
10, 20
1 King's Bench Walk, London EC4
p938 . . . . 020 7936 1500

Castle, Miss Susan Elizabeth MA M *Jul 1986*
10, 20, 22
33 Bedford Row, London WC1
p925 . . . . 020 7242 6476

Caswell, Mr Benjamin Cecil MA(Oxon); MA(Lond) M *Oct 1993*
8, 11, 22, 37, 30
No 6 Barristers Chambers, Leeds
p978 . . . . 0113 245 9763

Caswell, Mr Matthew MA M *May 1968*
15, 20, 40, 8, 11
11 King's Bench Walk, Leeds
p978 . . . . 0113 297 1200

Caswell, Miss Rebecca Mary MA(Oxon) M *Jan 1983*
23, 20, 37
11 King's Bench Walk, Leeds
p978 . . . . 0113 297 1200
No 6 Barristers Chambers, Leeds
p978 . . . . 0113 245 9763

CATCHPOLE, Mr Stuart P I *Jul 1987*
(Q.C.) *1, 36, 11, 7, 24, 40, 51, 26, 46, 31*
Thirty Nine Essex Street, London WC2
p932 . . . . 020 7832 1111

CATFORD, Mr Gordon B LLB(Lond) L *Jul 1980*
53, 30, 27, 12
Crown Office Chambers, London EC4
p929 . . . . 020 7797 8100

Catherwood, Shaen BA(Oxon) G *Jul 2000*
24, 18, 55, 51, 11, 12, 30
Devereux Chambers, London WC2
p930 . . . . 020 7353 7534

Cattan, Mr Philip David LLB(Manc) G *Nov 1970*
15
St Johns Buildings, Preston
p990 . . . . 01772 256100
St Johns Buildings, Chester
p974 . . . . 01244 323070
St Johns Buildings, Manchester
p985 . . . . 0161 214 1500
St Johns Buildings, Liverpool
p982 . . . . 0151 243 6000

CATTERMOLE, Ms Rebecca M *Oct 1999*
8, 11, 12, 22
Tanfield Chambers, London WC1
p951 . . . . 020 7421 5300

Cattermull, Ms Emma LLB(Hons) L *Oct 2004*
10, 12, 18, 30
East Anglian Chambers, Norwich
p988 . . . . 01603 617351
East Anglian Chambers, Colchester
p975 . . . . 01206 572756
East Anglian Chambers, Chelmsford
p973 . . . . 01245 215660
East Anglian Chambers, Ipswich
p976 . . . . 01473 214481

CATTON-NEWELL, Miss Sally G *Jul 2009*
10, 12, 20
Trinity Chambers, Chelmsford
p974 . . . . 01245 605040

Caudle, Mr John BA; Recorder M *Nov 1976*
15, 62
2 Bedford Row, London WC1
p924 . . . . 020 7440 8888

CAULFIELD, Ms Barbara I *Jun 1999*
10, 20
St Philips Chambers, Birmingham
p969 . . . . 0121 246 7000

Caun, Mr Lawrence MA(Oxon) L *Nov 1977*
12, 30, 40, 8, 88, 93
Lamb Chambers, London EC4
p941 . . . . 020 7797 8300

CAUSER, Mr John C BA; Gambia Bar 1982 I *Jul 1979*
15, 36, 12, 11, 62, 72
23 Essex Street, London WC2
p932 . . . . 020 7413 0353

CAVANAGH, Mr John MA(Oxon); LLM(Cantab); Recorder M *Nov 1985*
(Q.C.) *1, 11, 18, 19, 26, 36, 51, 55, 56*
11KBW, London EC4
p938 . . . . 020 7632 8500

Cavanagh, Ms Lorraine G *Jan 2000*
St Johns Buildings, Preston
p990 . . . . 01772 256100
St Johns Buildings, Chester
p974 . . . . 01244 323070
St Johns Buildings, Manchester
p985 . . . . 0161 214 1500
St Johns Buildings, Liverpool
p982 . . . . 0151 243 6000

Cave, Mr Jeremy LLB(Manc) M *Oct 1992*
12, 20, 22, 30
Crown Office Row Chambers, Brighton
p970 . . . . 01273 625625

Cave, Miss Patricia BA(Hons)(Manc) M *Jan 1989*
2, 20, 12, 10
36 Bedford Row, London WC1
p925 . . . . 020 7421 8000

Cavender, Mr David M *Jul 1993*
(Q.C.)
One Essex Court, London EC4
p931 . . . . 020 7583 2000

CAVENDER, Ms Susan BA(Hons) G *Oct 2004*
15, 25
Guildhall Chambers, Bristol
p970 . . . . 0117 930 9000

Cavin, Mr Paul G *Nov 1995*
15, 62
Atkinson Bevan Chambers, London EC4
p924 . . . . 020 7353 2112

CAWS, Mr Eian BA(Oxon) I *Nov 1974*
31, 36, 46
Landmark Chambers, London EC4
p941 . . . . 020 7430 1221

Cawsey, Barry I *Jul 2001*
Clerksroom - Administration Centre, Taunton
p993 . . . . 0845 083 3000

Cawsey, Ms Laura L *Nov 2004*
22, 15, 51, 70, 88, 96
Garden Court North Chambers, Manchester
p983 . . . . 0161 236 1840

Cawson, Mr Mark LLB; MA; Junior Counsel to the Crown(Provincial Panel); Recorder L *Jul 1982*
(Q.C.) *6, 8, 40, 11*
Exchange Chambers, Manchester
p983 . . . . 0161 833 2722
Exchange Chambers, Liverpool
p980 . . . . 0151 236 7747
Exchange Chambers, Leeds
p977 . . . . 0113 203 1970
New Square Chambers, London WC2
p943 . . . . 020 7419 8000

CAYFORD, Mr Philip LLB M *Jul 1975*
(Q.C.) *10, 20*
29 Bedford Row, London WC1
p925 . . . . 020 7404 1044

Cecil, Ms Joanne I *Jan 2005*
15, 1, 51, 21, 33
1 Pump Court, London EC4
p947 . . . . 020 7842 7070

Celikoz, Miss Tara LLB(Hons) M *Jan 2007*
15, 10, 20
Eastbourne Chambers, Eastbourne
p975 . . . . 01323 642102

CELLAN-JONES, Mr Deiniol BA(Oxon) M *Oct 1988*
10, 12, 20, 22, 30
1 King's Bench Walk, London EC4
p938 . . . . 020 7936 1500

CHACKO, Mr Thomas BA(Hons) I *Oct 2007*
37, 57, 58, 34
Pump Court Tax Chambers, London WC1
p948 . . . . 020 7414 8080

Chacksfield, Mr Mark Andrew BA(Cantab) M *Oct 1999*
13, 50
8 New Square, London WC2
p943 . . . . 020 7405 4321

CHADWICK, Mr Daniel M *Oct 2006*
15
25 Bedford Row, London WC1
p925 . . . . 020 7067 1500

Chadwick, Miss Joanna LLB M *Nov 1988*
20, 63, 10
No5 Chambers, Bristol
p971 . . . . 0845 210 5555
No5 Chambers, London EC4
p944 . . . . 0845 210 5555
No5 Chambers, Birmingham
p968 . . . . 0845 210 5555

Chaffin-Laird, Miss Olivia G *Jul 2001*
6, 8, 11, 97, 47, 67, 14, 38, 89, 63, 29, 40, 74
No5 Chambers, Bristol
p971 . . . . 0845 210 5555
No5 Chambers, London EC4
p944 . . . . 0845 210 5555
No5 Chambers, Birmingham
p968 . . . . 0845 210 5555

CHAGGAR, Mrs Maninder I *Jul 1992*
15, 23
No 8 Chambers, Birmingham
p968 . . . . 0121 236 5514

Chaisty, Mr Paul LLB(Nott'm); BCL(Oxon) L *Jul 1982*
(Q.C.) *8, 5, 6, 11, 24*
3 Stone Buildings, London WC2
p951 . . . . 020 7242 4937
Kings Chambers, Leeds
p978 . . . . 0113 242 1123
Kings Chambers, Manchester
p984 . . . . 0161 832 9082

Chaize, Mr Tristan I *Nov 1977*
5 Pump Court, London EC4
p947 . . . . 020 7353 2532 / 7583 7133

CHALKLEY, Ms Rebecca M *Jan 1999*
15, 36, 62
18 Red Lion Court, London EC4
p949 . . . . 020 7520 6000
18 Red Lion Court (Annexe), Chelmsford
p973 . . . . 01245 280880

CHALLACOMBE, Mr Thomas LLB G *Jul 2006*
12, 15, 20, 18
King's Bench Godolphin Chambers, Truro
p994 . . . . 0845 308 1551
King's Bench Godolphin Chambers, Plymouth
p990 . . . . 0845 308 1551

Challenger, Mr Colin Westcott LLB(Lond); MBA(Berkeley) I *Nov 1970*
12, 8, 7, 6, 11, 29, 40, 62
Lamb Chambers, London EC4
p941 . . . . 020 7797 8300

CHALLINOR, Mr Jonathan I *Nov 1998*
15
Cornwall Street Chambers, Birmingham
p967 . . . . 0121 233 7500

CHALLINOR, Mr Thomas G *Jan 2004*
Citadel Chambers, Birmingham
p967 . . . . 0121 233 8500

CHALMERS, Ms Suzanne BA(Oxon) G *Oct 1995*
24, 40, 30, 11, 7
Crown Office Chambers, London EC4
p929 . . . . 020 7797 8100

Chaloner, Mr Mark MA(Cantab) M *Jul 2002*
10, 20
12 College Place, Southampton
p992 . . . . 023 8032 0320

Chamberlain, Mr Kevin G *Aug 1965*
York Chambers, York
p995 . . . . 01904 620048
York Chambers, Newcastle upon Tyne
p987 . . . . 0191 206 4677

Chamberlain, Mr Martin BA(Hons)(Oxon); BLC(Oxon) G *Oct 1997*
11, 18, 19, 1, 44
Brick Court Chambers, London WC2
p927 . . . . 020 7379 3550

CHAMBERLAYNE, Mr Patrick MA(Cantab) I *Nov 1992*
(Q.C.) *20*
29 Bedford Row, London WC1
p925 . . . . 020 7404 1044

CHAMBERS, Mr Adam BA(Leeds); Deputy District Judge M *Jul 1989*
12, 11, 7, 30, 93
12 King's Bench Walk, London EC4
p940 . . . . 020 7583 0811

Chambers, Mr Dominic LLB G *Nov 1987*
(Q.C.)
Maitland Chambers, London WC2
p941 . . . . 020 7406 1200

Chambers, Ms Gaynor BSc G *Oct 1998*
3, 7, 11, 24, 40
Keating Chambers, London WC2
p938 . . . . 020 7544 2600

Chambers, Mr Jonathan MA(Oxon); BCL(Oxon); CPLS(QUB) I *Oct 1996*
Quadrant Chambers, London EC4
p948 . . . . 020 7583 4444

CHAMBERS, Mr Michael L *Jan 1980*
(Q.C.)
Farrar's Building, London EC4
p933 . . . . 020 7583 9241

Chambers, Ms Rachel M *Jan 2002*
Cloisters, London EC4
p928 . . . . 020 7827 4000

Champion, Ms Deborah Recorder G *Jul 1970*
15
2 Bedford Row, London WC1
p924 . . . . 020 7440 8888

CHAMPION, Miss Karina BA I *Jan 2005*
12, 11, 8, 18, 30, 25, 47, 40, 88
Oriel Chambers, Liverpool
p981 . . . . 0151 236 7191 / 236 4321
Oriel Chambers, Preston
p990 . . . . 01772 254764

Champion, Ms Rowena M *Feb 1990*
Field Court Chambers, London WC1
p933 . . . . 020 7405 6114

See p1010 for the Key to Work Categories

CHAN, Miss Abberlaine Dianne Pao Che LLB(Bris) G *Jul 1979*
15
9-12 Bell Yard Chambers, London WC2
p926 . . . . . 020 7400 1800

Chan, Evonnie M *Jan 2006*
20, 15
18 St John Street Chambers, Manchester
p985 . . . . . 0161 278 1800

Chan, Miss Rachel Siv Yee LLB I *Jul 2004*
15, 20
Staple Inn Chambers, London WC1
p951 . . . . . 020 7242 5240

CHAN, Miss Rebecca M *Nov 2006*
1, 22, 25, 26, 88, 93
Arden Chambers, London WC1
p923 . . . . . 020 7242 4244

Chan, Miss Susan BA(Oxon) G *Oct 1994*
King's Bench Chambers, Oxford
p989 . . . . . 01865 311066
13 King's Bench Walk, London EC4
p940 . . . . . 020 7353 7204

Chandarana, Yogain LLB(Hons) L *Jan 1997*
51, 15, 45
Nine Bedford Row, London WC1
p924 . . . . . 020 7489 2727

CHANDLER, Mr Alexander MA(Hons)(Oxon); DipLaw(Lond) M *Oct 1995*
10, 20
1 Garden Court, London EC4
p934 . . . . . 020 7797 7900

CHANDLER, Ms Kate LLB(Lond) I *Oct 1990*
30, 12
12 King's Bench Walk, London EC4
p940 . . . . . 020 7583 0811

Chandran, Miss Parosha LLB(Lond); LLM(Lond); Dip Human Rights L *Oct 1997*
1, 18, 51, 23, 27, 33, 55
1 Pump Court, London EC4
p947 . . . . . 020 7842 7070

CHAPLIN, Mr Adrian BA(Cantab); MA(Lond) G *Oct 1990*
12, 15, 25
9-12 Bell Yard Chambers, London WC2
p926 . . . . . 020 7400 1800

CHAPLIN, Ms Sophie M *Jan 2007*
4 King's Bench Walk, London EC4
p939 . . . . . 020 7822 7000

Chapman, Ms Claire BA(Hons) M *Nov 1991*
20, 12, 15
St Ives Chambers, Birmingham
p969 . . . . . 0121 236 0863

CHAPMAN, Ms Dawn L *Jan 2001*
15, 20, 70
Mitre House Chambers, London WC1
p942 . . . . . 020 7307 7100

Chapman, Ms Gemma M *Jan 2002*
12, 10, 20
Regency Chambers, Peterborough
p990 . . . . . 01733 315215

Chapman, Mr Graham I *Oct 1998*
8, 12, 24, 40
Four New Square, London WC2
p943 . . . . . 020 7822 2000

Chapman, Helen M *Jan 2006*
2 Pump Court, London EC4
p947 . . . . . 020 7353 5597

Chapman, Mr Jeffrey BA; LLM M *Nov 1989*
(Q.C.)
Fountain Court Chambers, London EC4
p934 . . . . . 020 7583 3335

CHAPMAN, Mr John L *Jul 2003*
15, 12, 20, 30
Pump Court Chambers, Swindon
p993 . . . . . 01793 539899
Pump Court Chambers, Winchester
p994 . . . . . 01962 868161
Pump Court Chambers, London EC4
p947 . . . . . 020 7353 0711

CHAPMAN, Miss Juliet LLB L *Jan 2009*
10, 20
Lamb Building, Brighton
p970 . . . . . 01273 820490
Lamb Building, London EC4
p940 . . . . . 020 7797 7788

Chapman, Mr Matthew LLB; LLM(Lond) G *Oct 1994*
12, 30, 47, 48, 59, 62
1 Chancery Lane, London WC2
p928 . . . . . 0845 634 6666

CHAPMAN, Mr Nicholas BSc; DipLaw I *Oct 1990*
20
29 Bedford Row, London WC1
p925 . . . . . 020 7404 1044
9-12 Bell Yard Chambers, London WC2
p926 . . . . . 020 7400 1800

Chapman, Miss Rebecca I *Nov 1990*
1, 23
Tooks Chambers, London EC4
p953 . . . . . 020 7842 7575

Chapman, Mr Richard G *Oct 1998*
5, 6, 7, 8, 13, 16, 18, 22, 24, 31, 32, 37
18 St John Street Chambers, Manchester
p985 . . . . . 0161 278 1800

Chapman, Ms Tracy BA(Hons)(B'ham); MSc(Oxon); GDL(Lond) M *Jul 2009*
10, 20
Coram Chambers, London EC1
p929 . . . . . 020 7092 3700

Chapman, Mr Vivian MA; LLM(Cantab); Recorder L *Jul 1970*
(Q.C.) *2, 8, 9, 29, 32, 14, 37, 40, 54, 88, 89, 93*
9 Stone Buildings Barristers Chambers, London WC2
p951 . . . . . 020 7404 5055

Chapman, Mr William G *Jul 2003*
15, 62, 12, 30, 53, 18
7 Bedford Row, London WC1
p924 . . . . . 020 7242 3555

CHAPPLE, Mr Malcolm Dundas BSc; FCIArb G *Nov 1975*
13, 11
New Square Chambers, London WC2
p943 . . . . . 020 7419 8000

Charalamides, Mr Leo I *Jul 1988*
1, 22, 25, 26, 46, 51, 56, 82, 83, 84, 88, 93
Ely Place Chambers, London EC1
p931 . . . . . 020 7400 9600

Charbit, Miss Valerie LLB(Hons) M *Oct 1992*
15, 62
2 Bedford Row, London WC1
p924 . . . . . 020 7440 8888

Charkham, Mr Graham BSc(Bris) I *Oct 1993*
3, 11, 12, 24, 35, 41
20 Essex Street, London WC2
p932 . . . . . 020 7842 1200

Charles, Miss Deborah BA(Hons) L *Oct 1996*
12, 15, 20, 22, 30, 40, 51
6-8 Mill Street, Maidstone
p982 . . . . . 01622 688094 / 688095
6 Pump Court, London EC4
p947 . . . . . 020 7797 8400

CHARLES, Mr Henry LLB; LLM(Lond) I *Nov 1987*
30, 40, 53
12 King's Bench Walk, London EC4
p940 . . . . . 020 7583 0811

Charles, Mr Simon LLB L *Jun 2004*
1, 6, 8, 11, 13, 22, 29, 32, 37, 88
18 St John Street Chambers, Manchester
p985 . . . . . 0161 278 1800

Charleton, Miss Laura G *Jul 2002*
15, 12
Stour Chambers, Canterbury
p972 . . . . . 01227 764899

Charlton, Mr Alexander MA(Hons)(St Andrews); DipLaw(City) M *Jul 1983*
(Q.C.) *3, 7, 11, 12, 24, 29, 40, 45*
4 Pump Court, London EC4
p947 . . . . . 020 7842 5555

Charlton, Mr Hugo BA G *Jan 1978*
1 Gray's Inn Square, London WC1
p935 . . . . . 020 7405 8946

Charlton, Mr Timothy BA(Oxon) I *Nov 1974*
(Q.C.) *24, 35, 11, 5, 41*
Brick Court Chambers, London WC2
p927 . . . . . 020 7379 3550

Charlwood, Mr Spike Llewellyn M *Nov 1994*
40
Hailsham Chambers, London EC4
p936 . . . . . 020 7643 5000

CHARMAN, Mr Andrew MA(Cantab) L *Nov 1994*
6, 8, 11, 29, 37, 97, 69, 81
St Philips Chambers, Birmingham
p969 . . . . . 0121 246 7000

Charnley, Miss Bethan L *Oct 2007*
Nine Bedford Row, London WC1
p924 . . . . . 020 7489 2727

CHASEMORE, Ms Catherine L *Jan 2004*
15
1 High Pavement, Nottingham
p988 . . . . . 0115 941 8218

Chatterjee, Miss Adreeja Julia BA(Hons)(Cantab) G *Nov 1997*
20, 10, 64
No5 Chambers, Bristol
p971 . . . . . 0845 210 5555
No5 Chambers, London EC4
p944 . . . . . 0845 210 5555
No5 Chambers, Birmingham
p968 . . . . . 0845 210 5555

Chatterjee, Miss Mira M *Nov 1973*
10, 20
4 Brick Court Chambers, London EC4
p927 . . . . . 020 7832 3200

Chatterjee, Mr Rangan MA(Cantab); M Phil(Cantab) L *Jul 2004*
40, 24, 7, 89, 11
4 Pump Court, London EC4
p947 . . . . . 020 7842 5555

CHATTERTON, Mr Mark LLB(Hons) G *Jul 1983*
30, 40, 12
7 Harrington Street Chambers, Liverpool
p981 . . . . . 0151 242 0707

Chaudary, Ms Ambereen L *Jan 2002*
96, 30, 53
3PB, London EC4
p946 . . . . . 020 7583 8055

Chaudhry, Dr Farooq Ahmad L *Jul 1970*
23, 63, 64
10 Springwater Avenue, Bury
p972 . . . . . 01204 886883

CHAUDHRY, Mehvish L *Oct 2008*
10, 20, 23
Renaissance Chambers, London WC1
p949 . . . . . 020 7404 1111

Chaudhry, Miss Sabuhi LLB(Hons)(Lond) L *Oct 1993*
10, 20
Coram Chambers, London EC1
p929 . . . . . 020 7092 3700

Chaudhry, Miss Saiqa MA(Cantab) I *Jul 2005*
20
18 St John Street Chambers, Manchester
p985 . . . . . 0161 278 1800

Chaudhry, Ms Zia LLB I *Nov 1991*
15, 12
St Johns Buildings, Preston
p990 . . . . . 01772 256100
St Johns Buildings, Chester
p974 . . . . . 01244 323070
St Johns Buildings, Manchester
p985 . . . . . 0161 214 1500
St Johns Buildings, Liverpool
p982 . . . . . 0151 243 6000

CHAUDHURI, Mr Avirup LLB M *Feb 1990*
15, 62, 95
187 Fleet Street, London EC4
p933 . . . . . 020 7430 7430

Chavasse, Miss Ann G *May 1971*
St Ives Chambers, Birmingham
p969 . . . . . 0121 236 0863

CHAWATAMA, Mr Sydney LLB(Hons)(Essex) M *Oct 1994*
12, 18, 20, 27, 30, 40, 53
1 Crown Office Row, London EC4
p929 . . . . . 020 7797 7500

CHAWDHERY, Miss Yasmin L *Oct 2005*
23, 51, 12, 10
Kenworthy's Chambers, Manchester
p984 . . . . . 0161 832 4036

CHAWLA, Mr Mukul LLB(Lond) G *Jul 1983*
(Q.C.) *15*
9-12 Bell Yard Chambers, London WC2
p926 . . . . . 020 7400 1800

Chawla, Mr Neil I *Jan 2000*
62, 23
No5 Chambers, Bristol
p971 . . . . . 0845 210 5555
No5 Chambers, London EC4
p944 . . . . . 0845 210 5555
No5 Chambers, Birmingham
p968 . . . . . 0845 210 5555

CHBAT, Miss Nadia LLB M *Nov 1996*
15, 23
4 King's Bench Walk, London EC4
p939 . . . . . 020 7822 7000

Cheema, Miss Parmjit-Kaur LLB; Junior Treasury Council G *Jul 1989*
15, 62
2 Hare Court, London EC4
p937 . . . . . 020 7353 5324

Cheetham, Mr Gareth L *Jan 2005*
St Ives Chambers, Birmingham
p969 . . . . . 0121 236 0863

Cheetham, Miss Lucy BA(Hons); DipLaw G *Oct 1999*
20, 10
4 Paper Buildings, London EC4
p946 . . . . . 020 7583 0816

Cheetham, Mr Simon M *Nov 1991*
11, 18
Old Square Chambers, Bristol
p971 . . . . . 0117 930 5100
Old Square Chambers, London WC1
p945 . . . . . 020 7269 0300

Chegwidden, Mr James LLB(Oxon) L *Jan 2008*
51, 18, 71, 55, 10, 97
3PB, London EC4
p946 . . . . . 020 7583 8055

Chelmick, Mr Timothy L *Jan 2004*
Four New Square, London WC2
p943 . . . . . 020 7822 2000

Chelvan, S I *Oct 1999*
No5 Chambers, Bristol
p971 . . . . . 0845 210 5555
No5 Chambers, London EC4
p944 . . . . . 0845 210 5555
No5 Chambers, Birmingham
p968 . . . . . 0845 210 5555

CHENG, Miss Serena LLB(Lond) L *Oct 2000*
3, 7, 11, 31, 40, 41, 43, 45, 49, 54, 61, 78, 74
Atkin Chambers, London WC1
p923 . . . . . 020 7404 0102

Chennells, Mr Mark MA(Jt Hons) G *Oct 2002*
3, 7, 11, 31, 40, 41, 43, 45, 49, 54, 61, 78, 74
Atkin Chambers, London WC1
p923 . . . . . 020 7404 0102

CHERN, Dr Cyril BArch(Hons)(Architecture & Engineering) G *Jan 1972*
74, 41, 7, 43, 3, 96, 40, 24
Crown Office Chambers, London EC4
p929 . . . . . 020 7797 8100

Cherrill, Mrs Beverley M *Nov 1996*
15
Westgate Chambers, Lewes
p980 . . . . . 01273 480510

Cherry, Mr John M G *Nov 1961*
(Q.C.) *53, 40, 30, 27*
Lamb Chambers, London EC4
p941 . . . . . 020 7797 8300

CHERRY, Mr Peter L *Mar 2003*
1, 41, 11, 12, 16, 49, 18, 29, 40
Chancery House Chambers, Leeds
p977 . . . . . 0113 244 6691

Chesner, Mr Howard LLB(Lond); MBA G *Jul 1995*
One Essex Court, London EC4
p931 . . . . . 020 7936 3030

CHESTER, Mark LLB L *Oct 2002*
30
Atlantic Chambers, Liverpool
p980 . . . . . 0151 236 4421

Chesters, Ms Colette L M *Mar 1996*
15
1 Pump Court, London EC4
p947 . . . . . 020 7842 7070

CHEVES, Mr Simon T BA(Dunelm) I *Jul 1980*
18, 30, 53, 55
Tanfield Chambers, London WC1
p951 . . . . . 020 7421 5300

Chhotu, Jasvant G *Jun 1979*
12, 15, 23
189 Randolph Avenue, London W9
p949 . . . . . 020 7328 0158

CHIBAFA, Mr Jonathan M *Nov 2006*
15, 62, 94, 18, 46
18 Red Lion Court, London EC4
p949 . . . . . 020 7520 6000
18 Red Lion Court (Annexe), Chelmsford
p973 . . . . . 01245 280880

CHICHESTER-CLARK, Mr Adam M *Oct 2000*
Exchange Chambers, Manchester
p983 . . . . . 0161 833 2722
Exchange Chambers, Liverpool
p980 . . . . . 0151 236 7747

13

Exchange Chambers, Leeds
p977 . . . . 0113 203 1970
13 Old Square Chambers, London WC2
p945 . . . . 020 7831 4445

Chidgey, Mr David M *Oct 2000*
15
Albion Chambers, Bristol
p970 . . . . 0117 927 2144

Chidgey, Miss Kate I *Jun 2006*
15
3 Temple Gardens, London EC4
p952 . . . . 020 7353 3102

CHIDLEY, Mr Matthew M *Jan 2008*
Furnival Chambers, London EC4
p934 . . . . 020 7405 3232

Child, Mr Andrew J BA(Cantab) L *Nov 1997*
6, 8, 11, 12, 22
3 Stone Buildings, London WC2
p951 . . . . 020 7242 4937

CHILD, Mr Jeremy BA(Hons); LLB(Hons) L *Mar 2003*
6, 8, 11, 22, 38, 40, 88
Enterprise Chambers, London WC2
p931 . . . . 020 7405 9471
Enterprise Chambers, Leeds
p977 . . . . 0113 246 0391
Enterprise Chambers, Newcastle upon Tyne
p987 . . . . 0191 222 3344

CHILD, Mr John BA; LLB(Cantab) L *Nov 1966*
8, 9, 32, 34, 37
Wilberforce Chambers, London WC2
p953 . . . . 020 7306 0102

CHINKIN, Professor Christine LLB(Hons)(Lond) L *Mar 2003*
33, 51, 49
Matrix Chambers, London WC1
p942 . . . . 020 7404 3447

Chinn, Mr Antony Recorder M *Nov 1972*
(Q.C.) *15, 51*
Nine Bedford Row, London WC1
p924 . . . . 020 7489 2727

CHINNER, Miss Fer I *Oct 1998*
Furnival Chambers, London EC4
p934 . . . . 020 7405 3232

Chinnock, Mrs Christina Frances LLB(Hons) M *Nov 1998*
20
Angel Chambers, Swansea
p992 . . . . 01792 464623

Chippeck, Mr Stephen LLB L *Jul 1988*
15, 20
5 King's Bench Walk, London EC4
p939 . . . . 020 7353 5638

Chippendale, Miss Emma L LLB(Hons) M *Jul 2002*
12, 20, 17
37 Park Square Chambers, Leeds
p978 . . . . 0113 243 9422

Chipperfield, Mr Jeremy I *Jan 1995*
1 Mitre Court Buildings, London EC4
p942 . . . . 020 7452 8900

CHIPPINDALL, Mr Adam LLB(Soton) G *Jul 1975*
30, 40, 53
Guildhall Chambers, Bristol
p970 . . . . 0117 930 9000

Chirico, Mr David L *Jan 2002*
23
1 Pump Court, London EC4
p947 . . . . 020 7842 7070

Chirnside, Mr Stewart Murray BA(Hons) I *Jul 2005*
5, 11, 12, 18, 62, 24, 30, 40
2 Temple Gardens, London EC4
p952 . . . . 020 7822 1200

CHISHOLM, Mr Malcolm MA(Cantab) I *Nov 1989*
10, 20
1 Garden Court, London EC4
p934 . . . . 020 7797 7900

CHIVERS, Mr David BA(Cantab) L *Jul 1983*
(Q.C.) *11, 38, 97*
Erskine Chambers, London WC2
p931 . . . . 020 7242 5532

CHOKOWRY, Katy Former Solicitor M *Oct 2003*
10, 20
Renaissance Chambers, London WC1
p949 . . . . 020 7404 1111

CHOO, Professor Andrew B Com; LLB(UNSW); DPhil(Oxon) I *Jul 2002*
51, 15
Matrix Chambers, London WC1
p942 . . . . 020 7404 3447

Choo Choy, Mr Alain I *Nov 1991*
(Q.C.)
One Essex Court, London EC4
p931 . . . . 020 7583 2000

CHOON KIAT WEE, Mr Paul G *Jan 2010*
5, 81, 24, 47, 3, 50, 18, 74, 45, 43, 7, 49, 52, 40, 48, 38, 97, 62, 41, 78, 35
3 Verulam Buildings, London WC1
p953 . . . . 020 7831 8441

Choongh, Dr Satnam LLB(Warw); D Phil(Oxon) L *Apr 1994*
1, 18, 31, 55, 26, 78, 54, 60, 61, 46
No5 Chambers, Bristol
p971 . . . . 0845 210 5555
No5 Chambers, London EC4
p944 . . . . 0845 210 5555
No5 Chambers, Birmingham
p968 . . . . 0845 210 5555

Choudhry, Kamran L *Oct 2001*
1, 15, 21, 33, 51, 18
Tooks Chambers, London EC4
p953 . . . . 020 7842 7575

CHOUDHURY, Mr Akhlaq BSc(Glasgow); LLB(Lond) I *Oct 1992*
1, 11, 18, 26, 51, 55, 73
11KBW, London EC4
p938 . . . . 020 7632 8500

Choudhury, Mrs Fareha LLB(Sussex) G *Oct 1995*
10, 20, 22, 12, 30, 26
42 Bedford Row, London WC1
p925 . . . . 020 7831 0222

Choudhury, Nafeesa I *Jan 1990*
Broad Chare Chambers, Newcastle upon Tyne
p986 . . . . 0191 232 0541

CHOUDHURY, Ms Sadiya BA; BSc L *May 2002*
37, 57, 58, 34
Pump Court Tax Chambers, London WC1
p948 . . . . 020 7414 8080

Chowdury, Mr Nazeer A BA; MPhil I *Jun 2002*
6, 47, 22, 26, 30, 40
Henderson Chambers, London EC4
p937 . . . . 020 7583 9020

CHRISTENSEN, Mr Carlton MSc; PhD I *Jul 1977*
6, 7, 8, 11, 12, 25, 29, 32, 37
10 King's Bench Walk, London EC4
p940 . . . . 020 7353 7742

Christian, Mr Neil MA(Hons) M *Oct 2005*
St Johns Buildings, Preston
p990 . . . . 01772 256100
St Johns Buildings, Chester
p974 . . . . 01244 323070
St Johns Buildings, Manchester
p985 . . . . 0161 214 1500
St Johns Buildings, Liverpool
p982 . . . . 0151 243 6000

Christie, Mr Aidan BA(Oxon); MA(Cantab); Recorder M *Jul 1988*
(Q.C.) *3, 7, 11, 12, 24, 40*
4 Pump Court, London EC4
p947 . . . . 020 7842 5555

Christie, Mr David H BComm I *Jul 1973*
8, 18, 11, 12, 29, 10
7 Bedford Row, London WC1
p924 . . . . 020 7242 3555

Christie, Mr Iain BA(Hons) I *Jul 1989*
16, 50, 51, 36, 56
5RB, London WC1
p948 . . . . 020 7242 2902

Christie, Miss Michelle LLB(Hons) M *Sep 1999*
12, 15, 20, 30
Northampton Chambers, Northampton
p988 . . . . 01604 636271

Christie, Mr Richard LLB(Manc) I *Jul 1986*
(Q.C.) *15, 12, 20*
2 Pump Court, London EC4
p947 . . . . 020 7353 5597

Christie, Mr Robert BA(Oxon) M *Jan 2006*
9, 97, 11, 47, 14, 38, 26, 40, 93, 32
Radcliffe Chambers, London WC2
p949 . . . . 020 7831 0081

CHRISTIE, Mr Simon LLB M *Feb 1988*
15
Chavasse Court Chambers, Liverpool
p980 . . . . 0151 229 2030

Christie-Brown, Ms Sarah M *Oct 1994*
53, 40, 27, 49
Hailsham Chambers, London EC4
p936 . . . . 020 7643 5000

Christopher, Mr Julian BA(Cantab) G *Nov 1988*
15, 62
5 Paper Buildings, London EC4
p946 . . . . 020 7583 6117

CHRISTOPHER-CHAMBERS, Gillian BA(Hons) M *Jul 2003*
11, 22, 12
Five Paper, London EC4
p946 . . . . 020 7815 3200

CHU, Miss Josephine LLB I *Oct 2007*
12, 18, 30
Bank House Chambers, Sheffield
p991 . . . . 0114 275 1223

Chudleigh, Ms Louise BA(Kent); Part-Time Employment Tribunal Chair L *Jul 1987*
18, 36, 56, 55, 51, 27, 48
Old Square Chambers, Bristol
p971 . . . . 0117 930 5100
Old Square Chambers, London WC1
p945 . . . . 020 7269 0300

Chukwuemeka, Mr John O BSc L *Nov 1994*
15, 20, 12, 30
St Johns Buildings, Preston
p990 . . . . 01772 256100
St Johns Buildings, Chester
p974 . . . . 01244 323070
St Johns Buildings, Manchester
p985 . . . . 0161 214 1500
St Johns Buildings, Liverpool
p982 . . . . 0151 243 6000

CHURCH, Ms Camilla MA(Hons)(Law) M *Nov 1998*
53, 12, 68, 84, 89
Thirty Nine Essex Street, London WC2
p932 . . . . 020 7832 1111

Church, Mr John BA L *Nov 1984*
10, 20
Field Court Chambers, London WC1
p933 . . . . 020 7405 6114

Chute, Ms Andrea LLB(Hons); LLM(Hons) M *Oct 1995*
18, 70, 55, 36
Rougemont Chambers, Exeter
p975 . . . . 01392 208484
Tooks Chambers, London EC4
p953 . . . . 020 7842 7575

Ciborowska, Clare BA(Hons) I *Jan 2009*
20, 18, 72, 30, 15, 70
Crown Office Row Chambers, Brighton
p970 . . . . 01273 625625

Ciumei, Mr Charles Gregg BA(Oxon) M *Oct 1991*
Essex Court Chambers, London WC2
p931 . . . . 020 7813 8000

CLAPHAM, Miss Penelope BA(Oxon) I *Jan 2008*
10, 20, 51
1 Garden Court, London EC4
p934 . . . . 020 7797 7900

Clappison, James G *Nov 1981*
Zenith Chambers, Leeds
p979 . . . . 0113 245 5438

CLARE, Ms Allison G *Oct 1992*
15, 62, 34, 36
18 Red Lion Court, London EC4
p949 . . . . 020 7520 6000
18 Red Lion Court (Annexe), Chelmsford
p973 . . . . 01245 280880

CLARE, Mr Michael G *Nov 1986*
15, 25, 36
Octagon House, Norwich
p988 . . . . 01603 623186

Clargo, Mr John MA(Oxon) M *Oct 1994*
11, 2, 88, 89, 97
King's Bench Chambers, Oxford
p989 . . . . 01865 311066
13 King's Bench Walk, London EC4
p940 . . . . 020 7353 7204
3PB, Oxford
p989 . . . . 01865 793736

Claridge, Miss Rachael LLB(Hons) I *Oct 1996*
10, 20
Crown Office Row Chambers, Brighton
p970 . . . . 01273 625625

CLARK, Mr Andrew R MA(Oxon) I *Oct 1994*
40, 8, 11, 7, 30, 25, 48, 12
9 St John Street Chambers, Manchester
p984 . . . . 0161 955 9000

Clark, Mr Dingle BSc(Soton) M *Jul 1981*
Goldsmith Chambers, London EC4
p935 . . . . 020 7353 6802

Clark, Miss Fiona MA(Cantab) M *Jul 1982*
13, 50, 56
8 New Square, London WC2
p943 . . . . 020 7405 4321

Clark, Miss Geraldine LLB(Hons) G *Jul 1988*
11, 3, 41, 5, 49, 24, 62, 40, 35
Serle Court, London WC2
p950 . . . . 020 7242 6105

Clark, Ms Julia E MA(Oxon); MA(Lond) G *Jul 1984*
3, 5, 6, 7, 8, 11, 13, 19, 22, 29, 32, 37, 38
Hogarth Chambers, London WC2
p937 . . . . 020 7404 0404

Clark, Mr Michael L *Jan 2005*
One Essex Court, London EC4
p931 . . . . 020 7583 2000

Clark, Mr Neil I *Jul 2007*
42 Bedford Row, London WC1
p925 . . . . 020 7831 0222

Clark, Mr Neil Andrew LLB(Leeds) I *Jul 1987*
15, 30
No 6 Barristers Chambers, Leeds
p978 . . . . 0113 245 9763

Clark, Mrs Patricia Jane LLB L *Nov 2009*
20, 10
15 Winckley Square, Preston
p991 . . . . 01772 252828

Clark, Mr Paul Robert LLB(L'pool) M *May 1994*
30
Exchange Chambers, Manchester
p983 . . . . 0161 833 2722
Exchange Chambers, Liverpool
p980 . . . . 0151 236 7747
Exchange Chambers, Leeds
p977 . . . . 0113 203 1970

Clark, Mr Peter I *Oct 2000*
2 Pump Court, London EC4
p947 . . . . 020 7353 5597

CLARK, Mr Peter Lestor BA(Oxon); DipLaw M *Nov 1988*
15
Carmelite Chambers, London EC4
p927 . . . . 020 7936 6300

Clark, Miss Rebecca LLB(Sheff) I *Jul 1989*
12, 25, 22, 30, 53
Exchange Chambers, Manchester
p983 . . . . 0161 833 2722
Exchange Chambers, Liverpool
p980 . . . . 0151 236 7747
Exchange Chambers, Leeds
p977 . . . . 0113 203 1970

CLARK, Mr Robert M *Jan 2002*
12
Bank House Chambers, Sheffield
p991 . . . . 0114 275 1223

Clark, Mr Tim LLB(Hons) I *Feb 1993*
15, 51, 62, 72
1 Inner Temple Lane, London EC4
p937 . . . . 020 7427 4400
23 Essex Street, London WC2
p932 . . . . 020 7413 0353

Clark, Mr Timothy M *Jul 1974*
2 New Street, Leicester
p979 . . . . 0116 262 5906

Clark, Ms Tonia Anne BSc(Hons); Deputy District Judge M *Jul 1986*
20, 10
3PB, Winchester
p994 . . . . 01962 868884

CLARK, Mr Wayne LLB(Lond); BCL(Oxon) M *Jul 1982*
Falcon Chambers, London EC4
p933 . . . . 020 7353 2484

Clarke, Miss Amanda M *Jul 1998*
10, 15, 20
Westgate Chambers, Lewes
p980 . . . . 01273 480510

CLARKE, Mr Andrew LLB; BCL; AKC; Accredited Mediator M *Jul 1980*
(Q.C.) *1, 3, 5, 6, 8, 11, 12, 13, 18, 29, 36, 49, 55*
Littleton Chambers, London EC4
p941 . . . . 020 7797 8600

Clarke, Miss Anna Victoria BA(Lond); BA(Oxon) I *Nov 1994*
8, 32, 37, 14, 40
5 Stone Buildings, London WC2
p951 . . . . 020 7242 6201

See p1010 for the Key to Work Categories

CLARKE, Miss Elizabeth LLB(Oxon); BA(Hons)(Cantab) *G Nov 1991*
10, 20
Queen Elizabeth Buildings, London EC4
p948 . . . . . 020 7797 7837

Clarke, Mr Gerard J P MA(Oxon) *M Jul 1986*
1, 16, 18, 36, 29, 51, 55, 56, 52, 50, 76, 89, 46
Blackstone Chambers, London EC4
p926 . . . . . 020 7583 1770

Clarke, Mr Ian *I Jan 2005*
53, 12, 22, 88, 26, 30, 40
1 Chancery Lane, London WC2
p928 . . . . . 0845 634 6666

Clarke, Mr Ivan George Robert LLB *G Nov 1973*
15, 7, 11, 12, 22, 30, 31, 47
5 Pump Court, London EC4
p947 . . . . . 020 7353 2532 / 7583 7133

CLARKE, Mr J Daniel *G Jul 2005*
11, 12, 30, 18, 40, 59, 88, 93
3 Hare Court, London EC4
p937 . . . . . 020 7415 7800

Clarke, Mr Jamie BA(Oxon) *G Nov 1995*
30, 40
Hardwicke, London WC2
p936 . . . . . 020 7242 2523

Clarke, Mr Jeremy *I Jul 1985*
15, 51
New Bailey Chambers, Preston
p990 . . . . . 01772 258087

Clarke, Mr Jonathan BSc(Hons) *I Oct 1999*
15, 62, 22
Exchange Chambers, Manchester
p983 . . . . . 0161 833 2722
Exchange Chambers, Liverpool
p980 . . . . . 0151 236 7747
Exchange Chambers, Leeds
p977 . . . . . 0113 203 1970
Old Square Chambers, Bristol
p971 . . . . . 0117 930 5100
Old Square Chambers, London WC1
p945 . . . . . 020 7269 0300

CLARKE, Miss Laura *M Jan 2003*
10, 20
St Mary's Chambers, Nottingham
p989 . . . . . 0115 950 3503

CLARKE, Lindsay BA(Hons) *G Jul 1999*
20, 12, 30, 62, 94, 67, 84
Oriel Chambers, Liverpool
p981 . . . . . 0151 236 7191 / 236 4321
Oriel Chambers, Preston
p990 . . . . . 01772 254764

Clarke, Miss Lisa LLB *G Oct 1995*
22, 30
Staple Inn Chambers, London WC1
p951 . . . . . 020 7242 5240

Clarke, Mr Malcolm LLB(Hons)(Coventry) *G Oct 1994*
12, 15, 22, 30
King's Bench Godolphin Chambers, Truro
p994 . . . . . 0845 308 1551
King's Bench Godolphin Chambers, Plymouth
p990 . . . . . 0845 308 1551

Clarke, Mr Michael *L Jan 2009*
St John's Chambers, Bristol
p972 . . . . . 0117 921 3456

Clarke, Miss Michelle LLB(Soton) *I Jul 1988*
2 King's Bench Walk, London EC4
p939 . . . . . 020 7353 1746

Clarke, Mr Nicholas *L Oct 2001*
15
18 St John Street Chambers, Manchester
p985 . . . . . 0161 278 1800
Bank House Chambers, Sheffield
p991 . . . . . 0114 275 1223
9 St John Street Chambers, Manchester
p984 . . . . . 0161 955 9000

CLARKE, Mr Patrick J BSc *G Oct 1997*
3, 7, 11, 31, 40, 41, 43, 45, 49, 54, 61, 78, 74
Atkin Chambers, London WC1
p923 . . . . . 020 7404 0102

Clarke, Mr Paul Sebastian MA *G Jan 1997*
8, 22, 40
Maitland Chambers, London WC2
p941 . . . . . 020 7406 1200

Clarke, Mr Rory BA(Cantab) *I Oct 1996*
1, 12, 15, 18, 22, 26, 31, 36
Cornerstone Barristers, London WC1
p929 . . . . . 020 7242 4986

Clarke, Ms Sarah BA(Oxon) *I Jan 2005*
18, 30, 53
3PB, Bristol
p971 . . . . . 0117 928 1520
3 Serjeants' Inn, London EC4
p950 . . . . . 020 7427 5000

CLARKE, Ms Susan LLB(Hons); LLM International Law *M Oct 1996*
12, 30, 40
Oriel Chambers, Liverpool
p981 . . . . . 0151 236 7191 / 236 4321
Oriel Chambers, Preston
p990 . . . . . 01772 254764

CLARKE, Mr Timothy J MA(Cantab) *M Oct 1992*
8, 30, 17, 20, 12
Cornwall Street Chambers, Birmingham
p967 . . . . . 0121 233 7500

CLARKSON, Mr Patrick Robert James *L Jul 1972*
(Q.C.) *31, 36, 46*
Landmark Chambers, London EC4
p941 . . . . . 020 7430 1221

Clarkson, Mr Stuart BA(L'pool) *G Nov 1987*
12, 15, 30
St Ives Chambers, Birmingham
p969 . . . . . 0121 236 0863

CLAXTON, Mr David *M Oct 2008*
15, 62, 18, 25
18 Red Lion Court, London EC4
p949 . . . . . 020 7520 6000
18 Red Lion Court (Annexe), Chelmsford
p973 . . . . . 01245 280880

CLAXTON, Mr Elroy G LLB(Hons); Recorder *I Jul 1983*
15, 36, 91, 72, 70
23 Essex Street, London WC2
p932 . . . . . 020 7413 0353

CLAXTON, Miss Judith LLB *M Oct 1990*
20, 10
St Mary's Chambers, Nottingham
p989 . . . . . 0115 950 3503

Clay, Mr Jonathan BSc; LLB *L Oct 1990*
1, 12, 22, 26, 31, 36
Cornerstone Barristers, London WC1
p929 . . . . . 020 7242 4986

Clay, Mr Robert D Phil(Oxon); MA(Oxon); DipLaw *I Jul 1989*
3, 7, 11, 31, 40, 41, 43, 45, 49, 54, 61, 78, 74
Atkin Chambers, London WC1
p923 . . . . . 020 7404 0102

Clayton, Mr Henry *M Jan 2007*
20, 10
4 Paper Buildings, London EC4
p946 . . . . . 020 7583 0816

Clayton, Mr Nigel LLB *I Jul 1987*
5, 6, 11, 22, 31, 40
Kings Chambers, Manchester
p984 . . . . . 0161 832 9082
Kings Chambers, Leeds
p978 . . . . . 0113 242 1123

CLAYTON, Mr Richard MA(Oxon); Recorder *M Nov 1977*
(Q.C.) *1, 51*
4-5 Gray's Inn Square, London WC1
p935 . . . . . 020 7404 5252

Clayton, Mr Stephen Charles *I May 1973*
15
Atkinson Bevan Chambers, London EC4
p924 . . . . . 020 7353 2112

Cleary, Mr James *M Nov 2003*
KCH Garden Square Chambers, Nottingham
p989 . . . . . 0115 941 8851
KCH Garden Square Chambers, Leicester
p979 . . . . . 0115 941 8851

Cleaver, Mr Tom BA(Cambs) *L Jan 2009*
1, 18, 19, 44, 11, 52
Blackstone Chambers, London EC4
p926 . . . . . 020 7583 1770

Cleaver, Mr Wayne *I Jul 1986*
Nine Bedford Row, London WC1
p924 . . . . . 020 7489 2727

Clee, Mr Christopher LLB(Wales); Recorder *G Jul 1983*
(Q.C.) *15*
Angel Chambers, Swansea
p992 . . . . . 01792 464623

Cleeve, Mr Thomas BSc *L Feb 1993*
12, 15, 22
33 Bedford Row, London WC1
p925 . . . . . 020 7242 6476

Clegg, Mr Adam BA(Hons) *G Nov 1994*
10, 12, 20, 38, 30, 76, 88
Stour Chambers, Canterbury
p972 . . . . . 01227 764899

CLEGG, Mr Simon LLB(Lond) *L Jul 1980*
8, 11, 22, 31, 40
St Philips Chambers, Birmingham
p969 . . . . . 0121 246 7000

Clegg, Mr William LLB(Hons); Recorder *G Jul 1972*
(Q.C.) *15, 36, 62*
2 Bedford Row, London WC1
p924 . . . . . 020 7440 8888

Clemens, Mr Adam *L Dec 1985*
1, 30, 53, 51, 73, 27, 40
7 Bedford Row, London WC1
p924 . . . . . 020 7242 3555

CLEMENT, Miss Joanne BA(Oxon); BCL *G Jan 2002*
1, 55, 51, 76, 26
11KBW, London EC4
p938 . . . . . 020 7632 8500

Clement, Mr Peter Guy LLM; LLB *I Nov 1988*
15
Atkinson Bevan Chambers, London EC4
p924 . . . . . 020 7353 2112

Clement, Mr Ryan W BSc(Hons) *M Oct 1996*
11, 18, 23, 41, 88
Conference Chambers, Harrow
p976 . . . . . 07958 421595

Clements, Miss Paula Kate LLB(Soton) *I Jul 1985*
10, 20
Guildford Chambers, Guildford
p975 . . . . . 01483 539131

Clemes, Mr Andrew LLB(Hons) *G Nov 1984*
6, 12, 15, 20, 22, 30
Angel Chambers, Swansea
p992 . . . . . 01792 464623

Clemitson, Miss Julie LLB(Newc) *I Nov 1991*
15, 12
Broad Chare Chambers, Newcastle upon Tyne
p986 . . . . . 0191 232 0541

Clews, Mr Richard Anthony LLB *G Jul 1986*
15
No 6 Barristers Chambers, Leeds
p978 . . . . . 0113 245 9763

Cliff, Mr Barry George LLB *L Jul 1988*
15, 12, 30
Regent Chambers, Hanley
p976 . . . . . 01782 286666

CLIFF, Miss Elizabeth Dunbar *M Jul 1975*
10, 15, 20
Chavasse Court Chambers, Liverpool
p980 . . . . . 0151 229 2030

Cliff, Mr Graham Hilton LLB; Recorder *M Jul 1973*
30, 53, 40, 94, 63, 39, 84
No5 Chambers, Bristol
p971 . . . . . 0845 210 5555
No5 Chambers, London EC4
p944 . . . . . 0845 210 5555
No5 Chambers, Birmingham
p968 . . . . . 0845 210 5555

Cliff, Mr Paul Richard LLB *G Oct 1992*
15, 12, 20, 23, 30, 25, 36
Regent Chambers, Hanley
p976 . . . . . 01782 286666

Clifford, Mr James BA(Oxon) *L Nov 1984*
Maitland Chambers, London WC2
p941 . . . . . 020 7406 1200

Clifford, Miss Victoria LLB *G Jul 2002*
10, 20, 63
No5 Chambers, Bristol
p971 . . . . . 0845 210 5555
No5 Chambers, London EC4
p944 . . . . . 0845 210 5555
No5 Chambers, Birmingham
p968 . . . . . 0845 210 5555

Clifton, Ms Jane BA(Oxon) *M Oct 2001*
11, 22, 30
Lamb Chambers, London EC4
p941 . . . . . 020 7797 8300

Climie, Mr Stephen BA *L Jul 1982*
30, 53, 15, 62, 84
King's Bench Godolphin Chambers, Truro
p994 . . . . . 0845 308 1551
King's Bench Godolphin Chambers, Plymouth
p990 . . . . . 0845 308 1551
Outer Temple Chambers, London WC2
p945 . . . . . 020 7353 6381

CLINE, Robert MA(Cantab) *G Oct 2002*
1, 15, 84, 51, 30
Atlantic Chambers, Liverpool
p980 . . . . . 0151 236 4421

CLIVE, Mr Nigel Philip Trevor LLB(Hons) *G Nov 1998*
15
Wilberforce Chambers, Hull
p976 . . . . . 01482 323264

Cloherty, Mr Adam *L Jan 2005*
XXIV Old Buildings, London WC2
p944 . . . . . 020 7691 2424

CLOSE, Mr Ben *L Jan 2009*
Citadel Chambers, Birmingham
p967 . . . . . 0121 233 8500

Close, Mr Douglas MA; BCL(Oxon) *L Nov 1991*
8, 37
Serle Court, London WC2
p950 . . . . . 020 7242 6105

Close, Mr Jon LLB *L Oct 1997*
72, 15, 70, 80, 82, 62
Exchange Chambers, Manchester
p983 . . . . . 0161 833 2722
Exchange Chambers, Liverpool
p980 . . . . . 0151 236 7747
Exchange Chambers, Leeds
p977 . . . . . 0113 203 1970

CLOUGH, Richard William Butler *I Nov 1971*
10, 20
Renaissance Chambers, London WC1
p949 . . . . . 020 7404 1111

Clover, Ms Sarah BA(Hons); LLM *L Nov 1993*
25, 31, 36, 26, 83, 46, 96, 49
No5 Chambers, Bristol
p971 . . . . . 0845 210 5555
No5 Chambers, London EC4
p944 . . . . . 0845 210 5555
No5 Chambers, Birmingham
p968 . . . . . 0845 210 5555

Clutten, Rebecca *I Jan 2008*
1, 12, 43, 76, 18, 46, 2, 22, 51, 23, 25, 26, 54, 31, 60, 36
Francis Taylor Building, London EC4
p934 . . . . . 020 7353 8415

CLUTTERBUCK, Mr Andrew BA(Oxon) *M Oct 1992*
6, 8, 11
4 Stone Buildings, London WC2
p951 . . . . . 020 7242 5524

Coade, Ms Georgina *G Jul 2005*
15, 20
No 6 Barristers Chambers, Leeds
p978 . . . . . 0113 245 9763

Coates, Mr George Alexander Nigel MA(Cantab) *M Nov 1990*
12, 15, 20
Guildford Chambers, Guildford
p975 . . . . . 01483 539131

Coates, Miss Holly *L Oct 2008*
10, 12, 18, 20, 88, 26, 30, 94
Becket Chambers, Canterbury
p972 . . . . . 01227 786331
Becket Chambers, Maidstone
p982 . . . . . 01622 230957

Coates, Mr John LLB *M Nov 1988*
15
1 Gray's Inn Square, London WC1
p935 . . . . . 020 7405 8946

COBB, Mr Stephen William Scott LLB(Hons)(L'pool) *I Jul 1985*
(Q.C.) *10, 20, 63, 1, 14*
1 Garden Court, London EC4
p934 . . . . . 020 7797 7900
Trinity (Newcastle) Chambers, Newcastle upon Tyne
p987 . . . . . 0191 232 1927
Trinity (Teesside) Chambers, Middlesbrough
p986 . . . . . 01642 247569

Cobbe, Mr Matthew LLB; MSc(Econ) *G Oct 1998*
15, 18, 30
9 Park Place, Cardiff
p973 . . . . . 029 2038 2731

Cobill, Mr Nicholas *M Jan 2003*
5, 6, 7, 11, 29, 88, 47, 67, 69, 81, 86, 89, 93, 97
No5 Chambers, Bristol
p971 . . . . . 0845 210 5555
No5 Chambers, London EC4
p944 . . . . . 0845 210 5555
No5 Chambers, Birmingham
p968 . . . . . 0845 210 5555

13

COBURN, Mr Michael BA(Oxon) *I Nov 1990*
(Q.C.) *3, 11, 12, 24, 35, 41*
20 Essex Street, London WC2
p932 . . . . . 020 7842 1200

Coccaro, Mr Carlo Eduardo LLB(Hons)(Southampton) *L Jul 2007*
12
Fenners Chambers, Cambridge
p972 . . . . . 01223 368761

COCKAYNE, Miss Kerry *L Jul 2002*
20, 10
St Mary's Chambers, Nottingham
p989 . . . . . 0115 950 3503

Cockerill, Miss Sara E MA(Oxon) *L Oct 1990*
(Q.C.)
Essex Court Chambers, London WC2
p931 . . . . . 020 7813 8000

COCKINGS, Mr Giles F S KSc(Hons); LLB(Hons) *M Oct 1996*
15
Furnival Chambers, London EC4
p934 . . . . . 020 7405 3232

COCKS, Mr David *L Jun 1961*
(Q.C.) *15, 36, 62, 46, 95*
18 Red Lion Court, London EC4
p949 . . . . . 020 7520 6000
18 Red Lion Court (Annexe), Chelmsford
p973 . . . . . 01245 280880

COE, Miss Rosalind Recorder *M Jan 1983*
(Q.C.) *10, 53, 20, 85, 26, 27, 30, 40*
7 Bedford Row, London WC1
p924 . . . . . 020 7242 3555

Coen, Ms Yvonne Anne MA; Recorder *M Nov 1982*
(Q.C.) *15, 20*
7 Bedford Row, London WC1
p924 . . . . . 020 7242 3555

Coffey, Mr John LLB(Lond); Recorder *M Nov 1970*
(Q.C.) *15, 62, 91*
3 Temple Gardens, London EC4
p952 . . . . . 020 7353 3102

Cogan, Mr Michael BA *M Feb 1986*
15, 20
6 King's Bench Walk, London EC4
p939 . . . . . 020 7583 0695 / 7353 4931

Coghill-Smith, Ms Abigail *G Nov 1997*
15, 20
33 Chancery Lane, London WC2
p928 . . . . . 020 7440 9950

COGHLAN, Mr Terence MA(Oxon); Recorder *I Dec 1968*
(Q.C.) *12, 27, 30, 36*
1 Crown Office Row, London EC4
p929 . . . . . 020 7797 7500

Coghlin, Mr Thomas *I Jan 1998*
11, 50, 56, 55, 18, 51, 30, 1
Cloisters, London EC4
p928 . . . . . 020 7827 4000

Cogin, Mr Leo BA(Hons); LLB(Hons) *M Oct 2000*
10, 20
4 Brick Court Chambers, London EC4
p927 . . . . . 020 7832 3200
Crown Office Row Chambers, Brighton
p970 . . . . . 01273 625625

Cogley, Mr Stephen William LLB(Hons) *G Nov 1984*
5, 6, 8, 11, 24, 89, 29, 40
Quadrant Chambers, London EC4
p948 . . . . . 020 7583 4444

Cohen, Miss Abigail LLB(Bham) *L Jan 2005*
Henderson Chambers, London EC4
p937 . . . . . 020 7583 9020

Cohen, Mr Edward MA(Cantab) *M Jul 1972*
1, 3, 5, 11, 18, 24, 29, 38, 62
11 Stone Buildings, London WC2
p951 . . . . . 020 7831 6381

COHEN, Mr Howard BA(Hons)(Oxon); MPhil(Cantab) *G Oct 1999*
30, 40, 12, 57
Farrar's Building, London EC4
p933 . . . . . 020 7583 9241

Cohen, Mr Jonathan BA *L Jul 1974*
(Q.C.) *10, 12, 20, 40*
4 Paper Buildings, London EC4
p946 . . . . . 020 7583 0816
Pump Court Chambers, Swindon
p993 . . . . . 01793 539899
Pump Court Chambers, Winchester
p994 . . . . . 01962 868161
Pump Court Chambers, London EC4
p947 . . . . . 020 7353 0711

Cohen, Mr Jonathan Michael BA(Oxon) *G Oct 1999*
11, 18
Cloisters, London EC4
p928 . . . . . 020 7827 4000
Littleton Chambers, London EC4
p941 . . . . . 020 7797 8600

Cohen, Ms Linda *M Jul 1985*
18, 12, 11, 22, 55
39 Windsor Road, London N3
p954 . . . . . 020 8349 9194

Cohen, Ms Marisa *I Jan 2010*
1 Pump Court, London EC4
p947 . . . . . 020 7842 7070

COHEN, Mr Michael *G Oct 1992*
15, 20, 23
10 King's Bench Walk, London EC4
p940 . . . . . 020 7353 7742

Cohen, Mr Raphael *L Jul 1981*
6, 8, 11, 12, 48, 18, 20, 62, 63, 29, 40
Broadway House Chambers, Leeds
p977 . . . . . 0113 246 2600
Broadway House Chambers, Bradford
p969 . . . . . 01274 722560

COHEN, Mr Ross *I Nov 2001*
Furnival Chambers, London EC4
p934 . . . . . 020 7405 3232

Cohen, Miss Samantha *I Nov 1995*
15, 51
Nine Bedford Row, London WC1
p924 . . . . . 020 7489 2727

Coke, Mr Edward LLB(Warw) *I Jul 1976*
15, 12, 30
St Ives Chambers, Birmingham
p969 . . . . . 0121 236 0863

Coker, Mr William John LLB; Recorder *I Jul 1973*
(Q.C.) *15, 62, 27*
7 Bedford Row, London WC1
p924 . . . . . 020 7242 3555

Colbey, Mr Richard LLB(Exon) *I Jul 1984*
11, 30, 7, 22, 40, 13
Guildhall Chambers, Portsmouth
p990 . . . . . 023 9275 2400
Lamb Chambers, London EC4
p941 . . . . . 020 7797 8300

Colborne, Miss Michelle Diane LLB *G May 1993*
(Q.C.) *15, 18, 30*
Broadway House Chambers, Leeds
p977 . . . . . 0113 246 2600
Broadway House Chambers, Bradford
p969 . . . . . 01274 722560

Coldrick, Mr Emmet *G Jan 2004*
11
Quadrant Chambers, London EC4
p948 . . . . . 020 7583 4444

COLE, Mr Edward MA(Oxon) *G Jul 1980*
Falcon Chambers, London EC4
p933 . . . . . 020 7353 2484

COLE, Ms Georgina BA(Hons)(Oxon); LLM *L Jul 2007*
1 Garden Court, London EC4
p934 . . . . . 020 7797 7900

COLE, Mr Gordon *I Jan 1974*
(Q.C.)
Furnival Chambers, London EC4
p934 . . . . . 020 7405 3232
Exchange Chambers, Manchester
p983 . . . . . 0161 833 2722
Exchange Chambers, Liverpool
p980 . . . . . 0151 236 7747
Exchange Chambers, Leeds
p977 . . . . . 0113 203 1970
Lombard Chambers, London EC1
p941 . . . . . 020 7107 2100

Cole, Mr Justin *I May 1992*
15, 13, 62, 18, 25
5 Paper Buildings, London EC4
p946 . . . . . 020 7583 6117

COLE, Miss Justine Amanda LLB *I Nov 1994*
15, 20
Bank House Chambers, Sheffield
p991 . . . . . 0114 275 1223

Cole, Mr Nicholas BSc(B'ham); CPE(Nott'm) *L Oct 1993*
10, 12, 15, 20, 22, 27, 30
St Ives Chambers, Birmingham
p969 . . . . . 0121 236 0863

Cole, Mr Richard LLB *G Oct 2000*
12, 15, 30
Civitas Law, Cardiff
p972 . . . . . 0845 071 3007

Cole, Mr Robert *M Jan 1991*
10, 20, 32, 40, 37
Broadway House Chambers, Leeds
p977 . . . . . 0113 246 2600
Broadway House Chambers, Bradford
p969 . . . . . 01274 722560

Cole-Wilson, Ms Lois BA(Hons); MA; DipLaw *I Nov 1995*
1 Gray's Inn Square, London WC1
p935 . . . . . 020 7405 8946

COLECLOUGH, Ms Suzanne *I Mar 2005*
20
St Philips Chambers, Birmingham
p969 . . . . . 0121 246 7000

Coleman, Mr Anthony J S MA(Oxon); Recorder *M Jul 1973*
30, 12
3PB, Winchester
p994 . . . . . 01962 868884

COLEMAN, Mr Bruce Robert LLB(Hons)(Bris) *I Jul 1972*
10, 20
1 Garden Court, London EC4
p934 . . . . . 020 7797 7900

Coleman, Mr Daniel *G Nov 1994*
1 Gray's Inn Square, London WC1
p935 . . . . . 020 7405 8946

Coleman, Miss Elizabeth J *I Jul 1985*
10, 20
4 Paper Buildings, London EC4
p946 . . . . . 020 7583 0816

Coleman, Mr Guy LLB(Hons) *I Nov 1998*
30
Lamb Chambers, London EC4
p941 . . . . . 020 7797 8300

Coleman, Mr Richard J L LLM(Yale); BA(Cantab) *L Feb 1994*
Fountain Court Chambers, London EC4
p934 . . . . . 020 7583 3335

COLES, Mr Steven MA(Cantab) *M Jul 1983*
74, 7, 11, 12, 24, 29, 40
Crown Office Chambers, London EC4
p929 . . . . . 020 7797 8100

Coles-Harrington, Miss Frances *L Jan 2001*
2 Pump Court, London EC4
p947 . . . . . 020 7353 5597

COLIN, Mr Giles BA(Dunelm); DipLaw *I Feb 1994*
12, 18, 20, 22, 30, 36
1 Crown Office Row, London EC4
p929 . . . . . 020 7797 7500

Collaco Moraes, Francis BA(Law) *L Jan 1985*
8, 11, 97, 38, 88, 29, 32, 93
3 Stone Buildings, London WC2
p951 . . . . . 020 7242 4937

Collard, Mr Michael LLB(Bris) *M Jul 1986*
5 Pump Court, London EC4
p947 . . . . . 020 7353 2532 / 7583 7133

COLLERY, Mr Shane *L Jul 1988*
15, 36, 62
18 Red Lion Court, London EC4
p949 . . . . . 020 7520 6000
18 Red Lion Court (Annexe), Chelmsford
p973 . . . . . 01245 280880

COLLETT, Mr Gavin Charles LLB(Hons) *I Oct 1993*
12, 15, 22, 31, 46, 47, 42
Rougemont Chambers, Exeter
p975 . . . . . 01392 208484

Collett, Mr Ivor DipLaw; BA(Hons) *M Nov 1995*
12, 30, 40, 53, 62, 24
1 Chancery Lane, London WC2
p928 . . . . . 0845 634 6666

Collett, Mr Michael BA(Oxon) *G Oct 1995*
3, 11, 12, 24, 35, 41
20 Essex Street, London WC2
p932 . . . . . 020 7842 1200

Colley, Dr Peter McLean BSc; PhD; LLB(Lond) *G Jul 1989*
13, 19, 44, 45, 48, 50
Hogarth Chambers, London WC2
p937 . . . . . 020 7404 0404

Collie, Mr Peter LLB(Hons) *M Nov 1994*
7, 40, 41, 49, 96, 74, 21, 3
No5 Chambers, Bristol
p971 . . . . . 0845 210 5555
No5 Chambers, London EC4
p944 . . . . . 0845 210 5555
No5 Chambers, Birmingham
p968 . . . . . 0845 210 5555

Collier, Miss Jane BA(Cantab); MBA(Lond) *M Nov 1994*
1, 11, 13, 29, 41, 51, 5, 81, 46, 76, 89
Blackstone Chambers, London EC4
p926 . . . . . 020 7583 1770

Collier, Mr John Greenwood MA; LLB(Cantab) *G Nov 1961*
20 Essex Street, London WC2
p932 . . . . . 020 7842 1200

Collier, Mr Martin MA(Oxon) *G Jul 1982*
8, 12, 20, 22, 31
Fenners Chambers, Cambridge
p972 . . . . . 01223 368761

Collingnon, Ms Laura *L Jan 1998*
Thomas More Chambers, London WC2
p952 . . . . . 020 7404 7000

Collings, Mr Andrew *G Nov 1987*
15, 20
5 King's Bench Walk, London EC4
p939 . . . . . 020 7353 5638

Collings, Mr Matthew G B LLB(Hons)(Lond) *L Jul 1985*
(Q.C.)
Maitland Chambers, London WC2
p941 . . . . . 020 7406 1200

Collings, Mr Nicholas LLB *G Nov 1997*
3, 7, 11, 31, 40, 41, 43, 45, 49, 54, 61, 78, 74
Atkin Chambers, London WC1
p923 . . . . . 020 7404 0102

Collingwood, Mr Timothy BA(Oxon); BCL *G Oct 1996*
6, 8, 11, 29, 37, 38, 62, 97
Serle Court, London WC2
p950 . . . . . 020 7242 6105

COLLINS, Mr Ben BA(Cantab) *M Nov 1996*
12, 18, 20, 27, 30, 40, 53, 56
1 Crown Office Row, London EC4
p929 . . . . . 020 7797 7500

Collins, Mrs Catherine *M Nov 2000*
Iscoed Chambers, Swansea
p993 . . . . . 01792 652988

COLLINS, Miss Deborah *G Jan 2007*
20
St Philips Chambers, Birmingham
p969 . . . . . 0121 246 7000

COLLINS, Ms Deirdre *I Nov 1999*
15, 20, 70
Mitre House Chambers, London WC1
p942 . . . . . 020 7307 7100

Collins, Mr James BA(Cantab) *G Feb 1995*
Essex Court Chambers, London WC2
p931 . . . . . 020 7813 8000

Collins, Miss Jennifer BSc(Hons); DipLaw *G Oct 1994*
10, 15, 20
Eastbourne Chambers, Eastbourne
p975 . . . . . 01323 642102

Collins, Mr John Irish Bar 1966; Australian Bar 1989 *M Jul 1967*
3, 6, 8, 10, 11, 12, 13, 15, 18, 20, 23, 25, 28, 29, 30, 31, 32, 36, 37
Westgate Chambers, Lewes
p980 . . . . . 01273 480510

Collins, John M *M Jul 1956*
2, 6, 8, 11, 12, 29, 30, 32, 37, 38, 40, 47, 53, 67, 84, 88, 93
Zenith Chambers, Leeds
p979 . . . . . 0113 245 5438

COLLINS, Mr Ken G W LLM; LLB(Hons) *I Oct 1996*
10, 20
29 Bedford Row, London WC1
p925 . . . . . 020 7404 1044

Collins, Miss Louisa *L Nov 2004*
15, 94, 84
Argent Chambers, London WC2
p923 . . . . . 020 7556 5500

COLLINS, Mr Michael SC; MA(NUI); LLM(NUI); LLM(PENN) *L Jan 1987*
11, 44, 19
Monckton Chambers, London WC1
p942 . . . . . 020 7405 7211
Temple Tax Chambers, London EC4
p952 . . . . . 020 7353 7884 / 7353 8982
No 6 Barristers Chambers, Leeds
p978 . . . . . 0113 245 9763

COLLINS, Ms Rosaleen LLB(Kent) *I Nov 1996*
15
Guildhall Chambers, Bristol
p970 . . . . . 0117 930 9000

See p1010 for the Key to Work Categories

COLLINS, Mrs Sally LLB M *Oct 2002*
10, 20
Wilberforce Chambers, Hull
p976 . . . . . 01482 323264

COLLINS, Miss Siobhan I *Jan 2005*
Citadel Chambers, Birmingham
p967 . . . . . 0121 233 8500

Collinson, Ms Alicia MA; M Phil(Oxon) M *Jul 1982*
20, 10, 40, 30, 63
Harcourt Chambers, London EC4
p936 . . . . . 0844 561 7135
Harcourt Chambers, Oxford
p989 . . . . . 0844 561 7135

Collis, Mr Michael MA(Cantab) I *Nov 2004*
15, 62, 70, 91
15 New Bridge Street Chambers, London EC4
p943 . . . . . 020 7842 1900

Colman, Mr Andrew LLB L *Jul 1980*
15, 62
2 Hare Court, London EC4
p937 . . . . . 020 7353 5324

Colover, Mr Robert Mark M *Nov 1975*
15, 62
4 Breams Buildings, London EC4
p927 . . . . . 020 7092 1900

Coltart, Mr Christopher BA; MA(Oxon) I *Nov 1998*
15, 62, 36
2 Hare Court, London EC4
p937 . . . . . 020 7353 5324

Colter, Lucy L *Jan 2008*
Four New Square, London WC2
p943 . . . . . 020 7822 2000

Colton, Mr Simon I *Nov 1999*
One Essex Court, London EC4
p931 . . . . . 020 7583 2000

COLVILLE, Mr Iain David LLB; Legal Advisor I *Jul 1989*
22, 31, 1, 26, 25
Arden Chambers, London WC1
p923 . . . . . 020 7242 4244

COMAISH, Mr Andrew J C MA M *Nov 1989*
18, 12, 7, 22, 13, 47
Wilberforce Chambers, Hull
p976 . . . . . 01482 323264

COMB, Mr David I *Oct 2005*
1, 15, 23, 46, 70
Trinity (Newcastle) Chambers, Newcastle upon Tyne
p987 . . . . . 0191 232 1927
Trinity (Teesside) Chambers, Middlesbrough
p986 . . . . . 01642 247569

COMERTON, Julie-Anne G *Jan 2003*
4 KBW, London EC4
p938 . . . . . 020 7822 8822

Comfort, Miss Polly-Anne LLB L *Feb 1988*
2 Dr Johnson's Buildings, London EC4
p930 . . . . . 020 7936 2613

Comiskey, Mr Reuben BA(Oxon) L *Nov 2002*
11, 6, 18, 38
11 Stone Buildings, London WC2
p951 . . . . . 020 7831 6381

Commins, Mr Andrew LLB M *Oct 2004*
20, 10
St John's Chambers, Bristol
p972 . . . . . 0117 921 3456

COMMON, Mr Hamish BVC; BEng L *Jul 2003*
15, 62
23 Essex Street, London WC2
p932 . . . . . 020 7413 0353

Compton, Mr Allan LLB(Hons) I *Nov 1994*
15, 62
2 Bedford Row, London WC1
p924 . . . . . 020 7440 8888

Compton, Mr Benjamin Recorder L *Nov 1979*
(Q.C.) *84, 30, 53*
Outer Temple Chambers, London WC2
p945 . . . . . 020 7353 6381

Compton, Mr Gareth MA(Cantab) M *Mar 1997*
30, 40, 68, 94
No5 Chambers, Bristol
p971 . . . . . 0845 210 5555
No5 Chambers, London EC4
p944 . . . . . 0845 210 5555
No5 Chambers, Birmingham
p968 . . . . . 0845 210 5555

Compton, Ms Justine M *Jan 2005*
1, 22, 51
1 Pump Court, London EC4
p947 . . . . . 020 7842 7070

Compton, Timothy BA I *Nov 1984*
15, 10, 20
12 College Place, Southampton
p992 . . . . . 023 8032 0320
Renaissance Chambers, London WC1
p949 . . . . . 020 7404 1111

COMPTON-RICKETT, Miss Mary LLB(Bris) G *Nov 1972*
20, 10
7 Harrington Street Chambers, Liverpool
p981 . . . . . 0151 242 0707

Comyn, Mr Timothy LLB(Hull) I *Jul 1980*
1, 26, 31, 60, 36
Francis Taylor Building, London EC4
p934 . . . . . 020 7353 8415

Concannon, Mr Timothy I *Jul 1993*
1, 6, 7, 8, 9, 10, 11, 12, 13, 15, 16, 18, 20, 22, 25, 27, 29, 30, 31, 36
Guildhall Chambers, Portsmouth
p990 . . . . . 023 9275 2400

CONE, Mr John LLB(L'pool) M *Jul 1975*
11, 38, 97
Erskine Chambers, London WC2
p931 . . . . . 020 7242 5532

CONEY, Mr Christopher Ronald Ramsden LLB(Soton) I *Jul 1979*
6, 7, 8, 11, 12, 22, 40, 55
Tanfield Chambers, London WC1
p951 . . . . . 020 7421 5300

CONLAN, Ms Tina G *Jul 2002*
22, 12
Arden Chambers, London WC1
p923 . . . . . 020 7242 4244

Conlon, Mr Michael I *Jul 1974*
(Q.C.) *34*
Temple Tax Chambers, London EC4
p952 . . . . . 020 7353 7884 / 7353 8982

Connell, Miss Amy M *Oct 2006*
10, 20
East Anglian Chambers, Norwich
p988 . . . . . 01603 617351
East Anglian Chambers, Colchester
p975 . . . . . 01206 572756
East Anglian Chambers, Chelmsford
p973 . . . . . 01245 215660
East Anglian Chambers, Ipswich
p976 . . . . . 01473 214481

Connell, Mr Edward BA(Jt Hons); DipLaw M *Oct 1996*
15
1 Inner Temple Lane, London EC4
p937 . . . . . 020 7427 4400
5 St Andrew's Hill, London EC4
p950 . . . . . 020 7332 5400

Connerty, Anthony MA; FCIArb I *Jul 1974*
3, 7, 11, 12, 41, 21, 40, 49, 67, 75, 78, 96
Lamb Chambers, London EC4
p941 . . . . . 020 7797 8300
Zenith Chambers, Leeds
p979 . . . . . 0113 245 5438

Connolly, Ms Barbara Winifred LLB M *Jul 1986*
10, 26, 20, 1, 63
7 Bedford Row, London WC1
p924 . . . . . 020 7242 3555

Connolly, Mr Dominic LLB M *Feb 1989*
12, 15, 22, 30, 20
5 St Andrew's Hill, London EC4
p950 . . . . . 020 7332 5400

CONNOLLY, Miss Joanne LLB M *Oct 1992*
12, 18, 30, 53, 55
9 St John Street Chambers, Manchester
p984 . . . . . 0161 955 9000

Connolly, Miss Martina L *Nov 1999*
12, 15, 20
11 King's Bench Walk, Leeds
p978 . . . . . 0113 297 1200

Connolly, Mr Oliver M *Jul 1997*
11, 12
36 Bedford Row, London WC1
p925 . . . . . 020 7421 8000

Connolly, Mr Simon LLB M *Jul 1981*
15, 62
3 Temple Gardens, London EC4
p952 . . . . . 020 7353 3102

Connolly, Mr Stephen L *Jan 2003*
5, 8, 11, 22, 29, 40, 36, 24, 6
Exchange Chambers, Manchester
p983 . . . . . 0161 833 2722
Exchange Chambers, Liverpool
p980 . . . . . 0151 236 7747
Exchange Chambers, Leeds
p977 . . . . . 0113 203 1970

Connolly, Mr Timothy BA(Plymouth) I *Mar 2004*
15, 30
St Johns Buildings, Preston
p990 . . . . . 01772 256100
St Johns Buildings, Chester
p974 . . . . . 01244 323070
St Johns Buildings, Manchester
p985 . . . . . 0161 214 1500
St Johns Buildings, Liverpool
p982 . . . . . 0151 243 6000

CONNOR, Mr Gino G *Nov 1974*
Furnival Chambers, London EC4
p934 . . . . . 020 7405 3232

Connor, Mr Mark LLB I *May 1994*
15
St Johns Buildings, Preston
p990 . . . . . 01772 256100
St Johns Buildings, Chester
p974 . . . . . 01244 323070
St Johns Buildings, Manchester
p985 . . . . . 0161 214 1500
St Johns Buildings, Liverpool
p982 . . . . . 0151 243 6000

CONNORS, Hannah I *Jan 2008*
Pump Court Chambers, Swindon
p993 . . . . . 01793 539899
Pump Court Chambers, Winchester
p994 . . . . . 01962 868161
Pump Court Chambers, London EC4
p947 . . . . . 020 7353 0711

CONNORS, Ms Jess G *Apr 2000*
1, 5, 11, 18, 40, 7
Thirty Nine Essex Street, London WC2
p932 . . . . . 020 7832 1111

Connors, Mrs Sophie M *Oct 2009*
20, 10
4 Paper Buildings, London EC4
p946 . . . . . 020 7583 0816

CONOLLY, Mr Oliver BA; PhD L *Oct 2003*
37, 57, 58, 34
Pump Court Tax Chambers, London WC1
p948 . . . . . 020 7414 8080

Conrad, Mr Alan BA; Recorder M *Jul 1976*
(Q.C.)
Lincoln House Chambers, Manchester
p984 . . . . . 0161 832 5701

CONRATH, Mr Philip G *Jul 1972*
10, 15, 20
Tanfield Chambers, London WC1
p951 . . . . . 020 7421 5300

CONSOLO, Dr Henrietta Katherine MBChB; BSc(Hons)(MedSci); MA; GDL M *Nov 2006*
30
12 King's Bench Walk, London EC4
p940 . . . . . 020 7583 0811

Constable, Mr Adam BA(Oxon) I *Jan 1995*
3, 7, 11, 24, 40
Keating Chambers, London WC2
p938 . . . . . 020 7544 2600

Constable, Mr John Martyn Chester LLB; LLM; MA G *Feb 1972*
1, 6, 8, 10, 47, 48, 18, 20, 22, 23, 63
Old Court Chambers, Middlesbrough
p986 . . . . . 01642 232523

Constantine, Mr Stephen M *Jan 1992*
15, 30, 70, 72
Old Court Chambers, Middlesbrough
p986 . . . . . 01642 232523

Convey, Mr Christopher L *Nov 1994*
33 Chancery Lane, London WC2
p928 . . . . . 020 7440 9950

Conway, Mr Charles LLB(Hons) M *Jul 1969*
15, 62
2 Bedford Row, London WC1
p924 . . . . . 020 7440 8888

Coode, Mr Jonathan BA(East Anglia) M *Jul 1984*
King's Bench Chambers, Oxford
p989 . . . . . 01865 311066
13 King's Bench Walk, London EC4
p940 . . . . . 020 7353 7204

COOK, Mr Alexander BA(Oxon); LLM(Washington) L *Oct 2008*
6, 11, 97, 62, 38
4 Stone Buildings, London WC2
p951 . . . . . 020 7242 5524

COOK, Miss Alison LLB(Manc) G *Feb 1989*
10, 20
St Philips Chambers, Birmingham
p969 . . . . . 0121 246 7000

Cook, Mr Christopher BSc; BCom; DipLaw I *Oct 1990*
6, 8, 11, 13, 29, 40, 16, 7, 38, 45, 47
Exchange Chambers, Manchester
p983 . . . . . 0161 833 2722
Exchange Chambers, Liverpool
p980 . . . . . 0151 236 7747
Exchange Chambers, Leeds
p977 . . . . . 0113 203 1970

COOK, Miss Emily L *Jan 2002*
15
25 Bedford Row, London WC1
p925 . . . . . 020 7067 1500

Cook, Mr Gary I *Jan 1989*
15
No 8 Chambers, Birmingham
p968 . . . . . 0121 236 5514

COOK, Mr Ian Reginald Blacklin BA(Lond) I *Nov 1994*
1, 10, 12, 20
1 King's Bench Walk, London EC4
p938 . . . . . 020 7936 1500

COOK, Ms Kate BA(Oxon); LLM(NYU) M *Nov 1990*
1, 19, 51, 46, 33
Matrix Chambers, London WC1
p942 . . . . . 020 7404 3447

Cook, Miss Katherine L *Jul 2007*
1 Hare Court, London EC4
p936 . . . . . 020 7797 7070

Cook, Ms Mary LLB(Cardiff) G *Jul 1982*
1, 12, 22, 26, 31, 8, 18, 25, 36, 29
Cornerstone Barristers, London WC1
p929 . . . . . 020 7242 4986

Cook, Mr Matthew M *Nov 1999*
One Essex Court, London EC4
p931 . . . . . 020 7583 2000

COOK, Mr Oliver James Alexander LLB(Aberystwyth) G *Oct 2004*
15
Chavasse Court Chambers, Liverpool
p980 . . . . . 0151 229 2030

Cook, Mr Paul LLB M *Nov 1992*
15, 62
Albion Chambers, Bristol
p970 . . . . . 0117 927 2144

Cook, Ms Tina Gail BA(Hons)(Oxon) M *Jul 1988*
1, 10, 26, 31
42 Bedford Row, London WC1
p925 . . . . . 020 7831 0222

COOKE, Miss Charlotte M *Jan 2008*
5, 6, 8, 11, 97, 38, 69
South Square, London WC1
p950 . . . . . 020 7696 9900

Cooke, Mr Duncan Matthew I *Mar 2010*
15
Atkinson Bevan Chambers, London EC4
p924 . . . . . 020 7353 2112

COOKE, Mr Peter LLB(Manc); LLM(Environmental Law)(DMU) L *Jul 1985*
11, 74, 48, 67, 18, 46, 82, 62, 84, 25, 54, 31, 36, 61
Cornwall Street Chambers, Birmingham
p967 . . . . . 0121 233 7500

Cooke, Mr Richard I *Jul 2005*
30, 68, 94
No5 Chambers, Bristol
p971 . . . . . 0845 210 5555
No5 Chambers, London EC4
p944 . . . . . 0845 210 5555
No5 Chambers, Birmingham
p968 . . . . . 0845 210 5555

COOKE, Mr Stephen G *Jan 2006*
3 Temple Gardens, London EC4
p952 . . . . . 020 7353 3102

COOKE, Mr Tom G *Mar 2006*
Pallant Chambers, Chichester
p974 . . . . . 01243 784538

13

Cooksley, Mr Nigel MA(Cantab); Chairman of BAR Council
CFA Panel I *Jul 1975*
(Q.C.) *27, 30, 53, 40, 56, 48*
Old Square Chambers, Bristol
p971 . . . . . 0117 930 5100
Old Square Chambers, London WC1
p945 . . . . . 020 7269 0300

Coombe, Mr Peter BA(Oxon) M *Nov 1993*
King's Bench Chambers, Oxford
p989 . . . . . 01865 311066
13 King's Bench Walk, London EC4
p940 . . . . . 020 7353 7204

Coombes, Mr Timothy J BA(Dunelm) I *Jul 1980*
10, 12, 15, 18, 20, 22, 25, 30
3PB, Bournemouth
p969 . . . . . 01202 292102

Coombes Davies, Mrs Mair BSc; BArch; PhD; Arbitrator; Adjudicator L *Jun 1988*
7, 22, 31
Civitas Law, Cardiff
p972 . . . . . 0845 071 3007

COONAN, Mr Kieran Recorder of the Crown Court (1996) G *Jul 1971*
(Q.C.) *53, 30*
1 Crown Office Row, London EC4
p929 . . . . . 020 7797 7500

Cooper, Mr Ben LLB; BVC L *Nov 2000*
18, 30, 53, 55, 36, 51
Old Square Chambers, Bristol
p971 . . . . . 0117 930 5100
Old Square Chambers, London WC1
p945 . . . . . 020 7269 0300
Doughty Street Chambers, London WC1
p930 . . . . . 020 7404 1313

Cooper, Miss Christine I *Jul 2006*
Field Court Chambers, London WC1
p933 . . . . . 020 7405 6114

Cooper, Miss Claire L *Jan 2002*
15, 62
5 St Andrew's Hill, London EC4
p950 . . . . . 020 7332 5400

Cooper, Ms Danielle L *Oct 1999*
15, 51
Tooks Chambers, London EC4
p953 . . . . . 020 7842 7575

Cooper, Mr Douglas I *Jan 2004*
St Johns Buildings, Preston
p990 . . . . . 01772 256100
St Johns Buildings, Chester
p974 . . . . . 01244 323070
St Johns Buildings, Manchester
p985 . . . . . 0161 214 1500
St Johns Buildings, Liverpool
p982 . . . . . 0151 243 6000

Cooper, Elisabeth M *Jan 2008*
St Johns Buildings, Preston
p990 . . . . . 01772 256100
St Johns Buildings, Chester
p974 . . . . . 01244 323070
St Johns Buildings, Manchester
p985 . . . . . 0161 214 1500
St Johns Buildings, Liverpool
p982 . . . . . 0151 243 6000

Cooper, Mr Gilead P MA(Oxon); DipLaw M *Nov 1983*
(Q.C.) *6, 8, 11, 22, 29, 32, 37, 9, 14, 40*
3 Stone Buildings, London WC2
p951 . . . . . 020 7242 4937

Cooper, Mr Ian Mark MA(History) M *Mar 1998*
5, 8, 11, 6, 40
Kings Chambers, Manchester
p984 . . . . . 0161 832 9082

COOPER, Mr John I *Jul 1985*
84, 30, 46, 47
Crown Office Chambers, London EC4
p929 . . . . . 020 7797 8100
25 Bedford Row, London WC1
p925 . . . . . 020 7067 1500

Cooper, Mr Jonathan G *Oct 1992* OBE
51, 12
Doughty Street Chambers, London WC1
p930 . . . . . 020 7404 1313

COOPER, Mr Mark BA(Cantab) L *Jan 2005*
12, 30, 62
Oriel Chambers, Liverpool
p981 . . . . . 0151 236 7191 / 236 4321
Oriel Chambers, Preston
p990 . . . . . 01772 254764
Kings Chambers, Leeds
p978 . . . . . 0113 242 1123

Cooper, Mr Nicholas LLB; DipEd I *Nov 1998*
1 Gray's Inn Square, London WC1
p935 . . . . . 020 7405 8946

Cooper, Mr Nigel LLB(Leeds); LLM(Lond); Dip EI(Amsterdam) L *Jul 1987*
19, 11, 24, 3, 35
Quadrant Chambers, London EC4
p948 . . . . . 020 7583 4444

Cooper, Mr Peter John G *Nov 1996*
St Ives Chambers, Birmingham
p969 . . . . . 0121 236 0863

Cooper, Ms Samantha G *Oct 2007*
Fenners Chambers, Cambridge
p972 . . . . . 01223 368761

Cooper, Miss Sarah Lucy BA(Hons)(Dunelm); DipLaw I *Nov 1993*
1, 7, 10, 12, 15, 20, 21, 23, 24, 26, 30, 31, 33
Thomas More Chambers, London WC2
p952 . . . . . 020 7404 7000

COPE, Siri BSc(Bris); CPE(City) I *Nov 1997*
6, 8, 9, 11, 14, 22, 29, 32, 37, 40
Falcon Chambers, London EC4
p933 . . . . . 020 7353 2484

Cope, Ms Stephanie LLB(Hons)(UWE) L *Jan 2008*
30
St John's Chambers, Bristol
p972 . . . . . 0117 921 3456

COPELAND, Mr Miles J S BA(Hons)(Cantab) L *Oct 2004*
13, 45
3 New Square, London WC2
p943 . . . . . 020 7405 1111

Copley, Mr James I *Oct 1997*
18, 23
4 Paper Buildings, London EC4
p946 . . . . . 020 7583 0816

Coplin, Mr Richard BA(Hons) M *Oct 1997*
3, 7, 11, 24, 40
Keating Chambers, London WC2
p938 . . . . . 020 7544 2600

COPPEL, Mr Jason BA(Oxon); LLM(EUI Florence) I *Nov 1994*
1, 11, 18, 19, 26, 51
11KBW, London EC4
p938 . . . . . 020 7632 8500

COPPEL, Mr Philip BA(Hons); LLB(ANU) L *Nov 1994*
(Q.C.) *1, 7, 11, 12, 26, 31, 18, 45, 46, 55*
4-5 Gray's Inn Square, London WC1
p935 . . . . . 020 7404 5252

Coppola, Miss Anna Francesca BA(Lond); DipLaw L *Nov 1996*
12, 13, 16, 18, 50, 51, 56
5RB, London WC1
p948 . . . . . 020 7242 2902

Corben, Mr Paul MA(Cantab); FCIArb G *Jul 1979*
3, 7, 11, 12, 18, 22, 24, 27, 29, 30
5 Pump Court, London EC4
p947 . . . . . 020 7353 2532 / 7583 7133

Corbett, James LLB; LLM(Exon); FCIArb I *Jul 1975*
(Q.C.) *8, 11, 18*
Serle Court, London WC2
p950 . . . . . 020 7242 6105
Zenith Chambers, Leeds
p979 . . . . . 0113 245 5438

Cordara, Mr Roderick C MA(Cantab); Counsel to the Department of Trade; SC (Australia) M *Jul 1975*
(Q.C.)
Essex Court Chambers, London WC2
p931 . . . . . 020 7813 8000

Cordery, Mr Philip G *Jan 2003*
New Court Chambers, Newcastle upon Tyne
p987 . . . . . 0191 232 1980

Cordey, Mr Dan G *Nov 1990*
York Chambers, York
p995 . . . . . 01904 620048
York Chambers, Newcastle upon Tyne
p987 . . . . . 0191 206 4677

Cordrey, Mr Thomas BA(Cantab)(Law) L *Jul 2006*
30, 18, 11, 12, 15, 24
Devereux Chambers, London WC2
p930 . . . . . 020 7353 7534

Corfield, Miss Louise BA(Hons) I *Oct 2008*
66, 6, 8, 11, 47, 67, 14, 55, 18, 38, 88, 89, 29, 32, 93, 37
No5 Chambers, Bristol
p971 . . . . . 0845 210 5555
No5 Chambers, London EC4
p944 . . . . . 0845 210 5555
No5 Chambers, Birmingham
p968 . . . . . 0845 210 5555

Corfield, Miss Sheelagh LLB(Bris) M *Jul 1975*
20, 10
St John's Chambers, Bristol
p972 . . . . . 0117 921 3456

Corkery, Mr Michael L *Nov 1949*
(Q.C.) *15, 62*
5 Paper Buildings, London EC4
p946 . . . . . 020 7583 6117

CORLESS, John MTheol(St Andrews) M *Nov 1984*
17, 25, 30, 40, 53
Atlantic Chambers, Liverpool
p980 . . . . . 0151 236 4421

CORNER, Mr Timothy Frank MA; BCL(Oxon) G *Nov 1981*
(Q.C.) *1, 46, 22, 26, 31, 51*
4-5 Gray's Inn Square, London WC1
p935 . . . . . 020 7404 5252

Cornwall, Miss Natalia BA M *Jul 2007*
15, 20, 30
Exchange Chambers, Manchester
p983 . . . . . 0161 833 2722
Exchange Chambers, Liverpool
p980 . . . . . 0151 236 7747
Exchange Chambers, Leeds
p977 . . . . . 0113 203 1970

Cornwall, Miss Virginia LLB(Hons) M *Oct 1990*
15
Albion Chambers, Bristol
p970 . . . . . 0117 927 2144
1 Inner Temple Lane, London EC4
p937 . . . . . 020 7427 4400

CORNWELL, Mr James Matthew BA(Oxon) M *Jan 2002*
1, 18, 26, 51, 55, 73, 76
11KBW, London EC4
p938 . . . . . 020 7632 8500

Corrie, Mr Matthew BA(Hons)(Manc) M *Jun 2006*
King's Bench Chambers, Oxford
p989 . . . . . 01865 311066
13 King's Bench Walk, London EC4
p940 . . . . . 020 7353 7204

CORRIGAN, Mr Peter A MA(Oxon) M *Jul 1973*
12, 15, 29, 30
Carmelite Chambers, London EC4
p927 . . . . . 020 7936 6300

Corrin, Ms Lucy LLB(Hons) M *Oct 2001*
51, 15
Doughty Street Chambers, London WC1
p930 . . . . . 020 7404 1313

Corsellis, Mr Nicholas LLB L *Jul 1992*
15, 25, 60, 62
3 Temple Gardens, London EC4
p952 . . . . . 020 7353 3102

CORY-WRIGHT, Mr Charles A. M *Feb 1984*
(Q.C.) *30, 24, 40, 53, 7*
Thirty Nine Essex Street, London WC2
p932 . . . . . 020 7832 1111

Cosedge, Mr Andrew John LLB(Exon) I *Jul 1972*
8, 9, 14, 29, 32, 34, 37, 54
3 Stone Buildings, London WC2
p951 . . . . . 020 7242 4937

Cosgrove, Mr Patrick J G *Jul 1976*
(Q.C.) *15*
Broad Chare Chambers, Newcastle upon Tyne
p986 . . . . . 0191 232 0541

Cosgrove, Mr Thomas James BA(Cantab) I *Oct 1994*
1, 11, 12, 15, 18, 20, 22, 26, 30, 31, 36
Cornerstone Barristers, London WC1
p929 . . . . . 020 7242 4986

COSTELLO, Mr Brian M *Jan 2007*
4 King's Bench Walk, London EC4
p939 . . . . . 020 7822 7000

Coster, Mr Ronald BSc(Lancs); DipLaw L *Jul 1989*
1, 8, 12, 22, 26, 30
42 Bedford Row, London WC1
p925 . . . . . 020 7831 0222

Cottage, Miss Rosina LLB(Bris) I *Nov 1988*
15, 62, 20, 65, 81, 39, 38, 84
9 Gough Square, London EC4
p935 . . . . . 020 7832 0500

Cotter, Mr Barry LLB(Lond) L *Jul 1985*
(Q.C.) *11, 27, 30, 36, 48, 53, 39*
Old Square Chambers, Bristol
p971 . . . . . 0117 930 5100
Old Square Chambers, London WC1
p945 . . . . . 020 7269 0300

Cotter, Mr Mark M *Nov 1994*
15
Holborn Chambers, London WC2
p937 . . . . . 020 7242 6060
5 St Andrew's Hill, London EC4
p950 . . . . . 020 7332 5400

Cotter, Mr Nicholas BA L *Oct 1999*
15, 84
1 Paper Buildings, London EC4
p946 . . . . . 020 7353 3728

Cotter, Miss Rachel M *Nov 1994*
20, 10
No5 Chambers, Bristol
p971 . . . . . 0845 210 5555
No5 Chambers, London EC4
p944 . . . . . 0845 210 5555
No5 Chambers, Birmingham
p968 . . . . . 0845 210 5555

COTTERELL, Mr David BSc L *Jan 2001*
Albion Chambers, Bristol
p970 . . . . . 0117 927 2144

Cotton, Miss Diana MA(Oxon) M *Jun 1964*
(Q.C.) *12, 15, 18, 27, 30, 36*
Devereux Chambers, London WC2
p930 . . . . . 020 7353 7534

COTTON, Ms Heidi E L *Jan 1998*
15
Bank House Chambers, Sheffield
p991 . . . . . 0114 275 1223

Cotton, Mr Stephen David LLB(Hons); LLM(City) L *Mar 1998*
10, 20
College Chambers, Southampton
p992 . . . . . 023 8023 0338

COTTRELL, Mr Matthew R LLB(Hons) G *Oct 1996*
12, 30, 22, 40, 11
Oriel Chambers, Liverpool
p981 . . . . . 0151 236 7191 / 236 4321
Oriel Chambers, Preston
p990 . . . . . 01772 254764

COTTRELL, Mr Stephen BA(Oxon) I *Oct 1998*
Temple Garden Chambers, London EC4
p952 . . . . . 020 7583 1315

Couch, Miss Elizabeth I *Jul 2003*
20, 10
4 Paper Buildings, London EC4
p946 . . . . . 020 7583 0816

Couch, Mr Stephen BA I *Mar 2005*
15
37 Park Square Chambers, Leeds
p978 . . . . . 0113 243 9422

Coughlan, Mr John M *Nov 1999*
30, 40, 53, 27, 12, 68, 94
No5 Chambers, Bristol
p971 . . . . . 0845 210 5555
No5 Chambers, London EC4
p944 . . . . . 0845 210 5555
No5 Chambers, Birmingham
p968 . . . . . 0845 210 5555

COUGHLIN, Ms Elizabeth M *Nov 1989*
Furnival Chambers, London EC4
p934 . . . . . 020 7405 3232

COUGHLIN, Mr Vincent M *Jul 1980*
(Q.C.) *72, 15, 62*
18 Red Lion Court, London EC4
p949 . . . . . 020 7520 6000
18 Red Lion Court (Annexe), Chelmsford
p973 . . . . . 01245 280880

COUGHTRIE, Mr Scott LLB(Hons) L *Jan 2000*
St Ives Chambers, Birmingham
p969 . . . . . 0121 236 0863

Coulter, Barry I *Nov 1985*
Clerksroom - Administration Centre, Taunton
p993 . . . . . 0845 083 3000

Counsell, Mr James H MA(Cantab) I *Jul 1984*
30, 53, 40, 81, 12, 5, 11, 8
Outer Temple Chambers, London WC2
p945 . . . . . 020 7353 6381

Counsell, Miss Lynne M BA; DipLaw I *Jul 1986*
8, 11, 22, 29, 32, 37, 2, 9, 14
9 Stone Buildings Barristers Chambers, London WC2
p951 . . . . . 020 7404 5055

COUPLAND, Mr Steven L *Nov 1993*
15
1 High Pavement, Nottingham
p988 . . . . . 0115 941 8218

See p1010 for the Key to Work Categories

Courtenay, Mr Charles P MA(Cantab) I *Jan 1999*
8, 22, 37, 40
Maitland Chambers, London WC2
p941 . . . . . 020 7406 1200

Courts, Mr Robert L *Jan 2003*
3PB, Oxford
p989 . . . . . 01865 793736

COUSENS, Mr Michael P L *Feb 1973*
Carmelite Chambers, London EC4
p927 . . . . . 020 7936 6300

Couser, Mr James LLB; LLM; BCL L *May 2000*
13 Old Square Chambers, London WC2
p945 . . . . . 020 7831 4445

Cousins, Mr Jeremy LLB; Deputy High Court Judge M *Jul 1977*
(Q.C.) *5, 11, 38, 69, 81, 97, 29, 37*
11 Stone Buildings, London WC2
p951 . . . . . 020 7831 6381

Coventry, Mr Charles LLB(Hons)(Bris) G *Jan 2007*
30, 18
St John's Chambers, Bristol
p972 . . . . . 0117 921 3456

Cover, Ms Martha BA; LLB(Lond) G *Nov 1979*
20, 10
Coram Chambers, London EC1
p929 . . . . . 020 7092 3700

COVINGTON, Miss Rebecca M *Mar 2006*
10, 20
St Mary's Chambers, Nottingham
p989 . . . . . 0115 950 3503

COWAN, Mr David M *Nov 2006*
1, 22, 26
Arden Chambers, London WC1
p923 . . . . . 020 7242 4244

COWAN, Mr Peter S M MA(Oxon); Recorder M *Jul 1980*
5, 7, 11, 12, 25, 29, 30, 36, 47, 40, 18, 96
Oriel Chambers, Liverpool
p981 . . . . . 0151 236 7191 / 236 4321
Oriel Chambers, Preston
p990 . . . . . 01772 254764

Coward, Mr John Stephen LLB; Recorder I *Apr 1964*
(Q.C.) *15*
7 Bedford Row, London WC1
p924 . . . . . 020 7242 3555

COWE, Ms Mary I *Nov 2006*
15
Guildhall Chambers, Bristol
p970 . . . . . 0117 930 9000

COWEN, Mr Gary LLB(Bris) I *Oct 1990*
Falcon Chambers, London EC4
p933 . . . . . 020 7353 2484

Cowen, Mr Jonathan BA(Oxon); DipLaw M *Nov 1983*
8, 12, 30, 20, 40, 14, 10
Chartlands Chambers, Northampton
p988 . . . . . 01604 603322
Field Court Chambers, London WC1
p933 . . . . . 020 7405 6114

Cowen, Mr Timothy BA(L'pool) I *Oct 1993*
8, 40
11 Stone Buildings, London WC2
p951 . . . . . 020 7831 6381

Cowey, Miss Sarah M *Oct 2006*
41, 24, 35, 61
7 King's Bench Walk, London EC4
p940 . . . . . 020 7910 8300

Cowley, Mr Robert LLB L *Oct 1992*
15
No 8 Chambers, Birmingham
p968 . . . . . 0121 236 5514

COWTON, Miss Catherine BA(Hons)(Cantab) M *Nov 1995*
20
Queen Elizabeth Buildings, London EC4
p948 . . . . . 020 7797 7837

Cox, Mr Bryan R LLB(Hons) M *Oct 1979*
(Q.C.) *12, 22, 1, 15, 30*
Park Court Chambers, Leeds
p978 . . . . . 0113 243 3277

COX, Mr Carwyn LLB(Hons)(Dunelm); PG Diplaw L *Oct 2002*
30, 18, 12, 15
Farrar's Building, London EC4
p933 . . . . . 020 7583 9241

Cox, Mr Dominic BA(Hons); CPE L *Oct 1994*
15, 95
Argent Chambers, London WC2
p923 . . . . . 020 7556 5500

Cox, Mr Geoffrey BA(Cantab) M *Jul 1982*
(Q.C.) *1, 12, 15, 16, 20, 36*
Thomas More Chambers, London WC2
p952 . . . . . 020 7404 7000

COX, Mr Jason LLB G *Oct 1992*
30, 11, 40, 53
Ropewalk Chambers, Nottingham
p989 . . . . . 0115 947 2581

Cox, Mr Jonathan L *Jan 2005*
KCH Garden Square Chambers, Nottingham
p989 . . . . . 0115 941 8851
KCH Garden Square Chambers, Leicester
p979 . . . . . 0115 941 8851

Cox, Mr Lindsay LLB(East Anglia) M *Jun 1984*
15
1 Paper Buildings, London EC4
p946 . . . . . 020 7353 3728

COX, Mr Nicholas BA(Oxon); MBA(Warw); Junior Counsel to the Crown (A) M *Oct 1992*
6, 8, 11, 29, 40
4 Stone Buildings, London WC2
p951 . . . . . 020 7242 5524

COX, Nigel John BA; MA; DipLaw I *Nov 1986*
10, 20
Renaissance Chambers, London WC1
p949 . . . . . 020 7404 1111

COX, Olivia M *Nov 2007*
Atlantic Chambers, Liverpool
p980 . . . . . 0151 236 4421

Cox, Mr Raymond Edwin BA(Oxon) G *Jul 1982*
(Q.C.)
Fountain Court Chambers, London EC4
p934 . . . . . 020 7583 3335

Cox, Miss Sian M *Jul 2008*
20, 10, 67
Harcourt Chambers, London EC4
p936 . . . . . 0844 561 7135
Harcourt Chambers, Oxford
p989 . . . . . 0844 561 7135

Cox, Mr Simon F LLB I *Nov 1992*
18, 23, 51
Doughty Street Chambers, London WC1
p930 . . . . . 020 7404 1313

Cox, Miss Sita BA M *Nov 1987*
7, 10, 12, 20, 30, 76, 93, 31
Stour Chambers, Canterbury
p972 . . . . . 01227 764899

COX, Miss Tamsin Victoria Elizabeth BA(Hons)(Oxon); CPE L *Oct 2005*
22
Falcon Chambers, London EC4
p933 . . . . . 020 7353 2484

Coxhill, Mr Fraser L *Jan 2004*
15
QEB Hollis Whiteman, London EC4
p948 . . . . . 020 7933 8855

Coyle, Mr Anthony LLB(Hons) L *Nov 2003*
Zenith Chambers, Leeds
p979 . . . . . 0113 245 5438

COYLE, Stephen M *Oct 1998*
10, 20
Renaissance Chambers, London WC1
p949 . . . . . 020 7404 1111

CRABB, Mr Richard Blechyndem M *Nov 1975*
15, 20, 30
Colleton Chambers, Exeter
p975 . . . . . 01392 274898

CRABB, Ms Samantha LLB I *Nov 1996*
3, 10, 12, 15, 18, 20, 25, 30
Citadel Chambers, Birmingham
p967 . . . . . 0121 233 8500

Crabtree, Mr Richard LLB G *Jul 1974*
15
3 Temple Gardens, London EC4
p952 . . . . . 020 7353 3102

Crabtree, Mr Simon J G LLB L *Nov 1988*
10, 20, 36
St Johns Buildings, Preston
p990 . . . . . 01772 256100
St Johns Buildings, Chester
p974 . . . . . 01244 323070
St Johns Buildings, Manchester
p985 . . . . . 0161 214 1500
St Johns Buildings, Liverpool
p982 . . . . . 0151 243 6000

CRADDOCK, Miss Xanthe BA(Hons)(Oxon) M *Oct 2000*
15, 12, 20
Trinity (Newcastle) Chambers, Newcastle upon Tyne
p987 . . . . . 0191 232 1927
Trinity (Teesside) Chambers, Middlesbrough
p986 . . . . . 01642 247569

CRAGG, Miss Janet L *Jul 2005*
20, 23, 10
Kenworthy's Chambers, Manchester
p984 . . . . . 0161 832 4036

Cragg, Mr Stephen J LLB; MA M *Nov 1996*
1, 22, 51, 21
Doughty Street Chambers, London WC1
p930 . . . . . 020 7404 1313

CRAIG, Mr Aubrey J I *Nov 1987*
5, 6, 8, 11, 12, 97, 47, 67, 38, 88, 32, 40, 93
Chancery House Chambers, Leeds
p977 . . . . . 0113 244 6691
St Philips Chambers, Birmingham
p969 . . . . . 0121 246 7000

CRAIG, Mr David BSc(Hons); MPhil(Cantab) I *Oct 1997*
18, 55
Essex Court Chambers, London WC2
p931 . . . . . 020 7813 8000

CRAIG, Mr Nicholas BA(Oxon) I *Oct 1998*
5, 11, 24, 35
3 Verulam Buildings, London WC1
p953 . . . . . 020 7831 8441

CRAIL, Miss Ross MA(Oxon) L *Jul 1986*
11, 22, 37
New Square Chambers, London WC2
p943 . . . . . 020 7419 8000

CRAMMOND, Mr Andrew LLB(Hons)(Durham) L *Jan 2008*
11, 18, 30, 63, 38, 8
Trinity (Newcastle) Chambers, Newcastle upon Tyne
p987 . . . . . 0191 232 1927
Trinity (Teesside) Chambers, Middlesbrough
p986 . . . . . 01642 247569

CRAMPIN, Miss Cecily Mary MA(Oxon); MSc(Manc); DPhil(Oxon); CPE; BVC M *Oct 2008*
11, 18, 93
Tanfield Chambers, London WC1
p951 . . . . . 020 7421 5300

Crampin, Mr Paul LLB M *Oct 1992*
15, 82, 62
Lamb Building, Brighton
p970 . . . . . 01273 820490
Lamb Building, London EC4
p940 . . . . . 020 7797 7788

Crampin, Mr Peter MA(Oxon) M *Nov 1976*
(Q.C.) *8, 9, 14, 22, 29, 32, 37, 40*
Radcliffe Chambers, London WC2
p949 . . . . . 020 7831 0081

Cramsie, Mr Sinclair James Beresford LLB(Lond) I *Nov 1988*
18
King's Bench Chambers, Oxford
p989 . . . . . 01865 311066
13 King's Bench Walk, London EC4
p940 . . . . . 020 7353 7204

Cran, Mr Mark LLB(Bris) G *Jul 1973*
(Q.C.) *25, 5, 11, 24, 19, 1*
Brick Court Chambers, London WC2
p927 . . . . . 020 7379 3550

Crane, Miss Denece Elizabeth LLB(Hons) L *Oct 1999*
12, 15, 25
4 Breams Buildings, London EC4
p927 . . . . . 020 7092 1900

Crane, Mr Michael BA(Oxon) M *Nov 1975*
(Q.C.)
Fountain Court Chambers, London EC4
p934 . . . . . 020 7583 3335

Crane, Miss Rebecca BSc(Hons) G *Oct 1998*
15, 12, 20, 10, 68, 70
36 Bedford Row, London WC1
p925 . . . . . 020 7421 8000

Crane, Ms Suzanne LLB(Hons) L *Nov 1995*
10, 12, 15, 18, 20, 30
4 Rowchester Court, Birmingham
p968 . . . . . 0121 233 2327

Cranfield, Mr James LLD(Hons)(Wales) I *Jan 2002*
15, 20
Albion Chambers, Bristol
p970 . . . . . 0117 927 2144

CRANFIELD, Mr Peter Anthony BA(Oxon); BCL G *Jul 1982*
2, 6, 8, 9, 11, 19, 22, 29, 32, 34, 37
3 Verulam Buildings, London WC1
p953 . . . . . 020 7831 8441

CRANFIELD, Mr Tony LLB M *Nov 1975*
12, 15, 20
Bank House Chambers, Sheffield
p991 . . . . . 0114 275 1223

Crangle, Miss Charlotte G *Jan 1995*
St Johns Buildings, Preston
p990 . . . . . 01772 256100
St Johns Buildings, Chester
p974 . . . . . 01244 323070
St Johns Buildings, Manchester
p985 . . . . . 0161 214 1500
St Johns Buildings, Liverpool
p982 . . . . . 0151 243 6000

Crangle, Mr Thomas G *Jul 2002*
40, 24, 7, 89, 11
4 Pump Court, London EC4
p947 . . . . . 020 7842 5555

Cranidge, Miss Ruth LLB(Hons) L *Oct 2001*
Park Court Chambers, Leeds
p978 . . . . . 0113 243 3277

Cranmer-Brown, Mr Michael Timothy BA(Oxon) M *Nov 1986*
15
KCH Garden Square Chambers, Nottingham
p989 . . . . . 0115 941 8851
KCH Garden Square Chambers, Leicester
p979 . . . . . 0115 941 8851

Cranny, Miss Amanda L *Nov 1984*
KCH Garden Square Chambers, Nottingham
p989 . . . . . 0115 941 8851
KCH Garden Square Chambers, Leicester
p979 . . . . . 0115 941 8851

CRANSTON-MORRIS, Mr Wayne LLB L *Jul 1986*
15, 36, 62, 72
23 Essex Street, London WC2
p932 . . . . . 020 7413 0353

CRAPPER, Ms Sadie G *Nov 2004*
Thirty Nine Essex Street, London WC2
p932 . . . . . 020 7832 1111

Crasnow, Ms Rachel M *Nov 1994*
55, 18, 30, 1, 51, 26
Cloisters, London EC4
p928 . . . . . 020 7827 4000

CRAVEN, Mr Edward L *Jan 2007*
Matrix Chambers, London WC1
p942 . . . . . 020 7404 3447

Craven, Mr Robert Michael BA; BCL G *Nov 1979*
8, 12, 15, 20, 22, 30
Iscoed Chambers, Swansea
p993 . . . . . 01792 652988

Crawford, Mr Colin LLB; LLM M *Jul 1997*
1, 26, 31, 46, 54
Kings Chambers, Leeds
p978 . . . . . 0113 242 1123
Kings Chambers, Manchester
p984 . . . . . 0161 832 9082

CRAWFORD, Miss Georgina Aynsley LLB I *Oct 2006*
18, 30
12 King's Bench Walk, London EC4
p940 . . . . . 020 7583 0811

Crawford, Mr Grant MA(Cantab) M *Jul 1974*
5, 6, 8, 11, 22, 29, 32, 34, 37, 40
Radcliffe Chambers, London WC2
p949 . . . . . 020 7831 0081

CRAWFORD, Professor James SC LLB; BA(Adelaide); D Phil(Oxon) G *Jun 1999*
33, 51, 46, 19
Matrix Chambers, London WC1
p942 . . . . . 020 7404 3447

CRAWFORD, Mr Lincoln LLB(Brunel); Recorder G *Nov 1977*
OBE
1, 11, 16, 18, 26, 31, 33, 23, 40, 53
12 King's Bench Walk, London EC4
p940 . . . . . 020 7583 0811

Crawford, Miss Marie LLB(Hons) L *Oct 1992*
10, 11, 12, 15, 20, 25, 36
Eastbourne Chambers, Eastbourne
p975 . . . . . 01323 642102

Crawford, Mr Robert MA(Cantab); Recorder L *Jul 1976*
12, 15, 30, 2, 25
15 Winckley Square, Preston
p991 . . . . . 01772 252828

CRAWFORD, Mr Shane LLB; LLM L *Oct 1996*
15, 18
St Philips Chambers, Birmingham
p969 . . . . . 0121 246 7000

13

CRAWLEY, Mr Gary Thomas LLB; LLM(Lond) *M Feb 1988*
10, 20
1 Garden Court, London EC4
p934 . . . . . . 020 7797 7900

CRAWLEY, Mr Kevin BSc; MA *G Jul 1998*
20, 10
Trinity (Newcastle) Chambers, Newcastle upon Tyne
p987 . . . . . . 0191 232 1927
Trinity (Teesside) Chambers, Middlesbrough
p986 . . . . . . 01642 247569

Crawshaw, Mr Simon BA(Hons); LLM *L Jul 2005*
3, 7, 11, 31, 40, 41, 43, 45, 49, 54, 61, 78, 74
Atkin Chambers, London WC1
p923 . . . . . . 020 7404 0102

Cray, Mr Timothy BA(Durham) *I Nov 1989*
15, 62
6 King's Bench Walk, London EC4
p939 . . . . . . 020 7583 0410

Crean, Mr Anthony BA *G Jul 1987*
(Q.C.) *31, 46, 54, 43, 60, 61, 78, 96*
No5 Chambers, Bristol
p971 . . . . . . 0845 210 5555
No5 Chambers, London EC4
p944 . . . . . . 0845 210 5555
No5 Chambers, Birmingham
p968 . . . . . . 0845 210 5555

Creer, Miss Andy *L Sep 2006*
88, 93
Hardwicke, London WC2
p936 . . . . . . 020 7242 2523

CREGAN, John-Paul BCL *M Nov 1990*
10, 12, 20, 36
Renaissance Chambers, London WC1
p949 . . . . . . 020 7404 1111

Crew, Ms Gillian *G Jan 1998*
53, 30, 26
Ely Place Chambers, London EC1
p931 . . . . . . 020 7400 9600

Criddle, Miss Betsan BA(Law); BVC(Inns of Court School of Law) *M Oct 2002*
18, 30
Old Square Chambers, Bristol
p971 . . . . . . 0117 930 5100
Old Square Chambers, London WC1
p945 . . . . . . 020 7269 0300

Cridland, Mr Simon James BA(Hons)(Cantab) *M Mar 1999*
12, 27, 30, 40, 53, 68, 85, 36
3 Serjeants' Inn, London EC4
p950 . . . . . . 020 7427 5000

CRIGMAN, Mr David Recorder *G Jul 1969*
(Q.C.) *15, 72, 70*
St Philips Chambers, Birmingham
p969 . . . . . . 0121 246 7000

Crilley, Mr Darrel *I Feb 1996*
12
St Johns Buildings, Preston
p990 . . . . . . 01772 256100
St Johns Buildings, Chester
p974 . . . . . . 01244 323070
St Johns Buildings, Manchester
p985 . . . . . . 0161 214 1500
St Johns Buildings, Liverpool
p982 . . . . . . 0151 243 6000

Crinion, Mr Charles *M Jan 2002*
1 Mitre Court Buildings, London EC4
p942 . . . . . . 020 7452 8900

Crinnion, Miss Neena *G Oct 1997*
15, 25, 94, 82, 62
Castle Chambers, Harrow
p976 . . . . . . 020 8423 6579
3 Temple Gardens, London EC4
p952 . . . . . . 020 7353 3102

Crispin, Mr Stephen *L Nov 2008*
20, 10, 67
Harcourt Chambers, London EC4
p936 . . . . . . 0844 561 7135
Harcourt Chambers, Oxford
p989 . . . . . . 0844 561 7135

Critchley, Mr John *G Jul 1985*
Field Court Chambers, London WC1
p933 . . . . . . 020 7405 6114

Croall, Mr Simon MA(Cantab) *M Nov 1986*
(Q.C.) *11, 3, 5, 24, 35*
Quadrant Chambers, London EC4
p948 . . . . . . 020 7583 4444

Croally, Mr Miles *M Nov 1987*
Field Court Chambers, London WC1
p933 . . . . . . 020 7405 6114

Crocker, Ms Beth *M Nov 2006*
15, 62, 70, 72, 80, 82, 89, 94
15 New Bridge Street Chambers, London EC4
p943 . . . . . . 020 7842 1900

Crockett, Mr Thomas *G Jan 2009*
53, 12, 22, 88, 26, 30, 40
1 Chancery Lane, London WC2
p928 . . . . . . 0845 634 6666

Cronshaw, Mr Michael MA(Oxon); MSc; DipLaw *M Oct 1993*
10, 20, 12, 18, 22, 24, 30, 40
3 Dr Johnson's Buildings, London EC4
p930 . . . . . . 020 7353 4854

Crookenden, Mr Simon R MA(Cantab); Recorder *G Nov 1975*
(Q.C.)
Essex Court Chambers, London WC2
p931 . . . . . . 020 7813 8000

Cropp, Mr Nicholas LLB; BCL *G Nov 1999*
1, 70, 72, 18, 80, 81, 62, 51, 21, 89
7 Bedford Row, London WC1
p924 . . . . . . 020 7242 3555

Crorie, Mr Ethu LLB(Hons)(LSE) *M Aug 2000*
15, 83, 12, 25
12 College Place, Southampton
p992 . . . . . . 023 8032 0320

Crosfill, Mr John *M Nov 1995*
Field Court Chambers, London WC1
p933 . . . . . . 020 7405 6114

Croskell, Mr Marcus BSc(Jt Hons) *L Jul 2003*
15
East Anglian Chambers, Norwich
p988 . . . . . . 01603 617351
East Anglian Chambers, Colchester
p975 . . . . . . 01206 572756
East Anglian Chambers, Chelmsford
p973 . . . . . . 01245 215660
East Anglian Chambers, Ipswich
p976 . . . . . . 01473 214481

Crosland, Mr James Benjamin MA *G Feb 1993*
15
Broadway House Chambers, Leeds
p977 . . . . . . 0113 246 2600
Broadway House Chambers, Bradford
p969 . . . . . . 01274 722560

Cross, Mr Anthony *G Jan 1982*
(Q.C.)
Lincoln House Chambers, Manchester
p984 . . . . . . 0161 832 5701

CROSS, Ms Caroline LLB *G Jan 2006*
1, 53, 67, 18, 46, 12, 85, 51, 26, 30, 40, 57, 68
1 Crown Office Row, London EC4
p929 . . . . . . 020 7797 7500

Cross, Mr James MA(Oxon) *G Jul 1985*
(Q.C.) *7, 11, 12, 24, 30*
4 Pump Court, London EC4
p947 . . . . . . 020 7842 5555

Cross, Ms Joanna BSc; MBCHB; DipLaw *L Oct 1992*
10, 12, 20, 30
Park Court Chambers, Leeds
p978 . . . . . . 0113 243 3277

Cross, Mr Paul BA *G Jul 1981*
12, 15, 16, 18, 22, 25, 30
New Court Chambers, Newcastle upon Tyne
p987 . . . . . . 0191 232 1980

Cross, Mr Richard BA(Hons)(Bris) *L Oct 1993*
Thomas More Chambers, London WC2
p952 . . . . . . 020 7404 7000

CROSS, Mr Tom *L Jan 2007*
1, 76, 18, 51
11KBW, London EC4
p938 . . . . . . 020 7632 8500

CROSSLEY, Mr Dominic *G Oct 2006*
5, 6, 8, 11, 12, 97, 67, 38, 88, 29, 40
Chancery House Chambers, Leeds
p977 . . . . . . 0113 244 6691

Crossley, Miss Joanne BA(Hons) *M Jan 1994*
20
St Pauls Chambers, Leeds
p979 . . . . . . 0113 245 5866

Crossley, Justin *I Nov 1993*
1, 22, 30
Zenith Chambers, Leeds
p979 . . . . . . 0113 245 5438

Crossley, Mr Steven R *I Nov 1992*
10, 68, 15, 70, 72, 85, 27
St Pauls Chambers, Leeds
p979 . . . . . . 0113 245 5866

CROSTHWAITE, Mr Graham BA(Oxon)(Jurisprudence) *I Nov 1995*
10, 20, 1, 30, 22, 2
1 King's Bench Walk, London EC4
p938 . . . . . . 020 7936 1500

Crow, Mr Charles *L Nov 1999*
30, 18, 55, 36, 62, 40, 68, 94
No5 Chambers, Bristol
p971 . . . . . . 0845 210 5555
No5 Chambers, London EC4
p944 . . . . . . 0845 210 5555
No5 Chambers, Birmingham
p968 . . . . . . 0845 210 5555

CROW, Mr Jonathan R BA(Oxon); First Treasury Counsel to the Crown *L Jul 1981*
(Q.C.) *1, 11*
4 Stone Buildings, London WC2
p951 . . . . . . 020 7242 5524

Crowe, Mr Cameron BA(Hons) *I Oct 2002*
1, 2, 10, 12, 18, 20, 15
36 Bedford Row, London WC1
p925 . . . . . . 020 7421 8000

Crowley, Mr Daniel FCIArb; BA; LLB(Hons)(QLD); BCL(OXON) *G Oct 1990*
7, 11, 12, 24, 30, 40, 41, 49, 3
2 Temple Gardens, London EC4
p952 . . . . . . 020 7822 1200

CROWLEY, Mrs Jane LLB; Recorder; Deputy High Court Judge *G Jul 1976*
(Q.C.) *10, 20*
1 Garden Court, London EC4
p934 . . . . . . 020 7797 7900
Thirty Park Place, Cardiff
p973 . . . . . . 029 2039 8421

Crowley, Miss Laura *I Jul 2005*
40, 24, 11, 7, 89
4 Pump Court, London EC4
p947 . . . . . . 020 7842 5555

Crowther, Mr Jeremy Gage *M Oct 1991*
53, 30, 70
9 Gough Square, London EC4
p935 . . . . . . 020 7832 0500

CROWTHER, Miss Sarah Helen *M Oct 1999*
11, 12, 18, 19, 59
3 Hare Court, London EC4
p937 . . . . . . 020 7415 7800

CROXFORD, Mr Ian LLB(Leics) *G Jul 1976*
(Q.C.) *1, 3, 7, 11, 12, 15, 18, 24, 25, 26, 56, 40, 62*
Wilberforce Chambers, London WC2
p953 . . . . . . 020 7306 0102

Croxford, Mr Thomas MA(Cantab) *M Oct 1992*
11, 18, 29, 55, 5, 81, 89
Blackstone Chambers, London EC4
p926 . . . . . . 020 7583 1770

Crozier, Rawdon R C *M Nov 1984*
King's Bench Godolphin Chambers, Truro
p994 . . . . . . 0845 308 1551
King's Bench Godolphin Chambers, Plymouth
p990 . . . . . . 0845 308 1551

Cruickshank, Miss Cynthia *L Nov 1968*
15, 20, 10
1 Gray's Inn Square, London WC1
p935 . . . . . . 020 7405 8946

Crystal, Mr Jonathan LLB(Lond) *M Jul 1972*
6, 8, 11, 12, 16, 50, 56
Cloisters, London EC4
p928 . . . . . . 020 7827 4000

CRYSTAL, Mr Michael LLB(Lond); BCL(Oxon) *M Nov 1970*
(Q.C.) *5, 6, 8, 11, 12, 24, 29, 40, 37, 38*
South Square, London WC1
p950 . . . . . . 020 7696 9900

CUDBY, Ms Markanza *M Oct 1983*
10, 20
1 King's Bench Walk, London EC4
p938 . . . . . . 020 7936 1500

Cuddigan, Mr Hugo Jonathan MA(Cantab) *M Nov 1995*
73, 50, 19, 45, 13, 52, 96, 41
11 South Square, London WC1
p950 . . . . . . 020 7405 1222

CUDDY, Natalie LLB(Hons) *I Jan 2004*
1, 10, 72, 15, 70, 76, 20, 63, 94
Atlantic Chambers, Liverpool
p980 . . . . . . 0151 236 4421

Cullen, Mr Edmund BA(Bris) *L Oct 1990*
Maitland Chambers, London WC2
p941 . . . . . . 020 7406 1200

Cullen, Mrs Felicity Ann LLB; LLM(Cantab) *L Jul 1985*
(Q.C.) *34, 57, 58*
Gray's Inn Tax Chambers, London WC1
p936 . . . . . . 020 7242 2642

CULLETON, Miss Louise LLB(UCL) *M Jan 2005*
15, 27, 36
23 Essex Street, London WC2
p932 . . . . . . 020 7413 0353

CULLEY, Miss Laura *L Oct 2006*
Citadel Chambers, Birmingham
p967 . . . . . . 0121 233 8500

Culver, Mr Edward LLB *I Jan 2005*
15, 46, 94, 25, 84, 96
Argent Chambers, London WC2
p923 . . . . . . 020 7556 5500

Cumberland, Miss Melanie BA(Oxon) *L Oct 2001*
15
6 King's Bench Walk, London EC4
p939 . . . . . . 020 7583 0410

Cummerson, Miss Romilly *M Oct 1998*
30, 53
Hardwicke, London WC2
p936 . . . . . . 020 7242 2523

Cumming, Mr Edward *L Jan 2006*
49, 41, 3, 5, 6, 8, 11, 97, 67, 62, 38, 24, 21, 89, 32, 40, 37
XXIV Old Buildings, London WC2
p944 . . . . . . 020 7691 2424

Cummings, Mr Brian MA(Cantab); Recorder(2005) *L Nov 1988*
(Q.C.) *15, 62, 72, 82*
Exchange Chambers, Manchester
p983 . . . . . . 0161 833 2722
Exchange Chambers, Liverpool
p980 . . . . . . 0151 236 7747
Exchange Chambers, Leeds
p977 . . . . . . 0113 203 1970

CUMMINGS, Miss Stephanie Anne *M Nov 2010*
30, 12, 18
Oriel Chambers, Liverpool
p981 . . . . . . 0151 236 7191 / 236 4321
Oriel Chambers, Preston
p990 . . . . . . 01772 254764

CUMMINS, Mr Brian Dominic LLB(Hons); LLM(Lond) *M Nov 1992*
30
Old Square Chambers, Bristol
p971 . . . . . . 0117 930 5100
Old Square Chambers, London WC1
p945 . . . . . . 020 7269 0300

CUNDY, Catherine *M Jan 2011*
9 St John Street Chambers, Manchester
p984 . . . . . . 0161 955 9000

Cunningham, Miss Elizabeth LLB(Bris) *M Oct 1995*
18
Albion Chambers, Bristol
p970 . . . . . . 0117 927 2144

Cunningham, Mr Graham T LLB(Hons) *G Jul 1976*
13, 43, 45, 49
Hardwicke, London WC2
p936 . . . . . . 020 7242 2523

Cunningham, Mr Mark BA(Oxon); Accredited Mediator *I Nov 1980*
(Q.C.) *2, 3, 5, 6, 8, 9, 11, 13, 22, 29, 32, 37*
Maitland Chambers, London WC2
p941 . . . . . . 020 7406 1200

Cunningham, Ms Naomi LLB(Reading); LLM(Bris) *G Jan 1994*
18
Outer Temple Chambers, London WC2
p945 . . . . . . 020 7353 6381

Cunnington, Mr David *L Jan 2005*
Old Square Chambers, London WC1
p945 . . . . . . 020 7269 0300

Curl, Mr Joseph BA; LLB *L Jan 2007*
8, 6, 67, 93, 38
9 Stone Buildings Barristers Chambers, London WC2
p951 . . . . . . 020 7404 5055

Curnow, Miss Ann LLB(Lond) *G Feb 1957*
(Q.C.) *15, 36*
6 King's Bench Walk, London EC4
p939 . . . . . . 020 7583 0410

Curran, Mr Leo MA(Oxon) *G Jul 1972*
7, 10, 12, 18, 20, 22, 26, 30, 27
3PB, Oxford
p989 . . . . . . 01865 793736

See p1010 for the Key to Work Categories

Curran, Mr Phillip C BA(Hons); Recorder L *May 1979*
Lincoln House Chambers, Manchester
p984 . . . . . 0161 832 5701

CURRER, Mr Paul J LLB M *Oct 2000*
15, 70
Trinity (Newcastle) Chambers, Newcastle upon Tyne
p987 . . . . . 0191 232 1927
Trinity (Teesside) Chambers, Middlesbrough
p986 . . . . . 01642 247569

Currie, Mr Fergus G *Mar 1997*
15, 18, 30, 55
Unity Street Chambers, Bristol
p972 . . . . . 0117 906 9789

CURRIE, Mr Heriot LLB G *Jan 1979*
(Q.C.) *1, 11, 44, 13, 19, 51, 57, 61*
Monckton Chambers, London WC1
p942 . . . . . 020 7405 7211

CURRY, Miss Caroline M *Nov 2003*
9 St John Street Chambers, Manchester
p984 . . . . . 0161 955 9000

Curry, Owen L *Oct 2010*
49, 41, 3, 5, 6, 8, 9, 11, 97, 67, 69, 78, 81, 62, 38, 21, 89, 96, 79, 29, 86, 32, 40, 93, 37
XXIV Old Buildings, London WC2
p944 . . . . . 020 7691 2424

CURSHAM, Mrs Georgina G *Jan 2007*
12, 30, 11, 40, 53, 22, 29
Ropewalk Chambers, Nottingham
p989 . . . . . 0115 947 2581

CURTIS, Mr Charles BA(Dunelm) L *Oct 1992*
Temple Garden Chambers, London EC4
p952 . . . . . 020 7583 1315

Curtis, Mr James MA(Oxon) I *Jul 1970*
(Q.C.) *15, 36, 62*
6 King's Bench Walk, London EC4
p939 . . . . . 020 7583 0410

Curtis, Mr Matthew LLB(Hons) M *Jul 2006*
6, 7, 8, 10, 11, 12, 47, 67, 15, 18, 20, 88, 30
College Chambers, Southampton
p992 . . . . . 023 8023 0338

CURTIS, Mr Michael BA(Oxon) M *Jan 1982*
(Q.C.) *74, 7, 11, 40, 3, 29*
Crown Office Chambers, London EC4
p929 . . . . . 020 7797 8100

CURTIS-RALEIGH, Mr Giles BA(Hons); MA; DipLaw; Recorder M *Oct 1992*
15, 25, 72
23 Essex Street, London WC2
p932 . . . . . 020 7413 0353

Curwen, Mr David BA G *Jul 1982*
12, 22, 30, 18, 48, 55
Unity Street Chambers, Bristol
p972 . . . . . 0117 906 9789

Cusworth, Mr Nicholas N C MA(Oxon) L *Nov 1986*
(Q.C.) *20, 10*
1 Hare Court, London EC4
p936 . . . . . 020 7797 7070

Cutler, Mr Anthony BSc(Hons)(Maths & Physics); CEng G *Jan 2007*
Clerksroom - Administration Centre, Taunton
p993 . . . . . 0845 083 3000

Cutress, Mr James BA(Oxon); BCL(Oxon); LLM(Harv) L *Oct 2000*
Fountain Court Chambers, London EC4
p934 . . . . . 020 7583 3335

D'Aguilar, Mr Hugh L *Nov 1998*
15, 23, 25
Staple Inn Chambers, London WC1
p951 . . . . . 020 7242 5240

D'Aigremont, Maitre Gilles L *Jul 1978*
21
1 Gray's Inn Square, London WC1
p935 . . . . . 020 7405 8946

d'Arcy, Miss Eleanor L *Oct 2008*
37, 8, 38, 88, 93
Kings Chambers, Leeds
p978 . . . . . 0113 242 1123
Kings Chambers, Manchester
p984 . . . . . 0161 832 9082

D'Arcy, Miss Louise I *Nov 1988*
15, 51
Nine Bedford Row, London WC1
p924 . . . . . 020 7489 2727

d'Arcy, Mr Michael I *Jul 2008*
One Essex Court, London EC4
p931 . . . . . 020 7583 2000

D'CRUZ, Miss Laura I *Nov 2006*
9 St John Street Chambers, Manchester
p984 . . . . . 0161 955 9000

D'CRUZ, Mr Rufus L *Oct 1993*
15, 62, 51
18 Red Lion Court, London EC4
p949 . . . . . 020 7520 6000
18 Red Lion Court (Annexe), Chelmsford
p973 . . . . . 01245 280880

D'CRUZ, Mr Rupert BA(Nott'm) L *Nov 1989*
11, 66, 97, 5, 40
Littleton Chambers, London EC4
p941 . . . . . 020 7797 8600

D'SOUZA, Ms Carolyn LLB(Lond); LLM(Harv) M *Oct 1994*
1, 18, 30, 40
12 King's Bench Walk, London EC4
p940 . . . . . 020 7583 0811

D'Souza, Mr Dominic BA(Lond); DipLaw; CPE(City) I *Nov 1993*
15, 62
Argent Chambers, London WC2
p923 . . . . . 020 7556 5500

Da Costa, Elissa BA; DipLaw M *Oct 1990*
Clerksroom - Administration Centre, Taunton
p993 . . . . . 0845 083 3000

da Costa, Ms Francisca LLB(Hons) M *Jan 2006*
72, 15, 30, 53, 20, 10
3PB, Bournemouth
p969 . . . . . 01202 292102

da Silva, Mr David MA(Oxon) M *Nov 1978*
3, 6, 8, 11, 12, 18, 22, 24, 35
3 Stone Buildings, London WC2
p951 . . . . . 020 7242 4937

Dabbs, Mr David LLB(Manc) L *Jul 1984*
5, 11, 47, 29, 40, 8, 12, 24, 37, 32
42 Bedford Row, London WC1
p925 . . . . . 020 7831 0222

Dable, Jeremy LLB G *Nov 1987*
Clerksroom - Administration Centre, Taunton
p993 . . . . . 0845 083 3000

Dacey, Mr Mark BA M *Nov 1985*
15
5 King's Bench Walk, London EC4
p939 . . . . . 020 7353 5638

Dacre, Mr Ian BA; MA M *Nov 1991*
15, 30, 12
New Bailey Chambers, Preston
p990 . . . . . 01772 258087

DAGG, Mr John D BSc(Dunelm); LLB(Lond); MCD(L'pool); MRTPI M *Jul 1980*
1, 31, 26, 25
Trinity Chambers, Chelmsford
p974 . . . . . 01245 605040

Dagnall, Ms Jane I *Jan 1987*
St Johns Buildings, Preston
p990 . . . . . 01772 256100
St Johns Buildings, Chester
p974 . . . . . 01244 323070
St Johns Buildings, Manchester
p985 . . . . . 0161 214 1500
St Johns Buildings, Liverpool
p982 . . . . . 0151 243 6000

Dagnall, Mr John Marshall Anthony BA; BCL(Oxon); Accredited Mediator L *Nov 1983*
1, 3, 5, 6, 7, 8, 9, 11, 12, 13, 14, 22, 24, 26, 28, 29, 31, 32, 37
Maitland Chambers, London WC2
p941 . . . . . 020 7406 1200

Dahlsen, Mr Peter LLB(Hons) G *Oct 1996*
2 Dr Johnson's Buildings, London EC4
p930 . . . . . 020 7936 2613

Daiches, Mr Michael Salis M *Jul 1977*
8, 12, 22, 26, 46, 7, 61
42 Bedford Row, London WC1
p925 . . . . . 020 7831 0222

Dainty, Miss Cheryl I *Jul 2006*
Kings Chambers, Leeds
p978 . . . . . 0113 242 1123
Kings Chambers, Manchester
p984 . . . . . 0161 832 9082

Dakyns, Miss Isabel BA(Oxon) L *Nov 1992*
15, 62, 25, 36, 16
6 King's Bench Walk, London EC4
p939 . . . . . 020 7583 0410

Dalal, Mr Rajen C J LLB(Hons) L *Sep 1991*
10, 12, 19, 20, 25
Cobden House Chambers, Manchester
p983 . . . . . 0161 833 6000

Dale, Mr Derrick BA(Cantab); LLM(Harv) M *Dec 1990*
(Q.C.)
Fountain Court Chambers, London EC4
p934 . . . . . 020 7583 3335

Dale, Mr Jonathan Paul G *Jan 1991*
8, 5, 6, 7, 13, 16, 18, 22, 24, 31, 37, 32
18 St John Street Chambers, Manchester
p985 . . . . . 0161 278 1800

Dale, Mr Julian LLB M *Nov 1991*
15, 91
Eastbourne Chambers, Eastbourne
p975 . . . . . 01323 642102

Dales, Mr Colin L *Jan 2007*
Clerksroom - Administration Centre, Taunton
p993 . . . . . 0845 083 3000

Daley, Mr Howard M BA(Hons)(Cantab) G *Oct 1997*
11, 8, 88, 67, 93
Lamb Chambers, London EC4
p941 . . . . . 020 7797 8300

Daley, Miss Nicola G *Jul 2000*
15, 62, 70, 72
Exchange Chambers, Manchester
p983 . . . . . 0161 833 2722
Exchange Chambers, Liverpool
p980 . . . . . 0151 236 7747
Exchange Chambers, Leeds
p977 . . . . . 0113 203 1970

Daley, Miss Sarah BA I *Jan 2007*
1, 51, 15, 18, 55, 23
Garden Court North Chambers, Manchester
p983 . . . . . 0161 236 1840

Dallas, Mr Andrew T A Recorder G *Nov 1978*
12, 15
No 6 Barristers Chambers, Leeds
p978 . . . . . 0113 245 9763

Dalling, Mr Robert M *Jan 2003*
15, 25
5 Paper Buildings, London EC4
p946 . . . . . 020 7583 6117

Daly, Ms Caoimhe MA(Law); LLM(Corporate Crime) I *Jan 2005*
15
QEB Hollis Whiteman, London EC4
p948 . . . . . 020 7933 8855

DALY, Mr David BA; LLB; AKC M *Jul 1979*
1, 18, 22, 26, 31, 38, 37, 23
Tanfield Chambers, London WC1
p951 . . . . . 020 7421 5300

Daly, Mr Nigel LLB(Lond) G *Jul 1979*
King's Bench Chambers, Oxford
p989 . . . . . 01865 311066
13 King's Bench Walk, London EC4
p940 . . . . . 020 7353 7204

Daly, Miss Orla Marie G *Nov 2000*
15
5 King's Bench Walk, London EC4
p939 . . . . . 020 7353 5638

DANCE, Mr Mathew L *Jul 2001*
15, 62
18 Red Lion Court, London EC4
p949 . . . . . 020 7520 6000
18 Red Lion Court (Annexe), Chelmsford
p973 . . . . . 01245 280880

DANCER, Miss Helen M *Jul 2001*
23, 15, 20
Guildford Chambers, Guildford
p975 . . . . . 01483 539131

Daneshyar, Mr Osama BA(Hons) I *Mar 1996*
15, 20, 23
Equity Chambers, Birmingham
p968 . . . . . 0121 233 2100

Daniel, Ms Hayley LLB I *Jan 2007*
20, 10
Temple Chambers, Newport
p988 . . . . . 01633 267403 / 255855
Temple Chambers, Cardiff
p973 . . . . . 029 2039 7364

Daniel, Mr Nigel LLB I *Nov 1988*
15, 62
4 Breams Buildings, London EC4
p927 . . . . . 020 7092 1900

Daniells-Smith, Mr Roger LLB M *Nov 1974*
1 Mitre Court Buildings, London EC4
p942 . . . . . 020 7452 8900

Daniels, Mr Ian L *Jan 1992*
30, 53, 18, 11, 22
Ely Place Chambers, London EC1
p931 . . . . . 020 7400 9600

DANIELS, Mr Nicholas LLB(Hons)(Bris) I *Feb 1988*
10, 20
1 Garden Court, London EC4
p934 . . . . . 020 7797 7900

Daniels, Miss Philipa BA(Hons) I *Dec 1995*
8, 11, 6
36 Bedford Row, London WC1
p925 . . . . . 020 7421 8000

Dann, Mr Jared MA(Oxon); CPE(Lond) M *Jan 2007*
4 KBW, London EC4
p938 . . . . . 020 7822 8822

Dannatt, Ms Lucinda MA(Oxon); PgDL I *Oct 2003*
15
4 Breams Buildings, London EC4
p927 . . . . . 020 7092 1900

Danton, Ms Kirstie LLB L *Jul 1999*
10, 20, 12
New Walk Chambers, Leicester
p979 . . . . . 0871 200 1298

Darbishire, Mr Adrian L *Nov 1993*
15, 25, 36
QEB Hollis Whiteman, London EC4
p948 . . . . . 020 7933 8855

DARBY, Miss Johanna Louise BA(Hons); MA(Theatre) M *Oct 2007*
12, 20, 18, 38, 94
Trinity (Newcastle) Chambers, Newcastle upon Tyne
p987 . . . . . 0191 232 1927
Trinity (Teesside) Chambers, Middlesbrough
p986 . . . . . 01642 247569

DARBY, Mr Patrick MA(Cantab) M *Jan 1978*
11, 15, 40, 37
St Philips Chambers, Birmingham
p969 . . . . . 0121 246 7000

DARBYSHIRE, Mr Robert MA; LLM L *Nov 1995*
5, 6, 8, 11, 22, 32, 37, 40
9 St John Street Chambers, Manchester
p984 . . . . . 0161 955 9000

DARDIS, Mrs Heather LLB(Wolv) L *Nov 2000*
30, 68, 94
Temple Garden Chambers, London EC4
p952 . . . . . 020 7583 1315

Darian, Ms Alice M *Jan 2006*
20, 10
Queen Square Chambers, Bristol
p972 . . . . . 0117 921 1966

Darian, Mrs Ann LLB M *Jul 1974*
20, 10
Queen Square Chambers, Bristol
p972 . . . . . 0117 921 1966

Darling, Mr Paul A BA; BCL(Oxon) M *Jul 1983*
(Q.C.) *3, 7, 11, 24, 40*
Keating Chambers, London WC2
p938 . . . . . 020 7544 2600

Darling, Miss Polly I *Nov 2000*
15, 51, 42
Nine Bedford Row, London WC1
p924 . . . . . 020 7489 2727

Darlington, Elizabeth BA(Hons) M *Oct 1998*
Zenith Chambers, Leeds
p979 . . . . . 0113 245 5438

Darlington-Pearce, Ms Susan I *Nov 1999*
22, 12
St Albans Chambers, St Albans
p992 . . . . . 01727 843383

Darlow, Miss Annabel MA(Cantab) M *Oct 1993*
15, 62
6 King's Bench Walk, London EC4
p939 . . . . . 020 7583 0410

Darnborough, Mr Daniel M *Jan 2006*
15, 94
Lamb Building, Brighton
p970 . . . . . 01273 820490
Lamb Building, London EC4
p940 . . . . . 020 7797 7788

Darroch, Fiona BA(Lond); CPE; LLM(Lond) I *Oct 1994*
46
Clerksroom - Administration Centre, Taunton
p993 . . . . . 0845 083 3000

DARTON, Mr Clifford BA(Oxon) M *Jul 1988*
6, 7, 22, 29, 12, 18, 11, 30, 32, 40
Pallant Chambers, Chichester
p974 . . . . . 01243 784538

13

Daruwalla, Miss Navaz LLB(Hons) M *Oct 1997*
15
2 Bedford Row, London WC1
p924 . . . . . 020 7440 8888

DARWIN, Ms Claire Louise MA(Hons)(Cantab); DipLaw(City) I *Oct 2005*
18, 76, 55, 1, 11, 67, 73, 19, 51, 6
Matrix Chambers, London WC1
p942 . . . . . 020 7404 3447

Das, Miss Kamala BA(Sussex); LLM(Lond) M *Nov 1975*
36, 10, 20
St John's Chambers, Bristol
p972 . . . . . 0117 921 3456

Dasani, Kajal M *Oct 2004*
New Walk Chambers, Leicester
p979 . . . . . 0871 200 1298

Dashani, Ms Sonal L *Nov 2002*
15, 62
15 New Bridge Street Chambers, London EC4
p943 . . . . . 020 7842 1900

Dashwood, Prof Alan I *Nov 1969*
(Q.C.) CBE*19*
Henderson Chambers, London EC4
p937 . . . . . 020 7583 9020

Date, Mr Julian M *Nov 1988*
Field Court Chambers, London WC1
p933 . . . . . 020 7405 6114

Datta, Mr Shomik BA(Oxon) G *Nov 2000*
12
42 Bedford Row, London WC1
p925 . . . . . 020 7831 0222

Dave, Miss Priya L *Oct 2006*
15
3 Temple Gardens, London EC4
p952 . . . . . 020 7353 3102

DAVENPORT, Mr Simon LLB I *Nov 1987*
(Q.C.) *11, 12, 24, 41, 59, 40*
3 Hare Court, London EC4
p937 . . . . . 020 7415 7800

Davey, Charles MA M *Feb 1989*
Clerksroom - Administration Centre, Taunton
p993 . . . . . 0845 083 3000

DAVEY, Miss Helen L *Jan 2008*
10, 20
St Mary's Chambers, Nottingham
p989 . . . . . 0115 950 3503

DAVEY, Mr Jonathan MA(Nott'm); Mphil(Cantab); DipLaw(City) L *Oct 2003*
6, 8, 11, 12, 18, 22, 29, 37, 40
Wilberforce Chambers, London WC2
p953 . . . . . 020 7306 0102

Davey, Miss Kate I *May 1988*
15
2 Pump Court, London EC4
p947 . . . . . 020 7353 5597

Davey, Mr Michael LLB(Lond); BCL(Oxon) G *Nov 1990*
3, 41, 4, 11, 46, 24, 35, 60
Quadrant Chambers, London EC4
p948 . . . . . 020 7583 4444

DAVEY, Michelle LLB(Hons) L *Nov 1993*
20
Atlantic Chambers, Liverpool
p980 . . . . . 0151 236 4421

Davey, Mr Neil M *Jul 1978*
(Q.C.) *15, 25*
39 Park Square, Leeds
p978 . . . . . 0113 245 6633
3 Temple Gardens, London EC4
p952 . . . . . 020 7353 3102

Davey, Mr Roger Lawrence LLB I *Feb 1978*
Charter Chambers, London WC1
p928 . . . . . 020 7618 4400

DAVEY, Mr Toby G *Jul 1977*
1, 26, 31, 23, 51, 18
4-5 Gray's Inn Square, London WC1
p935 . . . . . 020 7404 5252

David, Mr Alastair Robert Oulpe BA(Hons) L *Jul 2005*
18, 15, 89, 30, 20
New Walk Chambers, Leicester
p979 . . . . . 0871 200 1298
Pendragon Chambers, Swansea
p993 . . . . . 01792 411188

DAVIDGE, Miss Justine G *Jul 2001*
4 King's Bench Walk, London EC4
p939 . . . . . 020 7822 7000

DAVIDSON, Mr Andrew Edward G *Oct 2003*
Citadel Chambers, Birmingham
p967 . . . . . 0121 233 8500

Davidson, Mr Arthur M *Nov 1953*
(Q.C.) *11, 43, 56, 52*
Cloisters, London EC4
p928 . . . . . 020 7827 4000

Davidson, Ms Katharine M MA(Oxon) L *Nov 1987*
20, 10
1 Hare Court, London EC4
p936 . . . . . 020 7797 7070

Davidson, Ms Laura PhD(Cantab); MA(Hons)(Edin); PGCE(Oxon); DipLaw; LLM(Cantab) L *Oct 1996*
14, 63, 85, 1
No5 Chambers, Bristol
p971 . . . . . 0845 210 5555
No5 Chambers, London EC4
p944 . . . . . 0845 210 5555
No5 Chambers, Birmingham
p968 . . . . . 0845 210 5555

Davidson, Mr Nicholas Ranking BA(Cantab) I *Jul 1974*
(Q.C.) *41, 8, 12, 24, 40, 45*
Four New Square, London WC2
p943 . . . . . 020 7822 2000

Davidson, Dr Ranald LLB(Hons); MB; CHB(Edin) I *Nov 1996*
12, 27, 30, 40, 53, 1, 68, 85, 36
3 Serjeants' Inn, London EC4
p950 . . . . . 020 7427 5000

Davidson, Ms Sally LLB(Hons)(L'pool) I *Jul 2006*
8, 10, 12, 15, 55, 18, 20, 38, 88, 89, 30
College Chambers, Southampton
p992 . . . . . 023 8023 0338

Davie, Mr Michael LLB; Dip Phil(Oxon) M *Nov 1993*
(Q.C.) *5, 11, 12, 18, 22, 24, 25, 29*
4 Pump Court, London EC4
p947 . . . . . 020 7842 5555

Davies, Mr Adrian Michael MA(Cantab); LLM(Lond) L *Jul 1998*
6, 8, 12, 16, 22, 32, 40, 37
3 Dr Johnson's Buildings, London EC4
p930 . . . . . 020 7353 4854

Davies, Mr Andrew BA(Oxon) I *Jul 1988*
8, 11, 12, 40, 45, 50, 56, 59, 22, 51
Henderson Chambers, London EC4
p937 . . . . . 020 7583 9020

Davies, Miss Angharad LLB L *Oct 2000*
22, 6, 11, 30, 15, 8, 26, 32, 37, 38, 47, 88
Thirty Park Place, Cardiff
p973 . . . . . 029 2039 8421
York Chambers, York
p995 . . . . . 01904 620048
York Chambers, Newcastle upon Tyne
p987 . . . . . 0191 206 4677

Davies, Mr Anthony Recorder G *Jul 1971*
(Q.C.) *15*
1 Paper Buildings, London EC4
p946 . . . . . 020 7353 3728

Davies, Mr Benjamin Guy LLB(Law & French Law) L *Oct 1999*
30, 53
Thirty Park Place, Cardiff
p973 . . . . . 029 2039 8421

Davies, Miss Carol E LLB(Hons) M *Oct 1995*
6, 8, 10, 53, 11, 12, 67, 14, 20, 96, 88, 30, 32, 40
College Chambers, Southampton
p992 . . . . . 023 8023 0338
2 New Street, Leicester
p979 . . . . . 0116 262 5906

DAVIES, Miss Charlotte BA(Hons)(Oxon) L *Oct 2006*
18, 11, 12, 55, 6, 56
Littleton Chambers, London EC4
p941 . . . . . 020 7797 8600

Davies, Mr David G *Jan 2004*
Essex Court Chambers, London WC2
p931 . . . . . 020 7813 8000

DAVIES, Ms Deborah G *Nov 1993*
30, 12, 18, 40, 53
Ropewalk Chambers, Nottingham
p989 . . . . . 0115 947 2581

Davies, Mr E Huw LLB(Cardiff) G *Nov 1985*
(Q.C.)
Essex Court Chambers, London WC2
p931 . . . . . 020 7813 8000

DAVIES, Mr Edward BCL(Oxon); BA(Cantab) I *Jan 1998*
11, 38, 97
Erskine Chambers, London WC2
p931 . . . . . 020 7242 5532

Davies, Ms Emily J LLB(Wales) G *Nov 1989*
10, 12, 15, 20
9 Park Place, Cardiff
p973 . . . . . 029 2038 2731

Davies, Miss Emily Sparham LLB(Law with French) M *Jan 2000*
30, 22
Lamb Chambers, London EC4
p941 . . . . . 020 7797 8300

DAVIES, Mr George MA(Oxon) L *Nov 1998*
Temple Garden Chambers, London EC4
p952 . . . . . 020 7583 1315

Davies, Dr Gillian PhD L *Nov 1961* DL
13, 50, 19
Hogarth Chambers, London WC2
p937 . . . . . 020 7404 0404

Davies, Mr Graham J LLM(Lond) I *Nov 1971*
Charter Chambers, London WC1
p928 . . . . . 020 7618 4400

Davies, Mr Gregory BSc M *Jan 2005*
10, 20, 15
4 Brick Court Chambers, London EC4
p927 . . . . . 020 7832 3200

Davies, Mr Harold Rodney Olonindieh L *Jan 1978*
22, 88, 15
Redemption Chambers, London NW11
p949 . . . . . 020 8458 5486 / 07929 511917

Davies, Miss Helen BA(Cantab) I *Nov 1991*
11, 5, 24, 35, 1, 19, 44
Brick Court Chambers, London WC2
p927 . . . . . 020 7379 3550

DAVIES, Mr Huw P BA(Oxon); DipLaw G *Nov 1998*
30, 12, 18, 15, 36
Farrar's Building, London EC4
p933 . . . . . 020 7583 9241

Davies, Mr Iwan Rhun LLB; LLM; PhD G *Feb 1995*
11, 15, 20
Iscoed Chambers, Swansea
p993 . . . . . 01792 652988

Davies, Mr J Meirion LLB G *Jul 1975*
15
Temple Chambers, Newport
p988 . . . . . 01633 267403 / 255855
Temple Chambers, Cardiff
p973 . . . . . 029 2039 7364

DAVIES, Mr Jake BA(Cantab); CPE I *Oct 1997*
11, 18, 12, 47, 6, 40
Five Paper, London EC4
p946 . . . . . 020 7815 3200

DAVIES, Mr James LLB; LLM; BVC L *Jul 2009*
5, 6, 8, 9, 11, 29, 32, 37, 38, 66, 67, 69, 86, 88, 89, 93, 97
Enterprise Chambers, London WC2
p931 . . . . . 020 7405 9471
Enterprise Chambers, Leeds
p977 . . . . . 0113 246 0391
Enterprise Chambers, Newcastle upon Tyne
p987 . . . . . 0191 222 3344
3PB, Oxford
p989 . . . . . 01865 793736

DAVIES, Mr Jonathan MA(Cantab) M *Nov 1971*
15, 62, 95
187 Fleet Street, London EC4
p933 . . . . . 020 7430 7430

Davies, Mr Jonathan Huw MA; PgDL L *Jan 2003*
18, 30
Old Square Chambers, Bristol
p971 . . . . . 0117 930 5100
Old Square Chambers, London WC1
p945 . . . . . 020 7269 0300

DAVIES, Mr Jonathan Norval LLB(Lond) I *Jul 1981*
15, 25
9-12 Bell Yard Chambers, London WC2
p926 . . . . . 020 7400 1800

Davies, Miss Josephine L *Oct 2006*
49, 41, 3, 5, 11, 43, 47, 78, 24, 54, 35, 44
20 Essex Street, London WC2
p932 . . . . . 020 7842 1200

Davies, Mr Karl LLB; LLM(Cantab) I *Nov 1999*
19, 23
Cornerstone Barristers, London WC1
p929 . . . . . 020 7242 4986

Davies, Miss Lindsay Jane LLB(Wales); Assistant Recorder G *Jul 1975*
10, 20
Fenners Chambers, Cambridge
p972 . . . . . 01223 368761

Davies, Mr Max BSc M *Oct 2005*
20, 12
Temple Chambers, Newport
p988 . . . . . 01633 267403 / 255855
Temple Chambers, Cardiff
p973 . . . . . 029 2039 7364

DAVIES, Mr Michael M *Jul 1979*
15
7 Harrington Street Chambers, Liverpool
p981 . . . . . 0151 242 0707

DAVIES, Mr Nicholas BA I *Jul 1975*
30, 40, 12
Crown Office Chambers, London EC4
p929 . . . . . 020 7797 8100
Fenners Chambers, Cambridge
p972 . . . . . 01223 368761

Davies, Mr Nick BA(Hons)(Oxon) G *Jan 2006*
97, 20, 10, 30, 53
3PB, Oxford
p989 . . . . . 01865 793736

Davies, Mr Peter LLB L *Oct 1996*
15
9 Park Place, Cardiff
p973 . . . . . 029 2038 2731
7 Harrington Street Chambers, Liverpool
p981 . . . . . 0151 242 0707

Davies, Miss Rebecca L *Nov 1996*
10, 20
Westgate Chambers, Lewes
p980 . . . . . 01273 480510

Davies, Mr Rhodri M *Jul 1979*
(Q.C.)
One Essex Court, London EC4
p931 . . . . . 020 7583 2000

Davies, Mr Rhys G *Oct 2004*
15
No5 Chambers, Bristol
p971 . . . . . 0845 210 5555
No5 Chambers, London EC4
p944 . . . . . 0845 210 5555
No5 Chambers, Birmingham
p968 . . . . . 0845 210 5555

DAVIES, Mr Rupert G *Jan 2007*
30, 12, 15
18 St John Street Chambers, Manchester
p985 . . . . . 0161 278 1800

DAVIES, Ms Sarah Jane BA(Hons)(Cantab) I *Oct 1996*
1, 11, 18, 31, 26
4-5 Gray's Inn Square, London WC1
p935 . . . . . 020 7404 5252

Davies, Ms Sarah Jeannette BA(Hons)(Kent) G *Feb 1984*
10, 20
1 Pump Court, London EC4
p947 . . . . . 020 7842 7070

Davies, Miss Sian BA G *Oct 1999*
22, 23, 26
Cornerstone Barristers, London WC1
p929 . . . . . 020 7242 4986

DAVIES, Mr Stephen LLB(Lond); LLB M *Jul 1983*
(Q.C.) *6, 11, 38, 56, 97*
Guildhall Chambers, Bristol
p970 . . . . . 0117 930 9000

Davies, Mr Trevor Glyn G *Jul 1978*
30, 40, 53
9 Gough Square, London EC4
p935 . . . . . 020 7832 0500

Davies, Unime M *Jan 2006*
2 King's Bench Walk, London EC4
p939 . . . . . 020 7353 1746

DAVIES-JONES, Mr Jonathan MA(Cantab) M *Nov 1994*
5, 11, 24, 40
3 Verulam Buildings, London WC1
p953 . . . . . 020 7831 8441

Davis, Mr Adrian BSc; LLB G *Oct 1996*
22, 26, 30
Field Court Chambers, London WC1
p933 . . . . . 020 7405 6114

DAVIS, Mr Andrew LLB G *Oct 1996*
30, 11, 24, 96, 45, 40, 53
Crown Office Chambers, London EC4
p929 . . . . . 020 7797 8100

Davis, Mr Anthony BA(Dunelm) G *Nov 1986*
7, 12, 30
Broad Chare Chambers, Newcastle upon Tyne
p986 . . . . . 0191 232 0541

See p1010 for the Key to Work Categories

DAVIS, Mr Brendan MA(Oxon) G *Oct 1994*
12, 15, 18, 22, 23, 30
4 King's Bench Walk, London EC4
p939 . . . . . . 020 7822 7000

DAVIS, Miss Carol M *Oct 1996*
18, 11, 40, 12
Littleton Chambers, London EC4
p941 . . . . . . 020 7797 8600

DAVIS, Mr Glen MA(Oxon) M *Oct 1992*
(Q.C.) *5, 6, 8, 11, 12, 24, 29, 38, 81*
South Square, London WC1
p950 . . . . . . 020 7696 9900

DAVIS, Mr Greville LLB L *Jul 1976*
62, 15
Lombard Chambers, London EC1
p941 . . . . . . 020 7107 2100

Davis, Mr Jim Deputy District Judge (MC) G *Jul 1997*
15
Angel Chambers, Swansea
p992 . . . . . . 01792 464623

DAVIS, Mr Jonathan MA(Oxon); Head of Civil & Employment Team M *Dec 1983*
30, 53, 38, 84, 48, 6
Cornwall Street Chambers, Birmingham
p967 . . . . . . 0121 233 7500

DAVIS, Mr Justin LLB; BVC L *Oct 2003*
30, 12, 24, 11, 38, 84
Crown Office Chambers, London EC4
p929 . . . . . . 020 7797 8100

DAVIS, Miss Lucinda LLB(Hons) G *Jul 1981*
10, 20
Pallant Chambers, Chichester
p974 . . . . . . 01243 784538

DAVIS, Miss Lucy G *Nov 2003*
15, 20
Pump Court Chambers, Swindon
p993 . . . . . . 01793 539899
Pump Court Chambers, Winchester
p994 . . . . . . 01962 868161
Pump Court Chambers, London EC4
p947 . . . . . . 020 7353 0711

DAVIS, Mr Richard MA G *Oct 1992*
13
Hogarth Chambers, London WC2
p937 . . . . . . 020 7404 0404

Davis, Miss Sheilagh LLB(Lond) M *Feb 1974*
15, 25, 62
4 Breams Buildings, London EC4
p927 . . . . . . 020 7092 1900

DAVIS, Mr Simon MA(Cantab); DipLaw M *Oct 1990*
15, 25, 62, 84, 71
23 Essex Street, London WC2
p932 . . . . . . 020 7413 0353
St Philips Chambers, Birmingham
p969 . . . . . . 0121 246 7000

DAVIS-WHITE, Mr Malcolm BCL; MA(Oxon) M *Jul 1984*
(Q.C.) *6, 11*
4 Stone Buildings, London WC2
p951 . . . . . . 020 7242 5524

Davison, Miss Eleanor L *Nov 2003*
62, 15, 84, 18, 1
Outer Temple Chambers, London WC2
p945 . . . . . . 020 7353 6381

Davison, Mr Guy LLB L *Oct 1998*
15, 23, 10, 20, 12
1 Gray's Inn Square, London WC1
p935 . . . . . . 020 7405 8946

Davison, Mr James LLB(Hons)(Wales) G *Jan 1996*
11, 67, 74
3PB, London EC4
p946 . . . . . . 020 7583 8055

DAVISON, Mr Richard Harold BA(Oxon); Recorder G *Jul 1982*
30, 12, 18, 53
12 King's Bench Walk, London EC4
p940 . . . . . . 020 7583 0811

Davitt, Ms Paula LLB G *Oct 1988*
10, 20
St Johns Buildings, Preston
p990 . . . . . . 01772 256100
St Johns Buildings, Chester
p974 . . . . . . 01244 323070
St Johns Buildings, Manchester
p985 . . . . . . 0161 214 1500
St Johns Buildings, Liverpool
p982 . . . . . . 0151 243 6000

Davy, Mr Neil Geoffrey BA(Hons)(Oxon) M *Oct 2000*
12, 18, 30, 40, 53, 68, 85, 27, 36
3 Serjeants' Inn, London EC4
p950 . . . . . . 020 7427 5000

Daw, Mr Christopher LLB G *Nov 1993*
12, 15, 16, 28, 30, 38
18 St John Street Chambers, Manchester
p985 . . . . . . 0161 278 1800

Dawar, Mrs Archna L *Oct 1996*
20, 10, 30, 12, 18
Exchange Chambers, Manchester
p983 . . . . . . 0161 833 2722
Exchange Chambers, Liverpool
p980 . . . . . . 0151 236 7747
Exchange Chambers, Leeds
p977 . . . . . . 0113 203 1970

Dawes, Mr James Christopher BA(Dunelm); CPE I *Nov 1993*
15, 62
Atkinson Bevan Chambers, London EC4
p924 . . . . . . 020 7353 2112

Dawes, Ms Laura L *Oct 2001*
15, 30, 10, 53
7 Bedford Row, London WC1
p924 . . . . . . 020 7242 3555

DAWES, Simon LLB(L'pool) I *Oct 1990*
30
Atlantic Chambers, Liverpool
p980 . . . . . . 0151 236 4421

Dawson, Mr Adam LLB M *Oct 2000*
12, 30, 24, 49, 53
9 Gough Square, London EC4
p935 . . . . . . 020 7832 0500

Dawson, Mr Alexander William MA(Oxon) M *Jul 1969*
30
King's Bench Chambers, Oxford
p989 . . . . . . 01865 311066
13 King's Bench Walk, London EC4
p940 . . . . . . 020 7353 7204

Dawson, Miss Beatrice Grace L *Jan 2006*
15, 20, 30, 47, 48, 59
Broad Chare Chambers, Newcastle upon Tyne
p986 . . . . . . 0191 232 0541

DAWSON, Mr James LLB(Hons) I *Nov 1994*
53, 30, 67, 97, 18, 8, 93
Oriel Chambers, Liverpool
p981 . . . . . . 0151 236 7191 / 236 4321
Oriel Chambers, Preston
p990 . . . . . . 01772 254764
3PB, Winchester
p994 . . . . . . 01962 868884
2 Hare Court, London EC4
p937 . . . . . . 020 7353 5324

Dawson, Miss Judy MA(Cantab) G *Oct 1993*
15, 12, 30
Unity Street Chambers, Bristol
p972 . . . . . . 0117 906 9789

Dawson, Miss Rachael LLB(Hons) M *Jul 2007*
10, 20, 30, 12
Chartlands Chambers, Northampton
p988 . . . . . . 01604 603322

Day, Mr Andrew LLB(Hons) I *Oct 2003*
15, 12, 20, 30, 23
St Ives Chambers, Birmingham
p969 . . . . . . 0121 236 0863

Day, Miss Anneliese MA I *Oct 1996*
8, 12, 24, 40, 48, 18
Four New Square, London WC2
p943 . . . . . . 020 7822 2000

Day, Mr Dorian M *Jul 1987*
15, 20, 10, 12, 23, 18
Goldsmith Chambers, London EC4
p935 . . . . . . 020 7353 6802

DAY, Mr Douglas MA(Cantab); Dep.High Court Judge; Recorder L *Jul 1967*
(Q.C.) *15, 12*
Farrar's Building, London EC4
p933 . . . . . . 020 7583 9241

Day, Miss Robyn I *May 1997*
Guildhall Chambers, Portsmouth
p990 . . . . . . 023 9275 2400

DAYKIN, Emma I *Jan 2005*
23, 1, 18, 15
Mitre House Chambers, London WC1
p942 . . . . . . 020 7307 7100

DE BANZIE, Mr Robert G *Jan 2000*
Maidstone Chambers, Maidstone
p982 . . . . . . 01622 688592

De Berry, Mr Philip L *Oct 2003*
15
18 St John Street Chambers, Manchester
p985 . . . . . . 0161 278 1800

de Bono, Mr John BA(Oxon); MA(Oxon) G *Oct 1995*
53, 12, 68, 85, 27, 63, 30, 40
3 Serjeants' Inn, London EC4
p950 . . . . . . 020 7427 5000

De Burgos, Mr Jamie M A MA(Cantab) I *Jul 1973*
12, 10, 15, 20, 30, 27, 22
36 Bedford Row, London WC1
p925 . . . . . . 020 7421 8000

DE CORDOVA, Miss Gemma LLB I *Jan 2006*
12, 67, 18, 22, 88, 89, 93, 94, 6, 11
Tanfield Chambers, London WC1
p951 . . . . . . 020 7421 5300

de Freitas, Mr Anthony Peter Stanley MA(Oxon) I *Jul 1971*
11, 40, 24, 2
Hailsham Chambers, London EC4
p936 . . . . . . 020 7643 5000

De Freitas, Miss Melanie M *Nov 1995*
12, 15
3PB, Winchester
p994 . . . . . . 01962 868884

de Garr Robinson, Mr Anthony L *Jul 1987*
(Q.C.)
One Essex Court, London EC4
p931 . . . . . . 020 7583 2000

DE GREGORIO, Mr Michele BA; LLM I *Jul 2003*
74, 7, 11, 24, 30, 40
Crown Office Chambers, London EC4
p929 . . . . . . 020 7797 8100

De Haan, Mr Kevin I *Jul 1976*
(Q.C.) *47, 48, 25, 46*
Francis Taylor Building, London EC4
p934 . . . . . . 020 7353 8415

de la Mare, Mr Thomas O BA(Oxon); LLM(EUI) M *Oct 1995*
1, 11, 19, 43, 44, 51, 55, 89
Blackstone Chambers, London EC4
p926 . . . . . . 020 7583 1770

de la Poer, Mr Nicholas BA(Hons) G *Jul 2003*
Park Court Chambers, Leeds
p978 . . . . . . 0113 243 3277

De Lacy, Mr Richard MA(Cantab); FCIArb M *Jul 1976*
(Q.C.) *3, 5, 6, 11, 29, 40*
3 Stone Buildings, London WC2
p951 . . . . . . 020 7242 4937

de Lury, Mr Terence William FCIArb; FI PlantE; FI Brit E; Forensic Ceng G *Jul 1985*
3, 7, 22, 31
Court Yard Chambers, London SE9
p929 . . . . . . 020 7936 2710

De Marco, Mr Nick LLB(Hons) M *Jul 2001*
1, 18, 11, 56, 50, 52, 51, 89
Blackstone Chambers, London EC4
p926 . . . . . . 020 7583 1770

de Mello, Ramby LLB; LLM; MA L *Feb 1983*
1, 15, 71, 72, 55, 18, 19, 51, 23, 33, 95
6 King's Bench Walk, London EC4
p939 . . . . . . 020 7583 0695 / 7353 4931
No5 Chambers, Bristol
p971 . . . . . . 0845 210 5555
No5 Chambers, London EC4
p944 . . . . . . 0845 210 5555
No5 Chambers, Birmingham
p968 . . . . . . 0845 210 5555

DE MESTRE, Mr Andrew BA(Hons)(Cantab) M *Mar 1998*
5, 6, 11, 29
4 Stone Buildings, London WC2
p951 . . . . . . 020 7242 5524

de Mestre, Ms Lyndsey BA(Hons) L *Nov 1999*
5, 6, 8, 11, 29, 32, 37, 40, 59, 49, 62
XXIV Old Buildings, London WC2
p944 . . . . . . 020 7691 2424

DE MOLLER, Mr Andre I *Nov 1965*
11, 71, 72, 15
10 King's Bench Walk, London EC4
p940 . . . . . . 020 7353 7742

De Navarro, Frances I *Jan 2005*
St Johns Buildings, Preston
p990 . . . . . . 01772 256100
St Johns Buildings, Chester
p974 . . . . . . 01244 323070
St Johns Buildings, Manchester
p985 . . . . . . 0161 214 1500
St Johns Buildings, Liverpool
p982 . . . . . . 0151 243 6000

De Navarro, Mr Michael Anthony BA(Cantab) I *Jul 1968*
(Q.C.) *11, 24, 27, 30, 40, 53*
2 Temple Gardens, London EC4
p952 . . . . . . 020 7822 1200

De Oliveira, Mrs Liz L *Oct 2000*
20, 15, 23
No 8 Chambers, Birmingham
p968 . . . . . . 0121 236 5514

de Pourbaix, Mr Roman BA(Hons) L *Jan 2001*
5, 34, 32, 11, 6, 18, 20, 22, 23, 24, 37, 53, 88, 89, 97, 57, 58
Warwick House Chambers, London WC1
p953 . . . . . . 020 7430 2323

de Rohan, Mr Jonathan Stewart BA; DipLaw M *Jul 1989*
30, 56, 49, 12, 24, 40, 4, 36, 41, 59
2 Temple Gardens, London EC4
p952 . . . . . . 020 7822 1200

DE ROZARIEUX, Ms Louise L *Oct 1999*
15, 12, 20
Pump Court Chambers, Swindon
p993 . . . . . . 01793 539899
Pump Court Chambers, Winchester
p994 . . . . . . 01962 868161
Pump Court Chambers, London EC4
p947 . . . . . . 020 7353 0711

DE SILVA, Miss Camilla G *Oct 1999*
15, 51, 62
Nine Bedford Row, London WC1
p924 . . . . . . 020 7489 2727

De Silva, Sir Desmond M *Jul 1964*
(Q.C.) *15, 21, 56, 62, 71, 91, 28*
Argent Chambers, London WC2
p923 . . . . . . 020 7556 5500

De Silva, Harendra MA; LLM(Cantab); Recorder M *Jul 1970*
(Q.C.) *15, 62, 84*
Argent Chambers, London WC2
p923 . . . . . . 020 7556 5500

DE SILVA, Mr Niran BA(Oxon) L *Oct 1997*
6, 11, 12, 18, 40
Littleton Chambers, London EC4
p941 . . . . . . 020 7797 8600

de Souza, Mr Mark BSc(Lond); MBBS; DipLaw(City) G *Oct 2000*
1, 20, 22, 63, 10, 38
Coram Chambers, London EC1
p929 . . . . . . 020 7092 3700

DE VECCHI, Mr Tom I *Jan 2009*
11, 6, 81, 38, 62, 24
3 Verulam Buildings, London WC1
p953 . . . . . . 020 7831 8441

DE VERNEUIL SMITH, Mr Peter MA L *Jan 1998*
5, 41, 11, 62
3 Verulam Buildings, London WC1
p953 . . . . . . 020 7831 8441

de Waal, Mr John MA(Cantab) M *Oct 1992*
49, 11, 40, 93
Hardwicke, London WC2
p936 . . . . . . 020 7242 2523

de Wilde, Robin I *Jan 1971*
(Q.C.)
Clerksroom - Administration Centre, Taunton
p993 . . . . . . 0845 083 3000

De Zonie, Miss Jane M *Nov 1993*
14 Gray's Inn Square, London WC1
p936 . . . . . . 020 7242 0858

DEACOCK, Mr Adam Jason BA(Oxon) M *Nov 1991*
6, 8, 11, 62, 38
Pallant Chambers, Chichester
p974 . . . . . . 01243 784538
11 Stone Buildings, London WC2
p951 . . . . . . 020 7831 6381

Deacon, Ms Emma I *Nov 1993*
15, 62
5 Paper Buildings, London EC4
p946 . . . . . . 020 7583 6117

Deacon, Ms Jennifer I *Jul 2004*
8, 18, 30, 55, 68, 94
No5 Chambers, Bristol
p971 . . . . . . 0845 210 5555
No5 Chambers, London EC4
p944 . . . . . . 0845 210 5555
No5 Chambers, Birmingham
p968 . . . . . . 0845 210 5555

13

DEACON, Mr Robert LLB(Manc) G *Jul 1976*
5, 7, 8, 11, 13, 16, 24, 29
11 Stone Buildings, London WC2
p951 . . . . 020 7831 6381

DEAKIN, Mr Andrew BA(Phil); MPhil; CPE; BVC L *Jan 2006*
12, 33, 11, 1
Thirty Nine Essex Street, London WC2
p932 . . . . 020 7832 1111

DEAL, Ms Katherine Alison Frances M *Oct 1997*
12, 47, 30, 6, 59
3 Hare Court, London EC4
p937 . . . . 020 7415 7800

Deal, Mr Timothy LLB G *Jul 1988*
12, 15, 18, 36, 60
60 Moordown, London SE18
p943 . . . . 020 8856 8738

Dean, Mr Brian G *Nov 1994*
62, 15, 42, 70, 72, 91
No5 Chambers, Bristol
p971 . . . . 0845 210 5555
No5 Chambers, London EC4
p944 . . . . 0845 210 5555
No5 Chambers, Birmingham
p968 . . . . 0845 210 5555

DEAN, Ms Christine L *Jan 2007*
20
1 Pump Court, London EC4
p947 . . . . 020 7842 7070

Dean, Miss Elizabeth I *Jul 2006*
3 Temple Gardens, London EC4
p952 . . . . 020 7353 3102

Dean, Mr Jacob BA(Oxon) I *Oct 1995*
12, 13, 16, 11, 8, 50, 51, 56
5RB, London WC1
p948 . . . . 020 7242 2902

Dean, Mr James P L *Nov 1977*
Goldsmith Chambers, London EC4
p935 . . . . 020 7353 6802

Dean, Mr Nicholas LLB; Recorder L *Nov 1982*
(Q.C.) *15, 53, 62, 30*
7 Bedford Row, London WC1
p924 . . . . 020 7242 3555

DEAN, Mr Paul BA(Oxon); DipLaw I *Jul 1982*
53, 30, 18, 4, 11, 12, 3, 74, 7, 27, 39, 40
Crown Office Chambers, London EC4
p929 . . . . 020 7797 8100

DEAN, Mr Paul J I *Nov 2001*
11, 39, 97, 8
St Philips Chambers, Birmingham
p969 . . . . 0121 246 7000

Dean, Mr Peter T M *Nov 1987*
2, 12, 23, 63, 1
36 Bedford Row, London WC1
p925 . . . . 020 7421 8000

Dean, Miss Rosa M BA(Oxon) G *Oct 1993*
20, 12, 15, 10, 62
36 Bedford Row, London WC1
p925 . . . . 020 7421 8000

DEANS, Miss Jacqueline LLB L *Dec 1998*
10, 15, 20, 12
Chavasse Court Chambers, Liverpool
p980 . . . . 0151 229 2030

Dear, Mr Ian L *Jul 1999*
15
5 King's Bench Walk, London EC4
p939 . . . . 020 7353 5638

DEARING, Mr Anthony John LLB(Hons) M *Nov 1998*
4-5 Gray's Inn Square, London WC1
p935 . . . . 020 7404 5252

Deas, Ms Susan Margaret BA(Hons) G *Jul 1999*
10, 20
St Johns Buildings, Preston
p990 . . . . 01772 256100
St Johns Buildings, Chester
p974 . . . . 01244 323070
St Johns Buildings, Manchester
p985 . . . . 0161 214 1500
St Johns Buildings, Liverpool
p982 . . . . 0151 243 6000

Deb, Miss Shuvra I *Nov 2007*
8, 6, 38, 93, 97, 88, 18, 29
9 Stone Buildings Barristers Chambers, London WC2
p951 . . . . 020 7404 5055

Debattista, Professor Charles MA; BA; LLP M *Jul 2004*
41, 3, 11
Stone Chambers, London WC1
p951 . . . . 020 7440 6900

Dee, Mr Jonathan LLB(Bris) I *Nov 1989*
15, 22, 11, 18
KCH Garden Square Chambers, Nottingham
p989 . . . . 0115 941 8851
KCH Garden Square Chambers, Leicester
p979 . . . . 0115 941 8851

Deegan, Mr Jeffrey LLB I *Jul 1989*
12, 18, 20, 30
Fenners Chambers, Cambridge
p972 . . . . 01223 368761

Degun, Mr Jasvir M *Jan 2003*
One Essex Court, London EC4
p931 . . . . 020 7936 3030

Dehn, Mr Conrad Francis MA(Oxon) G *Jul 1952*
(Q.C.)
Fountain Court Chambers, London EC4
p934 . . . . 020 7583 3335

DEHON, Ms Estelle I *Jul 2005*
1, 31, 18, 26
4-5 Gray's Inn Square, London WC1
p935 . . . . 020 7404 5252

Deighan, Mr Patricia LLB(Hons) I *Jan 1996*
Chancery Chambers, London WC2
p928 . . . . 020 7405 6879

Deignan, Ms Mary-Teresa BSc; PhD M *Oct 1991*
Charter Chambers, London WC1
p928 . . . . 020 7618 4400

DEIN, Mr Jeremy LLB(Lond) M *Nov 1982*
(Q.C.) *15, 62*
25 Bedford Row, London WC1
p925 . . . . 020 7067 1500

DEKOVEN, Mr Ronald BA(Stanford); JD(Chicago) L *Jan 2009*
38, 5, 11
South Square, London WC1
p950 . . . . 020 7696 9900

DEL FABBRO, Mr Oscar BCom; Recorder G *Jul 1982*
15, 36, 11, 12, 34, 91, 72, 70
23 Essex Street, London WC2
p932 . . . . 020 7413 0353

Del Mese, Miss Francesca M BA(Hons)(East Anglia); CPE M *Jan 1998*
15
1 Pump Court, London EC4
p947 . . . . 020 7842 7070

Del Priore, Miss Assunta MA(Hons); CTE M *Oct 1998*
11, 12, 18, 30, 36, 55
Cobden House Chambers, Manchester
p983 . . . . 0161 833 6000
9 St John Street Chambers, Manchester
p984 . . . . 0161 955 9000

Delahunty, Ms Johanne Erica BA; MA(Oxon) M *Oct 1986*
(Q.C.) *20, 10*
4 Paper Buildings, London EC4
p946 . . . . 020 7583 0816

Delamere, Ms Isabel S BA(Hull) M *Nov 1985*
15, 36
4 Breams Buildings, London EC4
p927 . . . . 020 7092 1900

DELANEY, Mr Joe BA(Natural Sciences) M *Oct 2006*
13, 45
3 New Square, London WC2
p943 . . . . 020 7405 1111

DELANEY, Kenneth LLB(Hons) I *Oct 1996*
12, 30
Atlantic Chambers, Liverpool
p980 . . . . 0151 236 4421

Delany, Ms Francesca M *Oct 2006*
1 Mitre Court Buildings, London EC4
p942 . . . . 020 7452 8900

Demachkie, Mr Jamal BA(Jurisprudence)(Oxon) I *Jan 2004*
11, 88, 93, 8, 96
3PB, London EC4
p946 . . . . 020 7583 8055

Demetriou, Ms Marie-Eleni BA; BCL(Oxon) M *Nov 1995*
56, 1, 19, 11, 51
Brick Court Chambers, London WC2
p927 . . . . 020 7379 3550

Dempsey, Ms Karen LLB(Hons); LLM(Law) L *Jan 1996*
15, 60, 94, 62
3 Temple Gardens, London EC4
p952 . . . . 020 7353 3102

DEMPSTER, Miss Jennifer LLB(Hons) L *Apr 1993*
15, 62
18 Red Lion Court, London EC4
p949 . . . . 020 7520 6000
18 Red Lion Court (Annexe), Chelmsford
p973 . . . . 01245 280880

Dempster, Ms Tina G *Nov 1997*
15, 12, 20
11 King's Bench Walk, Leeds
p978 . . . . 0113 297 1200

DENCER, Mr Mark LLB(Lond) L *Apr 1978*
11, 22, 30
Tanfield Chambers, London WC1
p951 . . . . 020 7421 5300

Denehan, Mr Edward B A LLB(Warw) L *Jul 1981*
22, 40, 8
9 Stone Buildings Barristers Chambers, London WC2
p951 . . . . 020 7404 5055

DENHAM, Mr Ian BA(Oxon) M *Jul 2003*
30, 94, 6, 38, 88
9 St John Street Chambers, Manchester
p984 . . . . 0161 955 9000
18 St John Street Chambers, Manchester
p985 . . . . 0161 278 1800

Denholm, Mr Graham MA(Hons)(Glasgow); M Phil(Cantab); DipLaw M *Jul 2001*
23, 22
1 Pump Court, London EC4
p947 . . . . 020 7842 7070

DENIS-SMITH, Mr John G *Jan 1998*
Thirty Nine Essex Street, London WC2
p932 . . . . 020 7832 1111

Denison, Mr Simon MA(Cantab); Junior Treasury Counsel L *Nov 1984*
15
6 King's Bench Walk, London EC4
p939 . . . . 020 7583 0410

Denning, Ms Louisa G *Nov 1999*
30, 40, 68, 94
No5 Chambers, Bristol
p971 . . . . 0845 210 5555
No5 Chambers, London EC4
p944 . . . . 0845 210 5555
No5 Chambers, Birmingham
p968 . . . . 0845 210 5555

DENNIS, Mr Mark MA(Cantab); Senior Treasury Counsel M *Jul 1977*
15
6 King's Bench Walk, London EC4
p939 . . . . 020 7583 0410

Dennis, Ms Rebecca I *Nov 1993*
18, 30, 53, 68
Queen Square Chambers, Bristol
p972 . . . . 0117 921 1966

Dennison, Mr James BA I *Jul 1986*
15
2 Dr Johnson's Buildings, London EC4
p930 . . . . 020 7936 2613

Dennison, Mr Stephen LLB(Manc) M *Nov 1985*
(Q.C.) *3, 7, 11, 31, 40, 41, 43, 45, 49, 54, 61, 78, 74*
Atkin Chambers, London WC1
p923 . . . . 020 7404 0102

Denny, Mr Robin H A BA(Oxon) I *May 1969*
12, 15
York Chambers, York
p995 . . . . 01904 620048
York Chambers, Newcastle upon Tyne
p987 . . . . 0191 206 4677

Dennys, Mr Nicholas BA(Oxon); Recorder M *Nov 1975*
(Q.C.) *3, 7, 11, 31, 40, 41, 43, 45, 49, 54, 61, 78, 74*
Atkin Chambers, London WC1
p923 . . . . 020 7404 0102

DENT, Mr Adrian LLB(Hons) L *Jul 1974*
15
Fountain Chambers, Middlesbrough
p986 . . . . 01642 804040
39 Park Square, Leeds
p978 . . . . 0113 245 6633

Dent, Mr Kevin BA(Hons) G *Nov 1991*
12, 15, 20, 30
2 Dr Johnson's Buildings, London EC4
p930 . . . . 020 7936 2613

Dent, Ms Sally BA(Reading); DipLaw L *Jul 1989*
10, 11, 12, 15, 16, 20, 22, 30
1 Pump Court, London EC4
p947 . . . . 020 7842 7070

DENT, Mr Stephen LLB G *Nov 1991*
15
Guildhall Chambers, Bristol
p970 . . . . 0117 930 9000

Denton, Mr Douglas LLB(Hons); LLM(Cantab) L *Nov 1997*
St Johns Buildings, Preston
p990 . . . . 01772 256100
St Johns Buildings, Chester
p974 . . . . 01244 323070
St Johns Buildings, Manchester
p985 . . . . 0161 214 1500
St Johns Buildings, Liverpool
p982 . . . . 0151 243 6000

DENTON-COX, Mr Gregory LLB(Nott'm); Junior Counsel to the Crown (C) L *Jul 2000*
6, 11, 8, 29
4 Stone Buildings, London WC2
p951 . . . . 020 7242 5524

DENYER-GREEN, Mr Barry LLM(Lond); PhD M *Nov 1972*
Falcon Chambers, London EC4
p933 . . . . 020 7353 2484

DERBYSHIRE, Hugh LLB G *Jan 2004*
8, 1, 22, 51, 88, 25, 89, 26, 31, 93, 36
Atlantic Chambers, Liverpool
p980 . . . . 0151 236 4421

Derrington, Mr Jonathan BSc(City); CPE(UWE) I *Oct 1998*
18, 55, 11
No5 Chambers, Bristol
p971 . . . . 0845 210 5555
No5 Chambers, London EC4
p944 . . . . 0845 210 5555
No5 Chambers, Birmingham
p968 . . . . 0845 210 5555

DESAI, Mr Raj L *Jan 2010*
Matrix Chambers, London WC1
p942 . . . . 020 7404 3447

DESCHAMPSNEUFS, Miss Alice BA(Hons) I *Jul 1976*
20, 10
4 King's Bench Walk, London EC4
p939 . . . . 020 7822 7000

DESMOND, Mr Denis BA(L'pool) M *Nov 1974*
72, 15, 70, 25
Cornwall Street Chambers, Birmingham
p967 . . . . 0121 233 7500

Desouza, Mrs Josephine Claudia L *Nov 1992*
20, 23
12 Old Square, London WC2
p945 . . . . 020 7404 0875

Detter, Ms Ingrid DPhil(Oxon); Judge Stockholm High Court; Swedish Immigration Appeal Tribunal G *Jul 1978*
13 Old Square Chambers, London WC2
p945 . . . . 020 7831 4445

Devas, Ms Nicola G *Jan 2003*
15
1 Paper Buildings, London EC4
p946 . . . . 020 7353 3728

Devereux, Mr Edward BA(Hons)(Cantab) M *Oct 2001*
20, 10, 76, 18, 14
Harcourt Chambers, London EC4
p936 . . . . 0844 561 7135
Harcourt Chambers, Oxford
p989 . . . . 0844 561 7135

Devereux-Cooke, Mr Richard BA(Hons)(Oxon) M *Oct 1999*
12, 20, 22, 47
13 Old Square Chambers, London WC2
p945 . . . . 020 7831 4445

Devine, Mr Michael BA; LLM(International Business Studies) G *Oct 1995*
3, 11, 41, 12, 47, 48, 46, 13, 19, 21, 33
Rougemont Chambers, Exeter
p975 . . . . 01392 208484

Devlin, Mr Bernard LLB; LLM G *Nov 1980*
6, 11, 12, 19, 22, 29, 30, 37
5 St Andrew's Hill, London EC4
p950 . . . . 020 7332 5400

Devlin, Mr Jonathan Nicholas Ponton LLB(Hons) I *Nov 1978*
53, 48, 15, 70, 62, 84, 25, 30, 40, 60
St Pauls Chambers, Leeds
p979 . . . . 0113 245 5866

DEVLIN, Mr Thomas L *Jul 2009*
62, 15
23 Essex Street, London WC2
p932 . . . . 020 7413 0353

DEVLIN, Mr Timothy R BA(Lond); DipLaw L *Jul 1985*
15
Furnival Chambers, London EC4
p934 . . . . 020 7405 3232

See p1010 for the Key to Work Categories

DEVONSHIRE, Mr Simon BA(Oxon) G *Feb 1988*
(Q.C.) *11, 13, 18, 50, 55, 56*
11KBW, London EC4
p938 . . . . . 020 7632 8500

DEW, Mr Richard J LLB(Reading) I *Oct 1999*
8
Ten Old Square, London WC2
p945 . . . . . 020 7405 0758

Dewar, Miss Fiona BA(Oxon) L *Nov 2005*
Maitland Chambers, London WC2
p941 . . . . . 020 7406 1200

DEWHURST, Ms Eleanor MA(Oxon) M *Nov 2008*
Pallant Chambers, Chichester
p974 . . . . . 01243 784538

Dewi, Miss Cadi LLB; BVC G *Jan 2008*
15, 20, 23, 30
Angel Chambers, Swansea
p992 . . . . . 01792 464623

Dewsbery, Mr Richard LLB(Essex) I *Oct 1992*
10, 12, 15, 18, 20, 11
St Ives Chambers, Birmingham
p969 . . . . . 0121 236 0863

Dhadda, Miss Sukwinder L *Jan 2004*
2 King's Bench Walk, London EC4
p939 . . . . . 020 7353 1746

Dhadli, Mrs Perminder BA M *Nov 1984*
20
KCH Garden Square Chambers, Nottingham
p989 . . . . . 0115 941 8851
KCH Garden Square Chambers, Leicester
p979 . . . . . 0115 941 8851

Dhaliwal, Miss Davinder M *Nov 1990*
20, 23
No 8 Chambers, Birmingham
p968 . . . . . 0121 236 5514

Dhar, Siddharth M *Jan 2005*
Essex Court Chambers, London WC2
p931 . . . . . 020 7813 8000

Dhar, Mr Zeeshan LLB(Hons) L *Jan 1999*
18
Hardwicke, London WC2
p936 . . . . . 020 7242 2523

Dhillon, Mr Jasbir BA(Oxon); LLM(Harv) G *Oct 1996*
11, 5, 1, 24, 19, 44, 56
Brick Court Chambers, London WC2
p927 . . . . . 020 7379 3550

Dhir, Miss Anuja LLB(Dundee) G *Nov 1989*
15, 62
5 Paper Buildings, London EC4
p946 . . . . . 020 7583 6117

Di Francesco, Alex M *Jul 2008*
15, 94
Lamb Building, Brighton
p970 . . . . . 01273 820490
Lamb Building, London EC4
p940 . . . . . 020 7797 7788

di Mambro, Mr David LLB(Lond); MCIArb M *Nov 1973*
11, 22, 8
Radcliffe Chambers, London WC2
p949 . . . . . 020 7831 0081

Diamond, Miss Anna G *Nov 1995*
30, 53, 68, 46, 94
No5 Chambers, Bristol
p971 . . . . . 0845 210 5555
No5 Chambers, London EC4
p944 . . . . . 0845 210 5555
No5 Chambers, Birmingham
p968 . . . . . 0845 210 5555

DIAMOND, Mr Christopher LLB(Sheff) G *Nov 1975*
15
18 St John Street Chambers, Manchester
p985 . . . . . 0161 278 1800

Dias, Miss Julia Amanda MA(Cantab) I *Jul 1982*
(Q.C.) *11, 24, 35*
7 King's Bench Walk, London EC4
p940 . . . . . 020 7910 8300

Dias, Miss Sappho G *Nov 1982*
15
5 King's Bench Walk, London EC4
p939 . . . . . 020 7353 5638

Diaz, Ms Paula M *Oct 2000*
10, 20, 12
Field Court Chambers, London WC1
p933 . . . . . 020 7405 6114

Dick, Mr James Anthony M *Jan 2003*
15, 94
Bell Yard Chambers, London WC2
p926 . . . . . 020 7306 9292 / 7404 5138

Dick, Ms Julia B Tech(Bradford); DipLaw M *Nov 1988*
15, 30
Tooks Chambers, London EC4
p953 . . . . . 020 7842 7575

Dickason, Mr Robert James MKA(Cantab) L *Jan 2007*
53, 12, 15, 18, 85, 27, 30
Outer Temple Chambers, London WC2
p945 . . . . . 020 7353 6381

DICKER, Mr Robin BA; BCL(Oxon) M *Apr 1986*
(Q.C.) *5, 6, 8, 11, 12, 24, 29, 38*
South Square, London WC1
p950 . . . . . 020 7696 9900

DICKINSON, Mr Gregory D M G *Jul 1981*
(Q.C.) *15*
1 High Pavement, Nottingham
p988 . . . . . 0115 941 8218

Dickinson, Mr John BA(Oxon) M *Oct 1995*
5, 6, 8, 11, 29, 32, 37, 93, 40, 65, 88
St John's Chambers, Bristol
p972 . . . . . 0117 921 3456

Dickinson, Mr Jonathan LLB(Bris) I *Nov 1986*
8, 12, 15, 18, 20, 22, 25, 30
St Johns Buildings, Preston
p990 . . . . . 01772 256100
St Johns Buildings, Chester
p974 . . . . . 01244 323070
St Johns Buildings, Manchester
p985 . . . . . 0161 214 1500
St Johns Buildings, Liverpool
p982 . . . . . 0151 243 6000

DICKINSON, Miss Rosa I *Jan 2006*
11, 12, 30, 18
St Philips Chambers, Birmingham
p969 . . . . . 0121 246 7000

DICKINSON, Mr Russell BA(Hons); PGDL L *Jul 2002*
30, 20, 11, 22
9 St John Street Chambers, Manchester
p984 . . . . . 0161 955 9000

Dicks, Mr Anthony MA; LLB(Cantab) I *Nov 1961*
(Q.C.)
Essex Court Chambers, London WC2
p931 . . . . . 020 7813 8000

Dieu, Mr Hoa LLB G *Jan 2006*
12, 15, 20, 23
Temple Chambers, Newport
p988 . . . . . 01633 267403 / 255855
Temple Chambers, Cardiff
p973 . . . . . 029 2039 7364

DIGGLE, Mr Mark I *Oct 1996*
30, 11, 40, 53, 18
Ropewalk Chambers, Nottingham
p989 . . . . . 0115 947 2581

DIGNUM, Mr Marcus B M *Oct 1994*
11, 12, 30, 47, 40, 59
3 Hare Court, London EC4
p937 . . . . . 020 7415 7800

Dilliway-Parry, Mr Guy G *Jul 2002*
15, 91
5 King's Bench Walk, London EC4
p939 . . . . . 020 7353 5638

DILLON, Miss Clare M *Jan 1974*
20
St Philips Chambers, Birmingham
p969 . . . . . 0121 246 7000

Dilnot, Miss Anna LLB(Lond) L *Mar 2008*
8, 11, 37, 38, 67, 62
3 Stone Buildings, London WC2
p951 . . . . . 020 7242 4937

Dilworth, Mr Noel BA(Hons) I *Jul 2001*
12, 22, 24, 30
Henderson Chambers, London EC4
p937 . . . . . 020 7583 9020

DIN, Soofi P I L *Nov 1984*
11, 40, 22
Ropewalk Chambers, Nottingham
p989 . . . . . 0115 947 2581

Dinan-Hayward, Miss Deborah LLB(Hons) I *Jul 1988*
20
Albion Chambers, Bristol
p970 . . . . . 0117 927 2144

Dineen, Miss Maria LLB(Hons) I *Oct 1997*
15, 62
2 Bedford Row, London WC1
p924 . . . . . 020 7440 8888

DINGEMANS, Mr James M I *Jul 1987*
(Q.C.) *1, 41, 11, 12, 51, 30, 59*
3 Hare Court, London EC4
p937 . . . . . 020 7415 7800

Dingiswayo, Zani I *Jan 2001*
15
1 Pump Court, London EC4
p947 . . . . . 020 7842 7070

Dingle, Jonathan M *Jul 1986*
49
Clerksroom - Administration Centre, Taunton
p993 . . . . . 0845 083 3000

Dinkin, Mr Anthony BSc(Lond) L *Nov 1968*
(Q.C.) *1, 26, 31, 22*
Cornerstone Barristers, London WC1
p929 . . . . . 020 7242 4986

Dippenaar, Mr Daniel Jacobus LLB; BProc M *Jan 2007*
53, 12, 97, 30, 40
Lamb Chambers, London EC4
p941 . . . . . 020 7797 8300

Ditchburn, Mr John BA(Hons)(Oxon); BUC(ICSL) M *Jan 2007*
4 KBW, London EC4
p938 . . . . . 020 7822 8822

DITE, Mr Alexis I *Nov 2008*
15, 62, 94
18 Red Lion Court, London EC4
p949 . . . . . 020 7520 6000
18 Red Lion Court (Annexe), Chelmsford
p973 . . . . . 01245 280880

DIWAN, Mr Ricky BA(Cantab); LLM(Harv) L *Jan 1998*
Essex Court Chambers, London WC2
p931 . . . . . 020 7813 8000

DIXEY, Mr Ian I *Jan 1984*
15, 62, 84, 46
Guildhall Chambers, Bristol
p970 . . . . . 0117 930 9000

Dixon, Ms Annie LLB(Hons); RGN M *Nov 1991*
15, 10, 20
1 Pump Court, London EC4
p947 . . . . . 020 7842 7070

Dixon, Miss Claire Elizabeth BA(Oxon) G *Nov 2002*
Four New Square, London WC2
p943 . . . . . 020 7822 2000

Dixon, Ms Emma BA(Hons)(Cantab) G *Jan 1994*
1, 51, 55, 89, 46, 26, 70
Blackstone Chambers, London EC4
p926 . . . . . 020 7583 1770

Dixon, Mr Huw BA(Hons); LLM(Manc) L *Jan 1999*
12, 15, 30, 8
15 Winckley Square, Preston
p991 . . . . . 01772 252828

Dixon, Mr James L *Jan 2001*
18, 55
No5 Chambers, Bristol
p971 . . . . . 0845 210 5555
No5 Chambers, London EC4
p944 . . . . . 0845 210 5555
No5 Chambers, Birmingham
p968 . . . . . 0845 210 5555

DIXON, Mr John LLB(Hons) G *Nov 1995*
15, 12, 30, 36
St Johns Buildings, Preston
p990 . . . . . 01772 256100
St Johns Buildings, Chester
p974 . . . . . 01244 323070
St Johns Buildings, Manchester
p985 . . . . . 0161 214 1500
St Johns Buildings, Liverpool
p982 . . . . . 0151 243 6000

Dixon, Ralph BA(York) M *Nov 1980*
Clerksroom - Administration Centre, Taunton
p993 . . . . . 0845 083 3000

DIXON, Mr Rodney BA; LLB(Rhodes University, Cape Town) I *Mar 2000*
Temple Garden Chambers, London EC4
p952 . . . . . 020 7583 1315

DOBBY, Miss Helen M *Jan 2008*
4 King's Bench Walk, London EC4
p939 . . . . . 020 7822 7000

Dobie, Miss Lisa I *Jan 2006*
53, 12, 22, 88, 26, 30, 40
1 Chancery Lane, London WC2
p928 . . . . . 0845 634 6666

Dobkin, Mr Matthew G *Jan 2007*
20, 10, 67, 37, 11, 8
St Pauls Chambers, Leeds
p979 . . . . . 0113 245 5866

DOBSON, Ms Catherine I *Jan 2009*
1, 11, 12, 74, 67, 46, 23, 30, 95
Thirty Nine Essex Street, London WC2
p932 . . . . . 020 7832 1111

Dockery, Mr Paul LLB(Lond) G *Jul 1973*
15, 7
18 St John Street Chambers, Manchester
p985 . . . . . 0161 278 1800

Doctor, Mr Brian BCL; BA; LLB L *Jul 1991*
(Q.C.)
Fountain Court Chambers, London EC4
p934 . . . . . 020 7583 3335

Dodd, Mr John LLB(Hons); Recorder G *Nov 1979*
(Q.C.) *15, 62*
2 Bedford Row, London WC1
p924 . . . . . 020 7440 8888

Dodd, Ms Margaret Deputy Secretary M *Jul 1979*
2 Bedford Row, London WC1
p924 . . . . . 020 7440 8888

Dodd, Miss Sara LLB L *Jul 1987*
15
Exchange Chambers, Manchester
p983 . . . . . 0161 833 2722
Exchange Chambers, Liverpool
p980 . . . . . 0151 236 7747
Exchange Chambers, Leeds
p977 . . . . . 0113 203 1970

DODD, Miss Stephanie G *Jul 2001*
15
9-12 Bell Yard Chambers, London WC2
p926 . . . . . 020 7400 1800
Goldsmith Chambers, London EC4
p935 . . . . . 020 7353 6802

DODDS, Kate G *Jan 2000*
Fountain Chambers, Middlesbrough
p986 . . . . . 01642 804040

Dodds, Mr Shaun LLB G *Jul 1990*
15, 72, 70
Old Court Chambers, Middlesbrough
p986 . . . . . 01642 232523

Dodge, Mr Peter MA(Cantab) L *Oct 1992*
6, 8, 9, 11, 22, 29, 32, 37, 40
Radcliffe Chambers, London WC2
p949 . . . . . 020 7831 0081

DODGSON, Mr Lance M *Jan 2007*
12, 15, 20
Bank House Chambers, Sheffield
p991 . . . . . 0114 275 1223

Dodson, Joanna MA(Cantab) M *Nov 1971*
(Q.C.) *10, 20*
42 Bedford Row, London WC1
p925 . . . . . 020 7831 0222
Park Court Chambers, Leeds
p978 . . . . . 0113 243 3277
Renaissance Chambers, London WC1
p949 . . . . . 020 7404 1111

Doerries, Ms Chantal-Aimee MA(Cantab) M *Oct 1992*
(Q.C.) *3, 7, 11, 31, 40, 41, 43, 45, 49, 54, 61, 78, 74*
Atkin Chambers, London WC1
p923 . . . . . 020 7404 0102

DOHERTY, Mr Bernard M *Nov 1990*
30, 40, 53, 11, 24, 84
Thirty Nine Essex Street, London WC2
p932 . . . . . 020 7832 1111

DOHERTY, Mr Nicholas LLB L *Jul 1983*
4 King's Bench Walk, London EC4
p939 . . . . . 020 7822 7000

Dohmann, Miss Barbara G *Nov 1971*
(Q.C.) *3, 5, 8, 11, 12, 19, 24, 29, 36, 41, 50, 89, 81, 44, 21, 52*
Blackstone Chambers, London EC4
p926 . . . . . 020 7583 1770

Doig, Mr Gavin A LLB(Bris) L *Nov 1995*
15
New Court Chambers, Newcastle upon Tyne
p987 . . . . . 0191 232 1980

Dolan, Ms Bridget BSc(Hons); PhD; C Psychol M *Oct 1997*
12, 27, 30, 40, 63, 53, 68, 36
3 Serjeants' Inn, London EC4
p950 . . . . . 020 7427 5000

DOMENGE, Mrs Victoria Jane BA; DipLaw M *Nov 1993*
10, 20
29 Bedford Row, London WC1
p925 . . . . . 020 7404 1044

13

Donaldson, Mr David MA(Cantab) G *Nov 1968*
(Q.C.) *1, 3, 5, 8, 11, 12, 24, 29, 41, 44, 81, 89*
Blackstone Chambers, London EC4
p926 . . . 020 7583 1770

Donaldson, Ms Sarah I *Jul 2003*
12, 15, 20, 30, 59
18 St John Street Chambers, Manchester
p985 . . . 0161 278 1800

Donkin, Matthew LLB I *Jul 2004*
15, 70, 72, 91
Zenith Chambers, Leeds
p979 . . . 0113 245 5438

DONMALL, Mr Matthew BA(Cantab); MPhil L *Jan 2006*
12, 1, 51, 18, 53, 30, 46, 68, 57
1 Crown Office Row, London EC4
p929 . . . 020 7797 7500

Donne, Mr Anthony M M *Apr 1973*
(Q.C.)
King's Bench Godolphin Chambers, Truro
p994 . . . 0845 308 1551
King's Bench Godolphin Chambers, Plymouth
p990 . . . 0845 308 1551
Pump Court Chambers, Swindon
p993 . . . 01793 539899
Pump Court Chambers, Winchester
p994 . . . 01962 868161
Pump Court Chambers, London EC4
p947 . . . 020 7353 0711
2 King's Bench Walk, London EC4
p939 . . . 020 7353 1746
Queen Square Chambers, Bristol
p972 . . . 0117 921 1966

Donne, Mr Jeremy M *Nov 1978*
(Q.C.) *15, 25, 36*
QEB Hollis Whiteman, London EC4
p948 . . . 020 7933 8855

Donnellan, Mr Christopher J BA(Oxon) I *Jul 1981*
(Q.C.) *12, 15, 30, 62, 10, 86*
36 Bedford Row, London WC1
p925 . . . 020 7421 8000

Donnelley, Mr Lewis LLB(Hons) M *Jul 2008*
Zenith Chambers, Leeds
p979 . . . 0113 245 5438

Donnelly, Miss Catherine LLB(Dublin); BCL(Oxon); LLM(Harv); DPhil(Oxon) G *Nov 2003*
19, 51, 1, 44, 89
Blackstone Chambers, London EC4
p926 . . . 020 7583 1770

Donnelly, Mr John Patrick LLB(Hons) I *Nov 1983*
15, 62
2 Bedford Row, London WC1
p924 . . . 020 7440 8888

Donnelly, Miss Kathleen BA(Hons); Jurnis(Oxon) L *Jan 2005*
11, 33
Henderson Chambers, London EC4
p937 . . . 020 7583 9020

Donnelly, Mr Kevin G BA(Hons) L *Oct 1991*
Lincoln House Chambers, Manchester
p984 . . . 0161 832 5701

Donnelly, Mr Timothy LLB L *Jan 2004*
20
Broad Chare Chambers, Newcastle upon Tyne
p986 . . . 0191 232 0541

DONNELLY, Mr William G *Nov 1981*
15, 62, 94
Kenworthy's Chambers, Manchester
p984 . . . 0161 832 4036

Donoghue, Mr Steven M LLB(Wales) M *Oct 1992*
12, 15, 18
9 Park Place, Cardiff
p973 . . . 029 2038 2731

Donovan, Ms Alison MA(Oxon) M *Nov 1987*
10, 12, 20
Angel Chambers, Swansea
p992 . . . 01792 464623

Donovan, Miss Juliet BA(Hons) M *Jul 2002*
15
East Anglian Chambers, Norwich
p988 . . . 01603 617351
East Anglian Chambers, Colchester
p975 . . . 01206 572756
East Anglian Chambers, Chelmsford
p973 . . . 01245 215660
East Anglian Chambers, Ipswich
p976 . . . 01473 214481

DONOVAN, Scott BA(Dunelm) L *Jul 1975*
53, 27, 30, 40, 49, 1
Atlantic Chambers, Liverpool
p980 . . . 0151 236 4421
Cloisters, London EC4
p928 . . . 020 7827 4000

Dooher, Ms Nancy Helen LLB(Hons) L *Nov 1997*
11, 67, 97
Exchange Chambers, Manchester
p983 . . . 0161 833 2722
Exchange Chambers, Liverpool
p980 . . . 0151 236 7747
Exchange Chambers, Leeds
p977 . . . 0113 203 1970
3PB, Winchester
p994 . . . 01962 868884

Dooley, Mr Allan Recorder; Deputy District Judge L *Apr 1970*
30, 53, 40, 94, 68, 74
No5 Chambers, Bristol
p971 . . . 0845 210 5555
No5 Chambers, London EC4
p944 . . . 0845 210 5555
No5 Chambers, Birmingham
p968 . . . 0845 210 5555

Dooley, Ms Christine BA G *Jul 1980*
10, 15
2 Pump Court, London EC4
p947 . . . 020 7353 5597

Doran, Ms Catherine BA(Cantab) I *Jan 2008*
5, 11, 97, 47, 38, 40, 93, 37
Radcliffe Chambers, London WC2
p949 . . . 020 7831 0081

Doran, Mr Gerard G *Nov 1993*
Lincoln House Chambers, Manchester
p984 . . . 0161 832 5701

Dorman-O'Gowan, Mr Christopher P D BA(Newc) L *Nov 1979*
10, 15, 30
Broad Chare Chambers, Newcastle upon Tyne
p986 . . . 0191 232 0541

DORRELL, Miss Alison G G *Feb 1992*
15
Bank House Chambers, Sheffield
p991 . . . 0114 275 1223

Doswell, Mr Rupert LLB I *Oct 1996*
12, 15, 20
11 King's Bench Walk, Leeds
p978 . . . 0113 297 1200

Dougherty, Mr Charles BCL; BA(Oxon) M *Oct 1997*
7, 11, 12, 24, 40, 62
2 Temple Gardens, London EC4
p952 . . . 020 7822 1200

DOUGHERTY, Mr Nigel G *Oct 1993*
11, 38, 97
Erskine Chambers, London WC2
p931 . . . 020 7242 5532

Doughty, Mr Peter LLB(Cardiff) L *Jul 1988*
18, 55, 26
12 College Place, Southampton
p992 . . . 023 8032 0320

Douglas, Mr Colin LLM L *Oct 1998*
20, 10
Temple Chambers, Newport
p988 . . . 01633 267403 / 255855
Temple Chambers, Cardiff
p973 . . . 029 2039 7364

Douglas, Mr Michael BA(Hons)(Oxon); Recorder G *Nov 1974*
(Q.C.) *5, 7, 8, 11, 12, 24, 27, 22*
4 Pump Court, London EC4
p947 . . . 020 7842 5555

Douglas, Mr Stephen John LLB(Hons) I *Nov 1994*
30, 12, 53, 40
St Johns Buildings, Preston
p990 . . . 01772 256100
St Johns Buildings, Chester
p974 . . . 01244 323070
St Johns Buildings, Manchester
p985 . . . 0161 214 1500
St Johns Buildings, Liverpool
p982 . . . 0151 243 6000

DOUGLAS, Mr Zachary BA; LLB(Hons)(Melbourne); BCL(Oxon) G *Mar 2006*
49, 3, 41, 51, 11, 56, 33
Matrix Chambers, London WC1
p942 . . . 020 7404 3447

Douglas-Jones, Mr Benjamin LLB(Hons) G *Nov 1998*
15
5 Paper Buildings, London EC4
p946 . . . 020 7583 6117

Douthwaite, Mr Charles MA G *Jul 1977*
8, 12, 24, 40
Four New Square, London WC2
p943 . . . 020 7822 2000

DOVAR, Mr Daniel G *Jan 1997*
8, 11, 12, 22
Tanfield Chambers, London WC1
p951 . . . 020 7421 5300

Dove, Mr Ian Deputy High Court Judge; Recorder I *Jul 1986*
(Q.C.) *1, 31, 46, 78, 51, 54, 60, 61*
No5 Chambers, Bristol
p971 . . . 0845 210 5555
No5 Chambers, London EC4
p944 . . . 0845 210 5555
No5 Chambers, Birmingham
p968 . . . 0845 210 5555

Dow, Mr Kenneth BA(Exon) L *Nov 1970*
5 Pump Court, London EC4
p947 . . . 020 7353 2532 / 7583 7133

Dowden, Mr Andrew Philip BA(Hons); MPhil(Cantab) L *Jan 1991*
15, 20, 22, 25
Castle Chambers, Harrow
p976 . . . 020 8423 6579

DOWDING, Mr Nicholas MA(Cantab) I *Jul 1979*
(Q.C.)
Falcon Chambers, London EC4
p933 . . . 020 7353 2484

Dowley, Mr Dominic MA(Oxon) G *Jul 1983*
(Q.C.) *1, 3, 5, 7, 11, 24*
Serle Court, London WC2
p950 . . . 020 7242 6105

Down, Miss Barbara LLB(Hons) L *Nov 1999*
15
Westgate Chambers, Lewes
p980 . . . 01273 480510

Down, Miss Susan LLB M *Nov 1984*
10, 20
King's Bench Godolphin Chambers, Truro
p994 . . . 0845 308 1551
King's Bench Godolphin Chambers, Plymouth
p990 . . . 0845 308 1551

Downes, Ms Charlotte BA(Cantab); LLB; LLM; ACA L *May 1997*
6, 8, 11, 32, 37, 34
3 Stone Buildings, London WC2
p951 . . . 020 7242 4937

Downes, Mr Paul ACIB; BA(Oxon) G *Oct 1991*
(Q.C.) *5, 11, 1, 3, 24, 6, 40*
2 Temple Gardens, London EC4
p952 . . . 020 7822 1200

Downey, Miss Aileen Patricia L *Nov 1991*
20, 30, 53
9 Gough Square, London EC4
p935 . . . 020 7832 0500

DOWNEY, Mr B Raoul D BSc; DipLaw L *Jul 1988*
5, 6, 7, 8, 11, 12, 18, 22, 29
Littleton Chambers, London EC4
p941 . . . 020 7797 8600

DOWNEY, Neil BA(Hons)(Oxon) M *Mar 1997*
30, 11, 18, 68, 55
Atlantic Chambers, Liverpool
p980 . . . 0151 236 4421

DOWNHAM, Miss Gillian BSc(Soc Sci); DipSW; MA(Econ); DipLaw M *Nov 1993*
10, 20
1 Garden Court, London EC4
p934 . . . 020 7797 7900

DOWNIE, Mr Andrew BA; MA G *Nov 1990*
15, 20
7 Harrington Street Chambers, Liverpool
p981 . . . 0151 242 0707

Downing, Miss Emma MA(Hons) M *Jan 2002*
15, 20, 23, 30
Broadway House Chambers, Leeds
p977 . . . 0113 246 2600
Broadway House Chambers, Bradford
p969 . . . 01274 722560

DOWNS, Mr Martin BA(Oxon) I *Nov 1990*
12, 20, 30, 36, 18
1 Crown Office Row, London EC4
p929 . . . 020 7797 7500

Dowse, Ms Clare I *Jul 2002*
15, 62
3 Temple Gardens, London EC4
p952 . . . 020 7353 3102

DOYLE, Miss Holly L *Jan 2008*
11, 93, 38, 5, 40
Guildhall Chambers, Bristol
p970 . . . 0117 930 9000

Doyle, Mr James LLB M *Jul 1985*
15, 91
5 King's Bench Walk, London EC4
p939 . . . 020 7353 5638

Doyle, Mr Louis G LLB; LLM L *Nov 1996*
5, 6, 8, 11, 29, 32, 37, 40, 41
Kings Chambers, Leeds
p978 . . . 0113 242 1123
Kings Chambers, Manchester
p984 . . . 0161 832 9082

DOYLE, Mr Peter M *Jan 1975*
(Q.C.) *15, 62, 72*
25 Bedford Row, London WC1
p925 . . . 020 7067 1500

Doyle, Mr Shane BCL; LLB; Becon L *Jan 2001*
Essex Court Chambers, London WC2
p931 . . . 020 7813 8000

DRABBLE, Mr Richard BA(Cantab) I *Nov 1975*
(Q.C.) *1, 26, 31, 36, 23, 33*
Landmark Chambers, London EC4
p941 . . . 020 7430 1221

DRACASS, Mr Timothy LLB I *Oct 1998*
15, 18, 30
Pump Court Chambers, Swindon
p993 . . . 01793 539899
Pump Court Chambers, Winchester
p994 . . . 01962 868161
Pump Court Chambers, London EC4
p947 . . . 020 7353 0711

Dracos, Mr Marcos M *Jan 2005*
One Essex Court, London EC4
p931 . . . 020 7583 2000

Drake, Mr David BA; BCL(Oxon) I *Nov 1994*
6, 8, 11, 38, 40, 43, 62, 67
Serle Court, London WC2
p950 . . . 020 7242 6105

Drake, Mr James BA; LLB; LLM L *Jan 1998*
(Q.C.) *11, 35, 24*
7 King's Bench Walk, London EC4
p940 . . . 020 7910 8300

Drake, Miss Rachel Alexia LLB(Hons)(Brunel) M *Nov 1995*
15
King's Bench Chambers, Oxford
p989 . . . 01865 311066
13 King's Bench Walk, London EC4
p940 . . . 020 7353 7204

DRAKE, Ms Rebecca L *Jul 2007*
Thirty Nine Essex Street, London WC2
p932 . . . 020 7832 1111

Drake, Miss Sophie Helena LLB(Leics) G *Oct 1990*
10, 15, 20
Broadway House Chambers, Leeds
p977 . . . 0113 246 2600
Broadway House Chambers, Bradford
p969 . . . 01274 722560

DRAPER, Mr Guy M *Mar 2008*
Furnival Chambers, London EC4
p934 . . . 020 7405 3232

DRAPER, Mr Owain MA(Eng Lit); DipLaw L *Jan 2008*
44, 57, 19, 56, 1
Monckton Chambers, London WC1
p942 . . . 020 7405 7211

DRAY, Mr Martin LLB(Bris) G *Oct 1992*
Falcon Chambers, London EC4
p933 . . . 020 7353 2484

Draycott, Mr Christopher I *Jan 2005*
4 Breams Buildings, London EC4
p927 . . . 020 7092 1900

Draycott, Miss Natasha M *Jan 2005*
15
5 St Andrew's Hill, London EC4
p950 . . . 020 7332 5400

Draycott, Mr Paul G *Nov 1994*
18, 51, 23
Doughty Street Chambers, London WC1
p930 . . . 020 7404 1313

DRAYCOTT, Mr Simon M *Jul 1977*
(Q.C.) *15*
Citadel Chambers, Birmingham
p967 . . . 0121 233 8500

See p1010 for the Key to Work Categories

5 St Andrew's Hill, London EC4
p950 . . . . . 020 7332 5400

Drew, Mrs Cheryl G *Nov 1972*
6, 8, 10, 11, 12, 15, 20, 30, 32, 37
Warwick House Chambers, London WC1
p953 . . . . . 020 7430 2323

Drew, Mr Christopher Thomas LLB(Hons)(Lond) G *Nov 1969*
6, 7, 8, 10, 11, 12, 15, 20, 30, 88, 37
Warwick House Chambers, London WC1
p953 . . . . . 020 7430 2323

Drew, Ms Jane BA(Dunelm) M *Jul 1976*
20, 10, 37
Coram Chambers, London EC1
p929 . . . . . 020 7092 3700

Drew, Ms Sandhya G *Nov 1993*
1, 18, 55
Tooks Chambers, London EC4
p953 . . . . . 020 7842 7575

Drew, Mr Simon L *Nov 1987*
(Q.C.) *15, 62, 84, 39, 70, 72*
No5 Chambers, Bristol
p971 . . . . . 0845 210 5555
No5 Chambers, London EC4
p944 . . . . . 0845 210 5555
No5 Chambers, Birmingham
p968 . . . . . 0845 210 5555

DRING, Emma L *Jan 2009*
Cornerstone Barristers, London WC1
p929 . . . . . 020 7242 4986

Driscoll, Mr Michael BA; LLB(Cantab) M *Jul 1970*
(Q.C.) *1, 3, 5, 6, 7, 8, 9, 11, 12, 13, 14, 22, 24, 26, 28, 29, 31, 32, 37*
Maitland Chambers, London WC2
p941 . . . . . 020 7406 1200

Driver, Miss Emily Rose BA I *Oct 1988*
15, 10, 20, 76
Boston Manor Chambers, Brentford
p970 . . . . . 07980 328753

DRIVER, Mr Simon Gregory BA I *Nov 1991*
15, 62
7 Harrington Street Chambers, Liverpool
p981 . . . . . 0151 242 0707

DRIVER, Stuart MA(Oxon) G *Nov 1988*
(Q.C.) *15*
Atlantic Chambers, Liverpool
p980 . . . . . 0151 236 4421

Druce, Mr Michael MA(Cantab) I *Jul 1988*
1, 26, 28, 31, 36
Cornerstone Barristers, London WC1
p929 . . . . . 020 7242 4986

DRUMMOND, Mr Bruce BSc; LLM(New York) G *Oct 1992*
20, 11, 50, 52
Cornwall Street Chambers, Birmingham
p967 . . . . . 0121 233 7500

Drury, Miss Claire LLB(Hons)(Hull) L *Oct 2000*
15, 18, 23
4 Breams Buildings, London EC4
p927 . . . . . 020 7092 1900

Dry, Mr Nicholas D BA(Hons) L *Nov 1996*
62, 15, 72
St Pauls Chambers, Leeds
p979 . . . . . 0113 245 5866

Dryden, Mr Shaun L *Jan 1994*
15, 70, 72
Old Court Chambers, Middlesbrough
p986 . . . . . 01642 232523

Dsane, Miss Victoria T BA; LLB; MA(Business) M *Nov 1971*
61 Elm Grove, Sutton
p992 . . . . . 020 8643 9714

DU CANN, Mr Christian D L G *Jun 1982*
30, 24, 40, 53, 56, 12, 84
Thirty Nine Essex Street, London WC2
p932 . . . . . 020 7832 1111

DU PREEZ, Mr Robin I *Nov 1985*
15
18 Red Lion Court, London EC4
p949 . . . . . 020 7520 6000
18 Red Lion Court (Annexe), Chelmsford
p973 . . . . . 01245 280880

DUBBERY, Mr Mark M *Oct 1996*
10, 12, 15, 18, 20, 30, 40, 32
Pump Court Chambers, Swindon
p993 . . . . . 01793 539899
Pump Court Chambers, Winchester
p994 . . . . . 01962 868161
Pump Court Chambers, London EC4
p947 . . . . . 020 7353 0711

DUBIN, Mr Joshua MA(Cantab) M *Nov 1997*
12, 15, 18, 22, 47
1 Pump Court, London EC4
p947 . . . . . 020 7842 7070

Dubinsky, Ms Laura M *Oct 2002*
1, 51, 21
Doughty Street Chambers, London WC1
p930 . . . . . 020 7404 1313

Duck, Mr Michael LLB G *Nov 1988*
(Q.C.) *15, 62, 36, 68, 70, 72*
No5 Chambers, Bristol
p971 . . . . . 0845 210 5555
No5 Chambers, London EC4
p944 . . . . . 0845 210 5555
No5 Chambers, Birmingham
p968 . . . . . 0845 210 5555

Duckworth, Miss Emily MA(Cantab) I *Jul 2003*
6, 8, 11, 22
Kings Chambers, Leeds
p978 . . . . . 0113 242 1123
Kings Chambers, Manchester
p984 . . . . . 0161 832 9082

DUCKWORTH, Mr Nathaniel MA(Oxon) L *Oct 2002*
Falcon Chambers, London EC4
p933 . . . . . 020 7353 2484

DUCKWORTH, Mr Peter Arthur LLB; BA M *Nov 1971*
10, 20, 30
29 Bedford Row, London WC1
p925 . . . . . 020 7404 1044

DUDDRIDGE, Mr Robert BA(Oxon) L *Feb 1992*
8, 6, 11, 49, 40, 22, 38, 88
Enterprise Chambers, London WC2
p931 . . . . . 020 7405 9471
Enterprise Chambers, Leeds
p977 . . . . . 0113 246 0391
Enterprise Chambers, Newcastle upon Tyne
p987 . . . . . 0191 222 3344

Dudley, Mr Robert Michael MA(Cantab) G *Oct 1993*
15, 62
Exchange Chambers, Manchester
p983 . . . . . 0161 833 2722
Exchange Chambers, Liverpool
p980 . . . . . 0151 236 7747
Exchange Chambers, Leeds
p977 . . . . . 0113 203 1970

DUDLEY, Mr Thomas BA(Hons); GDL; BVC I *Jan 2008*
10, 20
1 Garden Court, London EC4
p934 . . . . . 020 7797 7900

Dudnikov, Mr Anton G *Jul 2008*
Essex Court Chambers, London WC2
p931 . . . . . 020 7813 8000

Duff, Mr Euan C MA(Cantab) I *Jul 1973*
15
Broad Chare Chambers, Newcastle upon Tyne
p986 . . . . . 0191 232 0541

Dufficy, Mr Conor M *Jul 2004*
15, 62, 12, 30
7 Bedford Row, London WC1
p924 . . . . . 020 7242 3555

DUFFIELD, Mr Stephen Michael BA(Oxon) G *Jul 1969*
15
Trinity (Newcastle) Chambers, Newcastle upon Tyne
p987 . . . . . 0191 232 1927
Trinity (Teesside) Chambers, Middlesbrough
p986 . . . . . 01642 247569

Duffy, Catherine I *Oct 2003*
15, 12, 30, 70, 72
Zenith Chambers, Leeds
p979 . . . . . 0113 245 5438

Duffy, Mr Derek J BA(Hons) G *Mar 1997*
12, 81, 15, 6, 29, 62, 84, 25
St Pauls Chambers, Leeds
p979 . . . . . 0113 245 5866

Duffy, Mr James L *Oct 2005*
Fountain Court Chambers, London EC4
p934 . . . . . 020 7583 3335

DUFFY, Mr Jonathan Bernard CPE; PGDL G *Oct 2002*
15
7 Harrington Street Chambers, Liverpool
p981 . . . . . 0151 242 0707

DUFFY, Mr Patrick BCL; MSE M *Jul 2007*
15, 62
23 Essex Street, London WC2
p932 . . . . . 020 7413 0353

DUGDALE, Mr Jeremy MA(Oxon) I *Oct 1992*
10, 15, 20
Octagon House, Norwich
p988 . . . . . 01603 623186

Dugdale, Nicholas BA; LLB(Auckland) M *Feb 1982*
Clerksroom - Administration Centre, Taunton
p993 . . . . . 0845 083 3000

Dugdale, Mr Paul LLB(Lond) G *Oct 1990*
2 King's Bench Walk, London EC4
p939 . . . . . 020 7353 1746

DUGGAN, Mr Michael BA; BCL; LLM G *Jul 1984*
3, 7, 11, 12, 18, 36
Littleton Chambers, London EC4
p941 . . . . . 020 7797 8600

Dulay, Miss Ranjeet I *Jan 1999*
15, 23
12 Old Square, London WC2
p945 . . . . . 020 7404 0875

Dumaresq, Ms Delia MA; DipLaw I *Jul 1984*
3, 7, 11, 31, 40, 41, 43, 45, 49, 54, 61, 78, 74
Atkin Chambers, London WC1
p923 . . . . . 020 7404 0102

Dumbill, Eric Alexander LLB G *Nov 1971*
Clerksroom - Administration Centre, Taunton
p993 . . . . . 0845 083 3000

Dummett, Miss Emily BA(Hons) M *Nov 2006*
15
2 Hare Court, London EC4
p937 . . . . . 020 7353 5324

Dumont, Mr Thomas MA(Cantab) G *Nov 1979*
5, 6, 8, 9, 29, 32, 37, 11, 14, 40
Radcliffe Chambers, London WC2
p949 . . . . . 020 7831 0081

Duncan, Mr Gareth L *Jan 2010*
20, 23, 15, 62, 30, 11
Thirty Park Place, Cardiff
p973 . . . . . 029 2039 8421

Duncan, Miss Hannah Gillian Isobella I *Oct 2002*
15
Atkinson Bevan Chambers, London EC4
p924 . . . . . 020 7353 2112

Duncan, Ms Nikki LLB G *Nov 1994*
15
King's Bench Chambers, Oxford
p989 . . . . . 01865 311066
13 King's Bench Walk, London EC4
p940 . . . . . 020 7353 7204

DUNHAM, Mr Nicholas BA(Hons)(Dunelm) M *Oct 1999*
15, 25
9-12 Bell Yard Chambers, London WC2
p926 . . . . . 020 7400 1800

Dunkels, Mr Paul Recorder I *May 1972*
(Q.C.) *12, 15, 25, 30, 36*
Walnut House Chambers, Exeter
p975 . . . . . 01392 279751

Dunkerton, Mrs Katie L *Jul 2008*
8, 11, 12
St John's Chambers, Bristol
p972 . . . . . 0117 921 3456

DUNKIN, Mr Oliver G *Oct 1999*
15, 25, 72, 70
23 Essex Street, London WC2
p932 . . . . . 020 7413 0353

Dunlop, Mr Hamish BA M *Nov 1991*
15, 20, 30
3PB, Bournemouth
p969 . . . . . 01202 292102

Dunlop, Mrs Patricia BL(Dublin); BA(Dublin)(Communication Studies) M *Jan 2009*
12, 15, 20, 25, 10, 30
Regency Chambers, Peterborough
p990 . . . . . 01733 315215

DUNLOP, Mr Rory BA; DipLaw L *Nov 2002*
40, 30, 18, 51, 46, 11, 1, 23
Thirty Nine Essex Street, London WC2
p932 . . . . . 020 7832 1111

DUNN, Ms Katherine L LLB L *Oct 1993*
15, 62, 63, 25
Trinity (Newcastle) Chambers, Newcastle upon Tyne
p987 . . . . . 0191 232 1927
Trinity (Teesside) Chambers, Middlesbrough
p986 . . . . . 01642 247569

DUNN, Miss Sarah L *Oct 1998*
34, 57, 58, 37
Pump Court Tax Chambers, London WC1
p948 . . . . . 020 7414 8080

DUNN, Mr Tom L *Jan 1998*
Maidstone Chambers, Maidstone
p982 . . . . . 01622 688592

DUNNE, Mr David M *Jul 2005*
30, 94, 47, 12, 15
7 Harrington Street Chambers, Liverpool
p981 . . . . . 0151 242 0707

Dunning, Mr Graham MA(Cantab); LLM(Harv) L *Jul 1982*
(Q.C.)
Essex Court Chambers, London WC2
p931 . . . . . 020 7813 8000

Dunning, Mr John BSc I *Jul 1973*
12, 15, 25
37 Park Square Chambers, Leeds
p978 . . . . . 0113 243 9422

Dunn-Shaw, Mr Jason L *Oct 1992*
15, 62, 16
6 King's Bench Walk, London EC4
p939 . . . . . 020 7583 0410

Dunseath, Katherine BSc(Hons) G *Jan 2008*
18, 20, 10, 53, 93, 71, 88, 8
3PB, Oxford
p989 . . . . . 01865 793736

DUNSTAN, Mr James P BA(Oxon) G *Jan 1995*
15, 62
St Philips Chambers, Birmingham
p969 . . . . . 0121 246 7000

Durance, Mr Alex BA(Hons) G *Nov 1997*
22, 23, 1, 70
Doughty Street Chambers, London WC1
p930 . . . . . 020 7404 1313

DURBER, Joanna L *Jan 2005*
4 King's Bench Walk, London EC4
p939 . . . . . 020 7822 7000

Durham Hall, Mr Christian BA(Hons); PDipLaw; LLM G *Jul 2009*
20
Broadway House Chambers, Leeds
p977 . . . . . 0113 246 2600
Broadway House Chambers, Bradford
p969 . . . . . 01274 722560

DUROSE, Mr David W L *Oct 1996*
1, 12, 15, 30
Furnival Chambers, London EC4
p934 . . . . . 020 7405 3232

DURR, Jude MA(Hons) I *Nov 1995*
15, 30, 70
Octagon House, Norwich
p988 . . . . . 01603 623186

DURRAN, Miss Alexia MA(Hons)(Cantab); Recorder M *Sep 1995*
15, 36, 25, 62
23 Essex Street, London WC2
p932 . . . . . 020 7413 0353

Durrant, Mr Charles I *Jul 2006*
15
3 Temple Gardens, London EC4
p952 . . . . . 020 7353 3102

Durston, Mr Jeremy LLB; BA(Commerce) I *Jan 2008*
15, 30, 12, 94
Exchange Chambers, Manchester
p983 . . . . . 0161 833 2722
Exchange Chambers, Liverpool
p980 . . . . . 0151 236 7747
Exchange Chambers, Leeds
p977 . . . . . 0113 203 1970

DUTCHMAN-SMITH, Mr Malcolm G *Feb 1995*
15
7 Harrington Street Chambers, Liverpool
p981 . . . . . 0151 242 0707

Duthie, Miss Catriona LLB; MSc(Notts) I *Jul 1981*
20, 10
St John's Chambers, Bristol
p972 . . . . . 0117 921 3456

Duthie, Mr Malcolm I *Jul 1989*
30, 53, 40, 94, 68
No5 Chambers, Bristol
p971 . . . . . 0845 210 5555
No5 Chambers, London EC4
p944 . . . . . 0845 210 5555
No5 Chambers, Birmingham
p968 . . . . . 0845 210 5555

13

DUTTA, Miss Nandini LLB M *Feb 1993*
10, 20, 64
No5 Chambers, Bristol
p971 . . . 0845 210 5555
No5 Chambers, London EC4
p944 . . . 0845 210 5555
No5 Chambers, Birmingham
p968 . . . 0845 210 5555

Dutton, Mr Timothy BA(Oxon) M *Nov 1979*
(Q.C.)
Fountain Court Chambers, London EC4
p934 . . . 020 7583 3335

Dutton, Mr Timothy Christopher BA(Durham) I *Jul 1985*
2, 8, 11, 22, 29, 40, 32, 36
Maitland Chambers, London WC2
p941 . . . 020 7406 1200

Duval, Mr Robert G *Nov 1979*
72, 15, 70
Albion Chambers, Bristol
p970 . . . 0117 927 2144

Duxbury, Sarah M *Mar 2010*
10, 20
East Anglian Chambers, Norwich
p988 . . . 01603 617351
East Anglian Chambers, Colchester
p975 . . . 01206 572756
East Anglian Chambers, Chelmsford
p973 . . . 01245 215660
East Anglian Chambers, Ipswich
p976 . . . 01473 214481

Duyvenbode, Mr Damian M *Nov 2001*
15, 46, 84
Argent Chambers, London WC2
p923 . . . 020 7556 5500

Dwomoh, Miss Elizabeth M *Oct 2005*
Lamb Chambers, London EC4
p941 . . . 020 7797 8300

DYAL, Miss Mandeep I *Jan 2008*
20
Cornwall Street Chambers, Birmingham
p967 . . . 0121 233 7500

DYBLE, Mr Steven M *Nov 1986*
15
18 Red Lion Court, London EC4
p949 . . . 020 7520 6000
18 Red Lion Court (Annexe), Chelmsford
p973 . . . 01245 280880

DYE, Mr Brian W MA(Oxon) M *Oct 1991*
Essex Court Chambers, London WC2
p931 . . . 020 7813 8000

Dye, Mr John I *Nov 2002*
Goldsmith Chambers, London EC4
p935 . . . 020 7353 6802

Dyer, Mr Allen BA(Hons)(Bris) I *Jul 1976*
7, 11, 12, 18, 20, 24, 36
4 Pump Court, London EC4
p947 . . . 020 7842 5555

Dyer, Mr Jacob Jackson BA(Hons) L *Nov 1995*
15, 30
15 Winckley Square, Preston
p991 . . . 01772 252828

Dyer, Mr Nigel I G BA(Dunelm) I *Feb 1982*
(Q.C.) *20, 10*
1 Hare Court, London EC4
p936 . . . 020 7797 7070

Dyer, Miss Shereen L *Oct 2003*
25, 15, 30
East Anglian Chambers, Norwich
p988 . . . 01603 617351
East Anglian Chambers, Colchester
p975 . . . 01206 572756
East Anglian Chambers, Chelmsford
p973 . . . 01245 215660
East Anglian Chambers, Ipswich
p976 . . . 01473 214481

Dyer, Mr Simon C BA(Kent) M *Jul 1987*
30, 18, 12, 53
Cloisters, London EC4
p928 . . . 020 7827 4000

Dykers, Miss C Joy BA G *Oct 1995*
15, 84, 62
Lamb Building, Brighton
p970 . . . 01273 820490
Lamb Building, London EC4
p940 . . . 020 7797 7788

DYMOND, Mr Andrew Mark MA(Oxon) M *Nov 1991*
1, 22, 26, 38, 51, 36
Arden Chambers, London WC1
p923 . . . 020 7242 4244

Dyson, Mr Daniel Bryn William LLB G *Nov 2007*
8, 18, 89, 40
King's Bench Godolphin Chambers, Truro
p994 . . . 0845 308 1551
King's Bench Godolphin Chambers, Plymouth
p990 . . . 0845 308 1551

EADIE, Miss Charlotte L *Oct 2003*
15, 62, 95
187 Fleet Street, London EC4
p933 . . . 020 7430 7430

Eadie, Mr James MA(Cantab) M *Jul 1984*
(Q.C.) *1, 3, 5, 11, 12, 24, 51, 41, 89, 81, 43, 36*
Blackstone Chambers, London EC4
p926 . . . 020 7583 1770

Eady, Ms Jennifer BA(Oxon); Part-Time Employment Tribunal Chair I *Jul 1989*
(Q.C.) *11, 18, 26, 36, 55, 1, 56, 51*
Old Square Chambers, Bristol
p971 . . . 0117 930 5100
Old Square Chambers, London WC1
p945 . . . 020 7269 0300

EAGLESTONE, Mr William M *Nov 2001*
15, 72, 70
23 Essex Street, London WC2
p932 . . . 020 7413 0353

Eales, Mr Darren G *Jan 2000*
56, 12, 18, 30, 40
2 Temple Gardens, London EC4
p952 . . . 020 7822 1200

EALES, Miss Hannah M *Nov 2003*
15, 62, 94
18 Red Lion Court, London EC4
p949 . . . 020 7520 6000
18 Red Lion Court (Annexe), Chelmsford
p973 . . . 01245 280880

EARDLEY, Mr Aidan BA(Hons)(Oxon) L *Nov 2002*
16, 52, 73
One Brick Court, London EC4
p927 . . . 020 7353 8845

Earlam, Mr Simon MA(Oxon); BCL(Oxon); Recorder G *Feb 1975*
30, 53, 40, 56, 68, 16, 96
Exchange Chambers, Manchester
p983 . . . 0161 833 2722
Exchange Chambers, Liverpool
p980 . . . 0151 236 7747
Exchange Chambers, Leeds
p977 . . . 0113 203 1970

Earle, Mr James Christopher BA(Hons); MA(Lond) G *Oct 1996*
Fenners Chambers, Cambridge
p972 . . . 01223 368761

Earle, Miss Judy M *Oct 1994*
12, 15
3PB, Bournemouth
p969 . . . 01202 292102

EARLEY, Ms Sarah Jane LLB(Hons) I *Oct 1998*
10, 20, 15
Pallant Chambers, Chichester
p974 . . . 01243 784538

East, Mr William BA(Oxon) L *Jan 2008*
8, 32, 37, 14, 38
5 Stone Buildings, London WC2
p951 . . . 020 7242 6201

EASTEAL, Mr Andrew Recorder I *Jul 1990*
62, 15
23 Essex Street, London WC2
p932 . . . 020 7413 0353

Easton, Miss Alison LLB(Hons)(B'ham) I *Nov 1994*
10, 20
Coram Chambers, London EC1
p929 . . . 020 7092 3700

Easton, Mr Jonathan LLB(Warw) G *Nov 1996*
1, 22, 26, 31, 36, 46, 54, 61
Kings Chambers, Leeds
p978 . . . 0113 242 1123
Kings Chambers, Manchester
p984 . . . 0161 832 9082

Eastwood, Mr Charles Peter BA(Oxon) L *Jul 1988*
12, 20, 30, 15
St Johns Buildings, Preston
p990 . . . 01772 256100
St Johns Buildings, Chester
p974 . . . 01244 323070
St Johns Buildings, Manchester
p985 . . . 0161 214 1500
St Johns Buildings, Liverpool
p982 . . . 0151 243 6000

Eastwood, Miss Charlotte LLB(Hons) M *Nov 2003*
15, 20, 30, 31
37 Park Square Chambers, Leeds
p978 . . . 0113 243 9422

EASTWOOD, Shannon LLB I *Oct 2007*
12, 30, 53, 15
Atlantic Chambers, Liverpool
p980 . . . 0151 236 4421

EATON, Miss Deborah A BSocSc(Keele); DipLaw(City) I *Jul 1985*
(Q.C.) *10, 20, 14, 49*
1 King's Bench Walk, London EC4
p938 . . . 020 7936 1500

Eaton, Mr Nigel T BA; BCL(Oxon) G *Nov 1991*
Essex Court Chambers, London WC2
p931 . . . 020 7813 8000

Eaton, Mr Tobias LLB L *Nov 2001*
15, 22, 26
Staple Inn Chambers, London WC1
p951 . . . 020 7242 5240

Eaton-Hart, Mr Andrew LLB(Hons)(Exon) G *Jul 1989*
12, 20, 11, 10, 30, 27, 18
Walnut House Chambers, Exeter
p975 . . . 01392 279751

EATON TURNER, Mr David LLB(Lond) L *Jul 1984*
6, 11, 5, 8
New Square Chambers, London WC2
p943 . . . 020 7419 8000

Eatwell, Tatyana I *Jul 2007*
15, 51
Tooks Chambers, London EC4
p953 . . . 020 7842 7575

EBORALL, Ms Charlotte M *Jan 2004*
5, 81, 38, 6, 24, 40, 62, 97
3 Verulam Buildings, London WC1
p953 . . . 020 7831 8441

ECKERSLEY, Mr Simon BA(Hons)(Oxon) L *May 1996*
15
1 High Pavement, Nottingham
p988 . . . 0115 941 8218

Ecob, Miss Joanne A F LLB(Newc) I *Jul 1985*
12, 30, 27, 40
36 Bedford Row, London WC1
p925 . . . 020 7421 8000

EDDY, Ms Katherine I *Jan 2009*
1, 18, 76, 51
11KBW, London EC4
p938 . . . 020 7632 8500

Edelman, Mr Colin MA(Cantab) M *Jul 1977*
(Q.C.) *11, 12, 24, 36, 3, 40*
Devereux Chambers, London WC2
p930 . . . 020 7353 7534

Edelman, Mr James L *Mar 2008*
One Essex Court, London EC4
p931 . . . 020 7583 2000

Edenborough, Mr James Scott M *Nov 2001*
15, 62
15 New Bridge Street Chambers, London EC4
p943 . . . 020 7842 1900

Edey, Mr Philip David BA(Oxon) G *Nov 1994*
(Q.C.) *3, 11, 12, 24, 35, 41*
20 Essex Street, London WC2
p932 . . . 020 7842 1200

Edge, Mr Alan BA(Hons)(History & English) L *Jul 2006*
15, 20, 10, 67
Argent Chambers, London WC2
p923 . . . 020 7556 5500

EDGE, Mr Andrew I *Oct 2003*
18, 55, 1, 11
11KBW, London EC4
p938 . . . 020 7632 8500

Edge, Miss Charlotte Louise BA(Oxon); GDL; BVC(Lond) L *Oct 2006*
6, 8, 11, 97, 32
3 Stone Buildings, London WC2
p951 . . . 020 7242 4937

Edge, Mr Ian LLM; BA M *Feb 1981*
3, 5, 12, 21, 33
3PB, London EC4
p946 . . . 020 7583 8055

Edge, Miss Romilly M *Jan 2005*
St Ives Chambers, Birmingham
p969 . . . 0121 236 0863

Edginton, Mr Horace Ronald RGN; LLB; LLM G *Nov 1984*
10, 20, 12
Becket Chambers, Canterbury
p972 . . . 01227 786331
Becket Chambers, Maidstone
p982 . . . 01622 230957

Edhem, Miss Emma G *Oct 1993*
11, 3, 96, 97, 89, 67, 79
No5 Chambers, Bristol
p971 . . . 0845 210 5555
No5 Chambers, London EC4
p944 . . . 0845 210 5555
No5 Chambers, Birmingham
p968 . . . 0845 210 5555

EDINGTON, Mrs Fiona A R BA(Hons) M *Oct 1998*
Thomas More Chambers, London WC2
p952 . . . 020 7404 7000

EDIS, Andrew BA(Oxon); MA(Oxon) M *Jul 1980*
(Q.C.) *5, 7, 8, 11, 15, 27, 29, 30, 40, 12, 53, 62*
Atlantic Chambers, Liverpool
p980 . . . 0151 236 4421

EDIS, Mr William BA(Oxon) L *Jul 1985*
(Q.C.) *12, 18, 27, 30, 1, 22*
1 Crown Office Row, London EC4
p929 . . . 020 7797 7500

Edmonds, Mr Michael PGDL; BA(Hons)(Philosophy) I *Aug 2000*
68, 72, 15, 70, 82, 62, 25, 84, 91, 94, 95
33 Bedford Row, London WC1
p925 . . . 020 7242 6476
15 New Bridge Street Chambers, London EC4
p943 . . . 020 7842 1900

EDMONDS, Ms Victoria G *Jul 2004*
20, 30, 12
St Philips Chambers, Birmingham
p969 . . . 0121 246 7000

Edmondson, Miss Harriet LLB(Hons)(Wales) G *Nov 1997*
12, 20
Thirty Park Place, Cardiff
p973 . . . 029 2039 8421

EDMUNDS, Miss Lisa LLB(Hons) I *Oct 2002*
15, 20, 62, 10
7 Harrington Street Chambers, Liverpool
p981 . . . 0151 242 0707

EDUSEI, Mr Francis I *Jul 1989*
15, 62, 70, 82
Kenworthy's Chambers, Manchester
p984 . . . 0161 832 4036

Edward, Sir David MA(Oxon); LLD(Edin) G *Jan 1962*
(Q.C.) *49, 96*
Blackstone Chambers, London EC4
p926 . . . 020 7583 1770

Edwards, Miss Ann Merērid LLB G *Sep 1991*
10, 20, 30
Paradise Chambers, Sheffield
p992 . . . 0114 273 8951

EDWARDS, Mr Anthony M *Nov 1999*
7, 11, 12, 22, 40
Chancery House Chambers, Leeds
p977 . . . 0113 244 6691

Edwards, Mr Charles Edwin M *Jan 2002*
Clapham Law Chambers, London SW1
p928 . . . 020 7978 8482 / 7642 5777

Edwards, Mr Christopher MA(Oxon); MA(UCL); BVC G *Jan 2006*
18, 30
Old Square Chambers, Bristol
p971 . . . 0117 930 5100
Old Square Chambers, London WC1
p945 . . . 020 7269 0300
3PB, London EC4
p946 . . . 020 7583 8055

Edwards, Mr Daniel L *Oct 1993*
York Chambers, York
p995 . . . 01904 620048
York Chambers, Newcastle upon Tyne
p987 . . . 0191 206 4677

Edwards, Mr David Leslie BA(Cantab) L *Jul 1989*
(Q.C.) *35, 11, 24, 5, 6, 3, 40*
7 King's Bench Walk, London EC4
p940 . . . 020 7910 8300

Edwards, Mr Denis M *Oct 2002*
1, 76, 15, 46, 22, 51, 23, 25, 26
Francis Taylor Building, London EC4
p934 . . . 020 7353 8415

See p1010 for the Key to Work Categories

Edwards, Mr Douglas LLB(B'ham); Dip EC Law(Lond) *L Nov 1992*
(Q.C.) *1, 12, 46, 22, 26, 31, 36, 25*
Francis Taylor Building, London EC4
p934 . . . . . 020 7353 8415

Edwards, Mr Glyn LLM(Cantab) *L Jul 1987*
30, 26
St John's Chambers, Bristol
p972 . . . . . 0117 921 3456

Edwards, Mr Heath LLB(Warw) *G Nov 1996*
12, 15, 18, 30
9 Park Place, Cardiff
p973 . . . . . 029 2038 2731

Edwards, Mr Huw *G Jan 2009*
St Johns Buildings, Preston
p990 . . . . . 01772 256100
St Johns Buildings, Chester
p974 . . . . . 01244 323070
St Johns Buildings, Manchester
p985 . . . . . 0161 214 1500
St Johns Buildings, Liverpool
p982 . . . . . 0151 243 6000

Edwards, Mr Iain *M Apr 2000*
1 Mitre Court Buildings, London EC4
p942 . . . . . 020 7452 8900

Edwards, Mr Jacob LLB *L Jan 2007*
15, 70
1 Paper Buildings, London EC4
p946 . . . . . 020 7353 3728

Edwards, Miss Jennifer *G Oct 1992*
King's Bench Chambers, Oxford
p989 . . . . . 01865 311066
13 King's Bench Walk, London EC4
p940 . . . . . 020 7353 7204
Charter Chambers, London WC1
p928 . . . . . 020 7618 4400

EDWARDS, Mr John David BA; Recorder *I Jul 1983*
15
St Philips Chambers, Birmingham
p969 . . . . . 0121 246 7000

Edwards, Mr Jonathan *L Nov 1994*
12, 15
Westgate Chambers, Lewes
p980 . . . . . 01273 480510

Edwards, Mrs Kate *M Oct 2006*
53, 30, 85, 27, 84, 40, 12
Outer Temple Chambers, London WC2
p945 . . . . . 020 7353 6381

EDWARDS, Mr Martin Richard BA(Hons); MA(Env Law) *I Nov 1995*
1, 46, 26, 31, 25, 28
Thirty Nine Essex Street, London WC2
p932 . . . . . 020 7832 1111

Edwards, Mr Matthew *G Jul 2006*
15
East Anglian Chambers, Norwich
p988 . . . . . 01603 617351
East Anglian Chambers, Colchester
p975 . . . . . 01206 572756
East Anglian Chambers, Chelmsford
p973 . . . . . 01245 215660
East Anglian Chambers, Ipswich
p976 . . . . . 01473 214481

Edwards, Mr Michael *I Jul 2010*
10, 14, 20
4 Paper Buildings, London EC4
p946 . . . . . 020 7583 0816

Edwards, Miss Nicola LLB(Hons) *L Nov 1991*
18, 20, 27, 30
12 Old Square, London WC2
p945 . . . . . 020 7404 0875

Edwards, Mr Nigel D H MA(Cantab) *L Jan 1999*
53, 8, 12, 30, 11, 40, 6, 5, 47, 48
Exchange Chambers, Manchester
p983 . . . . . 0161 833 2722
Exchange Chambers, Liverpool
p980 . . . . . 0151 236 7747
Exchange Chambers, Leeds
p977 . . . . . 0113 203 1970

Edwards, Mr Nigel Royston LLB(Sheff) *L Nov 1995*
10, 12, 72, 15, 81, 62, 25, 96, 31, 86, 36, 20
St Pauls Chambers, Leeds
p979 . . . . . 0113 245 5866

Edwards, Patricia *I Oct 2007*
49, 41, 3, 5, 11, 43, 47, 78, 24, 54, 35
20 Essex Street, London WC2
p932 . . . . . 020 7842 1200

Edwards, Mr Paul LLB(Hons) *L Mar 2002*
12, 20, 23
37 Park Square Chambers, Leeds
p978 . . . . . 0113 243 9422

Edwards, Mr Peter BA(Hons)(Law) *I Oct 1992*
1, 11, 12, 18, 30, 36, 34, 26, 27, 24, 40, 55
Devereux Chambers, London WC2
p930 . . . . . 020 7353 7534

EDWARDS, Mr Richard MA(Cantab); M Phil(Cantab) *M Oct 1993*
1, 46, 19, 51, 26, 28, 31, 36, 60
3 Verulam Buildings, London WC1
p953 . . . . . 020 7831 8441

EDWARDS, Miss Sarah *I Nov 1990*
12, 20, 30, 40
Queen Elizabeth Buildings, London EC4
p948 . . . . . 020 7797 7837

EDWARDS, Mr Simon MA(Cantab) *M Nov 1978*
11, 30, 40
Thirty Nine Essex Street, London WC2
p932 . . . . . 020 7832 1111

Edwards, Miss Susan LLB(Hons)(L'pool) *L Nov 1998*
12, 20
St Johns Buildings, Preston
p990 . . . . . 01772 256100
St Johns Buildings, Chester
p974 . . . . . 01244 323070
St Johns Buildings, Manchester
p985 . . . . . 0161 214 1500
St Johns Buildings, Liverpool
p982 . . . . . 0151 243 6000

EDWARDS, Mr William BA(Hons)(Cantab) *M Jan 2002*
5, 40, 6
3 Verulam Buildings, London WC1
p953 . . . . . 020 7831 8441

Edwards-Stuart, Miss Anna MA; D Phil *L Oct 2003*
73, 50, 19, 45, 13, 52, 96, 41
11 South Square, London WC1
p950 . . . . . 020 7405 1222

EELEY, Miss Rebecca BA(Hons) *M Mar 2001*
30, 18
9 St John Street Chambers, Manchester
p984 . . . . . 0161 955 9000

EGAN, Miss Caroline BA(Cantab) *G Nov 1993*
20, 10, 93
Cornwall Street Chambers, Birmingham
p967 . . . . . 0121 233 7500

Egan, Mr Eugene MA(Oxon) *L Oct 1993*
12, 15, 62
Thirty Park Place, Cardiff
p973 . . . . . 029 2039 8421

Egan, Mr Manus LLB *M Nov 1991*
5, 11, 12, 15, 18, 19, 23, 30
Thomas More Chambers, London WC2
p952 . . . . . 020 7404 7000

EGAN, Mr Michael Recorder *G Nov 1981*
(Q.C.) *15*
9-12 Bell Yard Chambers, London WC2
p926 . . . . . 020 7400 1800

EGBUNA, Mr Robert Obiora LLB *G Nov 1988*
15
1 High Pavement, Nottingham
p988 . . . . . 0115 941 8218

EGLETON, Mr Richard MA(Oxon) *G Jul 1981*
Pallant Chambers, Chichester
p974 . . . . . 01243 784538

Ehiribe, Ike LLB(Hons); BL; FCIArb; QDR *L Nov 1996*
7 Stone Buildings Intellectual Property, London WC2
p951 . . . . . 020 7242 8848

Eicke, Mr Tim LLB(Hons)(Dundee) *M Oct 1993*
(Q.C.)
Essex Court Chambers, London WC2
p931 . . . . . 020 7813 8000

EIDINOW, Mr John Samuel MA(Oxon) *M Nov 1992*
6, 8, 11, 32, 37
New Square Chambers, London WC2
p943 . . . . . 020 7419 8000

Eilledge, Miss Amanda MA(Oxon) *L Nov 1991*
8, 18, 38, 62
11 Stone Buildings, London WC2
p951 . . . . . 020 7831 6381

Ekaney, NKumbe LLB(Bris) *G Oct 1990*
(Q.C.) *20, 23*
Albion Chambers, Bristol
p970 . . . . . 0117 927 2144

Ekeledo, Ms Peggy *L Nov 2007*
20
Tooks Chambers, London EC4
p953 . . . . . 020 7842 7575

Eklund, Mr Graham BA *I May 1984*
(Q.C.) *11, 12, 24, 30, 40*
Four New Square, London WC2
p943 . . . . . 020 7822 2000

El-Falahi, Sami D MA(Oxon); MSc(Econ) *I Jul 1972*
3, 11, 21, 29, 35
International Law Chambers, London W2
p938 . . . . . 020 7221 5685 / 7352 6649

Elcombe, Mr Nicholas LLB; Pupil Supervisor *I Jul 1987*
20, 10, 12
East Anglian Chambers, Norwich
p988 . . . . . 01603 617351
East Anglian Chambers, Colchester
p975 . . . . . 01206 572756
East Anglian Chambers, Chelmsford
p973 . . . . . 01245 215660
East Anglian Chambers, Ipswich
p976 . . . . . 01473 214481

Elder, Miss Fiona Ann Morag LLB(Sheff) *G Jul 1988*
15, 45
Albion Chambers, Bristol
p970 . . . . . 0117 927 2144

Eldergill, Mr Edmund BA; DipLaw *I Nov 1991*
20, 10, 37
1 Pump Court, London EC4
p947 . . . . . 020 7842 7070

Eldridge, Mr Mark BA(Hons); DipLaw *G Jul 1982*
12, 15
114 Liverpool Road, London N1
p941 . . . . . 020 7226 9863

Eleftheriadis, Dr Pavlos BA(Athens) *L Jan 2006*
19, 51, 21, 1
Francis Taylor Building, London EC4
p934 . . . . . 020 7353 8415

Eley, Miss Joanne Mary BA *M Oct 1997*
15
1 Paper Buildings, London EC4
p946 . . . . . 020 7353 3728

Eley, Mr Jonathan BA *M Jun 1987*
KCH Garden Square Chambers, Nottingham
p989 . . . . . 0115 941 8851
KCH Garden Square Chambers, Leicester
p979 . . . . . 0115 941 8851

Elfield, Miss Laura *G Sep 1996*
18, 30
9 Gough Square, London EC4
p935 . . . . . 020 7832 0500

Elford, Ms Caroline *I Jan 2002*
10, 20, 40
Queen Square Chambers, Bristol
p972 . . . . . 0117 921 1966

ELIA, Miss Elena LLB(Hons) *M Oct 2009*
15, 27, 36
23 Essex Street, London WC2
p932 . . . . . 020 7413 0353

Elias, Mr David MA(Cantab) *I Nov 1994*
12, 15
9 Park Place, Cardiff
p973 . . . . . 029 2038 2731

ELIAS, Mr Gerard LLB; Dep.High Court Judge; Recorder *I Jul 1968*
(Q.C.) *15, 12, 36, 56*
Farrar's Building, London EC4
p933 . . . . . 020 7583 9241

Elias, Mr Robert W LLB *M Jul 1979*
Lincoln House Chambers, Manchester
p984 . . . . . 0161 832 5701

Eljadi, Mr Omar BA(Jurisprudence); BCL(Oxon) *M Jan 2009*
3, 7, 11, 31, 40, 41, 43, 45, 49, 54, 61, 78, 74
Atkin Chambers, London WC1
p923 . . . . . 020 7404 0102

Elkington, Mr Ben MA *G Oct 1996*
8, 12, 24, 40, 48, 18
Four New Square, London WC2
p943 . . . . . 020 7822 2000

ELLENBOGEN, Ms Naomi MA(Oxon); Accredited Mediator *G Oct 1992*
(Q.C.) *5, 6, 8, 11, 18, 12, 40*
Littleton Chambers, London EC4
p941 . . . . . 020 7797 8600

Elleray, Mr Anthony *I Jan 1977*
(Q.C.) *2, 41, 5, 6, 8, 9, 11, 49, 22, 24, 29, 32, 40, 57, 58, 37, 62*
Exchange Chambers, Manchester
p983 . . . . . 0161 833 2722
Exchange Chambers, Liverpool
p980 . . . . . 0151 236 7747
Exchange Chambers, Leeds
p977 . . . . . 0113 203 1970

Ellin, Miss Nina LLB(Lond) *I Nov 1994*
12, 15, 18, 20, 22, 51
6-8 Mill Street, Maidstone
p982 . . . . . 01622 688094 / 688095
6 Pump Court, London EC4
p947 . . . . . 020 7797 8400

Elliott, Mr Colin BSc(Lond); DipLaw(City) *G Jul 1987*
6, 8, 12, 14, 55, 18, 20, 22, 38, 88, 25, 89, 31, 40, 93, 36
King's Bench Godolphin Chambers, Truro
p994 . . . . . 0845 308 1551
King's Bench Godolphin Chambers, Plymouth
p990 . . . . . 0845 308 1551

Elliott, Mr Edward LLB *G Oct 2000*
Goldsmith Chambers, London EC4
p935 . . . . . 020 7353 6802

ELLIOTT, Mr Eric A Recorder *G Jul 1974*
(Q.C.) *15, 56*
Trinity (Newcastle) Chambers, Newcastle upon Tyne
p987 . . . . . 0191 232 1927
Trinity (Teesside) Chambers, Middlesbrough
p986 . . . . . 01642 247569

Elliott, Mr Jason *I Oct 1993*
Broad Chare Chambers, Newcastle upon Tyne
p986 . . . . . 0191 232 0541

Elliott, Miss Margot LLB(Newc) *G Nov 1989*
10, 12, 20, 1
Regency Chambers, Peterborough
p990 . . . . . 01733 315215

Elliott, Mr Mark BA(Hons) *L Oct 2007* 13
20, 10
3PB, Bournemouth
p969 . . . . . 01202 292102

ELLIOTT, Mr Nicholas LLB(Bris) *G Jul 1972*
(Q.C.) *5, 6, 11, 18, 24*
3 Verulam Buildings, London WC1
p953 . . . . . 020 7831 8441

Elliott, Mr Richard *M Oct 2001*
15
3 Temple Gardens, London EC4
p952 . . . . . 020 7353 3102

Elliott, Miss Sarah *G Nov 1996*
15, 51
Doughty Street Chambers, London WC1
p930 . . . . . 020 7404 1313

Elliott, Mr Steven *L Jul 2001*
One Essex Court, London EC4
p931 . . . . . 020 7583 2000

Elliott, Mr Timothy S MA(Oxon) *M Jul 1975*
(Q.C.) *3, 7, 11, 24, 40*
Keating Chambers, London WC2
p938 . . . . . 020 7544 2600

ELLIOTT, Miss Tracey LLB; LLM *G Jul 1986*
15
9-12 Bell Yard Chambers, London WC2
p926 . . . . . 020 7400 1800

ELLIS, Mr Aidan BA(Cantab) *M Jul 2005*
Temple Garden Chambers, London EC4
p952 . . . . . 020 7583 1315

ELLIS, Ms Catherine LLB(Hons) *L Jul 1987*
15, 12, 22, 30, 47, 18, 11, 40, 7, 88, 84, 67, 53, 68
Oriel Chambers, Liverpool
p981 . . . . . 0151 236 7191 / 236 4321
Oriel Chambers, Preston
p990 . . . . . 01772 254764

Ellis, Miss Catherine S LLB *M Jan 2003*
10, 67, 20, 22, 88, 93, 11
3 Dr Johnson's Buildings, London EC4
p930 . . . . . 020 7353 4854

Ellis, Ms Charlotte BA(Oxon) *M Oct 2001*
3, 7, 11, 24, 40
Keating Chambers, London WC2
p938 . . . . . 020 7544 2600

ELLIS, Miss Diana LLB *I Jul 1978*
(Q.C.) *15, 51, 21, 71*
25 Bedford Row, London WC1
p925 . . . . . 020 7067 1500

Ellis, Mr Henry L *Jan 2008*
Stone Chambers, London WC1
p951 . . . 020 7440 6900

Ellis, Ms Morag MA(Cantab) I *Jul 1984*
(Q.C.) *1, 12, 22, 26, 31, 8, 18, 25, 36, 29*
Cornerstone Barristers, London WC1
p929 . . . 020 7242 4986

Ellis, Dr Peter Mediator; Assistant Deputy Coroner M *Nov 1997*
53, 85, 27, 30, 68
7 Bedford Row, London WC1
p924 . . . 020 7242 3555

ELLIS, Miss Rachel L *Oct 2004*
15, 62, 95
187 Fleet Street, London EC4
p933 . . . 020 7430 7430

Ellis, Mr Roger John LLB; BSc(Lond) G *Jul 1962*
(Q.C.) *8*
King's Bench Chambers, Oxford
p989 . . . 01865 311066
13 King's Bench Walk, London EC4
p940 . . . 020 7353 7204

ELLIS, Miss Sarah LLB(Wales) G *Nov 1989*
15
9-12 Bell Yard Chambers, London WC2
p926 . . . 020 7400 1800

Ellison, Mr Mark G *Nov 1979*
(Q.C.) *15, 25, 36*
QEB Hollis Whiteman, London EC4
p948 . . . 020 7933 8855

Ellison, Mr Robert M *Oct 1996*
15
5 King's Bench Walk, London EC4
p939 . . . 020 7353 5638

Elmer, Mr Thomas M *Jul 2001*
12, 15, 62, 30
7 Bedford Row, London WC1
p924 . . . 020 7242 3555

Elton, Mr Edward LLB(Hons)(Lond) G *Jan 2000*
15, 25, 26, 62, 84, 91
12 College Place, Southampton
p992 . . . 023 8032 0320

Elton, Mr Edward S O LLB M *Nov 2000*
2 King's Bench Walk, London EC4
p939 . . . 020 7353 1746

Elvidge, Mr John G *Nov 1988*
(Q.C.)
York Chambers, York
p995 . . . 01904 620048
York Chambers, Newcastle upon Tyne
p987 . . . 0191 206 4677

ELVIN, Mr David BA; BCL(Oxon) M *Nov 1983*
(Q.C.) *1, 21, 26, 31, 33, 36, 93*
Landmark Chambers, London EC4
p941 . . . 020 7430 1221

ELWICK, Mr Bryan Martin LLB(Nott'm) M *Jul 1981*
15
1 High Pavement, Nottingham
p988 . . . 0115 941 8218

EMANUEL, Mr Mark BA(Hons) I *Nov 1985*
20
29 Bedford Row, London WC1
p925 . . . 020 7404 1044

Emerson, Mr Paul Michael LLB M *Jul 1984*
5, 6, 8, 11, 24, 29
Lamb Chambers, London EC4
p941 . . . 020 7797 8300

EMERSON, Mr William LLB(Hons) M *Nov 1992*
12, 15, 18, 22, 26, 30, 31, 36
Pallant Chambers, Chichester
p974 . . . 01243 784538

EMERY, Mr Philip Anthony M *Mar 2008*
30, 53
7 Harrington Street Chambers, Liverpool
p981 . . . 0151 242 0707

EMMANUEL, Ms Joy M *Oct 2001*
10, 76
Kenworthy's Chambers, Manchester
p984 . . . 0161 832 4036

EMMERSON, Mr Ben LLB(Bris) M *Nov 1986*
(Q.C.) *1, 15, 16, 36, 33, 12, 51, 19, 50, 11, 55*
Matrix Chambers, London WC1
p942 . . . 020 7404 3447

EMMERSON, Heather BA(Law) L *Oct 2009*
4-5 Gray's Inn Square, London WC1
p935 . . . 020 7404 5252

Emmett, Mr Laurence L *Jan 2004*
One Essex Court, London EC4
p931 . . . 020 7583 2000

Emslie, Mr Simon I *Jul 2007*
Albion Chambers, Bristol
p970 . . . 0117 927 2144

Engelman, Mr Mark BSc(Pharmacology); DipLaw(City) G *Nov 1987*
13, 11, 44, 45, 16, 39, 56
Hardwicke, London WC2
p936 . . . 020 7242 2523

Engelman, Mr Philip LLB(Lond) G *Jul 1979*
18, 11, 1, 38
Cloisters, London EC4
p928 . . . 020 7827 4000
Trinity (Newcastle) Chambers, Newcastle upon Tyne
p987 . . . 0191 232 1927
Trinity (Teesside) Chambers, Middlesbrough
p986 . . . 01642 247569

England, Laura M *Jan 2008*
St Johns Buildings, Preston
p990 . . . 01772 256100
St Johns Buildings, Chester
p974 . . . 01244 323070
St Johns Buildings, Manchester
p985 . . . 0161 214 1500
St Johns Buildings, Liverpool
p982 . . . 0151 243 6000

England, Mrs Lisa G *Jan 1992*
Guildhall Chambers, Portsmouth
p990 . . . 023 9275 2400

ENGLAND, Mr William I *Nov 1991*
15
Carmelite Chambers, London EC4
p927 . . . 020 7936 6300

Englehart, Mr Robert MA(Oxon); LLM(Harv) M *Nov 1969*
(Q.C.) *1, 3, 8, 11, 12, 13, 29, 36, 19, 41, 50, 52, 56, 89, 51*
Blackstone Chambers, London EC4
p926 . . . 020 7583 1770

English, Miss Caroline LLB(Hons) I *Nov 1989*
15, 27
4 Breams Buildings, London EC4
p927 . . . 020 7092 1900

ENGLISH, Ms Caroline I *Jul 1989*
Furnival Chambers, London EC4
p934 . . . 020 7405 3232

English, Mr Richard I *Mar 2003*
Lincoln House Chambers, Manchester
p984 . . . 0161 832 5701

English, Mr Robert I *Oct 1996*
15
1 Pump Court, London EC4
p947 . . . 020 7842 7070

Enoch, Mr Dafydd LLB(Bucks); Diplome d'L'tudes Juridiques G *Nov 1985*
(Q.C.) *15, 62, 27, 36*
Exchange Chambers, Manchester
p983 . . . 0161 833 2722
Exchange Chambers, Liverpool
p980 . . . 0151 236 7747
Exchange Chambers, Leeds
p977 . . . 0113 203 1970
23 Essex Street, London WC2
p932 . . . 020 7413 0353

Enonchong, Prof Nelson I *Jan 2006*
3, 35, 78, 21, 54, 5, 11
No5 Chambers, Bristol
p971 . . . 0845 210 5555
No5 Chambers, London EC4
p944 . . . 0845 210 5555
No5 Chambers, Birmingham
p968 . . . 0845 210 5555

ENSAFF, Mr Omar Sherif G *Oct 2000*
11, 8, 7, 6, 22, 29, 40, 64, 74, 96, 97
No5 Chambers, Bristol
p971 . . . 0845 210 5555
No5 Chambers, London EC4
p944 . . . 0845 210 5555
No5 Chambers, Birmingham
p968 . . . 0845 210 5555

ENTWISTLE, Mr Thomas G *Nov 2001*
8, 32, 22, 37, 14
5 Stone Buildings, London WC2
p951 . . . 020 7242 6201

EPHGRAVE, Ms Amy G *Oct 1997*
10, 20
Pump Court Chambers, Swindon
p993 . . . 01793 539899
Pump Court Chambers, Winchester
p994 . . . 01962 868161
Pump Court Chambers, London EC4
p947 . . . 020 7353 0711

EPSTEIN, Mr Michael LLB(Hons) M *Nov 1992*
15, 62
2 Bedford Row, London WC1
p924 . . . 020 7440 8888

Epstein, Mr Paul M *Nov 1988*
11, 43, 50, 55, 56, 18, 1, 26
Cloisters, London EC4
p928 . . . 020 7827 4000

ERIERA, Mr Anton BA(Hons)(Cantab); LLM(Harv) L *Jan 2010*
10, 20
29 Bedford Row, London WC1
p925 . . . 020 7404 1044

ERINLE, Miss Bonike L *Oct 2008*
12, 18, 30
Farrar's Building, London EC4
p933 . . . 020 7583 9241

Erlen, Miss Nicole G I *Jan 2007*
Paradise Chambers, Sheffield
p992 . . . 0114 273 8951

Escoriza, Miss Natalia MSc M *Nov 2002*
10, 20
Park Court Chambers, Leeds
p978 . . . 0113 243 3277

Espley, Miss Susan LLB(Leeds) G *Jul 1976*
10, 20, 51
Fenners Chambers, Cambridge
p972 . . . 01223 368761

Esprit, Mr Benoit BA; BSc I *Nov 1982*
23 Harries Road, Hayes
p976 . . . 020 8841 8236

Essex Williams, Mr David LLB(Wales); ACIB M *Jul 1975*
5, 15
9 Park Place, Cardiff
p973 . . . 029 2038 2731

ETHERINGTON, Mr David Recorder M *Nov 1979*
(Q.C.) *15, 36, 62*
18 Red Lion Court, London EC4
p949 . . . 020 7520 6000
18 Red Lion Court (Annexe), Chelmsford
p973 . . . 01245 280880

Etherton, Miss Gillian Felicity Amanda M *Jul 1988*
(Q.C.) *15*
Atkinson Bevan Chambers, London EC4
p924 . . . 020 7353 2112
1 Inner Temple Lane, London EC4
p937 . . . 020 7427 4400

Etiebet, Ms Peggy BA(Hons) G *Oct 2001*
22, 31, 26, 25, 23, 12
Cornerstone Barristers, London WC1
p929 . . . 020 7242 4986

Evans, Mr Alan MA; LLB(Cantab) L *Jul 1978*
1, 26, 31, 46, 54
Kings Chambers, Leeds
p978 . . . 0113 242 1123
Kings Chambers, Manchester
p984 . . . 0161 832 9082

EVANS, Mr Andrew L *Jan 2000*
25, 83, 30, 12
St Philips Chambers, Birmingham
p969 . . . 0121 246 7000
18 St John Street Chambers, Manchester
p985 . . . 0161 278 1800

EVANS, Mr Anthony G *Jan 1965*
(Q.C.)
Furnival Chambers, London EC4
p934 . . . 020 7405 3232

EVANS, Mr Bill M *Nov 1988*
15, 62, 95
187 Fleet Street, London EC4
p933 . . . 020 7430 7430

EVANS, Miss Catrin BA(Essex) I *Nov 1994*
16, 52, 73
One Brick Court, London EC4
p927 . . . 020 7353 8845

EVANS, Mr Charles M *Nov 1988*
Furnival Chambers, London EC4
p934 . . . 020 7405 3232

Evans, Mr David MA(Cantab) G *Mar 1996*
15, 30, 12, 18
Walnut House Chambers, Exeter
p975 . . . 01392 279751
33 Chancery Lane, London WC2
p928 . . . 020 7440 9950
QEB Hollis Whiteman, London EC4
p948 . . . 020 7933 8855
1 Crown Office Row, London EC4
p929 . . . 020 7797 7500

Evans, Mr David Gareth Evan LLB G *Jul 2008*
12, 15, 18, 20, 30, 91
9 Park Place, Cardiff
p973 . . . 029 2038 2731

Evans, Mr Dylan G *Apr 1989*
14 Gray's Inn Square, London WC1
p936 . . . 020 7242 0858

Evans, Miss Elwen Mair MA(Cantab) G *Jul 1980*
(Q.C.) *10, 12, 15, 20, 25, 30, 31, 36*
Iscoed Chambers, Swansea
p993 . . . 01792 652988

Evans, Mr Franklin St Clair Melville BA(Lancs) G *Nov 1981*
18, 30, 53
Field Court Chambers, London WC1
p933 . . . 020 7405 6114

Evans, Mr Gareth R W Recorder G *Nov 1973*
(Q.C.) *30, 53, 15, 42, 49, 56, 59, 62, 84, 46, 39, 94, 68*
No5 Chambers, Bristol
p971 . . . 0845 210 5555
No5 Chambers, London EC4
p944 . . . 0845 210 5555
No5 Chambers, Birmingham
p968 . . . 0845 210 5555

EVANS, Mr Gwynfor Owen MA(Cantab)(Social & Political Sciences); DipLaw(City) G *Jul 2007*
10, 20, 30, 94
Tanfield Chambers, London WC1
p951 . . . 020 7421 5300

Evans, Miss Helen BA(Hons)(Oxon) M *Aug 2001*
40, 12, 8, 24
Four New Square, London WC2
p943 . . . 020 7822 2000

Evans, Mr Hugh MA M *Nov 1987*
8, 12, 24, 40, 53
Four New Square, London WC2
p943 . . . 020 7822 2000

Evans, Mr Huw David BA(Hons) L *Jul 1985*
15, 62
Thirty Park Place, Cardiff
p973 . . . 029 2039 8421

EVANS, Mr James BA(Cantab); LLM(Lond) G *Nov 1991*
3, 5, 6, 11, 33, 40
3 Verulam Buildings, London WC1
p953 . . . 020 7831 8441
Temple Chambers, Newport
p988 . . . 01633 267403 / 255855
Temple Chambers, Cardiff
p973 . . . 029 2039 7364

Evans, Ms Jill G *Jul 1986*
15, 51, 91
Doughty Street Chambers, London WC1
p930 . . . 020 7404 1313

EVANS, Ms Joanne M *Oct 1998*
15, 51, 21
25 Bedford Row, London WC1
p925 . . . 020 7067 1500

EVANS, Mr John Wainwright I *Jan 1983*
15
St Philips Chambers, Birmingham
p969 . . . 0121 246 7000

EVANS, Mr Johnathan BA(Oxon) M *Nov 1994*
6, 8, 11, 22, 29, 40, 37, 32
Wilberforce Chambers, London WC2
p953 . . . 020 7306 0102

Evans, Ms Judi LLB M *Nov 1996*
10, 20, 31, 46, 48
St John's Chambers, Bristol
p972 . . . 0117 921 3456

Evans, Mr Julian M *Oct 1997*
15, 25, 36
QEB Hollis Whiteman, London EC4
p948 . . . 020 7933 8855

EVANS, Mr Lee J MA(Cantab) G *Nov 1996*
18, 30, 12
Farrar's Building, London EC4
p933 . . . 020 7583 9241

See p1010 for the Key to Work Categories

Evans, Mr Martin M *Nov 1989*
33 Chancery Lane, London WC2
p928 . . . 020 7440 9950

EVANS, Mr Michael Ritho LLB M *Nov 1988*
15
1 High Pavement, Nottingham
p988 . . . 0115 941 8218

Evans, Mr Nicholas LLB I *Jan 2001*
15, 62, 39
Staple Inn Chambers, London WC1
p951 . . . 020 7242 5240

Evans, Mr Paul LLB(Hons) G *Jan 2001*
2 Pump Court, London EC4
p947 . . . 020 7353 5597
No5 Chambers, Bristol
p971 . . . 0845 210 5555
No5 Chambers, London EC4
p944 . . . 0845 210 5555
No5 Chambers, Birmingham
p968 . . . 0845 210 5555

EVANS, Mr Paul Timothy BA(Oxon); MA(Oxon) G *Oct 1992*
15
Exchange Chambers, Manchester
p983 . . . 0161 833 2722
Exchange Chambers, Liverpool
p980 . . . 0151 236 7747
Exchange Chambers, Leeds
p977 . . . 0113 203 1970

Evans, Mr Philip L *Oct 1995*
15, 25, 36
QEB Hollis Whiteman, London EC4
p948 . . . 020 7933 8855

Evans, Mr Rhys G *Jan 2010*
20, 23, 15, 62, 30, 11
Thirty Park Place, Cardiff
p973 . . . 029 2039 8421

Evans, Mr Robert J MA(Cantab); LLB(Lond); CEng; MICE; FCIArb G *Jul 1989*
3, 7, 11, 24, 40
Keating Chambers, London WC2
p938 . . . 020 7544 2600

Evans, Mr Roger MA(Cantab) M *Nov 1970*
26, 17, 5, 18, 67, 32, 37, 93, 29
Harcourt Chambers, London EC4
p936 . . . 0844 561 7135
Harcourt Chambers, Oxford
p989 . . . 0844 561 7135

Evans, Miss Sarah I *Nov 2004*
10, 20
Southernhay Chambers, Exeter
p975 . . . 01392 255777

Evans, Mr Simeon BA(Hons) L *Jun 1997*
15, 70, 71, 72
St Johns Buildings, Preston
p990 . . . 01772 256100
St Johns Buildings, Chester
p974 . . . 01244 323070
St Johns Buildings, Manchester
p985 . . . 0161 214 1500
St Johns Buildings, Liverpool
p982 . . . 0151 243 6000

EVANS, Mr Stephen M *Oct 1992*
8, 22, 26, 93
Five Paper, London EC4
p946 . . . 020 7815 3200

Evans, Mr Steven M *Oct 1997*
15, 63, 62, 10, 70, 14
36 Bedford Row, London WC1
p925 . . . 020 7421 8000

EVANS, Ms Suzanne Marie BA(Oxon) M *Nov 1985*
10, 20
Oriel Chambers, Liverpool
p981 . . . 0151 236 7191 / 236 4321
Oriel Chambers, Preston
p990 . . . 01772 254764

EVANS, Mr T Gareth LLB(Hons)(Exon) M *Oct 1996*
12, 15, 25, 20, 42
Colleton Chambers, Exeter
p975 . . . 01392 274898

Evans, Mr Thomas L *Jan 2008*
Henderson Chambers, London EC4
p937 . . . 020 7583 9020

Evans, Mr Timothy BA(Hons)(Oxon) L *Jul 1979*
Maitland Chambers, London WC2
p941 . . . 020 7406 1200

Evans, Mr William G *Jan 1977*
11, 30
Ely Place Chambers, London EC1
p931 . . . 020 7400 9600

EVANS-GORDON, Ms Jane LLB(Reading) I *Nov 1992*
6, 8, 11, 22, 62
New Square Chambers, London WC2
p943 . . . 020 7419 8000

EVANS-TOVEY, Mr Jason R MA(Cantab); LLM G *Oct 1990*
40, 11, 24, 36
Crown Office Chambers, London EC4
p929 . . . 020 7797 8100

Eveleigh-Winstone, Ms Adelle G *Oct 2003*
31, 30, 20
New Walk Chambers, Leicester
p979 . . . 0871 200 1298

Everest, Mr Roger BA(Wales) G *Nov 1968*
15
Twinfirs, Pontyclun
p990 . . . 01443 229850

Evison, Mr John LLB(Lond) L *Jul 1974*
5 Pump Court, London EC4
p947 . . . 020 7353 2532 / 7583 7133

EWART, Mr David BA(Oxon) G *Nov 1987*
(Q.C.) *34, 58, 57*
Pump Court Tax Chambers, London WC1
p948 . . . 020 7414 8080

Ewing, Mr Hal MA(Cantab) G *Nov 1997*
12, 15, 30, 22, 23
KCH Garden Square Chambers, Nottingham
p989 . . . 0115 941 8851
KCH Garden Square Chambers, Leicester
p979 . . . 0115 941 8851

Ewins, Ms Catherine BA(Cantab) G *Nov 1995*
40, 53, 27, 30
Hailsham Chambers, London EC4
p936 . . . 020 7643 5000

EWINS, Mr James BA(Oxon) M *Jul 1996*
12, 20
Queen Elizabeth Buildings, London EC4
p948 . . . 020 7797 7837

Exall, Gordon L *Jul 1991*
30, 53, 68
Zenith Chambers, Leeds
p979 . . . 0113 245 5438

Exall, Rosemary M *Dec 2000*
21, 10
Zenith Chambers, Leeds
p979 . . . 0113 245 5438

Eyers, Mr Anthony BA(Hons)(Oxon) I *Nov 1994*
15
Exchange Chambers, Manchester
p983 . . . 0161 833 2722
Exchange Chambers, Liverpool
p980 . . . 0151 236 7747
Exchange Chambers, Leeds
p977 . . . 0113 203 1970

Eyre, Mr Giles LLB G *Jul 1974*
27, 30, 40, 96, 53
9 Gough Square, London EC4
p935 . . . 020 7832 0500

EYRE, Mr Stephen John Arthur Recorder I *Jul 1981*
11, 5, 6, 97, 38, 40, 93, 32, 37
St Philips Chambers, Birmingham
p969 . . . 0121 246 7000

Ezekiel, Miss Adina I *Apr 1997*
15, 62
6 King's Bench Walk, London EC4
p939 . . . 020 7583 0410

FACENNA, Mr Gerry MA(Cantab); LLB(Edin) L *Nov 2001*
11, 19, 46, 51, 1, 57
Monckton Chambers, London WC1
p942 . . . 020 7405 7211

FADIPE, Mr Gabriel BA(Kent); Mait en Droit(Bordeaux) I *Nov 1991*
5, 6, 8, 11, 47, 13, 62, 22, 40, 37
Wilberforce Chambers, London WC2
p953 . . . 020 7306 0102

Fagan, Ms Catherine G *Jan 1993*
15, 10, 12, 20, 25
Old Court Chambers, Middlesbrough
p986 . . . 01642 232523

Fagborun-Bennett, Ms Morayo I *Jul 2004*
22, 33, 18, 1
Hardwicke, London WC2
p936 . . . 020 7242 2523

FAGGIONATO, Miss Marina BA; LLM L *Jan 2006*
20, 12, 10
Queen Elizabeth Buildings, London EC4
p948 . . . 020 7797 7837

FAIN, Mr Carl Ian BA(Oxon) L *Oct 2001*
6, 11, 12, 47, 22, 23, 25, 30
Tanfield Chambers, London WC1
p951 . . . 020 7421 5300

Fairbank, Mr Nicholas MA(Cantab) L *Nov 1996*
12, 20
Becket Chambers, Canterbury
p972 . . . 01227 786331
Becket Chambers, Maidstone
p982 . . . 01622 230957

FAIRBURN, Mr George L *Mar 1995*
10, 20, 93
Cornwall Street Chambers, Birmingham
p967 . . . 0121 233 7500

Fairclough, Miss Lucy G *Oct 2005*
Northampton Chambers, Northampton
p988 . . . 01604 636271

Fairclough, Sara M *Jan 1992*
4 KBW, London EC4
p938 . . . 020 7822 8822

Fairhead, Mr John BA M *Nov 1978*
15
5 King's Bench Walk, London EC4
p939 . . . 020 7353 5638

Fairley, Miss Chloe BA(Hons)(Dublin) G *Oct 2004*
Park Court Chambers, Leeds
p978 . . . 0113 243 3277

Fairpo, Ms Anne G *Nov 2009*
13 Old Square Chambers, London WC2
p945 . . . 020 7831 4445

Falkenstein, Mr John Roy L *Aug 1996*
18, 55
Chambers of John Roy Falkenstein, Newcastle upon Tyne
p987 . . . 07973 776801

FALKOWSKI, Mr Damian LLDip G *Oct 1994*
31, 11, 5, 24, 40
4-5 Gray's Inn Square, London WC1
p935 . . . 020 7404 5252

Fallows, Miss Paula BA(Hons) L *Jul 1981*
10, 20
Cobden House Chambers, Manchester
p983 . . . 0161 833 6000

Fama, Mrs Gudrun BA(Hons); MA(Lond) G *Oct 1991*
10, 12, 15, 20, 22, 23
Two King's Bench Walk, London EC4
p939 . . . 020 7353 7202 / 7353 3909

FANCOURT, Mr Timothy MA(Cantab) L *Nov 1987*
(Q.C.)
Falcon Chambers, London EC4
p933 . . . 020 7353 2484

Fane, Miss Angela M *Nov 1992*
10, 20
Goldsmith Chambers, London EC4
p935 . . . 020 7353 6802

Fanneran, Michelle G *Jul 2003*
Clerksroom - Administration Centre, Taunton
p993 . . . 0845 083 3000

Fanshawe, Ms Lynn H C M *Oct 1999*
15
Castle Chambers, Harrow
p976 . . . 020 8423 6579

FAPOHUNDA, Kemi G *Jul 2002*
Furnival Chambers, London EC4
p934 . . . 020 7405 3232

Farara, Mr Gerard St Claire G *Jul 1977*
Outer Temple Chambers, London WC2
p945 . . . 020 7353 6381

Farazi, Ms Seema LLB(Hons); LLM L *Jul 2001*
51, 23, 21, 1
Doughty Street Chambers, London WC1
p930 . . . 020 7404 1313

Farber, Mr Martin G *Jul 1976*
5, 11, 24, 29, 40, 37
5 Stone Buildings, London WC2
p951 . . . 020 7242 6201

Farbey, Miss Judith BA(Hons)(Oxon); DipLaw M *Oct 1992*
23, 51, 21, 1
Doughty Street Chambers, London WC1
p930 . . . 020 7404 1313

FARLEY, Anna I *Jan 2002*
Maidstone Chambers, Maidstone
p982 . . . 01622 688592

Farley, Mr David BA(Hons) M *Jan 2001*
15, 56, 70, 71, 72
St Johns Buildings, Preston
p990 . . . 01772 256100
St Johns Buildings, Chester
p974 . . . 01244 323070
St Johns Buildings, Manchester
p985 . . . 0161 214 1500
St Johns Buildings, Liverpool
p982 . . . 0151 243 6000

Farley, Mr Roger LLB M *May 1974*
(Q.C.) *12, 15*
3PB, London EC4
p946 . . . 020 7583 8055
Cobden House Chambers, Manchester
p983 . . . 0161 833 6000

FARMER, Mr Gabriel G *Nov 1994*
30
Guildhall Chambers, Bristol
p970 . . . 0117 930 9000

Farmer, Mr John G *Nov 1970*
15, 84
1 Paper Buildings, London EC4
p946 . . . 020 7353 3728

Farmer, Mr Matthew BA(Lond); DipLaw I *Jun 1987*
15, 62
Atkinson Bevan Chambers, London EC4
p924 . . . 020 7353 2112

Farmer, Miss Sarah BA(Oxon) L *Nov 1991*
6, 10, 12, 15, 18, 20, 27, 30
Thomas More Chambers, London WC2
p952 . . . 020 7404 7000

Farnon, Ms Patricia R G LLB I *Nov 1986*
15, 20, 30
Tooks Chambers, London EC4
p953 . . . 020 7842 7575

Farnsworth, Miss Emma L *Nov 2000*
15, 12, 20, 23
11 King's Bench Walk, Leeds
p978 . . . 0113 297 1200

Farquhar, Ms Fiona I *Jan 2002*
20, 10, 18, 96
Queen Square Chambers, Bristol
p972 . . . 0117 921 1966

FARQUHARSON, Mr Jonathan BA(Dunelm) I *Jul 1988*
10, 12, 20, 30
Colleton Chambers, Exeter
p975 . . . 01392 274898

Farrell, Mr David LLB(Manc); Recorder I *Jul 1978*
(Q.C.) *12, 15, 22, 30, 62*
36 Bedford Row, London WC1
p925 . . . 020 7421 8000

Farrell, Mr Edmund G LLB(Leeds); LLM(Cantab); Dip Euro Law(Lond) G *Jul 1981*
8, 19, 20, 92
Cobden House Chambers, Manchester
p983 . . . 0161 833 6000
International Law Chambers, London W2
p938 . . . 020 7221 5685 / 7352 6649

Farrell, Ms Patricia I *Jul 1976*
Holborn Chambers, London WC2
p937 . . . 020 7242 6060

Farrelly, Miss Catherine LLB M *Nov 1999*
15
5 King's Bench Walk, London EC4
p939 . . . 020 7353 5638

FARRELLY, Mr Kevin BA(Cantab) M *May 1993*
6, 8, 22, 32
Ten Old Square, London WC2
p945 . . . 020 7405 0758

Farrer, Mr Adam LLB(Nott'm) G *Sep 1992*
30, 40, 68, 94
No5 Chambers, Bristol
p971 . . . 0845 210 5555
No5 Chambers, London EC4
p944 . . . 0845 210 5555
No5 Chambers, Birmingham
p968 . . . 0845 210 5555

Farrer, Mr David John MA(Cantab); Recorder M *Apr 1967*
(Q.C.) *15, 62*
7 Bedford Row, London WC1
p924 . . . 020 7242 3555

13

FARRIMOND, Miss Stephanie LLB(Essex) M *Jul 1987*
15, 62
18 Red Lion Court, London EC4
p949 ... 020 7520 6000
18 Red Lion Court (Annexe), Chelmsford
p973 ... 01245 280880

FARRINGTON, Mrs Gail G *Jul 2011*
10, 20
St Mary's Chambers, Nottingham
p989 ... 0115 950 3503

Farrington, Ms Gemma BA(Hons); CPE(Law) G *Oct 1994*
10, 20
Stour Chambers, Canterbury
p972 ... 01227 764899

Farrow, Mr Adrian John LLB M *Jul 1997*
15, 62, 84
Exchange Chambers, Manchester
p983 ... 0161 833 2722
Exchange Chambers, Liverpool
p980 ... 0151 236 7747
Exchange Chambers, Leeds
p977 ... 0113 203 1970

Fatima, Miss Shaheed LLB(Hons); LLM(Harv); BCL(Oxon) G *Oct 2001*
1, 18, 11, 51, 33, 50, 52, 89
Blackstone Chambers, London EC4
p926 ... 020 7583 1770

Faul, Mrs Anne LLB M *Oct 1996*
15, 25, 30, 40, 27
Nine Bedford Row, London WC1
p924 ... 020 7489 2727

FAULKNER, Mr Benjamin BA(Cantab) L *Jan 2008*
11, 93, 8
Wilberforce Chambers, London WC2
p953 ... 020 7306 0102

Faulks, Mr Edward MA(Oxon); FCIArb M *Nov 1973*
(Q.C.) *26, 30, 40, 51, 53, 10, 76, 63, 85, 27*
1 Chancery Lane, London WC2
p928 ... 0845 634 6666

FAULKS, Mr Samuel BA(Law)(Hons); LLB I *Oct 1997*
Fountain Chambers, Middlesbrough
p986 ... 01642 804040

Faure Walker, Miss Julia MA(Cantab) L *Jan 2004*
15
2 Hare Court, London EC4
p937 ... 020 7353 5324

FAUX, Mr Andrew John BA(Hons)(Hist); CPE; BVC I *Nov 1995*
18
Cornwall Street Chambers, Birmingham
p967 ... 0121 233 7500

Faux, Ms Rachel LLB(Nott'm) I *Oct 1997*
15, 20, 30
18 St John Street Chambers, Manchester
p985 ... 0161 278 1800

FAWCETT, Miss Michelle LLB(Hons)(Kent) I *Nov 1993*
15, 25
Furnival Chambers, London EC4
p934 ... 020 7405 3232

Fawcett, Mr Neil L *Jan 2006*
St Ives Chambers, Birmingham
p969 ... 0121 236 0863

FAZACKERLEY, Mr Tom Brian G *Oct 2010*
10, 20, 30, 12
Oriel Chambers, Liverpool
p981 ... 0151 236 7191 / 236 4321
Oriel Chambers, Preston
p990 ... 01772 254764

FEALY, Mr Michael M *May 1997*
One Essex Court, London EC4
p931 ... 020 7583 2000

Fear, Ms Claire M *Jan 2010*
12, 15, 23
Temple Chambers, Newport
p988 ... 01633 267403 / 255855
Temple Chambers, Cardiff
p973 ... 029 2039 7364

FEARNLEY, Mr Ben BA(Oxon)(Jurisprudence) M *Nov 2001*
20, 10
29 Bedford Row, London WC1
p925 ... 020 7404 1044

FEARON, Miss Sarah Louise BA(Hons) M *Nov 2000*
20, 10
Wilberforce Chambers, Hull
p976 ... 01482 323264

FEATHERBY, Mr William MA(Oxon); Recorder M *Nov 1978*
(Q.C.) *24, 30, 40, 53, 84*
12 King's Bench Walk, London EC4
p940 ... 020 7583 0811

Feder, Mr Ami LLB I *Jul 1965*
11, 15, 29, 82, 62
Lamb Building, Brighton
p970 ... 01273 820490
Lamb Building, London EC4
p940 ... 020 7797 7788

Feehan, Mr Frank T BA(Hons)(Cantab) L *Jul 1988*
(Q.C.) *10, 12, 20*
42 Bedford Row, London WC1
p925 ... 020 7831 0222

Feeney, Miss Katie I *Jul 2005*
30, 68, 94
No5 Chambers, Bristol
p971 ... 0845 210 5555
No5 Chambers, London EC4
p944 ... 0845 210 5555
No5 Chambers, Birmingham
p968 ... 0845 210 5555

FEENY, Mr Charles BA(Cantab) I *Nov 1977*
11, 18, 24, 25, 30, 31
St Johns Buildings, Preston
p990 ... 01772 256100
St Johns Buildings, Chester
p974 ... 01244 323070
St Johns Buildings, Manchester
p985 ... 0161 214 1500
St Johns Buildings, Liverpool
p982 ... 0151 243 6000

Feeny, Mr Jack BVC; GDL; MA; BA I *Jan 2005*
No5 Chambers, Bristol
p971 ... 0845 210 5555
No5 Chambers, London EC4
p944 ... 0845 210 5555
No5 Chambers, Birmingham
p968 ... 0845 210 5555

Feest, Mr Adam BA(Oxon) I *Feb 1994*
2 King's Bench Walk, London EC4
p939 ... 020 7353 1746

Feldman, Mr Matthew BA(Jt Hons)(Manc) I *Oct 1995*
22, 8, 12, 26
42 Bedford Row, London WC1
p925 ... 020 7831 0222

Feldschreiber, Dr Peter I *Aug 2000*
Four New Square, London WC2
p943 ... 020 7822 2000

Felix, Miss Alexandra LLB; LLM M *Oct 1999*
15, 36
QEB Hollis Whiteman, London EC4
p948 ... 020 7933 8855

FELL, Mr Alistair LLB; LLM M *Nov 1994*
62, 15, 36
18 Red Lion Court, London EC4
p949 ... 020 7520 6000
18 Red Lion Court (Annexe), Chelmsford
p973 ... 01245 280880

Fell, Mr Mark L *Jan 2004*
Radcliffe Chambers, London WC2
p949 ... 020 7831 0081

Fellows, Mr Philip BA(Hons) L *Jan 2007*
49, 5, 81, 11, 22, 38, 24, 93, 37
Hardwicke, London WC2
p936 ... 020 7242 2523

Felstead, Mr Christopher LLB(Wales) L *Oct 1998*
10, 20, 22
9 Park Place, Cardiff
p973 ... 029 2038 2731

Feltham, Mr Piers BA(Cantab) G *Jul 1985*
2, 5, 6, 8, 9, 11, 13, 14, 22, 29, 32, 37, 40
Radcliffe Chambers, London WC2
p949 ... 020 7831 0081

Felton, Mr Timothy J F LLB(Hons); Associate Member M *Jul 1977*
2, 46, 12, 18
Rougemont Chambers, Exeter
p975 ... 01392 208484

Femi-Ola, Mr John BA G *Nov 1985*
15, 62
3 Temple Gardens, London EC4
p952 ... 020 7353 3102

Fender, Mr Carl BA(Hons) M *Feb 1994*
12, 15, 20, 25, 30, 18, 24
Regency Chambers, Peterborough
p990 ... 01733 315215

FENHALLS, Mr Mark MA; MSc G *Oct 1992*
12, 15, 36, 62, 27
23 Essex Street, London WC2
p932 ... 020 7413 0353

Fenn, Mr Andrew BA G *Mar 2007*
3, 7, 11, 31, 40, 41, 43, 45, 49, 54, 61, 78, 74
Atkin Chambers, London WC1
p923 ... 020 7404 0102

Fenner, Mr Edward M *Jul 2000*
4 Breams Buildings, London EC4
p927 ... 020 7092 1900

FENNY, Mr Ian LLB(Reading) G *Jul 1978*
15, 36
Guildhall Chambers, Bristol
p970 ... 0117 930 9000

Fenston, Ms Felicia BA(Oxon) M *Nov 1994*
10, 12, 20, 22, 30, 48
Henderson Chambers, London EC4
p937 ... 020 7583 9020

FENTEM, Mr Ross BA; MD L *Nov 2003*
11, 5, 38, 93
Guildhall Chambers, Bristol
p970 ... 0117 930 9000

Fenton, Mr Adam BA(Oxon) I *Jul 1984*
(Q.C.) *3, 35, 19, 33, 24, 11, 40, 5*
7 King's Bench Walk, London EC4
p940 ... 020 7910 8300

Fenwick, Mr Justin MA I *Nov 1980*
(Q.C.) *41, 8, 12, 24, 40, 11, 48*
Four New Square, London WC2
p943 ... 020 7822 2000

Ferber, Miss Iris BA(Hons) I *Jan 2005*
1, 6, 8, 11, 18, 22, 25, 26, 55, 61
Cobden House Chambers, Manchester
p983 ... 0161 833 6000

Ferguson, Mr Christopher Mark M *May 1979*
10, 20
Court Yard Chambers, London SE9
p929 ... 020 7936 2710
Unity Street Chambers, Bristol
p972 ... 0117 906 9789

Ferguson, Miss Corina BA; CPE; LLM L *Jul 2003*
18, 30
Old Square Chambers, Bristol
p971 ... 0117 930 5100
Old Square Chambers, London WC1
p945 ... 020 7269 0300

Ferguson, Mr Craig Charles LLB M *Feb 1992*
15, 62, 25, 36
2 Hare Court, London EC4
p937 ... 020 7353 5324

Ferguson, Ms Eva BA M *Nov 1999*
40, 53, 11, 27
Hailsham Chambers, London EC4
p936 ... 020 7643 5000

Ferguson, Mr Frederick Morris Gifford BA(Oxon) M *Jul 1978*
62, 15, 65, 81, 39, 38, 84
9 Gough Square, London EC4
p935 ... 020 7832 0500

Ferguson, Mrs Katharine BA(Oxon) I *Feb 1995*
20, 30, 12
Fenners Chambers, Cambridge
p972 ... 01223 368761

Ferguson, Mr Stephen Michael MA(Oxon) I *Nov 1991*
15, 62, 42
2 Hare Court, London EC4
p937 ... 020 7353 5324

Ferm, Mr Rodney E BA(Oxon) M *Jul 1972*
7, 11, 18, 20, 30, 36, 15, 12, 16, 40
37 Park Square Chambers, Leeds
p978 ... 0113 243 9422

Fern, Mr Gary LLM; BEng(Hons) L *Oct 1992*
13, 19, 43, 44, 45, 50
7 Stone Buildings Intellectual Property, London WC2
p951 ... 020 7242 8848

Fernandes, Ms Suella MA(Hons); LLM M *Oct 2005*
11, 8, 37, 32, 1, 31, 22, 25, 23, 46
No5 Chambers, Bristol
p971 ... 0845 210 5555
No5 Chambers, London EC4
p944 ... 0845 210 5555
No5 Chambers, Birmingham
p968 ... 0845 210 5555

Fernando, Mr Giles Rudyard BA(Hons)(Jurisprudence) G *Mar 1998*
73, 50, 19, 45, 13, 52, 96, 41
11 South Square, London WC1
p950 ... 020 7405 1222

Fernando, Mr Pravin LLB; LLM(LSE) I *Oct 2009*
3 Serjeants' Inn, London EC4
p950 ... 020 7427 5000

Fernyhough, Mr Richard LLB(Lond); FCIArb; Recorder 1986 M *Nov 1970*
(Q.C.) *3, 7, 11, 24, 40*
Keating Chambers, London WC2
p938 ... 020 7544 2600

Ferrari, Mr Nicholas G *Nov 2005*
18, 15, 12, 47, 48, 38
Rougemont Chambers, Exeter
p975 ... 01392 208484

Ferrer, Mr Peter A BA(Cardiff); DipLaw(City) I *Mar 1998*
11, 35, 24, 5
Quadrant Chambers, London EC4
p948 ... 020 7583 4444

Ferrier, Ms Susan BSc(Wales) G *Jul 1985*
15
9 Park Place, Cardiff
p973 ... 029 2038 2731

Ferris, Ms Caitlin Tara BA(Leeds) I *Mar 1996*
10, 20
Coram Chambers, London EC1
p929 ... 020 7092 3700

FERRIS, Mr Shaun BA(Oxon) G *Nov 1985*
30, 40, 53, 27
Crown Office Chambers, London EC4
p929 ... 020 7797 8100

FERRO, Mr Jack BA(Oxon) I *Sep 1998*
30, 83, 40, 24, 11, 74, 7, 84, 36
Crown Office Chambers, London EC4
p929 ... 020 7797 8100

Fessal, Mr Ignatius LLB I *Nov 1981*
15
1 Mitre Court Buildings, London EC4
p942 ... 020 7452 8900

FETHERSTONHAUGH, Mr Guy BSc(Bris) I *Jul 1983*
(Q.C.)
Falcon Chambers, London EC4
p933 ... 020 7353 2484

Fetto, Mr Niazi MA(Cantab) I *Oct 1999*
18, 55, 30, 53, 12, 47, 48, 50, 51, 24, 40, 36
2 Temple Gardens, London EC4
p952 ... 020 7822 1200

Fewtrell, Mr Nicholas Austin LLB(Lond) I *Nov 1977*
30, 24, 11, 7, 18
18 St John Street Chambers, Manchester
p985 ... 0161 278 1800

ffitch, Nigel QVRM; TD G *Oct 1996*
Clerksroom - Administration Centre, Taunton
p993 ... 0845 083 3000

FIELD, Mr Julian LLB(Lond) G *Nov 1980*
30, 24, 74, 7, 11, 40
Crown Office Chambers, London EC4
p929 ... 020 7797 8100

Field, Mr Stephen A LLB(Lond) G *Nov 1993*
15, 31, 53, 51
1 Pump Court, London EC4
p947 ... 020 7842 7070

Fielding, Mr Janick I *Oct 1997*
15, 62, 84, 96
Argent Chambers, London WC2
p923 ... 020 7556 5500

FIELDING, Mr Stephen I *Jan 1974*
Pump Court Chambers, Swindon
p993 ... 01793 539899
Pump Court Chambers, Winchester
p994 ... 01962 868161
Pump Court Chambers, London EC4
p947 ... 020 7353 0711

FIELDSEND, Mr James LLB(Newc) L *Oct 1997*
88, 93
Tanfield Chambers, London WC1
p951 ... 020 7421 5300

Finch, Mr Thomas Michael L *Nov 1981*
12, 20, 18
Broad Chare Chambers, Newcastle upon Tyne
p986 ... 0191 232 0541

FINDLAY, Mr Archibald SC G *Jan 1999*
11, 41, 1, 31, 13, 33, 67
Thirty Nine Essex Street, London WC2
p932 ... 020 7832 1111

 See p1010 for the Key to Work Categories

Findlay, Mr James BA(Cantab) M *Nov 1984*
(Q.C.) *1, 12, 18, 22, 25, 26, 28, 30, 31, 36, 47*
Cornerstone Barristers, London WC1
p929 . . . . . 020 7242 4986

Finnigan, Mr Peter L *Jul 1979*
(Q.C.) *15, 25, 36*
QEB Hollis Whiteman, London EC4
p948 . . . . . 020 7933 8855

Finucane, Mr Brendan Godfrey Eamonn BSc(Hons); Recorder M *Jul 1976*
(Q.C.) *72, 15, 68, 62, 84, 85, 27, 86*
Outer Temple Chambers, London WC2
p945 . . . . . 020 7353 6381

Firbank, Mr Kit M *Oct 2005*
20
18 St John Street Chambers, Manchester
p985 . . . . . 0161 278 1800

Firth, Miss Alison MA(Oxon); MSc I *Nov 1980*
13, 16, 19
Ingenuity IP Chambers, London EC4
p937 . . . . . 020 7936 4474

Firth, Ms Georgina LLB M *Oct 1995*
23, 1, 51, 70
Garden Court North Chambers, Manchester
p983 . . . . . 0161 236 1840

FIRTH, Mr Mathew G *Jul 1991*
12, 20
Queen Elizabeth Buildings, London EC4
p948 . . . . . 020 7797 7837

Fish, Mr Lee L *Jan 2003*
New Court Chambers, Newcastle upon Tyne
p987 . . . . . 0191 232 1980

FISHER, Mr Andrew G *Jul 1980*
(Q.C.) *15, 25, 48, 51*
Citadel Chambers, Birmingham
p967 . . . . . 0121 233 8500

Fisher, Mr Craig LLB M *May 2004*
Regent Chambers, Hanley
p976 . . . . . 01782 286666

Fisher, Mr David G *Jul 1973*
(Q.C.) *15, 62*
6 King's Bench Walk, London EC4
p939 . . . . . 020 7583 0410
New Square Chambers, London WC2
p943 . . . . . 020 7419 8000

Fisher, Mr Jonathan G *Jul 1980*
(Q.C.) *57, 58, 71, 72, 81, 34*
Devereux Chambers, London WC2
p930 . . . . . 020 7353 7534

FISHER, Miss Justine LLB; LLM I *Nov 1994*
23, 1, 18
Mitre House Chambers, London WC1
p942 . . . . . 020 7307 7100

Fisher, Mr Martin G *Jan 1999*
1 Pump Court, London EC4
p947 . . . . . 020 7842 7070

Fisher, Ms Mel L *Jun 1985*
MFL Chambers, London N2
p941 . . . . .

FISHER, Mr Richard LLB(Lond); BCL(Oxon) L *Oct 2000*
5, 6, 8, 11, 97, 38
South Square, London WC1
p950 . . . . . 020 7696 9900
Doughty Street Chambers, London WC1
p930 . . . . . 020 7404 1313

FISHER, Sandra I *Nov 1993*
10, 20
Renaissance Chambers, London WC1
p949 . . . . . 020 7404 1111

Fisher, Mr Steve G *Jan 2000*
30
Kew Chambers, Kew
p976 . . . . . 0844 809 9991

FISHER, Mr Toby L *Jan 2008*
1, 46, 31, 93
Landmark Chambers, London EC4
p941 . . . . . 020 7430 1221

FISHWICK, Mr Gregory David Philip Kyle LLB(Hons)(Lond); BCL(Oxon) G *Oct 1996*
15, 62, 95
187 Fleet Street, London EC4
p933 . . . . . 020 7430 7430

Fitton, Mr Michael David Guy MA(Oxon) G *Nov 1991*
(Q.C.) *15, 62*
Albion Chambers, Bristol
p970 . . . . . 0117 927 2144

Fitton-Brown, Ms Rebeca LLB; Pupil Master I *Apr 1981*
20, 10
New Walk Chambers, Leicester
p979 . . . . . 0871 200 1298

FitzGerald, Mr Benedict L *Oct 2000*
15
QEB Hollis Whiteman, London EC4
p948 . . . . . 020 7933 8855

Fitzgerald, Mr Edward BA; MPhil; Recorder I *Nov 1978*
(Q.C.) *1, 14, 15, 33, 12, 51*
Doughty Street Chambers, London WC1
p930 . . . . . 020 7404 1313

FITZGERALD, Ms Elizabeth LLB(KCL) M *Jan 2001*
Falcon Chambers, London EC4
p933 . . . . . 020 7353 2484

FITZGERALD, Mr John I *Oct 1998*
Maidstone Chambers, Maidstone
p982 . . . . . 01622 688592

Fitzgerald, Mr John V BSc M *Jul 1971*
13, 16, 19, 44, 45, 50
Ingenuity IP Chambers, London EC4
p937 . . . . . 020 7936 4474
No 3 Fleet Street Chambers, London EC4
p944 . . . . . 020 7936 4474

FITZGERALD, Mr Michael Edward BA(Hons)(Lond) L *May 1979*
11, 51, 21, 1
Monckton Chambers, London WC1
p942 . . . . . 020 7405 7211

FitzGerald, Ms Susanna I *Jul 1973*
(Q.C.)
One Essex Court, London EC4
p931 . . . . . 020 7583 2000

Fitzgerald, Mr Toby Jonathan BSc(Bris) L *Oct 1993*
15
Atkinson Bevan Chambers, London EC4
p924 . . . . . 020 7353 2112

Fitzgibbon, Mr Francis BA(Oxon) M *Jan 1986*
15, 51
Doughty Street Chambers, London WC1
p930 . . . . . 020 7404 1313

FITZGIBBON, Mr Neil L *Nov 1989*
Carmelite Chambers, London EC4
p927 . . . . . 020 7936 6300

Fitzharris, Miss Ginnette LLB(Hons) L *Nov 1993*
10, 20
St Johns Buildings, Preston
p990 . . . . . 01772 256100
St Johns Buildings, Chester
p974 . . . . . 01244 323070
St Johns Buildings, Manchester
p985 . . . . . 0161 214 1500
St Johns Buildings, Liverpool
p982 . . . . . 0151 243 6000

Fitzherbert, Mr Francis Brian Royds L *Oct 2008*
15
Atkinson Bevan Chambers, London EC4
p924 . . . . . 020 7353 2112

Fitzpatrick, Mr Andrew LLB G *Jan 2003*
15, 51, 96
Garden Court North Chambers, Manchester
p983 . . . . . 0161 236 1840

FITZPATRICK, Miss Denise M *Jul 2000*
15, 94, 25
Kenworthy's Chambers, Manchester
p984 . . . . . 0161 832 4036

FITZPATRICK, Mr Francis MA; BCL(Oxon) I *Nov 1990*
34, 57, 58
11 New Square, London WC2
p943 . . . . . 020 7242 4017

Fitzpatrick, Mr Jerry BA; DipLaw M *Mar 1996*
20
Coram Chambers, London EC1
p929 . . . . . 020 7092 3700

Fitzpatrick, Mr Stephen L *Jan 2004*
2 Pump Court, London EC4
p947 . . . . . 020 7353 5597

FITZPATRICK, Mr Thomas A LLB L *Nov 1988*
15
9 St John Street Chambers, Manchester
p984 . . . . . 0161 955 9000

Flach, Mr Robert LLB M *Jan 1950*
15
2 Bedford Row, London WC1
p924 . . . . . 020 7440 8888

Flanagan, Ms Julia BA(Hons); DipLaw; CPE L *Oct 1993*
Charter Chambers, London WC1
p928 . . . . . 020 7618 4400

Flanagan, Mr Nicholas LLB(Hons) L *Jul 2004*
15, 18, 94
Cobden House Chambers, Manchester
p983 . . . . . 0161 833 6000

FLATTERY, Miss Amanda L *Oct 1993*
20, 10, 76
Kenworthy's Chambers, Manchester
p984 . . . . . 0161 832 4036

Flavin, Mr Marcus Benedict Sean BA; MSt(Oxon) L *Nov 2001*
Radcliffe Chambers, London WC2
p949 . . . . . 020 7831 0081

FLECK, Miss Helen L *Oct 2005*
15, 62, 95
187 Fleet Street, London EC4
p933 . . . . . 020 7430 7430

Fleck, Miss Nicola M *Nov 2006*
15
Atkinson Bevan Chambers, London EC4
p924 . . . . . 020 7353 2112

Fleming, Mr Adrian BA M *Nov 1991*
2 King's Bench Walk, London EC4
p939 . . . . . 020 7353 1746

Fleming, Mr Paul S G *Nov 1983*
12, 15, 62
37 Park Square Chambers, Leeds
p978 . . . . . 0113 243 9422

Flenley, Mr William BA; BCL; LLM M *Nov 1988*
40
Hailsham Chambers, London EC4
p936 . . . . . 020 7643 5000

Flesch, Mr Michael Charles LLB G *May 1963*
(Q.C.) *34, 57, 58*
Gray's Inn Tax Chambers, London WC1
p936 . . . . . 020 7242 2642

FLETCHER, Mr Andrew MA(Cantab) I *Nov 1980*
(Q.C.) *3, 5, 8, 11, 24, 40*
3 Verulam Buildings, London WC1
p953 . . . . . 020 7831 8441

FLETCHER, Mr Christopher Michael I *Nov 1984*
22, 36, 18, 10, 12, 20, 30
Octagon House, Norwich
p988 . . . . . 01603 623186

Fletcher, Mr David H MA(Cantab) G *Jul 1971*
8, 11, 18, 22, 26, 29, 31, 40, 55, 93, 25, 1, 46, 76
St John's Chambers, Bristol
p972 . . . . . 0117 921 3456

FLETCHER, Prof Ian F MA; LLM; PhD; LLD(Cantab); MCL(Tulane) L *Nov 1971*
South Square, London WC1
p950 . . . . . 020 7696 9900

Fletcher, Mr James M *Jan 2000*
15
5 St Andrew's Hill, London EC4
p950 . . . . . 020 7332 5400

FLETCHER, Mr Marcus Alexander BA(Law) M *Oct 1990*
10, 12, 15, 20, 22, 30, 38, 91
1 King's Bench Walk, London EC4
p938 . . . . . 020 7936 1500

FLETCHER, Matthew L *Mar 2003*
10, 12, 20, 23
Renaissance Chambers, London WC1
p949 . . . . . 020 7404 1111

Fletcher, Mr Stephen Jeffery M *Nov 1987*
18, 30, 32, 47, 88, 93
Broad Chare Chambers, Newcastle upon Tyne
p986 . . . . . 0191 232 0541

Fleurie, Mr Jean-Francois M *Jan 2003*
2 King's Bench Walk, London EC4
p939 . . . . . 020 7353 1746

FLEWITT, Mr Neil LLB(L'pool); Recorder M *Jul 1981*
(Q.C.) *15*
7 Harrington Street Chambers, Liverpool
p981 . . . . . 0151 242 0707

FLINN, Mr Matthew L *Jan 2010*
18, 53, 30, 40
1 Crown Office Row, London EC4
p929 . . . . . 020 7797 7500

Flint, Mr Charles MA(Cantab) M *Jul 1975*
(Q.C.) *1, 3, 5, 8, 11, 12, 24, 29, 36, 41, 49, 56, 89, 51, 81, 50, 52*
Blackstone Chambers, London EC4
p926 . . . . . 020 7583 1770

Flood, Mr David LLB M *Nov 1993*
7, 11, 12, 15, 18, 22, 24, 30, 40, 53
St Johns Buildings, Preston
p990 . . . . . 01772 256100
St Johns Buildings, Chester
p974 . . . . . 01244 323070
St Johns Buildings, Manchester
p985 . . . . . 0161 214 1500
St Johns Buildings, Liverpool
p982 . . . . . 0151 243 6000

FLOOD, Mr Diarmuid LLB L *Apr 1989*
22, 30, 15, 40, 88, 24, 38, 11
7 Harrington Street Chambers, Liverpool
p981 . . . . . 0151 242 0707

FLOOD, Mr Edward A MA(Oxon) M *Oct 2002*
10, 20
1 Garden Court, London EC4
p934 . . . . . 020 7797 7900

Flower, Mr Philip BA(Exon) I *Nov 1979*
6, 8, 11, 13, 18, 22, 30, 38
9 Stone Buildings Barristers Chambers, London WC2
p951 . . . . . 020 7404 5055

Flynn, Mr James BA(Oxon) M *Jul 1978*
(Q.C.) *19, 44, 1*
Brick Court Chambers, London WC2
p927 . . . . . 020 7379 3550

Flynn, Mr Steven G *Jan 2006*
Iscoed Chambers, Swansea
p993 . . . . . 01792 652988
St Johns Buildings, Preston
p990 . . . . . 01772 256100
St Johns Buildings, Chester
p974 . . . . . 01244 323070
St Johns Buildings, Manchester
p985 . . . . . 0161 214 1500
St Johns Buildings, Liverpool
p982 . . . . . 0151 243 6000

Flynn, Mr Vernon J H BA(Cantab) L *Oct 1991*
(Q.C.)
Essex Court Chambers, London WC2
p931 . . . . . 020 7813 8000

FODDER, Mr Martin BA; LLM I *Jul 1983*
18, 40, 55, 49
Littleton Chambers, London EC4
p941 . . . . . 020 7797 8600

Fogg, Mr Anthony G MSc G *Nov 1970*
15
Charter Chambers, London WC1
p928 . . . . . 020 7618 4400

Foinette, Mr Ian BA M *Nov 1986*
12, 15, 30
5 St Andrew's Hill, London EC4
p950 . . . . . 020 7332 5400

FOLEY, Miss Jane G *Jan 2002*
15
Trinity (Newcastle) Chambers, Newcastle upon Tyne
p987 . . . . . 0191 232 1927
Trinity (Teesside) Chambers, Middlesbrough
p986 . . . . . 01642 247569

FOLEY, Miss Sheila BA I *Nov 1988*
6, 11, 8, 29, 38
9 Stone Buildings Barristers Chambers, London WC2
p951 . . . . . 020 7404 5055

Folland, Mr David BSc L *Jan 1976*
15, 20, 25, 10, 30, 48
Victory Chambers, Carmarthen
p973 . . . . . 01994 231704
St David's Chambers, Swansea
p993 . . . . . 01792 644466

Follon, Daniel M *Jul 2003*
4 KBW, London EC4
p938 . . . . . 020 7822 8822

Fookes, Mr Robert MA(Cantab) L *Jul 1975*
1, 2, 26, 28, 31, 36, 61
Francis Taylor Building, London EC4
p934 . . . . . 020 7353 8415

Fooks, Mr Nicholas I *Jan 1978*
15, 62
5 Paper Buildings, London EC4
p946 . . . . . 020 7583 6117

13

Forbes, Mr Alex BA(Hons)(LSE) L *Oct 2003*
20, 10, 12, 30, 67
Harcourt Chambers, London EC4
p936 . . . . . 0844 561 7135
Harcourt Chambers, Oxford
p989 . . . . . 0844 561 7135

Forbes, Mr Peter LLB(Lond) I *Oct 1990*
1, 12, 15, 20, 22, 26, 30, 31, 51
6-8 Mill Street, Maidstone
p982 . . . . . 01622 688094 / 688095
6 Pump Court, London EC4
p947 . . . . . 020 7797 8400

Forbes, Sir Thayne LLB(UCL); LLM(UCL) I *Jan 1966*
(Q.C.) KB3, *7, 11, 31, 40, 41, 43, 45, 49, 54, 61, 72, 74*
Atkin Chambers, London WC1
p923 . . . . . 020 7404 0102

Forbes, Victoria I *Jan 2007*
15
Argent Chambers, London WC2
p923 . . . . . 020 7556 5500

Forbes Smith, Mr Henry M *Jan 2004*
One Essex Court, London EC4
p931 . . . . . 020 7583 2000

FORD, Mr Andrew BA(Hons) M *Oct 1997*
15, 36
7 Harrington Street Chambers, Liverpool
p981 . . . . . 0151 242 0707

Ford, Miss Caroline E G *Oct 1993*
10, 12, 15, 20
Paradise Chambers, Sheffield
p992 . . . . . 0114 273 8951
37 Park Square Chambers, Leeds
p978 . . . . . 0113 243 9422

FORD, Miss Charlotte Jennifer BA(Hons)(Cantab) L *Oct 2007*
8
New Square Chambers, London WC2
p943 . . . . . 020 7419 8000

Ford, Mr Gerard BSc; MA I *Jul 1986*
16, 10, 12, 47, 48, 20, 22, 63, 30
Old Court Chambers, Middlesbrough
p986 . . . . . 01642 232523

Ford, Mr Graeme LLB(Lond) I *Jul 1972*
15
5 King's Bench Walk, London EC4
p939 . . . . . 020 7353 5638

Ford, Mr Jeremy L *Oct 1996*
30, 11, 40
9 Gough Square, London EC4
p935 . . . . . 020 7832 0500

Ford, Mr Michael LLB(Hons); MA(Distinction) M *Jul 1992*
18, 1, 30, 55, 36, 51
Old Square Chambers, Bristol
p971 . . . . . 0117 930 5100
Old Square Chambers, London WC1
p945 . . . . . 020 7269 0300

Ford, Miss Monica LLB(L'pool) M *Jul 1984*
14 Gray's Inn Square, London WC1
p936 . . . . . 020 7242 0858

Ford, Mr Steven M *Nov 1992*
11, 30, 53, 26, 59, 76
7 Bedford Row, London WC1
p924 . . . . . 020 7242 3555

Ford, Mr Tom G *Jan 2008*
Essex Court Chambers, London WC2
p931 . . . . . 020 7813 8000

FORDE, Mr Martin BA; LLB(Oxon) M *Feb 1984*
(Q.C.) *12, 20, 27, 30*
1 Crown Office Row, London EC4
p929 . . . . . 020 7797 7500

FORDHAM, Ms Chloe I *Jul 2005*
Furnival Chambers, London EC4
p934 . . . . . 020 7405 3232

Fordham, Mrs Judith Deputy District Judge I *Jul 1991*
20
Exchange Chambers, Manchester
p983 . . . . . 0161 833 2722
Exchange Chambers, Liverpool
p980 . . . . . 0151 236 7747
Exchange Chambers, Leeds
p977 . . . . . 0113 203 1970

Fordham, Mr Michael BA(Oxon); BCL(Oxon); LLM(Virginia) G *Feb 1990*
(Q.C.) *1, 19, 26, 36, 46, 51, 89, 44, 23*
Blackstone Chambers, London EC4
p926 . . . . . 020 7583 1770

FORGAN, Mr Hugh BA(Cantab) L *Jan 1989*
15, 62, 34
23 Essex Street, London WC2
p932 . . . . . 020 7413 0353

Forlin, Mr Gerard LLB; LLM; M Phil G *Jun 1984*
(Q.C.) *4, 12, 15, 51, 60, 61*
Cornerstone Barristers, London WC1
p929 . . . . . 020 7242 4986

FORMBY, Ms Emily BA(Oxon) M *Nov 1993*
27, 30, 11
Thirty Nine Essex Street, London WC2
p932 . . . . . 020 7832 1111

Forrest, Mr Alastair MA(Oxon) G *Jul 1972*
30, 24, 20, 12
18 St John Street Chambers, Manchester
p985 . . . . . 0161 278 1800

Forrest, Mr Robert L *Jan 2007*
2 King's Bench Walk, London EC4
p939 . . . . . 020 7353 1746

FORSDICK, Mr David John BA G *Oct 1993*
Landmark Chambers, London EC4
p941 . . . . . 020 7430 1221

Forshall, Ms Isabella BA(Cantab) G *Feb 1982*
15, 51
Doughty Street Chambers, London WC1
p930 . . . . . 020 7404 1313

Forshaw, Miss Sarah LLB M *Nov 1987*
(Q.C.) *15*
5 King's Bench Walk, London EC4
p939 . . . . . 020 7353 5638

FORSHAW, Mr Simon MA(Hons)(Oxon) G *Mar 2004*
18, 55, 1, 11
11KBW, London EC4
p938 . . . . . 020 7632 8500

Forster, Mr Brian Clive LLB L *Jan 1977*
(Q.C.)
Charter Chambers, London WC1
p928 . . . . . 020 7618 4400

Forster, Ms Bridget I *Jan 2001*
31, 1, 94, 46, 30, 68
No5 Chambers, Bristol
p971 . . . . . 0845 210 5555
No5 Chambers, London EC4
p944 . . . . . 0845 210 5555
No5 Chambers, Birmingham
p968 . . . . . 0845 210 5555

FORSTER, Mr Michael W LLB(Lond) G *Feb 1984*
15, 12, 20, 10, 26, 25, 30, 40
12 College Place, Southampton
p992 . . . . . 023 8032 0320

Forster, Miss Sarah LLB; Dip M *Nov 1976*
14 Gray's Inn Square, London WC1
p936 . . . . . 020 7242 0858

FORSTER, Mr Thomas I *Nov 1993*
15, 36, 62, 46, 68, 84, 91
18 Red Lion Court, London EC4
p949 . . . . . 020 7520 6000
18 Red Lion Court (Annexe), Chelmsford
p973 . . . . . 01245 280880

FORSTER, Mr Timothy LLB M *Oct 1990*
15
Furnival Chambers, London EC4
p934 . . . . . 020 7405 3232

Forster-Jones, Mr Wilfred BA M *Nov 1976*
Chambers of Wilfred Forster-Jones, London WC1
p934 . . . . . 020 7831 0037

Forsyth, Mr Andrew I *Nov 1989*
15, 62
15 New Bridge Street Chambers, London EC4
p943 . . . . . 020 7842 1900

FORSYTH, Miss Julie Patricia LLB G *Jul 1983*
10, 15, 20
Chavasse Court Chambers, Liverpool
p980 . . . . . 0151 229 2030

FORSYTH, Ms Samantha I *Jul 1988*
Citadel Chambers, Birmingham
p967 . . . . . 0121 233 8500

Fortescue, Miss Kate M *Jan 2004*
2 King's Bench Walk, London EC4
p939 . . . . . 020 7353 1746

FORTSON, Mr Rudi LLB M *Nov 1976*
(Q.C.) *12, 15*
25 Bedford Row, London WC1
p925 . . . . . 020 7067 1500

Fortune, Mr Malcolm Donald Porter Recorder (1994) M *Jul 1972*
15, 25, 36, 53, 46, 84, 40
3 Serjeants' Inn, London EC4
p950 . . . . . 020 7427 5000

Fortune, Mr Peter BA; MA I *Jul 1978*
12, 15, 18, 30, 53
Guildhall Chambers, Portsmouth
p990 . . . . . 023 9275 2400

FORTUNE, Peter I *Jan 1978*
4 King's Bench Walk, London EC4
p939 . . . . . 020 7822 7000

Fortune, Mr Robert A LLB(Lond) M *Feb 1976*
(Q.C.) *15, 51*
Nine Bedford Row, London WC1
p924 . . . . . 020 7489 2727

FORWARD, Mr Barry Miles BSc(Econ); DipLaw G *Jul 1981*
15, 25
10 King's Bench Walk, London EC4
p940 . . . . . 020 7353 7742

Foskett, Miss Rosanna L *Jul 2008*
Maitland Chambers, London WC2
p941 . . . . . 020 7406 1200

FOSTER, Miss Alison L C I *Jul 1984*
(Q.C.) *1, 23, 26, 27, 36, 51, 57, 34, 85*
Thirty Nine Essex Street, London WC2
p932 . . . . . 020 7832 1111

FOSTER, Ms Catherine I *Jan 1986*
30
Crown Office Chambers, London EC4
p929 . . . . . 020 7797 8100

Foster, Mr Charles A MA(Cantab); VETMB; MRCVS; Recorder I *Oct 1988*
1, 12, 15, 27, 36, 40, 51, 53, 63, 30
Outer Temple Chambers, London WC2
p945 . . . . . 020 7353 6381

Foster, Mr Ian LLB L *Jul 1988*
8, 9, 11, 22, 29, 32, 37, 40
Exchange Chambers, Manchester
p983 . . . . . 0161 833 2722
Exchange Chambers, Liverpool
p980 . . . . . 0151 236 7747
Exchange Chambers, Leeds
p977 . . . . . 0113 203 1970

FOSTER, Mr Julien BA(Hons) M *Oct 1995*
10, 20
1 Garden Court, London EC4
p934 . . . . . 020 7797 7900
Goldsmith Chambers, London EC4
p935 . . . . . 020 7353 6802

FOSTER, Mr Peter LLB(Hons) M *Nov 1992*
18, 30, 40, 12, 47, 16
Oriel Chambers, Liverpool
p981 . . . . . 0151 236 7191 / 236 4321
Oriel Chambers, Preston
p990 . . . . . 01772 254764

Foster, Miss Rosalind Mary BA(Oxon) M *Nov 1969*
27, 36, 12, 63
2 Temple Gardens, London EC4
p952 . . . . . 020 7822 1200

Foster, Mr Simon M *Jul 1982*
2 King's Bench Walk, London EC4
p939 . . . . . 020 7353 1746

FOSTER, Miss Wendy BA(Cantab) I *Oct 2005*
15, 12, 10
Wilberforce Chambers, Hull
p976 . . . . . 01482 323264

FOSUHENE, Miss Amelia LLB M *Nov 1996*
Carmelite Chambers, London EC4
p927 . . . . . 020 7936 6300

Fottrell, Ms Deirdre May BA(Hons); LLM M *Oct 2001*
20, 10, 51
Coram Chambers, London EC1
p929 . . . . . 020 7092 3700

Foulkes, Mr Christopher D MA; LLB(Cantab) L *Oct 1994*
15, 36, 62
2 Hare Court, London EC4
p937 . . . . . 020 7353 5324

Foulkes, Miss Rebecca BA(Hons) L *Jul 2001*
20, 10
4 Paper Buildings, London EC4
p946 . . . . . 020 7583 0816

Foulser-McFarlane, Ms Jane LLM; Lead Counsel to Welsh Assembly Govt on IP G *Jan 1994*
12, 20, 13
Temple Chambers, Newport
p988 . . . . . 01633 267403 / 255855
Temple Chambers, Cardiff
p973 . . . . . 029 2039 7364

FOUND, Mr Tim LLB(Exon) L *Jul 2006*
30, 12
Farrar's Building, London EC4
p933 . . . . . 020 7583 9241

Fowler, Mr David L *Oct 2004*
Field Court Chambers, London WC1
p933 . . . . . 020 7405 6114

Fowler, Mr Edmund LLB G *Oct 1992*
15
5 King's Bench Walk, London EC4
p939 . . . . . 020 7353 5638

Fowler, Mr Richard MA(Hons)(Oxon); DPhil(Oxon) I *Jan 2003*
Maitland Chambers, London WC2
p941 . . . . . 020 7406 1200

Fowles, Mr Jonathan BA(Oxon); PGDL G *Jul 2004*
6, 8, 9, 11, 62, 29, 32, 40, 37
Serle Court, London WC2
p950 . . . . . 020 7242 6105

FOX, Ms Anna Katherine Helen LLB(Hons)(L'pool) M *Jul 1986*
10, 20
Oriel Chambers, Liverpool
p981 . . . . . 0151 236 7191 / 236 4321
Oriel Chambers, Preston
p990 . . . . . 01772 254764

FOX, Claire M *Oct 2003*
10, 20
Renaissance Chambers, London WC1
p949 . . . . . 020 7404 1111

Fox, Mr David L *Jul 2005*
Maitland Chambers, London WC2
p941 . . . . . 020 7406 1200

Fox, Mr John Harvey LLB(Lond); BDS I *Jul 1973*
10, 12, 20, 22, 30, 40, 49, 53, 96
Lamb Building, Brighton
p970 . . . . . 01273 820490
Lamb Building, London EC4
p940 . . . . . 020 7797 7788

Fox, Miss Katie MA(Oxon) I *Oct 2001*
12, 15, 20
6-8 Mill Street, Maidstone
p982 . . . . . 01622 688094 / 688095
6 Pump Court, London EC4
p947 . . . . . 020 7797 8400

Fox, Mr Martin George LLB M *Jul 1981*
15
Warwick House Chambers, London WC1
p953 . . . . . 020 7430 2323

FOX, Miss Nicola S BSc; MSc M *Oct 1996*
10, 20
1 Garden Court, London EC4
p934 . . . . . 020 7797 7900

Fox, Dr Simon I *Jan 1994*
27, 30, 53
No5 Chambers, Bristol
p971 . . . . . 0845 210 5555
No5 Chambers, London EC4
p944 . . . . . 0845 210 5555
No5 Chambers, Birmingham
p968 . . . . . 0845 210 5555
Exchange Chambers, Manchester
p983 . . . . . 0161 833 2722
Exchange Chambers, Liverpool
p980 . . . . . 0151 236 7747
Exchange Chambers, Leeds
p977 . . . . . 0113 203 1970

Foxton, Mr David A BA; BCL(Oxon) G *Feb 1989*
(Q.C.)
Essex Court Chambers, London WC2
p931 . . . . . 020 7813 8000

Foy, Mr John Leonard Recorder G *Jul 1969*
(Q.C.) *30, 53, 15, 40, 18*
9 Gough Square, London EC4
p935 . . . . . 020 7832 0500

Foyle, Mr Andrew L *Jan 2006*
One Essex Court, London EC4
p931 . . . . . 020 7583 2000

Frame, Mr Stuart LLB G *May 1997*
15, 7, 12, 18, 22, 26, 48
Staple Inn Chambers, London WC1
p951 . . . . . 020 7242 5240

Francis, Mr Andrew MA(Oxon) L *Nov 1977*
29, 32, 37, 40, 49, 93, 89, 8
Serle Court, London WC2
p950 . . . . . 020 7242 6105

See p1010 for the Key to Work Categories

FRANCIS, Mr Edward MA(Oxon) I *Nov 1995*
5, 6, 8, 11, 22, 29, 32, 37, 40, 38, 49, 88, 97
Enterprise Chambers, London WC2
p931 . . . . . 020 7405 9471
Enterprise Chambers, Leeds
p977 . . . . . 0113 246 0391
Enterprise Chambers, Newcastle upon Tyne
p987 . . . . . 0191 222 3344

FRANCIS, Mr Nicholas MA(Cantab); Assistant Recorder M *Jul 1981*
(Q.C.) *10, 20, 40*
29 Bedford Row, London WC1
p925 . . . . . 020 7404 1044

Francis, Mr Richard BA; MUKCFM G *Nov 1974*
8, 12, 20, 22, 30, 49
9 Park Place, Cardiff
p973 . . . . . 029 2038 2731

Francis, Mr Robert Anthony LLB(Exon) I *Jul 1973*
(Q.C.) *27, 30, 18, 12, 36, 40, 53, 63, 1, 85*
3 Serjeants' Inn, London EC4
p950 . . . . . 020 7427 5000

FRANCIS, Miss Victoria MA(Hons) M *Oct 2001*
20
29 Bedford Row, London WC1
p925 . . . . . 020 7404 1044

Franklin, Mr Edward Thomas Robert G *Jul 2006*
15
Atkinson Bevan Chambers, London EC4
p924 . . . . . 020 7353 2112

FRANKLIN, Miss Kim LLB(Warw) M *Nov 1984*
74, 7, 24, 11
Crown Office Chambers, London EC4
p929 . . . . . 020 7797 8100

FRANKLIN, Ms Rebecca L *Jul 2001*
20
St Philips Chambers, Birmingham
p969 . . . . . 0121 246 7000

Fraser, Mr Alan BSc; MSc; DipLaw G *Sep 1990*
1, 2, 15, 18, 22, 26, 28, 38
Charter Chambers, London WC1
p928 . . . . . 020 7618 4400

FRASER, Donald LLB I *Jul 2003*
97, 67, 38, 88, 37
Atlantic Chambers, Liverpool
p980 . . . . . 0151 236 4421

FRASER, Mr Orlando BA(Cantab) I *Nov 1994*
6, 11, 29
4 Stone Buildings, London WC2
p951 . . . . . 020 7242 5524

Fraser, Mr Peter D MA; LLM(Cantab); Recorder M *Nov 1989*
(Q.C.) *3, 7, 11, 31, 40, 41, 43, 45, 49, 54, 56, 61, 78, 74*
Atkin Chambers, London WC1
p923 . . . . . 020 7404 0102

FRASER, Mr Quintin M *Nov 2006*
94, 84, 68, 56, 67, 40, 53, 30, 24, 12, 1
Thirty Nine Essex Street, London WC2
p932 . . . . . 020 7832 1111

Fraser, Mr Vincent MA(Oxon) G *Jul 1981*
(Q.C.) *1, 26, 31, 46, 54*
Cornerstone Barristers, London WC1
p929 . . . . . 020 7242 4986
Kings Chambers, Leeds
p978 . . . . . 0113 242 1123
Kings Chambers, Manchester
p984 . . . . . 0161 832 9082

FRASER-URQUHART, Mr Andrew MA(Cantab) M *Oct 1993*
1, 11, 55, 18, 26, 31, 56
4-5 Gray's Inn Square, London WC1
p935 . . . . . 020 7404 5252

Frazer, Miss Alison G *Oct 1999*
18, 96, 20, 10
Queen Square Chambers, Bristol
p972 . . . . . 0117 921 1966

FRAZER, Ms Lucy MA(Cantab) M *Oct 1996*
5, 6, 8, 11, 40, 97, 38
South Square, London WC1
p950 . . . . . 020 7696 9900

Fredman, Prof Sandra G *Jan 2002*
Old Square Chambers, London WC1
p945 . . . . . 020 7269 0300

Freeborn, Ms Susan Christine BA(Cantab) G *Jul 1989*
53, 10, 30, 1
Outer Temple Chambers, London WC2
p945 . . . . . 020 7353 6381

Freedman, Mr Clive MA(Cantab); Accredited Mediator G *Jul 1978*
(Q.C.) *5, 6, 8, 11, 12, 18, 19, 24, 28, 36, 40, 44, 47, 49, 51, 55, 56*
Kings Chambers, Leeds
p978 . . . . . 0113 242 1123
Kings Chambers, Manchester
p984 . . . . . 0161 832 9082
Littleton Chambers, London EC4
p941 . . . . . 020 7797 8600

Freedman, Miss Michelle L *Jan 2002*
One Essex Court, London EC4
p931 . . . . . 020 7936 3030

FREEDMAN, Mr S Clive MA(Cantab) G *Jul 1975*
5, 40, 7, 43
3 Verulam Buildings, London WC1
p953 . . . . . 020 7831 8441

FREEMAN, Miss Emma I *Oct 2002*
10, 12, 30, 76, 20, 63, 8, 88, 40, 38, 32
7 Harrington Street Chambers, Liverpool
p981 . . . . . 0151 242 0707

FREEMAN, Ms Lisa L *Oct 2005*
Furnival Chambers, London EC4
p934 . . . . . 020 7405 3232

FREEMAN, Mr Peter LLB(Hons) M *Oct 1992*
30, 12, 53
Farrar's Building, London EC4
p933 . . . . . 020 7583 9241

Freeman, Ms Sally Jane LLB; Pupil Supervisor L *Nov 1995*
12, 20
East Anglian Chambers, Norwich
p988 . . . . . 01603 617351
East Anglian Chambers, Colchester
p975 . . . . . 01206 572756
East Anglian Chambers, Chelmsford
p973 . . . . . 01245 215660
East Anglian Chambers, Ipswich
p976 . . . . . 01473 214481

Freemantle, Miss Kate L *Jan 2003*
2 King's Bench Walk, London EC4
p939 . . . . . 020 7353 1746

Freeston, Miss Lynn Dip M; DipCam; BA(Canada); LLB(Hons) G *Oct 1996*
10, 20
Coram Chambers, London EC1
p929 . . . . . 020 7092 3700

Freman (nee Sampson), Miss Hannah MA(Hons)(Classics) L *Jul 2004*
18, 30, 36
Old Square Chambers, Bristol
p971 . . . . . 0117 930 5100
Old Square Chambers, London WC1
p945 . . . . . 020 7269 0300

French, Mr Hugh I *Oct 2004*
Atkinson Bevan Chambers, London EC4
p924 . . . . . 020 7353 2112

French, Mr Jonathan LLB(Hons); LLM L *Nov 1997*
6, 8, 11, 12, 97, 74, 47, 48, 67, 55, 18, 38, 96, 29, 40
Exchange Chambers, Manchester
p983 . . . . . 0161 833 2722
Exchange Chambers, Liverpool
p980 . . . . . 0151 236 7747
Exchange Chambers, Leeds
p977 . . . . . 0113 203 1970

French, Mr Louis MA(Oxon) I *Nov 1979*
12, 15, 25, 62, 42
Nine Bedford Row, London WC1
p924 . . . . . 020 7489 2727

FRENCH, Miss Lucie I *Jul 2008*
20
St Philips Chambers, Birmingham
p969 . . . . . 0121 246 7000

FRENCH, Mr Paul LLB(Wolv) I *Nov 1989*
6, 8, 11, 29, 38
Guildhall Chambers, Bristol
p970 . . . . . 0117 930 9000

Frew, Mr Bruce L *Jan 2005*
York Chambers, York
p995 . . . . . 01904 620048
York Chambers, Newcastle upon Tyne
p987 . . . . . 0191 206 4677

Fridd, Mr Nicholas MA(Oxon) I *Nov 1975*
15, 62
Albion Chambers, Bristol
p970 . . . . . 0117 927 2144
Bell Yard Chambers, London WC2
p926 . . . . . 020 7306 9292 / 7404 5138

FRIEDMAN, Mr Daniel BA(Hons)(Oxon); LLM(Lond) M *Oct 1996*
15, 12, 51, 56, 50, 19, 33, 1
Matrix Chambers, London WC1
p942 . . . . . 020 7404 3447

Friedman, Mr David MA(Oxon); BCL I *Jul 1968*
(Q.C.) *3, 7, 11, 12, 24, 78*
4 Pump Court, London EC4
p947 . . . . . 020 7842 5555

Friel, Mr John LLB G *Jul 1974*
1, 9, 26, 76
Hardwicke, London WC2
p936 . . . . . 020 7242 2523

Friel, Miss Michele E L *Jul 1991*
20, 10
No5 Chambers, Bristol
p971 . . . . . 0845 210 5555
No5 Chambers, London EC4
p944 . . . . . 0845 210 5555
No5 Chambers, Birmingham
p968 . . . . . 0845 210 5555

FRIER, Mr Daniel LLB; BVC G *Oct 2005*
15, 10, 20
Eastbourne Chambers, Eastbourne
p975 . . . . . 01323 642102

Frieze, Mr Daniel BA(Hons)(Theology); DipLaw G *Oct 1994*
5, 6, 12, 24, 29, 30, 36
St Johns Buildings, Preston
p990 . . . . . 01772 256100
St Johns Buildings, Chester
p974 . . . . . 01244 323070
St Johns Buildings, Manchester
p985 . . . . . 0161 214 1500
St Johns Buildings, Liverpool
p982 . . . . . 0151 243 6000

Frieze, Mr Robin Bennett LLB(Leeds) L *Jul 1985*
15
No 6 Barristers Chambers, Leeds
p978 . . . . . 0113 245 9763

FRIPP, Mr Eric William Burtin MA(Hons); LLM G *Oct 1994*
1, 18, 23
Mitre House Chambers, London WC1
p942 . . . . . 020 7307 7100

Friston, Dr Mark MA; BA M *Nov 1997*
27, 30, 53
Kings Chambers, Leeds
p978 . . . . . 0113 242 1123
Kings Chambers, Manchester
p984 . . . . . 0161 832 9082

Frith, Miss Alexandra L *Feb 1993*
6, 8, 11, 12, 18, 22, 29, 30, 32, 37
Westgate Chambers, Lewes
p980 . . . . . 01273 480510

Frith, Miss Heather Vivien M *Jul 1989*
10, 20
Pendragon Chambers, Swansea
p993 . . . . . 01792 411188

Frith, Mr Nicholas John LLB; LLM G *Oct 1992*
10, 20
37 Park Square Chambers, Leeds
p978 . . . . . 0113 243 9422

Frith, Mr Timothy MA(Hons); DipLaw M *Nov 1996*
65, 5, 11, 21, 56, 97, 38, 74, 24
Devereux Chambers, London WC2
p930 . . . . . 020 7353 7534

Fritz, Mr Dan McCourt BA(Cantab); DipLaw(City) L *Jan 2007*
6, 8, 9, 11, 97, 67, 38, 24, 88, 32, 37
Serle Court, London WC2
p950 . . . . . 020 7242 6105

FRODSHAM, Mr Alexander LLB(Hons) L *Oct 1996*
12, 11, 30, 62, 47
Oriel Chambers, Liverpool
p981 . . . . . 0151 236 7191 / 236 4321
Oriel Chambers, Preston
p990 . . . . . 01772 254764

FROST, Miss Angela G *Jan 2001*
30
12 King's Bench Walk, London EC4
p940 . . . . . 020 7583 0811

Frost, Ms Nicola I *Jan 2009*
20
3PB, Bristol
p971 . . . . . 0117 928 1520

Fry, Miss Eleanor M *Nov 2007*
Park Court Chambers, Leeds
p978 . . . . . 0113 243 3277

Fry, Mr Neil LLB(Hons)(Exon) I *Feb 1992*
10, 20, 30
Coram Chambers, London EC1
p929 . . . . . 020 7092 3700

Fryer, Mr Nigel LLB M *Nov 1999*
15, 84, 68, 46, 39, 62, 94, 36, 48, 26
Queen Square Chambers, Bristol
p972 . . . . . 0117 921 1966

FRYER-SPEDDING, Mr James LLB(Hons); BCL G *Feb 1994*
6, 8, 11, 22, 29, 32, 37, 40
9 St John Street Chambers, Manchester
p984 . . . . . 0161 955 9000

Fryman, Mr Neil M *Jul 1989*
15
Lincoln House Chambers, Manchester
p984 . . . . . 0161 832 5701

FRYMANN, Mr Andrew P LLB I *Nov 1995*
15, 62, 95
187 Fleet Street, London EC4
p933 . . . . . 020 7430 7430

Fuad, Mr Kerim LLB(Hons)(Lond) I *Nov 1992*
12, 20, 15, 30, 22, 18
1 Inner Temple Lane, London EC4
p937 . . . . . 020 7427 4400

Fudakowski, Katherine L *Jan 2008*
Old Square Chambers, Bristol
p971 . . . . . 0117 930 5100
Old Square Chambers, London WC1
p945 . . . . . 020 7269 0300

FUDGE, Miss Sally L *Nov 1998*
Furnival Chambers, London EC4
p934 . . . . . 020 7405 3232

FUGALLO, Mr Daniel M *Oct 1999*
15, 62
23 Essex Street, London WC2
p932 . . . . . 020 7413 0353

Fuller, Mr Alan Peter LLB G *Oct 1993*
15, 62, 48
Albion Chambers, Bristol
p970 . . . . . 0117 927 2144

FULLER, Mr Jonathan L *Oct 1977*
(Q.C.) *15, 62, 95*
187 Fleet Street, London EC4
p933 . . . . . 020 7430 7430

FULLER, Mr Simon BA(Cantab); LLM(Cornell); Associate Member L *Oct 2003*
8, 5, 6, 11, 97, 38
South Square, London WC1
p950 . . . . . 020 7696 9900

Fuller, Mr Steven M *Jul 2008*
1, 20
Field Court Chambers, London WC1
p933 . . . . . 020 7405 6114

Fuller, Mr Stuart Kenneth MA(Cantab) I *Mar 2007*
10, 20
Albion Chambers, Bristol
p970 . . . . . 0117 927 2144
4 Brick Court Chambers, London EC4
p927 . . . . . 020 7832 3200

Fullwood, Mr Adam BA; MA(Bris) G *Mar 1996*
Kings Chambers, Leeds
p978 . . . . . 0113 242 1123
Kings Chambers, Manchester
p984 . . . . . 0161 832 9082

FURBER, Mr John MA(Cantab) I *Jul 1973*
(Q.C.) *22, 31*
Wilberforce Chambers, London WC2
p953 . . . . . 020 7306 0102

FURLONG, Mr Richard L *Jul 1994*
15, 62
25 Bedford Row, London WC1
p925 . . . . . 020 7067 1500

Furmston, Prof Philip Michael G *Oct 1960*
3, 7, 11, 49, 41
Keating Chambers, London WC2
p938 . . . . . 020 7544 2600

Furness, Mr Jonathan MA(Cantab); Recorder G *Jun 1979*
(Q.C.) *10, 12, 20*
Thirty Park Place, Cardiff
p973 . . . . . 029 2039 8421

FURNESS, Mr Michael MA(Cantab); BCL(Oxon) L *Jul 1982*
(Q.C.) *8, 9, 11, 14, 22, 29, 32, 37, 40, 34, 58, 5*
Wilberforce Chambers, London WC2
p953 . . . . . 020 7306 0102

13

Furniss, Mr Richard MA(Cantab) M *Oct 1991*
53, 11, 12, 18, 30, 40
42 Bedford Row, London WC1
p925 . . . 020 7831 0222

Furst, Mr Stephen A BA(Oxon); LLB(Leeds); Recorder M *Jul 1975*
(Q.C.) *3, 7, 11, 24, 22, 40*
Keating Chambers, London WC2
p938 . . . 020 7544 2600

FURZE, Miss Caroline BA(Hons) L *Oct 1992*
6, 8, 9, 11, 14, 17, 32, 40, 37, 29
Wilberforce Chambers, London WC2
p953 . . . 020 7306 0102

GABB, Mr Charles H LLB M *Feb 1975*
15, 25, 62, 42, 91
Pump Court Chambers, Swindon
p993 . . . 01793 539899
Pump Court Chambers, Winchester
p994 . . . 01962 868161
Pump Court Chambers, London EC4
p947 . . . 020 7353 0711

GABBITAS, Mr Christopher L *Dec 2009*
15
1 High Pavement, Nottingham
p988 . . . 0115 941 8218

GADD, Mr Adam G *Jan 2004*
15, 20, 30, 12
Pump Court Chambers, Swindon
p993 . . . 01793 539899
Pump Court Chambers, Winchester
p994 . . . 01962 868161
Pump Court Chambers, London EC4
p947 . . . 020 7353 0711

GADD, Mr Michael BA L *Jul 1981*
5, 6, 8, 11, 29, 32, 37, 40, 41, 49, 62
XXIV Old Buildings, London WC2
p944 . . . 020 7691 2424

Gadsden, Mr Mark Jeremy BA(Oxon) M *Jul 1980*
15, 62
Atkinson Bevan Chambers, London EC4
p924 . . . 020 7353 2112

Gaisford, Mr Philip David LLB(Soton) G *Nov 1969*
36, 53, 85, 27, 40
3 Serjeants' Inn, London EC4
p950 . . . 020 7427 5000

Gaisman, Mr Jonathan N C BA; BCL(Oxon) I *Nov 1979*
(Q.C.) *3, 35, 19, 33, 24, 11, 5, 40*
7 King's Bench Walk, London EC4
p940 . . . 020 7910 8300

Gaitskell, Dr Robert PhD; BSc(Eng); FIEE; CEng; FCIArb; Recorder G *Jul 1978*
(Q.C.) *3, 7, 11, 24, 40*
Keating Chambers, London WC2
p938 . . . 020 7544 2600

Gal, Miss Sonia BA I *Nov 1982*
St Johns Buildings, Preston
p990 . . . 01772 256100
St Johns Buildings, Chester
p974 . . . 01244 323070
St Johns Buildings, Manchester
p985 . . . 0161 214 1500
St Johns Buildings, Liverpool
p982 . . . 0151 243 6000

Galberg, Mr Marc MA(Oxon) M *Jul 1982*
11, 18, 22
33 Bedford Row, London WC1
p925 . . . 020 7242 6476

Galbraith-Marten, Mr Jason M *Oct 1991*
55, 18, 19, 1, 51
Cloisters, London EC4
p928 . . . 020 7827 4000

Gale, Jocelin BA(Philosophy); GDL I *Jan 2009*
41, 25, 35, 61
7 King's Bench Walk, London EC4
p940 . . . 020 7910 8300

GALE, Mr Jonathan G *Oct 2009*
Chancery House Chambers, Leeds
p977 . . . 0113 244 6691

GALE, Mr Phillip BA; BCL L *Oct 2008*
6, 8, 11, 97, 67, 38, 88, 89, 29, 32, 40, 93, 37
Enterprise Chambers, London WC2
p931 . . . 020 7405 9471
Enterprise Chambers, Leeds
p977 . . . 0113 246 0391
Enterprise Chambers, Newcastle upon Tyne
p987 . . . 0191 222 3344

Gallacher, Kirsty G *Nov 2006*
10, 20
No5 Chambers, Bristol
p971 . . . 0845 210 5555
No5 Chambers, London EC4
p944 . . . 0845 210 5555
No5 Chambers, Birmingham
p968 . . . 0845 210 5555

GALLAFENT, Miss Kate BA(Cantab) G *Oct 1997*
1, 11, 18, 41, 51, 55, 89, 56, 50, 52, 3
Blackstone Chambers, London EC4
p926 . . . 020 7583 1770

GALLAGHER, Mr Brian LLB(Bris); BL I *Jul 1975*
7, 18, 30, 40, 53
12 King's Bench Walk, London EC4
p940 . . . 020 7583 0811

Gallagher, Ms Caoilfhionn L *Oct 2006*
51, 1, 15, 76, 21, 22
Doughty Street Chambers, London WC1
p930 . . . 020 7404 1313

Gallagher, Mr John BA(Lond); AKC G *Nov 1974*
30, 53, 11, 62, 24, 40, 37
Hardwicke, London WC2
p936 . . . 020 7242 2523

GALLAGHER, Miss Maria LLB(L'pool) I *Nov 1997*
20, 23, 18, 30
Pump Court Chambers, Swindon
p993 . . . 01793 539899
Pump Court Chambers, Winchester
p994 . . . 01962 868161
Pump Court Chambers, London EC4
p947 . . . 020 7353 0711

Gallagher, Mr Patrick LLB(Lond) G *Jul 1984*
10, 20
KCH Garden Square Chambers, Nottingham
p989 . . . 0115 941 8851
KCH Garden Square Chambers, Leicester
p979 . . . 0115 941 8851

GALLAGHER, Mr Stanley Harold LLB; BEc L *Feb 1994*
93, 88
Tanfield Chambers, London WC1
p951 . . . 020 7421 5300

Galley, Mrs Helen LLB G *Jul 1987*
5, 6, 8, 11, 22, 29, 32, 37, 14, 40, 49, 62
XXIV Old Buildings, London WC2
p944 . . . 020 7691 2424

GALLIVAN, Mr Terence BA; LLB I *Jul 1981*
63, 26, 51, 22, 18, 1, 12
Arden Chambers, London WC1
p923 . . . 020 7242 4244

GALLOWAY, Mr Malcolm BA I *Oct 1992*
15, 42
Colleton Chambers, Exeter
p975 . . . 01392 274898
Old Square Chambers, Bristol
p971 . . . 0117 930 5100
Old Square Chambers, London WC1
p945 . . . 020 7269 0300

Galloway, Miss Rachel G *Oct 2004*
30, 18, 94
Kings Chambers, Leeds
p978 . . . 0113 242 1123
Kings Chambers, Manchester
p984 . . . 0161 832 9082

Galvin, Mr Kieran LLB(Hons); BA(Hons) M *Nov 1996*
15, 62
2 Bedford Row, London WC1
p924 . . . 020 7440 8888

Galway-Cooper, Mr Philip I *Jan 1993*
5 St Andrew's Hill, London EC4
p950 . . . 020 7332 5400

GAMBLE, Ms Esther M *Jul 2001*
30, 11, 12
St Philips Chambers, Birmingham
p969 . . . 0121 246 7000

GAMBLE, Helen I *Jan 1998*
Fountain Chambers, Middlesbrough
p986 . . . 01642 804040

Gamble, Mr Jamie M *Nov 1999*
30, 40, 68, 94
No5 Chambers, Bristol
p971 . . . 0845 210 5555
No5 Chambers, London EC4
p944 . . . 0845 210 5555
No5 Chambers, Birmingham
p968 . . . 0845 210 5555

GAMMIE, Mr Malcolm M *Oct 1997*
(Q.C.)
One Essex Court, London EC4
p931 . . . 020 7583 2000

Gammon, Mrs Davina BA(Hons); Head of Chambers M *Jul 1979*
10, 12, 20
Stones Throw, Tenby
p993 . . . 01834 870174

Gandhi, Miss Paulene I *Oct 1995*
23, 57
12 Old Square, London WC2
p945 . . . 020 7404 0875
Renaissance Chambers, London WC1
p949 . . . 020 7404 1111

GANESAN, Muthupandi L *Oct 2003*
Furnival Chambers, London EC4
p934 . . . 020 7405 3232

GANNER, Mr Joseph M LLB I *Jul 1983*
15
Furnival Chambers, London EC4
p934 . . . 020 7405 3232

Gannon, Mr Kevin I *May 1993*
22
1 Pump Court, London EC4
p947 . . . 020 7842 7070

Ganteaume, Ms Natalie LLB(Hons) M *Nov 2001*
42 Bedford Row, London WC1
p925 . . . 020 7831 0222

Gape, Mr Christian M *Jul 2005*
10, 20, 22, 23
Southernhay Chambers, Exeter
p975 . . . 01392 255777

Garcha, Ajmer Singh BA L *Nov 1980*
10, 12, 15, 20, 22, 25
1 Argyle Road, Wolverhampton
p994 . . . 01902 561047

GARCHA, Mr Gurdeep Singh BA(Hons) L *Nov 1997*
15, 51
Citadel Chambers, Birmingham
p967 . . . 0121 233 8500

Garcha, Mr Sukdev M *Jan 2008*
15, 23
Paradise Chambers, Sheffield
p992 . . . 0114 273 8951

GARDEN, Mr Ian LLB(Hons) L *Jul 1989*
17
Oriel Chambers, Liverpool
p981 . . . 0151 236 7191 / 236 4321
Oriel Chambers, Preston
p990 . . . 01772 254764

Gardiner, Mr Bruce MA(Oxon) M *Nov 1994*
11, 12, 18, 30, 40
2 Temple Gardens, London EC4
p952 . . . 020 7822 1200

GARDINER, Miss Helen G *Oct 2007*
66, 6, 11, 12, 47, 67, 18, 38, 35
Chancery House Chambers, Leeds
p977 . . . 0113 244 6691

GARDINER, Mr John R MA; LLM(Cantab) M *Nov 1968*
(Q.C.) *34, 57, 58*
11 New Square, London WC2
p943 . . . 020 7242 4017

Gardiner, Ms Kerry M *Jan 2006*
18, 55, 48
Queen Square Chambers, Bristol
p972 . . . 0117 921 1966

GARDINER, Mr Sebastian I *Oct 1997*
15
25 Bedford Row, London WC1
p925 . . . 020 7067 1500

GARDNER, Mr Alan BA(Hons) M *Jan 1997*
15, 10, 12, 20, 30
1 King's Bench Walk, London EC4
p938 . . . 020 7936 1500

Gardner, Miss Eilidh LLB(Hons)(Newc) M *Oct 1997*
10, 20, 12
42 Bedford Row, London WC1
p925 . . . 020 7831 0222

Gardner, Miss Francesca LLB L *Oct 2004*
12, 27, 30
Kings Chambers, Leeds
p978 . . . 0113 242 1123
Kings Chambers, Manchester
p984 . . . 0161 832 9082

GARDNER, Mr Piers MA(Oxon) G *Mar 2000*
19, 51, 44
Monckton Chambers, London WC1
p942 . . . 020 7405 7211

Gargan, Miss Catherine J LLB(L'pool) M *Jul 1978*
10, 20, 26, 14
36 Bedford Row, London WC1
p925 . . . 020 7421 8000

Gargan, Mr Mark Patrick MA(Oxon); Recorder M *Jul 1983*
11, 30, 18, 40, 27, 49
No 6 Barristers Chambers, Leeds
p978 . . . 0113 245 9763

GARGITTER, Ms Emma L *Nov 2003*
15, 62, 94, 95
18 Red Lion Court, London EC4
p949 . . . 020 7520 6000
18 Red Lion Court (Annexe), Chelmsford
p973 . . . 01245 280880

GARLAND, Mr David LLB; AKC; LLM(Lond) M *Nov 1986*
11, 40, 5, 24, 35
Brick Court Chambers, London WC2
p927 . . . 020 7379 3550

GARLICK, Mr Paul M *Jan 1973*
(Q.C.)
Furnival Chambers, London EC4
p934 . . . 020 7405 3232

Garn, Miss Jennifer I *Jan 2006*
5 Paper Buildings, London EC4
p946 . . . 020 7583 6117

GARNER, Ms Sophie M *Oct 1990*
18, 55
St Philips Chambers, Birmingham
p969 . . . 0121 246 7000

GARNER, Mr Stephen G *Oct 1994*
30
Guildhall Chambers, Bristol
p970 . . . 0117 930 9000
Zenith Chambers, Leeds
p979 . . . 0113 245 5438

Garnham, Clare LLB G *Jan 2005*
10, 20, 23, 51, 55, 63, 64, 80
Zenith Chambers, Leeds
p979 . . . 0113 245 5438

GARNHAM, Mr Neil MA(Cantab); Recorder M *Jul 1982*
(Q.C.) *1, 18, 23, 27, 30, 40, 51, 53, 55, 56*
1 Crown Office Row, London EC4
p929 . . . 020 7797 7500

GARNIER, Mr Edward H MA(Oxon) M *Jul 1976*
(Q.C.) *16, 52, 73*
One Brick Court, London EC4
p927 . . . 020 7353 8845

Garrett, Miss Lucy BA(Hons); PGDL G *Oct 2001*
3, 24, 7, 40, 61
Keating Chambers, London WC2
p938 . . . 020 7544 2600

Garrett, Mr Luke BSc; MA G *Jul 2005*
30, 18, 11
Thirty Park Place, Cardiff
p973 . . . 029 2039 8421

GARRETT, Mr Michael Owen LLB(Hons) G *Jul 1967*
15, 62
St Philips Chambers, Birmingham
p969 . . . 0121 246 7000

Garrido, Mr Damian BA(Hons) M *Nov 1993*
20, 10
Harcourt Chambers, London EC4
p936 . . . 0844 561 7135
Harcourt Chambers, Oxford
p989 . . . 0844 561 7135

Garrod, Mr Neil LLB I *Jan 2000*
15, 23, 18
Warwick House Chambers, London WC1
p953 . . . 020 7430 2323

GARSIDE, Mr Charles G *Nov 1971*
(Q.C.) *11, 12, 15, 18, 30, 62, 1*
Bank House Chambers, Sheffield
p991 . . . 0114 275 1223
Nine Bedford Row, London WC1
p924 . . . 020 7489 2727
9 St John Street Chambers, Manchester
p984 . . . 0161 955 9000

Garside, Mr David LLB G *Nov 1982*
7, 10, 12, 15, 20, 22, 25, 26, 30
St Johns Buildings, Preston
p990 . . . 01772 256100
St Johns Buildings, Chester
p974 . . . 01244 323070
St Johns Buildings, Manchester
p985 . . . 0161 214 1500

See p1010 for the Key to Work Categories

St Johns Buildings, Liverpool
p982 . . . . . 0151 243 6000
Garside, Mr Mark I *Feb 1993*
10, 20
Exchange Chambers, Manchester
p983 . . . . . 0161 833 2722
Exchange Chambers, Liverpool
p980 . . . . . 0151 236 7747
Exchange Chambers, Leeds
p977 . . . . . 0113 203 1970
St Philips Chambers, Birmingham
p969 . . . . . 0121 246 7000
GARSON, Mr Robert I *Nov 1999*
15, 62
Furnival Chambers, London EC4
p934 . . . . . 020 7405 3232
GARTH, Mr Steven David G *Nov 1983*
15
Wilberforce Chambers, Hull
p976 . . . . . 01482 323264
Gartland, Ms Dorothea I *Jan 2004*
20, 10
4 Paper Buildings, London EC4
p946 . . . . . 020 7583 0816
GARVIE, Mr Carl L *Mar 2008*
11, 67, 40, 69
St Philips Chambers, Birmingham
p969 . . . . . 0121 246 7000
Garwood, Mr Joshua M *Jan 1992*
20, 10, 15
1 Pump Court, London EC4
p947 . . . . . 020 7842 7070
GASH, Mr Simon G *Jul 1977*
30, 40, 53
Ropewalk Chambers, Nottingham
p989 . . . . . 0115 947 2581
Gask, Mr Alex BA(Hons)(Oxon) M *Jan 2008*
15, 51, 23, 21, 52, 16, 70, 1
Doughty Street Chambers, London WC1
p930 . . . . . 020 7404 1313
GASPARRO, Julia L *Jul 1999*
10, 20, 23
Renaissance Chambers, London WC1
p949 . . . . . 020 7404 1111
Gassman, Miss Caroline LLB(Leeds) I *Jul 1974*
1 Mitre Court Buildings, London EC4
p942 . . . . . 020 7452 8900
GASTON, Mr Graeme LLB(Leeds) L *Jul 1991*
15, 12
Fountain Chambers, Middlesbrough
p986 . . . . . 01642 804040
Gasztowicz, Mr Steven LLB(Nott'm) G *Jul 1981*
(Q.C.) *1, 6, 8, 11, 12, 18, 22, 24, 26, 29, 30, 31, 36, 37, 40*
Cornerstone Barristers, London WC1
p929 . . . . . 020 7242 4986
GATENBY, Mr James LLB M *Oct 1994*
10, 20, 12
Chavasse Court Chambers, Liverpool
p980 . . . . . 0151 229 2030
Gates, Mr Harry BA(Hons); LLB L *Nov 2001*
20, 10
4 Paper Buildings, London EC4
p946 . . . . . 020 7583 0816
Gates, Miss Serena M *Jan 2001*
15
5 St Andrew's Hill, London EC4
p950 . . . . . 020 7332 5400
GATESHILL, Mr J Bernard MA; Recorder L *Jul 1972*
15, 53, 30, 40
Wilberforce Chambers, Hull
p976 . . . . . 01482 323264
Gatland, Mr Glenn LLB G *Nov 1972*
4, 12, 15
New Court Chambers, Newcastle upon Tyne
p987 . . . . . 0191 232 1980
Gatley, Mr Mark G *Oct 1993*
15, 62
Argent Chambers, London WC2
p923 . . . . . 020 7556 5500
GATTO, Ms Nicola LLB(Hons)(B'ham) M *Nov 1987*
15, 20, 25
9 St John Street Chambers, Manchester
p984 . . . . . 0161 955 9000
Gatty, Mr Daniel BA(Hons)(Econ) M *Aug 1990*
22, 5, 6, 7, 8, 11, 45, 29, 40, 37
Hardwicke, London WC2
p936 . . . . . 020 7242 2523
GAU, Mr Justin LLB(Lond) M *Jul 1989*
15, 36
Pump Court Chambers, Swindon
p993 . . . . . 01793 539899
Pump Court Chambers, Winchester
p994 . . . . . 01962 868161
Pump Court Chambers, London EC4
p947 . . . . . 020 7353 0711
Gault, Mr Simon LLB(Newc) G *Nov 1970*
35, 3, 24
Quadrant Chambers, London EC4
p948 . . . . . 020 7583 4444
GAUNT, Mr Jonathan BA(Oxon) L *Jul 1972*
(Q.C.)
Falcon Chambers, London EC4
p933 . . . . . 020 7353 2484
Gaunt, Miss Sarah LLB(Wales); M Phil(Cantab) L *Oct 1992*
15, 12, 22
36 Bedford Row, London WC1
p925 . . . . . 020 7421 8000
GAVAGHAN, Mr Jonathan BA; BCL(Oxon) L *Nov 1992*
1, 5, 6, 7, 8, 9, 11, 14, 18, 19, 22, 29, 32, 37
Ten Old Square, London WC2
p945 . . . . . 020 7405 0758
Gayford, Ms Justine LLB(Hons) M *Oct 2005*
10, 12, 20, 30
College Chambers, Southampton
p992 . . . . . 023 8023 0338
GEADAH, Mr Anthony LLB(KCL) G *Oct 2000*
10, 20
29 Bedford Row, London WC1
p925 . . . . . 020 7404 1044
GEARTY, Professor Conor BCL; LLB; PhD(Cantab) M *Jan 1995*
1, 42, 48, 15, 51, 25, 38, 50, 11, 55, 19, 33, 12
Matrix Chambers, London WC1
p942 . . . . . 020 7404 3447
Geary, Mr Gavin BA(Oxon) G *Feb 1989*
11, 35, 3, 24, 5, 40
7 King's Bench Walk, London EC4
p940 . . . . . 020 7910 8300
Gedge, Mr Simon MA(Oxon) I *Nov 1984*
15
1 Inner Temple Lane, London EC4
p937 . . . . . 020 7427 4400
Gedrych, Miss Janet LLB(Hons) G *Oct 2000*
15
Angel Chambers, Swansea
p992 . . . . . 01792 464623
Gee, Ms Caroline G *Jan 2003*
20
Exchange Chambers, Manchester
p983 . . . . . 0161 833 2722
Exchange Chambers, Liverpool
p980 . . . . . 0151 236 7747
Exchange Chambers, Leeds
p977 . . . . . 0113 203 1970
Gee, Mr Steven M MA(Oxon) M *Jul 1975*
(Q.C.) *3, 5, 8, 11, 35, 36*
Stone Chambers, London WC1
p951 . . . . . 020 7440 6900
GEE, Mr Toby BA(Cantab) I *Oct 1992*
53, 27, 40, 30, 84, 24, 11, 12, 74, 7, 96, 33
Crown Office Chambers, London EC4
p929 . . . . . 020 7797 8100
GEEKIE, Mr Charles LLB(Bris) I *Jul 1985*
(Q.C.) *10, 20*
1 Garden Court, London EC4
p934 . . . . . 020 7797 7900
St Mary's Chambers, Nottingham
p989 . . . . . 0115 950 3503
GEERING, Mr Ian Associate Member I *Nov 1974*
(Q.C.) *5, 11, 24, 40*
3 Verulam Buildings, London WC1
p953 . . . . . 020 7831 8441
GEESON, Mr Christopher G *Nov 1989*
15
1 High Pavement, Nottingham
p988 . . . . . 0115 941 8218
GEEY, Mr David S LLB; Recorder I *Jul 1970*
53, 30, 62, 15, 40, 21
7 Harrington Street Chambers, Liverpool
p981 . . . . . 0151 242 0707
Gelbart, Mr Geoffrey Alan BA; LLM L *Nov 1982*
6, 8
1 Gray's Inn Square, London WC1
p935 . . . . . 020 7405 8946
Genn, Ms Yvette BA; Dip I *Oct 1991*
1, 3, 8, 12, 13, 18, 22, 23, 26, 30, 36, 38, 51
Cloisters, London EC4
p928 . . . . . 020 7827 4000
GENNEY, Mr Paul W BDS M *May 1976*
15
Wilberforce Chambers, Hull
p976 . . . . . 01482 323264
GENTLEMAN, Mr Tom MA(Oxon) L *Jan 2005*
6, 11, 97, 62, 38
4 Stone Buildings, London WC2
p951 . . . . . 020 7242 5524
George, Mr Andrew MA(Oxon) G *Oct 1997*
1, 11, 24, 41, 5, 81, 52, 50, 56, 89
Blackstone Chambers, London EC4
p926 . . . . . 020 7583 1770
George, Mr Charles MA(Oxon) I *Jul 1974*
(Q.C.) *1, 12, 46, 17, 51, 26, 28, 31, 60, 36*
Francis Taylor Building, London EC4
p934 . . . . . 020 7353 8415
George, Mr Dean G *Jul 2002*
15, 62, 51
2 Bedford Row, London WC1
p924 . . . . . 020 7440 8888
George, Mr Donald E J G *Jul 1973*
15, 20, 22, 23, 18
Leone Chambers, Harrow
p976 . . . . . 020 8868 2736
George, Miss Eve LLB(Hons) I *Oct 1997*
15, 20
St Albans Chambers, St Albans
p992 . . . . . 01727 843383
George, Mr Mark BA(Cantab) I *Nov 1976*
(Q.C.) *15, 51, 36, 72, 70, 82, 62, 95*
Garden Court North Chambers, Manchester
p983 . . . . . 0161 236 1840
George, Mr Michael Robert LLB G *Dec 1990*
10, 12, 20, 24, 30
Goldsmith Chambers, London EC4
p935 . . . . . 020 7353 6802
George, Mr Nicholas LLB I *Jul 1983*
30, 8
New Walk Chambers, Leicester
p979 . . . . . 0871 200 1298
GEORGE, Miss Sarah BA(Cantab); Part-time Employment Tribunal Judge M *Oct 1991*
18, 55
St Philips Chambers, Birmingham
p969 . . . . . 0121 246 7000
George, Ms Susan LLB(Hons) G *Nov 1990*
10, 20
Coram Chambers, London EC1
p929 . . . . . 020 7092 3700
George, Mr Timothy David I *Oct 2000*
KCH Garden Square Chambers, Nottingham
p989 . . . . . 0115 941 8851
KCH Garden Square Chambers, Leicester
p979 . . . . . 0115 941 8851
Georgiou, Ms Angela LLB(Hons) I *Oct 1997*
12, 30, 53, 59
Cobden House Chambers, Manchester
p983 . . . . . 0161 833 6000
GERASIMIDIS, Mr Nicolas LLB(Hons) I *Nov 1988*
15, 62
Guildhall Chambers, Bristol
p970 . . . . . 0117 930 9000
Germain, Mr Richard I *Jul 1968*
15, 51
Nine Bedford Row, London WC1
p924 . . . . . 020 7489 2727
German, Miss Kelly LLB(Hons) L *Jul 2000*
12, 15, 20, 91
Eastbourne Chambers, Eastbourne
p975 . . . . . 01323 642102
Gerry, Ms Alison LLB; LLM I *Jan 2003*
1, 15, 51, 63, 22, 21
Doughty Street Chambers, London WC1
p930 . . . . . 020 7404 1313
Gerry, Miss Felicity M *Jan 1994*
95, 15, 62, 10, 63, 46
36 Bedford Row, London WC1
p925 . . . . . 020 7421 8000
2 New Street, Leicester
p979 . . . . . 0116 262 5906
Gersch, Mr Adam LLB(Hons) L *Oct 1993*
62, 15
Argent Chambers, London WC2
p923 . . . . . 020 7556 5500
GESER, Miss Anita G *Jul 1992*
Pallant Chambers, Chichester
p974 . . . . . 01243 784538
Ghaffar, Mr Arshad LLB(Hons)(Exeter); LLM(Cantab) M *Oct 1991*
3, 4, 5, 24, 11, 19, 35, 6, 49, 62
XXIV Old Buildings, London WC2
p944 . . . . . 020 7691 2424
Ghaffar, Mr Rasib LLB(Hons); LLM L *Jun 1995*
15, 20, 23
12 Old Square, London WC2
p945 . . . . . 020 7404 0875
GHALY, Mr Karim I *Jul 2001*
1, 11, 23, 30, 40
Thirty Nine Essex Street, London WC2
p932 . . . . . 020 7832 1111
GHOSH, Mr Julian LLB(Edin); LLM(Lond) L *Jul 1993*
(Q.C.) *34, 57, 58*
Pump Court Tax Chambers, London WC1
p948 . . . . . 020 7414 8080
GIBAUD, Miss Catherine BBusSc(Hons) G *Oct 1996*
5, 6, 11, 24, 40
3 Verulam Buildings, London WC1
p953 . . . . . 020 7831 8441
Gibb, Miss Fiona M LLB(B'ham); Barrister M *Jul 1983*
10, 20
Coram Chambers, London EC1
p929 . . . . . 020 7092 3700
GIBB, Ms Katherine Anne BA(Hons)(Oxon) G *Oct 1999*
8, 11, 40, 38, 18, 97
Guildhall Chambers, Bristol
p970 . . . . . 0117 930 9000
Gibbon, Ms Juliet LLB; Legal Advisor to Care Counsel for Wales; And NMC L *Jan 1994*
20, 10
Temple Chambers, Newport
p988 . . . . . 01633 267403 / 255855
Temple Chambers, Cardiff
p973 . . . . . 029 2039 7364
Gibbon, Mr Michael BA(Hons)(Oxon); MPhil(Cantab); Junior Counsel to Crown A Panel G *Nov 1993*
(Q.C.)
Maitland Chambers, London WC2
p941 . . . . . 020 7406 1200
Gibbon, Miss Zoe I *Jan 2009*
No 3 Fleet Street Chambers, London EC4
p944 . . . . . 020 7936 4474
Gibbons, Mr Christopher C BSc G *Jul 1977*
15, 20, 3, 6, 11, 18, 36, 22
4 Rowchester Court, Birmingham
p968 . . . . . 0121 233 2327
GIBBONS, Miss Ellodie I *Oct 1999*
67, 93, 88
Tanfield Chambers, London WC1
p951 . . . . . 020 7421 5300
Gibbons, Mr James Francis G *Jul 1974*
8, 11, 12, 18, 29
3 Stone Buildings, London WC2
p951 . . . . . 020 7242 4937
Gibbons, Miss Mary BA; DipLaw(City) L *Mar 1999*
3, 5, 6, 8, 11, 12, 49, 24, 35, 36
Stone Chambers, London WC1
p951 . . . . . 020 7440 6900
GIBBONS, Mr Orlando LLB(Lond) G *Nov 1982*
15
10 King's Bench Walk, London EC4
p940 . . . . . 020 7353 7742
Pallant Chambers, Chichester
p974 . . . . . 01243 784538
Gibbons, Mr Perrin M *Oct 1998*
30, 53, 11, 70, 40
9 Gough Square, London EC4
p935 . . . . . 020 7832 0500
Gibbons, Ms Sarah BA(B'ham) M *Nov 1987*
20, 10
Harcourt Chambers, London EC4
p936 . . . . . 0844 561 7135
Harcourt Chambers, Oxford
p989 . . . . . 0844 561 7135
Gibbs, Ms Georgina G *Jan 2000*
15, 84
1 Paper Buildings, London EC4
p946 . . . . . 020 7353 3728

13

Gibbs, Mrs Jocelyn LLB *L Nov 1972*
1 Mitre Court Buildings, London EC4
p942 . . . . . 020 7452 8900

Gibbs, Mr Philip LLB(Hons) *I Oct 1991*
15, 18, 56, 62
KCH Garden Square Chambers, Nottingham
p989 . . . . . 0115 941 8851
KCH Garden Square Chambers, Leicester
p979 . . . . . 0115 941 8851

Gibney, Mr Malcom T P LLB(Cardiff); Recorder *I Jul 1981*
15, 18, 26, 36, 70, 62, 25
12 College Place, Southampton
p992 . . . . . 023 8032 0320

GIBSON, Mr Arthur George *L Jul 1980*
15, 30, 62, 40, 51
7 Harrington Street Chambers, Liverpool
p981 . . . . . 0151 242 0707

Gibson, Mr Charles BA(Dunelm); Recorder *I Jul 1984*
(Q.C.) *1, 12, 24, 27, 30, 36, 40, 48*
Henderson Chambers, London EC4
p937 . . . . . 020 7583 9020

Gibson, Mr Christopher BA(Law); Recorder *M Oct 1976*
(Q.C.) *27, 51, 53, 30*
Doughty Street Chambers, London WC1
p930 . . . . . 020 7404 1313

Gibson, Miss Claire Michelle *L Oct 2004*
15, 20, 30, 47, 48, 59
Broad Chare Chambers, Newcastle upon Tyne
p986 . . . . . 0191 232 0541

Gibson, Mr John LLB(Durham) *I Nov 1991*
1, 12, 20, 22, 30, 36
36 Bedford Row, London WC1
p925 . . . . . 020 7421 8000

Gibson, Mr John Arthur LLB *L Nov 1993*
15, 25
St Johns Buildings, Preston
p990 . . . . . 01772 256100
St Johns Buildings, Chester
p974 . . . . . 01244 323070
St Johns Buildings, Manchester
p985 . . . . . 0161 214 1500
St Johns Buildings, Liverpool
p982 . . . . . 0151 243 6000

GIBSON, Mr Nicholas MA(Cantab); PgDL(Notts); LLM(Kings); Former Solicitor *L Jan 2009*
1, 3, 11, 18, 19, 33, 41, 43, 44, 47, 51, 56, 57, 61, 67, 80, 89
Matrix Chambers, London WC1
p942 . . . . . 020 7404 3447

Gibson-Lee, Mr David LLB *L Jul 1970*
15, 62, 12, 82, 94
Bell Yard Chambers, London WC2
p926 . . . . . 020 7306 9292 / 7404 5138

Giddens, Miss Sarah LLB *L Oct 1999*
15, 62
Atkinson Bevan Chambers, London EC4
p924 . . . . . 020 7353 2112

GIDNEY, Mr Jonathan *I Jun 1991*
18, 55
St Philips Chambers, Birmingham
p969 . . . . . 0121 246 7000

GIFFIN, Mr Nigel MA(Oxon) *I Nov 1986*
(Q.C.) *1, 11, 18, 19, 26, 36, 46, 55, 51*
11KBW, London EC4
p938 . . . . . 020 7632 8500

Gifford, Lord Anthony MA(Cantab) *M Jul 1962*
(Q.C.)
1 Mitre Court Buildings, London EC4
p942 . . . . . 020 7452 8900

GILBART, Mr Tom LLB *M Jan 2003*
15
9 St John Street Chambers, Manchester
p984 . . . . . 0161 955 9000

Gilbert, Mr Barry LLB(Hons); Dip Arabic *G Jul 1978*
15, 62
2 Bedford Row, London WC1
p924 . . . . . 020 7440 8888

GILBERT, Daniella *I Mar 2007*
10, 12, 72, 18, 20, 91, 42, 30, 32, 36
Pump Court Chambers, Swindon
p993 . . . . . 01793 539899
Pump Court Chambers, Winchester
p994 . . . . . 01962 868161
Pump Court Chambers, London EC4
p947 . . . . . 020 7353 0711

GILBERT, Mr Francis P BD; MA(Exon); Dip *L Jul 1980*
15, 25, 12, 62, 70
Mitre House Chambers, London WC1
p942 . . . . . 020 7307 7100

GILBERT, Mr Robert LLB(L'pool) *M Jul 1986*
10, 12, 15, 18, 20, 30
Fountain Chambers, Middlesbrough
p986 . . . . . 01642 804040

Gilberthorpe, Mr James *M Jan 2002*
53, 40, 30, 27
Hailsham Chambers, London EC4
p936 . . . . . 020 7643 5000

GILBERTSON, Ms Helen LLB(Hons) *M Nov 1993*
20
Octagon House, Norwich
p988 . . . . . 01603 623186

GILCHRIST, Mr David Somerled BA(Dunelm) *I Nov 1987*
5, 8, 11, 22, 6, 40
9 St John Street Chambers, Manchester
p984 . . . . . 0161 955 9000

GILCHRIST, Ms Naomi *I Jan 1996*
15, 25, 83, 47, 48, 46, 62
St Philips Chambers, Birmingham
p969 . . . . . 0121 246 7000

GILEAD, Miss Beryl L BA(Keele) *I Feb 1989*
10, 12, 20
St Mary's Chambers, Nottingham
p989 . . . . . 0115 950 3503

Giles, Mr David W LLB *L Nov 1988*
6, 8, 9, 15, 20, 22, 25, 37
1 Gray's Inn Square, London WC1
p935 . . . . . 020 7405 8946

GILES, Miss Molly LLB(Hons)(Dunelm) *G Jul 2005*
10, 20, 12, 93
Cornwall Street Chambers, Birmingham
p967 . . . . . 0121 233 7500

Giles, Mr Roger S *G Jul 1976*
31, 30, 46
No5 Chambers, Bristol
p971 . . . . . 0845 210 5555
No5 Chambers, London EC4
p944 . . . . . 0845 210 5555
No5 Chambers, Birmingham
p968 . . . . . 0845 210 5555

GILL, Mr Anthony *L Jan 2008*
1, 26, 30, 31, 48
Kings Chambers, Leeds
p978 . . . . . 0113 242 1123
Kings Chambers, Manchester
p984 . . . . . 0161 832 9082

GILL, Ms Baljinder BA *I Oct 1996*
20, 23, 51
10 King's Bench Walk, London EC4
p940 . . . . . 020 7353 7742

Gill, Gurnam BSc *M Nov 1978*
15, 20, 18, 23, 12
4 Rowchester Court, Birmingham
p968 . . . . . 0121 233 2327

Gill, Ms Jane *G Jul 1973*
Field Court Chambers, London WC1
p933 . . . . . 020 7405 6114

Gill, Mr Manjit *G Jul 1982*
(Q.C.) *1, 11, 71, 55, 14, 73, 18, 46, 19, 85, 51, 23, 21, 63, 33, 95, 36*
No5 Chambers, Bristol
p971 . . . . . 0845 210 5555
No5 Chambers, London EC4
p944 . . . . . 0845 210 5555
No5 Chambers, Birmingham
p968 . . . . . 0845 210 5555

GILL, Ms Meena BA(Hons)(Leics) *M Jul 1982*
20
Coram Chambers, London EC1
p929 . . . . . 020 7092 3700

Gill, Mr Ned LLB *M Jul 2004*
Iscoed Chambers, Swansea
p993 . . . . . 01792 652988

Gill, Miss Pamila LLB(Hons) *L Apr 1989*
10, 12, 15, 20, 30, 36
Goldsmith Chambers, London EC4
p935 . . . . . 020 7353 6802

Gill, Ms Tess BA(Manc); Part-Time Employment Tribunal Chair *L Feb 1990*
18, 19, 51, 26, 55, 36, 27, 10
Old Square Chambers, Bristol
p971 . . . . . 0117 930 5100
Old Square Chambers, London WC1
p945 . . . . . 020 7269 0300

Gillan, Ms Dominique LLB(Queens) *G Oct 1998*
10, 12, 15, 16, 20, 22, 25, 27, 30, 40
Guildford Chambers, Guildford
p975 . . . . . 01483 539131

Gillan, Shauna *L Jan 2006*
15
1 Pump Court, London EC4
p947 . . . . . 020 7842 7070

GILLARD, Miss Isabelle *M Jul 1980*
Carmelite Chambers, London EC4
p927 . . . . . 020 7936 6300

GILLESPIE, Miss Jane *I Oct 2001*
10, 20
St Mary's Chambers, Nottingham
p989 . . . . . 0115 950 3503

GILLET, Ms Emily LLB(Lond) *L Oct 2005*
8, 11
New Square Chambers, London WC2
p943 . . . . . 020 7419 8000

Gillett, Miss Amanda Josephine LLB(Hons)(Soton) *G Oct 1998*
10, 12, 14, 20, 63
College Chambers, Southampton
p992 . . . . . 023 8023 0338

Gillette, Mr John LLB *M Jul 1990*
15, 72, 70
Old Court Chambers, Middlesbrough
p986 . . . . . 01642 232523

Gilliatt, Ms Jacqueline BA(Hons)(Oxon); DipLaw *M Feb 1992*
20, 10, 76
4 Brick Court Chambers, London EC4
p927 . . . . . 020 7832 3200

Gillies, Miss Jennie MA(Cantab) *M Nov 2000*
40, 24, 7, 89
4 Pump Court, London EC4
p947 . . . . . 020 7842 5555

Gilliland, His Hon David *G Nov 1964*
(Q.C.)
Kings Chambers, Leeds
p978 . . . . . 0113 242 1123
Kings Chambers, Manchester
p984 . . . . . 0161 832 9082

GILLING, Denise LLB(Hons) *L Oct 1992*
8, 10, 12, 15, 20, 22, 23, 30
Renaissance Chambers, London WC1
p949 . . . . . 020 7404 1111

Gillis, Mr Richard *L Nov 1982*
(Q.C.)
One Essex Court, London EC4
p931 . . . . . 020 7583 2000

GILLMAN, Miss Rachel *G Jul 1988*
1 Garden Court, London EC4
p934 . . . . . 020 7797 7900

Gillott, Mr Paul Alan Anthony BA(Hons); CPE(City) *M Oct 1996*
12, 20, 30, 56, 25
15 Winckley Square, Preston
p991 . . . . . 01772 252828

GILLYON, Mr Philip MA(Cantab) *M Jul 1988*
11, 38, 97
Erskine Chambers, London WC2
p931 . . . . . 020 7242 5532

Gilman, Mr Jonathan C B MA(Oxon) *M Feb 1965*
(Q.C.)
Essex Court Chambers, London WC2
p931 . . . . . 020 7813 8000

Gilmore, Miss Alexandra *L Jul 2005*
Goldsmith Chambers, London EC4
p935 . . . . . 020 7353 6802

Gilmore, Miss Seanin MA *G Nov 1996*
8, 12, 24, 40
Four New Square, London WC2
p943 . . . . . 020 7822 2000

Gilmour, Miss Susan LLB(Hons) *I Nov 1994*
1, 6, 7, 8, 11, 12, 29, 31, 32, 36, 37, 40
Cobden House Chambers, Manchester
p983 . . . . . 0161 833 6000

Gilroy, Mr Paul LLB(Hons) *G Jul 1985*
(Q.C.) *18, 36*
Old Square Chambers, Bristol
p971 . . . . . 0117 930 5100
Old Square Chambers, London WC1
p945 . . . . . 020 7269 0300
9 St John Street Chambers, Manchester
p984 . . . . . 0161 955 9000

GIMLETTE, Mr John BA(Cantab) *I Nov 1986*
12, 20, 27, 30, 36
1 Crown Office Row, London EC4
p929 . . . . . 020 7797 7500

Gingell, Ms Melanie LLB(Lond) *M Jan 1988*
20, 10
Tooks Chambers, London EC4
p953 . . . . . 020 7842 7575

GINNIFF, Nigel LLB(Hull) *I Nov 1978*
34, 18, 55, 8
Atlantic Chambers, Liverpool
p980 . . . . . 0151 236 4421

Ginsburg, Mrs Amanda LLB *L Jul 1985*
10, 14, 20
37 Park Square Chambers, Leeds
p978 . . . . . 0113 243 9422

Gioserano, Mr Richard Stephen LLB(Newc) *G Nov 1992*
15, 18, 30
No 6 Barristers Chambers, Leeds
p978 . . . . . 0113 245 9763

GIOVANNETTI, Miss Lisa LLB *G Oct 1990*
(Q.C.) *1, 23, 51, 26, 14*
Thirty Nine Essex Street, London WC2
p932 . . . . . 020 7832 1111

Giovannini, Mrs Angela *G Nov 2000*
20, 63
Broad Chare Chambers, Newcastle upon Tyne
p986 . . . . . 0191 232 0541
Trinity (Newcastle) Chambers, Newcastle upon Tyne
p987 . . . . . 0191 232 1927
Trinity (Teesside) Chambers, Middlesbrough
p986 . . . . . 01642 247569

GIOVENE, Mr Laurence MA(Cantab) *L Jul 1962*
15
2 Pump Court, London EC4
p947 . . . . . 020 7353 5597

Giret, Ms Jane DipLaw *I Jul 1981*
(Q.C.) *5, 6, 8, 11, 38*
11 Stone Buildings, London WC2
p951 . . . . . 020 7831 6381

Girolami, Mr Paul Julian BA(Cantab); Deputy High Court Judge; Accredited Mediator *M Nov 1983*
(Q.C.)
Maitland Chambers, London WC2
p941 . . . . . 020 7406 1200

Gist, Mr Robin PgDL; BVC; MSci(Hons) *G Jul 2004*
11, 6, 38, 88, 30
Lamb Chambers, London EC4
p941 . . . . . 020 7797 8300

GITTINS, Mr Timothy James LLB; Recorder *M Oct 1990*
15, 46, 70
Trinity (Newcastle) Chambers, Newcastle upon Tyne
p987 . . . . . 0191 232 1927
Trinity (Teesside) Chambers, Middlesbrough
p986 . . . . . 01642 247569

GIZ, Ms Alev LLB(Hons)(Lond) *G Oct 1988*
10, 20, 51
1 Garden Court, London EC4
p934 . . . . . 020 7797 7900

Glaister-Young, Ms Shelly *I Jan 2004*
15, 20
Staple Inn Chambers, London WC1
p951 . . . . . 020 7242 5240

Glancy, Mr Robert MA(Cantab) *M Jul 1972*
(Q.C.) *1, 7, 11, 12, 24, 27, 30, 36, 40*
Devereux Chambers, London WC2
p930 . . . . . 020 7353 7534

Glanville, Miss Susan Elizabeth BA(Hons)(Lond) *I Oct 1991*
10, 20
3 Dr Johnson's Buildings, London EC4
p930 . . . . . 020 7353 4854

Glaser, Mr Michael Samson *M Oct 1998*
14 Gray's Inn Square, London WC1
p936 . . . . . 020 7242 0858

GLASGOW, Mr Edwin *G Nov 1969*
(Q.C.) *11, 12, 24, 30, 36, 40, 56, 51*
Thirty Nine Essex Street, London WC2
p932 . . . . . 020 7832 1111

Glasgow, Mr Oliver BA(Oxon) *M Nov 1995*
15, 62
2 Hare Court, London EC4
p937 . . . . . 020 7353 5324

See p1010 for the Key to Work Categories

Glass, Mr Anthony I *Jul 1965*
(Q.C.) *15, 25, 36*
QEB Hollis Whiteman, London EC4
p948 . . . . 020 7933 8855

GLASS, Miss Mary M *Oct 2001*
1, 23, 11, 51, 22
Five Paper, London EC4
p946 . . . . 020 7815 3200

Glass, Ms Mary Patricia G *Nov 2000*
23, 18, 15
Redemption Chambers, London NW11
p949 . . . . 020 8458 5486 / 07929 511917

GLASSBROOK, Mr Alexander BA(Bris) M *Oct 1995*
Temple Garden Chambers, London EC4
p952 . . . . 020 7583 1315

GLASSON, Mr Jonathan MA(Hons)(Oxon); Solicitor(Hons 1993); Former Solicitor M *Feb 1996*
1, 12, 53, 68, 71, 85, 23, 51, 27, 91, 30, 33, 95, 36, 48, 70, 84
Matrix Chambers, London WC1
p942 . . . . 020 7404 3447

Gledhill, Mr Andreas MA(Cambs) M *Nov 1992*
11, 5, 81
Blackstone Chambers, London EC4
p926 . . . . 020 7583 1770

Gledhill, Kris BA; LLM I *Jul 1989*
1, 27, 51
Camberwell Chambers, London SE5
p927 . . . . 020 7274 0830

Gledhill, Mr Orlando I *Oct 1998*
One Essex Court, London EC4
p931 . . . . 020 7583 2000

GLEN, Mr David MA(Hons)(Edin) M *Mar 2002*
16, 52, 73
One Brick Court, London EC4
p927 . . . . 020 7353 8845

Glen, Mr Ian LLB(Lond) G *Nov 1973*
(Q.C.) *1, 15, 25*
5 King's Bench Walk, London EC4
p939 . . . . 020 7353 5638

Glen, Mr Philip A LLB(Lond); Deputy District Judge M *Jul 1983*
22, 12, 88, 93
12 College Place, Southampton
p992 . . . . 023 8032 0320

Glennie, Mr Andrew MA(Oxon) M *Jul 1982*
26
King's Bench Chambers, Oxford
p989 . . . . 01865 311066

Glenser, Mr Peter I *Oct 1993*
Nine Bedford Row, London WC1
p924 . . . . 020 7489 2727

Glick, Mr Ian I *Nov 1970*
(Q.C.)
One Essex Court, London EC4
p931 . . . . 020 7583 2000

Gloag, Mr Angus LLB(Hons) I *Jan 1992*
11, 12, 47, 6, 30, 40, 36, 18, 38
1 Gray's Inn Square, London WC1
p935 . . . . 020 7405 8946
Rougemont Chambers, Exeter
p975 . . . . 01392 208484

Glover, Miss Anne-Marie BA(Hons); DipLaw M *Oct 2000*
10, 20, 63
Coram Chambers, London EC1
p929 . . . . 020 7092 3700

GLOVER, Mr Marc G *Jan 1999*
22, 12, 23
Tanfield Chambers, London WC1
p951 . . . . 020 7421 5300

Glover, Mr Richard BA(Cantab) I *Jul 1984*
(Q.C.) *1, 2, 26, 28, 31, 36, 43*
Francis Taylor Building, London EC4
p934 . . . . 020 7353 8415

Glover, Mr Stephen J LLB M *Jul 1978*
12, 20, 30, 40, 11, 53
37 Park Square Chambers, Leeds
p978 . . . . 0113 243 9422

Glyn, Mr Caspar LLB I *Nov 1992*
12, 18, 27, 30, 53, 55
Cloisters, London EC4
p928 . . . . 020 7827 4000

GLYNN, Ms Joanna BA M *Nov 1983*
(Q.C.) *68, 85, 27, 36*
1 Crown Office Row, London EC4
p929 . . . . 020 7797 7500

Glynn, Mr Stephen LLB(Bris) M *Oct 1990*
30, 40, 53
9 Gough Square, London EC4
p935 . . . . 020 7832 0500

Goatley, Mr Peter I *Jul 1992*
31, 26, 43, 78, 54, 60, 61, 46
No5 Chambers, Bristol
p971 . . . . 0845 210 5555
No5 Chambers, London EC4
p944 . . . . 0845 210 5555
No5 Chambers, Birmingham
p968 . . . . 0845 210 5555

GOBIR, Nuhu LLB(Wales); LLM M *Oct 1998*
12, 15, 23
9 Park Place, Cardiff
p973 . . . . 029 2038 2731

Goddard, Mr Andrew BA I *Nov 1985*
(Q.C.) *3, 7, 11, 31, 40, 41, 43, 45, 49, 54, 61, 78, 74*
Atkin Chambers, London WC1
p923 . . . . 020 7404 0102

Goddard, Mr Christopher LLB M *Jul 1973*
12, 27, 30, 53, 40
9 Gough Square, London EC4
p935 . . . . 020 7832 0500

GODDARD, Ms Katherine Lesley BA I *Nov 1987*
15
Bank House Chambers, Sheffield
p991 . . . . 0114 275 1223

Goddard, Mr Richard A BA(Hons) I *Mar 1999*
12, 24, 27, 30, 36, 40, 53, 56
Cobden House Chambers, Manchester
p983 . . . . 0161 833 6000

Goddard, Ms Suzanne LLB; Recorder G *Nov 1987*
(Q.C.)
Lincoln House Chambers, Manchester
p984 . . . . 0161 832 5701

GODFREY, Mr Christopher Nicholas L *Jan 1992*
10, 20
Colleton Chambers, Exeter
p975 . . . . 01392 274898

Godfrey, Miss Emma BA(Hons) L *Nov 1995*
Field Court Chambers, London WC1
p933 . . . . 020 7405 6114

Godfrey, Ms Hannah BA L *Jan 2004*
12, 18, 22, 30, 53, 55, 36, 38
Cloisters, London EC4
p928 . . . . 020 7827 4000

Godfrey, Mr Howard LLB(Hons)(Lond); Recorder M *Nov 1970*
(Q.C.) *15, 12, 62*
2 Bedford Row, London WC1
p924 . . . . 020 7440 8888

GODFREY, Mr John P BSc(Econ) G *May 1985*
20, 10
Wilberforce Chambers, Hull
p976 . . . . 01482 323264

Godfrey, Mr Lauren BA; LLB; BVC I *Jan 2007*
10, 15, 93, 11, 30, 56, 40, 26, 25, 32, 18, 88
Crown Office Row Chambers, Brighton
p970 . . . . 01273 625625

GODFREY, Mr Thomas I *Jul 2003*
23 Essex Street, London WC2
p932 . . . . 020 7413 0353

Godfrey, Mr Timothy M *Oct 1997*
15, 62, 70, 65, 39, 38, 81, 84
9 Gough Square, London EC4
p935 . . . . 020 7832 0500

Godsmark, Mr Nigel Graham LLB; Recorder M *Nov 1979*
(Q.C.) *53, 30, 15, 12, 27*
7 Bedford Row, London WC1
p924 . . . . 020 7242 3555

GODWIN, Mr William George Henry M *Nov 1986*
11, 7, 41, 40, 3
3 Hare Court, London EC4
p937 . . . . 020 7415 7800

Goff, Mr Anthony Thomas BA(Oxon) M *Jul 1978*
30
Exchange Chambers, Manchester
p983 . . . . 0161 833 2722
Exchange Chambers, Liverpool
p980 . . . . 0151 236 7747
Exchange Chambers, Leeds
p977 . . . . 0113 203 1970

Goh, Mr Allan Lee Guan LLB G *Jul 1984*
15, 62
4 Breams Buildings, London EC4
p927 . . . . 020 7092 1900

Goh, Ms Sue G *Mar 1997*
15, 20, 23
Redemption Chambers, London NW11
p949 . . . . 020 8458 5486 / 07929 511917

Gohil, Ms Pushpanjali M *Jul 2000*
15, 62, 84, 26, 94, 95
Queen Square Chambers, Bristol
p972 . . . . 0117 921 1966

Gold, Ms Debra BA(Oxon); DipLaw M *Jul 1985*
10, 20
Fenners Chambers, Cambridge
p972 . . . . 01223 368761

Gold, Mr Jeremy Recorder M *Jul 1977*
(Q.C.) *12, 15, 25, 30, 36*
Westgate Chambers, Lewes
p980 . . . . 01273 480510

Gold, Mr Richard BA(Oxon) I *Nov 2006*
8, 11, 38, 93, 5, 88, 32, 37
St John's Chambers, Bristol
p972 . . . . 0117 921 3456

Goldberg, Mr David Gerard LLM; LLB L *Jul 1971*
(Q.C.) *34, 57, 58*
Gray's Inn Tax Chambers, London WC1
p936 . . . . 020 7242 2642

Goldberg, Mr Jonathan MA; LLB(Cantab) M *Feb 1971*
(Q.C.) *8, 11, 12, 13, 15, 16, 21, 25*
Cobden House Chambers, Manchester
p983 . . . . 0161 833 6000

GOLDBERG, Mr Simon Ian BA(Oxon) M *Jul 1999*
11, 8, 18, 22, 38, 2, 88, 97
Trinity (Newcastle) Chambers, Newcastle upon Tyne
p987 . . . . 0191 232 1927
Trinity (Teesside) Chambers, Middlesbrough
p986 . . . . 01642 247569

GOLDBLATT, Mr Simon G *Jun 1953*
(Q.C.) *7, 11, 24*
Thirty Nine Essex Street, London WC2
p932 . . . . 020 7832 1111

Goldie, Miss Kate I *Oct 2004*
10, 20, 15
Albion Chambers, Bristol
p970 . . . . 0117 927 2144

Goldman, Mrs Linda M *Oct 1990*
Henderson Chambers, London EC4
p937 . . . . 020 7583 9020

GOLDREIN, Mr Iain S FRSA; MA(Cantab); Recorder I *Jul 1975*
(Q.C.) *30, 51, 23, 24, 53, 25, 40, 11*
7 Harrington Street Chambers, Liverpool
p981 . . . . 0151 242 0707

Goldring, Miss Jenny BA(Oxon) M *Nov 1993*
10, 12, 15, 30
5 St Andrew's Hill, London EC4
p950 . . . . 020 7332 5400

GOLDRING, Mr Jeremy BA(Oxon); MA(Yale) L *Oct 1996*
5, 6, 8, 11, 24, 29, 40, 97, 38
South Square, London WC1
p950 . . . . 020 7696 9900

Goldsack, Mr Ian G *May 1997*
12, 15, 30
Paradise Chambers, Sheffield
p992 . . . . 0114 273 8951

Goldsmith, Mr James G *Oct 2002*
One Essex Court, London EC4
p931 . . . . 020 7583 2000

Goldsmith, Mr Joseph L *Nov 2003*
8, 32, 22, 37, 14
5 Stone Buildings, London WC2
p951 . . . . 020 7242 6201

Goldstein, Miss Heather BA; LLDip M *Nov 1998*
15, 51
Nine Bedford Row, London WC1
p924 . . . . 020 7489 2727

Goldstein, Mr Wayne BA L *Jan 1999*
8
18 St John Street Chambers, Manchester
p985 . . . . 0161 278 1800

Goldstone, Mr David Julian MA(Cantab); BCL(Oxon); Treasury A Panel Counsel(Admiralty Junior) M *May 1986*
(Q.C.) *3, 5, 11, 35, 60*
Quadrant Chambers, London EC4
p948 . . . . 020 7583 4444

Goldstone, Mr Simon BA(Oxon)(Modern Languages) M *Jul 2004*
11, 62, 67, 40, 89, 24
4 Pump Court, London EC4
p947 . . . . 020 7842 5555

Goldwater, Mr Michael MA(Oxon) M *Jul 1977*
12, 15, 22, 27, 30, 36, 40, 51, 53
Cobden House Chambers, Manchester
p983 . . . . 0161 833 6000

Golinski, Mr Robert BA M *Oct 1990*
15
Exchange Chambers, Manchester
p983 . . . . 0161 833 2722
Exchange Chambers, Liverpool
p980 . . . . 0151 236 7747
Exchange Chambers, Leeds
p977 . . . . 0113 203 1970

Gollop, Katie BA(Oxon) G *Jan 1993*
53, 68, 18, 85, 27, 30, 40, 36
3 Serjeants' Inn, London EC4
p950 . . . . 020 7427 5000

Gomer, Mr Elis G *Jan 2008*
St Johns Buildings, Preston
p990 . . . . 01772 256100
St Johns Buildings, Chester
p974 . . . . 01244 323070
St Johns Buildings, Manchester
p985 . . . . 0161 214 1500
St Johns Buildings, Liverpool
p982 . . . . 0151 243 6000

GOMULKA, Mr Michael I *Jan 2002*
15
25 Bedford Row, London WC1
p925 . . . . 020 7067 1500

Goodall, Mr Charles BA(Hons)(Dunelm); DipLaw(City) I *Jul 1986*
16, 8, 17, 2, 38, 88, 32, 40, 93
Queen Square Chambers, Bristol
p972 . . . . 0117 921 1966

Goodall, Mr Patrick LLB(Soton); BSL I *Mar 1998*
Fountain Court Chambers, London EC4
p934 . . . . 020 7583 3335

Goodall, Miss Rachael BA(Hons)(Law & Politics) G *Jul 2000*
10, 20
3PB, Bournemouth
p969 . . . . 01202 292102

GOODBODY, Mr Peter James LLB(Hons)(Manc) L *Jul 1986*
5, 11, 18, 24, 29, 30, 12, 45, 6, 46
Oriel Chambers, Liverpool
p981 . . . . 0151 236 7191 / 236 4321
Oriel Chambers, Preston
p990 . . . . 01772 254764

Goode, Julian L *Jan 2006*
St Johns Buildings, Preston
p990 . . . . 01772 256100
St Johns Buildings, Chester
p974 . . . . 01244 323070
St Johns Buildings, Manchester
p985 . . . . 0161 214 1500
St Johns Buildings, Liverpool
p982 . . . . 0151 243 6000

Goode, Miss Rowena Margaret LLB; Recorder G *Jul 1974*
15
Exchange Chambers, Manchester
p983 . . . . 0161 833 2722
Exchange Chambers, Liverpool
p980 . . . . 0151 236 7747
Exchange Chambers, Leeds
p977 . . . . 0113 203 1970

Gooderham, Miss Elizabeth I *Jul 2001*
15, 20
Northampton Chambers, Northampton
p988 . . . . 01604 636271

GOODFELLOW, Mr Giles MA(Cantab); LLM M *Jul 1983*
(Q.C.) *34, 57, 58*
Pump Court Tax Chambers, London WC1
p948 . . . . 020 7414 8080

GOODFELLOW, Mr Nicholas BSc L *Jul 2009*
18, 11, 12, 55, 6, 56
Littleton Chambers, London EC4
p941 . . . . 020 7797 8600

Goodfellow, Mr Stephen BSc(Hons) M *Nov 1997*
18, 30, 22, 53, 41, 7, 12, 31, 40, 36
East Anglian Chambers, Norwich
p988 . . . . 01603 617351
East Anglian Chambers, Colchester
p975 . . . . 01206 572756

13

East Anglian Chambers, Chelmsford
p973 . . . . 01245 215660
East Anglian Chambers, Ipswich
p976 . . . . 01473 214481

Goodhead, Mr Thomas L *Jan 2010*
Clerksroom - Administration Centre, Taunton
p993 . . . . 0845 083 3000

Gooding, Miss Laura L *Jan 2001*
30, 15, 12, 18
Exchange Chambers, Manchester
p983 . . . . 0161 833 2722
Exchange Chambers, Liverpool
p980 . . . . 0151 236 7747
Exchange Chambers, Leeds
p977 . . . . 0113 203 1970

GOODISON, Mr Adam BA(Dunelm) M *Oct 1990*
5, 6, 8, 11, 12, 24, 29, 38
South Square, London WC1
p950 . . . . 020 7696 9900

Goodkin, Mr Daniel L *Oct 2008*
11, 12, 40, 24
4 Pump Court, London EC4
p947 . . . . 020 7842 5555

GOODLAD, Mr Grant LLB(B'ham) L *Nov 2006*
18, 30, 96
Farrar's Building, London EC4
p933 . . . . 020 7583 9241

GOODMAN, Mr Alex DipLaw; MA L *Jan 2003*
4-5 Gray's Inn Square, London WC1
p935 . . . . 020 7404 5252

Goodman, Mr Andrew LLB(Soton); ACIArb L *Jul 1978*
11, 22, 40, 49, 96
1 Chancery Lane, London WC2
p928 . . . . 0845 634 6666

Goodman, Miss Bernadette BA I *Nov 1983*
St Johns Buildings, Preston
p990 . . . . 01772 256100
St Johns Buildings, Chester
p974 . . . . 01244 323070
St Johns Buildings, Manchester
p985 . . . . 0161 214 1500
St Johns Buildings, Liverpool
p982 . . . . 0151 243 6000

GOODMAN, Mr Jonathan I *Nov 1999*
Octagon House, Norwich
p988 . . . . 01603 623186

Goodman, Mr Simon BA(Bris) G *Nov 1996*
15, 48, 84, 68, 46, 39, 62, 94, 36, 26
Queen Square Chambers, Bristol
p972 . . . . 0117 921 1966

Goodrich, Ms Siobhan G *Nov 1980*
3 Serjeants' Inn, London EC4
p950 . . . . 020 7427 5000

GOODWIN, Miss Caroline Tracy BA; Recorder I *Nov 1988*
15, 25, 2
Trinity (Newcastle) Chambers, Newcastle upon Tyne
p987 . . . . 0191 232 1927
Trinity (Teesside) Chambers, Middlesbrough
p986 . . . . 01642 247569

Goodwin, Ms Deirdre Evelyn LLB(Lond) G *Jul 1974*
King's Bench Chambers, Oxford
p989 . . . . 01865 311066
13 King's Bench Walk, London EC4
p940 . . . . 020 7353 7204

Goodwin, Mr Nicholas BA(Oxon) I *Oct 1995*
20, 10
Harcourt Chambers, London EC4
p936 . . . . 0844 561 7135
Harcourt Chambers, Oxford
p989 . . . . 0844 561 7135

Goodwin-Gill, Mr Guy BA(Oxon); MA(Oxon); DPhil(Oxon) I *Sep 1971*
33, 51, 1, 23, 89
Blackstone Chambers, London EC4
p926 . . . . 020 7583 1770

Goolamali, Ms Nina BA(Oxon) M *Oct 1995*
12, 27, 30, 24, 53
2 Temple Gardens, London EC4
p952 . . . . 020 7822 1200

Goold, Mr Alexander MA(Hons)(Cantab) L *Oct 1994*
6, 49, 11, 74, 40
Hardwicke, London WC2
p936 . . . . 020 7242 2523

Goose, Julian N LLB; Recorder L *Jul 1984*
(Q.C.) *15, 30, 62, 70, 72, 84*
Zenith Chambers, Leeds
p979 . . . . 0113 245 5438

Gorasia, Mr Paras I *Oct 2005*
30, 18, 81, 62, 84, 1
Kings Chambers, Leeds
p978 . . . . 0113 242 1123
Kings Chambers, Manchester
p984 . . . . 0161 832 9082

GORDON, Mr Ben I *Nov 2005*
Furnival Chambers, London EC4
p934 . . . . 020 7405 3232

Gordon, Miss Cathy LLB M *Jul 1989*
63, 14, 36
3 Wayside Green, Woodcote
p994 . . . . 01491 680722

Gordon, Ms Clare G *Jan 1995*
15
1 Pump Court, London EC4
p947 . . . . 020 7842 7070

Gordon, Mr James Cosmo Alexander M *Oct 2004*
15
Atkinson Bevan Chambers, London EC4
p924 . . . . 020 7353 2112

Gordon, Mr Jeremy LLB I *Jul 1974*
8, 11, 12, 30, 32, 37, 49, 96
Lamb Building, Brighton
p970 . . . . 01273 820490
Lamb Building, London EC4
p940 . . . . 020 7797 7788

Gordon, Mr Richard MA(Oxon); LLM(Lond) M *Jul 1972*
(Q.C.) *19, 1, 51*
Brick Court Chambers, London WC2
p927 . . . . 020 7379 3550

GORDON WALKER, Miss Emily Clare MA; PGDL M *Jul 2007*
18, 30
12 King's Bench Walk, London EC4
p940 . . . . 020 7583 0811

Gore, Mr Andrew Roger MA(Cantab); FCIArb; Deputy Chairman Agricultural Lands Tribunal M *Nov 1973*
1, 2, 8, 22, 26, 31
Fenners Chambers, Cambridge
p972 . . . . 01223 368761

Gore, Miss Keira BA(Hons); LLB M *Jan 2008*
1, 53, 12, 55, 18, 84, 30
Outer Temple Chambers, London WC2
p945 . . . . 020 7353 6381

Gore, Mr Mark M *Oct 1994*
10, 12, 14, 20, 30, 40
37 Park Square Chambers, Leeds
p978 . . . . 0113 243 9422

Gore, Miss Sally BA; MPhil; LLM; PhD I *Jul 2006*
14 Gray's Inn Square, London WC1
p936 . . . . 020 7242 0858

Gore, Mrs Susan Diana LLB(Hons)(UEA); BA(Hons)(Manc) M *Nov 1993*
10, 20
Coram Chambers, London EC1
p929 . . . . 020 7092 3700

GORTON, Carl BA(Hons) I *Nov 1999*
20
Atlantic Chambers, Liverpool
p980 . . . . 0151 236 4421

GORTON, Simon LLB I *Jul 1988*
(Q.C.) *18, 30*
Atlantic Chambers, Liverpool
p980 . . . . 0151 236 4421
Old Square Chambers, Bristol
p971 . . . . 0117 930 5100
Old Square Chambers, London WC1
p945 . . . . 020 7269 0300

GOSLING, Miss Deborah BA(Hons)(L'Pool) L *Mar 2004*
10, 12, 20
Chavasse Court Chambers, Liverpool
p980 . . . . 0151 229 2030

GOSLING, Mr Tom Adam L *Nov 2004*
8, 11, 12, 47, 18, 30, 40, 88
Oriel Chambers, Liverpool
p981 . . . . 0151 236 7191 / 236 4321
Oriel Chambers, Preston
p990 . . . . 01772 254764

GOTT, Mr Paul Andrew BA(Cantab); BCL(Oxon) L *Oct 1991*
Fountain Court Chambers, London EC4
p934 . . . . 020 7583 3335

Gottlieb, Mr David I *Nov 1988*
Thomas More Chambers, London WC2
p952 . . . . 020 7404 7000

Gotts, Miss Anna L *Jan 2001*
3, 11, 35, 24
7 King's Bench Walk, London EC4
p940 . . . . 020 7910 8300

Goudie, Mr Alex LLB I *Nov 2000*
15, 46, 84
Argent Chambers, London WC2
p923 . . . . 020 7556 5500

GOUDIE, Mr James LLB(Lond); FCIArb; Recorder; Deputy High Court Judge; President of National Security Panel of the Information Tribunal I *Jul 1970*
(Q.C.) *1, 11, 18, 19, 26, 50, 51, 55, 56*
11KBW, London EC4
p938 . . . . 020 7632 8500

Goudie, Mr W Martin P LLB(Hons)(Exeter) I *Oct 1996*
15, 12, 25
Charter Chambers, London WC1
p928 . . . . 020 7618 4400

Gough, Ms Emma I *Jan 2005*
York Chambers, York
p995 . . . . 01904 620048
York Chambers, Newcastle upon Tyne
p987 . . . . 0191 206 4677

GOUGH, Ms Karen Louise LLB I *Jul 1983*
41, 7, 40, 67
Thirty Nine Essex Street, London WC2
p932 . . . . 020 7832 1111

Gough, Mrs Sian LLB(Hons) G *Nov 2003*
10, 12, 20, 22, 8, 89, 96, 30, 37
College Chambers, Southampton
p992 . . . . 023 8023 0338

Gould, Mr Dennis MA(Cantab) M *Nov 1969*
25, 15
Charter Chambers, London WC1
p928 . . . . 020 7618 4400

GOULD, Mr James G *Jan 1997*
15
Bank House Chambers, Sheffield
p991 . . . . 0114 275 1223

GOULDING, Mr Jonathan LLB(Manc) I *Jul 1984*
15, 12, 39, 48, 59
Gough Square Chambers, London EC4
p935 . . . . 020 7353 0924

Goulding, Mr Paul MA; BCL(Oxon) M *Jul 1984*
(Q.C.) *1, 11, 12, 18, 19, 29, 36, 51, 55, 56, 89, 81, 5, 44*
Blackstone Chambers, London EC4
p926 . . . . 020 7583 1770

Gourgey, Mr Alan LLB(Bris) L *Jul 1984*
(Q.C.) *5, 6, 8, 11, 13, 29, 62*
11 Stone Buildings, London WC2
p951 . . . . 020 7831 6381

Gouriet, Mr Gerald William I *Jul 1974*
(Q.C.) *47, 48, 25, 46*
Francis Taylor Building, London EC4
p934 . . . . 020 7353 8415

GOURLAY, Miss Amanda Kirsten MA G *Jul 2004*
12, 20, 22, 30
Tanfield Chambers, London WC1
p951 . . . . 020 7421 5300

Gourley, Miss Claire MA(Cantab) M *Oct 1996*
30
Exchange Chambers, Manchester
p983 . . . . 0161 833 2722
Exchange Chambers, Liverpool
p980 . . . . 0151 236 7747
Exchange Chambers, Leeds
p977 . . . . 0113 203 1970

Gow, Mr Henry McCallion LLB; MA G *Oct 1995*
15, 42, 51
New Bailey Chambers, Preston
p990 . . . . 01772 258087

GOWEN, Mr Matthew LLB L *Oct 1992*
15, 36, 62, 68, 82
18 Red Lion Court, London EC4
p949 . . . . 020 7520 6000
18 Red Lion Court (Annexe), Chelmsford
p973 . . . . 01245 280880

Gower, Ms Helen MA(Oxon); LLM(Lond) M *Oct 1992*
18, 30, 55, 36
Old Square Chambers, Bristol
p971 . . . . 0117 930 5100
Old Square Chambers, London WC1
p945 . . . . 020 7269 0300

Gower, Mr Peter MA(Oxon) L *Jul 1985*
1, 12, 15, 26, 30, 31, 51
6-8 Mill Street, Maidstone
p982 . . . . 01622 688094 / 688095
6 Pump Court, London EC4
p947 . . . . 020 7797 8400

Goy, Mr David John Lister LLM M *May 1973*
(Q.C.) *34, 57, 58*
Gray's Inn Tax Chambers, London WC1
p936 . . . . 020 7242 2642

Gozem, Mr Guy LLB; Recorder M *Jul 1972*
(Q.C.)
Lincoln House Chambers, Manchester
p984 . . . . 0161 832 5701

Grabiner, Lord L *Nov 1968*
(Q.C.)
One Essex Court, London EC4
p931 . . . . 020 7583 2000

GRACE, Timothy BA(Hons)(Oxon) M *Nov 1993*
18, 30, 12, 40, 53, 84
Atlantic Chambers, Liverpool
p980 . . . . 0151 236 4421

GRAFFIUS, Mr Mark LLB M *Nov 1990*
15, 62, 95
187 Fleet Street, London EC4
p933 . . . . 020 7430 7430

Graham, Mrs Alana BA(Hons); LLB(Hons) L *Jan 1993*
Chambers of Alana Graham, Halesowen
p976 . . . . 01384 894560

GRAHAM, Ms Amina M *Jan 2010*
Furnival Chambers, London EC4
p934 . . . . 020 7405 3232

Graham, Mr Charles M *Nov 1986*
(Q.C.)
One Essex Court, London EC4
p931 . . . . 020 7583 2000

Graham, Ms Danielle G *Oct 2003*
20, 62, 31, 72, 15, 12
St Pauls Chambers, Leeds
p979 . . . . 0113 245 5866

Graham, Mr Gareth M *Jan 2006*
12, 47, 48, 55, 76, 18, 30, 94
Queen Square Chambers, Bristol
p972 . . . . 0117 921 1966

GRAHAM, Mr Michael J G BA(Hons) L *Mar 1999*
15, 2, 48, 91, 84
Trinity (Newcastle) Chambers, Newcastle upon Tyne
p987 . . . . 0191 232 1927
Trinity (Teesside) Chambers, Middlesbrough
p986 . . . . 01642 247569

Graham, Mr Roger M *Oct 1973*
30, 12, 97
Kew Chambers, Kew
p976 . . . . 0844 809 9991

Graham, Mr Stuart L *Jan 1996*
New Court Chambers, Newcastle upon Tyne
p987 . . . . 0191 232 1980

GRAHAM, Mr Thomas MA(Cantab) M *Nov 1985*
6, 11, 24, 29, 18, 8
New Square Chambers, London WC2
p943 . . . . 020 7419 8000

Graham Paul, Annabel M *Jan 2008*
1, 12, 43, 76, 18, 46, 2, 22, 51, 23, 25, 26, 54, 31, 60, 36
Francis Taylor Building, London EC4
p934 . . . . 020 7353 8415

Graham-Wells, Miss Alison BA(Hons)(Law & Sociology) I *Jul 1992*
34, 11, 38, 8, 1
Exchange Chambers, Manchester
p983 . . . . 0161 833 2722
Exchange Chambers, Liverpool
p980 . . . . 0151 236 7747
Exchange Chambers, Leeds
p977 . . . . 0113 203 1970

Grahame, Miss Nina BA; BVC M *Nov 1993*
72, 15, 70, 82, 62, 51, 91, 95
Garden Court North Chambers, Manchester
p983 . . . . 0161 236 1840

Grainger, Mr Alistair LLB(L'pool); LLM(Lond) I *Nov 1998*
King's Bench Chambers, Oxford
p989 . . . . 01865 311066
13 King's Bench Walk, London EC4
p940 . . . . 020 7353 7204

Grainger, Mr Ian I *Jul 1978*
One Essex Court, London EC4
p931 . . . . 020 7583 2000

 See p1010 for the Key to Work Categories

GRANGE, Ms Kate L *Nov 1998*
1, 7, 18, 56, 11, 23, 63, 76, 96, 14
Thirty Nine Essex Street, London WC2
p932 . . . . . 020 7832 1111

Granshaw, Ms Sara MA(Oxon) L *Oct 1991*
20, 10
Harcourt Chambers, London EC4
p936 . . . . . 0844 561 7135
Harcourt Chambers, Oxford
p989 . . . . . 0844 561 7135

GRANT, Chudi L *Nov 2002*
15, 62, 63, 70
Kenworthy's Chambers, Manchester
p984 . . . . . 0161 832 4036

Grant, Mr David E BA; BCL(Oxon) I *Mar 1999*
8, 18, 81, 29, 32, 42
Outer Temple Chambers, London WC2
p945 . . . . . 020 7353 6381

Grant, Mr Edward LLB I *Nov 1991*
20, 5, 21, 93, 67, 79, 86
No5 Chambers, Bristol
p971 . . . . . 0845 210 5555
No5 Chambers, London EC4
p944 . . . . . 0845 210 5555
No5 Chambers, Birmingham
p968 . . . . . 0845 210 5555
6-8 Mill Street, Maidstone
p982 . . . . . 01622 688094 / 688095
6 Pump Court, London EC4
p947 . . . . . 020 7797 8400

Grant, Mr Gary A BA(Oxon) M *Nov 1985*
12, 30, 26, 31, 54
12 College Place, Southampton
p992 . . . . . 023 8032 0320

Grant, Miss Jules BSc(Hons); MA M *Oct 1991*
10, 20
Crown Office Row Chambers, Brighton
p970 . . . . . 01273 625625

Grant, Miss Karen I *Jan 2004*
6 King's Bench Walk, London EC4
p939 . . . . . 020 7583 0695 / 7353 4931

GRANT, Mr Kenneth John BA(Hons) I *Mar 1998*
15, 30, 38, 62, 67
7 Harrington Street Chambers, Liverpool
p981 . . . . . 0151 242 0707

GRANT, Mr Marcus BA(Hons)(Reading) L *Oct 1993*
Temple Garden Chambers, London EC4
p952 . . . . . 020 7583 1315

Grant, Mr Murray I *Oct 2003*
King's Bench Chambers, Oxford
p989 . . . . . 01865 311066
13 King's Bench Walk, London EC4
p940 . . . . . 020 7353 7204

Grant, Miss Orla L *Jul 2005*
20, 10, 15
No5 Chambers, Bristol
p971 . . . . . 0845 210 5555
No5 Chambers, London EC4
p944 . . . . . 0845 210 5555
No5 Chambers, Birmingham
p968 . . . . . 0845 210 5555

GRANT, Miss Rebecca I *Jan 2008*
53, 12, 22, 88, 26, 30, 40
1 Chancery Lane, London WC2
p928 . . . . . 0845 634 6666

Grantham, Mr Andrew Timothy MA; BCL(Oxon) M *Oct 1991*
Kings Chambers, Leeds
p978 . . . . . 0113 242 1123
Kings Chambers, Manchester
p984 . . . . . 0161 832 9082

GRANVILLE STAFFORD, Mr Andrew MA(Cantab) G *Jul 1987*
30, 18, 12, 22, 31, 40
4 King's Bench Walk, London EC4
p939 . . . . . 020 7822 7000

Grasso, Ms Antonietta LLB(Hons) M *Nov 2004*
6, 8, 10, 11, 12, 47, 67, 15, 20, 22, 88, 30
College Chambers, Southampton
p992 . . . . . 023 8023 0338

Gration, Mr Michael I *Nov 2007*
20, 10
4 Paper Buildings, London EC4
p946 . . . . . 020 7583 0816

Grattage, Mr Stephen L *Nov 2000*
72, 15, 70
Exchange Chambers, Manchester
p983 . . . . . 0161 833 2722
Exchange Chambers, Liverpool
p980 . . . . . 0151 236 7747
Exchange Chambers, Leeds
p977 . . . . . 0113 203 1970

Gratwicke, Miss Susan Aileen LLB G *Nov 1976*
Chambers of Wilfred Forster-Jones, London WC1
p934 . . . . . 020 7831 0037
Lavenham Chambers, Sudbury
p992 . . . . . 01787 248247

Gray, Mr Gilbert LLB(Leeds) G *Nov 1953*
(Q.C.) *15, 25*
York Chambers, York
p995 . . . . . 01904 620048
York Chambers, Newcastle upon Tyne
p987 . . . . . 0191 206 4677

Gray, Miss Jennifer M *Oct 1992*
10, 20, 15
Westgate Chambers, Lewes
p980 . . . . . 01273 480510

Gray, Jennifer M *Jan 1992*
15, 20, 82
Lamb Building, Brighton
p970 . . . . . 01273 820490
Lamb Building, London EC4
p940 . . . . . 020 7797 7788

GRAY, Mr John MA L *Oct 2001*
12, 47, 11, 30, 40, 18, 62, 96, 53
Oriel Chambers, Liverpool
p981 . . . . . 0151 236 7191 / 236 4321
Oriel Chambers, Preston
p990 . . . . . 01772 254764

GRAY, Mr Justin H W BA(Hons) I *Nov 1993*
20, 10, 1, 63
Trinity (Newcastle) Chambers, Newcastle upon Tyne
p987 . . . . . 0191 232 1927
Trinity (Teesside) Chambers, Middlesbrough
p986 . . . . . 01642 247569

Gray, Miss Margaret BA; BCL(Oxon); LLM G *Feb 1998*
19, 1
Brick Court Chambers, London WC2
p927 . . . . . 020 7379 3550

Gray, Mr Mark J G *Nov 1996*
New Bailey Chambers, Preston
p990 . . . . . 01772 258087

Gray, Miss Nichola Jayne BA(Oxon) L *Jul 1991*
20
1 Hare Court, London EC4
p936 . . . . . 020 7797 7070

Gray, Mr Richard LLB M *Nov 1986*
15
St Johns Buildings, Preston
p990 . . . . . 01772 256100
St Johns Buildings, Chester
p974 . . . . . 01244 323070
St Johns Buildings, Manchester
p985 . . . . . 0161 214 1500
St Johns Buildings, Liverpool
p982 . . . . . 0151 243 6000

Gray, Mr Roger MA; DipLaw L *Jul 1984*
11, 12, 20, 30
5 Pump Court, London EC4
p947 . . . . . 020 7353 2532 / 7583 7133

Gray, Miss Ruth Elizabeth L *Jul 2000*
30, 47, 48, 59, 88
Broad Chare Chambers, Newcastle upon Tyne
p986 . . . . . 0191 232 0541

Gray, Mr Steven L *Nov 2000*
15, 12, 62, 30, 53
7 Bedford Row, London WC1
p924 . . . . . 020 7242 3555

Grayson, Mr Edward L *Jan 1948*
Chancery Chambers, London WC2
p928 . . . . . 020 7405 6879

GREANEY, Ms Nicola M *Nov 1999*
1, 7, 11, 12, 26, 30, 53, 51, 46, 31, 18, 55, 14, 67
Thirty Nine Essex Street, London WC2
p932 . . . . . 020 7832 1111

Greaney, Mr Paul Richard BA I *Oct 1993*
(Q.C.) *15, 62*
6 King's Bench Walk, London EC4
p939 . . . . . 020 7583 0410
Park Court Chambers, Leeds
p978 . . . . . 0113 243 3277

Greatorex, Helen I *Mar 1997*
18, 22, 88
Zenith Chambers, Leeds
p979 . . . . . 0113 245 5438

GREATOREX, Mr Paul BA(Hons) L *Nov 1999*
1, 11, 18, 23, 26, 31, 33, 36, 46, 51, 55, 56
4-5 Gray's Inn Square, London WC1
p935 . . . . . 020 7404 5252

Green, Ms Alison LLB; LLM(UCL) M *Jul 1974*
24, 11, 40, 49
2 Temple Gardens, London EC4
p952 . . . . . 020 7822 1200

Green, Sir Allan MA(Cantab); KCB I *Jun 1959*
(Q.C.) KCB*15, 36*
2 Hare Court, London EC4
p937 . . . . . 020 7353 5324

Green, Mr Andrew BA(Oxon) G *Jul 1974*
7, 8, 11, 12, 6
Thirty Park Place, Cardiff
p973 . . . . . 029 2039 8421
St Johns Buildings, Preston
p990 . . . . . 01772 256100
St Johns Buildings, Chester
p974 . . . . . 01244 323070
St Johns Buildings, Manchester
p985 . . . . . 0161 214 1500
St Johns Buildings, Liverpool
p982 . . . . . 0151 243 6000
Blackstone Chambers, London EC4
p926 . . . . . 020 7583 1770

GREEN, Mr Brian BA; BCL(Oxon) M *Nov 1980*
(Q.C.) *2, 8, 9, 14, 29, 32, 34, 37*
Wilberforce Chambers, London WC2
p953 . . . . . 020 7306 0102

Green, Mr Colin Richard BA(Hons); DipLaw L *Jul 1982*
2, 5, 6, 7, 8, 9, 11, 13, 14, 18, 24, 26, 32, 37, 40, 41
Cobden House Chambers, Manchester
p983 . . . . . 0161 833 6000

GREEN, David LLB(Lancs) L *Oct 1993*
6, 8, 9, 11, 29, 32, 37, 14, 2, 97, 38, 88, 40, 93, 34
Atlantic Chambers, Liverpool
p980 . . . . . 0151 236 4421

Green, Mr Dore BA(Oxon) L *May 1994*
7, 12, 30, 51, 40, 24
2 Temple Gardens, London EC4
p952 . . . . . 020 7822 1200

Green, Mr Garry I *Nov 1999*
15
Tooks Chambers, London EC4
p953 . . . . . 020 7842 7575

Green, Mr Jason MA; DipLaw(UCL) G *Oct 2001*
20, 10
Harcourt Chambers, London EC4
p936 . . . . . 0844 561 7135
Harcourt Chambers, Oxford
p989 . . . . . 0844 561 7135

Green, Mr Kenneth C BA(Hons) L *Jul 2001*
15, 18
Broadway House Chambers, Leeds
p977 . . . . . 0113 246 2600
Broadway House Chambers, Bradford
p969 . . . . . 01274 722560

GREEN, Miss Louise G *Jul 2009*
St James's Chambers, Manchester
p984 . . . . . 0161 834 7000

Green, Mr Mark BA(Hons)(Cantab) L *Jan 2006*
96, 18, 30, 53
3PB, London EC4
p946 . . . . . 020 7583 8055

Green, Mr Michael BA(Cantab) L *Jul 1987*
(Q.C.) *6, 8, 11*
Fountain Court Chambers, London EC4
p934 . . . . . 020 7583 3335

Green, Dr Nicholas LLB; LLM; PhD I *Jul 1986*
(Q.C.) *1, 19, 44*
Brick Court Chambers, London WC2
p927 . . . . . 020 7379 3550

Green, Mr Patrick BA(Cantab) M *Nov 1990*
7, 11, 12, 18, 19, 45, 49, 47, 51
Henderson Chambers, London EC4
p937 . . . . . 020 7583 9020

Green, Mr Robin LLB(Lond) I *Oct 1992*
1, 11, 12, 15, 18, 20, 22, 25, 26, 29, 30, 31, 36
Cornerstone Barristers, London WC1
p929 . . . . . 020 7242 4986

Green, Mr Roger LLB(Lond) L *Jul 1972*
15, 30, 18, 55
St Johns Buildings, Preston
p990 . . . . . 01772 256100
St Johns Buildings, Chester
p974 . . . . . 01244 323070
St Johns Buildings, Manchester
p985 . . . . . 0161 214 1500
St Johns Buildings, Liverpool
p982 . . . . . 0151 243 6000

Green, Mr Samuel BA(Hons) L *Oct 1998*
Park Court Chambers, Leeds
p978 . . . . . 0113 243 3277
3 Serjeants' Inn, London EC4
p950 . . . . . 020 7427 5000

GREEN, Mr Timothy G *Jan 1996*
15, 47, 48, 46, 25, 83, 62
St Philips Chambers, Birmingham
p969 . . . . . 0121 246 7000

GREEN, Ms Victoria LLB(Hons) G *Oct 1994*
10, 20, 96, 49
1 King's Bench Walk, London EC4
p938 . . . . . 020 7936 1500

GREEN, Mr William LLB(Hons) M *Jul 1998*
10, 15, 20, 25
Trinity Chambers, Chelmsford
p974 . . . . . 01245 605040

Greenan, Mr John G *Jul 1984*
15, 62
15 New Bridge Street Chambers, London EC4
p943 . . . . . 020 7842 1900

Greenan, Sarah G *Jul 1987*
20, 22, 32, 37, 88, 93
Zenith Chambers, Leeds
p979 . . . . . 0113 245 5438

GREENBOURNE, Mr John MA(Cantab) G *Jul 1978*
30, 40, 11, 12, 24, 27
Crown Office Chambers, London EC4
p929 . . . . . 020 7797 8100

Greene, Mr Maurice A BA(Hons) I *Nov 1982*
15, 26, 30, 12
St Johns Buildings, Preston
p990 . . . . . 01772 256100
St Johns Buildings, Chester
p974 . . . . . 01244 323070
St Johns Buildings, Manchester
p985 . . . . . 0161 214 1500
St Johns Buildings, Liverpool
p982 . . . . . 0151 243 6000

GREENE, Mr Paul LLB(Hons) M *Oct 1994*
Maidstone Chambers, Maidstone
p982 . . . . . 01622 688592

GREENFIELD, Mr Jeremy I *Oct 1995*
11, 12, 30, 88
7 Harrington Street Chambers, Liverpool
p981 . . . . . 0151 242 0707

GREENHALGH, Emma M *Jan 2010*
9 St John Street Chambers, Manchester
p984 . . . . . 0161 955 9000

Greenhalgh, Miss Jane BA(Hons) L *Nov 2004*
15
St Johns Buildings, Preston
p990 . . . . . 01772 256100
St Johns Buildings, Chester
p974 . . . . . 01244 323070
St Johns Buildings, Manchester
p985 . . . . . 0161 214 1500
St Johns Buildings, Liverpool
p982 . . . . . 0151 243 6000

GREENHILL, Mr Julian BA(Cantab); DipLaw I *Feb 1997*
6, 8, 11, 22, 29, 31, 32, 36, 37
Wilberforce Chambers, London WC2
p953 . . . . . 020 7306 0102

Greenslade, Mr Henry Michael BA(Law); BL(Irl); Parking Adjudicator; Commissioner for Oaths G *Nov 1982*
12, 15, 25
Two King's Bench Walk, London EC4
p939 . . . . . 020 7353 7202 / 7353 3909

GREENWOOD, Miss Celestine LLB(Hons) L *Oct 1991*
10, 15, 20
Chavasse Court Chambers, Liverpool
p980 . . . . . 0151 229 2030

GREENWOOD, Mr Paul Jerome BA; BCL(Oxon) L *Nov 1991*
6, 8, 11, 29
4 Stone Buildings, London WC2
p951 . . . . . 020 7242 5524

GREENWOOD, Miss Ruth BA(Hons) G *Oct 2003*
30, 53
12 King's Bench Walk, London EC4
p940 . . . . . 020 7583 0811

13

Gregg, Miss Rebecca LLB(Lancs) G *Jan 2003*
10, 20
Cobden House Chambers, Manchester
p983 .... 0161 833 6000

GREGO, Mr Kevin C G *Nov 2001*
Citadel Chambers, Birmingham
p967 .... 0121 233 8500

Gregory, Miss Ann-Marie LLB(Hons) M *Nov 1994*
10, 20
St Pauls Chambers, Leeds
p979 .... 0113 245 5866

GREGORY, Mr Barry G *Nov 1987*
Furnival Chambers, London EC4
p934 .... 020 7405 3232

Gregory, Mr James Hans BA G *Jul 1970*
Lincoln House Chambers, Manchester
p984 .... 0161 832 5701

GREGORY, Mr Julian MA(Cantab); BCL(Oxon) I *Nov 2000*
11, 44, 19, 46, 51, 1, 57
Monckton Chambers, London WC1
p942 .... 020 7405 7211

Gregory, Miss Karen BA M *Jul 1985*
20
Exchange Chambers, Manchester
p983 .... 0161 833 2722
Exchange Chambers, Liverpool
p980 .... 0151 236 7747
Exchange Chambers, Leeds
p977 .... 0113 203 1970

GREGORY, Mr Peter LLB; Recorder G *Jul 1982*
30, 40, 53, 24, 62, 84
7 Harrington Street Chambers, Liverpool
p981 .... 0151 242 0707

GREGORY, Mr Richard MA(Cantab) M *Oct 1993*
30, 40, 53, 18
Ropewalk Chambers, Nottingham
p989 .... 0115 947 2581
42 Bedford Row, London WC1
p925 .... 020 7831 0222

Gregory, Mr Rupert LLB(Hons) L *Jul 1998*
15
Argent Chambers, London WC2
p923 .... 020 7556 5500

GRENNAN, Mr Barry E L *Jul 1977*
15, 62, 94, 70, 72, 71, 82, 80
Kenworthy's Chambers, Manchester
p984 .... 0161 832 4036

Grennan, Ms Debbie G *Oct 1997*
18, 55
Queen Square Chambers, Bristol
p972 .... 0117 921 1966

Grewcock, Miss Penelope LLB(Hons)(Leics) M *Oct 2004*
11, 15, 18, 20
Fenners Chambers, Cambridge
p972 .... 01223 368761

GREY, Ms Eleanor G *Oct 1990*
(Q.C.) *1, 23, 26, 51, 36, 63, 85*
Thirty Nine Essex Street, London WC2
p932 .... 020 7832 1111

GREY, Mr Michael Henry John M *Nov 1975*
15, 51
Citadel Chambers, Birmingham
p967 .... 0121 233 8500

Grey, Mr Robert W BA(Lancs) G *Jul 1979*
12, 15, 20, 30
3PB, Bournemouth
p969 .... 01202 292102

Grey, Mr Robin G *Feb 1957*
(Q.C.) *15, 25, 36*
QEB Hollis Whiteman, London EC4
p948 .... 020 7933 8855

GREY, Miss Sharon I *Jan 2003*
20, 23, 36, 10
Octagon House, Norwich
p988 .... 01603 623186

Grey, Ms Siobhan BA G *Oct 1994*
15, 20
Charter Chambers, London WC1
p928 .... 020 7618 4400

Gribbin, Mr Liam I *Jul 2001*
15, 18, 20, 30
Fenners Chambers, Cambridge
p972 .... 01223 368761

Gribble, Mr Peter J G *Jul 1972*
12, 15, 25
Two King's Bench Walk, London EC4
p939 .... 020 7353 7202 / 7353 3909

GRICE, Mr A Kevin LLB(L'pool); Recorder G *Jul 1977*
7, 12, 22, 30, 18, 96, 24, 62, 53, 40, 46, 11, 47, 88
7 Harrington Street Chambers, Liverpool
p981 .... 0151 242 0707

GRICE, Miss Joanna MA(Cantab) M *Oct 1991*
10, 12, 15, 18, 20, 30, 38
1 King's Bench Walk, London EC4
p938 .... 020 7936 1500

Grice, Mr Timothy James MA(Oxon) M *Jul 1975*
30, 53
St John's Chambers, Bristol
p972 .... 0117 921 3456

Grief, Ms Alison LLB(Hons) I *Oct 1990*
20, 10
4 Paper Buildings, London EC4
p946 .... 020 7583 0816

Grier, Mr Warren LLB I *Nov 1989*
1, 6, 12, 47, 48, 13, 15, 20, 22, 25, 30, 72
Old Court Chambers, Middlesbrough
p986 .... 01642 232523

Grierson, Mr Jonathan M *Nov 1999*
10, 20, 25, 23
18 St John Street Chambers, Manchester
p985 .... 0161 278 1800

GRIEVE, Mr Dominic C R MA(Oxon) M *Nov 1980*
(Q.C.)
Temple Garden Chambers, London EC4
p952 .... 020 7583 1315

Grieve, Miss Kate Makepeace L *Jul 2006*
12, 46, 18, 30, 93, 15, 76, 10, 20
36 Bedford Row, London WC1
p925 .... 020 7421 8000

Grieve, Mr Michael BA; Recorder M *Nov 1975*
(Q.C.) *15, 16, 51*
Doughty Street Chambers, London WC1
p930 .... 020 7404 1313

Grieves-Smith, Mr Peter LLB(Leics) M *Nov 1989*
15, 62
6 King's Bench Walk, London EC4
p939 .... 020 7583 0410

Griffin, Miss Fiona E LLM; LLB G *Jul 2003*
Guildford Chambers, Guildford
p975 .... 01483 539131

Griffin, Mr Ian M *Nov 1997*
10, 20
4 Brick Court Chambers, London EC4
p927 .... 020 7832 3200

GRIFFIN, Miss Lynn LLB(Hons) G *Oct 1991*
13, 15, 36, 48, 27
23 Essex Street, London WC2
p932 .... 020 7413 0353

GRIFFIN, Miss Margaret BA(Hons)(Cantab); MA(Cantab) G *Jul 2004*
6, 8, 67, 14, 38, 88, 89, 32, 40, 93, 37
Enterprise Chambers, London WC2
p931 .... 020 7405 9471
Enterprise Chambers, Leeds
p977 .... 0113 246 0391
Enterprise Chambers, Newcastle upon Tyne
p987 .... 0191 222 3344

GRIFFIN, Mr Neil Patrick Luke LLB(Hons)(Lond) G *Oct 1996*
12, 15, 25, 26
9-12 Bell Yard Chambers, London WC2
p926 .... 020 7400 1800

Griffin, Mr Nicholas LLB(Bris) I *Oct 1992*
28, 15, 62, 25
5 Paper Buildings, London EC4
p946 .... 020 7583 6117

Griffiths, Mr Alan G *Feb 1981*
One Essex Court, London EC4
p931 .... 020 7583 2000

GRIFFITHS, Ms Alison LLB(Hons) I *Oct 2001*
23, 15, 30
4 King's Bench Walk, London EC4
p939 .... 020 7822 7000

GRIFFITHS, Mr Ben BA(Cantab) M *Oct 2004*
11, 38, 97
Erskine Chambers, London WC2
p931 .... 020 7242 5532

Griffiths, Mr Brian J BA(Law & Business) G *Nov 1999*
30, 40, 18
Kings Chambers, Leeds
p978 .... 0113 242 1123
Kings Chambers, Manchester
p984 .... 0161 832 9082
No 6 Barristers Chambers, Leeds
p978 .... 0113 245 9763

Griffiths, Mr Conrad LLB G *Nov 1986*
(Q.C.) *1, 11, 12, 18, 30*
Henderson Chambers, London EC4
p937 .... 020 7583 9020

GRIFFITHS, Mr Dafydd LLB G *Mar 1997*
10, 20
29 Bedford Row, London WC1
p925 .... 020 7404 1044

GRIFFITHS, Mr David I *Oct 2001*
30, 11, 93, 88, 49, 41
St Philips Chambers, Birmingham
p969 .... 0121 246 7000

Griffiths, Miss Emma G *Oct 1998*
20, 10
3PB, Oxford
p989 .... 01865 793736

Griffiths, Mrs Hayley LLB(Hons) I *Oct 1990*
3PB, Bournemouth
p969 .... 01202 292102

GRIFFITHS, Mr Hugh LLB I *Nov 1972*
Furnival Chambers, London EC4
p934 .... 020 7405 3232

Griffiths, Mr J Peter LLB; Recorder G *Oct 1970*
(Q.C.) *15, 27, 62*
2 Bedford Row, London WC1
p924 .... 020 7440 8888
Thirty Park Place, Cardiff
p973 .... 029 2039 8421

Griffiths, Mr Martin MA(Oxon); DipLaw I *Nov 1986*
(Q.C.)
Essex Court Chambers, London WC2
p931 .... 020 7813 8000

Griffiths, Mr Patrick MA(Oxon) G *Nov 1972*
15
Iscoed Chambers, Swansea
p993 .... 01792 652988

GRIFFITHS, Mr Peter R MA(Cantab) I *Jul 1977*
6, 8, 11, 29
4 Stone Buildings, London WC2
p951 .... 020 7242 5524

Griffiths, Mr Richard Stephen G *Nov 1983*
15, 30, 10, 20, 88, 25
Pendragon Chambers, Swansea
p993 .... 01792 411188

Griffiths, Mr Robert Norton LLB(Hons) M *May 1988*
15, 62, 42
12 College Place, Southampton
p992 .... 023 8032 0320

Griffiths, Mr Robin BA(Oxon); Dip Crim(Cantab) M *Nov 1970*
15
2 Dr Johnson's Buildings, London EC4
p930 .... 020 7936 2613

Griffiths, Mr Roger V LLB G *Jul 1983*
15
Temple Chambers, Newport
p988 .... 01633 267403 / 255855
Temple Chambers, Cardiff
p973 .... 029 2039 7364

Griffiths, Miss Tania BA(Hons); Recorder G *Jul 1982*
(Q.C.) *30, 15, 70, 12, 42, 56*
Exchange Chambers, Manchester
p983 .... 0161 833 2722
Exchange Chambers, Liverpool
p980 .... 0151 236 7747
Exchange Chambers, Leeds
p977 .... 0113 203 1970

GRIFFITHS, Mr W Robert MA; BCL(Oxon) M *Nov 1974*
(Q.C.) *1, 3, 51, 11, 19, 18, 61, 46, 24, 26*
4-5 Gray's Inn Square, London WC1
p935 .... 020 7404 5252

GRIME, Mr Andrew L *Oct 1997*
12, 15, 20, 32
Pump Court Chambers, Swindon
p993 .... 01793 539899
Pump Court Chambers, Winchester
p994 .... 01962 868161
Pump Court Chambers, London EC4
p947 .... 020 7353 0711

GRIME, Mr Stephen MA(Oxon); FCIArb M *Jan 1978*
(Q.C.)
2 Pump Court, London EC4
p947 .... 020 7353 5597

GRODZINSKI, Mr Sam MA(Oxon); Solicitor(1993) M *Mar 1996*
(Q.C.) *1, 11, 24, 30, 40, 7, 12, 23, 47, 53, 57, 51*
Matrix Chambers, London WC1
p942 .... 020 7404 3447

GROGAN, Miss Rose L *Jul 2010*
94, 93, 84, 78, 74, 67, 53, 51, 46, 41, 40, 31, 30, 26, 14, 12, 11, 1, 63
Thirty Nine Essex Street, London WC2
p932 .... 020 7832 1111

Groom, Mr Ian M *Nov 1990*
30, 40, 15, 12
Paradise Chambers, Sheffield
p992 .... 0114 273 8951

Groome, Mr David M *Nov 1987*
15, 48, 13, 39, 62, 25
QEB Hollis Whiteman, London EC4
p948 .... 020 7933 8855

Ground, Mr Richard William MA(Cantab) I *Oct 1994*
1, 12, 15, 18, 22, 26, 31, 36
Cornerstone Barristers, London WC1
p929 .... 020 7242 4986

Grout, Mr Christopher I *Jan 2007*
15 New Bridge Street Chambers, London EC4
p943 .... 020 7842 1900

GROVER, Mr Timothy I *Nov 1991*
30, 53
7 Harrington Street Chambers, Liverpool
p981 .... 0151 242 0707

GROVES, Mr Hugo LLB(Leics); LLM(Lond); Attorney - New York State G *Oct 1980*
6, 8, 11, 29, 40, 49, 38, 97
Enterprise Chambers, London WC2
p931 .... 020 7405 9471
Enterprise Chambers, Leeds
p977 .... 0113 246 0391
Enterprise Chambers, Newcastle upon Tyne
p987 .... 0191 222 3344

Grubb, Miss Cathrine M *Jan 2007*
Civitas Law, Cardiff
p972 .... 0845 071 3007

GRUCHY, Mr Simon M *May 1993*
Carmelite Chambers, London EC4
p927 .... 020 7936 6300

Gruder, Mr Jeffrey M *Jul 1977*
(Q.C.)
Essex Court Chambers, London WC2
p931 .... 020 7813 8000

GRUFFYDD, Mr John G *Feb 1992*
62, 12, 30, 40, 72, 15
Oriel Chambers, Liverpool
p981 .... 0151 236 7191 / 236 4321
Oriel Chambers, Preston
p990 .... 01772 254764

GRUFFYDD, Miss Sarah G *Jul 2003*
15, 12, 30
Oriel Chambers, Liverpool
p981 .... 0151 236 7191 / 236 4321
Oriel Chambers, Preston
p990 .... 01772 254764

GRUMBAR, Mr Paul BA(Nott'm) M *Nov 1974*
15, 62
Albion Chambers, Bristol
p970 .... 0117 927 2144

Grunberg, Angela I *Jan 1999*
One Essex Court, London EC4
p931 .... 020 7936 3030

Grundy, Ms Clare LLB(B'ham) G *Jul 1989*
12
St Johns Buildings, Preston
p990 .... 01772 256100
St Johns Buildings, Chester
p974 .... 01244 323070
St Johns Buildings, Manchester
p985 .... 0161 214 1500
St Johns Buildings, Liverpool
p982 .... 0151 243 6000

GRUNDY, Liam LLB(Hull); LLM(Cantab) I *Jul 1995*
8
Atlantic Chambers, Liverpool
p980 .... 0151 236 4421

Grundy, Mr Milton MA(Cantab) I *Nov 1954*
34
Gray's Inn Tax Chambers, London WC1
p936 .... 020 7242 2642

See p1010 for the Key to Work Categories

GRUNDY, Mr Nicholas MA(Cantab); MSc(Loughborough) *G Nov 1993*
22, 26, 51, 1, 8, 88, 93
Five Paper, London EC4
p946 . . . 020 7815 3200

GRUNDY, Mr Nigel MA(Oxon) *M Jul 1983*
11, 12, 18, 24, 30, 7, 36, 40
9 St John Street Chambers, Manchester
p984 . . . 0161 955 9000

Grundy, Mr Philip Michael David LLB(Cardiff) *M Jul 1980*
St Johns Buildings, Preston
p990 . . . 01772 256100
St Johns Buildings, Chester
p974 . . . 01244 323070
St Johns Buildings, Manchester
p985 . . . 0161 214 1500
St Johns Buildings, Liverpool
p982 . . . 0151 243 6000

GUEST, Mr Peter *I Jan 1971*
15, 62, 95
187 Fleet Street, London EC4
p933 . . . 020 7430 7430

GUILOFF, Ms Carolina *I Oct 1996*
15, 62
25 Bedford Row, London WC1
p925 . . . 020 7067 1500

Guirguis, Miss Sheren *I Jan 1996*
20, 10, 30, 12, 18
Exchange Chambers, Manchester
p983 . . . 0161 833 2722
Exchange Chambers, Liverpool
p980 . . . 0151 236 7747
Exchange Chambers, Leeds
p977 . . . 0113 203 1970

Guishard, Mr David E K LLB(Hons) *M Feb 1978*
15, 12, 22, 30
4 Rowchester Court, Birmingham
p968 . . . 0121 233 2327

Gullick, Mr Mathew *G Jan 2003*
3PB, London EC4
p946 . . . 020 7583 8055

GUMBEL, Ms Elizabeth Anne MA(Oxon) *I Nov 1974*
(Q.C.) *30, 53*
1 Crown Office Row, London EC4
p929 . . . 020 7797 7500

Gumbs, Miss Annette LLB *G Oct 1994*
12
St Johns Buildings, Preston
p990 . . . 01772 256100
St Johns Buildings, Chester
p974 . . . 01244 323070
St Johns Buildings, Manchester
p985 . . . 0161 214 1500
St Johns Buildings, Liverpool
p982 . . . 0151 243 6000

Gumsley, Mr Carl John LLB *I Nov 1989*
15, 27, 94
New Court Chambers, Newcastle upon Tyne
p987 . . . 0191 232 1980
Trinity (Newcastle) Chambers, Newcastle upon Tyne
p987 . . . 0191 232 1927
Trinity (Teesside) Chambers, Middlesbrough
p986 . . . 01642 247569

GUN CUNINGHAME, Mr Julian MA(Edin) *L Nov 1989*
11, 22, 29, 30, 40, 5, 6
Gough Square Chambers, London EC4
p935 . . . 020 7353 0924

GUNARATNA, Mr Kavan MA(Cantab) *L Nov 2004*
5, 6, 8, 11, 22, 29, 40, 38, 88
Enterprise Chambers, London WC2
p931 . . . 020 7405 9471
Enterprise Chambers, Leeds
p977 . . . 0113 246 0391
Enterprise Chambers, Newcastle upon Tyne
p987 . . . 0191 222 3344

Gunning, Mr Alexander LLB; LLM(Lond) *I Mar 1994*
7, 11, 12, 24, 40, 78
4 Pump Court, London EC4
p947 . . . 020 7842 5555

Gunstone, Mr Giles *M Jul 2007*
KCH Garden Square Chambers, Nottingham
p989 . . . 0115 941 8851
KCH Garden Square Chambers, Leicester
p979 . . . 0115 941 8851

GUNTHER, Miss Elizabeth *L Oct 1993*
10, 20
Pump Court Chambers, Swindon
p993 . . . 01793 539899
Pump Court Chambers, Winchester
p994 . . . 01962 868161
Pump Court Chambers, London EC4
p947 . . . 020 7353 0711

GUPTA, Mr Amit *G Jul 2006*
8, 11, 93, 30
St Philips Chambers, Birmingham
p969 . . . 0121 246 7000

Gupta, Miss Mamta *L Oct 2004*
30, 53, 68, 94
No5 Chambers, Bristol
p971 . . . 0845 210 5555
No5 Chambers, London EC4
p944 . . . 0845 210 5555
No5 Chambers, Birmingham
p968 . . . 0845 210 5555

GUPTA, Mr Teertha *I Nov 1990*
20, 10
4 Paper Buildings, London EC4
p946 . . . 020 7583 0816

Gurney, Mr Simon *I Jul 2006*
Lincoln House Chambers, Manchester
p984 . . . 0161 832 5701

Gurnham, Mr Paul BA(Hons)(Cantab) *L Jul 2004*
King's Bench Chambers, Oxford
p989 . . . 01865 311066
13 King's Bench Walk, London EC4
p940 . . . 020 7353 7204

GURSOY, Mr Ramiz A BA(Essex); DipLaw(City) *M Nov 1991*
15
18 Red Lion Court, London EC4
p949 . . . 020 7520 6000
18 Red Lion Court (Annexe), Chelmsford
p973 . . . 01245 280880

Guthrie, Ms Cara BA(Cantab) *I Jan 2000*
53, 30
Outer Temple Chambers, London WC2
p945 . . . 020 7353 6381

GUTHRIE, Mr James D *I Jul 1975*
(Q.C.) *11, 12, 51, 1, 41*
3 Hare Court, London EC4
p937 . . . 020 7415 7800

Gutteridge, Miss Beverley J *M Jul 1987*
36 Dunmore Road, London SW20
p930 . . . 07710 326130

Gutteridge, Mr Christopher LLB(Dunelm) *I Oct 2006*
15, 30, 12, 25, 22
Exchange Chambers, Manchester
p983 . . . 0161 833 2722
Exchange Chambers, Liverpool
p980 . . . 0151 236 7747
Exchange Chambers, Leeds
p977 . . . 0113 203 1970

GUY, Mr David BA(B'ham); FCIArb *G Jul 1972*
11, 45
Tanfield Chambers, London WC1
p951 . . . 020 7421 5300

Guy, Mr Richard Perran MA(Oxon) *I Nov 1970*
1, 6, 7, 8, 10, 12, 74, 47, 48, 67, 68, 14, 55, 76, 77, 18, 20, 2, 62, 51, 38, 89, 26, 31, 86, 32, 40, 93, 60, 36
King's Bench Godolphin Chambers, Truro
p994 . . . 0845 308 1551
King's Bench Godolphin Chambers, Plymouth
p990 . . . 0845 308 1551
Lamb Building, Brighton
p970 . . . 01273 820490
Lamb Building, London EC4
p940 . . . 020 7797 7788

Habboo, Miss Camille LLB *G Jul 1987*
14 Gray's Inn Square, London WC1
p936 . . . 020 7242 0858

Habel, Mrs Jessica Jennet MA(Oxon) *M Jul 1991*
20, 10
12 College Place, Southampton
p992 . . . 023 8032 0320

HABIB, Ms Shysta *L Jul 2002*
30, 89, 64
Kenworthy's Chambers, Manchester
p984 . . . 0161 832 4036

HACKER, Mr Richard D MA(Cantab); Licence Specialise en Droit European(Brussels) *L Nov 1977*
(Q.C.) *5, 6, 8, 11, 12, 24, 29, 38*
South Square, London WC1
p950 . . . 020 7696 9900

Hackett, Mr Martin John *M Jan 1995*
Lincoln House Chambers, Manchester
p984 . . . 0161 832 5701

Hackett, Mr Philip *M Oct 1978*
(Q.C.) *72, 15, 71, 84, 62*
Argent Chambers, London WC2
p923 . . . 020 7556 5500

Hacon, Mr Richard BSc *G Nov 1979*
73, 50, 19, 45, 13, 52, 96, 41
11 South Square, London WC1
p950 . . . 020 7405 1222

Hadden, Mr Rhys Thomas MA(Manc) *M Nov 2006*
Field Court Chambers, London WC1
p933 . . . 020 7405 6114

HADDON, Ms Clare *G Jan 1999*
30, 12, 40, 53
Ropewalk Chambers, Nottingham
p989 . . . 0115 947 2581

Haddon-Cave, Mr Charles MA(Cantab) *G Jul 1978*
(Q.C.) *36, 11, 35, 4, 24, 30*
Quadrant Chambers, London EC4
p948 . . . 020 7583 4444

Hadfield, Miss Charlotte LLB(Hons) *I Jan 1999*
96, 18, 93, 71
3PB, London EC4
p946 . . . 020 7583 8055

Hadgill, Mr Clinton LLB(Hons) *M Jan 1998*
15, 18, 12, 96
St Albans Chambers, St Albans
p992 . . . 01727 843383

Hadley, Mr Richard *G Oct 1997*
20, 10, 63
No5 Chambers, Bristol
p971 . . . 0845 210 5555
No5 Chambers, London EC4
p944 . . . 0845 210 5555
No5 Chambers, Birmingham
p968 . . . 0845 210 5555

HADLEY, Mr Steven Frank BA(Jt Hons)(Biblical Studies); BD; DipLaw *I Jul 1987*
15
9-12 Bell Yard Chambers, London WC2
p926 . . . 020 7400 1800
1 Inner Temple Lane, London EC4
p937 . . . 020 7427 4400

HADRILL, Mr Keith *L Jan 1977*
Furnival Chambers, London EC4
p934 . . . 020 7405 3232

HAEEMS, Mr David *I Mar 1996*
Carmelite Chambers, London EC4
p927 . . . 020 7936 6300

Hagen, Mr Dakis MA(Cantab); DipLaw *L Oct 2002*
6, 8, 9, 53, 11, 97, 67, 62, 38, 21, 32, 40, 37
Serle Court, London WC2
p950 . . . 020 7242 6105

Haggan, Mr Nicholas S Recorder *M Jul 1977*
(Q.C.) *15, 62, 48, 84, 39*
12 College Place, Southampton
p992 . . . 023 8032 0320

Haggerty, Miss Elizabeth Frances LLB *L Nov 1994*
22, 88, 93
Lamb Chambers, London EC4
p941 . . . 020 7797 8300

Haggis, Mr Andrew *M Mar 2007*
10, 20
St Johns Buildings, Preston
p990 . . . 01772 256100
St Johns Buildings, Chester
p974 . . . 01244 323070
St Johns Buildings, Manchester
p985 . . . 0161 214 1500
St Johns Buildings, Liverpool
p982 . . . 0151 243 6000

Hague, Mr Paul BA *L Jul 1983*
15
15 Winckley Square, Preston
p991 . . . 01772 252828

Haines, Mr Alex *L Jan 2007*
4 Breams Buildings, London EC4
p927 . . . 020 7092 1900

HAINES, Miss Hannah *L Feb 2005*
9 St John Street Chambers, Manchester
p984 . . . 0161 955 9000

HAISLEY, Mr Matthew LLB *L Oct 1999*
8, 11, 12, 47, 48, 30
9 St John Street Chambers, Manchester
p984 . . . 0161 955 9000

Hajimitsis, Anthony *I Nov 1984*
20
Zenith Chambers, Leeds
p979 . . . 0113 245 5438

Hakme, Mr Mustapha *M Aug 2000*
15, 51
Nine Bedford Row, London WC1
p924 . . . 020 7489 2727

Halden, Mr Angus Robert *M Oct 1999*
11, 12, 18, 25, 47, 48, 68, 55, 20, 39, 84, 85, 51, 89, 29, 40, 36
Queen Square Chambers, Bristol
p972 . . . 0117 921 1966

Hale, Mr Charles LLB(Hons) *M Oct 1992*
20, 30, 10, 12, 36
4 Paper Buildings, London EC4
p946 . . . 020 7583 0816

Hale, Mrs Grace LLM *G Mar 1998*
15
KCH Garden Square Chambers, Nottingham
p989 . . . 0115 941 8851
KCH Garden Square Chambers, Leicester
p979 . . . 0115 941 8851

Hale, Miss Rachel Paula *L Mar 2003*
20, 10
Pendragon Chambers, Swansea
p993 . . . 01792 411188

Hale, Mr Simon BA *G Jan 2006*
Hardwicke, London WC2
p936 . . . 020 7242 2523

Hale, Miss Victoria LLB(Hons) *M Jul 2006*
15
Argent Chambers, London WC2
p923 . . . 020 7556 5500

HALES, Ms Sally-Anne LLB *G Jul 1988*
15, 62, 36
18 Red Lion Court, London EC4
p949 . . . 020 7520 6000
18 Red Lion Court (Annexe), Chelmsford
p973 . . . 01245 280880

Halkerston, Miss Sally LLB(Hons) *M Oct 1994*
Atkinson Bevan Chambers, London EC4
p924 . . . 020 7353 2112

HALKYARD, Miss Kay LLB(Lond) *G Jul 1980*
10, 20
1 Garden Court, London EC4
p934 . . . 020 7797 7900

Hall, Mr Andrew LLB; MA; Solr(1980) *G Feb 1991*
(Q.C.) *15, 51*
Doughty Street Chambers, London WC1
p930 . . . 020 7404 1313

HALL, Miss Angela *G Jul 2000*
22, 26, 20, 8
Five Paper, London EC4
p946 . . . 020 7815 3200

Hall, David P *G Jul 1980*
15, 25, 30
Zenith Chambers, Leeds
p979 . . . 0113 245 5438

HALL, Miss Jacqueline *L Nov 1994*
15, 62, 84
18 Red Lion Court, London EC4
p949 . . . 020 7520 6000
18 Red Lion Court (Annexe), Chelmsford
p973 . . . 01245 280880

HALL, Mr James Edward LLB(Cardiff) *L Oct 2000*
8, 11, 12, 47, 67, 81, 62, 24, 88, 40, 93, 37
Cornwall Street Chambers, Birmingham
p967 . . . 0121 233 7500

Hall, Mr Jeremy J LLB *G Feb 1988*
10, 18, 20, 96
Becket Chambers, Canterbury
p972 . . . 01227 786331
Becket Chambers, Maidstone
p982 . . . 01622 230957

Hall, Ms Joanna Mary LLB(Lond) *I Nov 1973*
14 Gray's Inn Square, London WC1
p936 . . . 020 7242 0858

HALL, Mr Jonathan *G Jul 1994*
15, 25
9-12 Bell Yard Chambers, London WC2
p926 . . . 020 7400 1800

Hall, Mr Matthew BA(Oxon) *M Mar 1999*
5, 6, 11, 22
Kings Chambers, Leeds
p978 . . . 0113 242 1123

Kings Chambers, Manchester
p984 . . . . . 0161 832 9082

HALL, Mrs Melanie BA(Dunelm) I *Nov 1982*
(Q.C.) *1, 18, 11, 40, 51, 57*
Monckton Chambers, London WC1
p942 . . . . . 020 7405 7211

HALL, Mr Michael Richard LLB(Hons) I *Oct 1996*
15, 82, 39, 62
Pump Court Chambers, Swindon
p993 . . . . . 01793 539899
Pump Court Chambers, Winchester
p994 . . . . . 01962 868161
Pump Court Chambers, London EC4
p947 . . . . . 020 7353 0711

Hall, Mr Nicholas MA(Oxon) G *Jul 1973*
15
Westgate Chambers, Lewes
p980 . . . . . 01273 480510

HALL, Mr Nigel RMN; LLB I *Jul 2001*
15, 70, 63, 62, 73, 82, 25
Cornwall Street Chambers, Birmingham
p967 . . . . . 0121 233 7500
King's Bench Godolphin Chambers, Truro
p994 . . . . . 0845 308 1551
King's Bench Godolphin Chambers, Plymouth
p990 . . . . . 0845 308 1551

HALL, Mr Richard Andrew LLB(Soton) I *Nov 1995*
10, 20
Pump Court Chambers, Swindon
p993 . . . . . 01793 539899
Pump Court Chambers, Winchester
p994 . . . . . 01962 868161
Pump Court Chambers, London EC4
p947 . . . . . 020 7353 0711

HALL, Mr Robert LLB G *Oct 1997*
15, 70, 72
1 King's Bench Walk, London EC4
p938 . . . . . 020 7936 1500

Hall, Toby L *Jan 2008*
1 Pump Court, London EC4
p947 . . . . . 020 7842 7070

Hall, Mrs Yasmin L *Jan 1993*
Guildhall Chambers, Portsmouth
p990 . . . . . 023 9275 2400

Hall Taylor, Mr Alex BA(Hons)(Bris); DipLaw I *Oct 1996*
6, 8, 9, 11, 22, 29, 32, 37, 40, 12, 24
Four New Square, London WC2
p943 . . . . . 020 7822 2000

Hallam, Mr Jacob W MA(Cantab) G *Oct 1996*
15, 62, 16
6 King's Bench Walk, London EC4
p939 . . . . . 020 7583 0410

Hallett, Ms Katherine L *Jul 2006*
13 Old Square Chambers, London WC2
p945 . . . . . 020 7831 4445

Halliday, Mr Ian Nicolas LLB L *Nov 1989*
15, 62, 48, 84, 36
Queen Square Chambers, Bristol
p972 . . . . . 0117 921 1966

HALLIDAY, Mr Patrick BA(Hons)(Cantab)(Social & Political Sciences); DipLaw(City) G *Jan 2005*
1, 18, 55, 11, 26, 19, 36, 73
11KBW, London EC4
p938 . . . . . 020 7632 8500

HALLIDAY-DAVIS, Miss Lee I *Jul 1999*
Carmelite Chambers, London EC4
p927 . . . . . 020 7936 6300

Halligan, Mr Brendan BA; LLB M *Jan 1998*
6 King's Bench Walk, London EC4
p939 . . . . . 020 7583 0695 / 7353 4931

HALLIGAN, Mr Rodney LLB(Hons) G *Jul 1972*
15
7 Harrington Street Chambers, Liverpool
p981 . . . . . 0151 242 0707

Hallin, Mr Conrad BA(Hons) I *Jul 2004*
53, 12, 68, 18, 85, 27, 40, 36
3 Serjeants' Inn, London EC4
p950 . . . . . 020 7427 5000

Hallissey, Ms Caroline BA I *Feb 1990*
27, 30, 53
Outer Temple Chambers, London WC2
p945 . . . . . 020 7353 6381

Halliwell, Mr Mark BSc(Econ); Recorder L *Jun 1985*
5, 6, 8, 9, 11, 22, 29, 32, 37, 40
Kings Chambers, Leeds
p978 . . . . . 0113 242 1123
Kings Chambers, Manchester
p984 . . . . . 0161 832 9082

Halliwell, Mr Toby LLB M *Nov 1992*
15, 12, 18, 30, 55
Unity Street Chambers, Bristol
p972 . . . . . 0117 906 9789

Halloran, Miss Cathy L *Oct 1997*
15
Tooks Chambers, London EC4
p953 . . . . . 020 7842 7575

HALLORAN, Ms Ceilidh Ann MA L *Nov 1992*
12, 22, 1, 26
Arden Chambers, London WC1
p923 . . . . . 020 7242 4244

Hallowes, Mr Rupert J M BA(Bris); CPE I *Oct 1995*
12, 15, 20, 62
3 Temple Gardens, London EC4
p952 . . . . . 020 7353 3102

HALLWORTH, Mr Andrew G *Mar 2002*
Carmelite Chambers, London EC4
p927 . . . . . 020 7936 6300

Halpern, Mr David MA(Oxon) G *Jul 1978*
(Q.C.) *5, 6, 8, 11, 22, 29, 32, 37, 40, 12, 24*
Four New Square, London WC2
p943 . . . . . 020 7822 2000

Halsey, Mr Mark LLB(Hons)(Bris) I *Feb 1974*
15
2 Bedford Row, London WC1
p924 . . . . . 020 7440 8888

Halstead, Mr Robin Bernard BA(Oxon) I *Oct 1996*
20, 10, 23, 11, 12, 30, 22
One Essex Court, London EC4
p931 . . . . . 020 7936 3030

HAM, Mr Robert BCL(Oxon); BA M *Nov 1973*
(Q.C.) *8, 9, 14, 29, 32, 34, 37*
Wilberforce Chambers, London WC2
p953 . . . . . 020 7306 0102

Hamblin, Mr Nicholas L *Nov 1981*
15, 18, 12, 25, 23, 30, 36, 62
Westgate Chambers, Lewes
p980 . . . . . 01273 480510

HAMER, Mr Charles Former Solicitor M *Jan 2007*
Citadel Chambers, Birmingham
p967 . . . . . 0121 233 8500

Hamer, Mr George BSc(Lond); ARCS G *Nov 1974*
13, 50, 56
8 New Square, London WC2
p943 . . . . . 020 7405 4321

Hamer, Mr Kenneth M H Recorder I *Apr 1975*
6, 8, 12, 19, 27, 30, 40
Henderson Chambers, London EC4
p937 . . . . . 020 7583 9020

Hames, Mr Christopher LLB(Hons) I *Jul 1987*
20
4 Paper Buildings, London EC4
p946 . . . . . 020 7583 0816

Hamey, Mr John MA(Cantab) I *Jul 1979*
12, 30, 20, 53, 49, 63
East Anglian Chambers, Norwich
p988 . . . . . 01603 617351
East Anglian Chambers, Colchester
p975 . . . . . 01206 572756
East Anglian Chambers, Chelmsford
p973 . . . . . 01245 215660
East Anglian Chambers, Ipswich
p976 . . . . . 01473 214481

Hamid, Mrs Beebee Nass L *Jul 1980*
Clapham Law Chambers, London SW1
p928 . . . . . 020 7978 8482 / 7642 5777

HAMID, Ms Ruby L *Nov 2002*
15, 62, 34, 36, 46, 84
18 Red Lion Court, London EC4
p949 . . . . . 020 7520 6000
18 Red Lion Court (Annexe), Chelmsford
p973 . . . . . 01245 280880

HAMILL, Mr Hugh BA(UCD) I *Jul 1988*
24, 30, 40, 53, 74
12 King's Bench Walk, London EC4
p940 . . . . . 020 7583 0811

HAMILTON, Miss Amanda L *Jan 1995*
Furnival Chambers, London EC4
p934 . . . . . 020 7405 3232

Hamilton, Miss Caroline LLB M *Jul 1989*
15, 20
Two King's Bench Walk, London EC4
p939 . . . . . 020 7353 7202 / 7353 3909

HAMILTON, Ms Carolyn LLB G *Jul 1996*
10
1 King's Bench Walk, London EC4
p938 . . . . . 020 7936 1500

Hamilton, Mr Gavin BA(Oxon) G *Jul 1979*
40, 24, 41, 47, 37, 22
3PB, London EC4
p946 . . . . . 020 7583 8055

HAMILTON, Mr Jaime G *Nov 1993*
15
9 St John Street Chambers, Manchester
p984 . . . . . 0161 955 9000

Hamilton, Mr John C BSc(City); DipLaw G *Nov 1988*
15, 20, 18, 30
Field Court Chambers, London WC1
p933 . . . . . 020 7405 6114

Hamilton, Mr Nigel James I *Oct 2004*
15, 12
Broadway House Chambers, Leeds
p977 . . . . . 0113 246 2600
Broadway House Chambers, Bradford
p969 . . . . . 01274 722560

HAMILTON, Mrs Penelope Ann LLB; Partner G *Jul 1972*
34, 57
Pump Court Tax Chambers, London WC1
p948 . . . . . 020 7414 8080

Hamilton, Mr Peter BA(Rhodes); MA(Cantab) I *Feb 1968*
7, 12, 24, 81
4 Pump Court, London EC4
p947 . . . . . 020 7842 5555

Hamilton, Ms Philippa BA(Oxon); DipLaw(City) L *Oct 1996*
Fountain Court Chambers, London EC4
p934 . . . . . 020 7583 3335

HAMILTON, Mr William M *Nov 2008*
9 St John Street Chambers, Manchester
p984 . . . . . 0161 955 9000

Hamilton-Shield, Ms Anna LLB(Hons) M *Nov 1989*
15
Charter Chambers, London WC1
p928 . . . . . 020 7618 4400

Hamlin, Mr Patrick Lindop G *Nov 1970*
1, 3, 7, 11, 12, 26, 29, 31, 24, 40, 8
42 Bedford Row, London WC1
p925 . . . . . 020 7831 0222

Hammerton, Mr Alastair MA(Cantab); LLM I *Jul 1983*
24, 30, 40, 78, 62, 63, 26, 85
1 Chancery Lane, London WC2
p928 . . . . . 0845 634 6666

Hammett, Mr Michael LLB G *Nov 2001*
15
9 Park Place, Cardiff
p973 . . . . . 029 2038 2731

HAMMOND, Ms Claire LLB(Hons) L *Jul 2003*
53, 12, 47, 48, 18, 20, 22, 24, 30, 55, 36, 41
St James's Chambers, Manchester
p984 . . . . . 0161 834 7000

HAMMOND, Mr Fayaz LLB G *Oct 1999*
12, 20, 30, 23
St James's Chambers, Manchester
p984 . . . . . 0161 834 7000

HAMMOND, Mr Tim Mark MA; LLM L *Mar 2003*
6, 11, 12, 22, 30
Tanfield Chambers, London WC1
p951 . . . . . 020 7421 5300

Hampton, Mr Peter J G LLB(Hons); BVC G *Jan 2003*
15
Broadway House Chambers, Leeds
p977 . . . . . 0113 246 2600
Broadway House Chambers, Bradford
p969 . . . . . 01274 722560

Hanbury, Mr William LLB(Manc); P/T Immigration Judge/ Deputy Judge of Upper Tribunal (Immigration & Asylum Chamber) I *Nov 1985*
5, 6, 7, 8, 11, 12, 67, 22, 51, 23, 88, 89, 26, 29, 40, 60, 93, 1, 49, 74, 47, 14, 46, 2, 38, 31, 32, 36, 37
Exchange Chambers, Manchester
p983 . . . . . 0161 833 2722
Exchange Chambers, Liverpool
p980 . . . . . 0151 236 7747
Exchange Chambers, Leeds
p977 . . . . . 0113 203 1970

Hancock, Mr Christopher P MA(Cantab); LLM(Harv) M *Jul 1983*
(Q.C.) *3, 11, 12, 24, 35, 41*
20 Essex Street, London WC2
p932 . . . . . 020 7842 1200

Hancock, Ms Maria G *Nov 1995*
10, 20
Westgate Chambers, Lewes
p980 . . . . . 01273 480510

HANCOX, Miss Lisa I *Nov 2006*
15, 70, 62, 72, 39, 10, 68, 20, 94
Cornwall Street Chambers, Birmingham
p967 . . . . . 0121 233 7500

Hancox, Ms Sally BSc(Hons); DipLaw L *Nov 1996*
15, 62, 72
No5 Chambers, Bristol
p971 . . . . . 0845 210 5555
No5 Chambers, London EC4
p944 . . . . . 0845 210 5555
No5 Chambers, Birmingham
p968 . . . . . 0845 210 5555

Hand, Mr Anthony LLB(Lonf) L *Jul 1989*
10, 12, 20
College Chambers, Southampton
p992 . . . . . 023 8023 0338

Hand, Mr John LLB; LLM(Nott'm); Recorder; Bencher,Gray's Inn G *Jul 1972*
(Q.C.) *1, 18, 19, 27, 30, 36, 51, 55, 40, 46, 56*
Old Square Chambers, Bristol
p971 . . . . . 0117 930 5100

Hand, Mr Jonathan E S BA(Oxon) I *Nov 1990*
30, 40, 53
Outer Temple Chambers, London WC2
p945 . . . . . 020 7353 6381

Handa, Radhika I *Jul 2008*
10, 20
Coram Chambers, London EC1
p929 . . . . . 020 7092 3700

HANDY, Mr Benjamin L *Oct 2008*
15, 30
7 Harrington Street Chambers, Liverpool
p981 . . . . . 0151 242 0707

Handyside, Mr Richard Neil BCL; MA(Oxon) L *Oct 1993*
(Q.C.)
Fountain Court Chambers, London EC4
p934 . . . . . 020 7583 3335

HANIF, Ms Saima BA(Oxon) L *Jan 2002*
1, 51, 18, 31, 11, 26
4-5 Gray's Inn Square, London WC1
p935 . . . . . 020 7404 5252

HANKE, Mr Richard L *Jan 2006*
5, 81, 11, 28, 62, 50, 24
3 Verulam Buildings, London WC1
p953 . . . . . 020 7831 8441

HANKIN, Mr Jonas K M *Jan 1994*
15, 62, 84
St Philips Chambers, Birmingham
p969 . . . . . 0121 246 7000

Hanley, Miss Colleen BA(Jurisprudence); LLM(EUI) I *Jan 2003*
49, 41, 3, 5, 11, 43, 47, 78, 24, 54, 35, 44
20 Essex Street, London WC2
p932 . . . . . 020 7842 1200

Hanna, Mr Ronan BA; BCL I *Oct 2006*
3, 7, 11, 31, 40, 41, 43, 45, 49, 54, 61, 78, 74
Atkin Chambers, London WC1
p923 . . . . . 020 7404 0102

Hannaford, Ms Sarah J MA(Oxon) M *Jul 1989*
(Q.C.) *3, 7, 11, 24, 40*
Keating Chambers, London WC2
p938 . . . . . 020 7544 2600

HANNAM, Mr Timothy BA(Hons) G *Oct 1995*
12, 15, 22, 30
Citadel Chambers, Birmingham
p967 . . . . . 0121 233 8500

HANNETT, Ms Sarah LLM; LLB L *Jan 2003*
1, 46, 18, 22, 51, 26, 63, 31, 55
4-5 Gray's Inn Square, London WC1
p935 . . . . . 020 7404 5252

Hansen, Mr William BSc; MPhil(Cantab); Deputy Adjudicator to HM Land Registry L *Nov 1992*
8, 29, 88, 93, 7, 32, 37, 38, 47, 67, 89, 97
No5 Chambers, Bristol
p971 . . . . . 0845 210 5555
No5 Chambers, London EC4
p944 . . . . . 0845 210 5555
No5 Chambers, Birmingham
p968 . . . . . 0845 210 5555

Hanson, Mr Timothy I *Jan 1989*
11, 18, 20, 27, 47, 48
No5 Chambers, Bristol
p971 . . . . . 0845 210 5555

See p1010 for the Key to Work Categories

No5 Chambers, London EC4
p944 . . . 0845 210 5555
No5 Chambers, Birmingham
p968 . . . 0845 210 5555

HANTUSCH, Mr Robert Anthony MA(Cantab) I *Jul 1982*
5, 6, 7, 8, 11, 22, 24, 29, 32, 37, 40
3 Stone Buildings, London WC2
p951 . . . 020 7242 4937

Hapgood, Mr Mark LLB(Nott'm) G *Feb 1979*
(Q.C.) *11, 5, 40, 24*
Brick Court Chambers, London WC2
p927 . . . 020 7379 3550

Happe, Mr Dominic BA G *Nov 1993*
35, 41, 11, 24, 60, 3
Stone Chambers, London WC1
p951 . . . 020 7440 6900

Haque, Gazi Mosta Gawsal MA I *Jul 1970*
15, 20, 23, 25
Dollis Hill Chambers, London NW10
p930 . . . 020 8208 1663

HAQUE, Mr Muhammed L BA(Hons); MA L *Sep 1997*
30, 11, 84, 24, 40
Crown Office Chambers, London EC4
p929 . . . 020 7797 8100

HAQUE, Ms Sara M *Nov 2000*
15, 94, 63, 68, 62
Kenworthy's Chambers, Manchester
p984 . . . 0161 832 4036

Harbage, Mr William J H MA(Cantab) M *Jul 1983*
(Q.C.) *12, 15, 62, 63, 86, 68*
36 Bedford Row, London WC1
p925 . . . 020 7421 8000

Harbottle, Gwilym Thomas BA(Oxon) L *Nov 1987*
6, 8, 11, 12, 15, 18, 22, 25, 30
Hogarth Chambers, London WC2
p937 . . . 020 7404 0404

Harby, Mr David LLB(Hons); LLM(Lond) M *Jul 2006*
6, 7, 8, 10, 53, 11, 12, 97, 47, 67, 15, 20, 38, 25, 88, 30, 31, 32
College Chambers, Southampton
p992 . . . 023 8023 0338

Harden, Miss Claire M *Nov 2000*
72, 15, 62
9 Gough Square, London EC4
p935 . . . 020 7832 0500

Harding, Mr Ben I *Oct 2005*
11, 67, 24, 48, 5, 97
Kings Chambers, Leeds
p978 . . . 0113 242 1123
Kings Chambers, Manchester
p984 . . . 0161 832 9082

HARDING, Ms Cherry LLB(Lond) G *Nov 1978*
10, 20
1 King's Bench Walk, London EC4
p938 . . . 020 7936 1500

Harding, Mr Christopher LLB(Hons) I *Nov 1992*
Thomas More Chambers, London WC2
p952 . . . 020 7404 7000

Harding, Mr Jack M *Jan 2004*
59, 30, 40, 12, 53
1 Chancery Lane, London WC2
p928 . . . 0845 634 6666

Harding, Mr Mathew L *Oct 2002*
39 Park Square, Leeds
p978 . . . 0113 245 6633

Harding, Mr Richard A BA(Oxon) M *Oct 1992*
3, 7, 11, 24, 40
Keating Chambers, London WC2
p938 . . . 020 7544 2600

Harding, Mr Simon BA(Hons) M *Oct 1998*
18, 67, 12, 23, 22, 30
36 Bedford Row, London WC1
p925 . . . 020 7421 8000
Thomas More Chambers, London WC2
p952 . . . 020 7404 7000

HARDWICK, Mr Matthew MA(Cantab); Licence Specialise en Droit European(ULB) G *Oct 1994*
5, 6, 8, 11, 18, 40
3 Verulam Buildings, London WC1
p953 . . . 020 7831 8441

Hardy, Mrs Amanda LLB(Hons); LLM(Tax); AKC M *Nov 1993*
34, 37, 36, 29, 8, 9
15 Old Square, London WC2
p945 . . . 020 7242 2744

HARDY, Mrs Lisa Marie L *Jan 2011*
1 High Pavement, Nottingham
p988 . . . 0115 941 8218

Hardy, Mr Max I *Jan 2004*
Nine Bedford Row, London WC1
p924 . . . 020 7489 2727

HARDY, Dr Stephen L *Oct 2005*
9 St John Street Chambers, Manchester
p984 . . . 0161 955 9000

Hardyman, Mr Matthew BA(Hons); CPE L *Jan 1997*
15 New Bridge Street Chambers, London EC4
p943 . . . 020 7842 1900

Hare, Mr Ivan LLB(Lond); BCL(Oxon); LLM(Harv); MA(Cantab) G *Oct 1991*
1, 18, 11, 89
Blackstone Chambers, London EC4
p926 . . . 020 7583 1770

Haren, Ms Sarah BA(Oxon); BCL(Oxon) M *Jan 1999*
8, 32, 37, 14
5 Stone Buildings, London WC2
p951 . . . 020 7242 6201

Hargan, Mr Carl LLB(Hons) L *Nov 1995*
St Johns Buildings, Preston
p990 . . . 01772 256100
St Johns Buildings, Chester
p974 . . . 01244 323070
St Johns Buildings, Manchester
p985 . . . 0161 214 1500
St Johns Buildings, Liverpool
p982 . . . 0151 243 6000

HARGREAVES, Mr Benjamin LLB(Hons) L *Nov 1989*
10, 12, 15, 20, 25, 30
Carmelite Chambers, London EC4
p927 . . . 020 7936 6300

Hargreaves, Miss Sara LLB(Lond) M *Jul 1979*
1, 8, 11, 49, 22, 29, 40, 60, 36, 37
Radcliffe Chambers, London WC2
p949 . . . 020 7831 0081

Hargreaves, Mr Simon J BA(Oxon) I *Oct 1991*
3, 7, 11, 24, 40
Keating Chambers, London WC2
p938 . . . 020 7544 2600

Hargreaves, Ms Teresa L *Nov 1999*
30, 53, 62, 56, 63, 40, 27, 68, 94
No5 Chambers, Bristol
p971 . . . 0845 210 5555
No5 Chambers, London EC4
p944 . . . 0845 210 5555
No5 Chambers, Birmingham
p968 . . . 0845 210 5555

HARINGTON, Miss Amanda L *Jul 1989*
49, 41, 3, 5, 8, 11, 97, 67, 69, 81, 62, 38, 21, 89, 96, 79, 29, 86, 32, 40, 93, 37
XXIV Old Buildings, London WC2
p944 . . . 020 7691 2424

Harkus, Mr George MA; LLB I *Nov 1975*
12, 15, 20
Goldsmith Chambers, London EC4
p935 . . . 020 7353 6802

Harland, Mr Rob M *Oct 2006*
10, 20, 15, 18, 30, 12
7 Bedford Row, London WC1
p924 . . . 020 7242 3555

HARLING-PHILLIPS, Emma G *Jan 2009*
1, 46, 31, 93
Landmark Chambers, London EC4
p941 . . . 020 7430 1221

HARMAN, Miss Sarah Jane BA(Oxon); Junior Counsel to the Crown (A) L *Nov 1987*
6, 11, 29
4 Stone Buildings, London WC2
p951 . . . 020 7242 5524

Harmer, Miss Christine BA M *Jul 1973*
10, 20
Broad Chare Chambers, Newcastle upon Tyne
p986 . . . 0191 232 0541

HAROUNOFF, Mr David BA(Sussex) M *Nov 1984*
15
9-12 Bell Yard Chambers, London WC2
p926 . . . 020 7400 1800

HARPER, Mr Joseph BA; LLM(Lond) G *Jul 1970*
(Q.C.) *22, 31, 93*
Landmark Chambers, London EC4
p941 . . . 020 7430 1221
Trinity Chambers, Chelmsford
p974 . . . 01245 605040

Harper, Mr Mark BA(Cantab) L *Oct 1993*
5, 6, 7, 8, 9, 11, 22, 29, 32, 40, 41, 45, 49
Kings Chambers, Leeds
p978 . . . 0113 242 1123
Kings Chambers, Manchester
p984 . . . 0161 832 9082

HARPUM, Dr Charles LLD L *Jul 1976*
Falcon Chambers, London EC4
p933 . . . 020 7353 2484

HARRAP, Mr Giles Thresher LLB(Lond); Recorder I *Nov 1971*
8, 12, 20, 25, 30, 36, 27, 32, 49
Pump Court Chambers, Swindon
p993 . . . 01793 539899
Pump Court Chambers, Winchester
p994 . . . 01962 868161
Pump Court Chambers, London EC4
p947 . . . 020 7353 0711

HARRAP, Mr Robert BA(Hons)(UCL) I *Oct 1997*
23, 18, 22
Five Paper, London EC4
p946 . . . 020 7815 3200

HARRIES, Mr Mark L *Oct 1995*
Carmelite Chambers, London EC4
p927 . . . 020 7936 6300

Harrill, Ms Jayne BA(Hons) M *Oct 1990*
10, 20, 14
4 Brick Court Chambers, London EC4
p927 . . . 020 7832 3200

Harrington, Ms Clare LLB(Hons); LLM L *Oct 1998*
King's Bench Chambers, Oxford
p989 . . . 01865 311066
13 King's Bench Walk, London EC4
p940 . . . 020 7353 7204

HARRINGTON, Mr Patrick LLB(Lond); Recorder G *Nov 1973*
(Q.C.) *15, 12*
Farrar's Building, London EC4
p933 . . . 020 7583 9241

Harrington, Miss Rebecca G *Jan 2004*
12, 20, 36, 37, 8
Thirty Park Place, Cardiff
p973 . . . 029 2039 8421

HARRINGTON, Mr Timothy M G *Mar 1997*
15, 12, 51
Citadel Chambers, Birmingham
p967 . . . 0121 233 8500

HARRINGTON, Miss Tina Amanda BA(Hons) M *Oct 1985*
10, 20
Trinity Chambers, Chelmsford
p974 . . . 01245 605040

HARRIS, Mr Adrian LLB(Hons) I *Oct 2001*
23 Essex Street, London WC2
p932 . . . 020 7413 0353

Harris, Miss Alexandra LLB G *Jul 1989*
Holborn Chambers, London WC2
p937 . . . 020 7242 6060

Harris, Ms Amelia M *Jan 2006*
1 Hare Court, London EC4
p936 . . . 020 7797 7070

Harris, Miss Annemarie BA M *Jul 1975*
10, 12, 20
3 Dr Johnson's Buildings, London EC4
p930 . . . 020 7353 4854

HARRIS, Miss Caroline I *Nov 2004*
15, 10, 20
1 King's Bench Walk, London EC4
p938 . . . 020 7936 1500

HARRIS, Mr Christopher LLB; LLM(Leidan) L *Jan 2002*
6, 5, 24, 62, 50
3 Verulam Buildings, London WC1
p953 . . . 020 7831 8441

Harris, Miss Claire L *Oct 1998*
15, 23, 20
4 Rowchester Court, Birmingham
p968 . . . 0121 233 2327

HARRIS, Mr Craig M *Jul 2006*
Furnival Chambers, London EC4
p934 . . . 020 7405 3232

Harris, Mr David LLB(Hons) L *Jan 1997*
22, 30, 32, 96
St Albans Chambers, St Albans
p992 . . . 01727 843383

Harris, Mr David A BA G *Oct 1990*
10, 12, 15, 18, 20, 22, 30, 36
Iscoed Chambers, Swansea
p993 . . . 01792 652988

Harris, Mr David Raymond LLM(Lond); LLM; Head of Chambers L *Nov 1973*
34, 57, 58
Prince Henry's Chambers, London WC1
p947 . . . 020 7837 1645

Harris, Miss Eleanor MA(Cantab) M *Jan 2000*
20, 10
1 Hare Court, London EC4
p936 . . . 020 7797 7070

Harris, Ms Elizabeth LLB(Hons) I *Feb 1992*
10, 20
Angel Chambers, Swansea
p992 . . . 01792 464623

Harris, Miss Frances BA(Oxon) L *Jan 2005*
20, 10
Harcourt Chambers, London EC4
p936 . . . 0844 561 7135
Harcourt Chambers, Oxford
p989 . . . 0844 561 7135

Harris, Mr Glenn L *Oct 1994*
15, 62
4 Breams Buildings, London EC4
p927 . . . 020 7092 1900

Harris, Mr Ian I *Oct 1990*
15
Exchange Chambers, Manchester
p983 . . . 0161 833 2722
Exchange Chambers, Liverpool
p980 . . . 0151 236 7747
Exchange Chambers, Leeds
p977 . . . 0113 203 1970

Harris, Mr Jake LLB M *Jul 2000*
12, 15, 20, 22, 30, 18
Goldsmith Chambers, London EC4
p935 . . . 020 7353 6802

Harris, Mr James MA(Oxon) G *Nov 1975*
12, 22, 7, 8, 45
5 St Andrew's Hill, London EC4
p950 . . . 020 7332 5400

HARRIS, Mr Julian Gilbert M *Oct 1982*
15
Citadel Chambers, Birmingham
p967 . . . 0121 233 8500

HARRIS, Miss Katie LLB(Hons) I *Nov 2005*
20
Octagon House, Norwich
p988 . . . 01603 623186

Harris, Mr Lance L *Jan 2011*
Old Square Chambers, Bristol
p971 . . . 0117 930 5100
Old Square Chambers, London WC1
p945 . . . 020 7269 0300

Harris, Mr Lee I *Jan 1997*
No 3 Fleet Street Chambers, London EC4
p944 . . . 020 7936 4474
4 King's Bench Walk, London EC4
p939 . . . 020 7822 7000
Two King's Bench Walk, London EC4
p939 . . . 020 7353 7202 / 7353 3909

HARRIS, Miss Lucinda M *Jan 2004*
30, 18, 11, 12, 55, 24
Devereux Chambers, London WC2
p930 . . . 020 7353 7534

Harris, Mr Luke LLB(Lond) I *Jul 2001*
6, 8, 9, 11, 32, 37
3 Stone Buildings, London WC2
p951 . . . 020 7242 4937

HARRIS, Mr Micheal BA(Hons)(Cantab) M *Oct 1993*
51, 23
10 King's Bench Walk, London EC4
p940 . . . 020 7353 7742

Harris, Ms Michelle M *Jul 2000*
15
1 Pump Court, London EC4
p947 . . . 020 7842 7070

Harris, Mr Miles G *Oct 2003*
Four New Square, London WC2
p943 . . . 020 7822 2000

HARRIS, Mr Paul LLB(Cantab); LLM(Berkeley) G *Oct 1994*
(Q.C.) *1, 11, 12, 19, 40, 56, 44*
Monckton Chambers, London WC1
p942 . . . 020 7405 7211

Harris, Mr Peter M *Jul 1980*
Clerksroom - Administration Centre, Taunton
p993 . . . 0845 083 3000

Harris, Miss Philippa G *Jan 2005*
88, 20, 93, 37
Hardwicke, London WC2
p936 . . . 020 7242 2523

Harris, Ms Rebecca M *Oct 1997*
15, 25, 36
QEB Hollis Whiteman, London EC4
p948 . . . 020 7933 8855

Harris, Mr Roger C J BA(Exeter) I *Oct 1996*
12, 18, 24, 30, 53
2 Temple Gardens, London EC4
p952 . . . 020 7822 1200

HARRIS, Mr Russell James MA(Cantab) G *Nov 1986*
(Q.C.) *1, 26, 31, 36, 46*
Landmark Chambers, London EC4
p941 . . . 020 7430 1221

HARRIS, Miss Sarah BA(Hons) G *Jan 2007*
15, 27, 36
23 Essex Street, London WC2
p932 . . . 020 7413 0353

Harris, Ms Stella G *Nov 2002*
15
Tooks Chambers, London EC4
p953 . . . 020 7842 7575

Harris, Mr Wilbert A. BA; FCIArb; Head of Chambers I *Nov 1973*
12, 15, 20, 30, 23
4 Rowchester Court, Birmingham
p968 . . . 0121 233 2327

Harris-Jenkins, Mr Philip LLB(Hons); Recorder G *Nov 1990*
12, 15, 30, 23, 41
Angel Chambers, Swansea
p992 . . . 01792 464623

Harrison, Mr Anthony L *Jul 2004*
15, 51
Tooks Chambers, London EC4
p953 . . . 020 7842 7575

Harrison, Mr Carl LLB(Hons) G *Nov 1997*
15, 62
Thirty Park Place, Cardiff
p973 . . . 029 2039 8421

Harrison, Ms Caroline Marie Alice MA(Oxon); MA(Lond) L *Jul 1986*
53, 27, 30, 59, 24, 40, 12
2 Temple Gardens, London EC4
p952 . . . 020 7822 1200

HARRISON, Mr Christopher BA(Cantab) G *Nov 1988*
6, 11, 29, 40
4 Stone Buildings, London WC2
p951 . . . 020 7242 5524

Harrison, Esther I *Jan 2002*
KCH Garden Square Chambers, Nottingham
p989 . . . 0115 941 8851
KCH Garden Square Chambers, Leicester
p979 . . . 0115 941 8851

Harrison, Mr Gordon LLB I *Jan 1996*
15, 62, 2, 18
Argent Chambers, London WC2
p923 . . . 020 7556 5500

Harrison, Dr Graeme MA; DPhil; DipLaw I *Jan 1997*
10, 20, 30, 53
12 College Place, Southampton
p992 . . . 023 8032 0320

Harrison, Mr J Keith LLB L *Nov 1983*
12, 15, 30
St Johns Buildings, Preston
p990 . . . 01772 256100
St Johns Buildings, Chester
p974 . . . 01244 323070
St Johns Buildings, Manchester
p985 . . . 0161 214 1500
St Johns Buildings, Liverpool
p982 . . . 0151 243 6000

Harrison, Mr James BA(Hons); PGDL L *Nov 2002*
15, 62
2 Bedford Row, London WC1
p924 . . . 020 7440 8888

Harrison, Mr John Foster BA(Hons); MSocSc; LLB(Hons) L *Oct 1994*
53, 12, 47, 67, 68, 72, 15, 70, 62, 84, 85, 27, 31
St Pauls Chambers, Leeds
p979 . . . 0113 245 5866

Harrison, Mr Jon BA L *Mar 2003*
15, 70, 62, 82
Lamb Building, Brighton
p970 . . . 01273 820490
Lamb Building, London EC4
p940 . . . 020 7797 7788

Harrison, Miss Leona BA M *Nov 1993*
10, 12, 20, 30
St Johns Buildings, Preston
p990 . . . 01772 256100
St Johns Buildings, Chester
p974 . . . 01244 323070
St Johns Buildings, Manchester
p985 . . . 0161 214 1500
St Johns Buildings, Liverpool
p982 . . . 0151 243 6000

HARRISON, Mr Michael LLB(Hons) I *Jan 1979*
15
23 Essex Street, London WC2
p932 . . . 020 7413 0353

Harrison, Mr Nicholas BA(Oxon) L *Jul 1988*
Serle Court, London WC2
p950 . . . 020 7242 6105

Harrison, Mr Peter BA(Dunelm) I *Jul 1987*
1, 12, 15, 26, 30, 31, 46, 51
6-8 Mill Street, Maidstone
p982 . . . 01622 688094 / 688095
6 Pump Court, London EC4
p947 . . . 020 7797 8400

Harrison, Mr Peter John LLB M *Jul 1983*
12, 24, 30, 53
St Johns Buildings, Preston
p990 . . . 01772 256100
St Johns Buildings, Chester
p974 . . . 01244 323070
St Johns Buildings, Manchester
p985 . . . 0161 214 1500
St Johns Buildings, Liverpool
p982 . . . 0151 243 6000

Harrison, Miss Petra BA I *Jul 2004*
10, 15, 20
St Johns Buildings, Preston
p990 . . . 01772 256100
St Johns Buildings, Chester
p974 . . . 01244 323070
St Johns Buildings, Manchester
p985 . . . 0161 214 1500
St Johns Buildings, Liverpool
p982 . . . 0151 243 6000

Harrison, Ms Philomena BA(Hons); DipLaw M *Nov 1985*
11, 22, 40, 8
Maitland Chambers, London WC2
p941 . . . 020 7406 1200

HARRISON, Mr Piers L *Mar 1997*
8, 11, 12, 22
Tanfield Chambers, London WC1
p951 . . . 020 7421 5300

Harrison, Miss Rachel LLB(Hons) I *Nov 1993*
15, 20
Paradise Chambers, Sheffield
p992 . . . 0114 273 8951

Harrison, Mr Richard BA(Cantab) L *Nov 1991*
1, 11, 12, 18, 36, 24, 26, 27, 40, 55
Devereux Chambers, London WC2
p930 . . . 020 7353 7534

HARRISON, Mr Richard Tristan MA(Cantab) I *Nov 1993*
10, 20, 96, 49
1 King's Bench Walk, London EC4
p938 . . . 020 7936 1500

Harrison, Mr Robert John McIntosh LLB L *Feb 1988*
12, 30, 53
Thirty Park Place, Cardiff
p973 . . . 029 2039 8421

Harrison, Mr Roger Recorder G *Feb 1970*
15
1 Paper Buildings, London EC4
p946 . . . 020 7353 3728

Harrison, Miss Sally BSc G *Oct 1992*
(Q.C.)
St Johns Buildings, Preston
p990 . . . 01772 256100
St Johns Buildings, Chester
p974 . . . 01244 323070
St Johns Buildings, Manchester
p985 . . . 0161 214 1500
St Johns Buildings, Liverpool
p982 . . . 0151 243 6000

HARRISON, Ms Sarah LLB(Hons) L *Nov 1989*
8, 9, 32, 40, 37
St James's Chambers, Manchester
p984 . . . 0161 834 7000

Harrison, Miss Susan Kathryn LLB(Bris) M *Oct 1993*
12, 20, 30, 15
18 St John Street Chambers, Manchester
p985 . . . 0161 278 1800

HARRISON-HALL, Mr Giles Arthur MA(Oxon) G *Jul 1977*
30, 40, 11, 93, 53
St Philips Chambers, Birmingham
p969 . . . 0121 246 7000

Harrod, Mr Henry MA(Oxon) L *Jul 1963*
8, 9, 14, 22, 29, 37, 58, 40, 2
5 Stone Buildings, London WC2
p951 . . . 020 7242 6201

Harrop Griffiths, Mr Hilton BA(Manc) I *Jul 1978*
Field Court Chambers, London WC1
p933 . . . 020 7405 6114

Harry, Mr Timothy Hawkins MA; BCL(Oxon); Accredited Mediator L *Jul 1983*
1, 3, 5, 6, 7, 8, 9, 11, 12, 13, 14, 22, 24, 26, 28, 29, 31, 32, 37
Maitland Chambers, London WC2
p941 . . . 020 7406 1200

HARRY THOMAS, Miss Caroline Jane LLB; Recorder M *Feb 1981*
(Q.C.) *10, 12, 14, 20, 27, 30, 49*
Littleton Chambers, London EC4
p941 . . . 020 7797 8600

Hart, Ms Amanda M *Jul 2001*
51, 18, 55
Doughty Street Chambers, London WC1
p930 . . . 020 7404 1313

HART, Mr Colin MA(Oxon) M *Nov 1966*
7, 12, 15, 22, 23, 25, 30
10 King's Bench Walk, London EC4
p940 . . . 020 7353 7742

HART, Mr David BA(Cantab) M *Jul 1982*
(Q.C.) *1, 12, 27, 30, 31, 40, 42, 46, 51, 53*
1 Crown Office Row, London EC4
p929 . . . 020 7797 7500

Hart, Ms Jenny BA(Hons); LLB(Hons) M *Oct 1993*
15, 20
1 Inner Temple Lane, London EC4
p937 . . . 020 7427 4400

Hart, Mr Neil BA(Oxon); DipLaw(City) G *Jan 1998*
Essex Court Chambers, London WC2
p931 . . . 020 7813 8000

Hart, Mr Paul LLB G *Jul 1982*
10, 20
15 Winckley Square, Preston
p991 . . . 01772 252828

Hart-Leverton, Mr Colin G *May 1957*
(Q.C.)
1 Mitre Court Buildings, London EC4
p942 . . . 020 7452 8900

Harte, Mr John David LLB G *Jul 1967*
17, 31
Broad Chare Chambers, Newcastle upon Tyne
p986 . . . 0191 232 0541

Harte, Mr Patrick L *Oct 2006*
15, 94
3 Temple Gardens, London EC4
p952 . . . 020 7353 3102

HARTHAN, Mr Peter James BA; BVC I *Oct 2007*
15, 30
7 Harrington Street Chambers, Liverpool
p981 . . . 0151 242 0707

Hartley, Mr Anthony LLB G *Feb 1991*
23
No 8 Chambers, Birmingham
p968 . . . 0121 236 5514

Hartley, Bronia G *Jan 2006*
Zenith Chambers, Leeds
p979 . . . 0113 245 5438

HARTLEY, Miss Caroline M *Aug 2002*
20, 10
Pump Court Chambers, Swindon
p993 . . . 01793 539899
Pump Court Chambers, Winchester
p994 . . . 01962 868161
Pump Court Chambers, London EC4
p947 . . . 020 7353 0711

HARTLEY, Miss Charlotte G *Jul 2009*
10, 20, 15, 25, 22
1 King's Bench Walk, London EC4
p938 . . . 020 7936 1500

Hartley, Louise M *Jan 2008*
15 New Bridge Street Chambers, London EC4
p943 . . . 020 7842 1900

Hartley, Mr Richard A LLB(Hons); Recorder M *Jul 1985*
(Q.C.) *12, 30, 40, 53, 56*
Cobden House Chambers, Manchester
p983 . . . 0161 833 6000

HARTLEY, Mr Richard L C MA(Cantab) G *Jun 1956*
(Q.C.) *16, 52, 73*
One Brick Court, London EC4
p927 . . . 020 7353 8845

Hartley, Mr Timothy Guy LLB G *Jul 1970*
Park Court Chambers, Leeds
p978 . . . 0113 243 3277

Hartley-Davies, Mr Paul Kevil LLB; Recorder G *Jul 1977*
10, 12, 20, 25
Thirty Park Place, Cardiff
p973 . . . 029 2039 8421

Hartman, Mr Michael L *Nov 1975*
1, 5, 6, 7, 8, 11, 12, 13, 18, 22, 24, 30, 31, 32
Two King's Bench Walk, London EC4
p939 . . . 020 7353 7202 / 7353 3909

Hartshorn, Sabrina M *Nov 2001*
12, 15, 22, 30, 67
Zenith Chambers, Leeds
p979 . . . 0113 245 5438

HARTY, Mr Patrick BA(Cantab) L *Jan 2008*
11, 38, 97
Erskine Chambers, London WC2
p931 . . . 020 7242 5532

Harvey, Mr Colin G *Jan 1973*
York Chambers, York
p995 . . . 01904 620048
York Chambers, Newcastle upon Tyne
p987 . . . 0191 206 4677

Harvey, Mr John Gilbert LLB(Hons); Recorder G *Jan 1973*
30, 40, 53, 68, 94, 31, 46
No5 Chambers, Bristol
p971 . . . 0845 210 5555
No5 Chambers, London EC4
p944 . . . 0845 210 5555
No5 Chambers, Birmingham
p968 . . . 0845 210 5555

Harvey, Mr Jonathan BA(Cantab) I *Jul 1974*
12, 24, 27, 30, 40, 56
Henderson Chambers, London EC4
p937 . . . 020 7583 9020

Harvey, Miss Louise LLB(Hons) M *Jul 2000*
10, 12, 47, 20, 22, 25
College Chambers, Southampton
p992 . . . 023 8023 0338

Harvey, Ms Louise LLB L *Oct 1991*
20, 10
15 Winckley Square, Preston
p991 . . . 01772 252828

HARVEY, Mr Michael MA; LLB(Cantab); Recorder G *Jul 1966*
(Q.C.) *74, 3, 5, 7, 11, 12, 24, 40*
Crown Office Chambers, London EC4
p929 . . . 020 7797 8100

Harvey, Miss Shona LLB(Shef) M *Nov 1999*
11, 12, 30, 40, 88
East Anglian Chambers, Norwich
p988 . . . 01603 617351
East Anglian Chambers, Colchester
p975 . . . 01206 572756
East Anglian Chambers, Chelmsford
p973 . . . 01245 215660
East Anglian Chambers, Ipswich
p976 . . . 01473 214481

HARVEY, Mr Stephen G *Jul 1979*
(Q.C.) *15, 25, 62, 91*
18 Red Lion Court, London EC4
p949 . . . 020 7520 6000
18 Red Lion Court (Annexe), Chelmsford
p973 . . . 01245 280880

HARVEY, Mr Tristan M *Jan 2002*
20, 12, 10
Queen Elizabeth Buildings, London EC4
p948 . . . 020 7797 7837

Harvie, Mr Jonathan MA(Oxon) M *Jul 1973*
(Q.C.) *1, 3, 11, 12, 24, 29, 36, 40, 41, 89, 51, 62*
Blackstone Chambers, London EC4
p926 . . . 020 7583 1770

HARWOOD, Mr Richard MA; LLM(Cantab) M *Nov 1993*
1, 46, 26, 28, 31
Thirty Nine Essex Street, London WC2
p932 . . . 020 7832 1111

See p1010 for the Key to Work Categories

HARWOOD-GRAY, Mr Barry L *Nov 1998*
18, 56, 55
Kenworthy's Chambers, Manchester
p984 . . . 0161 832 4036

Hasan, Miss Ayesha LLM(Cantab) G *Jul 1987*
10, 20, 21
3 Dr Johnson's Buildings, London EC4
p930 . . . 020 7353 4854

HASELHURST, Ian LLB(L'pool) G *Jul 1976*
10, 15
Atlantic Chambers, Liverpool
p980 . . . 0151 236 4421

HASKELL, Mr James I *Nov 2004*
15
Guildhall Chambers, Bristol
p970 . . . 0117 930 9000

Haslam, Mr Andrew P Recorder G *Oct 1991*
15, 94, 62, 84, 72
St Pauls Chambers, Leeds
p979 . . . 0113 245 5866

Hasslacher, Mr James BA M *Nov 1993*
15
4 Breams Buildings, London EC4
p927 . . . 020 7092 1900

Hasson, Mr James I *Nov 2006*
New Walk Chambers, Leicester
p979 . . . 0871 200 1298

Hastings, Miss Frances M BA; DipLaw I *Oct 1990*
15, 20, 22, 30
Charter Chambers, London WC1
p928 . . . 020 7618 4400

Hatch, Miss Lisa Sharmila LLB(Hons); LLM M *May 1995*
30, 12, 21, 11, 22, 45
One Essex Court, London EC4
p931 . . . 020 7936 3030

Hatfield, Miss Sally BA(Oxon) I *Nov 1988*
27, 40, 53, 68, 1, 76
42 Bedford Row, London WC1
p925 . . . 020 7831 0222
Doughty Street Chambers, London WC1
p930 . . . 020 7404 1313
Byrom Street Chambers, Manchester
p983 . . . 0161 829 2100

Hatt, Mr James BA(Oxon) L *Oct 2003*
40, 24, 11, 89
4 Pump Court, London EC4
p947 . . . 020 7842 5555

HATT, Miss Samantha M *Nov 2000*
15, 25, 27, 36
23 Essex Street, London WC2
p932 . . . 020 7413 0353

Hattan, Mr Simon BSc; DipLaw(City) M *Jan 1999*
5, 8, 11, 62, 29, 40, 36, 81
Serle Court, London WC2
p950 . . . 020 7242 6105

Hatton, Mr Andrew I *Nov 1987*
15, 25
No 6 Barristers Chambers, Leeds
p978 . . . 0113 245 9763

Hatton, Mr David William LLB G *Jul 1976*
(Q.C.) *15, 62*
Park Court Chambers, Leeds
p978 . . . 0113 243 3277
Fountain Chambers, Middlesbrough
p986 . . . 01642 804040

Hatton, Miss Theresa LLB(Hons) L *Mar 1998*
15, 20, 10
Rougemont Chambers, Exeter
p975 . . . 01392 208484

HAUGHEY, Ms Caroline M *Nov 1999*
Furnival Chambers, London EC4
p934 . . . 020 7405 3232

Haughty, Mr Jeremy Nicholas LLB; LLM(Exon) L *Nov 1989*
30, 18, 12, 29, 22, 55, 37
Rougemont Chambers, Exeter
p975 . . . 01392 208484

HAUGSTAUD, Annelise L *Jan 1996*
Fountain Chambers, Middlesbrough
p986 . . . 01642 804040

Haukeland, Mr Martin DipLaw; BA M *Feb 1989*
15, 20, 22, 30
42 Bedford Row, London WC1
p925 . . . 020 7831 0222

HAVEN, Mr Kevin LLM(Lond); DipIPL(London); BA(Hons)(Kent) G *Jul 1982*
30
Pallant Chambers, Chichester
p974 . . . 01243 784538

Havenhand, Barry M *Oct 1976*
Clerksroom - Administration Centre, Taunton
p993 . . . 0845 083 3000

HAVERS, The Hon Philip BA(Cantab) I *Jul 1974*
(Q.C.) *1, 12, 26, 27, 30, 36, 40, 42, 46, 51, 53*
1 Crown Office Row, London EC4
p929 . . . 020 7797 7500
Crown Office Row Chambers, Brighton
p970 . . . 01273 625625

Hawes, Mr Neil LLB I *Nov 1989*
Charter Chambers, London WC1
p928 . . . 020 7618 4400

Hawkes, Ms Naomi MA(Hons)(Cantab) M *Oct 1994*
22, 26, 30
42 Bedford Row, London WC1
p925 . . . 020 7831 0222

Hawkin, Mr Benjamin M *Oct 1998*
23, 15
Two King's Bench Walk, London EC4
p939 . . . 020 7353 7202 / 7353 3909

HAWKINS, Miss Charlene BA(Oxon) M *Jul 2008*
18, 11, 12, 55, 6, 56
Littleton Chambers, London EC4
p941 . . . 020 7797 8600

HAWKINS, Mr David J G *Oct 1991*
20
Bank House Chambers, Sheffield
p991 . . . 0114 275 1223

HAWKINS, Mr James BA; LLM M *Jan 2003*
12, 11, 30
3 Hare Court, London EC4
p937 . . . 020 7415 7800

Hawkins, Miss Lucy BA(Hons); CPE L *Nov 1994*
St Ives Chambers, Birmingham
p969 . . . 0121 236 0863

Hawkins, Mr Quinn LLB(Hons) L *Jan 1999*
15, 36
2 Hare Court, London EC4
p937 . . . 020 7353 5324

Hawkins, Mr Robert MSc L *Jan 1998*
12, 15
Temple Chambers, Newport
p988 . . . 01633 267403 / 255855
Temple Chambers, Cardiff
p973 . . . 029 2039 7364

HAWKS, Mr Anthony Joseph Vincent LLB; Recorder M *Nov 1975*
15, 26, 48, 84, 62
Trinity (Newcastle) Chambers, Newcastle upon Tyne
p987 . . . 0191 232 1927
Trinity (Teesside) Chambers, Middlesbrough
p986 . . . 01642 247569

HAWKS, Mr James Philip BA(Oxon); MA(Toronto); MTh(Lond) G *Nov 2003*
15
Chavasse Court Chambers, Liverpool
p980 . . . 0151 229 2030

Hawley, Ms Carol LLB G *Oct 1990*
15, 51
Tooks Chambers, London EC4
p953 . . . 020 7842 7575

Haworth, Mr Richard A LLB I *Nov 1978*
15, 25
15 Winckley Square, Preston
p991 . . . 01772 252828

HAY, Mr Benjamin MA(Cantab) M *Jul 2004*
Temple Garden Chambers, London EC4
p952 . . . 020 7583 1315

Hay, Miss Deborah M *Apr 1991*
1, 76
Hardwicke, London WC2
p936 . . . 020 7242 2523

Hay, Ms Fiona Ruth BSc; BA(Exon) I *Nov 1989*
20
Harcourt Chambers, London EC4
p936 . . . 0844 561 7135
Harcourt Chambers, Oxford
p989 . . . 0844 561 7135

Hay, Mrs Georgia S LLB(Lond); FSWW I *Oct 1999*
20, 12, 6, 15, 32, 37
Abbey Chambers, Shepperton
p992 . . . 01932 560913

Hay, Mr Malcolm BA(Oxon) G *Nov 1972*
10, 20
3 Dr Johnson's Buildings, London EC4
p930 . . . 020 7353 4854

Hay, Mr Robin MA; LLB(Cantab) I *Nov 1964*
30, 11, 27, 40, 53, 6, 12, 36
Lamb Chambers, London EC4
p941 . . . 020 7797 8300

Hay, Miss Teresa M *Jul 2001*
15, 62
5 Paper Buildings, London EC4
p946 . . . 020 7583 6117

Haycroft, Mr Anthony Mark LLB(Reading); BCL(Oxon) M *Nov 1982*
12, 15, 30, 53, 27, 62
Outer Temple Chambers, London WC2
p945 . . . 020 7353 6381

Hayden, Mr Anthony M *Nov 1987*
(Q.C.)
1 Pump Court, London EC4
p947 . . . 020 7842 7070
St Johns Buildings, Preston
p990 . . . 01772 256100
St Johns Buildings, Chester
p974 . . . 01244 323070
St Johns Buildings, Manchester
p985 . . . 0161 214 1500
St Johns Buildings, Liverpool
p982 . . . 0151 243 6000

Haydon, Mr Alec G BA(Cantab); LLM(Harv) G *Oct 1993*
11, 35, 5, 24
Brick Court Chambers, London WC2
p927 . . . 020 7379 3550

Hayes, Ms Christine M *Nov 1999*
20
East Anglian Chambers, Norwich
p988 . . . 01603 617351
East Anglian Chambers, Colchester
p975 . . . 01206 572756
East Anglian Chambers, Chelmsford
p973 . . . 01245 215660
East Anglian Chambers, Ipswich
p976 . . . 01473 214481

Hayes, Mr Jerry LLB M *Nov 1977*
15, 25, 62, 91, 28
Argent Chambers, London WC2
p923 . . . 020 7556 5500

Hayes, John LLB L *Nov 1992*
10, 20
Zenith Chambers, Leeds
p979 . . . 0113 245 5438

HAYES, Miss Josephine MA(Oxon); LLM L *Jul 1980*
5, 6, 8, 9, 11, 14, 22, 29, 32, 37
Gough Square Chambers, London EC4
p935 . . . 020 7353 0924

Hayes, Mrs Kathryn E M *Jan 2000*
Paradise Chambers, Sheffield
p992 . . . 0114 273 8951

HAYES, Mr Paul L *Mar 2005*
56, 11, 41, 12, 40, 24, 1
Thirty Nine Essex Street, London WC2
p932 . . . 020 7832 1111

Hayes, Mr Richard LLB L *Oct 1995*
11, 12, 22, 18, 8, 6, 24, 29, 47, 55
Lamb Chambers, London EC4
p941 . . . 020 7797 8300

HAYGARTH, Mr Edmund Bruce LLB(Lond) G *Nov 1988*
15
Chavasse Court Chambers, Liverpool
p980 . . . 0151 229 2030

Hayhoe, The Honourable Crispin L *Jan 2004*
15, 38, 11, 93, 18
Warwick House Chambers, London WC1
p953 . . . 020 7430 2323

Hayhow, Mrs Lyndsay LLB(Hons) I *Nov 1990*
15, 62
3 Temple Gardens, London EC4
p952 . . . 020 7353 3102

Hayhurst, Mr Benjamin David LLB(Hons) G *Nov 2004*
2 Pump Court, London EC4
p947 . . . 020 7353 5597

Haymerle, Mr Friedrich I *Oct 2000*
15
Tooks Chambers, London EC4
p953 . . . 020 7842 7575

Hayne, Ms Janette BA(Hons) I *Nov 1991*
15
4 Breams Buildings, London EC4
p927 . . . 020 7092 1900

Haynes, Mr Matthew T B BA L *Nov 1991*
8, 11, 12, 15, 20, 22, 30, 37
St Ives Chambers, Birmingham
p969 . . . 0121 236 0863

Haynes, Mr Michael John LLB G *Jul 1979*
15, 62
2 Bedford Row, London WC1
p924 . . . 020 7440 8888

HAYNES, Mr Peter LLB(B'ham) G *Jul 1983*
(Q.C.) *15, 71, 62*
St Philips Chambers, Birmingham
p969 . . . 0121 246 7000

HAYNES, Miss Rebecca LLB; LLM(Lond) I *Nov 1994*
1, 2, 6, 11, 18, 19, 23, 40, 44, 57
Monckton Chambers, London WC1
p942 . . . 020 7405 7211

HAYTON, Mrs Linda LLB L *Nov 1975*
1, 12, 22, 26, 37
Arden Chambers, London WC1
p923 . . . 020 7242 4244

HAYWARD, Mr James M *Jan 1985*
20, 10, 12
Colleton Chambers, Exeter
p975 . . . 01392 274898

Hayward, Mr Peter M BA; BCL(Oxon) G *Jul 1974*
3, 24
30 Brooksby Street, London N1
p927 . . . 020 7607 3854

Haywood, Miss Janet BA; DipLaw I *Jul 1985*
10, 20
Guildford Chambers, Guildford
p975 . . . 01483 539131

HAYWOOD, Janette LLM(Lond); LLB(Cardiff) M *Nov 1977*
10, 20
Renaissance Chambers, London WC1
p949 . . . 020 7404 1111

Haywood, Jennifer MA; DipLaw L *Jul 2001*
8, 11
Serle Court, London WC2
p950 . . . 020 7242 6105
Zenith Chambers, Leeds
p979 . . . 0113 245 5438

HAYWOOD, Mr Marcus BA(Oxon) L *Nov 2002*
5, 6, 11, 8, 97, 38
South Square, London WC1
p950 . . . 020 7696 9900

Haywood, Mr Phil BA M *Mar 2001*
23, 51
Doughty Street Chambers, London WC1
p930 . . . 020 7404 1313

HEAD, Mr David BA(Hons)(Oxon) M *Nov 1997*
5, 6, 11, 40
3 Verulam Buildings, London WC1
p953 . . . 020 7831 8441

Head, Mr Peter James BA; MA(Cantab); LLB L *Oct 2008*
89, 5, 6, 8, 38
11 Stone Buildings, London WC2
p951 . . . 020 7831 6381

HEADLAN, Mr Roy LLB G *Nov 1983*
15
Furnival Chambers, London EC4
p934 . . . 020 7405 3232

Heal, Ms Madeleine LLM(LSE) L *Jan 1996*
13, 52, 44, 11
Hardwicke, London WC2
p936 . . . 020 7242 2523

HEALD, Mr Jeremy BSc(Hons)(Dunelm) M *Jan 2010*
13, 45
3 New Square, London WC2
p943 . . . 020 7405 1111

HEALEY, Mr Greville MA(Cantab); B Phil; D Phil(Oxon); DipLaw(City) I *Oct 2002*
Falcon Chambers, London EC4
p933 . . . 020 7353 2484

Healey, Ms Susan BA(Hons) M *Jul 1995*
10, 20
Crown Office Row Chambers, Brighton
p970 . . . 01273 625625

Healing, Ms Yvonne LLB(Hons) I *Jan 1987*
20, 10
18 St John Street Chambers, Manchester
p985 . . . 0161 278 1800

13

HEALY, Miss Alexandra MA(Cantab) G *Oct 1992*
(Q.C.) *15*
9-12 Bell Yard Chambers, London WC2
p926 . . . . . 020 7400 1800

Healy, Mr Sam G *Jul 1999*
York Chambers, York
p995 . . . . . 01904 620048
York Chambers, Newcastle upon Tyne
p987 . . . . . 0191 206 4677

Healy, Miss Sandra Ita BA; LLB M *Jul 2007*
41, 3, 5, 11, 78, 24, 40, 35
Stone Chambers, London WC1
p951 . . . . . 020 7440 6900

Healy, Ms Sioban BA(Oxon); LOM(Uni Chicago) I *Jul 1993*
(Q.C.) *3, 5, 11, 24, 35*
7 King's Bench Walk, London EC4
p940 . . . . . 020 7910 8300

Heap, Dr Emma BSc; MBBS; MRc Psych I *Nov 2004*
30, 40, 53, 22, 63, 27, 88, 89
Hailsham Chambers, London EC4
p936 . . . . . 020 7643 5000

Heap, Gerard G *Jan 1985*
Clerksroom - Administration Centre, Taunton
p993 . . . . . 0845 083 3000

Heard, Mr Jonathan M *Jan 2004*
18, 55, 48
Queen Square Chambers, Bristol
p972 . . . . . 0117 921 1966

HEARN, Mr Nicholas M *Jan 2007*
Furnival Chambers, London EC4
p934 . . . . . 020 7405 3232

HEARNDEN, Miss Alexis BA I *Oct 2005*
12, 1, 63, 30, 11, 7, 67, 26, 23, 14
Thirty Nine Essex Street, London WC2
p932 . . . . . 020 7832 1111

HEARNDEN, Mr Richard G *Mar 1998*
Furnival Chambers, London EC4
p934 . . . . . 020 7405 3232
5 Pump Court, London EC4
p947 . . . . . 020 7353 2532 / 7583 7133

HEARNE, Miss Juliet G *Jan 1989*
20, 10, 93
Cornwall Street Chambers, Birmingham
p967 . . . . . 0121 233 7500

HEATH, Mr Duncan MA; LLB; GDL; BVC L *Nov 2007*
6, 8, 11, 12, 14, 18, 29, 32, 37, 38, 40, 47, 66, 67, 88, 93
Enterprise Chambers, London WC2
p931 . . . . . 020 7405 9471
Enterprise Chambers, Leeds
p977 . . . . . 0113 246 0391
Enterprise Chambers, Newcastle upon Tyne
p987 . . . . . 0191 222 3344

HEATH, Mr Stephen BA(Cantab) L *Feb 1992*
18
Tanfield Chambers, London WC1
p951 . . . . . 020 7421 5300

HEATHCOTE WILLIAMS, Mr Nicholas MA(Cantab); Recorder I *Nov 1976*
(Q.C.) *12, 24, 30, 40*
12 King's Bench Walk, London EC4
p940 . . . . . 020 7583 0811

HEATHER, Mr Christopher MA(Cantab) M *Oct 1995*
22, 40, 8, 45, 47, 11
Tanfield Chambers, London WC1
p951 . . . . . 020 7421 5300

Heaton, Clive MA(Oxon); Recorder G *Jul 1992*
(Q.C.) *10*
Zenith Chambers, Leeds
p979 . . . . . 0113 245 5438

Heaton, Mr David MA(Cantab) M *Jul 1983*
(Q.C.) *30, 53, 42*
42 Bedford Row, London WC1
p925 . . . . . 020 7831 0222
Byrom Street Chambers, Manchester
p983 . . . . . 0161 829 2100

HEATON, Miss Laura Jane BA(Cantab) M *Nov 1998*
20
29 Bedford Row, London WC1
p925 . . . . . 020 7404 1044

HEATON-ARMSTRONG, Mr Anthony LLB G *Jul 1973*
15
9-12 Bell Yard Chambers, London WC2
p926 . . . . . 020 7400 1800

Heckscher, Mr William H LLB(Hons) I *Oct 2006*
20, 10, 14
Albion Chambers, Bristol
p970 . . . . . 0117 927 2144

Hedgecoe, Mr John Philip LLB(Hull) I *Nov 1972*
7, 12, 15, 30
St Johns Buildings, Preston
p990 . . . . . 01772 256100
St Johns Buildings, Chester
p974 . . . . . 01244 323070
St Johns Buildings, Manchester
p985 . . . . . 0161 214 1500
St Johns Buildings, Liverpool
p982 . . . . . 0151 243 6000

HEDLEY, Mr Richard P LLB(Leics); Recoreder M *Nov 1983*
11, 5, 40, 7, 26, 1, 29, 31
Ropewalk Chambers, Nottingham
p989 . . . . . 0115 947 2581

HEDWORTH, Mr Alan Toby MA(Cantab); Recorder 1991 I *Jul 1975*
(Q.C.) *15, 1, 31, 91*
Trinity (Teesside) Chambers, Middlesbrough
p986 . . . . . 01642 247569
Trinity (Newcastle) Chambers, Newcastle upon Tyne
p987 . . . . . 0191 232 1927

HEDWORTH, Mr Leonard BSc; DipLaw L *Jul 1979*
15
10 King's Bench Walk, London EC4
p940 . . . . . 020 7353 7742

HEDWORTH, Miss Rachel LLB I *Jul 1999*
15, 2, 48
Trinity (Newcastle) Chambers, Newcastle upon Tyne
p987 . . . . . 0191 232 1927
Trinity (Teesside) Chambers, Middlesbrough
p986 . . . . . 01642 247569

Heeley, Ms Michelle G *Jan 2001*
15, 25, 62, 70, 94
No5 Chambers, Bristol
p971 . . . . . 0845 210 5555
No5 Chambers, London EC4
p944 . . . . . 0845 210 5555
No5 Chambers, Birmingham
p968 . . . . . 0845 210 5555

HEER, Miss Deanna LLB(Hons) G *Jan 1994*
5 Paper Buildings, London EC4
p946 . . . . . 020 7583 6117

HEGARTY, Mr Kevin LLB(Newc); Recorder M *Nov 1982*
(Q.C.) *15, 46, 62, 84*
St Philips Chambers, Birmingham
p969 . . . . . 0121 246 7000

Heilbron, Miss Hilary MA(Oxon) G *Jul 1971*
(Q.C.) *11, 41*
Brick Court Chambers, London WC2
p927 . . . . . 020 7379 3550

Heimler, Mr George I *Jul 1978*
15, 18, 36, 38
4 Breams Buildings, London EC4
p927 . . . . . 020 7092 1900

HEINZ, Mr Volker I *Jan 1989*
41, 21
South Square, London WC1
p950 . . . . . 020 7696 9900

HELLEBRONTH, Miss Rosanna MA; BVC M *Oct 2004*
30, 68, 11
Crown Office Chambers, London EC4
p929 . . . . . 020 7797 8100

Hellens, Mr Matthew MA(Cantab) M *Oct 1992*
20, 10
3 Dr Johnson's Buildings, London EC4
p930 . . . . . 020 7353 4854

HELLER, Mrs Anne LLB(Hons); BA(Hons) M *Nov 1995*
51, 23
10 King's Bench Walk, London EC4
p940 . . . . . 020 7353 7742
12 Old Square, London WC2
p945 . . . . . 020 7404 0875

Hellman, Mr Stephen G I *Jul 1988*
33 Chancery Lane, London WC2
p928 . . . . . 020 7440 9950

HELME, Mr Ian BA(Hons) M *Jul 2005*
16, 52, 73
One Brick Court, London EC4
p927 . . . . . 020 7353 8845

HELME, Mr Ned BA; GDL; BVC L *Oct 2006*
1, 31, 55, 76, 51, 63, 25, 23
4-5 Gray's Inn Square, London WC1
p935 . . . . . 020 7404 5252

Helmi, Hala BA; MA M *Jan 2000*
15, 12, 30
3PB, London EC4
p946 . . . . . 020 7583 8055

HELMORE, Katie L *Jan 2009*
1, 46, 31, 93
Landmark Chambers, London EC4
p941 . . . . . 020 7430 1221

Hemerey, Ms Philippa G *Jan 2009*
1 Pump Court, London EC4
p947 . . . . . 020 7842 7070

HENDERSON, Mr Alasdair I *Jan 2009*
51, 18, 1, 68, 53, 30, 23, 33, 21, 12
1 Crown Office Row, London EC4
p929 . . . . . 020 7797 7500

Henderson, Mr Duncan L *Jan 2003*
13 Old Square Chambers, London WC2
p945 . . . . . 020 7831 4445

Henderson, Mr James LLB G *Nov 1997*
34, 57, 58, 37
Kings Chambers, Leeds
p978 . . . . . 0113 242 1123
Pump Court Tax Chambers, London WC1
p948 . . . . . 020 7414 8080
Kings Chambers, Manchester
p984 . . . . . 0161 832 9082

HENDERSON, Miss Josephine BSc(Hons); DipLaw I *Oct 1990*
22, 51, 26, 1
Five Paper, London EC4
p946 . . . . . 020 7815 3200

HENDERSON, Mr Lawrence LLB M *Nov 1990*
9-12 Bell Yard Chambers, London WC2
p926 . . . . . 020 7400 1800

Henderson, Mr Mark BA(Oxon) G *Oct 1994*
23, 51
Doughty Street Chambers, London WC1
p930 . . . . . 020 7404 1313

Henderson, Mr Neil BA I *Oct 2004*
3, 5, 6, 8, 11, 35
Stone Chambers, London WC1
p951 . . . . . 020 7440 6900

Henderson, Mr Simon BA(Durham) I *Oct 1993*
11, 12, 24, 30
4 Pump Court, London EC4
p947 . . . . . 020 7842 5555

Henderson, Mr William H BA(Cantab) I *Jul 1978*
8, 9, 32, 37, 40, 14
Serle Court, London WC2
p950 . . . . . 020 7242 6105

HENDRON, Mr Ashley L *Jan 2005*
Carmelite Chambers, London EC4
p927 . . . . . 020 7936 6300

Hendron, Mr Gerald James LLB(Hons)(Leeds) L *Oct 1992*
12, 15, 18, 20, 30, 11, 36
Broadway House Chambers, Leeds
p977 . . . . . 0113 246 2600
Broadway House Chambers, Bradford
p969 . . . . . 01274 722560

Hendry, Mrs Lucy I *Jan 1988*
3PB, Bournemouth
p969 . . . . . 01202 292102

Hendry, Mrs Sandra LLB G *Nov 1985*
10, 15, 20
Stour Chambers, Canterbury
p972 . . . . . 01227 764899

Hendy, Mr John LLB(Lond); LLM(Belfast); Bencher, Gray's Inn G *Jul 1971*
(Q.C.) *18, 19, 27, 30, 36, 51, 53, 55*
Old Square Chambers, Bristol
p971 . . . . . 0117 930 5100
Old Square Chambers, London WC1
p945 . . . . . 020 7269 0300

Hendy, Ms Pauline L *Nov 1985*
53, 30
Cloisters, London EC4
p928 . . . . . 020 7827 4000

Henke, Ms Ruth Sara Margaret MA(Oxon) I *Nov 1987*
(Q.C.) *1, 10, 20, 26, 14, 76, 63*
Thirty Park Place, Cardiff
p973 . . . . . 029 2039 8421

HENLEY, Mr Andrew M *Oct 1992*
15
Furnival Chambers, London EC4
p934 . . . . . 020 7405 3232

Henley, Miss Carly LLB L *Jul 2003*
10, 12, 20, 25, 30
Broad Chare Chambers, Newcastle upon Tyne
p986 . . . . . 0191 232 0541

HENLEY, Mr Christopher M G *Jul 1989*
Carmelite Chambers, London EC4
p927 . . . . . 020 7936 6300

Henley, Mark L *Oct 1994*
20, 30
Zenith Chambers, Leeds
p979 . . . . . 0113 245 5438

Henley, Mr Martin I *Oct 2004*
6 King's Bench Walk, London EC4
p939 . . . . . 020 7583 0695 / 7353 4931

HENNESSEY, Mr Patrick M *Jul 2010*
94, 84, 74, 68, 53, 42, 40, 30, 24, 11, 1
Thirty Nine Essex Street, London WC2
p932 . . . . . 020 7832 1111

Hennessey, Miss Tracey LLB(Hons) L *Jul 2001*
10, 20
12 College Place, Southampton
p992 . . . . . 023 8032 0320

HENNESSY, Ms Clare G *Jul 2009*
15, 62, 94
18 Red Lion Court, London EC4
p949 . . . . . 020 7520 6000
18 Red Lion Court (Annexe), Chelmsford
p973 . . . . . 01245 280880

HENNESSY, Ms Shirley BA(Oxon) L *Oct 1997*
12, 30, 22, 40, 96, 84, 88, 53
Oriel Chambers, Liverpool
p981 . . . . . 0151 236 7191 / 236 4321
Oriel Chambers, Preston
p990 . . . . . 01772 254764

HENRY, Miss Annette LLB G *Jul 1984*
15, 62, 72
25 Bedford Row, London WC1
p925 . . . . . 020 7067 1500

HENRY, Mr Delroy I *Oct 1999*
15, 51
Citadel Chambers, Birmingham
p967 . . . . . 0121 233 8500

Henry, Mr Edward L *Nov 1988*
15, 25, 36
QEB Hollis Whiteman, London EC4
p948 . . . . . 020 7933 8855

Henry, Mr Philip Ivan BA(Hons) G *Oct 1979*
62, 15, 65, 81, 39, 38, 84
9 Gough Square, London EC4
p935 . . . . . 020 7832 0500

Henry, Miss Winsome H BA M *Nov 1979*
10, 15, 20, 36
Staple Inn Chambers, London WC1
p951 . . . . . 020 7242 5240

Henshaw, Mr Andrew BA; MA(Cantab) I *Oct 2000*
11, 5, 1
Brick Court Chambers, London WC2
p927 . . . . . 020 7379 3550

Henson, Miss Christine BA(Jt Hons) M *Oct 1994*
15
Crown Office Row Chambers, Brighton
p970 . . . . . 01273 625625

Henson, Mr Graham G *Jul 1976*
15, 62, 72
No5 Chambers, Bristol
p971 . . . . . 0845 210 5555
No5 Chambers, London EC4
p944 . . . . . 0845 210 5555
No5 Chambers, Birmingham
p968 . . . . . 0845 210 5555

HENSTOCK-TURNER, Ms Sarah LLB(Hons); LLM M *Oct 2004*
10, 12, 18, 20, 30
College Chambers, Southampton
p992 . . . . . 023 8023 0338

Henthorn, Miss Kate LLB M *Mar 2005*
20
18 St John Street Chambers, Manchester
p985 . . . . . 0161 278 1800

Henton, Mr Paul I *Jan 2004*
Quadrant Chambers, London EC4
p948 . . . . . 020 7583 4444

Hepher, Mr Paul Arthur Richard MA(Oxon) G *Jan 1994*
20, 10
4 Paper Buildings, London EC4
p946 . . . . . 020 7583 0816

See p1010 for the Key to Work Categories

HEPPENSTALL, Miss Claire LLM(Lond) I *Nov 1990*
10, 20
1 Garden Court, London EC4
p934 . . . . . 020 7797 7900

HEPPENSTALL, Miss Rachael BSc(Hons) M *Aug 1997*
10, 20
9 St John Street Chambers, Manchester
p984 . . . . . 0161 955 9000

Heppinstall, Mr Adam BA(Hons)(Oxon) M *Oct 1999*
12, 22, 24, 30
Henderson Chambers, London EC4
p937 . . . . . 020 7583 9020

Hepworth, Miss Elizabeth G *Mar 2004*
20, 10, 3
3PB, Bournemouth
p969 . . . . . 01202 292102

Heraghty, Mr David BSc I *Oct 1995*
12, 15, 1
Tooks Chambers, London EC4
p953 . . . . . 020 7842 7575

Herberg, Mr Javan LLB(Lond); BCL(Oxon) L *Oct 1992*
(Q.C.) *1, 11, 24, 36, 51, 12, 89*
Blackstone Chambers, London EC4
p926 . . . . . 020 7583 1770

Herbert, Mr David G *Oct 1992*
2 New Street, Leicester
p979 . . . . . 0116 262 5906
XXIV Old Buildings, London WC2
p944 . . . . . 020 7691 2424

Herbert, Mr Donald Peter LLB G *Nov 1982* OBE
10, 15, 18, 20, 23, 51, 55
Tooks Chambers, London EC4
p953 . . . . . 020 7842 7575

HERBERT, Mr Douglas C LLB; Recorder M *Jul 1972*
30, 31, 40, 53
Ropewalk Chambers, Nottingham
p989 . . . . . 0115 947 2581

Herbert, Miss Jane G *Jan 2008*
10, 15, 20, 12, 30
Rougemont Chambers, Exeter
p975 . . . . . 01392 208484

HERBERT, Miss Kate G *Jan 2004*
12, 30, 11, 40, 53, 22, 29
Ropewalk Chambers, Nottingham
p989 . . . . . 0115 947 2581

Herbert, Mr Mark BA L *Jul 1974*
(Q.C.) *8, 9, 14, 34, 37, 57, 58, 96*
5 Stone Buildings, London WC2
p951 . . . . . 020 7242 6201

Herbert, Mrs Rebecca LLB I *Oct 1993*
12, 15
2 New Street, Leicester
p979 . . . . . 0116 262 5906

Herman, Mr Ray LLB I *Feb 1972*
15, 62
St Johns Buildings, Preston
p990 . . . . . 01772 256100
St Johns Buildings, Chester
p974 . . . . . 01244 323070
St Johns Buildings, Manchester
p985 . . . . . 0161 214 1500
St Johns Buildings, Liverpool
p982 . . . . . 0151 243 6000

Herman, Mr Saul I *Jul 2007*
15
3 Temple Gardens, London EC4
p952 . . . . . 020 7353 3102

Hermer, Mr Richard BA(Hons); DipLaw M *Oct 1993*
(Q.C.) *30, 27, 1, 22, 51, 71, 21*
Doughty Street Chambers, London WC1
p930 . . . . . 020 7404 1313

Herrity, Mr Peter BSc(Lond) L *Jul 1982*
15
Holborn Chambers, London WC2
p937 . . . . . 020 7242 6060

Herrmann, Mr Richard G *Jan 2004*
York Chambers, York
p995 . . . . . 01904 620048
York Chambers, Newcastle upon Tyne
p987 . . . . . 0191 206 4677

HERTZOG, Miss Frances Dawn LLB(L'pool) G *Nov 2001*
15, 62
7 Harrington Street Chambers, Liverpool
p981 . . . . . 0151 242 0707

Heslop, Mr Martin Sydney LLB; Recorder L *Jul 1972*
(Q.C.) *15, 25*
2 Hare Court, London EC4
p937 . . . . . 020 7353 5324

Hester, Mr Paul BA; DipLaw M *Jul 1989*
10, 12, 15, 20, 30
3PB, Bournemouth
p969 . . . . . 01202 292102

HETHERINGTON, Ms Tessa BA(Cantab); LLM(Harv) L *Jul 2004*
51, 18, 26, 1, 16, 55, 14, 36, 76
Matrix Chambers, London WC1
p942 . . . . . 020 7404 3447

Hevingham, Mr Paul G *Jan 2006*
No 8 Chambers, Birmingham
p968 . . . . . 0121 236 5514

HEWITT, Miss Alison B LLB(Lond) M *Jul 1984*
Temple Garden Chambers, London EC4
p952 . . . . . 020 7583 1315

Hewitt, Mr David BSc M *Jul 1991*
12, 15, 22, 20, 30, 18
5 St Andrew's Hill, London EC4
p950 . . . . . 020 7332 5400

Hewitt, Mr Edward LLB(Lond); BCL(Oxon) L *Jan 2007*
6, 8, 32, 37, 38, 86, 88, 93
9 Stone Buildings Barristers Chambers, London WC2
p951 . . . . . 020 7404 5055

Hewitt, Miss Wendy M *Nov 1999*
15, 62, 12
5 St Andrew's Hill, London EC4
p950 . . . . . 020 7332 5400

Hewson, Miss Barbara MA(Cantab); BA(Hons); DipLaw M *Nov 1985*
1, 11, 18, 19, 27, 40, 51, 63, 37
Hardwicke, London WC2
p936 . . . . . 020 7242 2523

Hext, Mr Neil LLB(Bris) G *Oct 1995*
12, 24, 30, 27, 40
Four New Square, London WC2
p943 . . . . . 020 7822 2000

Heybroek, Miss Jane Myrna LLB I *Jan 2003*
10, 15, 20, 23, 94
Bell Yard Chambers, London WC2
p926 . . . . . 020 7306 9292 / 7404 5138

Heylin, Mr Alexander M *Jan 2000*
15, 18
5 St Andrew's Hill, London EC4
p950 . . . . . 020 7332 5400

Heywood, Mr Mark G *Jul 1986*
15, 25, 70, 72, 62
No5 Chambers, Bristol
p971 . . . . . 0845 210 5555
No5 Chambers, London EC4
p944 . . . . . 0845 210 5555
No5 Chambers, Birmingham
p968 . . . . . 0845 210 5555
5 King's Bench Walk, London EC4
p939 . . . . . 020 7353 5638

Heywood, Mr Matthew LLB(Sussex) M *Jul 2006*
15, 20, 10
Eastbourne Chambers, Eastbourne
p975 . . . . . 01323 642102

Heywood, Mr Michael Edmondson BSc(Lond); FCIArb I *Jul 1975*
2, 5, 6, 8, 9, 11, 22, 29, 32, 40, 37
Radcliffe Chambers, London WC2
p949 . . . . . 020 7831 0081

HEYWORTH, Miss Alison BA(Hons) I *Mar 2001*
15
9 St John Street Chambers, Manchester
p984 . . . . . 0161 955 9000

Heyworth, Ms Catherine Louise LLB(Hons) I *Nov 1991*
10, 20, 76, 63
Thirty Park Place, Cardiff
p973 . . . . . 029 2039 8421

Hick, Mr Michael G *Oct 1995*
62, 15, 48, 13
5 Paper Buildings, London EC4
p946 . . . . . 020 7583 6117

Hickey, Mr Alexander Frederick BA(Hons)(Oxon) L *Jul 1995*
7, 40, 24, 78
4 Pump Court, London EC4
p947 . . . . . 020 7842 5555

Hickey, Mr Eugene L *Jul 1988*
15, 25, 62, 72
No5 Chambers, Bristol
p971 . . . . . 0845 210 5555
No5 Chambers, London EC4
p944 . . . . . 0845 210 5555
No5 Chambers, Birmingham
p968 . . . . . 0845 210 5555

HICKINBOTTOM, Miss Abigail BA I *Nov 2004*
Paradise Chambers, Sheffield
p992 . . . . . 0114 273 8951

Hickman, Mr Tom MA(Cantab); LLM(Toronto); Phd(Cantab) L *Oct 2003*
11, 1, 18, 51, 50, 52, 56, 19, 44, 23, 89, 95
Blackstone Chambers, London EC4
p926 . . . . . 020 7583 1770

Hicks, Mr Ben I *Jul 2001*
53, 12, 22, 25, 30, 40, 26
1 Chancery Lane, London WC2
p928 . . . . . 0845 634 6666

Hicks, Mr Edward MA(Cantab) M *Jan 2004*
11, 97, 47, 14, 38, 40, 93, 37
Radcliffe Chambers, London WC2
p949 . . . . . 020 7831 0081

Hicks, Mr Martin Leslie Arthur LLB(Lond) I *May 1977*
(Q.C.) *15, 62, 95*
2 Hare Court, London EC4
p937 . . . . . 020 7353 5324

Hicks, Mr Michael C BA(Cantab)(Nat Sci) I *Nov 1976*
13, 19, 44, 45, 48, 50
Hogarth Chambers, London WC2
p937 . . . . . 020 7404 0404

HICKS, Mr William David Anthony MA(Cantab) I *Jul 1975*
(Q.C.) *31, 36, 46*
Landmark Chambers, London EC4
p941 . . . . . 020 7430 1221

Hiddleston, Mr Adam LLB I *Oct 1990*
72, 15, 70
3PB, Winchester
p994 . . . . . 01962 868884

Higgins, Mr Adrian MA(Oxon) L *Oct 1990*
40
King's Bench Chambers, Oxford
p989 . . . . . 01865 311066
13 King's Bench Walk, London EC4
p940 . . . . . 020 7353 7204

Higgins, Mr Anthony BA(Hons)(Oxon); LLM(Lond) G *Nov 1978*
King's Bench Chambers, Oxford
p989 . . . . . 01865 311066
13 King's Bench Walk, London EC4
p940 . . . . . 020 7353 7204

Higgins, Mr Daniel Malcolm Buhlea MA(Cantab)(Law) I *Jan 2003*
15, 62
Nine Bedford Row, London WC1
p924 . . . . . 020 7489 2727

Higgins, Miss Gabrielle MA(Oxon) L *Jul 2002*
Maitland Chambers, London WC2
p941 . . . . . 020 7406 1200

Higgins, Miss Gillian G *Nov 1997*
Nine Bedford Row, London WC1
p924 . . . . . 020 7489 2727

Higgins, Mr Mark MA(Oxon) I *Jan 2005*
20, 10, 18, 12, 88
Harcourt Chambers, London EC4
p936 . . . . . 0844 561 7135
Harcourt Chambers, Oxford
p989 . . . . . 0844 561 7135

Higgins, Ms Nichola BA(Hons) L *Jul 2005*
15, 62
15 New Bridge Street Chambers, London EC4
p943 . . . . . 020 7842 1900

Higgins, Mr Rupert BA(Cantab); MA(Cantab) I *Oct 1991*
7, 11, 22, 49, 88, 38, 40, 93
Hardwicke, London WC2
p936 . . . . . 020 7242 2523

Higginson, Mr Peter LLB(Queens, Canada) I *Jul 1975*
Charter Chambers, London WC1
p928 . . . . . 020 7618 4400

HIGGINSON, Mr Timothy Nicholas B LLB; Accredited Mediator I *Nov 1977*
3, 5, 7, 8, 11, 12, 24, 29, 36, 40, 49
Littleton Chambers, London EC4
p941 . . . . . 020 7797 8600

Higginson, Mr William L *Oct 2001*
12, 15, 20
King's Bench Godolphin Chambers, Truro
p994 . . . . . 0845 308 1551
King's Bench Godolphin Chambers, Plymouth
p990 . . . . . 0845 308 1551

Higgo, Mr Justin BA(Oxon) G *Feb 1995*
5, 6, 8, 11, 12, 14, 32, 37, 40, 62
Serle Court, London WC2
p950 . . . . . 020 7242 6105

Higgs, Mr Jonathan BA M *Nov 1987*
(Q.C.) *15*
5 King's Bench Walk, London EC4
p939 . . . . . 020 7353 5638

Higgs, Miss Josephine Amy BA(Oxon) M *Nov 2000*
41, 5, 24
7 King's Bench Walk, London EC4
p940 . . . . . 020 7910 8300

Hignett, Mr Richard I *Nov 1995*
18, 55
No5 Chambers, Bristol
p971 . . . . . 0845 210 5555
No5 Chambers, London EC4
p944 . . . . . 0845 210 5555
No5 Chambers, Birmingham
p968 . . . . . 0845 210 5555

HIKMET, Miss Berin BSc(Bris) M *Oct 2000*
15, 21
Argent Chambers, London WC2
p923 . . . . . 020 7556 5500

Hildyard, Miss Marianna M *Nov 1977*
(Q.C.) *10, 20*
4 Brick Court Chambers, London EC4
p927 . . . . . 020 7832 3200

Hilken, Ms Alice Mary BA(Hons) M *Nov 1994*
22
1 Pump Court, London EC4
p947 . . . . . 020 7842 7070

HILL, Mr Gregory MA; BCL(Oxon) L *Jul 1972*
6, 8, 14, 22, 29, 11, 32, 34, 37
Ten Old Square, London WC2
p945 . . . . . 020 7405 0758

Hill, Ms Henrietta BA(Hons) I *Jan 1997*
12, 15, 18, 51, 1
Doughty Street Chambers, London WC1
p930 . . . . . 020 7404 1313

Hill, Mr James M LLB(Hons)(Manc) I *Jul 1984*
(Q.C.) *12, 15*
Broadway House Chambers, Leeds
p977 . . . . . 0113 246 2600
Fountain Chambers, Middlesbrough
p986 . . . . . 01642 804040
Broadway House Chambers, Bradford
p969 . . . . . 01274 722560

Hill, Mr Jonathan LLB(Hons) M *Oct 1997*
10, 20, 88, 25, 30
Pendragon Chambers, Swansea
p993 . . . . . 01792 411188

Hill, Mr Jonathon Bron L *Oct 2000*
13, 50, 45, 56
8 New Square, London WC2
p943 . . . . . 020 7405 4321

HILL, Mr Mark LLB M *Jul 1987*
(Q.C.) *1, 12, 11, 7, 31, 17, 29, 30, 32, 51*
9 St John Street Chambers, Manchester
p984 . . . . . 0161 955 9000
Pump Court Chambers, Swindon
p993 . . . . . 01793 539899
Pump Court Chambers, Winchester
p994 . . . . . 01962 868161
Pump Court Chambers, London EC4
p947 . . . . . 020 7353 0711

HILL, Mr Matthew BA(Hons); MSt; DipLaw I *Jan 2009*
51, 53, 18, 46, 68, 30, 56, 57, 58
1 Crown Office Row, London EC4
p929 . . . . . 020 7797 7500

HILL, Mr Max BA(Oxon) M *Nov 1987*
(Q.C.) *15, 62, 95, 68*
18 Red Lion Court, London EC4
p949 . . . . . 020 7520 6000
18 Red Lion Court (Annexe), Chelmsford
p973 . . . . . 01245 280880

HILL, Mr Michael BDS; DipCom Scd; PgDc G *Jun 2004*
11, 12, 38, 30, 53
Trinity (Newcastle) Chambers, Newcastle upon Tyne
p987 . . . . . 0191 232 1927
Trinity (Teesside) Chambers, Middlesbrough
p986 . . . . . 01642 247569

Hill, Miss Miranda M *Oct 1999*
15, 62, 36, 16
6 King's Bench Walk, London EC4
p939 . . . . . 020 7583 0410

13

Hill, Mr Nicholas Ian BA L *Oct 1993*
8, 11, 37, 22, 47, 6, 25
No 6 Barristers Chambers, Leeds
p978 . . . . . 0113 245 9763

Hill, Mr Piers LLB I *Jul 1987*
26, 31, 8, 37, 32, 22, 7
37 Park Square Chambers, Leeds
p978 . . . . . 0113 243 9422

HILL, Mr Raymond BA(Oxon) L *Oct 1992*
1, 18, 57
Monckton Chambers, London WC1
p942 . . . . . 020 7405 7211

HILL, Mr Richard Geoffrey BA(Cantab); Junior Counsel to the Crown (A) G *Oct 1993*
5, 6, 11, 29
4 Stone Buildings, London WC2
p951 . . . . . 020 7242 5524

HILL, Mr Thomas MA(Cantab) L *Jul 1988*
(Q.C.) *1, 46, 26, 28, 31*
4-5 Gray's Inn Square, London WC1
p935 . . . . . 020 7404 5252

Hill, Mr Timothy LLB(Lond); DLS; BCL(Oxon) M *Oct 1990*
(Q.C.) *11, 35, 3, 4, 5, 12, 24, 36, 40*
Stone Chambers, London WC1
p951 . . . . . 020 7440 6900

Hill-Baker, Mr Jeremy Robert LLB(Leeds); Recorder I *Jul 1983*
15
No 6 Barristers Chambers, Leeds
p978 . . . . . 0113 245 9763

HILL-SMITH, Mr Alexander George Levander MA; LLB; Immigration adjudicator G *Oct 1978*
New Square Chambers, London WC2
p943 . . . . . 020 7419 8000

HILLAS, Samantha LLB I *Oct 1996*
20, 10
Atlantic Chambers, Liverpool
p980 . . . . . 0151 236 4421

Hilliard, Miss Alexandra LLB M *Nov 1987*
(Q.C.) *5, 11, 97, 62, 38, 40, 81*
11 Stone Buildings, London WC2
p951 . . . . . 020 7831 6381

Hilliard, Miss Emma L *Jul 2006*
41, 24, 35, 61
7 King's Bench Walk, London EC4
p940 . . . . . 020 7910 8300

HILLIARD, Mr Jonathan BA; LLM(Cantab) L *Oct 2003*
6, 9, 11, 22, 29, 32, 34, 37, 40
Wilberforce Chambers, London WC2
p953 . . . . . 020 7306 0102

Hilliard, Mr Nicholas BA(Oxon); Senior Treasury Counsel M *Jul 1981*
15, 36
6 King's Bench Walk, London EC4
p939 . . . . . 020 7583 0410

HILLIER, Mr Andrew BA(Dublin) G *Jul 1972*
(Q.C.) *1, 12, 18, 19, 26, 27, 40, 55, 63*
11KBW, London EC4
p938 . . . . . 020 7632 8500

Hillier, Mr Nicholas Peter I *Jul 1982*
53, 30, 40
9 Gough Square, London EC4
p935 . . . . . 020 7832 0500

Hillier, Miss Victoria Jane G *Jul 2005*
15, 12, 22, 6
Civitas Law, Cardiff
p972 . . . . . 0845 071 3007

HILLIS, Mr John LLB G *Jul 1982*
12, 15
Bank House Chambers, Sheffield
p991 . . . . . 0114 275 1223

HILLMAN, Mr Basil MA(Mod) G *Nov 1968*
15
4 King's Bench Walk, London EC4
p939 . . . . . 020 7822 7000

HILLMAN, Mr Gerard G *Jan 1999*
15
Carmelite Chambers, London EC4
p927 . . . . . 020 7936 6300

Hillman, Mr Roger LLB(L'pool); Deputy District Judge G *Jul 1983*
20, 30, 18, 55
Exchange Chambers, Manchester
p983 . . . . . 0161 833 2722
Exchange Chambers, Liverpool
p980 . . . . . 0151 236 7747
Exchange Chambers, Leeds
p977 . . . . . 0113 203 1970

Hills, Mr Timothy James L *Jul 1968*
15
Albion Chambers, Bristol
p970 . . . . . 0117 927 2144

Hilton, Mr John M *Nov 1964*
(Q.C.) *15, 25, 36*
QEB Hollis Whiteman, London EC4
p948 . . . . . 020 7933 8855

Hilton, Mr Oliver James LLB(Lond) L *Jul 2002*
6, 8, 11, 32, 37
3 Stone Buildings, London WC2
p951 . . . . . 020 7242 4937

Hilton, Mr Simon BA(Oxon); Recorder G *Nov 1987*
11, 12, 30, 36, 47, 53
Kings Chambers, Leeds
p978 . . . . . 0113 242 1123
Kings Chambers, Manchester
p984 . . . . . 0161 832 9082

Himsworth, Ms Emma G *Oct 1993*
One Essex Court, London EC4
p931 . . . . . 020 7583 2000

Hinchcliffe, Prof Doreen PhD; LLB G *Nov 1953*
11, 20, 24
Argent Chambers, London WC2
p923 . . . . . 020 7556 5500
Renaissance Chambers, London WC1
p949 . . . . . 020 7404 1111

HINCHLIFFE, Mr Nicholas LLB; Recorder M *Nov 1980*
(Q.C.) *12, 27, 24, 30*
9 St John Street Chambers, Manchester
p984 . . . . . 0161 955 9000

HINCHLIFFE, Mr Thomas BA(Oxon) M *Oct 1997*
13
3 New Square, London WC2
p943 . . . . . 020 7405 1111

HIND, Mr Kenneth LLB(Hons) G *Jul 1973* CBE
15
Oriel Chambers, Liverpool
p981 . . . . . 0151 236 7191 / 236 4321
Oriel Chambers, Preston
p990 . . . . . 01772 254764

HINDMARSH, Mr Luke M *Mar 2007*
15
9-12 Bell Yard Chambers, London WC2
p926 . . . . . 020 7400 1800

Hinds, Oriel G LLB(Hons) I *Jul 1988*
96
Clerksroom - Administration Centre, Taunton
p993 . . . . . 0845 083 3000

HINGSTON, Mr Joe L *Jan 2007*
Carmelite Chambers, London EC4
p927 . . . . . 020 7936 6300

Hinks, Mr Frank MA; BCL(Oxon) L *Jul 1973*
(Q.C.) *8, 9, 14, 29, 32, 37, 40, 41, 93*
Serle Court, London WC2
p950 . . . . . 020 7242 6105

Hinks, Mr Philip Martyn LLB(Bris); BCL(Oxon) L *Oct 2008*
89, 5, 6, 8, 92, 38
11 Stone Buildings, London WC2
p951 . . . . . 020 7831 6381

Hiorns, Mr Roger Martin Fairchild M *Jul 1983*
30, 53
9 Gough Square, London EC4
p935 . . . . . 020 7832 0500

Hipkin, Mr John Leslie LLB G *Nov 1989*
10, 12, 15, 20, 30
Iscoed Chambers, Swansea
p993 . . . . . 01792 652988

Hirsch, Ms Georgina MBA G *Jan 2009*
18, 30
Devereux Chambers, London WC2
p930 . . . . . 020 7353 7534

Hirst (nee Clapham), Miss Catherine Victoria BA I *Jul 1999*
12, 15, 30, 20
Guildford Chambers, Guildford
p975 . . . . . 01483 539131

Hirst, Mr David MA(Cantab) G *Oct 2003*
13, 16, 50, 56
5RB, London WC1
p948 . . . . . 020 7242 2902

Hirst, Mr Jonathan MA(Cantab) I *Jul 1975*
(Q.C.) *11, 24, 5, 35, 41*
Brick Court Chambers, London WC2
p927 . . . . . 020 7379 3550

Hirst, Mr Karl I *Oct 1997*
30, 40, 53, 68, 94
No5 Chambers, Bristol
p971 . . . . . 0845 210 5555
No5 Chambers, London EC4
p944 . . . . . 0845 210 5555
No5 Chambers, Birmingham
p968 . . . . . 0845 210 5555

HIRST, Miss Kathryn LLB I *Nov 1986*
Furnival Chambers, London EC4
p934 . . . . . 020 7405 3232

Hirst, Ms Leonie I *Oct 2006*
18, 51, 23, 55, 76, 63
Tooks Chambers, London EC4
p953 . . . . . 020 7842 7575

Hirst, Miss Rebecca LLB(Hons) G *Nov 1999*
15, 25, 94
Cobden House Chambers, Manchester
p983 . . . . . 0161 833 6000

HIRST, Mr Simon David LLB; Recorder L *Oct 1993*
15, 20, 10
Wilberforce Chambers, Hull
p976 . . . . . 01482 323264

Hirst, Ms Susan M *Jan 2001*
New Court Chambers, Newcastle upon Tyne
p987 . . . . . 0191 232 1980

Hislop, Mr David LLB; NZ Bar(1979) G *Feb 1989*
15, 51, 91
Doughty Street Chambers, London WC1
p930 . . . . . 020 7404 1313

Hitchcock, Jodie-Jane M *Jan 2006*
15 New Bridge Street Chambers, London EC4
p943 . . . . . 020 7842 1900

Hitchcock, Ms Patricia I *Nov 1988*
53, 27, 30, 40
Cloisters, London EC4
p928 . . . . . 020 7827 4000

Hitchcock, Mr Richard Guy BA(Oxon) M *Nov 1989*
18, 8, 92
Outer Temple Chambers, London WC2
p945 . . . . . 020 7353 6381

Hitchens, Miss Erin BA(Cantab) L *Jan 2006*
49, 41, 3, 5, 6, 8, 11, 97, 67, 62, 38, 24, 21, 89, 32, 40, 37
XXIV Old Buildings, London WC2
p944 . . . . . 020 7691 2424

HITCHING, Ms Isabel M *Nov 1992*
11, 74, 12, 7, 24, 40, 41, 3, 96
Crown Office Chambers, London EC4
p929 . . . . . 020 7797 8100

HITCHMOUGH, Mr Andrew LLB I *Oct 1991*
34, 57, 58
Pump Court Tax Chambers, London WC1
p948 . . . . . 020 7414 8080

Ho, Mr Edward M *Jul 2009*
3, 5, 11, 78, 24, 35, 41, 49, 43, 47, 54
20 Essex Street, London WC2
p932 . . . . . 020 7842 1200

Hoare, Mr Gregory Blake LLB G *Nov 1992*
15
Exchange Chambers, Manchester
p983 . . . . . 0161 833 2722
Exchange Chambers, Liverpool
p980 . . . . . 0151 236 7747
Exchange Chambers, Leeds
p977 . . . . . 0113 203 1970

Hobbs, Mr Daniel S LLB(Hons) L *Oct 1998*
18, 55, 30, 40
13 King's Bench Walk, London EC4
p940 . . . . . 020 7353 7204

HOBBS, Ms Emma-Jane BA(Bris) G *Oct 1996*
Temple Garden Chambers, London EC4
p952 . . . . . 020 7583 1315

Hobbs, Mr Geoffrey I *Jul 1977*
(Q.C.)
One Essex Court, London EC4
p931 . . . . . 020 7583 2000

Hobbs, Miss Naomi LLB G *Oct 1993*
10, 20, 22
No 8 Chambers, Birmingham
p968 . . . . . 0121 236 5514

Hobbs, Mrs Ruth LLB(Hons); DipLaw; BVC L *Jul 2007*
15, 62, 70, 94
15 New Bridge Street Chambers, London EC4
p943 . . . . . 020 7842 1900

Hobcraft, Ms Gemma BA(Hons)(History); PGDipLaw; LLM(Human Rights Law) L *Jan 2006*
15, 51
Doughty Street Chambers, London WC1
p930 . . . . . 020 7404 1313

HOBHOUSE, Ms Helen BSocSc I *Oct 1990*
30, 18, 12
Farrar's Building, London EC4
p933 . . . . . 020 7583 9241

HOBSON, Mr Fred L *Jan 2005*
5, 81, 41, 11, 40
3 Verulam Buildings, London WC1
p953 . . . . . 020 7831 8441

HOBSON, Mr John LLM(Cantab) I *Jul 1980*
(Q.C.) *1, 22, 26, 28, 31, 36, 51*
4-5 Gray's Inn Square, London WC1
p935 . . . . . 020 7404 5252
Doughty Street Chambers, London WC1
p930 . . . . . 020 7404 1313

HOBSON, Miss Laura G *Jan 2003*
Citadel Chambers, Birmingham
p967 . . . . . 0121 233 8500

Hobson, Mr Paul G *Jul 2001*
Iscoed Chambers, Swansea
p993 . . . . . 01792 652988

Hobson, Miss Sally LLM I *Apr 1991*
15, 84, 48, 70
1 Paper Buildings, London EC4
p946 . . . . . 020 7353 3728

HOCHBERG, Mr Daniel Alan MA(Oxon) L *Jul 1982*
5, 8, 9, 11, 49, 22, 62, 29, 32, 40, 37
Wilberforce Chambers, London WC2
p953 . . . . . 020 7306 0102

Hochhauser, Mr Andrew R LLB; LLM(Lond) M *Jul 1977*
(Q.C.)
Essex Court Chambers, London WC2
p931 . . . . . 020 7813 8000

Hockman, Mr Stephen MA(Cantab) M *Jul 1970*
(Q.C.) *1, 12, 15, 26, 30, 31, 46, 51*
6-8 Mill Street, Maidstone
p982 . . . . . 01622 688094 / 688095
6 Pump Court, London EC4
p947 . . . . . 020 7797 8400
Regency Chambers, Peterborough
p990 . . . . . 01733 315215

HOCKNELL, Miss Laura I *Jan 2005*
Carmelite Chambers, London EC4
p927 . . . . . 020 7936 6300

Hockton, Mr Andrew Ian Callinhan BA M *Nov 1984*
53, 40, 27, 63, 85, 68
3 Serjeants' Inn, London EC4
p950 . . . . . 020 7427 5000

Hodder, Philip LLB(Hons) L *Mar 2005*
Clerksroom - Administration Centre, Taunton
p993 . . . . . 0845 083 3000

HODGES, Miss Victoria LLB G *Jul 1980*
10, 20
St Mary's Chambers, Nottingham
p989 . . . . . 0115 950 3503

HODGETTS, Miss Elizabeth BA(Hons) M *Nov 1998*
18, 55
St Philips Chambers, Birmingham
p969 . . . . . 0121 246 7000

Hodgetts, Mr Glen I *Nov 1995*
1, 23, 51
Tooks Chambers, London EC4
p953 . . . . . 020 7842 7575

Hodgkin, Harry John LLB(Hons); MCIArb M *Jul 1983*
93
Clerksroom - Administration Centre, Taunton
p993 . . . . . 0845 083 3000

Hodgkin, Rebecca L *Nov 1991*
88
Clerksroom - Administration Centre, Taunton
p993 . . . . . 0845 083 3000

Hodgkinson, Mr Paul George L *Jul 2002*
15
St Johns Buildings, Preston
p990 . . . . . 01772 256100
St Johns Buildings, Chester
p974 . . . . . 01244 323070
St Johns Buildings, Manchester
p985 . . . . . 0161 214 1500
St Johns Buildings, Liverpool
p982 . . . . . 0151 243 6000

See p1010 for the Key to Work Categories

HODGKINSON, Mr Robert I *Nov 1968*
15, 2
St Philips Chambers, Birmingham
p969 . . . . 0121 246 7000

HODGSON, Mrs Jane L L *Oct 2000*
22, 51, 36, 38, 31
Arden Chambers, London WC1
p923 . . . . 020 7242 4244

Hodgson, Miss Margaret Julia LLB(Warw) L *Jul 1975*
10, 20
St Ives Chambers, Birmingham
p969 . . . . 0121 236 0863

Hodgson, Mr Martin M *Jan 1980*
22
1 Pump Court, London EC4
p947 . . . . 020 7842 7070

Hodgson, Mr Timothy P I *Nov 1991*
30, 22, 18, 53
Cobden House Chambers, Manchester
p983 . . . . 0161 833 6000

Hodivala, Mr Jamas LLB(Hons) L *Oct 1998*
1, 15, 51, 62
2 Bedford Row, London WC1
p924 . . . . 020 7440 8888

Hodkinson, Mr Gary M *Jan 2010*
11, 18, 22, 30, 51, 55, 67
Lamb Building, Brighton
p970 . . . . 01273 820490
Lamb Building, London EC4
p940 . . . . 020 7797 7788

HODSON, Mr Matthew LLB(Hons)(Lond) L *Nov 2004*
30, 11, 18, 93
Farrar's Building, London EC4
p933 . . . . 020 7583 9241

Hodson, Mr Michael Dip Ed M *Feb 1977*
15
New Court Chambers, Newcastle upon Tyne
p987 . . . . 0191 232 1980

Hodson, Mr Peter I *Nov 1994*
15, 30, 40, 27, 94, 51, 96
Garden Court North Chambers, Manchester
p983 . . . . 0161 236 1840

Hoffman, Mr David A MA(Oxon); BCL L *Oct 1997*
8, 11, 6, 41, 67, 45, 38, 88, 29, 40, 93
18 St John Street Chambers, Manchester
p985 . . . . 0161 278 1800

Hoffmann, Ms Clare BA G *Oct 1990*
Serle Court, London WC2
p950 . . . . 020 7242 6105

Hofford, Mr Peter BA(Wales); LL Dip G *Nov 1979*
15
5 King's Bench Walk, London EC4
p939 . . . . 020 7353 5638

Hofmeyr, Mr Stephen Murray MA(Oxon) G *Jul 1982*
(Q.C.) *3, 35, 19, 33, 24, 5, 40, 11*
7 King's Bench Walk, London EC4
p940 . . . . 020 7910 8300

HOGAN, Mr Andrew I *Oct 1996*
1, 18, 30, 40, 53, 31
Ropewalk Chambers, Nottingham
p989 . . . . 0115 947 2581

Hogan, Miss Emma L *Oct 1996*
30, 18, 55, 68
No5 Chambers, Bristol
p971 . . . . 0845 210 5555
No5 Chambers, London EC4
p944 . . . . 0845 210 5555
No5 Chambers, Birmingham
p968 . . . . 0845 210 5555

HOGARTH, Mr Alistair G *Oct 2005*
30, 15, 20, 18
9 Gough Square, London EC4
p935 . . . . 020 7832 0500

HOGARTH, Mr Andrew MA(Cantab) L *Jul 1974*
(Q.C.) *18, 30, 40*
12 King's Bench Walk, London EC4
p940 . . . . 020 7583 0811

HOGBEN, Helen G *Jan 2006*
Fountain Chambers, Middlesbrough
p986 . . . . 01642 804040

Hogben, Mr Paul LLB(Hons) G *Nov 1993*
15
199 Kingsworth Road, Ashford
p967 . . . . 01233 645805

HOGG, The Hon Douglas Martin BA(Oxon) L *Jul 1968*
(Q.C.) MP
Carmelite Chambers, London EC4
p927 . . . . 020 7936 6300
37 Park Square Chambers, Leeds
p978 . . . . 0113 243 9422

HOGG, Mr James I *Jan 2006*
St James's Chambers, Manchester
p984 . . . . 0161 834 7000

HOILE, Miss Elinor L *Mar 2008*
30, 40, 38, 67, 53, 18, 88
Pallant Chambers, Chichester
p974 . . . . 01243 784538

HOLBECH, Mr Charles Edward BA(Hons)(Oxon) L *Jul 1988*
86, 93, 89, 37, 32
New Square Chambers, London WC2
p943 . . . . 020 7419 8000

HOLBORN, Mr David I *Oct 1991*
15, 70, 36
18 Red Lion Court, London EC4
p949 . . . . 020 7520 6000
18 Red Lion Court (Annexe), Chelmsford
p973 . . . . 01245 280880

HOLBORN, Mr Jack L *Jun 2008*
Thirty Nine Essex Street, London WC2
p932 . . . . 020 7832 1111

Holbrook, Mr Jon BA(Sheff); DipLaw I *Nov 1991*
22
Cornerstone Barristers, London WC1
p929 . . . . 020 7242 4986

Holden, Mr Andrew I *Nov 2007*
49, 41, 5, 6, 8, 11, 97, 67, 69, 81, 62, 38, 24, 21, 88, 89, 96, 29, 32, 40, 93, 33, 37
XXIV Old Buildings, London WC2
p944 . . . . 020 7691 2424

Holden, Mr Philip L *Oct 1994*
Lincoln House Chambers, Manchester
p984 . . . . 0161 832 5701

Holder, Miss Claire MA L *Jul 1978* OBE
15, 18, 20, 36
243 Westbourne Grove, London W11
p953 . . . . 020 7229 3819

Holder, Mr Simon LLB; LLM I *Jul 1989*
22, 30, 36, 40, 53, 68
St Johns Buildings, Preston
p990 . . . . 01772 256100
St Johns Buildings, Chester
p974 . . . . 01244 323070
St Johns Buildings, Manchester
p985 . . . . 0161 214 1500
St Johns Buildings, Liverpool
p982 . . . . 0151 243 6000

HOLDER, Mr Terence G *Jul 1984*
15, 18, 25, 36
Colleton Chambers, Exeter
p975 . . . . 01392 274898

HOLDERNESS, Kate G *Jan 2008*
11, 5, 81, 40, 62
3 Verulam Buildings, London WC1
p953 . . . . 020 7831 8441

HOLDSWORTH, Mr James MA(Oxon) M *Feb 1977*
Temple Garden Chambers, London EC4
p952 . . . . 020 7583 1315

HOLGATE, Mr David BA(Oxon) M *Jul 1978*
(Q.C.) *1, 21, 26, 31, 33, 36, 93*
Landmark Chambers, London EC4
p941 . . . . 020 7430 1221

HOLINER, Mr Drew Magister(Russia); GDL L *Jul 2005*
3, 11, 21, 33, 41, 51
Monckton Chambers, London WC1
p942 . . . . 020 7405 7211

Holl-Allen, Mr Jonathan MA; LLM(Cantab) I *Nov 1990*
27, 18, 30, 12, 1, 36, 40, 53, 68, 85, 63
3 Serjeants' Inn, London EC4
p950 . . . . 020 7427 5000

Holland, Mrs Annie BA(Law); RGN M *Nov 1994*
10, 20
King's Bench Godolphin Chambers, Truro
p994 . . . . 0845 308 1551
King's Bench Godolphin Chambers, Plymouth
p990 . . . . 0845 308 1551

Holland, Mr Charles Christopher I *Nov 1994*
8, 22, 25, 40, 88, 93, 97, 38
Broad Chare Chambers, Newcastle upon Tyne
p986 . . . . 0191 232 0541

Holland, Ms Charlotte Kate BA(Hons) L *Oct 1996*
15, 12, 20
Lincoln House Chambers, Manchester
p984 . . . . 0161 832 5701

HOLLAND, Mr David Moore MA(Cantab); LLM I *Jul 1986*
(Q.C.) *6, 12, 22, 11, 40, 93*
Landmark Chambers, London EC4
p941 . . . . 020 7430 1221

HOLLAND, Mrs Eleanor BA(Oxon); LLM L *Jan 2010*
6, 8, 11, 38
4 Stone Buildings, London WC2
p951 . . . . 020 7242 5524

HOLLAND, Mr Guy M *Mar 2001*
22, 88, 93
Five Paper, London EC4
p946 . . . . 020 7815 3200

Holland, Mr Jordan BA(Cantab) L *Oct 2009*
8, 32, 37, 14, 38
5 Stone Buildings, London WC2
p951 . . . . 020 7242 6201

HOLLAND, Ms Katharine Jane BA(Oxon); BCL(Oxon) M *Jul 1989*
(Q.C.) *93*
Landmark Chambers, London EC4
p941 . . . . 020 7430 1221

HOLLAND, Mr Michael Frederick Richard BA I *Nov 1984*
(Q.C.) *15*
9-12 Bell Yard Chambers, London WC2
p926 . . . . 020 7400 1800
2 Hare Court, London EC4
p937 . . . . 020 7353 5324

Holland, Mr Rick LLB; LLM G *Nov 1994*
Lincoln House Chambers, Manchester
p984 . . . . 0161 832 5701

Holland, Mrs Roberta BSc; LLB L *Nov 1989*
20, 10
12 College Place, Southampton
p992 . . . . 023 8032 0320

HOLLAND, Mr Russell PPE(Oxon); PG DipLaw L *Jan 2008*
18, 76, 30, 33, 31, 26, 12
12 King's Bench Walk, London EC4
p940 . . . . 020 7583 0811

HOLLAND, Mr William G *Jul 1982*
20, 10
Tanfield Chambers, London WC1
p951 . . . . 020 7421 5300

Hollander, Mr Charles MA(Cantab) G *Jul 1978*
(Q.C.) *56, 11, 5, 40*
Brick Court Chambers, London WC2
p927 . . . . 020 7379 3550

HOLLIMAN, Mr Adam LLB(Lond); BLC(Oxon) L *Jan 2005*
6, 11, 97, 62, 38
4 Stone Buildings, London WC2
p951 . . . . 020 7242 5524

HOLLINGTON, Mr Robin MA(Oxon); LLM L *Jul 1979*
(Q.C.) *6, 11, 29, 8, 38*
New Square Chambers, London WC2
p943 . . . . 020 7419 8000

Hollingworth, Mr Guy L *Oct 2001*
One Essex Court, London EC4
p931 . . . . 020 7583 2000

Hollins, Miss Catherine L *Jul 2007*
15, 20, 18, 30
No 6 Barristers Chambers, Leeds
p978 . . . . 0113 245 9763

HOLLIS, Mrs Kim LLB(Lond) G *Jul 1979*
(Q.C.) *15, 62*
25 Bedford Row, London WC1
p925 . . . . 020 7067 1500

Holloran, Miss Fiona LLB(Hons)(Warw) G *Nov 1989*
20
18 St John Street Chambers, Manchester
p985 . . . . 0161 278 1800

Hollow, Mr Paul John LLB(UEA); Deputy District Judge G *Nov 1981*
30, 20, 12, 53
Fenners Chambers, Cambridge
p972 . . . . 01223 368761

Holloway, Mr David G *Jul 1996*
3, 35, 78, 21, 54, 24, 96, 49, 97, 89, 11
No5 Chambers, Bristol
p971 . . . . 0845 210 5555
No5 Chambers, London EC4
p944 . . . . 0845 210 5555
No5 Chambers, Birmingham
p968 . . . . 0845 210 5555

HOLLOWAY, Mr Orlando LLB(Exon) L *Oct 2004*
42 Bedford Row, London WC1
p925 . . . . 020 7831 0222

Holloway, Ms Sharon BA(York); CPE(Staffs) I *Oct 1994*
15
1 Pump Court, London EC4
p947 . . . . 020 7842 7070

HOLLOWAY, Mr Timothy MA(Cantab) I *Nov 1991*
51, 12, 30, 40, 62, 96
Oriel Chambers, Liverpool
p981 . . . . 0151 236 7191 / 236 4321
Oriel Chambers, Preston
p990 . . . . 01772 254764

HOLLYOAK, Ms Kate LLB(Manc) G *Nov 1997*
10, 20
9 St John Street Chambers, Manchester
p984 . . . . 0161 955 9000

HOLME, Mr Gavin James BA(Leeds) I *Jan 1999*
4 King's Bench Walk, London EC4
p939 . . . . 020 7822 7000

HOLME, Ms Sophie M.ST(European Literature)(Oxon); BA(French & Linguistics)(Oxon) G *Jan 2009*
30, 53
Guildhall Chambers, Bristol
p970 . . . . 0117 930 9000

Holmes, Mr Andrew Christopher L *Jul 2000*
10, 12, 15, 20, 53, 30
Broad Chare Chambers, Newcastle upon Tyne
p986 . . . . 0191 232 0541

HOLMES, Miss Elisa MPhil; BCL; LLB(Hons); BA I *Nov 2003*
1, 9, 11, 44, 50, 19, 51, 55, 56
Monckton Chambers, London WC1
p942 . . . . 020 7405 7211

Holmes, Ms Helen I *Jul 2000*
15, 23
No 6 Barristers Chambers, Leeds
p978 . . . . 0113 245 9763

Holmes, Miss Jessica BA(Lond) I *Oct 2003*
15, 96
Argent Chambers, London WC2
p923 . . . . 020 7556 5500

Holmes, Mr Jon A PhD; MB; BCH G *Oct 1999*
53, 27, 30, 15, 62
Thirty Park Place, Cardiff
p973 . . . . 029 2039 8421

HOLMES, Mr Josh MA; BCL; LLM I *Jan 1997*
1, 44, 19, 57, 61
Monckton Chambers, London WC1
p942 . . . . 020 7405 7211

Holmes, Mr Justin I *Jan 1994*
Radcliffe Chambers, London WC2
p949 . . . . 020 7831 0081

HOLMES, Ms Martha Felicity BA; PGDL I *Jul 2003*
10, 20, 25, 22, 49, 96
1 King's Bench Walk, London EC4
p938 . . . . 020 7936 1500

Holmes, Mr Michael M *Oct 1999*
3, 35, 24, 11
7 King's Bench Walk, London EC4
p940 . . . . 020 7910 8300

HOLMES, Mr Rory M *Nov 2009*
30, 12, 11
Crown Office Chambers, London EC4
p929 . . . . 020 7797 8100

Holmes-Milner, Mr James MA(Cantab) M *Jul 1989*
12, 18, 22, 30, 40, 53, 14
9 Gough Square, London EC4
p935 . . . . 020 7832 0500

Holmes-Willis, Mrs Sarah M *Jul 1999*
York Chambers, York
p995 . . . . 01904 620048
York Chambers, Newcastle upon Tyne
p987 . . . . 0191 206 4677

Holroyd, Mr Charles BA G *Jan 1997*
11, 24, 35, 3
7 King's Bench Walk, London EC4
p940 . . . . 020 7910 8300

Holroyd, John J G *Nov 1989*
7, 31, 40, 41, 46, 49, 60, 61, 67, 93, 94, 96
Zenith Chambers, Leeds
p979 . . . . 0113 245 5438

HOLSGROVE, Mr Jonathan G *Jan 2011*
12, 30, 88
Bank House Chambers, Sheffield
p991 . . . . 0114 275 1223

13

Holsgrove, Lara M *Jan 1999*
St Johns Buildings, Preston
p990 . . . . . 01772 256100
St Johns Buildings, Chester
p974 . . . . . 01244 323070
St Johns Buildings, Manchester
p985 . . . . . 0161 214 1500
St Johns Buildings, Liverpool
p982 . . . . . 0151 243 6000

Holt, Ms Abigail BA(Oxon) L *Sep 1993*
30
Lincoln House Chambers, Manchester
p984 . . . . . 0161 832 5701

Holt, Mr Ben I *Oct 2006*
15
5 King's Bench Walk, London EC4
p939 . . . . . 020 7353 5638

Holt, Mr Craig G *Jan 2002*
20, 10
7 Bedford Row, London WC1
p924 . . . . . 020 7242 3555

Holt, Mrs Jane M *Oct 2006*
KCH Garden Square Chambers, Nottingham
p989 . . . . . 0115 941 8851
KCH Garden Square Chambers, Leicester
p979 . . . . . 0115 941 8851

Holt, Mr Julian BA M *Jan 1982*
15
St Johns Buildings, Preston
p990 . . . . . 01772 256100
St Johns Buildings, Chester
p974 . . . . . 01244 323070
St Johns Buildings, Manchester
p985 . . . . . 0161 214 1500
St Johns Buildings, Liverpool
p982 . . . . . 0151 243 6000

HOLT, Miss Karen Jane LLB(Leeds); Recorder L *Nov 1987*
15, 62, 72
23 Essex Street, London WC2
p932 . . . . . 020 7413 0353

Holt, Mr Matthew BA(Oxon) G *Oct 2001*
3, 7, 11, 24, 40
Keating Chambers, London WC2
p938 . . . . . 020 7544 2600

HOLT, Miss Sarah Louise LLB(Hons) M *Oct 1999*
15
7 Harrington Street Chambers, Liverpool
p981 . . . . . 0151 242 0707

Holtham, Ms Ruth BA; DipLaw M *Jan 2001*
62, 11, 40, 8, 38
Serle Court, London WC2
p950 . . . . . 020 7242 6105

Holwill, Mr Derek Paul Winsor MA(Cantab) G *Jul 1982*
53, 40, 27
Hailsham Chambers, London EC4
p936 . . . . . 020 7643 5000

Hone, Mr Barnaby LLB M *Jan 2006*
15, 70
1 Paper Buildings, London EC4
p946 . . . . . 020 7353 3728

Honey, Mr Richard BSc(Hons); Chartered Surveyor I *Jul 2003*
1, 46, 26, 31, 36
Francis Taylor Building, London EC4
p934 . . . . . 020 7353 8415

Honeyman, Ms Gillian BA(Bristol) G *Jul 2011*
10
Coram Chambers, London EC1
p929 . . . . . 020 7092 3700

Hood, Mr David I *Nov 1980*
90 Overstrand Mansions, London SW11
p946 . . . . . 020 7622 7415

HOOD, Mr Nigel Anthony BA(Hons); MBA I *Oct 1993*
62, 11, 8
New Square Chambers, London WC2
p943 . . . . . 020 7419 8000

Hookway, Aelred LLB G *Nov 1990*
10, 20
Zenith Chambers, Leeds
p979 . . . . . 0113 245 5438

Hoon, Notu I *Nov 1975*
15, 62
Argent Chambers, London WC2
p923 . . . . . 020 7556 5500

HOOPER, Mr Benjamin Richard BA(Oxon); CPE(City) I *Oct 2000*
1, 11, 18, 19, 23, 26, 51, 73
11KBW, London EC4
p938 . . . . . 020 7632 8500

HOOPER, Mr David BA M *Feb 1971*
(Q.C.) *12, 15, 25, 51*
25 Bedford Row, London WC1
p925 . . . . . 020 7067 1500

Hooper, Mr Martin C LLB(Hons) M *Jul 1988*
15
5 King's Bench Walk, London EC4
p939 . . . . . 020 7353 5638

Hope, Miss Heather LLB G *Oct 1993*
15, 25
Goldsmith Chambers, London EC4
p935 . . . . . 020 7353 6802

HOPE, Mr Ian S BA; CPE; DipLaw I *Nov 1996*
15, 27, 62
23 Essex Street, London WC2
p932 . . . . . 020 7413 0353

Hopkin, Mr William I *Aug 2000*
15, 9, 20, 36, 10, 68
Rougemont Chambers, Exeter
p975 . . . . . 01392 208484

Hopkins, Mr Adrian Mark BA(Oxon) L *Nov 1984*
(Q.C.) *12, 18, 27, 30, 36, 40, 53, 63, 85*
3 Serjeants' Inn, London EC4
p950 . . . . . 020 7427 5000

Hopkins, Mr John M *Apr 1963*
Maitland Chambers, London WC2
p941 . . . . . 020 7406 1200

Hopkins, Ms Julie BA(Hons)(Oxon) I *Jul 1999*
15
King's Bench Chambers, Oxford
p989 . . . . . 01865 311066

Hopkins, Mr Paul A LLB(B'ham) G *Jul 1989*
20, 10, 14, 37
9 Park Place, Cardiff
p973 . . . . . 029 2038 2731

Hopkins, Ms Phillipa M BA(Hons); BCL(Oxon) M *Oct 1994*
Essex Court Chambers, London WC2
p931 . . . . . 020 7813 8000

HOPKINS, Mr Robin L *Jul 2008*
1, 76, 18, 55, 73
11KBW, London EC4
p938 . . . . . 020 7632 8500

Hopkins, Mr Rowland LLB(Lond) I *Nov 1970*
12, 7, 22, 30, 8
4 Rowchester Court, Birmingham
p968 . . . . . 0121 233 2327

Hopkins, Mr Simeon I *Nov 1968*
5 Pump Court, London EC4
p947 . . . . . 020 7353 2532 / 7583 7133

Hopkinson, Miss Joy MA(Hons)(History/Politics); DipLaw(CPE) M *Jan 1999*
20, 10
4 Brick Court Chambers, London EC4
p927 . . . . . 020 7832 3200

HOPPER, Mr Stephen M *Jan 2001*
15, 62, 95
187 Fleet Street, London EC4
p933 . . . . . 020 7430 7430

Horan, Mr John BA(Cantab) I *Feb 1993*
1, 10, 12, 18, 26, 30
Cloisters, London EC4
p928 . . . . . 020 7827 4000

HORAN, Mr Stephen LLB; BA L *Nov 2002*
11, 38, 69, 97
Erskine Chambers, London WC2
p931 . . . . . 020 7242 5532

Horder, Mr Tom M *Jul 2004*
3PB, Bournemouth
p969 . . . . . 01202 292102

Horgan, Mr Tim I *Jul 1982*
15, 62
Argent Chambers, London WC2
p923 . . . . . 020 7556 5500

HORMAECHE, Miss Alejandra L *Jan 1998*
12, 30, 11, 22
Tanfield Chambers, London WC1
p951 . . . . . 020 7421 5300

Hornblower, Mrs Sarah G *Jul 2005*
18, 15, 20, 70, 2, 71
Rougemont Chambers, Exeter
p975 . . . . . 01392 208484

HORNE, Mr David LLB G *Jul 2009*
12, 15, 23
Bank House Chambers, Sheffield
p991 . . . . . 0114 275 1223

HORNE, Mr James M *Jan 2004*
15
Bank House Chambers, Sheffield
p991 . . . . . 0114 275 1223

HORNE, Mr Julian BA(Hons)(Oxon); BCL(Oxon) M *Sep 1998*
74, 30, 11, 24, 40, 53, 7, 84, 36
Crown Office Chambers, London EC4
p929 . . . . . 020 7797 8100
St John's Chambers, Bristol
p972 . . . . . 0117 921 3456

HORNE, Kenderik BA(Cantab) L *Mar 1996*
12, 15, 18, 22, 30, 47, 55, 53
Atlantic Chambers, Liverpool
p980 . . . . . 0151 236 4421

Horne, Mr Michael MA(Cantab) G *Oct 1992*
12, 27, 30, 40, 53, 68, 85
3 Serjeants' Inn, London EC4
p950 . . . . . 020 7427 5000

Horne, Mr Wilson LLB L *Oct 1992*
5, 11, 22, 40, 41
Kings Chambers, Leeds
p978 . . . . . 0113 242 1123
Kings Chambers, Manchester
p984 . . . . . 0161 832 9082

Horne-Roberts, Mrs Jennifer BA(Lond); DipLaw M *Nov 1976*
51, 1, 20
Goldsmith Chambers, London EC4
p935 . . . . . 020 7353 6802

Horner, Mr Robert I *Nov 1999*
12
3PB, Oxford
p989 . . . . . 01865 793736

Horner, Mr Robin L *Jul 1975*
8, 32, 88, 93
Broad Chare Chambers, Newcastle upon Tyne
p986 . . . . . 0191 232 0541

HORNSBY, Mr Walton Francis Petre BA(Oxon) L *Jul 1980*
10, 12, 15, 20
1 King's Bench Walk, London EC4
p938 . . . . . 020 7936 1500

HORROCKS, Mr Peter Leslie MA(Cantab) M *Nov 1977*
10, 20
1 Garden Court, London EC4
p934 . . . . . 020 7797 7900

Horseley, Mr Nicholas BA(Hons)(Cantab); LLB(Hons)(Lond) M *Oct 1998*
42 Bedford Row, London WC1
p925 . . . . . 020 7831 0222

Horsham, Miss Irene Ansa-Asare LLB; MBA L *Jul 2004*
15, 12, 20, 30, 18
9 Park Place, Cardiff
p973 . . . . . 029 2038 2731

Horsley, Mr Nicholas BA(Hons)(Cantab); LLB(Hons)(Lond) M *Oct 1998*
10
Coram Chambers, London EC1
p929 . . . . . 020 7092 3700

HORTON, Mr Mark V LLB M *Jul 1981*
10, 20
Colleton Chambers, Exeter
p975 . . . . . 01392 274898

HORTON, Mr Matthew MA; LLM(Cantab) M *Jul 1969*
(Q.C.) *31, 46, 1, 26*
Thirty Nine Essex Street, London WC2
p932 . . . . . 020 7832 1111

Horton, Mr Michael John Edward MA(Cantab) G *Nov 1993*
10, 20, 37
Coram Chambers, London EC1
p929 . . . . . 020 7092 3700

HORWOOD-SMART, Miss Rosamund Recorder I *Jul 1974*
(Q.C.) *15, 36, 68, 91*
18 Red Lion Court, London EC4
p949 . . . . . 020 7520 6000
18 Red Lion Court (Annexe), Chelmsford
p973 . . . . . 01245 280880

HOSFORD-TANNER, Mr J Michael BA; LLB I *Nov 1974*
10, 12, 20, 30
Queen Elizabeth Buildings, London EC4
p948 . . . . . 020 7797 7837

Hosking, Ms Ruth L *Nov 2002*
Quadrant Chambers, London EC4
p948 . . . . . 020 7583 4444

Hoskins, Mr Mark George MA; BCL(Oxon) G *Nov 1991*
19, 44, 56, 1, 51
Brick Court Chambers, London WC2
p927 . . . . . 020 7379 3550

HOSKINS, Mr Thomas L *Jan 2009*
15
9-12 Bell Yard Chambers, London WC2
p926 . . . . . 020 7400 1800

HOSKINS, Mr William G MA(Oxon) M *Nov 1980*
Temple Garden Chambers, London EC4
p952 . . . . . 020 7583 1315

HOSSAIN, Mr Ahmed LLB(Hons) G *Nov 1996*
72, 15, 71, 62
23 Essex Street, London WC2
p932 . . . . . 020 7413 0353
Westgate Chambers, Lewes
p980 . . . . . 01273 480510

HOSSAIN, Mr Mozammel I *Jan 2001*
15, 62, 95
187 Fleet Street, London EC4
p933 . . . . . 020 7430 7430

Hossain, Sa'ad G *Nov 1995*
One Essex Court, London EC4
p931 . . . . . 020 7583 2000

Hotten, Mr Christopher LLB; Recorder I *Nov 1972*
(Q.C.) *15, 62, 95, 70, 72*
No5 Chambers, Bristol
p971 . . . . . 0845 210 5555
No5 Chambers, London EC4
p944 . . . . . 0845 210 5555
No5 Chambers, Birmingham
p968 . . . . . 0845 210 5555

Hough, Mr Christopher LLB M *Jul 1981*
27, 30, 51, 53
Doughty Street Chambers, London WC1
p930 . . . . . 020 7404 1313

Hough, Mr Jonathan MA(Oxon) M *Oct 1997*
Four New Square, London WC2
p943 . . . . . 020 7822 2000

Houghton, Ms Lisa BA(Hons) G *May 1994*
10, 20
St Johns Buildings, Preston
p990 . . . . . 01772 256100
St Johns Buildings, Chester
p974 . . . . . 01244 323070
St Johns Buildings, Manchester
p985 . . . . . 0161 214 1500
St Johns Buildings, Liverpool
p982 . . . . . 0151 243 6000

HOUGHTON, Mr Peter BA(Hons); MPhil; DipLaw; CPE L *Oct 2005*
30, 24, 47, 40, 11
Crown Office Chambers, London EC4
p929 . . . . . 020 7797 8100

Houlder, Mr Bruce G *Jul 1969*
(Q.C.) *15, 62, 36*
6 King's Bench Walk, London EC4
p939 . . . . . 020 7583 0410

Houseman, Mr Stephen BA; BCL(Oxon) I *Nov 1995*
Essex Court Chambers, London WC2
p931 . . . . . 020 7813 8000

HOUSTON, Mr Andrew I *Nov 1989*
15
Pump Court Chambers, Swindon
p993 . . . . . 01793 539899
Pump Court Chambers, Winchester
p994 . . . . . 01962 868161
Pump Court Chambers, London EC4
p947 . . . . . 020 7353 0711

HOWARD, Amanda LLB(Hons) I *Nov 1994*
20, 30
Atlantic Chambers, Liverpool
p980 . . . . . 0151 236 4421

HOWARD, Ms Anneli MA(Oxon); BCL(Oxon) G *Jan 2002*
11, 44, 19, 1
Monckton Chambers, London WC1
p942 . . . . . 020 7405 7211

HOWARD, Mr Anthony LLB I *Oct 1992*
30, 12, 18, 40
9 St John Street Chambers, Manchester
p984 . . . . . 0161 955 9000

HOWARD, Mr Charles MA(Cantab) I *Jul 1975*
(Q.C.) *20, 27, 30, 10*
1 King's Bench Walk, London EC4
p938 . . . . . 020 7936 1500

See p1010 for the Key to Work Categories

Howard, Mr Graham L *Nov 1987*
Clerksroom - Administration Centre, Taunton
p993 . . . . . 0845 083 3000

Howard, Mr Ian LLB(Newc) L *Nov 1987*
15, 25
Broadway House Chambers, Leeds
p977 . . . . . 0113 246 2600
Broadway House Chambers, Bradford
p969 . . . . . 01274 722560

HOWARD, Ms Katrina G *Jan 2009*
13
3 New Square, London WC2
p943 . . . . . 020 7405 1111

Howard, Mr Mark LLB; LLM G *Jul 1980*
(Q.C.) *11, 3, 1, 40, 35, 5, 62, 24*
Brick Court Chambers, London WC2
p927 . . . . . 020 7379 3550

Howard, Michael N MA; BCL(Oxon) G *May 1971*
(Q.C.) *11, 4, 5, 24, 35, 3*
Quadrant Chambers, London EC4
p948 . . . . . 020 7583 4444

HOWARD, Ms Nicola M *Jul 1995*
15, 62
25 Bedford Row, London WC1
p925 . . . . . 020 7067 1500

Howard, Mr Robin William John MA(Oxon) M *Jan 1986*
Fenners Chambers, Cambridge
p972 . . . . . 01223 368761

Howard, Mr Steven I *Jan 2009*
20
3PB, Bournemouth
p969 . . . . . 01202 292102

Howarth, Mr Andrew BA(Oxon); DipLaw L *Nov 1988*
15, 25
36 Bedford Row, London WC1
p925 . . . . . 020 7421 8000

Howarth, Miss Kathryn L *Nov 2005*
51, 15, 10, 62, 70, 82, 23, 22
36 Bedford Row, London WC1
p925 . . . . . 020 7421 8000

Howd, Stephen BA(Oxon) M *Jul 1989*
66, 49, 5, 8, 11, 97, 47, 67, 80, 81, 62, 24, 88, 89, 96, 29, 40, 93
Zenith Chambers, Leeds
p979 . . . . . 0113 245 5438

HOWE, Mr Andrew LLB(Hons) L *Jan 2002*
12, 30, 15, 62
Oriel Chambers, Liverpool
p981 . . . . . 0151 236 7191 / 236 4321
Oriel Chambers, Preston
p990 . . . . . 01772 254764

HOWE, Mr Darren Francis G *Oct 1992*
20, 10
1 Garden Court, London EC4
p934 . . . . . 020 7797 7900

Howe, Mr Gavin BA(Hons) G *Nov 2003*
10, 12, 15, 20
Crown Office Row Chambers, Brighton
p970 . . . . . 01273 625625

Howe, Mr Martin MA(Cantab) M *Jul 1978*
(Q.C.) *13, 45, 50, 56, 43*
8 New Square, London WC2
p943 . . . . . 020 7405 4321

HOWE, Miss Penny BA(Cantab) I *Nov 1991*
10, 12, 20
Pump Court Chambers, Swindon
p993 . . . . . 01793 539899
Pump Court Chambers, Winchester
p994 . . . . . 01962 868161
Pump Court Chambers, London EC4
p947 . . . . . 020 7353 0711

Howe, Mr Robert MA(Cantab); BCL(Oxon) M *Nov 1988*
(Q.C.) *1, 3, 8, 11, 13, 18, 24, 29, 36, 41, 50, 56, 89, 21, 12, 52, 5, 81, 44, 19*
Blackstone Chambers, London EC4
p926 . . . . . 020 7583 1770

HOWE, Ruth BA(Hons) L *Oct 1983*
15, 20, 10
Atlantic Chambers, Liverpool
p980 . . . . . 0151 236 4421

Howe, Miss Sara L *Oct 1993*
15, 62
Westgate Chambers, Lewes
p980 . . . . . 01273 480510

Howe, Mr Timothy Jean-Paul BA(Oxon) M *Nov 1987*
(Q.C.)
Fountain Court Chambers, London EC4
p934 . . . . . 020 7583 3335

Howell, Miss Claire BA(Hons)(Oxon) I *Nov 2003*
1, 2, 10, 12, 20, 15, 62, 68, 63, 84
36 Bedford Row, London WC1
p925 . . . . . 020 7421 8000

Howell, Mr Jacques L *Oct 2000*
1 Mitre Court Buildings, London EC4
p942 . . . . . 020 7452 8900

Howell, Mr John BA(Oxon) M *Feb 1979*
(Q.C.) *1, 23, 26, 46, 51, 89, 76, 19, 44*
Blackstone Chambers, London EC4
p926 . . . . . 020 7583 1770

Howell-Jones, Mr Nicholas LLB G *Jul 2000*
St Ives Chambers, Birmingham
p969 . . . . . 0121 236 0863

Howell Williams, Mr Craig BA(Leeds) G *Jul 1983*
(Q.C.) *1, 26, 31, 36*
Francis Taylor Building, London EC4
p934 . . . . . 020 7353 8415

Howells, Miss Catherine LLB(L'pool); Recorder G *Jul 1989*
30, 53
Exchange Chambers, Manchester
p983 . . . . . 0161 833 2722
Exchange Chambers, Liverpool
p980 . . . . . 0151 236 7747
Exchange Chambers, Leeds
p977 . . . . . 0113 203 1970

Howells, Mr Christian James LLB(Hons)(Bris) I *Jul 2007*
30, 15, 23, 62
Thirty Park Place, Cardiff
p973 . . . . . 029 2039 8421

HOWELLS, Mr Geraint LLB(Brunel) G *Nov 2002*
48, 47, 11, 12
Gough Square Chambers, London EC4
p935 . . . . . 020 7353 0924

Howells, Mr James BA; MA; BCL M *Nov 1995*
3, 7, 11, 31, 40, 41, 43, 45, 49, 54, 61, 78, 74
Atkin Chambers, London WC1
p923 . . . . . 020 7404 0102

Howells, Miss Katherine BA(Hons)(Jurisprudence) G *Oct 1994*
30
Old Square Chambers, Bristol
p971 . . . . . 0117 930 5100
Old Square Chambers, London WC1
p945 . . . . . 020 7269 0300

Howells, Mr Stephen BA; LLB(Hons) M *Jul 2006*
41, 3, 5, 8, 11, 44, 48, 17, 18, 83, 35, 36
Stone Chambers, London WC1
p951 . . . . . 020 7440 6900

Howes, Miss Sally Margaret M *Nov 1983*
(Q.C.) *15*
Atkinson Bevan Chambers, London EC4
p924 . . . . . 020 7353 2112

Howie, Mr Keir BA(Jurisprudence) M *Jan 2010*
41, 25, 35, 61
7 King's Bench Walk, London EC4
p940 . . . . . 020 7910 8300

Howker, Mr David Thomas LLB I *Jul 1982*
(Q.C.) *15, 70, 72, 95, 84, 62, 39, 82, 71*
2 Hare Court, London EC4
p937 . . . . . 020 7353 5324
No5 Chambers, Bristol
p971 . . . . . 0845 210 5555
No5 Chambers, London EC4
p944 . . . . . 0845 210 5555
No5 Chambers, Birmingham
p968 . . . . . 0845 210 5555

Howlett, Mr James Anthony LLB(Bris); FCIA M *Jul 1980*
31, 18, 22, 30, 36, 7, 11, 8
KCH Garden Square Chambers, Nottingham
p989 . . . . . 0115 941 8851
KCH Garden Square Chambers, Leicester
p979 . . . . . 0115 941 8851

Howling, Mr Rex M *Jan 1991*
(Q.C.) *20, 10*
4 Paper Buildings, London EC4
p946 . . . . . 020 7583 0816

Hoyal, Ms Jane MA; LLB M *Nov 1976*
1, 10, 20
1 Pump Court, London EC4
p947 . . . . . 020 7842 7070

Hubbard, Mr Daniel L *Jul 2003*
One Essex Court, London EC4
p931 . . . . . 020 7583 2000

HUBBARD, Mr Mark Iain BA(Oxon) M *Nov 1991*
2, 5, 6, 8, 9, 11, 14, 22, 29, 32, 37
New Square Chambers, London WC2
p943 . . . . . 020 7419 8000

Hubbard, Mr Michael J MA; Recorder G *May 1972*
(Q.C.) *15*
1 Paper Buildings, London EC4
p946 . . . . . 020 7353 3728

Hubble, Mr Ben BA M *Nov 1992*
(Q.C.) *8, 12, 24, 40*
Four New Square, London WC2
p943 . . . . . 020 7822 2000

Huckle, Mr Theodore BA; LLM(Cantab) L *Jul 1985*
11, 15, 18, 29, 30, 40, 45, 49, 51, 53
Civitas Law, Cardiff
p972 . . . . . 0845 071 3007

Huda, Miss Abida Alia Jehan LLB(Hons) M *Nov 1989*
10, 20
1 Pump Court, London EC4
p947 . . . . . 020 7842 7070

HUDD, Miss Anne MA(Law); MA(Cantab) G *Oct 2000*
20, 30
29 Bedford Row, London WC1
p925 . . . . . 020 7404 1044

Hudson, Ms Abigail G *Jan 2003*
St Johns Buildings, Preston
p990 . . . . . 01772 256100
St Johns Buildings, Chester
p974 . . . . . 01244 323070
St Johns Buildings, Manchester
p985 . . . . . 0161 214 1500
St Johns Buildings, Liverpool
p982 . . . . . 0151 243 6000

Hudson, Mr Anthony LLB(Hons) M *Nov 1996*
16, 51, 52
Doughty Street Chambers, London WC1
p930 . . . . . 020 7404 1313

Hudson, Miss Chloe BA(Hons)(Oxon) L *Apr 2003*
Park Court Chambers, Leeds
p978 . . . . . 0113 243 3277

Hudson, Miss Elisabeth LLB G *Nov 1987*
10, 15, 20, 22, 30
3PB, Winchester
p994 . . . . . 01962 868884

HUDSON, Ms Emma MA L *Feb 1995*
10, 20
1 Garden Court, London EC4
p934 . . . . . 020 7797 7900

Hudson, Mr John LLB I *Nov 2006*
Zenith Chambers, Leeds
p979 . . . . . 0113 245 5438

Hudson, Miss Kate LLB M *Jul 1981*
20, 10
Coram Chambers, London EC1
p929 . . . . . 020 7092 3700

Huffer, Mr Ian G *Dec 1979*
18 St John Street Chambers, Manchester
p985 . . . . . 0161 278 1800

HUGGINS, Mrs Bianca LLB(Law & Government) G *Jul 2004*
12, 30, 88
Bank House Chambers, Sheffield
p991 . . . . . 0114 275 1223

Huggins, Mr Toby BSc M *Oct 1998*
15, 22, 30
Unity Street Chambers, Bristol
p972 . . . . . 0117 906 9789

Hugh-Jones, Mr George MA(Cantab) M *Nov 1983*
(Q.C.) *12, 27, 30, 36, 40, 53, 85, 63*
3 Serjeants' Inn, London EC4
p950 . . . . . 020 7427 5000

HUGHES, Mr Adrian MA(Oxon) M *Jul 1984*
(Q.C.) *7, 11, 45, 40, 3*
Thirty Nine Essex Street, London WC2
p932 . . . . . 020 7832 1111

Hughes, Miss Anna M *Jul 2008*
2 Temple Gardens, London EC4
p952 . . . . . 020 7822 1200

Hughes, Miss Anna Carina LLB(Hons); LLM M *Oct 2003*
15
Angel Chambers, Swansea
p992 . . . . . 01792 464623

Hughes, Ms Daisy M *Oct 1999*
10, 20, 63
Coram Chambers, London EC1
p929 . . . . . 020 7092 3700

Hughes, Mr David LLB I *Jul 1980*
15, 18, 51
Nine Bedford Row, London WC1
p924 . . . . . 020 7489 2727

Hughes, Mr David Gordon BA(Hons) M *Jan 1997*
1, 15, 16, 18, 26, 30, 48, 13
Thirty Park Place, Cardiff
p973 . . . . . 029 2039 8421

Hughes, Mr Dermot Francis LLB; LLM G *Nov 1993*
18, 12, 15, 30, 20
Paradise Chambers, Sheffield
p992 . . . . . 0114 273 8951

HUGHES, Dr Dominic Wyndham G *Jul 2001*
13
3 New Square, London WC2
p943 . . . . . 020 7405 1111

HUGHES, Miss Gabriel BA(Cantab) L *Apr 1978*
8, 9, 14, 32, 34, 37
Wilberforce Chambers, London WC2
p953 . . . . . 020 7306 0102

Hughes, Mr Gareth G *Nov 1985*
15
2 Pump Court, London EC4
p947 . . . . . 020 7353 5597

HUGHES, Mr Henry I *Oct 2003*
15, 62, 95
187 Fleet Street, London EC4
p933 . . . . . 020 7430 7430

Hughes, Mr Hywel LLB(Wales) G *Nov 1995*
15, 62
Thirty Park Place, Cardiff
p973 . . . . . 029 2039 8421

Hughes, Mr Ignatius LLB(Hons) M *Apr 1986*
(Q.C.) *15, 62*
Albion Chambers, Bristol
p970 . . . . . 0117 927 2144
Nine Bedford Row, London WC1
p924 . . . . . 020 7489 2727

Hughes, Mr Jason LLB(Hons)(L'pool) I *Jul 2009*
8, 10, 12, 15, 20, 38, 88, 89, 30
College Chambers, Southampton
p992 . . . . . 023 8023 0338

Hughes, Mrs Jessica BA L *Jan 1997*
5, 8, 11, 29, 32, 37, 40, 49, 6, 62
XXIV Old Buildings, London WC2
p944 . . . . . 020 7691 2424

HUGHES, Miss Joanna Elizabeth MA(Cantab) M *Jul 2007*
Temple Garden Chambers, London EC4
p952 . . . . . 020 7583 1315

HUGHES, Mrs Kathryn M *Mar 2003*
10, 20
Chavasse Court Chambers, Liverpool
p980 . . . . . 0151 229 2030

Hughes, Miss Kathryn Ann LLB(Bris) I *Nov 1992*
10, 20, 76, 63
Thirty Park Place, Cardiff
p973 . . . . . 029 2039 8421

Hughes, Leighton LLB; Part-Time Chairman SSAT I *Jul 1989*
15
Temple Chambers, Newport
p988 . . . . . 01633 267403 / 255855
Temple Chambers, Cardiff
p973 . . . . . 029 2039 7364

Hughes, Ms Mary I *Jan 1994*
20
1 Pump Court, London EC4
p947 . . . . . 020 7842 7070

Hughes, Miss Meryl Elizabeth LLB(Leeds Metropolitan) G *Nov 1987*
10, 15, 20
Fenners Chambers, Cambridge
p972 . . . . . 01223 368761

Hughes, Mr Paul BA(Hons) M *Oct 2001*
12, 30
Kings Chambers, Leeds
p978 . . . . . 0113 242 1123
Kings Chambers, Manchester
p984 . . . . . 0161 832 9082

HUGHES, Ms Rachel BA(Hons) G *Nov 1995*
12, 30, 62
Oriel Chambers, Liverpool
p981 . . . . . 0151 236 7191 / 236 4321
Oriel Chambers, Preston
p990 . . . . . 01772 254764

Hughes, Ms Ruth LLB L *Jan 2007*
8, 32, 37, 14, 38
5 Stone Buildings, London WC2
p951 . . . . . 020 7242 6201

13

Hughes, Mr Simon David BA(Oxon) G *May 1995*
3, 7, 11, 24, 40
Keating Chambers, London WC2
p938 . . . . 020 7544 2600

Hughes, Mr Simon Ieuan G *Oct 2003*
15, 22, 11, 30, 6
Civitas Law, Cardiff
p972 . . . . 0845 071 3007

HUGHES, Mr William BSc(Leics) G *Nov 1989*
12, 15, 25
9-12 Bell Yard Chambers, London WC2
p926 . . . . 020 7400 1800

Hughes, Mr Y Gwydion LLB(Wales) G *Nov 1994*
8, 11, 12, 32
9 Park Place, Cardiff
p973 . . . . 029 2038 2731

HUGHES-DEANE, Charlotte LLB(Hons) L *Nov 2002*
8
Atlantic Chambers, Liverpool
p980 . . . . 0151 236 4421

Hugheston-Roberts, Mr Justin M *Jan 1986*
15 New Bridge Street Chambers, London EC4
p943 . . . . 020 7842 1900

Hulme, Mr John BSc M *Nov 1983*
15, 25
Goldsmith Chambers, London EC4
p935 . . . . 020 7353 6802

HULSE, Ms Cecilia M *Nov 1998*
Mitre House Chambers, London WC1
p942 . . . . 020 7307 7100

Hummerstone, Miss Rebekah BA(Oxon) G *Jul 2002*
15
2 Hare Court, London EC4
p937 . . . . 020 7353 5324

Humphreys, Elizabeth M *Jan 2009*
Henderson Chambers, London EC4
p937 . . . . 020 7583 9020

Humphreys, Miss Jacqueline MA(Oxon) L *Oct 1994*
10, 20
St John's Chambers, Bristol
p972 . . . . 0117 921 3456

Humphreys, Mr Richard I *Jul 1986*
(Q.C.) *1, 12, 43, 46, 2, 25, 26, 54, 28, 31, 60, 36, 61*
Francis Taylor Building, London EC4
p934 . . . . 020 7353 8415
No5 Chambers, Bristol
p971 . . . . 0845 210 5555
No5 Chambers, London EC4
p944 . . . . 0845 210 5555
No5 Chambers, Birmingham
p968 . . . . 0845 210 5555

HUMPHRIES, Mr Michael LLB(Leics) I *Jul 1982*
(Q.C.) *1, 26, 28, 31, 36, 61, 54*
Francis Taylor Building, London EC4
p934 . . . . 020 7353 8415

Hunjan, Satinder P S Deputy High Court Judge; Recorder G *Jul 1984*
(Q.C.) *30, 53, 27, 39, 40, 41, 46, 48, 49, 50, 56, 94, 36*
No5 Chambers, Bristol
p971 . . . . 0845 210 5555
No5 Chambers, London EC4
p944 . . . . 0845 210 5555
No5 Chambers, Birmingham
p968 . . . . 0845 210 5555

Hunka, Mr Simon BSc; GDL; BVC M *Jul 2007*
15, 30, 62, 84, 39, 94
No5 Chambers, Bristol
p971 . . . . 0845 210 5555
No5 Chambers, London EC4
p944 . . . . 0845 210 5555
No5 Chambers, Birmingham
p968 . . . . 0845 210 5555

Hunt, Miss Alison M *Nov 2001*
12, 15, 10, 20
Regency Chambers, Peterborough
p990 . . . . 01733 315215

Hunt, Ms Alison J G *Jul 1986*
20, 10, 37
No 6 Barristers Chambers, Leeds
p978 . . . . 0113 245 9763

Hunt, Mr David MA(Cantab) G *Jul 1969*
(Q.C.) *3, 5, 8, 11, 12, 24, 29, 35, 41, 89*
Blackstone Chambers, London EC4
p926 . . . . 020 7583 1770

Hunt, Mr Quentin John BA; MA; CPE G *Oct 2000*
15, 62
2 Bedford Row, London WC1
p924 . . . . 020 7440 8888

Hunt, Mr Richard M LLB(Hons) L *Jul 1985*
15, 20
15 Winckley Square, Preston
p991 . . . . 01772 252828

HUNT, Mr Roderick MA(Cantab) M *Jul 1981*
15, 12
Fountain Chambers, Middlesbrough
p986 . . . . 01642 804040

HUNT, Mr Stephen MA(Oxon) L *Jul 1968*
6, 8, 9, 14, 22, 29, 32, 37, 40
4 Stone Buildings, London WC2
p951 . . . . 020 7242 5524

HUNTER, Miss Allison BA; LLM L *Jul 1986*
Furnival Chambers, London EC4
p934 . . . . 020 7405 3232

Hunter, Mr Andrew BA(Oxon); BCL(Oxon) M *Nov 1993*
1, 11, 29, 40, 41, 50, 56, 52, 62, 24, 81, 5, 89, 51
Blackstone Chambers, London EC4
p926 . . . . 020 7583 1770

Hunter, Mr Anthony BA(Oxon) I *Nov 1963*
5 Pump Court, London EC4
p947 . . . . 020 7353 2532 / 7583 7133

HUNTER, Miss Caroline Margaret BA(Oxon); Law Lecturer M *Nov 1985*
1, 22, 26, 51
Arden Chambers, London WC1
p923 . . . . 020 7242 4244

Hunter, Mr Geoffrey LLB(Newc) G *Feb 1979*
York Chambers, York
p995 . . . . 01904 620048
York Chambers, Newcastle upon Tyne
p987 . . . . 0191 206 4677

Hunter, Mr Ian G A MA; LLB(Cantab); LLM(Harv); Recorder and a Member of Gibraltar Bar I *Nov 1967*
(Q.C.)
Essex Court Chambers, London WC2
p931 . . . . 020 7813 8000

Hunter, Mr John LLB L *Feb 1991*
12, 15
1 Gray's Inn Square, London WC1
p935 . . . . 020 7405 8946
Kings Chambers, Leeds
p978 . . . . 0113 242 1123
Kings Chambers, Manchester
p984 . . . . 0161 832 9082

HUNTER, Miss Katherine LLB(Hons); M Phil(Cantab) G *Oct 1997*
15, 62, 72, 27, 36
23 Essex Street, London WC2
p932 . . . . 020 7413 0353

Hunter, Mr Martin BA(Cantab) L *Nov 1994*
Essex Court Chambers, London WC2
p931 . . . . 020 7813 8000

Hunter, Mr Peter Michael L *Jun 2000*
Goldsmith Chambers, London EC4
p935 . . . . 020 7353 6802

Hunter, Mr Robert Neil BVC; BA G *Oct 2000*
30, 84, 40
Devereux Chambers, London WC2
p930 . . . . 020 7353 7534

Hunter, Mr Simon G *Nov 2009*
13 Old Square Chambers, London WC2
p945 . . . . 020 7831 4445

Hunter, Miss Susan MA(Cantab); Diplaw I *Jul 1985*
10, 20
St John's Chambers, Bristol
p972 . . . . 0117 921 3456

Hunter, Mr Timothy I *Oct 1998*
15, 62
Atkinson Bevan Chambers, London EC4
p924 . . . . 020 7353 2112

Hunter, Mr William MA(Cantab) I *Jul 1972*
8, 22, 40, 26
1 Chancery Lane, London WC2
p928 . . . . 0845 634 6666

HUNTER, Mr Winston Ronald LLB(Leeds); Recorder; Deputy High Court Hudge L *Jul 1985*
(Q.C.) *53, 30, 12, 18, 56, 40*
Byrom Street Chambers, Manchester
p983 . . . . 0161 829 2100
42 Bedford Row, London WC1
p925 . . . . 020 7831 0222

HUNTLEY, Miss Clare Helen Patricia LLB(Warw) G *Jul 2000*
15
9-12 Bell Yard Chambers, London WC2
p926 . . . . 020 7400 1800

HURD, Mr James G *Oct 1994*
12, 18, 30, 55
St James's Chambers, Manchester
p984 . . . . 0161 834 7000

Hurlock, Mr John LLB(Hons) G *Oct 1993*
15, 62
2 Bedford Row, London WC1
p924 . . . . 020 7440 8888

Hurrion, Miss Sarah-Jane MA(Oxon) G *Jul 2000*
8, 11, 5, 38, 93, 32, 37, 6, 88
Unity Street Chambers, Bristol
p972 . . . . 0117 906 9789

HURST, Mr Andrew BA(Oxon); Recorder I *Nov 1992*
12, 15, 36, 27
23 Essex Street, London WC2
p932 . . . . 020 7413 0353

Hurst, Mr Brian MA(Oxon) M *Jul 1983*
8, 12, 11, 24, 22, 5
39 Park Square, Leeds
p978 . . . . 0113 245 6633

HURST, Mr Martin M *Jul 1985*
15
1 High Pavement, Nottingham
p988 . . . . 0115 941 8218

HURWORTH, Miss Jillian MA(Hons)(Cantab) I *Oct 1993*
10, 20, 51
1 Garden Court, London EC4
p934 . . . . 020 7797 7900

Husain, Miss Laureen L *Mar 1997*
15
2 Pump Court, London EC4
p947 . . . . 020 7353 5597

HUSAIN, Mr Raza BA(Hons)(Oxon); CPE(Lond) M *Oct 1993*
(Q.C.) *23, 15, 1, 19, 51, 36, 50, 27, 55, 33*
Matrix Chambers, London WC1
p942 . . . . 020 7404 3447

HUSBANDS, Miss Abigail M *Nov 2000*
25, 15, 27, 13
23 Essex Street, London WC2
p932 . . . . 020 7413 0353

Huseyin, Mr Martin BA(Sussex); DipLaw I *Nov 1988*
15, 22, 30
Tooks Chambers, London EC4
p953 . . . . 020 7842 7575

HUSSAIN, Mr Basharat G *Jan 1997*
20, 10, 93, 64
Cornwall Street Chambers, Birmingham
p967 . . . . 0121 233 7500

Hussain, Miss Fara M *Jan 2000*
15 New Bridge Street Chambers, London EC4
p943 . . . . 020 7842 1900

HUSSAIN, Miss Frida Khanam LLB(Hons) I *Oct 1995*
Furnival Chambers, London EC4
p934 . . . . 020 7405 3232

Hussain, Mr Ghulam LLB(Hons) I *Oct 1998*
12, 15, 18, 30, 25
Crown Office Row Chambers, Brighton
p970 . . . . 01273 625625

Hussain, Mr Gul Nawaz G *Jan 2000*
Park Court Chambers, Leeds
p978 . . . . 0113 243 3277

HUSSAIN, Mukhtar M *Jul 1971*
(Q.C.) *15*
Carmelite Chambers, London EC4
p927 . . . . 020 7936 6300
Lincoln House Chambers, Manchester
p984 . . . . 0161 832 5701

Hussain, Mr Rafaquat Mahmood BA M *Jan 1996*
15, 23, 22, 88
Bell Yard Chambers, London WC2
p926 . . . . 020 7306 9292 / 7404 5138

Hussain, Mr Riaz LLB G *Oct 2002*
3, 7, 11, 31, 40, 41, 43, 45, 49, 54, 61, 78, 74
Atkin Chambers, London WC1
p923 . . . . 020 7404 0102

Hussain, Miss Rukshanda LLB(Hons) G *Sep 1998*
10, 20, 15, 72
St Pauls Chambers, Leeds
p979 . . . . 0113 245 5866

Hussain, Tasaddat LLB(Hons)(Huddersfield) L *Nov 1998*
12, 20, 26, 30, 31, 41, 46, 47, 51
Broadway House Chambers, Leeds
p977 . . . . 0113 246 2600
Broadway House Chambers, Bradford
p969 . . . . 01274 722560

Hussain, Mr Zahid LLB(UWE) L *Jan 2001*
20, 10
St John's Chambers, Bristol
p972 . . . . 0117 921 3456

HUSSAIN, Zira L *Oct 1998*
20
St Philips Chambers, Birmingham
p969 . . . . 0121 246 7000

Hussein, Mr Tim LLB I *Jan 1993*
10, 20
1 Pump Court, London EC4
p947 . . . . 020 7842 7070

Hussey, Miss Ann Elizabeth BA M *May 1981*
1 Hare Court, London EC4
p936 . . . . 020 7797 7070

Huston, Mr Graham I *Feb 1991*
15, 62
7 Bedford Row, London WC1
p924 . . . . 020 7242 3555

Hutchin, Mr Edward LLB(Hons)(Notts) M *Oct 1996*
One Essex Court, London EC4
p931 . . . . 020 7936 3030
Temple Garden Chambers, London EC4
p952 . . . . 020 7583 1315

Hutchings, Mr Mark BSc(Hons); CPE G *Jan 2005*
Stour Chambers, Canterbury
p972 . . . . 01227 764899

HUTCHINGS, Mr Martin MA(Oxon) M *Feb 1986*
8, 22, 31, 40
Wilberforce Chambers, London WC2
p953 . . . . 020 7306 0102

Hutchings, Mr Matthew BA(Oxon); DipLaw I *Nov 1993*
1, 8, 22, 46
42 Bedford Row, London WC1
p925 . . . . 020 7831 0222

Hutchings, Mr Richard G *Jul 2001*
15
1 Inner Temple Lane, London EC4
p937 . . . . 020 7427 4400

Hutchison, Eleanor M *Jan 2007*
1 Pump Court, London EC4
p947 . . . . 020 7842 7070

Hutton, Mr Alexander BSc G *Oct 1992*
53, 27
Hailsham Chambers, London EC4
p936 . . . . 020 7643 5000

HUTTON, Miss Caroline MA(Cantab); FCIArb; Mediator (CEDR) M *Nov 1979*
2, 6, 7, 8, 22, 49, 88
Enterprise Chambers, London WC2
p931 . . . . 020 7405 9471
Enterprise Chambers, Leeds
p977 . . . . 0113 246 0391
Enterprise Chambers, Newcastle upon Tyne
p987 . . . . 0191 222 3344

Hutton, Miss Louise BA(Hons)(Oxon) I *Nov 1998*
Maitland Chambers, London WC2
p941 . . . . 020 7406 1200

HUYTON, Ms Katherine LLB(Hons) M *Nov 1999*
20, 12, 30, 62
Oriel Chambers, Liverpool
p981 . . . . 0151 236 7191 / 236 4321
Oriel Chambers, Preston
p990 . . . . 01772 254764

HYAM, Mr Jeremy BA(Hons) G *Nov 1995*
12, 18, 20, 22, 30
1 Crown Office Row, London EC4
p929 . . . . 020 7797 7500

Hyams, Mr Oliver LLB(Hons); Part Time Employment Tribunal Chairman M *Jan 1989*
18
Devereux Chambers, London WC2
p930 . . . . 020 7353 7534

HYDE, Mr Charles Gordon LLB(Hons)(Manc); Recorder M *Jul 1988*
(Q.C.) *20, 10*
Queen Elizabeth Buildings, London EC4
p948 . . . . 020 7797 7837

Hyde, Mr David BA(Hons); MBA; DipLaw L *Nov 1997*
Clapham Law Chambers, London SW1
p928 . . . . 020 7978 8482 / 7642 5777

See p1010 for the Key to Work Categories

Hyde, Ms Marcia BA(Leeds); MA; DipLaw I *Oct 1992*
10
Coram Chambers, London EC1
p929 . . . . . 020 7092 3700

HYDE, Mr Michael Thomas I *Nov 2006*
Mitre House Chambers, London WC1
p942 . . . . . 020 7307 7100

Hyde, Mr Sarah-Jane I *Jan 2002*
One Essex Court, London EC4
p931 . . . . . 020 7936 3030

Hyland, Mr Graham BA I *Jul 1978*
(Q.C.) *15, 62*
Broad Chare Chambers, Newcastle upon Tyne
p986 . . . . . 0191 232 0541

Hyland, Mr J Graham Keith BA(Newc); Recorder I *Jul 1978*
(Q.C.) *15*
Broadway House Chambers, Leeds
p977 . . . . . 0113 246 2600
Broadway House Chambers, Bradford
p969 . . . . . 01274 722560

Hylton, Miss Nasstassia I *Jul 2007*
20, 10, 67
Harcourt Chambers, London EC4
p936 . . . . . 0844 561 7135
Harcourt Chambers, Oxford
p989 . . . . . 0844 561 7135

Hymanson, Miss Deanna S LLB(Hons) M *Feb 1988*
19, 20
Cobden House Chambers, Manchester
p983 . . . . . 0161 833 6000

HYNES, Mr Paul L *Nov 1987*
(Q.C.) *15, 62, 51*
25 Bedford Row, London WC1
p925 . . . . . 020 7067 1500

Hytner, Mr Benet MA(Cantab) M *Feb 1952*
(Q.C.) *12, 30*
42 Bedford Row, London WC1
p925 . . . . . 020 7831 0222

IBEKWE, Ms Frances M *Mar 2008*
Furnival Chambers, London EC4
p934 . . . . . 020 7405 3232

IBRAHIM, Miss Sara Elise Lewis L *Oct 2006*
10, 11, 18, 30, 38
3 Hare Court, London EC4
p937 . . . . . 020 7415 7800

Ieuan, Mr Morris LLB(Lond) G *Jul 1979*
12, 15
9 Park Place, Cardiff
p973 . . . . . 029 2038 2731

IFE, Ms Linden MA(Oxon) M *Nov 1982*
5, 6, 8, 11, 24, 29, 40, 38, 49
Enterprise Chambers, London WC2
p931 . . . . . 020 7405 9471
Enterprise Chambers, Leeds
p977 . . . . . 0113 246 0391
Enterprise Chambers, Newcastle upon Tyne
p987 . . . . . 0191 222 3344

Iles, Mr David LLB(Lond) I *Jul 1977*
15, 72
No5 Chambers, Bristol
p971 . . . . . 0845 210 5555
No5 Chambers, London EC4
p944 . . . . . 0845 210 5555
No5 Chambers, Birmingham
p968 . . . . . 0845 210 5555

ILIFFE, Ms Kate L *Jan 2000*
15, 62
St Philips Chambers, Birmingham
p969 . . . . . 0121 246 7000

ILYAS, Mr Shaiba LLB; LLM L *Mar 1998*
5, 6, 8, 11, 22, 29, 40, 47, 49, 38, 88, 97
Enterprise Chambers, London WC2
p931 . . . . . 020 7405 9471
Enterprise Chambers, Leeds
p977 . . . . . 0113 246 0391
Enterprise Chambers, Newcastle upon Tyne
p987 . . . . . 0191 222 3344

Indulska, Naomi Lydia G *Jan 2006*
10, 20
Pendragon Chambers, Swansea
p993 . . . . . 01792 411188

Infield, Paul LLB(Sheff) I *Jul 1980*
29
Clerksroom - Administration Centre, Taunton
p993 . . . . . 0845 083 3000

INGHAM, Miss Elizabeth BA(Oxon) M *Nov 1989*
Colleton Chambers, Exeter
p975 . . . . . 01392 274898

Inglis, Mr Alan BA(Essex); MA(Warw); DipLaw; CQSW M *Jul 1989*
10, 20, 1, 37, 40, 58, 63
Coram Chambers, London EC1
p929 . . . . . 020 7092 3700

Inglis Jones, Mr Nigel John BA(Oxon) I *Nov 1954*
(Q.C.) *8, 92*
Outer Temple Chambers, London WC2
p945 . . . . . 020 7353 6381

Ingram, Mr Jonathan BA I *Jul 1984*
15
5 St Andrew's Hill, London EC4
p950 . . . . . 020 7332 5400

Ingram, Mr Nigel I *Jul 1972*
15, 62
2 Bedford Row, London WC1
p924 . . . . . 020 7440 8888

Innes, Mr Stephen G *Oct 2000*
8, 12, 24, 40
Four New Square, London WC2
p943 . . . . . 020 7822 2000

Inyundo, Mr Richard Kwame Swaka G *Mar 1997*
15
1 Inner Temple Lane, London EC4
p937 . . . . . 020 7427 4400

Iqbal, Mr Abdul S DipLaw(B'ham) G *Jan 1994*
15, 30
No 6 Barristers Chambers, Leeds
p978 . . . . . 0113 245 9763

Iqbal, Miss Samina L *Oct 1999*
23, 57
Two King's Bench Walk, London EC4
p939 . . . . . 020 7353 7202 / 7353 3909
Renaissance Chambers, London WC1
p949 . . . . . 020 7404 1111

IRVIN, Mr Peter BA(Oxon) G *Jul 1972*
11, 24, 5, 35, 62, 44
Brick Court Chambers, London WC2
p927 . . . . . 020 7379 3550

Irving, Miss Gillian BA(Hons)(Law) I *Jul 1984*
(Q.C.) *10, 12, 20, 30, 27*
15 Winckley Square, Preston
p991 . . . . . 01772 252828
1 Hare Court, London EC4
p936 . . . . . 020 7797 7070
9 St John Street Chambers, Manchester
p984 . . . . . 0161 955 9000

ISAAC, Mr Nicholas BA G *Oct 1993*
8, 88, 93
Tanfield Chambers, London WC1
p951 . . . . . 020 7421 5300

Isaac, Mr Sebastian L *Jan 2005*
One Essex Court, London EC4
p931 . . . . . 020 7583 2000

ISAACS, Mr Barry BA(Oxon); MA(Harv); ASA I *Oct 1994*
(Q.C.) *5, 6, 8, 11, 12, 24, 29, 38*
South Square, London WC1
p950 . . . . . 020 7696 9900

Isaacs, Miss Elizabeth L *Jan 1998*
St Ives Chambers, Birmingham
p969 . . . . . 0121 236 0863

Isaacs, Mr Oliver M *Jan 2000*
11, 50, 12, 18
3PB, London EC4
p946 . . . . . 020 7583 8055

Isaacs, Mr Paul Recorder M *Feb 1974*
20
Broadway House Chambers, Leeds
p977 . . . . . 0113 246 2600
Broadway House Chambers, Bradford
p969 . . . . . 01274 722560

Isherwood, Mr John MA(Cantab) G *Jul 1978*
12, 30, 53
Unity Street Chambers, Bristol
p972 . . . . . 0117 906 9789

ISLAM, Mr Mohammad M *Oct 2002*
15, 94
18 Red Lion Court, London EC4
p949 . . . . . 020 7520 6000
18 Red Lion Court (Annexe), Chelmsford
p973 . . . . . 01245 280880

ISLAM, Miss Naznin G *Oct 2000*
12, 15, 18, 20, 23
Pump Court Chambers, Swindon
p993 . . . . . 01793 539899
Pump Court Chambers, Winchester
p994 . . . . . 01962 868161
Pump Court Chambers, London EC4
p947 . . . . . 020 7353 0711

ISLAM, Mr Saiful L *Jan 2005*
3 Dr Johnson's Buildings, London EC4
p930 . . . . . 020 7353 4854

Ismail, Miss Nazmun LLB L *May 1992*
No5 Chambers, Bristol
p971 . . . . . 0845 210 5555
No5 Chambers, London EC4
p944 . . . . . 0845 210 5555
No5 Chambers, Birmingham
p968 . . . . . 0845 210 5555

ISMAIL, Ms Roxanne LLB(Lond) L *Nov 1993*
5, 6, 8, 11, 12, 24, 29
South Square, London WC1
p950 . . . . . 020 7696 9900

Israel, Mr Jeffrey Antony M *Oct 2000*
15
5 King's Bench Walk, London EC4
p939 . . . . . 020 7353 5638

ISSA, Ms Alexandra MA(Hons)(Oxon) L *Nov 1993*
Temple Garden Chambers, London EC4
p952 . . . . . 020 7583 1315

Itari Wills, Miss Alexandra I *Jan 2000*
No 3 Fleet Street Chambers, London EC4
p944 . . . . . 020 7936 4474

ITEN, Miss Corinne I *Oct 2006*
10, 15, 18, 20
Pump Court Chambers, Swindon
p993 . . . . . 01793 539899
Pump Court Chambers, Winchester
p994 . . . . . 01962 868161
Pump Court Chambers, London EC4
p947 . . . . . 020 7353 0711

IVENS, Miss Jemma L *Feb 1994*
1 Mitre Court Buildings, London EC4
p942 . . . . . 020 7452 8900

IVIMY, Miss Cecilia BA(Oxon) M *Nov 1995*
1, 11, 19, 26, 51
11KBW, London EC4
p938 . . . . . 020 7632 8500

IYENGAR, Ms Harini MA; BCL I *Oct 1999*
1, 18, 51, 26, 55, 36
11KBW, London EC4
p938 . . . . . 020 7632 8500

JACK, Mr Adrian MA(Oxon); Member New South Wales Bar; Munich Bar; Recorder M *Nov 1986*
6, 8, 11, 18, 22, 32, 40, 49, 38, 88, 97
Enterprise Chambers, London WC2
p931 . . . . . 020 7405 9471
Enterprise Chambers, Leeds
p977 . . . . . 0113 246 0391
Enterprise Chambers, Newcastle upon Tyne
p987 . . . . . 0191 222 3344

JACK, Mrs Angela LLB(Hons) I *Jan 1999*
22, 26
Five Paper, London EC4
p946 . . . . . 020 7815 3200

JACK, Mr Nicholas BSc(Manc) L *Jan 2003*
10, 20
Octagon House, Norwich
p988 . . . . . 01603 623186

Jacklin, Miss Susan BA(Dunelm) I *Nov 1980*
(Q.C.) *10, 20, 40*
Harcourt Chambers, London EC4
p936 . . . . . 0844 561 7135
Harcourt Chambers, Oxford
p989 . . . . . 0844 561 7135
St John's Chambers, Bristol
p972 . . . . . 0117 921 3456

Jackson, Mr Adrian MA(Cantab); MCIArb L *Oct 1990*
7, 11, 18, 22, 30, 40
Paradise Chambers, Sheffield
p992 . . . . . 0114 273 8951

JACKSON, Mr Andrew BA(Manc); DipLaw L *Jan 1986*
15, 62
St Philips Chambers, Birmingham
p969 . . . . . 0121 246 7000

Jackson, Mr Anthony Warren MA(Cantab); M Phil(Cantab); LLM(Illinois) I *Oct 1995*
12, 27, 40, 51, 1, 36
3 Serjeants' Inn, London EC4
p950 . . . . . 020 7427 5000

JACKSON, Ms Claire LLB(Hons) L *Mar 2002*
6, 8, 11, 22, 38, 40, 88, 97
Enterprise Chambers, London WC2
p931 . . . . . 020 7405 9471
Enterprise Chambers, Leeds
p977 . . . . . 0113 246 0391
Enterprise Chambers, Newcastle upon Tyne
p987 . . . . . 0191 222 3344

Jackson, Mr David G *Jul 1986*
15, 25, 12
St Ives Chambers, Birmingham
p969 . . . . . 0121 236 0863

Jackson, Miss Fiona I *Nov 1998*
33 Chancery Lane, London WC2
p928 . . . . . 020 7440 9950

Jackson, Ms Judith LLB; LLM I *Nov 1975*
(Q.C.) *1, 3, 5, 6, 7, 8, 9, 11, 12, 13, 14, 22, 24, 26, 28, 29, 31, 32, 37*
Maitland Chambers, London WC2
p941 . . . . . 020 7406 1200

Jackson, Mr Kevin BA(Hons) M *Nov 1984*
10, 20
Becket Chambers, Canterbury
p972 . . . . . 01227 786331
Becket Chambers, Maidstone
p982 . . . . . 01622 230957

Jackson, Mr Mark L *Jan 1997*
15
No 8 Chambers, Birmingham
p968 . . . . . 0121 236 5514

Jackson, Mr Matthew David Everard BA(Cantab) M *Jul 1986*
40, 53, 27
Hailsham Chambers, London EC4
p936 . . . . . 020 7643 5000

Jackson, Mr Myles LLB(Hons)(Lond); MA(York) L *Oct 1995*
Thomas More Chambers, London WC2
p952 . . . . . 020 7404 7000

JACKSON, Nicholas LLB(Newc) L *Nov 1992*
6, 8, 9, 11, 22, 29, 31, 32, 37
Atlantic Chambers, Liverpool
p980 . . . . . 0151 236 4421

Jackson, Mr Paul I *Jul 2002*
15
5 King's Bench Walk, London EC4
p939 . . . . . 020 7353 5638

JACKSON, Ms Philippa BA; GDL; BVC L *Oct 2008*
1, 31, 55, 76, 57, 63, 25, 23
4-5 Gray's Inn Square, London WC1
p935 . . . . . 020 7404 5252

Jackson, Ms Rosemary E LLB(Lond); AKC(Lond) M *Jul 1981*
(Q.C.) *3, 7, 11, 24, 40*
Keating Chambers, London WC2
p938 . . . . . 020 7544 2600

Jackson, Ms Samantha LLB(Hons); LLM M *Nov 1996*
20, 22, 88, 89, 26, 93
1 Chancery Lane, London WC2
p928 . . . . . 0845 634 6666

JACKSON, Mr Simon Recorder G *Jan 1982*
(Q.C.) *15, 30*
9 St John Street Chambers, Manchester
p984 . . . . . 0161 955 9000

Jackson, Mr Simon Malcolm Dermot LLB(Leeds) G *Nov 1982*
(Q.C.)
Park Court Chambers, Leeds
p978 . . . . . 0113 243 3277
Temple Garden Chambers, London EC4
p952 . . . . . 020 7583 1315

JACKSON, Ms Stephanie L LLB(Reading) I *Oct 1992*
7, 8, 22, 11, 40
12 King's Bench Walk, London EC4
p940 . . . . . 020 7583 0811

Jacob, Mr Isaac LLB; FCIArb; US Att(California); Recorder/ Assistant Parliamentary Boundary Commissioner L *Jul 1963*
5, 6, 8, 11, 13, 19, 29, 41, 44, 51, 38
9 Stone Buildings Barristers Chambers, London WC2
p951 . . . . . 020 7404 5055

Jacob, Mr Winston M *Jul 2005*
93, 11, 30
Lamb Chambers, London EC4
p941 . . . . . 020 7797 8300

Jacobs, Mr Alexander Marc G *Oct 1997*
St Ives Chambers, Birmingham
p969 . . . . . 0121 236 0863

Jacobs, Miss Amy M *Jan 2005*
St Ives Chambers, Birmingham
p969 . . . . . 0121 236 0863

13

JACOBS, Miss Claire LLB(Hons) G *Jul 1989*
15, 20, 10
4 King's Bench Walk, London EC4
p939 . . . . . 020 7822 7000

Jacobs, Sir Francis Geoffrey M *Jan 1964*
(Q.C.)
Fountain Court Chambers, London EC4
p934 . . . . . 020 7583 3335

Jacobs, Ms Linda BSc; LLM M *Jan 2000*
53, 12, 22, 27, 30, 38
Cloisters, London EC4
p928 . . . . . 020 7827 4000

Jacobs, Mr Nigel BA; LLM(Cantab) M *Nov 1983*
(Q.C.) *11, 35, 24, 3*
Quadrant Chambers, London EC4
p948 . . . . . 020 7583 4444

Jacobs, Mr Richard D BA(Cantab) M *Nov 1979*
(Q.C.)
Essex Court Chambers, London WC2
p931 . . . . . 020 7813 8000

Jacobs, Mr Robin BA(Hons) M *Jan 2006*
76, 33, 1
Hardwicke, London WC2
p936 . . . . . 020 7242 2523

JACOBSON, Mr Lawrence BA; LLB(UCT); DipLaw(PCL); Advocate of the Supreme Court SA G *Nov 1985*
30, 11, 40, 53
Five Paper, London EC4
p946 . . . . . 020 7815 3200

JACOBSON, Miss Mary Inge MA(Cantab); LLB(Hons)(Lond) M *Oct 1992*
12, 25, 30, 15
Maidstone Chambers, Maidstone
p982 . . . . . 01622 688592

Jacques, Mr Gareth Edward LLB(Hons) I *Jan 2007*
20, 12, 18, 10
Regency Chambers, Peterborough
p990 . . . . . 01733 315215

JACQUES, Mr Timothy M *Jan 2008*
12, 15, 11, 38, 30, 20, 10
Cornwall Street Chambers, Birmingham
p967 . . . . . 0121 233 7500

JAFFA, Mr Ronald LLB G *Jul 1974*
15
25 Bedford Row, London WC1
p925 . . . . . 020 7067 1500

Jafferjee, Mr Aftab Asger BA(Dunelm) I *Nov 1980*
(Q.C.) *15, 62*
Atkinson Bevan Chambers, London EC4
p924 . . . . . 020 7353 2112

Jaffey, Mr Ben MA(Cantab) M *Sep 1999*
1, 18, 11, 51, 5, 81, 50, 52, 56, 89
Blackstone Chambers, London EC4
p926 . . . . . 020 7583 1770

Jagadesham, Mr Vijay I *Jan 2004*
1, 22, 51, 23, 70
Garden Court North Chambers, Manchester
p983 . . . . . 0161 236 1840

Jagutpal, Mr Previn M *Oct 2005*
Guildford Chambers, Guildford
p975 . . . . . 01483 539131

Jahangir, Asma G *Jan 2000*
1 Pump Court, London EC4
p947 . . . . . 020 7842 7070

Jaisri, Shashi L *Jan 1995*
23, 22
12 Old Square, London WC2
p945 . . . . . 020 7404 0875

Jakens, Miss Claire BA; MPhil; DipLaw; Recorder M *Jul 1988*
10, 15, 20, 30, 36
Westgate Chambers, Lewes
p980 . . . . . 01273 480510

Jamal, Isabel L *Jan 2008*
8 New Square, London WC2
p943 . . . . . 020 7405 4321

James, Mr Alun Edward MA; BCL(Oxon) M *Nov 1986*
34, 36, 57, 58
Exchange Chambers, Manchester
p983 . . . . . 0161 833 2722
Exchange Chambers, Liverpool
p980 . . . . . 0151 236 7747
Exchange Chambers, Leeds
p977 . . . . . 0113 203 1970
Temple Tax Chambers, London EC4
p952 . . . . . 020 7353 7884 / 7353 8982

James, Mr Arthur Ronald Alfred LLB(Lond) M *Nov 1975*
1, 12, 13, 15, 18, 20, 22, 31, 36, 38
Abbey Chambers, Shepperton
p992 . . . . . 01932 560913

James, Mr Christopher LLB(Hons) G *Nov 1977*
20, 2
Angel Chambers, Swansea
p992 . . . . . 01792 464623
No5 Chambers, Bristol
p971 . . . . . 0845 210 5555
No5 Chambers, London EC4
p944 . . . . . 0845 210 5555
No5 Chambers, Birmingham
p968 . . . . . 0845 210 5555

James, Mr David BSc(Hons); LLB(Hons) I *Oct 1998*
15, 56, 70, 71, 72, 94
St Johns Buildings, Preston
p990 . . . . . 01772 256100
St Johns Buildings, Chester
p974 . . . . . 01244 323070
St Johns Buildings, Manchester
p985 . . . . . 0161 214 1500
St Johns Buildings, Liverpool
p982 . . . . . 0151 243 6000

JAMES, Mr Edward LLB I *Oct 2002*
12, 30, 11, 40, 53, 22, 29
Ropewalk Chambers, Nottingham
p989 . . . . . 0115 947 2581

JAMES, Mr Grahame G *Apr 1989*
15, 10, 20, 25, 30
Carmelite Chambers, London EC4
p927 . . . . . 020 7936 6300

James, Mr Henry G *Nov 1999*
King's Bench Chambers, Oxford
p989 . . . . . 01865 311066
13 King's Bench Walk, London EC4
p940 . . . . . 020 7353 7204

JAMES, Mr Ian G *Jul 1981*
15, 25, 36
Octagon House, Norwich
p988 . . . . . 01603 623186

JAMES, Mr Mark MA(Oxon) M *Nov 1987*
Temple Garden Chambers, London EC4
p952 . . . . . 020 7583 1315

JAMES, Mr Michael MA(Oxon); FCIArb; Mediator L *Feb 1976*
3, 5, 6, 8, 11, 18, 24, 29, 35, 40, 41, 49, 38, 88
Enterprise Chambers, London WC2
p931 . . . . . 020 7405 9471
Enterprise Chambers, Leeds
p977 . . . . . 0113 246 0391
Enterprise Chambers, Newcastle upon Tyne
p987 . . . . . 0191 222 3344

James, Mr Nicholas BA(Hons); CPE M *Jul 2001*
15, 62, 46, 84, 25
Argent Chambers, London WC2
p923 . . . . . 020 7556 5500

James, Rhodri I *Jul 2002*
15, 62
Lamb Building, Brighton
p970 . . . . . 01273 820490
Lamb Building, London EC4
p940 . . . . . 020 7797 7788

James, Mr Roddy L *Mar 1999*
Charter Chambers, London WC1
p928 . . . . . 020 7618 4400

James, Ms Sharon Ann Sarah LLB(Hons); LLM(Bris) G *Oct 1995*
20, 10
Angel Chambers, Swansea
p992 . . . . . 01792 464623

James, Mrs Venice I BA L *Jul 1983*
10, 15, 23, 12
No 8 Chambers, Birmingham
p968 . . . . . 0121 236 5514

James, Winston M *Oct 1999*
Clerksroom - Administration Centre, Taunton
p993 . . . . . 0845 083 3000

James-Moore, Siward L *Jul 2000*
KCH Garden Square Chambers, Nottingham
p989 . . . . . 0115 941 8851
KCH Garden Square Chambers, Leicester
p979 . . . . . 0115 941 8851

Jameson, Miss Antonia M *Nov 1999*
12
3PB, Bournemouth
p969 . . . . . 01202 292102

JAMESON, Mr Barnaby M *Nov 1993*
15, 95
18 Red Lion Court, London EC4
p949 . . . . . 020 7520 6000
18 Red Lion Court (Annexe), Chelmsford
p973 . . . . . 01245 280880

JAMESON, Mr Daniel M *Nov 2004*
Furnival Chambers, London EC4
p934 . . . . . 020 7405 3232

Jameson, Mr Rodney Mellor Maples BA(Eton) I *Jul 1976*
(Q.C.) *15*
4 Breams Buildings, London EC4
p927 . . . . . 020 7092 1900
No 6 Barristers Chambers, Leeds
p978 . . . . . 0113 245 9763

Jamieson, Stuart Owen BA(Cantab)(Law) G *Oct 2003*
10, 12, 20, 30
Zenith Chambers, Leeds
p979 . . . . . 0113 245 5438

Jamil, Miss Aisha LLB(Hons) L *Jan 1995*
15, 20, 10, 30
Broadway House Chambers, Leeds
p977 . . . . . 0113 246 2600
Broadway House Chambers, Bradford
p969 . . . . . 01274 722560

Jamil, Miss Yasmin LLB L *Nov 1998*
10, 20
4 Brick Court Chambers, London EC4
p927 . . . . . 020 7832 3200

Jan-Temmink, Mr Robert BA(Hons)(Cantab) M *Oct 1996*
49, 41, 5, 8, 11, 74, 67, 81, 92, 40
Outer Temple Chambers, London WC2
p945 . . . . . 020 7353 6381

Janes, Mr Jeremy BA(Bris) L *Nov 1992*
8, 15, 22, 30, 23
KCH Garden Square Chambers, Nottingham
p989 . . . . . 0115 941 8851
KCH Garden Square Chambers, Leicester
p979 . . . . . 0115 941 8851

Janner, Mr Daniel M *Jan 1980*
(Q.C.) *72, 15, 71, 70, 82, 62*
Exchange Chambers, Manchester
p983 . . . . . 0161 833 2722
Exchange Chambers, Liverpool
p980 . . . . . 0151 236 7747
Exchange Chambers, Leeds
p977 . . . . . 0113 203 1970
23 Essex Street, London WC2
p932 . . . . . 020 7413 0353

JANUSZ, Mr Pierre P M *Jul 1979*
11, 12, 24, 30, 59
3 Hare Court, London EC4
p937 . . . . . 020 7415 7800

JARMAIN, Mr Stephen Robert BSc; CPE M *Jul 2005*
20, 10
1 Garden Court, London EC4
p934 . . . . . 020 7797 7900

Jarman, Mr Christopher MA(Cantab) I *Jan 1976*
13 Old Square Chambers, London WC2
p945 . . . . . 020 7831 4445

Jarman, Mr Mark Christopher LLB(Hons) I *Nov 1989*
20, 10
4 Paper Buildings, London EC4
p946 . . . . . 020 7583 0816

Jarman, Mr Samuel I *Jul 1989*
4 KBW, London EC4
p938 . . . . . 020 7822 8822
Lombard Chambers, London EC1
p941 . . . . . 020 7107 2100

JARRON, Miss Stephanie BA L *May 1990*
88, 32, 93, 29
Enterprise Chambers, London WC2
p931 . . . . . 020 7405 9471
Enterprise Chambers, Leeds
p977 . . . . . 0113 246 0391
Enterprise Chambers, Newcastle upon Tyne
p987 . . . . . 0191 222 3344

JARVIS, Mr John MA(Cantab) L *Jul 1970*
(Q.C.) *3, 5, 6, 11, 24, 40*
3 Verulam Buildings, London WC1
p953 . . . . . 020 7831 8441

Jarvis, Mr Malcolm LLM(Cantab); LLD(Groningen) M *Oct 1998*
3, 11, 12, 19, 24, 35, 41
20 Essex Street, London WC2
p932 . . . . . 020 7842 1200

Jarvis, Mr Oliver I *Nov 1992*
72, 15, 70
Exchange Chambers, Manchester
p983 . . . . . 0161 833 2722
Exchange Chambers, Liverpool
p980 . . . . . 0151 236 7747
Exchange Chambers, Leeds
p977 . . . . . 0113 203 1970

JASPAL, Mr Kam L *Jan 2005*
12, 30, 11, 40, 53, 22, 29
Ropewalk Chambers, Nottingham
p989 . . . . . 0115 947 2581

Jay, Mr Grenville R MA(Cantab) I *Dec 1975*
Regent Chambers, Hanley
p976 . . . . . 01782 286666

JAY, Mr Robert M M *Jun 1981*
(Q.C.) *1, 30, 23, 12, 53, 51, 11, 76, 46, 31*
Thirty Nine Essex Street, London WC2
p932 . . . . . 020 7832 1111

JEANS, Mr Christopher LLB(Lond); BCL(Oxon); P/T Chairman of Employment Tribunal
P/T Chairman of Employment Tribunal G *Jul 1980*
(Q.C.) *18, 55, 36, 19*
11KBW, London EC4
p938 . . . . . 020 7632 8500

Jeary, Mr Stephen LLB I *Jul 1987*
15
Temple Chambers, Newport
p988 . . . . . 01633 267403 / 255855
Temple Chambers, Cardiff
p973 . . . . . 029 2039 7364

JEAVONS, Ms Anne M *Jan 2008*
11, 5, 35, 81, 40, 62, 38, 24
3 Verulam Buildings, London WC1
p953 . . . . . 020 7831 8441

Jebb, Mr Andrew John LLB(Hons); Deputy District Judge (Mags) G *Nov 1993*
15, 62
Exchange Chambers, Manchester
p983 . . . . . 0161 833 2722
Exchange Chambers, Liverpool
p980 . . . . . 0151 236 7747
Exchange Chambers, Leeds
p977 . . . . . 0113 203 1970

JEFFERIES, Mr Thomas BA(Dunelm) M *Nov 1981*
5, 6, 8, 11, 29, 32
Landmark Chambers, London EC4
p941 . . . . . 020 7430 1221

Jefferis, Mr Michael M *Jan 1976*
13 Old Square Chambers, London WC2
p945 . . . . . 020 7831 4445

Jefford, Ms Nerys A MA(Oxon); LLM(UVA) G *Nov 1986*
(Q.C.) *3, 7, 11, 19, 24, 40*
Keating Chambers, London WC2
p938 . . . . . 020 7544 2600

JEFFREYS, Mr Alan LLB; Recorder G *Jul 1970*
(Q.C.) *30, 40, 53*
Farrar's Building, London EC4
p933 . . . . . 020 7583 9241

JEGARAJAH, Shivani BA M *Jul 1993*
23
Renaissance Chambers, London WC1
p949 . . . . . 020 7404 1111

Jelf, Mr Simon E LLB(Hons) G *Oct 1996*
29
48 Bedford Row, London WC1
p926 . . . . . 020 7430 2005

Jenking-Rees, Ms Laura LLB(Hons) L *Mar 2002*
15, 20, 12
Guildhall Chambers, Portsmouth
p990 . . . . . 023 9275 2400

Jenkins, Mr Alan BA(Hons) M *Feb 1984*
15, 27, 62, 85, 81
Outer Temple Chambers, London WC2
p945 . . . . . 020 7353 6381

Jenkins, Mr Alun LLB G *May 1981*
Goldsmith Chambers, London EC4
p935 . . . . . 020 7353 6802
2 Bedford Row, London WC1
p924 . . . . . 020 7440 8888

Jenkins, Mr Benjamin LLB(Hons)(Cardiff) G *Jan 2004*
Albion Chambers, Bristol
p970 . . . . . 0117 927 2144

JENKINS, Miss Catherine Phillida BA(Keele) M *Nov 1990*
10, 20
1 Garden Court, London EC4
p934 . . . . . 020 7797 7900

See p1010 for the Key to Work Categories

Jenkins, Mr David Crofton *I Nov 1967*
2 King's Bench Walk, London EC4
p939 . . . . . 020 7353 1746

Jenkins, Mr Edward BA(Cantab) *M Jul 1977*
(Q.C.) *15, 62, 13, 48, 39*
5 Paper Buildings, London EC4
p946 . . . . . 020 7583 6117

Jenkins, Mr Hywel Iestyn LLB *I Jul 1974*
30, 12, 10, 53, 84, 62
Outer Temple Chambers, London WC2
p945 . . . . . 020 7353 6381

Jenkins, Mr James John LLB *G Nov 1974*
12, 15, 30, 40, 51, 53, 56
Iscoed Chambers, Swansea
p993 . . . . . 01792 652988

JENKINS, Miss Joanne Frances *M Jul 2009*
15, 10, 12
Wilberforce Chambers, Hull
p976 . . . . . 01482 323264

JENKINS, Miss Kim *G Jul 1982*
15, 62, 36, 46
18 Red Lion Court, London EC4
p949 . . . . . 020 7520 6000
18 Red Lion Court (Annexe), Chelmsford
p973 . . . . . 01245 280880

JENKINS, Mr Philip BA; PhD *M Jan 2003*
8, 11, 88, 29, 37, 38
St John's Chambers, Bristol
p972 . . . . . 0117 921 3456

Jenkins, Mr Rowan MA; D Phil *L Jul 1994*
15, 62, 48
Crown Office Row Chambers, Brighton
p970 . . . . . 01273 625625

Jenkins, Susan *G Oct 1998*
Angel Chambers, Swansea
p992 . . . . . 01792 464623

Jenkins, Mr T Alun LLB(Bris); Recorder *L Jul 1972*
(Q.C.) *15, 62, 71, 84*
Queen Square Chambers, Bristol
p972 . . . . . 0117 921 1966

JENKINSON, Mr Lee LLB(Hons) *G Mar 2001*
30, 53
7 Harrington Street Chambers, Liverpool
p981 . . . . . 0151 242 0707

Jennings, Mr Peter N *M Jul 1972*
4, 5, 8, 11, 22, 24, 29, 30, 32, 35
3PB, London EC4
p946 . . . . . 020 7583 8055

Jennings, Ms Sarah *I Jan 2009*
20, 10, 89, 47
Queen Square Chambers, Bristol
p972 . . . . . 0117 921 1966

Jenns, Mr Tim *L Jan 2009*
81, 5, 11, 24, 35, 41, 61
7 King's Bench Walk, London EC4
p940 . . . . . 020 7910 8300

JEPSON, Mrs Amanda LLB; LLM *G Oct 2005*
20, 10, 76, 30, 94, 36
Tanfield Chambers, London WC1
p951 . . . . . 020 7421 5300

Jeremy, Mr David Hugh Thomas *M Jul 1977*
(Q.C.) *12, 15, 36*
QEB Hollis Whiteman, London EC4
p948 . . . . . 020 7933 8855

Jerman, Mr Anthony BA(Lond); DipLaw *M Nov 1989*
10, 20
42 Bedford Row, London WC1
p925 . . . . . 020 7831 0222

Jerram, Ms Harriet A MA(Cantab) *G Oct 1998*
53, 30, 84, 1
Outer Temple Chambers, London WC2
p945 . . . . . 020 7353 6381

Jervis, Mr Christopher Robert MA(Oxon) *I Jul 1966*
15
Albion Chambers, Bristol
p970 . . . . . 0117 927 2144

Jess, Dr Digby C BSc; LLM; FCIArb; PhD; Chartered Arbitrator *G Jul 1978*
7, 11, 24, 40, 41
Exchange Chambers, Manchester
p983 . . . . . 0161 833 2722
Exchange Chambers, Liverpool
p980 . . . . . 0151 236 7747
Exchange Chambers, Leeds
p977 . . . . . 0113 203 1970

Jessel, Mrs Philippa BSc(Lond) *I Jul 1978*
15
6 King's Bench Walk, London EC4
p939 . . . . . 020 7583 0410

Jessop, Mr Stuart BSc(Hons) *G Jul 2002*
15, 51, 62, 1
Nine Bedford Row, London WC1
p924 . . . . . 020 7489 2727

JESURUM, Raphael *G Jan 2007*
15, 62, 70
Mitre House Chambers, London WC1
p942 . . . . . 020 7307 7100

JEWELL, Miss Charlotte *M Nov 1999*
20, 10
Tanfield Chambers, London WC1
p951 . . . . . 020 7421 5300

Jewell, Mr Matthew *L Nov 1989*
15
1 Paper Buildings, London EC4
p946 . . . . . 020 7353 3728

Jibowu, Mr Olumuyiwa A O LLB(Hons) *I Jan 1994*
Chancery Chambers, London WC2
p928 . . . . . 020 7405 6879

Jinadu, Mr Abdul-Lateef BA; LLM(Cantab) *M May 1995*
3, 7, 11, 24, 40
Keating Chambers, London WC2
p938 . . . . . 020 7544 2600

Joffe, Ms Natasha BA(Oxon) *G Oct 1992*
1, 11, 12, 18, 30, 36, 24, 26, 27, 40, 55, 51
Outer Temple Chambers, London WC2
p945 . . . . . 020 7353 6381

Joffe, Mr Victor MA(Cantab); LLB(Cantab) *M Nov 1975*
(Q.C.) *5, 6, 8, 11, 29, 37, 38, 56, 62, 97*
Serle Court, London WC2
p950 . . . . . 020 7242 6105

Johal, Miss Davinder *G Oct 1995*
Holborn Chambers, London WC2
p937 . . . . . 020 7242 6060

Johal, Miss Suki LLB(Hons) *M Nov 1991*
20, 32, 37
Hardwicke, London WC2
p936 . . . . . 020 7242 2523

John, Mr Benjamin MChem(Oxon) *I Jan 2002*
Maitland Chambers, London WC2
p941 . . . . . 020 7406 1200

John, Miss Charlotte BA(Hons); MA *M Jan 2008*
10, 20, 11, 18, 26, 30, 56, 32, 40, 93
Crown Office Row Chambers, Brighton
p970 . . . . . 01273 625625

John, Miss Emma Catrin LLB(Wales) *G Jun 1992*
12, 20, 10
Thirty Park Place, Cardiff
p973 . . . . . 029 2039 8421

JOHN, Miss Laura BA(Hons)(Oxon); CPE(City) *G Jan 2001*
5, 24, 6, 7, 45, 11
3 Verulam Buildings, London WC1
p953 . . . . . 020 7831 8441

JOHN, Miss Laura Elizabeth BCL(ECL); BA(Hons) *I Oct 2007*
1, 44, 11, 18, 46, 19, 51, 28, 33, 57, 61
Monckton Chambers, London WC1
p942 . . . . . 020 7405 7211

John, Mr Morgan *G Jan 2004*
11, 30, 93, 12, 88
Lamb Chambers, London EC4
p941 . . . . . 020 7797 8300

JOHN, Mr Peter C LLB(Hons) *I Nov 1989*
32, 11, 37, 22
Five Paper, London EC4
p946 . . . . . 020 7815 3200

John, Mr Simon *L Jul 1996*
6, 8, 11, 12, 18, 22, 23, 30, 37, 47, 48
Civitas Law, Cardiff
p972 . . . . . 0845 071 3007

Johns, Mr Alan Grant BA(Oxon) *G Oct 1994*
1, 3, 5, 6, 7, 8, 9, 11, 12, 13, 14, 22, 24, 26, 28, 29, 31, 32, 37
Maitland Chambers, London WC2
p941 . . . . . 020 7406 1200

Johnson, Mr Alan MA(Oxon) *M Jul 1971*
15
1 Gray's Inn Square, London WC1
p935 . . . . . 020 7405 8946

Johnson, Miss Amanda *G Oct 1992*
72, 15, 70
Exchange Chambers, Manchester
p983 . . . . . 0161 833 2722
Exchange Chambers, Liverpool
p980 . . . . . 0151 236 7747
Exchange Chambers, Leeds
p977 . . . . . 0113 203 1970
36 Bedford Row, London WC1
p925 . . . . . 020 7421 8000

JOHNSON, Mr Anthony BA(Oxon) *M Nov 2006*
Temple Garden Chambers, London EC4
p952 . . . . . 020 7583 1315

Johnson, Mrs Carolyn LLB *G Nov 1974*
10, 19, 20
Cobden House Chambers, Manchester
p983 . . . . . 0161 833 6000

JOHNSON, Christine LLB(Hons) *I Nov 1991*
10, 20
Atlantic Chambers, Liverpool
p980 . . . . . 0151 236 4421

Johnson, Mr Christopher *M Jul 1983*
1 Inner Temple Lane, London EC4
p937 . . . . . 020 7427 4400

JOHNSON, Miss Clara *I Nov 2005*
11, 12, 1, 30, 88, 93, 38, 59
3 Hare Court, London EC4
p937 . . . . . 020 7415 7800

Johnson, Mr Edwin Geoffrey BA(Oxon) *L Nov 1987*
(Q.C.) *1, 3, 5, 6, 7, 8, 9, 11, 12, 13, 22, 24, 26, 28, 29, 31, 32, 37*
Maitland Chambers, London WC2
p941 . . . . . 020 7406 1200

JOHNSON, Mr Gregory *I Dec 1998*
Carmelite Chambers, London EC4
p927 . . . . . 020 7936 6300

Johnson, Mr John Richard Henesey MA(Oxon); Dip B Admin(Manc); FFB *M Nov 1993*
6, 7, 10, 11, 12, 18, 20, 30, 31
Regent Chambers, Hanley
p976 . . . . . 01782 286666

Johnson, Ms Kathryn Margaret *G Jul 1989*
Lincoln House Chambers, Manchester
p984 . . . . . 0161 832 5701

Johnson, Miss Laura *G Nov 2001*
53, 12, 30, 40, 59, 22, 76, 26
1 Chancery Lane, London WC2
p928 . . . . . 0845 634 6666

Johnson, Mr Lindsay BSc(Brunel); MA(Lond) *I Oct 1997*
1, 22
Doughty Street Chambers, London WC1
p930 . . . . . 020 7404 1313

Johnson, Ms Melanie BSc(Hons) *M Oct 1996*
10, 20
1 Pump Court, London EC4
p947 . . . . . 020 7842 7070

Johnson, Mr Nicholas J *I Nov 1994*
15, 62, 36
Exchange Chambers, Manchester
p983 . . . . . 0161 833 2722
Exchange Chambers, Liverpool
p980 . . . . . 0151 236 7747
Exchange Chambers, Leeds
p977 . . . . . 0113 203 1970

JOHNSON, Mr Nicholas Robert BA; DipLaw *I Jul 1987*
(Q.C.) *15, 62*
7 Harrington Street Chambers, Liverpool
p981 . . . . . 0151 242 0707

Johnson, Mr Paul LLB(Brunel) *G Nov 2006*
41
Kings Chambers, Leeds
p978 . . . . . 0113 242 1123
Kings Chambers, Manchester
p984 . . . . . 0161 832 9082

Johnson, Mr Peter *I Jul 1986*
15, 30, 40
York Chambers, York
p995 . . . . . 01904 620048
York Chambers, Newcastle upon Tyne
p987 . . . . . 0191 206 4677

Johnson, Mr Roderick MA(Oxon) *L Nov 1975*
(Q.C.) *15, 62, 12*
Argent Chambers, London WC2
p923 . . . . . 020 7556 5500

JOHNSON, Sarah *L Oct 2001*
18, 55, 10
Kenworthy's Chambers, Manchester
p984 . . . . . 0161 832 4036

Johnson, Mr Simon LLB(Wales) *G Jul 1987*
20, 10, 76
Stour Chambers, Canterbury
p972 . . . . . 01227 764899
Enterprise Chambers, London WC2
p931 . . . . . 020 7405 9471
Enterprise Chambers, Leeds
p977 . . . . . 0113 246 0391
Enterprise Chambers, Newcastle upon Tyne
p987 . . . . . 0191 222 3344

Johnson, Ms Susannah *M Nov 1996*
20, 15, 12, 10
7 Bedford Row, London WC1
p924 . . . . . 020 7242 3555

Johnson, Ms Zoe *I Oct 1990*
15, 25, 36
QEB Hollis Whiteman, London EC4
p948 . . . . . 020 7933 8855

JOHNSTON, Miss Annie LLB *I Nov 1990*
15, 84
Carmelite Chambers, London EC4
p927 . . . . . 020 7936 6300

JOHNSTON, Mr Anthony BA(Hons)(Cantab) *M Nov 1993*
30, 15, 18, 55
St Philips Chambers, Birmingham
p969 . . . . . 0121 246 7000

Johnston, Ms Carey *M Jul 1977*
(Q.C.) *15, 62, 36*
Queen Square Chambers, Bristol
p972 . . . . . 0117 921 1966
18 Red Lion Court, London EC4
p949 . . . . . 020 7520 6000
18 Red Lion Court (Annexe), Chelmsford
p973 . . . . . 01245 280880

JOHNSTON, Mr Christopher MA(Cantab) *G Nov 1990*
(Q.C.) *27, 18, 30, 12, 40, 53, 68, 85, 63, 36*
3 Serjeants' Inn, London EC4
p950 . . . . . 020 7427 5000

Johnston, Ms Justine LLB(Hons)(Lond); BA(Comm)(Aust) *M Oct 1997*
20
4 Paper Buildings, London EC4
p946 . . . . . 020 7583 0816

Johnston, Miss Sarah LLB(Hons) *G Jul 2004*
15
Exchange Chambers, Manchester
p983 . . . . . 0161 833 2722
Exchange Chambers, Liverpool
p980 . . . . . 0151 236 7747
Exchange Chambers, Leeds
p977 . . . . . 0113 203 1970

Johnstone, Mr Mark LLB; MSc *I Jul 1984*
20, 10
4 Paper Buildings, London EC4
p946 . . . . . 020 7583 0816

JOLLIFFE, Mr John BA(Hons) *I Jan 2005*
1, 53, 18, 46, 27, 51, 30, 40, 56, 36, 57
1 Crown Office Row, London EC4
p929 . . . . . 020 7797 7500

Jolliffe, Ms Victoria *L Nov 2005*
16, 13, 50, 56, 73, 51
5RB, London WC1
p948 . . . . . 020 7242 2902

Jolly, Miss Schona *G Oct 1999*
18, 23, 30, 53, 1, 19, 55, 51
Cloisters, London EC4
p928 . . . . . 020 7827 4000

Jonathan-Jones, Mr Gareth *I Jan 1991*
20, 10
Thirty Park Place, Cardiff
p973 . . . . . 029 2039 8421

Jones, Mr Alun J BSc(Hons) *L Jul 2003*
11, 12, 48, 67, 72, 15, 70, 81, 62, 31, 36, 8
St Pauls Chambers, Leeds
p979 . . . . . 0113 245 5866

Jones, Mr Andrew LLB(Hons) *I Oct 1996*
12, 30, 15, 62
Thirty Park Place, Cardiff
p973 . . . . . 029 2039 8421

Jones, Ms Anika *G Mar 2002*
15, 23
1 Mitre Court Buildings, London EC4
p942 . . . . . 020 7452 8900
12 Old Square, London WC2
p945 . . . . . 020 7404 0875

13

Jones, Mr Benjamin LLB M *Feb 1993*
15, 18, 20, 22, 30
St Johns Buildings, Preston
p990 . . . . 01772 256100
St Johns Buildings, Chester
p974 . . . . 01244 323070
St Johns Buildings, Manchester
p985 . . . . 0161 214 1500
St Johns Buildings, Liverpool
p982 . . . . 0151 243 6000

Jones, Bronwen M *Jul 2009*
10, 20
Tooks Chambers, London EC4
p953 . . . . 020 7842 7575

JONES, Miss Carolyn LLB(Lond) L *Oct 1995*
20
St Philips Chambers, Birmingham
p969 . . . . 0121 246 7000

JONES, Ms Charlotte MA(Cantab) M *Jul 1982*
53
Crown Office Chambers, London EC4
p929 . . . . 020 7797 8100

Jones, Mrs Cheryl S LLB; Deputy District Judge G *Oct 1996*
20, 37, 38, 88, 93, 40, 97
No5 Chambers, Bristol
p971 . . . . 0845 210 5555
No5 Chambers, London EC4
p944 . . . . 0845 210 5555
No5 Chambers, Birmingham
p968 . . . . 0845 210 5555

Jones, Mr Christopher LLB(Hons) G *Jul 2004*
8, 37, 11, 13, 40, 32, 7, 88
St John's Chambers, Bristol
p972 . . . . 0117 921 3456

JONES, Miss Claire L *Jan 1999*
10, 12, 15, 20
Chavasse Court Chambers, Liverpool
p980 . . . . 0151 229 2030

JONES, Mr Clive Hugh BA(Oxon)(Jurisprudence) M *Jul 1981*
6, 11, 22, 26
New Square Chambers, London WC2
p943 . . . . 020 7419 8000

Jones, Mr Craig I *Nov 2003*
Iscoed Chambers, Swansea
p993 . . . . 01792 652988

Jones, Mr Daniel LLB(Lond) G *Mar 2002*
15, 70, 46, 84
Argent Chambers, London WC2
p923 . . . . 020 7556 5500
Charter Chambers, London WC1
p928 . . . . 020 7618 4400

Jones, Mr David Nicholas LLB(Lond) G *Jul 1985*
10, 15, 18, 20, 30, 36, 40
Broadway House Chambers, Leeds
p977 . . . . 0113 246 2600
Broadway House Chambers, Bradford
p969 . . . . 01274 722560

Jones, Mr Edward Bartley BA(Oxon) L *Jul 1975*
(Q.C.) *6, 8, 11, 29, 32, 37, 2, 41, 5, 9, 18, 22, 51, 24, 26, 40, 66, 97, 38, 67, 93, 88*
Exchange Chambers, Manchester
p983 . . . . 0161 833 2722
Exchange Chambers, Liverpool
p980 . . . . 0151 236 7747
Exchange Chambers, Leeds
p977 . . . . 0113 203 1970

JONES, Miss Eleri MA(Cantab); BVC M *Jan 2009*
10, 20
1 Garden Court, London EC4
p934 . . . . 020 7797 7900

Jones, Ms Elizabeth BA(Cantab) M *Nov 1984*
(Q.C.)
Serle Court, London WC2
p950 . . . . 020 7242 6105

Jones, Ms Emilie M *Jan 2005*
Four New Square, London WC2
p943 . . . . 020 7822 2000

Jones, Miss Emma I *Jul 2010*
One Essex Court, London EC4
p931 . . . . 020 7583 2000

Jones, Mr Emyr BA; MPhil G *Oct 1999*
12, 30, 15, 18
9 Park Place, Cardiff
p973 . . . . 029 2038 2731

Jones, Mr Francis MA(Oxon) I *Jul 1980*
12, 15, 38
Iscoed Chambers, Swansea
p993 . . . . 01792 652988

Jones, Mr Gareth I *Jan 1991*
Civitas Law, Cardiff
p972 . . . . 0845 071 3007
Lincoln House Chambers, Manchester
p984 . . . . 0161 832 5701

Jones, Mr Geraint MA(Cantab) M *Jul 1976*
(Q.C.) *8*
New Walk Chambers, Leicester
p979 . . . . 0871 200 1298
9 St John Street Chambers, Manchester
p984 . . . . 0161 955 9000
Tanfield Chambers, London WC1
p951 . . . . 020 7421 5300

Jones, Mr Geraint Martyn MA; LLM(Cantab); Chairman Rent Assessment Committee G *Nov 1972*
8, 11, 18, 31, 32, 37
Fenners Chambers, Cambridge
p972 . . . . 01223 368761

JONES, Mr Gerald William LLB G *Jul 1995*
15
7 Harrington Street Chambers, Liverpool
p981 . . . . 0151 242 0707

JONES, Ms Gillian L *Oct 1996*
15, 62, 34, 36
18 Red Lion Court, London EC4
p949 . . . . 020 7520 6000
18 Red Lion Court (Annexe), Chelmsford
p973 . . . . 01245 280880

JONES, Mr Gregory MA(Oxon); LLM(Lond) L *Nov 1991*
1, 46, 51, 26, 28, 31, 36, 60
Francis Taylor Building, London EC4
p934 . . . . 020 7353 8415

JONES, Mr Howard BA(Cantab) G *Oct 1992*
15
Carmelite Chambers, London EC4
p927 . . . . 020 7936 6300

JONES, Mr Huw LLB(Hons) L *Jan 1997*
20
St Philips Chambers, Birmingham
p969 . . . . 0121 246 7000

Jones, Ms Jacinta G *Jul 2002*
1 Mitre Court Buildings, London EC4
p942 . . . . 020 7452 8900

Jones, Mr Jeffrey LLB(Wales) G *Jul 2003*
15, 62
Thirty Park Place, Cardiff
p973 . . . . 029 2039 8421

Jones, Miss Jennifer BA(Oxon); BVC L *Oct 2003*
54, 3, 7, 11, 31, 40, 41, 43, 45, 49, 61, 78, 74
Atkin Chambers, London WC1
p923 . . . . 020 7404 0102

Jones, Mr John R W D L *Jan 1992*
51, 15, 91, 71
Doughty Street Chambers, London WC1
p930 . . . . 020 7404 1313

JONES, Mr John Richard LLB M *Jul 1981*
(Q.C.) *15, 62, 30, 12, 70, 10, 56, 68*
Carmelite Chambers, London EC4
p927 . . . . 020 7936 6300
Exchange Chambers, Manchester
p983 . . . . 0161 833 2722
Exchange Chambers, Liverpool
p980 . . . . 0151 236 7747
Exchange Chambers, Leeds
p977 . . . . 0113 203 1970

Jones, Mr Jonathan L *Oct 1994*
30, 40, 53, 68, 94
No5 Chambers, Bristol
p971 . . . . 0845 210 5555
No5 Chambers, London EC4
p944 . . . . 0845 210 5555
No5 Chambers, Birmingham
p968 . . . . 0845 210 5555

JONES, Miss Katie Laura G *Oct 2003*
Lincoln House Chambers, Manchester
p984 . . . . 0161 832 5701

Jones, Miss Kay Mary BA(Sussex) G *Jul 1974*
10, 20, 37
Field Court Chambers, London WC1
p933 . . . . 020 7405 6114

JONES, Mr Kevin M *Jan 2003*
15
Bank House Chambers, Sheffield
p991 . . . . 0114 275 1223

Jones, Mr Laurence G *Oct 1997*
15
Temple Chambers, Newport
p988 . . . . 01633 267403 / 255855
Temple Chambers, Cardiff
p973 . . . . 029 2039 7364

JONES, Miss Louise MA(Oxon) M *Jul 2004*
Temple Garden Chambers, London EC4
p952 . . . . 020 7583 1315

Jones, Mr Mark BA(Oxon) L *Nov 2000*
3, 11, 12, 47, 24, 35, 36
Stone Chambers, London WC1
p951 . . . . 020 7440 6900
St Ives Chambers, Birmingham
p969 . . . . 0121 236 0863

Jones, Mr Mark Simeon MA M *Jul 1997*
7, 8, 12, 47, 67, 16, 18, 88, 89, 32, 93, 37
3 Dr Johnson's Buildings, London EC4
p930 . . . . 020 7353 4854

Jones, Mr Michael LLB(Hons); BCL(Oxon) L *Jan 2006*
34, 57, 58
Gray's Inn Tax Chambers, London WC1
p936 . . . . 020 7242 2642
Cobden House Chambers, Manchester
p983 . . . . 0161 833 6000

Jones, Mr Michael Adrian Lyster BA I *Jul 1972*
12, 15, 20
Guildford Chambers, Guildford
p975 . . . . 01483 539131

JONES, Mr Michael Wyn G *Mar 1999*
15
7 Harrington Street Chambers, Liverpool
p981 . . . . 0151 242 0707

Jones, Mr Nathan Richard L *Jul 2008*
23, 15, 12, 18, 20, 30, 62
Thirty Park Place, Cardiff
p973 . . . . 029 2039 8421

Jones, Mr Nicholas David BSc(Wales)(Econ); LLM(Cantab) G *Nov 1987*
30, 44, 53
Civitas Law, Cardiff
p972 . . . . 0845 071 3007

Jones, Mr Nigel G *Jul 1976*
(Q.C.) *18, 8, 40, 49, 11, 24*
Hardwicke, London WC2
p936 . . . . 020 7242 2523

Jones, Mr Oliver I *Nov 1998*
20, 10
4 Paper Buildings, London EC4
p946 . . . . 020 7583 0816

Jones, Mr Paul Alan BA(Hons) I *Jul 1981*
15, 26, 48
Staple Inn Chambers, London WC1
p951 . . . . 020 7242 5240

Jones, Mr Philip MA; BCL(Oxon); LLM L *Jul 1985*
(Q.C.)
Serle Court, London WC2
p950 . . . . 020 7242 6105

Jones, Mr Philip A M *Nov 1990*
27, 22, 20, 15, 30, 93, 53, 18, 40, 11
9 Gough Square, London EC4
p935 . . . . 020 7832 0500

Jones, Philip Walter G *Jan 2007*
Clerksroom - Administration Centre, Taunton
p993 . . . . 0845 083 3000

Jones, Miss Rhian G *Jul 2008*
12, 20, 10
Thirty Park Place, Cardiff
p973 . . . . 029 2039 8421

JONES, Miss Rhiannon I *Nov 1993*
30, 40, 53
Farrar's Building, London EC4
p933 . . . . 020 7583 9241

Jones, Mr Rhys LLB(Hons) G *Nov 1998*
15, 10
Angel Chambers, Swansea
p992 . . . . 01792 464623
33 Bedford Row, London WC1
p925 . . . . 020 7242 6476

JONES, Mr Richard Gwyn BA(Hons) I *Oct 2003*
20, 10
1 Garden Court, London EC4
p934 . . . . 020 7797 7900

Jones, Mr Richard H F LLB G *Jul 1984*
15, 25
4 Breams Buildings, London EC4
p927 . . . . 020 7092 1900

Jones, Mr Richard Henry MA(Oxon); Recorder I *Nov 1972*
(Q.C.) *11, 41, 47, 24, 5, 29, 6, 8, 7, 18, 55, 21, 49, 67, 69, 74, 75, 79, 81, 86, 87, 88, 89, 93, 96, 97*
No5 Chambers, Bristol
p971 . . . . 0845 210 5555
No5 Chambers, London EC4
p944 . . . . 0845 210 5555
No5 Chambers, Birmingham
p968 . . . . 0845 210 5555

Jones, Mr Rupert MA(Oxon) M *Oct 2000*
71, 72
3PB, London EC4
p946 . . . . 020 7583 8055

Jones, Miss Ruth I *Jan 2004*
Nine Bedford Row, London WC1
p924 . . . . 020 7489 2727

JONES, Mr Samuel LLB G *Jan 2008*
15
Guildhall Chambers, Bristol
p970 . . . . 0117 930 9000

Jones, Miss Sarah L *Nov 1996*
2 King's Bench Walk, London EC4
p939 . . . . 020 7353 1746
Pump Court Chambers, Swindon
p993 . . . . 01793 539899
Pump Court Chambers, Winchester
p994 . . . . 01962 868161
Pump Court Chambers, London EC4
p947 . . . . 020 7353 0711

JONES, Mr Sean BA; BCL(Oxon) I *Oct 1991*
1, 11, 18, 19, 55, 56
11KBW, London EC4
p938 . . . . 020 7632 8500

Jones, Miss Sian Scott MA(Cantab); Assistant Deputy Coroner L *Oct 1998*
30
Exchange Chambers, Manchester
p983 . . . . 0161 833 2722
Exchange Chambers, Liverpool
p980 . . . . 0151 236 7747
Exchange Chambers, Leeds
p977 . . . . 0113 203 1970

Jones, Mr Steffan R G *Nov 1997*
10, 20
Temple Chambers, Newport
p988 . . . . 01633 267403 / 255855
Temple Chambers, Cardiff
p973 . . . . 029 2039 7364

JONES, Mr Stephen MA(Oxon) I *Nov 1978*
8, 12, 22, 51
Pump Court Chambers, Swindon
p993 . . . . 01793 539899
Pump Court Chambers, Winchester
p994 . . . . 01962 868161
Pump Court Chambers, London EC4
p947 . . . . 020 7353 0711

Jones, Mr Stewart E MA(Oxon) G *Nov 1972*
(Q.C.) *15, 25*
King's Bench Godolphin Chambers, Truro
p994 . . . . 0845 308 1551
King's Bench Godolphin Chambers, Plymouth
p990 . . . . 0845 308 1551
3PB, London EC4
p946 . . . . 020 7583 8055

Jones, Miss Susannah LLB(Lond) G *Nov 1999*
3, 11, 12, 24, 35, 41
20 Essex Street, London WC2
p932 . . . . 020 7842 1200
Octagon House, Norwich
p988 . . . . 01603 623186

JONES, Mr Timothy LLB; FRSA; FCIArb; FGS I *Jul 1975*
31, 46, 54, 51, 43, 60, 61, 78, 96, 49
No5 Chambers, Bristol
p971 . . . . 0845 210 5555
No5 Chambers, London EC4
p944 . . . . 0845 210 5555
No5 Chambers, Birmingham
p968 . . . . 0845 210 5555

Jones, Mr Tristan MA(Hons)(Oxon); MPA(Harv); DipLaw G *Jan 2006*
1, 11, 18, 51, 44, 19, 96, 49, 89
Blackstone Chambers, London EC4
p926 . . . . 020 7583 1770

Jones, Miss Victoria LLB(Hons)(French) L *Oct 2003*
93, 8, 13, 97
3PB, Bristol
p971 . . . . 0117 928 1520

See p1010 for the Key to Work Categories

Jones, Mr William John Recorder *I Nov 1972*
15, 62
2 Hare Court, London EC4
p937 ... 020 7353 5324

Jones, Miss Ximena *M Jan 2007*
2 King's Bench Walk, London EC4
p939 ... 020 7353 1746

Jones-Fenleigh, Miss Harriet *L Jul 2007*
Fountain Court Chambers, London EC4
p934 ... 020 7583 3335

JORDAN, Mr Andrew *I Jan 2008*
Furnival Chambers, London EC4
p934 ... 020 7405 3232

Jordan, Ms Ruth BA; MPhil; PhD; DipLaw; Junior Counsel to the Crown (C Panel) *I Oct 2001*
6, 8, 11, 62, 37, 40, 38, 97
Serle Court, London WC2
p950 ... 020 7242 6105

Jordash, Mr Wayne *M Oct 1995*
15, 51, 1
Doughty Street Chambers, London WC1
p930 ... 020 7404 1313

JORY, Mr Hugh BA(Cantab) *L Oct 1992*
5, 6, 8, 11, 29, 40, 49, 38
Enterprise Chambers, London WC2
p931 ... 020 7405 9471
Enterprise Chambers, Leeds
p977 ... 0113 246 0391
Enterprise Chambers, Newcastle upon Tyne
p987 ... 0191 222 3344

JORY, Mr Richard Norman BA(Hons)(Reading) *M Nov 1993*
15
9-12 Bell Yard Chambers, London WC2
p926 ... 020 7400 1800

Joseph, Mr Andrew BA(Hons) *G Jan 2004*
12, 30, 36, 18
Thirty Park Place, Cardiff
p973 ... 029 2039 8421

JOSEPH, Mr Charles Henry BA; FCIArb *L Jul 1980*
41, 6, 7, 8, 11, 12, 49, 29, 32, 37, 40, 38, 93
Tanfield Chambers, London WC1
p951 ... 020 7421 5300

Joseph, Mr David P MA(Cantab) *M Nov 1984*
(Q.C.)
Essex Court Chambers, London WC2
p931 ... 020 7813 8000

Joseph, Ms Elizabeth Ann Ayodele BA; LLM(Lond) *G Jul 1983*
10, 15, 18, 20, 23
66 Daubeney Road, London E5
p930 ... 020 8985 3030

Joseph, Mr Henry LLB(Hons) *M Nov 1998*
15, 62
3 Temple Gardens, London EC4
p952 ... 020 7353 3102

Joseph, Mr Paul *I Oct 1992*
3, 5, 6, 8, 11, 24, 40, 41, 47, 48, 49, 62, 16, 89, 96, 93, 97
No5 Chambers, Bristol
p971 ... 0845 210 5555
No5 Chambers, London EC4
p944 ... 0845 210 5555
No5 Chambers, Birmingham
p968 ... 0845 210 5555

JOSEPH, Ms Sandradee *I Jan 1998*
13 Old Square Chambers, London WC2
p945 ... 020 7831 4445

Joseph, Miss Wendy MA(Cantab) *G Nov 1975*
(Q.C.) *15, 62*
6 King's Bench Walk, London EC4
p939 ... 020 7583 0410

JOSEPHS, Ms Jennifer *M Jul 2000*
15, 62
St Philips Chambers, Birmingham
p969 ... 0121 246 7000

Joshi, Mr Pramod Kumar LLB(Hons); MBA(Sheff) *I Nov 1992*
3, 11, 12, 18, 20, 22, 25, 27, 29, 30, 34, 36, 40
One Essex Court, London EC4
p931 ... 020 7936 3030

JOSHI, Mr Raj *I Jul 1983*
15, 36
18 Red Lion Court, London EC4
p949 ... 020 7520 6000
18 Red Lion Court (Annexe), Chelmsford
p973 ... 01245 280880

JOSLING, Mr William *L Nov 1995*
37 Park Square Chambers, Leeds
p978 ... 0113 243 9422

Josty, Mr David BSc(Hons); MSc *G Jul 2002*
10, 12, 20, 30
College Chambers, Southampton
p992 ... 023 8023 0338

JOURDAN, Mr Stephen MA(Cantab) *G Nov 1989*
(Q.C.)
Falcon Chambers, London EC4
p933 ... 020 7353 2484

Jowell, Mr Daniel *M Nov 1995*
11, 44, 24, 56, 5
Brick Court Chambers, London WC2
p927 ... 020 7379 3550

Jowell, Mr Jeffrey BA; LLB; LLM; MA(Oxon) *M Feb 1965*
(Q.C.) *1, 19, 26, 51, 96, 49, 89*
Blackstone Chambers, London EC4
p926 ... 020 7583 1770

Jowett, Mr Christian *G Oct 1999*
12, 15, 23, 30
Temple Chambers, Newport
p988 ... 01633 267403 / 255855
Temple Chambers, Cardiff
p973 ... 029 2039 7364

Jowitt, Mr Matthew BA(Oxon) *M Nov 1994*
15, 62
7 Bedford Row, London WC1
p924 ... 020 7242 3555

Joy, Mr Michael *M Nov 1997*
Field Court Chambers, London WC1
p933 ... 020 7405 6114

JOYCE, Ms Abigail *I Oct 1998*
15
1 High Pavement, Nottingham
p988 ... 0115 941 8218

JOYCE, Mr Peter Stuart Langford *I Jul 1968*
(Q.C.) *15*
1 High Pavement, Nottingham
p988 ... 0115 941 8218

JUBB, Brian Patrick *G Nov 1971*
1, 8, 10, 12, 15, 20, 26
Renaissance Chambers, London WC1
p949 ... 020 7404 1111

Jubb, Mr David *I Oct 2002*
Goldsmith Chambers, London EC4
p935 ... 020 7353 6802

Judd, Ms Frances MA(Cantab) *M Jul 1984*
(Q.C.) *20, 10*
Harcourt Chambers, London EC4
p936 ... 0844 561 7135
Harcourt Chambers, Oxford
p989 ... 0844 561 7135

Judge, Mr Andrew John *M Jul 1986*
15, 31
Westgate Chambers, Lewes
p980 ... 01273 480510

Judge, Mr Charles BA *I Jul 1981*
15, 62
5 Paper Buildings, London EC4
p946 ... 020 7583 6117

Judge, Ms Parveen *L Mar 2001*
1 Mitre Court Buildings, London EC4
p942 ... 020 7452 8900

Julien, Miss Christine *I Nov 1991*
20
Guildford Chambers, Guildford
p975 ... 01483 539131

Jupp, Mr Jeffrey BA(Worcs) *I Nov 1994*
18, 30, 11, 55
7 Bedford Row, London WC1
p924 ... 020 7242 3555

JUSS, Prof Satvinder Singh *G Nov 1989*
1, 51, 23, 76, 41, 3
3 Hare Court, London EC4
p937 ... 020 7415 7800

Kabra, Miss Madhavi *M Jul 2008*
1 Hare Court, London EC4
p936 ... 020 7797 7070

Kabweru-Namulemu, Miss Karen *L Jul 2001*
KCH Garden Square Chambers, Nottingham
p989 ... 0115 941 8851
KCH Garden Square Chambers, Leicester
p979 ... 0115 941 8851

Kadri, Sibghat *I Nov 1969*
(Q.C.) *15, 23, 12*
6 King's Bench Walk, London EC4
p939 ... 020 7583 0695 / 7353 4931

Kajue, Miss Soria LLB; LLM *M Jan 2001*
20
18 St John Street Chambers, Manchester
p985 ... 0161 278 1800

Kaler, Ms Manjeet LLB(Hons)(Middx) *M Feb 1993*
10, 20
1 Pump Court, London EC4
p947 ... 020 7842 7070

KALFON, Mr Olivier BSc(LSE) *I Oct 2003*
5, 6, 8, 11, 22, 29, 40, 38, 88, 97
Enterprise Chambers, London WC2
p931 ... 020 7405 9471
Enterprise Chambers, Leeds
p977 ... 0113 246 0391
Enterprise Chambers, Newcastle upon Tyne
p987 ... 0191 222 3344

KAMAL, Setu *L Jan 2004*
St James's Chambers, Manchester
p984 ... 0161 834 7000

Kamill, Miss Louise Naima Rachel LLB; Recorder *I Jul 1974*
15, 62
2 Hare Court, London EC4
p937 ... 020 7353 5324

Kamlish, Mr Stephen BA *G Jul 1979*
(Q.C.) *15, 25*
Tooks Chambers, London EC4
p953 ... 020 7842 7575

KAMM, Miss Rachel *L Oct 2006*
1, 18, 11, 55, 51, 26, 76
11KBW, London EC4
p938 ... 020 7632 8500

KANE, Mr Adam BA(Hons)(Oxon) *G Nov 1993*
15, 62
Carmelite Chambers, London EC4
p927 ... 020 7936 6300

KANE, Gillian *G Jan 2002*
Fountain Chambers, Middlesbrough
p986 ... 01642 804040

KAPOOR, Mr Shaman LLM(Lond) *L Oct 1999*
18, 22, 12, 20, 15
Temple Garden Chambers, London EC4
p952 ... 020 7583 1315

KARAS, Mr Jonathan MA(Oxon) *M Jul 1986*
(Q.C.) *1, 8, 22, 51, 26, 31*
Wilberforce Chambers, London WC2
p953 ... 020 7306 0102

Karia, Mr Chirag MA(Cantab); LLM *L Nov 1988*
5, 6, 24, 41, 46
Quadrant Chambers, London EC4
p948 ... 020 7583 4444

Karim, Mr Sam *G Nov 2002*
1, 33, 51, 55, 63, 76, 30, 23
Kings Chambers, Leeds
p978 ... 0113 242 1123
Kings Chambers, Manchester
p984 ... 0161 832 9082

Kark, Mr Tom *I Jul 1982*
15, 25, 36
QEB Hollis Whiteman, London EC4
p948 ... 020 7933 8855

Karmy-Jones, Miss Riel *L Nov 1995*
72, 15, 62, 36
2 Hare Court, London EC4
p937 ... 020 7353 5324
18 Red Lion Court, London EC4
p949 ... 020 7520 6000
18 Red Lion Court (Annexe), Chelmsford
p973 ... 01245 280880

KARNIK, Mr Mikhil *G Jan 2006*
Central Chambers, Manchester
p983 ... 0161 236 1133

Karseras, Miss Anastasia *G Oct 2000*
12, 53, 5, 6, 11, 47, 13, 16, 50, 27, 56, 30, 40
2 Temple Gardens, London EC4
p952 ... 020 7822 1200

Karu, Mr Lee BA(Hons) *L Jan 1985*
15, 51, 62
Nine Bedford Row, London WC1
p924 ... 020 7489 2727

KASASIAN, Miss Laura BA(Hons)(Sussex) *M Jan 2002*
11, 12, 30, 18, 84, 70, 55
Cornwall Street Chambers, Birmingham
p967 ... 0121 233 7500

KATKOWSKI, Mr Christopher MA; LLB(Cantab) *G Feb 1982*
(Q.C.) *31, 36, 46*
Landmark Chambers, London EC4
p941 ... 020 7430 1221

Katrak, Mr Cyrus Pesi LLB *G Oct 1991*
30, 53
3PB, London EC4
p946 ... 020 7583 8055

KATYAR, Mr Arun LLB(Hons) *L Nov 1993*
30
12 King's Bench Walk, London EC4
p940 ... 020 7583 0811

KATZ, Mr Philip MA(Oxon); Recorder *M Nov 1976*
(Q.C.) *15*
9-12 Bell Yard Chambers, London WC2
p926 ... 020 7400 1800

Kaufmann, Ms Phillippa LLB; MA *G Oct 1991*
1, 12, 15, 18, 22, 30, 38, 51
Doughty Street Chambers, London WC1
p930 ... 020 7404 1313

KAUL, Miss Kalyani *M Jul 1983*
(Q.C.) *15*
9-12 Bell Yard Chambers, London WC2
p926 ... 020 7400 1800

Kaur, Miss Harinder LLB(Hons); LLM; BVC *I Jan 1995*
10, 20, 30, 40, 14
7 Bedford Row, London WC1
p924 ... 020 7242 3555

Kaur, Lukhvinder LLB *I Nov 2000*
20
18 St John Street Chambers, Manchester
p985 ... 0161 278 1800

Kavanagh, Mrs Jennifer LLB(Hons) *L Oct 1993*
20, 12, 18, 23, 15
Henley Chambers, Henley-on-Thames
p976 ... 01491 636000

KAY, Mr Dominic BSc(Hons); DipLaw(CPE) *G Oct 1997*
36, 84, 30, 47
Crown Office Chambers, London EC4
p929 ... 020 7797 8100

Kay, Mr Steven LLB *I Nov 1977*
(Q.C.) *15, 51, 21, 33*
Nine Bedford Row, London WC1
p924 ... 020 7489 2727

KAYNE, Mr Adrian LLB(Hons) *I Jul 1989*
15
Carmelite Chambers, London EC4
p927 ... 020 7936 6300

Kaza, Miss Ajanta LLB(Hons) *L Nov 1998*
15, 51
1 Pump Court, London EC4
p947 ... 020 7842 7070

KAZAKOS, Mr Leon *I Oct 1999*
15, 62, 95
187 Fleet Street, London EC4
p933 ... 020 7430 7430

KAZANTZIS, Mr Philip *I Mar 1998*
15, 62, 95
187 Fleet Street, London EC4
p933 ... 020 7430 7430

Keal, Mr John *L Jan 2004*
15
5 St Andrew's Hill, London EC4
p950 ... 020 7332 5400

Kealey, Mr Gavin Sean BA(Oxon) *I Feb 1977*
(Q.C.) *3, 35, 19, 33, 24, 5, 40, 11*
7 King's Bench Walk, London EC4
p940 ... 020 7910 8300

Kealey, Simon LLB *I Apr 1991*
15, 62, 68, 70, 71, 72, 82
Zenith Chambers, Leeds
p979 ... 0113 245 5438

Kearl, Mr Guy A BA(Hons); Recorder 1999 *M Sep 1982*
(Q.C.) *15, 62, 84, 81, 48*
2 Bedford Row, London WC1
p924 ... 020 7440 8888
St Pauls Chambers, Leeds
p979 ... 0113 245 5866

Kearney, Mr Andrew BA(Oxon) *I Jan 2007*
8, 11, 5, 7, 74, 93, 96
St John's Chambers, Bristol
p972 ... 0117 921 3456

KEARNEY, Mr John *M Nov 1994*
15
Furnival Chambers, London EC4
p934 ... 020 7405 3232

Kearney, Mr Robert I *Nov 1996*
Lincoln House Chambers, Manchester
p984 . . . . . 0161 832 5701

Kearney, Mr Seamus LLB G *Feb 1992*
10, 20, 32, 37, 25, 14
Lamb Building, Brighton
p970 . . . . . 01273 820490
Lamb Building, London EC4
p940 . . . . . 020 7797 7788

KEATING, Mr Dermot I *Nov 1997*
15, 62
25 Bedford Row, London WC1
p925 . . . . . 020 7067 1500

Keay, Prof Andrew Associate Member L *Mar 2010*
8, 97, 38
Kings Chambers, Leeds
p978 . . . . . 0113 242 1123
Kings Chambers, Manchester
p984 . . . . . 0161 832 9082

Kee, Mr Peter William BA; LLM M *Jul 1983*
15, 22, 30, 26, 12, 6, 25, 18, 5, 94
Becket Chambers, Canterbury
p972 . . . . . 01227 786331
Becket Chambers, Maidstone
p982 . . . . . 01622 230957

Keegan, Mr Leslie M *Nov 1989*
53, 30, 10, 27, 85
7 Bedford Row, London WC1
p924 . . . . . 020 7242 3555

Keehan, Mr Michael LLB M *Jul 1982*
(Q.C.) *10, 20*
Queen Square Chambers, Bristol
p972 . . . . . 0117 921 1966
St Ives Chambers, Birmingham
p969 . . . . . 0121 236 0863

Keel, Mr Douglas MA(Oxon); DipLaw; FCA; Associate Member L *Oct 1997*
57, 58
11 Stone Buildings, London WC2
p951 . . . . . 020 7831 6381

Keeling, Mr Adrian BA I *Oct 1990*
(Q.C.) *15, 62, 36, 68*
No5 Chambers, Bristol
p971 . . . . . 0845 210 5555
No5 Chambers, London EC4
p944 . . . . . 0845 210 5555
No5 Chambers, Birmingham
p968 . . . . . 0845 210 5555

Keeling-Roberts, Mr Sam BA(Hons); ARCM; MA(Law) I *Jul 2005*
22, 8, 11
Cobden House Chambers, Manchester
p983 . . . . . 0161 833 6000

KEEN, Mr Graeme LLB M *Mar 1995*
Landmark Chambers, London EC4
p941 . . . . . 020 7430 1221

Keen, Mr Richard LLB(Hons)(Edin); Dean of Faculty 2007 M *Jan 1980*
(Q.C.) *1, 51, 81, 89, 11*
Blackstone Chambers, London EC4
p926 . . . . . 020 7583 1770

KEEN, Mr Spencer M *Jan 1998*
Pump Court Chambers, Swindon
p993 . . . . . 01793 539899
Pump Court Chambers, Winchester
p994 . . . . . 01962 868161
Pump Court Chambers, London EC4
p947 . . . . . 020 7353 0711

KEENE, Mrs Gillian Margaret BA(Oxon) G *Nov 1980*
30, 18, 12
Farrar's Building, London EC4
p933 . . . . . 020 7583 9241

Keene, Mr Rory M *Dec 2001*
15, 1, 25, 62, 13, 48
5 Paper Buildings, London EC4
p946 . . . . . 020 7583 6117

KEFFORD, Mr Anthony BSc M *Nov 1980*
10, 20
Octagon House, Norwich
p988 . . . . . 01603 623186

KEIGHLEY, Miss Anna M *Jan 2006*
15, 62, 95
187 Fleet Street, London EC4
p933 . . . . . 020 7430 7430

Keith, Mr Alistair BA(Lond) M *Nov 1974*
5 Pump Court, London EC4
p947 . . . . . 020 7353 2532 / 7583 7133

Keith, Mr Ben L *Jan 2004*
15, 12
5 St Andrew's Hill, London EC4
p950 . . . . . 020 7332 5400

Kelbrick, Mr Anthony M BA; Recorder G *Jul 1992*
15
No 6 Barristers Chambers, Leeds
p978 . . . . . 0113 245 9763

KELEHER, Mr Paul G *Jul 1980*
(Q.C.) *15, 62*
25 Bedford Row, London WC1
p925 . . . . . 020 7067 1500

KELLAR, Mr Robert BA(Hons)(Oxon); LLM(Cantab) G *Jan 1999*
12, 18, 30, 40, 55
1 Crown Office Row, London EC4
p929 . . . . . 020 7797 7500

Kelleher, Mr Benedict Peter John LLB; MSc(Bris) I *Nov 1994*
15, 62
Atkinson Bevan Chambers, London EC4
p924 . . . . . 020 7353 2112

Kelleher, Ms Katherine BA(Hons) L *Jul 2000*
15, 82, 62, 84
Lamb Building, Brighton
p970 . . . . . 01273 820490
Lamb Building, London EC4
p940 . . . . . 020 7797 7788

Keller, Mr Ciaran MA(Oxon) L *Jul 2004*
Maitland Chambers, London WC2
p941 . . . . . 020 7406 1200

Kellett, Mr Charles M *Nov 1971*
15
1 Paper Buildings, London EC4
p946 . . . . . 020 7353 3728

Kelly, Mrs Amy Louise BA(Hons) M *Nov 2000*
18, 30, 31, 32, 37, 88, 93
12 College Place, Southampton
p992 . . . . . 023 8032 0320

Kelly, Mr Ben L *Jan 2006*
St Johns Buildings, Preston
p990 . . . . . 01772 256100
St Johns Buildings, Chester
p974 . . . . . 01244 323070
St Johns Buildings, Manchester
p985 . . . . . 0161 214 1500
St Johns Buildings, Liverpool
p982 . . . . . 0151 243 6000

Kelly, Mr Brendan Damien LLB; Recorder G *Jul 1988*
(Q.C.) *15, 62, 36*
2 Hare Court, London EC4
p937 . . . . . 020 7353 5324

Kelly, Mr Eamonn I *Oct 1997*
15
Two King's Bench Walk, London EC4
p939 . . . . . 020 7353 7202 / 7353 3909
No 3 Fleet Street Chambers, London EC4
p944 . . . . . 020 7936 4474

KELLY, Ms Emma Deputy District Judge L *Oct 1997*
11, 88, 93, 30
St Philips Chambers, Birmingham
p969 . . . . . 0121 246 7000

Kelly, Miss Gemma BA(Hons) I *Nov 2007*
20, 10, 67
Harcourt Chambers, London EC4
p936 . . . . . 0844 561 7135
Harcourt Chambers, Oxford
p989 . . . . . 0844 561 7135

KELLY, Mr Geoffrey LLB M *Feb 1992*
10, 12, 15, 20, 22, 30, 7
Pump Court Chambers, Swindon
p993 . . . . . 01793 539899
Pump Court Chambers, Winchester
p994 . . . . . 01962 868161
Pump Court Chambers, London EC4
p947 . . . . . 020 7353 0711

Kelly, Geraldine G *Mar 1996*
15, 62, 72, 80, 82, 91
Zenith Chambers, Leeds
p979 . . . . . 0113 245 5438

Kelly, Mr Mark LLB(Bris) G *Nov 1985*
15, 18, 19, 36, 30, 11, 8, 62, 84, 39, 68, 70, 72, 91, 42
No5 Chambers, Bristol
p971 . . . . . 0845 210 5555
No5 Chambers, London EC4
p944 . . . . . 0845 210 5555
No5 Chambers, Birmingham
p968 . . . . . 0845 210 5555

Kelly, Mr Martyn MA(Oxon) I *Nov 1972*
15
9 Park Place, Cardiff
p973 . . . . . 029 2038 2731

KELLY, Mr Matthias BA(Hons); LLB; Recorder G *Feb 1979*
(Q.C.) *1, 53, 18, 30, 36, 40, 84*
Thirty Nine Essex Street, London WC2
p932 . . . . . 020 7832 1111

Kelly, Mr Richard BA G *Oct 1994*
25, 15, 62
East Anglian Chambers, Norwich
p988 . . . . . 01603 617351
East Anglian Chambers, Colchester
p975 . . . . . 01206 572756
East Anglian Chambers, Chelmsford
p973 . . . . . 01245 215660
East Anglian Chambers, Ipswich
p976 . . . . . 01473 214481

KELLY, Mr Sean MA(Cantab) G *Jan 1990*
41, 5, 6, 7, 8, 9, 11, 44, 13, 14, 22, 24, 29, 32, 40, 37
St James's Chambers, Manchester
p984 . . . . . 0161 834 7000

Kelly, Mr Shaw M M *Oct 1997*
12, 15, 22
Staple Inn Chambers, London WC1
p951 . . . . . 020 7242 5240

Kelly, Miss Siobhan G *Oct 1995*
12, 15, 30, 40
Paradise Chambers, Sheffield
p992 . . . . . 0114 273 8951

Kelly, Ms Siobhan Frances BA(Hons) M *Oct 1995*
10, 20
Coram Chambers, London EC1
p929 . . . . . 020 7092 3700

KELSEY, Miss Katherine BA(Hons) L *Jul 2003*
10, 20, 49, 14, 96
1 King's Bench Walk, London EC4
p938 . . . . . 020 7936 1500

Kelsey-Fry, Mr John G *Nov 1978*
(Q.C.)
Cloth Fair Chambers, London EC1
p928 . . . . . 020 7710 6444

Kember, Mr Richard MA M *Oct 1993*
12, 22, 20, 10, 18, 53, 40
9 Park Place, Cardiff
p973 . . . . . 029 2038 2731

Kemp, Mr Christopher Mark MA(Oxon); DipLaw; Recorder M *Nov 1984*
30, 53, 40
Outer Temple Chambers, London WC2
p945 . . . . . 020 7353 6381

KEMP, Mr Edward William LLB; Maitrise en Droit; LLM I *Jan 2005*
18, 30, 55
12 King's Bench Walk, London EC4
p940 . . . . . 020 7583 0811

KEMP, Mr James LLB; LLM I *Jan 1999*
8, 11, 38, 20, 63, 30
Trinity (Newcastle) Chambers, Newcastle upon Tyne
p987 . . . . . 0191 232 1927
Trinity (Teesside) Chambers, Middlesbrough
p986 . . . . . 01642 247569

KEMP, Mr Stephen Richard BA(Hons) L *Oct 1995*
1 High Pavement, Nottingham
p988 . . . . . 0115 941 8218

Kempe, Ms Dianna M *Jan 2001*
1 Pump Court, London EC4
p947 . . . . . 020 7842 7070

Kempster, Mr Toby LLB(Leics) I *Jul 1980*
18, 30, 36, 40, 55, 51, 26
Old Square Chambers, Bristol
p971 . . . . . 0117 930 5100
Old Square Chambers, London WC1
p945 . . . . . 020 7269 0300

Kendal, Mr Timothy LLB(Hons) G *Oct 1985*
15, 62
2 Bedford Row, London WC1
p924 . . . . . 020 7440 8888

KENDALL, Mr Joel BA(Oxon) M *Oct 1993*
12, 18, 24, 30, 53, 56, 84
12 King's Bench Walk, London EC4
p940 . . . . . 020 7583 0811

Kendrick, Mr Dominic John MA(Cantab) M *Jul 1981*
(Q.C.) *3, 35, 19, 33, 24, 11, 5, 40*
7 King's Bench Walk, London EC4
p940 . . . . . 020 7910 8300

KENDRICK, Miss Julia BA(Oxon); CPE(City); Junior Tenant M *Oct 2005*
30, 53, 40, 11, 84, 38
Crown Office Chambers, London EC4
p929 . . . . . 020 7797 8100

Kenefick, Mr Timothy BA(Cantab) G *Oct 1996*
41, 5, 11, 24, 35, 40
7 King's Bench Walk, London EC4
p940 . . . . . 020 7910 8300

Keniston, Miss Zosia BA(Hons)(Oxon) L *Jul 2004*
15, 20, 18, 10, 12
12 College Place, Southampton
p992 . . . . . 023 8032 0320

KENNEDY, Mr Andrew BA; DipLaw M *Jan 1989*
53, 36, 40, 63, 30, 1, 51, 27
1 Crown Office Row, London EC4
p929 . . . . . 020 7797 7500

KENNEDY, Mr Christopher BA(Cantab) G *Jul 1989*
(Q.C.) *12, 18, 26, 30, 24, 40*
9 St John Street Chambers, Manchester
p984 . . . . . 0161 955 9000

Kennedy, Miss Fleur Jennifer MA L *Oct 2005*
20
Field Court Chambers, London WC1
p933 . . . . . 020 7405 6114

Kennedy, Ms Helena G *Jul 1972*
(Q.C.) *15, 51*
Doughty Street Chambers, London WC1
p930 . . . . . 020 7404 1313

Kennedy, Miss Lucy M *Oct 2000*
15, 25, 36
QEB Hollis Whiteman, London EC4
p948 . . . . . 020 7933 8855

Kennedy, Mr Matthew A BSc G *Nov 1981*
15, 51
Nine Bedford Row, London WC1
p924 . . . . . 020 7489 2727

Kennedy, Mr Michael LLB M *May 1985*
10, 20
St Johns Buildings, Preston
p990 . . . . . 01772 256100
St Johns Buildings, Chester
p974 . . . . . 01244 323070
St Johns Buildings, Manchester
p985 . . . . . 0161 214 1500
St Johns Buildings, Liverpool
p982 . . . . . 0151 243 6000
New Square Chambers, London WC2
p943 . . . . . 020 7419 8000

Kennedy, Mr P Nicholas D LLB L *Jul 1977*
12, 15, 30
15 Winckley Square, Preston
p991 . . . . . 01772 252828

Kennedy, Mr Stuart L *Oct 1999*
3PB, London EC4
p946 . . . . . 020 7583 8055

Kennedy-McGregor, Ms Marilyn BA(Dunelm) G *Jul 1989*
6, 8, 11, 37, 62
11 Stone Buildings, London WC2
p951 . . . . . 020 7831 6381

Kennelly, Mr Brian MA(Cantab); European Law Degree(Brussels) M *Sep 1999*
1, 11, 19, 51, 44, 5, 81, 56, 43, 21, 89
Blackstone Chambers, London EC4
p926 . . . . . 020 7583 1770

KENNING, Mr Thomas BSc(Hons) L *Feb 1989*
15
Citadel Chambers, Birmingham
p967 . . . . . 0121 233 8500

Kenny, Ms Caroline I *Oct 2006*
8, 32, 37, 14
5 Stone Buildings, London WC2
p951 . . . . . 020 7242 6201

Kenny, Miss Charlotte BA(Hull); DipLaw(City) G *Nov 1993*
15
Exchange Chambers, Manchester
p983 . . . . . 0161 833 2722
Exchange Chambers, Liverpool
p980 . . . . . 0151 236 7747
Exchange Chambers, Leeds
p977 . . . . . 0113 203 1970

Kenny, Mr Christian I *Jan 2003*
1 Hare Court, London EC4
p936 . . . . . 020 7797 7070

See p1010 for the Key to Work Categories

Kenny, Mr David J BA(Philosophy) *M Nov 1982*
12, 27, 30, 53, 56
Cobden House Chambers, Manchester
p983 .... 0161 833 6000

Kenny, Mr Edward *M Jan 2009*
12, 22, 20, 88, 30, 15
Becket Chambers, Canterbury
p972 .... 01227 786331
Becket Chambers, Maidstone
p982 .... 01622 230957

Kenny, Mr Julian BA(Oxon) *G Nov 1997*
3, 11, 12, 24, 35, 41
20 Essex Street, London WC2
p932 .... 020 7842 1200

Kenny, Mr Martin *I Jan 1997*
10, 20, 15
Walnut House Chambers, Exeter
p975 .... 01392 279751

Kenny, Mr Stephen Charles Wilfred MA; BCL(Oxon) *I Jul 1987*
(Q.C.) *3, 35, 19, 33, 24, 5, 11, 40*
7 King's Bench Walk, London EC4
p940 .... 020 7910 8300

KENT, Mr Alan LLB *I Nov 1986*
(Q.C.) *15, 11, 36*
23 Essex Street, London WC2
p932 .... 020 7413 0353

KENT, Mr Michael BA; Recorder *M Jul 1975*
(Q.C.) *30, 40, 53, 1, 57, 27, 31, 11, 12*
Crown Office Chambers, London EC4
p929 .... 020 7797 8100

Kent, Mr Peter LLB *G Nov 1978*
7, 8, 10, 11, 12, 18, 20, 22, 29, 30, 31
3PB, Oxford
p989 .... 01865 793736

Kent, Mr Rupert Haworth Harcourt *M Nov 2006*
15
Atkinson Bevan Chambers, London EC4
p924 .... 020 7353 2112

KENTRIDGE, Ms Janet LLM(LSE); BA(Hons); LLB; LLM(Witwatersrand); MA(Oxon); LLM(LSE) *L Jul 1999*
1, 11, 26, 51, 55, 41, 89
Matrix Chambers, London WC1
p942 .... 020 7404 3447

Kentridge, Sir Sydney MA(Oxon); BA(Wit) *L Jul 1977*
(Q.C.) *24, 1, 11*
Brick Court Chambers, London WC2
p927 .... 020 7379 3550

KENWARD, Mr Tim David MA(Oxon) *G Nov 1987*
18, 30, 11, 76, 26, 1, 51, 36, 67
7 Harrington Street Chambers, Liverpool
p981 .... 0151 242 0707

Kenyon, Miss Flavia *L Oct 2005*
15
3 Temple Gardens, London EC4
p952 .... 020 7353 3102

KENYON, Ms Laura *I Nov 2009*
15, 62, 94
18 Red Lion Court, London EC4
p949 .... 020 7520 6000
18 Red Lion Court (Annexe), Chelmsford
p973 .... 01245 280880

KEOGH, Mr Andrew *I Nov 1978*
15, 25, 62
No5 Chambers, Bristol
p971 .... 0845 210 5555
No5 Chambers, London EC4
p944 .... 0845 210 5555
No5 Chambers, Birmingham
p968 .... 0845 210 5555

KER-REID, Mr John MA(Cantab) *I Nov 1974*
10, 12, 20, 30, 25
Pump Court Chambers, Swindon
p993 .... 01793 539899
Pump Court Chambers, Winchester
p994 .... 01962 868161
Pump Court Chambers, London EC4
p947 .... 020 7353 0711

Kerins, Mr Charles *M Oct 1984*
Outer Temple Chambers, London WC2
p945 .... 020 7353 6381

Kerner, Ms Angela LLB *I Jul 1965*
15, 94
Bell Yard Chambers, London WC2
p926 .... 020 7306 9292 / 7404 5138

Kerr, Mr Christopher *M Nov 1988*
2 Pump Court, London EC4
p947 .... 020 7353 5597

Kerr, Mr Derek William LLB(Hons) *M Oct 1994*
30, 18, 88, 93
Lamb Chambers, London EC4
p941 .... 020 7797 8300

Kerr, Dr Joanna MA(Hons); PhD *G Oct 2001*
18, 30, 17, 12
Lamb Chambers, London EC4
p941 .... 020 7797 8300

Kerr, Mr Neil *I Oct 2001*
12, 20, 22
3 Dr Johnson's Buildings, London EC4
p930 .... 020 7353 4854

KERR, Mr Patrick *G Oct 2006*
30, 12, 53, 67, 59, 56, 94, 40
12 King's Bench Walk, London EC4
p940 .... 020 7583 0811

Kerr, Mr Simon MA *L Jan 1997*
5, 35, 24, 40, 11, 3, 19
7 King's Bench Walk, London EC4
p940 .... 020 7910 8300

Kerr, Mr Stuart *I Nov 1995*
1 Mitre Court Buildings, London EC4
p942 .... 020 7452 8900

KERR, Mr Tim BA(Oxon); P/T Chairman of Employment Tribunal *G Nov 1983*
(Q.C.) *1, 16, 18, 51, 26, 40, 55, 56, 36*
11KBW, London EC4
p938 .... 020 7632 8500

KERRIGAN, Mr Herbert MA(Keele); LLB(Aberdeen) *M Jul 1990*
(Q.C.) *12, 15, 27, 36*
9-12 Bell Yard Chambers, London WC2
p926 .... 020 7400 1800

KERRUISH-JONES, Mr Matthew BA(Hons)(Russian Studies); DipLaw *L Nov 2003*
12, 15, 30
Farrar's Building, London EC4
p933 .... 020 7583 9241

Kershaw, Mr Andrew Recorder *M Jan 1975*
15
Broadway House Chambers, Leeds
p977 .... 0113 246 2600
Broadway House Chambers, Bradford
p969 .... 01274 722560

Kershaw, Mr Dean *L Oct 1995*
15, 23, 62, 72
No5 Chambers, Bristol
p971 .... 0845 210 5555
No5 Chambers, London EC4
p944 .... 0845 210 5555
No5 Chambers, Birmingham
p968 .... 0845 210 5555
4 Rowchester Court, Birmingham
p968 .... 0121 233 2327

KERSHEN, Mr Lawrence *M Jul 1967*
(Q.C.) *1, 15, 11, 12, 16, 22, 24, 29, 37, 40, 41, 49, 51, 56*
Tooks Chambers, London EC4
p953 .... 020 7842 7575

Kesselman, Dr Neville MA; Dr Jur; LLD; Head of Chambers *G Jul 1970*
15, 17, 51
Chambers of Dr Neville Kesselman, London NW4
p938 .... 020 8203 4711

Kessler, Mr James R MA(Oxon) *L Jul 1984*
(Q.C.) *34, 37, 36, 29, 8, 9*
15 Old Square, London WC2
p945 .... 020 7242 2744

Key, Mr Paul LLB; PhD(Oxon) *I Jan 1997*
1, 3, 4, 5, 6, 8, 11, 13, 18, 19, 21, 24, 29, 33, 34, 35, 36
Essex Court Chambers, London WC2
p931 .... 020 7813 8000

Keyes, Mr Grant *G Jul 2007*
Northampton Chambers, Northampton
p988 .... 01604 636271

Keyser, Mr Andrew MA(Oxon); Recorder *M Nov 1986*
(Q.C.) *12, 8, 11, 29, 5, 40*
9 Park Place, Cardiff
p973 .... 029 2038 2731

Khalid, Mr Saleem *L May 2001*
12, 53, 22, 30, 40, 59
1 Chancery Lane, London WC2
p928 .... 0845 634 6666

Khalil, Karim Recorder *L Jul 1984*
(Q.C.) *15, 84*
1 Paper Buildings, London EC4
p946 .... 020 7353 3728

Khalique, Miss Nageena *G Oct 1994*
1, 53, 68, 14, 85, 22, 51, 25, 26, 27, 63
No5 Chambers, Bristol
p971 .... 0845 210 5555
No5 Chambers, London EC4
p944 .... 0845 210 5555
No5 Chambers, Birmingham
p968 .... 0845 210 5555

KHAMISA, Mr Mohammed J BA(Hons)(Lond) *M Nov 1985*
(Q.C.) *15*
Charter Chambers, London WC1
p928 .... 020 7618 4400

Khan, Miss Aisha *L Oct 2002*
15
Nine Bedford Row, London WC1
p924 .... 020 7489 2727

KHAN, Mr Ashraf *M Jan 1999*
15, 62
23 Essex Street, London WC2
p932 .... 020 7413 0353

KHAN, Mr B Jamil LLB *L Jul 1986*
1, 10, 12, 20, 22, 26, 30, 51
7 Harrington Street Chambers, Liverpool
p981 .... 0151 242 0707

KHAN, Mr Changez LLB; LLM; Maîtrise en Droit *L Jul 2008*
12, 18, 30
Farrar's Building, London EC4
p933 .... 020 7583 9241

Khan, Mr Farhaz *M Oct 2005*
30, 18, 81, 62, 84, 1
Outer Temple Chambers, London WC2
p945 .... 020 7353 6381

Khan, Mr Hassan *L Nov 1999*
20, 10
4 Paper Buildings, London EC4
p946 .... 020 7583 0816

KHAN, Miss Helen M G LLB *M Nov 1990*
10, 15, 20
Pump Court Chambers, Swindon
p993 .... 01793 539899
Pump Court Chambers, Winchester
p994 .... 01962 868161
Pump Court Chambers, London EC4
p947 .... 020 7353 0711

Khan, Mr Imran LLB(Hons) *L Nov 2001*
12, 15
St Albans Chambers, St Albans
p992 .... 01727 843383

Khan, Mr Karim A A LLB(Lond) *L Oct 1992*
(Q.C.)
2 Hare Court, London EC4
p937 .... 020 7353 5324
Temple Garden Chambers, London EC4
p952 .... 020 7583 1315

Khan, Mr Mahmood Shafi BA; MA; LLB *L Feb 1994*
1, 11, 12, 15, 20, 22, 23, 26, 30, 51, 64, 67, 88, 89
Luton Chambers, Luton
p982 .... 01582 598394

Khan, Mr Mohammad Tayab LLM(Lond); MA(Cantab) *L Feb 1972*
15, 20, 23, 36
Melbury House, Oadby
p989 ....

KHAN, Mr Mohammed Asif *L Nov 1983*
23
Citadel Chambers, Birmingham
p967 .... 0121 233 8500

Khan, Mr Muhammed Babar LLB(Hons) *I Jan 1999*
Chancery Chambers, London WC2
p928 .... 020 7405 6879

Khan, Ruwena LLB(Hons) *I Jul 2005*
12, 67, 15, 30, 62, 22, 61, 72, 80, 84, 88, 89, 94
Zenith Chambers, Leeds
p979 .... 0113 245 5438

Khan, Ms Sabina LLB(Hons) *M Feb 1999*
23, 18
Angel Chambers, Swansea
p992 .... 01792 464623
4 King's Bench Walk, London EC4
p939 .... 020 7822 7000

Khan, Mr Shaukat LLB *L May 1971*
Chambers of Mr S A Khan, Kingston upon Thames
p977 .... 020 8541 3875

KHAN, Miss Shazia *L Jul 2000*
23, 1, 51
Kenworthy's Chambers, Manchester
p984 .... 0161 832 4036

Khan, Shokat LLB; LLM *M Nov 1979*
12, 20, 23, 30, 53
Kings Chambers, Leeds
p978 .... 0113 242 1123
Kings Chambers, Manchester
p984 .... 0161 832 9082

Khan, Mr Tahir Zaffar LLB *L Jul 1986*
(Q.C.) *12, 15, 23, 26*
Broadway House Chambers, Leeds
p977 .... 0113 246 2600
Broadway House Chambers, Bradford
p969 .... 01274 722560

Khandker, Miss Monisha *M Jul 2005*
Albion Chambers, Bristol
p970 .... 0117 927 2144

KHANGURE, Mr Avtar BA; LLM(Cantab); Recorder *G Nov 1985*
(Q.C.) *6, 7, 11, 8*
St Philips Chambers, Birmingham
p969 .... 0121 246 7000

KHANNA, Ms Priyadarshani LLB(Hons) *I Oct 2001*
15, 62
18 Red Lion Court, London EC4
p949 .... 020 7520 6000
18 Red Lion Court (Annexe), Chelmsford
p973 .... 01245 280880

Khanzada, Ms Najma LLB *I Nov 1992*
15
1 Pump Court, London EC4
p947 .... 020 7842 7070

Khatoon, Ms Najma LLB *I Nov 1986*
10, 12, 15, 20, 22
Goldsmith Chambers, London EC4
p935 .... 020 7353 6802

Khawar, Aftab LLB *G Jul 1983*
1, 30, 23, 12, 15, 10
St Johns Buildings, Preston
p990 .... 01772 256100
St Johns Buildings, Chester
p974 .... 01244 323070
St Johns Buildings, Manchester
p985 .... 0161 214 1500
St Johns Buildings, Liverpool
p982 .... 0151 243 6000

Khayum, Mr Zulfikar LLB(Hons); PgDip(BVC); BCL *G Oct 2006*
3, 7, 11, 31, 40, 41, 43, 45, 49, 54, 61, 78
Atkin Chambers, London WC1
p923 .... 020 7404 0102

Khubber, Mr Ranjiv *M Nov 1994*
1, 23, 51
1 Pump Court, London EC4
p947 .... 020 7842 7070

Khurshid, Mr Jawdat BA(Oxon) *L Oct 1994*
3, 11, 24, 33, 35
7 King's Bench Walk, London EC4
p940 .... 020 7910 8300

Kiai, Gilda *G Jan 2004*
15
1 Pump Court, London EC4
p947 .... 020 7842 7070

KIBLING, Mr Thomas LLB *M Nov 1990*
55, 18, 51, 1, 11, 19, 33
Matrix Chambers, London WC1
p942 .... 020 7404 3447

KIDD, Miss Joanne *L Oct 1995*
Fountain Chambers, Middlesbrough
p986 .... 01642 804040

KIDD, Mr Peter LLB(Hons) *L Jul 1987*
20, 40, 10, 30, 88, 8, 38
7 Harrington Street Chambers, Liverpool
p981 .... 0151 242 0707

Kilcoyne, Mr Desmond LLB(Soton); LLM(Lond) *I May 1990*
22, 26
42 Bedford Row, London WC1
p925 .... 020 7831 0222

KILCOYNE, Mr Paul A J LLB(B'ham) *L Nov 1985*
Temple Garden Chambers, London EC4
p952 .... 020 7583 1315

Killalea, Mr Stephen LLB *M Jul 1981*
(Q.C.) *12, 15, 27, 30, 36, 53*
Devereux Chambers, London WC2
p930 .... 020 7353 7534

13

KILLEEN, Mr Simon LLB; Recorder I *Jul 1984*
15, 20, 30
7 Harrington Street Chambers, Liverpool
p981 . . . . . 0151 242 0707

Killen, Geoffrey LLB I *Oct 1990*
Clerksroom - Administration Centre, Taunton
p993 . . . . . 0845 083 3000

Kilpatrick, Miss Alyson LLB; College of Europe Bruges M *Jul 1991*
1, 8, 12, 22, 26, 28, 36, 51
Cobden House Chambers, Manchester
p983 . . . . . 0161 833 6000

Kilroy, Ms Charlotte BA(Hons)(Oxon); DipLaw(City) I *Jan 1999*
76, 23, 33, 1
Doughty Street Chambers, London WC1
p930 . . . . . 020 7404 1313

Kilvington, Miss Sarah BA(Oxon) M *Oct 1999*
20
18 St John Street Chambers, Manchester
p985 . . . . . 0161 278 1800

Kilvington, Mr Simon Charles BA(Oxon) L *Nov 1995*
15, 18, 30
18 St John Street Chambers, Manchester
p985 . . . . . 0161 278 1800

Kimbell, Mr John Ashley MA; M Phil(Cantab) I *Nov 1995*
4, 5, 11, 24
Quadrant Chambers, London EC4
p948 . . . . . 020 7583 4444

Kimblin, Mr Richard M *Jul 1998*
31, 26, 46, 48, 61, 43, 54, 23, 78
No5 Chambers, Bristol
p971 . . . . . 0845 210 5555
No5 Chambers, London EC4
p944 . . . . . 0845 210 5555
No5 Chambers, Birmingham
p968 . . . . . 0845 210 5555

KIME, Mr Matthew BA(Oxon)(Chemistry with Biophysics); DPhil(Oxon); LLB(Lond); NATO/SERC Post Doctoral Research Fellow(Yale) G *Jul 1988*
13, 16, 19, 44, 45
Ingenuity IP Chambers, London EC4
p937 . . . . . 020 7936 4474
No 3 Fleet Street Chambers, London EC4
p944 . . . . . 020 7936 4474

Kimmins, Mr Charles Dominic BA(Cantab) I *Nov 1994*
(Q.C.) *3, 11, 12, 24, 35, 41*
20 Essex Street, London WC2
p932 . . . . . 020 7842 1200

Kimsey, Mr Mark Fenton LLB I *Oct 1990*
15
Castle Chambers, Harrow
p976 . . . . . 020 8423 6579

KINCH, Mr Christopher MA(Oxon); Recorder L *Jul 1976*
(Q.C.) *15, 36, 11, 62, 72*
23 Essex Street, London WC2
p932 . . . . . 020 7413 0353

KINCH, Miss Hannah LLB(Hons)(LSE) M *Jan 2006*
15, 62, 27, 36
23 Essex Street, London WC2
p932 . . . . . 020 7413 0353

King, Mr Adam I *Jan 2005*
15
QEB Hollis Whiteman, London EC4
p948 . . . . . 020 7933 8855

King, Mr Charles LLB(Hons) M *Nov 1995*
Lamb Chambers, London EC4
p941 . . . . . 020 7797 8300

King, Mr Edmund BA(Oxon) I *Nov 1999*
Essex Court Chambers, London WC2
p931 . . . . . 020 7813 8000

King, Miss Emma BA(Hons)(Oxon); DipLaw I *Nov 1999*
15, 62
2 Bedford Row, London WC1
p924 . . . . . 020 7440 8888

King, Miss Fawzia BA M *Nov 1985*
10, 20
42 Bedford Row, London WC1
p925 . . . . . 020 7831 0222

King, Mr Gelaga LLB(Hons); Recorder G *Jul 1985*
15, 62
2 Bedford Row, London WC1
p924 . . . . . 020 7440 8888

King, Mr Henry MA(Oxon); ACA I *Nov 1998*
Fountain Court Chambers, London EC4
p934 . . . . . 020 7583 3335

King, Mr John I *Jan 1983*
Nine Bedford Row, London WC1
p924 . . . . . 020 7489 2727
12 King's Bench Walk, London EC4
p940 . . . . . 020 7583 0811

KING, Miss Judith MA M *Jul 2002*
Maidstone Chambers, Maidstone
p982 . . . . . 01622 688592

KING, Ms Julia I *Jul 1998*
15
1 High Pavement, Nottingham
p988 . . . . . 0115 941 8218

King, Mr Karl BA(Hons) G *Nov 1985*
30, 88, 22, 93
Hardwicke, London WC2
p936 . . . . . 020 7242 2523

King, Mr Mark BSc(Lond) I *Oct 1997*
53, 30
Lamb Chambers, London EC4
p941 . . . . . 020 7797 8300

King, Mr Michael MA G *Jul 1971*
6, 8, 11, 29, 32, 37, 40, 5, 14, 41, 9, 49, 62
XXIV Old Buildings, London WC2
p944 . . . . . 020 7691 2424

KING, Mr Neil MA(Oxon) I *Jul 1980*
(Q.C.) *1, 2, 26, 28, 31, 36, 46*
Landmark Chambers, London EC4
p941 . . . . . 020 7430 1221

King, Mr Oliver LLB G *Jul 2001*
12, 15, 23
St Johns Buildings, Preston
p990 . . . . . 01772 256100
St Johns Buildings, Chester
p974 . . . . . 01244 323070
St Johns Buildings, Manchester
p985 . . . . . 0161 214 1500
St Johns Buildings, Liverpool
p982 . . . . . 0151 243 6000

KING, Mr Philip BA I *Nov 1974*
(Q.C.) *15, 62, 95*
187 Fleet Street, London EC4
p933 . . . . . 020 7430 7430

KING, Mr Richard BA(Dunelm) I *Jul 1978*
96
Five Paper, London EC4
p946 . . . . . 020 7815 3200

King, Miss Samantha MA(Cantab) M *Nov 1990*
20, 10
4 Paper Buildings, London EC4
p946 . . . . . 020 7583 0816

King, Mr Simon Paul BA; Recorder I *Nov 1987*
41, 30, 40, 84, 53
7 Bedford Row, London WC1
p924 . . . . . 020 7242 3555

King-Smith, Mr James BA(Oxon) M *Nov 1980*
18, 20, 22, 30, 36, 40
Crown Office Row Chambers, Brighton
p970 . . . . . 01273 625625

KING-UNDERWOOD, Mr Gregory M *Oct 2002*
Carmelite Chambers, London EC4
p927 . . . . . 020 7936 6300

Kingerley, Mr Martin LLB(Hons) L *Jul 1999*
2, 10, 20, 63
36 Bedford Row, London WC1
p925 . . . . . 020 7421 8000

Kinghorn, Miss Helen MA(Cantab) M *Jul 2006*
67, 22, 88, 84, 30, 94, 12, 18
Lamb Chambers, London EC4
p941 . . . . . 020 7797 8300

Kingscote, Mr Geoffrey BA(Oxon); MPhil(Cantab) I *Nov 1993*
10, 20
1 Hare Court, London EC4
p936 . . . . . 020 7797 7070

Kingsley, Mr Daniel MA(Cantab) L *Oct 1994*
10, 20, 22
1 Pump Court, London EC4
p947 . . . . . 020 7842 7070

Kingsley, Mr Richard LLB I *Jul 1977*
14 Gray's Inn Square, London WC1
p936 . . . . . 020 7242 0858

Kingston, Mr Martin M *Apr 1972*
(Q.C.) *31, 46, 54, 43, 60, 61, 78*
No5 Chambers, Bristol
p971 . . . . . 0845 210 5555
No5 Chambers, London EC4
p944 . . . . . 0845 210 5555
No5 Chambers, Birmingham
p968 . . . . . 0845 210 5555

KINGSWELL, Miss Gemma I *Jul 2008*
15, 62, 94
18 Red Lion Court, London EC4
p949 . . . . . 020 7520 6000
18 Red Lion Court (Annexe), Chelmsford
p973 . . . . . 01245 280880

KINLOCH-JONES, Miss Caroline CPE(Bris) I *Nov 2002*
10, 20
12 College Place, Southampton
p992 . . . . . 023 8032 0320

Kinnear, Miss Elise BA(Hons)(Oxon) G *Oct 2003*
Field Court Chambers, London WC1
p933 . . . . . 020 7405 6114

KINNEAR, Mr Jonathan S LLB(Hons)(Newc) G *Oct 1994*
15
9-12 Bell Yard Chambers, London WC2
p926 . . . . . 020 7400 1800

Kinnier, Mr Andrew MA(Cantab) M *Oct 1996*
11, 12, 18, 19, 22, 30, 36, 51
Henderson Chambers, London EC4
p937 . . . . . 020 7583 9020

KINSKY, Mr Cyril BA(Cantab) M *Nov 1988*
(Q.C.) *40, 24, 3, 11*
3 Verulam Buildings, London WC1
p953 . . . . . 020 7831 8441

Kinsler, Ms Marie-Louise I *Jan 1992*
11, 19, 24
2 Temple Gardens, London EC4
p952 . . . . . 020 7822 1200

Kirby, Mr James G *Oct 1994*
15
Tooks Chambers, London EC4
p953 . . . . . 020 7842 7575

Kirby, Mr Peter LLB(Hons) I *Jul 1989*
40, 18, 11, 49, 88, 24
Hardwicke, London WC2
p936 . . . . . 020 7242 2523

Kirby, Miss Rhian Faith LLB L *Oct 2000*
10, 20
Thirty Park Place, Cardiff
p973 . . . . . 029 2039 8421

Kirby, Miss Ruth M *Oct 1994*
20, 10
4 Paper Buildings, London EC4
p946 . . . . . 020 7583 0816

KIRK, Mr Anthony LLB(Lond) G *Jan 1981*
(Q.C.) *20, 10, 12, 49, 96*
1 King's Bench Walk, London EC4
p938 . . . . . 020 7936 1500

Kirk, Mr Graeme I *Jun 2001*
One Essex Court, London EC4
p931 . . . . . 020 7936 3030

Kirk, Mr Jonathan LLB(Hons) L *Nov 1995*
(Q.C.) *12, 15, 39, 48, 59*
36 Bedford Row, London WC1
p925 . . . . . 020 7421 8000
Gough Square Chambers, London EC4
p935 . . . . . 020 7353 0924

Kirk, Mr Thomas LLB(Hons) L *Jul 2007*
6, 8, 11, 12, 15, 18, 30, 32, 37, 38, 55, 67, 76, 94
12 College Place, Southampton
p992 . . . . . 023 8032 0320

Kirkwood, Mr Edward LLB(Exeter) I *Nov 1999*
20, 10
Harcourt Chambers, London EC4
p936 . . . . . 0844 561 7135
Harcourt Chambers, Oxford
p989 . . . . . 0844 561 7135

Kirtley, Mr Paul G MA(Cantab) M *Jul 1982*
Exchange Chambers, Manchester
p983 . . . . . 0161 833 2722
Exchange Chambers, Liverpool
p980 . . . . . 0151 236 7747
Exchange Chambers, Leeds
p977 . . . . . 0113 203 1970

Kishore, Mr Paul LLB; BA; ACP; ACIArb L *Nov 1982*
Chancery Chambers, London WC2
p928 . . . . . 020 7405 6879

KISSER, Miss Amy I *Jul 2009*
10, 20
Queen Elizabeth Buildings, London EC4
p948 . . . . . 020 7797 7837

KISSIN, Miss Clare MA M *Oct 2009*
16, 52, 73
One Brick Court, London EC4
p927 . . . . . 020 7353 8845

Kitchener, Mr Neil M *Nov 1991*
(Q.C.)
One Essex Court, London EC4
p931 . . . . . 020 7583 2000

Kitchin, Miss Louise BA(Hons) M *Oct 1998*
15
Lincoln House Chambers, Manchester
p984 . . . . . 0161 832 5701

KITCHING, Mrs Kossar LLB I *Jan 1999*
20, 10, 63
Trinity (Newcastle) Chambers, Newcastle upon Tyne
p987 . . . . . 0191 232 1927
Trinity (Teesside) Chambers, Middlesbrough
p986 . . . . . 01642 247569

Kitzing, Miss Susanna M *Jan 2005*
Park Court Chambers, Leeds
p978 . . . . . 0113 243 3277

Kivdeh, Mr Sean M *Oct 1992*
1 Mitre Court Buildings, London EC4
p942 . . . . . 020 7452 8900

KLEIN, Mr Jonathan LLB; BCL; Junior Counsel to the Crown (Regional) L *Oct 1992*
2, 8, 12, 22, 32, 37, 40, 49, 88
Enterprise Chambers, London WC2
p931 . . . . . 020 7405 9471
Enterprise Chambers, Leeds
p977 . . . . . 0113 246 0391
Enterprise Chambers, Newcastle upon Tyne
p987 . . . . . 0191 222 3344

Kloss, Mr Alexander BA G *Oct 1993*
12, 10, 20
St Johns Buildings, Preston
p990 . . . . . 01772 256100
St Johns Buildings, Chester
p974 . . . . . 01244 323070
St Johns Buildings, Manchester
p985 . . . . . 0161 214 1500
St Johns Buildings, Liverpool
p982 . . . . . 0151 243 6000

Kloss, Mrs Diana Mary G *Jul 1986*
18, 19, 27
St Johns Buildings, Preston
p990 . . . . . 01772 256100
St Johns Buildings, Chester
p974 . . . . . 01244 323070
St Johns Buildings, Manchester
p985 . . . . . 0161 214 1500
St Johns Buildings, Liverpool
p982 . . . . . 0151 243 6000

KNAGG, Mr Christopher G *Nov 2005*
12, 30, 18
7 Harrington Street Chambers, Liverpool
p981 . . . . . 0151 242 0707

Knapp, Ms Sophie BA(Lond) G *Feb 1990*
20
3PB, Bournemouth
p969 . . . . . 01202 292102

KNAPP, Mr Stephen LLB(Hons) G *Jul 1986*
30, 25, 12, 40, 76
7 Harrington Street Chambers, Liverpool
p981 . . . . . 0151 242 0707

Knapton, Ms Sarah BA(Leeds) M *Jun 2007*
8, 11, 1, 22, 31, 46
St John's Chambers, Bristol
p972 . . . . . 0117 921 3456

KNIBBE, Mr Jorren BA; LLM M *Oct 2005*
1, 19, 34, 44, 46
Monckton Chambers, London WC1
p942 . . . . . 020 7405 7211

Knifton, Mr David Alan LLB(Hons); Recorder I *Jul 1986*
30, 53
Exchange Chambers, Manchester
p983 . . . . . 0161 833 2722
Exchange Chambers, Liverpool
p980 . . . . . 0151 236 7747
Exchange Chambers, Leeds
p977 . . . . . 0113 203 1970

Knight, Miss Adrienne G *Jan 1981*
15, 62
3 Temple Gardens, London EC4
p952 . . . . . 020 7353 3102

See p1010 for the Key to Work Categories

KNIGHT, Ms Alexia M *Jan 2007*
5, 81, 62, 38, 97, 13, 24
3 Verulam Buildings, London WC1
p953 . . . . . 020 7831 8441

Knight, Miss Caroline LLB; Dip d'Etudes Jur Fr I *Jul 1985*
12, 15, 20, 25, 30
5 St Andrew's Hill, London EC4
p950 . . . . . 020 7332 5400

KNIGHT, Mr Christopher I *Jan 2008*
11KBW, London EC4
p938 . . . . . 020 7632 8500

Knight, Mr Edward MA; ACA L *Nov 1999*
5, 6, 8, 11, 29, 32, 37, 40, 59, 49, 62
XXIV Old Buildings, London WC2
p944 . . . . . 020 7691 2424

Knight, Emma L *Jul 2008*
13 Old Square Chambers, London WC2
p945 . . . . . 020 7831 4445

Knight, Heidi MA(Cantab); BA(Law) L *Jan 2001*
53, 68, 85, 27, 30, 36
3 Serjeants' Inn, London EC4
p950 . . . . . 020 7427 5000

Knight, Ms Jennifer LLB G *Oct 1996*
15
Atkinson Bevan Chambers, London EC4
p924 . . . . . 020 7353 2112

KNIGHT, Keith G *Jan 1969*
4 King's Bench Walk, London EC4
p939 . . . . . 020 7822 7000

Knight, Mr Peter M *Nov 2005*
Westgate Chambers, Lewes
p980 . . . . . 01273 480510

KNIGHT, Ms Sarah M *Jul 1996*
15
1 High Pavement, Nottingham
p988 . . . . . 0115 941 8218

KNIGHTS, Ms Samantha BA(Hons)(Oxon); DipLaw; LLM L *Nov 1996*
11, 51, 6, 1, 41, 55, 76, 23, 38, 33
Matrix Chambers, London WC1
p942 . . . . . 020 7404 3447

Knott, Ms Helen CQSW M *Jul 2002*
10, 18, 20
4 Brick Court Chambers, London EC4
p927 . . . . . 020 7832 3200

KNOTT, Mr James BA(Warwick) I *Jan 2008*
6, 11, 97, 62, 38
4 Stone Buildings, London WC2
p951 . . . . . 020 7242 5524

Knott, Ms Samantha LLB(Warw) L *Jan 2005*
11, 30, 56, 26, 31, 25, 32
Crown Office Row Chambers, Brighton
p970 . . . . . 01273 625625

Knotts, Miss Carol LLB(Hons) I *Nov 1996*
No5 Chambers, Bristol
p971 . . . . . 0845 210 5555
No5 Chambers, London EC4
p944 . . . . . 0845 210 5555
No5 Chambers, Birmingham
p968 . . . . . 0845 210 5555

Knowles, Miss Catherine BA(Hons)(Oxon) M *Jul 2004*
Park Court Chambers, Leeds
p978 . . . . . 0113 243 3277

KNOWLES, Gwynneth BA; MSc G *Nov 1993*
(Q.C.) *20, 10*
Atlantic Chambers, Liverpool
p980 . . . . . 0151 236 4421

KNOWLES, Mr Julian BA(Oxon); CPE I *Nov 1994*
(Q.C.) *15, 1, 33, 51, 12, 21, 19, 23, 26*
Matrix Chambers, London WC1
p942 . . . . . 020 7404 3447

Knowles, Miss Linsey MA(Hons) L *Jul 2000*
15, 20
6-8 Mill Street, Maidstone
p982 . . . . . 01622 688094 / 688095
6 Pump Court, London EC4
p947 . . . . . 020 7797 8400

Knowles, Mr Mark LLB M *Nov 1989*
KCH Garden Square Chambers, Nottingham
p989 . . . . . 0115 941 8851
KCH Garden Square Chambers, Leicester
p979 . . . . . 0115 941 8851

Knowles, Mr Michael LLB(Hons) M *Oct 2000*
15, 94
Cobden House Chambers, Manchester
p983 . . . . . 0161 833 6000

KNOWLES, Mr Robin St J MA(Cantab) M *Jul 1982*
(Q.C.) CBE*5, 6, 8, 11, 12, 24, 29, 4, 9, 40, 38*
South Square, London WC1
p950 . . . . . 020 7696 9900

KNOX, Mr Christopher John BA(Dunelm); Recorder I *Jul 1974*
12, 15, 20, 30, 27, 40, 1, 38, 2, 11, 63
Trinity (Newcastle) Chambers, Newcastle upon Tyne
p987 . . . . . 0191 232 1927
Trinity (Teesside) Chambers, Middlesbrough
p986 . . . . . 01642 247569

KNOX, Mr Henry MA(Hons); PhD G *Jan 2000*
5, 11, 24, 40, 6, 50
3 Verulam Buildings, London WC1
p953 . . . . . 020 7831 8441

KNOX, Mr Simon C Peter M *Nov 1983*
(Q.C.) *11, 12, 22, 24*
3 Hare Court, London EC4
p937 . . . . . 020 7415 7800

Kochnari, Kate LLB I *Jan 2008*
Stour Chambers, Canterbury
p972 . . . . . 01227 764899

Kodagoda, Fritz L *Nov 1993*
15, 23
12 Old Square, London WC2
p945 . . . . . 020 7404 0875

KOGAN, Mr Barry I *Jul 1973*
Carmelite Chambers, London EC4
p927 . . . . . 020 7936 6300

Kokelaar, Mr Sebastian L *Jul 2004*
13 Old Square Chambers, London WC2
p945 . . . . . 020 7831 4445

Kolhatkar, Mr Ishan BSc(Hons)(Lond) M *Oct 2002*
15, 36
2 Hare Court, London EC4
p937 . . . . . 020 7353 5324

KOLINSKY, Mr Daniel I *Oct 1998*
Landmark Chambers, London EC4
p941 . . . . . 020 7430 1221

KOLODYNSKI, Mr Stefan L *Oct 1993*
15, 62, 91, 88
St Philips Chambers, Birmingham
p969 . . . . . 0121 246 7000

Kolvin, Mr Philip BA(Oxon) I *Jul 1988*
(Q.C.) *1, 12, 22, 25, 26, 31, 18, 30*
Cornerstone Barristers, London WC1
p929 . . . . . 020 7242 4986

Kong, Mr Senghin M *Jul 2008*
15
5 King's Bench Walk, London EC4
p939 . . . . . 020 7353 5638

KORDA, Mr Anthony LLB(Lond) I *Jan 1988*
15, 62, 95
187 Fleet Street, London EC4
p933 . . . . . 020 7430 7430

Korn, Mr Anthony G *Nov 1978*
18, 55
No5 Chambers, Bristol
p971 . . . . . 0845 210 5555
No5 Chambers, London EC4
p944 . . . . . 0845 210 5555
No5 Chambers, Birmingham
p968 . . . . . 0845 210 5555

KORN, Mr Richard Adam I *Nov 1992*
12, 30, 53, 10, 40, 85, 27, 68
7 Bedford Row, London WC1
p924 . . . . . 020 7242 3555

Korner, Ms Joanna I *Nov 1974*
(Q.C.) CMG*15, 62, 36*
6 King's Bench Walk, London EC4
p939 . . . . . 020 7583 0410

Korniej, Ms Rebekah LLB(Hons) M *Oct 1999*
15, 20
East Anglian Chambers, Norwich
p988 . . . . . 01603 617351
East Anglian Chambers, Colchester
p975 . . . . . 01206 572756
East Anglian Chambers, Chelmsford
p973 . . . . . 01245 215660
East Anglian Chambers, Ipswich
p976 . . . . . 01473 214481

Korobowicz, Ms Natalia W I *Oct 2004*
20, 10
No 6 Barristers Chambers, Leeds
p978 . . . . . 0113 245 9763

Korol, Ms Kathryn M *Mar 1996*
20, 10
15 Winckley Square, Preston
p991 . . . . . 01772 252828

Kotak, Mr Raggi BA I *Mar 2000*
23, 20
1 Pump Court, London EC4
p947 . . . . . 020 7842 7070

Kothari, Miss Sima LLB G *Oct 1992*
10, 20
Coram Chambers, London EC1
p929 . . . . . 020 7092 3700

KOTZEVA, Miss Anna MA(Cantab) M *Oct 1998*
Temple Garden Chambers, London EC4
p952 . . . . . 020 7583 1315

KOVATS, Mr Steven M *Jul 1989*
(Q.C.) *1, 23, 51, 85, 26, 19*
Thirty Nine Essex Street, London WC2
p932 . . . . . 020 7832 1111

KRAMER, Mr Adam G *Jan 2004*
11, 5, 62, 24, 40
3 Verulam Buildings, London WC1
p953 . . . . . 020 7831 8441

KREISBERGER, Miss Ronit MA(Oxon)(Jurisprudence); BCL G *Jan 1999*
44, 19, 51, 1, 18, 56, 61
Monckton Chambers, London WC1
p942 . . . . . 020 7405 7211

Krikler, Mr Alexander Richard BA; CPE M *Nov 1995*
15
4 Breams Buildings, London EC4
p927 . . . . . 020 7092 1900

KRISH, Miss Doushka LLB(Hons) M *Jun 1991*
10, 20
1 Garden Court, London EC4
p934 . . . . . 020 7797 7900

Krishnan, Ms Davina LLB(Hons) L *Jul 2004*
20, 10
St Albans Chambers, St Albans
p992 . . . . . 01727 843383

Krolick, Mr Ivan LLB(Dunelm); FCIArb G *Nov 1966*
8, 11, 12, 13, 15, 16, 30, 31, 40, 95
Lamb Building, Brighton
p970 . . . . . 01273 820490
Lamb Building, London EC4
p940 . . . . . 020 7797 7788

KUBIK, Ms Heidi LLB(Nott'm) L *Jan 1993*
15, 62
St Philips Chambers, Birmingham
p969 . . . . . 0121 246 7000

Kulkarni, Mr Yash MA(Cantab) L *Jan 1998*
7, 11, 12, 35
Quadrant Chambers, London EC4
p948 . . . . . 020 7583 4444

Kumeta, Miss Jennifer BA(Hons) M *Oct 2005*
20, 94
Cobden House Chambers, Manchester
p983 . . . . . 0161 833 6000

King's Bench Godolphin Chambers, Truro
p994 . . . . . 0845 308 1551
King's Bench Godolphin Chambers, Plymouth
p990 . . . . . 0845 308 1551

Kumi, Mr Ishmael Job MA(Oxon); Maitrise(Sorbonne) G *Nov 1977*
1, 10, 12, 15, 18, 20, 21, 23, 30, 32
Cromwell-Ayeh-Kumi Chambers, London W3
p929 . . . . . 020 8740 6982

Kurji, Miss Fatim I *Jan 2003*
8, 11, 22, 55, 6, 18, 12, 30, 40, 53, 68, 94
No5 Chambers, Bristol
p971 . . . . . 0845 210 5555
No5 Chambers, London EC4
p944 . . . . . 0845 210 5555
No5 Chambers, Birmingham
p968 . . . . . 0845 210 5555

KURZNER, Miss Emma M *Feb 1999*
15, 62, 95
187 Fleet Street, London EC4
p933 . . . . . 020 7430 7430

KUSHNER, Miss Martine LLB(Hons)(B'ham); Recorder M *Jul 1980*
10, 20
St Philips Chambers, Birmingham
p969 . . . . . 0121 246 7000

Kverndal, Mr Simon MA(Cantab) M *Nov 1982*
(Q.C.) *11, 35, 3*
Quadrant Chambers, London EC4
p948 . . . . . 020 7583 4444

Kwiatkowski, Mr Feliks Jerzy M *Jul 1977*
30, 11, 97, 47, 67
Kew Chambers, Kew
p976 . . . . . 0844 809 9991

Kyriakides, Ms Tina MA(Cantab) L *Jul 1984*
5, 6, 8, 11, 24, 29, 38
11 Stone Buildings, London WC2
p951 . . . . . 020 7831 6381

Kyte, Mr Peter L *Jul 1970*
(Q.C.) *15, 25, 36*
QEB Hollis Whiteman, London EC4
p948 . . . . . 020 7933 8855

LACHKOVIC, Mr James LLB(Hull) G *Nov 1987*
15, 62, 95
187 Fleet Street, London EC4
p933 . . . . . 020 7430 7430

LACOB, Ms Lisa G *Jan 2004*
5, 81, 40, 45
3 Verulam Buildings, London WC1
p953 . . . . . 020 7831 8441

LACY, Mr Brian L *Nov 2006*
6, 8, 11, 97, 67, 18, 38, 89
Littleton Chambers, London EC4
p941 . . . . . 020 7797 8600

Ladak, Miss Tahera LLB(Essex) G *Nov 1986*
10, 20
1 Pump Court, London EC4
p947 . . . . . 020 7842 7070

LADDIE, Mr James BA(Hons)(Cantab) M *Nov 1995*
11, 43, 50, 56, 18, 1, 51, 55
Matrix Chambers, London WC1
p942 . . . . . 020 7404 3447

Lahiffe, Mr Martin Patrick Joseph BA M *Nov 1984*
15, 18, 62, 70
3 Temple Gardens, London EC4
p952 . . . . . 020 7353 3102

Laidlaw, Mr Jonathan James LLB; Recorder; Senior Treasury Counsel I *Jul 1982*
(Q.C.) *15, 62, 25, 96*
2 Hare Court, London EC4
p937 . . . . . 020 7353 5324

Laing, Ms Christine LLB; Recorder L *Jan 1984*
(Q.C.) *15, 62*
3 Temple Gardens, London EC4
p952 . . . . . 020 7353 3102

LAING, Miss Elisabeth BA(Cantab); Recorder M *Jul 1980*
(Q.C.) *1, 11, 18, 19, 26, 63, 51, 23*
11KBW, London EC4
p938 . . . . . 020 7632 8500

LAIRD, Mr Francis LLB(Newc); Recorder G *Jan 1986*
(Q.C.) *15, 62*
St Philips Chambers, Birmingham
p969 . . . . . 0121 246 7000

Lake, Mr James LLB I *Oct 2005*
15, 12, 20, 10, 62, 56
St Pauls Chambers, Leeds
p979 . . . . . 0113 245 5866

Lakha, Abbas BA I *Nov 1984*
(Q.C.) *15, 51, 62*
Nine Bedford Row, London WC1
p924 . . . . . 020 7489 2727

LAKHA, Mr Shabbir LLB(Hons); M Phil(Cantab) L *Jul 1989*
1, 11, 12, 18, 29, 30, 36, 24
Farrar's Building, London EC4
p933 . . . . . 020 7583 9241

Lakin, Mr Paul LLB(Hons) M *Jul 2000*
8, 81, 38, 29, 40, 93, 37
Kings Chambers, Leeds
p978 . . . . . 0113 242 1123
Kings Chambers, Manchester
p984 . . . . . 0161 832 9082

Lakin, Ms Tracy I *Oct 1993*
12, 15, 20, 22, 30
St Ives Chambers, Birmingham
p969 . . . . . 0121 236 0863

LAL, Mr Sanjay LLB(Hons)(Lond); LLM L *Oct 1993*
23, 15
4 King's Bench Walk, London EC4
p939 . . . . . 020 7822 7000

LALL, Mr Tarlochan LLB; LLM(Tax); CTA M *Jan 2010*
57
Monckton Chambers, London WC1
p942 . . . . . 020 7405 7211

13

Lallane, Mr Bernard I *Jul 1994*
Holborn Chambers, London WC2
p937 . . . . . 020 7242 6060

Lallie, Ranjit Singh L *Jan 1997*
15, 25, 62
Equity Chambers, Birmingham
p968 . . . . . 0121 233 2100

Lally, Mr Harbinder Singh L *Jan 1997*
15, 25, 84, 68, 82, 39, 70
No5 Chambers, Bristol
p971 . . . . . 0845 210 5555
No5 Chambers, London EC4
p944 . . . . . 0845 210 5555
No5 Chambers, Birmingham
p968 . . . . . 0845 210 5555

LAMB, Mr David S M *Nov 1987*
15, 18
York Chambers, York
p995 . . . . . 01904 620048
York Chambers, Newcastle upon Tyne
p987 . . . . . 0191 206 4677

Lamb, Mr Edward L *Oct 2006*
30, 15, 18, 93, 20, 11, 70
9 Gough Square, London EC4
p935 . . . . . 020 7832 0500

Lamb, Mr Eric LLB(L'pool); Recorder L *Jul 1975*
15
Exchange Chambers, Manchester
p983 . . . . . 0161 833 2722
Exchange Chambers, Liverpool
p980 . . . . . 0151 236 7747
Exchange Chambers, Leeds
p977 . . . . . 0113 203 1970

Lamb, Mr Henry I *Jan 2004*
14 Gray's Inn Square, London WC1
p936 . . . . . 020 7242 0858

Lamb, Mr Jeffrey BA; MA M *Oct 1992*
15
Westgate Chambers, Lewes
p980 . . . . . 01273 480510

Lamb, Mr John BA M *May 1990*
15
1 Pump Court, London EC4
p947 . . . . . 020 7842 7070

Lamb, Ms Maria Jane Recorder G *Nov 1984*
15
1 Paper Buildings, London EC4
p946 . . . . . 020 7353 3728

Lamb, Mr Robert Glasson MA(Cantab) M *Jul 1973*
93
King's Bench Chambers, Oxford
p989 . . . . . 01865 311066
13 King's Bench Walk, London EC4
p940 . . . . . 020 7353 7204

Lamballe, Miss Victoria Jane M *Jul 2002*
15, 1, 47, 70, 72
Old Court Chambers, Middlesbrough
p986 . . . . . 01642 232523

LAMBERT, Mrs Alison M *Jul 2005*
15, 12, 25
Trinity Chambers, Chelmsford
p974 . . . . . 01245 605040

LAMBERT, Ms Christina MA(Hons) I *Jan 1988*
(Q.C.) *53, 36, 40, 63, 30, 1, 51, 27*
1 Crown Office Row, London EC4
p929 . . . . . 020 7797 7500

LAMBERT, Mr Nigel R W Recorder G *Nov 1974*
(Q.C.)
Carmelite Chambers, London EC4
p927 . . . . . 020 7936 6300

LAMBERT, Ms Sarah BA(Oxon) G *Oct 1994*
12, 18, 20, 27, 30, 40, 53
1 Crown Office Row, London EC4
p929 . . . . . 020 7797 7500

LAMBERT, Ms Suzanne BA; AB L *Oct 2002*
1, 53, 12, 46, 18, 19, 27, 30, 31, 40, 55
1 Crown Office Row, London EC4
p929 . . . . . 020 7797 7500

LAMBERTSON, Ms Siobhan M *Nov 2007*
11, 24, 30, 68
Crown Office Chambers, London EC4
p929 . . . . . 020 7797 8100

Lamberty, Mr Mark BCL; MA(Oxon) I *Nov 1970*
15
St Johns Buildings, Preston
p990 . . . . . 01772 256100
St Johns Buildings, Chester
p974 . . . . . 01244 323070
St Johns Buildings, Manchester
p985 . . . . . 0161 214 1500
St Johns Buildings, Liverpool
p982 . . . . . 0151 243 6000

Lambis, Mr Marios P BA(Hons); DipLaw M *Nov 1989*
15, 62, 44
International Law Chambers, London W2
p938 . . . . . 020 7221 5685 / 7352 6649
2 Hare Court, London EC4
p937 . . . . . 020 7353 5324

Lamming, Mr David LLB(Lond); LLM(Lond) G *Nov 1972*
1, 12, 15, 18, 20, 22, 26, 30, 31
Cornerstone Barristers, London WC1
p929 . . . . . 020 7242 4986

Lamont, Mr Calum MA(Cantab); MPhil I *Jan 2004*
7, 24, 40
Keating Chambers, London WC2
p938 . . . . . 020 7544 2600

LAMONT, Miss Camilla MA(Oxon); BCL M *Nov 1995*
2, 5, 6, 8, 9, 11, 14, 22, 32, 37, 40
Landmark Chambers, London EC4
p941 . . . . . 020 7430 1221

Lams, Mr Barnabus BA; MA G *Oct 1995*
23, 12, 15
4 Brick Court Chambers, London EC4
p927 . . . . . 020 7832 3200

Lancaster, Mr Roger LLB(Hons) M *Nov 2002*
31
Kings Chambers, Leeds
p978 . . . . . 0113 242 1123
Kings Chambers, Manchester
p984 . . . . . 0161 832 9082

LANCHESTER, Mr Martin MA(Cantab) M *Jan 2001*
15
Guildhall Chambers, Bristol
p970 . . . . . 0117 930 9000

Land, Mr Peter MA(Cantab); GDL M *Oct 2007*
3, 7, 11, 31, 40, 41, 43, 45, 49, 54, 61, 78, 74
Atkin Chambers, London WC1
p923 . . . . . 020 7404 0102

Landale, Miss Tina Jeanette Recorder M *Jul 1988*
15
Exchange Chambers, Manchester
p983 . . . . . 0161 833 2722
Exchange Chambers, Liverpool
p980 . . . . . 0151 236 7747
Exchange Chambers, Leeds
p977 . . . . . 0113 203 1970

Landau, Mr Toby MA; BCL(Oxon); LLM(Harv) M *Oct 1993*
(Q.C.)
Essex Court Chambers, London WC2
p931 . . . . . 020 7813 8000

LANDER, Mr Charles Gideon LLB(Leeds) L *Nov 1993*
15
Chavasse Court Chambers, Liverpool
p980 . . . . . 0151 229 2030

Lander, Mr Richard LLB L *Oct 1993*
5, 6, 7, 8, 9, 11, 22, 29, 32, 40, 41, 49
Kings Chambers, Leeds
p978 . . . . . 0113 242 1123
Kings Chambers, Manchester
p984 . . . . . 0161 832 9082

Landsbury, Mr Alan G *Jun 1975*
4 Breams Buildings, London EC4
p927 . . . . . 020 7092 1900

Lane, Mr Andrew L *Oct 1999*
22, 93, 1, 88, 37
Hardwicke, London WC2
p936 . . . . . 020 7242 2523

Lane, Mr Christopher Paul BA L *Nov 2002*
15, 23, 30
No 8 Chambers, Birmingham
p968 . . . . . 0121 236 5514

Lane, Ms Lindsay BA(Cantab) M *Oct 1996*
13, 50, 56
8 New Square, London WC2
p943 . . . . . 020 7405 4321

Lane, Mr Michael BA(Cantab) M *Jul 1983*
22, 31, 18, 12, 26
East Anglian Chambers, Norwich
p988 . . . . . 01603 617351
East Anglian Chambers, Colchester
p975 . . . . . 01206 572756
East Anglian Chambers, Chelmsford
p973 . . . . . 01245 215660
East Anglian Chambers, Ipswich
p976 . . . . . 01473 214481

LANE, Mr Patrick SC BA; LLB; Senior Counsel - South Africa 1993 G *Oct 1997*
7, 41, 67, 11, 38, 40, 5, 24, 88, 54
Thirty Nine Essex Street, London WC2
p932 . . . . . 020 7832 1111

Lane, Miss Rachel Caroline LLB(Hons) L *Nov 2002*
12, 15, 20
2 King's Bench Walk, London EC4
p939 . . . . . 020 7353 1746

Lane, Mr Simon Charles LLM I *Jul 2002*
12, 11, 29, 22, 30
Rougemont Chambers, Exeter
p975 . . . . . 01392 208484

LANEY, Miss Anna LLB; BVC L *Oct 1998*
74, 7, 41, 96, 40, 11
Crown Office Chambers, London EC4
p929 . . . . . 020 7797 8100

Lang, Miss Beverley BA(Oxon) I *Nov 1978*
(Q.C.) *1, 18, 19, 23, 26, 51, 55, 89*
Blackstone Chambers, London EC4
p926 . . . . . 020 7583 1770

Langdale, Mr Adrian Mark LLB G *Mar 1996*
15, 62, 72
7 Bedford Row, London WC1
p924 . . . . . 020 7242 3555

Langdale, Miss Rachel LLB; M Phil M *Oct 1990*
(Q.C.) *10, 20, 1*
7 Bedford Row, London WC1
p924 . . . . . 020 7242 3555

Langdale, Mr Timothy L *Jul 1966*
(Q.C.)
Cloth Fair Chambers, London EC1
p928 . . . . . 020 7710 6444

LANGDON, Mr Andrew LLB(Bris) M *Jul 1986*
(Q.C.) *15, 84, 26*
Guildhall Chambers, Bristol
p970 . . . . . 0117 930 9000

LANGDON, Ms Katie Jane LLB(Hons); LLM(Industrial & Commercial Law) M *Jan 2007*
10, 11, 12, 20, 30, 38, 18, 47, 55, 67, 88, 93
Cornwall Street Chambers, Birmingham
p967 . . . . . 0121 233 7500

Langford, Miss Abigail LLB(Hons) L *Nov 2005*
15
Broadway House Chambers, Leeds
p977 . . . . . 0113 246 2600
Broadway House Chambers, Bradford
p969 . . . . . 01274 722560

Langford, Ms Sarah BA G *Jan 2005*
72, 15, 71, 30, 10, 20
3PB, Winchester
p994 . . . . . 01962 868884

LANGHAM, Mr Richard Geoffrey BA(Oxon) L *Nov 1986*
1, 26, 31
Landmark Chambers, London EC4
p941 . . . . . 020 7430 1221

LANGHORN, Mr Alex M *Jan 2010*
9 St John Street Chambers, Manchester
p984 . . . . . 0161 955 9000

Langley, Mr Charles BA(Hons) M *Oct 1999*
15, 62
2 Bedford Row, London WC1
p924 . . . . . 020 7440 8888

LANGLEY, Miss Sarah L *Nov 2001*
10, 20, 30, 67, 47, 88
7 Harrington Street Chambers, Liverpool
p981 . . . . . 0151 242 0707

Langlois, Mrs Nicole LLB(Exeter) L *May 2008*
49, 6, 8, 11, 97, 67, 62, 38, 24, 21, 89, 96, 32, 40, 37
XXIV Old Buildings, London WC2
p944 . . . . . 020 7691 2424

Langlois, Mr Peter John LLB L *Oct 1991*
11, 8, 6, 45, 29, 31, 32
Unity Street Chambers, Bristol
p972 . . . . . 0117 906 9789

Langridge, Ms Niki LLB(Hons)(Sheff) L *Nov 1993*
10, 20
Coram Chambers, London EC1
p929 . . . . . 020 7092 3700

Langrish, Mr Adam LLB(Hons)(L'pool) I *Jul 2006*
10, 12, 15, 18, 20, 88, 30
College Chambers, Southampton
p992 . . . . . 023 8023 0338

Langstaff, Mr Brian M *Jul 1971*
(Q.C.) *53, 18, 19, 27, 30, 1, 55*
Cloisters, London EC4
p928 . . . . . 020 7827 4000

Laprell, Mr Mark BA(Oxon) G *Nov 1979*
30, 27, 20, 7, 24, 12
18 St John Street Chambers, Manchester
p985 . . . . . 0161 278 1800

Larizadeh, Mr Cyrus BA(Kent); Dip de Droit Francais(Bordeaux) I *Nov 1992*
20, 12, 23
4 Paper Buildings, London EC4
p946 . . . . . 020 7583 0816

Larkin, Mr Sean I *Jul 1987*
15, 25, 36
QEB Hollis Whiteman, London EC4
p948 . . . . . 020 7933 8855

Larton, Miss Claire L *Jan 2005*
15
Broadway House Chambers, Leeds
p977 . . . . . 0113 246 2600
Broadway House Chambers, Bradford
p969 . . . . . 01274 722560

LASCELLES, Mr David MA(Cantab); BCL(Oxon) L *Nov 2003*
11, 5, 6, 18, 97, 67, 38, 40, 66
Littleton Chambers, London EC4
p941 . . . . . 020 7797 8600

Lashbrook, Miss Kellie LLB I *Jul 2001*
10, 20
3 Dr Johnson's Buildings, London EC4
p930 . . . . . 020 7353 4854

LASK, Mr Benjamin Bela David BA; BVC M *Nov 2003*
44, 1, 47, 19, 51, 56
Monckton Chambers, London WC1
p942 . . . . . 020 7405 7211

Lasker, Mr Jeremy S LLB(B'ham) I *Jul 1976*
12, 15, 21, 30
Lincoln House Chambers, Manchester
p984 . . . . . 0161 832 5701

LASOK, Mr Paul MA(Cantab); LLM; PhD M *Jul 1977*
(Q.C.) *1, 19, 44, 57*
Monckton Chambers, London WC1
p942 . . . . . 020 7405 7211

Last, Peter L *Oct 1995*
94
Clerksroom - Administration Centre, Taunton
p993 . . . . . 0845 083 3000

Latham, Mr Kevin M *Oct 2007*
30, 12
Kings Chambers, Leeds
p978 . . . . . 0113 242 1123
Kings Chambers, Manchester
p984 . . . . . 0161 832 9082

LATHAM, Mr Michael LLB(L'pool) G *Nov 1975*
15
Furnival Chambers, London EC4
p934 . . . . . 020 7405 3232

Latham, Mr Richard Brunton LLB; Recorder I *Jul 1971*
(Q.C.) *15, 62, 36*
7 Bedford Row, London WC1
p924 . . . . . 020 7242 3555

Latham, Mr Robert MA(Cantab) M *Jul 1976*
1, 22, 51
Doughty Street Chambers, London WC1
p930 . . . . . 020 7404 1313

LATIF, Mr Mohammed LLB(Hons) L *Jul 1985*
15, 62
St Philips Chambers, Birmingham
p969 . . . . . 0121 246 7000

Latimer, Mr Andrew BA; BCL G *Nov 1995*
5, 6, 8, 11, 29, 37, 40, 49
Kings Chambers, Leeds
p978 . . . . . 0113 242 1123
Kings Chambers, Manchester
p984 . . . . . 0161 832 9082

Latimer-Sayer, Mr William Laurence LLB; MA G *Oct 1995*
30, 53
Cloisters, London EC4
p928 . . . . . 020 7827 4000

Lattimer, Miss Justine I *Apr 1992*
St Ives Chambers, Birmingham
p969 . . . . . 0121 236 0863

See p1010 for the Key to Work Categories

Lau, Mr Martin MA(UCL) *M Jan 1996*
Essex Court Chambers, London WC2
p931 . . . . . 020 7813 8000

Lau, Sarah *L Oct 1998*
Academy Chambers, London N2
p923 . . . . . 07979 265321

Lau, Miss Vanessa LLB(Hons) *M Mar 2005*
20
18 St John Street Chambers, Manchester
p985 . . . . . 0161 278 1800

LAUGHLAND, Mr James BA(Kent) *I Nov 1991*
Temple Garden Chambers, London EC4
p952 . . . . . 020 7583 1315

LAUGHTON, Mr Samuel BA(Cantab) *M Feb 1992*
22, 8, 32
Ten Old Square, London WC2
p945 . . . . . 020 7405 0758

LAUGHTON, Ms Victoria *L Apr 1998*
23, 18
Mitre House Chambers, London WC1
p942 . . . . . 020 7307 7100

LAURENCE, Mr George F MA; BA(Cape Town)(Oxon) *M Nov 1972*
(Q.C.) *1, 8, 2, 88, 26*
New Square Chambers, London WC2
p943 . . . . . 020 7419 8000

Lauterpacht, Sir Elihu MA; LLM(Cantab) *G Nov 1950*
(Q.C.) CBE*33, 41*
20 Essex Street, London WC2
p932 . . . . . 020 7842 1200

Lavender, Mr Nicholas MA(Cantab); BCL(Oxon); ACIArb *I Jul 1989*
(Q.C.) *3, 5, 7, 11, 24, 40, 51*
Serle Court, London WC2
p950 . . . . . 020 7242 6105

Lavers, Mr Michael BA; DipLaw(City) *M Oct 1990*
Charter Chambers, London WC1
p928 . . . . . 020 7618 4400

Lavery, Mr Michael LLB(Hons) *G Feb 1990*
62, 15, 85, 72, 71
Exchange Chambers, Manchester
p983 . . . . . 0161 833 2722
Exchange Chambers, Liverpool
p980 . . . . . 0151 236 7747
Exchange Chambers, Leeds
p977 . . . . . 0113 203 1970

Lavy, Mr Matthew MA(Cantab); PhD(Cantab) *L Jul 2004*
40, 24, 45, 11, 89
4 Pump Court, London EC4
p947 . . . . . 020 7842 5555

Law, Miss Charlotte *M Oct 2005*
30, 18, 94
Kings Chambers, Leeds
p978 . . . . . 0113 242 1123
Kings Chambers, Manchester
p984 . . . . . 0161 832 9082

LAW, Ms Helen LLB(Birm); LLM(Leiden) *G Oct 2005*
15, 51, 1, 55, 33, 70, 71, 72
Matrix Chambers, London WC1
p942 . . . . . 020 7404 3447

Law, Mr John BA(Oxon); DipLaw(City) *L Oct 1996*
12, 15, 22, 25, 30, 40
33 Bedford Row, London WC1
p925 . . . . . 020 7242 6476

Lawler, Mr Joseph Gerard *M Nov 1978*
8, 30, 15
Chambers of J G Lawler, Widnes
p994 . . . . . 0151 424 3246

Lawley, Frances *L Jan 2007*
Zenith Chambers, Leeds
p979 . . . . . 0113 245 5438

Lawrence, Mr Benjamin *L Jan 2003*
St Johns Buildings, Preston
p990 . . . . . 01772 256100
St Johns Buildings, Chester
p974 . . . . . 01244 323070
St Johns Buildings, Manchester
p985 . . . . . 0161 214 1500
St Johns Buildings, Liverpool
p982 . . . . . 0151 243 6000

Lawrence, Dr Heather B D Phil; MA(Oxon) *M Oct 1990*
41, 73, 50, 19, 45, 13, 52, 96
11 South Square, London WC1
p950 . . . . . 020 7405 1222

Lawrence, Mr Nalla LLB(Hons); Deputy District Judge; Immigrations Adjudicator & Special Adjudicator (Part Time); Pupil Master *M May 1987*
10, 12, 18, 20, 22, 23, 25
New Walk Chambers, Leicester
p979 . . . . . 0871 200 1298

LAWRENCE, Mr Nigel *L Jul 1988*
30, 53, 84
7 Harrington Street Chambers, Liverpool
p981 . . . . . 0151 242 0707

Lawrence, Mr Patrick John Tristram BA(Oxon) *I Feb 1985*
(Q.C.)
Four New Square, London WC2
p943 . . . . . 020 7822 2000

Lawrence, Miss Rachel C LLB(Hons)(Lond) *I Nov 1992*
15, 84, 94
Argent Chambers, London WC2
p923 . . . . . 020 7556 5500

LAWRENCE, Miss Soraya *I Jan 1999*
Carmelite Chambers, London EC4
p927 . . . . . 020 7936 6300

LAWRENSON, Ms Sarah *M Oct 2003*
St James's Chambers, Manchester
p984 . . . . . 0161 834 7000
Zenith Chambers, Leeds
p979 . . . . . 0113 245 5438

Lawrie, Mr Ian LLB(Hons); Recorder *G Nov 1985*
(Q.C.) *72, 15, 71, 46*
3PB, London EC4
p946 . . . . . 020 7583 8055

Laws, Miss Eleanor BA(B'ham) *I Oct 1990*
(Q.C.) *15, 51*
Exchange Chambers, Manchester
p983 . . . . . 0161 833 2722
Exchange Chambers, Liverpool
p980 . . . . . 0151 236 7747
Exchange Chambers, Leeds
p977 . . . . . 0113 203 1970
6-8 Mill Street, Maidstone
p982 . . . . . 01622 688094 / 688095
6 Pump Court, London EC4
p947 . . . . . 020 7797 8400

Laws, Mr Simon BA(York) *I Oct 1991*
(Q.C.) *15*
6 King's Bench Walk, London EC4
p939 . . . . . 020 7583 0410
Walnut House Chambers, Exeter
p975 . . . . . 01392 279751

Lawson, Mr Andrew *I Jan 1995*
St Johns Buildings, Preston
p990 . . . . . 01772 256100
St Johns Buildings, Chester
p974 . . . . . 01244 323070
St Johns Buildings, Manchester
p985 . . . . . 0161 214 1500
St Johns Buildings, Liverpool
p982 . . . . . 0151 243 6000

Lawson, Mr Daniel BA(Oxon); MA(Lond) *I Oct 1994*
11, 12, 20, 22, 30
9 Gough Square, London EC4
p935 . . . . . 020 7832 0500

Lawson, Mr David A BA(Hons)(Oxon); LLM(Lond); CPE *M Jul 2000*
76, 18, 85, 51, 1
Hardwicke, London WC2
p936 . . . . . 020 7242 2523

Lawson, Ms Elizabeth A LLB *I Jul 1969*
(Q.C.) *20, 10*
1 Pump Court, London EC4
p947 . . . . . 020 7842 7070

LAWSON, Mr Matthew *G Oct 1995*
Carmelite Chambers, London EC4
p927 . . . . . 020 7936 6300

Lawson, Mr Robert BA(Oxon); DipLaw *I Nov 1989*
(Q.C.) *4, 11, 24, 36, 40*
Quadrant Chambers, London EC4
p948 . . . . . 020 7583 4444

LAWSON, Miss Sara *I Oct 1990*
15, 36, 62, 84
18 Red Lion Court, London EC4
p949 . . . . . 020 7520 6000
18 Red Lion Court (Annexe), Chelmsford
p973 . . . . . 01245 280880

LAWSON-ROGERS, Mr Stuart LLB(Hons) *G Jul 1969*
(Q.C.) *15, 36, 11, 12*
7 Harrington Street Chambers, Liverpool
p981 . . . . . 0151 242 0707

Lawton, Mr Paul LLB(Hons); Recorder *L Nov 1987*
15
Lincoln House Chambers, Manchester
p984 . . . . . 0161 832 5701

Lay, Ms Georgia *L Jan 2007*
30, 12, 47
Queen Square Chambers, Bristol
p972 . . . . . 0117 921 1966

Layne, Mr Ronald *L Jan 1992*
15, 18, 22, 23, 30
12 Old Square, London WC2
p945 . . . . . 020 7404 0875

Layton, Mr Alexander William MA(Oxon) *M Jul 1976*
(Q.C.) *3, 11, 12, 19, 24*
20 Essex Street, London WC2
p932 . . . . . 020 7842 1200

LAZARIDES, Mr Marcus DPhil *M Nov 1999*
10, 20
Queen Elizabeth Buildings, London EC4
p948 . . . . . 020 7797 7837

LAZARUS, Mr Grant P LLB(Cardiff) *G Nov 1981*
10, 12, 16, 20, 22, 24, 26, 30, 53, 40, 88, 94
7 Harrington Street Chambers, Liverpool
p981 . . . . . 0151 242 0707

Lazarus, Ms Mary Helen MA(Cantab) *M Oct 1991*
10, 18, 26, 12, 20
42 Bedford Row, London WC1
p925 . . . . . 020 7831 0222

LAZARUS, Mr Michael MA(Cantab) *M Nov 1987*
2, 5, 11, 24
3 Verulam Buildings, London WC1
p953 . . . . . 020 7831 8441

LAZARUS, Mr Robert MB; ChB; LLB *I Oct 2004*
53, 1, 63, 27, 23, 30, 11, 18, 85
Thirty Nine Essex Street, London WC2
p932 . . . . . 020 7832 1111

Lazur, Mr Thomas BA(Bris); GDL; BUC *I Nov 2005*
7, 11, 24, 40
Keating Chambers, London WC2
p938 . . . . . 020 7544 2600

Le Foe, Ms Sarah *M Nov 1989*
15
1 Inner Temple Lane, London EC4
p937 . . . . . 020 7427 4400

LE POIDEVIN, Mr Nicholas MA; LLB(Cantab) *M Nov 1975*
(Q.C.) *8, 11, 22, 37, 40*
New Square Chambers, London WC2
p943 . . . . . 020 7419 8000

Le Prevost, Mrs Aviva BA(Hons)(Manc); DipLaw *I Nov 1990*
20
Crown Office Row Chambers, Brighton
p970 . . . . . 01273 625625
Westgate Chambers, Lewes
p980 . . . . . 01273 480510

Leabeater, Mr James BA(Oxon) *L Oct 1999*
11, 12, 40
4 Pump Court, London EC4
p947 . . . . . 020 7842 5555

Leach, Mr Alexander *I Dec 2001*
Lincoln House Chambers, Manchester
p984 . . . . . 0161 832 5701

Leach, Mr Douglas *I Jan 2003*
18, 55
Queen Square Chambers, Bristol
p972 . . . . . 0117 921 1966

Leach, Ms Natasha *L Jan 2000*
St Johns Buildings, Preston
p990 . . . . . 01772 256100
St Johns Buildings, Chester
p974 . . . . . 01244 323070
St Johns Buildings, Manchester
p985 . . . . . 0161 214 1500
St Johns Buildings, Liverpool
p982 . . . . . 0151 243 6000

Leach, Mr Robin Anthony Langley MA(St Andrews) *L Jul 1979*
72, 15
3PB, Bournemouth
p969 . . . . . 01202 292102

LEACH, Mr Stuart *G Jun 2004*
12, 15, 20, 42, 91
Pump Court Chambers, Swindon
p993 . . . . . 01793 539899
Pump Court Chambers, Winchester
p994 . . . . . 01962 868161
Pump Court Chambers, London EC4
p947 . . . . . 020 7353 0711

LEADER, Miss Lucy LLB(Hons) *L Oct 2002*
20, 12, 18, 6, 10, 67, 55, 22, 38, 88, 30, 32, 36, 37
Angel Chambers, Swansea
p992 . . . . . 01792 464623

Leader, Mr Timothy James BSc(Hons); MA; MRTPI *M Oct 1994*
12, 26, 31, 46
Clerksroom - Administration Centre, Taunton
p993 . . . . . 0845 083 3000

Leafe, Mr Daniel LLB(Hons) *G Jul 1996*
20
Albion Chambers, Bristol
p970 . . . . . 0117 927 2144

LEAHY, Miss Blair BA(York); MA(Essex) *I Jun 2001*
6, 11, 5, 8, 97, 38, 40
South Square, London WC1
p950 . . . . . 020 7696 9900

LEAKE, Laban *M Oct 1996*
Furnival Chambers, London EC4
p934 . . . . . 020 7405 3232

LEAKE, Mr Stephen *M Jan 2002*
Carmelite Chambers, London EC4
p927 . . . . . 020 7936 6300

LEAN, Ms Jacqueline *G Jul 2007*
1, 46, 31, 93
Landmark Chambers, London EC4
p941 . . . . . 020 7430 1221

LEAR, Miss Estelle Christine LLB(Hons) *L Jul 2006*
10, 20
Tanfield Chambers, London WC1
p951 . . . . . 020 7421 5300

LEARMONTH, Mr Alexander Robert Magnus BA(Oxon)(Jurisprudence) *L Oct 2000*
11, 8, 37
New Square Chambers, London WC2
p943 . . . . . 020 7419 8000

Leaver, Mr Peter *L Jul 1967*
(Q.C.)
One Essex Court, London EC4
p931 . . . . . 020 7583 2000

13

Leavesley, Miss Laura Mariel LLB(Hons) *I Jul 2005*
12, 67, 15, 18, 80, 20, 88, 30, 37
Angel Chambers, Swansea
p992 . . . . . 01792 464623

Leckie, Mr James Harry Laird MA; LLM; FCIArb *G Jul 1964*
2, 3, 7, 4, 12, 5, 6, 8, 9, 11, 14, 18, 21, 24, 29, 31, 32, 37, 40, 46, 49, 62, 66, 67, 88, 89, 96
Westleigh Chambers, Langport
p977 . . . . . 01458 251261

Leckie, James Harry Laird *G Jan 1964*
41
Clerksroom - Administration Centre, Taunton
p993 . . . . . 0845 083 3000

LeCointe, Ms Elpha LLB *L Nov 1988*
10, 20
Coram Chambers, London EC1
p929 . . . . . 020 7092 3700

LEDDEN, Mr Thomas *G Nov 2009*
15, 12
Wilberforce Chambers, Hull
p976 . . . . . 01482 323264

LEDERMAN, Mr David *I Jan 1966*
(Q.C.) *12, 15, 25, 36*
Carmelite Chambers, London EC4
p927 . . . . . 020 7936 6300

Lederman, Mr Howard BA(Hons)(Oxon) *G Jul 1982*
8, 22, 40, 12, 30
42 Bedford Row, London WC1
p925 . . . . . 020 7831 0222

LEDGISTER, Mr Roy LLB *I Nov 2005*
15
25 Bedford Row, London WC1
p925 . . . . . 020 7067 1500

Ledward, Ms Jocelyn *M Jan 1999*
15, 25
QEB Hollis Whiteman, London EC4
p948 . . . . . 020 7933 8855

LEE, Annabel *M Jan 2010*
4-5 Gray's Inn Square, London WC1
p935 . . . . . 020 7404 5252

Lee, Mr David C BA(Hons)(Cantab); AB(Harv) *G Jul 1973*
12, 15, 20, 30, 26, 31
36 Bedford Row, London WC1
p925 . . . . . 020 7421 8000

LEE, Gordon *M Jan 1998*
15, 23, 18, 12
Mitre House Chambers, London WC1
p942 . . . . . 020 7307 7100

Lee, Mr Ian LLM G *Jul 1973*
11, 12, 18, 27, 30, 36, 24, 40, 26, 53, 55
Devereux Chambers, London WC2
p930 . . . 020 7353 7534

LEE, Ms Jennifer L *Jan 2007*
10, 12, 72, 18, 20, 91, 42, 30, 32, 36
Pump Court Chambers, Swindon
p993 . . . 01793 539899
Pump Court Chambers, Winchester
p994 . . . 01962 868161
Pump Court Chambers, London EC4
p947 . . . 020 7353 0711

LEE, Miss Jessica BA(Hons)(Lond); MP M *Oct 2000*
10, 20
St Mary's Chambers, Nottingham
p989 . . . 0115 950 3503

Lee, Mr Jonathan James Wilton BEng(Sheff) G *Oct 1993*
3, 7, 11, 24, 40
Keating Chambers, London WC2
p938 . . . 020 7544 2600

Lee, Miss Krista MA; BSc(Hons); BCL L *Nov 1996*
7, 11, 24, 40
Keating Chambers, London WC2
p938 . . . 020 7544 2600

LEE, Mr Michael L *Jan 2009*
18, 76, 51, 1
11KBW, London EC4
p938 . . . 020 7632 8500
4 Breams Buildings, London EC4
p927 . . . 020 7092 1900

LEE, Miss Rebecca L *Oct 2005*
15, 62, 95
187 Fleet Street, London EC4
p933 . . . 020 7430 7430

Lee, Ms Rosslyn G *Nov 1987*
York Chambers, York
p995 . . . 01904 620048
York Chambers, Newcastle upon Tyne
p987 . . . 0191 206 4677

Lee, Miss Sarah BA(Oxon); BCL M *Nov 1990*
11, 44, 1, 24, 19
Brick Court Chambers, London WC2
p927 . . . 020 7379 3550

Lee, Miss Sarah Jane LLB L *Jan 2002*
15, 12, 20
15 Winckley Square, Preston
p991 . . . 01772 252828

Lee, Miss Taryn J I *Jul 1992*
10, 20
37 Park Square Chambers, Leeds
p978 . . . 0113 243 9422

LEECH, Mr Benedict BA; DipLaw I *Jan 1997*
30, 40, 53
12 King's Bench Walk, London EC4
p940 . . . 020 7583 0811

Leech, Mr Geoffrey Anthony BSc(Hons); DIS; CPE L *Nov 1992*
12, 18, 20, 30, 40, 45, 47, 49, 51, 55
Advolex Chambers, Croydon
p975 . . . 0871 717 7321

LEECH, Mr Stewart MA(Oxon) L *Oct 1992*
(Q.C.) *12, 20*
Queen Elizabeth Buildings, London EC4
p948 . . . 020 7797 7837

Leech, Mr Thomas Alexander Crispin BA; BCL(Oxon); Accredited Mediator M *Nov 1988*
(Q.C.) *1, 3, 5, 6, 7, 8, 9, 11, 12, 13, 14, 22, 24, 26, 28, 29, 31, 32, 37*
Maitland Chambers, London WC2
p941 . . . 020 7406 1200

LEEMING, Miss Lucinda BA(Hons) M *Jan 1999*
15
9 St John Street Chambers, Manchester
p984 . . . 0161 955 9000

LEEMING, Mr Michael LLB; Recorder I *Jul 1983*
15
9 St John Street Chambers, Manchester
p984 . . . 0161 955 9000

Leene, Miss Sharon LLB G *Oct 1996*
15
St Johns Buildings, Preston
p990 . . . 01772 256100
St Johns Buildings, Chester
p974 . . . 01244 323070
St Johns Buildings, Manchester
p985 . . . 0161 214 1500
St Johns Buildings, Liverpool
p982 . . . 0151 243 6000

Leeper, Mr Thomas R G M *Nov 1991*
Outer Temple Chambers, London WC2
p945 . . . 020 7353 6381
St John's Chambers, Bristol
p972 . . . 0117 921 3456

Lees, Miss Charlotte LLB(Hons); LLM(Hons) L *Nov 2001*
15, 20, 10, 70
12 College Place, Southampton
p992 . . . 023 8032 0320

LEES, Miss Elisabeth L *Oct 2002*
15, 13
23 Essex Street, London WC2
p932 . . . 020 7413 0353

LEES, Mr Kester BCL; LLB(Hons); BA(Hons) I *Jan 2010*
38, 40, 88, 93
Falcon Chambers, London EC4
p933 . . . 020 7353 2484

LEGALLAIS, Mr James M *Oct 2005*
6, 11, 47
Five Paper, London EC4
p946 . . . 020 7815 3200

Legard, Mr Edward G *Oct 1996*
York Chambers, York
p995 . . . 01904 620048
York Chambers, Newcastle upon Tyne
p987 . . . 0191 206 4677

Leggatt, Mr George MA(Cantab) M *Jul 1983*
(Q.C.) *11, 35, 5, 24, 40, 41*
Brick Court Chambers, London WC2
p927 . . . 020 7379 3550

Legge, Mr Henry BA(Oxon) M *Nov 1993*
8, 14, 29, 32, 37, 40
5 Stone Buildings, London WC2
p951 . . . 020 7242 6201

LeGrice, Mr Valentine M *Jan 1977*
(Q.C.)
1 Hare Court, London EC4
p936 . . . 020 7797 7070

Leigh, Mr Kevin LLB(Hons) L *Nov 1986*
8, 11, 1, 31, 46, 51, 67, 25, 93, 96, 49
6-8 Mill Street, Maidstone
p982 . . . 01622 688094 / 688095
No5 Chambers, Bristol
p971 . . . 0845 210 5555
No5 Chambers, London EC4
p944 . . . 0845 210 5555
No5 Chambers, Birmingham
p968 . . . 0845 210 5555
6 Pump Court, London EC4
p947 . . . 020 7797 8400

Leigh, Prof Leonard I *May 1993*
2 Pump Court, London EC4
p947 . . . 020 7353 5597

LEIGH, Ms Samantha BA(Hons) I *Nov 1995*
15, 62
18 Red Lion Court, London EC4
p949 . . . 020 7520 6000
18 Red Lion Court (Annexe), Chelmsford
p973 . . . 01245 280880

Leigh, Miss Sarah I *Jan 1984*
20
Cobden House Chambers, Manchester
p983 . . . 0161 833 6000

LEIGHTON, Peter I *Jan 1966*
4 King's Bench Walk, London EC4
p939 . . . 020 7822 7000

LEIGHTON WILLIAMS, Mr John MA; LLB; Dep. High Court Judge; Recorder G *Apr 1964*
(Q.C.) *30, 53, 12*
Farrar's Building, London EC4
p933 . . . 020 7583 9241

LEIPER, Mr Richard LLB; M Jur G *Oct 1996*
1, 11, 18, 19, 26, 51, 55
11KBW, London EC4
p938 . . . 020 7632 8500

Leist, Mr Ian I *Jul 1981*
15, 62, 36, 1
2 Hare Court, London EC4
p937 . . . 020 7353 5324

LEIVESLEY, Miss Julie LLM L *Nov 2000*
10, 20, 51, 23
Five Paper, London EC4
p946 . . . 020 7815 3200

Lemer, Mr Saul G *Jan 2007*
One Essex Court, London EC4
p931 . . . 020 7583 2000

LEMMY, Mr Michael LLB(Hons) M *Jan 1994*
11, 22, 30, 53
9 St John Street Chambers, Manchester
p984 . . . 0161 955 9000

Lemon, Ms Jane Katherine BA(Oxon) I *Nov 1993*
3, 7, 11, 24, 40
Keating Chambers, London WC2
p938 . . . 020 7544 2600

Lemos, Ms Marika MA(Hons) M *Oct 2002*
Gray's Inn Tax Chambers, London WC1
p936 . . . 020 7242 2642

LENEHAN, Miss Emma G *Jan 2006*
10, 20, 93
Cornwall Street Chambers, Birmingham
p967 . . . 0121 233 7500

Lennard, Mr Stephen LLB G *Jul 1976*
18, 40, 11, 93
Hardwicke, London WC2
p936 . . . 020 7242 2523

LENNON, Mr Desmond Joseph BA G *Nov 1986*
15
7 Harrington Street Chambers, Liverpool
p981 . . . 0151 242 0707

LENNON, Mr Jonathan BA(Hons) L *Mar 1997*
15, 72, 70, 62
23 Essex Street, London WC2
p932 . . . 020 7413 0353

Lennon, Miss Karen I *Jan 2003*
York Chambers, York
p995 . . . 01904 620048
York Chambers, Newcastle upon Tyne
p987 . . . 0191 206 4677

Lenon, Mr Andrew L *Nov 1982*
(Q.C.)
One Essex Court, London EC4
p931 . . . 020 7583 2000

Leonard, Mr Anthony I *Jul 1978*
(Q.C.) *15, 62*
6 King's Bench Walk, London EC4
p939 . . . 020 7583 0410

Leonard, Miss Claire I *Jan 2009*
St John's Chambers, Bristol
p972 . . . 0117 921 3456

Leonard, Mrs Edna BSc G *Oct 1992*
15
KCH Garden Square Chambers, Nottingham
p989 . . . 0115 941 8851
KCH Garden Square Chambers, Leicester
p979 . . . 0115 941 8851

Leonard, Mr James BA(Hons) I *Jan 1989*
15, 81, 62, 36
Outer Temple Chambers, London WC2
p945 . . . 020 7353 6381

Leonard, Ms Patricia BCL; BVC L *Jan 2007*
30, 53, 68, 67, 11, 15, 18
7 Bedford Row, London WC1
p924 . . . 020 7242 3555

Leonard, Mr Robert BA(Dublin) I *Jul 1976*
30, 88, 11, 20, 40, 93, 37
Hardwicke, London WC2
p936 . . . 020 7242 2523

Leong, Mr Andrew LLB(Bris) M *Oct 1998*
20, 10
Harcourt Chambers, London EC4
p936 . . . 0844 561 7135
Harcourt Chambers, Oxford
p989 . . . 0844 561 7135

Leong, Ms Jacqueline QC (Hong Kong) I *Jul 1970*
1 Hare Court, London EC4
p936 . . . 020 7797 7070

Leong, Mr Simon M *Jan 2001*
15
New Bailey Chambers, Preston
p990 . . . 01772 258087

Lerego, Mr Michael MA; BCL(Oxon) I *Jul 1972*
(Q.C.)
Fountain Court Chambers, London EC4
p934 . . . 020 7583 3335

Leslie, Miss Clare BA(Oxon) M *Jan 2002*
15, 63, 70, 62, 84
Lamb Building, Brighton
p970 . . . 01273 820490
Lamb Building, London EC4
p940 . . . 020 7797 7788

Leslie, Mr James LLB M *Jan 2004*
15, 12, 20, 30
No5 Chambers, Bristol
p971 . . . 0845 210 5555
No5 Chambers, London EC4
p944 . . . 0845 210 5555
No5 Chambers, Birmingham
p968 . . . 0845 210 5555

Leslie, Miss Marie BA(Hons) I *Jan 2000*
10, 20
Albion Chambers, Bristol
p970 . . . 0117 927 2144

Leslie, Mr Stephen W L *Feb 1971*
(Q.C.) *15*
Cobden House Chambers, Manchester
p983 . . . 0161 833 6000
Furnival Chambers, London EC4
p934 . . . 020 7405 3232

LESTER, Miss Maya BA(Cantab); MA L *Nov 2000*
11, 19, 1, 51, 44
Brick Court Chambers, London WC2
p927 . . . 020 7379 3550

Lester of Herne Hill, Lord Anthony BA(Cantab); LLM(Harv) L *Feb 1963*
(Q.C.) *1, 11, 18, 26, 28, 36, 19, 51, 55, 89*
Blackstone Chambers, London EC4
p926 . . . 020 7583 1770

LETMAN, Mr Paul BSc M *Jul 1987*
7, 8, 11, 12, 22
3 Hare Court, London EC4
p937 . . . 020 7415 7800

Lett, Mr Brian Recorder I *Nov 1971*
(Q.C.) *15, 62*
Argent Chambers, London WC2
p923 . . . 020 7556 5500

Levene, Mr Anthony M *Jul 1993*
Holborn Chambers, London WC2
p937 . . . 020 7242 6060

LEVENE, Miss Rachael G *Oct 2006*
9 St John Street Chambers, Manchester
p984 . . . 0161 955 9000

LEVENE, Mr Simon MA(Cantab); Recorder M *Jul 1977*
30, 53, 42, 32
12 King's Bench Walk, London EC4
p940 . . . 020 7583 0811

LEVER, Sir Jeremy MA(Oxon) G *Nov 1957*
(Q.C.) *1, 19, 44, 61, 57*
Monckton Chambers, London WC1
p942 . . . 020 7405 7211

Levett, Miss Francesca L *Oct 1997*
15, 12, 30, 62
5 St Andrew's Hill, London EC4
p950 . . . 020 7332 5400

LEVETT, Mr Martyn BSc M *Nov 1978*
15, 82, 25, 84
18 Red Lion Court, London EC4
p949 . . . 020 7520 6000
18 Red Lion Court (Annexe), Chelmsford
p973 . . . 01245 280880

Levey, Mr Edward MA(Cantab); BCL(Oxon) I *Nov 1999*
Fountain Court Chambers, London EC4
p934 . . . 020 7583 3335

Levinson, Miss Jemma G *Oct 2001*
1 Mitre Court Buildings, London EC4
p942 . . . 020 7452 8900

LEVINSON, Mr Justin LLB(Hons) M *Oct 1994*
30, 53, 40, 26, 56, 22
1 Crown Office Row, London EC4
p929 . . . 020 7797 7500

Leviseur, Mr Nicholas T MA(Oxon) G *Nov 1979*
5, 8, 11, 13, 16, 20, 22, 24, 29, 30
3PB, London EC4
p946 . . . 020 7583 8055

Levy, Mr Jacob I *Jul 1986*
30, 40, 53
9 Gough Square, London EC4
p935 . . . 020 7832 0500

Levy, Mr Michael LLB(Hons) G *Nov 1979*
15, 62
2 Bedford Row, London WC1
p924 . . . 020 7440 8888

See p1010 for the Key to Work Categories

LEVY, Mr Neil LLB(Exon) L *Nov 1986*
5, 11, 38, 6, 40
Guildhall Chambers, Bristol
p970 . . . . . 0117 930 9000

Levy, Mr Robert M *Jan 2003*
(Q.C.) *8, 11, 97, 38, 21, 93, 79*
Queen Square Chambers, Bristol
p972 . . . . . 0117 921 1966
New Square Chambers, London WC2
p943 . . . . . 020 7419 8000

LEWERS, Mr Nigel MA(Oxon) G *Nov 1986*
30, 40, 53
12 King's Bench Walk, London EC4
p940 . . . . . 020 7583 0811

Lewin, Mr Nicholas BA G *Jul 1989*
King's Bench Godolphin Chambers, Truro
p994 . . . . . 0845 308 1551
King's Bench Godolphin Chambers, Plymouth
p990 . . . . . 0845 308 1551

Lewington, Miss Francesca MA(Hons)(Jurisprudence) I *Jan 2001*
15, 88, 26, 25, 68, 85
Crown Office Row Chambers, Brighton
p970 . . . . . 01273 625625

Lewis, Mr Adam MA(Cantab) G *Jul 1985*
(Q.C.) *1, 8, 11, 16, 19, 56, 51, 44, 89*
Blackstone Chambers, London EC4
p926 . . . . . 020 7583 1770

Lewis, Miss Alex BA M *Nov 1990*
15, 62
2 Hare Court, London EC4
p937 . . . . . 020 7353 5324

Lewis, Mr Andrew BA(Oxon) M *Nov 1986*
15, 12, 30
4 Breams Buildings, London EC4
p927 . . . . . 020 7092 1900
Byrom Street Chambers, Manchester
p983 . . . . . 0161 829 2100

Lewis, Mr Christopher David BA(Oxon); BCL M *Nov 1998*
3, 7, 11, 31, 40, 41, 43, 45, 49, 54, 61, 78, 74
Atkin Chambers, London WC1
p923 . . . . . 020 7404 0102

LEWIS, Mr Clive MA(Cantab); LLM(Dalhousie); Recorder; First junior counsel to the national assembly of Wales M *Nov 1987*
(Q.C.) *1, 19, 51, 26, 55, 61*
11KBW, London EC4
p938 . . . . . 020 7632 8500

LEWIS, Mr Daniel BA M *Jan 2003*
59, 11, 12, 30, 22
3 Hare Court, London EC4
p937 . . . . . 020 7415 7800

Lewis, Miss Danielle Soraya LLB(Hons) L *Nov 1995*
10, 20
Coram Chambers, London EC1
p929 . . . . . 020 7092 3700

Lewis, Mr Darren Eurwyn LLB(Hons) I *Oct 2004*
30, 18
St John's Chambers, Bristol
p972 . . . . . 0117 921 3456

Lewis, Mr David LLB L *Jan 1997*
30, 49, 11, 74, 18, 24
Hardwicke, London WC2
p936 . . . . . 020 7242 2523
20 Essex Street, London WC2
p932 . . . . . 020 7842 1200

Lewis, Mr Dominic I *Jul 2000*
15, 48, 13, 25
5 Paper Buildings, London EC4
p946 . . . . . 020 7583 6117

Lewis, Mr Edward T G Prosecuting Counsel to DHSS G *Jul 1972*
15, 16, 25
4 Breams Buildings, London EC4
p927 . . . . . 020 7092 1900

LEWIS, Mr Gwion G *Apr 2005*
1, 46, 31, 36, 51
Landmark Chambers, London EC4
p941 . . . . . 020 7430 1221

LEWIS, Mr Jeremy BA(Oxon); BCL L *May 1992*
1, 6, 8, 22, 11, 12, 18, 19, 40
Littleton Chambers, London EC4
p941 . . . . . 020 7797 8600

Lewis, Ms Joanna M *Jan 2004*
30, 53, 48, 68
Queen Square Chambers, Bristol
p972 . . . . . 0117 921 1966

Lewis, Mr Jonathan MA(Jurisprudence)(Oxon) M *Jan 2007*
Henderson Chambers, London EC4
p937 . . . . . 020 7583 9020

Lewis, Mr Jonathan M LLB(Hons)(Manc) I *Mar 1996*
6, 89, 74, 38, 40, 11, 97
4 Pump Court, London EC4
p947 . . . . . 020 7842 5555

LEWIS, Katherine I *Jan 2009*
Maidstone Chambers, Maidstone
p982 . . . . . 01622 688592

Lewis, Miss Marian LLB(Hons) M *Nov 1977*
15, 12, 62
Thirty Park Place, Cardiff
p973 . . . . . 029 2039 8421

LEWIS, Mr Max BA(Hons) G *Jan 2002*
10, 20
29 Bedford Row, London WC1
p925 . . . . . 020 7404 1044

Lewis, Mr Meyric BA(Bris) G *Nov 1986*
1, 46, 51, 26, 31, 36, 60
Francis Taylor Building, London EC4
p934 . . . . . 020 7353 8415

Lewis, Mr Owen P LLB(Wales); LLM(Cantab) M *Jul 1985*
12, 30, 22, 20, 15, 18, 53
9 Park Place, Cardiff
p973 . . . . . 029 2038 2731

Lewis, Paul BA(Leeds) M *Jul 2007*
10, 20, 18
St John's Chambers, Bristol
p972 . . . . . 0117 921 3456

LEWIS, Mr Paul Keith LLB(Hons)(Leics) G *Feb 1981*
(Q.C.) *15, 84, 56*
Farrar's Building, London EC4
p933 . . . . . 020 7583 9241
Thirty Park Place, Cardiff
p973 . . . . . 029 2039 8421

LEWIS, Ms Rachael M *Nov 2006*
9 St John Street Chambers, Manchester
p984 . . . . . 0161 955 9000

LEWIS, Mr Raymond M *Jul 1971*
Furnival Chambers, London EC4
p934 . . . . . 020 7405 3232

Lewis, Mr Robert MA; BCL(Oxon) G *Nov 1996*
1, 18, 22, 25, 26, 30, 31, 36, 46, 48, 51, 55, 61
Radcliffe Chambers, London WC2
p949 . . . . . 020 7831 0081

LEWIS, Mr Robin Arwel I *Nov 1991*
20, 12, 15
St Philips Chambers, Birmingham
p969 . . . . . 0121 246 7000

Lewis, Prof Roy LLB; MSc(Lond); Employment Tribunal Part-Time Chairman L *May 1992*
18, 55, 41, 49, 51, 35, 26
Old Square Chambers, Bristol
p971 . . . . . 0117 930 5100
Old Square Chambers, London WC1
p945 . . . . . 020 7269 0300

LEWIS, Miss Sara MA(Hons) L *Jan 1996*
9 St John Street Chambers, Manchester
p984 . . . . . 0161 955 9000

LEWIS, Sara I *Jan 2007*
8, 11, 12, 22
Tanfield Chambers, London WC1
p951 . . . . . 020 7421 5300

LEWIS, Miss Sarah MA(TCD) M *Jul 2006*
15, 91, 62, 68, 94
18 Red Lion Court, London EC4
p949 . . . . . 020 7520 6000
18 Red Lion Court (Annexe), Chelmsford
p973 . . . . . 01245 280880

Lewis, Miss Sarah Louise M *Nov 1995*
10, 20, 18
4 Paper Buildings, London EC4
p946 . . . . . 020 7583 0816

Lewison, Mr Josh L *Jan 2005*
Radcliffe Chambers, London WC2
p949 . . . . . 020 7831 0081

LEWSLEY, Mr Christopher BSc; PhD; CEng; MI Struct E L *Jul 1976*
31, 36, 46
Landmark Chambers, London EC4
p941 . . . . . 020 7430 1221

LEWTHWAITE, Ms Joanne LLB(Hons) I *Oct 1990*
15
Oriel Chambers, Liverpool
p981 . . . . . 0151 236 7191 / 236 4321
Oriel Chambers, Preston
p990 . . . . . 01772 254764

LEY, Mr N Spencer MA(Cantab) M *Jul 1985*
30, 53, 12
Farrar's Building, London EC4
p933 . . . . . 020 7583 9241

Ley-Morgan, Mr Mark John BSc; LLB(Lond) G *Nov 1994*
12, 30, 40, 18, 53, 68, 85, 27
3 Serjeants' Inn, London EC4
p950 . . . . . 020 7427 5000

Lickley, Mr Nigel J D LLB(Lond); Recorder; Leader of Western Circuit (2010) G *Jul 1983*
(Q.C.) *12, 15, 30, 31*
3PB, Winchester
p994 . . . . . 01962 868884

Lidbury, Mr David I *Oct 2006*
10, 20, 22, 23
Southernhay Chambers, Exeter
p975 . . . . . 01392 255777

Liddell, Mr Richard M *Nov 1999*
8, 12, 24, 40
Four New Square, London WC2
p943 . . . . . 020 7822 2000

LIDDIARD, Mr Martin I *Jan 1989*
Carmelite Chambers, London EC4
p927 . . . . . 020 7936 6300
No5 Chambers, Bristol
p971 . . . . . 0845 210 5555
No5 Chambers, London EC4
p944 . . . . . 0845 210 5555
No5 Chambers, Birmingham
p968 . . . . . 0845 210 5555

LIEBERMAN, Gemma M *Jan 2007*
Kings Chambers, Leeds
p978 . . . . . 0113 242 1123
Kings Chambers, Manchester
p984 . . . . . 0161 832 9082

LIEBRECHT, Mr Michael BA(Oxon); LLM(Cantab) I *Nov 1989*
20
1 Garden Court, London EC4
p934 . . . . . 020 7797 7900

LIEVEN, Ms Nathalie BA(Cantab) G *Jul 1989*
(Q.C.) *1, 31, 36, 26, 46*
Landmark Chambers, London EC4
p941 . . . . . 020 7430 1221

Light, Prof Roy G *Oct 1992*
15, 25, 1
St John's Chambers, Bristol
p972 . . . . . 0117 921 3456

Lightfoot, Mr Jeremy BA(Hons)(Oxon) L *Jul 2006*
41, 5, 6, 8, 11, 97, 67, 24, 89, 96, 35, 60
Stone Chambers, London WC1
p951 . . . . . 020 7440 6900

Lightman, Mr Daniel BA(Oxon) L *Oct 1995*
6, 8, 11, 32, 40, 37, 38, 97
Serle Court, London WC2
p950 . . . . . 020 7242 6105

Lightwing, Mr Stuart LLB; MBA; FCIS; MCMI; FRSA:FCIArb M *Jul 1972*
18, 30, 20, 40
Counsels Chambers, Yarm
p994 . . . . . 01642 650550

Lillington, Mr Simon BA(Hons)(Law)(Anglia Ruskin); LLM(Lond) M *Nov 1980*
8, 20, 96
College Chambers, Southampton
p992 . . . . . 023 8023 0338
Renaissance Chambers, London WC1
p949 . . . . . 020 7404 1111

LILLY, Mr Donald BA(Oxon); BCL M *Jan 2006*
6, 11, 97, 62, 38
4 Stone Buildings, London WC2
p951 . . . . . 020 7242 5524

Limb, Mr Christopher LLB(Hons) G *Jul 1975*
18 St John Street Chambers, Manchester
p985 . . . . . 0161 278 1800

LIMB, Mr Patrick M *Jul 1987*
(Q.C.) *30, 40, 53*
Ropewalk Chambers, Nottingham
p989 . . . . . 0115 947 2581

Limbrey, Mr Bernard Martin MSc(City) M *Nov 1980*
12, 20, 32, 47
3 Dr Johnson's Buildings, London EC4
p930 . . . . . 020 7353 4854

Lin, Miss Esther MA(Oxon) M *Jan 2002*
5, 6, 8, 11, 22, 29, 40, 36, 24
Exchange Chambers, Manchester
p983 . . . . . 0161 833 2722
Exchange Chambers, Liverpool
p980 . . . . . 0151 236 7747
Exchange Chambers, Leeds
p977 . . . . . 0113 203 1970

Lince, Miss Elizabeth LLB(Hons) M *Jul 2007*
10, 20, 30, 12
Chartlands Chambers, Northampton
p988 . . . . . 01604 603322

LINDEN, Mr Thomas BA(Jurisprudence); BCL(Oxon) G *Nov 1989*
(Q.C.) *18, 26, 36, 55, 51, 1, 12, 56, 50, 11, 29*
Matrix Chambers, London WC1
p942 . . . . . 020 7404 3447

Lindesay, Ms Elizabeth G *Jan 2009*
41, 24, 35, 61, 40, 21, 11
7 King's Bench Walk, London EC4
p940 . . . . . 020 7910 8300

Lindfield, Miss Gemma I *Oct 2002*
15, 71
7 Bedford Row, London WC1
p924 . . . . . 020 7242 3555

Lindop, Ms Sarah G *Nov 1989*
15
1 Inner Temple Lane, London EC4
p937 . . . . . 020 7427 4400
Westgate Chambers, Lewes
p980 . . . . . 01273 480510

LINDQVIST, Mr Andrew M *Nov 1968*
6, 8, 12, 18, 20, 22, 26, 30
Octagon House, Norwich
p988 . . . . . 01603 623186

LINDSAY, Mr Alistair David MA(Cantab); PhD(Cantab) I *Nov 1993*
44, 11
Monckton Chambers, London WC1
p942 . . . . . 020 7405 7211

LINDSAY, Mr Fraser M *Jul 2006*
15, 12, 26
7 Harrington Street Chambers, Liverpool
p981 . . . . . 0151 242 0707

Lindsay, Mr Jeremy M H LLB(Hons) G *Jul 1986*
15, 36
37 Park Square Chambers, Leeds
p978 . . . . . 0113 243 9422

LINDSAY STRUGO, Ms Andrea BA I *Jan 2003*
1, 53, 12, 46, 47, 18, 19, 51, 23, 27, 30, 31, 40, 55, 36
1 Crown Office Row, London EC4
p929 . . . . . 020 7797 7500

Lindsey, Miss Amy M *Jan 2001*
12, 10, 20, 15, 53, 30
Regency Chambers, Peterborough
p990 . . . . . 01733 315215

LINDSEY, Miss Susan BSc; DipArch; MSc I *Nov 1997*
74, 7, 3, 41, 40, 11
Crown Office Chambers, London EC4
p929 . . . . . 020 7797 8100

Line, Alex G *Jan 2009*
3PB, London EC4
p946 . . . . . 020 7583 8055

LINEHAN, Mr Stephen Recorder L *Jan 1970*
(Q.C.) *15, 62, 82, 83, 72, 70*
St Philips Chambers, Birmingham
p969 . . . . . 0121 246 7000

Ling, Ms Naomi BA(Oxon) M *Mar 2002*
18, 30, 8, 92
Outer Temple Chambers, London WC2
p945 . . . . . 020 7353 6381

Linklater, Ms Lisa I *Oct 1995*
5, 6, 11, 29, 40, 8, 38, 97
Exchange Chambers, Manchester
p983 . . . . . 0161 833 2722
Exchange Chambers, Liverpool
p980 . . . . . 0151 236 7747
Exchange Chambers, Leeds
p977 . . . . . 0113 203 1970

LINNEMANN, Mr Bernard BA(Dublin) G *Jan 1980*
15
St Philips Chambers, Birmingham
p969 . . . . . 0121 246 7000

LINSTEAD, Mr Peter James MA(Oxon) G *Oct 1994*
11, 12, 18, 30, 55, 36
Tanfield Chambers, London WC1
p951 . . . . . 020 7421 5300

Lintott, Mr David J G *Oct 1996*
1, 12, 15, 18, 22, 26, 31, 36
Cornerstone Barristers, London WC1
p929 . . . . . 020 7242 4986

Lippiatt, Mr Huw G *Mar 2010*
York Chambers, York
p995 . . . . . 01904 620048
York Chambers, Newcastle upon Tyne
p987 . . . . . 0191 206 4677

Lippold, Mrs Sarah I *Nov 1999*
King's Bench Chambers, Oxford
p989 . . . . . 01865 311066
13 King's Bench Walk, London EC4
p940 . . . . . 020 7353 7204

Lissack, Mr Richard A I *Nov 1978*
(Q.C.) *30, 53, 40, 15, 26, 13, 81, 62, 56*
Outer Temple Chambers, London WC2
p945 . . . . . 020 7353 6381

LISTER, Miss Caroline BSc(Lond) M *Nov 1980*
10, 12, 20
1 King's Bench Walk, London EC4
p938 . . . . . 020 7936 1500

LISTER, Mr Daniel I *Jan 2009*
23 Essex Street, London WC2
p932 . . . . . 020 7413 0353

Lithman, Mr Nigel BA; LLB(Hons); Recorder I *Nov 1976*
(Q.C.) *15, 62, 36*
2 Bedford Row, London WC1
p924 . . . . . 020 7440 8888

Little, Ms Helen LLB(Lancs)(ELS) L *Oct 1999*
20, 10
Harcourt Chambers, London EC4
p936 . . . . . 0844 561 7135
Harcourt Chambers, Oxford
p989 . . . . . 0844 561 7135

LITTLE, Mr Ian BA(Oxon); DipLaw(City) M *Feb 1989*
18, 30, 36
9 St John Street Chambers, Manchester
p984 . . . . . 0161 955 9000

Little, Mr Richard John MA(Oxon) I *Jul 2000*
20
42 Bedford Row, London WC1
p925 . . . . . 020 7831 0222

Little, Mr Tom M *Oct 1997*
65, 81, 39, 38, 84, 62, 15, 70, 30
9 Gough Square, London EC4
p935 . . . . . 020 7832 0500

LITTLER, Miss Anna L *Jan 2008*
New Square Chambers, London WC2
p943 . . . . . 020 7419 8000

Littler, Mr Martin LLB(Hons) G *Nov 1989*
1, 7, 12, 22, 27, 30, 40, 53
Cobden House Chambers, Manchester
p983 . . . . . 0161 833 6000

Littler, Mr Richard LLB(Hons) G *May 1994*
15
Exchange Chambers, Manchester
p983 . . . . . 0161 833 2722
Exchange Chambers, Liverpool
p980 . . . . . 0151 236 7747
Exchange Chambers, Leeds
p977 . . . . . 0113 203 1970

Littlewood, Ms Rebecca M LLB(Soton) I *Nov 1988*
10, 12, 20
1 Pump Court, London EC4
p947 . . . . . 020 7842 7070

Littlewood, Mr Robert BA(Hons); DipLaw I *Oct 1993*
10, 20, 14
4 Paper Buildings, London EC4
p946 . . . . . 020 7583 0816

Littman, Mr Jeffrey James MA(Cantab) M *Jul 1974*
8, 11
9 Park Place, Cardiff
p973 . . . . . 029 2038 2731

LITTON, Mr John LLB(Soton) M *Jul 1989*
(Q.C.) *1, 21, 31, 33, 36, 46, 93*
Landmark Chambers, London EC4
p941 . . . . . 020 7430 1221

Livesey, Mr John W A LLB(Bris) L *Nov 1990*
18, 30, 31
Albion Chambers, Bristol
p970 . . . . . 0117 927 2144

Livesey, Ms Kate MA(Cantab) M *Nov 2001*
40, 24, 11, 89, 7
4 Pump Court, London EC4
p947 . . . . . 020 7842 5555

LIVESLEY, Rhian LLB G *Jul 2000*
20
Atlantic Chambers, Liverpool
p980 . . . . . 0151 236 4421

Living, Mr Marc Stephen M *Oct 1983*
8, 18, 22, 37
Holborn Chambers, London WC2
p937 . . . . . 020 7242 6060
Pallant Chambers, Chichester
p974 . . . . . 01243 784538

LIVINGSTON, Mr John LLM; BA G *Jul 1980*
15
2 Bedford Row, London WC1
p924 . . . . . 020 7440 8888

Livingston, Mr Richard M *Oct 2006*
Kings Chambers, Leeds
p978 . . . . . 0113 242 1123
Kings Chambers, Manchester
p984 . . . . . 0161 832 9082

Livingstone, Mr Douglas LLB I *Nov 1989*
6, 7, 8, 10, 11, 12, 15, 18, 20, 22, 24, 25, 26, 27, 29, 30
Goldsmith Chambers, London EC4
p935 . . . . . 020 7353 6802

Livingstone, Mr Simon LLB I *Oct 1990*
Thomas More Chambers, London WC2
p952 . . . . . 020 7404 7000

Lixenberg, Mr Marc BA(Hons) G *Jul 2005*
3, 7, 11, 31, 40, 41, 43, 45, 49, 54, 61, 78, 74
Atkin Chambers, London WC1
p923 . . . . . 020 7404 0102

Llewellyn, Mr Charles LLB(Hons) G *Jul 1978*
10, 12, 15, 20, 22, 23, 30
Staple Inn Chambers, London WC1
p951 . . . . . 020 7242 5240

Lloyd, Mr David G B BA(Hons)(Law & Econ) G *Jan 1998*
12, 15, 41, 47
St David's Chambers, Swansea
p993 . . . . . 01792 644466

Lloyd, Mr Francis I *Jul 1987*
15, 62
15 New Bridge Street Chambers, London EC4
p943 . . . . . 020 7842 1900

Lloyd, Ms Gaynor Elizabeth LLB L *Oct 1992*
20, 31, 10
St Johns Buildings, Preston
p990 . . . . . 01772 256100
St Johns Buildings, Chester
p974 . . . . . 01244 323070
St Johns Buildings, Manchester
p985 . . . . . 0161 214 1500
St Johns Buildings, Liverpool
p982 . . . . . 0151 243 6000

Lloyd, His Honour Humphrey MA; LLB(Dublin) I *Jul 1963*
(Q.C.) *3, 7, 11, 31, 40, 41, 43, 45, 49, 54, 61, 78, 74*
Atkin Chambers, London WC1
p923 . . . . . 020 7404 0102

Lloyd, Mr John Nesbitt MA; LLB(Exeter); BA(Natal) I *Nov 1988*
31, 1, 12, 26, 22, 9, 40, 49, 28, 25
Rougemont Chambers, Exeter
p975 . . . . . 01392 208484

Lloyd, Mr Julian MA; LLM G *Jul 1985*
7, 10, 12, 15, 18, 20, 22, 25, 26, 30
St Johns Buildings, Preston
p990 . . . . . 01772 256100
St Johns Buildings, Chester
p974 . . . . . 01244 323070
St Johns Buildings, Manchester
p985 . . . . . 0161 214 1500
St Johns Buildings, Liverpool
p982 . . . . . 0151 243 6000

Lloyd, Miss Rhiannon LLB(Hons) I *Oct 2002*
20, 10
4 Paper Buildings, London EC4
p946 . . . . . 020 7583 0816

LLOYD, Ms Sarah M *Jul 2005*
15
1 High Pavement, Nottingham
p988 . . . . . 0115 941 8218

Lloyd, Mr Stephen M *Jul 1971*
1, 6, 8, 9, 11, 13, 22, 29, 31, 32, 36, 37, 14, 40
13 Old Square Chambers, London WC2
p945 . . . . . 020 7831 4445

Lloyd-Eley, Mr Andrew LLB M *Nov 1979*
15, 62
2 Hare Court, London EC4
p937 . . . . . 020 7353 5324

Lloyd-Jones, Mr John B BA(Hons)(Dunelm) I *Nov 1993*
12, 15, 10, 62
36 Bedford Row, London WC1
p925 . . . . . 020 7421 8000

Lloyd-Nesling, Miss Tracey LLB(Hons)(Bucks) M *Jul 1988*
15, 62
Thirty Park Place, Cardiff
p973 . . . . . 029 2039 8421

Lo, Mr Bernard I *Nov 1991*
Field Court Chambers, London WC1
p933 . . . . . 020 7405 6114

Loades, Mr Jonathan C M *Nov 1986*
53, 62, 15, 30, 40, 70, 65, 81, 39, 84, 38
9 Gough Square, London EC4
p935 . . . . . 020 7832 0500

Lobbenberg, Mr Nicholas BA(Oxon) G *Nov 1987*
15, 23, 25, 36
4 Breams Buildings, London EC4
p927 . . . . . 020 7092 1900

Lock, Mr David G *Nov 1985*
(Q.C.) *1, 14, 76, 85, 22, 51, 26, 27, 63, 68, 28*
No5 Chambers, Bristol
p971 . . . . . 0845 210 5555
No5 Chambers, London EC4
p944 . . . . . 0845 210 5555
No5 Chambers, Birmingham
p968 . . . . . 0845 210 5555

LOCKEY, Mr John C G MA(Cantab); LLM(Harv) M *Jun 1987*
(Q.C.)
Essex Court Chambers, London WC2
p931 . . . . . 020 7813 8000

LOCKHART, Mr Andrew LLB(Hons)(Lond); Recorder L *Oct 1991*
(Q.C.) *15, 62, 84, 91*
St Philips Chambers, Birmingham
p969 . . . . . 0121 246 7000

LOCKHART-MUMMERY, Mr Christopher BA(Cantab) I *Jul 1971*
(Q.C.) *31, 46, 36*
Landmark Chambers, London EC4
p941 . . . . . 020 7430 1221

Lockyer, Miss Jane LLB G *Jul 1970*
15, 51
Nine Bedford Row, London WC1
p924 . . . . . 020 7489 2727

Lodder, Mr Peter LLB(Hons); Recorder M *Jul 1981*
(Q.C.) *15, 62*
2 Bedford Row, London WC1
p924 . . . . . 020 7440 8888

Lodge, Mr Adam LLB(Hons)(UWE) G *Oct 1996*
15, 12
18 St John Street Chambers, Manchester
p985 . . . . . 0161 278 1800

LODGE, Mr Anton James Corduff MA(Cantab) G *Nov 1966*
(Q.C.)
Furnival Chambers, London EC4
p934 . . . . . 020 7405 3232
Park Court Chambers, Leeds
p978 . . . . . 0113 243 3277

Lody, Mr Stuart T BA(Hons) G *Nov 1991*
15
KCH Garden Square Chambers, Nottingham
p989 . . . . . 0115 941 8851
KCH Garden Square Chambers, Leicester
p979 . . . . . 0115 941 8851

Loeb, Miss Dinah M *Nov 2004*
20, 10
Westgate Chambers, Lewes
p980 . . . . . 01273 480510

Lofthouse, Mr John C M *Nov 1979*
2 King's Bench Walk, London EC4
p939 . . . . . 020 7353 1746

Lofthouse, Mr Simon LLB(Lond); Recorder G *Jul 1988*
(Q.C.) *3, 7, 11, 31, 40, 41, 43, 45, 49, 54, 61, 78, 74*
Atkin Chambers, London WC1
p923 . . . . . 020 7404 0102

LOFTUS, Miss Teresa Anne Martine LLB(Hull) L *Mar 1995*
15, 62
7 Harrington Street Chambers, Liverpool
p981 . . . . . 0151 242 0707

Logan, Mr Graeme BVC M *Oct 1998*
72, 15, 42, 91
15 New Bridge Street Chambers, London EC4
p943 . . . . . 020 7842 1900

Logan, Ms Maura LLB I *Jul 1971*
15, 20
St John's Chambers, Altrincham
p967 . . . . . 0161 980 7379

LOGAN, Ms Rachel BA(Hons)(Oxon); MA(Columbia); DipLaw I *Jan 2008*
23, 1, 51, 33, 21, 56, 3, 55, 76, 46, 19, 70, 71, 91
Matrix Chambers, London WC1
p942 . . . . . 020 7404 3447

Logsdon, Mr Michael Anthony LLB I *Feb 1988*
15, 62
2 Hare Court, London EC4
p937 . . . . . 020 7353 5324

Lohmus, Mr Michael G *Jan 2005*
St Ives Chambers, Birmingham
p969 . . . . . 0121 236 0863

Loke, Miss Siew BA G *Jul 2003*
15, 70, 23
Lamb Building, Brighton
p970 . . . . . 01273 820490
Lamb Building, London EC4
p940 . . . . . 020 7797 7788

Lomas, Mr Mark S BA M *Jul 1983*
12, 15, 22, 26, 29, 30
3PB, Winchester
p994 . . . . . 01962 868884

LOMAS, Miss Sophie Victoria I *Oct 2006*
Citadel Chambers, Birmingham
p967 . . . . . 0121 233 8500

Lomnicka, Miss Eva MA; LLB M *Jul 1974*
5, 8, 12, 24, 40, 48
Four New Square, London WC2
p943 . . . . . 020 7822 2000

Long, Mr Andrew I *Jul 1981*
15, 30, 53
St Johns Buildings, Preston
p990 . . . . . 01772 256100
St Johns Buildings, Chester
p974 . . . . . 01244 323070
St Johns Buildings, Manchester
p985 . . . . . 0161 214 1500
St Johns Buildings, Liverpool
p982 . . . . . 0151 243 6000

Long, Mr Ben I *Nov 2000*
10, 12, 15, 20, 51
Guildford Chambers, Guildford
p975 . . . . . 01483 539131

Long, Mr Benjamin M *Jan 2006*
2 King's Bench Walk, London EC4
p939 . . . . . 020 7353 1746
Pump Court Chambers, Swindon
p993 . . . . . 01793 539899
Pump Court Chambers, Winchester
p994 . . . . . 01962 868161
Pump Court Chambers, London EC4
p947 . . . . . 020 7353 0711

LONGMORE, Mrs Beatrice I *Jul 2006*
42 Bedford Row, London WC1
p925 . . . . . 020 7831 0222

Longstaff, Mr Benjamin BA(Maths) G *Jan 2009*
13, 8
Hogarth Chambers, London WC2
p937 . . . . . 020 7404 0404

Longworth, Mr Antony Stephen BA(Oxon) M *Jul 1978*
12, 15, 20, 10, 30
St Johns Buildings, Preston
p990 . . . . . 01772 256100
St Johns Buildings, Chester
p974 . . . . . 01244 323070
St Johns Buildings, Manchester
p985 . . . . . 0161 214 1500
St Johns Buildings, Liverpool
p982 . . . . . 0151 243 6000

Lonsdale, Mr David BA(Oxon) I *Nov 1988*
11, 12, 22, 29, 30, 40
33 Bedford Row, London WC1
p925 . . . . . 020 7242 6476

Lonsdale, Miss Marion G *Jul 1984*
Academy Chambers, London N2
p923 . . . . . 07979 265321

See p1010 for the Key to Work Categories

LOOSEMOORE, Mrs Mary BSc(Hons)(Econ) *I May 1992*
10, 20
Pallant Chambers, Chichester
p974 . . . . . 01243 784538

Lopez, Mr Juan *L Oct 2002*
1, 46, 25, 26, 31, 36
Francis Taylor Building, London EC4
p934 . . . . . 020 7353 8415

Lopez, Mr Paul Anthony LLB(B'ham) *M Jul 1982*
30, 10, 11, 12, 15, 27
St Ives Chambers, Birmingham
p969 . . . . . 0121 236 0863

Lopian, Dr Jonathan B MA(Cantab); PhD(Cantab) *M Nov 1994*
5, 6, 8, 11, 29, 38
11 Stone Buildings, London WC2
p951 . . . . . 020 7831 6381

Loraine, Miss Kara *M Jan 2006*
26, 51, 36, 46, 18, 55, 48, 49, 53
Old Square Chambers, London WC1
p945 . . . . . 020 7269 0300

LORAM, Miss Mary LLM *I Nov 1995*
51
Citadel Chambers, Birmingham
p967 . . . . . 0121 233 8500

Lord, Mr Andrew *G Oct 1999*
15, 20, 30
Paradise Chambers, Sheffield
p992 . . . . . 0114 273 8951

Lord, Mr David William LLB(Bris) *M Jul 1987*
(Q.C.) *6, 5, 8, 11, 13, 22, 24, 29, 37, 50, 56*
3 Stone Buildings, London WC2
p951 . . . . . 020 7242 4937

Lord, Mr Richard MA(Cantab) *I Nov 1981*
(Q.C.) *35, 40, 11, 24*
Brick Court Chambers, London WC2
p927 . . . . . 020 7379 3550

Lord, Mr Timothy M MA(Cantab) *I Nov 1992*
11, 24, 40
Brick Court Chambers, London WC2
p927 . . . . . 020 7379 3550

LORENZO, Ms Claudia *I Apr 1991*
10, 20
Pump Court Chambers, Swindon
p993 . . . . . 01793 539899
Pump Court Chambers, Winchester
p994 . . . . . 01962 868161
Pump Court Chambers, London EC4
p947 . . . . . 020 7353 0711

LORIE, Mr Andrew BA(Hons)(UWE); CPE(Westminster) *M Oct 1996*
3PB, Winchester
p994 . . . . . 01962 868884

Lorne, Miss Victoria *L Jan 2005*
12, 18, 30, 10, 15, 23, 76
36 Bedford Row, London WC1
p925 . . . . . 020 7421 8000

Loughran, Ms Gemma *I Nov 2008*
1 Pump Court, London EC4
p947 . . . . . 020 7842 7070

Louis, Miss Angela *L Jan 2002*
Clapham Law Chambers, London SW1
p928 . . . . . 020 7978 8482 / 7642 5777

Love, Mr Dudley Mark BSc(Lond); Director *G Nov 1979*
15, 20
2 Dr Johnson's Buildings, London EC4
p930 . . . . . 020 7936 2613

Love, Miss Sharon Anne *G Jan 1997*
15, 23, 20
12 Old Square, London WC2
p945 . . . . . 020 7404 0875

LOVEDAY, Mr David *I Nov 2007*
18, 76, 1, 63
4-5 Gray's Inn Square, London WC1
p935 . . . . . 020 7404 5252

LOVEDAY, Mr Mark Allen BA(Kent) *I Jul 1986*
88, 93, 40, 89, 36, 26
Tanfield Chambers, London WC1
p951 . . . . . 020 7421 5300

LOVELAND, Mr Ian BA; LLM; DPhil *I Mar 2001*
1, 22, 26
Arden Chambers, London WC1
p923 . . . . . 020 7242 4244

Lovell-Pank, Mr Dorian *I Jul 1971*
(Q.C.) *15, 36, 62*
6 King's Bench Walk, London EC4
p939 . . . . . 020 7583 0410

LOVERIDGE, Mr Andrew R LLB(Newc); Recorder *L Jul 1983*
10, 20
7 Harrington Street Chambers, Liverpool
p981 . . . . . 0151 242 0707

LOWE, Mr Anthony Marshall MA(Oxon) *M Jul 1976*
10, 93, 20
Cornwall Street Chambers, Birmingham
p967 . . . . . 0121 233 7500

Lowe, Mr Christopher *M Jul 2001*
KCH Garden Square Chambers, Nottingham
p989 . . . . . 0115 941 8851
KCH Garden Square Chambers, Leicester
p979 . . . . . 0115 941 8851

Lowe, Mr Craig LLB(Hons)(Lond) *L Oct 1994*
15
Paradise Chambers, Sheffield
p992 . . . . . 0114 273 8951

Lowe, Mr David MA(Cantab) *G Nov 2008*
11, 18, 33
Blackstone Chambers, London EC4
p926 . . . . . 020 7583 1770
13 Old Square Chambers, London WC2
p945 . . . . . 020 7831 4445

Lowe, Miss Elizabeth MA(Oxon); BA(Hons)(Oxon) *M Nov 1999*
15, 62, 96
Argent Chambers, London WC2
p923 . . . . . 020 7556 5500

Lowe, Miss Emma BSc(Surrey); Non-Practising Door Tenant *G Oct 1996*
15, 62
2 Hare Court, London EC4
p937 . . . . . 020 7353 5324

Lowe, Mr Geoffrey LLB *G Jul 1975*
15
St Johns Buildings, Preston
p990 . . . . . 01772 256100
St Johns Buildings, Chester
p974 . . . . . 01244 323070
St Johns Buildings, Manchester
p985 . . . . . 0161 214 1500
St Johns Buildings, Liverpool
p982 . . . . . 0151 243 6000

Lowe, Mr Jonathan LLB(Hons) *L Mar 2008*
5, 6, 11, 67, 38, 24, 89, 96, 40, 37
Exchange Chambers, Manchester
p983 . . . . . 0161 833 2722
Exchange Chambers, Liverpool
p980 . . . . . 0151 236 7747
Exchange Chambers, Leeds
p977 . . . . . 0113 203 1970

Lowe, Mr Mark LLB(Leics) *G Jul 1972*
(Q.C.) *1, 28, 31, 12, 18, 22, 26, 46*
Cornerstone Barristers, London WC1
p929 . . . . . 020 7242 4986

Lowe, Mr Matthew LLB(Exon) *I Nov 1991*
12, 15, 18
36 Bedford Row, London WC1
p925 . . . . . 020 7421 8000

Lowe, Mr Mungo *M Jan 2003*
13 Old Square Chambers, London WC2
p945 . . . . . 020 7831 4445

LOWE, Mr Rupert *I Nov 1998*
15, 46, 84, 62
Guildhall Chambers, Bristol
p970 . . . . . 0117 930 9000

LOWE, Mr Thomas LLB(Lond); LLB(Cantab) *I Nov 1985*
(Q.C.) *3, 5, 6, 11, 12, 15, 18, 29, 30, 40, 62*
Wilberforce Chambers, London WC2
p953 . . . . . 020 7306 0102

Lowe, Prof Vaughan LLB; LLM; PhD *G Oct 1993*
(Q.C.)
Essex Court Chambers, London WC2
p931 . . . . . 020 7813 8000

Lowe, Mr William LLB(Newc) *I Jul 1972*
(Q.C.) *15, 30, 84*
Paradise Chambers, Sheffield
p992 . . . . . 0114 273 8951
York Chambers, York
p995 . . . . . 01904 620048
York Chambers, Newcastle upon Tyne
p987 . . . . . 0191 206 4677

LOWENSTEIN, Mr Paul LLB(Hons)(Manc); LLM(Cantab); CEDR *M Nov 1988*
(Q.C.) *3, 5, 6, 8, 11, 24, 40, 45*
3 Verulam Buildings, London WC1
p953 . . . . . 020 7831 8441

Lownds, Mr Peter BSc(Hons) *G Nov 1998*
15, 51, 91, 62
Doughty Street Chambers, London WC1
p930 . . . . . 020 7404 1313

Lowne, Mr Stephen BA *I Jul 1981*
15
KCH Garden Square Chambers, Nottingham
p989 . . . . . 0115 941 8851
KCH Garden Square Chambers, Leicester
p979 . . . . . 0115 941 8851

Lucas, Miss Bridget A BA(Oxon) *I Nov 1989*
Fountain Court Chambers, London EC4
p934 . . . . . 020 7583 3335

Lucas, Mr Edward *M Oct 1991*
15
9 Gough Square, London EC4
p935 . . . . . 020 7832 0500

Lucas, Ms Felicie LLB *M Oct 1999*
20, 10
Temple Chambers, Newport
p988 . . . . . 01633 267403 / 255855
Temple Chambers, Cardiff
p973 . . . . . 029 2039 7364

Lucas, Ms Joanna *G Jan 2004*
20, 10, 30, 96
Queen Square Chambers, Bristol
p972 . . . . . 0117 921 1966

Lucas, Mr John *M Oct 1995*
Goldsmith Chambers, London EC4
p935 . . . . . 020 7353 6802

LUCAS, Mr Noel BSc(Lond); Recorder *M Jul 1979*
(Q.C.) *15, 36, 62, 95*
18 Red Lion Court, London EC4
p949 . . . . . 020 7520 6000
18 Red Lion Court (Annexe), Chelmsford
p973 . . . . . 01245 280880

LUCEY, Miss Anne-Marie *M Nov 2005*
20, 10, 15, 70, 26, 12
Trinity Chambers, Chelmsford
p974 . . . . . 01245 605040

LUCK, Ms Julie-Anne *L Jul 2006*
30, 89, 12, 49, 96, 24
Kenworthy's Chambers, Manchester
p984 . . . . . 0161 832 4036

Luckhurst, Mr Paul BA(Oxon); MPhil(Cantab) *L Jan 2009*
1, 11, 19, 44, 56, 52, 18
Blackstone Chambers, London EC4
p926 . . . . . 020 7583 1770

Lucking, Mrs Adrienne *M Jan 1989*
15, 62, 63
36 Bedford Row, London WC1
p925 . . . . . 020 7421 8000

LUCRAFT, Mr Mark *I Jul 1984*
(Q.C.) *15, 36, 62, 94, 34, 84*
18 Red Lion Court, London EC4
p949 . . . . . 020 7520 6000
18 Red Lion Court (Annexe), Chelmsford
p973 . . . . . 01245 280880

LUDBROOK, Mr Timothy LLB(Hons) *I Oct 1996*
13 Old Square Chambers, London WC2
p945 . . . . . 020 7831 4445

Ludlow, Mr Craig LLB *L Jan 2002*
12, 15, 23
3PB, Bournemouth
p969 . . . . . 01202 292102

Lugg, Ms Elizabeth Claire BA(Hons)(Dunelm) *G Oct 1994*
10, 12, 15, 20, 30
Broad Chare Chambers, Newcastle upon Tyne
p986 . . . . . 0191 232 0541

LUGSDIN, Mr Martin *M Nov 2005*
10
Kenworthy's Chambers, Manchester
p984 . . . . . 0161 832 4036

Lule, Ms Jacqueline *M Oct 1999*
1 Mitre Court Buildings, London EC4
p942 . . . . . 020 7452 8900

Lumbers, Miss Kate *I Oct 1999*
15, 10, 20, 18
7 Bedford Row, London WC1
p924 . . . . . 020 7242 3555

Lumley, Mr Nicholas *L Oct 1992*
Park Court Chambers, Leeds
p978 . . . . . 0113 243 3277

LUMSDON, Miss Kate BA; CPE(Lond) *M Oct 1993*
12, 72, 15, 62
23 Essex Street, London WC2
p932 . . . . . 020 7413 0353
2 King's Bench Walk, London EC4
p939 . . . . . 020 7353 1746

LUND, Celia LLB(Reading) *L Nov 1988*
6, 7, 8, 9, 11, 14, 22, 29, 31, 32, 37
Atlantic Chambers, Liverpool
p980 . . . . . 0151 236 4421

Lundie, Mr Christopher MA(Cantab); Diploma in European Law *I Nov 1991*
5, 40, 22, 11, 12, 41, 24
2 Temple Gardens, London EC4
p952 . . . . . 020 7822 1200

LYCOURGOU, Miss Olive *G Jan 1997*
4 King's Bench Walk, London EC4
p939 . . . . . 020 7822 7000

Lydiard, Mr Andrew BA(Oxon); LLM *I Jul 1980*
(Q.C.) *11, 5, 35, 19, 24, 1*
Brick Court Chambers, London WC2
p927 . . . . . 020 7379 3550

Lykiarpoulos, Mr Andrew *M Oct 2004*
13, 50
8 New Square, London WC2
p943 . . . . . 020 7405 4321

Lyle, Miss Helen *I Jul 2006*
Nine Bedford Row, London WC1
p924 . . . . . 020 7489 2727

LYNAGH, Mr Richard LLB; Recorder *G Jul 1975*
(Q.C.) *11, 12, 24, 27, 30, 40, 53*
Crown Office Chambers, London EC4
p929 . . . . . 020 7797 8100

LYNCH, Mr Adrian LLB(Lond); Recorder *G Nov 1983*
(Q.C.) *1, 5, 18, 19, 26, 29, 36, 55*
11KBW, London EC4
p938 . . . . . 020 7632 8500

Lynch, Mr Ben BA(Oxon); LLM(Columbia) *M Oct 2001*
24, 18, 55, 51, 11, 12
Devereux Chambers, London WC2
p930 . . . . . 020 7353 7534

Lynch, Mr John *G Jan 2008*
15, 36
QEB Hollis Whiteman, London EC4
p948 . . . . . 020 7933 8855

LYNCH, Miss Patricia Recorder *I Nov 1979*
(Q.C.) *15, 36*
18 Red Lion Court, London EC4
p949 . . . . . 020 7520 6000
18 Red Lion Court (Annexe), Chelmsford
p973 . . . . . 01245 280880

Lynch, Mr Patrick BEd(Lond); DipLaw *I Jul 1988*
15
Guildhall Chambers, Portsmouth
p990 . . . . . 023 9275 2400

Lynch, Mr Peter BSc; Dip *L Jul 1985*
10, 20, 91
4 Brick Court Chambers, London EC4
p927 . . . . . 020 7832 3200

Lyndon-Stanford, Mr Michael Andrew Flemying MA(Cantab); Deputy High Court Judge *I Feb 1962*
(Q.C.)
Maitland Chambers, London WC2
p941 . . . . . 020 7406 1200

LYNE, Mr Mark MA(Cantab) *I Jul 1981*
11, 10, 20
Five Paper, London EC4
p946 . . . . . 020 7815 3200

LYNESS, Mr Scott Edward LLB *L Oct 1996*
1, 8, 22, 26, 31, 36
Landmark Chambers, London EC4
p941 . . . . . 020 7430 1221

Lyon, Mr Gavin *M Jan 2006*
Northampton Chambers, Northampton
p988 . . . . . 01604 636271

Lyon, Mrs Shane *M Nov 1976*
King's Bench Godolphin Chambers, Truro
p994 . . . . . 0845 308 1551
King's Bench Godolphin Chambers, Plymouth
p990 . . . . . 0845 308 1551

Lyon, Mr Stephen LLB(Hons) *I Jul 1987*
20
4 Paper Buildings, London EC4
p946 . . . . . 020 7583 0816

LYONS, Mr Andrew I *Jul 2002*
12, 30, 11, 40, 53, 22, 29
Ropewalk Chambers, Nottingham
p989 . . . . 0115 947 2581

Lyons, Miss Christina L *Jul 2004*
53, 11, 12, 18, 85, 26, 27, 30, 55, 40
7 Bedford Row, London WC1
p924 . . . . 020 7242 3555

Lyons, Mr David M *May 1987*
2 Pump Court, London EC4
p947 . . . . 020 7353 5597

LYONS, Mr John BA(Dunelm); DipLaw M *Jul 1986*
15, 62
18 Red Lion Court, London EC4
p949 . . . . 020 7520 6000
18 Red Lion Court (Annexe), Chelmsford
p973 . . . . 01245 280880

LYONS, Miss Tara M *Oct 2005*
10, 15, 18, 20
Pump Court Chambers, Swindon
p993 . . . . 01793 539899
Pump Court Chambers, Winchester
p994 . . . . 01962 868161
Pump Court Chambers, London EC4
p947 . . . . 020 7353 0711

LYONS, Mr Timothy LLB(Bris); LLM; PhD(Lond) I *Jul 1980*
(Q.C.) *57, 58, 11, 19, 81*
4-5 Gray's Inn Square, London WC1
p935 . . . . 020 7404 5252
15 Old Square, London WC2
p945 . . . . 020 7242 2744
St James's Chambers, Manchester
p984 . . . . 0161 834 7000
Zenith Chambers, Leeds
p979 . . . . 0113 245 5438

MABB, Mr David MA(Cantab) L *Jul 1979*
(Q.C.) *11, 38, 97*
Erskine Chambers, London WC2
p931 . . . . 020 7242 5532

Mably, Mr Louis L *Apr 1997*
15, 62
6 King's Bench Walk, London EC4
p939 . . . . 020 7583 0410

MABON, Mrs Jane LLB G *Jul 1998*
12, 30, 53, 25, 18, 20
9 St John Street Chambers, Manchester
p984 . . . . 0161 955 9000

MacAdam, Mr Jason LLB(Hons) L *Nov 1990*
15, 72, 70
Exchange Chambers, Manchester
p983 . . . . 0161 833 2722
Exchange Chambers, Liverpool
p980 . . . . 0151 236 7747
Exchange Chambers, Leeds
p977 . . . . 0113 203 1970
St Pauls Chambers, Leeds
p979 . . . . 0113 245 5866

MACAULAY, Mr Jack L *Oct 2009*
30, 12, 11
Crown Office Chambers, London EC4
p929 . . . . 020 7797 8100

Maccabe, Mr Irvine MA(Cantab) G *Nov 1983*
18, 55
No5 Chambers, Bristol
p971 . . . . 0845 210 5555
No5 Chambers, London EC4
p944 . . . . 0845 210 5555
No5 Chambers, Birmingham
p968 . . . . 0845 210 5555

MacDonald, Ms Ailsa M *Jan 2000*
New Court Chambers, Newcastle upon Tyne
p987 . . . . 0191 232 1980

Macdonald, Mr Alexander L *Jan 2001*
3, 35, 24, 11
7 King's Bench Walk, London EC4
p940 . . . . 020 7910 8300

MACDONALD, Ms Alison BA(Cantab); BCL(Oxon) G *Jan 2000*
1, 51, 12, 15
Matrix Chambers, London WC1
p942 . . . . 020 7404 3447

MACDONALD, Mr Alistair BA(Hons)(Nott'm); Recorder I *Nov 1995*
(Q.C.) *20, 22, 24, 12*
St Philips Chambers, Birmingham
p969 . . . . 0121 246 7000

MacDonald, Mr Alistair Neil BSc G *Jul 1983*
(Q.C.) *15, 62*
Park Court Chambers, Leeds
p978 . . . . 0113 243 3277

MACDONALD, Mr Iain BA(Oxon) M *Jul 1996*
11, 12, 39, 47, 48, 59
Gough Square Chambers, London EC4
p935 . . . . 020 7353 0924

Macdonald, Mr Ian Alexander MA; LLB(Cantab) M *Feb 1963*
(Q.C.) *15, 1, 23, 51, 95*
Garden Court North Chambers, Manchester
p983 . . . . 0161 236 1840

MACDONALD, Mr James I *Jan 2005*
5, 62, 41
3 Verulam Buildings, London WC1
p953 . . . . 020 7831 8441

MACDONALD, Mr John MA(Cantab) L *Jun 1955*
(Q.C.) *1*
New Square Chambers, London WC2
p943 . . . . 020 7419 8000

MACDONALD, Lord Ken I *Jul 1978*
(Q.C.) KB1, *15, 16, 56, 62, 71, 72, 95*
Matrix Chambers, London WC1
p942 . . . . 020 7404 3447

Macdonald, Miss Sheila LLB; PhD M *Feb 1993*
22, 20, 40, 37, 7, 11, 6
KCH Garden Square Chambers, Nottingham
p989 . . . . 0115 941 8851
KCH Garden Square Chambers, Leicester
p979 . . . . 0115 941 8851

MacDonald Eggers, Mr Peter LLB; LLM M *Jul 1999*
(Q.C.) *3, 11, 24, 41, 35*
7 King's Bench Walk, London EC4
p940 . . . . 020 7910 8300

MacEvilly, Mr Conn LLB; LLM I *Jan 1997*
97, 11, 18, 69, 81, 6, 38, 93
9 Stone Buildings Barristers Chambers, London WC2
p951 . . . . 020 7404 5055

Macey-Dare, Mr Thomas MA; LLM(Cantab); LLM(Cornell) M *Feb 1994*
3, 35, 24, 11, 40
Quadrant Chambers, London EC4
p948 . . . . 020 7583 4444

MACFARLANE, Mr Andrew Lennox I *May 1995*
Colleton Chambers, Exeter
p975 . . . . 01392 274898

MacFaul, Mr Donald William LLB(Hons); MICS I *Mar 1998*
Broad Chare Chambers, Newcastle upon Tyne
p986 . . . . 0191 232 0541

MacGregor, Mr Craig L *Jan 1997*
Cobden House Chambers, Manchester
p983 . . . . 0161 833 6000

Machell, Mr John LLB(Soton) I *Oct 1993*
8, 11, 97, 38, 37, 29
Serle Court, London WC2
p950 . . . . 020 7242 6105

MACHELL, Mr Raymond D MA; LLB(Cantab); Deputy High Court Hudge G *Jul 1973*
(Q.C.) *30, 12, 53, 40*
Byrom Street Chambers, Manchester
p983 . . . . 0161 829 2100
42 Bedford Row, London WC1
p925 . . . . 020 7831 0222

MACHIN, Mr Charles Kim MA(Oxon) L *Nov 1973*
5, 6, 8, 9, 11, 18, 29, 32, 37
St James's Chambers, Manchester
p984 . . . . 0161 834 7000

MACHIN, Mr Graham Edward G *Jul 1965*
31, 26, 40, 7, 11, 1
Ropewalk Chambers, Nottingham
p989 . . . . 0115 947 2581

MACHIN, Ms Susan LLB(Hons)(Lancs) I *Jul 1999*
1, 14, 18, 63
Chavasse Court Chambers, Liverpool
p980 . . . . 0151 229 2030

Mackay, Mr Archie M *Jan 2003*
15
5 Paper Buildings, London EC4
p946 . . . . 020 7583 6117

MacKean, Miss Sarah MA(Oxon); DipLaw I *Nov 1992*
10, 14, 77, 20, 63
King's Bench Godolphin Chambers, Truro
p994 . . . . 0845 308 1551
King's Bench Godolphin Chambers, Plymouth
p990 . . . . 0845 308 1551

Mackenzie, Mr Alasdair G *Jan 2004*
1, 51, 22, 23
Doughty Street Chambers, London WC1
p930 . . . . 020 7404 1313

MACKENZIE, Miss Julie L *Nov 1978*
10, 20
Pump Court Chambers, Swindon
p993 . . . . 01793 539899
Pump Court Chambers, Winchester
p994 . . . . 01962 868161
Pump Court Chambers, London EC4
p947 . . . . 020 7353 0711

MACKENZIE, Mr Robert G *Jan 1996*
One Essex Court, London EC4
p931 . . . . 020 7936 3030

Mackeson, Miss Antoinette L *Oct 1993*
15, 51
Nine Bedford Row, London WC1
p924 . . . . 020 7489 2727

Mackie, Ms Jeannie BA(Hons)(Cantab) I *Jul 1995*
15, 51
Doughty Street Chambers, London WC1
p930 . . . . 020 7404 1313

MACKINNON, Laura I *Jan 2009*
15
9-12 Bell Yard Chambers, London WC2
p926 . . . . 020 7400 1800

MacKinnon, Ms Lucy L *Jul 2003*
11, 53, 40, 30, 27
Hailsham Chambers, London EC4
p936 . . . . 020 7643 5000

MacKinnon, Mr Thomas LLB; LLM M *Jul 1982*
1 Mitre Court Buildings, London EC4
p942 . . . . 020 7452 8900

Mackley, Mr David BA(Hons) L *Oct 1997*
20
18 St John Street Chambers, Manchester
p985 . . . . 0161 278 1800

Mackworth, Ms Julia I *Jul 1999*
1 Gray's Inn Square, London WC1
p935 . . . . 020 7405 8946

Maclachlan, Ms Esther M *Jul 2005*
18, 20, 15, 30, 40, 70, 11, 93
9 Gough Square, London EC4
p935 . . . . 020 7832 0500

MACLAREN, Miss Catriona BA(Cantab) I *Oct 1993*
10, 18, 20, 55
Tanfield Chambers, London WC1
p951 . . . . 020 7421 5300

Maclean, Mr Alan BA(Oxon) G *Nov 1993*
24, 11, 1, 51
Brick Court Chambers, London WC2
p927 . . . . 020 7379 3550

MacLean, Mr Kenneth G *May 1985*
(Q.C.)
One Essex Court, London EC4
p931 . . . . 020 7583 2000

MACLEAN, Mr Niall L *Jul 2008*
30
12 King's Bench Walk, London EC4
p940 . . . . 020 7583 0811

Macleod, Mr Duncan M *Jul 1980*
62, 30, 53, 40, 70, 65, 81, 39, 84, 38
9 Gough Square, London EC4
p935 . . . . 020 7832 0500

MACLEOD, Ms Elena LLB(Exeter) L *Jul 2007*
1 Garden Court, London EC4
p934 . . . . 020 7797 7900

MACLEOD, Mr Murdo LLB(Hons)(Aberdeen) M *Jul 1994*
(Q.C.)
Temple Garden Chambers, London EC4
p952 . . . . 020 7583 1315

Maclynn, Miss Louise BA G *Jan 2001*
20, 10
4 Brick Court Chambers, London EC4
p927 . . . . 020 7832 3200

MACMANUS, Miss Sabha L *Jan 2008*
Carmelite Chambers, London EC4
p927 . . . . 020 7936 6300

MACNAB, Mr Andrew MA; LLM(Cantab) M *Jul 1986*
11, 19, 40, 44
Monckton Chambers, London WC1
p942 . . . . 020 7405 7211

MacPhail, Mr Andrew MA(Hons)(Edin) M *Jan 2007*
18
3PB, Oxford
p989 . . . . 01865 793736

MACPHERSON, Mr Alexander BA(Oxon); DipLaw(City) M *Nov 2000*
74, 7, 30, 11, 40
Crown Office Chambers, London EC4
p929 . . . . 020 7797 8100

MACPHERSON, Mr Angus MA(Cantab) I *Jul 1977*
12, 27, 30
Temple Garden Chambers, London EC4
p952 . . . . 020 7583 1315

Macpherson, Mr Duncan BA(Hons) M *May 1994*
One Essex Court, London EC4
p931 . . . . 020 7936 3030

MACRO, Miss Morwenna LLB(Hons) I *Jul 2002*
6, 8, 11, 47
Five Paper, London EC4
p946 . . . . 020 7815 3200

MacWhannell, Mr Iain M *Jan 2006*
71, 57, 58, 19, 72
3PB, London EC4
p946 . . . . 020 7583 8055

MADAN, Mr Pankaj MA(Hons)(Cantab); Law Tripos; Deputy District Judge M *Jan 1997*
30, 53, 84, 27
12 King's Bench Walk, London EC4
p940 . . . . 020 7583 0811

Madan, Pankaj M *Sep 1997*
11, 30, 47
Zenith Chambers, Leeds
p979 . . . . 0113 245 5438

Maddan, Mr Archie BA(Hons) G *Nov 1993*
7, 8, 12, 26, 46, 49, 22, 84, 88, 25
5 Pump Court, London EC4
p947 . . . . 020 7353 2532 / 7583 7133

MADDEN, Mr John Andrew I *Aug 1997*
15, 62, 95
187 Fleet Street, London EC4
p933 . . . . 020 7430 7430

Madderson, Miss Naomi M LLB(Hons) G *Oct 2003*
12, 15, 20
37 Park Square Chambers, Leeds
p978 . . . . 0113 243 9422

Maddison, Mr David LLB G *Oct 1995*
10, 12, 15, 19, 20, 30
Cobden House Chambers, Manchester
p983 . . . . 0161 833 6000

MADDISON, Mr Matthew LLB(Hons); BVC M *Jul 2010*
6, 8, 11, 22, 29, 32, 37, 38, 40, 45, 47, 66, 67, 88, 93, 97
Enterprise Chambers, London WC2
p931 . . . . 020 7405 9471
Enterprise Chambers, Leeds
p977 . . . . 0113 246 0391
Enterprise Chambers, Newcastle upon Tyne
p987 . . . . 0191 222 3344

Maddison, Mr Simon I *Jan 2008*
St Johns Buildings, Preston
p990 . . . . 01772 256100
St Johns Buildings, Chester
p974 . . . . 01244 323070
St Johns Buildings, Manchester
p985 . . . . 0161 214 1500
St Johns Buildings, Liverpool
p982 . . . . 0151 243 6000

MADGE-WYLD, Mr Sam M *Oct 2008*
1, 22, 26, 88, 93
Arden Chambers, London WC1
p923 . . . . 020 7242 4244

Magarian, Mr Michael BA(Cantab) G *Jul 1988*
(Q.C.) *15*
Tooks Chambers, London EC4
p953 . . . . 020 7842 7575

Magee, Mr Mike MA(Cantab); DipLaw I *Oct 1997*
12, 15, 18
Fenners Chambers, Cambridge
p972 . . . . 01223 368761

MAGEE, Miss Rosein BA(Hons) G *Oct 1994*
12, 10, 15, 20
Pallant Chambers, Chichester
p974 . . . . 01243 784538

Maggs, Mr Patrick I *Oct 1996*
62, 15
15 New Bridge Street Chambers, London EC4
p943 . . . . 020 7842 1900

See p1010 for the Key to Work Categories

Maginn, Miss Olivia LLB L *Jan 1998*
25, 15
New Walk Chambers, Leicester
p979 ... 0871 200 1298

Maguire, Mr Andrew LLB(Hull) I *Nov 1988*
11, 22, 30, 31, 46
Exchange Chambers, Manchester
p983 ... 0161 833 2722
Exchange Chambers, Liverpool
p980 ... 0151 236 7747
Exchange Chambers, Leeds
p977 ... 0113 203 1970
St Philips Chambers, Birmingham
p969 ... 0121 246 7000

Maguire, Mr Benn BA(Hons); MA I *Nov 1994*
15
QEB Hollis Whiteman, London EC4
p948 ... 020 7933 8855

Maguire, Clodagh I *Jan 2003*
St Johns Buildings, Preston
p990 ... 01772 256100
St Johns Buildings, Chester
p974 ... 01244 323070
St Johns Buildings, Manchester
p985 ... 0161 214 1500
St Johns Buildings, Liverpool
p982 ... 0151 243 6000

Maguire, Mr Stephen M *Mar 2007*
Kings Chambers, Leeds
p978 ... 0113 242 1123
Kings Chambers, Manchester
p984 ... 0161 832 9082

MAHER, Ms Felicity I *Jan 2006*
5, 81, 11, 62, 40, 6, 38
3 Verulam Buildings, London WC1
p953 ... 020 7831 8441

Maher, Mrs Martha BCL; LLB(Cork) I *Jan 1987*
97, 38, 11, 8
St John's Chambers, Bristol
p972 ... 0117 921 3456

Maher, Mr Michael BA(Hons); LLM G *Nov 1995*
15, 18
Nine Bedford Row, London WC1
p924 ... 020 7489 2727
Exchange Chambers, Manchester
p983 ... 0161 833 2722
Exchange Chambers, Liverpool
p980 ... 0151 236 7747
Exchange Chambers, Leeds
p977 ... 0113 203 1970

Mahmood, Mr Abid LLB I *Oct 1992*
1, 8, 10, 11, 12, 15, 18, 20, 22, 30, 40, 47, 51, 53, 14, 95, 62
No5 Chambers, Bristol
p971 ... 0845 210 5555
No5 Chambers, London EC4
p944 ... 0845 210 5555
No5 Chambers, Birmingham
p968 ... 0845 210 5555

Mahmood, Ghazan LLB(Hons) I *Sep 1997*
5, 6, 8, 11, 18, 29, 40, 47
St Johns Buildings, Preston
p990 ... 01772 256100
St Johns Buildings, Chester
p974 ... 01244 323070
St Johns Buildings, Manchester
p985 ... 0161 214 1500
St Johns Buildings, Liverpool
p982 ... 0151 243 6000

Mahmood, Mr Imran M *Jan 1992*
15, 20
Holborn Chambers, London WC2
p937 ... 020 7242 6060
5 Pump Court, London EC4
p947 ... 020 7353 2532 / 7583 7133

MAHMOOD, Miss Saleema G *Nov 1999*
Carmelite Chambers, London EC4
p927 ... 020 7936 6300

Mahmud, Saamir G *Jan 1996*
10, 20
1 Pump Court, London EC4
p947 ... 020 7842 7070

MAHMUTAJ, Miss Klentiana LLB(Hons); LLM M *Jul 2005*
15, 62, 51, 94
18 Red Lion Court, London EC4
p949 ... 020 7520 6000
18 Red Lion Court (Annexe), Chelmsford
p973 ... 01245 280880

Mahood, Miss Emma-Jane G *Jul 2001*
20
9 Gough Square, London EC4
p935 ... 020 7832 0500

Maidment, Mr Kieran LLB; MA G *Nov 1989*
15, 16, 51
Doughty Street Chambers, London WC1
p930 ... 020 7404 1313

Mailer, Mr Clifford M *Jul 1987*
Goldsmith Chambers, London EC4
p935 ... 020 7353 6802

MAIN THOMPSON, Dermot G *Jul 1977*
10, 12, 20, 26, 30
Renaissance Chambers, London WC1
p949 ... 020 7404 1111

Mainds, Mr Sam A G Recorder I *Feb 1977*
12, 15, 30
36 Bedford Row, London WC1
p925 ... 020 7421 8000

Mainwaring, Henry L *Jan 2001*
Clerksroom - Administration Centre, Taunton
p993 ... 0845 083 3000

Mairs, Mr Robin LLB; LLM G *Oct 1992*
72, 15, 62
St Pauls Chambers, Leeds
p979 ... 0113 245 5866

Maitland, Mr Andrew H R L *Jul 1970*
King's Bench Godolphin Chambers, Truro
p994 ... 0845 308 1551
King's Bench Godolphin Chambers, Plymouth
p990 ... 0845 308 1551

Maitland-Jones, Mr Mark MA(Edin) M *Nov 1986*
King's Bench Chambers, Oxford
p989 ... 01865 311066
13 King's Bench Walk, London EC4
p940 ... 020 7353 7204

Majumdar, Mr Shantanu BA(Oxon) M *Nov 1992*
5, 81, 97, 11, 38, 40
Radcliffe Chambers, London WC2
p949 ... 020 7831 0081

Maka, Mr Isaac L *Nov 1998*
23, 12, 15
Two King's Bench Walk, London EC4
p939 ... 020 7353 7202 / 7353 3909

Makepeace, Mr Peter L *Jul 1988*
York Chambers, York
p995 ... 01904 620048
York Chambers, Newcastle upon Tyne
p987 ... 0191 206 4677

Makey, Mr Christopher LLB(Lond) M *Jul 1975*
12, 18, 30, 36, 40, 53, 48, 1, 49
Old Square Chambers, Bristol
p971 ... 0117 930 5100
Old Square Chambers, London WC1
p945 ... 020 7269 0300

Malam, Mr James G *Jan 2002*
7, 24, 40
St Johns Buildings, Preston
p990 ... 01772 256100
St Johns Buildings, Chester
p974 ... 01244 323070
St Johns Buildings, Manchester
p985 ... 0161 214 1500
St Johns Buildings, Liverpool
p982 ... 0151 243 6000

Malcolm, Mr Alistair Recorder I *Feb 1971*
(Q.C.) *15, 84*
1 Paper Buildings, London EC4
p946 ... 020 7353 3728

Malcolm, Miss Jane BSc(Hons); DipLaw M *Jul 2005*
King's Bench Chambers, Oxford
p989 ... 01865 311066
13 King's Bench Walk, London EC4
p940 ... 020 7353 7204

Malcolm, Miss Rosalind M *Jul 1977*
6, 8, 12, 15
Guildford Chambers, Guildford
p975 ... 01483 539131

MALE, Mr John BA(Cantab) L *Jul 1976*
(Q.C.) *31, 93*
Landmark Chambers, London EC4
p941 ... 020 7430 1221

MALEK, Mr Ali MA(Oxon); BCL G *Jul 1980*
(Q.C.) *3, 5, 6, 11, 40*
3 Verulam Buildings, London WC1
p953 ... 020 7831 8441

MALEK, Mr Hodge M MA(Oxon); BCL G *Jul 1983*
(Q.C.) *1, 3, 5, 11, 15, 24, 37*
4-5 Gray's Inn Square, London WC1
p935 ... 020 7404 5252

Males, Mr Stephen M MA(Cantab) M *Jul 1978*
(Q.C.) *3, 11, 12, 24, 35, 41*
20 Essex Street, London WC2
p932 ... 020 7842 1200

MALEY, Mr William G *Jul 1982*
15
25 Bedford Row, London WC1
p925 ... 020 7067 1500

Malhotra, Miss Mehtab LLB; LLM L *Oct 1996*
15, 20, 22, 23
12 Old Square, London WC2
p945 ... 020 7404 0875

MALHOTRA, Priya I *Jan 2007*
25 Bedford Row, London WC1
p925 ... 020 7067 1500

Malik, Mr Ahmed G *Jan 2008*
Clapham Law Chambers, London SW1
p928 ... 020 7978 8482 / 7642 5777

Malik, Mr Amjad R BA; LLM(UCL) L *Nov 1987*
22, 15, 12, 62
36 Bedford Row, London WC1
p925 ... 020 7421 8000

Malik, Mr Omar L LLB(Soton) I *Nov 1990*
18, 20, 10
12 College Place, Southampton
p992 ... 023 8032 0320

Malik, Miss Sarah LLB(Hons); BVC L *Nov 1999*
18, 33, 1
Hardwicke, London WC2
p936 ... 020 7242 2523

Mallalieu, Baroness Ann MA; LLB(Cantab) I *Jul 1970*
(Q.C.) *15, 62, 36*
6 King's Bench Walk, London EC4
p939 ... 020 7583 0410

Mallalieu, Mr Roger LLB M *Nov 1998*
40, 53, 27
Four New Square, London WC2
p943 ... 020 7822 2000

Mallett, Miss Sarah Victoria LLB(Sheff) I *Nov 1988*
12, 15, 20
11 King's Bench Walk, Leeds
p978 ... 0113 297 1200

Mallett, Mr Simon Jeremy LLB(Sheff) I *Jul 1986*
15, 30, 20, 11, 18
11 King's Bench Walk, Leeds
p978 ... 0113 297 1200

Mallick, Miss Nabila LLB(Hons); LLM G *Oct 1992*
1, 23, 18, 55
No5 Chambers, Bristol
p971 ... 0845 210 5555
No5 Chambers, London EC4
p944 ... 0845 210 5555
No5 Chambers, Birmingham
p968 ... 0845 210 5555

Mallin, Mr Max MA(Cantab) I *Oct 1993*
5, 18, 19, 24, 29, 62
11 Stone Buildings, London WC2
p951 ... 020 7831 6381

MALLINCKRODT, Ms Sophie MA(Cantab) L *Jul 1999*
5, 6, 11, 24, 40
3 Verulam Buildings, London WC1
p953 ... 020 7831 8441

MALLISON, Miss Kate M *Nov 1974*
15
4 King's Bench Walk, London EC4
p939 ... 020 7822 7000

MALLON, Miss Joanna BA(Hons) L *Oct 1996*
30, 20
7 Harrington Street Chambers, Liverpool
p981 ... 0151 242 0707

MALLORY, Miss Kathrine BA(Hons) I *Jan 1998*
30, 53
9 St John Street Chambers, Manchester
p984 ... 0161 955 9000

Malone, Mr David John BSc(Hons); DipLaw G *Oct 1998*
12, 68, 72, 15, 71, 70, 46, 82, 62, 83, 51, 25, 26, 63, 91, 28, 40, 94, 56, 95, 36
1 Gray's Inn Square, London WC1
p935 ... 020 7405 8946

Malone, Mr Michael G *Nov 1975*
One Essex Court, London EC4
p931 ... 020 7583 2000

MALTZ, Mr Ben L *Nov 1998*
12, 22, 40, 8
Five Paper, London EC4
p946 ... 020 7815 3200

MALYNICZ, Mr Simon LLB; MA; BA I *Oct 1997*
13
3 New Square, London WC2
p943 ... 020 7405 1111

Manasse, Dr Paul G *Nov 1995*
20
18 St John Street Chambers, Manchester
p985 ... 0161 278 1800

MANDALIA, Mr Vinesh I *Jan 1997*
20, 30, 23
St Philips Chambers, Birmingham
p969 ... 0121 246 7000

Mandel, Mr Richard G *Jul 1972*
15, 62
4 Breams Buildings, London EC4
p927 ... 020 7092 1900

Mander, Mr Marcus MA M *Jan 2005*
41, 11, 24, 40, 35
7 King's Bench Walk, London EC4
p940 ... 020 7910 8300

Mangat, Dr Tejina BSc; MBBS M *Oct 1990*
30, 53, 27
Hailsham Chambers, London EC4
p936 ... 020 7643 5000

MANKAU, Mrs Louise LLB(Edin); LLM(Maastricht) L *Jan 2005*
11, 18, 30, 93
Tanfield Chambers, London WC1
p951 ... 020 7421 5300

MANKNELL, Mr David BA; BCL M *Nov 2001*
18, 30, 53, 1
1 Crown Office Row, London EC4
p929 ... 020 7797 7500

Manley, Mr David BA; Recorder I *Jul 1981*
(Q.C.) *1, 26, 31, 46, 54*
Kings Chambers, Leeds
p978 ... 0113 242 1123
Kings Chambers, Manchester
p984 ... 0161 832 9082

Manley, Miss Lesley BA M *Nov 1983*
15
1 Inner Temple Lane, London EC4
p937 ... 020 7427 4400

Manley, Mr Oliver BA(Hons) G *Jul 2005*
12, 18, 20, 23, 30, 36
Thirty Park Place, Cardiff
p973 ... 029 2039 8421

Mann, Mr Christopher BA(Hons)(Oxon) L *Oct 1998*
30, 53, 38
King's Bench Chambers, Oxford
p989 ... 01865 311066
13 King's Bench Walk, London EC4
p940 ... 020 7353 7204

Mann, Miss Daya Lucienne L *Feb 1995*
10, 20, 22, 23
Southernhay Chambers, Exeter
p975 ... 01392 255777

Mann, Mr Ian L *Oct 2000*
King's Bench Chambers, Oxford
p989 ... 01865 311066

Mann, Mr Jasvir M *Jan 1990*
15, 62, 72
No5 Chambers, Bristol
p971 ... 0845 210 5555
No5 Chambers, London EC4
p944 ... 0845 210 5555
No5 Chambers, Birmingham
p968 ... 0845 210 5555

MANN, Mr Jonathan LLB I *Nov 1989*
15
25 Bedford Row, London WC1
p925 ... 020 7067 1500

Mann, Mr Martin G *Jul 1968*
(Q.C.) *5, 6, 8, 11, 29, 32, 37, 40, 41, 62, 49*
XXIV Old Buildings, London WC2
p944 ... 020 7691 2424

MANN, Mr Paul BA G *Nov 1980*
(Q.C.) *15*
1 High Pavement, Nottingham
p988 ... 0115 941 8218

Mann, Miss Rebecca LLB(Leics) G *Jan 1995*
20, 10
Pendragon Chambers, Swansea
p993 ... 01792 411188

13

Mann, Miss Sara LLB(Hons) M *Nov 1994*
10, 20, 30
St Johns Buildings, Preston
p990 . . . . . 01772 256100
St Johns Buildings, Chester
p974 . . . . . 01244 323070
St Johns Buildings, Manchester
p985 . . . . . 0161 214 1500
St Johns Buildings, Liverpool
p982 . . . . . 0151 243 6000

MANNERING, Mr Stephen L *Nov 2011*
10, 20
St Mary's Chambers, Nottingham
p989 . . . . . 0115 950 3503

MANNING, Mr Jonathan David Grant MA(Cantab) I *Jul 1989*
1, 12, 22, 26, 36, 51, 46
Arden Chambers, London WC1
p923 . . . . . 020 7242 4244

Manning, Miss Ruth LLB G *Oct 1993*
No 8 Chambers, Birmingham
p968 . . . . . 0121 236 5514

MANNION, Ms Amy I *Oct 2003*
9-12 Bell Yard Chambers, London WC2
p926 . . . . . 020 7400 1800

Mansell, Mr Jason I *Jan 1991*
15, 62, 73
7 Bedford Row, London WC1
p924 . . . . . 020 7242 3555

Mansell, Miss Rebecca Lily G *Jul 2005*
12, 22, 6, 20
Civitas Law, Cardiff
p972 . . . . . 0845 071 3007

Mansell, Mr Richard Austin LLB(Essex) G *Nov 1991*
(Q.C.) *15*
No 6 Barristers Chambers, Leeds
p978 . . . . . 0113 245 9763

Mansfield, Mr Ben I *Jan 2005*
KCH Garden Square Chambers, Nottingham
p989 . . . . . 0115 941 8851
KCH Garden Square Chambers, Leicester
p979 . . . . . 0115 941 8851

MANSFIELD, Mr Gavin MA(Cantab); Accredited Mediator M *Nov 1992*
8, 12, 7, 18, 5, 22, 30
Littleton Chambers, London EC4
p941 . . . . . 020 7797 8600

MANSFIELD, Hon Guy MA(Oxon); Recorder M *Nov 1972*
(Q.C.) *12, 20, 27, 30, 1, 36, 40, 51, 53*
1 Crown Office Row, London EC4
p929 . . . . . 020 7797 7500

Mansfield, Mr Michael BA G *Nov 1967*
(Q.C.) *16, 15, 1, 36, 51*
Tooks Chambers, London EC4
p953 . . . . . 020 7842 7575

Mansfield, Ms Nadia I *Nov 2006*
10, 20, 22, 23, 30
KCH Garden Square Chambers, Nottingham
p989 . . . . . 0115 941 8851
KCH Garden Square Chambers, Leicester
p979 . . . . . 0115 941 8851

Mansoor, Ms Parveen I *Nov 1996*
1 Mitre Court Buildings, London EC4
p942 . . . . . 020 7452 8900

MANSOORI, Ms Sara LLB(Hons) L *Nov 1997*
1, 12, 67, 73, 16, 50, 51, 87, 52, 89
Matrix Chambers, London WC1
p942 . . . . . 020 7404 3447

MANT, Mr Peter BA(History); CPE; BVC I *Jan 2006*
1, 12, 11, 33, 14
Thirty Nine Essex Street, London WC2
p932 . . . . . 020 7832 1111

MANTLE, Mr Peter BA(Oxon); LLM(Cantab) I *Jul 1989*
3, 6, 11, 30, 40, 57
Monckton Chambers, London WC1
p942 . . . . . 020 7405 7211

Mantle, Mr Philip BA(Oxon) L *Jan 2002*
11, 12, 30, 6, 22, 29, 40, 93, 97, 87, 81, 5, 74
No5 Chambers, Bristol
p971 . . . . . 0845 210 5555
No5 Chambers, London EC4
p944 . . . . . 0845 210 5555
No5 Chambers, Birmingham
p968 . . . . . 0845 210 5555

Manyarara, Miss Natsai G *Jul 2001*
20, 23
12 Old Square, London WC2
p945 . . . . . 020 7404 0875

MANZONI, Mr Charles M *Jul 1988*
(Q.C.) *7, 11, 40, 3, 49, 46, 31, 69, 24, 61*
Thirty Nine Essex Street, London WC2
p932 . . . . . 020 7832 1111

Maqsood, Ms Kalsoom LLB(Hons) M *Oct 1998*
10, 20
3PB, Oxford
p989 . . . . . 01865 793736
18 St John Street Chambers, Manchester
p985 . . . . . 0161 278 1800

Maqsood, Miss Zabeda LLB(Derby) G *Nov 1996*
15, 20, 12
15 Winckley Square, Preston
p991 . . . . . 01772 252828

Marcus, Mr Peter BA M *Jul 2004*
Zenith Chambers, Leeds
p979 . . . . . 0113 245 5438

MARCUS, Ms Rachel BA(Oxon) I *Jan 2005*
1, 53, 18, 46, 27, 51, 30, 57, 12
1 Crown Office Row, London EC4
p929 . . . . . 020 7797 7500

Mardner, Miss Sharn I *Jan 2003*
15, 12, 20, 23, 94
Bell Yard Chambers, London WC2
p926 . . . . . 020 7306 9292 / 7404 5138

Margo, Mr Saul L *Oct 2005*
30, 18, 31, 62, 84, 1
Outer Temple Chambers, London WC2
p945 . . . . . 020 7353 6381

Margolin, Mr Daniel BA(Oxon); Junior Counsel to Crown B Panel G *Nov 1995*
8, 9, 22, 37, 40
Maitland Chambers, London WC2
p941 . . . . . 020 7406 1200

Margree, Miss Sarah L *Oct 1996*
15, 30, 12, 20, 23
11 King's Bench Walk, Leeds
p978 . . . . . 0113 297 1200

MARKANDYA, Miss Susannah MA(Edinburgh) I *Oct 2005*
5, 6, 8, 11, 22, 29, 40, 38, 88
Enterprise Chambers, London WC2
p931 . . . . . 020 7405 9471
Enterprise Chambers, Leeds
p977 . . . . . 0113 246 0391
Enterprise Chambers, Newcastle upon Tyne
p987 . . . . . 0191 222 3344

Markham, Miss Andrea LLB G *Jan 2000*
20
18 St John Street Chambers, Manchester
p985 . . . . . 0161 278 1800

MARKHAM, Miss Anna MA(Oxon); ACA L *Oct 1996*
6, 11, 29
4 Stone Buildings, London WC2
p951 . . . . . 020 7242 5524

Markham, Miss Hannah Megan BA(Hons); MA(Lond) L *Jul 1998*
20, 10, 81, 63
36 Bedford Row, London WC1
p925 . . . . . 020 7421 8000

MARKLEW, Mr Lee BA(Sheff) G *Jan 1993*
15, 62, 84
St Philips Chambers, Birmingham
p969 . . . . . 0121 246 7000

MARKS, Mr David M MA; BCL(Oxon) G *Nov 1974*
(Q.C.) *5, 6, 8, 11, 24, 29, 4, 21, 38*
South Square, London WC1
p950 . . . . . 020 7696 9900

Marks, Ms Jacqueline BA; Deputy District Judge (Principal Registry) M *Jul 1984*
10, 20
Coram Chambers, London EC1
p929 . . . . . 020 7092 3700

Marks, Mr Jonathan BA(Oxon) I *Jul 1975*
(Q.C.) *7, 11, 12, 20, 24, 30*
4 Pump Court, London EC4
p947 . . . . . 020 7842 5555

MARKS, Mr Jonathan H MA(Oxon); BCL I *Oct 1992*
5, 11, 40, 1, 47, 19, 26, 29, 51, 50, 44, 46, 33
Matrix Chambers, London WC1
p942 . . . . . 020 7404 3447

Marks, Ms Katherine M *Oct 1998*
15, 20, 25
Staple Inn Chambers, London WC1
p951 . . . . . 020 7242 5240

MARKS, Mr Lewis BA(Oxon) M *Jul 1984*
(Q.C.) *20*
Queen Elizabeth Buildings, London EC4
p948 . . . . . 020 7797 7837

Marks, Mr Richard G *Jul 1975*
(Q.C.) *15*
33 Chancery Lane, London WC2
p928 . . . . . 020 7440 9950
St Johns Buildings, Preston
p990 . . . . . 01772 256100
St Johns Buildings, Chester
p974 . . . . . 01244 323070
St Johns Buildings, Manchester
p985 . . . . . 0161 214 1500
St Johns Buildings, Liverpool
p982 . . . . . 0151 243 6000

Marks Moore, Mr Douglas BA(Belfast) G *Nov 1979*
15, 62
6 King's Bench Walk, London EC4
p939 . . . . . 020 7583 0410

Markus, Ms Kate LLB G *Nov 1981*
1, 18, 22, 26, 36, 51
Doughty Street Chambers, London WC1
p930 . . . . . 020 7404 1313

Marland, Mr Timothy I *Jul 2002*
Quadrant Chambers, London EC4
p948 . . . . . 020 7583 4444

Marley, Miss Sarah LLB(Hons) L *Oct 1995*
20, 10
Coram Chambers, London EC1
p929 . . . . . 020 7092 3700

Marney, Mr Nicholas LLB(Hons)(Lond) M *Jul 2002*
15, 91, 46, 84
Argent Chambers, London WC2
p923 . . . . . 020 7556 5500

MARNHAM, Miss Michelle J I *Nov 1994*
22, 30, 11, 12
Tanfield Chambers, London WC1
p951 . . . . . 020 7421 5300

MARQUAND, Mr Charles MA(Oxon); Dip ECLaw(Lond) I *Nov 1987*
1, 6, 11, 29
4 Stone Buildings, London WC2
p951 . . . . . 020 7242 5524

Marquis, Mr Piers BA(Warwick) G *Jul 2001*
18, 55, 22, 70
Doughty Street Chambers, London WC1
p930 . . . . . 020 7404 1313

Marrin, Mr John MA(Cantab); FCIArb; Recorder & Deputy High Court Judge, TCC I *Nov 1974*
(Q.C.) *3, 7, 11, 24, 40*
Keating Chambers, London WC2
p938 . . . . . 020 7544 2600

Marriott, Mr Jamie LLB G *Jul 2003*
30
Cobden House Chambers, Manchester
p983 . . . . . 0161 833 6000

MARRS, Mr Andrew I *Nov 1995*
36, 15, 62, 63
Kenworthy's Chambers, Manchester
p984 . . . . . 0161 832 4036

Marsden, Mr Andrew LLB(Oxon) L *May 1994*
8, 11, 29, 40, 97
St John's Chambers, Bristol
p972 . . . . . 0117 921 3456
East Anglian Chambers, Norwich
p988 . . . . . 01603 617351
East Anglian Chambers, Colchester
p975 . . . . . 01206 572756
East Anglian Chambers, Chelmsford
p973 . . . . . 01245 215660
East Anglian Chambers, Ipswich
p976 . . . . . 01473 214481

Marsden-Lynch, Mr John Francis BA(Sydney); LLB(Lond); MA(Lond) M *Nov 1988*
15
Westgate Chambers, Lewes
p980 . . . . . 01273 480510

Marsh, Miss Carolyn LLB(Bris) I *Jul 1985*
Charter Chambers, London WC1
p928 . . . . . 020 7618 4400

Marsh, Miss Elizabeth A BA(Hons) G *Nov 1979*
(Q.C.) *15, 51, 62, 34*
Nine Bedford Row, London WC1
p924 . . . . . 020 7489 2727

Marsh, Mr Graham Ian LLB L *Oct 2004*
12, 20, 94
Foregate Chambers, Kidderminster
p976 . . . . . 07760 766152

MARSH, Mr John G *Jul 1977*
15, 70, 72, 82
Kenworthy's Chambers, Manchester
p984 . . . . . 0161 832 4036

Marsh, Miss Nancy I *Jul 2008*
10, 15, 20, 62
Argent Chambers, London WC2
p923 . . . . . 020 7556 5500

MARSHALL, Mr Andrew LLB(Lond); Recorder I *Jul 1986*
15, 36, 62, 84
18 Red Lion Court, London EC4
p949 . . . . . 020 7520 6000
18 Red Lion Court (Annexe), Chelmsford
p973 . . . . . 01245 280880

Marshall, Mr David L *Jan 1981*
3PB, London EC4
p946 . . . . . 020 7583 8055

Marshall, Mr Derek LLB(Soton) I *Jun 1980*
6, 7, 8, 53, 11, 12, 97, 67, 18, 20, 38, 88, 30, 32, 96, 40
College Chambers, Southampton
p992 . . . . . 023 8023 0338

Marshall, Mrs Elizabeth Suzanne MA(Oxon); LLM(Lond) I *Oct 1995*
12, 15, 20, 22, 30, 18
Iscoed Chambers, Swansea
p993 . . . . . 01792 652988

MARSHALL, Miss Eloise M K S BA(Hons) G *Oct 1994*
15, 36, 62, 72
23 Essex Street, London WC2
p932 . . . . . 020 7413 0353

Marshall, Miss Laura J M *Jul 2001*
Paradise Chambers, Sheffield
p992 . . . . . 0114 273 8951

Marshall, Lucy M *Jan 2005*
St Johns Buildings, Preston
p990 . . . . . 01772 256100
St Johns Buildings, Chester
p974 . . . . . 01244 323070
St Johns Buildings, Manchester
p985 . . . . . 0161 214 1500
St Johns Buildings, Liverpool
p982 . . . . . 0151 243 6000

MARSHALL, Mr Paul BA(Cantab) I *Jan 1991*
24, 5, 11, 62, 35
4-5 Gray's Inn Square, London WC1
p935 . . . . . 020 7404 5252

Marshall, Mr Peter D LLB(Hons)(Warw) L *Nov 1991*
15, 62
4 Breams Buildings, London EC4
p927 . . . . . 020 7092 1900

MARSHALL, Mr Philip LLB(L'pool) G *Jul 1989*
10, 12, 20
1 King's Bench Walk, London EC4
p938 . . . . . 020 7936 1500
Serle Court, London WC2
p950 . . . . . 020 7242 6105

Marshall, Mr Philip Derek MA M *Nov 1975*
12, 15, 18, 25, 30, 31, 36, 27, 40, 53, 55
Iscoed Chambers, Swansea
p993 . . . . . 01792 652988

Marshall, Ms Vanessa LLB G *Nov 1994*
53, 30, 15, 85, 40, 27
7 Bedford Row, London WC1
p924 . . . . . 020 7242 3555

MARSHALL-ANDREWS, Mr Robert Graham LLB(Bris); Recorder G *Feb 1967*
(Q.C.) MP
Carmelite Chambers, London EC4
p927 . . . . . 020 7936 6300

Marshall-Bain, Miss Lydia G *Jan 1998*
Clapham Law Chambers, London SW1
p928 . . . . . 020 7978 8482 / 7642 5777

Marten, Mr Hedley MA(Cantab) L *Nov 1966*
8, 5, 6, 22, 32, 40, 37, 2, 11
Radcliffe Chambers, London WC2
p949 . . . . . 020 7831 0081

See p1010 for the Key to Work Categories

Martignetti, Mr Ian LLB I *Nov 1990*
1, 7, 8, 11, 12, 22, 29, 30, 32, 20, 24, 25, 26
Regency Chambers, Peterborough
p990 . . . . 01733 315215

Martin, Mr Bradley LLB(Leics) L *Oct 1990*
30, 40, 48, 53, 27
2 Temple Gardens, London EC4
p952 . . . . 020 7822 1200

MARTIN, Mr Dale LLB(Hons) I *Oct 1997*
6, 11, 12, 18, 40
Littleton Chambers, London EC4
p941 . . . . 020 7797 8600

Martin, Mr David I *Oct 1969*
15, 62
Queen Square Chambers, Bristol
p972 . . . . 0117 921 1966

Martin, Ms Dianne LLB(B'ham) G *Jun 1992*
10, 20
St John's Chambers, Bristol
p972 . . . . 0117 921 3456

MARTIN, Mrs Emma L *Jan 2002*
15, 20, 10, 12
Octagon Chambers, Taunton
p993 . . . . 01823 331919

Martin, Mr Gerard James MA(Cantab) M *Jul 1978*
(Q.C.) *30, 53*
Exchange Chambers, Manchester
p983 . . . . 0161 833 2722
Exchange Chambers, Liverpool
p980 . . . . 0151 236 7747
Exchange Chambers, Leeds
p977 . . . . 0113 203 1970
12 King's Bench Walk, London EC4
p940 . . . . 020 7583 0811

Martin, Miss Jade M *Oct 2003*
15, 12, 20
East Anglian Chambers, Norwich
p988 . . . . 01603 617351
East Anglian Chambers, Colchester
p975 . . . . 01206 572756
East Anglian Chambers, Chelmsford
p973 . . . . 01245 215660
East Anglian Chambers, Ipswich
p976 . . . . 01473 214481

Martin, Mr James LLB L *Mar 2003*
62, 15
5 King's Bench Walk, London EC4
p939 . . . . 020 7353 5638

MARTIN, Mr John MA(Cantab) L *Jul 1972*
(Q.C.) *5, 6, 7, 8, 9, 11, 22, 29, 40*
Wilberforce Chambers, London WC2
p953 . . . . 020 7306 0102

MARTIN, Mr Jonathan BA(Hons) M *Nov 1994*
51, 23
10 King's Bench Walk, London EC4
p940 . . . . 020 7353 7742

Martin, Josephine L *Jan 2008*
Four New Square, London WC2
p943 . . . . 020 7822 2000

Martin, Mrs Nicola LLB I *Jan 1982*
20, 10
3PB, Oxford
p989 . . . . 01865 793736

MARTIN, Mr Piers I *Oct 1997*
18, 30, 40, 55, 20
4 King's Bench Walk, London EC4
p939 . . . . 020 7822 7000

Martin, Ms Rebecca L *Jan 2002*
15
1 Pump Court, London EC4
p947 . . . . 020 7842 7070

Martin, Mr Richard H B BSc(Econ) I *Nov 1978*
12, 15, 30, 27, 6
4 Rowchester Court, Birmingham
p968 . . . . 0121 233 2327

MARTIN, Mr Roy LLB(Glasgow) L *Jul 1990*
(Q.C.) *31, 46*
Landmark Chambers, London EC4
p941 . . . . 020 7430 1221

Martin, Miss Sarah I *Mar 2008*
41, 24, 35, 61
7 King's Bench Walk, London EC4
p940 . . . . 020 7910 8300

Martin, Mr Stuart LLB; LLM L *Oct 2007*
20
18 St John Street Chambers, Manchester
p985 . . . . 0161 278 1800

MARTIN, Mr William GDL; BVC(College of Law) G *Nov 2010*
15
9-12 Bell Yard Chambers, London WC2
p926 . . . . 020 7400 1800

Martin-Clark, Mr David BA(Oxon)(Jurisprudence) G *Jun 1961*
41, 3, 11, 21, 35, 36, 49, 24
Stone Chambers, London WC1
p951 . . . . 020 7440 6900

MARVEN, Mr Robert BA M *Oct 1994*
47, 24, 1
Thirty Nine Essex Street, London WC2
p932 . . . . 020 7832 1111

MARWICK, Mr James L *Jan 2008*
8, 11, 18, 30, 38, 31, 2
Trinity (Newcastle) Chambers, Newcastle upon Tyne
p987 . . . . 0191 232 1927
Trinity (Teesside) Chambers, Middlesbrough
p986 . . . . 01642 247569

MARZEC, Ms Alexandra LLB(Warw) M *Nov 1990*
16, 13, 50, 51
5RB, London WC1
p948 . . . . 020 7242 2902

Masefield, Mr Roger LLB(Cantab); BCL(Oxon) M *Jan 1994*
11, 5, 40, 24
Brick Court Chambers, London WC2
p927 . . . . 020 7379 3550

Mashembo, Mrs Carol LLB(Hons)(Exon); PGDipLaw(City); BVC(Inns of Court School of Law) L *Oct 1999*
53, 30, 20
St John's Chambers, Bristol
p972 . . . . 0117 921 3456

Masih, Mrs Harleen M *Jul 1999*
20, 23
No 8 Chambers, Birmingham
p968 . . . . 0121 236 5514

Maskrey, Mr Simeon Andrew LLB; Recorder, Deputy High Court Judge I *Jul 1977*
(Q.C.) *53, 30, 26, 27, 40*
7 Bedford Row, London WC1
p924 . . . . 020 7242 3555

Mason, Mr David LLB(Leics); Recorder I *Jul 1986*
(Q.C.) *15, 62, 36, 68, 70, 72*
No5 Chambers, Bristol
p971 . . . . 0845 210 5555
No5 Chambers, London EC4
p944 . . . . 0845 210 5555
No5 Chambers, Birmingham
p968 . . . . 0845 210 5555

Mason, Mr David Hugh Rothwell LLB(Nott'm) M *Feb 1984*
18
Broad Chare Chambers, Newcastle upon Tyne
p986 . . . . 0191 232 0541

MASON, Mr David John LLB G *Jul 1979*
12, 20
Bank House Chambers, Sheffield
p991 . . . . 0114 275 1223

Mason, Mr James G *Jul 1967*
Goldsmith Chambers, London EC4
p935 . . . . 020 7353 6802

MASON, Mr John J LLB(Lond) I *Nov 1971*
11, 88, 30, 40, 93, 97, 48, 12
Cornwall Street Chambers, Birmingham
p967 . . . . 0121 233 7500

Mason, Mr Nicholas BA G *Jul 1984*
Park Court Chambers, Leeds
p978 . . . . 0113 243 3277

MASON, Mr Patrick I *Oct 1997*
42, 15
Octagon Chambers, Taunton
p993 . . . . 01823 331919

Mason, Mr Stephen BA(Hons); MA; LLM; PGCE(FE) M *Jan 1988*
45, 87
St Pauls Chambers, Leeds
p979 . . . . 0113 245 5866

MASOOD, Miss Hafsah M *Oct 2006*
12, 18, 30, 40, 51, 23, 59
3 Hare Court, London EC4
p937 . . . . 020 7415 7800

Massarella, Mr David M *Nov 1999*
55, 18, 30, 51, 36
Cloisters, London EC4
p928 . . . . 020 7827 4000

Massey, Miss Stella M BA; PGCE M *Feb 1990*
10, 12, 15, 18, 20, 22, 23, 30, 36, 38
Central Chambers, Manchester
p983 . . . . 0161 236 1133

MASSEY, Mr William BA(Oxon) M *Jul 1977*
(Q.C.) *34, 57, 58, 37*
Pump Court Tax Chambers, London WC1
p948 . . . . 020 7414 8080

Massih, Mr Michel LLB M *Nov 1979*
(Q.C.) *15, 62, 51*
Tooks Chambers, London EC4
p953 . . . . 020 7842 7575

Masters, Mr Alan B R LLB M *Jul 1979*
12, 15, 20, 22, 30, 31, 36, 40, 53, 1, 18, 51, 25
1 Pump Court, London EC4
p947 . . . . 020 7842 7070

Masters, Mr Jonathan BA(Hons)(African History)(Lond); GDL(College of Law, Lond); BVC(College of Law, Lond) M *Jan 2009*
Fenners Chambers, Cambridge
p972 . . . . 01223 368761

MASTERS, Mr Lee BA M *Nov 1984*
15, 18
Citadel Chambers, Birmingham
p967 . . . . 0121 233 8500

Masters, Ms Sara Alayna MA(Cantab) M *Oct 1993*
3, 11, 12, 19, 24, 35, 41
20 Essex Street, London WC2
p932 . . . . 020 7842 1200

Matharoo, Miss Reena BA; LLM(Lond) L *Aug 1998*
Field Court Chambers, London WC1
p933 . . . . 020 7405 6114

MATHER, Ms Alison L *Oct 1997*
15, 63, 36, 68
Kenworthy's Chambers, Manchester
p984 . . . . 0161 832 4036

MATHER, Mr Brian G *Jul 2002*
20, 10, 63
Trinity (Newcastle) Chambers, Newcastle upon Tyne
p987 . . . . 0191 232 1927
Trinity (Teesside) Chambers, Middlesbrough
p986 . . . . 01642 247569

MATHER, Mr James David MA L *Oct 2006*
11, 8
Serle Court, London WC2
p950 . . . . 020 7242 6105

MATHER, Miss Kate LLB(Hons)(Lond) G *Oct 1990*
10, 20, 51
1 Garden Court, London EC4
p934 . . . . 020 7797 7900

MATHER, Mr Nicholas I S BA(Hons); DipLaw M *Oct 1998*
10, 12, 15, 20, 51
Furnival Chambers, London EC4
p934 . . . . 020 7405 3232

Mather-Lees, Mr Michael Anthony LLB(Lond) I *Feb 1981*
15, 62
Thirty Park Place, Cardiff
p973 . . . . 029 2039 8421

Mathers, Ms Wendy MA(Oxon) I *Jan 2005*
9, 97, 11, 47, 14, 38, 92, 40, 93, 37
Radcliffe Chambers, London WC2
p949 . . . . 020 7831 0081

MATHEW, Miss Nergis-Anne BSc(Hons) I *Nov 1981*
10, 20
St Philips Chambers, Birmingham
p969 . . . . 0121 246 7000

Mathew, Mr Oscar MA(English Lit)(Edin) M *Jul 2009*
30
Lamb Chambers, London EC4
p941 . . . . 020 7797 8300

MATHEW, Mr Robin BA(Dublin) L *Nov 1974*
(Q.C.) *34*
New Square Chambers, London WC2
p943 . . . . 020 7419 8000

Mathews, Mr Deni BSc; LLB G *Jul 1996*
15, 20, 12
King's Bench Godolphin Chambers, Truro
p994 . . . . 0845 308 1551
King's Bench Godolphin Chambers, Plymouth
p990 . . . . 0845 308 1551

Mathieson, Mr Guy BA M *Oct 1993*
12
St Johns Buildings, Preston
p990 . . . . 01772 256100
St Johns Buildings, Chester
p974 . . . . 01244 323070
St Johns Buildings, Manchester
p985 . . . . 0161 214 1500
St Johns Buildings, Liverpool
p982 . . . . 0151 243 6000

MATON, Mr Neil Foster M *Nov 2001*
20, 30, 37
Pallant Chambers, Chichester
p974 . . . . 01243 784538

Matovu, Mr Daniel BA(Oxon) I *Nov 1985*
18, 30, 55, 12
2 Temple Gardens, London EC4
p952 . . . . 020 7822 1200

Matovu, Mr Harry BA(Oxon) I *Jul 1988*
11, 24
Brick Court Chambers, London WC2
p927 . . . . 020 7379 3550

Matthew, Mr Alfred David Hugh MA; Dip G *Nov 1987*
15, 62
7 Bedford Row, London WC1
p924 . . . . 020 7242 3555

Matthews, Miss Claire I *Nov 1998*
15, 84
1 Paper Buildings, London EC4
p946 . . . . 020 7353 3728

MATTHEWS, Mr Dennis LLM M *Jul 1973*
53, 40, 12, 24, 30, 36, 39, 27
Crown Office Chambers, London EC4
p929 . . . . 020 7797 8100

Matthews, Mr Duncan H R BA(Oxon) G *Nov 1986*
(Q.C.) *3, 11, 12, 24, 35, 41*
20 Essex Street, London WC2
p932 . . . . 020 7842 1200

MATTHEWS, Janek P MA(Cantab); FCA G *Jul 1972*
34, 57, 58
Pump Court Tax Chambers, London WC1
p948 . . . . 020 7414 8080

Matthews, Mr Julian David LLB; Recorder G *Jul 1979*
53, 30, 40, 27, 84, 85
7 Bedford Row, London WC1
p924 . . . . 020 7242 3555

MATTHEWS, Miss Lisa G *Nov 1974*
Furnival Chambers, London EC4
p934 . . . . 020 7405 3232

Matthews, Ms Lynne I *Nov 1987*
15, 62, 48, 84, 36
Queen Square Chambers, Bristol
p972 . . . . 0117 921 1966

Matthews, Miss Nicola LLB M *Jan 2002*
15, 20, 18, 22, 23, 88
Staple Inn Chambers, London WC1
p951 . . . . 020 7242 5240

Matthews, Mr Richard BA; MA(Cantab) I *Feb 1989*
15, 62
2 Bedford Row, London WC1
p924 . . . . 020 7440 8888

Matthews-Stroud, Miss Jacqueline LLB(Bris) G *Nov 1984*
10, 15, 20
36 Bedford Row, London WC1
p925 . . . . 020 7421 8000

Matthewson, Mr Scott BA(Lond); DipLaw I *Oct 1996*
12, 53, 30, 18, 40, 49
42 Bedford Row, London WC1
p925 . . . . 020 7831 0222

Matthias, Mr David H BA I *Jul 1980*
(Q.C.) *1, 12, 13, 18, 22, 25, 26, 36, 40, 41, 47, 51*
Cornerstone Barristers, London WC1
p929 . . . . 020 7242 4986

Matuk, Miss Helen LLB G *Jun 1990*
10, 20
Walnut House Chambers, Exeter
p975 . . . . 01392 279751

MAUGER, Miss Shanti BA(Oxon) I *Oct 1996*
5, 6, 8, 11, 22, 29, 40, 47, 49, 38, 88, 97
Enterprise Chambers, London WC2
p931 . . . . 020 7405 9471
Enterprise Chambers, Leeds
p977 . . . . 0113 246 0391
Enterprise Chambers, Newcastle upon Tyne
p987 . . . . 0191 222 3344

MAUGHAM, Jolyon LLB(Dunelm) M *Mar 1997*
34, 57, 58
11 New Square, London WC2
p943 . . . . 020 7242 4017

MAULADAD, Miss Farrah LLB M *Oct 1999*
30, 53
Crown Office Chambers, London EC4
p929 . . . . 020 7797 8100

13

Maunder, Mr David M *Dec 1993*
15, 62, 48, 39, 84, 26, 95, 94
Queen Square Chambers, Bristol
p972 . . . . . 0117 921 1966

MAURICI, Mr James Patrick BA(Oxon) I *Nov 1996*
Landmark Chambers, London EC4
p941 . . . . . 020 7430 1221

Mawdsley, Mr Matthew LLB(Hons) I *Nov 1991*
12, 18, 22, 30
St Johns Buildings, Preston
p990 . . . . . 01772 256100
St Johns Buildings, Chester
p974 . . . . . 01244 323070
St Johns Buildings, Manchester
p985 . . . . . 0161 214 1500
St Johns Buildings, Liverpool
p982 . . . . . 0151 243 6000

Mawhinney, Mr Richard Martin BA(Oxon) M *Nov 1977*
13, 30, 40, 11, 67
Outer Temple Chambers, London WC2
p945 . . . . . 020 7353 6381

Mawrey, Ms Eleanor G *Jul 2001*
62, 15, 65, 39, 38, 81, 84
9 Gough Square, London EC4
p935 . . . . . 020 7832 0500

Mawrey, Mr Richard MA(Oxon); Recorder; Deputy High Court Judge G *Feb 1964*
(Q.C.) *1, 3, 11, 26, 40, 47, 51*
Henderson Chambers, London EC4
p937 . . . . . 020 7583 9020

Max, Ms Sally BA(Cantab) L *Oct 1991*
20
Harcourt Chambers, London EC4
p936 . . . . . 0844 561 7135
Harcourt Chambers, Oxford
p989 . . . . . 0844 561 7135

Maxwell, Mr Adrian Robert MA(Oxon) M *Jan 1993*
1, 84, 22, 15, 25, 42, 91
St John's Chambers, Bristol
p972 . . . . . 0117 921 3456

MAXWELL, Mr David Part-time Employment Tribunal Judge I *Feb 1994*
18, 30, 55
St Philips Chambers, Birmingham
p969 . . . . . 0121 246 7000

Maxwell, Miss Judith Mary Angela LLB(B'ham) L *Jul 1988*
22, 1
3 Dr Johnson's Buildings, London EC4
p930 . . . . . 020 7353 4854

Maxwell Lewis, Mr Cameron M *Jul 1974*
49, 11, 8, 44
Lamb Chambers, London EC4
p941 . . . . . 020 7797 8300

MAXWELL-SCOTT, Mr James H BA(Cantab); BCL G *Nov 1995*
84, 36, 68, 24, 30, 53, 40, 12
Crown Office Chambers, London EC4
p929 . . . . . 020 7797 8100

May, Miss Charlotte BA(Oxon) I *Nov 1995*
13, 50
8 New Square, London WC2
p943 . . . . . 020 7405 4321

May, Mr Christopher MA(Cantab) M *Nov 1983*
6, 12, 15, 11
5 St Andrew's Hill, London EC4
p950 . . . . . 020 7332 5400

MAY, Miss Nicola G *Nov 1993*
15, 70, 84, 68
18 Red Lion Court, London EC4
p949 . . . . . 020 7520 6000
18 Red Lion Court (Annexe), Chelmsford
p973 . . . . . 01245 280880

MAY, Mr Nigel BA; Dip(Cantab) I *Jul 1974*
15
Furnival Chambers, London EC4
p934 . . . . . 020 7405 3232

May, Mrs Patricia R Recorder G *Jul 1965*
15, 51
Nine Bedford Row, London WC1
p924 . . . . . 020 7489 2727

Mayall, Mr David MA(Cantab) G *Jul 1979*
8, 11, 12, 18, 22, 29, 30, 40
Lamb Chambers, London EC4
p941 . . . . . 020 7797 8300

Maycock, Miss Elizabeth BA(Warw) I *Jan 1996*
20, 10
Chartlands Chambers, Northampton
p988 . . . . . 01604 603322

MAYES, Mr Ian BA; Recorder M *Jul 1974*
(Q.C.) *11, 12, 18, 29, 34, 36, 3, 5, 16, 24, 41*
Littleton Chambers, London EC4
p941 . . . . . 020 7797 8600

Mayhew, Ms Alice LLB(Exeter); LLM(Cantab) I *Dec 2001*
24, 30, 18, 55, 51, 11, 12
Devereux Chambers, London WC2
p930 . . . . . 020 7353 7534

MAYHEW, Mr David I *Nov 2011*
81, 1
Thirty Nine Essex Street, London WC2
p932 . . . . . 020 7832 1111

Mayhew, Miss Judith LLB(Hons) M *Jul 2000*
10, 12, 20, 22, 15, 18
3 Dr Johnson's Buildings, London EC4
p930 . . . . . 020 7353 4854

MAYNARD, Mr Christopher BA; DipLaw G *Jan 1988*
8, 11, 88, 29, 32, 37
Tanfield Chambers, London WC1
p951 . . . . . 020 7421 5300
Goldsmith Chambers, London EC4
p935 . . . . . 020 7353 6802

Maynard, Mr Matthew LLB(Hons) I *Nov 2003*
12, 15, 20, 30
Northampton Chambers, Northampton
p988 . . . . . 01604 636271

Maynard, Miss Sandra I *Oct 1998*
15, 23, 20
4 Rowchester Court, Birmingham
p968 . . . . . 0121 233 2327

Maynard-Connor, Mr Giles LLB(Lancs) I *Nov 1992*
5, 6, 11, 29, 40, 8, 38, 97
Exchange Chambers, Manchester
p983 . . . . . 0161 833 2722
Exchange Chambers, Liverpool
p980 . . . . . 0151 236 7747
Exchange Chambers, Leeds
p977 . . . . . 0113 203 1970
13 Old Square Chambers, London WC2
p945 . . . . . 020 7831 4445

MAYO, Mr Simon BA I *Nov 1985*
(Q.C.) *15, 62, 95*
187 Fleet Street, London EC4
p933 . . . . . 020 7430 7430

Mayoh, Ms Michelle L *Jul 2003*
8, 11, 22, 38, 56, 89, 97
Kings Chambers, Leeds
p978 . . . . . 0113 242 1123
Kings Chambers, Manchester
p984 . . . . . 0161 832 9082

Mazzag, Mr Anthony MA L *Nov 1996*
12, 27, 30, 40, 53
Cobden House Chambers, Manchester
p983 . . . . . 0161 833 6000

McAllister, Mr Robert I *Oct 2002*
30, 70, 40, 53, 93, 11, 20
9 Gough Square, London EC4
p935 . . . . . 020 7832 0500

MCARDLE, Ms Isabel BA(Hons) L *Jul 2008*
53, 51, 57, 58, 26, 67, 30, 18
1 Crown Office Row, London EC4
p929 . . . . . 020 7797 7500

MCATASNEY, Ms Philippa LLB(Lond) L *Nov 1985*
(Q.C.)
Furnival Chambers, London EC4
p934 . . . . . 020 7405 3232

McAvock, Miss Gabrielle L *Oct 1996*
2 King's Bench Walk, London EC4
p939 . . . . . 020 7353 1746

McBeam, Mr Hamish L *Jan 2002*
30, 18, 89
Queen Square Chambers, Bristol
p972 . . . . . 0117 921 1966

McBride, Mr Gavin M *Sep 1996*
30, 53, 25
Kings Chambers, Leeds
p978 . . . . . 0113 242 1123
Kings Chambers, Manchester
p984 . . . . . 0161 832 9082

MCBRIDE, Mr Jeremy LLB I *Nov 2004*
1, 51, 33
Monckton Chambers, London WC1
p942 . . . . . 020 7405 7211

McBrinn, Ms Diane MA(Hons) G *Jul 2002*
20, 10
Hardwicke, London WC2
p936 . . . . . 020 7242 2523

MCCABE, Miss Louise Assistant Deputy Coroner I *Oct 1996*
20, 12
St Philips Chambers, Birmingham
p969 . . . . . 0121 246 7000

MCCAFFERTY, Miss Jane BA(Cantab); LLM(Cantab) M *Nov 1998*
1, 12, 18, 19, 26, 55, 76
11KBW, London EC4
p938 . . . . . 020 7632 8500

MCCAFFERTY, Mr John A MA(Glasgow); PGC(Lond); CPE(Guildhall) G *Jul 2000*
1, 22, 26
Arden Chambers, London WC1
p923 . . . . . 020 7242 4244

McCafferty, Ms Lynne BA(Oxon) M *Oct 1997*
7, 12, 45, 24
4 Pump Court, London EC4
p947 . . . . . 020 7842 5555

McCain, Mr Charles Stuart M *Oct 2002*
20
Broad Chare Chambers, Newcastle upon Tyne
p986 . . . . . 0191 232 0541

McCall, Mr Christopher H BA(Hons)(Oxon) L *Nov 1966*
(Q.C.) *8, 9, 14, 32, 34, 37*
Maitland Chambers, London WC2
p941 . . . . . 020 7406 1200

McCall, Mr Duncan BA(Oxon) G *Feb 1988*
(Q.C.) *7, 11, 12, 24, 40, 78, 45*
4 Pump Court, London EC4
p947 . . . . . 020 7842 5555

McCalla, Mr Tarquin BA(Hons)(Hull) L *Oct 1994*
15, 20, 30
Charter Chambers, London WC1
p928 . . . . . 020 7618 4400

McCallum, Louise G *May 1999*
10, 20
Zenith Chambers, Leeds
p979 . . . . . 0113 245 5438

McCambley, Ms Dawn L *Oct 2005*
8, 11, 6, 38
11 Stone Buildings, London WC2
p951 . . . . . 020 7831 6381

McCandless, Mr Paul L *Nov 1991*
2 New Street, Leicester
p979 . . . . . 0116 262 5906

McCann, Ms Claire I *Oct 2000*
18, 55, 23, 1, 30, 51, 36
Cloisters, London EC4
p928 . . . . . 020 7827 4000

MCCANN, Katie LLB; LPC L *Oct 2009*
20
Atlantic Chambers, Liverpool
p980 . . . . . 0151 236 4421

McCann, Miss Sarah L *Jan 2001*
1, 5, 88, 11, 74, 38, 24, 40, 93, 37
Hardwicke, London WC2
p936 . . . . . 020 7242 2523

McCarroll, Ms Isobel G *Nov 2001*
4 Breams Buildings, London EC4
p927 . . . . . 020 7092 1900

McCarroll, Mr John Johnston LLB(Dublin) I *Nov 1988*
8, 11, 37, 32, 5, 6, 29
Exchange Chambers, Manchester
p983 . . . . . 0161 833 2722
Exchange Chambers, Liverpool
p980 . . . . . 0151 236 7747
Exchange Chambers, Leeds
p977 . . . . . 0113 203 1970

McCarthy, Mr Damian M *May 1994*
12, 18, 30, 55, 26
Cloisters, London EC4
p928 . . . . . 020 7827 4000

McCarthy, Miss Hui Ling BSc(Hons) I *Jul 2005*
Gray's Inn Tax Chambers, London WC1
p936 . . . . . 020 7242 2642

MCCARTHY, Keelin G *Jan 2007*
23
Mitre House Chambers, London WC1
p942 . . . . . 020 7307 7100

McCarthy, Miss Mary LLB(Hons)(Oxon) M *Oct 1994*
12, 15
Walnut House Chambers, Exeter
p975 . . . . . 01392 279751

McCarthy, Mr Roger J BA G *Jul 1975*
(Q.C.) *20, 10, 63, 26, 1, 51, 36*
Coram Chambers, London EC1
p929 . . . . . 020 7092 3700

McCartney, Mr Kevin M *Nov 1991*
5 Paper Buildings, London EC4
p946 . . . . . 020 7583 6117

McCartney, Mr Peter LLB I *Nov 1983*
72, 15
Regent Chambers, Hanley
p976 . . . . . 01782 286666

McCaughran, Mr John G *Jul 1982*
(Q.C.)
One Essex Court, London EC4
p931 . . . . . 020 7583 2000

MCCAUL, Mr Colin LLB G *Jul 1978*
(Q.C.) *30, 40, 53, 46, 84*
Thirty Nine Essex Street, London WC2
p932 . . . . . 020 7832 1111

McClelland, Mr James L *Jul 2004*
Fountain Court Chambers, London EC4
p934 . . . . . 020 7583 3335

MCCLEMENT, Ms Lynette I *Jan 2002*
Citadel Chambers, Birmingham
p967 . . . . . 0121 233 8500

McClenaghan, Miss Frances L *Jan 2009*
53, 12, 22, 88, 26, 30, 40
1 Chancery Lane, London WC2
p928 . . . . . 0845 634 6666

McClory, Ms Elizabeth I *Jan 2005*
New Court Chambers, Newcastle upon Tyne
p987 . . . . . 0191 232 1980

McCloskey, Miss Louise G *Oct 2002*
15
St Johns Buildings, Preston
p990 . . . . . 01772 256100
St Johns Buildings, Chester
p974 . . . . . 01244 323070
St Johns Buildings, Manchester
p985 . . . . . 0161 214 1500
St Johns Buildings, Liverpool
p982 . . . . . 0151 243 6000

MCCLUGGAGE, Mr Brian MA(Cantab); LLM(Toronto) M *Oct 1995*
18, 24, 30
9 St John Street Chambers, Manchester
p984 . . . . . 0161 955 9000

McCluskey, Mr Alec BA(Oxon) I *Oct 2005*
Maitland Chambers, London WC2
p941 . . . . . 020 7406 1200

MCCLUSKEY, Mr Mark G *Jul 2001*
10, 20
St Mary's Chambers, Nottingham
p989 . . . . . 0115 950 3503

MCCOLGAN, Professor Aileen BA(Hons)(Cantab); LLM L *Jan 2001*
51, 55, 1, 18, 22, 26, 52, 73, 76, 11, 12, 14, 19, 48, 70
Matrix Chambers, London WC1
p942 . . . . . 020 7404 3447

MCCOLGAN, Ms Caroline BVC; GDL; BA(Modern History) I *Jan 2010*
30, 11, 40, 24
Crown Office Chambers, London EC4
p929 . . . . . 020 7797 8100

McCombie, Mr Fergus BA(Hons) G *Oct 1999*
18, 30, 15
St Albans Chambers, St Albans
p992 . . . . . 01727 843383

MCCONNELL, Mr Christopher MA(Oxon) L *Jul 1979*
10, 20, 18
4 King's Bench Walk, London EC4
p939 . . . . . 020 7822 7000

McCormack, Mr Alan LLB L *Oct 1990*
10, 12, 15, 18, 20, 22, 30
Staple Inn Chambers, London WC1
p951 . . . . . 020 7242 5240

McCormack, Mr Ben G *Nov 2005*
22, 51, 88, 1
Garden Court North Chambers, Manchester
p983 . . . . . 0161 236 1840

McCormack, Ms Helen LLB M *Feb 1986*
15, 62
15 New Bridge Street Chambers, London EC4
p943 . . . . . 020 7842 1900

See p1010 for the Key to Work Categories

McCormack, Mr Philip Alexander LLB(Wales) G *Oct 1994*
20, 10
42 Bedford Row, London WC1
p925 . . . . 020 7831 0222

MCCORMACK, Miss Theresa I *Jul 2002*
20
St Philips Chambers, Birmingham
p969 . . . . 0121 246 7000

McCormick, Ms Alison Claire BA(Oxon) M *Nov 1988*
30, 53
Outer Temple Chambers, London WC2
p945 . . . . 020 7353 6381

McCormick, Dr Paul MA; M Phil; D Phil(Oxon) M *Jul 1983*
1, 6, 7, 8, 10, 11, 12, 15, 16, 18, 20, 22, 27, 30
Hampshire Chambers, Portsmouth
p990 . . . . 023 9282 6636 / 9229 7144

McCormick, Mr William LLB G *Jul 1985*
(Q.C.) *11, 12, 22, 30, 15, 16, 56, 18*
Ely Place Chambers, London EC1
p931 . . . . 020 7400 9600

McCoubrey, Mr Robin MA I *Jul 2000*
15, 16
6 King's Bench Walk, London EC4
p939 . . . . 020 7583 0410

MCCOURT, Mr Christopher LLB I *Nov 1993*
40, 20
1 King's Bench Walk, London EC4
p938 . . . . 020 7936 1500

McCoy, Mr Gerard LLB; MSc M *Nov 1986*
(Q.C.) *1, 5, 21, 6, 15*
Argent Chambers, London WC2
p923 . . . . 020 7556 5500

MCCRACKEN, Mr Jamie LLB(Hons); LLM M *Nov 1998*
12, 15, 11, 18, 57, 58, 38, 70, 50, 52
Cornwall Street Chambers, Birmingham
p967 . . . . 0121 233 7500

McCracken, Mr Robert MA(Oxon) I *Jul 1973*
(Q.C.) *1, 46, 51, 26, 28, 31, 36*
Francis Taylor Building, London EC4
p934 . . . . 020 7353 8415

MCCRAE, Miss Fiona LLB G *Jul 1986*
23, 20
Trinity (Newcastle) Chambers, Newcastle upon Tyne
p987 . . . . 0191 232 1927
Trinity (Teesside) Chambers, Middlesbrough
p986 . . . . 01642 247569

MCCREATH, Mr James BA I *Jul 2009*
11, 41, 8, 88, 92, 40, 93
Wilberforce Chambers, London WC2
p953 . . . . 020 7306 0102

McCredie, Ms Fionnula MA(Brunel) M *Oct 1992*
3, 7, 11, 24, 40
Keating Chambers, London WC2
p938 . . . . 020 7544 2600

McCrindell, Mr James BSc(Hons)(Lond) M *Oct 1993*
15
1 Pump Court, London EC4
p947 . . . . 020 7842 7070

McCrudden, Prof Christopher LLB(QUB); LLM(Yale); DPhil(Oxon) G *Oct 1995*
18, 33, 51
Blackstone Chambers, London EC4
p926 . . . . 020 7583 1770

McCue, Mr Donald MA(Cantab) L *Jul 1974*
5, 7, 8, 11, 13, 62
11 Stone Buildings, London WC2
p951 . . . . 020 7831 6381

MCCULLOCH, Mr Niall BA(Oxon); MA(Dundee) L *Oct 2000*
6, 8, 11, 40, 21, 38, 97
Enterprise Chambers, London WC2
p931 . . . . 020 7405 9471
Enterprise Chambers, Leeds
p977 . . . . 0113 246 0391
Enterprise Chambers, Newcastle upon Tyne
p987 . . . . 0191 222 3344

McCulloch-James, Ms Melissa I *Oct 1999*
22, 20
6 King's Bench Walk, London EC4
p939 . . . . 020 7583 0695 / 7353 4931

MCCULLOUGH, Mr Angus BA M *Oct 1990*
(Q.C.) *12, 30, 36, 18, 27, 1, 23, 46, 51, 53*
1 Crown Office Row, London EC4
p929 . . . . 020 7797 7500

McCullough, Miss Louise Clare LLB(Hons) M *Oct 1991*
15, 30, 20, 10
Lamb Building, Brighton
p970 . . . . 01273 820490
Lamb Building, London EC4
p940 . . . . 020 7797 7788

McCune, Mr Rodney James LLB(Hons) L *Nov 2000*
Goldsmith Chambers, London EC4
p935 . . . . 020 7353 6802

Mcdermott, Mr Frazer I *Mar 2004*
20
Broad Chare Chambers, Newcastle upon Tyne
p986 . . . . 0191 232 0541

McDermott, Mr Gerard Francis LLB M *Jul 1978*
(Q.C.) *18, 27, 30, 36, 40, 53, 55*
Outer Temple Chambers, London WC2
p945 . . . . 020 7353 6381
9 St John Street Chambers, Manchester
p984 . . . . 0161 955 9000

MCDERMOTT, Mr John Raymond LLB G *Nov 1976*
(Q.C.) *10, 15, 20, 25*
Chavasse Court Chambers, Liverpool
p980 . . . . 0151 229 2030

McDevitt, Mr Colin John BSc(Hons); DipLaw(City) I *Oct 1995*
18, 30, 40, 11
3PB, Winchester
p994 . . . . 01962 868884

McDonagh, Mr Matthew LLB(Hons) M *Oct 1994*
15, 62, 91, 41, 36, 27
1 Inner Temple Lane, London EC4
p937 . . . . 020 7427 4400

23 Essex Street, London WC2
p932 . . . . 020 7413 0353

MCDONALD, Mr Andrew LLB G *Jul 1971*
12, 30
7 Harrington Street Chambers, Liverpool
p981 . . . . 0151 242 0707

McDonald, Mr Brent G *Oct 2000*
Old Square Chambers, Bristol
p971 . . . . 0117 930 5100
Old Square Chambers, London WC1
p945 . . . . 020 7269 0300

McDonald, Mr George L *Jan 2007*
Four New Square, London WC2
p943 . . . . 020 7822 2000

McDonald, Ms Janet LLB G *Jul 1984*
15
9 Park Place, Cardiff
p973 . . . . 029 2038 2731

McDonald, Mr John William MA; FRSA; FCIArb M *Nov 1981*
2, 11, 7, 24, 22, 30, 12, 40
2 Temple Gardens, London EC4
p952 . . . . 020 7822 1200

MCDONALD, Lawrence LLB(Hons) I *Oct 1996*
8, 11, 93, 88, 1, 38, 40, 31
Atlantic Chambers, Liverpool
p980 . . . . 0151 236 4421

MCDONALD, Ms Margaret I *Nov 2000*
30, 96, 89
Kenworthy's Chambers, Manchester
p984 . . . . 0161 832 4036

McDonald, Mr Mark I *Jan 1997*
15
1 Pump Court, London EC4
p947 . . . . 020 7842 7070

McDonald, Mrs Melanie G *Jan 1990*
No5 Chambers, Bristol
p971 . . . . 0845 210 5555
No5 Chambers, London EC4
p944 . . . . 0845 210 5555
No5 Chambers, Birmingham
p968 . . . . 0845 210 5555

MCDONALD, Mr Paul LLB(Hons) L *Jul 1975*
15
9 St John Street Chambers, Manchester
p984 . . . . 0161 955 9000

McDonald, Miss Rachael L *Nov 2000*
20, 8
Alpha Court Chambers, Leamington Spa
p977 . . . . 0800 634 9650 / 01926 886412

McDonnell, Mr Conrad MA(Oxon) L *Oct 1994*
34, 57, 58
Gray's Inn Tax Chambers, London WC1
p936 . . . . 020 7242 2642

McDonnell, Miss Constance MA(Oxon) L *Jul 2000*
6, 8, 11, 14, 38, 88, 32, 93, 37
3 Stone Buildings, London WC2
p951 . . . . 020 7242 4937

McDonnell, Mr John MA(Oxon); LLM(Harv) L *Jul 1968*
(Q.C.) *5, 6, 8, 9, 11, 12, 49, 50, 22, 29, 32, 40, 36, 37, 56*
13 Old Square Chambers, London WC2
p945 . . . . 020 7831 4445

McDonnell, Mr Martin M *Jan 1997*
12, 15
Warwick House Chambers, London WC1
p953 . . . . 020 7430 2323

McDowell, Mr Daniel Robin LLB; MPhil(Cantab) G *Oct 2001*
20, 15, 12, 11, 2, 1
36 Bedford Row, London WC1
p925 . . . . 020 7421 8000

McElduff, Mr Barry L *Jan 2003*
2 King's Bench Walk, London EC4
p939 . . . . 020 7353 1746

MCELEAVY, Mr Peter G *Jan 1999*
10, 20
1 Garden Court, London EC4
p934 . . . . 020 7797 7900

MCFARLAND, Miss Denise MA(Cantab) I *Jul 1987*
13, 50, 48, 96
3 New Square, London WC2
p943 . . . . 020 7405 1111

MCFARLANE, Mr Alastair D J LLB(Reading) M *Jul 1985*
30, 22, 25, 7, 18
Temple Garden Chambers, London EC4
p952 . . . . 020 7583 1315

MCFARLANE, Ms Cynthia M *Nov 2003*
23, 51, 15, 18, 20, 10, 12
10 King's Bench Walk, London EC4
p940 . . . . 020 7353 7742

MCGAHEY, Ms Cathryn MA(Cantab) I *Nov 1990*
Temple Garden Chambers, London EC4
p952 . . . . 020 7583 1315

McGahey, Ms Elizabeth BA(Wales) I *Oct 1994*
12, 20, 10
Thirty Park Place, Cardiff
p973 . . . . 029 2039 8421

McGarry, Mr Steven L *Mar 2005*
St Johns Buildings, Preston
p990 . . . . 01772 256100
St Johns Buildings, Chester
p974 . . . . 01244 323070
St Johns Buildings, Manchester
p985 . . . . 0161 214 1500
St Johns Buildings, Liverpool
p982 . . . . 0151 243 6000

McGee, Mr Andrew BA(Jurisprudence); BCL L *Nov 1998*
5, 6, 8, 11, 24, 29, 40
Kings Chambers, Leeds
p978 . . . . 0113 242 1123
Kings Chambers, Manchester
p984 . . . . 0161 832 9082
2 Bedford Row, London WC1
p924 . . . . 020 7440 8888

MCGEE, Miss Tamala LLB(Hons); LLM L *Oct 1995*
12, 15, 38, 18, 1, 30, 23
4 King's Bench Walk, London EC4
p939 . . . . 020 7822 7000

McGeorge, Mr Anthony William MA(Cantab) I *Nov 1969*
King's Bench Chambers, Oxford
p989 . . . . 01865 311066
13 King's Bench Walk, London EC4
p940 . . . . 020 7353 7204

McGhee, Mr John Alexander MA(Oxon) L *Jul 1984*
(Q.C.) *1, 3, 5, 6, 7, 8, 9, 11, 12, 13, 14, 22, 24, 26, 28, 29, 31, 32, 37*
Maitland Chambers, London WC2
p941 . . . . 020 7406 1200

McGhee, Mr Philip G *Jan 2003*
15
QEB Hollis Whiteman, London EC4
p948 . . . . 020 7933 8855

McGhee, Mr Stuart LLB; LLM(Dunelm) L *Mar 2000*
10, 12, 20
College Chambers, Southampton
p992 . . . . 023 8023 0338

McGinty, Mr Robert Fraser BA(Oxon) I *Nov 1994*
6, 8, 18, 22, 26, 30, 37, 40, 47, 12
St Johns Buildings, Preston
p990 . . . . 01772 256100
St Johns Buildings, Chester
p974 . . . . 01244 323070
St Johns Buildings, Manchester
p985 . . . . 0161 214 1500
St Johns Buildings, Liverpool
p982 . . . . 0151 243 6000

McGonigal, Mr David Ambrose BA G *Jul 1982*
15
Broadway House Chambers, Leeds
p977 . . . . 0113 246 2600
Broadway House Chambers, Bradford
p969 . . . . 01274 722560

MCGOWAN, Miss Laura G *Jan 2006*
Carmelite Chambers, London EC4
p927 . . . . 020 7936 6300

McGowan, Miss Maura LLB(Hons); Recorder M *Nov 1980*
(Q.C.) *15, 62*
2 Bedford Row, London WC1
p924 . . . . 020 7440 8888

McGrath, Mr Andrew J G *Jul 1983*
30, 53, 18, 55, 68, 94
No5 Chambers, Bristol
p971 . . . . 0845 210 5555
No5 Chambers, London EC4
p944 . . . . 0845 210 5555
No5 Chambers, Birmingham
p968 . . . . 0845 210 5555

MCGRATH, Ms Elizabeth LLB(Hull) I *Nov 1987*
20
St Philips Chambers, Birmingham
p969 . . . . 0121 246 7000

MCGRATH, Mr Frank MA M *Oct 1995*
15, 62, 13
23 Essex Street, London WC2
p932 . . . . 020 7413 0353
1 Inner Temple Lane, London EC4
p937 . . . . 020 7427 4400

MCGRATH, Mr Paul LLB(Lond) G *Oct 1997*
Temple Garden Chambers, London EC4
p952 . . . . 020 7583 1315

McGrath, Mr Paul A BA(Hons); BCL(Oxon) I *Nov 1994*
(Q.C.)
Essex Court Chambers, London WC2
p931 . . . . 020 7813 8000

MCGRATH, Miss Siobhan Evelyn BA(Sussex) M *Jul 1982*
1, 22, 36
Arden Chambers, London WC1
p923 . . . . 020 7242 4244

MCGREGOR, Mr Alistair J LLB(Lond) M *Jul 1974*
(Q.C.) *3, 5, 11, 13, 18, 29*
11KBW, London EC4
p938 . . . . 020 7632 8500

McGregor, Mr Harvey DCL; MA(Oxon); SJD(Harv) I *Feb 1955*
(Q.C.) *49, 30, 40*
Hailsham Chambers, London EC4
p936 . . . . 020 7643 5000

MCGUINNESS, Mr John BA(Lond); Recorder L *Jul 1980*
(Q.C.) *15, 25, 26*
9-12 Bell Yard Chambers, London WC2
p926 . . . . 020 7400 1800

McGuire, Mr Bryan Nicholas LLB(Lond); M Phil M *Jul 1983*
(Q.C.)
Cornerstone Barristers, London WC1
p929 . . . . 020 7242 4986

MCGUIRE, Miss Deirdre LLB(Hons) I *Nov 1983*
10, 15, 20
7 Harrington Street Chambers, Liverpool
p981 . . . . 0151 242 0707

MCGUIRE, Mr Donal Patrick LLB(L'pool); BL(Dublin) G *Jul 1983*
15
Lombard Chambers, London EC1
p941 . . . . 020 7107 2100

McGurk, Dr Brendan M *Jan 2004*
Four New Square, London WC2
p943 . . . . 020 7822 2000

McHugh, David LLB(Hons) L *Oct 1994*
Clerksroom - Administration Centre, Taunton
p993 . . . . 0845 083 3000

MCHUGH, Mr Kelan I *Oct 2007*
10, 20, 15, 25, 22
1 King's Bench Walk, London EC4
p938 . . . . 020 7936 1500

Mchugh, Miss Pauline Mary MA(Cantab) G *Nov 1995*
20
St Johns Buildings, Preston
p990 . . . . 01772 256100
St Johns Buildings, Chester
p974 . . . . 01244 323070

13

St Johns Buildings, Manchester
p985 . . . . 0161 214 1500
St Johns Buildings, Liverpool
p982 . . . . 0151 243 6000

McIlroy, Mr David I *Nov 1995*
12, 15, 18, 25, 30, 51
3PB, London EC4
p946 . . . . 020 7583 8055

MCILWAIN, Mr Sylvester L *Jul 1985*
1 Garden Court, London EC4
p934 . . . . 020 7797 7900
14 Gray's Inn Square, London WC1
p936 . . . . 020 7242 0858

McIntosh, Ms Jacqueline I *Apr 1987*
1 Mitre Court Buildings, London EC4
p942 . . . . 020 7452 8900

McIntosh, Miss Melanie L *Sep 2002*
31, 26, 15, 20, 88, 5, 32, 10, 6, 30
Becket Chambers, Canterbury
p972 . . . . 01227 786331
Becket Chambers, Maidstone
p982 . . . . 01622 230957

McKay, Mr Christopher LLB; Deputy District Judge (Civil) G *Nov 1976*
20, 12
Temple Chambers, Newport
p988 . . . . .01633 267403 / 255855
Temple Chambers, Cardiff
p973 . . . . 029 2039 7364

MCKECHNIE, Miss Emily BA(Hons)(Cantab); LLM(Cantab) L *Jan 2005*
6, 8, 11, 22, 40, 37
Wilberforce Chambers, London WC2
p953 . . . . 020 7306 0102

McKechnie, Mrs Gail G *Jul 2007*
10, 20, 27
Southernhay Chambers, Exeter
p975 . . . . 01392 255777

McKechnie, Mr Stuart I *Oct 1997*
30, 53
9 Gough Square, London EC4
p935 . . . . 020 7832 0500

McKee, Mr Hugh A BA(Hons)(Law) M *Nov 1983*
15, 30
St Johns Buildings, Preston
p990 . . . . 01772 256100
St Johns Buildings, Chester
p974 . . . . 01244 323070
St Johns Buildings, Manchester
p985 . . . . 0161 214 1500
St Johns Buildings, Liverpool
p982 . . . . 0151 243 6000

McKeever, Miss Frances LLM(B'ham) G *Jul 1988*
15
3 Temple Gardens, London EC4
p952 . . . . 020 7353 3102

MCKENDRICK, Mr Ewan LLB(Edin); MA; BCL(Oxon) M *Mar 1998*
11, 40
3 Verulam Buildings, London WC1
p953 . . . . 020 7831 8441

McKendrick, Mr John LLB; LLM; MSc(Oxon); Part-time Tribunal Judge I *Nov 1999*
1, 55, 76, 85, 51, 26, 63, 36
Outer Temple Chambers, London WC2
p945 . . . . 020 7353 6381

McKenna, Miss Anna BA(Hons)(Leeds) M *Nov 1994*
10, 18, 20, 30, 12
42 Bedford Row, London WC1
p925 . . . . 020 7831 0222

McKenna, Mr Brian LLB(L'pool) M *Jun 1983*
15
St Johns Buildings, Preston
p990 . . . . 01772 256100
St Johns Buildings, Chester
p974 . . . . 01244 323070
St Johns Buildings, Manchester
p985 . . . . 0161 214 1500
St Johns Buildings, Liverpool
p982 . . . . 0151 243 6000

MCKENZIE, Miss Lesley Sharon L *Jan 1983*
10, 20, 63
Trinity (Newcastle) Chambers, Newcastle upon Tyne
p987 . . . . 0191 232 1927
Trinity (Teesside) Chambers, Middlesbrough
p986 . . . . 01642 247569

MCKENZIE SMITH, Catherine I *Nov 1960*
12, 11, 6, 21
10 King's Bench Walk, London EC4
p940 . . . . 020 7353 7742

MCKEON, Mr James LLB(Hons) L *Nov 1982*
30, 40, 53, 84
7 Harrington Street Chambers, Liverpool
p981 . . . . 0151 242 0707

McKeone, Ms Mary LLB G *Feb 1986*
15, 51, 72, 70, 82, 62, 96
Garden Court North Chambers, Manchester
p983 . . . . 0161 236 1840

MCKEOWN, Mr Paul Michael Gerard LLB; LLM G *Nov 1998*
15
Mitre House Chambers, London WC1
p942 . . . . 020 7307 7100

MCKEOWN, Ms Sarah BA(Hons) M *Nov 1998*
12, 22, 8, 30
Arden Chambers, London WC1
p923 . . . . 020 7242 4244

Mckie, Ms Suzanne LLB(Hons) I *Nov 1991*
18, 55
Devereux Chambers, London WC2
p930 . . . . 020 7353 7534

McKinlay, Kate M *Oct 2001*
15, 12, 20
Zenith Chambers, Leeds
p979 . . . . 0113 245 5438

MCKINLAY, Miss Kirsty LLB(Hons) L *Mar 2001*
30
9 St John Street Chambers, Manchester
p984 . . . . 0161 955 9000

McKinlay, Miss Vanessa Jane LLB(UWE) M *Oct 2000*
30, 53
St John's Chambers, Bristol
p972 . . . . 0117 921 3456

McKinley, Mr Gregor Charles BA(QUB); DipLaw G *Oct 1992*
10, 15, 20, 22, 23, 25, 30
Holborn Chambers, London WC2
p937 . . . . 020 7242 6060

McKinney, Nicola G *Jan 2004*
4 KBW, London EC4
p938 . . . . 020 7822 8822

MCLACHLAN, Mr David Robert LLB(Hons); LLM I *Oct 1996*
15
7 Harrington Street Chambers, Liverpool
p981 . . . . 0151 242 0707

McLaren, The Hon Michael Duncan BA(Cantab) M *Nov 1981*
(Q.C.)
Fountain Court Chambers, London EC4
p934 . . . . 020 7583 3335

McLarnon, Mr Neil L *Jan 2004*
5, 6, 8, 11, 49, 62, 29, 32, 40, 37
XXIV Old Buildings, London WC2
p944 . . . . 020 7691 2424

McLaughlin, Mr Andrew BA(York) M *Nov 1993*
30, 18, 53
St John's Chambers, Bristol
p972 . . . . 0117 921 3456

McLaughlin, Miss Karen BA M *Jul 1982*
20
Crown Office Row Chambers, Brighton
p970 . . . . 01273 625625

McLaughlin, Victoria G *Jan 2004*
Guildford Chambers, Guildford
p975 . . . . 01483 539131

MCLEOD, Mr Iain I *Jul 1969*
30, 20, 12, 36
3 Hare Court, London EC4
p937 . . . . 020 7415 7800

McLernon, Mr James M *Jan 2007*
Northampton Chambers, Northampton
p988 . . . . 01604 636271

McLevy, Miss Tracey L *Nov 1993*
Goldsmith Chambers, London EC4
p935 . . . . 020 7353 6802

McLinden, Mr John NZ Bar (1975) I *Apr 1975*
Field Court Chambers, London WC1
p933 . . . . 020 7405 6114

McLorinan, Miss Hayley I *Jul 2008*
2 Temple Gardens, London EC4
p952 . . . . 020 7822 1200

McLoughlin, Mr Ian CPE; BSc; SCI L *Nov 1993*
40, 6, 18, 22
4 Breams Buildings, London EC4
p927 . . . . 020 7092 1900

MCLOUGHLIN, Mr Kevin MA(Sheff) M *May 2007*
Temple Garden Chambers, London EC4
p952 . . . . 020 7583 1315

McMahon, Heather M *Jan 1999*
40, 30, 11
Hailsham Chambers, London EC4
p936 . . . . 020 7643 5000

MCMANUS, Mr J Richard MA(Cantab) M *Jul 1982*
(Q.C.) *1, 4, 51, 11, 19, 18, 24, 26, 40, 55*
4-5 Gray's Inn Square, London WC1
p935 . . . . 020 7404 5252

McMaster, Mr Peter LLB(Lond) M *Jul 1981*
(Q.C.) *3, 5, 11, 44, 19, 29, 40*
Serle Court, London WC2
p950 . . . . 020 7242 6105

McMeekin, Mr Ian BA(Hons) M *Jan 1987*
15, 62
Lincoln House Chambers, Manchester
p984 . . . . 0161 832 5701

MCMEEL, Mr Gerard BCL; MA(Oxon) I *Nov 1993*
5, 11, 40, 81
Guildhall Chambers, Bristol
p970 . . . . 0117 930 9000

McMillan, Ms Carol M *Jan 1996*
10, 20
Westgate Chambers, Lewes
p980 . . . . 01273 480510

McMullan, Ms Laura Christina LLB(Exeter) I *Nov 2004*
10, 20
Coram Chambers, London EC1
p929 . . . . 020 7092 3700

McMullan, Mr Manus BA(Oxon) M *Nov 1994*
(Q.C.) *3, 7, 11, 31, 40, 41, 43, 45, 49, 54, 61, 78, 74*
Atkin Chambers, London WC1
p923 . . . . 020 7404 0102

McMurray, Ms N M *Jun 2001*
McMurray Chambers, Bromley
p972 . . . . 020 7566 8244

MCMURTRIE, Mr Christopher G *Jul 2003*
12, 20, 30
Oriel Chambers, Liverpool
p981 . . . . 0151 236 7191 / 236 4321
Oriel Chambers, Preston
p990 . . . . 01772 254764

MCNAB, Miss Mhairi M *Jul 1974*
14 Gray's Inn Square, London WC1
p936 . . . . 020 7242 0858

McNair, Duncan M *Jul 2003*
Clerksroom - Administration Centre, Taunton
p993 . . . . 0845 083 3000

McNair-Wilson, Ms Laura MA; CPE G *Nov 2007*
30, 18, 11, 12, 55, 24
Devereux Chambers, London WC2
p930 . . . . 020 7353 7534
Matrix Chambers, London WC1
p942 . . . . 020 7404 3447

McNall, Dr Christopher M *Jan 2005*
8, 11, 22, 5, 6, 7, 13, 16, 24, 37, 32, 20
18 St John Street Chambers, Manchester
p985 . . . . 0161 278 1800

McNally, Mr Stephen BA; PGDL G *Nov 2003*
15, 30
Exchange Chambers, Manchester
p983 . . . . 0161 833 2722
Exchange Chambers, Liverpool
p980 . . . . 0151 236 7747
Exchange Chambers, Leeds
p977 . . . . 0113 203 1970

MCNAMARA, Mr Andrew LLB; BA(Leeds/Soton) I *Nov 1992*
30, 40, 53, 18
Ropewalk Chambers, Nottingham
p989 . . . . 0115 947 2581

MCNAMARA, Mr James BA I *May 1990*
15
1 High Pavement, Nottingham
p988 . . . . 0115 941 8218

McNamara, Mr Stephen G *Jul 2008*
Kings Chambers, Leeds
p978 . . . . 0113 242 1123
Kings Chambers, Manchester
p984 . . . . 0161 832 9082

McNeill, Mr David I *Jan 2003*
15
5 St Andrew's Hill, London EC4
p950 . . . . 020 7332 5400

McNeill, Ms Jane BA(Oxon); DipLaw(City); Part-Time Employment Tribunal Chair L *Nov 1982*
(Q.C.) *18, 27, 30, 36, 53, 55, 51*
Old Square Chambers, Bristol
p971 . . . . 0117 930 5100
Old Square Chambers, London WC1
p945 . . . . 020 7269 0300

McNeill, Mr John Seddon BSc G *Jul 1974*
30, 12, 53
St Johns Buildings, Preston
p990 . . . . 01772 256100
St Johns Buildings, Chester
p974 . . . . 01244 323070
St Johns Buildings, Manchester
p985 . . . . 0161 214 1500
St Johns Buildings, Liverpool
p982 . . . . 0151 243 6000

McNerney, Mr Kevin I *Jan 1992*
St Johns Buildings, Preston
p990 . . . . 01772 256100
St Johns Buildings, Chester
p974 . . . . 01244 323070
St Johns Buildings, Manchester
p985 . . . . 0161 214 1500
St Johns Buildings, Liverpool
p982 . . . . 0151 243 6000

McNicholas, Mr Eamon BA(Hons); DipLaw(City) L *Oct 1994*
34
Temple Tax Chambers, London EC4
p952 . . . . .020 7353 7884 / 7353 8982

MCNIFF, Mr Matthew G *Oct 1992*
15, 25
18 Red Lion Court, London EC4
p949 . . . . 020 7520 6000
18 Red Lion Court (Annexe), Chelmsford
p973 . . . . 01245 280880

MCNULTY, Mr Lawrence BA; BCL M *Nov 1985*
15
Tooks Chambers, London EC4
p953 . . . . 020 7842 7575

McParland, Mr Michael BA(Oxon) I *Jul 1983*
40, 46, 26, 31, 50, 56
Quadrant Chambers, London EC4
p948 . . . . 020 7583 4444

MCPHERSON, Mr George I *Jan 2003*
24, 5, 40, 50
3 Verulam Buildings, London WC1
p953 . . . . 020 7831 8441

McPherson, Mr Graeme MA G *Nov 1993*
(Q.C.) *8, 12, 24, 40*
Four New Square, London WC2
p943 . . . . 020 7822 2000

McQuail, Ms Katherine BA(Oxon) M *Nov 1989*
8, 11, 14, 22, 29, 32, 37, 40
Radcliffe Chambers, London WC2
p949 . . . . 020 7831 0081

MCQUATER, Mr Ewan MA(Cantab) M *Jul 1985*
(Q.C.) *5, 6, 11, 40*
3 Verulam Buildings, London WC1
p953 . . . . 020 7831 8441

McSorley, Miss Hannah I *Nov 2009*
Guildford Chambers, Guildford
p975 . . . . 01483 539131

McTague, Miss Meghann Rose BA I *Oct 2004*
15, 25, 36, 39, 48
2 Temple Gardens, London EC4
p952 . . . . 020 7822 1200

MCVAY, Ms Bridget I *Feb 1990*
20, 23
Octagon Chambers, Taunton
p993 . . . . 01823 331919

Meacher, Miss Alison LLB(Hons)(Law with Politics) L *Nov 1998*
22, 51, 63, 93, 88
Hardwicke, London WC2
p936 . . . . 020 7242 2523

MEACHIN, Miss Vanessa LLB(Hons); Recorder I *Oct 1990*
20
St Philips Chambers, Birmingham
p969 . . . . 0121 246 7000

Mead, Mr Larry M *Jan 1977*
11
4 Rowchester Court, Birmingham
p968 . . . . 0121 233 2327

Mead, Mr Philip LLB(B'ham); LLM(Florence) L *Jul 1989*
18, 30, 46, 59, 36, 48, 55, 51
Old Square Chambers, Bristol
p971 . . . . 0117 930 5100

 See p1010 for the Key to Work Categories

Old Square Chambers, London WC1
p945 . . . . . 020 7269 0300

Meade, Mr Richard L *Nov 1991*
(Q.C.) *13, 45, 50, 56*
8 New Square, London WC2
p943 . . . . . 020 7405 4321

Meadowcroft, Mr Stephen G *Jan 1973*
(Q.C.) *15*
Exchange Chambers, Manchester
p983 . . . . . 0161 833 2722
Exchange Chambers, Liverpool
p980 . . . . . 0151 236 7747
Exchange Chambers, Leeds
p977 . . . . . 0113 203 1970

MEADWAY, Miss Susannah BA(Oxon) M *Jul 1988*
8, 9, 14, 22, 32, 34, 37
Ten Old Square, London WC2
p945 . . . . . 020 7405 0758

Meager, Ms Rowena L *Jul 2007*
31, 46, 60, 78
No5 Chambers, Bristol
p971 . . . . . 0845 210 5555
No5 Chambers, London EC4
p944 . . . . . 0845 210 5555
No5 Chambers, Birmingham
p968 . . . . . 0845 210 5555

MEAKIN, Mr Ian G *Nov 1991*
49, 41, 3, 8, 9, 11, 97, 67, 62, 24, 21, 89, 56
XXIV Old Buildings, London WC2
p944 . . . . . 020 7691 2424

Meares, Mr Nigel BA(Cantab) M *Nov 1975*
8, 11, 13, 29, 32, 37, 62
11 Stone Buildings, London WC2
p951 . . . . . 020 7831 6381

Medcroft, Mr Nicholas LLB L *Sep 1998*
5, 11, 81, 84, 62
Outer Temple Chambers, London WC2
p945 . . . . . 020 7353 6381

MEDD, Mr James MA(Cantab) M *Jul 1985*
40, 24, 30, 74, 7, 11, 12, 36, 27
Crown Office Chambers, London EC4
p929 . . . . . 020 7797 8100

Medhurst, Mr David Charles LLB G *Nov 1969*
8, 11, 12, 15, 18, 19, 22, 23
4 Brick Court Chambers, London EC4
p927 . . . . . 020 7832 3200

Medland, Mr Simon BA(Hull); DipLaw M *Oct 1991*
(Q.C.) *15, 36*
Exchange Chambers, Manchester
p983 . . . . . 0161 833 2722
Exchange Chambers, Liverpool
p980 . . . . . 0151 236 7747
Exchange Chambers, Leeds
p977 . . . . . 0113 203 1970

MEECH, Miss Jennifer MA(Cantab); GDL M *Oct 2008*
66, 49, 6, 8, 11, 97, 47, 67, 62, 22, 38, 88, 89, 29, 32, 40, 93, 37
Enterprise Chambers, London WC2
p931 . . . . . 020 7405 9471
Enterprise Chambers, Leeds
p977 . . . . . 0113 246 0391
Enterprise Chambers, Newcastle upon Tyne
p987 . . . . . 0191 222 3344

MEEGAN, Mr Trevor L *Jan 2000*
Citadel Chambers, Birmingham
p967 . . . . . 0121 233 8500

MEEK, Ms Susan G *Nov 1997*
Furnival Chambers, London EC4
p934 . . . . . 020 7405 3232

MEEKE, Mr R Martin J LLB G *Jul 1973*
(Q.C.) *15, 18, 20, 25*
Colleton Chambers, Exeter
p975 . . . . . 01392 274898

Megyery, Ayshea Khatune LLB(Leeds) M *Oct 1997*
15, 20
No 6 Barristers Chambers, Leeds
p978 . . . . . 0113 245 9763

Mehigan, Mr James LLB(Hons)(Dublin); MPhil(Cantab); PhD(Open) M *Nov 2008*
15, 51
Tooks Chambers, London EC4
p953 . . . . . 020 7842 7575

Mehigan, Mr Simon L *Jul 1980*
(Q.C.) *44, 18, 25, 49*
Francis Taylor Building, London EC4
p934 . . . . . 020 7353 8415

MEHRZAD, Mr John MA; DEA; M.St(Oxon) I *Oct 2005*
Littleton Chambers, London EC4
p941 . . . . . 020 7797 8600

Mehta, Miss Anita LLB(Hons) L *Oct 2002*
15
Crown Office Row Chambers, Brighton
p970 . . . . . 01273 625625
Westgate Chambers, Lewes
p980 . . . . . 01273 480510

Mehta, Mr Nikhil LLB(Hons)(Bris) L *Jan 1976*
34, 57, 58
Gray's Inn Tax Chambers, London WC1
p936 . . . . . 020 7242 2642

Mehta, Mr Sailesh L *Jul 1986*
72, 15, 62, 46, 34
1 Gray's Inn Square, London WC1
p935 . . . . . 020 7405 8946
2 Hare Court, London EC4
p937 . . . . . 020 7353 5324
18 Red Lion Court, London EC4
p949 . . . . . 020 7520 6000
18 Red Lion Court (Annexe), Chelmsford
p973 . . . . . 01245 280880

MEICHEN, Mr Jonathan I *Jan 2006*
18, 12
St Philips Chambers, Birmingham
p969 . . . . . 0121 246 7000

Meikle, Mr Robert LLB(B'ham) G *Jul 1970*
15
Goldsmith Chambers, London EC4
p935 . . . . . 020 7353 6802

Mejzner, Mr Stephen LLB M *Nov 1978*
15, 25
Charter Chambers, London WC1
p928 . . . . . 020 7618 4400

MELLO, Mr Michael J MA G *Jul 1972*
(Q.C.)
Ten Old Square, London WC2
p945 . . . . . 020 7405 0758

MELLOR, Mr Christopher LLB; BA; BVC M *Nov 1999*
1, 12, 51, 53, 30, 40, 34
1 Crown Office Row, London EC4
p929 . . . . . 020 7797 7500

Mellor, Faye M *Jan 2005*
KCH Garden Square Chambers, Nottingham
p989 . . . . . 0115 941 8851
KCH Garden Square Chambers, Leicester
p979 . . . . . 0115 941 8851

Mellor, Mr James MA(Cantab) M *Jul 1986*
(Q.C.) *13, 45, 50, 56*
8 New Square, London WC2
p943 . . . . . 020 7405 4321

Mellor, Miss Rachel L *Jan 2004*
8, 10, 47, 48, 55, 18, 20, 38, 88, 25, 30, 94
Broadway House Chambers, Leeds
p977 . . . . . 0113 246 2600
Broadway House Chambers, Bradford
p969 . . . . . 01274 722560

Melly, Miss Kama M *Jan 1997*
15, 20, 10
No 6 Barristers Chambers, Leeds
p978 . . . . . 0113 245 9763

Melton, Mr Christopher LLB(Bris) G *Jul 1982*
(Q.C.) *53, 30, 12, 15, 27, 36, 40*
42 Bedford Row, London WC1
p925 . . . . . 020 7831 0222
Byrom Street Chambers, Manchester
p983 . . . . . 0161 829 2100

Melville, Miss Elizabeth E J BA(Hons)(Oxon); DipLaw G *Oct 1994*
18, 30, 53, 36, 55, 51
Old Square Chambers, Bristol
p971 . . . . . 0117 930 5100
Old Square Chambers, London WC1
p945 . . . . . 020 7269 0300

MELVILLE, Mr Richard David I *Jul 1975*
(Q.C.) *40, 30, 11, 53*
Thirty Nine Essex Street, London WC2
p932 . . . . . 020 7832 1111

Melville-Shreeve, Mr Michael LLB(Exon); Deputy District Judge G *Jul 1986*
6, 7, 20, 12, 18, 29, 30, 27
Walnut House Chambers, Exeter
p975 . . . . . 01392 279751

Melwani, Miss Poonam MA(Cantab) I *Nov 1989*
11, 35, 3, 24, 30, 4
Quadrant Chambers, London EC4
p948 . . . . . 020 7583 4444

MENARY, Mr Andrew BA(Hons)(Law) I *Nov 1982*
(Q.C.) *15, 62, 30, 84*
Furnival Chambers, London EC4
p934 . . . . . 020 7405 3232
7 Harrington Street Chambers, Liverpool
p981 . . . . . 0151 242 0707

Menashy, Miss Michelle G *Oct 2003*
One Essex Court, London EC4
p931 . . . . . 020 7583 2000

MENDELLE, Mr Paul LLB L *Jul 1981*
(Q.C.) *15, 62, 36*
25 Bedford Row, London WC1
p925 . . . . . 020 7067 1500

Mendelson, Mr Maurice MA(Oxon); D Phil L *Nov 1965*
(Q.C.) *33, 51, 89*
Blackstone Chambers, London EC4
p926 . . . . . 020 7583 1770

Mendes Da Costa, Mr David I *Nov 1976*
20, 23, 30, 8, 22, 11
Two King's Bench Walk, London EC4
p939 . . . . . 020 7353 7202 / 7353 3909

Mendoza, Mr Colin BA; LLM I *Nov 1983*
30, 15, 11, 25, 18, 27, 20
Devereux Chambers, London WC2
p930 . . . . . 020 7353 7534

MENDOZA, Miss Elizabeth Kagaba I *Jul 1999*
23, 1, 20, 63
Trinity (Newcastle) Chambers, Newcastle upon Tyne
p987 . . . . . 0191 232 1927
Trinity (Teesside) Chambers, Middlesbrough
p986 . . . . . 01642 247569

MENSAH, Miss Lorraine S L LLB(Hons) G *Oct 1997*
23, 18, 12, 30
St Johns Buildings, Preston
p990 . . . . . 01772 256100
St Johns Buildings, Chester
p974 . . . . . 01244 323070
St Johns Buildings, Manchester
p985 . . . . . 0161 214 1500
St Johns Buildings, Liverpool
p982 . . . . . 0151 243 6000

MENSAH, Martin LLB I *Oct 2004*
15, 76, 18
Atlantic Chambers, Liverpool
p980 . . . . . 0151 236 4421

Menzies, Mr Gordon MA(Cantab) I *Oct 1998*
12, 15, 20, 22, 26, 30, 31
6-8 Mill Street, Maidstone
p982 . . . . . 01622 688094 / 688095
6 Pump Court, London EC4
p947 . . . . . 020 7797 8400

Menzies, Mr Jennifer LLB(Hons)(L'pool) L *Oct 2002*
20, 12
St Johns Buildings, Preston
p990 . . . . . 01772 256100
St Johns Buildings, Chester
p974 . . . . . 01244 323070
St Johns Buildings, Manchester
p985 . . . . . 0161 214 1500
St Johns Buildings, Liverpool
p982 . . . . . 0151 243 6000

Menzies, Mr Richard MA(Cantab) M *Nov 1993*
12, 30, 40, 53
Lamb Chambers, London EC4
p941 . . . . . 020 7797 8300

Mercer, Mr David BA(Oxon); DipLaw L *Jul 1980*
20, 30, 18, 27, 12, 53, 40, 47
St Johns Buildings, Preston
p990 . . . . . 01772 256100
St Johns Buildings, Chester
p974 . . . . . 01244 323070
St Johns Buildings, Manchester
p985 . . . . . 0161 214 1500
St Johns Buildings, Liverpool
p982 . . . . . 0151 243 6000

Mercer, Mr Geoffrey LLB(Soton); Recorder I *Nov 1975*
(Q.C.) *12, 15, 25, 27, 30*
Walnut House Chambers, Exeter
p975 . . . . . 01392 279751

Mercer, Mr Hugh MA(Cantab) M *Jul 1985*
(Q.C.)
Essex Court Chambers, London WC2
p931 . . . . . 020 7813 8000

MERCER, Mr Ian L *Oct 2001*
10, 12, 15, 20
Chavasse Court Chambers, Liverpool
p980 . . . . . 0151 229 2030

Mercer, Miss Kirsten LLB(Hons) I *Jan 2006*
Park Court Chambers, Leeds
p978 . . . . . 0113 243 3277

MEREDITH, Ms Catherine Amy G *Jan 2008*
23, 15
Mitre House Chambers, London WC1
p942 . . . . . 020 7307 7100

MEREDITH, Mr Christopher LLB I *Jul 1988*
Furnival Chambers, London EC4
p934 . . . . . 020 7405 3232

Meredith, Miss Clare LLB; BVC L *Oct 2000*
20, 10, 86
36 Bedford Row, London WC1
p925 . . . . . 020 7421 8000

Meredith, Mr George G *Jul 1969*
10, 20
King's Bench Godolphin Chambers, Truro
p994 . . . . . 0845 308 1551
King's Bench Godolphin Chambers, Plymouth
p990 . . . . . 0845 308 1551

Meredith, Mr Philip Granville BA(Dunelm) I *Jul 1979*
15
Westgate Chambers, Lewes
p980 . . . . . 01273 480510

MEREDITH-HARDY, Mr John MA(Hons)(St Andrews) I *Jun 1989*
30, 53, 40, 12
Farrar's Building, London EC4
p933 . . . . . 020 7583 9241

Merrett, Ms Louise Ann BA(Cantab) G *Nov 1995*
Fountain Court Chambers, London EC4
p934 . . . . . 020 7583 3335

MERRICK, Miss Nicola LLB G *Nov 1983*
Furnival Chambers, London EC4
p934 . . . . . 020 7405 3232

Merrigan, Mr David MA(Oxon) L *Jul 2004*
20, 10, 96
Lamb Building, Brighton
p970 . . . . . 01273 820490
Lamb Building, London EC4
p940 . . . . . 020 7797 7788

Merry, Mr Hugh G LLB(Bris) I *Jul 1979*
15, 10, 20, 12, 18, 22, 30
12 College Place, Southampton
p992 . . . . . 023 8032 0320

MERRYLEES, Mr Gavin LLB(Lond) G *Nov 1964*
10, 12, 20, 30, 32, 37, 23
Tanfield Chambers, London WC1
p951 . . . . . 020 7421 5300

MERZ, Mr Richard LLB(Soton); Recorder I *Jul 1972*
15
9-12 Bell Yard Chambers, London WC2
p926 . . . . . 020 7400 1800

MESSLING, Mr Lawrence David BA(Keele) M *Jul 1983*
20
St Philips Chambers, Birmingham
p969 . . . . . 0121 246 7000

METAXA, William M *Nov 1995*
10, 20
Renaissance Chambers, London WC1
p949 . . . . . 020 7404 1111

Metcalf, Miss Louise I *Oct 1997*
30, 12, 53
Exchange Chambers, Manchester
p983 . . . . . 0161 833 2722
Exchange Chambers, Liverpool
p980 . . . . . 0151 236 7747
Exchange Chambers, Leeds
p977 . . . . . 0113 203 1970

Metcalfe, Mr Ian LLB(Hons) M *Nov 1985*
15
Cobden House Chambers, Manchester
p983 . . . . . 0161 833 6000

METHUEN, Mr Richard Recorder L *Nov 1972*
(Q.C.) *30, 40, 53, 94, 96*
12 King's Bench Walk, London EC4
p940 . . . . . 020 7583 0811

Mettam, Miss Hannah I *Nov 2006*
Northampton Chambers, Northampton
p988 . . . . . 01604 636271

Metzer, Mr Anthony MA(Hons)(Oxon); Recorder M *Jan 1987*
1, 12, 15, 62
Argent Chambers, London WC2
p923 . . . . . 020 7556 5500

Mew, Mr Graeme BA; LLB(Windsor) I *Jul 1982*
8, 12, 24, 40, 56, 41
Four New Square, London WC2
p943 . . . . . 020 7822 2000

Meyer, Miss Birgitta BA(Cantab) M *Nov 1992*
6, 8, 11, 38
11 Stone Buildings, London WC2
p951 . . . . . 020 7831 6381

Meyer, Miss Lorna I *Jul 1986*
(Q.C.) *20, 10, 63*
No5 Chambers, Bristol
p971 . . . . . 0845 210 5555
No5 Chambers, London EC4
p944 . . . . . 0845 210 5555
No5 Chambers, Birmingham
p968 . . . . . 0845 210 5555

MIAH, Mr Zacharias LLM; LLB I *Nov 1990*
Carmelite Chambers, London EC4
p927 . . . . . 020 7936 6300

Miall, Mr Hugh L *Jul 2009*
13 Old Square Chambers, London WC2
p945 . . . . . 020 7831 4445

Mian, Mr Naeem BA(Hons) I *Oct 2002*
15, 51, 36, 63, 1
Tooks Chambers, London EC4
p953 . . . . . 020 7842 7575

Mian, Miss Najma G *Jan 2006*
St Ives Chambers, Birmingham
p969 . . . . . 0121 236 0863

MICAH, Carol L *Jan 2009*
10, 63
Kenworthy's Chambers, Manchester
p984 . . . . . 0161 832 4036

Michael, Mr Nicholas LLB(Hons); LLM M *Jul 2003*
11, 22, 30, 53
East Anglian Chambers, Norwich
p988 . . . . . 01603 617351
East Anglian Chambers, Colchester
p975 . . . . . 01206 572756
East Anglian Chambers, Chelmsford
p973 . . . . . 01245 215660
East Anglian Chambers, Ipswich
p976 . . . . . 01473 214481

Michael, Mr Simon LLB(Lond) M *Nov 1978*
30, 40, 53, 68, 97
No5 Chambers, Bristol
p971 . . . . . 0845 210 5555
No5 Chambers, London EC4
p944 . . . . . 0845 210 5555
No5 Chambers, Birmingham
p968 . . . . . 0845 210 5555

Michaels, Ms Amanda L BA(Dunelm); MA(Bruges) G *Jul 1981*
6, 8, 11, 13, 19, 22, 29, 32, 37
Hogarth Chambers, London WC2
p937 . . . . . 020 7404 0404

Michalos, Miss Christina Antigone Diana LLB; MA G *Nov 1994*
13, 50, 51, 56
5RB, London WC1
p948 . . . . . 020 7242 2902

Michell, Mr Paul MA(Cantab); DipLaw(City) M *Nov 1991*
1, 11, 12, 18, 30, 40, 55
Cloisters, London EC4
p928 . . . . . 020 7827 4000

MIDDLETON, Ms Caroline BA; DipLaw I *Oct 2002*
20, 10
1 Garden Court, London EC4
p934 . . . . . 020 7797 7900

MIDDLETON, Mr Christopher LLB(Nott'm) I *Jan 2002*
46, 12, 30, 18, 47, 62, 22, 40
Oriel Chambers, Liverpool
p981 . . . . . 0151 236 7191 / 236 4321
Oriel Chambers, Preston
p990 . . . . . 01772 254764

Middleton, Miss Claire LLB(Hons)(Newc) L *Oct 1991*
10, 12, 15, 20, 30
Broad Chare Chambers, Newcastle upon Tyne
p986 . . . . . 0191 232 0541

Middleton, Ms Di I *Oct 1997*
15
Tooks Chambers, London EC4
p953 . . . . . 020 7842 7575

Middleton, Mr Joseph BSc; LLB I *Nov 1997*
1, 51, 23, 15, 33
Doughty Street Chambers, London WC1
p930 . . . . . 020 7404 1313

Midgley, Mr Andrew BA(Hons)(English) G *Oct 2000*
18
Old Square Chambers, Bristol
p971 . . . . . 0117 930 5100
Old Square Chambers, London WC1
p945 . . . . . 020 7269 0300

Midgley, Miss Anna BA(Hons)(Cantab) M *Oct 2005*
10, 12, 15, 18, 20, 30
Albion Chambers, Bristol
p970 . . . . . 0117 927 2144

Midwinter, Mr Stephen BA(Hons); LLM(Law) M *Jul 2002*
11, 24, 5, 1, 19
Brick Court Chambers, London WC2
p927 . . . . . 020 7379 3550

Mildon, Mr David W MA; LLB(Cantab) M *Jul 1980*
(Q.C.)
Essex Court Chambers, London WC2
p931 . . . . . 020 7813 8000

Miles, Mr Edward Napier Tremayne BA(Oxon) I *Feb 1989*
30, 53
Lamb Chambers, London EC4
p941 . . . . . 020 7797 8300

MILES, Miss Nicola LLB(Hons) L *Oct 1999*
15, 10, 20
7 Harrington Street Chambers, Liverpool
p981 . . . . . 0151 242 0707

Miles, Mr Richard Iain BA(Kingston) G *Nov 1997*
12, 18, 22, 25, 30, 47
One Essex Court, London EC4
p931 . . . . . 020 7936 3030

MILES, Mr Robert J BA(Oxon); BCL L *Nov 1987*
(Q.C.) *6, 11, 29*
4 Stone Buildings, London WC2
p951 . . . . . 020 7242 5524

MILFORD, Mr Julian Robert BA(Oxon) M *Jul 2000*
1, 18, 26, 51, 55
11KBW, London EC4
p938 . . . . . 020 7632 8500

Mill, Mr Ian MA(Cantab) M *Jul 1981*
(Q.C.) *3, 11, 12, 13, 24, 29, 36, 50, 56, 41, 62, 40, 89*
Blackstone Chambers, London EC4
p926 . . . . . 020 7583 1770

Millar, Mr Gavin BA L *Jul 1981*
(Q.C.) *1, 12, 16, 18, 26, 51*
Doughty Street Chambers, London WC1
p930 . . . . . 020 7404 1313

Miller, Miss Amanda I *Jul 2005*
20
Broad Chare Chambers, Newcastle upon Tyne
p986 . . . . . 0191 232 0541

Miller, Mr Andrew LLB(Soton); FCIArb I *Jul 1989*
7, 11, 12, 24, 30, 40, 41
2 Temple Gardens, London EC4
p952 . . . . . 020 7822 1200

Miller, Mr Christopher LLB L *Oct 1998*
14 Gray's Inn Square, London WC1
p936 . . . . . 020 7242 0858

Miller, Mr Daniel BA(Hons)(Philosophy) L *Jan 2005*
20, 10
Crown Office Row Chambers, Brighton
p970 . . . . . 01273 625625

MILLER, Mr David LLB(Hons) I *Oct 1998*
Furnival Chambers, London EC4
p934 . . . . . 020 7405 3232

Miller, Mr Ian LLB(Hons) G *Oct 1999*
12, 30, 40, 53, 22, 59
1 Chancery Lane, London WC2
p928 . . . . . 0845 634 6666
Broadway House Chambers, Leeds
p977 . . . . . 0113 246 2600
Broadway House Chambers, Bradford
p969 . . . . . 01274 722560

Miller, Mr Jonathan BA(Hons)(Oxon) M *Nov 1996*
1, 6, 11, 12, 13, 18, 29, 31, 33
One Essex Court, London EC4
p931 . . . . . 020 7936 3030

Miller, Miss Kate BA(Hons)(Dunelm) G *Jul 2003*
15, 10, 12, 20, 25
East Anglian Chambers, Norwich
p988 . . . . . 01603 617351
East Anglian Chambers, Colchester
p975 . . . . . 01206 572756
East Anglian Chambers, Chelmsford
p973 . . . . . 01245 215660
East Anglian Chambers, Ipswich
p976 . . . . . 01473 214481

MILLER, Mr Keith G *Jan 1973*
Fountain Chambers, Middlesbrough
p986 . . . . . 01642 804040

Miller, Mr Nicholas LLB; Former solicitor (1985) I *Jul 1994*
20
St John's Chambers, Bristol
p972 . . . . . 0117 921 3456

MILLER, Mr Paul W MA; Recorder L *Jul 1974*
30, 12, 29, 18, 88
Wilberforce Chambers, Hull
p976 . . . . . 01482 323264

Miller, Mr Peter LLB(Lond) L *Oct 1993*
1, 11, 12, 15, 18, 20, 22, 25, 26, 29, 30, 31, 36
Cornerstone Barristers, London WC1
p929 . . . . . 020 7242 4986

MILLER, Mr Richard Hugh BSc M *Jul 1976*
(Q.C.) *13, 19, 44*
3 New Square, London WC2
p943 . . . . . 020 7405 1111

Miller, Mr Richard James LLB G *Oct 1991*
10, 20
Temple Chambers, Newport
p988 . . . . . 01633 267403 / 255855
Temple Chambers, Cardiff
p973 . . . . . 029 2039 7364

Miller, Miss Sarah Elizabeth Barbara G *Nov 1971*
3, 11, 35
Stone Chambers, London WC1
p951 . . . . . 020 7440 6900

Miller, Mr Simon LLB(Hons) L *Oct 1996*
20, 10, 14, 63
Harcourt Chambers, London EC4
p936 . . . . . 0844 561 7135
Harcourt Chambers, Oxford
p989 . . . . . 0844 561 7135

MILLER, Mr Stephen BA(Oxon); Recorder M *Jul 1971*
(Q.C.) *12, 20, 27, 30, 36, 53, 40, 49*
1 Crown Office Row, London EC4
p929 . . . . . 020 7797 7500

MILLER, Ms Wendy M *Jan 2001*
Citadel Chambers, Birmingham
p967 . . . . . 0121 233 8500

Millett, Mr Kenneth James LLB I *Jul 1988*
15, 62
2 Hare Court, London EC4
p937 . . . . . 020 7353 5324

Millett, Mr Richard L BA(Cantab) L *Jul 1985*
(Q.C.)
Essex Court Chambers, London WC2
p931 . . . . . 020 7813 8000

Milligan, Mr Iain MA(Cantab) I *Jul 1973*
(Q.C.) *3, 11, 12, 24, 35, 41, 61*
20 Essex Street, London WC2
p932 . . . . . 020 7842 1200

Milliken-Smith, Mr Mark LLB(Hons)(Bris); Recorder G *Nov 1986*
(Q.C.) *15, 62*
2 Bedford Row, London WC1
p924 . . . . . 020 7440 8888

Millin, Ms Leslie M LLB G *Nov 1988*
Clerksroom - Administration Centre, Taunton
p993 . . . . . 0845 083 3000

MILLINGTON, Mr Christopher John Recorder G *Jul 1976*
(Q.C.) *15, 62, 82, 72, 70*
St Philips Chambers, Birmingham
p969 . . . . . 0121 246 7000

MILLINGTON, Mr Joseph LLB; MPhil I *Jan 2009*
10, 11, 15, 20
St Philips Chambers, Birmingham
p969 . . . . . 0121 246 7000

Millington, Mr Oliver G *Jul 2003*
30, 53, 70, 93, 20, 15, 18
9 Gough Square, London EC4
p935 . . . . . 020 7832 0500

MILLS, Mr Alexander G *Jul 2004*
15, 13, 62
23 Essex Street, London WC2
p932 . . . . . 020 7413 0353

Mills, Miss Barbara LLB(Hull) I *Oct 1990*
10, 20
4 Paper Buildings, London EC4
p946 . . . . . 020 7583 0816

MILLS, Mr Ben I *Oct 2000*
15, 84, 62, 25, 48
St Philips Chambers, Birmingham
p969 . . . . . 0121 246 7000

Mills, Corey LLB M *Nov 1987*
10, 20, 12
Becket Chambers, Canterbury
p972 . . . . . 01227 786331
Becket Chambers, Maidstone
p982 . . . . . 01622 230957

MILLS, Mr Kristian LLB(Hons) M *Oct 1998*
12, 30, 22, 48, 1, 38, 11, 8, 18
Trinity (Newcastle) Chambers, Newcastle upon Tyne
p987 . . . . . 0191 232 1927
Trinity (Teesside) Chambers, Middlesbrough
p986 . . . . . 01642 247569

MILLS, Mr Simon MA(Cantab) L *Nov 1994*
11, 6, 5, 62
Five Paper, London EC4
p946 . . . . . 020 7815 3200

MILLS, Mr Stuart LLB(Hons) M *Oct 1992*
15, 12, 62, 51, 30
Oriel Chambers, Liverpool
p981 . . . . . 0151 236 7191 / 236 4321
Oriel Chambers, Preston
p990 . . . . . 01772 254764

Milmo, Mr Patrick Helenus MA(Cantab) M *Jul 1962*
(Q.C.) *13, 16, 36, 50, 51, 56*
5RB, London WC1
p948 . . . . . 020 7242 2902

MILNE, Mr Alexander G *Nov 1981*
(Q.C.) *15, 36, 62, 71, 91*
18 Red Lion Court, London EC4
p949 . . . . . 020 7520 6000
18 Red Lion Court (Annexe), Chelmsford
p973 . . . . . 01245 280880

MILNE, Mrs Arlene M *Jan 1999*
20, 30
Cobden House Chambers, Manchester
p983 . . . . . 0161 833 6000

MILNE, Mr David C FCA; MA(Oxon) L *Jul 1970*
(Q.C.) *34, 57*
Pump Court Tax Chambers, London WC1
p948 . . . . . 020 7414 8080

Milne, Mr Duncan MPhil(Cantab); BA(Hons)(York) L *Oct 2007*
72, 15, 70, 83, 84, 25, 91
12 College Place, Southampton
p992 . . . . . 023 8032 0320

Milne, Mr Michael BA; FRICS; FCIArb L *Jul 1987*
7, 41, 49
Resolution Chambers, Malvern
p982 . . . . . 01684 541008

MILNE, Mr Richard MA(Hons)(Oxon); DipLaw M *Oct 1992*
15, 36, 27, 62
23 Essex Street, London WC2
p932 . . . . . 020 7413 0353

Milner, Mr Alexander Nathan BA(Hons)(Modern & Medieval Languages); BVC; MA L *Oct 2006*
Fountain Court Chambers, London EC4
p934 . . . . . 020 7583 3335

Milner, Mr Jonathan LLB(Lond) I *Jul 1977*
1, 22, 26, 31, 36
Francis Taylor Building, London EC4
p934 . . . . . 020 7353 8415

Milner, Mr Nicolas G *Mar 1996*
Holborn Chambers, London WC2
p937 . . . . . 020 7242 6060

Milnes, Mr Simon G *Oct 2005*
41, 5, 35, 11, 36, 49, 3, 43, 47, 78, 24, 54
20 Essex Street, London WC2
p932 . . . . . 020 7842 1200

Milsom, Ms Catherine M LLB(Crime); BA(Hons) I *Nov 1994*
15, 62, 84, 20, 67, 10
Argent Chambers, London WC2
p923 . . . . . 020 7556 5500

Minihan, Mr Sean G *Nov 1988*
15, 36
4 Breams Buildings, London EC4
p927 . . . . . 020 7092 1900

Minto, Miss Amanada M *Nov 2009*
Guildford Chambers, Guildford
p975 . . . . . 01483 539131

Mintz, Mr Simon BA(Hons) I *Nov 1996*
15, 20
St Johns Buildings, Preston
p990 . . . . . 01772 256100

See p1010 for the Key to Work Categories

St Johns Buildings, Chester
p974 . . . . 01244 323070
St Johns Buildings, Manchester
p985 . . . . 0161 214 1500
St Johns Buildings, Liverpool
p982 . . . . 0151 243 6000

Mirchandani, Ms Sian MA; DipLaw — *I Oct 1997*
8, 12, 24, 40
Four New Square, London WC2
p943 . . . . 020 7822 2000

Miric, Mr Robin LLB — *G Jul 1978*
15, 12, 62
4 Breams Buildings, London EC4
p927 . . . . 020 7092 1900

Mirwitch, Miss Jane D LLM(Lond) — *M Nov 1974*
15, 51
Nine Bedford Row, London WC1
p924 . . . . 020 7489 2727

Mirza, Mr Mussadak BA(Hons); MSc(Oxon) — *M Jan 2004*
12, 15, 30
Cobden House Chambers, Manchester
p983 . . . . 0161 833 6000

Mishcon, Ms Jane Malca MA(Oxon) — *G Jul 1979*
53, 40, 27, 30, 49
Hailsham Chambers, London EC4
p936 . . . . 020 7643 5000

MISKIN, Mr Charles MA(Oxon); Recorder — *G Jul 1975*
(Q.C.) *15, 36, 25, 62, 46*
23 Essex Street, London WC2
p932 . . . . 020 7413 0353

Miskin, Miss Claire M LLM(Lond); Recorder — *M Nov 1970*
18, 22, 26, 40
3 Dr Johnson's Buildings, London EC4
p930 . . . . 020 7353 4854

Misner, Mr Philip LLB — *M Jul 1984*
15, 36
4 Breams Buildings, London EC4
p927 . . . . 020 7092 1900

MISRA, Miss Eleena BA(Oxon) — *M Jul 2001*
6, 11, 12, 18, 55
Littleton Chambers, London EC4
p941 . . . . 020 7797 8600

Mitchell, Mr Alistair LLB(Hons) — *M Oct 1997*
15, 20, 12, 11, 18, 30
49 Chambers, Bridgnorth
p970 . . . . 01746 761545
Foregate Chambers, Kidderminster
p976 . . . . 07760 766152

Mitchell, Mr Andrew BL — *G Jul 1976*
(Q.C.) *15*
33 Chancery Lane, London WC2
p928 . . . . 020 7440 9950

Mitchell, Mr Andrew Edward BCL(Oxon); LLB(Cantab) — *M Nov 1992*
Fountain Court Chambers, London EC4
p934 . . . . 020 7583 3335

Mitchell, Mr Andrew Jonathan Mills LLB(Leeds) — *L Nov 1991*
8, 11, 22, 30, 49
No 6 Barristers Chambers, Leeds
p978 . . . . 0113 245 9763

Mitchell, Mr Brenton Dip Crim — *L Jul 1973 OBE*
15, 94
Bell Yard Chambers, London WC2
p926 . . . . 020 7306 9292 / 7404 5138

Mitchell, Mr Christian BSc(Hons); PgDL — *M Jul 2001*
Guildford Chambers, Guildford
p975 . . . . 01483 539131

Mitchell, Mr David — *I Jan 2004*
18, 11, 26, 22, 30, 53, 40
Ely Place Chambers, London EC1
p931 . . . . 020 7400 9600
No5 Chambers, Bristol
p971 . . . . 0845 210 5555
No5 Chambers, London EC4
p944 . . . . 0845 210 5555
No5 Chambers, Birmingham
p968 . . . . 0845 210 5555

MITCHELL, Mr Frank LLB(Trinity College Dublin); AITI — *G Jan 2010*
57
Monckton Chambers, London WC1
p942 . . . . 020 7405 7211

MITCHELL, Mr Gregory BA(Hons); PhD(Lond) — *G Jul 1979*
(Q.C.) *5, 6, 11, 13, 18, 24, 40*
3 Verulam Buildings, London WC1
p953 . . . . 020 7831 8441

Mitchell, Mr Jack — *I Oct 1994*
3PB, Oxford
p989 . . . . 01865 793736

Mitchell, Miss Janet Vivien BA — *M Feb 1978*
10, 20
4 Brick Court Chambers, London EC4
p927 . . . . 020 7832 3200

MITCHELL, Mr Jonathan — *G Nov 1992*
30, 53, 1, 31
Ropewalk Chambers, Nottingham
p989 . . . . 0115 947 2581
25 Bedford Row, London WC1
p925 . . . . 020 7067 1500

Mitchell, Mr Jonathon — *G Mar 1998*
1 Gray's Inn Square, London WC1
p935 . . . . 020 7405 8946

Mitchell, Miss Julianna LLB(Hons)(B'ham); BCL(Oxon) — *L Oct 1994*
12, 18, 19, 22, 30, 51
Henderson Chambers, London EC4
p937 . . . . 020 7583 9020

Mitchell, Mr Keith A BA(Hons)(Law) — *I Nov 1981*
15, 36
33 Chancery Lane, London WC2
p928 . . . . 020 7440 9950

Mitchell, Ms Lesley BSc(Hons); DipLaw — *I Nov 1987*
20
Stapleton Lodge, Brentford
p970 . . . . 020 8568 2164

Mitchell, Mr Nigel C LLB(Lond) — *L Feb 1978*
12, 15, 30
3PB, Bournemouth
p969 . . . . 01202 292102

Mitchell, Mr Paul MA; PhD — *L Oct 1999*
40, 11
Hailsham Chambers, London EC4
p936 . . . . 020 7643 5000

MITCHELL, Mr Peter LLB(Lond) — *I Oct 1996*
20
29 Bedford Row, London WC1
p925 . . . . 020 7404 1044

MITCHELL, Miss Rebecca LLB — *G Oct 2000*
10, 20
1 Garden Court, London EC4
p934 . . . . 020 7797 7900
14 Gray's Inn Square, London WC1
p936 . . . . 020 7242 0858

Mitchell, Mr Ronald — *I Jan 1973*
New Court Chambers, Newcastle upon Tyne
p987 . . . . 0191 232 1980

MITCHELL, Mr Tom MA(Oxon) — *L Oct 1995*
15, 12
Fountain Chambers, Middlesbrough
p986 . . . . 01642 804040

MITCHESON, Mr Thomas George BA(Cantab) — *I Nov 1996*
13, 45
3 New Square, London WC2
p943 . . . . 020 7405 1111

MITFORD, Mr Christopher — *M Nov 2001*
1, 15, 63, 91, 96
Trinity (Newcastle) Chambers, Newcastle upon Tyne
p987 . . . . 0191 232 1927
Trinity (Teesside) Chambers, Middlesbrough
p986 . . . . 01642 247569

MITROPHANOUS, Miss Eleni BA(Cantab); BCL(Oxon); LLM(European Inst); DPhil(Oxon) — *I Oct 1999*
11, 44, 1, 18, 19, 51, 34, 48, 67, 57
Matrix Chambers, London WC1
p942 . . . . 020 7404 3447

Mitropoulos, Chris MA(Cantab) — *L Mar 1997*
12, 15, 22, 23
5 Pump Court, London EC4
p947 . . . . 020 7353 2532 / 7583 7133

Mitropoulos, Miss Georgia BA(Wales); DipLaw — *G Jul 1989*
10, 20
Coram Chambers, London EC1
p929 . . . . 020 7092 3700

Mittell, Miss Jodie LLB(Hons) — *I Jul 2004*
15, 70, 48, 25
12 College Place, Southampton
p992 . . . . 023 8032 0320

Moat, Mr Richard BA(Oxon) — *L Jul 1985*
30, 68, 94, 53, 56
No5 Chambers, Bristol
p971 . . . . 0845 210 5555
No5 Chambers, London EC4
p944 . . . . 0845 210 5555
No5 Chambers, Birmingham
p968 . . . . 0845 210 5555

MOATE, Jennifer BA(Oxon) — *M Jul 2006*
10, 20, 22, 26, 88
Five Paper, London EC4
p946 . . . . 020 7815 3200

Mobbs, Mr Richard — *L Jan 2007*
15, 23, 94
Lamb Building, Brighton
p970 . . . . 01273 820490
Lamb Building, London EC4
p940 . . . . 020 7797 7788

MODGIL, Sangita — *G Oct 1990*
Carmelite Chambers, London EC4
p927 . . . . 020 7936 6300

Modgill, Mr Alexander Jeffrey LLB; LLM — *L Feb 2002*
30, 20, 12
Broadway House Chambers, Leeds
p977 . . . . 0113 246 2600
Broadway House Chambers, Bradford
p969 . . . . 01274 722560

MODHA, Mr Niraj — *L Jan 2010*
8, 11, 12, 22
Tanfield Chambers, London WC1
p951 . . . . 020 7421 5300

Moelwyn-Williams, Miss Anna Charlotte BA; LLB — *G Jul 2006*
12, 15, 18, 20, 30
9 Park Place, Cardiff
p973 . . . . 029 2038 2731

Moeran, Mr Fenner Orlando BSc(Bris) — *L Nov 1996*
6, 8, 9, 11, 12, 18, 22, 29, 32, 37, 38, 40
3 Stone Buildings, London WC2
p951 . . . . 020 7242 4937

MOFFETT, Mr Jonathan BA; LLM(Cantab); MA — *I Oct 1996*
1, 11, 18, 31, 26, 36, 51, 55, 56, 61
4-5 Gray's Inn Square, London WC1
p935 . . . . 020 7404 5252

Moffett, Mr William BA(Hons)(Cantab) — *G Sep 2000*
6, 8, 11, 22, 29, 32, 37
Radcliffe Chambers, London WC2
p949 . . . . 020 7831 0081

Moger, Mr Christopher LLB(Bris); Recorder — *I Jul 1972*
(Q.C.) *3, 7, 11, 12, 24, 25, 83*
4 Pump Court, London EC4
p947 . . . . 020 7842 5555

Mohammad, Mr Nazar — *G Jan 2008*
No 3 Fleet Street Chambers, London EC4
p944 . . . . 020 7936 4474

MOHAMMED, Mr Iqbal — *M Jan 2007*
11, 20, 18
St Philips Chambers, Birmingham
p969 . . . . 0121 246 7000

MOHAMMED, Mr Rashad LLB(Hons) — *L Jul 2004*
62, 15
23 Essex Street, London WC2
p932 . . . . 020 7413 0353

MOHINDRU, Mr Anurag — *M Jan 2003*
Lombard Chambers, London EC1
p941 . . . . 020 7107 2100

Mohsin, Miss Andlub — *L Jan 2006*
6 King's Bench Walk, London EC4
p939 . . . . 020 7583 0695 / 7353 4931

Mohyuddin, Mr David Niaz LLB(Hons)(B'ham) — *L Oct 1999*
5, 6, 8, 11, 29, 40, 36, 34, 38, 49, 96, 56
Exchange Chambers, Manchester
p983 . . . . 0161 833 2722
Exchange Chambers, Liverpool
p980 . . . . 0151 236 7747
Exchange Chambers, Leeds
p977 . . . . 0113 203 1970
13 Old Square Chambers, London WC2
p945 . . . . 020 7831 4445

MOKAL, Prof Riz PhD(UCL); BCL(Oxon); LLB(UCL); BSc(Pb) — *G Nov 1997*
11, 6, 5
South Square, London WC1
p950 . . . . 020 7696 9900

MOLD, Mr Andrew MA(Cantab); LLM(Harv) — *L Oct 2003*
41, 5, 6, 8, 9, 11, 12, 49, 62, 22, 29, 32, 40, 34, 58, 37
Wilberforce Chambers, London WC2
p953 . . . . 020 7306 0102

Moll, Mr Christian — *M Jul 1986*
30, 15, 22, 25, 36, 20
Blackfriars Chambers, London EC4
p926 . . . . 020 7353 7400

MOLL, Mr Louis-Peter — *M Oct 1998*
15
18 Red Lion Court, London EC4
p949 . . . . 020 7520 6000
18 Red Lion Court (Annexe), Chelmsford
p973 . . . . 01245 280880

MOLLOY, Mr Andrew — *G Jan 2004*
15, 70, 91
St Ives Chambers, Birmingham
p969 . . . . 0121 236 0863

Molloy, Mr Kevin Anthony Joseph — *M Mar 1999*
15
1 Inner Temple Lane, London EC4
p937 . . . . 020 7427 4400

Moloney, Mr Tim — *M Nov 1993*
(Q.C.) *15, 51*
Tooks Chambers, London EC4
p953 . . . . 020 7842 7575

MOLYNEUX, Mr Brent BA(Oxon); DipLaw — *L Feb 1994*
10, 20
29 Bedford Row, London WC1
p925 . . . . 020 7404 1044

MOLYNEUX, Mr Simon Rowley BSc(Lond); MPhil — *I Apr 1986*
15, 25
Carmelite Chambers, London EC4
p927 . . . . 020 7936 6300

MOMTAZ, Mr Sam LLB — *L Nov 1995*
10, 20
1 Garden Court, London EC4
p934 . . . . 020 7797 7900

MONAGHAN, Ms Karon LLB — *I Jul 1989*
(Q.C.) *22, 26, 18, 30, 36, 1, 19, 51, 55, 33, 23, 38*
Matrix Chambers, London WC1
p942 . . . . 020 7404 3447

MONAGHAN, Mr Mark — *L Jul 1987*
15, 61
9 St John Street Chambers, Manchester
p984 . . . . 0161 955 9000
Angel Chambers, Swansea
p992 . . . . 01792 464623

Monaghan, Ms Susan — *I Oct 1995*
1, 23
No5 Chambers, Bristol
p971 . . . . 0845 210 5555
No5 Chambers, London EC4
p944 . . . . 0845 210 5555
No5 Chambers, Birmingham
p968 . . . . 0845 210 5555

MONAH, Ms Helen Anne — *L Nov 1996*
10, 20
1 Pump Court, London EC4
p947 . . . . 020 7842 7070

Mondair, Mr Rashpal — *M Jun 1995*
No 8 Chambers, Birmingham
p968 . . . . 0121 236 5514

Monday, Ms Martha BA(Hons); LLM — *M Oct 1998*
18, 20, 10
Stour Chambers, Canterbury
p972 . . . . 01227 764899

Monk, Mr David BA; LLM — *M Jul 1991*
18
New Walk Chambers, Leicester
p979 . . . . 0871 200 1298
2 New Street, Leicester
p979 . . . . 0116 262 5906

MONKCOM, Mr Stephen Philip BA(Oxon) — *M Nov 1974*
1, 25
Tanfield Chambers, London WC1
p951 . . . . 020 7421 5300

Monnington, Mr Bruce MA; LLM; DipLaw — *I Sep 1989*
Fenners Chambers, Cambridge
p972 . . . . 01223 368761

Monson, The Hon Andrew MA(Oxon) — *M Sep 1983*
12, 13, 16, 50, 51, 36, 56
5RB, London WC1
p948 . . . . 020 7242 2902

Montagu-Smith, Mr Tom — *L Oct 2001*
66, 49, 41, 3, 5, 6, 7, 8, 11, 97, 67, 69, 62, 38, 24, 21, 89, 96, 29, 40
XXIV Old Buildings, London WC2
p944 . . . . 020 7691 2424

Montaldo, Mr Neil — *L Mar 2002*
St Johns Buildings, Preston
p990 . . . . 01772 256100
St Johns Buildings, Chester
p974 . . . . 01244 323070

St Johns Buildings, Manchester
p985 . . . . . 0161 214 1500
St Johns Buildings, Liverpool
p982 . . . . . 0151 243 6000

MONTGOMERY, Miss Clare P LLB(Lond); Recorder(2000); Deputy High Court Judge(2003); Judge Court of Appeal Guernsey and Jersey (2008) G *Nov 1980*
(Q.C.) *1, 15, 16, 51, 34, 6, 11, 29, 19, 50, 33*
Matrix Chambers, London WC1
p942 . . . . . 020 7404 3447

MONTGOMERY, Prof John Warwick M *Oct 1984*
Ten Old Square, London WC2
p945 . . . . . 020 7405 0758

MONTGOMERY, Miss Kristina LLB(Hons); Recorder M *Jan 1993*
15, 62
St Philips Chambers, Birmingham
p969 . . . . . 0121 246 7000

Montrose, Mr Stuart I *May 1972*
15
Tooks Chambers, London EC4
p953 . . . . . 020 7842 7575

Monty, Mr Simon LLB I *Jul 1982*
(Q.C.) *8, 12, 24, 40, 45*
Four New Square, London WC2
p943 . . . . . 020 7822 2000

Moody, Mr Neil MA(Oxon) G *Nov 1989*
(Q.C.) *12, 24, 30, 40*
2 Temple Gardens, London EC4
p952 . . . . . 020 7822 1200

Moody-Stuart, Mr Thomas BA(Cantab) M *Nov 1995*
13, 50
8 New Square, London WC2
p943 . . . . . 020 7405 4321

Moollan, Mr Salim BA(Cantab) M *Jan 1998*
Essex Court Chambers, London WC2
p931 . . . . . 020 7813 8000

Moon, Mr Philip Charles Angus MA(Cantab) M *Nov 1986*
(Q.C.) *27, 7, 18, 11, 36, 40, 53, 85*
3 Serjeants' Inn, London EC4
p950 . . . . . 020 7427 5000

Moonan, Miss Caroline L *Mar 1997*
1 Gray's Inn Square, London WC1
p935 . . . . . 020 7405 8946

Mooney, Mr Giles G *Nov 1998*
30, 11, 62, 70, 53, 65, 81, 84, 38, 39
9 Gough Square, London EC4
p935 . . . . . 020 7832 0500

Mooney, Mr Stephen John LLB(Hull) I *Nov 1987*
15, 23, 62
Albion Chambers, Bristol
p970 . . . . . 0117 927 2144

Moor, Mr Philip D MA(Oxon) I *Jul 1982*
(Q.C.) *20, 10*
1 Hare Court, London EC4
p936 . . . . . 020 7797 7070

Moor, Ms Sarah BA(Cantab) M *Oct 1991*
18, 55, 51, 46, 36, 56, 26
Old Square Chambers, Bristol
p971 . . . . . 0117 930 5100
Old Square Chambers, London WC1
p945 . . . . . 020 7269 0300

MOORE, Miss Alison MA(Hons)(Oxon) M *Nov 1994*
10, 20
1 Garden Court, London EC4
p934 . . . . . 020 7797 7900
14 Gray's Inn Square, London WC1
p936 . . . . . 020 7242 0858

Moore, Mr Andrew David BA(Manc); PhD(Manc) I *Oct 1996*
15, 20, 30
18 St John Street Chambers, Manchester
p985 . . . . . 0161 278 1800

Moore, Mr Anthony L *Jul 1984*
39 Park Square, Leeds
p978 . . . . . 0113 245 6633

Moore, Mr Arthur James BA(Oxon) G *Oct 1992*
1, 11, 12, 22, 25, 30
Hardwicke, London WC2
p936 . . . . . 020 7242 2523

Moore, Mrs Finola BA; MA; Cert Ed L *Jul 1988*
10, 20
4 Brick Court Chambers, London EC4
p927 . . . . . 020 7832 3200

MOORE, Mr George I *Jan 1970*
11KBW, London EC4
p938 . . . . . 020 7632 8500

Moore, Mr Guy G *Jul 2006*
20
Temple Chambers, Newport
p988 . . . . . 01633 267403 / 255855
Temple Chambers, Cardiff
p973 . . . . . 029 2039 7364

MOORE, Miss Katharine Elizabeth BA(Cantab); Recorder M *Oct 1995*
15, 23, 36, 70
Octagon House, Norwich
p988 . . . . . 01603 623186

Moore, Miss Kirstie Elizabeth LLB(KCL); LLM(Sheff) M *Oct 1994*
10, 11, 12, 15, 18, 20, 25, 30, 36
Regent Chambers, Hanley
p976 . . . . . 01782 286666

MOORE, Mr Martin BA(Oxon) L *Jul 1982*
(Q.C.) *11, 38, 97*
Erskine Chambers, London WC2
p931 . . . . . 020 7242 5532

Moore, Mr Miranda J BSc L *Jul 1983*
(Q.C.) *15, 62, 48*
5 Paper Buildings, London EC4
p946 . . . . . 020 7583 6117

Moore, Miss Natalie L *Jan 2007*
Quadrant Chambers, London EC4
p948 . . . . . 020 7583 4444

MOORE, Mr Neil LLB(Nott'm) G *Jul 1986*
15, 62
23 Essex Street, London WC2
p932 . . . . . 020 7413 0353
King's Bench Chambers, Oxford
p989 . . . . . 01865 311066

Moore, Nicola L *Jan 1993*
KCH Garden Square Chambers, Nottingham
p989 . . . . . 0115 941 8851
KCH Garden Square Chambers, Leicester
p979 . . . . . 0115 941 8851

MOORE, Mr Oliver G *Mar 2005*
30
Guildhall Chambers, Bristol
p970 . . . . . 0117 930 9000

MOORE, Mr Richard MA(Oxon) L *Oct 1992*
8, 11, 37, 32, 6, 22
St James's Chambers, Manchester
p984 . . . . . 0161 834 7000

Moore, Mr Roderick A LLB I *Nov 1993*
18, 20, 86
Outer Temple Chambers, London WC2
p945 . . . . . 020 7353 6381
Pump Court Chambers, Swindon
p993 . . . . . 01793 539899
Pump Court Chambers, Winchester
p994 . . . . . 01962 868161
Pump Court Chambers, London EC4
p947 . . . . . 020 7353 0711

Moore, Mr Roger A LLB; LLM L *Jul 1969*
10, 12, 15, 18, 20, 30, 36
New Court Chambers, Newcastle upon Tyne
p987 . . . . . 0191 232 1980

MOORE, Miss Sarah MA; LLM(Cantab); Part-Time Chairman of Employment Tribunal M *Nov 1990*
1, 19, 51, 55, 56, 36, 26, 18, 44
11KBW, London EC4
p938 . . . . . 020 7632 8500

Moores, Mr Timothy K LLB(Bris) L *Jul 1987*
15, 30, 70, 72, 25
12 College Place, Southampton
p992 . . . . . 023 8032 0320

MOORHOUSE, Mr Brendon LLB(Hons) M *Nov 1992*
15, 46, 84
Guildhall Chambers, Bristol
p970 . . . . . 0117 930 9000

Mootien, Ms Davina G *Jan 2004*
4 Breams Buildings, London EC4
p927 . . . . . 020 7092 1900

Moradifar, Mr Kambiz LLB(Lond) G *Nov 1998*
20, 10
St John's Chambers, Bristol
p972 . . . . . 0117 921 3456

MORAN, Mr Andrew MA(Oxon) G *Nov 1976*
(Q.C.) *11, 35, 30, 79, 40, 53, 81*
7 Harrington Street Chambers, Liverpool
p981 . . . . . 0151 242 0707
Serle Court, London WC2
p950 . . . . . 020 7242 6105

Moran, Mr Christopher M *Jan 2007*
1 Mitre Court Buildings, London EC4
p942 . . . . . 020 7452 8900
39 Park Square, Leeds
p978 . . . . . 0113 245 6633

Moran, Mr Patrick LLB(Hons) I *Oct 1997*
15, 25, 36, 39, 42, 51, 62, 70, 71, 72, 84, 91, 94, 95
15 New Bridge Street Chambers, London EC4
p943 . . . . . 020 7842 1900

Moran, Mr Thomas LLB G *Oct 1996*
15, 12
New Court Chambers, Newcastle upon Tyne
p987 . . . . . 0191 232 1980

Moran, Mr Vincent MA(Cantab) G *Oct 1991*
7, 22, 30, 40
Keating Chambers, London WC2
p938 . . . . . 020 7544 2600

Morcom, Mr Christopher MA(Cantab) M *Jul 1963*
(Q.C.) *13*
Hogarth Chambers, London WC2
p937 . . . . . 020 7404 0404

MORE O'FERRALL, Geraldine M *Jul 1983*
10, 15, 20, 32
Renaissance Chambers, London WC1
p949 . . . . . 020 7404 1111

Moreland, Miss Penelope Jane MA(Cantab) G *Jul 1986*
10, 12, 15, 20
New Court Chambers, Newcastle upon Tyne
p987 . . . . . 0191 232 1980

Morelli, Miss Luisa T BA(Hons) M *Nov 1993*
10, 20
Crown Office Row Chambers, Brighton
p970 . . . . . 01273 625625

Moretto, Mr Robert Salvatore I *Oct 2000*
30, 18
Old Square Chambers, Bristol
p971 . . . . . 0117 930 5100
Old Square Chambers, London WC1
p945 . . . . . 020 7269 0300

Morgan, Mr Adam G *Jan 1996*
15, 18, 62
Argent Chambers, London WC2
p923 . . . . . 020 7556 5500
Charter Chambers, London WC1
p928 . . . . . 020 7618 4400

Morgan, Ms Adrienne BA(Hons) G *Nov 1978*
18, 55
No5 Chambers, Bristol
p971 . . . . . 0845 210 5555
No5 Chambers, London EC4
p944 . . . . . 0845 210 5555
No5 Chambers, Birmingham
p968 . . . . . 0845 210 5555

Morgan, Miss Alison M *Nov 2000*
15
6 King's Bench Walk, London EC4
p939 . . . . . 020 7583 0410

MORGAN, Mr Charles MA(Cantab); FCIArb; Junior Counsel to the Crown (Regional) M *Jul 1978*
5, 7, 8, 11, 22, 24, 26, 29, 40, 41, 46, 54, 61, 49, 38, 88
Enterprise Chambers, London WC2
p931 . . . . . 020 7405 9471
Enterprise Chambers, Leeds
p977 . . . . . 0113 246 0391
Enterprise Chambers, Newcastle upon Tyne
p987 . . . . . 0191 222 3344

Morgan, Mr Christopher LLB M *Oct 1987*
15, 84
1 Paper Buildings, London EC4
p946 . . . . . 020 7353 3728

MORGAN, Mr Colin BA(Oxon) M *Nov 1989*
1, 12, 18, 20, 22, 30, 10
Pallant Chambers, Chichester
p974 . . . . . 01243 784538

Morgan, Mr David John M *Nov 1998*
23
12 Old Square, London WC2
p945 . . . . . 020 7404 0875

Morgan, Mr Dylan R LLB(CNAA) G *Jul 1986*
20, 10
12 College Place, Southampton
p992 . . . . . 023 8032 0320

MORGAN, Mr Edward LLB; LLM L *Jul 1989*
18, 8, 11, 40
9 St John Street Chambers, Manchester
p984 . . . . . 0161 955 9000

Morgan, Miss Gemma BA(Cantab)(Law); BCL(Oxon) M *Jan 2006*
Quadrant Chambers, London EC4
p948 . . . . . 020 7583 4444

MORGAN, Mr James BA(Hons)(Cantab); Recorder I *Oct 1996*
6, 11, 12, 22, 5, 67, 38, 40
St Philips Chambers, Birmingham
p969 . . . . . 0121 246 7000

MORGAN, Mr Jamie I *Aug 2006*
38, 30, 11, 18
Trinity (Newcastle) Chambers, Newcastle upon Tyne
p987 . . . . . 0191 232 1927
Trinity (Teesside) Chambers, Middlesbrough
p986 . . . . . 01642 247569

MORGAN, Mr Jeremy BA(Oxon); BA(Kent) M *Apr 1989*
(Q.C.) *1, 26, 31, 40, 41, 51, 46*
Thirty Nine Essex Street, London WC2
p932 . . . . . 020 7832 1111

Morgan, Miss Katie LLB(Hons) I *Aug 2002*
12, 20, 10
Thirty Park Place, Cardiff
p973 . . . . . 029 2039 8421

MORGAN, Mr Lloyd John BAAppSc; LLB; MBA M *Mar 1999*
15
Chavasse Court Chambers, Liverpool
p980 . . . . . 0151 229 2030

Morgan, Ms Lynne LLB; Recorder (Family Law) M *Jul 1984*
20, 10
Temple Chambers, Newport
p988 . . . . . 01633 267403 / 255855
Temple Chambers, Cardiff
p973 . . . . . 029 2039 7364

Morgan, Mr Matt L *Jan 2004*
2 Pump Court, London EC4
p947 . . . . . 020 7353 5597

Morgan, Mr Richard LLB(Bucks); LLM(Cantab) G *Nov 1988*
(Q.C.)
Maitland Chambers, London WC2
p941 . . . . . 020 7406 1200

MORGAN, Miss Sarah Mary LLB(Hons) G *Nov 1988*
(Q.C.) *10, 20, 26*
1 Garden Court, London EC4
p934 . . . . . 020 7797 7900

Morgan, Mr Simon G *Nov 1988*
15, 36, 42, 48, 84, 62, 68, 46, 82
St John's Chambers, Bristol
p972 . . . . . 0117 921 3456

MORGAN, Mr Stephen Francis LLB(Warw); MA(Nott'm) G *Nov 1983*
Landmark Chambers, London EC4
p941 . . . . . 020 7430 1221

Morgan, Miss Victoria I *Jan 2005*
Thomas More Chambers, London WC2
p952 . . . . . 020 7404 7000

MORGANS, Mr John Morgan LLB(Hons) M *Nov 1996*
15, 25, 36
Octagon House, Norwich
p988 . . . . . 01603 623186

Moriarty, Mr Stephen BCL; MA(Oxon) M *Nov 1986*
(Q.C.)
Fountain Court Chambers, London EC4
p934 . . . . . 020 7583 3335

Morland, Miss Camille BA(Hons) G *Nov 1996*
12, 15, 20, 30
Broadway House Chambers, Leeds
p977 . . . . . 0113 246 2600
Broadway House Chambers, Bradford
p969 . . . . . 01274 722560

MORLEY, Mr Iain Charles MA(Oxon) I *Jul 1988*
(Q.C.) *15, 25, 36, 62*
23 Essex Street, London WC2
p932 . . . . . 020 7413 0353

MORLEY, Miss Kate I *Oct 2004*
10, 15, 20, 70
Chavasse Court Chambers, Liverpool
p980 . . . . . 0151 229 2030
Bank House Chambers, Sheffield
p991 . . . . . 0114 275 1223

MORLEY, Miss Laura M *Jul 2006*
20, 10
4 Paper Buildings, London EC4
p946 . . . . . 020 7583 0816

Morley, Mr Stephen LLB(Hons)(Westminster) I *Oct 1996*
40, 25, 68, 30
3 Serjeants' Inn, London EC4
p950 . . . . . 020 7427 5000

See p1010 for the Key to Work Categories

Morpuss, Mr Guy LLB(B'ham) *L Oct 1991*
(Q.C.) *3, 11, 12, 24, 35, 41*
20 Essex Street, London WC2
p932 . . . . . 020 7842 1200

MORRELL, Miss Roxanne T LLB(Hons) *M Jun 1996*
Carmelite Chambers, London EC4
p927 . . . . . 020 7936 6300

MORRIS, Mr Anthony *G Nov 1986*
15, 63
Kenworthy's Chambers, Manchester
p984 . . . . . 0161 832 4036

Morris, Mr Arthur Rowland *G Jan 1997*
12, 15, 20
Eastbourne Chambers, Eastbourne
p975 . . . . . 01323 642102

Morris, Miss Bella BA(Jurisprudence); BVC *M Oct 2000*
30, 18, 55, 36, 53, 46, 51, 40
Old Square Chambers, Bristol
p971 . . . . . 0117 930 5100
Old Square Chambers, London WC1
p945 . . . . . 020 7269 0300

MORRIS, Mr Ben LLB(Hons)(L'pool) *M Oct 1996*
15
Chavasse Court Chambers, Liverpool
p980 . . . . . 0151 229 2030

MORRIS, Mr Benjamin Francis Joseph LLB(Hons) *L Jan 2004*
9 St John Street Chambers, Manchester
p984 . . . . . 0161 955 9000

Morris, Miss Brenda BSc *M Jul 1978*
14 Gray's Inn Square, London WC1
p936 . . . . . 020 7242 0858

MORRIS, Mr Brendan *M Jul 1985*
15, 36, 62
18 Red Lion Court, London EC4
p949 . . . . . 020 7520 6000
18 Red Lion Court (Annexe), Chelmsford
p973 . . . . . 01245 280880

MORRIS, Ms Christina BA *G Nov 1983*
10, 20
Coram Chambers, London EC1
p929 . . . . . 020 7092 3700

Morris, Mr David LLB(Bris) *I Oct 1976*
15, 27, 85
Outer Temple Chambers, London WC2
p945 . . . . . 020 7353 6381

MORRIS, Ms Fenella BA(Hons)(Oxon); DipLaw(City) *M Oct 1990*
1, 26, 27, 51, 55, 85, 63, 76, 96, 14
Thirty Nine Essex Street, London WC2
p932 . . . . . 020 7832 1111

MORRIS, Professor Gillian LLB(Bris); PhD(Cantab) *I Jan 1997*
18, 49
Matrix Chambers, London WC1
p942 . . . . . 020 7404 3447

Morris, Mr Michael BSc *G Jun 1984*
15, 12
Goldsmith Chambers, London EC4
p935 . . . . . 020 7353 6802

Morris, Mr Paul H *L Nov 1986*
York Chambers, York
p995 . . . . . 01904 620048
York Chambers, Newcastle upon Tyne
p987 . . . . . 0191 206 4677

Morris, Mr Peter BA; MA *I Oct 2000*
23, 33, 51, 18
Doughty Street Chambers, London WC1
p930 . . . . . 020 7404 1313

Morris, Mr Philip *M Jul 2011*
39 Park Square, Leeds
p978 . . . . . 0113 245 6633

Morris, Mr Phillip BA(Oxon)(Law) *G Jul 2003*
12, 15, 18, 30
9 Park Place, Cardiff
p973 . . . . . 029 2038 2731

Morris, Mr Stephen N MA(Cantab) *L Jul 1981*
(Q.C.) *1, 3, 11, 12, 19, 24, 35, 41, 44*
20 Essex Street, London WC2
p932 . . . . . 020 7842 1200

Morris-Coole, Mr Christopher LLB(Lond); BSc; GI Biol; FRSA; Recorder *I Jul 1974*
12, 30, 46, 40, 53, 56
Crown Office Row Chambers, Brighton
p970 . . . . . 01273 625625

Morris of Aberavon KG, Rt Hon Lord Recorder *G Feb 1954*
(Q.C.) MP*15*
2 Bedford Row, London WC1
p924 . . . . . 020 7440 8888

Morrison, Ms Andrea LLB *I Jun 2000*
15
York Chambers, York
p995 . . . . . 01904 620048
York Chambers, Newcastle upon Tyne
p987 . . . . . 0191 206 4677

Morrison, Mr Christopher Quentin *I Nov 1986*
15, 72, 70
Old Court Chambers, Middlesbrough
p986 . . . . . 01642 232523

Morrison, Mr Giles *M Jan 2002*
15, 62
15 New Bridge Street Chambers, London EC4
p943 . . . . . 020 7842 1900

Morrison, Mr Matthew John MA(Oxon); Jurisprudence; Batchelor of Civil Law *L Jan 2004*
8, 11
Serle Court, London WC2
p950 . . . . . 020 7242 6105

Morse, Mr Andrew Philip Richard BSocSc(Hons) *G Jul 2000*
15, 30, 12, 62
Thirty Park Place, Cardiff
p973 . . . . . 029 2039 8421

MORSE, Mr Malcolm George McEwan MA(Cantab); Recorder *I Jul 1967*
15, 62
St Philips Chambers, Birmingham
p969 . . . . . 0121 246 7000

MORSHEAD, Mr Timothy BA(Oxon) *L Feb 1995*
(Q.C.) *93*
Landmark Chambers, London EC4
p941 . . . . . 020 7430 1221

Mort, Mr Justin BA(Dunelm) *M Nov 1994*
12, 24, 7, 40
Keating Chambers, London WC2
p938 . . . . . 020 7544 2600

MORTIMER, Mr Barry BA; MA(Cantab) *M Oct 1956*
(Q.C.)
South Square, London WC1
p950 . . . . . 020 7696 9900

Mortimer, Ms Sophie BA; CP; DipLaw *L Nov 1996*
12, 30, 40, 53, 76, 26
1 Chancery Lane, London WC2
p928 . . . . . 0845 634 6666

MORTIMORE, Mr Simon LLB(Exon) *I Jul 1972*
(Q.C.) *5, 6, 8, 11, 12, 24, 29, 97, 38*
South Square, London WC1
p950 . . . . . 020 7696 9900

MORTON, Mr David *I Nov 1999*
15
Kenworthy's Chambers, Manchester
p984 . . . . . 0161 832 4036

MORTON, Mr Gary MA; BSc(Econ); DipLaw *G May 1993*
18
Pump Court Chambers, Swindon
p993 . . . . . 01793 539899
Pump Court Chambers, Winchester
p994 . . . . . 01962 868161
Pump Court Chambers, London EC4
p947 . . . . . 020 7353 0711

MORTON, Mr Keith BSc(Hull); DipLaw *L Oct 1990*
(Q.C.)
Temple Garden Chambers, London EC4
p952 . . . . . 020 7583 1315

MORTON, Mr Peter LLM *M Oct 1988*
30, 53, 40, 84, 11, 29
Crown Office Chambers, London EC4
p929 . . . . . 020 7797 8100

Morton, Miss Rachel Joanna Eaden LLB(Hons)(Warw); LLM(LSE) *L Feb 1995*
10, 20
4 Brick Court Chambers, London EC4
p927 . . . . . 020 7832 3200

Morton, Miss Rowan *L Jan 2004*
Guildford Chambers, Guildford
p975 . . . . . 01483 539131

Morton Jack, Mr Henry *L Jul 2009*
30, 24
2 Temple Gardens, London EC4
p952 . . . . . 020 7822 1200

Morwood, Mr Boyd BA(Hons)(Keels); LLB *M Jan 1996*
Hardwicke, London WC2
p936 . . . . . 020 7242 2523

MOSELEY, Ms Julie LLB *I Oct 1992*
20
St Philips Chambers, Birmingham
p969 . . . . . 0121 246 7000

MOSER, Mr Philip Curt Harold *I Oct 1992*
19, 40, 11
Monckton Chambers, London WC1
p942 . . . . . 020 7405 7211

MOSES, Mr Stephen *G Nov 1997*
Furnival Chambers, London EC4
p934 . . . . . 020 7405 3232

Moss, Mr Christopher *L Oct 2002*
12, 15, 22, 30
St Johns Buildings, Preston
p990 . . . . . 01772 256100
St Johns Buildings, Chester
p974 . . . . . 01244 323070
St Johns Buildings, Manchester
p985 . . . . . 0161 214 1500
St Johns Buildings, Liverpool
p982 . . . . . 0151 243 6000

Moss, Mr Edward *I Jan 2005*
72, 15, 70
Exchange Chambers, Manchester
p983 . . . . . 0161 833 2722
Exchange Chambers, Liverpool
p980 . . . . . 0151 236 7747
Exchange Chambers, Leeds
p977 . . . . . 0113 203 1970

MOSS, Mr Gabriel MA; BCL(Oxon) *L Jul 1974*
(Q.C.) *5, 6, 8, 11, 12, 24, 29, 38*
South Square, London WC1
p950 . . . . . 020 7696 9900

MOSS, Ms Joanne R MA(Cantab); LLM(Lond); FCIArb *I Jul 1976*
Falcon Chambers, London EC4
p933 . . . . . 020 7353 2484

Moss, Miss Karen *M Jan 2002*
3PB, London EC4
p946 . . . . . 020 7583 8055

MOSS, Mr Nicholas MA(Cantab) *M Nov 1995*
Temple Garden Chambers, London EC4
p952 . . . . . 020 7583 1315

Moss, Mr Norman William LLB(Hons); DipLaw(Lond) *I Oct 1990*
10, 20
3 Dr Johnson's Buildings, London EC4
p930 . . . . . 020 7353 4854

MOSS, Richard *M Jan 2005*
4 King's Bench Walk, London EC4
p939 . . . . . 020 7822 7000

Mostafa, Miss Margia *L Oct 1999*
2 Pump Court, London EC4
p947 . . . . . 020 7353 5597

Mosteshar, Dr Sa'id BSc; MSc; DPhil; Attorney(Calif) *L Jul 1975*
13, 33
Hardwicke, London WC2
p936 . . . . . 020 7242 2523

Mostyn, Mr Piers BSc(Hons)(Bris); DipLaw *M Nov 1989*
15
Tooks Chambers, London EC4
p953 . . . . . 020 7842 7575

Motraghi, Miss Nadia MA(Oxon); LLM(Harv) *G Jul 2004*
18, 30
Old Square Chambers, Bristol
p971 . . . . . 0117 930 5100
Old Square Chambers, London WC1
p945 . . . . . 020 7269 0300

Mott, Geoffrey Edward BA; DipLaw *G Jul 1982*
40
Clerksroom - Administration Centre, Taunton
p993 . . . . . 0845 083 3000

Mott, Mr Philip Charles MA(Oxon) *I Jul 1970*
(Q.C.) *12, 15, 71, 84, 63, 62*
Outer Temple Chambers, London WC2
p945 . . . . . 020 7353 6381

Mott, Mr Richard *M Jan 2006*
One Essex Court, London EC4
p931 . . . . . 020 7583 2000

MOTTRAM, Miss Cheryl *L Oct 2002*
15
Kenworthy's Chambers, Manchester
p984 . . . . . 0161 832 4036

MOTZ, Stephanie *G Jan 2007*
23, 18
Mitre House Chambers, London WC1
p942 . . . . . 020 7307 7100

MOULD, Mr Timothy BA(Oxon) *G Jul 1987*
(Q.C.) *1, 21, 31, 36, 46*
Landmark Chambers, London EC4
p941 . . . . . 020 7430 1221

Moulder, Mr Paul J LLB(Hons) *L Oct 1997*
12, 15, 20, 25, 30
Guildford Chambers, Guildford
p975 . . . . . 01483 539131

Moulder, Miss Pauline M *L Jul 1983*
8, 10, 20, 22
Broad Chare Chambers, Newcastle upon Tyne
p986 . . . . . 0191 232 0541

MOULES, Mr Richard *M Jan 2005*
Landmark Chambers, London EC4
p941 . . . . . 020 7430 1221

Moulson, Mr Peter LLB; MA *G Jul 1992*
12, 15
No 6 Barristers Chambers, Leeds
p978 . . . . . 0113 245 9763

MOUNTFIELD, Ms Helen BA(Oxon); DipLaw(City); Dip(European Law) *G Jul 1991*
(Q.C.) *1, 10, 49, 73, 55, 76, 77, 18, 46, 9, 85, 22, 51, 26, 96, 33*
Matrix Chambers, London WC1
p942 . . . . . 020 7404 3447

Mountford, Mr Tom BA(Oxon) *L Jan 2009*
11, 1, 18, 19, 44, 52, 56
Blackstone Chambers, London EC4
p926 . . . . . 020 7583 1770

Mousley, Mr Timothy T Recorder *M Jul 1979*
(Q.C.) *15*
2 King's Bench Walk, London EC4
p939 . . . . . 020 7353 1746

Mousley, Mr William *M Jul 1986*
2 King's Bench Walk, London EC4
p939 . . . . . 020 7353 1746

Moverley Smith, Mr Stephen MA *M Feb 1985*
(Q.C.) *5, 6, 8, 11, 29, 32, 37, 40, 36, 41, 62, 49*
XXIV Old Buildings, London WC2
p944 . . . . . 020 7691 2424

MOWSCHENSON, Mr Terence BA(Lond); BCL(Oxon); Recorder *M Jul 1977*
(Q.C.) *3, 5, 6, 8, 11, 12, 21, 24, 29, 36, 40, 41, 47, 49, 62*
Wilberforce Chambers, London WC2
p953 . . . . . 020 7306 0102

Moxon Browne, Mr Robert William BA(Oxon) *G Jul 1969*
(Q.C.) *11, 7, 3, 8, 24, 12, 30, 40*
2 Temple Gardens, London EC4
p952 . . . . . 020 7822 1200

MOYS, Mr Clive MA(Hons) *L Jul 1998*
Pallant Chambers, Chichester
p974 . . . . . 01243 784538
Radcliffe Chambers, London WC2
p949 . . . . . 020 7831 0081

MOYS, Miss Laura *G Jul 2008*
10, 20, 15, 25, 22
1 King's Bench Walk, London EC4
p938 . . . . . 020 7936 1500

Mtetwa, Ms Beatrice *L Jan 2002*
1 Pump Court, London EC4
p947 . . . . . 020 7842 7070

Mugliston, Mr Adam *L Oct 2008*
York Chambers, York
p995 . . . . . 01904 620048
York Chambers, Newcastle upon Tyne
p987 . . . . . 0191 206 4677

Muhammad, Ms Tamara *M Jul 1998*
1 Pump Court, London EC4
p947 . . . . . 020 7842 7070

Muir, Miss Nicola *I Nov 1998*
22, 40, 93
Hardwicke, London WC2
p936 . . . . . 020 7242 2523

MUIR-WILSON, Miss Louise *M Jan 1999*
Carmelite Chambers, London EC4
p927 . . . . . 020 7936 6300

Mukherjee, Abhijeet LLB *M Feb 1995*
53, 30, 68, 85, 27
Outer Temple Chambers, London WC2
p945 . . . . . 020 7353 6381

MUKHERJEE, Mr Avik *G Jul 1990*
15
1 High Pavement, Nottingham
p988 . . . . . 0115 941 8218

13

Mukherjee, Mr Tublu I *Jan 1996*
51, 23
Doughty Street Chambers, London WC1
p930 . . . . 020 7404 1313

Mulcahy, Miss Jane S BA(Lond) M *Oct 1995*
1, 18, 50, 51, 55, 89, 56, 96, 49, 52
Blackstone Chambers, London EC4
p926 . . . . 020 7583 1770

Mulcahy, Miss Leigh-Ann Maria BA(Cantab) I *Oct 1993*
(Q.C.) *6, 12, 18, 11, 24, 30, 8, 40, 48, 51*
Four New Square, London WC2
p943 . . . . 020 7822 2000

MULDERIG, Mr Joseph LLB(Hons) L *Jan 2002*
12, 47, 30, 18, 40, 55, 36, 53
St James's Chambers, Manchester
p984 . . . . 0161 834 7000

Mulholland, Miss Helen M LLB M *Oct 1999*
12, 18, 30, 53, 55
Kings Chambers, Leeds
p978 . . . . 0113 242 1123
Kings Chambers, Manchester
p984 . . . . 0161 832 9082

Mulholland, Mr James I *Jul 1986*
(Q.C.) *15, 62*
15 New Bridge Street Chambers, London EC4
p943 . . . . 020 7842 1900

MULHOLLAND, Mr Michael MA(Oxon); Dip Crim(Cantab) G *Sep 1976*
30, 20, 1, 18, 40, 53, 11, 47, 29
St James's Chambers, Manchester
p984 . . . . 0161 834 7000

Mullan, Mr Rory G *Jul 2000*
34, 37, 36, 29, 8, 9
15 Old Square, London WC2
p945 . . . . 020 7242 2744

Mullany, Mr Nicholas I *Oct 2007*
53, 68, 85, 27, 63, 30, 40, 36
3 Serjeants' Inn, London EC4
p950 . . . . 020 7427 5000

Mullee, Mr Brendan LLB(Hons) M *Oct 1996*
22, 1
Hardwicke, London WC2
p936 . . . . 020 7242 2523

Mullen, Miss Jayne LLB(Cardiff) G *Jul 1989*
10, 15, 18, 20
St Ives Chambers, Birmingham
p969 . . . . 0121 236 0863

Mullen, Mr Mark BA(Dunelm); PGDL L *Jul 2001*
8, 9, 37
Radcliffe Chambers, London WC2
p949 . . . . 020 7831 0081

Mullen, Mr Patrick A MA(Cantab) G *Jul 1967*
15, 62, 46, 84
Argent Chambers, London WC2
p923 . . . . 020 7556 5500

Mullen, Mr Peter BA(Lond) L *Jul 1977*
1 Mitre Court Buildings, London EC4
p942 . . . . 020 7452 8900

MULLER, Antonie MA(Cantab) M *Jul 1990*
15, 30
Citadel Chambers, Birmingham
p967 . . . . 0121 233 8500

Muller, Mr Franz Joseph LLB(Hons) G *Feb 1961*
(Q.C.) *12, 15*
36 Bedford Row, London WC1
p925 . . . . 020 7421 8000
11 King's Bench Walk, Leeds
p978 . . . . 0113 297 1200

Mulligan, Ms Ann BA(Hons) G *Jul 1989*
15 New Bridge Street Chambers, London EC4
p943 . . . . 020 7842 1900

Mullins, Mr Mark BA I *Nov 1995*
15
5 St Andrew's Hill, London EC4
p950 . . . . 020 7332 5400
Outer Temple Chambers, London WC2
p945 . . . . 020 7353 6381

MULLIS, Mr Roger BA(Oxon); BCL L *Nov 1987*
5, 6, 8, 9, 11, 40, 22, 29, 32, 37
Pallant Chambers, Chichester
p974 . . . . 01243 784538
Radcliffe Chambers, London WC2
p949 . . . . 020 7831 0081

MULRENNAN, Miss Maria H A BA(Sussex); LLM(Nott'm) I *Nov 1990*
20, 10
St Mary's Chambers, Nottingham
p989 . . . . 0115 950 3503

Mulrooney, Mr Mark BA(Kent); MPhil(Cantab); P/T President of Mental Health Review Tribunal M *Jul 1988*
30
Exchange Chambers, Manchester
p983 . . . . 0161 833 2722
Exchange Chambers, Liverpool
p980 . . . . 0151 236 7747
Exchange Chambers, Leeds
p977 . . . . 0113 203 1970

Mumford, Mr David MA(Hons)(Oxon) L *Oct 2000*
Maitland Chambers, London WC2
p941 . . . . 020 7406 1200

MUMFORD, Mr Richard MA(Cantab); LLM(EUI) L *Nov 2004*
1, 53, 12, 47, 18, 19, 39, 51, 23, 27, 63, 30, 40, 36
1 Crown Office Row, London EC4
p929 . . . . 020 7797 7500

Munby, Mr Thomas BA(Hons) I *Oct 2006*
Maitland Chambers, London WC2
p941 . . . . 020 7406 1200

Munday, Mr Andrew LLB(Hons); Recorder M *Nov 1973*
(Q.C.) *15, 62*
2 Bedford Row, London WC1
p924 . . . . 020 7440 8888

Munday, Mr Gareth M *Nov 2000*
72, 15, 62
9 Gough Square, London EC4
p935 . . . . 020 7832 0500

Munden, Mr Richard LLB(Hons) L *Oct 2003*
13, 16, 50, 56
5RB, London WC1
p948 . . . . 020 7242 2902

MUNDY, Mr Robert M *Jul 2008*
11, 18
St Philips Chambers, Birmingham
p969 . . . . 0121 246 7000

Munir, Dr A Edward MA; PhD G *Jun 1956*
1, 12, 26
5 St Andrew's Hill, London EC4
p950 . . . . 020 7332 5400

Munro, Mr Campell M *Jul 2006*
1 Mitre Court Buildings, London EC4
p942 . . . . 020 7452 8900

MUNRO, Mr David G *Nov 2001*
15, 62, 94
St Philips Chambers, Birmingham
p969 . . . . 0121 246 7000

Munro, Mr Iain BA(Oxon)(Modern History) L *Jan 2009*
11, 12, 40, 24, 89, 74
4 Pump Court, London EC4
p947 . . . . 020 7842 5555

Munro, Mr Joshua Neil G *Jul 2001*
12, 11, 40
Hailsham Chambers, London EC4
p936 . . . . 020 7643 5000

MUNRO, Mr Kenneth S MA(Cantab) I *Nov 1973*
7, 12, 22
New Square Chambers, London WC2
p943 . . . . 020 7419 8000

MUNRO, Ms Sarah M *Oct 1990*
15
1 High Pavement, Nottingham
p988 . . . . 0115 941 8218

Munroe, Ms Allison BA M *Oct 1992*
15, 10, 20, 36
Tooks Chambers, London EC4
p953 . . . . 020 7842 7575

Munt, Mr Alastair LLB; LLM; M Phil G *Jul 1989*
15, 36, 23
KCH Garden Square Chambers, Nottingham
p989 . . . . 0115 941 8851
KCH Garden Square Chambers, Leicester
p979 . . . . 0115 941 8851

Muquit, Mr Mohammed Shuyeb I *Jan 1998*
23
12 Old Square, London WC2
p945 . . . . 020 7404 0875

Murch, Mr Stephen LLB(Hons)(Bucks) L *Oct 1991*
7, 8, 11, 12, 22, 29, 40, 41
42 Bedford Row, London WC1
p925 . . . . 020 7831 0222

Murdin, Mr Liam BA(Hons)(Salford) L *Jul 1998*
11, 30, 12, 20, 40, 53
St Johns Buildings, Preston
p990 . . . . 01772 256100
St Johns Buildings, Chester
p974 . . . . 01244 323070
St Johns Buildings, Manchester
p985 . . . . 0161 214 1500
St Johns Buildings, Liverpool
p982 . . . . 0151 243 6000

Murkin, Ms Sandria I *Oct 2004*
20, 10
Becket Chambers, Canterbury
p972 . . . . 01227 786331
Becket Chambers, Maidstone
p982 . . . . 01622 230957

MURPHY, Mr Damian MA(Cantab) M *Jul 2001*
5, 6, 8, 11, 29, 38, 40, 97
Enterprise Chambers, London WC2
p931 . . . . 020 7405 9471
Enterprise Chambers, Leeds
p977 . . . . 0113 246 0391
Enterprise Chambers, Newcastle upon Tyne
p987 . . . . 0191 222 3344

MURPHY, Miss Emer BA(Law & French) I *Jan 2009*
Wilberforce Chambers, London WC2
p953 . . . . 020 7306 0102

Murphy, Heather L *Jan 2009*
49, 41, 3, 5, 6, 8, 9, 11, 97, 67, 69, 78, 81, 62, 38, 21, 89, 96, 79, 29, 86, 32, 40, 43, 56, 37
XXIV Old Buildings, London WC2
p944 . . . . 020 7691 2424

Murphy, Mr Ian LLB(Hons)(LSE); Recorder; Bencher M *Jul 1972*
(Q.C.) *30, 40, 15, 53*
9 Park Place, Cardiff
p973 . . . . 029 2038 2731
Farrar's Building, London EC4
p933 . . . . 020 7583 9241

Murphy, Ms Jasmine LLB(Hons) G *Jul 2002*
30, 40
Hardwicke, London WC2
p936 . . . . 020 7242 2523

MURPHY, Miss Martina G *Jan 1998*
18, 30, 55
Tanfield Chambers, London WC1
p951 . . . . 020 7421 5300

Murphy, Miss Melissa Rosalind Gillian BA M *Nov 2001*
1, 12, 18, 22, 51, 26, 31
Cornerstone Barristers, London WC1
p929 . . . . 020 7242 4986

MURPHY, Mr Michael I *Jan 1990*
72, 15, 71, 70, 23
10 King's Bench Walk, London EC4
p940 . . . . 020 7353 7742

Murphy, Nicola G *Oct 1995*
4 KBW, London EC4
p938 . . . . 020 7822 8822

MURPHY, Miss Olivia BA(Hons); PGDL; BVC M *Mar 2001*
20, 37
Tanfield Chambers, London WC1
p951 . . . . 020 7421 5300

Murphy, Mr Paul G *Jul 2004*
St Johns Buildings, Preston
p990 . . . . 01772 256100
St Johns Buildings, Chester
p974 . . . . 01244 323070
St Johns Buildings, Manchester
p985 . . . . 0161 214 1500
St Johns Buildings, Liverpool
p982 . . . . 0151 243 6000

MURPHY, Mr Peter LLB(Hons)(Leics); Recorder G *Nov 1980*
(Q.C.) *15, 12*
Farrar's Building, London EC4
p933 . . . . 020 7583 9241

Murphy, Mr Peter John LLB; Recorder G *May 1980*
(Q.C.) *15, 62*
Thirty Park Place, Cardiff
p973 . . . . 029 2039 8421

Murphy, Ms Sheila M *Oct 1992*
Holborn Chambers, London WC2
p937 . . . . 020 7242 6060

MURRAY, Mr Anil P LLB M *Jul 1989*
15
Wilberforce Chambers, Hull
p976 . . . . 01482 323264

MURRAY, Ashley C LLB(Hons); Recorder M *Jul 1974*
20
Oriel Chambers, Liverpool
p981 . . . . 0151 236 7191 / 236 4321
Oriel Chambers, Preston
p990 . . . . 01772 254764

Murray, Miss Carole M *Nov 1989*
3, 35, 78, 21, 54, 79
No5 Chambers, Bristol
p971 . . . . 0845 210 5555
No5 Chambers, London EC4
p944 . . . . 0845 210 5555
No5 Chambers, Birmingham
p968 . . . . 0845 210 5555

MURRAY, Mr Charles I *Mar 2005*
12, 11, 30, 8, 47, 15, 22, 29, 36, 18
Rougemont Chambers, Exeter
p975 . . . . 01392 208484

Murray, Mr David John BCL(Oxon); BA(Hons) L *Jul 2004*
Fountain Court Chambers, London EC4
p934 . . . . 020 7583 3335

Murray, Miss Elizabeth I *Oct 2005*
30, 20, 15
18 St John Street Chambers, Manchester
p985 . . . . 0161 278 1800

MURRAY, Mr Harvey M *Jan 2004*
Fountain Chambers, Middlesbrough
p986 . . . . 01642 804040

Murray, Miss Joanne M *Mar 2006*
30, 15, 12
St Pauls Chambers, Leeds
p979 . . . . 0113 245 5866

Murray, Ms Judith BA(Hons)(Oxon) M *Oct 1994*
20, 10
4 Paper Buildings, London EC4
p946 . . . . 020 7583 0816

Murray, Miss Lucy L *May 1997*
12, 23
Charter Chambers, London WC1
p928 . . . . 020 7618 4400

Murray, Miss Rebecca L *Jan 2001*
Temple Tax Chambers, London EC4
p952 . . . . .020 7353 7884 / 7353 8982

Murray, Mr Simon I *Oct 2000*
1, 12, 44, 18, 51, 88, 26, 30
1 Chancery Lane, London WC2
p928 . . . . 0845 634 6666

Murray, Simon I *Jan 2008*
St Johns Buildings, Preston
p990 . . . . 01772 256100
St Johns Buildings, Chester
p974 . . . . 01244 323070
St Johns Buildings, Manchester
p985 . . . . 0161 214 1500
St Johns Buildings, Liverpool
p982 . . . . 0151 243 6000

Murray, Mr Stephen John LLB(Hons) I *Aug 1986*
20, 12
18 St John Street Chambers, Manchester
p985 . . . . 0161 278 1800

Murray-Smith, Mr James BA(Law) M *May 1990*
1 Mitre Court Buildings, London EC4
p942 . . . . 020 7452 8900

Musaheb, Mr Kevin LLM(Hons) M *Jan 1990*
1, 5, 6, 7, 8, 11, 12, 22, 24, 25, 26, 29, 31, 32, 36, 37, 40, 41, 57
Cobden House Chambers, Manchester
p983 . . . . 0161 833 6000

Musgrave, Ms Anarkali Literae Humaniores(Oxon) I *Jan 2005*
18, 30, 53
3PB, Oxford
p989 . . . . 01865 793736

Musgrave, Ms Kerry LLB(Hons) M *Nov 1992*
96, 71, 70, 72, 40
3PB, London EC4
p946 . . . . 020 7583 8055

Mushtaq, Erimnaz I *Jan 2000*
1, 91, 15
Doughty Street Chambers, London WC1
p930 . . . . 020 7404 1313

Mussa, Miss Azreen LLB(Hons)(Leics) M *Oct 2003*
6, 10, 12, 15, 18, 20, 30, 94
Fenners Chambers, Cambridge
p972 . . . . 01223 368761

Mussa, Mr Hanif BA(Cantab); DipLaw I *Jul 2007*
1, 11, 18, 51, 89
Blackstone Chambers, London EC4
p926 . . . . 020 7583 1770

See p1010 for the Key to Work Categories

Mustafa, Miss Hala LLB M *Jun 2004*
20, 10
4 Brick Court Chambers, London EC4
p927 . . . . . . 020 7832 3200
Crown Office Row Chambers, Brighton
p970 . . . . . . 01273 625625

Mustafa, Mr Jehad M *Nov 2007*
15
1 Paper Buildings, London EC4
p946 . . . . . . 020 7353 3728

Mustakim, Mr Al L *May 1997*
23
Two King's Bench Walk, London EC4
p939 . . . . . . 020 7353 7202 / 7353 3909
No 3 Fleet Street Chambers, London EC4
p944 . . . . . . 020 7936 4474

Mustard, Ms Lorraine LLB L *Oct 1999*
15, 23
Broad Chare Chambers, Newcastle upon Tyne
p986 . . . . . . 0191 232 0541

Muth, Ms Susanne LLB; CPE; LLM I *Jul 1998*
5, 6, 8, 11, 18, 22, 29, 40
St Johns Buildings, Preston
p990 . . . . . . 01772 256100
St Johns Buildings, Chester
p974 . . . . . . 01244 323070
St Johns Buildings, Manchester
p985 . . . . . . 0161 214 1500
St Johns Buildings, Liverpool
p982 . . . . . . 0151 243 6000

Myatt, Mr Charles BA(Dunelm) G *Oct 1993*
15
1 Paper Buildings, London EC4
p946 . . . . . . 020 7353 3728

Myers, Mr Benjamin I *Nov 1994*
72, 15, 70
Exchange Chambers, Manchester
p983 . . . . . . 0161 833 2722
Exchange Chambers, Liverpool
p980 . . . . . . 0151 236 7747
Exchange Chambers, Leeds
p977 . . . . . . 0113 203 1970

Myers, John LLB I *Mar 2007*
10, 20
Zenith Chambers, Leeds
p979 . . . . . . 0113 245 5438

Myers, Mr Rupert I *Nov 2008*
15
East Anglian Chambers, Norwich
p988 . . . . . . 01603 617351
East Anglian Chambers, Colchester
p975 . . . . . . 01206 572756
East Anglian Chambers, Chelmsford
p973 . . . . . . 01245 215660
East Anglian Chambers, Ipswich
p976 . . . . . . 01473 214481

Myers, Mr Simon M *Nov 1987*
15, 25
Broadway House Chambers, Leeds
p977 . . . . . . 0113 246 2600
Broadway House Chambers, Bradford
p969 . . . . . . 01274 722560

Myerson, Mr Simon MA(Cantab) M *Jan 1986*
(Q.C.) *62, 11, 15, 8, 53, 70, 72, 27*
42 Bedford Row, London WC1
p925 . . . . . . 020 7831 0222
Byrom Street Chambers, Manchester
p983 . . . . . . 0161 829 2100
St Pauls Chambers, Leeds
p979 . . . . . . 0113 245 5866

MYHILL, Mr David BA(Hons); BVC L *Nov 2006*
11, 74, 24, 30, 84, 40
Crown Office Chambers, London EC4
p929 . . . . . . 020 7797 8100

Mylonas, Mr Michael John LLB(Bucks) G *Jul 1988*
12, 27, 30, 40, 53, 68, 85, 63, 46, 84
3 Serjeants' Inn, London EC4
p950 . . . . . . 020 7427 5000

Mylvaganam, Mr Paul BA(Hons)(Oxon); CPE(Lond) M *Nov 1993*
15, 16, 19, 51, 62, 84
Argent Chambers, London WC2
p923 . . . . . . 020 7556 5500

Mynors, Dr Charles MA(Cantab); MA(Sheff); Dip EC Law(Lond); FRTPI; MRICS M *Nov 1988*
1, 12, 46, 26, 31, 17
Francis Taylor Building, London EC4
p934 . . . . . . 020 7353 8415

MYTTON, Mr Paul L *Jul 1982*
15, 62, 84
St Philips Chambers, Birmingham
p969 . . . . . . 0121 246 7000

Nabi, Mr Zia U LLB(Hons)(Essex) M *Nov 1991*
11, 22, 18, 30
1 Pump Court, London EC4
p947 . . . . . . 020 7842 7070

NABIJOU, Miss Sherry BSc(Leeds) I *Oct 1996*
7, 8, 15, 20, 22, 31
10 King's Bench Walk, London EC4
p940 . . . . . . 020 7353 7742

Nadeem, Mr Afshan LLM(Hons); LLM L *Jan 2005*
Park Court Chambers, Leeds
p978 . . . . . . 0113 243 3277

Nadin, Mr James L *Oct 2002*
One Essex Court, London EC4
p931 . . . . . . 020 7583 2000

NAGPAL, Mr Deepak BA(Oxon)(Jurisprudence); BCL(Oxon) L *Oct 2002*
10, 20
1 King's Bench Walk, London EC4
p938 . . . . . . 020 7936 1500

Naik, Gaurang Ramamlal BSc; DipLaw G *Jul 1985*
11, 22, 30, 15, 62, 65, 81, 39, 38, 84
9 Gough Square, London EC4
p935 . . . . . . 020 7832 0500

Naik, Mr Timothy G *Nov 1994*
Holborn Chambers, London WC2
p937 . . . . . . 020 7242 6060

Naish, Mr Christopher LLB I *Jul 1980*
10, 20
Southernhay Chambers, Exeter
p975 . . . . . . 01392 255777

NAJIB, Mr Shakil Mohammed L *Oct 1999*
6, 8, 11, 12, 97, 38
St Philips Chambers, Birmingham
p969 . . . . . . 0121 246 7000

Nall-Cain, Mr Richard LLM; LLB(Hons) I *Jan 1997*
30, 40, 53, 22, 31, 96
St Albans Chambers, St Albans
p992 . . . . . . 01727 843383

Nambisan, Mr Deepak LLM(Harv); BA(Cantab) G *Oct 1998*
Fountain Court Chambers, London EC4
p934 . . . . . . 020 7583 3335

Nance, Mr Francis G *Nov 1970*
15
Exchange Chambers, Manchester
p983 . . . . . . 0161 833 2722
Exchange Chambers, Liverpool
p980 . . . . . . 0151 236 7747
Exchange Chambers, Leeds
p977 . . . . . . 0113 203 1970

NAPTHINE, Mr David Robert Guy BA I *Nov 1979*
15
1 High Pavement, Nottingham
p988 . . . . . . 0115 941 8218

Narain, Mr Benjamin M *Jan 1999*
15, 51, 91
Doughty Street Chambers, London WC1
p930 . . . . . . 020 7404 1313

Narayan, Mr Harry Recorder L *Nov 1970*
15, 23
Cobden House Chambers, Manchester
p983 . . . . . . 0161 833 6000

Nardecchia, Mr Nicholas MA(Cantab) M *Nov 1974*
1, 26, 28, 31, 22
Cornerstone Barristers, London WC1
p929 . . . . . . 020 7242 4986

NARDELL, Mr Gordon LLB(Hons) I *Nov 1995*
(Q.C.) *1, 46, 19, 51, 26, 28, 31*
Thirty Nine Essex Street, London WC2
p932 . . . . . . 020 7832 1111

Nartey, Miss Elizabeth M *Jan 2003*
10, 15, 20, 62
Argent Chambers, London WC2
p923 . . . . . . 020 7556 5500
33 Bedford Row, London WC1
p925 . . . . . . 020 7242 6476

Nash, Miss Alice I *Jan 2006*
40, 27, 53, 30, 11
Hailsham Chambers, London EC4
p936 . . . . . . 020 7643 5000

Nash, Miss Emma I *Oct 2001*
15
2 Pump Court, London EC4
p947 . . . . . . 020 7353 5597

NASH, Mr Jonathan BA(Oxon) G *Nov 1986*
(Q.C.) *3, 5, 6, 11, 24, 40*
3 Verulam Buildings, London WC1
p953 . . . . . . 020 7831 8441

Nash, Laura L *Jan 2009*
St Johns Buildings, Preston
p990 . . . . . . 01772 256100
St Johns Buildings, Chester
p974 . . . . . . 01244 323070
St Johns Buildings, Manchester
p985 . . . . . . 0161 214 1500
St Johns Buildings, Liverpool
p982 . . . . . . 0151 243 6000

Nashashibi, Mr Anwar David BA(Hons) M *Nov 1995*
12, 15, 20, 62, 26
7 Bedford Row, London WC1
p924 . . . . . . 020 7242 3555

Nasir, Dr Jamal Jamil BA; PhD(Lond); LLB L *Jan 1948*
3, 21, 23, 33
2 Stone Buildings, London WC2
p951 . . . . . . 020 7405 3818

Nassar, Ms Victoria BSc; PGCL G *Feb 1994*
23
Fortis Green Chambers, London N2
p934 . . . . . . 020 8883 8117

Nathan, Miss Aparna LLB; LLM M *Nov 1994*
34, 57, 58
Gray's Inn Tax Chambers, London WC1
p936 . . . . . . 020 7242 2642

Nathan, Mr David LLB(Hons)(Manc) M *Oct 1971*
(Q.C.) *15, 62*
Argent Chambers, London WC2
p923 . . . . . . 020 7556 5500

Nathan, David Associate Tenant M *Nov 1971*
(Q.C.) *15, 62*
Zenith Chambers, Leeds
p979 . . . . . . 0113 245 5438

Nathan, Mr Stephen MA(Oxon) M *Nov 1969*
(Q.C.) *8, 11, 12, 24, 29, 25, 41, 52, 89, 49, 50, 3*
Blackstone Chambers, London EC4
p926 . . . . . . 020 7583 1770

Nathwani, Mr Rishi M *Jul 2006*
15
5 King's Bench Walk, London EC4
p939 . . . . . . 020 7353 5638

NAUGHTON, Miss Lianne Eve I *Oct 1999*
30, 84
7 Harrington Street Chambers, Liverpool
p981 . . . . . . 0151 242 0707

Naughton, Mr Philip Anthony LLB(Nott'm) G *Apr 1970*
(Q.C.) *3, 7, 11, 12, 18, 27, 40, 96, 41*
3 Serjeants' Inn, London EC4
p950 . . . . . . 020 7427 5000

Naughton, Mr Sebastian BA(Bris) G *Nov 1999*
12
42 Bedford Row, London WC1
p925 . . . . . . 020 7831 0222

Nawaz, Mr Mohammed LLB; LLM(Cantab) L *Nov 1995*
Lincoln House Chambers, Manchester
p984 . . . . . . 0161 832 5701

Nawbatt, Mr Akash BA(Cantab) G *Jun 1999*
24, 18, 55, 51, 11, 12, 30
Devereux Chambers, London WC2
p930 . . . . . . 020 7353 7534

Naylor, Dr Kevin MB; ChB; LLB(Hons); LLM L *Oct 1992*
12, 27, 30, 53, 89, 96, 68, 84, 85
Exchange Chambers, Manchester
p983 . . . . . . 0161 833 2722
Exchange Chambers, Liverpool
p980 . . . . . . 0151 236 7747
Exchange Chambers, Leeds
p977 . . . . . . 0113 203 1970

Naylor, Mr Martyn MA(Cantab) I *Jul 2009*
11, 12, 40, 24, 89, 74, 35, 79
4 Pump Court, London EC4
p947 . . . . . . 020 7842 5555

NAZARETH, Melanie Bernadette BSc(Lond); DipLaw I *Jul 1984*
10, 20
Renaissance Chambers, London WC1
p949 . . . . . . 020 7404 1111

Ndlovu, Mr Lazarus BA; LLM(Lond) I *Jul 1979*
15, 20, 23, 25
12 Old Square, London WC2
p945 . . . . . . 020 7404 0875

Neal, Prof Alan LLB G *Jul 1975*
2 New Street, Leicester
p979 . . . . . . 0116 262 5906

Neale, Miss Fiona Rosalind LLB(Lond) M *Jul 1981*
27, 30, 36, 40, 53, 68, 85
3 Serjeants' Inn, London EC4
p950 . . . . . . 020 7427 5000

Neale, Mr Nicholas L BA G *Jul 1972*
15
Paradise Chambers, Sheffield
p992 . . . . . . 0114 273 8951

Neale, Mr Stuart MA(Cantab) M *Jul 1976*
15, 16, 62, 70
Cobden House Chambers, Manchester
p983 . . . . . . 0161 833 6000

NEAMAN, Mr Sam L Accredited Mediator I *Jul 1988*
5, 11, 12, 18, 27, 40, 30, 49
Littleton Chambers, London EC4
p941 . . . . . . 020 7797 8600

Neathey, Ms Rona BA I *Nov 1990*
10, 20, 22
6 King's Bench Walk, London EC4
p939 . . . . . . 020 7583 0695 / 7353 4931

NEAVES, Mr Andrew LLB(Leics) G *Jul 1977*
20, 51
St Philips Chambers, Birmingham
p969 . . . . . . 0121 246 7000

NEENAN, Ms Caroline BA(Hons)(Oxon); LLM G *Oct 1998*
1, 12, 18, 23, 27, 30, 40, 51, 53, 55
1 Crown Office Row, London EC4
p929 . . . . . . 020 7797 7500

NEILL, Mr Daniel L *Nov 2008*
30, 53
Guildhall Chambers, Bristol
p970 . . . . . . 0117 930 9000

Neill, Ms Emily BA(Oxon) I *Jan 2008*
11, 18, 19, 44, 1, 33
Blackstone Chambers, London EC4
p926 . . . . . . 020 7583 1770

Neill, Mr Robert LLB(Hons)(Lond) M *Jul 1975*
15, 25, 26, 31
2 Bedford Row, London WC1
p924 . . . . . . 020 7440 8888

Neill, Mr Robin LLB(Bucks) G *Jul 1979*
7, 8, 11, 38, 93, 96
St John's Chambers, Bristol
p972 . . . . . . 0117 921 3456

Neish, Mr Andrew MA(Hons)(St Andrews); DipLaw(City) L *Jul 1988*
(Q.C.) *3, 11, 12, 24, 78*
4 Pump Court, London EC4
p947 . . . . . . 020 7842 5555

Nejranowski, Miss Tessa M *Jan 2005*
15, 62
5 St Andrew's Hill, London EC4
p950 . . . . . . 020 7332 5400

Nelson, Mr Cairns LLB G *Jan 1987*
(Q.C.) *15, 62*
Exchange Chambers, Manchester
p983 . . . . . . 0161 833 2722
Exchange Chambers, Liverpool
p980 . . . . . . 0151 236 7747
Exchange Chambers, Leeds
p977 . . . . . . 0113 203 1970
23 Essex Street, London WC2
p932 . . . . . . 020 7413 0353

Nelson, Mr Giles BSc(Bris) I *Feb 1995*
72, 15, 70
Albion Chambers, Bristol
p970 . . . . . . 0117 927 2144

Nelson, Miss Linda LLB(Exeter) G *Jul 2000*
12, 18, 22, 30, 60, 53
9 Gough Square, London EC4
p935 . . . . . . 020 7832 0500

NELSON, Miss Michelle LLB; BSc M *Nov 1994*
15, 62, 51
18 Red Lion Court, London EC4
p949 . . . . . . 020 7520 6000
18 Red Lion Court (Annexe), Chelmsford
p973 . . . . . . 01245 280880

NELSON, Mr Vincent I *Nov 1980*
(Q.C.) *11, 24, 56, 7, 5, 97, 52*
Thirty Nine Essex Street, London WC2
p932 . . . . 020 7832 1111

Nereshraaj, Mr Srikantharajah MA(Hons)(Edin); LLB(Hons)(Lond) G *Jun 2007*
15, 51
Tooks Chambers, London EC4
p953 . . . . 020 7842 7575

NERESSIAN, Mr Tiran Junior Counsel to the Crown (C) L *Nov 2002*
6, 8, 11, 29
4 Stone Buildings, London WC2
p951 . . . . 020 7242 5524

Nesbitt, Mr Timothy LLM(Lond) M *Feb 1991*
30, 84, 1, 60
Outer Temple Chambers, London WC2
p945 . . . . 020 7353 6381

Neuberger, Mr Edmund MEng(Oxon); GDL(City); BVC L *Jul 2008*
3, 7, 11, 31, 40, 41, 43, 45, 49, 54, 61, 78, 74
Atkin Chambers, London WC1
p923 . . . . 020 7404 0102

Neubert, Mr Jolyon LLB M *Jul 1989*
15, 12, 22
1 Gray's Inn Square, London WC1
p935 . . . . 020 7405 8946

Nevill, Miss Penelope M *Jul 2010*
33, 21, 3, 19, 41, 12
20 Essex Street, London WC2
p932 . . . . 020 7842 1200

NEVILLE, Mr Stephen MA(Cantab) M *Nov 1986*
5, 6, 11, 18, 22, 29, 12, 40, 47, 59
Gough Square Chambers, London EC4
p935 . . . . 020 7353 0924

NEVILLE-CLARKE, Mr Sebastian A B BA(Oxon) I *Nov 1973*
7, 31, 22, 11, 36
3 Hare Court, London EC4
p937 . . . . 020 7415 7800

Newbegin, Miss Nicola M *Jan 2009*
26, 51, 36, 46, 18, 55, 48, 49, 53
Old Square Chambers, London WC1
p945 . . . . 020 7269 0300

Newberry, Mr Clive I *Jul 1978*
(Q.C.) *1, 25, 26, 31, 36, 46, 28*
Francis Taylor Building, London EC4
p934 . . . . 020 7353 8415

NEWBERY, Ms Freya MA(Cantab); Recorder M *Nov 1986*
30, 40
12 King's Bench Walk, London EC4
p940 . . . . 020 7583 0811

NEWBOLD, Mr Michael I *Jul 2004*
15
9-12 Bell Yard Chambers, London WC2
p926 . . . . 020 7400 1800

Newbon, Mr Ian LLB(Leeds) M *Feb 1977*
7, 10, 11, 12, 18, 20, 22, 23, 24, 25, 27, 30, 31, 36, 15, 40
Broadway House Chambers, Leeds
p977 . . . . 0113 246 2600
Broadway House Chambers, Bradford
p969 . . . . 01274 722560

Newcomb, Mr Quinton LLB M *Jul 2005*
15
1 Paper Buildings, London EC4
p946 . . . . 020 7353 3728

Newcombe, Mr Andrew BA(Dunelm) M *Jul 1987*
(Q.C.) *1, 26, 31, 60, 36, 61*
Francis Taylor Building, London EC4
p934 . . . . 020 7353 8415

Newcombe, Mr Paul LLB I *Feb 1991*
15, 72, 70
Old Court Chambers, Middlesbrough
p986 . . . . 01642 232523

Newell, Miss Charlotte LLB(Newc) G *Oct 1994*
15
5 King's Bench Walk, London EC4
p939 . . . . 020 7353 5638

Newell, Mr Giles M *Mar 2007*
15
Tooks Chambers, London EC4
p953 . . . . 020 7842 7575

Newey, Mr Guy MA; LLM(Cantab); Deputy High Court Judge, Acting Deemster IoM M *Jul 1982*
(Q.C.)
Maitland Chambers, London WC2
p941 . . . . 020 7406 1200

Newman, Mr Alan Recorder; Attorney at Law State Bar of California, USA M *Nov 1968*
(Q.C.) *15, 11, 12, 69, 62, 21, 1, 41, 96*
Argent Chambers, London WC2
p923 . . . . 020 7556 5500

Newman, Miss Anya I *Jan 2007*
St Ives Chambers, Birmingham
p969 . . . . 0121 236 0863

Newman, Austin I *Jan 1987*
15, 30
Zenith Chambers, Leeds
p979 . . . . 0113 245 5438

Newman, Miss Catherine Mary LLB(Hons)(Lond); Recorder; Lt. Bailiff in the Royal Courts of Guernsey; Deputy High Court Judge; Accredited Mediator M *Jul 1979*
(Q.C.)
Maitland Chambers, London WC2
p941 . . . . 020 7406 1200

NEWMAN, Mr Christopher I *Jan 2003*
5, 11, 18, 29, 55, 50, 97
Littleton Chambers, London EC4
p941 . . . . 020 7797 8600

Newman, Mr James G *Jul 2000*
8, 11, 12, 97, 47, 67, 88, 89, 30, 40, 93
Ely Place Chambers, London EC1
p931 . . . . 020 7400 9600
5 Pump Court, London EC4
p947 . . . . 020 7353 2532 / 7583 7133

Newman, Mr Paul MA(Cantab) G *Jan 1982*
96, 93, 8, 74
3PB, Bristol
p971 . . . . 0117 928 1520
Wilberforce Chambers, London WC2
p953 . . . . 020 7306 0102

NEWMAN, Mr Peter I *Jul 2005*
10, 20, 25, 22
1 King's Bench Walk, London EC4
p938 . . . . 020 7936 1500

Newman, Mr Philip DipIcArb; LLM(Lond); FCIArb G *Nov 1977*
3, 8, 11, 29, 36
42 Bedford Row, London WC1
p925 . . . . 020 7831 0222

Newman, Mr Timothy BA(Keele) G *Jul 1981*
30, 40, 53, 94, 68
No5 Chambers, Bristol
p971 . . . . 0845 210 5555
No5 Chambers, London EC4
p944 . . . . 0845 210 5555
No5 Chambers, Birmingham
p968 . . . . 0845 210 5555

NEWNHAM, Ms Mary BA; PGDL L *Nov 2003*
30, 18, 53, 40
12 King's Bench Walk, London EC4
p940 . . . . 020 7583 0811

Newport, Mr Ian LLB(Hons); LLM G *Oct 2000*
10, 12, 47, 20, 30, 31
College Chambers, Southampton
p992 . . . . 023 8023 0338

Newport, Mr Michael BSc M *Jul 1999*
15, 55, 82, 62
Lamb Building, Brighton
p970 . . . . 01273 820490
Lamb Building, London EC4
p940 . . . . 020 7797 7788

NEWSOM, Mr George MA(Oxon); FCIArb L *Nov 1973*
8, 17, 37, 93, 49
Guildhall Chambers, Bristol
p970 . . . . 0117 930 9000

Newstead, Ms Jennifer Elizabeth BA; MA; DipLaw G *Nov 2003*
11, 30, 8, 22
St Johns Buildings, Preston
p990 . . . . 01772 256100
St Johns Buildings, Chester
p974 . . . . 01244 323070
St Johns Buildings, Manchester
p985 . . . . 0161 214 1500
St Johns Buildings, Liverpool
p982 . . . . 0151 243 6000

Newton, Mrs Alexandra L *Mar 2007*
10, 20
15 Winckley Square, Preston
p991 . . . . 01772 252828

Newton, Miss Alice BA(Hons) I *Jul 2009*
15, 12
East Anglian Chambers, Norwich
p988 . . . . 01603 617351
East Anglian Chambers, Colchester
p975 . . . . 01206 572756
East Anglian Chambers, Chelmsford
p973 . . . . 01245 215660
East Anglian Chambers, Ipswich
p976 . . . . 01473 214481

NEWTON, Mr Andrew MA(Oxon); DipLaw(City) I *Nov 1991*
15, 62, 95
187 Fleet Street, London EC4
p933 . . . . 020 7430 7430

Newton, Mr Benjamin BA(Oxon); PGDL(City) L *Jan 2004*
51, 15, 91
Doughty Street Chambers, London WC1
p930 . . . . 020 7404 1313

NEWTON, Mr Clive MA(Oxon); BCL(Oxon) M *Nov 1968*
(Q.C.) *10, 11, 12, 20*
1 King's Bench Walk, London EC4
p938 . . . . 020 7936 1500

Newton, Miss Katharine LLB; LLM M *Oct 1999*
18, 30, 36, 51, 53, 55
Old Square Chambers, Bristol
p971 . . . . 0117 930 5100
Old Square Chambers, London WC1
p945 . . . . 020 7269 0300

Newton, Miss Laura LLB(Hons)(Dunelm); BCL M *Oct 2009*
89, 5, 6, 8, 38
11 Stone Buildings, London WC2
p951 . . . . 020 7831 6381

Newton, Mr Philip BA; LLM; Dip(Human Rights) M *Jul 1984*
10, 20, 51
Becket Chambers, Canterbury
p972 . . . . 01227 786331
Becket Chambers, Maidstone
p982 . . . . 01622 230957

Newton, Mr Stuart R J BA(Hons) M *Nov 1993*
15
Paradise Chambers, Sheffield
p992 . . . . 0114 273 8951

NEWTON-PRICE, Mr James BA M *Oct 1992*
15, 30, 12, 42, 91
Pump Court Chambers, Swindon
p993 . . . . 01793 539899
Pump Court Chambers, Winchester
p994 . . . . 01962 868161
Pump Court Chambers, London EC4
p947 . . . . 020 7353 0711

Ng, Mr Jern-Fei L *Jan 2002*
Essex Court Chambers, London WC2
p931 . . . . 020 7813 8000

NI GHRALAIGH, Ms Blinne BA(Cantab); DipLaw L *Nov 2005*
1, 15, 70, 71, 51, 55, 76, 21, 33, 72
Matrix Chambers, London WC1
p942 . . . . 020 7404 3447

NIAZ, Miss Anisa M *Oct 2004*
18, 23
Kenworthy's Chambers, Manchester
p984 . . . . 0161 832 4036

NICE, Sir Geoffrey MA(Oxon); Recorder I *Jul 1971*
(Q.C.)
Temple Garden Chambers, London EC4
p952 . . . . 020 7583 1315

Nichol, Mr Simon B BSc L *May 1994*
15, 70
Cobden House Chambers, Manchester
p983 . . . . 0161 833 6000

Nicholas, Mr Garvin LLB(Hons) I *Jan 2001*
30, 18, 20, 93, 97, 1, 88
3PB, London EC4
p946 . . . . 020 7583 8055

Nicholes, Ms Catherine LLB(Lond) I *May 1977*
20, 10
Coram Chambers, London EC1
p929 . . . . 020 7092 3700

NICHOLLS, Mr Benjamin G *Jan 1978*
Citadel Chambers, Birmingham
p967 . . . . 0121 233 8500

Nicholls, Mr David BA(Oxon) L *Dec 2002*
6, 11
11 Stone Buildings, London WC2
p951 . . . . 020 7831 6381

Nicholls, Ms Elizabeth J BA(Hons); Recorder I *Jul 1984*
Lincoln House Chambers, Manchester
p984 . . . . 0161 832 5701

Nicholls, Mr Jack BA(Dunelm) I *Nov 1991*
5 Pump Court, London EC4
p947 . . . . 020 7353 2532 / 7583 7133

NICHOLLS, Ms Jane LLB(Hons) I *Nov 1989*
10, 20
Oriel Chambers, Liverpool
p981 . . . . 0151 236 7191 / 236 4321
Oriel Chambers, Preston
p990 . . . . 01772 254764

Nicholls, Mr John Peter MA(Hons)(Cantab) L *Jul 1986*
(Q.C.)
Maitland Chambers, London WC2
p941 . . . . 020 7406 1200

Nicholls, Mr Michael John Gadsby M *Nov 1975*
(Q.C.) *20, 10*
Broad Chare Chambers, Newcastle upon Tyne
p986 . . . . 0191 232 0541
1 Hare Court, London EC4
p936 . . . . 020 7797 7070

NICHOLLS, Mr Paul LLB(Sheff); BCL(Oxon) I *Oct 1992*
1, 11, 18, 19, 26, 55
11KBW, London EC4
p938 . . . . 020 7632 8500

Nicholls, Mr Samuel David LLB; LLM I *Nov 2006*
18, 30, 11
Devereux Chambers, London WC2
p930 . . . . 020 7353 7534

NICHOLS, Mr Stuart LLB(Hons)(Leics) L *Nov 1989*
1 Garden Court, London EC4
p934 . . . . 020 7797 7900

Nicholson, Ms Amy L *Dec 1999*
Lincoln House Chambers, Manchester
p984 . . . . 0161 832 5701

Nicholson, Dr Brian BEng(Hons); PhD L *Jul 2000*
73, 50, 19, 45, 13, 52, 96, 41
11 South Square, London WC1
p950 . . . . 020 7405 1222

Nicholson, Mr Edward M *Nov 1993*
1, 51, 23
No5 Chambers, Bristol
p971 . . . . 0845 210 5555
No5 Chambers, London EC4
p944 . . . . 0845 210 5555
No5 Chambers, Birmingham
p968 . . . . 0845 210 5555

NICHOLSON, Mr Jeremy MA(Cantab) M *Jul 1977*
(Q.C.) *7, 11, 12, 22, 24, 78*
4 Pump Court, London EC4
p947 . . . . 020 7842 5555

NICHOLSON, Mr John G *Jul 2004*
23, 1, 51
Kenworthy's Chambers, Manchester
p984 . . . . 0161 832 4036

Nicholson, Mr Michael LLB(UCL) M *Jan 1993*
30
Old Square Chambers, Bristol
p971 . . . . 0117 930 5100
Old Square Chambers, London WC1
p945 . . . . 020 7269 0300

NICHOLSON, Miss Rosalind V MA(Oxon); Tenant G *Jul 1987*
6, 11, 29
4 Stone Buildings, London WC2
p951 . . . . 020 7242 5524

Nicholson, Mr Thomas Edward Cyril G *Jul 2001*
15
Atkinson Bevan Chambers, London EC4
p924 . . . . 020 7353 2112

Nicholson Pratt, Mr Tom LLB(Hons) L *Nov 1986*
15, 62
15 New Bridge Street Chambers, London EC4
p943 . . . . 020 7842 1900

Nickless, Mr Jason LLB(Hons); LLM(Dunelm) G *Oct 2001*
6, 7, 8, 10, 53, 11, 12, 47, 67, 20, 22, 38, 88, 30
College Chambers, Southampton
p992 . . . . 023 8023 0338

Nicklin, Mr Andrew M *Jul 2010*
12, 15, 72
East Anglian Chambers, Norwich
p988 . . . . 01603 617351
East Anglian Chambers, Colchester
p975 . . . . 01206 572756
East Anglian Chambers, Chelmsford
p973 . . . . 01245 215660
East Anglian Chambers, Ipswich
p976 . . . . 01473 214481

Nicklin, Mr Matthew LLB(Hons)(Newc) L *Nov 1993*
13, 16, 50, 51
5RB, London WC1
p948 . . . . 020 7242 2902

See p1010 for the Key to Work Categories

Nicol, Mr Andrew R BA I *Nov 1991*
8, 12, 24, 40
Four New Square, London WC2
p943 . . . . 020 7822 2000

Nicol, Mr Nicholas K LLB(Lond) I *Nov 1986*
1, 12, 18, 22, 26, 28, 33, 39
1 Pump Court, London EC4
p947 . . . . 020 7842 7070

Nicol, Mr Stuart LLB(Lond) L *Nov 1994*
King's Bench Chambers, Oxford
p989 . . . . 01865 311066
13 King's Bench Walk, London EC4
p940 . . . . 020 7353 7204

Nield, Ms Zoe LLB G *Oct 1998*
Lincoln House Chambers, Manchester
p984 . . . . 0161 832 5701

Nijabat, Sharma B LLB; LLM M *Nov 1993*
10, 20
Paradise Chambers, Sheffield
p992 . . . . 0114 273 8951

Nisbett, Mr James T LLB L *Jun 1973*
12, 15, 23, 30, 38
7 Westmeath Avenue, Leicester
p979 . . . . 0116 212 8497

Nissen, Mr Alexander D LLB(Manc); FCIAM M *Jul 1985*
(Q.C.) *3, 7, 11, 24, 40*
Keating Chambers, London WC2
p938 . . . . 020 7544 2600

NIXON, Miss Abigail Recorder I *Oct 1991*
Citadel Chambers, Birmingham
p967 . . . . 0121 233 8500

Nixon, Mr Andrew G *Jun 2006*
St Pauls Chambers, Leeds
p979 . . . . 0113 245 5866

NIXON, Mr Colin BA(Natal) L *Jul 1973*
30, 40, 53, 11, 24
Crown Office Chambers, London EC4
p929 . . . . 020 7797 8100

Nixon, Ms Elaine L *Jul 2003*
20, 10
Temple Chambers, Newport
p988 . . . . .01633 267403 / 255855
Temple Chambers, Cardiff
p973 . . . . 029 2039 7364

NOBLE, Mr Andrew LLB(Hons)(Manc); FRICS; FCIArb; Mediator L *Nov 1992*
6, 7, 8, 11, 22, 40, 41, 49, 38, 88, 97
Enterprise Chambers, London WC2
p931 . . . . 020 7405 9471
Enterprise Chambers, Leeds
p977 . . . . 0113 246 0391
Enterprise Chambers, Newcastle upon Tyne
p987 . . . . 0191 222 3344

NOBLE, Mr Arthur BA(Dublin); Recorder I *Jul 1965*
15
Chavasse Court Chambers, Liverpool
p980 . . . . 0151 229 2030

Noble, Mr Philip R I *Jul 1978*
10, 12, 15, 20, 22, 23, 25, 30
Thomas More Chambers, London WC2
p952 . . . . 020 7404 7000

NOBLE, Mr Roderick G G *Nov 1977*
30, 40, 53
Thirty Nine Essex Street, London WC2
p932 . . . . 020 7832 1111

Noble, Mr Will G *Jul 2000*
Nine Bedford Row, London WC1
p924 . . . . 020 7489 2727

Nock, Mr Reginald Stanley LLB; LLM; FTII L *Nov 1968*
34, 37, 36, 29, 8, 9
15 Old Square, London WC2
p945 . . . . 020 7242 2744

Nolan, Mr Benjamin M *Jul 1971*
(Q.C.) *15, 62, 94, 84, 30*
Broad Chare Chambers, Newcastle upon Tyne
p986 . . . . 0191 232 0541
15 New Bridge Street Chambers, London EC4
p943 . . . . 020 7842 1900
St Pauls Chambers, Leeds
p979 . . . . 0113 245 5866
Kenworthy's Chambers, Manchester
p984 . . . . 0161 832 4036

Nolan, Mr Damian Francis BSc(Jt Hons)(Econ) L *Nov 1994*
Hardwicke Scholar
15, 62
Exchange Chambers, Manchester
p983 . . . . 0161 833 2722
Exchange Chambers, Liverpool
p980 . . . . 0151 236 7747
Exchange Chambers, Leeds
p977 . . . . 0113 203 1970

NOLAN, Mr Dominic L *Jul 1985*
(Q.C.)
Ropewalk Chambers, Nottingham
p989 . . . . 0115 947 2581

Nolan, Miss Georgina M *Jul 2006*
15, 20, 30, 47, 48, 59
Broad Chare Chambers, Newcastle upon Tyne
p986 . . . . 0191 232 0541

Nolan, Mr Michael MA(Oxon) M *Jul 1981*
11, 24, 35, 5, 3
Quadrant Chambers, London EC4
p948 . . . . 020 7583 4444

NOLAN, Mr Richard BA; MA(Cantab) M *Jul 1999*
11, 38, 97
Erskine Chambers, London WC2
p931 . . . . 020 7242 5532

Nolten, Miss Sonia Jayne MA(Oxon); Master of Studies(Oxon) I *Nov 2002*
5, 11, 24
2 Temple Gardens, London EC4
p952 . . . . 020 7822 1200

Norbury, Mr Hugh BA(Oxon); LLM L *Nov 1995*
5, 6, 8, 11, 62, 40, 37, 29, 61
Serle Court, London WC2
p950 . . . . 020 7242 6105

Norie-Miller, Mr Jeffery LLB(Soton) I *Jul 1996*
15, 70, 26
12 College Place, Southampton
p992 . . . . 023 8032 0320

Norman, Mr Ben LLB(Hons) G *Jan 2000*
30
18 St John Street Chambers, Manchester
p985 . . . . 0161 278 1800

Norman, Miss Elizabeth MA(Cantab) M *Oct 1977*
18, 15, 23, 22
4 Rowchester Court, Birmingham
p968 . . . . 0121 233 2327

Norman, Mr James M *Nov 2000*
15, 48, 13, 25
5 Paper Buildings, London EC4
p946 . . . . 020 7583 6117

Norman, Mr Jared M *Nov 2001*
Field Court Chambers, London WC1
p933 . . . . 020 7405 6114

Norman, Mr John LLB(Lond) L *Nov 1979*
24, 30, 40, 46, 76, 62, 26
1 Chancery Lane, London WC2
p928 . . . . 0845 634 6666

Norman, Mr Michael BA(Cantab); LLB(Cantab); Recorder G *Feb 1971*
3, 5, 6, 7, 10, 12, 20, 21, 22, 24, 25, 26, 29, 30, 31
3PB, Bournemouth
p969 . . . . 01202 292102

Norman, Mr Richard G *Jan 2009*
St John's Chambers, Bristol
p972 . . . . 0117 921 3456

Normington, Mr James I *Jan 2005*
Park Court Chambers, Leeds
p978 . . . . 0113 243 3277

Norris, Mr Adam I *Jan 2002*
15
3PB, London EC4
p946 . . . . 020 7583 8055

Norris, Mr Andrew James BSc(Hons); DipLaw M *Nov 1995*
13, 50
Hogarth Chambers, London WC2
p937 . . . . 020 7404 0404

Norris, Mr J Geraint MA(Oxon); BA(Oxon) L *Jul 1980*
10, 12, 20, 25
Albion Chambers, Bristol
p970 . . . . 0117 927 2144

Norris, Mr James LLB I *May 1984*
15, 12, 23
Goldsmith Chambers, London EC4
p935 . . . . 020 7353 6802

NORRIS, Ms Josephine G *Jul 2008*
1, 11, 12, 74, 46, 19, 84, 30, 40, 94
Thirty Nine Essex Street, London WC2
p932 . . . . 020 7832 1111

NORRIS, Mr Paul H BA(Oxon) M *Nov 1963*
11, 40, 29
Five Paper, London EC4
p946 . . . . 020 7815 3200

NORRIS, Mr William MA(Oxon) M *Jul 1974*
(Q.C.) *30, 56, 53, 40, 46, 84, 36*
Thirty Nine Essex Street, London WC2
p932 . . . . 020 7832 1111

NORRMAN, Ms Edith I *Nov 2000*
Furnival Chambers, London EC4
p934 . . . . 020 7405 3232

North, Ms Claire LLB I *Oct 2003*
20, 10
Temple Chambers, Newport
p988 . . . . .01633 267403 / 255855
Temple Chambers, Cardiff
p973 . . . . 029 2039 7364

North, Sir Peter I *May 1992*
(Q.C.) *3, 33*
20 Essex Street, London WC2
p932 . . . . 020 7842 1200

NORTHALL, Mr Daniel BA(Law) L *Jan 2004*
9 St John Street Chambers, Manchester
p984 . . . . 0161 955 9000

NORTON, Mr Andrew David BSc(Soton); CPE; DipLaw I *Oct 1992*
10, 20
1 Garden Court, London EC4
p934 . . . . 020 7797 7900

Norton, Miss Heather M *Nov 1988*
15, 25, 36
QEB Hollis Whiteman, London EC4
p948 . . . . 020 7933 8855

Norton, Mr Richard LLB L *Nov 1992*
12, 15, 20
St Johns Buildings, Preston
p990 . . . . 01772 256100
St Johns Buildings, Chester
p974 . . . . 01244 323070
St Johns Buildings, Manchester
p985 . . . . 0161 214 1500
St Johns Buildings, Liverpool
p982 . . . . 0151 243 6000

Norton-Taylor, Mr Hugo I *Oct 2000*
23, 51, 1, 14, 76
36 Bedford Row, London WC1
p925 . . . . 020 7421 8000

Nosworthy, Mr Harry M *Oct 2010*
10, 14, 20
4 Paper Buildings, London EC4
p946 . . . . 020 7583 0816

NOSWORTHY, Mr Jonathan M *Nov 2000*
20
St Philips Chambers, Birmingham
p969 . . . . 0121 246 7000

Nother, Mr Daniel BA(Hons)(Oxon) I *Nov 1994*
10, 53, 11, 12, 67, 20, 96, 88, 30
College Chambers, Southampton
p992 . . . . 023 8023 0338

Nott, Miss Emma G *Nov 1995*
Goldsmith Chambers, London EC4
p935 . . . . 020 7353 6802

Nourse, Mr Edmund L *Nov 1994*
One Essex Court, London EC4
p931 . . . . 020 7583 2000

NOWELL, Ms Katie LLB L *Nov 1996*
18, 30, 40, 53, 55
9 St John Street Chambers, Manchester
p984 . . . . 0161 955 9000

NOWINSKI, Mr Richard BA; LLM M *Jun 1977*
3, 11, 33, 35
Tanfield Chambers, London WC1
p951 . . . . 020 7421 5300

Nowland, Mr Lee L *Jan 1997*
30
Cobden House Chambers, Manchester
p983 . . . . 0161 833 6000

NSUGBE, Mr Oba E LLB(Hull); Recorder G *Jul 1985*
(Q.C.) *12, 15, 30, 21, 62*
Pump Court Chambers, Swindon
p993 . . . . 01793 539899
Pump Court Chambers, Winchester
p994 . . . . 01962 868161
Pump Court Chambers, London EC4
p947 . . . . 020 7353 0711

NUGEE, Mr Christopher BA(Oxon); Recorder I *Jul 1983*
(Q.C.) *6, 8, 9, 11, 22, 32, 40, 54*
Wilberforce Chambers, London WC2
p953 . . . . 020 7306 0102

NUGEE, Mr Edward MA(Oxon) I *Jun 1955*
(Q.C.) TD*8, 9, 22, 32, 40, 37, 29*
Wilberforce Chambers, London WC2
p953 . . . . 020 7306 0102

Nugent, Mr Colm BA(Kent) I *Oct 1992*
30, 22, 18, 49, 88, 40
Hardwicke, London WC2
p936 . . . . 020 7242 2523

Nurse, Mr Gordon MA(Cantab) M *Nov 1973*
8, 9, 11, 22, 29, 32, 37, 40
Radcliffe Chambers, London WC2
p949 . . . . 020 7831 0081

NUSSEY, Mr Richard BA; Dep.Q.B.Manter L *Nov 1971*
30, 40, 12
Farrar's Building, London EC4
p933 . . . . 020 7583 9241

Nuttall, Mr Andrew P LLB(Hons) L *Nov 1978*
Lincoln House Chambers, Manchester
p984 . . . . 0161 832 5701

NUTTER, Mr Julian LLB(Hons) G *Jan 1979*
15, 62
7 Harrington Street Chambers, Liverpool
p981 . . . . 0151 242 0707

Nuvoloni, Mr Stefano LLB; MA I *Nov 1994*
10, 20, 14
4 Paper Buildings, London EC4
p946 . . . . 020 7583 0816
St Ives Chambers, Birmingham
p969 . . . . 0121 236 0863

Nwosu, Miss Sheryl M *Nov 2000*
4 Breams Buildings, London EC4
p927 . . . . 020 7092 1900

O'Brien, Mr Bernard Nicholas MA(Dublin) M *Jul 1968*
15, 4
Albion Chambers, Bristol
p970 . . . . 0117 927 2144

O'BRIEN, Mr David M *Nov 1994*
20, 10
Trinity Chambers, Chelmsford
p974 . . . . 01245 605040

O'Brien, Mr Dermod Patrick MA(Oxon) I *Jul 1962*
(Q.C.) *24, 30, 7, 12, 1, 40, 41*
2 Temple Gardens, London EC4
p952 . . . . 020 7822 1200

O'Brien, Mr Joseph I *Jan 1989*
Broad Chare Chambers, Newcastle upon Tyne
p986 . . . . 0191 232 0541

O'Brien, Mr Joseph P A P LLB I *Nov 1989*
8, 11, 12, 20, 30
Paradise Chambers, Sheffield
p992 . . . . 0114 273 8951

O'Brien, Mr Liam M *Jan 2007*
72, 15, 82, 51, 30
Old Court Chambers, Middlesbrough
p986 . . . . 01642 232523

O'Brien, Mr Michael M *Jan 1987*
1, 63, 14, 26, 28, 85
No5 Chambers, Bristol
p971 . . . . 0845 210 5555
No5 Chambers, London EC4
p944 . . . . 0845 210 5555
No5 Chambers, Birmingham
p968 . . . . 0845 210 5555

O'BRIEN, Miss Niamh Katrina LLB M *Nov 1998*
8, 12, 22, 30
Lamb Chambers, London EC4
p941 . . . . 020 7797 8300

O'Brien, Mr Nicholas BA; DipLaw M *Nov 1985*
18, 20, 22, 30, 63
Coram Chambers, London EC1
p929 . . . . 020 7092 3700
10 King's Bench Walk, London EC4
p940 . . . . 020 7353 7742

O'Brien, Mr Paul BA(Manc) G *Nov 1974*
15, 30, 27, 20, 12
18 St John Street Chambers, Manchester
p985 . . . . 0161 278 1800

O'Brien, Mr Richard L *Jan 2005*
Four New Square, London WC2
p943 . . . . 020 7822 2000

13

O'Brien, Ms Sarah LLB(Hull) I *Jul 1998*
22, 11, 51, 88, 26, 93, 1
Exchange Chambers, Manchester
p983 . . . . . 0161 833 2722
Exchange Chambers, Liverpool
p980 . . . . . 0151 236 7747
Exchange Chambers, Leeds
p977 . . . . . 0113 203 1970

O'BRIEN, Mr Sean L *Oct 2001*
11, 18, 93
St Philips Chambers, Birmingham
p969 . . . . . 0121 246 7000

O'Byrne, Mr Andrew G *Jul 1978*
(Q.C.) *15*
St Johns Buildings, Preston
p990 . . . . . 01772 256100
St Johns Buildings, Chester
p974 . . . . . 01244 323070
St Johns Buildings, Manchester
p985 . . . . . 0161 214 1500
St Johns Buildings, Liverpool
p982 . . . . . 0151 243 6000

O'Ceallaigh, Greg I *Jan 2006*
1 Pump Court, London EC4
p947 . . . . . 020 7842 7070

O'Connell, Miss Joanna G *Oct 2003*
1, 2, 10, 12, 18, 20, 15
36 Bedford Row, London WC1
p925 . . . . . 020 7421 8000

O'CONNOR, Mr Andrew MA(Cantab) G *Oct 1996*
Temple Garden Chambers, London EC4
p952 . . . . . 020 7583 1315

O'Connor, Miss Charlotte I *Oct 1999*
15, 51, 42
Nine Bedford Row, London WC1
p924 . . . . . 020 7489 2727

O'CONNOR, Mr Ged MA(Oxon) L *Sep 1993*
15
23 Essex Street, London WC2
p932 . . . . . 020 7413 0353

O'Connor, Mr Gerard L *Nov 1993*
15, 62
4 Breams Buildings, London EC4
p927 . . . . . 020 7092 1900

O'Connor, Mr Patrick M J LLB(Lond) I *Nov 1970*
(Q.C.) *1, 12, 15, 51*
Doughty Street Chambers, London WC1
p930 . . . . . 020 7404 1313

O'Dair, Mr Richard G *Nov 1987*
12, 11, 18, 23, 30, 40, 31, 1, 2
36 Bedford Row, London WC1
p925 . . . . . 020 7421 8000

O'Dempsey, Mr Declan John BA(Cantab); DipLaw M *Nov 1987*
12, 18, 23, 53, 55, 19, 27, 30, 1, 51, 26
Cloisters, London EC4
p928 . . . . . 020 7827 4000

O'Doherty, Mr Paul BA(Hons) M *Jan 2000*
7, 11, 6
3PB, London EC4
p946 . . . . . 020 7583 8055

O'Donnell, Mr Duncan G *Oct 1992*
15
1 Paper Buildings, London EC4
p946 . . . . . 020 7353 3728

O'DONNELL, Mr Iain L *Jul 2000*
30, 18, 6, 12, 25, 8, 16, 22, 26, 7
1 Crown Office Row, London EC4
p929 . . . . . 020 7797 7500

O'DONOGHUE, Mr Hugh M *Oct 2004*
Carmelite Chambers, London EC4
p927 . . . . . 020 7936 6300

O'DONOGHUE, Miss Lisa BCL; BVC; LLM G *Jan 2008*
10, 20
1 Garden Court, London EC4
p934 . . . . . 020 7797 7900

O'DONOHOE, Mr Anthony Francis LLB; Recorder M *Jul 1983*
10, 15, 20, 12, 18, 22, 24, 25, 30, 36
Chavasse Court Chambers, Liverpool
p980 . . . . . 0151 229 2030

O'Donohoe, Mr Thomas BA(Hons)(Oxon) L *Jan 2007*
11, 97, 18, 30, 53
3PB, London EC4
p946 . . . . . 020 7583 8055

O'DONOHUE, Miss Katherine G *Jul 2006*
15, 20, 12
7 Harrington Street Chambers, Liverpool
p981 . . . . . 0151 242 0707

O'Donovan, Mr Hugh G *Jan 1975*
Quadrant Chambers, London EC4
p948 . . . . . 020 7583 4444

O'Donovan, Mr Kevin M *Jul 1978*
18, 30, 53, 40, 55, 56, 94, 38
No5 Chambers, Bristol
p971 . . . . . 0845 210 5555
No5 Chambers, London EC4
p944 . . . . . 0845 210 5555
No5 Chambers, Birmingham
p968 . . . . . 0845 210 5555

O'DONOVAN, Mr Ronan Daniel James L *Oct 1995*
10, 12, 20
14 Gray's Inn Square, London WC1
p936 . . . . . 020 7242 0858

O'DRISCOLL, Ms Patricia M *Oct 2006*
Pump Court Chambers, Swindon
p993 . . . . . 01793 539899
Pump Court Chambers, Winchester
p994 . . . . . 01962 868161
Pump Court Chambers, London EC4
p947 . . . . . 020 7353 0711

O'FARRELL, Ms Finola M BA(Dunelm) I *Jul 1983*
(Q.C.) *3, 7, 11, 24, 40*
Keating Chambers, London WC2
p938 . . . . . 020 7544 2600

O'FLAHERTY, Mr John BA(Hons); CRE; MLitt; DipLaw M *Oct 2001*
44, 11, 15, 19, 23, 1
Matrix Chambers, London WC1
p942 . . . . . 020 7404 3447

O'GORMAN, Mr Christopher G *Jan 1987*
72, 15, 51, 27, 46, 31, 48, 62, 94
Cornwall Street Chambers, Birmingham
p967 . . . . . 0121 233 7500

O'GRADY, Mr Matthew G *Aug 2010*
10, 20
St Mary's Chambers, Nottingham
p989 . . . . . 0115 950 3503

O'HAGAN, Ms Rachael I *Oct 2006*
61, 36, 93, 40, 89, 24, 67, 74, 11, 73, 41, 49
Thirty Nine Essex Street, London WC2
p932 . . . . . 020 7832 1111

O'Hagan, Miss Sophie Maria LLM; LLB M *Jan 1996*
10, 12, 15, 18, 20, 23, 30
Regent Chambers, Hanley
p976 . . . . . 01782 286666

O'Hara, Miss Sarah MA(Cantab) M *Jul 1984*
10, 12, 15, 20, 22, 30
3PB, Winchester
p994 . . . . . 01962 868884

O'Kane, Miss Sarah M *Oct 2001*
15, 23, 25, 94
Argent Chambers, London WC2
p923 . . . . . 020 7556 5500

O'KEEFFE, Mr Darren MA(Oxon) I *Jul 1984*
12, 30, 40, 47, 51, 46
Oriel Chambers, Liverpool
p981 . . . . . 0151 236 7191 / 236 4321
Oriel Chambers, Preston
p990 . . . . . 01772 254764

O'Leary, Mr Brendan M *Oct 2007*
15
18 St John Street Chambers, Manchester
p985 . . . . . 0161 278 1800

O'LEARY, Mr John M *Jul 2010*
15
7 Harrington Street Chambers, Liverpool
p981 . . . . . 0151 242 0707

O'Leary, Miss Michele LLB(Hons) G *Nov 1983*
10, 20
1 Pump Court, London EC4
p947 . . . . . 020 7842 7070

O'Leary, Mr Robert Michael LLB(Cardiff) I *Oct 1990*
6, 8, 11, 12, 22, 24, 29, 30, 37, 40, 53
Civitas Law, Cardiff
p972 . . . . . 0845 071 3007

O'Leary, Mr Samuel L *Jan 2007*
One Essex Court, London EC4
p931 . . . . . 020 7583 2000

O'Mahony, Mr David I *Oct 2000*
15, 12, 62
7 Bedford Row, London WC1
p924 . . . . . 020 7242 3555

O'Mahony, Mr Jonathan Solomon BA(TCD); MPhil(Cantab) I *Nov 2000*
8, 6, 38, 93, 88
9 Stone Buildings Barristers Chambers, London WC2
p951 . . . . . 020 7404 5055

O'Malley, Ms Helen L *Oct 1991*
Holborn Chambers, London WC2
p937 . . . . . 020 7242 6060

O'Malley, Miss Julie LLB(Sheff) G *Nov 1983*
20, 10, 49, 96
Lamb Building, Brighton
p970 . . . . . 01273 820490
Lamb Building, London EC4
p940 . . . . . 020 7797 7788

O'Malley, Miss Laura L *Jan 2007*
Northampton Chambers, Northampton
p988 . . . . . 01604 636271

O'NEILL, Mr Aidan LLB(Hons)(Edin); LLM(Hons)(Sydney); LLM(Florence) I *Jul 1996*
(Q.C.) *1, 18, 19, 51*
Matrix Chambers, London WC1
p942 . . . . . 020 7404 3447

O'Neill, Mr Brian P LLB; Recorder; Secretary of Criminal Bar Association G *Nov 1987*
15, 25, 62
2 Hare Court, London EC4
p937 . . . . . 020 7353 5324

O'Neill, Mr Jonathan I *Jan 2007*
11, 67, 18, 55, 46, 31, 36, 12
Rougemont Chambers, Exeter
p975 . . . . . 01392 208484

O'Neill, Ms Louise BA(Dublin); LLM(Cantab) G *Feb 1989*
10, 12, 20
St John's Chambers, Bristol
p972 . . . . . 0117 921 3456

O'NEILL, Mr Michael I *Jan 2006*
St James's Chambers, Manchester
p984 . . . . . 0161 834 7000
York Chambers, York
p995 . . . . . 01904 620048
York Chambers, Newcastle upon Tyne
p987 . . . . . 0191 206 4677

O'NEILL, Miss Sally LLB G *Nov 1976*
(Q.C.)
Furnival Chambers, London EC4
p934 . . . . . 020 7405 3232

O'REILLY, Miss Beth LLB L *Oct 2000*
15, 62
25 Bedford Row, London WC1
p925 . . . . . 020 7067 1500

O'Reilly, Miss Catherine Mary LLB G *Oct 1998*
10, 12, 15, 18, 20, 30, 36
Regent Chambers, Hanley
p976 . . . . . 01782 286666

O'Reilly, Miss Niamh LLB(Dublin); BCL(Oxon) M *Jan 2007*
40, 27, 30
Hailsham Chambers, London EC4
p936 . . . . . 020 7643 5000

O'RIORDAN, Mr Thomas BA; BSc; PhD I *Jan 1993*
11, 5, 81
4-5 Gray's Inn Square, London WC1
p935 . . . . . 020 7404 5252

O'Rourke, Miss Mary Bernadette LLB(Lond); Cert des Hautes Etudes Europeennes G *Nov 1981*
(Q.C.) *1, 3, 18, 27, 36, 40, 56, 53, 85*
3 Serjeants' Inn, London EC4
p950 . . . . . 020 7427 5000

O'Ryan, Mr Rory M *Mar 2000*
23, 22, 51, 88, 1
Garden Court North Chambers, Manchester
p983 . . . . . 0161 236 1840

O'Shea, Miss Joanne LLB(Hons) M *Nov 2000*
10, 20
No 8 Chambers, Birmingham
p968 . . . . . 0121 236 5514

O'SHEA, Mr Paul Andrew LLB I *Jun 1989*
15
Bank House Chambers, Sheffield
p991 . . . . . 0114 275 1223

O'Sullivan, Mr Bernard MA(Cantab) I *Jul 1971*
10, 12, 20, 51
Henderson Chambers, London EC4
p937 . . . . . 020 7583 9020

O'SULLIVAN, Mr Derek L *Jan 1990*
30, 40, 24, 84
Thirty Nine Essex Street, London WC2
p932 . . . . . 020 7832 1111

O'SULLIVAN, Mr John LLB(Warw) M *Jul 1984*
20, 14, 63
Trinity (Newcastle) Chambers, Newcastle upon Tyne
p987 . . . . . 0191 232 1927
Trinity (Teesside) Chambers, Middlesbrough
p986 . . . . . 01642 247569

O'Sullivan, Mr Michael Morton MA(Cantab); BCL(Oxon) L *Jul 1986*
8, 14, 32, 37, 40
5 Stone Buildings, London WC2
p951 . . . . . 020 7242 6201

O'Sullivan, Mr Richard I *May 1999*
1 Mitre Court Buildings, London EC4
p942 . . . . . 020 7452 8900
East Anglian Chambers, Norwich
p988 . . . . . 01603 617351
East Anglian Chambers, Colchester
p975 . . . . . 01206 572756
East Anglian Chambers, Chelmsford
p973 . . . . . 01245 215660
East Anglian Chambers, Ipswich
p976 . . . . . 01473 214481

O'Sullivan, Mr Robert LLB(Lond) L *Jul 1988*
15, 62, 48, 13, 39, 25
5 Paper Buildings, London EC4
p946 . . . . . 020 7583 6117

O'Sullivan, Mr Sean MA(Oxon) I *Nov 1997*
7, 11, 12, 78, 40, 35
4 Pump Court, London EC4
p947 . . . . . 020 7842 5555

O'Sullivan, Ms Zoe M *Oct 1993*
One Essex Court, London EC4
p931 . . . . . 020 7583 2000

O'Toole, Mr Bartholomew BSc; LL Dip M *Nov 1980*
15, 20
5 King's Bench Walk, London EC4
p939 . . . . . 020 7353 5638

O'Toole, Mr Simon Gerard BA; DipLaw I *Jul 1984*
5 Pump Court, London EC4
p947 . . . . . 020 7353 2532 / 7583 7133

OAKES, Ms Alison Denise BA I *Nov 1996*
Landmark Chambers, London EC4
p941 . . . . . 020 7430 1221

Oakes, Mr Christopher N BEng(Hons); DipLaw L *Oct 1996*
7, 12, 30
Cobden House Chambers, Manchester
p983 . . . . . 0161 833 6000

Oakes, Mr Richard LLB(Hons) M *Oct 2007*
68, 30, 94, 62
No5 Chambers, Bristol
p971 . . . . . 0845 210 5555
No5 Chambers, London EC4
p944 . . . . . 0845 210 5555
No5 Chambers, Birmingham
p968 . . . . . 0845 210 5555

Oakes, Miss Victoria I *Jan 2005*
5 Paper Buildings, London EC4
p946 . . . . . 020 7583 6117

Oakeshott, Miss Rachel I *Jan 2006*
One Essex Court, London EC4
p931 . . . . . 020 7583 2000

Oakley, Miss Louise BA(Hons) M *Jul 2001*
15, 62
2 Bedford Row, London WC1
p924 . . . . . 020 7440 8888

Oakley, Mr Paul LLB(Hons); MSc G *Nov 1995*
6, 8, 11, 12, 13, 22, 30, 53
One Essex Court, London EC4
p931 . . . . . 020 7936 3030

Oates, Mr John Richard G *Jul 1987*
10, 12, 15, 18, 20, 22, 25, 26, 30
St Johns Buildings, Preston
p990 . . . . . 01772 256100
St Johns Buildings, Chester
p974 . . . . . 01244 323070
St Johns Buildings, Manchester
p985 . . . . . 0161 214 1500
St Johns Buildings, Liverpool
p982 . . . . . 0151 243 6000

See p1010 for the Key to Work Categories

Obi-Ezekpazu, Ms Maureen G *Jan 2008*
20
Tooks Chambers, London EC4
p953 . . . 020 7842 7575

OBORNE, Miss Jennifer I *Jan 2007*
Carmelite Chambers, London EC4
p927 . . . 020 7936 6300

Obuka, Miss Obi I *Oct 1993*
10, 12, 15, 20, 23
Two King's Bench Walk, London EC4
p939 . . . 020 7353 7202 / 7353 3909

Ocan, Ms Akidi BA(Hons); Barrister M *Jul 1982*
12, 20, 26
Gray's Inn Chambers, London WC1
p935 . . . 07976 426871

Odell, Mr Alex BA(Hons)(Eng Lit) L *Oct 2007*
5 Paper Buildings, London EC4
p946 . . . 020 7583 6117

ODGERS, Mr John BA(Oxon) G *Oct 1990*
5, 6, 11, 40
3 Verulam Buildings, London WC1
p953 . . . 020 7831 8441

ODITAH, Mr Fidelis MA; BCL; D Phil(Oxon) L *Nov 1992*
(Q.C.) *5, 6, 8, 11, 12, 24, 29, 38*
South Square, London WC1
p950 . . . 020 7696 9900

Offeh, Mr John LLB(Hons)(Lond) I *Nov 1969*
12, 22, 23, 20, 15, 18
12 Old Square, London WC2
p945 . . . 020 7404 0875

OFFENBACH, Mr Roger I *Jun 1978*
15
25 Bedford Row, London WC1
p925 . . . 020 7067 1500

Offer, Mr Alex MA; DipLaw M *Oct 1998*
Park Court Chambers, Leeds
p978 . . . 0113 243 3277

Oganah, Ms Janet M *Jul 2007*
42 Bedford Row, London WC1
p925 . . . 020 7831 0222

Ogden, Mr Thomas L *Jan 2008*
Four New Square, London WC2
p943 . . . 020 7822 2000

Ogle, Miss Rebecca I *Jan 1989*
10, 20, 37
Southernhay Chambers, Exeter
p975 . . . 01392 255777

Oguntayo, Tosin MA(Cantab); LLB(Hons); LLM(Lond) M *Nov 2001*
20
Hardwicke, London WC2
p936 . . . 020 7242 2523

Ohrenstein, Mr Dov MA(Cantab) G *Oct 1995*
5, 6, 8, 9, 11, 22, 32, 37, 40, 29
Radcliffe Chambers, London WC2
p949 . . . 020 7831 0081

Ohringer, Mr Adam M *Jan 2001*
18, 30, 21
Cloisters, London EC4
p928 . . . 020 7827 4000

OJUITIKU, Mrs Kemi L *Jan 1994*
4 King's Bench Walk, London EC4
p939 . . . 020 7822 7000

Okai, Mr Anthony I *Jul 1973*
23, 15, 20, 18
12 Old Square, London WC2
p945 . . . 020 7404 0875

Oke, Lanre MA(Oxon) L *Jun 1979*
15, 23, 50
Kingsway Chambers, London EC4
p940 . . . 020 7404 2357
12 Old Square, London WC2
p945 . . . 020 7404 0875

Okewale, Mr Tunde I *Jan 2007*
4 Breams Buildings, London EC4
p927 . . . 020 7092 1900

Okine, Miss Julie L *Oct 1996*
Goldsmith Chambers, London EC4
p935 . . . 020 7353 6802

OKOYA, Mr William Ebikise LLM(Lond); LLB(Cardiff) G *Nov 1989*
22, 26, 38, 11, 1, 51, 47, 46
Arden Chambers, London WC1
p923 . . . 020 7242 4244

Okoye, Ms Joy BA G *Jul 1981*
10, 12, 15, 18, 20, 22, 30, 36, 41
Gray's Inn Chambers, London WC1
p935 . . . 07976 426871

Olbourne, Mr Ben BEC; BA; LLB; LLM I *Nov 2003*
49, 41, 3, 5, 11, 43, 47, 78, 24, 54, 35
20 Essex Street, London WC2
p932 . . . 020 7842 1200

OLDFIELD, Ms Jane M *Oct 2004*
15, 62, 68, 94
18 Red Lion Court, London EC4
p949 . . . 020 7520 6000
18 Red Lion Court (Annexe), Chelmsford
p973 . . . 01245 280880

OLDHAM, Mrs Frances G *Jul 1977*
(Q.C.) *51, 15, 10, 20, 70, 68, 63, 86, 62*
37 Park Square Chambers, Leeds
p978 . . . 0113 243 9422
36 Bedford Row, London WC1
p925 . . . 020 7421 8000

OLDHAM, Mrs Jane BA; MA(Cantab) M *Jul 1985*
1, 26, 11, 73
11KBW, London EC4
p938 . . . 020 7632 8500

OLDHAM, Mr Peter BA(Cantab); DipLaw(City) G *Oct 1990*
(Q.C.) *1, 18, 19, 26, 55, 51, 76*
11KBW, London EC4
p938 . . . 020 7632 8500

Oldland, Mr Andrew MSc(Lond); DipLaw(City) I *Nov 1990*
(Q.C.) *11, 15, 25*
6 King's Bench Walk, London EC4
p939 . . . 020 7583 0410
Walnut House Chambers, Exeter
p975 . . . 01392 279751

OLIVER, Mr Andrew L *Nov 1993*
12, 15, 36, 70
Octagon House, Norwich
p988 . . . 01603 623186

Oliver, Mr Crispin Arthur MA M *Nov 1990*
10, 20
York Chambers, York
p995 . . . 01904 620048
York Chambers, Newcastle upon Tyne
p987 . . . 0191 206 4677

Oliver, The Hon David BA(Cantab); Licence Special en droit European L *Jul 1972*
(Q.C.)
13 Old Square Chambers, London WC2
p945 . . . 020 7831 4445

OLIVER, Mr Harry BA(Oxon) G *Nov 1999*
10, 12, 20, 96, 49
1 King's Bench Walk, London EC4
p938 . . . 020 7936 1500

Oliver, Mr Michael R MA I *Jul 1977*
15, 62
15 New Bridge Street Chambers, London EC4
p943 . . . 020 7842 1900

Oliver, Mr Peter MB; BS L *Jul 2002*
40, 24, 11, 89
4 Pump Court, London EC4
p947 . . . 020 7842 5555

OLLECH, Mr Joseph BSc(LSE) L *Oct 2007*
Falcon Chambers, London EC4
p933 . . . 020 7353 2484

Ollennu, Ashitey Kwame Nii-Amaa L *Jul 1981*
12, 67, 68, 15, 11, 23, 20, 62, 22, 51, 18, 8, 88
Redemption Chambers, London NW11
p949 . . . 020 8458 5486 / 07929 511917

Olleson, Mr Simon L *Jan 2002*
13 Old Square Chambers, London WC2
p945 . . . 020 7831 4445

OLLEY, Ms Katherine I *Oct 1999*
Landmark Chambers, London EC4
p941 . . . 020 7430 1221

Omambala, Ijeoma BA(Cantab); MPhil G *Apr 1989*
18, 23, 30, 51, 55, 36, 1, 49
Old Square Chambers, Bristol
p971 . . . 0117 930 5100
Old Square Chambers, London WC1
p945 . . . 020 7269 0300

OMIDEYI, Ms Anu L *Jul 2001*
15
Furnival Chambers, London EC4
p934 . . . 020 7405 3232

Omran-Baber, Mr Waheed G *Nov 1999*
15
New Bailey Chambers, Preston
p990 . . . 01772 258087

ONABAJO, Teniola M *Jan 2010*
5, 81, 24, 47, 40
3 Verulam Buildings, London WC1
p953 . . . 020 7831 8441

Onalaja, Mr James L *Jan 2004*
2 Pump Court, London EC4
p947 . . . 020 7353 5597

Ong, Miss Grace Y LLB(Hons)(Lond); Pupil Supervisor L *Jul 1985*
15, 21, 62, 20, 10, 67, 12
Argent Chambers, London WC2
p923 . . . 020 7556 5500

Onions, Mr Jeffery M *Jul 1981*
(Q.C.)
One Essex Court, London EC4
p931 . . . 020 7583 2000

Onipede, Dr Victor ACIB; MBA; LLB(Hons); PhD L *Jan 2000*
Chancery Chambers, London WC2
p928 . . . 020 7405 6879

ONSLOW, Mr Andrew BA(Oxon) M *Jul 1982*
(Q.C.) *3, 11, 5, 40*
3 Verulam Buildings, London WC1
p953 . . . 020 7831 8441

Onslow, Mr Richard MA(Oxon); Recorder I *Jul 1982*
72, 15, 71, 70
3PB, Winchester
p994 . . . 01962 868884

Onslow, Mr Robert BA(Oxon) L *Oct 1991*
13, 43, 45
8 New Square, London WC2
p943 . . . 020 7405 4321

ONUAGULUCHI, Jones I *Feb 1971*
15, 12
10 King's Bench Walk, London EC4
p940 . . . 020 7353 7742

Oon, Miss Pamela Beng Sue LLB I *Jul 1982*
15
Charter Chambers, London WC1
p928 . . . 020 7618 4400

Openshaw, Miss Samantha LLB(Hons) L *Jan 2005*
11, 18, 30
Cobden House Chambers, Manchester
p983 . . . 0161 833 6000

Oppenheim, Mr Robin BA; DipLaw M *Nov 1988*
(Q.C.) *1, 12, 16, 26, 27, 30, 36, 51, 53*
Doughty Street Chambers, London WC1
p930 . . . 020 7404 1313

Oppenheimer, Miss Tamara Helen BA(Hons); BCL(Oxon) I *Oct 2002*
Fountain Court Chambers, London EC4
p934 . . . 020 7583 3335

Opperman, Mr Guy T LLB M *Nov 1989*
12, 15, 30, 51
3PB, London EC4
p946 . . . 020 7583 8055

Oram, Mr Seb MA(Hons)(Cantab) L *Jan 2007*
8, 93, 38
3PB, London EC4
p946 . . . 020 7583 8055

ORCHARD, Mr Anthony I *Oct 1991*
(Q.C.)
Carmelite Chambers, London EC4
p927 . . . 020 7936 6300

ORCHARD, Miss Cathlyn BA(Hons) L *Jan 1999*
15, 12
Citadel Chambers, Birmingham
p967 . . . 0121 233 8500

Orchover, Ms Frances BA(Hons)(Lond); DipLaw M *Jul 1989*
15, 20
Coram Chambers, London EC1
p929 . . . 020 7092 3700

ORME, Miss Emily BA(Hons) L *Jul 2003*
22, 1
Arden Chambers, London WC1
p923 . . . 020 7242 4244

Orme, Mr Richard L *Oct 1993*
15
St Johns Buildings, Preston
p990 . . . 01772 256100
St Johns Buildings, Chester
p974 . . . 01244 323070
St Johns Buildings, Manchester
p985 . . . 0161 214 1500
St Johns Buildings, Liverpool
p982 . . . 0151 243 6000

Ormondroyd, Mr Cain L *Jan 2007*
1, 12, 46, 25, 26, 54, 31, 36
Francis Taylor Building, London EC4
p934 . . . 020 7353 8415

Ormond-Walshe, Ms Sarah BSc(Hons); DipLaw M *Nov 2001*
42 Bedford Row, London WC1
p925 . . . 020 7831 0222

Ornsby, Miss Suzanne LLB(Lond) M *Nov 1986*
31, 1, 26, 36, 22
Francis Taylor Building, London EC4
p934 . . . 020 7353 8415

Orr, Mr Craig Wyndham MA(Cantab); BCL M *Jul 1986*
(Q.C.)
Fountain Court Chambers, London EC4
p934 . . . 020 7583 3335

Orr, Mr Julian LLB(Hons) L *Oct 1995*
12, 24, 30, 40, 53, 56
Cobden House Chambers, Manchester
p983 . . . 0161 833 6000

ORR, Mr Matthew L *Oct 2004*
15, 62, 68, 94
18 Red Lion Court, London EC4
p949 . . . 020 7520 6000
18 Red Lion Court (Annexe), Chelmsford
p973 . . . 01245 280880

ORSULIK, Mr Michael BA; LLM(Lond) M *Nov 1978*
15
9-12 Bell Yard Chambers, London WC2
p926 . . . 020 7400 1800

Osborne, Miss Jane L *Apr 2000*
15
Atkinson Bevan Chambers, London EC4
p924 . . . 020 7353 2112

Osborne, Ms Katie M *Nov 1993*
Holborn Chambers, London WC2
p937 . . . 020 7242 6060

Osborne, Mr Richard I *Nov 2005*
40, 24, 11, 89
4 Pump Court, London EC4
p947 . . . 020 7842 5555

Oscroft, Mr Daniel M *Nov 2003*
15, 62, 25, 94
No5 Chambers, Bristol
p971 . . . 0845 210 5555
No5 Chambers, London EC4
p944 . . . 0845 210 5555
No5 Chambers, Birmingham
p968 . . . 0845 210 5555

OSCROFT, Jennifer M *Jan 2006*
Cornerstone Barristers, London WC1
p929 . . . 020 7242 4986

OSEPCIU, Miss Ligia BA(Cantab); LLM(Cornell) L *Jan 2008*
44, 7, 1, 57, 19
Monckton Chambers, London WC1
p942 . . . 020 7405 7211

OSLER, Miss Victoria Louise BA(Hons); CPE M *Nov 2001*
22, 26, 31
Arden Chambers, London WC1
p923 . . . 020 7242 4244

Osman, Mr Faisal L *Mar 2002*
15
33 Chancery Lane, London WC2
p928 . . . 020 7440 9950

OSMAN, Mr Nabeel M *Jan 2008*
15, 62, 95
187 Fleet Street, London EC4
p933 . . . 020 7430 7430

OSMAN, Mr Osman LLB(Hons) I *Feb 1995*
15, 72, 62
25 Bedford Row, London WC1
p925 . . . 020 7067 1500

Osmund-Smith, Miss Thea LLB I *Jan 2010*
No5 Chambers, Bristol
p971 . . . 0845 210 5555
No5 Chambers, London EC4
p944 . . . 0845 210 5555
No5 Chambers, Birmingham
p968 . . . 0845 210 5555

13

Ossack, Mrs Tanya Rachelle Elise Dip Criminol; MA Socio-leg; Dip Commun Studies *G Oct 1993*
15, 70, 62
3 Temple Gardens, London EC4
p952 . . . . 020 7353 3102

Otton-Goulder, Miss Catharine MA(Oxon) *L Nov 1983*
(Q.C.) *11, 5*
Brick Court Chambers, London WC2
p927 . . . . 020 7379 3550

Otty, Mr Timothy John MA(Cantab) *L Oct 1990*
(Q.C.) *1, 11, 51, 33, 89*
Blackstone Chambers, London EC4
p926 . . . . 020 7583 1770
Doughty Street Chambers, London WC1
p930 . . . . 020 7404 1313

Otwal, Mr Mukhtiar LLB *L Nov 1991*
6, 8, 11, 12, 22, 30, 40, 53, 47
33 Bedford Row, London WC1
p925 . . . . 020 7242 6476

OUDKERK, Mr Daniel Richard LLB(Bris) *I Nov 1992*
(Q.C.) *1, 11, 18, 55*
11KBW, London EC4
p938 . . . . 020 7632 8500

Oughton, Mr Richard Donald MA(Cantab); LLM(Penn); Member of the Irish Bar *L Jul 1978*
8, 11, 22, 32, 37, 58
Cobden House Chambers, Manchester
p983 . . . . 0161 833 6000

Oultram, Mr Jonathan LLB(Hons) *M Nov 1988*
12, 15, 62, 94, 70, 84
Cobden House Chambers, Manchester
p983 . . . . 0161 833 6000

OUTHWAITE, Ms Wendy BA(Oxon); Lic Spec en Droit Europeen(Brux); MA *L May 1990*
(Q.C.) *1, 12, 19, 27, 30, 39, 51, 53, 18*
1 Crown Office Row, London EC4
p929 . . . . 020 7797 7500

OUTTERSIDE, Mr David *I Jul 2004*
15
1 High Pavement, Nottingham
p988 . . . . 0115 941 8218

Ouwehand, Mr Martin BEc; LLB(Melbourne) *L Oct 2002*
11, 6, 38
11 Stone Buildings, London WC2
p951 . . . . 020 7831 6381

Ovey, Ms Elizabeth BA(Oxon) *M Jul 1978*
8, 9, 29, 32, 37, 40
Radcliffe Chambers, London WC2
p949 . . . . 020 7831 0081

OWEN, Miss Carys *L Oct 2002*
15, 62, 91
18 Red Lion Court, London EC4
p949 . . . . 020 7520 6000
18 Red Lion Court (Annexe), Chelmsford
p973 . . . . 01245 280880

OWEN, Mr Daniel R S BA(Oxon); MSc(Newc); DipLaw(City) *M Oct 1999*
46
Fenners Chambers, Cambridge
p972 . . . . 01223 368761

OWEN, Mr David *G Jul 1981*
15
7 Harrington Street Chambers, Liverpool
p981 . . . . 0151 242 0707

Owen, Mr David C BA(Oxon) *M Nov 1983*
(Q.C.) *3, 11, 12, 24, 35, 41*
20 Essex Street, London WC2
p932 . . . . 020 7842 1200

Owen, Miss Denise *G Oct 2003*
20, 10
No5 Chambers, Bristol
p971 . . . . 0845 210 5555
No5 Chambers, London EC4
p944 . . . . 0845 210 5555
No5 Chambers, Birmingham
p968 . . . . 0845 210 5555

OWEN, Mr Eric LLB *G Nov 1969*
1, 17, 26, 31, 46
Kings Chambers, Leeds
p978 . . . . 0113 242 1123
Kings Chambers, Manchester
p984 . . . . 0161 832 9082

Owen, Miss Gail LLB *G Nov 1980*
10, 20
St Johns Buildings, Preston
p990 . . . . 01772 256100
St Johns Buildings, Chester
p974 . . . . 01244 323070
St Johns Buildings, Manchester
p985 . . . . 0161 214 1500
St Johns Buildings, Liverpool
p982 . . . . 0151 243 6000

Owen, Miss Glenda Caroline LLB(Hons); LLM(Bris) *G Jul 2002*
6, 15, 20, 22, 30, 41
Angel Chambers, Swansea
p992 . . . . 01792 464623

OWEN, Mr Jonathan *I Jan 2004*
12, 30, 11, 40, 53, 22, 29
Ropewalk Chambers, Nottingham
p989 . . . . 0115 947 2581

Owen, Ms Sara BA *I Oct 1995*
20, 10
Temple Chambers, Newport
p988 . . . . .01633 267403 / 255855
Temple Chambers, Cardiff
p973 . . . . 029 2039 7364

OWEN, Mr Tim BA; DipLaw(LSE); Recorder of the Crown Court (2006); Deputy High Court Judge (2010) *M Jul 1983*
(Q.C.) *1, 12, 15, 19, 33, 36, 6, 51, 56, 50, 70, 71*
Matrix Chambers, London WC1
p942 . . . . 020 7404 3447

Owen, Wendy Jane *M Jan 2002*
St Johns Buildings, Preston
p990 . . . . 01772 256100
St Johns Buildings, Chester
p974 . . . . 01244 323070
St Johns Buildings, Manchester
p985 . . . . 0161 214 1500
St Johns Buildings, Liverpool
p982 . . . . 0151 243 6000

Owen-Easey, Neil *G Jan 2007*
St Johns Buildings, Preston
p990 . . . . 01772 256100
St Johns Buildings, Chester
p974 . . . . 01244 323070
St Johns Buildings, Manchester
p985 . . . . 0161 214 1500
St Johns Buildings, Liverpool
p982 . . . . 0151 243 6000

Owen-Thomas, Mr Richard *M Nov 2000*
King's Bench Chambers, Oxford
p989 . . . . 01865 311066
13 King's Bench Walk, London EC4
p940 . . . . 020 7353 7204

Owens, Miss Elspeth BA(Oxon) *M Oct 2007*
11, 12, 40, 24, 35, 41, 67, 74, 78, 79, 89
4 Pump Court, London EC4
p947 . . . . 020 7842 5555

OWENS, Mrs Lucy BA(Hons)(Law & Sociology) *M Oct 1997*
20
29 Bedford Row, London WC1
p925 . . . . 020 7404 1044

Owosu-Yianoma, Mr David *I Sep 1992*
1 Mitre Court Buildings, London EC4
p942 . . . . 020 7452 8900

Oxlade, Miss Joanne LLB(Coventry) *M Jul 1988*
12, 20, 22, 30, 32, 37
33 Bedford Row, London WC1
p925 . . . . 020 7242 6476

OZIN, Mr Paul David BA(Oxon) *M Nov 1987*
15, 36, 11, 62, 27, 63, 46
23 Essex Street, London WC2
p932 . . . . 020 7413 0353

OZWELL, Miss Kate *L Nov 2007*
10, 20, 15, 25, 22
1 King's Bench Walk, London EC4
p938 . . . . 020 7936 1500

PACEY, Mr Thomas *G Nov 2008*
30, 18
12 King's Bench Walk, London EC4
p940 . . . . 020 7583 0811

Packman, Miss Claire BA(Oxon) *I Oct 1996*
12, 18, 40, 24
4 Pump Court, London EC4
p947 . . . . 020 7842 5555

Padfield, Miss Alison Mary BA(Oxon); Lic Spec Dr Eur(Brussels); BCL(Oxon) *L Oct 1992*
3, 5, 6, 11, 12, 19, 21, 24, 29, 40, 55, 51
Devereux Chambers, London WC2
p930 . . . . 020 7353 7534

Padley, Miss Clare BA(Cantab) *I Oct 1991*
30, 20, 11, 93
9 Gough Square, London EC4
p935 . . . . 020 7832 0500

Page, Miss Adrienne BA(Kent) *M Jul 1974*
(Q.C.) *16, 13, 50, 51*
5RB, London WC1
p948 . . . . 020 7242 2902

PAGE, Mr Douglas *L Jan 2003*
Carmelite Chambers, London EC4
p927 . . . . 020 7936 6300

Page, Mr Hugo MA(Cantab) *I Nov 1977*
(Q.C.) *3, 11, 12, 13, 24, 29, 36, 40, 41, 35, 89, 62, 4*
Blackstone Chambers, London EC4
p926 . . . . 020 7583 1770

Page, Mrs Jane LLB *I Jul 1982*
10, 20
Chartlands Chambers, Northampton
p988 . . . . 01604 603322

PAGE, Mr Jonathan R T DipLaw *M Oct 1996*
Carmelite Chambers, London EC4
p927 . . . . 020 7936 6300

PAGE, Mr Nigel B LLB(Lond) *G Jul 1976*
10, 20
St Mary's Chambers, Nottingham
p989 . . . . 0115 950 3503

Page, Ms Philippa BA(Lond) *G Nov 1999*
15, 46, 84, 96
Argent Chambers, London WC2
p923 . . . . 020 7556 5500

PAGE, Miss Rebecca BA(Cantab) *G Nov 2001*
6, 8, 11, 22, 21, 38, 40, 88, 97
Enterprise Chambers, London WC2
p931 . . . . 020 7405 9471
Enterprise Chambers, Leeds
p977 . . . . 0113 246 0391
Enterprise Chambers, Newcastle upon Tyne
p987 . . . . 0191 222 3344

PAGET, Miss Henrietta BA(Worcs) *I Oct 1999*
15
9-12 Bell Yard Chambers, London WC2
p926 . . . . 020 7400 1800

PAGETT, Helen *I Jul 2008*
30, 11, 24
Crown Office Chambers, London EC4
p929 . . . . 020 7797 8100

PAIN, Mr Kevin MA(Oxon) *G Jan 1994*
Pallant Chambers, Chichester
p974 . . . . 01243 784538

Paine, Mr Douglas *L Oct 2009*
One Essex Court, London EC4
p931 . . . . 020 7583 2000

PAINES, Mr Nicholas MA(Oxon); Licence Speciale En Droit Europeen(Brux) *G Apr 1978*
(Q.C.) *1, 18, 19, 44, 51, 57*
Monckton Chambers, London WC1
p942 . . . . 020 7405 7211

PAKROOH, Ramin *L Oct 1996*
15
Guildhall Chambers, Bristol
p970 . . . . 0117 930 9000

PALEY, Miss Ruth *G Oct 2003*
15, 62, 13
23 Essex Street, London WC2
p932 . . . . 020 7413 0353

Palfrey, Mr Montague LLB(Bucks) *M Nov 1985*
22
3PB, London EC4
p946 . . . . 020 7583 8055

PALIN, Miss Sarah BA(Oxon) *M Nov 1999*
16
One Brick Court, London EC4
p927 . . . . 020 7353 8845

PALLO, Mr Simon *G Jan 2003*
12, 15, 20
Bank House Chambers, Sheffield
p991 . . . . 0114 275 1223

PALMER, Mr Adrian MA(Cantab) *M Jul 1972*
(Q.C.) *11, 12, 30, 40*
Guildhall Chambers, Bristol
p970 . . . . 0117 930 9000

Palmer, Ms Anya BA(Hons) *I Jan 1999*
18, 36, 51, 55
Old Square Chambers, Bristol
p971 . . . . 0117 930 5100
Old Square Chambers, London WC1
p945 . . . . 020 7269 0300

Palmer, Miss Briony Madelaine BA(Hons); MA; MSt; GDL; BVC *I Jul 2009*
6, 10, 12, 20, 22, 38, 88
3 Dr Johnson's Buildings, London EC4
p930 . . . . 020 7353 4854

Palmer, Ms Claire *L Jan 2003*
Thomas More Chambers, London WC2
p952 . . . . 020 7404 7000

Palmer, Mr Edward James LLB(Hons); LLM *L Jul 2000*
15, 20, 12, 23
Regent Chambers, Hanley
p976 . . . . 01782 286666

Palmer, Mr Howard William Arthur MA(Oxon) *I Jul 1977*
(Q.C.) *7, 24, 30, 12, 40, 41, 53, 21, 46*
2 Temple Gardens, London EC4
p952 . . . . 020 7822 1200

PALMER, Mr Iain *M Nov 1999*
23
Renaissance Chambers, London WC1
p949 . . . . 020 7404 1111

PALMER, Mr Ian Frarlyn LLB(Hons) *M Nov 1999*
23, 12, 18, 51
10 King's Bench Walk, London EC4
p940 . . . . 020 7353 7742

Palmer, Mr James BA(Cantab) *M Nov 1983*
12, 18, 24, 27, 30, 40, 47, 51
Henderson Chambers, London EC4
p937 . . . . 020 7583 9020

Palmer, Mr Martin MA(Hons)(Oxon) *I Jul 2003*
18, 11, 56
Cloisters, London EC4
p928 . . . . 020 7827 4000
Littleton Chambers, London EC4
p941 . . . . 020 7797 8600

Palmer (nee Biggs), Miss Nicola *M Jul 2001*
15
Westgate Chambers, Lewes
p980 . . . . 01273 480510

Palmer, Prof Norman Ernest MA; BCL(Oxon) *G Jul 1973*
(Q.C.) *7, 12, 24, 47, 48, 41*
3 Stone Buildings, London WC2
p951 . . . . 020 7242 4937
York Chambers, York
p995 . . . . 01904 620048
York Chambers, Newcastle upon Tyne
p987 . . . . 0191 206 4677

PALMER, Mr Robert H BA(Hons)(Oxon); DipLaw(City) *G Oct 1998*
1, 23, 31, 26, 76, 46, 51, 19
Monckton Chambers, London WC1
p942 . . . . 020 7405 7211

Palmer, Dr Stephanie LLB; LLM; SJD *M Sep 2000*
51, 33, 1
Blackstone Chambers, London EC4
p926 . . . . 020 7583 1770

PALMER, Ms Suzanne *M Nov 1995*
18, 30, 22, 36
4 King's Bench Walk, London EC4
p939 . . . . 020 7822 7000

PALMER, Mr Timothy N J *M Jul 1982*
15
1 High Pavement, Nottingham
p988 . . . . 0115 941 8218

Palser, Miss Elaine Jaqueline BBusSc(CapeTown); MA(Cantab); MA(Oxon) *M Oct 2002*
8, 11, 40, 6, 32, 37, 14, 38, 67, 96
9 Stone Buildings Barristers Chambers, London WC2
p951 . . . . 020 7404 5055

Paltenghi, Mr Mark LLB(Brunel) *M Jul 1979*
15, 62
Atkinson Bevan Chambers, London EC4
p924 . . . . 020 7353 2112

Panagiotopoulou, Miss Sophie LLB *M Nov 1995*
10, 15, 20, 23, 25
Staple Inn Chambers, London WC1
p951 . . . . 020 7242 5240

Panagiotopoulou, Miss Tania *M Oct 1994*
10, 23, 25
Staple Inn Chambers, London WC1
p951 . . . . 020 7242 5240

PANAYI, Mr Pavlos *G Oct 1995*
Carmelite Chambers, London EC4
p927 . . . . 020 7936 6300

Pandey, Mr Reuben BA(Hons)(Oxon); BCL(Oxon)(Jurisprudence) *L Jan 1996*
12, 6, 15, 11
Abbey Chambers, Shepperton
p992 . . . . 01932 560913

See p1010 for the Key to Work Categories

Panesar, Mr Deshpal Singh LLB(LSE) I *Jan 1993*
18
Old Square Chambers, Bristol
p971 . . . . . 0117 930 5100
Old Square Chambers, London WC1
p945 . . . . . 020 7269 0300

PANESAR, Mr Rashvinder G *Jan 2004*
Lombard Chambers, London EC1
p941 . . . . . 020 7107 2100

Pangraz, Theo M *Jan 2007*
11
Clerksroom - Administration Centre, Taunton
p993 . . . . . 0845 083 3000

Pannick, Lord David MA(Oxon); BCL(Oxon) G *Jul 1979*
(Q.C.) *1, 18, 19, 23, 26, 28, 36, 51, 55, 56, 89, 43*
Blackstone Chambers, London EC4
p926 . . . . . 020 7583 1770

PANTON, Mr Alastair H MA I *Oct 1996*
11, 12, 22, 30, 88, 32, 37
10 King's Bench Walk, London EC4
p940 . . . . . 020 7353 7742

PANTON, Mr Tom L *Jul 2002*
40, 12, 53, 30
Ropewalk Chambers, Nottingham
p989 . . . . . 0115 947 2581

Papadopoulos, Mr Socrates BA I *Jan 2001*
41, 3, 5, 11, 43, 47, 49, 24, 54, 35, 61
20 Essex Street, London WC2
p932 . . . . . 020 7842 1200

Papazian, Miss Cliona BA; LLB; MA I *Nov 1994*
10, 20, 37
4 Paper Buildings, London EC4
p946 . . . . . 020 7583 0816

PARAMJORTHY, Mr Nishan L *Nov 1999*
23, 57
Renaissance Chambers, London WC1
p949 . . . . . 020 7404 1111

PARATHALINGAM, Miss Amrisha L *Jan 2004*
15, 20, 30, 11, 67, 38
St Philips Chambers, Birmingham
p969 . . . . . 0121 246 7000

PARDOE, Mr Rupert MA(Cantab) I *Jul 1984*
36, 15, 25, 72, 62
23 Essex Street, London WC2
p932 . . . . . 020 7413 0353

Pare, Mr Christopher M *Jan 2006*
St Johns Buildings, Preston
p990 . . . . . 01772 256100
St Johns Buildings, Chester
p974 . . . . . 01244 323070
St Johns Buildings, Manchester
p985 . . . . . 0161 214 1500
St Johns Buildings, Liverpool
p982 . . . . . 0151 243 6000

PARFITT, Mr Matthew L *Nov 2005*
11, 38, 97
Erskine Chambers, London WC2
p931 . . . . . 020 7242 5532

Parham, Sam M *Jan 2000*
15
1 Pump Court, London EC4
p947 . . . . . 020 7842 7070

Parish, Mr Stephen A B Recorder I *Jul 1966*
2 King's Bench Walk, London EC4
p939 . . . . . 020 7353 1746

Park, Mr David L *Jul 1992*
31, 26, 54, 78, 46
No5 Chambers, Bristol
p971 . . . . . 0845 210 5555
No5 Chambers, London EC4
p944 . . . . . 0845 210 5555
No5 Chambers, Birmingham
p968 . . . . . 0845 210 5555

PARKE, Genevieve M *Jan 2006*
One Essex Court, London EC4
p931 . . . . . 020 7936 3030

PARKER, Mr Alan P G *May 1995*
15, 10, 51
Citadel Chambers, Birmingham
p967 . . . . . 0121 233 8500

Parker, Mr Benjamin M *Jan 2000*
3, 11, 24, 35
7 King's Bench Walk, London EC4
p940 . . . . . 020 7910 8300

Parker, Mr Christopher LLB; Recorder G *Jul 1986*
(Q.C.) *12, 15, 22, 30*
3PB, Winchester
p994 . . . . . 01962 868884

Parker, Mr Christopher R BCL; MA(Oxon); LLM(Harv) L *Dec 1984*
(Q.C.)
Maitland Chambers, London WC2
p941 . . . . . 020 7406 1200

Parker, Ms Karen PG DipLaw; BSc Chem; RGN I *Jul 2001*
15, 8, 53, 12, 18, 20, 22, 30, 40, 37
Guildhall Chambers, Portsmouth
p990 . . . . . 023 9275 2400

PARKER, Mr Matthew BA(Cantab) M *Oct 1997*
3, 5, 11, 40, 41
3 Verulam Buildings, London WC1
p953 . . . . . 020 7831 8441

Parker, Mr Paul MA M *Jul 1986*
8, 12, 24, 40, 45
Four New Square, London WC2
p943 . . . . . 020 7822 2000

PARKER, Mr Steven N LLB; Deputy District Judge G *Nov 1987*
10, 30, 20, 27, 12, 40, 53
7 Harrington Street Chambers, Liverpool
p981 . . . . . 0151 242 0707

Parker, Miss Wendy M *Jul 1978*
49, 5, 88, 11, 38, 40, 93, 37
Hardwicke, London WC2
p936 . . . . . 020 7242 2523

Parkin, Ms Fiona Jane LLB(Exon); LLM(Cantab) I *Oct 1993*
(Q.C.) *3, 7, 11, 31, 40, 41, 43, 45, 49, 54, 61, 78, 74*
Atkin Chambers, London WC1
p923 . . . . . 020 7404 0102

Parkin, Mr Timothy C LLB I *Nov 1971*
15, 8, 30, 37
New Court Chambers, Newcastle upon Tyne
p987 . . . . . 0191 232 1980

PARKINS, Mr Graham Recorder I *Jul 1972*
(Q.C.) *15, 62*
18 Red Lion Court, London EC4
p949 . . . . . 020 7520 6000
18 Red Lion Court (Annexe), Chelmsford
p973 . . . . . 01245 280880

PARKINSON, Mr Andrew CPE; BVC; BA(History) L *Jan 2010*
Landmark Chambers, London EC4
p941 . . . . . 020 7430 1221

Parkinson, William H LLB L *Oct 1997*
Clerksroom - Administration Centre, Taunton
p993 . . . . . 0845 083 3000

Parmar, Miss Chetna G *Jan 2003*
30, 22
Cobden House Chambers, Manchester
p983 . . . . . 0161 833 6000

Parnell, Ms Cherie LLB M *Nov 2000*
10, 20
East Anglian Chambers, Norwich
p988 . . . . . 01603 617351
East Anglian Chambers, Colchester
p975 . . . . . 01206 572756
East Anglian Chambers, Chelmsford
p973 . . . . . 01245 215660
East Anglian Chambers, Ipswich
p976 . . . . . 01473 214481

Parr, Mr John E LLB M *Nov 1989*
30
Cobden House Chambers, Manchester
p983 . . . . . 0161 833 6000

PARR, Judith I *Feb 1994*
10, 20
Renaissance Chambers, London WC1
p949 . . . . . 020 7404 1111

PARR, Miss Margaret BA(Law)(Oxon)(Jurisprudence) L *Mar 2008*
10, 20, 15
Oriel Chambers, Liverpool
p981 . . . . . 0151 236 7191 / 236 4321
Oriel Chambers, Preston
p990 . . . . . 01772 254764

Parrish, Mr Samuel LLB I *Feb 1962*
12, 15, 30, 31, 36
3PB, London EC4
p946 . . . . . 020 7583 8055

Parroy, Mr Michael BA(Oxon); Recorder M *Nov 1969*
(Q.C.) *7, 12, 15, 30*
3PB, London EC4
p946 . . . . . 020 7583 8055

Parry, Miss Angharad G *Oct 2002*
41, 3, 5, 24, 44, 11, 51, 33
20 Essex Street, London WC2
p932 . . . . . 020 7842 1200

PARRY, Mr Charles LLB(Lond) M *Nov 1973*
15, 22, 25, 49, 84
Pump Court Chambers, Swindon
p993 . . . . . 01793 539899
Pump Court Chambers, Winchester
p994 . . . . . 01962 868161
Pump Court Chambers, London EC4
p947 . . . . . 020 7353 0711

Parry, Ms Clare M *Jan 2005*
Cornerstone Barristers, London WC1
p929 . . . . . 020 7242 4986

Parry, Mr Philip L *Jan 1995*
St Johns Buildings, Preston
p990 . . . . . 01772 256100
St Johns Buildings, Chester
p974 . . . . . 01244 323070
St Johns Buildings, Manchester
p985 . . . . . 0161 214 1500
St Johns Buildings, Liverpool
p982 . . . . . 0151 243 6000

Parry, Miss Sian Rachel LLB(Wales) G *Oct 1994*
10, 20
9 Park Place, Cardiff
p973 . . . . . 029 2038 2731

Parry, Mr Simon LLB I *Nov 1997*
15
St Johns Buildings, Preston
p990 . . . . . 01772 256100
St Johns Buildings, Chester
p974 . . . . . 01244 323070
St Johns Buildings, Manchester
p985 . . . . . 0161 214 1500
St Johns Buildings, Liverpool
p982 . . . . . 0151 243 6000

Parry-Evans, Ms Mary BCL; MA(Oxon) I *Jun 1953*
15, 62
Thirty Park Place, Cardiff
p973 . . . . . 029 2039 8421

Parry-Jones, Ms Carole Ann LLB(Hons)(Westminster) M *Nov 1992*
10, 20, 12
East Anglian Chambers, Norwich
p988 . . . . . 01603 617351
East Anglian Chambers, Colchester
p975 . . . . . 01206 572756
East Anglian Chambers, Chelmsford
p973 . . . . . 01245 215660
East Anglian Chambers, Ipswich
p976 . . . . . 01473 214481

PARRY-JONES, Mr John Trevor LLB G *Feb 1992*
10, 15, 20, 62
7 Harrington Street Chambers, Liverpool
p981 . . . . . 0151 242 0707

Parsley, Mr Charles Ronald LLB(Exon) I *Jul 1973*
1, 8, 10, 20, 31, 32, 37, 14
Thirty Park Place, Cardiff
p973 . . . . . 029 2039 8421

Parsons, Mr Andrew James LLB(Hons)(Lond); FCIArb I *Jul 1985*
65, 66, 49, 41, 5, 7, 8, 53, 11, 12, 97, 44, 67, 69, 80, 20, 81, 38, 24, 88, 89, 96, 29, 92, 30, 40, 93, 35, 36, 37
Portsmouth Barristers Chambers, Portsmouth
p990 . . . . . 023 9283 1292

Parsons, Mr Glen L *Jan 1999*
Park Court Chambers, Leeds
p978 . . . . . 0113 243 3277

Parsons, Mr Luke LLB(Bris) I *Jul 1985*
(Q.C.) *11, 24, 5, 35, 3*
Quadrant Chambers, London EC4
p948 . . . . . 020 7583 4444

PARSONS, Miss Naomi I *Oct 2008*
15, 62, 94
18 Red Lion Court, London EC4
p949 . . . . . 020 7520 6000
18 Red Lion Court (Annexe), Chelmsford
p973 . . . . . 01245 280880

PARTINGTON, Miss Lisa LLB I *Jul 1989*
20, 10, 12, 15, 38
St Johns Buildings, Preston
p990 . . . . . 01772 256100
St Johns Buildings, Chester
p974 . . . . . 01244 323070
St Johns Buildings, Manchester
p985 . . . . . 0161 214 1500
St Johns Buildings, Liverpool
p982 . . . . . 0151 243 6000

PARTINGTON, Prof Thomas BA; LLB; Professor of Law University of Bristol M *Nov 1984*
1, 22, 88
Arden Chambers, London WC1
p923 . . . . . 020 7242 4244

Partridge, Mr Ian MA(Oxon); Deputy Master I *Jul 1979*
3, 5, 6, 7, 8, 11, 13, 18, 22, 23, 24, 29, 31, 32
3PB, London EC4
p946 . . . . . 020 7583 8055

Partridge, Dr Richard Charles MBBch; LLB(Hons)(Cardiff) L *Nov 1994*
27, 30, 12, 40, 53, 68, 85, 63
3 Serjeants' Inn, London EC4
p950 . . . . . 020 7427 5000

Paruk, Miss Saira BA(Oxon)(Law with French); BCL(Oxon) L *Jan 2004*
Quadrant Chambers, London EC4
p948 . . . . . 020 7583 4444

Pascall, Mr Matthew Stephen BA M *Jul 1984*
12, 15, 22, 8, 48
Guildford Chambers, Guildford
p975 . . . . . 01483 539131

PASCOE, Mr Martin BA; BCL(Oxon) L *Jul 1977*
(Q.C.) *5, 6, 8, 11, 12, 24, 29, 38*
South Square, London WC1
p950 . . . . . 020 7696 9900

Pascoe, Mr Nigel I *Jul 1966*
(Q.C.) *15, 62*
Queen Square Chambers, Bristol
p972 . . . . . 0117 921 1966
Pump Court Chambers, Swindon
p993 . . . . . 01793 539899
Pump Court Chambers, Winchester
p994 . . . . . 01962 868161
Pump Court Chambers, London EC4
p947 . . . . . 020 7353 0711

Pass, Mr Geoffrey LLB M *Jul 1975*
13, 22, 32, 37
Kings Chambers, Leeds
p978 . . . . . 0113 242 1123
Kings Chambers, Manchester
p984 . . . . . 0161 832 9082

PASSFIELD, Mr Simon LLB(Hons)(Notts); BVC(BPP) G *Jul 2009*
38, 89, 5, 11
Guildhall Chambers, Bristol
p970 . . . . . 0117 930 9000

Patel, Elyas Mohammed LLB; LLM(Cantab) G *Nov 1991*
Park Court Chambers, Leeds
p978 . . . . . 0113 243 3277

PATEL, Miss Gita I *Jul 1988*
23, 51, 1
Kenworthy's Chambers, Manchester
p984 . . . . . 0161 832 4036

Patel, Miss Hanisha L *Oct 2002*
15, 62
7 Bedford Row, London WC1
p924 . . . . . 020 7242 3555

Patel, Jai G *Oct 1999*
15, 62
4 Breams Buildings, London EC4
p927 . . . . . 020 7092 1900

Patel, Jayantilal BSc(Hons); ARILS I *Nov 1999*
12, 15, 22, 23
189 Randolph Avenue, London W9
p949 . . . . . 020 7328 0158

Patel, Miss Naina BA(Hons)(Oxon); MPP(Harv) I *Oct 2005*
1, 11, 18, 51, 33, 44, 19, 89
Blackstone Chambers, London EC4
p926 . . . . . 020 7583 1770

PATEL, Mr Parishil M *Nov 1996*
30, 40, 12, 1, 18, 55, 63, 23, 51, 67, 7, 14
Thirty Nine Essex Street, London WC2
p932 . . . . . 020 7832 1111

Patel, Shail I *Jan 2006*
Four New Square, London WC2
p943 . . . . . 020 7822 2000

PATEL, Mr Yasin G *Jul 2002*
15, 70
25 Bedford Row, London WC1
p925 . . . . . 020 7067 1500

13

Paterson, Miss Fiona BA(Law) M *Mar 2003*
1, 53, 12, 68, 85, 27, 30, 40, 36, 96
3 Serjeants' Inn, London EC4
p950 . . . . . 020 7427 5000

Pathak, Pankaj MA(Cantab); LLM(Lond) L *Oct 1992*
2 Dr Johnson's Buildings, London EC4
p930 . . . . . 020 7936 2613

PATIENCE, James BA(Hons) M *Jan 2007*
1, 7, 12, 47, 48, 67, 15, 84, 89, 30
Atlantic Chambers, Liverpool
p980 . . . . . 0151 236 4421

PATON, Miss Danielle I *Jul 2007*
15, 20, 30
7 Harrington Street Chambers, Liverpool
p981 . . . . . 0151 242 0707

PATON, Mr Ewan W MA; BCL(Oxon) I *Oct 1996*
8, 93, 37, 32, 41
Guildhall Chambers, Bristol
p970 . . . . . 0117 930 9000

Paton, Mr Ian M *Apr 1975*
15, 25, 36
QEB Hollis Whiteman, London EC4
p948 . . . . . 020 7933 8855

Paton-Philip, Mr Richard G *Jan 2004*
Nine Bedford Row, London WC1
p924 . . . . . 020 7489 2727

PATRY HOSKINS, Ms Carine I *Jul 1999*
Landmark Chambers, London EC4
p941 . . . . . 020 7430 1221

Patten, Mr Benedict Joseph BA(Oxon) M *Jul 1986*
(Q.C.) *8, 12, 24, 40, 18*
Four New Square, London WC2
p943 . . . . . 020 7822 2000

Patterson, Miss Anna Louise M *Oct 2004*
15, 20, 30, 12
15 Winckley Square, Preston
p991 . . . . . 01772 252828

Patterson, Mr Gareth BA(Cantab) G *Jul 1995*
15, 25, 62
6 King's Bench Walk, London EC4
p939 . . . . . 020 7583 0410

PATTERSON, Mr Stewart BA(Oxon); Recorder M *Nov 1967*
7, 15, 20, 35, 12, 10, 62, 49
Pump Court Chambers, Swindon
p993 . . . . . 01793 539899
Pump Court Chambers, Winchester
p994 . . . . . 01962 868161
Pump Court Chambers, London EC4
p947 . . . . . 020 7353 0711

Pattinson, Miss Catherine G *Jan 2000*
2 King's Bench Walk, London EC4
p939 . . . . . 020 7353 1746

Patton, Mr Conall G *Jan 2004*
One Essex Court, London EC4
p931 . . . . . 020 7583 2000

Patton, Mr Robin BA I *Jul 1983*
12, 15
New Court Chambers, Newcastle upon Tyne
p987 . . . . . 0191 232 1980

Paul, Mr John I *Apr 1972*
Eastern Chambers, London N2
p930 . . . . .

Paul, Mr Matthew BA(Oxon); CPE I *Oct 2000*
15, 91, 84
Argent Chambers, London WC2
p923 . . . . . 020 7556 5500

Paulin, Mr Michael BA(Hons); MPhil I *Jan 2007*
18, 72, 71
3PB, London EC4
p946 . . . . . 020 7583 8055

Pavlou, Mr Paul LLB(Hons) L *Nov 1993*
10, 20
4 Brick Court Chambers, London EC4
p927 . . . . . 020 7832 3200

PAWSON, Mr Robert Edward BA; MA(Lond) I *Nov 1994*
15, 12, 62, 25, 42, 91
Pump Court Chambers, Swindon
p993 . . . . . 01793 539899
Pump Court Chambers, Winchester
p994 . . . . . 01962 868161
Pump Court Chambers, London EC4
p947 . . . . . 020 7353 0711

PAXTON, Mr Christopher LLB(Hons) G *Nov 1991*
15, 62, 84
18 Red Lion Court, London EC4
p949 . . . . . 020 7520 6000
18 Red Lion Court (Annexe), Chelmsford
p973 . . . . . 01245 280880

PAY, Mr Adrian BA(Oxon) M *Nov 1999*
8, 6, 22
New Square Chambers, London WC2
p943 . . . . . 020 7419 8000

Payne, Mr David G *Jun 2003*
10, 20, 15
No 8 Chambers, Birmingham
p968 . . . . . 0121 236 5514

PAYNE, Mr Geoff I *Nov 2000*
15, 62
25 Bedford Row, London WC1
p925 . . . . . 020 7067 1500

Payne, Mr Johnathan G *Jan 1997*
53, 30, 11, 40, 18
Ely Place Chambers, London EC1
p931 . . . . . 020 7400 9600

PAYNE, Mr Tom M *Oct 1998*
15, 62
18 Red Lion Court, London EC4
p949 . . . . . 020 7520 6000
18 Red Lion Court (Annexe), Chelmsford
p973 . . . . . 01245 280880

PAYTON, Mr Alexander MA(Oxon) L *Nov 1998*
8, 30, 12
Alpha Court Chambers, Leamington Spa
p977 . . . . . 0800 634 9650 / 01926 886412

Payton, Mr Clifford MA; BCL(Oxon) I *Jul 1972*
8, 11, 40, 38
Alpha Court Chambers, Leamington Spa
p977 . . . . . 0800 634 9650 / 01926 886412

PEACOCK, Mr Ian MA(Cantab) G *Oct 1990*
11, 22, 26, 40
New Square Chambers, London WC2
p943 . . . . . 020 7419 8000

PEACOCK, Mr Jonathan David MA(Oxon) M *Jul 1987*
(Q.C.) *34, 57, 58*
11 New Square, London WC2
p943 . . . . . 020 7242 4017

Peacock, Miss Lisa Jayne MA(Cantab) L *Oct 1992*
10, 12, 20, 22
3 Dr Johnson's Buildings, London EC4
p930 . . . . . 020 7353 4854

Peacock, Mr Nicholas G *Oct 1992*
40, 53, 30, 27
Hailsham Chambers, London EC4
p936 . . . . . 020 7643 5000
Maitland Chambers, London WC2
p941 . . . . . 020 7406 1200

Peacocke, Mrs Teresa Rosen BA(Mich); MA L *Nov 1982*
5, 6, 8, 11, 22, 24, 29, 32, 37, 40
3 Stone Buildings, London WC2
p951 . . . . . 020 7242 4937

Pearce, Miss Emma L *Jul 2006*
King's Bench Godolphin Chambers, Truro
p994 . . . . . 0845 308 1551
King's Bench Godolphin Chambers, Plymouth
p990 . . . . . 0845 308 1551

Pearce, Mr Ivan G *Oct 1994*
33 Chancery Lane, London WC2
p928 . . . . . 020 7440 9950

Pearce, Mr Luke L *Nov 2007*
49, 41, 3, 5, 11, 43, 47, 78, 24, 54, 35
20 Essex Street, London WC2
p932 . . . . . 020 7842 1200

Pearce, Ms Nicola M *Jan 2002*
3PB, Bournemouth
p969 . . . . . 01202 292102

Pearce, Mr Richard BA(Cantab) M *Jul 1985*
53, 12, 30
42 Bedford Row, London WC1
p925 . . . . . 020 7831 0222
Byrom Street Chambers, Manchester
p983 . . . . . 0161 829 2100

Pearce, Mr Robert E MA; BCL(Oxon) M *Jul 1977*
(Q.C.) *2, 6, 8, 11, 14, 22, 29, 32, 37, 5, 9, 40*
Radcliffe Chambers, London WC2
p949 . . . . . 020 7831 0081

Pearce-Smith, Mr James MA(Cantab) I *Jan 2002*
11, 8, 40, 29, 6, 7, 93, 32, 37, 74, 5, 88
St John's Chambers, Bristol
p972 . . . . . 0117 921 3456

Pearman, Mr Lee Charles LLB; LLM M *Jul 2003*
20, 10, 91, 15
4 Brick Court Chambers, London EC4
p927 . . . . . 020 7832 3200

Pearman, Mr Scott M *Jan 1999*
11, 18, 29, 16
Ely Place Chambers, London EC1
p931 . . . . . 020 7400 9600

PEARS, Derrick A MA(Oxon) I *Jul 1975*
10, 12
Tanfield Chambers, London WC1
p951 . . . . . 020 7421 5300

Pearson, Mr Adam M *Oct 2000*
12, 15, 26, 10, 62
36 Bedford Row, London WC1
p925 . . . . . 020 7421 8000

Pearson, Miss Carolyn LLB G *Nov 1990*
12, 20, 22
14 Gray's Inn Square, London WC1
p936 . . . . . 020 7242 0858
Stour Chambers, Canterbury
p972 . . . . . 01227 764899

Pearson, Mr Christopher I *Oct 1995*
13, 11, 50
Lamb Chambers, London EC4
p941 . . . . . 020 7797 8300

Pearson, Ms Elizabeth Anne LLB(Bris) I *Oct 1999*
12, 30, 15
9 Park Place, Cardiff
p973 . . . . . 029 2038 2731

Pearson, Miss Rebecca LLB(Hons) G *Oct 1999*
12, 18, 22, 30, 51, 55, 59
Cobden House Chambers, Manchester
p983 . . . . . 0161 833 6000

PEARSON, Mr Thomas Adam Spencer BA; LLB(Cantab) M *Nov 1969*
49, 41, 96
Pump Court Chambers, Swindon
p993 . . . . . 01793 539899
Pump Court Chambers, Winchester
p994 . . . . . 01962 868161
Pump Court Chambers, London EC4
p947 . . . . . 020 7353 0711

Pease, Ms Alexandra LLM M *Nov 1999*
23, 15, 62
Lamb Building, Brighton
p970 . . . . . 01273 820490
Lamb Building, London EC4
p940 . . . . . 020 7797 7788

Peat, Mr Charlie G *Jan 2003*
15, 20
1 Pump Court, London EC4
p947 . . . . . 020 7842 7070

Peat, Mr Richard G *Jan 1993*
13 Old Square Chambers, London WC2
p945 . . . . . 020 7831 4445

PECK, Ms Catherine LLB(B'ham) G *Nov 1995*
24, 30, 53
12 King's Bench Walk, London EC4
p940 . . . . . 020 7583 0811

Peckham, Ms Jane LLB(Hons) I *Jan 1999*
12, 20, 22, 30, 10, 6
Crown Office Row Chambers, Brighton
p970 . . . . . 01273 625625

Pedro, Mr Terry Adebisi LLB(Hons)(Lond) M *Oct 1996*
15
1 Pump Court, London EC4
p947 . . . . . 020 7842 7070

PEEBLES, Mr Andrew MA(Cantab) I *Nov 1987*
12, 18, 11, 36, 30
Farrar's Building, London EC4
p933 . . . . . 020 7583 9241

PEEL, Mr Robert BA(Oxon); DipLaw M *Nov 1990*
(Q.C.) *10, 20, 30*
29 Bedford Row, London WC1
p925 . . . . . 020 7404 1044

Peers, Miss Heather BA(Dunelm); MPhil(Cantab) G *Oct 1991*
10, 20
King's Bench Godolphin Chambers, Truro
p994 . . . . . 0845 308 1551
King's Bench Godolphin Chambers, Plymouth
p990 . . . . . 0845 308 1551

Peers, Miss Nicola Jane BA(Oxon) I *Oct 1996*
12, 15, 20, 30
Broadway House Chambers, Leeds
p977 . . . . . 0113 246 2600
Broadway House Chambers, Bradford
p969 . . . . . 01274 722560

Peet, Mr Andrew I *Oct 1991*
2 New Street, Leicester
p979 . . . . . 0116 262 5906

PEIRSON, Mr Oliver LLB L *Oct 1993*
15, 20, 30, 10, 12, 18
Pump Court Chambers, Swindon
p993 . . . . . 01793 539899
Pump Court Chambers, Winchester
p994 . . . . . 01962 868161
Pump Court Chambers, London EC4
p947 . . . . . 020 7353 0711

Pelling, Mr Alexander MA(Dundee); D Phil(Oxon) M *Oct 1995*
4, 5, 6, 8, 40, 37, 11, 49, 62, 25
XXIV Old Buildings, London WC2
p944 . . . . . 020 7691 2424

Pema, Anesh M *Nov 1994*
12, 24, 37, 40, 88, 94
Zenith Chambers, Leeds
p979 . . . . . 0113 245 5438

Pemberton, Miss Jessica L I *Jan 2007*
Paradise Chambers, Sheffield
p992 . . . . . 0114 273 8951

PEMBERTON, Miss Lydia L *Jul 2006*
8, 11
St Philips Chambers, Birmingham
p969 . . . . . 0121 246 7000

PEMBERTON, Ms Yolanda L *Mar 2002*
20
St Philips Chambers, Birmingham
p969 . . . . . 0121 246 7000

Pendlebury, Mr Jeremy BA I *Jul 1980*
53, 30, 40, 27, 84, 85
7 Bedford Row, London WC1
p924 . . . . . 020 7242 3555

PENGELLY, Ms Sarah I *Oct 1996*
1, 22, 26, 88, 93
Arden Chambers, London WC1
p923 . . . . . 020 7242 4244

Penn, Mr Jon I *Mar 1996*
1 Mitre Court Buildings, London EC4
p942 . . . . . 020 7452 8900

PENNI, Miss Sally G *Oct 2000*
15, 25, 18, 63, 55
Kenworthy's Chambers, Manchester
p984 . . . . . 0161 832 4036

Pennicott, Mr Ian BA; LLM(Cantab); Member of Hong Kong Bar M *Jul 1982*
(Q.C.) *3, 7, 11, 24, 40*
Keating Chambers, London WC2
p938 . . . . . 020 7544 2600

Pennifer, Ms Kelly LLB; Maitrise en Droit M *Nov 1994*
41, 7, 11, 47, 18, 24, 40, 3, 5, 8, 12, 51, 55, 35, 61, 66, 67, 74, 89
Exchange Chambers, Manchester
p983 . . . . . 0161 833 2722
Exchange Chambers, Liverpool
p980 . . . . . 0151 236 7747
Exchange Chambers, Leeds
p977 . . . . . 0113 203 1970

Pennington Legh, Mr Jonathan I *Oct 2000*
Field Court Chambers, London WC1
p933 . . . . . 020 7405 6114

Penny, Miss Abigail M *Oct 1999*
15, 62, 51
4 Breams Buildings, London EC4
p927 . . . . . 020 7092 1900

Penny, Mr Duncan M *Oct 1992*
15, 62, 16
6 King's Bench Walk, London EC4
p939 . . . . . 020 7583 0410

Penny, Mr Tim LLB(Bris) I *Jul 1988*
8, 11, 13, 62
11 Stone Buildings, London WC2
p951 . . . . . 020 7831 6381

PENTOL, Mr Simon LLB(Lond) M *Nov 1982*
15, 62, 56
25 Bedford Row, London WC1
p925 . . . . . 020 7067 1500

Pepper, Miss Judith Leah LLB; LLM M *Oct 1999*
20, 10
4 Brick Court Chambers, London EC4
p927 . . . . . 020 7832 3200

PEPPER, Miss Theresa Recorder G *Nov 1973*
10, 15, 20
Chavasse Court Chambers, Liverpool
p980 . . . . . 0151 229 2030

See p1010 for the Key to Work Categories

Pepperall, Mr Edward Brian LLB(B'ham) L *Jul 1989*
11, 18, 30, 55, 8, 53, 97, 75
2 Temple Gardens, London EC4
p952 . . . . . 020 7822 1200
St Philips Chambers, Birmingham
p969 . . . . . 0121 246 7000

PERCIVAL, Mr Robert Eldon MA(Cantab) I *Nov 1971*
30, 20, 53
Five Paper, London EC4
p946 . . . . . 020 7815 3200

Pereira, Mr James MA(Cantab); LLM(Lond) M *Oct 1996*
1, 46, 51, 26, 31, 36
Francis Taylor Building, London EC4
p934 . . . . . 020 7353 8415

PERETZ, Mr George BA(Oxon) M *Sep 1990*
11, 19, 44
Monckton Chambers, London WC1
p942 . . . . . 020 7405 7211

Perfect, Mr Andrew BA(Hons)(Manc) I *Jan 2007*
11, 18, 30, 76, 89
3PB, London EC4
p946 . . . . . 020 7583 8055

Perhar, Mr Simon G *Oct 1997*
15, 22, 25, 20, 11, 18, 63
Ely Place Chambers, London EC1
p931 . . . . . 020 7400 9600

Perian, Mr Steven LLB(Lond) L *Nov 1987*
15, 62, 25
3 Temple Gardens, London EC4
p952 . . . . . 020 7353 3102

Perkins, Mr Alistair G BA(Keele) M *Jul 1986*
10, 20, 30, 12
4 Paper Buildings, London EC4
p946 . . . . . 020 7583 0816

PERKINS, Joanna BA(Hons); LLM(Cantab); DPhil(Oxon) M *Jan 2001*
81, 5
South Square, London WC1
p950 . . . . . 020 7696 9900

Perkins, Ms Marianne G *Jan 1997*
13 Old Square Chambers, London WC2
p945 . . . . . 020 7831 4445

Perkins, Simon LLB G *Nov 1999*
68, 15, 72, 71, 70, 82, 23, 91, 94
Zenith Chambers, Leeds
p979 . . . . . 0113 245 5438

Perkins, Miss Victoria L *Nov 2002*
30, 18, 27, 53, 85, 26
7 Bedford Row, London WC1
p924 . . . . . 020 7242 3555

PERKOFF, Mr Richard Michael MA(Oxon); Accredited Mediator M *Jul 1971*
3, 5, 6, 7, 8, 11, 12, 24, 29, 41, 49
Littleton Chambers, London EC4
p941 . . . . . 020 7797 8600

Perplus, Miss Stephanie BA; DipLaw L *Oct 2008*
20, 10
15 Winckley Square, Preston
p991 . . . . . 01772 252828

Perrins, Mr Gregory I *Oct 1997*
15, 84, 43
1 Paper Buildings, London EC4
p946 . . . . . 020 7353 3728

PERRINS, Miss Jennifer L *Jul 2004*
10, 20, 15, 25, 22
1 King's Bench Walk, London EC4
p938 . . . . . 020 7936 1500

PERRINS, Mr Philip LLB(Hons); LLM(Cantab) M *Jan 2002*
10, 20
1 Garden Court, London EC4
p934 . . . . . 020 7797 7900

Perry, Miss Cleo G *Oct 2000*
20, 10
4 Paper Buildings, London EC4
p946 . . . . . 020 7583 0816

Perry, Mr David LLB; MA(Leics); Standing Counsel to DTI; Senior Treasury Counsel L *Jul 1980*
15, 12, 36, 25
6 King's Bench Walk, London EC4
p939 . . . . . 020 7583 0410

PERRY, Mr Derek G *Jan 2006*
10, 15, 20, 30, 40, 94
Octagon Chambers, Taunton
p993 . . . . . 01823 331919

Perry, Miss Jacqueline MA(Oxon) G *May 1975*
(Q.C.) *30, 40, 24, 53, 12, 49*
2 Temple Gardens, London EC4
p952 . . . . . 020 7822 1200

PERRY, Mrs Naomi Melanie BA(B'ham) M *Jul 1974*
4 King's Bench Walk, London EC4
p939 . . . . . 020 7822 7000

Persey, Mr Lionel Edward LLB; DJEF G *Jul 1981*
(Q.C.) *3, 41, 4, 11, 24, 35, 60*
Quadrant Chambers, London EC4
p948 . . . . . 020 7583 4444

PERSHAD, Mr Rohan Anthony LLB(Lond) L *Oct 1991*
(Q.C.) *24, 30, 53, 11, 7, 40*
Thirty Nine Essex Street, London WC2
p932 . . . . . 020 7832 1111

Persson, Mr Matthew MA I *Nov 2003*
20, 8, 11, 10, 22, 32, 37
4 Paper Buildings, London EC4
p946 . . . . . 020 7583 0816

Pester, Mr Iain BA(Oxon); BCL L *Nov 1999*
11, 6, 62, 38
11 Stone Buildings, London WC2
p951 . . . . . 020 7831 6381

Petchey, Mr Philip MA(Oxon) M *Jul 1976*
1, 12, 46, 17, 26, 28, 31, 36
Francis Taylor Building, London EC4
p934 . . . . . 020 7353 8415

Peters, Mr David BA(Cantab) M *Jan 2005*
6, 8, 11, 38
11 Stone Buildings, London WC2
p951 . . . . . 020 7831 6381

PETERS, Mr Edward MA(Cantab) M *Nov 1998*
Falcon Chambers, London EC4
p933 . . . . . 020 7353 2484

PETERS, Ms Georgina MA(Cantab) L *Jul 2005*
8, 5, 6, 11, 97, 38
South Square, London WC1
p950 . . . . . 020 7696 9900

PETERS, Mr Nigel Recorder L *Jul 1976*
(Q.C.) *15, 25, 62, 95, 36*
18 Red Lion Court, London EC4
p949 . . . . . 020 7520 6000
18 Red Lion Court (Annexe), Chelmsford
p973 . . . . . 01245 280880

Petersen, Mr Lewis Neil M *Jul 1993*
2 Dr Johnson's Buildings, London EC4
p930 . . . . . 020 7936 2613

Petersen, Mr Thomas L *Jul 2004*
Goldsmith Chambers, London EC4
p935 . . . . . 020 7353 6802

Peterson, Miss Geri BA M *Oct 1997*
23, 12, 49, 96
Lamb Building, Brighton
p970 . . . . . 01273 820490
Lamb Building, London EC4
p940 . . . . . 020 7797 7788

Petherbridge, Ms Bridget G *Oct 2002*
15
QEB Hollis Whiteman, London EC4
p948 . . . . . 020 7933 8855

Petkovic, Mr James L *Jul 2009*
One Essex Court, London EC4
p931 . . . . . 020 7583 2000

Peto, Mr Anthony MA(Oxon); BCL(Oxon) M *Feb 1985*
(Q.C.) *5, 6, 11, 13, 24, 29, 36, 41, 62, 12, 81, 89*
Blackstone Chambers, London EC4
p926 . . . . . 020 7583 1770

Petrou, Ms Mandy G *Aug 2006*
Petrou Chambers, Barnet
p967 . . . . . 020 7566 8244

Petterson, Mr Andrew M *Oct 2004*
72, 15, 70
Exchange Chambers, Manchester
p983 . . . . . 0161 833 2722
Exchange Chambers, Liverpool
p980 . . . . . 0151 236 7747
Exchange Chambers, Leeds
p977 . . . . . 0113 203 1970

Pettican, Mr Kevin BA; BCL(Oxon) I *Jan 1994*
41, 11, 18, 62
11 Stone Buildings, London WC2
p951 . . . . . 020 7831 6381

Pettit, Mr Sean BA(Hons) I *Oct 1997*
1 Pump Court, London EC4
p947 . . . . . 020 7842 7070

Pettitt, Mr Robert M *Jul 2002*
12, 15, 20, 30
Northampton Chambers, Northampton
p988 . . . . . 01604 636271

Petts, Mr Peter Simon Tinsley LLB(Hons)(Lond) I *Oct 1998*
93, 40
42 Bedford Row, London WC1
p925 . . . . . 020 7831 0222
Hardwicke, London WC2
p936 . . . . . 020 7242 2523

PETTS, Mr Timothy BA; M Jur(Oxon); Recorder I *Oct 1996*
12, 30, 40
12 King's Bench Walk, London EC4
p940 . . . . . 020 7583 0811

PHELAN, Margaret Former Solicitor I *Oct 1993*
Renaissance Chambers, London WC1
p949 . . . . . 020 7404 1111

PHELAN, Miss Sarah Jane BA(Hons) I *Nov 1999*
10, 12, 15, 20
Chavasse Court Chambers, Liverpool
p980 . . . . . 0151 229 2030

Phelps, Ms Rosalind J BA; BCL(Oxon); Dip(French Law)(Paris) L *Nov 1998*
Fountain Court Chambers, London EC4
p934 . . . . . 020 7583 3335

Phile-Ebosie, Miss Shelia LLB(Nigeria); LLM(Lond) G *Nov 1988*
42 Bedford Row, London WC1
p925 . . . . . 020 7831 0222

Philipps, Mr Guy Wogan BA(Oxon); DipLaw I *Jul 1986*
(Q.C.)
Fountain Court Chambers, London EC4
p934 . . . . . 020 7583 3335

PHILIPS, Mr David MA(Oxon); Deputy High Court Judge, Recorder, Bencher of Gray's Inn; Director of Disability Law Service G *Nov 1976*
(Q.C.) *8, 11, 29, 56, 60*
Wilberforce Chambers, London WC2
p953 . . . . . 020 7306 0102

Phillimore, Ms Sarah L *Oct 1994*
St John's Chambers, Bristol
p972 . . . . . 0117 921 3456

PHILLIPS, Mr Andrew BA(Oxon); MA(Cantab) M *Jul 1978*
40, 24, 74, 7, 30, 11, 12, 3
Crown Office Chambers, London EC4
p929 . . . . . 020 7797 8100

Phillips, Ms Emma M *Nov 2001*
1 Pump Court, London EC4
p947 . . . . . 020 7842 7070

Phillips, Mr Frank LLB L *Nov 1972*
15, 25
Iscoed Chambers, Swansea
p993 . . . . . 01792 652988

PHILLIPS, Mr Henry L *Jan 2008*
5, 6, 8, 11, 97, 38, 69
South Square, London WC1
p950 . . . . . 020 7696 9900

PHILLIPS, Miss Jane R BA(Oxon) I *Jul 1989*
16, 52, 73
One Brick Court, London EC4
p927 . . . . . 020 7353 8845

Phillips, Mr Jeremy BA(Hons)(English Lit) I *Oct 2004*
1, 22, 25, 26, 31, 36, 47, 48
Francis Taylor Building, London EC4
p934 . . . . . 020 7353 8415

PHILLIPS, Mr Jonathan Mark BA(Cantab) I *Nov 1991*
5, 6, 11, 40
3 Verulam Buildings, London WC1
p953 . . . . . 020 7831 8441

Phillips, Miss Katie BA(Oxon) L *Jul 2002*
42 Bedford Row, London WC1
p925 . . . . . 020 7831 0222

PHILLIPS, Mr Mark LLB; LLM(Brist) I *Jul 1984*
(Q.C.) *5, 6, 11, 24, 29, 40, 56, 38*
South Square, London WC1
p950 . . . . . 020 7696 9900

Phillips, Mr Matthew BA(Oxon) L *Nov 1993*
30, 53, 56
Outer Temple Chambers, London WC2
p945 . . . . . 020 7353 6381

Phillips, Mr Michael Charles LLB(Lond) M *Feb 1980*
10, 20
Lamb Building, Brighton
p970 . . . . . 01273 820490
Lamb Building, London EC4
p940 . . . . . 020 7797 7788

Phillips, Ms Moira G *Jan 1989*
20, 10, 63
No5 Chambers, Bristol
p971 . . . . . 0845 210 5555
No5 Chambers, London EC4
p944 . . . . . 0845 210 5555
No5 Chambers, Birmingham
p968 . . . . . 0845 210 5555

PHILLIPS, Mr Nevil David BA(Soton); DipLaw(City); LLM(Lond) G *Oct 1992*
3, 35, 24, 11
Quadrant Chambers, London EC4
p948 . . . . . 020 7583 4444

Phillips, Mr Oliver BA(Classics); MA M *Jul 2009*
Maitland Chambers, London WC2
p941 . . . . . 020 7406 1200

Phillips, Mr Paul Stuart LLB(Wales) G *Feb 1991*
12, 15, 23, 25, 36
Charter Chambers, London WC1
p928 . . . . . 020 7618 4400

Phillips, Mr Richard MA(Cantab) I *Nov 1970*
(Q.C.) *1, 26, 31, 25, 36*
Francis Taylor Building, London EC4
p934 . . . . . 020 7353 8415

PHILLIPS, Mr Rory MA(Cantab) I *Jul 1984*
(Q.C.) *3, 7, 11, 24, 40*
3 Verulam Buildings, London WC1
p953 . . . . . 020 7831 8441

PHILLIPS, Miss Ruth LLB(Hons) M *Jul 2001*
20, 15
Trinity (Newcastle) Chambers, Newcastle upon Tyne
p987 . . . . . 0191 232 1927
Trinity (Teesside) Chambers, Middlesbrough
p986 . . . . . 01642 247569

Phillips, Mr Simon Benjamin BA; LLM I *Jul 1985*
(Q.C.) *1, 15, 25, 46, 56, 62, 84*
Francis Taylor Building, London EC4
p934 . . . . . 020 7353 8415
Park Court Chambers, Leeds
p978 . . . . . 0113 243 3277

PHILLIPS, Mr Simon David BA(Cantab) I *Oct 1996*
15, 62, 71, 91
St Philips Chambers, Birmingham
p969 . . . . . 0121 246 7000

PHILLIPS, Mr Stephen BA(Oxon) G *Jul 1984*
(Q.C.) *3, 5, 6, 11, 40*
3 Verulam Buildings, London WC1
p953 . . . . . 020 7831 8441

Phillips, Stephen J BA(Oxon); BCL L *Oct 1993*
(Q.C.) *3, 4, 5, 11, 24, 33, 35, 40*
7 King's Bench Walk, London EC4
p940 . . . . . 020 7910 8300

Phillips, Mr William Bernard MA(Oxon) I *Jul 1970*
30, 40, 12, 27, 11
Paradise Chambers, Sheffield
p992 . . . . . 0114 273 8951

Phillipson, Nicola L *Jun 1999*
30, 22, 88
Zenith Chambers, Leeds
p979 . . . . . 0113 245 5438

Phillpot, Mr Hereward BA(York); Dip(EC Law)(Lond) G *Nov 1997*
1, 26, 31, 36
Francis Taylor Building, London EC4
p934 . . . . . 020 7353 8415

Philo, Mr Noel P MA(Oxon) G *Feb 1975*
15
KCH Garden Square Chambers, Nottingham
p989 . . . . . 0115 941 8851
KCH Garden Square Chambers, Leicester
p979 . . . . . 0115 941 8851

PHILPOTT, Mr Fred LLB(Lond) G *Jul 1974*
39, 47, 48, 59
Gough Square Chambers, London EC4
p935 . . . . . 020 7353 0924

Philpotts, Mr Robert John BA; MPhil; Recorder G *Oct 1990*
15, 62
Thirty Park Place, Cardiff
p973 . . . . . 029 2039 8421

Phipps, Mr Charles MA M *Nov 1992*
8, 12, 24, 40
Four New Square, London WC2
p943 . . . . . 020 7822 2000

13

PHIPPS, Mr Sandy L *Jan 2008*
5, 81, 11
3 Verulam Buildings, London WC1
p953 . . . . . 020 7831 8441

PHIPPS, Miss Sarah Elizabeth BA(Oxon) L *Nov 1997*
12, 20
Queen Elizabeth Buildings, London EC4
p948 . . . . . 020 7797 7837

PHYSSAS, Claire L *Oct 2004*
23, 51
Renaissance Chambers, London WC1
p949 . . . . . 020 7404 1111

Piasecki, Ms Emma G *Jan 2001*
New Court Chambers, Newcastle upon Tyne
p987 . . . . . 0191 232 1980

Pickard, Miss Kathryn MA(Cantab); BCL(Oxon) I *Oct 2002*
73, 50, 19, 45, 13, 52, 96, 41
11 South Square, London WC1
p950 . . . . . 020 7405 1222

PICKAVANCE, Mr Graham LLB G *Nov 1973*
10, 15, 20, 26, 31
Chavasse Court Chambers, Liverpool
p980 . . . . . 0151 229 2030

PICKAVANCE, Mr Michael J LLB(Hons) M *Jul 1974*
12, 30
7 Harrington Street Chambers, Liverpool
p981 . . . . . 0151 242 0707

Picken, Mr James G *Oct 2004*
St Ives Chambers, Birmingham
p969 . . . . . 0121 236 0863

Picken, Mr Simon Derek LLB(Cardiff); LLM(Cantab) M *Jul 1989*
(Q.C.) *3, 35, 11, 24, 6, 40*
7 King's Bench Walk, London EC4
p940 . . . . . 020 7910 8300

PICKERING, Andrew MA(Cantab) L *Nov 1987*
53, 12, 67, 84, 24, 30, 40, 94, 56, 59, 89
Atlantic Chambers, Liverpool
p980 . . . . . 0151 236 4421
12 King's Bench Walk, London EC4
p940 . . . . . 020 7583 0811

PICKERING, Mr James BSc(Soton) M *Oct 1991*
6, 7, 8, 11, 13, 22, 29, 32, 37, 40, 49, 38, 88, 97
Enterprise Chambers, London WC2
p931 . . . . . 020 7405 9471
Enterprise Chambers, Leeds
p977 . . . . . 0113 246 0391
Enterprise Chambers, Newcastle upon Tyne
p987 . . . . . 0191 222 3344

PICKERING, Mr Leon L *Jul 2010*
8, 37, 93
Ten Old Square, London WC2
p945 . . . . . 020 7405 0758

Pickering, Mr Murray A MA(NZ); LLM(Lond) I *Nov 1963*
(Q.C.) *3, 11, 12, 24, 35, 41*
20 Essex Street, London WC2
p932 . . . . . 020 7842 1200

PICKERING, Miss Rebecca I *Jul 2007*
15, 23
Kenworthy's Chambers, Manchester
p984 . . . . . 0161 832 4036

PICKERING, Mr Simon T LLB; MA I *Oct 1996*
7, 8, 12, 47, 88, 10, 20
Wilberforce Chambers, Hull
p976 . . . . . 01482 323264

PICKERSGILL, Mr David LLB(Hons) M *Nov 1996*
15, 62
18 Red Lion Court, London EC4
p949 . . . . . 020 7520 6000
18 Red Lion Court (Annexe), Chelmsford
p973 . . . . . 01245 280880

PICKFORD, Mr Meredith MA(Cantab) M *Oct 1999*
1, 11, 19, 44, 46, 51, 56, 57
Monckton Chambers, London WC1
p942 . . . . . 020 7405 7211

PICKLES, Mr Simon Robert MA(Cantab) I *Jul 1978*
26, 31
Landmark Chambers, London EC4
p941 . . . . . 020 7430 1221

Pickthall, Ms Claire LLB G *Nov 1999*
15
Temple Chambers, Newport
p988 . . . . . 01633 267403 / 255855
Temple Chambers, Cardiff
p973 . . . . . 029 2039 7364

Pickup, Ms Alison BA; MA M *Jan 2007*
18, 55, 22, 51, 23, 63, 1, 70
Doughty Street Chambers, London WC1
p930 . . . . . 020 7404 1313

Pickup, Mr David I *Jul 1984*
12, 15, 19, 25
St Johns Buildings, Preston
p990 . . . . . 01772 256100
St Johns Buildings, Chester
p974 . . . . . 01244 323070
St Johns Buildings, Manchester
p985 . . . . . 0161 214 1500
St Johns Buildings, Liverpool
p982 . . . . . 0151 243 6000

Pickup, Mr James K MA(Oxon); BCL; Recorder G *Jul 1976*
(Q.C.) *15, 62*
2 Hare Court, London EC4
p937 . . . . . 020 7353 5324
Lincoln House Chambers, Manchester
p984 . . . . . 0161 832 5701

Picton, Mr Julian Mark BA(Oxon) M *Feb 1988*
40, 30, 53, 27
Hailsham Chambers, London EC4
p936 . . . . . 020 7643 5000

Piears, Miss Angela BA; LLM M *Oct 2001*
30, 52
Cobden House Chambers, Manchester
p983 . . . . . 0161 833 6000

PIERCY, Ms Arlette L *Nov 1990*
1, 15, 18, 30
25 Bedford Row, London WC1
p925 . . . . . 020 7067 1500

Pierpoint, Ms Katherine LLB L *Oct 1998*
Lincoln House Chambers, Manchester
p984 . . . . . 0161 832 5701

Pievsky, Mr David BA(Cantab); MPhil(Cantab) I *Jul 2001*
1, 18, 11, 51, 23, 89
Blackstone Chambers, London EC4
p926 . . . . . 020 7583 1770

Pigot, Miss Diana BA(Lond) I *Nov 1978*
15
2 Pump Court, London EC4
p947 . . . . . 020 7353 5597

PIGOTT, Ms Frances G *Oct 1994*
11, 7, 88, 93
St Philips Chambers, Birmingham
p969 . . . . . 0121 246 7000

Pigram, Mr Christopher Stuart BA(Hons); Pupil Supervisor G *Jul 2000*
11, 22, 18, 30, 12, 6, 47, 29, 40, 55, 37
East Anglian Chambers, Norwich
p988 . . . . . 01603 617351
East Anglian Chambers, Colchester
p975 . . . . . 01206 572756
East Anglian Chambers, Chelmsford
p973 . . . . . 01245 215660
East Anglian Chambers, Ipswich
p976 . . . . . 01473 214481

Pike, Mr Jeremy LLB; LLM M *Jul 2001*
1, 12, 46, 18, 25, 26, 31, 36, 61, 51, 54, 28, 60
Francis Taylor Building, London EC4
p934 . . . . . 020 7353 8415

Pike, Olivia M *Jan 2008*
10, 20, 30
Thirty Park Place, Cardiff
p973 . . . . . 029 2039 8421

Pilbrow, Mr Fionn I *Jan 2001*
11, 35, 5, 24, 1
Brick Court Chambers, London WC2
p927 . . . . . 020 7379 3550

Pilgerstorfer, Mr Marcus BA(Hons)(English Law; German Law); Bar Vocational Course; BPP Law School M *Jan 2002*
30, 18
Old Square Chambers, Bristol
p971 . . . . . 0117 930 5100
Old Square Chambers, London WC1
p945 . . . . . 020 7269 0300

Pilkington, Miss Abigail Jane BA(Hons)(Dunelm); PGDL(bpp) I *Jul 2008*
Fenners Chambers, Cambridge
p972 . . . . . 01223 368761

PILLAI, Mr Rajesh BA(Hons)(Oxon); BA(Hons)(Cantab); LLM(NYU); NY Bar 2003 M *Jan 2002*
5, 62, 6, 24, 50, 40
3 Verulam Buildings, London WC1
p953 . . . . . 020 7831 8441

Pilling, Miss Annabel BA(Lond) M *Oct 1995*
15, 62, 16
6 King's Bench Walk, London EC4
p939 . . . . . 020 7583 0410

Pilling, Mr Benjamin MA(Oxon) I *Nov 1997*
7, 11, 12, 5, 24, 40
4 Pump Court, London EC4
p947 . . . . . 020 7842 5555

Pillow, Mr Nathan BA(Oxon) G *Jan 1997*
1, 2, 4, 5, 6, 8, 11, 13, 18, 19, 21, 24, 29, 33, 34, 35, 36
Essex Court Chambers, London WC2
p931 . . . . . 020 7813 8000

PIMLOTT, Mr Charles BA(Cantab); Junior Tenant M *Nov 2001*
74, 7, 40, 24, 11
Crown Office Chambers, London EC4
p929 . . . . . 020 7797 8100

PIMM, Mr Peter J BA(Bris); Recorder G *Apr 1991*
12, 15, 20
Bank House Chambers, Sheffield
p991 . . . . . 0114 275 1223

PINDER, Sarah Former Solicitor M *Oct 2006*
10, 20, 23
Renaissance Chambers, London WC1
p949 . . . . . 020 7404 1111

Pine, Miss Mika M *Nov 2007*
15
East Anglian Chambers, Norwich
p988 . . . . . 01603 617351
East Anglian Chambers, Colchester
p975 . . . . . 01206 572756
East Anglian Chambers, Chelmsford
p973 . . . . . 01245 215660
East Anglian Chambers, Ipswich
p976 . . . . . 01473 214481

Pine-Coffin, Miss Margaret A BA(Leeds)(Law) I *Jul 1981*
20, 10, 63
12 College Place, Southampton
p992 . . . . . 023 8032 0320

Pines Richman, Ms Helene BA(Penn); JD(George Washington) M *Jul 1992*
5, 6, 8, 9, 11, 21, 22, 29, 31, 32, 34, 37
Stour Chambers, Canterbury
p972 . . . . . 01227 764899

Pinfold, Mr Martin M *Jan 1981*
15
9 Gough Square, London EC4
p935 . . . . . 020 7832 0500

Pini, Mr John BA; Recorder G *Jul 1981*
(Q.C.) *15, 62*
7 Bedford Row, London WC1
p924 . . . . . 020 7242 3555

Pinkham, Mrs Joy G *Jan 1993*
10, 20
Chartlands Chambers, Northampton
p988 . . . . . 01604 603322

PINKNEY, Mr Giles LLB G *Nov 1978*
12, 20
Fountain Chambers, Middlesbrough
p986 . . . . . 01642 804040

Pinnell, Mr David LLB G *Mar 2008*
15
Temple Chambers, Newport
p988 . . . . . 01633 267403 / 255855
Temple Chambers, Cardiff
p973 . . . . . 029 2039 7364

Pinnock, Mr Earl M *Nov 2003*
15, 62, 72, 94
No5 Chambers, Bristol
p971 . . . . . 0845 210 5555
No5 Chambers, London EC4
p944 . . . . . 0845 210 5555
No5 Chambers, Birmingham
p968 . . . . . 0845 210 5555

PINTO, Miss Amanda BA M *Nov 1983*
(Q.C.) *15, 62, 13*
5 Paper Buildings, London EC4
p946 . . . . . 020 7583 6117

Pipe, Mr Adam LLM M *Oct 1999*
23
No 8 Chambers, Birmingham
p968 . . . . . 0121 236 5514

PIPE, Mr Gregory L *Oct 1995*
3, 7, 8, 12, 18, 24, 36, 40, 41, 47, 49, 51, 55, 11, 29
Chancery House Chambers, Leeds
p977 . . . . . 0113 244 6691

Piper, Mr Angus BA L *Nov 1991*
12, 30, 40, 53, 62, 24, 26, 85
1 Chancery Lane, London WC2
p928 . . . . . 0845 634 6666

Pirani, Mr Rohan C MA(Oxon); BCL(Oxon); LLM(Toronto) M *Oct 1995*
18, 30, 36, 27, 55
Old Square Chambers, Bristol
p971 . . . . . 0117 930 5100
Old Square Chambers, London WC1
p945 . . . . . 020 7269 0300

Piskolti, Miss Catherine L *Jul 2003*
20
3 Dr Johnson's Buildings, London EC4
p930 . . . . . 020 7353 4854

Pitchers, Mr Henry BA(Oxon) I *Nov 1996*
30, 40, 68, 94
No5 Chambers, Bristol
p971 . . . . . 0845 210 5555
No5 Chambers, London EC4
p944 . . . . . 0845 210 5555
No5 Chambers, Birmingham
p968 . . . . . 0845 210 5555

Pithers, Mr Clive Robert LLB(Reading) G *Feb 1989*
8, 10, 12, 20, 22, 31, 36, 38
Fenners Chambers, Cambridge
p972 . . . . . 01223 368761

PITMAN, Ms Laura L *Oct 2000*
15
1 High Pavement, Nottingham
p988 . . . . . 0115 941 8218

Pitt, Mr Daniel C BSc; CPE I *Oct 1995*
20
Fenners Chambers, Cambridge
p972 . . . . . 01223 368761

PITT-LEWIS, Mrs Janet MA(Oxon) M *Jul 1976*
15, 10, 20, 93, 12
Cornwall Street Chambers, Birmingham
p967 . . . . . 0121 233 7500

PITT-PAYNE, Mr Timothy BA; BCL(Oxon) I *Nov 1989*
(Q.C.) *1, 11, 18, 19, 40, 73, 26*
11KBW, London EC4
p938 . . . . . 020 7632 8500

PITTAWAY, Miss Amanda M LLB(B'ham) G *Jul 1980*
20, 10, 93
Cornwall Street Chambers, Birmingham
p967 . . . . . 0121 233 7500

Pittaway, Mr David MA(Cantab); FCIArb I *Jul 1977*
(Q.C.) *30, 40, 27, 53*
Hailsham Chambers, London EC4
p936 . . . . . 020 7643 5000

Pitter, Mr Jason LLB G *Jun 1994*
Park Court Chambers, Leeds
p978 . . . . . 0113 243 3277

Pitts, Miss Charlotte LLB(Soton) I *Oct 1999*
20, 23
Albion Chambers, Bristol
p970 . . . . . 0117 927 2144

PITTS, Miss Emily I *Jan 2000*
15, 12
Colleton Chambers, Exeter
p975 . . . . . 01392 274898

Pitts, Mr Keith M *Oct 1997*
74, 18, 67, 97, 11, 40, 88, 38, 12
Chambers of Mr Keith Pitts, Royston
p991 . . . . . 01763 287760

Piyadasa, Miss Susan LLB L *Jan 1994*
4 Breams Buildings, London EC4
p927 . . . . . 020 7092 1900

PLANGE, Janet LLB(B'ham) G *Jul 1981*
10, 20
Renaissance Chambers, London WC1
p949 . . . . . 020 7404 1111

Plant, Ms April LLB L *Oct 2002*
15, 37
East Anglian Chambers, Norwich
p988 . . . . . 01603 617351
East Anglian Chambers, Colchester
p975 . . . . . 01206 572756
East Anglian Chambers, Chelmsford
p973 . . . . . 01245 215660
East Anglian Chambers, Ipswich
p976 . . . . . 01473 214481

See p1010 for the Key to Work Categories

Plant, Dr Glen MA(Oxon); PhD(Lond); Dip Hague Ac Int Law I *Jul 1985*
20 Essex Street, London WC2
p932 . . . 020 7842 1200

PLANT, Mr James Richard BA(Hons)(L'Pool); PG DipLaw M *Nov 2004*
30, 12
Farrar's Building, London EC4
p933 . . . 020 7583 9241

Plaschkes, Ms Sarah I *Jul 1988*
15, 25, 36
QEB Hollis Whiteman, London EC4
p948 . . . 020 7933 8855

PLATFORD, Mr Graham BA(Nott'm) G *Nov 1970*
11, 40, 29
Five Paper, London EC4
p946 . . . 020 7815 3200

PLATT, Mr David W MA(Cantab) M *Jul 1987*
(Q.C.) *30, 24, 84, 40, 31, 36, 11, 46*
Crown Office Chambers, London EC4
p929 . . . 020 7797 8100

Platt, Miss Eleanor Frances LLB G *Feb 1960*
(Q.C.)
Eastbourne Chambers, Eastbourne
p975 . . . 01323 642102
1 Garden Court, London EC4
p934 . . . 020 7797 7900

PLATT, Miss Heather L *Oct 2002*
18, 20, 12
Pump Court Chambers, Swindon
p993 . . . 01793 539899
Pump Court Chambers, Winchester
p994 . . . 01962 868161
Pump Court Chambers, London EC4
p947 . . . 020 7353 0711

PLATT, Mr Stephen M *Jan 1994*
62, 5, 69, 75, 81, 21, 29, 57
23 Essex Street, London WC2
p932 . . . 020 7413 0353

Platts, Mr Robert LLB(Hons); MSc; Recorder L *Jul 1973*
Lincoln House Chambers, Manchester
p984 . . . 0161 832 5701

Platts Mills, Mr Mark MA(Oxon) I *Jul 1974*
(Q.C.) *13, 50*
8 New Square, London WC2
p943 . . . 020 7405 4321

Plaut, Mr Simon M MA(Law) L *Oct 1997*
18, 30
Kings Chambers, Leeds
p978 . . . 0113 242 1123
Kings Chambers, Manchester
p984 . . . 0161 832 9082

Pleeth, Mr Edward LLB(UEA) I *Jul 2005*
18, 27, 53, 68, 85, 30, 40, 36
3 Serjeants' Inn, London EC4
p950 . . . 020 7427 5000

PLEMING, Mr Nigel I *Feb 1971*
(Q.C.) *1, 36, 26, 23, 46, 51, 34*
Thirty Nine Essex Street, London WC2
p932 . . . 020 7832 1111

Pliener, Mr David M *Nov 1996*
49, 11, 74, 38, 24, 40, 93, 88
Hardwicke, London WC2
p936 . . . 020 7242 2523

Plimmer, Ms Melanie LLB(Hons); LLM G *Mar 1996*
23, 1, 10, 18, 55, 36, 51
Kings Chambers, Leeds
p978 . . . 0113 242 1123
Kings Chambers, Manchester
p984 . . . 0161 832 9082

PLOWDEN, Ms Selena BA(Hons); DipLaw I *Oct 1991*
53, 30, 63
Guildhall Chambers, Bristol
p970 . . . 0117 930 9000

PLUNKETT, Mr Raymond LLB(Hons)(B'ham) G *Jan 2004*
10, 20, 68
Cornwall Street Chambers, Birmingham
p967 . . . 0121 233 7500

POCOCK, Mr Christopher BA(Oxon) I *Jul 1984*
(Q.C.) *10, 20, 96, 49*
1 King's Bench Walk, London EC4
p938 . . . 020 7936 1500

Pocock, Mr Louis John G *Jan 1997*
Chancery Chambers, London WC2
p928 . . . 020 7405 6879

Pointer, Mr Martin J LLB G *Jul 1976*
(Q.C.) *20, 10*
1 Hare Court, London EC4
p936 . . . 020 7797 7070

Pojur, Mr David LLB M *Nov 2001*
15, 12, 23
St Johns Buildings, Preston
p990 . . . 01772 256100
St Johns Buildings, Chester
p974 . . . 01244 323070
St Johns Buildings, Manchester
p985 . . . 0161 214 1500
St Johns Buildings, Liverpool
p982 . . . 0151 243 6000

POKU, Miss Mary Laureen LLB(Hons) L *Nov 1993*
15, 62
9-12 Bell Yard Chambers, London WC2
p926 . . . 020 7400 1800

Pole, Mr Tim BA M *Jul 2001*
10, 20, 15, 62, 84, 39, 23, 94, 72, 70
No5 Chambers, Bristol
p971 . . . 0845 210 5555
No5 Chambers, London EC4
p944 . . . 0845 210 5555
No5 Chambers, Birmingham
p968 . . . 0845 210 5555

Polglase, Mr David S BA(Hons)(Oxon) M *Oct 1993*
15, 22, 30
St Johns Buildings, Preston
p990 . . . 01772 256100
St Johns Buildings, Chester
p974 . . . 01244 323070
St Johns Buildings, Manchester
p985 . . . 0161 214 1500
St Johns Buildings, Liverpool
p982 . . . 0151 243 6000

Pollard, Miss Joanna MA(Cantab) G *Nov 1993*
1, 11, 13, 40, 41, 50, 52, 33, 21, 12, 89
Blackstone Chambers, London EC4
p926 . . . 020 7583 1770

Polley, Mr Alexander I *Jan 2005*
One Essex Court, London EC4
p931 . . . 020 7583 2000

POLLI, Mr Timothy M *Jan 1997*
11, 12, 22, 8
Tanfield Chambers, London WC1
p951 . . . 020 7421 5300

Pollock, Mr Gordon MA; LLB(Cantab); Recorder G *Nov 1968*
(Q.C.)
Essex Court Chambers, London WC2
p931 . . . 020 7813 8000

Pollock, Miss Hilary LLB I *Nov 1993*
Goldsmith Chambers, London EC4
p935 . . . 020 7353 6802

Polnay, Mr Jonathan BA(Hons)(Cantab) M *Nov 2000*
15
5 King's Bench Walk, London EC4
p939 . . . 020 7353 5638

Polson, Mr Alistair MA(Hons)(Glasgow); DipLaw M *Nov 1989*
15, 12
1 Pump Court, London EC4
p947 . . . 020 7842 7070

POMFRET, Mr Brad L *Jan 2004*
St James's Chambers, Manchester
p984 . . . 0161 834 7000

Pons, Mr Gary G *Jan 1995*
15
5 St Andrew's Hill, London EC4
p950 . . . 020 7332 5400

Ponter, Mr Ian BA(Keele); LLM(Aberdeen) M *Oct 1993*
1, 3, 26, 31, 46, 54
Kings Chambers, Leeds
p978 . . . 0113 242 1123
Kings Chambers, Manchester
p984 . . . 0161 832 9082

Poole, Mr Nigel BA(Hons)(Oxon) M *Nov 1989*
30, 53, 36
Kings Chambers, Leeds
p978 . . . 0113 242 1123
Kings Chambers, Manchester
p984 . . . 0161 832 9082

POOLE, Mr Tom I *Jan 2001*
11, 30, 12, 51, 18, 59
3 Hare Court, London EC4
p937 . . . 020 7415 7800

Poole, Mr William M *Jan 2004*
St Johns Buildings, Preston
p990 . . . 01772 256100
St Johns Buildings, Chester
p974 . . . 01244 323070
St Johns Buildings, Manchester
p985 . . . 0161 214 1500
St Johns Buildings, Liverpool
p982 . . . 0151 243 6000

Pooles, Mr Michael LLB(Lond) I *Jul 1978*
(Q.C.) *40, 24, 30*
Hailsham Chambers, London EC4
p936 . . . 020 7643 5000

POOTS, Ms Laura BA(Hons)(Jurisprudence) M *Jan 2007*
37, 57, 58, 34
Pump Court Tax Chambers, London WC1
p948 . . . 020 7414 8080

Popat, Prashant BA(Oxon) G *Feb 1992*
(Q.C.) *12, 18, 22, 30, 36, 40, 47, 48*
Henderson Chambers, London EC4
p937 . . . 020 7583 9020

Popat, Mr Surendra LLB(Lond); LLM L *Jul 1969*
12, 15
Two King's Bench Walk, London EC4
p939 . . . 020 7353 7202 / 7353 3909

Pope, Ms Heather BA I *Jul 1977*
20, 10
1 Hare Court, London EC4
p936 . . . 020 7797 7070

Pope, Ms Sarah L *Jul 2006*
14 Gray's Inn Square, London WC1
p936 . . . 020 7242 0858

Pople, Miss Alison LLB(Hons) M *Nov 1993*
15, 62
2 Bedford Row, London WC1
p924 . . . 020 7440 8888

Popplewell, Mr Andrew MA(Cantab) I *Nov 1981*
(Q.C.) *11, 18, 24, 35, 5*
Brick Court Chambers, London WC2
p927 . . . 020 7379 3550

POPPLEWELL, Mr Simon BA(Oxon) G *Oct 2000*
11, 12, 47, 48, 18, 39, 22
Gough Square Chambers, London EC4
p935 . . . 020 7353 0924

Porten, Mr Anthony BA(Cantab) I *Jul 1969*
(Q.C.) *1, 25, 26, 31, 46, 22*
Cornerstone Barristers, London WC1
p929 . . . 020 7242 4986

Porter, Ms Alexandra M *Jan 2002*
Thomas More Chambers, London WC2
p952 . . . 020 7404 7000

PORTER, Mr David LLB(Manc) L *Jul 1980*
2, 6, 8, 9, 11, 13, 22, 29, 32, 37
St James's Chambers, Manchester
p984 . . . 0161 834 7000

Porter, Ms Joanne Emily I *Nov 2010*
Stour Chambers, Canterbury
p972 . . . 01227 764899

Porter, Mr Martin Hugh MA(Cantab); LLM(Cantab) I *Jul 1986*
(Q.C.) *4, 24, 30, 1, 12, 40, 27, 51, 53*
2 Temple Gardens, London EC4
p952 . . . 020 7822 1200

PORTER, Mr Nigel MA; LLM(Cantab) M *Nov 1994*
1, 11, 18, 26, 55
11KBW, London EC4
p938 . . . 020 7632 8500

PORTER-BRYANT, Mr Matthew Seymour LLB(Hons) M *Nov 1999*
30, 53
Guildhall Chambers, Bristol
p970 . . . 0117 930 9000

Porter-Phillips, Mrs Clare LLB(Hons) L *Mar 2001*
12, 15, 20
St Johns Buildings, Preston
p990 . . . 01772 256100
St Johns Buildings, Chester
p974 . . . 01244 323070
St Johns Buildings, Manchester
p985 . . . 0161 214 1500
St Johns Buildings, Liverpool
p982 . . . 0151 243 6000

POSNER, Gabrielle Recorder I *Jul 1984*
10, 20
Renaissance Chambers, London WC1
p949 . . . 020 7404 1111

Post, Mr Andrew BA; DipLaw M *Jul 1988*
40, 27, 53
Hailsham Chambers, London EC4
p936 . . . 020 7643 5000

Posta, Mr Adrian M *Oct 1996*
20, 30
Albion Chambers, Bristol
p970 . . . 0117 927 2144

Pote, Mr Andrew Thomas LLB; DMS G *Nov 1983*
20
King's Bench Chambers, Oxford
p989 . . . 01865 311066
13 King's Bench Walk, London EC4
p940 . . . 020 7353 7204

Potter, Ms Alison MA(Oxon) M *Feb 1987*
40, 31, 11
4 Pump Court, London EC4
p947 . . . 020 7842 5555

Potter, Mr Anthony BA(Hons) G *Jul 1994*
15, 25, 62, 72, 94
No5 Chambers, Bristol
p971 . . . 0845 210 5555
No5 Chambers, London EC4
p944 . . . 0845 210 5555
No5 Chambers, Birmingham
p968 . . . 0845 210 5555

Potter, Mr Charlie BA(Cantab); DipLaw G *Jul 2007*
1, 51, 11, 18, 50, 52, 56
Blackstone Chambers, London EC4
p926 . . . 020 7583 1770

Potter, Mr David LLB(Hons) L *Oct 1990*
15, 62
Exchange Chambers, Manchester
p983 . . . 0161 833 2722
Exchange Chambers, Liverpool
p980 . . . 0151 236 7747
Exchange Chambers, Leeds
p977 . . . 0113 203 1970

POTTER, Mr Harry MA; M Phil(Cantab); LLB G *Oct 1993*
15
25 Bedford Row, London WC1
p925 . . . 020 7067 1500

Potter, Mr Ian Edward James LLB I *Nov 2001*
15, 25
Eastbourne Chambers, Eastbourne
p975 . . . 01323 642102

Potter, Ms Louise MA(Oxon) I *Nov 1993*
20
Harcourt Chambers, London EC4
p936 . . . 0844 561 7135
Harcourt Chambers, Oxford
p989 . . . 0844 561 7135

Potter, Mr Timothy L *Jan 2005*
10, 20, 23, 15
4 Brick Court Chambers, London EC4
p927 . . . 020 7832 3200

Pottinger, Mr Gavin BSc(Hons)(Econ)(Lond); DipLaw I *Oct 1991*
12, 15
4 Breams Buildings, London EC4
p927 . . . 020 7092 1900

Pottle, Miss Emilie LLB; BVC L *Jan 2008*
20, 15, 18, 30, 51, 76
36 Bedford Row, London WC1
p925 . . . 020 7421 8000

POTTS, Mr James BA G *Oct 1994*
11, 38, 97
Erskine Chambers, London WC2
p931 . . . 020 7242 5532

POTTS, Mr Richard LLB(Hons) I *Nov 1991*
15
18 Red Lion Court, London EC4
p949 . . . 020 7520 6000
18 Red Lion Court (Annexe), Chelmsford
p973 . . . 01245 280880

POTTS, Warren BA(Hons) M *Jul 1995*
11, 40, 22, 47, 12
St James's Chambers, Manchester
p984 . . . 0161 834 7000
Zenith Chambers, Leeds
p979 . . . 0113 245 5438

Poulet, Ms Rebecca L *Nov 1975*
(Q.C.) *15, 25, 36*
QEB Hollis Whiteman, London EC4
p948 . . . 020 7933 8855

Pounder, Ms Esther I *Jul 2003*
30, 53, 70, 15, 20, 18, 93
9 Gough Square, London EC4
p935 . . . 020 7832 0500

13

POUNDER, Mr Gerard LLB(Lond); BA L *Jul 1980*
15, 62, 36, 68
18 Red Lion Court, London EC4
p949 . . . . 020 7520 6000
18 Red Lion Court (Annexe), Chelmsford
p973 . . . . 01245 280880

Pounds, Miss Caroline BA(Law with French Law) L *Jan 2003*
11, 35
Quadrant Chambers, London EC4
p948 . . . . 020 7583 4444

POVALL, Mr David L *Jul 2000*
15, 72, 70
23 Essex Street, London WC2
p932 . . . . 020 7413 0353

Povoas, Mr Nigel LLB(Hons) L *Oct 1998*
15, 12, 30, 18
7 Bedford Row, London WC1
p924 . . . . 020 7242 3555

POVOAS, Mr Simon LLB(Hons); MA L *Oct 1996*
10, 12, 15, 20, 22, 30
Chavasse Court Chambers, Liverpool
p980 . . . . 0151 229 2030

Powell, Mr Andrew G *Nov 2008*
10, 20
4 Paper Buildings, London EC4
p946 . . . . 020 7583 0816

Powell, Mr Bernard Hilson BSc; PhD G *Oct 1991*
12, 15, 30
Temple Chambers, Newport
p988 . . . . 01633 267403 / 255855
Temple Chambers, Cardiff
p973 . . . . 029 2039 7364

POWELL, Ms Charlotte I *Jul 2005*
Furnival Chambers, London EC4
p934 . . . . 020 7405 3232

Powell, Ms Debra BA(Nott'm) M *Oct 1995*
27, 12, 30, 40, 63, 53, 68, 85
3 Serjeants' Inn, London EC4
p950 . . . . 020 7427 5000

Powell, Mr Frederick Mansell LLB(Hons) L *Nov 1999*
6, 10, 12, 15, 20, 22, 30
Regent Chambers, Hanley
p976 . . . . 01782 286666

Powell, Mr Giles G *Jan 1990*
Old Square Chambers, London WC1
p945 . . . . 020 7269 0300

Powell, Mr John Lewis MA; LLB M *Jul 1974*
(Q.C.) *41, 5, 8, 12, 24, 40, 11*
Four New Square, London WC2
p943 . . . . 020 7822 2000

Powell, Ms Katie M *Jan 2005*
Four New Square, London WC2
p943 . . . . 020 7822 2000

Powell, Ms Leona MA(Oxon) M *Jul 2000*
11
Blackstone Chambers, London EC4
p926 . . . . 020 7583 1770

Powell, Miss Michelle LLB I *Jul 2001*
20, 25, 10, 14
Lamb Building, Brighton
p970 . . . . 01273 820490
Lamb Building, London EC4
p940 . . . . 020 7797 7788

Powell, Mr Oliver LLB(Hons) G *Jan 2006*
72, 15, 71
3PB, London EC4
p946 . . . . 020 7583 8055

Powell, Mr Richard M *Jul 1989*
10, 20, 23
Southernhay Chambers, Exeter
p975 . . . . 01392 255777

POWELL, Mr Robin I *Nov 1993*
20, 10, 30, 18
Tanfield Chambers, London WC1
p951 . . . . 020 7421 5300

Powell, Mr William L *Nov 1971*
12, 46, 13, 15, 18, 22, 23, 25, 26, 30, 31
Regency Chambers, Peterborough
p990 . . . . 01733 315215

POWER, Ms Alexia G *Oct 1992*
15
Furnival Chambers, London EC4
p934 . . . . 020 7405 3232

Power, Ms Elizabeth I *Jan 1996*
15, 62, 72
No5 Chambers, Bristol
p971 . . . . 0845 210 5555
No5 Chambers, London EC4
p944 . . . . 0845 210 5555
No5 Chambers, Birmingham
p968 . . . . 0845 210 5555

POWER, Ms Eloise BA(Cantab) G *Jan 2002*
27, 30
Doughty Street Chambers, London WC1
p930 . . . . 020 7404 1313

POWER, Miss Erica MA(Cantab) L *Oct 1990*
11, 12, 27, 30, 53, 40, 84
Crown Office Chambers, London EC4
p929 . . . . 020 7797 8100

POWER, Miss Laurie-Anne LLB(Hons) M *Oct 2000*
Carmelite Chambers, London EC4
p927 . . . . 020 7936 6300

Power, Mr Lawrence M *Oct 1995*
4 KBW, London EC4
p938 . . . . 020 7822 8822

Power, Mr Lewis LLB G *Oct 1990*
(Q.C.) *15, 95, 84, 82*
Lamb Building, Brighton
p970 . . . . 01273 820490
Lamb Building, London EC4
p940 . . . . 020 7797 7788

Power, Mr Nicholas L *Jul 2004*
10, 20, 32, 40, 37
Broadway House Chambers, Leeds
p977 . . . . 0113 246 2600
Broadway House Chambers, Bradford
p969 . . . . 01274 722560

POWER, Mr Nigel John LLB I *Nov 1992*
(Q.C.) *15, 62, 91*
7 Harrington Street Chambers, Liverpool
p981 . . . . 0151 242 0707

Power, Mr Richard L *Oct 2007*
Fountain Court Chambers, London EC4
p934 . . . . 020 7583 3335
Lamb Chambers, London EC4
p941 . . . . 020 7797 8300

Powers, Dr Michael J BSc(Lond); MBBS L *Jul 1979*
(Q.C.) *53*
Clerksroom - Administration Centre, Taunton
p993 . . . . 0845 083 3000

Powis, Miss Lucy LLB G *Oct 1992*
12, 30, 53
Kings Chambers, Leeds
p978 . . . . 0113 242 1123
Kings Chambers, Manchester
p984 . . . . 0161 832 9082

POWIS, Miss Samantha L *Nov 1984*
Citadel Chambers, Birmingham
p967 . . . . 0121 233 8500

Powles, Mr Stephen I *Oct 1997*
15, 51, 33, 1, 91
Doughty Street Chambers, London WC1
p930 . . . . 020 7404 1313

Powlesland, Mr Paul M *Oct 2009*
11, 12, 18, 30, 89
Ely Place Chambers, London EC1
p931 . . . . 020 7400 9600

Pownall, Mr Orlando Recorder M *Jul 1975*
(Q.C.) *15, 95*
2 Hare Court, London EC4
p937 . . . . 020 7353 5324

Poynor, Miss Bryony MSc; BA L *Jan 2009*
51, 23, 1, 21, 20, 15
Garden Court North Chambers, Manchester
p983 . . . . 0161 236 1840

Prager, Miss Sarah LLB(Nott'm) L *Oct 1997*
30, 59, 12, 22
1 Chancery Lane, London WC2
p928 . . . . 0845 634 6666

Prand, Dr Annette B MA(Cantab); Dr iur I *Nov 1995*
11, 12, 22, 40, 38, 6, 93, 97
Lamb Chambers, London EC4
p941 . . . . 020 7797 8300

PRATLEY, Miss Michelle LLM; BA; LLB L *Jan 2006*
1, 76, 18, 63
4-5 Gray's Inn Square, London WC1
p935 . . . . 020 7404 5252

Pratt, Mr Ashley LLB G *Oct 2006*
Zenith Chambers, Leeds
p979 . . . . 0113 245 5438

Pratt, Mr Jake LLB(Hons) L *Oct 2004*
8, 11, 12, 47, 67, 14, 38, 88, 89, 63, 30, 31, 40, 93, 94, 36
Angel Chambers, Swansea
p992 . . . . 01792 464623

Pratt, Mrs Patricia LLB L *Oct 1991*
10, 12, 20
St Johns Buildings, Preston
p990 . . . . 01772 256100
St Johns Buildings, Chester
p974 . . . . 01244 323070
St Johns Buildings, Manchester
p985 . . . . 0161 214 1500
St Johns Buildings, Liverpool
p982 . . . . 0151 243 6000

PRATT, Mr Richard Camden MA(Oxon) G *Jul 1970*
(Q.C.) *10, 12, 15, 20, 27, 30, 31, 36*
1 King's Bench Walk, London EC4
p938 . . . . 020 7936 1500

PRATT, Mr Richard J BA G *Jul 1980*
(Q.C.) *18, 15, 25, 30, 12, 62*
Lombard Chambers, London EC1
p941 . . . . 020 7107 2100
7 Harrington Street Chambers, Liverpool
p981 . . . . 0151 242 0707

Preece, Miss Nicola G *Jan 2006*
Iscoed Chambers, Swansea
p993 . . . . 01792 652988

Preen, Miss Catherine LLB(Lond) M *Nov 1988*
10, 20
St Ives Chambers, Birmingham
p969 . . . . 0121 236 0863

PRENTICE, Prof Dan L *Nov 1982*
11, 38, 97
Erskine Chambers, London WC2
p931 . . . . 020 7242 5532

PRENTIS, Mr Sebastian MA M *Oct 1996*
8, 11, 6, 29
New Square Chambers, London WC2
p943 . . . . 020 7419 8000

Prescott, Mr Peter R K BSc(Lond) L *Nov 1970*
(Q.C.) *13, 45, 50, 56*
8 New Square, London WC2
p943 . . . . 020 7405 4321

Presland, Mr Frederick James Adrian BA(Hons)(East Anglia) G *Jul 1985*
10, 20, 22
1 Pump Court, London EC4
p947 . . . . 020 7842 7070

Presland, Ms Samantha BA(Oxon) M *Jan 2000*
53, 30
Outer Temple Chambers, London WC2
p945 . . . . 020 7353 6381

Pressdee, Mr Piers MA(Cantab) M *Oct 1991*
(Q.C.) *10*
Harcourt Chambers, London EC4
p936 . . . . 0844 561 7135
Harcourt Chambers, Oxford
p989 . . . . 0844 561 7135

Pressman, Mr Bernard LLM M *Nov 2004*
11, 12, 18, 30, 93
Lamb Chambers, London EC4
p941 . . . . 020 7797 8300

Prest, Mr Charles I *Nov 2005*
20, 10
No 6 Barristers Chambers, Leeds
p978 . . . . 0113 245 9763

PRESTON, Mr Darren LLB G *Oct 1991*
12, 15, 20
9 St John Street Chambers, Manchester
p984 . . . . 0161 955 9000

Preston, Mr David L *Jan 1992*
18, 11
Ely Place Chambers, London EC1
p931 . . . . 020 7400 9600

Preston, Mr Dominic BA(Lond); DipLaw(City) I *Feb 1995*
1, 22, 51
Doughty Street Chambers, London WC1
p930 . . . . 020 7404 1313

Preston, Mr Hugh BA(Hons); DipLaw M *Oct 1994*
12, 30, 40, 11, 18, 42, 53
7 Bedford Row, London WC1
p924 . . . . 020 7242 3555

PRESTON, Miss Kim BSc(Hons); DipLaw I *Nov 1991*
15, 20, 10
4 King's Bench Walk, London EC4
p939 . . . . 020 7822 7000

PRESTON, Lewis BA(Cantab) M *Jul 2007*
11, 97, 6, 38, 24
Five Paper, London EC4
p946 . . . . 020 7815 3200

Preston, Nicholas MA G *Jul 1986*
6
Clerksroom - Administration Centre, Taunton
p993 . . . . 0845 083 3000

Preston, Ms Nicola L *Jul 1992*
8, 9, 14, 32, 34, 37, 40, 57, 56, 93, 89
No5 Chambers, Bristol
p971 . . . . 0845 210 5555
No5 Chambers, London EC4
p944 . . . . 0845 210 5555
No5 Chambers, Birmingham
p968 . . . . 0845 210 5555

PRESTWICH, Mr Andrew G *Nov 1986*
30, 40, 53
Ropewalk Chambers, Nottingham
p989 . . . . 0115 947 2581

PRETSELL, Mr James BA(Bris) G *Nov 1998*
30, 18, 12
Farrar's Building, London EC4
p933 . . . . 020 7583 9241

Pretzell, Mr Andreas LLM M *Oct 1997*
15, 23, 18, 49, 55, 96
Lamb Building, Brighton
p970 . . . . 01273 820490
Lamb Building, London EC4
p940 . . . . 020 7797 7788

Price, Mr Charles LLB(Hons); LLM M *Nov 1999*
18, 55, 23
No5 Chambers, Bristol
p971 . . . . 0845 210 5555
No5 Chambers, London EC4
p944 . . . . 0845 210 5555
No5 Chambers, Birmingham
p968 . . . . 0845 210 5555

Price, Ms Clare LLB; LLM M *Jul 1988*
53, 40, 30, 27
Hailsham Chambers, London EC4
p936 . . . . 020 7643 5000

PRICE, Miss Collette BA(Hons)(Cantab) G *Nov 1997*
12, 15
Fountain Chambers, Middlesbrough
p986 . . . . 01642 804040

PRICE, Miss Emma Charlotte Louisa BA(Exeter) G *Oct 2007*
Temple Garden Chambers, London EC4
p952 . . . . 020 7583 1315

PRICE, Mr Evan LLB(Hons) M *Oct 1997*
8
Ten Old Square, London WC2
p945 . . . . 020 7405 0758

Price, Mr James BA(Oxon) I *Jul 1974*
(Q.C.) *13, 16, 50, 51*
5RB, London WC1
p948 . . . . 020 7242 2902

PRICE, Mr John BA(Oxon); Recorder I *Jul 1982*
(Q.C.) *15, 36, 11, 12, 4, 91*
23 Essex Street, London WC2
p932 . . . . 020 7413 0353

Price, Mr Jonathan M *Oct 2004*
6, 8, 11, 12, 16, 18, 22, 25, 30
Ely Place Chambers, London EC1
p931 . . . . 020 7400 9600

PRICE, Mr Leolin MA(Oxon) M *Nov 1949*
(Q.C.) CBE*1, 3, 5, 6, 8, 9, 11, 19, 22, 24, 29, 32, 34, 37*
Ten Old Square, London WC2
p945 . . . . 020 7405 0758

Price, Mrs Louise M *Nov 1972*
20
Albion Chambers, Bristol
p970 . . . . 0117 927 2144

Price, Mr Nicholas G *Nov 1987*
York Chambers, York
p995 . . . . 01904 620048
York Chambers, Newcastle upon Tyne
p987 . . . . 0191 206 4677

Price, Miss Rachael I *Nov 1994*
10, 20
No5 Chambers, Bristol
p971 . . . . 0845 210 5555
No5 Chambers, London EC4
p944 . . . . 0845 210 5555
No5 Chambers, Birmingham
p968 . . . . 0845 210 5555

See p1010 for the Key to Work Categories

PRICE, Mr Richard L *Mar 2011*
9 St John Street Chambers, Manchester
p984 . . . . . 0161 955 9000

PRICE, Mr Richard M LLB(Lond); Accredited Mediator G *Nov 1969*
(Q.C.) OBE*1, 11, 12, 13, 26, 27, 28, 29, 16, 49*
Littleton Chambers, London EC4
p941 . . . . . 020 7797 8600
Park Court Chambers, Leeds
p978 . . . . . 0113 243 3277

PRICE, Mr Roderick I *Jan 1971*
15, 62, 95
187 Fleet Street, London EC4
p933 . . . . . 020 7430 7430

PRICE, Mr Thomas LLB(Hons)(Soton) I *Nov 1985*
(Q.C.) *15, 36*
25 Bedford Row, London WC1
p925 . . . . . 020 7067 1500

PRICE LEWIS, Mr Rhodri MA(Oxon); Dip Crim(Cantab) M *Jul 1975*
(Q.C.) *31, 36, 46*
Landmark Chambers, London EC4
p941 . . . . . 020 7430 1221

Price-Marmion, Miss Alexandra M *Oct 2002*
2 Pump Court, London EC4
p947 . . . . . 020 7353 5597

PRICE ROWLANDS, Mr Gwynn I *May 1985*
4 King's Bench Walk, London EC4
p939 . . . . . 020 7822 7000
St Ives Chambers, Birmingham
p969 . . . . . 0121 236 0863
Foregate Chambers, Kidderminster
p976 . . . . . 07760 766152

Priday, Mr Charles N B BA(Oxon) M *Nov 1982*
3, 35, 19, 33, 24, 11, 5, 40
7 King's Bench Walk, London EC4
p940 . . . . . 020 7910 8300

Priestley, Mr Roderick BSc(Hons) G *Nov 1996*
Lincoln House Chambers, Manchester
p984 . . . . . 0161 832 5701

Primost, Mr Norman LLB(Lond) M *Jul 1954*
5 Pump Court, London EC4
p947 . . . . . 020 7353 2532 / 7583 7133

PRINCE, Miss Laura LLB(Hons) L *Jun 2003*
18, 67, 51, 55
Matrix Chambers, London WC1
p942 . . . . . 020 7404 3447

PRINGLE, Mr Ian MA(Cantab) G *Jul 1979*
(Q.C.) *15, 62*
Guildhall Chambers, Bristol
p970 . . . . . 0117 930 9000

PRINGLE, Mr Watson BA(Oxon) I *Jul 2005*
8, 11
New Square Chambers, London WC2
p943 . . . . . 020 7419 8000

PRINN, Miss Helen M *Oct 1993*
3, 10, 12, 15, 20, 22, 30
Octagon House, Norwich
p988 . . . . . 01603 623186

PRIOR, Charles BA(Hons)(Oxon) L *Oct 1995*
30, 1, 7, 11, 40, 63, 67, 76, 84, 94
Atlantic Chambers, Liverpool
p980 . . . . . 0151 236 4421

Pritchard, Miss Cecilia M *Jan 1998*
15, 67, 6
New Bailey Chambers, Preston
p990 . . . . . 01772 258087

PRITCHARD, Mr Geoffrey PhD M *Nov 1998*
13, 50, 45, 41
3 New Square, London WC2
p943 . . . . . 020 7405 1111

Pritchard, Miss Sarah LLB G *Oct 1993*
12, 30, 53
Kings Chambers, Leeds
p978 . . . . . 0113 242 1123
Kings Chambers, Manchester
p984 . . . . . 0161 832 9082
St Ives Chambers, Birmingham
p969 . . . . . 0121 236 0863

Pritchard, Mr Simon MA(Oxon) L *Jul 2007*
1, 11, 18, 51, 50, 52, 56, 89
Blackstone Chambers, London EC4
p926 . . . . . 020 7583 1770

Pritchett, Mr Stephen LLB L *Jun 1989*
6, 8, 22, 32, 37, 40
Kings Chambers, Leeds
p978 . . . . . 0113 242 1123
Kings Chambers, Manchester
p984 . . . . . 0161 832 9082

Privett, Mr Simon Recorder M *Jul 1976*
15
1 Paper Buildings, London EC4
p946 . . . . . 020 7353 3728

Probert, Miss Sarah LLB(Hons) M *Nov 2000*
15, 12, 20
15 Winckley Square, Preston
p991 . . . . . 01772 252828

Probyn, Miss Jane LLB(Hons); Recorder (SE) 2003 M *Feb 1988*
20, 10
4 Paper Buildings, London EC4
p946 . . . . . 020 7583 0816

PROCHASKA, Miss Elizabeth BA; LLB; BCL I *Jan 2007*
1, 18, 22, 23, 51, 63, 70, 76
Matrix Chambers, London WC1
p942 . . . . . 020 7404 3447

PROCTER, Mr Alfred George Haydn LLB M *Jul 2005*
20, 10
1 Garden Court, London EC4
p934 . . . . . 020 7797 7900

Procter, Mr Michael BA(Hons) G *Nov 1993*
15
Fenners Chambers, Cambridge
p972 . . . . . 01223 368761

Proghoulis, Mr Phillip I *Nov 1963*
Roehampton Chambers, London SW15
p949 . . . . . 020 8788 1238

Prokofiev, Mr Sergey L *Jul 2004*
Lincoln House Chambers, Manchester
p984 . . . . . 0161 832 5701

PROOPS, Miss Anya BA(Cantab); PhD(Lond) I *Oct 1998*
1, 18, 19, 26, 55, 73
11KBW, London EC4
p938 . . . . . 020 7632 8500

Proops, Miss Helen M *Jul 1986*
York Chambers, York
p995 . . . . . 01904 620048
York Chambers, Newcastle upon Tyne
p987 . . . . . 0191 206 4677

Prosser, Mr Anthony LLB I *Jul 1985*
12, 15, 30, 36
5 St Andrew's Hill, London EC4
p950 . . . . . 020 7332 5400

PROSSER, Mr Kevin LLB; BCL(Oxon) L *Jul 1982*
(Q.C.) *34, 57, 58*
Pump Court Tax Chambers, London WC1
p948 . . . . . 020 7414 8080

PRYCE, Mr Gary D BA(Cantab); LLM(Virginia) L *Oct 1997*
8, 22, 18
New Square Chambers, London WC2
p943 . . . . . 020 7419 8000

Pryce, Mr Gregory H BA(Wolv) G *Jul 1988*
10, 20
36 Bedford Row, London WC1
p925 . . . . . 020 7421 8000

PRYNNE, Mr Andrew LLB(Soton) M *Jul 1975*
(Q.C.)
Temple Garden Chambers, London EC4
p952 . . . . . 020 7583 1315

Pryor, Mr Michael LLB I *Oct 1992*
1, 3, 5, 6, 7, 8, 9, 11, 12, 13, 14, 22, 24, 26, 28, 29, 31, 32, 37
Maitland Chambers, London WC2
p941 . . . . . 020 7406 1200

Przybylska, Miss Sarah BA(Hons) M *Oct 2006*
15
2 Hare Court, London EC4
p937 . . . . . 020 7353 5324

Puar, Mr Mikhael LLB(Hons) G *Jan 2006*
15, 30, 18, 22
Thirty Park Place, Cardiff
p973 . . . . . 029 2039 8421

Pugh, Mr Charles G *Jan 1975*
Old Square Chambers, Bristol
p971 . . . . . 0117 930 5100
Old Square Chambers, London WC1
p945 . . . . . 020 7269 0300

Pugh, Mr David LLB(Hons)(Shef) M *Oct 2008*
8, 10, 12, 15, 20, 38, 88, 89, 30
College Chambers, Southampton
p992 . . . . . 023 8023 0338

PUGH, Miss Helen Elizabeth I *Oct 2008*
10, 11, 30, 88, 93, 38, 59
3 Hare Court, London EC4
p937 . . . . . 020 7415 7800

Pugh, Mr John LLB(Hons) L *Jul 1972*
5, 11, 47, 7, 89, 48
John Pugh's Chambers, Liverpool
p981 . . . . . 0151 236 5415

PUGH-SMITH, Mr John MA(Oxon) G *Jul 1977*
26, 31, 46, 1, 96
Thirty Nine Essex Street, London WC2
p932 . . . . . 020 7832 1111

PULLE, Miss Roshani BSc(LSE) M *Jan 2007*
15, 62, 27
23 Essex Street, London WC2
p932 . . . . . 020 7413 0353

Pullen, Mr Timothy BSc; CPE M *Nov 1993*
1, 55, 18, 51, 89, 26
Doughty Street Chambers, London WC1
p930 . . . . . 020 7404 1313
King's Bench Godolphin Chambers, Truro
p994 . . . . . 0845 308 1551
King's Bench Godolphin Chambers, Plymouth
p990 . . . . . 0845 308 1551

Pulling, Mr Dean LLB(Hons)(Wales) M *Nov 1993*
15
Angel Chambers, Swansea
p992 . . . . . 01792 464623
Iscoed Chambers, Swansea
p993 . . . . . 01792 652988

Pulman, Mr George F MA(Cantab) M *Jul 1972*
(Q.C.) *27, 30, 20, 53*
Hardwicke, London WC2
p936 . . . . . 020 7242 2523
Stour Chambers, Canterbury
p972 . . . . . 01227 764899

PUNIA, Raj L *Jan 1999*
15
St Philips Chambers, Birmingham
p969 . . . . . 0121 246 7000

PUNJANI, Miss Yasmin L *Jan 2000*
15, 62, 95
187 Fleet Street, London EC4
p933 . . . . . 020 7430 7430

Punt, Dr Jonathan MBBS I *Jul 2005*
53, 20, 30, 68, 94, 40
No5 Chambers, Bristol
p971 . . . . . 0845 210 5555
No5 Chambers, London EC4
p944 . . . . . 0845 210 5555
No5 Chambers, Birmingham
p968 . . . . . 0845 210 5555

PURCELL, Miss Deirdre Marie LLB(Hons) L *Nov 2000*
30, 12, 62, 47, 67, 88
Oriel Chambers, Liverpool
p981 . . . . . 0151 236 7191 / 236 4321
Oriel Chambers, Preston
p990 . . . . . 01772 254764

PURCELL, Mr Gregor L *Oct 1997*
15
1 High Pavement, Nottingham
p988 . . . . . 0115 941 8218

PURCHAS, Mr Christopher Patrick Brooks MA(Cantab); Recorder I *Jul 1966*
(Q.C.) *12, 24, 30, 40, 53, 84*
Crown Office Chambers, London EC4
p929 . . . . . 020 7797 8100

Purchas, Mr James MA(Cantab) I *Oct 1997*
7, 12, 40, 81
4 Pump Court, London EC4
p947 . . . . . 020 7842 5555

Purchas, Mr Robin MA(Cantab) I *Nov 1968*
(Q.C.) *1, 26, 28, 31, 36, 54, 60*
Francis Taylor Building, London EC4
p934 . . . . . 020 7353 8415

PURCHASE, Mr Mathew BA(Hons)(Oxon); CPE; BVC L *Jan 2002*
1, 18, 51, 26, 55, 76
Matrix Chambers, London WC1
p942 . . . . . 020 7404 3447

PURDIE, Mr Robert LLB(Hons) M *Jul 1979*
37, 17, 20
4 King's Bench Walk, London EC4
p939 . . . . . 020 7822 7000

Purdy, Miss Catherine I *Jan 1997*
12, 15
3PB, Winchester
p994 . . . . . 01962 868884

PURKIS, Mr Simon I *Oct 2008*
10, 12, 72, 18, 20, 91, 42, 30, 32, 36
Pump Court Chambers, Swindon
p993 . . . . . 01793 539899
Pump Court Chambers, Winchester
p994 . . . . . 01962 868161
Pump Court Chambers, London EC4
p947 . . . . . 020 7353 0711

PURKISS, Miss Kate BA(Lond); DipLaw L *Jul 1988*
10, 20
Coram Chambers, London EC1
p929 . . . . . 020 7092 3700

Purnell, Ms Catherine I *Oct 1999*
15, 48, 13
5 Paper Buildings, London EC4
p946 . . . . . 020 7583 6117

Purnell, Mr James MA(Hons); PGDL M *Oct 2002*
5, 6, 8, 11, 12, 47, 18, 22, 30, 40, 59, 26
Henderson Chambers, London EC4
p937 . . . . . 020 7583 9020

Purnell, Mr Nicholas MA(Cantab) M *Jul 1968*
(Q.C.) *15, 36, 11, 25, 62*
Cloth Fair Chambers, London EC1
p928 . . . . . 020 7710 6444

Purnell, Mr Paul Oliver I *Nov 1962*
(Q.C.) *15, 62*
Farringdon Chambers, London SE1
p933 . . . . . 020 7089 5700

Purss, Mr C Nairn I *Oct 1999*
10, 20
4 Brick Court Chambers, London EC4
p927 . . . . . 020 7832 3200

Purves, Mr Gavin B LLB(Brunel); DEI(Amsterdam); Accredited mediator G *Jul 1979*
5, 6, 8, 12, 13, 15, 19, 32, 37, 49, 31, 50, 45, 75, 96, 29, 93
Swan House, London W13
p951 . . . . . 020 8998 3035

PURVES, Mr Robert M *Jan 2007*
81
3 Verulam Buildings, London WC1
p953 . . . . . 020 7831 8441

Purvis, Mr Iain MA; BCL G *Jul 1986*
(Q.C.) *41, 73, 50, 19, 45, 13, 52, 96*
11 South Square, London WC1
p950 . . . . . 020 7405 1222

Pusey, Mr William James LLB(Leeds) I *Nov 1977*
30, 40, 68, 94
No5 Chambers, Bristol
p971 . . . . . 0845 210 5555
No5 Chambers, London EC4
p944 . . . . . 0845 210 5555
No5 Chambers, Birmingham
p968 . . . . . 0845 210 5555

PUZEY, Mr James LLB I *Jul 1990*
15, 34, 84
St Philips Chambers, Birmingham
p969 . . . . . 0121 246 7000

Pye, Mr Derek LLB(Hons); FRICS; FCIArb L *Jul 2008*
3, 7, 40, 41, 49, 96, 74
No5 Chambers, Bristol
p971 . . . . . 0845 210 5555
No5 Chambers, London EC4
p944 . . . . . 0845 210 5555
No5 Chambers, Birmingham
p968 . . . . . 0845 210 5555
Zenith Chambers, Leeds
p979 . . . . . 0113 245 5438

Pye, Miss Jayne M BA(Hons) M *May 1995*
10, 20
37 Park Square Chambers, Leeds
p978 . . . . . 0113 243 9422

PYLE, Miss Susan LLB(Newc) G *Nov 1985*
1 Garden Court, London EC4
p934 . . . . . 020 7797 7900

Pymont, Mr Christopher Howard MA(Oxon); Recorder; Deputy High Court Judge G *Jul 1979*
(Q.C.)
Maitland Chambers, London WC2
p941 . . . . . 020 7406 1200

Pyne, Mr Russell I *Nov 1991*
2 King's Bench Walk, London EC4
p939 . . . . . 020 7353 1746

Qadri, Khalid M *Nov 1993*
Holborn Chambers, London WC2
p937 . . . . . 020 7242 6060

13

QAZI, Mr Ayaz G *Jan 1993*
Carmelite Chambers, London EC4
p927 . . . 020 7936 6300

Quddus, Khandakar Abdul MA I *Jul 1968*
15, 12, 20, 23
19 Chestnut Drive, Pinner
p990 . . . 020 8866 7603

QUEGAN, Mr Peter QVRM; TD I *Jul 2010*
30, 89, 12, 67, 42, 91, 40
Kenworthy's Chambers, Manchester
p984 . . . 0161 832 4036

QUEST, Mr David MA(Cantab) G *Oct 1993*
3, 5, 6, 11, 40
3 Verulam Buildings, London WC1
p953 . . . 020 7831 8441

Quigley, Mr Conor LLB; Dip EurINT; MA(Lond) G *Nov 1985*
(Q.C.) *19, 1, 44*
Brick Court Chambers, London WC2
p927 . . . 020 7379 3550

Quigley, Ms Louise I *Jan 2003*
St Johns Buildings, Preston
p990 . . . 01772 256100
St Johns Buildings, Chester
p974 . . . 01244 323070
St Johns Buildings, Manchester
p985 . . . 0161 214 1500
St Johns Buildings, Liverpool
p982 . . . 0151 243 6000

QUINEY, Mr Ben BA; BCL(Oxon) G *Mar 1998*
24, 74, 7, 40, 41, 12, 97
Crown Office Chambers, London EC4
p929 . . . 020 7797 8100

QUINLAN, Mr Christopher John LLB I *Nov 1992*
(Q.C.) *15, 12, 56, 46, 84*
Guildhall Chambers, Bristol
p970 . . . 0117 930 9000

Quinn, Mr Chris M *Oct 1992*
11, 43, 50, 56, 55, 18, 1, 26, 40, 51, 13, 16
Cloisters, London EC4
p928 . . . 020 7827 4000
Littleton Chambers, London EC4
p941 . . . 020 7797 8600

QUINN, Michelle I *Jan 2005*
Clerksroom - Administration Centre, Taunton
p993 . . . 0845 083 3000

Quinn, Miss Susan G *Jun 1983*
10, 20
4 Brick Court Chambers, London EC4
p927 . . . 020 7832 3200

Quinn, Miss Victoria K BA(Hons); CPE L *Oct 1995*
Thomas More Chambers, London WC2
p952 . . . 020 7404 7000

Quinney, Miss Nicola T BA G *Jan 2001*
15, 12, 30
Paradise Chambers, Sheffield
p992 . . . 0114 273 8951

Quint, Mrs Francesca LLB; AKC; TEP; Qual Mediator G *Jul 1970*
8, 9, 22, 32, 37, 40, 49, 58
Radcliffe Chambers, London WC2
p949 . . . 020 7831 0081

Quinton, Mr Thomas I *Oct 1997*
15, 62, 28, 25
5 Paper Buildings, London EC4
p946 . . . 020 7583 6117

Quirk, Mr Iain LLB(Nott'm) L *Oct 2002*
Essex Court Chambers, London WC2
p931 . . . 020 7813 8000

QUIRKE, Mr Gerard M *Nov 1988*
Citadel Chambers, Birmingham
p967 . . . 0121 233 8500

QUIRKE, Mr James K BA(Oxon) G *Nov 1974*
6, 25, 32, 37, 40
St Philips Chambers, Birmingham
p969 . . . 0121 246 7000

Qureshi, Mr Abdul-Saleem BA; LLB M *Jul 1972*
1, 3, 12, 15, 20, 21, 23, 22, 18, 55
Barclay Chambers, London E11
p924 . . . 020 8558 2289 / 8558 3849

Qureshi, Mr Khawar LLB; LLM(Cantab) M *Jul 1990*
(Q.C.) *1, 3, 5, 7, 8, 11, 12, 24, 26, 28, 29, 33*
Serle Court, London WC2
p950 . . . 020 7242 6105

QURESHI, Mr Tanveer L *Jan 2000*
15, 18
25 Bedford Row, London WC1
p925 . . . 020 7067 1500

Rabaiotti, Miss Catherine I *Mar 2002*
15
5 Paper Buildings, London EC4
p946 . . . 020 7583 6117

Rabinowitz, Mr Laurence M *Nov 1987*
(Q.C.)
One Essex Court, London EC4
p931 . . . 020 7583 2000

Radburn, Mr Mark Charles Crispin L *Oct 1991*
30, 53, 40, 94, 68
No5 Chambers, Bristol
p971 . . . 0845 210 5555
No5 Chambers, London EC4
p944 . . . 0845 210 5555
No5 Chambers, Birmingham
p968 . . . 0845 210 5555

RADCLIFFE, Mr Andrew Allen BA(Oxon); Recorder M *Nov 1975*
(Q.C.) *15, 62*
2 Hare Court, London EC4
p937 . . . 020 7353 5324

Radcliffe, Ms Emily G *Oct 2003*
62, 65, 81, 39, 38, 84, 30, 70, 20, 18, 53
9 Gough Square, London EC4
p935 . . . 020 7832 0500

Radcliffe, Mr Francis Charles Joseph MA(Cantab) G *Nov 1962*
15
11 King's Bench Walk, Leeds
p978 . . . 0113 297 1200

Radcliffe, Miss Pamela Joan C LLB(Hons) G *Jul 1979*
Holborn Chambers, London WC2
p937 . . . 020 7242 6060

Radcliffe, Ms Sheila Mary M *Jul 2003*
10, 20
Temple Chambers, Newport
p988 . . . 01633 267403 / 255855
Temple Chambers, Cardiff
p973 . . . 029 2039 7364

RADEVSKY, Mr Anthony LLB(Soton) I *Jul 1978*
12, 22
Falcon Chambers, London EC4
p933 . . . 020 7353 2484

RADFORD, Ms Althea Jane L *Jan 2009*
23, 15
Mitre House Chambers, London WC1
p942 . . . 020 7307 7100

RADFORD, Mrs Nadine L *Jan 1974*
(Q.C.)
187 Fleet Street, London EC4
p933 . . . 020 7430 7430

RADLEY-GARDNER, Mr Oliver BA G *Jan 2003*
Falcon Chambers, London EC4
p933 . . . 020 7353 2484

RADSTONE, Mr Matthew M *Jan 2005*
25 Bedford Row, London WC1
p925 . . . 020 7067 1500

RAE, Mr James I *Jul 1976*
15
7 Harrington Street Chambers, Liverpool
p981 . . . 0151 242 0707

Raeside, Mr Mark BA; MPhil(Cantab) M *Nov 1982*
(Q.C.) *3, 7, 11, 31, 40, 41, 43, 45, 49, 54, 61, 78, 74*
Atkin Chambers, London WC1
p923 . . . 020 7404 0102

Rafati, Mr Ali LLB G *Nov 1993*
King's Bench Godolphin Chambers, Truro
p994 . . . 0845 308 1551
King's Bench Godolphin Chambers, Plymouth
p990 . . . 0845 308 1551

Rafferty, Miss Angela L *Feb 1995*
15, 84
1 Paper Buildings, London EC4
p946 . . . 020 7353 3728

RAFFERTY, Mr Stuart G *Jul 1975*
(Q.C.) *15*
Furnival Chambers, London EC4
p934 . . . 020 7405 3232
1 High Pavement, Nottingham
p988 . . . 0115 941 8218

RAFFIN, Mr Charles BA(Hons)(Oxon) M *Jan 2005*
Hardwicke, London WC2
p936 . . . 020 7242 2523

Rafter, Miss Lauren BA(Hons); LLB; BVC I *Oct 2007*
12, 15, 71, 18, 33, 30, 20
7 Bedford Row, London WC1
p924 . . . 020 7242 3555

RAGGATT, Mr Timothy LLB(Lond); Recorder I *Jan 1972*
(Q.C.) *15, 62*
4 King's Bench Walk, London EC4
p939 . . . 020 7822 7000
St Philips Chambers, Birmingham
p969 . . . 0121 246 7000

Rahman, Mr Anis MA; DipLaw; Dip Shipping I *Nov 1990*
18, 20, 23
12 Old Square, London WC2
p945 . . . 020 7404 0875

Rahman, Miss Khadiua I *Jan 2000*
No 3 Fleet Street Chambers, London EC4
p944 . . . 020 7936 4474

Rahman, Mr Sami LLB(Hons) L *Oct 1996*
18, 12, 29
Field Court Chambers, London WC1
p933 . . . 020 7405 6114

RAHMAN, Ms Shaheen BA G *Nov 1996*
12, 18, 20, 23, 27, 30, 40
1 Crown Office Row, London EC4
p929 . . . 020 7797 7500

Rahman, Miss Tahmina LLB(Lond) L *Jan 2001*
15, 20, 30
4 Brick Court Chambers, London EC4
p927 . . . 020 7832 3200

RAHMAN, Yaqub BA(Oxon); Recorder G *Oct 1991*
12, 18, 30, 40, 46, 47, 11, 7, 57, 67, 84
Oriel Chambers, Liverpool
p981 . . . 0151 236 7191 / 236 4321
Oriel Chambers, Preston
p990 . . . 01772 254764

Rahman, Zia L *Jan 2006*
Clerksroom - Administration Centre, Taunton
p993 . . . 0845 083 3000

RAI, Amarjit Singh LLB M *Jul 1989*
11, 30, 93, 88, 12
St Philips Chambers, Birmingham
p969 . . . 0121 246 7000

Rai, Miss Puneet BA L *Jan 2004*
Thomas More Chambers, London WC2
p952 . . . 020 7404 7000

RAI, Miss Sonia BPharm(Hons) G *Oct 1998*
8, 22, 26, 93
Five Paper, London EC4
p946 . . . 020 7815 3200

Railton, Mr David BA(Oxon) G *Jul 1979*
(Q.C.)
Fountain Court Chambers, London EC4
p934 . . . 020 7583 3335

RAINEY, Miss Angela I *Nov 2009*
94, 85, 84, 56, 53, 51, 40, 30, 23, 1
Thirty Nine Essex Street, London WC2
p932 . . . 020 7832 1111

RAINEY, Mr Kieran G *Jan 2004*
Fountain Chambers, Middlesbrough
p986 . . . 01642 804040

RAINEY, Mr Philip LLB; MCIArb M *Oct 1990*
(Q.C.) *8, 41, 88, 93*
Tanfield Chambers, London WC1
p951 . . . 020 7421 5300

Rainey, Mr Simon MA(Cantab); Licence Specialise en Droit European(Brussels) L *Jul 1982*
(Q.C.) *11, 35, 24, 3, 5, 19*
Quadrant Chambers, London EC4
p948 . . . 020 7583 4444

Rainsford, Mr Mark David LLB; LSE L *Nov 1985*
(Q.C.)
33 Chancery Lane, London WC2
p928 . . . 020 7440 9950

Raitt, Miss Kate L *Jul 2009*
York Chambers, York
p995 . . . 01904 620048
York Chambers, Newcastle upon Tyne
p987 . . . 0191 206 4677

RAJAH, Mr Eason LLB(Nott'm) G *Jul 1989*
(Q.C.) *5, 6, 7, 8, 9, 11, 14, 21, 22, 29, 32, 34, 37*
Ten Old Square, London WC2
p945 . . . 020 7405 0758

RAJGOPAUL, Mr Craig MA I *Nov 2010*
18, 11, 12, 55, 6, 56
Littleton Chambers, London EC4
p941 . . . 020 7797 8600

Ralph, Mr Craig LLB(Hons) M *Jan 2002*
Kings Chambers, Leeds
p978 . . . 0113 242 1123
Kings Chambers, Manchester
p984 . . . 0161 832 9082

RALSTON, Mr William LLB(Hons) I *Oct 2000*
15, 12, 18, 10, 20, 30, 67, 88, 38, 40, 84, 11, 26, 51
7 Harrington Street Chambers, Liverpool
p981 . . . 0151 242 0707

RAMADHAN, Miss Lubeya LLB(Hons) M *Jul 2000*
15
Pump Court Chambers, Swindon
p993 . . . 01793 539899
Pump Court Chambers, Winchester
p994 . . . 01962 868161
Pump Court Chambers, London EC4
p947 . . . 020 7353 0711

Ramasamy, Selva I *Nov 1992*
15, 25, 36
QEB Hollis Whiteman, London EC4
p948 . . . 020 7933 8855

Ramble, Mr Don LLB M *Nov 1998*
15
5 St Andrew's Hill, London EC4
p950 . . . 020 7332 5400

Ramdas-Harsia, Mr Rohan M *Nov 1999*
15, 20, 23
1 Pump Court, London EC4
p947 . . . 020 7842 7070

RAMEL, Stefan LLB; LLM; BVC I *Oct 2002*
11, 6, 5, 38, 97
Guildhall Chambers, Bristol
p970 . . . 0117 930 9000

Ramlogan, Mr Oudit L *Jan 1960*
Chancery Chambers, London WC2
p928 . . . 020 7405 6879

RAMPTON, Mr Richard BA(Oxon) I *Nov 1965*
(Q.C.) *16, 52, 73*
One Brick Court, London EC4
p927 . . . 020 7353 8845

RAMSAHOYE, Miss Indira L *Nov 1980*
10, 20
29 Bedford Row, London WC1
p925 . . . 020 7404 1044

RAMSDEN, Mr James LLB(Hons) M *Nov 1987*
11, 24, 29, 1, 5, 26, 8, 18, 3, 40
4-5 Gray's Inn Square, London WC1
p935 . . . 020 7404 5252

Ramsden, Miss Veronica Mary LLB(Wales) G *Jul 1979*
15, 25
Staple Inn Chambers, London WC1
p951 . . . 020 7242 5240

Rana, Mr M Akram L *Jan 1995*
Clapham Law Chambers, London SW1
p928 . . . 020 7978 8482 / 7642 5777

Ranales-Cotos, Ms Tina LLB; BCL(Oxon) L *Oct 1999*
5, 6, 8, 11, 13, 18, 19, 55
Kings Chambers, Leeds
p978 . . . 0113 242 1123
Kings Chambers, Manchester
p984 . . . 0161 832 9082

Ranatunga, Mr Asitha Nandika MA I *Oct 2001*
1, 12, 18, 22, 26, 31, 51
Cornerstone Barristers, London WC1
p929 . . . 020 7242 4986

Randall, Mr John MA(Cantab); Recorder; Deputy HC Judge L *Jul 1978*
(Q.C.) *1, 6, 8, 11, 31*
Maitland Chambers, London WC2
p941 . . . 020 7406 1200
St Philips Chambers, Birmingham
p969 . . . 0121 246 7000

Randall, Mr Louise E BA(Keele) M *Jul 1988*
3, 7, 11, 24, 40
Keating Chambers, London WC2
p938 . . . 020 7544 2600

Randall, Mr Nicholas LLB M *Oct 1990*
11, 12, 18, 36, 1, 26, 55
Devereux Chambers, London WC2
p930 . . . 020 7353 7534

RANDALL, Ms Rebecca G *Jul 2005*
15
25 Bedford Row, London WC1
p925 . . . 020 7067 1500

See p1010 for the Key to Work Categories

Randhawa, Miss Ravinder L *Nov 1995*
York Chambers, York
p995 . . . . 01904 620048
York Chambers, Newcastle upon Tyne
p987 . . . . 0191 206 4677

Randolph, Mr Fergus LLB(Bucks) M *Jul 1985*
19, 1, 11, 44
Brick Court Chambers, London WC2
p927 . . . . 020 7379 3550

Rankin, Mr James I *Jul 1983*
25
Francis Taylor Building, London EC4
p934 . . . . 020 7353 8415

RANKIN, Ms Jane L *Jan 2000*
12, 18, 24, 30
12 King's Bench Walk, London EC4
p940 . . . . 020 7583 0811

RANKIN, Mr William K LLB(Hons) G *Oct 1994*
12, 30, 40, 62, 84
Oriel Chambers, Liverpool
p981 . . . . 0151 236 7191 / 236 4321
Oriel Chambers, Preston
p990 . . . . 01772 254764

Raphael, Mr Thomas M *Nov 1999*
3, 11, 12, 24, 35, 41
20 Essex Street, London WC2
p932 . . . . 020 7842 1200

RAPP, Mr Michael BA(Bris) I *Jul 2002*
Temple Garden Chambers, London EC4
p952 . . . . 020 7583 1315

RASHID, Mr Haroon LLB; MA L *Mar 1999*
23, 30, 53, 12, 47
St James's Chambers, Manchester
p984 . . . . 0161 834 7000

Rashid, Mr Mirza Abdul BA; MA(Political Science); LLB(Hons) L *Nov 1981*
15, 23
Commonwealth Chambers, Birmingham
p967 . . . . 0121 446 5732

Rashid, Mr Waqas L *Jan 2006*
20, 12, 30, 10
Chartlands Chambers, Northampton
p988 . . . . 01604 603322

RASIAH, Mr Nathan I *Jan 2007*
15, 62
23 Essex Street, London WC2
p932 . . . . 020 7413 0353

RASOUL, Ms Miriam LLM(Dunelm) L *Jul 2001*
23, 1
Trinity (Newcastle) Chambers, Newcastle upon Tyne
p987 . . . . 0191 232 1927
Trinity (Teesside) Chambers, Middlesbrough
p986 . . . . 01642 247569

Rasul, Ms Lubna LLB(Hons) M *Jan 1997*
10, 20, 15
St Albans Chambers, St Albans
p992 . . . . 01727 843383

Ratcliffe, Miss Anne BSc; DipLaw I *Feb 1981*
5 Pump Court, London EC4
p947 . . . . 020 7353 2532 / 7583 7133

Ratcliffe, Ms Frances L *Jan 2002*
Radcliffe Chambers, London WC2
p949 . . . . 020 7831 0081

RATCLIFFE, Mr Peter BA(Hons); MA(Nott'm) M *Oct 1998*
3, 5, 11, 13, 35, 40, 50
3 Verulam Buildings, London WC1
p953 . . . . 020 7831 8441

Rathmell, Mr Robin BA I *Oct 2006*
8, 11, 97, 38, 93, 37, 67, 40
Serle Court, London WC2
p950 . . . . 020 7242 6105

RATHOD, Mr Pritesh LLB(Hons) M *Jan 2006*
1, 53, 67, 18, 46, 85, 51, 26, 30, 40, 57
1 Crown Office Row, London EC4
p929 . . . . 020 7797 7500

Rathour, Miss Delvinder Kaur PG DipLaw(UWE) G *Nov 2005*
12, 15, 18, 20, 88, 25, 52
Warwick House Chambers, London WC1
p953 . . . . 020 7430 2323

Ratledge, Mr John MPhil(Cantab) L *Jun 1999*
12
St Johns Buildings, Preston
p990 . . . . 01772 256100
St Johns Buildings, Chester
p974 . . . . 01244 323070
St Johns Buildings, Manchester
p985 . . . . 0161 214 1500
St Johns Buildings, Liverpool
p982 . . . . 0151 243 6000

Ratliff, Mr Peter L *Oct 2003*
15
6 King's Bench Walk, London EC4
p939 . . . . 020 7583 0410

Raudnitz, Mr Paul I *Nov 1994*
15, 25, 36
Charter Chambers, London WC1
p928 . . . . 020 7618 4400
QEB Hollis Whiteman, London EC4
p948 . . . . 020 7933 8855

RAW, Mr Edward MA(Oxon) I *Jul 1963*
23, 15, 51, 62, 96
Tanfield Chambers, London WC1
p951 . . . . 020 7421 5300

Rawal, Anita M *Jan 2004*
10, 20
Lamb Building, Brighton
p970 . . . . 01273 820490
Lamb Building, London EC4
p940 . . . . 020 7797 7788

Rawat, Mr Bilal BSc(Hons) M *Oct 1995*
12, 1, 36, 10, 20, 68
7 Bedford Row, London WC1
p924 . . . . 020 7242 3555

RAWAT, Miss Houzla M *Oct 2001*
Carmelite Chambers, London EC4
p927 . . . . 020 7936 6300

Rawcliffe, Mr Mark BA(Hons)(Oxon); DipLaw; LLM M *Jan 1996*
20, 10
4 Brick Court Chambers, London EC4
p927 . . . . 020 7832 3200

Rawley, Mr Alan David MA(Oxon) M *Jun 1958*
(Q.C.) *30, 84, 27, 1, 53, 15, 71, 62*
Outer Temple Chambers, London WC2
p945 . . . . 020 7353 6381

Rawley, Miss Dominique BA(Cantab) M *Oct 1991*
3, 7, 11, 31, 40, 41, 43, 45, 49, 54, 61, 78, 74
Atkin Chambers, London WC1
p923 . . . . 020 7404 0102

Rawlings, Carrie-Ann I *Oct 2005*
King's Bench Godolphin Chambers, Truro
p994 . . . . 0845 308 1551
King's Bench Godolphin Chambers, Plymouth
p990 . . . . 0845 308 1551

Rawlings, Mr Clive I *Oct 1994*
1, 12, 22, 33, 40
Hardwicke, London WC2
p936 . . . . 020 7242 2523

RAWLINSON, Mr Michael LLB(Manc) I *Dec 1991*
(Q.C.) *30, 53*
12 King's Bench Walk, London EC4
p940 . . . . 020 7583 0811
Kings Chambers, Leeds
p978 . . . . 0113 242 1123
Kings Chambers, Manchester
p984 . . . . 0161 832 9082

Rawlinson, Mr Michael John LLB(Hons) L *Jan 2002*
15, 12
Paradise Chambers, Sheffield
p992 . . . . 0114 273 8951

Ray, Mr Jonathan Richard BA G *Jul 1980*
12, 15
Thomas More Chambers, London WC2
p952 . . . . 020 7404 7000

Ray, Mr Simon BA(Dunelm) G *Nov 2001*
15
6 King's Bench Walk, London EC4
p939 . . . . 020 7583 0410

Ray-Crosby, Miss Irena BA(Oxon) M *Nov 1990*
15, 63
6 King's Bench Walk, London EC4
p939 . . . . 020 7583 0410
Westgate Chambers, Lewes
p980 . . . . 01273 480510

RAYMENT, Mr Benedick M MA(Hons); BCL(Oxon) I *Jun 1996*
1, 43, 44, 19, 51, 36, 61, 38, 56
Monckton Chambers, London WC1
p942 . . . . 020 7405 7211

Rayner, Ms Catherine G *Oct 1989*
18
Tooks Chambers, London EC4
p953 . . . . 020 7842 7575

Rayner, Miss Emily M *Jul 2009*
20, 10, 67
Harcourt Chambers, London EC4
p936 . . . . 0844 561 7135
Harcourt Chambers, Oxford
p989 . . . . 0844 561 7135

Rayner James, Mr Jonathan E MA; LLM(Cantab); Lic Spec en Droit European; Recorder L *Nov 1971*
(Q.C.) *3, 5, 6, 8, 11, 13, 19, 22, 29, 32, 36, 37*
Hogarth Chambers, London WC2
p937 . . . . 020 7404 0404

RAYNOR, Mr Keith LLB(Hons); Recorder L *Oct 1995*
62, 15
23 Essex Street, London WC2
p932 . . . . 020 7413 0353

Rayson, Miss Jane G *Jul 1982*
20, 10
4 Paper Buildings, London EC4
p946 . . . . 020 7583 0816

Rea, Ms Karen BA(Law); RGN; MCIArb; Deputy District Judge; Legal Chairman FHSAA G *Jul 1980*
27, 30, 53, 40, 36
Queen Square Chambers, Bristol
p972 . . . . 0117 921 1966

READ, Mr Daniel BA(Hons)(EngLit); GDL; BVC G *Oct 2006*
12, 30
Farrar's Building, London EC4
p933 . . . . 020 7583 9241

READ, Miss Emily MA(Cantab) M *Jul 2007*
12 King's Bench Walk, London EC4
p940 . . . . 020 7583 0811

Read, Mr Graham Stephen MA(Cantab) G *Jul 1981*
(Q.C.) *11, 24, 40, 7, 1, 29, 26*
Devereux Chambers, London WC2
p930 . . . . 020 7353 7534

Read, Simon LLB I *Nov 1989*
22, 1, 26, 88, 93
Zenith Chambers, Leeds
p979 . . . . 0113 245 5438

READE, Mr David J LLB; Accredited Mediator M *Jul 1983*
(Q.C.) *5, 6, 11, 12, 18, 22, 27, 30, 40, 55, 49*
Littleton Chambers, London EC4
p941 . . . . 020 7797 8600

READE, Mr Kevin LLB(Hons) G *Jul 1983*
20, 10
7 Harrington Street Chambers, Liverpool
p981 . . . . 0151 242 0707

Readhead, Mr Simon BCL; MA(Oxon) M *Jul 1979*
(Q.C.) *30, 40, 51, 53, 27, 85*
1 Chancery Lane, London WC2
p928 . . . . 0845 634 6666

READINGS, Mr Douglas George MA(Cantab); Recorder M *Jul 1972*
8, 11, 22, 31
St Philips Chambers, Birmingham
p969 . . . . 0121 246 7000

READY, Miss Hannah BA(Cantab) L *Oct 2010*
16, 52, 73
One Brick Court, London EC4
p927 . . . . 020 7353 8845

Real, Miss Kirsty LLB(Hons)(Nott'm) I *Oct 1996*
15, 18, 23, 63
Albion Chambers, Bristol
p970 . . . . 0117 927 2144

REANEY, Miss Janet E MA(Cantab) M *Jul 1987*
1, 10, 12, 15, 20, 30, 26, 48
7 Harrington Street Chambers, Liverpool
p981 . . . . 0151 242 0707

REARDON, Miss Madeleine BA(Oxon) M *Nov 2001*
10, 20, 12, 49, 14
1 King's Bench Walk, London EC4
p938 . . . . 020 7936 1500

Rebane, Ms Lena Marie MA; BVC L *Mar 2006*
12, 67, 97, 18, 22, 89
12 College Place, Southampton
p992 . . . . 023 8032 0320

Record, Miss Celia M *Mar 1998*
23, 20, 10, 15
Two King's Bench Walk, London EC4
p939 . . . . 020 7353 7202 / 7353 3909

Rector, Ms Penelope LLB(Hons) G *Nov 1980*
15, 62
5 Paper Buildings, London EC4
p946 . . . . 020 7583 6117

REDDIFORD, Mr Anthony LLB I *Nov 1991*
30, 53
Guildhall Chambers, Bristol
p970 . . . . 0117 930 9000

REDDISH, Mr John MA(Oxon) M *Jan 1973*
10, 12, 20, 30
1 King's Bench Walk, London EC4
p938 . . . . 020 7936 1500

Redfern, Mr Alan M *May 1995*
One Essex Court, London EC4
p931 . . . . 020 7583 2000

Redfern, Mr Michael Howard LLB I *Jul 1970*
(Q.C.) *30, 12*
St Johns Buildings, Preston
p990 . . . . 01772 256100
St Johns Buildings, Chester
p974 . . . . 01244 323070
St Johns Buildings, Manchester
p985 . . . . 0161 214 1500
St Johns Buildings, Liverpool
p982 . . . . 0151 243 6000

Redford, Miss Jessica K BA(Hons); DipLaw I *Nov 1994*
10, 20, 12, 30, 22
3 Dr Johnson's Buildings, London EC4
p930 . . . . 020 7353 4854

REDGRAVE, Mr Adrian LLB(Exon); Recorder I *Oct 1968*
(Q.C.)
Citadel Chambers, Birmingham
p967 . . . . 0121 233 8500

Redgrave, Mr William Alexander BA I *Oct 1995*
12, 15, 62
7 Bedford Row, London WC1
p924 . . . . 020 7242 3555

REDHEAD, Mr Leroy LLB; LLM; Dip L *Nov 1982*
15
25 Bedford Row, London WC1
p925 . . . . 020 7067 1500

Redley, Clive I *Nov 2010*
10, 20
Tooks Chambers, London EC4
p953 . . . . 020 7842 7575

Redmayne, Mr Simon BA(Oxon) I *Jul 1982*
11, 27, 12, 6, 7, 18, 22, 29
East Anglian Chambers, Norwich
p988 . . . . 01603 617351
East Anglian Chambers, Colchester
p975 . . . . 01206 572756
East Anglian Chambers, Chelmsford
p973 . . . . 01245 215660
East Anglian Chambers, Ipswich
p976 . . . . 01473 214481

Redmond, Mr David M *Oct 2006*
15, 12
St Albans Chambers, St Albans
p992 . . . . 01727 843383

REDMOND, Miss Helen LLB; LLM G *Jan 1999*
11, 22, 32, 40
9 St John Street Chambers, Manchester
p984 . . . . 0161 955 9000

REDMOND, Mr Jack G *Jan 2009*
15, 20, 30, 11
St Philips Chambers, Birmingham
p969 . . . . 0121 246 7000

REDMOND, Mr Stephen BA(Hons) G *Jul 1975*
11, 12, 15, 30
Citadel Chambers, Birmingham
p967 . . . . 0121 233 8500

Redpath, Mr Scott M *Jan 1996*
5, 6, 8, 11, 22, 29, 40, 36, 24, 18
Exchange Chambers, Manchester
p983 . . . . 0161 833 2722
Exchange Chambers, Liverpool
p980 . . . . 0151 236 7747
Exchange Chambers, Leeds
p977 . . . . 0113 203 1970
Temple Tax Chambers, London EC4
p952 . . . . 020 7353 7884 / 7353 8982

Redpath-Stevens, Mr Alastair Y BSc(Bris) M *Jan 1998*
22
Hardwicke, London WC2
p936 . . . . 020 7242 2523

Redston, Ms Anne M *Jan 2009*
Temple Tax Chambers, London EC4
p952 . . . . 020 7353 7884 / 7353 8982

13

REECE, Mr Brian LLB(Lond) M *Jul 1974*
15, 62, 95
187 Fleet Street, London EC4
p933 . . . 020 7430 7430

REECE, Mr Jason G *Nov 2000*
10, 20
St Mary's Chambers, Nottingham
p989 . . . 0115 950 3503

Reece, Mr Rupert BA(Cantab) I *Oct 1992*
1, 3, 7, 11, 12, 24, 30, 33, 40
2 Temple Gardens, London EC4
p952 . . . 020 7822 1200

REED, Mrs Claire G *Oct 2009*
15, 10
Wilberforce Chambers, Hull
p976 . . . 01482 323264

Reed, Mr Jeremy MA(Cantab) M *Oct 1997*
13, 19, 44, 45, 48, 50
Hogarth Chambers, London WC2
p937 . . . 020 7404 0404

Reed, Mr Julian LLB I *Nov 1991*
20, 10, 12, 30, 18, 37, 47
9 Park Place, Cardiff
p973 . . . 029 2038 2731

Reed, Mrs Lucy BVC; ISCL; PG DipLaw; CPE; MRES; BA(Hons)(Exon) L *Oct 2002*
20, 10
St John's Chambers, Bristol
p972 . . . 0117 921 3456

REED, Mr Matthew MA(Cantab); MA(City) M *Nov 1995*
1, 22, 26, 28, 31, 40
Landmark Chambers, London EC4
p941 . . . 020 7430 1221

Reed, Mr Paul LLB(Hons); MSc; ACIArb I *Jul 1988*
(Q.C.) *40, 11*
Hardwicke, London WC2
p936 . . . 020 7242 2523

Reed, Miss Penelope LLB(Lond) I *Jul 1983*
(Q.C.) *8, 9, 14, 32, 34, 37, 57, 58*
5 Stone Buildings, London WC2
p951 . . . 020 7242 6201

Reed, Mr Piers Knowle Moorehouse L *Nov 1974*
15, 25, 26, 36, 62, 39, 82
3 Temple Gardens, London EC4
p952 . . . 020 7353 3102

REED, Mr Rupert BA(Cantab); MA(Cantab); LLB(Harv) L *May 1996*
3, 5, 6, 8, 9, 11, 12, 49, 24, 29, 32, 40, 37
Wilberforce Chambers, London WC2
p953 . . . 020 7306 0102

Reed, Mr Simon BA; DipLaw; Pupil Master G *Mar 1998*
8, 30, 31, 22
New Walk Chambers, Leicester
p979 . . . 0871 200 1298

Reed, Mr Steven I *Jul 2005*
5, 6, 8, 11, 97, 44, 67, 73, 16, 50, 45, 41, 13, 52, 87
No5 Chambers, Bristol
p971 . . . 0845 210 5555
No5 Chambers, London EC4
p944 . . . 0845 210 5555
No5 Chambers, Birmingham
p968 . . . 0845 210 5555

REED, Ms Susan Catherine LLB I *Jul 1984*
10, 26, 63
7 Bedford Row, London WC1
p924 . . . 020 7242 3555

Reeder, Mr John LLM(Lond); PhD(B'ham) G *Jul 1971*
(Q.C.) *3, 11, 35*
Stone Chambers, London WC1
p951 . . . 020 7440 6900

Reeder, Mr Stephen M *Oct 1991*
1, 22, 51
Doughty Street Chambers, London WC1
p930 . . . 020 7404 1313

Reeds, Gareth L *Oct 2001*
Academy Chambers, London N2
p923 . . . 07979 265321

Rees, Ms Caroline LLB G *Oct 1994*
15, 62
Thirty Park Place, Cardiff
p973 . . . 029 2039 8421

Rees, Mr David Benjamin BA(Oxon) L *Oct 1994*
8, 14, 29, 32, 37, 40
5 Stone Buildings, London WC2
p951 . . . 020 7242 6201

Rees, Mr Edward LLB G *Feb 1973*
(Q.C.) *1, 15, 51*
Doughty Street Chambers, London WC1
p930 . . . 020 7404 1313

REES, Mr Gareth G *Jul 1981*
(Q.C.) *72, 15, 71, 70, 62, 56, 69, 36*
23 Essex Street, London WC2
p932 . . . 020 7413 0353

REES, Mr Hefin BA(Hons) I *Nov 1992*
30, 12, 18, 22
Thirty Nine Essex Street, London WC2
p932 . . . 020 7832 1111

Rees, Mr Ieuan BSc(Econ) G *Nov 1982*
15
Angel Chambers, Swansea
p992 . . . 01792 464623

Rees, Mr James G *Oct 1994*
8, 10, 20, 30
Southernhay Chambers, Exeter
p975 . . . 01392 255777

Rees, Mr John Charles BA(Cantab); LLB; LLM L *Jul 1972*
(Q.C.) *15, 62, 84*
Exchange Chambers, Manchester
p983 . . . 0161 833 2722
Exchange Chambers, Liverpool
p980 . . . 0151 236 7747
Exchange Chambers, Leeds
p977 . . . 0113 203 1970
Furnival Chambers, London EC4
p934 . . . 020 7405 3232

Rees, Mr Jonathan I *Oct 2000*
15, 62, 25
5 Paper Buildings, London EC4
p946 . . . 020 7583 6117
2 Hare Court, London EC4
p937 . . . 020 7353 5324

Rees, Mr Matthew LLB(Hons) G *Oct 1996*
Angel Chambers, Swansea
p992 . . . 01792 464623

Rees, Ms Naomi LLB(Hons)(UCL) M *Jan 2006*
11, 97, 72, 15, 70, 30, 53
3PB, Winchester
p994 . . . 01962 868884

Rees, Mr Owen Huw LLB(Wales) G *Jul 1983*
10, 15, 20, 25, 30
Iscoed Chambers, Swansea
p993 . . . 01792 652988

REES, Mr Paul MA; M Phil; BCL G *Nov 1980*
(Q.C.) *1, 12, 23, 27, 30, 31, 36*
1 Crown Office Row, London EC4
p929 . . . 020 7797 7500

Rees, Mr Robert Charles David BA; LLB; FCIArb; Pupil Master M *Feb 1978*
40, 30, 10, 20, 22, 8
New Walk Chambers, Leicester
p979 . . . 0871 200 1298

Rees, Mr Stephen Robert Tristram LLB G *Nov 1979*
12, 15, 18, 20, 25, 30, 36
Iscoed Chambers, Swansea
p993 . . . 01792 652988

Reese, Mr Colin MA(Cantab); Recorder G *Jul 1973*
(Q.C.) *3, 7, 11, 31, 40, 41, 43, 45, 49, 54, 61, 78, 74*
Atkin Chambers, London WC1
p923 . . . 020 7404 0102

Reeve, Mr Matthew MA(Cantab) I *Nov 1987*
24, 4, 40, 18, 11
Quadrant Chambers, London EC4
p948 . . . 020 7583 4444

Reeve, Miss Veronica BA(Oxon) I *Jun 2004*
15, 82, 62
Lamb Building, Brighton
p970 . . . 01273 820490
Lamb Building, London EC4
p940 . . . 020 7797 7788

Reevell, Miss Louise L *Oct 2001*
39 Park Square, Leeds
p978 . . . 0113 245 6633

Reevell, Mr Simon L *Oct 1990*
15, 30, 53
39 Park Square, Leeds
p978 . . . 0113 245 6633

REEVES, Miss Sian MA(Cantab) G *Jul 2006*
Temple Garden Chambers, London EC4
p952 . . . 020 7583 1315

Reeves-Croft, Mr Christopher M *Nov 1992*
20, 15, 96
St Albans Chambers, St Albans
p992 . . . 01727 843383

Reffin, Ms Clare M *Jul 1981*
One Essex Court, London EC4
p931 . . . 020 7583 2000

Regan, Mr David MA(Oxon); DipLaw I *Nov 1994*
18, 30, 53
St John's Chambers, Bristol
p972 . . . 0117 921 3456

Regan, Mrs Sarah L *Oct 2000*
15, 62
Albion Chambers, Bristol
p970 . . . 0117 927 2144

Reid, Mr David G *Nov 1994*
12, 15
3PB, Winchester
p994 . . . 01962 868884

Reid, Mr Dickon I *Nov 2005*
15, 91
5 King's Bench Walk, London EC4
p939 . . . 020 7353 5638

Reid, Mr Errol G *Feb 1978*
Clapham Law Chambers, London SW1
p928 . . . 020 7978 8482 / 7642 5777

REID, Miss Helen LLB(Hons) L *Jul 2005*
6, 11, 47
Five Paper, London EC4
p946 . . . 020 7815 3200

Reid, Miss Jacqueline BSc; MPhil M *Oct 1992*
41, 73, 50, 19, 45, 13, 52, 96
11 South Square, London WC1
p950 . . . 020 7405 1222

Reid, Mr James Gordon LLB(Hons); FCIArb I *Jan 1980*
(Q.C.) *3, 7, 11, 31, 40, 41, 43, 45, 49, 54, 61, 78, 74*
Atkin Chambers, London WC1
p923 . . . 020 7404 0102

REID, Mr Martin L *Nov 2003*
15, 30, 12
7 Harrington Street Chambers, Liverpool
p981 . . . 0151 242 0707

Reid, Mr Paul C MA(Cantab); Recorder G *Jul 1973*
(Q.C.)
Lincoln House Chambers, Manchester
p984 . . . 0161 832 5701

Reid, Mr Paul William MA(Cantab) I *Jul 1975*
King's Bench Chambers, Oxford
p989 . . . 01865 311066
13 King's Bench Walk, London EC4
p940 . . . 020 7353 7204
Park Court Chambers, Leeds
p978 . . . 0113 243 3277

Reid, Miss Sarah LLB(Law with Hispanic) L *Sep 2004*
1, 12, 18, 31, 26
Kings Chambers, Leeds
p978 . . . 0113 242 1123
Kings Chambers, Manchester
p984 . . . 0161 832 9082

REID, Mr Sebastian BA(Lond) G *Jul 1982*
22, 30, 20, 25, 47
Tanfield Chambers, London WC1
p951 . . . 020 7421 5300

Reilly, Miss Ffyon I *Sep 1999*
Castle Chambers, Harrow
p976 . . . 020 8423 6579

Reindorf, Miss Akua M *Nov 1999*
55, 18, 1, 51, 36
Cloisters, London EC4
p928 . . . 020 7827 4000

Renfree, Mr Peter LLB(Hons) M *Jan 1992*
10, 13, 18, 20, 22, 27, 29, 30, 40
Harbour Court Chambers, Southampton
p992 . . . 01489 557999

Renouf, Mr Gerard MA(Dublin) I *Jul 1977*
12, 15
2 Pump Court, London EC4
p947 . . . 020 7353 5597

Renouf, Mr Mark M *Oct 1994*
18, 11
No5 Chambers, Bristol
p971 . . . 0845 210 5555
No5 Chambers, London EC4
p944 . . . 0845 210 5555
No5 Chambers, Birmingham
p968 . . . 0845 210 5555

RENSTEN, Ms Katy BA(Cantab); CPE I *Jul 2010*
10, 20
Coram Chambers, London EC1
p929 . . . 020 7092 3700

RENTON, The Hon Clare L *Nov 1972*
10, 14, 20
29 Bedford Row, London WC1
p925 . . . 020 7404 1044

Renton, Miss Jacqueline M *Jul 2007*
20, 10
4 Paper Buildings, London EC4
p946 . . . 020 7583 0816

Renvoize, Mr Edward L *Oct 2004*
15, 30
No 6 Barristers Chambers, Leeds
p978 . . . 0113 245 9763

Repper, Miss Elizabeth LLB; LLM I *Jan 2002*
7, 24, 40
Keating Chambers, London WC2
p938 . . . 020 7544 2600

REQUENA, Mr Stephen I *Oct 1997*
15, 62
18 Red Lion Court, London EC4
p949 . . . 020 7520 6000
18 Red Lion Court (Annexe), Chelmsford
p973 . . . 01245 280880

RESTELL, Mr Piers LLB(Lee) Hons M *Jul 2002*
Maidstone Chambers, Maidstone
p982 . . . 01622 688592

Revere, Miss Carla I *Jan 2001*
33 Bedford Row, London WC1
p925 . . . 020 7242 6476

Reynold, Mr Frederic BA(Oxon); Bencher, Gray's Inn G *Jul 1960*
(Q.C.) *1, 11, 18, 26, 36, 40, 51, 55*
Old Square Chambers, Bristol
p971 . . . 0117 930 5100
Old Square Chambers, London WC1
p945 . . . 020 7269 0300

REYNOLDS, Mr Adrian L BA(Oxon); Recorder G *Nov 1982*
15, 30
1 High Pavement, Nottingham
p988 . . . 0115 941 8218

REYNOLDS, Miss Charlotte M *Oct 2001*
30, 40, 53, 18, 12, 47, 22, 59, 38
12 King's Bench Walk, London EC4
p940 . . . 020 7583 0811

Reynolds, Prof Francis DCL; FBA I *Feb 1961*
(Q.C.) *3, 11, 35, 40, 41*
7 King's Bench Walk, London EC4
p940 . . . 020 7910 8300

Reynolds, Mr Gary William BSc(Hons) L *Nov 1994*
7, 12, 15, 22, 30
St Johns Buildings, Preston
p990 . . . 01772 256100
St Johns Buildings, Chester
p974 . . . 01244 323070
St Johns Buildings, Manchester
p985 . . . 0161 214 1500
St Johns Buildings, Liverpool
p982 . . . 0151 243 6000

REYNOLDS, Mr Kirk MA(Cantab) M *Jul 1974*
(Q.C.)
Falcon Chambers, London EC4
p933 . . . 020 7353 2484

Reynolds, Mr Richard BA(Hons)(Oxon); GDL; LLM; BVC M *Jul 2007*
18, 23, 51
Tooks Chambers, London EC4
p953 . . . 020 7842 7575

REYNOLDS, Mr Stephen Alan BA; Former Solicitor I *Nov 1987*
20
29 Bedford Row, London WC1
p925 . . . 020 7404 1044

Reza, Mr Hashim M *Jul 1981*
Field Court Chambers, London WC1
p933 . . . 020 7405 6114

RHEE, Miss Deok Joo BA; BCL(Oxon); BVC G *Oct 1998*
1, 11, 47, 46, 19, 51, 26, 55, 31
11KBW, London EC4
p938 . . . 020 7632 8500

Rhind, Mr Mark A LLB M *May 1989*
15
Exchange Chambers, Manchester
p983 . . . 0161 833 2722
Exchange Chambers, Liverpool
p980 . . . 0151 236 7747

See p1010 for the Key to Work Categories

Exchange Chambers, Leeds
p977 . . . 0113 203 1970

Rhodes, Ms Amanda L *May 1990*
10, 20
Holborn Chambers, London WC2
p937 . . . 020 7242 6060

Rhodes, Mr David BA(Hons); MPhil M *Jul 2002*
15, 51, 91, 62
Doughty Street Chambers, London WC1
p930 . . . 020 7404 1313

Rhodes, Mr Nicholas LLB L *Jul 1981*
15
Charter Chambers, London WC1
p928 . . . 020 7618 4400

Rhodes, Mr Robert Elliott MA(Oxon) I *Jul 1968*
(Q.C.) *1, 11, 12, 15, 34, 5, 71, 81, 62, 49*
Outer Temple Chambers, London WC2
p945 . . . 020 7353 6381

Rhodri, Mr James I *Jul 2002*
15
Westgate Chambers, Lewes
p980 . . . 01273 480510

Rhone-Adrien, Miss Paula LLB I *Oct 1998*
20, 56, 10, 55, 14, 96
Lamb Building, Brighton
p970 . . . 01273 820490
Lamb Building, London EC4
p940 . . . 020 7797 7788

Rhys, Miss Megan J I *Nov 1994*
12, 20, 30
Paradise Chambers, Sheffield
p992 . . . 0114 273 8951

Rice, Mr Christopher BA(Hons) M *Jul 1991*
10, 20
Crown Office Row Chambers, Brighton
p970 . . . 01273 625625

Rich, Miss A Barbara MA(Cantab) G *Oct 1990*
6, 8, 14, 29, 37, 40, 32, 93
5 Stone Buildings, London WC2
p951 . . . 020 7242 6201

RICH, Mr Jonathan BA(Cantab) M *Dec 1989*
11, 22, 47, 15, 24
Five Paper, London EC4
p946 . . . 020 7815 3200

Richards, Mr Alan I *Oct 2004*
15
5 Paper Buildings, London EC4
p946 . . . 020 7583 6117

Richards, Ms Catherine LLB(Hons) L *Nov 2000*
Iscoed Chambers, Swansea
p993 . . . 01792 652988

Richards, Mr Cennydd BA(Oxon) G *Oct 1999*
20, 22, 12, 10, 6, 37
Angel Chambers, Swansea
p992 . . . 01792 464623

RICHARDS, Ms Elizabeth M *Oct 2001*
20
St Philips Chambers, Birmingham
p969 . . . 0121 246 7000

Richards, Mr Hugh I *Nov 1992*
31, 26, 1, 60, 54, 78, 46
No5 Chambers, Bristol
p971 . . . 0845 210 5555
No5 Chambers, London EC4
p944 . . . 0845 210 5555
No5 Chambers, Birmingham
p968 . . . 0845 210 5555

RICHARDS, Mr Ian BA L *Nov 1971*
34, 57, 58
Pump Court Tax Chambers, London WC1
p948 . . . 020 7414 8080

RICHARDS, Ms Jennifer M *Oct 1991*
(Q.C.) *1, 26, 19, 51, 63, 85, 23, 76, 14*
Thirty Nine Essex Street, London WC2
p932 . . . 020 7832 1111

Richards, Dr Jonathan Nicholas MB; ChB M *Nov 1995*
53, 27, 30, 40
King's Bench Godolphin Chambers, Truro
p994 . . . 0845 308 1551
King's Bench Godolphin Chambers, Plymouth
p990 . . . 0845 308 1551
Lamb Chambers, London EC4
p941 . . . 020 7797 8300

Richards, Mr Stephan BA M *May 1993*
15
Queen Square Chambers, Bristol
p972 . . . 0117 921 1966

Richards, Mr Tom BA(Hons)(Oxon); DipLaw G *Jan 2006*
1, 11, 18, 51, 50, 52, 56, 89
Blackstone Chambers, London EC4
p926 . . . 020 7583 1770

Richardson, Miss Anne L LLB(B'ham) I *Jul 1986*
10, 15, 20
Broad Chare Chambers, Newcastle upon Tyne
p986 . . . 0191 232 0541

Richardson, Mr Garth M *Jul 1975*
15, 20, 30, 42, 18, 70, 91
Rougemont Chambers, Exeter
p975 . . . 01392 208484

Richardson, Mr Giles BA(Oxon); BCL(Oxon) I *Oct 1997*
6, 8, 11, 29, 32, 37, 62
Serle Court, London WC2
p950 . . . 020 7242 6105

RICHARDSON, Mr Grahame M *Jul 2001*
10, 20
Trinity Chambers, Chelmsford
p974 . . . 01245 605040

RICHARDSON, Mr James LLB; LLM; Dip Crim(Cantab) G *Jul 1975*
(Q.C.) *15, 36, 11, 25*
23 Essex Street, London WC2
p932 . . . 020 7413 0353

RICHARDSON, Mr James David LLB G *Nov 1982*
20
Trinity (Newcastle) Chambers, Newcastle upon Tyne
p987 . . . 0191 232 1927
Trinity (Teesside) Chambers, Middlesbrough
p986 . . . 01642 247569

Richardson, Mr Jeremy William LLB(Lond); Recorder I *Jul 1980*
(Q.C.) *15, 30, 40, 20, 10*
11 King's Bench Walk, Leeds
p978 . . . 0113 297 1200

Richardson, Mr Matthew G *Oct 2006*
Henderson Chambers, London EC4
p937 . . . 020 7583 9020

Richardson, Miss Rebecca BVC; LLM(Lond); LLB(Hons) M *Oct 2003*
30
Hardwicke, London WC2
p936 . . . 020 7242 2523

Riches, Mr Philip BA(Cantab) I *Nov 2001*
11, 44, 78, 21, 35, 41, 62, 5
Stone Chambers, London WC1
p951 . . . 020 7440 6900

Richman, Mrs Helene Pines BA(Hons)(Penn)(Bio Eng); JD M *Jul 1992*
5, 6, 9, 11, 13, 21, 22, 29, 31, 32, 34, 37
9 Stone Buildings Barristers Chambers, London WC2
p951 . . . 020 7404 5055

Richmond, Mr Bernard Grant LLB; Recorder M *Jul 1988*
(Q.C.) *15, 23, 1, 18, 36, 38, 56, 68*
Lamb Building, Brighton
p970 . . . 01273 820490
Lamb Building, London EC4
p940 . . . 020 7797 7788

Richmond, Mr Paul I *Oct 1998*
1 Mitre Court Buildings, London EC4
p942 . . . 020 7452 8900

RICKARBY, Mr William LLB(L'pool) G *Nov 1975*
72, 15, 70, 46
Cornwall Street Chambers, Birmingham
p967 . . . 0121 233 7500

RICKARD, Mr Marcus I *Jul 2000*
72, 15, 62, 34
18 Red Lion Court, London EC4
p949 . . . 020 7520 6000
18 Red Lion Court (Annexe), Chelmsford
p973 . . . 01245 280880

RICKARD, Ms Susanna BA(Hons)(Cantab) M *Jul 2009*
3 Serjeants' Inn, London EC4
p950 . . . 020 7427 5000

Rickards, Mr James I *Mar 2002*
92, 11, 40
Outer Temple Chambers, London WC2
p945 . . . 020 7353 6381

Ricks, Mr Richard LLB; LLM L *Oct 1999*
6, 15, 22, 25
St Albans Chambers, St Albans
p992 . . . 01727 843383

RIDD, Mr Ian BA(Oxon) M *Jul 1975*
8, 11, 7, 18, 40
Farrar's Building, London EC4
p933 . . . 020 7583 9241

Ridgway, Mr Philip M *Nov 1986*
34, 57, 58
Temple Tax Chambers, London EC4
p952 . . . 020 7353 7884 / 7353 8982

RIDING, Mr Henry LLB(L'pool) M *Jul 1981*
15
7 Harrington Street Chambers, Liverpool
p981 . . . 0151 242 0707

RIDLEY, Ms Samantha I *Jul 2009*
10, 20, 15, 25, 22
1 King's Bench Walk, London EC4
p938 . . . 020 7936 1500

Ridout, Frances M *Jan 2007*
15 New Bridge Street Chambers, London EC4
p943 . . . 020 7842 1900

RIGBY, Mr Terence LLB(Nott'm); BCL; Recorder G *May 1971*
12, 18, 30, 20, 15
9 St John Street Chambers, Manchester
p984 . . . 0161 955 9000

RIGBY, Miss Victoria PG DipLaw M *Jan 2000*
18, 30
9 St John Street Chambers, Manchester
p984 . . . 0161 955 9000

RIGGS, Ms Samantha G *Oct 1996*
15, 46, 62
25 Bedford Row, London WC1
p925 . . . 020 7067 1500

RIGNEY, Mr Andrew BA(Cantab) G *Oct 1992*
(Q.C.) *74, 7, 11, 24, 40, 4*
Crown Office Chambers, London EC4
p929 . . . 020 7797 8100

RILEY, Miss Christine LLB G *Jul 1974*
10, 20
9 St John Street Chambers, Manchester
p984 . . . 0161 955 9000

RILEY, Miss Davinia I *Jan 2004*
15, 11, 20, 30
St Philips Chambers, Birmingham
p969 . . . 0121 246 7000

Riley, Miss Geraldine LLB(Hons) L *Jan 2002*
4, 15, 94
Cobden House Chambers, Manchester
p983 . . . 0161 833 6000

Riley, Mr Jamie MA(Cantab) L *Nov 1995*
5, 18, 19, 24, 29, 38, 62
11 Stone Buildings, London WC2
p951 . . . 020 7831 6381

RILEY, Mr John BA(Hons) M *Nov 1983*
15
23 Essex Street, London WC2
p932 . . . 020 7413 0353

Riley-Smith, Mr Toby MA(Cantab) M *Nov 1995*
11, 12, 18, 22, 30, 47, 48, 51
Henderson Chambers, London EC4
p937 . . . 020 7583 9020

RIMMER, Mr Anthony G *Jul 1983*
15, 62, 95
187 Fleet Street, London EC4
p933 . . . 020 7430 7430

Rimmer, Miss Catherine LLB G *Jul 2004*
10, 15, 20, 18
St Johns Buildings, Preston
p990 . . . 01772 256100
St Johns Buildings, Chester
p974 . . . 01244 323070
St Johns Buildings, Manchester
p985 . . . 0161 214 1500
St Johns Buildings, Liverpool
p982 . . . 0151 243 6000

RIMMER, Mr Nicholas L *Jul 2004*
15, 13, 62
23 Essex Street, London WC2
p932 . . . 020 7413 0353

Riordan, Mr Kevin BCL G *Nov 1972*
15, 25, 31
Iscoed Chambers, Swansea
p993 . . . 01792 652988

RIORDAN, Mr Stephen LLB I *Jul 1972*
(Q.C.) *15*
7 Harrington Street Chambers, Liverpool
p981 . . . 0151 242 0707

RIPLEY, Mr Michael BA(Hons)(Dunelm); DipLaw(City) L *Jan 2008*
34, 57, 58
11 New Square, London WC2
p943 . . . 020 7242 4017

Rippon, Mrs Amanda Jayne G *Oct 1993*
Broad Chare Chambers, Newcastle upon Tyne
p986 . . . 0191 232 0541

Rippon, Louise Jane LLB(Hons); LLM M *Jun 2000*
34, 57, 58
Temple Tax Chambers, London EC4
p952 . . . 020 7353 7884 / 7353 8982
Zenith Chambers, Leeds
p979 . . . 0113 245 5438

RIPPON, Mr Simon John G *Nov 1996*
Citadel Chambers, Birmingham
p967 . . . 0121 233 8500

Risoli, Mr Andreá LLB(Cardiff) G *Jan 2005*
18
Old Square Chambers, Bristol
p971 . . . 0117 930 5100
Old Square Chambers, London WC1
p945 . . . 020 7269 0300

Ritchie, Mr Andrew MA(Cantab) I *Jan 1985*
10, 30, 29, 12, 36, 40, 53
9 Gough Square, London EC4
p935 . . . 020 7832 0500

Ritchie, Mr Richard BA M *Jul 1978*
5, 6, 8, 11, 29, 32, 37, 36, 49, 62
XXIV Old Buildings, London WC2
p944 . . . 020 7691 2424

Ritchie, Miss Shauna LLB(Hons) L *Nov 2000*
15, 62
2 Bedford Row, London WC1
p924 . . . 020 7440 8888

RITCHIE, Mr Stuart BA(Hons)(Oxon) M *Oct 1995*
18, 11, 40, 6
Littleton Chambers, London EC4
p941 . . . 020 7797 8600

Rivalland, Mr Marc-Edouard B Com; LLB; LLM M *Jul 1987*
11, 30, 40, 53
1 Chancery Lane, London WC2
p928 . . . 0845 634 6666

Rivers, Mr David LLM; BA G *Jan 2002*
30
Old Square Chambers, Bristol
p971 . . . 0117 930 5100
Old Square Chambers, London WC1
p945 . . . 020 7269 0300

RIVERS MANSFIELD, Mrs Suzanne M *Jul 2010*
St James's Chambers, Manchester
p984 . . . 0161 834 7000

RIVETT, Mr James MA(Cantab); Mphil L *Nov 2004*
37, 57, 58, 34
Pump Court Tax Chambers, London WC1
p948 . . . 020 7414 8080

Riza, Mr Alper Recorder G *Nov 1973*
(Q.C.)
Goldsmith Chambers, London EC4
p935 . . . 020 7353 6802

Roach, Miss Jacqueline Alison LLB(Hons)(Kent) M *Oct 1996*
20
Crown Office Row Chambers, Brighton
p970 . . . 01273 625625

ROBB, Mr Adam BA; BCL I *Nov 1995*
1, 7, 11, 51, 24, 26
Thirty Nine Essex Street, London WC2
p932 . . . 020 7832 1111

ROBBINS, Mr Ian Geoffrey LLB M *Feb 1991*
10, 20
1 Garden Court, London EC4
p934 . . . 020 7797 7900

Roberston, Mr Andrew M *Jul 1975*
(Q.C.) *53, 62, 15, 30, 70*
9 Gough Square, London EC4
p935 . . . 020 7832 0500

Roberts, Mr Allan M *Jan 2004*
18, 55, 36, 96, 74, 48, 88, 89, 29, 40
Queen Square Chambers, Bristol
p972 . . . 0117 921 1966

ROBERTS, Miss Beverly M *Jan 1998*
4 King's Bench Walk, London EC4
p939 . . . 020 7822 7000

ROBERTS, Miss Catherine MA; LLM(Cantab) *L Nov 1986*
11, 38, 97
Erskine Chambers, London WC2
p931 . . . . . 020 7242 5532

ROBERTS, Miss Clare LLB *M Nov 1988*
1, 11, 22, 26, 88
Arden Chambers, London WC1
p923 . . . . . 020 7242 4244

Roberts, Elliw *G Jan 2009*
St Johns Buildings, Preston
p990 . . . . . 01772 256100
St Johns Buildings, Chester
p974 . . . . . 01244 323070
St Johns Buildings, Manchester
p985 . . . . . 0161 214 1500
St Johns Buildings, Liverpool
p982 . . . . . 0151 243 6000

Roberts, Miss Gemma *G Oct 2006*
5, 6, 8, 11, 97, 67, 38, 24, 88, 29, 93, 18, 55, 30, 68, 94
No5 Chambers, Bristol
p971 . . . . . 0845 210 5555
No5 Chambers, London EC4
p944 . . . . . 0845 210 5555
No5 Chambers, Birmingham
p968 . . . . . 0845 210 5555

ROBERTS, Mr Hilary LLB *G Nov 1978*
15
Temple Chambers, Newport
p988 . . . . . 01633 267403 / 255855
Temple Chambers, Cardiff
p973 . . . . . 029 2039 7364

ROBERTS, Mr James BA(Oxon) *G Oct 1993*
10, 12, 20, 30, 36, 49, 96
1 King's Bench Walk, London EC4
p938 . . . . . 020 7936 1500

ROBERTS, Mrs Jennifer LLB *I Jul 1988*
(Q.C.) *20*
Queen Elizabeth Buildings, London EC4
p948 . . . . . 020 7797 7837

Roberts, Dr John FCIArb; QC; DCL *G Nov 1969*
(Q.C.)
Warwick House Chambers, London WC1
p953 . . . . . 020 7430 2323

ROBERTS, Dr Julian BA; MA; PhD(Cantab) *L Jul 1987*
Ten Old Square, London WC2
p945 . . . . . 020 7405 0758

Roberts, Ms Lisa LLB *L Oct 1993*
Lincoln House Chambers, Manchester
p984 . . . . . 0161 832 5701

Roberts, Mr Marc *I Nov 1984*
6, 7, 8, 10, 11, 13, 16, 18
4 Brick Court Chambers, London EC4
p927 . . . . . 020 7832 3200

ROBERTS, Mr Mark LLB(Hons) *G Mar 2001*
30
7 Harrington Street Chambers, Liverpool
p981 . . . . . 0151 242 0707

Roberts, Mr Mark Vaughan LLB(Hons) *I Sep 1991*
7, 10, 12, 15, 18, 20, 22, 25, 26, 30
St Johns Buildings, Preston
p990 . . . . . 01772 256100
St Johns Buildings, Chester
p974 . . . . . 01244 323070
St Johns Buildings, Manchester
p985 . . . . . 0161 214 1500
St Johns Buildings, Liverpool
p982 . . . . . 0151 243 6000

Roberts, Mr Matthew J P LLB(Hons); LLM *G Oct 1994*
15
9 Park Place, Cardiff
p973 . . . . . 029 2038 2731

Roberts, Ms Patricia LLB(L'pool) *G Nov 1987*
10, 20, 12
14 Gray's Inn Square, London WC1
p936 . . . . . 020 7242 0858

Roberts, Mr Philip *I Oct 1996*
One Essex Court, London EC4
p931 . . . . . 020 7583 2000

Roberts, Mr Richard BA(Oxon); MPhil(Cantab) *L Jan 2006*
Henderson Chambers, London EC4
p937 . . . . . 020 7583 9020

Roberts, Mr Simon *G Jan 1975*
1 Pump Court, London EC4
p947 . . . . . 020 7842 7070

Roberts, Mr Stephen BA(Hons); LLM *L Jan 2002*
18, 20, 49, 10, 40, 96, 56
Queen Square Chambers, Bristol
p972 . . . . . 0117 921 1966

ROBERTS, Mr Stuart *M Nov 1994*
Chancery House Chambers, Leeds
p977 . . . . . 0113 244 6691

ROBERTS, Mr Timothy LLB *G Jul 1978*
(Q.C.) *15, 62*
Fountain Chambers, Middlesbrough
p986 . . . . . 01642 804040

ROBERTSHAW, Mr Charles BSc(Hons); ARCS; LLB(Hons) *M Nov 2007*
12 King's Bench Walk, London EC4
p940 . . . . . 020 7583 0811

Robertshaw, Mr Martin *M Nov 1977*
12, 15, 30
39 Park Square, Leeds
p978 . . . . . 0113 245 6633

Robertson, Mr Aidan BA; LLM(Cantab) *M Jul 1995*
19, 44, 1
Brick Court Chambers, London WC2
p927 . . . . . 020 7379 3550

Robertson, Miss Alice *G Oct 1996*
King's Bench Chambers, Oxford
p989 . . . . . 01865 311066
13 King's Bench Walk, London EC4
p940 . . . . . 020 7353 7204

Robertson, Mr Andrew James MA(Cantab); Recorder *M Jul 1975*
(Q.C.) *15, 12, 30, 40, 53*
11 King's Bench Walk, Leeds
p978 . . . . . 0113 297 1200

Robertson, Mr Geoffrey BA; LLB; BCL; Recorder, Joint Head of Chambers *M Jul 1973*
(Q.C.) *1, 15, 16, 21, 33, 36, 51, 52*
Doughty Street Chambers, London WC1
p930 . . . . . 020 7404 1313

Robertson, Jollyon LLB *M Feb 1983*
15, 62
4 Breams Buildings, London EC4
p927 . . . . . 020 7092 1900

Robertson, Mary *L Jun 2005*
42 Bedford Row, London WC1
p925 . . . . . 020 7831 0222

Robertson, Nicole *L Jan 2007*
Henderson Chambers, London EC4
p937 . . . . . 020 7583 9020

Robertson, Ms Patricia BA(Oxon) *I Nov 1988*
(Q.C.)
Fountain Court Chambers, London EC4
p934 . . . . . 020 7583 3335

Robertson, Ms Sally *I Nov 1995*
55, 18, 30, 1, 36, 26, 51
Cloisters, London EC4
p928 . . . . . 020 7827 4000

Robins, Miss Imogen LLB *I Nov 1991*
3PB, Winchester
p994 . . . . . 01962 868884

ROBINS, Mr Stephen BA(Oxon) *L Nov 2001*
5, 6, 8, 11, 47, 62, 29, 40, 97, 38
South Square, London WC1
p950 . . . . . 020 7696 9900

Robinson, Ali *L Jul 1978*
10
Clerksroom - Administration Centre, Taunton
p993 . . . . . 0845 083 3000

Robinson, Ms Claire BA *G Oct 1991*
Charter Chambers, London WC1
p928 . . . . . 020 7618 4400

ROBINSON, Mr Daniel *G Jul 2010*
15, 62, 94
18 Red Lion Court, London EC4
p949 . . . . . 020 7520 6000
18 Red Lion Court (Annexe), Chelmsford
p973 . . . . . 01245 280880
Falcon Chambers, London EC4
p933 . . . . . 020 7353 2484

Robinson, Mr Daniel M BSc(Hons) *L Nov 1993*
15
5 King's Bench Walk, London EC4
p939 . . . . . 020 7353 5638

ROBINSON, Mr Graham *M Jul 2009*
9 St John Street Chambers, Manchester
p984 . . . . . 0161 955 9000

Robinson, Mr James *M Oct 1992*
York Chambers, York
p995 . . . . . 01904 620048
York Chambers, Newcastle upon Tyne
p987 . . . . . 0191 206 4677

Robinson, Ms Karen BA(Hons)(Cantab) *L Sep 2000*
15, 62, 36
2 Hare Court, London EC4
p937 . . . . . 020 7353 5324

Robinson, Miss Katherine *G Jul 2002*
15, 20
No 6 Barristers Chambers, Leeds
p978 . . . . . 0113 245 9763

ROBINSON, Miss Kirsty MA(Hons) *G Oct 2003*
10, 12, 15, 20
Chavasse Court Chambers, Liverpool
p980 . . . . . 0151 229 2030

ROBINSON, Ms Laura BSc; PGDL *I Oct 2001*
18, 67, 55, 30
Tanfield Chambers, London WC1
p951 . . . . . 020 7421 5300

Robinson, Mr Matthew *I Jan 1994*
10, 20, 25, 36
Chartlands Chambers, Northampton
p988 . . . . . 01604 603322

Robinson, Mr Nicholas *I Jan 2006*
72, 15, 71, 70, 18
3PB, Bournemouth
p969 . . . . . 01202 292102
Ropewalk Chambers, Nottingham
p989 . . . . . 0115 947 2581

ROBINSON, Mr Nick *L Jan 2007*
4 Breams Buildings, London EC4
p927 . . . . . 020 7092 1900

Robinson, Mr Sam *M Nov 2002*
15, 51
Tooks Chambers, London EC4
p953 . . . . . 020 7842 7575

Robinson, Miss Sara J LLB *I Nov 1994*
Paradise Chambers, Sheffield
p992 . . . . . 0114 273 8951

ROBINSON, Mr Stephen M BA *G Nov 1999*
15
Wilberforce Chambers, Hull
p976 . . . . . 01482 323264

Robinson, Miss Tanya LLB(Soton) *I Nov 1997*
12, 15, 20, 30, 51
6-8 Mill Street, Maidstone
p982 . . . . . 01622 688094 / 688095
6 Pump Court, London EC4
p947 . . . . . 020 7797 8400

Robinson, Mr Thomas MA(Oxon) *L Jan 2003*
6, 8, 11, 18, 38
11 Stone Buildings, London WC2
p951 . . . . . 020 7831 6381

Robinson-Young, Mr David *L Jul 1999*
18
Broad Chare Chambers, Newcastle upon Tyne
p986 . . . . . 0191 232 0541

Roblin, Laraine A LLB(Hons)(Wales) *L Jul 1981*
20, 10
Iscoed Chambers, Swansea
p993 . . . . . 01792 652988

ROBSON, Mr Alexander BA(Hons)(Cantab)(Law) *M Jul 2006*
18, 11, 12, 6, 55, 56
Littleton Chambers, London EC4
p941 . . . . . 020 7797 8600

Robson, Mr Barry James *G Jul 2004*
New Court Chambers, Newcastle upon Tyne
p987 . . . . . 0191 232 1980

Robson, Mr David Ernest Henry MA(Oxon) *I Feb 1965*
(Q.C.) *15, 25, 10, 36, 12*
New Court Chambers, Newcastle upon Tyne
p987 . . . . . 0191 232 1980

Robson, Mr Jeremy *M Oct 1999*
KCH Garden Square Chambers, Nottingham
p989 . . . . . 0115 941 8851
KCH Garden Square Chambers, Leicester
p979 . . . . . 0115 941 8851

ROBSON, Mr John Malcolm LLB(Lond); FCIArb; Part-time Chairman Appeals Service *I Jul 1974*
3, 5, 6, 7, 8, 11, 12, 20, 22, 31, 32, 40, 41, 47, 51, 37
Arden Chambers, London WC1
p923 . . . . . 020 7242 4244

Robson, Mrs Sarah LLB(Hons) *I Jul 2002*
30, 8
Alpha Court Chambers, Leamington Spa
p977 . . . . . 0800 634 9650 / 01926 886412

Roche, Mr Brendan BA(Oxon) *G Jul 1989*
10, 18, 20, 26, 30, 53, 76
7 Bedford Row, London WC1
p924 . . . . . 020 7242 3555

ROCHE, Maria *I Jan 2010*
18, 53, 30, 40
1 Crown Office Row, London EC4
p929 . . . . . 020 7797 7500

Roche, Mr Patrick Recorder *M Jul 1977*
1, 10, 15, 18, 20, 22, 30, 36
Tooks Chambers, London EC4
p953 . . . . . 020 7842 7575

ROCHFORD, Mr Thomas Nicholas Beverley MA(Cantab); Recorder *I Jul 1984*
11, 18, 22, 30, 12, 40, 29, 53
St Philips Chambers, Birmingham
p969 . . . . . 0121 246 7000

Roddick, Miss Helen BA *G Jul 2004*
12, 15, 18, 30
9 Park Place, Cardiff
p973 . . . . . 029 2038 2731

Roddick, Mr Winston LLB; LLM; Recorder *G Nov 1968*
(Q.C.) *CB1, 8, 11, 12, 15, 22, 26, 31, 60, 36, 37, 27, 25, 40*
9 Park Place, Cardiff
p973 . . . . . 029 2038 2731

RODERICK, Mr David BA(Hons)(Manc); MA(Lond); LLM *M Oct 2005*
12, 18, 30
Farrar's Building, London EC4
p933 . . . . . 020 7583 9241

RODGER, Mr Jonathan LLB; LLM(Lond) *M Nov 1999*
6, 8, 11, 22, 40, 38, 88, 97
Enterprise Chambers, London WC2
p931 . . . . . 020 7405 9471
Enterprise Chambers, Leeds
p977 . . . . . 0113 246 0391
Enterprise Chambers, Newcastle upon Tyne
p987 . . . . . 0191 222 3344

RODGER, Mr Martin BA(Oxon) *M Jul 1986*
(Q.C.)
Falcon Chambers, London EC4
p933 . . . . . 020 7353 2484

RODGER, Miss Senay LLB(Hons)(East Anglia) *L Oct 1999*
30, 18, 12
Farrar's Building, London EC4
p933 . . . . . 020 7583 9241

Rodgers, Mr Benedict *I Nov 2007*
20, 15, 30
9 Gough Square, London EC4
p935 . . . . . 020 7832 0500

Rodgers, Ms June MA(Dublin); MA(Oxon) *M Nov 1971*
20, 10, 17, 37
Harcourt Chambers, London EC4
p936 . . . . . 0844 561 7135
Harcourt Chambers, Oxford
p989 . . . . . 0844 561 7135

Rodham, Miss Susan Anne LLB *G Nov 1989*
15, 20
5 King's Bench Walk, London EC4
p939 . . . . . 020 7353 5638

Rodikis, Miss Joanna *M Oct 1993*
St Johns Buildings, Preston
p990 . . . . . 01772 256100
St Johns Buildings, Chester
p974 . . . . . 01244 323070
St Johns Buildings, Manchester
p985 . . . . . 0161 214 1500
St Johns Buildings, Liverpool
p982 . . . . . 0151 243 6000

RODWAY, Miss Susan *M Jul 1981*
(Q.C.) *27, 53, 30, 40, 56, 76*
Thirty Nine Essex Street, London WC2
p932 . . . . . 020 7832 1111

ROE, Mr Thomas BA(Cantab) *M Nov 1995*
11, 12, 30, 18
3 Hare Court, London EC4
p937 . . . . . 020 7415 7800

Roebuck, Mr Roy *G Nov 1974*
15, 62, 94
Bell Yard Chambers, London WC2
p926 . . . . . 020 7306 9292 / 7404 5138

See p1010 for the Key to Work Categories

ROGERS, Miss Amy L *Jan 2007*
1, 55, 18, 73
11KBW, London EC4
p938 . . . 020 7632 8500

Rogers, Ms Beverly-Ann LLB(Lond) M *Jul 1978*
8, 9, 14, 96, 29, 32, 40, 93, 37
Serle Court, London WC2
p950 . . . 020 7242 6105

ROGERS, Mr Christopher Thomas BA(Hons)(Cantab) M *Jul 2004*
6, 11, 47
Five Paper, London EC4
p946 . . . 020 7815 3200

Rogers, Miss Christy MA(Cantab) M *Nov 1999*
13, 16, 44, 50
Ingenuity IP Chambers, London EC4
p937 . . . 020 7936 4474
No 3 Fleet Street Chambers, London EC4
p944 . . . 020 7936 4474

ROGERS, Mr Daniel BA(Hons) I *Oct 1997*
30, 22, 47, 53, 40, 67, 88
7 Harrington Street Chambers, Liverpool
p981 . . . 0151 242 0707

Rogers, Mr Don H LLB(Hons) M *Nov 1991*
15, 36, 12, 25
Goldsmith Chambers, London EC4
p935 . . . 020 7353 6802

Rogers, Mr Gregory Charles BA G *Nov 1992*
12, 15, 20, 30
St Ives Chambers, Birmingham
p969 . . . 0121 236 0863

Rogers, Miss Heather M *Jul 1983*
(Q.C.) *16, 50*
Doughty Street Chambers, London WC1
p930 . . . 020 7404 1313

ROGERS, Mr Ian Paul MA(Oxon); LLM(EUI) G *Nov 1995*
1, 5, 11, 12, 47, 18, 50, 19, 21, 62, 51, 24, 33, 55, 56, 59
Monckton Chambers, London WC1
p942 . . . 020 7405 7211

Rogers, Mr Jonathan M *Oct 2000*
30, 15, 12, 62, 95, 25
Exchange Chambers, Manchester
p983 . . . 0161 833 2722
Exchange Chambers, Liverpool
p980 . . . 0151 236 7747
Exchange Chambers, Leeds
p977 . . . 0113 203 1970

ROGERS, Miss Kate LLB I *Jan 2009*
10, 11, 15, 20
St Philips Chambers, Birmingham
p969 . . . 0121 246 7000

Rogers, Mr Ken I *Nov 1999*
6 King's Bench Walk, London EC4
p939 . . . 020 7583 0695 / 7353 4931

ROGERS, Mr Michael LLB(Hons) G *Jul 2002*
15, 18, 70
Mitre House Chambers, London WC1
p942 . . . 020 7307 7100

Rogers, Mr Paul LLB(Hons) I *Nov 1989*
15, 62, 84
Outer Temple Chambers, London WC2
p945 . . . 020 7353 6381

ROGERS, Miss Shona I *Oct 1998*
10, 20, 96, 49
1 King's Bench Walk, London EC4
p938 . . . 020 7936 1500

ROGERSON, Ms Judith BA L *Jul 2003*
1, 53, 51, 27, 30, 40, 36, 12
1 Crown Office Row, London EC4
p929 . . . 020 7797 7500

Rohrer, Mr Kerron I *Oct 2005*
15, 30, 12, 22, 53
Exchange Chambers, Manchester
p983 . . . 0161 833 2722
Exchange Chambers, Liverpool
p980 . . . 0151 236 7747
Exchange Chambers, Leeds
p977 . . . 0113 203 1970

Rolfe, Mr Patrick LLB(Lond) M *Nov 1987*
6, 11, 24, 29, 40, 8, 93
5 Stone Buildings, London WC2
p951 . . . 020 7242 6201

ROLLIN, Mr Aron M *Jan 2004*
Carmelite Chambers, London EC4
p927 . . . 020 7936 6300

Rollinson, Mr Darryn LLB(Hons) L *Jul 2001*
15, 62
15 New Bridge Street Chambers, London EC4
p943 . . . 020 7842 1900

ROMANS, Mr Philip MA G *Nov 1982*
15
Furnival Chambers, London EC4
p934 . . . 020 7405 3232

Romney, Miss Daphne BA(Cantab) I *Nov 1979*
51, 55, 18, 11, 43, 50, 56, 52
Cloisters, London EC4
p928 . . . 020 7827 4000

RONG, Miss Rochelle L *Jan 2005*
12, 30, 11, 40, 53, 22, 29
Ropewalk Chambers, Nottingham
p989 . . . 0115 947 2581

Roochove, Mr Mark BSc G *Oct 1994*
2 Pump Court, London EC4
p947 . . . 020 7353 5597

Rook, Miss Rachel L *Jan 2006*
15, 23, 20, 12
Paradise Chambers, Sheffield
p992 . . . 0114 273 8951

Rook, Mr Stuart Alan G *Oct 2006*
30, 47, 48, 59
Broad Chare Chambers, Newcastle upon Tyne
p986 . . . 0191 232 0541

Rooke, Mr Alex L *Jan 2001*
15, 62
5 St Andrew's Hill, London EC4
p950 . . . 020 7332 5400

Rooney, Mr Paul LLB I *Jan 2007*
15, 36
QEB Hollis Whiteman, London EC4
p948 . . . 020 7933 8855

Roots, Mr Guy MA(Oxon) M *Jul 1969*
(Q.C.) *1, 25, 26, 28, 31, 36*
Francis Taylor Building, London EC4
p934 . . . 020 7353 8415

ROQUES, Mr Michael G *Nov 2000*
4 King's Bench Walk, London EC4
p939 . . . 020 7822 7000

Rosario, Mr Desmond D L I *Nov 1990*
15
Paradise Chambers, Sheffield
p992 . . . 0114 273 8951

Roscoe, Mr Mark L *Oct 1999*
1 Mitre Court Buildings, London EC4
p942 . . . 020 7452 8900

ROSE, Mr Anthony Kenneth LLM M *Nov 1978*
10, 15, 18, 20, 22, 23, 25, 26, 30, 31, 36
Chavasse Court Chambers, Liverpool
p980 . . . 0151 229 2030

Rose, Mr Christopher L *Jan 1999*
New Court Chambers, Newcastle upon Tyne
p987 . . . 0191 232 1980

Rose, Mr David Leslie MA; LLB(Cantab) M *Jul 1977*
8, 11, 37, 40, 22, 6, 49, 32
No 6 Barristers Chambers, Leeds
p978 . . . 0113 245 9763

Rose, Miss Dinah BA(Oxon) G *Jul 1989*
(Q.C.) *1, 18, 19, 23, 36, 51, 55, 56, 89, 43, 44*
Blackstone Chambers, London EC4
p926 . . . 020 7583 1770

Rose, Mr Jonathon LLB M *Nov 1986*
15, 18, 12, 7, 6, 22
Charter Chambers, London WC1
p928 . . . 020 7618 4400

Rose, Mr Neil G *Jan 2007*
Northampton Chambers, Northampton
p988 . . . 01604 636271

Rose, Mr Paul LLB(Reading) G *Nov 1981*
(Q.C.) *18, 27, 30, 36, 56, 55, 51, 53, 26*
Old Square Chambers, Bristol
p971 . . . 0117 930 5100
Old Square Chambers, London WC1
p945 . . . 020 7269 0300

ROSE, Mr Stephen BA(Oxon) G *Nov 1995*
15, 62, 68
18 Red Lion Court, London EC4
p949 . . . 020 7520 6000
18 Red Lion Court (Annexe), Chelmsford
p973 . . . 01245 280880

Rose, Mr Will I *Jul 2007*
King's Bench Godolphin Chambers, Truro
p994 . . . 0845 308 1551
King's Bench Godolphin Chambers, Plymouth
p990 . . . 0845 308 1551

Rosefield, Ms Laura M *Jul 2003*
15
6 King's Bench Walk, London EC4
p939 . . . 020 7583 0410

ROSEMAN, Mr Gideon I *Jul 2007*
8
Ten Old Square, London WC2
p945 . . . 020 7405 0758

Rosenblatt, Mr Jeremy LLB(Hons)(LSE) G *Jul 1985*
42 Bedford Row, London WC1
p925 . . . 020 7831 0222

ROSENTHAL, Mr Adam BA(Oxon) G *Oct 1999*
Falcon Chambers, London EC4
p933 . . . 020 7353 2484

Rosenthal, Mr Dennis G *Nov 2009*
Henderson Chambers, London EC4
p937 . . . 020 7583 9020

Ross, Mr David LLB M *Nov 1974*
15
5 St Andrew's Hill, London EC4
p950 . . . 020 7332 5400

Ross, Mr Gordon MacRae LLB I *Jul 1986*
15, 36, 62
3 Temple Gardens, London EC4
p952 . . . 020 7353 3102

Ross, Mr Iain I *Nov 1991*
12, 18, 19, 20, 22, 24, 25, 29, 30
3PB, Bournemouth
p969 . . . 01202 292102

ROSS, Mr James G *Nov 2001*
Maidstone Chambers, Maidstone
p982 . . . 01622 688592
Gough Square Chambers, London EC4
p935 . . . 020 7353 0924

Ross, Mr John G LLM(Lond) I *Jul 1971*
(Q.C.) *24, 30, 40, 53, 48, 62, 26*
1 Chancery Lane, London WC2
p928 . . . 0845 634 6666

Ross, Mr Neil BA(Hons) G *Oct 2006*
15, 62, 70, 94
15 New Bridge Street Chambers, London EC4
p943 . . . 020 7842 1900

Ross, Mr Sidney LLB; MSc; PhD(Lond) M *Jul 1983*
1, 8, 32, 36, 37
11 Stone Buildings, London WC2
p951 . . . 020 7831 6381

Ross, Simon LLB(Hons) L *Nov 1999*
6, 12, 30, 40, 38, 47, 67, 89, 94
Zenith Chambers, Leeds
p979 . . . 0113 245 5438

Ross, Mr Tony G *Jan 1991*
22
1 Pump Court, London EC4
p947 . . . 020 7842 7070

ROSS MARTYN, Mr John Greaves MA(Cantab); LLM(Cantab) M *Oct 1969*
37, 8
New Square Chambers, London WC2
p943 . . . 020 7419 8000

Ross-Munro, Mr Colin W G MA(Cantab) M *Jun 1951*
(Q.C.) *5, 8, 11, 12, 24, 36, 3, 41, 89*
Blackstone Chambers, London EC4
p926 . . . 020 7583 1770

Rothwell, Miss Joanne I *Oct 1993*
1, 51, 23
No5 Chambers, Bristol
p971 . . . 0845 210 5555
No5 Chambers, London EC4
p944 . . . 0845 210 5555
No5 Chambers, Birmingham
p968 . . . 0845 210 5555

ROUCH, Mr Peter Christopher G *Jul 1972*
(Q.C.) *15, 62*
3 Temple Gardens, London EC4
p952 . . . 020 7353 3102
Iscoed Chambers, Swansea
p993 . . . 01792 652988

Rouch, Mr Robin BA(Hons) G *Nov 1999*
15, 12, 18
Iscoed Chambers, Swansea
p993 . . . 01792 652988

Rought-Brooks, Ms Hannah LLB M *Mar 1999*
10, 20
Tooks Chambers, London EC4
p953 . . . 020 7842 7575

Roughton, Mr Ashley Wentworth BSc(Lond); DipLaw; BSc(Eng); PhD(Cantab) I *Oct 1992*
13, 15, 19, 44
Hogarth Chambers, London WC2
p937 . . . 020 7404 0404

ROUSE, Mr James G *Jul 2000*
15, 62, 95
187 Fleet Street, London EC4
p933 . . . 020 7430 7430

Rouse, Mr Justin Recorder L *Jul 1982*
15, 51, 62
Nine Bedford Row, London WC1
p924 . . . 020 7489 2727

Roussak, Mr Jeremy Brian MA; MB; B CHIR(Cantab); FRCS(Edin) M *Oct 1996*
30, 40, 53
St Johns Buildings, Preston
p990 . . . 01772 256100
St Johns Buildings, Chester
p974 . . . 01244 323070
St Johns Buildings, Manchester
p985 . . . 0161 214 1500
St Johns Buildings, Liverpool
p982 . . . 0151 243 6000

ROUTLEDGE, Mr Shaun LLB(Hons) G *Nov 1988*
15, 25, 48
Trinity (Newcastle) Chambers, Newcastle upon Tyne
p987 . . . 0191 232 1927
Trinity (Teesside) Chambers, Middlesbrough
p986 . . . 01642 247569

Routley, Mr Patrick MA(Cantab) I *Jul 1979*
10, 17, 20, 32, 37, 30, 12
Goldsmith Chambers, London EC4
p935 . . . 020 7353 6802

Row, Mr Charles BA(Hons) L *Oct 1993*
15, 48, 62, 68, 39, 84, 94, 95, 36
Queen Square Chambers, Bristol
p972 . . . 0117 921 1966

Rowe, Ms Freya E B BA(Oxon) I *Oct 1996*
Thomas More Chambers, London WC2
p952 . . . 020 7404 7000

ROWE, Miss Judith May LLB(Lond) G *Jul 1979*
(Q.C.) *10, 20*
1 Garden Court, London EC4
p934 . . . 020 7797 7900

Rowell, Mr David Stewart BA(Oxon) G *Jul 1972*
8, 9, 29, 34, 37, 58, 88, 93
9 Stone Buildings Barristers Chambers, London WC2
p951 . . . 020 7404 5055

Rowell, Mr George MA(Oxon); DipLaw; MA(City) L *Jan 2004*
18, 57, 8, 11
St John's Chambers, Bristol
p972 . . . 0117 921 3456

Rowland, Mr Nicholas BA(Bris) I *Jun 1988*
12, 15
3PB, Winchester
p994 . . . 01962 868884

Rowland, Mr Robin Frank LLB; Recorder M *Nov 1977*
10, 20, 2
No5 Chambers, Bristol
p971 . . . 0845 210 5555
No5 Chambers, London EC4
p944 . . . 0845 210 5555
No5 Chambers, Birmingham
p968 . . . 0845 210 5555

Rowlands, Mr David P LLB(Manc) M *Nov 1988*
10, 12, 15, 20
Broad Chare Chambers, Newcastle upon Tyne
p986 . . . 0191 232 0541

Rowlands, Mr Mark BA(Hons)(Oxon) G *Nov 1990*
3, 7, 11, 24, 40
Keating Chambers, London WC2
p938 . . . 020 7544 2600
1 Pump Court, London EC4
p947 . . . 020 7842 7070

Rowlands, Miss Sara G *Jan 2001*
20, 30, 8
Iscoed Chambers, Swansea
p993 . . . 01792 652988
Pallant Chambers, Chichester
p974 . . . 01243 784538

13

ROWLEY, Mr James MA(Cantab); DipLaw *L Jul 1987*
(Q.C.) *53, 27, 30, 56, 42*
42 Bedford Row, London WC1
p925 . . . . 020 7831 0222
Byrom Street Chambers, Manchester
p983 . . . . 0161 829 2100

Rowley, Miss Jane LLB *G Jul 1988*
15
Temple Chambers, Newport
p988 . . . . 01633 267403 / 255855
Temple Chambers, Cardiff
p973 . . . . 029 2039 7364

Rowley, Mr Karl John BA(Hons) *M Nov 1994*
20
St Johns Buildings, Preston
p990 . . . . 01772 256100
St Johns Buildings, Chester
p974 . . . . 01244 323070
St Johns Buildings, Manchester
p985 . . . . 0161 214 1500
St Johns Buildings, Liverpool
p982 . . . . 0151 243 6000

Rowley, Mr Keith LLB(Lond) *G Jul 1979*
(Q.C.) *5, 6, 8, 11, 22, 29, 40*
Radcliffe Chambers, London WC2
p949 . . . . 020 7831 0081

Rowley, Miss Rachel *M Nov 1997*
20, 10, 63
No5 Chambers, Bristol
p971 . . . . 0845 210 5555
No5 Chambers, London EC4
p944 . . . . 0845 210 5555
No5 Chambers, Birmingham
p968 . . . . 0845 210 5555

ROWLING, Miss Fiona *I Jan 1980*
15
Westgate Chambers, Lewes
p980 . . . . 01273 480510

ROWLINSON, Miss Wendy BA(Hons) *G Jul 1981*
10, 20
Pallant Chambers, Chichester
p974 . . . . 01243 784538

Rowntree, Mr Edward BA(Hons)(Oxon) *L Apr 1996*
Hardwicke, London WC2
p936 . . . . 020 7242 2523

Rowsell, Miss Claire LLB(Hons)(Wales) *M Feb 1991*
20
Albion Chambers, Bristol
p970 . . . . 0117 927 2144

Roxburgh, Mr Alan BA(Oxon); DipLaw(City) *M Oct 1992*
11, 35, 24, 5
Brick Court Chambers, London WC2
p927 . . . . 020 7379 3550

ROY, Mr Andrew MA; LLB(Hons) *L Jul 2002*
53, 12, 24, 40, 30, 56, 59, 67, 89
12 King's Bench Walk, London EC4
p940 . . . . 020 7583 0811

Royce, Mr Darryl BA *G Nov 1976*
3, 7, 11, 31, 40, 41, 43, 45, 49, 54, 61, 78, 74
Atkin Chambers, London WC1
p923 . . . . 020 7404 0102

Royle, Mr Charles *L Oct 1997*
Goldsmith Chambers, London EC4
p935 . . . . 020 7353 6802

Royle, Mr Chris LLB; MA *L Jul 2009*
6, 11, 12, 18, 38, 43, 45, 47, 67, 75, 87, 93, 97
Exchange Chambers, Manchester
p983 . . . . 0161 833 2722
Exchange Chambers, Liverpool
p980 . . . . 0151 236 7747
Exchange Chambers, Leeds
p977 . . . . 0113 203 1970

Rozier, Mr James Ian *M Jan 2007*
11, 12, 18, 46, 55, 38
Rougemont Chambers, Exeter
p975 . . . . 01392 208484

Rubens, Miss Jacqueline *L Nov 1989*
1 Pump Court, London EC4
p947 . . . . 020 7842 7070

Rubin, Mr Stephen Charles MA(Oxon) *M Jul 1977*
(Q.C.)
Fountain Court Chambers, London EC4
p934 . . . . 020 7583 3335

Ruck, Miss Mary Ida MA(Lond) *G Oct 1993*
63, 27, 53, 30, 84, 51
42 Bedford Row, London WC1
p925 . . . . 020 7831 0222
Byrom Street Chambers, Manchester
p983 . . . . 0161 829 2100

RUCK KEENE, Mr Alexander BA(Hons); MA(Hons) *L Oct 2002*
1, 11, 31, 46, 51, 18, 30, 40, 23, 63, 85, 26, 12, 67, 14
Thirty Nine Essex Street, London WC2
p932 . . . . 020 7832 1111

Rudd, Mr Matthew *I Nov 1994*
10, 12, 67, 18, 20, 32, 40
Broadway House Chambers, Leeds
p977 . . . . 0113 246 2600
Broadway House Chambers, Bradford
p969 . . . . 01274 722560

Rudd, Mr Michael *I Jan 2002*
15, 31, 20, 23
36 Bedford Row, London WC1
p925 . . . . 020 7421 8000

RUDD, Mr Oliver BA(Oxon)(Biological Sciences) *L Jan 2009*
30, 18, 12
12 King's Bench Walk, London EC4
p940 . . . . 020 7583 0811

Rudd, Miss Zoe LLB(Hons) *G Jul 2003*
10, 12, 18, 20, 63
College Chambers, Southampton
p992 . . . . 023 8023 0338

Rudeloff, Walter *M Jan 1990*
4 KBW, London EC4
p938 . . . . 020 7822 8822

Rudman, Ms Sara LLB(Hons)(Exon) *I Nov 1992*
20, 10
Pendragon Chambers, Swansea
p993 . . . . 01792 411188

RUDOLF, Mr Nathaniel *M Nov 1996*
15, 62
25 Bedford Row, London WC1
p925 . . . . 020 7067 1500

Rudston, Mr Neville *M Jan 2000*
15
1 Pump Court, London EC4
p947 . . . . 020 7842 7070

RUFFELL, Mr Mark BA(Hons)(Lond); DipLaw *M Nov 1992*
15, 42, 25, 91
Pump Court Chambers, Swindon
p993 . . . . 01793 539899
Pump Court Chambers, Winchester
p994 . . . . 01962 868161
Pump Court Chambers, London EC4
p947 . . . . 020 7353 0711

Rule, Mr Jonathan Daniel *G Oct 1993*
8
Palmyra Chambers, Warrington
p994 . . . . 01925 444919

Rumfitt, Mr Nigel John BA(Oxon); BCL; Recorder *G Jul 1974*
(Q.C.) *15, 84*
7 Bedford Row, London WC1
p924 . . . . 020 7242 3555

RUMNEY, Mr Conrad MA *I Feb 1988*
1, 7, 8, 11, 12, 22, 26, 31, 40
St Philips Chambers, Birmingham
p969 . . . . 0121 246 7000

Rupasinha, Mr Sunil LLB *I Nov 1983*
15
5 St Andrew's Hill, London EC4
p950 . . . . 020 7332 5400

Rush, Mr Craig LLB(Hons) *I Nov 1989*
15, 62
2 Bedford Row, London WC1
p924 . . . . 020 7440 8888

Rushbrooke, Mr Justin MA(Oxon) *M Jul 1992*
11, 12, 13, 16, 50, 51
5RB, London WC1
p948 . . . . 020 7242 2902

Rushton, Mr Jonathon *I Nov 1997*
12, 46, 31, 93, 22, 70
36 Bedford Row, London WC1
p925 . . . . 020 7421 8000

RUSHTON, Ms Nicola Jane BA(Cantab); LLM(Dalhousie Canada) *G Oct 1993*
11, 30, 40
Five Paper, London EC4
p946 . . . . 020 7815 3200

Rushworth, Mr Adam *L Nov 2010*
One Essex Court, London EC4
p931 . . . . 020 7583 2000

Rushworth, Miss Georgina BA(York); MA *L Oct 2007*
10, 20
Coram Chambers, London EC1
p929 . . . . 020 7092 3700

RUSSELL, Ms Alison *G Jul 1983*
(Q.C.) *10, 20*
1 Garden Court, London EC4
p934 . . . . 020 7797 7900
Pump Court Chambers, Swindon
p993 . . . . 01793 539899
Pump Court Chambers, Winchester
p994 . . . . 01962 868161
Pump Court Chambers, London EC4
p947 . . . . 020 7353 0711

RUSSELL, Mr Christopher John LLB(Exon) *G Nov 1982*
12, 24, 30, 40, 49
2 Temple Gardens, London EC4
p952 . . . . 020 7822 1200

Russell, Miss Fern *M Oct 1994*
2 King's Bench Walk, London EC4
p939 . . . . 020 7353 1746

RUSSELL, Mr Graham *I Nov 2004*
Citadel Chambers, Birmingham
p967 . . . . 0121 233 8500

Russell, Mr Guy BA *G Nov 1985*
10, 12, 15
Westgate Chambers, Lewes
p980 . . . . 01273 480510

Russell, Ms Jane *G Nov 2004*
18
Tooks Chambers, London EC4
p953 . . . . 020 7842 7575

Russell, Mr Jeremy BA; LLM(Lond) *M Nov 1975*
(Q.C.) *11, 35, 4, 24*
Quadrant Chambers, London EC4
p948 . . . . 020 7583 4444

Russell, Mr John BA(Oxon) *M Oct 1993*
4, 24, 5, 40, 11, 35
Quadrant Chambers, London EC4
p948 . . . . 020 7583 4444

Russell, Mr Martin Howard LLB *I Nov 1977*
6, 7, 8, 10, 11, 12, 13, 15, 16, 18
Field Court Chambers, London WC1
p933 . . . . 020 7405 6114

RUSSELL, Mr Paul BA(Dunelm) *M Jul 1984*
(Q.C.) *12, 24, 30, 40, 47, 53*
12 King's Bench Walk, London EC4
p940 . . . . 020 7583 0811

Russell, Ms Rachel MA(Oxon) *G Oct 2001*
30
St John's Chambers, Bristol
p972 . . . . 0117 921 3456

Russell, Mr Tom *I Jan 2004*
6, 8, 12, 18, 22, 30, 40, 36, 37
KCH Garden Square Chambers, Nottingham
p989 . . . . 0115 941 8851
KCH Garden Square Chambers, Leicester
p979 . . . . 0115 941 8851

Russell Flint, Mr Simon BA(Hons) *I Nov 1980*
(Q.C.) *15, 36, 62, 72, 70*
Eastbourne Chambers, Eastbourne
p975 . . . . 01323 642102
23 Essex Street, London WC2
p932 . . . . 020 7413 0353

Russell-Mitra, Ms Jessica *M Jan 2003*
1 Mitre Court Buildings, London EC4
p942 . . . . 020 7452 8900

Russen, Mr Jonathan LLB(Wales); LLM(Hons)(Cantab) *L Jul 1986*
(Q.C.) *6, 8, 11, 37*
Maitland Chambers, London WC2
p941 . . . . 020 7406 1200

Rustom, Mr Shiraz *M Oct 1998*
1 Mitre Court Buildings, London EC4
p942 . . . . 020 7452 8900

Rutherford, Miss Emma LLB(Hons) *M Nov 2002*
15, 23, 12
No 8 Chambers, Birmingham
p968 . . . . 0121 236 5514

RUTHERFORD, Mr Martin *L Oct 1990*
Furnival Chambers, London EC4
p934 . . . . 020 7405 3232

Rutledge, Mr Kelvin Albert LLB(Essex); LLM *M Jul 1989*
8, 22, 26
Cornerstone Barristers, London WC1
p929 . . . . 020 7242 4986

RUTTER, Mr Andrew M LLB *M Jul 1990*
15, 25, 48
Trinity (Newcastle) Chambers, Newcastle upon Tyne
p987 . . . . 0191 232 1927
Trinity (Teesside) Chambers, Middlesbrough
p986 . . . . 01642 247569

Ruttle, Mr Stephen BA(Cantab) *G Nov 1976*
(Q.C.) *24, 35, 41*
Brick Court Chambers, London WC2
p927 . . . . 020 7379 3550

Ryan, Mr David Patrick BA *G Nov 1985*
15, 62
3 Temple Gardens, London EC4
p952 . . . . 020 7353 3102

Ryan, Miss Fiona *G Mar 2009*
5 King's Bench Walk, London EC4
p939 . . . . 020 7353 5638

Ryan, Mr Liam Michael LLB(Durham); LLM(Notts) *I Jan 2007*
4, 6, 8, 11, 12, 13, 16, 18, 24, 25, 27, 30, 36, 37, 38, 40, 47, 48, 52, 53, 55, 66, 67, 68, 74, 84
Ely Place Chambers, London EC1
p931 . . . . 020 7400 9600

RYAN, Nicholas BA(Lond) *G Jan 1984*
15, 20
Atlantic Chambers, Liverpool
p980 . . . . 0151 236 4421

Ryan, Mr Richard *G Oct 2004*
41, 74, 38
Hardwicke, London WC2
p936 . . . . 020 7242 2523

Ryder, Mr John BA(Hons) *I Nov 1980*
(Q.C.) *15, 25, 62*
6 King's Bench Walk, London EC4
p939 . . . . 020 7583 0410

RYDER, Mr Matthew LLB(Hons)(Cantab); LLM(Columbia) *G Oct 1992*
(Q.C.) *1, 12, 15, 51, 56, 55, 18, 70, 71, 72, 73, 80, 95*
Matrix Chambers, London WC1
p942 . . . . 020 7404 3447

Rylands, Ms Elizabeth *M Jan 1973*
20
18 St John Street Chambers, Manchester
p985 . . . . 0161 278 1800

Ryle, Ms Kate *I Aug 2002*
5 Pump Court, London EC4
p947 . . . . 020 7353 2532 / 7583 7133

Sabben-Clare, Ms Rebecca BA(Oxon) *G Oct 1993*
3, 4, 5, 11, 24, 35, 40
7 King's Bench Walk, London EC4
p940 . . . . 020 7910 8300

Sabido, Mr John *L Jul 1976*
Goldsmith Chambers, London EC4
p935 . . . . 020 7353 6802

Sabiston, Mr Peter LLB *G Feb 1992*
15, 70, 72
Old Court Chambers, Middlesbrough
p986 . . . . 01642 232523

SABRY, Karim S BA(Hons) *I Oct 1992*
30, 22, 23
9 St John Street Chambers, Manchester
p984 . . . . 0161 955 9000

SACHDEVA, Mr Vikram *I Oct 1998*
1, 7, 11, 18, 51, 27, 53, 31, 55, 56, 36, 76, 63
Thirty Nine Essex Street, London WC2
p932 . . . . 020 7832 1111

Sackman, Sarah *I Jan 2008*
1, 12, 43, 76, 18, 46, 2, 22, 51, 23, 25, 26, 54, 31, 60, 36
Francis Taylor Building, London EC4
p934 . . . . 020 7353 8415

Sadd, Mr Patrick *M Nov 1984*
30, 53, 1, 60
Outer Temple Chambers, London WC2
p945 . . . . 020 7353 6381

SADIQ, Mr Faisel *I Oct 2000*
1, 22, 19, 51, 26, 31
Arden Chambers, London WC1
p923 . . . . 020 7242 4244

Sadiq, Mr Tariq BA(Hons)(Kent) *G Jul 1993*
18, 55
Devereux Chambers, London WC2
p930 . . . . 020 7353 7534
St Philips Chambers, Birmingham
p969 . . . . 0121 246 7000

Sadler, Miss Rhiannon *M Jul 2004*
Westgate Chambers, Lewes
p980 . . . . 01273 480510

See p1010 for the Key to Work Categories

SAGAR, Mr Leigh BA(North London) L *Jul 1983*
11, 37, 57, 58
New Square Chambers, London WC2
p943 . . . 020 7419 8000

SAGE, Mr Richard BA(Hons); CPE L *Nov 2006*
74, 7, 40, 11, 24, 30
Crown Office Chambers, London EC4
p929 . . . 020 7797 8100

SAHONTE, Rajinder Kumar LLB(Hons) L *Nov 1986*
8, 32, 37, 93, 11
Guildhall Chambers, Bristol
p970 . . . 0117 930 9000

SAHU, Mr Mark LLB(Hons); LLM M *Nov 1995*
15, 18, 12, 70
Mitre House Chambers, London WC1
p942 . . . 020 7307 7100

Said, Mr Sebastian William St.John BA(Hons); BCL(Oxon) I *Nov 2004*
Fountain Court Chambers, London EC4
p934 . . . 020 7583 3335

Saifee, Mr Faisal M *Jan 2003*
89
Thomas More Chambers, London WC2
p952 . . . 020 7404 7000

SAIFOLAHI, Ms Sanaz L *Jul 2000*
23, 51
Renaissance Chambers, London WC1
p949 . . . 020 7404 1111

Saini, Mr Pushpinder MA(Oxon); BCL(Oxon) G *Oct 1991*
(Q.C.) *1, 8, 11, 12, 19, 23, 29, 50, 51, 56, 89, 52, 5, 81, 44*
Blackstone Chambers, London EC4
p926 . . . 020 7583 1770

Sajid, Ahmer LLB(Hons) L *Nov 1998*
12
Clerksroom - Administration Centre, Taunton
p993 . . . 0845 083 3000

Sakr, Ms Farida M *Jan 2005*
4 Breams Buildings, London EC4
p927 . . . 020 7092 1900

SALAKO, Miss Toyin M *Nov 1998*
15, 25, 62, 70, 72
23 Essex Street, London WC2
p932 . . . 020 7413 0353

SALIS, Robert M *Jan 1999*
4 King's Bench Walk, London EC4
p939 . . . 020 7822 7000

Sallar, Tara M *Jan 2007*
Clerksroom - Administration Centre, Taunton
p993 . . . 0845 083 3000

Sallon, Mr Christopher Recorder G *Jul 1973*
(Q.C.) *15, 51*
Doughty Street Chambers, London WC1
p930 . . . 020 7404 1313

Salmman, Mr Hashim LLB L *Jan 2005*
15
Temple Chambers, Newport
p988 . . . 01633 267403 / 255855
Temple Chambers, Cardiff
p973 . . . 029 2039 7364

SALMON, Mr Charles Nathan LLB I *Nov 1972*
(Q.C.) *15, 72, 62*
25 Bedford Row, London WC1
p925 . . . 020 7067 1500

SALMON, Mr Jonathan Carl LLB; Deputy District Judge I *Nov 1987*
30, 46, 84, 88
St Philips Chambers, Birmingham
p969 . . . 0121 246 7000

SALMON, Mr Kevin MA G *Oct 1984*
10, 12, 20
St Mary's Chambers, Nottingham
p989 . . . 0115 950 3503

SALMON, Miss Sarah L *Jun 2007*
1, 22, 26, 88, 93
Arden Chambers, London WC1
p923 . . . 020 7242 4244

Saloman, Mr Timothy P D BA(Oxon) M *Nov 1975*
(Q.C.) *3, 35, 33, 11, 24, 5, 40*
7 King's Bench Walk, London EC4
p940 . . . 020 7910 8300

Salter, Mr Adrian MA(Cantab) M *Jul 1973*
5, 6, 8, 11, 13, 16, 24, 29
11 Stone Buildings, London WC2
p951 . . . 020 7831 6381

Salter, Mr Michael G *Oct 1999*
18, 55, 30, 89, 11
Ely Place Chambers, London EC1
p931 . . . 020 7400 9600

SALTER, Mr Richard MA(Oxon); ACIArb I *Jul 1975*
(Q.C.) *3, 5, 6, 11, 13, 18, 24, 40*
3 Verulam Buildings, London WC1
p953 . . . 020 7831 8441

Salter, Miss Sibby MA(Cantab) M *Oct 1991*
15, 18, 20, 22, 25, 62
3 Temple Gardens, London EC4
p952 . . . 020 7353 3102

Salzedo, Mr Simon BA(Oxon); ACA; DipLaw L *Jan 1995*
11, 40, 5, 24, 35
Brick Court Chambers, London WC2
p927 . . . 020 7379 3550

SAMEK, Mr Charles MA(Oxon); Accredited Mediator M *Nov 1989*
(Q.C.) *5, 6, 7, 8, 11, 18, 29, 13, 36, 49*
Littleton Chambers, London EC4
p941 . . . 020 7797 8600

Samiloff, Mr Julian David BSc; LLM I *May 1988*
10, 12, 15, 20, 23, 33
Wight Chambers, Newport
p988 . . . 01983 522828 / 07976 512823

SAMIMI, Ms Maryam M *Jul 1994*
23
Mitre House Chambers, London WC1
p942 . . . 020 7307 7100

Sammy, Ms Natasha L *Jan 2006*
1 Pump Court, London EC4
p947 . . . 020 7842 7070

Sampson, Mr Graeme William LLB G *Nov 1981*
31, 74, 40, 96
3PB, London EC4
p946 . . . 020 7583 8055

Sampson, Mr Jonathan R MA(Cantab) M *Oct 1997*
20, 10
Harcourt Chambers, London EC4
p936 . . . 0844 561 7135
Harcourt Chambers, Oxford
p989 . . . 0844 561 7135

Sampson, Dr Timothy L *Jan 2000*
One Essex Court, London EC4
p931 . . . 020 7936 3030

Samra, Miss Sharn L *Nov 2002*
10, 12, 18, 23
Broadway House Chambers, Leeds
p977 . . . 0113 246 2600
Broadway House Chambers, Bradford
p969 . . . 01274 722560

Samson, Mr John I *Jan 2001*
16
Ely Place Chambers, London EC1
p931 . . . 020 7400 9600

Samuel, Mr Adam I *Jul 2003*
Old Square Chambers, Bristol
p971 . . . 0117 930 5100
Old Square Chambers, London WC1
p945 . . . 020 7269 0300

Samuel, Ms Ana I *Jul 2004*
18, 30
St Johns Buildings, Preston
p990 . . . 01772 256100
St Johns Buildings, Chester
p974 . . . 01244 323070
St Johns Buildings, Manchester
p985 . . . 0161 214 1500
St Johns Buildings, Liverpool
p982 . . . 0151 243 6000

Samuel, Mr Gerwyn MA(Oxon) G *Jul 1986*
53, 27, 51, 30
Doughty Street Chambers, London WC1
p930 . . . 020 7404 1313

SAMUEL, Mr Glyn LLB L *Oct 1991*
12, 15, 30
St Philips Chambers, Birmingham
p969 . . . 0121 246 7000

Samuel, Miss Jacqueline Eleanor LLB G *Jul 1971*
15
2 Hare Court, London EC4
p937 . . . 020 7353 5324

SAMUEL, Mr Richard G G MA; LLB M *Jan 1996*
11, 18
3 Hare Court, London EC4
p937 . . . 020 7415 7800

Samuel, Mr Tim M *Jan 2005*
6 King's Bench Walk, London EC4
p939 . . . 020 7583 0695 / 7353 4931

SAMUEL, Mr Zimran M *Nov 2008*
9 St John Street Chambers, Manchester
p984 . . . 0161 955 9000

Samuels, Mr Jeffrey K M *Jul 1988*
(Q.C.) *15*
St Johns Buildings, Preston
p990 . . . 01772 256100
St Johns Buildings, Chester
p974 . . . 01244 323070
St Johns Buildings, Manchester
p985 . . . 0161 214 1500
St Johns Buildings, Liverpool
p982 . . . 0151 243 6000

SAMUELS, Ms Leslie BA(Cantab); MA; Deputy District Judge G *Jul 1989*
(Q.C.) *10, 12, 15, 18, 20, 25, 30, 49*
Pump Court Chambers, Swindon
p993 . . . 01793 539899
Pump Court Chambers, Winchester
p994 . . . 01962 868161
Pump Court Chambers, London EC4
p947 . . . 020 7353 0711

SAMUELS, Mr Thomas David BA(Oxon) L *Jan 2009*
Gough Square Chambers, London EC4
p935 . . . 020 7353 0924

Sandbach, Miss Carly I *Jul 2006*
5, 6, 8, 11, 22, 29, 40, 36, 24, 66, 97, 47, 67, 69, 62, 38, 89, 96, 93, 56
Exchange Chambers, Manchester
p983 . . . 0161 833 2722
Exchange Chambers, Liverpool
p980 . . . 0151 236 7747
Exchange Chambers, Leeds
p977 . . . 0113 203 1970

Sandbrook-Hughes, Mr Stewert BSc(Econ); DipLaw L *Nov 1980*
25, 29, 30, 31, 10, 12, 20, 15
Iscoed Chambers, Swansea
p993 . . . 01792 652988

SANDELL, Mr Adam BA(Oxon); BM BCh(Oxon); LLB(Lond); MSc(Oxon); MRCGP L *Jul 2008*
1, 23, 33, 36, 51, 55, 63, 70, 77, 27, 85, 68
Matrix Chambers, London WC1
p942 . . . 020 7404 3447

Sandells, Miss Nicole BA(Oxon) I *Nov 1994*
5, 8, 11, 14, 22, 29, 32, 37, 40, 12, 24
Four New Square, London WC2
p943 . . . 020 7822 2000

Sander, Ms Amy M *Jan 2006*
Essex Court Chambers, London WC2
p931 . . . 020 7813 8000

Sandercock, Ms Natalie BA(Hons); PGDipLaw M *Sep 2000*
12, 47, 20, 30, 63, 76
Thirty Park Place, Cardiff
p973 . . . 029 2039 8421

Sanders, Mr Damian LLB M *Nov 1988*
10, 12, 20
St Johns Buildings, Preston
p990 . . . 01772 256100
St Johns Buildings, Chester
p974 . . . 01244 323070
St Johns Buildings, Manchester
p985 . . . 0161 214 1500
St Johns Buildings, Liverpool
p982 . . . 0151 243 6000

SANDERS, Mr Oliver LLB; BCL I *Jul 1995*
1, 42, 53, 12, 51, 26, 30, 31, 40
1 Crown Office Row, London EC4
p929 . . . 020 7797 7500

SANDERSON, Mr David F BA I *Nov 1985*
30, 40, 53
12 King's Bench Walk, London EC4
p940 . . . 020 7583 0811

Sanderson, Miss Eleanor MA(Oxon); DipLaw I *Jul 2005*
15, 62
2 Bedford Row, London WC1
p924 . . . 020 7440 8888

SANDFORD, Mr Robert M *Jan 1999*
15
Bank House Chambers, Sheffield
p991 . . . 0114 275 1223

Sandford, Mr Simon G *Nov 1979*
15, 20
5 King's Bench Walk, London EC4
p939 . . . 020 7353 5638

SANDHAM, Mr James Andrew LLB; LLM(Commercial) L *Mar 2002*
1, 8, 12, 22, 26
Arden Chambers, London WC1
p923 . . . 020 7242 4244

Sandhu, Mr Harpreet Singh G *Jul 2005*
15, 62, 84, 39, 94, 70, 72, 71
No5 Chambers, Bristol
p971 . . . 0845 210 5555
No5 Chambers, London EC4
p944 . . . 0845 210 5555
No5 Chambers, Birmingham
p968 . . . 0845 210 5555

SANDHU, Sunit BA; LLB(Hons) M *Feb 1990*
15, 25, 62
Equity Chambers, Birmingham
p968 . . . 0121 233 2100

Sandiford, Mr David BA(Oxon) G *Oct 1995*
30, 53, 25, 51
Cobden House Chambers, Manchester
p983 . . . 0161 833 6000

Sandiford, Mr Jonathan LLB(Newc); Recorder G *Oct 1992*
72, 15, 62, 70, 68
St Pauls Chambers, Leeds
p979 . . . 0113 245 5866

SANDS, Professor Philippe MA; LLM(Cantab) M *Nov 1985*
(Q.C.) *3, 19, 33, 51, 46, 21, 11, 1*
Matrix Chambers, London WC1
p942 . . . 020 7404 3447

SANDYS, Mr Neil I *Oct 1998*
15, 27, 34
23 Essex Street, London WC2
p932 . . . 020 7413 0353

Sanghera, Ms Sharan BA(Hons)(Oxon) M *Jan 2009*
30, 18, 12
3PB, London EC4
p946 . . . 020 7583 8055

SANGSTER, Mr Nigel H LLB M *Nov 1976*
(Q.C.) *15, 62*
25 Bedford Row, London WC1
p925 . . . 020 7067 1500
St Pauls Chambers, Leeds
p979 . . . 0113 245 5866

Santmera, Miss Louise G *Oct 2002*
15, 23, 18
New Bailey Chambers, Preston
p990 . . . 01772 258087

Saoul, Mr Daniel L *Jan 2008*
Four New Square, London WC2
p943 . . . 020 7822 2000

SAPIECHA, Mr David J LLB(Hons) M *Oct 1990*
15, 25, 12, 51
Colleton Chambers, Exeter
p975 . . . 01392 274898

Sapnara, Ms Khatun LLB(Lond) M *Nov 1990*
10, 20
Coram Chambers, London EC1
p929 . . . 020 7092 3700

Sapsard, Jamal LLB L *Jul 1987*
12, 15, 20, 22, 34, 25
2 Dr Johnson's Buildings, London EC4
p930 . . . 020 7936 2613

Sapsford, Mr Philip I *Nov 1974*
(Q.C.)
Goldsmith Chambers, London EC4
p935 . . . 020 7353 6802

Sapstead, Miss Louise L *Jul 2004*
10
KCH Garden Square Chambers, Nottingham
p989 . . . 0115 941 8851
KCH Garden Square Chambers, Leicester
p979 . . . 0115 941 8851

SAPWELL, Mr Timothy L *Jan 1997*
15, 82, 25, 70, 62, 91
Cornwall Street Chambers, Birmingham
p967 . . . 0121 233 7500

SAREEN, Mr Ellis M *Oct 2008*
15
9-12 Bell Yard Chambers, London WC2
p926 . . . 020 7400 1800

SARGINSON, Ms Jane M *Mar 2000*
15, 62
St Philips Chambers, Birmingham
p969 . . . 0121 246 7000

13

Sarll, Mr Richard M *Oct 2005*
41, 24, 35, 61
7 King's Bench Walk, London EC4
p940 . . . . . 020 7910 8300

Sarooshi, Mr Dan M *Jan 2005*
Essex Court Chambers, London WC2
p931 . . . . . 020 7813 8000

Sartin, Mr Leon LLM(Hons) M *Nov 1997*
8, 32, 9, 37, 14
5 Stone Buildings, London WC2
p951 . . . . . 020 7242 6201

Sasse, Mr Toby LLB(Exon) M *Jul 1988*
30, 22, 27, 15, 20, 18, 12
18 St John Street Chambers, Manchester
p985 . . . . . 0161 278 1800

Sastry, Mr Bob LLB(Hons) I *Oct 1996*
15, 56, 70, 71, 72
St Johns Buildings, Preston
p990 . . . . . 01772 256100
St Johns Buildings, Chester
p974 . . . . . 01244 323070
St Johns Buildings, Manchester
p985 . . . . . 0161 214 1500
St Johns Buildings, Liverpool
p982 . . . . . 0151 243 6000

SAUL, Ms Sonya G *Jan 2002*
15, 62
23 Essex Street, London WC2
p932 . . . . . 020 7413 0353

Saunders, Denise I *Jan 2008*
15, 20, 10
Crown Office Row Chambers, Brighton
p970 . . . . . 01273 625625

SAUNDERS, Ms Emma G *Nov 1994*
1, 22, 26, 88, 93
Arden Chambers, London WC1
p923 . . . . . 020 7242 4244

Saunders, Mr Kevin G *Jan 2003*
St Ives Chambers, Birmingham
p969 . . . . . 0121 236 0863

Saunders, Mr Mark I *Oct 2002*
20, 10
No 6 Barristers Chambers, Leeds
p978 . . . . . 0113 245 9763

Saunders, Mr Nicholas Joseph LLB(Hull); LLM(Cantab) M *Jul 1989*
4, 11, 35
Clerksroom - Administration Centre, Taunton
p993 . . . . . 0845 083 3000
Fenners Chambers, Cambridge
p972 . . . . . 01223 368761

Saunders, Mr William Anthony LLB(B'ham) G *Nov 1980*
15, 62
3 Temple Gardens, London EC4
p952 . . . . . 020 7353 3102

Saunders, Miss Zoe BA(Bris) G *Oct 2003*
20, 10
St John's Chambers, Bristol
p972 . . . . . 0117 921 3456

Saunderson, Miss Emily PGDL; BA G *Jul 2005*
12, 30, 24, 18, 40
2 Temple Gardens, London EC4
p952 . . . . . 020 7822 1200

Saunt, Ms Linda P MA I *Nov 1986*
33 Chancery Lane, London WC2
p928 . . . . . 020 7440 9950

Sauvain, Mr Stephen MA; LLB L *Jul 1977*
(Q.C.) *1, 26, 28, 31, 36*
Cornerstone Barristers, London WC1
p929 . . . . . 020 7242 4986
Kings Chambers, Leeds
p978 . . . . . 0113 242 1123
Kings Chambers, Manchester
p984 . . . . . 0161 832 9082

Savage, Ms Amanda M *Nov 1999*
8, 12, 24, 40
Four New Square, London WC2
p943 . . . . . 020 7822 2000

SAVAGE, Mr Jonathan LLB(Hons) G *Jan 2003*
15
9 St John Street Chambers, Manchester
p984 . . . . . 0161 955 9000

Savage, Miss Mai-Ling Carmen Pilar BD(Lond); DipLaw I *Oct 1998*
10, 18, 22, 20, 51, 1, 63
14 Gray's Inn Square, London WC1
p936 . . . . . 020 7242 0858

Savage, Mr Timothy LLB I *Nov 1991*
15
Paradise Chambers, Sheffield
p992 . . . . . 0114 273 8951

Savill, Mr Peter John BA(Hons) I *Nov 1995*
30, 12, 25, 27, 15, 42, 18, 48, 22
12 College Place, Southampton
p992 . . . . . 023 8032 0320

Savvides, Miss Maria BA(Hons) M *Jul 1986*
10, 15, 20
Northampton Chambers, Northampton
p988 . . . . . 01604 636271

SAWTELL, Mr David L *Jan 2005*
4 King's Bench Walk, London EC4
p939 . . . . . 020 7822 7000

SAWYER, Mr Edward BA(Oxon) M *Oct 2001*
6, 8, 9, 11, 12, 22, 29, 32, 37, 40
Wilberforce Chambers, London WC2
p953 . . . . . 020 7306 0102

SAWYER, Mr Jamie LLB; LLM I *Oct 2003*
15, 62, 94
18 Red Lion Court, London EC4
p949 . . . . . 020 7520 6000
18 Red Lion Court (Annexe), Chelmsford
p973 . . . . . 01245 280880

Sawyer, Ms Katrine M *Jul 1996*
19
Hailsham Chambers, London EC4
p936 . . . . . 020 7643 5000

Sawyerr, Miss Sharon LLB(Leics) I *Nov 1992*
10, 20
Coram Chambers, London EC1
p929 . . . . . 020 7092 3700

SAXBY, Mr Daniel James BA M *Nov 2000*
11, 12, 18, 59, 30, 6
3 Hare Court, London EC4
p937 . . . . . 020 7415 7800

Saxby, Mr Oliver LLB(Soton) I *Nov 1992*
12, 15, 18, 20, 22, 51
6-8 Mill Street, Maidstone
p982 . . . . . 01622 688094 / 688095
6 Pump Court, London EC4
p947 . . . . . 020 7797 8400

SAXENA, Miss Hannah M *Mar 2010*
12, 18, 30, 36
Farrar's Building, London EC4
p933 . . . . . 020 7583 9241

Saxton, Ms Nicola Helen MA(Cantab) I *Nov 1992*
20
St Pauls Chambers, Leeds
p979 . . . . . 0113 245 5866

SAY, Mr Bradley John LLB(Newc) I *Nov 1993*
11, 12, 22, 47, 48
Gough Square Chambers, London EC4
p935 . . . . . 020 7353 0924

Sayed, Miss Ruby LLB(Hons) I *Mar 1999*
10, 20
1 Pump Court, London EC4
p947 . . . . . 020 7842 7070

Sayeed, Mr Muhammad Abu BA I *Jul 1973*
10 Highlever Road, London W10
p937 . . . . . 020 8969 8514

SAYER, Mr Peter MA(Cantab) M *Jul 1975*
5, 11, 47, 48, 59
Gough Square Chambers, London EC4
p935 . . . . . 020 7353 0924

SAYER, Mr Sebastian L *Jul 2007*
15
9-12 Bell Yard Chambers, London WC2
p926 . . . . . 020 7400 1800

SCAMARDELLA, Mr Rossano BA(Hons) G *Nov 1998*
72, 15, 71, 62
23 Essex Street, London WC2
p932 . . . . . 020 7413 0353

Scannell, Mr David I *Jan 2003*
19, 44, 1, 11
Brick Court Chambers, London WC2
p927 . . . . . 020 7379 3550

Schaff, Mr Alistair Graham MA(Cantab) I *Jul 1983*
(Q.C.) *35, 3, 11, 24, 40, 5*
7 King's Bench Walk, London EC4
p940 . . . . . 020 7910 8300

SCHAMA, Mr Lee M *Nov 2003*
15, 20, 23
10 King's Bench Walk, London EC4
p940 . . . . . 020 7353 7742

SCHAW MILLER, Mr Stephen BA(Oxon); DipLaw I *Nov 1988*
6, 11, 12, 24
New Square Chambers, London WC2
p943 . . . . . 020 7419 8000

Scher, Mr Laurie M *Jul 2008*
Maitland Chambers, London WC2
p941 . . . . . 020 7406 1200

SCHERBEL-BALL, Mr Jonathan BA(Hons)(Oxon) M *Oct 2010*
16, 52, 73
One Brick Court, London EC4
p927 . . . . . 020 7353 8845

SCHMITZ, Mr David Reuben BA; Mediator L *Nov 1976*
5, 6, 8, 11, 22, 12
Ten Old Square, London WC2
p945 . . . . . 020 7405 0758

Schofield, Mr James John MA(Oxon) G *Jul 2004*
10, 20
Coram Chambers, London EC1
p929 . . . . . 020 7092 3700

Schofield, Mr Peter BA G *Nov 1982*
15, 25
New Court Chambers, Newcastle upon Tyne
p987 . . . . . 0191 232 1980

Schofield, Mr Thomas LLB L *Oct 2001*
15, 62, 94, 70, 72
No5 Chambers, Bristol
p971 . . . . . 0845 210 5555
No5 Chambers, London EC4
p944 . . . . . 0845 210 5555
No5 Chambers, Birmingham
p968 . . . . . 0845 210 5555

Scholes, Mr Michael LLB(Hons) I *Jan 1996*
15
Exchange Chambers, Manchester
p983 . . . . . 0161 833 2722
Exchange Chambers, Liverpool
p980 . . . . . 0151 236 7747
Exchange Chambers, Leeds
p977 . . . . . 0113 203 1970

Schoneveld, Mr Frank LLB I *Jul 1992*
Henderson Chambers, London EC4
p937 . . . . . 020 7583 9020

Schutzer-Weissman, Ms Esther M *Oct 2000*
15, 16
6 King's Bench Walk, London EC4
p939 . . . . . 020 7583 0410

Schwarz, Mr Jonathan S BA; LLB(Wits); LLM(Berkeley); FTII M *Mar 1998*
57
Temple Tax Chambers, London EC4
p952 . . . . . 020 7353 7884 / 7353 8982

SCHWENK, Mr Mark M *Jul 2001*
23, 1, 51
Kenworthy's Chambers, Manchester
p984 . . . . . 0161 832 4036

Scolding, Ms Fiona MA G *Jan 1996*
Hardwicke, London WC2
p936 . . . . . 020 7242 2523

Scorey, Mr David BA(Oxon) L *Jun 1997*
1, 2, 4, 5, 6, 8, 11, 13, 18, 19, 21, 24, 29, 33, 34, 35, 36
Essex Court Chambers, London WC2
p931 . . . . . 020 7813 8000

Scotland, Baroness M *Oct 1977*
(Q.C.) *10, 20*
4 Paper Buildings, London EC4
p946 . . . . . 020 7583 0816

Scotland, Ms Maria Lyn BSc; MA; CPE; BVC G *Oct 1995*
20, 10
7 Bedford Row, London WC1
p924 . . . . . 020 7242 3555

Scott, Miss Alexandra G *Jul 1983*
2 New Street, Leicester
p979 . . . . . 0116 262 5906

Scott, Mr Andrew M *Nov 2000*
15
18 St John Street Chambers, Manchester
p985 . . . . . 0161 278 1800

Scott, Mr Charles LLB; FCIArb M *Jul 1980*
2, 6, 7, 8, 11, 12, 22, 24, 29, 30
13 King's Bench Walk, London EC4
p940 . . . . . 020 7353 7204

SCOTT, Miss Gemma MA(Hons) I *Jan 2005*
30, 18, 12
12 King's Bench Walk, London EC4
p940 . . . . . 020 7583 0811

Scott, Mr Ian BA(Newc); MSc(Lond) L *Oct 1991*
18, 26, 30, 36, 55, 51, 56
Old Square Chambers, Bristol
p971 . . . . . 0117 930 5100
Old Square Chambers, London WC1
p945 . . . . . 020 7269 0300

SCOTT, Miss January LLB(Hons) G *Jul 2000*
30, 40, 12
Wilberforce Chambers, Hull
p976 . . . . . 01482 323264

Scott, Ms Jennifer I *Jul 2006*
30, 15, 20, 18, 93, 11, 53
9 Gough Square, London EC4
p935 . . . . . 020 7832 0500

SCOTT, Ms Katharine M *Jun 2000*
1, 12, 51, 23, 27, 30, 63, 76, 14
Thirty Nine Essex Street, London WC2
p932 . . . . . 020 7832 1111

SCOTT, Ms Laura L *Jul 2001*
10, 20, 18
Tanfield Chambers, London WC1
p951 . . . . . 020 7421 5300

Scott, Louise M *Jan 2006*
St Johns Buildings, Preston
p990 . . . . . 01772 256100
St Johns Buildings, Chester
p974 . . . . . 01244 323070
St Johns Buildings, Manchester
p985 . . . . . 0161 214 1500
St Johns Buildings, Liverpool
p982 . . . . . 0151 243 6000

SCOTT, Mr Matthew BA I *Nov 1985*
10, 12, 15, 23, 25, 42
Pump Court Chambers, Swindon
p993 . . . . . 01793 539899
Pump Court Chambers, Winchester
p994 . . . . . 01962 868161
Pump Court Chambers, London EC4
p947 . . . . . 020 7353 0711

Scott, Mr Richard Michael M *Jul 1997*
15
5 St Andrew's Hill, London EC4
p950 . . . . . 020 7332 5400

Scott, Mr Stuart I *Jan 1998*
20, 10
1 Pump Court, London EC4
p947 . . . . . 020 7842 7070

SCOTT, Ms Tiffany BA(Oxon) M *Jul 1998*
8, 9, 11, 12, 22, 32, 37, 40
Wilberforce Chambers, London WC2
p953 . . . . . 020 7306 0102

SCOTT, Mr Timothy John Whittaker MA(Oxon) G *Nov 1975*
(Q.C.) *10, 20*
29 Bedford Row, London WC1
p925 . . . . . 020 7404 1044

Scott-Beckett, Miss Alissa LLB I *Jul 2000*
15, 62, 20
Eastbourne Chambers, Eastbourne
p975 . . . . . 01323 642102

SCOTT BELL, Mrs Rosalind Sara LLB; General Medical Council Legal Assessor M *Oct 1993*
15, 25, 63, 48, 84
Trinity (Teesside) Chambers, Middlesbrough
p986 . . . . . 01642 247569
Trinity (Newcastle) Chambers, Newcastle upon Tyne
p987 . . . . . 0191 232 1927

Scott Holland, Mr Gideon MA(Oxon) L *Jul 1999*
3, 7, 11, 24, 40
Keating Chambers, London WC2
p938 . . . . . 020 7544 2600

Scott-Jones, Miss Alison LLB(Hons) M *Feb 1991*
10, 15, 20
No 8 Chambers, Birmingham
p968 . . . . . 0121 236 5514

Scott-Manderson, Mr Marcus C W BA; BCL(Oxon) L *Jul 1980*
(Q.C.) *10, 20, 23*
4 Paper Buildings, London EC4
p946 . . . . . 020 7583 0816

See p1010 for the Key to Work Categories

Screeche-Powell, Ms Genevieve BA(Hons) G *Oct 1997*
12, 22, 26
Field Court Chambers, London WC1
p933 . . . . . 020 7405 6114

Scriven, Miss Pamela I *Jan 1970*
(Q.C.)
Broad Chare Chambers, Newcastle upon Tyne
p986 . . . . . 0191 232 0541
1 King's Bench Walk, London EC4
p938 . . . . . 020 7936 1500

Scully, Ms Jennifer M *Jul 2006*
10, 20
St Johns Buildings, Preston
p990 . . . . . 01772 256100
St Johns Buildings, Chester
p974 . . . . . 01244 323070
St Johns Buildings, Manchester
p985 . . . . . 0161 214 1500
St Johns Buildings, Liverpool
p982 . . . . . 0151 243 6000

SCUTT, Mr David BA(Hons)(Keele) M *Nov 1989*
15
9-12 Bell Yard Chambers, London WC2
p926 . . . . . 020 7400 1800

SEABROOK, Mr Richard M LLB I *Jul 1987*
30, 18, 40, 53
Ropewalk Chambers, Nottingham
p989 . . . . . 0115 947 2581

SEABROOK, Mr Robert LLB; Recorder M *Jun 1964*
(Q.C.) *12, 27, 30, 36, 53, 20, 40*
1 Crown Office Row, London EC4
p929 . . . . . 020 7797 7500

Seagrim, Mr William LLB G *Jul 2007*
15, 12, 20, 30, 18
9 Park Place, Cardiff
p973 . . . . . 029 2038 2731

Seal, Mr Julius Damien L *Nov 1967*
12, 15, 22
189 Randolph Avenue, London W9
p949 . . . . . 020 7328 0158

Seal, Mr Kevin LLB G *Jan 1998*
15
Temple Chambers, Newport
p988 . . . . . 01633 267403 / 255855
Temple Chambers, Cardiff
p973 . . . . . 029 2039 7364

Seal, Ms Philippa L *Nov 2008*
Lamb Chambers, London EC4
p941 . . . . . 020 7797 8300

Seaman, Miss Jennifer BA(Oxon); BCL(Oxon) L *Jan 2007*
6, 8, 11, 67, 38, 32, 93, 37
3 Stone Buildings, London WC2
p951 . . . . . 020 7242 4937

Sear, Miss Joanne LLB(Cardiff) G *Jul 2004*
King's Bench Chambers, Oxford
p989 . . . . . 01865 311066
13 King's Bench Walk, London EC4
p940 . . . . . 020 7353 7204

Sear, Mr Richard M *Jan 2005*
1 Hare Court, London EC4
p936 . . . . . 020 7797 7070

SEARLE, Mr Barrie LLB(Hons)(L'pool); Recorder; Legal Assessor M *Jul 1975*
10, 12, 20, 27, 30, 36, 53
St James's Chambers, Manchester
p984 . . . . . 0161 834 7000

Searle, Miss Corinne LLB(Lond); Recorder G *Jul 1982*
10, 20
Walnut House Chambers, Exeter
p975 . . . . . 01392 279751

Searle, Mr Jason Ario Xavier LLB(Hons) M *Oct 1993*
18
St Johns Buildings, Preston
p990 . . . . . 01772 256100
St Johns Buildings, Chester
p974 . . . . . 01244 323070
St Johns Buildings, Manchester
p985 . . . . . 0161 214 1500
St Johns Buildings, Liverpool
p982 . . . . . 0151 243 6000

Sears, Mr David MA(Oxon) M *Nov 1984*
(Q.C.) *3, 7, 11, 31, 40, 41, 43, 45, 49, 54, 61, 78, 74*
Four New Square, London WC2
p943 . . . . . 020 7822 2000

Seaward, Mr Martin V BA(Durham) G *Nov 1978*
1, 40, 22, 26, 53, 30, 36, 55
Cloisters, London EC4
p928 . . . . . 020 7827 4000

SEDDON, Miss Dorothy LLB(B'ham) M *Jul 1974*
20, 10
Cornwall Street Chambers, Birmingham
p967 . . . . . 0121 233 7500

Seeboruth, Mr Royln Jean-Paul LLB(Hons) M *Oct 1986*
Chambers of Royln Seeboruth, Aylesbury
p967 . . . . . 01296 393329

SEED, Mr Stephen Nicholas G *Oct 1991*
30, 40
7 Harrington Street Chambers, Liverpool
p981 . . . . . 0151 242 0707

SEEHRA, Ms Amarjit LLB(Hons) G *Oct 1999*
23, 30, 51
10 King's Bench Walk, London EC4
p940 . . . . . 020 7353 7742

Seelig, Mr Leo L *Nov 2007*
15
Atkinson Bevan Chambers, London EC4
p924 . . . . . 020 7353 2112

Seely, Mr Jonathan I *Jan 1987*
15
1 Paper Buildings, London EC4
p946 . . . . . 020 7353 3728

Sefi, Mr Benedict BA(Oxon) I *Jul 1972*
37, 29, 88, 20, 8
Harcourt Chambers, London EC4
p936 . . . . . 0844 561 7135
Harcourt Chambers, Oxford
p989 . . . . . 0844 561 7135

SEFTON, Ms Joanne I *Jul 2002*
6, 11, 12, 18, 55
Littleton Chambers, London EC4
p941 . . . . . 020 7797 8600

SEFTON, Mr Mark BA(Cantab) M *Nov 1996*
8, 22, 6, 40, 11
Falcon Chambers, London EC4
p933 . . . . . 020 7353 2484

Sefton, Mr Nicholas Edward G *Jul 2004*
15, 20
Pendragon Chambers, Swansea
p993 . . . . . 01792 411188

Sefton-Smith, Mr Lloyd BA(Lond); DipLaw L *Oct 1993*
1, 7, 8, 12, 45, 49, 22, 24, 30, 31, 40, 37, 14
Lamb Chambers, London EC4
p941 . . . . . 020 7797 8300

Segal, Mr Oliver BA(Oxon); MA(Lond) M *Oct 1992*
(Q.C.) *18, 26, 36, 55, 1, 51, 48, 56*
Old Square Chambers, Bristol
p971 . . . . . 0117 930 5100
Old Square Chambers, London WC1
p945 . . . . . 020 7269 0300

SEGAL, Miss Sharon LLB(Queen Mary & Westfield) I *Oct 2000*
10, 20
1 Garden Court, London EC4
p934 . . . . . 020 7797 7900

Segan, Mr James BA(Oxon); DipLaw I *Nov 2004*
11, 1, 18, 51, 19, 44, 56, 50, 52, 43, 89
Blackstone Chambers, London EC4
p926 . . . . . 020 7583 1770

SEIFERT, Ms Victoria M *Oct 2002*
1, 22, 26, 88, 93
Arden Chambers, London WC1
p923 . . . . . 020 7242 4244

SEITLER, Deborah I *Nov 1991*
10, 20
Renaissance Chambers, London WC1
p949 . . . . . 020 7404 1111

SEITLER, Mr Jonathan BA(Oxon); DipLaw I *Nov 1985*
(Q.C.) *41, 8, 40, 22*
Wilberforce Chambers, London WC2
p953 . . . . . 020 7306 0102

Selby, Andrew G *Nov 1997*
15, 84, 62
Lamb Building, Brighton
p970 . . . . . 01273 820490
Lamb Building, London EC4
p940 . . . . . 020 7797 7788
Westgate Chambers, Lewes
p980 . . . . . 01273 480510

Selby, Mr Jonathan BA(Hons)(Cantab) G *Nov 1999*
3, 7, 11, 24, 40
Keating Chambers, London WC2
p938 . . . . . 020 7544 2600

Selby, Mr Lawrence BA(Hons) G *Oct 1997*
15, 51, 62
Nine Bedford Row, London WC1
p924 . . . . . 020 7489 2727

SELBY, Miss Sarah G *Oct 1998*
15
9-12 Bell Yard Chambers, London WC2
p926 . . . . . 020 7400 1800

Self, Mr Gary BA(Hons); Part-time Employment Judge L *Oct 1991*
10, 12, 18, 20, 32
College Chambers, Southampton
p992 . . . . . 023 8023 0338

Selfe, Mr Michael R Recorder M *Nov 1965*
2 King's Bench Walk, London EC4
p939 . . . . . 020 7353 1746

SELLARS, Michael BA(Dunelm) I *Jul 1980*
10, 20
Atlantic Chambers, Liverpool
p980 . . . . . 0151 236 4421

SELLERS, Graham LLB(Hons); LLM M *Oct 1990*
66, 5, 6, 7, 8, 11, 97, 67, 14, 38, 24, 88, 96, 29, 31, 32, 40, 93, 34, 37
Atlantic Chambers, Liverpool
p980 . . . . . 0151 236 4421

SELLERS, Mr Robin St John LLB(Reading) I *Nov 1994*
15, 62
23 Essex Street, London WC2
p932 . . . . . 020 7413 0353

Sellick, Mr Llewelyn M *Jul 1973*
King's Bench Godolphin Chambers, Truro
p994 . . . . . 0845 308 1551
King's Bench Godolphin Chambers, Plymouth
p990 . . . . . 0845 308 1551

Sells, Mr Oliver I *Jul 1972*
(Q.C.) *15, 62*
5 Paper Buildings, London EC4
p946 . . . . . 020 7583 6117

SELMAN, Miss Elizabeth LLB(Lond) I *Nov 1989*
10, 20, 12
1 King's Bench Walk, London EC4
p938 . . . . . 020 7936 1500

Selvaratnam, Miss Vasanti LLB; LLM(Lond) M *Jul 1983*
(Q.C.) *3, 11, 35, 36, 5, 24, 40*
Stone Chambers, London WC1
p951 . . . . . 020 7440 6900

Selway, Ms Kate BA(Hons)(Bris); DPhil(Oxon); Junior Counsel to the Crown I *Nov 1995*
5, 8, 9, 11, 22, 29, 32, 34, 37, 40
Radcliffe Chambers, London WC2
p949 . . . . . 020 7831 0081

SELWAY, Mr Michael M *Nov 2007*
93, 11, 38
Guildhall Chambers, Bristol
p970 . . . . . 0117 930 9000

SELWYN SHARPE, Mr Richard LLB(Bris) L *Nov 1985*
6, 8, 11, 22, 47, 40, 37
New Square Chambers, London WC2
p943 . . . . . 020 7419 8000
St James's Chambers, Manchester
p984 . . . . . 0161 834 7000

SEMKEN, Mr Christopher MA(Oxon) L *Jul 1977*
8, 9, 11, 14, 22, 32, 37
New Square Chambers, London WC2
p943 . . . . . 020 7419 8000

Semple, Mr Gordon G *Oct 2003*
10, 20
No 6 Barristers Chambers, Leeds
p978 . . . . . 0113 245 9763

Sen, Mr Aditya Kumar MA; LLB(Cantab); BA(Hons)(Delhi); FCA L *Jul 1977*
3, 7, 8, 11
Coram Chambers, London EC1
p929 . . . . . 020 7092 3700

Sen Gupta, Ms Diya MA(Cantab) I *Oct 2000*
18
Blackstone Chambers, London EC4
p926 . . . . . 020 7583 1770

SENDALL, Mr Antony MA(Cantab) L *Jul 1984*
11, 18, 12, 36
Littleton Chambers, London EC4
p941 . . . . . 020 7797 8600

Senior, Mr Anthony James LLB(Hons) L *Jul 2002*
30, 47, 48
Broad Chare Chambers, Newcastle upon Tyne
p986 . . . . . 0191 232 0541

Senior, Mr Mark LLB(Hons); MA G *Jul 2002*
20, 10
St Johns Buildings, Preston
p990 . . . . . 01772 256100
St Johns Buildings, Chester
p974 . . . . . 01244 323070
St Johns Buildings, Manchester
p985 . . . . . 0161 214 1500
St Johns Buildings, Liverpool
p982 . . . . . 0151 243 6000

Sethi, Mr Mohinderpal MA(Oxon) M *Jan 1996*
18, 30, 55, 59, 51
Devereux Chambers, London WC2
p930 . . . . . 020 7353 7534

Sethi, Miss Natasha LLM; LLB M *Jan 2001*
Henderson Chambers, London EC4
p937 . . . . . 020 7583 9020

Sethi, Ms Rita I *Nov 2000*
23
Tooks Chambers, London EC4
p953 . . . . . 020 7842 7575

Setright, Mr Henry John M *Nov 1979*
(Q.C.) *20, 10*
4 Paper Buildings, London EC4
p946 . . . . . 020 7583 0816

Seymour, Ms Lydia BA(Oxon) I *Oct 1997*
18, 55
Outer Temple Chambers, London WC2
p945 . . . . . 020 7353 6381

SEYMOUR, Mr Mark William MA(Cantab) M *Oct 1992*
15, 25, 26
9-12 Bell Yard Chambers, London WC2
p926 . . . . . 020 7400 1800

SEYMOUR, Mr Thomas MA(Cantab) I *Jul 1975*
8, 22, 29, 32, 40
Wilberforce Chambers, London WC2
p953 . . . . . 020 7306 0102

SHACKLEFORD, Miss Susan BA(Lond) I *Oct 1980*
20
Octagon House, Norwich
p988 . . . . . 01603 623186

13

Shadarevian, Mr Paul BA; DipLaw G *Jul 1984*
1, 22, 26, 31, 46
Cornerstone Barristers, London WC1
p929 . . . . . 020 7242 4986

Shah, Akhil MA(Cantab) I *Nov 1990*
(Q.C.) *4, 18, 40*
Fountain Court Chambers, London EC4
p934 . . . . . 020 7583 3335

Shah, Mr Bajul BA; BCL L *Oct 1996*
6, 8, 11, 29, 32, 37, 40, 5, 4, 59, 49, 62
XXIV Old Buildings, London WC2
p944 . . . . . 020 7691 2424

Shah, Ferdous L *Jul 1969*
23
1 Garfield Road, London SW11
p935 . . . . . 020 7228 1137

Shah, Mr Jilan M *Jan 2001*
Conference Chambers, Harrow
p976 . . . . . 07958 421595

Shah, Miss Nehali M *Oct 2008*
One Essex Court, London EC4
p931 . . . . . 020 7583 2000

Shah, Mr Neil LLB(Hons)(LSE) M *Jul 2008*
10, 20
Coram Chambers, London EC1
p929 . . . . . 020 7092 3700

Shah, Ms Roshnee M *Oct 1998*
Charter Chambers, London WC1
p928 . . . . . 020 7618 4400

SHAH, Ms Shilpa LLB; LLM L *Jul 1998*
30, 40, 53, 18
Ropewalk Chambers, Nottingham
p989 . . . . . 0115 947 2581

Shah Begum, Ms Monwara L *Mar 2004*
1 Mitre Court Buildings, London EC4
p942 . . . . . 020 7452 8900

SHAHBAHRAMI, Miss Tara I *Oct 2006*
1, 18, 11, 51, 55, 26, 76
11KBW, London EC4
p938 . . . . . 020 7632 8500

Shaikh, Miss Semaab L *Nov 2002*
10, 20, 23
Broadway House Chambers, Leeds
p977 . . . . . 0113 246 2600
Broadway House Chambers, Bradford
p969 . . . . . 01274 722560

SHAKOOR, Mr Tariq Bin BA I *Feb 1992*
15, 72, 70, 82, 25
Cornwall Street Chambers, Birmingham
p967 . . . . . 0121 233 7500

Shaldon, Miss Nicola MA; LLB M *Oct 1994*
8, 12, 24, 40
Four New Square, London WC2
p943 . . . . . 020 7822 2000

Shalom, Miss Miriam M *Jul 2003*
Field Court Chambers, London WC1
p933 . . . . . 020 7405 6114

Shamash, Miss Anne BA G *Nov 1986*
15, 10, 20, 30
Tooks Chambers, London EC4
p953 . . . . . 020 7842 7575

Shamim, Mr Mohammed L *Jan 1975*
Clapham Law Chambers, London SW1
p928 . . . . . 020 7978 8482 / 7642 5777

SHANDRO, Mr Sandy MA(Alberta); MA(McGill); BCL; MA(Oxon) L *Jan 2008*
38, 5, 11
South Square, London WC1
p950 . . . . . 020 7696 9900

Shankardass, Vijay BSc(Delhi); MA; LLM(Cantab) L *May 1972*
Maitland Chambers, London WC2
p941 . . . . . 020 7406 1200

Shannon, Mr Eric BA(Oxon) M *Nov 1974*
11, 16, 18, 6, 26, 27, 30, 13, 31, 12, 53, 40, 55
St Johns Buildings, Preston
p990 . . . . . 01772 256100
St Johns Buildings, Chester
p974 . . . . . 01244 323070
St Johns Buildings, Manchester
p985 . . . . . 0161 214 1500
St Johns Buildings, Liverpool
p982 . . . . . 0151 243 6000

Shannon, Ms Nicola MA M *Oct 1997*
15, 25, 62, 82
Lamb Building, Brighton
p970 . . . . . 01273 820490
Lamb Building, London EC4
p940 . . . . . 020 7797 7788

Shannon, Mr Simon I *Mar 1999*
15, 62
3 Temple Gardens, London EC4
p952 . . . . . 020 7353 3102

SHANT, Ms Nirmal Kanta LLB; Recorder; Master Grays Inn Chair of The Midlands Society of Asian Lawyers G *Jul 1984*
(Q.C.) *15, 62*
23 Essex Street, London WC2
p932 . . . . . 020 7413 0353

SHAPIRO, Mr Daniel I *Oct 1999*
11, 40, 24, 78, 74, 7
Crown Office Chambers, London EC4
p929 . . . . . 020 7797 8100

Shapiro, Mr Selwyn I *Jul 1979*
2 King's Bench Walk, London EC4
p939 . . . . . 020 7353 1746

Sharghy, Ms Pegah I *Jan 1998*
20
Crown Office Row Chambers, Brighton
p970 . . . . . 01273 625625

Sharghy, Mr Shahram L *Jul 2000*
30, 93, 11, 20, 62, 65, 81, 84, 38, 39, 53
9 Gough Square, London EC4
p935 . . . . . 020 7832 0500

Sharif, Ms Nadia J BA(Hons) L *Nov 1985*
31, 46, 60
No5 Chambers, Bristol
p971 . . . . . 0845 210 5555
No5 Chambers, London EC4
p944 . . . . . 0845 210 5555
No5 Chambers, Birmingham
p968 . . . . . 0845 210 5555

SHARKEY, Mr Paul LLB(Hons); MSc M *Nov 2000*
15
9-12 Bell Yard Chambers, London WC2
p926 . . . . . 020 7400 1800

SHARLAND, Mr Andrew LLB(Hons)(Lond); LLM; BCL G *Oct 1996*
1, 55, 26, 18, 11, 19, 51, 31
4-5 Gray's Inn Square, London WC1
p935 . . . . . 020 7404 5252

SHARMA, Mr Jamie I *Jan 2005*
15, 62, 95
187 Fleet Street, London EC4
p933 . . . . . 020 7430 7430

SHARMA, Miss Neelam L *Jun 2000*
15, 62, 95
187 Fleet Street, London EC4
p933 . . . . . 020 7430 7430

SHARMA, Pavan M *Jan 1993*
Lombard Chambers, London EC1
p941 . . . . . 020 7107 2100

Sharma, Rakhee LLB(Lond) G *Jan 1995*
12, 15
Kingsway Chambers, London EC4
p940 . . . . . 020 7404 2357

Sharma, Mrs Suman LLB(Hons) M *Jan 1994*
15, 23, 62
Warwick House Chambers, London WC1
p953 . . . . . 020 7430 2323

Sharma, Ms Sunyana I *Jan 2006*
30, 53, 72, 15, 70, 8, 93
3PB, Bournemouth
p969 . . . . . 01202 292102

Sharman, Mr Brian G *Jan 2004*
2 King's Bench Walk, London EC4
p939 . . . . . 020 7353 1746

SHARMAN, Mr Mark L *Jan 2004*
15, 12
Cornwall Street Chambers, Birmingham
p967 . . . . . 0121 233 7500

Sharp, Mr Christopher MA(Oxon) I *Jul 1975*
(Q.C.) *10, 12, 20, 30, 40, 53*
Harcourt Chambers, London EC4
p936 . . . . . 0844 561 7135
Harcourt Chambers, Oxford
p989 . . . . . 0844 561 7135
St John's Chambers, Bristol
p972 . . . . . 0117 921 3456

SHARP, Mr David BA(Oxon); MA; DipLaw M *Nov 1986*
20, 30, 10
Tanfield Chambers, London WC1
p951 . . . . . 020 7421 5300

SHARPE, Dr David Irish Bar (1999) I *Nov 2004*
53, 30, 68, 27, 40, 85
12 King's Bench Walk, London EC4
p940 . . . . . 020 7583 0811

Sharpe, Mr Dennis I *Jul 1976*
Field Court Chambers, London WC1
p933 . . . . . 020 7405 6114

Sharpe, Mr Harry M *Jan 2010*
49, 41, 3, 5, 6, 8, 9, 11, 97, 67, 69, 78, 81, 62, 38, 21, 89, 96, 79, 29, 86, 32, 40, 43, 56, 37
XXIV Old Buildings, London WC2
p944 . . . . . 020 7691 2424

SHARPE, Malcolm LLB(Sheff); LLM(Belfast) L *Jul 1989*
10, 20
Atlantic Chambers, Liverpool
p980 . . . . . 0151 236 4421

Sharpe, Mr Martin Laurence BA(Hons); MA M *Nov 1989*
Park Court Chambers, Leeds
p978 . . . . . 0113 243 3277

Sharpe, Mr Richard MA(Oxon) M *Jan 2002*
15, 62
33 Bedford Row, London WC1
p925 . . . . . 020 7242 6476
23 Essex Street, London WC2
p932 . . . . . 020 7413 0353

Sharpe, Mr Thomas L *May 1976*
(Q.C.)
One Essex Court, London EC4
p931 . . . . . 020 7583 2000

SHARPE, Mr Timothy MA(Cantab) L *Oct 2002*
Temple Garden Chambers, London EC4
p952 . . . . . 020 7583 1315

Sharples, Mr John BA(Oxon); LLM(Cantab); LLM(Pennsylvania) M *Nov 1992*
8, 22, 29, 32, 37, 93, 88
St John's Chambers, Bristol
p972 . . . . . 0117 921 3456

Shaw, Mr Andrew L *Mar 1998*
15, 91
1 Paper Buildings, London EC4
p946 . . . . . 020 7353 3728

Shaw, Miss Annabel G *Jul 2002*
Four New Square, London WC2
p943 . . . . . 020 7822 2000

SHAW, Mr Antony BA(Oxon); Recorder M *Jul 1975*
(Q.C.) *15, 62*
18 Red Lion Court, London EC4
p949 . . . . . 020 7520 6000
18 Red Lion Court (Annexe), Chelmsford
p973 . . . . . 01245 280880

SHAW, Mr Benjamin BCL(Oxon) L *Nov 2002*
11, 38, 97
Erskine Chambers, London WC2
p931 . . . . . 020 7242 5532

Shaw, Miss Elizabeth M *Nov 1996*
37 Park Square Chambers, Leeds
p978 . . . . . 0113 243 9422

Shaw, Howard James M *Oct 1999*
15, 70, 72
Zenith Chambers, Leeds
p979 . . . . . 0113 245 5438

Shaw, Mr James I *Jan 1988*
20, 10
4 Paper Buildings, London EC4
p946 . . . . . 020 7583 0816

Shaw, Miss Joanna M *Jan 2000*
One Essex Court, London EC4
p931 . . . . . 020 7936 3030

SHAW, Mr John Howard LLB(Lond); Member Bar of Ireland I *Jul 1973*
(Q.C.) *20, 30, 40*
29 Bedford Row, London WC1
p925 . . . . . 020 7404 1044

Shaw, Jonathan I *Jan 2008*
Zenith Chambers, Leeds
p979 . . . . . 0113 245 5438

Shaw, Mr Julian LLB(Wales) G *Sep 1984*
7, 10, 12, 15, 18, 20, 22, 25, 26, 30
St Johns Buildings, Preston
p990 . . . . . 01772 256100
St Johns Buildings, Chester
p974 . . . . . 01244 323070
St Johns Buildings, Manchester
p985 . . . . . 0161 214 1500
St Johns Buildings, Liverpool
p982 . . . . . 0151 243 6000

Shaw, Prof Malcolm N LLB; LLM; PhD G *Jul 1988*
(Q.C.)
Essex Court Chambers, London WC2
p931 . . . . . 020 7813 8000

Shaw, Mr Mark BA(Dunelm); LLM(Cantab) I *Jul 1987*
(Q.C.) *1, 19, 23, 26, 36, 51, 89, 96, 49, 95*
Blackstone Chambers, London EC4
p926 . . . . . 020 7583 1770

SHAW, Mr Michael John LLB(Hons) M *Jan 1994*
15
9-12 Bell Yard Chambers, London WC2
p926 . . . . . 020 7400 1800

Shaw, Mrs Nicola BA(Hons) L *Oct 1992*
20
Broad Chare Chambers, Newcastle upon Tyne
p986 . . . . . 0191 232 0541
Trinity (Newcastle) Chambers, Newcastle upon Tyne
p987 . . . . . 0191 232 1927
15 Winckley Square, Preston
p991 . . . . . 01772 252828
Trinity (Teesside) Chambers, Middlesbrough
p986 . . . . . 01642 247569

Shaw, Ms Nicola BCL; BA(Oxon) I *Nov 1995*
Gray's Inn Tax Chambers, London WC1
p936 . . . . . 020 7242 2642

Shaw, Mr Peter M BA(Hons)(Manc) M *Nov 1995*
6, 40, 38, 5
9 Stone Buildings Barristers Chambers, London WC2
p951 . . . . . 020 7404 5055

SHAW, Mr Robert M *Jan 2008*
25 Bedford Row, London WC1
p925 . . . . . 020 7067 1500

Shaw, Mr Samuel Benjamin Barnaby M *Nov 1996*
15, 84, 91
1 Paper Buildings, London EC4
p946 . . . . . 020 7353 3728

SHAY, Mr Stephen BA(Oxon) M *Nov 1984*
6, 11, 15, 12, 18, 22, 30, 72, 70, 62, 40
1 King's Bench Walk, London EC4
p938 . . . . . 020 7936 1500

SHEA, Ms Caroline MA(Cantab) M *Nov 1994*
Falcon Chambers, London EC4
p933 . . . . . 020 7353 2484

Shears, Mr Philip Peter LLB; Recorder I *Nov 1972*
(Q.C.) *15, 20, 62*
7 Bedford Row, London WC1
p924 . . . . . 020 7242 3555

Sheehan, Mr James M *Oct 2008*
Maitland Chambers, London WC2
p941 . . . . . 020 7406 1200

Sheehan, Mr Malcolm MA(Oxon) L *Oct 1993*
10, 12, 18, 20, 22, 24, 30, 40, 47, 48, 51
Henderson Chambers, London EC4
p937 . . . . . 020 7583 9020

Sheehan, Mr Michael M *Oct 2010*
10, 20
East Anglian Chambers, Norwich
p988 . . . . . 01603 617351
East Anglian Chambers, Colchester
p975 . . . . . 01206 572756
East Anglian Chambers, Chelmsford
p973 . . . . . 01245 215660
East Anglian Chambers, Ipswich
p976 . . . . . 01473 214481

SHEFF, Miss Janine M *Jan 1983*
15, 36, 20, 70, 68
18 Red Lion Court, London EC4
p949 . . . . . 020 7520 6000
18 Red Lion Court (Annexe), Chelmsford
p973 . . . . . 01245 280880

SHEFTEL, Mr Andrew Lawson Baylies BA(Oxon)(Law) I *Nov 2004*
3, 41, 4, 18, 30, 12, 47, 22
Tanfield Chambers, London WC1
p951 . . . . . 020 7421 5300

SHEIKH, Mr Irshad L *Mar 1983*
15, 62, 95
187 Fleet Street, London EC4
p933 . . . . . 020 7430 7430

Sheikh, Ms Saira Kabir BA; LLB; LLM I *Nov 2000*
1, 12, 46, 18, 21, 25, 26, 31, 36, 61, 51, 54, 28, 60
Francis Taylor Building, London EC4
p934 . . . . . 020 7353 8415

Shekerdemian, Ms Marcia MA(Cantab) M *Jul 1987*
5, 6, 11, 38
11 Stone Buildings, London WC2
p951 . . . . . 020 7831 6381

SHELDON, Mr Clive BA(Cantab); LLM(Penn) I *Nov 1991*
(Q.C.) *1, 11, 18, 26, 55, 51, 76, 96*
11KBW, London EC4
p938 . . . . . 020 7632 8500

SHELDON, Mr Neil MA(Cantab) G *Nov 1998*
1, 12, 18, 30, 40, 47
1 Crown Office Row, London EC4
p929 . . . . . 020 7797 7500

SHELDON, Mr Richard M MA(Cantab) G *Jul 1979*
(Q.C.) *5, 6, 8, 11, 12, 24, 29, 38*
South Square, London WC1
p950 . . . . . 020 7696 9900

SHELDON, Mr Richard Neil LLB L *Jul 1984*
12, 15
Bank House Chambers, Sheffield
p991 . . . . . 0114 275 1223

Sheldrake, Miss Christine LLB(Lond); Deputy District Judge M *Jul 1977*
10, 20
Coram Chambers, London EC1
p929 . . . . . 020 7092 3700

Shellard, Mr Robin BA(Wales); DipLaw I *Nov 1992*
15, 48, 62, 68, 82, 39, 84, 94, 95, 36
Queen Square Chambers, Bristol
p972 . . . . . 0117 921 1966

SHELLEY, Mr Dominic G *Jul 2003*
15
1 High Pavement, Nottingham
p988 . . . . . 0115 941 8218

Shelton, Mr Gordon Edward LLB(Leics); Recorder I *Nov 1981*
12, 15, 18, 20, 22, 25, 30, 36, 24, 27
Broadway House Chambers, Leeds
p977 . . . . . 0113 246 2600
Broadway House Chambers, Bradford
p969 . . . . . 01274 722560

Shenton, Miss Rachel LLB(Hons)(Lancs) M *Nov 1993*
15
18 St John Street Chambers, Manchester
p985 . . . . . 0161 278 1800

SHENTON, Miss Suzanne LLB(Hons)(Manc) M *Jul 1973*
10, 20
1 Garden Court, London EC4
p934 . . . . . 020 7797 7900

See p1010 for the Key to Work Categories

Shepherd, Mr Jim BA(Hons); DipLaw(City) *M Oct 1998*
1, 22, 51
Doughty Street Chambers, London WC1
p930 . . . . 020 7404 1313

Shepherd, Miss Jude LLB(Hons)(Derby) *L Oct 1996*
12, 55, 18, 22
42 Bedford Row, London WC1
p925 . . . . 020 7831 0222

Shepherd, Mr Philip BSc(Econ) *G Nov 1975*
(Q.C.) *3, 4, 5, 6, 8, 11, 29, 35, 40, 24, 41, 59, 49, 62*
XXIV Old Buildings, London WC2
p944 . . . . 020 7691 2424

Shepherd, Mr Richard LLB(Hons)(Wales) *M Jan 2001*
Albion Chambers, Bristol
p970 . . . . 0117 927 2144

Shepherd, Mr Thomas Paul LLB(Bris); BCL(Oxon) *L Oct 2008*
89, 5, 6, 8, 38
11 Stone Buildings, London WC2
p951 . . . . 020 7831 6381

Sheppard, Mr Tim *I Nov 1995*
1, 18, 31, 55, 34, 46, 26
No5 Chambers, Bristol
p971 . . . . 0845 210 5555
No5 Chambers, London EC4
p944 . . . . 0845 210 5555
No5 Chambers, Birmingham
p968 . . . . 0845 210 5555

SHEPPARD-JONES, Miss Victoria *G Jan 2005*
Carmelite Chambers, London EC4
p927 . . . . 020 7936 6300

Sher, Mr Adam *L Oct 2007*
Fountain Court Chambers, London EC4
p934 . . . . 020 7583 3335

Sher, Miss Shamim *L Jun 1995*
23
12 Old Square, London WC2
p945 . . . . 020 7404 0875

SHERBORN, Miss Natalie *G Nov 2000*
25 Bedford Row, London WC1
p925 . . . . 020 7067 1500

Sherborne, Mr David Alexander BA(Oxon) *G Oct 1992*
13, 16, 50, 51, 56
5RB, London WC1
p948 . . . . 020 7242 2902

SHERIDAN, Miss Amber MA(Hons)(Politics) *M Jan 2008*
10, 20
29 Bedford Row, London WC1
p925 . . . . 020 7404 1044

SHERIDAN, Mr Matthew *G Jul 2000*
6, 11, 12, 44, 47, 18, 40, 55
Littleton Chambers, London EC4
p941 . . . . 020 7797 8600

SHERIDAN, Mr Maurice LLM(Cantab) *M Jul 1984*
19, 61, 1, 2, 41, 3, 46, 49, 51, 11, 26
Matrix Chambers, London WC1
p942 . . . . 020 7404 3447

Sheridan, Mr Norman LLM *M Oct 1990*
19, 46, 21
Sheridan Chambers, Radlett
p991 . . . . 01923 856345

Sheridan, Mr Paul LLB *L Jul 1984*
30, 51
Cobden House Chambers, Manchester
p983 . . . . 0161 833 6000

Sheridan, Mr Robert *L Nov 2001*
8, 32, 37, 12, 6
Southernhay Chambers, Exeter
p975 . . . . 01392 255777

Sheridan, Mr Shane P B *I Feb 1973*
15, 51
Nine Bedford Row, London WC1
p924 . . . . 020 7489 2727

Sheriff, Mr Andrew MA; DipLaw *M Jan 2000*
18, 22, 12
3PB, Oxford
p989 . . . . 01865 793736

Sheriff, Mr Simon *I Nov 1999*
Goldsmith Chambers, London EC4
p935 . . . . 020 7353 6802

Sherman, Mr Robert LLB *G Jul 1977*
14, 40, 49, 53, 96, 30
Charter Chambers, London WC1
p928 . . . . 020 7618 4400
Lamb Building, Brighton
p970 . . . . 01273 820490
Lamb Building, London EC4
p940 . . . . 020 7797 7788

SHERMAN, Ms Susan Elizabeth LLB *M Nov 1993*
10, 12, 15, 18, 20, 22, 30, 36
Chavasse Court Chambers, Liverpool
p980 . . . . 0151 229 2030

SHERRARD, Mr Charles LLB *M Nov 1986*
Furnival Chambers, London EC4
p934 . . . . 020 7405 3232

SHERRATT, Mr Mathew LLB; LLM *I Oct 1994*
Carmelite Chambers, London EC4
p927 . . . . 020 7936 6300
Thomas More Chambers, London WC2
p952 . . . . 020 7404 7000

SHERRY, Mr Eamonn LLB *G Nov 1990*
12, 15, 25, 38
Carmelite Chambers, London EC4
p927 . . . . 020 7936 6300

Sherry, Mr Michael Gabriel MA(Oxon); ACA A *G Nov 1978*
34
Temple Tax Chambers, London EC4
p952 . . . . 020 7353 7884 / 7353 8982

SHERWIN, Miss Deborah LLB(Exon) *I Jul 1979*
12, 15
Fountain Chambers, Middlesbrough
p986 . . . . 01642 804040

Sherwood, Miss Hannah BA(Hons) *M Jul 2002*
Park Court Chambers, Leeds
p978 . . . . 0113 243 3277

Shetty, Rajeev *I Jan 1996*
30, 70, 11, 65, 39, 84, 81, 38, 62, 15, 53
9 Gough Square, London EC4
p935 . . . . 020 7832 0500

SHIBLI, Faraz *I Nov 2007*
15, 23, 51
10 King's Bench Walk, London EC4
p940 . . . . 020 7353 7742

Shield, Miss Deborah LLB *I Nov 1991*
10, 20
42 Bedford Row, London WC1
p925 . . . . 020 7831 0222

Shields, Mr Josh *M Mar 2000*
5, 6, 8, 11, 22, 29, 40, 34, 7, 9, 14, 32, 37, 38, 63, 66, 67, 77, 88, 89, 93, 96, 97
Exchange Chambers, Manchester
p983 . . . . 0161 833 2722
Exchange Chambers, Liverpool
p980 . . . . 0151 236 7747
Exchange Chambers, Leeds
p977 . . . . 0113 203 1970

SHIELDS, Miss Sonja M *G Jul 1977*
Carmelite Chambers, London EC4
p927 . . . . 020 7936 6300

Shikder, Kutub MBE *L Nov 1990*
Tower Hamlets Barristers Chambers, London E1
p953 . . . . 020 7377 8090

Shillingford, Ms Julia *M Jan 2002*
3PB, Oxford
p989 . . . . 01865 793736

SHIPWRIGHT, Mr Adrian BCL; MA(Oxon) *M Feb 1993*
Pump Court Tax Chambers, London WC1
p948 . . . . 020 7414 8080

Shires, Mr Gareth Richard BA(Oxon); LLB *L Jul 2007*
67, 15, 88, 30
Exchange Chambers, Manchester
p983 . . . . 0161 833 2722
Exchange Chambers, Liverpool
p980 . . . . 0151 236 7747
Exchange Chambers, Leeds
p977 . . . . 0113 203 1970

Shirley, Mr James LLB; Bcl *M Nov 2002*
41, 5, 8, 11, 30, 35
Stone Chambers, London WC1
p951 . . . . 020 7440 6900

Shirley, Ms Lynne LLB *M Jul 2002*
15
East Anglian Chambers, Norwich
p988 . . . . 01603 617351
East Anglian Chambers, Colchester
p975 . . . . 01206 572756
East Anglian Chambers, Chelmsford
p973 . . . . 01245 215660
East Anglian Chambers, Ipswich
p976 . . . . 01473 214481

Shiu, Miss Ming Yee BA(Cantab); LLM *M Oct 2000*
12, 5, 11, 24, 18
2 Temple Gardens, London EC4
p952 . . . . 020 7822 1200

SHIVJI, Mr Sharif BSc(Econ) *L Jul 2001*
6, 8, 11, 29
4 Stone Buildings, London WC2
p951 . . . . 020 7242 5524

SHOKER, Mr Chanvir *M Jan 2006*
12, 15, 20, 10, 93
Cornwall Street Chambers, Birmingham
p967 . . . . 0121 233 7500

SHOKER, Mr Makhan Singh LLB *I May 1981*
15, 23
St Philips Chambers, Birmingham
p969 . . . . 0121 246 7000

SHOLICAR, Ms Ann LLB(Hons) *L Nov 2000*
Oriel Chambers, Liverpool
p981 . . . . 0151 236 7191 / 236 4321
Oriel Chambers, Preston
p990 . . . . 01772 254764

Shore, Miss Victoria Louise *L Nov 2005*
13, 16, 50, 56, 73, 51
5RB, London WC1
p948 . . . . 020 7242 2902

Shorey, Miss Carrie *M Jul 2006*
Nine Bedford Row, London WC1
p924 . . . . 020 7489 2727

Shorrock, Mr Michael *I Jul 1966*
(Q.C.) *12, 25, 15, 11, 30, 27*
St Johns Buildings, Preston
p990 . . . . 01772 256100
St Johns Buildings, Chester
p974 . . . . 01244 323070
St Johns Buildings, Manchester
p985 . . . . 0161 214 1500
St Johns Buildings, Liverpool
p982 . . . . 0151 243 6000
Atkinson Bevan Chambers, London EC4
p924 . . . . 020 7353 2112

Short, Mr Andrew LLB(Bris) *G Nov 1990*
(Q.C.) *1, 22, 18, 92*
Outer Temple Chambers, London WC2
p945 . . . . 020 7353 6381

SHORT, Miss Anna MA(Cantab) *G Nov 1997*
12, 22, 23, 30
St James's Chambers, Manchester
p984 . . . . 0161 834 7000

SHORT, Harriet *G Jan 2007*
23
Mitre House Chambers, London WC1
p942 . . . . 020 7307 7100

SHORT, Ms Mandy *M Jul 2003*
20
Tanfield Chambers, London WC1
p951 . . . . 020 7421 5300

Shotton, Miss Sophie MA(Hons)(Law)(Cantab) *I Oct 1999*
15, 25, 42, 48, 51, 62, 70, 71, 72, 80, 82, 91, 94, 95
15 New Bridge Street Chambers, London EC4
p943 . . . . 020 7842 1900

SHRAVAT, Mr Neelo *M Nov 2002*
15, 20, 30
Pump Court Chambers, Swindon
p993 . . . . 01793 539899
Pump Court Chambers, Winchester
p994 . . . . 01962 868161
Pump Court Chambers, London EC4
p947 . . . . 020 7353 0711

SHRIMPTON, Miss Claire Alison LLB(Hull) *I Jul 1983*
15, 10, 20
Guildford Chambers, Guildford
p975 . . . . 01483 539131

SHROFF, Mr Cyrus *G Jul 1983*
15
18 Red Lion Court, London EC4
p949 . . . . 020 7520 6000
18 Red Lion Court (Annexe), Chelmsford
p973 . . . . 01245 280880

SHUMAN, Miss Karen Ann Elizabeth *L Jan 1991*
93, 22, 32, 88, 8
1 Chancery Lane, London WC2
p928 . . . . 0845 634 6666

SHUTTLEWORTH, Mr Timothy William LLB(L'pool) *G Jul 1971*
10, 20, 63, 77
Tanfield Chambers, London WC1
p951 . . . . 020 7421 5300

Siberry, Mr W Richard MA; LLB(Cantab) *M Jul 1974*
(Q.C.)
Essex Court Chambers, London WC2
p931 . . . . 020 7813 8000

Sibson, Ms Clare MA(Cantab) *M Oct 1997*
Cloth Fair Chambers, London EC1
p928 . . . . 020 7710 6444

Siddall, Mr Nicholas BA(Cantab) *M Oct 1997*
12, 18, 30, 47, 53, 55
Kings Chambers, Leeds
p978 . . . . 0113 242 1123
Kings Chambers, Manchester
p984 . . . . 0161 832 9082

Siddiqi, Mr Faizul Aqtab LLB; Barrister *L Jul 1990*
8, 9, 10, 11, 12, 13, 18, 20, 21, 23, 40, 47, 49, 51, 64
Justice Court Chambers, Leicester
p979 . . . . 024 7632 5859

Siddle, Mr Trevor Brian LLB *G Oct 1991*
12, 15, 18, 20, 25, 30
Goldsmith Chambers, London EC4
p935 . . . . 020 7353 6802

SIDHU, Navjot *L Nov 1993*
15, 95
25 Bedford Row, London WC1
p925 . . . . 020 7067 1500

Sidhu, Sukhwant LLB(Lond) *L Oct 1996*
12, 18, 20, 23
One Essex Court, London EC4
p931 . . . . 020 7936 3030

SIDHU-BRAR, Mr Sean LLB(Hons) *G Oct 1991*
15
Citadel Chambers, Birmingham
p967 . . . . 0121 233 8500

SIGEE, Peter MA; LLB(Hons) *M Nov 2002*
49, 12, 67, 68, 18, 62, 84, 24, 89, 30, 40, 94, 59
Atlantic Chambers, Liverpool
p980 . . . . 0151 236 4421

Silcock, Mr Ian LLB(Hons); MSc(IT) *M Oct 1997*
13
Hardwicke, London WC2
p936 . . . . 020 7242 2523

SILVA, Mr Jerome *I Oct 2001*
4 King's Bench Walk, London EC4
p939 . . . . 020 7822 7000

Silver, Ms Nadia *M Nov 2001*
12, 20, 15, 18, 2, 1, 63, 62
36 Bedford Row, London WC1
p925 . . . . 020 7421 8000

Silver, Ms Tamsin BSc *G Nov 2002*
1 Mitre Court Buildings, London EC4
p942 . . . . 020 7452 8900

Silverleaf, Mr Michael BSc *G May 1980*
(Q.C.) *41, 73, 50, 19, 45, 13, 52, 96*
11 South Square, London WC1
p950 . . . . 020 7405 1222

Silvester, Mr Bruce Ross LLB(Lond) *I Jul 1983*
30, 27, 26, 25, 20, 7, 1
Devereux Chambers, London WC2
p930 . . . . 020 7353 7534

Simcock, Miss Sarah Louise BA(Hons)(Oxon) *I Jan 2001*
27, 30, 18, 53, 68, 85, 40, 36
3 Serjeants' Inn, London EC4
p950 . . . . 020 7427 5000

SIMISON, Mr Jeremy Charles BCom(Hons) *I Oct 1993*
10, 20, 89, 18
Trinity Chambers, Chelmsford
p974 . . . . 01245 605040

Simkin, Mr Iain BA(Hons) *I Feb 1995*
15, 70, 71, 72
St Johns Buildings, Preston
p990 . . . . 01772 256100
St Johns Buildings, Chester
p974 . . . . 01244 323070
St Johns Buildings, Manchester
p985 . . . . 0161 214 1500
St Johns Buildings, Liverpool
p982 . . . . 0151 243 6000

Simler, Miss Ingrid MA(Cantab) *I Jul 1987*
(Q.C.) *11, 12, 18, 36, 24, 26, 19, 40, 55, 51*
Devereux Chambers, London WC2
p930 . . . . 020 7353 7534

Simmonds, Ms Alexandra *G Oct 1998*
12, 15, 30
St Johns Buildings, Preston
p990 . . . . 01772 256100
St Johns Buildings, Chester
p974 . . . . 01244 323070

St Johns Buildings, Manchester
p985 . . . . . 0161 214 1500
St Johns Buildings, Liverpool
p982 . . . . . 0151 243 6000

Simmonds, Mr Andrew John MA(Cantab) M *Nov 1980*
(Q.C.) *8, 29, 32, 37, 40, 92*
5 Stone Buildings, London WC2
p951 . . . . . 020 7242 6201

Simon, Mr Michael LLB(L'pool) I *Nov 1992*
1, 10, 18, 20, 49, 55
4 Paper Buildings, London EC4
p946 . . . . . 020 7583 0816

Simons, Mr Kane BA(Hons); LLM L *Oct 2007*
30, 12, 15, 94
18 St John Street Chambers, Manchester
p985 . . . . . 0161 278 1800

Simons, Mr Richard G LLB(Hons) G *Feb 1991*
Lincoln House Chambers, Manchester
p984 . . . . . 0161 832 5701

SIMONS, Mr Zack I *Jan 2009*
Thirty Nine Essex Street, London WC2
p932 . . . . . 020 7832 1111

SIMOR, Miss Jessica MA(Oxon); Dip EU Law M *Nov 1992*
1, 19, 23, 11, 44, 46, 26, 51, 55, 33
Matrix Chambers, London WC1
p942 . . . . . 020 7404 3447

SIMPSON, Mr David BA(Hons)(Oxon) G *Jan 2003*
5, 81, 40, 62
3 Verulam Buildings, London WC1
p953 . . . . . 020 7831 8441

SIMPSON, Mr Edwin MA; BCL(Oxon) L *Nov 1990*
26, 31, 60
New Square Chambers, London WC2
p943 . . . . . 020 7419 8000

Simpson, Mr Graeme M *Jan 1994*
St Ives Chambers, Birmingham
p969 . . . . . 0121 236 0863

SIMPSON, Miss Hannah LLB(Hons) M *Oct 2000*
10, 20
St Mary's Chambers, Nottingham
p989 . . . . . 0115 950 3503

Simpson, Ian LLB(Hons) L *Oct 1997*
Clerksroom - Administration Centre, Taunton
p993 . . . . . 0845 083 3000

Simpson, Ms Jacqueline I *Jan 2006*
18, 53, 40, 11, 30
Hailsham Chambers, London EC4
p936 . . . . . 020 7643 5000

Simpson, Mr Mark MA(Oxon); DipLaw; Ec Law M *Oct 1992*
(Q.C.)
Fountain Court Chambers, London EC4
p934 . . . . . 020 7583 3335

SIMPSON, Ms Melanie G *Jan 1998*
15
25 Bedford Row, London WC1
p925 . . . . . 020 7067 1500

Simpson, Mr Paul Richard LLB L *Jul 1980*
20, 30
New Bailey Chambers, Preston
p990 . . . . . 01772 258087

Simpson, Ms Raquel LLB(Lond) I *Oct 1990*
15
18 St John Street Chambers, Manchester
p985 . . . . . 0161 278 1800

Sims, Mr Guy BA I *Jul 2000*
8, 12, 15, 18, 30, 45
Fenners Chambers, Cambridge
p972 . . . . . 01223 368761

SIMS, Mr Hugh L *Oct 1999*
6, 8, 11, 40, 41, 49, 56, 38, 97
Guildhall Chambers, Bristol
p970 . . . . . 0117 930 9000

Sinai, Mr Ali Reza G *Jan 1997*
18, 11, 22, 33
Ely Place Chambers, London EC1
p931 . . . . . 020 7400 9600

Sinclair, Ms Caroline I *Jan 2005*
20
1 Pump Court, London EC4
p947 . . . . . 020 7842 7070

SINCLAIR, Mr Duncan L *Sep 1996*
1, 11, 12, 19, 39, 44, 61, 78, 79
Thirty Nine Essex Street, London WC2
p932 . . . . . 020 7832 1111

Sinclair, Miss Fiona MA I *Jul 1989*
8, 12, 24, 40
Four New Square, London WC2
p943 . . . . . 020 7822 2000

Sinclair, Mr Graham LLB(Lond); Part time Chairman LVTRAC G *Jul 1979*
22, 6, 12, 46, 8, 49, 26, 29, 32, 40, 37
East Anglian Chambers, Norwich
p988 . . . . . 01603 617351
East Anglian Chambers, Colchester
p975 . . . . . 01206 572756
East Anglian Chambers, Chelmsford
p973 . . . . . 01245 215660
East Anglian Chambers, Ipswich
p976 . . . . . 01473 214481

Sinclair, Mr Jean-Paul MA(Cantab) M *Feb 1989*
20, 10
33 Bedford Row, London WC1
p925 . . . . . 020 7242 6476

Sinclair, Mr Paul MA(Hons); LLM(Harv) M *Jan 1997*
Fountain Court Chambers, London EC4
p934 . . . . . 020 7583 3335

SINCLAIR, Mr Philip G *Nov 1995*
Maidstone Chambers, Maidstone
p982 . . . . . 01622 688592

Singer, Mr Andrew BA(Cantab); Panel of TEBAR Adjudicators G *Nov 1990*
7, 40, 41
Kings Chambers, Leeds
p978 . . . . . 0113 242 1123
Kings Chambers, Manchester
p984 . . . . . 0161 832 9082

Singer, Mr Nicholas BA(Cantab) G *Jul 2006*
42 Bedford Row, London WC1
p925 . . . . . 020 7831 0222

Singer, Mr Philip MA; LLM(Cantab) I *Feb 1964*
(Q.C.) *15*
2 Pump Court, London EC4
p947 . . . . . 020 7353 5597

SINGER, Ms Samantha LLB(Hons) G *Jul 2004*
20, 51, 12, 10
Queen Elizabeth Buildings, London EC4
p948 . . . . . 020 7797 7837

Singh, Balbir LLB L *Jul 1984*
15, 25, 62
Equity Chambers, Birmingham
p968 . . . . . 0121 233 2100

SINGH, Mr Dapinderpaul M *Jul 2000*
62, 15
23 Essex Street, London WC2
p932 . . . . . 020 7413 0353
Park Court Chambers, Leeds
p978 . . . . . 0113 243 3277

SINGH, Gurdial L *Jan 1989*
15
Bank House Chambers, Sheffield
p991 . . . . . 0114 275 1223

Singh, Mr Karamjit L *Mar 2000*
St Ives Chambers, Birmingham
p969 . . . . . 0121 236 0863

Singh, Mr Kuldip M *Jul 1975*
(Q.C.)
Serle Court, London WC2
p950 . . . . . 020 7242 6105

Singh, Ms Ranjana M *Oct 1995*
Holborn Chambers, London WC2
p937 . . . . . 020 7242 6060

Singh, Mr Sandesh LLB(Hons) I *Oct 2004*
15
2 Bedford Row, London WC1
p924 . . . . . 020 7440 8888

SINGH, Mr Sarabjit BA(Oxon) L *Oct 2001*
1, 53, 12, 18, 51, 27, 30, 57
1 Crown Office Row, London EC4
p929 . . . . . 020 7797 7500

Singh, Mr Talbir G *Jan 1997*
15, 18, 55, 25, 62, 94
No5 Chambers, Bristol
p971 . . . . . 0845 210 5555
No5 Chambers, London EC4
p944 . . . . . 0845 210 5555
No5 Chambers, Birmingham
p968 . . . . . 0845 210 5555

SINGLA, Nikki MA(Oxon); BCL M *Jul 2000*
1, 41, 5, 6, 7, 8, 9, 11, 45, 47, 13, 16, 18, 50, 62, 29, 40
Wilberforce Chambers, London WC2
p953 . . . . . 020 7306 0102

SINGLETON, Mr Barry MA(Cantab) G *Jul 1968*
(Q.C.) *10, 20, 96, 49*
1 King's Bench Walk, London EC4
p938 . . . . . 020 7936 1500

Singleton, Mr Michael LLB(Leics) M *Jul 1987*
12, 16, 22, 30
St Ives Chambers, Birmingham
p969 . . . . . 0121 236 0863

Singleton, Ms Sarah BA(Oxon) M *Jul 1983*
(Q.C.)
1 Pump Court, London EC4
p947 . . . . . 020 7842 7070
St Johns Buildings, Preston
p990 . . . . . 01772 256100
St Johns Buildings, Chester
p974 . . . . . 01244 323070
St Johns Buildings, Manchester
p985 . . . . . 0161 214 1500
St Johns Buildings, Liverpool
p982 . . . . . 0151 243 6000

Sinker, Mr Andrew LLB(Hons) L *Oct 1991*
15, 30, 20, 47
New Bailey Chambers, Preston
p990 . . . . . 01772 258087

Sinnatt, Mr Simon BA(York)(History); CPE(Sussex) L *Oct 1993*
6, 8, 12, 22, 26, 31, 40, 37
Crown Office Row Chambers, Brighton
p970 . . . . . 01273 625625

SIRIKANDA, Morgan BA M *Jan 2002*
20, 10
Queen Elizabeth Buildings, London EC4
p948 . . . . . 020 7797 7837

Sisley, Mr Timothy Julian Crispin BA(Hons)(Lond) M *Jul 1989*
6, 8, 11, 18, 7, 29, 47, 38
9 Stone Buildings Barristers Chambers, London WC2
p951 . . . . . 020 7404 5055

SISSONS, Mr Philip BA; BCL I *Nov 2005*
Falcon Chambers, London EC4
p933 . . . . . 020 7353 2484

Siva, Mr Kannan BA(Hons) G *Nov 1996*
15, 70, 72
Albion Chambers, Bristol
p970 . . . . . 0117 927 2144

Sjolin, Miss Catarina LLM; BA(Cantab) G *Nov 1998*
23, 15, 12, 10, 62, 63
36 Bedford Row, London WC1
p925 . . . . . 020 7421 8000

Sjostrand, Ekaterina I *Jan 2003*
13 Old Square Chambers, London WC2
p945 . . . . . 020 7831 4445

Skeate, Ian L *Jan 2002*
Clerksroom - Administration Centre, Taunton
p993 . . . . . 0845 083 3000

SKELLEY, Mr Michael BA(Oxon) I *Oct 1991*
15, 62
18 Red Lion Court, London EC4
p949 . . . . . 020 7520 6000
18 Red Lion Court (Annexe), Chelmsford
p973 . . . . . 01245 280880

Skellorn, Ms Kathryn MA(Oxon) G *Nov 1993*
10, 20, 18
St John's Chambers, Bristol
p972 . . . . . 0117 921 3456

Skelly, Mr Andrew LLB(Hons) I *Oct 1994*
11, 12, 22, 29, 31, 40, 93, 37
Hardwicke, London WC2
p936 . . . . . 020 7242 2523

Skelt, Mr Ian L *Jul 1994*
15, 30, 8, 23
11 King's Bench Walk, Leeds
p978 . . . . . 0113 297 1200

SKELTON, Mr Peter M *Oct 1997*
53, 30, 51, 1, 68
1 Crown Office Row, London EC4
p929 . . . . . 020 7797 7500

Skerrett, Ms Katy BA(Oxon); Tenant M *Oct 1999*
1, 12, 15, 18, 22, 26, 31, 36
Cornerstone Barristers, London WC1
p929 . . . . . 020 7242 4986

SKILBECK, Ms Jennifer BSc; MSc; DipLaw L *Oct 1991*
1, 19, 44
Monckton Chambers, London WC1
p942 . . . . . 020 7405 7211

Skinner, Mr Andrew LLB(Hons) L *Jul 2000*
10, 12, 20
College Chambers, Southampton
p992 . . . . . 023 8023 0338

SKINNER, Miss Lorna MA(Cantab) M *Nov 1997*
16, 51, 50, 52, 73, 89
Matrix Chambers, London WC1
p942 . . . . . 020 7404 3447

Skittrell, Miss Elaine M *Jan 1999*
Park Court Chambers, Leeds
p978 . . . . . 0113 243 3277

Skyner, Mr Robert M *Mar 2003*
39 Park Square, Leeds
p978 . . . . . 0113 245 6633

Slack, Mr Henry L *Oct 1999*
30, 53
Hardwicke, London WC2
p936 . . . . . 020 7242 2523

Slack, Mr Kevin John MA(Cantab) G *Oct 1997*
15, 25, 36, 62
Exchange Chambers, Manchester
p983 . . . . . 0161 833 2722
Exchange Chambers, Liverpool
p980 . . . . . 0151 236 7747
Exchange Chambers, Leeds
p977 . . . . . 0113 203 1970

Slade, Mr Richard BA(Cantab) L *Nov 1987*
11, 24, 40, 5
Brick Court Chambers, London WC2
p927 . . . . . 020 7379 3550

Slater, Miss Alison M *Nov 1996*
Charter Chambers, London WC1
p928 . . . . . 020 7618 4400

SLATER, Miss Julie LLB L *Jul 1988*
10, 20, 93
Cornwall Street Chambers, Birmingham
p967 . . . . . 0121 233 7500

Slater, Mr Justin MA(Cantab) I *Jul 1999*
10, 20
7 Bedford Row, London WC1
p924 . . . . . 020 7242 3555

Slater, Mr Matthew James BA(Oxon); Treasury Counsel M *Nov 2005*
8, 11, 1, 34
3 Stone Buildings, London WC2
p951 . . . . . 020 7242 4937

Slater, Mr Michael N I *Jul 1983*
15, 30, 12
Paradise Chambers, Sheffield
p992 . . . . . 0114 273 8951

Slatter, Ms Alexis BSc; MA; DipLaw; PGDipLaw I *Nov 1999*
23, 51, 76, 63, 1
Tooks Chambers, London EC4
p953 . . . . . 020 7842 7575

Slaughter, Mr Andrew M *Oct 1993* MP
Lamb Chambers, London EC4
p941 . . . . . 020 7797 8300

Slaughter, Miss Jessica M *Jul 2009*
12, 15, 72
East Anglian Chambers, Norwich
p988 . . . . . 01603 617351
East Anglian Chambers, Colchester
p975 . . . . . 01206 572756
East Anglian Chambers, Chelmsford
p973 . . . . . 01245 215660
East Anglian Chambers, Ipswich
p976 . . . . . 01473 214481

Slee, Lydia LLB M *Jan 2007*
Stour Chambers, Canterbury
p972 . . . . . 01227 764899

SLEEMAN, Miss Rachel LLB(Hons); AKC G *Nov 1996*
11, 6, 24, 29, 47, 12
Five Paper, London EC4
p946 . . . . . 020 7815 3200

Sleeman, Ms Susan I *Oct 2001*
51, 18, 27, 30, 55
Doughty Street Chambers, London WC1
p930 . . . . . 020 7404 1313

Sleightholme, Mr John T LLB G *Nov 1982*
14, 15, 25, 30, 36, 37, 12
37 Park Square Chambers, Leeds
p978 . . . . . 0113 243 9422

Sleight, Mr Nigel L *Oct 1998*
12, 15, 10, 20
Regency Chambers, Peterborough
p990 . . . . . 01733 315215

 See p1010 for the Key to Work Categories

SLOANE, Miss Valentina BA G *Oct 2000*
11, 44, 19, 51, 57
Monckton Chambers, London WC1
p942 . . . . . 020 7405 7211
Sloboda, Mr Nicholas L *Jan 2007*
One Essex Court, London EC4
p931 . . . . . 020 7583 2000
Slomnicka, Miss Barbara Irene LLB G *Nov 1976*
14 Gray's Inn Square, London WC1
p936 . . . . . 020 7242 0858
Slow, Miss Camille LLB(Bris) M *Jul 2002*
3, 7, 11, 31, 40, 41, 43, 45, 49, 54, 61, 78, 74
Atkin Chambers, London WC1
p923 . . . . . 020 7404 0102
Smales, Mrs Suzanne LLB I *Nov 1990*
15, 20, 10
No 6 Barristers Chambers, Leeds
p978 . . . . . 0113 245 9763
Small, Arlene Ann-Marie LLB(Hons) M *Oct 1997*
Clerksroom - Administration Centre, Taunton
p993 . . . . . 0845 083 3000
Small, Miss Gina BA L *Oct 1991*
King's Bench Godolphin Chambers, Truro
p994 . . . . . 0845 308 1551
King's Bench Godolphin Chambers, Plymouth
p990 . . . . . 0845 308 1551
SMALL, Mr Jonathan BA(Nott'm) L *Oct 1990*
(Q.C.)
Falcon Chambers, London EC4
p933 . . . . . 020 7353 2484
Small, Ms Penelope I *Oct 1992*
33 Chancery Lane, London WC2
p928 . . . . . 020 7440 9950
SMALLER, Miss Elizabeth BA; DipLaw; CPE(Hons) G *Oct 1995*
15
9-12 Bell Yard Chambers, London WC2
p926 . . . . . 020 7400 1800
1 Inner Temple Lane, London EC4
p937 . . . . . 020 7427 4400
Smallwood, Ms Anne E M *Nov 1977*
20, 10, 2
No5 Chambers, Bristol
p971 . . . . . 0845 210 5555
No5 Chambers, London EC4
p944 . . . . . 0845 210 5555
No5 Chambers, Birmingham
p968 . . . . . 0845 210 5555
SMALLWOOD, Mr Robert L *Nov 1994*
30, 40, 68, 94
No5 Chambers, Bristol
p971 . . . . . 0845 210 5555
No5 Chambers, London EC4
p944 . . . . . 0845 210 5555
No5 Chambers, Birmingham
p968 . . . . . 0845 210 5555
SMART, Miss Jacqueline Ann LLB M *Nov 1981*
2, 6, 8, 22, 37, 32, 40, 38
Trinity (Newcastle) Chambers, Newcastle upon Tyne
p987 . . . . . 0191 232 1927
Trinity (Teesside) Chambers, Middlesbrough
p986 . . . . . 01642 247569
Smart, Mr John Andrew C BSc(Bris); DipLaw(City) M *Nov 1989*
6, 8, 11, 22, 32, 34, 37, 9, 40, 57, 58, 51, 29, 14
9 Stone Buildings Barristers Chambers, London WC2
p951 . . . . . 020 7404 5055
Smart, Miss Julia G *Oct 1993*
Goldsmith Chambers, London EC4
p935 . . . . . 020 7353 6802
Smart, Mr Neil Assistant Deputy Coroner L *May 1998*
34, 57, 58, 53, 21, 68, 40, 13
Exchange Chambers, Manchester
p983 . . . . . 0161 833 2722
Exchange Chambers, Liverpool
p980 . . . . . 0151 236 7747
Exchange Chambers, Leeds
p977 . . . . . 0113 203 1970
Smart, Mr Roger LLB I *Jul 1989*
15, 25, 36
QEB Hollis Whiteman, London EC4
p948 . . . . . 020 7933 8855
Smith, Ms Abigail L *Oct 2003*
23, 51
Tooks Chambers, London EC4
p953 . . . . . 020 7842 7575
Smith, Mr Adam BA(Oxon) G *Nov 2001*
6, 8, 11, 22, 32, 37, 40
Maitland Chambers, London WC2
p941 . . . . . 020 7406 1200
Crown Office Row Chambers, Brighton
p970 . . . . . 01273 625625
Smith, Mr Alan Arthur M *Jul 1981*
27, 53, 30, 40
Old Square Chambers, Bristol
p971 . . . . . 0117 930 5100
Old Square Chambers, London WC1
p945 . . . . . 020 7269 0300
SMITH, Mr Alastair BA(Manc) I *Oct 2001*
15
9-12 Bell Yard Chambers, London WC2
p926 . . . . . 020 7400 1800
SMITH, Mr Alisdair LLB(Lond) G *Jul 1981*
15, 62, 25
9-12 Bell Yard Chambers, London WC2
p926 . . . . . 020 7400 1800
SMITH, Mr Andrew LLB(Hons); DipLP G *Jan 1988*
(Q.C.) *30, 40, 53, 8, 11, 84*
Crown Office Chambers, London EC4
p929 . . . . . 020 7797 8100
Matrix Chambers, London WC1
p942 . . . . . 020 7404 3447
SMITH, Mr Andrew D LLB M *Oct 1991* MBE; TD
12, 15, 20
Bank House Chambers, Sheffield
p991 . . . . . 0114 275 1223

SMITH, Mr Andrew Duncan BA(Oxon); Recorder M *Oct 1997*
15, 62, 84
St Philips Chambers, Birmingham
p969 . . . . . 0121 246 7000
Smith, Mr Andrew William LLB(Hons) L *Oct 1996*
15, 62
Exchange Chambers, Manchester
p983 . . . . . 0161 833 2722
Exchange Chambers, Liverpool
p980 . . . . . 0151 236 7747
Exchange Chambers, Leeds
p977 . . . . . 0113 203 1970
Smith, Prof Anthony M *May 1992*
16, 50, 51
5RB, London WC1
p948 . . . . . 020 7242 2902
Smith, Mr Antony I *Jan 1958*
(Q.C.) *15, 31, 46, 70, 72*
No5 Chambers, Bristol
p971 . . . . . 0845 210 5555
No5 Chambers, London EC4
p944 . . . . . 0845 210 5555
No5 Chambers, Birmingham
p968 . . . . . 0845 210 5555
SMITH, Mr Benjamin I *Oct 1997*
Goldsmith Chambers, London EC4
p935 . . . . . 020 7353 6802
Smith, Miss Caroline BA(Politics Social Policy); CPE; BVC I *Jul 2003*
20, 23, 10
Broad Chare Chambers, Newcastle upon Tyne
p986 . . . . . 0191 232 0541
Smith, Mr Charles BA(Oxon); MSt(Oxon) L *Jan 2002*
Maitland Chambers, London WC2
p941 . . . . . 020 7406 1200
Smith, Chris LLB L *Jan 1997*
15, 71, 72, 80
Zenith Chambers, Leeds
p979 . . . . . 0113 245 5438
Smith, Mr Christopher LLB(Soton) I *Jul 1989*
(Q.C.)
Essex Court Chambers, London WC2
p931 . . . . . 020 7813 8000
Smith, Mr Christopher M BA(Hons) I *Oct 1999*
11, 35, 24, 5
Quadrant Chambers, London EC4
p948 . . . . . 020 7583 4444
SMITH, Mr David LLB(Brunel); LLM(Lond) I *Nov 1980*
Landmark Chambers, London EC4
p941 . . . . . 020 7430 1221
9-12 Bell Yard Chambers, London WC2
p926 . . . . . 020 7400 1800
SMITH, Mr Duncan LLB I *Jul 1979*
15
York Chambers, York
p995 . . . . . 01904 620048
York Chambers, Newcastle upon Tyne
p987 . . . . . 0191 206 4677
Smith, Miss Emma LLB(Leics); MA(Lond) L *Oct 1995*
18, 30, 27, 53, 55, 36
Old Square Chambers, Bristol
p971 . . . . . 0117 930 5100
Old Square Chambers, London WC1
p945 . . . . . 020 7269 0300
Furnival Chambers, London EC4
p934 . . . . . 020 7405 3232
5 Pump Court, London EC4
p947 . . . . . 020 7353 2532 / 7583 7133
SMITH, Miss Fiona G *Nov 2009*
15, 12
East Anglian Chambers, Norwich
p988 . . . . . 01603 617351
East Anglian Chambers, Colchester
p975 . . . . . 01206 572756
East Anglian Chambers, Chelmsford
p973 . . . . . 01245 215660
East Anglian Chambers, Ipswich
p976 . . . . . 01473 214481
SMITH, Mr Graham LLB(Hons) I *Oct 1999*
15
23 Essex Street, London WC2
p932 . . . . . 020 7413 0353
Smith, Mr Howard BA(Oxon) I *Jul 1986*
5, 6, 8, 9, 11, 22, 24, 32, 37, 29, 40
Radcliffe Chambers, London WC2
p949 . . . . . 020 7831 0081
Smith, Mr Jamie MA L *Oct 1995*
8, 12, 24, 40, 53
Four New Square, London WC2
p943 . . . . . 020 7822 2000
Smith, Mrs Jane I *Jan 2007*
10, 20
Southernhay Chambers, Exeter
p975 . . . . . 01392 255777
SMITH, Mr Jason LLB M *Jul 1989*
15
7 Harrington Street Chambers, Liverpool
p981 . . . . . 0151 242 0707
Smith, Ms Jennie I *Jan 2002*
York Chambers, York
p995 . . . . . 01904 620048
York Chambers, Newcastle upon Tyne
p987 . . . . . 0191 206 4677
SMITH, Miss Joan M *Oct 2002*
1, 8, 15, 30, 91, 25
Trinity (Newcastle) Chambers, Newcastle upon Tyne
p987 . . . . . 0191 232 1927
Trinity (Teesside) Chambers, Middlesbrough
p986 . . . . . 01642 247569
SMITH, Ms Joanna BA(Oxon) L *Nov 1990*
(Q.C.) *1, 11, 12, 15, 18, 22, 25, 26, 29, 36, 6, 7, 40*
Wilberforce Chambers, London WC2
p953 . . . . . 020 7306 0102
SMITH, Mr Joel I *Jul 2002*
Furnival Chambers, London EC4
p934 . . . . . 020 7405 3232

SMITH, Mr Jonathan LLB(Hons) G *Jan 1992*
1, 6, 8, 11, 47, 22, 26, 29, 32
St James's Chambers, Manchester
p984 . . . . . 0161 834 7000
Smith, Mr Julian LLB I *Nov 1991*
12, 15, 20, 30
New Court Chambers, Newcastle upon Tyne
p987 . . . . . 0191 232 1980
SMITH, Ms Kassie BA(Oxon); BCL I *Nov 1995*
1, 18, 19, 23, 40, 44, 51, 46
Monckton Chambers, London WC1
p942 . . . . . 020 7405 7211
Smith, Miss Kate LLB; BVC G *Jan 2008*
15, 20, 23, 30
Angel Chambers, Swansea
p992 . . . . . 01792 464623
Smith, Ms Kerry Ann L *Jul 2002*
23, 18, 55, 51
Garden Court North Chambers, Manchester
p983 . . . . . 0161 236 1840
SMITH, Mr Leonard G *Jan 1986*
(Q.C.)
Carmelite Chambers, London EC4
p927 . . . . . 020 7936 6300
SMITH, Miss Leonorah I *Nov 1993*
10, 20
Pump Court Chambers, Swindon
p993 . . . . . 01793 539899
Pump Court Chambers, Winchester
p994 . . . . . 01962 868161
Pump Court Chambers, London EC4
p947 . . . . . 020 7353 0711
SMITH, Mr Marcus Alexander BCL; BA(Oxon) L *Oct 1991*
(Q.C.)
Fountain Court Chambers, London EC4
p934 . . . . . 020 7583 3335
SMITH, Miss Marion LLB; LLM G *Jul 1981*
11, 40, 52
Thirty Nine Essex Street, London WC2
p932 . . . . . 020 7832 1111
Smith, Mr Mark V MA(Cantab) L *Jul 1981*
Essex Court Chambers, London WC2
p931 . . . . . 020 7813 8000
Smith, Mr Matthew MA L *Oct 1991*
18
Kings Chambers, Leeds
p978 . . . . . 0113 242 1123
Kings Chambers, Manchester
p984 . . . . . 0161 832 9082
15 Winckley Square, Preston
p991 . . . . . 01772 252828
Maitland Chambers, London WC2
p941 . . . . . 020 7406 1200
Smith, Mr Michael I *Nov 2008*
13 Old Square Chambers, London WC2
p945 . . . . . 020 7831 4445
Kenworthy's Chambers, Manchester
p984 . . . . . 0161 832 4036
Smith, Mr Michael Anthony LLB(Newc); Recorder I *Jul 1980*
15, 27, 30
No 6 Barristers Chambers, Leeds
p978 . . . . . 0113 245 9763
Smith, Mr Nick L *Jan 1988*
Nick Smith Barrister, London SE5
p950 . . . . . 020 7566 8244
Smith, Dr Nathan L *Jan 2007*
Kings Chambers, Leeds
p978 . . . . . 0113 242 1123
Kings Chambers, Manchester
p984 . . . . . 0161 832 9082
SMITH, Mr Nicholas BA G *Oct 1994*
15, 34, 62
St Philips Chambers, Birmingham
p969 . . . . . 0121 246 7000
Queen Square Chambers, Bristol
p972 . . . . . 0117 921 1966
Smith, Mr Paul BA(Hons) G *Oct 2002*
St Johns Buildings, Preston
p990 . . . . . 01772 256100
St Johns Buildings, Chester
p974 . . . . . 01244 323070
St Johns Buildings, Manchester
p985 . . . . . 0161 214 1500
St Johns Buildings, Liverpool
p982 . . . . . 0151 243 6000
Broadway House Chambers, Leeds
p977 . . . . . 0113 246 2600
Broadway House Chambers, Bradford
p969 . . . . . 01274 722560
Smith, Dr Peter L *Jun 1993*
Radcliffe Chambers, London WC2
p949 . . . . . 020 7831 0081
Smith, Ms Rachel L *Oct 1990*
Lincoln House Chambers, Manchester
p984 . . . . . 0161 832 5701
Trinity (Newcastle) Chambers, Newcastle upon Tyne
p987 . . . . . 0191 232 1927
Trinity (Teesside) Chambers, Middlesbrough
p986 . . . . . 01642 247569
Smith, Ms Rebecca Ellen L *Jan 2002*
15, 70, 72
St Johns Buildings, Preston
p990 . . . . . 01772 256100
St Johns Buildings, Chester
p974 . . . . . 01244 323070
St Johns Buildings, Manchester
p985 . . . . . 0161 214 1500
St Johns Buildings, Liverpool
p982 . . . . . 0151 243 6000
SMITH, Mr Richard BA(Hons)(Cantab) I *Oct 1999*
1, 12, 18, 27, 30, 40, 53, 56
1 Crown Office Row, London EC4
p929 . . . . . 020 7797 7500
Guildhall Chambers, Bristol
p970 . . . . . 0117 930 9000

13

Octagon Chambers, Taunton
p993 . . . . . 01823 331919

SMITH, Mr Robert G *Oct 2005*
9 St John Street Chambers, Manchester
p984 . . . . . 0161 955 9000
St Pauls Chambers, Leeds
p979 . . . . . 0113 245 5866

Smith, Mr Robert Clive MA(Cantab) M *Jul 1974*
12, 20
RCS Chambers, Rotherham
p991 . . . . . 01709 814147

Smith, Mr Robert Steen LLB I *Jul 1971*
(Q.C.)
Park Court Chambers, Leeds
p978 . . . . . 0113 243 3277

SMITH, Mr Roger D H LLM(B'ham) G *Feb 1972*
(Q.C.) *15, 46*
Cornwall Street Chambers, Birmingham
p967 . . . . . 0121 233 7500

Smith, Mr Roger Gavin A MA(Oxon) M *Oct 1981*
20, 10
1 Hare Court, London EC4
p936 . . . . . 020 7797 7070

Smith, Mr Roger H T BA(Oxon) G *Nov 1968*
11, 30, 22, 40, 29, 32, 67, 88, 89, 93
No5 Chambers, Bristol
p971 . . . . . 0845 210 5555
No5 Chambers, London EC4
p944 . . . . . 0845 210 5555
No5 Chambers, Birmingham
p968 . . . . . 0845 210 5555

SMITH, Ms Sally LLB(Lond) I *Nov 1977*
(Q.C.) *12, 27, 30, 18*
1 Crown Office Row, London EC4
p929 . . . . . 020 7797 7500

SMITH, Mr Scott G *Jan 2003*
15
Fountain Chambers, Middlesbrough
p986 . . . . . 01642 804040

SMITH, Mr Shaun M G *Jul 1981*
(Q.C.) *15*
Bank House Chambers, Sheffield
p991 . . . . . 0114 275 1223
1 High Pavement, Nottingham
p988 . . . . . 0115 941 8218

SMITH, Mr Simon LLB(Sheff) G *Nov 1981*
15, 62
3 Temple Gardens, London EC4
p952 . . . . . 020 7353 3102

SMITH, Sophie LLB(Hons)(L'pool) L *Oct 1999*
15, 20
Atlantic Chambers, Liverpool
p980 . . . . . 0151 236 4421

SMITH, Miss Stephanie BA L *Nov 2004*
1, 7, 22, 26, 32
Arden Chambers, London WC1
p923 . . . . . 020 7242 4244

SMITH, Mr Stephen BA(Oxon) M *Jul 1983*
(Q.C.) *6, 11, 8*
New Square Chambers, London WC2
p943 . . . . . 020 7419 8000

SMITH, Mr Tom BA; LLM(Cantab) M *Oct 1999*
5, 6, 8, 11, 24, 97, 38
South Square, London WC1
p950 . . . . . 020 7696 9900

SMITH, Mr Tyrone G *May 1994*
15
25 Bedford Row, London WC1
p925 . . . . . 020 7067 1500

Smithburn, Prof John Eric BS; MA; JD M *Nov 1989*
1 Hare Court, London EC4
p936 . . . . . 020 7797 7070

Smithers, Dr Roger Howard BSc; PhD; DipLaw I *Nov 1990*
37, 11
Clerksroom - Administration Centre, Taunton
p993 . . . . . 0845 083 3000
Guildford Chambers, Guildford
p975 . . . . . 01483 539131

SMITTEN, Mr Ben M *Jan 1999*
15, 62
25 Bedford Row, London WC1
p925 . . . . . 020 7067 1500

Smouha, Mr Joe MA(Cantab); LLM(New York) M *Jul 1986*
(Q.C.)
Essex Court Chambers, London WC2
p931 . . . . . 020 7813 8000

Smoult-Hawtree, Ms Karen G *Jun 2000*
York Chambers, York
p995 . . . . . 01904 620048
York Chambers, Newcastle upon Tyne
p987 . . . . . 0191 206 4677

Smout, Mr Will L *Jan 2005*
Guildford Chambers, Guildford
p975 . . . . . 01483 539131

Smullen, Mrs Marion LLB(Lond); BA G *Mar 1985*
15
1 Inner Temple Lane, London EC4
p937 . . . . . 020 7427 4400

Smyth, Mr Christopher G *Jan 2006*
48, 15, 39, 62, 84, 88, 26, 93, 94
Queen Square Chambers, Bristol
p972 . . . . . 0117 921 1966

Smyth, Mr Jack LLB M *Oct 2007*
84, 30, 31, 46, 23, 1, 78, 60
No5 Chambers, Bristol
p971 . . . . . 0845 210 5555
No5 Chambers, London EC4
p944 . . . . . 0845 210 5555
No5 Chambers, Birmingham
p968 . . . . . 0845 210 5555

Smyth, Mr Stephen Mark James A Recorder I *Jul 1974*
15
Atkinson Bevan Chambers, London EC4
p924 . . . . . 020 7353 2112

SNARR, Mr Matthew LLB(Hons) I *Jan 2001*
30, 53
9 St John Street Chambers, Manchester
p984 . . . . . 0161 955 9000

SNELL, Mr John BA(Oxon); DipLaw L *Oct 1991*
7, 30, 53, 11, 12, 24, 27, 33, 1, 3, 8, 22, 40
Guildhall Chambers, Bristol
p970 . . . . . 0117 930 9000
2 Temple Gardens, London EC4
p952 . . . . . 020 7822 1200
New Walk Chambers, Leicester
p979 . . . . . 0871 200 1298

Snelling, Mr Charles William LLB(King's College) M *Oct 2005*
Fenners Chambers, Cambridge
p972 . . . . . 01223 368761

SNELUS, Mr James I *Oct 1999*
10, 12, 20
St Mary's Chambers, Nottingham
p989 . . . . . 0115 950 3503

Snider, Mr John MA(Oxon); MBA(WIT) M *Jul 1982*
Essex Court Chambers, London WC2
p931 . . . . . 020 7813 8000

Snook, Mr Harry I *Nov 2006*
15, 12
St Albans Chambers, St Albans
p992 . . . . . 01727 843383

Snook, Mr Sean BA L *Jan 2000*
41, 3, 5, 11, 43, 47, 49, 24, 54, 35, 61
20 Essex Street, London WC2
p932 . . . . . 020 7842 1200

SNOWDEN, Mr Richard MA(Cantab); LLM(Harv) L *Jun 1986*
(Q.C.) *11, 38, 97*
Erskine Chambers, London WC2
p931 . . . . . 020 7242 5532

SNOWDEN, Mr Steven BA(Nott'm) I *Jul 1989*
30, 53, 40, 24, 11, 12
Crown Office Chambers, London EC4
p929 . . . . . 020 7797 8100

Snowdon, Miss Martine L *Oct 2000*
30, 15, 12, 22, 62
Exchange Chambers, Manchester
p983 . . . . . 0161 833 2722
Exchange Chambers, Liverpool
p980 . . . . . 0151 236 7747
Exchange Chambers, Leeds
p977 . . . . . 0113 203 1970

Soares, Mr Patrick C LLB; LLM(Lond) L *Nov 1983*
34, 57, 58
Gray's Inn Tax Chambers, London WC1
p936 . . . . . 020 7242 2642

Sofaer, Miss Moira BSc(Lond) M *Jul 1975*
10, 12, 15, 20, 22, 30
1 Gray's Inn Square, London WC1
p935 . . . . . 020 7405 8946
1 Mitre Court Buildings, London EC4
p942 . . . . . 020 7452 8900

Sokol, Mr Christopher John Francis MA(Cantab) L *Jul 1975*
34, 37, 36, 29, 8, 9
15 Old Square, London WC2
p945 . . . . . 020 7242 2744

SOLE, Miss Emma BA(Oxon) I *Oct 2005*
30, 18
Farrar's Building, London EC4
p933 . . . . . 020 7583 9241

Solley, Mr Stephen I *Nov 1969*
(Q.C.)
Charter Chambers, London WC1
p928 . . . . . 020 7618 4400

Solomon, Mr Adam Jonathan MA(Oxon); MA(Sussex); DipLaw(City) G *Oct 1998*
11, 76, 18
Cloisters, London EC4
p928 . . . . . 020 7827 4000
Littleton Chambers, London EC4
p941 . . . . . 020 7797 8600

Solomon, Mr Reuben L *Jan 1992*
15, 18, 23
12 Old Square, London WC2
p945 . . . . . 020 7404 0875

Solomon, Miss Susan MA(Oxon) M *Jul 1967*
3PB, London EC4
p946 . . . . . 020 7583 8055

SOMERVILLE, Mr Bryce E MA(Cantab) M *Jul 1980*
20, 93, 25
Cornwall Street Chambers, Birmingham
p967 . . . . . 0121 233 7500

Sonaike, Kola I *Jan 1998*
One Essex Court, London EC4
p931 . . . . . 020 7936 3030

Sones, Mr Richard LLB I *Nov 1969*
15, 25
5 King's Bench Walk, London EC4
p939 . . . . . 020 7353 5638

Soole, Mr Michael MA(Oxon) I *Jul 1977*
(Q.C.) *5, 12, 41, 8, 24, 40*
Four New Square, London WC2
p943 . . . . . 020 7822 2000

Soor, Smair Singh LLB(Kingston) G *Jul 1988*
18, 55
7 Bedford Row, London WC1
p924 . . . . . 020 7242 3555

Soppitt, Mr Nigel G *Jan 1996*
15, 70, 72
Old Court Chambers, Middlesbrough
p986 . . . . . 01642 232523

Sorel-Cameron, Mr Matthew M *Oct 2009*
15, 12
East Anglian Chambers, Norwich
p988 . . . . . 01603 617351
East Anglian Chambers, Colchester
p975 . . . . . 01206 572756
East Anglian Chambers, Chelmsford
p973 . . . . . 01245 215660
East Anglian Chambers, Ipswich
p976 . . . . . 01473 214481

Soubry, Ms Anna LLB(Hons) I *Nov 1995*
15
KCH Garden Square Chambers, Nottingham
p989 . . . . . 0115 941 8851
KCH Garden Square Chambers, Leicester
p979 . . . . . 0115 941 8851

Soule, Miss Natalie L *Oct 2008*
15, 20
5 King's Bench Walk, London EC4
p939 . . . . . 020 7353 5638

Southern, Mr David Boardman LLB(Hons)(Lond); MA; M Phil; D Phil(Oxon) L *Jan 1982*
34
Temple Tax Chambers, London EC4
p952 . . . . . 020 7353 7884 / 7353 8982

Southern, Miss Emma Catherine LLB(Hons) L *Jan 2006*
15, 18, 20, 10
12 College Place, Southampton
p992 . . . . . 023 8032 0320

Southern, Mr Richard Michael MA(Cantab) M *Nov 1987*
(Q.C.) *3, 35, 19, 33, 24, 5, 11, 40*
7 King's Bench Walk, London EC4
p940 . . . . . 020 7910 8300

Southey, Mr David Hugh Recorder I *Nov 1996*
(Q.C.) *23, 15, 1, 51*
Tooks Chambers, London EC4
p953 . . . . . 020 7842 7575

SOUTHGATE, Mr Jonathan Blake LLB M *Nov 1992*
10, 20
29 Bedford Row, London WC1
p925 . . . . . 020 7404 1044

Sowden, Ms Lucy LLB(Hons) I *Jul 2006*
Zenith Chambers, Leeds
p979 . . . . . 0113 245 5438

SOWERSBY, Mr Robert MA(History & Anthropology)(UCL) G *Jan 2000*
30, 53
Guildhall Chambers, Bristol
p970 . . . . . 0117 930 9000

Spackman, Mr Mark A LLB(Leics) L *Nov 1986*
8, 12, 11, 15, 6, 18, 22, 30
Iscoed Chambers, Swansea
p993 . . . . . 01792 652988

SPAIN, Mr Timothy Harrisson LLB G *Jul 1983*
10, 12, 20, 1, 63, 14
Trinity (Newcastle) Chambers, Newcastle upon Tyne
p987 . . . . . 0191 232 1927
Trinity (Teesside) Chambers, Middlesbrough
p986 . . . . . 01642 247569

Spalton, Mr George L *Jan 2004*
Four New Square, London WC2
p943 . . . . . 020 7822 2000

Sparks, Ms Paula LLB G *Oct 1994*
30, 53, 27, 51
Doughty Street Chambers, London WC1
p930 . . . . . 020 7404 1313

Sparling, Mr Charlie I *Jan 2006*
26, 51, 36, 46, 18, 55, 48, 49, 53
Old Square Chambers, London WC1
p945 . . . . . 020 7269 0300

Speaight, Mr Anthony MA(Oxon) M *Jul 1973*
(Q.C.) *7, 11, 12, 40, 81, 78*
4 Pump Court, London EC4
p947 . . . . . 020 7842 5555

Speakman, Mr Lee BA(Hons) M *Jul 2009*
12, 15, 20, 30
Exchange Chambers, Manchester
p983 . . . . . 0161 833 2722
Exchange Chambers, Liverpool
p980 . . . . . 0151 236 7747
Exchange Chambers, Leeds
p977 . . . . . 0113 203 1970

Spear, Miss Sarah I *Oct 1997*
12
St Johns Buildings, Preston
p990 . . . . . 01772 256100
St Johns Buildings, Chester
p974 . . . . . 01244 323070
St Johns Buildings, Manchester
p985 . . . . . 0161 214 1500
St Johns Buildings, Liverpool
p982 . . . . . 0151 243 6000

SPEARING, Miss Rachel M LLB(Hons) I *Nov 1999*
15, 62, 84
Pump Court Chambers, Swindon
p993 . . . . . 01793 539899
Pump Court Chambers, Winchester
p994 . . . . . 01962 868161
Pump Court Chambers, London EC4
p947 . . . . . 020 7353 0711

SPEARMAN, Mr Richard MA(Cantab) M *Nov 1977*
(Q.C.) *8, 11, 12, 13, 16, 18, 24, 40, 41, 50, 51, 56*
4-5 Gray's Inn Square, London WC1
p935 . . . . . 020 7404 5252

SPEARS, Miss Katharine M *Jan 2005*
Carmelite Chambers, London EC4
p927 . . . . . 020 7936 6300

SPEARS, Ms Portia G *Jan 1992*
30
12 King's Bench Walk, London EC4
p940 . . . . . 020 7583 0811

Speck, Mr Adrian MA(Cantab) G *Oct 1993*
13, 45, 50, 56
8 New Square, London WC2
p943 . . . . . 020 7405 4321

SPEED, Mr Ian G *Oct 2000*
15, 62
St Philips Chambers, Birmingham
p969 . . . . . 0121 246 7000

Speker, Mr Adam BA(Hons)(Bris) M *Oct 1999*
13, 16, 50, 51, 18, 56
5RB, London WC1
p948 . . . . . 020 7242 2902

See p1010 for the Key to Work Categories

Spence, Ms Elizabeth MA G *Jul 2006*
20, 30, 18, 76, 10, 23, 88, 12, 94
Stour Chambers, Canterbury
p972 . . . . . 01227 764899

Spence, Miss Gemma-Louise L *Jul 2007*
15, 12, 20
East Anglian Chambers, Norwich
p988 . . . . . 01603 617351
East Anglian Chambers, Colchester
p975 . . . . . 01206 572756
East Anglian Chambers, Chelmsford
p973 . . . . . 01245 215660
East Anglian Chambers, Ipswich
p976 . . . . . 01473 214481

SPENCE, Mr Simon I *Jul 1985*
(Q.C.) *15, 84*
18 Red Lion Court, London EC4
p949 . . . . . 020 7520 6000
18 Red Lion Court (Annexe), Chelmsford
p973 . . . . . 01245 280880

SPENCE, Mr Stephen G *Jul 1983*
15, 84, 4, 91
1 Paper Buildings, London EC4
p946 . . . . . 020 7353 3728

Spencer, Mr Andrew G *Jan 2004*
59, 30, 40, 12, 93, 53
1 Chancery Lane, London WC2
p928 . . . . . 0845 634 6666

Spencer, Miss Anna G *Jan 2004*
14 Gray's Inn Square, London WC1
p936 . . . . . 020 7242 0858

SPENCER, Sir Derek Harold MA; BCL(Oxon) G *Feb 1961*
(Q.C.) *15, 62, 95*
18 Red Lion Court, London EC4
p949 . . . . . 020 7520 6000
18 Red Lion Court (Annexe), Chelmsford
p973 . . . . . 01245 280880

Spencer, Mr Joseph G *Jul 2001*
12, 15, 20
11 King's Bench Walk, Leeds
p978 . . . . . 0113 297 1200

Spencer, Miss Lara L *Jul 2000*
12, 18, 22, 53
Walnut House Chambers, Exeter
p975 . . . . . 01392 279751

Spencer, Mr Martin Benedict BCL; MA(Oxon) I *Jul 1979*
(Q.C.) *27, 53, 30*
Hailsham Chambers, London EC4
p936 . . . . . 020 7643 5000

SPENCER, Mr Michael MA(Oxon) I *Jul 1970*
(Q.C.) *30, 36, 84, 53*
Crown Office Chambers, London EC4
p929 . . . . . 020 7797 8100

Spencer, Mr Paul I *Nov 1965*
2 New Street, Leicester
p979 . . . . . 0116 262 5906

Spencer, Mr Paul Anthony LLB M *Nov 1988*
1, 27, 85, 53, 68, 63, 40, 96
Cloisters, London EC4
p928 . . . . . 020 7827 4000
3 Serjeants' Inn, London EC4
p950 . . . . . 020 7427 5000

Spencer, Mr Shaun LLB L *Jan 2005*
12, 20, 22, 30, 46, 10, 47, 88
St Johns Buildings, Preston
p990 . . . . . 01772 256100
St Johns Buildings, Chester
p974 . . . . . 01244 323070
St Johns Buildings, Manchester
p985 . . . . . 0161 214 1500
St Johns Buildings, Liverpool
p982 . . . . . 0151 243 6000

Spencer, Mr Timothy John MA(Cantab); Recorder M *Jul 1982*
(Q.C.) *15, 62*
7 Bedford Row, London WC1
p924 . . . . . 020 7242 3555

SPENCER BERNARD, Mr Robert MA(Oxon); Recorder of the Crown Court I *Nov 1969*
15, 12
4 King's Bench Walk, London EC4
p939 . . . . . 020 7822 7000

SPENCER-LEWIS, Mr Neville MA(Oxon) I *Jul 1970*
5, 11, 30, 47, 53
12 King's Bench Walk, London EC4
p940 . . . . . 020 7583 0811

Spens, Mr David I *Jan 1973*
(Q.C.) *15*
6 King's Bench Walk, London EC4
p939 . . . . . 020 7583 0410

SPENWYN, Miss Marie G *Jan 1999*
Carmelite Chambers, London EC4
p927 . . . . . 020 7936 6300

Spicer, Mr Jonathan BA(Hons)(Cantab) I *Oct 1995*
62, 15, 34, 18, 30, 67
36 Bedford Row, London WC1
p925 . . . . . 020 7421 8000

Spicer, Miss Rachel BA(Oxon) M *Jan 2002*
1 Hare Court, London EC4
p936 . . . . . 020 7797 7070

Spink, Mr Andrew Murray MA(Cantab); Recorder M *Nov 1985*
(Q.C.) *53, 30, 40, 92*
Outer Temple Chambers, London WC2
p945 . . . . . 020 7353 6381

Spink, Mr Peter John William G *Jul 1979*
15, 70, 62
12 College Place, Southampton
p992 . . . . . 023 8032 0320

Spinks, Mr Roderick LLB(Sheff) I *Jan 1997*
12, 20, 30, 38
Fenners Chambers, Cambridge
p972 . . . . . 01223 368761

Spitz, Mr Derek L *Nov 2001*
One Essex Court, London EC4
p931 . . . . . 020 7583 2000

SPOLLON, Mr Guy BA G *Nov 1976*
20
St Philips Chambers, Birmingham
p969 . . . . . 0121 246 7000

Spooner, Miss Judith LLB(Hons) M *Jul 1987*
10, 20
14 Gray's Inn Square, London WC1
p936 . . . . . 020 7242 0858

Sprack, Mr John M *Jul 1984*
1 Pump Court, London EC4
p947 . . . . . 020 7842 7070

SPRAGG, Mr Robert M *Jan 2003*
15, 62, 25
Trinity (Newcastle) Chambers, Newcastle upon Tyne
p987 . . . . . 0191 232 1927
Trinity (Teesside) Chambers, Middlesbrough
p986 . . . . . 01642 247569

SPRATLING, Ms Anne BA(Cantab) L *Jul 1980*
20, 10
Coram Chambers, London EC1
p929 . . . . . 020 7092 3700

Spratt, Mr Christopher David LLB(Dundee) G *Nov 1986*
97, 8, 29, 5, 38, 93, 37, 18
33 Bedford Row, London WC1
p925 . . . . . 020 7242 6476
9 Stone Buildings Barristers Chambers, London WC2
p951 . . . . . 020 7404 5055

SPRATT-DAWSON, Ms Josephine LLB(Hons) G *Oct 1993*
8, 10, 11, 12, 20, 29, 30, 32, 37, 40, 89
Trinity Chambers, Chelmsford
p974 . . . . . 01245 605040

SPREADBOROUGH, Mr Paul G *Oct 2002*
Furnival Chambers, London EC4
p934 . . . . . 020 7405 3232

SPRINZ, Miss Lucy BA(Hons) I *Jan 2008*
10, 20, 51
1 Garden Court, London EC4
p934 . . . . . 020 7797 7900

Sproson, Miss Eileen G *Jan 2005*
2 King's Bench Walk, London EC4
p939 . . . . . 020 7353 1746

Sproull, Mr Nicholas LLB G *Nov 1992*
12, 18, 20, 30
Albion Chambers, Bristol
p970 . . . . . 0117 927 2144

SPURLING, Mr Rudolph I *Jan 2007*
23, 51, 12, 88
10 King's Bench Walk, London EC4
p940 . . . . . 020 7353 7742

SQUIRES, Mr Daniel MA(Cantab); LLM(Harv) M *Nov 1998*
1, 12, 46, 16, 18, 19, 51, 55, 36, 27, 23, 33, 26, 76
Matrix Chambers, London WC1
p942 . . . . . 020 7404 3447

Squirrell, Mr Benjamin I *Oct 1990*
15, 62
Nine Bedford Row, London WC1
p924 . . . . . 020 7489 2727

St Louis, Mr Brian LLB; LLM M *Oct 1994*
15, 18
15 New Bridge Street Chambers, London EC4
p943 . . . . . 020 7842 1900

St Quintin, Mr Thomas Christopher MA(Cantab); MSci I *Jan 2006*
Hogarth Chambers, London WC2
p937 . . . . . 020 7404 0404

St Ville, Mr James MA(Cantab); CEng; MIEE G *Oct 1995*
13, 45
8 New Square, London WC2
p943 . . . . . 020 7405 4321

Stables, Mr Christopher LLB(L'pool) G *Oct 1990*
15, 70, 72, 80, 62, 84, 95
Exchange Chambers, Manchester
p983 . . . . . 0161 833 2722
Exchange Chambers, Liverpool
p980 . . . . . 0151 236 7747
Exchange Chambers, Leeds
p977 . . . . . 0113 203 1970

Stables, Mr Gordon L *Oct 1995*
15, 20, 30
Paradise Chambers, Sheffield
p992 . . . . . 0114 273 8951

Stacey, Mr Dan G *Oct 1996*
11, 40
Hailsham Chambers, London EC4
p936 . . . . . 020 7643 5000

STACEY, Ms Myriam LLB(Bris) I *Oct 1998*
5, 6, 8, 11, 22, 29, 32, 37, 47
Landmark Chambers, London EC4
p941 . . . . . 020 7430 1221

STADDON, Ms Claire LLB(Lond) M *Jul 1985*
6, 8, 11, 62
New Square Chambers, London WC2
p943 . . . . . 020 7419 8000

STADDON, Mr Paul BSc(Econ) I *Jul 1976*
6, 8, 11, 22, 40, 18, 47
Tanfield Chambers, London WC1
p951 . . . . . 020 7421 5300

Staff, Mr Marcus BA I *Oct 1994*
5, 6, 8, 11, 21, 3, 41, 49, 62
XXIV Old Buildings, London WC2
p944 . . . . . 020 7691 2424

STAFFORD, Mr Andrew MA(Cantab) M *Jul 1980*
(Q.C.) *11, 18, 40, 38, 47, 56, 96*
Littleton Chambers, London EC4
p941 . . . . . 020 7797 8600
Trinity (Newcastle) Chambers, Newcastle upon Tyne
p987 . . . . . 0191 232 1927
Trinity (Teesside) Chambers, Middlesbrough
p986 . . . . . 01642 247569

STAFFORD, Dr Paul MA(Oxon); D Phil(Oxon) G *Nov 1987*
5, 6, 7, 11, 29
Ten Old Square, London WC2
p945 . . . . . 020 7405 0758

STAFFORD-MICHAEL, Mr Simon LLB(Bris) G *Nov 1982*
15, 11
Lombard Chambers, London EC1
p941 . . . . . 020 7107 2100

Stage, Mr Peter James LLB L *Jul 1971*
15, 62
4 Breams Buildings, London EC4
p927 . . . . . 020 7092 1900

Stagg, Mr Paul LLB(Warw) G *Nov 1994*
22, 51, 30, 40, 26, 10
1 Chancery Lane, London WC2
p928 . . . . . 0845 634 6666

Stagi, Miss Alexandra F V MA(Cantab) L *Nov 1997*
11, 12, 22, 30, 40
Lamb Chambers, London EC4
p941 . . . . . 020 7797 8300

STAKER, Mr Christopher BA; DPhil M *Oct 2003*
33, 19, 1, 51, 23, 46, 71, 41, 34
Thirty Nine Essex Street, London WC2
p932 . . . . . 020 7832 1111

Staley, Miss Helen L *Mar 1997*
12, 15, 20, 30, 40, 41
Castle Chambers, Harrow
p976 . . . . . 020 8423 6579

Stallworthy, Mr Nicolas MA(Oxon); BCL M *Oct 1993*
(Q.C.) *92, 40, 8, 37, 81, 11*
Outer Temple Chambers, London WC2
p945 . . . . . 020 7353 6381

Stamford, Ms Susan Deborah LLB(Hons)(Lond) M *Oct 1997*
10, 20
Coram Chambers, London EC1
p929 . . . . . 020 7092 3700

STAMP, Ms Abigail LLB; BVC G *Oct 2004*
30, 53
Guildhall Chambers, Bristol
p970 . . . . . 0117 930 9000

Stanage, Mr Nick MA I *Jan 1997*
1, 15, 23
Doughty Street Chambers, London WC1
p930 . . . . . 020 7404 1313

STANBURY, Mrs Louise L *Jan 2004*
20
Bank House Chambers, Sheffield
p991 . . . . . 0114 275 1223

Stanbury, Mr Matthew LLB G *Jan 2004*
1, 15, 51
Garden Court North Chambers, Manchester
p983 . . . . . 0161 236 1840

Stancombe, Mr Barry LLB(Lond) G *Jul 1983*
11, 18, 40
3PB, London EC4
p946 . . . . . 020 7583 8055

Standfast, Mr Philip Arthur BA(Sheff) I *Jul 1980*
15, 12, 18, 36, 70, 68, 84
St Pauls Chambers, Leeds
p979 . . . . . 0113 245 5866

Stanford, Mr Tony L *Nov 1996*
4 Breams Buildings, London EC4
p927 . . . . . 020 7092 1900

Stanger, Mr Mark Fullerton LLB(Hons) M *Jan 1998*
15, 30
33 Bedford Row, London WC1
p925 . . . . . 020 7242 6476
Oriel Chambers, Liverpool
p981 . . . . . 0151 236 7191 / 236 4321
Oriel Chambers, Preston
p990 . . . . . 01772 254764

Stangoe, Miss Heather Elizabeth I *Oct 2001*
15
Atkinson Bevan Chambers, London EC4
p924 . . . . . 020 7353 2112

Stanistreet, Miss Penelope BA(Hons); DipLww(Lond) L *Oct 1993*
15, 20
Paradise Chambers, Sheffield
p992 . . . . . 0114 273 8951

STANLEY, Mrs Gillian BA; DipLaw M *Jul 2001*
10, 20
1 Garden Court, London EC4
p934 . . . . . 020 7797 7900

Stanley, Mr Paul BA(Cantab); LLM(Harv) M *Oct 1993*
(Q.C.)
Essex Court Chambers, London WC2
p931 . . . . . 020 7813 8000

Stanniland, Mr Jonathan LLB I *Nov 1993*
72, 15, 70
Albion Chambers, Bristol
p970 . . . . . 0117 927 2144
Unity Street Chambers, Bristol
p972 . . . . . 0117 906 9789

Stansby, Ms Alexandra M *Nov 1985*
20
18 St John Street Chambers, Manchester
p985 . . . . . 0161 278 1800

Stansfield, Mr Piers A LLB(Bris) I *Nov 1993*
3, 7, 11, 24, 40
Keating Chambers, London WC2
p938 . . . . . 020 7544 2600

Stanton, Miss Lisa MA(Cantab) I *Oct 1993*
10, 15, 20
St Albans Chambers, St Albans
p992 . . . . . 01727 843383

STANZEL, Ms Sarah Astrid LLB(Hons); LLM I *Jul 1999*
18
Tanfield Chambers, London WC1
p951 . . . . . 020 7421 5300

STAPLETON, Miss Elaine LLM; BCL I *Nov 1997*
Carmelite Chambers, London EC4
p927 . . . . . 020 7936 6300

STARCEVIC, Petar LLB(Bris) I *Jul 1983*
8, 11, 18, 22, 30, 40
St Philips Chambers, Birmingham
p969 . . . . . 0121 246 7000

13

Stark, Mr James LLB(Hons) M *Jan 1998*
22, 26, 30, 55, 51, 1, 88, 73
Garden Court North Chambers, Manchester
p983 . . . . . 0161 236 1840

Starks, Mr Nicholas LLB I *Aug 1989*
St Ives Chambers, Birmingham
p969 . . . . . 0121 236 0863

START, Miss Angharad BA(Dunelm) L *Nov 1988*
2, 5, 6, 8, 9, 11, 14, 21, 29, 32, 37, 40
3 Verulam Buildings, London WC1
p953 . . . . . 020 7831 8441

STARTE, Mr Harvey N A MA(Cantab) G *Nov 1985*
16, 52, 73
One Brick Court, London EC4
p927 . . . . . 020 7353 8845

Staunton, Mr Ulick LLB(Lond) M *Jul 1984*
6, 8, 9, 11, 22, 29, 32, 37, 14, 40
Radcliffe Chambers, London WC2
p949 . . . . . 020 7831 0081

Stavrou, Miss Xenia LLB(Hons)(Lond) M *Nov 1998*
15, 20
5 King's Bench Walk, London EC4
p939 . . . . . 020 7353 5638

Stead, Mr Richard MA(Cantab) M *Jul 1979*
7, 12, 30, 40, 74, 11, 96
St John's Chambers, Bristol
p972 . . . . . 0117 921 3456

Stead, Mr Timothy Harold BA; Recorder G *Nov 1979*
15, 30
No 6 Barristers Chambers, Leeds
p978 . . . . . 0113 245 9763

Steadman, Mr Russell Charles BA(Hons) I *Nov 1995*
10, 20
3 Dr Johnson's Buildings, London EC4
p930 . . . . . 020 7353 4854

Stedman, Mr Aryan M *Nov 1997*
23, 12, 15
Two King's Bench Walk, London EC4
p939 . . . . . 020 7353 7202 / 7353 3909

STEEL, Mr John BSc(Dunelm) G *Jul 1978*
(Q.C.) *1, 31*
4-5 Gray's Inn Square, London WC1
p935 . . . . . 020 7404 5252

Steele, Mr Iain MA(Cantab); BCL(Oxon) I *Oct 2005*
1, 11, 18, 51, 89
Blackstone Chambers, London EC4
p926 . . . . . 020 7583 1770

Steele, Ms Jennifer LLB M *Jul 2002*
31, 20, 30
New Walk Chambers, Leicester
p979 . . . . . 0871 200 1298

Steele, Miss Laura C I *Oct 1996*
12, 15, 20, 23, 30, 36
Castle Chambers, Harrow
p976 . . . . . 020 8423 6579

Steen, Mr Martin Gamper LLB(Lond) I *Jul 1976*
15, 62
Albion Chambers, Bristol
p970 . . . . . 0117 927 2144

STEER, Mr David BA(Hons)(Law); Recorder; Leader of The Northern Circuit 2002-2004 I *Nov 1974*
(Q.C.) *15*
7 Harrington Street Chambers, Liverpool
p981 . . . . . 0151 242 0707

Steer, Mr Richard BA; PG DipLaw G *Jan 2001*
11, 12, 47, 67, 15, 18, 30, 36, 24
Angel Chambers, Swansea
p992 . . . . . 01792 464623

Stein, Mr Alexander LLB G *Jul 1998*
15, 30, 6, 7, 13, 31, 39, 45, 46, 48, 51, 62, 84, 94, 72, 70, 71
No5 Chambers, Bristol
p971 . . . . . 0845 210 5555
No5 Chambers, London EC4
p944 . . . . . 0845 210 5555
No5 Chambers, Birmingham
p968 . . . . . 0845 210 5555

STEINBERG, Mr Harry BA(Cantab) G *Nov 1997*
7, 22, 30, 40, 47
12 King's Bench Walk, London EC4
p940 . . . . . 020 7583 0811

Steinert, Mr Jonathan BA(Oxon) M *Feb 1986*
7, 8, 11, 12, 40, 45, 50, 56, 22
Henderson Chambers, London EC4
p937 . . . . . 020 7583 9020

Steinfeld, Mr Alan BA; LLB L *Nov 1968*
(Q.C.) *5, 6, 8, 9, 11, 29, 32, 37, 40, 41, 49, 62*
XXIV Old Buildings, London WC2
p944 . . . . . 020 7691 2424

STEINFELD, Ms Charlotte L *Oct 2004*
12, 15, 20, 30, 31
10 King's Bench Walk, London EC4
p940 . . . . . 020 7353 7742

STELLING, Mr Nigel Roy I *Jul 1987*
15, 51
Citadel Chambers, Birmingham
p967 . . . . . 0121 233 8500

Stemp, Mr Scott LLB I *Oct 2000*
15, 26, 31, 42, 48, 84, 62
12 College Place, Southampton
p992 . . . . . 023 8032 0320

Stenning, Mr James L *Jan 2006*
Clerksroom - Administration Centre, Taunton
p993 . . . . . 0845 083 3000

Stephens, Mr Andrew L *Jul 2004*
Westgate Chambers, Lewes
p980 . . . . . 01273 480510

Stephens, Miss Jessica UWA; BCom; LLB L *Jan 2001*
3, 7, 11, 24, 40
Keating Chambers, London WC2
p938 . . . . . 020 7544 2600

Stephens, Mr John Lewis BA(Oxon) M *Jul 1975*
8, 5, 6, 11, 29, 49, 62, 32, 37
XXIV Old Buildings, London WC2
p944 . . . . . 020 7691 2424

Stephens, Mr Mark M *Nov 1998*
1 Mitre Court Buildings, London EC4
p942 . . . . . 020 7452 8900

Stephens, Mr Michael BA(Hons) I *Jul 1983*
St Ives Chambers, Birmingham
p969 . . . . . 0121 236 0863

Stephens, Mr Richard L *Jan 2008*
Cobden House Chambers, Manchester
p983 . . . . . 0161 833 6000

Stephenson, Mr Benedict MA(Oxon) L *Jul 1973*
15
3PB, London EC4
p946 . . . . . 020 7583 8055

Stephenson, Mr Christopher MA(Hons)(Edin) L *Nov 1994*
30, 53, 70
9 Gough Square, London EC4
p935 . . . . . 020 7832 0500

Stephenson, Mr Geoffrey FCII G *Nov 1971*
1, 12, 15, 22, 24, 26, 28, 30, 31, 36
Cornerstone Barristers, London WC1
p929 . . . . . 020 7242 4986

STEPHENSON, Ms Lisa BA(Oxon); Masters in European Law; Free University of Brussels L *Oct 1999*
12, 18, 24, 30, 47
12 King's Bench Walk, London EC4
p940 . . . . . 020 7583 0811

Stephenson, Mr Mark G *Nov 1997*
72, 15, 70
Exchange Chambers, Manchester
p983 . . . . . 0161 833 2722
Exchange Chambers, Liverpool
p980 . . . . . 0151 236 7747
Exchange Chambers, Leeds
p977 . . . . . 0113 203 1970

STEPHENSON, Mr Paul LLB(Hons); LLM M *Oct 1990*
13, 19, 44, 45, 47, 48
St James's Chambers, Manchester
p984 . . . . . 0161 834 7000

Stephenson, Mr Simon LLB(Hons) I *Jul 2005*
10, 47, 67, 72, 15, 70, 18, 20, 30, 94, 36
Angel Chambers, Swansea
p992 . . . . . 01792 464623

STERLING, Robert MA(Cantab) G *Jul 1970*
1, 5, 6, 8, 9, 11, 13, 14, 22, 29, 32, 34, 37, 40
New Square Chambers, London WC2
p943 . . . . . 020 7419 8000
St James's Chambers, Manchester
p984 . . . . . 0161 834 7000
Zenith Chambers, Leeds
p979 . . . . . 0113 245 5438

Sterling, Miss Valerie LLB(Hons) G *Jul 1981*
Park Court Chambers, Leeds
p978 . . . . . 0113 243 3277

Stern, Mr David LLB(Lond); LLM(Cantab); Associate Member L *Jul 1989*
11 Stone Buildings, London WC2
p951 . . . . . 020 7831 6381

STERN, Ms Kristina I *Nov 1996*
30, 27, 40, 12, 1, 51, 53, 36, 63
Thirty Nine Essex Street, London WC2
p932 . . . . . 020 7832 1111

Stern, Mr Mark Richard Alexander BA; MA L *Feb 1988*
15, 20
2 Dr Johnson's Buildings, London EC4
p930 . . . . . 020 7936 2613

STERN, Mr Thomas G *Nov 1995*
Maidstone Chambers, Maidstone
p982 . . . . . 01622 688592

STERNBERG, Mr Daniel G *Oct 2006*
15
9-12 Bell Yard Chambers, London WC2
p926 . . . . . 020 7400 1800

Sternberg, Mr Michael V MA; LLM(Cantab) G *Jul 1975*
(Q.C.) *10, 20*
4 Paper Buildings, London EC4
p946 . . . . . 020 7583 0816

Stevens, Mr Andrew MA(Cantab) L *Jan 2007*
3, 11, 24, 35, 40, 41, 78, 79, 89
4 Pump Court, London EC4
p947 . . . . . 020 7842 5555

Stevens, Miss Hanne BA(Hons) M *Jul 2002*
15
2 Hare Court, London EC4
p937 . . . . . 020 7353 5324

Stevens, Ms Hazel BA(Hons) L *Jul 2001*
15, 20, 12, 10, 11
East Anglian Chambers, Norwich
p988 . . . . . 01603 617351
East Anglian Chambers, Colchester
p975 . . . . . 01206 572756
East Anglian Chambers, Chelmsford
p973 . . . . . 01245 215660
East Anglian Chambers, Ipswich
p976 . . . . . 01473 214481

Stevens, Miss Heather LLB M *Jan 2009*
15
Lamb Building, Brighton
p970 . . . . . 01273 820490
Lamb Building, London EC4
p940 . . . . . 020 7797 7788

STEVENS, Mr Henry BA; LLB I *Oct 2002*
11, 93, 38
Guildhall Chambers, Bristol
p970 . . . . . 0117 930 9000

STEVENS, Mr Howard M *Oct 1990*
12, 30, 40, 59
3 Hare Court, London EC4
p937 . . . . . 020 7415 7800

Stevens, Mr Mark I *Jul 1998*
15
1 Inner Temple Lane, London EC4
p937 . . . . . 020 7427 4400

Stevens, Miss Sarah Louise L *Nov 2002*
19, 11, 24
Brick Court Chambers, London WC2
p927 . . . . . 020 7379 3550

Stevens, Mr Stuart S G *Jul 1970*
Holborn Chambers, London WC2
p937 . . . . . 020 7242 6060

Stevens-Hoare, Ms Michelle LLB; LLM M *Jul 1986*
40, 22, 49, 11, 88, 93, 37
Hardwicke, London WC2
p936 . . . . . 020 7242 2523

STEVENSON, Mr Daniel L *Oct 2002*
15
9-12 Bell Yard Chambers, London WC2
p926 . . . . . 020 7400 1800

STEVENSON, Mr John Melford MA(Oxon) I *Nov 1975*
30, 40, 53, 24, 27, 11, 12
Crown Office Chambers, London EC4
p929 . . . . . 020 7797 8100

STEVENSON, Ms Monica M *Jan 2004*
15
25 Bedford Row, London WC1
p925 . . . . . 020 7067 1500

STEVENSON, Mr Paul Anthony MA(Oxon); DipLaw M *Oct 2006*
6, 8, 12, 47, 67, 18, 38, 88, 89, 40, 93
Tanfield Chambers, London WC1
p951 . . . . . 020 7421 5300

Stevenson, Mr Peter I *Jan 2008*
Stone Chambers, London WC1
p951 . . . . . 020 7440 6900

STEVENSON, Mr William MA(Oxon); Recorder L *Nov 1968*
(Q.C.) *24, 40, 53, 30, 11, 27*
Crown Office Chambers, London EC4
p929 . . . . . 020 7797 8100

Stevenson-Watt, Mr Neville William MA(Cantab); LLB M *Nov 1985*
20
Crown Office Row Chambers, Brighton
p970 . . . . . 01273 625625

Steward, Miss Claire BA(Hons) L *Nov 2002*
12, 18, 30
Kings Chambers, Leeds
p978 . . . . . 0113 242 1123
Kings Chambers, Manchester
p984 . . . . . 0161 832 9082

STEWARD, Mr Mark BA(Hons) I *Oct 2002*
10, 15, 20, 30, 12
Chavasse Court Chambers, Liverpool
p980 . . . . . 0151 229 2030

Stewart, Mr Alexander J BA; BCL(Oxon) G *Jul 1975*
3, 5, 6, 8, 11, 12, 18, 29, 37
Hogarth Chambers, London WC2
p937 . . . . . 020 7404 0404

Stewart, Miss Lindsey MA(Oxon) L *Nov 1983*
Maitland Chambers, London WC2
p941 . . . . . 020 7406 1200

Stewart, Mr Nicholas BA; C Dip AF I *Jul 1971*
(Q.C.) *1, 3, 5, 6, 8, 9, 11, 12, 14, 16, 18, 19, 22, 24, 29, 32, 36, 37, 38*
Ely Place Chambers, London EC1
p931 . . . . . 020 7400 9600

Stewart, Mr Paul BA(Belfast) G *Jul 1975*
18, 27, 30, 36, 40, 53, 13, 55, 67, 84, 85
Lamb Chambers, London EC4
p941 . . . . . 020 7797 8300

Stewart, Mr Roger MA I *Jul 1986*
(Q.C.) *41, 8, 12, 24, 40, 11*
Four New Square, London WC2
p943 . . . . . 020 7822 2000

STEWART, Mr Toby M *Jul 1989*
30, 40, 53
Ropewalk Chambers, Nottingham
p989 . . . . . 0115 947 2581

STEWART SMITH, Mr Rodney W BA; LLB(Cantab) M *Jun 1964*
8, 9, 11, 14, 22, 29, 31, 32, 37
New Square Chambers, London WC2
p943 . . . . . 020 7419 8000

STEYN, Miss Karen BA(Hons)(L'pool); DipLaw(City); Dip(EC Law) M *Nov 1995*
1, 19, 51, 23, 25, 26, 55, 73
11KBW, London EC4
p938 . . . . . 020 7632 8500

Steynor, Mr Alan C MA(Cantab); ACIArb; Recorder G *Jul 1975*
3, 7, 11, 24, 40
Keating Chambers, London WC2
p938 . . . . . 020 7544 2600

Stickler, Miss Rebecca BA(Oxon)(Law Studies in Europe(French Law)) M *Oct 2007*
10, 20, 1, 8, 32, 47
Thirty Park Place, Cardiff
p973 . . . . . 029 2039 8421

STILGOE, Mr Rufus BA; CPE I *Nov 1994*
15, 36, 25, 34
23 Essex Street, London WC2
p932 . . . . . 020 7413 0353

STILITZ, Mr Daniel BA(Oxon); MA(City) L *Oct 1992*
(Q.C.) *1, 11, 18, 26, 51, 55, 49, 96*
11KBW, London EC4
p938 . . . . . 020 7632 8500

Stimpson, Mr Christopher MA M *Jan 1999*
15, 62
Atkinson Bevan Chambers, London EC4
p924 . . . . . 020 7353 2112

STINCHCOMBE, Mr Paul MA(Cantab); LLM(Harv) L *Jul 1985*
(Q.C.) *1, 51, 22, 26, 56, 31*
4-5 Gray's Inn Square, London WC1
p935 . . . . . 020 7404 5252

Stirling, Mr Christopher W I *Oct 1993*
Field Court Chambers, London WC1
p933 . . . . . 020 7405 6114

See p1010 for the Key to Work Categories

Stirling, Mr Simon BA(Hons) G *Nov 1989*
15, 51, 39, 63
Nine Bedford Row, London WC1
p924 . . . 020 7489 2727

Stobart, Mrs Tracey LLB M *Jan 1995*
15
KCH Garden Square Chambers, Nottingham
p989 . . . 0115 941 8851
KCH Garden Square Chambers, Leicester
p979 . . . 0115 941 8851

STOCKER, Mr John Crispin LLB(Exon); LLM(Cantab) I *Nov 1985*
20
1 Garden Court, London EC4
p934 . . . 020 7797 7900

STOCKILL, Mr David L *Jul 1985*
8, 29, 93, 88, 97, 36, 89
St Philips Chambers, Birmingham
p969 . . . 0121 246 7000

Stockley, Miss Ruth LLB L *Jul 1988*
1, 26, 31, 46, 54
Kings Chambers, Leeds
p978 . . . 0113 242 1123
Kings Chambers, Manchester
p984 . . . 0161 832 9082

STOCKWELL, Mr Graham Clive LLB I *Nov 1988*
15
1 High Pavement, Nottingham
p988 . . . 0115 941 8218

Stockwell, Mr Matthew LLB(Hons); LLM(Dublin) G *Oct 1998*
1, 11, 12, 18, 27, 30, 47, 59, 22, 26
St Johns Buildings, Preston
p990 . . . 01772 256100
St Johns Buildings, Chester
p974 . . . 01244 323070
St Johns Buildings, Manchester
p985 . . . 0161 214 1500
St Johns Buildings, Liverpool
p982 . . . 0151 243 6000

STOKELL, Mr Robert BA(Oxon) L *Oct 1995*
11, 74, 7, 40, 24, 30
Crown Office Chambers, London EC4
p929 . . . 020 7797 8100

Stoker, Mr Graham LLB; LLM(Lond) M *Nov 1977*
1, 26, 31, 22, 36
Cornerstone Barristers, London WC1
p929 . . . 020 7242 4986

STOKES, Ms Mary MA(Oxon); LLM(Harv) L *Jul 1989*
11, 38, 81, 97
Erskine Chambers, London WC2
p931 . . . 020 7242 5532

Stoll, Mr James I *Nov 1994*
No5 Chambers, Bristol
p971 . . . 0845 210 5555
No5 Chambers, London EC4
p944 . . . 0845 210 5555
No5 Chambers, Birmingham
p968 . . . 0845 210 5555

STONE, Caroline MA(Hons)(Cantab) M *Jan 2005*
71, 18, 30, 53, 72, 97, 11
3PB, London EC4
p946 . . . 020 7583 8055

Stone, Mr Christopher Mark MA(Oxon); MA(Intl Affairs) L *Oct 2007*
18, 30, 56
Devereux Chambers, London WC2
p930 . . . 020 7353 7534

Stone, Mr Joseph I *Jan 1989*
51, 15, 62
Doughty Street Chambers, London WC1
p930 . . . 020 7404 1313
2 Dr Johnson's Buildings, London EC4
p930 . . . 020 7936 2613

STONE, Miss Judith BA(Hons)(Oxon); CPE I *Jan 2003*
18, 1, 26, 55, 76, 73
11KBW, London EC4
p938 . . . 020 7632 8500

Stone, Ms Kate I *Oct 2004*
15, 18, 55, 51, 72, 70, 1, 96
Garden Court North Chambers, Manchester
p983 . . . 0161 236 1840

STONE, Miss Lucy MA(Cantab) M *Jul 1983*
(Q.C.) *10, 20*
Queen Elizabeth Buildings, London EC4
p948 . . . 020 7797 7837

Stone, Mr Russell I *Jan 1992*
11, 30, 53
Ely Place Chambers, London EC1
p931 . . . 020 7400 9600

STONE, Ms Sally BA I *Nov 1994*
10, 20
1 Garden Court, London EC4
p934 . . . 020 7797 7900

Stone, Mr Turlough I *Nov 2004*
Quadrant Chambers, London EC4
p948 . . . 020 7583 4444

STONEFROST, Ms Hilary MSc(Lond) M *Nov 1991*
5, 6, 8, 11, 12, 24, 29, 56
South Square, London WC1
p950 . . . 020 7696 9900

Stoner, Mr Christopher P BA L *Oct 1991*
40, 56, 88, 93
Serle Court, London WC2
p950 . . . 020 7242 6105

STONOR, Mr Nicholas William LLB(Lond) M *Oct 1993*
10, 20, 63
Trinity (Newcastle) Chambers, Newcastle upon Tyne
p987 . . . 0191 232 1927
Trinity (Teesside) Chambers, Middlesbrough
p986 . . . 01642 247569

Stopa, Mr Christopher M *Nov 1976*
2 King's Bench Walk, London EC4
p939 . . . 020 7353 1746

Stopps, Miss Natalie MA(Cantab); DipLaw(City) G *Jul 2000*
Fountain Court Chambers, London EC4
p934 . . . 020 7583 3335

Storey, Mr Jeremy MA(Cantab); Recorder I *Jul 1974*
(Q.C.) *3, 5, 7, 11, 12, 24*
4 Pump Court, London EC4
p947 . . . 020 7842 5555

STOREY, Mr Paul BA L *Nov 1982*
(Q.C.) *20, 10*
29 Bedford Row, London WC1
p925 . . . 020 7404 1044
Regency Chambers, Peterborough
p990 . . . 01733 315215
Southernhay Chambers, Exeter
p975 . . . 01392 255777

Storey, Mr Richard L *Nov 2005*
15, 94
3 Temple Gardens, London EC4
p952 . . . 020 7353 3102

Storey, Tom BA(Oxon) G *Feb 1993*
15, 62, 72
Zenith Chambers, Leeds
p979 . . . 0113 245 5438

Stork, Mr Brian Raymond LLB(Lond) I *Jul 1981*
15, 62
3 Temple Gardens, London EC4
p952 . . . 020 7353 3102

Storrie, Mr Timothy BA(Oxon) M *Oct 1993*
15, 30
Lincoln House Chambers, Manchester
p984 . . . 0161 832 5701

STORY-REA, Mrs Alexa LLB(Hons) M *Feb 1990*
10, 20
29 Bedford Row, London WC1
p925 . . . 020 7404 1044

Stotesbury, Mr David Charles LLB(Lond); MA(Cantab) G *Feb 1980*
1, 26, 15, 18
21 Lauderdale Tower, London EC2
p941 . . . 020 7920 9308

Stott, Mr Matthew M *Oct 2005*
6, 8, 10, 11, 97, 47, 67, 20, 38, 88, 25, 30, 32, 40, 94
Broadway House Chambers, Leeds
p977 . . . 0113 246 2600
Broadway House Chambers, Bradford
p969 . . . 01274 722560
Field Court Chambers, London WC1
p933 . . . 020 7405 6114

Stott, Mr Philip M *Jan 2004*
15
QEB Hollis Whiteman, London EC4
p948 . . . 020 7933 8855

STOUT, Miss Holly BA(Hons); CPE; DipLaw; BVC L *Jul 2003*
18, 1, 11, 55, 26, 76, 73
11KBW, London EC4
p938 . . . 020 7632 8500

Strachan, Miss Elaine M *Nov 1995*
18, 30, 20, 10
3PB, Oxford
p989 . . . 01865 793736

STRACHAN, Mr James BA(Hons)(Oxon) M *Oct 1996*
1, 11, 31, 18, 26, 12, 25, 46, 47, 51, 54, 56, 61
4-5 Gray's Inn Square, London WC1
p935 . . . 020 7404 5252

STRACHAN, Mr Mark I *Jul 1969*
(Q.C.) *11, 30, 41, 12, 40, 59*
3 Hare Court, London EC4
p937 . . . 020 7415 7800

Stradling, Mr Michael Donat MA(Cantab) G *Nov 1998*
15
4 Breams Buildings, London EC4
p927 . . . 020 7092 1900

STRAKER, Mr Timothy MA(Cantab) G *Jul 1977*
(Q.C.) *1, 18, 22, 26, 27, 28, 31, 36, 25, 12, 51, 60, 61, 41*
4-5 Gray's Inn Square, London WC1
p935 . . . 020 7404 5252

Stranex, Mr Andrew BA(Hons) G *Jul 2000*
91, 72, 15, 12, 70
St Pauls Chambers, Leeds
p979 . . . 0113 245 5866

STRANG, Mr Robert I *Jan 2003*
22, 11, 12, 30, 59
3 Hare Court, London EC4
p937 . . . 020 7415 7800

Strange, Miss Jessica LLB(Hons) I *Jun 2003*
Zenith Chambers, Leeds
p979 . . . 0113 245 5438

Stratford, Miss Jemima BA(Oxon); DipLaw M *Oct 1993*
19, 51, 1
Brick Court Chambers, London WC2
p927 . . . 020 7379 3550

Strauss, Mr Nicholas M *Nov 1965*
(Q.C.)
One Essex Court, London EC4
p931 . . . 020 7583 2000

Straw, Mr Adam G *Oct 2004*
18, 22, 63, 23, 55, 51
Tooks Chambers, London EC4
p953 . . . 020 7842 7575

Straw, Mr Jonathan LLB M *Oct 1992*
15
KCH Garden Square Chambers, Nottingham
p989 . . . 0115 941 8851
KCH Garden Square Chambers, Leicester
p979 . . . 0115 941 8851

Streatfeild-James, Mr David BA(Oxon) I *Jul 1986*
(Q.C.) *3, 7, 11, 31, 40, 41, 43, 45, 49, 54, 61, 78, 74*
Atkin Chambers, London WC1
p923 . . . 020 7404 0102

Street, Miss Amy Caroline MA(Lond) I *Oct 2002*
12, 53, 27, 30, 40, 1, 68, 18, 85, 63, 36
3 Serjeants' Inn, London EC4
p950 . . . 020 7427 5000

STREET, Miss Charlotte G *Jul 2003*
18, 12, 20, 30
Pump Court Chambers, Swindon
p993 . . . 01793 539899
Pump Court Chambers, Winchester
p994 . . . 01962 868161
Pump Court Chambers, London EC4
p947 . . . 020 7353 0711

STRELITZ, Mr Paul LLB(Hons) L *Nov 2005*
15, 12
East Anglian Chambers, Norwich
p988 . . . 01603 617351
East Anglian Chambers, Colchester
p975 . . . 01206 572756
East Anglian Chambers, Chelmsford
p973 . . . 01245 215660
East Anglian Chambers, Ipswich
p976 . . . 01473 214481

STRIDE, Mr Lionel BSc(Aston) L *Oct 2005*
Temple Garden Chambers, London EC4
p952 . . . 020 7583 1315

Stringer, Ms Jacinta Maria Rockingham BA(Hons); MA G *Nov 1999*
15, 70
Cobden House Chambers, Manchester
p983 . . . 0161 833 6000
1 Inner Temple Lane, London EC4
p937 . . . 020 7427 4400

Stringer, Mr Leon BSc(Hons); DipLaw L *Oct 1996*
20, 10
15 Winckley Square, Preston
p991 . . . 01772 252828

Stringer, Ms Rosie M *Jan 2002*
St Johns Buildings, Preston
p990 . . . 01772 256100
St Johns Buildings, Chester
p974 . . . 01244 323070
St Johns Buildings, Manchester
p985 . . . 0161 214 1500
St Johns Buildings, Liverpool
p982 . . . 0151 243 6000

Strong, Mr Adrian G *Jul 2001*
12, 15, 20
11 King's Bench Walk, Leeds
p978 . . . 0113 297 1200

Strong, Mr Ben M *Nov 2001*
One Essex Court, London EC4
p931 . . . 020 7583 2000

Strongman, Mrs Carol L *Sep 2003*
10, 20
No 8 Chambers, Birmingham
p968 . . . 0121 236 5514

Stroud, Miss Amy I *Nov 2004*
6, 8, 11, 12, 16, 18, 22, 25, 30
Ely Place Chambers, London EC1
p931 . . . 020 7400 9600

Strudwick, Ms Linda L *Jul 1973*
15, 25, 36
QEB Hollis Whiteman, London EC4
p948 . . . 020 7933 8855

Strutt, Mr Martin BA(Cantab) I *Nov 1981*
7, 8, 11, 12, 13, 18, 22, 25, 29, 30
3PB, Oxford
p989 . . . 01865 793736

STUART, Mr Bruce G *Nov 1977*
15, 62
Lombard Chambers, London EC1
p941 . . . 020 7107 2100

Stuart, Mr Douglas Mark G *Nov 1985*
Lincoln House Chambers, Manchester
p984 . . . 0161 832 5701

Stuart, Mr James BA(Cantab) G *Oct 1990*
11, 18, 22, 29, 6, 40
Lamb Chambers, London EC4
p941 . . . 020 7797 8300

Stuart-Lofthouse, Michelle BA L *Nov 2001*
15, 22, 25, 30, 88
Zenith Chambers, Leeds
p979 . . . 0113 245 5438

Stuart-Smith, Mr Jeremy Hugh MA(Cantab) G *Jul 1978*
(Q.C.) *11, 24, 12, 27, 36, 33, 40*
Four New Square, London WC2
p943 . . . 020 7822 2000

Stubbs, Mr Andrew J LLB; Recorder L *Jul 1988*
(Q.C.) *12, 15, 62, 84, 48*
St Pauls Chambers, Leeds
p979 . . . 0113 245 5866

Stubbs, Miss Rebecca MA(Hons)(Cantab) M *Oct 1994*
Maitland Chambers, London WC2
p941 . . . 020 7406 1200

STUBBS, Mr Richard L *Jul 2005*
1, 38, 2, 11, 8, 18
Trinity (Newcastle) Chambers, Newcastle upon Tyne
p987 . . . 0191 232 1927
Trinity (Teesside) Chambers, Middlesbrough
p986 . . . 01642 247569

STUCKEY, Miss Kathryn I *Oct 2004*
39 Park Square, Leeds
p978 . . . 0113 245 6633

STUDER, Mr Mark BA(Oxon) L *Jul 1976*
2, 8, 9, 14, 32, 34, 37, 40
Wilberforce Chambers, London WC2
p953 . . . 020 7306 0102

Sturman, Mr Jim LLB(Hons) G *Jul 1982*
(Q.C.) *15, 62, 56*
2 Bedford Row, London WC1
p924 . . . 020 7440 8888

Styles, Mr Clive R LLB(Hons) G *Oct 1990*
10, 20, 30, 12, 53, 40, 32
Becket Chambers, Canterbury
p972 . . . 01227 786331
Becket Chambers, Maidstone
p982 . . . 01622 230957

13

Styles, Ms Margaret BA(Hons)(Oxon) M *Oct 2000*
20, 10
Harcourt Chambers, London EC4
p936 . . . . . 0844 561 7135
Harcourt Chambers, Oxford
p989 . . . . . 0844 561 7135

Styles, Mr Mark Patrick LLB I *Jul 1988*
15, 30
Broad Chare Chambers, Newcastle upon Tyne
p986 . . . . . 0191 232 0541

SUGAR, Mr Simon LLB(Warw) M *Dec 1990*
1 Garden Court, London EC4
p934 . . . . . 020 7797 7900

SUGARMAN, Mr Jason I *Jul 1995*
12, 15
9-12 Bell Yard Chambers, London WC2
p926 . . . . . 020 7400 1800

Sukhbir, Singh Bassra M *May 1993*
15
No 6 Barristers Chambers, Leeds
p978 . . . . . 0113 245 9763

SULLIVAN, Mr James William BSc; MPhil; PGDL I *Oct 2005*
30, 18
12 King's Bench Walk, London EC4
p940 . . . . . 020 7583 0811

SULLIVAN, Mr Liam L *Jul 2009*
10, 12, 15, 20
Trinity Chambers, Chelmsford
p974 . . . . . 01245 605040

Sullivan, Miss Linda Elizabeth BA; Recorder M *Jul 1973*
(Q.C.) *15, 30, 27, 10*
Goldsmith Chambers, London EC4
p935 . . . . . 020 7353 6802

Sullivan, Mr Mark M *Jan 1997*
12, 15
3PB, Winchester
p994 . . . . . 01962 868884

Sullivan, Mr Michael LLB(Manc) I *Jul 1983*
(Q.C.) *5, 11, 12*
One Essex Court, London EC4
p931 . . . . . 020 7583 2000

Sullivan, Mr Sean BA(Oxon) I *Jun 2004*
15
Nine Bedford Row, London WC1
p924 . . . . . 020 7489 2727

Sultan, Ms Neelim G *Apr 1993*
1 Mitre Court Buildings, London EC4
p942 . . . . . 020 7452 8900

Sumeray, Ms Caroline M *Jan 1993*
15, 62
No5 Chambers, Bristol
p971 . . . . . 0845 210 5555
No5 Chambers, London EC4
p944 . . . . . 0845 210 5555
No5 Chambers, Birmingham
p968 . . . . . 0845 210 5555

SUMMERS, Miss Allison L *Oct 2000*
12, 62, 15, 20, 34
36 Bedford Row, London WC1
p925 . . . . . 020 7421 8000

SUMMERS, Mr Gary BA(Hons) G *Nov 1985*
72, 15, 62, 27, 36
23 Essex Street, London WC2
p932 . . . . . 020 7413 0353

SUMMERS, Mr John Emrys BA; LLM L *Oct 2004*
Falcon Chambers, London EC4
p933 . . . . . 020 7353 2484

SUMMERS, Mr Mark LLB(Hons) I *Nov 1996*
1, 72, 15, 71, 95, 19, 21, 33, 51, 62, 70, 80, 82
Matrix Chambers, London WC1
p942 . . . . . 020 7404 3447

Sumnall, Miss Charlene L *Jan 2003*
15, 25
5 Paper Buildings, London EC4
p946 . . . . . 020 7583 6117

SUMNER, Daian LLB; BVC; PGCE G *Jan 2004*
8, 11
Atlantic Chambers, Liverpool
p980 . . . . . 0151 236 4421

Sumner, Miss Emma Jane BA I *Oct 1999*
1 Hare Court, London EC4
p936 . . . . . 020 7797 7070

Sumption, Mr Jonathan MA(Oxon) I *Jul 1975*
(Q.C.) *11, 5, 24, 35, 1*
Brick Court Chambers, London WC2
p927 . . . . . 020 7379 3550

Surtees-Jones, Mr Christopher LLB(Hons) I *Oct 1997*
15, 62
4 Breams Buildings, London EC4
p927 . . . . . 020 7092 1900

Susman, Mr Peter Joseph MA(Oxon); BA(Hons); Recorder, Deputy Technology Court Judge I *Nov 1966*
(Q.C.) *1, 45, 7, 11, 26, 40, 47, 51*
Henderson Chambers, London EC4
p937 . . . . . 020 7583 9020

SUTCLIFFE, Mr Andrew MA(Oxon) I *Nov 1983*
(Q.C.) *5, 6, 11, 13, 40*
3 Verulam Buildings, London WC1
p953 . . . . . 020 7831 8441

Suterwalla, Mr Azeem I *Jan 2004*
1, 22, 26, 63, 51
Doughty Street Chambers, London WC1
p930 . . . . . 020 7404 1313

SUTHERLAND, Mr Jamie BA(Hons); MPhil L *Jan 2010*
88, 93
Falcon Chambers, London EC4
p933 . . . . . 020 7353 2484

Sutherland, Miss Jessica BA; LLM M *Oct 2003*
11, 24, 35
7 King's Bench Walk, London EC4
p940 . . . . . 020 7910 8300

Sutherland, Mr Paul MA M *Nov 1992*
8, 12, 24, 40, 45
Four New Square, London WC2
p943 . . . . . 020 7822 2000

Sutherland, Miss Sara L *Oct 2004*
30
Exchange Chambers, Manchester
p983 . . . . . 0161 833 2722
Exchange Chambers, Liverpool
p980 . . . . . 0151 236 7747
Exchange Chambers, Leeds
p977 . . . . . 0113 203 1970

Sutherland, Miss Yvonne L *Jul 2001*
King's Bench Godolphin Chambers, Truro
p994 . . . . . 0845 308 1551
King's Bench Godolphin Chambers, Plymouth
p990 . . . . . 0845 308 1551

Sutton, Mr Clive LLB(Hons) I *Jul 1987*
10, 15, 20
Fenners Chambers, Cambridge
p972 . . . . . 01223 368761

Sutton, Ms Emma G *Jan 2006*
10, 20, 63, 1, 12, 14, 76, 26, 77
Thirty Park Place, Cardiff
p973 . . . . . 029 2039 8421

SUTTON, Mr Keith A LLB G *Nov 1988*
12, 15, 18, 25, 30, 26, 62
7 Harrington Street Chambers, Liverpool
p981 . . . . . 0151 242 0707

Sutton, Mr Mark BA; DipLaw(Lond); Employment Tribunal: Part-time Chairman M *Jul 1982*
(Q.C.) *11, 18, 12, 36, 40, 51, 55*
Old Square Chambers, Bristol
p971 . . . . . 0117 930 5100
Old Square Chambers, London WC1
p945 . . . . . 020 7269 0300

Sutton, Mr Paul E LLB(Lond) M *Jul 1973*
Holborn Chambers, London WC2
p937 . . . . . 020 7242 6060

Sutton, Mr Philip LLB I *Nov 1971*
15, 62, 12, 82, 94
Bell Yard Chambers, London WC2
p926 . . . . . 020 7306 9292 / 7404 5138

Sutton, Rebecca I *Jan 2004*
St Johns Buildings, Preston
p990 . . . . . 01772 256100
St Johns Buildings, Chester
p974 . . . . . 01244 323070
St Johns Buildings, Manchester
p985 . . . . . 0161 214 1500
St Johns Buildings, Liverpool
p982 . . . . . 0151 243 6000

SUTTON, Mr Richard Recorder M *Jul 1969*
(Q.C.) *15, 36, 62*
18 Red Lion Court, London EC4
p949 . . . . . 020 7520 6000
18 Red Lion Court (Annexe), Chelmsford
p973 . . . . . 01245 280880

Sutton-Mattocks, Mr Christopher MA(Oxon) M *Jul 1975*
15, 25, 62, 68, 36
Argent Chambers, London WC2
p923 . . . . . 020 7556 5500

SWAIN, Miss Jacqueline LLB(Hons) L *Oct 1998*
30, 68, 67
7 Harrington Street Chambers, Liverpool
p981 . . . . . 0151 242 0707

SWAIN, Mr Jon BSc L *Nov 1983*
15
Furnival Chambers, London EC4
p934 . . . . . 020 7405 3232

Swainston, Mr Michael MA(Cantab) L *Nov 1985*
(Q.C.) *11, 24, 5, 35, 1, 41*
Brick Court Chambers, London WC2
p927 . . . . . 020 7379 3550

SWAN, Jennifer M *Oct 2009*
10, 20
Renaissance Chambers, London WC1
p949 . . . . . 020 7404 1111

Swaroop, Sudhanshu MA(Cantab); BCL(Oxon) I *Oct 1997*
1, 3, 11, 12, 19, 24, 35, 41
20 Essex Street, London WC2
p932 . . . . . 020 7842 1200

Sweeney, Mr Christian LLB G *Oct 1992*
12, 18, 19, 20, 22, 30
3PB, Oxford
p989 . . . . . 01865 793736

Sweeney, Ms Linda Mary M *Nov 1999*
10, 12, 14, 18, 20, 30, 51
St Johns Buildings, Preston
p990 . . . . . 01772 256100
St Johns Buildings, Chester
p974 . . . . . 01244 323070
St Johns Buildings, Manchester
p985 . . . . . 0161 214 1500
St Johns Buildings, Liverpool
p982 . . . . . 0151 243 6000

SWEENEY, Miss Lydia BA(Manc) I *Oct 2002*
Temple Garden Chambers, London EC4
p952 . . . . . 020 7583 1315

Sweeney, Mr Nigel LLB M *Jul 1976*
(Q.C.) *15, 62, 36*
6 King's Bench Walk, London EC4
p939 . . . . . 020 7583 0410

SWEET, Ms Louise G *Jun 1994*
Carmelite Chambers, London EC4
p927 . . . . . 020 7936 6300

Sweeting, Mr Derek Anthony BA(Cantab); Recorder G *Jul 1983*
(Q.C.) *7, 53, 30, 40, 84, 42, 91, 45*
7 Bedford Row, London WC1
p924 . . . . . 020 7242 3555

SWEETING, Ms Margaret MA(KCL) L *Jan 1996*
20, 63, 14
Trinity (Newcastle) Chambers, Newcastle upon Tyne
p987 . . . . . 0191 232 1927
Trinity (Teesside) Chambers, Middlesbrough
p986 . . . . . 01642 247569

SWIFT, Mr John MA(Oxon) I *Nov 1965*
(Q.C.) *44, 43*
Monckton Chambers, London WC1
p942 . . . . . 020 7405 7211

SWIFT, Mr Jonathan M BA(Oxon); LLM(Cantab); First Treasury Council I *Jul 1989*
(Q.C.) *1, 11, 18, 19, 26, 29, 51, 55, 96*
11KBW, London EC4
p938 . . . . . 020 7632 8500

SWIFT, Mr Jonathan Peter LLB(Hons)(Lond); Member Western Circuit; Bar European Group; FLBA I *Nov 1977*
10, 20, 53
29 Bedford Row, London WC1
p925 . . . . . 020 7404 1044

SWIFT, Mr Malcolm Robin LLB; AKC(KCL) G *Jul 1970*
(Q.C.) *15*
Wilberforce Chambers, Hull
p976 . . . . . 01482 323264

Swift, Miss Valeria L *Oct 2003*
15, 20, 91
5 King's Bench Walk, London EC4
p939 . . . . . 020 7353 5638

SWINNERTON, Mr David L *Nov 1995*
15, 62, 48, 18, 55, 70
Cornwall Street Chambers, Birmingham
p967 . . . . . 0121 233 7500

Swinstead, Mr David L L *Jul 1970*
12, 15, 7, 30
3PB, Winchester
p994 . . . . . 01962 868884

Swirsky, Mr Adam BSc(Hons)(Econ); MSc M *Nov 1989*
1, 11, 18, 22, 30
Lamb Chambers, London EC4
p941 . . . . . 020 7797 8300

Swirsky, Mr Joshua Max Bradbury BA(Dunelm) M *Nov 1987*
1, 8, 22
Field Court Chambers, London WC1
p933 . . . . . 020 7405 6114

Switalski, Mr Stephen I *Mar 2006*
20, 10
No 6 Barristers Chambers, Leeds
p978 . . . . . 0113 245 9763

Swoboda, John-Paul LLB(Hons) G *Jul 2006*
20, 30, 22, 15
Zenith Chambers, Leeds
p979 . . . . . 0113 245 5438

SYED, Gulzar G *Jul 1983*
15, 20
Bank House Chambers, Sheffield
p991 . . . . . 0114 275 1223

Syed, Miss Maryam LLB(Hons) L *Oct 1993*
15, 20, 10
7 Bedford Row, London WC1
p924 . . . . . 020 7242 3555
2 Dr Johnson's Buildings, London EC4
p930 . . . . . 020 7936 2613

Syed, Mr Mohammad Ali L *Jul 1970* MBE
15, 23
Park Avenue Chambers, Mitcham
p986 . . . . . 020 8648 1684

SYED, Safora L *Jan 2000*
15, 70
Mitre House Chambers, London WC1
p942 . . . . . 020 7307 7100

Syfret, Mr Nicholas MA(Cantab) M *Oct 1979*
(Q.C.) *15, 62*
King's Bench Chambers, Oxford
p989 . . . . . 01865 311066
13 King's Bench Walk, London EC4
p940 . . . . . 020 7353 7204
Citadel Chambers, Birmingham
p967 . . . . . 0121 233 8500

Sykes, Caroline Jayne G *Jan 2004*
10, 20, 7, 53, 88, 25, 30
Pendragon Chambers, Swansea
p993 . . . . . 01792 411188

Sykes, Mr Laurent MA; ACA G *Jan 2007*
34, 57, 58
Gray's Inn Tax Chambers, London WC1
p936 . . . . . 020 7242 2642

Symington, Ms Anna LLB(Dunelm) I *Oct 2002*
30
St John's Chambers, Bristol
p972 . . . . . 0117 921 3456

SYMMS, Miss Kate BA(Cantab) G *Mar 1990*
10, 12, 20, 25, 30, 96
7 Harrington Street Chambers, Liverpool
p981 . . . . . 0151 242 0707

SYMONS, Mr Christopher BA(Kent) M *Jul 1972*
(Q.C.) *3, 7, 11, 24, 40*
3 Verulam Buildings, London WC1
p953 . . . . . 020 7831 8441

Syril, Mr George L *Jul 1980*
12, 67, 20, 23, 88, 89, 94, 36, 30, 51, 10, 18
Willesden Chambers, London NW10
p954 . . . . . 020 8965 8856

Szerard, Mr Andrei Michael LLB(Hons) I *Apr 1986*
10, 20
3 Dr Johnson's Buildings, London EC4
p930 . . . . . 020 7353 4854

SZWED, Miss Elizabeth LLB(Leeds) M *Jul 1974*
10, 20
1 Garden Court, London EC4
p934 . . . . . 020 7797 7900

TABACHNIK, Mr Andrew MA; LLM I *Nov 1991*
1, 11, 12, 44, 18, 6, 31
4-5 Gray's Inn Square, London WC1
p935 . . . . . 020 7404 5252

TABARI, Mr Ali-Reza LLB(Durham) I *Nov 2006*
11, 18, 23, 25, 30, 38, 46, 47, 48, 84
St Philips Chambers, Birmingham
p969 . . . . . 0121 246 7000

 See p1010 for the Key to Work Categories

Tackaberry, Mr John MA; LLB; FCIArb; FFB *G Jul 1967*
(Q.C.) *7, 78, 81, 11, 3, 49, 41, 89, 96*
Arbitration Chambers, London NW5
p923 . . . . 020 7267 2137
Thirty Nine Essex Street, London WC2
p932 . . . . 020 7832 1111
Unity Street Chambers, Bristol
p972 . . . . 0117 906 9789

TACZALSKI, Mr Carlo BA(Law); BVC *M Jan 2010*
11, 40, 24, 30
Crown Office Chambers, London EC4
p929 . . . . 020 7797 8100

Tafadar, Ms Sultana *L Mar 2005*
15, 51
Tooks Chambers, London EC4
p953 . . . . 020 7842 7575

TAFT, Mr Christopher LLB(Hons) *M Nov 1997*
18, 30, 53
St James's Chambers, Manchester
p984 . . . . 0161 834 7000

TAGGART, Mr Nicholas LLB(Lond); BCL(Oxon) *M Oct 1991*
Landmark Chambers, London EC4
p941 . . . . 020 7430 1221

TAGHDISSIAN, Mr James *G Oct 2005*
Colleton Chambers, Exeter
p975 . . . . 01392 274898

Tahta, Ms Natasha *I Jan 1998*
15, 25
QEB Hollis Whiteman, London EC4
p948 . . . . 020 7933 8855

TAI, Miss Farzana *M Jul 2003*
15, 8, 10, 11, 12, 22, 30
Pallant Chambers, Chichester
p974 . . . . 01243 784538

Tait, Mr Andrew MA(Oxon) *I Jul 1981*
(Q.C.) *1, 26, 31, 36, 60*
Francis Taylor Building, London EC4
p934 . . . . 020 7353 8415

Tait, Mr Don BA *I Feb 1987*
72, 15, 70
Albion Chambers, Bristol
p970 . . . . 0117 927 2144

Takatsuki, Miss Yuli *L Jan 2007*
73, 16, 50, 51, 13, 56
5RB, London WC1
p948 . . . . 020 7242 2902

TALACCHI, Mr Carlo LLM *L Jul 1986*
15, 23, 20
10 King's Bench Walk, London EC4
p940 . . . . 020 7353 7742

Talbot, Miss Ann-Marie LLB *M Oct 2006*
72, 15, 70, 88, 23
Staple Inn Chambers, London WC1
p951 . . . . 020 7242 5240

Talbot, Mr Kennedy *G Nov 1984*
33 Chancery Lane, London WC2
p928 . . . . 020 7440 9950

Talbot, Mr Kevin LLB(Hons) *M Jul 1970*
20, 15, 12
15 Winckley Square, Preston
p991 . . . . 01772 252828

Talbot, Miss Nicola *L Oct 2007*
15
1 Paper Buildings, London EC4
p946 . . . . 020 7353 3728

Talbot, Mr Patrick MA(Oxon); Recorder *L Jul 1969*
(Q.C.) *6, 8, 9, 11, 14, 22, 24, 29, 32, 37, 40, 41, 49, 56, 62*
Serle Court, London WC2
p950 . . . . 020 7242 6105

Talbot-Bagnall, Mr John LLB(Hons) *I Nov 1988*
10, 12, 15, 20
2 Dr Johnson's Buildings, London EC4
p930 . . . . 020 7936 2613

Talbot Rice, Mrs Elspeth BA *L Oct 1990*
(Q.C.) *5, 6, 8, 11, 22, 29, 32, 37, 40, 41, 49, 62*
XXIV Old Buildings, London WC2
p944 . . . . 020 7691 2424

Talbott, Mr Ross LLB(Hons) *M Jan 2008*
15, 10, 20
Eastbourne Chambers, Eastbourne
p975 . . . . 01323 642102

TALLENTIRE, Ms Jennifer LLB; BVC *L Jul 2000*
15
Guildhall Chambers, Bristol
p970 . . . . 0117 930 9000

TALLON, Mr John FCA *M Jul 1975*
(Q.C.) *34, 57, 58*
Pump Court Tax Chambers, London WC1
p948 . . . . 020 7414 8080

Talmon, Prof Stefan *L Jul 2007*
20 Essex Street, London WC2
p932 . . . . 020 7842 1200

TAM, Mr Robin B K MA(Cantab); Member of Hong Kong Bar *M Jul 1986*
(Q.C.)
Temple Garden Chambers, London EC4
p952 . . . . 020 7583 1315

TAMBLING, Mr Richard BA(Hons); LLB(Hons) *M Oct 2005*
10, 20
1 Garden Court, London EC4
p934 . . . . 020 7797 7900

Tamblyn, Mr Nathan BA(Oxon) *G Nov 1999*
11, 35, 24, 5
Quadrant Chambers, London EC4
p948 . . . . 020 7583 4444

TAMLYN, Mr Lloyd BA(Cantab) *G Nov 1991*
5, 6, 8, 11, 12, 24, 29, 38
South Square, London WC1
p950 . . . . 020 7696 9900

Tan, Charlotte *M Jul 2008*
49, 41, 3, 5, 11, 43, 47, 78, 24, 54, 35
20 Essex Street, London WC2
p932 . . . . 020 7842 1200

Tanchel, Ms Vivienne LLB(Hons) *M Jan 2005*
15, 36
2 Hare Court, London EC4
p937 . . . . 020 7353 5324

TANKEL, Mr Benjamin BA(History); GDL *M Nov 2009*
4-5 Gray's Inn Square, London WC1
p935 . . . . 020 7404 5252

Tankel, Mrs Ruth *M Jul 1990*
10, 20
15 Winckley Square, Preston
p991 . . . . 01772 252828

TANNEY, Mr Anthony BA(Durham); M Jur *L Nov 1994*
Falcon Chambers, London EC4
p933 . . . . 020 7353 2484

TANSEY, Rock B LLB(Bris); Dip Soc(Bris) *L Jul 1966*
(Q.C.) *15, 19, 51*
25 Bedford Row, London WC1
p925 . . . . 020 7067 1500

Tapper, Miss Lucy *M Nov 2002*
King's Bench Chambers, Oxford
p989 . . . . 01865 311066

Tapper, Mr Paul *M Jan 1991*
20, 40, 10
Chartlands Chambers, Northampton
p988 . . . . 01604 603322

Tappin, Dr Michael BSc; DPhil(Oxon) *M Oct 1991*
(Q.C.) *13, 50*
8 New Square, London WC2
p943 . . . . 020 7405 4321

Tapsell, Mr Paul LLB(Lancs) *M Oct 1991*
12, 15, 18, 26, 31, 22, 62, 25, 88
Becket Chambers, Canterbury
p972 . . . . 01227 786331
Becket Chambers, Maidstone
p982 . . . . 01622 230957

Tapson, Miss Lesley LLB(Newc) *G Nov 1982*
20, 10
Field Court Chambers, London WC1
p933 . . . . 020 7405 6114

TARBITT, Mr Nicholas E H LLB *I Jul 1988*
30, 84, 13, 56, 52, 50, 12
Cornwall Street Chambers, Birmingham
p967 . . . . 0121 233 7500

Tarr, Miss Beverly LLB *M Oct 1995*
15
2 Pump Court, London EC4
p947 . . . . 020 7353 5597

TASKEEN, Mr Wasim LLB(Hons) *L Jan 1998*
6, 8, 11, 47, 22
St James's Chambers, Manchester
p984 . . . . 0161 834 7000

TASKIS, Miss Catherine BA(Oxon); BCL(Oxon) *I Oct 1995*
Falcon Chambers, London EC4
p933 . . . . 020 7353 2484

TATFORD, Mr Warwick Henry Patrick BA(Hons)(Oxon) *L Nov 1993*
15, 12, 25, 26
9-12 Bell Yard Chambers, London WC2
p926 . . . . 020 7400 1800

TATLOW, Mr Nicholas BA(Wales) *G May 1996*
15
Citadel Chambers, Birmingham
p967 . . . . 0121 233 8500

Tattersall, Mr Geoffrey Frank MA(Oxon); Recorder; Judge of Appeal(Isle Of Man) *L Jul 1970*
(Q.C.) *30, 12, 53, 1, 17, 40*
42 Bedford Row, London WC1
p925 . . . . 020 7831 0222
Byrom Street Chambers, Manchester
p983 . . . . 0161 829 2100

Tattersall, Mr Simon Mark Rogers LLB(Lond); Deputy District Judge *M Nov 1977*
10, 12, 20, 30
Fenners Chambers, Cambridge
p972 . . . . 01223 368761

TATTON-BENNETT, Mr Alex *G Oct 2007*
10, 20, 15, 25, 22
1 King's Bench Walk, London EC4
p938 . . . . 020 7936 1500

TATTON-BROWN, Mr Daniel N MA(Oxon); Treasury Counsel *M Oct 1994*
11, 12, 18, 40
Littleton Chambers, London EC4
p941 . . . . 020 7797 8600

TAUBE, Mr Simon MA(Oxon) *M Jul 1980*
(Q.C.) *6, 8, 9, 14, 22, 32, 34, 37*
Ten Old Square, London WC2
p945 . . . . 020 7405 0758

Taurah, Sheila LLB *L Oct 1991*
20
Clerksroom - Administration Centre, Taunton
p993 . . . . 0845 083 3000

Tautz, Mr William *G Nov 2004*
20
Tooks Chambers, London EC4
p953 . . . . 020 7842 7575

Tavares, Mr Nathan W BSc(Hons)(Eng) *M Oct 1992*
40, 53, 30
Outer Temple Chambers, London WC2
p945 . . . . 020 7353 6381

Taverner, Mr Marcus L LLB(Leics); LLM(Lond); ACIArb *G Jul 1981*
(Q.C.) *3, 7, 11, 24, 40*
Keating Chambers, London WC2
p938 . . . . 020 7544 2600

TAWFIK, Miss Nicola MA(Hons) *M Jan 2010*
Pallant Chambers, Chichester
p974 . . . . 01243 784538

Taylor, Mr Alan Jeremy BA(Hons); LLB(Hons); DipLaw; MPhil *L Nov 1986*
Park Court Chambers, Leeds
p978 . . . . 0113 243 3277

Taylor, Mr Alex BA; DipLaw *I Oct 2000*
Park Court Chambers, Leeds
p978 . . . . 0113 243 3277

Taylor, Mr Andrew BSc(Cantab)(Econ) *G Jan 1984*
15, 62
Thirty Park Place, Cardiff
p973 . . . . 029 2039 8421

Taylor, Mr Andrew Peter BA(Hons) *G Nov 1989*
11, 12, 18, 20, 22, 30
KCH Garden Square Chambers, Nottingham
p989 . . . . 0115 941 8851
KCH Garden Square Chambers, Leicester
p979 . . . . 0115 941 8851

Taylor, Miss Araba Arba Kurankyiwa MA(Cantab) *M Jul 1985*
8, 17, 32, 37, 40, 77, 86, 89, 93
Fenners Chambers, Cambridge
p972 . . . . 01223 368761

TAYLOR, Mr Charles LLB(Hons) *M Jul 1974*
1, 5, 8, 11, 7, 13, 18, 24, 27, 29, 30, 40
Pallant Chambers, Chichester
p974 . . . . 01243 784538

Taylor, Mr Christian *L Jan 2003*
30, 12
Exchange Chambers, Manchester
p983 . . . . 0161 833 2722
Exchange Chambers, Liverpool
p980 . . . . 0151 236 7747
Exchange Chambers, Leeds
p977 . . . . 0113 203 1970

Taylor, Mr Christopher BA *G Nov 1982*
30, 53
Queen Square Chambers, Bristol
p972 . . . . 0117 921 1966

Taylor, Mr David LLB *G Jul 1986*
6, 10, 11, 12, 15, 20, 30
Charter Chambers, London WC1
p928 . . . . 020 7618 4400
37 Park Square Chambers, Leeds
p978 . . . . 0113 243 9422
No5 Chambers, Bristol
p971 . . . . 0845 210 5555
No5 Chambers, London EC4
p944 . . . . 0845 210 5555
No5 Chambers, Birmingham
p968 . . . . 0845 210 5555

Taylor, Mr David Christopher LLB(Hons); PGDip *L Oct 1998*
30, 53, 12
St Johns Buildings, Preston
p990 . . . . 01772 256100
St Johns Buildings, Chester
p974 . . . . 01244 323070
St Johns Buildings, Manchester
p985 . . . . 0161 214 1500
St Johns Buildings, Liverpool
p982 . . . . 0151 243 6000

Taylor, Mr Douglas BA(Hons); Deputy District Judge/Judge of Mental Health Tribunal *M Jan 1981*
10, 12, 20, 63
College Chambers, Southampton
p992 . . . . 023 8023 0338

Taylor, Miss Gemma Mary LLB(Lond) *I Feb 1988*
10, 12, 20
42 Bedford Row, London WC1
p925 . . . . 020 7831 0222

Taylor, Mr Gregg BA *M Jul 1974*
(Q.C.) *15*
9 Park Place, Cardiff
p973 . . . . 029 2038 2731

Taylor, Mr Jason *M Dec 1995*
15, 62
Albion Chambers, Bristol
p970 . . . . 0117 927 2144

Taylor, Mr John Charles BA(Cantab) *M Oct 1993*
Fountain Court Chambers, London EC4
p934 . . . . 020 7583 3335

Taylor, Mr Jonathan LLB *M Nov 1991*
10, 12, 20
St Johns Buildings, Preston
p990 . . . . 01772 256100
St Johns Buildings, Chester
p974 . . . . 01244 323070
St Johns Buildings, Manchester
p985 . . . . 0161 214 1500
St Johns Buildings, Liverpool
p982 . . . . 0151 243 6000

Taylor, Mr Julian *M Jul 1986*
15
St Johns Buildings, Preston
p990 . . . . 01772 256100
St Johns Buildings, Chester
p974 . . . . 01244 323070
St Johns Buildings, Manchester
p985 . . . . 0161 214 1500
St Johns Buildings, Liverpool
p982 . . . . 0151 243 6000

Taylor, Miss Julie LLB(Hons) *I Nov 1992*
15
15 Winckley Square, Preston
p991 . . . . 01772 252828

Taylor, Miss Kathryn *L Jul 2005*
20, 10
No5 Chambers, Bristol
p971 . . . . 0845 210 5555
No5 Chambers, London EC4
p944 . . . . 0845 210 5555
No5 Chambers, Birmingham
p968 . . . . 0845 210 5555

TAYLOR, Miss Kitty *M Oct 1992*
15
No 6 Barristers Chambers, Leeds
p978 . . . . 0113 245 9763

Taylor, Miss Linda *I Oct 1998*
20, 10, 22
Westgate Chambers, Lewes
p980 . . . . 01273 480510

13

TAYLOR, Mr Mark M *Jul 2010*
10, 20
Trinity Chambers, Chelmsford
p974 . . . . . 01245 605040

TAYLOR, Mr Martin BA M *Jul 1988*
Carmelite Chambers, London EC4
p927 . . . . . 020 7936 6300

Taylor, Ms Mary-Jane BSc(Natal); LLB(Hons)(Sussex); LLM(East Anglia) I *Oct 2003*
10, 20
Coram Chambers, London EC1
p929 . . . . . 020 7092 3700

Taylor, Miss Maureen J LLB(Hons) L *Nov 1993*
12, 15, 30, 20, 22, 10
5 Pump Court, London EC4
p947 . . . . . 020 7353 2532 / 7583 7133

Taylor, Mr Michael BA(Oxon) M *Nov 1996*
12, 45, 7, 40
4 Pump Court, London EC4
p947 . . . . . 020 7842 5555

Taylor, Mr Nigel LLB I *Jul 1993*
15, 62, 23, 48, 20
Crown Office Row Chambers, Brighton
p970 . . . . . 01273 625625

Taylor, Mr Paul G *Jan 1985*
15, 1, 48
Exchange Chambers, Manchester
p983 . . . . . 0161 833 2722
Exchange Chambers, Liverpool
p980 . . . . . 0151 236 7747
Exchange Chambers, Leeds
p977 . . . . . 0113 203 1970
Doughty Street Chambers, London WC1
p930 . . . . . 020 7404 1313

Taylor, Mr Phillip LLB(Hons)(Lond); PGCE L *Jan 2001* MBE
15, 26, 42, 6, 31
Abbey Chambers, Shepperton
p992 . . . . . 01932 560913

Taylor, Mr Phillip Brian LLB(Lond); PGCE L *Nov 1991* MBE
1, 12, 13, 15, 18, 20, 22, 31, 36, 38
Richmond Green Chambers, Richmond upon Thames
p991 . . . . . 020 8948 4801

TAYLOR, Miss Rebecca BA(Oxon) G *Oct 2001*
74, 7, 40, 24, 11
Crown Office Chambers, London EC4
p929 . . . . . 020 7797 8100
St John's Chambers, Bristol
p972 . . . . . 0117 921 3456

TAYLOR, Mr Reuben LLB(Wales) G *Oct 1990*
1, 26, 28, 31, 36
Landmark Chambers, London EC4
p941 . . . . . 020 7430 1221

Taylor, Mr Rhys LLB; Part-Time Chairman of Residential Property Tribunal I *Nov 1996*
20, 12
Temple Chambers, Newport
p988 . . . . . 01633 267403 / 255855
Temple Chambers, Cardiff
p973 . . . . . 029 2039 7364

Taylor, Mr Rufus M *Oct 1998*
2 King's Bench Walk, London EC4
p939 . . . . . 020 7353 1746

Taylor, Miss Ruth M *Jul 2010*
30
Kings Chambers, Leeds
p978 . . . . . 0113 242 1123
Kings Chambers, Manchester
p984 . . . . . 0161 832 9082

Taylor, Mr Simon BSc(Hons); DipLaw(City) I *Oct 1993*
62, 12
33 Chancery Lane, London WC2
p928 . . . . . 020 7440 9950

Taylor, Dr Simon W MA(Cantab); MB; B Chir M *Jul 1984*
(Q.C.) *27, 30, 1, 53*
Cloisters, London EC4
p928 . . . . . 020 7827 4000

TAYLOR, Miss Susan Recorder M *Jan 1987*
20, 63
Trinity (Newcastle) Chambers, Newcastle upon Tyne
p987 . . . . . 0191 232 1927
Trinity (Teesside) Chambers, Middlesbrough
p986 . . . . . 01642 247569

TAYLOR, Ms Susan BEd(Hons); MA(Essex); MEd(Leeds) L *Oct 1996*
20, 23, 51
10 King's Bench Walk, London EC4
p940 . . . . . 020 7353 7742
12 Old Square, London WC2
p945 . . . . . 020 7404 0875

TAYLOR, Teresa G *Jan 1994*
Fountain Chambers, Middlesbrough
p986 . . . . . 01642 804040

TAYLOR, Mr William M *Jul 1990*
(Q.C.) *12, 15*
Carmelite Chambers, London EC4
p927 . . . . . 020 7936 6300

TAYLOR, Mrs Yvonne M LLB(Northumbria) I *Jul 1998*
15, 20, 10, 91, 48
Trinity (Newcastle) Chambers, Newcastle upon Tyne
p987 . . . . . 0191 232 1927
Trinity (Teesside) Chambers, Middlesbrough
p986 . . . . . 01642 247569

TAYLOR, Ms Zoe BA(Cantab) G *Oct 1998*
12, 18, 20, 23, 27, 30, 40
1 Crown Office Row, London EC4
p929 . . . . . 020 7797 7500

Tayton, Miss Lynn M LLB(Lond) G *Jul 1981*
(Q.C.) *12, 15, 20, 10*
36 Bedford Row, London WC1
p925 . . . . . 020 7421 8000

TEACHER, Miss Petra BVC I *Jan 2006*
10, 20
29 Bedford Row, London WC1
p925 . . . . . 020 7404 1044

Tedd, Mr Rex MA; BCL; Deputy High Court Judge; Recorder I *Feb 1970*
(Q.C.) *15, 62, 31, 46, 42, 84, 39, 95, 91, 70, 71, 72*
No5 Chambers, Bristol
p971 . . . . . 0845 210 5555
No5 Chambers, London EC4
p944 . . . . . 0845 210 5555
No5 Chambers, Birmingham
p968 . . . . . 0845 210 5555

Tedore, Ms Amanda M *Oct 1992*
15
1 Inner Temple Lane, London EC4
p937 . . . . . 020 7427 4400

Tee, Mr Greg I *Jul 1999*
10, 12, 15, 22, 30
Guildford Chambers, Guildford
p975 . . . . . 01483 539131

Teggin, Miss Victoria BA(Lond); DipLaw I *Nov 1990*
10, 51, 18, 30
3 Dr Johnson's Buildings, London EC4
p930 . . . . . 020 7353 4854

Tehrani, Mr Christopher I LLB I *Nov 1990*
12, 15, 18, 36, 38
Park Court Chambers, Leeds
p978 . . . . . 0113 243 3277

Teji, Miss Usha LLB(Lond) L *Jul 1981*
10, 12, 20
1 Pump Court, London EC4
p947 . . . . . 020 7842 7070

Telford, Mr Peter BA L *Jul 1985*
12, 22, 30, 23, 47, 11, 18, 51
Southernhay Chambers, Exeter
p975 . . . . . 01392 255777

Temkin, Mr David BA(Hons)(Oxon); PGCE I *Jul 2000*
72, 15, 18, 62, 83, 84, 25, 26, 36
Exchange Chambers, Manchester
p983 . . . . . 0161 833 2722
Exchange Chambers, Liverpool
p980 . . . . . 0151 236 7747
Exchange Chambers, Leeds
p977 . . . . . 0113 203 1970

Temple, Mr Adam M *Jul 2008*
11, 12, 40, 24
4 Pump Court, London EC4
p947 . . . . . 020 7842 5555

Temple, Mr Anthony MA(Oxon); Recorder; Dep High Court judge I *Jul 1968*
(Q.C.) *3, 7, 11, 12, 24, 25, 30, 36*
4 Pump Court, London EC4
p947 . . . . . 020 7842 5555

Temple, Mr Benjamin I *Oct 1997*
15
5 King's Bench Walk, London EC4
p939 . . . . . 020 7353 5638

TEMPLE, Ms Booan BSc; DipLaw M *Jan 2001*
1, 12, 15, 18, 23, 51, 55, 36, 38
Matrix Chambers, London WC1
p942 . . . . . 020 7404 3447

Temple, Miss Eleanor LLB I *Jul 2000*
5, 6, 8, 11, 22, 40
Kings Chambers, Leeds
p978 . . . . . 0113 242 1123
Kings Chambers, Manchester
p984 . . . . . 0161 832 9082

TEMPLE, Miss Michelle J L *Oct 1992*
11, 8, 12, 63, 2
Trinity (Newcastle) Chambers, Newcastle upon Tyne
p987 . . . . . 0191 232 1927
Trinity (Teesside) Chambers, Middlesbrough
p986 . . . . . 01642 247569

TEMPLE, Miss Rachel BA G *Nov 2004*
10, 20
Chavasse Court Chambers, Liverpool
p980 . . . . . 0151 229 2030

Temple, Mr Victor I *Jul 1971*
(Q.C.) *15, 36, 62*
6 King's Bench Walk, London EC4
p939 . . . . . 020 7583 0410

Temple-Bone, Miss Gillian BA(Hons) G *Nov 1978*
15, 20, 26, 10
36 Bedford Row, London WC1
p925 . . . . . 020 7421 8000

Templeman, Miss Clare LLB I *Nov 2004*
10, 20, 30
Angel Chambers, Swansea
p992 . . . . . 01792 464623

Templeman, Mr Mark J MA; BCL(Oxon) M *Nov 1981*
(Q.C.)
Essex Court Chambers, London WC2
p931 . . . . . 020 7813 8000

Templeman, The Hon Michael Richard MA(Oxon) L *Nov 1973*
8, 32, 37, 40
Guildford Chambers, Guildford
p975 . . . . . 01483 539131

TEMPLETON, Mr Joseph BA(Cantab) M *Jan 2006*
15
23 Essex Street, London WC2
p932 . . . . . 020 7413 0353

TENNET, Mr Michael MA(Oxon) I *Jul 1985*
(Q.C.) *6, 8, 11, 29, 37, 40*
Wilberforce Chambers, London WC2
p953 . . . . . 020 7306 0102

TER HAAR, Miss Camilla MA I *Jul 2005*
6, 11
Five Paper, London EC4
p946 . . . . . 020 7815 3200

TER HAAR, Mr Roger BA(Oxon) I *Jul 1974*
(Q.C.) *74, 1, 3, 7, 12, 18, 23, 24, 31, 40, 78, 11, 45, 76*
Crown Office Chambers, London EC4
p929 . . . . . 020 7797 8100

Terris, Ms Sally BA(Hons)(Cantab) M *Nov 1997*
10, 20
Park Court Chambers, Leeds
p978 . . . . . 0113 243 3277

Terry, Mr Jeffrey LLB; MA L *Jul 1976*
11, 24, 40, 97, 5, 29, 37, 93, 41, 96
Kings Chambers, Leeds
p978 . . . . . 0113 242 1123
Kings Chambers, Manchester
p984 . . . . . 0161 832 9082

Tether, Ms Melanie MA(Oxon) G *Nov 1995*
18, 36, 55, 51, 1
Old Square Chambers, Bristol
p971 . . . . . 0117 930 5100
Old Square Chambers, London WC1
p945 . . . . . 020 7269 0300

Tetlow, Mr Bernard BA; LLM(Cantab) M *Nov 1984*
15, 30, 12, 25, 36
Charter Chambers, London WC1
p928 . . . . . 020 7618 4400

Tetlow, Mr Richard M *Jul 2006*
11, 30, 5, 6, 8, 12, 47, 67, 97, 84, 38, 89, 40, 94
Exchange Chambers, Manchester
p983 . . . . . 0161 833 2722
Exchange Chambers, Liverpool
p980 . . . . . 0151 236 7747
Exchange Chambers, Leeds
p977 . . . . . 0113 203 1970

TETTEY, Mr Stephen G *Mar 2010*
23, 15, 62, 51
Kenworthy's Chambers, Manchester
p984 . . . . . 0161 832 4036

Thacker, Mr James G *Nov 2001*
72, 15, 65
9 Gough Square, London EC4
p935 . . . . . 020 7832 0500

THACKRAY, Mr John R LLB L *Oct 1994*
15
Wilberforce Chambers, Hull
p976 . . . . . 01482 323264

THAIN, Miss Ashley I *Oct 1996*
10, 20
1 King's Bench Walk, London EC4
p938 . . . . . 020 7936 1500

Thanki, Bankim MA(Oxon) M *Jul 1988*
(Q.C.)
Fountain Court Chambers, London EC4
p934 . . . . . 020 7583 3335

Tharoo, Safia LLB I *Jul 2004*
42 Bedford Row, London WC1
p925 . . . . . 020 7831 0222

THATCHER, Mr Richard I *Jul 1989*
15
1 High Pavement, Nottingham
p988 . . . . . 0115 941 8218

Theis, Miss Lucy Morgan LLB(B'ham) G *Jul 1982*
(Q.C.)
Field Court Chambers, London WC1
p933 . . . . . 020 7405 6114

THELEN, Ms Jennifer JD; BPhil I *Nov 2007*
1, 31, 55, 76, 51, 63, 25, 23
4-5 Gray's Inn Square, London WC1
p935 . . . . . 020 7404 5252

Thind, Miss Anita LLB I *Nov 1988*
10, 12, 20, 30, 27, 26, 31
Regency Chambers, Peterborough
p990 . . . . . 01733 315215

Thirlwall, Ms Kathryn Mary BA; Recorder L *Jul 1982*
(Q.C.) *53, 30, 26, 18, 20, 10, 1*
7 Bedford Row, London WC1
p924 . . . . . 020 7242 3555

Thistle, Mr Dean Terence L *Dec 2010*
12, 22, 20, 88, 30, 15
Becket Chambers, Canterbury
p972 . . . . . 01227 786331
Becket Chambers, Maidstone
p982 . . . . . 01622 230957

THOM, Mr James MA(Oxon); BCL(Oxon); Recorder L *Nov 1974*
(Q.C.) *8, 22, 40, 56*
New Square Chambers, London WC2
p943 . . . . . 020 7419 8000

THOMANN, Mr Colin I *Jul 1999*
1, 7, 11, 12, 18, 19, 51, 30, 31, 46
Thirty Nine Essex Street, London WC2
p932 . . . . . 020 7832 1111

Thomas, Mr Andrew BA G *Jul 1989*
(Q.C.) *15, 18, 22, 53, 30, 40, 36, 31, 46*
Lincoln House Chambers, Manchester
p984 . . . . . 0161 832 5701
Brick Court Chambers, London WC2
p927 . . . . . 020 7379 3550

Thomas, Ms Anna MA(Oxon) I *Nov 1995*
18, 55, 30, 1, 51
Devereux Chambers, London WC2
p930 . . . . . 020 7353 7534

Thomas, Mr Arron LLB(Hons) L *Oct 2005*
20
18 St John Street Chambers, Manchester
p985 . . . . . 0161 278 1800

Thomas, Mr Bryan LLB; ACLIA G *Jul 1978*
12, 15, 30
Civitas Law, Cardiff
p972 . . . . . 0845 071 3007

THOMAS, Mr Charles BA(Oxon); DipLaw(Westminster) M *Oct 1990*
15
Guildhall Chambers, Bristol
p970 . . . . . 0117 930 9000

Thomas, Ms Christina LLB I *Feb 1994*
20, 10
Temple Chambers, Newport
p988 . . . . . 01633 267403 / 255855
Temple Chambers, Cardiff
p973 . . . . . 029 2039 7364

See p1010 for the Key to Work Categories

Thomas, Mr Christopher S BA; PhD; Dip de Droit Compare; Recorder L *Jul 1973*
(Q.C.) *3, 7, 11, 24, 40*
Keating Chambers, London WC2
p938 . . . . . 020 7544 2600

Thomas, Miss Claire LLB(Hull) I *Oct 1998*
15, 30
New Bailey Chambers, Preston
p990 . . . . . 01772 258087

THOMAS, Mr Clive BA(Cardiff) G *Jul 2005*
30, 53, 12
Farrar's Building, London EC4
p933 . . . . . 020 7583 9241

Thomas, Mr Daniel James M *Jul 2005*
Lincoln House Chambers, Manchester
p984 . . . . . 0161 832 5701

Thomas, Dr David Arthur LLD L *Feb 1992*
(Q.C.) *15*
2 Bedford Row, London WC1
p924 . . . . . 020 7440 8888

Thomas, Mr David C L *Oct 2009*
11, 24
2 Temple Gardens, London EC4
p952 . . . . . 020 7822 1200

Thomas, Dr David Keith I *Jan 2003*
53, 30, 27, 63, 40, 68, 77
Rougemont Chambers, Exeter
p975 . . . . . 01392 208484

THOMAS, Miss Dawn Marie L *Oct 2001*
9 St John Street Chambers, Manchester
p984 . . . . . 0161 955 9000

Thomas, Mr Dominic G *Sep 1998*
Charter Chambers, London WC1
p928 . . . . . 020 7618 4400

Thomas, Mr Dyfed L L BA(Oxon) M *Oct 1992*
15
Angel Chambers, Swansea
p992 . . . . . 01792 464623

Thomas, Mr Gareth LLB(Wales) I *Oct 1993*
8, 31, 30, 22
9 Park Place, Cardiff
p973 . . . . . 029 2038 2731

THOMAS, Gareth LLB; ACII G *Jul 1977*
1, 18, 20, 24, 30, 12, 22, 25, 40
Atlantic Chambers, Liverpool
p980 . . . . . 0151 236 4421

Thomas, Mr George L BA(Cantab) G *Oct 1995*
12, 18, 27, 30, 40, 53, 68, 85, 46, 84, 1
3 Serjeants' Inn, London EC4
p950 . . . . . 020 7427 5000

Thomas, Miss Jacqueline L LLB(Hons) L *Oct 2000*
20, 15
37 Park Square Chambers, Leeds
p978 . . . . . 0113 243 9422

Thomas, Mr James M *Jan 1999*
KCH Garden Square Chambers, Nottingham
p989 . . . . . 0115 941 8851
KCH Garden Square Chambers, Leicester
p979 . . . . . 0115 941 8851

Thomas, Miss Kate LLB G *Nov 1994*
12, 47, 15, 53, 30
No 8 Chambers, Birmingham
p968 . . . . . 0121 236 5514

Thomas, Mr Keith BA(Oxon) G *Jul 1969*
15, 30, 31, 36, 26
New Bailey Chambers, Preston
p990 . . . . . 01772 258087
New Bailey Chambers, Liverpool
p981 . . . . . 0151 236 9402

Thomas, Mrs Laura L *Jan 2003*
20
18 St John Street Chambers, Manchester
p985 . . . . . 0161 278 1800

Thomas, Ms Lisa LLB(Wales); LLM M *Oct 1998*
20
9 Park Place, Cardiff
p973 . . . . . 029 2038 2731

Thomas, Lord Martin G *Jan 1970*
(Q.C.) OBE*10, 15, 20*
No 8 Chambers, Birmingham
p968 . . . . . 0121 236 5514

Thomas, Mr Michael G *Mar 2000*
34, 57, 58
Gray's Inn Tax Chambers, London WC1
p936 . . . . . 020 7242 2642

Thomas, Mr Michael D BA; LLB(Lond) M *Nov 1955*
(Q.C.) CMG
Essex Court Chambers, London WC2
p931 . . . . . 020 7813 8000

Thomas, Mr Nigel Matthew LLB(Wales); LLB(Cantab); Recorder; Accredited Mediator L *Jul 1976*
Maitland Chambers, London WC2
p941 . . . . . 020 7406 1200

THOMAS, Mr Owain BA(Oxon); BCL I *Oct 1995*
18, 12, 30, 1, 27, 40, 46, 47, 51, 53, 55, 57
1 Crown Office Row, London EC4
p929 . . . . . 020 7797 7500

Thomas, Mr Owen BA(Oxon); LLM(Wales) G *Oct 1994*
20, 15, 12, 10
9 Park Place, Cardiff
p973 . . . . . 029 2038 2731

Thomas, Mr Paul Huw MA(Cantab) G *Jul 1979*
(Q.C.) *15, 25, 30, 53*
Iscoed Chambers, Swansea
p993 . . . . . 01792 652988

Thomas, Mrs Paula Angelique PDGL; MA L *Jan 2009*
12, 15, 20, 25, 10, 30
Regency Chambers, Peterborough
p990 . . . . . 01733 315215

Thomas, Miss Rebecca BA(Cantab) I *Nov 1999*
12, 18, 55, 22
42 Bedford Row, London WC1
p925 . . . . . 020 7831 0222

Thomas, Mr Richard MA(Oxon); MA(City) I *Oct 2002*
51, 15, 91, 1, 62
Doughty Street Chambers, London WC1
p930 . . . . . 020 7404 1313

Thomas, Mr Robert MA(Cantab); BCL(Oxon); Lic Sp Dr Eur(Br) L *Nov 1992*
11, 35, 3, 19, 24
Quadrant Chambers, London EC4
p948 . . . . . 020 7583 4444

Thomas, Mr Roger I *Jul 2001*
St Ives Chambers, Birmingham
p969 . . . . . 0121 236 0863
Equity Chambers, Birmingham
p968 . . . . . 0121 233 2100
4 King's Bench Walk, London EC4
p939 . . . . . 020 7822 7000
9 Park Place, Cardiff
p973 . . . . . 029 2038 2731

THOMAS, Mr Roger C MA; BCL(Oxon) L *Jul 1979*
34, 57, 58
Pump Court Tax Chambers, London WC1
p948 . . . . . 020 7414 8080

Thomas, Mr Simon I *Oct 1995*
15, 62
7 Bedford Row, London WC1
p924 . . . . . 020 7242 3555

THOMAS, Mr Stephen Edward Owen LLB(Hons); Recorder G *Jul 1980*
15, 62, 84
St Philips Chambers, Birmingham
p969 . . . . . 0121 246 7000

Thomas, Mr Steven LLB G *Feb 1993*
15
Temple Chambers, Newport
p988 . . . . . 01633 267403 / 255855
Temple Chambers, Cardiff
p973 . . . . . 029 2039 7364

THOMAS, Mr Timothy L *Jan 2002*
Lombard Chambers, London EC1
p941 . . . . . 020 7107 2100

Thomas, Mr William David MA(Oxon); BA(Oxon) M *Jul 1982*
(Q.C.) *3, 7, 8, 11, 12, 24, 33, 40*
Keating Chambers, London WC2
p938 . . . . . 020 7544 2600

Thomas of Gresford, Lord Martin Recorder G *Nov 1967*
(Q.C.) MBE
Goldsmith Chambers, London EC4
p935 . . . . . 020 7353 6802

Thomas-Symonds, Mr Nicklaus L *Oct 2004*
12, 15, 22, 26, 30, 6
Civitas Law, Cardiff
p972 . . . . . 0845 071 3007

THOMPSON, Mr Andrew G *Oct 1991*
15, 62
18 Red Lion Court, London EC4
p949 . . . . . 020 7520 6000
18 Red Lion Court (Annexe), Chelmsford
p973 . . . . . 01245 280880
Tanfield Chambers, London WC1
p951 . . . . . 020 7421 5300
Erskine Chambers, London WC2
p931 . . . . . 020 7242 5532

Thompson, Mr Antony M *Oct 2002*
41, 3, 5, 4, 11, 43, 44, 45, 48, 24, 54, 40, 33
20 Essex Street, London WC2
p932 . . . . . 020 7842 1200

THOMPSON, Miss Blondel Marguerittle LLB M *Jul 1987*
15
St Philips Chambers, Birmingham
p969 . . . . . 0121 246 7000

Thompson, Miss Clare LLB M *Oct 1998*
37 Park Square Chambers, Leeds
p978 . . . . . 0113 243 9422

Thompson, Mr Collingwood Forster James LLB; Recorder M *Jul 1975*
(Q.C.) *15, 62*
7 Bedford Row, London WC1
p924 . . . . . 020 7242 3555

Thompson, Mr Gareth G *Jan 2005*
St Johns Buildings, Preston
p990 . . . . . 01772 256100
St Johns Buildings, Chester
p974 . . . . . 01244 323070
St Johns Buildings, Manchester
p985 . . . . . 0161 214 1500
St Johns Buildings, Liverpool
p982 . . . . . 0151 243 6000

Thompson, Mr Howard Neil L *Jul 1982*
30, 40, 68, 94
No5 Chambers, Bristol
p971 . . . . . 0845 210 5555
No5 Chambers, London EC4
p944 . . . . . 0845 210 5555
No5 Chambers, Birmingham
p968 . . . . . 0845 210 5555

THOMPSON, Mr James BA(Cantab); BVC M *Jul 2005*
7, 11, 24, 40
Keating Chambers, London WC2
p938 . . . . . 020 7544 2600

Thompson, Mr Jonathan Richard LLM(Cantab); MA I *Oct 1990*
12, 20, 30, 10, 23
St Johns Buildings, Preston
p990 . . . . . 01772 256100
St Johns Buildings, Chester
p974 . . . . . 01244 323070
St Johns Buildings, Manchester
p985 . . . . . 0161 214 1500
St Johns Buildings, Liverpool
p982 . . . . . 0151 243 6000

Thompson, Miss Lindsey C G *Nov 1995*
15
Atkinson Bevan Chambers, London EC4
p924 . . . . . 020 7353 2112

Thompson, Mr Lyall I *Jan 1995*
4 Breams Buildings, London EC4
p927 . . . . . 020 7092 1900
Goldsmith Chambers, London EC4
p935 . . . . . 020 7353 6802

Thompson, Mr Patrick LLB(Manc) G *Oct 1990*
15, 12
St Johns Buildings, Preston
p990 . . . . . 01772 256100
St Johns Buildings, Chester
p974 . . . . . 01244 323070
St Johns Buildings, Manchester
p985 . . . . . 0161 214 1500
St Johns Buildings, Liverpool
p982 . . . . . 0151 243 6000

Thompson, Ms Pauline M *Jul 1998*
15
5 King's Bench Walk, London EC4
p939 . . . . . 020 7353 5638

Thompson, Mr Philip Nigel G *Jul 2000*
18, 88
Pendragon Chambers, Swansea
p993 . . . . . 01792 411188

THOMPSON, Polly BA(Hons) M *Nov 1990*
10, 20
Renaissance Chambers, London WC1
p949 . . . . . 020 7404 1111
Stour Chambers, Canterbury
p972 . . . . . 01227 764899

THOMPSON, Mr Rhodri MA; Phil(Oxon) M *Jul 1989*
(Q.C.) *1, 19, 2, 51, 44, 46, 39, 26, 56, 50, 11, 55, 23, 33, 60, 61, 81*
Matrix Chambers, London WC1
p942 . . . . . 020 7404 3447

THOMPSON, Mr Richard Anthony LLB(Hons) M *Jul 2007*
15
Wilberforce Chambers, Hull
p976 . . . . . 01482 323264

Thompson, Miss Sally CPE M *Oct 1994*
15, 62, 96
Atkinson Bevan Chambers, London EC4
p924 . . . . . 020 7353 2112

Thompson, Mr Steven BA(Hons) I *Oct 1996*
6, 8, 11, 29, 32, 37, 40, 5, 4, 59, 49, 62, 38
XXIV Old Buildings, London WC2
p944 . . . . . 020 7691 2424

THOMPSON, Mrs Zoe LLB M *Jan 1999*
8, 11, 12, 47, 48, 19, 30
9 St John Street Chambers, Manchester
p984 . . . . . 0161 955 9000

Thomson, Dr David MB; ChB; LLB(Hons); LLM L *Nov 1994*
27, 30, 12, 53, 59, 56
1 Chancery Lane, London WC2
p928 . . . . . 0845 634 6666

THOMSON, Miss Louise BA; DipLaw L *Nov 1996*
30
12 King's Bench Walk, London EC4
p940 . . . . . 020 7583 0811

Thomson, Mr Mark MSci(Glasgow); MSc(Cantab) L *Jan 2006*
5, 9, 97, 11, 47, 38, 40, 93, 37
Radcliffe Chambers, London WC2
p949 . . . . . 020 7831 0081

Thomson, Mr Martin Haldane Ahmad LLB(Hons); GDL G *Jul 1979*
9, 18, 37, 51, 55, 64
Wynne Chambers, London NW6
p954 . . . . . 020 3239 6964

THOMSON, Vanessa L *Dec 1997*
15
9 St John Street Chambers, Manchester
p984 . . . . . 0161 955 9000

THORLEY, Mr Simon Joe MA(Oxon)(Jurisprudence) I *Jul 1972*
(Q.C.) *13, 3, 19, 44, 41*
3 New Square, London WC2
p943 . . . . . 020 7405 1111

Thorne, Ms Katy I *Nov 1994*
Tooks Chambers, London EC4
p953 . . . . . 020 7842 7575

Thorne, Miss Sarah Louise LLB(Hons) M *Nov 1995*
15
Westgate Chambers, Lewes
p980 . . . . . 01273 480510

Thorne, Mr Timothy MA(Oxon) G *Nov 1987*
15
33 Bedford Row, London WC1
p925 . . . . . 020 7242 6476

THORNE, Miss Zoe LLB(Hons) L *Jul 1999*
20, 10, 36
7 Harrington Street Chambers, Liverpool
p981 . . . . . 0151 242 0707

THORNETT, Mr Gary Deputy District Judge; Former Solicitor M *Oct 1991*
30, 12, 53, 84, 27
12 King's Bench Walk, London EC4
p940 . . . . . 020 7583 0811

THORNHILL, Mr Andrew Robert BA(Oxon) M *Jul 1969*
(Q.C.) *34, 57, 58, 37*
Pump Court Tax Chambers, London WC1
p948 . . . . . 020 7414 8080

THORNLEY, Miss Hannah BA(Cantab); BCL(Oxon) M *Oct 2003*
5, 6, 11, 8, 97, 38
South Square, London WC1
p950 . . . . . 020 7696 9900

THORNTON, Mr Andrew James LLB L *Nov 1994*
11, 38, 97
Erskine Chambers, London WC2
p931 . . . . . 020 7242 5532

Thornton, Mrs Delia LLB(Notts) L *Oct 1999*
20, 10
St John's Chambers, Bristol
p972 . . . . . 0117 921 3456

Thornton, Mr John Robert G *Jun 2002*
20, 10, 94
Stour Chambers, Canterbury
p972 . . . . . 01227 764899

13

THORNTON, Ms Justine L *Feb 1994*
31, 46, 1, 78, 84, 61, 26
Thirty Nine Essex Street, London WC2
p932 . . . . 020 7832 1111

Thornton, Mr Stephen G *Jan 2003*
York Chambers, York
p995 . . . . 01904 620048
York Chambers, Newcastle upon Tyne
p987 . . . . 0191 206 4677

Thorogood, Mr Bernard Recorder G *Jul 1986*
15, 73, 17, 46, 2, 82, 39, 62, 84, 42, 91, 56, 68
No5 Chambers, Bristol
p971 . . . . 0845 210 5555
No5 Chambers, London EC4
p944 . . . . 0845 210 5555
No5 Chambers, Birmingham
p968 . . . . 0845 210 5555

Thorowgood, Mr Max L *Nov 1995*
Field Court Chambers, London WC1
p933 . . . . 020 7405 6114

THORPE, Mr Alexander I *Nov 1995*
20, 12
Queen Elizabeth Buildings, London EC4
p948 . . . . 020 7797 7837

Threlfall, Mr George G *Jan 1972*
15, 62, 48, 84, 36
Queen Square Chambers, Bristol
p972 . . . . 0117 921 1966

Thwaites, Mr Ronald G *Nov 1970*
(Q.C.) *12, 15, 16, 36*
Ely Place Chambers, London EC1
p931 . . . . 020 7400 9600

Thyne, Mr Richard M L *Jan 2002*
15, 12, 30
Paradise Chambers, Sheffield
p992 . . . . 0114 273 8951

Tibbitts, Mr Simon I *Jan 2006*
18, 55, 30, 48
Queen Square Chambers, Bristol
p972 . . . . 0117 921 1966

Ticciati, Mr Oliver MA(Cantab) I *Jul 1979*
7, 12, 24, 30
4 Pump Court, London EC4
p947 . . . . 020 7842 5555

Ticehurst, Mr Joss I *Jan 2006*
15, 30, 22, 12, 10
Walnut House Chambers, Exeter
p975 . . . . 01392 279751

TIDBURY, Mr Andrew BA(Cantab) I *Jul 1976*
10, 12, 20
Queen Elizabeth Buildings, London EC4
p948 . . . . 020 7797 7837

Tidmarsh, Mr Christopher Ralph Francis BA(Oxon) L *Nov 1985*
(Q.C.) *8, 29, 32, 37, 40*
5 Stone Buildings, London WC2
p951 . . . . 020 7242 6201

TILBURY, Mr James G *Jan 1996*
Carmelite Chambers, London EC4
p927 . . . . 020 7936 6300

Tilley, Mr Gareth LLB(Sydney); BA; BCL(Oxon) L *Jan 2007*
8, 11, 62
Serle Court, London WC2
p950 . . . . 020 7242 6105

Tillyard, Mr James H H BSc; Recorder M *Jun 1978*
(Q.C.) *10, 12, 20*
Thirty Park Place, Cardiff
p973 . . . . 029 2039 8421

TIMMINS, Miss Nicola MA; LLM(Cantab) G *Oct 2008*
6, 11, 97, 62, 38
4 Stone Buildings, London WC2
p951 . . . . 020 7242 5524

TIMSON, Mr Corin I *Nov 1994*
23, 1, 51
Kenworthy's Chambers, Manchester
p984 . . . . 0161 832 4036

TINDAL, Mr Jim Deputy District Judge; Part-time Employment Tribunal Judge L *Nov 2002*
30, 22, 18, 76, 55
St Philips Chambers, Birmingham
p969 . . . . 0121 246 7000

TINDALL, Mr Paul R BA(Hons); LLM G *Oct 1999*
6, 47, 11, 22, 40, 51
St James's Chambers, Manchester
p984 . . . . 0161 834 7000

TINKLER, David BA(Hons) L *Oct 2004*
15, 12, 18, 30
Atlantic Chambers, Liverpool
p980 . . . . 0151 236 4421

TINNION, Mr Antoine BA(Cantab); MA(Oxon); LLM(Harv) L *Nov 2004*
11, 18, 8, 38, 88
Trinity (Newcastle) Chambers, Newcastle upon Tyne
p987 . . . . 0191 232 1927
Trinity (Teesside) Chambers, Middlesbrough
p986 . . . . 01642 247569

Tipples, Miss Amanda J MA(Cantab); Recorder, Junior Counsel to Crown A Panel G *Oct 1991*
(Q.C.)
Maitland Chambers, London WC2
p941 . . . . 020 7406 1200

Titchmarsh, Miss Katharine LLB(Hons) L *Nov 1998*
12, 30, 53
Exchange Chambers, Manchester
p983 . . . . 0161 833 2722
Exchange Chambers, Liverpool
p980 . . . . 0151 236 7747
Exchange Chambers, Leeds
p977 . . . . 0113 203 1970

Titmuss, Mr Jonathan BA(Hons)(Lond) L *Nov 2001*
93, 86, 11
42 Bedford Row, London WC1
p925 . . . . 020 7831 0222
Hardwicke, London WC2
p936 . . . . 020 7242 2523

TITUS, Miss Francesca M *Jul 2003*
Carmelite Chambers, London EC4
p927 . . . . 020 7936 6300

TIVADAR, Mr Daniel M *Nov 2005*
1, 11, 12, 18, 30, 51, 38
3 Hare Court, London EC4
p937 . . . . 020 7415 7800

Tiwana, Mr Ekwall Singh M *Jan 1988*
15, 25, 62
No5 Chambers, Bristol
p971 . . . . 0845 210 5555
No5 Chambers, London EC4
p944 . . . . 0845 210 5555
No5 Chambers, Birmingham
p968 . . . . 0845 210 5555

TKACZYNSKA, Ms Anna M *Jul 2008*
22, 76, 51
Hardwicke, London WC2
p936 . . . . 020 7242 2523

Toal, Mr David LLB(Hons) G *Feb 1990*
15
Exchange Chambers, Manchester
p983 . . . . 0161 833 2722
Exchange Chambers, Liverpool
p980 . . . . 0151 236 7747
Exchange Chambers, Leeds
p977 . . . . 0113 203 1970

TOBIN, Mr Daniel LLB(Hons) M *Oct 1994*
30
12 King's Bench Walk, London EC4
p940 . . . . 020 7583 0811

TOBIN, Kezia M *Oct 2010*
23, 20, 10
Renaissance Chambers, London WC1
p949 . . . . 020 7404 1111

Toch, Miss Joanna LLB; Mediator M *Oct 1988*
Lamb Building, Brighton
p970 . . . . 01273 820490
Lamb Building, London EC4
p940 . . . . 020 7797 7788

TOD, Mr Jonathan Alan LLB(Hons) I *Nov 1990*
20
29 Bedford Row, London WC1
p925 . . . . 020 7404 1044

Todd, Miss Bridget G *Jan 2001*
15, 62
5 St Andrew's Hill, London EC4
p950 . . . . 020 7332 5400

Todd, Mrs Elisabeth Helen Margaret LLB(Lond) M *Oct 1990*
20, 10
1 Hare Court, London EC4
p936 . . . . 020 7797 7070

TODD, Mr James G *Nov 1990*
18, 24, 30, 84
Thirty Nine Essex Street, London WC2
p932 . . . . 020 7832 1111

Todd, Mr Martin I *Nov 1991*
York Chambers, York
p995 . . . . 01904 620048
York Chambers, Newcastle upon Tyne
p987 . . . . 0191 206 4677

TODD, Mr Michael BA(Keele) L *Jul 1977*
(Q.C.) *11, 38, 97*
Erskine Chambers, London WC2
p931 . . . . 020 7242 5532

Todd, Mr Richard F BA(Oxon) M *Jul 1988*
(Q.C.) *20, 10*
1 Hare Court, London EC4
p936 . . . . 020 7797 7070

TODD, Ms Susan G *Oct 1991*
20
St Philips Chambers, Birmingham
p969 . . . . 0121 246 7000

Todman, Ms Deborah LLB(Hons) G *Oct 1991*
42 Bedford Row, London WC1
p925 . . . . 020 7831 0222

TOLANEY, Ms Sonia MA(Oxon) M *Oct 1995*
(Q.C.) *5, 6, 11, 19, 24, 40*
3 Verulam Buildings, London WC1
p953 . . . . 020 7831 8441

Toledano, Mr Daniel I *Oct 1993*
(Q.C.)
One Essex Court, London EC4
p931 . . . . 020 7583 2000

Tolkien, Mr Simon BA M *Jul 1994*
15
2 Dr Johnson's Buildings, London EC4
p930 . . . . 020 7936 2613

Tolley, Mr Adam Richard BSc(Oxon) L *Oct 1994*
Fountain Court Chambers, London EC4
p934 . . . . 020 7583 3335

Tolson, Mr Robin Recorder M *Oct 1994*
(Q.C.) *10, 20, 51*
Southernhay Chambers, Exeter
p975 . . . . 01392 255777

Tolson, Mr Robin Stewart I *Nov 1980*
(Q.C.)
Outer Temple Chambers, London WC2
p945 . . . . 020 7353 6381
St John's Chambers, Bristol
p972 . . . . 0117 921 3456

TOMAN, Miss Cristin BSc(Hons)(Western Australia); LLB L *Jan 2004*
5, 6, 8, 11, 22, 29, 40, 38, 88
Enterprise Chambers, London WC2
p931 . . . . 020 7405 9471
Enterprise Chambers, Leeds
p977 . . . . 0113 246 0391
Enterprise Chambers, Newcastle upon Tyne
p987 . . . . 0191 222 3344

Tomassi, Mr Mark David BA M *Nov 1981*
15
Charter Chambers, London WC1
p928 . . . . 020 7618 4400

Tomlinson, Miss Elizabeth LLB; LLM(Cantab) I *Jul 2004*
20, 10
Harcourt Chambers, London EC4
p936 . . . . 0844 561 7135
Harcourt Chambers, Oxford
p989 . . . . 0844 561 7135

TOMLINSON, Mr Hugh BA(Oxon); MA(Sussex) G *Nov 1983*
(Q.C.) *16, 40, 12, 11, 1, 8, 9, 47, 48, 18, 19, 51, 26, 55, 56, 50, 15, 33*
Matrix Chambers, London WC1
p942 . . . . 020 7404 3447

Tomlinson, Mr Michael M *Jan 2002*
3PB, Bournemouth
p969 . . . . 01202 292102

Tompkins, Miss Kate BA(Hons)(Sheff) L *Jul 2003*
1, 2, 10, 12, 18, 20, 15
36 Bedford Row, London WC1
p925 . . . . 020 7421 8000

Tompkinson, Deborah A MA(Oxon); LLB M *Nov 1984*
45
Clerksroom - Administration Centre, Taunton
p993 . . . . 0845 083 3000

Toms, Mr Nicholas LLM(Hons); LLM(Cantab) M *Nov 1996*
18, 51, 22, 27, 30, 1
Doughty Street Chambers, London WC1
p930 . . . . 020 7404 1313

Toms, Mr Paul G *Jan 2003*
41, 5, 11, 24, 35
Quadrant Chambers, London EC4
p948 . . . . 020 7583 4444

TOMSON, Mr Alastair MA(Cantab) L *Jan 2004*
6, 11, 97, 62, 38
4 Stone Buildings, London WC2
p951 . . . . 020 7242 5524

Toney, Miss Rachel BA(Oxon) L *Nov 1998*
3, 11, 12, 18, 35, 55
Stone Chambers, London WC1
p951 . . . . 020 7440 6900

TONGE, Mr Christopher I *Jan 1988*
15
Bank House Chambers, Sheffield
p991 . . . . 0114 275 1223

TONNA, Mr John BA(Oxon) G *Jul 1974*
12, 39, 27, 53, 30, 48, 40
Thirty Nine Essex Street, London WC2
p932 . . . . 020 7832 1111

TOOGOOD, Miss Claire Victoria M *Oct 1995*
53, 30
Crown Office Chambers, London EC4
p929 . . . . 020 7797 8100

Toogood, Mr John LLM G *Jul 1957* QPM
15
4 KBW, London EC4
p938 . . . . 020 7822 8822

Toogood, Katherine G *Jan 1998*
4 KBW, London EC4
p938 . . . . 020 7822 8822

Toomey, Mr Kevin G *Jul 2004*
15, 25, 62
2 Bedford Row, London WC1
p924 . . . . 020 7440 8888

Toone, Mr Robert I *Oct 1993*
30, 8, 34
11 King's Bench Walk, Leeds
p978 . . . . 0113 297 1200

Topal, Mr Erol LLB M *Jul 1998*
7, 12, 47, 18, 22, 29, 55
Lamb Chambers, London EC4
p941 . . . . 020 7797 8300

Topham, Mr Geoffrey John BA(Cantab) L *Jun 1964*
8, 37
3 Stone Buildings, London WC2
p951 . . . . 020 7242 4937

Topham, Mr John David LLB(Lond) G *Jul 1970*
15, 18, 25, 46, 48
Broadway House Chambers, Leeds
p977 . . . . 0113 246 2600
Broadway House Chambers, Bradford
p969 . . . . 01274 722560

Topliss, Miss Megan G *Nov 1994*
3PB, Winchester
p994 . . . . 01962 868884

Topolski, Mr Michael Recorder I *Apr 1986*
(Q.C.) *15, 36, 51*
Tooks Chambers, London EC4
p953 . . . . 020 7842 7575

Topping, Miss Caroline MA(Cantab) M *Oct 1984*
10, 12, 20, 51
6-8 Mill Street, Maidstone
p982 . . . . 01622 688094 / 688095
6 Pump Court, London EC4
p947 . . . . 020 7797 8400

Torode, Miss Joanna Dorothea BA(Hons)(Politics) M *Nov 2006*
33 Chancery Lane, London WC2
p928 . . . . 020 7440 9950

TOUBE, Ms Felicity BA; BCL(Oxon) I *Nov 1995*
(Q.C.) *5, 6, 8, 11, 12, 24, 29, 37, 40, 38*
South Square, London WC1
p950 . . . . 020 7696 9900

TOWERS, Mr Martin LLB G *Oct 1996*
15
Fountain Chambers, Middlesbrough
p986 . . . . 01642 804040

Towler, Mr Peter J H MA(Cantab); FCIArb; Recorder M *Jul 1974*
31, 26, 11, 22, 36, 15, 62
12 College Place, Southampton
p992 . . . . 023 8032 0320

Townend, Mr Samuel L *Oct 1999*
3, 7, 11, 24, 40
Keating Chambers, London WC2
p938 . . . . 020 7544 2600

See p1010 for the Key to Work Categories

TOWNSEND, Mr Edmund LLB; LLM M *Mar 2006*
12, 18, 30
Farrar's Building, London EC4
p933 . . . . 020 7583 9241

Townsend, Mrs Harriet BSc M *Nov 1992*
1, 11, 12, 15, 18, 20, 22, 25, 26, 29, 30, 31, 36
Cornerstone Barristers, London WC1
p929 . . . . 020 7242 4986

TOWNSEND, Mr James MA(Oxon) I *Jul 1980*
30, 62, 53
Guildhall Chambers, Bristol
p970 . . . . 0117 930 9000

TOZER, Miss Stephanie BA(Hons)(Oxon) L *Oct 1996*
6, 8, 11, 22, 32, 37, 40
Falcon Chambers, London EC4
p933 . . . . 020 7353 2484

Tozzi, Mr Nigel LLB(Exon) G *Jul 1980*
(Q.C.) *8, 11, 12, 24, 25, 36*
4 Pump Court, London EC4
p947 . . . . 020 7842 5555

TOZZI, Miss Sarah LLB(Hons)(Reading) I *Oct 1998*
30, 18, 12
Farrar's Building, London EC4
p933 . . . . 020 7583 9241

Trace, Mr Anthony John MA(Hons)(Cantab) L *Jul 1981*
(Q.C.)
Maitland Chambers, London WC2
p941 . . . . 020 7406 1200

Tracey, Ms Helen L *Jan 2001*
1 Pump Court, London EC4
p947 . . . . 020 7842 7070

Tracy Forster, Ms Jane LLB(Hons) I *Jul 1975*
18, 53, 27
Hailsham Chambers, London EC4
p936 . . . . 020 7643 5000

TRAFFORD, Mr Mark BA(Hons)(History & Politics) I *May 1992*
12, 72, 15, 62, 20, 67
23 Essex Street, London WC2
p932 . . . . 020 7413 0353
2 King's Bench Walk, London EC4
p939 . . . . 020 7353 1746

TRAIN, Sophie M *Jul 2005*
10, 20
Renaissance Chambers, London WC1
p949 . . . . 020 7404 1111

Travers, Mr Daniel LLB L *Oct 1999*
15, 62
Exchange Chambers, Manchester
p983 . . . . 0161 833 2722
Exchange Chambers, Liverpool
p980 . . . . 0151 236 7747
Exchange Chambers, Leeds
p977 . . . . 0113 203 1970

Travers, Mr David LLB(Lond); LLM; AKC M *Jul 1981*
1, 15, 26, 31, 39, 46, 48, 49, 51, 53
6-8 Mill Street, Maidstone
p982 . . . . 01622 688094 / 688095
6 Pump Court, London EC4
p947 . . . . 020 7797 8400

TRAVERS, Mr Hugh MA(Cantab); MSc; Employment Tribunal Chairman M *Nov 1988*
7, 10, 12, 15, 20, 30
Pump Court Chambers, Swindon
p993 . . . . 01793 539899
Pump Court Chambers, Winchester
p994 . . . . 01962 868161
Pump Court Chambers, London EC4
p947 . . . . 020 7353 0711

Traversi, Mr John S D A MA(Oxon) G *Jul 1977*
15, 51, 62
Nine Bedford Row, London WC1
p924 . . . . 020 7489 2727

Traynor, Mr David BA(Oxon) L *Oct 2002*
12, 15
15 Winckley Square, Preston
p991 . . . . 01772 252828

TREADWELL, Mr Brian L *Oct 2006*
15
7 Harrington Street Chambers, Liverpool
p981 . . . . 0151 242 0707

Treasure, Mr Francis MA(Oxon) G *Feb 1980*
42 Bedford Row, London WC1
p925 . . . . 020 7831 0222

Tregear, Mr Francis BA M *Jul 1980*
(Q.C.) *5, 6, 8, 11, 29, 32, 37, 40, 24, 56, 49, 62, 25*
XXIV Old Buildings, London WC2
p944 . . . . 020 7691 2424

TREGIDGO, Mr Marc M *Jul 2002*
4 King's Bench Walk, London EC4
p939 . . . . 020 7822 7000

TREGILGAS-DAVEY, Mr Marcus G *Feb 1993*
12, 15, 30, 42, 91
Pump Court Chambers, Swindon
p993 . . . . 01793 539899
Pump Court Chambers, Winchester
p994 . . . . 01962 868161
Pump Court Chambers, London EC4
p947 . . . . 020 7353 0711

TREGONING, Mr Bruce BA(Hons); DipLaw M *Jan 2009*
20
Crown Office Row Chambers, Brighton
p970 . . . . 01273 625625

Treharne, Miss Jennet LLB(Hons)(Lond) M *Oct 1975*
15
Thirty Park Place, Cardiff
p973 . . . . 029 2039 8421

Trembath, Mr Graham LLB M *Jul 1978*
(Q.C.) *15, 62*
5 Paper Buildings, London EC4
p946 . . . . 020 7583 6117

Treneer, Mr Mark BA(Soton); DipLaw; MA I *Jul 1987*
6, 7, 8, 12, 22, 29, 30, 31, 18
Walnut House Chambers, Exeter
p975 . . . . 01392 279751

TREPTE, Mr Peter-Armin BA(Hons); Lic En Dr; PhD; FCIArb; MCIPS G *Jul 1987*
19, 11
Littleton Chambers, London EC4
p941 . . . . 020 7797 8600

Tresman, Mr Lewis Robert Simon LLB(Reading) G *Nov 1980*
7, 10, 12, 15, 20, 22, 29, 30, 36, 37, 27, 18
Staple Inn Chambers, London WC1
p951 . . . . 020 7242 5240

Tresman, Miss Sarah M *Oct 2008*
49, 41, 3, 5, 11, 43, 47, 78, 24, 54, 35
20 Essex Street, London WC2
p932 . . . . 020 7842 1200

Trevelyan Thomas, Mr Adrian MA(Cantab) G *Jul 1974*
1, 26, 28, 31
Cornerstone Barristers, London WC1
p929 . . . . 020 7242 4986

TREVERTON-JONES, Mr Gregory Recorder I *Nov 1977*
(Q.C.) *1, 30, 56, 51, 12, 84, 36*
Thirty Nine Essex Street, London WC2
p932 . . . . 020 7832 1111

Trevis, Robert LLB I *Apr 1990*
Clerksroom - Administration Centre, Taunton
p993 . . . . 0845 083 3000

TRIDIMAS, Professor Takis LLB(Athens); LLM; PhD(Cantab) M *Jan 2000*
19, 1, 51, 33, 3, 15
Matrix Chambers, London WC1
p942 . . . . 020 7404 3447

Trigg, Mr Miles Haddon I *Jul 1987*
12, 15, 25, 62
4 Breams Buildings, London EC4
p927 . . . . 020 7092 1900

Trigger, Mr Simon M *Nov 2000*
53, 12, 22, 30, 40, 59, 24
1 Chancery Lane, London WC2
p928 . . . . 0845 634 6666

TRIMMER, Miss Carol Jane LLB G *Nov 1993*
20, 10
Wilberforce Chambers, Hull
p976 . . . . 01482 323264

Trimmer, Mr Stuart LLB(Lond) G *Jul 1977*
(Q.C.) *15*
4 Breams Buildings, London EC4
p927 . . . . 020 7092 1900

Tritton, Mr Guy H BSc(Dunelm); DipLaw I *Jul 1987*
11, 13, 19, 50, 45
Hogarth Chambers, London WC2
p937 . . . . 020 7404 0404

TROLLOPE, Mr Andrew I *Nov 1971*
(Q.C.) *15, 62, 95*
187 Fleet Street, London EC4
p933 . . . . 020 7430 7430

Troman, Mr Carl L *Jul 2001*
Four New Square, London WC2
p943 . . . . 020 7822 2000

TROMANS, Mr Stephen MA(Cantab) I *Jul 1999*
(Q.C.) *1, 26, 31, 46, 61, 78*
Thirty Nine Essex Street, London WC2
p932 . . . . 020 7832 1111

Troop, Mr Paul Benjamin LLB(Hons)(B'ham) L *Aug 1998*
10, 19, 36, 55, 51
Tooks Chambers, London EC4
p953 . . . . 020 7842 7575

Trory, Mr Henry I *Jan 2003*
York Chambers, York
p995 . . . . 01904 620048
York Chambers, Newcastle upon Tyne
p987 . . . . 0191 206 4677

TROTTER, Miss Helen G *Oct 2004*
15, 12, 20
Pump Court Chambers, Swindon
p993 . . . . 01793 539899
Pump Court Chambers, Winchester
p994 . . . . 01962 868161
Pump Court Chambers, London EC4
p947 . . . . 020 7353 0711

TROUP, Mr Alex MA(Oxon) G *Nov 1998*
8, 11, 40, 93, 37, 32, 88, 24
St John's Chambers, Bristol
p972 . . . . 0117 921 3456

TROUP, Miss Rachel L *Nov 2005*
15
Pump Court Chambers, Swindon
p993 . . . . 01793 539899
Pump Court Chambers, Winchester
p994 . . . . 01962 868161
Pump Court Chambers, London EC4
p947 . . . . 020 7353 0711

TROWELL, Mr Stephen BA(Oxon); DPhil(Oxon) M *Oct 1995*
20, 10
1 Hare Court, London EC4
p936 . . . . 020 7797 7070

TROWER, Mr William S P MA(Oxon) L *Jul 1983*
(Q.C.) *5, 6, 8, 11, 12, 24, 29, 40, 38*
South Square, London WC1
p950 . . . . 020 7696 9900

Trowler, Ms Rebecca BSc G *Oct 1995*
15, 1, 51
Doughty Street Chambers, London WC1
p930 . . . . 020 7404 1313

Troy, Mrs Jill Mary MA(Oxon) M *Jul 1986*
10, 20, 37
No 6 Barristers Chambers, Leeds
p978 . . . . 0113 245 9763

Troy, Ms Karen L *Jan 1981*
11, 24, 19, 29, 40, 5, 6, 47, 7, 66, 38, 97
Exchange Chambers, Manchester
p983 . . . . 0161 833 2722
Exchange Chambers, Liverpool
p980 . . . . 0151 236 7747
Exchange Chambers, Leeds
p977 . . . . 0113 203 1970

Trumper, Miss Sarah BA(Hons); DipLaw L *Nov 1996*
10, 20
Southernhay Chambers, Exeter
p975 . . . . 01392 255777

Trumpington, Mr John Henry BA M *Feb 1985*
8, 10, 12, 15, 20, 22, 23, 25, 30, 36, 37
Staple Inn Chambers, London WC1
p951 . . . . 020 7242 5240

TRUSCOTT, Ms Caroline LLB L *Nov 1998*
30
Thirty Nine Essex Street, London WC2
p932 . . . . 020 7832 1111

Truscott, Mr Ian LLB(Edin); LLM(Leeds); Called in Scotland 1988 G *Nov 1995*
(Q.C.) *18, 36, 51, 19*
Old Square Chambers, Bristol
p971 . . . . 0117 930 5100
Old Square Chambers, London WC1
p945 . . . . 020 7269 0300

Trusted, Mr Harry MA(Cantab) I *Jul 1985*
53, 30, 40
Outer Temple Chambers, London WC2
p945 . . . . 020 7353 6381

Tselentis, Mr Michael SC; BCL(Oxon); BA; LLB(Cape Town) G *Oct 1995*
(Q.C.) *3, 4, 11, 12, 24, 35, 41*
20 Essex Street, London WC2
p932 . . . . 020 7842 1200

Tuck, Miss Rebecca L BA(Oxon) G *Oct 1998*
18, 30, 55, 36, 51
Old Square Chambers, Bristol
p971 . . . . 0117 930 5100
Old Square Chambers, London WC1
p945 . . . . 020 7269 0300

TUCKER, Mr Andrew R S LLB(Sheff) M *Jul 1977*
15, 70, 39, 46
Cornwall Street Chambers, Birmingham
p967 . . . . 0121 233 7500

Tucker, Mr Ashley Russell BA M *Nov 1990*
Park Court Chambers, Leeds
p978 . . . . 0113 243 3277

Tucker, Mr Ian BSc M *Jul 2010*
5, 6, 8, 11, 38, 47, 67
Exchange Chambers, Manchester
p983 . . . . 0161 833 2722
Exchange Chambers, Liverpool
p980 . . . . 0151 236 7747
Exchange Chambers, Leeds
p977 . . . . 0113 203 1970

Tucker, Mr James G *Oct 2004*
15, 62
Queen Square Chambers, Bristol
p972 . . . . 0117 921 1966

TUCKER, Ms Lorraine M *Nov 1982*
15, 62
18 Red Lion Court, London EC4
p949 . . . . 020 7520 6000
18 Red Lion Court (Annexe), Chelmsford
p973 . . . . 01245 280880

TUCKER, Mr Lynton A MA; BCL(Oxon) L *Feb 1971*
8, 37
New Square Chambers, London WC2
p943 . . . . 020 7419 8000

Tucker, Mr Nicholas J BA I *Oct 1993*
15, 47, 48, 62, 84, 70, 22, 88
12 College Place, Southampton
p992 . . . . 023 8032 0320

Tucker, Mr Paul BA(Cantab) G *Nov 1990*
(Q.C.) *1, 26, 31, 46, 54*
Kings Chambers, Leeds
p978 . . . . 0113 242 1123
Kings Chambers, Manchester
p984 . . . . 0161 832 9082

Tucker, Dr Peter Louis MA G *Nov 1970*
15, 23
Leone Chambers, Harrow
p976 . . . . 020 8868 2736

Tucker, Sir Richard L *Jan 1954*
(Q.C.) *41*
No5 Chambers, Bristol
p971 . . . . 0845 210 5555
No5 Chambers, London EC4
p944 . . . . 0845 210 5555
No5 Chambers, Birmingham
p968 . . . . 0845 210 5555

TUDOR-EVANS, Mr Quintin L *Jul 1977*
30, 24, 40, 53
12 King's Bench Walk, London EC4
p940 . . . . 020 7583 0811

Tueje, Ms Patricia I *Jan 1999*
22
1 Pump Court, London EC4
p947 . . . . 020 7842 7070

Tughan, Mr John LLB(L'pool) I *Nov 1991*
20, 10
4 Paper Buildings, London EC4
p946 . . . . 020 7583 0816

Tully, Ms Anne Margaret MA; LLM(Cantab) G *Nov 1989*
6, 7, 8, 11, 12, 18, 22, 27, 30, 32, 36
Eastbourne Chambers, Eastbourne
p975 . . . . 01323 642102

TULLY, Mr Philip M *Oct 2000*
15, 62
7 Harrington Street Chambers, Liverpool
p981 . . . . 0151 242 0707

TULLY, Mr Ray BA I *Nov 1987*
15, 62
Guildhall Chambers, Bristol
p970 . . . . 0117 930 9000

Tunkel, Mr Alan Michael BA(Oxon) M *Jul 1976*
6, 7, 8, 9, 11, 12, 22, 29, 32, 40, 37
3 Stone Buildings, London WC2
p951 . . . . 020 7242 4937

13

Tunley, James L *Jan 2007*
4 KBW, London EC4
p938 . . . . . 020 7822 8822

Turcan, Mr Henry W MA(Oxon) I *Jul 1965*
4 Paper Buildings, London EC4
p946 . . . . . 020 7583 0816

TURKSON, Tetteh G *Oct 1998*
15, 72
23 Essex Street, London WC2
p932 . . . . . 020 7413 0353

Turnbull, Miss Helen BA(Oxon) I *Jan 2004*
11, 30
Lamb Chambers, London EC4
p941 . . . . . 020 7797 8300

Turner, Miss Abigail M *Jan 2006*
Northampton Chambers, Northampton
p988 . . . . . 01604 636271

Turner, Mr Adam L *Oct 2008*
41, 24, 35, 61
7 King's Bench Walk, London EC4
p940 . . . . . 020 7910 8300

Turner, Mr Alan Joseph G *Oct 1984*
Academy Chambers, London N2
p923 . . . . . 07979 265321

Turner, Andrew L *Nov 2010*
Clerksroom - Administration Centre, Taunton
p993 . . . . . 0845 083 3000

Turner, Miss Annabel LLB(Hons) I *Jul 2003*
10, 20, 18
4 Paper Buildings, London EC4
p946 . . . . . 020 7583 0816

Turner, Mr David BA(Cantab) G *Nov 1992*
(Q.C.)
Four New Square, London WC2
p943 . . . . . 020 7822 2000

TURNER, Mr James LLB(Hull) I *Jul 1976*
(Q.C.) *1, 10, 12, 15, 20, 31, 36, 8, 96, 49*
1 King's Bench Walk, London EC4
p938 . . . . . 020 7936 1500

Turner, Mr James M BA(Dunelm); LM(Tubingen); MIL I *Jul 1990*
11, 35, 3, 24
Quadrant Chambers, London EC4
p948 . . . . . 020 7583 4444

Turner, Mr James Paul I *Jul 2001*
10, 20, 67
14 Gray's Inn Square, London WC1
p936 . . . . . 020 7242 0858
Harcourt Chambers, London EC4
p936 . . . . . 0844 561 7135
Harcourt Chambers, Oxford
p989 . . . . . 0844 561 7135

Turner, Mr Jonathan MA(Cantab) G *Feb 1982*
13 Old Square Chambers, London WC2
p945 . . . . . 020 7831 4445
Exchange Chambers, Manchester
p983 . . . . . 0161 833 2722
Exchange Chambers, Liverpool
p980 . . . . . 0151 236 7747
Exchange Chambers, Leeds
p977 . . . . . 0113 203 1970
6 King's Bench Walk, London EC4
p939 . . . . . 020 7583 0410
Argent Chambers, London WC2
p923 . . . . . 020 7556 5500
5 St Andrew's Hill, London EC4
p950 . . . . . 020 7332 5400
Monckton Chambers, London WC1
p942 . . . . . 020 7405 7211

TURNER, Dr Justin John PhD(Cantab); AFrc DipLaw; Vet Med(Lond) M *Nov 1992*
(Q.C.) *13, 3, 19, 44*
3 New Square, London WC2
p943 . . . . . 020 7405 1111

TURNER, Mr Justyn I *Jan 2001*
4 King's Bench Walk, London EC4
p939 . . . . . 020 7822 7000

TURNER, Mr Mark G BA(Oxon); Recorder G *Jul 1981*
(Q.C.) *30, 24, 84, 27, 46*
Crown Office Chambers, London EC4
p929 . . . . . 020 7797 8100

Turner, Mr Mathew G *Oct 2003*
15, 25, 62, 70, 71, 72, 80, 94
15 New Bridge Street Chambers, London EC4
p943 . . . . . 020 7842 1900

TURNER, Miss Nicola LLB(Hons) G *Nov 1995*
20, 10
7 Harrington Street Chambers, Liverpool
p981 . . . . . 0151 242 0707

TURNER, Mr Paul I *Nov 1998*
51, 23, 10, 20
10 King's Bench Walk, London EC4
p940 . . . . . 020 7353 7742

Turner, Mrs Taryn Jones LLB G *Feb 1990*
Park Court Chambers, Leeds
p978 . . . . . 0113 243 3277

TURNEY, Mr Richard G *Jan 2007*
1, 46, 31, 93
Landmark Chambers, London EC4
p941 . . . . . 020 7430 1221

TURNILL, Mr Evan LLB(Hons) G *Sep 2003*
Pallant Chambers, Chichester
p974 . . . . . 01243 784538

Turrall-Clarke, Mr Robert MA(Oxon); AInstArb M *Jun 1971*
31, 26
Mayfair Chambers, London W1
p942 . . . . . 01428 681666

TURTON, Mr Andrew Philip LLB M *Jul 1977*
Carmelite Chambers, London EC4
p927 . . . . . 020 7936 6300

TURTON, Mr Philip G *Nov 1989*
30, 40, 53
Ropewalk Chambers, Nottingham
p989 . . . . . 0115 947 2581

TURTON, Robin I *Jan 1996*
Fountain Chambers, Middlesbrough
p986 . . . . . 01642 804040

TUTT, Mr Richard LLB M *Jul 2000*
12, 15, 18, 30
Pump Court Chambers, Swindon
p993 . . . . . 01793 539899
Pump Court Chambers, Winchester
p994 . . . . . 01962 868161
Pump Court Chambers, London EC4
p947 . . . . . 020 7353 0711

Tuttiett, Miss Emily LLB G *Oct 2004*
12, 15, 20, 30
9 Park Place, Cardiff
p973 . . . . . 029 2038 2731

Tweedy, Miss Laura LLB(Hons) L *Jan 2007*
88, 22, 51, 93, 37
Hardwicke, London WC2
p936 . . . . . 020 7242 2523

Twigger, Mr Andrew Mark BA(Oxon) I *Nov 1994*
6, 8, 11, 29, 32, 37, 24, 40
3 Stone Buildings, London WC2
p951 . . . . . 020 7242 4937

Twist, Mr Stephen M *Jul 1979*
York Chambers, York
p995 . . . . . 01904 620048
York Chambers, Newcastle upon Tyne
p987 . . . . . 0191 206 4677

Twomey, Mr Mark James LLB(Bris) I *Nov 1990*
10, 20, 88
Coram Chambers, London EC1
p929 . . . . . 020 7092 3700

Twomlow, Mr Richard MA(Cantab); Recorder G *Jul 1976*
15
9 Park Place, Cardiff
p973 . . . . . 029 2038 2731

TWYDELL, Ms Cherry BA(Hons) M *Jun 1985*
10, 20, 89, 36, 37, 32
Trinity Chambers, Chelmsford
p974 . . . . . 01245 605040

Tyack, Mr David MA(Oxon) M *Nov 1994*
53, 30, 40, 68, 94
Exchange Chambers, Manchester
p983 . . . . . 0161 833 2722
Exchange Chambers, Liverpool
p980 . . . . . 0151 236 7747
Exchange Chambers, Leeds
p977 . . . . . 0113 203 1970
No5 Chambers, Bristol
p971 . . . . . 0845 210 5555
No5 Chambers, London EC4
p944 . . . . . 0845 210 5555
No5 Chambers, Birmingham
p968 . . . . . 0845 210 5555

Tyers-Smith, Mr Peter LLB(Hons); LPC L *Nov 2005*
5, 6, 8, 11, 97, 67, 38, 24, 88, 29, 93
No5 Chambers, Bristol
p971 . . . . . 0845 210 5555
No5 Chambers, London EC4
p944 . . . . . 0845 210 5555
No5 Chambers, Birmingham
p968 . . . . . 0845 210 5555

TYLER, Katherine I *Jan 2009*
15
9-12 Bell Yard Chambers, London WC2
p926 . . . . . 020 7400 1800

Tyler, Mr Paul M *Jan 1997*
St Johns Buildings, Preston
p990 . . . . . 01772 256100
St Johns Buildings, Chester
p974 . . . . . 01244 323070
St Johns Buildings, Manchester
p985 . . . . . 0161 214 1500
St Johns Buildings, Liverpool
p982 . . . . . 0151 243 6000

Tyler, Ms Sarah BSc(Bristol) I *Oct 2009*
10, 20
Coram Chambers, London EC1
p929 . . . . . 020 7092 3700

Tyler, Mr Thomas LLB(Hons) L *Oct 1996*
10, 20
4 Brick Court Chambers, London EC4
p927 . . . . . 020 7832 3200

Tyler, Mr William J BA(Hons)(Oxon); MA(Oxon) I *Jan 1996*
10, 12, 15, 20, 30, 22
36 Bedford Row, London WC1
p925 . . . . . 020 7421 8000

Tyrell, Mr Glen LLB I *Jul 1977*
8, 12, 24, 40, 30
Four New Square, London WC2
p943 . . . . . 020 7822 2000

TYRELL, Mr Richard G *Oct 1993*
84, 18
Crown Office Chambers, London EC4
p929 . . . . . 020 7797 8100

Tyson, Mr Richard BA(Exon) I *Nov 1975*
7, 8, 10, 12, 18, 20, 22, 23, 30, 36
3PB, Bristol
p971 . . . . . 0117 928 1520

Tyson, Thomas David LLB(Hons) G *Oct 1995*
22, 30
Zenith Chambers, Leeds
p979 . . . . . 0113 245 5438

Tythcott, Ms Elisabeth LLB(Huddersfield) I *Nov 1989*
1, 6, 8, 11, 13, 22, 29, 32, 37
18 St John Street Chambers, Manchester
p985 . . . . . 0161 278 1800

TYZACK, Mr William M *Jan 2007*
10, 20
Queen Elizabeth Buildings, London EC4
p948 . . . . . 020 7797 7837

Uberoi, Mr Michael M *Jun 2004*
1, 18, 30, 84, 81
Outer Temple Chambers, London WC2
p945 . . . . . 020 7353 6381

Udom, Miss Ini L *Jan 2002*
15, 62
5 St Andrew's Hill, London EC4
p950 . . . . . 020 7332 5400

Uduje, Mr Benjamin Elliot LLB(Hons) M *Nov 1992*
18, 22, 30, 51, 55, 12, 11
42 Bedford Row, London WC1
p925 . . . . . 020 7831 0222

Uff, Mr David C G *Jul 1981*
6, 8, 11, 47, 24, 29, 5, 22
St Johns Buildings, Preston
p990 . . . . . 01772 256100
St Johns Buildings, Chester
p974 . . . . . 01244 323070
St Johns Buildings, Manchester
p985 . . . . . 0161 214 1500
St Johns Buildings, Liverpool
p982 . . . . . 0151 243 6000

Uff, Mr John F CBE; PhD; BScEng; FICE; CEng; FCIArb; Recorder; Deputy Judge, TCC G *Jul 1970*
(Q.C.) *3, 7, 11, 24, 40*
Keating Chambers, London WC2
p938 . . . . . 020 7544 2600

Ul Haq, Miss Yasmeen LLB I *Jan 2008*
10, 20
Lamb Building, Brighton
p970 . . . . . 01273 820490
Lamb Building, London EC4
p940 . . . . . 020 7797 7788

ULLSTEIN, Mr Augustus Rupert Patrick Anthony LLB I *Jul 1970*
(Q.C.) *12, 30, 40, 24, 48*
Thirty Nine Essex Street, London WC2
p932 . . . . . 020 7832 1111

Ulyatt, Mr Craig Owen L *Jul 2008*
Fountain Court Chambers, London EC4
p934 . . . . . 020 7583 3335

Ume, Mr Cyril Obiora LLB(Lond); ACIArb L *Jul 1972*
12, 15, 11, 3, 6, 20, 18, 33, 35, 23
12 Old Square, London WC2
p945 . . . . . 020 7404 0875

Underhill, Ms Allison LLB(Hons) G *Oct 1997*
10, 20
East Anglian Chambers, Norwich
p988 . . . . . 01603 617351
East Anglian Chambers, Colchester
p975 . . . . . 01206 572756
East Anglian Chambers, Chelmsford
p973 . . . . . 01245 215660
East Anglian Chambers, Ipswich
p976 . . . . . 01473 214481

Underhill, Mr Gareth L *Oct 1995*
15, 62
4 Breams Buildings, London EC4
p927 . . . . . 020 7092 1900

Underhill, Mr Jonathan I *Jan 2008*
12, 15, 20, 23
Temple Chambers, Newport
p988 . . . . . 01633 267403 / 255855
Temple Chambers, Cardiff
p973 . . . . . 029 2039 7364

UNDERWOOD, Mr Ashley Grenville LLB(Lond) G *Jul 1976*
(Q.C.) *1, 26, 93*
Landmark Chambers, London EC4
p941 . . . . . 020 7430 1221

Underwood, Mr Dean MA(Oxon); LLB(Wales) M *Oct 2002*
22, 93, 1
Hardwicke, London WC2
p936 . . . . . 020 7242 2523

Underwood, Mr Robert A BA(De Montfort) L *Jul 1986*
12, 15, 26
36 Bedford Row, London WC1
p925 . . . . . 020 7421 8000

Unigwe, Mr Sylvester Emefiena ACII; LLB(Hons) L *Jan 1972*
Chancery Chambers, London WC2
p928 . . . . . 020 7405 6879

UNSWORTH, Mr Ian LLB(Hons) L *Oct 1992*
(Q.C.) *15, 62, 56*
7 Harrington Street Chambers, Liverpool
p981 . . . . . 0151 242 0707

UNTERHALTER, Mr David SC; MA(Cantab); LLB(Wits); BCL(Oxon) G *Jan 2009*
11, 44, 1, 3
Monckton Chambers, London WC1
p942 . . . . . 020 7405 7211

Unthank, Miss Nina M *Jul 2001*
12, 18, 53, 13, 16, 11, 50, 24, 30, 40, 56
2 Temple Gardens, London EC4
p952 . . . . . 020 7822 1200

UNWIN, Mr Greg M *Jan 2008*
15, 62, 95
187 Fleet Street, London EC4
p933 . . . . . 020 7430 7430

Upex, Prof Robert M *Jul 1973*
18
Old Square Chambers, Bristol
p971 . . . . . 0117 930 5100
Old Square Chambers, London WC1
p945 . . . . . 020 7269 0300

UPSON, Mr Michael James LLB L *Oct 1993*
12, 15
Bank House Chambers, Sheffield
p991 . . . . . 0114 275 1223

UPTON, Mr Alexander L *Jan 2004*
15, 62
23 Essex Street, London WC2
p932 . . . . . 020 7413 0353

UPTON, Mr John G *Jan 1998*
4 King's Bench Walk, London EC4
p939 . . . . . 020 7822 7000

UPTON, Mr Jonathan G *Jan 2004*
8, 11, 12, 22
Tanfield Chambers, London WC1
p951 . . . . . 020 7421 5300

See p1010 for the Key to Work Categories

Upton, Miss Rebecca BA(Hons) G *Jul 1999*
12, 15, 20, 91
Eastbourne Chambers, Eastbourne
p975 . . . . 01323 642102

Upton, Mr William MA; LLM(Cantab) I *Nov 1990*
1, 12, 19, 26, 28, 31, 46, 51, 60
6-8 Mill Street, Maidstone
p982 . . . . 01622 688094 / 688095
6 Pump Court, London EC4
p947 . . . . 020 7797 8400

Upward, Mr Patrick Charles LLB(Hons) I *Jul 1972*
(Q.C.) *15, 42, 62, 63, 70, 71, 72, 82, 83, 91, 94, 95*
Broad Chare Chambers, Newcastle upon Tyne
p986 . . . . 0191 232 0541
15 New Bridge Street Chambers, London EC4
p943 . . . . 020 7842 1900

URELL, Miss Kate LLB; EUR(Hons)(French); LLM(Cantab) M *Nov 2002*
Gough Square Chambers, London EC4
p935 . . . . 020 7353 0924

Urqhart, Miss Catherine M *Oct 2010*
6, 12, 18, 22, 25, 30, 38, 47, 55, 67, 68, 84, 88, 89, 93, 97
Ely Place Chambers, London EC1
p931 . . . . 020 7400 9600

Urquhart, Mr Andrew BA(Oxon) M *Nov 1963*
22, 30, 11, 15
36 Bedford Row, London WC1
p925 . . . . 020 7421 8000

Urquhart, Miss Doris BA(Hons) M *Apr 1968*
10, 20
Westgate Chambers, Lewes
p980 . . . . 01273 480510

Urwin, Mr Tom MSc(LSE); BA M *Jan 2007*
Fenners Chambers, Cambridge
p972 . . . . 01223 368761

Usher, Mr Neil M *Oct 1993*
15, 22
Lincoln House Chambers, Manchester
p984 . . . . 0161 832 5701

Utley, Mr Charles M *Nov 1979*
53, 30, 40
42 Bedford Row, London WC1
p925 . . . . 020 7831 0222

Uttley, Mr Stephen BA(Hons) I *Apr 1986*
Park Court Chambers, Leeds
p978 . . . . 0113 243 3277

VAHIB, Miss Ayse M *Jan 2003*
12
Colleton Chambers, Exeter
p975 . . . . 01392 274898

Vaitilingam, Mr Adam MA(Cantab) M *Nov 1987*
(Q.C.) *15, 18, 30, 12*
Albion Chambers, Bristol
p970 . . . . 0117 927 2144

VAJDA, Mr Christopher MA(Cantab); Licence Specialise en Droit European G *Jul 1979*
(Q.C.) *1, 18, 19, 44, 51, 57*
Monckton Chambers, London WC1
p942 . . . . 020 7405 7211

Vakil, Mr Jimmy LLB M *Oct 1993*
15, 12, 20, 22
Staple Inn Chambers, London WC1
p951 . . . . 020 7242 5240

Valder, Mr Paul BA I *Nov 1994*
15
5 St Andrew's Hill, London EC4
p950 . . . . 020 7332 5400

VALENTIN, Mr Ben BA; BCL(Oxon); LLM(Cornell) I *Nov 1995*
5, 6, 8, 11, 12, 24, 29
South Square, London WC1
p950 . . . . 020 7696 9900

Valentine, Mr Donald MA; LLB(Cantab); Dr Jur Utrecht L *Jun 1956*
3, 7, 11, 31, 40, 41, 43, 45, 49, 54, 61, 78, 74
Atkin Chambers, London WC1
p923 . . . . 020 7404 0102

VALENTINE, Justin BSc(Hons) M *Oct 1999*
1, 53, 47, 48, 67, 68, 62, 84, 85, 89, 27, 30, 40, 94
Atlantic Chambers, Liverpool
p980 . . . . 0151 236 4421

Valios, Mr Nicholas I *Jan 1964*
(Q.C.)
No 8 Chambers, Birmingham
p968 . . . . 0121 236 5514

Valios, Mr Nicholas P I *Jun 1964*
(Q.C.) *11, 30, 18, 15, 12, 7, 31, 3*
4 Breams Buildings, London EC4
p927 . . . . 020 7092 1900

Valks, Mr Michael LLB(Hons) G *Oct 1994*
10, 20
Eastbourne Chambers, Eastbourne
p975 . . . . 01323 642102

Vallack, Miss Julie Ann LLB G *Oct 1993*
10, 20
St David's Chambers, Swansea
p993 . . . . 01792 644466

VALLAT, Mr Richard BA G *Oct 1997*
34, 57, 58, 37
Pump Court Tax Chambers, London WC1
p948 . . . . 020 7414 8080

Vallejo, Miss Jacqueline M *Apr 1997*
15, 51
Tooks Chambers, London EC4
p953 . . . . 020 7842 7575

VALLEY, Ms Helen M *Oct 1990*
15, 20
25 Bedford Row, London WC1
p925 . . . . 020 7067 1500

Valli, Yunis LLB(Leeds) L *Jul 1995*
15, 30
No 6 Barristers Chambers, Leeds
p978 . . . . 0113 245 9763

Van Besouw, Mr Eufron LLB M *Nov 1988*
10, 20
Chartlands Chambers, Northampton
p988 . . . . 01604 603322

VAN DER BOSCH, Miss Zoe G *Jan 1999*
15, 62
23 Essex Street, London WC2
p932 . . . . 020 7413 0353

Van Der Haer, Ms Audrey LLB(Hons) G *Oct 2001*
St Johns Buildings, Preston
p990 . . . . 01772 256100
St Johns Buildings, Chester
p974 . . . . 01244 323070
St Johns Buildings, Manchester
p985 . . . . 0161 214 1500
St Johns Buildings, Liverpool
p982 . . . . 0151 243 6000

Van der Leij, Ms Martina BA; MSc; PhD(Lond) I *Jul 2001*
King's Bench Chambers, Oxford
p989 . . . . 01865 311066
13 King's Bench Walk, London EC4
p940 . . . . 020 7353 7204

Van Der Zwart, Mr Mark Andrew LLB(Essex) M *Feb 1988*
15
KCH Garden Square Chambers, Nottingham
p989 . . . . 0115 941 8851
KCH Garden Square Chambers, Leicester
p979 . . . . 0115 941 8851

van Overdijk, Mrs Claire L *Jan 2003*
1, 14, 70, 11, 93, 38, 21, 67, 63
No5 Chambers, Bristol
p971 . . . . 0845 210 5555
No5 Chambers, London EC4
p944 . . . . 0845 210 5555
No5 Chambers, Birmingham
p968 . . . . 0845 210 5555

VAN ROL, Miss Katherine LLB L *Jul 2002*
10, 20
4 Paper Buildings, London EC4
p946 . . . . 020 7583 0816

VAN SANTE, Mr Theodor I *Jan 2009*
21, 5, 81, 97, 38, 40, 45, 62, 41
3 Verulam Buildings, London WC1
p953 . . . . 020 7831 8441

VAN TONDER, Mr Gerard BA; LLB M *Nov 1990*
6, 11, 29
New Square Chambers, London WC2
p943 . . . . 020 7419 8000

Vanderpump, Henry I *Jan 2007*
St Johns Buildings, Preston
p990 . . . . 01772 256100
St Johns Buildings, Chester
p974 . . . . 01244 323070
St Johns Buildings, Manchester
p985 . . . . 0161 214 1500
St Johns Buildings, Liverpool
p982 . . . . 0151 243 6000

VANDYCK, Mr William BA(Cantab) L *Jul 1988*
30, 24, 40, 53, 27, 18, 11, 12
Crown Office Chambers, London EC4
p929 . . . . 020 7797 8100

VANE, Mr Christopher John Fletcher MA(Cantab) I *Nov 1976*
2, 6, 8, 22, 32, 37, 40, 38, 88
Trinity (Newcastle) Chambers, Newcastle upon Tyne
p987 . . . . 0191 232 1927
Trinity (Teesside) Chambers, Middlesbrough
p986 . . . . 01642 247569

Vanhegan, Mr Mark MA L *Nov 1990*
(Q.C.) *41, 73, 50, 19, 45, 13, 52, 96*
11 South Square, London WC1
p950 . . . . 020 7405 1222

VANHEGAN, Mr Toby MA; LLM M *Oct 1996*
22, 23, 1, 51
Arden Chambers, London WC1
p923 . . . . 020 7242 4244

VANN, Mr Harry BA(Hons); BVC M *Oct 2003*
84, 46, 30, 53, 40
Crown Office Chambers, London EC4
p929 . . . . 020 7797 8100

VANSTONE, Mr Grant M *Jan 1988*
15, 62, 95
187 Fleet Street, London EC4
p933 . . . . 020 7430 7430

VANSTONE, Miss Rebecca I *Jan 2006*
15, 62
23 Essex Street, London WC2
p932 . . . . 020 7413 0353

Vardon, Mr Richard LLB(B'ham) G *Nov 1985*
15, 30, 18
18 St John Street Chambers, Manchester
p985 . . . . 0161 278 1800

VARLE, Miss Stephanie L *Jul 2009*
15, 12, 89, 67
Kenworthy's Chambers, Manchester
p984 . . . . 0161 832 4036

Varma, Mr Rahul I *Nov 2007*
Lamb Chambers, London EC4
p941 . . . . 020 7797 8300

Varty, Ms Louise Jane LLB G *Nov 1986*
53, 27, 85
7 Bedford Row, London WC1
p924 . . . . 020 7242 3555

Vass, Mr Hugh BA G *Nov 1983*
15, 91
1 Paper Buildings, London EC4
p946 . . . . 020 7353 3728

Vassall-Adams, Mr Guy M *Nov 2000*
51, 52, 16, 1
Doughty Street Chambers, London WC1
p930 . . . . 020 7404 1313

Vater, Mr John BA(Oxon) G *Feb 1995*
10, 63
Harcourt Chambers, London EC4
p936 . . . . 0844 561 7135
Harcourt Chambers, Oxford
p989 . . . . 0844 561 7135

Vaughan, Mr David MA(Cantab) I *Nov 1963*
(Q.C.) CBE*19, 1*
Brick Court Chambers, London WC2
p927 . . . . 020 7379 3550

Vaughan, Mr Simon P LLB(Hons) G *Nov 1989*
30, 15, 11
Exchange Chambers, Manchester
p983 . . . . 0161 833 2722
Exchange Chambers, Liverpool
p980 . . . . 0151 236 7747
Exchange Chambers, Leeds
p977 . . . . 0113 203 1970

Vaughan, Mr Terence Paul BSc(Hons); CEng; MICE; FCIArb M *Oct 1996*
7, 30
Fenners Chambers, Cambridge
p972 . . . . 01223 368761

Vaughan Jones, Ms Sarah J MA(Cantab) M *Jul 1983*
(Q.C.) *12, 27, 30, 36, 40*
2 Temple Gardens, London EC4
p952 . . . . 020 7822 1200

Vaughan-Neil, Ms Kate BA(Oxon); LLM(Cantab) I *Oct 1994*
4, 11, 12, 40
4 Pump Court, London EC4
p947 . . . . 020 7842 5555

Vaughan-Williams, Mr Laurence LLB(Hons); Advocate (Isle of Man) L *Oct 1988*
1, 58, 8
13 Old Square Chambers, London WC2
p945 . . . . 020 7831 4445

Vavrecka, Mr David LLB; LLM M *Oct 1992*
20, 10, 63, 76
Coram Chambers, London EC1
p929 . . . . 020 7092 3700

VEASEY-PUGH, Mr Jonathan L *Jul 2005*
15, 94, 70, 25
Cornwall Street Chambers, Birmingham
p967 . . . . 0121 233 7500

Veeder, Mr Van V MA(Cantab) I *Nov 1971*
(Q.C.)
Essex Court Chambers, London WC2
p931 . . . . 020 7813 8000

Veitch, Mr Steven L *Nov 2007*
KCH Garden Square Chambers, Nottingham
p989 . . . . 0115 941 8851
KCH Garden Square Chambers, Leicester
p979 . . . . 0115 941 8851

Venables, Mr Robert MA(Oxon); LLM M *Jul 1973*
(Q.C.) *34, 37, 36, 29, 8, 9*
15 Old Square, London WC2
p945 . . . . 020 7242 2744

Vencatachellum, Ms Glenda Roxande BA(Law & Criminology) M *Oct 1996*
15, 23
4 Rowchester Court, Birmingham
p968 . . . . 0121 233 2327

Venn, Ms Sarah LLB(B'ham) G *Jul 2002*
30
Hardwicke, London WC2
p936 . . . . 020 7242 2523

VENTHAM, Mr Tony BSc(Econ); BA(Hons); DipLaw M *Apr 1991*
15
Carmelite Chambers, London EC4
p927 . . . . 020 7936 6300

Venturi, Mr Gary M *Oct 1996*
2 King's Bench Walk, London EC4
p939 . . . . 020 7353 1746

Verdan, Mr Alex I *Jan 1987*
(Q.C.)
4 Paper Buildings, London EC4
p946 . . . . 020 7583 0816

Verdirame, Dr Guglielmo I *Mar 2006*
3, 33
20 Essex Street, London WC2
p932 . . . . 020 7842 1200

VERDUYN, Mr Anthony BA(Hons)(Dunelm); DPhil(Oxon); Recorder L *Oct 1993*
22, 12, 47, 6, 59, 88, 93
St Philips Chambers, Birmingham
p969 . . . . 0121 246 7000

Vere-Hodge, Mr Michael G *Nov 1970*
(Q.C.) *8, 15, 72*
King's Bench Godolphin Chambers, Truro
p994 . . . . 0845 308 1551
King's Bench Godolphin Chambers, Plymouth
p990 . . . . 0845 308 1551
3PB, London EC4
p946 . . . . 020 7583 8055
Unity Street Chambers, Bristol
p972 . . . . 0117 906 9789

Vernon, Mr Elliot L *Oct 2001*
8, 6, 11, 15, 18, 30, 32
Two King's Bench Walk, London EC4
p939 . . . . 020 7353 7202 / 7353 3909
No 3 Fleet Street Chambers, London EC4
p944 . . . . 020 7936 4474

Vernon, Mr Robert L *Nov 2002*
12, 30, 15, 18
9 Park Place, Cardiff
p973 . . . . 029 2038 2731

VERNON-ASIMENG, Miss Kathryn BA; GDL M *Jan 2009*
10, 11, 15, 20
St Philips Chambers, Birmingham
p969 . . . . 0121 246 7000

VICARY, Miss Joanna BA(Hons)(Law) M *Jan 2003*
11, 8
9 St John Street Chambers, Manchester
p984 . . . . 0161 955 9000

VICKERS, Mr Craig I *Jul 2008*
10, 12, 15, 20
Trinity Chambers, Chelmsford
p974 . . . . 01245 605040

13

For a range of specialised Legal Services please refer to Section 20

Vickers, Mr Edmund *M Nov 1993*
15, 62
Nine Bedford Row, London WC1
p924 . . . 020 7489 2727

Vickers, Mr Guy BA(Oxon) *M Nov 1986*
5, 6, 7, 8, 11, 12, 24, 29, 32, 40, 37, 30, 53, 67, 84, 93, 88
Exchange Chambers, Manchester
p983 . . . 0161 833 2722
Exchange Chambers, Liverpool
p980 . . . 0151 236 7747
Exchange Chambers, Leeds
p977 . . . 0113 203 1970

Vickers, Miss Rachel *L Nov 1992*
53, 30
Outer Temple Chambers, London WC2
p945 . . . 020 7353 6381

Vickery, Mr Neil MA(Cantab) *G Jul 1985*
King's Bench Chambers, Oxford
p989 . . . 01865 311066
13 King's Bench Walk, London EC4
p940 . . . 020 7353 7204

VIGARS, Ms Anna L BA(Oxon) *G Nov 1996*
15, 84, 46, 26
Guildhall Chambers, Bristol
p970 . . . 0117 930 9000

VILLAGE, Mr Peter LLB(Hons)(Leeds) *I Jul 1983*
(Q.C.) *1, 3, 22, 46, 26, 28, 31*
4-5 Gray's Inn Square, London WC1
p935 . . . 020 7404 5252

Villarosa, Tina BA; LLB *M Jul 1995*
Clerksroom - Administration Centre, Taunton
p993 . . . 0845 083 3000

Vinall, Mr Mark BA(Oxon) *I Jul 2002*
1, 18, 51, 89
Blackstone Chambers, London EC4
p926 . . . 020 7583 1770

VINCENT, Ms Joanna MA(Cantab); Deputy District Judge *M Oct 1998*
12, 30, 40, 24, 67
12 King's Bench Walk, London EC4
p940 . . . 020 7583 0811

VINCENT, Mr Patrick BA(Bris) *M Oct 1992*
7, 24, 30, 40
12 King's Bench Walk, London EC4
p940 . . . 020 7583 0811

Vindis, Ms Tara *I Nov 1996*
30, 20, 70, 53
9 Gough Square, London EC4
p935 . . . 020 7832 0500

Vine, Mr Aidan MA(Cornell); BA(Oxon) *M Oct 1995*
20, 10, 51, 40
Harcourt Chambers, London EC4
p936 . . . 0844 561 7135
Harcourt Chambers, Oxford
p989 . . . 0844 561 7135

Vine, Ms Catriona BA; LLB; LLM *M Jul 2002*
1 Pump Court, London EC4
p947 . . . 020 7842 7070

Vine, Ms Sarah BA(B'ham); CPE *I Jan 1997*
2 Pump Court, London EC4
p947 . . . 020 7353 5597

Vineall, Mr Nicholas MA(Cantab); MA(Pittsburgh) *M Nov 1988*
(Q.C.) *7, 11, 12, 18, 40, 81, 78*
4 Pump Court, London EC4
p947 . . . 020 7842 5555

Vines, Mr Anthony BA(Cantab) *G Nov 1993*
15, 39, 46, 47, 48, 59
Civitas Law, Cardiff
p972 . . . 0845 071 3007

VINEY, Mr Richard BA; LLM(Cantab); Deputy District Judge *M Feb 1994*
7, 11, 18, 22, 30, 40
12 King's Bench Walk, London EC4
p940 . . . 020 7583 0811

Vinson, Mr Andrew BA(Hons) *M Jul 2000*
5, 6, 8, 11, 47, 22, 32, 40, 7, 29, 37, 66, 38, 97, 88, 93
Exchange Chambers, Manchester
p983 . . . 0161 833 2722
Exchange Chambers, Liverpool
p980 . . . 0151 236 7747
Exchange Chambers, Leeds
p977 . . . 0113 203 1970

Vir Singh, Miss Sylvia BEd(Hons); LLB(Hons) *M Jul 2001*
St Johns Buildings, Preston
p990 . . . 01772 256100
St Johns Buildings, Chester
p974 . . . 01244 323070
St Johns Buildings, Manchester
p985 . . . 0161 214 1500
St Johns Buildings, Liverpool
p982 . . . 0151 243 6000

VIRGO, Mr John MA(Oxon) *I Jul 1983*
8, 12, 38, 40, 49, 88, 93, 81, 11, 5
Guildhall Chambers, Bristol
p970 . . . 0117 930 9000

Virk, Sundeep *G Nov 2004*
6 King's Bench Walk, London EC4
p939 . . . 020 7583 0695 / 7353 4931

Vissian, Mrs Hena BA(Hons) *L Oct 2002*
20
Chartlands Chambers, Northampton
p988 . . . 01604 603322

Vodanovic, Vilma LLB *G Oct 2002*
12, 22, 30, 47, 59, 67, 81, 84, 88, 94
Zenith Chambers, Leeds
p979 . . . 0113 245 5438

Voelcker, Ms Harriet BA(Hons) *G Jul 2003*
20
East Anglian Chambers, Norwich
p988 . . . 01603 617351
East Anglian Chambers, Colchester
p975 . . . 01206 572756
East Anglian Chambers, Chelmsford
p973 . . . 01245 215660
East Anglian Chambers, Ipswich
p976 . . . 01473 214481

Vokes, Mr Stephen *L Jan 1989*
23
No 8 Chambers, Birmingham
p968 . . . 0121 236 5514
4 Rowchester Court, Birmingham
p968 . . . 0121 233 2327

VOLLENWEIDER, Amiot BSc(Hons) *G Oct 2000*
10, 12, 15, 20
Chavasse Court Chambers, Liverpool
p980 . . . 0151 229 2030

Volz, Mr Karl *M Nov 1993*
2 Pump Court, London EC4
p947 . . . 020 7353 5597

Von Berg, Mr Piers GDL; BVC; MA *G Jan 2009*
20, 15, 18, 30, 51, 76
36 Bedford Row, London WC1
p925 . . . 020 7421 8000

Vonberg, Mr Thomas LLB(Hons)(Durham) *M Nov 2004*
30, 53
Devereux Chambers, London WC2
p930 . . . 020 7353 7534

VOOGHT, Miss Abbey *I Jan 2006*
4 King's Bench Walk, London EC4
p939 . . . 020 7822 7000

Vullo, Mr Stephen LLB(Hons) *M Oct 1996*
15, 62
2 Bedford Row, London WC1
p924 . . . 020 7440 8888

Wacek, Kim Marie *M Nov 2003*
4 KBW, London EC4
p938 . . . 020 7822 8822
Clerksroom - Administration Centre, Taunton
p993 . . . 0845 083 3000

Waddell, Ms Philippa *L Jan 2004*
St Johns Buildings, Preston
p990 . . . 01772 256100
St Johns Buildings, Chester
p974 . . . 01244 323070
St Johns Buildings, Manchester
p985 . . . 0161 214 1500
St Johns Buildings, Liverpool
p982 . . . 0151 243 6000

WADDINGTON, Mr James Recorder *G Jul 1983*
15, 62
9-12 Bell Yard Chambers, London WC2
p926 . . . 020 7400 1800

Wade, Ms Clare BA; DipLaw *I Jul 1990*
15
Charter Chambers, London WC1
p928 . . . 020 7618 4400

Wade, Mr Ian MA(Cantab) *G Nov 1977*
15, 62
5 Paper Buildings, London EC4
p946 . . . 020 7583 6117

Wade, Miss Rebecca LLB(Hons) *G Nov 2003*
12, 15, 20, 30
Northampton Chambers, Northampton
p988 . . . 01604 636271

Wadge, Mr Richard BA(Hons)(Law) *G Mar 1997*
15, 20
Broad Chare Chambers, Newcastle upon Tyne
p986 . . . 0191 232 0541
New Court Chambers, Newcastle upon Tyne
p987 . . . 0191 232 1980

Wadoodi, Miss Aisha LLB(Newc) *M May 1994*
12, 15, 20
York Chambers, York
p995 . . . 01904 620048
York Chambers, Newcastle upon Tyne
p987 . . . 0191 206 4677

Wadsley, Mr Peter MA; LLB(Cantab) *M Jun 1984*
1, 12, 25, 26, 31, 48
St John's Chambers, Bristol
p972 . . . 0117 921 3456

WAGNER, Mr Adam MA(Oxon) *I Jan 2007*
51, 18, 53, 30, 67, 11, 46, 68, 57, 58
1 Crown Office Row, London EC4
p929 . . . 020 7797 7500

WAGSTAFFE, Mr Christopher David LLB(Hons) *I Nov 1992*
(Q.C.) *10, 20*
29 Bedford Row, London WC1
p925 . . . 020 7404 1044

Waheed, Erum *L Jan 1995*
23
12 Old Square, London WC2
p945 . . . 020 7404 0875

Wahiwala, Mr Amrik *M Jul 2003*
15, 12
East Anglian Chambers, Norwich
p988 . . . 01603 617351
East Anglian Chambers, Colchester
p975 . . . 01206 572756
East Anglian Chambers, Chelmsford
p973 . . . 01245 215660
East Anglian Chambers, Ipswich
p976 . . . 01473 214481

Waine, Lydia LLB *L Jan 2007*
15, 70
1 Paper Buildings, London EC4
p946 . . . 020 7353 3728

Wainwright, Mr Jeremy *G Oct 1990*
15, 18, 25, 36, 62
Lamb Building, Brighton
p970 . . . 01273 820490
Lamb Building, London EC4
p940 . . . 020 7797 7788
Westgate Chambers, Lewes
p980 . . . 01273 480510

WAINWRIGHT, Mr Patrick MA(Oxon) *L Oct 1994*
20
St Philips Chambers, Birmingham
p969 . . . 0121 246 7000

Wainwright, Mr Scott LLB(Hons) *M Oct 2006*
72, 70, 91, 68, 30
2 Pump Court, London EC4
p947 . . . 020 7353 5597

WAITE, Mr Jonathan MA(Cantab) *I Jul 1978*
(Q.C.) *30, 27, 11, 24, 36, 40, 12, 84*
Crown Office Chambers, London EC4
p929 . . . 020 7797 8100

Waite, Mr Kiril *G Jan 1997*
11, 12, 24, 30, 40, 59
1 Chancery Lane, London WC2
p928 . . . 0845 634 6666

Waithe, Mr John LLB(Lond); LLM; MA *L Jul 1972*
11, 12, 13, 15, 19, 18, 22, 30, 23
12 Old Square, London WC2
p945 . . . 020 7404 0875

Wakefield, Ms Victoria *G Jan 2003*
19, 1, 11, 44
Brick Court Chambers, London WC2
p927 . . . 020 7379 3550

Wakerley, Mr Paul LLB(Hons) *G Nov 1990*
15, 36
QEB Hollis Whiteman, London EC4
p948 . . . 020 7933 8855

WALBANK, Mr David MA(Cantab) *I Nov 1987*
15, 62, 34
18 Red Lion Court, London EC4
p949 . . . 020 7520 6000
18 Red Lion Court (Annexe), Chelmsford
p973 . . . 01245 280880

WALD, Mr Richard MA(Edin); DipLaw(KCL) *G Nov 1997*
1, 26, 28, 31, 46
Thirty Nine Essex Street, London WC2
p932 . . . 020 7832 1111

WALDEN-SMITH, Mr David MA(Cantab) *L Jul 1985*
20, 30, 10
29 Bedford Row, London WC1
p925 . . . 020 7404 1044
6-8 Mill Street, Maidstone
p982 . . . 01622 688094 / 688095
6 Pump Court, London EC4
p947 . . . 020 7797 8400

WALDER, Mr Aaron LLB; M Phil *I Jan 2002*
93
Landmark Chambers, London EC4
p941 . . . 020 7430 1221

Waldron, Ms Lorraine *G Jan 2004*
20, 10
1 Pump Court, London EC4
p947 . . . 020 7842 7070

Waldron, Mr William F LLB(Wales); Recorder(2000) *G Nov 1986*
(Q.C.) *30, 96, 56*
Exchange Chambers, Manchester
p983 . . . 0161 833 2722
Exchange Chambers, Liverpool
p980 . . . 0151 236 7747
Exchange Chambers, Leeds
p977 . . . 0113 203 1970

WALE, Elizabeth BA(Hons); PGDipLaw *I Jul 2004*
53, 30, 67, 1, 40, 47
Atlantic Chambers, Liverpool
p980 . . . 0151 236 4421
2 Temple Gardens, London EC4
p952 . . . 020 7822 1200

Wales, Mr Andrew BA(Cantab); LLM *G Nov 1992*
1, 6, 11, 18, 19, 24, 26, 3, 35, 40
7 King's Bench Walk, London EC4
p940 . . . 020 7910 8300

WALES, Mr Matthew BA *I Oct 1993*
6, 8, 11, 32, 37, 88, 93
Guildhall Chambers, Bristol
p970 . . . 0117 930 9000

WALFORD, Mr Philip MMath; DipLaw(City) *L Jan 2003*
34, 57, 58
11 New Square, London WC2
p943 . . . 020 7242 4017

Walford, Mr Richard LLB(Exon) *M Jul 1984*
3, 6, 8, 11
Serle Court, London WC2
p950 . . . 020 7242 6105

Walji, Miss Shabnam *G Jul 2001*
12, 15, 20, 22, 30
Regency Chambers, Peterborough
p990 . . . 01733 315215

Walker, Mr Adam Nigel LLB(Hons) *L Jul 2000*
11, 18, 53, 30, 40
Lamb Chambers, London EC4
p941 . . . 020 7797 8300

Walker, Mr Allister David LLB(Hons) *I Nov 1990*
15
5 St Andrew's Hill, London EC4
p950 . . . 020 7332 5400

Walker, Miss Amelia MA(Hons) *I Jan 2007*
49, 11, 24, 74, 40
Hardwicke, London WC2
p936 . . . 020 7242 2523

Walker, Mr Andrew LLB(Hons) *I Oct 1998*
10, 15, 20, 36, 41
Broad Chare Chambers, Newcastle upon Tyne
p986 . . . 0191 232 0541

WALKER, Mr Andrew Greenfield MA(Cantab); Mediator *L Jul 1975*
5, 6, 8, 11, 22, 29, 32, 37
Ten Old Square, London WC2
p945 . . . 020 7405 0758

Walker, Mr Bruce *G Nov 1994*
8, 9, 11, 22, 29, 32, 37, 40
Exchange Chambers, Manchester
p983 . . . 0161 833 2722
Exchange Chambers, Liverpool
p980 . . . 0151 236 7747
Exchange Chambers, Leeds
p977 . . . 0113 203 1970

Walker, Mr Christopher D B MA(Cantab) *M Nov 1990*
18, 30, 53, 48, 55, 40
Old Square Chambers, Bristol
p971 . . . 0117 930 5100
Old Square Chambers, London WC1
p945 . . . 020 7269 0300

See p1010 for the Key to Work Categories

Walker, Mr Damien L *Jan 2006*
Essex Court Chambers, London WC2
p931 . . . . . 020 7813 8000

WALKER, Mrs Elizabeth BA(Hons)(Dunelm) G *Oct 1994*
20
St Philips Chambers, Birmingham
p969 . . . . . 0121 246 7000

WALKER, Mrs Fiona LLB I *Jul 1998*
20, 10
Trinity (Newcastle) Chambers, Newcastle upon Tyne
p987 . . . . . 0191 232 1927
Trinity (Teesside) Chambers, Middlesbrough
p986 . . . . . 01642 247569

WALKER, Mrs Fiona L LLB I *Feb 1992*
12, 15, 20
Bank House Chambers, Sheffield
p991 . . . . . 0114 275 1223

WALKER, Mr James LLB(Hons) L *Oct 1994*
12, 15, 30
Carmelite Chambers, London EC4
p927 . . . . . 020 7936 6300

Walker, Miss Jane BA(Oxon) M *Jul 1987*
10, 12, 20, 30
St Johns Buildings, Preston
p990 . . . . . 01772 256100
St Johns Buildings, Chester
p974 . . . . . 01244 323070
St Johns Buildings, Manchester
p985 . . . . . 0161 214 1500
St Johns Buildings, Liverpool
p982 . . . . . 0151 243 6000
43 Eglantine Road, London SW18
p930 . . . . . 020 8874 3469

WALKER, Mr Jonathan L *Jan 1997*
Fountain Chambers, Middlesbrough
p986 . . . . . 01642 804040

WALKER, Ms Lucy LPC; CPC; BA M *Jan 2008*
5, 11
Guildhall Chambers, Bristol
p970 . . . . . 0117 930 9000

Walker, Ms Maria-Amalia BA(UCL); MA(City) I *Oct 2003*
42 Bedford Row, London WC1
p925 . . . . . 020 7831 0222

WALKER, Mr Mark J M *Nov 1986*
12, 18, 25, 30, 36, 40, 47, 24, 51, 55, 11, 48
Chancery House Chambers, Leeds
p977 . . . . . 0113 244 6691

Walker, Mr Michael M *Jan 2008*
10, 20, 15, 11, 18, 26, 30, 56, 40, 93
Crown Office Row Chambers, Brighton
p970 . . . . . 01273 625625

Walker, Mr Nicholas LLB(Hons) L *Oct 1998*
15
Exchange Chambers, Manchester
p983 . . . . . 0161 833 2722
Exchange Chambers, Liverpool
p980 . . . . . 0151 236 7747
Exchange Chambers, Leeds
p977 . . . . . 0113 203 1970

Walker, Mr Paul L *Oct 1993*
15
5 King's Bench Walk, London EC4
p939 . . . . . 020 7353 5638

Walker, Pauline M *Jul 2008*
New Walk Chambers, Leicester
p979 . . . . . 0871 200 1298

WALKER, Mr Ronald LLB(Lond); Recorder G *Jul 1962*
(Q.C.) *11, 24, 30, 40, 41, 47, 49, 74, 96*
12 King's Bench Walk, London EC4
p940 . . . . . 020 7583 0811

Walker, Mr Steven John LLB L *Oct 1993*
3, 7, 11, 31, 40, 41, 43, 45, 49, 54, 61, 78, 74
Atkin Chambers, London WC1
p923 . . . . . 020 7404 0102

WALKER, Mr Steven Peter LLB(Hons); DipLP; ACIArb M *Mar 2008*
41
Tanfield Chambers, London WC1
p951 . . . . . 020 7421 5300

Walker, Mr Timothy John MA(Cantab) I *Jul 1984*
12, 30, 18, 40, 11, 8
7 Bedford Row, London WC1
p924 . . . . . 020 7242 3555

Walker-Kane, Mr Jonathan G *Jul 1994*
20
Broadway House Chambers, Leeds
p977 . . . . . 0113 246 2600
Broadway House Chambers, Bradford
p969 . . . . . 01274 722560

Walker-McKevitt, Miss Emma G *Jul 2006*
14 Gray's Inn Square, London WC1
p936 . . . . . 020 7242 0858

Walker-Nolan, Mr Ben LLB M *Mar 2002*
12, 18, 23
Thomas More Chambers, London WC2
p952 . . . . . 020 7404 7000

WALKLING, Mr Tom L *Jan 2001*
15, 62
St Philips Chambers, Birmingham
p969 . . . . . 0121 246 7000

Wall, Mr Christopher LLB(Hons) L *Nov 1987*
10, 20, 96
Becket Chambers, Canterbury
p972 . . . . . 01227 786331
Becket Chambers, Maidstone
p982 . . . . . 01622 230957

Wall, Miss Jacqueline LLB(Hons) G *Jul 1986*
20, 10
15 Winckley Square, Preston
p991 . . . . . 01772 252828

WALL, Mr Mark MA(Cantab) L *Nov 1985*
(Q.C.) *15*
Citadel Chambers, Birmingham
p967 . . . . . 0121 233 8500

Wallace, Mr Andrew LLB G *Nov 1988*
15, 62, 23, 72
No5 Chambers, Bristol
p971 . . . . . 0845 210 5555
No5 Chambers, London EC4
p944 . . . . . 0845 210 5555
No5 Chambers, Birmingham
p968 . . . . . 0845 210 5555

Wallace, Miss Ann LLB I *Jul 1979*
10, 20
King's Bench Godolphin Chambers, Truro
p994 . . . . . 0845 308 1551
King's Bench Godolphin Chambers, Plymouth
p990 . . . . . 0845 308 1551

Wallace, Mr Hugh G *Nov 1993*
15, 25
9 Park Place, Cardiff
p973 . . . . . 029 2038 2731

Wallace, Ms Nicola BA(Hons) I *Oct 2006*
King's Bench Chambers, Oxford
p989 . . . . . 01865 311066
13 King's Bench Walk, London EC4
p940 . . . . . 020 7353 7204
4 Paper Buildings, London EC4
p946 . . . . . 020 7583 0816

Wallbanks, Miss Joanne LLB M *May 1997*
72, 15
Regent Chambers, Hanley
p976 . . . . . 01782 286666

Waller, Mr Richard B BA G *Oct 1994*
3, 11, 24, 35, 4, 5
7 King's Bench Walk, London EC4
p940 . . . . . 020 7910 8300

WALLINGTON, Mr Peter MA; LLM(Cantab); P/T Chairman of employment tribunal G *Jul 1987*
(Q.C.) *1, 18, 19, 24, 26, 55*
11KBW, London EC4
p938 . . . . . 020 7632 8500

WALLINGTON, Mr Richard MA(Cantab) M *Jul 1972*
8, 9, 22, 32, 34, 37
Ten Old Square, London WC2
p945 . . . . . 020 7405 0758

Walls, Mr Kevin Andrew G *Jan 1999*
15, 62
4 Breams Buildings, London EC4
p927 . . . . . 020 7092 1900

Walmisley, Mrs Lisa M *Jul 2000*
47, 67, 81, 24, 29, 40, 8, 11, 56, 97, 38, 89, 5, 6, 74
Kings Chambers, Leeds
p978 . . . . . 0113 242 1123
Kings Chambers, Manchester
p984 . . . . . 0161 832 9082

Walmsley, Mr Alan BSc(Leics) I *Nov 1991*
15
5 King's Bench Walk, London EC4
p939 . . . . . 020 7353 5638

WALMSLEY, Mr James MA(Oxon); GDL(City) L *Jan 2008*
Wilberforce Chambers, London WC2
p953 . . . . . 020 7306 0102

Walmsley, Mr Keith I *Jul 1973*
30, 53
1 Chancery Lane, London WC2
p928 . . . . . 0845 634 6666

Walsh, Ms Annie I *Oct 1993*
Holborn Chambers, London WC2
p937 . . . . . 020 7242 6060

Walsh, Mr Darren I *Oct 1997*
48, 12
Queen Square Chambers, Bristol
p972 . . . . . 0117 921 1966

Walsh, Mr David I *Jan 2007*
Quadrant Chambers, London EC4
p948 . . . . . 020 7583 4444

Walsh, Mr Jack L *Jan 2006*
2 Pump Court, London EC4
p947 . . . . . 020 7353 5597

Walsh, Mr John L BA; LLB; MA I *Nov 1993*
21, 23, 51
Doughty Street Chambers, London WC1
p930 . . . . . 020 7404 1313

Walsh, Miss Kathryn LLB(Hons) M *Nov 2008*
Broadway House Chambers, Leeds
p977 . . . . . 0113 246 2600
Broadway House Chambers, Bradford
p969 . . . . . 01274 722560

Walsh, Mr Kevin L *Mar 2003*
4 Breams Buildings, London EC4
p927 . . . . . 020 7092 1900

Walsh, Miss Martha M *Nov 2000*
15, 23
Westgate Chambers, Lewes
p980 . . . . . 01273 480510

WALSH, Mr Michael M *Jan 2006*
8, 11, 12, 22
Tanfield Chambers, London WC1
p951 . . . . . 020 7421 5300

Walsh, Miss Moira BSc(Hons) M *Jul 2000*
Northampton Chambers, Northampton
p988 . . . . . 01604 636271

Walsh, Ms Patricia C LLB(Hons) L *Nov 1993*
20, 10
East Anglian Chambers, Norwich
p988 . . . . . 01603 617351
East Anglian Chambers, Colchester
p975 . . . . . 01206 572756
East Anglian Chambers, Chelmsford
p973 . . . . . 01245 215660
East Anglian Chambers, Ipswich
p976 . . . . . 01473 214481

Walsh, Mr Peter Anthony Joseph LLB(Lond) M *Nov 1978*
15, 71, 70, 72
15 New Bridge Street Chambers, London EC4
p943 . . . . . 020 7842 1900

WALSH, Mr Peter P BA(Hons) G *May 1982*
15
Trinity (Newcastle) Chambers, Newcastle upon Tyne
p987 . . . . . 0191 232 1927
Trinity (Teesside) Chambers, Middlesbrough
p986 . . . . . 01642 247569

Walsh, Ms Rosie M *Jan 2006*
15, 48, 39, 84, 26, 36, 94
Queen Square Chambers, Bristol
p972 . . . . . 0117 921 1966

WALSH, Mr Steven James Franklin BA; LLB(Cantab) L *Feb 1965*
5, 6, 8, 12, 29, 32, 37, 53, 40
Five Paper, London EC4
p946 . . . . . 020 7815 3200

WALSH, Mr Timothy Edmund BA I *Oct 2000*
8, 12, 93, 37, 88
Guildhall Chambers, Bristol
p970 . . . . . 0117 930 9000

Walters, Mr Edmund BA(Bris); DipLaw M *Nov 1991*
25
King's Bench Chambers, Oxford
p989 . . . . . 01865 311066
13 King's Bench Walk, London EC4
p940 . . . . . 020 7353 7204

Walters, Mr Geraint W LLB(Wales); Recorder G *Nov 1981*
12, 15, 18
Angel Chambers, Swansea
p992 . . . . . 01792 464623

Walters, Mr Graham MA(Oxon) G *Apr 1986*
11, 17, 22, 25, 29, 31, 18, 26
Civitas Law, Cardiff
p972 . . . . . 0845 071 3007

Walters, Mr John Latimer MA(Oxon) M *Jul 1977*
(Q.C.) *34, 57, 58*
Gray's Inn Tax Chambers, London WC1
p936 . . . . . 020 7242 2642

Walters, Mr Jonathan LLB(Wales) I *Jul 1984*
12, 18, 25, 30, 36, 55
Civitas Law, Cardiff
p972 . . . . . 0845 071 3007

Walters, Miss Vivian BA(Hons)(Leics) M *Nov 1991*
15
5 St Andrew's Hill, London EC4
p950 . . . . . 020 7332 5400

Walthall, Mr Arron I *Jan 2005*
Cobden House Chambers, Manchester
p983 . . . . . 0161 833 6000

Walton, Mr Alastair H BA(Oxon) L *Jul 1977*
Maitland Chambers, London WC2
p941 . . . . . 020 7406 1200

Walton, Miss Carolyn Margery LLM(Lond); Accredited Mediator G *Jul 1980*
5, 6, 7, 11
Maitland Chambers, London WC2
p941 . . . . . 020 7406 1200

WALTON, Mr Robert MA(Hons)DipLaw L *Jan 1999*
Landmark Chambers, London EC4
p941 . . . . . 020 7430 1221

Warburton, Ms Julie LLB(Lond) M *Oct 1993*
15
KCH Garden Square Chambers, Nottingham
p989 . . . . . 0115 941 8851
KCH Garden Square Chambers, Leicester
p979 . . . . . 0115 941 8851

Warby, Mr Mark MA(Oxon) G *Nov 1981*
(Q.C.) *16, 13, 11, 36, 50, 51, 56*
5RB, London WC1
p948 . . . . . 020 7242 2902

WARD, Miss Alexandra L *Jul 2000*
15
9-12 Bell Yard Chambers, London WC2
p926 . . . . . 020 7400 1800

Ward, Mr Andrew John BA; BCL(Oxon) M *Jul 2000*
30, 11
Exchange Chambers, Manchester
p983 . . . . . 0161 833 2722
Exchange Chambers, Liverpool
p980 . . . . . 0151 236 7747
Exchange Chambers, Leeds
p977 . . . . . 0113 203 1970

WARD, Ms Anne G *Nov 1997*
12, 15, 20, 32
Pump Court Chambers, Swindon
p993 . . . . . 01793 539899
Pump Court Chambers, Winchester
p994 . . . . . 01962 868161
Pump Court Chambers, London EC4
p947 . . . . . 020 7353 0711

WARD, Mr David L *Jul 2004*
39 Park Square, Leeds
p978 . . . . . 0113 245 6633

WARD, Miss Galina BA(Hons)(Law with German Law) G *Mar 2000*
1, 12, 22, 51, 23, 40, 30
Landmark Chambers, London EC4
p941 . . . . . 020 7430 1221

Ward, Mr Henry MEng M *Nov 2000*
13, 50
8 New Square, London WC2
p943 . . . . . 020 7405 4321

Ward, Mr Johnny L *Jan 2007*
Kings Chambers, Leeds
p978 . . . . . 0113 242 1123
Kings Chambers, Manchester
p984 . . . . . 0161 832 9082

WARD, Miss Kelly M *Jan 2001*
20
Pallant Chambers, Chichester
p974 . . . . . 01243 784538

Ward, Mr Martin BA(Warw) L *Oct 1992*
12, 18, 20
Guildford Chambers, Guildford
p975 . . . . . 01483 539131

13

Ward, Mr Peter LLB(Lond) I *Oct 1996*
18
Chambers of Mr Peter Ward, London WC2
p953 . . . . . 020 3402 2152

Ward, Mr Robert L *Jan 2007*
15 New Bridge Street Chambers, London EC4
p943 . . . . . 020 7842 1900

WARD, Mr Simon John LLB(B'ham); Recorder I *Jul 1986*
15, 62
St Philips Chambers, Birmingham
p969 . . . . . 0121 246 7000

Ward, Mr Simon K M *Nov 1984*
15, 34, 46, 62, 84
Argent Chambers, London WC2
p923 . . . . . 020 7556 5500

WARD, Mr Tim MA(Oxon) G *Oct 1994*
(Q.C.) *1, 11, 19, 23, 51, 46, 57, 44*
Monckton Chambers, London WC1
p942 . . . . . 020 7405 7211

Ward, Mr Trevor LLB(CNAA); MSc(Lond) M *Apr 1991*
26, 31
12 College Place, Southampton
p992 . . . . . 023 8032 0320

Ward, Mr Vincent M *Jan 1998*
New Court Chambers, Newcastle upon Tyne
p987 . . . . . 0191 232 1980

WARDELL, Mr John LLB(Exon); M Phil(Cantab) G *Jul 1979*
(Q.C.) *11, 22, 40, 18*
Wilberforce Chambers, London WC2
p953 . . . . . 020 7306 0102

Wardlow, Mr John G *Jul 1971*
30, 12, 10, 20, 40
East Anglian Chambers, Norwich
p988 . . . . . 01603 617351
East Anglian Chambers, Ipswich
p976 . . . . . 01473 214481
East Anglian Chambers, Colchester
p975 . . . . . 01206 572756
East Anglian Chambers, Chelmsford
p973 . . . . . 01245 215660

Warne, Mr Peter I *Oct 1993*
15, 25, 36
Lincoln House Chambers, Manchester
p984 . . . . . 0161 832 5701

WARNER, Mr Anthony Charles Broughton G *Jul 1979*
Citadel Chambers, Birmingham
p967 . . . . . 0121 233 8500

WARNER, Mr David LLB(Hons) G *Oct 1996*
11, 40, 88, 93
St Philips Chambers, Birmingham
p969 . . . . . 0121 246 7000

WARNER, Mr Malcolm BSc L *Jul 1979*
8, 11, 29, 32, 37, 93, 97, 88
Guildhall Chambers, Bristol
p970 . . . . . 0117 930 9000

Warner, Miss Pamela BA(Hons)(Law) G *Feb 1985*
10
Coram Chambers, London EC1
p929 . . . . . 020 7092 3700

Warnock, Mr Andrew BA(Cantab) I *Nov 1993*
26, 30, 40, 24, 10, 76, 53, 51, 85
1 Chancery Lane, London WC2
p928 . . . . . 0845 634 6666

Warnock-Smith, Mrs Shan LLM(Lond) G *Jul 1971*
(Q.C.) *8, 9, 14, 32, 34, 37, 96*
5 Stone Buildings, London WC2
p951 . . . . . 020 7242 6201

Warren, Miss Camille EMA; BA I *Jan 2008*
1, 15, 22, 51, 23
Garden Court North Chambers, Manchester
p983 . . . . . 0161 236 1840

WARREN, Mr Michael MA(Oxon) M *Nov 1971*
6, 8, 10, 12, 15, 20, 22, 30
1 King's Bench Walk, London EC4
p938 . . . . . 020 7936 1500

Warren, Mr Philip G *May 1988*
15, 62, 48, 84, 36
Queen Square Chambers, Bristol
p972 . . . . . 0117 921 1966

WARREN, Mr Rupert BA(Oxon); DipLaw(City) G *Oct 1994*
1, 2, 22, 26, 28, 31, 36
Landmark Chambers, London EC4
p941 . . . . . 020 7430 1221

Warrender, Ms Nichola Mary LLB(Bris); BA(Hons) I *Nov 1995*
11, 24, 5, 40, 18, 59, 89, 30
Quadrant Chambers, London EC4
p948 . . . . . 020 7583 4444

Warrents, Daniel L *Oct 2010*
49, 41, 3, 5, 6, 8, 9, 11, 97, 67, 69, 78, 81, 62, 38, 21, 89, 96, 79, 29, 86, 32, 40, 43, 56, 37
XXIV Old Buildings, London WC2
p944 . . . . . 020 7691 2424

Warrick, Mr Paul Terence Philip I *Jul 1972*
11, 12, 26, 35, 67
Law Office of Paul Warrick, London SW10
p953 . . . . . 020 7795 1122

Warrington, Mr John L *Jul 2000*
15
5 St Andrew's Hill, London EC4
p950 . . . . . 020 7332 5400

Warshaw, Mr Justin MA(Oxon) G *Nov 1995*
20, 10
1 Hare Court, London EC4
p936 . . . . . 020 7797 7070

Warwick, Ms Joanna L *Jan 2004*
15
QEB Hollis Whiteman, London EC4
p948 . . . . . 020 7933 8855

WASS, Krystelle I *Mar 2007*
15, 23, 51
10 King's Bench Walk, London EC4
p940 . . . . . 020 7353 7742

Wass, Miss Sasha G *Nov 1981*
(Q.C.) *15, 62, 36*
6 King's Bench Walk, London EC4
p939 . . . . . 020 7583 0410

Wastall, Mr Andrew BA(Hons); LLB(Hons) G *Oct 2005*
Park Court Chambers, Leeds
p978 . . . . . 0113 243 3277

Wastall, Mrs Rebecca L *Oct 2002*
15
East Anglian Chambers, Norwich
p988 . . . . . 01603 617351
East Anglian Chambers, Colchester
p975 . . . . . 01206 572756
East Anglian Chambers, Chelmsford
p973 . . . . . 01245 215660
East Anglian Chambers, Ipswich
p976 . . . . . 01473 214481

WASTELL, Mr Robert BA(Oxon) L *Jul 2004*
1, 53, 12, 18, 51, 23, 27, 30, 40, 55, 56, 36
1 Crown Office Row, London EC4
p929 . . . . . 020 7797 7500

Waterman, Mr Adrian LLB(Hons) I *Jun 1988*
(Q.C.) *15, 62, 51*
11 King's Bench Walk, Leeds
p978 . . . . . 0113 297 1200
Tooks Chambers, London EC4
p953 . . . . . 020 7842 7575

Waters, Mr David Recorder M *May 1973*
(Q.C.) *15, 96*
2 Hare Court, London EC4
p937 . . . . . 020 7353 5324

Waters, Mr John Clough Pupil Supervisor L *May 1974*
20, 10
East Anglian Chambers, Norwich
p988 . . . . . 01603 617351
East Anglian Chambers, Colchester
p975 . . . . . 01206 572756
East Anglian Chambers, Chelmsford
p973 . . . . . 01245 215660
East Anglian Chambers, Ipswich
p976 . . . . . 01473 214481

Waters, Mr Julian P MA(Cantab) M *Nov 1986*
24, 30, 40, 85, 26, 62
1 Chancery Lane, London WC2
p928 . . . . . 0845 634 6666

Waters, Mr Malcolm MA; BCL(Oxon) L *Jul 1977*
(Q.C.) *8, 9, 11, 32, 37, 5, 40, 47*
Radcliffe Chambers, London WC2
p949 . . . . . 020 7831 0081

Waters, Ms Sarah LLB(Hons)(Newc) M *Oct 1999*
15, 30, 62
Thirty Park Place, Cardiff
p973 . . . . . 029 2039 8421

Waterson, Ms Anna I *Jan 2007*
1 Mitre Court Buildings, London EC4
p942 . . . . . 020 7452 8900

WATERWORTH, Mr Michael Christopher BA(Cantab) L *Oct 1994*
6, 8, 9, 22, 29, 32, 34, 37
Ten Old Square, London WC2
p945 . . . . . 020 7405 0758

WATKIN, Mr Toby Paul I *Oct 1996*
93
Landmark Chambers, London EC4
p941 . . . . . 020 7430 1221

Watkin, Mr Tony M *Oct 1998*
St Ives Chambers, Birmingham
p969 . . . . . 0121 236 0863

Watkins, Mr Adam G *Jul 2004*
St Johns Buildings, Preston
p990 . . . . . 01772 256100
St Johns Buildings, Chester
p974 . . . . . 01244 323070
St Johns Buildings, Manchester
p985 . . . . . 0161 214 1500
St Johns Buildings, Liverpool
p982 . . . . . 0151 243 6000

WATKINS, Mr Guy Thomas LLB(Hons) L *Oct 1999*
18, 30, 11, 93
Farrar's Building, London EC4
p933 . . . . . 020 7583 9241

Watkins, Mr Michael L *Oct 2009*
One Essex Court, London EC4
p931 . . . . . 020 7583 2000

Watkins, Miss Rachel M *Oct 1998*
20, 10
Chartlands Chambers, Northampton
p988 . . . . . 01604 603322

WATKINSON, Mr Howard L *Oct 2006*
15
9-12 Bell Yard Chambers, London WC2
p926 . . . . . 020 7400 1800

Watson, Mr Alaric BA(Bris); PhD(Lond) M *Oct 1997*
6, 8, 40, 38
11 Stone Buildings, London WC2
p951 . . . . . 020 7831 6381

WATSON, Mr Antony Edward Douglas MA(Cantab) I *Nov 1968*
(Q.C.) *13, 3, 19, 44, 41*
3 New Square, London WC2
p943 . . . . . 020 7405 1111

WATSON, Mr Christopher I *Jul 2003*
20, 30
St Philips Chambers, Birmingham
p969 . . . . . 0121 246 7000

Watson, Ms Claire LLB L *Nov 1991*
15
East Anglian Chambers, Norwich
p988 . . . . . 01603 617351
East Anglian Chambers, Colchester
p975 . . . . . 01206 572756
East Anglian Chambers, Chelmsford
p973 . . . . . 01245 215660
East Anglian Chambers, Ipswich
p976 . . . . . 01473 214481

Watson, Miss Claire Elizabeth BA(Hons) M *Jan 2001*
27, 30, 53, 12, 40, 68, 85, 36
3 Serjeants' Inn, London EC4
p950 . . . . . 020 7427 5000

Watson, Mr David W M *Oct 1990*
15
St Johns Buildings, Preston
p990 . . . . . 01772 256100
St Johns Buildings, Chester
p974 . . . . . 01244 323070
St Johns Buildings, Manchester
p985 . . . . . 0161 214 1500
St Johns Buildings, Liverpool
p982 . . . . . 0151 243 6000

Watson, Mr Dennis Recorder I *Jul 1985*
(Q.C.)
Lincoln House Chambers, Manchester
p984 . . . . . 0161 832 5701

Watson, Mr Duncan BA(Hons)(Cardiff) I *Oct 1997*
20, 12, 30
Westgate Chambers, Lewes
p980 . . . . . 01273 480510

Watson, Mr Francis Paul G *Nov 1978*
(Q.C.) *15, 84*
Paradise Chambers, Sheffield
p992 . . . . . 0114 273 8951

WATSON, Mr Graham L *Oct 1996*
18
Colleton Chambers, Exeter
p975 . . . . . 01392 274898

WATSON, Mr Hal M *Nov 2002*
15
9-12 Bell Yard Chambers, London WC2
p926 . . . . . 020 7400 1800

Watson, Mr Ian David BA(Brown); JD(Columbia) L *Jul 2005*
8, 21, 32, 37, 58
3 Stone Buildings, London WC2
p951 . . . . . 020 7242 4937

Watson, Miss Isabelle BA(Hons)(Cantab); DipLaw M *Nov 1991*
20, 10
4 Brick Court Chambers, London EC4
p927 . . . . . 020 7832 3200

Watson, Mr James MA(Cantab) M *Nov 1979*
(Q.C.) *27, 30, 18, 12, 40, 1, 53, 85, 68, 96*
3 Serjeants' Inn, London EC4
p950 . . . . . 020 7427 5000

Watson, Ms Kirstie A LLB(Hons) M *Oct 1995*
15, 12, 70, 72
St Pauls Chambers, Leeds
p979 . . . . . 0113 245 5866

Watson, Mr Mark BA(Oxon) G *Jul 1994*
10, 12, 15, 20, 51
6-8 Mill Street, Maidstone
p982 . . . . . 01622 688094 / 688095
6 Pump Court, London EC4
p947 . . . . . 020 7797 8400
KCH Garden Square Chambers, Nottingham
p989 . . . . . 0115 941 8851
KCH Garden Square Chambers, Leicester
p979 . . . . . 0115 941 8851

Watson, Mr Paul BA; Recorder G *Nov 1978*
(Q.C.) *15, 51, 42*
Nine Bedford Row, London WC1
p924 . . . . . 020 7489 2727

Watson, Ms Philippa MA(Dublin); LLB; PhD(Cantab) M *Jul 1988*
Essex Court Chambers, London WC2
p931 . . . . . 020 7813 8000

Watson, Miss Sarah L *Jan 2002*
24, 18, 55, 51, 11, 12
Devereux Chambers, London WC2
p930 . . . . . 020 7353 7534

Watson, Miss Sharon BA(Hons) M *Nov 1994*
15
15 Winckley Square, Preston
p991 . . . . . 01772 252828

WATSON, Mr Tom BA(Hons); MA I *Oct 1990*
15
Chavasse Court Chambers, Liverpool
p980 . . . . . 0151 229 2030

Watson-Gandy, Prof Mark LLB I *Oct 1990*
3, 11, 21, 29, 5
13 Old Square Chambers, London WC2
p945 . . . . . 020 7831 4445

Watt, Miss Katherine Anna Mary BA(Hons); MPhil(Cantab) M *Oct 2002*
Fountain Court Chambers, London EC4
p934 . . . . . 020 7583 3335

WATT-PRINGLE, Mr Jonathan BCL(Oxon); BA; LLB(Stellenbosch) M *Jul 1987*
(Q.C.) *30, 53, 12*
Farrar's Building, London EC4
p933 . . . . . 020 7583 9241

WATTERS, Miss Sarah Louise LLB L *Oct 2007*
15, 30, 94, 20, 67
7 Harrington Street Chambers, Liverpool
p981 . . . . . 0151 242 0707

Watthey, Mr James BA; BCL G *Nov 2000*
49, 5, 11, 74, 24, 40, 35
Hardwicke, London WC2
p936 . . . . . 020 7242 2523

WATTS, Miss Andrea L *Oct 2006*
10, 20, 15, 25, 22
1 King's Bench Walk, London EC4
p938 . . . . . 020 7936 1500

WATTS, Mr Darren BSc(Hons) M *Oct 2005*
10, 20
Tanfield Chambers, London WC1
p951 . . . . . 020 7421 5300

WATTS, Mr Lawrence I *Jul 1988*
Citadel Chambers, Birmingham
p967 . . . . . 0121 233 8500

WAUGH, Mr Andrew Peter BSc G *Jul 1982*
(Q.C.) *13, 19, 3, 44*
3 New Square, London WC2
p943 . . . . . 020 7405 1111

See p1010 for the Key to Work Categories

Waugh, Miss Jane LLB I *Nov 1992*
12, 15, 20
New Court Chambers, Newcastle upon Tyne
p987 . . . . . 0191 232 1980

Way, Mr Ian BA(Lond) I *Nov 1988*
15
KCH Garden Square Chambers, Nottingham
p989 . . . . . 0115 941 8851
KCH Garden Square Chambers, Leicester
p979 . . . . . 0115 941 8851

Way, Mr Patrick BA L *Nov 1994*
34, 57, 58
Gray's Inn Tax Chambers, London WC1
p936 . . . . . 020 7242 2642

Waylen, Mr Barnaby J MA(Cantab) I *Jul 1968*
15
4 Breams Buildings, London EC4
p927 . . . . . 020 7092 1900

Wayne, Mr Nicholas BA(Hons)(Oxon) M *Jul 1994*
12, 18, 20, 15
Argent Chambers, London WC2
p923 . . . . . 020 7556 5500
1 Gray's Inn Square, London WC1
p935 . . . . . 020 7405 8946

Weale, Mr James I *Jan 2007*
6, 8, 97, 44, 37, 38, 24, 88, 40, 32
3 Stone Buildings, London WC2
p951 . . . . . 020 7242 4937

Weatherby, Mr Peter BSc(Hons) G *Nov 1992*
15, 1, 62, 51, 82, 72, 70, 36
Garden Court North Chambers, Manchester
p983 . . . . . 0161 236 1840

WEATHERILL, Mr Bernard BA(Law) G *Nov 1974*
(Q.C.) *5, 8, 11, 29, 32, 40, 37*
Pallant Chambers, Chichester
p974 . . . . . 01243 784538
Enterprise Chambers, London WC2
p931 . . . . . 020 7405 9471
Enterprise Chambers, Leeds
p977 . . . . . 0113 246 0391
Enterprise Chambers, Newcastle upon Tyne
p987 . . . . . 0191 222 3344

Weaver, Miss Elizabeth LLB L *Jul 1982*
5, 6, 8, 11, 29, 32, 37, 40, 41, 49, 62
XXIV Old Buildings, London WC2
p944 . . . . . 020 7691 2424

WEAVER, Mr Matthew L *Nov 2002*
11, 97, 38, 67, 8
St Philips Chambers, Birmingham
p969 . . . . . 0121 246 7000

WEAVER, Miss Victoria G *Jul 2006*
15, 62, 95
187 Fleet Street, London EC4
p933 . . . . . 020 7430 7430

Webb, Mr Geraint BA(Oxon) I *Oct 1995*
12, 18, 22, 30, 48, 51
Henderson Chambers, London EC4
p937 . . . . . 020 7583 9020

WEBB, Miss Holly MA(Oxon) L *Nov 2006*
15, 27, 36
23 Essex Street, London WC2
p932 . . . . . 020 7413 0353

Webb, Miss Lorraine BA(Hons) M *Jul 1980*
15, 25, 62, 26
Roxwell Chambers, Chelmsford
p974 . . . . . 01245 248341

Webb, Victoria M *Jan 2009*
Old Square Chambers, Bristol
p971 . . . . . 0117 930 5100
Old Square Chambers, London WC1
p945 . . . . . 020 7269 0300

Webb, Mr William BA(Cantab); BCL; LLM L *Jul 2005*
7, 11, 24, 40
Keating Chambers, London WC2
p938 . . . . . 020 7544 2600

Webber, Mr Dominic Denzil Fernandez BA(Hons); DipLaw G *Nov 1985*
15
5 King's Bench Walk, London EC4
p939 . . . . . 020 7353 5638

Webber, Ms Ruth LLB(Bris) L *Jul 2006*
42 Bedford Row, London WC1
p925 . . . . . 020 7831 0222

Webster, Mr Alistair S BA(Oxon) M *Jul 1976*
(Q.C.)
33 Chancery Lane, London WC2
p928 . . . . . 020 7440 9950
Lincoln House Chambers, Manchester
p984 . . . . . 0161 832 5701

WEBSTER, Miss Barbara L *Oct 2005*
15, 62
7 Harrington Street Chambers, Liverpool
p981 . . . . . 0151 242 0707

WEBSTER, Mr David M *Jan 1998*
15
Bank House Chambers, Sheffield
p991 . . . . . 0114 275 1223
Temple Chambers, Newport
p988 . . . . . 01633 267403 / 255855
Temple Chambers, Cardiff
p973 . . . . . 029 2039 7364

WEBSTER, Keith G *Jul 2006*
4 King's Bench Walk, London EC4
p939 . . . . . 020 7822 7000

Webster, Miss Sarah M *Jul 2006*
10, 15, 20
Staple Inn Chambers, London WC1
p951 . . . . . 020 7242 5240

WEBSTER, Miss Shelley L *Jan 2002*
Carmelite Chambers, London EC4
p927 . . . . . 020 7936 6300

Webster, Mr Simon BA I *Jan 1997*
10, 20
1 Hare Court, London EC4
p936 . . . . . 020 7797 7070

Webster, Mr William H LLB(Bris) M *Jul 1975*
8, 11, 40, 47, 38, 88, 26, 29, 32
12 College Place, Southampton
p992 . . . . . 023 8032 0320

Weddell, Mr Geoffrey D A I *Jan 1989*
26, 30, 12, 48, 51, 40
1 Chancery Lane, London WC2
p928 . . . . . 0845 634 6666

WEDDERSPOON, Miss Rachel LLB M *Oct 1993*
12, 18, 24, 30, 36
9 St John Street Chambers, Manchester
p984 . . . . . 0161 955 9000

Weddle, Mr Steven G *Nov 1977*
27, 30, 53
Hardwicke, London WC2
p936 . . . . . 020 7242 2523

Weeden, Mr Ross M *Oct 1996*
12, 15, 25, 23, 94
Bell Yard Chambers, London WC2
p926 . . . . . 020 7306 9292 / 7404 5138

Weedon, Mr Rupert Stuart M *Jan 2006*
10, 15, 20, 12, 18, 94, 30, 88
Eastbourne Chambers, Eastbourne
p975 . . . . . 01323 642102

WEEKES, Miss Anesta BA(Hons); Recorder G *Jul 1981*
(Q.C.) *15, 41, 36, 62, 72, 70*
23 Essex Street, London WC2
p932 . . . . . 020 7413 0353

Weekes, Mr Mark L *Nov 1999*
15, 62, 16
6 King's Bench Walk, London EC4
p939 . . . . . 020 7583 0410

Weekes, Mr Robert MA(Hons)(Cantab); LLM(NYU) M *Oct 2003*
1, 11, 18, 50, 52, 56, 51, 89
Blackstone Chambers, London EC4
p926 . . . . . 020 7583 1770

WEEKES, Mr Thomas Charles BA(Oxon); BCL(Oxon) I *Oct 1995*
Landmark Chambers, London EC4
p941 . . . . . 020 7430 1221

Weeks, Miss Janet LLB(Exeter) I *Nov 1994*
15, 62
5 Paper Buildings, London EC4
p946 . . . . . 020 7583 6117

Weereratne, Ms Aswini BSc; DipLaw G *Jul 1986*
1, 12, 14, 30, 36, 38, 51, 53
Doughty Street Chambers, London WC1
p930 . . . . . 020 7404 1313

Weetch, Mr Oliver M *Jul 2000*
15
1 Inner Temple Lane, London EC4
p937 . . . . . 020 7427 4400

Weetman, Mr Gareth G *Oct 1999*
12, 15, 62, 30, 53
7 Bedford Row, London WC1
p924 . . . . . 020 7242 3555

WEHRLE, Ms Jacqueline LLB L *Nov 1984*
10, 20
29 Bedford Row, London WC1
p925 . . . . . 020 7404 1044

WEINIGER, Noah LLB; Former Solicitor admitted 1969 G *Nov 1984*
1, 8, 10, 12, 20, 22, 23, 26, 32, 36
Renaissance Chambers, London WC1
p949 . . . . . 020 7404 1111

Weir, Miss Claire BA(Cantab); LLM(Harv) M *Sep 1998*
1, 11, 18, 19, 51, 55, 23, 89
Blackstone Chambers, London EC4
p926 . . . . . 020 7583 1770

Weir, Mr Darren LLB(Hons) M *Oct 1998*
15
Stour Chambers, Canterbury
p972 . . . . . 01227 764899

WEIR, Miss Olivia BA(Hons) I *Nov 1995*
12, 20, 30
Bank House Chambers, Sheffield
p991 . . . . . 0114 275 1223

Weir, Mr Robert MA M *Nov 1992*
(Q.C.) *12, 30, 27, 53*
Devereux Chambers, London WC2
p930 . . . . . 020 7353 7534

Weisman, Mr Malcolm MA(Oxon) M *Jun 1961* OBE
15
1 Gray's Inn Square, London WC1
p935 . . . . . 020 7405 8946

Weiss, Mr Alfred GDL; BVC L *Oct 2006*
11, 12, 18, 29, 30, 47, 55, 67
Exchange Chambers, Manchester
p983 . . . . . 0161 833 2722
Exchange Chambers, Liverpool
p980 . . . . . 0151 236 7747
Exchange Chambers, Leeds
p977 . . . . . 0113 203 1970
Zenith Chambers, Leeds
p979 . . . . . 0113 245 5438

Weisselberg, Mr Tom MA(Oxon); DipLaw(City) I *Oct 1995*
1, 11, 18, 40, 41, 50, 55, 56, 51, 43, 81, 5, 3, 52, 62, 89
Blackstone Chambers, London EC4
p926 . . . . . 020 7583 1770

Weitzman, Mr Adam BA; MA(Manc) M *Nov 1993*
30, 18, 15, 26, 62, 76, 53
7 Bedford Row, London WC1
p924 . . . . . 020 7242 3555

WEITZMAN, Mr Thomas BA(Oxon) G *Jul 1984*
(Q.C.) *3, 11, 24, 40*
3 Verulam Buildings, London WC1
p953 . . . . . 020 7831 8441

Welch, Mr Voldi M *Oct 2008*
St Pauls Chambers, Leeds
p979 . . . . . 0113 245 5866

Welfare, Mr Damien Francis John BA; MSc I *Jul 2001*
26, 31, 1
Cornerstone Barristers, London WC1
p929 . . . . . 020 7242 4986

Weller, Ms Sophie G *Jan 2005*
Cornerstone Barristers, London WC1
p929 . . . . . 020 7242 4986

Wellfare, Miss Aimee Mia L *Oct 2004*
15
3 Temple Gardens, London EC4
p952 . . . . . 020 7353 3102

Wellings, Mr Oliver I *Jan 2001*
2 King's Bench Walk, London EC4
p939 . . . . . 020 7353 1746

Wells, Miss Camilla BA(Hons) I *Nov 1998*
20, 10
Crown Office Row Chambers, Brighton
p970 . . . . . 01273 625625

Wells, Mr Casper John Mowlem BA M *Oct 2000*
Goldsmith Chambers, London EC4
p935 . . . . . 020 7353 6802

Wells, Mr Chris I *Jan 2007*
10, 12, 15, 20, 30
KCH Garden Square Chambers, Nottingham
p989 . . . . . 0115 941 8851
KCH Garden Square Chambers, Leicester
p979 . . . . . 0115 941 8851

WELLS, Mr Colin BSc; DipLaw; MA I *Nov 1987*
1, 15, 18, 30
25 Bedford Row, London WC1
p925 . . . . . 020 7067 1500

WELLS, Mr Graham MA(Oxon); Recorder M *Jul 1982*
40, 30, 12, 47, 51, 96
Oriel Chambers, Liverpool
p981 . . . . . 0151 236 7191 / 236 4321
Oriel Chambers, Preston
p990 . . . . . 01772 254764

Wells, Mr Jason L *Jan 2007*
53, 30
18 St John Street Chambers, Manchester
p985 . . . . . 0161 278 1800

Wells, Mrs Jessica BCL; BA L *Jan 2004*
Essex Court Chambers, London WC2
p931 . . . . . 020 7813 8000

Wells, Mr Nathan BA(Oxon); LLM(Cantab) L *Oct 2000*
6, 8, 11, 22, 32, 37
Radcliffe Chambers, London WC2
p949 . . . . . 020 7831 0081

Wells, Mr Nicholas BA(Cantab) L *Nov 1990*
15, 20
1 Gray's Inn Square, London WC1
p935 . . . . . 020 7405 8946

Welsh, Mr James Anthony Kirkman BA(Hons)(Dunelm); DipLaw M *Nov 1994*
10, 15, 20, 62, 1, 42
Nine Bedford Row, London WC1
p924 . . . . . 020 7489 2727

WENBAN-SMITH, Mr Mungo L *Jan 2004*
1, 18, 22
4-5 Gray's Inn Square, London WC1
p935 . . . . . 020 7404 5252

WENTWORTH, Miss Annabel BA(Hons); DipLaw I *Oct 1990*
10, 20
29 Bedford Row, London WC1
p925 . . . . . 020 7404 1044

Wernham, Mr Stewart LLB(Hons)(Lond) M *Jul 1984*
20, 10
Goldsmith Chambers, London EC4
p935 . . . . . 020 7353 6802

West, Mr Colin BA; BCL(Oxon) I *Oct 1999*
11, 19
Brick Court Chambers, London WC2
p927 . . . . . 020 7379 3550

WEST, Mr Ewan MA; DPHIL(Oxon); MBA(Cranfield); LLB(Lond) L *Jan 2006*
1, 19, 26, 44, 55, 57, 60, 61
Monckton Chambers, London WC1
p942 . . . . . 020 7405 7211

WEST, Mr Ian I *Jan 1985*
15
Fountain Chambers, Middlesbrough
p986 . . . . . 01642 804040

WEST, Mr Ian Herbert LLB M *Nov 1996*
15, 12
Bank House Chambers, Sheffield
p991 . . . . . 0114 275 1223

West, Mr John R M *Dec 1965*
8, 11, 2
No5 Chambers, Bristol
p971 . . . . . 0845 210 5555
No5 Chambers, London EC4
p944 . . . . . 0845 210 5555
No5 Chambers, Birmingham
p968 . . . . . 0845 210 5555

WEST, Ms Laura G *Nov 2006*
1, 7, 22, 26, 32
Arden Chambers, London WC1
p923 . . . . . 020 7242 4244

West, Mr Lawrence LLM; LLB; BA; Recorder G *May 1979*
(Q.C.) *12, 24, 26, 27, 30, 48, 51*
Henderson Chambers, London EC4
p937 . . . . . 020 7583 9020

West, Mr Mark MA; LLM(Cantab) M *Jul 1987*
6, 8, 9, 22, 32, 37, 11, 29, 40
Radcliffe Chambers, London WC2
p949 . . . . . 020 7831 0081

West, Mr Mark R LLB(Bris); Recorder; Mediator I *May 1973*
93, 88, 8, 40, 31, 96, 2, 7, 74
Lamb Chambers, London EC4
p941 . . . . . 020 7797 8300

WEST, Mr Matthew MA; BCL; Attorney - New York State M *Nov 2000*
6, 8, 11, 40, 49, 38, 88, 97
Enterprise Chambers, London WC2
p931 . . . . . 020 7405 9471
Enterprise Chambers, Leeds
p977 . . . . . 0113 246 0391
Enterprise Chambers, Newcastle upon Tyne
p987 . . . . . 0191 222 3344

West, Mr Patrick MA(Oxon) L *Jan 2007*
30
St John's Chambers, Bristol
p972 . . . . 0117 921 3456

West-Knights, Mr Laurence James MA(Cantab) G *Nov 1977*
(Q.C.) *11, 49*
Hailsham Chambers, London EC4
p936 . . . . 020 7643 5000

Westaway, Mr Ned L *Jan 2009*
1, 12, 43, 76, 18, 46, 2, 22, 51, 23, 25, 26, 54, 31, 60, 36
Francis Taylor Building, London EC4
p934 . . . . 020 7353 8415

Westcott, Mr David Guy BA(Oxon); BCL M *Nov 1982*
(Q.C.) *30, 53, 40*
Outer Temple Chambers, London WC2
p945 . . . . 020 7353 6381

WESTERN, Mr Adam G *Oct 1997*
15, 48, 51
Citadel Chambers, Birmingham
p967 . . . . 0121 233 8500

Westgate, Mr Martin BA M *Nov 1985*
1, 12, 18, 22, 26, 27, 25, 30, 51, 53
Doughty Street Chambers, London WC1
p930 . . . . 020 7404 1313

WESTLEY, Mr Nicholas BA(Hons) L *Oct 2005*
20, 12, 10
Queen Elizabeth Buildings, London EC4
p948 . . . . 020 7797 7837

Westmoreland Smith, Mr Mark CPE; BPP L *Jan 2006*
1, 12, 46, 25, 26, 54, 31, 36
Francis Taylor Building, London EC4
p934 . . . . 020 7353 8415

Weston, Ms Amanda LLB I *Oct 1995*
23, 1
Tooks Chambers, London EC4
p953 . . . . 020 7842 7575

Weston, Mr James Paul Radovic BSc; MPhil; GDL; BVC L *Jan 2007*
72, 15, 71, 70, 30, 53, 12, 40, 10, 20, 62, 84
7 Bedford Row, London WC1
p924 . . . . 020 7242 3555

Weston, Mr Jeremy LLB I *Nov 1991*
St Ives Chambers, Birmingham
p969 . . . . 0121 236 0863

Weston, Mr Louis L *Nov 1994*
15, 30, 12
3PB, Winchester
p994 . . . . 01962 868884

Westwood, Mr Andrew MA(Oxon); Junior Counsel to the Crown (B Panel) I *Nov 1994*
Maitland Chambers, London WC2
p941 . . . . 020 7406 1200

Whaites, Miss Louise LLB(Hons) G *Nov 1994*
15
1 Inner Temple Lane, London EC4
p937 . . . . 020 7427 4400

Whaites, Ms Louise LLB G *Jan 1994*
15
Exchange Chambers, Manchester
p983 . . . . 0161 833 2722
Exchange Chambers, Liverpool
p980 . . . . 0151 236 7747
Exchange Chambers, Leeds
p977 . . . . 0113 203 1970

Whalan, Mr Mark BA; DipLaw M *Nov 1988*
12, 22, 25, 30, 36, 40, 93, 53
9 Gough Square, London EC4
p935 . . . . 020 7832 0500

WHALE, Mr Stephen DipLaw G *Oct 1999*
1, 11, 18, 19, 51, 31
4-5 Gray's Inn Square, London WC1
p935 . . . . 020 7404 5252

WHALLEY, Miss Alison LLB(Hons) L *Nov 2000*
15
7 Harrington Street Chambers, Liverpool
p981 . . . . 0151 242 0707

Whatley, Mr Paul LLB L *Oct 2002*
3, 6, 7, 8, 12, 13, 22, 24, 26, 29, 33, 37, 38, 40, 45, 47, 48
Cobden House Chambers, Manchester
p983 . . . . 0161 833 6000

Whawell, Miss Leesha L *Jul 2005*
3 Temple Gardens, London EC4
p952 . . . . 020 7353 3102

Wheater, Mr Michael LLB; LLM L *Oct 2003*
8, 11, 49, 74, 38, 24, 40, 93
Hardwicke, London WC2
p936 . . . . 020 7242 2523

Wheatley, Mr Geraint BA(Oxon) G *Sep 2001*
5, 8, 11, 22, 40, 6, 32, 29
Kings Chambers, Leeds
p978 . . . . 0113 242 1123
Kings Chambers, Manchester
p984 . . . . 0161 832 9082

WHEATLEY, Ms Jane G *Jan 2007*
20
Bank House Chambers, Sheffield
p991 . . . . 0114 275 1223

Wheatley, Mr Robin Pearse Recorder I *Jul 1971*
15, 19, 51, 62
Argent Chambers, London WC2
p923 . . . . 020 7556 5500

Wheatley, Mr Simon D J LLB(Brunel); Deputy Judge Advocate Courts Martial M *Jul 1979*
53, 30, 40, 42, 91, 84, 85, 27
7 Bedford Row, London WC1
p924 . . . . 020 7242 3555

Wheatly, Mr Ian LLB I *Nov 1977*
5, 7, 15, 22, 25, 30
Charter Chambers, London WC1
p928 . . . . 020 7618 4400

WHEELDON, Miss Sarah Helen Dip; MA G *Oct 1990*
10, 20
St James's Chambers, Manchester
p984 . . . . 0161 834 7000

Wheeler, Mr Andrew L *Jul 1988*
15, 62
7 Bedford Row, London WC1
p924 . . . . 020 7242 3555

Wheeler, Mr Giles LLM(Cantab); BA(Cantab) M *Oct 1998*
Fountain Court Chambers, London EC4
p934 . . . . 020 7583 3335

WHEELER, Ms Marina BA(Cantab); MA G *Nov 1987*
18, 19, 33, 51, 1, 20, 55
1 Crown Office Row, London EC4
p929 . . . . 020 7797 7500

Wheeler, Mr Richard I *Jul 2004*
3PB, Winchester
p994 . . . . 01962 868884

Wheetman, Mr Alan LLB(Hons) M *Oct 1995*
15
East Anglian Chambers, Norwich
p988 . . . . 01603 617351
East Anglian Chambers, Colchester
p975 . . . . 01206 572756
East Anglian Chambers, Chelmsford
p973 . . . . 01245 215660
East Anglian Chambers, Ipswich
p976 . . . . 01473 214481

Whelan, Mr Christopher LLB; PhD M *Jan 2001*
18
3PB, Oxford
p989 . . . . 01865 793736

WHELAN, Mr Geoff G *Mar 1996*
15
Kenworthy's Chambers, Manchester
p984 . . . . 0161 832 4036

Whelan, Miss Roma LLB G *May 1981*
10, 20
4 Brick Court Chambers, London EC4
p927 . . . . 020 7832 3200

WHIPPLE, Ms Philippa MA(Oxon) M *Nov 1994*
(Q.C.) *1, 12, 18, 20, 22, 27, 30, 36, 53, 57*
1 Crown Office Row, London EC4
p929 . . . . 020 7797 7500

Whippman, Mrs Constance BA; MA(Pennsylvania) G *Nov 1978*
10, 20, 22
33 Bedford Row, London WC1
p925 . . . . 020 7242 6476

Whitaker, Ms Quincy BA(Oxon) M *Oct 1991*
1, 12, 15, 51
Doughty Street Chambers, London WC1
p930 . . . . 020 7404 1313

Whitaker, Mr Stephen L *Nov 1970*
6, 8, 9, 11, 14, 29, 32, 37, 2, 93, 97, 40, 92, 88, 38
No5 Chambers, Bristol
p971 . . . . 0845 210 5555
No5 Chambers, London EC4
p944 . . . . 0845 210 5555
No5 Chambers, Birmingham
p968 . . . . 0845 210 5555

WHITCOMBE, Mr Mark D BA(Oxon); BCL(Oxon) M *Nov 1994*
18, 36, 55, 51
Old Square Chambers, Bristol
p971 . . . . 0117 930 5100
Old Square Chambers, London WC1
p945 . . . . 020 7269 0300

White, Miss Abigail Claire LLB(Hons)(B'ham) L *Jan 2000*
15
5 St Andrew's Hill, London EC4
p950 . . . . 020 7332 5400

White, Miss Amanda G *Nov 1976*
No 8 Chambers, Birmingham
p968 . . . . 0121 236 5514

White, Mr Andrew LLB(Wales) L *Jul 1980*
(Q.C.) *3, 7, 11, 31, 40, 41, 43, 45, 49, 54, 61, 78, 74*
Atkin Chambers, London WC1
p923 . . . . 020 7404 0102

WHITE, Mr Antony MA(Cantab) M *Nov 1983*
(Q.C.) *1, 6, 8, 11, 12, 47, 48, 16, 18, 50, 51, 36, 26*
Matrix Chambers, London WC1
p942 . . . . 020 7404 3447

White, Mr Barry G *Jan 2004*
15, 30, 22, 11, 12
Walnut House Chambers, Exeter
p975 . . . . 01392 279751

White, Ms Ceri G *Jan 2002*
20, 10
4 Paper Buildings, London EC4
p946 . . . . 020 7583 0816

WHITE, Mr Daniel G *Oct 2003*
Citadel Chambers, Birmingham
p967 . . . . 0121 233 8500

WHITE, Mr David BA(Sheff) I *Jul 2009*
Temple Garden Chambers, London EC4
p952 . . . . 020 7583 1315
12 King's Bench Walk, London EC4
p940 . . . . 020 7583 0811

White, Mrs Debra LLB(Hons) G *Oct 2005*
St Johns Buildings, Preston
p990 . . . . 01772 256100
St Johns Buildings, Chester
p974 . . . . 01244 323070
St Johns Buildings, Manchester
p985 . . . . 0161 214 1500
St Johns Buildings, Liverpool
p982 . . . . 0151 243 6000

White, Miss Elizabeth MA(Bristol) I *Jul 2006*
11, 15
East Anglian Chambers, Norwich
p988 . . . . 01603 617351
East Anglian Chambers, Colchester
p975 . . . . 01206 572756
East Anglian Chambers, Chelmsford
p973 . . . . 01245 215660
East Anglian Chambers, Ipswich
p976 . . . . 01473 214481

White, Miss Gemma LLB(Lond); Maitre en Droit(Paris); BCL(Oxon) I *Nov 1994*
1, 11, 13, 51, 55, 89
Blackstone Chambers, London EC4
p926 . . . . 020 7583 1770

WHITE, Helen M *Oct 2001*
10, 20
Renaissance Chambers, London WC1
p949 . . . . 020 7404 1111

White, Ms Helena BA(Hons)(Oxon) M *Jan 2007*
Hardwicke, London WC2
p936 . . . . 020 7242 2523

WHITE, Mr Jeremy G *Jun 1976*
34, 57, 58
Pump Court Tax Chambers, London WC1
p948 . . . . 020 7414 8080

White, Mr Matthew J BA(Oxon) G *Oct 1997*
30, 18
St John's Chambers, Bristol
p972 . . . . 0117 921 3456

WHITE, Mr Oliver BA I *Jul 2001*
5, 11, 18, 29, 55, 50, 97
Littleton Chambers, London EC4
p941 . . . . 020 7797 8600

White, Mr Peter-John BA I *Jul 1977*
8, 12, 20, 22, 30
Chambers of Tanya and Peter-John White, Bedford
p967 . . . . 01234 870004

WHITE, Ms Rachel M *Nov 2000*
15, 68
Kenworthy's Chambers, Manchester
p984 . . . . 0161 832 4036

WHITE, Mr Robert Douglas LLB(LSE) I *Nov 1993*
1, 26, 51, 31
4-5 Gray's Inn Square, London WC1
p935 . . . . 020 7404 5252

White, Mr Robin BSc; ARCS; LLB G *Oct 1995*
18, 30, 11, 12
Old Square Chambers, London WC1
p945 . . . . 020 7269 0300

WHITE, Mr Sasha MA(Cantab) I *Oct 1991*
Landmark Chambers, London EC4
p941 . . . . 020 7430 1221

WHITE, Ms Shelley BA(Oxon); BCL(Oxon) M *Oct 2003*
8, 11, 38, 93
New Square Chambers, London WC2
p943 . . . . 020 7419 8000

White, Mr Steven BA(Hons) I *Jan 1998*
Park Court Chambers, Leeds
p978 . . . . 0113 243 3277

White, Mrs Tanya BA M *Feb 1983*
20, 23
Chambers of Tanya and Peter-John White, Bedford
p967 . . . . 01234 870004

White, Mr Timothy BA(Hons)(Law) M *Jul 1978*
10, 12, 27, 30, 40, 53
Cobden House Chambers, Manchester
p983 . . . . 0161 833 6000

WHITEHALL, Mr Mark LLB I *Jul 1983*
10, 12, 15, 18, 20, 22, 30, 36
Colleton Chambers, Exeter
p975 . . . . 01392 274898

WHITEHEAD, Mr Darron LLB(Hons) I *Nov 1995*
15, 62
St Philips Chambers, Birmingham
p969 . . . . 0121 246 7000

Whitehead, Mr Tom BA(Law) I *Oct 2002*
11, 41, 44, 30, 35, 60, 5
Stone Chambers, London WC1
p951 . . . . 020 7440 6900

Whitehouse, Mr Christopher J BA; BCL(Oxon); BA(Lond) I *Feb 1972*
8, 32, 34, 37, 58
5 Stone Buildings, London WC2
p951 . . . . 020 7242 6201

Whitehouse, Miss Sarah L *Oct 1993*
15, 62, 16, 25
6 King's Bench Walk, London EC4
p939 . . . . 020 7583 0410

Whitehouse, Mr Stuart LLB M *Jul 1987*
Goldsmith Chambers, London EC4
p935 . . . . 020 7353 6802

Whitehouse-Vaux, Mr William Edward Dr. jur.(Bologna) I *Nov 1977*
3, 35, 11, 12
Stone Chambers, London WC1
p951 . . . . 020 7440 6900

WHITEHURST, Mr Ian LLB(Hull) I *Nov 1994*
15
7 Harrington Street Chambers, Liverpool
p981 . . . . 0151 242 0707

Whiteman, Mr Peter L *Sep 1967*
(Q.C.) *34*
QEB Hollis Whiteman, London EC4
p948 . . . . 020 7933 8855

Whitfield, Mr Simon MA(Cantab) L *Jul 2009*
66, 49, 41, 5, 6, 7, 8, 11, 97, 74, 47, 48, 67, 38, 89, 26, 96, 29, 40, 93, 61, 37
Exchange Chambers, Manchester
p983 . . . . 0161 833 2722
Exchange Chambers, Liverpool
p980 . . . . 0151 236 7747
Exchange Chambers, Leeds
p977 . . . . 0113 203 1970

Whitley, Mr Jonathan Denton LLB I *Nov 1993*
12, 15
Castle Chambers, Harrow
p976 . . . . 020 8423 6579

Whittaker, Mr David BA; DipLaw; Recorder M *Nov 1986*
15, 62
Nine Bedford Row, London WC1
p924 . . . . 020 7489 2727

See p1010 for the Key to Work Categories

Whittaker, Miss Isobel I *Oct 2002*
6 King's Bench Walk, London EC4
p939 . . . . 020 7583 0695 / 7353 4931

WHITTAKER, Miss Nadia I *Jul 2007*
30, 12, 11
Crown Office Chambers, London EC4
p929 . . . . 020 7797 8100

Whittaker, Mr Robert LLB(Lond) M *Jul 1977*
15, 31, 25, 26
3 Temple Gardens, London EC4
p952 . . . . 020 7353 3102

Whittaker, Prof Simon BCL(Oxon); MA(Oxon); DPhil(Oxon); DCL(Oxon) L *Jan 1987*
Blackstone Chambers, London EC4
p926 . . . . 020 7583 1770

Whittam, Miss Samantha M *Nov 1995*
14 Gray's Inn Square, London WC1
p936 . . . . 020 7242 0858

WHITTING, Mr John BA(Oxon); LLM(Lond) M *Oct 1991*
(Q.C.) *12, 27, 30, 40, 53*
1 Crown Office Row, London EC4
p929 . . . . 020 7797 7500

Whittle, Dr Henry BSc; PhD G *Jul 1975*
73, 50, 19, 45, 13, 52, 96, 41
11 South Square, London WC1
p950 . . . . 020 7405 1222

Whittle-Martin, Miss Lucia M *Jan 1985*
3PB, London EC4
p946 . . . . 020 7583 8055

Whittlestone, Ms Kim M *Oct 1994*
15
Exchange Chambers, Manchester
p983 . . . . 0161 833 2722
Exchange Chambers, Liverpool
p980 . . . . 0151 236 7747
Exchange Chambers, Leeds
p977 . . . . 0113 203 1970

Whittock, Mr Robert L *Oct 2006*
30, 13, 38, 45
Clerksroom - Administration Centre, Taunton
p993 . . . . 0845 083 3000
Kew Chambers, Kew
p976 . . . . 0844 809 9991

Whyatt, Mr Michael LLB G *Feb 1992*
7, 12, 30, 31, 11, 20, 22
15 Winckley Square, Preston
p991 . . . . 01772 252828

WHYTE, Anne BA(Hons) G *Feb 1993*
(Q.C.) *1, 53, 72, 15, 18, 82, 62, 30, 95*
Atlantic Chambers, Liverpool
p980 . . . . 0151 236 4421

Whyte, Mr James PhD(Cantab); BA(Cantab) L *Oct 2005*
13, 50
8 New Square, London WC2
p943 . . . . 020 7405 4321

Whyte, Miss Monica BA(Hons); LLM I *Oct 1996*
12, 30, 53
42 Bedford Row, London WC1
p925 . . . . 020 7831 0222

WIBBERLEY, Mr James L *Jan 2009*
12, 30, 11, 40, 53, 22, 29
Ropewalk Chambers, Nottingham
p989 . . . . 0115 947 2581

Wibberley, Lucie G *Jan 2005*
1 Pump Court, London EC4
p947 . . . . 020 7842 7070

WICKENS, Mr Simon L *Oct 1998*
15, 20
Maidstone Chambers, Maidstone
p982 . . . . 01622 688592

WICKINS, Miss Stefanie LLB(Hons); LLM L *Nov 1994*
11, 20, 10, 12, 22, 40, 30
Trinity Chambers, Chelmsford
p974 . . . . 01245 605040

WICKS, Mr David BA(Hons) M *Jul 1989*
18, 20, 51
Pump Court Chambers, Swindon
p993 . . . . 01793 539899
Pump Court Chambers, Winchester
p994 . . . . 01962 868161
Pump Court Chambers, London EC4
p947 . . . . 020 7353 0711

WICKS, Ms Joanne BA; BCL(Oxon) L *Nov 1990*
(Q.C.) *5, 8, 14, 49, 22, 29, 32, 40, 37*
Wilberforce Chambers, London WC2
p953 . . . . 020 7306 0102

Wicks, Lucinda M *Nov 2006*
10, 20
Coram Chambers, London EC1
p929 . . . . 020 7092 3700

Wicks, Mr Raymond CIArb I *Oct 1997*
3, 7, 41, 40
Prince Henry's Chambers, London WC1
p947 . . . . 020 7837 1645

Widdett, Miss Ceri L BA G *Nov 1994*
Park Court Chambers, Leeds
p978 . . . . 0113 243 3277

Widdup, Mr Stanley Jeffrey Recorder G *Nov 1973*
8, 10, 12, 15, 18, 20, 40, 26
Guildford Chambers, Guildford
p975 . . . . 01483 539131

Wiggans, Miss Amanda J LLB M *Nov 1986*
15, 10, 20, 18, 30, 3, 35, 12
4 Rowchester Court, Birmingham
p968 . . . . 0121 233 2327

Wigglesworth, Mr Raymond LLB(Manc) G *Jul 1974*
(Q.C.) *15, 30*
18 St John Street Chambers, Manchester
p985 . . . . 0161 278 1800

Wigglesworth, Mr Timothy Robin M *Jul 2007*
30, 32, 47, 48, 88, 93
Broad Chare Chambers, Newcastle upon Tyne
p986 . . . . 0191 232 0541

Wightwick, Mr Iain BSc I *Nov 1985*
12, 22, 26, 30, 88
Unity Street Chambers, Bristol
p972 . . . . 0117 906 9789

Wigin, Miss Caroline Rosemary BA I *Jul 1984*
Park Court Chambers, Leeds
p978 . . . . 0113 243 3277

Wigley, Miss Jenny BA(Hons)(Cantab) M *Nov 2000*
31, 36, 46, 25, 1, 60
No5 Chambers, Bristol
p971 . . . . 0845 210 5555
No5 Chambers, London EC4
p944 . . . . 0845 210 5555
No5 Chambers, Birmingham
p968 . . . . 0845 210 5555

WIGLEY, Mr Joseph M *Jan 2010*
6, 8, 11, 38
4 Stone Buildings, London WC2
p951 . . . . 020 7242 5524

Wigley, Miss Rachel G *Nov 1997*
15
St Albans Chambers, St Albans
p992 . . . . 01727 843383

Wignall, Mr Gordon Part Time Employment Tribunal Chairman G *Oct 1987*
18, 40, 55, 30, 31, 46, 1, 78, 24, 47, 48, 49, 67, 74, 81, 86, 88, 89, 93, 96, 97
No5 Chambers, Bristol
p971 . . . . 0845 210 5555
No5 Chambers, London EC4
p944 . . . . 0845 210 5555
No5 Chambers, Birmingham
p968 . . . . 0845 210 5555

WIGODER, Hon Justin D Phil; MA(Oxon) G *Jul 1977*
15
1 High Pavement, Nottingham
p988 . . . . 0115 941 8218

WIJEYARATNE, Mr Asela Lochana Neville L *Nov 2008*
10, 11, 18, 30, 40, 38, 88, 93
3 Hare Court, London EC4
p937 . . . . 020 7415 7800

Wilby, Mr David C MA(Cantab); Recorder I *Jul 1974*
(Q.C.) *27, 30, 40, 46, 53, 48, 36*
Old Square Chambers, Bristol
p971 . . . . 0117 930 5100
Old Square Chambers, London WC1
p945 . . . . 020 7269 0300

Wilcken, Mr Anthony M *Nov 1966*
15, 25, 36
QEB Hollis Whiteman, London EC4
p948 . . . . 020 7933 8855

Wilcock, Mr Peter LLB(Lond) I *Jul 1988*
15, 30, 12, 36, 51
Tooks Chambers, London EC4
p953 . . . . 020 7842 7575

WILCOX, Mr Lawrence L *Sep 1996*
15, 42, 18, 36
Octagon Chambers, Taunton
p993 . . . . 01823 331919

WILD, Mr Simon Peter BA(Lond) I *Jul 1977*
15, 25
9-12 Bell Yard Chambers, London WC2
p926 . . . . 020 7400 1800

Wild, Mr Steven LLB(Hons) G *Oct 1994*
10, 12, 15, 20, 30, 36
St Johns Buildings, Preston
p990 . . . . 01772 256100
St Johns Buildings, Chester
p974 . . . . 01244 323070
St Johns Buildings, Manchester
p985 . . . . 0161 214 1500
St Johns Buildings, Liverpool
p982 . . . . 0151 243 6000

WILDE, Miss Carmel LLB(Hons)(Manc Met)(Law with French) I *Oct 2004*
10, 15, 20, 30
Chavasse Court Chambers, Liverpool
p980 . . . . 0151 229 2030

WILES, Ms Ellen I *Oct 2007*
Thirty Nine Essex Street, London WC2
p932 . . . . 020 7832 1111

WILEY, Miss Francesca BA(Oxon); MA(Oxon) G *May 1996*
20, 10, 51
1 Garden Court, London EC4
p934 . . . . 020 7797 7900

WILFORD, Ellis G *Jan 2006*
23
Mitre House Chambers, London WC1
p942 . . . . 020 7307 7100

WILKEN, Mr Sean M *Nov 1991*
(Q.C.) *1, 11, 7, 51, 19, 24, 49, 78, 52, 23*
Thirty Nine Essex Street, London WC2
p932 . . . . 020 7832 1111

Wilkes, Miss Alison M *Oct 2005*
15
5 King's Bench Walk, London EC4
p939 . . . . 020 7353 5638

Wilkins, Mr Andrew MA(Oxon) L *Oct 1995*
15, 46, 48, 62
Castle Chambers, Harrow
p976 . . . . 020 8423 6579
Cornwall Street Chambers, Birmingham
p967 . . . . 0121 233 7500

Wilkins, Miss Chloe LLB(Cardiff) G *Jan 2006*
20, 10, 67
Harcourt Chambers, London EC4
p936 . . . . 0844 561 7135
Harcourt Chambers, Oxford
p989 . . . . 0844 561 7135

WILKINS, Mr Christopher BA(Oxon) L *May 1993*
Pallant Chambers, Chichester
p974 . . . . 01243 784538

Wilkins, Mrs Liz L *Mar 1985*
Ellerton Chambers, Dagenham
p975 . . . .

WILKINS, Miss Susan L *Jul 2004*
10, 20, 96, 49
1 King's Bench Walk, London EC4
p938 . . . . 020 7936 1500

Wilkins, Mr Thomas A BSc M *Nov 1993*
15
Atkinson Bevan Chambers, London EC4
p924 . . . . 020 7353 2112

Wilkinson, Mr Francis M *Oct 2001*
Field Court Chambers, London WC1
p933 . . . . 020 7405 6114

Wilkinson, Miss Helen BA(Hons)(Law) M *Jul 2007*
20, 10, 67
Harcourt Chambers, London EC4
p936 . . . . 0844 561 7135
Harcourt Chambers, Oxford
p989 . . . . 0844 561 7135

Wilkinson, Miss Kate M *Oct 1998*
15, 62
6 King's Bench Walk, London EC4
p939 . . . . 020 7583 0410

Wilkinson, Mr Marc L *Oct 1992*
8, 11, 24, 6, 5, 12, 47, 67, 69, 38, 88, 29, 40, 93
No5 Chambers, Bristol
p971 . . . . 0845 210 5555
No5 Chambers, London EC4
p944 . . . . 0845 210 5555
No5 Chambers, Birmingham
p968 . . . . 0845 210 5555

WILKINSON, Mr Michael I *Jan 2006*
8, 11, 88, 67, 38, 40, 37
18 St John Street Chambers, Manchester
p985 . . . . 0161 278 1800

WILKINSON, Mr Michael John LLB G *Jul 1979*
15
Trinity (Newcastle) Chambers, Newcastle upon Tyne
p987 . . . . 0191 232 1927
Trinity (Teesside) Chambers, Middlesbrough
p986 . . . . 01642 247569

Wilkinson, Mr Nicholas M *Jan 2006*
1 Hare Court, London EC4
p936 . . . . 020 7797 7070

WILKINSON, Mr Nigel MA(Oxon); Recorder M *Jul 1972*
(Q.C.)
Temple Garden Chambers, London EC4
p952 . . . . 020 7583 1315

Wilkinson, Mr Paul LLB G *Jul 2001*
30, 47, 48, 88, 93
Broad Chare Chambers, Newcastle upon Tyne
p986 . . . . 0191 232 0541

Wilkinson, Mr Peter G *Jul 2003*
1 Pump Court, London EC4
p947 . . . . 020 7842 7070

WILKINSON, Mr Richard LLB(Hons)(Bris) L *Oct 1992*
Temple Garden Chambers, London EC4
p952 . . . . 020 7583 1315

Wilkinson, Miss Sarah MA(Oxon); DPhil(Oxon) G *Jul 2003*
1, 11, 18, 51, 89
Blackstone Chambers, London EC4
p926 . . . . 020 7583 1770

WILKINSON, Miss Tiffany I *Nov 2003*
10, 20, 89
Trinity Chambers, Chelmsford
p974 . . . . 01245 605040

Wilkinson, Mr Timothy I *Jan 2006*
St Johns Buildings, Preston
p990 . . . . 01772 256100
St Johns Buildings, Chester
p974 . . . . 01244 323070
St Johns Buildings, Manchester
p985 . . . . 0161 214 1500
St Johns Buildings, Liverpool
p982 . . . . 0151 243 6000

Will, Mr Gerhardt M *Jun 2001*
30, 18, 20
7 Bedford Row, London WC1
p924 . . . . 020 7242 3555

Willan, Mr James G *Jan 2006*
Essex Court Chambers, London WC2
p931 . . . . 020 7813 8000

Willard, Mr Neville LLB(Lond) G *Jul 1976*
15, 51
6-8 Mill Street, Maidstone
p982 . . . . 01622 688094 / 688095
6 Pump Court, London EC4
p947 . . . . 020 7797 8400

WILLBOURNE, Miss Caroline BA(Lond) I *Nov 1970*
10, 20
1 Garden Court, London EC4
p934 . . . . 020 7797 7900

Willcock, Miss Rachel BA(Cantab) I *Jan 2008*
11, 18, 30, 56, 40, 93
Crown Office Row Chambers, Brighton
p970 . . . . 01273 625625

WILLCOCKS, Miss Hannah M *Jul 2001*
15, 94, 62
18 Red Lion Court, London EC4
p949 . . . . 020 7520 6000
18 Red Lion Court (Annexe), Chelmsford
p973 . . . . 01245 280880

WILLE, Mr Andrew BA(Hons)(Oxon); DipLaw L *Oct 1998*
30, 53, 18, 11
Farrar's Building, London EC4
p933 . . . . 020 7583 9241

Willems, Mr Marc P BA(Hons); Recorder L *Nov 1990*
11, 12, 14, 24, 27, 30, 35, 36, 40, 53, 56
Cobden House Chambers, Manchester
p983 . . . . 0161 833 6000

Willer, Mr Robert G *Jan 1970*
30, 40, 53
Ely Place Chambers, London EC1
p931 . . . . 020 7400 9600

13

Willets, Mr Glenn M *Nov 2000*
8, 11, 6, 29, 40, 32, 37, 38, 47, 67, 88, 89, 93, 97, 96
No5 Chambers, Bristol
p971 . . . . . 0845 210 5555
No5 Chambers, London EC4
p944 . . . . . 0845 210 5555
No5 Chambers, Birmingham
p968 . . . . . 0845 210 5555

WILLETTS, Mr Andrew LLB M *Jan 1997*
8, 20, 10, 30, 11
King's Bench Godolphin Chambers, Truro
p994 . . . . . 0845 308 1551
King's Bench Godolphin Chambers, Plymouth
p990 . . . . . 0845 308 1551
New Walk Chambers, Leicester
p979 . . . . . 0871 200 1298

WILLIAMS, Mr A John MA(Cantab) L *Jul 1983*
30, 84, 25, 46
Crown Office Chambers, London EC4
p929 . . . . . 020 7797 8100

WILLIAMS, Mr Alexander MA(Cantab) M *Jan 2004*
11, 12, 18, 30, 68, 36, 51, 67, 73, 84, 34, 1
Oriel Chambers, Liverpool
p981 . . . . . 0151 236 7191 / 236 4321
Oriel Chambers, Preston
p990 . . . . . 01772 254764
3 Temple Gardens, London EC4
p952 . . . . . 020 7353 3102

Williams, Miss Alison BA(UCL) G *Oct 2004*
20, 10
Harcourt Chambers, London EC4
p936 . . . . . 0844 561 7135
Harcourt Chambers, Oxford
p989 . . . . . 0844 561 7135

WILLIAMS, Andrew LLB(B'ham) G *Nov 1994*
8, 88, 32, 40, 93, 37
Atlantic Chambers, Liverpool
p980 . . . . . 0151 236 4421

WILLIAMS, Miss Anna LLB(Hons) G *Nov 1990*
10, 20
Trinity Chambers, Chelmsford
p974 . . . . . 01245 605040

Williams, Ms Anne M *Mar 2005*
KCH Garden Square Chambers, Nottingham
p989 . . . . . 0115 941 8851
KCH Garden Square Chambers, Leicester
p979 . . . . . 0115 941 8851

WILLIAMS, Mr Ben L *Jan 2006*
12, 15, 48, 30
St Philips Chambers, Birmingham
p969 . . . . . 0121 246 7000

Williams, Mr Ben D LLB(Newc) M *Jan 2001*
15, 18, 48
Kings Chambers, Leeds
p978 . . . . . 0113 242 1123
Kings Chambers, Manchester
p984 . . . . . 0161 832 9082

WILLIAMS, Mr Benjamin MA(Oxon) L *Nov 1994*
11, 24, 40, 47
Thirty Nine Essex Street, London WC2
p932 . . . . . 020 7832 1111

Williams, Miss Carys Ellen LLB L *Oct 2007*
15, 12, 20, 30, 18, 8
9 Park Place, Cardiff
p973 . . . . . 029 2038 2731

Williams, Miss Cassie M *Jan 2002*
39 Park Square, Leeds
p978 . . . . . 0113 245 6633

Williams, Miss Cerys G *Jul 2008*
10, 20
St Johns Buildings, Preston
p990 . . . . . 01772 256100
St Johns Buildings, Chester
p974 . . . . . 01244 323070
St Johns Buildings, Manchester
p985 . . . . . 0161 214 1500
St Johns Buildings, Liverpool
p982 . . . . . 0151 243 6000

Williams, Mr Christopher P LLB I *Feb 1988*
1, 22, 51, 23
Tooks Chambers, London EC4
p953 . . . . . 020 7842 7575

Williams, Miss Claire LLB(Hons) G *Jan 2004*
12, 20, 10
Thirty Park Place, Cardiff
p973 . . . . . 029 2039 8421

Williams, Mr David B LLB I *Oct 1990*
20, 30, 10
4 Paper Buildings, London EC4
p946 . . . . . 020 7583 0816
Nine Bedford Row, London WC1
p924 . . . . . 020 7489 2727

WILLIAMS, Mr David Henry BA(Hons); Recorder G *Feb 1990*
15
Chavasse Court Chambers, Liverpool
p980 . . . . . 0151 229 2030

Williams, Mr Eifion LLB G *Oct 2000*
20, 10
Temple Chambers, Newport
p988 . . . . . 01633 267403 / 255855
Temple Chambers, Cardiff
p973 . . . . . 029 2039 7364

Williams, Felicity LLM; LLB L *Nov 2000*
1, 15, 70, 51
Tooks Chambers, London EC4
p953 . . . . . 020 7842 7575

Williams, Mr Graeme MA(Oxon) I *Jun 1959*
(Q.C.)
King's Bench Chambers, Oxford
p989 . . . . . 01865 311066

WILLIAMS, Mr Graham LLB(Hons) M *Jan 2002*
30, 12, 62, 96
Oriel Chambers, Liverpool
p981 . . . . . 0151 236 7191 / 236 4321
Oriel Chambers, Preston
p990 . . . . . 01772 254764

WILLIAMS, Mr Greg LLB L *Jan 2006*
18, 20, 93, 22
4 King's Bench Walk, London EC4
p939 . . . . . 020 7822 7000

WILLIAMS, Mr Guy BA(Hons)(Oxon); DipLaw(City) I *Jul 2000*
1, 2, 22, 26, 28, 31, 36
Landmark Chambers, London EC4
p941 . . . . . 020 7430 1221

Williams, Ms Heather LLB G *Jul 1985*
(Q.C.) *1, 12, 16, 18, 22, 38, 51, 53*
Doughty Street Chambers, London WC1
p930 . . . . . 020 7404 1313

WILLIAMS, Miss Heledd Llwyd G *Oct 1999*
20
St Philips Chambers, Birmingham
p969 . . . . . 0121 246 7000

Williams, Miss Helen LLB(Hons) I *Jul 2000*
20, 23
Broadway House Chambers, Leeds
p977 . . . . . 0113 246 2600
Broadway House Chambers, Bradford
p969 . . . . . 01274 722560
29 Bedford Row, London WC1
p925 . . . . . 020 7404 1044

Williams, Hermione M *Jan 2008*
18, 55, 2, 5, 6, 7, 8, 11, 38, 32, 37, 47, 61, 67, 69, 89, 93, 97
No5 Chambers, Bristol
p971 . . . . . 0845 210 5555
No5 Chambers, London EC4
p944 . . . . . 0845 210 5555
No5 Chambers, Birmingham
p968 . . . . . 0845 210 5555

WILLIAMS, Mr Hugh BA(Lond) G *Jul 1992*
King's Bench Chambers, Oxford
p989 . . . . . 01865 311066
13 King's Bench Walk, London EC4
p940 . . . . . 020 7353 7204

Williams, Ms Joanne I *Oct 1999*
12, 26, 30
Civitas Law, Cardiff
p972 . . . . . 0845 071 3007

Williams, Mr John Robert Selwyn LLB; Recorder M *Nov 1973*
15, 62
Atkinson Bevan Chambers, London EC4
p924 . . . . . 020 7353 2112

Williams, Miss Juliet I *Nov 1998*
10, 20
Southernhay Chambers, Exeter
p975 . . . . . 01392 255777

Williams, Miss June I *Jan 1999*
10, 20, 12
No 8 Chambers, Birmingham
p968 . . . . . 0121 236 5514

Williams, Mr Karl LLB(Lond) M *Jul 1982*
12, 15, 36, 30
9 Park Place, Cardiff
p973 . . . . . 029 2038 2731

Williams, Mr Lloyd LLB; Recorder I *Jul 1981*
(Q.C.) *30, 12, 53, 84*
Thirty Park Place, Cardiff
p973 . . . . . 029 2039 8421

Williams, Mr Mark G *Oct 1998*
6, 8, 12, 47, 22, 24, 40, 30, 18, 53, 55, 48
Queen Square Chambers, Bristol
p972 . . . . . 0117 921 1966

Williams, Mr Meyrick LLB(Hons); LLM I *Jan 2003*
15, 62, 46, 84
Argent Chambers, London WC2
p923 . . . . . 020 7556 5500

Williams, Miss Micaila LLB(Hons) I *Jul 2004*
15
East Anglian Chambers, Norwich
p988 . . . . . 01603 617351
East Anglian Chambers, Colchester
p975 . . . . . 01206 572756
East Anglian Chambers, Chelmsford
p973 . . . . . 01245 215660
East Anglian Chambers, Ipswich
p976 . . . . . 01473 214481

Williams, Mr Micheal I *Jan 2005*
2 King's Bench Walk, London EC4
p939 . . . . . 020 7353 1746

WILLIAMS, Mr Neal Moreton LLB L *Nov 1984*
15
St Philips Chambers, Birmingham
p969 . . . . . 0121 246 7000

Williams, Ms Nicola L *Nov 1985*
15, 30
1 Mitre Court Buildings, London EC4
p942 . . . . . 020 7452 8900

Williams, Mr Owen LLB(Wales) G *Sep 2000*
12, 15, 30
9 Park Place, Cardiff
p973 . . . . . 029 2038 2731

Williams, Mr Owen J M *Jul 1974*
15, 51
Nine Bedford Row, London WC1
p924 . . . . . 020 7489 2727

Williams, Mr Paul I *Jan 1994*
Park Court Chambers, Leeds
p978 . . . . . 0113 243 3277

Williams, Mr Philip I *Apr 2005*
1, 25, 31, 46, 72, 15, 71, 70, 94, 11
No5 Chambers, Bristol
p971 . . . . . 0845 210 5555
No5 Chambers, London EC4
p944 . . . . . 0845 210 5555
No5 Chambers, Birmingham
p968 . . . . . 0845 210 5555

WILLIAMS, Mr Rhodri BA(Oxon); DipLaw G *Jul 1987*
(Q.C.) *1, 19, 26*
Henderson Chambers, London EC4
p937 . . . . . 020 7583 9020
Thirty Park Place, Cardiff
p973 . . . . . 029 2039 8421

WILLIAMS, Mr Rhys LLM M *Nov 2007*
88, 93, 22
Five Paper, London EC4
p946 . . . . . 020 7815 3200

WILLIAMS, Mr Robert Brychan James MA; BCL M *Jan 2000*
1, 11, 41, 44, 19
Monckton Chambers, London WC1
p942 . . . . . 020 7405 7211

Williams, Mr Simon LLB M *Jan 1984*
40, 11, 8, 22
Radcliffe Chambers, London WC2
p949 . . . . . 020 7831 0081

Williams, Ms Susan LLB(Bris) M *Nov 1978*
10, 15, 20
Charter Chambers, London WC1
p928 . . . . . 020 7618 4400

Williams, Mr Timothy BA M *Nov 2003*
Fenners Chambers, Cambridge
p972 . . . . . 01223 368761

Williams, Mr Vincent MA(Cantab) M *Jul 1985*
12, 30, 40, 70
9 Gough Square, London EC4
p935 . . . . . 020 7832 0500

Williams, Ms Zillah LLB(Hons) L *Nov 1997*
15
St Johns Buildings, Preston
p990 . . . . . 01772 256100
St Johns Buildings, Chester
p974 . . . . . 01244 323070
St Johns Buildings, Manchester
p985 . . . . . 0161 214 1500
St Johns Buildings, Liverpool
p982 . . . . . 0151 243 6000

Williamson, Mr Adrian J G H MA(Cantab) M *Nov 1983*
(Q.C.) *3, 7, 11, 24, 40*
Keating Chambers, London WC2
p938 . . . . . 020 7544 2600

WILLIAMSON, Miss Bridget BA(Oxon) L *Feb 1993*
5, 6, 8, 11, 29, 40, 49, 38, 88, 97
Enterprise Chambers, London WC2
p931 . . . . . 020 7405 9471
Enterprise Chambers, Leeds
p977 . . . . . 0113 246 0391
Enterprise Chambers, Newcastle upon Tyne
p987 . . . . . 0191 222 3344

Williamson, Miss Melanie J I *Oct 1990*
8, 11
No 6 Barristers Chambers, Leeds
p978 . . . . . 0113 245 9763

WILLIAMSON, Nicholas M *Mar 2009*
Pump Court Chambers, Swindon
p993 . . . . . 01793 539899
Pump Court Chambers, Winchester
p994 . . . . . 01962 868161
Pump Court Chambers, London EC4
p947 . . . . . 020 7353 0711

WILLIAMSON, Mr Oliver Jack MSc(Hons)(Lond); PGDL(Lond) M *Jul 2008*
18, 53, 68, 85, 27, 30, 40, 36
3 Serjeants' Inn, London EC4
p950 . . . . . 020 7427 5000

WILLIAMSON, Mr Patrick I *Nov 1989*
15
Kenworthy's Chambers, Manchester
p984 . . . . . 0161 832 4036

Willink, Mr David Christopher MA; LLM(Cantab) M *Nov 2004*
12, 22, 30, 11, 17, 67, 88
Lamb Chambers, London EC4
p941 . . . . . 020 7797 8300

WILLINS, Mr Andrew Jan LLB(Hons) G *Jul 2000*
49, 30, 40
29 Bedford Row, London WC1
p925 . . . . . 020 7404 1044

Willis, Miss Pearl LLB(Hons) I *Jul 1986*
15, 10, 20, 36
Fenners Chambers, Cambridge
p972 . . . . . 01223 368761

Willis, Mr Tony L *Jan 2004*
Brick Court Chambers, London WC2
p927 . . . . . 020 7379 3550

Willitts, Mr Timothy L LLB(Hons) G *Nov 1989*
12, 27, 30, 36, 40, 53, 56
Cobden House Chambers, Manchester
p983 . . . . . 0161 833 6000

Willmer, Mr Stephen M *Nov 2004*
15, 25, 84, 46
Argent Chambers, London WC2
p923 . . . . . 020 7556 5500

Willmott, Mr Oliver M *Jan 2002*
15, 62, 48, 84, 26, 36, 51, 94
Queen Square Chambers, Bristol
p972 . . . . . 0117 921 1966

Willoughby, Mr James M *Jan 2005*
York Chambers, York
p995 . . . . . 01904 620048
York Chambers, Newcastle upon Tyne
p987 . . . . . 0191 206 4677

Wills, Ms Janice LLB(Hons) L *Oct 1991*
20
18 St John Street Chambers, Manchester
p985 . . . . . 0161 278 1800

WILLS, Mr Jonathan Stuart L *Jan 2006*
1, 46, 31, 93
Landmark Chambers, London EC4
p941 . . . . . 020 7430 1221

Wills Goldingham, Ms Claire L M LLB(B'ham) I *Jul 1988*
20, 23
Albion Chambers, Bristol
p970 . . . . . 0117 927 2144

WILLSON, Mr William MA(Oxon) L *Oct 2006*
8, 5, 6, 11, 97, 38
South Square, London WC1
p950 . . . . . 020 7696 9900

See p1010 for the Key to Work Categories

Willsteed, Miss Elizabeth I *Nov 2004*
22, 23, 88, 12, 10, 20
Southernhay Chambers, Exeter
p975 . . . . . 01392 255777

WILMOT-SMITH, Mr Richard M *Jul 1978*
(Q.C.) *3, 11, 7, 40, 24, 61, 78*
Thirty Nine Essex Street, London WC2
p932 . . . . . 020 7832 1111

Wilmshurst, Mr Paul M *Jan 2007*
8, 22, 1, 12, 88
12 College Place, Southampton
p992 . . . . . 023 8032 0320

Wilshire, Mr Simon G *Jul 1994*
8, 10, 12, 15, 20, 22, 24, 29, 30
4 Breams Buildings, London EC4
p927 . . . . . 020 7092 1900

Wilson, Mr Adam LLB(Lond) I *Nov 1994*
20, 10
No 6 Barristers Chambers, Leeds
p978 . . . . . 0113 245 9763

WILSON, Mr Alan I *Nov 2005*
15, 62, 63, 18, 55, 10, 76, 30, 89
Kenworthy's Chambers, Manchester
p984 . . . . . 0161 832 4036

Wilson, Mr Alasdair John LLB(Wales) G *Nov 1988*
12, 22, 38
Fenners Chambers, Cambridge
p972 . . . . . 01223 368761

Wilson, Mr Alastair MA(Cantab) M *Jul 1968*
(Q.C.) *13, 19, 44, 45, 48, 50*
Hogarth Chambers, London WC2
p937 . . . . . 020 7404 0404

Wilson, Andrew G *Nov 1995*
6, 12, 15, 30, 22
Zenith Chambers, Leeds
p979 . . . . . 0113 245 5438

WILSON, Mr Andrew James BSc(Hons)(Leeds) M *Jun 2005*
15, 12
Wilberforce Chambers, Hull
p976 . . . . . 01482 323264

Wilson, Miss Charmaine I *Jul 2003*
15, 22, 30
Westgate Chambers, Lewes
p980 . . . . . 01273 480510

Wilson, Mr Christopher LLB(L'pool); Recorder G *Jul 1980*
11, 93, 96, 30, 40
9 Gough Square, London EC4
p935 . . . . . 020 7832 0500

WILSON, Mr David LLB G *Oct 1996*
15, 62
18 Red Lion Court, London EC4
p949 . . . . . 020 7520 6000
18 Red Lion Court (Annexe), Chelmsford
p973 . . . . . 01245 280880

Wilson, Miss Elizabeth LLB(Hons) G *Nov 1989*
10, 12, 20
One Essex Court, London EC4
p931 . . . . . 020 7936 3030
Pump Court Tax Chambers, London WC1
p948 . . . . . 020 7414 8080

WILSON, Mr Gerald BA(Oxon) G *Nov 1989*
20, 93
Tanfield Chambers, London WC1
p951 . . . . . 020 7421 5300

WILSON, Mr Graeme I *Feb 1987*
Furnival Chambers, London EC4
p934 . . . . . 020 7405 3232

Wilson, Miss Hannah MA(Hons)(Cantab) L *Jan 2005*
Henderson Chambers, London EC4
p937 . . . . . 020 7583 9020

Wilson, Ms Helen G *Oct 2004*
10, 18, 20, 63
St Johns Buildings, Preston
p990 . . . . . 01772 256100
St Johns Buildings, Chester
p974 . . . . . 01244 323070
St Johns Buildings, Manchester
p985 . . . . . 0161 214 1500
St Johns Buildings, Liverpool
p982 . . . . . 0151 243 6000

WILSON, Mr Ian MA(Cantab); LLM(Cantab) M *Oct 1995*
5, 6, 11, 19, 24, 40
3 Verulam Buildings, London WC1
p953 . . . . . 020 7831 8441

Wilson, Miss Jennifer Mary Pentreath LLB(Hons) G *Jul 1979*
68, 72, 15, 96
King's Bench Godolphin Chambers, Truro
p994 . . . . . 0845 308 1551
King's Bench Godolphin Chambers, Plymouth
p990 . . . . . 0845 308 1551

Wilson, Mr John I *Jan 1981*
1 Hare Court, London EC4
p936 . . . . . 020 7797 7070

Wilson, Mr Jonathan BA(Hons) L *Mar 2005*
10, 20
37 Park Square Chambers, Leeds
p978 . . . . . 0113 243 9422

WILSON, Mr Julian BA(Oxon) I *Oct 1997*
11, 18, 40
11KBW, London EC4
p938 . . . . . 020 7632 8500

WILSON, Ms Kate BA(Hons); MPhil I *Nov 2005*
16, 52, 73
One Brick Court, London EC4
p927 . . . . . 020 7353 8845

WILSON, Katrina L *Jul 2007*
15
1 High Pavement, Nottingham
p988 . . . . . 0115 941 8218

Wilson, Mr Lachlan I *Oct 1996*
3PB, London EC4
p946 . . . . . 020 7583 8055

WILSON, Lisa I *Jan 2008*
Furnival Chambers, London EC4
p934 . . . . . 020 7405 3232

Wilson, Mr Martin LLB(Nott'm); Recorder M *Nov 1963*
(Q.C.) *15, 62*
7 Bedford Row, London WC1
p924 . . . . . 020 7242 3555

Wilson, Mr Myles LLB L *Oct 1993*
15
St Johns Buildings, Preston
p990 . . . . . 01772 256100
St Johns Buildings, Chester
p974 . . . . . 01244 323070
St Johns Buildings, Manchester
p985 . . . . . 0161 214 1500
St Johns Buildings, Liverpool
p982 . . . . . 0151 243 6000

Wilson, Mr Paul BA(Hons) L *Jan 1989*
18, 30, 55
Broadway House Chambers, Leeds
p977 . . . . . 0113 246 2600
Broadway House Chambers, Bradford
p969 . . . . . 01274 722560

Wilson, Ms Rebekah M *Nov 1998*
10, 20, 18
Tooks Chambers, London EC4
p953 . . . . . 020 7842 7575

Wilson, Mr Richard LLB(Sheff); LLM M *Nov 1996*
8, 37, 32, 40, 36, 62, 38, 58, 79
3 Stone Buildings, London WC2
p951 . . . . . 020 7242 4937

Wilson, Mr Richard C BA(Sussex); LLM(Cantab) L *Nov 1981*
(Q.C.) *11, 12, 18, 22, 30, 36*
36 Bedford Row, London WC1
p925 . . . . . 020 7421 8000

Wilson, Mr Scott LLB L *Nov 1993*
12, 15, 62, 70
St Pauls Chambers, Leeds
p979 . . . . . 0113 245 5866

Wilson, Mr Steven I *Jul 1999*
15
1 Inner Temple Lane, London EC4
p937 . . . . . 020 7427 4400

WILSON, Miss Thea MA(Cantab); LLM(Hons) I *Jul 2008*
12 King's Bench Walk, London EC4
p940 . . . . . 020 7583 0811

Wilson, Miss Victoria G *Jul 2002*
Goldsmith Chambers, London EC4
p935 . . . . . 020 7353 6802

Wilson-Barnes, Lucy BA(Warw); Associate Tenant I *Jul 1989*
6, 8, 11, 22, 32, 37, 40, 2, 9, 29
Zenith Chambers, Leeds
p979 . . . . . 0113 245 5438
St James's Chambers, Manchester
p984 . . . . . 0161 834 7000

Wilson-Smith, Mr Christopher G *Nov 1965*
(Q.C.) *30, 53, 15, 40, 84, 62*
Outer Temple Chambers, London WC2
p945 . . . . . 020 7353 6381

Wilton, Mr Simon G *Oct 1993*
40, 11
Hailsham Chambers, London EC4
p936 . . . . . 020 7643 5000

Wiltshire, Mrs Hannah LLB(Hons) G *Oct 1998*
10, 12, 15, 20, 30
Albion Chambers, Bristol
p970 . . . . . 0117 927 2144

WINBERG, Mr Stephen A I *Nov 1974*
Furnival Chambers, London EC4
p934 . . . . . 020 7405 3232

Winchester, Mr Leonard Clive Allyn BCom; LLB L *Jul 2002*
18, 44, 24, 22
Lamb Chambers, London EC4
p941 . . . . . 020 7797 8300

Windle, Miss Victoria MA(Cantab) I *Nov 2001*
1, 18, 11, 3, 41, 51, 56, 89
Blackstone Chambers, London EC4
p926 . . . . . 020 7583 1770

WINDSOR, Miss Emily MA; DSU(Paris) I *Oct 1995*
Falcon Chambers, London EC4
p933 . . . . . 020 7353 2484

Winfield, Mr Joshua MA(Oxon) I *Oct 2001*
8, 9, 37, 32, 6
Radcliffe Chambers, London WC2
p949 . . . . . 020 7831 0081

Wing, Mr Christopher J BSc; BA G *Jul 1985*
15, 91, 71
1 Paper Buildings, London EC4
p946 . . . . . 020 7353 3728

Wing, Mr James BA(Hons) L *Oct 2002*
15, 94, 70
3 Temple Gardens, London EC4
p952 . . . . . 020 7353 3102

WINGERT, Rachel Thomas LLM(Lond) M *Jul 1980*
10, 20
Renaissance Chambers, London WC1
p949 . . . . . 020 7404 1111

Wingrave, Mr Michael M *Jul 2001*
30, 40, 53, 2, 68, 94, 20, 24
No5 Chambers, Bristol
p971 . . . . . 0845 210 5555
No5 Chambers, London EC4
p944 . . . . . 0845 210 5555
No5 Chambers, Birmingham
p968 . . . . . 0845 210 5555

WINN-SMITH, Mr Matthew MA(Oxon) L *Mar 2003*
11, 12, 22, 30, 88, 93
Lamb Chambers, London EC4
p941 . . . . . 020 7797 8300

WINSER, Mr Crispin BA(Hons); BVC I *Oct 2003*
74, 7, 24, 40, 11
Crown Office Chambers, London EC4
p929 . . . . . 020 7797 8100

WINSHIP, Mr Julian LLB G *Oct 1995*
15
Furnival Chambers, London EC4
p934 . . . . . 020 7405 3232

Winslett, Mr Frank M *Mar 2004*
15, 20, 12
Westgate Chambers, Lewes
p980 . . . . . 01273 480510

WINSTANLEY, Miss Alice L *Jan 2006*
15, 20
St Philips Chambers, Birmingham
p969 . . . . . 0121 246 7000

WINSTON, Miss Naomi LLB(Leics) M *Jan 2006*
8
Ten Old Square, London WC2
p945 . . . . . 020 7405 0758

Winstone, Ms Hilary LLB(Hons) G *Oct 1998*
18, 30, 48, 50, 55, 36
Old Square Chambers, Bristol
p971 . . . . . 0117 930 5100
Old Square Chambers, London WC1
p945 . . . . . 020 7269 0300

WINT, Mr Peter G *Mar 2007*
10, 15, 20
Chavasse Court Chambers, Liverpool
p980 . . . . . 0151 229 2030

Winter, Mr Alexander BA(Hons)(Oxon) M *Jul 2003*
Maitland Chambers, London WC2
p941 . . . . . 020 7406 1200

Winter, Mr Ian I *Jul 1988*
Cloth Fair Chambers, London EC1
p928 . . . . . 020 7710 6444

Winter, Louise L *Jul 2009*
New Walk Chambers, Leicester
p979 . . . . . 0871 200 1298

Winter, Ms Melanie M *Nov 1996*
15
9 Gough Square, London EC4
p935 . . . . . 020 7832 0500

Wise, Mr Ian BA G *Nov 1992*
1, 26, 19, 51
Doughty Street Chambers, London WC1
p930 . . . . . 020 7404 1313

WISE, Leslie M FCA M *Nov 1985*
12, 15, 11
10 King's Bench Walk, London EC4
p940 . . . . . 020 7353 7742

WISE, Mr Oliver BA(Cantab) L *Jul 1981*
10, 12, 20, 30, 56
Queen Elizabeth Buildings, London EC4
p948 . . . . . 020 7797 7837

WISEMAN, Mr Adam I *Nov 1994*
15, 84
18 Red Lion Court, London EC4
p949 . . . . . 020 7520 6000
18 Red Lion Court (Annexe), Chelmsford
p973 . . . . . 01245 280880

WITCOMB, Mr Henry BA(Dunelm) L *Apr 1989*
30, 53
1 Crown Office Row, London EC4
p929 . . . . . 020 7797 7500

Witherington, Ms Gemma BA(Hons) I *Jan 2008*
Hardwicke, London WC2
p936 . . . . . 020 7242 2523

Withers, Ms Michelle J M LLB(Wales) I *Jul 1991*
20
9 Park Place, Cardiff
p973 . . . . . 029 2038 2731
Thirty Park Place, Cardiff
p973 . . . . . 029 2039 8421

Withey, Mr Richard I *Jan 1996*
Guildhall Chambers, Portsmouth
p990 . . . . . 023 9275 2400

Withington, Mr Angus Richard BA(Hons) G *Nov 1995*
18, 55, 11, 30
Henderson Chambers, London EC4
p937 . . . . . 020 7583 9020

Withyman, Mr Jim M *Jun 1999*
York Chambers, York
p995 . . . . . 01904 620048
York Chambers, Newcastle upon Tyne
p987 . . . . . 0191 206 4677

WOERNER, Mr Steven M *Nov 2006*
30, 94, 12
7 Harrington Street Chambers, Liverpool
p981 . . . . . 0151 242 0707

Wolanski, Mr Adam MA(Cantab) L *Feb 1995*
12, 13, 16, 18, 50, 51
5RB, London WC1
p948 . . . . . 020 7242 2902

Wolchover, Mr Chaim David Hirsch G *Jul 1971*
15
Ridgeway Chambers, London NW11
p949 . . . . . 020 8455 2939

WOLFE, Mr David BSc; M Eng; PhD(Cantab); DipLaw(City) M *Nov 1992*
1, 4, 51, 12, 55, 46, 45, 25, 26, 31, 36, 38, 50, 27, 19, 33
Matrix Chambers, London WC1
p942 . . . . . 020 7404 3447

Wolfe, Ms Madeline Louise I *Oct 1998*
15
1 Inner Temple Lane, London EC4
p937 . . . . . 020 7427 4400

WOLFE, Ms Tara I *Nov 2000*
23, 15
Guildhall Chambers, Bristol
p970 . . . . . 0117 930 9000

WOLFENDEN, Mr Peter LLB(Hons) M *Jul 2007*
12, 30, 62
Oriel Chambers, Liverpool
p981 . . . . . 0151 236 7191 / 236 4321
Oriel Chambers, Preston
p990 . . . . . 01772 254764

Wolff, Mr Michael LLB G *Jun 1964*
15
St Johns Buildings, Preston
p990 . . . . . 01772 256100
St Johns Buildings, Chester
p974 . . . . . 01244 323070

13

St Johns Buildings, Manchester
p985 . . . . . 0161 214 1500
St Johns Buildings, Liverpool
p982 . . . . . 0151 243 6000

Wolfson, Mr David BA(Cantab) *I Nov 1992*
(Q.C.) *5, 6, 11, 40*
One Essex Court, London EC4
p931 . . . . . 020 7583 2000

Wolkind, Mr Michael *M Nov 1976*
(Q.C.) *15*
2 Bedford Row, London WC1
p924 . . . . . 020 7440 8888

Wollner, Mr Ernest John DipLaw *I Nov 1988*
4, 12, 15, 21, 22, 23
21 Lauderdale Tower, London EC2
p941 . . . . . 020 7920 9308

WOLSTENHOLME, Mr Alan *L Jul 1989*
15, 62, 21, 84
Kenworthy's Chambers, Manchester
p984 . . . . . 0161 832 4036

Wolstenholme, Ms Helen *L Nov 2002*
12, 30, 40, 18
2 Temple Gardens, London EC4
p952 . . . . . 020 7822 1200

Wolton, Mr Harry *G Dec 1969*
(Q.C.) *31, 46*
No5 Chambers, Bristol
p971 . . . . . 0845 210 5555
No5 Chambers, London EC4
p944 . . . . . 0845 210 5555
No5 Chambers, Birmingham
p968 . . . . . 0845 210 5555

WONG, Miss Natasha Pui-Wai *M Nov 1993*
15, 62, 95
187 Fleet Street, London EC4
p933 . . . . . 020 7430 7430

Wonnacott, Mr Mark A LLB(Lond) *L Jul 1989*
22
Maitland Chambers, London WC2
p941 . . . . . 020 7406 1200

Wood, Mr Benjamin *L Jan 2005*
Four New Square, London WC2
p943 . . . . . 020 7822 2000

Wood, Miss Catherine LLB(Lond) *M Jul 1985*
(Q.C.) *10, 20*
4 Paper Buildings, London EC4
p946 . . . . . 020 7583 0816

Wood, Mr Christopher M MA(Oxon); DESu(Aix-Marseille 3) *M Feb 1986*
20, 10
1 Hare Court, London EC4
p936 . . . . . 020 7797 7070

WOOD, Mr Daniel *L Jan 2008*
12, 30, 11, 40, 53, 22, 29
Ropewalk Chambers, Nottingham
p989 . . . . . 0115 947 2581
7 Harrington Street Chambers, Liverpool
p981 . . . . . 0151 242 0707

WOOD, Mr Derek MA; BCL(Oxon); FCIArb *M Feb 1964*
(Q.C.) CBE
Falcon Chambers, London EC4
p933 . . . . . 020 7353 2484

Wood, Ms Emily *M Jan 2006*
Essex Court Chambers, London WC2
p931 . . . . . 020 7813 8000

Wood, Mr Graeme MA; LLM(Cantab) *M Jul 1968*
8, 22, 32
New Bailey Chambers, Preston
p990 . . . . . 01772 258087

Wood, Mr Graham LLB *M Jul 1979*
(Q.C.) *15, 30*
3PB, London EC4
p946 . . . . . 020 7583 8055

Wood, Hannah *L Jan 2007*
St Johns Buildings, Preston
p990 . . . . . 01772 256100
St Johns Buildings, Chester
p974 . . . . . 01244 323070
St Johns Buildings, Manchester
p985 . . . . . 0161 214 1500
St Johns Buildings, Liverpool
p982 . . . . . 0151 243 6000

Wood, Mr James LLB; Recorder *M Nov 1975*
(Q.C.) *1, 12, 15, 16, 51*
Doughty Street Chambers, London WC1
p930 . . . . . 020 7404 1313

WOOD, Mr James M LLB(Wales) *L Jan 1989*
15, 82, 25
Cornwall Street Chambers, Birmingham
p967 . . . . . 0121 233 7500

Wood, Miss Joanna LLB *I Nov 1989*
10, 20
Angel Chambers, Swansea
p992 . . . . . 01792 464623

Wood, Ms Joanna *M Jan 1996*
20, 23
1 Pump Court, London EC4
p947 . . . . . 020 7842 7070

WOOD, Miss Katherine LLB *M Jul 2002*
12, 20, 30, 38, 11, 8
Trinity (Newcastle) Chambers, Newcastle upon Tyne
p987 . . . . . 0191 232 1927
Trinity (Teesside) Chambers, Middlesbrough
p986 . . . . . 01642 247569

Wood, Ms Katie *I Jul 2001*
20, 10
4 Paper Buildings, London EC4
p946 . . . . . 020 7583 0816

Wood, Miss Lana Claire MA(Cantab); BCL(Oxon) *G Oct 1993*
88, 93, 2
9 Stone Buildings Barristers Chambers, London WC2
p951 . . . . . 020 7404 5055

Wood, Mr Martin John MA(Cantab) *I Jul 1973*
10, 12, 20, 22, 28, 30, 25, 40
Broadway House Chambers, Leeds
p977 . . . . . 0113 246 2600
Broadway House Chambers, Bradford
p969 . . . . . 01274 722560

Wood, Mr Michael BA(Sheff); LLB(Sheff) *L Nov 1989*
11, 24, 19, 29, 35, 40, 4
Exchange Chambers, Manchester
p983 . . . . . 0161 833 2722
Exchange Chambers, Liverpool
p980 . . . . . 0151 236 7747
Exchange Chambers, Leeds
p977 . . . . . 0113 203 1970
Carmelite Chambers, London EC4
p927 . . . . . 020 7936 6300

Wood, Sir Michael *M Jan 1968*
20 Essex Street, London WC2
p932 . . . . . 020 7842 1200

Wood, Miss Natalie *M Jul 2001*
2 King's Bench Walk, London EC4
p939 . . . . . 020 7353 1746

WOOD, Mr Nicholas A *I Jul 1970*
1, 22, 40, 8, 12, 30
Five Paper, London EC4
p946 . . . . . 020 7815 3200

Wood, Mrs Penelope LLB(Hons)(Lond) *L Apr 1999*
10, 20, 62
36 Bedford Row, London WC1
p925 . . . . . 020 7421 8000

WOOD, Mr Percy MA(Cantab) *G Feb 1961*
15, 23
St James's Chambers, Manchester
p984 . . . . . 0161 834 7000

Wood, Mr Richard BA(Hons) *G Nov 1995*
15, 18, 30, 42, 7, 12, 39, 62, 40, 55
East Anglian Chambers, Norwich
p988 . . . . . 01603 617351
East Anglian Chambers, Colchester
p975 . . . . . 01206 572756
East Anglian Chambers, Chelmsford
p973 . . . . . 01245 215660
East Anglian Chambers, Ipswich
p976 . . . . . 01473 214481

Wood, Miss Sarah *I Jan 1996*
15, 62
7 Bedford Row, London WC1
p924 . . . . . 020 7242 3555

Wood, Mr Simon BSc; MA *M Oct 2001*
12, 15, 31
6-8 Mill Street, Maidstone
p982 . . . . . 01622 688094 / 688095
6 Pump Court, London EC4
p947 . . . . . 020 7797 8400

Wood, Mr Stephen LLB(Huddersfield) *I Nov 1991*
1, 12, 15, 26, 30
Broadway House Chambers, Leeds
p977 . . . . . 0113 246 2600
Broadway House Chambers, Bradford
p969 . . . . . 01274 722560

Wood, Mr Thomas LLB(Hons)(Lond) *L Oct 2002*
42 Bedford Row, London WC1
p925 . . . . . 020 7831 0222

Wood, Mr William BA; BCL(Oxon); LLM(Harv) *M Nov 1980*
(Q.C.) *4, 11, 19, 41, 24, 40*
Brick Court Chambers, London WC2
p927 . . . . . 020 7379 3550

WOODALL, Mr Peter LLB *M Jul 1983*
15
Carmelite Chambers, London EC4
p927 . . . . . 020 7936 6300

WOODBRIDGE, Mr Julian LLB(Warw) *M Nov 1981*
12, 15, 20, 40, 62, 70, 72
1 King's Bench Walk, London EC4
p938 . . . . . 020 7936 1500

WOODBRIDGE, Miss Victoria BA(Hons)(Lond) *L Oct 1998*
53, 30, 40, 11
Crown Office Chambers, London EC4
p929 . . . . . 020 7797 8100

Woodcock, Mr Jonathan *M Nov 1981*
15
4 Breams Buildings, London EC4
p927 . . . . . 020 7092 1900
3 Temple Gardens, London EC4
p952 . . . . . 020 7353 3102

Woodcock, Mr Robert LLB *I Feb 1978*
(Q.C.) *15, 62*
Broad Chare Chambers, Newcastle upon Tyne
p986 . . . . . 0191 232 0541
Kenworthy's Chambers, Manchester
p984 . . . . . 0161 832 4036
New Court Chambers, Newcastle upon Tyne
p987 . . . . . 0191 232 1980

Woodcraft, Ms Elizabeth *M Jul 1980*
20, 10, 1
Tooks Chambers, London EC4
p953 . . . . . 020 7842 7575

WOODHALL, Mr Gary *G Oct 1997*
15
9 St John Street Chambers, Manchester
p984 . . . . . 0161 955 9000

Woodham, Ms Samantha *I Jan 2006*
20, 10
4 Paper Buildings, London EC4
p946 . . . . . 020 7583 0816

Woodhead, Mr George Byron *L Nov 2009*
Guildford Chambers, Guildford
p975 . . . . . 01483 539131

Woodhouse, Mr Alaric LLB *L Jul 2003*
15, 22, 6, 12, 26
Staple Inn Chambers, London WC1
p951 . . . . . 020 7242 5240

Woodhouse, Mr Charles LLB(Hons) *M Oct 1997*
30, 15, 53
Old Square Chambers, Bristol
p971 . . . . . 0117 930 5100
Old Square Chambers, London WC1
p945 . . . . . 020 7269 0300

Woodhouse, Mr Nigel LLB(Hons) *G Nov 1997*
King's Bench Chambers, Oxford
p989 . . . . . 01865 311066
13 King's Bench Walk, London EC4
p940 . . . . . 020 7353 7204

Wooding, Mr Oliver *M Jan 2009*
St John's Chambers, Bristol
p972 . . . . . 0117 921 3456

WOODLEY, Miss Sonia *G Jul 1968*
(Q.C.)
Furnival Chambers, London EC4
p934 . . . . . 020 7405 3232

WOODS, Mr Alex *L Jan 2007*
15, 62, 95
187 Fleet Street, London EC4
p933 . . . . . 020 7430 7430

Woods, Miss Danielle *M Oct 2009*
20, 10
15 Winckley Square, Preston
p991 . . . . . 01772 252828

Woods, Mr George BA(Oxon) *M Mar 2003*
12, 40, 24, 89
4 Pump Court, London EC4
p947 . . . . . 020 7842 5555

Woods, Ms Leanne BA(Hons)(Oxon); LLM(Penn) *I Oct 2005*
27, 30, 18, 63, 53, 68, 85, 40, 36
3 Serjeants' Inn, London EC4
p950 . . . . . 020 7427 5000

Woods, Ms Rachel Helen LLB(Hons) *G Oct 1992*
15
Exchange Chambers, Manchester
p983 . . . . . 0161 833 2722
Exchange Chambers, Liverpool
p980 . . . . . 0151 236 7747
Exchange Chambers, Leeds
p977 . . . . . 0113 203 1970

WOODS, Mr Terence LLB(Lond) *M Nov 1989*
15, 62, 95
187 Fleet Street, London EC4
p933 . . . . . 020 7430 7430

WOODWARD, Mr Jeremy LLB(Hons) *I Nov 1996*
Pallant Chambers, Chichester
p974 . . . . . 01243 784538

WOODWARD, Miss Joanne LLB(Hons) *G Nov 1989*
9 St John Street Chambers, Manchester
p984 . . . . . 0161 955 9000

Woodward, Mr John LLB *L Nov 1984*
15
15 Winckley Square, Preston
p991 . . . . . 01772 252828

Woodward-Carlton, Mr Damian BSc; MA(Dunelm) *I Oct 1995*
10, 20, 27, 26
42 Bedford Row, London WC1
p925 . . . . . 020 7831 0222

Woolf, Mr Eliot C A MA(Cantab) *I Oct 1993*
30, 53, 40
Outer Temple Chambers, London WC2
p945 . . . . . 020 7353 6381

Woolf, Lord Harry LLB(Lond); LLD(Hon) *I Oct 1955*
49, 41, 96
Blackstone Chambers, London EC4
p926 . . . . . 020 7583 1770

WOOLF, The Hon Jeremy BA; LLM(Cantab) *I Jul 1986*
34, 57, 58, 37
Pump Court Tax Chambers, London WC1
p948 . . . . . 020 7414 8080

Woolf, Mr Steven LLB(Hons) *I Jul 1989*
22, 11, 49, 88, 40, 93
Hardwicke, London WC2
p936 . . . . . 020 7242 2523

WOOLFE, Mr Philip John MA; BA; BCL *L Oct 2004*
1, 19, 57, 44, 11
Monckton Chambers, London WC1
p942 . . . . . 020 7405 7211

WOOLFENDEN, Ivan BA(Oxon) *M Jul 1986*
18, 25, 30, 55, 53
Atlantic Chambers, Liverpool
p980 . . . . . 0151 236 4421

WOOLGAR, Mr Dermot LLB *I Jul 1988*
74, 7, 12, 22, 30, 11, 1, 6, 38, 5, 93, 40
Crown Office Chambers, London EC4
p929 . . . . . 020 7797 8100

WOOLHOUSE, Mr Oliver LLB(Hons)(Leicester) *I Nov 1996*
15, 70
Cornwall Street Chambers, Birmingham
p967 . . . . . 0121 233 7500

WOOLLEY, Mr David Rorie MA(Cantab) *M Jul 1962*
(Q.C.) *31, 46*
Landmark Chambers, London EC4
p941 . . . . . 020 7430 1221

Woolrich, Miss Sarah *M Nov 1994*
York Chambers, York
p995 . . . . . 01904 620048
York Chambers, Newcastle upon Tyne
p987 . . . . . 0191 206 4677

Wordsworth, Mr Filo Jones BL; LLM; MBA; MScIT *M Jan 1986*
Chambers of Wilfred Forster-Jones, London WC1
p934 . . . . . 020 7831 0037

Wordsworth, Philippa LLB *G Oct 1995*
10, 20, 36
Zenith Chambers, Leeds
p979 . . . . . 0113 245 5438

Wordsworth, Mr Samuel *L Jan 1997*
Essex Court Chambers, London WC2
p931 . . . . . 020 7813 8000

Worlock, Mr Simon *M Jul 1975*
10, 20, 15, 25
No5 Chambers, Bristol
p971 . . . . . 0845 210 5555
No5 Chambers, London EC4
p944 . . . . . 0845 210 5555

 See p1010 for the Key to Work Categories

No5 Chambers, Birmingham
p968 . . . . 0845 210 5555

WORMINGTON, Mr Jim G *Jan 2007*
QEB Hollis Whiteman, London EC4
p948 . . . . 020 7933 8855

Wormington, Mr Timothy Michael BA; BCL(Oxon) M *Nov 1977*
Fountain Court Chambers, London EC4
p934 . . . . 020 7583 3335

Worrall, Ms Anna LLB M *Nov 1959*
(Q.C.) *15, 62, 82*
Lamb Building, Brighton
p970 . . . . 01273 820490
Lamb Building, London EC4
p940 . . . . 020 7797 7788

Worrall, John R G G *Jul 1984*
10, 15, 18, 20, 44, 89
Zenith Chambers, Leeds
p979 . . . . 0113 245 5438

Worrall, Mr Philip G *Jan 2001*
12, 30, 88
Foregate Chambers, Kidderminster
p976 . . . . 07760 766152
Kew Chambers, Kew
p976 . . . . 0844 809 9991

Worsley, Ms Charlotte H G M *Oct 2002*
15, 20, 10
No 6 Barristers Chambers, Leeds
p978 . . . . 0113 245 9763

WORSLEY, Mr Mark LLB(Hons); Member of New York Bar I *Nov 1994*
12, 15, 18
Guildhall Chambers, Bristol
p970 . . . . 0117 930 9000

Worsley, Mr Michael I *Jun 1955*
(Q.C.) *15*
6 King's Bench Walk, London EC4
p939 . . . . 020 7583 0410

Worsley, Nicholas M *Oct 1998*
15, 70, 72, 51, 62
Zenith Chambers, Leeds
p979 . . . . 0113 245 5438

WORTHEN, Mr Thomas BA; BCL G *Jul 2007*
8, 38, 88, 7, 97, 53, 40
Pallant Chambers, Chichester
p974 . . . . 01243 784538

WORTHINGTON, Prof Sarah LLB(Qld); PhD(Cantab) M *Mar 2005*
(Q.C.) *6, 5, 11*
South Square, London WC1
p950 . . . . 020 7696 9900

WORTHINGTON, Mr Stephen MA(Cantab); Recorder G *Nov 1976*
(Q.C.) *7, 24, 30, 40, 46*
12 King's Bench Walk, London EC4
p940 . . . . 020 7583 0811

Worthley, Mr Andrew LLB(Hons) L *Oct 2004*
12, 8, 18, 10, 20, 22, 37, 67
Rougemont Chambers, Exeter
p975 . . . . 01392 208484

Wortley, Ms Natalie G *Jan 1999*
New Court Chambers, Newcastle upon Tyne
p987 . . . . 0191 232 1980

Worton, Ms Louise LLB I *Jan 2000*
15, 12, 18, 22
3PB, Oxford
p989 . . . . 01865 793736

Wrack, Mr Nick I *Mar 1997*
15
Tooks Chambers, London EC4
p953 . . . . 020 7842 7575

Wraight, Mr Oliver BA(Cantab) M *Oct 1998*
20, 10
Harcourt Chambers, London EC4
p936 . . . . 0844 561 7135
Harcourt Chambers, Oxford
p989 . . . . 0844 561 7135

Wraight, Mr William MRCS(Eng) L *Jul 2009*
30, 53
2 Temple Gardens, London EC4
p952 . . . . 020 7822 1200

WRAITH, Mr Nigel M *Jul 2004*
15, 12, 20
Colleton Chambers, Exeter
p975 . . . . 01392 274898

WREN, Mr Andrew John M *Jul 2005*
10, 20
St Mary's Chambers, Nottingham
p989 . . . . 0115 950 3503

WRENN, Ms Helen BA(Hons) I *Nov 1994*
20, 10
7 Harrington Street Chambers, Liverpool
p981 . . . . 0151 242 0707

Wright, Ms Abigail Mary Barbara BA(Hons)(Oxon) M *Oct 2000*
11, 12, 22, 30
Lamb Chambers, London EC4
p941 . . . . 020 7797 8300

Wright, Mr Alastair BA(Oxon); DipLaw L *Dec 1991*
12
St Johns Buildings, Preston
p990 . . . . 01772 256100
St Johns Buildings, Chester
p974 . . . . 01244 323070
St Johns Buildings, Manchester
p985 . . . . 0161 214 1500
St Johns Buildings, Liverpool
p982 . . . . 0151 243 6000

Wright, Mr Alex LLB(Hons)(Manc) I *Nov 1997*
15, 62, 25
Argent Chambers, London WC2
p923 . . . . 020 7556 5500

Wright, Mr Alexander MA(Cantab) M *Jul 2007*
11, 40, 24, 3, 35, 79
4 Pump Court, London EC4
p947 . . . . 020 7842 5555

WRIGHT, Mr Caley Denis Alastair BA(Oxon); MA(Oxon) L *Jul 2008*
New Square Chambers, London WC2
p943 . . . . 020 7419 8000

Wright, Miss Clare LLB(Bris) I *Oct 1995*
12, 15, 20, 31, 46, 51
6-8 Mill Street, Maidstone
p982 . . . . 01622 688094 / 688095
6 Pump Court, London EC4
p947 . . . . 020 7797 8400

Wright, Mr Colin LLB(Leics) M *Jul 1987*
3, 5, 6, 8, 11, 19, 21, 24, 29, 35
Stone Chambers, London WC1
p951 . . . . 020 7440 6900

WRIGHT, Mr Ian BSc(Dundee); LLB(Leics) M *Nov 1983*
18, 55, 36
Five Paper, London EC4
p946 . . . . 020 7815 3200

Wright, Mr Ian Bernard LLB(Hons)(Wales) M *Nov 1994*
15
Iscoed Chambers, Swansea
p993 . . . . 01792 652988

WRIGHT, Mr Ian F G DipLaw; BSc(Hons); MSc; DIC; CEng; MICE; MIStructE I *Jul 1989*
40, 74, 7
Crown Office Chambers, London EC4
p929 . . . . 020 7797 8100

Wright, Mr Jeremy I *Oct 1996*
15
No5 Chambers, Bristol
p971 . . . . 0845 210 5555
No5 Chambers, London EC4
p944 . . . . 0845 210 5555
No5 Chambers, Birmingham
p968 . . . . 0845 210 5555

WRIGHT, Mr Jeremy J I *Jul 1970*
King's Bench Godolphin Chambers, Truro
p994 . . . . 0845 308 1551
King's Bench Godolphin Chambers, Plymouth
p990 . . . . 0845 308 1551
2 King's Bench Walk, London EC4
p939 . . . . 020 7353 1746

Wright, Mr Jonathan Nicholas M *Oct 1997*
15
Castle Chambers, Harrow
p976 . . . . 020 8423 6579

WRIGHT, Miss Lisa I *Jan 2007*
4 King's Bench Walk, London EC4
p939 . . . . 020 7822 7000

WRIGHT, Mr Paul I *Oct 2003*
20, 10
7 Harrington Street Chambers, Liverpool
p981 . . . . 0151 242 0707
Brick Court Chambers, London WC2
p927 . . . . 020 7379 3550

Wright, Mr Peter D LLB(Hons) I *Jul 1981*
(Q.C.) *15, 95*
2 Hare Court, London EC4
p937 . . . . 020 7353 5324
Lincoln House Chambers, Manchester
p984 . . . . 0161 832 5701

Wright, Mr Richard G *Oct 1998*
15
No 6 Barristers Chambers, Leeds
p978 . . . . 0113 245 9763

Wright, Miss Sarah G *Oct 1984*
10, 15, 20
Paradise Chambers, Sheffield
p992 . . . . 0114 273 8951

Wright, Mr Stuart LLB(Hons) I *Jul 2000*
6, 7, 12, 22, 25, 30, 26, 31
Crown Office Row Chambers, Brighton
p970 . . . . 01273 625625

Wright, Mr Thomas I *Jul 2001*
2 King's Bench Walk, London EC4
p939 . . . . 020 7353 1746

WRIGHT, Mr Trevor LLB M *Nov 1992*
15
Maidstone Chambers, Maidstone
p982 . . . . 01622 688592
5 St Andrew's Hill, London EC4
p950 . . . . 020 7332 5400

Wright, Mrs Yasmin LLB(Hons) I *Nov 1990*
20, 23
Cobden House Chambers, Manchester
p983 . . . . 0161 833 6000

WROTTESLEY, Miss Angela I *Jan 1999*
12, 15
Bank House Chambers, Sheffield
p991 . . . . 0114 275 1223

Wurtzel, Mr David I MA(Cantab); MA(Lond) M *Nov 1974*
15, 20, 30
Charter Chambers, London WC1
p928 . . . . 020 7618 4400

Wyand, Mr Roger MA(Cantab); Recorder, Deputy High Court Judge M *May 1973*
(Q.C.) *13*
Hogarth Chambers, London WC2
p937 . . . . 020 7404 0404

Wyatt, Mr Anthony LLB(Hons) M *Mar 2002*
15, 62
2 Bedford Row, London WC1
p924 . . . . 020 7440 8888

Wyatt, Mr Derrick MA; LLB(Cantab); JD(Chicago) L *Jul 1972*
(Q.C.) *19*
Brick Court Chambers, London WC2
p927 . . . . 020 7379 3550

Wyatt, Mr Mark M *Jul 1976*
12, 15, 18, 20, 30
2 New Street, Leicester
p979 . . . . 0116 262 5906

Wyeth, Mr Mark Charles BA; LLM; ACIArb I *Jul 1983*
(Q.C.) *15, 12, 18, 30*
5 Paper Buildings, London EC4
p946 . . . . 020 7583 6117

Wyeth, Mr Stephen I *Jan 2010*
18
3PB, Winchester
p994 . . . . 01962 868884

Wygas, Mr Luke MA; MEng M *Nov 2004*
6, 11, 24, 38, 40, 41, 78, 88
4 Pump Court, London EC4
p947 . . . . 020 7842 5555

Wyles, Miss Lucy MA(Oxon) L *Oct 1994*
12, 19, 24, 30
2 Temple Gardens, London EC4
p952 . . . . 020 7822 1200

Wylie, Mr Neil LLB G *Nov 1996*
12, 18, 22, 30
KCH Garden Square Chambers, Nottingham
p989 . . . . 0115 941 8851
KCH Garden Square Chambers, Leicester
p979 . . . . 0115 941 8851

Wyn Jones, Mr Robert L *Jan 1993*
15
Exchange Chambers, Manchester
p983 . . . . 0161 833 2722
Exchange Chambers, Liverpool
p980 . . . . 0151 236 7747
Exchange Chambers, Leeds
p977 . . . . 0113 203 1970

Wynn, Mr Toby LLB(Lond) G *Jul 1982*
1
11 King's Bench Walk, Leeds
p978 . . . . 0113 297 1200

Wynne, Ashley LLB G *Nov 1990*
20, 2
No5 Chambers, Bristol
p971 . . . . 0845 210 5555
No5 Chambers, London EC4
p944 . . . . 0845 210 5555
No5 Chambers, Birmingham
p968 . . . . 0845 210 5555

WYNNE, Mr James LLM M *Jul 2002*
18, 11, 5, 6, 12, 55, 89
Littleton Chambers, London EC4
p941 . . . . 020 7797 8600

Wynne Jones, Mr Martin MA; LLB I *Nov 1977*
1 Mitre Court Buildings, London EC4
p942 . . . . 020 7452 8900

Wynter, Mr Colin LLB; M Phil I *Nov 1984*
(Q.C.) *11, 12, 18, 27, 36, 24, 3, 40*
Devereux Chambers, London WC2
p930 . . . . 020 7353 7534

Xydias, Mr Nicholas L *Oct 1992*
30, 40, 68, 94
No5 Chambers, Bristol
p971 . . . . 0845 210 5555
No5 Chambers, London EC4
p944 . . . . 0845 210 5555
No5 Chambers, Birmingham
p968 . . . . 0845 210 5555

YAKUBU, Mr Emmanuel Mahama LLB(Lond) M *Jul 1970*
5 Barnsbury Close, New Malden
p986 . . . . 020 8949 7748

YANG, Miss Zizhen BA(Hons) L *Jan 2009*
37, 57, 58, 34
Pump Court Tax Chambers, London WC1
p948 . . . . 020 7414 8080

YARROW, Miss Charlotte L *Oct 1999*
Furnival Chambers, London EC4
p934 . . . . 020 7405 3232

Yasnik, Mr Ram I *Nov 1965*
23, 20, 8, 10, 22, 30
Two King's Bench Walk, London EC4
p939 . . . . 020 7353 7202 / 7353 3909

Yasseri, Miss Yasmin MA(Hons); LLM I *Jul 2005*
5, 6, 8, 11, 97, 67, 38, 24, 88, 29, 93
No5 Chambers, Bristol
p971 . . . . 0845 210 5555
No5 Chambers, London EC4
p944 . . . . 0845 210 5555
No5 Chambers, Birmingham
p968 . . . . 0845 210 5555

YATES, Mr David MA(Cantab); DipLaw(City) L *Jan 2004*
37, 57, 58, 34
Pump Court Tax Chambers, London WC1
p948 . . . . 020 7414 8080

YATES, Ms Katrina L *Oct 2006*
1, 46, 31, 93
Landmark Chambers, London EC4
p941 . . . . 020 7430 1221

Yates, Mr Nicholas BA(Cantab) I *Oct 1996*
20
1 Hare Court, London EC4
p936 . . . . 020 7797 7070

Yates, Miss Victoria M *Nov 2006*
15, 62, 84, 39, 18, 55
No5 Chambers, Bristol
p971 . . . . 0845 210 5555
No5 Chambers, London EC4
p944 . . . . 0845 210 5555
No5 Chambers, Birmingham
p968 . . . . 0845 210 5555

YEARWOOD, Mr Jeffrey BA I *Nov 1975*
15
1 Mitre Court Buildings, London EC4
p942 . . . . 020 7452 8900

Yeatman, Ms Trudi I *Jan 2006*
13 King's Bench Walk, London EC4
p940 . . . . 020 7353 7204

Yeboah, Yaa LLB(Ghana); LLM(Harv) G *Nov 1977*
20, 12, 23
Tooks Chambers, London EC4
p953 . . . . 020 7842 7575

Yeginsu, Can I *Jan 2007*
Four New Square, London WC2
p943 . . . . 020 7822 2000

Yell, Mr Nicholas LLB(Lond) M *Jul 1979*
12, 30, 40, 53, 11, 67, 85, 27, 63
1 Chancery Lane, London WC2
p928 . . . . 0845 634 6666

YEO, Colin M *Mar 2002*
23, 20, 10
Renaissance Chambers, London WC1
p949 . . . . 020 7404 1111

Yeo, Mr Nik BA; LLB(Melbourne); BCL(Oxon) M *Nov 2000*
Fountain Court Chambers, London EC4
p934 . . . . 020 7583 3335

Yeung, Mr Stuart I *Nov 1999*
15, 20
Northampton Chambers, Northampton
p988 . . . . 01604 636271

Yip, Mrs Amanda BA; Recorder G *Dec 1991*
(Q.C.) *30, 53, 56, 96*
Exchange Chambers, Manchester
p983 . . . . 0161 833 2722
Exchange Chambers, Liverpool
p980 . . . . 0151 236 7747
Exchange Chambers, Leeds
p977 . . . . 0113 203 1970

Yong, Miss Pearl L *Nov 1993*
23, 57
Two King's Bench Walk, London EC4
p939 . . . . 020 7353 7202 / 7353 3909
Renaissance Chambers, London WC1
p949 . . . . 020 7404 1111

YORKE, Mr Richard BA(Hons)(Shef) M *Oct 2006*
10, 20
Coram Chambers, London EC1
p929 . . . . 020 7092 3700

Youll, Miss Joanna Isabel LLB(Lond) G *Nov 1989*
Field Court Chambers, London WC1
p933 . . . . 020 7405 6114

Young, Mr Andrew Charles Alexander BA(Hons); MSE; CPE; GDL L *Nov 2008*
10, 11, 12, 67, 15, 18, 20, 88, 94
7 Bedford Row, London WC1
p924 . . . . 020 7242 3555

YOUNG, Mr Andrew G L *Jul 1977*
11, 12, 18, 22, 24, 36, 59
3 Hare Court, London EC4
p937 . . . . 020 7415 7800

Young, Mr Andrew Paul L *Jan 1992*
58, 57, 34
Prince Henry's Chambers, London WC1
p947 . . . . 020 7837 1645

Young, Mr Christopher M *Oct 1997*
31, 46, 84, 26, 78, 54, 60, 61
No5 Chambers, Bristol
p971 . . . . 0845 210 5555
No5 Chambers, London EC4
p944 . . . . 0845 210 5555
No5 Chambers, Birmingham
p968 . . . . 0845 210 5555

YOUNG, Mr David BA(Hons); LLM M *Jul 1986*
Nine Bedford Row, London WC1
p924 . . . . 020 7489 2727
Park Court Chambers, Leeds
p978 . . . . 0113 243 3277

Young, Mr Lee LLB(Hons) M *Oct 1991*
20, 10, 11, 40, 30
Guildhall Chambers, Portsmouth
p990 . . . . 023 9275 2400

Young, Mr Martin LLB; LLM M *Nov 1984*
8, 11, 18, 36, 40, 47, 55, 88, 93, 31, 25, 38
9 Stone Buildings Barristers Chambers, London WC2
p951 . . . . 020 7404 5055

YOUNG, Miss Rachel I *Jan 2006*
12, 30, 11, 40, 53, 22, 29
Ropewalk Chambers, Nottingham
p989 . . . . 0115 947 2581

Young, Miss Rebecca Leah LLB(Hons) I *Nov 1993*
10, 12, 15, 20, 30, 18
39 Park Square, Leeds
p978 . . . . 0113 245 6633

Young, Mr Simon MA(Hons) I *Nov 1998*
11, 12, 18, 30, 40, 53, 55
Kings Chambers, Leeds
p978 . . . . 0113 242 1123
Kings Chambers, Manchester
p984 . . . . 0161 832 9082

Young, Mr Timothy BA; BCL(Oxon) G *Jul 1977*
(Q.C.) *3, 11, 12, 24, 35, 41*
20 Essex Street, London WC2
p932 . . . . 020 7842 1200

YOUNIS, Miss Saima I *Nov 2008*
10, 20
Queen Elizabeth Buildings, London EC4
p948 . . . . 020 7797 7837

YOUSHANI, Elahe L *Jan 2005*
St James's Chambers, Manchester
p984 . . . . 0161 834 7000

YULE, Miss Stephanie L *Oct 2005*
10, 12, 20, 30
Trinity Chambers, Chelmsford
p974 . . . . 01245 605040

Zabihi, Mrs Tanya LLB(Hons); Diploma in Child Protection G *Jun 1988*
20, 10
3PB, Bristol
p971 . . . . 0117 928 1520

ZACAROLI, Mr Antony BA; BCL(Oxon) M *Nov 1987*
(Q.C.) *5, 6, 8, 11, 12, 24, 29, 38*
South Square, London WC1
p950 . . . . 020 7696 9900

ZAFFUTO, Ms Rosa M *Jan 2000*
Lombard Chambers, London EC1
p941 . . . . 020 7107 2100

Zakers, Mr Franklyn R LLB(Hons) L *Nov 1999*
Park Court Chambers, Leeds
p978 . . . . 0113 243 3277

Zaman, Mr Mohammed Khalil LLB(Warw) G *Jul 1985*
(Q.C.) *22, 7, 11, 8, 18*
Hardwicke, London WC2
p936 . . . . 020 7242 2523
St Philips Chambers, Birmingham
p969 . . . . 0121 246 7000

Zaman, Miss Shazma M *Nov 2003*
37 Park Square Chambers, Leeds
p978 . . . . 0113 243 9422

Zeb, Miss Emma LLB(Lond) I *Jul 1998*
30, 53
St John's Chambers, Bristol
p972 . . . . 0117 921 3456

Zeitlin, Mr Derek J L *Jul 1974*
15, 51, 62, 34
Nine Bedford Row, London WC1
p924 . . . . 020 7489 2727

ZELIN, Mr Geoffrey MA(Cantab) M *Jul 1984*
5, 6, 8, 11, 22, 29, 40, 49, 38, 88
Enterprise Chambers, London WC2
p931 . . . . 020 7405 9471
Enterprise Chambers, Leeds
p977 . . . . 0113 246 0391
Enterprise Chambers, Newcastle upon Tyne
p987 . . . . 0191 222 3344

Zellick, Mr Adam BA(Cantab) M *Oct 2000*
Fountain Court Chambers, London EC4
p934 . . . . 020 7583 3335

Zentar, Dr Remy LLD G *Jul 1997*
20, 10, 14
St Johns Buildings, Preston
p990 . . . . 01772 256100
St Johns Buildings, Chester
p974 . . . . 01244 323070
St Johns Buildings, Manchester
p985 . . . . 0161 214 1500
St Johns Buildings, Liverpool
p982 . . . . 0151 243 6000

Zentler-Munro, Ms Ruth I *Nov 2004*
15, 62
15 New Bridge Street Chambers, London EC4
p943 . . . . 020 7842 1900

Zimbler, Miss Alexia L *Oct 1993*
Broad Chare Chambers, Newcastle upon Tyne
p986 . . . . 0191 232 0541
Maidstone Chambers, Maidstone
p982 . . . . 01622 688592

ZOEST, Miss Jacqueline G *Nov 1995*
Carmelite Chambers, London EC4
p927 . . . . 020 7936 6300

Zorbas, Mr Panos C L *Jun 1964*
15
Argent Chambers, London WC2
p923 . . . . 020 7556 5500

Zoubir, Adam L *Jan 2005*
4 KBW, London EC4
p938 . . . . 020 7822 8822

ZWART, Mr Christiaan I *Oct 1997*
1, 7, 26, 31, 46, 11, 25, 61, 34
Thirty Nine Essex Street, London WC2
p932 . . . . 020 7832 1111

See p1010 for the Key to Work Categories

EMPLOYED BARRISTERS, ENGLAND & WALES – A-Z

Abbasi, Miss Lubna L *Jan 2001*
BA(Hons); LLM. Northamptonshire Magistrates Courts, Regents Pavilion, Summerhouse Road, Moulton Park, Northampton, Northamptonshire NN3 6AS *Tel:*01604 497000 *Fax:*01536 497010 Court Clerk

Adam, Mrs Feroza Nazeem Shah-e M *Nov 1984*
BA(Hons)(Law); Barrister. Windsor & Maidenhead Borough Council, Town Hall, St Ives Road, Maidenhead, Windsor & Maidenhead SL6 1RF *Tel:*01628 798888 *Fax:*01628 796408 *Dx:*6422 MAIDENHEAD. Contracts Lawyer

Adams, Mrs Linda J I *Nov 1994*
LLB; Barrister. The Automobile Association, Group Legal Services, Fanum House 9, Basing View, Basingstoke, Hampshire RG21 4EA *Tel:*01256 491588 *Fax:*01256 494666

Adams, Mrs Louise Ann L *Nov 1982*
BA. Anthos London Ltd, 4th Floor, Eagle House, London SW1Y 6EE *Tel:*020 7024 3500 *Fax:*020 7024 3501 Director

Adcock, Thomas C A I *Nov 1974*
Treasury Solicitors Department, 7th Floor, One Kemble Street, London WC2B 4TS *Tel:*020 7210 3000 *Fax:*020 7210 3004 *Dx:*123242 KINGSWAY.

Adutt, James I L *Oct 1992*
Treasury Solicitors Department, 7th Floor, One Kemble Street, London WC2B 4TS *Tel:*020 7210 3000 *Fax:*020 7210 3004 *Dx:*123242 KINGSWAY.

Aga, Ms Kamini I *Jul 2004*
Bolton Magistrates Court, The Courts, Civic Centre, PO Box 24, Bolton, Greater Manchester BL1 1QX *Tel:*01204 558200 *Fax:*01204 364373 *Dx:*707360 BOLTON 6. Trainee Legal Adviser

Ahmad, Mirza Farakh Navid G *Jul 1984*
BSocSc(Hons); MBA; LLM. Birmingham City Council Legal & Democratic Services, Ingleby House, 11-14 Cannon Street, Birmingham, West Midlands B2 5EN *Tel:*0121 303 2066 *Fax:*0121 303 1312 *Dx:*13053 BIRMINGHAM.

Alderman, Richard G *Jan 1974*
LLB. Serious Fraud Office, Elm House, 10-16 Elm Street, London WC1X 0BJ *Tel:*020 7239 7272 *Fax:*020 7837 1689 *Dx:*135896 LONDON GRAY'S INN ROAD. *E-mail:*public.enquiries@sfo.gsi.gov.uk Director

Allan, Robert John L *Jun 1980*
BA(Hons)(Law). Haringey Magistrates Legal Advisers Office, The Court House, Bishops Road off Archway Road, Highgate, London N6 4HS *Tel:*0845 601 3600 *Fax:*020 8273 3838 *Dx:*123550 HIGHGATE 3. *E-mail:*firstname.secondname@hmcourts-service.gsi.gov.uk Director of Legal Services

Allbless, Edward M *Jul 1990*
MA(Oxon). South Bank University, Faculty of Law & Business, 103 Borough Road, Southwark, London SE1 0AA *Tel:*020 7277 1091 Lecturer in Commercial Law

Allen, Neil Edward I *Feb 1993*
Wokingham District Council, PO Box 152 , Civic Offices, Shute End, Wokingham RG40 1WJ *Tel:*0118 974 6000 *Fax:*0118 974 6542 *Dx:*33506 WOKINGHAM. Senior Lawyer

Allott, Stephen Antony G *Oct 1981*
McKinsey and Co, No 1 Jeremy Street, London SW1Y 4UH *Tel:*020 7839 8040 *Fax:*020 7873 9777 Associate

Amir, Ms Nasim G *Nov 1990*
Department for Business, Enterprise and Regulatory Reform, 1 Victoria Street, London SW1H 0ET *Tel:*020 7215 0105

Andrews, Ms Christalla G *Jul 1982*
BA(Hons)(Business Law). Society of Lloyd's, One Lime Street, London EC3M 7HA *Tel:*020 7327 1000 *Fax:*020 7626 2389 Commercial Team Manager

Ansari, Javed L *Oct 2003*
LLB(Hons)(Law). London Borough of Haringey, Legal Services, Alexandra House, 10 Station Road, Haringey, London N22 4TR *Tel:*020 8489 0000 *Fax:*020 8489 3835 / 5984 *Dx:*35651 WOOD GREEN 1.

Armitage, Roderick Donald M *Feb 1979*
FCIS. Confederation of British Industry, Centre Point, 103 New Oxford Street, London WC1A 1DU *Tel:*020 7379 8044 *Fax:*020 7836 1114 *E-mail:*rod.armitage@cbi.org.uk Head of Company Affairs

Arthur, Robin Anthony G *Nov 1976*
LLB. Parmentier Arthur, 7 The Waits, St Ives, Cambridgeshire PE27 5BY *Tel:*01480 465522 *Fax:*01480 461221 *E-mail:*robin.arthur@parmentierarthur.com Managing Director

Ashbee, Matthew Noel Dominic M *Jul 1974*
LLB; LLM(Lond). Bromley College of Further & Higher Education, Rookery Lane, Bromley, Kent BR2 8HE *Tel:*020 8295 7000 *Fax:*020 8595 7099 *E-mail:*info@bromley.ac.uk Course Tutor of Legal Executive Courses

Atherton-Ham, James L *Oct 1993*
LLB(Hons). National Grid PLC, National Grid Park, Warwick Technology Park, Gallows Hill, Warwick, Warwickshire CV34 6DA *Tel:*01926 653000 *Fax:*01926 654378 Senior Counsel Work: 18,22,30,32,12,20

Aylett, Anthony P M M *May 1971*
Treasury Solicitors Department, 7th Floor, One Kemble Street, London WC2B 4TS *Tel:*020 7210 3000 *Fax:*020 7210 3004 *Dx:*123242 KINGSWAY.

Bacon, Stephen F T G *Jul 1969*
LLB; AKC. Express Newspapers PLC, Ludgate House, 245 Blackfriars Road, Southwark, London SE1 9UX *Tel:*020 7922 7785 *Fax:*020 7922 7967 Legal Adviser

Baggs, David John L *Nov 1975*
LLB. Borough of Poole, Legal and Democratic Services, Room 159, Civic Centre, Poole BH15 2RU *Tel:*01202 262808 *Fax:*01202 262818 *Dx:*123820 POOLE 7. *E-mail:*dhamerton@poole.gov.uk Employed Barrister

Baker, Leslie G *Mar 2004*
LLB(Hons). Essex County Council, County Hall, Market Road, Chelmsford, Essex CM1 1LX *Tel:*0845 743 0430 *Fax:*01245 352710 *Dx:*123300 CHELMSFORD 7. Barrister

Ball, Andrew Charles Manton G *Nov 1979*
LLB. Touche Ross & Co, Hill House, 1 Little New Street, London EC4A 3TR *Tel:*020 7936 3000 ext: 012 *Fax:*020 7583 8517 VAT Partner

Barber, Philip G *Nov 1991*
LLB. Harehills & Chapeltown Law Centre, 263 Roundhay Road, Leeds, West Yorkshire LS8 4HS *Tel:*0113 249 1100 Lawyer Work: 1,47,22,51,88,89,63,93

Barker, Ramsey M *Nov 1989*
LLB; DMS. Furness & District Petty Sessional Division, Magistrates' Court, Abbey Road, Barrow-in-Furness, Cumbria LA14 5QX *Tel:*01229 820161 *Fax:*01229 870287 *Dx:*63909 BARROW-IN-FURNESS. Barrister

Barnato, Michael I *Nov 1978*
BA(Econ); MA(Econ); ACIS. Strategy and Marketing Partners, 17 St Matthew's Avenue, Surbiton, Surrey KT6 6JJ *Tel:*020 8399 7595 *Fax:*020 8390 5950 *E-mail:*mike@strategy-partners.co.uk Director

Barton, Charles N I *Jul 1986*
Treasury Solicitors Department, 7th Floor, One Kemble Street, London WC2B 4TS *Tel:*020 7210 3000 *Fax:*020 7210 3004 *Dx:*123242 KINGSWAY.

Barton, Nigel John L *Jul 1977*
BA. Citibank N A, Promenade Level, Cabot Place East, Canary Wharf, London E14 4QS *Tel:*020 7500 5000 Vice President

Basaran, Mrs Sandra J G *Jul 1984*
LLB(Hons). Consolidated Financial Insurance, Building 11, Chiswick Park, Chiswick High Road, London W4 5XR *Tel:*020 8380 3000 *Fax:*020 8380 3065 Group Legal Director

Bazley, Stuart Richard M *Nov 1991*
LLB. Irish Life Assurance PLC, The Irish Life Centre, Victoria Street, St Albans, Hertfordshire AL1 5TF *Tel:*01727 817000 *Fax:*01727 848924 Head of Legal & Compliance

Beach, Nicholas P M *Nov 1983*
Treasury Solicitors Department, 7th Floor, One Kemble Street, London WC2B 4TS *Tel:*020 7210 3000 *Fax:*020 7210 3004 *Dx:*123242 KINGSWAY.

Beardmore, Ms Alison Claire G *Oct 1991*
LLB(Hons). Central & South West Staffordshire Magistrates Court, The Court House, South Walls, Stafford, Staffordshire ST16 3DW *Tel:*01785 223144 *Fax:*01785 258508 *Dx:*14575 STAFFORD 1. Area Legal Manager

Beecroft, Ms Kirstie I *Feb 1994*
LLB(Hons). Essex County Council, County Hall, Market Road, Chelmsford, Essex CM1 1LX *Tel:*0845 743 0430 *Fax:*01245 352710 *Dx:*123300 CHELMSFORD 7. Principal Barrister Work: 15,20

Benney, Mark W I *Jul 1982*
Treasury Solicitors Department, 7th Floor, One Kemble Street, London WC2B 4TS *Tel:*020 7210 3000 *Fax:*020 7210 3004 *Dx:*123242 KINGSWAY.

Betteley, Jason P I *Oct 1990*
Treasury Solicitors Department, 7th Floor, One Kemble Street, London WC2B 4TS *Tel:*020 7210 3000 *Fax:*020 7210 3004 *Dx:*123242 KINGSWAY.

Bhogal, Kashminder S L *Nov 1981*
LLB(Hons). Southall Rights Ltd, 54 High Street, Southall, Middlesex UB1 3DB *Tel:*020 8571 4920 *Fax:*020 8571 9584 Director

Blackburn, LT Cmmdr (RNR) George Richard I *Nov 1948*
MA(Cantab); ALAM; ARAESoc; VRD. Kings Park Management Co Ltd, 1 Shannon Way, Kings Park, Pevensey Bay Road, Eastbourne, East Sussex BN23 6UA *Tel:*01323 769978 Company Secretary/Consultant (BACFI Member)

Blair, Ms Linda Susan G *Oct 1993*
Barrister; LLB(Hons). Royal Borough of Kingston upon Thames, Guildhall, High Street, Kingston upon Thames, Surrey KT1 1EU *Tel:*020 8546 2121 *Fax:*020 8547 5127 *Dx:*31515 KINGSTON UPON THAMES. Principal Housing Lawyer

Block, Oliver G *Oct 2002*
LLB; PG Dip Professional Legal Skills. North Devon District Council, Civic Centre, North Walk, Barnstaple, Devon EX31 1EA *Tel:*01271 327711 *Fax:*01271 388261 *E-mail:*info@northdevon.gov.uk Planning Lawyer

Bloyce, Miss Samantha Jeanette G *Nov 1997*
LLB(Hons); Barrister. HM Revenue & Customs, Solicitor's Office, Ralli Quays (West), 3 Stanley Street, Salford, Greater Manchester M60 9LB *Tel:*0870 785 8545 *Fax:*0870 785 8528 *Dx:*742371 SALFORD 20. Senior Lawyer

Blythe, Mark Andrew I *Nov 1966*
BCL; MA(Oxon). Treasury Solicitors Department, 7th Floor, One Kemble Street, London WC2B 4TS *Tel:*020 7210 3000 *Fax:*020 7210 3004 *Dx:*123242 KINGSWAY.

Bog, Graham Taylor M *Jul 1976*
LLB. Intertek Testing Services, 25 Saville Row, London W1S 2ES *Tel:*020 7396 3400 Regional Director-Europe, Middle East & Africa

Boissezon, Miss Corinne L M M *Jul 2003*
LLB(Hons). The Magistrates' Courts' Commission, The Magistrates' Court Brent, 448 High Road, Church End, London NW10 2DZ *Tel:*020 8451 2425 *Fax:*020 8451 6227 Employed barrister

Bousher, Stephen G *Nov 1975*
H M Revenue & Customs, Somerset House, Strand, London WC2R 1LB Barrister

Boustred, Mrs Anne Mary I *Jul 1995*
LLB(Hons). Luton Borough Council, Town Hall, George Street, Luton, Luton LU1 2BQ *Tel:*01582 546000 *Fax:*01582 546994 *Dx:*5926 LUTON. Senior Lawyer

Bowler, Christopher G *Jul 1978*
LLB(Hons). Her Majesty's Courts Service Bury St Edmunds, Justices Clerks Office, Shire Hall, Bury St Edmunds, Suffolk IP33 1HF *Tel:*01284 352300 *Fax:*01284 352343; Peterborough Magistrates Court, Bridge Street, Peterborough PE1 1ED *Tel:*01223 314311 *Fax:*01733 313749 *Dx:*702304 PETERBOROUGH 8. Justices' Clerk / Barrister

Boyd, David John G *Jan 1963*
(Q.C.) 1982 Hewlett-Packard Ltd, Amen Corner, Cain Road, Bracknell, Bracknell Forest RG12 1HN *Tel:*01344 360000 *Fax:*01344 362224 Director, Legal Services

13

Braby-Pavitt, Ms Lynne G *Nov 1986*
LLB(Hons). Essex County Council, County Hall, Market Road, Chelmsford, Essex CM1 1LX *Tel:*0845 743 0430 *Fax:*01245 352710 *Dx:*123300 CHELMSFORD 7. Principal Barrister

Braggins, James R J G *Jul 1972*
Treasury Solicitors Department, 7th Floor, One Kemble Street, London WC2B 4TS *Tel:*020 7210 3000 *Fax:*020 7210 3004 *Dx:*123242 KINGSWAY.

Brett-Holt, Ms Alex L *Jul 1973*
Department for Business, Enterprise and Regulatory Reform, 1 Victoria Street, London SW1H 0ET *Tel:*020 7215 0105

Brewster, David John G *Jan 1961*
MA(Cantab). Investment Management Regulatory Organisation, 25 The North Colonnade, Canary Wharf, London E14 5HS *Tel:*020 7066 1000 *Fax:*020 7066 1099 Legal Adviser

Brinkworth, Paul Gregory L *Oct 1990*
BA. Serious Fraud Office, Elm House, 10-16 Elm Street, London WC1X 0BJ *Tel:*020 7239 7272 *Fax:*020 7837 1689 *Dx:*135896 LONDON GRAY'S INN ROAD. *E-mail:*public.enquiries@sfo.gsi.gov.uk Case Controller Work: 15

Broadway, Dennis I *Oct 1993*
LLB. School of Law, University Park, Nottingham NG7 2RD *Tel:*0115 951 5700 *Fax:*0115 951 5696

Brough, Simon G *May 1987*
BA(Hons). Clerk to Sheffield Justices, Magistrates Court, Castle Street, Sheffield, South Yorkshire S3 8LU *Tel:*0114 276 0760 *Fax:*0114 272 0129 *Dx:*10599 SHEFFIELD. Principal Legal Adviser

Brown, David Charles M *Feb 1993*
BSc(Hons). Birmingham City Council Legal & Democratic Services, Ingleby House, 11-14 Cannon Street, Birmingham, West Midlands B2 5EN *Tel:*0121 303 2066 *Fax:*0121 303 1312 *Dx:*13053 BIRMINGHAM.

Brown, Mrs Elaine Maude M *Jul 1983*
LLB(Lond); LLM(Lond). Office of the Public Guardian, Archway Tower, 2 Junction Road, London N19 5SZ *Tel:*020 7664 7000 *Fax:*020 7664 7705 *Dx:*141150 ARCHWAY 2. Deputy Legal Adviser

Brown, Mrs Wendy Pamela L *Feb 1994*
LLB(Hons); LLM. Eastgate Assistance Ltd, Eastgate House, Stephenson Road, The Business Park, Colchester, Essex CO4 4QR *Tel:*0870 523 4500 *Fax:*0870 523 4508 *Dx:*3626 COLCHESTER. Barrister

Bugeja, Albert John L *Nov 1981*
BA(Hons). Rochford District Council, Council Offices, 3-19 South Street, Rochford, Essex SS4 1BW *Tel:*01702 546366 *Fax:*01702 545737 *Dx:*39751 ROCHFORD. *E-mail:*legal.services@rochford.gov.uk

Burling, Julian Michael G *Jul 1976*
MA; LLB(Cantab). Society of Lloyd's, One Lime Street, London EC3M 7HA *Tel:*020 7327 1000 *Fax:*020 7626 2389 Counse to Lloyd's

Burman, Keith William M *Jul 1984*
SBStJ. Greenwich Magistrates Court, 9 Blackheath Road, Greenwich, London SE10 8PG *Tel:*020 8276 1341 *Fax:*020 8276 1399 *Dx:*35203 GREENWICH WEST. Bench Legal Manager

Burrows, Mrs Carole J G *Apr 1989*
Central & South West Staffordshire Magistrates Court, The Court House, South Walls, Stafford, Staffordshire ST16 3DW *Tel:*01785 223144 *Fax:*01785 258508 *Dx:*14575 STAFFORD 1. Senior Legal Adviser

Burton, Raymond G *Nov 1968*
Department for Business, Enterprise and Regulatory Reform, 1 Victoria Street, London SW1H 0ET *Tel:*020 7215 0105

Busby, David John M *Oct 1966*
LLB. Tioxide Group Ltd, Haverton Hill Road, Billingham, Stockton-on-Tees TS23 1PS *Tel:*020 7602 7121 *Fax:*020 8784 0019 Company Secretary

Butcher, Michael Joseph G *Jul 1975*
Central Railway, Chichester House, 278/282 High Holborn, London WC1V 7HA *Tel:*020 7404 1888 *Fax:*020 7404 1868 Managing Director & General Counsel

Byrne, Kevin M M *Nov 1983*
BA(Law). Great Yarmouth Magistrates Court, Magistrates Court House, North Quay, Great Yarmouth, Norfolk NR30 1PW *Tel:*01493 849800 *Fax:*01493 852169 *Dx:*139400 GREAT YARMOUTH 3. *E-mail:*greatyarmouth.court@hmcourts-service.gsi.gov.uk Bench Legal Adviser

Callender Smith, Robin G *Jul 1977*
LLB. Thames Magistrates Court, 58 Bow Road, London E3 4DJ *Tel:*020 8980 1000 *Fax:*020 8980 0670 *Dx:*55654 BOW. Youth Justices' Clerk

Caller, Mitchell Bernard M *Sept 1997*
BA(Hons)(Oxon). JP Morgan Chase Bank, 125 London Wall, London EC2Y 5AJ *Tel:*020 7777 2000 *Fax:*020 7777 3141 Vice president of UK Legal Department

Calvert, Philip Alan M *Sept 1977*
BA. Sea Containers Services Ltd, Sea Containers House, 20 Upper Ground, Blackfriars, Southwark, London SE1 9PF *Tel:*020 7805 5202 *Fax:*020 7805 5912 Director Legal Services

Cam, David Edward M *May 1981*
BA. Blackpool Pleasure Beach Group, 525 Promenade, Blackpool FY4 1EZ *Tel:*01253 341033 *Fax:*01253 401098 Group Company Secretary and Director

Cane, Lindsay David I *Sept 1981*
BA; MA. Oxford City Council, Town Hall, Blueboar Street, Oxford, Oxfordshire OX1 1BX *Tel:*01865 249811 *Fax:*01865 252694 Barrister

Carey-Yard, Gordon Michael G *Nov 1982*
LLB(Hons). Metropolitan Police Directorate of Legal Services, First Floor, Victoria Block, New Scotland Yard, London SW1H 0BG *Tel:*020 7230 7210 *Fax:*020 7230 7209 Senior Lawyer

Carney, Ms Julie M *Nov 1990*
Department for Business, Enterprise and Regulatory Reform, 1 Victoria Street, London SW1H 0ET *Tel:*020 7215 0105

Carpenter, Michael C L I *Jul 1971*
Treasury Solicitors Department, 7th Floor, One Kemble Street, London WC2B 4TS *Tel:*020 7210 3000 *Fax:*020 7210 3004 *Dx:*123242 KINGSWAY.

Carr, Mrs Linda M *Jul 2002*
LLB(Hons). South Tyneside Magistrates Court, Millbank, Secretan Way, South Shields, Tyne & Wear NE33 1RG *Tel:*0191 455 8800 *Fax:*0191 427 4499 Legal Adviser

Carter, Robert James I *Jul 1995*
BSc(Hons). Shell International Ltd, Shell Centre, York Road, London SE1 7NA *Tel:*020 7934 1234 *Fax:*020 7934 3023 *Dx:*473 LONDON/CHANCERY LN. *E-mail:*l.dalsgaard@shell.com Associate Legal Counsel, IP

Case, Mrs Sally A I *Oct 1996*
LLB. RSPCA, Wilberforce Way, Southwater, Horsham, West Sussex RH13 9RS *Tel:*0870 010 1181 *Fax:*0870 753 0048 *Dx:*57628 HORSHAM 6. *E-mail:*legal_services@rspca.org.uk Head of Society Prosecutions

Casely-Hayford, Ms Margaret G *Jul 1983*
John Lewis plc, Corporate Offices, Partnership House, Carlisle Place, London SW1P 1BX *Tel:*020 7828 1000 *Fax:*020 7592 6566 Director Of Legal Services And Company Director

Chambers, Michael L *Nov 1966*
BA. Chambers and Partners, 74 Long Lane, Tower Hamlets, London EC1A 9ET *Tel:*020 7315 8996 *Fax:*020 7315 8998

Champness, Andrew P M *Oct 1998*
PGCE; LLB. Gloucestershire Magistrates' Courts, PO Box 9051, Gloucester, Gloucestershire GL1 2XG *Tel:*01452 420100 *Fax:*01452 833551 / 833555 *Dx:*9866 GLOUCESTER 5. Barrister

Chandler, Miss Esme Katherine I *Jul 1982*
LLB(B'ham). The College of Law, 14 Store Street, Bloomsbury, London WC1E 7DE *Tel:*0800 289997 Senior Lecturer

Chaplin, Richard James M *Feb 1992*
LLB(Hons); LLM(Cantab); PG Dip EC Company Law. Hess Ltd, Level 9, The Adelphi Building, 1-11 John Adam Street, London WC2N 6AG *Tel:*020 7331 3000 *Fax:*020 7331 3004 Assistant General Counsel

Chapman, David N M *Nov 1989*
LLB. Pembrokeshire Magistrates' Court, Clerks Office, Penffynnon, Hawthorn Rise, Haverfordwest, Pembrokeshire SA61 2AZ *Tel:*01437 772090 *Fax:*01437 768662 *Dx:*99613 HAVERFORDWEST 2.

Charvonia, Arthur James M *Nov 1999*
LLB. Waveney District Council, Town Hall, High Street, Lowestoft, Suffolk NR32 1HS *Tel:*01502 562111 *Fax:*01502 589327 *Dx:*41220 LOWESTOFT. Principal Solicitor

Choudhury, Bhaskar L *Nov 1988*
BSc; BA; MSc; LLB; ACMA. Eastgate Assistance Ltd, Eastgate House, Stephenson Road, The Business Park, Colchester, Essex CO4 4QR *Tel:*0870 523 4500 *Fax:*0870 523 4508 *Dx:*3626 COLCHESTER. Barrister

Chowdhury, Atiqur Rahman L *Mar 1999*
LLB(Lond); LLM(Lond). The Newspaper Society, St Andrews House, 18-20 St Andrews Street, London EC4A 3AY *Tel:*020 7632 7400 *Fax:*020 7632 7401 *E-mail:*ns@newspapersoc.org.uk Legal Adviser(Advertising & Regulating Affairs)

Churaman, Miss Debbie M *Nov 1984*
Department for Business, Enterprise and Regulatory Reform, 1 Victoria Street, London SW1H 0ET *Tel:*020 7215 0105

Cleary, Edmund G *Apr 1986*
BA(Law). Sunderland Magistrates Court, Gillbridge Avenue, Sunderland, Tyne & Wear SR1 3AP *Tel:*0191 514 1621 *Fax:*0191 565 8564 *Dx:*67757 SUNDERLAND.

Cluett, Ms Deborah Mary L *Jan 1983*
City of London Corporation, Guildhall, London EC2P 2EJ *Tel:*020 7606 3030 *Fax:*020 7332 1992 *Dx:*121783 GUILDHALL. Chief Legal Assistant

Cole, Martin David I *Nov 1994*
Financial Services Authority, 25 The North Colonnade, Canary Wharf, London E14 5HS *Tel:*020 7066 1000 Work: 8,18,22,25,30,40

Collier-Wright, Charles Edward H M *Jul 1976*
BA(Hons). Trinity Mirror PLC, One Canada Square, Canary Wharf, London E14 5AP *Tel:*020 7293 3934 *Fax:*020 7293 3613 Group Legal Manager

Conceicao, Carlos M *Jul 1987*
Department for Business, Enterprise and Regulatory Reform, 1 Victoria Street, London SW1H 0ET *Tel:*020 7215 0105

Cooper, James J I *Jul 1986*
Treasury Solicitors Department, 7th Floor, One Kemble Street, London WC2B 4TS *Tel:*020 7210 3000 *Fax:*020 7210 3004 *Dx:*123242 KINGSWAY.

Cooper, Ms Susan I *Oct 1990*
BSc(Hons); Diplaw. Financial Services Authority, 25 The North Colonnade, Canary Wharf, London E14 5HS *Tel:*020 7066 1000

Coward, Ms Antoinette I *Nov 1994*
LLB(Hons). Birmingham City Council Legal & Democratic Services, Ingleby House, 11-14 Cannon Street, Birmingham, West Midlands B2 5EN *Tel:*0121 303 2066 *Fax:*0121 303 1312 *Dx:*13053 BIRMINGHAM.

Coyte, Anthony C M *Nov 1984*
BA. Towry Law PLC, Towry Law House, The Western Centre, Western Road, Bracknell, Bracknell Forest RG12 1TL *Tel:*01344 828000 *Fax:*01344 828001 *E-mail:*dainslie@towrylaw.com Technical Director

Crockford, Gary Brett I *Nov 1980*
BA. Chartered Association of Certified Accountants, 29 Lincolns Inn Fields, London WC2A 3EE *Tel:*020 7242 6855

Croft, Ms Caroline G *Nov 1991*
BA(Oxon). Department for Business, Enterprise and Regulatory Reform, 1 Victoria Street, London SW1H 0ET *Tel:*020 7215 0105

Curtis, Ms Rebecca I *Oct 1993*
BSc; CPE. Bristol City Council, Legal Department, Council House, College Green, Bristol BS1 5TR *Tel:*0117 922 2000 *Fax:*0117 922 2172 *Dx:*7827. Barrister

Curtis, Richard Anthony I *Jul 1984*
LLM(Lond). Essex County Council, County Hall, Market Road, Chelmsford, Essex CM1 1LX *Tel:*0845 743 0430 *Fax:*01245 352710 *Dx:*123300 CHELMSFORD 7.; Fraud Investigation Group, 50 Ludgate Hill, London EC4M 7EX *Tel:*020 7273 8000 *Fax:*020 7329 8164 *Dx:*300850 LUDGATE. Team Manager

Cyrus, Willan Julius L *Nov 1984*
BA; DipLaw. Reading Borough Council, Civic Offices, Civic Centre, Reading RG1 7AE *Tel:*01734 875444 *Fax:*01734 752786; Reading Borough Council, Civic Offices, Civic Centre, Reading RG1 7AE *Tel:*0118 939 0900 *Fax:*0118 939 0767 *Dx:*40124 READING (CASTLE STREET). Barrister

D'Souza, Miss Mavis Mathilda Ursula M *Nov 1985*
Informa Publishing Group Ltd, Telephone House, 69-77 Paul Street, London EC2A 4LQ *Tel:*020 7553 1000 *Fax:*020 7553 1100 Editor-Lloyd's Law Reports

Dabbs, Ian G *Oct 1993*
LLB(Hons). Clerk to Sheffield Justices, Magistrates Court, Castle Street, Sheffield, South Yorkshire S3 8LU *Tel:*0114 276 0760 *Fax:*0114 272 0129 *Dx:*10599 SHEFFIELD. Senior Legal Adviser

Daber, Timothy Mark G *Nov 1981*
LLB(Hons); MCMI. Cambridge Magistrates Court, The Court House, Lion Yard, Cambridge, Cambridgeshire CB2 3NA *Tel:*01223 314311 *Fax:*01223 355237 *Dx:*131966 CAMBRIDGE. Clerk to the Justices

Dalby, Marc I *Jul 1986*
MA(Oxon). Merck Sharp & Dohme Ltd, Hertford Road, Hoddesdon, Hertfordshire EN11 9BU *Tel:*01992 452509 *Fax:*01992 470189 Legal Director

Daniels, Miss Tanya Collette L *Nov 1985*
LLB(Exon). Fujitsu Technology Solutions International Limited, Grafton House, Grafton Way, Basingstoke, Hampshire RG22 6HY *Tel:*01256 865100 *Fax:*01256 865106 *E-mail:*tanya_daniels@uk.ftsi.fujitsu.com Legal Director EMEA

Davies, Frederick George I *Jul 1979*
BA(Hons). Peterborough Magistrates Court, Bridge Street, Peterborough PE1 1ED *Tel:*01223 314311 *Fax:*01733 313749 *Dx:*702304 PETERBOROUGH 8.

Davies, Martin John G *Jul 1975*
LLB; LLM. Financial Services Authority, 25 The North Colonnade, Canary Wharf, London E14 5HS *Tel:*020 7066 1000

Davies, Mrs Rachel G *Jul 1995*
LLB(Hons). HM Courts Service Dorset Area, The Law Courts, Stafford Road, Bournemouth BH1 1LA *Tel:*01202 745309 *Fax:*01202 711999 Clerk to the Justices

Davies, Robin Hunkin I *Nov 1960*
LLB. Kiafield (Developments) Ltd, 21 Humes Avenue, Hanwell, London W7 2LJ *Tel:*020 8840 6571 *Fax:*020 8579 0790 Director

Davis, Miss Marcia G *Jul 1992*
Milton Keynes Magistrates Court, 301 Silbury Boulevard, Witan Gate East, Milton Keynes MK9 2AJ *Tel:*0870 241 2819 *Fax:*01908 451146 *Dx:*54462 MILTON KEYNES. Deputy Justices' Clerk

Davison, Andrew Michael M *Nov 1986*
DipLaw. Doncaster Magistrates Court, The Law Courts, College Road, PO Box 49, Doncaster, South Yorkshire DN1 3HT *Tel:*01302 366711 *Fax:*01302 347359 *Dx:*12574 DONCASTER 1.

Dawson, Peter Henry M *Feb 1976*
MA; LLB(Lond). Beauville Ltd, Ashburton Lodge, Broadmead Road, Send, Woking, Surrey GU23 7AD *Tel:*01604 643173 *Fax:*01604 643173 Company Secretary

De Val, Peter R I *Nov 1988*
Treasury Solicitors Department, 7th Floor, One Kemble Street, London WC2B 4TS *Tel:*020 7210 3000 *Fax:*020 7210 3004 *Dx:*123242 KINGSWAY.

Dearing, Anthony John M *Nov 1998*
LLB(Hons). Financial Services Authority, 25 The North Colonnade, Canary Wharf, London E14 5HS *Tel:*020 7066 1000

Denham, Grey I *Nov 1972*
LLB(Lond). GKN PLC (Legal Dept), PO Box 55, Ipsley House, Ipsley Church Lane, Redditch, Worcestershire B98 0TL *Tel:*01527 517715 *Fax:*01527 533470 Group Secretary

Diaper, Malcolm John G *Nov 1978*
LLB; DMA. North West Leicestershire District Council, Council Offices, Whitwick Road, Coalville, Leicestershire LE67 3FJ *Tel:*01530 454545 *Fax:*01530 454506 *Dx:*23662 COALVILLE.

Diaper, Ms Ruth G *Feb 1991*
LLB. Department for Business, Enterprise and Regulatory Reform, 1 Victoria Street, London SW1H 0ET *Tel:*020 7215 0105 Work: 12,15

Dickson, Ian I *Nov 1978*
LLB. Cimage International Ltd, 1000 Great West Road, Brentford, Middlesex TW8 9DW *Tel:*020 8232 2555 *Fax:*020 8758 9388 Director, Commercial & Legal Services

Dingwall, Richard A G *Oct 1991*
LLB. Department for Business, Enterprise and Regulatory Reform, 1 Victoria Street, London SW1H 0ET *Tel:*020 7215 0105

Dodgshon, Simon M *Jul 1986*
BA(Hons); DMS; Barrister. Stockport Magistrates Court, The Courthouse, Edward Street, Stockport, Greater Manchester SK1 3NF *Tel:*0161 477 2020 *Fax:*0161 474 1115 *Dx:*708280 STOCKPORT. Head of Legal Services

Dodson, Timothy C G *Jan 1980*
LLB(Hons); MBA. Cardiff Magistrates Court, Magistrates' Clerks Office, Fitzalan Place, Cardiff CF24 0RZ *Tel:*029 2046 3040

Donnabella, Miss Rosemary M *Feb 1991*
LLB. Serious Fraud Office, Elm House, 10-16 Elm Street, London WC1X 0BJ *Tel:*020 7239 7272 *Fax:*020 7837 1689 *Dx:*135896 LONDON GRAY'S INN ROAD. *E-mail:*public.enquiries@sfo.gsi.gov.uk

Dowling, Carl G *Jan 1998*
Department for Business, Enterprise and Regulatory Reform, 1 Victoria Street, London SW1H 0ET *Tel:*020 7215 0105

Draper, Norman H I *Nov 1978*
BA(Hons). St Helens Magistrates Court, The Court House, Corporation Street, St Helens, Merseyside WA10 1SZ *Tel:*01744 20244 *Fax:*01744 451697 *Dx:*19488 ST HELENS.

Duffield, Mrs Janet Rachel M *Nov 1990*
LLB. Pontefract Magistrates Court, Court House, Front Street, Pontefract, West Yorkshire WF8 1BW *Tel:*01977 691600 *Fax:*01977 691610

Duncan, Ms Denise G *Jan 1985*
LLB; DMS; CTP. South Western Magistrates Court, 176a Lavender Hill, London SW11 1JU *Tel:*020 7805 1447 *Fax:*020 7805 1448 *Dx:*58559 CLAPHAM JUNCTION.

Dunstan, Mrs Tessa J M *Nov 1967*
Department for Business, Enterprise and Regulatory Reform, 1 Victoria Street, London SW1H 0ET *Tel:*020 7215 0105

Eccles, Alan Michael M *Jul 1981*
Dudley Magistrates Court, The Inhedge, Dudley, West Midlands DY1 1RY *Tel:*01384 211411 / 211414 *Fax:*01384 211415 *Dx:*12769 DUDLEY. Clerk to the Justices

Ellis, Ms Rebecca I *Nov 1992*
Department for Business, Enterprise and Regulatory Reform, 1 Victoria Street, London SW1H 0ET *Tel:*020 7215 0105

Emeruwa, John I *Jul 1989*
LLM. Department for Business, Enterprise and Regulatory Reform, 1 Victoria Street, London SW1H 0ET *Tel:*020 7215 0105

Emmitt, Ms Louise G *Oct 1997*
BA(Hons)(Law). South Wales Police, Police Headquarters, Cowbridge Road, Bridgend CF31 3SU *Tel:*01656 869476 *Fax:*01656 302103 Litigation Lawyer

Engelman, Mark G *Nov 1987*
BSc(Pharmacology); DipLaw(City). The Body Shop International PLC, Watersmead Business Park, Littlehampton, West Sussex BN17 6LS *Tel:*01903 731500 *Fax:*01903 731275 Work: 13,11,44,45,16,39,56

Evans, Crispin James Mark I *Jul 1977*
BA. Universal Polygram, 8 St James Square, London SW1Y 4JU *Tel:*020 7747 4000 Director of Legal and Business Affairs

Evans, Peter W M *Nov 1994*
LLB. Department for Business, Enterprise and Regulatory Reform, 1 Victoria Street, London SW1H 0ET *Tel:*020 7215 0105

Eyres, Raymond John I *Nov 1973*
LLB; MA; MBA. Cummins Engine Company Ltd, Unit 1b, Uniongate, Ridgeway Trading Estate, Iver, Buckinghamshire SL0 9HX *Tel:*020 8700 6920 *Fax:*020 8949 5604 Director and Company Secretary

Falk, Andrew Michael Pope I *Feb 1977*
MA(Cantab). Metropolitan Police Directorate of Legal Services, First Floor, Victoria Block, New Scotland Yard, London SW1H 0BG *Tel:*020 7230 7210 *Fax:*020 7230 7209 Senior Lawyer

Farooq, Mohammed Khan L *Oct 1993*
LLB(Hons). Dudley Metropolitan Borough Council, Legal & Property Services, 5 Ednam Road, Dudley, West Midlands DY1 1HL *Tel:*01384 815326 *Fax:*01384 815325 *Dx:*12767 DUDLEY. *E-mail:*legal@vin1.dudley.gov.uk Senior Lawyer

Farrell, Peter Stephen L *Jul 1976*
LLB. Prysmian Cables & Systems Ltd, Chickenhall Lane, Eastleigh, Hampshire SO50 6YU *Tel:*023 8029 5321 *Fax:*023 8029 5317

Faulkner, Ms Angela M *Oct 1987*
LLB(Hons). Norwich Union Life, 2 Rougier Street, York YO90 1UU *Tel:*01904 452210 *Fax:*01904 452856 Barrister

Fedrick, Mrs Janet G *Nov 1974*
Environment Agency (Thames Region), Kings Meadow House, Kings Meadow Road, Reading RG1 8DQ *Tel:*0870 850 6506 *Fax:*0118 950 0388 *Dx:*121325 READING. Prosecution Barrister

See p1010 for the Key to Work Categories

Fenwick, Daniel Fitzgerald L *Oct 1993*
BA(Hons). London Borough of Greenwich Legal Services, 5th Floor , Riverside House , Woolwich High Street, Greenwich, London SE18 6DN *Tel:*020 8921 5123 *Fax:*020 8921 5556 *Dx:*400851 WOOLWICH 5. Senior Lawyer

Fitzpatrick, Desmond Christopher I *Jul 1983*
BA(Hons); DipLaw; Dip(EU Law). Society of Lloyd's, One Lime Street, London EC3M 7HA *Tel:*020 7327 1000 *Fax:*020 7626 2389 Barrister

Flinders, Harold D G *Feb 1981*
BA(Hons). Kellogg Brown & Root (UK) Ltd, Hill Park Court, Springfield Drive, Leatherhead, Surrey KT22 7NL *Tel:*01372 865000 *Fax:*01372 866951 Barrister

Flood, John M *Jul 1975*
LLB. H M Revenue & Customs, Somerset House, Strand, London WC2R 1LB Head of Tax Litigation

Fluker, Ms Christine Louise G *Nov 1976*
MA; LLB(Cantab). De La Rue PLC, De La Rue House, Viables, Basingstoke, Hampshire RG22 4BS *Tel:*01256 605000 *E-mail:*louise.fluker@delarue.com

Forman, Ian M *Nov 1984*
LLB. Department for Business, Enterprise and Regulatory Reform, 1 Victoria Street, London SW1H 0ET *Tel:*020 7215 0105

Fowler, Miss Tracey I *Feb 1994*
LLB(Hons). Metropolitan Police Directorate of Legal Services, First Floor, Victoria Block, New Scotland Yard, London SW1H 0BG *Tel:*020 7230 7210 *Fax:*020 7230 7209 Senior Lawyer

Frankham, David Mark G *Feb 1988*
MBA. Plymouth Justices' Clerk, Magistrates Court, St Andrew Street, Plymouth PL1 2DP *Tel:*01752 206200 *Fax:*01752 206194

Fraser, Anthony K L *Nov 1986*
Treasury Solicitors Department, 7th Floor, One Kemble Street, London WC2B 4TS *Tel:*020 7210 3000 *Fax:*020 7210 3004 *Dx:*123242 KINGSWAY.

French, Ralph John L *Oct 1964*
OBE. Eco Enterprises Ltd Ecoforest Ltd, Orchard Villa, Amersham Road, Chesham, Buckinghamshire HP5 1NE *Tel:*01494 792799 *Fax:*01494 792790 Chairman

Frieze, Mrs Jennie Rochelle G *Aug 2007*
LLB(Hons). The Environment Agency (North West Region [HQ]), PO Box 12, Richard Fairclough House, Knutsford Road, Warrington WA4 1HG *Tel:*01925 653999 *Fax:*01925 574736 *Dx:*709290 WARRINGTON 5. *E-mail:*nick.webb@environment.agency.gov.uk Principal Counsel

Fuller, Mrs Adele Susannah L *Mar 1996*
RSPCA, Wilberforce Way, Southwater, Horsham, West Sussex RH13 9RS *Tel:*0870 010 1181 *Fax:*0870 753 0048 *Dx:*57628 HORSHAM 6. *E-mail:*legal_sevices@rspca.org.uk Charity Lawyer

Furneaux, Mrs Marivere Wallace L *Jan 1950*
Crown Yard Properties Ltd, 72 Queens Gate, London SW7 5JT *Tel:*020 7370 4900 Managing Director

Gallagher, Mrs Margaret S I *Jul 1989*
Treasury Solicitors Department, 7th Floor, One Kemble Street, London WC2B 4TS *Tel:*020 7210 3000 *Fax:*020 7210 3004 *Dx:*123242 KINGSWAY.

Gamble, Neil Robert L *Mar 1998*
Serious Fraud Office, Elm House, 10-16 Elm Street, London WC1X 0BJ *Tel:*020 7239 7272 *Fax:*020 7837 1689 *Dx:*135896 LONDON GRAY'S INN ROAD. *E-mail:*public.enquiries@sfo.gsi.gov.uk Investigative Lawyer

Garland-Collins, Francis M *May 1974*
Basildon Magistrates Court, The Court House, Great Oaks, Basildon, Essex SS14 1EH *Tel:*01268 363400 *Fax:*01268 363497 *E-mail:*basildon@essex-mcc.gov.uk; Grays Magistrates Court, The Court House, Orsett Road, Grays, Thurrock RM17 5SB *Tel:*01245 313300 *Fax:*01245 313399 *Dx:*151020 CHELMSFORD 17. *E-mail:*basildon@essex-mcc.gov.uk Clerk to Magistrates

Gautama, Ms Nisha M *Nov 1988*
LLB. Brent Magistrates Court, Church End, 448 High Road, London NW10 2DZ *Tel:*020 8451 7111 *Fax:*020 8451 2040 *Dx:*110850 WILLESDEN 2.

George, Mrs Valerie I *Jan 1983*
LLB(Hons). Rutland County Council, Catmose, Oakham, Rutland LE15 6HP *Tel:*01572 722577 *Fax:*01572 758307 *Dx:*28340 OAKHAM. *E-mail:*legal@rutland.gov.uk

Geraghty, Miss Toni M *Oct 1993*
LLB(Hons). Lincolnshire County Council Resources- Legal Services, County Offices, Newland, Lincoln, Lincolnshire LN1 1YP *Tel:*01522 552222 *Fax:*01522 552138 *Dx:*701680 LINCOLN 5. Solicitor

Gibbs, David G *Jan 1984*
Central Hertfordshire Magistrates Court, Justice Clerks Office, The Court House, Civic Centre, St Albans, Hertfordshire AL1 3LB *Tel:*01727 816822 *Fax:*01727 816829 *Dx:*6172 ST ALBANS.; West Hertfordshire Magistrates Court, The Court House, Clarendon Road, Watford, Hertfordshire WD17 1ST *Tel:*01923 297500 *Fax:*01923 297528 *Dx:*51509 WATFORD 2.

Gondal, Ms Sofia Bashir M *Nov 1994*
LLB(Hons); LLM. Hounslow Law Centre Ltd, 51 Lampton Road, Hounslow, Middlesex TW3 1JG *Tel:*020 8570 9505 *Fax:*020 8572 0730 Immigration Advisate / Senior Caseworker Work: 23,15,12,36,38

Goodman, David R G *Nov 1983*
Central & South West Staffordshire Magistrates Court, The Court House, South Walls, Stafford, Staffordshire ST16 3DW *Tel:*01785 223144 *Fax:*01785 258508 *Dx:*14575 STAFFORD 1. Justices' Clerk

Graham, Alexander Donald I *Feb 1975*
LLB. Norwich Union Life, 2 Rougier Street, York YO90 1UU *Tel:*01904 452210 *Fax:*01904 452856 Legal Services Manager

Graham, Jeremy J M G *Nov 1984*
LLB(Hons). Gateshead Magistrates Court, Warwick Street, Gateshead, Tyne & Wear NE8 1DT *Tel:*0191 477 5821 *Fax:*0191 478 7825 *Dx:*67783 GATESHEAD 3. Deputy Clerk to the Justices (Legal)

Graham-Wells, Miss Alison I *Jul 1992*
BA(Hons)(Law & Sociology). HM Revenue & Customs, Solicitor's Office, Ralli Quays (West), 3 Stanley Street, Salford, Greater Manchester M60 9LB *Tel:*0870 785 8545 *Fax:*0870 785 8528 *Dx:*742371 SALFORD 20. Senior Lawyer Work: 34,11,38,8,1

Grayson, Stephen I *Nov 1990*
BA. Department for Business, Enterprise and Regulatory Reform, 1 Victoria Street, London SW1H 0ET *Tel:*020 7215 0105

Green, Philip John L *Jul 1999*
LLB(Hons). Eastgate Assistance Ltd, Eastgate House, Stephenson Road, The Business Park, Colchester, Essex CO4 4QR *Tel:*0870 523 4500 *Fax:*0870 523 4508 *Dx:*3626 COLCHESTER. Barrister

Gretton, Ms Joanne Claire I *Nov 1997*
LLB(Hons). Telent PLC, New Century Park, PO Box 53, Coventry, West Midlands CV3 1HJ *Tel:*024 7656 2000 *Fax:*024 7656 7000 General Counsel Work: 13

Grier, Warren I *Nov 1989*
LLB. Sunderland Magistrates Court, Gillbridge Avenue, Sunderland, Tyne & Wear SR1 3AP *Tel:*0191 514 1621 *Fax:*0191 565 8564 *Dx:*67757 SUNDERLAND. Court Clerk Work: 1,6,12,47,48,13,15,20,22,25,30,72

Griffiths, Gareth V L *Oct 1999*
LLB(Hons). MBNA Europe Bank Ltd, Chester Business Park, Chester, Cheshire CH4 9FB *Tel:*01244 672002 *Fax:*01244 672044

Grimshaw, David M *Nov 1975*
BA(Cantab); MA(Business Law); MBA(Legal Practice). ConocoPhillips (UK) Ltd, Portman House, 2 Portman Street, London W1H 6DU *Tel:*020 7408 6000 *Fax:*020 7408 6466

Grundy, Ms Stephanie C M *Jul 1983*
Treasury Solicitors Department, 7th Floor, One Kemble Street, London WC2B 4TS *Tel:*020 7210 3000 *Fax:*020 7210 3004 *Dx:*123242 KINGSWAY.

Gulliford, Jonathan R M *Jan 1992*
LLM. RAC Motoring Services, RAC House, Great Park Road, Bradley Stoke, Bristol BS32 4QN *Tel:*0870 553 3533 *Fax:*01454 208222 Legal Implementation Manager

Guy, Ian G *Nov 1988*
BA(Hons). Neath Port Talbot County Borough Council, Civic Centre, Port Talbot, Neath Port Talbot SA11 3QZ *Tel:*01639 763333 *Fax:*01639 763370 *Dx:*135226 PORT TALBOT 2.

Hall, Amory J A I *Nov 1989*
LLB(Hons). Bolton Magistrates Court, The Courts, Civic Centre, PO Box 24, Bolton, Greater Manchester BL1 1QX *Tel:*01204 558200 *Fax:*01204 364373 *Dx:*707360 BOLTON 6.

Hall, Eric Michael L *Nov 1986*
DML. Bromley Magistrates Court, The Court House, 1 London Road, Bromley, Kent BR1 1RA *Tel:*0845 601 3600 *Fax:*020 8437 3506 *Dx:*119601 BROMLEY 8. Legal Advisor

Hallam, Nigel Edwin G *Jul 1987*
DMS; CTP; MCMI. Southern Derbyshire Magistrates' Court, St Mary's Gate, Derby DE1 3JR *Tel:*01332 362000 *Fax:*01332 333181 *Dx:*707570 DERBY 8.

Hambley, Ms Elizabeth I *Nov 1992*
Treasury Solicitors Department, 7th Floor, One Kemble Street, London WC2B 4TS *Tel:*020 7210 3000 *Fax:*020 7210 3004 *Dx:*123242 KINGSWAY.

Hamilton, Mrs Penelope Ann G *Jul 1972*
LLB. PricewaterhouseCoopers LLP, 1 Embankment Place, London WC2N 6NN *Tel:*020 7583 5000 *Fax:*020 7822 4652 Partner Work: 34,57

Hamilton, Patrick Joseph Martin G *Nov 1980*
Uxbridge Magistrates Court, Harefield Road, Uxbridge, Middlesex UB8 1PQ *Tel:*01895 230771 *Fax:*01895 274280

Hamper, Andrew J P M *Sept 1991*
LLB. JP Morgan Chase Bank, 125 London Wall, London EC2Y 5AJ *Tel:*020 7777 2000 *Fax:*020 7777 3141 Legal Counsel FX & Derivatives

Hanratty, Miss Judith Christine I *Jan 1987*
LLB; LLM. British Petroleum Co PLC, Britannic House, 1 Finsbury Circus, London EC2M 7BA *Tel:*020 7496 4000 *Fax:*020 7496 4630 Company Secretary

Harding, Miss Jennifer Ann M *Jan 1990*
BA(Hons)(Ancient History). Black Rock, 33 King William Street, London EC4R 9AS *Tel:*020 7743 3000 *Fax:*020 7743 1064 Vice President

Harper-Ward, Miss Victoria I *Oct 2004*
The Magistrates' Courts' Commission, The Magistrates' Court Brent, 448 High Road, Church End, London NW10 2DZ *Tel:*020 8451 2425 *Fax:*020 8451 6227 Trainee Legal Advisor

Harrison, Trevor Kenneth I *Jul 1978*
LLB. Wold Fuel Services Europe Ltd, Wells House, 15-17 Elmfield Road, Bromley, Kent BR1 1LT *Tel:*020 8315 7777 *Fax:*020 8315 7788 *E-mail:*trevor.harrison@wfscorp.com Group Legal Advisor

Harrles, John Christopher Nicholas I *Jul 2003*
BA(Hons); MA; LLM. EEF Western, Engineer's House, The Promenade, Clifton Down, Bristol BS8 3NB *Tel:*0117 906 4800 *Fax:*0117 973 6010 *E-mail:*mktg@eef-west.org.uk Employed Barrister

Harwood, Miss Susan Mary Josephine M *Nov 1988*
BA(Hons); DipLaw. Department for Business, Enterprise and Regulatory Reform, 1 Victoria Street, London SW1H 0ET *Tel:*020 7215 0105 Work: 1,15,30,36

Hatcher, Mark M *Nov 1978*
MA. PricewaterhouseCoopers LLP, 1 Embankment Place, London WC2N 6NN *Tel:*020 7583 5000 *Fax:*020 7822 4652 Head of Public Affairs Consultancy

Hatt, Miss Rebecca May L *Jul 2004*
Severn Trent Water Ltd, 2297 Coventry Road, Birmingham, West Midlands B26 3PU *Tel:*0121 722 4000 *Fax:*0121 722 4228 *Dx:*21806 SHELDON. *E-mail:*professionalservices@severntrent.co.uk

Havard, Nigel George G *Mar 1998*
BA(Hons). City & County of Swansea, Legal Services, County Hall, Oystermouth Road, Swansea SA1 3SN *Tel:*01792 636000 *Fax:*01792 636340 *Dx:*82807 SWANSEA 2. Directorate Lawyer-Regeneration

Hawkings, Richard I *Jan 1986*
BA(Law). Kellogg Brown & Root (UK) Ltd, Hill Park Court, Springfield Drive, Leatherhead, Surrey KT22 7NL *Tel:*01372 865000 *Fax:*01372 866951 Senior Counsel

Haycock, Mrs Anne G *Nov 1986*
DML. Reading Borough Council, Civic Offices, Civic Centre, Reading RG1 7AE *Tel:*0118 939 0900 *Fax:*0118 939 0767 *Dx:*40124 READING (CASTLE STREET).

Haydock, James William I *Feb 1984*
DML. Clerk to the Justices, Wigan Magistrates Court, Darlington Street, Wigan, Greater Manchester WN1 1DW *Tel:*01942 405405 *Fax:*01942 405444

Hemming, Martin J G *Jul 1972*
Treasury Solicitors Department, 7th Floor, One Kemble Street, London WC2B 4TS *Tel:*020 7210 3000 *Fax:*020 7210 3004 *Dx:*123242 KINGSWAY.

Herbert-Young, Nicholas M *May 1988*
LLB(Hons); LLM(Merit); FP1-2. Financial Services Authority, 25 The North Colonnade, Canary Wharf, London E14 5HS *Tel:*020 7066 1000

Hewitson, Ms Melanie J M *Oct 1996*
LLB. Armstrong World Industries Ltd, Armstrong House, 38 Market Square, Uxbridge, Middlesex UB8 1NG *Tel:*01895 202095 *Fax:*01895 256869 European Legal Adviser

Hickman, Ms Jane G *Nov 1983*
BA; DipLaw; BAK. Metropolitan Police Directorate of Legal Services, First Floor, Victoria Block, New Scotland Yard, London SW1H 0BG *Tel:*020 7230 7210 *Fax:*020 7230 7209 Senior Lawyer

Hill, David Lewis M *Oct 1992*
MA(Cantab). Bank Of Ireland UK Financial Services, PO Box 27, Temple Quay, Bristol BS99 7AX *Tel:*0117 979 2222 *Fax:*0117 929 1115 *Dx:*98850 BRISTOL. Legal Adviser

Hirst, Richard Dodsworth M *Nov 1981*
MA(Oxon). AT&T ISTEL, Highfield House, Headless Cross Drive, Headless Cross, Redditch, Worcestershire B97 5ED *Tel:*01527 518181 *Fax:*01527 493593 Divisional Legal Adviser

Hobkirk, Miss Kirsten Anna M *Nov 2002*
LLB(Hons); BUC. Wycombe & Beaconsfield Magistrates Court, Easton Street, High Wycombe, Buckinghamshire HP11 1LR *Tel:*01494 651035 *Fax:*01494 651030 *Dx:*97883 HIGH WYCOMBE 3. *E-mail:*wycombe.magistrates@hmcourts-service.gsi.gov.uk Legal Adviser

Holland, Richard David G *Nov 1987*
DML. South Cheshire Magistrates Court, Law Courts, Civic Centre, Crewe, Cheshire CW1 2DT *Tel:*0870 162 6261 *Fax:*01270 589357 Legal Manager

Hooper, Graham Boucher L *Jul 1984*
LLB(Hons); DMS. Nottingham Magistrates Court, Carrington Street, Nottingham NG2 1EE *Tel:*0115 955 8111 *Fax:*0115 955 8139 *Dx:*719030 NOTTINGHAM 32. Justice's Clerk

Hopper, Martyn John M *Nov 1991*
BA(Hons); LLM. Financial Services Authority, 25 The North Colonnade, Canary Wharf, London E14 5HS *Tel:*020 7066 1000

House, Christopher L *Nov 1976*
Treasury Solicitors Department, 7th Floor, One Kemble Street, London WC2B 4TS *Tel:*020 7210 3000 *Fax:*020 7210 3004 *Dx:*123242 KINGSWAY.

Housego, Nigel William L *Nov 1989*
LLB(Hons). Eastgate Assistance Ltd, Eastgate House, Stephenson Road, The Business Park, Colchester, Essex CO4 4QR *Tel:*0870 523 4500 *Fax:*0870 523 4508 *Dx:*3626 COLCHESTER. Barrister

Howard, Ms Rebecca Alexandra M *Oct 1991*
BSc(Econ)(LSE). Tower Hamlets Law Centre, 214 Whitechapel Road, Tower Hamlets, London E1 1BJ *Tel:*020 7247 8998 *Fax:*020 7247 9424

Howe, Mrs Alison F M *Oct 1998*
LLB. London Borough of Wandsworth, Administration Department, The Town Hall, Wandsworth High Street, Wandsworth, London SW18 2PU *Tel:*020 8871 6000 *Fax:*020 8871 7506 *Dx:*59054 WANDSWORTH NORTH. *E-mail:*legal@wandsworth.gov.uk

Hughes, Miss Gwyneth E L *Nov 1992*
Treasury Solicitors Department, 7th Floor, One Kemble Street, London WC2B 4TS *Tel:*020 7210 3000 *Fax:*020 7210 3004 *Dx:*123242 KINGSWAY.

Hui, Ms Carol G *Nov 1985*
LLB; PCLL. Transport Development Group PLC, Windsor House, 50 Victoria Street, Westminster, London SW1H 0NR *Tel:*020 7222 7411 *Fax:*020 7222 2806 *E-mail:*huic@tdg.co.uk Director of Legal Services & Group Company Secretary

Huma, Ms Zill-E L *Nov 2002*
LLB(Hons); PGDL(BVC). Bolton Magistrates Court, The Courts, Civic Centre, PO Box 24, Bolton, Greater Manchester BL1 1QX *Tel:*01204 558200 *Fax:*01204 364373 *Dx:*707360 BOLTON 6. Trainee Legal Advisor

Humphreys, Mrs Rosalind G *Jan 1999*
MA(Cantab). Corby Borough Council, Grosvenor House, George Street, Corby, Northamptonshire NN17 1QB *Tel:*01536 402551 *Fax:*01536 464109 *Dx:*12915 CORBY. Housing Lawyer

Hunt, Miss Sharon Louise M *Oct 2001*
LLB; LLM. Wakefield Metropolitan District Council, County Hall, Bond Street, Wakefield, West Yorkshire WF1 2QW *Tel:*01924 306090 *Fax:*01924 305243

Hurst, Ms Claire M *Oct 1999*
LLB(Hons). Eastgate Assistance Ltd, Eastgate House, Stephenson Road, The Business Park, Colchester, Essex CO4 4QR *Tel:*0870 523 4500 *Fax:*0870 523 4508 *Dx:*3626 COLCHESTER. Legal Advisor - Employment

Hussain, M Altaf M *Jul 1970*
MA; LLB. Cambridge House Legal Centre, Cambridge House, 137 Camberwell Road, London SE5 0HF *Tel:*020 7703 3051 / 7701 9499 *Fax:*020 7277 0401

Iles, Adrian I *Jul 1980*
MA(Cantab). National Institutions of the Church of England, Legal Office, Church House, Great Smith Street, Westminster, London SW1P 3AZ *Tel:*020 7898 1000 *Fax:*020 7898 1718 *Dx:*148403 WESTMINSTER 5. *E-mail:*legal@c-of-e.org.uk Designated Officer Under the Clergy Discipline Measure 2003 Work: 7,20,37,22

Incledon, Mrs Claire Frances I *Nov 1990*
Pembrokeshire County Council, County Hall, Haverfordwest, Pembrokeshire SA61 1TP *Tel:*01437 764551 *Fax:*01437 776476 *Dx:*98295 HAVERFORDWEST. Principal Advocate

Insua, Miss Leah Margaret M *Nov 2001*
LLB(Law with Spanish). Solihull Magistrates Court, The Courthouse, Homer Road, Solihull, West Midlands B91 3RD *Tel:*0121 705 8101 *Fax:*0121 711 2045 *Dx:*708350 SOLIHULL 14. Legal Adviser

Jackson, Stephen Malcolm G *Jul 1975*
LLB. Bristol Claims & Property Consultants, 27 Westbury Road, Westbury-on-Trym, Bristol BS9 3AX *Tel:*0117 962 4665 *E-mail:*di.jackson@tinyonline.co.uk Senior Partner

13

Jameson, Ms Carolyn L *Mar 2002*
LLB(Hons). Novell UK Ltd, Novell House, 1 Arlington Square, Downshire Way, Bracknell, Bracknell Forest RG12 1WA *Tel:*01344 724000 *Fax:*01344 724250 *E-mail:*ncurphey@novell.com Legal Counsel

Jamieson-Hesk, Mrs Debra I *Nov 1996*
LLB(Hons). Portsmouth City Council, Civic Offices, Guildhall Square, Portsmouth PO1 2PX *Tel:*023 9283 4034 *Fax:*023 9283 4076 *Dx:*2244 PORTSMOUTH. Barrister

Jeffreys, Ms Rosemary A G *Jul 1978*
Treasury Solicitors Department, 7th Floor, One Kemble Street, London WC2B 4TS *Tel:*020 7210 3000 *Fax:*020 7210 3004 *Dx:*123242 KINGSWAY.

Jennings, Mrs Caroline P M *Jul 1989*
Dip ML; DipLaw; DIPMS. Northamptonshire Magistrates Courts, Regents Pavilion, Summerhouse Road, Moulton Park, Northampton, Northamptonshire NN3 6AS *Tel:*01604 497000 *Fax:*01536 497010 Deputy Clerk to the Justices

John-Charles, Lee L *Nov 1985*
Treasury Solicitors Department, 7th Floor, One Kemble Street, London WC2B 4TS *Tel:*020 7210 3000 *Fax:*020 7210 3004 *Dx:*123242 KINGSWAY.

Jones, Gareth Alun M *Oct 1997*
BVC. East Sussex County Council, County Hall, St Anne's Crescent, Lewes, East Sussex BN7 1SG *Tel:*01273 481000 *Fax:*01273 473321 *Dx:*97482 LEWES 3. Solicitor

Jones, Mrs Jorina M *Jul 1986*
BA(Hons). Department for Business, Enterprise and Regulatory Reform, 1 Victoria Street, London SW1H 0ET *Tel:*020 7215 0105

Jones, Robert Ffrancon Wyn L *Nov 1993*
BA(Hons); LLB. Cyngor Sir Ynys Mon (Isle of Anglesey County Council), Council Offices, Llangefni, Anglesey LL77 7TW *Tel:*01248 750057 *Fax:*01248 752132 *Dx:*701771 LLANGEFNI. Barrister Work: 15

Jones, Ms Sian E L *Jul 1981*
LLB; DMS. Teesside Magistrates Court, Teesside Law Courts, Victoria Square, Middlesbrough TS1 2AS *Tel:*01642 240301 *Fax:*01642 224010 *Dx:*60562 MIDDLESBROUGH. *E-mail:*postbox@hmcourts-service.gsi.gov.uk

Jones, Simon David G *Nov 1985*
LLB. Reigate & Banstead Borough Council, Town Hall, Reigate, Surrey RH2 0SH *Tel:*01737 276000 *Fax:*01737 276070 *Dx:*54102 REIGATE 2. Legal Services Manager

Kale, Samuel Meano L *Jul 1987*
LLB; MA. Bank of Scotland Legal Operations, 155 Bishopsgate, London EC2M 3YB *Tel:*0870 600 5000 *Fax:*01422 334453 Senior Legal Adviser

Karpinski, Ms Jan M *Dec 1976*
Bank Of Ireland UK Financial Services, PO Box 27, Temple Quay, Bristol BS99 7AX *Tel:*0117 979 2222 *Fax:*0117 929 1115 *Dx:*98850 BRISTOL.

Kaye, David G *Nov 1989*
MBA; DML; DMS; FInstCPD; FInstLM. North Lincolnshire Magistrates Court, Justices Clerks Office, Corporation Road, Scunthorpe, North Lincolnshire DN15 6QB *Tel:*01724 281100 *Fax:*01724 281890 *Dx:*14727 SCUNTHORPE. Principal Legal Adviser

Kaye, Jeremy Robin I *Jul 1962*
MA; FCIS. Secure Trust Banking Group PLC, Arhuthand House, 20 Ropemaker Street, London EC2Y 9AR *Tel:*020 7012 2400 *Fax:*020 7012 2401 Secretary

Kelly, Ms Ruth I *Jan 1998*
Department for Business, Enterprise and Regulatory Reform, 1 Victoria Street, London SW1H 0ET *Tel:*020 7215 0105

Kennedy, Paul Gilbert L *Nov 1991*
MA(Cantab); FIA; FCII; ACCA; ACIArb. Financial Services Authority, 25 The North Colonnade, Canary Wharf, London E14 5HS *Tel:*020 7066 1000 Work: 5,6,11,18,24,34

Khan, Noor- Ul Muzamil G *Nov 1993*
Institute of Chartered Accountants in England & Wales, Level 1, Metropolitan House, 321 Avebury Boulevard, Milton Keynes MK9 2FZ *Tel:*01908 248100 *Fax:*01908 248088 *Dx:*31427 MILTON KEYNES. *E-mail:*generalenquiries@icaew.com Barrister

Kielty, Ms A Marion G *Nov 1988*
LLB. Northamptonshire County Council, County Hall, George Row, Northampton, Northamptonshire NN1 1DN *Tel:*01604 236236 *Fax:*01604 237167 *Dx:*12481 NORTHAMPTON.

Kindred, Frank P G *Jul 1985*
BSc(Hons); MSc. British Telecommunications PLC, PPC5A, BT Centre, 81 Newgate Street, Tower Hamlets, London EC1A 7AJ *Tel:*020 7356 6181 *Fax:*01332 577374 *E-mail:*suzanne.ridley@bt.com Intellectual Property Counsel

King, Charles M *Nov 1995*
LLB(Hons). Gloucester Law Centre, 75-81 Eastgate Street, Gloucester, Gloucestershire GL1 1PN *Tel:*01452 423492 *Fax:*01452 387594 *E-mail:*admin@gloucesterlawcentre.co.uk Barrister

King, Geoffrey G *Jan 1968*
LLB(Lond). Financial Services Authority, 25 The North Colonnade, Canary Wharf, London E14 5HS *Tel:*020 7066 1000

Kinghorn, Andrew G *Nov 1991*
LLB(Hons). New Forest District Council, Appletree Court, Lyndhurst, Hampshire SO43 7PA *Tel:*023 8028 5000 *Fax:*023 8028 5543 *Dx:*123010 LYNDHURST 2. Barrister Work: 12,15,18,20,30

Klausner, Isidor M *Nov 1981*
LLM; DRS EC(Rotterdam). Stancroft Trust Ltd, Bride House, 20 Bride Lane, London EC4Y 8DX *Tel:*020 7583 3808 *Fax:*020 7583 5912 Director

Klein, Prof Silviu Thomas Rudolf M *Nov 1979*
LLB(Hons)(Lond); FCIOB; Cert Ed. Specialist Engineering Contractors Group, ESCA House, 34 Palace Court, Westminster, London W2 4JG *Tel:*020 7313 4920 *Fax:*020 7727 9268 *E-mail:*rklein@hvca.org.uk Chief Executive

Knowles, Philip Jonathan G *Jul 1982*
LLB; DMS. Justices Clerks Office, Magistrates Court, Walton Street, Aylesbury, Buckinghamshire HP21 7QZ *Tel:*01296 554300 *Fax:*01296 554340 *Dx:*149920 AYLESBURY 10.; Milton Keynes Magistrates Court, 301 Silbury Boulevard, Witan Gate East, Milton Keynes MK9 2AJ *Tel:*0870 241 2819 *Fax:*01908 451146 *Dx:*54462 MILTON KEYNES.

Kong, Miss Ming G *Jan 1997*
Department for Business, Enterprise and Regulatory Reform, 1 Victoria Street, London SW1H 0ET *Tel:*020 7215 0105

La Neice, Jeremy M *Jan 1973*
LLB(Manc). Financial Services Authority, 25 The North Colonnade, Canary Wharf, London E14 5HS *Tel:*020 7066 1000

Lai, Ms Iy Lee M *Jul 1989*
BA(Hons)(Soc Sci). Peterborough Magistrates Court, Bridge Street, Peterborough PE1 1ED *Tel:*01223 314311 *Fax:*01733 313749 *Dx:*702304 PETERBOROUGH 8. Principal Court Clerk

Lamb, Miss Janina C L *Mar 2001*
McClure Naismith, Equitable House, 47 King William Street, London EC4R 9AF *Tel:*020 7929 3770 *Fax:*020 7929 3466 *Dx:*764 LONDON/CITY. *E-mail:*london@mcmlurenaismith.com

Lambert, Nigel A D M *Jul 1975*
Treasury Solicitors Department, 7th Floor, One Kemble Street, London WC2B 4TS *Tel:*020 7210 3000 *Fax:*020 7210 3004 *Dx:*123242 KINGSWAY.

Lassman, Malcolm Arnold M *Jul 1955*
LLB; FCA. PPS Rotaprint, 720 Tudoe Estate, Abbey Road, London NW10 7UN *Tel:*020 8908 1111 *Fax:*020 8908 3212 Director & Company Secretary

Lawson, Martin Jeffery L *Feb 1994*
LLB; DMS. Eastgate Assistance Ltd, Eastgate House, Stephenson Road, The Business Park, Colchester, Essex CO4 4QR *Tel:*0870 523 4500 *Fax:*0870 523 4508 *Dx:*3626 COLCHESTER. Barrister

Lawunmi, Ms Doyin I *Nov 1984*
Department for Business, Enterprise and Regulatory Reform, 1 Victoria Street, London SW1H 0ET *Tel:*020 7215 0105

Leathes, Michael S G *Jul 1970*
BA; LLM. British American Tobacco, Globe House, 4 Temple Place, London WC2R 2PG *Tel:*020 7845 1000 *Fax:*020 7845 2783

Lees, Gordon C G *Jul 1979*
York Magistrates, Clifford Street, York YO1 9RE *Tel:*01757 293500 *Fax:*01757 293501 Clerk to Justices

Lenihan, Martin John M *Jul 1983*
BA(Hons); LLM; ACIArb. Skanska UK PLC, Maple Cross House, Denham Way, Maple Cross, Rickmansworth, Hertfordshire WD3 9SW *Tel:*01923 776666 *Fax:*01923 423864 Legal Adviser

Lester, Alan Nicholas I *Jul 1984*
MA(Hons)(Oxon)(Jurisprudence). John Lewis plc, Corporate Offices, Partnership House, Carlisle Place, London SW1P 1BX *Tel:*020 7828 1000 *Fax:*020 7592 6566 Principal Lawyer (Personnel)

Lewis, Mrs Christina M *Oct 1997*
LLB(Hons). Orange PCS Ltd, St James Court, Great Park Road, Bradley Stoke, Bristol BS32 4QJ *Tel:*0870 376 8888 *Fax:*01454 618501

Lewis, Ms Jacqueline Ann L *Jan 1992*
BSc; DipLaw. British Waterways Board, 64 Clarendon Road, Watford, Hertfordshire WD17 1DA *Tel:*01923 226422 *Fax:*01923 201378 Head of Legal

Lewis, James Andrew G *Jul 2004*
LLB. Cardiff Magistrates Court, Magistrates' Clerks Office, Fitzalan Place, Cardiff CF24 0RZ *Tel:*029 2046 3040 Court Legal Advisor

Licata, Joseph M *Jul 1981*
BA(Hons)(Law); MBA. Northamptonshire Magistrates Courts, Regents Pavilion, Summerhouse Road, Moulton Park, Northampton, Northamptonshire NN3 6AS *Tel:*01604 497000 *Fax:*01536 497010 Bench Legal Adviser

Lisgarten, Miss Barbara I *Nov 2000*
LLB. Dacorum Borough Council, Civic Centre, Marlowes, Dacorum Borough, Hemel Hempstead, Hertfordshire HP1 1HH *Tel:*01442 228000 *Fax:*01442 228746 *Dx:*8804 HEMEL HEMPSTEAD. Litigation Barrister (Team Member)

Litchfield, Miss Sarah K G *Feb 1992*
BA(Oxon). Department for Business, Enterprise and Regulatory Reform, 1 Victoria Street, London SW1H 0ET *Tel:*020 7215 0105

Lloyd, Reginald W L *Nov 1993*
LLM. Eastgate Assistance Ltd, Eastgate House, Stephenson Road, The Business Park, Colchester, Essex CO4 4QR *Tel:*0870 523 4500 *Fax:*0870 523 4508 *Dx:*3626 COLCHESTER. Barrister

Love, Ms Kathy Lee I *Nov 1976*
BA; LLM(Cantab). Shell International Ltd, Shell Centre, York Road, London SE1 7NA *Tel:*020 7934 1234 *Fax:*020 7934 3023 *Dx:*473 LONDON/CHANCERY LN. *E-mail:*l.dalsgaard@shell.com Senior Legal Counsel

Lucas, Daniel L *Nov 2004*
LLB(Hons); PGCert; PGDipLP. Eastleigh Borough Council, Civic Offices, Leigh Road, Eastleigh, Hampshire SO50 9YN *Tel:*023 8068 8068 *Fax:*023 8062 9277 *Dx:*122381 EASTLEIGH 2. Lawyer (Planning & Litigation)

Lyons, Mrs Ruth M *Nov 1981*
Department for Business, Enterprise and Regulatory Reform, 1 Victoria Street, London SW1H 0ET *Tel:*020 7215 0105

McArdle, Kevin Edward M *Nov 1989*
BSc; LLB; RGN. Merck Sharp & Dohme Ltd, Hertford Road, Hoddesdon, Hertfordshire EN11 9BU *Tel:*01992 452509 *Fax:*01992 470189 Legal Officer

McCabe, Miss Yvonne Catherine I *Nov 1986*
LLB. Rentokil Initial PLC, City Link, The Meadows River Bank, Camberley, Surrey GU17 9AB *Tel:*01276 606200 *Fax:*01276 606299 General Manager

McCafferty, Miss Elaine G *Jan 1979*
LLB; ACIB. Metropolitan Police Directorate of Legal Services, First Floor, Victoria Block, New Scotland Yard, London SW1H 0BG *Tel:*020 7230 7210 *Fax:*020 7230 7209 Senior Lawyer

McCann, Miss Catryn L *Jan 1988*
LLB(Hons); LLM. Bromley Magistrates Court, The Court House, 1 London Road, Bromley, Kent BR1 1RA *Tel:*0845 601 3600 *Fax:*020 8437 3506 *Dx:*119601 BROMLEY 8. Legal Adviser

McConnell, Mrs Christine Maria G *Oct 1999*
LLB(Hons). Clerk to Sheffield Justices, Magistrates Court, Castle Street, Sheffield, South Yorkshire S3 8LU *Tel:*0114 276 0760 *Fax:*0114 272 0129 *Dx:*10599 SHEFFIELD. Senior Legal Adviser: Sheffield Magistrates court

McCreath, Ms Fiona G *Oct 1991*
LLB(Hons); Barrister at Law. Southampton City Council, Civic Centre, Southampton SO14 7LY *Tel:*023 8022 3855 *Fax:*023 8083 2308

McGibbon, Eric John Wallace G *Jul 1978*
LLB(Lond). Royal Mail Group, 100 Victoria Embankment, London EC4V 0HQ *Tel:*020 7250 2468

McGregor, Rev Alexander L *Jan 1996*
MA(Oxon). National Institutions of the Church of England, Legal Office, Church House, Great Smith Street, Westminster, London SW1P 3AZ *Tel:*020 7898 1000 *Fax:*020 7898 1718 *Dx:*148403 WESTMINSTER 5. *E-mail:*legal@c-of-e.org.uk Barrister

McHugo, Christopher Benedict M *May 1978*
MA; FCA. Association of British Insurers, 51 Gresham Street, London EC2V 7HQ *Tel:*020 7600 3333 *Fax:*020 7696 8997 Taxation Manager

McLean, Ms Isabella L *Nov 1997*
LLB; LLM. Eastgate Assistance Ltd, Eastgate House, Stephenson Road, The Business Park, Colchester, Essex CO4 4QR *Tel:*0870 523 4500 *Fax:*0870 523 4508 *Dx:*3626 COLCHESTER. Barrister

McMillan, Ms Fiona I *Oct 1993*
LLB(Hons); Dip LG. South Cambridgeshire District Council, South Cambridgeshire Hall, Cambourne Business Park, Cambourne, Cambridge, Cambridgeshire CB23 6EA *Tel:*0845 045 0500 *Fax:*01954 713150 *Dx:*729500 CAMBRIDGE 15. *E-mail:*scdc@scambs.gov.uk Senior Lawyer Work: 18,22,31

Mahy, Ms Helen Margaret M *Jul 1982*
National Grid PLC, National Grid Park, Warwick Technology Park, Gallows Hill, Warwick, Warwickshire CV34 6DA *Tel:*01926 653000 *Fax:*01926 654378 Group Company Secretary & General Counsel

Makele, Ibrahim Daniel I *Nov 1992*
BA; LLM. Consolidated Financial Insurance, Building 11, Chiswick Park, Chiswick High Road, London W4 5XR *Tel:*020 8380 3000 *Fax:*020 8380 3065 Senior Counsel - International

Malone, Tony I *Jul 1998*
LLB; LLM; BAR. Warwickshire County Council, Shire Hall, Warwick, Warwickshire CV34 4RR *Tel:*01926 410410 *Fax:*01926 412946 *Dx:*723362 WARWICK 5. Senior Solicitor & Chartered Secretary

Manning Nee Sefton, Mrs Claire-Louise I *Oct 1997*
BA(Hons); AKC. Enfield Magistrates Court, The Court House, Lordship Lane, Tottenham, London N17 6RT *Tel:*020 8808 5411 *Fax:*020 8885 4343 *Dx:*134490 TOTTENHAM 3. Legal Adviser

Marshall, Mrs Alison Jean I *Nov 1987*
LLB(Hons). Southern Derbyshire Magistrates' Court, St Mary's Gate, Derby DE1 3JR *Tel:*01332 362000 *Fax:*01332 333181 *Dx:*707570 DERBY 8.

Martin, Ms Jill L *Nov 1993*
LLB; LLM; LLD. Office of the Public Guardian, Archway Tower, 2 Junction Road, London N19 5SZ *Tel:*020 7664 7000 *Fax:*020 7664 7705 *Dx:*141150 ARCHWAY 2. Legal Adviser to the Public Guardian Work: 8,9,22,37

Matondo, Mukulu L *Mar 2002*
LLB; Bar Finals. Equality and Human Rights Commission, St Dunstan's House, 201-211 Borough High Street, Westminster, London SE1 1GZ *Tel:*020 7939 0000 *Fax:*020 7939 0001

Maxwell, Anthony Michael Lockhart M *Feb 1985*
LLB; MRIN; MRAeS; Cert Air & Spac. Airclaims Ltd, Cardinal Point, Newall Road, Heathrow Airport, Hounslow, Middlesex TW6 2AS *Tel:*020 8897 1066 *Fax:*020 8897 0300 Legal Officer

Mayhew-Arnold, Michael Charles John I *Nov 1983*
LLB(Hons). Ansbacher & Co Ltd, Two London Bridge, London SE1 9RA *Tel:*020 7089 4700 *Fax:*020 7089 4895; Ansbacher & Co Ltd, Two London Bridge, London SE1 9RA *Tel:*020 7089 4700 *Fax:*020 7089 4895

Mayne, Miss Caroline Margaret I *Nov 1984*
LLB. Society of Lloyd's, One Lime Street, London EC3M 7HA *Tel:*020 7327 1000 *Fax:*020 7626 2389 Litigation Team Manager

Mear, Ms Lynn G *Jan 1981*
Department for Business, Enterprise and Regulatory Reform, 1 Victoria Street, London SW1H 0ET *Tel:*020 7215 0105

Medland, Miss Elizabeth Ellen L *Mar 2001*
LLB(Hons); BVC. Central & South West Staffordshire Magistrates Court, The Court House, South Walls, Stafford, Staffordshire ST16 3DW *Tel:*01785 223144 *Fax:*01785 258508 *Dx:*14575 STAFFORD 1. Senior Legal Advisor

Meeke, Mrs Beverley A G *Jul 1973*
LLB(Hons). Environment Agency (South West Region), Manley House, Kestrel Way, Exeter, Devon EX2 7LQ *Tel:*0870 850 6506 *Fax:*01392 442112 *Dx:*121350 EXETER 12. Principal Counsel

Mehan, Miss Meena Kumari L *Nov 2002*
LLB(Hons); DMS. Northamptonshire Magistrates Courts, Regents Pavilion, Summerhouse Road, Moulton Park, Northampton, Northamptonshire NN3 6AS *Tel:*01604 497000 *Fax:*01536 497010 Court Clerk, Non Practising Barrister, Solicitor

Melhuish-Hancock, Simon G *Jul 1981*
LLB. Corus Group Limited, 30 Millbank, Westminster, London SW1P 4WY *Tel:*020 7717 4523 *Fax:*020 7717 4642 *E-mail:*helen.matheson@corusgroup.com Corporate Lawyer

Messeter, Mrs Ulanta Ann G *Apr 1991*
BEd; LLB. Bromley Magistrates Court, The Court House, 1 London Road, Bromley, Kent BR1 1RA *Tel:*0845 601 3600 *Fax:*020 8437 3506 *Dx:*119601 BROMLEY 8. Legal Advisor

Middleton, Daniel John G *Mar 2005*
LLB; BA; BVC. Severn Trent Water Ltd, 2297 Coventry Road, Birmingham, West Midlands B26 3PU *Tel:*0121 722 4000 *Fax:*0121 722 4228 *Dx:*21806 SHELDON. *E-mail:*professionalservices@severntrent.co.uk Commercial Lawyer

Miles, William F G *Jul 1976*
LLB. Slough Magistrates Court, Chalvey Park (Off Windsor Road), Slough SL1 2HJ *Tel:*01753 521345 *Fax:*01753 693296

Milligan, Scott G M *Jul 1975*
MA(Oxon). Department for Business, Enterprise and Regulatory Reform, 1 Victoria Street, London SW1H 0ET *Tel:*020 7215 0105

Mills, Ms Julie Ann I *Jul 1986*
Bath & Wansdyke Magistrates Court, North Parade Road, Bath, Bath & North East Somerset BA1 5AF *Tel:*01225 463281 *Fax:*01225 420225 Deputy Clerk to the Justices

See p1010 for the Key to Work Categories

Mitchell, Mrs Karen Joy G *Jan 1982*
LLB. Clerk to the Justices, Wigan Magistrates Court, Darlington Street, Wigan, Greater Manchester WN1 1DW *Tel:*01942 405405 *Fax:*01942 405444; Wigan and Leigh Magistrates' Court, Darlington Street, Wigan, Greater Manchester WN1 1DW *Tel:*01942 405405 *Fax:*01942 405444

Mitchell, Miss Tracey Jane L *Apr 1999*
LLB(Hons). Northamptonshire Magistrates Courts, Regents Pavilion, Summerhouse Road, Moulton Park, Northampton, Northamptonshire NN3 6AS *Tel:*01604 497000 *Fax:*01536 497010 Court Clerk

Miyajima, Ms Mitsue L *Jan 1997*
BA; ACIB; LLDip; Barrister. Mitsubishi Securities International PLC, Legal Department, 6 Broadgate, London EC2M 2AA *Tel:*020 7577 2804 *Fax:*020 7577 2872 Senior Manager

Moodliar, Nuns G *Feb 1982*
LLM. Hertz Europe Ltd, 11 Vine Street, Uxbridge, Hounslow, Middlesex UB8 1QE *Tel:*01895 553500 *Fax:*01895 553728 Vice President, Legal & Corporate Affairs

Morgan, Miss Katie I *Aug 2002*
LLB(Hons). The College of Law, 14 Store Street, Bloomsbury, London WC1E 7DE *Tel:*0800 289997 Work: 12,20,10

Morris, Mrs Helen Elizabeth G *Nov 1996*
LLB(Lond). Crown Prosecution Service Merseyside, 7th Floor, Royal Liver Building, Pier Head, Liverpool, Merseyside L3 1HN *Tel:*0151 239 6400 *Fax:*0151 239 6410 *Dx:*700596 LIVERPOOL 4. Work: 10,15,20

Morris-Marsham, Ms Margaret Lindelia L *Jan 1967*
PricewaterhouseCoopers LLP, 1 Embankment Place, London WC2N 6NN *Tel:*020 7583 5000 *Fax:*020 7822 4652 Manager

Morrison, Humphrey I *Jul 1973*
Treasury Solicitors Department, 7th Floor, One Kemble Street, London WC2B 4TS *Tel:*020 7210 3000 *Fax:*020 7210 3004 *Dx:*123242 KINGSWAY.

Morse, Miss B G *Jan 1978*
City of Westminster Magistrates' Court, 70 Horseferry Road, Westminster, London SW1P 2AX *Tel:*020 7805 1008 *Fax:*020 7805 1193 *Dx:*120551 VICTORIA 6. Justices' Clerk

Mottram, Paul Richard M *Dec 1995*
LLB(Hons); CLE. Trinity Mirror PLC, One Canada Square, Canary Wharf, London E14 5AP *Tel:*020 7293 3934 *Fax:*020 7293 3613 Legal Adviser

Muttukumaru, Christopher Peter Jayantha G *Nov 1974*
MA(Oxon). CB. Department for Transport, Great Minster House, 76 Marsham Street, London SW1P 4DR *Tel:*020 7944 8300. *Fax:*020 7944 9622 The Legal Advisor & Legal Services Director

Nasser, Ms Shafi M *Nov 1988*
Treasury Solicitors Department, 7th Floor, One Kemble Street, London WC2B 4TS *Tel:*020 7210 3000 *Fax:*020 7210 3004 *Dx:*123242 KINGSWAY.

Nawbatt, Lal M *Jan 1972*
Department for Business, Enterprise and Regulatory Reform, 1 Victoria Street, London SW1H 0ET *Tel:*020 7215 0105

Needham, Christopher E M *Nov 1974*
LLB(Hons). Unisys Insurance Services Limited, 101 Old Hall Street, Liverpool, Merseyside L3 9BD *Tel:*0151 328 2918 *Fax:*0151 328 2976 Senior Legal Adviser

Nevshehir-Owen, Ms Carolyn Elisabeth I *Nov 1990*
BA; ACIArb; FLand Inst. N D N Owen Ltd, 3 The Spinney, Beccles, Suffolk NR34 7DF *Tel:*01508 548613 *Fax:*01508 548613 Director

Newman, Miss Susan Alexandra L *Jul 1980*
Cambridge Magistrates Court, The Court House, Lion Yard, Cambridge, Cambridgeshire CB2 3NA *Tel:*01223 314311 *Fax:*01223 355237 *Dx:*131966 CAMBRIDGE.

Norris, Charles J L *Jul 1986*
LLB; LLM. Department for Business, Enterprise and Regulatory Reform, 1 Victoria Street, London SW1H 0ET *Tel:*020 7215 0105

Norris, Paul Francis M *Nov 1977*
BA; LLM. M M & K Ltd, 1 Bengal Court, Birchin Lane, London EC3V 9DD *Tel:*020 7283 7200 *Fax:*020 7283 4119 *E-mail:*info@mm-k.com Managing Director

Nunan, Matthew M *Jan 1996*
LLB. Department for Business, Enterprise and Regulatory Reform, 1 Victoria Street, London SW1H 0ET *Tel:*020 7215 0105

Nwanodi, Anthony C K E G *Nov 1987*
Treasury Solicitors Department, 7th Floor, One Kemble Street, London WC2B 4TS *Tel:*020 7210 3000 *Fax:*020 7210 3004 *Dx:*123242 KINGSWAY.

O'Flynn, Miss Elizabeth N I *Feb 1965*
LLB. Department for Business, Enterprise and Regulatory Reform, 1 Victoria Street, London SW1H 0ET *Tel:*020 7215 0105

Oates, Laurence C M *Jul 1968*
Official Solicitor and Public Trustee, 81 Chancery Lane, London WC2A 1DD *Tel:*020 7911 7127 *Fax:*020 7911 7105 *Dx:*0012 LONDON/CHANCERY LN. *E-mail:*enquiries@offsol.gsi.gov.uk Official Solicitor to the Supreme Court & Public Trustee

Ocan, Ms Akidi M *Jul 1984*
BA(Hons). Surrey County Council, County Hall, Penrhyn Road, Kingston upon Thames, Surrey KT1 2DN *Tel:*020 8541 9088 *Fax:*020 8541 9115 *Dx:*31509 KINGSTON UPON THAMES. Senior Community Care Lawyer

Ogilvie Smals, Rufus Alexander M *Nov 1973*
MA(Cantab); Dip European Integration (Amsterdam). GKN PLC (Legal Dept), PO Box 55, Ipsley House, Ipsley Church Lane, Redditch, Worcestershire B98 0TL *Tel:*01527 517715 *Fax:*01527 533470 Head of Legal Dept

Okposuogu, Miss Tessa L *Mar 2002*
LLB(Hons). Havering Magistrates' Court, Court House, 19 Main Road, Romford, Essex RM1 3BH *Tel:*0845 601 3600 *Fax:*01708 794270 *Dx:*131527 ROMFORD 8. Legal Adviser

Oldham, Mark M *Jun 1984*
BA. United Biscuits (UK) Ltd, Hayes Park, Hayes End Road, Hayes, Middlesex UB4 8EE *Tel:*020 8234 5000 *Fax:*020 8734 5555

Oliver, Mrs Marcia Frances M *Nov 1984*
LLB. Visit Britain, Thames Tower, Black's Road, Hammersmith, London W6 9EL *Tel:*020 8563 3325 *Fax:*020 8748 0123 *E-mail:*marcia.oliver@visitbritain.org

Oogaragh, Jason I *Nov 1998*
LLB(Hons). AXA UK PLC, 5 Old Broad Street, London E22N 1AD *Tel:*020 7920 5900 *Fax:*020 7920 5224 Legal Adviser

Osborne, Ms Jennifer L *Nov 1992*
LLB(Hons); Barrister. Joint Council for the Welfare of Immigrants, 115 Old Street, Islington, London EC1V 9JR *Tel:*020 7251 8708

Outram, Mrs Louise Ann M *Jul 1989*
BA(Hons). Merseytravel, Hatton Garden, 24 Hatton Garden, Liverpool, Merseyside L3 2AN *Tel:*0151 224 7020 *Fax:*0151 474 2001

Owen, Paul I *Jul 1998*
LLB(Hons). Knowsley Magistrates' Court, Court House, Lathom Road, Huyton, Liverpool, Merseyside L36 9XY *Tel:*0151 489 4400 Legal Advisor

Owen, Mrs Tracey Rebecca M *Jul 1984*
LLB. Institute of Chartered Accountants in England & Wales, Level 1, Metropolitan House, 321 Avebury Boulevard, Milton Keynes MK9 2FZ *Tel:*01908 248100 *Fax:*01908 248088 *Dx:*31427 MILTON KEYNES. *E-mail:*generalenquiries@icaew.com Head of Legal Services

Owens, Gareth Richard G *Nov 1993*
LLB. Shrewsbury and Atcham Borough Council, The Guildhall, Frankwell Quay, Shrewsbury, Shropshire SY3 8HQ *Tel:*01743 281000 *Fax:*01743 281040 *E-mail:*legal@shrewsbury-atcham.gov.uk; West Wiltshire District Council, Bradley Road, Trowbridge, Wiltshire BA14 0RD *Tel:*01225 770396 *Fax:*01225 761053 *Dx:*116891 TROWBRIDGE 3. Democratic & Legal Services Manager

Page, Matthew C M *Feb 1986*
MA; MSc. Weymouth & Portland Borough Council, Council Offices, North Quay, Weymouth, Dorset DT4 8TA *Tel:*01305 838000 *Fax:*01305 838289 Senior Lawyer

Painter, Ian David L *Nov 1993*
BA(Hons); Barrister. HM Revenue & Customs, Solicitor's Office, Ralli Quays (West), 3 Stanley Street, Salford, Greater Manchester M60 9LB *Tel:*0870 785 8545 *Fax:*0870 785 8528 *Dx:*742371 SALFORD 20. Senior Lawyer Work: 15,18,22

Parasram, Ms Isabelle G *Jan 1995*
Department for Business, Enterprise and Regulatory Reform, 1 Victoria Street, London SW1H 0ET *Tel:*020 7215 0105

Parkins, Miss Diane G *Feb 1986*
Bedfordshire County Council, County Hall, Cauldwell Street, Bedford, Bedfordshire MK42 9AP *Tel:*01234 363222 *Fax:*01234 228619 *Dx:*117105 BEDFORD 4. Barrister

Pearce, Marcus Stewart I *Jul 1972*
Wycombe & Beaconsfield Magistrates Court, Easton Street, High Wycombe, Buckinghamshire HP11 1LR *Tel:*01494 651035 *Fax:*01494 651030 *Dx:*97883 HIGH WYCOMBE 3. *E-mail:*wycombe.magistrates@hmcourts-service.gsi.gov.uk Work: 15

Perkins, Richard C I *Nov 1972*
MA(Oxon). Department for Business, Enterprise and Regulatory Reform, 1 Victoria Street, London SW1H 0ET *Tel:*020 7215 0105

Pervez, Miss Asma M *Oct 2002*
LLB(Hons). Northamptonshire Magistrates Courts, Regents Pavilion, Summerhouse Road, Moulton Park, Northampton, Northamptonshire NN3 6AS *Tel:*01604 497000 *Fax:*01536 497010 Court Clerk

Petty, Christopher R W M *Nov 1976*
MA(Cantab). AstraZeneca, Alderley House, Alderley Park, Macclesfield, Cheshire SK10 4TF *Tel:*01625 582828 *Fax:*01625 585618 Assistant General Counsel

Phillips, Alfred William I *Nov 1998*
BA(Hons); LLB(Hons). HM Revenue & Customs, Solicitor's Office, Ralli Quays (West), 3 Stanley Street, Salford, Greater Manchester M60 9LB *Tel:*0870 785 8545 *Fax:*0870 785 8528 *Dx:*742371 SALFORD 20. Lawyer

Pigott, Mrs Sarah Jane Elizabeth I *Jul 1998*
LLB; LLM; BVC. Shell International Ltd, Shell Centre, York Road, London SE1 7NA *Tel:*020 7934 1234 *Fax:*020 7934 3023 *Dx:*473 LONDON/CHANCERY LN. *E-mail:*l.dalsgaard@shell.com Legal Counsel

Pikett, Christopher M *Nov 1976*
LLB(Hons). 3M United Kingdom PLC, 3M Centre, Cain Road, Bracknell, Bracknell Forest RG12 8HT *Tel:*0870 536 0036 *Fax:*01344 858278 General Manager Legal Affairs & Company Secretary Work: 11,22,13

Pilkington, Aubrey Alfred St John M *Nov 1982*
LLB(Hons). South Lincolnshire Magistrates Courts, Justices Clerks Office, Harlaxton Road, Grantham, Lincolnshire NG31 6SB *Tel:*01476 563438 *Fax:*01476 567200 *Dx:*711100 GRANTHAM 4. Justices Clerk

Polledri, Ms Elisabetta L *Jul 1989*
Treasury Solicitors Department, 7th Floor, One Kemble Street, London WC2B 4TS *Tel:*020 7210 3000 *Fax:*020 7210 3004 *Dx:*123242 KINGSWAY.

Povey, Ms Caroline I *Oct 1998*
Department for Business, Enterprise and Regulatory Reform, 1 Victoria Street, London SW1H 0ET *Tel:*020 7215 0105

Poxon, Philip L *Jul 1985*
LLB. Austin Power Service, Power House, Silverlink Business Park, Newcastle upon Tyne, Tyne & Wear NE28 9ND *Tel:*0191 295 2000 *Fax:*0191 295 2011 Legal and Commercial Manager

Price, Jonathan Nicholas I *Nov 1989*
LLB(Hons); MBA. Northamptonshire Magistrates Courts, Regents Pavilion, Summerhouse Road, Moulton Park, Northampton, Northamptonshire NN3 6AS *Tel:*01604 497000 *Fax:*01536 497010 Deputy Clerk to the Justices

Prince, Raymond L *Jul 1985*
BA(Hons). London Borough of Haringey, Legal Services, Alexandra House, 10 Station Road, Haringey, London N22 4TR *Tel:*020 8489 0000 *Fax:*020 8489 3835 / 5984 *Dx:*35651 WOOD GREEN 1. Principal Lawyer

Pryer, David G *Nov 1982*
MCMI; FInstCPD. Justices Clerks Office, The Court House, Beaumont Street, Hexham, Northumberland NE46 3NB *Tel:*01434 603248 *Fax:*01434 609378; South East Northumberland Magistrates Court, Magistrates' Clerks Office, Law Courts, Bedlington, Northumberland NE22 7LX *Tel:*01670 531100 *Fax:*01670 820133 *Dx:*62705 BEDLINGTON. *E-mail:*david.pryer@hmcourts-service.gsi.gov.uk; Tynedale Magistrates Court, The Courthouse, Beaumont Street, Hexham, Northumberland NE46 3NB *Tel:*01434 603248 *Fax:*01434 609378 *Dx:*68720 HEXHAM. Clerk to the Justices

Puckrin, Arthur William G *Sept 1966*
LLB(Lond); FCIS; MBIM. Romanby Finance Ltd, 3 Romanby Gardens, Middlesbrough TS5 8BW *Tel:*01642 593807 Director

Radway, Mrs Margaret L *Jan 1979*
South Lincolnshire Magistrates Courts, Justices Clerks Office, Harlaxton Road, Grantham, Lincolnshire NG31 6SB *Tel:*01476 563438 *Fax:*01476 567200 *Dx:*711100 GRANTHAM 4. Court Clerk

Rajagopal, Ms Samantha Jane I *Nov 2002*
LLB(Hons). Northamptonshire Magistrates Courts, Regents Pavilion, Summerhouse Road, Moulton Park, Northampton, Northamptonshire NN3 6AS *Tel:*01604 497000 *Fax:*01536 497010 Court Clerk, Solicitor

Ramsey, Ms Jane M *Jul 1989*
BA(Hons); MSc. Merton Council Legal Services, Merton Civic Centre, London Road, Morden, Surrey SM4 5DX *Tel:*020 8543 2222 *Fax:*020 8543 7126 *Dx:*41650 MORDEN. Head of Legal Services

Rasaiah, Ms Santha M *Jul 1983*
BA(Oxon). The Newspaper Society, St Andrews House, 18-20 St Andrews Street, London EC4A 3AY *Tel:*020 7632 7400 *Fax:*020 7632 7401 *E-mail:*ns@newspapersoc.org.uk Political Editorial & Regulatory Affairs Director

Ratcliffe, Steven James G *Nov 1984*
LLB(Hons). Lincolnshire County Council Resources - Legal Services, County Offices, Newland, Lincoln, Lincolnshire LN1 1YP *Tel:*01522 552222 *Fax:*01522 552138 *Dx:*701680 LINCOLN 5. Solicitor

Rayne, Miss Tracy M *Jan 2002*
Newcastle Upon Tyne City Council, Civic Centre, Barras Bridge, Newcastle upon Tyne, Tyne & Wear NE99 2BN *Tel:*0191 232 8520 *Fax:*0191 277 7127 *Dx:*62552 JESMOND.

Rees-Lewis, Miss Megan L *Oct 2001*
LLB. Swansea Magistrates Court, Grove Place, Swansea SA1 5DB *Tel:*01792 655171 *Fax:*01792 651066 Trainee Legal Advisor

Reihill, Mark G *Nov 1996*
MA(Hons); PG Dip. Birmingham City Council Legal & Democratic Services, Ingleby House, 11-14 Cannon Street, Birmingham, West Midlands B2 5EN *Tel:*0121 303 2066 *Fax:*0121 303 1312 *Dx:*13053 BIRMINGHAM.

Rennell, Nigel John Nicholas L *Nov 1990*
BA(Hons)(Law). Wycombe & Beaconsfield Magistrates Court, Easton Street, High Wycombe, Buckinghamshire HP11 1LR *Tel:*01494 651035 *Fax:*01494 651030 *Dx:*97883 HIGH WYCOMBE 3. *E-mail:*wycombe.magistrates@hmcourts-service.gsi.gov.uk

Richardson, Philip Martin L *Jul 1988*
MA; LLB. Nuneaton and Bedworth Borough Council, Town Hall, Coton Road, Nuneaton, Warwickshire CV11 5AA *Tel:*024 7637 6376 *Fax:*024 7637 6238 *Dx:*16458 NUNEATON. *E-mail:*philip.richardson@nuneaton-bedworthbc.gov.uk Head of Legal Services

Richmond, David Andrew I *Nov 1993*
LIB(Hons). Croydon Magistrates Court, Barclay Road, Croydon, Surrey CR9 3NG *Tel:*020 8603 0476 *Fax:*020 8680 9801 *Dx:*97474 CROYDON 6. Branch Legal Manager

Rodger, Mark Stuart G *Jan 1983*
LLB. Birmingham City Council Legal & Democratic Services, Ingleby House, 11-14 Cannon Street, Birmingham, West Midlands B2 5EN *Tel:*0121 303 2066 *Fax:*0121 303 1312 *Dx:*13053 BIRMINGHAM. Barrister

Roopra, Ravinder Singh L *Nov 1996*
LLB(Hons). Eastgate Assistance Ltd, Eastgate House, Stephenson Road, The Business Park, Colchester, Essex CO4 4QR *Tel:*0870 523 4500 *Fax:*0870 523 4508 *Dx:*3626 COLCHESTER. Barrister

Roper, Frank S D M *Oct 1975*
National Grid PLC, National Grid Park, Warwick Technology Park, Gallows Hill, Warwick, Warwickshire CV34 6DA *Tel:*01926 653000 *Fax:*01926 654378

Rose, Ms Vivien G *Jul 1984*
MA(Cantab); BCL(Oxon). Treasury Solicitors Department, 7th Floor, One Kemble Street, London WC2B 4TS *Tel:*020 7210 3000 *Fax:*020 7210 3004 *Dx:*123242 KINGSWAY.

Rowan, Michael Anthony I *Nov 1991*
LLB(Hons). Kennet District Council, Browfort, Bath Road, Devizes, Wiltshire SN10 2AT *Tel:*01380 724911 *Fax:*01380 720835 *Dx:*42909 DEVIZES. *E-mail:*kentishtowncab@camdencabservice.org.uk

Rowbottom, Stephen Peter G *Feb 1983*
LLB(Hons); MBA. North Tyneside Council, Quadrant, The Silverlink North, Cobalt Business Park, Newcastle upon Tyne, Tyne & Wear NE27 0BY *Tel:*0191 643 5000 *Fax:*0191 643 2430 Lawyer

Rowlands, Ian Richard M *Nov 1986*
BSc(Hons). Ajilon Group Ltd, 33 Regent Street, London SW1Y 4NB *Tel:*020 7440 2010 *Fax:*020 7440 2012 Group Legal Director

Royce-Lewis, Ms Christine Alison M *Nov 1982*
BA; MSc. Visa Europe, PO Box 39662, London W2 6WH *Tel:*020 7937 8111 *Fax:*020 7937 0877 Senior Vice President & Senior Legal Adviser

Rundle, Simon M M *Nov 1998*
BA. Environment Agency (South West Region), Manley House, Kestrel Way, Exeter, Devon EX2 7LQ *Tel:*0870 850 6506 *Fax:*01392 442112 *Dx:*121350 EXETER 12. Principal Counsel

Russell, Geoffrey David I *Jun 1997*
Nottinghamshire County Council Legal Services Division, Centenary House, 1 Wilford Lane, West Bridgford, Nottinghamshire NG2 7QZ *Tel:*0115 977 3478 *Fax:*0115 977 3815 *Dx:*723420 NOTTINGHAM.

Russell, Miss Veena Maya G *Jul 1976*
LLB. Diamond Trading Company, 17 Charterhouse Street, London EC1N 6RA *Tel:*020 7404 4444 *Fax:*020 7430 3445 Legal Adviser

Rylands, Keith William M *Nov 1979*
LLB(Lond). Crown Prosecution Service Essex, County House, 100 New London Road, Chelmsford, Essex CM2 0RG *Tel:*01245 455800 *Fax:*01245 455964 *Dx:*139160 CHELMSFORD 11.

Sachs, Mrs Anne Marie G *Jul 1978*
LLM. Department for Business, Enterprise and Regulatory Reform, 1 Victoria Street, London SW1H 0ET *Tel:*020 7215 0105

13

Samnadda, Ms Julie K M *Nov 1986*
Department for Business, Enterprise and Regulatory Reform, 1 Victoria Street, London SW1H 0ET *Tel:*020 7215 0105

Sands, Miss Sarah Rebecca M *Nov 1998*
BA(Hons); LLM. Ashby-de-la-Zouch Petty Sessional Division, Clerks Office, Vaughan Street, Coalville, Leicestershire LE67 3DP *Tel:*01530 810661 *Fax:*01530 813427; Hinckley Magistrates Court, Upper Bond Street, Hinckley, Leicestershire LE10 1NZ Legal Advisor Work: 15,20,41,12

Sansam, Miss Heather R G *Jul 1980*
Warley Magistrates Court, Law Courts, Oldbury Ringway, Sandwell, Warley, West Midlands B69 4JN Acting Clerk to the Justices

Saunt, Ms Linda P I *Nov 1986*
MA. Department for Business, Enterprise and Regulatory Reform, 1 Victoria Street, London SW1H 0ET *Tel:*020 7215 0105

Schofield, Peter Graham L *Nov 1988*
BA. EEF, Broadway House, Tothill Street, Westminster, London SW1H 9NQ *Tel:*020 7222 7777 *Fax:*020 7222 2782 Director of Employment Policy

Scott, Ms Charlotte Elizabeth G *Nov 2005*
LLB; BVC. Redbridge Magistrates Court, 850 Cranbrook Road, Barkingside, Ilford, Essex IG6 1HW *Tel:*0845 601 3600 *Fax:*020 8550 2101 *Dx:*99327 BARKINGSIDE. Barrister

Scott, Trevor P G *Oct 1996*
LLB(Hons). Slough Borough Council, Town Hall, Bath Road, Slough SL1 3UQ *Tel:*01753 552288 *Fax:*01753 875183 *Dx:*42270 SLOUGH WEST.; Wealden District Council, Council Offices, Pine Grove, Wealden, Crowborough, East Sussex TN6 1DH *Tel:*01892 653311 *Fax:*01892 602223 *Dx:*36860 CROWBOROUGH. Barrister

Searle, Ms Frances Anne G *Nov 1979*
BA(Hons)(Linguistics & German). South Western Magistrates Court, 176a Lavender Hill, London SW11 1JU *Tel:*020 7805 1447 *Fax:*020 7805 1448 *Dx:*58559 CLAPHAM JUNCTION. Assistant Justices Clerk (Youth Justice)

Seculer, Anthony Roy M *May 1985*
BSc(Econ). Vale of Glamorgan Magistrates Court, Thompson Street, Barry, Vale of Glamorgan CF63 4SX *Tel:*01446 737491 *Fax:*01446 732743

Sehrawat, Sahib Ram M *Jan 1979*
Land Registry - Croydon Office, Trafalgar House, 1 Bedford Park, Croydon, Surrey CR0 2AQ *Tel:*020 8388 3288 *Fax:*020 8781 9110 *Dx:*2699 CROYDON 3. *E-mail:*croydon.office@landregistry.gsi.gov.uk Barrister

Shah, Miss Sheilja M *Oct 1994*
LLB(Hons); LLM. Department for Business, Enterprise and Regulatory Reform, 1 Victoria Street, London SW1H 0ET *Tel:*020 7215 0105

Shaw, Mrs Leslie M G *Jan 1998*
RAC Motoring Services, RAC House, Great Park Road, Bradley Stoke, Bristol BS32 4QN *Tel:*0870 553 3533 *Fax:*01454 208222

Shaw, Peter Vernon Hugh L *Nov 1993*
BA(Hons). Eastgate Assistance Ltd, Eastgate House, Stephenson Road, The Business Park, Colchester, Essex CO4 4QR *Tel:*0870 523 4500 *Fax:*0870 523 4508 *Dx:*3626 COLCHESTER. Barrister

Shipsey, Miss Helen I *Nov 1991*
LLB(Lond). Country Land and Business Association Ltd, 16 Belgrave Square, London SW1X 8PQ *Tel:*020 7235 0511 *Fax:*020 7235 4696 Senior Legal Adviser

Shoulders, Paul M *Feb 1998*
DMS; MBA. Bury Magistrates Court, The Courthouse, Tenters Street, Bury, Greater Manchester BL9 0HX *Tel:*0161 447 8600 *Fax:*0161 447 8630 *Dx:*707370 BURY.

Shriplin, Miss Katy M *Jul 1984*
LLB. Department for Business, Enterprise and Regulatory Reform, 1 Victoria Street, London SW1H 0ET *Tel:*020 7215 0105

Shropshire, Miss Alison E M L *Nov 1979*
BA; LLM. B A A PLC, Heathrow Point West, 234 Bath Road, Hayes, Middlesex UB3 5AP *Tel:*0870 000 0123 *Fax:*020 8745 4290

Sidhu, Ravi I *Feb 1988*
Crown Prosecution Service Thames Valley, The Courtyard, Lombard Street, Abingdon, Oxfordshire OX14 5SE *Tel:*01235 551900 *Fax:*01235 551901 *Dx:*35859 ABINGDON.

Sembhi, Gurdeep Singh I *Jan 2003*
Corby Borough Council, Grosvenor House, George Street, Corby, Northamptonshire NN17 1QB *Tel:*01536 402551 *Fax:*01536 464109 *Dx:*12915 CORBY. Senior Legal Officer

Slaney, Ms Louise P I *Sept 1990*
LLB. Swindon Borough Council, Civic Offices, Euclid Street, Swindon SN1 2JH *Tel:*01793 463000 *Fax:*01793 490420 *Dx:*133055 SWINDON 16.

Smith, Mark W M *Jul 1982*
BA. Department for Business, Enterprise and Regulatory Reform, 1 Victoria Street, London SW1H 0ET *Tel:*020 7215 0105

Smith, Michael R G *Nov 1987*
Treasury Solicitors Department, 7th Floor, One Kemble Street, London WC2B 4TS *Tel:*020 7210 3000 *Fax:*020 7210 3004 *Dx:*123242 KINGSWAY.

Snell, John Bernard L *Jul 1972*
BA(Oxon). Romney Hythe & Dymchurch Light Railway Company, New Romney Station, New Romney, Kent TN28 8PL *Tel:*01679 62353 *Fax:*01679 63591 Company Secretary

Snowdon, Peter I *Oct 1997*
LLB(Hons); LLM. Financial Services Authority, 25 The North Colonnade, Canary Wharf, London E14 5HS *Tel:*020 7066 1000

Sofat, Sushil Kumar L *Jul 1960*
BSc; BSc(Tech); C Chem; FRSC. British Pest Control Association, 44 Greenacres, Leverstock Green, Hemel Hempstead, Hertfordshire HP2 4NA *Tel:*01442 257579 *Fax:*01442 404735 Legal Adviser

Southgate, Miss Marie Dawn L *Oct 1997*
LLB. Peterborough City Council, Town Hall, Bridge Street, Peterborough PE1 1HG *Tel:*01733 747474 *Fax:*01733 452524 *Dx:*12310 PETERBOROUGH. Barrister

Sparkes, Peter I *Dec 1991*
Ipswich Borough Council, Grafton House, 15-17 Russell Road, Ipswich, Suffolk IP1 2DE *Tel:*01473 432000 *Fax:*01473 432326 *Dx:*3225 IPSWICH. *E-mail:*legal@ipswich.gov.uk Barrister

Spencer, Miss Francoise G *Feb 1993*
LLB. Department for Business, Enterprise and Regulatory Reform, 1 Victoria Street, London SW1H 0ET *Tel:*020 7215 0105

Spicer, David Leslie G *Nov 1973*
Nottinghamshire County Council Legal Services Division, Centenary House, 1 Wilford Lane, West Bridgford, Nottinghamshire NG2 7QZ *Tel:*0115 977 3478 *Fax:*0115 977 3815 *Dx:*723420 NOTTINGHAM.

Stanley, David M *Oct 2001*
Taylor Nelson Sofres PLC, AGB House, Westgate, Ealing, London W5 1UA *Tel:*020 8967 4348 *Fax:*020 8967 4058 *E-mail:*john.stobart@tnsofres.com Legal Counsel

Stewart, Andrew M *Jul 1983*
BA(Hons). Department for Business, Enterprise and Regulatory Reform, 1 Victoria Street, London SW1H 0ET *Tel:*020 7215 0105

Stewart, Ms Victoria J I *Feb 1990*
LLB(Hons). Derby Hospitals NHS Foundation Trust, Derby City General Hospital, Uttoxeter Road, Derby DE22 3NE *Tel:*01332 785419 *Fax:*01332 788671 *E-mail:*victoria.stewart@derbyhospitals.nhs.uk Non-Practising

Stibbs, Michael John Parker M *Oct 1982*
BA(Hons). Great Yarmouth Magistrates Court, Magistrates Court House, North Quay, Great Yarmouth, Norfolk NR30 1PW *Tel:*01493 849800 *Fax:*01493 852169 *Dx:*139400 GREAT YARMOUTH 3. *E-mail:*greatyarmouth.court@hmcourts-service.gsi.gov.uk Legal Team Leader

Stokes, Paul Gwynne L *Oct 1998*
LLB(Hons). Hardwicke Scholar. HSBC Legal Department, 8th Floor, 12 Calthorpe Road, Edgbaston, Birmingham, West Midlands B15 1QZ *Tel:*0121 455 2740 *Fax:*0121 455 2770 *Dx:*712633 BIRMINGHAM 32.

Stoplar, David G *Jul 1982*
LLB. Civil Aviation Authority, CAA House, 45-59 Kingsway, London WC2B 6TE *Tel:*020 7453 6162 *Fax:*020 7453 6163

Suddaby, John I *Nov 1990*
BA(Hons); DipLaw. London Borough of Haringey, Legal Services, Alexandra House, 10 Station Road, Haringey, London N22 4TR *Tel:*020 8489 0000 *Fax:*020 8489 3835 / 5984 *Dx:*35651 WOOD GREEN 1. Deputy Head of Legal & Monitoring Officer Work: 10,18,20,30,36

Sugrue, Miss Claire M *Oct 1985*
LLB(Hons). Universal-Island Records Ltd, 22 St Peters Square, London W6 9NW *Tel:*020 8741 1511 / 5300 *Fax:*020 8741 8781 / 8748 1998 Director, Legal & Business Affairs

Sullivan, Mrs Debra L *Nov 1988*
LLB; Maitrise en Droit. British American Tobacco, Globe House, 4 Temple Place, London WC2R 2PG *Tel:*020 7845 1000 *Fax:*020 7845 2783

Sutcliff, Miss E L L *Aug 1995*
BSc. Gateshead Magistrates Court, Warwick Street, Gateshead, Tyne & Wear NE8 1DT *Tel:*0191 477 5821 *Fax:*0191 478 7825 *Dx:*67783 GATESHEAD 3. Justices Clerk Assistant

Sutherland, Ms Alison Jane Benham G *Nov 1981*
MA(Cantab). Local Government Association, Local Government House, Smith Square, Westminster, London SW1P 3HZ *Tel:*020 7664 3000 *Fax:*020 7664 3030 *Dx:*119450 CLERKENWELL 3. *E-mail:*info@lga.gov.uk

Swinhoe, Luke I *Dec 1987*
BA(Hons); DipLaw; LLM. Darlington Borough Council, Town Hall, Feethams, Darlington DL1 5QT *Tel:*01325 388055 *Fax:*01325 388318 *Dx:*69280 DARLINGTON 6. Barrister

Syed, Mohammed Hussain L *Nov 1989*
BA(Hons); Barrister; Solicitor. Shell International Ltd, Shell Centre, York Road, London SE1 7NA *Tel:*020 7934 1234 *Fax:*020 7934 3023 *Dx:*473 LONDON/CHANCERY LN. *E-mail:*l.dalsgaard@shell.com

Tackie, Abraham M *Nov 1983*
RMN; BA; LLM. Middlesex University, Faculty of Law, The Burroughs, Hendon, London NW4 4BT *Tel:*020 8411 5555 Lecturer

Tailby, Christopher Russell I *Nov 1971*
PricewaterhouseCoopers LLP, Cornwall Court, 19 Cornwall Street, Birmingham, West Midlands B3 2DT *Tel:*0121 200 3000 *Fax:*0121 200 2464

Tate, Miss Phillipa Susan Anne G *Nov 2000*
Hertfordshire County Council, County Hall, Pegs Lane, Hertford, Hertfordshire SG13 8DQ *Tel:*01992 555555 *Fax:*01992 555541 *Dx:*145781 HERTFORD 4. Barrister

Taylor, C Paul L *Nov 1990*
LLB(Hons). Environment Agency (Anglian Region), Kingfisher House, Goldhay Way, Orton Goldhay, Peterborough PE2 5ZR *Tel:*01733 371811 *Fax:*01733 231840 *Dx:*701640 ORTON GOLDHAY. Counsel

Taylor, Howard G *Jan 1986*
Northamptonshire Magistrates Courts, Regents Pavilion, Summerhouse Road, Moulton Park, Northampton, Northamptonshire NN3 6AS *Tel:*01604 497000 *Fax:*01536 497010 BLA

Thomas, Ms Belinda Jane M *Oct 1991*
BA(Hons)(French/Political Science); DipLaw. Serious Fraud Office, Elm House, 10-16 Elm Street, London WC1X 0BJ *Tel:*020 7239 7272 *Fax:*020 7837 1689 *Dx:*135896 LONDON GRAY'S INN ROAD. *E-mail:*public.enquiries@sfo.gsi.gov.uk Policy Lawyer; SFO

Thomas, Ian David M *Jul 1965*
MA. IFPI Secretariat, 10 Piccadilly, London W1J 0DD *Tel:*020 7878 7900 *Fax:*020 7878 7950 *E-mail:*info@ifpi.org Consultant

Thomlinson, Peter Robert L *Jul 1981*
BA; LLM. Mitsubishi Electric Europe B V, Travellers Lane, Hatfield, Hertfordshire AL10 8XB *Tel:*01707 276100 Legal Adviser

Thomson, Ms Meredith Drewe G *Jan 1975*
BA(Hons). E E F South, Station Road, Hook, Hampshire RG27 9TL *Tel:*01256 763969 *Fax:*01256 768530 *E-mail:*info@eef-south.org.uk Legal Adviser

Thomson, Peter M *Jul 1966*
MA(Oxon). Chartered Institute of Purchasing & Supplies, Gaston House, Easton on the Hill, Stamford, Lincolnshire PE9 3NZ *Tel:*01780 756777 *Fax:*01780 757610 Director General

Thornhill, Ms Teresa M *Jul 1986*
BA(Oxon); DipLaw(City); MA(Lond). Bristol City Council, Legal Department, Council House, College Green, Bristol BS1 5TR *Tel:*0117 922 2000 *Fax:*0117 922 2172 *Dx:*7827. Barrister Work: 10

Tookey, Michael L *Nov 1992*
LLB. The College of Law, 14 Store Street, Bloomsbury, London WC1E 7DE *Tel:*0800 289997 Senior Lecturer Work: 22,29,30

Underhill, Ms Caroline G *Jan 1982*
Avon & Bristol Law Centre, 2 Moon Street, Stokes Croft, Bristol BS2 8QE *Tel:*0117 924 8662 *Fax:*0117 924 8020 *E-mail:*mail@ablc.demon.co.uk

Uwemedimo, David Brian L *Jul 1986*
BA; LLB. Performing Right Society Ltd, Copyright House, 29-33 Berners Street, London W1P 4AA *Tel:*020 7580 5544 *Fax:*020 7306 4650

Vahey, Philip I *Nov 1986*
MBA. Her Majesty's Courts Service Lewes, Area Directors Office, The Court House, Friars Walk, Lewes, East Sussex BN7 2PG *Tel:*01273 409160 *Fax:*01273 480413 *E-mail:*philip.vahey@hmcourts-service.gsi.gov.uk Director of Legal Services

Vose, Martin I *Jul 1983*
LLB(Hons). City of London Magistrates Court, 1 Queen Victoria Street, London EC4N 4XY *Tel:*020 7332 1830 *Fax:*020 7332 1493 *Dx:*98943 CHEAPSIDE 2.

Walcott, Mrs Eunice L *Oct 1998*
LLB(Hons). Walsall Metropolitan Borough Council, Legal Services, Civic Centre, Darwall Street, Walsall, West Midlands WS1 1TP *Tel:*01922 650000 *Fax:*01922 646142 *Dx:*12149 WALSALL. *E-mail:*coxt@walsall.gov.uk Barrister

Walcott, Stephen J M *May 1998*
RAC Motoring Services, RAC House, Great Park Road, Bradley Stoke, Bristol BS32 4QN *Tel:*0870 553 3533 *Fax:*01454 208222 Corporate Legal Advisor

Walford, Justin Hugh I *Jul 1981*
BA. Express Newspapers PLC, Ludgate House, 245 Blackfriars Road, Southwark, London SE1 9UX *Tel:*020 7922 7785 *Fax:*020 7922 7967

Walker, Miss Annabel Sarah M *Mar 2001*
MA(Hons). Shell International Ltd, Shell Centre, York Road, London SE1 7NA *Tel:*020 7934 1234 *Fax:*020 7934 3023 *Dx:*473 LONDON/CHANCERY LN. *E-mail:*l.dalsgaard@shell.com Legal Counsel Work: 12,22,24,30

Walker, Miss Hazel Louise G *Nov 1982*
BA(Hons). Network Rail, 40 Melton Street, London NW1 2EE *Tel:*020 7557 8000 *Fax:*020 7557 9000 *Dx:*133075 EUSTON 3.

Walker, Murray L *Nov 1985*
LLB. St John's Innovation Centre, Cowley Road, Cambridge, Cambridgeshire CB4 4WS *Tel:*01223 420252 *Fax:*01223 420844

Wallace, Philip G *Nov 1994*
BA(Hons). Financial Services Authority, 25 The North Colonnade, Canary Wharf, London E14 5HS *Tel:*020 7066 1000

Walmsley, Keith G *Jul 1972*
LLB; FCIS. The London Law Agency Ltd, 69 Southampton Row, London WC1B 4ET *Tel:*020 7353 9471 *Fax:*0870 432 0663 *Dx:*1053 LONDON/CHANCERY LN. *E-mail:*info@londonlaw.co.uk Legal Adviser

Walsh, Gregory F A L *Feb 1991*
LLB(Hons); Bar Finals. BUPA, BUPA House, 15-19 Bloomsbury Way, London WC1A 2BA *Tel:*020 7656 2305 *Fax:*020 7656 2725 Head of Legal, Membership

Wannell, Colin D I *Oct 2001*
BSc(Econ); FCII; CPE; BVC. BP Oil International Ltd, International Headquarters, 1 St James's Square, London SW1Y 4PD *Tel:*020 7496 4000 *Fax:*020 7496 4630

Ward, Miss Nicola M *Nov 2001*
Unisys Insurance Services Limited, 101 Old Hall Street, Liverpool, Merseyside L3 9BD *Tel:*0151 328 2918 *Fax:*0151 328 2976 Legal Adviser

Ward, Peter I *Oct 1996*
LLB(Lond). Metropolitan Police Directorate of Legal Services, First Floor, Victoria Block, New Scotland Yard, London SW1H 0BG *Tel:*020 7230 7210 *Fax:*020 7230 7209 Lawyer Work: 18

Warner-Price, Ms Kim E G *Sept 1982*
LLB(Hons). Cheltenham & Gloucester PLC, Chief Office, Barnett Way, Gloucester, Gloucestershire GL4 3RL *Tel:*01452 372372 *Fax:*01452 375570 *Dx:*55251 GLOUCESTER 2. *E-mail:*cglegal@cglegal.demon.co.uk Senior Lawyer

Watkins, Owen David L *Jul 1986*
MA; D Phil(Oxon); MA(City)(Law). Financial Services Authority, 25 The North Colonnade, Canary Wharf, London E14 5HS *Tel:*020 7066 1000

Watson, Nick G *Jun 1986*
LLB; LLM; MBA. Leicester Market Harborough & Lutterworth Petty Sessional Division, Leicester Magistrates Court, Pocklingtons Walk, Leicester LE1 9BE *Tel:*0116 255 3666 *Fax:*0116 254 5851 *Dx:*10828 LEICESTER 1. Clerk to the Justices

Weeks, Stephen Thomas L *Jul 1978*
MA(Cantab). Freemans PLC, Lavender House, 139 Clapham Road, London SW9 0HR *Tel:*020 7735 7644 *Fax:*020 7820 2769 Company Secretary

Welch, Bryan I *Jul 1975*
MA(Cantab). Department for Business, Enterprise and Regulatory Reform, 1 Victoria Street, London SW1H 0ET *Tel:*020 7215 0105

West, David M *Jul 1977*
LLB(Hons). United Kingdom Atomic Energy Authority, Legal Department, Building 521, Harwell, Didcot, Oxfordshire OX11 0RA *Tel:*01235 436984 *Fax:*01235 436850 *E-mail:*david.west@ukaea.org.uk Head of Legal Services

Weston, Steven M *Jul 1975*
LLB(Hons). BP Oil International Ltd, International Headquarters, 1 St James's Square, London SW1Y 4PD *Tel:*020 7496 4000 *Fax:*020 7496 4630 Managing Counsel (Europe)

Whale, Stephen J T G *Feb 1986*
MBA. Montgomeryshire Justices Clerks Office, PO Box 105, Mansion House, 24 Severn Street, Welshpool, Powys SY21 7UX *Tel:*01267 220523

White, Ms Catherine R G *Jan 1977*
LLB. Pembrokeshire Magistrates' Court, Clerks Office, Penffynnon, Hawthorn Rise, Haverfordwest, Pembrokeshire SA61 2AZ *Tel:*01437 772090 *Fax:*01437 768662 *Dx:*99613 HAVERFORDWEST 2.

See p1010 for the Key to Work Categories

Wignall, Julian D M *Jul 1975*
LLB; MBA. City of London Magistrates Court, 1 Queen Victoria Street, London EC4N 4XY *Tel:*020 7332 1830 *Fax:*020 7332 1493 *Dx:*98943 CHEAPSIDE 2.

Willey, Stuart M *Jun 1979*
BA(Hons). Financial Services Authority, 25 The North Colonnade, Canary Wharf, London E14 5HS *Tel:*020 7066 1000

Williams, Miss Elaine Denise G *Jul 1982*
BA; LLM; MBA; F Inst D. Transferry Shipping Co Ltd, Transferry House, Arterial Road, Hornchurch, Essex RM11 3UT *Tel:*01277 232342 *Fax:*01277 222320 *Dx:*44257 PONTYPOOL. *E-mail:*duncan.forbes@torfaen.gov.uk Director

Williams, Simon L *Jan 1993*
Department for Business, Enterprise and Regulatory Reform, 1 Victoria Street, London SW1H 0ET *Tel:*020 7215 0105

Willis-Jones, William Mark M *Nov 1982*
BSc; DipLaw. Armstrong World Industries Ltd, Armstrong House, 38 Market Square, Uxbridge, Middlesex UB8 1NG *Tel:*01895 202095 *Fax:*01895 256869 Deputy General Counsel - International

Wilson, Miss Hilary Margaret G *Nov 1974*
MA(Cantab). Skanska UK PLC, Maple Cross House, Denham Way, Maple Cross, Rickmansworth, Hertfordshire WD3 9SW *Tel:*01923 776666 *Fax:*01923 423864

Wilson, Julian M *Oct 1994*
BSc(Hons); CPE. Durham County Council, Corporate Services, County Hall, Durham, Co Durham DH1 5UL *Tel:*0191 383 3513 *Fax:*0191 383 4455 *Dx:*722100 DURHAM 16. *E-mail:*elizabeth.wilson@durham.gov.uk

Wilson, Miss Marion J M *Oct 1991*
LLB(Hons). Worcestershire County Council, County Hall, Spetchley Road, Worcester, Worcestershire WR5 2NP *Tel:*01905 766335 *Fax:*01905 766677 *Dx:*29941 WORCESTER 2. *E-mail:*legalservices@worcestershire.gov.uk Barrister Work: 12,15,20

Wilson, Terence John L *Nov 1982*
LLB. Newark & Sherwood District Council, Kelham Hall, Kelham, Newark, Nottinghamshire NG23 5QX *Tel:*01636 650000 *Fax:*01636 655239

Winfield, Miss Sarah I *Oct 1990*
LLB(Hons). Metropolitan Police Directorate of Legal Services, First Floor, Victoria Block, New Scotland Yard, London SW1H 0BG *Tel:*020 7230 7210 *Fax:*020 7230 7209 Senior Lawyer Work: 1,6,11,12,15,18,22,23,26,30,31,36,38

Winkley, Julian Patrick M *Jan 1983*
BA(Hons); Barrister. HM Revenue & Customs, Solicitor's Office, Ralli Quays (West), 3 Stanley Street, Salford, Greater Manchester M60 9LB *Tel:*0870 785 8545 *Fax:*0870 785 8528 *Dx:*742371 SALFORD 20. Senior Lawyer

Withington, Neil Robert M *Jul 1981*
MA(Oxon); BCL. British American Tobacco, Globe House, 4 Temple Place, London WC2R 2PG *Tel:*020 7845 1000 *Fax:*020 7845 2783 Legal Director and General Counsel

Woodhull, Ms Anuita I *May 1995*
LLB. Shell International Ltd, Shell Centre, York Road, London SE1 7NA *Tel:*020 7934 1234 *Fax:*020 7934 3023 *Dx:*473 LONDON/CHANCERY LN. *E-mail:*l.dalsgaard@shell.com Senior Legal Counsel

Woolley, Mrs Diana Rosemary G *Jul 1962*
LLB. Omnicon UK PLC, 12 Bishop's Bridge Road, Westminster, London W2 6AA *Tel:*020 7258 3838 *Fax:*020 7258 4383 Group Company Secretary

Worrall, Mrs Judith M *Oct 1992*
National Grid PLC, National Grid Park, Warwick Technology Park, Gallows Hill, Warwick, Warwickshire CV34 6DA *Tel:*01926 653000 *Fax:*01926 654378

Worrall, Miss Sara L *Nov 1998*
LLB; BVC. Government Legal Service, 11th Floor, Lower Castle Street, Castle Mead, Bristol BS1 3AG *Tel:*0845 300 0793 Lawyer

Wright, Mark John M *Oct 1997*
LLB(Hons); LLM. HSBC Legal Department, 8th Floor, 12 Calthorpe Road, Edgbaston, Birmingham, West Midlands B15 1QZ *Tel:*0121 455 2740 *Fax:*0121 455 2770 *Dx:*712633 BIRMINGHAM 32. Legal Adviser

Wynn Davies, Arthur Geraint M *Nov 1971*
LLB(Wales). Telegraph Media Group, 111 Buckingham Palace Road, London SW1W 0DT *Tel:*020 7931 3131 Legal Manager

Young, Barry I *Nov 1968*
LLB; FPMI. M M & K Ltd, 1 Bengal Court, Birchin Lane, London EC3V 9DD *Tel:*020 7283 7200 *Fax:*020 7283 4119 *E-mail:*info@mm-k.com Barrister

Yousuf, Ms Farah L *Jul 1985*
BA(Law). Brent Magistrates Court, Church End, 448 High Road, London NW10 2DZ *Tel:*020 8451 7111 *Fax:*020 8451 2040 *Dx:*110850 WILLESDEN 2.

Zaman, Mrs Sajadia L *Nov 1985*
BA(Law). Stockport Metropolitan Borough Council, Mount Tabor, Mottram Street, Stockport, Greater Manchester SK1 3PA *Tel:*0161 480 4949 *Fax:*0161 477 9835 *Dx:*22605 STOCKPORT 2. Senior Lawyer

SECTION 14

BARRISTERS

NORTHERN IRELAND

CONTENTS

INDIVIDUAL BARRISTERS, NORTHERN IRELAND – A-Z

The General Council of the Bar of Northern Ireland
The Bar Library
91 Chichester Street
Belfast
BT1 3JQ

Tel: 028 9056 2349
Fax: 028 9056 2350
E-mail: admin@barcouncil-ni.org.uk
Web: www.barlibrary.com

Name	Year
Aiken, Joseph	*1999M*
Aldworth, Philip	*1981M*
Alexander, Ms Karon	*1995M*
Allen, Ms Mary	*2009M*
Anderson, James	*2011M*
Anderson, Miss Michelle	*2002M*
Anthony, Gordon	*2011M*
Anyadike-Danes, Mrs Monye (Q.C.)	*1997M*
Askin, Ms Leona	*1998M*
Atchison, Wayne	*2002M*
Auret, Ms Nicola	*1990M*
Austin, Miss Breige	*2007M*
Babington, Andrew	*1985T*
Bacon, Paul	*1999M*
Barlow, Mark	*2006H*
Barr, Dane	*2009M*
Barr, Liam	*1979M*
Bassett, Mark	*2010M*
Beattie, Stewart (Q.C.)	*1986M*
Bentley, Ronnie (Q.C.)	*1974M*
Bernard, Malachy	*2005M*
Berry, Gregory (Q.C.)	*1989M*
Berry, Michael	*1980M*
Best, Harry	*1999H*
Best, Miss Rachel	*2006M*
Blackburn, Alan	*1976M*
Blackburn, Robert	*2000M*
Blythe, Miss Rhyannon	*2008M*
Boal, Ms Lindsay	*1997M*
Bonnar, Gavin	*1991M*
Bowman, Miss Shellee	*2009M*
Boyd, Dennis	*1982M*
Boyd, Michael	*2001M*
Boyd, Mrs Stephanie	*2001M*
Boyle, Paul	*1985M*
Bradley, Ms Suzanne	*1978M*
Brady, Ms Amanda	*1986M*
Brady, Bernard	*1994M*
Brady, Ms Grainne	*2011M*
Brady, James	*1997M*
Brangam, Alva (Q.C.)	*1978M*
Bready, Michael	*2000M*
Breen, Ms Michele	*2009M*
Brennan, Anthony	*2001M*
Brennen, Paul	*1999M*
Brolly, Joe	*1992M*
Brown, Andrew	*2005M*
Brown, George	*1988M*
Brown, Ms Lee	*1997M*
Brown, Miss Michelle	*2010M*
Browne, Jonathan	*1997M*
Brownlie, Andrew	*2005M*
Burns, Paul	*2009M*
Byrne, Conor	*2002M*
Byrne, Justin	*1997M*
Cahill, Tom (Q.C.)	*1957T*
Cairns, Gavyn	*2002M*
Campbell, Ms Conagh	*2007M*
Campbell, Conor	*1990M*
Campbell, Dawson	*2009M*
Campbell, Miss Gerarda	*2008M*
Campbell, Michael	*1990M*
Campbell, Taylor	*1981M*
Canavan, Miss Claire	*2007M*
Carlin, Miss Seana	*2010M*
Carson, Ms Margaret	*2008M*
Cartmill, David	*1980M*
Casey, Ms Lisa	*2004M*
Caslin, Miss Siobhan	*2011M*
Cavanagh, Ms Caroline	*2009M*
Chambers, Michael	*2005M*
Chapman, Stephen	*2005M*
Chesney, George	*1983M*
Clarke, Ms Alex	*2009M*
Clarke, Miss Laura	*2011M*
Clayton, John	*2010M*
Cleland, Conor	*1995M*
Cleland, Eric	*2006M*
Coey, Miss Leanne	*2011M*
Coghlin, Richard	*2006M*
Coiley, Peter	*2003M*
Cole, Miss Kirsty	*2011M*
Coll, Miss Katie	*2007M*
Coll, Peter	*1996M*
Collins, Ms Claire	*1997M*
Collins, Jonathan	*1999M*
Colmer, Adrian	*1994M*
Colton, Adrian (Q.C.)	*1983M*
Comerton, Alan (Q.C.)	*1963M*
Comerton, Ms Jill	*1993M*
Conlon, Kevin (Q.C.)	*1976M*
Conlon, Mark	*2002M*
Connell, Russell	*1979M*
Connolly, Ms Fionnuala	*1996M*
Connolly, Jonathan	*2003M*
Connolly, Ms Martina	*1997M*
Connolly, Ms Mary	*2000M*
Connolly, Paddy	*1978M*
Connor, Neil	*1993M*
Copeland, Michael	*1983M*
Corkey, Matthew	*2008M*
Corrigan, Aidan Barry	*2010M*
Corrigan, Aiden	*1980M*
Coulter, Ms Nicola	*2010M*
Coyle, Christopher	*2007M*
Coyle, John	*1990T*
Crawford, Andrew	*1990M*
Cregan, Miss Rosena	*2011M*
Creighton, Ms Dawn	*1986M*
Croft, Mrs Cheryl	*1998H*
Cunningham, Alan	*2003M*
Cunningham, Miss Kate	*1997M*
Curran, Luke	*2000M*
Cush, Peter	*1971M*
Daly, Ronan	*1994M*
Dargan, Ms Brenda	*1986M*
Davey, Gerry	*1979M*
Davidson, Miss Wendy	*2000M*
Dellow-Perry, Ms Emma Jane	*2010M*
Denvir, Ms Ciara	*1995M*
Denvir, Kevin	*1979M*
Devine, Sean	*2006M*
Devlin, Brendan	*1996M*
Devlin, Miss Catherine	*2011M*
Devlin, Eoghan	*2001M*
Devlin, Miss Niamh	*2005M*
Devlin, Miss Una	*2009M*
Dillon, Noel	*1988M*
Dinsmore, Mrs Margaret-Ann (Q.C.)	*1980M*
Doherty, Ms Fiona	*1997M*
Doherty, Miss Kelly	*2006M*
Doherty, Michael	*2011M*
Doherty, Ms Sarah	*2011M*
Doherty, Sean	*2001M*
Doherty, Sean Gerard	*2007M*
Donaghy, Gareth	*2001M*
Donaghy, Rory	*1996M*
Donald, Ms Denise	*2008M*
Donaldson, Marcus	*2006M*
Donnelly, Ms Cathy	*1977M*
Doran, Michael	*2011M*
Doran, Sean	*1987M*
Dornan, Philip	*1978M*
Douglas, Miss Lisa	*2007M*
Dowd, Roger	*1991M*
Dowey, John	*2005M*
Downey, Ms Roisin	*2008M*
Duffy, Gavan (Q.C.)	*1991M*
Duffy, Michael	*1988M*
Dunford, Craig	*2000M*
Dunlop, David	*1998M*
Dunlop, Jonathan	*1996M*
Dunn, Campbell	*1978M*
Dunn, Michael	*1987M*
Durkan, Miss Mary	*2004M*
Edmondson, Douglas	*1997M*
Egan, Michael	*1989M*
Elliott, Miss Daphne	*1984M*
Elliott, Fraser (Q.C.)	*1966M*
Elliott, Stephen	*1984M*
Ellis, Miss Rosalind	*2007M*
Ellison, Miss Julia (known as Julie)	*2011M*
Ennis, Miss Ciara	*2001M*
Fahy, Desmond	*1999M*
Farrell, Donal	*2002M*
Farrell, Mark	*1994M*
Farrell, Miss Rachel	*2001M*
Farrelly, Francis	*1978M*
Fee, Brian (Q.C.)	*1978M*
Fee, Dermot (Q.C.)	*1975M*
Fee, Ms Fiona	*2009M*
Fee, Miss Nessa	*2006M*
Fee, Rory	*2007M*
Ferran, Paul	*1977M*
Ferriss, Tim (Q.C.)	*1968M*
Ferrity, Patrick	*1980M*
Finegan, Ms Anne	*1978M*
Finlay, Ms Kate	*1982M*
Fisher, Ms Sian	*2008M*
Fitzpatrick, Bernard	*1986M*
Fitzpatrick, Stephen	*2010T*
Fitzpatrick, Thomas	*1994M*
Fitzsimons, Ms Cathy	*2008M*
Flanagan, Colm	*2003M*
Flanagan, Donal	*1997M*
Flanagan, Miss Julie	*2002M*
Forde, Michael	*2009M*
Foster, Eamon	*2008M*
Foster, Paul	*2000M*
Fox, Neil	*2000M*
Friel, Oisin	*2011M*
Friers, Mrs Fiona	*2004M*
Gallagher, James (Q.C.)	*1972M*
Gallagher, John	*2008M*
Gallagher, Miss Suzanne	*2005M*
Gibson, Barry	*1983M*
Gibson, Christopher	*2009M*
Gibson, Ms Heather (Q.C.)	*1983M*
Gibson, Keith	*1999M*
Gilkeson, Ms Janice	*2009M*
Gillespie, Conor	*1994M*
Gillespie, Jack	*1980M*
Gilmore, Stephen	*2007M*
Girvan, Peter	*2005M*
Gogarty, Alain	*1979M*
Good, Patrick (Q.C.)	*1983M*
Gormley, Barry	*1998M*
Goss, Craig	*2004M*
Gowdy, William	*2006M*
Grainger, Gerry	*1981M*
Grant, Eugene (Q.C.)	*1975M*
Grattan, Mrs Sheena	*1999M*
Greene, Richard	*1994M*
Gregan, Ms Hayley	*1995M*
Gribben, Kyle	*2011M*
Haddick, Mrs Joan	*2003M*
Hagan, Colm	*2003M*
Halleron, Damien	*2011M*
Ham, Stephen	*1999M*

14

Name	Year
Hamill, Conor	1990M
Hamill, Michael	1977M
Hanna, Nicolas (Q.C.)	1973M
Hannigan, Ms Joanne	1998M
Harkin, Aidan	1980M
Harvey, Arthur (Q.C.)	1972M
Harvey, Ciaran	1999H
Harvey, Miss Deborah	2006M
Haughey, John	1998M
Heaney, Mark	2001H
Hendron, Miss Roisin	2001M
Henry, Colin	1983M
Henry, Ed	2009M
Henry, Philip	2003M
Heraghty, David	2003M
Higgins, Adrian	1999M
Higgins, Ms Mary (Q.C.)	1984M
Hill, Charles (Q.C.)	1959M
Hill, Miss Fiona	2010M
Hill, Norman	1984M
Hill, Rick	2009M
Hindley, Stewart	2005M
Hogg, Christopher	2009M
Holmes, Chris	1990M
Holmes, Conor	2009M
Hopkins, Peter	2007M
Hopley, David (Q.C.)	1979M
Horner, Mark (Q.C.)	1979M
Houston, Ms Denise	1984M
Huddleston, Karl	2010M
Hughes, Miss Cathy	2001M
Humphreys, Michael (Q.C.)	1994M
Hunt, Niall	1987M
Hunter, David (Q.C.)	1971M
Hunter, John	1986M
Hutton, Dessie	1998M
Hyland, Miss Laura	2007M
Hyland, Miss Marie-Therese	2001M
Hyndman, Miss Kelly	2007M
Ievers, Mrs Laura	1997M
Irvine, Malcolm	2005M
Irvine, Peter (Q.C.)	1982M
Jennings, Ms Lisa	2002H
Johnston, James	1997M
Jones, Miss Ashleigh	2008M
Jones, Nick	2004M
Jones, Ms Susan	2010M
Jordan, Miss Deborah	1994M
Jordan, Ms Katie	2009M
Kane, Alan (Q.C.)	1981M
Kane, Ms Maxine	1991M
Kearney, John (Q.C.)	1989M
Kearney, Paul	2011M
Kearney, Seamus	2002T
Keegan, Brian	1998M
Keegan, Mrs Siobhan (Q.C.)	1994M
Keenan, Colm (Q.C.)	1980M
Kelley, Miss Severina	2011M
Kelly, Ms Elaine	1991M
Kelly, Ms Maire	2010M
Kelso, Stephen	1993M
Kennedy, Brian (Q.C.)	1978M
Kennedy, Ms Fiona	1992M
Kennedy, Dr Iryna	2005M
Kennedy, Joseph	2003M
Kennedy, Ms Roisin	2009M
Keogh, Michael	1989H
Kerr, Gordon (Q.C.)	1976M
Kerr, Ms Nicola	1993M
Kerrin, Andrew	2006M
Kidd, Ms Julia	2005M
Kiley, Ms Denise	2008M
Killen, Ms Orla	2010M
Killen, Miss Shona	2011M
Kilpatrick, Ms Alyson	1998M
King, Peter	1994T
Kinnen, Jeremy	2007M
Kinney, Ms Sara	1991M
Kirkwood, Ms Jennifer	2008M
Kitson, Mrs Tessa	1978M
Lamont, Ms Fiona	1978M
Lannon, Seamus	2002M
Larkin, Ms Eileen	1995M
Larkin, John (Q.C.)	1986M
Lavery, Finbar	2000M
Lavery, Jim (Q.C.)	1973M
Lavery, Ms Joanne	2002M
Lavery, Ms Melissa	2005M
Lavery, Michael	1990M
Lavery, Michael (Q.C.)	1956M
Lavery, Ms Naomh	2003M
Lavery, Ronan (Q.C.)	1993T
Law, Stephen	1993M
Lenaghan, Ms Clare	1991M
Lennon, Mark	1982M
Lewis, Mrs Mary	1988M
Lewis, Paul	1978M
Lindsay, Mrs Jill	1996M
Lindsay, Joel	1992M
Litvack, Mrs Marianne	2000M
Lockhart, Brett (Q.C.)	1982M
Logan, Miss Eileen	2001H
Logue, Miss Emma	2006M
Logue, Mrs Kathryn M	2004T
Long, Michael (Q.C.)	1975M
Lowry, Jonathan	1988M
Lundy, Brian	2001M
Lunny, Conor	2005M
Lunny, Donal	1998M
Lunny, Dr Tony	1983M
Lynch, Miss Frances	2002M
Lyttle, Paddy (Q.C.)	1978M
Macartney, Brian	1975M
MacCreanor, Charles (Q.C.)	1989M
Macdonald, Barry (Q.C.)	1979M
Mack, Geoffrey	1979M
MacKenzie, Ms Claire	1999M
MacMahon, Hugh	1987M
Magee, Andrew	2000M
Magill, Kevin	1997H
Magill, Peter	1978M
Maginness MLA, Alban	1976M
Maguire, Conor	2000M
Maguire, Paul (Q.C.)	1978M
Maguire, Ms Tara	2007M
Mahaffey, Ms Sheena	1992M
Mallon, Jim	1977M
Mallon, Kieran (Q.C.)	1985M
Mannis, Glenn	2009M
Marlow, Ronan	2010M
Martin, Nigel	1986M
Martin, Ms Roisin	2003M
Mateer, Philip (Q.C.)	1981M
Matthews, Ms Agnes Jane	1985M
Matthews, Miss Angela	2011M
Matthews, Neale	1987M
Maxwell, John (AJS)	1984M
Maxwell, Michael	1973M
McAleavey, Miss Katharine	2004M
McAleer, Fintan	2006M
McAleer, Michael	1997M
McAlinden, Gerry (Q.C.)	1986M
McAlinden, Paul	2003M
McAlister, David	1976M
McAllister, Ryan	2005M
McArdle, Eamonn	1996M
McAreavey, Ms Louise	1986M
McAteer, Ivor	1990M
McAteer, Philip	1997M
McAughey, David	1986M
McBride, Ms Denise (Q.C.)	1989M
McBrien, David	1982M
McCabe, Thomas	2009M
McCaffrey, Miss Jessica	2006M
McCain, Ms Joanne	2009M
McCann, Joseph	2003M
McCann, Martin	1981M
McCartney, Brian (Q.C.)	1983M
McCartney, Miss Niamh	2004M
McCaughey, Ronan	2009M
McCausland, Robert	2011M
McCausland, Ms Sara	2009M
McClean, David	1996M
McClean, Ronan	2011M
McCleave, Terence	2010M
McCloskey, Miss Caroline	2001M
McColgan, Ms Donna (Q.C.)	1986M
McCollum, Ciaran	1998M
McCollum, Liam (Q.C.)	1985M
McComb, Michael	1973H
McCombe, Nigel	1983M
McConkey, Richard	2001M
McCormick, Miss Rachael	2011M
McCormick, Mrs RoseAnne	1989M
McCracken, Michael	2005M
McCrea, Michael	1983M
McCreanor, Tom	1988M
McCrissican, Ms Patricia	2008M
McCrory, Billy (Q.C.)	1976M
McCrudden, Gary	1977M
McCrudden, John (Q.C.)	1975M
McCrudden, Laurence (Q.C.)	1977M
McCullagh, Miss Ciara	1992M
McCullough, Miss Geraldine	2001M
McDermott, Ms Eilis (Q.C.)	1974M
McDermott, Miss Marie-Claire	2002M
McDonald, Terry (Q.C.)	1976M
McDonnell, Martin	1981M
McDowell, Ms Alison	1998M
McDowell, David	1999H
McEvoy, Joseph	1985M
McEvoy, Ms Leona	2010M
McEvoy, Mark	2001M
McEvoy, Philip	2000M
McEwen, Mark	1986M
McFarland, Paul	1993M
McGahan, Ms Orlagh	2003M
McGarrity, Mark	2004M
McGarvey, Michael	2003M
McGaughey, Mrs Gillian	1988M
McGill, Miss Laura	2004M
McGinley, Miss Helen	2001M
McGivern, Ms Anne	1989M
McGleenan, Dr Tony (Q.C.)	1997M
McGowan, Aidan	2011M
McGowan, Malachy	2007M
McGrane, Miss Catherine	2007M
McGrath, John	2010M
McGrath, Miss Karen	2011M
McGregor, Ms Ruth	1996M
McGrenera, Ms Noelle (Q.C.)	1978M
McGuckin, Karl	2011M
McGuckin, Ms Sarah	2010M
McGuigan, Miss Derval	1989M
McGuigan, Gregory (Q.C.)	1991M
McGuinness, Andrew	1998M
McGuinness, Miss Ann (Q.C.)	1985M
McGurk, Mrs Una	2002M
McHugh, Miss Anna	2011M
McHugh, Gareth	1993M
McHugh, Ms Mary	2001M
McIlroy, Miss Julie	2007M
McIvor, Ms Daren	2008M
McKay, Mrs Catherine	1988M
McKay, Charles (Q.C.)	1976M
McKeagney, Ms Sinead	1994M
McKee, Brian	1990M
McKee, Ms Kathy	1999H
McKeever, John	2006M
McKelvey, Ross	1987M
McKenna, Barry	2003M
McKenna, Eugene	2010H
McKenna, Ms Tara	1996M
McKeown, David	2008M
McKeown, Guillaume	2009M
McKernan, Ms Paula	2005M
McKillop, Tommy	1980M
McLaughlin, Kieran	2010M
McLaughlin, Miss Laura	2011M
McLaughlin, Paul	1997M
McMahon, Ken (Q.C.)	1969H
McMahon, Ms Laura	2005M
McMillen, David (Q.C.)	1985M
McMullan, Ms Victoria	2010M
McNally, Miss Aisling	2011M
McNamee, Rory	1997H
McNeill, Seamus	1985M
McNicholl, Miss Emer	2011M
McNulty, Miss Fiona	2001M
McNulty, James (Q.C.)	1968M
McQuitty, Steven	2005M
McStay, Liam	1993M
McTaggart, Stuart	2001M
McVeigh, Ms Joanne	2005M
McVeigh, Ms Paula	2009M
Mercer, Jonathan	1982M
Millar, Robert	1987M
Milliken, James	2008M
Millinson, Christopher	1981M
Miskelly, Vincent	2009M
Molloy, Steven	2001M
Montague, Turlough (Q.C.)	1982M
Montgomery, Andrew	1994M
Mooney, Dean	2004M
Mooney, Stephen	2003M
Mooney, Terence (Q.C.)	1971M
Moore, Neil	1996M
Moran, Ms Lisa	1997M
Morgan, Martin	1995M
Moriarty, Andrew	1998M
Morrissey, John	1987M
Morrissey, John Joseph	2006M
Morrow, Mervyn (Q.C.)	1970M
Mortimer, William	1978M
Mulgrew, Marcus	2000M
Mulholland, Miss Maria	2010M
Mulholland, Mark (Q.C.)	1993M
Mullally, Ms Maria	1993M
Mullan, Conor	2003M
Mullan, Miss Maeve	2007M
Mullan, Sean	2010M
Mulqueen, Barry	1995M

Name	Year
Murnaghan, Mrs Neasa	1996M
Murphy, Ciaran (Q.C.)	1985M
Murphy, Ms Grainne	1992M
Murphy, Miss Louise	2000M
Murray, Miss Blaithin	2006M
Nash, Raymond	1995M
Neeson, Maurice	1977M
Neeson, Michael	2007M
Nugent, Blaine	2009M
Nugent, Plunkett	2006M
O'Brien, Luke	2010T
O'Brien, Martin	1989M
O'Brien, Michael	2008M
O'Connor, Hugh	1990M
O'Connor, John Peter	2001M
O'Connor, Miss Siobhan	2004M
O'Donoghue, Frank (Q.C.)	1985M
O'Flaherty, Ms Sinead	2000M
O'Grady, Ms Adele	1992M
O'Hara, John (Q.C.)	1979M
O'Hare, Dr Brendan	1989M
O'Hare, John	1988M
O'Hare, Kevin	1985M
O'Hare, Kevin Francis	2007M
O'Hare, Sean	1998M
O'Kane, Conor	1991M
O'Kane, Mrs Fiona	2005M
O'Kane, Patrick	2000M
O'Kane, Ms Paula	1982M
O'Keeffe, Joseph	2004M
O'Neill, Conn	2005M
O'Neill, Damien	2004M
O'Neill, Ms Kerri	2009M
O'Neill, William	1991M
O'Reilly, Francis	1972M
O'Reilly, Ms Sarah	2004M
O'Rourke, Martin (Q.C.)	1987M
O'Sullivan, Brian	2009M
Orbinson, William (Q.C.)	1988M
Orr, Ms Jackie (Q.C.)	1976M
Orr, John (Q.C.)	1973M
Orr, Mark (Q.C.)	1980M
Overing, Miss Tracy	2004M
Park, Jonathan	1993M
Patterson, Sean	1995M
Patton, Craig	2004M
Pauley, Mrs Jackie	1989M
Phillips, Miss Heather	2004M
Phillips, Neil	1999M
Pinkerton, Ms Natalie	2010M
Pollock, Ms Lisa	2008M
Potter, Gary	1982M
Potter, Michael	1988M
Power, Mel	1985M
Purvis, Gareth	1992M
Quinlivan, Ms Karen (Q.C.)	1993M
Quinn, Declan	2000M
Quinn, Fintan	1981M
Quinn, Ms Lauren	2008M
Quinn, Nigel	1982M
Quinn, Mrs Nuala	1984M
Quinn, Stephen (Q.C.)	1977M
Rafferty, John	2011M
Rafferty, John	1992M
Rafferty, Neil	1990M
Rafferty, Steffan	2009M
Rainey, Paul	2010M
Ramsey, Paul (Q.C.)	1977M
Ramsey, Ms Sarah	1993M
Ranaghan, Ms Paula	1984M
Rea, Bobbie	1997H
Rea, Conan	1997M
Reel, Mark	1996M
Reid, David (James)	2003M
Reid, David John	2006M
Reid, Simon	1994M
Rice, Miss Melanie	2004M
Richards, Neil	2007M
Ringland, Christopher	2010M
Ringland, David (Q.C.)	1978M
Ringland, Terry	1984M
Ritchie, Stephen	1978M
Ritchie, Timothy	2000M
Robinson, Miss Claire	2001M
Robinson, Gavin	2008M
Robinson, Keith	1996M
Robinson, Ms Linda	1996T
Robinson, Mark	1999M
Rodgers, Martin (Q.C.)	1975M
Rodgers, Paul	1996M
Rooney, Kevin (Q.C.)	1983M
Ross, Miss Victoria	2002M
Rountree, Ms Nicola	2009M
Russell, David	1991M
Ryan, Ms Eithne	1996M
Ryan, Miss Rosy	2001M
Sands, Aidan	1998M
Savage, Patrick	2009M
Sayers, Donal	1997M
Scoffield, David (Q.C.)	1999M
Scullion, Andrew	2011M
Sefton, Peter	1983M
Sharpe, Dr David	1999M
Shaw, Michael	1984M
Shaw, Stephen (Q.C.)	1980M
Sheil, Michael	2004M
Sherrard, Christopher	2001M
Shields, JonPaul	1995M
Shields, Richard	2002M
Sholdis, Ms Carole	1986M
Simpson, Gerald (Q.C.)	1974M
Simpson, Ms Jacqueline	1987M
Simpson, Ms Suzanne	1998M
Singer, Miss Vicky	2011M
Sinton, William	2009M
Sloane, Miss Emma	2004M
Smith, Anthony	1999H
Smith, Ms Christine (Q.C.)	1985M
Smith, Ciaran	2007M
Smyth, Miss Aileen	2007M
Smyth, Ms Lynn	2010M
Smyth, Ms Moira	1995M
Smyth, Paul	2009M
Smyth, Richard	2003M
Smyth, Sean	1984M
Solomon, Richard	2011M
Spence, Stuart	1981M
Steele, Miss Caroline	2000M
Steer, Robin	1994M
Stevenson, Douglas	2009M
Stewart, Alan	2006M
Stewart, John	1980M
Stitt, Michael (Q.C.)	1975M
Sweeney, Ms Noreen	1986M
Swift, Felix	2000M
Taggart, Patrick	1997M
Talbot, Gordon	1974M
Tannahill, Ian	1990M
Taylor, Patrick	2005M
Thompson, Aaron	2002M
Tierney, Ms Caoimhe	2009M
Tierney, Michael	2010M
Todd, Eamon	1996M
Toner, Henry (Q.C.)	1976M
Toolan, James	1980M
Trainor, Miss Aisling	2007M
Trainor, Miss Shauna	2001H
Turkington, Ian	1995M
Valentine, Barry	1974M
Vance, Miss Laura	2006M
Vials, Dr Cora	2011M
Walker, Ms Suzanne	2007M
Walkingshaw, Ms Sarah	2003M
Wall, Benedict	2009M
Wallace, Christopher	2010M
Walsh, Ms Margaret (Q.C.)	1980M
Ward, Michael	2011M
Warnock, Timothy	2004M
Watt, Graeme	2001M
Watterson, Ms Rebecca	2010M
Weatherhead, Miss Louise	1998H
Weir, Richard (Q.C.)	1979M
White, Ciaran	2003H
Williamson, Jonathan	2010M
Williamson-Graham, Ms Anita	2003M
Willis, Aaron	2009M
Wolfe, Martin	1994M

SECTION 15

PROFESSIONAL, EDUCATIONAL, REGULATORY AND OTHER BODIES

CONTENTS

ASSOCIATION OF LAW COSTS DRAFTSMEN

ALCD COUNCIL
Michael Bacon
Deborah Burke
Simon Gibbs
Jon Williams

Administrative Secretary
Mrs D Pattenden
Herringbone House, Lion Road, Palgrave,
Diss, Norfolk, IP22 1AL
DX: 42520 DISS
Tel: 020 3174 0967
Fax: 01379 651647
Email: enquiries@costslawyer.co.uk

Please direct all paper communications via the Administrative Secretary to the address shown above.

Chairman
Mr Iain Stark
Email: iainstark@btconnect.com

Vice-Chairman
Miss Victoria Hopkins
Email: vicechairman@costslawyer.co.uk

Secretary
Mr John Hocking
Email: honsec@costslawyer.co.uk

Treasurer
Mr Michael Kain
Email: michael.kain@kain-knight.co.uk

Educational Development Officer
Mr Murray Heining
Email: edo@costslawyer.co.uk

COST LAWYERS

Abbott, P
Pinsent Masons LLP, 30 Crown Place, London EC2A 4ES

Ackroyd, M
DLA Piper UK LLP, 1 St Paul's Place, Sheffield, South Yorkshire S1 2JX
Tel: 0800 111 111

Adams, P L
RBS Cost Drafting Department, PO Box 636, Bromley, Kent BR1 1WF
Tel: 0208 285 8759

Adams, J S
FBC Manby Bowdler LLP Solicitors, 6-10 George Street, Snow Hill, Wolverhampton, West Midlands WV2 4DN
Tel: 01902 578000

Adat, S
Adat Law Costs Drafting, 18 Beveren Close, Fleet, Hampshire GU51 2UB
Tel: .... 01252 810221 Mob: 07765 434056

Addicott, C
Kain Knight, 1, 2 & 4 Priors, London Road, Bishop's Stortford, Hertfordshire CM23 5ED
Tel: 01279 755552

Addison, L
28 Cornfield Close, Bomere Heath, Shrewsbury, Shropshire SY4 3PA
Tel: 01939 291274

Aitken, T
PI Costing Plc, Robson House, 4 Regent Terrace, South Parade, Doncaster, South Yorkshire DN1 2EE
Tel: 01302 386698

Alden, S
Slaughter & May, 1 Bunhill Row, London EC1Y 8YY

Aldrich, R
Bridge Mcfarland Solicitors, 19 Tentercroft Street, Lincoln, Lincolnshire LN5 7DB
Tel: 01522 518888

Allen, R K
Liddell & Co, 20 Balgores Square, Gidea Park, Romford, Essex RM2 6AU
Tel: 01708 775999

Allen, B
Acumension Ltd, No1 Universal Square, Devonshire Street North, Manchester, Greater Manchester M12 6AH
Tel: 0161 277 5100

Anderson, K
Banner Jones Solicitors, 24 Glumangate, Chesterfield, Derbyshire S40 1UA
Tel: 01246 560547

Andrew, L
Coles Miller Solicitors LLP, 44/46 Parkstone Road, Poole BH15 2PG
Tel: 01202 673011

Anker, B
Kain Knight, Regis House, 9 Dane John Works, Gordon Road, Canterbury, Kent CT1 3PP
Tel: 01227 786499

Appleyard, J
Hill Dickinson LLP, City Plaza, Pinfold Street, Sheffield, South Yorkshire S1 2GU
Tel: 0114 229 7907

Arbon-Donovan, L J
Knapp Richardson, 3rd Floor, Chancery House, 53-64 Chancery Lane, London WC2A 1QU
Tel: 0207 831 9082

Arlidge, C
Clyde & Co LLP, 1 Stoke Road, Guildford, Surrey GU1 4HW
Tel: 01483 555488

Armson, A J C
SPH Costing Services Ltd, Suites 3-6, Leyland House, Lancashire Business Park, Centurion Way Park, Leyland, Lancashire PR26 6TY
Tel: 01772 435550

Armstrong, R A
Compass Costs Consultants Ltd, King's Business Park, King's Drive, Prescot, Merseyside L34 1PJ
Tel: 0151 481 4477

Armstrong, M
Winckworth Sherwood Solicitors, Minerva House, 5 Montague Close, London SE1 9BB
Tel: 0207 593 5142

Arnot, D
Crown Costs Consultants Ltd, The Red House, 74 High Street, Bushey, Hertfordshire WD23 3HE
Tel: 020 8838 7110

Arter, P
Temple Chambers, 3-7 Temple Avenue, London EC4Y 0HP
Tel: 020 7353 1165

Arter, P
Temple Chambers, 3-7 Temple Avenue, London EC4Y 0HP
Tel: 0207 353 1165

Ashley, A
AJA Legal Services, 26 Midfield Way, Orpington, Kent BR5 2QJ
Tel: 020 8302 2467

Attwood, D
The John M Hayes Partnership, White House, 111 New Street, Birmingham, West Midlands B2 4EU
Tel: 0121 643 0001

Averill, S J
Phoenix Legal Services Ltd, 4th Floor, Windsor House, Windsor Lane, Cardiff CF10 3DE
Tel: 029 2066 8664

Avis, P
Masters Legal Costs Services LLP, 3-4 New Street, Bishopsgate, London EC2M 4HD
Tel: 0207 929 4344

Ayliffe, T
Irwin Mitchell Solicitors, Bauhaus, Rosseti Place, 27 Quay Street, Manchester, Greater Manchester M3 4AW
Tel: 0870 1500 100

Bacon, A C R
A & M Bacon Limited, 300 Eastrea Road, Whittlesey, Peterborough, Cambridgeshire PE7 2AR
Tel: 01733 350880

Bacon, M
A & M Bacon Limited, 300 Eastrea Road, Whittlesey, Peterborough, Cambridgeshire PE7 2AR
Tel: 01733 350880

Baker, R
Complete Cost Consultants Ltd, Hendra, Tremethick Cross, Penzance, Cornwall TR20 8UD
Tel: 01736 330229

Baller, J
18 Jengar Close, Burnell Road, Sutton, Surrey SM1 4DE
Tel: 0208 401 1301

Banks, R
Kain Knight, 1, 2 & 4 Priors, London Road, Bishop's Stortford, Hertfordshire CM23 5ED
Tel: 01279 755552

Banyard, M
The John M Hayes Partnership, 26-28 Churchill Way, Cardiff CF10 2DY
Tel: 02920 394043

Barker, M
Claimant Costs Recovery Limited, PO Box 385, Plymouth PL1 9BT
Tel: 01752 424841

Barnett, A
19 Burgess Close, Haynes, Bedford, Bedfordshire MK45 3PB
Tel: 01234 381642

Barrett, J
Treasury Solicitors, One Kemble Street, London WC2B 4TS
Tel: 0207 210 2958

Barron, M
Jennings Legal Services, Clifford House, Clifford Court, Cooper Way, Parkhouse, Carlisle, Cumbria CA3 0HG
Tel: 0870 7777 100

Barry, A M
Compass Cost Consultants Ltd, Compass House, Kings Business Park, Kings Drive, Prescot, Merseyside L34 1PJ
Tel: 0151 481 4489

Battison, S
36 Church Way, Weston Favell, Northampton, Northamptonshire NN3 3BX
Tel: 01604 633008

Beadle, S
Beadle Procter Costs Consultants, 81 New Wanstead, London E11 2SA
Tel: 020 8309 9907

Bedford, E
Kings Chambers, Manchester, Greater Manchester M3 3FT
Tel: 0161 832 9082

Bell, K
Irwin Mitchell Solicitors, Riverside East, 2 Millsands, Sheffield, South Yorkshire S3 8DT
Tel: 0870 1500 100

Bellamy, J
Joe Bellamy & Associates, Suite 12a, Sheffield Design Studios, 40 Ball Street, Sheffield, South Yorkshire S3 8DB
Tel: 0114 263 4131

Bennett, D F
45 Central Avenue, Ashingdon, Rochford, Essex SS4 3BG
Tel: 01702 543121

Bennett, B
Crouch Law Costs Services Ltd, 156a Station Road, Burnham-On-Crouch, Essex CM0 8NY
Tel: 01621 784481

Bennetts, A
73 Retallick Meadows, St Austell, Cornwall PL25 3BY
Tel: 01726 64729

Best, D S
17 Coryton Rise, Whitchurch, Cardiff CF14 7EJ
Tel: 029 20521096

Bingham, P J
34 Beechway, Bexley, Kent DA5 3DG
Tel: 020 8303 0133

Bingham, M
P J Bingham & Co, 68 Berkeley Avenue, Bexleyheath, Kent DA7 4UB
Tel: 020 8301 4190

Bintley, K
Keith Bintley Limited, 96 Stortford Hall Park, Bishop's Stortford, Hertfordshire CM23 5AN
Tel: .... 01279 501273 Mob: 078108 14890

Birks, H
Harry Birks Legal Costing Services, The Barn, 5 Rectory Road, Sutton Coldfield, West Midlands B75 7AJ
Tel: 0121 355 6525

Black, I
Ian Black & Associates, Suite 6, Saville Exchange, Howard Street, North Shields, Tyne & Wear NE30 1SE
Tel: 0191 257 3595

Blore, J
10 Mill Road, Waterlooville, Hampshire PO7 7AR
Tel: 02392 753575

Blower, J
2 Navigation Street, Measham, Swadlincote, Derbyshire DE12 7LW
Tel: 01530 272413

Bone, R
13 Sands Way, Woodford Green, Essex IG8 8EJ
Tel: 0208 505 7416

Booth, J
Harry Birks Legal Costing Services, 5 Rectory Road, Sutton Coldfield, West Midlands B75 7AJ
Tel: 0121 355 6525

Booth, Y
Keoghs LLP, 2 The Parklands, Bolton, Greater Manchester BL6 4SE

Bowden, P M
Masters Legal Costs Services LLP, 3-4 New Street, Bishopsgate, London EC2M 4TP
Tel: 020 7929 4344

Bowyer, J
Borneos Solicitors, Dixon House, 77-97 Harpur Street, Bedford, Bedfordshire MK40 2SY
Tel: 01234 353221

Boyd, D A
Penlan House, Maentwrog, Blaenau Ffestiniog, Gwynedd LL41 4HN
Tel: 0207 481 0010

Boyle, D S
Temple Chambers, 3-7 Temple Avenue, London EC4Y 0HP
Tel: 0207 353 1165

Brace, R
Crouch Law Costs Services Ltd, 156a Station Road, Burnham-On-Crouch, Essex CM0 8HJ
Tel: 01621 784481

Bracewell, P
JPN Consultancy, Europa House, Barcroft Street, Bury, Greater Manchester BL9 5BT
Tel: 0161 447 8889

Brasher, A
A B Costings, 2 Ferndale Close, Newmarket, Newmarket, Suffolk CB8 7DZ
Tel: 01638 668859

Brennan, J
Gibbins Costs Lawyers, Freemans House, Liquorice Way, Pontefract, West Yorkshire WF8 1DN
Tel: 01977 701938

Brett, A
Crown Costs Consultants Ltd, The Red House, 74 High Street, Bushey, Hertfordshire WD23 3HE
Tel: 020 8838 7110

Brett, N
Recoverx LLP, No1 Universal Square, Devonshire Street, Manchester, Greater Manchester M12 6JH
Tel: 0161 276 2000

Brewer, A
Aileen Brewer Costing Ltd, 6 Somerville Road, Daventry, Northamptonshire NN11 4RT
Tel: 01327 878161

Bridge, K
Burroughs Day Solicitors, 14 Charlotte Street, Bristol BS1 5PT
Tel: 0117 930 7574

Brooks, M
Tollers LLP, 2 Castilian Street, Northampton, Northamptonshire NN1 1JX
Tel: 01604 258558
Brown, S
Hampton House, Ashwater, Beaworthy, Devon EX21 5EF
Tel: 01409 211451
Brown, P
Carter Brown & Co, Garstang Business & Community Centre, High Street, Garstang, Preston, Lancashire PR3 1EB
Tel: 01995 601212
Brown, M
QM Legal Costs, Mercury Court, Tithebarn Street, Liverpool, Merseyside L2 2QP
Tel: 0870 402 7812
Brown, J
Acumension Ltd, No1 Universal Square, Devonshire Street North, Manchester, Greater Manchester M12 6JH
Tel: 0161 277 5105
Buchan, A J
AJB Legal Services, 32a Newgate Street, Morpeth, Northumberland NE61 1BA
Tel: 01670 515500
Buchan, R
Willis Legal Services Ltd, Panasonic Building, Christchurch Road., Baglan Industrial Park, Port Talbot, Neath Port Talbot SA12 7BZ
Tel: 01639 813030
Buckley, A
Prentice Shaw, Commerce Centre, Canal Wharf, Chesterfield, Derbyshire S41 7NA
Tel: 0845 094 9374
Budworth, J
Studio 104, Mill Studio Business Centre, Crane Mead, Ware, Hertfordshire SG12 9PY
Tel: 01920 444321
Bull, S
187 Montrose Avenue, Welling, Kent DA16 2QT
Tel: 0208 856 5029
Bullock, C
Paragon Costs Solutions, The Paragon Counterslip, Bristol BS1 6BX
Tel: 0117 9309529
Burke, D
Deborah Burke Costing Ltd, Equity House, 47 Burton Street, Melton Mowbray, Leicestershire LE13 1AF
Tel: 01664 482866
Burnett, P
Ringrose Law, Endeavour House, 3 Gilbert Drive, Boston, Lincolnshire PE21 7TR
Tel: 01205 311511
Burroughs, A J
Hogan Lovells International LLP, Atlantic House, Holborn Viaduct, London EC1A 2FG
Tel: 020 7296 2000
Burton, S
Bird & Co, 15 Castlegate, Grantham, Lincolnshire NG31 6SE
Tel: 01476 591711
Butler, C
Kain Knight, Carpenters Hall, Throgmorton Avenue, London EC2N 2JJ
Tel: 0207 825 9057
Button, E A
Johnson & Johnson, Third Floor, The Senate, Southernhay Gardens, Exeter, Devon EX1 1UG
Tel: 01392 267267
Byrne, M
Crown Costs Consultants Ltd, First Floor, 74 High Street, Bushey, Hertfordshire WD23 3HE
Tel: 020 8838 7110
Caddick, J A
Thompsons Solicitors, Grove House, 55 Lowlands Road, Harrow, Middlesex HA1 3AP
Tel: 0208 872 8600
Callaghan, M
MC Legal Costing Services, Suite F, Main Street, Gibraltar,
Tel: 00 350 200 46060
Cape, J
Calculus Legal Costs Ltd, Number Fourteen, Slaidburn Crescent, Southport, Merseyside PR9 9YF
Tel: 01704 508240
Carlisle, P J
Honey Bee Cottage, Sandy Lane North, Irby, Merseyside CH61 4XX
Tel: .... 0151 648 4014 / 07808 078525
Carroll, F
The John M Hayes Partnership, 61 Park Street, Bristol BS1 5NU
Tel: 0117 929 4000
Carter, M E
19 Eleanor Road, Bengeo, Hertford, Hertfordshire SG14 3DN
Tel: 01992 552702
Carter, P T
9 Grennell Close, Sutton, Surrey SM1 3LU
Tel: 020 8641 0729
Cassin, P
124 Woodside Road, Amersham, Buckinghamshire HP6 6NP
Tel: 01494 725593
Chalk, C
Shrublands, Henny Street, Great Henny, Sudbury, Suffolk CO10 7LS
Tel: 01787 267850
Chard, A
1 Richmond Road, Basingstoke, Hampshire RG21 2NX
Tel: 01256 363944
Christie, J
Porcelain Cottage, 10 Severn Street, Worcester, Worcestershire WR1 2ND
Tel: 01905 611141
Church, G
Abbey Law, 18 Hanover Square, London W1S 1HX
Tel: 0207 147 9943
Clark, G
Woodfines LLP, 16 St Cuthberts Street, Bedford, Bedfordshire
Tel: 01234 270600

Clegg, G
Dobbs House, High Bickington, Devon EX37 9BH
Tel: 01769 560446
Clement, M
P J Gibbins & Co, Freeman House, Liquorice Way, Pontefract, West Yorkshire WF8 1DN
Tel: 01977 701938
Clifford, N
Neil Clifford & Co, Suite 5, Springfield House, Water Lane, Wilmslow, Cheshire SK9 5BG
Tel: 01625 549993
Clivery, M
Clivery Barr & Co, 56a College Road, Crosby, Liverpool, Merseyside L23 0RP
Tel: 0151 931 1004
Cobb, T
Hay Farm, Wessington, Alfreton, Derbyshire DE55 6BY
Tel: 0870 1500 100
Coker, O
Just Costs Solicitors, Central Court, 25 Southampton Buildings, London WC2A 1AL
Tel: 0207 758 2160
Coleman, P
25 Cranborne Gardens, Upminster, Essex RM14 2YT
Tel: .... 01708 220708 Mob: 07768 862648
Coleman, K
SPH Costing Services Ltd, Suites 3-6, Leyland House, Lancashire Business Park, Centurion Way Park, Leyland, Lancashire PR26 6TY
Tel: 01772 435550
Collins, D M
Matthew Harman & Partners, Ardenham Lane House, Ardenham Lane, Aylesbury, Buckinghamshire HP19 8AA
Tel: 01296 390000
Collins, B A
8 Lyndhurst Road, Crosby, Merseyside L23 9TW
Tel: 0151 242 6873
Connelly, R
Child & Child Solicitors, 14 Grosvenor Crescent, London SW1X 7EE
Tel: 0207 201 3556
Cookson, P
P A Gibbins & Co, Freemans House, Liquorice Way, Pontefract, West Yorkshire WF8 1DN
Tel: 01977 601423
Cooper, C
Kingsley Napley LLP, Knights Quarter, 14 St Johns Lane, London EC1M 4AJ
Tel: 020 7814 1200
Cooper, D P
Taylor Rose Law LLP, Northminster House, Northminster Road, Peterborough, Cambridgeshire PE1 1UA
Tel: 01733 333333
Corbin, S
Barron House, Overbury, Tewkesbury, Gloucestershire GL20 7NT
Tel: 01386 725665
Corness, K
Acumension Ltd, No1 Universal Square, Devonshire Street North, Manchester, Greater Manchester M12 6JH
Tel: 0161 277 5144
Corrie, C
Johnson & Johnson, Third Floor, The Senate, Southernhay Gardens, Exeter, Devon EX1 1UG
Tel: 01392 267267
Cosgrove, I
Cosgrove Costing Agency, Pinetree Centre, Durham Road, Birtley, Chester-le-Street, Co Durham DH3 2TD
Tel: 0191 492 8204
Costa, K
14 Tempsford, Welwyn Garden City, Hertfordshire AL7 2PB
Tel: .... 01707 392450 Mob: 07733 254986
Cottenham, P F
Cottenhams, 8 Hazel Drive, Burn Bridge, Harrogate, North Yorkshire HG3 1NY
Tel: 01423 870209
Cousins, C
A & M Bacon Limited, 300 Eastrea Road, Whittlesey, Peterborough, Cambridgeshire PE7 2AR
Tel: 01733 350880
Cramer-Wright, C
Ince & Co, International House, 1 St Katherine's Way, London E1W 1AY
Tel: 020 7481 0010
Crewe, N
278 Windham Road, Bournemouth BH1 4QU
Tel: 01202 399369
Currah, A
Weightmans LLP, First Floor, St Philips Point, 47 Cannon Street, Birmingham, West Midlands B2 5EF
Tel: .... 0121 200 8129 Ext: 8129
Curtis, S
Berrymans Lace Mawer LLP, Salisbury House, London Wall, London EC2M 5QN
Tel: 020 7865 8508
Daley, L
Sills & Betteridge LLP, 46 Silver Street, Lincoln, Lincolnshire LN2 1ED
Tel: 01522 542211
Damon, S
Borneos Solicitors, 77-97 Harpur Street, Bedford, Bedfordshire MK40 3SY
Tel: 01234 353221
Davies, V
Cost Chambers Ltd, 25a Cemetery Road, Southport, Merseyside PR8 6RH
Tel: 01704 50 40 90
Davies, T
North West Law Ltd, Queens House, Queens Road, Chester, Cheshire CH1 3BQ
Tel: 01244 317543
Davies, S
Evolution Costs, Highpoint, Highfield Street, Liverpool, Merseyside L3 6AA
Tel: 0151 242 0960

Davison, A P J
A D Consulting, 57 Abbotsford Gardens, Woodford Green, Essex IG8 9HP
Tel: 020 8559 0777
Dawes, B
Stephensons, 26 Union Street, Leigh, Greater Manchester WN7 1AT
Tel: 01942 777777
Dawson, S
DWF LLP, Bridgewater Place, Water Lane, Leeds, West Yorkshire LS11 5DY
Tel: .... 0113 261 6118 / 07736 908568
De Rose, H
Hogan Lovells International LLP, Atlantic House, Holborn Viaduct, London EC1A 2FG
Tel: 020 7296 2000
Dean, A
Denovo Legal Costs Consultants, 60 Lombard Street, London EC3V 9EA
Tel: 020 3170 8989
Dean, S
29 Valentine Way, Off Penfold Lane, Great Billing, Northampton, Northamptonshire NN3 9XD
Tel: 01604 409735
Deane, M C
Macfarlanes, 10 Norwich Street, London EC4A 1BD
Tel: 0207 831 9222
Devine, S L
Irwin Mitchell Solicitors, Riverside East, 2 Millsands, Sheffield, South Yorkshire S3 8DT
Tel: .... 0870 1500 100 Ext: 4135
Dickinson, L D
West End Farm, Greenhead Lane, Bentham, North Yorkshire LA2 7ES
Tel: 01524 263222
Dixon, L
Just Costs Solicitors, Dunston Innovation Centre, Dunston Road, Chesterfield, Derbyshire S41 8NG
Tel: 01246 267961
Dixon, J
Silver Fitzgerald Solicitors & Advocates, 15-17 Castle Street, Cambridge, Cambridgeshire CB3 0AH
Tel: 01223 562001
Dobbs, P R
24 Beresford Road, Chingford, London E4 6EE
Tel: 0208 529 8097
Donnell, C
Burnetts Solicitors, Montgomery Way, Rosehill, Carlisle, Cumbria CA1 2RW
Tel: 01228 552222
Donoghue, D
Budworth & Nolan, 1 Little Mount Sion, Tunbridge Wells, Kent TN1 1YS
Tel: 01892 557890
Dullay, I
Beachcroft LLP, Nine Brindley Place, 4 Oozells Square, Birmingham, West Midlands
Tel: 0121 698 5381
Dunn, J
5 Capricorn Road, Manchester, Greater Manchester M9 7JA
Tel: 07971 486184
Durham, I
I & C Associates Ltd, 8 Wyre Close, Haddenham, Aylesbury, Buckinghamshire HP17 8AU
Tel: 01844 291522
Dwyer, M W
RBS Cost Drafting Department, PO Box 636, Bromley, Kent BR1 1WF
Tel: 0208 285 8528
Eadon, H
Irwin Mitchell Solicitors, Riverside East, 2 Millsands, Sheffield, South Yorkshire S3 8DT
Tel: 0870 1500 100
Earl, D F
Wensum Law Costs Ltd, 5 St Mary S House, Duke Street, Norwich, Norfolk NR3 1QA
Tel: 01603 633500
Ede, D
Curtis House, 34 Third Avenue, Brighton, Brighton & Hove BN3 2PD
Tel: 01273 703000
Edinboro, J
23 Goodwin Drive, Sidcup, Kent DA14 4NX
Tel: 07581 377539
Edwards, R
Williams Associates, T109, Titan House, Cardiff Bay Business Centre, Lewis Road, Ocean Park, Cardiff CF24 5BS
Tel: 029 2045 0772
Edwards, J
Berrymans Lace Mawer LLP, Salisbury House, London Wall, London EC2M 5QN
Tel: 020 7638 2811
Ellam, D
P A Gibbins & Co, Freemans House, Liquorice Way, Pontefract, West Yorkshire WF8 1DN
Tel: 01977 701938
Ellis, A
Ellis Grant Law Costs Consultants, 11 High Street, Wanstead, London E11 2AA
Tel: 020 8518 8484
Ellison, L
R Costings Ltd The Old Chapel, St Johns Court, East Street, St Ives, Cambridgeshire PE27 5PD
Tel: 01480 463499
Emery, P
Kain Knight, The Old Maltings, Hockerill Street, Bishop's Stortford, Hertfordshire CM23 2ED
Tel: 01279 504975
Evans, L M
North West Law Ltd, Queens House, Queens Road, Chester, Cheshire CH1 3BQ
Tel: 01244 317543
Fallaize, B
RWF Costs, The Mount, Hill Crescent, Haverhill, Suffolk CB9 0DF
Tel: 07989 922842

Farmer, G
Geoff Farmer & Co, 1a St Margaret S Drive, Chesterfield, Derbyshire S40 4SY
Tel: 01246 202541
Farthing, J
Dickinson Dees LLP, St Ann's Wharf, 112 Quayside, Newcastle Upon Tyne, Tyne & Wear NE1 3DX
Tel: 0191 2799042
Fensom, K
Mews Cottage Archways, Castle Street, Aylesbury, Buckinghamshire HP20 2RE
Tel: 01296 432430
Final, I
R Pain & Co, 93a Hivings Hill, Chesham, Buckinghamshire HP5 2PJ
Tel: 01494 771133
Finn, K
Apartment 2, Windermere House, Mossley Hill Drive, Liverpool, Merseyside L17 0ES
Tel: 0844 579 6885
Fisher, S
Vindex Legal Costs, PO Box 178, Deeside, Flintshire CH5 9AU
Tel: 01244 525731
Fitsell, M
Just Costs Solicitors, Central Court, 25 Southampton Buildings, London WC2A 1AL
Tel: 0207 758 2171
Fitzgerald, J
Fitzgerald Legal Costs Limited, 21 Ingleside Close, Park Road, Beckenham, Kent BR3 1QU
Tel: 0208 594 3762
Fitzpatrick, J
Jennings Legal Services, Clifford House, Clifford Court, Cooper Way, Parkhouse, Carlisle, Cumbria CA3 0JG
Tel: 0870 7777 100
Flatman, N A
Tri Star Costs Limited, Forum House, Kings Park, Knowsley, Prescot, Merseyside L34 1BH
Tel: 0151 949 5111
Fletcher, M S
Glaisyers Solicitors LLP, One St James's Square, Manchester, Greater Manchester M2 6DN
Tel: 0161 833 5671
Forman, H
Harvey Ingram LLP, 20 New Walk, Leicester LE1 6TX
Tel: 0116 254 5454
Francis, R
Ince & Co, International House, 1 St Katherine's Way, London E1W 1AY
Tel: 0207 481 0010
Francis, J
8 Harry Pay Close, Kennington, Ashford, Kent TN24 9PX
Tel: 01233 647840
Franks, R
4 Dimmock Close, Leighton Buzzard, Bedfordshire LU7 4RY
Tel: 01442 828090
Freeman, M
Lyons Davidson, Victoria House, 51 Victoria Street, Bristol BS1 6AD
Tel: 0117 9046000
Frost, D
R Costings Ltd, The Old Chapel, St John's Court, East Street, St Ives, Cambridgeshire PE27 5PD
Tel: 01480 463499
Frost, C
Civil & Commercial Costs Lawyers Ltd, 5 New York Street, Manchester, Greater Manchester M1 4JB
Tel: 0161 255 2788
Garriock, N C
Anvil Cottage, 38 Quartermile Road, Busbridge, Godalming, Surrey GU7 1TJ
Tel: 01483 429852
Gerrard, T W
North West Law Ltd, Queens House, Queens Road, Chester, Cheshire CH1 3BQ
Tel: 01244 317543
Gibb, T
Budworth & Nolan, 1 Little Mount Sion, Tunbridge Wells, Kent TN1 1YS
Tel: 01892 557890
Gibb, G A
267 South Lane, New Malden, Surrey KT3 5RP
Tel: 0208 942 5927
Gibbins, R
P A Gibbins & Co, Freemans House, Liquorice Way, Pontefract, West Yorkshire WF8 1DN
Tel: .... 01977 601424 / 701938
Gibbs, S T B
Gibbs Wyatt Stone, 68 Clarendon Drive, London SW15 1AH
Tel: 0207 096 0937
Gilbert, I
Irwin Mitchell Solicitors, Riverside East, 2 Millsands, Sheffield, South Yorkshire S3 8DT
Tel: 0870 1500 100
Gill, S
26 Wraglings, Beldams Lane, Bishop's Stortford, Hertfordshire CM23 5TB
Tel: .... 01279 755485 / 07947 883398
Gillmore, M
Temple Drafting Ltd, PO Box 2241, Pewsey, Wiltshire SN9 6PW
Tel: 01672 851297
Ginnaw, G R
Norton Rose LLP, 3 More London Riverside, London SE1 2AQ
Tel: 020 7283 6000
Goddard, D
18 Beaconsfield Road, Altrincham, Greater Manchester WA14 5LQ
Tel: 0161 233 0452
Goodwin, M R
Goodwin Malatesta Legal Costs Services Ltd, 134-136 High Street, Epping, Essex CM16 4AG
Tel: 01992 574846
Gordon, J
44 The Avenue, Wroxham, Norwich, Norfolk NR12 8TR
Tel: 01603 783787

Graham, D M
39 Knowle Road, Mirfield, Leeds, West Yorkshire WF14 8DJ
Tel: 01924 513375
Gray, A D
Reed Smith LLP, The Broadgate Tower, 20 Primrose Street, London EC2A 2RS
Tel: 020 3116 2947
Gray, R S
Dickinson Dees LLP, St Ann's Wharf, 112 Quayside, Newcastle Upon Tyne, Tyne & Wear NE1 3DX
Tel: 0191 279 9641
Green, S A
Irwin Mitchell Solicitors, St Peters House, Hartshead, Sheffield, South Yorkshire S1 2EL
Tel: 0870 1500 100
Green, C
Bisley Moorside Farm, Moorside Road, Edgworth, Bolton, Greater Manchester BL7 0JZ
Tel: 01204 852225
Greenhalgh, A D
I B Costings Limited, 51 Queen Street, Gt Harwood, Blackburn, Blackburn BB6 7QP
Tel: 01254 883545
Greenslade, S A
Matthew Harman & Partners, Ardenham Lane House, Ardenham Lane, Aylesbury, Buckinghamshire HP19 8AA
Tel: 01296 390000
Grimes, B A
48 Russet Drive, Little Billing, Northampton, Northamptonshire NN3 9TU
Tel: 01604 401126
Groombridge, R J
Empire Costs Ltd, 5th Floor, 63 St. Mary Axe, London EC3A 8AA
Tel: 0207 743 8663
Gurnett, A
Marash House, 2 Brook Street, Tring, Hertfordshire HP23 5ED
Tel: 01442 890877
Gustard, C
Just Costs Solicitors, Trident One, Styal Road, Manchester, Greater Manchester M22 5XB
Tel: 0161 435 6069
Hale, A
Masters Legal Costs Services LLP, 3-4 New Street, Bishopsgate, London EC2M 4HD
Tel: 020 7929 4344
Hall, D G
David G Hall & Associates, 14 Marvels Lane Lee, London SE12 9PA
Tel: 0208 857 0333
Hallett, R J
Waterlow Costs Drafting, 6-8 Underwood Street, London N1 7JQ
Tel: 020 7250 3350
Hamblin, R
Westwind, 6 Craw Park, Brampton, Cumbria CA8 1UZ
Hammond, A J
A J Hammond & Co, Brooklands, 21 Lansdown Road, Sidcup, Kent DA14 4EF
Tel: 020 8300 4578
Hanlon, B
Legal Costs Negotiators Ltd, Armstrong House, 1 Houston Park, Salford Quays, Manchester, Greater Manchester M50 2RP
Tel: 0161 742 4555
Hardcastle, M
PH Costs Solutions, Garden Studios, 11-15 Betterton Street, London WC2H 9BP
Tel: 0207 866 5408
Harkin, F
23 Walker Court, Cambridge, Cambridgeshire CB4 2RU
Tel: 01223 501459
Harman, M
Matthew Harman & Partners, Ardenham Lane House, Ardenham Lane, Aylesbury, Buckinghamshire HP19 8AA
Tel: 01296 390000
Harper, S
Masters Legal Costs Services LLP, 3-4 New Street, Bishopsgate, London EC2M 4HD
Tel: 020 7929 4344
Harris, V
Northwest Costing, 38 Bertram Drive, Meols, Wirral, Merseyside CH47 0LH
Tel: 0151 632 4072
Harrison, J R
51a High Street, Thrapston, Kettering, Northamptonshire NN14 4JJ
Tel: 01832 732988
Hartley, S
Compass Costs Consultants Ltd, King's Business Park, King's Drive, Prescot, Merseyside L34 1PJ
Tel: 0151 481 4488
Hassey, K
Beachcroft LLP, Nine Brindley Place, 4 Oozells Square, Birmingham, West Midlands B1 2HE
Tel: 0121 698 5291
Heathcote, B
18 Shaw Lane, Barnsley, South Yorkshire S70 6EH
Tel: 01977 701938
Heawood, J
Just Costs Solicitors, Central Court, 25 Southampton Buildings, London WC2A 1AL
Tel: 020 7758 2155
Hegley, G K
Imperial Costing, 2 Ducketts Wharf, 107-109 South Street, Bishop's Stortford, Hertfordshire CM23 3AR
Tel: 01279 466733
Heining, M
52 Station Road, Woburn Sands, Milton Keynes MK17 8RU
Tel: .... 01908 282892 / 07851 058746
Herlihy, P
Law Costs Consultancy Service Ltd, 19 Hayling Avenue, Little Paxton, St Neots, Cambridgeshire PE19 4HG
Tel: 01480 403316
Hesketh, R
Keoghs LLP, 2 The Parklands, Bolton, Greater Manchester BL6 4SE
Tel: 01204 677000

Hickman, J
Hickmans Law Costs Draftsmen, 107 Coast Drive, Greatstone, Tunbridge Wells, Kent TN28 8NR
Tel: 01797 366400
Higginbotham, S P
SPH Costing Services Ltd, Suites 3-6, Leyland House, Lancashire Business Park, Centurion Way, Leyland, Lancashire PR26 6TY
Tel: 01772 435550
Higgins, G
Law Costs Solutions Ltd, 5 Priors, London Road, Bishop's Stortford, Hertfordshire CM23 5ED
Tel: 01279 504975
Hipgrave, K
136 Glengall Road, Woodford Green, Essex IG8 0DS
Tel: .... 0208 504 3407 / 07963 840351
Hocking, J
North West Law Ltd, Queens House, Queens Road, Chester, Cheshire CH1 3BQ
Tel: 01244 317543
Hocking, J
North West Law Ltd, Queens House, Queens Road, Chester, Cheshire CH1 3BQ
Tel: 01244 317543
Holland, J
Masters Legal Costs Services LLP, 3-4 New Street, Bishopsgate, London EC2M 4HD
Tel: 0207 929 4344
Holliday, J
Jennings Law LLP Solicitors, Clifford House, Clifford Court, Cooper Way, Parkhouse, Carlisle, Cumbria CA3 0JG
Tel: 0845 450 5551
Holmes, D
26 Brook Crescent, Chingford, London E4 9EP
Tel: 0208 771 2131
Homersham, M
Cost Advocates Ltd, 3rd Floor, 40 Dukes Place, London EC3A 7NH
Tel: 0870 402 7891
Hook, M D
Holman Fenwick Willan LLP, Friary Court, 65 Crutched Friars, London EC3N 2AE
Tel: 0207 264 8411
Hopkins, V
Deborah Burke Costing Ltd, Palamos House, 66/67 High Street, Lymington, Hampshire SO41 9AL
Tel: 01590 679777
Hornby, M
Southern Costings, Satis House, 3 Havisham Road, Chalk, Gravesend, Kent DA12 4UW
Tel: 01474 743021
Houghton, S
Law Costs, Black Bull Cottage, St. Michael's Lane, Bolton-Le-Sands, Carnforth, Lancashire LA5 8DP
Tel: 01524 823275
Houlan, P
Hempsons, Hempsons House, 40 Villiers Street, London WC2N 6NJ
Tel: 0207 839 0278
Hounslow, N
Law Costs Solutions Ltd, 5 Priors, London Road, Bishop's Stortford, Hertfordshire CM23 5ED
Tel: 01279 504975
Howey, S
HM Law Cost Draftsmen, Graphic House, 73-75 Gammons Lane, Watford, Hertfordshire WD24 5TU
Tel: 01923 242345
Hoyle, L
Eversheds, 1 Callaghan Square, Cardiff CF10 5BT
Tel: 02920 477346
Hoyle, M
Phoenix Legal Services Ltd, 4th Floor, Windsor House, Windsor Lane, Cardiff CF10 3DE
Tel: 02920 668664
Hunt, R
Red Hall Walk, Leeds, West Yorkshire LS14 1EB
Tel: 0113 205 6300
Ison, J
27 Birch Court, Llay, Wrexham LL12 0TY
Israel, D
DSI Law Costs Draftsman, DSI House, 37 Leicester Road, Salford, Greater Manchester M7 4AS
Tel: 0161 708 8645
Ivory, J
Kain Knight, 1, 2 & 4 Priors, London Road, Bishop's Stortford, Hertfordshire CM23 5ED
Tel: 01279 505974
Jack, R
West Lakes Legal Costs Ltd, 2 Europe Way, Cockermouth, Cumbria CA13 0RJ
Tel: 07980 300940
Jago, A
Just Costs Solicitors, Central Court, 25 Southampton Buildings, London WC2A 1AL
Tel: 0207 758 2157
Jefferson, P
39 Midhurst Road, Benton, Newcastle Upon Tyne, Tyne & Wear NE12 9NU
Tel: 0191 270 0784
Jepson, S
Costs Lawyer, Loudoun House, Main Street, Eastwell, Leicester, Leicestershire LE14 4EH
Tel: 01949 860368
Jethwa, C
GLCS, Suite 11, 86 Euston Street, High Wycombe, Buckinghamshire HP11 1LT
Tel: 01494 527100
Johnson, D A
Johnson & Johnson, 8 Church Street, St Austell, Cornwall PL25 5PQ
Tel: 01726 64729
Johnson, D
26 Mill Lane, Bold Heath, Widnes, Cheshire WA8 3UU
Tel: 07808 771 333

Johnston, S
Godfrey Wright Law Costs Draftsmen, Halifax House, 93/101 Bridge Street, Manchester, Greater Manchester M3 2GX
Tel: 0161 819 5021

Jones, G
Laskey House, Laskey Lane, Thelwall, Warrington, Cheshire WA4 2TF
Tel: 07947 485093

Jones, S
Matthew Harman & Partners, Ardenham Lane House, Ardenham Lane, Aylesbury, Buckinghamshire HP19 8AA
Tel: 01296 390000

Jones, O B J
Civil & Commercial Costs Lawyers Ltd, 40-43 Chancery Lane, London EC4A 1NE
Tel: 0207 831 3003

Jones, W D
PO Box 625, 244 Main Street, Gibraltar,
Tel: 00 350 200 48438

Jones, P
R Costings Ltd, The Old Chapel, St Johns Court, East Street, St Ives, Cambridgeshire PE27 5PD
Tel: 01480 463499

Judge, T
Clyde & Co LLP, 1 Stoke Road, Guildford, Surrey GU1 4HW
Tel: 01483 555426

Kain, M
Kain Knight, 1, 2 & 4 Priors, London Road, Bishop's Stortford, Hertfordshire CM23 5ED
Tel: 01279 505974

Kain, M B
Kain Knight, 1, 2 & 4 Priors, London Road, Bishop's Stortford, Hertfordshire CM23 5ED
Tel: .... 01279 504975 / 506741

Kann, L
30 Park Grove, Edgware, Middlesex HA8 7SJ
Tel: 0208 958 9506

Keegan, N A D
Barlow Lyde & Gilbert LLP, Beaufort House, 15 St Botolph Street, London EC3A 7NJ
Tel: 0207 643 7037

Kelly, S
Irwin Mitchell Solicitors, Riverside East, 2 Millsands, Sheffield, South Yorkshire S3 8DT
Tel: 0870 1500 100

Kendall, P
2 Meadow Park, Trewoon, St Austell, Cornwall PL25 5SR
Tel: 01726 64729

Kendall, F
Masters Legal Costs Services LLP, 3-4 New Street, Bishopsgate, London EC2M 4TP
Tel: 020 7929 4344

Kendry, S
Costs Consultant, 263 Church Street, Westhoughton, Bolton, Greater Manchester BL5 3BL
Tel: 07963 568855

Kenyon, S
Jennings Legal Services, Clifford House, Clifford Court, Cooper Way, Parkhouse, Carlisle, Cumbria CA3 0JG
Tel: 0870 7777 100

Key, C
Keelys Solicitors, 30-34 Curtain Road, London EC2A 3NZ
Tel: 0207 422 8669

Kiernan, D
QM Costs, Mercury Court, Tithebarn Street, Liverpool, Merseyside L2 2QP
Tel: 0151 475 8555

Killeen, M J
The French Connection - Legal Costs Solutions, The Barn, Norton Paddox Lane, Norton Lindsey, Warwick, Warwickshire CV35 8JA
Tel: 0776 4987591

Kimpton, J
38 Kingsway, South Woodham Ferrers, Chelmsford, Essex CM3 5QH
Tel: 01245 325036

Kinder-Naylor, S
Wilkinson Woodward, 11 Fountain Street, Halifax, West Yorkshire HX1 1LU
Tel: 01422 339600

Kirby, M
Goodwin Malatesta Legal Costs Services Ltd, 82-84 Epping High Street, Epping, Essex CM16 4AE
Tel: 01992 574846

Kittle, K
The Kittle Partnership Ltd, Unit 1, 6 Freebournes Road, Witham, Essex CM8 3UN
Tel: 01376 511716

Knight, M
Costs Lawyer Network Limited, 37 Magnaville Road, Bishop's Stortford, Hertfordshire CM23 4DN
Tel: 01279 758427

Knight, G
GK Law Costs, Broad Street, Chesham, Buckinghamshire HP5 3EA
Tel: 01494 580686

Knight, J
Costs Lawyer Network Limited, 10 Hillcrest View, Basildon, Essex SS16 4QU
Tel: 01268 550448

Knight, G J
Costs Lawyer Network Limited, 2 Emblems, Great Dunmow, Essex CM6 2AG
Tel: 01371 879930

Knock, B
Email: .... knockbob@hotmail.com

Lamble, R
Claimant Costs Recovery Limited, PO Box 385, Plymouth PL1 9BT
Tel: 0845 872 8898

Lavelle, J
The John M Hayes Partnership, 1 Park Court Mews, Park Place, Cardiff CF10 3DQ
Tel: 029 2039 4043

Lavender, P
97 Burdon Lane, Cheam, Sutton, Surrey SM2 7BZ
Tel: 0208 643 0579

Leakey, P
Kain Knight, The Old Maltings, Hockerill Street, Bishop's Stortford, Hertfordshire CM23 2ED
Tel: 01279 504975

Lee, N
Paragon Costs Solutions, The Paragon Counterslip, Bristol BS1 6BX
Tel: 0117 9309528

Lee, H J
28 Lydiate Lane, Thornton, Liverpool, Merseyside L23 1TP
Tel: 0151 931 3291

Leggott, C
Hempsons, The Exchange, Station Parade, Harrogate, North Yorkshire HG1 1DY
Tel: 01423 522331

Lesslie, M
Irwin Mitchell Solicitors, Riverside East, 2 Millsands, Sheffield, South Yorkshire S3 8DT
Tel: 0870 1500 100

Levene, K J
30 Crown Place, London EC2A 4ES
Tel: 07710 169919

Levin, J
Knapp Richardson, 3rd Floor, Chancery House, 53-64 Chancery Lane, London WC2A 1QU
Tel: 0207 831 9082

Lewis, G
4 Dan-Yr-Ardd, Castle View, Caerphilly CF83 1TS
Tel: 02920 851775

Lewis, J
Williams Associates, T109, Titan House, Cardiff Bay Business Centre, Lewis Road, Ocean Park, Cardiff CF24 5BS
Tel: 02920 450772

Ley, R
Empire Costs Ltd, Suite B, 5th Floor, 63 St Mary Axe, London EC3A 8AA
Tel: 0207 743 8660

Liburd, A
Kain Knight, Carpenters Hall, Throgmorton Avenue, London EC2N 2JJ
Tel: 0203 215 1011

Lines, J
Lauben Legal Services Ltd, 229 Botley Road, Chesham, Buckinghamshire HP5 1XY
Tel: 01494 786565

Little, F
Costsmaster, Ardenham Lane House, Ardenham Lane, Aylesbury, Buckinghamshire HP19 8AA
Tel: 01494 837889

Livingstone, A
Annette Livingstone & Associates Ltd, The Ship, 1 West Street, Banwell, North Somerset BS29 6DA
Tel: 01934 825845

Locke, J
Williams Associates, T109, Titan House, Cardiff Bay Business Centre, Lewis Road, Ocean Park, Cardiff CF24 5BS
Tel: 02920 450772

Longman, J A
28 Canon Woods Way, The Orchards, Kennington, Ashford, Kent TN24 9QY
Tel: 020 7623 2011

Lord, J
Cost Advocates Ltd, 1st Floor, Dukes House, 32-38 Dukes Place, London EC3A 7LP
Tel: 0870 402 7871

Love, E
Kennedys Law LLP, Ventana House, 2 Concourse Way, Sheaf Street, Sheffield, South Yorkshire S1 2BJ
Tel: 0114 253 2048

Ludlam, M
Acumension Ltd, No1 Universal Square, Devonshire Street North, Manchester, Greater Manchester M12 6JH
Tel: 0161 277 5114

Ludman, J
3 Downs Wood, Vigo, Meopham, Kent DA13 0SQ
Tel: 07809 151 534

Lumby, D
Masters Legal Costs Services LLP, 3-4 New Street, Bishopsgate, London EC2M 4HD
Tel: 020 7929 4344

Mahoney, A P
Hugh James Solicitors, Hodge House, 114-116 St Mary Street, Cardiff CF10 1DY
Tel: 02920 224871

Mahoney, M
Cost Advocates Ltd, 3rd Floor, 40 Dukes Place, London EC3A 7NH
Tel: 0870 402 7511

Malatesta, D
Goodwin Malatesta Legal Costs Services Ltd, 134-136 High Street, Epping, Essex CM16 4AG
Tel: 01992 574846

Male, L
Costs Draftsman & Consultant, 65 Bramble Grove, Stamford, Lincolnshire PE9 4BL
Tel: 01780 480803

Manley, R
113 Inkerman Road, Knaphill, Woking, Surrey GU21 2BQ
Tel: 07780 666418

Mannix, M J
Temple Chambers, 3-7 Temple Avenue, London EC4Y 0HP
Tel: 020 7353 1165

Marcus, L
Ford & Warren Solicitors, Westgate Point, Westgate, Leeds, West Yorkshire LS1 2AX
Tel: 0113 243 6601

Marshall, S
JSP Solicitors, 10/12 Algitha Road, Skegness, Lincolnshire PE25 2AG
Tel: 01754 762252

Mccarthy, P
RMR legal, Suite 4b, Century Buildings, Blackfriars House, The Parsonage, Manchester, Greater Manchester M3 2JA
Tel: 0161 834 5444

Mccarthy, D M J
McCarthys Legal Costs, 9 Ayletts Broomfield, Chelmsford, Essex CM1 7LE
Tel: 01245 442544

Mccombe-Russell, A
RMR legal, Suite 4b, Century Buildings, Blackfriars House, The Parsonage, Manchester, Greater Manchester M3 2JA
Tel: 0161 834 5444

Mccormack, K J
2 Llys Gwynsryn, Bryncoch, Neath, Neath Port Talbot SA10 7UB
Tel: 01639 633543

Mcdonnell, N
Just Costs Solicitors, Trident One, Trident Business Park, Styal Road, Manchester, Greater Manchester M22 5XB
Tel: 0161 435 6069

Mcglashan, S C
7 Rydal Close, Stukeley Meadows, Huntingdon, Cambridgeshire PE29 6UF
Tel: 020 7090 4356

Mckay, R
DLA Piper UK LLP, 1 St Paul's Place, Sheffield, South Yorkshire S1 2JX
Tel: 0114 283 3032

Merrell, P
Freshfields Bruckhaus Derringer, 65 Fleet Street, London EC4Y 1HS
Tel: 020 7936 4000

Merrick, N
16 Wood Street, Horwich, Bolton, Greater Manchester BL6 6BN
Tel: 01704 381223

Middlemiss, I R
Hogan Lovells International LLP, Atlantic House, Holborn Viaduct, London EC1A 2FG
Tel: 0207 296 2000

Middleton, C
Suite 3, On Site Lodge, 9 Mansfield Road, Eastwood, Nottingham NG16 3AR
Tel: 01773 767503

Middleton, J
19 Priory Farm Road, Hatfield Peverell, Chelmsford, Essex CM3 2NJ
Tel: 0207 839 0278

Millard, N
Millards Costs Consultants, Aspect Court, 4 Temple Row, Birmingham, West Midlands B2 5HG
Tel: 0845 508 1951

Mistri, J
HM Law Cost Draftsmen, Graphic House, 73-75 Gammons Lane, Watford, Hertfordshire WD24 5TU
Tel: 01923 242345

Mistry-Johnson, H
Eversheds, 1 Callaghan Square, Cardiff CF10 5BT
Tel: 02920 471147

Monaghan, M
Abacus Law Costs Consultants, Studio 33, 4th Floor, 1-13 Adler Street, London E1 1EG
Tel: .... 0207 392 2044 Mob: 07967 555 924

Moran, D
Donal J Moran & Associates Ltd, 78 York Street, London W1H 1DP
Tel: 020 7127 5288

Moreton, T
TM Costings Ltd, Suffolk House, 54-55 The Green, Wooburn Green, Buckingham, Buckinghamshire HP10 0EU
Tel: 01494 616122

Morgan, R
Bromiley Holcroft Solicitors, Calderhurst House, 143-149 Bispham Road, Southport, Merseyside PR9 7BL
Tel: 0870 236 0000

Morgan, J
Willis Legal Services Ltd, Panasonic Building, Christchurch Road, Baglan Industrial Park, Port Talbot, Neath Port Talbot SA12 7BZ
Tel: 01639 813030

Morris, M
Victory Legal Costs Solicitors, 18 High Street, Fareham, Hampshire PO16 7AF
Tel: 0844 9801690

Morrison, V
Crown Costs Consultants Ltd, Knoll House, 30 Macclesfield Road, Wilmslow, Cheshire SK9 2AF
Tel: .... 0845 533 3102 Mob: 07815 111959

Morton, M
147 Hermon Hill, South Woodford, London E18 1QQ
Tel: 0207 691 4076

Moss, J D
Matthew Harman & Partners, Ardenham Lane House, Ardenham Lane, Aylesbury, Buckinghamshire HP19 8AA
Tel: 01296 390000

Moxon, I
PI Costing Plc, Robson House, 4 Regent Terrace, South Parade, Doncaster, South Yorkshire DN1 2EE
Tel: 01302 343666

Mujaddadi, R
Just Costs Solicitors, Central Court, 25 Southampton Buildings, London WC2A 1AL
Tel: 0207 758 2174

Murphy, J
Costs Lawyer, Latton Bush Centre, Southern Way, Harlow, Essex CM18 7BL
Tel: 0207 626 1188

Murray, S L
Keelys Solicitors, 30-34 Curtain Road, London EC2A 3NZ
Tel: 0207 422 8686

Muttett, D C
13 Spurrell Avenue, Bexley, Kent DA5 2HA
Tel: 01322 528637

Muxworthy, J
Cosgrove Costing Agency, Pinetree Centre, Durham Road, Birtley, Chester-le-Street, Co Durham DH3 2TD
Tel: 0191 492 8204

Naisbitt, D
Just Costs Solicitors, Central Court, 25 Southampton Buildings, London WC2A 1AL
Tel: 020 7758 2155
Nash, S
GLCS, Suite 11, 86 Easton Street, High Wycombe, Buckinghamshire HP11 1LT
Tel: 01494 527100
Neale, A
Clifford Chance LLP, 10 Upper Bank Street, London E14 5JJ
Tel: 0207 006 1000
Neary, C
Pannone LLP, 123 Deansgate, Manchester, Greater Manchester M3 2BU
Tel: 0161 909 3000
Neil, K
Just Costs Solicitors, Central Court, 25 Southampton Buildings, London WC2A 1AL
Tel: 0207 758 2170
Nelson, C
North West Law Ltd, Queens House, Queens Road, Chester, Cheshire CH1 3BQ
Tel: 01244 317543
Newberry, G
Eversheds, 1 Callaghan Square, Cardiff CF10 5BT
Tel: 0845 498 7220
Newby, E
Bindmans LLP, 275 Gray's Inn Road, London
Tel: 0207 833 4433
Newton, M
Johnson & Johnson, Third Floor, The Senate, Southernhay Gardens, Exeter, Devon EX1 1UG
Tel: 01392 267267
Nicholls, L
Bolt Burdon Kemp, Providence House, Providence Place, Islington, London N1 0NT
Tel: 0800 389 0385
Nichols, P
Irwin Mitchell Solicitors, Riverside East, 2 Millsands, Sheffield, South Yorkshire S3 8DT
Tel: 0870 1500 100
Noakes, S
Profin Cost Solutions Ltd, 24 Holmwood Ave, Shenfield, Chelmsford, Essex CM15 8QS
Tel: 01277 202357
Nolan, C
Budworth & Nolan, 1 Little Mount Sion, Tunbridge Wells, Kent TN1 1YS
Tel: 01892 557890
Nolan, L
Bromleys Solicitors LLP, 50 Wellington Road, Ashton-Under-Lyne, Greater Manchester OL6 6XL
Tel: 0161 330 6821
Norcott, J E
14 Meadow View, Areley Kings, Stourport-on-Severn, Worcestershire DY13 OJS
O'Connor, D
Barlow Lyde & Gilbert LLP, Beaufort House, 15 St Botolph Street, London EC3A 7NJ
O'Neill, E
Crown Costs Consultants Ltd, The Red House, 74 High Street, Bushey, Hertfordshire WD23 3HE
Tel: 020 8838 7110
O'Rourke, S
Kain Knight, 1, 2 & 4 Priors, London Road, Bishop's Stortford, Hertfordshire CM23 5ED
Tel: 01279 755552
Osborn, J H
Costsmanager, 3 Oxford Court, Bishopsgate, Manchester, Greater Manchester M2 3WQ
Tel: .... 0161 200 8464 Mob: 07990 970458
Overton, N
Overtons Costs Consultants, 42 Oakwood Drive, Billericay, Essex CM12 0SA
Tel: 07768 691298
Page, S J
PH Costs Solutions, Garden Studios, 11-15 Betterton Street, London WC2H 9BP
Tel: .... 0207 866 5407 Mob: 07944 862208
Paget, C
Law Costs Solutions Ltd, 5 Priors, London Road, Bishop's Stortford, Hertfordshire CM23 5ED
Tel: 01279 504975
Pain, R
R Pain & Co, 93a Hivings Hill, Chesham, Buckinghamshire HP5 2PJ
Tel: 01494 771133
Parker, K
HM Law Cost Draftsmen, Graphic House, 73-75 Gammons Lane, Watford, Hertfordshire WD24 5TU
Tel: 01923 242345
Parness, R
Paramount Legal Costs Ltd, Rural Enterprise Centre, Redhills, Penrith, Cumbria CA11 0DT
Tel: 01768 213072
Passalaris, M
Just Costs Solicitors, Central Court, 25 Southampton Buildings, London WC2A 1AL
Tel: 0207 758 2172
Pattinson, A
17 The Landway, Kemsing, Sevenoaks, Kent TN15 6TG
Tel: 01732 760152
Paveley, J
TCP Richings, Basilica Suite, 334 Southend Road, Wickford, Essex SS11 8QS
Tel: 01268 572320
Pearce, T
Langley, Chapel Street, Rocklands, Attleborough, Norfolk NR17 1UJ
Tel: 01953 483472
Pearce, T B
Holly Lodge, Middletown Lane, East Budleigh, Budleigh Salterton, Devon EX9 7EQ
Tel: 01395 444422

Pearlgood, S
Law Costs Solutions Ltd, 5 Priors, London Road, Bishop's Stortford, Hertfordshire CM23 5ED
Tel: 01279 715669
Pearson, D
23 Field Close, Chesham, Buckinghamshire HP5 3LB
Tel: 01494 786804
Pennington, J
JPN Consultancy, Europa House, Barcroft Street, Bury, Greater Manchester BL9 5BT
Tel: 0161 447 8889
Perch, D
HM Law Cost Draftsmen, Graphic House, 73-75 Gammons Lane, Watford, Hertfordshire WD24 5TU
Tel: 01923 242345
Perkins, R
Law Costs Drafting Ltd, 72 Gloucester Avenue, Maldon, Essex CM9 6LA
Tel: 01621 855622
Peterson, D
D Peterson Ltd, The Plaza, 6th Floor, 100 Old Hall Street, Liverpool, Merseyside L3 9QJ
Tel: 0151 600 5168
Petrecz, B T
Keoghs LLP, 2 The Parklands, Bolton, Greater Manchester BL6 4SE
Tel: 01204 677000
Phillips, J
CC Law Ltd, 14 Museum Place, Cardiff
Tel: 02920 382205
Phillips, K
Williams Associates, T109, Titan House, Cardiff Bay Business Centre, Lewis Road, Ocean Park, Cardiff CF24 5BS
Tel: 02921 600 521
Philpott, S L
Oak Edge Lodge, Oak Edge Lane, Tansley, Matlock, Derbyshire DE4 5FQ
Tel: 01629 57334
Pickett, M
9 Brompton Meadows, Brompton Regis, Somerset TA22 9PD
Tel: 01398 371633
Pickett, N
Old Barn, Postern Park Farm, Postern Lane, Tonbridge, Kent TN11 OQS
Tel: 01732 353090
Platnauer, D J
Masters Legal Costs Services LLP, 3-4 New Street, Bishopsgate, London EC2M 4HD
Tel: 0207 929 4344
Platts, R
Irwin Mitchell Solicitors, Riverside East, 2 Millsands, Sheffield, South Yorkshire S3 8DT
Tel: 0870 1500 100
Plunkett, J
14 Burcott Road, Wells, Somerset BA5 2EQ
Tel: .... 01380 733 327 Mob: 07935 752355
Popplewell, W
Equity Law Costing, 107-111 Fleet Street, London EC4A 2AB
Tel: 0207 936 9749
Popplewell, S
Equity Law Costing, The Barn Cowels Lane, Lindsell, Great Dunmow, Essex CM6 3QG
Tel: 01371 870595
Portch, N
Studio 33, 1-13 Alder Street, London E1 1EG
Tel: 0207 392 2044
Powell, J
38 Hawkshill, Dellfield, St Albans, Hertfordshire AL1 5HU
Tel: 01604 258570
Power, E
Just Costs Solicitors, Trident One, Styal Road, Manchester, Greater Manchester M22 5XB
Tel: 0161 435 6549
Price, D
Willis Legal Services Ltd, Panasonic Building, Christchurch Road, Baglan Industrial Park, Port Talbot, Neath Port Talbot SA12 7BZ
Tel: 01639 813030
Procter, A A J
Beadle Procter Costs Consultants, 81 New Wanstead, London E11 2SA
Tel: 0208 530 4997
Purchas, J
DLA Piper UK LLP, Princes Exchange, Princes Square, Leeds, West Yorkshire LS1 4BY
Tel: 0113 369 2474
Pyrah, J
The John M Hayes Partnership, 1st Floor, Front Suite, Graphic House, 14-16 Sussex Road, Haywards Heath, West Sussex RH16 4EA
Tel: 01444 440489
Qureshi, M
RBS Cost Drafting Department, PO Box 636, Bromley, Kent BR1 1WF
Tel: 0208 285 8763
Rabbitte, P
Dickinson & Rabbitte Ltd, 40a Gordon Road, West Bridgford, Nottinghamshire NG2 5NL
Tel: 0115 9826394
Rawlinson, M
QC Law Costs Draftsmen & Consultants, 8 Warwick Court, Gray's Inn, London WC1R 5DJ
Tel: 0207 430 0150
Reader, P J
Carter-Ruck, 6 St Andrew Street, London EC4A 3AE
Tel: 0207 353 5005
Reason, P
R Costings Ltd, The Old Chapel, St Johns Court, East Street, St Ives, Cambridgeshire PE27 5PD
Tel: 01480 463499
Reeve, L
Weightmans LLP, First Floor, St Philips Point, 47 Cannon Street, Birmingham, West Midlands B2 5EF
Tel: 0121 632 6100

Reynolds, A J
Group Litigation Costs Services Ltd, 86 Easton Street, High Wycombe, Buckinghamshire HP11 1LT
Tel: 01494 527100
Richards, S
J J Berry & Co, 207 South Street, Romford, Essex RM1 1QL
Tel: 01708 767013
Richardson, M
10 Wymering Road, Aylesbury, Buckinghamshire HP21 9KP
Tel: 01296 484874
Richings, J W
TCP Richings, 4th Floor, 68 Great Eastern Street, London EC2A 3JT
Tel: 020 7729 7750
Rigney, J
Clyde & Co LLP, 51 Eastcheap, London EC3M 1JP
Tel: 0207 648 1883
Riley, B
27a Springfield Road, Wigan, Greater Manchester WN6 7AT
Tel: 01942 321826
Riordan, J J
Riordan Associates, 50 Jefferson Drive, Rainham, Gillingham, Kent ME8 0DB
Tel: 01634 230962
Riordan, D P
Riordan Associates, Otterburn House, 10-12 Bromley Road, Beckenham, Kent BR3 5JE
Tel: 020 8650 8002
Riordan, B J
Riordan Associates, 50 Jefferson Drive, Rainham, Gillingham, Kent ME8 ODB
Tel: 01634 230962
Robbins, F
RMR legal, Suite 4b, Century Buildings, Blackfriars House, The Parsonage, Manchester, Greater Manchester M3 2JA
Tel: 0161 834 5444
Roberts, B C
Law Costs Drafting Services, 3 Hall Lane, Lydiate, Liverpool, Merseyside L31 4HN
Tel: 0151 526 0569
Roberts, O
Abacus Costs Consultancy Limited, 25/26 Neptune Court, Vanguard Way, Cardiff CF24 5PJ
Tel: .... 02920 475680 Mob: 0750 4653145
Roberts, P L
North West Law Ltd, Queens House, Queens Road, Chester, Cheshire CH1 3BQ
Tel: 01244 317543
Robins, J
J Robins & Co, 26 Clarence Road, Grays, Essex RM17 6QJ
Tel: 01375 390566
Robotham, P
104 Derwent Road, Stirchley, Birmingham, West Midlands B30 2US
Tel: 0121 200 7577
Robson, R
R Costings Ltd, The Old Chapel, St Johns Court, East Street, St Ives, Cambridgeshire PE27 5PD
Tel: 01480 463499
Rolfe, P
10 Little Warren Close, Guildford, Surrey GU4 8PW
Tel: 01483 302135
Rooney, A
HM Law Cost Draftsmen, Graphic House, 73-75 Gammons Lane, Watford, Hertfordshire WD24 5TU
Tel: 01923 242345
Rouane, M
Irwin Mitchell Solicitors, Riverside East, 2 Millsands, Sheffield, South Yorkshire S3 8DT
Tel: 0870 1500 100
Rowan, R
Rowan Legal Costs Ltd, Wallsend, Newcastle, Tyneside NE28 8SS
Tel: 0191 262 8040
Ryan, P
North West Law Ltd, Queens House, Queens Road, Chester, Cheshire CH1 3BQ
Tel: 01244 317543
Salliss, D N
69 Brixham Road, Welling, Kent DA16 1EH
Tel: 020 8304 5598
Sankey, M G
Oak Gate, 45b Hayes Way, Park Langley, Beckenham, Kent BR3 6RJ
Tel: 0208 650 1059
Scott, K J
7 Falconers Field, Roundwood Park, Harpenden, Bath & North East Somerset AL5 3EU
Tel: 01582 713532
Scott, J C
Matthew Harman & Partners, 17 Mulberry Place, Pinnell Road, London SE9 6AR
Tel: 020 8850 2122
Senior, M R
Joe Bellamy & Associates, Suite 12a, Sheffield Design Studios, 40 Ball Street, Sheffield, South Yorkshire S3 8DB
Tel: 0114 263 4131
Seville, D
Peter Brearley & Co Solicitors, 22 Sanderson House, Station Road, Horsforth, Leeds, West Yorkshire LS18 5NT
Tel: 0113 259 1761
Shotton, S
Irwin Mitchell Solicitors, Riverside East, 2 Millsands, Sheffield, South Yorkshire S3 8DT
Tel: .... 0870 1500 100 Ext: 4079
Sing, P
D W Costs Ltd, Spindle Ridge, Sun Hill, Fawkham, Longfield, Kent DA3 8NU
Tel: 0207 583 2622
Singleton, C
Cost Chambers Ltd, 25a Cemetery Road, Southport, Merseyside PR8 6RH
Tel: 01704 504090
Smith, E
3 Valley Fold, Bradford, West Yorkshire BD13 2LF
Tel: 01274 813640

Smith, M
Irwin Mitchell Solicitors, Imperial House, 31 Temple Street, Birmingham, West Midlands B2 5DB
Tel: 0870 1500 100
Snell, C
2 The Glebe, Stone, Aylesbury, Buckinghamshire HP17 8RH
Tel: 01296 747036
Snooks, N
Acumension Ltd, Universal House, Devonshire Street North, Manchester, Greater Manchester M12 6JH
Tel: 0161 277 5116
Sorrel, J
Clyde & Co LLP, 51 Eastcheap, London EC3M 1JP
Tel: 020 7623 1244
Spanyol, T
Masters Legal Costs Services LLP, 3-4 New Street, Bishopsgate, London EC2M 4HD
Tel: 0207 929 4344
Speight, A
CC Law Ltd, 14 Museum Place, Cardiff CF10 3BH
Tel: 029 2038 2205
Squires, J
Squires Costs, 6 Lilybank Close, Matlock, Derbyshire DE4 3EH
Tel: .... 0845 6435 908 Mob: 07766 101784
Sra, J
Legal Costs Practitioners, Suite 250, 15-17 Caledonian Road, London N1 9DX
Tel: 0844 991 9897
Stab, J
Kain Knight, Carpenters Hall, Throgmorton Avenue, London EC2N 2JJ
Tel: 0203 215 1011
Stainton, C
Thompsons Solicitors, Grove House, 55 Lowlands Road, Harrow, Middlesex HA1 3AP
Tel: 0208 872 8600
Staples, J
24 Lymington Avenue, Clacton-On-Sea, Colchester, Essex CO15 4PJ
Tel: 01920 444321
Stapleton, A T
Holman Fenwick Willan LLP, Friary Court, 65 Crutched Friars, London EC3N 2AE
Tel: 0207 264 8000
Stark, I
Stark Costing Services, Unit 44, Symonds Farm Business Park, Risby, Bury St Edmunds, Suffolk IP28 6RE
Tel: 01284 811831
Stedman, K
Kain Knight, Regis House, 9 Dane John Works, Gordon Road, Canterbury, Kent CT1 3PP
Tel: 01227 786499
Stettler, H
147 Arundel Road, Peacehaven, East Sussex BN10 8HP
Tel: 01273 580324
Stevens, A D
80 Dukes Avenue, Theydon Bois, Epping, Essex CM16 7HF
Tel: 0207 591 3334
Stevens, G
Maghull Business Centre, 1 Liverpool Road North, Maghull, Merseyside L31 2HB
Tel: 01704 892876
Storey, D G W
90 Avalon Road, Orpington, Kent BR6 9BA
Tel: 016898 20223
Stott, C
Hugh James Solicitors, Hodge House, 114-116 St Mary Street, Cardiff CF10 1DY
Tel: 02920 224871
Street, R D
DF LLP, Bridgewater Place, Water Lane, Leeds, West Yorkshire LS11 5DY
Tel: 0113 261 6099
Strickland, E
Token House, Token House Yard, London EC2R 7AS
Tel: .... 0207 073 2600 / 07724 286 900
Sudra, D
32 Wensley Avenue, Woodford Green, Essex IG8 9HE
Tel: 020 8505 7613
Swallow, D
Century Consultants Limited, 7 Trent Business Centre, Trent Park, Eastern Avenue, Lichfield, Staffordshire WS13 6RR
Tel: 01543 442 167
Swan, K
Meruit Costs, Lyons Davidson Solicitors, Victoria House, 51 Victoria Street, Bristol BS1 6AD
Tel: 0117 904 6000
Taylor, A
North West Law Ltd, Queens House, Queens Road, Chester, Cheshire CH1 3BQ
Tel: 01244 317543
Taylor, R
Williams Associates, T109, Titan House, Cardiff Bay Business Centre, Lewis Road, Ocean Park, Cardiff CF24 5BS
Tel: 02920 450772
Tebay, S
Alpha Legal Costing Services, 31 Hawksworth Drive, Menston, Ilkley, West Yorkshire LS29 6HP
Tel: .... 01943 876857 Mob: 07912 639034
Terry, M J
Herbert Smith, Exchange House, Primrose Street, London EC2A 2HS
Tel: 020 7374 8000
Thomas, A
Civil & Commercial Costs Lawyers Ltd, 40-43 Chancery Lane, London EC4A 1NE
Tel: 0207 269 2618
Thomas, C
Keeble Hawson, Old Cathedral Vicarage, St James Row, Sheffield, South Yorkshire S1 1XA
Tel: 0114 2906212
Thomas, J
Trerose Cottage, Old Road, Liskeard, Cornwall PL14 6DH
Tel: 01752 675141
Thomas, Z B
Z B Thomas Costing Services, Cockshed Llanwrin, Machynlleth, Powys SY20 8QJ
Tel: 01650 511578
Thompson, L
DWF LLP, Bridgewater Place, Water Lane, Leeds, West Yorkshire LS11 5DY
Tel: 0113 261 6076
Thompson, S
Keelys Solicitors, 30-34 Curtain Road, London EC2A 3NZ
Tel: 0207 422 8673
Thurley, K
Goodwin Malatesta Legal Costs Services Ltd, 134-136 High Street, Epping, Essex CM16 4AG
Tel: 01992 574846
Thurley, N D
Masters Legal Costs Services LLP, 3-4 New Street, Bishopsgate, London EC4M 2TP
Tel: 020 7929 4344
Tollitt, A J
North West Law Ltd, Queens House, Queens Road, Chester, Cheshire CH1 3BQ
Tel: 01244 317543
Townsend, S
Kiteleys Solicitors, 7 St Stephens Court, 15-17 St Stephens Road, Bournemouth BH2 6LA
Tel: 01202 299992
Townshend, K
10 Garnett Drive, Easton, Norwich, Norfolk NR9 5FB
Tel: 07764 322 956
Tully, J
Treasury Solicitors, One Kemble Street, London WC2B 4TS
Tel: 0207 210 3186
Turpin, A
16 Rue Danton, Port Vendres, 666600
Tel: 07932 141524
Tyler, M
Civil & Commercial Costs Lawyers Ltd, 40-43 Chancery Lane, London EC4A 1NE
Tel: 0207 269 2602
Upton, D
Kain Knight, 1, 2 & 4 Priors, London Road, Bishop's Stortford, Hertfordshire CM23 5ED
Tel: 01279 755552
Varney, B
11 Clarke Crescent, Kennington, Ashford, Kent TN24 9SA
Tel: .... 01233 650717 Mob: 07770 661669
Vessey, E
Canna, Forest Road, East Horsley, Surrey KT24 5BT
Tel: 01483 284838
Vickery, M
10 Sheepscroft, Cepen Park North, Chippenham, Wiltshire SN14 6YJ
Tel: 01249 463797
Virji, A N
Pictons Solicitors LLP, 28 Dunstable Road, Luton, Bedfordshire LU1 1DY
Tel: 01582 878560
Vodden, A
Hempsons, West One, Forth Banks, Newcastle Upon Tyne, Tyne & Wear NE1 3PA
Tel: 0191 230 6044
Wade, S
Wake Smith LLP, 6 Campo Lane, Sheffield, South Yorkshire S1 2EF
Tel: 0114 266 6660
Walkden, P
Irwin Mitchell Solicitors, Riverside East, 2 Millsands, Sheffield, South Yorkshire S3 8DT
Tel: 0870 1500 100
Walker, L
Hill Dickinson LLP, City Plaza, Pinfold Street, Sheffield, South Yorkshire S1 2GU
Tel: 0114 229 7926
Wallis, D C S
D W Costs Ltd, Spindle Ridge, Sun Hill, Fawkham, Longfield, Kent DA3 8NU
Tel: 020 7583 2622
Walmsley, J
Gibbins Costs Lawyers, Freeman House, Liquorice Way, Pontefract, West Yorkshire WF8 1DN
Tel: 01977 781651
Walmsley, C
PI Costing Plc, Robson House, 4 Regent Terrace, South Parade, Doncaster, South Yorkshire DN1 2EE
Tel: 01302 343666
Walsh, S
North West Law Ltd, Queens House, Queens Road, Chester, Cheshire CH1 3BQ
Tel: 01244 317543
Walsh, T
Oracle Costs Consultants, 71 Corporation Street, St Helens, Merseyside WA10 1SX
Tel: 01744 762011
Walters, L
The John M Hayes Partnership, 1st Floor, Front Suite, Graphic House, 14-16 Sussex Road, Haywards Heath, West Sussex RH16 4EA
Tel: 01444 440489
Walton, P
Masters Legal Costs Services LLP, 3-4 New Street, Bishopsgate, London EC2M 4HD
Tel: 020 7929 4344
Walton, I R
Masters Legal Costs Services LLP, 3-4 New Street, Bishopsgate, London EC2M 4HD
Tel: .... 0207 929 4344 / 4041
Watkins, B
Eversheds, 1 Callaghan Square, Cardiff CF10 5BT
Tel: 0845 497 9797
Webb, A
North West Law Ltd, Queens House, Queens Road, Chester, Cheshire CH1 3BQ
Tel: 01244 317543
Welfare, C S
Accounting & Management Services, 19 Coleshill Street, Sutton Coldfield, West Midlands B72 1SD
Tel: 0121 355 6032
Westacott, D
33 First Avenue, Dursley, Gloucestershire GL11 4NW
Tel: 07761 107057
Whitaker, V
Irwin Mitchell Solicitors, Riverside East, 2 Millsands, Sheffield, South Yorkshire S3 8DT
Tel: 0870 1500 100
White, D
14 Silverdale Crescent, Alderholt, Fordingbridge, Hampshire SP6 3JZ
Tel: 01425 653316
White, P A
14 Fordyce Close, Emerson Park, Hornchurch, Essex RM11 3LE
Tel: 01708 453730
White, R
Cost Advocates Ltd, 40 Dukes Place, 1st Floor, London EC3A 7NH
Tel: 0870 402 7871
White, L
Irwin Mitchell Solicitors, Riverside East, 2 Millsands, Sheffield, South Yorkshire S3 8DT
Tel: 0870 1500 100
White, J
Cricketers Cottage, Cricketers Lane, Herongate, Brentwood, Essex CM13 3QB
Tel: 0207 626 1111
Whittaker, G
Carlisle Legal Costing, Bourne House, Milbourne Street, Carlisle, Cumbria CA2 5XF
Tel: 01228 635545
Whyke, L
Just Costs Solicitors, 1 City Square, Leeds, West Yorkshire LS1 2ES
Tel: 0113 366 3193
Willett, M
Freshfields, 65 Fleet Street, London EC4Y 1HS
Tel: 020 7936 4000
Williams, J
Williams Associates, Titan House, Cardiff Bay Business Centre, Lewis Road, Ocean Park, Cardiff CF24 5BS
Tel: 029 2045 0772
Williams, R N
Reed Smith LLP, The Broadgate Tower, 20 Primrose Street, London EC2A 2RS
Tel: 020 3116 3000
Willis, D J
Willis Legal Services Ltd, Panasonic Building, Christchurch Road, Baglan Industrial Park, Port Talbot, Neath Port Talbot SA12 7BZ
Tel: 01639 813030
Wilson, J
Analysis Professional Legal Costing Services, Prospect Cottage, Rye Hill, Rye, East Sussex TN31 7NH
Tel: 01797 225353
Wilson, D M
Masters Legal Costs Services LLP, 3-4 New Street, Bishopsgate, London EC2M 4HD
Tel: 020 7929 4344
Winsor, J
61 Church Street, Micheldever, Winchester, Hampshire SO21 3DB
Tel: 01962 774385
Winyard, T
TM Costings Ltd, Suffolk House, 54-55 The Green, Wooburn Green, Buckingham, Buckinghamshire HP10 0EU
Tel: 01494 616122
Wonnacott, K
14 Monarch Terrace, West Malling, Kent ME19 4NP
Tel: 01732 874 994
Wood, K
Acumen Costs, Josephs Well, Hanover Walk, Leeds, West Yorkshire LS3 1AB
Tel: 0844 984 5261
Worman, M
Worman & Co, 14 Canute Close, Canewdon, Rochford, Essex SS4 3PX
Tel: 01702 258907
Wright, S J
Godfrey Wright Law Costs Draftsmen, 93/101 Bridge Street, Manchester, Greater Manchester M3 2GX
Tel: 0161 819 5021
Zarait, N
Just Costs Solicitors, Pall Mall Court, 61-67 King Street, Manchester, Greater Manchester M2 4PD
Tel: 0161 618 1095

THE BARRISTERS' BENEVOLENT ASSOCIATION
Founded 1873

To help needy and deserving Members of the English Bar who are or have been in practice in England or Wales, their husbands or wives, widows or widowers, children and in exceptional circumstances, dependants.

CLC
(COUNCIL FOR LICENSED CONVEYANCERS)

16-18 Glebe Road, Chelmsford, Essex CM1 1QG Tel: 01245 349599 Fax: 01245 341300
Email: clc@clc-uk.org Web: www.clc-uk.org

THE COUNCIL

Chief Executive of the Council
Mr Victor Olowe

Council Members
Ms Anna Bradley - Chair
Mr Alex Clark
Mr Rob Gurney
Mr John Jones
Mr George Kidd
Miss Jan Smith
Mr John Wells

Training

The basic educational requirement for registration as a CLC student is four GCSE passes, or equivalent, in English Language and three other approved subjects at grades A, B or C. Students who are employed in conveyancing within a licensed conveyancer's or solicitor's practice and mature students over 25 years with relevant practical experience may also be accepted. Students who have completed the recognised equivalent ILEX or Law Society examinations may apply and be granted exemption from some subjects.

The CLC examinations are in two parts, Foundation and Finals. The Foundation comprises two assignment based modules which are assessed: Introduction to Conveyancing & Introduction to Law & Legal Method plus two examinations, Land Law & Law of Contract (both examined at degree level). The Final comprises three examination subjects: Accounts; Conveyancing Law & Practice and Landlord & Tenant (all examinations at professional level).

Tuition for the CLC Examinations is available from a number of colleges throughout England and Wales or through distance learning direct from the CLC.

Probate is also regulated by CLC. When a student has completed the course to be a licensed conveyancer, they can study for the addition of the probate qualification.

Rules and Guidance Notes

The CLC's Rules, Regulations and Guidance Notes are set out in full on the CLC website www.clc-uk.org/rules_guidance.php. They explain the standards of behaviour, education and training all applicants must achieve to be issued with a licence to act as a licensed conveyancer. The Conduct Rules set high standards for licensed conveyancers and CLC regulated practices (including those they employ) to ensure that clients receive a good standard of service with appropriate levels of protection and, where things go wrong, clients are told what will be done.

CONDUCT RULES 2009

Made on 21 January 2009 by the Council for Licensed Conveyancers with the concurrence of the Secretary of State pursuant to section 20, section 32 and section 38(1) Administration of Justice Act 1985 and section 53 and schedule 8 Courts and Legal Services Act 1990.

CONTENTS

1. CITATIONS

1.1 These Rules regulating the professional practice, conduct and discipline of Licensed Conveyancers may be cited as the Licensed Conveyancers' Conduct Rules 2009 and shall come into force on 31 March 2009 on which date the Licensed Conveyancers' Conduct Rules 2005 shall cease to have effect, but without prejudice to any matter arising under those Rules then current.

1.2 Republished 6th October 2010 due to 5.2.10 amendment, as required by new complaints signposting requirements.

2. INTERPRETATION

2.1 In these Rules:
- The first letter of any term defined appears in capitals in these Rules.
- Unless the contrary intention appears, words importing the masculine gender include the feminine and neuter, words in the singular include the plural and words in the plural include the singular.

"1985 Act"
Administration of Justice Act 1985;

"the Council"
the Council for Licensed Conveyancers established under section 12 of the 1985 Act;

"Council's Rules"
the Licensed Conveyancers' Conduct Rules 2009 and any other rules made by the Council;

"the Council's Statutory Duty"
to ensure that the standards of competence and professional conduct among persons who practise as Licensed Conveyancers are sufficient to secure adequate protection for consumers, and that the Conveyancing Services provided by such persons are provided both economically and efficiently;

"Client"
any person or persons for whom a Licensed Conveyancer acts in the provision of Regulated Services;

"Communications"
include communications sent by or on behalf of a Licensed Conveyancer or Recognised Body by post, by a telecommunication system or by other means whilst in an electronic form;

"Company"
has the meaning given by section 735(1) of the Companies Act 1985;

"Compensation Fund"
the fund out of which grants and other payments are made by the Council for the purposes set out at section 21(2) of the 1985 Act;.

"Control"
strategic management, risk management, accounting and financial controls (including supervisory and audit functions);

"Conveyancing Services"
the preparation of transfers, conveyances, contracts and other documents in connection with, and other services ancillary to, the disposition or acquisition of estates or interests in land;

"Durable Medium"
the means by which information is stored in a way accessible for future reference for no less than the period prescribed by the Council and which allows the unchanged reproduction of the information stored;

"Guidance Notes"
guidance issued by the Council to facilitate compliance with the Council's Rules;

"Indemnity Policy"
the insurance policy authorised by the Licensed Conveyancers' Indemnity Rules;

"Legal Regulators"
the Council, the Law Society, the General Council of the Bar, the Master of the Faculties, the Institute of Legal Executives, the Chartered Institute of Patent Attorneys, the Institute of Trade Mark Attorneys, the Association of Law Costs Draftsmen and such other bodies which may be authorised to regulate providers of Reserved Legal Services;

"Licence"
a licence to practise as a Licensed Conveyancer issued by the Council;

"Licensed Conveyancer"
a person who holds a Licence;

"Limited Liability Partnership"
a body corporate formed by being incorporated under the Limited Liability Partnerships Act 2000 recognised by the Council under section 32 of the 1985 Act to provide Regulated Services;

"Limited Liability Partnerships Act 2000"
the Limited Liability Partnerships Act 2000, the Limited Liability Partnerships Regulations 2001 and any other regulations made under that Act;

"LLP Member"
a member of a Limited Liability Partnership;

"Manager"
in relation to a Recognised Body, means a person who is:
(a) a member of the Recognised Body, if the Recognised Body is a Company and its affairs are managed by its members;
(b) a director of the Recognised Body, if the Recognised Body is a Company and paragraph (a) does not apply;
(c) a partner, if the Recognised Body is a partnership;
(d) a LLP member, if the Recognised Body is a Limited Liability Partnership;
(e) a member of its governing body, if the Recognised Body is an unincorporated body (other than a partnership); and
(f) a Licensed Conveyancer, if sub-paragraphs (a)-(e) do not apply and the affairs of the Recognised Body are not managed by another Licensed Conveyancer;

"Permitted Person"
a solicitor regulated by the Law Society, a barrister regulated by the General Council of the Bar, a notary public regulated by the Master of the Faculties, a fellow regulated by the Institute of Legal Executives, a patent attorney regulated by the Chartered Institute of Patent Attorneys, a trade mark attorney regulated by the Institute of Trade Mark Attorneys, a law costs draftsman regulated by the Association of Law Costs Draftsmen and such other individuals authorised by any other Legal Regulator to provide Reserved Legal Services;

"Probate Services"
services limited to the drawing or preparation of any papers on which to found or oppose a grant of probate or grant of letters of administration and the administration of the estate of a deceased person;

"Qualified Person"
a Licensed Conveyancer; or a Permitted Person;

"Recognised Body"
a body recognised by the Council under section 32 of the 1985 Act to provide Regulated Services to the public;

"Regulated Services"
Conveyancing Services and such other services, including Probate Services, in respect of which a Licensed Conveyancer is regulated by the Council;

"Reserved Legal Services"
the right to conduct litigation, rights of audience, probate services, administration of oaths, notarial activities and conveyancing services.

3. ENTITLEMENT TO PROVIDE REGULATED SERVICES

3.1 A Licensed Conveyancer must

3.1.1 comply with the Council's Rules which relate to that Licensed Conveyancer;

3.1.2 ensure that the Recognised Body of which he is a Manager complies with the Council's Rules which relate to that Recognised Body.

3.2 A Licensed Conveyancer must:

3.2.1 comply with the Guidance Notes unless he has good reason for not doing so in the particular circumstances;

3.2.2 ensure that the Recognised Body of which he is a Manager complies with the Guidance Notes unless it has good reason for not doing so in the particular circumstances.

3.3 A Licensed Conveyancer shall only provide Regulated Services to the public:-

3.3.1 as a Manager of a Recognised Body; or

3.3.2 as a Manager of a body regulated by a Legal Regulator other than the Council; or

3.3.3 If neither rule 3.3.1 nor rule 3.3.2 is applicable, as an employee of a Recognised Body or of a body regulated by a Legal Regulator other than the Council.

3.4 A Manager who is not a Licensed Conveyancer must:

3.4.1 comply with the Council's Rules so far as they relate to the provision of Regulated Services and is treated for this purpose as a Licensed Conveyancer;

3.4.2 ensure that the Recognised Body of which he is a Manager complies with the Council's Rules in the provision of Regulated Services.

3.5 Control of a Recognised Body must be from a permanent fixed address in England or Wales.

3.6 All Communications must include:-

3.6.1 the principal address of the Recognised Body;

3.6.2 the names of the Managers of a Recognised Body (identifying each Manager who is a Licensed Conveyancer); and

3.6.3 the words "Regulated by the Council for Licensed Conveyancers".

3.7 There must be displayed at the principal office of a Recognised Body:-

3.7.1 the current Licence of any Manager who is a Licensed Conveyancer;

3.7.2 the current certificate of recognition issued by the Council.

3.8 There must be displayed at each branch office of a Recognised Body:-

3.8.1 a duplicate of the current licence of any Manager who is a Licensed Conveyancer;

3.8.2 a duplicate of the current certificate of recognition issued by the Council;

3.8.3 a notice giving the address of the principal office of the Recognised Body.

4. CONDUCT OF A LICENSED CONVEYANCER

4.1 A Licensed Conveyancer must:-

4.1.1 act with integrity and honesty;

4.1.2 act with reasonable care, skill and diligence;

4.1.3 not take, and must not permit anyone on his behalf to take, any action which may bring disrepute to the profession;

4.1.4 comply with a direction of the Council;

4.1.5 neither directly nor indirectly discriminate against nor treat less favourably any person because of their ethnic or national origin, sex, sexual orientation, marital status, religion, education, age or disability;

4.2 A Licensed Conveyancer must obtain permission from the Council before offering Regulated Services:

4.2.1 as a new business;

4.2.2 in an body regulated by a Legal Regulator other than the Council; or

4.2.3 through a Recognised Body with a Manager who is not a Licensed Conveyancer.

4.3 A Licensed Conveyancer must when practising in an body regulated by a Legal Regulator other than the Council:

4.3.1 comply with the rules of that Legal Regulator to the extent that they differ from the Council's Rules save that at all times the Licensed Conveyancer must comply with rule 4.1;

4.3.2 at all times keep paramount the interests of the Client except as required by law or by the rules of that Legal Regulator; and

4.3.3 keep confidential all information about the Client except as authorised by the Client or as required by law or by the rules of that Legal Regulator;

4.3.4 when acting in matters not regulated by the Council, not communicate in a way which states or implies he is undertaking the work as a Licensed Conveyancer.

4.4 A Licensed Conveyancer must when offering or providing Regulated Services through a Recognised Body:

4.4.1 ensure that all the Managers and employees of the Recognised Body comply with the Council's Rules where they apply;

4.4.2 when acting as a Licensed Conveyancer only accept instructions to act in a matter which is regulated by the Council;

4.4.3 when acting in matters not regulated by the Council, not communicate in a way which states or implies he is undertaking the work as a Licensed Conveyancer;

4.4.4 when undertaking work which is not regulated by the Council or by another Legal Regulator, inform the Client in writing that such work is not so regulated and that it is not covered by indemnity insurance taken out in accordance with the Council's Rules;

4.4.5 immediately notify the Council in writing of any breach of the Council's Rules by him or by any of the Managers or employees of the Recognised Body;

4.4.6 not conduct himself in a manner which he knows or has reasonable grounds for suspecting will result in a breach by the Licensed Conveyancer of the law or of the Council's Rules;

4.4.7 comply fully with any undertaking given by him, the Recognised Body or any employee of that Recognised Body;

4.4.8 never give false or misleading information relating to the provision of Regulated Services to any person;

4.4.9 promptly comply with any request for information made by the Council as authorised by statute or by the Council's Rules;

4.4.10 promptly notify the Council in writing of any facts or matters which may give rise to a claim under the Council's Compensation Fund;

4.4.11 promptly notify his insurers in writing of any facts or matters which may give rise to a claim under the Council's Indemnity Policy;

4.4.12 cease to provide Regulated Services for any period for which the current evidence of insurance issued to the Recognised Body has been avoided.

4.5 With the exception of unsolicited telephone calls or unsolicited visits a Licensed Conveyancer or a Manager may promote Regulated Services through any means provided that a person may freely choose a practitioner to act on his behalf.

4.6 A Recognised Body must:-

4.6.1 conduct business under a name which is not misleading;

4.6.2 ensure all Regulated Services are either carried out by or effectively supervised and directed by a Qualified Person;

4.6.3 keep information and records relating to Regulated Services safe on a Durable Medium;

4.6.4 have in place an appropriate written complaints procedure;

4.6.5 have in place appropriate management arrangements and systems to ensure compliance with the Council's Rules.

4.6.6 comply promptly with any request for information or documents made by the Council to enable it:

4.6.6.1 or the insurers of the Indemnity Policy, to determine the Recognised Body's contribution to the Indemnity Policy;

4.6.6.2 to determine the amount of the Recognised Body's contribution to the Council's compensation fund; and

4.6.6.3 to act in accordance with the Council's Statutory Duty, including without limitation for the purpose of ascertaining whether it is or has been in breach of any of the Council's Rules.

5. CONDUCT TOWARDS CLIENTS

5.1 A Licensed Conveyancer must:-

5.1.1 at all times keep paramount the interests of the Client except as required by law or by the Council's Rules;

5.1.2 keep confidential all information about the Client Except as authorised by the Client or as required by law or the Council's Rules;

5.1.3 not accept instructions from a person nor continue to act for any Client whose interests conflict directly or indirectly with his own or those of the Recognised Body, or with those of any other Client;

5.1.4 cease acting in any matter if the Client so instructs.

5.2 A Licensed Conveyancer, in the provision of Regulated Services, must:-

5.2.1 except as permitted in guidance issued by the Council, act only for one Client in a matter unless each Client is informed in writing in advance that the Recognised Body has been asked to act for another Client; each Client is at all times represented by different Qualified Persons and those Qualified Persons conduct themselves in the matter as though they were members of different entities;

5.2.2 on the granting or redemption of a mortgage not act for himself nor for any Client prohibited by the instructions of any lender;

5.2.3 only accept instructions within his professional competence;

5.2.4 only undertake matters within his professional competence;

5.2.5 advise a Client to seek legal or other advice where a matter is beyond his professional competence;

5.2.6 only seek to exclude or limit liability with the informed written consent of the Client;

5.2.7 ensure that all Communications are clear, fair and not misleading;

5.2.8 disclose to a Client in writing, as soon as they are known to the Licensed Conveyancer, the existence and amount of any sum payable by or to the Licensed Conveyancer arising, whether directly or indirectly, from the Client's instructions;

5.2.9 keep safe Client information and records on a Durable Medium until delivered to the Client or disposed of in accordance with guidance issued by the Council;

5.2.10 before or when accepting instructions, set out in writing to the Client the terms on which instructions are accepted, an estimate of costs and the Recognised Body's complaints procedure; this information must also include the client's right to complain to the Legal Ombudsman at the conclusion of the com plaint process, the time limits for doing so and full details about how to contact the Legal Ombudsman.

5.2.11 where a complaint is received comply with the Recognised Body's complaints procedure;

5.2.12 keep the Client properly informed;

5.2.13 not delay completion because his fees are outstanding (for this purpose fees do not include disbursements);

5.2.14 with the authority of his seller Client at once disclose in writing to all prospective buyers any instruction to submit contracts to more than one prospective buyer: if the seller Client refuses to give such authority immediately cease to act.

5.3 After giving its Client reasonable notice in writing with reasons a Recognised Body may cease acting in any matter where it is reasonable for it to do so.

6. REQUIREMENT TO REPORT

6.1 A Recognised Body shall immediately notify the Council in writing if it intends to employ or pay or if it becomes aware that it is employing or paying any person to whom Rule 6.2 applies.

6.2 A Recognised Body shall not, except with the written permission of the Council, employ or pay or continue to employ or pay any person to provide Regulated Services who is known to that Recognised Body:-

6.2.1 to be subject to an Order revoking or suspending his Licence or disqualifying him from holding a Licence;

6.2.2 to be convicted of a criminal offence involving fraud, dishonesty or deception or an indictable offence which has not been spent by virtue of a period of rehabilitation without offending under the Rehabilitation of Offenders Act 1974.

6.2.3 to have had the Council's powers of intervention under the 1985 Act exercised against him, against a body in which he was a principal, partner or employee or against a Recognised Body in which he was a Manager or employee;

6.2.4 as a member of another profession, to have had an Order made against him by his professional body (other than an Order which provides only for the payment of costs by him); or

6.2.5 to be subject to an Order under section 43(2) Solicitors' Act 1974., or to have been found guilty of an offence under section 44(1), (1A), (1B) or (1C) of that Act.

6.3 A Licensed Conveyancer must immediately notify the Council in writing if to his knowledge he or any Manager in the Recognised Body:-

6.3.1 is a person to whom any of the provisions of Rule 6.2 applies;

6.3.2 has failed to satisfy a civil judgement;

6.3.3 is an undischarged bankrupt or has made a composition or arrangement with creditors unless:

(i) the bankruptcy is annulled either on the ground that he ought not to have been adjudged bankrupt or, where he is not subject to a bankruptcy restrictions order or interim order, on the ground that his debts have been paid in full on the date of annulment; or

(ii) in the case of a composition or arrangement with his creditors, he pays his debts in full on the date on which payment is completed or on the expiration of five years from the date on which the terms of the deeds of composition or arrangement are fulfilled;

6.3.4 has been a director of a company which has gone into liquidation on the grounds of insolvency;

6.3.5 has been a Licensed Conveyancer in, or Manager of, a Recognised Body which has had a certificate of recognition refused, revoked or made subject to conditions;

6.3.6 has had an order made against him by a Legal Regulator;

6.3.7 was, in relation to a body which is the subject of an order made by a Legal Regulator, a Licensed Conveyancer or a Manager at the time of the act or omission complained of;

6.3.8 lacks capacity (within the meaning of the Mental Capacity Act 2005) and powers under section 15 to 20 or section 48 of that Act have been exercised in relation to that person.

7. INSPECTION AND DISCIPLINARY CONSEQUENCES

7.1 In order to monitor compliance with the Council's Rules, a Licensed Conveyancer must at the time and place fixed by the Council produce to any person appointed by the Council all information held on a Durable Medium relating to his Practice (to include his records, papers, files and financial accounts) reasonably required to enable the preparation of a report to the Council.

7.2 A report made following an inspection under Rule 7.1 may be used as part of any investigation under section 24 Administration of Justice Act 1985.

7.3 If it appears to the Council that there has been a contravention of any of the Council's Rules a Licensed Conveyancer is liable to disciplinary proceedings and sanction under section 24 and 26 Administration of Justice Act 1985 (as amended by the Courts and Legal Services Act 1990) and a Recognised Body is liable to disciplinary proceedings under Schedule

LICENSED CONVEYANCERS

Key to symbols

* = Full Licence

This listing is based on information from both the spring and autumn editorial mailings. It is not a comprehensive list nor is it, in any way, associated with information held by the Council for Licensed Conveyancers.

Bedfordshire

Curl, Kalpana*
Austin & Carnley Albion Chambers High Street Leighton Buzzard Bedfordshire LU7 1DP *Tel:* 01525 372140 *Fax:* 01525 851554 *Dx:* 90805 LEIGHTON BUZZARD

Rogers, Stephen L*
Austin & Carnley Albion Chambers High Street Leighton Buzzard Bedfordshire LU7 1DP *Tel:* 01525 372140 *Fax:* 01525 851554 *Dx:* 90805 LEIGHTON BUZZARD

Belfast

Hart, Kevin E*
Hart & Co 4th Floor Causeway Tower 9 James Street South Belfast BT2 8DN *Tel:* 028 9032 3545 *Fax:* 028 9024 5005 *Dx:* 446NR BELFAST

Hart, Kevin P*
Hart & Co 4th Floor Causeway Tower 9 James Street South Belfast BT2 8DN *Tel:* 028 9032 3545 *Fax:* 028 9024 5005 *Dx:* 446NR BELFAST

Hart, Martin C*
Hart & Co 4th Floor Causeway Tower 9 James Street South Belfast BT2 8DN *Tel:* 028 9032 3545 *Fax:* 028 9024 5005 *Dx:* 446NR BELFAST

Jordan, Claire M*
Hart & Co 4th Floor Causeway Tower 9 James Street South Belfast BT2 8DN *Tel:* 028 9032 3545 *Fax:* 028 9024 5005 *Dx:* 446NR BELFAST

Blackburn

Acklam, David Ian*
Acklam Bond Noor 2 Strawberry Bank Blackburn BB2 6AA *Tel:* 01254 56068 *Fax:* 01254 677415 *Dx:* 17980 BLACKBURN

Blackpool

Baker, Philip
Easthams Solicitors Limited Continental House 292-302 Church Street Blackpool FY1 3QA *Tel:* 0800 032 1432 *Fax:* 0844 855 4405 *Dx:* 714600 BLACKPOOL 6

Wareng, Pamela*
Easthams Solicitors Limited Continental House 292-302 Church Street Blackpool FY1 3QA *Tel:* 0800 032 1432 *Fax:* 0844 855 4405 *Dx:* 714600 BLACKPOOL 6

Bracknell Forest

Robinault, Jacqueline S
Kite Griffin Brooke House High Street Bracknell Bracknell Forest RG12 1LL *Tel:* 01344 425637 *Fax:* 01344 423536 *Dx:* 33604 BRACKNELL

Brighton & Hove

Clemons, Madeline
Arscotts 54 Lansdowne Place Hove Brighton & Hove BN3 1FG *Tel:* 01273 735289 *Fax:* 01273 325091 *Dx:* 59281 HOVE

Edgar, Amanda Christina*
Edward Harte LLP 6 Pavilion Parade Brighton Brighton & Hove BN2 1RA *Tel:* 01273 662750 *Fax:* 01273 662755 *Dx:* 36651 BRIGHTON 2

Bristol

O'Malley, Claire Louise*
Cooke Painter Limited 26 & 32 Gilda Parade Wells Road Whitchurch Bristol BS14 9HY *Tel:* 01275 835569 *Fax:* 01275 540050

Porter, Stephen George*
Cooke Painter Limited 314 Wells Road Knowle Bristol BS4 2QG *Tel:* 0117 977 7403 *Fax:* 0117 972 3658 *Dx:* 119404 KNOWLE

Buckinghamshire

Couser, Robin Edward
B P Collins LLP Collins House 32-38 Station Road Gerrards Cross Buckinghamshire SL9 8EL *Tel:* 01753 889995 *Fax:* 01753 889851 *Dx:* 40256 GERRARDS CROSS

Pullen, Julia Pamela
Wilkins Lincoln House 6 Church Street Aylesbury Buckinghamshire HP20 2QS *Tel:* 01296 424681 *Fax:* 01296 426213 *Dx:* 4104 AYLESBURY

Cardiff

Askins, Karen*
Berry Smith LLP Haywood House Dumfries Place Cardiff CF10 3GA *Tel:* 029 2034 5511 *Fax:* 029 2034 5945 *Dx:* 33097 CARDIFF 1

Cheshire

Watkinson, Justine Michelle
Hillyer McKeown LLP Murlain House Union Street Chester Cheshire CH1 1QP *Tel:* 01244 318131 *Fax:* 01244 344749 *Dx:* 22153 CHESTER

Co Londonderry

Blaney, Patricia*
Blaney & Diamond 15 Kirk Avenue Magherafelt Co Londonderry BT45 6BT *Tel:* 028 7930 0660 *Fax:* 028 7930 0662

Douglas, Richard*
R G Connell & Son 13 Main Street Limavady Co Londonderry BT49 0EP *Tel:* 028 7772 2617 *Fax:* 028 7772 2447 *Dx:* 3501NR LIMAVADY

Cornwall

Marchese, Karina M A
Merricks Formerly Merrick Kelleher Cross Street Wadebridge Cornwall PL27 7DT *Tel:* 01208 812068 / 813104 *Fax:* 01208 814186 *Dx:* 81701 WADEBRIDGE

Cumbria

Winer, Judith M*
Beaty & Co 1 Victoria Place High Street Wigton Cumbria CA7 9PJ *Tel:* 01697 342121 *Fax:* 01697 344697 *Dx:* 714665 WIGTON

Derbyshire

Box, Shani
Sharp & Partners 43 Market Place Long Eaton Derbyshire NG10 1JL *Tel:* 0115 973 4111 *Fax:* 0115 946 2627

Devon

Gregory, Angela
Tozers 2-3 Orchard Gardens Teignmouth Devon TQ14 8DR *Tel:* 01626 772376 *Fax:* 01626 770317 *Dx:* 82051 TEIGNMOUTH

East Riding of Yorkshire

Holehouse, Sally
Stuart Smith & Burnett 16 Wellington Road Bridlington East Riding of Yorkshire YO15 2BG *Tel:* 01262 678128 *Fax:* 01262 400012 *Dx:* 61900 BRIDLINGTON

Spooner, Suzanne
Stuart Smith & Burnett 16 Wellington Road Bridlington East Riding of Yorkshire YO15 2BG *Tel:* 01262 678128 *Fax:* 01262 400012 *Dx:* 61900 BRIDLINGTON

East Sussex

Hovey, David C
Adams & Remers Trinity House School Hill Lewes East Sussex BN7 2NN *Tel:* 01273 480616 *Fax:* 01273 480618 *Dx:* 3100 LEWES 1

Mitchell, John J
Adams & Remers Trinity House School Hill Lewes East Sussex BN7 2NN *Tel:* 01273 480616 *Fax:* 01273 480618 *Dx:* 3100 LEWES 1

Wickens, Nicholas R
Gaby Hardwicke 33 The Avenue Eastbourne East Sussex BN21 3YD *Tel:* 01323 435900 *Fax:* 01323 435921 *Dx:* 6916 EASTBOURNE

Essex

Beard, Leslie Clive
Ellisons London House 45 Kingsway Dovercourt Harwich Essex CO12 3JU *Tel:* 01255 502428 *Fax:* 01255 504651 *Dx:* 49503 HARWICH (DOVERCOURT)

Bloom, Linda*
Pinney Talfourd LLP 52 Station Road Upminster Essex RM14 2TU *Tel:* 01708 229444 *Fax:* 01708 228163 *Dx:* 35555 UPMINSTER

Curtis, Kerry
MacLeish Littlestone Cowan 23 Longbridge Road Barking Essex IG11 8TN *Tel:* 020 8514 3000 *Fax:* 020 8507 1191 *Dx:* 8504 BARKING

Eagle, Paul J
Bawtrees LLP 65 Newland Street Witham Essex CM8 1AB *Tel:* 01376 513491 *Fax:* 01376 510713 *Dx:* 33400 WITHAM

Hill, David J
Holmes & Hills LLP Dale Chambers Bocking End Braintree Essex CM7 9AJ *Tel:* 01376 320456 *Fax:* 01376 342156 *Dx:* 56200 BRAINTREE 1

Holland, Elaine
Birkett Long LLP One Legg Street Chelmsford Essex CM1 1JS *Tel:* 01245 453800 *Fax:* 01245 453801 *Dx:* 3394 CHELMSFORD

Linton, Joanne Mandy
Michael Cullen & Partners 102 High Street Billericay Essex CM12 9BY *Tel:* 01277 623132 *Fax:* 01277 630098 *Dx:* 32200 BILLERICAY

Lynn, Valerie
Reeves Fisher & Sams 47 Crown Street Brentwood Essex CM14 4BD *Tel:* 01277 202500 *Dx:* 50121 BRENTWOOD

Phillips, John A*
Reeves Fisher & Sams 47 Crown Street Brentwood Essex CM14 4BD *Tel:* 01277 202500 *Dx:* 50121 BRENTWOOD

Powell, Christopher A*
Powells 21 New Pier Street Walton-on-the-Naze Essex CO14 8ED *Tel:* 01255 675698 *Fax:* 01255 679372 *Dx:* 54401 FRINTON-ON-SEA

Rayner, Annette
Ellisons 143 Connaught Avenue Frinton-on-Sea Essex CO13 9AB *Tel:* 01255 851000 *Fax:* 01255 850041

Stuart, Richard G
Reeves Fisher & Sams 47 Crown Street Brentwood Essex CM14 4BD *Tel:* 01277 202500 *Dx:* 50121 BRENTWOOD

Taylor, Nicola*
Taylors Legal 184 Manor Road Chigwell Ilford Essex IG7 5PZ *Tel:* 020 8501 4959 *Fax:* 020 8501 3008 *Dx:* 154760 CHIGWELL

Greater Manchester

Allen, Catherine*
SAS Daniels LLP 30 Greek Street Stockport Greater Manchester SK3 8AD *Tel:* 0161 475 7676 *Fax:* 0161 475 7677

Carter, Deborah K
Howarth Goodman 8 King Street Manchester Greater Manchester M60 8HG *Tel:* 0161 832 5068 *Fax:* 0161 819 7878 *Dx:* 14308 MANCHESTER

Fearn, Julie
Adam F Greenhalgh & Co Mawdsley Chambers 20 Mawdsley Street Bolton Greater Manchester BL1 1LE *Tel:* 0845 074 3491 *Fax:* 01204 364611 *Dx:* 24148 BOLTON 1

Finch, Hannah
Russell & Russell Churchill House Wood Street Bolton Greater Manchester BL1 1EE *Tel:* 01204 399299 *Fax:* 01204 389223 *Dx:* 24146 BOLTON 1

Freeman, Margaret
Alker & Ball 29-33 King Street Wigan Greater Manchester WN1 1EG *Tel:* 01942 246241 *Fax:* 01942 820086 *Dx:* 19315 WIGAN

Hinchliffe, Roger M*
Pearson Hinchliffe Albion House 31 Queen Street Oldham Greater Manchester OL1 1RD *Tel:* 0161 785 3500 *Fax:* 0161 624 2589 *Dx:* 23615 OLDHAM

Kerrigan, Debra Jayne
Russell & Russell Churchill House Wood Street Bolton Greater Manchester BL1 1EE *Tel:* 01204 399299 *Fax:* 01204 389223 *Dx:* 24146 BOLTON 1

Naylor, Janine
Russell & Russell Churchill House Wood Street Bolton Greater Manchester BL1 1EE *Tel:* 01204 399299 *Fax:* 01204 389223 *Dx:* 24146 BOLTON 1

Nelson, Amanda Patricia
Birchall Blackburn LLP 20 Kennedy Street Manchester Greater Manchester M2 4BY *Tel:* 0161 236 0662 *Fax:* 0161 236 0687 *Dx:* 718168 MANCHESTER 3

Nield, Laura Elizabeth*
Rowley Dickinson Halifax House 93-101 Bridge Street Manchester Greater Manchester M3 2GX *Tel:* 0161 834 4215 *Fax:* 0161 834 5153 *Dx:* 14332 MANCHESTER 1

Pearson, A John*
Pearson Hinchliffe Albion House 31 Queen Street Oldham Greater Manchester OL1 1RD *Tel:* 0161 785 3500 *Fax:* 0161 624 2589 *Dx:* 23615 OLDHAM

Pitt, Michael*
Pearson Hinchliffe Albion House 31 Queen Street Oldham Greater Manchester OL1 1RD *Tel:* 0161 785 3500 *Fax:* 0161 624 2589 *Dx:* 23615 OLDHAM

Hampshire

Barlow, John T*
Barker Son & Isherwood LLP 32 High Street Andover Hampshire SP10 1NT *Tel:* 01264 353411 *Fax:* 01264 356549 *Dx:* 90303 ANDOVER

Rigby, Lisa
Brain Chase Coles Haymarket House 20-24 Wote Street Basingstoke Hampshire RG21 7NL *Tel:* 01256 354481 *Fax:* 01256 841432 *Dx:* 3005 BASINGSTOKE

Rolfe, Gary*
Dutton Gregory Trussell House 23 St Peters Street Winchester Hampshire SO23 8BT *Tel:* 01962 844333 *Fax:* 01962 863582 *Dx:* 2515 WINCHESTER

Hertfordshire

Dawson, Belinda*
HRJ Law LLP 7-8 Portmill Lane Hitchin Hertfordshire SG5 1AS *Tel:* 01462 628888 *Fax:* 01462 631233 *Dx:* 7100 HITCHIN

Green, Michael W
Maffey & Brentnall 149 The Parade Watford Hertfordshire WD17 1NB *Tel:* 01923 234607 *Fax:* 01923 818500 *Dx:* 4512 WATFORD

Kent

Hitch, Pauline A
Gullands 16 Mill Street Maidstone Kent ME15 6XT *Tel:* 01622 678341 *Fax:* 01622 757735 *Dx:* 51973 MAIDSTONE 2

Warley, Simon Nicholas
Whitehead Monckton Monckton House 72 King Street Maidstone Kent ME14 1BL *Tel:* 01622 698000 *Fax:* 01622 690050 *Dx:* 4807 MAIDSTONE 1

Lancashire

Acklam, David Ian*
Acklam Bond Noor Equity Chambers 10-12 St James Street Accrington Lancashire BB5 1LY *Tel:* 01254 872272 *Fax:* 01254 233370 *Dx:* 23766 ACCRINGTON

Alveston, Julie C
Farleys Solicitors LLP 12-18 Willow Street Accrington Lancashire BB5 1LP *Tel:* 01254 367853 *Fax:* 01254 235468 *Dx:* 23753 ACCRINGTON

Bugler, Maggie*
Walker Foster Craven House Newtown Barnoldswick Lancashire BB18 5UQ *Tel:* 01282 812340 *Fax:* 01282 812331 *Dx:* 18553 BARNOLDSWICK

Clegg, Paul A*
Dickinson Parker Hill 22 Derby Street Ormskirk Lancashire L39 2BZ *Tel:* 01695 574201 *Fax:* 01695 579986 *Dx:* 21254 ORMSKIRK

Thurnhill, Joseph A*
Thurnhills Charnley House 13 Winckley Square Preston Lancashire PR1 2JT *Tel:* 01772 251762 *Fax:* 01772 561319 *Dx:* 17135 PRESTON
Thurnhills Cross House Market Place Garstang Lancashire PR3 1ZA *Tel:* 01995 603142 *Fax:* 01995 600163

Leicester

Kinson, Lesley Lorraine
Spearing Waite LLP 41 Friar Lane Leicester LE1 5RB *Tel:* 0116 262 4225 *Fax:* 0116 251 2009 *Dx:* 10837 LEICESTER 1

Leicestershire

Livsey, Gavin
JS Law 37 The Point Market Harborough Leicestershire LE16 7QU *Tel:* 0870 380 4000 *Fax:* 0870 755 3270

Lincolnshire

Foyster, Robin C*
Langleys Olympic House Doddington Road Lincoln Lincolnshire LN6 3SE *Tel:* 01522 888555 *Fax:* 01522 888556 *Dx:* 700678 NORTH HYKEHAM 2

London

Allen, Catherine J*
Edwards Angell Palmer & Dodge Dashwood 69 Old Broad Street London EC2M 1QS *Tel:* 020 7583 4055 *Fax:* 020 7353 7377 *Dx:* 103 LONDON/CHANCERY LN

Bailey, Madelaine E
Armstrong & Co 2 Dartmouth Road Forest Hill London SE23 3XU *Tel:* 020 8699 3477 *Fax:* 020 8291 3645 *Dx:* 34400 FOREST HILL

Gorst, Jonathan*
Bryan Cave 88 Wood Street London EC2V 7AJ *Tel:* 020 7207 1100 *Fax:* 020 7207 1881

Jackson, Rachel L
Unsworth Rose 19 Princess Road Regents Park Camden London NW1 8JR *Tel:* 020 7483 4411 *Fax:* 020 7586 9388 *Dx:* 96852 PRIMROSE HILL

Jones, Belinda J
Unsworth Rose 19 Princess Road Regents Park Camden London NW1 8JR *Tel:* 020 7483 4411 *Fax:* 020 7586 9388 *Dx:* 96852 PRIMROSE HILL

Killick, Michael
South Square 3-4 South Square Gray's Inn London WC1R 5HP *Tel:* 020 7696 9900 *Fax:* 020 7696 9911 *Dx:* 338 LONDON/CHANCERY LANE

Liveras, Savakis Kyriacou*
Protopapas Queens House 180 Tottenham Court Road London W1T 7PD *Tel:* 020 7636 2100 *Fax:* 020 7636 2101 *Dx:* 134203 LONDON/TOTTENHAM COURT ROAD 2

May, Angela
9-12 Bell Yard Chambers London WC2A 2JR *Tel:* 020 7400 1800 *Fax:* 020 7404 1405 *Dx:* 390 LONDON/ CHANCERY LANE

Mythen, Thomas Anthony
Hanne & Co St Johns Chambers 1c St Johns Hill Clapham Junction London SW11 1TN *Tel:* 020 7228 0017 *Fax:* 020 7326 8300 *Dx:* 58550 CLAPHAM JUNCTION

Nolan, Fionnuala*
Pini Franco LLP 22-24 Ely Place London EC1N 6TE *Tel:* 020 7566 3140 *Fax:* 020 7566 3144 *Dx:* 487 LONDON/ CHANCERY LN

Schindler, Alan A
Myers Fletcher & Gordon 15 Cambridge Court 210 Shepherds Bush Road Hammersmith London W6 7NJ *Tel:* 020 7610 4433 *Fax:* 020 7610 4455 *Dx:* 46761 HAMMERSMITH 3

Wright, Anne Elizabeth*
Lawrence Stephens 4th Floor Morley House 26-30 Holborn Viaduct London EC1A 2AT *Tel:* 020 7935 1211 *Fax:* 020 7935 1213

Medway Towns

Johnston, Alan*
Stephens & Son LLP Rome House 39-41 Railway Street Chatham Medway Towns ME4 4RP *Tel:* 01634 811444 *Fax:* 01634 831532 *Dx:* 6700 CHATHAM 1

Merseyside

Mitchell, Joanne*
Hillyer McKeown LLP 2 Church Road Bebington Merseyside CH63 7PH *Tel:* 0151 645 4255 *Fax:* 0151 644 1905 *Dx:* 18282 BEBINGTON

Thompson, Tracy*
Morecrofts Solicitors LLP 2 Crown Buildings Liverpool Road Crosby Merseyside L23 5SR *Tel:* 0151 924 9234 *Fax:* 0151 931 3165 *Dx:* 20410 CROSBY

Middlesex

Clothier, Robert J*
Hodders The Triangle 311 Harrow Road Wembley Middlesex HA9 6BD *Tel:* 020 8902 9604 *Fax:* 020 8903 4906 *Dx:* 51154 WEMBLEY PARK

Tomlin, Alec
Bonnetts Solicitors LLP 33 Bath Road Hounslow Middlesex TW3 3BW *Tel:* 020 8570 5286 *Fax:* 020 8570 8531 *Dx:* 3501 HOUNSLOW

Milton Keynes

Sidney, Emma Jeanne*
Geoffrey Leaver Solicitors LLP 251 Upper 3rd Street Bouverie Square Milton Keynes MK9 1DR *Tel:* 01908 692769 *Fax:* 01908 692772 *Dx:* 54460 MILTON KEYNES 1

Monmouthshire

Vargas, Katherine Jane Bladen
Marie Dark Solicitors Rose Cottage Chapel Lane Pwllmeyrric Chepstow Monmouthshire NP16 6JU *Tel:* 01291 621638 *Fax:* 01291 622102

North East Lincolnshire

Goddard, Clifford D
Bridge McFarland 19 South St Mary's Gate Grimsby North East Lincolnshire DN31 1JE *Tel:* 01472 311711 *Fax:* 01472 311500 *Dx:* 13507 GRIMSBY 1

King, Philip John
Paul Rudd Riverhead Chambers 9 New Street Grimsby North East Lincolnshire DN31 1HQ *Tel:* 01472 350881 *Fax:* 01472 242234 *Dx:* 13521 GRIMSBY 1

North Lincolnshire

Wingate, Margaret A
Mason Baggott & Garton 13-19 Wells Street Scunthorpe North Lincolnshire DN15 6HN *Tel:* 01724 868611 *Fax:* 01724 280433 *Dx:* 14707 SCUNTHORPE

North Yorkshire

Grunwell, Nicola
Pinkney Grunwells Lawyers LLP 64 Westborough Scarborough North Yorkshire YO11 1TS *Tel:* 01723 352125 *Fax:* 01723 500023 *Dx:* 61807 SCARBOROUGH

Mawer, Beverley Mary
Bywaters Topham Phillips LLP 17 Hornbeam Square South Hornbeam Business Park Harrogate North Yorkshire HG2 8NB *Tel:* 01423 879556 *Fax:* 01423 874142 *Dx:* 11961 HARROGATE 1

Northamptonshire

Green, Sally Margaret*
Vincent Sykes & Higham LLP Montague House Chancery Lane Thrapston Northamptonshire NN14 4LN *Tel:* 01832 732161 *Fax:* 01832 733701 *Dx:* 701612 THRAPSTON

Nottingham

Box, Shani
Sharp & Partners 6 Weekday Cross Nottingham NG1 2GF *Tel:* 0115 959 0055 *Fax:* 0115 959 0099 *Dx:* 10019 NOTTINGHAM 1

Nottinghamshire

Yates, Frances*
Larken & Co 10 Lombard Street Newark Nottinghamshire NG24 1XE *Tel:* 01636 703333 *Fax:* 01636 706649 *Dx:* 11803 NEWARK

Oxfordshire

Bacchus, Simon K*
Darbys Solicitors LLP 52 New Inn Hall Street Oxford Oxfordshire OX1 2DN *Tel:* 01865 811700 *Fax:* 01865 811777 *Dx:* 145840 OXFORD 6

Evans, Barbara*
Stanger Stacey & Mason 35a High Street Witney Oxfordshire OX28 6HP *Tel:* 01993 776491 *Fax:* 01993 702059 *Dx:* 40201 WITNEY

Maw, Janet
Alfred Truman The Old Court House 5 Sheep Street Bicester Oxfordshire OX26 6JB *Tel:* 01869 252761 *Fax:* 01869 246619 *Dx:* 40150 BICESTER

Peterborough

Palmann, Marion I*
Pirie Palmann Priestgate House 3-7 Priestgate Peterborough PE1 1JN *Tel:* 01733 427799 *Fax:* 01733 427277 *Dx:* 12335 PETERBOROUGH

Poole

Bowman, Simon*
Bowman & Co 203 Ashley Road Parkstone Poole BH14 9DL *Tel:* 01202 716171 *Fax:* 01202 716032 *Dx:* 92902 PARKSTONE 2

Powys

Evans, Avril
Milwyn Jenkins Cranford House 1 Severn Square Newtown Powys SY16 2AG *Tel:* 01686 626218 *Fax:* 01686 610047 *Dx:* 29231 NEWTOWN (POWYS)

Haughton, Alison
PCB Solicitors LLP Barclays Bank Chambers 8 Broad Street Knighton Powys LD7 1BL *Tel:* 01547 520254

Shropshire

Ashton, Karen Michelle*
Wace Morgan 1-2 Belmont Shrewsbury Shropshire SY1 1TD *Tel:* 01743 280100 *Fax:* 01743 280111 *Dx:* 19718 SHREWSBURY

Chesters, Simon J
FBC Manby Bowdler LLP Routh House Hall Court Hall Park Way Telford Shropshire TF3 4NJ *Tel:* 01952 292129 *Fax:* 01952 291716 *Dx:* 707201 TELFORD 4

Somerset

Keate, Anne*
Broomhead & Saul 11 & 13 East Street Ilminster Somerset TA19 0AE *Tel:* 01460 57056 *Fax:* 01460 54846 *Dx:* 95803 ILMINSTER

Rossiter, Peter Stephen*
Peter Rossiter & Co 9-11 Abingdon Street Burnham-on-Sea Somerset TA8 1PH *Tel:* 01278 780143 *Fax:* 01278 793143

South Yorkshire

Fitzgerald, Ann*
Arthur Jackson & Co 4 Ash Mount Doncaster Gate Rotherham South Yorkshire S65 1DQ *Tel:* 01709 363876 *Fax:* 01709 829928 *Dx:* 12608 ROTHERHAM

Foy, Malcolm Clive*
Malcolm C Foy & Co 52 Hallgate Doncaster South Yorkshire DN1 3PB *Tel:* 01302 340005 *Fax:* 01302 322283 *Dx:* 28698 DONCASTER 2
Malcolm C Foy & Co 2 Upper Millgate Rotherham South Yorkshire S60 1PF *Tel:* 01709 836866 *Fax:* 01709 836755 *Dx:* 12607 ROTHERHAM

Rawlings, Anthony B
Paul Bullen & Co 5 Copley Road Doncaster South Yorkshire DN1 2PE *Tel:* 01302 819000 *Fax:* 01302 812500 *Dx:* 28683 DONCASTER 2

Winfield, Linda A
Foys Solicitors 102-112 Burncross Chapeltown Sheffield South Yorkshire S35 1TG *Tel:* 0114 246 7609 *Fax:* 0114 240 2625 *Dx:* 19836 CHAPELTOWN

Southend-on-Sea

Nickolls, Alan R
Paul Robinson Solicitors The Old Bank 470-474 London Road Westcliff-on-Sea Southend-on-Sea SS0 9LD *Tel:* 01702 338338 *Fax:* 01702 354032 *Dx:* 100808 WESTCLIFF-ON-SEA 1

Suffolk

Robinson, Margaret Jane
Stevens 25 High Street Haverhill Suffolk CB9 8AD *Tel:* 01440 762511 *Fax:* 01440 703873 *Dx:* 80351 HAVERHILL

Surrey

Gray, Linda*
Nichols Marcy Dawson 77 High Street Walton-on-Thames Surrey KT12 1DR *Tel:* 01932 219500 *Fax:* 01932 220549 *Dx:* 80001 WALTON-ON-THAMES

Tite, Jennifer Anne*
Sheppersons 1 Massetts Road Horley Surrey RH6 7PR *Tel:* 01293 772424 *Fax:* 01293 785642 *Dx:* 200402 HORLEY

Swindon

Brockington, Roger Francis
Clark Holt Hardwick House Prospect Place Swindon SN1 3LJ *Tel:* 01793 617444 *Fax:* 01793 617436 *Dx:* 38606 SWINDON 2

Thurrock

Lander, David*
Hattens Solicitors 90 Orsett Road Grays Thurrock RM17 5ER *Tel:* 01375 374851 / 373516 *Fax:* 01375 374332 *Dx:* 54000 GRAYS

Torbay

Wilkinson, David
Eastleys The Manor Office Victoria Street Paignton Torbay TQ4 5DW *Tel:* 01803 559257 *Fax:* 01803 558625 *Dx:* 100603 PAIGNTON

Vale of Glamorgan

Pearce, Helen*
J A Hughes Centenary House King Square Barry Vale of Glamorgan CF62 8HB *Tel:* 01446 411000 *Fax:* 01446 411010 *Dx:* 38550 BARRY

West Midlands

Dodd, Peter H*
Stables & Co 70 High Street Halesowen West Midlands B63 3BA *Tel:* 0121 585 3820 *Fax:* 0121 501 2211

Evans, Barbara*
CMHT Solicitors 41 Anchor Road Aldridge Walsall West Midlands WS9 8PT *Tel:* 01922 743525 *Fax:* 01922 743164 *Dx:* 29192 ALDRIDGE

Gibbins, Roland Clive
Howell & Co 1341 Stratford Road Hall Green Birmingham West Midlands B28 9HW *Tel:* 0121 778 5031 *Fax:* 0121 777 3967 *Dx:* 714513 HALL GREEN 2

West Sussex

Horlock, Philip
Edward Hayes LLP 236 Chichester Road Bognor Regis West Sussex PO21 5BA *Tel:* 01243 822655 *Fax:* 01243 827647 *Dx:* 30307 CHICHESTER

Lewis, Anthony James*
Green Wright Chalton Annis Churchill Court 112 The Street Rustington West Sussex BN16 3DA *Tel:* 01903 774131 *Fax:* 01903 778444 *Dx:* 55100 RUSTINGTON
Green Wright Chalton Annis 13-14 Liverpool Terrace Worthing West Sussex BN11 1TQ *Tel:* 01903 234064 *Fax:* 01903 200743 *Dx:* 3722 WORTHING

Phillips, Melvin I*
Mayo Wynne Baxter LLP The Studio 43-45 Cantelupe Road East Grinstead West Sussex RH19 3BL *Tel:* 01342 310600 *Fax:* 01342 410020 *Dx:* 300206 EAST GRINSTEAD

Waite, Douglas H
Edward Hayes LLP 236 Chichester Road Bognor Regis West Sussex PO21 5BA *Tel:* 01243 822655 *Fax:* 01243 827647 *Dx:* 30307 CHICHESTER

Watson, Graham J*
Edward Hayes LLP 14 Shore Road East Wittering Chichester West Sussex PO20 8DZ *Tel:* 01243 672124 *Fax:* 01243 672818 *Dx:* 30307 CHICHESTER

West Yorkshire

Beedle, Joan E
Holroyd & Co 27 Market Street Milnsbridge Huddersfield West Yorkshire HD3 4ND *Tel:* 01484 645464 *Fax:* 01484 460087

Fox, Ann*
Worger Howcroft Skipton Chambers Chapel Lane Bingley West Yorkshire BD16 2NG *Tel:* 01274 511246 *Fax:* 01274 511258 *Dx:* 21105 BINGLEY 2

Gable, Heather*
Ison Harrison 29 Main Street Garforth West Yorkshire LS25 1DS *Tel:* 0113 286 1455 *Fax:* 0113 287 3014 *Dx:* 29766 GARFORTH

Sagu, Parminder S
Patel & Bhatoa National House 951 Leeds Road Bradford West Yorkshire BD3 8JB *Tel:* 01274 669023 *Fax:* 01274 656151 *Dx:* 721740 BRADFORD 19

Shackleton, Lynda J
Ramsdens Solicitors 102 Huddersfield Road Holmfirth West Yorkshire HD9 3AX *Tel:* 01484 690040 *Fax:* 01484 685641

Tottie, Elaine
Bury & Walkers LLP 4 Butts Court Leeds West Yorkshire LS1 5JS *Tel:* 0113 244 4227 *Fax:* 0113 246 5965 *Dx:* 12048 LEEDS 1

Windsor & Maidenhead

Evans, Margaret
Abbott Lloyd Howorth Minster Court 22-30 York Road Maidenhead Windsor & Maidenhead SL6 1SF *Tel:* 01628 798800 *Fax:* 0871 210 0041 *Dx:* 6412 MAIDENHEAD

Worcestershire

Atkinson, Emma*
County Conveyancing 1st Floor 14-15 Church Green East Redditch Worcestershire B98 8BP *Tel:* 01527 591964

Atkinson, John R E*
County Conveyancing 1st Floor 14-15 Church Green East Redditch Worcestershire B98 8BP *Tel:* 01527 591964

Chadd, Sue
Thomas Guise 5 Foregate Street Worcester Worcestershire WR1 1DB *Tel:* 01905 723131 *Fax:* 01905 723312 *Dx:* 716284 WORCESTER

York

Foyster, Robin C*
Langleys Queen's House Micklegate York YO1 6WG *Tel:* 01904 610886 *Fax:* 01904 611086 *Dx:* 720620 YORK 21

THE INSTITUTE OF LEGAL EXECUTIVES (ILEX)

Kempston Manor, Kempston, Bedford MK42 7AB

President

Miss Susan A. Silver F.Inst.L.Ex.,
SDA Consultants, Cheshire

Vice-President

Mr Nicholas Hanning F.Inst.L.Ex.,
Reynolds Williams Solicitors, Dorset

Deputy-President

Mr Stephen Gowland F.Inst.L.Ex.,
ILS Solicitors, Durham

ILEX Council Members

Mr Keith M. Barrett F.Inst.L.Ex., Irwin Mitchell, London
Miss Gillian Birchnall F.Inst.L.Ex., Gorman Hamilton Solicitors, Newcastle
Mr Mark Bishop F.Inst.L.Ex., C J Jones Solicitors LLP, London
Mr Martin Callan F.Inst.L.Ex., Martin Callan Limited, London
Mr David Edwards F.Inst.L.Ex., St Albans District Council, Hertfordshire
Mrs Frances Edwards F.Inst.L.Ex.,Caswell Jones, Wales
Miss Judith Gordon-Nichols F.Inst.L.Ex., Beachcroft LLP, Bristol
Mrs Lesley Graham F.Inst.L.Ex., Sheldon Davidson, Manchester
Mrs Julie Hughes F.Inst.L.Ex., United Utilities PLC, Warrington
Mrs Victoria L. Loughnane F.Inst.L.Ex., HBJ Gateley Wareing LLP, Leicester
Mr Kevin McCarthy F.Inst.L.Ex., Hugh James, Cardiff
Mr David M. McGrady F.Inst.L.Ex., Gregsons Solicitors, London
Ms Janine E. Moore F.Inst.L.Ex., Purdys Solicitors, Cambridge
Ms Rachael N. Palmer F.Inst.L.Ex., Blakemores Solicitors, Birmingham
Mr Roger Ralph F.Inst.L.Ex., Campbell Chambers Solicitors, London
Mr Mark A. Reeves F.Inst.L.Ex., Myer Wolff Solicitors, Hull
Mrs Dawn Slow F.Inst.L.Ex., Harvey Ingram LLP, Leicester

Chief Executive

Diane Burleigh

The Institute of Legal Executives (ILEX) is the professional body which represents 22,000 trainee and practicing Legal Executives. Its role is to enhance the standing of Legal Executives in the legal profession. ILEX works closely with Government and the Ministry of Justice (MoJ) and is recognised in England and Wales as one of the three core regulators of the legal profession alongside barristers and solicitors.

ILEX provides a cost effective route to obtaining law qualifications and a career in law which is open to all. Study is through full/part time courses and distance learning available from ILEX Tutorial College (ITC). Legal Executives are Fellows of the Institute who have completed the ILEX Professional Higher Diploma in Law and Practice and the required period of a qualifying employment.

Legal Executive lawyers specialise in a particular area of law, which means the everyday work of a Legal Executive lawyer is similar to that of a solicitor.

With rights of audience in civil, criminal and family proceedings, those Fellows who train and qualify as Legal Executive Advocates can represent their clients in the County Court, Family Proceedings Court, Magistrates' Court, Youth Court, Coroners Court and in most Tribunals depending on the area of law in which they practise.

Legal Executive lawyers are eligible for judicial appointments and partnerships in Legal Disciplinary Practices (LDPs).

ILEX is an approved regulator for litigation rights for Associate Prosecutors, enabling associate prosecutors in the Crown Prosecution Service to exercise litigation and advocacy rights in the Magistrates' Courts under the stewardship of an approved regulator.

FELLOWS EMPLOYED IN LONDON

E1
Ahmad, Tariq Mahmood (TV Edwards)
Britton, Richard (McCormacks)
David, Jeannette Vilma (Reynolds Porter Chamberlain LLP)
Hunter, Martin John (Reynolds Porter Chamberlain LLP)
Lee, Dennis (St Paul International Insurance Co Ltd)
Mondol, Mohammed Fazlul (Capital Solicitors LLP)
Morton-Curtis, Rachel (Alzheimers Society)
Porter, Floyd Ramsey (Miles & Partners)
Spence, Cislyn (McMillan Hamilton McCarthy)
Thompson, Vivien (Kennedy Cater Legal)
Westwood, Martin (Reynolds Porter Chamberlain LLP)

E4
Ang, Erwin Cheng Chye (The Scout Association)

E6
Bruce, Emily Maria (London Borough of Newham)
Deuchars, Innes James (Edwards Duthie)
Donovan, Richard Andrew (Jacobs Solicitors)
Harrison, Kevin Gerard (Edell Jones & Lessers)
Stewart, Sally Ann Therese (Corporate Services Department)

E8
Abbott, Robert James (London Borough of Hackney)
Aloba, Deborah Elizabeth (Lucas & Co)
Enukora, Lorna (London Borough of Hackney)
George-Elliott, Anora (Hackney Borough Council)
Knowlden, Christine Elizabeth (London Borough of Hackney)

E9
Kaur, Harbens (Homerton Hospital)

E11
Procter, Andrew Arthur John (Beadle Procter Costs Consultants)

E13
Mclaughlin, David (Edwards Duthie)

E14
Arram Frsa, Joyce Muriel (Alexander JLO)
Brahmbhatt, Himadri Doli (London Borough of Tower Hamlets)
Froy, Sarah Louise (Financial Ombudsman Service)
Hastings-Prosser, Harriet (Financial Ombudsman Service)
Kingwell, Adrian James (Clifford Chance LLP)
Lazarus, Elizabeth (Exchange Tower)
Llewellyn, Anisa Gracine (Vance Harris LLP)

E15
Ajayi, Elizabeth Oluyemisi (Crown Prosecution Service)
Doshi, Lauren (Crown Prosecution Service)
Ijiwoye-Adeyemo, Oluwatoyin Tolu Temitope (JDS Solicitors)
Khan, Nasir (Bowling & Co)
Mehmet, Ercan Salih (Bowling & Co)
Murray, Arabella Josephine (Bowling & Co)

E17
Carty, Hemerdy Danny (Ascham Homes)
Cohen, Michelle Diana (London Borough of Waltham Forest)
Davies, Philip Andrew (London Borough of Waltham Forest)
Ferguson, Mark James (London Borough of Waltham Forest)
Mullett, James Robert (London Borough of Waltham Forest)
Sasdev, Kaushika (Sasdev & Co)
Terrode, Claudette Marie (Cartwright Cunningham Haselgrove & Co)

EC1
Andrews, Jennifer Sharon (Royal Mail Group)
Angel, Stuart James (Rollingsons Solicitors)
Barrett, Keith Martin (Irwin Mitchell LLP)
Batrick, Lesley Clare (Alexander Harris)
Begley, Sally Anne Jane (Irwin Mitchell LLP)
Bishop, Mark (C J Jones)
Canale, Zena Joy (Lovells)
Edge, Robert John (Irwin Mitchell LLP)
Egles, Michael John (Bowen Egles LLP)
Fairburn, Stephen Victor (C J Jones solicitors LLP)
Finniss, Gary Keith (Kingsley Napley)
Gilbey, Louise Victoria Ann (CMS Cameron Mckenna)
Howe, Nicola (Irwin Mitchell LLP)
Hurd, Alison Louise (Chan Neill Solicitors)
McCarthy, John James (Liddigans LLP)
Naude, Susanna (Irwin Mitchell LLP)
Richardson, Yanthe (Josiah-Lake Gardiner Solicitors)
Robinson, Eileen Rose (Balsara & Co)
Shakallis, Prodromos (Carter Lemon Camerons LLP)
Shapiro, Michael (GSC Solicitors)
Smith, Nicola (Webster Dixon LLP)
Snape, David Michael (CMS Cameron Mckenna)
Swainston, Victoria Clare (CMS Cameron Mckenna)
Taylor, Philip Thomas Bradley (Royal Mail Group)
Thomas, David Kenneth (Simpson Millar)
Upton, Rachel Louise (Abrahams Dresden)
Wicks, Gary John (Squire & Co)

EC2
Achampong - Kyei, Andrew (DLA Piper UK LLP)
Baker, Barbara Georgina (Weil Gotshal & Manges)
Bellinger, David William (Herbert Smith)
Braude, Michael (Corporation of London)
Carney, Phillip Trevor (Berrymans Lace Mawer)
Culkin, Natalie Anne (Linklaters LLP)
De Sousa, Usha (Ashurst LLP)
Fieldhouse, Claire Michelle (MWB)
Galan, Maria Luisa (Gide Loyrette Nouel)
Garousha, Abeer (Weil Gotshal & Manges)
Green, Maria (Allen & Overy)
Hannon, Mairead Ann (Orrick Herrington & Sutcliffe (Europe) LLP)
Harris, Maureen (Simmons & Simmons)
Harrison, Sally Frances (Orrick Herrington & Sutcliffe (Europe) LLP)
Haughton, Andrea Nicola (Reed Smith LLP)
Hodges, Dawn Jeanette (Osborne Clarke)
Howlett, Richard Peter (The Corporation of London)
Jenkins, Karen (Druces & Attlee)
Keliris, Costa Peter (Squire Sanders Hammonds)
Kemp, Daren John (Sidley Austin)
Kyriazis, Elizabeth Anne (DLA Piper UK LLP)
Leech, Alistair (A J Colvin)
Lodge, Gemma Anita (DLA Piper UK LLP)
Mccarthy, Donna Claire (Devonshires Solicitors)
Pitt, Allen Kenneth (Pritchard Englefield)
Quinlan, Brendan Mark (G T Stewart Solicitors)
Ramsey, Georgina Elizabeth (Finch Rating Ltd)
Randall-Gray, Claire Catherine (G T Stewart Solicitors)
Reed, Suzie-Jane (Sidley Austin)
Ryan, Michelle Emily (DLA Piper UK LLP)
Scott, Jennifer (Corporation of London)
Seal, Mary Josephine (AXA UK Plc)
Sheppard, Ian Peter (Berrymans Lace Mawer)
Shorter, Maria (Squire Sanders Hammonds)
Viner, Sarah Jane (UBS Investment Bank)
Voss, Louisa Elizabeth (Alexander Forbes Services Limited)
Westbrook, Malcolm Bruce (Hextalls Limited)
Wood, David John (Lattey & Dawe Solicitors)
Woodcock, Katie (Pinsent Masons LLP)
Yip, King Ying Lili (Squire Sanders Hammonds)

EC3
Bains, Harminder (Field Fisher Waterhouse LLP)
Bass, Graeme Peter (The Parabis Group)
Bearryman, Samantha Jennie (Clyde & Co LLP)
Berry, Carole Elizabeth (Rollingsons Solicitors)
Carter, Robert David (Kennedys)
Conway, Grant (Barlow Lyde & Gilbert)
Crockford, Richard David (Kennedys)
Earle, Richard Leslie (Field Fisher Waterhouse LLP)
Fennelly, Patrick (AIG Europe (UK) Ltd)
Ferris, Christine Anita (Greenwood Solicitors)
Finlay, Allan Robert (Kennedys)
Gammon, Mark David (Barlow Lyde & Gilbert)
Garrett, Tracey Elaine (Capita London Market Services)
Gheerawo Skilbeck, Melissa (Trowers & Hamlins)
Gorvett, Maxine Ann (Kennedys)
Hancock, Alison Jane (Sprecher Grier Halberstam LLP)
Henson, Jennifer (Prolegal Ltd)
Hobbs, Debbie Louise (Clyde & Co LLP)
Jeremiah, Keith Valentine (Barclays PLC)
Lewis, Robert Windsor (Kennedys)
Mahboob, Saira Parveen (Trowers & Hamlins)
Murphy, Steven John (Kennedys)
Mussington, Keithly Alexander James (Clyde & Co LLP)
Palmer, John Robert (Barlow Lyde & Gilbert)
Patyal, Amarjit (Mills & Reeve)
Platt, Jayne Mary (Blake Turner & Co)
Salvatore, Emma (Trowers & Hamlins)
Sandhar, Sukhvir Kaur (Beachcroft LLP)
Seear, Colin Xavier Christopher (Munich R E General Services Ltd)
Surry, Frederick Arthur (Richards Butler LLP)
Walker, Peter Mark (Willis Group)
Watson, Emma Louise (Prolegal Ltd)
Wheeler, Joanne (Rollingsons Solicitors)
Willett, Gillian Elizabeth (Blake Turner & Co)
Williams, Mandy Louise (Kennedys)

EC4
Ashton, Elaine (Levison Meltzer Pigott)
Banson, Victoria (Jones Day)
Bennett, Herbert Montagu (Charles Russell Business Services)
Bignell, Julie Anne (Blackrock Investment Management (UK) Ltd)
Bittner, Sally-Ann Lisa (Martineau Johnson)
Brocklehurst, Benedict Louis Daniel (Byrne & Partners Solicitors)
Brown, Janet Rosemary (Weightmans LLP)
Burke, Anthony Simon (Peters And Peters)
Colquhoun, Iain (Thomas Eggar LLP)
Connolly, John James (Cannings Connolly)
Cooper, Joyce (Maxwell Winward LLP)
Cotter, James Joseph (Dewar Hogan)
Craig, Laurie (McGuireWoods London LLP)
Days, Simon Alexander (Maxwell Winward LLP)
Drawwater, Marilyn Pamela (Royal Mail Legal Services)
Ebberson, Ann Yvonne (Rosling King)
Faggetter, Julia Marion (Royds)
Fish, Miles (Berwin Leighton Paisner LLP)
Fox, Robert (Nicholson Graham & Jones)
Golding, Denis John (Thomas Eggar LLP)
Helliwell, Karen Jean (Beachcroft LLP)
Hillier, Martha Jane (SJ Berwin LLP)
Holyoake, Vivienne Lara (CRBS)
Jackson, Robert (Sebastians)
Lawson, Dawn (Harcus Sinclair)
Layode, Cynthia Omololu (Nesta)
Lee, Mary Lilian (Berwin Leighton Paisner LLP)
Lewiston, Michelle Louise (Speechly Bircham LLP)
Lindsay, Ricky Christopher (DWF LLP)
Lodhi, Yassar Mohammad (Beachcroft LLP)
Manning, James Anthony (DWF LLP)
Martin, Claire Caroline (Goodman Derrick)
Maxwell, Alan Robert (Withers LLP)
Mclean, Vivienne Jean (Mayer Brown International LLP)

Neate, Janet Barbara (Royds)
Page, Sandra Pamela (Veale Wasbrough Vizards)
Patel, Reena (Weightmans LLP)
Perry, Catherine (Crowell & Moring)
Philpot, Roger Charles (Taylor Wessing)
Pipkin, David Alan (Davies Arnold Cooper)
Rixson, Karen Mary Joyce (Denton Wilde Sapte)
Speller, Peter Andrew (Royal Mail Legal Services)
Sweeney, Victoria Clare (Beachcroft LLP)
Tallentire, Emma Louise (Veale Wasbrough Vizards)
Taylor, Claudius Adesholay (Crown Prosecution Service)
Thomas, Adella Lillian Adina (DWF LLP)
Tilfourd, Diana Margaret (Withers LLP)
Toth, Karen (Macfarlanes)
Turner, Jonathan Lewis (Speechly Bircham LLP)
Verow, Daniel Paul (DWF LLP)
Walton, Yvonne Stephanie (Bower Cotton & Bower)
Wilson, Derek (Beachcroft LLP)
Windell, Lorraine Yvonne (Horwich Cohen Coghlan Solicitors)
Worrell, Malcolm Elvis (Thomas Eggar LLP)

N1

Ellerman, Deborah Louise (CW Publishing Limited)
Fox, Jonathan Beaumont (London Borough of Islington)
Legge, Keith Harold (London Borough of Islington)
Mustafa, Senol (London Borough of Islington)
Pathak, Rajesh (London Borough of Islington)

N3

Cohen, Shirley Louise (OGR Stock Denton)
Del Vecchio, Nicholas (Hugh Jones & Co)
Dervish, Erdogan (Hugh Jones & Co)
Mittleman, Felicity Shareen (Lloyd Platt & Co)
Thorne, William Edwin (Newman Law)

N4

Senadheera, Dinu (Shanthi & Co)

N5

Ladwa, Smita (London Borough of Islington)
Pascal, Hilma May (Homes For Islington)

N6

Davidson, Maria (Elizabeth M Millar)

N7

Baker, Peter Heywood (Alban Gould Baker & Co)

N8

Greaney, Rita (T R Taner & Co)
Parry, Gwynn Tecwyn (Cramer Pelmont Solicitors)

N9

Brown, Christina Ana (McKenzie Solicitors)

N11

O'Hara, John Patrick (The London Borough of Barnet)

N12

Economides, Mario (Yanakas Votsis Associates)
Michael, Michael Louis (The Cyprus Popular Bank Ltd)
O'Connell, Maria Dawn (Matthew Gold & Co)
Sparrow, Marilyn (Galbraith Branley Solicitors)

N13

Christodoulou, Andrea Michelle (Watermans Solicitors)

N15

Kemiki, Davina Ojuolape (Dozie & Co Solicitors)
Nolan, Susan Kim Claire (Andre Grant & Co)

N16

Lomas, Stephen (London Borough of Hackney)

N17

Canavan, James Michael (Fairbairn Smith & Co)
Mcclory, Hazel Jean (Enfield Magistrates Court)
Tuohy, Gemma (Porters)
Whitbread, Ian (Wilson & Co Solicitors)

N18

Kalpakiotis, Panagiotis Peter (Barnett Alexander Conway Ingram Solicitors)

N22

Duguid, Tracy Ann (Haringey Council)
Nafi, Semiha (Levenes Solicitors)
Thomas, Gillian Jacqueline (Haringey Council)

NW1

Borris, Mischa Anna (White & Co)
Damgaard, Pia Trier (Hodge Jones & Allen LLP)
Dunning, Aiden John (CBS Outdoor Ltd)
Galewski, Elizabeth Anne (Network Rail)
Joseph, Claire Louise (Unsworth Rose)
Malaktos, Daisy (Associated Press Television News)
Palmer-Head, Catherine Dianne (London Borough of Camden)

NW3

Carr, Barry Brian (Newton & Co)
Hare, Patricia Ann (CKFT)
Wright, Christopher Andrew (CKFT)

NW4

Callum-Clarke, Annette Marie Wisdom (Darryl Ingram Solicitors)
Walia-Rodrigo, Vandana (London Borough of Barnet)

NW5

Ebulue, Emmanuel Reginald (Immigration Consultation Services Ltd)
Grandy, Florence Fiona (Lewis Nedas)
Olley, Katy (TNT Solicitors)

NW6

Cinque, Mark John (JD Spicer & Co)
Riordan, Sandra Mary (Powell Spencer & Partners)

NW9

Newstead-Smith, Charlotte Elizabeth (HBG Construction Ltd)
Ramkissoon, Mavis (Crown Prosecution Service)
Raphael, Nadia (Chesham & Co)

NW11

Botelho, Anthony Joseph (Meer & Co)

SE1

Chisholm, Ruth (Shell International Ltd)
Collins, Jane Elizabeth (St Ives Plc)
Donovan, John Daniel (Crown Prosecution Service)
Fleet, John Frederick (London Fire & Emergency Planning Authority)
Franklin, Lisa-Jane (Anthony Gold Solicitors)
Harrison, Lidia Helena-Maria (The Royal British Legion)
Harrison, Alan Joseph (Lawrence Graham LLP)
Little, Katie Rebecca (Winckworth Sherwood LLP)
Mark, Ian Lionel (Southwark Council)
O'Flaherty, Kevin Peter (Britannia Steam Ship Insurance)
O'Reilly, Jill Margaret (Winckworth Sherwood LLP)
Pauling, Julia Ann (Financial Times)
Paynter, Marie Ita Louise (Landau Zeffertt Weir Solicitors)
Pereira, John Maximus (Jury Central Summoning Bureau)
Richards, Christopher Sydney (London Fire & Emergency Planning Authority)
Smith, Edmund Allen (Peabody Trust)
Thomas, Maria (Practical Law Company Ltd)
Thurgill, Lauren (Lawrence Graham LLP)
Tiwana, Charanjit (Crown Prosecution Service)
Woolven, Amanda Jane (The Oakley Shee Partnership Solicitors)

SE5

Caspersz, Johann Dirk Modeste (London Borough of Southwark)
Farrell, Charlotte (London Borough of Southwark)
O'Connell, Bryan William Thomas (Samuel Ross Solicitors)
Scutt, Sarah Jane (London Borough of Southwark)
Shillingford, Judy Deborah (London Borough of Southwark)

SE6

Dixon, Patricia Eileen (London Borough of Lewisham)
Head, Oliver James (Morrison Spowart)
Shanahan, Fiona Dolores (London Borough of Lewisham)

SE8

Connell, Lisa Sarah (Macauley Smith & Co)
Foster, Anne-Marie Adana (J B Wheatley & Co)

SE10

Dear, Michael Brian (Grant Saw)
Walker, Rosemary Diana Jean (Grant Saw)

SE11

Spring, Wayne (Fisher Meredith)

SE13

Harris, Michael (Marsh Brown & Co)

SE14

Smith, Hillary (Mackesys Solicitors)

SE15

Barron, Andrew David (Glazer Delmar)

SE16

Flanagan, Patrick Thomas (Attridge Solicitors)

SE18

Mathieson, Kerry Jane (London Borough of Greenwich Social Services Department)

SE19

Bowey, Karen Mary (Amphlett Lissimore Bagshaws LLP)
Cole, Patricia Frances (Amphlett Lissimore Bagshaws LLP)
Lawrence, Linda Ann (Bagshaws)
Ludlow, Rachel Marie (Amphlett Lissimore Bagshaws LLP)
Robertson, Lynsey (Amphlett Lissimore Bagshaws LLP)

SE22

Boyle, Peter Nicholas (G T Stewart Solicitors)

SW1

Atkinson, John William (Currey & Co LLP)
Boyce, Sharron Anne (Janes Solicitors)
Brown, Anne Carol (Child & Child)
Cheater, Jill Freda (Radcliffes Le Brasseur)
D' Monte, Helen Martine (Bircham Dyson Bell)
D'Monte, Bernard (Bircham Dyson Bell)
Duguid, Judith Claire (Lee & Pembertons)
Flurry, Teresa Joy (Radcliffes Le Brasseur)
Gilchrist, Sally Anne (Metropolitan Police)
Hill, Rosalind Margaret (Nabarro LLP)
Hilton, Richard John (DEFRA)
Huseyin, Serda (Crown Prosecution Service)
Lewis, Pamela Gay (William Sturges & Co)
Mahany, Sara-Jayne (Winckworth Sherwood LLP)
Maynard, Linda Clare (DEFRA)
Nihill, Kim Frances (Janes Solicitors)
Shephard, David Anthony (Department of Transport)
Simpson, Laura Jane (Metropolitan Police)
Tully, James Daniel (HM Treasury)
Turpin, Neil Dudley (Lee Bolton Monier-Williams)
Tyrrell, Claire Lisa (Piper Smith Watton LLP)

SW2

Allen, Joy Susan (London Borough of Lambeth)

SW4

Dickinson, Belinda Sonia Elizabeth (QAS Ltd)
Jupp, Brenda Dawn (Streathers)

SW6

Rapp, Neil Richard (David Tagg & Co)

SW9

James, Hubert (Brixton Law Centre)
Obi, Aloysius Igwebuike (Golding Doves Limited)

SW11

Horner, Wayne Andrew (Attridge Solicitors)
Walker, James Peter (Geo H Gibson & Co)

SW12

Griffin, Thelma Mary (Viridian Housing)
Sukul, Savita Jagwantie (SJS Solicitors)

SW15

Johal, Narinder Kaur (Russell Cooke LLP)
Lahillonne, Kieron Patrick (Slater Bradley & Co)
Morley, Alison (Capsticks Solicitors LLP)
Reed, Paul Trevor (Russell Cooke LLP)
Solomon, Lewis Maurice (Hotelplan Ltd)

SW16

Lindsay, Donovan Joseph (Anthony Gold Solicitors)

SW17

Acharya, Dina (AP Law)
Killeen, Anne Marie (Threshold Housing Advice)
Kistoo-Sancho, Paula Ulita (Ashok Patel & Co)
Weeraratne, Sandhya Deeptika (Roelens Solicitors)

SW18

Dennis, Phillipa Jane (Corsellis)
Wilson, Lisa Michelle (London Borough of Wandsworth)

SW19

Denton, Daniel Simon (Thompsons Solicitors)
Greenham, Diana Frances (Ashworths Solicitors)
Haynes, David George (Daviesmorgante Law Limited)
McDonald, Rachel Katherine (Act International)
McGrady, David Matthew Jude (Gregsons Solicitors)

W1

Ahmed, Shalim (Sterling Estate)
Arneja, Penny Priya (Davenport Lyons)
Atkinson, Peter Robert (Gordon Dadds)
Bortoft, Arron Pierre (Sears Tooth Solicitors)
Bown, Anthony John (Jeffrey Green Russell)
Calvert, Thomas Harry (Fremantle Media)
Chatterley, Kim Steven (Harbottle & Lewis)
Church, Susan Helen (Forsters LLP)
Cox, Alison Claire (Glovers)
Daly, Jessie (Paul L Simon)
Dhaliwal, Sharanjit Kaur (Kingfield)
Dias, Rexford Edwin (Glovers)
Fisher, Jane Marian (Phillip Ross & Co)
Fowler, Daniel (PJ Law)
Gaughan, Flora Ann (Jeffrey Green Russell)
Gilbert, Paul Samuel (Finers Stephens Innocent LLP)
Haggis, Rachel Kathryn (PCB Lawyers LLP)
Hall, Kerrie-Louise (Ketley Miller Joels LLP)
Harfield, Susan (Ove Arup & Partners)
Hensman, Donna Patricia (Jeffrey Green Russell)
Johnson, Vanwyck (Forsters LLP)
Kataria, Kokila Anju (Seddons Solicitors)
Ling, Peter George (Howard Kennedy)
Loobey, Colette (C H Hausmann & Co)
Maginn, Terence William (Lithgow Pepper & Eldridge)
Mathieson, Jamie (Fladgate Fielder)
Mccall, Joyce (Boodle Hatfield)
McCoy, Jacqueline (Berkeley Law Limited)
Morgan, Tracey Elaine (Magrath LLP)
Mott, Lesley Anne (Forsters LLP)
Munroe, Sherrie (Seddons Solictors)
Onisiforou, Joanna (Jeffrey Green Russell)
Owusu, Harriet (Forsters LLP)
Pryke, Gillian Elizabeth (Boodle Hatfield)
Puckering, Deirdre (Phillip Ross & Co)
Russell, Carly Anne (Howard Kennedy)
Scott, Mark Anthony (Finers Stephens Innocent LLP)
Sweeney, Kathleen Ann (Jacobs Allen Hammond Solicitors)
Tolliday, Gregg Richard (Lee & Thompson)
Walsh, Martin Gerald (Victor Lissack Roscoe & Coleman)
Wood, Jonathan Alan (Wallace & Partners)

W2

Comiskey, Carmel Ann (Visa Europe)
Pomeroy, Valerie Ann (AK20 Nobel UK Ltd)

W3

Tingling, Emma Clare (Ledgisters Solicitors)

W4

Lines, Deniece Elizabeth (Bruce Weir Webber & Co)

W5

Bram, Julie (London Borough of Ealing)
Catt, Hannah Victoria (Winckworth Sherwood LLP)
Charalambous, Harris Kyriacou (Prince Evans Solicitors)
Creffield, Donna Mary (London Borough of Ealing)
Hart, Guy Richard (London Borough of Ealing)
Richardson, Michael Anthony (London Borough of Ealing)
Underwood, Dawn Elizabeth (Prince Evans Solicitors)
Wheeler, Denis Eric (London Borough of Ealing)

W6

Bradley, Margaret Maria (Hubbard Pegman & Whitney LLP)
Cairns, Melanie (The Walt Disney Co Ltd)
Cunningham, John Michael (Hubbard Pegman & Whitney LLP)
Nelson, Lenora (London Borough of Hammersmith & Fulham)
Ricketts, Myrna Elaine (FMW Law Ltd)
Trotman, Winston Fitzpatrick (London Borough of Hammersmith & Fulham)

W8
Bell, David Patrick (Royal Borough of Kensington & Chelsea)
Brockhurst Leacock, Julia Marjorie (Dorothy A Hurrell)
Chan, Judy Suk-Mui (Royal Borough of Kensington & Chelsea)
Thacker, Janet Stephanie (Alan Edwards & Co)

W9
Khan, Alia (Knights Solicitors LLP)

W12
Georgestone, Okang Frances (Davis Thomas Solicitors)
Newman, Clive Anthony (London Borough of Hammersmith & Fulham)

W13
Sidhu, Ranjit Kaur (EDC Lord & Co)

W14
Getley, Scott Paul (Universal Music)
Lambert, Rachel Elizabeth (Stringfellow & Co)

WC1
Bailie, Mandy (Nabarro LLP)
Barber, Christopher Charles (Gregory Rowcliffe & Milners)
Barnett, Marina Teresa (Memery Crystal)
Blake, Esther Vinnetta (Russell Jones & Walker)
Bowes-Smith, Oliver William (Greenwoods Solicitors)
Bowyer, Ian Richard (Gregory Rowcliffe & Milners)
Burn, Wendy Louise (Collyer Bristow LLP)
Callaghan, Sarah Elizabeth (Mishcon De Reya)
Collyer, Mark Henry (Competition Appeal Tribunal)
Cooper, Carly Louise (General Chiropractic Council)
Dhillon, Sarup (Tucker Turner Kingsley Wood & Co)
Ellison, Daniel Benjamin (Mishcon De Reya)
Foster, David Reginald (Hyde Mahon Bridges)
Francis, Glenis Olga (Wedlake Bell LLP)
Gilligan, David William (Russell Jones & Walker)
Girard, Lynne Mary (Sharpe Pritchard)
Gorman, Michael Francis (Collyer Bristow LLP)
Greenaway, Sandra (Chartered Institute of Arbitrators)
Hamer, Suzanne Caroline (Teacher Stern Selby)
Hayton, Martin Leonard (Burton Woods)
Houghton, Barry Frank (Collyer Bristow LLP)
Kelly, Frances Kay (Cumberland Ellis LLP)
Loram, Melanie Kim (Lawson Cruttenden & Co)
Malcolm, Leisha (Metropolitan Police)
Merritt, Francis Peter (Collyer Bristow LLP)
Miller, Christine Margaret (Moon Beever)
Milwood-Henry, Angela Marie (NHS Litigation Authority)
Mouricette, Elizabeth (London Borough of Camden)
North, Ruth Margaret (Mishcon De Reya)
Philpott, Elizabeth Sarah (Gregory Rowcliffe & Milners)
Pratt, Peter James (Collyer Bristow LLP)
Preston, Pauline Anne (Warren Murton)
Richmond, Amanda (Greenwoods Solicitors)
Seery, Frances Margaret Maria (Bazley White & Co)
Sharples, Peter Clive Dougal (Gregory Rowcliffe & Milners)
Smith, Graham Albert (Pattison And Brewer)
Stephenson, Kenneth Maurice (Tucker Turner Kingsley Wood)
Thomson, Alexandra Marie (Butcher Burns)
Williams, Anthony John (Lord Chancellors Department)
Yates, Margaret Frances (The Law Society)

WC2
Barry, John Richard (Hunters)
Beazleigh, Gary Scott (Rollingsons Solicitors)
Blanking, Roger Frederick (Maples Teesdale)
Boyce, Cheryl Alverine Pamela (Farrer & Co LLP)
Brades, Keith James (Lawrence Graham LLP)
Brooker, Jane Elizabeth (Foster-Brimm Consulting UK Ltd)
Bruce, Michael Ernest (Payne Hicks Beach)
Calnan, Diane Margaret (Burton Copeland)
Christopher, Lance Russell (Payne Hicks Beach)
Clark, Caroline Christine (BBC Active)
Cook, Stephanie (Official Solicitors Office)
Deritis, Claire Fiona (The Law Society)
Dickens, Anne (William Blakeney)
Duffy, Michael John (Lawrence Graham LLP)
Duxbury, Richard Mark (Fentons Solicitors LLP)
Easton, Michelle Leslie Linda (Hempsons Solicitors)
Graham-Bolt, Audrey Natasha (B K J Lewis)
Greenhalgh, Juliet Louise (Seth Lovis & Co Solicitors)
Heading, Rachel Victoria (Corker Binning Solicitors)
Holloway, Lucy (PricewaterhouseCoopers Legal LLP)
Howe, Carole Ann (Farrer & Co LLP)
Isbister, David William (Belvederes)
Jackson, Daniel Terry (Payne Hicks Beach)
Killeen, Monika (Reynolds Dawson)
Kristensen, Emma Caroline (Rollingsons Solicitors)
Liburd, Sharon Germaine (Association of Teachers & Lecturers)
Lux, Gary Michael (Clintons Solicitors)
Lynch, Michael Roger Thomas (Watmores)
Maddock, John Richard (Hunters)
Mawlabaux, Adrian (Fladgate LLP)
Mehmet, Sermet Ali (Fletcher Day LLP)
Mitchell, Yvonne Ivorene (Farrer & Co LLP)
Morgan, Deborah Jane (KPM Solicitors LLP)
Murray, Natasha Ann (Burton Copeland)
O'Gara, Hugh Anthony (The Law Society)
Palfrey, John Ronald (Memery Crystal)
Ralph, Valerie Susan (The Law Society)
Rose, Karen Elizabeth (Seth Lovis & Co Solicitors)
Rush, Tara (Lawrence Graham LLP)
Shaw, Laurence Joseph (Fentons Solicitors LLP)
Smith, Michelle Clark (Fladgate LLP)
St Paul, Brenda Maria (British American Tobacco PLC)
Stevens, Peter William (Maxwell Batley)
Stock, Jacqueline (Department For Work and Pensions)
Street, Kenneth Geoffrey (Farrer & Co LLP)
Trott, Andrew Paul (Plexus Law)
Turner, Daniel (Watmores)

FELLOWS EMPLOYED IN ENGLAND AND WALES

ABERDARE, Rhondda Cynon Taff
Carr-Ferguson, Sharon Rose (Hughes & Jenkins)
Herbert, Karen (Georgeand D'Ambra Solicitors)

ABERGAVENNY, Monmouthshire
Davies, Louise Claire (Morgans Solicitors)
Edwards, Julie (R George Davies & Co)
Jury, Zoe Amanda (Gabb & Co)
Llewellyn, Rhian Elizabeth (Gabb & Co)
Theaker, Elaine Alison (Advantage Legal)

ABERGELE, Conwy
Jones, Eleri (Howell Jones & Company)
Malam, Alison Patricia (A P Malam)

ABERYSTWYTH, Ceredigion
Clow, Helen Frances (Alun Thomas & John Solicitors)

ABINGDON, Oxfordshire
Bradford, Sharon Rachel (Slade Legal)
Davies, Angela Joycelen (Withy King Solicitors)
Dyer, Sarah Janet (Slade Legal)
Fry, Laura Anne (Marshall & Galpin Solicitors)
Makin, Jennifer Laura (Slade Legal)
Simcock, Claire Louise (Franklins)

ACCRINGTON, Lancashire
Grundy, Trevor (Hyndburn Borough Council)
Meeks, Julie (Acklam Bond Solicitors)
Scully, Deborah Ann (Farleys Solicitors)

ADDLESTONE, Surrey
Murphy, Karen Virginia (Broadway Mallyan Ltd)

ALCESTER, Warwickshire
Fitter, Samantha (Imivision Ltd)

ALDERSHOT, Hampshire
Beauclerk, Christopher (Taylor Street Solicitors)
Bell, Anna Cristina (Pinto Potts)
Berry, Robert Arnold (Bakers Solicitors)
Cross, Hayleigh Laura (Taylor Street Solicitors)
James, Philip John (Pinto Potts)
Pankhurst, Amanda Jayne (Taylor Street Solicitors)
Thacker, Patricia Anne (Tanner & Taylor)
Thorne, Sara Jane (Hill & Company)

ALFRETON, Derbyshire
Fasey, Joanne Mandy (Chapman & Chubb Solicitors)

ALTRINCHAM, Greater Manchester
Akka, Anthony Abraham (The Deli)
Poole, Victoria Jane (Gaskells)
Rose, Hilary (William H Lill & Co)

AMERSHAM, Buckinghamshire
Durkin, Michele Anne (Lennon Solicitors Ltd)
Koo, Helen Christine (Chiltern District Council)

AMESBURY, Wiltshire
Coles, Natalie (Richard Griffiths & Co)

ANDOVER, Hampshire
Barr, Rachel Dawn (Bakers Son & Isherwood LLP)
Bearfoot, Sally Elizabeth (Bonallack & Bishop)
Cumberlin, Linda Jane Angela (Bonallack & Bishop)
Daubney, Alison Jane (Bull & Co Solicitors)
Newton, Karen Jane (Bakers Son & Isherwood LLP)

ARUNDEL, West Sussex
Knott, Caralyn (Green Wright Chalton Annis)

ASCOT, Windsor & Maidenhead
Broomer, Jennifer Catherine (Key Equipment Finance Ltd)
Somerville, James Neil (Ascot Lawyers)

ASHBY DE LA ZOUCH, Leicestershire
Payne, Amanda Elaine (Fishers Solicitors)
Robotham, Andrew Brian (Blakemores Solicitors)
Wilding, Alison Catherine (Fishers Solicitors)

ASHFORD, Kent
Ball, Daniel (Martin Tolhurst Partnership)
Drawbridge, Gordon Edmund (G Drawbridge)
Driscoll, Cheryl (Sharpe & Co)
Ford, Kacy Marie (Hallett & Co)
Foreman, Catherine Patricia (Ashford Borough Council)
Howard, James Alan (Kingsford Flower & Pain)
Laker, Samantha Louise (Sharpe & Co)
Manuel, Clive Robert (Kingsford Flower & Pain)
Prosser, Valerie Joy (Girlings Solicitors)
Smith, Susan Patricia (Ashford Borough Council)

ASHINGTON, Northumberland
Peoples, Nicola (Adams Hetherington)

ASHTON-UNDER-LYNE, Greater Manchester
Campbell, Barbara (Rupert Wood & Son)
Charnock, Neil (Tameside Metropolitan Borough Council)
Davies, Helen Cecilia (New Charter Homes Limited)
Grainger, Raymond (Tameside Metropolitan Borough Council)
Murray, Linda Christine (Tameside Metropolitan Borough Council)
Nolan, Louise Ann (Bromley Solicitors LLP)
O'Shea, Pauline (Tameside Metropolitan Borough Council)
Page, Russell John (Tameside Metropolitan Borough Council)
Pretl, Beverley (Bromley Solicitors LLP)
Tarnowski, Anna Christina (Bromley Solicitors LLP)
Thompson, Victoria Lorraine (Thornley Solicitors)
Whitehead, Stuart Richard (New Charter Homes Limited)
Wilson, Paul Andrew (New Charter Homes Limited)

ATHERSTONE, Warwickshire
Brough, Adrian (North Warwickshire Borough Council)

ATTLEBOROUGH, Norfolk
Brooks, Deborah Jane (Greenland Houchen Pomeroy)
Folwell, Patricia Ann (Moroneys)

AXMINSTER, Devon
Bricknell, Tina (Scott Rowe)

AYLESBURY, Buckinghamshire
Bateman, Joanne (Parrott & Coales)
Beaujeux, Jennifer Elizabeth (Parrott & Coales)
Caprio, Jennifer Louise (Buckinghamshire County Council)
Cauldwell, Patricia Maxine (Buckinghamshire County Council)
Cayless, Joanne Claire (Buckinghamshire County Council)
Dwyer, Jane Rosalind (Parrott & Coales)
Hunt, Jill Penelope (Parrott & Coales)
Juett, Pamela (Buckinghamshire County Council)
King, Eleanor Jane (Parrott & Coales)
Lock, Mary Caroline (Buckinghamshire County Council)
Molyneux, Susan Angela (Buckinghamshire County Council)
Murton, Lesley (Matthew Harman & Partners)
Sykes, Kathryn Sarah (Pickup & Scott Solicitors)
Todd, Kim Susan (Buckinghamshire County Council)

BAKEWELL, Derbyshire
Anderson, Catherine Ann (Franklin & Co)
Clegg, Carol Jane (Goodwin Cockerton & Colhoun)
Gray, Nicola (Franklin & Co)
Judge, Eugene William (Peak District National Park Authority)
Mcclenaghan, Glenn Henry (Cockertons)

BALDOCK, Hertfordshire
Kingham, Kate (Oldhams Solicitors)

BANBURY, Oxfordshire
Barker, Ann Elizabeth (Spratt Endicott)
Bowling, Lisa Jane (Leport & Co)
Bradford, Susan Janet (Bower & Bailey)
Calcott, Sioban (Brethertons LLP)
Gardner, Peter David (Spratt Endicott)
Hawtin, Richard Gary (Cherwell District Council)
Jackson, Samantha Maria (Brethertons LLP)
Plant, Danielle Lesley (Leport & Co)
Ray, Jacqueline Anne (Brethertons LLP)
Upton, Annette Clare (Johnson & Gaunt)
Wyeth, Keith Charles (Aplins)

BANSTEAD, Surrey
Porteous, Suzanne Mary (Quality Solicitors Copley Clark)
West, Karen Pamela (Copley Clark & Bennett)

BARKING, Essex
Bradstreet, Carole Evelyn (Sternberg Reed Solicitors)
Brown, Claire (London Borough of Barking & Dagenham)
Jeffs, Neil Bryan Philip (Sternberg Reed Solicitors)
Mansbridge, Amanda Claire (Sternberg Reed Solicitors)
McGrath, Zoe (Sternberg Reed Solicitors)
O'Mahony, Declan (Corinthian Insurance)
Small, Donna Marcelle (Sternberg Reed Solicitors)

BARMOUTH, Gwynedd
Phipps-Owen, Janice Ann (Breese Gwyndaf Solicitors)

BARNARD CASTLE, Co Durham
Mcgarry, Michael Bernard (McGarry & Co)

BARNET, Hertfordshire
Chapman, Fleur Elizabeth (Black Horse Ltd)
Marsh, Olga (Steven Dean Magac & Co)
Reid, Anne Margaret (Parkes Wilshire Johnson)
Reid, Jacqueline Ometa (HM Corroners Court)
Skitt, Amanda Sarah (Black Horse Ltd)
Smart, Angela Dennise (AMV Law)
Versani, Ashok (Black Horse Ltd)

BARNOLDSWICK, Lancashire
Mcgee, Helen Joan (Cendant VRG)

BARNSLEY, South Yorkshire
Addy, Stephen (Raleys Solicitors)
Baines, Andrew Gordon (Howard & Co)
Brook, Gaynor Louise (Pennine Law)
Brookes, Karen Julie (Atteys Solicitors)
Brown, Matthew James (Raleys Solicitors)
Cooke, Colin Kenneth (Raleys Solicitors)
Glossop, Stephen (Newman & Bond)
Haigh, Joanne (Raleys Solicitors)
Hanby, Julie (Elmhirst & Maxton)
Jennings, Susan Carole (Bury & Walkers LLP)
Lawton, Janet (Peace Revitt Solicitors)
Mackfall, Laura Josephine (Howard & Co)
Mcdonnell, Caroline Louise (Milners Solicitors)
Needham, Joanne (Barnsley Metropolitan Borough Council)
Nicholson, Benjamin Brian (Bury & Walkers LLP)
O'Sullivan, Taryn Louise (Howard & Co)
Painting, Susan Jean (Atteys Solicitors)
Stacey, Beverley (Atteys Solicitors)
Urpeth, Julie Anne (L A Steel Solicitors)
Wake, Amanda Jane (G V Hale & Co)
Woodhouse, John (Raleys Solicitors)

BARNSTAPLE, Devon
Coombes, Sadie Lorraine (Slee Blackwell)
Dorey, Staci Marie (Toller Beattie LLP)
Parr, Rebecca Louise (Samuels Solicitors)
Prosser, Beverley (North Devon District Council)
Randall, Donna Maria (Toller Beattie LLP)
Townsend, Marion Lesley (Slee Blackwell)

BARROW-IN-FURNESS, Cumbria
Greenwood, Stephen Robert (Poole Townsend)
Mellen, June Theresa (Mellen & Company)
Scott, Jacqueline (Denby & Co Solicitors)

BARRY, Vale of Glamorgan
Bridge, Carey Diane (James & Lloyd)
Guttridge, Linda Margaret (Myer Cohen Morgan)
Moyle, John Paul (Colin Jones Solicitor)
Panayiotiou, Joanne (J A Hughes)
Vincent, Susan (Vale of Glamorgan Council)
Woods, Susan Margaret (J A Hughes Solicitors)

BASILDON, Essex
Maryon, James Alexander (Martin Nossel & Co)
Smith, Lyndsey (Basildon District Council)

BASINGSTOKE, Hampshire
Andruszewski, Luke (Shoosmiths)
Bristow, Karen Marie (Shoosmiths)
Brooker, Nicola Jane (Phillips Solicitors)
Bundy, Maria Christine (Basingstoke & Deane Borough Council)
Carver, Joanne Elizabeth (Shoosmiths)
Clarkson, Tamarind Johann (Shoosmiths)
Clifton, Kirsty (Shoosmiths)
Crouch, Nicole Sian (Spencers Lawyers Ltd)
Earle, Nicholas Spencer (Henleys)
Emery, Lisa (Shoosmiths)
Glover, Amanda Frances (Shoosmiths)
Hayward, Elizabeth Ann (Shoosmiths)
Howell, Caroline (Coomber Rich Solicitors)
Johnson, Elizabeth (Motorola Ltd)
Kuhanen, Sarah Louise (Lamb Brooks)
Leach, Clare (Phillips Solicitors)
Levy, Jennifer Marie (Basingstoke & Deane Borough Council)
Mansbridge, Joanna Louise (Basingstoke & Deane Borough Council)
Milton, Katherine Ann (Shoosmiths)
Moore, Stephanie Dawn (Shoosmiths)
Morrison, Carol Anne (Lamb Brooks)
Pendry-Clark, Janine Marie (Phillips Solicitors)
Pilbeam, Emma Marie (Willis Chandler)
Poynter, Sarah Anne (Shoosmiths)
Proctor, Amanda Jane (Shoosmiths)
Richards, Emma Louise (Lamb Brooks)
Richards, Simon (Shoosmiths)
Rowland, Samantha Lillian (Shoosmiths)
Selby-Short, Nicola (Amery Parkes & Co)
Smith, Elena Maria (Shoosmiths)

BATH, Bath & North East Somerset
Austin, Carol Ann (Withy King Solicitors)
Back, Marion Patricia (Thring Townsend Lee & Pembertons)
Bentley, Karen Jane (Bishop Longbotham & Bagnall)
Clements, Caroline (Complete)
Cooke, Laura Jayne (Stone King LLP)
Crawshaw, Emma Jayne (Mowbray & Woodward)
Eldridge, Kathryn Jane (Bath & North East Somerset Council)
Elias, Simon Mark (Bath & North East Somerset Council)
Gilbert, Honor Patricia (Thring Townsend Lee & Pembertons)
Goodridge, Sarah Louise (Withy King Solicitors)
Haines, Susan Anne (FDC Law Solicitors)
Hall, Helen Elizabeth (Whithy King Solicitors)
Hill, David Patrick (Mogers Solicitors LLP)
Hosier, Polly (Kings Court Trust Corporation)
Jones, Caroline Mary Margaret (Withy King Solicitors)
Meadows, Helen Sandra (Ministry of Defence)
Murray, Julie Anne (Stone King LLP)
Nunn, Heather Elizabeth (Ministry of Defence)
Pearce, Rachel Louisa (Mowbray Woodwards)
Pitman, Elaine Linda (FDC Law Solicitors)
Powell, Emma Jane (Bath & North East Somerset Council)
Robbins, Wendy (Bath & North East Somerset Council)
Robinson, Rebecca (Thatcher & Hallam)
Sage, Mark Philip (Mogers Solicitors LLP)
Spicer, Carol (Leech & Co Solicitors)
Staniforth, Helen Elizabeth (De Ops South-Lms3B)
Thomas, Susan Anne (Withy King Solicitors)
Veale, Hayley (Thatcher & Hallam)
Wardle, Kathrine (Ministry of Defence)
Weeks, Clive Philip (Withy King Solicitors)
Winkler, Geraldine Nicola (Stone King LLP)
Wyatt, Alison (Wessex Water Plc)

BATLEY, West Yorkshire
Betts, Joanne Claire (Brearleys)
Bird, Emily Jayne (Brearleys)

BATTLE, East Sussex
Greenwell, Gillian Patricia (Herringtons)

BEBINGTON, Merseyside
Elias, Susan Carol (Hillyer Mckeown Solicitors)

BECCLES, Suffolk
Bagshaw, Joanne Louise (Norton Peskett Solicitors)
Muskett, Brenda (Mears Hobbs & Durrant)
Smith, Gilliane Mary (Chamberlins Solicitors)
Wardle, Andrew Charles (Norton Peskett Solicitors)

BECKENHAM, Kent
Castell, Ross (Jbs Solicitors)
Gasson, Claire Louise (JBS Solicitors)
Lee, Julie (Pritchard Joyce & Hinds)
Turkel, Jacqueline Anne (Pritchard Joyce & Hinds)

BEDALE, North Yorkshire
Johnson, Alison Mary (Eccles Heddon & Co)

BEDFORD, Bedfordshire
Betts, Tracey Jayne (Bedfordshire County Council)
Bishop, Deborah Ann (Davidson-Smith & Co Solicitors)
Brown, Janet (Sharman Law LLP)
Burn, Kelly Anne (Park Woodfine Heald Mellows LLP)
Cartledge, Debra Lyn (Woodfines LLP)
Exton, Leslie (Sharman Law LLP)
Furr, Hannah Louise (Woodfines LLP)
Guest, Paula Jane (First Defence)
Gurney, Barbara Mary (Bedfordshire Magistrates Court Committee)
Johashen, Emma Louise (First Defence)
Milne, Lesley Anne (Park Woodfine Heald Mellows LLP)
Mirza, Shanaz B (Bedford Borough Council)
Noble, Yvonne Denise (Harvey Ingram Borneos)
Poole, Nichola Jane (Park Woodfine Heald Mellows LLP)
Redford, Malcolm Dyson (Woodfines LLP)
Ribbans, Janet Winifred (Palmers Solicitors)
Rigby, Heather (Bedford Borough Council)
Sanders, Nicola Dawn (Park Woodfine Heald Mellows LLP)
Swannell, Lisa Jayne (Bedfordshire County Council)
Walker, David John (Woodfines LLP)
Warren, Lynn (Lawtons Ltd)
Wetherilt, Bryan Ronald (Park Woodfine Heald Mellows LLP)

BEESTON, Nottinghamshire
Roberts, Sarah Louise (Maclaren Warner)
Warren, Jane Louise (German & Soar)

BELPER, Derbyshire
Smith, Rosemary Alison (Briggs Sayer & Co)

BENFLEET, Essex
Lord, Roderick James (Nairnsey Fisher & Lewis)

BERKHAMSTED, Hertfordshire
Cooper, Meg Ruby (Sumner & Tabor)
Dolling, Debra Ann (Graham Spittle)
Tinworth, Wendy Mary (Harrowell & Atkins)

BERWICK-ON-TWEED, Northumberland
Mcgurk, Linda Greig (Sanderson Mccreath & Edney)

BEVERLEY, East Riding of Yorkshire
Brown, Thelma Susan (East Yorkshire Magistates' Courts)
Goodison, Michael (East Riding of Yorkshire Council)
Leaning, Cheryl (Quality Solicitors Lockings)
Mansell, Robert James (East Riding of Yorkshire Council)
Milner, Teresa Ellen (East Riding of Yorkshire Council)
Parker, Stephen Thomas (East Riding of Yorkshire Council)
Williams, David James (East Riding of Yorkshire Council)
Winter, Andrew John (East Riding of Yorkshire Council)

BEXHILL-ON-SEA, East Sussex
Cahill, Arthur Manouk (Lyons Davidson Solicitors)
Duke, Gaynor Denise (Lyons Davidson Solicitors)
Eaton, Andrew (Rother District Council)
Langridge, Wendy May (Gaby Hardwicke)
McCarthy, Vanessa Jean (Gaby Hardwicke)
Saunders, Sylvia Marguerite (Gaby Hardwicke)
Still, Wendy Hilary (Fynmores)

BEXLEY, Kent
Inman, Julie Rae (Graham Dawson & Co)
Prowse, Helen (Prowse Probate & Trustee Services Limited)
Wells, Margot Anne (Graham Dawson & Co)

BEXLEYHEATH, Kent
Bouchard, Lesley Ann (Howarth Scott)
Coxall, Matthew Neil (Thos Boyd Whyte)
Harris, Emma (T G Baynes Solicitors)
Hodges, Hazel Linda (The Woolwich)
Kennett, Michael John (Bexley Borough Council)
Lane, Shaun Robert (Bexley Borough Council)
North, Martin Leonard (Aletta Shaw Solicitors)
Sparrow, Laura Alexandra (T G Baynes Solicitors)
Stewart, Leon Gary (Thomas Boyd White)

BICESTER, Oxfordshire
Friend, Christina Jayne (Bowerman & Partners)
Griffiths, Peppy Joyce Sheelagh (Neasham Lloyd Partnership)

BIDEFORD, Devon
Balman, Sharon Magaret (Peter Peter & Wright)
Bennett, Jayne Mary (Peter Peter & Wright)
Edwards, Priscilla Perry (Peter Peter & Wright)
Horrell, Lucinda Rose (Seldons Solicitors)
Lawrence, Stuart John (Slee Blackwell)
Manser, Judith (Slee Blackwell)
Mitchell, Geoffrey Ian (Seldons Solicitors)
Nicholls, Richard James (Seldons Solicitors)
Russell, Sarah Frances (Seldons Solicitors)

BIGGLESWADE, Bedfordshire
Mccutcheon, Teresa Clare (Motley & Hope)

BILLERICAY, Essex
Cook, Natalie Dawn (Jervis Jerman)
Lohan, Bronda (E Edwards Son & Noice)
Packman, Anastasia (Michael Cullen & Partners)

BILLINGHAM, Stockton-on-Tees
Graham, Christopher (Huntsman Tioxide)

BINGLEY, West Yorkshire
Goodall, Andrew Charles (Bradford & Bingley PLC)
Thompson, Mark David (Bradford & Bingley PLC)
Turner, Kathleen Ann (Kathleen A Turner)

BIRKENHEAD, Merseyside
Bennett, Shirley-Ann (Fanshaw Porter & Hazlehurst)
Coggins, Philip Charles (Carpenters Solicitors)
Dagnall, Philomena (Lees Solicitors LLP)
Davies, Diane Michelle (Camp Solicitors)
Hallett, Sharron (Carpenters Solicitors)
Harvey, Matthew (Kirwans Solicitors)
Hick, Martin Christopher Sampson (The Specter Partnership)
Jackson, Sharon (Carpenters Solicitors)
Keenan, Marcella (Ballam Delaney Hunt)
Lea, Joanne Mary (Camp Solicitors)
Lunt, Katha Johanna (Roberts Moore Nicholas Jones)
Macintosh-Jones, Lynne (Camp Solicitors)
Mahmood, Julia Rose (Lees Solicitors LLP)
Roberts, Rachel Anne (Statement Services Ltd)
Roberts, Simon Nicholas (Carpenters Solicitors)
Robertson, Elizabeth Sara (Brian Camp & Co)
Shackleton, Alison Jane (Statement Services Ltd)
Skillen-Smith, Jennifer Brigitte (Lees Solicitors LLP)
Smyth, Joanne Elizabeth (Carpenters Solicitors)
Swanson, Lynne Marie (Percy Hughes & Roberts)
Taylor, Kristel (Roberts Moore Nicholas Jones)
Walsh, Gail (Kirwans Solicitors)
Williams, Louise (Carpenters Solicitors)

BIRMINGHAM, West Midlands
Abbasi, Mohammed Naheem (Aman Solicitor Advocates)
Adams, Sarah Elizabeth (Buller Jeffries Solicitors)
Akhtar, Shabir (Kingswood Solicitors)
Arnold, Natalie (Tyndallwoods Solicitors)
Ashcroft, Paul (Beachcroft LLP)
Astbury, Keith Roger (Glaisyers Solicitors)
Azam, Rehana (Beachcroft LLP)
Bains, Rajdeep Kaur (Immigration Law Consultants Ltd)
Baker, Lisa Elizabeth (Wragge & Co LLP)
Ball, Anita Valerie (Shakespeare Putsman LLP)
Ball, Elizabeth Jane (Eyre & Co)
Barnes, Samantha Louise (Blakemores Solicitors)
Barston, Faye Alexandra (Beachcroft LLP)
Bates, Cassandra (Dass Solicitors)
Beet, Daniel John (John Morgan)
Beggan, Nicola Louise (Tyndallwoods Solicitors)
Bevington, Sarah Louise (SMB Wills)
Bhati, Gurvinder (Bollin Legal Associates)
Bird, Graham Phillip (Glaisyers Solicitors)
Birks, Matthew Charles (Jonas Raybloom & Co)
Blyth, Alison (Irwin Mitchell LLP)
Bolton, Kerry Ann (K Knight)
Brain, Adam John (Beachcroft LLP)
Brookes, Philip Timothy James (Cogent Solicitors)
Brooks, Jennifer Eleanor (Irwin Mitchell LLP)
Brown, Michael Raymond (Martineau Johnson)
Brueton, Elizabeth Jane (Wragge & Co LLP)
Bull, Natalie (Wragge & Co LLP)
Burns, Peter John (West Midlands Police Authority)
Burton, Saul (Weightmans LLP)
Butterfield, Claire Elizabeth (Challinors Solicitors)
Caddy, Lindsey (Eversheds LLP)
Callow, Rachel Louise (Bickley Wheatley & Co)
Caluan, Nicola Della (Eversheds LLP)
Candelent, Heather (Evans Derry Binnon)
Carroll, Richard Michael (Three Spires Solicitors)
Carter, Denise Lorraine (Shakespeare Putsman LLP)
Chahal, Rajinder (Shoosmiths)
Chaplin, Paul (Robin Simon LLP)
Chapman, Marina Catherine (Eversheds LLP)
Clark, David (Beachcroft LLP)
Clarke, Soraya Susan Catherine (David Warren Jones)
Collins, Valerie Joy (Eyre & Co)
Comiskey, Clare (Irwin Mitchell LLP)
Cooling, Lucy (Martineau Johnson)
Cooper, Anne Deborah (Mills & Reeve)
Copland, Nigel Gerard (HSBC)
Cordiner-Tomkins, Michelle Frances (England Stickland)
Cornelius, Samantha Jane (Tuckers Solicitors)
Cranshaw, Paul Francis (Severn Trent Water Ltd)
Creedon, Tracey Anne (Eversheds LLP)
Crook, Claire Frances (Shoosmiths)
Dadley, Jessica Ann (Berrymans Lace Mawer)
Darer, Lynda Ann (Purcell & Parker Solicitors)
Day, Peter Stephen (Howell & Co Solicitors)
Deeming, Anne Dorothy (Putsman)
Devgun, Perminder Singh (Amery Parkes Solicitors)
Didehban, Tammy (Wragge & Co LLP)
Doal, Samita (Jonas Raybloom & Co)
Doore, Jayne Kirstie (Shakespeare Putsman LLP)
Drayton, Christopher Michael (Shakespeare Putsman LLP)
Drinkwater, Emma (Brimingham & Solihull Mental Health NHS Foundation Trust)
Dyer, Maria (Lloyds Private Banking Ltd)
Edge, John Andrew (James Pearce & Co)
Edwards, Oaslyn Barbara (James Pearce & Co)
Elmore, Susan Ann (Wragge & Co LLP)
Else, Esther (The Dm Partnership)
Elwell, Kate (Wragge & Co LLP)
Fellows, Andrea Susan (Carvill & Johnson Solicitors LLP)
Fieldhouse, Robert Douglas (Birmingham City Council)
Fisher, David John (Thompsons Solicitors)
Fitzsimon, John Bartholomew (Beachcroft LLP)
Foster, Richard James (Pinsent Masons LLP)
Fox, Nicolas John (HSBC)
Franklin, Rebecca Anne (Irwin Mitchell LLP)
Fulford, Jacqueline Frances (Beachcroft LLP)
Giles, Timothy Mark (Pearson Rowe)
Gill, Nisha (Beachcroft LLP)
Gillespie, Anne (Shakespeare Putsman LLP)
Grace, Joanne Susan (Wragge & Co LLP)
Grego, Deborah (Irwin Mitchell LLP)
Gregory, Clare (Eversheds LLP)
Grice, Gillian Margaret (Roskell Davies & Co)
Griffin, Michael Paul (Irwin Mitchell LLP)
Grosvenor, Louise (Beachcroft LLP)
Guest, Emma Jane (Beachcroft LLP)
Hancox, Lynette (Hadgkiss Hughes & Beale)
Hare, Jaclyn Elizabeth (Wragge & Co LLP)
Harper, Rachel Louise (Kenneth Curtis & Co)
Harrison, Rebecca Ann (Eversheds LLP)
Harvey, Elizabeth (Berrymans Lace Mawer)
Hassell, Kelly Eve (Irwin Mitchell LLP)
Hawthorne, Amanda Marie (Wragge & Co LLP)
Hawthorne, Michelle Tracey (Mills & Reeve)
Hayward-Higham, Jane Margaret (Glaisyers Solicitors)
Head, Barbara Ann (Weightmans LLP)
Henbest, Gemma Louise (Beachcroft LLP)
Hendry, Mark Stephen (Beachcroft LLP)

Higley, Jacqueline Mary (Kennedys)
Hiley, Samantha (Berrymans Lace Mawer)
Hill, Katherine Elizabeth (Lane & Co)
Hill, Lisa Victoria (Wragge & Co LLP)
Hodson, Samantha Jane (Glaisyers Solicitors)
Holland, Amanda Dawn (Divorce & Family Law Practice)
Homer, Wayne Paul (Shakespeare Putsman LLP)
Hopwood, Sarah Louise (Weightmans LLP)
Hughes, Siobhan Marie (HSBC)
Hull, Janice Monica (Tyndallwoods Solicitors)
Hume, Kathryn Helen (Kennedys)
Ibrahim, Samantha (Bollin Legal Associates)
Jagpal, Raman Kumar (DLA Piper UK LLP)
Jeffcott, Amie Louise (Thompsons Solicitors)
Jerome, Anne Elizabeth (Roskell Davies & Co)
Jevons, Emma Louise (Weightmans LLP)
Jevons, Gavin Michael (Blakemores Solicitors)
Jones, Catharine Anne (Blakemores Solicitors)
Jones, Katie Elizabeth (Irwin Mitchell LLP)
Joseph, Claire Helen (Beachcroft LLP)
Kaur, Inderjit (Winchesters Solicitors)
Kenny, Peter James (HSBC)
Keogh, Imelda Mary (Beachcroft LLP)
Khan, Aliya (Tyndallwoods Solicitors)
Khatkar, Mandip Singh (Harbans Singh & Co)
King, Elaine Rosemary (Chief Legal Officer)
Kumari, Kulbhoosan (Birmingham City Council)
Lacey, Karen Ann (Townshends LLP)
Land, Susan Martina (Wragge & Co LLP)
Langford, Stuart Alan (Glaisyers Solicitors)
Larkin, Derek William (Mary Monson Solicitors)
Le-Monnier, Adrian Davy (Weightmans LLP)
Liggins, Julie Kristina (Wragge & Co LLP)
Lloyd, Victoria Anne (Eversheds LLP)
Loxton, Alexandra Joy (Anthony Collins Solicitors LLP)
MacRae, Rachel Ann (Eversheds LLP)
Maguire, Laura Anne (Eversheds LLP)
Marytsch, Rebecca Sian (Eversheds LLP)
Mason, Lisa Marie (Wragge & Co LLP)
McGill, Sarah Louise (Beachcroft LLP)
Mchugh, Helen Jane (Mills & Reeve)
McMillan-Ridley, Michelle (John Morgan)
Merchant, Maslen (Hadgkiss Hughes & Beale)
Moorhouse, Rose-Marie (Challinors Solicitors)
Morries, Jennifer Janine (Cobbetts Employee Services)
Munkacsi, Sylvia (Birmingham City Council)
Murtagh, Amanda (Waters & Co Solicitors)
Newbold, Jason (HSBC)
O'Neill, Deborah (Squire Sanders Hammonds)
O'Rourke, Charlotte Emma (HSBC)
Orton, Michelle Lesley (HSBC)
Osman, Kenneth David (James Pearce & Co)
Palmer, Joanne Patricia (Thompsons Solicitors)
Palmer, Rachael Nicola (Blakemores Solicitors)
Palser, Sarah Jane Elizabeth (Irwin Mitchell LLP)
Pape, Robert James (Child Support Solutions)
Peel, Yvonne (Thompsons Solicitors)
Pleece, Claire Hope (Eversheds LLP)
Postings, Nicola Claire (HSBC)
Pratt, Kate Sarah (Irwin Mitchell LLP)
Pumphrey, Benjamin Thomas (Capsticks Solicitors LLP)
Rafique, Naveedah (Wragge & Co LLP)
Randhawa, Ravinder Kaur (Wragge & Co LLP)
Rani, Asha (The Family Firm)
Raybone, Michelle Anne (Weightmans LLP)
Reeves, Kathryn Ann (Shoosmiths)
Reynolds, John (British Telecom PLC)
Richmond, Emma Joy (Beachcroft LLP)
Roache, Lucille Patricia (Beachcroft LLP)
Roberts, Janet Anne (Eversheds LLP)
Rogers, Rebecca Ann Lesley (Cobbetts Employee Services)
Rolls, Catherine Mary (Mian & Co Solicitors)
Ross, Neil Andrew (Glaisyers Solicitors)
Rowe, Richard Paul (Beachcroft LLP)
Rowlands, Penny Elizabeth (Wragge & Co LLP)
Russell, Liam Paul (Eversheds LLP)
Ryan, Mary Geraldine (Eversheds LLP)
Ryder, Anita Rosemary (Bourne Jaffa & Co)
Salt, Tracey (Bourne Jaffa & Co)
Sandel, Tracey Jayne (Centro)
Sanders, Carol Lesley (Shakespeare Putsman LLP)
Santy, Steven Phillip (Sydney Mitchell LLP)
Savage, Victoria Louise (Wragge & Co LLP)
Scotter, Faye (Evans Derry Binnon)
Sedgwick, Louisa Elizabeth (EEF West Midlands)
Shaheen, Refeat (Beachcroft LLP)
Shenton, Sarah Jane (Carvers Solicitors)
Shepherd, Lorraine (Evans Derry Binnon)
Shipstone, Donna Victoria (Anthony Collins Solicitors LLP)
Shriane, Gerardine Julie (Glaisyers Solicitors)
Silvester, Carol Ann (Tyndallwoods Solicitors)
Sinclair, Jennifer Irene (Young & Lee)
Singh, Satnam (HSBC)
Smith, Kieley Louise (Beachcroft LLP)
Smith, Paul Michael (Browne Jacobson LLP)
Southall, Paul Malcolm (Canty & Co Solicitors)
Spicer, Keith Gordon (Thompsons Solicitors)
Standley, Tristan Joseph (Wragge & Co LLP)
Styles, Emma Louise (Wragge & Co LLP)
Styles, Stephen Victor (Buller Jeffries Solicitors)
Sullivan, David Paul (Eversheds LLP)
Sutton, Laurence Anthony (Crown Prosecution Service)
Symes, Sian (Eversheds LLP)
Takhi, Barinder Kaur (Beachcroft LLP)
Taylor, Christine (Eversheds LLP)
Thorpe, Valerie Anne (The Firm)
Tougher, Donna Lisa (The Wilkes Partnership)
Uppal, Dhanbir (Sydney Mitchell LLP)
Vale, Michael Stephen (Else Solicitors LLP)
Walker, Zoe (HBJ Gateley Wareing LLP)
Warrington, Pauline June (Michael Green & Co)
Waters, Suzanne Claire (Birmingham City Council)
Welch, Gemma Louise (Wragge & Co LLP)
Wharton, Naomi (HSBC)
Wilkins, Lesley-Ann (Eversheds LLP)
Williams, Claire (Wragge & Co LLP)
Williams, David Joseph (Gordon Jones & Co)
Wilson, Lorna Drummond (Eversheds LLP)
Wilson, Susan Ann (Wragge & Co LLP)
Wright, Joanne Patricia (Buller Jeffries Solicitors)
Wright, Patricia Yvonne (Wragge & Co LLP)
Young, Caroline Samantha (Blair Allison & Co)

BISHOP AUCKLAND, Co Durham
Morland, Elaine (Anthony Walters & Co)
Sayers, Linda Joan (Meikles)

BISHOPS CASTLE, Shropshire
Pugh, Nicola Jane (Snows Solicitors)

BISHOPS CLEEVE, Gloucestershire
Lilley, Carolyn (David Billingham & Partners)

BISHOP'S STORTFORD, Hertfordshire
Connell, David Henry (East Hertfordshire District Council)
Finnegan, Dee Anne (Pellys LLP)
Kain, Michael Bernard (Kainknight Ltd)
Mills, Faith Jacqueline (Nockolds Solicitors LLP)
Pleasance, Terence William (Stanley Tee & Co)
Rogers, Joanne Claire (Nockolds Solicitors LLP)
Ward, Heather (Breeze & Wyles Solicitors LLP)
Wichett, Karen Ann (Breeze & Wyles Solicitors LLP)

BLACKBURN, Blackburn
Addicott, Raymond Stanley (Twin Valley Homes Ltd)
Atkinson, Lisa Natalie (Forbes Solicitors)
Beal, David (Forbes Solicitors)
Brooks, Helen Ruth (Farleys Solicitors)
Bullock, Carole Anne (Taylors Solicitors)
Devlin, Adelle (Forbes Solicitors)
Dickinson-Jones, Colleen Rose (Roebucks Solicitors)
Downes, Ruth (Farleys Solicitors)
Duckworth, Ellie (Hardman Wood Solicitors)
Ellahi, Mussarat (Blackburn with Darwen Borough Council)
Garner, Emma Louise (Forbes Solicitors)
Higson, Philippa Margaret (Farleys Solicitors)
McIlwaine, Carol Anne (Nigel Holden & Co)
New, Theresa Ann (Blakewater Solicitors)
Reid, Karen Deborah (Haworth & Nuttall)
Smith, Diane Elizabeth (Watson Ramsbottom Partnership)
Williams, Sara (Watson Ramsbottom Partnership)

BLACKPOOL, Blackpool
Ashcroft, Ann (Wylie Kay)
Banks, Elaine (Blackhurst Budd LLP)
Bennett, Lynda (Blackpool Borough Council)
Cocker, Nicola Clare (Berrys Solicitors)
Cowburn, Deborah Anne (Blackpool Borough Council)
Coyle, John Anthony (Leslie Harris Priestley & Fisher)
Dewhurst, Nicola (Barker Booth & Eastwood)
Donoghue, Susan Ann (Napthens LLP)
Flynn, Joanne Sally (Cooper Nimmo)
Gill, Lorraine Susan (Roland Robinsons & Fentons)
Howard, Mary Sian (Atkinson Cave & Stuart)
Hunter, Sara Judith (Blackpool Borough Council)
Jenkins, Nicola (Wylie Kay)
Johnson, David (Taylor Poole)
Laffin, Carol Pamela (Snipelaw)
Leonard, Suzanne (John Budd & Co)
Moore, Marie Louise (Blackpool & the Fylde College)
Mugford, Suzanne Jane (Cobains Solicitors)
Reid, Fiona (Ascroft Whiteside)
Sawkill, Amy (Easthams)
Smith, Pamela Grace (Crown Prosecution Service)
Stollard, Leslie Philip (Cobains Solicitors)
Whitehouse, Elaine Frances (Inghams)

BLACKWOOD, Caerphilly
Bray, Sandra Irene (Trevor Griffiths & Co)
James, Linda Anne (Granville-West Solicitors)

BLAENAU FFESTINIOG, Gwynedd
Pearce, Susan (Alwena Jones & Jones)

BLANDFORD FORUM, Dorset
Clarke, Fiona (Blanchards Bailey LLP)
Guppy, Jessica (Blanchards Bailey LLP)
Herbert, Michael John (Blanchards Bailey LLP)
Pattle, Samantha Marie (Blanchards Bailey LLP)
Wareham, Trudy (Grenville J Walker)

BLYTH, Northumberland
Earl, Dennis (Blyth Valley Borough Council)

BODMIN, Cornwall
Bridges, Sarah Elizabeth Jane (C & I Chisholm)
O'Callaghan, Teresa Jane (C Nicholls)
Ovey, Gary (Sproull Solicitors LLP)
Rowan, Julie Dawn (Sproull Solicitors LLP)
Whitehead, Pippa Michelle (C & I Chisholm)

BOGNOR REGIS, West Sussex
Aldred, Sandra (Wannop Fox Staffurth & Bray)
Bartlett, Amanda (Wannop Fox Staffurth & Bray)
Bodington, Claire Elizabeth (Wannop Fox Staffurth & Bray)
Churcher, Julie Maria (Citizens Advice Bureau)
Hall, David (David Hall)
Hodges, Tracy Ann (Rita Sen Solicitors)
Holden, Susan (George Ide LLP)
Lowe, David Michael (Wannop Fox Staffurth & Bray)
Medlock, Denise Anne (Wannop Fox Staffurth & Bray)
Yates, Kristina Joanne (Nigel Seed Solicitor)

BOLTON, Greater Manchester
Bennett, Janet Anne (Bolton Metropolitan Borough Council)
Berry, Karen Louise (Keoghs Solicitors LLP)
Butler, Sarah Elizabeth (Keoghs Solicitors LLP)
Chisnall, Alan Denis (Keoghs Solicitors LLP)
Cooney, Lisa Jane (MRH Solicitors Ltd)
Cordock, Emma Louise (Adam F Greenhalgh & Co)
Dale, Anthony (Keoghs Solicitors LLP)
Dalecki, Diane Marie (Keoghs Solicitors LLP)
Eckersley, Peter James (Serious Law)
Fletcher, Carl David (Adam F Greenhalgh & Co)
Fray, Rodney Duncan (Allansons Solicitors)
Geary, Aidan Richard (Keoghs Solicitors LLP)
Halai, Anitaben Premji (Asons Solicitors)
Harrison, Katherine Esther (Keoghs Solicitors LLP)
Haslam, Tracy Marie (Adam F Greenhalgh & Co)
Hayes, Carol (Fieldings Porter Solicitors)
Hazeldine, Janice (Stephensons Solicitors LLP)
Heywood, Shirley (Keoghs Solicitors LLP)
Johnston, Karen (Royal College of Nursing)
Latham, Tracy (Keoghs Solicitors LLP)
Martin, Julian Robert (Keoghs Solicitors LLP)
Mcgovern, Helen Jayne (Keoghs Solicitors LLP)
Melody, Caroline (Keoghs Solicitors LLP)
Mitchell, Angela Diane (Bolton Metropolitan Borough Council)
Morris, Caroline (Serious Law)
Morris, Robert Graham (Keoghs Solicitors LLP)
Newton, Andrea Louise (Keoghs Solicitors LLP)
Nield, Marie (Russell & Russell)
Painter, Kimberley Anne (Bolton Metropolitan Borough Council)
Perks, Andrew James (Fieldings Porter Solicitors)
Phillips, Stephanie (Waring & Co Solicitors)
Potter, Alvin Philip (Hills Solicitors)
Ruck, Matthew John (Keoghs Solicitors LLP)
Sanderson, Kay (Keoghs Solicitors LLP)
Sayers, Sarah Elizabeth (Kippax Beaumont Lewis)
Scholar, Andrew Clive (Keoghs Solicitors LLP)
Spillane, Maeve Ceclia (Keoghs Solicitors LLP)
Syddall, Jonathan (Serious Law)
Webster, Philippa Jane (Keoghs Solicitors LLP)
Weir, Christopher John (Waring & Co Solicitors)
Whitaker, Billie-Jean (Keoghs Solicitors LLP)
Witherington, Abbie Louise (Keoghs Solicitors LLP)
Woolham, Catherine Jayne (Keoghs Solicitors LLP)
Woolley, Eric John (Keoghs Solicitors LLP)

BOOTLE, Merseyside
Astles, Neil George (Sefton Metropolitan Borough Council)
Beatty, Jane (Sefton Metropolitan Borough Council)
Friday, Gary (Citizens Advice Bureau)
Loughlin, Andrew David (Sefton Metropolitan Borough Council)
Reynolds, Tracy Joanne (James Murray Solicitors)
Staunton, Clare Marion (One Vision Housing)

BOREHAMWOOD, Hertfordshire
Bellotte, Vicki Lyn (Freedman Sharman & Co)
Blank, Jane (Hertsmere Borough Council)
Clark, Linda Helen (Hertsmere Borough Council)
Doherty, Verne Adele (B K Ellis & Co)

BOSTON, Lincolnshire
Berry, Linda Ruth (Morley Brown & Co)
Butler, Christine Bernadette (Chattertons Solicitors)
Dawson, Andrew (Chattertons Solicitors)
French, Karen (Richard Tinn Solicitor)
Gaches, Pamela Ann (Ringrose Law Solicitors)
Jordan, Tracey Ann Denise (Jebb & Tunnard)
Robinson, Stephen Neal (Ringrose Law Solicitors)
Simpson, Steven (Chattertons Solicitors)
Sparkes, Tina Louise (Bambridges Solicitors)
Webb, Robert Andrew (Chattertons Solicitors)
Wilson, Carol June (Chattertons Solicitors)
Woods, Luisa Kate (Ringrose Law Solicitors)

BOURNE, Lincolnshire
Grundy, Alison Ruth (Suremove)
Ramm, Kate Vanessa (Suremove)

BOURNE END, Buckinghamshire
De Franco, Gianfranco (Brittons)
Krykant, Teresa Rachel (Browns Solicitors)
Smith, Laura (Browns Solicitors)

BOURNEMOUTH, Bournemouth
Albritton, Anne Margaret (Coles Miller Solicitors LLP)
Andrews, Susan Karen (Ellis Jones)
Beck, Lucy Claire (Avis & Cutmore)
Bostock, Sandra Marion (Ellis Jones)
Campbell, Fiona Mary (Bournemouth & Poole College)
Clarke, Joanne Elizabeth (Lester Aldridge LLP)
Coleman, Julie Elizabeth (Lester Aldridge LLP)
Crewe, Nicholas Cary (E W Marshall Harvey & Dalton)
Cross, Keith Leslie (Preston & Redman)
Day, Michelle Louise (Lester Aldridge LLP)
Dellar, Amy (Humphries Kirk)
Derwish, Sarah Lynne (Laceys)
Dolbear, Anthony John (Horsey Lightly Fynn)
Doulton, Myra Susan (Aldridge & Brownlee)
Dytham, Lisa (Crown Prosecution Service)
Elford, Victoria Anne (Harold G Walker & Company)
France, Sharon Janet (Aldridge & Brownlee)
Fulmer, Zara Jade Susan (Borough of Bournemouth)
Grainger, Victoria Mary (Lester Aldridge LLP)
Gregory, Roger Jeremy (Dibbens)
Hickman, Susan Margaret (Rawlins Davy)
Holden, Leigh (David Hurley Associates)
Jones, Christine Patricia (Coles Miller Solicitors LLP)
Jones, Susan Mary (Humphries Kirk)
Lawrence, Graham Douglas (Preston & Redman)
Lloyd, Alison Jane (Coles Miller Solicitors LLP)
Lorrimer, Iain James (Solomons)
Martin, Anne (Aldridge & Brownlee)
Mcnamara, Johanne (Bournemouth Borough Council)
Mitcham, Lynn Patricia (Ellis Jones)
Morris, Robbi-Louise (Gales)

15

Pearce, Deborah Ann (Laceys)
Pitt, Karen Lyn (Aldridge & Brownlee)
Reeves, Jacqueline Ann (Lester Aldridge LLP)
Regler, Sarah (Aldridge & Brownlee)
Sargent, David Charles (Nationwide Building Society)
Smith, Jacqueline Ann (Aldridge & Brownlee)
Thomas, Jane Victoria (Lester Aldridge LLP)
Tucker, Lynette Anne (Ellis Jones)
Wells, Marion Joan (Horsey Lightly Fynn)
Wilkins, Sarah Louise (Horsey Lightly Fynn)
Willmott, Rebecca Louise (Matthew & Matthew)
Youings, Rebecca Claire (Grenville J Walker)

BRACKNELL, Bracknell Forest

Adamczyk, Malgorzata (Panasonic UK Limited)
Atkin, Dean (GMAC-RFC Ltd)
Holcombe, Andrew Christopher (Ascot Lawyers)
Kite, Deborah (Kite Griffin)
Robinault, Jacqueline Shirley (Kite Griffin)
Smith, Louise Anne (Brooker Alexander Speed)
Thompson, Natalie (Ascot Lawyers)
White, Gillian Mary (Wilson & Berry)
Witherington, Lucy Ann (3M United Kingdom)

BRADFORD, West Yorkshire

Allen, Susan Kay (Alastair Bateman& Co)
Austick, Philip (Last Cawthra Feather LLP)
Baker, Justene Marie (Gordons LLP)
Barrott, Carole Elizabeth (Bradford Metropolitan District Council)
Broadley, Pamela (Optima Legal Services Ltd)
Broady, Karen Rosina (Eaton & Co)
Brough, Lisa Anne (Gordons LLP)
Brown, George Roland (Thomas Cook Tour Operations Ltd)
Butt, Shazia (Hammonds Direct)
Butterfield, Janet Anne (Stachiw Bashir Green Solicitors)
Chadwick, Sally (Bradford Metropolitan District Council)
Chapman, Joanne (Optima Legal Services Ltd)
Colleran, Marie (Gordons LLP)
Collins, Amyas Hugh (Yorkshire Building Society)
Coop, Dilys Wendy (Bradford Metropolitan District Council)
Dimmock, Sarah Louise (West Yorkshire Fire Service)
Foulds, Peter Joseph (Provident Financial Management)
Fox, Adam Steven (Drydens Ltd)
Fox, Katherine Louise (Last Cawthra Feather LLP)
Giedrojt, Sharon Jayne (Optima Legal Services Ltd)
Gill, Mark Richard (Yorkshire Building Society)
Hardy, Simon Nicholas (Provident Personnel Credit Limited)
Horne, Laura Dianne (Makin Dixon Solicitors)
Howard, Dawn Sylvia (Yorkshire Building Society)
James, Sara Michelle Woodrow (Gordons LLP)
Jarvis, Davina (Optima Legal Services Ltd)
Kenyon, Jane Elizabeth (Bradford Metropolitan District Council)
MacGregor, Julie (Last Cawthra Feather LLP)
Mann, Lynette Virginia (Optima Legal Services Ltd)
Matheson, Hugh Roy Roger (Incommunities)
Mcgurk, Melanie Jane (Bradford Metropolitan District Council)
McLuckie, Tracy Ann (Legal & Democratic Services Licencing & Local Land Charges)
Middlemass, Stephanie (Williscroft & Co)
Moorhouse, Richard David (Philippa Murray & Co)
Parkinson, Frankie Hannah (Gordons LLP)
Rashid, Sofia (Needhams Solicitors)
Richards, James (Optima Legal Services Ltd)
Rigby, Shirley (Optima Legal Services Ltd)
Sanders, Kay Elizabeth (Bradford Metropolitan District Council)
Schulman, Dennis Ashley (Bradford Metropolitan District Council)
Scott, Philip Sydney (Last Cawthra Feather LLP)
Smith, Kathryn Joyce (Incommunities)
Sparling, Rachel Leanne (Petherbridge Bassra Solcitors)
Stevens, Paul Martin (Thomas Cook Tour Operations Ltd)
Stirling, Deborah (Yorkshire Water Services Ltd)
Tildesley, Sarah Jayne (Optima Legal Services Ltd)
White, Kathryn Ann (Eaton & Co)
Williams, Craig (Runhams LLP)
Williams, Elizabeth Helen (Eaton & Co)

BRADFORD-ON-AVON, Wiltshire

Gudge, Nicholas Leonard (McCloy Legal)

BRAINTREE, Essex

Broad, Maria Louise (Holmes & Hills LLP)
Burder, Sarah Ann (Braintree District Council)
Clark, Terence Desmond (Holmes & Hills LLP)
Hill, David John (Holmes & Hills LLP)
Hitchcock, Adrian Michael (Steed & Steed LLP)
Housden, Sharon Louise (Shergroup Limited)
Hull, Sara (Smith Law Partnership)
Lawson, Sheila Murray (Steed & Steed LLP)
Reid, Emma Claire (Boyd Carter)
Wisbey, Emma Louise (Braintree District Council)
Woolf, Anna Louise (Holmes & Hills LLP)

BRANDON, Suffolk

Robinson, Lisa-Marie (Rudlings & Wakelam)

BRAUNTON, Devon

Andrews, David (Slee Blackwell)
Osment, Beverley Claire (Taylors Solicitors)
Plummer, Catherine Sarah (Taylors Solicitors)
Saunders, Catherine (Taylors Solicitors)

BRECON, Powys

Sims, Louise (Keppe Rofer Solicitors)
Treen, Claire Denise (Shelter Cymru)
Williams, Fiona Jane (Woodland & Co Solicitors)

BRENTWOOD, Essex

Carr, Sandra Bridget (Sanders Witherspoon LLP)
Johnston, Janette (Landons)
Lowe, Judith Anne (Countrywide Property Lawyers)
Mcguire, David Andrew (Wortley Byers)
Oddy, Kevin Russell (Sanders Witherspoon LLP)
Plumb, Rosalind Ann (Wortley Byers)
Smith, Simon (Scannells Solicitors)
Tappenden, Anne Frances (Sanders Witherspoon LLP)
Tring, Aileen Thomasina (Sanders Witherspoon LLP)

BRIDGEND, Bridgend

Bayliss, Emma Margaret (David & Snape)
Bebb, Michelle Louise (Runnet & Co)
Lee, Andrea (Bridgend County Borough Council)
Morgan, Claire Joanne (David Prosser & Co)
Roberts, Sally Anne (Rosser Thomas Lewis)
Smith, Alisa Jane (Sian Thomas & Co)
Williams, Hayden (Barry Y Jones & Co)

BRIDGNORTH, Shropshire

Raymont, David Richard (FBC Manby Bowdler Solicitors)

BRIDGWATER, Somerset

Bawdon, Clare (Alletsons)
Bennett, Caroline Jane (Pardoes Solicitors)
Corran, Suzanne Hillary (Sedgemoor District Council)
Keirle, Janet Lorraine (Barrington & Sons)
Mills, Judith Anne (Pardoes Solicitors)
Osborne, Nigel David (Sedgemoor District Council)
Scobie, Cindy Jane (Pardoes Solicitors)
Vucicevic, Goran (Alletsons)
Waddon, Heidi-Marie (Ash Clifford & Co)
Welch, Lesley Winifred (Ash Clifford & Co)

BRIDPORT, Dorset

Blair, Lindsey Anne (Milne & Lyall)
Rendell, Paul Nigel (Kitson & Trotman)

BRIERLEY HILL, West Midlands

Bartlett, Susan Margaret (Stephenson)
Berry, Peter James (Inland Revenue)
Cash, Dawn Ann (Waldrons Solicitors)
Mapp, David Stanley (Chelsfield Ltd)
Nightingale, David John (Higgs & Sons Solicitors)
Oliver-Ward, Justine Lisa (Regulatory LLP)
Rowley, Sharon Julie (Higgs & Sons Solicitors)
Young, Melanie Jayne (Waldrons Solicitors)

BRIGG, North Lincolnshire

Havard, Susan Jane (Mason Baggott & Garton)
Langley, Julie Anne (Mason Baggott & Garton)

BRIGHOUSE, West Yorkshire

Pickard, Nadine (Michael A Taylor Solicitors)

BRIGHTON, Brighton & Hove

Allen, Jill Anne (Diebel & Allen)
Baxter, Paula (DMH Stallard LLP)
Budd, Sharleen (DMH Stallard LLP)
Clark, Gemma Barbara (DMH Stallard LLP)
Cole, Jane (Sussex Law Ltd)
Diplock, Susan (Griffith Smith Farrington Webb Solicitors)
Dodgson, Fiona (ASB Law)
Edwards, Diane Jean (Tennant & Knight Solicitors)
Fuller, Jacqueline (Tennant & Knight Solicitors)
Gowen, Darina Mary (Healys Solicitors)
Helm, Marcella (Spearpoint Franks Solicitors)
Hopley, Clare (Dean Wilson LLP)
Kenneally, Jeanette Mary (Wedd Daniel Solicitors)
Leedham, Felicity Sophia (DMH Stallard LLP)
Mallett, Elaine Wendy (Diebel & Allen)
McGinley, Mirren Ann (DMH Stallard LLP)
Rawson, Mary Eveline (Griffith Smith Farrington Webb Solicitors)
Roper, Terence Michael (DMH Stallard LLP)
Rowe, Carole Margaret (Fitzhugh Gates)
Rowe, Samantha Justine (Harney & Wells)
Sawyer, Kathryn (Healys Solicitors)
Seymour, Anthony Brett (Dakers Seymour & Co)
Shepherd, Victoria (Howlett Clarke Solicitors LLP)
Smith, Catherine Verity Margaret (DMH Stallard LLP)
Warford, Philip Craig (Renaissance Legal)
White, Hilary Claire (Mayo Wynne Baxter LLP)
Whittle, Sara Helen (Griffith Smith Farrington Webb Solicitors)

BRISTOL, Bristol

Adams, Joanne (Lyons Davidson Solicitors)
Addicott, Darren (The Co-Operative Trust Corporation - Legal Services)
Adlem, Christine (Fleet Solicitors LLP)
Allchorne, Peter James (Beachcroft LLP)
Alldis, Coralie-Kate (TLT LLP)
Amos, Tracey Jane (Brain Sinnott & Co)
Attewell-Smith, Judith Catherine (Lyons Davidson Solicitors)
Augustus, Martin John (Scrase Employment Solictors)
Aullybocus, Zahrah (Bevan Brittan LLP)
Baggs, Victoria (Direct Line Insurance)
Banwell, Sasha Denise (Bobbetts Mackan)
Barnett, Marian Josephine (TLT LLP)
Barton, Sarah Elizabeth (Lyons Davidson Solicitors)
Batley, Olivia Wendy (Bristol City Council)
Bennet, Catherine Anne (David Burrows)
Beynon, Cathryn Jane (Bevan Brittan LLP)
Bigwood, Anya Jane (DAS Legal Expenses)
Blunden, Julie Teresa (Bank of Ireland)
Bowling, Angela Louise (Beachcroft LLP)
Bradley, Tracey Anne (Orange PCS Ltd)
Bradshaw, Kirsty (Beachcroft LLP)
Bridges, Jacqueline Marie (Thompson Solicitors)
Brightman, Judith Claire (Lyons Davidson Solicitors)
Britton, Hazel (Clarke Willmott LLP)
Broadway, Kirsty (Pattison & Brewer)
Brookman, Mark Robin (Osborne Clarke)
Brown, Melanie Jane (Clarke Willmott LLP)
Brown, Ruth (DAS Legal Expenses)
Browne, Rebecca Claire (Peter Browne Solicitor)
Bull, Simon William (Bennetts Solicitors)
Bunting, Christine Doris (Quality Solicitors Burroughs Day)
Bushnell, Melanie (CW Law Solicitors)
Cashmore, Kate (The Co-Operative Trust Corporation - Legal Services)
Castiglione, Alexandra Cathryn Louise (Kirby Sheppard)
Cawsey, Sharon (Wards Solicitors)
Chalmers, Eric Christopher (Lyons Davidson Solicitors)
Chapman, Jacqueline Anne (The Co-Operative Trust Corporation - Legal Services)
Charalambou, Charalambous (Quality Solicitors Burroughs Day)
Christie, Kathryn Alison (Osborne Clarke)
Chun, Jacqueline Beverley (Brain Sinnott & Co)
Clatworthy, Natasha Kelly (Lyons Davidson Solicitors)
Coghlan-Forbes, Alexandra Jayne (Computershare Invester Services PLC)
Collins, Jennifer (Kelcey & Hall)
Collins, Sarah Frances (Bristol Law Society)
Comley, Sarah Margaret (Lyons Davidson Solicitors)
Constantinou, Constantinos (Bristol City Council)
Coombs, Neil (DAS Legal Expenses)
Cox, Grace Elizabeth (Davies & Partners)
Cox, Joanna Louise (Davies & Partners)
Croft, Dawn Marie (Cameron Mckenna)
Crosby, Caughlin Caroline (Barcan Woodward)
Cross, Helen Elizabeth (TLT LLP)
Curtis, Jacqueline Claire Louise (Henriques Griffiths & Co)
Cuthbertson, Sophie Amelia (Cartwright Insurance Partners)
Dallen, Helen Elizabeth (Royal Bank of Scotland Insurance)
Dauncey, Jessica (TLT LLP)
Davey, Kathryn Gail (Stafford Eales)
Davies, Susan (Bath & North East Somerset District Council)
Davis, Sarah (Quality Solicitors Burroughs Day)
Denford, Robin Geoffrey (Bristol City Council)
Dennis, Katie Patricia Grace (CIP Solicitors)
Dilleigh, Elizabeth Julia (David Gist Solicitors)
Dowell, Sarah Frances (Thompson Solicitors)
Dowling, Alicia Jane (Clarke Willmott LLP)
Downing, Paula Ruth (Barcan Woodward)
Duggan, Timothy David (Fire Safe Ltd)
Dunlop, Angela Mary (TLT LLP)
Durrant, Holly Charlotte (Burges Salmon LLP)
East, Emma Jane (Thompson Solicitors)
Eley, Agnes Clare (Lyons Davidson Solicitors)
England, June Anne (Bennetts Solicitors)
Evans, Claudia Rose (Lyons Davidson Solicitors)
Evans, Harriet Jane (Beachcroft LLP)
Evans, Laura Ann (Clarke Willmott LLP)
Evens, Katie (Henriques Griffiths & Co)
Eyers, Rachel Christine (Metcalfes Solicitors)
Fear, Linda Anne (M C Hullah & Co)
Francis-Thompson, Natasha (The Co-Operative Trust Corporation - Legal Services)
Fuidge, Paulette Angela (Bank of Ireland)
Gait, Tracey Ann (TLT LLP)
Garside, James Alexander (Veale Wasbrough Vizards)
Gilling, Rosemary Susan (TLT Solicitors)
Gitsom, Kelly Samantha (Foster & Partners)
Gordon-Nichols, Judith Leanne (Beachcroft LLP)
Goulding, Geoffrey Mark (Wards Solicitors)
Graham, Claire (Bush & Bush)
Green, Sarah (Lyons Davidson Solicitors)
Grey, Emily Louise (Beachcroft LLP)
Grove, Alexander James (Direct Line Insurance)
Gurnsey, Caroline (Lyons Davidson Solicitors)
Hackford, Kelly Louise (TLT LLP)
Hanham, Benjamin James (TLT LLP)
Harris, Catherine Louise (Lyons Davidson Solicitors)
Harris, Joanne Louise (TLT LLP)
Harris, Joshua Liam (Beachcroft LLP)
Harrison, Anna-Marie (Quality Solicitors Burroughs Day)
Hartnoll, Janet Mary (Bristol City Council)
Harvey, Thomas (Bank of Ireland)
Head, Lynsey Anne (Lyons Davidson Solicitors)
Head, Michelle Jane (Osborne Clarke)
Hicks, Sally Louise (Allianz Cornhill Legal Protection)
Hiett, Rebecca Ann (Taylor Wimpey UK Ltd)
Hill, Judith Helen (Culpan Williams LLP)
Hill, Nadine Tanya (The Co-Operative Trust Corporation - Legal Services)
Hillman, Paula (Metcalfes Solicitors)
Hingley, Gregory Neil (Osborne Clarke)
Howarth, Adele Alice (TLT LLP)
Howe, Sarah-Jane Emily (Ocean Property Lawyers)
Hoyle, Gemma Louise (The Co-operative Legal Services)
Hudson, Helen Elizabeth (Cartwright Insurance Partners)
Huggett, Matthew John (EEF Western)
Hullah, Jens Thomas (Quality Solicitors Burroughs Day)
Hurley, Kim Louise (Lyons Davidson Solicitors)
Ivaldi, Damian Peter (Lyons Davidson Solicitors)
Ivaldi, Sarah Louise (Lyons Davidson Solicitors)
Jenkins, Teaghan (The Co-Operative Trust Corporation - Legal Services)
Johnson, Jennifer Mary (Kirby Sheppard)
Jones, Barbara Anne (AMD Solicitors)
Jones, Jacqueline Anna (Lyons Davidson Solicitors)
Jones, Karen Vivien (Bevan Ashford Solicitors)
Jones, Kelly Anne (David Gist Solicitors)
Jones, Robert Malcolm (Pinstripe)
Jordon, Heidi Melanie (Burges Salmon LLP)
Joyce, Louise (John A Neil)
Keating, Stacey Ann (Veale Wasbrough Vizards)
Kitching, Jacqueline Louise (Parkhouse & Co)
Korn, Lydia Melanie (Wards Solicitors)
Lambourne, Vanessa Louise (Berrymans Lace Mawer)
Lane, Estelle Lynne (CW Law Solicitors)
Lansdown, Katrina Dawn (Lyons Davidson Solicitors)
Large, Jennifer Anne (Direct Line Insurance)
Lawrence, Angela (Fussell Wright & Co)
Lawrence, Julia Anne (TLT LLP)
Leach, Susan (Palser Crossman)
Leaker, Victoria Anne (Lyons Davidson Solicitors)
Lippiatt, Jessica Emma (Barcan Woodward)
Lopes, Marcia (Lyons Davidson Solicitors)
Lynn, Laura Rebecca (AMD Solicitors)

Lyons, Susan Marion (Osborne Clarke)
Magor, Sarah Louise (Clarke Willmott LLP)
Marsh, Oliver (Lyons Davidson Solicitors)
Maybee, Kelly (NFU Mutual Insurance Society)
Mazelin, Michelle (The Co-Operative Trust Corporation - Legal Services)
Mcanaspie, Helen Leone Mary (Morgan Cole Solicitors)
McDermott, Terry Daniel (TLT LLP)
McDonald, Robert (Wards Solicitors)
Mcnerney, Emma Jane (TLT LLP)
Mills, Natalie Yvette (TLT LLP)
Minnion, Samuel Jason (Russell Jones & Walker)
Mizen, Sarah (Paul Stevens & Co)
Moloney, Aneurin Anthony (Metcalfes Solicitors)
Morcombe, Yvette Michelle (Murray Roach)
Morgan, Louise (TLT LLP)
Morgan, Philippa (Lyons Davidson Solicitors)
Morris, Nadia Terese (Beachcroft LLP)
Morrison, Sonia Yvonne (Quality Solicitors Burroughs Day)
Nairne, Katie (Clarke Willmott LLP)
Neal, Lucy Rebecca (Lyons Davidson Solicitors)
New-Richards, Meryl (Lyons Davidson Solicitors)
North, Asha (Cameron Mckenna)
Ogden, Mark Charles (The Law Shop)
Patterson, Amanda Teresa (Trumps)
Peacock, Michelle Joanne (Clarke Willmott LLP)
Pearn, Justine Alison (Veale Wasbrough Vizards)
Peets, Roger (Lyons Davidson Solicitors)
Perrett, Shona Claire (Direct Line Insurance)
Peters, Debra Jane (Allianz Cornhill Legal Protection)
Phillips, Kara (Quality Solicitors Burroughs Day)
Pickford, Kariann Marie (DAS Legal Expenses)
Piper, Samantha (Meade-King Solicitors)
Pirooz, Hossein (Lyons Davidson Solicitors)
Pople, Elizabeth Margaret (Wards Solicitors)
Powell-Jones, Pauline Angela (Thompson Solicitors)
Pratt, Kim Elizabeth (Kirby Sheppard)
Quemper, Jerome Paul (DAS Legal Expenses)
Raisbeck, Kathryn Dorothy (Direct Line Insurance)
Randall, Rebecca Elaine (Osborne Clarke)
Raymond, Kerry (Davies & Partners)
Rendle, Karen Jane (Lyons Davidson Solicitors)
Rhodes, Ian Jeffrey (Bevan Brittan LLP)
Riches, Lynn (Veale Wasbrough Vizards)
Roe, Jacqueline Ann (Veale Wasbrough Vizards)
Rogers, John Anthony (DAS Legal Expenses)
Rollings, Nathan Lee (Burges Salmon LLP)
Rosewarne, Tracy Louise (Meade-King Solicitors)
Rowe, Diane Jacqueline (Osborne Clarke)
Rowe, Sarah (Clarke Willmott LLP)
Rzeznicki, Susan Heather (Gregg Latchams WRH)
Saunders, Mandy (Lyons Davidson Solicitors)
Savill, Julia Margaret (M C Hullah & Co)
Scammell, Alison Marie (Brain Sinnott & Co)
Seawert, Caron Nicola (Veale Wasbrough Vizards)
Sefton, Janet (Quality Solicitors Burroughs Day)
Shardelow, Beth Marie (Royal Bank of Scotland Insurance)
Shorland, Georgina (Bevan Ashford Solicitors)
Simmons, Carol Margaret (Rodney King & Partners)
Smith, Jane Elizabeth (Devereux & Co)
Snell, Karal Elaine (Lyons Davidson Solicitors)
Sobers, Nigel (DAS Legal Expenses)
Spear, Donna Marie (Sheppards)
Splaine, Julie Carolyn (Barcan Woodward)
Staley, Christine (David Cross & Co)
Stell, Abbigail Jenny Laura (Pattinson & Brewer)
Stevens, Gemma Louise (Legal Services Commission)
Stewart, Michael (Osborne Clarke)
Sunderland, June (Places For People)
Tancell, Andrew George (Veale Wasbrough Vizards)
Tanner, Emily Irene (Beachcroft LLP)
Taylor, Keith Ronald (Burges Salmon LLP)
Taylor, Nikki Amy (CW Law Solicitors)
Terry, Mary (Davis Wood)
Thatcher, Kellie Jeanette (Veale Wasbrough Vizards)
Thomas, Bonnie Elizabeth (Metcalfes Solicitors)
Thompson, Samantha Claire (Allianz Cornhill Legal Protection)
Thompson, Suzanne (TLT LLP)
Tickner, Craig Michael (Aidan Wood & Company)
Tovey, Nicola Claire (George Wimpey Bristol)
Tranfield, Sharon Louise (CIP Solicitors)
Treasure, David Stewart (Beachcroft LLP)
Trevett, Sarah Leigh (Lyons Davidson Solicitors)
Tucker, Claire Eve (Osborne Clarke)
Tuckwell, Christine Sarah (Bevans)
Turner, Sarah (Quality Solicitors Burroughs Day)
Vellender, Jane (Direct Line Insurance)
Wainford, Lisa Marie (Bristol City Council)
Wallace, Suzanne Lindsey (TLT LLP)
Warner, Mary Louise (Davis Wood)
Weeks, Lyndon (Churchill Insurance)
Whitaker, Robert James (TLT LLP)
Wicks, Suzanne Marie (Lyons Davidson Solicitors)
Wilcox, Peter (Bristol City Council)
Wilkinson, Rebecca Lucy (CMS Cameron Mckenna)
Willding, Sarah Louise (Clarke Willmott LLP)
Williams, Helen Christina (TLT LLP)
Williams, Jayne Henrietta (Allianz Cornhill Legal Protection)
Williams, Tanya Louise (DAS Legal Expenses)
Williams, Tristan Lee (Burges Salmon LLP)
Winton, Andrea Helen (Metcalfes Solicitors)
Withers, Barrie John (Whittuck Taylor & Caines)
Worsley, Daniel Martin (Veale Wasbrough Vizards)
Wright, David Anthony (Clarke Willmott LLP)
Wright, Sarah Louise (The Co-Operative Trust Corporation - Legal Services)
Wygladala, Clair Alexandre (David Burrows)

BROADSTONE, Dorset

Allen, Teresa Marie (Bruce Curtis Turner)
Cooke, Gaynor Gillian (Coles Miller Solicitors LLP)
Reeves, Jennifer Louise (Coles Miller Solicitors LLP)

BROADWAY, Worcestershire

Perry, Kate (Antony A Holmes)

BROMLEY, Kent

Barnes, David John (Churchill Insurance)
Benson, Mark Allan John (MTA Solicitors LLP)
Bitz, Emma Caroline (MTA Solicitors LLP)
Cheeseman, June Alison (CSG / Michael Taylor & Associates)
Churchill, Amy Elizabeth (Marsons Solicitors)
Day, Denise Maria (Solex Legal Services)
Edwards, Michelle Gaynor (MTA Solicitors LLP)
Galea, Maria-Pia Lukarda (London Borough of Bromley)
Head, James Sebastian (Thackray Williams)
Hill, Richard (Batchelors)
Johnstone, Karen Elizabeth (Michael Taylor Associates)
Josef, Claire (Thackray Williams)
Lawrence, Katherine (Wellers Solicitors)
Linnell, Stephanie Ann (MTA Solicitors LLP)
Matthews, Lynda (The London Borough of Bromley)
Missing, Helen (Wellers Solicitors)
Morgan, Rebecca Anne (First Title)
Nolan, Terence John (Medway Wholesale Meats)
Oliver, Michael Godfrey (Trans Law)
Paris, Raheli Mkengwa (London Borough of Bromley)
Pitt, Louise (MTA Solicitors LLP)
Proudlove, Christine Ann (First Title)
Roach, Robert Francis (Hillary Stephenson Solicitors)
Rose, Nathalie Anne (Cogent Solicitors)
Saunders, Clair Suzann (MTA Solicitors LLP)
Saunders, Nicola (MTA Solicitors LLP)
Thompson, Karl Ellington (Phoenix Community Housing)
Weir, Graeme John (Thackray Williams)
Williams, Arthur David (Churchill Insurance)
Young, Raymond (MTA Solicitors LLP)

BROMSGROVE, Worcestershire

Felton, Claire Louise (Bromsgrove District Council)
Herbert, Joanne Lesley (Thomas Horton & Sons)
Horan, Yvonne Lesley (Thomas Horton & Sons)
Reeves, Sally (Thomas Horton & Sons)
Shorte, Fiona (S C Gray Solicitors)
Sodhi, Kamaldeep (Bromsgrove District Council)
Sultana, Rasma (Bromsgrove District Council)

BUCKHURST HILL, Essex

O'Shea, Karen Lee (Diamonds)

BUDE, Cornwall

Curnow, Martin John (Paul Finn Solicitors)
Gliddon, Patricia Irene (Peter Peter & Wright)
Piper, Sharon Catherine (Finn And Busby)

BURNHAM-ON-SEA, Somerset

Cromey, Barbara Jill (Holley & Steer)
Phillips, Alison Jean (Henry Nevill & Co)

BURNLEY, Lancashire

Barker, Emma Victoria (Burnley Borough Council)
Berry, Denise Annette (Burnley Borough Council)
Culshaw, Amanda Kathryn (Smith & Smith)
Greenwood, Alison Leigh (Waddington & Co)
Harris, Catherine Jane (Pollard Bower & Co)
Harvey, Shelley Alice (Farnworths Solicitors)
Kendall, Katharine Jean (Donald Race & Newton)
Partington, Kay (Southerns)
Rayward, Tina Louise (Smith Jones)
Ridgway, Jacqueline (Burnley Borough Council)
Sturrock, Donna Marie (Southern Jobling & Ashworth)

BURSLEM, Staffordshire

Mcintyre, Pauline Elaine (Arthur Boulton & Son Solicitors)
Whitmore, Natalie (Arthur Boulton & Son Solicitors)

BURTON-ON-TRENT, Staffordshire

Davis, Russell Michael (Trent & Dove Housing Ltd)
Fellows, John (John Fellows Legal Services)
Footitt, Julie (Talbot & Co)
Ford, Bridget Margaret (Burton Hospital NHS Trust)
Gould, Harold (R W Skinner & Son)
Hayward, Karen Ann (Timms Solicitors)
Jackson, Adrian Timothy (Frank E L Spiers)
Roe, Susan Jayne (The Smith Partnership)
Vorley, Helen (Astle Paterson Ltd)

BURY, Greater Manchester

Ali, Saada Miriam (Bury Metropolitan Borough Council)
Baxendale, Joanne Ruth (Bury Metropolitan Borough Council)
Carse, David Everton (Bury Metropolitan Borough Council)
Cohn, Gillian Kathryn (Bury Metropolitan Borough Council)
Deakin, Ruth (Northgate Arinso Employer Services)
Foulkes, Kathryn Elizabeth (Bury Metropolitan Borough Council)
Press, Dominic Michael (Bury Metropolitan Borough Council)
Simmonds, Laura Katharine (Butcher & Barlow LLP)
Stanton, Angela Louise (Bury Metropolitan Borough Council)
Swinnerton, Christine (Bury Metropolitan Borough Council)
Vinden, Catherine Louise (Bury Metropolitan Borough Council)
Walker, Vivienne Louise (Bury Metropolitan Borough Council)
Wrigley, Paula Ann (GLP Solicitors)

BURY ST EDMUNDS, Suffolk

Blackwell, Tracey Diane (Ashton Graham Solicitors)
Callender, Teresa (Ashton Graham Solicitors)
Lock, Sarah Jane (Ashton Graham Solicitors)
Read, Laura Jade (Ashton Graham Solicitors)
Austin, Christopher William (Greene & Greene)
Benfield, Marie Helen (Hayward Moon)
Callender, Karen Elizabeth Evelyn (Greene & Greene)
Cardy, Julia Dawn (Greene & Greene)
Carnegie, Alasdair Lyon (Partridge & Wilson)
Clark, Nicola Jane (McCarthy & Booty)
Dulieu, Nigel Henry (St Edmundsbury Borough Council)
Ellis, Elizabeth Anne (MPH Solicitors)
Evans, Jacqueline Karen (Suffolk Constabulary)
Halliday, Teresa Ann (St Edmundsbury Borough Council)
Harvey, Juliet Rose (Greene & Greene)
Lee, Rosemary Sarah (Gross & Co)
Marsh, Jean Patricia (St Edmundsbury Borough Council)
Quy, Steven (Gross & Co)
Renshaw-Fox, Timothy (Greene & Greene)
Sanger, Joanne Elizabeth (Cunningham John Solicitors)
Smith, Rebecca Jane (Partridge & Wilson)
Woodhouse, Graham Nicholas (Cunningham John Solicitors)

BUSHEY, Hertfordshire

Madley, Lucy (BSG Solicitors)

BUXTON, Derbyshire

Bassett, Erica Kirsten (Cooper Sons Hartley & Williams)
Milner, Joanne Elizabeth (Derbyshire Constabulary)

CAERNARFON, Gwynedd

Hughes, Elisabeth Eirian (Pritchard Jones Evans Lane)
Thomas, Gwenan (Gwynedd County Council)

CAERPHILLY, Caerphilly

Carey-Evans, Amanda (DAS Legal Expenses)
Davies, Julie (Evans & Greaves Solicitors)
Edwards, Frances (Caswell Jones Partnership)
Morgan, Michelle (Caswell Jones Partnership)
Oakes, Andrew John (DAS Legal Expenses)
Williams, Lesleyann (Michael Leighton Jones)
Williams, Mathew (DAS Legal Expenses)

CALDICOT, Monmouthshire

Bader, Carolyne (Granville-West Solicitors)
Lewis, Amanda Elizabeth (Twomlows Solicitors)

CAMBERLEY, Surrey

Holmes, Annari (Herrington & Carmichael LLP)
Keighley, Ruth Fiona (Herrington & Carmichael LLP)
Whittington, Richard Charles (Herrington & Carmichael LLP)

CAMBORNE, Cornwall

Eathorne, Sara Louise (Cornwall Council)
Lewin, Neil John (Howell Hylton Solicitors)
Masi, Maria-Anne Frances (Walters & Barbary)
Massetti, Christine Violet (Howell Hylton Solicitors)
Perry, Alan Robert (Cornwall Council)
Robinson, Brenda Susan (Nalders Solicitors)

CAMBRIDGE, Cambridgeshire

Carter, Lorna Elizabeth (Hewitson Becke & Shaw)
Clarke, Karen Elizabeth (Miller Sands)
Davies, Jonathan (Taylor Vinters)
East, Camilla Mary (Mills & Reeve)
Franks, Sarah Ann (Mills & Reeve)
Gadney, Elaine (Mills & Reeve)
Gummer, Simon John (Tee Lorimers)
Harvey, Anna Elisabeth (Harvey Camford LLP)
Hunt, Emma Louise (Kester Cunningham John Solicitors)
Jessiman, Jacqueline Ann (Ginn & Co)
Jones, Glyn Thomas (Mills & Reeve)
Lebish, Nicola Elaine (Mills & Reeve)
Mader, Gary Max (Miller & Sands)
Mead, Sharon (Taylor Vinters)
Moore, Janine Elizabeth (Purdys Solicitors)
Murphy, Amanda Elaine (Taylor Vinters)
Murphy, Faye Emma (Miller Sands)
Murphy, Helen Michaela (Barr Ellison)
North, Shelley Rose (Taylor Vinters)
Nunn, Tracey Jayne (Cambridgeshire County Council)
Parmar, Hemlata (Thomson Webb & Corfield)
Rattenbury, Ian John (Eversheds LLP)
Richmond, Virginia Ellen (Webb & Partners)
Ridgeon, Helen Louise (Irena Spence & Co)
Robinson, Daryl Lee (Barr Ellison)
Sculthorpe, Hayley Jane (Arm Ltd)
Sharman, Nathan Lee (Legal Services Commission)
Somerton, Michaela Louise (Matthews Winter & Bullock)
Symes, Pamela Irene (Hewitson Becke & Shaw)
Truin, Emma Jane (Taylor Vinters)
Turner, David Paul (Taylor Vinters)
Walker, Jennifer Elizabeth (Tee Lorimers)
White, Angela Victoria (Eversheds LLP)
Williams, Jason (Cambridgeshire County Council)
Wright, John Francis (Thomson Webb & Corfield)

CANNOCK, Staffordshire

Bamborough, Marilyn Patricia (Dunham Guest & Lyons)
Fairs, Elizabeth (Ansons LLP)
Goucher, John Barry (Gardner Iliff & Dowding)
Holgate, Alexa Lara (Ansons LLP)
Phillips, Helen Margaret (Gardner Iliff & Dowding)
Saha, Emma Louise (Gardner Iliff & Dowding)
Tatton, Dawn Rosemary (Jewels Solicitors)
Tomasik, Julie (Ansons LLP)

CANTERBURY, Kent

Abbott, Michael John (Beadle Pitt & Gottschalk)
Adams, Natasha Anne (Gardner Croft)
Beake, Ann Pauline (Lexica Law)
Cole, Dawn Heather (Robinsons Solicitors)
Duke, Kelly Rebecca (Furley Page Solicitors LLP)
Fearn, Kay (Gardner Croft)
Fowler, Lynda Mary (Robinsons Solicitors)
Gilmour, Ian Alexander (Furley Page Solicitors LLP)
Man, Shoueng (Girlings Solicitors)
Newman, Heather Dawn (Lexica Law)
Radlett, Susan Patricia (Gardner Croft)
Sahathevan, Dawn Emma (Robinsons Solicitors)
Selsby, Sharon Fenella (Gardner Croft)
Smith, Amanda Louise (Furley Page Solicitors LLP)
Stephens, John Charles (Lexica Law)
Trevett, Susan Margaret (Canterbury City Council)
Turner, Una (Fairwather & Co Solicitors)
Webb, Cheryl (Robinsons Solicitors)
Wickenden, Susan Anne (Furley Page Solicitors LLP)

15

CANVEY ISLAND, Essex
Marsh, Roland Jonathan (Hook & Partners)

CARDIFF, Cardiff
Abell, Jean Elizabeth (Morgan Cole Solicitors)
Aldridge, Natasha (O'Brien Lewis & James)
Archer - Williams, Hefin Wynne (Leo Abse & Cohen)
Bagnall, Melanie Jane (New Law Solicitors LLP)
Bennett, Lara Elizabeth (Leo Abse & Cohen)
Blain, Jessie Bethan (Hugh James)
Bowen, Diane (Davies Pritchard & Weatherill)
Bowler, June Alyson (Morgan Cole Solicitors)
Brenchley, Vanessa (Charles Crookes)
Brooks, Glenn Howard (Confreys)
Brooks, Lena Rosamund May (Hugh James)
Brown, Kelly-Marie (Dolmans)
Canham, Cheryl Selina (Cardiff County Council)
Colvin, Jennifer Susan (Hugh James)
Cooke, David Charles (Crown Prosecution Service)
Cosslett, Maria Elizabeth (Loosemores)
Crouch, Gillian Marie (Leo Abse & Cohen)
Davies, Alexandra Louise (Leo Abse & Cohen)
Dyer, Lynwen Margaret (Countrywide Property Lawyers)
Evans, Dianne (Wendy & Hopkins)
Evans, Matthew Stuart (Secure Law)
Evans, Natalie Louise (Kings Legal)
Eyre, Peter (National Assembly for Wales)
Fitzgerald, Stephen James (Geldards LLP)
Fitzherbert, Sally Ruth (Phoenix Legal Services)
Fullard, Karen Dawn (Cardiff County Council)
Galeozzie, Louis Arthur (Eversheds LLP)
Goodridge, Bethan (McTaggart Solicitors)
Gower, Phillip William (Simpson Millar LLP)
Green, Jonathan Paul (Morgan Cole Solicitors)
Griffiths, Janine (Martyn Prowel Solicitors)
Hawkins, Ria Jayne (National Assembly for Wales)
Haynes, Delyth Joy (Leo Abse & Cohen)
Healan, Catherine (M & A Solicitors LLP)
Hevicon, Craig Michael (Berrymans Lace Mawer)
Hounsell, Rebecca May (Rubin Lewis O'Brien)
Howlett, Gareth Victor (Capital Law LLP)
James, Sarah Elizabeth (O'Brien Lewis & James)
James, Sian Marie (National Assembly for Wales)
John, Victoria (Countrywide Property Lawyers)
Jones, Andrew Clark (Shelter Cymru)
Jones, Glenys (Ellisons & Co Solicitors)
Jones, Marlene Shirley (Thompson Solicitors)
Jones, Vicki (Hugh James)
Kinsey, Mandy (Hugh James)
Kitchen, Susan Marie (Hugh James)
Lewis, Anna Breony (New Law Solicitors LLP)
Lewis, Lorna Jane (Cardiff County Council)
Lloyd, Leon Anthony (Hugh James)
Lloyd-Williams, Gillian Anne (Morgans Solicitors & Advocates)
Malpass, Danielle Marie (Hugh James)
Marshall, Elaine Mia (Kings Legal)
Mason, Fay (Countrywide Property Lawyers)
Matthews, Laura Gwendolen (Huttons)
McCarthy, Kevin Michael (Hugh James)
Mcmullen, Philomena Bridie (Countrywide Property Lawyers)
Morgan, Ellen Louise (Crown Prosecution Service)
Morgan, Michelle Ann (Hugh James)
Morgan, Susanna Louise (Hugh James)
Morse, Hiedi Rebecca (Countrywide Property Lawyers)
Mumford, Christopher Paul (Connect Utilities Ltd)
Nash, Clare (Thompsons Solicitors)
Nelms, Aileen Julie (Hugh James)
Newton, Stephanie Jane (Western Power Distribution)
Pain, Kerry Jayne (Cardiff County Council)
Planchant, Andrea Louise (Geldards LLP)
Pritchard, Jenna louise (Cardiff County Council)
Quinn, Tegen (Hugh James)
Rees, Jane (Berry Smith)
Rees-Perrin, Annette Allyson (Morgan Cole Solicitors)
Roberts, Judith Elizabeth (Eversheds LLP)
Shah, Johanna (Cunningham Lindsey)
Shirley, Helen (Martyn Prowel Solicitors)
Simpson, Ann (Dolmans)
Spiteri, Paul Anthony (Hugh James)
Stuckey, Cherry Robyrda (Freed & Co Solicitors)
Thomas, Amy Rebecca (Thompsons Solicitors)
Thomas, Philippa Andrea (Morgans Solicitors & Advocates)
Thomas, Scott Edward (New Law Solicitors LLP)
Thomas, Sharon (Eversheds LLP)
Thompson, Catherine Elizabeth (Morgans Solicitors & Advocates)
Turner, Stephen Richard (New Law Solicitors LLP)
Uwins, Michael George Stephen (Countrywide Property Lawyers)
Voyle, David (Hugh James)
Walters, Vikki (New Law Solicitors LLP)
Watts, Rachel Leanne (Morgan Cole Solicitors)
Wheeler, Natalie (Leo Abse & Cohen)
White, Helen (Environment Agency)
Wright, Natasha Cleony Ann (Thomas Simon Solicitors)

CARLISLE, Cumbria
Ashbridge, Colin (Cumbria County Council)
Baxter, Kim (Cumbria County Council)
Brown, Stephen Richard (Carlisle City Council)
Coady, Rebecca Kerr (Bell Park Kerridge Solicitors)
Dunstan, Sharon (Baines Wilson Solicitors)
Forster, Andrea Jane (Butterworths Solicitors)
Herbert, Gillian Elizabeth (A Neat Law Costing)
Hilton, Martin Richard (Bell Park Kerridge Solicitors)
Hind, Susan Jeannine (Cumbria County Council)
Hutchinson, Lynn Marie (Burnetts Solicitors)
Jennings, Susan Margaret (Jennings Law LLP Solicitors)
Jobling, Anita Lesley (Atkinson Ritson)
Keegan, Gabriel Alex (K J Commons & Co)
Mortimer, Moira Jane (Bendles Solicitors)
Oliver, Jane Elizabeth (Cumbria County Council)
Winder, Robert (Burnetts Solicitors)

CARMARTHEN, Carmathenshire
James, Lydia Ruth (Andrew Markham & Co)

CARNFORTH, Lancashire
Hill, Julie Anne (Ratcliffe & Bibby)
Oldfield, Simon James (Oldfields Solicitors)

CARSHALTON, Surrey
Rogan, Julia Anne (McMillan Williams Solicitors)
Virdee, Lisa Marie (McMillan Williams Solicitors)

CASTLE CARY, Somerset
Hayter, Judy Anne (Dyne Drewett Solicitors)

CASTLEFORD, West Yorkshire
Burton, Andrew Neil (CE Electric UK)
Tomlinson, Darren James (Emsleys Solicitors)

CATERHAM, Surrey
Ball, Karen Jean (Dollman & Pritchard)
Holbrook, Julian Brendon (Dollman & Pritchard)
Woof, Louise Michelle (Dollman & Pritchard)

CATTERICK GARRISON, North Yorkshire
Carter, Richard Leonard (Scotts Wright Solicitors)

CHAPEL-EN-LE-FRITH, Derbyshire
Jackson, Bruce Stuart (High Peak Legal Services)
Miller, Carol Lynn (High Peak Borough Council)
Smith, Julie (High Peak Borough Council)

CHARD, Somerset
Lamb, John Kenneth (Beviss & Beckingsale Solicitors)

CHATHAM, Kent
Eastland, Christopher Derek Charles (Kingsley Smith & Co)
Gregory, Maxine (Furley Page LLP)
Ingram, David (Winch & Winch)
Kingman, Martin Paul (Furley Page LLP)
Murchie, Carol Ann (Dakers Green Brett)
Payne, Elaine Margaret (Winch & Winch)
Robins, Tracey Louise (Furley Page LLP)
Squire, Shirley (Kent Reliance)

CHATTERIS, Cambridgeshire
Wilding, Michael John (Cartwrights)

CHEADLE, Greater Manchester
Bilsborrow, Karen Marie (Simpsons Solicitors)
Lovett, Doreen (Andrew J Taylor)
Massey, Keith Frederick (Simpsons Solicitors)
Mycroft, Robert Albert (Financial and Legal Insurance Company Ltd)
Selbie, Emma Jane (Andrew J Taylor)

CHELMSFORD, Essex
Allen, Ian Jeffrey Bruce (Crown Prosecution Service)
Argent, Teresa Ann (Essex County Council)
Basimi, Deanie Lynda (Essex County Council)
Begum, Rashid (Essex County Council)
Brown, Mira (Essex County Council)
Butterfield, Gemma (Council For Licensed Conveyancers)
Buxton-Smith, Susan Tina (Wortley Redmayne & Kershaw)
Catling, Sheila (Essex County Council)
Chambers, John Philip (Essex County Council)
Cherry, Vivien Jane (Silverbeck Rymer Solicitors)
Connick, Laura Margaret (Leonard Gray LLP)
Davis, Antonia Chantal (Just Law Limited)
Dhanda, Bakhsh (Gepp & Sons)
East, Andrew Leonard (Prettys Solicitors)
Farrant, Gayle Dorinda (Nigel Broadhead Mynard)
Fisher, Louise Emma (Wollastons)
Freeman, Judith Mary (Hill & Abbott Solicitors)
French, Claire Louise (Crown Prosecution Service)
Galloway, Korah (Essex County Council)
Greenwood, Natalie Jane (Thompsons Solicitors)
Hole, Jo-Anne (Chelmsford Borough Council)
Hughes, Angela (Crown Prosecution Service)
Jones, Felicity Gayle (Silverbeck Rymer Solicitors)
Kempster, Caroline Ann (Hill & Abbott Solicitors)
Kresner, Helen Louise (Cofunds Ltd)
Lawrence, Lynette Jane (Birketts LLP)
Mason, Henry Barrie (Gepp & Sons)
McEachern, Victoria Elizabeth (RSA Insurance)
Mcfayden, Kathleen Ann (Hill & Abbott Solicitors)
Moore, John Stanley (Essex County Council)
Moorey, John Robert (Leonard Gray LLP)
Roberts, Julie Holland (Essex County Council)
Sharpe, Julie Karen (Just Law Limited)
Sheppard, Keith Edward Stuart (Thompson Solicitors)
Simpson, Helen (Essex County Council)
Tuck, Patricia Carol (Colemans)
Turner, Lorna Jane (Just Law Limited)
Waters, Deborah Wendy (Essex County Council)
White, Peter Richard (Kennedys)
Yung, Sze-Kwok Stanislaus (Stan Young Legal Translator)

CHELTENHAM, Gloucestershire
Bilton, Julia Louise (Rickerbys Solicitors LLP)
Brindley, Janeen (Rickerbys Solicitors LLP)
Brunsdon, Trula Katy (Willians Services Limited)
Burke, Peter John (Alpha Legal Services)
Collett, Ian Charles (Kendall & Davies)
Cook, Jamie Nicholas (Nick Hutchinson & Co)
Cottell, Emma Jane (BPL Solicitors Ltd)
Curr, James Andrew (Yorkshire Building Society)
Davies, John Simon David Hampton (Davis Gregory Solicitors)
Hanman, Jane (Dowty Group Services Limited)
Harrison, Helen Margaret Rendell (Rickerbys Solicitors LLP)
Hart, Andrew Wallace (Bailey McIlquham)
Hewitt, Neil Fraser (Kendall & Davies)
Hughes, Andrea Joy (Davis Gregory Solicitors)
Knight, Tracey Bettina (Yorkshire Building Society)
Menell, Daniel David (Ross Aldridge LLP)
Morgan, Joanna (Hughes Paddison)
Pascoe, Susan Jessica (Charles Russell Business Services)
Procter, Rosemary Elizabeth (Hunts Solicitors)
Richardson, Nicholas John (Willians Services Limited)
Sears, Kathryn Louise (Town & Country Property Lawyer)
Shipp, Robert (Ross Aldridge LLP)
Summers, Lindsey Jane (BPL Solicitors Ltd)
Talbot, Dean Vincent (Ross Aldridge LLP)
Turvey, Susan Kathryn (Yorkshire Building Society)
Wheeler, Timothy John (Davis Gregory Solicitors)
Williams, Clare Jill (Capita Life and Pensions Services Ltd)
Wingate, Claire Lucy (Shires Law)
Young, Mary (AT @ Law Solicitors)

CHEPSTOW, Monmouthshire
James, Melanie Anne (Francis & Co)
Willis, Nicola Elizabeth (Marie Dark Solicitors)

CHESHAM, Buckinghamshire
Fisher, Helen Joanne (Rachael Matthews Solicitors)
Page, Carole Ann (Blaser Mills)
Phelan, Angela Margaret (Richardson Smith & Co)
Piggott, Jacqueline Ann (Lennon Solicitors Ltd)
Quilter, Karen Ann (Lennon Solicitors Ltd)
Ralph, Roger George (Richardson Smith & Co)

CHESHUNT, Hertfordshire
Cox, John (Broxbourne Borough Council)
Dobbs, Christine Frances (Broxbourne Borough Council)
Henderson, Cathryn Marjorie (Curwens Solicitors)
Sims, Hilary Claire (Gisby Harrison)

CHESTER, Cheshire
Bate, Sian (Cullimore Dutton)
Coslett, Michelle Victoria (Walker Smith Way Ltd)
Edwards, Karen Lorraine (Russell & Russell)
Gregory, Yvonne Jacintha (Cheshire County Council)
Heath, Pamela Jane (Cheshire West & Chester Council)
Homfray-Davies, Edwina (LMS)
Jenkinson, Paula Jayne (Walker Smith Way Ltd)
Jennions, Jane Susan (Cheshire County Council)
Jones, Samantha Jane (Knight McGold Solicitors)
Kenworthy, Hilary (Cheshire County Council)
Keryakoplis, John (Cheshire County Council)
Kingaby, Karen (Cheshire County Council)
Langley-Cole, Tara (Steggles Solicitors)
Llewellyn-Bell, Richard Ewan (Ellis Whittam Ltd)
Moore, Ian (Cheshire West & Chester Council)
Packham, Lynda Samantha (Cheshire County Council)
Phillips, Corinna Clare (Russell & Russell)
Purnell, Joanne Claire (Hillyer Mckeown Solicitors)
Richards, Sally Mair (Walker Smith Way Ltd)
Ryan, Sarah Jane (LMS)
Sutton, Llinos Tegai (Cullimore Dutton)
Taylor, Robert David (Cheshire County Council)
Tollitt, Andrew John (North West Law Services)
Turner, Catherine Mary (Lees Solicitors LLP)
Tyler, Paul (Lees Solicitors LLP)
Walton, Lisa Jayne (Hawker Beechcraft Services Ltd)
Wilkinson, Deborah Anne (Debrorah Wilkinson & Co)
Woods, Christopher (Mercury Legal LLP)

CHESTERFIELD, Derbyshire
Ainsworth, Sally Ann (North East Derbyshire District Council)
Barlow, Rachel Claire (Banner Jones)
Barwick, Ashley Cooper (Anderson Partnership)
Bellamy, Jillian Marie (Capital Insolvency Services Ltd)
Brooks, Steven (Your Lawyers)
Brown, Rachel (CS2 Lawyers Ltd)
Chambers, Louisa (CS2 Lawyers Ltd)
Chapell, Adelle (Chesterfield Borough Council)
Corbridge, Jody Abigail (CS2 Lawyers Ltd)
Croft-Rayner, Craig (CS2 Lawyers Ltd)
Difelice, Vicky Margaret (Chesterfield Borough Council)
Farmer, Geoffrey (Geoff Farmer & Co)
Ferguson, Janet (Banner Jones)
Froggatt, Nicola Joanne (CS2 Lawyers Ltd)
Gittins, Jane (CS2 Lawyers Ltd)
Goodall, Jenny Clare (CS2 Lawyers Ltd)
Harthill, Nicholas (Your Lawyers)
Hayes, Shelagh Mary (Anderson Partnership)
Haythorne, Lisa Margaret (Chesterfield Law Centre)
Hollingworth, Neil (CS2 Lawyers Ltd)
Hopkinson, Rebecca (CS2 Lawyers Ltd)
Hunt, Laura (CS2 Lawyers Ltd)
Jenkins, Clare Louise (CS2 Lawyers Ltd)
Kidd, Caroline Sonia Louise (Banner Jones)
Leggott, Catherine Helen (Just Costs Solicitors)
Lukic, Zoe Ann (CS2 Lawyers Ltd)
Montgomery, Andrew John (Chesterfield Law Centre)
Neal, Jemma Louise (CS2 Lawyers Ltd)
O'Brien, John (Cutts Shiers Solicitors)
O'Connor, Lisa Joanne (Prince Family Law)
Owen, Amanda Danniella (CS2 Lawyers Ltd)
Pearson, Gemma Louise (Cutts Shiers Solicitors)
Pritchard, Lynda Elizabeth (CS2 Lawyers Ltd)
Randall, Susan (CS2 Lawyers Ltd)
Reynolds, Helen Elizabeth (CS2 Lawyers Ltd)
Robinson, Stephanie (CS2 Lawyers Ltd)
Sadler, Sarah Louise (CS2 Lawyers Ltd)
Sargent, Steven Gregory (CS2 Lawyers Ltd)
Seaston, Shelley Marie (CS2 Lawyers Ltd)
Smedley, Julia Lindsey (CS2 Lawyers Ltd)
Smitheringale, Amy Elizabeth (CS2 Lawyers Ltd)
Stevenson, Hannah (CS2 Lawyers Ltd)
Tagg, Roger Carlton (Kelly & Anderson)
Tomlinson, Stuart Michael (The District of Bolsover)
Weeden, Paula Elizabeth Julia (CS2 Lawyers Ltd)
Whittle, Jonathan William (Your Lawyers)
Whyman, Shelley (BRM Solicitors)
Woodhead, David Andrew (Roger Woodhead & Alan Hoole)
Woodward, Sarah Louise (Prince Family Law)

CHESTER-LE-STREET, Co Durham
Crowther, Nicola Louise (Gordon Brown Associates)
Humes, Kenneth (Nigel J Humes & Co)
Laws, Geoffrey (Gordon Brown Associates)
O'Neill, Joanne Marie (Gordon Brown Associates)

CHICHESTER, West Sussex
Allemand, Miranda Jane (Crown Prosecution Service)
Angel, Catherine May (Thomas Eggar LLP)
Ayling, Richard (Wannop Fox Staffurth & Bray)
Ball, Sarah Tracey Anne (Thomas Eggar LLP)
Butler, Margaret Ellen (West Sussex County Council)
Clarke, Alison Jane (SMR Solicitors)
Coates, Emma Margaret (CK Solicitors)
Cole, Anne Tryphena (West Sussex County Council)
Colwell, Louise Emma (Edward Hayes LLP)
Evans, Lucie Ann (West Sussex County Council)
Freeman, Susan Anne (Thomas Eggar LLP)
Green, Katherine Patricia (SMR Solicitors)
Holdsworth, Deborah Elizabeth (Edward Hayes LLP)
James, Stuart Richard (George Ide LLP)
Keeping, Hilary Jane (Thomas Eggar LLP)
Laurence, Carol Anne (The Owen Kenny Partnership)
Oxley, Sandy (Private Client Legal Services)
Powell, Olga (Thomas Eggar LLP)
Ralph, Paul Anthony (Thomas Eggar LLP)
Roberts, Judy Marjorie (Chichester District Council)
Robinson, Nigel James (West Sussex County Council)
Rogers, Sonja (Edward Hayes LLP)
Rowley, Gail Amanda (West Sussex County Council)
Sharpe, Peter Gerald (West Sussex County Council)
Shine, Stephen (George Ide LLP)
Solieri, Paula Michele (Edward Hayes LLP)
Southward, Kerry Louise (West Sussex County Council)
Wallis, Ruth Rebecca (Thomas Eggar LLP)

CHIPPENHAM, Wiltshire
Berry, Peter Simon (Forrester & Forrester)
Henty, Karina Mary (Forrester & Forrester)
Hood, Victoria Louise (Jan Anton Czul Solicitors)
Wheatley, Heather Mary (Jeary & Lewis)
Whelan, Anita Dawn (Forrester & Forrester)
Wootten, Christopher George (North Wiltshire District Coun.)

CHISLEHURST, Kent
Barnes, Deirdre Ann (Thackray Williams)
Carter, Ronald Thomas Eric (Carters Law Services)
Huffey, Trevor Gary (Preston Mellor Harrison)

CHORLEY, Lancashire
Hobday, Margaret Joan (Whitehead & Co Solicitors)
Jackson, Fiona Marie (Kevills Solicitors)
Kelly, Rachel (Forbes Solicitors)
Nicholl, Maureen Elizabeth (Marsden Rawsthorn LLP)

CHRISTCHURCH, Dorset
Atkinson, John Christopher (Billens & Co Solicitors)
Bessant, Susan Vyna (Christchurch Borough Council)
Chisholm, Dawn (Frettens LLP)
Colver, Jane Catherine (Spectrum Housing Group)
Flood, Joanne Lisa (Christchurch Borough Council)
Golds, Susan Lesley (Harman & Co)
Johnson, Mandy Laura (Frettens LLP)
King, Emma Jayne (Harold G Walker & Company)
Lankester, Sheila (Truman Moore)
Varley, Heather Carol (Frettens LLP)
Walton, David (Frettens LLP)

CHURCH STRETTON, Shropshire
Evans, Samantha Helen (PCB Solicitors)

CINDERFORD, Gloucestershire
Pugh, Emma Louise (Gwyn James & Co)

CIRENCESTER, Gloucestershire
Calderhead, Elizabeth Jane (Residential Property Lawyers Ltd)
Holder, Jean Christina (Wilmot & Co Solicitors LLP)
Mackness, Ruth Louise (Sewell Mullings Logie LLP)
Marriott, Anne (Cotswold District Council)
Nairn, Catherine Ruth (Sewell Mullings Logie LLP)
Potter, Amy Helen (Tanners Solicitors LLP)
Wannell, Heather Mary (Alison Fielden & Co Solicitors)

CLACTON-ON-SEA, Essex
Brennan, Mary Ann Teresa (Powis & Co)
Chapman, Kim Joan (Pleass Thomson & Co)

CLECKHEATON, West Yorkshire
Hudson, Linda Mary (Cadmans)
Rudd, Vivienne (Cadmans)

CLEVEDON, North Somerset
Lockett, Lisa Catherine (Medreport Ltd)
Noble, David Jonathan (J R Brown & Co)
Woodward, Sarah Louise (Wards Solicitors)

CLITHEROE, Lancashire
Barrett, Catherine Margaret (Holdsworth Taylor Solicitors)
Cowking, Deborah Grace (Holdsworth Taylor Solicitors)
Wilson, Frederick Thomas (Holdsworth Taylor Solicitors)

COALVILLE, Leicestershire
Barltrop, Gareth Roger (Crane & Walton)
Basra, Mukesh Kumar (Mander Cruickshank LLP)
Channon, Lisa Joanne (Josiah Hincks Solicitor)

COBHAM, Surrey
Bentley, Teresa (Mundays)
Palmer, Lorna Catherine (Mundays)
Smart, Anita Caroline (Mundays)
Spring, Amanda Kelly (Mundays)
Tatlock, Karen Elizabeth (Lowrie & Co)
Townsend, Ursula Helene (Hart Brown & Co)
Wilton, Charlotte Evelyn (Mundays)

COCKERMOUTH, Cumbria
Lancaster, John (Waugh & Musgrave)

COCKFOSTERS, Hertfordshire
Purday, Dorothy Ann (Anthony Samuels & Co)

COLCHESTER, Essex
Auton, Sharon Ann (Thompson Smith & Puxon)
Bear, Alison Jane (Birkett Long LLP)
Birch, Yvonne (Amicus Legal Ltd)
Bland, Paula Maria (Fisher Jones Greenwood LLP)
Byford, Sheena (Ellisons Solicitors)
Conway, Rebecca Ann (Arc Legal Assistance)
Coppock, Anthony William (Thompson Smith & Puxon)
Crosby, Sheila Jane (John Fowlers LLP)
Davey, Margaret (Birkett Long LLP)
Dowding, Caroline Elizabeth Anne (Birkett Long LLP)
Essex, Richard David (Colchester Borough Council)
Foley, Deborah Ann (Fisher Jones Greenwood LLP)
Garthwaite, Stephen Robert (Ellisons Solicitors)
Gray, Caroline (Fisher Jones Greenwood LLP)
Hardy, Lorraine Ann (Birkett Long LLP)
Harper, Emma Kate (Birkett Long LLP)
Hempstead, Rebecca (John Fowlers LLP)
Hosking, Alison Margaret (John Fowlers LLP)
Knocker, Marion Eleanor (Fisher Jones Greenwood LLP)
Lawrence, Stephen David (Ellisons Solicitors)
Longbottom, Zoe Jane (Birkett Long LLP)
Longshaw, Bernadette (GoodyBurrett)
Mcglade, Carol Ann (Hiscox Underwriting Group Services Ltd)
Mullis, Susan Kathleen (GoodyBurrett)
Munro, Lisa Jane (Fisher Jones Greenwood LLP)
Pearce, Lee (Ellisons Solicitors)
Royle, Judith (Legal Assistance Direct)
Samuel, Christopher John (Colchester Borough Council)
Snook, Jane Anne (Fisher Jones Greenwood LLP)
Straughan, Rebekah (Colchester Borough Council)
Twitchett, John Lewin (Legal Assistance Direct)
Wair, Sven Michael (Fisher Jones Greenwood LLP)
Walker, Victoria Margaret Ann (Hiscox Underwriting Group Services Ltd)
Weavers, Andrew Charles (Colchester Borough Council)
Webb, Wendy Rose (John Fowlers LLP)
Wilkins, Julian Paul (Colchester Borough Council)
Wilsher, David John (Ellisons Solicitors)
Wombwell, Kathryn Louise (Fisher Jones Greenwood LLP)

COLNE, Lancashire
Howfield, Amanda Marie (Farnworth Shaw Solicitors)
Oates, Patricia Lynne (Steele & Son)
Sharp, Gillian (Nolan Grice Solicitors)

COLWYN BAY, Conwy
Evans, Christine (Bone & Payne)
Williams, Diane Elizabeth (Bone & Payne)

CONGLETON, Cheshire
Bedford, Gillian (Gladman Developments Ltd)
Gowin, Helen (SAS Daniels LLP)
Jones, Kerry Louise (Daniels)
Mcdonald, Teressa Simone (Wincham Investments Ltd)

CONSETT, Co Durham
Brown, Alan (Swinburne Snowball & Jackson)

CONWY, Conwy
Jones, Lisa Karen (Conwy County Borough Council)
Owen, Thomas Richard (Conwy County Borough Council)

CORBY, Northamptonshire
Bland, Melanie (Tollers LLP)
Chambers, Adrian Paul (Seatons Solicitors)
Cousins, Andrew David (Tollers LLP)
Marlow, Amanda Elizabeth (Tollers LLP)
McKimmie, Gemma Louise (Seatons Solicitors)
Riddle, Michael Charles (Lamb & Holmes)

COVENTRY, West Midlands
Andrews, Sally Anne (Alsters Kelley Solicitors)
Avern, Sarah Louise (Band Hatton & Co)
Avis, Neill Desmond (Rotherham & Co)
Barnett, Julie (Alsters Kelley Solicitors)
Bates, Graham Martin (Coltman Warner Cranston)
Berry, Stephanie (Keoghs Solicitors LLP)
Bhika-Jacobs, Anastasia (Heer Manak Solicitors)
Birta, Linda Ann (Angel & Co)
Browett, Natalie (Coltman Warner Cranston)
Bryden, Maxine (Coventry City Council)
Bull, Peter Michael (Ward & Rider)
Burman, Sarah Joan (Jaguar Cars Ltd)
Butler, Katherine Jayne (Alsters Kelley Solicitors)
Calcott, Julie Ann (Band Hatton & Co)
Davoile, Darren Robert (Coltman Warner Cranston)
Dobson, Maria Jane (Ward & Rider)
Docking, Abigail Victoria (Penmans Solicitors LLP)
Evans, Victoria Jane (Crown Prosecution Service)
Fisher, Julie (Smith & Wells)
Frampton, Jacqueline Anne (Penmans Solicitors LLP)
Gay, Julie Dawn (City Secretary's Department)
Gheent, Parminder (Alsters Kelley Solicitors)
Gladdy, Lisa Jayne (Band Hatton & Co)
Goodridge, Linda Anne (Sarginsons)
Harris, Tracy (Walsgrave Hospital)
Hartigan, Maria Catherine (Meridian Private Client LLP)
Hobson, Daniel Adam (Coventry City Council)
Hudson, Raymond (Ward & Rider)
Jaggard-Inglis, Claudette Michaela (Woolley & Co Solicitors)
Jones, Elgar Haydn (Alsters Kelley Solicitors)
Jones, Susan Mary (Keoghs Solicitors LLP)
Kaur, Baljit Anita (Ward & Rider)
Lord, Wendy (Newsome Vaughan)
Lucking, Anna (Coltman Warner Cranston)
Mulgrew, Angela Mary (Mander Hadley & Co)
Mulryne, Philip James (Ward & Rider)
Palmer, Helen Elizabeth (Ward & Rider)
Parkes, Robert (City Secretary's Department)
Plant, Nicola Jane (Coltman Warner Cranston)
Reynolds, Katrina (Coventry City Council)
Roper, Saira Jade Elizabeth (SRS Investigations Ltd)
Ross, Karen Derecia (Button Legal LLP)
Smith, Diane Mary (Varley Hibbs & Co)
Walker, Faye (Local Government Ombudsman)
Weaver, Gregory Edward (Mander Hadley & Co)
Wood, Emma Louise (Coltman Warner Cranston)

COWBRIDGE, Vale of Glamorgan
Stock, Tina Stephanie (Peter Davies Solicitors)

CRAWLEY, West Sussex
Baily, Linda Ann (Anthony Morris)
Carr, Kevin Peter (Crawley Borough Council)
Drewitt, Ian Richard (Lewis & Dick Solicitors)
Fawcett, Shaun Patrick (Crawley Citizen Advice Bureau)
Haines, Jeanine Louise (Oliver Bebb)
Harrison, Susan Elizabeth (ASB Law)
Lawrence, Lindsey Anne (CGD Veritas Services UK Ltd)
Lee, Heather Nicole (DMH Stallard LLP)
Lee, Paula (DMH Stallard LLP)
Lovatt, John Paul (Stevens Drake)
Peck, Susan Eveline (Thomas Eggar LLP)
Tallamy, Claire Louise (Thomas Eggar LLP)
Tipper, Susan Helen Louise (Stevens Drake)
Trory, Theresa Lynda (DMH Stallard LLP)
Whitney, Claire Louise (DMH Stallard LLP)
Willis, Katie Elizabeth (Russell & Co Solicitors)

CREDITON, Devon
Sharratt, Susan (Charlesworth Nicholls & Co)

CREWE, Cheshire
Collins, Gillian (Poole Alcock LLP)
Everall, Philip (Hall Smith Whittingham)
Hamilton-Fey, Ian Richard (Hibbert Durrad Moxon LLP)
Manning, Jonathan Henry (Hibbert Durrad Moxon LLP)
Millington, Deborah Jane (David Lago & Co)
Mould, Tracey Margaret (Thorneycroft & Co)
Price, Thomas (Hibbert Durrad Moxon LLP)
Pridding, Justine Susan (Bentley Motors Ltd)

CREWKERNE, Somerset
Broughton, Alison Sheila (Poole & Co LLP)
Charter, Claire Alison (The Stokes Partnership)
Mace, Karen Louise (The Stokes Partnership)
Mcintyre, Nicola Ann (The Stokes Partnership)
Morris, Lisa Juliet (Poole & Co LLP)

CRICKHOWELL, Powys
Main, Ruth Elizabeth (Gabb & Co)

CROMER, Norfolk
Bain, Douglas John (North Norfolk District Council)
Howe, Roger Michael (North Norfolk District Council)

CROOK, Co Durham
Parsley, Lori-Beth (Smith Rodham)
Salmon, Susan Margaret (Smith Rodham)

CROSBY, Merseyside
Holloway, Maureen (Morecrofts LLP)
Kerrigan, Claire Louise (Morecrofts LLP)

CROWBOROUGH, East Sussex
Camp, Susan Melanie (Vance Harris LLP)

CROWTHORNE, Bracknell Forest
Chivers, Amanda Jane (Rowberry Morris LLP)

CROYDON, Surrey
Armstrong, Kirsty June (Rymill Solicitors)
Backhouse, William Douglas (Ormerods Solicitors)
Barnett, Joelle Daphne Cecilia (Plexus Law)
Besfor, Kenneth John (Ormerods Solicitors)
Camlett, Paul Simon Martin (Plexus Law)
Colyer, Natalie (Blackfords LLP)
Cooksley, Daniella Dawn (Parabis Ltd)
Deguara, George John (Blackfords LLP)
Dolling, Alistair James (Parabis Ltd)
Edwards, Deborah Elaine (Rymill Solicitors)
Firby, Kenneth Charles (Parabis Ltd)
Floor, Stephanie Jane (Parabis Ltd)
Fraser, Jenny Helena (London Borough of Croydon)
Hallmark, Joanne Elizabeth (Plexus Law)
Hamilton, Kathleen Letitia (Andersons Solicitors)
Harvey, Garry Wayne (Parabis Ltd)
Henry, Marsha Michelle (Ormerods Solicitors)
Houghton, Danny John (Abbey Legal Protection)
Hunter, Michael Francis (Ormerods Solicitors)
James, Roger John (McMillan Williams Solicitors)
Johnston, Nichola Charlotte (Morgan Cole Solicitors)
Lock, Wayne (Gowens LLP)
Loizou, Andrew (Cook & Partners)
Newby, Helen Marion (The Refugee Legal Centre)
Preest, Helen Louise (Plexus Law)
Reynolds, Jean Mary (Consignia)
Service, Amanda Jane (Plexus Law)
Sinclair-Wheeler, Amanda Lesley Louise (Royal & Sun Alliance)
Slinger, Valerie (Grants Solicitors)
Stapleton, Margaret Anne (Blackfords LLP)
Symonds, Heather (Atkins Hope LLP)
Turner, Paul Andrew (Barnes Harrild & Dyer)
Ward, Christine Betty Edith (Gowen & Stevens Solicitors)
Wright, Philip Charles (Cogent Law)

CULLOMPTON, Devon
Davis, Helen Louise (Dunn & Baker)

CWMBRAN, Torfaen
Hancock, Stephen Keith (Gwent Magistrates Court)
Williams, Claire Louise (Monmouthshire County Council)

DAGENHAM, Essex
Wilson-Adams, Angela Rosalind (Metropolitan Police)

DALTON-IN-FURNESS, Cumbria
Mease, Jean (Livingstons Solicitors)
Ritchie, Sharon Andrea (Livingstons Solicitors)

DARLINGTON, Co Durham
Allison, Stephen (Darlington Borough Council)
Childs, Denis Anthony (Close Thornton LLP)
Leach, Peter (Blackett Hart & Pratt LLP)
Martin, Jacqueline (Durham Constabulary)
Noble, Adrian David (Close Thornton LLP)
Parry, Lisa Jayne (Donnelly McArdle Adamson)
Short, Janice Louise (Donnelly McArdle Adamson)
Smith, Sarah Elizabeth (Northgate Vehicle Hire Ltd)
Way, Andrew Peter (Latimer Hinks Solicitors)
Wood, Yvonne (Darlington Borough Council)
Young, Karen Marie (Hodgsons & Mortimer)

DARTFORD, Kent
Hanagan, Christopher John (Cook Taylor & Woodhouse)
Henning, Helen Jane (T G Baynes Solicitors)
Jones, Gloria Anne (Hitchman & Co)
Kelly, Pramabelle Marie (Dartford Borough Council)
Meader, Timothy Alexander (Weightmans LLP)
Patrick, Dennis Stephen (Weightmans LLP)
Trailor, Jill Elizabeth (Baily & Goff)
Webb, Keith Douglas (Dartford Borough Council)
Webb, Thelma Mary (T G Baynes Solicitors)

DAVENTRY, Northamptonshire
Beswick, Rhiannon Kyra (Rollasons Solicitors)
Caddoo, Joanne Helen (Rollasons Solicitors)
Davies, Claire Helen (DHL)
Green, Lynsey Yvonne (Simply Conveyancing)
Lister, Felicity Donna (Rollasons Solicitors)
Perkins, Samantha Jane (Simply Conveyancing)

DAWLISH, Devon
Gould, Susan Jane (Legal & Contract Services Ltd)

DEAL, Kent
Dickinson, Carley Gemma (Sandra C Palmer)

DEESIDE, Flintshire
Clarke, Lesley Katrina (Cyril Jones & Co)
Hodge, Donna Loretta (Lampkin & Co Solicitors)

DENBIGH, Denbighshire
Jenkins, Dawne Louise (Gamlins)

DENHAM, Buckinghamshire
Clarke, Elizabeth Anne (Intercontinental Hotels Group Emea)

DENTON, Greater Manchester
Flynn, Susan Elaine (Sainsburys)

DERBY, Derby
Anderson, Lydia (Geldards LLP)
Athey, Kirsty Dieke (Bakewells Solicitors)
Boultbee, Alison (Timms Solicitors)
Bradley, Michael John (John M Lewis & Co Ltd)
Brammer, Michelle Louise (Eddowes Waldron Solicitors)
Bridges, Joanna Claire (Eddowes Waldron Solicitors)
Butterworth, Sandra Jane (Moody & Woolley)
Chadwick, Amy Louise (Moody & Woolley)
Clayton, Andrea Jane (Flint Bishop)
Davies, Joanne Clare (Eddowes Waldron Solicitors)
Fisher, John Anthony (Edwards Geldard)
Fraser, Donna Julie (Geldards LLP)
Gilbert, Jonathan Charles (Flint Bishop)
Gilbert, Linda (Eddowes Waldron Solicitors)
Goodacre, Maria (Bemrose & Ling)
Griffiths, David John (Flint Bishop)
Griffiths, Helen Claire (Crown Prosecution Service)
Hilliard, Sara Jane Elizabeth (Timms Solicitors)
Holmes, Rachael Margaret (Flint Bishop)
Hopkins, Linda Mary (John M Lewis & Co Ltd)
Howlett, Sandra Diane Ruth (Flint Bishop)
Jacks, Sonya Ursula (Freeth Cartwright LLP)
Jones, Robert Alan (Flint Bishop)
Junor, Linda (Derby City Council)
Kimpton, Yvette (Derby City Council)
Knott, Elizabeth Jane (John M Lewis & Co Ltd)
Leadlay, Victoria (Bemrose & Ling)
Lennox, Trevor Paul (Flint Bishop)
Lowe, Sharon Marie (Edwards Geldard)
Marshall, Marianne (Flint Bishop)
Marshall, Stuart Ian (Flint Bishop)
Meacham, Sarah (Alexander & Co)
Milward-Hyde, Joanne (Flint Bishop)
Pook, Anne (Moody & Woolley)
Rhodes, Janet Ann (Freeth Cartwright LLP)
Riley, Janet Elizabeth (The Smith Partnership)
Ritchie, Claire Kirby (Flint Bishop)
Roe, Susan Julie (Underwood Vinecombe Solicitors)
Ruddock, Teresa Lorraine (Bakewells Solicitors)
Scott, Shelley Anne (Nelsons)
Shipley, Stuart John (Eddowes Waldron Solicitors)
Simpson, Joanne (Pinders)
Spenceley-Stevens, Penelope Ann (Flint Bishop)
Tunstall, Kathryn Louise (Flint Bishop)
Wasteney, Alison Clare (Derby City Council)
West, Lynn Suzanne (Bombardier Transportation (UK) Ltd)
White, Mary (Taylor Simpson & Mosley Solicitors)
Wilmot, Tracey Jane (Powergens PLC Legal)
Woodcock, Justine Louise (Alexander & Co)
Woodward, Rebecca Mary (Robinsons)
Yates, Lavinia Ann (L Yates Locum Sevices)

DEREHAM, Norfolk
Gotterson, Donna Marie (Hood Vores & Allwood)
Molony, Rosemary Joy (W F Smith & Co)

DEVIZES, Wiltshire
Hill, Naomi Ellen (Awdry Bailey & Douglas Solicitors)
Johnson, Edwin Peter (Awdry Bailey & Douglas Solicitors)
Lovesey, Sara Louisa (Awdry Bailey & Douglas Solicitors)
Nash, Frances Helen (Audrey Bailey & Douglas)
Philo, April Estelle Louise (Awdry Bailey & Douglas Solicitors)
Radley, Emma (Wansbroughs Solicitors)
Tambling, Karen Edith (Sarsen Housing Association)
Turley, Ronna Louise (Audrey Bailey & Douglas)

DEWSBURY, West Yorkshire
Badat, Rafik Ahmed (Disken & Co)
Cairns, Mark Patrick (Ashmans Solicitors)
Deans, Raymond John (Ashmans Solicitors)
Lindley, Katherine (Jordans Solicitors)
Pearson, Wendy (Whitfield Hallam Goodall)
Smithhurst, Danielle (Chadwick Lawrence LLP)

DIDCOT, Oxfordshire
Gotch, Penelope Jane (Soha Housing Ltd)
Merritt, Louise Claire (Slade Legal)
Miller, Elizabeth Pauline (Slade Legal)

DISS, Norfolk
Bacon, Karen Elizabeth (Steeles Law LLP)
Spraggons, Lucy Helen (Comer & Crawley)
Wenham, Katherine Ruth (Overburys & Raymond Thompson)

DONCASTER, South Yorkshire
Ahmed, Qaiser Mahmood (Foys Solicitors)
Ajimati, Jocelyn Ann (Doncaster Metropolitan Borough Council)
Alderson, Alison (Doncaster Metropolitan Borough Council)
Boughen, Christine (The Byrne Practice Solicitors)
Bradley, Veranne (Bridge Sanderson Munro)
Brocklesby, Simon Charles (Mason Baggott & Garton)
Butterworth, Shrene Ann (Atherton Godfrey Solicitors)
Connor, Helan Lisa (Atherton Godfrey Solicitors)
Cook, Jodie (Atherton Godfrey Solicitors)
Dawson, Lisa Ruth (Atherton Godfrey Solicitors)
Fowler, Michelle Louise (Atteys Solicitors)
Freeman, Catherine (Atherton Godfrey Solicitors)
Gallagher, Michael Anthony (Beresford & Long)
Goodwin, Denise Ann (Doncaster Metropolitan Borough Council)
Harvey, Philip Roger (Doncaster Metropolitan Borough Council)
Hilt, Susan Karen (Taylor Bracewell)
Hissey, Elaine (Atherton Godfrey Solicitors)
Holden, Stella Andrea (Atteys Solicitors)
Homar, Kellymarie Elsie (Atherton Godfrey Solicitors)
Hoyle, Lynn (Glade Dale Group Ltd)
Hughes, Dawn (Atteys Solicitors)
Hutchinson, Susan Frances (Dawson & Burgess)
Jackson, Jane Ann (Atherton Godfrey Solicitors)
Lambert, Lynn (Bridge Sanderson Munro)
Lee, Janet (Atherton Godfrey Solicitors)
Murray, Julie (Kenyon Son & Craddock)
Paddey, Jane Elizabeth (Doncaster Metropolitan Borough Council)
Platts, Susan Christine (Malcolm C Foy & Co)
Ranns, Paul David (Doncaster Metropolitan Borough Council)
Stones, Mary (Doncaster Metropolitan Borough Council)
Sykes, Mandy (P I Costing)
Taylor, Lisa Louise (Keeble Hawson)
Taylor, Nicola (Taylor Bracewell)
Teare, Richard (Shaw & Co Solicitors)
Toseland, Susan Elizabeth (Dawson & Burgess)
Walton, Mark David (Atteys Solicitors)
Ward, Gillian (Atherton Godfrey Solicitors)
Youngs, Sara Elizabeth (Doncaster Metropolitan Borough Council)

DORCHESTER, Dorset
Dufty, Timothy Richard (BPL Solicitors Ltd)
Fraser, Donna Louise Jean (BPL Solicitors Ltd)
Hooper, Claire Jayne (BPL Solicitors Ltd)
Jenner, Diane (Battens Solicitors)
Jullens, Charles Russell Hogarth (Dorset County Council (Dorset Enterprise System))
Mason, Caroline (West Dorset District Council)
Meggs, Sarah Lorraine (Dorset County Council (Dorset Enterprise System))
Middleton, Jacqueline (BPL Solicitors Ltd)
Mudford, Claire Anna (Humphries Kirk)
Pawsey, Fiona (Humphries Kirk)
Pemberton, Christopher Lee (Porter Dodson Solicitors)
Ricketts, Suzanne Jane (West Dorset District Council)
Way, Amanda Jayne (BPL Solicitors Ltd)
Wilson, Michelle Wendy (Blanchards Bailey LLP)

DORKING, Surrey
Bushell, Amanda Jane (Downs Solicitors LLP)
Callcut, Christina Alison (Hart Scales & Hodges)
Harris, Christopher (Mole Valley District Council)
Stoneman, Petra Jeannette (Mole Valley District Council)
Sumpter, Diane Hainsworth (Downs Solicitors LLP)

DOVER, Kent
Atkins, Michelle Jayne (Dover District Council)
Chivers, Ian Patrick (Castle Law Costing Ltd)
Claringbold, Mervyn Roy (Dover District Council)
Goodwin, Kay (Frederic Hall & Co)
Horton, Robert Andrew Bassett (Singleton Saunders Floord)
Stringer, Claire (Frederic Hall & Co)

DOWNHAM MARKET, Norfolk
Gregory, Sarah Jane (Fraser Dawbarns Solicitors)

DROITWICH, Worcestershire
Edmondson, Ian Michael (Crown Prosecution Service)
Green, Lynn Patricia (Parkinson Wright)
Harding, Laura Jane (MFG Solicitors)
Warren, Suzanne (Parkinson Wright)

DUDLEY, West Midlands
Amos, Keith Colin (Talbots Solicitors LLP)
Bradley, Martin (Silks Solicitors)
Burton, Lisa Diane (Talbots Solicitors LLP)
Dyke, Laura Jayne (Higgs and Sons / Hison Services)
Ghera, Linda Davee (Dudley Metropolitan Borough Council)
Giedrojc, Mark Julian (Dudley Metropolitan Borough Council)
Hill, Stephen Derek (Ward Dewhurst Solicitors)
Palmer, Leigh David (Rentokil Initial PLC)
Sefton, Helen Jane (Dudley Metropolitan Borough Council)
Spicer-Dent, Helen Louise (Dudley Metropolitan Borough Council)
Talbot, Michelle Louise (Dudley Metropolitan Borough Council)
Taylor, Danny (Silks Solicitors)
Timms, Gail (M R Timms & Co)
Wallage, Sandra Mary (Dudley Metropolitan Borough Council)
Whitehouse, Claire Louise (William Wright & Son)
Wilcox, Mandy Jane (Dudley Metropolitan Borough Council)
Woodhouse, Alison (Dudley Metropolitan Borough Council)

DUNSTABLE, Bedfordshire
Gentles, William Anderson (Franklins Solicitors LLP)
Marshall, Sara-Jo (Knowles Benning Solicitors)

DURHAM, Co Durham
Collins, Mark Andrew (Swinburne Maddison)
Doyle, Christopher (Northumbrian Water Limited)
Gowland, Stephen David (ILS Solicitors)
Hill, Kathleen (Swinburne Maddison)
Lee, Terry (Swinburne Maddison)
Norvell, Christine Margaret (Browell Smith & Co Solicitors)
Potts, Janet (Welcome Financial Services Ltd)
Thompson, Allison (Riley Langdon Solicitors Co)
Wilson, Barbara Ann (Blackett Hart & Pratt LLP)

EAST GRINSTEAD, West Sussex
Dorrington, Pamela Ann (Waughs)
Phillips, Melvin Ian (Allen Ticehurst Solicitors)
Purcell, Helen Denise (Rentokil Initial UK Ltd)
Wilmot, Carole Anne (Pearless De Rougemont & Co)

EAST MOLESEY, Surrey
Whittle, Elizabeth Susan (Kenwright Walker Wyllie)

EASTBOURNE, East Sussex
Ashley-Smith, Ian Charles (Heringtons)
Bell, Janet Susan (Gaby Hardwicke)
Comber, Robin Edwin (Lawson Lewis & Company)
Cox, Robert Paul (Stephen Rimmer & Co)
Crumbie, Masayo (Lawson Lewis & Company)
Dalton, Joseph Spencer (Stephen Rimmer & Co)
Day, Tina Ann Maria (Stephen Rimmer & Co)
Haniver, Christine Anne (Cornfield Law LLP)
Macdonald, Emma Claire (Rodney Warren & Company)
Messer, Pat Tracy (East Sussex County Council)
Parrington, Joni Kristina (Lawson Lewis & Company)
Pelling, Pamela Barbara (Gaby Hardwicke)
Priestman, Sarah Louise (Cornfield Law LLP)
Sharpin, Adrian Mark (Hillman Smart & Spicer)
Trott, Michael Charles (Stephen Rimmer & Co)
Wood, Rachel Emma (Hart Reade Solicitors)

EASTLEIGH, Hampshire
Brotherwood, David William John (George Wimpey Southern Ltd)
Butler, Fiona Gordon (Ageas Insurance Limited)
Cottrell, Daniel Mark (Knight & Co)
Foster, Amanda Lorraine (Knight & Co)
Francis, Claire Louise (Blake Lapthorn)
Garrity, Sharon Lesley (Blake Lapthorn)
Hayden, Karen Anne (Blake Lapthorn)
Jordan, Jacqueline Alexandra (Blake Lapthorn)
Joyce, Alison (Gammon Piercy & Gaiger Solicitors)
Metcalfe, Susan (Alliance Legal Costs Ltd)
O'Connell, Elizabeth Jane (First Wessex Housing Group Ltd)
Peters, Mandy (Royal Yachting Association)
Scanlan, Marlene Grace (Clarke Willmott LLP)

EASTWOOD, Nottinghamshire
Brown, Lynne (Maclaren Warner)

EBBW VALE, Blaenau Gwent
James, Rhiannon (Behr & Co)
Wheeler, Michael Christopher (Gartsides)

EDENBRIDGE, Kent
Hylands, Tina Yvonne (Hamways Walker Owens Solicitors)

EDGWARE, Middlesex
Addleman, Carolyn Jane (Stock Fraser Cukier)
Cameron, Dennis Alphonso (Wayne Leighton Berger)

EGHAM, Surrey
Rixon, Pamela Joan (Spectris PLC)

ELLESMERE PORT, Cheshire
Pickett, Sian Patricia (Legal Marketing Services Ltd)

ELY, Cambridgeshire
Battersby, Christine Elizabeth (Hall Ennion & Young)
Camp, Margaret Anne (East Cambridgeshire District Council)
Carpenter, Karen Esme (Archer & Archer)
Compton, Rachel (Archer & Archer)
Hughes, Carolyn Jayne (Archer & Archer)
Long, Adrian John (Archer & Archer)

EMSWORTH, Hampshire
Prew, David Michael (Belcher Frost & Co)

ENFIELD, Middlesex
Addison, Debbie Ann (London Borough of Enfield)
Baffa, Gennaro Giuseppe (Shepherd Harris & Co)
Canfield, Sarah (Shepherd Harris & Co)
Clarke, Michael Donald (Singletons Austin Ryder)
Coleran, Darren (Av Rillo & Co Solicitors)
Cook, Claire Rose (Martin Shepherd & Co)
Creevy, Duncan Frederick (London Borough of Enfield)
Davies, Mark Neil (Shepherd Harris & Co)
Foster, Beryl (Lee Valley Park Information Service)
Gazioglu, Canev (Martin Shepherd & Co)
Gibbs, Deborah Jane (Martin Shepherd & Co)

Lissner, Peter Paul Simon (Curwens Solicitors)
Marti, Nigel Jose (Bernard Pearce & Co)
Weller, Vivienne Elizabeth (London Borough of Enfield)
Wills, Clare Diane (Vanderpump & Sykes)

EPPING, Essex

Oakley, Graeme Alston (Epping Forest District Council)
O'Donnell, Tara (Foskett Marr Gadsby & Head)
Rose, Ruth (Epping Forest District Council)
Searl, Elizabeth Jane (Foskett Marr Gadsby & Head)

EPSOM, Surrey

Browne, Thomas Norman (Bowles & Co)
Dove, Leonie Carole Anne (Gumersalls)
Langrish, Heidi Caroline (Brett Holt Solicitors)
Sims, Victoria Anne (Lewis & Dick Solicitors)

EVESHAM, Worcestershire

Edgecombe, Richard Paul (Plexus Law)
Jacques, David Hugh (Cox & Hodgetts)
Pharo, Daniel Graham (Everatt & Co Solicitors)
Workman, Christopher Nigel (Everatt & Co Solicitors)

EWELL, Surrey

Hurst, Roger Albert James (Lewis & Dick Solicitors)

EXETER, Devon

Abbott, Richard Charles (Pennon Group PLC)
Alexander, Sally Patricia (Foot Anstey Solicitors)
Annal, Anne-Marie (Exeter City Council)
Atkinson, Lynne (Ashfords Solicitors)
Bates, Alan Carey (Veitch Penny)
Beechen, Robert (Devon County Council)
Bennett, Peter John (Gilbert Stephens)
Bloor, Abbigale Louise (Stones Solicitors)
Burgess, Jessica Ann (Gilbert Stephens)
Chetwood, Deborah Jane (Hartnell & Co)
Cobern, David Adrian (Hartnell & Co)
Croome, Tina Louise (Bond Pearce LLP)
Cunningham, Louise Margaret (Foot Anstey Solicitors)
Davey, Caroline Teresa (Devon County Council)
Davies, Mark Granville (Stewart Title Limited)
Davis, Elaine (Crosse & Crosse)
Douglas, Judith Mary Anne (Environment Agency)
Down, Melissa (Dunn & Baker)
Dumbiotis, Andrew (Police Federation)
Dumble, Katherine Elizabeth (Ashfords Solicitors)
Edwards, Susan Margaret (Exeter City Council)
Foulkes, Edward George (Tozers LLP)
Garty, John Leonard (Foot Anstey Solicitors)
Gaywood, Peter James (Crosse & Crosse)
Grantham, Edwin Michael John (Dunn & Baker)
Gratwick, Jill Margaret (Devon & Cornwall Constabulary)
Green, Michelle Ann (Thompsons Solicitors)
Griffiths-Jones, Julie Ann (Michelmores LLP)
Hadley, Janette Linda (Exeter City Council)
Hall, Matthew Charles (Echo South West)
Harris, Caroline Margaret (Tozers LLP)
Hart, Donna (Hartnell & Co)
Hasyn, Michael George (Environment Agency)
Hearn, Emma Victoria (Veitch Penny)
Hedditch, Nichola Jane (Stones Solicitors)
Hogg, Claire Louise (Gilbert Stephens)
Hooper, Chantale Mary Jane (Foot Anstey Solicitors)
Hornby, Rebecca Louise (Lloyds Private Banking Ltd)
Johnson, Elizabeth Jane (Ashfords Solicitors)
Johnson, Michelle (Exeter City Council)
Jones, Jemma Rachel (Ashfords Solicitors)
Kendall, Elizabeth Mary (Veitch Penny)
Kitchen, Nicholas Joseph (Johnson & Johnson)
Laver, Martin James (Tozers LLP)
Laws, Anita Florence (Cartridges)
Matravers, Katy (The Royal College of Nursing)
Matthews, Victoria Elizabeth (Cartridges)
Mccurry, Naomi Ruth (Gilbert Stephens)
McIntyre, Christine Janet (Devon County Council)
Morse, Christopher Neil (Stephens & Scown)
Moxham, Linda Patricia (Foot Anstey Solicitors)
Newis, Shaun Robert (Ford Simey LLP)
Newman, Eugenie Elizabeth (Thompsons Solicitors)
Page, Philip (Michelmores LLP)
Parsons, Helen Mary (The Royal College of Nursing)
Rainford, Amanda Jayne (Stones Solicitors)
Read-Brown, Jillian Dorothy (Hartnell & Co)
Sage, Suzanne Marie (Trinity Advocates)
Smith, Patricia Anne (Ashfords Solicitors)
Sparks, Gemma Mary Louise (Hartnell & Co)
Starkey, Alison (Michelmores LLP)
Stevinson, Amanda (Crosse & Crosse)
Strudwick, Emma Claire (Rundle Walker)
Sussex, Amelia Jane (J & S Pope Solicitors)
Tregale, Sarah Jane (Ford Simey LLP)
Tremlett, Susan Deborah (Devon County Council)
Turner, Susan (Tozers LLP)
Vaughan, Judith Ann (Ashfords Solicitors)
Voysey, Gary Nigel (Kitsons LLP)
Walker, Andrew James (Bond Pearce LLP)
Walker, Cyndy Mary (Cartridges)
Warren, Joseph George (Tozers LLP)
Watts, Pippa (Crosse & Crosse)
Weatherhogg, Timothy Giles (Dunn & Baker)
Westbrook, Paula Jayne (Environment Agency)
Westcott, Elizabeth Anne (Foot Anstey Solicitors)
Willows, Tracy Amanda (Stones Solicitors)
Wood, Claire Ellen (Veitch Penny)

EXMOUTH, Devon

Brice, Trevor Paul (Every & Philips)
Chappell, Roger Christopher (Exmouth Property Rentals)
Jones, Susan Tracey (Every & Philips)
Pring, Gordon William (Vine Orchards)
Strong, Nicholas (Every & Philips)

FAKENHAM, Norfolk

Ewings, David John (Butcher Andrews)
Sheldrake, Nicholas (Hayes & Storr)
Walker, Susan Christine (Hayes & Storr)

FALMOUTH, Cornwall

Binny, Julie Clair (Preston Goldburn)
Bourguignon, Sarah Helen (Hine Downing)
Burley, Sharon Jane (Nalder & Son)
Eslick, Louise Elizabeth (Hine Downing)
Fisher, Joanne (Hine Downing)
Lilley, Julia Anne (Bray & Dilks)
Roberts, Luke Samuel Peter (Hine Downing)
Sidgwick, Peter Benson (Nalder & Son)
Sleeman, Victoria Kate (Hine Downing)
Wheeler, Geoffrey Michael (Vivian Thomas & Jervis)

FAREHAM, Hampshire

Chapman, Louise (Blake Lapthorn)
Costello, Tracey Anne (Victory Legal Costs Solicitors)
Day, Tina (Coffin Mew LLP)
Debenham, Eve-Marie (Blake Lapthorn)
Donovan, Julie Corrinne (Blake Lapthorn)
Jenkins, Ian Robert (Blake Lapthorn)
King, Barry Michael (Glanvilles Solicitors)
Knight, Claire Louise (Warner Goodman LLP)
Lindsey, Simon (Palser Grossman)
Locke, Claire Louise (Brutton & Co)
Miller, Douglas James (Coffin Mew LLP)
Miller, Raymond George (Ray Miller Locum Services)
Patel, Sadhana (Glanvilles Solicitors)
Paxton, Janet Ann (Glanvilles Solicitors)
Pierre-Powell, Sarah (Blake Lapthorn)
Rowlands, Diane Wendy (Now Legal Solicitors)
Taylor, Sabina (Shoosmiths)
Watson, Mark Charles (Glanvilles Solicitors)
Webb, Martin (Brutton & Co)
Yarnold, Karen Evelyn (Coffin Mew LLP)

FARNBOROUGH, Hampshire

Elliott, Joanna Louise (Woodford Stauffer)
Haulkory, Davina (Bakers Solicitors)
Stanton, Carol Judith (Bakers Solicitors)

FARNHAM, Surrey

Baigent, Christine Margaret (Tanner & Taylor)
Butler, Carole Anne (Bells Solicitors)
Duffy, Kevin Gerard (Hadfields)

FELIXSTOWE, Suffolk

Pearson, Sharon Alane (Ashton Graham Solicitors)
Svoboda, Kristie Leigh (Margary & Miller)
Wade, Nadine (Ashton Graham Solicitors)

FERNDOWN, Dorset

Degan, Andrew Colin Christopher (Wetheralls Solicitors)

FERRYHILL, Co Durham

Corrigan, James Russell (Ferryhill Town Council)

FILEY, North Yorkshire

Pynn, Sarah Jane (Thorpe & Co)

FLEET, Hampshire

Willmott, Susan Jane (Neale Turk)

FOLKESTONE, Kent

Burrows, Diana June (The Compensation Clinic)
Cuffe, Rachel Sara Louise (Plexus Law)
Espline, Philip (Saga Group Ltd)
Medler, Graham Brian (Rootes & Alliott)
Richards, Alison Jane (Shepway District Council)

FORMBY, Merseyside

Owen, Alison Dorothy (Birchall Blackburn)

FRIMLEY, Surrey

Hood, June Elizabeth (Brooks & Partners Solicitors)
Sturman, Victoria Rose Lydia (Brooks & Partners Solicitors)
Temple, Ian David (Brooks & Partners Solicitors)

FRINTON-ON-SEA, Essex

Brookes, Shirley Ann (Sparling Benham & Brough)

FRODSHAM, Cheshire

Amos, Ian Yul (Parry & Company)

FROME, Somerset

Turner, Carolyn Heather (FDC Law)

GAINSBOROUGH, Lincolnshire

Barrett, Samantha Jane (Andrew Jay & Co)
Bembridge, Graham Ronald (Andrew Jay & Co)
Bishop, Peter Howard (Burton & Dyson Solicitors)
Dubut, Philip David (Andrew Jay & Co)
Gleadell, Matthew James (Burton & Dyson Solicitors)

GATESHEAD, Tyne & Wear

Bailey, Kate Noemi (Gateshead Metropolitan Borough Council)
Cook, John (Cinnamon Property Lawyers)
Donnelly, Pamela Christine (Gateshead Metropolitan Borough Council)
Lamb, Fiona Elizabeth (Cinnamon Property Lawyers)
Manvell, Louise (Gateshead Metropolitan Borough Council)
Mckinnon, Victoria Louise (Jacksons Solicitors)
Parlett, Karyn Lesley (The Borough Council Of Gateshead)
Pearson, Kimberley Dawn (Thomas Magnay & Co)
Ramsay, Judith Elaine (Gateshead Metropolitan Borough Council)
Russell, Joanne (Halliday Reeves)
Willis, Lynn (The Borough Council of Gateshead)

GATWICK, West Sussex

Brown, Sarah Louise (Initial Aviation Security)
Christmas, Anna Marie (Rentokil Initial PLC)

GILLINGHAM, Kent

Bird, Michelle Diane (Bassets)
Hassell, Sarah Catherine (Hawkridge & Co)
Kennett, Christopher Edward (Hawkridge & Co)
Langley, Carolyne June (V E White & Co)
Mencattelli, Mark John (Bassets)
Petts, Keith Eric (Bassets)
Swann, Rachel Christina (Davis Simmonds & Donaghey Solicitors)

GLASTONBURY, Somerset

Talbot, Elizabeth Amy (Gould & Swayne Solicitors)

GLOSSOP, Derbyshire

Bunting, Paul Michael (Aspinall Wright & Co)
Hanson, Samantha (Bakers Solicitors)
Leech, Michelle Ann (Aspinall Wright & Co)

GLOUCESTER, Gloucestershire

Bawden, Carolyn Jane (Gloucestershire County Council)
Bonser, Clare Marie (Gloucestershire County Council)
Boucher, Bridgette Lynette (Gloucestershire County Council)
Butler, Annabel (Gloucestershire County Council)
Clair, Alison Jane (Cheltenham & Gloucester PLC)
Ellerington, Janet Susan (Gloucestershire County Council)
Emsley, Katie Elizabeth (Langley Wellington Solicitors)
Gilbert, Viva Grace (Gloucester City Council)
Goode, Adam (Ageas)
Gunn, Lesley Anne (Dee & Griffin)
Hartwell, Lian (Allen Hoole Solicitors)
Hitchings, Claire Fiona (Gloucester City Council)
Hunt, Joanne (Gloucestershire Royal NHS Trust)
James, Susan Elizabeth (Langley Wellington Solicitors)
Jenkins, Julian Huw (Dee & Griffin)
Joyner, Carole Joan (Gloucestershire County Council)
Lines, Geoffrey Dennis (Cheltenham & Gloucester PLC)
Long, Julie (Rowbis)
Lycett, Winifred Joy (Iacopi Palmer Solicitors)
Moores, June Patricia (Gloucestershire County Council)
Moseley, Iona (Gloucester City Council)
Nooney, Melanie Jayne (Message Labs Ltd)
Ody, Georgina Ann (Gloucestershire Royal NHS Trust)
Pennington, Lesley Theresa (Equilaw)
Roberts, Martin John (Tayntons (LS) Ltd)
Robinson, Sara Jayne (Treasures)
Rule, Steven James (Tayntons (LS) Ltd)
Sofoluwe, Oluseyi (Gloucestershire County Council)
Thomas, Dawn Elizabeth (A & J Professional Services)
Tribe, Kathryn Anne (Thomas Legal Group)
Tye, Jane Louise (Gloucester City Council)
Waller, Sandra (Langley Wellington Solicitors)
Whiting, Simon (Madge Lloyd & Gibson Solicitors)

GODALMING, Surrey

Austen, Claire Louise (Penningtons Solicitors LLP)
Beswick, Deborah Ann (Hart Brown)
Greenfield, Sarah Jane (Barlow Robbins LLP)
Kemp, Gemma (Hart Brown)
Mccann, Laura Jane (Penningtons Solicitors LLP)
Neill, Anne Eveline (Downs Solicitors LLP)
Nuckowski, Josephine Charlotte (Barlow Robbins LLP)
Taylor, Kay Elizabeth (Penningtons Solicitors LLP)
Thomas, Anne Marie (Hart Brown)

GOOLE, East Riding of Yorkshire

Flowers, Joanna Louise (Heptonstalls LLP)

GOSFORTH, Tyne & Wear

Foster, Janet (McKeag & Co Solicitors)
Stanley, Carol Anne (Entec UK Ltd)

GOSPORT, Hampshire

Dennington, Natalie Jayne (Bill Charlton Solicitor Ltd)
Paul, Andrew John (Coffin Mew LLP)

GRANTHAM, Lincolnshire

Barker, Ena Muriel (Chattertons Solicitors)
Billing, Helen Clair (The Woodland Trust)
Booth, Jane Lesley (South Kesteven District Council)
Braithwaite, Mandy Patricia (South Kesteven District Council)
Carley, Alan (Fraser Wise & Co)
Carratt, Yvonne (JMP Solicitors)
Earth, John Thomas (Chattertons Solicitors)
Exton, Susan Joan (Ringrose Law Solicitors)
Gill, Nicola Jane (The Woodland Trust)
Hardy, Shelley Catherine (South Kesteven District Council)
Lambley, Denhys (Chattertons Solicitors)
Silvester, Samantha (JMP Solicitors)
Smart, Jason Andrew (JMP Solicitors)

GRAVESEND, Kent

Khan-Sherwani, Farukh Naeem (Farrukh Sherwani & Co Sols)
Ray, Sandra Christine (King Prior & Co)
Sewak, Shanida (Hatten Wyatt)
Smith, David George (Hatten Wyatt)
Wallis, Karen (Patrick Lawrence Solicitors)
White, Keith David (Martin Tolhurst Partnership)

GRAYS, Essex

Kemp, Barbara May (Margaret Reynolds)
Mcmillan, Andrea Jane (Sternberg Reed Solicitors)

GREAT DUNMOW, Essex

Kane, Elaine (Stanley Tee & Co)
Popplewell, Suzanna Victoria (Equity Law Costing)

GREAT YARMOUTH, Norfolk

Austin, Neil (Gordon Dean Solicitors)
Bean, Michelle Ann (Norton Peskett Solicitors)
Berry, Lesley Anne (Lucas & Wyllys)
Boyce, Emma (Norton Peskett Solicitors)
Breeze, Matthew David (Norton Peskett Solicitors)
Fleming, Amanda Dianne (Chamberlins Solicitors)
Gregory, Paul Jonathan (Norton Peskett Solicitors)
Griffen, Leanne (Norton Peskett Solicitors)

Hurren, Victoria Jayne (England & Co)
Mcnair, Julie Margaret (Hopton on Sea Parish Council)
Russell, Emma (Norton Peskett Solicitors)
Smith, Vicky Louisa (England & Co)
Spray, Tanith Rebecca (Lucas & Wyllys)
Wiseman, Nicholas Mark (Woolley & Co Solicitors)

GRIMSBY, North East Lincolnshire
Adams, Margaret Jean (Margaret Adams Law)
Barney, Danielle Louise (Bridge McFarland Solicitors)
Beedham, Gemma Victoria (Wilkin Chapman Group Ltd)
Bennett-Ryan, Catherine Vivien (Wilkin Chapman Group Ltd)
Briggs, Joshua Lee (Wilkin Chapman Group Ltd)
Broddley, Madeline Claire (Wilkin Chapman Group Ltd)
Buckingham, Denise Elaine (Beetenson & Gibbon Solicitors)
Bulbeck, Gary Simon (Roy Foreman & Co Solicitors)
Goddard, Clifford David (Bridge McFarland Solicitors)
Hasthorpe, Wendy (Paul Rudd Solicitors)
Hennegan, Steve Paul (Wilkin Chapman Group Ltd)
Hudson, Kathryn Mary (Bridge McFarland Solicitors)
King, Philip John (Paul Rudd Solicitors)
Lacy, Susan Lesley (Wilkin Chapman Group Ltd)
Langton, John Howard (Beetenson & Gibbon Solicitors)
Marshall, Richard Charles (North East Lincolnshire Borough Council)
Noton, Benna Louise (Wilkin Chapman Group Ltd)
Swallow, Hayley Anne (Bridge McFarland Solicitors)
Taylor, John Robert (Bates & Mountain)
Vincent, Paul Roland (Wilkin Chapman Group Ltd)

GUILDFORD, Surrey
Ashford, Elizabeth Louise (Barlow Robbins LLP)
Bell, Jane (Wheltons Solicitors)
Brown, Jessica Hannah (Crisp & Co)
Clark, Lora (Wheltons Solicitors)
Durman, Nigella Margaret (Karslakes Solicitors)
Gillespie, Sonya Rebecca (Barlow Robbins LLP)
Harrison, Beverley Jane (Clyde & Co LLP)
Hollingdale, Margaret Patricia (Guildford Borough Council)
Johnson, Katherine Louise (Barlow Robbins LLP)
Jones, Alison (Stevens & Bolton LLP)
Lawson, Lucy Ellen (Barlow Robbins LLP)
Margrave, Jennifer Christine (Margraves Solicitors)
McGarrigle, Laura (Barlow Robbins LLP)
Owen, Zoe Louise (GCL Solicitors)
Parker, Hannah Louise (MWA Solicitors)
Paterson, Louise Nicola (GCL Solicitors)
Pearson, Louise Joan (Clyde & Co LLP)
Richards, Gemma (Barlow Robbins LLP)
Rolfe, Philip Henry (Clyde & Co LLP)
Veitch, Rita Daphne (Childlaw Partnerships)
Wilson, Simon Louis (GCL Solicitors)

HADLEIGH, Suffolk
Bennett, Mark James (Babergh Borough Council)

HAILSHAM, East Sussex
Woodland, Clare Louise (Cooper Carter Claremont)

HALESOWEN, West Midlands
Bott, Phillip (Stables & Co)
Malpass, Steven William (M J Darby & Co)
Price, Richard Eric (Challinors White & Billingham)

HALESWORTH, Suffolk
Jones, Emma Marne (Norton Peskett Solicitors)
Salmon, Sally Marie (Norton Peskett Solicitors)
Utting, Teresa Ruth (Allens Solicitors)

HALIFAX, West Yorkshire
Barraclough, Julia Suzanne (Rsa Legal North)
Binns, Lee Andrew (Jubb Longbothams)
Byrne, Gerard Patrick (Halifax PLC)
Craven, Yvonne (Rsa Legal North)
Ferrett, John Michael (Calderdale Metropolitan Borough Council)
Gilligan, Diane (Chadwick Lawrence LLP)
Graham, Pamela Ann (Parabis Ltd)
Hall, Nicola (Makin Dixon Solicitors)
Jeffreys, Tracey Jane (Makin Dixon Solicitors)
Khanna, Sarah Simi (Wilkinson Woodward Inc Boococks)
Kinder-Naylor, Samantha (Wilkinson Woodward Inc Boococks)
Lockwood, Darryl John (Switalskis Solicitors LLP)
Masters, Clive John Richard (Wilkinson Woodward Inc Boococks)
Mckenna, Thomas John (Calderdale Metropolitan Borough Council)
Scanlon, Sara Gillian (Wilkinson Woodward Inc Boococks)
Woolford, Susan Margaret (Wilkinson Woodward Inc Boococks)

HALSTEAD, Essex
Abbott, Deborah Ann (Holmes & Hills LLP)
Dixey, David (Holmes & Hills LLP)
Emmins, Kathleen Ann (Holmes & Hills LLP)

HARLOW, Essex
Alexander, Mark Hayden (Harlow District Council)
Barr, Robin Maurice (EAME International Recoveries)
Bradford, Sarah Jane (Harlow District Council)
Cole, Leigh Patricia (Attwaters Solicitors)
Galvin, Julie Louise (Harlow District Council)
Holmes, Stephanie Jean (Attwaters Solicitors)
Mitchell, Wayne Neil (Harlow District Council)
Nuttall, Leanne (Attwaters Solicitors)

HARPENDEN, Bath & North East Somerset
Griffiths, Janet Hector (Taylor Walton Solicitors)
Kidd, Trevor (Neves)

HARROGATE, North Yorkshire
Barnicoat, Kathryn Ruth (Barber Titley)
Broadhead, Joanna Denise (Raworths LLP)
Chilton, William Andrew (Covance Laboratories Ltd)
Crabtree, Christopher Mark (Powell Eddison Freeman & Wilks)
Cunningham, Sarah Jane (Ashworth Law)
Fagan, Mark Andrew (Berwins LLP)
Gibbon, David Ian (Barber Titley)
Gregory, Helen Louise (Raworths LLP)
Hinds, Selena Kate (Raworths LLP)
Overton, Michael (Powell Eddison Freeman & Wilks)
Ruddy, Hannah (McCormicks)
Williams, Jayne Rosemary (Harrogate Borough Council)

HARROW, Middlesex
Abrahams, Gail Helma (Harold Benjamin)
Castle, Andrew David (Blaser Mills)
Clarke, Serena Lorraine (London Borough of Harrow)
Cole, Derek Stanley (Sayers)
Grimes, Gemma Amanda (Harold Benjamin)
Halai, Arti (Bovis Lend Lease Ltd)
Haling, Nadeem Hamza (Crown Prosecution Service)
Kynaston, Terence William (ALD Legal Ltd)
Laltoo, Beresford Ramrikha (Blatchfords Solicitors)
McEachron, Elaine Sonia (London Borough of Harrow)
Mehta, Rashmika (Atul Shah Solicitors)
Patel, Prabha (Kotecha & Company)
Wilkins, Laura (Camerons Jones Solicitors)
Winterton, Richard (Burrows)

HARTLEPOOL, Hartlepool
Boynton, Helen (Smith & Graham)
Bradford, Andrea Mary (Tilly Bailey & Irvine)
Coates, Pauline (Tilly Bailey & Irvine)
Dodgson, Natalie (Tilly Bailey & Irvine)
Harrison, Lisa (Tilly Bailey & Irvine)
Kinnersley, Michelle (Hartlepool Borough Council)
Moore, Sheila (TMJ Legal Services LLP)
Newton, Pauline (Hartlepool Borough Council)
Nottingham, Terena Maria (Donnelly Adamson)
Richardson, Joyce (Richardson's Real Estate)
Robinson, Lynne Marie (Smith & Graham)

HASLEMERE, Surrey
Nye, Wendy Karen (Burley & Geach Solicitors)

HASTINGS, East Sussex
Barkshire-Jones, Christine Jennifer (Hastings Borough Council)
Clark, Hayley Ann (Gaby Hardwicke)
Eley, Claire Louise (Gaby Hardwicke)
Laker, Joanne (Morgan & Lamplugh Solicitors)
Monaghan, Helen (Hastings Borough Council)
Nevey, Elizabeth Margaret (Funnell & Perring)
Upton, Diana Christine (Morgan & Lamplugh Solicitors)

HATFIELD, Hertfordshire
Codd, Carmel Margretta (T-Mobile (UK) Ltd)
Perring, Guy Levett (T-Mobile (UK) Ltd)

HATHERSAGE, Derbyshire
Meldrum, Jane Margaret (Favell Smith & Lawson)
Watts, Meriet Debra Jane Craig (Favell Smith & Lawson)

HAVANT, Hampshire
Bradley, Patricia Ann (Glanvilles Solicitors)
Cox, Karen Teresa (Glanvilles Solicitors)
Gard, Tracy Ann (Glanvilles Solicitors)
Poil, Margaret Ann (Guinness Hermitage Ltd)
Raine-Cooper, Janine Caroline (Dyer Burdett & Co)

HAVERFORDWEST, Pembrokeshire
Watson, Priscilla Margaret (Pembrokeshire County Council)

HAVERHILL, Suffolk
Bilinski, Anton (Adams Harrison)
Mealing, Catherine Jane (Adams Harrison)

HAYES, Middlesex
Anthony, Anita (Desor & Co Solicitors)
Bragg, David John (EDC Lord & Co)
Dahl, Emma (United Biscuits)
Elliott, Christine Doris (EDC Lord & Co)
Veja, Gita (Veja & Co Solicitors)

HAYLE, Cornwall
Harwood, Susan (Vingoe Lloyd Solicitors)

HAY-ON-WYE, Powys
Harris, Michael Edward (Williams Beales & Co)

HAYWARDS HEATH, West Sussex
Baker, Geoffrey Gordon (Colemans)
Collick, Paul Anthony (Mid Sussex District Council)
Cooper, Janet Anne (Colemans)
Kirkham, Patricia Anne (Waugh & Company)
Lacey, Katherine Anna (Hamnett Osborne Tisshaw)
Silk, Wendy Ann (Colemans)
Tompkins, Allison (Colemans)
Whitington, Heidi Jane (Europ Assistance)

HEATHFIELD, East Sussex
Burdett, Claire Linda (Repex Ltd)
Lane, Clare (H & R Hughes Solicitors LLP)
Sands, Patricia (H & R Hughes Solicitors LLP)

HEBDEN BRIDGE, West Yorkshire
Fowler, Paul Alan (Duffy & Co)

HECKMONDWIKE, West Yorkshire
Brayshaw, Caroline Elizabeth (Stanley Hays Solicitors)

HELSTON, Cornwall
Blenard, Teresa May (Vingoe Lloyd)
Van Den Berg, Jennifer Lesley (Randle Thomas)
Willey, Janice Wendy (Randle Thomas)

HEMEL HEMPSTEAD, Hertfordshire
Bell, Clive Antony (Dacorum Borough Council)
Green, Madeleine Mary (Dacorum Borough Council)
Khan, Natasha (DSG Retail Ltd)
Mackay, Julie Karen (Carr Hepburn Solicitors)
Pym, Sandra Kathryn (Kodak Ltd)
White, Martin Donald (Pickworths)

HENFIELD, West Sussex
Harris, Mary Ann (Griffith Smith Farrington Webb Solicitors)

HENGOED, Caerphilly
Bushell, Simon (Caerphilly County Borough Council)
Davies, Jacqueline (Caerphilly County Borough Council)
Dredge, Amy Louisa (Caerphilly County Borough Council)
Jones, Catherine Bernadette (Caerphilly County Borough Council)
Lane, Lisa Jane (Caerphilly County Borough Council)
Ruddock, Susan Ann (Caerphilly County Borough Council)

HENLEY-ON-THAMES, Oxfordshire
Marshall, Sandra (The Head Partnership)
O'Leary, Mary (The Head Partnership)

HEREFORD, Herefordshire
Cook, Diane Frances (Gordon Lutton & Co)
Davies, Lorraine (T A Matthews Solicitors)
Davies, Stacey (Gabbs & Co)
Dunham, Linden Trevor (County of Herefordshire District Council)
Evans, Samantha Jane (Herefordshire Council)
Farmer, Teresa Ann (Herefordshire Council)
Gray, Rachel Louise (Beaumonts)
Hughes, Bridget Anne (Beaumonts)
Jones, Michael Anthony Lewis (The County Herefordshire Distirct Council)
Kulakowski, Trecilla Jane (Practice Ltd)
Leyshon-James, Susan Helen (County of Herefordshire District Council)
Morlidge, Judith Elizabeth (Jaanette Hill & Co)
Rudd, Susan Ann (T A Matthews Solicitors)
Smith, Samantha Clare (Herefordshire Council)
Watts, Martin (County of Herefordshire District Council)
Williams, Hellen (Shawcross & Co)

HERNE BAY, Kent
Farrow, Louise (Girlings Solicitors)
Mountain, Louise (Parry Law)
Neeve, Christopher John (Girlings Solicitors)

HERTFORD, Hertfordshire
Aspland, Ann Georgina (Richard Long & Co)
Bearne, Abigail Esther (Hertfordshire Constabulary)
Bertram, Carole Anne (Jameson & Hill)
Cable, Nicola Jane (Jameson & Hill)
Davis, Hester (Hertfordshire County Council)
Galley, Alaina Lynn (Hertfordshire County Council)
Hobdell, Nicola Tara (Alistair Meldrum & Co)
Murray, Linda Margaret Susan (Hertfordshire County Council)
Pearson, Claire (Hertfordshire County Council)
Pointer, Trevor John (Which?)
Workman, Rosalyn (Longmores Solicitors)
Wright, Rita Janet (Breeze & Wyles Solicitors LLP)

HESSLE, East Riding of Yorkshire
Hill, Joanne Elizabeth (Ingrams Solicitors)
Parker, Audrey Anne (Ingrams Solicitors)

HEXHAM, Northumberland
Asquith, Rosemary (Marston Harbottle)
Samuel, Rona Dawn (Robert Lewis & Co)

HEYWOOD, Greater Manchester
Young, Maureen Williamson (Temperley Taylor)

HIGH WYCOMBE, Buckinghamshire
Bamber, Tonya Mary (The Guinness Trust)
Blay, Linda Jane (Allan Janes LLP)
Braathen, Lena Anne (Blaser Mills)
Couchman, Anita Lydia (Fendom Dawson & Partners)
Harriman, Richard Charles (Allan Janes LLP)
Lloyd, Emma Louise (Fairweather Whillis & Toghill)
Martyr, Robert John (Wycombe District Council)
Smith, Lisamarie Jacqueline (Blaser Mills)
Wolfe, Albert Richard (Davis & Co)

HIGHAM FERRERS, Northamptonshire
Skiplorne, Vincent Edward (Wilson Browne LLP)

HILLINGDON, Middlesex
Moran, Denis Gerard Michael (Rakhi Vaid)
Sondhi, Manjit (Rakhi Vaid)

HINCKLEY, Leicestershire
Birt, Wendy (Hinckley & Rugby Building Society)
Bradshaw, Jeffrey Andrew (First Assist Group Ltd)
Brogan, Janet Mary (Bray & Bray Solicitors)
Holland, Claire Helen (Pilgrim & Webster)
Skelton, Carl Barry (GS Solicitors)
Vallis, Sharon (Mander Cruickshank LLP)
Wright, Amanda Leah (Lester Dixon Jeffcome)

HINDHEAD, Surrey
Ferguson, Rebecca Lucie (MacPhersons Burley & Geach)

HITCHIN, Hertfordshire
Brown, David (Hawkins Russell Jones LLP)
Searle, Carol Ann (Hawkins Russell Jones LLP)
Tudball, Alan George (Hawkins Russell Jones LLP)

HODDESDON, Hertfordshire
Ewer, Robert Charles (CPM)

HOLBEACH, Lincolnshire
Pacey, Helen Lesley (Mossop & Bowser)

HOLSWORTHY, Devon
Bromell, Susan Elizabeth (Peter Peter & Wright)
Smith, David Andrew (Peter Peter & Wright)

HOLT, Norfolk
Arnup, Jane (Hayes & Storr)

HONITON, Devon
Hunt, Ian David (Everys Solicitors)
Land, Paula Susan (Everys Solicitors)
Manley, Penelope Ann (Everys Solicitors)

HOOK, Hampshire
Bottomley, Helen Louise (Wills Chandler Beech)
Prince, Emma Jane (Virgin Media)

HORLEY, Surrey
Walker, Catherine Rachel (Goodall Barnett James)
Windibank, Deborah Louise (Goodhand & Forsyth)

HORNCASTLE, Lincolnshire
Plaskitt, Nigel (Wilkin Chapman Group Ltd)

HORNCHURCH, Essex
Fisher, Alan Frederick (Reeve Fisher & Sands)
Green, Stephen Francis Peter (Pinney Talfourd LLP)
Harnetty, Michael (Moss & Coleman)
Kerley, Alison (Scott & Co)
Morgan, Gillian Anne (Moss & Coleman)
Nickless, Katie (Pinney Talfourd LLP)

HORSHAM, West Sussex
Allen, Kate (Sittons Solicitors)
Bastick, Suzanne Patricia (Rawlison Butler LLP)
Byng, Helen Suzanne (Paul Davidson Taylor)
Cobbett, Sarah (Royal & Sun Alliance)
Fenn, Jayne (The College of Richard Collyer)
Franzmann, Jennifer (RSPCA)
Harwood, Anne (Horsham District Council)
Kaplan, Anne Louise (Paul Davidson Taylor)
Matthews, Barbara Anne (Rawlison Butler LLP)

HOUGHTON-LE-SPRING, Tyne & Wear
Mitchell, Gillian Anne (Gordon Brown Associates)

HOUNSLOW, Middlesex
Brown, Kelly Louise (BAA Airports Ltd)
Farquhar, Anita Mary (Bonnetts Solicitors)
Lartey, Veronica (Ash Solicitors)

HOVE, Brighton & Hove
Batten, Leonard Roy (Brighton & Hove Council)
Copus, Glenn Anne (Brighton & Hove Council)
Harrington, Paul Antony (Bunkers LLP)
Harris, Peter George (Engleharts)
Knowles-Ley, Caroline Sarah (Lloyds TSB)
Macdonald, Linda Jane (Brian Mackrell & Co)
Mager, Elizabeth Hall (Woolley Bevis & Diplock)
Pack, Andrew Paul (Brighton & Hove Council)
Prosser, Alan (Bishop & Light Solicitors)
Thomas, Michael Francis (SCM Solicitors)

HUDDERSFIELD, West Yorkshire
Allen, Johanna Ruth (Ridley & Hall)
Barraclough, Emma Jane (Chadwick Lawrence LLP)
Bromley, Lynne (Ramsdens Solicitors)
Harrop, Katie Victoria Beatrice (Kirklees Metropolitan Council)
Martin, Anne (Kirklees Metropolitan Council)
Mcgregor, Malcolm Ross (Armitage Sykes & Hinchcliffe)
Milner, Vicky (Grieves Solicitors)
Moore, Judith Margaret (Ramsdens Solicitors)
Moss, Philip (Grieves Solicitors)
Ptycia, Stefan (West Yorkshire Accountancy Services)
Raynor, Lee (Eaton Smith)
Tollick, Clare Anne (Armitage Sykes & Hinchcliffe)
Warnes, Lesley Ann (Kirklees Metropolitan Council)
Watson, Janet Susan (Ridley & Hall)
Wells, Alexander Philip (Grieves Solicitors)
Withington, Alison May (Armitage Sykes & Hinchcliffe)

HULL, Kingston Upon Hull
Barratt, Lesley Carole (The Max Gold Partnership)
Brown, Michael Iain (Stamp Jackson & Procter Solicitors)
Burton, Melanie Jayne (David Porter & Co)
Coggin, Matthew John (The Max Gold Partnership)
Cook, Elizabeth (Ward Scott)
Cowell, Julie Anne (Hull City Council)
Davis, Geoffrey Arthur (Sandersons Solicitors)
Dent, Gillian Elizabeth (Andrew M Jackson)
Edmiston, Christine Anne (Stamp Jackson & Procter Solicitors)
Grant, Lisa Marie (Neil Hudgell Solicitors)
Hale, Alison (Sandersons Solicitors)
Kemp, Debra Anne (Humberside Police)
Khan, Kristina Dawn (Payne & Payne Solicitors)
Laverack, Sara Jane (Kingston Upon Hull City Council)
Lazenby, Catherine Anne (Graham & Rosen Solicitors)
Mcmaster, Nicola Jean (Myer Wolff Solicitors)
Midwinter, Heather Laura (Sandersons Solicitors)
Moore, Michael John (Kingston Upon Hull City Council)
Moore, Vicki (Kingston Upon Hull City Council)
Reeves, Mark Anthony (Myer Wolff Solicitors)
Richardson, Kenneth Paul (Hamers)
Robinson, Jill (Williamsons Solicitors)
Robinson, Mark Andrew (Wescot Credit Services)
Rylands, Shaun Michael (Stamp Jackson & Procter Solicitors)
Smith, Richard Graham (Williamsons Solicitors)
Snow, Rebecca (Neil Hudgell Solicitors)
Stark, Heather Dawn (Kingston Upon Hull City Council)
Swinn, Rachel (Andrew M Jackson)
Taylor, Deborah Suzanne (Harland Turnbull & Roberts)
Taylor, Lorraine (Bridge McFarland Solicitors)
Ward, Claire Louise (Andrew M Jackson)
Wilkinson, Adele Lesley (Andrew M Jackson)
Woodcock, Jane (Neil Hudgell Solicitors)

HUNGERFORD, West Berkshire
Bacchus, Dawn Louise (National Trainers Federation)

HUNSTANTON, Norfolk
Sopp, Carol Anne (SJP Solicitors)

HUNTINGDON, Cambridgeshire
Adamante, Rosangela (Stevensons Solicitors)
Asquith, Annette Mary (Leeds Day Solicitors)
Cuthbert, Christopher Osborne (RPM Legal)
Dear, Julie Deborah (Copleys)
Judd, Paula Annette (Serjeant & Son)
Mardell, Adrian James (The Crown Prosecution Service)
McCulloch, Joanne Patricia (Huntingdonshire District Council)
Rae, Minna Katarina (Leeds Day Solicitors)
Smith, Abby Marie (Leeds Day Solicitors)

HYDE, Greater Manchester
Burgess, Brian (Pluck Andrew & Co)
Deaville, Patricia Lynda (Pluck Andrew & Co)

ILFORD, Essex
Aswani, Rita (Bailey Nicholson Grayson Solicitors)
Bonich, Lorens Ernest (Edwards Duthie)
Brown, Patricia Eileen (Alan Winter Peace & Co)
Downes, Pam (Taylors Legal Solicitors)
Ellmore, Cynthia (London Borough of Redbridge)
Gupta, Sujata (Davis Solicitors LLP)
Okebu, Deborah Sharah (Bailey Nicholson Grayson Solicitors)
Sandhu, Pervinder (London Borough of Redbridge)

ILKESTON, Derbyshire
Dutton, Susan Margaret (Robinsons Solicitors)
Milne, Stephen (Robinsons Solicitors)

ILMINSTER, Somerset
Creech, Gerald Herbert (Broomhead & Saul)
Gray, Diane (Grays Legal Services)
Lock, Alison Mary (Baker & Duke)
Lowe, Sally (Broomhead & Saul)
Nobbs, Jennifer Ruth (Baker & Duke)

INGATESTONE, Essex
Ford, Terence Arthur (Iliffes Booth Bennett Solicitors)

IPSWICH, Suffolk
Abbott, Stephen John (Jackaman Smith & Mulley)
Bailey, Katherine Ann (Suffolk County Council)
Baker, Joanna Lynne (Maddocks Lusher & Matthews)
Barnard, Lucy (Tinkler Solicitors)
Blowers, Jane (Cash Genie UK Ltd)
Brice, Barry Kevin (AXA Liabilities Managers UK)
Bush, Howard John (Gotelee)
Collins, Karen Heather (Ashton Graham Solicitors)
Dawson, Pamela Rose (Birketts LLP)
Denton-Cardew, Lorna Catherine (Blocks)
Driver, Cheryl Louise (Suffolk County Council)
Durrell, Hilary Christine (Jackaman Smith & Mulley)
Farthing, Simon Daniel (Birketts LLP)
Fosker, Elaine Marie (Eversheds LLP)
French, Nigel William (Employment & Business Law)
Green, Christopher Stewart (Prettys Solicitors)
Gynn, John William (Birketts LLP)
Hogger, Angela (Ashton Graham Solicitors)
Jacobs, Andrew Paul (Andrew Jacobs Conveyancing)
Kean, Claire Jayne (Jackaman Smith & Mulley)
Kingham, Jennie Louise Stephanie (Ashton Graham Solicitors)
Mason, Christopher John (Bates Wells & Braithwaite)
Mcconnell, Kevin Hugh (Eversheds LLP)
McGrath, Corinne (Suffolk County Council)
Moffat, Christine Elizabeth (Jackaman Smith & Mulley)
Moss, Jade (Prettys Solicitors)
Mullane, Sian Megan Ruth (Gotelee)
Nield, Martin Douglas (Barricella Hughes Solicitors)
Oliver, Hazel Anne (Watkins Stewart & Ross)
Osborn, Linda Frances (Ashton Graham Solicitors)
Parker, Kelly (Birketts LLP)
Phillips, Beverley (Jackaman Smith & Mulley)
Phillips, Pauline Elizabeth (Birketts LLP)
Porter, Emma Louisa (Attwells Solicitors LLP)
Pryke, Rhonda Lynn (Gotelee)
Richards, Michael Paul (Birketts LLP)
Robinson, Anita Jean (Eversheds LLP)
Spurgeon, Bernice Clare (Ashton Graham Solicitors)
Squire, Martin William (Birketts LLP)
Swan, Jennifer (Gotelee)
Taylor, Janis Lindsay (Jackaman Smith & Mulley)
Threadkell, Susan Clare (Saunders Goodin Riddleston)
Trembath, Linda Bridget (Gotelee)
Yarrow-Smith, Diane Iris (Wolsey Probate)

IVYBRIDGE, Devon
Bishop, Philippa Louise (Clark & Weeks)
Webb, Jo-Anne Claire (Howard & Over)

JARROW, Tyne & Wear
Kulkarni, Sonia Margaret (Geoffrey Forrester & Co)
Stonley, Michelle (Geoffrey Forrester & Co)

KEIGHLEY, West Yorkshire
Blackwell, Keith Andrew (Blackwells Solicitors)
Jones, Julie Ann (Burr Sugden Solicitor)
Newstead, Richard Jeremy (W & G Burr Sugden & Co)
Southgate, Karen Josephine (John J Halliwell & Co Solicitors)

KEMPSTON, Bedfordshire
Remnant, Neil (Hilliers HRW Solicitors LLP)

KENDAL, Cumbria
Fisher, Suzanne Melanie (Hayton Winkley Solicitors)
Fletcher, Sara Tracey (Thomson Wilson Pattinson)
Hill, Martyn Stewart (Thomson Wilson Pattinson)

KENILWORTH, Warwickshire
Jones, Lyndsey Louisa (Penmans Solicitors LLP)
Leach, Susan (N R Wilson)
Patel, Dharmista (National Farmers Union)
Rolf, Alison Jane (Penmans Solicitors LLP)
Saunders, Janice Lynn (Penmans Solicitors LLP)

KETTERING, Northamptonshire
Austin, Sarah Elizabeth (Tollers LLP)
Farrington, Roy James (E Surv Ltd)
Fleming, Clare (Kettering Borough Council)
Futer, Paula Ann (Wilson Browne LLP)
King, Gaynor Louise (Wilson Browne LLP)
Marshall, Carol (Wilson Browne LLP)
Osborne-Richardson, Faye Louise (Lamb & Holmes)
Penn, Janis (Wilson Browne LLP)
Walton, Karon Ann (Tollers LLP)

KEYNSHAM, Bath & North East Somerset
Bennett, Geraldine Mary (Mowbray Woodwards)
Biddlecombe, Andrew John (Bath & North East Somerset Council)
Earl, Hilary Anne (Mowbray Woodwards)

KIDDERMINSTER, Worcestershire
Calder, Gillian Louise (Thursfields LLP)
Fowler, Deborah Jayne (DJF Consultancy)
Goodman, Julie Margaret (Thursfields LLP)
Hill, Alison Jane (Talbots Solicitors LLP)
Rowley, Paul Andrew (Painters Solicitors)
Ward, Katie Suzanne (Thursfields LLP)
Watkins, Gillian Rachel (Painters Solicitors)
Watson, Sarah Elizabeth (Prescotts)

KIDLINGTON, Oxfordshire
Cuss, Trevor George (George Cuss)
Perkins, Lisa (Thames Valley Police)
Stafford, Timothy (Thames Valley Police)
Waskett, Vicki Teresa (Thames Valley Police)

KINGS LYNN, Norfolk
Bentley, Charlotte Grace (Fraser Dawbarns Solicitors)
Bloye, Gerald Charles (Fraser Dawbarns Solicitors)
Bowler, Lynn Julie (Ward Gethin Solicitors)
Bullen, Jacqueline Beverley (Kings Lynn West Norfolk Council)
Butcher, Andrea Dawn (Ward Gethin Solicitors)
Campion, Teresa Jane (Borough Council Kings Lynn & West Norfolk)
Chase, Beverly Anne (Fraser Dawbarns Solicitors)
Curl, Suzanne Joy (Kenneth Bush & Co)
Dennis, Diane Jessie (Borough Council Kings Lynn & West Norfolk)
Edmunds, Phillipa Karen (Kenneth Bush & Co)
Egginton, Melanie Jane (Ward Gethin Solicitors)
Faivelowitz, Kim Louise (Ward Gethin Solicitors)
Jahangir, Lyndis Elizabeth (Kenneth Bush & Co)
Oderinde, Marian (Queen Elizabeth Hospital)
Payne, Dean Mervin (Hawkins Russell Jones LLP)
Pearman, Robert Charles (Ward Gethin Solicitors)
Raven, Diane (Fraser Dawbarns Solicitors)
Rawson, Sandra May (Ward Gethin Solicitors)
Robson, Melanie Jacqueline (Hayes & Storr)
Savill, Joy Elizabeth (Hawkins Russell Jones LLP)

KINGSBRIDGE, Devon
Basham, Paula Jane (Bartons)
Elliot-Smith, Mark Arnold (Beers LLP)
Godwin, Rusty (Beers LLP)
Heard, Kristy Jean (Bartons)
Hems, Sonia (Beers LLP)
Houston, Robert Bernard (Beers LLP)
Kovacic, Nicola Jayne (Bartons)
Luscombe, Gail June (Beers LLP)
Potter, Mandy Louise (Bartons)
Saunders, Helen Julia (Beers LLP)

KINGSTON UPON THAMES, Surrey
Allen, Philip John (Surrey County Council)
Baxendale, Robert James (Royal Borough of Kingston Upon Thames)
Brissett, Michelle Louise (Colemans-CTTS LLP)
Caines, Michelle (Surrey County Council)
Clark, Lucy (Carter Bells Solicitors)
Derby, Tessa Joy (CAB)
Harrison, Pamela (Kingston University)
Jennings-Christensen, Stephanie Gabrielle (Surrey County Council)
Joseph, Sally-Ann (Rose & Rose Solicitors)
Kennedy, Karen Leanne (Surrey County Council)
Mcbride, Terence Malcolm (Colemans-CTTS LLP)
Mcconachie, Jacqueline Ann (Colemans-CTTS LLP)
Mcdermott, Gloria Jean (Russell Cooke Potter & Chapman)
Mills, Yvonne Irene (Colemans-CTTS LLP)
Petchey, Andrew Edward (Howell Jones Solicitors)
Sassone, Hannah Elizabeth (Colemans-CTTS LLP)
Thornton, Tracey Marie (Howell Jones Solicitors)

KINGSWINFORD, West Midlands
Boddey, Yvonne Jane (Higgs & Sons Solicitors)
Hotchkiss, Peter Charles (M C Albion)

KIRKBY-IN-ASHFIELD, Nottinghamshire
Arbon, Rosemary Ann (Ashfield District Council)
Armiger, Joanne Gail (Ashfield District Council)
Oxby, Michele (Ashfield District Council)

KNARESBOROUGH, North Yorkshire
Birchell, Claire Louise (Steel & Co)
Wilson, Dawn Rachel (Greenwood Solicitors)

LANCASTER, Lancashire
Cockram, Pamela (Oglethorpe Sturton & Gillibrand)
Duckworth, Carol Patricia (Lancaster City Council)
Holmes, Jacqueline Norma (Douglas Clift & Solicitors)
Housley, Hayley (Oglethorpe Sturton & Gillibrand)
Lamb, Dawn (Holden Solicitors)
McCabe, Liza Diane (Holden Solicitors)
Nelis, Maria Lesley (Jobling & Knape)

LAUNCESTON, Cornwall
Cousens, Shirley Maureen (Parnalls Solicitors)
Crockford, Louise (Peters Langford Davies Solicitors)
Cummings, Linda Jane (Parnalls Solicitors)

15

Cummings, Mark Stephen (Parnalls Solicitors)
Davey, Emma Louise (Peters Langford Davies Solicitors)
Johnson, Natasha Louise (Peters Langford Davies Solicitors)
Plummer, Georgia Rose (Peters Langford Davies Solicitors)

LEAMINGTON SPA, Warwickshire

Arthur, Alison Barbara (Solicitors Regulation Authority)
Ball, Jacqueline Linda (Alsters Kelley Solicitors)
Bansil, Harjinder Singh (Solicitors Regulation Authority)
Bishop, Rachel Louise (Wright Hassall LLP)
Collett, Rachel Jane (Wright Hassall LLP)
Elliott, Michael David (Solicitors Regulation Authority)
England, Paul Alan (Blythe Liggins)
Gennard, Rachel Jayne (The Law Society)
Gill, Kamaljit Kaur (Blythe Liggins)
Grant, Sandra Anne (Wright Hassall LLP)
Grieve, Stephanie Anne (Field Overell Solicitors)
Griffin-Phelps, Stacey (The Law Society)
Hill, Alison Jane (Solicitors Regulation Authority)
Holmes, Janice Tracey (The Law Society)
Hopkins, Gemma Louise (Blythe Liggins)
Jackson, Gillian Anne (Wright Hassall LLP)
Kowalski, Zoe Anne (Solicitors Regulation Authority)
Longbottom, Melanie Jane (Solicitors Regulation Authority)
Macleod, Sushma (Wright Hassall LLP)
Martin, Andrew Philip (Wright Hassall LLP)
Mitchell, Amanda Jane (Solicitors Regulation Authority)
Mobley, Zoe Marie (Solicitors Regulation Authority)
Newman, Shona (Ollerenshaw Solicitors)
Sheasby, Louise Anne (Blythe Liggins)
Shimmin, Carole-Ann (Solicitors Regulation Authority)
Smallwood, David Allan (Solicitors Regulation Authority)
Southall, Stuart (Wright Hassall LLP)
Spencer, Russell Neville (Wright Hassall LLP)
Timothy, Melanie (The Law Society)
Upstone, Emma Louise (Blythe Liggins)
Wade, Sarah (Solicitors Regulation Authority)

LEATHERHEAD, Surrey

Crosby, Susan Elaine (TWM Solicitors LLP)
D'Cruz, Agnes Mary (Toshiba Carrier)
Dempsey, Susan Jane (Online Medical Reports Ltd)
Gould, Sonia (Hedleys)

LEDBURY, Herefordshire

Gardiner, Linda May (DF Legal LLP)
Glasper, Paul John (Ecclesiastical)
Gummery, Emma Jane (Masefield Solicitors LLP)
Longmore, Helen Diane (Masefield Solicitors LLP)

LEE-ON-THE-SOLENT, Hampshire

Mawson, Stuart Lionel (Churchers Solicitors)

LEEDS, West Yorkshire

Adams, Sally Anne (Plexus Law)
Ainscough, Ian Stuart (Shulmans Solicitors)
Bacon, Geraldine Jane (Plexus Law)
Ballad, Maxwell John (DLA Piper UK LLP)
Beaumont, Jenny (Leeds City Council)
Beaumont, Matin John (Medical Protection Society)
Bell, James Duncan (Beachcroft LLP)
Bell, Kenneth David (Leeds City Council)
Birch, Helen Louise (Addleshaw Goddard LLP)
Blakemore, Patricia Ann (Walton & Co)
Boland, Claire (Walker Morris Solicitors)
Boyce, Stephen Riley (Praxis Partners Solicitors)
Branchflower, Lynne Patricia (Bury & Walkers LLP)
Brooksbank, Emma Clare (Henry Hyams & Co)
Brown, Sarah Ann (Enact Conveyancing)
Bruce, Antonia Jane (Keeble Hawson)
Burton, Julie Ann (Addleshaw Goddard LLP)
Bush, Richard David (Henry Hyams & Co)
Butler, Jane (Asset Finance)
Campbell, Lyndon Stuart (Simpson Millar LLP)
Carey, Janice Susan (Wrigleys Solicitors)
Chapman, Lisa Claire (Enact Direct Legal Solutions)
Childs, Paul (Walker Morris Solicitors)
Churm, Paula (Walton & Co)
Clayton, George Francis (Gorman Hamilton Solicitors)
Comer, Jamie Michael (Plexus Law)
Conaghan, Ciaran Joseph (Harrison Bundey & Co)
Conwell, Paula Michelle (The Medical Protection Society)
Coulthard, Richard David (Michael Lewin Solicitors Ltd)
Cousins, Emma (Morrish & Co)
Davis, Julie Dawn (Shulmans Solicitors)
Elliott, Julie Anne (Irwin Mitchell LLP)
Evans, Stacey Michelle (Keeble Hawson)
Finlay, Kirsty Louise (Pathway Residential Property Lawyers)
Forbes, Linda Mary (Lester Morrill)
Fry, Jessica Elizabeth (Stapleton Gardner & Co)
Gee, Rachel Clare (Blacks Solicitors LLP)
Gilks, Emma Louise (Irwin Mitchell LLP)
Gledhill, Melanie (Cogent Law)
Grainger, Jacqueline (Irwin Mitchell LLP)
Grainger, Malcolm (Grahame Stowe Bateson & Co)
Grimshaw, Karl (Shelter)
Hale, Glynis Mary (Emsleys Solicitors)
Hammond, Lorraine (Beachcroft LLP)
Handley, Nicola Alexandra (Irwin Mitchell LLP)
Hanson, Timothy James (Lyons Davidson Solicitors)
Harrop, Sarah Victoria (Shulmans Solicitors)
Harvey, Natalie Michelle (Thompsons Solicitors)
Helliwell, Simon Anthony (Ison Harrison & Co)
Holmes, Margaret Anne (Shulmans Solicitors)
Horton, Andrew Wilson (DLA Piper UK LLP)
Hoskin, Christopher James (PricewaterhouseCoopers)
Howard, Andrew Richard (Clarion Solicitors LLP)
Howe, Beverley Jane (Cogent Law)
Hudson, Karen Julie (Levi Solicitors LLP)
Hudson, Susan (Lupton Fawcett LLP)
Johnson, Alex (Crown Prosecution Service)
Jones, David Ashley Blount (Leeds City Council)
Kamillo-Price, Emma Jane (Leeds City Council)
Kane, Geraldine Mary (Ison Harrison & Co)
Kauser, Nageena (Fairfax Solicitors Limited)
King, Clare Louise (Clarion Solicitors LLP)
Kirkbright, Karen Elizabeth (Enact Conveyancing)
Knapton, Sabrina Jayne (Shulmans Solicitors)
Ladlow, Janet Susan (Godlove Pearlman)
Law, Joanne Louisa (Thompsons Solicitors)
Lea, Lauren Claire (Walker Morris Solicitors)
Leadill, Adam (Zermansky & Partners)
Leppington, Sally Anne (Callcredit Ltd)
Lownsbrough, Stephen John (Blacks Solicitors LLP)
Marshall, Andrew Damian (Addleshaw Goddard LLP)
Marshall, Ronald Michael (Russell Jones & Walker)
Martin, Victoria Georgina (Blacks Solicitors LLP)
Maynard, Dawn Louise (Shulmans Solicitors)
McKay, Charlotte (Walton & Co)
McLaughlin, Hilary (Thompsons Solicitors)
Milner, Emma Jane (Emsleys Solicitors)
Minchin, Sarah (Lee & Priestley)
Minshull, Louise (Addleshaw Goddard LLP)
Moran, Kevin (Leeds City Council)
Moynihan, Karen Patricia (Emsleys Solicitors)
Newsome, Charlotte Lesley (Enact Conveyancing)
Nortcliffe, Donna Maria (Emsleys Solicitors)
Norton, Andrew Paul (Norton Connor Solicitors)
Oldroyd, Stephen (Richardson & Co Solicitors)
Oseland, Francesca (Cogent Law)
Parmar, Amit (Beachcroft LLP)
Pashley, Stephen (Squire Sanders & Dempsey (UK) LLP)
Patel, Sahida (Mintons Solicitors)
Plummer, Dianne (John Howe & Co)
Priston, Jason David (Gorman Hamilton Solicitors)
Proctor, Andrew Mark (Plexus Law)
Raines, Joanne (Keeble Hawson)
Rathod, Alka (Walker Morris Solicitors)
Richmond, Colin (Gorman Hamilton Solicitors)
Rowe, Jacqueline Imelda (Lupton Fawcett LLP)
Ryatt, Akwal (Stapleton Gardner & Co)
Seddon, Maria (Levi Solicitors LLP)
Senior, Richard Ian (Fairfax Solicitors Limited)
Shaw, Anna Sian (Ward Hadaway Solicitors)
Shiels, Matthew James (Gorman Hamilton Solicitors)
Simpson, Julie (YFM Group)
Smith, Jo-Ann (Cousins Tyrer)
Stokes, Gemma Louise (Irwin Mitchell LLP)
Stokes, Robert William (Praxis Partners Solicitors)
Stone, Catherine Louise (Lupton Fawcett LLP)
Stringer, Tracey (Ison Harrison & Co)
Sykes, April Rosemary (Plexus Law)
Tallant, James (Beachcroft LLP)
Tarbuck, John Michael (Shulmans Solicitors)
Tasker, Yvonne (Aedas)
Taylor, Laura Denise (Switalskis Solicitors LLP)
Thompson, Kenneth (Leeds City Council)
Thorley, Joanne (Cobbetts Employee Services)
Upson, Claire Louise (Irwin Mitchell LLP)
Wadwell, Richard Douglas (Beachcroft LLP)
Walker, Gillian Margaret (Lansdowne & Co Solicitors)
Welsh, Owen (Plexus Law)
West, Stephen Julian (Gorman Hamilton Solicitors)
Whitworth, Michael (DWF LLP)
Willson, Jill (Beachcroft LLP)
Wood, Katharine (Plexus Law)
Woods, Zoe Michelle (Irwin Mitchell LLP)
Woolford, Stephen John (Thompsons Solicitors)
Wright, Sara Louise (Praxis Partners Solicitors)

LEEK, Staffordshire

Bevington, Sarah Ann (Uprights Solicitors)
Brown, Julia Ann (Bowcock & Pursaill)
Harrison, Gillian (A H Brooks & Co)
Hough, Melissa Jane (Carney Solicitors)
Lawton-Martin, Rebecca (Tinsdills Solicitors)
Marsh, Jeanette (Staffordshire Moorlands District Council)
Penaluna, Michelle Anita (Uprights Solicitors)
Sharratt, Samantha Jayne (Britannia Building Society)

LEICESTER, Leicester

Ali, Emma (Harvey Ingram LLP)
Allen, Jacqueline (Davis & Co)
Ashcroft, Joanne Emma (Crown Prosection Service)
Ashton, Cheryl Louise (Spearing Waite Solicitors)
Bacon, Lisa Mandy (Barlows)
Bettany, Beverley Anne (R P Robinson)
Bevan, Marie (Premier Property Lawyers Ltd)
Billett, Tina Mandy (Bradshaw & Hollingworth)
Bird, Felicity (Bray & Bray Solicitors)
Brewer, Sylvia Caroline (Billson & Sharp)
Cave, Susan Jane (Dews Witcomb)
Clarke, Arthur David (Dixon Coles & Goddard)
Clewlow, Richard John (Harvey Ingram Borneos)
Cook, Claire Elizabeth (Spearing Waite Solicitors)
Cox, Lisa Jane (Harvey Ingram Borneos)
Dable, Maureen Elizabeth (Quality Solicitors Wilson Browne)
Daniels, Louise Georgina Mary (MHM Solicitors Ltd)
Denath, Aiyub Ismail (David & Co)
Dhami, Kalvinder (Leicester City Council)
Dunkley, Karl Michael (Michael Hill Partnership)
Eley, Graham John (Alliance & Leicester PLC)
Essat, Faizal (Leicestershire County Council)
Evans, Jacqueline Sarah Orgill (MHM Solicitors Ltd)
Fairbrother, Lucy Caroline (Geoffrey Tew & Co)
Fidler, John Robert (Crane & Walton)
Frith, Caroline Susan (Leicester City Council)
Girach, Lubna (Gateley LLP)
Gowtage, Tony John (Rich & Carr)
Griffin, Karen Jane (Harvey Ingram Borneos)
Grimbley, Cheryl Yvette (Leicester City Council)
Handley, Deborah (Black & Co)
Hardy, Karen Yvonne (Bray & Bray Solicitors)
Harrison, Sarah (Leicester City Council)
Heys, Beverley Anne (Bray & Bray Solicitors)
Hives, Lorna Philliday (Weightmans LLP)
Hocking, Dianne (Lawson West Solicitors Ltd)
Hodges, Carol Angela (Bray & Bray Solicitors)
Humphreys, Sally Ann (Leicester City Council)
Iliffe, Zoe Verena Elizabeth (Leicester City Council)
Johnson, Ian (Crown Prosecution Service)
Johnson, Richard Peter (Harvey Ingram Borneos)
Kadri, Mohammed Ibrahim (Harvey Ingram Borneos)
Kinson, Lesley Lorraine (Spearing Waite Solicitors)
Kirton, Susan Andrea (Rich & Carr)
Knight, Beverley Ann (Andrew M Ford Solicitors)
Loughnane, Victoria (Gateley LLP)
Mawson, Lawrence (Leicester City Council)
Mcivor, John Michael (Leicester City Council)
Measures, John Umberto (Harvey Ingram Borneos)
Metson, Susan Josephine (Leicester City Council)
Muttock, Alison (Rich & Carr)
Myers, Suzanne (Nelsons)
Oldershaw, Mark Andrew (Howes Percival LLP)
Parsons, Jayne Maria (BHW Commercial Solicitors)
Patel, Madhumati Jayant (Leicester City Council)
Patel, Mohsina (Leicester City Council)
Rahman, Waheed (Leicester City Council)
Rainbow, Jeremy Mark (Leicester City Council)
Raj, Rita Devi (Lawson West Solicitors Ltd)
Rawle, Marcia Angela (Spearing Waite Solicitors)
Ridgway, Vickki Lorraine (Lawson West Solicitors Ltd)
Roberts, Susan Elizabeth (Affinity Law LLP)
Rogers, Angela Mary (Roberts Rose Partnership)
Sanderson, Helen Susan (Quality Solicitors Wilson Browne)
Scothern, Jennifer Michelle (Home-Start UK)
Shoebotham, Peter John (Smith Partnership)
Skinner, Jacqueline Sandra (Leicester City Council)
Slow, Dawn (Harvey Ingram LLP)
Snowdon, Alexandra (Leicester City Council)
Steer, David Anthony (Harding & Barnett)
Stephens, Sandra Valerie (Hawley & Rodgers)
Strelzyn, Linda Beverley (Harvey Ingram Borneos)
Swift, Pauline Angela (Leicestershire County Council)
Taylor, Rebecca Jane (Harvey Ingram Borneos)
Vallance, Julie Rose (Harvey Ingram Borneos)
Vickers, Wayne Jason (Harvey Ingram Borneos)
Walczak, Helen Marie (Harvey Ingram Borneos)
Ward, Lucy Rebecca (Spearing Waite Solicitors)
Warner, Alexandra Judith (Blaby District Council)
Wells, John Arthur (Roberts Rose Partnership)
Wesson, Rebecca Claire (Harvey Ingram Borneos)
Whale, Frank Robert (Harvey Ingram Borneos)
Wood, Stephen (Emerson Process Management)
Wynne, Wendy Irene (R G Frisby & Small)

LEIGH, Greater Manchester

Brown, Vanessa (Widdows Mason Solicitors)
Day, Lauren Marie (Stephensons Solicitors LLP)
Gregory, Susan (Widdows Mason Solicitors)
Sargeant, Emma Clare (Widdows Mason Solicitors)

LEIGH-ON-SEA, Essex

Cottis, Anita Rosalie Elizabeth (Cooper & Lingard)
Lander, Colin Trevor (Frederick W Goodson)
Martin, Michael John (Cooper & Lingard)
Willis, Beverley Jane (Giles Wilson Solicitors)

LEIGHTON BUZZARD, Bedfordshire

Crook, Sarah Louise (Osborne Morris & Morgan)

LEISTON, Suffolk

Watson, Rachel Louise (Fairweather Stephenson & Co.)

LEOMINSTER, Herefordshire

Brown, Henrietta Lucy (Gabbs Solicitors LLP)
Walker, Anthony Michael (The County of Hertfordshire)

LETCHWORTH, Hertfordshire

Pearson, Melanie Sara (Michael Hall)

LEWES, East Sussex

Bailey, Simon George (East Sussex County Council)
Burton-Durham, Lisa Jane (Mayo Wynne Baxter LLP)
Chrismas, Sonia Jane (Beverley Ogden & Co)
Ferguson, Deanne Jane (Sarah Edmunds Legal Solicitors)
Gamble, Claire (Mayo Wynne Baxter LLP)
Mead, Stephen (Adams & Remers)
Mitchell, John Joseph (Adams & Remers)
Oliver, Jill Lyrrs (Lewes Smith Solicitors)
Taylor, Sally (East Sussex County Council)
Wade, Yvonne Elizabeth Mary (Blaker Son & Young)

LEYLAND, Lancashire

Bird, Julie Elizabeth (Birchall Blackburn)
Lloyd, Jemma Louise (Solicitor Direct)

LICHFIELD, Staffordshire

Patterson, Gillian Elizabeth (Keelys Solicitors)

LINCOLN, Lincolnshire

Anderson, Keely Jayne (Lincolnshire County Council)
Armitage, Karen Jane (Andrew & Co Solicitors)
Ashton, Ann-Marie (Lincolnshire Police Authority)
Basham, Katie (Lincolnshire County Council)
Bell, Denise (Langleys Solicitors)
Bezak, Caroline Maria (McKinnells Solicitors)
Biskup, Sheila Ann (Wilkin Chapman Group Ltd)
Brown, Jo-Anna Catherine (Dale & Co)
Cammack, Charlotte Kim (Lincolnshire County Council)
Clare, Victoria Ann (Adie O'Reilly)
Coddington, Jayne Lesley (Sills & Betteridge LLP)
Commons, Debbie Edwina (Chattertons Solicitors)
Curtis, Stuart (Burton & Co Solicitors)
Dennis, Leah-Marie (Langleys Solicitors)
Gash, Stephanie Jane (McKinnells Solicitors)
Gibson, Euan Crawford (Lincolnshire County Council)
Gray, Joanna Mary (Dale & Co)
Gray, Lisa Jane (Langleys Solicitors)

Hardy, Peter David (Langleys Solicitors)
Harris, Gemma (Lincolnshire County Constabulary)
Hart, Sarah-Anne (Anthony Clark & Co)
Hodgson, Julie Margaret (Sills & Betteridge LLP)
Hunt, Justine (Dale & Co)
King, Astasia Helena (Langleys Solicitors)
Lynes, Mark (Langleys Solicitors)
Maw, Victoria Lisa (Wilkin Chapman Group Ltd)
Merrikin, Sarah Hessell (McKinnells Solicitors)
Morley, Andrew David (McKinnells Solicitors)
Motley, Karen Marie (Sills & Betteridge LLP)
Murphy, Helen Catherine (Langleys Solicitors)
Overend, Jennifer (Burton & Co Solicitors)
Parkes, Paul (Langleys Solicitors)
Poucher, Neil (Lincolnshire County Council)
Pringle, Lorraine Mandy (Crown Prosecution Service)
Race, Felicity Nicola (McKinnells Solicitors)
Rodgers, Lesley Elizabeth (Lindum Group Ltd)
Shillitto, Anne (Andrew & Co Solicitors)
Somers-Wells, Joanne Mary (Bridge McFarland Solicitors)
Storey, Joanna Louise (Ringrose Law Solicitors)
Subden, Sarah Elizabeth (HR Solutions (GB) Limited)
Taylor, Hayley Joanne (Ringrose Law Solicitors)

LISKEARD, Cornwall

Glencross, Susan (Coodes Solicitors)
May, Michele (Earl & Crocker)
Woodhead, Paul (Cornwall Council)

LISS, Hampshire

Moore, Patricia Ann (Harveys)

LITTLEHAMPTON, West Sussex

Atkinson, Helen Jane (Arvin District Council)
Byrnes, Nadine Rosalind (E J Moyle Solicitors)
Dunks, Alan Raymond (E J Moyle Solicitors)
Formaggia, Alison Margaret (Green Wright Chalton Annis)
Sugden, Sally (Arun District Council)

LIVERPOOL, Merseyside

Alty, Joanne (Thomas R Jones & Son)
Baker, Alison Jane (Armstrong Solicitors)
Balfry, William Simon (DWF LLP)
Bancroft, Elenid Tayson (Hill Dickinson LLP)
Banks, Carole (DLA Piper UK LLP)
Barry, Viktoria Louise (Hill Dickinson LLP)
Bauress, Louise Marie (Keith Levin & Co)
Behn, Russell John (DWF LLP)
Behn, Wendy (DWF LLP)
Benson, Lee Russell (Lee Lloyd Whitley)
Benson, Louise Jane (Hertzog & Associates)
Birchall, Elizabeth Jean (Minards Pavlou Solicitors)
Blackwall, John Christopher (Murphy Hodgkinson Solicitors)
Bratsanos, Dawn (Allan Pilch & Co)
Buckley, Joanna Frances (PCJ Solicitors)
Byrne, Paul (Liverpool City Council)
Byrne, Simon Christopher (Unisys Insurance Services Ltd)
Candlish, Joanne (Thompsons Solicitors)
Carey, Janine (Thompsons Solicitors)
Catherall, Hayley (MSB Solicitors)
Claeys BA (Hons), Gary Thomas (Silverbeck Rymer Solicitors)
Croot, Karen Babara (DWF LLP)
Dalzell, Susan Patricia (Weightmans LLP)
Daniels, Helen (Weightmans LLP)
Darlington, Carol Elaine (DWF LLP)
Davies, Patricia Georgina (Bell Lamb & Joynson Family Mediation)
Doran, Anne Marie (DWF LLP)
Dougherty, Ronald Joseph (JST Lawyers)
Driscoll, Lorraine Marie (Berrymans Lace Mawer)
Duffy, Amanda Jane (Thompsons Solicitors)
Edwards, Kimberley (Jackson & Canter)
Ellis-Jones, Dawn Angela (Murphy Hodgkinson Solicitors)
English, Shirley Ann (David Phillips & Partners)
Erickson, Stephen Alan (Cobleys Solicitors)
Evans, Katharine Louise (Bartletts Solicitors)
Fazakerley, Christine (Maxwell Entwistle & Byrne)
Finlay, Arthur (Hill Dickinson LLP)
Fisher, Jonathan (E Rex Makin & Co)
Flaherty, Alison Jane (Gregory Abrams)
Flaherty, Lee (EAD Solicitors)
Foley, Anthony (Brabners Chaffe Street LLP)
Ford, Susan Margaret (Liverpool Womens Hospital)
Garlick, Clare Margaret (Michael Wafer)
Gormley, Lisa Grace (Thompsons Solicitors)
Grimsditch, David Roger (Berrymans Lace Mawer)
Gullon, Beverley (Edwards Abrams Doherty Solicitors)
Gutteridge, Hazel Susannah (Weightmans LLP)
Haddock, Nina (Hendersons Solicitors)
Halewood, Christopher Mark (Berrymans Lace Mawer)
Hamer, Linda (Stephen D Brine)
Hargreaves, Kirsten Marie (Silverbeck Rymer Solicitors)
Hassey, Kevin Thomas (Weightmans LLP)
Haver, Patricia Alice (Bermans Solicitors)
Henderson, Michele Susan (MSB Solicitors)
Henshall, Hilary Muriel (Maxwell Hodge)
Higgins, Lucy Maye (Royal & Sun Alliance)
Hignett, Mark Andrew (Cogent)
Horrocks, Louise Kathryn (Goldsmith Williams)
Hughes, Julie (Goldsmith Williams)
Johnson, Mark Andrew (EAD Solicitors)
Jones, John Edward (Goldsmith Williams)
Joughin, Dawn Barbara (Canter Levin & Berg)
Kielty, Tracy Marie (Weightmans LLP)
Lanceley, Gaynor (Morecrofts LLP)
Lawler, Eve Marie (Royal & Sun Alliance)
Leece, Paula Donna (Hill Dickinson LLP)
Link, Katy Jayne (Edwards Abrams Doherty Solicitors)
Lockwood, Susan Jane (Berrymans Lace Mawer)
Macmichael, Sandra (Weightmans LLP)
Maesschalck, Charles (Hill Dickinson LLP)
Malcolm, Rosemary Jane (Thompsons Solicitors)
Marsters, Suzanne Elizebeth (Maxwell Entwistle & Byrne)
Mcgowan, Michael Ian (Q M Legal Costs)
Mcguinness, James William (EAD Solicitors)
Miller, Helen Elizabeth (DBH Service Business Centres Ltd)
Mistry, Dharmista (Cogent)
Morris, Rachel Nadia (DWF LLP)
Nelson, Theressa Maria (Thompsons Solicitors)
New, Philip Stephen Ernest (Edwards Abrams Doherty Solicitors)
Newnes, Anita (The Dures Partnership Solicitors)
Newton, Michael (Goldsmith Williams)
Overton, Jean Annette (Robinsons Solicitors)
Pearson, Aaron James (Weightmans LLP)
Phillips, Anita (Lime Pictures (Hollyoaks) Ltd)
Pilch, Allan Francis (Allan Pilch & Co)
Pratt, Michael (Maxwell Entwistle & Byrne)
Purcell, Debra Anne (Liverpool City Council)
Radford, Patricia Mary (Berrymans Lace Mawer)
Rainford, John Gerard (Royal & Sun Alliance)
Rice, Patrick (Weightmans LLP)
Roberts, Nicola Jane (Liverpool City Council)
Roberts, Philip Bradley (Wilson Cowie & Dillion Solicitors)
Rooney, Denise (Weightmans LLP)
Rose, Cheryl Anne (Weightmans LLP)
Rowlands, Edward Graham (Edwards Abrams Doherty Solicitors)
Rutherford, Margaret (Yaffe Jackson Ostrin)
Scholes, Gemma Elizabeth (Morecrofts Solicitors)
Scothern, Sarah (Canter Levin & Berg)
Smallwood, Jonathan (Jackson & Canter LLP)
Squires, Linda Irene (Silverbeck Rymer Solictors)
Stanton, Caroline Jane Jackson (Wafer Phillips Solicitors)
Taylor, Julie (Cornish Forfar & Allen)
Traynier, Angela (Canter Levin & Berg)
Turner, Shirley Ann (Goldsmith Williams)
Tyrer, Elaine (Silverbeck Rymer Solicitors)
Watling, Julie Christine (Mersey Travel)
Watts, Amanda Jane (Murphy Hodgkinson Solicitors)
Whitelaw, Lisa Jane (Halliwells LLP)
Wild, John Christohper (Royal & Sun Alliance)
Wilkes, Angela Tracy (DWF LLP)
Williams, Gaynor Marie (J B Leitch & Co LLP)
Wilson, Maria (Royal & Sun Alliance)
Wood, Lisa Patricia (Rees Roberts Solicitors)
Woods, Gayle Janine (Maxwell Hodge)
Wray, Julie Anne (Cogent)

LLANBEDR, Gwynedd

Stephens, Henriette Erna Lore (Wills Galore)

LLANDRINDOD WELLS, Powys

Eales, Graham Martin (Powys County Council)
Foster, David Christopher (Powys County Council)

LLANELLI, Carmarthenshire

Barry, Rhian (Jennings Solicitors)
Bell, Antoinette Bernadette (Randell Lloyd & Martin)
Hammond, Lynwen (Jennings Solicitors)
Hughes, Susan Alice (Davies Parsons Allchurch Solicitors)
Necke, Maria Teresa (Davies Parsons Allchurch Solicitors)
Richards, Anne (Jennings Solicitors)

LLANGEFNI, Anglesey

Jones, Elfed (Anglesey County Council)

LLANIDLOES, Powys

Foulkes, Adrian (Milwyn Jenkins & Jenkins)

LONGFIELD, Kent

Saunders, John William (John W Saunders)

LOSTWITHIEL, Cornwall

Fowler, Susan Jayne (A P Bassett Solicitors)

LOUGHBOROUGH, Leicestershire

Adkin, Suzanne Elizabeth (3M Health Care Ltd)
Andrews, Martyn Frederick (Clerk To The Justices)
Frisby, Michelle (Hawley & Rodgers)
Leafe, Christopher (Latham & Co Solicitors)
Neal, George Martin (Moss Solicitors)
Payne, Susannah Kathleen (Straw & Pearce)
Stokes, Elizabeth Mary (Straw & Pearce)
Swinfield, Clare Louise (Prusinski & Co)
Wharton, Wendy Barbara (Straw & Pearce)

LOUTH, Lincolnshire

Flower, Carol Pauline (Bridge Mcfarland Hadden Owen)
Goldsbrough, Christine (Bridge McFarland Solicitors)
Rawling, Allison (Bridge Mcfarland Hadden Owen)

LOWESTOFT, Suffolk

Bagley, Jill (Nicholsons Solicitors)
Bissett, Alistair David (Waveney District Council)
Dunster, Jacqueline Lorraine (Waveney District Council)
Fulcher, Lynne (Norton Peskett Solicitors)
Hosty, Michelle Sylvia (HKB Wiltshires)
Hughes, Paul Francis (Nicholsons Solicitors)
Mason, Nicola Melissa (Norton Peskett Solicitors)
O'Flaherty, Paul Martin (Norton Peskett Solicitors)
Oxborough, Lisa Marie (Norton Peskett Solicitors)
Rodgers, Linda Susan (Mears Hobbs & Durrant)
Sayer, Louise (Waveney District Council)
Taylor, Helen Ann (Mears Hobbs & Durrant)
Vicente, Jaclina Louise (Norton Peskett Solicitors)

LUDLOW, Shropshire

Davies, Elizabeth Mary (Woolley & Co Solicitors)
Maxwell, Claire (Greens Solicitors)
Pryke, Roland Lionel (Morgans Solicitors)

LUTON, Bedfordshire

Collins, Caroline (Taylor Walton Solicitors)
Deacon, Angela Mary (Lawtons Solicitors)
Gildon, Christine Ann (Barnard & Tomlin)
Hafeez, Aqeela Naz (Kewley Radley Solicitors)
Harries, Stuart (Pictons Solicitors LLP)
Herring, Deborah Anne (Adams Moore Solicitors Ltd)
Jennings, Olwen Nelia (Paul Norton & Co Solicitors)
Jones, Christine (Solomon Levy & Co)
Lomas, Kerry Anne (Pictons Solicitors LLP)
Merris, David William (Luton Borough Council)
Moxey, Tricia (Knowles Benning Solicitors)
Schaverien, Dorothy Glenys (TUI UK)
Vyse, Gillian Margaret (Machins)

LUTTERWORTH, Leicestershire

Money, Alison (Timpson Estates Department)
Reynolds, Jennifer (Headleys Solicitors)

LYDNEY, Gloucestershire

Hodgson, Nigel John (Francis & Co)
Spokes, Janet Elizabeth (Francis & Co)

LYMINGTON, Hampshire

Sherlock, Janice Christine (Moore & Blatch Solicitors)

LYTHAM ST ANNES, Lancashire

Bullough, Julie (Coupe Bradbury)
Calvert, Sally Ann (Linder Myers)
Hoggarth, Angela Louise (Dickson Haslam)
Holmes, Clare Jane (Fylde Borough Council)
Matthews, Donna Victoria (Dickson Haslam)
Morris, Sian Louise (Linder Myers)
Pangburn, Gary Frank (Fylde Borough Council)
Rabaiotti, Jayne (Coupe Bradbury)

MACCLESFIELD, Cheshire

Adams, Diane Elizabeth (Hague Lambert)
Barker, George Percy (Cheshire Peaks & Plains Housing Trust)
Belfield, Mark David (Thorneycroft & Co Solicitors)
Cheetham, Charlotte (Thorneycroft & Co Solicitors)
Fox, Vicky (Cheshire Peaks & Plains Housing Trust)
Frame, Mathew James (Wains Solicitors)
Jones, Christina Louise (Daniels)
Smith, Emma Louise (Daniels)
Thompson, Anna-Maria Franchesca (Bollin Legal Associates)
Woods, Nicola Ann (Thorneycroft & Co Solicitors)

MAIDENHEAD, Windsor & Maidenhead

Baker, Lesley Margaret (Lambda)
Barwise, Alan George (Royal Borough of Windsor & Maidenhead)
Buckeridge, Stephanie Jane (Heath Buckeridge)
Lamprell, Joan Lesley (Royal Borough of Windsor & Maidenhead)
Warnes, Alan Leslie (Heath Buckeridge)

MAIDSTONE, Kent

Abdey, Paul Michael (Brachers LLP)
Alabaster, Nichola (Brachers LLP)
Beadle, Jacqueline Lesley (Gulland & Gulland)
Beasley, Sarah Jane (Kent County Council)
Blundell, Clare (Kent County Council)
Bowles, Dorothy Vivien (Berry & Berry)
Butler, Malcolm John Robert (Malcolm Butler & Co Solicitors)
Carrim, Kim (Kennedys)
Carter, Kerry Helen (Burroughs Solicitors)
Cockrill, Kizzy Dee (Berry & Berry)
Cogger, Joanne Marie (Berry & Berry)
Crawford, Stella June (The Quest Partnership)
Fleet, Mark Richard (Whitehead Monckton)
Gibbons, Myles Anthony (Kent County Council)
Gilbert, Amber Claudine (Brachers LLP)
Gore, Mark Alan (Brachers LLP)
Grantham, Deborah Lorraine (Davies Lavery)
Grimsey, Susan Laura (Burroughs Solicitors)
Gymer, Timothy Andrew (Watson Nevill)
Hampshire, Annette Caroline (Brachers LLP)
Harrison, Linda Carol (Kent County Council)
Hawgood, Terence Robert (ASB Law)
Hayes, Diane (The Kent County Council)
Johncock, Kevin Michael (Berry & Berry)
Johnson, Emily Serwa (Kent County Council)
Littlemore, John Peter (Maidstone Borough Council)
Long, Nicholas (Gulland & Gulland)
Moore, Shirley Dawn (Brachers LLP)
Morris, Stephen David (Brachers LLP)
Sinclair, Laura (ASB Law)
Sweeting, Julia Clare (Kent County Council)
Theodorou, Kristen (Whitehead Monckton)
Thompson, Robert Philip (Brachers LLP)
Townsend, Kim Mandy (Fishers Solicitors)
Vickerman, Karina (Kent County Council)
Warman, Garry James (Whitehead Monckton)
West, Alison Mary (The Kent County Council)

MALDON, Essex

Fosbrook, Ann Florence (Crick & Freeman Solicitors)
Naylor, Maureen Lana (Bright & Sons Solicitors)

MALMESBURY, Wiltshire

Badminton, Susan Jane (Forrester & Forrester)

MALTON, North Yorkshire

Barker, Paul Aidan (Crombie Wilkinson)
Smith, Lynne Diane (Pearsons & Ward)

MALVERN, Worcestershire

Braithwaite, Tamsin May (Gaynor Smith Owen & Co)
Mcmahon, Elaine Margaret (Gaynor Smith Owen & Co)
Morton, Julie (Whatley Recordon)
Vale, Helen Elizabeth (Gaynor Smith Owen & Co)
Wilson, Yvonne Carol (Whatley Recordon)

MANCHESTER, Greater Manchester

Adams, Emma Patricia (Fentons Solicitors LLP)
Almeida, Amber (Berrymans Lace Mawer)
Anson, Rosemary Alison (Leigh Day & Co)
Arora, Ashi (Davis Blank Furniss)
Ashcroft, Melanie Jane (Maidments)
Aspa, Janet (Pabla & Pabla Solicitors)
Barnes, Sara Jayne (Kuit Steinart Levy Solicitors)
Barron, Ruth (Cobbetts LLP)

15

Bateman, Tina Clare (Davies Wallis Foyster)
Beddows, Christina (Thompsons Solicitors)
Bickford, Michael John Peirson (Countrywide Property Lawyers)
Biddle, Rachel Elizabeth (Thompsons Solicitors)
Bingham, Richard (Trafford Council)
Black, John (Co-operative Insurance Society Ltd)
Booth, Karen (Ralli Solicitors)
Boshell, Louise Ann (DWF LLP)
Boyd, Cate (Michael Taylor Associates)
Boyle, Mary Martina (Chance Hunter LLP)
Brandolani, Luigi Mario (Bournes Law Ltd)
Bridges, Alexandra (DWF LLP)
Brushett, Laura-Jayne (Arrow Global)
Budsworth, Craig (Glaisyers Solicitors)
Bull, Sarah Kathryn (Cunninghams Solicitors)
Burgess, Vicky (JMW Solicitors)
Burnside, Renee Catherine (Michael Taylor Associates)
Carroll, Paul (Hargreaves Farrell & Hobbs Solicitors)
Cartain, John Peter Bernard (Thompsons Solicitors)
Cartland, Margaret (Manchester City Council)
Cartwright, Stuart James (JMW Solicitors)
Chapman, Alison Mary (Manchester Airport PLC)
Chapman, Gillian (Thompsons Solicitors)
Cheetham, Sian Louise (Manchester City Council)
Church, Catharine Alice (Complete Claims Ltd)
Chynoweth, Philip (George Davies Solicitors LLP)
Clayton, Norma Clarice (Addleshaw Goddard LLP)
Cole, Stephen Hugh (Colemans-CTTS LLP)
Collins, Karen (Donns Solicitors)
Combe, Karen (Thompsons Solicitors)
Congdon, Kathryn Ann (Slater Heelis Collier Littler)
Corfe, Gaynor Dawn (Manchester City Council)
Cowling, Jennifer Jayne (Manchester Airport PLC)
Coyle, Martin (Berrymans Lace Mawer)
Coyne, Sarah Jane (Pannone LLP)
Dalton, Jacqueline Adele (Russell Jones & Walker)
Davenport, Phillip James (Central Manchester Healthcare Trust)
Davies, Annette Bridgette (Keith Dyson Solicitors)
Delaney, David Fenton (Field Cunningham & Co)
Devoy, Helen Louise (Horwich Farrelly Solicitors)
Dillon, Natelia Jean (The Connexion Partnership)
Donlan, Kirsty Joanne (Lopian Wagner)
Doswell, Jennifer Anne (Churchill Insurance)
Dunn, Elaine (Manchester City Council)
Edmondson, Clare Jenna (DWF LLP)
Elliott, Christopher (Betesh Partnership)
Entwistle, Jill (Linder Myers)
Evans, Rebecca Jane (Barlow Lyde & Gilbert)
Fahy, Yvonne Sandra (Manchester City Council)
Fairweather, Karen Ann (Tranters Solicitors)
Farrell, Michelle Louise (Thompsons Solicitors)
Fereday, Hayley Anne (Ricksons Solicitors)
Firth, Janet (Bermans Solicitors)
Fitzpatrick, Alan Joseph (Rowley Dickinson)
Fitzpatrick, Jenny (Beachcroft LLP)
Flavell, Mark Jonathan (Berrymans Lace Mawer)
Fleming, John Stephen (Halliwells LLP)
Fletcher, Rachel Ann (Beachcroft LLP)
Foley, David (DWF LLP)
Francis, Tanya (Addleshaw Goddard LLP)
Gage, Nicola (The Connexion Partnership)
Gallagher, Michelle (Weightmans LLP)
Gardner - Boyes, Joanne (Irwin Mitchell LLP)
Gillooley, Robin Sean (Olliers Solicitors)
Golland, Lisa Jayne (Birchall Blackburn)
Goss, Clare Alexandra (Rowley Dickinson)
Gould, Justine (Michael Taylor Associates)
Graham, Lesley Carroll (Sheldon Davidson)
Grebenar, William (Horwich Cohen Coghlan Solicitors)
Green, David Anthony (Manchester City Council)
Gregory, Josephine (Shirley Kelly Solicitors)
Griffiths, Jill (Thompsons Solicitors)
Hackett, Deborah Elizabeth (Countrywide Property Lawyers)
Hardy, Anne (Barlow Lyde & Gilbert)
Harris, Maxine (Gateley LLP)
Hartley, Angela (Kennedys)
Hartley, Sarah Louise (Whittles Solicitors)
Haselum, Richard Graham (The Connexion Partnership)
Hayes, Karen Patricia (Fentons Solicitors LLP)
Haynes, John Edward (Plexus Law)
Hearty, Brendan William (Manchester City Council)
Hegarty, Gavin (Hill Dickinson LLP)
Hill, Gillian (Trowers & Hamlins)
Hilton, Andrea Kathryn (DLA Piper UK LLP)
Hoey, Susan Lyn (Co-operative Insurance Society Ltd)
Home, Nicola Jane (Countrywide Property Lawyers)
Horton, Gary Nicholas (Co-operative Insurance Society Ltd)
Hudson, Anthony Francis (Manchester City Council)
Humphries, Suzanne Marie (Thompsons Solicitors)
Hynan, Wendy Elizabeth (Pannone LLP)
Isaacs, Graham (Hill Dickinson LLP)
Johnson, David (Johnson Yates Ltd)
Jones, Clare Marie (Horwich Farrelly Solicitors)
Jones, David Robert (Pannone LLP)
Jones, Gary (Irwin Mitchell LLP)
Jones, Mark (Goodman Harvey)
Jones, Susan (Michael Taylor Associates)
Kendrick, Angela Mary (Countrywide Property Lawyers)
Kent, Anthony (Cobbetts LLP)
Khan, Tahira Nageen (Manchester City Council)
Latham, Wendy Marian (Cobbetts LLP)
Lawrence, Deborah (Manchester City Council)
Leigh, Christopher Geoffrey (Halliwells LLP)
Lewis, Joanne Ellen (Berrymans Lace Mawer)
Lewis, Michelle (Dennison Greer Solicitors)
Lindsay, Rebecca (Glaisyers Solicitors)
Linehan, Kim (Colemans-CTTS LLP)
Lloyd-Jones, John (The Connexion Partnership)
Lofters, Beverley Ann (Berrymans Lace Mawer)
Loftus, Victoria Gail (Wythenshawe Law Centre)
Lomas, Sharon Elizabeth (Greenwoods Solicitors)
Long, Amanda Mary (Olliers Solicitors)
Maisuria-Kenny, Rekha (Weightmans LLP)
Marr, Tracy Joyce (Manchester City Council)
Martin, Barbara Lesley (Co-operative UK)
Martin, Victoria Jane (Sheldon Davidson)
Martyniak, Lee Anthony (Leech & Co Solicitors)
Masud, Elizabeth Ann (Co-operative Insurance Society Ltd)
McCabe, Sharon Lynda (Beachcroft LLP)
McCann, Kevin Andrew (Leech & Co Solicitors)
McCarthy, Sarah Louise (Halliwells LLP)
McElroy, Patricia (Fruhman Davies & Co)
McGeown, Deirdre Janice (Halliwells LLP)
Mcghie, Michael John (Pannone LLP)
Mcgladdery, Paul William (Nexus Solicitors)
Mcgrath, Christopher Thomas (Addleshaw Goddard LLP)
Mchugh, John James (Manchester City Council)
Medhurst, Linda Hazel (Berry & Berry)
Metcalf, Kim Tracey (Irwin Mitchell LLP)
Mohan, Allison Marina (Thompsons Solicitors)
Molyneaux, Ann Marie (Pannone LLP)
Moore, Zoe (Leech & Co Solicitors)
Moore, Zoe Louise (Hammonds Solicitors)
Moses, Kevin Wyn (Donns Solicitors)
Mullins, Jonathan Paul (Plexus Law)
Murfin, Joanna (Berrymans Lace Mawer)
Murphy, Shelley (A Hodari & Co)
Naylor, Elizabeth Frances (Mohindra Maini LLP)
Newall, Carrie (Pannone LLP)
Newstead, Peter John (Beachcroft LLP)
Nicholson, Deborah Michelle (Richard Nelson Solicitors)
Noble, Anne Marie (Berrymans Lace Mawer)
Nunn, Craig Robert (Berrymans Lace Mawer)
O'Kane, Ruth Elizabeth (Countrywide Property Lawyers)
O'Keefe, Janet (Olliers Solicitors)
Oliver, Matthew Graham (Sheldon Davidson)
Owen, Jacqueline Yvette (Manchester City Council)
Paramor, Jonathan (Manchester City Council)
Parrott, Claire Louise (Tuckers Solicitors)
Patel, Charulata (Jones Maidment Wilson)
Paterson, Robert (Gruber Garratt Solicitors)
Peacock, David John (Manchester City Council)
Pickering, Gena (HL Interactive LLP)
Picton, Hazel (Crofton Solicitors)
Piper, Colin (Peel Holdings Limited)
Podesta, Zoe (HL Interactive LLP)
Pringle, Karen Frances (Keoghs Solicitors LLP)
Quinney, Neil Richard (Greenwoods Solicitors)
Rainsford, Brendan (Manchester City Council)
Raja, Asfa Rahman (Keoghs Solicitors LLP)
Rawson, Kathy (Cobbetts LLP)
Reid, Ian (Mercer Ltd)
Rennie, Janice (Manchester City Council)
Rigby, Andrea Jane (Plexus Law)
Roberts, Tracy Ann (Co-operative Group (Cws) Ltd)
Robertson, Wai Ying (The Connexion Partnership)
Robinson, Gerald William (Manchester Airport PLC)
Robinson, Kerry Lisa (Abacus Solicitors)
Ross, Jennifer (HL Interactive LLP)
Ross, Natasha Marcia (Pannone LLP)
Rowland, Adrian Nicholas (Beachcroft LLP)
Rowlands, Bridget Ann (Co-operative Insurance Society Ltd)
Salih, Gulderen (Pannone LLP)
Scale, Laura Wendie (Horwich Cohen Coghlan Solicitors)
Scott, Jason (Addleshaw Goddard LLP)
Scragg, Simon Carl (Shoosmiths)
Senogles, Jeffrey Colin (Steve Asuelime)
Shaw, Darren (Shoosmiths)
Shaw, Helen Patricia (Hugh Potter & Co)
Shiers, Kellie Marie (Berrymans Lace Mawer)
Simpson, Tracy Anne (Countrywide Property Lawyers)
St. Romaine, Clare Helen (Avalon Solicitors)
Statham, Julie Ann May (Keith Dyson Solicitors)
Stock, Shirley Lynne (Clear Law Solicitors)
Stone, William Anthony (Joan Ferguson & Co)
Stones, Craig Allan (Burrows Bussin)
Sykes, Karen Lesley (Pannone LLP)
Szabo, Szilvia (Leech & Co Solicitors)
Tann, Steve (Halliwells LLP)
Tapper, Claire (Burton Copeland)
Tarling, Andrew David (Pannone LLP)
Taylor, Janet Anne (Fentons Solicitors LLP)
Thomas, Daniel (Betesh Partnership)
Till, Andrea Claire (Thompsons Solicitors)
Tomlinson, Elizabeth Anne (Manchester Airport PLC)
Urquhart, Andrew Iain Peter (Pabla & Pabla Solicitors)
Vinton, Sarah Louise (Rowlands)
Walker, Laura Denise (Cobbetts LLP)
Wallace, Lisa (Leech & Co Solicitors)
Walmsley, Timothy Joseph (GMPTE)
Warmisham, Carol (DLA Piper UK LLP)
Watt, Rebecca Jane (Michael Taylor Associates)
Welsh, Peter John (University of Manchester Institute of Science & Technology (UMIST))
White, Paul Marcus (Barlow Lyde & Gilbert)
White, Susan Jane (Greater Manchester Police)
Wilkinson, Sarah Louise (Manchester City Council)
Williams, Lynda (Pannone LLP)
Winter, Pamela (Michael Alexander)
Wise, Nicola (Cogents Solicitors (RBS Insurance))
Wolstenhulme, Ian Robert (Leech & Co Solicitors)
Wood, Derek Alan (Hammonds Solicitors)
Woods, David James (Addleshaw Goddard LLP)
Woodward, David (Halliwells LLP)
Worrall, Tracey (Pannone LLP)
Wrigley, Emma (Pannone LLP)
Yearsley, Lynne Irene (Bannister Preston)
Young, Helen Jane (Cobbetts LLP)
Young, Peter Russell (Hillis Solicitors)

MANNINGTREE, Essex
Morsley, Susan Janice (Sparling Benham & Brough)

MANSFIELD, Nottinghamshire
Dale, Richard Alexander (Shacklocks)
Dodd, David Warren (The Coal Authority)
Green, Rosalynde (Harrop White Vallance & Dawson)
Hayes, John Samuel (Elliot Mather LLP)
Illsley, Robert (Elliot Mather LLP)
Liversidge, Priscilla Ann (Bryan & Armstrong)
Lodder, Lisa Jane (Hopkins Solicitors LLP)
Mason, Tina (Harrop White Vallance & Dawson)
Morris, Claire (Harrop White Vallance & Dawson)
Mowat, Victoria Emily (Bilton Hammond)
Scott, Kevin (Mansfield District Council)
Sheridan, Beth (Hopkin & Sons)
Staves, Glyn (Elliot Mather LLP)
Walker, Catherine Mary (Bryan & Armstrong)
White, Pamela (MH Legal)
Wright, Dean Douglas (Mansfield District Council)

MARCH, Cambridgeshire
Godfrey, Timothy James (Bowser Ollard & Bentley)
Jenkins, Lucy Ann (Fenland District Council)

MARGATE, Kent
Baird, Jane Somerville (Marsden Duncan)
Cowell, Brian John (Girlings Solicitors)
Durrant, Richard John (Boys & Maughan)
Huckstepp, Andrea (Boys & Maughan)
Lovelock, Simon Edward (Boys & Maughan)
Woods, Sarah Vanessa (Barnes Marsland)

MARKET DEEPING, Lincolnshire
Markwick, Karen Anne (Double & Megson)

MARKET DRAYTON, Shropshire
Wisniewski, Gemma Louise (Muller Dairies UK Ltd)

MARKET HARBOROUGH, Leicestershire
Alvey, Rachel (Hefford Johnson & Co)
Barson, David (Bray & Bray Solicitors)

MARLBOROUGH, Wiltshire
Snook, Karen (Withy King Solicitors)
Vassie, Rebecca Claire (Awdry Bailey & Douglas Solicitors)

MARYPORT, Cumbria
Oliphant, Diane (Milburns Solicitors)

MATLOCK, Derbyshire
Blackshaw, Kathryn Julie (Lovedays Solicitors)
Marriott, Angela (Derbyshire County Council)
Pearson, Shirley (Derbyshire County Council)
Wildgoose, Charles Frederick (Lovedays Solicitors)
Wilson, Julie (Derbyshire County Council)

MELTON MOWBRAY, Leicestershire
Cragg, Derek Stanley (Oldham Marsh Page Flavell)
Hill, Christine Anne (Latham & Co Solicitors)
Jepson, Stephen Paul (S Jepson)
Mcconnell, Nancy Joy (Oldham Marsh Page Flavell)

MERTHYR TYDFIL, Merthyr Tydfil
Egglestone, Susanne (North Glamorgan Nhs Trust)
Evans, Philip Anthony (Reynold John Mayoiet Solicitor)
Gibbs, Rachel Louise (The Gwyn George Partnership)
Parry, Ann (Merthyr Valleys Homes)
Thomas, Michelle Marie (The Gwyn George Partnership)

MIDDLESBROUGH, Middlesbrough
Bass, Alison Mary (Askew Bunting Solicitors)
Davison, Diane (Thompson Solicitors)
Dowson, Claire Louise (NAS Recruitment Ltd)
Fenwick, Lorraine (Middlesbrough Borough Council)
Garbutt, Timothy Vincent (Freers Solicitors)
Grainger, Jacqueline Sharon (Appleby Hope & Matthews)
Gray, Angela Maria (Middlesbrough Borough Council)
Holmes, Emma Louise (Macks Solicitors)
Hook, Janice Boyd (Thompson Solicitors)
Ingledew, Andrea (Appleby Hope & Matthews)
Phillips, Michelle Dawn (Cleveland Constabulary)
Routledge, Robert William (Watson Woodhouse Solicitors)
Shepherd, Tracey Louise (Macks Solicitors)
Spink, Abbilee (Askew Bunting Solicitors)
Thomson, Mary Margaret (University of Teesside)
Turner, Sarah Louise (Watson Woodhouse Solicitors)
Watson, Margaret (Kitching Kneale & Co)

MIDDLETON, Greater Manchester
Bennett, Julie Christine (Allison & Reilly Solicitors)
Broadbent, Alison Jane (Sedgwick Phelan & Partners)
Nuttall, Karen (Temperley Taylor)

MIDHURST, West Sussex
Pye, Jessica Lesley (MacDonald Oates LLP)

MILDENHALL, Suffolk
Orton, Jane Elizabeth (Forest Heath District Council)
Scott, Suzanne Elizabeth (Bendall & Sons)

MILFORD HAVEN, Pembrokeshire
Noble, Helen Jane (Noble Harbour Solicitors)

MILNTHORPE, Cumbria
Horne, Sara Louise (Poole Townsend)

MILTON KEYNES, Milton Keynes
Bamber, Brian John (Milton Keynes Council)
Bogle, Larisa Maria (Motor Insurers Bureau)
Cain, Clare Madeline (Adams Moore Solicitors Ltd)
Clark, Paul Robert (BP PLC)
Condliffe, Julie (Denton Wilde Sapte)
Cufaude, Alan Robert (Abbey National)
Dobson, Victoria Joy (EMW Law LLP)
Elam, Martin Norman (Fennemores Solicitors)
Fernandes, Carolyn Marie (Howes Percival LLP)
Hancox, Bernard John (Shoosmiths)

Higgins, Denise Louise (Woodfines LLP)
Hurst, Michelle (Adams Moore Solicitors Ltd)
Mansell, James (Greenwoods Soliticors)
Marchant, Leonora (Citizens Advice Bureau)
McConnachie, Lisa Maxine (EMW Law LLP)
Millar, Dawn Julia (Heald Solicitors)
Organ, Andrew Peter (Crawford & Company)
Ovenden, Nicola Joyce (Greenwoods Soliticors)
Pearson, Patricia Anne (Shoosmiths)
Richards, Keith Nicholas (SNR Denton)
Sanders, Lindsey (Crawford & Company)
Shillingford, Charlene Claire (Howes Percival LLP)
Sims, Laura Jane (Borneo Linnells Solicitors)
Smith, Teresa Ann (Pictons Solicitors LLP)
Southall, Anna Marie (Denton Wilde Sapte)
Summerling, Ann (Geoffrey Leaver)
Taylor, Deborah Helen (Countrywide Surveyors)
Ubhi, Surinder Singh (Denton Wilde Sapte)
Wager, Louise (Denton Wilde Sapte)
Wright, Denise (English Partnerships)
Zeineh, Barbro Harriet (Franklins Solicitors LLP)

MIRFIELD, West Yorkshire
Ward, Peter (Hellewell Pasley & Brewer)

MITCHAM, Surrey
Khan, Muhammed Abdul Muid (Rest Harrow Solicitors)

MOLD, Flintshire
Higgins, Carol Jean (Flintshire County Council)

MONMOUTH, Monmouthshire
Lord, Richard William (Alan Curtis)
Rudall, Wayne (Alan Curtis)

MORDEN, Surrey
Heffernan, Andrew Martin (London Borough of Merton)
Phelan, Paul Michael (London Borough of Merton)

MORECAMBE, Lancashire
Baines, Anthony Robin (Wright & Lord Solicitors)
Crookes, Janice (Whiteside & Knowles)
Hardman, Susan Ann (Birchall Blackburn)
Hicks, Christine (Carol Hill Conveyancing)
Hill, Carol (Carol Hill Conveyancing)
Hodgson, Gina (Jobling & Knape)
Mort, Kenneth (Locum)
Pearson, Jennifer Patricia (Richard Bagguley Solicitors)
Ribbons, Sarah Louise (Bannister Bates & Son)

MORETON-IN-MARSH, Gloucestershire
Jackson, Alan Charles (Independent Trust Corporation Ltd)

MORPETH, Northumberland
Dunlop, Maureen Mcarthur (Wholley Goodings)
Jackson, Linda (Northumberland County Council)

MUCH WENLOCK, Shropshire
Davies, Kelly Elizabeth (Fodens Solicitors)
Mercer, Claire Francesca (Fodens Solicitors)

NAILSEA, North Somerset
Simmons, Alison (Simmons)

NANTWICH, Cheshire
Hilton, Claire Louise (Hall Smith Whittingham)
McVeigh, Tracy (Poole Alcock LLP)

NEATH, Neath Port Talbot
Burbage, Elisabeth (Hutchinson Thomas)
Phillips, Helen (Hutchinson Thomas)
Pickering, Sandra May (Hutchinson Thomas)
Street, Sioned Euroswydd (Hutchinson Thomas)

NEEDHAM MARKET, Suffolk
Iacobucci, Joseph Pasquale (Mid Suffolk District Council)

NELSON, Lancashire
Ashworth, Tracy Louise (Marsden Building Society)
Calderbank, Linda Ann (Pendle Borough Council)
Ghosh, Ira Helen (Pendle Borough Council)
Harkley, Helen Jean (Steele Ford & Newton)
Hunt, David James (Farnworth Shaw Solicitors)
Kay, Barbara Christine (Pendle Borough Council)
Nutter, Julia (Farnworth Shaw Solicitors)
Rushton, Nicola Joy (Donald Race & Newton)
Thomson, Helen (Steele Ford & Newton)

NEW MALDEN, Surrey
Blunden, Graham John (Lyons Davidson Solicitors)
Herbert, William John (Lyons Davidson Solicitors)
Rawicz, Lidia Joanna (Lyons Davidson Solicitors)
Smith, Clive (Lyons Davidson Solicitors)
Trathen, Marcus Jonathan (Lyons Davidson Solicitors)

NEW MILTON, Hampshire
Barton, Sandra Elizabeth (Peverel Management Services Ltd)
Edgar, Keith Alan (Peverey Management Services Ltd)
Herd, Ann Elizabeth (Heppenstalls)
Scaife, Arthur Thomas (Lamb & Smart)

NEW OLLERTON, Nottinghamshire
Sleigh, Peter Henry (Jakes & Co)

NEWARK, Nottinghamshire
Clayton, Audrey Elaine (Tallents)
Gatheral, Sally Elizabeth (Locum)
Tasker, Rebecca Irene (Bird & Co)
Walters, Caroline Margaret (Payne Gamage Colton & Franks)

NEWBURY, West Berkshire
Booroff, Nicola Jayne (Mills & Bann)
Dear, Joshua Liam Russell (Horsey Lightly Fynn)
Fisher, Terence Frederick (Charles Hoile)
Hartwell, Ian Malcolm (Burton Stancliffe & Co)
House, Sarah Louise (West Berkshire District Council)
Matthews, Eric John (Vodafone Group)
Monger, Suzanne Angela (Burton Stancliffe & Co)
Pook, Simon Alan (Charles Lucas & Marshall)
Savage, Lucy Anne (Gardner Leader LLP)
Sherman, Michele (West Berkshire District Council)
Shipp, Andrew James (Gardner Leader LLP)

NEWCASTLE UNDER LYME, Staffordshire
Alcock, Jayne (Knights Solicitors LLP)
Birchall, Michelle Susan (Brown & Corbishley Solicitors)
Court, Catherine (Knights Solicitors LLP)
Dean, Gary (Tinsdills Solicitors)
Farrell, Janet (Brown & Corbishley Solicitors)
Forrester, Paul David (Knights Solicitors LLP)
Hill, Godfrey Alexander (Knights Solicitors LLP)
Washington, Paul Rushley (Newcastle Under Lyme Borough Council)
Washington, Susan Elizabeth (Aspire Housing)
White, Barbara (Knights Solicitors LLP)

NEWCASTLE UPON TYNE, Tyne & Wear
Adams, Claire Helen (Centre for Life)
Alexander, Vicki (Wallers Solicitors)
Appleyard, Pauline (Ward Hadaway Solicitors)
Arkle, Barry (Hay & Kilner)
Attle, James Raymond (Sintons LLP)
Barton, John Robert (North Tyneside Council)
Birchnall, Gillian (Gorman Hamilton Solicitors)
Boakes, Julie (Dickinson Dees LLP)
Borthwick, Kara Marie (Haswell & Cornberg)
Bouri, Jane Peggy Anne (Harish C Bouri)
Bowskill, Linda Carol (Dickinson Dees LLP)
Brooks, Beverley (Beachcroft LLP)
Brown, Hilary Ann (Ward Hadaway Solicitors)
Brown, Lynne (Optima Legal Services Ltd)
Bruce, Elaine (Gorman Hamilton Solicitors)
Burton, Adam (Browell Smith & Co Solicitors)
Carmichael, Jacqueline (Carmichael & Heathfield)
Catchpole, Dawn Marie (Russell Jones & Walker)
Chapman, Fiona (Eversheds LLP)
Christian, Susan (Newcastle Upon Tyne City Council)
Clark, Christine (Newcastle Upon Tyne City Council)
Clark, Paul Anthony (Dickinson Dees LLP)
Collins, Angela (Thompsons Solicitors)
Compton, Robert Thomas (Watson Burton LLP)
Connelly, Chantel Lucy (Beachcroft LLP)
Connelly, Gill (Thompsons Solicitors)
Cowen, Kathryn Louise (Neon Legal)
Craig, Michael Howard (The Care Quality Commission)
Craig, Philip (North Tyneside Council)
Currie, Graham Laurence (Eversheds LLP)
Dawson, Carol Anne (National Probation Service)
Devine, Debra Anne (Sintons LLP)
Devlin, Susan (Davies Bell & Reed)
Douglas, Mark Richard (Crutes Law Firm)
Eisner, Frederick Steven (Wallers Solicitors)
Ferguson, Leigh (Watson Burton LLP)
Foggett, Maureen (Newcastle Upon Tyne City Council)
Forster, Margaret (Wallers Solicitors)
Francis, Julie (Crutes Law Firm)
Freeman, Neil (Dickinson Dees LLP)
Gibson, Yvonne (Dickinson Dees LLP)
Graham, Catriona (Dickinson Dees LLP)
Harding, Sarah Louise (Silk Family Law)
Hay, Nicola Elizabeth (Dickinson Dees LLP)
Haywood, Nicola Ann (Gorman Hamilton Solicitors)
Herron, Sharon Maria (Newcastle Upon Tyne City Council)
Hetherington, Craig Gavin (Sintons LLP)
Hind, Julie (Ward Hadaway Solicitors)
Jackson, Simon David (Shaw & Co Solicitors)
Jehan, Christopher Stuart (Gorman Hamilton Solicitors)
Jobson, Sarah Louise (Dickinson Dees LLP)
Knipe, David James (Browell Smith & Co Solicitors)
Latham, William James (Nexus Solicitors)
Lawler, Kenneth (Sintons LLP)
Lees, Pamela Sharon (North Tyneside Council)
Lott, Christine Jeanette (Northumbria Police)
Lund, Simon Christopher (Ward Hadaway Solicitors)
Mann, Philip (Crutes Law Firm)
Mason, Robert (Pearson Caulfield)
Matthews, Carol Isobel (Beecham Peacock)
McFall, James Ian (Thompsons Solicitors)
McIvor, Debra Ann (Thompsons Solicitors)
Mole, David John (Thompsons Solicitors)
Nellist, Emma Elizabeth (Newcastle Upon Tyne City Council)
O'Mahony, Ranjit Kaur (Thompsons Solicitors)
Orr, Kirsty Ailsa (Muckle LLP)
Petrie, Steven David (Watson Burton LLP)
Priestman, Tracey (Sintons LLP)
Proud, Helen (Sintons LLP)
Ramsay, Kathleen Ann (Northumbria Police)
Redhead, Linda Ann (Thompsons Solicitors)
Reid-Mitchell, Michelle (Thompsons Solicitors)
Richardson, Gillian (Gorman Hamilton Solicitors)
Ridley, Isabell (Kidd Spoor Harper)
Robson, Caroline (Irwin Mitchell LLP)
Russell, Joan Hunter (Sintons LLP)
Scott, Anthony (Thompsons Solicitors)
Seery, Ann May (Beecham Peacock)
Shearer, Selina (Kidd Spoor Harper)
Simpson, Angela Claire (Beecham Peacock)
Simpson, Matthew George (EAGA PLC)
Stockwell, Michelle Ann (Hay & Kilner)
Tate, Kim (Dickinson Dees LLP)
Thompson, John Robert (Crutes Law Firm)
Vaughan, Helen Louise (Dickinson Dees LLP)
Vipond, Laura Anne (Blackett Hart & Pratt LLP)
Waldron, Helen (Gorman Hamilton Solicitors)
Ward, Carole Elizabeth (Ward Hadaway Solicitors)
Waugh, Nicola (Thompsons Solicitors)
Waugh, Tamsin (Winn Solicitors Ltd)
Webb, Amanda (Care Quality Commision)
Webb, Hazel (Thompsons Solicitors)
Williamson, Louise Jean (Watson Burton LLP)
Wood, Debby (Sintons LLP)

NEWMARKET, Suffolk
Gooch, Julia Mary (Hodson Margetts & Charles)
Hawkes, Georgina Jane (Hempsted Property & Probate Lawyers)
Howard, Joanne Elizabeth (National Farmers Union)
Knappett, Lisa Marie (Edmondson Hall)
Loke, Katherine Tracey (Oslers)

NEWPORT, Isle of Wight
Ambler, Deborah Christine (Eldridges Solicitors)
Barnes, Angela Ruth (Gartside Harding & Davies)
Barry, Helen (Watkins & Gunn)
Batstone, Jade (B2 From Beachcroft)
Brake, Brian Malcolm (Keith Traves Solicitor)
Bubenzer, Kristin (Gartside Harding & Davies)
Chambers, Emma Louise (Glanvilles Solicitors)
Christofi, Helen (Jacklyn Dawson)
Clark, Ian Woodrow (Eldridges Solicitors)
Cooper, Sonia Adonna (Isle of Wight Council)
Dash, Maria (Howells LLP)
Davies, Colin John (Harding Evans Ltd)
Dyer, Hilary Jane (Jerome & Co)
Edwards, Janine (Newport Borough Council)
Edwards, Tracey Jayne (Quality Solicitors hpjv)
Ford, Claire Louise (Convey Law)
Hands, Victoria Jane (Harding Evans Ltd)
Harding, Susan Jean (Everett Tomlin Lloyd & Pratt)
Harris, Karen Marie (Monmouthshire Buliding Society)
Harrison, Tracy Elaine (Crown Prosecution Service)
Hayward, Susan Florence (Isle of Wight Council)
Howells, Ceri (Convey Law)
James, Mark Edward (Gareth Driscoll Solicitors)
James, Stephen Foster (Glanvilles Solicitors)
Jones, Claire (Newport Borough Council)
Lapping, Beth (John W Davies & Co)
Murphy, Jonathan Paul (Isle of Wight Council)
Parish, Clive Anthony (Crown Prosecution Service)
Parry, Andrew Frank (Robin H Jones & Co)
Sadler, Josephine (Roger James Clements & Panting)
Stephens, Robert James (Reconvey)
Thorne, Justin Patrick (Isle of Wight Council)
Williams, Andrew John (Lloyds TSB Insurance)
Williams, Linda Christine (Premier Risk Solutions Ltd)
Zorrilla, Renee (Harding Evans Ltd)

NEWPORT PAGNELL, Buckinghamshire
Rose, Michael John (Harvey Ingram Borneos)

NEWQUAY, Cornwall
Allen, Stephanie Jane (Coodes Solicitors)
Hilton, James Robert (Ralph & Co)
Kendall, Lesley Drever (Coodes Solicitors)
Roberts, Lowenna Jayne (Coodes Solicitors)
Walker, Christopher John (Greenways)

NEWTON ABBOT, Devon
Aggett, Joanne Louise (WBW Solicitors)
Barnard, Karen (WBW Solicitors)
Davis, Heather Jean (Karen O'Neill)
Faulkner, Kay Elaine (Kellock & Johnson)
Gilderslleve, Ellen Sabine (Teign Housing)
Goodwin, Helen (Woollcombe Beer Watts)
Hargreaves, Richard Peter (WBW Solicitors)
Jennings, Caroline Louise (WBW Solicitors)
Linnitt, Christopher Craig (Linnitts Solicitors)
Macfie, Nina (Karen O'Neill)

NEWTON-LE-WILLOWS, Merseyside
Gowen, Susan Lesley (Michael W Halsall)
Hennen, Gemma Kay (Michael W Halsall)
Murray, Clare (Michael W Halsall)
Williams, Caroline Anne (Michael W Halsall)

NEWTOWN, Powys
Macken, Nicola Joanne (Williams Gittins & Tomley)

NORTH SHIELDS, Tyne & Wear
Bradley, Darryn (Kidd Spoor Taylor)
Cresser, Emma (Hadaway & Hadaway)
Robertson, Helen Louise (Hadaway & Hadaway)
Robson, Peter Robert (Kidd Spoor Taylor)

NORTH WALSHAM, Norfolk
Rollingson, Patricia (Hansells Solicitors)

NORTHALLERTON, North Yorkshire
Beddis-Jennings, Catherine Anne (North Yorkshire County Council)
Giffin, Harry John (North Yorkshire County Council)
Meynell, Howard Frederick (Calder Meynell)
Watson, Andrea Louise (North Yorkshire County Council)

NORTHAMPTON, Northamptonshire
Brown, Hayley Anne (Shoosmiths)
Chivers, Nina Martina (Tollers Solicitors)
Cliffe, Susan Mary (Hewitsons Solicitors)
Cook, Lorraine Melissa (Tollers Solicitors)
Copus, Desnee Claire Louise (Shoosmiths)
Edgley, Teresa Michelle (Wilson Browne LLP)
Hargrave, Simone Anne (Hewitsons Solicitors)
Harper, Sarah Louise (Shoosmiths)
Hutchings, Simon Paul (Shoosmiths)
Jordan, Susan (Woodford Robinson)
Keating, Lisa Jayne (Shoosmiths)
Knox, Graham (Goodchild Vizard & Smart)
Kooner, Jasvinder (DW Solicitors)
Kyprianides, Clare Elizabeth (Shoosmiths)
Maccarthy, Diana (Northampton College)
Male, Veronica Mercedes (Shoosmiths)
Murray, Jayne Marie (Wilson Browne LLP)
Neal-Jones, Sandra Jane (Persimmon Homes Ltd)
Nixon, Carolyn Susan Mary (Northamptonshire County Council)
Parish, Robert Andrew (Shoosmiths)

Parsons, Nicholas Jeremy (Borneo Hughes Martell Solicitors)
Percival, Julie Mary (Community Law Service)
Read, David Frank (Hewitsons Solicitors)
Reece, Patricia Frances (Paul Montgomery Solicitors)
Reed, Roger Harry (Tollers Solicitors)
Robinson, Nicola Simone (Norbet Dentressangle Holdings Ltd)
Scammell, Catherine (Howes Percival LLP)
Simpson, Claudette (Shoosmiths)
Smith, Christine Ann (Northamptonshire County Council)
Smith, George Arthur (Tollers Solicitors)
Stephenson, Jaqueline Audrey (Shoosmiths)
Stevens, Trudi (Summers Nigh Law LLP)
Treacy, Michelle Louise (Shoosmiths)
Tricker, James Walter (Goodchild Vizard & Smart)
Webb, Margaret (Redrow Homes)
White-Robinson, Timothy (Shoosmiths)

NORTHWICH, Cheshire

Birtles, Geoffrey (Dixon Keogh & Johnson)
Foundation, Julie (Moss Haselhurst Solicitors)
Kemp, Jeannette (Moss Haselhurst Solicitors)
Riley, Donna Louise (Poole Alcock LLP)

NORTHWOOD, Middlesex

Rush, Ruth Alison Linda (Seabourne Lawley Solicitors)

NORWICH, Norfolk

Alfieri, Emma (Steeles Law LLP)
Andrews, Sally Ann (Steeles Law LLP)
Ashby, David John (Aviva Legal Services)
Bales, Denise (Norfolk County Council)
Beard, Gemma Jane (Aviva)
Beck, Aileen Janine (Rogers & Norton)
Bee, John Anthony (Morgan Jones & Pett)
Bell, Steven Christian (Norfolk County Council)
Bergin, Martha Violet (Aviva)
Bird, Alison Creina (Godfrey Morgan Solicitors)
Bowen, Darren John (Leathes Prior)
Bransby, Simon Michael (Morgan Jones & Pett)
Brighton, Wendy Elizabeth (Capron & Helliwell)
Brown, Sarah Catherine (Steeles Law LLP)
Carter, Suzanne (Aviva)
Casey, Geraldine Ann (Norfolk County Council)
Chandler, Brenda Jane (Hansells Solicitors)
Clarke, Jane Margaret (Eversheds LLP)
Cole, Victoria Caroline (Norfolk County Council)
Coleman, Melissa (Mills & Reeve)
Cushing, Julie Edith (Eversheds LLP)
Devaney, Michael Jeremy (Crown Prosecution Service)
Duncan, Rosalind Anne (Overburys Solicitors)
Easey, Elizabeth (Norfolk County Council)
Edwards, Rebecca Ann (Cozens-Hardy LLP)
Ellis, Kirstin Charlotte (Norfolk County Council)
Endersby, Julie Dawn (Howes Percival LLP)
Fowler, Rebecca Jane (Clapham & Collinge Solicitors)
George, Jennifer Rose (Jennifer Easter Ltd)
Green, Christopher (Norwich Union)
Greeves, Lisa Nicole (Cozens-Hardy LLP)
Hall, Lorna (Norfolk County Council)
Hardiment, Joy Christine (Eversheds LLP)
Hardy, David Andrew (Aviva Legal Services)
Harmer, Richard (Motor Plus Ltd)
Hartley, Louise Jane (Norfolk County Council)
Head, Sharon Jane (Norfolk County Council)
Holmes, Kathryn Hope (Norfolk County Council)
Holt, Victoria April (Fosters Solicitors)
Howlett, Andrew (Norfolk County Council)
Ireland, Angela Karen (Steeles Law LLP)
Larner, Julie Ann (Aviva PLC Legal Services)
Larwood, Maria Frances (Rogers & Norton)
Leeds, Roslyn Joanne (Overburys Solicitors)
Leggoe, Gillian Lesley (Fosters Solicitors)
Lewis, Garydd Francis (Aviva)
Marshall, Linda (Greenland Houchen Pomeroy)
Mayes, Joanne Shelagh (Hatch Brenner Solicitors)
Meacock, Amy Louise (Fosters Solicitors)
Mickleburgh, Jane Carolyn (Willcox & Lewis)
Moore, Debra Lesley (Aviva)
Mower, Sarah Joan (Howes Percival LLP)
Newman, Margaret (Aviva Legal Services)
O'Kane, Jane Louise (Eversheds LLP)
Parker, Claire Victoria (Allan Rutherford Solicitors)
Percival, David John (Greenland Houchen Pomeroy)
Pritty, Faith Philomena (Hatch Brenner Solicitors)
Rackham, Sally Joy (South Norfolk District Council)
Richards, Melissa Louise (Howes Percival LLP)
Risk, Victoria Helen Maria (Mills & Reeve)
Robinson, Dereth Louise (Aviva Legal Services)
Robinson, Ian Edward (Aviva PLC Legal Services)
Rowe, Kurt (Aviva)
Russell, Marguerite (Fosters Solicitors)
Savage, Laura Anne (Leathes Prior)
Sawyer, Susan (Fosters Solicitors)
Schofield, Nicholas Roy (Aviva)
Slaughter, Jennifer Ann (Aviva)
Smith, Andrew Brooks (Motor Plus Ltd)
Smith, Harvey Graham (Aviva)
Smith, Nikki Marie (Norfolk County Council)
Starkings, Emma Jayne (Story & Robinson)
Starling, Carolyn Jane (Kester Cunningham John Solicitors)
Stevens, Teresa Susan (Aviva PLC Legal Services)
Summerhayes, Sara Annette (Aviva)
Vettraino, Tina Wendy (Norfolk County Council)
Ward, Wendy Lynne (Universal Asset Protection)
Williamson, Tracy Louise (Chambers & Co)
Wright, Julia Carolyn (Aviva Legal Services)
Wright, Sarah Jane (Greenland Houchen Pomeroy)
Yaxley, Sally Danielle (Steeles Law LLP)
Young, Michael John (Broadland Probate Services Ltd)

NOTTINGHAM, Nottinghamshire

Baguley, Ian David (Actons Solicitors)
Ball, Susan Maureen (Nottinghamshire County Council)
Bannister, Deborah (Martin Smalley & Co)
Birch, Lorraine Jane (Nottinghamshire County Council)
Bramley, Jane (Browne Jacobson LLP)
Brammer, Karen Ann (Nelsons Solicitors LLP)
Brennan, Antoinette Mary (Eversheds LLP)
Brown, Amanda Jane (Nottingham Family Law Associates)
Brown, Carole Elizabeth (Freeth Cartwright LLP)
Brown, Kerry Ann (Rothera Dowson)
Brown, Sophia (Nottingham City Council)
Castledine, Adrian (Robert Barber & Sons)
Collins, Sarah Ruth (Nottinghamshire County Council)
Cook, Sally Elizabeth (Browne Jacobson LLP)
Cottam, Carl Adrian (Browne Jacobson LLP)
Davis, Jane Elizabeth Monkal (Nelsons Solicitors LLP)
Dickerson, Claire (Blusource)
Dobson, Eloise (Nottingham City Council)
Elliott, Gwendoline Mary (Hugh Young Solicitors)
Emeleus-Moreton, Rebecca Louise (Sharp & Partners)
Franks, Yvonne Patience (Campion & Co)
Freeman, Carol Susan (Massers Solicitors)
Fryer, Stephen Paul (Nottingham City Council)
Garton, Mandy Joanne (SGC)
Geary, Jennifer Jane (Ellis Fermor & Negus)
Goff, Rachael Emma (Freeth Cartwright LLP)
Goode, Matthew Charles (Challinors Solicitors)
Graham, Peter Thomas (Nottingham City Council)
Grainger, Mary Letticia (Freeth Cartwright LLP)
Green, Hilary Rose (Newark & Sherwood District Council)
Greenwood, Julie Anne (Freeth Cartwright LLP)
Hallam, Claire Louise (Freeth Cartwright LLP)
Hallam, Neil (Nottinghamshire Constabulary)
Hayes, Anne Marie (Sheltons)
Ingram, Lisa Maria (Newark & Sherwood District Council)
Jackson, Pamela Pauline (Ashton Bond Gigg)
Jackson, Peter Nicholas (Geffery Parker Vorne)
Jackson, Wendy (Tallents Godfrey Solicitors)
Javens, Joanne Elaine (Nottingham City Council)
Keeling, Joanne Lesley (Gregsons)
Kendrick, Claire Louise (Campion & Co)
Landells, Nicholas John (Poppleston Allen Solicitors)
Langley, Katherine Georgina (Nelson Business Defence)
Lawrence, Petrona Michelle (Robert Barber & Sons)
Lees-Collier, Sarah Elizabeth (Gladstone Solicitors)
Lowe, Claire Marie (Fraser Brown)
Madden, Laura Georgina (Berryman Shacklock LLP)
Magill, Joanne Louise (Sheltons)
Makings, June Marie (Actons Solicitors)
Miles, David Peter (Crown Prosecution Service)
Money, Howard Lanham (Young & Pearce)
Nashed, Andrew Hamilton (Geldards LLP)
Naylor, Janis (Jackson Quinn)
O'Shea, Michelle (Michelle O'Shea & CO)
Pabla, Jacqueline Elaine (Yates & Co)
Peacock, John David (Sheltons)
Pottle, Sarah Jane (Fraser Brown)
Price, Christina (Nottingham City Council)
Randall, Glenda Joan (Campion & Co)
Rayson, Susan Maeve (Hawley & Rodgers)
Redfern, Kerry (Nelsons Solicitors LLP)
Richardson, Alison Marina (Sharp & Partners)
Rippon, Victoria Claire (Browne Jacobson LLP)
Sams, Sandra Vanessa (Actons Solicitors)
Severn, Laura Jane (Brady Solicitors)
Simpson, Sallyann (Massers Solicitors)
Smith, David Charles (Nottingham City Council)
Swain, Ruth Louise (Actons Solicitors)
Swainson-Jenkins, Tara (Thompsons Solicitors)
Talks, Ian (Sheltons)
Taylor, Stella Marie (Berryman Shacklock LLP)
Thomas, Clive Herbert Jenkin (Edwards Clegg)
Tomlinson, Deena Alison (Browne Jacobson LLP)
Townroe, Claire (Actons Solicitors)
Tyas, Justine Andrea (Actons Solicitors)
Ubhi, Rajvinder Kaur (Browne Jacobson LLP)
Waddon, Sarah Ellen May (Shoosmiths)
Walton, Lorraine Ann (Nelsons Solicitors LLP)
Watchorn, Elizabeth Jane (Sheltons)
Watkinson, Brian Kevin (Sheltons)
Watson, Tracy Ann (Freeth Cartwright LLP)
Wilbraham, Louise Marie (Browne Jacobson LLP)
Wilson, Karen Louise (Ellis Fermor & Negus)
Wilson, Linda Anne (Browne Jacobson LLP)
Wiss, Jennifer Lorraine (Academic Answers Ltd)
Young, Michelle Ann (Rothera Dowson)

NUNEATON, Warwickshire

Burton, Katherine Ann (LDJ Solicitors)
Ellis, Myles John (Imperium Law LLP)
Hewitt, Sharon Elaine (Cocks Lloyd & Co)
Hickman, Robert Thomas (LDJ Solicitors)
Howes Marsden, Donna Julie (Holland & Barrett Ltd)
Kahrman, Claire Ann (Nuneaton & Bedworth Borough Council)
Monahan, Jennifer Diana (Cocks Lloyd & Co)
Pearson, Andrea Dawn (Nuneaton & Bedworth Borough Council)
Prewett, Gloria (LDJ Solicitors)
Reynolds, Audrey Elizabeth (Cocks Lloyd & Co)
Stokes, Rebecca Louise (Nuneaton & Bedworth Borough Council)

OAKHAM, Rutland

Joseph, Nigel (Rutland County Council)
Patel, Selina (Associa Ltd)
Smith, Harry (Paul Browne)
Thompson-O'Connor, Mark Anthony (Thompson O'Connor Employment Services)

OLDBURY, West Midlands

Lambe, Marie Louise (Sandwell Metropolitian Borough Council)
Nickless, Stephen (Silks Solicitors)
Ogunshakin, Ifeolu Olumide (Sandwell Metropolitian Borough Council)

OLDHAM, Greater Manchester

Bradbury, Cassandra Louise (Stirling Law)
Chisholm, Douglas (Oldham Borough Council)
Crompton, Tracy (Hinchliffe)
Etherington, Keith (Mellor & Jackson)
Godfrey, Robert David (Mellor Heargreaves)
Howard, Daniel Alex (Oldham Borough Council)
Issa, Johanna (Oldham Borough Council)
Shakeshaft, Alison (Cuttle & Co Solicitors)
Swarbrick, Patricia (First Choice Homes)

OLNEY, Buckinghamshire

Adamson, Lesley Karen (J Gerrard & Allen)
Hill, Carol Elizabeth (Parish Family Law)

ORMSKIRK, Lancashire

Dickinson, Andrew John (Mooney Everett Solicitors)
Read, Susan Elizabeth (Brighouse Wolff)
Ward, Susan Carol (Mooney Everett Solicitors)
Waters, Craig James (John Cunningham Associates)

ORPINGTON, Kent

Cosford, Stephen Mark (Thomas Dunton & Co)
Haines, Jonathan (Thomas Dunton & Co)
Harris, David John (Clarkson Wright & Jakes)
Hill, Zena Jane (Dilworth Lamb & Co)
Jarrett, Victoria Lesley (Clarkson Wright & Jakes)
Sargeant, Carly Jane (Clarkson Wright & Jakes)
Simmonds, Michael (Clarkson Wright & Jakes)
Sykes, Sophie Abigail (Dilworth Lamb & Co)
Westcott, Catherine Anne (Thomas Dunton & Co)

OSWESTRY, Shropshire

Davies, Kaye Teresa (Lanyon Bowdler Solicitors)
Foden, David George (Lanyon Bowdler Solicitors)
Law, Terence Denselow (Gwilym Hughes & Partners)
Lewis, Ella Myfanwy (Crampton Pym & Lewis)
Pickstock, Jennifer Mary (Crampton Pym & Lewis)
Powell, Valerie Joan (Lanyon Bowdler Solicitors)

OTLEY, West Yorkshire

Butterill, Susan Margaret (Savage Crangle)

OTTERY ST MARY, Devon

Bowden, Tracy (Gilbert Stephens)

OXFORD, Oxfordshire

Atherstone, Linda (Barlow Lyde & Gilbert)
Beegoo, Amanda (Darbys Solicitors LLP)
Benfield, Caroline Kathleen (Isis Innovation Ltd)
Brooke, Catherine Mary (Manches LLP)
Collings, Sandra Jane (Whetter Duckworth Fowler)
Coltman, Alison (Warneford Hospital)
Cribbin, Daniel Peter (Oxford Radcliffe Hospital)
Daniels, James Thomas (Diplomatic Counciló)
Denham, Lorna Rose (Wilsons Solicitors LLP)
Dhaliwal, Kamaljeet Kaur (Oxford Radclife Hospital)
Duce, Tracy Angela (Oxfordshire County Council)
Einon, Kevin James (Oxford City Council)
Foster, Tina Marie (Withy King Solicitors)
Garland, Sarah Jayne (Morgan Cole Solicitors)
Gilbert, Maxine Lesley (HMG Law LLP)
Hickley, Kathryn Linda Susan (Boodle Hatfield)
Hubbert, Chloe Lorraine (Morgan Cole Solicitors)
King, Lorraine Anne (Truemans)
Masters, Denise Joy (Truemans)
Matharu, Tim Satwant (Oxfordshire County Council)
Neptune, Marilyn Lavonne (Blake Lapthorn)
O'Driscoll, Charlotte Katie (Henmans LLP)
Page, Alison Amanda (Challenor Gardiner)
Peacock, Karen (Plainlaw Solicitors)
Phillips, Jacqueline Louise (Darbys Solicitors LLP)
Rogers, Deborah Louise (Whetter Duckworth Fowler)
Stone, Andrew Paul (Oxfordshire County Council)
Sutton, Ann Mary (Henmans LLP)
Williams, Sally Anne (Withy King Solicitors)

OXTED, Surrey

Barker, Ruth Lillian (Tandridge District Council)
Coles, Caroline Dorothea (Hepburns Solicitors)

PAIGNTON, Devon

Caddell, Alison Jayne (Hooper & Wollen)
Collett, Rebecca Claire (Knapman & Co)
Kellow, Yvonne Mary (Eastleys Solicitors)
Miles, Peter (Roger Richard)
Milton, Lynne Rachel (Knapman & Co)
Winders, Anne Elizabeth (Gowmans)

PEACEHAVEN, East Sussex

Davies, Nicola Claire (Lawson Lewis & Company)
Jones, Nicola Christiane (Barwells Solicitors)

PENARTH, Vale of Glamorgan

Hughes-Lewis, Rachel Jane (Alan Simons & Co)
Lawrence, Catherine Mary (Merrils)

PENRITH, Cumbria

Brunskill, Alan (Gaynham King & Mellor Solicitors)
Bulman, Sharon Marie (Cartmell Shepherd)
Dixon, Cynthia (Eden District Council)
Hallatt, Elizabeth Janet (Cumbria Constabulary)
Keiller, Heather Louise (Cumbria Constabulary)
Naylor, Judith Ann (Arnison & Co)
Swarbrick, Sarah Louise (Cumbria Constabulary)

PENTRE, Rhondda Cynon Taff

Lane, Karan Elizabeth (Rhondda Cynon Taff County Borough Council)

PENZANCE, Cornwall

Barlow, Jane Elizabeth (J B Wills)
Carruthers, Karen Anne (Vivian Thomas & Jervis)
Deere, Louise (Boase Bennetts & James)
Gilbert, Jacqueline Miriam (Cornwall Council)
Hawkins, Michelle Haesung (Coodes Solicitors)

Mansell, Simon John Richard (Cornwall Council)
Mckinley, Carole Glennie Tregembo (Vivian Thomas & Jervis)
Sleeman, Jonathan Mark (Cornwall Council)
Thomas-James, Judith Denise (Penwith Citizens Advice Bureau)
White, Karen Jennifer (Borlase & Venning)
Wright, Mary-Jane (Nalders Solicitors)

PERSHORE, Worcestershire

Harris, Gemma Louise (Wychavon District Council)
O'Connor, Jemma Louise (Thomson Bancks & Co)
Wall, Chrys Louise (Thomson Bancks & Co)

PETERBOROUGH, Peterborough

Abbott, Michelle Margaret (Peterborough City Council)
Ahmed, Israr (Peterborough City Council)
Allen, Alison Elizabeth (Terrells LLP)
Barber, Alwen (Greenwoods Solicitors)
Berry, Daniel (Vincent Sykes)
Bosworth, Brian (Pearl Assurance PLC)
Cooper, David Paul (Taylor Rose Law)
Daniels, Emma Louise (BGL Group Ltd)
Ford, Christopher James (Peterborough City Council)
Glen, Donald Peter (HHG Services Ltd)
Griffiths, Ruth (Peterborough City Council)
Harrison, Beverley anne (Buckles Solicitors LLP)
Ide, Conway John (HC Solicitors)
Isaac, Julie (Buckles Solicitors LLP)
Jackson, Alan Peter (Amp Services Ltd)
Keates, Heather Fiona (Pirie Palmann)
Knight, Lesley Anne (Hegarty LLP)
Martin, Toby Frances (Lord Chancellors Department)
Newell, Jenny Paulette (HC Solicitors)
Nutt, Jayne (Greenwoods Solicitors)
O'Connor Long, David Leslie (Peterborough City Council)
O'Reilly, Wendy Maureen (Greenwoods Solicitors)
Pender, Kimberley Jean (Hegarty LLP)
Rands, Katherine Ann (Hegarty LLP)
Rawlings, Coralie Anne (Roythorne Christmas Solicitors)
Smith, Elliot James (Peterborough City Council)
Smith, Glenn Flavio (Glenn Smith & Co)
Webb, Amanda (Taylor Rose Law)
Welton, Margaret (Peterborough City Council)
Woods, Kirsty Estelle (Waller Needham & Green)

PETERSFIELD, Hampshire

Mann, Rosalind Honor (Mackarness & Lunt)
Parr, Michael Richard (Mackarness & Lunt)
Williams, Jillian Elizabeth (MacDonald Oates LLP)

PETWORTH, West Sussex

Cappelli, Lynda Joan (Gardner Thorpe Solicitors)

PICKERING, North Yorkshire

Skaife, Helen Elizabeth (Ellis Lakin & Co)

PINNER, Middlesex

Nicholls, Jacqueline Ann (E M Collins & Co)
Shah, Sunita (Jsk Law)

PLYMOUTH, Plymouth

Bailey, Catherine Helene (Gill Akaster Solicitors)
Baker, Alison Kay (Gill Akaster Solicitors)
Bedford, James Ian (Gard & Co)
Boardman, Alexandra Elizabeth (Plymouth City Council (Legal Services))
Bradbury, Deborah Jayne (Plymouth City Council (Legal Services))
Burch, Jacqueline (Plymouth City Council (Legal Services))
Canham, Catherine Denise (Wolferstans Solicitors)
Chapman, Philomena Sushila (Plymouth City Council (Legal Services))
Cobb, Nicola Jane (Bond Pearce LLP)
Coles, Susannah Louise (Russell Worth Solicitors)
Connor, Lesley Ann (Plymouth City Council (Legal Services))
Cotterill, Melanie Elizabeth (Wolferstans Solicitors)
Crane, Stephen Nicholas (Plymouth City Council (Legal Services))
Damarell, Danny Nicholas (Plymouth Community Homes)
Day, Sharon Louise (Plymouth City Council (Legal Services))
Dunn, Emma Kate (Thompsons Solicitors)
Eliadis, Alexander Charles (Thompsons Solicitors)
Ellard, Nancy Elizabeth (The Plymouth Legal Practice)
Furlong, Michelle Jane (Russell Worth Solicitors)
Gilbert, Andrea (Plymouth City Council (Legal Services))
Gilding, Samantha Emma (Plymouth City Council (Legal Services))
Giles, Rebecca Mary (Wolferstans Solicitors)
Gillbanks, Ann (Plymouth City Council (Legal Services))
Gray, Mark (Thompsons Solicitors)
Hallard, Helen (Evans Harvey Solicitors)
Jarvis, Alan Frederick (Plant Solicitors)
Kua, Jane Melanie (Wolferstans Solicitors)
Lamerton, Sharon (Devon Law Centre)
Langsworthy, Mark David (Foot Anstey Solicitors)
Lawrence, Mark (Plymouth City Council (Legal Services))
Ling, Sharon Rosalynd (Lyons Davidson Solicitors)
Ludlow-Ockelford, Julia Allison (Bright LLP)
Marshall, Janet Elizabeth (Sitters & Co)
Mccormick, Alison Jayne (Gill Akaster Solicitors)
McLay, Krista Jennet (Lyons Davidson Solicitors)
Mead, David Paul (Thompsons Solicitors)
Messham, John Arthur Charles (Bond Pearce LLP)
Moulding, Joan (Gill Akaster Solicitors)
Perrins, Dawn (Foot Anstey Solicitors)
Radmore, Kerry Anne (Gill Akaster Solicitors)
Reddish, Julie Ann (CCR Ltd)
Rees, Sian (Thompsons Solicitors)
Rimron, Joanna May Patricia (Plymouth City Council (Legal Services))
Roberts, Jennifer Teresa (Plymouth City Council (Legal Services))
Rowlands, Julia Bridget (Gill Akaster Solicitors)
Rundle, Julie Ann (Plymouth City Council (Legal Services))
Russell, Melanie Jane (Nash & Co)
Stroud, Caroline Ann (Thompson & Jackson)
Tassart, Peter Geoffrey (Beers LLP)
Timbrell, Angela Mary (Woollcombe Yonge Solicitors)
Vigus, Louise Marie (Thornleys)
Wallis, Susan Elizabeth (Plymouth City Council (Legal Services))
Watt, Mary Mckay (Alan Harris)
Wheeler, Helen Elizabeth (Nash & Co)
White, Paul Timothy (Wolferstans Solicitors)
Wilkinson, Lydia Frances (Clark & Weeks)
Williams, Elizabeth (Wolferstans Solicitors)
Williams, Ronald David (Plymouth City Council (Legal Services))
Williams, Susan Margaret (Thompson & Jackson)
Williams, Tracy (Bond Pearce LLP)

PONTEFRACT, West Yorkshire

Dawson, Paul Aaron (Hartley & Worstenholme)
Garside, Claire Louise (Hartley & Worstenholme)
Knox, Alison Jane (Moxon & Barker)
Phillips, David John (Carters Solicitors)
Ward, Caroline (Heptonstalls LLP)

PONTYCLUN, Rhondda Cynon Taff

Smith, Kristy Louise (David W Harris & Co)
Williams, Sarah-Jane (David W Harris & Co)

PONTYPOOL, Torfaen

Grubb, Angela Linda (Torfaen Borough Council)
Partington, Gillian (Everett Tomlin Lloyd & Pratt)
Poulsom, Lyndsay Ann (Everett Tomlin Lloyd & Pratt)
Williams, Nicola Jane (Torfaen Borough Council)

PONTYPRIDD, Rhondda Cynon Taff

Davies, Jodie Elise (Spicketts Battrick)
Harris, Paul Julian (Devonalds Solicitors)
Lewis, Marie (Devonalds Solicitors)
Weston, Celia (Devonalds Solicitors)

POOLE, Poole

Bantten, Diane (Acquit Limited)
Bennett, Kim Marie (RWPS LLP)
Brown, Jennetta Mary (Trevanions)
Davies, Helen (Jacobs & Reeves)
Funnell, Joanne Marie Elaine (Coles Miller Solicitors LLP)
Gosling, Sarah Jane (RWPS LLP)
Hanning, Nicholas Anthony (RWPS LLP)
Haynes, Sandra (O'Haras)
Hefferin, Justine Marie (Trevanions)
Hitchings, Bryan Robert (Jacobs & Reeves)
Jackson, Maria Christina (Dickinson Manser)
McKnight, Eanna Hazel (Coles Miller Solicitors LLP)
McQueen, Samantha Jane (RWPS LLP)
Parsons, Tracey Anne (Dickinson Manser)
Redfern, Louise Georgina (Borough of Poole)
Richards, Sarah Louise (Dickinson Manser)
Ridgley, Mary Russell (Bruce Lance & Co)
Robbins, Louise Rachel (Dickinson Manser)
Stratton, Julie Patricia (Coles Miller Solicitors LLP)
Templeton, Alison Ruth (Ellis Jones)
Vincent, Diane Elizabeth (Dickinson Manser)
Whiting, Michelle Louise (Laceys)
Woodward, Marcella Gay (RWPS LLP)

PORT TALBOT, Neath Port Talbot

Clark, Karen Louise (Neath Port Talbot County Borough Council)
James, Julie Ann (Kevin Lane & Co)
Jones, Stephen Nigel (Neath Port Talbot County Borough Council)

PORTSMOUTH, Portsmouth

Adamson, Amanda Jane (Coffin Mew LLP)
Blakey, Paul Marsden (Stokes Solicitors LLP)
Burden, Susan May (Hayward Baker Solicitors)
Caparco, Nicola Marie (Wessex Solicitors Chambers)
Cox, Nicola (Coffin Mew LLP)
Elloway, Mark David (Blake Lapthorn)
Farnham, Michael John (Portsmouth City Council)
Foulger, Susan Margaret (Blake Lapthorn)
Gent, Beverley Jane (Stokes Solicitors LLP)
Gilholm, Joanne (Churchers Solicitors)
Harrison, Karen Jane (Andrew & Andrew Solicitors)
Hayden, Veronica (Warner Goodman LLP)
Jenkins, Susan Diane (Blake Lapthorn)
Lee, Gary Alan (Hayward Baker Solicitors)
Lee, Paul Richard (Larcomes LLP Solicitors)
Longden-Thurgood, Leesa (Coffin Mew LLP)
Mansbridge, Kaye Marie (Blake Lapthorn)
Mcclure, Tracy (Hayward Baker Solicitors)
Mckee, Ann Jennifer (Bramsdon & Childs)
Moger, Elizabeth Jane (Bolitho Way Solicitors)
Nail, Peter John (Portsmouth City Council)
Parish, Charlotte Claire (Gurney Champion & Co)
Peach, Ian Edward (Verisona Solicitors)
Peach, Robert Leslie (Coffin Mew LLP)
Phillips, Sandra Elizabeth (Larcomes LLP Solicitors)
Powell, Christopher Guy (Stokes Solicitors LLP)
Richardson, Kevin (Biscoes Solicitors)
Russell, Delia Lilie (Saulet & Co)
Schofield, Sonia Helen (Portsmouth City Council)
Shepherd, Emma Jane (Stokes Solicitors LLP)
Smith, Christine Sarah (Churchers Solicitors)
Spriggs, Alison Jane (Hayward Baker Solicitors)
Taylor, John Sydney (Bramsdon & Childs)
Tidman, Paul Brian (Biscoes Solicitors)
Wilson, Judie Rosina (Verisona Solicitors)
Winslade, Paul John (Warner Goodman LLP)
Worthington, Joanne Louise (Groupama UK Services Ltd)

POTTERS BAR, Hertfordshire

Stoneham, Kerry (CLFIS (UK) Ltd)
Wood, Felicity Anne Elizabeth (Rhy Law LLP)

POULTON-LE-FYLDE, Lancashire

Greener, Catherine Irene (Wyre Borough Council)

PRESCOT, Merseyside

Beet, Adrian (Knowsley Housing Trust)
Flatman, Nicola Ann (Tri Star Costs Limited)

PRESTON, Lancashire

Aldridge, Sean Geoffrey (Napthens LLP)
Baron, Shena Anys (Roscoes)
Birstall, Jayne Louise (Meloy Whittle Robinson)
Dodgin, Emma (Meloy Whittle Robinson)
Fernandez, Anthony John (Preston City Council)
Graveson, Gillian (DWF)
Jairath, Shilpi (Emmetts Solicitors Limited)
Jones, Victoria Elizabeth (Peter Rickson & Partners)
Kiley, Lyndsey (Marsden Rawsthorn LLP)
Lee, Catherine Ruth (Lancashire County Council)
McClean, Joanna (Meloy Whittle Robinson)
Moorby, Howard John (Meloy Whittle Robinson)
Palmi, Janet (Peter Rickson & Partners)
Piontek, Karen Joanne (Lonsdales Solicitors)
Pitteway, Marianne Jane (Care Quality Commission)
Risby, Stephen (ATM Solicitors Ltd)
Roberts, Sandra Adele (Forbes Solicitors)
Sheppard, Mervyn James (Preston City Council)
Starr, Susan Mary (Crown Prosecution Service)
Taylor, Prema (Napthens LLP)
Wallis, Glenn Peter (The Ellen Court Partnership)
Wilson, Amanda Margaret (Napthens LLP)
Winters, Fiona Carmel (Lancashire County Council)
Young, Leeza (Lancashire County Council)

PRINCES RISBOROUGH, Buckinghamshire

Wright, Kirsty Louise (O'Neill Wright Nash)

PUDSEY, West Yorkshire

Ryan, Lynda Audrey (Ryan Property Law LLP)

PULBOROUGH, West Sussex

Knight, Sandra Denise (Anderson Longmore & Higham)

RAINHAM, Kent

Derham, Michelle Claire (John Morley & Co)
Reeves, Kirsten (Beckett Solicitors)

RAMSGATE, Kent

Sims, Ann (Marsden Douglas)

RAYLEIGH, Essex

Adams, Robert Arthur (Rudds)

READING, Reading

Alexander, Claire Margaret (Reading Borough Council)
Amor, Lynda Susan (Boyes Turner Solicitors)
Andrews, Sarah Louise (Morgan Cole Solicitors)
Baillie, Siobhan Kathleen (Pitmans Solicitors LLP)
Beavon, Ian Robert (Rowberry Morris LLP)
Brown, Rachel Colette (Pitmans Solicitors LLP)
Caballero, Marjorie Florence (Collins Dryland & Thorowgood)
Causer, Danielle Allison (Boyes Turner Solicitors)
Challinger, Sara (Mastek UK Ltd)
Cole, Joanne Faye (Morgan Cole Solicitors)
Cole, Petuna Angela (Reading Borough Council)
Colegrove, David John (Reading Borough Council)
Coltman, Caroline (Transportation Claims Ltd)
Cook, Claire Louise Maria (Scottish & Southern Energy PLC)
Cooper, Karen Lisa (Verizon Business)
Czajkowski, Adrian James Jan (Ratcliffe Duce & Gammer)
Duggan, Deborah Tracy (Rowberry Morris LLP)
Eighteen, Rachel Louise (British Gas PLC)
Fenty, Sallie Anne (Dexter Montague & Partners)
Francis, Lissa Kerrie (Shoosmiths)
Gillbe, Sarah Christina (Bowles & Co)
Harratt, Lydia (Pitmans Solicitors LLP)
Harte, Claire Louise (Boyes Turner Solicitors)
Hookway, Sarah-Jane Courtenay (Blandy & Blandy LLP)
Kent, Sarah Elizabeth (Morgan Cole Solicitors)
Kurowski, Andrew Paul (Foster Wheeler Energy Ltd)
Lamb, Madeleine Josette (The Head Partnership)
Long, Rena Eva (Thames Water Property Services Ltd)
Loveday, Helen (Osborne Clarke)
Massey, Angela (Rowberry Morris LLP)
Morwood-Leyland, Alice Mary Teresa (McNulty & UK PLC)
Newton, Sylvia Ann (Boyes Turner Solicitors)
Prater, Matthew Leslie (Thompson & Leatherdale)
Sanderson, Rosamund Lilian Margaret (Richard Wilson & Co)
Seigne, Stephanie Barrie (Royal Berkshire & Battle)
Snow, Francesca Louise (Johnsons Solicitors LLP)
Strawbridge, Julie Dawn (Emptoris Inc)
Strudwick, Julie Anne (Blandy & Blandy LLP)
Surey, Katie Emma Veronica (Field Seymour Parkes)
Thakrar, Meta (Johnsons Solicitors LLP)
Tingay, Joanne Frances (Verizon Business)
Tow, Alison Deborah (Boyes Turner Solicitors)
Warren, Rona Marcia (Huntswood (CTC) Ltd)
Watson, Helen Margaret (Olswang)
Wise, Neil John Webster (Environment Agency)
Wood, Jacqueline (Shoosmiths)

REDCAR, Redcar & Cleveland

Benson, Sarah Louise (Brown Beer Nixon Mallon)
Crooks, Irene (Askews)
Tait, Sharon (Brown Beer Nixon Mallon)
Wild, Danielle (Bousfield Gaskin)

REDDITCH, Worcestershire

Bartlett, Sarah Elizabeth Jane (The Law Society)
Calvert, Tracey Anne (The Law Society)
Middleton-Cassini, Stephen Mark (Solicitors Regulation Authority)
Phillips, Theresia Linda (Redditch Borough Council)
Whitehouse, John (The Law Society)

REDHILL, Surrey

Barlow, Siobhan Elizabeth (Robert Gray & Co)
Davis, Philip John (Gray Hooper Holt LLP)
Furst, Helen Anne (St Paul International Insurance Co)

15

Humphrey, Mandy Gail (Morrisons LLP)
Morrison, Diane (Morrisons LLP)
Peck, Anne Margaret (Goodhand & Forsyth)
Piper, Emma (Goodhand & Forsyth)
Shouler, Nadine Leanne (Goodhand & Forsyth)

REDRUTH, Cornwall
Cole, Jane Marie (Thurstan Hoskin & Partners)
Ferguson, Susan (Grylls & Paige Solicitors)
Gates, Alan James (Thurstan Hoskin & Partners)
Hillson, Emma Victoria (Smith Leaming Criminal Advocates)
Meteyard, John (Thurstan Hoskin & Partners)

REIGATE, Surrey
George, Sally Barbara (TWM Solicitors LLP)
Hunter-Rowe, Cara (Sheppersons)
Patel, Sital (1st Credit Ltd)

RETFORD, Nottinghamshire
Carey, Stephen (Tracey Barlow Furniss & Co)
Henderson, Victoria (Jones & Company Solicitors)
Hood, Derith Valerie (Tracey Barlow Furniss & Co)
Hudson, Rachel Louise (Jones & Co)
Pilgrim, Helen Claire (Jackson Quinn)

RHYL, Denbighshire
Bohanna, Susan (Humphrys Dawson)
May, Susan (Gamlins)
Reeve, Andrew John (Gamlins)

RICHMOND, North Yorkshire
Hutchinson, Colin Michael (Hunton & Garget)
Moore-Saxton, Michelle Marie (Calvert Smith & Sutcliffe)
Skillcorn, Rhapsody Angel (Saunders & Company)
West, Patricia Marie Renee (Hudsons Hart & Borrows)

RICKMANSWORTH, Hertfordshire
Carter, Geraldine (Blaser Mills)
Paxton, Judith Audrey (Blaser Mills)
White, Caroline Jane (Darlington Hardcastles)

RINGWOOD, Hampshire
Barnes, Susan Jane (Letchers Solicitors)
Boyling, Stephen Ronald (Meesons)
Lowe, Sharala (Ellis Jones)
Pask, Shirley Ann (Letchers Solicitors)
Willey, Samuel (Ellis Jones)

RIPLEY, Derbyshire
Bristol, Claire Juliet (Ellis Fermor & Negus)
Fox, Angela Sally (Amber Valley Borough Council)
Leam, Jill (Ellis Fermor & Negus)
Owen, Jennifer Diane (Amber Valley Borough Council)
Seddon, Sarah Louise (EG Legal)
Whittaker, Diane (Amber Vale Housing Ltd)
Winter, Catherine Marie (Amber Valley Borough Council)

RIPON, North Yorkshire
Windross, Sandra (Eccles Heddon & Co)
Wood, Adele Carol (Eccles Heddon & Co)
Young, Charles William Peter (Hutchinson & Buchanan)

ROCHDALE, Greater Manchester
Asghar, Lynn (Rochdale Metropolitan Borough Council)
Astridge, Joanne (Molesworth Bright Clegg Solicitors)
Butterfield, Karen Ann (Rochdale Boroughwide Housing)
Ferguson-Black, Tracey Ann (St Vincents Housing Association)
Halfpenny, Sharon Lesley Mary (AST Hampsons Solicitors)
Judge, Michael John (My Judge Property Lawyers)
Leach, Helen Elizabeth (Rochdale Metropolitan Borough Council)
Ledger, James Adam (Alfred Ledger & Sons)
Ledger, Nancy Patricia (Alfred Ledger & Sons)
Leeming, Susan (Molesworth Bright Clegg Solicitors)
Lund, Diane Louise (Rochdale Metropolitan Borough Council)
Moore, Terence Peter (Rochdale Metropolitan Borough Council)
Rhodes, Lesley Jane (Molesworth Bright Clegg Solicitors)
Scholes, Victoria (Michael Salt Solicitors)
Sharp, Deborah Ann (Rochdale Metropolitan Borough Council)
Shaw, Donna (Rochdale Metropolitan Borough Council)
Smith, Loretta Antonia (Rochdale Metropolitan Borough Council)
Wells, Annette (Rochdale Metropolitan Borough Council)
Wilson, Tracy Dawn (Molesworth Bright Clegg Solicitors)

ROCHESTER, Kent
Brier, Timothy James (Bassets)
Foster, Sarah Jane (Chris & Simmonds Solicitors)
Funnell, Margaret Edna (Bassets)
Graham, Barbara Susan (Medway Council)

ROMFORD, Essex
Bowell, Janette (Liddell & Co)
Daly, Jemma Louise (Sternberg Reed Solicitors)
Fernand, Kathleen (Sternberg Reed Solicitors)
Heary, Lisa Catherine (Sternberg Reed Solicitors)
Hillstead, Helen (Sternberg Reed Solicitors)
Holmes, Marilyn Joyce (David Charnley And Company)
Ioannou-Cherry, Andrea (London Borough of Havering)
Jones, Paula Christine (Capstick Dale & Partners)
Leland, Edward (Leland & Co)
Roast, Louise Laura (Liddell & Co)
Stuart, Helen Estelle (Leland & Co)
Weatherby, Louise Anne (Paul Martin & Co Solicitors)
Whaley, Joanna Nadine (Kenneth Elliott & Rowe)

ROMSEY, Hampshire
Holiday, Susanne Jennifer (Footners)
Slade, Peter Leonard (Kirklands)
Smith, Geoffrey Charles (Bells Solicitors)

ROSS-ON-WYE, Herefordshire
Bullock, Deborah Jane (Okell & Stewart)
Jennings, Emma Victoria (Shawcross & Co)
Kendrick, John Leslie (Kendrick Planning Ltd)

ROTHERHAM, South Yorkshire
Bates, Deborah Anne (Howells LLP)
Case, Victoria Jane (Malcolm C Foy & Co)
Davis, Marie (Tierney & Co Solicitors)
Driffill, Clare Rachel (Norrie Waite & Slater)
Ferrill, Roy (Foys Solicitors)
Lowry, Dawn Susan (Howells LLP)
Smith, Susan Tessa (Bradford & Son)
Watson, Roselyn (Rotherham Borough Council)
Weaver, Rachel Anne (Wilford Smith & Co)
Wragg, Helen (Howells LLP)

ROYSTON, Hertfordshire
Browning, Thomas (The Walkers Partners)

RUGBY, Warwickshire
Allen, Marian Elizabeth (Rugby Borough Council)
Austin, Kate Elizabeth (Brethertons LLP)
Dyer, Trevor Raymond (Brethertons LLP)
Hillman, Karen Dawn (Rugby Borough Council)
Jenkinson, Diane Ethel (Brethertons LLP)
Macleod, Torquil Alexander (Brethertons LLP)
Ritchie, Deborah Jayne (Rugby Borough Council)
Spencer, Dean Stephen (Morgan Solicitors)

RUGELEY, Staffordshire
Berry, Linda Gail (Pickering & Butters)
Peplow, Jane (Hand Morgan & Owen)

RUISLIP, Middlesex
Allen, Catherine Anne (Glenisters Solicitors)
Allsop, Rosalind (Bird & Lovibond Solicitors)
Gourdin, Norma Mary (Adare on Communications Ltd)
Nelson, Amy Cyprian Sinead (David Durn & Co Solicitors)

RUNCORN, Cheshire
Achilles, Catherine Jayne (Butcher & Barlow LLP)
Lloyd, Lynsey Ann (Hough & Co)

RUSTINGTON, West Sussex
Lyne, Richard Colin (Warwick & Barker)

RUTHIN, Denbighshire
Earlam, Phillipa Ann (Denbighshire County Council)
Woodward, Emma Caroline (Denbighshire County Council)

RYDE, Isle of Wight
Lloyd, Emma Jane (Heyes Samuels Solicitors)

SAFFRON WALDEN, Essex
Arnold, Andrew Philip Patrick (Pellys LLP)
Dalby, Kim Louise (Adams Harrison)
Furlong, Sarah Kathryn (Adams Harrison)
Horseman, Sarah Louise (Stevens)
O'Marra, Stefonie Anita (Stevens)
Wilmott, Helen Olive (Heckford Norton Solicitors)

SALE, Greater Manchester
Bowers, Janet (Bannister Preston)
Carney, Maralyn Lesley (Rothwell & Evans)
Chadderton, Karen (Slater Heelis Collier Littler)
Douglas, Mark Graham (Balfour Beatty Construction Ltd)
Earle, Zoe Ann (DGMW Solicitors)
Raj, Pritham Singh (Slater Heelis Collier Littler)
Shaoul-Leonard, Charmaine Juliet (ATM Solicitors)
Slack, David (Slater Heelis Collier Littler)

SALFORD, Greater Manchester
Dargon, Carly (Clifford Poole & Co)
Goddard, Hazel (Ralli Solicitors)
Halstead, Emma Jane (GLP Solicitors)
Holroyd, Angela Marie (Aughton Ainsworth Solicitors)
Howard, Gareth Edward (Kristina Harrison Solicitors)
Lavelle, Gillian Amanda (Stephensons Solicitors LLP)
Prosser, Elaine (Ralli Solicitors)
Robinson, Darrell (The Rose Partnership)
White, Helen (Robert Lizar Solicitors)

SALISBURY, Wiltshire
Adams, Neil David (Parker Bullen)
Cemm, Hazel (Parker Bullen)
Chandler, Caroline Anne (Bonallack & Bishop)
Cooper-Gray, Michelle Annette (Ranson Houghton)
Daley, Gregory (Rowanmoor Pensions Ltd)
Dooling, Angela Michelle Beverley (Whitehead Vizard)
George, Matthew Stanley Edward (Richard Griffiths & Co)
Hoare, Ruth (Parker Bullen)
Hunton, Pauline Jeniffer (Trethowans Solicitors)
Langdown, Victoria Louise (Sampson Coward)
Male, Kate Joanne (Inspire Family Solicitors & Mediators Ltd)
Parsons, Sarah Rebecca (Trethowans Solicitors)
Room, Frances Elizabeth (Wilsons Solicitors LLP)
Shucksmith, Jenny Ann (Trethowans Solicitors)
Smith, Angela (Bonallack & Bishop)
Trappes-Lomax, Amanda Jayne (Bonallack & Bishop)
Wyeth, Rosemary Alison (Trethowans Solicitors)

SALTASH, Cornwall
Zoffman, Sarah Ann (Nicholls & Sainsbury)

SANDWICH, Kent
Barnett, Christine Margaret (Emmerson Brown & Brown)

SANDY, Bedfordshire
Champion, Barbara Teresa (Woodfines LLP)
Thompson, Andrea (Woodfines LLP)

SCARBOROUGH, North Yorkshire
Baines, Andrew Stuart (Thorpe & Co)
Bairstow, Christopher Paul (Thorpe & Co)
Davis, Deborah Jacqueline (Pinkney Grunwells Lawyers LLP)
Fenby, Deborah Jane (Thorpe & Co)
Jeffels, Alison Jayne (North Yorkshire Law)
Jerome, Robert Anthony (Pinkney Grunwells Lawyers LLP)
Morris, Paula Jan (Scarborough Borough Council)
Plant, Dawn Alison (Pinkney Grunwells Lawyers LLP)
Richardson, Margaret (B & C Solicitors)
Sellars, Hanna Kirsten (Pinkney Grunwells Lawyers LLP)
Sherwood, Carol (Pinkney Grunwells Lawyers LLP)
Smith, Melanie Sara (Thorpe & Co)
White, Patricia Mary (Pinkney Grunwells Lawyers LLP)
Winter, Helen Louise (Tubbs & Co Solicitors)

SCUNTHORPE, North Lincolnshire
Fisher, Elizabeth Diane (Hett Stubbs & Kemp)
Kelly, Catherine Alice (North Lincolnshire Homes Ltd)
Mitchell, Ann (Bradbury Roberts & Raby)
Moore, Nichola Ann (Heptonstalls LLP)
Platts, Steven Robert (Sergeant & Collins)
Summerland, Caroline Elizabeth (Sergeant & Collins)
Wingate, Margaret Ann (Mason Baggott & Garton)

SEAFORD, East Sussex
Cremore, Michael Alan (Barwells Solicitors)
Stanyard, Karen Jane (Rix & Kay Solicitors)

SEAHAM, Co Durham
Mccoy, Vickie (Kenneth M Barrow & Co)

SELBY, North Yorkshire
Sands, Christina Margaret (Blackstones LLP)

SELSDON, Surrey
Micklewright, Kevin Robert (DKLL)

SEVENOAKS, Kent
Challis, Cyril Henry (Knocker & Foskett)
Heath, Julie Ann (District Council of Sevenoaks)
Randall, Harriet Caroline (Evans Main)
Smith, Jennifer Ann (Knocker & Foskett)
Spain, Rosalyn Sandra (Evans Main)

SHAFTESBURY, Dorset
Doman, Caroline Jane (Farnfield & Nicholls)
Watson, Guy (Farnfield & Nicholls)

SHEERNESS, Kent
Reardon, Ian (Peter Clough & Co)

SHEFFIELD, South Yorkshire
Alam, Surat (Howells LLP)
Auckland, Amanda Elizabeth (Electric Works)
Bailey, Benjamin Mark (Graysons Solicitors)
Bate, Louise Emily (Ashton Morton Slack LLP)
Bedford, Paul (DLA Piper UK LLP)
Bond, Annette (Irwin Mitchell LLP)
Bower, Jennifer (Ashton Morton Slack LLP)
Bracewell, Claire (Irwin Mitchell LLP)
Brodrick, Zoe (Irwin Mitchell LLP)
Brown, David Michael (Wake Smith & Tofields)
Brown, Karen Sally (Irwin Mitchell LLP)
Brownhill, Sarah Gemma (Irwin Mitchell LLP)
Buckley, Marianne (Irwin Mitchell LLP)
Bullivant, Philip (Irwin Mitchell LLP)
Carder, David Peter (Irwin Mitchell LLP)
Cartwright, Amy-Jo (Graysons Solicitors)
Clarke, Richard David (Graysons Solicitors)
Cockerham, Olivia Fleur (Irwin Mitchell LLP)
Cowan, Laura Natalya (Irwin Mitchell LLP)
Cowley, Amanda Jane (Wake Smith & Tofields)
Cox, Rae Emma (Irwin Mitchell LLP)
Crabtree, Frances Helen (Irwin Mitchell LLP)
Crossland, Victoria Elsie (Irwin Mitchell LLP)
Davies, Angela Louise (Thompsons Solicitors)
Davies, Sophie Louise (Irwin Mitchell LLP)
Davis, Jodie Michelle (Irwin Mitchell LLP)
Davis, Ryan Lee (Kennedys)
Denton, Sarah Jayne (Irwin Mitchell LLP)
Duggan, Linsey May (Norrie Waite & Slater)
Eddison, Jillian (Best Solicitors)
Fedak, Myron Roman (Irwin Mitchell LLP)
Fenton, Graham Anthony (Bray & Co Solicitors)
Flynn, Lucy Helen (Graysons Solicitors)
Forder, Rebecca Elizabeth (Irwin Mitchell LLP)
Foster, Clare Michelle (Iron Monger Curtis Ltd)
Fry, Jacqueline Anne (Unity Law Ltd)
Gregory, Alison Jayne (Irwin Mitchell LLP)
Hague, Keith Graham (Irwin Mitchell LLP)
Hayward, Martyn Edward (Irwin Mitchell LLP)
Howarth, Alison Jane (Irwin Mitchell LLP)
Hussain, Aansa Iram (Irwin Mitchell LLP)
Hutchison, Helen Marie (Irwin Mitchell LLP)
Jepson, Caroline Gail (Irwin Mitchell LLP)
Johnson, Tammy (Keeble Hawson)
Kirkham, David (Graysons Solicitors)
Kirtley, Jayne Elizabeth (Irwin Mitchell LLP)
Lee, Angela (Sheffield City Council)
Leonard, Matthew John (Irwin Mitchell LLP)
Lindley, Michelle Claire (Foys Solicitors)
Marriott, Teresa Clare (Thompsons Solicitors)
Marshall, Simon (Ashton Morton Slack LLP)
Martin, Deborah (Irwin Mitchell LLP)
McNally, Emma Jane (Irwin Mitchell LLP)
Moran, Donna-Jane (Graysons Solicitors)
Morley, Caroline Rose-Anne (Keeble Hawson)
Morris, Kelly (Irwin Mitchell LLP)
Nazar Sheikh, Ashia (Thompsons Solicitors)
New, Carey (Norrie Waite & Slater)
Newbould, Carol Linda (Favell Smith & Lawson)
Noreen, Anjum (Wrigleys Solicitors)
Oxley, Andrew Peter (Ashton Morton Slack LLP)
Parden, James Peter (Irwin Mitchell LLP)
Parsons, David John (Henry Boot Homes Ltd)
Perry, Brygida (Irwin Mitchell LLP)
Pitts, Nigel Antony (Benson Clegg Solicitors)
Porter, Katherine Louise Dawn (Taylor & Emmet)
Powell, Claire Simone (Keeble Hawson)
Presky, Sheila (Keeble Hawson)

Price, Elizabeth Louise (Kennedys)
Rice, Kerry Lisa (Keeble Hawson)
Ridge, Ann Juliet (Howells LLP)
Roberts, Fay Elise (Keeble Hawson)
Roberts, Lisa Caroline (Wake Smith & Tofields)
Robinson, Laura Kate (Irwin Mitchell LLP)
Roebuck, Paul Kenton (Taylor & Emmet)
Rose, Leanne (Keeble Hawson)
Round, Zoe Ann (Irwin Mitchell LLP)
Rushforth, Jennifer Heather (Howells LLP)
Sammans, Mark Jonathan (Graysons Solicitors)
Sandford, Joanne (Howells LLP)
Sargesson, Sally (Irwin Mitchell LLP)
Sawyer, Rachael (Lewis Francis Blackburn)
Scholey, Joanna Margaret (Sheffield City Council)
Shelton, Catherine Elizabeth (Watson Esam & Co)
Shepherdson, Nicola (Thompsons Solicitors)
Simmonds, Karen Lynne (Thompsons Solicitors)
Smallwood, Janet (South Yorkshire Passenger Transport Executive)
Smith, Donna Louise (Irwin Mitchell LLP)
Stockdale, Sharron (Taylor & Emmet)
Storrie, Linda Janet (Michael Ward)
Sweet, Fiona (Keeble Hawson)
Talbot, Shaun Patrick (Wake Smith & Co)
Taylor, Richard Winston (Proddow Mackay Solicitors)
Thompson, Stephen Robert (Wake Smith & Tofields)
Thorpe, Laura Louise Sanders (Proddow Mackay Solicitors)
Townsend, Alicia Claire (Irwin Mitchell LLP)
Turner, Donna Marie (Nabarro LLP)
Walker, David Graham (Irwin Mitchell LLP)
Watkinson, Alexander (Bell & Buxton Solicitors)
White, Laura Jane (Taylor & Emmet)
Wilkinson, Suzanne Jane (DLA Piper UK LLP)
Wilson, Keeley (Norrie Waite & Slater)
Winfield, Linda Anne (Foys Solicitors)
Winter, Sally (Taylor & Emmet)
Wrigley, Stanley Trevor (Rosalind Watchorn)

SHEFFORD, Bedfordshire

Bradbury, Elaine Julie (Central Bedfordshire Council)
Couchman, Geraldine Mary (Noble Solicitors)
Foster, Jane Linda (Central Bedfordshire Council)
Grace, Jane (Central Bedfordshire Council)
Howitt, Lorraine Diane (Central Bedfordshire Council)
Kennedy, Ruth Alexandra (Noble Solicitors)
Mcmahon, Gillian (Central Bedfordshire Council)

SHEPTON MALLET, Somerset

Burr, Cara (Dyne Drewett Solicitors)
Field, Paul Justin (Dyne Drewett Solicitors)
James, Helen Francis (Dyne Drewett Solicitors)

SHERBORNE, Dorset

Dickman, Vanessa Ann (Maclachlan Solicitors)
Vaughan-Jackson, Jennifer Sarah (Porter Dodson Solicitors)
Woolley, Cathryn Ann (Dyne Drewett Solicitors)

SHERINGHAM, Norfolk

Dawe, Susan Jean (Clapham & Collinge Solicitors)
Howell, Peter Raymond (Hansells Solicitors)
Kelly, Marie Ann (Hayes & Storr)
Pennell, Dawn Michelle (Hansells Solicitors)
Ward, Lesley Jane (Silver & Ward Solicitors LLP)

SHIFNAL, Shropshire

Walding, Annette Mary (Nettie Walding Mediation)

SHOREHAM-BY-SEA, West Sussex

Stockbridge, Peter John Lawrence (Advr District Council)

SHREWSBURY, Shropshire

Adams, David John (PCB Solicitors)
Bell, Alison (Hatchers Solicitors)
Bukhari, Saleem Tony (Howard Shah Solicitors)
Clancy, Deborah Dawn (West Mercia Constabulary)
Cole, Davina Elizabeth (Terry Jones Solicitors)
Davies, Paul Irving (Crown Prosecution Service)
Day, Michael John (Michael Day)
Evans, Esther Alexandra (Hatchers Solicitors)
Hindley, Nicola Anne (Shropshire County Council)
Hope, Sarah Elizabeth (Lanyon Bowdler Solicitors)
Hyland, Elise Patricia (Lanyon Bowdler Solicitors)
Jackson, Sandra (PCB Solicitors)
Leighton, Beverley Ann (SLC Solicitors)
Lloyd, Sarah Dorothy (Shopshire County Council)
Morris, Linda Mary (Shropshire County Council)
Myatt, Joy (1st Class Legal Ltd)
Owen, Lydia Susan (SLC Solicitors)
Pearce, Nicola Jane (Wace Morgan)
Thomas, Joanne (Hatchers Solicitors)

SIDCUP, Kent

Greig, Ross (Nelson Guest & Partners)
Hugo, Jeremy Kevin (Walsey Morris & Kennedy)
Shittu, Johnson Ometunde (Crown Prosecution Service)
Turner, Hayley Jayne (T G Baynes Solicitors)

SITTINGBOURNE, Kent

Cable, Richard (Jarmans Solicitors)
Harvey, Robert Herbert Frederick (Davis Simmonds & Donaghey Solicitors)
Seaward, Christian John (Swale Borough Council)
Yates, Rosemary June (Jarmans Solicitors)

SKEGNESS, Lincolnshire

Blackbourne, John Frederick (Norman Green)
Faunt, Christopher Paul (Bridge McFarland Solicitors)
Foster, Robert Arthur (Hodgkinsons Solicitors Ltd)
Gregory, Louise Clare (JSP Solicitors)
Johnson, Emma Lucy (Fearsons Solicitors)
Needham, Amanda Jane (JSP Solicitors)
Onyemah, Christine Margaret (JSP Solicitors)
Patten, Joanne Lisa (Fearsons Solicitors)
Skinner, Julian Richard Osborne (The James Smith Partnership)
Toon, Paul Martin (Fearsons Solicitors)
Walker, Andrew Stewart (Fearsons Solicitors)
Walker, Angela Mary (Fearsons Solicitors)

SKELMERSDALE, Lancashire

Green, Steven (R J Gill & Co)
Martell, Susannah Jane (Scott Rees & Co)
Palin, Raymond Thomas (Scott Rees & Co)
Roberts, Claire Louise (Brighouse Wolff)
Rusby, Clare (Scott Rees & Co)
Scully, Anthony Philip (R J Gill & Co)
Sharples, Emma Elizabeth Catherine (Scott Rees & Co)
Sloane, Deborah (Scott Rees & Co)
Smith, Royston Francis (Scott Rees & Co)
Thompson, Wayne Anthony (Scott Rees & Co)
Walker, Christopher (Scott Rees & Co)
Wilson, Justine Samantha (Scott Rees & Co)

SKIPTON, North Yorkshire

Akroyd, Helen (Mewies Solicitors)
Fawcett, Joseph Leslie (Charlesworth Wood & Brown)
Fitzmaurice, Christine (Craven District Council)
Rothwell, Lisa Jane (Makin Dixon Solicitors)
Scales, Joann Elizabeth (Armstrong Luty Solicitors)
Woodley, Martyn (J P Mewies & Co)

SLEAFORD, Lincolnshire

Bescoby, Nigel (Burton & Co Solicitors)
Chidlow, Joanne Claire (Chattertons Solicitors)
Cullen, Sandra Joan (Chattertons Solicitors)
Wilson, Karen Angela (Ringrose Law Solicitors)

SLOUGH, Slough

Ball, Amanda Jane (Slough Borough Council)
Collard, Alan Ronald (Barrett & Thomson)
Dale, Sukhjit Kaur (Martin Murray & Associates)
Elliott, Barry Stanley (Michael Page International)
Fullerton, Simon James (Chebsey & Co)
Gregory, Linda Maria (South Bucks District Council)
MacDiarmid, Helen Louise (Chebsey & Co)
Mistry, Jyoti (Owen White Solicitors)
O'Connor, Christine Susan (Martin Murray & Associates)
Orr, Bridget Ann (Owen White Solicitors)
Rance, Zoe (Martin Murray & Associates)
Smith, Jacqueline (Chebsey & Co)

SMETHWICK, West Midlands

Nicholls, Paul Victor (Nicholls Brimble Solicitors)

SOLIHULL, West Midlands

Case, Rosemary Diana (Millichips Solicitors)
Coall, Margaret Mary (Whiting & Purches Solicitors)
Coombs, Gillian Margaret (Lodders Solicitors LLP)
Creed, Tracy (Probate Solicitors Ltd)
Goldsby, Lynne Carol (Williamson & Soden)
Gormley, Deborah Lesley (Richard Nelson Business Defence Solicitors)
Gregg, Jayne Louise (Williamson & Soden)
Gregory, Paul (Lyons Davidson Solicitors)
Lees, Verity Anne (Williamson & Soden)
Loughrey, Terence Patrick (Terence Loughrey Consultancy)
Mottram, Steven William (Standley & Co)
O'Brien, Dorothy Agnes (Lodders Solicitors LLP)
Panchal, Anita (Hill Hofstetter)
Puar, Elizabeth Caroline (Lyons Davidson Solicitors)
Rea, Norman Conway (Sydney Mitchell LLP)
Rogers, Diane Jean (Fentimans)
Round, Clare (Caterpillar Financial Services (UK) Ltd)
Sadiq, Asif (National Grid)
Savage, Clare Louise (Lyons Davidson Solicitors)
Sheils, Louise Simone (Standley & Co)
Simmonds, Rachel (Harris Cooper Walsh)
Smith, Jane Elizabeth (Sydney Mitchell LLP)
Stokes, Marion Winifred (Standley & Co)
Twinning, Emma Jayne (Convey & Complete)
Wallace, Robert John (Lyons Davidson Solicitors)
Whitehead, Peter Rupert (NMB Group PLC)
Withers, Donna Louise (Enterprise Inns PLC)

SOMERTON, Somerset

Buck, Tina Jane (Chubb Bulleid)

SOUTH CROYDON, Surrey

Thompson, Gordon Henry James (Chappell & Thompson Legal Serv)

SOUTH MOLTON, Devon

Dennis, Barbara May (Slee Blackwell)

SOUTH SHIELDS, Tyne & Wear

Boyes, Rozann Margherita (Patterson Glenton & Stacey)
Bridge, Julie Margaret (Aileen Tallintire Solicitors)
Butler, Alison Jane (Robson Palmer)
Dunkerton, Denise Emma (G E Downs)
Grady, Paula (Terence Carney)
Hamblett, Claire (Borough of South Tyneside)
Pearce, Leeanne (Graeme Cook Solicitors)

SOUTHALL, Middlesex

Cheema, Kalwinder Kaur (David Shine Kharbanda)

SOUTHAMPTON, Southampton

Azib, Ferkhendah Jabeen (Lamport Bassitt)
Bailey, Emma (Access Law)
Bailey, Norman Charles (Placidi & Co Solicitors)
Best, Claire Louise (Bond Pearce LLP)
Boote, Kimmo Noel (Lamport Bassitt)
Boyce, James (Moore & Blatch Solicitors)
Brislane, Christine Marie (Southampton City Council)
Brooke, Fiona Catherine (Moore & Blatch Solicitors)
Burden, Nicola Joanna (Thomas Eggar LLP)
Caines, Rebecca (Paris Smith LLP)
Cameroo, Simon (Ewing Hickman & Clark)
Chainey, Peter (Paris Smith LLP)
Clarke, Kenneth Ian (Ewing Hickman & Clark)
Coats, Caroline Mary (Caroline Coats Solicitors)
Cottrell, Kelly-Anne (Eric Robinson & Co Ltd)
Dale, Caroline Paula (Eberts Solicitors)
Davies, Paul Thomas (Christopher Green Mccarrahers)
De Montjoie Rudolf, Bethany Clare (Warner Goodman LLP)
Dempsey, Sarah Jayne (State Securities PLC)
Evans, Jason David (Payne Marsh Stillwell)
Fanstone, Karen Louise (Hannides & Co)
Fisher, Louise (Hampshire Constabulary)
Francis, Pamela Mary (Clarke Willmott LLP)
Fuller, Allison Jane (Paris Smith LLP)
Gilmour, Susan Pamela (Lamport Bassitt)
Green, Edward Charles Hawrsmore (Coffin Mew LLP)
Green, Nichola Louise (Carnival UK)
Guilfoyle, Jeremy Paul (State Securities PLC)
Hall, Karen Louise (State Securities PLC)
Head, Jonathan (Clarke Willmott LLP)
Hewlett-Stamper, Sharon (Beeton Edwards LLP)
Holliss, Christopher Anthony James (Paris Smith LLP)
Howett, Carly (Lamport Bassitt)
Jeanes, Samantha Louise (Abels Solicitors)
Kemper, Chantelle (Lamport Bassitt)
King, Nicola Jayne (CDI Anderselite Ltd)
Land, Melanie Jane (Leonard & Co)
Legg, Karen Marie (Ewing Hickman & Clark)
Lodwick, Justine (Southampton City Council)
Lush, Karen Jane (Trethowans Solicitors)
McDonough, Alanna Louise (Bond Pearce LLP)
Mitchell, Tracy Elizabeth (Lamport Bassitt)
Mockford, Jacqueline Suzanne (Bond Pearce LLP)
Moore, Susan (Paris Smith LLP)
Munden, Andrew John (Warner Goodman LLP)
Parsons, Simon Edward (School of Law)
Peake, Angus David (Lamport Bassitt)
Perry, Lisa (Moore & Blatch Solicitors)
Poulter, Lucy Vivienne (Moore & Blatch Solicitors)
Powell, Carol Vesta (Coffin Mew LLP)
Pym, Beverley Ann (Eric Robinson Solicitors)
Smallbones, Tracy Anita (Bond Pearce LLP)
Smith, Helen Sarah (Bond Pearce LLP)
Smith, Julie (Southampton City Council)
Smith, Sandra Claire Marie (Clarke Willmott LLP)
Squires, Ralph Anthony (Paris Smith LLP)
Stafford, Stephen Wayne (Paris Smith LLP)
Stalker, Christina Ann (Moore & Blatch Solicitors)
Stevenson, Alexandra Jane (Thomas Eggar LLP)
Thomas, Siobhan Claire (Moore & Blatch Solicitors)
Thornton, Christopher Matthew (Southampton City Council)
Todd, Melanie Claire (Berrymans Lace Mawer)
Usher, Susan Jayne (Lester Aldridge LLP)
Waghorn, Elizabeth Jane (Moore & Blatch Solicitors)
Wall, Cristine Elizabeth (Trethowans Solicitors)
Watts, Karen Heather (Moore & Blatch Solicitors)
Whitfield, Steven (Eric Robinson Solicitors)
Woods, Jamie (Thomas Eggar LLP)

SOUTHEND-ON-SEA, Essex

Bennett-White, Clare (BTMK Solicitors LLP)
Farrow, Karen Angela (White & Co Solicitors)
Fedarb, Charlotte Claire (BTMK Solicitors LLP)
Garnett, Juliet Ann (GW Conveyancing Services)
Lee, Edward David (Kloosmans)
O'Connell, Tessa Frances (Southend-on-Sea Borough Council)
Whitcombe, Deborah Ann (BTMK Solicitors LLP)

SOUTHPORT, Merseyside

Brady, Gillian (Barnetts Solicitors)
Carter, Clare Elizabeth (Barnetts Solicitors)
Clark, Andrew (Fletchers Solicitors Limited)
Eyton, Julia Elizabeth (Fletchers Solicitors Limited)
Farrar, Jenny (JFA Legal Ltd)
Jones, Dawn (Barnetts Solicitors)
Kelty, Helen Elizabeth (Legal Director)
Kilby, Mavis Rosamond (Brighouses)
Noble, Susan (Sefton Metropolitan Borough Council)
Owen, Nicola Joanne (Fletchers Solicitors Limited)
Parker, Ian David (Merseyside Police)
Rowe, Sarah-Kate (Bromiley Holcroft Ltd)
Seasman, Angela Pauline (Sefton Metropolitan Borough Council)
Townsend, Fiona Vanessa (Sefton Metropolitan Borough Council)

SOUTHSEA, Hampshire

Strong, Rebecca Jane (Rowe Sparkes Partnership)

SPALDING, Lincolnshire

Berridge, Heather Mary (South Holland District Council)
Edwards, Timothy Richard (Roythorne & Co Solicitors)
Ingrey, Nicholas Guy (Roythorne & Co Solicitors)
King, Kay (Calthrops)
Redford, Mansel (Chattertons Solicitors)
Smith, Claire Michelle (Maples & Son)
Stinson, Mark (South Holland District Council)
Stokes, Peter Robert (Knipe Miller & Co)

SPENNYMOOR, Co Durham

Billingham, Hilary (Meikles)

SPILSBY, Lincolnshire

Hunt, Paul John (Sills & Betteridge LLP)

ST ALBANS, Hertfordshire

Broadhead, Richard Stephen (McKeowns Solicitors)
Brooks, Janet (Crown Prosecution Service)
Dale, Daljit (Taylor Walton Solicitors)
Docking, Keith Robin (SA Law LLP)
Edwards, David John (St Albans District Council)
Harvey, Michael John (SA Law)
Hildreth-Bell, Michael Frank (McKeowns Solicitors)
Kenneford, Stephen Richard (SA Law)
Mccarthy, Anne Michelle (Brethertons LLP)
O'Neill, Angela Felicity (Debenhams Ottaway)
Ranger, Clare Louise (Brethertons LLP)
Robson, Louise (City Lawyers)

Towler, Simon Charles Kendall (McKeowns Solicitors)
Walduck, Glyn Burley (National Pharmaceutical Assoc)

ST ASAPH, Denbighshire
Eyres, Alan (Qioptiq Ltd)

ST AUSTELL, Cornwall
Clemo, Andrea Jane (Charles French & Co Solicitors)
Coad, Martyn Shaun (Stephens & Scown)
Fitchett, Johanna Lee (Nalders Solicitors)
Hendry, Catherine (Nalders Solicitors)
Morgan, Joanna Margaret (Stephens & Scown)
Owens, George (Nalders Solicitors)
Read, Donna Louise (Brains Solicitors)
Robinson, Frederick Michael (Graham & Graham)
Seed, Kris (Stephens & Scown)
Slaney, Julie Anne (Stephens & Scown)
Vincent, Joanna Mary (Brains Solicitors)
Winch, Jacqueline Anne (Johnson & Johnson)

ST HELENS, Merseyside
Edgar, Michelle Marie (Canter Levin & Berg)
Ellis, David John (St Helens College)
Hesketh, Colette (Hattons Solicitors)
Hunt, Nicola Jane (The Mortgage Choice)
Roberts, Ann (Pilkington PLC)
Sims, Sharon (St Helens Metropolitan Borough Council)
Spence, Geraldine (Nulty Moffitt & Co)
Tickle, Marie Louise (Barrow & Cook)

ST IVES, Cornwall
Woon, Lesley Anne (Chellew With Nicholas Simpson)

ST LEONARDS-ON-SEA, East Sussex
Benzies, Gail Elaine (Conveyancing Direct)
Dunn, Karen Sandra (Conveyancing Direct)
Gillard, Mary Alison (Menneer Shuttleworth)
Saxelby, Diana Michelle (Fitzgraham Solicitors)

STAFFORD, Staffordshire
Abbott, Hazel (Mid Staffordshire General Hospital)
Cooper, Robert Stanley (Hand Morgan & Owen)
Dalton, Paula Louise (Staffordshire County Council)
Dean, Sarah Louise (Staffordshire County Council)
Lane, David Alan (Pickering & Butters)
Lomas, Keith James (Keith Lomas & Company)
Mahmood, Khalid (Staffordshire County Council)
Morgan, Heather Patricia (Staffordshire County Council)
Morley, Stephen John (Staffordshire County Council)
Perry, Julie Anne Cooper (Nowell Meller)
Price, Bridget Elaine (Hutsby Mees)
Simpson, Julie Ann (Stafford Borough Council)
Smith, Diana Louise (Staffordshire County Council)
Sutherland, Beverly (Staffordshire County Council)
Wain, Julie (Hand Morgan & Owen)
Young, Rhiannon Mair (Staffordshire County Council)

STAINES, Middlesex
Lewis, Sharron Janet (Rowberry Morris LLP)
Marland, Clare Margaret (Spelthorne Borough Council)

STAMFORD, Lincolnshire
Laycock, Gillian Mary (Stapleton & Son)
Thompson, Julia Dawn (Kelham & Sons)
Varley, Constance Madeleine (Daltons)

STANLEY, Co Durham
Donnelly, Christine (Derwentside Homes Limited)
Holliday, Helen (Power Scott Solicitors)

STANMORE, Middlesex
Englander, Derek Julian (Kirkwoods)
Fellows, John Douglas (BES Solicitors)
Hamilton-Bruce, Barbara Claire (Accident Advice Helpline)
Turney, Stuart David (SLP Solicitors)

STEVENAGE, Hertfordshire
Coates, Ann (Hamilton Davies)
Kaskar, Ruksana (Heckford Norton Solicitors)
Lucas, Paul (Friis & Radstone Solicitors)
Swann, Melanie Jayne (Haldanes)

STEYNING, West Sussex
Jenkinson, Lesley Ann (Leonard F T Warner)

STOCKBRIDGE, Hampshire
Hendy, Davina Rachel (Brockmans Solicitors)

STOCKPORT, Greater Manchester
Allen, Justine Louise (Mortons Solicitors)
Barker, Karen Blanche (SAS Daniels LLP)
Brittain, Duncan Baker (Stockport Metropolitan Borough Council)
Cartwright, Julia Joanne (Parkers Solicitors)
Connelly, Jacqueline Ann (Stockport Metropolitan Borough Council)
Grundy, Amanda Claire (O'Neill Patient Solicitors LLP)
Hayes, Kerry Ann (Delta Legal)
Jerdin, Caroline Elizabeth (Lea & Co)
Loseby, Alison Debra (The Clarke Partnership)
Mcgrail, Thomas Anthony (Lea & Co)
Nuttall, Ruth Charlotte (Belshaws Solicitors)

STOCKTON, Greater Manchester
Beacom, Wendy (Jacksons Law Firm LLP)
Brown, Alison Dawn (Jacksons Law Firm LLP)
Dent, Nicholas Brian (Jacksons Law Firm LLP)
Joel, Toby Matthew (Jacksons Law Firm LLP)
Saffin, Teresa Mary (Jacksons Law Firm LLP)
Scoones, Eleni Rose Liza (Jacksons Law Firm LLP)

STOCKTON-ON-TEES, Stockton-on-Tees
Butler, Raymond Derek (Archers Solicitors LLP)
Dalzell, Nicola (Archers Solicitors LLP)
Delaney, Joanne (Tilly Bailey & Irvine)
Edwards, Wendy (Archers Solicitors LLP)
Elstob, Helen Mary (Tilly Bailey & Irvine)
Gray, Mathew (NAS Advocates Ltd)
Griffiths, Susan Elizabeth (Berrymans Lace Mawer)
Hanratty, Anthony (Vickers Chisman Wishlade)
Martin, Helen Jane (Archers Solicitors LLP)
Medd, Karl Christopher (Crutes Law Firm)
Mudd, Alison Jane (Stockton-on-Tees Borough Council)
Powton, Briony Margaret (Berrymans Lace Mawer)
Tate, Helen (Archers Solicitors LLP)
Tribe, James Wilfred (Cochranes Law Firm)
Tully, Brian James (Cohen Hewitts Solicitors)
Tunney, Carol Audrey (Stockton-on-Tees Borough Council)
Webster, Lynda (Stockton-on-Tees Borough Council)
Williamson, Rachel Jane (Cochranes Law Firm)

STOKE-ON-TRENT, Stoke-on-Trent
Austin, Melony (Grindeys LLP)
Barber, Debra Jane (Stoke-on-Trent City Council)
Begg, Josephine (Wooliscroft Solicitors)
Bostock, Karen (Tinsdills Solicitors)
Bourne, Amanda Louise (Tinsdills Solicitors)
Bryan, Craig Kenneth (Tinsdills Solicitors)
Carr, Zoe Jo (Stoke-on-Trent City Council)
Chambers, Jane Louise (Tinsdills Solicitors)
Croft, Patricia Ann (Beswicks Solicitors)
Gilbert, Nicola Marie (Thompsons Solicitors)
Hague, Joanne Marie (Lichfield Reynolds)
Hodgson, Deborah Teresa (Leslie N Dodd & Co)
Holdcroft, Mandy (Woolliscrofts Solicitors)
Jones, Anita Maria (WWRD (United Kingdom) Ltd)
Jones, Samantha Jane (Stoke-on-Trent City Council)
Joughin, Lynn (Stevens Solicitors)
Knott, Hilary Anne (Tinsdills Solicitors)
Mierzwa, Stephanie Sarah (Charltons Solicitors)
Pinnell, Katherine (Grindeys LLP)
Riley, Charlotte Jane (Beswicks Solicitors)
Roberts, Deborah Ann (Thompsons Solicitors)
Shaw, Adele Diane (Dicksons Solicitors)
Simcock, Donna Ann (Thompsons Solicitors)
Smith, Heather Catherine (Stoke-on-Trent City Council)
Sykes, Rebecca Jane (Dicksons Solicitors)
Wade, Angela Dawn (Stevens)
Wheeldon, Michelle Jane (Stoke-on-Trent City Council)
White, Heather Joy (Young & Co Solicitors)

STONE, Staffordshire
Carnall, Beverley Louise (Eric Whitehead & Co)

STOURBRIDGE, West Midlands
Barnbrook, Jennifer Alison (Talbots Solicitors LLP)
Compson, Sharon (Wall James Chappell)
Godbehere, Judith Ann (Wall James Chappell)
Gray, Karen Julia (Talbots Solicitors LLP)
Holliday, Jayne (Talbots Solicitors LLP)
Marriott, Clare Lorraine (Wall James Chappell)
Oakley, Sharon (Talbots Solicitors LLP)

STOURPORT-ON-SEVERN, Worcestershire
Smith, Caroline Susan (Painters Solicitors)
Yates, Keith Albert (Lumsdons Solicitors LLP)

STOWMARKET, Suffolk
Alexander, Ingrid Elaine (Haywards Solicitors)
Goodenough, Louise Ellen (Haywards Solicitors)
Lambillion, Ruth Claire (Haywards Solicitors)
Lewis, Gerald Ivor (Gudgeons Prentice)
Simpson, John Colin (Haywards Solicitors)

STRATFORD-UPON-AVON, Warwickshire
Barnacle, Terena Louise (Geoffrey Parker & Bourne)
Brudenell, Cheryl (Lodders Solicitors LLP)
Chaplin, Jeremy Hugh (Geoffrey Parker & Bourne)
Dipper, Gillian Rachel (Jackson West Solicitors)
Evans, Janet (Stratford-upon-Avon District Council)
Fielding, Elizabeth Marion (Independent Trust Corporation Ltd)
Hill, Brent Jonathan (Geoffrey Parker & Bourne)
Nash, Macer John (Stratford-upon-Avon District Council)
Podmore, Lisa Marie (Lodders Solicitors LLP)
Robinson, Alexandra Janet (Lodders Solicitors LLP)
Scott, Sarah Melody Jayne (Needham & James LLP)
Smith, Kelly Louise (Independent Trust Corporation Ltd)
Sutherland, Susan Angela (Geoffrey Parker & Bourne)

STREET, Somerset
Moon, Patricia (Gould & Swayne Solicitors)

STRETFORD, Greater Manchester
Daley, Cassandra (Colemans-CTTS LLP)
Ginley, Emma Charlotte (Simpson Millar)
Lomax, Simon John (Simpson Millar)
Partington, Walter (Trafford Borough Council)
Rhodes, Michelle Dawn (Simpson Millar)
Taylor, Lucy Claire (Colemans-CTTS LLP)
Wright, Lisa Jane (Simpson Millar)

STROOD, Medway Towns
Mellins, Jan (Legal Services Medway Council)

STROUD, Gloucestershire
Inder, Patricia June (AT @ Law Solicitors)
Lewis, Leah Joanne (Winterbotham Smith Penley LLP)
Rogers, Elizabeth Jane (Stroud District Council)
Stephens, Elizabeth Jayne (Stroud & Swindon Building Society)

SUDBURY, Suffolk
Damant, Alison Jane (Bates Wells & Braithwaite)
Foster, Harvey Andrew Harcourt (Steed & Steed LLP)
Goulding, Karen (Steed & Steed LLP)

SUNBURY-ON-THAMES, Middlesex
Dulay, Harvinder (Chubb Fire Ltd)

SUNDERLAND, Tyne & Wear
Buckett, Elaine (McKenzie Bell)
Coulson, David (Arriva Plc)
Grant, Valda Patricia (Transcare Law)
Halliday, Julie Ann (Sunderland District Council)
Hammond, Gillian Ann (Cullen Hammond)
Heavisides, Neil Ian (Longdon Walker & Renny)
Henry, Alison (Richard Reed & Co)
Morrison, Barbara Anne (Brian Mackenow & Co Solicitors)
Murray, Valerie (Brian Mackenow & Co Solicitors)
Stoker, Hayley (Ben Hoare Bell)
Taylor, Debra Ann (McArdles Solicitors)
Taylor, Karen Ann (Sunderland District Council)
Truscott, Malcolm Leopold (Hedleys & Co)
Walls, Richard Peter (Hedleys & Co)
Wicks, Gale (Arriva Plc)
Wood, Barry Cosmo (Richard Reed & Co)

SUNNINGDALE, Windsor & Maidenhead
Allday, Danielle Joanne (Tanner & Taylor)
Grier, Victoria Louise (Campbell Hooper & Co)

SURBITON, Surrey
Bransgrove, Jane Louise (Chivers Easton Brown)
Butler, Chantal Frederika (Malcolm Johnson & Co)
Graham-Taylor, Rebecca Jane Emily (Malcolm Johnson & Co)

SUTTON, Surrey
Blackwell, Matthew (London Borough of Sutton)
Culleton, Noreen Josephine (McGlinchey & Co)
Dobson, Robert William (Pryce Woodrow)
Fox, Michael Lawrence (Brand & Co)
Gowar, Tracy (W H Matthews)
Johnson, Hazel Ruth (CRM Law LLP)
Kennard, Simon James (De Brett Solicitors)
McCaulay, Jacqueline Ann (Brand & Co)
Shuttle, Susan (Quality Solicitors Copley Clark)
Stanton, Tracy Louise (Quality Solicitors Copley Clark)
White, Gayle Elizabeth (Quality Solicitors Copley Clark)

SUTTON COLDFIELD, West Midlands
Byrne, Angela Maria (AEW Litigation Solicitors)
Cunningham, June Denise (Will Harrington & Co)
Dugard, Jacqueline Mary (Eddowes Perry & Osbourne)
Goode, Jane (Lawtrain)
Hazel, Jane Elizabeth (French & Co Solicitors)
Sezer, Claire (Central Law Training)
Vernon, Elizabeth Amelia Olivia (Woollastons Solicitors)
Wall, Louise Elizabeth (AEW Litigation Solicitors)
Woakes, Alison Jane (AEW Litigation Solicitors)
Woollaston, Laura Kay (Woollastons Solicitors)

SWADLINCOTE, Derbyshire
Kaur, Ardip (South Derbyshire District Council)
Sharman, Alicia Ann (Timms Solicitors)
Smith, Joy May (Timms Solicitors)
Wood, Andrew John (Timms Solicitors)

SWAFFHAM, Norfolk
Hewitt, Diane Elizabeth (Ward Gethin Solicitors)

SWANLEY, Kent
Hart, Elizabeth (Bishop Akers & Co)

SWANSEA, Swansea
Brooks, Heather Jane (Neath Port Talbot County Bouough Council)
Chalke, Ann Marie (Peter Williams & Co)
Davies, Nicholas John (Graham Evans & Partners)
Duff, Stuart Alexander (City & County of Swansea)
Edwards, Helen Louise (South Wales Constabulary)
Fuge, Shelly Marie (John Collins & Partners LLP)
Hayes, Eve Victoria (Graham Evans & Partners)
Howell, Deborah (City & County of Swansea)
Huxtable, Phillip (Graham Evans & Partners)
Jones, Kate (City & County of Swansea)
Jones, Robert Michael (Morgan Cole Solicitors)
Miles, Sara Non Ann (Howells LLP)
Moore, Elizabeth Ruth (Morgan Cole Solicitors)
Northey, Andrea Elizabeth (Smith Llewelyn Partnership)
O'Brien, Geraldine (City & County of Swansea)
Owen-Smith, Catherine Anne (City & County of Swansea)
Parkin, Wendy Mary (City & County of Swansea)
Patel, Pratima (Kearns & Co)
Phippen, Sarah (Davies Parsons Allchurch Solicitors)
Plumb, Jennifer (City & County of Swansea)
Rogers, Mary Elizabeth (Beor Wilson & Lloyd)
Spanner, Lesley Ann (City & County of Swansea)
Stevens, Sian Claire (City & County of Swansea)
Thyer-Hughes, Sarah Louise (City & County of Swansea)
Waldie, Anne Louise (City & County of Swansea)
Whelan, Lynne (John Collins & Partners LLP)
Wills, Frederick Jonathan (City & County of Swansea)

SWINDON, Swindon
Browning, Janice Lesley (Hale & Hopkins)
Butcher, Julie Ann (Bevirs)
Chamberlain, Kim (McEwens)
Clarke, Joanne (Arval P H H Ltd)
Cooke, Sarah Janet (Zurich Financial Services)
Coyle, Rachel (Swindon Borough Council)
Davison, Tara Alexandra (Fullagar Brooks Solicitors)
Gingell, Betty (PHH International Ltd)
Goodenough, Anne Patricia (McEwens)
Hewins, Jane Mary (Carter Read & Dove)
Hunt, Caroline Anne (The Hillman Partnership)
Leigh, Janine Roberta (Thames Water Utilities Limited)
Lewis, Sian (Lemon Solicitors LLP)
Maggs, Glenice Elaine (Milliken Solicitors)
Miles, Kathryn Anne (Cartus Ltd)
Mills, Maureen Joyce (Heath Lambert Group)
Morter, Emma Louise (Bevirs)
Pound, Adrian Mark (Stanley Security Solutions Ltd)
Simpkins, Barbara Anne (Nationwide Building Society)
Stacey, Elaine (Pooley Solicitors LLP)
Stiles, Ellen (Thring Townsend Lee & Pembertons)
Thorpe, Natasha Jayne (Swindon Borough Council)

Titcombe, Tracy Marie (Nationwide Building Society)
Treloar, Lesley Alison (Nationwide Building Society)
Warr, Harry Graeme (Lemon Solicitors LLP)
Warwick, Heidi Ingrid (Bishop Longbotham & Bagnall)
Watkins, Patricia Bernadette (Lemon Solicitors LLP)
Watson, Elizabeth Ann (Hale & Hopkins)

SWINTON, Greater Manchester
Hulse, Lauren (Salford City Council)
Jones, Angela (Salford City Council)
Roberts, Andrew (Salford City Council)

TADLEY, Hampshire
Greenwood, Helen Anne (Rowberry Morris LLP)

TAMWORTH, Staffordshire
Botting, Helen Rachel (Foseco International Ltd)
Parnham, Maurice Howard (Tamworth Borough Council)
Redfern, Colin Anthony (Rutherfords)
Stanton, Corinne Rosemary (Garner Canning Ltd)
Tremeer, Alison Maxine (South Staffordshire Family Mediation Services)
Tyler, Louise Jane (Rutherfords)
Wengraf, Catherine Louise (Rutherfords)

TAUNTON, Somerset
Abbott, Lisa Jane (Somerset County Council)
Alexander, Caroline (Clarke Willmott LLP)
Bedford, Graham Denis (Foot Anstey Solicitors)
Blyth, Mary Sanders (Harris Fowler Solicitors)
Boyce, Philip William James (Boyce & Company)
Candy, Janet (Fleet Solicitors LLP)
Chapman, Karen Louise (Clarke Willmott LLP)
Cooke, Peter Alan (Porter Dodson LLP)
Crossman, Linda Carole (Somerset County Council)
Dibble, Jemma Claire (Foot Anstey Solicitors)
Dodds, Hannah Louise (Kevin Shearn Family Law Pracitce)
Dunlop, Jane Mary (Clarke Willmott LLP)
Dymond, Teresa Mary (Pardoes Solicitors)
Eiserbeck, Kerry Jane (Bevan Ashford Solicitors)
Grant, Helen Louise (Risdon Hosegood)
Grice, Frances Melanie (Butler & Co)
Hockey, Richard Andrew (Somerset County Council)
Hoysted, Stuart William (Clarke Willmott LLP)
Jones, Andrew Richard (Somerset County Council)
Keniston, Suzanne Jane (Somerset County Council)
Langford, Amy Rachel (Pardoes Solicitors)
Mills, Samantha Claire (Foot Anstey Solicitors)
Morren, Jonathan Scott (Taunton Deane Borough Council)
Newstead, Carole Diane (Foot Anstey Solicitors)
Nicholls, Kathryn (Clarke Willmott LLP)
Pitt, Brenda Ruth (Risdon Hosegood)
Pollard, Andrea Joanne (Broomhead & Saul)
Pritchard, Janet Linda (Westco Conveyancing Services)
Rhodes, Sarah (Crown Prosecution Service)
Roberts, Philip Edward (Clarke Willmott LLP)
Shobbrook, Martin John (Ashfords Solicitors)
Stevens, Suzanne Lynda (Broomhead & Saul)
Stockton, Geoffrey (Harris Fowler Solicitors)
Van Zyl, Emma Louise (Harris Fowler Solicitors)
Vining, Margaret (Clarke Willmott LLP)
White, Kathryn Rose (Clarke Willmott LLP)

TAVISTOCK, Devon
Haggett, Stephen Charles (H & C Lawyers Ltd)
Kenyon, Annabel Teresa (West Devon Borough Council)
Pettit, Sophia Mary (Ann Pointer)

TEDDINGTON, Middlesex
Chin, Melissa (Redmans Solicitors)

TEIGNMOUTH, Devon
Grimshaw, Gwen (Scott Richards)
Halfyard, Suzanne Marie (Tozers LLP)
Marsland, Alison (Scott Richards)
Matthews, Wendy Michelle (Self Employed)
Thulborn, Susan Lorraine (Tozers LLP)

TELFORD, Shropshire
Anderson, Joyce (MFG Solicitors)
Begum, Nasrin (Parry Carver Solicitors)
Blair, Lisa Marie (Lanyon Bowdler Solicitors)
Christie, Ceri Dittany (Lanyon Bowdler Solicitors)
Cotton, Sharon (Green & Co)
Cureton, Karen Jean (Clarkes Solicitors)
Davies, Andrew Paul (MFG Solicitors LLP)
Dix, Helen Jane (Telford & Wrekin District Council)
Hale, Hannah Rachael (Poole & Co LLP)
Jarvis, Ruth Angela Elizabeth (Telford Wills & Probate)
Kirk, Abigail Ruth (Parry Carver Solicitors)
Link, Stephen Wayne (Wright & Mcmillan Bennet)
Mears, Sarah (Martin Kaye Solicitors)
Pickering, Nichola Jane (Martin Kaye Solicitors)
Pitchford, Clare Elizabeth (Martin Kaye Solicitors)
Sans, Gary Stephen Whitney (Lanyon Bowdler Solicitors)
Schultz, Maria Elizabeth (Telford & Wrekin District Council)
Shanahan, Susan Tansy (National Farmers Union)
Shaw, Liane (Telford & Wrekin District Council)
Thompson, Peter Leslie (Wright & McMillan Bennett)
Wellings, Amy Clare (Wright & Mcmillan Bennet)
Wickstead, Amanda Jayne (Martin Kaye Solicitors)
Wickstead, Kathrine Lynette (Green & Co)
Williams, Amy (Barn Farm CP School)

TENBURY WELLS, Worcestershire
Hopewell, Sharon Louise (Norris & Miles)

TENTERDEN, Kent
Hails, Laura (Pengelly & Rylands)

TETBURY, Gloucestershire
Scotford, Linda Jane (Richard T Bate & Co)

TEWKESBURY, Gloucestershire
Eager, Jonathan (Thomson & Badham)
Halliwell, Sarah Elizabeth (Tewkesbury Borough Council)
Sumnall, Vincent Kenneth (DF Legal LLP)

THATCHAM, West Berkshire
Kaxe, Garry (Henwick Properties)

THETFORD, Norfolk
Allison, Sharon Jane (Cunningham John Solicitors)
Brazier, Vickie Olive (Rudlings & Wakelan)
Campbell, Lorraine Dawn (Metcalfe Copeman & Pettefar)
Crossley, Julie (Cunningham John Solicitors)
Gleave, Timothy (Kester Cunningham John Solicitors)
Hendriks, Paul Lawrence William Louis (Metcalfe Copeman & Pettefar)
Lloyd, Deborah Ann (Cunningham John Solicitors)
Parker, Simon John (Kester Cunningham John Solicitors)
Stickland, Ruth Louise (Rudlings & Wakelan)
Taylor, Teresa Joanne (W F Smith & Co)
Ware, Nicholas Charles (Lloyd & Co)
Young, Geoffrey Alan (Rudlings & Wakelan)

THIRSK, North Yorkshire
Bleanch, Sara Lee (Shirtcliffe & Co)
Dallinson, Robert (Hileys Solicitors)

THORNBURY, South Gloucestershire
Storey, Christine Elizabeth (South Gloucestershire Council)
Tucker, Lynne Elizabeth (South Gloucestershire Council)

THORNE, South Yorkshire
Baxter, Terrence (Bridge Sanderson Munro)

TIPTON, West Midlands
Richards, Christine (Dennings Solicitors)

TIVERTON, Devon
Bright, Jane Clare (Ashfords Solicitors)
Hall, Polly (Mid Devon District Council)

TONBRIDGE, Kent
Cole, Karen (Warners Law LLP)
Dance, John Paul (Clarke Kiernan)
Dumbleton-Moore, Catherine Helen Elizabeth (EMD Law LLP)
Kneebone, Melissa Jane (Clarke Kiernan)
Marshall, Amanda Louise (Clarke Kiernan)
Ollett, Elizabeth Marie (Warners Law LLP)
Short, Lorraine Ann (Warners Law LLP)
Steele-Williams, Maria Lesley (Clarke Kiernan)
Wills, Carina Mary (Clarke Kiernan)
Worth, Leslene (Travel Insurance Facilities PLC)

TONYPANDY, Rhondda Cynon Taff
Jones, Melissa Ann (Graeme John)
Smith, Helen Jane (Devonalds Solicitors)

TORQUAY, Devon
Buckley, Julie (Hooper & Wollen)
Cable, Andrew Duncan (Bynes)
Coish, Andrea Marie (Woollcombe Beer Watts)
Cotton, Felicity (Almy & Thomas)
Dunn, Stephen Nicholas (Torbay Council)
Ellicott, David (Bynes)
Gilles, Anthony Andrew (Almy & Thomas)
Green, Jacqueline-Ann Bell (Hooper & Wollen)
Groom, Sally Ann (Somerville & Savage)
Hardy, Carole (Torbay Council)
Maries, Mark Simon (Torbay Council)
Nolan, Brigit Clare (Hooper & Wollen)
Osborne, Lisa Maria (Somerville & Savage)
Penfold, Michael Edward (Kitsons LLP)
Stokes, Mark Ian (Hooper & Wollen)
Wagstaff, Deborah Michelle (Kitsons LLP)

TOTNES, Devon
Anthony, Susan Jennifer (Recompense Ltd)
Hall, Kim Denise (Windeatts)
Hammond, Amanda (Recompense Ltd)
Harris, Wendy (Windeatts)
Huxham, Ian (Recompense Ltd)
Malthouse, Rebecca (Recompense Ltd)
Miles, Colin (South Hams District Council)
Snell, Roger Martin (Recompense Ltd)
Watson, Beverley Ann (Windeatts)

TOWCESTER, Northamptonshire
Schofield, Alina (Towcester Family Law Practice)

TREHARRIS, Merthyr Tydfil
Humphreys, Rachel (Dwr Cymru Welsh Water)
Williams, Louise Ann (Dwr Cymru Welsh Water)

TROWBRIDGE, Wiltshire
Coombs, Barbara Mary (Wiltshire County Council)
Dagger, Judith Mary (Bishop Longbotham & Bagnall)
Dagger, Julian John Kingsley (Bishop Longbotham & Bagnall)
Gale, Kevin (Wiltshire County Council)
Handsley, Sarah (Wiltshire County Council)
Holder, Christine Merilyn (Wiltshire County Council)
New, Alison Clare (Bishop Longbotham & Bagnall)
Purnell, Keith Bernard (Sylvester & Mackett)
Worsnop, Anne Rachel (Wiltshire County Council)

TRURO, Cornwall
Ager, Sandra (John Boyle & Co)
Barnes, Martine (CCET)
Buckley, Vivienne Kay (Stephens & Scown)
Cailleach, Teri (Stephens & Scown)
Chaney, Katherine Elowan (Cornwall Law)
Coia, Julian Max (Follett Stock Solicitors)
Conroy, Benjamin Thomas (Conroys Solicitors)
Copeland, Andrew Paul (Crown Prosecution Service)
Cowsill, Jean Ann (Cornwall Council)
Fearns, Rebecca Susanna (Chris Harrison Law)
Folkard, Gerald (Cornwall Council)
Gilbert, Michelle Anne (Nalders Solicitors)
Harris, Jason Lee (Stephens & Scown)
Heane, Johanna Louise (Chris Harrison Law)
Jones, Sophie Charlotte (Coodes Solicitors)
Keeler, Lynn Ann (Nalders Solictors)
Marshall, Mary Elizabeth (Nalders Solicitors)
Mitchell, Shellie (Cornwall Council)
Morris, Peggy Elizabeth (Chris Harrison Law)
Ormerod, Vanessa May (Cornwall Council)
Pritchard, Karen Jayne (Coodes Solicitors)
Standing, Rebecca Elaine (Coodes Solicitors)
Symes, Hayley Louise (Stephens & Scown)
Tew, Hannah Charlotte (Nalders Solicitors)
Vercoe, Hayley Kay (Truro & Penwith College)
Webster, Danielle Marie (Cornwall Law)
Wilton, Ann Marie (Follett Stock Solicitors)

TUNBRIDGE WELLS, Kent
Aldridge, Claire (Cripps Harries Hall LLP)
Clement, Jonathan Mark (Thomson Snell & Passmore)
Currie, Susan Elizbeth (Thomson Snell & Passmore)
Embley, Keith John (Tunbridge Wells Borough Council)
Foster, Lynne (Thomson Snell & Passmore)
Fox, Vincent James (Lloyds TSB Private Banking Ltd)
Fuller, Joanne Claire (Keogh Caisley Solicitors)
Gabay, Julie Ann (Thomson Snell & Passmore)
Gilbert, Stuart John (Berry & Berry)
Grant, Clair Marie (Cripps Harries Hall LLP)
Greig, Clare (Cripps Harries Hall LLP)
Hawkes, Jennifer Louise (Thomson Snell & Passmore)
Hebditch, Frances Gail (Cripps Harries Hall LLP)
Herbert, Jonathan (Thomson Snell & Passmore)
Kirwan, Stacey (Cripps Harries Hall LLP)
Lambert, Susan Anne (Thomson Snell & Passmore)
Patman, Rebecca (Cripps Harries Hall LLP)
Paxton, Amy Joanna (Thomson Snell & Passmore)
Rumm, David John (Rumm Employment)
Trevaskis, Sally Elizabeth (Cripps Harries Hall LLP)

TWICKENHAM, Middlesex
Burn, Alison Jean (London Borough of Richmond)
Forster, Jacqueline Kay (Stone Rowe Brewer)
Wilson, Anthony Nigel (Read & Co)

UCKFIELD, East Sussex
Binge, Julie Patricia (Dawson Hart LLP)
Braham, Marie-Francesca Anya (Rix & Kay Solicitors)
Edwards, Kirsten Elizabeth Ann (Dawson Hart LLP)
Hollands, Jan (Dawson Hart LLP)
Kay, Sharon Lesley (Rix & Kay Solicitors)
Morcom, Wendy (Rix & Kay Solicitors)
Morison, Valli Maryanne (Rix & Kay Solicitors)
Sparks, Alison Jane (Dawson Hart LLP)
Wilson, Jonathan Paul (Dawson Hart LLP)

ULVERSTON, Cumbria
Harrison, Stephanie Victoria (Hart Jackson & Sons)

UXBRIDGE, Middlesex
Almeida, Mary Ernestine (London Borough of Hillingdon)
Blackburn, Arthur James (London Borough of Hillingdon)
Brown, Anthony Robert (South Bucks District Council)
Cox, Maria (Iliffes Booth Bennett Solicitors)
Dunkley, Andrew James (Turbervilles Solicitors)
Kennedy, Louise Ann (Network Appliance Ltd)
Kotecha, Roopa (IBB Solicitors)
Lovegrove, Ginnette Ann (Hurstriver Ltd)
Millson, Ian David (Ally Lindsay Solicitors)
Munro, Kerrie (London Borough of Hillingdon)
Robins, Maxine (London Borough of Hillingdon)
Smith, Jason Winston (Iliffes Booth Bennett Solicitors)
Stooke, Andrew (Sterling Commerce (UK) Ltd)
Thompson, Laura Louise (IBB Solicitors)
Trivedi, Anjna (London Borough of Hillingdon)
Underhill, Malcolm David (Iliffes Booth Bennett Solicitors)
Walsh, Cheryl Sandra (Xerox Ltd)

VERWOOD, Dorset
Edwards, Deanne (MJP Law)

WADEBRIDGE, Cornwall
Blake, Philip John (Cornwall Council)

WAKEFIELD, West Yorkshire
Atkinson, Jayne Amy (Switalskis Solicitors LLP)
Barker, Adele Marie (Beaumont Legal)
Bartle, Sarah Louise (Wakefield Metropolitan District Council)
Box, Peter (Wakefield Metropolitan District Council)
Brown, Kirstin Linzi (Hewshaw Pratt Solicitors)
Deacon, Jason Neil (Green Williamson)
Dowson, Mary Teresa (Wakefield Metropolitan District Council)
Handy, Patrick Lawrence (Wakefield Metropolitan District Council)
Hinchliffe, Steven (City of Wakefield Metropolitan District Council)
Honeybone, Andrea (Minster Law Ltd)
Johnson, Richard Thomas (Switalskis Solicitors LLP)
Lovell, Lisa Marie (Switalskis Solicitors LLP)
Mcdonald, Linsey Anne (Switalskis Solicitors LLP)
Monaghan, Carolyn Louise (Hiutson Wittrick Solicitors)
Newsam, Rebecca (Wakefield Metropolitan District Council)
Peacock, Adrian John (Wakefield Metropolitan District Council)
Ridley, Lorraine (Green Williamson)

WALKDEN, Greater Manchester
Peaty, Joanne Marie Oldfield (Widdows Pilling & Co)

WALLASEY, Merseyside
Best, David Miles (Metropolitan Borough of Wirral)
Coburn, Phillip (Burd Ward Solicitors)
Fitzpatrick, Sean Anthony Paul (Metropolitan Borough of Wirral)
Mciver, Tracey Anne (Thomas A Higgins & Co)

Mead, Paul Gregory (Burd Ward Solicitors)
Prowse, Andrea (Thomas A Higgins & Co)

WALLINGFORD, Oxfordshire
Baker, Susan Jean (South Oxfordshire District Council)
Crosthwaite, Hazel Helen (Ratcliffe Duce & Gammer)
Shepherd, Nigel Paul (South Oxfordshire District Council)

WALLINGTON, Surrey
Cooper, Gavin John (Carpenter & Co)

WALLSEND, Tyne & Wear
Coldron, Graham John (North Tyneside Metropolitan Borough Council)
Harris, Lynn (The Associate Law Firm)

WALSALL, West Midlands
Bethell, Heather Jane (Walsall Metropolitan Borough Council)
Brindley, Hannah (Enoch Evans LLP)
Burgoyne, Paul Roy (Burgoyne & Co)
Clark, Janette (Walsall Housing Group)
Coleman, Lesley Jane (Jennings Perks & Co)
Doyle, Michael Stuart (Enoch Evans LLP)
Durkin, Elaine Angela (P J Wilson & Co)
Edmondson, Julie (Walsall Metropolitan Borough Council)
Foy, Lynn (Clive Shepherd & Co)
Greatrix, Daniel William (Enoch Evans LLP)
Green, Stephanie (CMHT)
Greenwood, Stephen Leslie (Greenwood & Co)
Harris, Paul Edward (Edmunds & Co Solicitors)
Havercroft, Brian Charles (Marston Group Limited)
Hunt, Kerry Anne (Enoch Evans LLP)
Myatt, Samantha Leann (Bradin Trubshaw Partnership)
Neylan, Suzanne Jane (Lane & Co)
O'Connor, James Gerald Vincent (Walsall Metropolitan Borough Council)
Ross, Kay (Colemans-CTTS LLP)
Rowley, Ralph (Walsall Metropolitan Borough Council)
Wentworth, Clare Louise (Enoch Evans LLP)

WALTHAM ABBEY, Essex
Adams, Leonie Kate (DJK Solicitors)
Gildir, Feride (Lingualaw Ltd)
Unger, Keith Colin (Townsend Family Law solicitors)

WALTHAM CROSS, Hertfordshire
Buckle, Stuart James (Tesco Stores Ltd)
King, Diana Elizabeth (Borough of Broxbourne)
Pegna, Carlo Colombo (Master Collections)

WALTON-ON-THAMES, Surrey
Wicks, Martin William (Arc (Europe) Ltd)

WANTAGE, Oxfordshire
Waller, Jacqueline Bernice (Charles Lucas & Marshall)
Wilkins, Amanda Jane (Angel Wilkins)

WAREHAM, Dorset
Clayton, Suzanne Frances (Humphries Kirk)
Eaves, Pauline Joan (Neville-Jones & Co Solicitors)
Hardy, Linda Karen (Neville-Jones & Co Solicitors)
Poole, Marion (Humphries Kirk)
Pullen, Rachel Clare (Neville-Jones & Co Solicitors)
Ryder, Veronica Jeanne (Humphries Kirk)

WARLEY, West Midlands
Bufton, Mervyn Raymond (George Green LLP)
Ford, Susan (George Green LLP)
Russell, Lesley Pauline (Hearne & Co)

WARMINSTER, Wiltshire
Ayrton, Joanne (Middleton & Upsall)
Clifford, Angela Celia (Edward Moore Solicitors)
Coombes, Pina Tauinaola (Edward Moore Solicitors)
Damurakis, Joanna Vicky (Middleton & Upsall)
King, Valerie Susanne (Middleton & Upsall)

WARRINGTON, Cheshire
Bedouet, Christelle Martine (Colin Watson & Co)
Boardman, Patricia Mary (Dootsons LLP)
Brierley, Neil Peter (United Utilities Plc)
Butler, Lesley Karen (Forshaws Davies Ridgway LLP)
Daniels, Kathryn Marie (Forshaws Solicitors LLP)
Down, Penny (Steimhoff UK Group)
Ennis-Bratchell, Joanne Louise (United Utilities Plc)
Flanagan, Julie Anne (United Utilities Plc)
Gaughran, Colm John (Warrington Borough Council)
Hicks, Emma (Forshaws Davies Ridgway LLP)
Hill, Darren Antony (United Utilities Plc)
Hogg, Sarah (Alpha Biolabs)
Hughes, Julie Anne (United Utilities Plc)
Hunter, Jane Rebecca (Steels Solicitors)
Iball, Timothy Mansergh (Willetts Marsden Solicitors)
Jones, Sera Adeline (Forshaws Davies Ridgway LLP)
King, Christine Elizabeth (Warrington Borough Council)
Martin, Adele (Dalgarno Solicitors)
Melia, Raymond (Fiona Bruce & Co)
Morgan, Jane Elizabeth (National Rivers Authority)
Munro, Natalie Marie (DWF LLP)
Ogden, Hilary Levern (Frank Howard Solicitors)
Oleszczuk, Julie Dawn (Rowlinsons)
Owens, Brian Charles (Forshaws Davies Ridgway LLP)
Pointon, Adrian Paul (Dalgarno Solicitors)
Stockley, Alison June (V T Nuclear Services Ltd)
Sutton, Peter Edward (Warrington Borough Council)
Wilson, Suzanne (Widdows Mason)

WARWICK, Warwickshire
Bhambra, Harjinder Kaur (Warwickshire County Council)
Cammish, Serena Louise (Warwickshire County Council)
Ford, Emma (Warwickshire County Council)
Freeth, Alison Claire (Warwickshire County Council)
Gillett, Nicola Jane (Moore & Tibbits)
Jarrett, Nicole Marie (Warwickshire County Council)
Martin, Tania Louise (Penmans Solicitors LLP)
Wallington, Sheila Ann (Moore & Tibbits)
Williamson, Christine Heather (Warwickshire County Council)
Zikking, Linda Jane (Warwickshire County Council)

WASHINGTON, Tyne & Wear
Allen, Brenda (George Mills)
Gibson, Muriel (Swinburne & Jackson LLP)
Reece, Donna (K Boswell & Co)
White, Emily Hannah (Mills Donkin & Co Solicitors)

WATERLOO, Merseyside
Blanchard, Sophie Alexandra (Bell & Co)

WATERLOOVILLE, Hampshire
Blore, James Edward Frederick (Warner Goodman LLP)
Bulmer, Debbie Louise (Verisona Solicitors)
Coffin, Karen Elizabeth (Biscoes Solicitors)
Richardson, Kristy (Biscoes Solicitors)
Williams, Selina Victoria (Biscoes Solicitors)

WATFORD, Hertfordshire
Bunton, Joanna Katie (Matthew Arnold & Baldwin LLP)
Bush, Malcolm (BT PLC)
Doherty, Tracie Jane (Taylor Woodrow Construction)
Dunn, Claire Michelle (Regus)
Hanlon, Jacqueline Margaret (Matthew Arnold & Baldwin LLP)
Healey, Michelle Marianne (Matthew Arnold & Baldwin LLP)
McManus, Patricia (Matthew Arnold & Baldwin LLP)
Mead, Collette (Collins Solicitors)
Neilson, Fiona (Matthew Arnold & Baldwin LLP)
Pendry, David Marc (Camelot Group PLC)
Simpson, Thomas David (GE Money Home Lending)
Wahlgren, Caroline Sarah (Matthew Arnold & Baldwin LLP)
Webster, Michelle Claire (Matthew Arnold & Baldwin LLP)
Williams, Alison Jane (Murphy & Co)

WELLING, Kent
Crook, Kim Jonathan (Hadfield & Co Solicitors)

WELLINGBOROUGH, Northamptonshire
Grimster, Jonathan Paul (NFU Mutual Insurance Society Ltd)

WELLINGTON, Shropshire
Gallagher, David Ian (Gallaghers)
Isaac, Nigel John (Porter Dodson Solicitors)

WELLS, Somerset
Hayes, Valerie Joyce (Harris & Harris)

WELLS-NEXT-THE-SEA, Norfolk
Weston, Laura Marie (Hayes & Storr)

WELSHPOOL, Powys
Harris, Ruth Elena (Harrisons)

WELWYN GARDEN CITY, Hertfordshire
Coventry, Joanna Mary (Ewart Price)
Hunt, Nigel Geoffrey (Ewart Price)
Lane, Christopher Dennis (Crane & Staples)
Lowe, Zoe Ann (Ewart Price)
Robertson, Mandy Elizabeth (Roche Products Limited)
Robinson-Smith, David (Welwyn Hatfield District Council)
Waring, Angela Jane (Welwyn Hatfield District Council)

WEMBLEY, Middlesex
Burnell, Louise Teresa (Metropolitan Police)
Namasivayam, Arunthathi (Genga & Co)
Ndirika, Evelyn Nkiruka (Templeton Legal Services)

WEST BROMWICH, West Midlands
Bartleet-Cross, Susan Lyn (West Bromwich Building Society)
Bassi, Sukhjit (UKIC Immigration Lawyers)
Brown, Audrey Euthilda (Challinors Solicitors)
Gaffey, Kimberley (Challinors Solicitors)
Howell, Richard George (Challinors Solicitors)
Mason, Philip Potter (Challinors Solicitors)

WEST BYFLEET, Surrey
Jackson, Jodie (Larkin & James)

WEST DRAYTON, Middlesex
Keniston, John Gerald (Richard L Brady Esq)

WEST MALLING, Kent
Cochrane, Clifford John (Tonbridge & Malling Borough Council)
Lattin, Susan Wendy (Vertex Law LLP)

WESTBURY, Wiltshire
Carleton, Sandra Julie (Pinniger Finch & Co)
Mckellar, Jennifer Elizabeth (The Jolly Williams Partnership)
Reeves, Anthony Richard (Pinniger Finch & Co)

WESTCLIFF-ON-SEA, Essex
Briggs, Yvonne Maria (Park Legal Service)
Cohen, Marilyn (Paul Robinson & Co)
Dunne, Valerie Ann (Law Hurst & Taylor)
Lowen, Annette Jayne (Paul Robinson & Co)
Parker, David Harold (Scott Jefferies)
Plant, Polly (Paul Robinson & Co)
Tobin, Gillian Margaret (Jefferies Essex LLP)

WESTERHAM, Kent
Humphreys, Judith Mary (Elgee Pinks Solicitors)
Main, Nicola Ann (Sharratts London)
Sayers, Douglas Albert (Brunswick Law)

WESTON SUPER MARE, North Somerset
Angelinetta, Karen (Berry Redmond & Robinson Solicitors)
Barnes, Valerie Irene (Gordon & Penny)
Blackman, Claire Anne (Wards Solicitors)
Carter, Janet Mary (Hall Ward & Fox)
Castle, Stewart Scott (John Hodge Solicitors)
Kourdoulos, Caroline (Berry Redmond & Robinson Solicitors)
Mackey, Hugh Stephen (John Hodge Solicitors)
Mapstone, Andrea Christine (Personal Estate Planning Legal Services)
Martin, David (The Cheque Exchange)
Meadows, Sally Jane (Berry Redmond & Robinson Solicitors)
Moore, Gillian Elizabeth (Powells)
Penwill, Sylvie (Wards Solicitors)
Press, Christopher Alexander (Chawner Grey & Co)
Rees, Simon James (Baker Rees)
Rudd, Julie Ann (John Hodge Solicitors)
Rylands, Deborah Caroline (Berry Redmond & Robinson Solicitors)
Wheeler, Pandora-May (Wards Solicitors)

WEYBRIDGE, Surrey
Digby, Ruth Anne (Gosling & Wilkinson)
Sapsed, Victoria Claire (Guillaumes Gosling & Wilkinson)
Tigwell, Alex Peter (Guillaumes Gosling & Wilkinson)

WEYMOUTH, Dorset
Adams, Marie (Mustoe Shorter Solicitors)
Arnold, Lindsey Yvonne (Pengillys)
O'Brien, Karen Susan (Simon Lacey Law Associates)

WHICKHAM, Tyne & Wear
Ross, Peter (Peter Ross & Co)

WHITBY, North Yorkshire
Allan, Beverley Pamela Ann (North Yorkshire Law)
Herbert, Rosemarie (North Yorkshire Law)
Lewis, Maureen (Thorpe & Co)

WHITCHURCH, Shorpshire
Brown, Nicola Ann (David Manning & Co)
Sandford, Maureen Rose (Henry Lees Solicitors)

WHITEHAVEN, Cumbria
Bestford, Louisa Elizabeth (HFT Gough & Co)
Herbert, Jacqueline (HFT Gough & Co)
Jewell, Marlene (Copeland Borough Council)
O'Neill, Joann (HFT Gough & Co)

WHITLEY BAY, Tyne & Wear
Scott, Diane Elizabeth (Williamsons)

WHITSTABLE, Kent
Alp, David William (The Parry Sharratt Partnership)
Cuckow, Sarah Louise (Kent County Council Legal & Democratic Services)
Kury, Rachel Wendy (Chaucer Insurance Ltd)
Lawrie, Andrew Robert (Pocock's Solicitors of Whitstable LLP)
Sansom, Jacqui (Kent County Council)
Sissons, Gillian (Kent County Council Legal & Democratic Services)

WIDNES, Cheshire
Hanson, Alison Ruth (Halton Borough Council)
Howard, Peter Anthony (Byrne Frodsham & Co)

WIGAN, Greater Manchester
Battye, Jonathan Mark (Wigan Metropolitan Borough Council)
Bourne, Kathryn Ann (Healds Solicitors)
Bowen, Michelle Susanne (Healds Solicitors)
Foster, Claire Louise (Wigan Metropolitan Borough Council)
Foster, Peter (Healds Solicitors)
Freeman, Margaret (Alker & Ball)
Fulford, Susan Yvonne (Wigan Metropolitan Borough Council)
Hodgkinson, Jessica Catherine (Wigan Metropolitan Borough Council)
Holland, Constance Helen (Wigan Metropolitan Borough Council)
Mcguire, Andrew Thomas (Wigan Metropolitan Borough Council)
Mitchell, John (Wigan Metropolitan Borough Council)
Nicholls, Julie Catherine (Wigan Metropolitan Borough Council)
Shaw, Ian Duncan (Wigan Metropolitan Borough Council)

WIGTON, Cumbria
Harrod, Catherine Mary (Beaty & Co)

WILLENHALL, West Midlands
Bennett, Julie Ann Louise (Foster Baxter Cooksey)
Buxton, Sandra Ann (Foster Baxter Cooksey)
Gallear, Gemma Marie (Foster Baxter Cooksey)
Hall, Kevin Arthur (Excalibur Investigations)
Kibble, Elaine Ann (Foster Baxter Cooksey)
Paul, Balbir Kaur (Ian Henery & Co Solicitors)
Sankey, Claire Rebecca (Foster Baxter Cooksey)
Walton, Elena Maria (Foster Baxter Cooksey)
Winwood, Mark Philip James (Foster Baxter Cooksey)

WILMSLOW, Cheshire
Briggs, Christopher (Roberts Jackson Solicitors)
Mason, Judith Anne (Bott & Co)
Smith, Julie Lesley (Hilary Meredith Solicitors)
Warburton, Michael Stanley Peter (Information Commissioner)

WIMBORNE, Dorset
Newnham, Angela Jane (Newnham & Jordan Solicitors)

WINCHESTER, Hampshire
Armstrong, Melanie Christel Annegreta (Shentons)
Boarder, Julie Ann (Dutton Gregory LLP Solicitors)
Fine, Sarah Jane (Beachcroft LLP)
George, Alan Douglas (Dutton Gregory LLP Solicitors)
Gook, Joanna Helena (Hampshire County Council)
Harrington, Catherine Danielle (Penfold & McPherson Solicitors)
Jeanes, Gemma Katherine (Hampshire County Council)
Lewis-Manning, Clare (Beachcroft LLP)
Mcloughlin, Nicola Louise (Penfold & McPherson Solicitors)
Noyce, Patricia Anne (Dutton Gregory LLP Solicitors)
Read, Richard Michael (Hampshire Constabulary)
Richards, Sarah Jane (Hampshire County Council)
Taylor, David John (Beachcroft LLP)
Tett, Alison Ruth (Hampshire County Council)
Turl, Kathryn Jean (Egglestones)
Wankling, Stephane Jane (Blake Lapthorn)
Wilson, Tracey Ann (Winchester City Council)

WINDSOR, Windsor & Maidenhead
A'Court, Lynette Ann (A'Court & Co)

Chapman, Briony (Charles Coleman & Co)
Lewis, Lisa Annette (Appleby Shaw)

WINSCOMBE, North Somerset
Dawson, Vanessa Caroline (Berry Redmond & Robinson Solicitors)

WINSFORD, Cheshire
Birdsey, Janice Susan (Moss Haselhurst Solicitors)
Rose, Jacqueline Ann (Cheshire Constabulary)

WINSLOW, Buckinghamshire
Killen, Marcia Joanne (ASK Legal LLP)

WIRRAL, Merseyside
Carless, Nicola (Fosters Solicitors)
Gauller, Clare Patricia (Ian C Free)
Hesketh, Angela (Lees Lloyd Whitley)
Moody-Smith, Victoria Myra Elizabeth (A Halsall & Co)
Stonehouse, Graham Stephen (Maxwell Entwistle & Byrne)

WISBECH, Cambridgeshire
Benner, Yvonne (Metcalfe Copeman & Pettefar)
Bridgeland, Sarah (Fraser Dawbarns Solicitors)
Cross, Kieren Edward (Fraser Dawbarns Solicitors)
Davies, Nunziata (Malletts Solicitors)
Garner, Linda Susannah (Metcalfe Copeman & Pettefar)
Groome, Ian James (Bowser Ollard & Bentley)
Jarvis, Helen May (Fraser Dawbarns Solicitors)
Lamb, Sarah (Fraser Dawbarns Solicitors)
Sharp, David Franklin (Cartwright Cunningham)
Spencer, Catherine (Fraser Dawbarns Solicitors)
Walker, Claire Louise (Metcalfe Copeman & Pettefar)

WITHAM, Essex
Eagle, Paul John (Bawtrees LLP)
King, Tracy Patricia (Bawtrees LLP)

WITNEY, Oxfordshire
Savin, Susan Michelle (Lee Chadwick & Co)

WOKING, Surrey
Crossman, Allison Pamela (Countrywide Property Lawyers)
Hamilton, Mary Clarke (Woking Borough Council)
Lucas, Jacqueline Margaret (Lyons & Co)
Lyons, Lynda Ellen (Lyons & Co)
Mccormick, Nicholas Ian (Woking Borough Council)
Mouser, Alison Jane (W Davies & Son)

WOKINGHAM, Wokingham
Cross, Alison Jane (Clifton Ingram LLP)
Elsmore-Wickens, Barbara Kate (Ratcliffe Duce & Gammer)
Jones, Emma Elizabeth (Charles Platel Solicitors)
Lilley, Tracey Jane (Wokingham District Council)
Mills, Nicholas Charles Adrian (Esporta)
Pizzardi, Natalie (Wokingham District Council)
Pratt, Carole Ann (Wokingham District Council)
Smith, Pauline Anne (Herrington & Carmichael LLP)
Swanton, Natasha Daisy (Charles Platel Solicitors)
Taylor, Helen Ruth (Sage (UK) Ltd)
Webb, Sarah Louise (Charles Platel Solicitors)

WOLVERHAMPTON, West Midlands
Baldwin, Robert Leonard (Wolverhampton City Council)
Beddows, Emma Jean (DBL Talbots LLP)
Bramley, Jacqueline Anne (Wolverhampton City Council)
Breakwell, Sallyann (DBL Talbots LLP)
Cockfield, David Alan George (Wolverhampton City Council)
Cummings, David Michael (DBL Talbots LLP)
Fisher, James Adrian (Forest Costing Service)
Gwilt, Jane Elizabeth (Rees Page)
Harper, Victoria Anne (FBC Manby Bowdler Solicitors)
Harvey-Pittaway, Annette Jane (Wolverhampton City Council)
Jeffs, Anthony (DBL Talbots LLP)
Lane, Tracey Ann (FBC Manby Bowdler Solicitors)
Law, Lisa Marie (Foster Haxter Cooksey)
Lewis, Christine Anne (Stevens Solicitors)
Meese, Linda June (Wolverhampton City Council)
Poole, Susan (FBC Manby Bowdler Solicitors)
Price, Paula (Lloyds Banking Group)
Probert, Clive John (Geoffrey T Smith & Co)
Rahman, Jarna (Thorne Beckett & Crofts)
Rice, Timothy (NM Legal Ltd)
Richards, Donna (Wolverhampton City Council)
Roberts, Kevin Michael (Wolverhampton City Council)
Sherry, James Dominic (Wolverhampton City Council)
Sidhu, Harminder (Wolverhampton City Council)
Smith, Rita (Rose Williams & Partners)
Spittle, Marie Louise (FBC Manby Bowdler Solicitors)
Trott, Martin Charles Harvey (Wolverhampton City Council)
Verlander, Andrew James Edward (FBC Manby Bowdler Solicitors)
Watts, Alexandra (Wolverhampton CAB)

WOODBRIDGE, Suffolk
Hayles, Ian Paul (Gross & Cujel)
Posford, Veronica Gillian (Suffolk Coastal District Council)

WOODFORD GREEN, Essex
Dacosta, Tracy Kim (Cartwright Cunningham)
Goldstein, Mark (Cartwright Cunningham)

WOOTTON BASSETT, Wiltshire
Baylies, Deborah Jane (Awdry Bailey & Douglas Solicitors)
Burton, Maxine Julie (Bevirs)
Hotchkiss, Timothy Michael (Awdry Bailey & Douglas Solicitors)
Neve, David James (Bevirs)
Seviour, Jenny Aileen (Bevirs)

WORCESTER, Worcestershire
Beard, Veronica (Hallmark Hulme)
Bragg-Walker, Lynda Jane (Hallmark Hulme)
Cobbett, Judith May (Parkinson Wright)
Coley, Georgina (Worcester City Council)
Freer-Ward, Theresa Ann (John Stallard & Co)
Marks, Eleanor Ann (Worcestershire County Council)
Norcott, Jane Emma (Harrison Clark Services Ltd)
Norman, Justine Elizabeth (Bubble Employment Law Solutions)
Normington, Marianne Amy (Harrison Clark Services Ltd)
Perkins, Laura Jane (Hamer Childs)
Piper, Amanda Clare (Morton Fisher)
Redding, Laura Pearl (Parkinson Wright)
Sanders, Hayley Jayne (Harrison Clark Services Ltd)
Strutton, Amber Louise (Harrison Clark Services Ltd)
Vaughan, Victor Graham (March & Edwards)
Weston, Amanda Jane (West Mercia Police Authority)

WORCESTER PARK, Surrey
Spicer, Jennifer (Vivash Hunt)
Strouvalis, Susan Bridget (Vivash Hunt)
Wale, Julie Ann (Brett Holt Solicitors)

WORKINGTON, Cumbria
Collinson, David John (K J Commons & Co)
Collinson, Gillian (Allerdale Borough Council)
Gear, Trevor (Allerdale Borough Council)
Graham, Mark Stephen (Kevin Commons & Co)
Hill, Kathryn Alison (Milburns Solicitors)
Porthouse, Victoria Patricia (Milburns Solicitors)
Sharp, Alison Eleanor (Milburns Solicitors)
Thompson, Lorraine Annette (K J Commons & Co)

WORKSOP, Nottinghamshire
Brady, Susan Mary (Ilett & Clark)
Hallam, Jill (Richmonds)
Liddle, Charles (Wilkinson Hardware Stores Limited)
Machin, Jane (Ilett & Clark)

WORSLEY, Greater Manchester
Davies, Christine Olwen (Berry & Berry)
Murphy, Rachel (Berry & Berry)

WORTHING, West Sussex
Bilbrough, Peter John (Environment Agency)
Blackford, Rowena Jane (Thomas Eggar LLP)
Campbell, Louise (Thomas Eggar LLP)
Carter, Sara (Naunton Lynch Hall)
Comins, Amy Louise (Thomas Eggar LLP)
Cowley, Rosemarie (Green Wright Chalton Annis)
Dickson, Malcolm (Green Wright Chalton Annis)
Dickson, Michael Charles (Miller Parris)
Emery, Nicola (Southern Water Services Limited)
Firman, Erica Janet (A R Brown & Co)
Fitzgerald, Malcolm Seamus Dexter (Coole & Haddock)
Flanagan, Shelley-Ann (Worthing Borough Council)
Gaden, Sarah Louise (Richardsons Solicitors)
Gawman, Sarah Elizabeth (Thomas Eggar LLP)
Gifford, Jacqueline Carole (Bennett Griffin & Partners)
Goodwin, Sarah Louise (Thomas Eggar LLP)
Green, Emma Louise (Southern Water Services Limited)
Gregg, Hannah (Thomas Eggar LLP)
Grover, Duncan Peter (Adur & Worthing Councils)
Hemsley, Sara Jane (Rosemary E Hensby)
Holland, Patricia (A R Brown & Co)
Hooper, Selena (Malcolm Wilson & Cobby)
Kendall, Keziah Elizabeth (Mortimer Clarke Solicitors)
Lawrence, Gemma Frances (Thomas Eggar LLP)
Mace, Rebecca Diane (Rosemary E Hensby)
Mason, Kathleen (Environment Agency)
Moore, Helen Louise (Green Wright Chalton Annis)
Parker, Susan Ann (Burnard Brazier Tisdall)
Rice, Brenda (Lings Solicitors)
Rixon, Wendy Anne (Thomas Eggar LLP)
Rogers, Tracey Jean (Sussex Defence Solicitors)
Stace, Sarah (Burnard Brazier Tisdall)
Stephenson, Patricia Eyton (Bennett Griffin & Partners)
Stringer, Joanne Rebecca (Williamson Macdougal & Campbell)
Sumner, Shirley Carole (Miller Parris)
Tambini, Janice Patricia (Miller Parris)
Townend, Stephen Guy (Malcolm Wilson & Cobby)
Varndell, Roger Clive (Worthing Borough Council)
Watson, Judy Anne (Thomas Eggar LLP)
Webb, Caroline Ann (Coole & Haddock)
West, Gema Nicole (NLH Solicitors LLP)
Wheatland, Mary Jane (Thomas Eggar LLP)
Whitehurst, Marguerite (Thomas Eggar LLP)
Wimble, Freda (Miller Parris)
Young, Kelly Ann (Southern Water Services Limited)

WREXHAM, Wrexham
ApThomas, Jane (Allington Hughes)
Fisher, Virginia Sian (Cyril Jones & Co)
Henderson, Christine Doris (Allington Hughes)
Powell, Tracey Elizabeth (Allington Hughes)
Rogers, Sarah Louise (Gittins Mcdonald Solicitors)
Stace, Alison Dawn (Allington Hughes)

YATELEY, Hampshire
Thomas, Joanna Harriet (Davies Blunden & Evans)

YEOVIL, Somerset
Caller, Gemma Leanne (Porter Dodson LLP)
Cassidy, Michelle (Porter Dodson LLP)
Chislett, Ann Catherine (Somerset District Council)
Coppard, Robert Charles (Porter Dodson LLP)
Crabb, Rowena Jayne (Porter Dodson LLP)
Creek, Lynda Joy (South Somerset Homes Ltd)
Crowther, Julie Anne (Yarlington Housing Group)
Defries, Gayle Frances (Porter Dodson LLP)
De-Maria, Simone Kerry (Gareth Webb & Co)
Eaves, Louise Anne (Morton Law Associates)
Elliott, Karen (Porter Dodson LLP)
Eveleigh, Lesley Anne (Porter Dodson LLP)
Goddard, Paula Marie (Somerset District Council)
Hansford, Nicholas James (Porter Dodson LLP)
Hooper, Carol Ann (Church House Investments Ltd)
Knight, Victoria Louisa (Battens Solicitors)
MacDonald, Natasha Alita (Law Ltd)
March, David George (Battens Solicitors)
Margetts, Joanne (Law Ltd)
Moughal, Zara (Law Ltd)
Osborne, Deborah Margaret (Porter Dodson LLP)
Randall, Robert Charles (Battens Solicitors)
Reed, Suzanna Louise (Porter Dodson LLP)
Rouse, Deborah Ann (Law Ltd)
Rowe, Jason Peter (South Somerset District Council)
Smith, Samantha Ann (Porter Dodson LLP)
Watkin, Peter Terence (Battens Solicitors)
Whitsun-Jones, Nicholas (South Somerset District Council)
Woodland, Gina Mary (Law Ltd)

YORK, York
Asomaning, Nancy (Langleys Solicitors)
Bacon, Angela Kerry (Harland & Co)
Bamforth, Dianna (Ingrams Solicitors)
Colley, Jennifer Tracy (City of York Council)
Cottam, Sally Marie (Langleys Solicitors)
Cruddas, Michelle Ann (Harrowells LLP)
Dale, Gemma Louise (Minster Law Ltd)
Dunn, Matthew Edward (Minster Law Ltd)
Fergueson, Isabel Serena (Ingrams Solicitors)
Gardner, Susan Patricia (Hague & Dixon)
Gibbs, David Stephen Anthony (Minster Law Ltd)
Gibson, Fiona (Sykes Lee & Brydson)
Hallowes, Michelle (Minster Law Ltd)
Hardcastle, Joanna Fay (Langleys Solicitors)
Hobson, Sandra Elizabeth (Herthertons LLP)
Holliday, David (Council of The City of York)
Hurst, Caroline (Langleys Solicitors)
Jessop, Carol Ann (Langleys Solicitors)
Kilbride, Mark (Minster Law Ltd)
Kilkenny, Juliette Aimee (Crombie Wilkinson)
Langton, Tina Louise (Denison Till Solicitors)
Long, Anthony John (Minster Law Ltd)
Main, Diane (Persimmon PLC)
Major, Emma Louise (Denison Till Solicitors)
Massey, Emma Louise (Langleys Solicitors)
McCormick, Karen (Harrowells LLP)
Mcgall, Catherine Ann (Harrowells LLP)
Mckellar, Stuart Ian (Norwich Union)
Meakin, Margaret Anne (Crown Prosecution Service)
Munro, Stephen Ian (Robertsons)
Oxley, Janice (Langleys Solicitors)
Plowman, June Elizabeth (Harrowells LLP)
Robinson, Malcolm Stuart (Rollits LLP)
Salisbury, Emma Jane (Persimmon PLC)
Sayer, Sandra (Chris Sayer Solicitor)
Scott, Elizabeth Anne (Langleys Solicitors)
Stubley, Lucinda Jane Elizabeth (Guest Walker & Co)
Tindall, Susan Marie (Langleys Solicitors)
Weston, Alison (Minster Law Ltd)
Wilson, Timothy Andrew (Ison Harrison & Co)
Wylie, Ian Davey (Langleys Solicitors)

FELLOWS EMPLOYED ABROAD

AUSTRALIA
Dunn, Karen (CGU Insurance)
Nesbeth, Marco Patrick (Moray & Agnew Lawyers)
Norris, Sharon Debrah (Dwyer Durack Lawyer)

BAHAMAS
Gittens, Kelsey Loren (Higgs & Johnson)
Ingraham, Shellyn Stephanie (The National Insurance Board)

BERMUDA
Addington, David John (Mello Jones & Martin)
Dakin, Coral (Codan Trust Company Ltd)
Dwyer, Dennis William (Hector Wakefield Dwyer)
Hourston, John Kelvin (Christopher E Swan & Co)
Pickard, Naomi Utah (Conyers Dill & Pearman)

BOTSWANA
McMahon, Finola Margaret (Osei-Ofei Swabi & Co)

CHANNEL ISLANDS
Boxall, Rebecca Charlotte (HM Attorney General)
Buckley, Lewis James Lees (Carey Olsen)
Jackson, Stephen John Hamilton (Spec Savers Optical Group)
Lanyon, Paula (Ozannes)
Le Prevost, Lynette Ann (Kleinwort Benson (Guernsey) Ltd)
Terry, Suzanne Marie (Mourant Services Ltd)

CYPRUS
Polycarpou, Andrew (Polycarpou & Polycarpou)

FRANCE
Sinclair, John Charles (Famille Sinclair)

GIBRALTAR
Frendo, Georgina (Hassans)
Kassam, Nell Bernadette (J A Evans Solicitors)
Lugaro, Isabella (Hassans)
Walker, Nicola Louise (Hassans)

GREECE
Billowes, Paul Timothy (Ince & Co)
Roumpea, Afroditi (Panagiotopoulos N & A Legal)

HONG KONG
Cheung, Wai Chi (Erwin Young Chu & Law)
Chiang, Siu-Shing Shing (Clyde & Co LLP)
Chung, Chi Kong (Wong & Partners Solicitors)
Fu, Willy Kin Chi (Jennifer Wu-Scharsig Solicitor)
Fung, Kwok Hung (Toyo Mall Ltd)
Shea, Ying Fai (Anthony Kwan & Co)
Tse, Kwong Pan William (Marie Tsang Dustin Chan & Co)
Wong, Chun Ming Kenny (Liu Choi & Chan)
Wong, Li Ying (Sony Corporation of Hong Kong Ltd.)

Wong, Anthony Chi Keung (Wilkinson & Grist)
Yau, Leong Sau (Lec Ng & Lau)
Young, Colin (Slaughter & May)

IRELAND
Kadeba, Margaret Omolara (Allied Irish Banks PLC)

NORTHERN IRELAND
Thomas, Nicola Jayne (J W McNinch & Son)

ISLE OF MAN
Craine, Margaret (Dickinson Cruickshank & Co)
Denham, Gaynor Nicole (Carter Jones Mcdonald)
Hall, Chrisina Joy (Cains Gordon Bell - Advocates)
Ledger, Ruth Jean (Carters Advocates)
Myerscough, Deborah (Kelly Luft Stanley & Ashton)
Sellors, Janice Elizabeth (Judy Thornley Advocate)
Todd, Raymond (Isle of Man Government)
Towndrow, Susan Elizabeth (Gelling Johnson Farrant)
Young, Carol Ann (Mann & Partners)

SCOTLAND
Weatherhead, Elaine Robertson (Scottish & Newcatsle International Ltd)

SINGAPORE
Ray, Jonathan Paul (Watson Farley & Williams LLP)

SWITZERLAND
Mehmet, Engin (Dr Vosseler)
Scanes, Louise Ruth (Celgene International Sûrl)

TURKS & CAICOS ISLANDS
Humar, Louise Rachel (Lyons Davidson Solicitors)

UKRAINE
Harris, Susan Mary (Shoosmiths)

UNITED STATES OF AMERICA
Coletta, Anthony Edward (Solicitors Regulation Authority)
Genner, Gareth Neville (Coles Barton LLP)

UNITES ARAB EMIRATES
Cleaves, Melissa (TDIC)
Manning, Paul Roderick (Galadari & Associates)
Marshall, Christine Ann (Abu Dhabi Aircraft Technologies LLC)
Scott, Steven James (Emirates Nuclear Energy Corporation)

WEST INDIES
Hadfield, Samantha Jayne (Millar Simmons O'Sullivan)

NOTARIES

The Court of Faculties of the Lord Archbishop of Canterbury is responsible for the appointment, admission and enrolment of all Notaries in England and Wales. The Master of the Faculties is the office-holder in charge. His regulatory role has been confirmed by the Legal Services Act 2007.

Following the passing of the Access to Justice Act 1999 (s.53) the jurisdiction of the Scriveners Company has been abolished and all notaries appointed to practise in England and Wales may practise throughout those countries including central London. Scrivener notaries are indicated by an *. The majority of notaries in England and Wales are also solicitors, although the profession is open to other legally experienced and qualified persons. Scrivener notaries (practising mostly in central London) specialise in international law and are fluent in a number of foreign languages and, additionally, undertake translation work.

The particular function of notaries in England and Wales is to prepare and certify the execution of legal documents for use abroad but they may also undertake domestic probate and conveyancing in their own right and hold full indemnity and fidelity insurance.

Details of the required qualifications for admission and appointment as a notary are available from:

The Registrar
The Faculty Office
1 The Sanctuary
Westminster
London SW1P 3JT
Telephone: 020 7222 5381 Ext 7168
Email: faculty.office@1thesanctuary.com
Website: www.facultyoffice.org.uk

LONDON

Ablitt, R H, Mr, Ablitts, 24 Metro Business Centre, Kangley Bridge Road, Penge, London SE26 5BW *Tel:* 020 8776 8783

Adili, J S, Mr, Steel & Shamash, 12 Baylis Road, Waterloo, London SE1 7AA *Tel:* 020 7803 3999

Albury, S A, Ms, Mischon De Reya, Summit House, 12 Red Lion Square, Kingsway, London WC1R 4QD *Tel:* 020 7440 7042

Ali, K, Mr, Kuddus Solicitors, 2 Whitechapel Road, Tower Hamlets, London E1 1EW *Tel:* 020 7247 5476

Anand, S, Mrs, Alan Edwards & Co, 192-196 Campden Hill Road, Notting Hill Gate, London W8 7TH *Tel:* 020 7221 7644

Arrenberg, K F, Mr, Parker Arrenberg, 37 Rushey Green, Catford, London SE6 4AS *Tel:* 020 8695 2330

Baker, K F C, Mr, Croft Baker, Capital Tower, 91 Waterloo Road, London SE1 8RT *Tel:* 020 7736 9520

Baker, P H, Mr, Alban Gould Baker, 405/7 Holloway Road, Holloway, London N7 6HG *Tel:* 020 7607 7269

Banks, J, Mr, 69 Shalimar Gardens, Acton, London W3 9JG *Tel:* 020 8896 3992

Barker, T L, Mr, 1st Floor, South Point House, 321 Chase Road, Southgate, London N14 6JT *Tel:* 020 7009 0030

Barnett, M F, Mr, Cramer Pelmont Solicitors, 33 Cavendish Square, London W1G 0PW *Tel:* 020 7016 3016

Battu, B K, Mr, Huggins Lewis Foskett, 5/6 The Shrubberies, George Lane, South Woodford, London E18 1BG *Tel:* 020 8989 3000

Berioli, M J, *Ms, John Venn & Sons, 95 Aldwych, London WC2B 4JF *Tel:* 020 7395 4300

Bernier, C B, Mr, Hartnells, 24 Landells Road, East Dulwich, London SE22 9PG *Tel:* 07960 301202

Biggs, N W, Mr, 40 South Hill Park, Hampstead, London NW3 2SJ *Tel:* 020 7794 4659

Bond, R T J, Mr, Speechly Bircham LLP, 6 New Street Square, London EC4A 3LX *Tel:* 020 7427 6660

Bower, J G, Mr, 15 Golders Green Crescent, Golders Green, London NW11 8LA *Tel:* 020 8455 8366

Brooks, B G C, *Mr, Cheeswrights, Bankside House, 107 Leadenhall Street, London EC3A 4HA *Tel:* 020 7623 9477

Buchner, M E, *Mr, De Pinna, 35 Piccadilly, London W1J OLJ *Tel:* 020 7208 2900

Burgess, J B, *Mr, Cheeswrights, Bankside House, 107 Leadenhall Street, London EC3A 4AF *Tel:* 020 7623 9477

Burton, P K, Mr, Rice-Jones & Smiths, 7 Ely Place, London EC1N 6RY *Tel:* 020 7242 6017

Campbell, R M, *Miss, Cheeswrights, Bankside House, 107 Leadenhall Street, London EC3A 4HA *Tel:* 020 7623 9477

Carey, D J, Mr, Suite 400, Temple Chambers, 3-7 Temple Avenue, London EC4Y 0HP *Tel:* 020 7504 1299 / 07973 625118

Carter, L S, Ms, Howard Kennedy, 19 Cavendish Square, London W1A 2AW *Tel:* 020 7546 8881

Ceolin, E A, *Ms, Saville & Co, One Carey Lane, London EC2V 8AE *Tel:* 020 7776 9823

Charlton, M A, Mr, De Pinna, 35 Piccadilly, London W1J OLJ *Tel:* 020 7208 2900

Claudet, A J, *Mr, Cheeswrights, Bankside House, 107 Leadenhall Street, London EC3A 4HA *Tel:* 020 7623 9477

Corless, A, *Mrs, John Venn, 95 Aldwych, London WC2B 4JF *Tel:* 020 7395 4300

Coutts, J P, *Mr, John Venn, 95 Aldwych, London WC2B 4JF *Tel:* 020 7395 4300

Craik, R P G, Mr, Richard Craik, Orion Park A, Northfield Avenue, Ealing, London W13 9SJ *Tel:* 020 8840 9524

Croft, A R, Mr, Solicitors First LLP, 240 Balham High Road, Balham, London SW17 7AW *Tel:* 020 8673 0116

da Costa, J-P, Mr, Sherrards Solicitors, 47 Marylebone Lane, London W1U 2NT *Tel:* 020 7563 9800

Davies, S T, Ms, 6 Princes Avenue, Gunnersbury Park, London W3 8LS *Tel:* 07984 610 696

Davies, S L, Ms, Watson Marshal, 4 Castle Row, Horticultural Place, Chiswick, London W4 4JQ *Tel:* 020 8987 0100

Dona Martin, M J, Mr, Manuel Martin Associates, 92 New Cavendish Street, London W1W 6XJ *Tel:* 020 7631 5161

Fawcett, D N L, *Mr, De Pinna, 35 Piccadilly, London W1J OLJ *Tel:* 020 7308 2900

Fearnside, J K, Mrs, Nabarro LLP, Lacon House, Theobald's Road, Holborn, London WC1X 8RW *Tel:* 020 7524 6093

Figueiredo, A X D R, Mr, Figueiredo & Bailey, Rivington House, 82 Great Eastern Street, London EC2A 3JF *Tel:* 020 7739 5599

Fisher, J A, Mr, Fishers, 180 Piccadilly, London W1J 9HF *Tel:* 020 7917 9575 / 07789 872839

Fogan, E F A, *Miss, De Pinna, 35 Piccadilly, London W1J OLJ *Tel:* 020 7208 2900

Frame, I R, Mr, Imison & Co, Salisbury House, London Wall, London EC2M 5QQ *Tel:* 020 7448 4860

Frimston, R M, Mr, Russell-Cooke LLP, 2 Putney Hill, Putney, London SW15 6AB *Tel:* 020 8394 6217

Gardiner, E, *Mr, Cheeswrights, Bankside House, 107 Leadenhall Street, London EC3A 4AF *Tel:* 020 7623 9477

Godden, S J, Mrs, Grant Saw, Norman House, 110-114 Norman Road, Greenwich, London SE10 9EH *Tel:* 020 8858 6971

Godoy Gomez, M T, *Ms, De Pinna, 35 Piccadilly, London W1J OLJ *Tel:* 020 7208 2910

Gonzalez, M V, *Ms, John Venn, 95 Aldwych, London WC2B 4JF *Tel:* 020 7395 4300

Grafton, A, *Ms, Cheeswrights, Bankside House, 107 Leadenhall Street, London EC3A 4HA *Tel:* 020 7623 9477

Grewal, T S, Mr, Hcl Hanne & Co, St John's Chambers, 1c St John's Hill, Battersea, London SW11 1TN *Tel:* 020 7228 0017

Gupta, G K, Mr, Gupta & Partners, 99 High Street, Harlesden, London NW10 4TS *Tel:* 020 8838 0008

Guthrie, C D, Mr, Notary Co Uk Ltd, Grosvenor Gardens House, 35-37 Grosvenor Gardens, Belgravia, London SW1W 0BS *Tel:* 020 7630 1777

Harris, C D, Mr, Harris & Co, Sovereign House, 1 Albert Place, Finchley, London N3 1QB *Tel:* 020 8346 1155

Hartwig, H J, Mr, Hartwig, 15 William Mews, Knightsbridge, London SW1X 9HF *Tel:* 020 7235 1504

Heinz, V G, Dr, 3/4 South Square, Gray's Inn, London WC1R 5HP *Tel:* 020 7696 6451

Henriquez, M I, Ms, Isabel Henríquez Notary Public, 3rd Floor, Cannongate House, 64 Cannon Street, London EC4N 6AE *Tel:* 07951 127418

Higgins, C G, *Mr, Saville & Co, One Carey Lane, London EC2V 8AE *Tel:* 020 7776 9828

Hon, T M S, Ms, DKLM LLP Solicitors, City House, 3 Cranwood Street, London EC1V 9PE *Tel:* 020 7549 7886 / 07880 870169

Hooke, B W, *Mr, John Newton & Sons, 68 Lombard Street, London EC3V 9LJ *Tel:* 020 7626 6068

Hunter, S A, Mr, Amphlett Chatterton, Greystoke House, 80-86 Westow Street, Crystal Palace, London SE19 3RW *Tel:* 020 8771 5254

Husain, S, Mr, H & S Notary Practice Ltd, Unit 4, Palace Court, 250 Finchley Road, Hampstead, London NW3 4DN *Tel:* 020 7433 3338

Hyde-Vaamonde, L N, *Mr, Cheeswrights, Bankside House, 107 Leadenhall Street, London EC3A 4HA *Tel:* 020 7623 9477

Imison, E E, *Miss, Imison & Co, Salisbury House, London Wall, London EC2M 5QQ *Tel:* 020 7448 4862

Journeaux, P A, *Mr, De Pinna, 35 Piccadilly, London W1J 0LJ *Tel:* 020 7208 2900

Kennair, W B, *Mr, John Venn, 95 Aldwych, London WC2B 4JF *Tel:* 020 7395 4300

Kerss, R S, *Mr, Saville & Co, One Carey Lane, London EC2V 8AE *Tel:* 020 7776 9829

Kherdin, N, Ms, K D Law, 3rd Floor, Warnford Court, 29 Throgmorton Street, London EC2N 2AT *Tel:* 020 7947 4494

Kober-Smith, M J, Mr, Kober-Smith & Associates, 6 Carlos Place, London W1K 3AP *Tel:* 020 7499 2605

Kostick, J, Mr, Kostick Hanan Herskovic LLP, 1 Egerton Road, Stamford Hill, London N16 6UE *Tel:* 020 8826 2131

Kuhn, M P, Mr, Hartwig, One Heddon Street, London W1B 4BD *Tel:* 020 7470 7131

Labovitch, S J R, *Mr, De Pinna, 35 Piccadilly, London W1J 0LJ *Tel:* 020 7208 2900

Lee-Kong, N S, Ms, Duncan Lewis, Woburn House, 155 Falcon Road, Clapham Junction, London SW11 2PD *Tel:* 020 7014 7319 / 07721 339507

Legister, M E, Mr, Huggins Lewis Foskett, 5/6 The Shrubberies, George Lane, South Woodford, London E18 1BG *Tel:* 020 8989 3000

Legister, M P, Mr, 239 Burntwood Lane, Tooting, London SW17 0AW *Tel:* 07940 524047

Lindley, M R, Mr, Streathers, 128 Wigmore Street, London W1U 3SA *Tel:* 020 7034 4207

Lindsay, B, Mrs, Bibi Gadwah, Ground Floor, Snowdon House, 223 Marsh Wall, Canary Wharf, London E14 9PG *Tel:* 020 7531 7420

Livingston, C M, Mrs, Laytons, Carmelite, 50 Victoria Embankment, London EC4Y 0LS *Tel:* 020 7842 8087

Loosley, R J, Mr, Fasken Martineau LLP, 5th Floor, 17 Hanover Square, Mayfair, London W1S 1HU *Tel:* 020 7917 8500

Lowry, O T, Mr, 9 Devonshire Square, Bishopsgate, London EC2M 4YF *Tel:* 020 3178 5781 / 07867 970076

Lusty, R M, Ms, Rowena Lusty NP, 33A Madeley Road, Ealing, London W5 2LS *Tel:* 0844 736 5776 / 07522 804666

Lyons, K A, Ms, Freshfields Bruckhaus Deringer LLP, 65 Fleet Street, London EC4Y 1HS *Tel:* 020 7427 3830

Mace, M A, Mr, Gates & Partners, 5th Floor, Capital House, 85 King William Street, London EC4N 7BL *Tel:* 020 7337 0300

MacNab, A J, *Mr, Saville & Co, One Carey Lane, London EC2V 8AE *Tel:* 020 7920 0000

Mahony, D, Mr, Parker Arrenberg, 37 Rushey Green, Catford, London SE6 4AS *Tel:* 020 8695 2330

Manika, K, *Ms, Saville & Co, One Carey Lane, London EC2V 8AE *Tel:* 020 7776 9800

Marriott, S J, Mrs, Charles Russell LLP, 5 Fleet Place, London EC4M 7RD *Tel:* 020 7203 5267

Mason, H C, Ms, Withers, 16 Old Bailey, London EC4M 7EG *Tel:* 020 7597 6308

McDonnell, L J, Ms, E G Arghyrakis & Co, 11 Bouverie Street, London EC4Y 8DP *Tel:* 020 7353 2302 / 07967 724446

Milburn, S J, *Mrs, Saville & Co, One Carey Lane, London EC2V 8AE *Tel:* 020 7776 9800

Miller, G E P, Mr, Miller Law Practice, 4A Topsfield Parade, Crouch End, London N8 8PR *Tel:* 020 8340 2953

Milligan, J K, *Mr, De Pinna, 35 Piccadilly, London W1J OLJ *Tel:* 020 7208 2900

Miranda, S, Mrs, Howard Kennedy, 19 Cavendish Square, London W1A 2AW *Tel:* 020 7546 8919

Mireles Romero, A-R, Ms, Mireles Romero, 2 London Wall Buildings, London EC2M 5UU *Tel:* 020 7448 5256

Mitchell, E L, Ms, Fishers, 180 Piccadilly, London W1J 9HF *Tel:* 020 7917 9575

Moody, R E R, *Mr, De Pinna, 35 Piccadilly, London W1J OLJ *Tel:* 020 7208 2900

Morris, A M, Miss, May Morris & Co, 9B Perry Vale, Sydenham, London SE23 2NE *Tel:* 020 8699 1000

Newton, L M, Mrs, Ashworths, 12 Compton Road, Wimbledon, London SW19 7QD *Tel:* 020 8417 8006

O'Connor, P J, Mr, C L Clemo & Co, 4th Floor, 131-133 Cannon Street, London EC4N 5AX *Tel:* 020 7929 3044

O'Donnell, T P, Mr, 27 Clements Lane, London EC4N 7AE *Tel:* 020 3207 9058 / 07773 731321

Okagbue, L U M, Ms, Pascalides & Co, 243 Grays Inn Road, Camden, London WC1X 8RB *Tel:* 020 7837 0049 / 07985 405640

Osagie, S I, Dr, Tsys International, 10 Chiswell Street, London EC1Y 4UQ *Tel:* 020 7160 9427

Osborn, S, Miss, 29 Homefield Road, Chiswick, London W4 2LW *Tel:* 020 8995 5139

Pay, J E S, Ms, 15 Golders Green Crescent, Golders Green, London NW11 8LA *Tel:* 020 8455 8366

Pinto, J E P, Mr, Office 345, Craven House, 121 Kingsway, Holborn, London WC2B 6PA *Tel:* 020 7953 8185

Plant, N J, Mrs, Pemberton Greenish LLP, 45 Cadogan Gardens, Chelsea, London SW3 2AQ *Tel:* 020 7591 3333

Preuveneers, B, Mr, Notary Co Uk Ltd, Grosvenor Gardens House, 35-37 Grosvenor Gardens, Victoria, London SW1W 0BS *Tel:* 020 7630 1777

Pryke, M D, Mr, Wallace LLP, One Portland Place, Mayfair, London W1B 1PN *Tel:* 020 7636 4422

Quaradeghini, M-L, Ms, Addleshaw Goddard LLP, Milton Gate, 60 Chiswell Street, London EC1Y 4AG *Tel:* 020 7160 3179

Ready, N P, *Mr, Cheeswrights, Bankside House, 107 Leadenhall Street, London EC3A 4HA *Tel:* 020 7623 9477

Reeve, J M, *Mrs, John Venn, 95 Aldwych, London WC2B 4JF *Tel:* 020 7395 4300

Rice, D, Miss, Dolores Rice, Rm 303, Phoenix House, 24 High Street, Wanstead, London E11 2AQ *Tel:* 020 8530 3085 / 07746 474240

Rios-Ternero, M E I, Ms, 19 Shepherd's Hill, Highgate, London N6 5QJ *Tel:* 020 8347 8431 / 07879 635093

Roberts, D T, Mr, Prichard Englefield, 14 New Street, London EC2M 4HE *Tel:* 020 7972 9720

Robinson, A W S, Mr, M K Soni Notaries, 6 Breams Buildings, London EC4A 1QL *Tel:* 020 7856 9099 / 07919 737392

Robinson, A N, *Mr, De Pinna, 35 Piccadilly, London W1J OLJ *Tel:* 020 7208 2900

Rogers, I A, *Mr, Cheeswrights, Bankside House, 107 Leadenhall Street, London EC3A 4HA *Tel:* 020 7623 9477

Rose, A P, Mr, Carpenter Rose, 26 The Broadway, Mill Hill, London NW7 3NL *Tel:* 020 8906 0088

Royal, T J, Mr, Royal & Co, 9 Devonshire Square, London EC2M 4YF *Tel:* 020 7147 9950

Salinger, P K, Mr, Salinger, 15 High Street, Kensington, London W8 5NP *Tel:* 020 7937 8524

Sandhu, G S, Mr, Lloyd & Assoc LLP, 35 Thurloe Street, South Kensington, London SW7 2LQ *Tel:* 020 7589 9599 / 0795 6186648

Saville, R J, *Mr, Saville & Co, One Carey Lane, London EC2V 8AE *Tel:* 020 7776 9800

Scott, M, *Ms, Cheeswrights, Bankside House, 107 Leadenhall Street, London EC3A 4HA *Tel:* 020 7623 9477

Sharkawi, H, Mr, H & S Notary Practice Ltd, Unit 4, Palace Court, 250 Finchley Road, Hampstead, London NW3 4DN *Tel:* 020 7433 3338

Simms, L R W, Mr, Advocates Atlantic LLP, 4th Floor, Hamilton House, Mabledon Place, Bloomsbury, London WC1H 9BB *Tel:* 020 7953 0293

Smith, F A, Miss, Forsters LLP, 31 Hill Street, Mayfair, London W1J 5LS *Tel:* 020 7836 8570

Soni, M K, Mr, M K Soni Notaries, 6 Breams Buildings, London EC4A 1QL *Tel:* 0845 888 0011

Spear, B A, Mr, Bulcraigs, 2 Replingham Road, Southfields, London SW18 5LS *Tel:* 020 8870 2207

Sreekumar, K S, Mr, Jacobs Solicitors, 451 Barking Road, East Ham, London E6 2JX *Tel:* 020 8821 9222

Stanyer, A F, Ms, Cumberland Ellis LLP, Atrium Court, 15 Jockey's Field, Holborn, London WC1R 4QR *Tel:* 020 7242 0422

Stone, D A, Mr, Simmons & Simmons, City Point, 1 Ropemaker Street, London EC2Y 9SS *Tel:* 020 7825 4098

Stone, F S, Ms, Notable Services LLP, 33 Wigmore Street, London W1V 1AU *Tel:* 020 7034 5204

Taqi, A N, Mr, Virgo Solicitors, Imperial House, 64 Willoughby Lane, Tottenham, London N17 0SP *Tel:* 020 8885 3999

Taylor, D, Mr, Hcl Hanne & Co, 1c St John's Hill, Battersea, London SW11 1TN *Tel:* 020 7228 0017

Thompson, N A, *Mr, Saville & Co, One Carey Lane, London EC2V 8AE *Tel:* 020 7776 9800

Thornton, J M, Mr, Russell-Cooke LLP, 2 Putney Hill, Putney, London SW15 6AB *Tel:* 020 8394 6521

Tilly, P J, Mr, Sibley Germain LLP, 1 Kentish Buildings, Borough High Street, London SE1 1NP *Tel:* 020 3195 7272

Toth, J E G A, Mr, Rochman Landau, Accurist House, 44 Baker Street, London W1U 7AL *Tel:* 020 7544 2424

Troup, D S F, Mr, Bennett Welch, 77A Westow Hill, Crystal Palace, London SE19 1TY *Tel:* 020 8670 6141

Trousset, N M R, Ms, De Pinna, 35 Piccadilly, London W1J OLJ *Tel:* 020 7208 2922

Vanner, J I, Mr, Saville & Co, One Carey Lane, London EC2V 8AE *Tel:* 020 7920 0000

von Tersch, N F M, Mrs, Dodd-Lewis, 18 Tranquil Vale, Blackheath, London SE3 0AZ *Tel:* 020 8852 1255

Wallace, P J, Mr, Anthony Gold, Lloyds Bank Chambers, 186 High Road, Streatham, London SW16 1BG *Tel:* 020 7940 4000 / 07712 677475

Ward, M V, Mr, Gregsons, St Christopher's House, 19 Tabor Grove, Wimbledon, London SW19 4EX *Tel:* 020 8946 1173

Wedgwood, D E, Mr, Anthony Gold, The Counting House, 53 Tooley Street, London SE1 2QN *Tel:* 020 7940 4000

Wilkins, J T, Mr, Devereaux Solicitors, Oldebourne House, 46/47 Chancery Lane, High Holborn, London WC2A 1JE *Tel:* 020 7242 7766

Wilkinson, E, *Ms, Cheeswrights, Bankside House, 107 Leadenhall Street, London EC3A 4AF *Tel:* 020 7623 9477

Wood, R F, Mr, Maple House, 149 Tottenham Court Road, London W1T 7BN *Tel:* 07886 306000

Young, E L, Mr, Sutton-Mattocks & Co LLP, 152 Chiswick Road, Chiswick, London W4 1PT *Tel:* 020 8166 0720

younghusband, M, Mr, Kuddus Solicitors, Unit 102, 21-31 Shacklewell Lane, Tower Hamlets, London E8 2DA *Tel:* 020 7241 0560

COUNTRY

Aberystwyth, Ceredigion

Morris, W G, Mr, Morris & Bates, PO Box 1, Ffordd Alexandra, Aberystwyth SY23 1PT *Tel:* 01970 625566

Abingdon, Oxfordshire

Ess, M N E, Mr, Brook Street Des Roches, 25 Milton Park, Abingdon OX14 4SH *Tel:* 01235 836600

Shaw, N P S, Mr, Franklins, Walton House, 15 Ock Street, Abingdon OX14 5AN *Tel:* 01235 553222

Alton, Hampshire

Acworth, S H A, Mr, Downie & Gadban, 100 High Street, Alton GU34 1ER *Tel:* 01420 82879

Altrincham, Greater Manchester

O'Donnell, J, Mr, 145A Ashley Road, Hale, Altrincham WA14 2UW *Tel:* 0161 728 8227

Ampthill, Bedfordshire

Northey, A W, Mr, Sharman Law LLP, 88 Dunstable Street, Ampthill MK45 2JR *Tel:* 01525 750750

Andover, Hampshire

Deverill, I M, Mrs, Parker Bullen LLP, 8 Newbury Street, Andover SP10 1DW *Tel:* 01264 400 500

Marshall, M L K, Mrs, Taskers Arch, Foundry Road, Anna Valley, Andover SP11 7NE *Tel:* 07540 704878

Walker, S T Q, Mr, Talbot Walker LLP, 16 Bridge Street, Andover SP10 1BJ *Tel:* 01264 721705

Ashford, Kent

Sharp, L L, Ms, Girlings, 4th Floor, Stourside Place, Station Road, Ashford TN23 1PP *Tel:* 01233 664 711

Aylesbury, Buckinghamshire

Couzens, J R, Mr, Parrott & Coales LLP, The Friarage, 25a Rickford's Hill, Aylesbury HP20 2RT *Tel:* 01296 318536

Cragg, D J, Mr, Mulberry Hill, Shupps Lane, Chearsley, Aylesbury HP18 0DE *Tel:* 01844 208112

Bala, Gwynedd

Davies, H L, Mr, Hywel Davies & Co, 74 High Street, Bala LL23 7BH *Tel:* 01678 520307

Banbury, Oxfordshire

Henshaw, R J, Mr, Aplins, 36 West Bar, Banbury OX16 9RU *Tel:* 01295 251234

Scott Andrews, A, Mr, Aplins, 36 West Bar, Banbury OX16 9RU *Tel:* 01295 251234

Bangor, Gwynedd

Davis, M H R, Mr, Carter Vincent Jones Davis, The Port House, Port Penrhyn, Bangor LL57 4HN *Tel:* 01248 362551

Barking, Essex

Bains, R K, Mrs, Bains Cohen LLP, 61a East Street, Barking IG11 8EJ *Tel:* 020 8252 7373

Barnet, Hertfordshire

Symon, W Y W, Mrs, Egmont Solicitors, 13 Ibsley Way, Cockfosters, Barnet EN4 9EY *Tel:* 07952 890833 / 020 7788 9688

Ward, S D, Mr, Derrick Bridges, 12 Wood Street, Barnet EN5 4BQ *Tel:* 020 8449 7326

Weldhen, R L, Mr, Derrick Bridges, 12 Wood Street, Barnet EN5 4BQ *Tel:* 020 8449 7326

Barnsley, South Yorkshire

Alliott, S P, Mr, Atteys Commercial, 31 Regent Street, Barnsley S70 2HJ *Tel:* 01226 212345

Wright, S P, Mr, Newman & Bond, 35 Church Street, Barnsley S70 2AP *Tel:* 01226 213434

Barnstaple, Devon

Oerton, M T, Mr, 22 Boutport Street, Barnstaple EX31 1RP *Tel:* 01271 378686

Barrow-in-Furness, Cumbria

Murray, J R F, Mr, Brown & Murray, 127 Ramsden Square, Barrow-in-Furness LA14 1XA *Tel:* 01229 820021

Barton-upon-Humber, North Lincolnshire

Pettifer, B W B, Mr, Cob Hall, Priestgate, Barton-upon-Humber DN18 5ET *Tel:* 01652 632248

Basildon, Essex

King, A B, Mr, Anthony King, Southgate House, Town Square, Basildon SS14 1BN *Tel:* 01268 240400

Basingstoke, Hampshire

Bradley, A M, Mr, Goldings, London Road, Basingstoke RG21 4AN *Tel:* 01256 478119

Coles, J M, Mr, Brain Chase Coles, Haymarket House, 20/24 Wote Street, Basingstoke RG21 1NL *Tel:* 01256 354481

Innes-Ker, R, Mr, Lamb Brooks, Victoria House, 39 Winchester Street, Basingstoke RG21 7EQ *Tel:* 01256 844888

Shedden, G R, Mr, 6 Weston Close, Upton Grey, Basingstoke RG25 2RX *Tel:* 01256 861955

Bath, Bath & North East Somerset

Macer, C A, Mr, Withy King, 4 Dowding Road, Bath BA1 6QJ *Tel:* 07831 718727

Mortimer, A J, Mr, Stone King Sewell LLP, 13 Queen Square, Bath BA1 2HJ *Tel:* 01225 337599

Sigournay, D, Mr, Thring Townsend Lee & Pembertons, Midland Bridge Road, Bath BA1 2HQ *Tel:* 01225 340064

Thring, J J, Mr, Thring Townsend Lee & Pembertons, Midland Bridge Road, Bath BA1 2HQ *Tel:* 01225 340099

Beckenham, Kent

Wilson, A, Mr, Tinklin Springall, 9/11 Rectory Road, Beckenham BR3 1JB *Tel:* 020 8289 9448

Bedford, Bedfordshire

Codrington, I C, Mr, Sharman Law LLP, 1 Harpur Street, Bedford MK40 1PF *Tel:* 01234 303030

Cook, S H, Mr, Sharman Law LLP, 1 Harpur Street, Bedford MK40 1PF *Tel:* 01234 303030

Gregory, F E, Ms, Sharman Law LLP, 1 Harpur Street, Bedford MK40 1PF *Tel:* 01234 303030

Kambli, S M, Mr, Premier Solicitors LLP, Mayfair House, 11 Lurke Street, Bedford MK40 3HZ *Tel:* 01234 348198

Berkhamsted, Hertfordshire

Williamson, P S, Mr, Paul S Williamson, 16 Priory Gardens, Berkhamsted HP4 2DS *Tel:* 01442 862475

Bideford, Devon

Clark, M, Mr, Chanter Ferguson, 17 The Quay, Bideford EX39 2EN *Tel:* 01237 478751

Ferguson, J J, Mr, Chanter Ferguson, 17 The Quay, Bideford EX39 2EN *Tel:* 01237 478751

Biggleswade, Bedfordshire

Whiddett, D StJ, Mr, Brignalls Balderston Warren, 2 London Road, Biggleswade SG18 8EP *Tel:* 01767 313813

Birmingham, West Midlands

Blakemore, A V, Mr, Shakespeares, Somerset House, 37 Temple Street, Birmingham B2 5DJ *Tel:* 0121 237 3000

Carslake, H B, Mr, Martineau, No1 Colmore Square, Birmingham B4 6AA *Tel:* 0870 763 2000

Gandham, M K, Mrs, BMG Solicitors, 3 Birmingham Road, Great Barr, Birmingham B43 6NW *Tel:* 0121 358 8855

Hughes, J B, Mr, Shakespeare Putsman, Somerset House, 37 Temple Street, Birmingham B2 5DJ *Tel:* 0845 620 9556

Ismail, F, Miss, Sydney Mitchell LLP, Apsley House, 35 Waterloo Street, Birmingham B2 5TJ *Tel:* 0121 698 2200

Lowe, P T, Mr, Challinors, Edmund House, 12-22 Newhall Street, Birmingham B3 3EF *Tel:* 0121 212 9393

Manning-Cox, A R, Mr, Wragge & Co LLP, 55 Colmore Row, Birmingham B3 2AS *Tel:* 0121 233 1000

Padhiar, R A, Mr, Carltons, 503 Coventry Road, Small Heath, Birmingham B10 0LN *Tel:* 0121 766 7447

Pinsent, M R, Mr, Fieldgate House, 61 Wellington Road, Edgbaston, Birmingham B15 2ER *Tel:* 0121 440 1733

Sangha, H S, Mr, Murria Solicitors, Court Chmbrs, 180 Corporation Street, Birmingham B4 6UD *Tel:* 0121 200 2818

Saunders, G S, Mr, Irwin Mitchell LLP, Imperial House, 31 Temple Street, Birmingham B2 5DB *Tel:* 0121 214 6577

Singh, H, Mr, Harbans Singh & Co, 366-372 Soho Road, Handsworth, Birmingham B21 9QL *Tel:* 0121 250 1673

Stocks, M G M, Mr, Blackhams, Lancaster House, 67 Newhall Street, Birmingham B3 1NR *Tel:* 0121 233 6900

Bishop's Stortford, Hertfordshire

Belcher, N J, Mr, Nockolds LLP, 6 Market Square, Bishop's Stortford CM23 3UZ *Tel:* 01279 755 777

Fraser, M R, Mr, Breeze & Wyles LLP, 11 Ducketts Wharf, South Street, Bishop's Stortford CM23 3AR *Tel:* 01279 715333

Lever, A, Mrs, Pothecary Witham Weld, White Horse Court, North Street, Bishop's Stortford CM23 2LD *Tel:* 01279 506421

Lockyer, S M, Ms, Trust Solicitors Limited, 41 Dane Park, Bishop's Stortford CM23 2PR *Tel:* 01279 655232

O'Brien, B C, Mr, Breeze & Wyles LLP, 11 Ducketts Wharf, South Street, Bishop's Stortford CM23 3AR *Tel:* 01279 715333

Robins, A K W, Mr, Legal Support Services, 1 New Cottages, Butlers Hall Lane, Thorley, Bishop's Stortford CM23 4BL *Tel:* 01279 507355

Blackburn, Blackburn

Holden, A N, Mr, Nigel Holden & Co, Richmond House, 16 Richmond Terrace, Blackburn BB1 7BQ *Tel:* 01254 841412

Hoyle, T A, Mr, Roebucks, 12 Richmond Terrace, Blackburn BB1 7BG *Tel:* 01254 274000

Parsonage, N D, Mr, Solomon Partnership LLP, 20 Strawberry Bank, Blackburn BB2 6AA *Tel:* 01254 667358

Blackpool, Blackpool

Sloman, E R, Mr, Blackhurst Budd LLP, 22 Edward Street, Blackpool FY1 1BA *Tel:* 01253 629300

Bletchley, Milton Keynes

Fuller, S J, Ms, Austin Ray Solicitors, 102 Queensway, Bletchley MK2 2RX *Tel:* 01908 644644

Bognor Regis, West Sussex

Poupart, N K, Mr, Wannop Fox Staffurth & Bray, York Road Chambers, Bognor Regis PO21 1LT *Tel:* 01243 872599

Bolton, Greater Manchester

Arkwright, D P, Mr, Cyril Morris Arkwright, Churchgate House, 30 Churchgate, Bolton BL1 1HS *Tel:* 01204 535261

Boroughbridge, North Yorkshire

Fitzgerald-Hart, M E, Mr, Fitzgerald-Harts, Claro Chambers, Boroughbridge YO519LD *Tel:* 01423 322312

Bournemouth, Bournemouth

Alahakoon, N J, Mr, Aldridge Brownlee, 89 Wimborne Road, Winton, Bournemouth BH3 7AW *Tel:* 01202 526343

Glazier, B E, Mr, Lester Aldridge LLP, Russell House, 31 Oxford Road, Bournemouth BH8 8EX *Tel:* 01202 786186

Graham, S D, Ms, Horsey Lightly Fynn, 3 Poole Road, Bournemouth BH2 5QJ *Tel:* 01202 551991

Howe, J P, Mr, Lester Aldridge LLP, Russell House, 31 Oxford Road, Bournemouth BH8 8EX *Tel:* 01202 786151

Neville-Jones, D J E, Mr, Preston & Redman, Hinton House, Hinton Road, Bournemouth BH1 2EN *Tel:* 01202 292424

Nightingale, S C, Mr, Horsey Lightly Fynn, 3 Poole Road, Bournemouth BN2 5QJ *Tel:* 01202 551991

Wells, A C P, Mr, Buchanan & Llewellyn, 52A Poole Road, Westbourne, Bournemouth BH4 9EP *Tel:* 01202 752525

Whitham, R W, Mr, 89 Wimborne Road, Winton, Bournemouth BH3 7AW *Tel:* 01202 526343 / 01202 422839

Bradford, West Yorkshire

Chamberlain, N J, Mr, Gordons LLP, Forward House, 8 Duke Street, Bradford BD1 3QX *Tel:* 01274 202157

Enderby, K I, Mr, Gordons LLP, Forward House, 8 Duke Street, Bradford BD1 3LX *Tel:* 01274 202202

Bramhall, Greater Manchester

Kelly, J S, Mr, Butcher & Barlow, 205 Moss Lane, Bramhall SK7 1BA *Tel:* 0161 439 8228

Brentwood, Essex

Lightowler, M, Mr, Wortley Byers LLP, Cathedral Place, Brentwood CM14 4ES *Tel:* 01277 268333

Bridport, Dorset

Harvey, M A, Mr, Nantes, 36 East Street, Bridport DT6 3LH *Tel:* 01308 422313

Lobb, A St J, Mr, Nantes, 36 East Street, Bridport DT6 3LH *Tel:* 01308 422313

Brighton, Brighton & Hove

Edwards, P C, Ms, Rix & Kay Solicitors LLP, 37 Frederick Place, Brighton BN1 4EA *Tel:* 01273 225606

Evans, N J, Mr, Griffith Smith Farrington Webb, 47 Old Steyne, Brighton BN1 1NW *Tel:* 01273 384042

Bristol

Bailey, K A, Mrs, Henriques Griffiths Solicitors, 107 High Street, Winterbourne, Bristol BS36 1RD *Tel:* 01454 855458

Brown, S, Mrs, Osborne Clarke Owa, 2 Temple Back East, Temple Quay, Bristol BS1 6EG *Tel:* 0117 917 3052

Burke, K M, Mr, Aventria House, Stock Lane, Lower Langford, Bristol BS40 5QB *Tel:* 0845 519 4982

Gisby, S J, Mr, Stephen Gisby & Co, Park House, 10 Park Street, Bristol BS1 5HX *Tel:* 0117 915 4562

Gregg, A D M, Mr, Gregg Latchams WRH, 7 Queen Square, Bristol BS1 4JE *Tel:* 0117 906 9400

Gupwell, M J, Mr, Gregg Latchams WRH, 7 Queen Square, Bristol BS1 4JE *Tel:* 0117 906 9400

James, A R G, Mr, Osborne Clarke Owa, 2 Temple Back East, Temple Quay, Bristol BS1 6EG *Tel:* 0117 917 3000

Leung, W H A, Ms, Leung & Co, Albert House, 111 Victoria Street, Bristol BS1 6AX *Tel:* 0117 920 9230

Pyper, T E, Mr, TLT LLP, Stock Farm, Littleton-upon-Severn, Bristol BS35 1NL *Tel:* 0117 917 7800 / 07802 419451

Weeks, S R, Mr, Jasmin Cottage, Stowey, Bishop Sutton, Bristol BS39 5TH *Tel:* 01275 333167

White, M R, Mr, Peter Browne Solicitors, 48 Gloucester Road, Bishopston, Bristol BS7 8BH *Tel:* 0117 944 1966 / 07758 160409

Buckingham, Buckinghamshire

Corner, R H G, Mr, Rodney Corner, Old Brewery House, 4 Castle Street, Buckingham MK18 1BS *Tel:* 01280 822217

Bude, Cornwall

Helman, D S, Mr, Busbys, The Strand, Bude EX23 8TJ *Tel:* 01288 359000

Buntingford, Hertfordshire
Hill, C J, Mr, CJH, Friars Grange, Offley Green, Rushden, Buntingford SG9 0TF *Tel:* 07973 781670

Burgess Hill, West Sussex
Oakley, A J, Mr, Bennett Oakley & Partners, 13 Mill Road, Burgess Hill RH15 8DN *Tel:* 01444 235232

Burnley, Lancashire
Lambert, D, Mr, Donald Rance & Newton, 5/7 Hargreaves Street, Burnley BB11 1EN *Tel:* 01282 433241 / 01282 864500

Burton-on-Trent, Staffordshire
Astle, E M, Mr, Astle Paterson Ltd, 181 Horninglow Street, Burton-on-Trent DE14 1NJ *Tel:* 01283 531366

Paterson, J C, Miss, Astle Paterson Ltd, 181 Horninglow Street, Burton-on-Trent DE14 1NJ *Tel:* 01283 531366

Perry, D P, Mr, Timms, 7/8 Lichfield Street, Burton-on-Trent DE14 3RE *Tel:* 01283 561531

Scragg, P W, Mr, 7 Ratcliffe Avenue, Branston, Burton-on-Trent DE14 3DA *Tel:* 01283 517952

Bury, Greater Manchester
Dawson, C F, Mr, "Greystones", Redisher Lane, Hawkshaw, Bury BL8 4HX *Tel:* 01204 884042

Higham, A R, Mr, Butcher & Barlow, 2-6 Bank Street, Bury BL9 0DL *Tel:* 0161 764 4062

Bury St Edmunds, Suffolk
Batt, M D, Mr, Greene & Greene, 80 Guildhall Street, Bury St Edmunds IP33 1QB *Tel:* 01284 762211

Jones, M A, Mr, Able Bishop & Co, Selwyn Chambers, Sampson House, The Street, Woolpit, Bury St Edmunds IP30 9QN *Tel:* 01359 245141

Thomson, C J, Mr, Greene & Greene, 80 Guildhall Street, Bury St Edmunds IP33 1QB *Tel:* 01284 717412

Callington, Cornwall
Anderson, G C, Mrs, Blight Broad & Skinnard, George Place, Callington PL17 7JH *Tel:* 07891 454130

Calne, Wiltshire
Figueiredo, I M L, Miss, Goughs, The Strand, Calne SN11 0JU *Tel:* 01249 812086

Camborne, Cornwall
Jacoby, J D, Mr, Alister Pilling, Hal an Truth, Drym Lane, Praze-an-Beeble, Camborne TR14 0NU *Tel:* 01209 831269

Cambridge, Cambridgeshire
Burton, N R, Mr, Mills & Reeves LLP, 112 Hills Road, Cambridge CB2 1PH *Tel:* 01223 222455

Fletcher, P C, Mr, Somerton & Fletcher, The Trapezium, 186A Victoria Road, Cambridge CB4 3LG *Tel:* 01223 448736

Gittins, P, Mr, 18 Priory Street, Cambridge CB4 3QH *Tel:* 01223 351302

Hindmarsh, J D, Mr, King & Co, St Andrew's House, 59 St Andrew's Street, Cambridge CB2 3DD *Tel:* 01223 365432

Horwood-Smart, A P, Mr, Taylor Vinters, Merlin Place, Milton Road, Cambridge CB4 4DP *Tel:* 01223 225209

Huskinson, A P, Mr, King & Co, 59 St Andrew's Street, Cambridge CB2 3DD *Tel:* 01223 365432

Solon, P C M, Mr, Mills & Reeves LLP, 112 Hills Road, Cambridge CB2 1PH *Tel:* 01223 222290

Stanfield, G, Mr, Eversheds LLP, Kett House, 1 Station Road, Cambridge CB1 2JY *Tel:* 0845 497 3806

Wheeler, G A P, Mr, Taylor Vinters, Merlin Place, Milton Road, Cambridge CB4 4DP *Tel:* 01223 423444

Canterbury, Kent
Byrne, C J, Mr, Girlings, Bowyck House, Boyke Lane, Rhodes Minnis, Canterbury CT4 6XN *Tel:* 07742 289934

Johnson, A M, Mr, Johnson & Garzon, 29 St George's Place, Canterbury CT1 1UT *Tel:* 01227 479479 / 01227 479794

Wolfe, S E A, Mr, Furley Page, 39 St Margaret's Street, Canterbury CT1 2TX *Tel:* 01227 763939

Cardiff, Cardiff
Baggott, M J, Mr, MLM Cartwright, Pendragon House, Fitzalan Court, Newport Road, Cardiff CF24 0BA *Tel:* 029 2046 2562

Brain, J L, Mr, 5 Cefn Llan, Pentyrch, Cardiff CF15 9QX *Tel:* 029 2089 1488

Crookes, R F, Mr, Charles Crookes, 51 The Parade, Cardiff CF24 3AB *Tel:* 029 2049 1271

Fisher, R J H, Mr, Charles Crookes Jones, 51 The Parade, Cardiff CF24 3AB *Tel:* 029 2049 1271

Lado, R A, Mr, Charles Crookes, 51 The Parade, Cardiff CF24 3AB *Tel:* 029 2049 1271

Mortimer, F A, Mrs, 36 Church Road, Whitchurch, Cardiff CF14 2EA *Tel:* 029 2022 5472

Carlisle, Cumbria
Attenborough, C A, Mr, Bendles, 22 Portland Square, Carlisle CA1 1PE *Tel:* 01228 522215

Carmarthen, Carmarthenshire
Hitchcock, R T, Mr, Steel & Hitchcock, 9 Quay Street, Carmarthen SA31 3JT *Tel:* 01267 236781

Chandlers Ford, Hampshire
Bowers, N J M, Mr, 8 Cumberland Avenue, Chandlers Ford SO53 2JX *Tel:* 023 8026 8100

Townsend, H R A, Mr, Blake Lapthorn, New Kings Court, Tollgate, Chandlers Ford SO53 3LG *Tel:* 023 8085 7457

Chelmsford, Essex
Allen, P C, Mr, Birkett Long LLP, Number One Legg Street, Chelmsford CM1 1JS *Tel:* 01245 453813

Cook, N D, Mr, Brierly Place, 160 New London Road, Chelmsford CM2 0AP *Tel:* 01245 344371

Nutt, J H, Mr, 101 Humber Road, Chelmsford CM1 7PG *Tel:* 01245 287400

Cheltenham, Gloucestershire
Engelbrecht, P N, Mr, Rickerbys LLP, Ellenborough House, Wellington Street, Cheltenham GL50 1YD *Tel:* 01242 246429

Howarth, T C, Mr, Davis Gregory, 25 Rodney Road, Cheltenham GL50 1HX *Tel:* 01242 235202

Srodon, L B, Miss, Davis Gregory, 25 Rodney Road, Cheltenham GL50 1HX *Tel:* 01242 235202

Chepstow, Monmouthshire
Propert, J P, Mr, Properts, Corner Cottage, The Square, Magor, Chepstow NP26 3EP *Tel:* 01633 882282

Propert, J E, Mrs, Properts, Albion Chambers, Albion Square, Chepstow NP16 5DA *Tel:* 01291 627268

Chesham, Buckinghamshire
Silverman, M D, Mr, IBB Solicitors, The Bury, Church Street, Chesham HP5 1JE *Tel:* 01494 790041

Cheshunt, Hertfordshire
Jackson, C H, Mr, Gisby Harrison, Goffs Oak House, 617 Goffs Oak Lane, Goffs Oak, Cheshunt EN7 5HG *Tel:* 01707 878342

Chessington, Surrey
Orbell, J L, Ms, 60 Grange Road, Chessington KT9 1EY *Tel:* 020 8391 4809

Chester, Cheshire
Edwards, D S M, Mr, Aaron & Partners LLP, 5/7 Grosvenor Court, Foregate Street, Chester CH1 1HG *Tel:* 01244 405555

Holliday, A S, Mr, Matthews Lewis & Co, Martins Bank Chambers, 31 Hooley Road, Hooley, Chester CH2 3NF *Tel:* 01244 327750

Pointon, C T, Mr, Aaron & Partners LLP, 5/7 Grosvenor Court, Foregate Street, Chester CH1 1HG *Tel:* 01244 405555

Chesterfield, Cheshire
Gordon, S, Mr, Banner Jones, 24 Glumangate, Chesterfield S40 1UA *Tel:* 01246 560560

Shiers, R A, Mr, Brm Solicitors, Gray Court, 99 Saltergate, Chesterfield S40 1LD *Tel:* 01246 555111

Chichester, West Sussex
Humphreys, M T, Mr, Charles Hill Hubbard, 27-28 Southgate, Chichester PO19 1ES *Tel:* 01243 781000

Standish, E J, Miss, Elaine Standish & Co, Holly House, 133 Almondington Lane, Earnley, Chichester PO20 7JR *Tel:* 01243 511222

Winskell, F H, Ms, Stone Milward Rapers, 50 Westgate, Chichester PO19 3HE *Tel:* 01243 780211

Chorley, Lancashire
Martin, I A D, Mr, I Anthony D Martin, Alderley House, Andertons Mill, Heskin, Chorley PR7 5PY *Tel:* 01257 451383

Christchurch, Dorset
Kerr, A R, Mr, Kerr & Co, 4 Millhams Street, Christchurch BH23 1DW *Tel:* 01202 487878

Spurling, J, Mr, Spurlings, 2A Church Street, Christchurch BH23 1BW *Tel:* 01202 473321

Church Stretton, Shropshire
Scarratt, J P, Mr, Lawley House, Smethcott, Church Stretton SY6 6NX *Tel:* 01694 751396

Cirencester, Gloucestershire
Fielden, A J, Mrs, Alison Fielden, The Gatehouse, Dollar Street, Cirencester GL7 2AN *Tel:* 01285 653261

Jenkins, E G J, Mr, Old Manor Barn, Shorncote, Cirencester GL7 6DE *Tel:* 01285 869+M205062

Clacton-on-Sea, Essex
Harper, L M, Ms, Thompson Smith & Puxon, 39-41 Station Road, Clacton-on-Sea CO15 1RN *Tel:* 01206 574431

Clitheroe, Lancashire
Dearing, I B, Mr, Stanley House, Lowergate, Clitheroe BB7 1AD *Tel:* 01200 426811

Cockermouth, Cumbria
Dunn, J M W, Mr, Brockbank Curwen Cain & Hall, Northam House, 71 Main Street, Cockermouth CA13 9JS *Tel:* 01900 827222

Pratley, S G, Mr, Brockbank Curwen Cain & Hall, Northam House, Main Street, Cockermouth CA13 9JS *Tel:* 01900 827222

Colchester, Essex
Ballard, B R, Mr, Birkett Long LLP, 42 Crouch Street, Colchester CO3 3HH *Tel:* 01206 217327

Cammack, D J, Mr, Birkett Long LLP, Essex House, 42 Crouch Street, Colchester CO3 3HH *Tel:* 01206 217311

Winward, J A, Mrs, Ellisons Solicitors, Headgate Court, Head Street, Colchester CO1 1NP *Tel:* 01206 764477

Coleshill, Warwickshire
Christensen, C F, Mrs, Townsends, Clinton House, High Street, Coleshill B46 3BP *Tel:* 01675 467333

Colwyn Bay, Conwy
Sandham, M S, Mr, Bone & Payne LLP, 2 Cadwgan Road, Old Colwyn, Colwyn Bay LI29 9PU *Tel:* 01492 515371 / 01492 514198

Consett, Co Durham
Cowie, J, Ms, Swinburne Snowball & Jackson, 2 Edith Street, Consett DH8 5DW *Tel:* 01207 502532

Corby, Northamptonshire
Rogers, B C, Mr, Tollers, 2 Exchange Court, Cottingham Road, Corby NN17 1TY *Tel:* 01536 276727

Corsham, Wiltshire
Brown, A, Mr, May Cottage, Henley Lane, Corsham SN13 8DB *Tel:* 01225 740097

Coventry, West Midlands
Kelley, R J, Mr, Alsters Kelley, 1 Manor Terrace, Friars Road, Coventry CV1 2NU *Tel:* 0844 561 0100

Cranbrook, Kent
Piper, R D, Mr, Buss Murton Law LLP, 31 High Street, Cranbrook TN17 3EE *Tel:* 01580 712215

Cranleigh, Surrey
Oliver, G R, Mr, TWM Solicitors LLP, Broadoak House, Horsham Road, Cranleigh GU6 8DJ *Tel:* 01483 273515

Crawley, West Sussex
Armitage, C D, Ms, Thomas Eggar LLP, Belmont House, Station Way, Crawley RH10 1JA *Tel:* 01293 742764 / 07795 023731

Beach, K J, Mr, Preuveneers LLP, 9 The Boulevard, Crawley RH10 1UR *Tel:* 01293 518074

Bennett, G S, Mr, James B Bennett, Nightingale House, 1-3 Brighton Road, Crawley RH10 6AE *Tel:* 01293 544044

Buckland, E L, Mrs, Dmh Stallard, Gainsborough House, Pegler Way, Crawley RH11 7FZ *Tel:* 01293 605198

Camps, M P, Mr, Thomas Eggar LLP, Belmont House, Station Way, Crawley RH10 1JA *Tel:* 01293 742736

Ladd, E C, Ms, Stevens Drake, 117/119 High Street, Crawley RH10 1YN *Tel:* 01293 596982

MacLeod, I H O, Mr, Thomas Eggar LLP, Belmont House, Station Way, Crawley RH10 1JA *Tel:* 01293 742880

Newell, K J, Mr, James B Bennett, Nightingale House, 1/3 Brighton Road, Crawley RH10 6AE *Tel:* 01293 544044

Pearson, H P N, Mr, Thomas Eggar LLP, Belmont House, Station Way, Crawley RH10 1JA *Tel:* 01293 742710

Penn, G P, Mr, Stevens Drake, 117/119 High Street, Crawley RH10 1YN *Tel:* 01293 596900

Crewkerne, Somerset
Bollington, D I, Mr, Stokes Partnership, Kingfisher House, Market Square, Crewkerne TA18 7LH *Tel:* 01460 279279

Crickhowell, Powys
Vaughan, W N P, Mr, Pembridge House, Llanbedr, Crickhowell NP8 1SR *Tel:* 01873 811753 / 07770 394114

Crosby, Merseyside
Howard, D S, Mr, Black Norman, 67/71 Coronation Road, Crosby L23 5RH *Tel:* 0151 931 2777

Crowborough, East Sussex
West, T J, Mr, Vance Harris LLP, 1 Beacon Road, Crowborough TN6 1AF *Tel:* 01892 783296

Crowthorne, Bracknell Forest
Buckland, J D, Mr, 22 Wiltshire Avenue, Crowthorne RG45 6NG *Tel:* 01344 777481

Croydon, Surrey
Ashley, S E, Mrs, Atkins Hope LLP, 74-78 North End, Croydon CR9 1SD *Tel:* 020 8680 5018

Aspden, J, Miss, Hartwig, 4 Dingwall Road, Croydon CR9 3RG *Tel:* 020 8681 2893

Barnes, E C L, Mrs, Hartwigs, 4 Dingwall Road, Croydon CR9 3RG *Tel:* 020 8681 2893

Darlington, Darlington
Blackett, P R, Mr, Blackett Hart & Pratt LLP, Westgate House, Faverdale, Darlington DL3 0PZ *Tel:* 01325 466794

Wood, A L, Mr, Blackett Hart & Pratt LLP, Westgate House, Faverdale, Darlington DL3 0PZ *Tel:* 01325 466794

Dartford, Kent
Ryder, R D, Mr, Vizards Wyeth, Riverside House, Anchor Boulevard, Crossways, Dartford DA2 6SL *Tel:* 020 7903 5570

Derby, Derby
Jinks, M G, Mr, Bakewells, 64 Friar Gate, Derby DE1 1DJ *Tel:* 01332 648507

Marson, J, Mrs, Moody & Woolley, 40 St Mary's Gate, Derby DE1 3JZ *Tel:* 01332 344221

Patten, R A, Mr, Edwards Geldard, Number One Pride Place, Pride Park, Derby DE24 8QR *Tel:* 01332 556377

Robotham, T C, Mr, Robotham & Co, 3 St Mary's Gate, Derby DE1 3JE *Tel:* 01332 346018

Sanghera, G, Mrs, 2nd Floor, Stuart House, Green Lane, Derby DE1 1RS *Tel:* 01332 228709

Doncaster, South Yorkshire
Pashley, A, Mrs, Malcolm C Foy & Co, 51 Hallgate, Doncaster DN1 3PB *Tel:* 01302 340005

Dorking, Surrey
Dalgetty, E, Ms, Downs Solicitors LLP, 156 High Street, Dorking RH4 1BQ *Tel:* 01306 502251

Grant, A J, Mr, Hart Scales & Hodges, 159 High Street, Dorking RH4 1AD *Tel:* 01306 884432

Thomas, S E, Miss, Downs, 156 High Street, Dorking RH4 1BQ *Tel:* 01306 502248

Dunstable, Bedfordshire
Morton, D R, Mr, Morton Solicitors, 75 West Street, Dunstable LU6 1ST *Tel:* 01582 501243

Dursley, Gloucestershire
Penley, J F, Mr, Winterbotham Smith Penleys LLP, 26 Long Street, Dursley GL11 4JA *Tel:* 01453 541940

East Grinstead, West Sussex
Hodkin, P D, Mr, Hodkin & Co, 42-44 Copthorne Road, Felbridge, East Grinstead RH19 2NS *Tel:* 01342 325765

East Horsley, Surrey
Hughes, C A R, Mr, Hedleys, 6 Bishopsmead Parade, East Horsley KT24 6SR *Tel:* 01483 284567

Taylor, R S, Mr, Headleys, 6 Bishopsmead Parade, East Horsley KT24 6SR *Tel:* 01483 284567

East Molesey, Surrey
Rivers, P A, Mrs, Robertson Rivers, Mole Cottage, 23 Creek Road, Hampton Court, East Molesey KT8 9BE *Tel:* 020 8979 6077

Robertson, D B, Mr, Robertson Rivers, Mole Cottage, 23 Creek Road, Hampton Court, East Molesey KT8 9BE *Tel:* 020 8979 6077

Eastbourne, East Sussex
Howes, J J Q, Mr, Cornfield Law, 47 Cornfield Road, Eastbourne BN21 4QN *Tel:* 01323 412512

O'Driscoll, R D, Mr, 37 Westdown House, Hartington Place, Eastbourne BN21 3BW *Tel:* 01323 720200

Edgware, Middlesex
Leong, S S W, Mr, Sunny Leong & Co, Premier House, 112 Station Road, Edgware HA8 7BJ *Tel:* 020 8951 5656

Egham, Surrey
Jamison, N D, Mr, Horne Engall Freeman, 47A High Street, Egham TW20 9ES *Tel:* 01784 432292

Epping, Essex
Smith, G E, Mr, Whiskers LLP, 265 High Street, Epping CM16 4BS *Tel:* 01992 561111

Epsom, Surrey
Harding, N P, Mr, TWM Solicitors LLP, King's Shade Walk, 123 High Street, Epsom KT19 8AU *Tel:* 01372 729555

Palmer, C B, Mr, Gumersalls, The White House, 16 Waterloo Road, Epsom KT19 8AZ *Tel:* 01372 721122

Pawley, L A, Ms, Gumersalls, The White House, 16 Waterloo Road, Epsom KT19 8AZ *Tel:* 01372 721122

Ewell, Surrey
Poolman, T E, Miss, Harold Bell & Co, Devon House, 174 Kingston Road, Ewell KT19 0SD *Tel:* 020 8393 0231

Stallwood, D A, Miss, Danewood Associates Ltd, 52 Court Farm Avenue, Ewell KT19 0HF *Tel:* 07917 540517

Exeter, Devon
Bowman, L M, Ms, Everys, Hertford House, Southernhay Gardens, Exeter EX1 1NP *Tel:* 01392 477983

Butcher, C N, Mr, Michelmores LLP, Woodwater House, Pynes Hill, Exeter EX2 5WR *Tel:* 01392 688688

Jaffa, A R, Mr, Foot Anstey, Senate Court, Southernhay Gardens, Exeter EX1 1NT *Tel:* 01392 411221

Martin, M G, Mr, WBW Solicitors LLP, County Chambers, 75 Queen Street, Exeter EX4 3RX *Tel:* 01392 202404

Pettit, J E, Mr, Ashfords, Ashford House, Grenadier Road, Southernhay, Exeter EX1 3LH *Tel:* 01392 333844

Farnborough, Hampshire
Rowe, D P, Mr, Davies Blunden & Evan, 43/45 Victoria Road, Farnborough GU14 7PD *Tel:* 01252 541633

Savage, D J, Mr, David Savage & Co, Ridgway Chambers, 16 Clockhouse Road, Farnborough GU14 7QY *Tel:* 01252 372858

Farnham, Surrey
Meyjes, G D C, Mr, Clifford Cowling, 9-10 Upper Church Lane, Farnham GU9 7PW *Tel:* 01252 725006

Ferndown, Dorset
Mills, J F, Mr, Allington Eames Ltd, Arena Business Centre, 9 Nimrod Way, Ferndown BH21 7SH *Tel:* 01202 862444

Fishguard, Pembrokeshire
Cross, P W S, Mr, Walter Williams, Sycamore Lodge, Hamilton Street, Fishguard SA65 9HL *Tel:* 01348 873223

Folkestone, Kent
Isaacson, A P, Mr, Rootes & Alliott, 27 Cheriton Gardens, Folkestone CT20 2AR *Tel:* 01303 851100

Mappledoram, G R, Mr, 23 Albany Road, Capel-le-Ferne, Folkestone CT18 7LA *Tel:* 07967 102709

Gainsborough, Lincolnshire
Westcott, P G, Mr, Burton & Dyson, 22 Market Place, Gainsborough DN21 2BZ *Tel:* 01427 616143

Gerrards Cross, Buckinghamshire
Wilkinson, P D, Mr, B P Collins, Collins House, 32/38 Station Road, Gerrards Cross SL9 8EL *Tel:* 01753 278665

Gillingham, Medway Towns
Smith, M P, Mr, Bassets, 31/35 Balmoral Road, Gillingham ME7 4QB *Tel:* 01634 575464

Glossop, Derbyshire
Wright, A M, Mr, Aspinall Wright, Notary House, 65 High Street West, Glossop SK13 8AZ *Tel:* 01457 854645

Gloucester, Gloucestershire
McMurtrie, P M, Mr, Walk Farm, Moorend Road, Eldersfield, Gloucester GL19 4NS *Tel:* 01452 840373

Rivers, C H, Mr, Treasures, 17 St John's Lane, Gloucester GL1 2AZ *Tel:* 01452 525351

Godalming, Surrey
Graham-Smith, D, Mr, Penningtons LLP, Highfield, Brighton Road, Godalming GU7 1NF *Tel:* 01483 791800 / 07957 422334

Herrington, D E, Mrs, Goodyear Blackie Herrington LLP, Elm House, Tanshire Park, Shackleford Road, Godalming GU8 6LB *Tel:* 01252 704000 / 07808 760252

Purser, C N K, Mrs, Barlow Robbins, Church House, 30 Church Street, Godalming GU7 1EP *Tel:* 01483 417120

Goring, Oxfordshire
Howell-Pryce, J B, Mr, Richard Wilson, Cymbal House, High Street, Goring RG8 9AU *Tel:* 01491 879100

Gosforth, Tyne & Wear
Appleby, R S, Mr, 48 Elmfield Road, Gosforth NE3 4BB *Tel:* 0191 285 2557

Hilton, C J, Mr, 20 North Avenue, Gosforth NE3 4DQ *Tel:* 0191 285 1534

Gravesend, Kent
du ROCHER, K M, Ms, Hatten Wyatt LLP, 51-54 Wrotham Road, Gravesend DA12 1BD *Tel:* 01474 351199

Gill, J S, Mr, Hatten Wyatt LLP, 51/54 Windmill Street, Gravesend DA12 1BD *Tel:* 01474 351199

Rothwell, P S, Mr, Martin Tolhurst, 7 Wrotham Road, Gravesend DA11 0PD *Tel:* 01474 325531

Grays, Thurrock
Ward, C M H, Mr, T A Capron, Milton House, 68 Orsett Road, Grays RM17 5EJ *Tel:* 01375 378331

Great Dunmow, Essex
Chapman, M R, Mr, Wade & Davies, 28 High Street, Great Dunmow CM6 1AH *Tel:* 01371 872816

Great Yarmouth, Norfolk
Gibbons, J R, Mr, Norton Peskett, 141 King Street, Great Yarmouth NR30 2PQ *Tel:* 01493 849223

Swanston, R R, Mr, Lucas & Wyllys, 11 Queen Street, Great Yarmouth NR30 2QW *Tel:* 01493 855555

Young, D G, Mr, HKB Wiltshires, 16/17 South Quay, Great Yarmouth NR30 2RA *Tel:* 01493 855676

Greenford, Middlesex
Singh, H, Mr, HS Law Solicitors, Allied Sainif House, 412 Greenford Road, Greenford UB6 9AH *Tel:* 020 8578 5688 / 020 8578 5689

Grimsby, North East Lincolnshire
Sheridan, P R, Mr, Wilkin Chapman LLP, PO Box 16, Town Hall Square, Grimsby DN31 1HE *Tel:* 01472 262626

Wilson, C B, Mr, Bates & Mountain, The Old Courthouse, 42 Brighowgate, Grimsby DN32 0QW *Tel:* 01472 357291

Guildford, Surrey
Jackson, A M, Mr, 3 Ashcroft, Shalford, Guildford GU4 8JT *Tel:* 01483 572757

O'Loughlin, A B P, Mr, TWM Solicitors LLP, The Tunsgate, 128 High Street, Guildford GU1 3HH *Tel:* 01483 565771

Pfister, C H, Mr, Awb Partnership LLP, "Braemar", 3 & 5 Jenner Road, Guildford GU1 3AQ *Tel:* 01483 302345

Servian, P D, Mr, Awb Partnership LLP, "Braemar", 3 & 5 Jenner Road, Guildford GU1 3AQ *Tel:* 01483 302345

Hale, Greater Manchester
Moss, J H, Mr, 145a Ashley Road, Hale WA14 2UW *Tel:* 0161 928 8227

Halifax, West Yorkshire
Cawthorn, M S, Mrs, Wilkinson Woodward, 11 Fountain Street, Halifax HX1 1LU *Tel:* 01422 339600

Horsman, D M, Mr, Jaque Royd Hall, Green Lane, Shelf, Halifax HX3 7TX *Tel:* 01274 676300

Harlow, Essex
Spencer, B R, Mr, 51 St John's Avenue, Harlow CM17 0BA *Tel:* 07968 123437

Harpenden, Hertfordshire
Simpson, R I, Mr, Neves, 2 Sun Lane, Harpenden AL5 4ET *Tel:* 01582 715234

Harrogate, North Yorkshire
Holmes, F M, Mr, Bywaters Topham Phillips, 6 Raglan Street, Harrogate HG1 1NB *Tel:* 01423 566777

Nelson, M, Ms, Bywaters Topham Phillips, 6 Raglan Street, Harrogate HG1 1NB *Tel:* 01423 566777 / 07795 226262

Harrow, Middlesex
Colwill, M, Mrs, 24 Hillbury Avenue, Harrow HA3 8EW *Tel:* 020 8907 2699

Hartlepool, Hartlepool
Barber, A, Mrs, Tilly Bailey & Irvine LLP, York Chambers, York Road, Hartlepool TS26 9DP *Tel:* 01429 264101

Harwich, Essex
Ward, R J H, Mr, Hanslip Ward & Co Ltd, 193 Main Road, Dovercourt, Harwich CO12 3PQ *Tel:* 01255 502366

Haslemere, Surrey
Farley, B E, Mr, Potter Owtram Peck, 42 West Street, Haslemere GU27 2AN *Tel:* 01428 642321

Hinchliffe, E H, Ms, Potter Owtram Peck, 42 West Street, Haslemere GU27 2AN *Tel:* 01428 642321

Loveless, S C, Mr, Potter Owtram Peck, 42 West Street, Haslemere GU27 2AN *Tel:* 01428 642321

Hastings, East Sussex
Langdon, C M F, Mr, Young Coles Langdon, Langham House, Albert Road, Hastings TN34 1QT *Tel:* 01424 437878

Havant, Hampshire
Small, C G, Mr, Langstone Gate, Solent Road, Havant PO9 1TR *Tel:* 023 9249 2300 / 07958 525019

Haverfordwest, Pembrokeshire
Cook, A G, Mr, Giddanmu, Musselwick, St Ishmaels, Haverfordwest SA62 3TJ *Tel:* 01646 636237

Hayes, Middlesex
Cooke, C, Mr, E D C Lord & Co, Link House, 1200 Uxbridge Road, Hayes UB4 8JD *Tel:* 020 8998 9988

Jariwalla, H, Mr, 6 Dunsmore Close, Hayes UB4 9RJ *Tel:* 07931 590778

Sehmi, C, Ms, J S Law, KBC Hayes Exchange, 23 Clayton Road, Hayes UB3 1AN *Tel:* 020 8817 1004

Haywards Heath, West Sussex
Benner, P C, Mr, Houseman Benner, Commercial House, 52 Perrymount Road, Haywards Heath RH16 3DT *Tel:* 01444 414081

Heathfield, East Sussex
Penticost, R F, Mr, H & R Hughes, 27A High Street, Heathfield TN21 8JR *Tel:* 01435 890101

Hebden Bridge, West Yorkshire
Lee, D J L, Mr, Finn Gledhill, 29 West End, Hebden Bridge HX7 8UQ *Tel:* 01422 842451 / 01422 330000

Henley-on-Thames, Oxfordshire
Prevost, S E, Mrs, Mercers, 50A Bell Street, Henley-on-Thames RG9 2BG *Tel:* 01491 572138

Hessle, East Riding of Yorkshire
Wharmby, S M, Ms, Devine Law, Suite 2, Stable Court, Hesslewood Country Business Park, Ferriby Road, Hessle HU13 0LH *Tel:* 01482 212077

High Wycombe, Buckinghamshire
Finn, S D, Mr, Stephen Finn, Shepherds Hey, 31 Amersham Hill Drive, High Wycombe HP13 6QX *Tel:* 01494 533862 / 07776 330035

Firth, E, Mrs, Browns Solicitors, 10 Brands Hill Avenue, High Wycombe HP13 5QA *Tel:* 01494 521856

Higham Ferrers, Northamptonshire
Hawkins, R A, Miss, Wilson Browne LLP, The Manor House, 12 Market Square, Higham Ferrers NN10 8BT *Tel:* 01933 410000

Wicks, D P, Mr, Wilson Browne LLP, Manor House, Market Square, Higham Ferrers NN10 8BT *Tel:* 01933 410000

Hinckley, Leicestershire
Healey, M B, Mr, Thomas Flavell & Sons, Church Walk, Hinckley LE10 1DN *Tel:* 01455 610747

Hitchin, Hertfordshire
Howard, D R, Mr, Hawkins Russell Jones, 7/8 Portmill Lane, Hitchin SG5 1AS *Tel:* 01462 628888

Holsworthy, Devon
Bodley, K F, Mr, Moorfield House, Brandis Corner, Holsworthy EX22 7YD *Tel:* 01409 221460

Holyhead, Anglesey
Hughes, D E C, Mr, T R Evans Hughes, Victoria Chambers, Holyhead LL65 1UR *Tel:* 01407 762204

Honiton, Devon
Ryden, G P, Mrs, Everys, 46 New Street, Honiton EX14 1BY *Tel:* 01404 43431

Hornchurch, Essex
O'Connell, M T, Mr, Crown House, 40 North Street, Hornchurch RM1 1EW *Tel:* 01708 511000

Horsham, West Sussex
Gadd, G D E, Mrs, Gillian Gadd & Co, The Courtyard, 30 Worthing Road, Horsham RH12 1SL *Tel:* 01403 262520 / 07708 426408

Hounslow, Middlesex
Evans, D L, Ms, Shergill & Co, 22 Bath Road, Hounslow TW3 3EB *Tel:* 020 8570 2323

Rahman, L, Mr, 1st Floor, Unit 1, Red Lion Court, Alexandra Road, Hounslow TW3 1JS *Tel:* 07940 020255

Shergill, G S, Mr, Shergill & Co, 22 Bath Road, Hounslow TW3 3EB *Tel:* 020 8570 2323

Hove, Brighton & Hove
Jones, O B, Mrs, 24 Shirley Street, Hove BN3 3WJ *Tel:* 01273 724726

Latham, J M, Mrs, Burnand Brazier Tisdall, 39 Church Road, Hove BN3 2BU *Tel:* 01273 734022

Huddersfield, West Yorkshire
Blakeborough, D, Mr, Eaton Smith, 14 High Street, Huddersfield HD1 2HA *Tel:* 01484 821434

Cash, S A, Mrs, Ridley & Hall, Queens House, 35 Market Street, Huddersfield HD1 2HL *Tel:* 01484 538421

Cornes, J W M, Mr, Ramsdens Solicitors LLP, Ramsden Street, Huddersfield HD1 2TH *Tel:* 01484 821554

Garnett, H J, Miss, Baxter Caulfield, 13 Station Street, Huddersfield HD1 1LY *Tel:* 01484 519519

Pendlebury, A E, Ms, Eaton Smith Llp, 14 High Street, Huddersfield HD1 2HA *Tel:* 01484 821334

Hull, Kingston upon Hull
Gilyott, F H, Mr, Andrew Kingston & Co, Lowgate House, Lowgate, Hull HU1 1EL *Tel:* 01482 216217

Hammond, D J, Mr, Andrew Jackson, Essex House, Manor Street, Hull HU1 1XH *Tel:* 01482 601295

Nettleton, G W, Mr, Ward Scott LLP, Wyke Chambers, 7 Silver Street, Hull HU1 1HT *Tel:* 01482 489870

Oakes, N L, Mr, Quality Solicitors Lockings, St. Mary's Court, Lowgate, Hull HU1 1YG *Tel:* 01482 300200

Taylor, S W, Mr, Andrew Jackson, Essex House, Manor Street, Hull HU1 1XH *Tel:* 01482 325242

Walker, S, Mr, Gosschalks, Queens Gardens, Hull HU1 3DZ *Tel:* 01482 324252

Ward, D J, Mr, Andrew Jackson, Essex House, Manor Street, Hull HU1 1XH *Tel:* 01482 325242

Hungerford, West Berkshire
Drake, R W S, Mr, Dickens Hopgood & Chidley LLP, The Old School House, 42 High Street, Hungerford RG17 0NF *Tel:* 01488 683555

Hythe, Hampshire
Knight, M I, Mr, Waring Partnership LLP, 8 Marsh Parade, Hythe SO45 6AN *Tel:* 023 8084 9381

Moorhead, R H V, Mr, Henry Moorhead, 2 Stade Street, Hythe CT21 6DB *Tel:* 01303 262525

Ilford, Essex
Dhillon, R P S, Mr, Dhillons, 26 Cameron Road, Seven Kings, Ilford IG3 8LB *Tel:* 020 8262 6565

Tatem, S K, Mrs, Edward Oliver & Bellis, 19 Broadway Market, Fencepiece Road, Ilford IG6 2JW *Tel:* 020 8500 4168

Ipswich, Suffolk
Long, L M, Miss, Blocks Solicitors, 2-6 Arcade Street, Ipswich IP1 1EL *Tel:* 01473 343906

Riddett, J D, Mr, Blocks, Arcade Chambers, 2-6 Arcade Street, Ipswich IP1 1EL *Tel:* 01473 343901

Ross, D R, Mr, Watkins Stewart Ross, 18 Lower Brook Street, Ipswich IP4 1AP *Tel:* 01473 226266

Schoop, J R, Mr, Prettys, Elm House, 25 Elm Street, Ipswich IP1 2AD *Tel:* 01473 232121

Isleworth, Middlesex
Brice, A L, Ms, 9 Wighton Mews, London Road, Isleworth TW7 4DZ *Tel:* 020 8568 6607

Kendal, Cumbria
Taylor, M E P, Mrs, Ramree, Brigsteer Road, Kendal LA9 5DY *Tel:* 01539 728929

Kettering, Northamptonshire
Lamb, J E, Mr, Lamb & Holmes, West Street, Kettering NN15 0AZ *Tel:* 01536 513195

Reed, M P, Mr, Lamb & Holmes, West Street, Kettering NN15 0AZ *Tel:* 01536 513195

Kidderminster, Worcestershire
Morrissy, S A, Ms, Thursfields, 14 Church Street, Kidderminster DY10 2AJ *Tel:* 01562 820575

Parker, J T, Mr, MFG Solicitors LLP, Adam House, Birmingham Road, Kidderminster DY10 2SA *Tel:* 01562 820181

King's Lynn, Norfolk
Gethin, J S, Mr, Hayes & Storr, The Old Court House, County Court Road, King's Lynn PE30 5EJ *Tel:* 01553 778900
Page, C L, Ms, Ward Gethin, 10-12 Tuesday Market Place, King's Lynn PE30 1JT *Tel:* 01553 660033
Scott, S L, Ms, Ward Gethin, 8-12 Tuesday Market Place, King's Lynn PE30 1JT *Tel:* 01553 660033

Kingston upon Thames, Surrey
de Veuve, D T, Mr, W H Matthews & Co, 19 Penrhyn Road, Kingston upon Thames KT1 2BZ *Tel:* 020 8549 0264
Hoyle, J B, Ms, Palmers, 89/91 Clarence Street, Kingston upon Thames KT1 1QY *Tel:* 020 8549 7444 / 020 8547 2117
Studdert-Kennedy, D A, Mr, Coleman & Betts, 85-87 Clarence Street, Kingston upon Thames KT1 1RB *Tel:* 020 8549 4402

Kirkham, Lancashire
Green, G R, Mr, Dickson Haslam, 12/14 Station Road, Kirkham PR4 2AS *Tel:* 01772 685109

Knowle, West Midlands
Standley, R W M, Mr, Standley & Co, 1612 High Street, Knowle B93 0JU *Tel:* 01564 776287

Knutsford, Cheshire
Armstrong, S D, Mr, The Orchard, School Lane, Ollerton, Knutsford WA16 8SJ *Tel:* 01565 652777 / 07540 861412

Lancaster, Lancashire
Pollock, A M, Mr, Joseph A Jones & Co, 6 Fenton Street, Lancaster LA1 1TE *Tel:* 01524 63371

Lancing, West Sussex
Allen, A J R, Mr, Dmh Stallard, "Southerly", Mount Way, Lancing BN15 0QD *Tel:* 01903 755070 / 07786 168693

Leamington Spa, Warwickshire
Armitage, R M, Mr, Field Overell, 42 Warwick Street, Leamington Spa CV32 5JS *Tel:* 01926 422101
Homer, S C, Mr, Field Overell, 42 Warwick Street, Leamington Spa CV32 5JS *Tel:* 01926 422101
McKenzie, T C I, Mr, Wright Hassall LLP, Olympus House, Olympus Avenue, Leamington Spa CV34 6BF *Tel:* 01926 886688

Leatherhead, Surrey
Bagnall, D W, Mr, TWM Solicitors LLP, Sweech House, Gravel Hill, Leatherhead KT22 7HF *Tel:* 01372 372227

Ledbury, Warwickshire
Brooks, R J, Mr, The Mount, Much Marcle, Ledbury HR8 2NB *Tel:* 01531 660628 / 07768 332049

Leeds, West Yorkshire
Atkinson, C H P, Mr, Suite E7.3, Joseph's Well, Park Lane, Leeds LS3 1AB *Tel:* 0113 816 0116 / 0872 115 5614
Beckett, K A, Ms, 266 West Park Drive West, Leeds LS8 2BD *Tel:* 07812 540414
Frieze, S A, Mr, Brooke North LLP, Crown House, Great George Street, Leeds LS1 3BR *Tel:* 0113 297 9000
Green, J Mark, Mr, Cobbetts LLP, No1 Whitehall Riverside, Leeds LS1 4BN *Tel:* 0845 404 2404
Lee, P J, Mr, Beachcroft LLP, 7 Park Square East, Leeds LS1 2LW *Tel:* 0113 251 4700 / 0113 251 4900
Watson, G, Mr, Brooke North LLP, Crown House, Great George Street, Leeds LS1 3BR *Tel:* 0113 297 9000
Wilson, A H, Mr, Cobbetts LLP, 1 Whitehall Riverside, Leeds LS1 4BN *Tel:* 0845 404 1536

Leicester, Leicester
Mansfield, E A, Ms, Harts, 146 Melton Road, Leicester LE4 5EG *Tel:* 0116 266 6665
McCallister, S, Mr, Salusburys Harding & Barnett, 14 New Street, Leicester LE1 5NE *Tel:* 0116 262 9033
McLauchlan, J K, Mr, Spearing Waite, 41 Friar Lane, Leicester LE1 5RB *Tel:* 0116 242 1207
Moore, T F, Mr, Trevor F Moore & Co, The Cottage, 71 High Street, Ibstock, Leicester LE67 6LH *Tel:* 01530 261719
Tyler, W A, Mr, W A Tyler & Co, 9 Station Road, Cropston, Leicester LE7 7HG *Tel:* 0116 236 2171
Woolfe, S H, Mr, Harvey Ingram LLP, 20 New Walk, Leicester LE1 6TX *Tel:* 0116 257 4403

Leigh, Greater Manchester
Aldersley, J A, Mr, Butcher & Barlow, 34 Railway Road, Leigh WN7 4AU *Tel:* 01942 674144

Leighton Buzzard, Bedfordshire
Smith, M T, Mr, Old Coach House, Old Road, Linslade, Leighton Buzzard LU7 2RB *Tel:* 01525 374183

Leominster, Herefordshire
Grazier, S N J, Mrs, Gabbs LLP, 26A Broad Street, Leominster HR6 8BS *Tel:* 01568 616333

Letchworth, Hertfordshire
Balsom, G, Mr, Brignalls Balderston Warren, Broadway Chambers, Station Place, Letchworth SG6 3AB *Tel:* 01462 482248
Garling, V R H, Mr, Brignalls Balderston Warren, Broadway Chambers, Station Place, Letchworth SG6 3AB *Tel:* 01462 482248
Hall, R M, Mr, Michael Hall, Abbeyhill Broadway, Letchworth SG6 3PT *Tel:* 01462 674767

Lewes, East Sussex
Bayley, J C L, Mr, Adams & Remers, Trinity House, School Hill, Lewes BN7 2NN *Tel:* 01273 480616

Lichfield, Staffordshire
Sira, G S, Mr, G S Sira, 33 Market Street, Lichfield WS13 6LA *Tel:* 01543 254382

Lincoln, Lincolnshire
Ashmore, C, Ms, Sills & Betteridge, 46 Silver Street, Lincoln LN2 1ED *Tel:* 07581 185292
Horner, P J, Mr, Langleys, Olympic House, Doddington Road, Lincoln LN6 8SE *Tel:* 01522 508730
Phillips, G I, Mr, Sills & Betteridge, 46 Silver Street, Lincoln LN2 1ED *Tel:* 01522 542211
Wheeler, C M A, Miss, Andrew & Co LLP, St Swithin's Court, 1 Flavian Road, Nettleham Road, Lincoln LN2 4GR *Tel:* 01522 781472

Liphook, Hampshire
Jackson, K E, Ms, Didlaw Solicitors, 24 Longmoor Road, Liphook GU30 7NY *Tel:* 01428 724685

Littlehampton, West Sussex
Baker, S E, Ms, Staffurth & Bray, 36 High Street, Littlehampton BN17 5ED *Tel:* 01903 721112

Liverpool, Merseyside
Arden, R H, Mr, Hill Dickinson LLP, No1 St Paul's Square, Liverpool L3 9SJ *Tel:* 0151 600 8820
Bishop, D C, Mr, David Bishop & Co, Horton House, Exchange Flags, Liverpool L37 2YL *Tel:* 0151 600 3088
Blaquiere, A D, Mr, DWF LLP, 5 St Paul's Square, Old Hall Street, Liverpool L3 9AE *Tel:* 07798 700448
Fisher, I A, Mr, Husband Forwood Morgan, 26 Exchange Street East, Liverpool L2 3PH *Tel:* 0151 236 9626
Freeman, G C, Mr, The Dures Partnership LLP, 21 Cheapside, Liverpool L2 2DY *Tel:* 0151 242 5111
Gibson, J P R, Mr, Hill Dickinson LLP, No1 St Paul's Square, Liverpool L3 9SJ *Tel:* 0151 600 8149
Jeffs, A L, Ms, DWF LLP, 5 St Paul's Square, Old Hall Street, Liverpool L3 9AE *Tel:* 07720 996117
Morton, C J, Mr, Husband Forwood Morgan, 26 Exchange Street East, Liverpool L2 3PH *Tel:* 0151 236 9626
Sandiford, D H, Mr, EAD Solicitors LLP, Prospect House, Columbus Quay, Riverside Drive, Liverpool L3 4DB *Tel:* 0151 735 1000
Welsh, V B, Mr, 66 Beech Lane, Allerton, Liverpool L18 3ER *Tel:* 0151 724 1855
Wignall, S J, Mr, Hill Dickinson LLP, No1 St Paul's Square, Liverpool L3 9SJ *Tel:* 0151 600 8197

Llandrindod Wells, Powys
Margrave-Jones, C V, Mr, Margraves, Old Court Chambers, Spa Road, Llandrindod Wells LD1 5EY *Tel:* 01597 825565

Llanidloes, Powys
Ransford, C W, Mr, Milwyn Jenkins & Jenkins, Mid Wales House, Great Oak Street, Llanidloes SY18 6BN *Tel:* 01686 412166

Llantwit Major, Vale of Glamorgan
Buckworth, J E, Mrs, 95 Llanmaes Road, Llantwit Major, Llantwit Major CF61 2XE *Tel:* 01446 794029 / 07787 049044

Long Eaton, Derbyshire
Cobbett, M S, Mr, Ellis-Fermor Negus, 35 Derby Road, Long Eaton NG10 1LU *Tel:* 0115 972 5222

Longfield, Kent
Saunders, J W, Mr, Timbercroft, The Drive, Longfield DA3 7LX *Tel:* 01474 706207 / 07980 225130

Loughborough, Leicestershire
Kirkman, T H, Mr, Latham & Co, Charnwood House, 2 & 4 Forest Road, Loughborough LE11 3NP *Tel:* 01509 238822

Louth, Lincolnshire
Day, P D, Mr, Wilkin Chapman LLP, 17 Cornmarket, Louth LN11 9QA *Tel:* 01507 350162

Luton, Luton
McEvoy, M T, Miss, Neves, 8 George Street West, Luton LU1 2DA *Tel:* 01582 725311
Singh-Takhar, S, Mr, GCA Solicitors, Ground Floor, Langham House West, 29-37 Mill Street, Luton LU1 2NA *Tel:* 01582 410041

Lymington, Hampshire
Dew, M P, Mr, Twynham House, 64 High Street, Lymington SO41 9AL *Tel:* 01590 677888 / 07528 179411

Lymm, Warrington
Nolan, B V, Mrs, 26 Oughtrington Crescent, Lymm WA13 9JD *Tel:* 01925 759387

Lytham, Lancashire
Hardy, R N, Mr, Senior Calveley Hardy, 8 Hastings Place, Lytham FY8 5NA *Tel:* 01253 733333
Jealous, A W, Mr, Alfred Jealous, 5A Wood Street, Lytham FY8 1PX *Tel:* 01253 723207
Stott, G M, Mr, Blackledge & Co, 33 Church Road, Lytham FY8 5LL *Tel:* 01253 730070

Macclesfield, Cheshire
Cusack, J P, Mr, 103 Pierce Street, Macclesfield SK11 6EX *Tel:* 01625 879657 / 0797 332 9791

Maidenhead, Windsor & Maidenhead
Jackson, D J, Mr, Heath Buckeridge, 23 Queen Street, Maidenhead SL6 1JN *Tel:* 01628 502332
Kidd, J D, Mr, Kidd & Co, Weir Bank, Bray-on-Thames, Maidenhead SL6 2ED *Tel:* 01628 762762
Watney, A P M, Mr, Kidd Rapinet, 33 Queen Street, Maidenhead SL6 1NB *Tel:* 01628 621301

Maidstone, Kent
Astley, A G, Mr, Gullands, 16 Mill Street, Maidstone ME15 6XT *Tel:* 01622 678341
Goode, J A, Ms, Whitehead Monckton, Monckton House, 72 King Street, Maidstone ME14 1BL *Tel:* 01622 698047
Rogers, R P, Mr, Whitehead Monckton, 72 King Street, Maidstone ME14 1BL *Tel:* 01622 698000

Malmesbury, Wiltshire
Gill, A J, Mr, Forrester & Forrester, 59 High Street, Malmesbury SN16 9AH *Tel:* 01666 827703

Manchester, Greater Manchester
Braude, E A, Ms, Pannone LLP, 12 Deansgate, Manchester M3 2BU *Tel:* 0161 909 3000
Bushell, G R, Mr, Cobbetts LLP, 58 Mosley Street, Manchester M2 3HZ *Tel:* 0845 165 5255
Cohen, H P, Mr, Livingstone & Co, Blackfriars House, Parsonage, Manchester M3 2JA *Tel:* 0161 833 0578 / 07785 725407
Copestake, M J, Mr, Cobbetts LLP, 58 Mosley Street, Manchester M2 3HZ *Tel:* 0845 165 5497
Gower-Jones, J R, Mr, Pannone LLP, 123 Deansgate, Manchester M3 2BU *Tel:* 0161 909 3000
Hughes, G A, Mr, Birchall Blackburn, 20 Kennedy Street, Manchester M2 4BY *Tel:* 0161 238 5631
Rowe, C, Mr, Aaron & Partners, Pall Mall Court, 61-67 King Street, Manchester M2 4PD *Tel:* 07935 795845 / 0161 618 1400
Stone, A H M, Mr, Cobbetts LLP, 58 Mosley Street, Manchester M2 3HZ *Tel:* 0845 165 5249
Weinberg, A G, Mr, Kuit Steinart Levy, 3 St Mary's Parsonage, Manchester M3 2RD *Tel:* 0161 838 7811
Wilcock, R K, Mr, R K Wilcock, Peter House, Oxford Street, Manchester M1 5AN *Tel:* 0161 602 3395
Wright, A M, Mr, Cobbetts LLP, 58 Mosley Street, Manchester M2 3HZ *Tel:* 0845 165 5013
Yiu, S T W, Mr, David Yip & Co, First Floor, 59-61 Faulkner Street, Manchester M1 4FF *Tel:* 0161 236 1880

March, Cambridgeshire
Orbell, J H, Mr, Bowser Ollard & Bentley, Market Square, March PE15 9JQ *Tel:* 01354 652606

Margate, Kent
Rodd, P J, Mr, Boys & Maughan, India House, Hawley Street, Margate CT9 1PZ *Tel:* 01843 234000

Matlock, Derbyshire
Handforth, M C, Mr, Heny Loveday & Keighley, Crown Chambers, Bank Road, Matlock DE4 3AQ *Tel:* 01629 583142

Middlesbrough, Middlesbrough
Wilkinson, D A, Mr, Newbys, 100 Borough Road, Middlesbrough TS1 2HJ *Tel:* 01642 247717

Midhurst, West Sussex
Bevis, M G, Mr, Bevis Rowntree, Sheep Lane, Midhurst GU29 9NS *Tel:* 01730 812201

Midsomer Norton, Bath & North East Somerset
Hallam, E W L, Mr, Thatcher Hallam, Island House, Midsomer Norton BA3 2HJ *Tel:* 01761 414646

Milton Keynes, Milton Keynes
Brooks, A G, Mr, City Law Ltd, 5a Copperhouse Court, Caldecotte, Milton Keynes MK7 8NL *Tel:* 01908 369333 / 01908 369344
Evans, M J, Mr, 60 Huntley Crescent, Milton Keynes MK9 3FY *Tel:* 07801 354727
Harrison, P J, Mr, Kingsley David, 5 Whittle Court, Knowlhill, Milton Keynes MK5 8FT *Tel:* 01908 325555
Pobjoy, G P, Mr, Heald Solicitors, Ashton House, 471 Silbury Boulevard, Milton Keynes MK9 2AH *Tel:* 01908 662277

Minehead, Somerset
Mullis, J E, Mr, Thorne Segar, 3 Bancks Street, Minehead TA24 5DE *Tel:* 01643 703234

Mirfield, West Yorkshire
Whitfield, J, Mr, Ramsden Whitfield Hallam, 7 King Street, Mirfield WF14 8AW *Tel:* 01924 499251

Mitcham, Surrey
Sethi, S K, Mrs, Preuveneers LLP, 103-105 London Road, Mitcham CR4 2JA *Tel:* 020 8646 4885

Montgomery, Powys
Anton-Stephens, H D, Mr, White House, Arthur Street, Montgomery SY15 6RA *Tel:* 01686 624604

Neath, Neath Port Talbot
Morris, R W A, Mr, Hutchinson Thomas, Pendrill Court, 119 London Road, Neath SA11 1LF *Tel:* 01639 645061
Thomas, R M E, Mr, Hutchinson Thomas, Pendrill Court, 119 London Road, Neath SA11 1LF *Tel:* 01639 645061
Williams, R, Ms, Hutchinson Thomas, Pendrill Court, 119 London Road, Neath SA11 2SL *Tel:* 01639 640529

New Milton, Hampshire
Jennings, A M, Mrs, Heppenstalls, 82 Station Road, New Milton BH25 6LG *Tel:* 01425 610078
Stafford, A J, Mr, Brook Oliver, 10 Mallard Buildings, Station Road, New Milton BH25 6HY *Tel:* 01425 616809

Newbury, West Berkshire
Phillips, S L, Ms, Thomas Eggar LLP, Newbury House, 20 Kings Road West, Newbury RG14 5XR *Tel:* 01635 571000

Newcastle under Lyme, Staffordshire
Brian, A C, Mr, Tinsdills, 15-19 Marsh Parade, Newcastle under Lyme ST5 1BT *Tel:* 01782 612311
Stephenson, R A M, Mr, Knights LLP, The Bramptons, Newcastle under Lyme ST5 0QW *Tel:* 01782 619225

Newcastle upon Tyne, Tyne & Wear
Bowyer, J, Mr, Gibson & Co, 77 West Road, Denton Burn, Newcastle upon Tyne NE15 6PR *Tel:* 07860 725159
Fairclough, L A, Ms, Ward Hadaway, Sandgate House, 102 Quayside, Newcastle upon Tyne NE1 3DX *Tel:* 0191 204 4095
Kemp, J R, Mr, Eversheds LLP, Central Square South, Orchard Street, Newcastle upon Tyne NE1 3XX *Tel:* 0845 497 6346
Priestley, D S, Mr, PO Box 53, Ponteland, Newcastle upon Tyne NE18 0YZ *Tel:* 01661 886701
Ridley, G W, Mr, The Grange, Middlepart Farm, Belsey, Newcastle upon Tyne NE20 0HB *Tel:* 01661 881111
Sim, P McG, Mr, Mills & Co, Milburn House, Dean Street, Newcastle upon Tyne NE1 1LE *Tel:* 0191 233 2222

Newent, Gloucestershire
Wyatt, D F, Mr, David Wyatt, Fawler House, Newent GL18 1EA *Tel:* 01531 820127

Newmarket, Suffolk
Skelton, M N, Mr, Milburn House, The Street, Moulton, Newmarket CB8 8R2 *Tel:* 01638 750563

Newport, Isle of Wight
Samuelson, C K, Mr, Glanvilles LLP, St Cross Business Park, Newport PO30 1SA *Tel:* 01983 527878
Westmacott, J, Mrs, Venners, Merstone, Newport PO30 3DE *Tel:* 01983 528955 / 07516 403581

Newquay, Cornwall
Stephens, A Paul, Mr, Greenways, 19 St Michael's Road, Newquay TR7 1LL *Tel:* 01637 872361

Newton Abbot, Devon

Luscombe, F L, Ms, WBW Solicitors LLP, Church House, Queen Street, Newton Abbot TQ12 2QP *Tel:* 01626 202404

Newton-le-Willows, Merseyside

O'Connell, J B, Mr, 19 Ashton Road, Newton-le-Willows WA12 0AG *Tel:* 01925 226190

Northampton, Northamptonshire

Frost, A E, Mrs, Martin Adams & Mccoll, 300 Wellingborough Road, Northampton NN1 4EP *Tel:* 01604 634123

Orton-Jones, D M, Mr, Shoosmiths, 68 High Street, Harpole, Northampton NN7 4BS *Tel:* 01604 830332

Vaughan, C J, Mr, Scott Fowler, Old Church Chambers, 23 Sandhill Road, St James, Northampton NN5 5LH *Tel:* 01604 750506

Northwich, Cheshire

Pickup, J B, Mr, Moss Haselhurst, 2 Castle Street, Northwich CW8 1AB *Tel:* 01606 74301

Seaman, M A, Mr, 2-2A The Bull Ring, Northwich CW8 2JS *Tel:* 01606 352219

Norwich, Norfolk

Chadd, R J, Mr, Leathes Prior, 74 The Close, Norwich NR1 4DR *Tel:* 01603 281102

Eagle, T, Mr, Hansells, 13 The Close, Norwich NR1 4DS *Tel:* 01603 751970

Guthrie, R N, Mr, Leathes Prior, 74 The Close, Norwich NR1 4DR *Tel:* 01603 281121

Hansell, A P, Mr, Leathes Prior, 42 Branksome Road, Norwich NR4 6SW *Tel:* 01603 453433

Lubbock, N C, Mr, Steeles Law LLP, 3 Norwich Business Park, Whiting Road, Norwich NR4 6DJ *Tel:* 01603 598022

Masterson, M L, Miss, 16 Lime Tree Road, Norwich NR2 2NQ *Tel:* 01603 453550

Smith, G H, Mr, Hansells, 13 The Close, Norwich NR1 4DS *Tel:* 01603 275844

Stockings, J L, Mrs, Hansells, 13 The Close, Norwich NR1 4DS *Tel:* 01603 751982

Nottingham, Nottingham

Cullen, C N, Mr, Freeth Cartwright LLP, Cumberland Court, 80 Mount Street, Nottingham NG1 6HH *Tel:* 0115 936 9385

Foulds, M A, Mr, Rothera Dowson, 956 Woodborough Road, Mapperley, Nottingham NG3 5QS *Tel:* 0115 952 0900

Gogia, S P, Mr, Notary Desk, 368 Broxtowe Lane, Aspley, Nottingham NG8 5ND *Tel:* 0115 929 9777 / 07960 283653

Grosberg, R D, Mr, Nelsons, Pennine House, 8 Stanford Street, Nottingham NG1 7BQ *Tel:* 0115 989 5219

Hammond, R B, Mr, Rothera Dowson, 2 Kayes Walk, Stoney Street, Nottingham NG1 1PZ *Tel:* 0115 910 0600

Syziu, D, Ms, Fraser Brown, 84 Friar Lane, Nottingham NG1 6ED *Tel:* 0115 988 8722

Nuneaton, Warwickshire

Bull, A J E, Mr, Alsters Kelley, 3 Dugdale Street, Nuneaton CV11 5QQ *Tel:* 0844 561 0100

Dosanj, K, Mrs, Cocks Lloyd, Riversley House, Coton Road, Nuneaton CV11 5TX *Tel:* 024 7664 2732

Oadby, Leicester

Holt, A J N, Mr, 49 London Road, Oadby LE2 5DN *Tel:* 0116 210 8731 / 07776 240257

Oldham, Greater Manchester

Smith, J D, Mr, Wrigley Claydon, 29/33 Union Street, Oldham OL1 1HH *Tel:* 0161 624 6811

Orpington, Kent

Giblin, P J, Mr, Clarkson Wright & Jakes LLP, Valiant House, 12 Knoll Rise, Orpington BR56 0PG *Tel:* 01689 887887

North, M A, Mr, Clarkson Wright & Jakes LLP, Valiant House, 12 Knoll Rise, Orpington BR6 0PG *Tel:* 01689 887887

Seldon, L J A, Mr, Bramley House, Mill Court, Penshurst Road, Bidborough, Orpington TN3 0XN *Tel:* 01892 514594

Wright, A C, Mr, Clarkson Wright & Jakes LLP, Valiant House, 12 Knoll Rise, Orpington BR6 0PG *Tel:* 01689 887887

Oxford, Oxfordshire

Burn, M J, Mr, Oxford Employment Law, 7200 The Quorum, Oxford Business Park North, Oxford OX4 2JZ *Tel:* 01865 487136

Capel, S P B, Mr, Henmans LLP, 5000 Oxford Business Park South, Oxford OX4 2BH *Tel:* 01865 781000 / 01865 778669

Chater, C A, Mrs, Hadleigh House, Hinksey Hill, Oxford OX1 5BE *Tel:* 01865 326914

Ewens, S E, Mr, HMG Law LLP, 126 High Street, Oxford OX1 4DG *Tel:* 01865 244661

Owens, N D, Mr, Blake Lapthorn, Seacourt Tower, West Way, Oxford OX2 0FB *Tel:* 01865 989120

Saunders, J S, Mr, Blake Lapthorn, Seacourt Tower, West Way, Oxford OX2 0FB *Tel:* 01865 248607

Woodward, K S, Miss, Morgan Cole LLP, Buxton Court, 3 West Way, Oxford OX2 0SZ *Tel:* 01865 262633

Pembroke, Pembrokeshire

Roache, P J, Mr, 12 Meyrick Street, Pembroke Dock, Pembroke SA72 6UT *Tel:* 01646 682603

Penrith, Cumbria

Richardson, J M, Mr, Arnison & Company, 1 St Andrews Place, Penrith CA11 7AW *Tel:* 01768 862007

Penryn, Cornwall

Rose, C A, Mr, Christopher Rose, 24 Lower Market Street, Penryn TR10 8BG *Tel:* 01326 372461

Peterborough, Peterborough

Browne, L J G, Mr, 26 Priestgate, Peterborough PE1 1WG *Tel:* 01733 865021

Monsell, C N, Mr, Buckles Solicitors LLP, Grant House, 101 Bourges Boulevard, Peterborough PE1 1NG *Tel:* 01733 888878

Petersfield, Hampshire

O'Flynn, P D A, Mr, Daltons, Lyndum House, 12 High Street, Petersfield GU32 3JG *Tel:* 01730 262816

Spencer, A M T, Mr, Macdonald Oates LLP, Walltree Court, St Peter's Road, Petersfield GU32 3HT *Tel:* 01730 268211 / 07733 397298

Plymouth, Plymouth

Collier, C C, Ms, The Surgery, 44A Sutherland Road, Mutley, Plymouth PL4 6BN *Tel:* 01752 666972

Coveney, N D, Mr, Foot Anstey, 4 North East Quay, Sutton Harbour, Plymouth PL4 0BN *Tel:* 01752 675000

Daniel, W A, Mr, Thompson & Jackson, 4/5 St Lawrence Road, Plymouth PL4 6HR *Tel:* 01752 665037

Dennerly, R E, Mr, Wolferstans, 60/66 North Hill, Plymouth PL4 8EP *Tel:* 01752 292212

Gabbitass, D J L, Mr, Wolferstans, Depford Chambers, 60/66 North Hill, Plymouth PL4 8EP *Tel:* 01752 663295

Searle, D I, Mr, Bright LLP, Studio 5-11, 5 Millbay Road, Plymouth PL1 3LF *Tel:* 07921 846000 / 01752 388884

Stitson, R B, Mr, Stroud Stitson, North Hill House, 119 North Hill, Plymouth PL4 8JY *Tel:* 01752 660066

Stroud, G B, Mr, Stroud Stitson, North Hill House, 119 North Hill, Plymouth PL4 8JY *Tel:* 01752 660066

Pocklington, East Riding of Yorkshire

Wood, J M, Mr, Wood Sherwood, 6-10 Railway Street, Pocklington YO4 2QZ *Tel:* 01759 302791

Pontefract, West Yorkshire

Wilton, C, Mr, Hartley Worstenholme, Gillygate Chambers, 10 Gillygate, Pontefract WF8 1PQ *Tel:* 01977 732222

Poole, Poole

Richardson, J, Mr, 1 Brunstead Place, Poole BH12 1EW *Tel:* 01202 768928

Wintle, P, Mr, Jacobs & Reeves, Beechurst, 153 High Street, Poole BH15 1AU *Tel:* 07964 666378

Portsmouth, Portsmouth

Blake, C S, Mr, Blake Lapthorn, Harbour Court, Compass Road, North Harbour, Portsmouth PO6 4ST *Tel:* 023 9222 1122

Cobbett, J R G, Mr, Biscoes, Kingston Place, 62-68 Kingston Crescent, Portsmouth PO2 8AQ *Tel:* 023 9266 0261

Collins, D A, Mr, Blake Lapthorn, Harbour Court, Compass Road, North Harbour, Portsmouth PO6 4ST *Tel:* 023 9222 1122

Heath, C W, Mr, Biscoes, 62/68 Kingston Crescent, North End, Portsmouth PO2 8AQ *Tel:* 023 9266 0261

Profit, M D J, Mr, Blake Lapthorn, Harbour Court, Compass Road, North Harbour, Portsmouth PO6 4ST *Tel:* 023 9222 1122

Russell, D W, Mr, Blake Lapthorn, Harbour Court, Compass Road, North Harbour, Portsmouth PO6 4ST *Tel:* 023 9222 1122

Stone, R E, Mr, Allens, 15 Landport Terrace, Portsmouth PO1 2QS *Tel:* 023 9282 2411

Poulton-le-Fylde, Lancashire

Lawson, P J, Mr, Mill Farm, 14 Little Poulton Lane, Poulton-le-Fylde FY6 7ET *Tel:* 01253 892600

Preston, Lancashire

Wilson, F E, Miss, 5B Barnfield Way, Millennium City Park, Fulwood, Preston PR2 5DB *Tel:* 01772 794680

Prestwich, Greater Manchester

Latimer, S R, Mr, Latimer Lee LLP, 35 Bury New Road, Sedgley Park, Prestwich M25 9JY *Tel:* 0161 798 9000

Latimer, J F, Ms, Latimer Lee LLP, 35 Bury New Road, Sedgley Park, Prestwich M25 9JY *Tel:* 0161 798 9000

Pwllheli, Gwynedd

Owen, I E, Mr, Robyns-Owen, 36 High Street, Pwllheli LL53 5RY *Tel:* 01758 613177

Radlett, Hertfordshire

Elgood, G D A, Mr, Debenhams Ottaway, 48 Wattling Street, Radlett WD7 7NN *Tel:* 01923 857171

Hayes, P, Mr, Debenhams Ottaway, 48 Watling Street, Radlett WD7 7NN *Tel:* 01923 857171

Radstock, Bath & North East Somerset

Orme, J G, Mr, Elm Tree Farm, Litton, Radstock BA3 4PS *Tel:* 01761 241285

Rainham, Medway Towns

Norrington, R H, Mr, Sackvilles, 12 The Broadway, Rainham RM13 9YL *Tel:* 01708 552804

Ramsgate, Kent

Daniel, M R M, Mr, Daniel & Edwards, 44/46 Queen Street, Ramsgate CT11 9EF *Tel:* 01843 594651

Reading, Reading

D'Arcy, P B, Mr, Blandy & Blandy, 1 Friar Street, Reading RG1 1DA *Tel:* 0118 951 6821

Few, D J, Mr, Friar Street Notaries, One Friar Street, Reading RG1 1DA *Tel:* 0118 951 6858

Griffiths, R G, Mr, Blandy & Blandy, 1 Friar Street, Reading RG1 1DA *Tel:* 0118 951 6852

Hutt, P M, Mr, Field Seymour Parkes, The Old Coroner's Court, 1 London Street, Reading RG1 4QW *Tel:* 0118 951 6200

Mann, M J, Ms, Field Seymour Parkes, The Old Coroner's Court, 1 London Street, Reading RG1 4QW *Tel:* 0118 951 6301

Matharoo, S, Mr, Friar Street Notaries, 1 Friar Street, Reading RG1 1DA *Tel:* 0118 951 6921

Retford, Nottinghamshire

Browne, M E, Mr, Jones & Co, Canon Square, Retford DN22 6PB *Tel:* 01777 703827

Oddy, V J, Mr, Old Shippen, Lound Low Road, Sutton cum Lound, Retford DN22 8PN *Tel:* 01777 702436 / 07767 306477

Rhyl, Denbighshire

Salisbury, R A, Mr, Gamlins, 31/37 Russell Road, Rhyl LL18 3DB *Tel:* 01745 343500

Richmond, Surrey

Thompson-Haughton, B, Miss, Dixon Ward, 16 The Green, Richmond TW9 1QD *Tel:* 020 8940 4051

Rickmansworth, Hertfordshire

Young, C J, Mr, 141 New Road, Croxley Green, Rickmansworth WD3 3EN *Tel:* 01923 775531

Ripon, North Yorkshire

Balmforth, J R, Mr, Tunnard & Co, Cathedral Chambers, 4 Kirkgate, Ripon HG4 1PA *Tel:* 01765 600755

Rochdale, Greater Manchester

Everett, D, Mr, 1 Heald Cottages, Off Judith Street, Lowerfold, Rochdale OL12 7HS *Tel:* 01706 645271 / 07818 602237

Rochester, Medway Towns

Tadhunter, S J, Ms, Bassets, 156 High Street, Rochester ME1 1ET *Tel:* 01634 400161

Romford, Essex

Ramsey, R E, Mr, Kenneth Elliott Rowe, Enterprise House, 18 Eastern Road, Romford RM1 3PJ *Tel:* 01708 757575

Romsey, Hampshire

Webb, P J W, Mr, Bells, 5 Market Place, Romsey SO51 8XF *Tel:* 01794 513328

Ross-on-Wye, Herefordshire

Shawcross, K R, Mr, Shawcross & Co, 6 High Street, Ross-on-Wye HR9 5HL *Tel:* 01989 562377

Rossendale, Lancashire

Foster, C S, Mr, Walkers, 574 Bacup Road, Waterfoot, Rossendale BB4 7QN *Tel:* 01706 213565

Rotherham, South Yorkshire

Coupland, D W, Mr, Foys, Church Steps, All Saints Square, Rotherham S60 1QD *Tel:* 01709 373799

Rugby, Warwickshire

Bailey, R F, Mr, Fullers, 24 Albert Street, Rugby CV21 2RT *Tel:* 01788 811213

Hardingham, P A, Mr, 41 Dorset Close, Cawston, Rugby CV22 7RB *Tel:* 01788 522334

Saffron Walden, Essex

Luckes, R J, Mr, Heckford Norton, 18 Hill Street, Saffron Walden CB10 1JD *Tel:* 01799 522636

Sale, Greater Manchester

Smith, G, Mr, Lawsmiths, 1st Floor, Dominion House, Sibson Road, Sale M33 7PP *Tel:* 0161 972 7700

Salisbury, Wiltshire

Carnegy, C D, Mr, Bonallack & Bishop, Rougemont House, Rougemount Close, Manor Road, Salisbury SP1 1LY *Tel:* 01722 422300

Lello, J M, Mr, Parker Bullen LLP, 45 Castle Street, Salisbury SP1 3SS *Tel:* 01722 412000

Lonergan, J M, Mrs, Wilsons LLP, Steynings House, Summerlock Approach, Salisbury SP2 7RJ *Tel:* 01722 427733

Sykes, R W, Mr, Parker Bullen LLP, 45 Castle Street, Salisbury SP1 3SS *Tel:* 01722 412000

Walker, D M, Mr, William Bache & Co, 4 Oakridge Office Park, Whaddon, Salisbury SP5 3HT *Tel:* 01722 713370

Sandbach, Cheshire

Barlow, C J M, Mr, Butcher & Barlow, 31 Middlewich Road, Sandbach CW11 1HW *Tel:* 01270 762521

Sandwich, Kent

Turner, J A, Mr, Emmerson Brown & Brown, 1 Potter Street, Sandwich CT13 9DR *Tel:* 01304 612444

Sandy, Bedfordshire

Hall, B A, Mr, Woodfines LLP, 6 Bedford Road, Sandy SG19 1EN *Tel:* 01767 680251

Scarborough, North Yorkshire

Garvey, F M, Mr, Tubbs & Co, 106 Victoria Road, Scarborough YO11 1SL *Tel:* 01723 352666

Sevenoaks, Kent

Barratt, N R M, Mr, Warners Law LLP, 16 South Park, Sevenoaks TN13 1AN *Tel:* 01732 747902

Wright, N C, Mr, Lovells Cottage, 9 Hollybush Lane, Sevenoaks TN13 3UN *Tel:* 01732 457060

Sheerness, Kent

Clough, P J I, Mr, Peter Clough, 13/15 Minster Road, Halfway, Sheerness ME12 3JE *Tel:* 01795 669299

Sheffield, South Yorkshire

Coffey, D P, Mr, Graysons, 4-12 Paradise Square, Sheffield S1 1TB *Tel:* 0114 272 9184

Downs, R J, Mrs, Keeble Hawson LLP, Old Cathedral Vicarage, St James Row, Sheffield S1 1XA *Tel:* 0114 290 6239

Pickford, R W G, Mr, Graysons, 4-12 Paradise Square, Sheffield S1 1TB *Tel:* 0114 272 9184

Wagner, E R, Mr, Anglo-Spanish Law, 6 Lower Burch Row, Eyam, Hope Valley, Sheffield S32 5QF *Tel:* 01433 631508

Sherborne, Dorset

Harris, R P H, Mr, Cobblers, Greenhill, Sherborne DT9 4EP *Tel:* 01935 389535

Shoreham-by-Sea, West Sussex

Barry, Q, Mr, Lawson Lewis & Co, 9 Mill Lane, Shoreham-by-Sea BN43 5AG *Tel:* 01273 455753

Hunt, H P, Mr, Fitzhugh Gates, 23-25 High Street, Shoreham-by-Sea BN4 5EE *Tel:* 01273 467470

Shrewsbury, Shropshire

Turner, S J, Ms, 3 College Hill, Shrewsbury SY1 1LT *Tel:* 01743 272771 / 07708 137002

Sittingbourne, Kent

Cramp, D W, Mr, Dudley Cramp, 42 High Street, Sittingbourne ME10 4PB *Tel:* 01795 420024

Skipton, North Yorkshire

Crangle, P J, Mr, Savage Crangle, 15 High Street, Skipton BD23 1AJ *Tel:* 01756 794611

Slough, Slough

Dhariwal, V, Mrs, Slough Solicitors LLP, 24 High Street, Slough SL1 1EQ *Tel:* 01753 535422

Kumeri, S, Ms, S & V Solicitors & Notaries, Abbey House, 18-24 Stoke Road, Slough SL2 5AG *Tel:* 01753 722130 / 07767 637582

Smethwick, West Midlands
Sahni, H S, Mr, Sahni & Co, 104 High Street, Smethwick B66 1AA *Tel:* 0121 558 5222

Solihull, West Midlands
Kimberley, P R, Mr, Williamson & Soden, Stanton House, 54 Stratford Road, Shirley, Solihull B90 3LS *Tel:* 0121 733 8000

McSheen-Bailey, C A, Mrs, Forum Law Solicitors, Avon House, 435 Stratford Road, Shirley, Solihull B90 4AA *Tel:* 0121 506 8191 / 07740 280441

South Shields, Tyne & Wear
Dodds, W N, Mr, 19 Hepscott Terrace, South Shields NE33 4TH *Tel:* 0191 456 3381

Southall, Middlesex
Bansal, R T, Mr, Bansal & Co, 2nd Floor, 92a The Broadway, Southall UB1 1QF *Tel:* 020 3118 2063

Jung, V, Ms, Jung & Co Solicitors, 41 North Road, Southall UB1 2JL *Tel:* 020 8813 8996

Southampton, Southampton
Caplen, A H A, Mr, Abels, 6 College Place, London Road, Southampton SO9 4ZE *Tel:* 023 8022 0317

Caton, M J, Mr, Moore & Blatch, 11 The Avenue, Southampton SO17 1XF *Tel:* 023 8071 8016

Coats, C M, Ms, Marston House, Blackfield Road, Blackfield, Southampton SO45 1WD *Tel:* 023 8089 0919 / 07540 585547

Gordon, I L, Mr, Paris Smith LLP, No1 London Road, Southampton SO15 2AE *Tel:* 023 8048 2482

Pugh, N M, Mr, Bond Pearce LLP, Oceana House, 39-49 Commercial Road, Southampton SO15 1GA *Tel:* 0845 415 8342

Smith, R G H, Mr, Paris Smith LLP, No1 London Road, Southampton SO15 2AE *Tel:* 023 8048 2482

Southend-on-Sea, Southend-on-Sea
Hurrell, A P, Mr, Andrew Hurrell, 198 The Broadway, Thorpe Bay, Southend-on-Sea SS1 3EU *Tel:* 01702 582030

Southport, Merseyside
Jacklin, R, Mr, Richard Jacklin & Co, 38 Houghton Street, Southport PR9 0PQ *Tel:* 01704 500024

Williamson, J M, Mrs, Cook & Talbot, St George's Place, 140 Lord Street, Southport PR9 0AH *Tel:* 01704 535216

Southwell, Nottinghamshire
Watts, J R, Ms, Tallents, 2 Westgate, Southwell NG25 0JJ *Tel:* 01636 813411

Southwold, Suffolk
Mantin, K, Ms, Mantins Solicitors & Notaries, 82 High Street, Southwold IP18 6DP *Tel:* 01502 724750

Spalding, Lincolnshire
Smith, G C H, Mr, Roythornes, Enterprise Way, Pinchbeck, Spalding PE11 3YR *Tel:* 01775 842500

St Albans, Hertfordshire
Barnes, P N, Mr, 36 Beaumont Avenue, St Albans AL1 4JT *Tel:* 01727 868857 / 07854 609978

Foy, J D, Mr, Debenhams Ottaway, Ivy House, 107 St Peter's Street, St Albans AL1 3EW *Tel:* 01727 837161

St Austell, Cornwall
Nicholls, A H L, Mrs, Stephens & Scown, 3 Cross Lane, St Austell PL25 4AX *Tel:* 01726 74433

St Helens, Merseyside
Unsworth, A K, Mr, Norton & Co, 499 Warrington Road, Rainhill, St Helens L35 0LR *Tel:* 0151 426 7001

St Ives, Cambridgeshire
Few, J E, Mr, Eaton & Few, 8 The Meadow, St Ives PE27 4LG *Tel:* 01480 301558

Stafford, Staffordshire
Harris, S P, Mr, Hand Morgan & Owen, 17 Martin Street, Stafford ST16 2LF *Tel:* 01785 211411

Jewels, M A, Mr, Jewels, Victoria Chambers, 15 Victoria Road, Stafford ST16 2BY *Tel:* 01785 602030

Stalybridge, Greater Manchester
Holden, P E, Mr, Thompson & Cooke LLP, 12 Stamford Street, Stalybridge SK15 1LA *Tel:* 0161 338 2614

Stamford, Lincolnshire
Jeffery, J W, Mr, 61 Cedar Road, Stamford PE9 2JJ *Tel:* 01780 765591

Vipan, R F M, Mr, 4 Baxters Lane, Easton on the Hill, Stamford PE9 3NH *Tel:* 01780 751869

Stockport, Greater Manchester
Glassey, N J A, Mr, Stevenson Glassey Solicitors, 13 Leamington Road, Houldsworth Square, Reddish, Stockport SK5 6BD *Tel:* 0161 443 1395

Harney, N J, Mr, Nightingales Solicitors Ltd, 127 Buxton Road, High Lane, Stockport SK6 8DX *Tel:* 01663 764038

Houlker, R B, Mr, Harney & Houlker, 127 Buxton Road, High Lane, Stockport SK6 8DX *Tel:* 01663 764038

Stockton-on-Tees, Stockton-on-Tees
Irons, R G, Mr, Archers Law LLP, Lakeside House, Kingfisher Way, Stockton-on-Tees TS18 3NB *Tel:* 01642 636500

Pacey, F J, Mr, Newbys, 10 Finkle Street, Stockton-on-Tees TS18 1AS *Tel:* 01642 673733

Robinson, S A, Mr, Blackett Hart Pratt LLP, 2 Kingfisher Way, Preston Farm, Stockton-on-Tees TS18 3EX *Tel:* 01642 672770

Stokesley, North Yorkshire
Rathmell, A C, Mrs, Thorp Parker, Martin House, 13 High Street, Stokesley TS9 5AD *Tel:* 01642 711354

Stourbridge, West Midlands
Allery, P R, Mr, Old Swinford, 9 Joyberry Drive, Stourbridge DY8 2EF *Tel:* 01384 374972

Fatchett, G W, Mr, Regulatory Legal Solicitors, Brindley House, Engine Lane, Lye, Stourbridge DY9 7AQ *Tel:* 01384 426400

Stratford-upon-Avon, Warwickshire
McMahon, A M, Ms, Anne Mcmahon, PO Box 4929, Welford on Avon, Stratford-upon-Avon CV37 1GS *Tel:* 01789 750142

Ollis, R W, Mr, Lodders Solicitors LLP, 10 Elm Court, Stratford-upon-Avon CV37 6PA *Tel:* 01789 206131 / 07771 850525

West, G, Mrs, Jackson West, The Old Pump House, Clifford Mill, Clifford Chambers, Stratford-upon-Avon CV37 8HR *Tel:* 01789 204020

Street, Somerset
Evans, M J, Mr, Chubb Bulleid Ltd, Strode House, 10 Leigh Road, Street BA16 0HA *Tel:* 01759 836100 / 01458 440640

Sudbury, Suffolk
Sneezum, D F, Mr, Steed & Steed, 6 Gainsborough Street, Sudbury CO10 2ET *Tel:* 01787 373387

Sunbury-on-Thames, Middlesex
Canarapen, T, Mrs, Rigby Golding LLP, 57 Staines Road West, Sunbury-on-Thames TW16 7AU *Tel:* 01932 765741

Webster, S, Miss, Rigby Golding LLP, 57 Staines Road West, Sunbury-on-Thames TW16 7AU *Tel:* 01932 765741

Sunderland, Tyne & Wear
Shaw, M C, Mr, 52 John Street, Sunderland SR1 1QN *Tel:* 0191 567 1851

Surbiton, Surrey
MacLaverty, R P, Mr, 40 Cleaveland Road, Surbiton KT6 4AH *Tel:* 07720 057640

Sutton, Surrey
Porter, A R M, Mr, Porter & Co, 40 Benhill Avenue, Sutton SM1 4DA *Tel:* 020 8643 5111

Sutton Coldfield, West Midlands
Delacroix-Humphreys, L H, Mrs, 12 Rocklands Drive, Four Oaks, Sutton Coldfield B75 6SP *Tel:* 07783 410196

Khara, B K, Mrs, Jordans, 29 The Range, Streetly, Sutton Coldfield B74 2BE *Tel:* 0121 580 9375

Sutton-in-Ashfield, Nottinghamshire
Slade, A T, Mr, Fidler & Pepper, 1 Low Street, Sutton-in-Ashfield NG17 1DH *Tel:* 01623 451145

Sutton-on-Sea, Lincolnshire
Houltby, R W B, Mr, Wilkin Chapman LLP, 44 High Street, Sutton-on-Sea LN12 2HB *Tel:* 01507 443077

Swanage, Dorset
Griffin, P, Mr, Neville-Jones & Co, 52/54 Station Road, Swanage BH19 1AF *Tel:* 01929 422666

Swansea
Jenkins, D M, Mr, Trevor Thomas Scott Jenkins, Central Chambers, Clydach, Swansea SA6 5EX *Tel:* 01792 843821

Morgan, K, Mr, Douglas-Jones Mercer, Mallard Way, 16 Axis Court, Swansea Vale, Swansea SA7 0AJ *Tel:* 01792 656501

Swindon, Swindon
Gregory, M R A, Mr, Withy King, Vectis Court, 4-6 Newport Street, Swindon SN1 3DX *Tel:* 01793 401052

Martin, P A, Ms, Andrews Martin, 6 Little London Court, Old Town, Swindon SN1 3HY *Tel:* 01793 641707

Martin, R A, Mr, Andrews Martin, 6 Little London Court, Old Town, Swindon SN1 5PD *Tel:* 01793 641707

Wyldbore-Smith, W F, Mr, Thring Townsend Lee & Pembertons, 6 Drakes Meadow, Penny Lane, Swindon SN3 3LL *Tel:* 020 7766 5666

Tamworth, Staffordshire
Garner, K G W, Mr, Garner Canning, 11 Aldergate, Tamworth B79 7DL *Tel:* 01827 314004

Tarporley, Cheshire
Driver, J, Mr, Hibberts LLP, Avenue Buildings, High Street, Tarporley CW6 0AZ *Tel:* 01829 733338

Taunton, Somerset
McVay, A J, Ms, Old Bartletts, Fore Street, Milverton, Taunton TA4 1JX *Tel:* 01823 401118

Pulvermacher, F M, Mr, 6 Higher Vexford, Lydeard St Lawrence, Taunton TA4 3QF *Tel:* 01984 656457

Russ, T J, Mr, Clarke Willmott LLP, Blackbrook Gate, Blackbrook Park Avenue, Taunton TA1 2PG *Tel:* 0845 209 1155

Sinclair, J E H, Mrs, Acorn Solicitors, 1st & 2nd Floors, 41 High Street, Taunton TA1 3PN *Tel:* 01823 273010 / 07540 723760

Thorne, S G, Mr, Clarke Willmott LLP, Blackbrook Gate, Blackbrook Park Avenue, Taunton TA1 2PG *Tel:* 0845 209 1105

Telford, Shropshire
Bridgman, M N E, Mr, Elliott Bridgman Solicitors, 10 Court Street, Madeley, Telford TF7 5EB *Tel:* 01952 684544

Edwards, H M, Mr, Terry Jones, 7 Hollinswood Court, Stafford Park 1, Telford TF3 3DE *Tel:* 01952 297979

Tenterden, Kent
Chapman, T J, Mr, Pengelly & Rylands, 39/41 High Street, Tenterden TN30 6BJ *Tel:* 01233 860216

Thetford, Norfolk
Plummer, J E, Mr, Act Solicitors, 2 White Hart Street, Thetford IP24 1AD *Tel:* 01842 765577

Thorpe Bay, Southend-on-Sea
Raffan, P M, Mr, 35 Thrope Bay Gardens, Thorpe Bay SS1 3NR *Tel:* 01702 587896

Tilehurst, Reading
Fursman, W, Mr, Collins Dryland Thorowgood, 81/83 School Road, Tilehurst RG3 5AT *Tel:* 0118 942 2448

Tonbridge, Kent
Smith, P A, Mr, Warners Law LLP, Bank House, Bank Street, Tonbridge TN9 1BL *Tel:* 01732 770660

Warner, C J, Mr, Warners Law LLP, Bank House, Bank Street, Tonbridge TN9 1BL *Tel:* 01732 375315

Torquay, Torbay
Davis, E K, Mrs, 10 Court Road, Chelston, Torquay TQ2 6SE *Tel:* 01803 607662

Forward, G A, Mr, Kitsons LLP, Minerva House, Orchard Way, Edginwell Park, Torquay TQ2 7FA *Tel:* 01803 202020

Richards, E M J, Mr, Hooper & Wollen, Carlton House, 30 The Terrace, Torquay TQ1 1BS *Tel:* 01803 213251

Turner, H M, Mr, Room 6, Cary Chambers, 1 Palk Street, Torquay TQ2 5EL *Tel:* 01803 213806

Towcester, Northamptonshire
Alton Honeywell, K M S, Mr, Arnold Thomson, 205 Watling Street West, Towcester NN12 6BX *Tel:* 01327 350266

Guille, D J, Mr, Shepherd & Co, 184 Watling Street East, Towcester NN12 6DB *Tel:* 01327 350185

Tring, Hertfordshire
Bateson, G V, Mr, Odd Spring, Stocks Road, Aldbury, Tring HP23 5RU *Tel:* 01442 851209

Truro, Cornwall
Dexter, P J, Mr, Coodes, Elizabeth House, Castle Street, Truro TR1 3AP *Tel:* 01872 261614

Murdoch, G I, Mr, Stephens & Scown, Osprey House, Malpas Road, Truro TR1 1UT *Tel:* 01872 265100

Tandy, D A, Mr, Frogmore House, Frog Lane, Tregony, Truro TR2 5RX *Tel:* 01872 530488

Tunbridge Wells, Kent
Caisley, A G, Mr, Keogh Caisley, Kenwood House, 1 Upper Grosvenor Road, Tunbridge Wells TN1 2EL *Tel:* 01892 548411

Green, F G, Mr, Thomson Snell Passmore, 3 Lonsdale Gardens, Tunbridge Wells TN1 1NX *Tel:* 01892 701237

Langridge, C J, Mr, Cripps Harries Hall LLP, Wallside House, 12 Mount Ephraim Road, Tunbridge Wells TN1 1EG *Tel:* 01892 515121

Leney, S D, Mr, Cripps Harries Hall LLP, Wallside House, 12 Mount Ephraim Road, Tunbridge Wells TN1 1EG *Tel:* 01892 506005

Lister, S D, Miss, Thompson Snell & Passmore, 3 Lonsdale Gardens, Tunbridge Wells TN1 1NX *Tel:* 01892 701394

Twickenham, Middlesex
Andrews, S R, Mr, 14 St Peters Road, St Margarets, Twickenham TW1 1QX *Tel:* 020 8744 1243

McDowell, A J, Mrs, 25 Erncroft Way, Twickenham TW1 1DA *Tel:* 020 8891 1566

Warner, V J, Mr, Anderson & Co, 49 Moormead Road, St Margarets, Twickenham TW1 1JS *Tel:* 020 8892 0092

Ulverston, Cumbria
Raymond, P J, Mr, Lin Crag Farm, Blawith, Ulverston LA12 8EH *Tel:* 01229 885437 / 07971 149302

Wakefield, West Yorkshire
Box, L M, Mrs, Dixon Coles & Gill, Bank House, Burton Street, Wakefield WF1 2DA *Tel:* 01924 373467

Rodgers, T W, Mr, Chadwick Lawrence LLP, Paragon Point, Red Wall Crescent, Paragon Business Village, Wakefield WF1 2DF *Tel:* 01924 379078

Wilding, J H, Mrs, Dixon Coles & Gill, 22 Westfield Road, Horbury, Wakefield WF1 2DA *Tel:* 01924 263166

Walsall, West Midlands
Meere, R, Mr, Enoch Evans LLP, St Paul's Chambers, 6/9 Hatherton Road, Walsall WS1 1XS *Tel:* 01922 720333

Sarai, R K, Mrs, 15 Angelica Close, Walsall WS5 4RP *Tel:* 07808 966715

Tutt, S K N S, Miss, HSC Solicitors, 4 Sprngvale Avenue, Walsall WS5 3QB *Tel:* 07957 106119

Walton-on-Thames, Surrey
Samuels, A D, Mr, Crane Cottage, The King's Drive, Walton-on-Thames KT12 4BA *Tel:* 07769 900565

Wantage, Oxfordshire
Mellor, J L, Miss, Amblers End, East Hendred, Wantage OX12 8LG *Tel:* 07808 862163

Wareham, Dorset
Cross, S D, Mr, Humphries Kirk, Glebe House, North Street, Wareham BH20 4AN *Tel:* 01929 552141

Warlingham, Surrey
Bowness, P S, Lord, Streeter Marshall, 416 Limpsfield Road, Warlingham CR6 9LA *Tel:* 01883 622433

Warminster, Wiltshire
Hindle, H I, Mrs, Middleton & Upsall LLP, East Gate House, 94 East Street, Warminster BA12 9BG *Tel:* 01985 214444

Warrington, Warrington
Poyner, S M, Mr, Forshaws Davies Ridgway LLP, 1-5 Palmyra Square, Warrington WA1 1DF *Tel:* 01925 230000

Royle, C A, Mr, Forshaws Davies Ridgway LLP, 21 Palmyra Square, Warrington WA1 1DF *Tel:* 01925 230000

Warwick, Warwickshire
Markham, A G, Mr, 6 Farriers Court, Wasperton, Warwick CV35 8EB *Tel:* 07787 401551

Mason, M A, Mrs, Biddle Mason & Co, Close Tower, Brownley Green Lane, Beausale, Warwick CV35 7PD *Tel:* 01926 484264

Wealdstone, Middlesex
Down, S J, Mr, Harrow Solicitors & Advocates, 5/7 Masons Avenue, Wealdstone HA3 5AH *Tel:* 020 8863 0788

Wellingborough, Northamptonshire
Carter, L, Ms, Wilson Browne LLP, 60b Oxford Street, Wellingborough NN8 4JJ *Tel:* 01933 279000

Wells-next-the-Sea, Norfolk
Marshall, M L, Ms, Hayes & Storr, Chancery Lane, The Buttlands, Wells-next-the-Sea NR23 1ER *Tel:* 01328 710210

Wembley, Middlesex
Bunce-Linsell, J A, Mrs, J A Bunce & Co, 235 Preston Road, Wembley HA9 8PE *Tel:* 020 8904 2229

West Bromwich, West Midlands
Edwards, J R, Mr, Clark Brookes, 2 Lombard Street West, West Bromwich B70 8EH *Tel:* 0121 553 2576
Porter, B R, Mr, Challinors Solicitors, Guardian House, Cronehills Linkway, West Bromwich B70 8SW *Tel:* 0121 553 3211 / 07538 021062
Sutton, A, Mr, Baches, Lombard House, Cronehills Linkway, West Bromwich B70 7PL *Tel:* 0121 553 3286

West Malling, Kent
Mayor, K L, Mrs, Vertex Law LLP, 23 King's Hill Avenue, Kings Hill, West Malling ME19 4UA *Tel:* 01732 224009

Weston-super-Mare, North Somerset
Kirkhope, J, Mr, John Kirkhope & Co, 33 Clarence Park North, Weston-super-Mare BS23 4AW *Tel:* 01934 644647

Wetherby, West Yorkshire
Dyson, N R, Mr, Hart Law LLP, 63 St James Street, Wetherby LS22 6RS *Tel:* 01937 547010

Weybridge, Surrey
Meadows, F E P, Mr, Meadows Fraser LLP, 56 Church Street, Weybridge KT13 8DP *Tel:* 01932 852057
Meadows, P P, Mr, Meadows Fraser LLP, 56 Church Street, Weybridge KT13 8DP *Tel:* 01932 852057

Whitefield, Greater Manchester
Price, P J, Mr, PO Box 357, Whitefield M45 7XF *Tel:* 07746 150055 / 0161 796 5493

Wigan, Greater Manchester
Houghton, S E, Ms, Houghton Pigot & Co, 25 Bridgeman Terrace, Wigan WN1 1TD *Tel:* 01942 241288
McAreavey, J B, Mr, Unsworth & Wood, 23 King Street, Wigan WN1 1EQ *Tel:* 01942 242400

Wigton, Cumbria
Hawks, E J, Mr, Beaty & Co, 1 Victoria Place, High Street, Wigton CA7 9PJ *Tel:* 016973 42121

Willenhall, West Midlands
Kumar, S, Mr, Rowland Tildesley Harris, 1 Rose Hill, Willenhall WV13 2AR *Tel:* 01902 366571 / 01902 608097

Wilmslow, Cheshire
Haworth, V A, Miss, 6 Highfield Crescent, Wilmslow SK9 2JL *Tel:* 01625 529404

Wincanton, Somerset
Beresford, R E, Mrs, Dyne Drewett LLP, Market Place, Wincanton BA9 9AB *Tel:* 01963 32374

Winchester, Hampshire
Hune-Schushmyn, P, Mr, Flat 195, 80 High Street, Winchester SO23 9AT
Nichols, C D, Mr, Godwins, 12 St Thomas Street, Winchester SO23 9HF *Tel:* 01962 841484
Radakin, L, Mrs, Meadowlands, Bridge Lane, Shawford, Winchester SO21 2BL *Tel:* 01962 717331 / 07789 433849
Tomsett, M J, Mr, Holdcroft, 8 Campion Way, Kings Worthy, Winchester SO23 7QP *Tel:* 01962 881857
Urquhart, R A D, Mr, 24 Little Hayes Lane, Itchen Abbas, Winchester SO21 1XA *Tel:* 01962 779579

Windermere, Cumbria
Crompton, J R M, Mr, Thomson Wilson Pattinson, Stonecliffe, Lake Road, Windermere LA23 3AR *Tel:* 01539 442233

Windsor, Windsor & Maidenhead
Jones, P H, Mr, Charsley Harrison LLP, Windsor House, Victoria Street, Windsor SL4 1EN *Tel:* 01753 851591

Wirral, Merseyside
Holland, B K, Mr, Butts Mead, 6 East Farm Mews, Caldy, Wirral CH48 1QB *Tel:* 0151 625 3131 / 07831 835360
Walker, M G, Mr, Glenthorne, Little Storeton Lane, Storeton, Wirral CH63 6HP *Tel:* 0151 608 3396

Witham, Essex
Hart, R W, Mr, Roger Hart, 24 Collingwood Road, Witham CM8 2DX *Tel:* 01376 519048
Martin, V E, Ms, Bright & Sons, 87-91 Newland Street, Witham CM8 1AD *Tel:* 01376 512338

Woking, Surrey
Bate, J R C, Mr, Buglear Bate, 31 Guildford Road, Woking GU22 7QQ *Tel:* 01483 715527

Wolverhampton, West Midlands
Braitch, L S, Mr, Braitch Solicitors, 28 Chapel Ash, Wolverhampton WV3 0TN *Tel:* 01902 711200
Carter, W S C, Mr, Underhill Langley & Wright, 7 Waterloo Road, Wolverhampton WV1 4DW *Tel:* 01902 420261
Nock, K J, Mr, Underhill Langley & Wright, 7 Waterloo Road, Wolverhampton WV1 4DW *Tel:* 01902 423431
Thompson, S E, Miss, Dallow & Dallow, 23 Waterloo Road, Wolverhampton WV1 4TJ *Tel:* 01902 427001 / 01902 420208

Woodbridge, Suffolk
Bird, C J, Mr, Marshall Hatchick, 22 Church Street, Woodbridge IP12 1DH *Tel:* 01394 388411
Humphreys, J, Miss, Marshall Hatchick, 22 Church Street, Woodbridge IP12 1DH *Tel:* 01394 388411
Leach, S M J, Mr, Margary Miller, 19 Church Street, Woodbridge IP12 1DS *Tel:* 01394 382777

Woodford Green, Esses
Thirsk, S B, Mr, Thirsk Winton LLP, 445 High Road, Woodford Green IG8 0XE *Tel:* 020 8505 4777
Winton, J M, Mr, Thirsk Winton LLP, 445 High Road, Woodford Green IG8 0XE *Tel:* 020 8505 4777

Woodhall, Lincolnshire
Mace, I T J, Mr, Abbotslea, 16 Abbey Drive, Woodhall Spa, Woodhall LN10 6QU *Tel:* 01526 353548

Worcester, Worcestershire
Huskinson, M G, Mr, March & Edwards, 8 Sansome Walk, Worcester WR1 1LW *Tel:* 01905 723561
Sprake, R M, Mr, March & Edwards, 8 Sansome Walk, Worcester WR1 1LW *Tel:* 01905 723561
Wright, C J, Mr, 50 Bevere Close, Bevere, Worcester WR3 7QL *Tel:* 07971 833707 / 01905 381787

Worthing, West Sussex
Kent, R H, Mr, Marsh Ferriman, Southfield House, 11 Liverpool Gardens, Worthing BN11 1SD *Tel:* 01903 228200
Laverick, P M, Mr, Shelley House, 23 Warwick Street, Worthing BN113DG *Tel:* 01903 883205

Wrexham, Wrexham
Newnes, A N, Mr, Humphrys & Co, 26 Chester Street, Wrexham LL13 8BG *Tel:* 01978 313399

York, York
Lennox, L P M, Mr, Denison Till, Stamford House, Piccadilly, York YO1 9PP *Tel:* 01904 623487
Oakley, M D, Mr, Michael D Oakley, Rose Cottage, Oswaldkirk, York YO62 5XT *Tel:* 01439 788339
Taylor, R, Mr, Langleys, Queens House, Micklegate, York YO1 6WG *Tel:* 01904 610886

LEGAL OMBUDSMAN

PO Box 15870
Birmingham
B3 9EB
Tel: 0121 245 3100
Email:enquiries@legalombudsman.org.uk
Helpline: 0300 555 0333

Chief Ombudsman
Adam Sampson

Deputy Chief Ombudsman
Gary Garland

Director of Operations
Liz Shepherd

Director of Finance and Business Services
Rob Hezel

Head of External Affairs
Alison Robinson

SOLICITORS BENEVOLENT ASSOCIATION

Founded 1858

PATRON

HER MAJESTY THE QUEEN

Vice Patron

Clive Anderson

President

President of the Law Society

The objects of the Association are to provide relief and assistance for persons in need who are or have been admitted to the Roll of Solicitors for England and Wales or who are or have been married to Solicitors so admitted or who are dependants of Solicitors so admitted.

Chairman
David Biddle

Vice-Chairman
Michael Gillman

Auditors
Baker Tilly

Secretary
John Platt

Trustees
The Solicitors Benevolent Association Trustees

Bankers
National Westminster Bank PLC, Law Courts, Temple Bar Branch, 217 Strand, London WC2R 1AL

Stockbrokers
Rensburg Sheppards

Membership
Annual Subscription £60

Life Membership
£600 or £300 post-retirement

Forms of membership may be obtained from the office of the Association:

1 Jaggard Way
London SW12 8SG

Tel: 020 8675 6440
Fax: 020 8675 6441
DX: 41608 Balham
Email: sec@sba.org.uk
Web: www.sba.org.uk

Members of the Association are distinguished in the Solicitors' and Barristers' Directory and Diary thus §

Registered Charity Number 1124512

SECTION 16

GENERAL REFERENCE

CONTENTS

16

COURTS & OFFICES

CONTENTS

JUDICIAL COMMITTEE OF THE PRIVY COUNCIL

Office
Parliament Square, London SW1P 3BD

The Judicial Committee of the Privy Council consists of past and present Lords of Appeal in Ordinary ("Law Lords") and Justices of the Supreme Court, and such other members of the Privy Council as shall from time to time hold or have held 'high judicial office' in the United Kingdom as defined in the Appellate Jurisdiction Acts 1876 and 1877. There is an age limit of 75 on membership of the Judicial Committee.

The Lords of Appeal in Ordinary
Lord Phillips of Worth Matravers
Lord Hope of Craighead
Lord Saville of Newdigate
Lord Rodger of Earlsferry
Lord Walker of Gestingthorpe
Baroness Hale of Richmond
Lord Brown of Eaton-under-Heywood
Lord Mance
Lord Collins of Mapesbury
Lord Kerr of Tonaghmore
Lord Clarke of Stone-cum-Ebony
Sir John Dyson SCJ

By virtue of the Judicial Committee Amendment Act 1895 as amended by the Appellate Jurisdiction Act 1908 the Judicial Committee also includes the following members:

Floissac, The Rt. Hon. Sir Vincent (St. Lucia)
Zacca, The Rt. Hon. Edward (Jamaica/Bahamas)
Byron, The Rt. Hon. Sir Dennis (Eastern Caribbean Court)
De la Bastide, The Rt. Hon Mr Justice Michael (Caribbean Court of Justice)
Sawyer, The Rt. Hon. Dame Joan (Bahamas)

Acting Registrar of the Privy Council
di Mambro, Mrs L

Chief Clerk
Lindsay, Mrs J A

Second Clerk
Condon, Miss S E

THE MINISTRY OF JUSTICE

102 Petty France, London SW1H 9AJ Tel: 020 3334 3555 Fax: 020 3334 4455 Email: general.queries@justice.gsi.gov.uk Web: www.justice.gov.uk

All email addresses unless indicated are firstname.secondname@justice.gsi.gov.uk

Permanent Secretary
Sir Suma Chakrabarti KCB
Tel: 020 3334 3708

Private Secretary
Ben Connah
Tel: 020 3334 3934

Diary Secretary
Jane Genuardi
Tel: 020 3334 3709

CORPORATE PERFORMANCE GROUP

DIRECTOR GENERALS
Ann Beasley
Tel: 020 3334 6505

Jonathan Slater
Tel: 020 3334 2824

FINANCE GROUP
Director General
Ann Beasley
Tel: 020 3334 6505

DIRECTOR, PROCUREMENT
Vincent Godfrey
Tel:0207 217 5433

DIRECTOR, SHARED SERVICES
Gerry Smith
Tel: 07530 264384

DIRECTOR, FINANCIAL PERFORMANCE
Craig Watkins
Tel: 020 3334 4794

CHIEF INFORMATION OFFICER
Andy Nelson
Tel: 020 3334 6025

DIRECTOR, ICT PROGRAMME & PROJECT DELIVERY
Nick Ramsay
Tel: 020 3334 3224

IT DIRECTOR, ACCESS TO JUSTICE
Paul Shipley
Tel: 020 3334 5363

IT DIRECTOR, HQ & ASSOCIATED OFFICES
Arwa'a Abdulla
Tel: 020 3334 5975

IT DIRECTOR, NATIONAL OFFENDER MANAGEMENT SERVICES
Martin Bellamy
Tel: 020 7217 6156

TRANSFORMING JUSTICE

DIRECTOR GENERAL
Jonathan Slater
Tel: 020 3334 2824

DIRECTOR, HUMAN RESOURCES
Chris Ball
Tel: 020 3334 2659

DIRECTOR, GROUP HR
Neil Hayward
Tel: 020 3334 2679

DIRECTOR, STRATEGIC ESTATES
John Aspinall
Tel: 020 3334 5423

DIRECTOR, STRATEGY AND CHANGE
Peter Thomas
Tel: 020 3334 5280

DIRECTOR, COMMUNICATIONS
Clare Harbord
Tel: 020 3334 3550

ACTING HEAD OF NEWS
Rob Smith
Tel: 020 3334 3505

ACTING DEPUTY HEAD OF NEWS
Simon Steel
Tel: 020 3334 3510

CHIEF PRESS OFFICERS
Debbie Kirby
Tel: 020 3334 3520

Stuart Green
Tel: 020 3334 3509

Fran Murphy
Tel: 020 3334 3532

Victoria Buxton
Tel: 020 3334 3541

Eve Shuttleworth
020 3334 3539

LAWS, RIGHTS AND INTERNATIONAL DESK
Press Officers
Katherine Hyde
Tel: 020 3334 3537

Nicole Valentinuzzi
Tel: 020 3334 3547

CIVIL, FAMILY AND LEGAL AID DESK
Senior Press Officer
Peter Morris
Tel: 020 3334 3531

JUSTICE DESK
Senior Press Officer
Becky Dearden
Tel: 020 3334 3528

Senior Press Officer
Cubby Fox
Tel: 020 3334 3516

OFFENDER MANAGEMENT DESK
Senior Press Officer
Vacant

PROBATION AND PUBLIC PROTECTION DESK

Senior Press Officer
Joanna Jacobson
Tel: 020 3334 3523

LAW, RIGHTS AND INTERNATIONAL

16

DIRECTOR GENERAL
Sharon White
Tel: 020 3334 2296

DIRECTOR, INFORMATION
Belinda Crowe
Tel: 020 3334 3789

DIRECTOR, HUMAN RIGHTS AND INTERNATIONAL
Catriona Laing
Tel: 020 3334 5145

DIRECTORS, LEGAL
Rosemary Davies
Tel: 020 3334 4737

Jane Hill
Tel: 020 3334 4753

DEVOLUTION DIRECTOR GENERAL
Jim Gallagher
020 3334 3009

ACCESS TO JUSTICE

DIRECTOR GENERAL
Peter Handcock CBE
Tel: 020 3334 3012

HMCS OPERATIONS AND PERFORMANCE
Shaun McNally
Tel: 020 3334 4011

DIRECTOR, IT
Paul Shipley
Tel: 020 3334 5363

DIRECTOR, HR
Chris Ball
Tel: 020 3334 2659

CHIEF EXECUTIVE, HER MAJESTY'S COURT SERVICE
Peter Handcock
Tel: 020 3334 3012

CHIEF EXECUTIVE, TRIBUNALS SERVICE
Kevin Sadler
Tel: 020 3334 3400

PUBLIC GUARDIAN AND CHIEF EXECUTIVE, OFFICE OF THE PUBLIC GUARDIAN
Martin John
Tel: 020 7664 7604

HEAD, SPONSORSHIP AND PERFORMANCE UNIT
Pat Lloyd
Tel: 020 3334 4021

NATIONAL OFFENDER MANAGEMENT SERVICE

DIRECTOR GENERAL
Michael Spurr
Tel: 0300 047 5163

CHIEF OPERATING OFFICER
Vacant

DIRECTOR, COMMISSIONING AND OPERATIONAL POLICY
Ian Porée
Tel: 020 7217 2964

DIRECTOR, FINANCE AND PERFORMANCE
Vacant

DIRECTOR, HUMAN RESOURCES
Robin Wilkinson
Tel: 020 7217 2950

DIRECTOR, IT
Martin Bellamy
Tel: 020 7217 6156

DIRECTOR, HIGH SECURITY PRISONS
Danny McAllister CBE
Tel: 020 7217 2888

JUSTICE POLICY GROUP

DIRECTOR GENERAL
Helen Edwards
Tel: 020 3334 6273

CIVIL FAMILY AND LEGAL AID POLICY
Sarah Albon
Tel: 020 3334 6273

CRIMINAL LAW, SENTENCING AND YOUTH JUSTICE POLICY
Helen Judge
Tel: 020 3334 4303

OFFENDER MANAGEMENT STRATEGY
Julie Taylor
Tel: 020 3334 2496

RESEARCH AND ANALYSIS
Rebecca Endean
Tel: 020 3334 3498

OFFICE FOR CRIMINAL JUSTICE REFORM DELIVERY AND COMMUNICATIONS
Catherine Lee
Tel: 020 3334 2250

Crown Office
House of Lords, Westminster, London SW1A 0PW Tel: 020 7219 4687 Website: www.crownoffice.gov.uk

Clerk of the Crown in Chancery
Sir Suma Chakrabarti KCB
Tel: 020 3334 3703
Fax: 020 3334 3710
Email: psecretary1@justice.gsi.gov.uk

Deputy Clerk of the Crown and of the Chamber
Ian Denyer
Tel: 020 7219 4687
Fax: 020 7210 2957
Email: ian.denyer@justice.gsi.gov.uk

ASSOCIATED OFFICES

SCOTLAND OFFICE
Alisdair McIntosh
Tel: 020 7270 6769 / 0131-244 9006

WALES OFFICE
Fiona Adams-Jones
Tel: 020 7270 0558

JUDICIAL OFFICE FOR ENGLAND AND WALES
Anne Sharp
Tel: 020 7947 7960

LAW COMMISSION
Mark Ormerod
Tel: 020 3334 0250

SUPREME COURT
Jenny Rowe
Tel: 020 7960 1906

THE NATIONAL ARCHIVES
Oliver Morley
Tel: 0208 392 5220

OFFICE OF THE OFFICIAL SOLICITORS AND PUBLIC TRUSTEE
Alistair Pitblado
Tel: 020 7911 7116

JUDICIAL STUDIES BOARD
Joint Executive Directors
Magy Piggott / Judith Killick
Tel: 020 3334 0700

EXECUTIVE AGENCIES

HM Courts Service - HMCS
HM Land Registry
National Archives
National Offender Management Service
Office of the Public Guardian
Tribunals Service

Non-Department Public Bodies sponsored by the Ministry of Justice

EXECUTIVE
Criminal Cases Review Commission - CCRC
Criminal Injuries Compensation Authority - CICA
Independent Monitoring Boards of Prisons and Immigration Removal Centres
Judicial Appointments Commission - JAC
Legal Services Board - LSB
Legal Services Commission - LSC
Office of the Information Commisioner
Parole Board for England and Wales
Probation Trusts
Youth Justice Board for England and Wales - YJB

ADVISORY
Administrative Justice and Tribunals Council
Advisory Committee on Civil Costs
Advisory Committees on Justices of the Peace in England and Wales
Advisory Council on National Records and Archives
Advisory Council on Public Sector Information - APPSI
Court Boards
Civil Justice Council
Civil Procedure Rule Committee
Criminal Procedure Rule Committee
Crown Court Rule Committee
Family Justice Council
Family Procedure Rule Committee
Independent Advisory Council on Deaths in Custody
Insolvency Rules Committee
Land Registration Rule Committee
Law Commission
Sentencing Council for England & Wales
Tribunal Procedure Committee
Victims Advisory Panel
Prison Service Pay Review Body

OTHER NON-EXECUTIVE BODIES:
Assessor For Compensation For Miscarriages of Justice - independent statutory
Courts Fund Office - independent statutory
Judicial Appointments and Conduct Ombudsman - independent statutory
Judicial Office of England and Wales - independent (part of MoJ)
Legal Services Ombudsman - independent statutory
Magistrates' Court Rule Committee - other
Office for Judicial Complaints - independent (part of MoJ)
Office of the Legal Services Ombudsman - Independent Statutory
Official Solicitor and Public Trustee - Independent Statutory
Prisons and Probation Ombudsman - Independent non-statutory
HM Inspection of Courts Administration - Independent Statutory
HM Inspectorate of Prisons - Independent Statutory
HM Inspectorate of Probation - Independent Statutory

Public Guardian Board - Independent Statutory Restraint Accreditation Board - Advisory other UK Supreme Court -Non-Ministerial Dept

CROWN PROSECUTION SERVICE

The Crown Prosecution Service (CPS) is the Government Department responsible for prosecuting people in England and Wales who have been charged by the police with a criminal offence. Created by the Prosecution of Offences Act 1985, we are an independent body that works closely with the police.

The head of the Crown Prosecution Service is the Director of Public Prosecutions (the Director) Keir Starmer QC. The CPS is Superintended by the Attorney General, who is responsible to Parliament for the Service.

With headquarters based in London, York and Birmingham, we operate under a structure of 42 geographical Areas in England and Wales. These Areas correspond with the boundaries of 43 police forces in England and Wales with the CPS London Area covering the operational boundaries of both City of London and Metropolitan Police Forces. Each Area is headed by a Chief Crown Prosecutor (CCP) who is responsible for prosecutions within the Area. In London the CCP is supported by London Sector Directors. Although CCP's are directly accountable for their Areas, most of the responsibilities for the efficient and effective administration of the Area fall to the Area Business Managers.

A new 43rd Area, CPS Direct, is also headed by a Chief Crown Prosecutor providing out-of-hours charging advice to the police.

The Crown Prosecution Service is the principal prosecuting authority in England and Wales. We are responsible for advising the police on cases for possible prosecution, reviewing cases submitted by the police, determining the charge in all but minor cases, preparing cases for court and the presentation of cases at court. The role of the Service is to prosecute cases firmly, fairly and effectively when there is sufficient evidence to provide a realistic prospect of conviction and when it is in the public interest to do so.

Headquarters (London)
50 Ludgate Hill, London EC4M 7EX Tel: 020 7796 8000, Public Enquiry Point Tel: 020 7796 8500, DX: 300850 LUDGATE EC4 Email:enquiries@cps.gsi.gov.uk, complaints@cps.gsi.gov.uk, Website: www.cps.gov.uk

Director of Public Prosecutions
Starmer, Q.C., Keir

Chief Executive
Lewis, Peter

Principal Legal Adviser
Levitt, Alison

Director of Policy
Hunt, Nick

Head of Organised Crime
Milford, Alun

Head of Special Crime Division
Clements, Simon

Head of Counter-Terrorism
Hemming, Sue

Director, Business Information Systems
Jones, David

Director, Human Resources
Summerfield, Mark

Director, Finance
Staff, Paul

Chief Operating Officer, Operations
Kennedy, Mike

Head of Strategic Communication
Teare, Pam

CHIEF CROWN PROSECUTORS (Area Offices)

Avon and Somerset
Hughes, Barry
Tel: 0117 930 2859 Fax: 0117 930 2806 DX: 78120 BRISTOL

Bedfordshire
Newcombe, Richard
Tel: 01582 816601 Fax: 01582 816678 DX: 120503 LUTON 6

Cambridgeshire
Ferguson, Frank
Tel: 01480 825201 Fax: 01480 825205 DX: 123223 HUNTINGDON 5

Cheshire
Lindley, Claire
Tel: 01244 408614 Fax: 01244 408660 DX: 20019 CHESTER

Cleveland
Wareham, Gerry
Tel: 01642 204501 Fax: 01642 204502 DX: 60551 MIDDLESBROUGH 12

Cumbria
Long, Christopher
Tel: 01228 882902 Fax: 01228 882927 DX: 63032 CARLISLE

Derbyshire
Gunn, Brian
Tel: 01332 614002 Fax: 01332 614009 DX: 725818 DERBY 22

Devon and Cornwall
Easton, Tracy
Tel: 01392 288010 Fax: 01392 288008 DX: 135606 EXETER 16

Dorset
Brown, Kate
Tel: 01202 498702 Fax: 01202 498860 DX: 7699 BOURNEMOUTH

Durham
Enzor, Chris
Tel: 0191 383 5825 Fax: 0191 383 5801 DX: 60227 DURHAM

Dyfed Powys
Jenkins, Iwan
Tel: 01267 242108 Fax: 01267 242133 DX: 742440 CARMARTHEN 9

Essex
Caley, Ken
Tel: 01245 455801 Fax: 01245 455964 DX: 139160 CHELMSFORD 11

Gloucestershire
Cook, Victoria
Tel: 01452 872401 Fax: 01452 872406 DX: 7544 GLOUCESTER

Greater Manchester
Holt, John
Tel: 0161 827 4702 Fax: 0161 827 4932 DX: 710288 MANCHESTER 3

Gwent
Brisbane, Jim
Tel: 01633 261101 Fax: 01633 261106 DX: 743270 CWMBRAN 4

Hampshire & Isle of White
Hawkins, Nick
Tel: 023 8067 3866 Fax: 023 8067 3854 DX: 148581 EASTLEIGH 4

Hertfordshire
Robinson, David
Tel: 01727 798766 Fax: 01727 798796 DX: 120650 ST ALBANS 7

Humberside
Petchey, Barbara
Tel: 01482 621004 Fax: 01482 621003 DX: 743480 Hull 21

Kent
Coe-Salazar, Roger
Tel: 01622 356318 Fax: 01622 356340 DX: 4830 MAIDSTONE

Lancashire
Rushton, Ian
Tel: 01772 208100 Fax: 01772 278277 DX: 723740 PRESTON 20

Leicestershire
Crowley, Richard
Tel: 0116 222 2222 Fax: 0116 262 4713 DX: 10899 LEICESTER 1

Lincolnshire
Chappell, Steve
Tel: 01522 585902 Fax: 01522 585959 DX: 15562 LINCOLN 4

London
Saunders, Alison
Tel: 020 7796 8653 Fax: 020 77103447 DX: 300850 LUDGATE EC4

Merseyside
Whittaker, Paul
Tel: 0151 239 6435 Fax: 0151 239 6410 DX: 700596 LIVERPOOL 4

Norfolk
Baxter, Andrew
Tel: 01603 693002 Fax: 01603 693001 DX: 5299 NORWICH

Northamptonshire
Richardson, Patricia
Tel: 01604 823686 Fax: 01604 823669 DX: 18512 NORTHAMPTON

Northumbria
Williams, Wendy
Tel: 0191 260 4228 Fax: 0191 260 4241 DX: 61006 NEWCASTLE UPON TYNE

North Wales
Price, Nick
Tel: 01978 436031 Fax: 01978 346069 DX: 723100 WREXHAM 5

North Yorkshire
Tait, Xanthe
Tel: 01904 731760 Fax: 01904 731764 DX: 729960 YORK 29

Nottinghamshire
Walker, Judith
Tel: 0115 852 3311 Fax: 0115 852 3314 DX: 729100 NOTTINGHAM 48

South Wales
Brisbane, Jim
Tel: 029 2080 3901 Fax: 029 2080 3906 DX: 33056 CARDIFF 1

South Yorkshire
Hussain, Naheed
Tel: 0114 229 8605 Fax: 0114 229 8606 DX: 711830 SHEFFIELD 18

Staffordshire
Beltrami, Ed
Tel: 01782 664560 Fax: 01782 664555 DX: 701706 HANLEY 2

Suffolk
Abrahams, Paula
Tel: 01473 282144 Fax: 01473 282101 DX: 3266 IPSWICH

Surrey
Ragnauth, Portia
Tel: 01483 468205 Fax: 01483 468202 DX: 122041 GUILDFORD 10

Sussex
Narwal, Jaswant
Tel: 01273 765602 Fax: 01273 765607 DX: 149840 HOVE 6

Thames Valley
Ubhey, Baljit
Tel: 01189 513265 Fax: 01235 551971 DX: 40104 READING

Warwickshire
Siddique, Zafar
Tel: 01926 455000 Fax: 01926 455003 DX: 11881 LEAMINGTON SPA

West Mercia
Chapman, Colin
Tel: 01905 825001 Fax: 01905 825100 DX: 179491 DROITWICH 4

West Midlands
Ireland, Harry
Tel: 0121 262 1301 Fax: 0121 262 1307 DX: 719540 BIRMINGHAM 45

West Yorkshire
Franklin, Neil
Tel: 0113 290 2962 Fax: 0113 290 2707 DX: 26435 LEEDS PARK SQUARE

Wiltshire
Montague, John
Tel: 01249 766111 Fax: 01249 766102 DX: 98644 CHIPPENHAM 2

CPS Direct
Goldman, Martin
Tel: 01904 545594
Fax: 01904 545698
DX: 65204 YORK 6

THE ROYAL COURTS OF JUSTICE

The Strand, London, WC2A 2LL Tel: 020 7947 6000

Director
Thompson, D

THE SUPREME COURT OF THE UNITED KINGDOM

The Supreme Court is now the final court of appeal for all United Kingdom civil cases, and criminal cases from England, Wales and Northern Ireland. It replaced the Appellate Committee of the House of Lords in October 2009 and hears appeals on arguable points of law, concentrating on cases of the greatest public and constitutional importance.

Justices of the Supreme Court
The Rt. Hon Lord Phillips
The Rt. Hon Lord Hope
The Rt. Hon Lord Rodger
The Rt. Hon Lord Walker
The Rt. Hon Baroness Hale
The Rt. Hon Lord Brown
The Rt. Hon Lord Mance
The Rt. Hon Lord Collins
The Rt. Hon Lord Kerr
The Rt. Hon Lord Clarke

Chief Executive
Rowe, Jenny

Registrar
di Mambro, Louise

COURT OF APPEAL

EX-OFFICIO JUDGES

The Lord Chief Justice of England & Wales
The Master of the Rolls
The President of the Queen's Bench Division
The President of the Family Division
The Chancellor of the High Court

The Lord Chief Justice of England & Wales
The Rt. Hon. Lord Judge (2008)
Clerk: Francis, Mrs L

Private Secretary
Jeffery, Ms A

Senior Personal Secretary
Souris, Miss M

The Master of the Rolls
Clarke, The Rt. Hon. Sir David Neuberger
Clerk: Lister, Mr G

Private Secretary
Farr, Mr P

Senior Personal Secretary
Roberts, Ms N

Lords Justice
Pill, The Rt. Hon. Sir Malcolm Thomas (1995)
Ward, The Rt. Hon. Sir Alan Hilton (1995)
Thorpe, Sir Mathew Alexander (Deputy Head of Family Justice and Head of International Family Law) (1995)
Mummery, The Rt. Hon. Sir John Frank (1996)
Laws, The Rt. Hon. Sir John Grant McKenzie (1999)
Sedley, The Rt. Hon. Sir Stephen John (1999)
Rix, The Rt. Hon. Sir Bernard Anthony (2000)
Arden, Dame Mary Howarth, DBE (2000)
Longmore, The Rt. Hon. Sir Andrew Centlivres (2001)
Carnwath, The Rt. Hon. Sir Robert John Anderson, CVO (Senior President of Tribunals) (2002)
Smith, Dame Janet Hilary, DBE (2002)
Thomas, The Rt. Hon. Sir Roger John Laughame (Vice-President of the Queen's Bench Division) (2003)
Jacob, The Rt. Hon. Sir Robert Raphael Hayim (Robin) (2003)
Kay, The Rt. Hon. Sir Maurice Ralph (Vice-President Civil Division of the Court of Appeal) (2004)
Hooper, The Rt. Hon. Sir Anthony (2004)
Lloyd, The Rt. Hon. Sir Timothy Andrew Wigram (2005)
Moore-Bick, The Rt. Hon. Sir Martin James (Deputy Head of Civil Justice) (2005)
Wilson, The Rt. Hon. Sir Nicholas Allan Roy (2005)
Moses, The Rt. Hon. Sir Alan George (2005)
Richards, The Rt. Hon. Sir Stephen Price (2005)
Hallett, Dame Heather Carol, DBE (Chair of the Judicial Studies Board) (2005)
Hughes, The Rt. Hon. Sir Anthony Philip Gilson (Vice-President, Criminal Division of the Court of Appeal) (2006)
Leveson, The Rt. Hon. Sir Brian Henry (Chairman of the Sentencing Council) (2006)
Toulson, The Rt. Hon. Sir Roger Grenfell (2007)
Rimer, The Rt. Hon. Sir Colin Percy Farquharson (2007)
Burnton, The Rt. Hon. Sir Stanley Jeffrey (2008)
Etherton, The Rt. Hon. Sir Terence Michael Elkan Barnet (2008)
Jackson, The Rt. Hon. Sir Rupert Matthew (2008)
Goldring, The Rt. Hon. Sir John Bernard (The Senior Presiding Judge) (2008)
Aikens, The Rt. Hon. Sir Richard John Pearson (2008)
Sullivan, The Rt. Hon. Sir Jeremy Mirth (2009)
Elias, The Rt. Hon. Sir Patrick (2009)
Patten, Sir Nicholas John (2009)
Munby, Sir James Lawrence (Chairman of the Law Commission) (2009)
Pitchford, Sir Christopher John (2010)
Black, Dame Jill Margaret, D.B.E. (2010)
Tomlinson, Sir Stephen Miles (2010)
Gross, Sir Peter Henry (2010)

COURT OF APPEAL CIVIL DIVISION

Royal Courts of Justice, Room E307, The Strand, WC2A 2LL Tel: 020 7947 7882 Fax: 020 7947 6740 DX: RCJ 44450 Strand

Head of Civil Appeals
Venne, Roger

COURT OF APPEAL CRIMINAL DIVISION & COURTS-MARTIAL APPEAL COURT

Royal Courts of Justice, The Strand, London WC2A 2LL Tel: 020 7947 6000 DX: RCJ 44450 Strand

Registrar
Master Venne

HIGH COURT OF JUSTICE

CHANCERY DIVISION

The Chancellor of the High Court
Morritt, The Rt. Hon. Sir Robert Andrew, CVO (2000)
Clerk: Glasgow, Ms S

Private Secretary
Bancroft-Rimmer, Miss M

Senior Personal Secretary
Harbert, Miss E

Chancery Judges
Smith, The Hon. Sir Peter Winston (2002)
Lewison, The Hon. Sir Kim Martin Jordan (2003)
Richards, The Hon. Sir David Anthony Stewart (2003)
Mann, The Hon. Sir George Anthony (2004)
Warren, The Hon. Sir Nicholas Roger (2005)
Kitchin, The Hon. Sir David James Tyson (2005)
Briggs, The Hon. Sir Michael Townley Featherstone (2006)
Henderson, The Hon. Sir Launcelot Dinadin James (2007)
Morgan, The Hon. Sir Paul Hyacinth (2007)
Norris, The Hon. Sir Alastair Hubert (2007)
Barling, The Hon. Sir Gerald Edward (2007)
Floyd, The Hon. Sir Christopher David (2007)
Sales, The Hon. Sir Philip James (2008)
Proudman, Dame Rosemary Susan (2008)
Arnold, The Hon. Sir Richard David (2008)
Roth, The Hon. Sir Peter Marcel (2009)
Vos, The Hon. Sir Geoffrey Charles (2009)
Newey, The Hon. Sir Guy Richard (2010)

Chancery Listing Officer
Bell, D A (Room WG04)

Chancery Chambers Registry
Thomas More Building, Royal Courts of Justice, The Strand, London WC2A 2LL Tel: 020 7947 6148 Fax: 020 947 7422 DX: RCJ 44450 Strand

Chief Master
Winegarten, J I

Masters
Moncaster, J A
Bragge, N W
Bowles, T J
Price, N S
Teverson, P

Head of Chancery Operations
Stickings, S

Court Manager Chancery Chambers
O'Brien, Mrs P

Deputy Court Manager
Uddin, M

Offices
Thomas More Building, Royal Courts of Justice, The Strand, London WC2A 2LL DX: RCJ 44450 Strand

Judges of the Court of Appeal in Bankruptcy
The Master of The Rolls

The Lords Justices and Other Members of The Court of Appeal

Judges
Rt. Hon. The Vice-Chancellor
Blackburne, The Hon. Sir William Anthony
Smith,The Hon Sir Peter Winston
Lewison, The Hon Sir Kim Martin Jordan
Richards, The Hon Sir David Anthony Stewart
Mann, The Hon Sir George Anthony
Warren, The Hon Sir Nicholas Roger
Kitchin, The Hon Sir David James Tyson
Briggs, The Hon Sir Michael Townley Featherstone
Henderson, The Hon Sir Launcelot Dinadin James
Morgan, The Hon Sir Paul Hyacinth
Norris, The Hon Sir Alastair Hubert
Barling, The Hon Sir Gerald Edward
Floyd, The Hon Sir Christopher David
Sales, The Hon Sir Philip James
Proudman, Dame Rosemary Susan
Arnold, The Hon Sir Richard David
Tomlinson, The Hon Sir Stephen Miles
Gross, The Hon. Sir Peter Henry

BANKRUPTCY AND COMPANIES COURT

Chief Registrar
Baister, S

Registrars
Simmonds, J
Jacques, G
Derrett, C
Nicholls, P
Barber, S A

Head of Chancery Operations
Stickings, S

Court Manager
O'Brien, Mrs P

Operational Manager Bankruptcy
Walker, S

Operational Manager Companies
Langdon, L

Companies Case Worker
Butcher, B

Taxing Master
One of the Taxing Masters of the Supreme Court

COURT OF PROTECTION

Office
Archway Tower, 2 Junction Road, London N19 5SZ Tel: 0300 456 4600 Fax: 020 7664 7705

Senior Judge
Lush, D

District Judges
Ralton, A
Eldergill, A
Hilder, C
Batten, E

Court Manager
Bradshaw, G

Deputy Court Managers
Batey, J
Hamilton, R
Prempeh, F

THE INSOLVENCY SERVICE

Office
21 Bloomsbury Street, London WC1B 3SS Tel: 0845602 9848

Regional Directors

Anglia
Smith, A
2nd Floor, Abbeygate House, 164-167 East Road, Cambridge CB1 1DB Tel: 01223 445323 Fax: 01223 445320

South East
Chapman, D A
5th Floor, Zone C, 21 Bloomsbury Street, London WC1B 3SS Tel: 020 7637 6397 Fax: 020 7291 6889

Midlands
Howard, K J
4th Floor West, Wellington House, Wellington Street, Leicester LE1 6HL Tel: 0116 279 5840 Fax: 0116 279 5833

North East
Mcreath, C
3rd Floor, 1 City Walk, Leeds LS11 9DA Tel: 0113 200 6000 Fax: 0113 200 6099

North West
Evison, R J
2nd Floor, 3 Piccadilly Place, London Road, Manchester M1 3BN Tel: 0161 234 8452 Fax: 0161 234 8500

South West
Ashcroft, P A
3rd Floor, Senate Court, Southernhay Gardens, Exeter, EX1 1UG Tel: 01392 436886 Fax: 01392 889675

London / Public Interest Unit
Chapman, D A
5th Floor, Zone C, 21 Bloomsbury Street, London WC1B 3SS Tel: 020 7637 6397 Fax: 020 7291 6889

QUEEN'S BENCH DIVISION

The President of the Queen's Bench Division
May, The Rt. Hon. Sir Anthony Tristram Kenneth (2008)
Clerk: McDonald, Mrs G

Private Secretary
Parker, Mr J

Senior Personal Secretary
Fidler, Miss M

Judges
McKinnon, The Hon Sir Stuart Neil (1988)
Collins, The Hon Sir Andrew David (1994)
Butterfield, The Hon Sir Alexander Neil Logie (1995)
Eady, The Hon Sir David (1997)
Penry-Davey, The Hon Sir David Herbert (1997)
Steel, The Hon Sir David William (1998)
Bratza, The Hon Sir Nicholas Dusan (Judge of the European Court of Human Rights) (1998)
Burton, The Hon Sir Michael John (1998)
Silber, The Hon Sir Stephen Robert (1999)
Rafferty, Dame Ann Judith, DBE (2000)
Henriques, The Hon Sir Richard Henry Quixano (2000)
Smith, The Hon Sir Andrew Charles (2000)
Pitchford, The Hon Sir Christopher John (2000)
Ouseley, The Hon Sir Duncan Brian Walter (2000)
McCombe, The Hon Sir Richard George Bramwell (2001)
Jack, The Hon Sir Raymond Evan (2001)
Owen, The Hon Sir Robert Michael (2001)
Mackay, The Hon Sir Colin Crichton (2001)
Mitting, The Hon Sir John Edward (2001)
Evans, The Hon Sir David Roderick (2001)
Davis, The Hon Sir Nigel Anthony Lamert (2001)
Keith, The Hon Sir Brian Richard (2001)
Cooke, The Hon Sir Jeremy Lionel (2001)
Field, The Hon Sir Richard Alan (2002)
Treacy, The Hon Sir Colman Maurice (2002)
Simon, The Hon Sir Peregrine Charles Hugo (2002)
Royce, Sir Roger John (2002)
Cox, Dame Laura Mary, DBE (2002)
Fulford, The Hon Sir Adrian Bruce (2002)
Beatson, The Hon Sir Jack (2003)
Tugendhat, The Hon Sir Michael George (2003)
Clarke, The Hon Sir David Clive (2003)
Gloster, Dame Elizabeth, DBE (2004)
Bean, The Hon Sir David Michael (2004)
Wilkie, The Hon Sir Alan Fraser (2004)
Dobbs, Dame Linda Penelope, DBE (2004)
Walker, The Hon Sir Paul James (2004)
Calvert-Smith, The Hon Sir David (2005)
Clarke, The Hon Sir Christopher Simon Courternay Stephenson (2005)
Openshaw, The Hon Sir Charles Peter Lawford (2005)
Swift, Dame Caroline Jane, DBE (2005)
Langstaff, The Hon Sir Brian Frederick James (2005)
Lloyd Jones, The Hon Sir David (2005)
Ramsey, The Hon Sir Vivian Arthur (2005)
Underhill, The Hon Sir Nicholas Edward (2006)
Irwin, The Hon Sir Stephen John (2006)
Teare, The Hon Sir Nigel John Martin (2006)
Williams, The Hon Sir John Griffith (2007)
Williams, The Hon Sir Wyn Lewis (2007)
King, The Hon Sir Timothy Roger Alan (2007)
Saunders, The Hon Sir John Henry Boulton (2007)
Flaux, The Hon Sir Julian Martin (2007)
Stadlen, The Hon Nicholas Felix (2007)
Akenhead, The Hon Robert (2007)
Foskett, The Hon David Robert (2007)
Blake, The Hon Sir Nicholas John Gorrod (2007)
Cranston, The Hon Sir Ross Frederick (2007)
Coulson, The Hon Sir Peter David William (2008)
Maddison, The Hon Sir David (2008)
Plender, The Hon Sir Richard Owen (2008)
Blair, The Hon Sir William James Lynton (2008)
MacDuff, The Hon Sir Alistair Geoffrey (2008)
Burnett, The Hon Sir Ian Duncan (2008)
Slade, Dame Elizabeth Ann DBE (2008)
Hamblen, The Hon Sir Nicholas Archibald (2008)
Hickinbottom, The Hon Sir Gary Robert (2009)
Holroyde, The Hon Sir Timothy Victor (2009)
Sharp, Dame Victoria Madeline DBE (2009)
Nicol, The Hon Andrew George Lindsay (2009)
Edwards-Stuart, The Hon Sir Antony James Cobham (2009)

Senior Master & Queen's Remembrancer
Whitaker, S

PA Senior Master
Edwards, Miss C

Masters
Leslie, H J
Yoxall, B J
Fontaine, B J
Eyre, P G A
Roberts, R J L
Eastman, R
Kay, R J
McCloud, V
Foster, I H

Masters Secretary
Osei-Asiamah, Miss J

Head of Court Support (QBD Administrative Court)
Fairweather, Mr K

Court Manager
Ryan, Mrs J

Deputy Court Manager
Pycock, Mr S

ADMIRALTY, COMMERCIAL & MERCANTILE COURT

Office
East Block Basement, Royal Courts of Justice, The Strand WC2A 2LL DX: RCJ 44450 Strand

Registrar
Kay, J

Admiralty Marshal and Court Manager
Houghton, K

Listing Officer
Hodgson, A

FAMILY DIVISION

President
Wall, The Rt. Hon. Sir Nicholas (2005)

Private Secretary
Sprague, Miss S

Clerk
Curtis, Mr J

Secretary
Leung, Ms S

Judges
Singer, The Hon. Sir Jan Peter John (1993)
Bennett, The Hon. Sir Hugh Peter Derwyn (1995)
Holman, The Hon. Sir Edward James (1995)
Hogg, Dame Mary Claire, DBE (1995)
Charles, The Hon. Sir Arthur William Hessin (1998)
Bodey, The Hon. Sir David Roderick Lessiter (1999)
Coleridge, The Hon. Sir Paul James Duke (2000)
Hedley, The Hon. Sir Mark (2002)
Pauffley, Dame Anna Evelyn Hamilton, DBE (2003)
Wood, The Hon. Sir Roderic Lionel James (2004)
Baron, Dame Florence Jacquelene, DBE (2004)
Ryder, The Hon. Sir Ernest Nigel (2004)
McFarlane, The Hon. Sir Andrew Ewart (2005)
Macur, Dame Julia Wendy, DBE (2005)
Moylan, The Hon. Sir Andrew Gregory (2007)
King, Dame Eleanor Warwick, DBE (2008)
Parker, Dame Judith Mary Frances, DBE (2008)
Baker, The Hon Sir Jonathan Leslie (2009)
Mostyn, The Hon Sir Nicholas Anthony Joseph Ghislain (2010)
Jackson, The Hon Sir Peter Arthur Brian (2010)

Office
Principal Registry of the Family Division, First Avenue House, 42-49 High Holborn, London WC1V 6NP Tel: 020 7947 6000

Family Court Manager
Risk, J (Acting in place of Munro, R)

Senior District Judge
Waller, P A

District Judges
Aitken, Mrs A E
Bassett-Cross, A R
Berry, M C
Bowman, Miss S M
Bradley, Miss H C
Cushing, Miss P
Gibson, Y
Gordon-Saker, L
Greene, P L
Harper, R S
Hess, E
MacGregor, Mrs H M
Malik, K T
Redgrave, Mrs D
Reid, Mrs C O
Roberts, Mrs L D

Robinson, R J
Simmonds, C
Walker, S M
White, K J

Clerk of The Rules and Orders
Bowstead, Miss C

Queen's Proctor
Nursaw, J

Assistant Queen's Proctor
Hood, I

Probate Service
Thomas More Building, Royal Courts of Justice, Strand, London WC2A 2LL Tel: 020 7947 7389

Director, Probate Service
Smith, H

THE CROWN COURT

CROWN COURT & OFFICE ADDRESSES

*Combined Court Centre

Circuit

Aylesbury Crown Court ....SE
County Hall, Market Square, Aylesbury, Buckinghamshire HP20 1XD Tel: 01296 434401 Fax: 01296 435665 DX: 157430 AYLESBURY 11

*Basildon Combined Court ....SE
The Gore, Basildon, Essex SS14 2BU Tel: 01268 458000 Fax: 01268 458100 DX: 97633 BASILDON 5

Birmingham Crown Court ....M
Queen Elizabeth II Law Courts, 1 Newton Street, Birmingham, West Midlands B4 7NA Tel: 0121 681 3300 Fax: 0121 681 3370 DX: 702033 BIRMINGHAM 8

Blackfriars Crown Court......................London
1-15 Pocock Street, London SE1 0BJ Tel: 020 7922 5800 Fax: 020 7922 5827 DX: 400800 LAMBETH 3

*Bolton Combined Court Centre ....NW
The Law Courts, Blackhorse Street, Bolton, Greater Manchester BL1 1SU Tel: 01204 392881 Fax: 01204 363204 DX: 702610 BOLTON 3

Bournemouth Crown Court......................SW
Courts of Justice, Deansleigh Road, Bournemouth, Dorset BH7 7DS Tel: 01202 502800 Fax: 01202 502801 DX: 98420 BOURNEMOUTH 4

*Bradford Combined Court Centre ....NE
Bradford Law Courts, Exchange Square, Drake Street, Bradford, West Yorkshire BD1 1JA Tel: 01274 840274 Fax: 01274 840275 DX: 702083 BRADFORD 2

Bristol Crown Court.................................SW
The Law Courts, Small Street, Bristol BS1 1DA Tel: 0117 976 3030 Fax: 0117 976 3026 DX: 78128 BRISTOL

*Burnley Combined Court Centre ....NW
The Law Courts, Hammerton Street, Burnley, Lancashire BB11 1XD Tel: 01282 855300 Fax: 01282 414911 DX: 724940 BURNLEY 4

Bury St Edmunds Crown Court.................SE
Shire Hall, Bury St Edmunds, Suffolk IP33 1HF Tel: 01473 228585 Fax: 01473 228560

Caernarfon Crown Court ....Wales
Caernarfon Criminal Justice Centre, Llanberis Road, Caernarfon, Gwynedd LL55 2DF Tel: 01352 707340 Fax: 01352 753874 DX: 744382 CAERNARFON 6

Cambridge Crown Court ....SE
The Court House, 83 East Road, Cambridge, Cambridgeshire CB1 1BT Tel: 01223 488321 Fax: 01223 488333 DX: 97365 CAMBRIDGE 2

*Canterbury Combined Court Centre.........SE
Canterbury Combined Court, The Law Courts, Chaucer Road, Canterbury, Kent CT1 1ZA Tel: 01227 819200 Fax: 01227 819329 DX: 99710 CANTERBURY 3

Cardiff Crown Court ....Wales
The Law Courts, Cathays Park, Cardiff, South Wales CF10 3PG Tel: 029 2067 8730 Fax: 029 2067 8732 DX: 99450 CARDIFF 5

*Carlisle Combined Court Centre ....NW
Courts of Justice, Earl Street, Carlisle, Cumbria CA1 1DJ Tel: 01228 882120 Fax: 01228 590588 DX: 65331 CARLISLE 2

Carmarthen Crown Court ....Wales
The Guildhall, Guildhall Square, Carmarthen, Carmarthenshire SA31 1PR Tel: 01792 637000 Fax: 01792 637049

Central Criminal Court.......................London
Old Bailey, London EC4M 7EH Tel: 020 7248 3277 Fax: 020 7192 2671 DX: 46700 OLD BAILEY

Chelmsford Crown Court ....SE
PO Box 9, New Street, Chelmsford, Essex CM1 1EL Tel: 01245 603000 Fax: 01245 603011 DX: 97375 CHELMSFORD 3

Chester Crown Court..............................NW
The Castle, Chester, Cheshire CH1 2AN DX: 702527 CHESTER 5

*Chichester Combined Court Centre ....SE
Southgate, Chichester, West Sussex PO19 1SX Tel: 01243 520742 Fax: 01243 538252 DX: 97460 CHICHESTER 2

*Coventry Combined Court Centre ....M
140 Much Park Street, Coventry, West Midlands CV1 2SN Tel: 024 7653 6166 Fax: 024 7652 0443 DX: 701580 COVENTRY 5

Croydon Crown Court.........................London
The Law Courts, Altyre Road, Croydon, Surrey CR9 5AB Tel: 020 8410 4700 Fax: 020 8781 1007 DX: 97473 CROYDON 6

*Derby Combined Court Centre ....M
Morledge, Derby, Derbyshire DE1 2XE Tel: 01332 622600 Fax: 01332 622543 DX: 724060 DERBY 21

Dolgellau Crown Court ....Wales
The County Hall, Dolgellau, Gwynedd Tel: 01352 707340 Fax: 01352 753874

Doncaster Crown Court..........................NE
College Road, Doncaster, South Yorkshire DN1 3HS Tel: 01302 322211 Fax: 01302 329471 DX: 703001 DONCASTER 5

Dorchester Crown Court.........................SW
County Hall, Colliston Park, Dorchester, Dorset DT1 1XJ Tel: 01305 265867 Fax: 01305 251867

Durham Crown Court...............................NE
The Law Courts, Old Elvet, Durham, County Durham DH1 3HW Tel: 0191 386 6714 Fax: 0191 383 0605 DX: 65112 DURHAM 4

*Exeter Combined Court Centre ....SW
Southernhay Gardens, Exeter, Devon EX1 1UH Tel: 01392 415300 Fax: 01392 415642 DX: 98440 EXETER 2

Gloucester Crown Court ....SW
Gloucestershire Crown Courthouse, Longsmith Street, Gloucester, Gloucestershire GL1 2TS Tel: 01452 420100 Fax: 01452 833557

*Great Grimsby Combined Court Centre...NE
Town Hall Square, Grimsby, Lincolnshire DN31 1HX Tel: 01472 265250 Fax: 01472 265251 DX: 702007 GRIMSBY 3

Guildford Crown Court ....SE
Bedford Road, Guildford, Surrey GU1 4ST Tel: 01483 468500 Fax: 01483 579545 DX: 97862 GUILDFORD 5

Harrow Crown Court..........................London
Hailsham Drive, off Headstone Drive, Harrow HA1 4TU Tel: 020 8424 2294 Fax: 020 8424 2209 DX: 97335 HARROW 5

Hereford Crown Court ....M
The Shirehall, St Peter's Square, Hereford, Herefordshire HR1 2HY Tel: 01432 276118 Fax: 01432 274350 DX: 719262 WORCESTER 1

Inner London Crown Court ....London
Sessions House, Newington Causeway, London SE1 6AZ Tel: 020 7234 3100 Fax: 020 7234 3287 DX: 97345 SOUTHWARK 3

Ipswich Crown Court................................SE
The Courthouse, 1 Russell Road, Ipswich Suffolk IP1 2AG Tel: 01473 228585 Fax: 01473 228560 DX: 729480 IPSWICH 19

Isleworth Crown Court.......................London
36 Ridgeway Road, Isleworth, London TW7 5LP Tel: 020 8380 4500 Fax: 020 8568 5368 DX: 97420 ISLEWORTH 1

King's Lynn Crown Court ....SE
The Court House, College Lane, King's Lynn, Norfolk PE30 1PQ Tel: 01553 760847 Fax: 01553 772873

*Kingston-upon-Hull Combined Court Centre. ....NE
Lowgate, Humberside HU1 2EZ Tel: 01482 586161 Fax: 01482 588527 DX: 703010 HULL 5

Kingston-upon-Thames Crown Court ....London
6-8 Penrhyn Road, Kingston-upon-Thames, Surrey KT1 2BB Tel: 020 8240 2500 Fax: 020 8240 2675 DX: 97430 KINGSTON-UPON-THAMES 2

Knutsford Crown Court ....NW
Sessions House, Toft Road, Knutsford, Cheshire WA16 0PB Tel: 01565 624020 Fax: 01565 624029

16

Lancaster Crown Court............................NW
Castle Hill, Lancaster, Lancashire LA1 1YJ Tel: 01772 844700 Fax: 01772 832476

*Leeds Combined Court Centre ....NE
The Court House, 1 Oxford Row, Leeds, West Yorkshire LS1 3BG Tel: 0113 306 2800 DX: 703016 LEEDS 6

Leicester Crown Court ....M
90 Wellington Street, Leicester, Leicestershire LE1 6HG Tel: 0116 222 5800 Fax: 0116 222 5888 DX: 10880 LEICESTER 3

*Lewes Combined Court Centre ....SE
The Law Courts, High Street, Lewes, East Sussex BN7 1YB Tel: 01273 480400 Fax: 01273 485269 DX: 97395 LEWES 4

Lincoln Crown Court ....M
The Castle, Castle Hill, Lincoln, Lincolnshire LN1 3GA Tel: 01522 525222 Fax: 01522 543962 DX: 722500 LINCOLN 11

Liverpool Crown Court.............................NW
The Queen Elizabeth II Law Courts, Derby Square, Liverpool, Merseyside L2 1XA Tel: 0151 473 7373 Fax: 0151 471 1000 DX: 740880 LIVERPOOL 22

Luton Crown Court....................................SE
7 George Street, Luton, Bedfordshire LU1 2AA Tel: 01582 522000 Fax: 01582 522001 DX: 120500 LUTON 6

*Maidstone Combined Court Centre..........SE
The Law Courts, Barker Road, Maidstone, Kent ME16 8EQ Tel: 01622 202000 Fax: 01622 202001 DX: 130065 MAIDSTONE 7

Manchester Crown Court (Crown Square) ....NW
Courts of Justice, Crown Square, Manchester, Greater Manchester M3 3FL Tel: 0161 954 1800 Fax: 0161 954 1705 DX: 702538 MANCHESTER 11

Manchester Crown Court (Minshull St) ....NW
The Court House, Minshull Street, Manchester, Greater Manchester M1 3FS Tel: 0161 954 7500 Fax: 0161 954 7600 DX: 724860 MANCHESTER 43

*Merthyr Tydfil Combined Court Centre.......... ....Wales
The Law Courts, Glebeland Place, Merthyr Tydfil, South Wales CF47 8BH Tel: 01685 727600 Fax: 01685 727703 DX: 99582 MERTHYR TYDFIL 2

Mold Crown Court.................................Wales
The Law Courts, Mold, Flintshire CH7 1AE Tel: 01352 707340 Fax: 01352 753874 DX: 702521 MOLD 2

*Newcastle-upon-Tyne Combined Court Centre ....NE
The Law Courts, The Quayside, Newcastle-upon-Tyne, Tyne & Wear NE1 3LA Tel: 0191 201 2000 Fax: 0191 201 2001 DX: 65127 NEWCASTLE-UPON-TYNE 2

*Newport (Isle of Wight) Crown and County Court ....SW
The Law Courts, 1 Quay Street, Newport, Isle of Wight PO30 5YT Tel: 01983 535 100 Fax: 01983 554 977 DX: 98460 NEWPORT IW2

Newport (South Wales) Crown Court ...Wales
The Law Courts, Faulkner Road, Newport, Gwent NP20 4PR Tel: 01633 266211 Fax: 01633 216824 DX: 99460 NEWPORT 1/2

*Northampton Combined Court ....M
85/87 Lady's Lane, Northampton, Northamptonshire NN1 3HQ Tel: 01604 470400 Fax: 01604 232398 DX: 725380 NORTHAMPTON 21

*Norwich Combined Court Centre ....SE
The Law Courts, Bishopgate, Norwich, Norfolk NR3 1UR Tel: 01603 728200 Fax: 01603 760863 DX: 97385 NORWICH 5

Nottingham Crown Court ....M
60 Canal Street, Nottingham, Nottinghamshire NG1 7EL Tel: 0115 910 3551 Fax: 0115 910 3599 DX: 702383 NOTTINGHAM 7

*Oxford Combined Court Centre................SE
St Aldates, Oxford, Oxfordshire OX1 1TL Tel: 01865 264200 Fax: 01865 264253 DX: 96450 OXFORD 4

*Peterborough Combined Court Centre.....SE
Crown Buildings, Rivergate, Peterborough, Cambridgeshire PE1 1EJ Tel: 01733 349161 Fax: 01733 891563 DX: 702302 PETERBOROUGH 8

*Plymouth Combined Court ....SW
The Law Courts, 10 Armada Way, Plymouth, Devon PL1 2ER Tel: 01752 677400 Fax: 01752 208292 DX: 98470 PLYMOUTH 7

*Portsmouth Combined Court Centre.......SW
The Courts of Justice, Winston Churchill Avenue, Portsmouth, Hampshire PO1 2EB Tel: 023 9289 3000 Fax: 023 9282 6385 DX: 98490 PORTSMOUTH 5

*Preston Combined Court Centre.............NW
The Law Courts, Openshaw Place, Ring Way, Preston, Lancashire PR1 2LL Tel: 01772 844700 Fax: 01772 844759 DX 702660 PRESTON 5

Preston Crown Court (Sessions House) ..NW
Sessions House, Lancaster Road, Preston, Lancashire PR1 2PD Tel: 01772 844700 Fax: 01772 844759 DX: 702660 PRESTON 5

Reading Crown Court ....SE
Old Shire Hall, The Forbury, Reading RG1 3EH Tel: 0118 967 4400 Fax: 0118 967 4444 DX: 97440 READING 5

*Sheffield Combined Court Centre ....NE
The Law Courts, 50 West Bar, Sheffield, South Yorkshire S3 8PH Tel: 0114 281 2400 Fax: 0114 281 2425 DX: 703028 SHEFFIELD 6

Shrewsbury Crown Court ....M
The Shirehall, Abbey Foregate, Shrewsbury, Shropshire SY2 6LU Tel: 01743 260820 Fax: 01743 244236 DX: 702022 SHREWSBURY 2

Snaresbrook Crown Court.................London
75 Hollybush Hill, Snaresbrook, London E11 1QW Tel: 020 8530 0000 Fax: 020 8530 0072 DX: 98240 WANSTEAD 2

*Southampton Combined Court Centre....SW
The Courts of Justice, London Road, Southampton, Hampshire SO15 2XQ Tel: 023 8021 3200 Fax: 023 8021 3234 DX: 111000 SOUTHAMPTON 11

Southend Crown Court ....SE
The Court House, Victoria Avenue, Southend-on-Sea, Essex SS2 6EG Tel: 01268 458000 Fax: 01268 458100

Southwark Crown Court ....London
1 English Grounds (off Battlebridge Lane), Southwark, London SE1 2HU Tel: 020 7522 7200 Fax: 020 7522 7300 DX: 39913 LONDON BRIDGE SOUTH

St Albans Crown Court ....SE
The Court Building, Bricket Road, St Albans, Hertfordshire AL1 3JW Tel: 01727 753220 Fax: 01727 753221 DX: 99700 ST ALBANS 3

*Stafford Combined Court Centre ....M
Victoria Square, Stafford, Staffordshire ST16 2QQ Tel: 01785 610730 Fax: 01785 213250 DX: 703190 STAFFORD 4

*Stoke-on-Trent Combined Court ....M
Bethesda Street, Hanley, Stoke-on-Trent, Staffordshire ST1 3BP Tel: 01782 854000 Fax: 01782 854021 DX: 703360 HANLEY 3

Swansea Crown Court.........................Wales
The Law Courts, St Helen's Road, Swansea, South Wales SA1 4PF Tel: 01792 637000 Fax: 01792 637049 DX: 99540 SWANSEA 4

*Swindon Combined Court ....SW
The Law Courts, Islington Street, Swindon, Wiltshire SN1 2HG Tel: 01793 690500 Fax: 01793 690555 DX: 98430 SWINDON 5

Taunton Crown Court...............................SW
The Shire Hall, Shuttern, Taunton, Somerset TA1 4EU Tel: 01823 281100 Fax: 01823 322116 DX: 98410 TAUNTON 2

*Teesside Combined Court Centre............NE
Russell Street, Middlesbrough, Cleveland TS1 2AE Tel: 01642 340000 Fax: 01642 340002 DX: 65152 MIDDLESBROUGH 2

Truro Crown Court ....SW
Courts of Justice, Edward Street, Truro, Cornwall TR1 2PB Tel: 01872 267420 Fax: 01872 261550 DX: 135396 TRURO 2

*Warwick Combined Court ....M
Warwickshire Justice Centre, Newbold Terrace, Leamington Spa, Warwickshire CV32 4EL Tel: 01926 682100

Welshpool Crown Court......................Wales
Town Hall, Welshpool, Powys SY2 7TQ Tel: 01352 707340 Fax: 01352 753874

*Weymouth and Dorchester Combined Court Centre ....SW
Westwey House, Westwey Road, Weymouth, Dorset DT4 8TE Tel: 01305 265867 Fax: 01305 251867 DX: 98820 WEYMOUTH 3

*Winchester Combined Court Centre ....SW
The Law Courts, Winchester, Hampshire SO23 9EL Tel: 01962 814100 Fax: 01962 853821 DX: 98520 WINCHESTER 3

*Wolverhampton Combined Court Centre ...M
Pipers Row, Wolverhampton, West Midlands WV1 3LQ Tel: 01902 481000 Fax: 01902 481001 DX: 702019 WOLVERHAMPTON 4

Wood Green Crown Court ....London
Woodall House, Lordship Lane, Wood Green, London N22 5LF Tel: 020 8826 4100 Fax: 020 8826 4217 DX: 130346 WOOD GREEN 3

Woolwich Crown Court ....London
2 Belmarsh Road, London SE28 0EY Tel: 020 8312 7000 Fax: 020 8312 7078 DX: 117650 Woolwich 7

*Worcester Combined Court ....M
The Shirehall, Foregate Street, Worcester, Worcestershire WR1 1EQ Tel: 01905 730823 Fax: 01905 730810 DX: 721120 WORCESTER 11

York Crown Court ....NE
The Castle, York, North Yorkshire YO1 9WZ Tel: 01904 645121 Fax: 01904 611689 DX: 65162 YORK 3

CIRCUIT JUDGES

	Circuit
Addison, His Hon. Judge	SE
Ader, His Hon. Judge	SE
Ainley, His Hon. Judge	SE
Alexander, His Hon. Judge, QC	M
Allweis, His Hon. Judge	N
Altman, His Hon. Judge	SE
Ambrose, His Hon. Judge	W
Anderson, His Hon. Judge	SE
Ansell, His Hon. Judge	SE
Anthony, His Hon. Judge	SE
Appleby, His Hon. Judge	N
Appleton, His Hon. Judge	N
Armitage, His Hon. Judge, QC	N
Armstrong, His Hon. Judge	NE
Arran, His Hon. Judge	SE
Arthur, His Hon. Judge Sir Gavyn	SE
Ashurst, His Hon. Judge	NE
Atherton, His Hon. Judge	N
Atkins, His Hon. Judge	SE
Atkinson, Her Hon. Judge	SE
Aubrey, His Hon. Judge, QC	N
Badley, Her Hon. Judge	N
Bailey, His Hon. Judge	SE
Baker, His Hon. Judge	N
Baker, His Hon. Judge Michael, QC	SE
Ball, His Hon. Judge, QC	SE
Barber, His Hon. Judge	NE
Barclay, His Hon. Judge	W
Barham, His Hon. Judge	SE
Barker, His Hon. Judge, QC	SE
Barnes, Her Hon. Judge	SE
Barnett, His Hon. Judge Kevin	N
Barnett, His Hon. Judge Andrew	W
Barratt, His Hon. Judge	SE
Bartfield, His Hon. Judge	NE
Bate, His Hon. Judge	SE
Batty, His Hon. Judge Christopher	NE
Batty, His Hon. Judge, QC	N
Baucher, Her Hon. Judge	SE
Beaumont, His Hon. Judge, QC	SE
Beddoe, His Hon. Judge	SE
Beech, Her Hon. Judge	SE
Behar, His Hon. Judge	SE
Behrens, His Hon. Judge	NE
Belcher, Her Hon. Judge Penelope	NE
Bellamy, His Hon. Judge	M
Bennett, His Hon. Judge Dudley	M
Benson, His Hon. Judge Peter	NE
de Bertodano, Her Hon.	M
Bevan, His Hon. Judge, QC	SE
Bidder, His Hon. Judge, QC	Wales
Bing, His Hon. Judge	SE
Binning, His Hon. Judge	SE
Birtles, His Hon. Judge	SE
Birts, His Hon. Judge, QC	SE
Bishop, His Hon. Judge	SE
Black, Her Hon. Judge	W
Blackett, His Hon. Judge	SE
Blacksell, His Hon. Judge, QC	SE
Blake, His Hon. Judge	N
Bloom, His Hon. Judge, QC	N
Boggis, His Hon. Judge, QC	W
Bolton, Her Hon. Judge	NE
Bond, His Hon. Judge	W
Boney, His Hon. Judge, QC	W
Booth, His Hon. Judge	N
Boulton, His Hon. Judge	N
Bowers, His Hon. Judge	NE
Brasse, Her Hon. Judge	SE
Brasse, His Hon. Judge	SE
Bray, His Hon. Judge	M
Briggs, His Hon. Judge	NE
Bright, His Hon. Judge, QC	SE
Bromilow, His Hon. Judge	W
Brooke, His Hon. Judge, QC	SE
Brown, His Hon. Judge Robert	M
Brown, His Hon. Judge Simon, QC	M
Brown, His Hon. Judge Mark	N
Brown, His Hon. Judge	N
Brown, is Hon. Judge Richard, DL	SE
Browne, His Hon. Judge, QC	SE
Buckingham, Her Hon. Judge	NE
Bullimore, His Hon. Judge	NE
Burford, His Hon. Judge, QC	W
Burgess, His Hon. Judge	M
Burke, His Hon. Judge Jeffrey, QC	SE
Burn, His Hon. Judge	SE
Burrell, His Hon. Judge, QC	W
Bush, Her Hon. Judge	M
Butler, Her Hon. Judge, QC	M
Butler, His Hon. Judge	N
Byers, His Hon. Judge	SE
Byrne, His Hon. Judge	N
Caddick, His Hon. Judge	SE
Cahill, Her Hon. Judge, QC	NE
Cameron, Her Hon. Judge	SE
Campbell, His Hon. Judge Andrew	SE
Cardinal, His Hon. Judge	M
Carey, His Hon. Judge	SE
Carr, His Hon. Judge Peter	M
Carr, Her Hon. Judge, QC	NE
Carr, His Hon. Judge Simon	SE
Carroll, His Hon. Judge	SE
Cartlidge, His Hon. Judge	NE
Case, Her Hon. Judge	N
Catterson, Her Hon. Judge	SE
Caulfield, His Hon. Judge	N
Cavell, His Hon. Judge	M
Challinor, His Hon. Judge	M
Chambers, His Hon. Judge, QC	Wales
Chapple, His Hon. Judge	SE
Clark, His Hon. Judge Peter	SE
Clark, His Hon. Judge Harvey, QC	W
Clarke, His Hon. Judge	N
Clarke, His Hon. Judge Peter, QC	SE
Clayson, His Hon. Judge	N
Cleary, His Hon. Judge	M
Cliffe, His Hon. Judge	NE
Clifton, His Hon. Judge	N
Coates, His Hon. Judge	M
Coates, Her Hon. Judge	SE
Cockroft, His Hon. Judge	NE
Coleman, His Hon. Judge	SE
Colgan, His Hon. Judge	SE
Collender, His Hon. Judge, QC	SE
Collier, His Hon. Judge, QC	NE
Collins, His Hon. Judge, CBE	SE
Coltart, His Hon. Judge	SE
Compston, His Hon. Judge	SE
Cooke, His Hon. Judge	M
Cooke, His Hon. Judge, QC	Wales
Copley, His Hon. Judge	SE
Coppel, Her Hon. Judge	N
Corbett, Her Hon. Judge	SE
Cornwall, His Hon. Judge	N
Corrie, His Hon. Judge	SE
Cottle, His Hon. Judge	W
Cowell, His Hon. Judge	SE
Cox, Her Hon. Judge	SE
Critchlow, His Hon. Judge	SE
Crocker, His Hon. Judge	SE
Cryan, His Hon. Judge	SE
Curl, His Hon. Judge	SE
Curran, His Hon. Judge Patrick, QC	Wales
Curran, His Hon. Judge	Wales
Cutler, His Hon. Judge	W
Daley, Her Hon. Judge	N
Dangor, Her Hon. Judge	SE
Darling, His Hon. Judge	SE
Darlow, His Hon. Judge	W
Darroch, His Hon. Judge	SE
Darwall Smith, His Hon. Judge	W
Darwall Smith, Her Hon. Judge	W
Davies, Her Hon. Judge Jacqueline	NE
Davies, His Hon. Judge Stephen	N
Davies, His Hon. Judge Huw	Wales
Davis, His Hon. Judge William, QC	M
Davis, His Hon. Judge	SE
De Haas, Her Hon. Judge, QC	N
De Mille, His Hon. Judge	SE
Dedman, His Hon. Judge	SE
Deeley, Her Hon. Judge	M
Denniss, His Hon. Judge	SE
Denyer, His Hon. Judge, QC	Wales
Devaux, His Hon. Judge	SE
Diehl, His Hon. Judge, QC	Wales
Dight, His Hon. Judge	SE
Dixon, His Hon. Judge	W
Dobkin, His Hon. Judge	NE
Dodds, His Hon. Judge	N
Dodgson, His Hon. Judge	SE
Downes, His Hon. Judge	SE
Downing, Her Hon. Judge	SE
Dowse, His Hon. Judge	NE
Dudley, His Hon. Judge	M
Duggan, His Hon. Judge	M
Durham Hall, His Hon. Judge, QC	NE
Dutton, His Hon. Judge	N
Eades, His Hon. Judge	M
Eaglestone, Her Hon. Judge	N
Eccles, His Hon. Judge, QC	M
Edmunds, His Hon. Judge, QC	SE
Edwards, His Hon. Judge, DL	N
Ellis, His Hon. Judge	SE
Elly, His Hon. Judge	SE
Elwen, His Hon. Judge	W
Enright, His Hon. Judge	SE
Evans, His Hon. Judge	NE
Everall, His Hon. Judge, QC	SE
Everett, His Hon. Judge	N
Faber, His Hon. Judge	M
Faber, Her Hon. Judge	SE
Farmer, His Hon. Judge, QC	Wales
Faulks, His Hon. Judge	NE
Fenn, His Hon. Judge	SE
Field, His Hon. Judge	W
Finnerty, Her Hon. Judge	NE
Fisher, Her Hon. Judge	M
Flahive, His Hon. Judge	SE
Fletcher, His Hon. Judge David	N
Ford, His Hon. Judge, QC	W
Forrester, Her Hon. Judge	N
Forrester, His Hon. Judge	SE
Forster, His Hon. Judge, QC	NE
Foster, His Hon. Judge, QC	N
Foster, His Hon. Judge Richard	SE
Fowler, His Hon. Judge	M
Fox, His Hon. Judge, QC	E
Fraser, His Hon. Judge	SE
Freeland, His Hon. Judge, QC	SE
Furness, His Hon. Judge	Wales
Fysh, His Hon. Judge, QC	SE
Gaskell, His Hon. Judge	Wales
Geake, His Hon. Judge	N
Gee, His Hon. Judge Anthony, QC	N

16

Name	Circuit
George, His Hon. Judge	N
Gerald, His Hon. Judge	SE
Gibson, His Hon. Judge Jonathan	N
Gibson, His Hon. Judge	SE
Gilbart, His Hon. Judge, QC	N
Gilbert, His Hon. Judge, QC	W
Gilmour, His Hon. Judge, QC	N
Gledhill, His Hon. Judge, QC	SE
Glenn, His Hon. Judge	M
Globe, His Hon. Judge	NW
Gold, His Hon. Judge, QC	SE
Goldsack, His Hon. Judge, QC	NE
Goldstaub, His Hon. Judge, QC	SE
Goldstone, His Hon. Judge, QC	N
Goodin, His Hon. Judge	SE
Gordon, His Hon. Judge	SE
Gosling, His Hon. Judge	M
Goss, His Hon. Judge, QC	NE
Goymer, His Hon. Judge	SE
Graham, His Hon. Judge	SE
Grainger, His Hon. Judge	SE
Grant, His Hon. Judge David	M
Grant, His Hon. Judge	NE
Gratwicke, His Hon. Judge	SE
Greenwood, His Hon. Judge Alan	SE
Gregory, His Hon. Judge	M
Griffith, His Hon. Judge	SE
Griffith-Jones, His Hon. Judge	M
Griffith-Jones, His Hon. Judge David	SE
Griggs, His Hon. Judge	W
Grobel, His Hon. Judge	SE
Guggenheim, Her Hon. Judge, QC	SE
Gullick, His Hon. Judge	NE
Hagen, Her Hon. Judge	W
Halbert, His Hon. Judge	N
Hale, His Hon. Judge	N
Hall, His Hon. Judge Victor	M
Hall, His Hon. Judge	SE
Hallam, Her Hon. Judge	NE
Hallon, Her Hon. Judge	SE
Hamilton, His Hon. Judge Andrew	M
Hamilton, His Hon. Judge Iain	N
Hamilton, His Hon. Judge	SE
Hammerton, Her Hon. Judge	SE
Hammond, His Hon. Judge	M
Hampton, Her Hon. Judge	M
Hand, His Hon. Judge	SE
Hardy, His Hon. Judge	SE
Harington, His Hon. Judge	W
Harris, His Hon. Judge	N
Harris, Her Hon. Judge	SE
Harris, Her Hon. Judge Joanne	SE
Harris, His Hon. Judge Charles, QC	SE
Harrow, His Hon. Judge	W
Hart, His Hon. Judge	W
Havelock-Allan, His Hon. Judge	W
Hawkesworth, His Hon. Judge, QC	NE
Hawkesworth, His Hon. Judge Gareth	SE
Hawkins, His Hon. Judge	SE
Haworth, His Hon. Judge Jonathan	SE
Hayward, His Hon. Judge	SE
Hayward Smith, His Hon. Judge, QC	SE
Head, His Hon. Judge	M
Heath, His Hon. Judge	M
Hegarty, His Hon. Judge, QC	N
Henderson, His Hon. Judge	M
Henry, His Hon. Judge	W
Henshell, His Hon. Judge	N
Hernandez, His Hon. Judge	N
Hetherington, His Hon. Judge	W
Heywood, His Hon. Judge	Wales
Higgins, His Hon. Judge	SE
Hillen, His Hon. Judge	SE
Hindley, Her Hon. Judge, QC	M
Hodge, His Hon. Judge, QC	N
Hodson, His Hon. Judge	M
Hodson, His Hon. Judge	NE
Hoffman, His Hon. Judge	NE
Hollis, His Hon. Judge	SE
Holloway, His Hon. Judge	N
Holman, His Hon. Judge	N
Holt, His Hon. Judge Stephen	SE
Holt, His Hon. Judge	SE
Hone, His Hon. Judge, QC	SE
Hooper, His Hon. Judge, QC	M
Hooton, His Hon. Judge	W
Hope, His Hon. Judge	W
Hopkins, His Hon. Judge, QC	Wales
Hopmeier, His Hon. Judge	SE
Hornby, His Hon. Judge	SE
Horowitz, His Hon. Judge, QC	SE
Horton, His Hon. Judge	W
Hudson, Her Hon. Judge	NE
Hughes, Her Hon. Judge	M
Hughes, His Hon. Judge, QC	NW
Hughes, Her Hon. Judge	SE
Hughes, His Hon. Judge	SE
Hughes, His Hon. Judge	Wales
Hughes, His Hon. Judge Dafydd	Wales
Hughes, His Hon. Judge, QC	Wales
Hughes, His Hon. Judge, QC	W
Hull, His Hon. Judge	N
Hunt, His Hon. Judge	NE
Huskinson, His Hon. Judge	SE
Ibbotson, His Hon. Judge	NE
Inglis, His Hon. Judge	M
Inman, His Hon. Judge Melbourne, QC	M
Issard-Davies, His Hon. Judge	SE
Jack, His Hon. Judge	NE
Jacobs, His Hon. Judge	SE
James, His Hon. Judge	N
James, His Hon. Judge Simon	SE
Jarman, His Hon. Judge, QC	Wales
Jarvis, His Hon. Judge	W
Jenkins, His Hon. Judge	M
John, His Hon. Judge	SE
John, His Hon. Judge Terence	Wales
Johnson, His Hon. Judge	SE
Jones, His Hon. Judge Peter	NE
Jones, His Hon. Judge Nicholas	SE
Jones, His Hon. Judge Gareth	Wales
Jones, His Hon. Judge	W
Joseph, Her Hon. Judge Wendy, QC	SE
Joy, His Hon. Judge	SE
Juckes, His Hon. Judge, QC	M
Kamil, His Hon. Judge	NE
Kamill, Her Hon. Judge	SE
Karsten, His Hon. Judge, QC	SE
Karu, Her Hon. Judge	SE
Katkhuda, His Hon. Judge	SE
Kay, His Hon. Judge, QC	SE
Kaye, His Hon. Judge, TD, QC	NE
Keen, His Hon. Judge, QC	NE
Kemp, His Hon. Judge	SE
Kennedy, His Hon. Judge	SE
Kent, Her Hon. Judge	SE
Kershaw, Her Hon. Judge, QC	NE
Khayat, His Hon. Judge, QC	SE
Khokhar, His Hon. Judge Mushtaq	N
King, His Hon. Judge	SE
King, His Hon. Judge Timothy	SE
Kirkham, Her Hon. Judge	M
Knight, His Hon. Judge, QC	SE
Knopf, His Hon. Judge	N
Knowles, His Hon. Judge, QC	N
Knowles, Her Hon. Judge	SE
Kramer, His Hon. Judge, QC	SE
Kushner, Her Hon. Judge Lindsey, QC	N
Lafferty, His Hon. Judge	SE
Lakin, His Hon. Judge	N
Lamb, His Hon. Judge, QC	SE
Lambert, His Hon. Judge	W
Lancaster, His Hon. Judge	NE
Langan, His Hon. Judge, QC	NE
Lawler, His Hon. Judge, QC	NE
Lawson, His Hon. Judge, QC	SE
Lea, His Hon. Judge	M
Leeming, His Hon. Judge Ian, QC	W
Lees, Her Hon. Judge	SE
Leonard, His Hon. Judge, QC	SE
Lever, His Hon. Judge	N
Levy, Her Hon. Judge	SE
Lewis, His Hon. Judge	N
Lewis, His Hon. Judge Jeffrey	N
Llewellyn-Jones, His Hon. Judge, QC	Wales
Lloyd, Her Hon. Judge Heather	N
Lochrane, His Hon.	SE
Lodge, His Hon. Judge	SE
Longbotham, His Hon. Judge	W
Longman, His Hon. Judge Michael	W
Loraine-Smith, His Hon. Judge	SE
Lowcock, His Hon. Judge	N
Lowden, His Hon. Judge	NE
Lowen, His Hon. Judge	SE
Ludlow, Her Hon. Judge	SE
Lunt, Her Hon. Judge	N
Lyon, Her Hon. Judge Christina	N
Lyon, His Hon. Judge	N
Lyons, His Hon. Judge, CBE	SE
Macdonald, His Hon. Judge, QC	SE
Macgill, His Hon. Judge	NE
MacKay, His Hon. Judge	N
Mackie, His Hon. Judge, CBE, QC	SE
Madge, His Hon. Judge	SE
Main, His Hon. Judge, QC	N
Marks Moore, His Hon. Judge	SE
Marron, His Hon. Judge, QC	SE
Marshall, Her Hon. Judge Hazel, QC	SE
Marshall, Her Hon. Judge Katharine	W
Marson, His Hon. Judge, QC	NE
Marston, His Hon. Judge	W
Martin, His Hon. Judge	M
Martineau, His Hon. Judge	SE
Masterman, His Hon. Judge	Wales
Matheson, His Hon. Judge, QC	SE
Matthews, His Hon. Judge Phillip	SE
Matthews, Her Hon. Judge, QC	SE
Maxwell, His Hon. Judge	M
May, Her Hon. Judge	SE
Mayer, Her Hon. Judge	SE
Mayo, His Hon. Judge	M
McCahill, His Hon. Judge, QC	W
McCallum, His Hon. Judge	NE
McCreath, His Hon. Judge	M
McDowall, His Hon. Judge	SE
McGregor-Johnson, His Hon. Judge	SE
McIntyre, His Hon. Judge	SE
McKenna, His Hon. Judge	M
McKinnon, His Hon. Judge	SE
McKittrick, His Hon. Judge	SE
McMullen, His Hon. Judge, QC	SE
Mensah, Her Hon. Judge	SE
Meston, His Hon. Judge, QC	W
Metcalf, His Hon. Judge	M
Mettyear, His Hon. Judge	NE
Mifflin, Her Hon. Judge	Wales
Milford, His Hon. Judge, QC	NE
Million, His Hon. Judge	SE
Milmo, His Hon. Judge, QC	M
Mitchell, His Hon. Judge	M
Mitchell, His Hon. Judge Nicolas	M
Mitchell, His Hon. Judge Christopher	S
Mitchell, His Hon. Judge David	SE
Mitchell, His Hon. Judge Fergus	SE
Mitchell, His Hon. Judge John	SE
Mithani, His Hon. Judge	M
Moir, Her Hon. Judge	NE
Mole, His Hon. Judge, QC	SE
Moloney, His Hon. Judge, QC	SE
Molyneux, Her Hon. Judge	SE
Mooncey, His Hon. Judge	M
Moore, His Hon. Judge	NE
Moorhouse, His Hon. Judge	NE
Morgan, His Hon. Judge Hugh	SE

Judge	Circuit
Morgan, His Hon. Judge David Wynn	Wales
Morris, His Hon. Judge Sean	M
Morris, His Hon. Judge William	N
Morris, His Hon. Judge Anthony, QC	SE
Morris, His Hon. Judge	Wales
Morrison, His Hon. Judge, OBE, QC	M
Morrison, His Hon. Judge Fraser	SE
Morrow, His Hon. Judge Graham, QC	N
Mort, His Hon. Judge	N
Moss, His Hon. Judge Peter	SE
Moss, His Hon. Judge	SE
Mowat, Her Hon. Judge	SE
Murdoch, His Hon. Judge, QC	SE
Murfitt, Her Hon. Judge	SE
Murphy, His Hon. Judge, QC	NE
Murphy, His Hon. Judge Peter	SE
Nash, His Hon. Judge	SE
Nathan, His Hon. Judge	SE
Nawaz, His Hon. Judge	M
Neligan, His Hon. Judge John	W
Newell, His Hon. Judge	N
Newton, Her Hon. Judge	N
Newton, His Hon. Judge	SE
Niblett, His Hon. Judge	SE
Nield, Her Hon. Judge	N
Norrie, Her Hon. Judge	SE
O'Brien, His Hon. Judge	SE
O'Dwyer, His Hon. Judge	SE
O'Leary, His Hon. Judge	N
Oliver-Jones, His Hon. Judge, QC	M
O'Mahony, His Hon. Judge	SE
O'Malley, His Hon. Judge, DL	W
Onions, His Hon. Judge	M
Oppenheimer, His Hon. Judge	SE
Orme, His Hon. Judge	M
O'Rorke, His Hon. Judge	M
Orrell, His Hon. Judge	M
O'Sullivan, His Hon. Judge	SE
Overbury, His Hon. Judge	SE
Owen, His Hon. Judge Robert, QC	M
Owen, His Hon. Judge	SE
Paget, His Hon. Judge, QC	SE
Pardoe, His Hon. Judge, QC	SE
Parker, His Hon. Judge	M
Parkes, His Hon. Judge, QC	SE
Parmoor (formerly His Honour Judge Crips), His Hon. Judge The Lord	SE
Parry, Her Hon. Judge	Wales
Patience, His Hon. Judge, QC	SE
Pawlak, His Hon. Judge	SE
Pearce-Higgins, His Hon. Judge, QC	M
Pearl, His Hon. Judge	SE
Pearl, Her Hon. Judge	SE
Pearson, His Hon. Judge	W
Pegden, His Hon. Judge, QC	SE
Pelling, His Hon. Judge, QC	N
Pert, His Hon. Judge, QC	M
Phillips, His Hon. Judge	N
Philpot, His Hon. Judge	SE
Phipps, His Hon. Judge	N
Picton, His Hon. Judge	W
Pillay, His Hon. Judge	SE
Pitts, His Hon. Judge	SE
Platt, His Hon. Judge	SE
Platts, His Hon. Judge	N
Plumstead, Her Hon. Judge	SE
Plumstead, His Hon. Judge	SE
Plunkett, His Hon. Judge	M
Polden, His Hon. Judge	SE
Pontius, His Hon. Judge	SE
Powles, His Hon. Judge, QC	SE
Pratt, His Hon. Judge	SE
Price, His Hon. Judge David	M
Price, His Hon. Judge	SE
Price, His Hon. Judge, Esq, QC	SE
Price, His Hon. Judge Richard	W
Prince, His Hon. Judge	NE
Pugsley, His Hon. Judge	M
Purle, His Hon. Judge, QC	M
Radford, His Hon. Judge	SE
Ralls, His Hon. Judge	W
Rawkins, His Hon. Judge	N
Raynor, His Hon. Judge, QC	N
Reddihough, His Hon. Judge	SE
Redgrave, Her Hon. Judge	SE
Rees, His Hon. Judge Wyn	Wales
Rees, Her Hon. Judge	Wales
Reid, His Hon. Judge, QC	SE
Rennie, His Hon. Judge	SE
Richards, His Hon. Judge Jeremy	SE
Richards, His Hon. Judge Philip	Wales
Richardson, His Hon. Judge Jeremy, QC	NE
Richardson, His Hon. Judge	SE
Risius, His Hon. Judge, CB	SE
Rivlin, His Hon. Judge, QC	SE
Roach, His Hon. Judge	W
Robbins, His Hon. Judge	SE
Roberts, His Hon. Judge	N
Roberts, His Hon. Judge Mervyn	S
Roberts, His Hon. Judge, QC	SE
Robertshaw, Her Hon. Judge	W
Robinson, His Hon. Judge	NE
Robinson, Her Hon. Judge Alice	SE
Roddy, Her Hon. Judge	N
Rogers, His Hon. Judge Mark	M
Rogers, His Hon. Judge, QC	Wales
Rook, His Hon. Judge, QC	SE
Rose, His Hon. Judge	NE
Ross, His Hon. Judge	M
Rudland, His Hon. Judge	N
Rumbelow, His Hon. Judge	N
Rundell, His Hon. Judge	M
Russell, His Hon. Judge, QC	N
Rutherford, His Hon. Judge	W
Rylance, His Hon. Judge John	SE
Saggerson, His Hon. Judge	SE
Salomonsen, His Hon. Judge	M
Sanders, His Hon. Judge	SE
Scarratt, His Hon. Judge	SE
Scott-Gall, His Hon. Judge	SE
Serota, His Hon. Judge, QC	SE
Seymour, His Hon. Judge	SE
Seys-Llewellyn, His Hon. Judge, QC	Wales
Shanks, His Hon. Judge	SE
Sheridan, His Hon. Judge	SE
Shipley, Her Hon. Judge Jane	NE
Shorrock, His Hon. Judge	SE
Simpkiss, His Hon. Judge	SE
Sleeman, His Hon. Judge	SE
Smith, His Hon. Judge Adrian	N
Smith, Her Hon. Judge Zoe, QC	SE
Southwell, His Hon. Judge Edward	E
Spencer, His Hon. Judge, QC	NE
Spencer, His Hon. Judge Shaun, QC	NE
St John-Stevens, His Hon. Judge	SE
Statman, His Hon. Judge	SE
Steiger, His Hon. Judge, QC	N
Stephens, His Hon. Judge, QC	SE
Stewart, His Hon. Judge, QC	NE
Stewart, His Hon. Judge, QC	N
Stewart, His Hon. Judge	SE
Stokes, His Hon. Judge Michael, QC	M
Stone, His Hon. Judge, QC	SE
Stow, His Hon. Judge	SE
Styler, His Hon. Judge	M
Sullivan, Her Hon. Judge Jane	SE
Sullivan, Her Hon. Judge, QC	W
Swanson, His Hon. Judge	NE
Swift, His Hon. Judge	N
Swindells, Her Hon. Judge, QC	M
Sycamore, His Hon. Judge	N
Tabor, His Hon. Judge	W
Tain, His Hon. Judge	SE
Tanzer, His Hon. Judge	SE
Tapping, Her Hon. Judge	SE
Taylor, His Hon. Judge John	NE
Taylor, His Hon. Judge Michael	NE
Taylor, Her Hon. Judge Deborah	SE
Teague, His Hon. Judge, QC	N
Teare, His Hon. Judge	M
Testar, His Hon. Judge	SE
Tetlow, His Hon. Judge	N
Thomas, His Hon. Judge Patrick, QC	M
Thomas, Her Hon. Judge	M
Thomas, His Hon. Judge Roger, QC	N
Thomas, His Hon. Judge Paul, QC	Wales
Thomas, His Hon. Judge Keith	Wales
Thompson, His Hon. Judge	SE
Thorn, His Hon. Judge, QC	NE
Thornton, His Hon. Judge, QC	SE
Thornton, His Hon. Judge Peter, QC	SE
Ticehurst, His Hon. Judge	W
Tonking, His Hon. Judge	M
Toulmin, His Hon. Judge, CMG, QC	SE
Tremberg, His Hon. Judge	NE
Trevor-Jones, His Hon. Judge	M
Trigger, His Hon. Judge	N
Turner, His Hon. Judge, QC	SE
Tyrer, His Hon. Judge	SE
Tyzack, His Hon. Judge	W
Van Der Bijl, His Hon. Judge	SE
Vincent, His Hon. Judge	W
Vosper, His Hon. Judge, QC	Wales
Waddicor, Her Hon. Judge	SE
Wade, His Hon. Judge	W
Wadsworth, His Hon. Judge, QC	S
Waine, His Hon. Judge	M
Wait, His Hon. Judge	M
Wakefield, His Hon. Judge	SE
Waksman, His Hon. Judge, QC	N
Walford, His Hon. Judge	NE
Waller, His Hon. Judge	SE
Wallwork, His Hon. Judge	N
Walsh, His Hon. Judge Martin	M
Walsh, His Hon. Judge	NE
Walton, His Hon. Judge	NE
Warner, His Hon. Judge	M
Warner, His Hon. Judge Stephen	SE
Warnock, His Hon. Judge	N
Wassall, His Hon. Judge	W
Watson, Her Hon. Judge Hilary	M
Watson, Her Hon. Judge	N
Webb, His Hon. Judge Nicholas	M
Webb, His Hon. Judge	SE
Welchman, His Hon. Judge	SE
Whitburn, His Hon. Judge	NE
White, His Hon. Judge Graham	W
Wide, His Hon. Judge, QC	M
Wiggs, His Hon. Judge	W
Wilcox, His Hon. Judge	SE
Wildblood, His Hon. Judge, QC	W
Wilkinson, His Hon. Judge	SE
Williams, Her Hon. Judge	SE
Williams, Her Hon. Judge Sally	SE
Winstanley, His Hon. Judge	SE
Wolstenholme, His Hon. Judge	NE
Wood, His Hon. Judge	NE
Wood, His Hon. Judge Simon	NE
Wood, His Hon. Judge, QC	SE
Wood, His Hon. Judge Nicholas	SE
Woodward, His Hon. Judge Nicholas	N
Woolman, His Hon. Judge	N
Worsley, His Hon. Judge	SE
Worsley, His Hon. Judge, QC	SE
Worster, His Hon. Judge	M
Wright, His Hon. Judge	N
Wright, Her Hon. Judge Catherine	SE
Wright, His Hon. Judge Peter	SE
Wulwik, His Hon. Judge	SE
Yelton, His Hon. Judge	SE
Zeidman, His Hon. Judge, QC	SE

COUNTY COURTS

COURTS BY TOWN

** Combined Court*

‡ Admiralty
Ψ Adoption
† Bankruptcy
Ω Care
^ Chancery
≠ District Registry
§ Divorce
Φ Family Work
 # Race Relations

LONDON

Bow Ψ Φ
96 Romford Road, London E15 4EG Tel: 020 8536 5200 Fax: 020 8503 1152 DX: 97490 STRATFORD (LONDON) 2

Brentford Φ §
Alexandra Road, High Street, Brentford, Middlesex TW8 0JJ Tel: 020 8231 8940 Fax: 020 8568 2401 DX: 97840 BRENTFORD 2

Bromley Ψ Φ §
Court House, College Road, Bromley, Kent BR1 3PX Tel: 020 8290 9620 Fax: 020 8313 9624 DX: 98080 BROMLEY 2

Central London ^ #
13 - 14 Park Crescent, London W1B 1HT Tel: 020 7917 5000 Fax: 020 7917 5014 DX: 97325 REGENTS PARK 2

Clerkenwell and Shoreditch § Φ
The Gee Street Courthouse, 29 - 41 Gee Street, London EC1V 3RE Tel: 020 7250 7200 Fax: 020 7250 7250 DX: 121000 SHOREDITCH 2

Croydon § ≠ †
The Law Courts, Altyre Road, Croydon, Surrey CR9 5AB Tel: 020 8410 4797 Fax: 020 8760 0432 DX: 97470 CROYDON 6

Edmonton Φ
Court House, 59 Fore Street, Edmonton, London N18 2TN Tel: 020 8884 6500 / 6560 Fax: 020 8803 0564 / 8887 0413 DX: 136686 EDMONTON 3

Ilford Φ
Buckingham Road, Ilford, Essex IG1 1TP Tel: 020 8477 1920 Fax: 020 8553 2824 DX: 97510 ILFORD 3

Kingston-upon-Thames † Φ
St James Road, Kingston-upon-Thames, Surrey KT1 2AD Tel: 020 8972 8700 Fax: 020 8547 1426 DX: 97890 KINGSTON-UPON-THAMES 3

Lambeth Φ
Court House, Cleaver Street, Kennington Road, SE11 4DZ Tel: 020 7091 4410 Fax: 020 7587 1951 DX: 145020 KENNINGTON 2

Mayor's and City of London ‡
Guildhall Buildings, Basinghall Street, London EC2V 5AR Tel: 020 7796 5400 Fax: 020 7796 5424 DX: 97520 MOORGATE EC2

Romford Φ †
2a Oaklands Avenue, Romford, Essex RM1 4DP Tel: 01708 775353 Fax: 01708 756653 DX: 97530 ROMFORD 2

Uxbridge Φ §
501 Uxbridge Road, Hayes, Middlesex UB4 8HL Tel: 020 8756 3520 Fax: 020 8561 2020 DX: 44658 HAYES (MIDDLESEX)

Wandsworth Φ
76-78 Upper Richmond Road, Putney, London SW15 2SU Tel: 020 8333 4351 Fax: 020 8877 9854 DX: 97540 PUTNEY 2

West London
West London Courthouse, 181 Talgarth Road, Hammersmith, London W6 8DN Tel: 020 8600 6868 Fax: 020 8600 6860 DX: 97550 HAMMERSMITH 8

Willesden Φ
9 Acton Lane, Harlesden, London NW10 8SB Tel: 020 8963 8200 Fax: 020 8453 0946 DX: 97560 HARLESDEN 2

Woolwich Φ
165 Powis Street, Woolwich, London SE18 6JW Tel: 020 8301 8700 Fax: 020 8316 4842 DX: 123450 WOOLWICH 8

COUNTRY

Circuit

Aberdare † — Wales
The Court House, Cwmbach Road, Aberdare, Glamorgan CF44 0JE Tel: 01685 888575 Fax: 01685 883413 DX: 99582 MERTHYR TYDFIL 2

Aberystwyth Ψ § † ≠ — Wales
Edleston House, Queens Road, Aberystwyth, Ceredigion SY23 2HP Tel: 01970 636370 Fax: 01970 625985 DX: 99560 ABERYSTWYTH 2

Accrington § Φ — NW
Bradshawgate House, 1 Oak Street, Accrington, Lancashire BB5 1EQ Tel: 01254 237490 / 398173 Fax: 01254 393869 DX: 702645 ACCRINGTON 2

Aldershot and Farnham Φ § — SW
78-82 Victoria Road, Aldershot, Hampshire GU11 1SS Tel: 01252 796800 Fax: 01252 345705 DX: 98530 ALDERSHOT 2

Altrincham § — NW
Trafford Courthouse, Ashton Lane, Sale, Cheshire M33 7WX Tel: 0161 975 4760 Fax: 0161 975 4761 DX: 708292 SALE 6

Ashford — SE
Ground Floor, The Court House, Tufton Street, Ashford, Kent TN23 1QQ Tel: 01233 632464 Fax: 01233 612786 DX: 98060 ASHFORD (KENT) 3

Aylesbury † — SE
Walton Street, Aylesbury, Buckinghamshire HP21 7QZ Tel: 01296 554326 / 27 Fax: 01296 554320 DX: 97820 AYLESBURY 10

Banbury † — E
The Court House, Warwick Road, Banbury, Oxfordshire OX16 2AW Tel: 01295 452090 Fax: 01295 452051 DX: 701967 BANBURY 2

Barnsley § Φ † — NE
12 Regent Street, Barnsley, South Yorkshire S70 2EW Tel: 01226 777550 Fax: 01226 779126 DX: 702080 BARNSLEY 3

Barnstaple Φ † — SW
8th Floor, The Law Courts, Civic Centre, Barnstaple, Devon EX31 1DX Tel: 01271 340410 Fax: 01271 340415 DX: 98560 BARNSTAPLE 2

Barrow-in-Furness ‡ § † Φ — NW
Barrow Law Courts, Abbey Road, Barrow-in-Furness, Cumbria LA14 5QX Tel: 01229 840370 Fax: 01229 840371 DX: 65210 BARROW-IN-FURNESS 2

***Basildon** — SE
The Gore, Basildon, Essex SS14 2BU Tel: 0844 892 4000 Fax: 01268 458100 DX: 97633 BASILDON 5

Basingstoke Φ — SW
3rd Floor, Grosvenor House, Basing View, Basingstoke, Hampshire RG21 4HG Tel: 01256 318200 Fax: 01256 318225 DX: 98570 BASINGSTOKE 3

Bath § † Φ — SW
The Law Courts, North Parade Road, Bath, Somerset BA1 5AF Tel: 01225 476730 Fax: 01225 476724 DX: 98580 BATH 2

Bedford ≠ † Φ § — SE
Shire Hall, 3 St Paul's Square, Bedford, Bedfordshire MK40 1SQ Tel: 0844 892 0550 Fax: 01234 319026 DX: 97590 BEDFORD 11

Birkenhead ≠ § Φ † — NW
76 Hamilton Street, Birkenhead, Merseyside CH41 5EN Tel: 0151 666 5800 Fax: 0151 666 5873 DX: 725000 BIRKENHEAD 10

Birmingham ^ # ‡ † — M
Priory Courts, 33 Bull Street, Birmingham, West Midlands B4 6DS Tel: 0121 681 4441 DX: 701987 BIRMINGHAM 7

Bishop Auckland § Φ — NE
Woodhouse Close, Bishop Auckland, Co. Durham DL14 6LD Tel: 01388 660251 Fax: 01388 660264 DX: 65100 BISHOP AUCKLAND 2

Blackburn § † Φ ≠ Ω — NW
64 Victoria Street, Blackburn, Lancashire BB1 6DJ Tel: 01254 299852 Fax: 01254 692712 DX: 702650 BLACKBURN 4

Blackpool Φ † § ≠ — NW
The Law Courts, Chapel Street, Blackpool, Lancashire FY1 5RJ Tel: 01253 754020 Fax: 01253 295255 DX: 724900 BLACKPOOL 10

Blackwood † ≠ § — Wales
8 Hall Street, Blackwood, South Wales NP12 1NY Tel: 01495 238200 Fax: 01495 238203 DX: 99470 BLACKWOOD 2

Bodmin Ψ Φ § — SW
The Law Courts, Launceston Road, Bodmin, Cornwall PL31 2AL Tel: 01208 261580 Fax: 01208 77255 DX: 136846 BODMIN 2

***Bolton** Φ † — NW
The Law Courts, Blackhorse Street, Bolton, Greater Manchester BL1 1SU Tel: 01204 392881 Fax: 01204 373706 DX: 702610 BOLTON 3

Boston Φ † M
Boston Court House, 55 Norfolk Street, Boston, Lincolnshire PE21 6PE Tel: 01205 366080 Fax: 01205 311692 DX: 701922 BOSTON 2

Bournemouth Ψ § † SW
Courts of Justice, Deansleigh Road, Bournemouth, Dorset BH7 7DS Tel: 01202 502800 Fax: 01202 502801 DX: 98420 BOURNEMOUTH 4

Bow
See London

***Bradford** † § Φ NE
Bradford Law Courts, Exchange Square, Drake Street, Bradford, West Yorkshire BD1 1JA Tel: 01274 840274 Fax: 01274 840275 DX: 702083 BRADFORD 2

Brecon Ψ § Φ Wales
Cambrian Way, Brecon, Powys LD3 7HR Tel: 01874 622993 Fax: 01874 622441 DX: 124340 BRECON 2

Brentford
See London

Bridgend Wales
Sunnyside, Bridgend, South Wales CF31 4AJ Tel: 01656 673833 Fax: 01656 647124 DX: 99750 BRIDGEND 2

Brighton ≠ Φ † SE
William Street, Brighton,East Sussex BN2 0RF Tel: 01273 674421 Fax: 01273 602138 DX: 98070 BRIGHTON 3

Brighton County & Family Proceedings Court Ψ § Φ SE
1 Edward Street, Brighton, East Sussex BN2 0JD Tel: 01273 811333 Fax: 01273 607638 DX: 142600 BRIGHTON 12

Bristol † § Φ # ^ ‡ Ψ SW
Bristol Civil Justice Centre, 2 Redcliff Street, Bristol BS1 6GR Tel: 0117 366 4800 Fax: 0117 366 4801 DX: 95903 BRISTOL 3

Bromley
See London

***Burnley** Φ § † NW
The Law Courts, Hammerton Street, Burnley, Lancashire BB11 1XD Tel: 01282 855300 Fax: 01282 414911 DX: 724940 BURNLEY 4

Burton-upon-Trent Φ † M
165 Station Street, Burton-upon-Trent, Staffordshire DE14 1BP Tel: 01283 568241 Fax: 01283 517245 DX: 702044 BURTON-UPON-TRENT 3

Bury § Φ † NW
Tenters Street, Bury, Greater Manchester BL9 0HX Tel: 0161 447 8699 Fax: 0161 763 4995 DX: 702615 BURY 2

Bury St Edmunds § Φ † SE
Triton House, Entrance B, St Andrews Street (N), Bury St Edmunds, Suffolk IP33 1TR Tel: 0844 892 4000 Fax: 01284 702687 DX: 97640 BURY ST EDMUNDS 3

Buxton M
Peak Buildings, Terrace Road, Buxton, Derbyshire SK17 6DY Tel: 01332 622600 Fax: 01332 622543

Caernarfon Ψ § ≠ † Wales
Llanberis Road, Caernarfon, Gwynedd LL55 2DF Tel: 01286 684600 Fax: 01286 678965 DX: 702483 CAERNARFON 2

Cambridge § Ψ # † SE
2 Park Street, Cardiff, South Wales CF10 1ET Tel: 0844 892 4000 Fax: 01223 224590 DX: 99500 CARDIFF 6

***Canterbury** § Φ ‡ Ψ # ≠ † SE
The Law Courts, Chaucer Road, Canterbury, Kent CT1 1ZA Tel: 01227 819200 Fax: 01227 819283 DX: 99710 CANTERBURY 3

Cardiff Ψ Ω ≠ § † Wales
2 Park Street, Cardiff, South Wales CF10 1ET Tel: 029 2037 6400 Fax: 029 2037 6475 DX: 99500 CARDIFF 6

***Carlisle** † ≠ Ψ § Φ NW
Courts of Justice, Earl Street, Carlisle, Cumbria CA1 1DJ Tel: 01228 882140 Fax: 01228 590588 DX: 65331 CARLISLE 2

Carmarthen § † ≠ Wales
The Guildhall, Guildhall Square, Carmarthen, Carmarthenshire SA31 1PR Tel: 01267 228010 Fax: 01267 221844 DX: 99570 CARMARTHEN 2

Central London
See London

Chelmsford § Φ † Ψ SE
Priory Place, New London Road, Chelmsford, Essex CM2 0PP Tel: 0844 892 4000 Fax: 01245 295395 DX: 97660 CHELMSFORD 4

Cheltenham † SW
1st Floor, Cheltenham Magistrates Court, St Georges Road, Cheltenham, Gloucestershire GL50 3PF Tel: 01452 834991 Fax: 01452 834923

Chester § Φ Ψ ^ ≠ † NW
Trident House, Little St John Street, Chester, Cheshire CH1 1SN Tel: 01244 404200 Fax: 01244 404300 DX: 702460 CHESTER 4

Chesterfield Φ † M
St Mary's Gate, Chesterfield, Derbyshire S41 7TD Tel: 01246 501200 Fax: 01246 501205 DX: 703160 CHESTERFIELD 3

***Chichester** Φ SE
Southgate, Chichester, West Sussex PO19 1SX Tel: 01243 520700 Fax: 01243 533756 DX: 97460 CHICHESTER 2

Chorley § NW
59 St Thomas's Road, Chorley, Lancashire PR7 1JE Tel: 01257 262778 Fax: 01257 232843 DX: 702655 CHORLEY 3

Clerkenwell & Shoreditch
See London

Colchester ≠ Φ † SE
Falkland House, 25 Southway, Colchester, Essex CO3 3EG Tel: 0844 892 4000 Fax: 01206 717250 DX: 97670 COLCHESTER 3

Consett § Φ NE
Victoria Road, Consett, County Durham DH8 5AU Tel: 01207 502854 Fax: 01207 582626 DX: 65106 CONSETT 2

Conwy and Colwyn Wales
Conwy Road, Llandudno, Conwy LL30 1GA Tel: 01745 352940 Fax: 01745 336726

***Coventry** Ψ Φ † Ω M
140 Much Park Street, Coventry, West Midlands CV1 2SN Tel: 0300 123 5577 Fax: 024 7652 0443 DX: 701580 COVENTRY 5

Crewe ≠ § Φ † NW
The Law Courts, Civic Centre, Crewe, Cheshire CW1 2DP Tel: 01270 539300 Fax: 01270 216344 DX: 702504 CREWE 2

Croydon
See London

Darlington Φ † NE
4 Coniscliffe Road, Darlington, County Durham DL3 7RL Tel: 01325 463224 Fax: 01325 362829 DX: 65109 DARLINGTON 3

Dartford § Φ SE
Home Gardens, Dartford, Kent DA1 1DX Tel: 01322 627600 Fax: 01322 270902 DX: 98090 DARTFORD 2

***Derby** Ψ Φ † M
Morledge, Derby, Derbyshire DE1 2XE Tel: 01332 622600 Fax: 01332622543 DX: 724060 DERBY 21

Dewsbury § Φ † NE
County Court House, Eightlands Road, Dewsbury, West Yorkshire WF13 2PE Tel: 01924 465860 Fax: 01924 456419 DX: 702086 DEWSBURY 2

Doncaster Φ † NE
74 Waterdale, Doncaster, South Yorkshire DN1 3BT Tel: 01302 381730 Fax: 01302 768090 DX: 702089 DONCASTER 4

Dudley Φ † M
Harbour Buildings, Waterfront West, Brierley Hill, Dudley, West Midlands DY5 1LN Tel: 01384 480799 Fax: 01384 482799 DX: 701949 DUDLEY 2

Durham § Φ † SW
Civil and Family Justice Centre, Green Lane, Old Elvet, Durham, County Durham DH1 3RG Tel: 0191 375 1840 Fax: 0191 375 1844 DX: 65115 DURHAM 5

Eastbourne Φ † SE
The Law Courts, Old Orchard Road, Eastbourne, East Sussex BN21 4UN Tel: 01323 727518 Fax: 01323 649372 DX: 98110 EASTBOURNE 2

Edmonton
See London

Epsom § Φ SE
Epsom Point, 84-90 East Street, Epsom, Surrey KT17 1HF Tel: 01372 721801 Fax: 01372 734229 DX: 97850 EPSOM 3

Evesham M
1st Floor, 87 High Street, Evesham, Worcestershire WR11 4EE Tel: 01386 442287 Fax: 01386 49203 DX: 70910 EVESHAM 3

***Exeter** † Φ SW
Southernhay Gardens, Exeter, Devon EX1 1UH Tel: 01392 415300 Fax: 01392 415642 DX: 98440 EXETER 2

Gateshead § Φ NE
Gateshead Law Courts, Warwick Street, Gateshead, Tyne & Wear NE8 1DT Tel: 0191 477 5821 Fax: 0191 440 7209 DX: 742120 GATESHEAD 6

Gloucester Ψ § Φ † SW
Kimbrose Way, Gloucester, Gloucestershire GL1 2DE Tel: 01452 834900 Fax: 01452 834923 DX: 98660 GLOUCESTER 5

Grantham M
Harlaxton Road, Grantham, Lincolnshire NG31 7SB Tel: 01476 539030 Fax: 01476 539040 DX: 711102 GRANTHAM 4

***Great Grimsby § Φ †** NE
Town Hall Square, Grimsby, Lincolnshire DN31 1HX Tel: 01472 265200 Fax: 01472 265201 DX: 702007 GRIMSBY 3

Guildford § Φ Ψ † SE
The Law Courts, Mary Road, Guildford, Surrey GU1 4PS Tel: 01483 405300 Fax: 01483 300031 DX: 97860 GUILDFORD 5

Halifax Φ † NE
Prescott Street, Halifax, West Yorkshire HX1 2JJ Tel: 01422 344700 Fax: 01422 360132 DX: 702095 HALIFAX 2

Harlow § Φ SE
Gate House, The High, Harlow, Essex CM20 1UW Tel: 0844 892 4000 Fax: 01279 451110 DX: 97700 HARLOW 2

Harrogate Φ † § ≠ NE
2 Victoria Avenue, Harrogate, North Yorkshire HG1 1EL Tel: 01423 503921 Fax: 01423 528679 DX: 702098 HARROGATE 3

Hartlepool § Φ NE
The Law Courts, Victoria Road, Hartlepool, Cleveland TS24 8BS Tel: 01429 268198 Fax: 01429 862550 DX: 65121 HARTLEPOOL 2

Hastings Φ † SE
The Law Courts, Bohemia Road, Hastings, East Sussex TN34 1QX Tel: 01424 710280 Fax: 01424 421585 DX: 98150 HASTINGS 2

Haverfordwest § † ≠ Wales
Penffynnon, Hawthorn Rise, Haverfordwest, Dyfed SA61 2AX Tel: 01437 772060 Fax: 01437 769222 DX: 99610 HAVERFORDWEST

Hereford Φ † M
1st Floor, Barclays Bank Chambers, 1-3 Broad Street, Hereford, Herefordshire HR4 9BA Tel: 01432 357233 Fax: 01432 352593 DX: 701904 HEREFORD 2

Hertford † Φ § SE
4th Floor, Sovereign House, Hale Road, Hertford, Hertfordshire SG13 8DY Tel: 0844 892 0550 Fax: 01992 501274 DX: 97710 HERTFORD 2

High Wycombe SE
The Law Courts, Ground Floor, Easton Street, High Wycombe, Buckinghamshire HP11 1LR Tel: 0118 987 0508 Fax: 01494 651030 DX: 98010 READING 6

Hitchin § Φ SE
Park House, 1-12 Old Park Road, Hitchin, Hertfordshire SG5 2JR Tel: 0844 892 0550 Fax: 01462 445444 DX: 97720 HITCHIN 2

Horsham Φ SE
The Law Courts, Hurst Road, Horsham, West Sussex RH12 2EU Tel: 01403 252474 Fax: 01403 258844 DX: 98170 HORSHAM 2

Huddersfield † NE
Queensgate House, Queensgate, Huddersfield, West Yorkshire HD1 2RR Tel: 01484 421043 Fax: 01484 426366 DX: 703013 HUDDERSFIELD 2

Ilford
See London

Ipswich † SE
8 Arcade Street, Ipswich, Suffolk IP1 1EJ Tel: 0844 892 4000 Fax: 01473 251797 DX: 97730 IPSWICH 3

Keighley Φ NE
County Court House, North Street, Keighley, West Yorkshire BD21 3SH Tel: 01535 602803 Fax: 01535 610549

Kendal § ≠ † NW
The Court House, Burneside Road, Kendal, Cumbria LA9 4NF Tel: 01539 721218 Fax: 01539 733840 DX: 63450 KENDAL 2

Kettering M
Dryland Street, Kettering, Northamptonshire NN16 0BE Tel: 01536 512471 Fax: 01536 416857 DX: 701886 KETTERING 2

Kidderminster † M
Comberton Place, Kidderminster, Worcestershire DY10 1QT Tel: 01562 514 000 Fax: 01562 514 084

King's Lynn † § Φ SE
Chequer House, 12 King Street, King's Lynn, Norfolk PE30 1ES Tel: 0844 892 4000 Fax: 01553 769824 DX: 97740 KING'S LYNN 2

***Kingston-upon-Hull Φ †** NE
Lowgate, Humberside HU1 2EZ Tel: 01482 586161 Fax: 01482 588527 DX: 703010 HULL 5

Kingston-Upon-Thames
See London

Lambeth
See London

Lancaster Ψ Ω § † NW
2nd Floor, Mitre House, Church Street, Lancaster, Lancashire LA1 1UZ Tel: 01524 68112 Fax: 01524 846478 DX: 145880 LANCASTER 2

***Leeds ‡ ^ # † §** NE
The Court House, 1 Oxford Row, Leeds, West Yorkshire LS1 3BG Tel: 0113 306 2800 DX: 703016 LEEDS 6

Leicester Ψ § † M
90 Wellington Street, Leicester, Leicestershire LE1 6HG Tel: 0116 222 5700 Fax: 0116 222 5763 DX: 17401 LEICESTER 3

Leigh § Φ NW
Darlington Street, Wigan, Greater Manchester WN1 1DW Tel: 01942 405405 Fax: 01942 405459 DX: 702555 LEIGH 2

***Lewes** SE
The Law Courts, High Street, Lewes, East Sussex BN7 1YB Tel: 01273 480400 Fax: 01273 485269 DX: 97395 LEWES 4

Lincoln Φ † M
360 High Street, Lincoln, Lincolnshire LN5 7PS Tel: 01522 551500 Fax: 01522 551551 DX: 703231 LINCOLN 6

Liverpool ≠ § Φ † NW
35 Vernon Street, Liverpool, Merseyside L2 2BX Tel: 0151 296 2200 Fax: 0151 296 2201 DX: 702600 LIVERPOOL 5

Llanelli § Φ Wales
2nd Floor, Court Buildings, Town Hall Square, Llanelli, Carmarthenshire SA15 3AL Tel: 01554 757171 Fax: 01554 758079 DX: 99510 LLANELLI 2

Llangefni § † Ψ ≠ Wales
Glanhwfa Road, Llangefni, Isle of Anglesey LL77 7EN Tel: 01248 750225 Fax: 01248 750778 DX: 702480 LLANGEFNI 2

Lowestoft § Φ SE
Old Nelson Street, Lowestoft, Suffolk NR32 1HJ Tel: 0844 892 4000 Fax: 01502 513875 DX: 97750 LOWESTOFT 2

Ludlow M
Guild Hall, Mill Street, Ludlow, Shropshire SY8 1BB DX: 702013 LUDLOW 2

Luton Φ § ≠ † Ψ Ω SE
2nd Floor, Cresta House, Alma Street, Luton, Bedfordshire LU1 2PU Tel: 0844 892 0550 DX: 97760 LUTON 4

Macclesfield Ψ Φ † ≠ NW
2nd Floor, Silk House, Park Green, Macclesfield, Cheshire SK11 7NA Tel: 01625 412800 Fax: 01625 501262 DX: 702498 MACCLESFIELD 3

***Maidstone Φ § †** SE
The Law Courts, Barker Road, Maidstone, Kent ME16 8EQ Tel: 01622 202000 Fax: 01622 202002 DX: 130065 MAIDSTONE 7

Manchester ‡ Ψ † ^ ≠ § Φ # NW
Manchester Civil Justice Centre, 1 Bridge Street West, Manchester, Greater Manchester M60 9DJ Tel: 0161 240 5000 Fax: 0161 240 5397 DX: 724783 MANCHESTER 44

Mansfield Φ M
Beech House, 58 Commercial Gate, Mansfield, Nottinghamshire NG18 1EU Tel: 01623 656406 Fax: 01623 626561 DX: 702180 MANSFIELD 3

Mayor's & City of London
See London

Medway ‡ Ψ § † SE
Anchorage House, 47-67 High Street, Chatham, Kent ME4 4DW Tel: 01634 887900 Fax: 01634 811332 DX: 98180 CHATHAM 4

Melton Mowbray M
The Court House, Norman Way, Melton Mowbray, Leicestershire LE13 1NH Tel: 01664 485100 Fax: 01664 501869 DX: 701937 MELTON MOWBRAY 2

***Merthyr Tydfil Φ †** Wales
The Law Courts, Glebeland Place, Merthyr Tydfil, South Wales CF47 8BH Tel: 01685 727600 Fax: 01685 727703 DX: 99582 MERTHYR TYDFIL 2

***Middlesbrough †** NE
The Law Courts, Russell Street, Middlesbrough, Cleveland TS1 2AE Tel: 01642 340000 Fax: 01642 340002 DX: 65152 MIDDLESBROUGH 2

Milton Keynes ≠ § † Ψ Ω SE
351 Silbury Boulevard (Rear), Witan Gate East, Central Milton Keynes, Buckinghamshire
MK9 2DT Tel: 01908 302800 / 01 Fax: 01908 230063 DX: 136266 MILTON KEYNES 6

Mold † ≠ Wales
Law Courts, Civic Centre, Mold, Flintshire CH7 1AE Tel: 01978 296140 Fax: 01978 290677 DX: 702521 MOLD 2

Morpeth and Berwick § Φ NE
Fountain House, Newmarket, Morpeth, Northumberland NE61 1LA Tel: 01670 512221 Fax:
01670 504188 DX: 65124 MORPETH 2

Neath and Port Talbot § † Wales
Forster Road, Neath, South Wales SA11 3BN Tel: 01639 642267 Fax: 01639 633505 DX: 99550 NEATH 2

Newark M
Beech House, 58 Commercial Gate, Mansfield, Nottinghamshire NG18 1EU Tel: 01623 656406 DX: 702180 MANSFIELD 3

Newbury † SE
The Court House, Mill Lane, Newbury, Berkshire RG14 5QS Tel: 01635 642210 Fax: 01635 529580 DX: 30816 NEWBURY 1

***Newcastle-upon-Tyne Φ § Ψ ≠ †** NE
The Law Courts, The Quayside, Newcastle-upon-Tyne, Tyne & Wear NE1 3LA Tel: 0191 201 2000 Fax: 0191 201 2001 DX: 65127 NEWCASTLE-UPON-TYNE 2

Newport (Gwent) Ψ Ω ≠ § † Wales
5th Floor Clarence House, Clarence Place, Newport, Gwent NP19 7AA Tel: 01633 245040 Fax: 01633 245041 DX: 99480 NEWPORT (SOUTH WALES) 4

***Newport (Isle of Wight) † § Φ** SW
The Law Courts, 1 Quay Street, Newport, Isle of Wight PO30 5YT Tel: 01983 535 100 Fax: 01983 821 039 DX: 98460 NEWPORT IW2

North Shields § NE
Kings Court, Earl Grey Way, Royal Quays, North Shields, Tyne & Wear NE29 6AR Tel: 0191 2982339 Fax: 0191 2982337 DX: 65137 NORTH SHIELDS 2

***Northampton Ω Φ †** M
85/87 Lady's Lane, Northampton, Northamptonshire NN1 3HQ Tel: 01604 470400 Fax: 01604 232398 DX: 725380 NORTHAMPTON 21

***Northwich Φ** NW
The Court House, Chester Way, Northwich, Cheshire Tel: 01606 338508 Fax: 01606 48740

***Norwich ≠ † Φ** SE
The Law Courts, Bishopgate, Norwich, Norfolk NR3 1UR Tel: 0844 892 4000 Fax: 01603 760863 DX: 97385 NORWICH 5

Nottingham ≠ Ω # † M
60 Canal Street, Nottingham, Nottinghamshire NG1 7EJ Tel: 0115 910 3500 DX: 702380 NOTTINGHAM 7

Nuneaton M
Warwickshire Justice Centre, PO Box 3878, Vicarage Street, Nuneaton, Warwickshire CV11 4JU Tel: 0300 123 5577 Fax: 024 7635 2835 DX: 701940 NUNEATON 2

Oldham Φ † NW
New Radcliffe Street, Oldham, Greater Manchester OL1 1NL Tel: 0161 290 4200 Fax: 0161 290 4222 DX: 702595 OLDHAM 2

Oswestry M
The Court House, Holbache Road, Oswestry, Shropshire SY11 1RP Tel: 01691 652127 Fax: 01691 658902

***Oxford Ψ Φ § † ≠ Ω** SE
St Aldates, Oxford, Oxfordshire OX1 1TL Tel: 01865 264200 Fax: 01865 790773 DX: 96450 OXFORD 4

Penrith Φ NW
The Court House, Lowther Terrace, Penrith, Cumbria CA11 7QL Tel: 01228 882140 Fax: 01228 590588

Penzance § Φ SW
Trevear, Alverton Terrace, Penzance, Cornwall TR18 4GH Tel: 01872 267460 Fax: 01872 222348

***Peterborough Φ †** SE
Crown Buildings, Rivergate, Peterborough, Cambridgeshire PE1 1EJ Tel: 0844 892 4000 Fax: 01733 557348 DX: 702302 PETERBOROUGH 8

***Plymouth † Φ §** SW
The Law Courts, 10 Armada Way, Plymouth, Devon PL1 2ER Tel: 01752 677400
DX: 98470 PLYMOUTH 7

Pontefract Φ § NE
Horsefair House, Horsefair, Pontefract, West Yorkshire WF8 1RJ Tel: 01977 702357 Fax: 01977 600204 DX: 703022 PONTEFRACT 2

Pontypool Wales
Park Road, Riverside, Pontypool, Torfaen, South Wales NP4 6NZ Tel: 01495 238215 Fax: 01495 238203

Pontypridd † Ψ Ω Φ § Wales
The Courthouse, Courthouse Street, Pontypridd, Rhondda Cynon Taff CF37 1JR Tel: 01443 490800 Fax: 01443 480305 DX: 99620 PONTYPRIDD 2

Poole SW
The Law Courts, Civic Centre, Park Road, Poole, Dorset BH15 2NS Tel: 01202 741150 Fax: 01202 747245 DX: 98700 POOLE 4

***Portsmouth ‡ Ψ § Φ Ω †** SW
The Courts of Justice, Winston Churchill Avenue, Portsmouth, Hampshire PO1 2EB Tel: 023 9289 3000 Fax: 023 9282 6385 DX: 98490 PORTSMOUTH 5

***Preston ^ Φ § †** NW
The Law Courts, Openshaw Place, Ring Way, Preston, Lancashire PR1 2LL Tel: 01772 844700 Fax: 01772 844710 DX: 702660 PRESTON 5

Rawtenstall Φ § NW
1 Grange Street, Rawtenstall, Lancashire BB4 7RT Tel: 01706 214614 Fax: 01706 219814 DX: 702565 RAWTENSTALL 2

Reading ≠ Φ Ψ † Ω SE
160-163 Friar Street, Reading RG1 1HE Tel: 0118 987 0500 Fax: 0118 987 0555 DX: 98010 READING 6

Redditch M
13 Church Road, Redditch, Worcestershire B97 4AB Tel: 01527 67822 Fax: 01527 65791 DX: 701880 REDDITCH 2

Reigate SE
The Law Courts, Hatchlends Road, Redhill, Surrey RH1 6BL Tel: 01737 763637 Fax: 01737 766917 DX: 98020 REDHILL WEST

Rhyl Ψ ≠ § Φ † Ω Wales
The Courthouse, Clwyd Street, Rhyl, Denbighshire LL18 3LA Tel: 01745 352940 Fax: 01745 336726 DX: 702489 RHYL 2

Romford
See London

Rotherham § Φ NE
Rotherham Law Courts, The Statutes, PO Box 15, Rotherham, South Yorkshire S60 1YW Tel: 01709 839339 Fax: 01709 788414 DX: 703025 ROTHERHAM 4

Rugby M
The New Courthouse, Newbold Road, Rugby, Warwickshire CV21 2LQ Tel: 0300 123 5577 Fax: 01788 866004 DX: 701934 RUGBY 2

Salford Φ § † NW
Prince William House, Peel Cross Road (off Eccles New Road), Salford, Greater Manchester M5 4RR Tel: 0161 7457511 Fax: 0161 7457202 DX: 702630 SALFORD 5

Salisbury † ≠ Φ SE
Wilton Road, Salisbury, Wiltshire SP2 7EP Tel: 01722 345200 Fax: 01722 345201 DX: 98500 SALISBURY 2

Scarborough Φ ≠ § † NE
Pavilion House, Valley Bridge Road, Scarborough, North Yorkshire YO11 2JS Tel: 01723 366361 Fax: 01723 501992 DX: 65140 SCARBOROUGH 2

Scunthorpe § † NE
Scunthorpe Court Centre, Laneham Street, Scunthorpe, Humberside DN15 6JY Tel: 01724 281100 Fax: 01724 281890 DX: 742212 SCUNTHORPE 10

***Sheffield Ω ≠ Φ †** NE
The Law Courts, 50 West Bar, Sheffield, South Yorkshire S3 8PH Tel: 0114 281 2400 Fax: 0114 281 2425 DX: 703028 SHEFFIELD 6

Shrewsbury ≠ § Φ † M
4th Floor, Cambrian Business Centre, Chester Street, Shrewsbury, Shropshire SY1 1NA Tel: 01743 289069 Fax: 01743 237954 DX: 702047 SHREWSBURY 3

Skegness M
55 Norfolk Street, Boston, Lincolnshire PE21 6PE Tel: 01205 366080 Fax: 01205 311692 DX: 701922 BOSTON 2

Skipton Φ NE
The Court House, Otley Street, Skipton, North Yorkshire BD23 1RH Tel: 01756 692650 Fax: 01756 692655 DX: 703031 SKIPTON 2

Slough Φ † § SE
The Law Courts, Windsor Road, Slough SL1 2HE Tel: 01753 690300 Fax: 01753 575990 DX: 98030 SLOUGH 3

South Shields ≠ § Φ NE
Millbank, Secretan Way, South Shields, Tyne & Wear NE33 1RG Tel: 0191 4563343 Fax: 0191 4274499 DX: 65143 SOUTH SHIELDS 3

***Southampton** ‡ Ψ § Φ † SW
The Courts of Justice, London Road, Southampton, Hampshire SO15 2XQ Tel: 023 8021 3200 Fax: 023 8021 3222 DX: 111000 SOUTHAMPTON 11

Southend Φ § ≠ † SE
Tylers House, Tylers Avenue, Southend-on-Sea, Essex SS1 2AW Tel: 0844 892 4000 Fax: 01702 603090 DX: 97780 SOUTHEND 2

Southport § Φ NW
Dukes House, 34 Hoghton Street, Southport, Merseyside PR9 0PU Tel: 01704 531541 Fax: 01704 542487 DX: 702580 SOUTHPORT 2

St Albans † SE
The Court Building, Bricket Road, St Albans, Hertfordshire AL13JW Tel: 0844 892 0550 Fax: 01727 753234 DX: 97770 ST ALBANS 2

St Helens § Φ NW
1st Floor, Rexmore House, Cotham Street, St Helens, Merseyside WA10 1SE Tel: 01744 27544 Fax: 01744 20484 DX: 725020 ST HELENS 4

***Stafford** Φ † M
Victoria Square, Stafford, Staffordshire ST16 2QQ Tel: 01785 610730 Fax: 01785 213250 DX: 703190 STAFFORD 4

Staines § Φ SE
The Law Courts, Knowle Green, Staines, Middlesex TW18 1XH Tel: 01784 895900 Fax: 01784 895530 DX: 98040 STAINES 2

Stockport † Φ NW
5th Floor, Heron House, Wellington Street, Stockport SK1 3DJ Tel: 0161 474 7707 Fax: 0161 476 3129 DX: 702620 STOCKPORT 4

***Stoke-on-Trent** Ψ Ω § Φ † M
Bethesda Street, Hanley, Stoke-on-Trent, Staffordshire ST1 3BP Tel: 01782 854000 Fax: 01782 854046 DX: 703360 HANLEY 3

Stourbridge † M
7 Hagley Road, Stourbridge, West Midlands DY8 1QL Tel: 01384 394232 Fax: 01384 441736 DX: 701889 STOURBRIDGE 2

Stratford-upon-Avon M
5 Elm Court, Arden Street, Stratford-upon-Avon, Warwickshire CV37 6PA Tel: 0300 123 5577 Fax: 01789 414973 DX: 701998 STRATFORD UPON AVON 3

Sunderland § Φ Ψ Ω † NE
44 John Street, Sunderland, Tyne & Wear SR1 1RB Tel: 0191 5680750 Fax: 0191 5143028 DX: 65149 SUNDERLAND 2

Swansea Ψ ≠ § † Ω Wales
Caravella House, Quay West, Quay Street, Swansea, South Wales SA1 1SP Tel: 01792 485800 Fax: 01792 485810 DX: 99740 SWANSEA 5

***Swindon** Ψ Ω § Φ † SW
The Law Courts, Islington Street, Swindon, Wiltshire SN1 2HG Tel: 01793 690500 Fax: 01793 690555 DX: 98430 SWINDON 5

Tameside § † NW
PO Box 166, Henry Square, Ashton-Under-Lyne, Lancashire OL6 7TP Tel: 0161 331 5614 Fax: 0161 331 5649 DX: 702625 ASHTON-UNDER-LYNE 2

Tamworth M
The Court House, Spinning School Lane, Tamworth, Staffordshire B79 7AN Tel: 01827 305910 Fax: 01827 303823 DX: 702016 TAMWORTH 2

Taunton Ψ Φ † SW
The Shire Hall, Taunton, Somerset TA1 4EU Tel: 01823 281110 DX: 98410 TAUNTON 2

***Teesside** Φ ≠ NE
Russell Street, Middlesbrough, Cleveland TS1 2AE Tel: 01642 340000 Fax: 01642 340002 DX: 65152 MIDDLESBROUGH 2

Telford Φ M
Telford Square, Malinsgate, Town Centre, Telford, Shropshire TF3 4JP Tel: 01952 238280 Fax: 01952 291601 DX: 701976 TELFORD 3

Thanet ≠ Φ § SE
The Court House, 2nd Floor, Cecil Square, Margate, Kent CT9 1RL Tel: 01843 221722 Fax: 01843 222730 DX: 98210 CLIFTONVILLE 2

Torquay and Newton Abbot † Φ ≠ W
The Willows, Nicholson Road, Torquay Devon, TQ2 7AZ Tel: 01803 616791 Fax: 01803 616795 DX: 98740 TORQUAY 4

Trowbridge Φ § SW
Ground Floor, Clarks Mill, Stallard Street, Trowbridge, Wiltshire BA14 8DB Tel: 01225 752101 Fax: 01225 776638 DX: 98750 TROWBRIDGE 2

Truro Ψ Ω Φ † SW
Courts of Justice, Edward Street, Truro, Cornwall TR1 2PB Tel: 01872 267460 Fax: 01872 222348 DX: 135396 TRURO 2

Tunbridge Wells ≠ § † SE
Merevale House, 42-46 London Road, Tunbridge Wells, Kent TN1 1DP Tel: 01892 700150 Fax: 01892 513676 DX: 98220 TUNBRIDGE WELLS 3

Uxbridge
See London

Wakefield § Φ † NE
Crown House, 127 Kirkgate, Wakefield, West Yorkshire WF1 1JW Tel: 01924 370268 Fax: 01924 200818 DX: 703040 WAKEFIELD 3

Walsall Φ † M
Bridge House, Bridge Street, Walsall, West Midlands WS1 1JQ Tel: 01922 728855 Fax: 01922 728891 DX: 701943 WALSALL 2

Wandsworth
See London

Warrington & Runcorn Φ Ψ ≠ † NW
Law Courts, Legh Street, Warrington, Cheshire WA1 1UR Tel: 01925 256700 Fax: 01925 413335 DX: 702501 WARRINGTON 3

***Warwick** † M
Warwickshire Justice Centre, Newbold Terrace, Leamington Spa, Warwickshire CV32 4EL Tel: 01926 682100

Watford Φ Ω SE
3rd Floor, Cassiobury House, 11-19 Station Road, Watford, Hertfordshire WD17 1EZ Tel: 0844 892 0550 Fax: 01923 699479 DX: 122740 WATFORD 5

Wellingborough M
Lothersdale House, West Villa Road, Wellingborough, Northamptonshire NN8 4NF Tel: 01933 226168 Fax: 01933 272977 DX: 701883 WELLINGBOROUGH 2

Welshpool and Newtown § † Ψ ≠ Wales
The Mansion House, 24 Severn Street, Welshpool, Powys SY21 7UX Tel: 01938 552004 Fax: 01938 555395 DX: 702524 WELSHPOOL 2

West London
See London

Weston-Super-Mare Φ SW
North Somerset Courthouse, The Hedges, St Georges, Weston-Super-Mare, Avon BS22 7BB Tel: 01934 528686 Fax: 01934 528594 DX: 152361 WESTON SUPER MARE 5

***Weymouth and Dorchester** ≠ § Φ † SW
Westwey House, Westwey Road, Weymouth, Dorset DT4 8TE Tel: 01305 752510 Fax: 01305 788293 DX: 98820 WEYMOUTH 3

Whitehaven ‡ § Φ † NW
Old Town Hall, Duke Street, Whitehaven, Cumbria CA28 7NU Tel: 01946 67788 Fax: 01946 691219 DX: 63990 WHITEHAVEN 2

Wigan § Φ † NW
Wigan and Leigh Courthouse, Darlington Street, Wigan, Greater Manchester WN1 1DW Tel: 01942 405405 Fax: 01942 405499 DX: 724820 WIGAN 9

***Winchester** ≠ § Φ † SW
The Law Courts, Winchester, Hampshire SO23 9EL Tel: 01962 814100 Fax: 01962 853821 DX: 98520 WINCHESTER 3

***Wolverhampton** Ψ Ω § † M
Pipers Row, Wolverhampton, West Midlands WV1 3LQ Tel: 01902 481000 Fax: 01902 481001 DX: 702019 WOLVERHAMPTON 4

Woolwich
See London

***Worcester** Ψ Ω Φ † M
The Shirehall, Foregate Street, Worcester, Worcestershire WR1 1EQ Tel: 01905 730823 Fax: 01905 730810 DX: 721120 WORCESTER 11

Worksop M
The Court House, 30 Potter Street, Worksop, Nottinghamshire S80 2AJ Tel: 01623 656406 Fax: 01623 626561 DX: 702180 MANSFIELD 3

Worthing § Φ SE
The Law Courts, Christchurch Road, Worthing, West Sussex BN11 1JD Tel: 01903 221920 Fax: 01903 235559 DX: 98230 WORTHING 4

Wrexham Ψ † Ω ≠ § Wales
Crown Buildings, 31 Chester Street, Wrexham, Denbighshire LL13 8XN Tel: 01978 296140 Fax: 01978 290677 DX: 721921 WREXHAM 4

Yeovil § Φ † SW
22 Hendford, Yeovil, Somerset BA20 2QD Tel: 01935 382150 Fax: 01935 410004 DX: 98830 YEOVIL 2

York Φ § † NE
Piccadilly House, 55 Piccadilly, York, North Yorkshire YO1 9WL Tel: 01904 688550 Fax: 01904 679963 DX: 65165 YORK 4

DISTRICT JUDGES

	Circuit
Ackroyd, District Judge Robert	N
Ackroyd, District Judge Charles, TD, RD	W
Adam, District Judge	W
Ainsworth, District Judge	W
Alderson, District Judge	NE
Allen, District Judge	SE
Anderson, District Judge	NE
Anson, District Judge	N
Arkless, District Judge	NE
Armon-Jones, District Judge	SE
Arnold, District Judge	W
Ashton, District Judge	N
Ashworth, District Judge	SE
Asokan, District Judge	M
Asplin, District Judge	W
Atherton, District Judge	NE
Atkinson, District Judge	M
Avent, District Judge	S
Avi, District Judge	SE
Ayers, District Judge	SE
Babbington, District Judge	NE
Backhouse, District Judge	SE
Baddeley, District Judge	M
Baker, District Judge	N
Banks, District Judge	SE
Barraclough, District Judge	NE
Batcup, District Judge	SE
Bazley White, District Judge	SE
Beale, District Judge	M
Beattie, District Judge	SE
Beck, District Judge	SE
Bedford, District Judge	NE
Bellamy, District Judge	N
Bennett, District Judge	N
Besford, District Judge	NE
Birchall, District Judge	SE
Birkby, District Judge	NE
Bishop, District Judge	SE
Blunsdon, District Judge	SE
Booth, District Judge	NE
Bowles, District Judge	SE
Brazier, District Judge	N
Brett, District Judge	SE
Britton, District Judge	W
Brookes, District Judge	W
Brooks, District Judge	SE
Brown, District Judge	M
Bryce, District Judge	N
Buchan, District Judge	NE
Buckley, District Judge	N
Bull, District Judge	M
Bullock, District Judge	NE
Burgess, District Judge Gerald	SE
Burgess, District Judge Linda	SE
Burn, District Judge	SE
Butler, District Judge	M
Buxton, District Judge	NE
Cahill, District Judge	N
Carney, District Judge	W
Carr, District Judge	SE
Carron, District Judge	W
Carson, District Judge	Wales
Cawood, District Judge	W
Chapman, District Judge Richard	M
Chapman, District Judge David	N
Chaudhuri, District Judge	SE
Chesterfield, District Judge	NE
Chrispin, District Judge	SE
Clark, District Judge Bryony	NE
Clark, District Judge John	N
Clegg, District Judge	N
Codlin-Tate, District Judge	W
Coffey, District Judge	N
Cohen, District Judge Edward	SE
Cohen, District Judge Lawrence	SE
Cole, District Judge Barrie	SE
Collier, District Judge	SE
Cooper, District Judge Christopher	M
Cooper, District Judge Susan	SE
Cooper, District Judge Malcolm	W
Corkill, District Judge	NE
Corrigan, District Judge	W
Cotterill, District Judge	M
Cross, District Judge	SE
Crowe, District Judge	M
Crowley, District Judge	M
Cuthbertson, District Judge	NE
Dabezies, District Judge	SE
Dancey, District Judge	W
Daniel, District Judge	W
Darbyshire, District Judge	SE
Davidson, District Judge	SE
Davies, District Judge Tony	M
Davies, District Judge Lloyd	Wales
Dawson, District Judge	Wales
Devlin, District Judge	SE
Dignan, District Judge	N
Dixon, District Judge	SE
Doel, District Judge	Wales
Douce, District Judge	M
Dowding, District Judge	M
Dowell, District Judge	W
Dowling, District Judge	M
Doyle, District Judge	N
Dudley, District Judge	SE
Duerden, District Judge	N
Eaton, District Judge	M
Edwards, District Judge Geoff	NE
Edwards, District Judge Carlton	SE
Ellery, District Judge	M
Ellington, District Judge	Wales
England, District Judge	M
Evans, District Judge Claire	N
Evans, District Judge Ian	SE
Evans, District Judge Peter	Wales
Evans, District Judge Rachel	Wales
Exton, District Judge	W
Eynon, District Judge	SE
Fairclough, District Judge	N
Fairwood, District Judge	NE
Farquhar, District Judge	SE
Fawcett, District Judge	SE
Field, District Judge	SE
Fine, District Judge	SE
Fitzgerald, District Judge	N
Flanagan, District Judge	NE
Flood, District Judge	M
Forrester, District Judge	N
Fox, District Judge	N
Fraser, District Judge	Wales
Freeborough, District Judge	SE
Freeman, District Judge Christopher	N
Freeman, District Judge John	W
Gailey, District Judge	M
Gamba, District Judge	SE
Garland-Thomas, District Judge	Wales
Gatter, District Judge	SE
Geddes, District Judge	N
George, District Judge	M
Gerlis, District Judge	SE
Gilchrist, District Judge	SE
Giles, District Judge	NE
Gilham, District Judge	N
Gill, District Judge	SE
Gittens, District Judge	SE
Glentworth, District Judge	NE
Glover, District Judge	SE
Goddard, District Judge	W
Godwin, District Judge	Wales
Gold, District Judge	SE
Gosnell, District Judge	N
Goudie, District Judge	NE
Grand, District Judge	W
Green, District Judge	SE
Gregory, District Judge	SE
Griffith, District Judge	M
Griffiths, District Judge	N
Griggs, District Judge	W
Grosse, District Judge	SE
Guinan, District Judge	SE
Habershon, District Judge	SE
Haigh, District Judge	N
Hale, District Judge	M
Hall, District Judge	NE
Hallett, District Judge	SE
Hamilton, District Judge	SE
Handley, District Judge	NE
Harrison, District Judge Nicola	N
Harrison, District Judge Anthony	N
Harvey, District Judge	W
Hayes, District Judge	SE
Hearne, District Judge	M
Heath, District Judge	NE
Hebblethwaite, District Judge	SE
Hendicott, District Judge	Wales
Henry, District Judge	SE
Henson, District Judge	SE
Henthorn, District Judge	N
Heyworth, District Judge	N
Hickinbottom, District Judge	NE
Hickman, District Judge	SE
Hicks, District Judge	SE
Hill, District Judge Robert	NE
Hill, District Judge Timothy	NE
Horan, District Judge	N
Hovington, District Judge	N
Howard, District Judge	NE
Hudson, District Judge	M
Humphreys-Roberts, District Judge	N
Hurley, District Judge	W
Ilsley, District Judge	M
Ingram, District Judge	M
Jabbar, District Judge Rasheeda	M
Jacey, District Judge	SE
Jack, District Judge	M
Jackson, District Judge Phillip	NE
Jackson, District Judge Stephen	N
Jackson, District Judge Nigel	SE
Jackson, District Judge Susan	SE
Jackson, District Judge William	SE
James, District Judge	W
Jenkins, District Judge Alan	SE
Jenkins, District Judge Tim	SE
Jenkins, District Judge Peter	Wales
Johns, District Judge	SE
Johnson, District Judge	N
Jolly, District Judge	W
Jones, District Judge Andrew	M
Jones, District Judge Alison	N
Jones, District Judge Ralph	N

16

Jones, District Judge S	SE
Jones-Evans, District Judge	Wales
Jordan, District Judge	NE
Karp, District Judge	SE
Kemp, District Judge	SE
Kesterton, District Judge	M
Khan, District Judge	N
King, District Judge	W
Kirby, District Judge	SE
Kirkham, District Judge	NE
Knifton, District Judge	N
Kubiak, District Judge	SE
Langley, District Judge	SE
Large, District Judge	NE
Lascelles, District Judge	NE
Law, District Judge	N
Lawton, District Judge	NE
Lee, District Judge	SE
Lethem, District Judge	SE
Lettall, District Judge	N
Letts, District Judge	SE
Levey, District Judge	SE
Levinson, District Judge	SE
Lewis, District Judge	Wales
Lightman, District Judge	SE
Lingard, District Judge	NE
Liston, District Judge	SE
Little, District Judge	N
Llewellyn, District Judge, OBE	Wales
Loomba, District Judge	NE
Lord, District Judge	NE
Lovecy, District Judge	M
Lynch, District Judge	M
MacKenzie, District Judge	M
Mainwaring-Taylor, District Judge, TD	NE
Manners, District Judge	SE
Manuel, District Judge	W
Marin, District Judge	SE
Marley, District Judge	NE
Marston, District Judge	M
Matharu, District Judge	N
Matthews, District Judge	SE
Maughan, District Judge	M
Maw, District Judge	M
McCulloch, District Judge	SE
McHale, District Judge	M
McLoughlin, District Judge	SE
Meredith, District Judge	W
Merrick, District Judge	SE
Merriman, District Judge	M
Middleton, District Judge	W
Mildred, District Judge	W
Millard, District Judge David	M
Millard, District Judge Lesley	SE
Mills, District Judge	SE
Millward, District Judge	SE
Mitchell, District Judge	SE
Mitchell, District Judge	W
Molle, District Judge	SE
Moon, District Judge	W
Moreton, District Judge	W
Morgan, District Judge	NE
Morley, District Judge	SE
Mornington, District Judge	NE
Morris, District Judge	SE
Mort, District Judge	NE
Mullis, District Judge	SE
Murdoch, District Judge	M
Naqvi, District Judge, TD	SE
Naylor, District Judge	W
Neaves, District Judge	N
Newman, District Judge	N
Nicholson, District Judge	SE
Nicolle, District Judge	M
Nield, District Judge	M
Nightingale, District Judge L	SE
Nisa, District Judge	SE
North, District Judge	Wales
Obodai, District Judge	N
Oldham, District Judge	NE
Oliver, District Judge	M
O'Neill, District Judge	N
O'Regan, District Judge	M
Osborne, District Judge	N
Owen, District Judge	M
Park, District Judge	N
Parker, District Judge Maureen	SE
Parker, District Judge Tim	SE
Parnell, District Judge	SE
Parry, District Judge	M
Pates, District Judge	N
Payne, District Judge	SE
Peake, District Judge	N
Pearce, District Judge	SE
Pearl, District Judge	SE
Pelly, District Judge	SE
Perry, District Judge	Wales
Perusko, District Judge	SE
Pescod, District Judge	NE
Phillips, District Judge	Wales
Pickup, District Judge	N
Plaskow, District Judge	SE
Pollard, District Judge	SE
Powell, District Judge	NE
Price, District Judge	SE
Pugh, District Judge	N
Raeside, District Judge	SE
Ralton, District Judge	SE
Rank, District Judge	M
Read, District Judge	W
Reed, District Judge	NE
Reeson, District Judge	M
Reeves, District Judge	Wales
Regan, District Judge	Wales
Relph, District Judge L	NW
Rhodes, District Judge John	SE
Richardson, District Judge	NE
Richmond, District Judge	N
Ridgway, District Judge	M
Robertson, District Judge	NE
Robinson, District Judge John T	SE
Rodgers, District Judge	NE
Rogers, District Judge Mark	M
Rogers, District Judge Stephen C	M
Rogers, District Judge Stephen E	SE
Rogers, District Judge Philip	SE
Rowe, District Judge	W
Rowley, District Judge	SE
Royall, District Judge	SE
Rutherford, District Judge	W
Rutland, District Judge	SE
Ryan, District Judge	SE
Saffman, District Judge	NE
Sandercock, District Judge	Wales
Sanderson, District Judge	N
Sanghera, District Judge	M
Savage, District Judge	M
Schroeder, District Judge	M
Sehdev, District Judge	M
Sethi, District Judge	SE
Shanks, District Judge	SE
Shaw, District Judge	N
Sheldrake, District Judge, TD	M
Silverman, District Judge	SE
Silverman, District Judge Geoffrey	SE
Silverwood-Cope, District Judge	SE
Simpson, District Judge	N
Singleton, District Judge	W
Slim, District Judge	NE
Smart, District Judge	N
Smedley, District Judge	N
Smith, District Judge Graeme	N
Smith, District Judge Simon	N
Smith, District Judge Geoffrey	SE
Smith, District Judge Brian	W
Southcombe, District Judge	SE
Sparrow, District Judge Robert	SE
Sparrow, District Judge John	W
Spencer, District Judge	NE
Stamenkovich, District Judge	M
Stapely, District Judge	NE
Stark, District Judge	M
Stary, District Judge	SE
Steel, District Judge	SE
Stephens, District Judge	N
Stephenson, District Judge	SE
Sterlini, District Judge	SE
Stewart, District Judge	SE
Stocken, District Judge	NE
Stockton, District Judge	N
Stone, District Judge David Martin Charles	SE
Stonier, District Judge	N
Sturdy, District Judge	SE
Swan, District Judge	N
Swindley, District Judge	N
Sykes, District Judge	N
Talbot, District Judge	N
Taylor, District Judge Adam	SE
Taylor, District Judge James	SE
Taylor, District Judge John	SE
Taylor, District Judge Marjory	Wales
Thomas, District Judge Andrew	SE
Thomas, District Judge John	Wales
Thomas, District Judge Alan	W
Thomas, District Judge J Lee	W
Thompson, District Judge	NE
Thorp, District Judge	NE
Tilbury, District Judge	SE
Toombs, District Judge	M
Travers, District Judge	N
Traynor, District Judge	NE
Trent, District Judge	SE
Trigg, District Judge	SE
Tromans, District Judge	W
Truman, District Judge	M
Turner, District Judge	N
Venables, District Judge	M
Vokes, District Judge	SE
Wainwright, District Judge	W
Wakem, District Judge	SE
Walker, District Judge Michael, CBE	Royal Courts of Justice
Walker, District Judge Andrew	W
Wall, District Judge	M
Wallace, District Judge	N
Waterworth, District Judge	W
Watkins, District Judge	W
Watson, District Judge Sarah	M
Watson, District Judge Paul	M
Watson, District Judge Brian	W
Weaver, District Judge	Wales
Weintroub, District Judge	W
Weston, District Judge	NE
Wharton, District Judge	SE
Wheeler, District Judge	N
White, District Judge David	SE
White, District Judge	W
Whitehurst, District Judge	M
Wicks, District Judge	SE
Wilding, District Judge	SE
Wildsmith, District Judge	NE
Wilkinson, District Judge	SE
Williams, District Judge	Wales
Willis, District Judge	M
Williscroft, District Judge	M
Wilson, District Judge	W
Wood, District Judge	NE
Woodhead, District Judge	NE
Worthington, District Judge	SE
Wright, District Judge Susan	N
Wright, District Judge Jane	SE
Young, District Judge	NE
Zimmels, District Judge	SE

MAGISTRATES' COURTS

LONDON

Senior District Judge (Chief Magistrate)
Vacant

Deputy Senior District Judge
Deputy Chief Magistrate
Wickham, Miss D

The Chief Magistrates Office
City of Westminster Magistrates Court, 70 Horseferry Road, London SW1P 2AX

Floating Judges attached to CMO
Tempia, Miss N

City of Westminster Magistrates Court
70 Horseferry Road, London SW1P 2AX Tel: 020 7805 1008 Fax: 020 7805 1193 DX: 120551 VICTORIA 6
Purdy, Q
Snow, M
Evans, H.N.
Riddle H.
Tubbs, Miss C S R
Roscoe, Miss E

West London Division

West London Magistrates Court
181 Talgarth Road, London W6 8DN Tel: 0845 601 3600 Fax: 020 8700 9344 DX: 124800 HAMMERSMITH
Sweet, A
Lachhar, Miss D
Philips, J
Simpson, D (Youth Magistrate)
Coleman, J (Youth Magistrate)
Williams, Miss S
Clark, P

East Central Division

Highbury Corner Magistrates Court
51 Holloway Road, London N7 8JA Tel: 020 7506 3147 Fax: 020 7506 3191
Perkins, J
Baker, I
Mcphee, R
Henderson, J

Thames Division
Justices' Clerk

Thames Magistrates Court
58 Bow Road, London E3 4DJ Tel: 0845 601 3600 Fax: 020 8271 1251 DX: 55654 BOW
Read, M
Comyns, Mrs J
Rose, Miss A M
McIvor, Miss J

South Western Magistrates Court
Justices' Clerk

South Western Magistrates Court
176A Lavender Hill, London SW11 1JU Tel: 0845 601 3600 Fax: 020 7805 1448 DX: 58559 CLAPHAM JUNCTION
Grant, K
Barnes, B
Bayne, Ms S

South Central Division
Justices' Clerk

Camberwell Green Magistrates Court
15 D'Eynsford Road, Camberwell Green, London SE5 7UP Tel: 020 7805 9801 DX: 35305 CAMBERWELL GREEN
Baldwin, Mr A
Sawetz, Miss A
Green, Miss S
Zani, J
Ikram, T

Tower Bridge Magistrates Court
211 Tooley Street, London SE1 2JY Tel: 020 7805 6724 DX: 35305 CAMBERWELL GREEN
Black, C S F
Somjee, S
Stone, T

South Eastern Division
Justices' Clerk

Greenwich Magistrates Courts
9 Blackheath Road, Greenwich, London SE10 8PG Tel: 020 8276 1301 DX: 35203 GREENWICH WEST

Woolwich Magistrates Court
Market Street, Woolwich, London SE18 6QY Tel: 020 8271 9000

Belmarsh Magistrates Court
4 Belmarsh Road, London SE28 0HA Tel: 020 8271 9098
Lynch, D
Hamilton A.
Barrie, Miss F.

Inner London and City Family Proceedings Court
Justices' Clerk
Damazer, Miss A

Inner London and City Family Proceedings Court
59/65 Wells Street, London W1A 3AE Tel: 020 7805 3401
Crichton, N (Family Magistrate)
Wain, P

DISTRICT JUDGES (MAGISTRATES' COURTS)

	Circuit
Workman, Senior District Judge, CBE	Chief Magistrate's Office
Wickham, Deputy Senior District Judge	Chief Magistrate's Court
Abelson, District Judge	N
Alderson, District Judge	M
Allison, District Judge	SE
Anderson, District Judge	NE
Arbuthnot, District Judge	Chief Magistrate's Office
Arnold, District Judge	W
Baker, District Judge Diana Margaret	N
Baker, District Judge Ian Michael	SE
Baldwin, District Judge	SE
Barnes, District Judge	SE
Barrie, District Judge	SE
Bayne, District Judge	W
Bennett, District Judge	NE
Berg, District Judge	N
Black, District Judge	SE
Blake, District Judge	M
Bopa-Rai, District Judge	W
Bouch, District Judge	NE
Brailsford, District Judge	NW
Brown, District Judge	W
Browne, District Judge	NE
Browning, District Judge	SE
Cadbury, District Judge	M
Callaway, District Judge	SE
Carr, District Judge	SE
Chalk, District Judge	N
Charles, District Judge	Wales
Chatelier, District Judge	N
Chinery, District Judge	M
Clancy, District Judge	N
Clark, District Judge	SE
Coleman, District Judge	SE
Coleman, District Judge	SE
Comyns, District Judge	SE
Cooper, District Judge Morris	M
Cooper, District Judge David Anthony	SE
Cooper, District Judge Simon Nicholas	W
Crabtree, District Judge, OBE	SE
Crichton, District Judge	SE
Curtis, District Judge	NE
Daber, District Judge	Chief Magistrate's Office
Darnton, District Judge	NE
Davison, District Judge	M
Dawson, District Judge Celia Anne	SE
Dawson, District Judge Stephen Eric	SE
Day, District Judge	SE
Devas, District Judge	M
Driver, District Judge	NE
Earl, District Judge	NE
Ede, District Judge	SE
Elsey, District Judge	NE
Evans, District Judge Anthony Thomas	SE
Evans, District Judge Henry Nicholas	SE
Farmer, District Judge	W
Finestein, District Judge	N
Foster, District Judge	NE
Friel, District Judge	M
Gillespie, District Judge	M
Gillibrand, District Judge	W
Gott, District Judge	SE
Goulborn, District Judge	M
Grant, District Judge	W
Gray, District Judge	SE
Green, District Judge	SE
Hadfield, District Judge	NE
Hamilton, District Judge	Chief Magistrate's Court
Harris, District Judge	M
Harrison, District Judge	NE
Henderson, District Judge	SE
Hickey, District Judge	NE
Holland, District Judge	M
House, District Judge	W
Hunter, District Judge	SE
Ikram, District Judge	SE
Jabbit, District Judge	M
Jellema, District Judge	M
Kelly, District Judge	SE
Kitson, District Judge	NE
Knight, District Judge	N
Lachhar, District Judge	SE
Leigh-Smith, District Judge	SE
Lloyd, District Judge	N
Lomax, District Judge	N
Lynch, District Judge	SE
Mallon, District Judge	NE
Manning-Davies, District Judge	Wales
McIvor, District Judge	SE
McPhee, District Judge	SE
Mellanby, District Judge	SE
Meredith, District Judge	M
Morgan, District Judge Bruce	M
Morgan, District Judge Loraine	W
Morris, District Judge	M
Mottram, District Judge	M
Nuttall, District Judge	M
Parsons, District Judge Graham Colin	SE
Parsons, District Judge David Huw	W
Pattinson, District Judge	SE

16

Perkins, District Judge SE
Philips, District Judge SE
Prowse, District Judge N
Purdy, District Judge SE
Qureshi, District Judge Khalid Jamil M
Qureshi, District Judge Shamim Ahmed M
Read, District Judge SE
Richardson, District Judge N
Riddle, District Judge SE
Roscoe, District Judge SE
Rose, District Judge SE
Rosenberg, District Judge NE
Rutherford, District Judge NE
Sanders, District Judge N
Sawetz, District Judge SE
Shaw, District Judge Wales
Shelvey, District Judge N
Sheraton, District Judge SE
Simpson, District Judge SE
Sims, District Judge SE
Snow, District Judge SE
Somjee, District Judge SE
Stobart, District Judge M
Stone, District Judge SE
Sweet, District Judge SE
Taylor, District Judge M
Thomas, District Judge NE
Tubbs, District Judge SE
Vickers, District Judge SE
Wain, District Judge SE
Walker, District Judge NE
Wallis, District Judge SE
Ward, District Judge N
Watkins, District Judge Wales
Watkins, District Judge Jill Wales
Wheeler, District Judge M
Wilkinson, District Judge M
Williams, District Judge Susan Frances SE
Williams, District Judge Richard Evan Huw Wales
Wood, District Judge NE
Woollard, District Judge W
Wright, District Judge Chief Magistrate's Office
Zani, District Judge SE
Zara, District Judge M

TRIBUNALS

TRIBUNALS SERVICE

The Tribunals Service is a government agency that provides common administrative support to the main central government tribunals. The Tribunals Service is an executive agency of the Ministry of Justice (MoJ) and it's launch was the biggest change to the tribunals system in this country in almost half a century.

Tribunals are an important part of the justice system, handling more cases each year than the ordinary civil courts, many involving the most vulnerable people in our society.

Senior President of Tribunals
Carnworth, Robert, The Hon. Sir CVO

Chief Executive
Sadler, Kevin

AGRICULTURAL LAND TRIBUNALS

OFFICE
Government Buildings (Block 3), Burghill Road, Westbury-on-Trym, Bristol BS10 6NJ Tel: 0300 060 1379 Fax: 0300 060 2186 Email: ray.gilbey@defra.gsi.gov.uk

ALT Secretary
Gilbey, Mr R J

SOUTH WESTERN REGION
(Old county of) Avon, Cornwall, Devon, Dorset, Gloucestershire, Somerset, Wiltshire, Isles of Scilly

SOUTH EASTERN REGION
Berkshire, Buckinghamshire, East Sussex, Hampshire, Isle of Wight, Kent, Oxfordshire, Surrey, West Sussex, *London Boroughs south of River Thames including Richmond upon Thames*

EASTERN REGION
Bedfordshire, Cambridgeshire, Essex, Hertfordshire, Lincolnshire, Norfolk, Northamptonshire, Suffolk, *London Boroughs north of the River Thames except Richmond upon Thames*

OFFICE
DEFRA Buildings, Electra Way, Crewe, Cheshire CW1 6GJ Tel: 01270 754156 Fax: 01270 754163 Email: michael.baker@defra.gsi.gov.uk

ALT Secretary
Baker, Mr M

NORTHERN REGION
Cumbria, Durham, Northumberland, Tyne & Wear, Tees Valley

YORKSHIRE AND HUMBERSIDE REGION
North Yorkshire, West Yorkshire, (Old county of) Humberside, South Yorkshire

WESTERN REGION
Cheshire, Greater Manchester, Lancashire, Merseyside, Shropshire, Staffordshire

MIDLANDS REGION
Derbyshire, Herefordshire & Worcestershire, Leicestershire, Nottinghamshire, Warwickshire, West Midlands

OFFICE
Government Buildings, Spa Road, Llandrindod Wells, Powys LD1 5HA Tel: 01597 828281 Fax: 01597 828385

ALT Secretary
Davies, Mrs C A

WELSH REGION
Gwynedd, Clwyd, Dyfed, Gwent, Powys, Mid/South & West Glamorgan, Flintshire.

SPECIAL COMMISSIONERS

Office
15/19 Bedford Avenue, London WC1B 3AS Tel: 020 7612 9700 Fax: 020 7436 4150

Presiding Special Commissioner
Oliver, His Hon. Stephen, Q.C.

Clerk
Lester, R P

FIRST TIER TAX TRIBUNALS

Office
45 Bedford Square, London WC1B 3DN Tel: 020 7612 9700 Fax: 020 7436 4150

President
Oliver, Sir Stephen Q.C.

Registrar
Kennerley, June

London Tribunal Centre

Office
45 Bedford Square, London WC1B 3DN Tel: 020 7612 9706 Fax: 020 7436 4150

Edinburgh Tribunal Centre

Office
George House, 126 George Street, Edinburgh EH2 4HH Tel: 0131 271 4330 Fax: 0131 271 4399

Manchester Tribunal Centre

Office
Alexandra House, 14-22 The Parsonage, Manchester M3 2JA Tel: 0161 833 5110 Fax: 0161 833 5151

COPYRIGHT TRIBUNAL

Office
2nd Floor, 21 Bloomsbury Street, London WC1B 3HB Tel: 020 7034 2836 Fax: 020 7034 2826 Website: www.ipo.gov.uk/ctribunal.htm Email: copyright.tribunal@ipo.gov.uk

Chairman
Birff, His Hon. Judge, Q.C.

Secretary
Worley, Catherine
Email: catherine.worley@ipo.gov.uk

EMPLOYMENT TRIBUNALS SERVICE

Policy Office for Employment Tribunals
5th Floor, Victory House, 30-34 Kingsway, London WC2B 6EX Tel: 020 7273 8666 Fax: 020 7273 8670 Web: www.tribunals.gov.uk

Hearings do not take place at this office.

EMPLOYMENT APPEAL TRIBUNALS

Established by the Employment Protection Act 1975 as a Superior Court of Record

England & Wales
Audit House, 58 Victoria Embankment, London EC4Y 0DS Tel: 020 7273 1041 Fax: 020 7273 1045 Email: londoneat@tribunals.gsi.gov.uk Web: www.employmentappeals.gov.uk

Scotland
52 Melville Street, Edinburgh EH3 7HF Tel: 0131 225 3963 Fax: 0131 220 6694 Email: edinburgheat@tribunals.gsi.gov.uk

President
Underhill, The Hon. Mr Justice

Nominated Judges
Smith, The Hon. Lady (Scotland)
Burton, The Hon. Mr Justice

Langstaff, The Hon. Mr Justice
Underhill, The Hon. Mr Justice
Wilkie, The Hon. Mr Justice
Bean, The Hon. Mr Justice
Keith, The Hon. Mr Justice
Cox, The Hon. Mrs Justice
Slade, The Hon. Mrs Justice

Registrar
Donleavy, Ms P

Central Office
Audit House, 58 Victoria Embankment, London EC4Y 0DS Tel: 020 7273 1041

Divisional Office
52 Melville Street, Edinburgh EH3 7HF Tel: 0131 225 3963

Section 9 Judges
Clark, His Hon. Judge Peter
McMullen Q.C., His Hon. Judge
Ansell, His Hon. Judge
Serota Q.C., His Hon. Judge
Richardson, His Hon. Judge
Birtles, His Hon. Judge
Burke Q.C., His Hon. Judge
Pugsley, His Hon. Judge D
Altman, His Hon. Judge J

PUBLIC REGISTERS OF APPLICATIONS & DECISIONS

England & Wales
100 Southgate Street, Bury St. Edmunds IP33 2AQ Tel: 01284 762171

Scotland
Eagle Building, 215 Bothwell Street, Glasgow G2 7TS Tel: 0141 204 0730

EMPLOYMENT TRIBUNALS

Aberdeen
Atholl House, 84-88 Guild Street, Aberdeen AB11 6LT Tel: 01224 593137 Fax: 01224 593138 DX: AB77 ABERDEEN

Ashford
Ashford House, County Square Shopping Centre, Ashford, Kent TN23 1YB Tel: 01233 621346 Fax: 01233 624423 DX: 157160 ASHFORD (KENT) 8

Bedford
8-10 Howard Street, Bedford MK40 3HS Tel: 01234 351306 Fax: 01234 352315 DX: 157150 BEDFORD 11

Birmingham
Phoenix House, 1-3 Newhall Street, Birmingham B3 3NH Tel: 0121 236 6051 Fax: 0121 236 6029

Brighton
Hilton Brighton Metropole, Kings Road, Brighton BN1 2FU Tel: 023 8071 6400 Fax: 023 8063 5506

Bristol
The Crescent Centre, Temple Back, Bristol BS1 6EZ Tel: 0117 929 8261 Fax: 0117 925 3452

Bury St Edmunds
100 Southgate Street, Bury St Edmunds, Suffolk IP33 2AQ Tel: 01284 762171 Fax: 01284 706064

Cardiff
Caradog House, 1-6 St Andrews Place, Cardiff CF10 3BE Tel: 029 2067 8100 Fax: 029 2022 5906

Dundee
Ground Floor, Block C, Caledonian House, Green Market, Dundee DD1 4QX Tel: 01382 221578 Fax: 01382 227136

Edinburgh
54-56 Melville Street, Edinburgh EH3 7HF Tel: 0131 226 5584 Fax: 0131 220 6847DX: ED147 EDINBURGH

Exeter
Keble House, Southernhay Gardens, Exeter EX1 1NT Tel: 01392 279665 Fax: 01392 430063

Glasgow
Eagle Building, 215 Bothwell Street, Glasgow G2 7TS Tel: 0141 204 0730 Fax: 0141 204 0732 DX: 590003 GLASGOW 17

Leeds
4th Floor, City Exchange, 11 Albion Street, Leeds LS1 5ES Tel: 0113 245 9741 Fax: 0113 242 8843 DX: 742940 LEEDS 75

Leicester
Kings Court, 5a New Walk, Leicester LE1 6TE Tel: 0116 255 0099 Fax: 0116 255 6099

Liverpool
1st Floor, Cunard Building, Pier Head, Liverpool L3 1TS Tel: 0151 236 9397 Fax: 0151 231 1484 DX: 715720 LIVERPOOL 14

London Central
Victory House, 30-34 Kingsway, London WC2B 6EX Tel: 020 7273 8603 Fax: 020 7273 8686 DX: 141420 BLOOMSBURY 7

London East
East London Tribunal Service, Anchorage House, 2 Clove Crescent, London E14 2BE Tel: 020 7538 6161 Fax: 020 7538 6210

London South
Montague Court, 101 London Road, Croydon CR0 2RF Tel: 020 8667 9131 Fax: 020 8649 9470 DX: 155062 CROYDON 39

Manchester
Alexandra House, 14-22 The Parsonage, Manchester M3 2JA Tel: 0161 833 6100 Fax: 0161 832 0249

Newcastle
Quayside House, 110 Quayside, Newcastle-upon-Tyne NE1 3DX Tel: 0191 260 6900 Fax: 0191 222 1680 DX: 742283 NEWCASTLE UPON TYNE 35

Nottingham
3rd Floor, Byron House, 2a Maid Marion Way, Nottingham NG1 6HS Tel: 0115 947 5701 Fax: 0115 950 7612

Reading
30-31 Friar Street, Reading RG1 1DX Tel: 0118 959 4917 Fax: 0118 956 8066

Sheffield
14 East Parade, Sheffield S1 2ET Tel: 0114 276 0348 Fax: 0114 276 2551

Shrewsbury
Prospect House, Belle Vue Road, Shrewsbury SY3 7NR Tel: 01743 358341 Fax: 01743 244186

Southampton
Duke's Keep, Marsh Lane, Southampton SO14 3EX Tel: 023 8071 6400 Fax: 023 8063 5506

Watford
Radius House, 51 Clarendon Road, Watford WD17 1HU Tel: 01923 281750 Fax: 01923 281781

IMMIGRATION AND ASYLUM CHAMBER OF THE FIRST TIER AND UPPER TRIBUNAL

SENIOR JUDICIARY

President
Blake, The Hon Mr Justice

Deputy President
Ockelton, Mr C M G

Legal Senior Immigration Judges
Allen, Mr D K
Chalkley, Mr R
Eshun, Ms K E
Freeman, Mr J G
Gill, Ms D K
Gleeson, Mrs J A
Goldstein, Mr N H
Grubb, Dr A
Jarvis, Ms C
Jordan, Mr A
Kekic, Dr R
King, Mr P D
Lane, Mr C N
Lane, Mr P R
Latter, Mr H J
Macleman, Mr H
Mather, Mr C P
McGeachy, Mr A L
McKee, Mr R A
Nichols, Mrs J E
Perkins, Mr J D
Southern, Mr P D
Spencer, Mr P A
Storey, Dr H H
Taylor, Mrs D E
Ward, Mrs S M
Warr, Mr G
Waumsley, Mr L V

Acting President of the First Tier Tribunal
Arfon-Jones, Miss E

ADMINISTRATION SUPPORT CENTRE
Asylum & Immigration Tribunal, Arnhem House, 31 Waterloo Way, Leicester LE1 6LR Tel: 0845 600 0877 Fax: 0116 249 4130 Email: customer.service@tribunals.gsi.gov.uk

16

REGIONAL OFFICES

BELFAST
The Old Town Hall Building, 80 Victoria Street, Belfast BT1 3FA

BIRMINGHAM OFFICE
2nd Floor, Sheldon Court, 1 Wagon Lane, Birmingham , West Midlands B26 3DU Tel: 0121 685 3300 Fax: 0121 742 4142

Resident Senior Immigration Judge
Renton, Mr N

BRADFORD
Phoenix House, Rushton Avenue, Thornbury, Bradford BD3 7BH

Resident Senior Immigration Judge
Roberts, Mrs C E

FIELD HOUSE
Field House, 15 Breams Buildings, London EC4A 1DZ

Resident Senior Immigration Judge
Southern, Mr P D

GLASGOW
4th Floor, Eagle Building, 215 Bothwell Street, Glasgow, Scotland G2 7EZ

Resident Senior Immigration Judge
Deans, Mr M

HARMONDSWORTH
AIT Harmondsworth, Colnbrook-By-Pass, Harmondsworth, Middlesex UB7 0HD

HATTON CROSS
York House, 2/3 Dukes Green Avenue, Feltham, Middlesex TW14 0LS

Resident Senior Immigration Judge
Clements, Mr M A

LONDON
Taylor House, 88 Roseberry Avenue, London EC1R 4QU

Resident Senior Immigration Judge
Pinkerton, Mr F T

MANCHESTER
AIT Piccadilly Exchange, 1st Floor, Piccadilly Exchange, Piccadilly Plaza, Manchester M1 4AH

Resident Senior Immigration Judge
Conway, Mr D

NEWPORT
Columbus House, Langstone Business Park, Chepstow Road, Newport NP18 2LX

Resident Senior Immigration Judge
Poole, Mr N R

NORTH SHIELDS
Kings Court, Royal Quays, Earl Grey Way, North Shields NE29 6AR

Resident Senior Immigration Judge
Hanson, Mr C J

STOKE-ON-TRENT
Bennett House, Town Road, Hanley, Stoke-on-Trent ST1 2QB

Resident Senior Immigration Judge
Martin, Mrs C J

SURBITON
Sessions House, 17 Ewell Road, Surbiton, Surrey KT6 6AQ

WALSALL OFFICE
2nd Floor, Bridge House, 47 Bridge Street, Walsall WS1 1HZ

YARL'S WOOD
AIT Yarl's Wood, Hearing Centre A, Twinwoods Road, Clapham, Bedfordshire, MK41 6HL

PATENTS COURT

Senior Patents Judges
Kitchin, Mr Justice

Clerk in charge of Patents Court List
Mr Doug Bell, Chancery Listing Officer Tel: 020 7947 6690/6778 Fax: 0870 739 5869

Judges
Lewison, Hon. Mr Justice
Mann, Hon. Mr Justice
Warren, Hon. Mr Justice
Morgan, Hon. Mr Justice
Norris, Hon. Mr Justice
Floyd, Hon. Mr Justice
Arnold, Hon. Mr Justice

WAR PENSIONS AND ARMED FORCES COMPENSATION

Office
Tribunals Service, 5th Floor, Fox Court, 14 Grays Inn Road, London WC2X 8HN Tel: 020 3206 0701 Fax: 020 3206 0702 Email: armedforces.chamber@tribunals.gsi.gov.uk

President
Bano, Judge Andrew

Tribunal Manager
Farren, Mr Paul

UPPER TRIBUNALS ADMINISTRATIVE APPEALS CHAMBERS

London Office
5th Floor, Chichester Rents, 81 Chancery Lane, London WC2A 3DD Tel: 020 7911 7085

Chambers President
Justice Walker

Judges
Levenson, H
Bano, A
Jupp, Mrs E
Jacobs, E
Ward, C
Howell, P, Q.C.
Pacey, S
Williams, D
Powell, P
Pearl, D
Wikely, N
Lane, S
Lloyd-Davies, A
Rowland, M
Mesher, J
Turnbull, C
May, D J, Q.C. (Scot)
Gamble, A

Tribunal Manager
Ranaweera, Emma

Edinburgh Office
George House, 126 George Street, Edinburgh EH2 4HH Tel: 0131 271 4310

Secretary
Niven, Mrs S

THE SOLICITORS DISCIPLINARY TRIBUNAL *(CONSTITUTED UNDER THE SOLICITORS ACT 1974)*

Solicitor Members
Barnecutt, J N, President
Isaacs, A H
Gibson, A G, TD
Bamford, R B
Gaynor-Smith, A
Leverton, D J
Stanley, Mrs E
Chesterton, J C
Spooner, A
Holmes, A
Gilford, L
Cullen, Miss T
Davies, J P
Todner, Ms K
Wolfe, I R
Duncan, K
Banks, Miss A
Nicholas, R
Devonish, Miss J
Green, D
Lucking, Miss N
Glass, D
Richards, E
Martineau, Miss J
Pearson, N
Potts, D
Fanning, M
Nally, E
Sibley, M
Prigg, R
Tinkler, S
Housego, P
Thompson, Miss K
Hegarty, R
Murray, C
Astle, J
Ghosh, A

Lay Members
Bonham-Carter, Lady
Marlow, D E
Baughan, M C
Pickering, Mrs C
Gilbertson, D, QPM
Fisher, G
Taylor, M G, CBE
Murray-Chandra, Mrs V
Jackson, J
Gordon, Mrs S
Howe, Mr S
Marquez, Mr R
Wyatt, Mr P
Chavda, Mrs N
Palayiwa, M
Hallam, M
Barnett, Miss L
Hill, S
Slack, R
McMahon-Hathway, Mrs L

Clerk
Humble, Mrs S (Solicitor)
3rd Floor, Gate House, 1 Farringdon Street, London EC4M 7NS

FIRST-TIER TRIBUNAL (TRANSPORT), UPPER TRIBUNAL TRAFFIC COMMISSIONER APPEALS, LANDS TRIBUNAL (THE LANDS CHAMBER OF THE UPPER TRIBUNAL) & FIRST-TIER TRIBUNAL (IMMIGRATION SERVICES)

Transport Tribunal Office
Victory House, 7th Floor, 30-34 Kingsway, London WC2B 6EX Hours: 9.00am to 5.00pm

Principal Judge
Brodrick , His Hon. Judge Michael

Tribunal Manager
Webb, Kim

Lands Tribunal Office

3rd Floor, 43-45 Bedford Square, London WC1B 3DN Hours 9:00am to 5:00pm

Chamber President
Bartlett, G, Q.C.

Registrars (to whom all communications should be addressed)
Scannell, Donald
Rozanski, Stella

Tribunal Manager
Farr, Laura

Immigration Services Tribunal Office

Victory House, 7th Floor, 30-34 Kingsway, London WC2B 6EX Hours: 9.00am to 5.00pm

Principal Judge
Marriott, Mr George

Tribunal Manager
Webb, Kim

RESIDENTIAL PROPERTY TRIBUNAL SERVICE

National Helpline: 0845 600 3178
Website: www.rpts.gov.uk

Senior President
McGrath, Ms Siobhan

Chief Executive
Ross, Mr Michael

The Residential Property Tribunal Service is the umbrella organisation covering the five Rent Assessment Panels in England which, in turn, provide Rent Assessment Committees, Rent Tribunals, Leasehold Valuation Tribunals, and Residential Property Tribunals. These provide an accessible, efficient and relatively informal tribunal service to the private rented and leasehold housing market, enabling disputes to be settled simply and quickly.

London Rent Assessment Panel

President
McGrath, Ms Siobhan

Vice Presidents
Barran, Ms Veronica
Hamilton-Farey, Ms Aileen
Andrew, Mr Angus

Regional Manager
Frost, Mr Peter
10 Alfred Place, London WC1E 7LR Tel: 020 7446 7700 Fax: 020 7637 1250 Email: london.rap@communities.gsi.gov.uk

Midland Rent Assessment Panel

President
Duffy, Mr Simon

Vice Presidents
Cooper, Mr Timothy
Gravells, Prof Nigel Paul

Regional Manager
Whale, Mrs Sara
2nd Floor, Louisa House, 92-93 Edward Street, Birmingham B1 2RA Tel: 0845 100 2615 / 0121 236 7837 Fax: 0121 236 9337 Email: midland.rap@communities.gsi.gov.uk

Southern Rent Assessment Panel

President
Tarling, Mr John

Vice Presidents
McAllister, Mr John Stanley
Agnew, Mr Donald

Regional Manager
May, Mr Jim
1st Floor, Midland House, 1 Market Avenue, Chichester, West Sussex, PO19 1JU Tel: 0845 100 2617 or 01243 779394 Fax: 01243 779389 Email: southern.rap@communities.gsi.gov.uk

Eastern Rent Assessment Panel

President
Edgington, Mr Bruce

Vice Presidents
Brown, Mr David S

Regional Manager
Allbut, Mr Mark
Unit C4, Quern House, Mill Court, Great Shelford, Cambridge CB22 5LD Tel: 0845 100 2616 / 01223 841524 Fax: 01223 843224 Email: eastern.rap@communities.gsi.gov.uk

Northern Rent Assessment Panel

President
Davey, Mr Martin

Vice Presidents
Robertson, Mr Alan
Thornton-Firkin, Ms Elizabeth
Bennett, Mr Laurence

Regional Manager
Whipp, Ms Beatrice
1st Floor, 5 New York Street, Manchester M1 4JB Tel: 0845 100 2614 / 0161 237 9491 Fax: 0161 237 3656 Email: northern.rap@communities.gsi.gov.uk

CORONERS

The Coroners' Society of England and Wales, HM Coroners Court, The Cotton Exchange, Old Hall Street, Liverpool L3 9UF

President 2010/2011
Johnson, Christopher
HM Coroner for The County of Merseyside, Wirral District

Honorary Secretary
Rebello, André J A
HM Coroner for the City of Liverpool
(The Hon. Secretary has overall control of the affairs of the Society - Subject to the Direction of the Council)

ENGLAND

AVON

Acting Coroner – M A Voisin - 2010
Police Station, Southmead Road,Southmead, Bristol BS10 4DW Tel: 0117 945 4822 Fax: 0117 945 4857

Police Station, Walliscote Road, Weston Supermare BS23 1NY Tel: 01934 638128 Fax: 01934 638119

Central Police Station, Manvers Street, Bath BA1 1JN Tel: 01225 842552 Fax: 01225 420413

BEDFORDSHIRE & LUTON

Coroner - D S Morris - 1992
8 Goldington Road, Bedford MK40 3NF Tel: 01234 273011 Fax: 01234 273014

HM Coroner's Office, 1st Floor, Suite 2, Jansel House, Hitchin Road, Luton LU2 7XH Tel: 01234 270443 Fax: 01582 481261

BERKSHIRE

East Berkshire

Coroner - P Bedford - 1999 (2004)
Wexham Park Hospital Mortuary, Wexham Park Hospital, Wexham Street, Slough, SL2 4HL Tel: 01753 633000 Ext: 3732 Fax: 01753 633221

Bracknell Police Station, The Broadway, Bracknell RG12 1AD Tel: 01344 823432 Fax: 01344 823499 / 01628 645635

The Mortuary, Royal Berkshire Hospital, London Road, Reading RG1 5AN Tel: 0118 986 3116 Fax: 0118 975 6594

Police Station, Mill Lane, Newbury RG14 5QU Tel: 01635 264745 Fax: 01635 264651

BUCKINGHAMSHIRE

Buckinghamshire

Coroner - R A Hulett - 1991 (1997)
Police Station, Queen Victoria Road, High Wycombe HP11 1BE Tel: 01494 686180 Fax: 01494 686012

Police Station, Aylesbury HP21 7LA Tel: 01296 396116 Fax: 01296 396036

Milton Keynes

Coroner - R H G Corner - 1976 (1997)
Milton Keynes Police Station, 302 North Row, Witan Gate East, Central Milton Keynes MK9 2DS Tel: 01908 686031 Fax: 01908 686187

CAMBRIDGESHIRE

South & West Cambridgeshire

Coroner - D S Morris - 1987
Lawrence Court, Princes Street, Huntingdon PE29 3PA Tel: 0345 045 1364 Fax: 01480 372777

North and East

Coroner - W R Morris - 1982
Lawrence Court, Princes Street, Huntingdon PE29 3PA Tel: 0345 045 1364 Fax: 01480 372777

CHESHIRE

Coroner - N L Rheinberg - 1992 (1999)
East Annexe, Town Hall, Sankey Street, Chester WA1 1UH Fax: 01925 442470

Chester
Tel: 01925 442473

Crewe
Tel: 01925 442481

Macclesfield
Tel: 01925 442478

Warrington
Tel: 01925 442475

CLEVELAND

Teesside

Coroner - M J F Sheffield - 1969
Newham House, 96-98 Borough Road, Middlesbrough TS1 2HJ Tel: 01642 243221 Fax: 01642 248031

Hartlepool

Coroner - C W M Donnelly - 1997
Newham House, 96-98 Borough Road, Middlesbrough TS1 2HJ Tel: 01642 243221 Fax: 01642 248031

CORNWALL

Coroner - E E Carlyon - 2000 (2001)
Truro Police Station, Tregolls Road, Truro TR1 1PY Tel: 01872 326210 Fax: 01872 326209

ISLES OF SCILLY

Coroner - I Arrow - 2003 (2006)
Cary Chambers, 1 Palk Street, Torquay TQ2 5EL Tel: 01803 380705 Fax: 01803 380704

CUMBRIA

South & East Cumbria & Furness

Coroner - I Smith - 1990 (2003)
Central Police Station, Market Street, Barrow-in-Furness LA14 2LE Tel: 01229 848868 Fax: 01229 848899

Western Cumbria

Coroner - D Roberts - 2009
38/42 Lowther Street, Whitehaven CA28 7JU Tel: 01946 692461/3 Fax: 01946 692015

DERBYSHIRE

Derby & South

Coroner - R W Hunter - 2007
St Katherine's House, St Mary's Wharf, Mansfield Road, Derby DE1 1TQ Tel: 01332 613014 Fax: 01332 294942 Email: derby.coroner@btopenworld.com

Scarsdale and High Peak

Coroner - R W Hunter- 2007 (2009)
69 Saltergate, Chesterfield S40 1JS Tel: 01246 201391 Fax: 01246 273058 Email: derby.coroner@btopenworld.com

DEVON

Exeter and Greater Devon

Coroner - E A Earland - 2003
Devon & Cornwall Constabulary, Heavitree Road, Exeter EX1 2LR Tel: 01392 451771 Fax: 01392 451656

Devon & Cornwall Constabulary, North Walk, Barnstaple EX31 1DQ Tel: 01271 341257 Fax: 01271 341255

Plymouth and South West Devon

Coroner - I M Arrow - 2003 (2007)
Cary Chambers, 1 Palk Street, Torquay TQ2 5EL Tel: 01803 380705 Fax: 01803 380704

Torbay and South

Coroner - I M Arrow - 2003
Cary Chambers, 1 Palk Street, Torquay TQ2 5EL Tel: 01803 380705 Fax: 01803 380704

DORSET

Bournemouth, Poole & Eastern Dorset

Coroner - S S Payne - 2000
The Coroner's Court, Stafford Road, Bournemouth BH1 1PA Tel: 01202 310049 Fax: 01202 780423

Western Dorset

Coroner - M C Johnston - 1979
The Coroner's Office, The Plocks, Blandford Forum DT11 7QB Tel: 01305 223033 Fax: 01258 455747

DURHAM

South

Coroner - A Tweedie - 1997 (2004)
Police Office, St Cuthberts Way, Darlington DL1 5LW Tel: 01325 742183 Fax: 01325 742183

Police Office, Woodhouse Lane, Bishop Auckland DL14 6LB Tel: 01388 603566 Fax: 01325 742323

North

Coroner - A Tweedie - 1997
The Police Station, New Elvet, Durham City DH1 3AQ Tel: 0191 375 2818

The Police Station, Stanley DH9 0BL Tel: 0191 375 2824

ESSEX

Coroner - C Beasley-Murray - 2000

Essex & Thurrock

New Bridge House, 60-68 New London Road, Chelmsford, Essex CM2 0PD Tel: 01245 506763 Fax: 01245 357335

Southern and South East

Coroner - P Dean - 1992
New Bridge House, 60-68 New London Road, Chelmsford, Essex CM2 0PD Tel: 01245 506763 Fax: 01245 357335

GLOUCESTERSHIRE

Cheltenham

Coroner - A C Crickmore - 2003 (2005)
County Offices, St George's Road, Cheltenham GL50 3PF Tel: 01242 221064 Fax: 01242 226575

Gloucester

Coroner - A C Crickmore - 2003
Maitland House, Spa Road, Gloucester, GL1 1VY Tel: 01452 305661 Fax: 01452 307935

HAMPSHIRE

Central Hampshire

Coroner - G A Short - 1991
New King's Court, Tollgate, Chandlers Ford SO53 3LG Tel: 023 8085 7447/8

North East Hampshire

Coroner - A M Bradley - 1989
Police Station, London Road, Basingstoke RG21 4AG Tel: 01256 473111 Fax: 01256 405001

Portsmouth and South East Hampshire

Coroner - D C Horsley - 2003
Coroner's Office, The Guildhall, Guildhall Square, Portsmouth PO1 2AJ Tel: 023 9268 8328/9 Fax: 023 9268 8331

Southampton

Coroner - K S Wiseman - 1993
Coroner's Office, Police Station, Civic Centre, Southampton SO14 7LG Tel: 023 8067 4266 Fax: 023 8022 3631

HEREFORDSHIRE

Coroner - D M Halpern - 1994
The Police Station, Bath Street, Hereford HR1 2HT Tel: 01432 276422 Fax: 01432 279006

HERTFORDSHIRE

Coroner - E G Thomas - 1993 (2004)
Hertfordshire Coroner's Unit, The Old Court House, St Albans Road East, Hatfield AL10 0ES Tel: 01707 897401/7 Fax: 01707 897399

ISLE OF WIGHT

Coroner - J A Matthews - 1994
3-9 Quay Street, Newport PO30 5BB Tel: 01983 520697 Fax: 01983 527678

KENT

Central & South East Kent

Coroner - H R Redman - 1999
Ashford Police Station, Tufton Street, Ashford TN23 1BT Tel: 01233 896242 Fax: 01233 896449

Police Station, Bouverie Road West, Folkestone CT20 2RW Tel: 01303 289147 Fax: 01303 289439

Mid Kent & Medway

Coroner - R J Sykes - 1986
Police Station, Palace Avenue, Maidstone ME15 6NF Tel: 01622 604115 Fax: 01622 604119

Medway Maritime Hospital, Windmill Road, Gillingham ME7 5NY

North East Kent

Coroner - R M Cobb- 1983 (2001)
Margate Police Station, Fort Hill, Margate CT9 1HL Tel: 01843 222170/171/173/128/153 Fax: 01843 222172

North West Kent

Coroner - R L Hatch - 1997
Tunbridge Wells Police Station, Crescent Road, Tunbridge Wells TN1 2OU Tel: 01892 502171 Fax: 01892 502172

North Kent Police Station, Thames Way, Northfleet, Gravesend DA11 8BD Tel: 01474 366481 Fax: 01474 366489

LANCASHIRE

Blackburn

Coroner - M Singleton - 1999
Lancashire Constabulary, Eastern Div HQ, Greenbank, Blackburn BB1 3HT Tel: 01254 294116 Fax: 01254 294563

The Royal Blackburn Hospital, Haslingdon Road, Blackburn BB2 3HH

Blackpool & Fylde

Coroner - A Hind (2004)
Lancashire Constabulary, Bonny Street, Blackpool FY1 5RL Tel: 01253 604207

East Lancashire

Coroner - R G Taylor (2002)
General Hospital, Burnley BB10 2PQ Tel: 01282 804508 Fax: 01282 474508

Preston & West

Coroner - J R H Adeley - 2005
Coroners Court, 2 Faraday Court, Faraday Drive, Fulwood, Preston PR2 9NB Tel: 01772 703700 Fax: 01772 704422

LEICESTERSHIRE

City & South

Coroner - C E Mason - 2009
The Town Hall, Town Hall Square, Leicester LE1 9BG Tel: 0116 225 2534 Fax: 0116 225 2537

North Leicestershire

Coroner - T H Kirkman - 2000
34 Wood Gate, Loughborough LE11 2TY Tel: 01509 268748 Fax: 01509 210744

LINCOLNSHIRE

Boston & Spalding

Coroner - M Taylor - 1989
Boston Police Station, Lincoln Lane, Boston PE21 8QS Tel: 01205 312217 Fax: 01205 312353

West Lincolnshire

Coroner - S P G Fisher - 2009
Divisional Police HQ, Swingbridge Road, Grantham NG31 7XT Tel: 01476 403217 Fax 01476 403219

North & Grimsby

Coroner - P Kelly - 2008
The Coroner's Office, The Town Hall, Knoll Street, Cleethorpes DN35 8LN Tel: 01472 324005 Fax: 01472 324007

Louth & Spilsby

Coroner - S P G Fisher - 1994
Police Station, Lincoln Lane, Boston PE21 8QS Tel: 01205 312330 Fax: 01205 312353

Stamford

Coroner - G S Ryall - 1975
Lincolnshire Police Divisional HQ, St Catherine's Road, Grantham NG31 9DD Tel: 01476 403217 Fax: 01476 403219

LONDON

City of London

Coroner - P Matthews - 2002
City of London Coroner's Court, 1 Walbrook Wharf, 78-83 Upper Thames Street, London EC4R 3TD Tel: 020 7332 1598 Fax: 020 7601 2714

East London

Coroner - E Stearns - 1998
Coroners Court, Queens Road, Walthamstow, London E17 8QP Tel: 020 8496 5000 Fax: 020 8496 3378

Inner North London

Coroner - A S Reid - 2002
St Pancras Coroner's Court, Camley Street, London NW1 0PP Tel: 020 7387 4882 Fax: 020 7383 2485

Poplar Coroner's Court, 127 Poplar High Street, London E14 0AE Tel: 020 7987 3614 Fax: 020 7538 0565

Inner South London

Coroner - *to be appointed*
Southwark Coroner's Court, 1 Tennis Street, London SE1 1YD Tel: 020 7089 6380 Fax: 020 7378 8401

Lewisham and Greenwich Office, 3 Devonshire Drive, Greenwich, London SE10 8LF Tel: 020 8692 0530 Fax: 020 8691 8832

Inner West London

Coroner - P A Knapman - 1980
Westminster Coroner's Court, 65 Horseferry Road, London SW1P 2ED Tel: 020 7834 6515 Fax: 020 7828 2837

Battersea Office, 48 Falcon Road, London SW11 2LR Tel: 020 7228 6044 Fax: 020 7738 0640

North London

Coroner - A Walker - 2007
Hornsey Coroner's Court, Myddelton Road, Hornsey, London N8 7PY Tel: 020 8348 4411 Fax: 020 8347 5229

Edgware Police Station, Whitchurch Lane, Edgware, Middlesex HA8 6LA Tel: 020 8733 3567

South London

Coroner - R N Palmer - 2001
Coroner's Court, Barclay Road, Croydon CR9 3NE Tel: 020 8681 5019 Fax: 020 8686 3491

Croydon and Sutton Office, 150 Thornton Road, Thornton Heath, CR7 6BB Tel: 020 8684 2758 Fax: 020 8684 2796

Bromley and Bexley Office, Kingfisher House, 21-23 Elmfield Road, Bromley BR1 1LT Tel: 020 8315 7580 Fax: 020 8315 7588

West London

Coroner - Alison M Thompson - 2000
West London Coroner's Court, 25 Bagleys Lane, Fulham, London SW6 2QA Tel: 020 8753 6800/2 Fax: 020 8753 6803

Hammersmith, Fulham & Hounslow Office, 25 Bagleys Lane, Fulham, London SW6 2QA Tel: 020 8753 6804/9

Kingston Office, Kingston Hospital, Wolverton Avenue, Kingston KT2 7QB Tel: 020 8934 2649/50 Fax: 020 8934 3097

Uxbridge Office, Hillingdon Mortuary, Kingston Lane, Uxbridge UB8 3PN Tel: 01895 237286 Fax: 01895 257047

GREATER MANCHESTER

Manchester

Coroner - N Meadows - 2006
HM Coroners Office, Crown Square, Manchester M60 1PR Tel: 0161 830 4222 Fax: 0161 830 4328/9

North Manchester

Coroner - S R Nelson - 2002
Rochdale Police Station Tel: 0161 856 8497

Bury Police Station Tel: 0161 856 8097

Oldham Police Station Tel: 0161 856 8820

South Manchester

Coroner - J S Pollard - 1995
Coroner's Court, Mount Tabor, Mottram Street, Stockport SK1 3PA Tel: 0161 474 3993 Fax: 0161 474 3994

West Manchester

Coroner - J Leeming - 2001
Paderborn House, Civic Centre, Howell Croft North, Bolton BL1 1JW Tel: 01204 527322 Fax: 01204 387674

MERSEYSIDE

Sefton, Knowsley & St. Helens

Coroner - C K Sumner - 1998
Sefton North and South, Southport Police Station, Law Courts, Southport Tel: 0151 7773 4800

Whiston & St Helens

Coroners Officer, Whiston Hospital, Whiston L35 5DR Tel: 0151 430 1238 / 426 6694

Liverpool

Coroner - André J A Rebello - 1994 (1999)
HM Coroner's Court, The Cotton Exchange, Old Hall Street, Liverpool L3 9UF Tel: 0151 233 4701/8 Fax: 0151 233 4710

Wirral

Coroner - C W Johnson - 1988
The Concourse, Grange Road, West Kirby, Wirral CH48 4DZ Tel: 0151 625 2207/5042 Fax: 0151 625 9477

NORFOLK

Coroner - W J Armstrong - 1996 (2010)
69 – 75 Thorpe Road, Norwich NR1 1UA

Officers:

Senior – Loraine Marshall	Tel: 01603 276490
Sue Ross	Tel: 01603 276491
Haley Fitzpatrick	Tel: 01603 276491
Ian Whittaker	Tel: 01603 276496
Paul Chapman	Tel: 01603 276495

NORTHAMPTONSHIRE

Coroner - A Pember -1994

Northampton

Campbell Square Police Station, Northampton NN1 3EB Tel: 01604 703618 Fax: 01604 703716

Kettering

Kettering Police Station, London Road, Kettering NN15 7PQ Tel: 01536 534827 Fax: 01536 534717

NORTHUMBERLAND

North Northumberland

Coroner - Anthony Brown - 2008
17 Church Street, Berwick-upon-Tweed, TD15 1EE Tel: 01289 304318 Fax: 01289 303591

South Northumberland

Coroner - E Armstrong - 2003
Hexham Police Station, Northumbria Police, SW Area Command, Shaftoe Leazes, Hexham NE46 3DG Tel: 01661 861454 Fax: 01661 861458

Blyth & Bedlington Police Station, Northumbria Police, SE Area Command, 104 Station Road, Ashington NE63 8HD Tel: 01661 872555 Ext: 61654 Fax: 01661 861688

NOTTINGHAMSHIRE

Coroner - N D Chapman - 1993
50 Carrington Street, Nottingham NG1 7FG Tel: 0115 941 2322 Fax: 0115 950 0141

OXFORDSHIRE

Oxford

Coroner - N G Gardiner - 1981
The Old School House, High Street, Cumnor, Oxford OX3 9DU Tel: 01865 861912 Fax: 01865 864207

PETERBOROUGH

Coroner - G S RYALL - 1977
Bridge Street Police Station, Peterborough PE1 1EQ Tel: 01733 424450/9 Fax: 01733 424405

THE ROYAL HOUSEHOLD

Coroner - M J C Burgess - 2002
49 Ormond Avenue, Hampton TW12 2RY Tel: 07968 832075

SHROPSHIRE

Telford and Wrekin

Coroner - J P Ellery – 2003 (2009)
Wellington Police Station, Victoria Road, Wellington, Telford TF1 1LQ Tel: 01952 214818/47 Fax: 01952 214833

Mid and North Shropshire

Coroner - J P Ellery - 2003
West Mercia Constabulary, Police HQ, Clive Road, Monkmoor, Shrewsbury SY2 5RW Tel: 01743 237445 Fax: 01743 264879

South Shropshire

Coroner - A F T Sibcy - 1984
The Police Station, Lower Galdeford, Ludlow SY8 1FA Tel: 0845 744 4888 Ext: 4608 Fax: 01743 264736

SOMERSET

Eastern

Coroner - T Williams - 1999
Police Station, 23 Commercial Road, Shepton Mallett BA4 5BH Tel: 01935 402312 Fax: 01935 402311

Western

Coroner - M R Rose - 1986
The Police Station, Shuttern, Taunton TA1 3QA Tel: 01823 363262 Fax: 01823 363215

STAFFORDSHIRE

Stoke-on-Trent & North Staffordshire

Coroner - I S Smith - 2001 (2003)
Coroner's Court & Chambers, 547 Hartshill Road, Hartshill, Stoke-on-Trent ST4 6HF Tel: 01782 234793 Fax: 01782 234783

South Staffordshire

Coroner - A A Haigh - 2000

Stafford

Stafford Borough Police Station, Eastgate Street, Stafford ST16 2DQ Tel: 01785 234083 Fax: 01785 234063

Cannock

Stafford Borough Police Station, Eastgate Street, Stafford ST16 2DQ Tel: 01785 234019

Burton-on-Trent

Burton Police Station, Horninglow, Burton-on-Trent DE14 1PA Tel: 01785 234783 Fax: 01785 234783

SUFFOLK

Greater Suffolk

Coroner - P Dean - 2002
Ipswich Police Station, Civic Drive, Ipswich IP1 2AW Tel: 01473 383167 Fax: 01473 281300

SURREY

Coroner - M J C Burgess - 1986
Coroner's Court, Station Approach, Woking GU22 7AP Tel: 01483 637300 Fax: 01483 634814

SUSSEX

East Sussex

Coroner - A R Craze - 1998

Hastings & Rother District Police Station, Bohemia Road, Hastings TN34 1BT Tel: 01424 456009 Fax: 01424 456096

Wealden, Eastbourne and Lewes District Police Station, Hailsham BN27 1AB Tel: 01323 414067 Fax: 01323 414038

Brighton & Hove

Coroner - V Hamilton-Deeley - 1997
Brighton Police Station, John Street, Brighton BN2 2LA Tel: 01273 665572/25/04 Fax: 01273 665543

West Sussex

Coroner - P A Schofield - 2008
Police Station, Kingsham Road, Chichester PO19 8AD Tel: 01243 520217 Fax: 01243 520354

Centenary House, Durrington Lane, Worthing BN13 2PQ Tel: 01243 843508 Fax: 01243 843566

Police Station, Bolnore Road, Haywards Heath RH16 4BA Tel: 01444 445808 Fax: 01444 445955

Police Station, Hurst Road, Horsham RH12 2DJ Tel: 01243 520286 Fax: 01243 520514

TYNE AND WEAR

South Tyneside

Coroner - T Carney - 2001
Northumbria Police HQ, Keppel Street, South Shields NE33 1LX Tel: 0191 510 2020 Fax: 0191 563 5139

Northumbria Police HQ, High West Street, Gateshead NE8 1BN Tel: 0191 221 9054 Fax: 0191 221 9188

Newcastle upon Tyne

Coroner - D Mitford - 1998
Coroner's Department Civic Centre, Barras Bridge, Newcastle Upon Tyne NE1 8PS Tel: 0191 277 7280 Fax: 0191 261 2952

North Tyneside

Coroner - E Armstrong - 2003
Police Station, Northumbria Police, Tynemouth Area Command, Upper Pearson Street, North Shields NE30 1AB Tel: 01661 872555 Ext: 63054 Fax: 01661 863177

Sunderland

Coroner - D Winter - 2003
Sunderland Civic Centre, Burdon Road, Sunderland SR2 7DN Tel: 0191 5617839/40/41/42/43 Fax: 0191 553 7803

WARWICKSHIRE

Coroner - S McGovern - 2007

Leamington Spa

The Police Station, Priory Road, Warwick CV34 4NA Tel: 01926 684349 Fax: 01926 684326

Stratford upon Avon

The Police Station, Rother Street, Stratford Upon Avon CV37 6RD Tel: 01789 444521 Fax: 01926 444688

Nuneaton

Bedworth Police Station, King Street, Bedworth CV12 8NH Tel: 024 7648 3361 Fax: 024 7648 3392

Rugby

County Police Office, Newbold Road, Rugby CV21 2DH Tel: 01788 853749 Fax: 01788 853869

WEST MIDLANDS

Birmingham and Solihull

Coroner - A K Cotter - 1984 (2001)
HM Coroner's Court, 50 Newton Street, Birmingham B4 6NE Tel: 0121 303 3920 Fax: 0121 233 4841

Black Country

Coroner - R J Balmain - 2000 (2004)
Crocketts Lane, Smethwick B66 3BS Tel: 0845 352 7483 Fax: 0845 352 7487

Coventry

Coroner - S McGovern - 2007
Police HQ, Little Park Street, Coventry CV1 2JX Tel: 024 7653 9018 Fax: 024 7653 9804

Wolverhampton

Coroner - R J Allen - 2001
Coroner's Court, Civic Centre, St Peter's Square, Wolverhampton WV1 1SD Tel: 01902 554599 Fax: 01902 551438

WILTSHIRE & SWINDON

Coroner - D W G Ridley - 2009
Divisional Pol. HQ, Wilton Road, Salisbury SP2 7HNR Tel: 01722 435293 Fax: 01722 435291

Divisional Police HQ, Hampton Park West, Melksham SN12 6QQ Tel: 01249 449633 Fax: 01249 449626

Swindon Police Station, Gablecross, Shrivenham Road, South Marston, Swindon SN3 4RB Tel: 01793 507841 Fax: 01793 507840

WORCESTERSHIRE

Coroner - G U Williams - 2007
HM Coroner's Office, Police Station, Castle Street, Worcester WR1 2JQ Tel: 01905 331026 Fax: 01905 331025

Alexandra Hospital Mortuary, Woodrow, Redditch B98 7UB Tel: 01527 512045 Fax: 01527 512130

YORK

Coroner - W D F Coverdale - 1987 (1998)
North Yorkshire Police Divisional HQ, Fulford Road, York YO1 4BY Tel: 01904 669332

York District Hospital, Wigginton Road, York YO3 7HE Tel: 01904 726804

YORKSHIRE NORTH

East

Coroner - M D Oakley - 1979
Scarborough Police Station, Northway, Scarborough DL7 8BR Tel: 01723 509332 Fax: 01723 509813

72 High Street, Northallerton DL7 8ES Tel: 01609 789458

West

Coroner - R Turnbull - 2010
Richmond Area, Northallerton Police Station, High Street, Northallerton DL7 8BR Tel: 01609 789458 Fax: 01609 789413

Harrogate Area, Harrogate Police Station, North Park Road, Harrogate HG1 5PJ Tel: 01423 539332 Fax: 01423 539324

Craven Area, Skipton Police Station, Potholme Road YO8 4QQ Tel: 01756 539701 Fax: 01756 539713

Selby Area, Selby Police Station, Portholme Road YO8 4QQ Tel: 01904 669654 Fax: 01904 669651

YORKSHIRE SOUTH

East

Coroner - N J Mundy - 2009
Doncaster Coroner's Court and Office, 5 Union Street (off St Sepulchre Gate West), Doncaster DN1 3AE Tel: 01302 385031 Fax: 01302 364833

Rotherham

The Police Station, Main Street, Rotherham S60 1QU Tel: 01709 832031 Fax: 01709 832185

West

Coroner - C P Dorries - 1991
Barnsley Police Station, Churchfields, Barnsley S70 2DL Tel: 01226 736031 Fax: 01226 736295

Medico-Legal Centre, Watery Street, Sheffield S3 7ET Tel: 0114 273 8721 Fax: 0114 272 6247

YORKSHIRE WEST

East

Coroner - D Hinchcliffe - 1993

Wakefield

71 Northgate, Wakefield WF1 3BS Tel: 01924 293270/3265/2684/2683 Fax: 01924 302184

Leeds

Symons House, Belgrave Street, Leeds LS2 8DD Tel: 0113 397 0607/3/2/6/4/0 Fax: 0113 245 4892

West

Coroner - R L Whittaker - 1996

Bradford

West Yorkshire Police, Central HQ, The Tyrls, Bradford BD1 1TR Tel: 01274 373037

Keighley

The Mortuary, Airedale General Hospital, Skipton Road, Steeton, Keighley BD20 6TD Tel: 01535 293481

Dewsbury

West Yorkshire Police, Dewsbury Division, Aldams Road, Dewsbury WF12 8AR Tel: 01924 431070

Huddersfield

West Yorkshire Police, Huddersfield Division, Castlegate, Huddersfield HD1 2NJ Tel: 01484 436700

Halifax

HM Coroner's Office, 8 Carlton Street, Halifax HX1 2AL Tel: 01422 354606

YORKSHIRE EAST

East Riding & Kingston Upon Hull

Coroner - G M Saul - 1998
Coroner's Court and Office, Essex House, Manor Street, Kingston upon Hull HU1 1YU Tel: 01482 613009 Fax: 01482 613020

WALES

CARMARTHENSHIRE

Coroner - W J Owen - 1987
Dyfed-Powys Police HQ, Waunlanyrafon, Llanelli, Dyfed SA15 3AA Tel: 01554 772222 Fax: 01554 741118

The Police Station, Friars Park, Carmarthen, Dyfed SA31 3AW Tel: 01267 232000 Fax: 01267 234262

CEREDIGION

Coroner - P L Brunton - 1989
Aberystwyth Police Station, Boulevard St Brieuc, Aberystwyth SY23 1PH Tel: 01970 612791 Fax: 01970 625985

GLAMORGAN

Bridgend & Glamorgan Valleys

Coroner - P Maddox – 2008 (2007)
Coroner's Office, Rock Grounds, Aberdare CF44 7AE Tel: 01685 885202 Fax: 01685 885222

Cardiff & Vale of Glamorgan

Coroner - M E Hassell - 2005
Cardiff Central Police Station, Cathays Park, Cardiff CF10 3NN Tel: 029 2022 2111 Fax: 029 2023 3886

Neath Port Talbot

Coroner - P Rogers – 2008 (2004)
Coroner's Office, Neath Police Station, Gnoll Park Road, Neath SA11 3BW Tel: 01792 562784

Coroner's Offic, Civic Centre, Oystermouth Road, Swansea SA1 3SN

Swansea

Coroner – P Rogers - 2004
Swansea Central Police Station, Grove Place, Swansea SA1 5DF Tel: 01792 450698 Fax: 01792 555577

GWENT

Coroner - D T Bowen - 1984
Victoria Chambers, 11 Clytha Park Rd, Newport, Gwent NP9 4PB Tel: 01633 264194 Fax: 01633 841146

NORTH EAST & NORTH WALES

Coroner - J B Hughes - 1982
Marbel House, Overton Arcade, High Street, Wrexham LL13 8LL Tel: 01978 357775

NORTH WEST WALES

Coroner - D Pritchard Jones - 1984
Bereavement Unit, Ysbyty Gwynedd, Penrhos Road, Bangor, Gwynned LL57 2PW Tel: 01248 384170 Fax: 01248 384170

PEMBROKESHIRE

Coroner - M S Howells - 1980
Police Station, Charles Street, Milford Haven SA73 1SA Tel: 01646 697375 Fax: 01646 690607

POWYS

Coroner - P Maddox - 2007
Divisional Police HQ, Plas y Ffynnon, Cambrian Way, Brecon LD3 7HP Tel: 0845 330 200 Ext: 681 Fax: 01874 620024

N.B. The year appearing next to each Coroner's name signifies the year of first appointment. A year appearing thereafter in brackets signifies the date of the current appointment

ECCLESIASTICAL COURTS

ARCHES COURT OF CANTERBURY

Registry
16 Beaumont Street, Oxford OX1 2LZ

Dean of the Arches
George, The Rt. Wor. Charles R, Q.C.

Registrar
Rees, The Rev. Canon John

VICAR GENERAL'S OFFICE OF THE PROVINCE OF CANTERBURY

Office
16 Beaumont Street, Oxford OX1 2LZ
Hours: 10am to 4pm

Vicar-General
Briden, The Rt. Wor. Timothy

Joint Registrars
Rees, The Rev. Canon John
Slack, Mr Stephen

CHANCERY COURT OF YORK

Registry
Stamford House, Piccadilly, York YO1 9PP

Auditor
George, The Rt. Wor. Charles R, Q.C.

Registrar
Lennox, Mr L P M

VICAR-GENERAL'S OFFICE OF THE PROVINCE OF YORK

Office
Stamford House, Piccadilly, York YO1 9PP

Vicar-General
Coningsby, The Rt Wor. T A, Q.C.
Leyfields, Elmore Road, Chipstead, Surrey CR5 3SG

Registrar
Lennox, Mr L P M
Slack, Mr Stephen (Provincial Elections)

DISCIPLINARY TRIBUNALS ESTABLISHED UNDER THE CLERGY DISCIPLINE MEASURE 2003

President of the Tribunals
Mummery, Rt Hon Lord Justice John

Deputy President
Bullimore, His Hon Judge John

Registrar of Tribunals for the Province of Canterbury
Rees, Rev. Canon John

Registrar of Tribunals for the Province of York
Lennox, Mr Lionel

Designated Officer
Iles, Mr Adrian
c/o The Legal Office, Church House, Great Smith Street, London SW1P 3AZ

THE COURT OF ECCLESIASTICAL CAUSES RESERVED

Registrar (Province of Canterbury)
Rees, The Rev. Canon John
16 Beaumont Street, Oxford OX1 2LZ

Registrar (Province of York)
Lennox, Mr L P M
Stamford House, Piccadilly, York YO1 9PP

COURT OF FACULTIES

Office
1 The Sanctuary, Westminster, London SW1P 3JT Principal Registry for Marriage Licences (Special and Common) for England and Wales. Appointment of Notaries Public in England and Wales. Hours: 10am to 4pm, Mon to Fri

Master of the Faculties
George, The Rt. Wor. Charles R, Q.C.

Registrar
Beesley, Mr P F B

CONSISTORY COURTS

PROVINCE OF CANTERBURY

CANTERBURY *(Commissary Court)*

Commissary General
Walker, His Hon. Judge Richard
1 Whiteoaks, Sutton Lane, Barnstead, Surrey SM7 3SA

Registrar
Carew-Jones, Mr Owen
Minerva House, 5 Montague Close, London SE1 9BB

LONDON

Chancellor
Seed, His Hon. Judge Nigel, Q.C.
3 Paper Buildings, Temple, London EC4Y 7EU

Registrar
Morris, Mr P
Minerva House, 5 Montague Close, London SE1 9BB

WINCHESTER

Chancellor
Clark, The Wor. Christopher, Q.C.
3 Pump Court, London EC4Y 7AJ

Registrar
Johnson, Mr A
Diocesan Registry, Minster Chambers, 42 Castle Street, Salisbury, Wiltshire SP1 3TX

BATH AND WELLS

Chancellor
Briden, The Wor. T J
Lamb Chambers, Lamb Building, London EC4Y 7AS

Registrar
Berry, Mr T
Diocesan Registry, 14 Market Place, Wells, Somerset BA5 2RE

BIRMINGHAM

Chancellor
Cardinal, The Wor. M
Martineau Johnson, No 1 Colmore Square, Birmingham B4 6PP

Registrar
Carslake, Mr H
Martineau Johnson, No 1 Colmore Square, Birmingham B4 6PP

BRISTOL

Chancellor
Behrens, The Wor. Dr James
Serle Court, 6 New Square, London WC2A 3QS

Registrar
Berry, Mr T
Diocesan Registry, 14 Market Place, Wells, Somerset BA5 2RE

CHELMSFORD

Chancellor
Pulman, The Wor. George, Q.C.
Hardwicke Building, New Square, Lincoln's Inn, London WC2A 3SB

Registrar
Hood, Mr B J
53a New Street, Chelmsford CM1 1NE

CHICHESTER

Chancellor
Hill, The Wor. Prof. Mark
3 Pump Court, Temple, London EC4Y 7AJ

Registrar
Stapleton, John
The Corn Exchange, Baffins Lane, Chichester, West Sussex PO19 1GE

COVENTRY

Chancellor
Eyre, The Wor. Stephen
St Philips Chambers, 55 Temple Row, Birmingham B2 5LS

Registrar
Dumbleton, D J
Diocesan Registry, 8-9 The Quadrant, Coventry CV1 2EL

DERBY

Chancellor
Bullimore, The Wor. John
The Rectory, 14 Grange Drive, Elmey, Huddersfield HD8 9SF

Registrar
Waldron, Mrs Nadine
Derby Church House, Full Street, Derby DE1 3DR

ELY

Chancellor
Gage, The Rt. Hon. & Wor. W M, Q.C.
2 Harcourt Buildings, Temple, London EC4Y 9DB

Registrar
Beesley, Mr P F B
1 The Sanctuary, Westminster, London SW1P 3JT

EUROPE

Chancellor
Hill, The Wor. Mark
3 Pump Court, London EC4Y 7AJ

Registrar
Hargreaves-Smith, Mr Aiden
14 Tufton Street, London SW1P 3QZ

EXETER

Chancellor
McFarlane, The Wor. A
Diocesan Registry, Woodwater House, Pynes Hill, Exeter EX2 5WR

Registrar
Follett, Mr M
Diocesan Registry, Woodwater House, Pynes Hill, Exeter EX2 5WR

GLOUCESTER

Chancellor
Rogers, The Wor. D J
2 Harcourt Buildings, Temple, London EC4Y 9DB

Registrar
Peak, Mr C G
Diocesan Registry, 34 Brunswick Road, Gloucester GL1 1JW

GUILDFORD

Chancellor
Jordan, The Wor. Andrew
11 Fairlawn Avenue, Chiswick, London W4 5DF

Registrar
Beesley, Mr P F B
1 The Sanctuary, Westminster, London SW1P 3JT

HEREFORD

Chancellor
Kaye, The Wor. R, Q.C.
24 Old Buildings, Lincoln's Inn, London WC2A 3UP

Registrar
Beesley, Mr P F B
1 The Sanctuary, Westminster, London SW1P 3JT

LEICESTER

Chancellor
Behrens, The Wor. Dr James
Serle Court, 6 New Square, Lincoln's Inn, London WC2A 3QS

Registrar
Kirkman, The Rev. Trevor
Latham & Co, Charnwood House, 2 Forest Road, Loughborough LE1 3NP

LICHFIELD

Chancellor
Coates, His Hon. Judge Marten
1 Old Barn House Mews, Hill Top, Longdon Green, Lichfield WS15 7LD

Registrars
Blackie, Mr N
FBC Manby Bowdler LLP, Routh House, Hall Court, Hall Parkway, Telford TF3 4NQ

LINCOLN

Chancellor
Bishop, The Wor. Mark
c/o Chatterton House, 2 Low Moor Road, Doddington Road, Lincoln LN6 3JY

Registrar
Mockford, Caroline
Chatterton House, 2 Low Moor Road, Doddington Road, Lincoln LN6 3JY

NORWICH

Chancellor
Downes, His Hon. Judge Paul
Hoveton House, Wroxham, Norwich NR12 8JE

Registrar
Jones, Mr Stuart
Birketts LLP, Kingfisher House, 1 Gilders Way, Norwich NR3 1UB

OXFORD

Chancellor
Bursell, His Hon. The Wor. and Rev Canon Rupert, Q.C.
c/o 16 Beaumont Street, Oxford OX1 2LZ

Registrar
Rees, The Rev. Canon J
16 Beaumont Street, Oxford OX1 2LZ

PETERBOROUGH

Chancellor
Pittaway, The Wor. David, Q.C.
c/o Diocesan Registry, 4 Holywell Way, Longthorpe, Peterborough PE3 6SS

Registrar
Hemingray, The Reverend Raymond
Diocesan Registry, 4 Holywell Way, Longthorpe, Peterborough PE3 6SS

PORTSMOUTH

Chancellor
Clarke, The Wor. Christopher, Q.C.
31 Southgate Street, Winchester SO23 9EE

Registrar
Tyler, Miss H A G
Diocesan Registry, West End House, 288 West Street, Fareham, Hampshire PO16 0AJ

ROCHESTER

Chancellor
Gallagher, The Wor. John
c/o Minerva House, 5 Montague Close, London SE1 9BB

Registrar
Carew-Jones, Mr Owen
Minerva House, 5 Montague Close, London SE1 9BB

ST ALBANS

Chancellor
Kaye, The Wor. Roger, Q.C.
Holywell Lodge, 41 Holywell Hill, St Albans Hertfordshire AL1 1HE

Registrar
Cheetham, Mr D N
Holywell Lodge, 41 Holywell Hill, St. Albans, Hertfordshire AL1 1HE

ST EDMUNDSBURY & IPSWICH

Chancellor
Blofeld, The Hon. Mr Justice, Q.C.
22-23 Museum Street, Ipswich IP1 1HZ

Registrar
Hall, Mr J
22-23 Museum Street, Ipswich IP1 1HZ

SALISBURY

Chancellor
Wiggs, His Hon. Judge Samuel
The Rookery, 72 Ansty, Wiltshire SP3 5QD

Registrar
Johnson, Mr A
Diocesan Registry, Minster Chambers, 42 Castle Street, Salisbury, Wiltshire SP1 3TX

SOUTHWARK

Chancellor
Petchey, Mr P
Minerva House, 5 Montague Close, London SE1 9BB

Registrar
Morris, Mr P
Minerva House, 5 Montague Close, London SE1 9BB

TRURO

Chancellor
Briden, The Wor. Timothy
Lamb Chambers, Lamb Building, London EC4Y 7AS

Registrar
Follett, Mr M J
Woodwater House, Pynes Hill, Exeter EX2 5WR

WORCESTER

Chancellor
Mynors, The Wor. C
2 Harcourt Buildings, Temple EC4Y 9DB

Registrar
Huskinson, Mr M
8 Sansome Walk, Worcester WR1 1LN

PROVINCE OF YORK

YORK

Chancellor
Collier, His Hon. Judge Peter, Q.C.
c/o Diocesan Registry, Stamford House, Piccadilly, York YO1 9PP

Registrar
Lennox, L P M
Diocesan Registry, Stamford House, Piccadilly, York YO1 9PP

DURHAM

Chancellor
Bursell, His Hon. The Wor. & Rev. Canon Dr R, Q.C.
Brookside, 74 Church Road, Winscombe, Avon BS25 1BP

Registrar
Monckton-Milnes, Hilary
56 North Bondgate, Bishop Auckland, Durham DL14 7PG

BLACKBURN

Chancellor
Bullimore, The Wor. J
14 Grange Drive, Emley, Huddersfield HD8 9SF

Registrar
Hoyle, Mr T A
Diocesan Registry, Cathedral Close, Blackburn BB1 5AA

BRADFORD

Chancellor
Walford, His Hon. Judge J de G
Ingerthorpe Cottage, Thwaites Lane, Markington, North Yorkshire HG3 3PS

Registrar
Foskett, Mr Peter
14 Piccadilly, Bradford, West Yorkshire BD1 3LX

CARLISLE

Chancellor
Tattersall, The Wor. Geoffrey, Q.C.
The Woodlands, Lostcok, Bolton BL6 4JD

Registrar
Lowdon, Mrs B J
The Cube, Barrack Road, Newcastle-Upon-Tyne NE4 6DB

CHESTER

Chancellor
Turner, The Wor. D, Q.C.
14 Grays Inn Square, London WC1R 5JD

Registrar
McFall, Helen
Diocesan Registry, The Friars, 20 White Friars, Chester CH1 1PS

LIVERPOOL

Chancellor
Hedley, The Wor. Sir Justice Mark
Royal Courts of Justice, Strand, London WC2A 2LL

Registrar
Dellar, Mr Howard
1 The Sanctuary, Westminster, London SW1P 3JT

MANCHESTER

Chancellor
Tattersall, The Wor. Geoffrey, Q.C.
The Woodlands, Lostock, Bolton BL6 4JD

Registrar
Monks, Jane
Diocesan Church House, 90 Deansgate, Manchester M3 2GH

NEWCASTLE

Chancellor
McLean, The Wor. Prof. D, Q.C.
6 Burnt Stones Close, Sheffield S10 5TS

Registrar
Lowdon, Mrs B J
The Cube, Barrack Road, Newcastle-Upon-Tyne NE4 6DB

RIPON & LEEDS

Chancellor
Grenfell, The Wor. S
St John's House, Sharow Lane, Ripon HG4 5BN

Joint Registrars
Tunnard, Mr C T & Harding, Mrs Nicola
Ripon Diocesan Registry, Cathedral Chambers, 4 Kirkgate, Ripon HG4 1PA

SHEFFIELD

Chancellor
McClean, The Wor. Prof. D, Q.C.
6 Burnt Stones Close, Sheffield, S10 5TS

Registrar
Vidler, Mr A
68 Clarkehouse Road, Sheffield S10 2LJ

SODOR AND MAN

Vicar General and Chancellor
Faulds, The Wor. C
30 Athol Street, Douglas, Isle of Man IM1 1JA

Registrar
Mann, Mr T A
49 Victoria Street, Douglas, Isle of Man IM1 1LB

SOUTHWELL & NOTTINGHAM

Chancellor
Box, The Wor. Mrs Linda M
Diocesan Registry, Dunham House, Westgate, Southwell, Nottinghamshire NG25 0JL

Registrar
Hodson, Canon C
Diocesan Registry, Dunham House, Westgate, Southwell, Nottinghamshire NG25 0JL

WAKEFIELD

Chancellor
Downes, The Wor. Paul

Joint Registrars
Gill, Mr Julian & Wilding, Mrs Julia
Diocesan Registry, Bank House, Burton Street, Wakefield WF1 2DA

ISLE OF MAN JUDICIARY & COURTS

High Court of Justice of the Isle of Man
Court of General Gaol Delivery
Courts of Summary Jurisdiction

Office
Hall of the Society, 27 Hope Street, Douglas, Isle of Man IM1 1AR Tel: 01624 662910 Fax: 01624 662910 Email: enquiries@iomlawsociety.co.im Web: www.iomlawsociety.co.im

President
Wild Esq, J J

Vice President
Stanley Esq, J B T

Council Members
Kerruish Esq, E P
Carter Esq, J P B
Caine Esq, S F
O'Riordan, Esq K
Dougherty Esq, M
Bird Esq, C (Associate Member)
Cain Esq, S

Secretary
Christian, Mrs G
Tel: 01624 662910

Chief Executive Officer
O'Rourke Ms J
Tel: 01624 679231
Email: jo@iomlawsociety.co.im

Treasurer
Weatherill Esq, L J
Tel/Fax: 01624 674994

Finance Manger
Alletson, Mrs T A
Tel: 01624 679232
Email: taa@iomlawsociety.co.im

Administrator
Cushnie, Mrs L
Tel/Fax: 01624 662910
Email: lc@iomlawsociety.co.im

Compliance Manager
Christie Mrs E
Tel: 01624 679223
Email: ejc@iomlawsociety.co.im

JUDGES AND COURT OFFICERS

H M First Deemster and Clerk of the Rolls
Doyle, His Hon. Deemster D C

H M Second Deemster
To be appointed

H M Deputy Deemster
Corlett, His Hon. Deputy Deemster A T K

H M Judge of Appeal
Tattersall, His Hon. Judge of Appeal Deemster

ATTORNEY GENERALS CHAMBERS

H M Attorney General
Corlett Esq, J

Legislative Draftsmen
Boyde Esq, M E

Legal Officers
Hughes, J
Watts, Ms L
Norman, Ms M
Braidwood, Ms R
Griffin Esq, D
Harding Esq, S
Helfrich, Ms H
Warrilow, Miss M
Murray, Mrs E
Bermingham Esq, D
Davey Esq, P
Bullas, Esq J
Neale, Esq S
Benson, Esq M

General Registry
Office of the High Court and Registry for Deeds and Companies

Chief Registrar
Cregeen Esq, S

ECCLESIASTICAL & CONSISTORY COURT

Vicar-General
Faulds, Clare

Diocesan Registrar
Callow Esq, C J

HIGH BAILIFF'S COURT

High Bailiff of Douglas and Castletown and of Ramsey and Peel
Needham, His Wor. The High Bailiff J

Deputy High Bailiff of Douglas and Castletown and of Ramsey and Peel
Montgomerie Esq, A A

JERSEY JUDICIARY & COURTS

THE ROYAL COURT OF JERSEY

Office
Bailiffs Chambers, Royal Court House, St Helier, Jersey JE1 1DD Tel: 01534 441100

Bailiff
Birt, M C St J

Deputy Bailiff
Bailhache, W J

Commissioners of the Royal Court
Bailhache, Sir Philip
Blair, Q.C., B.G.D.
Clyde-Smith,J.A.
Page, H.W.B.
Pitchers, Sir Christopher
Scriven, Miss P, Q.C.

Jurats
De Veulle, P J, OBE
Tibbo, J C
Le Breton, J L
Clapham, Mrs J
King, Mrs L J
Le Cornu, S J
Morgan, P J
Liddiard, Mr J R P F
Fisher, G W
Kerley, R J
Marrett-Crosby, S
Nicolle, P

Court of Appeal
Bailiff of Jersey
Deputy Bailiff of Jersey
Beloff, The Hon Michael, Q.C. (Blackstone Chambers)
Sumption, J P C, Q.C. (7-8 Essex Street)
Nutting, Sir John, Bt., Q.C.
Steel, Dame Heather
Rowland, Sir Geoffrey, Bailiff of Guernsey
Jones, M S, Q.C.
McNeill, J W, Q.C.
Martin J V, Q.C.
Montgomery, Clare, Q.C.
Pleming, N, Q.C.
Bailhache, Sir Philip
(The Judicial Committee of the Privy Council exercises final appellate jurisdiction in the island.)

Attorney General
Le Cocq, T, Q.C.

Solicitor General
Sharp, H, Q.C.

Crown Advocates
Baker, S
Belhomme, A
Fitz, S
Gollop, J
Jowitt, M
Lacey, B
Macrae, R
Morley-Kirk, R
O'Connell, M
Pedley, R
Robinson, A
Santos Costa, N
Sharpe, S
Whelan, C
Yates, C

Judicial Greffier
Wilkins, M

Deputy Judicial Greffier
Matthews, P

Viscount
Wilkins, M

Deputy Viscount
de Gruchy, P

MAGISTRATES' COURT GREFFE

Magistrate
Falle, R (Acting Magistrate)

Assistant Magistrate
Shaw, Mrs B

Relief Magistrates
Olsen, A
Boxall, G
Le Cornu, D
Harris, P
Santos Costa, N
Mourant, P

PRACTISING ADVOCATES & SOLICITORS

In Jersey Advocates act as both Barristers and Solicitors

Advocates

Amy, R, Ogier, PO Box 404, Whiteley Chambers, Don Street, St Helier JE4 9WG
Backhurst, M J
Baglin, C R, Bedell Cristin, PO Box 75, 26 New Street, St Helier JE4 8PP
Bailhache, P M
Baker, S M, Bakerplatt, PO Box 842, 2 Mulcaster Street, St Helier JE4 0US
Baker, K S
Bale, J F, Verraslaw, Third Floor, 22 Hill Street, St Helier JE2 4YE
Banks, D J, Jersey Financial Services Commission, PO Box 267, 14-18 Castle Street, St Helier JE4 8TP
Barbour, G J, Bedell Cristin, PO Box 75, 26 New Street, St Helier JE4 8PP
Begg, A P, Andrew Begg & Co, 2 Britannia Place, Bath Street, St Helier JE2 4SU
Belhomme, A J, Law Officers' Department, Morier House, Halkett Place, St Helier JE1 1DD

16

Bell, J W R, Carey Olsen, 47 The Esplanade, St Helier JE1 0BD
Benest, D J, Appleby, PO Box 207, 13/14 Esplanade, St Helier JE1 1BD
Benest, F J, Benest & Syvret, Royal Court Chambers, 10 Hill Street, St Helier JE1 1BS
Benest, N S H, Benest & Syvret, Royal Court Chambers, 10 Hill Street, St Helier JE1 1BS
Benest, C V E, Mourant Ozannes, PO Box 87, 22 Grenville Street, St Helier JE4 8PX
Benjamin, W, Appleby, PO Box 207, 13/14 Esplanade, St Helier JE1 1BD
Berry, K C J, Backhurst Dorey & Crane, 24 Sand Street, St Helier JE2 3QF
Bertram, P A, Ogier, PO Box 404, Whiteley Chambers, Don Street, St Helier JE4 9WG
Binnington, A R, Mourant Ozannes, PO Box 87, 22 Grenville Street, St Helier JE4 8PX
Birbeck, M J, Bedell Cristin, PO Box 75, 26 New Street, St Helier JE4 8PP
Birtwistle, D J, Mourant Ozannes, PO Box 87, 22 Grenville Street, St Helier JE4 8PX
Blakeley, O A, Blakeley Legal, Lincoln Chambers, 31 Broad Street, St Helier JE2 3RR
Blomfield, Z G, Viberts, PO Box 737, Pirouet House, Union Street, St Helier JE4 8ZQ
Boddie, R S, Carey Olsen, 47 The Esplanade, St Helier JE1 0BD
Boxall, G R, Appleby, PO Box 207, 13/14 Esplanade, St Helier JE1 1BD
Brambilla, C C, Mourant Ozannes, PO Box 87, 22 Grenville Street, St Helier JE4 8PX
Bridge, A J
Bridgeford, W A M
Brown, H E
Buckley, L J, Carey Olsen, 47 The Esplanade, St Helier JE1 0BD
Burns, E L, Bedell Cristin, PO Box 75, 26 New Street, St Helier JE4 8PP
Byrne, P, Bedell Cristin, PO Box 75, 26 New Street, St Helier JE4 8PP
Byrne, C, Ogier, PO Box 404, Whiteley Chambers, Don Street, St Helier JE4 9WG
Cadin, D M, Bedell Cristin, PO Box 75, 26 New Street, St Helier JE4 8PP
Campbell, J A, Bedell Cristin, PO Box 75, 26 New Street, St Helier JE4 8PP
Carus, A, Bedell Cristin, PO Box 75, 26 New Street, St Helier JE4 8PP
Chambers, M B, Mourant Ozannes, PO Box 87, 22 Grenville Street, St Helier JE4 8PX
Chapman, N J
Clapham, M H, Ogier, PO Box 404, Whiteley Chambers, Don Street, St Helier JE4 9WG
Clark, N L, Appleby, PO Box 207, 13/14 Esplanade, St Helier JE1 1BD
Clarke, A J, Le Gallais & Luce, PO Box 696, 6 Hill Street, St Helier JE4 8YX
Clyde-Smith, J A
Colley, R E, Viberts, PO Box 737, Pirouet House, Union Street, St Helier JE4 8ZQ
Coltman, G E S, Carey Olsen, 47 The Esplanade, St Helier JE1 0BD
Cook, G A, Appleby, PO Box 207, 13/14 Esplanade, St Helier JE1 1BD
Cook, M W, Mourant Ozannes, PO Box 87, 22 Grenville Street, St Helier JE4 8PX
Corbel, D A, Bedell Cristin, PO Box 75, 26 New Street, St Helier JE4 8PP
Corbin, G R P, Mourant Ozannes, PO Box 87, 22 Grenville Street, St Helier JE4 8PX
Crane, S J, Backhurst Dorey & Crane, 24 Sand Street, St Helier JE2 3QF
Cushen, H M
Cushen, P R
Cushing, M P, Appleby, PO Box 207, 13/14 Esplanade, St Helier JE1 1BD
Daggett, R J, Ogier, PO Box 404, Whiteley Chambers, Don Street, St Helier JE4 9WG
Dart, A O, Bedell Cristin, PO Box 75, 26 New Street, St Helier JE4 8PP
Davies, C R G, Backhurst Dorey & Crane, 24 Sand Street, St Helier JE2 3QF
Davies, N C, Mourant Ozannes, PO Box 87, 22 Grenville Street, St Helier JE4 8PX
Davies, C L I
De Gruchy, P P D, BNP Paribas Jersey Branch, PO Box 158, Anley Street, St Helier JE4 8RD
Dempsey, V M, Law Officers' Department, Morier House, Halkett Place, St Helier JE1 1DD
Dessain, A J N, Bedell Cristin, PO Box 75, 26 New Street, St Helier JE4 8PP
Dickinson, J S, Dickinson Gleeson, Second Floor, Charles House, Charles Street, St Helier JE2 4SF
Dixon, K O, Carey Olsen, 47 The Esplanade, St Helier JE1 0BD
Dorey, C J, Backhurst Dorey & Crane, 24 Sand Street, St Helier JE2 3QF
Dorgan, D B, Crill Canavan, 40 Don Street, St Helier JE1 4XD
Drew, S T, Benest & Syvret, Royal Court Chambers, 10 Hill Street, St Helier JE1 1BS
Drummond, A C S, Appleby, PO Box 207, 13/14 Esplanade, St Helier JE1 1BD
Dunlop, M T, Bedell Cristin, PO Box 75, 26 New Street, St Helier JE4 8PP
Dutôt, C R, Law Officers' Department, Morier House, Halkett Place, St Helier JE1 1DD
Eccles, M, Mourant Ozannes, PO Box 87, 22 Grenville Street, St Helier JE4 8PX
Ecobichon, M S, Carey Olsen, 47 The Esplanade, St Helier JE1 0BD
Edge, K J, Ogier, PO Box 404, Whiteley Chambers, Don Street, St Helier JE4 9WG
Edwards, S A, Ogier, PO Box 404, Whiteley Chambers, Don Street, St Helier JE4 9WG
Falle, R A, Bois & Bois, PO Box 429, 4 Bond Street, St Helier JE4 5QR
Field, A D, Ogier, PO Box 404, Whiteley Chambers, Don Street, St Helier JE4 9WG
Fielding, R G S, D'Angibau Willmot, 40 Haven Road, Canford Cliffs, Poole BH13 7LP
Fitz, S E, Ogier, PO Box 404, Whiteley Chambers, Don Street, St Helier JE4 9WG
Fitzgerald, S, Carey Olsen, 47 The Esplanade, St Helier JE1 0BD
Fletcher, L C, Ogier, PO Box 404, Whiteley Chambers, Don Street, St Helier JE4 9WG
Fogarty, C M, Ogier, PO Box 404, Whiteley Chambers, Don Street, St Helier JE4 9WG
Fox, J A, Carey Olsen, 47 The Esplanade, St Helier JE1 0BD
Franckel, S A, Franckel Law, PO Box 128, St Andrew's Studios, 3 St Andrew's Place, St Helier JE4 9QW
Garfield Bennett, E C, Bedell Cristin, PO Box 75, 26 New Street, St Helier JE4 8PP
Garner, A J R
Gaudin, J H, Walkers, PO Box 72, Walker House, 28-34 Hill Street, St Helier JE4 8PN
German, P G, Carey Olsen, 47 The Esplanade, St Helier JE1 0BD
Gerwat, R C, Bedell Cristin, PO Box 75, 26 New Street, St Helier JE4 8PP
Giffard, P H
Gilbert, D, Crill Canavan, 40 Don Street, St Helier JE1 4XD
Gilley, M J, Ogier, PO Box 404, Whiteley Chambers, Don Street, St Helier JE4 9WG
Gleeson, J M P, Bedell Cristin, PO Box 75, 26 New Street, St Helier JE4 8PP
Godden, M R, Sinels, PO Box 595, 79 Bath Street, St Helier JE4 9XE
Gollop, J C, Walkers, PO Box 72, Walker House, 28-34 Hill Street, St Helier JE4 8PN
Goulborn, M C, Bois & Bois, PO Box 429, 4 Bond Street, St Helier JE4 5QR
Gould, L M
Gould, S M, Mourant Ozannes, PO Box 87, 22 Grenville Street, St Helier JE4 8PX
Grace, W, Carey Olsen, 47 The Esplanade, St Helier JE1 0BD
Grace, J M, Mourant Ozannes, PO Box 87, 22 Grenville Street, St Helier JE4 8PX
Guillaume, M I, Ogier, PO Box 404, Whiteley Chambers, Don Street, St Helier JE4 9WG
Habin, S J
Haines, M J, Mourant Ozannes, PO Box 87, 22 Grenville Street, St Helier JE4 8PX
Hall, C, Viberts, PO Box 737, Pirouet House, Union Street, St Helier JE4 8ZQ
Hamel, K M, Mourant Ozannes, PO Box 87, 22 Grenville Street, St Helier JE4 8PX
Hamilton, M L, Mourant Ozannes, PO Box 87, 22 Grenville Street, St Helier JE4 8PX
Hamon, F C
Hancock, S A, Carey Olsen, 47 The Esplanade, St Helier JE1 0BD
Hanson, T V R, Hanson Renouf, Regency House, Regent Road, Hill Street, St Helier JE2 4UZ
Harris, M E, Mourant Ozannes, PO Box 87, 22 Grenville Street, St Helier JE4 8PX
Harris, P C
Harvey-Hills, J, Mourant Ozannes, PO Box 87, 22 Grenville Street, St Helier JE4 8PX
Hawgood, J N F
Heath, H J, Lempriere Whittaker Renouf, PO Box 581, Rutland House, Pitt Street, St Helier JE4 0YL
Herbert, T J, Mourant Ozannes, PO Box 87, 22 Grenville Street, St Helier JE4 8PX
Hewer, F W, BNY Mellon
Hill, J E, Mourant Ozannes, PO Box 87, 22 Grenville Street, St Helier JE4 8PX
Hollywood, S M, Bedell Cristin, PO Box 75, 26 New Street, St Helier JE4 8PP
Hollywood, E L, Law Officers' Department, Morier House, Halkett Place, St Helier JE1 1DD
Hopwood, D J, Bedell Cristin, PO Box 75, 26 New Street, St Helier JE4 8PP
Howard, Z J, Bedell Cristin, PO Box 75, 26 New Street, St Helier JE4 8PP
Howard, S R G, Howard Law, 31 Pier Road, St Helier JE4 8PW
Howe, J J, Ogier, PO Box 404, Whiteley Chambers, Don Street, St Helier JE4 9WG
Hoy, A D, Voisin, Templar House, Don Road, St Helier JE1 1AW
Huelin, S M, Mourant Ozannes, PO Box 87, 22 Grenville Street, St Helier JE4 8PX
Hunter, A J, Bedell Cristin, PO Box 75, 26 New Street, St Helier JE4 8PP
James, P D, Crill Canavan, 40 Don Street, St Helier JE1 4XD
Jeffrey, M G, Carey Olsen, 47 The Esplanade, St Helier JE1 0BD
Johns, S K, Ogier, PO Box 404, Whiteley Chambers, Don Street, St Helier JE4 9WG
Jones, I C, Carey Olsen, 47 The Esplanade, St Helier JE1 0BD
Jordan, E L, Bakerplatt, PO Box 842, 2 Mulcaster Street, St Helier JE4 0US
Journeaux, N F, Carey Olsen, 47 The Esplanade, St Helier JE1 0BD
Jowitt, M T, Mourant Ozannes, PO Box 87, 22 Grenville Street, St Helier JE4 8PX
Kelleher, J D, Carey Olsen, 47 The Esplanade, St Helier JE1 0BD
Kerr, C, Carey Olsen, 47 The Esplanade, St Helier JE1 0BD
Kershaw, N J, Ogier, PO Box 404, Whiteley Chambers, Don Street, St Helier JE4 9WG
Khiani, R

Kosofsky, E, Carey Olsen, 47 The Esplanade, St Helier JE1 0BD
Labesse, J P
Lacey, B H, Mourant Ozannes, PO Box 87, 22 Grenville Street, St Helier JE4 8PX
Landick, P S, Ogier, PO Box 404, Whiteley Chambers, Don Street, St Helier JE4 9WG
Lang, D J, Appleby, PO Box 207, 13/14 Esplanade, St Helier JE1 1BD
Langlois, N M
Lawrence, K J, Ogier, PO Box 404, Whiteley Chambers, Don Street, St Helier JE4 9WG
Lawrence, J M, Viberts, PO Box 737, Pirouet House, Union Street, St Helier JE4 8ZQ
Layzell, E M, Mourant Ozannes, PO Box 87, 22 Grenville Street, St Helier JE4 8PX
Le Cocq, T J, Law Officers' Department, Morier House, Halkett Place, St Helier JE1 1DD
Le Cornu, D E, Hanson Renouf, Regency House, Regent Road, Hill Street, St Helier JE2 4UZ
Le Cornu, P J, Ogier, PO Box 404, Whiteley Chambers, Don Street, St Helier JE4 9WG
Le Cras, P R
Le Guillou, E J, Carey Olsen, 47 The Esplanade, St Helier JE1 0BD
Le Maistre, D P, Crill Canavan, 40 Don Street, St Helier JE1 4XD
Le Marquand, B I
Le Quesne, D F, Viberts, PO Box 737, Pirouet House, Union Street, St Helier JE4 8ZQ
Le Sueur, D G, Bedell Cristin, PO Box 75, 26 New Street, St Helier JE4 8PP
Lempriere, R
Lewis, M P G, Appleby, PO Box 207, 13/14 Esplanade, St Helier JE1 1BD
Lincoln, B J, Mourant Ozannes, PO Box 87, 22 Grenville Street, St Helier JE4 8PX
Livingstone, P M, Jenners, PO Box 260, Broad Street Chambers, 4 & 6 Broad Street, St Helier JE4 8TS
Mackereth, E C P, Ogier, PO Box 404, Whiteley Chambers, Don Street, St Helier JE4 9WG
MacRae, R J, Carey Olsen, 47 The Esplanade, St Helier JE1 0BD
Malyn, T J
Marks, S D, Carey Olsen, 47 The Esplanade, St Helier JE1 0BD
Martin, J C, Le Moulinet
Matthams, P J, Carey Olsen, 47 The Esplanade, St Helier JE1 0BD
Matthews, P, Judicial Greffe, Royal Court House, Royal Square, St Helier JE1 1JG
McCallum, A K
Meiklejohn, S A, Ogier, PO Box 404, Whiteley Chambers, Don Street, St Helier JE4 9WG
Melia, J D, Walkers, PO Box 72, Walker House, 28-34 Hill Street, St Helier JE4 8PN
Metcalfe, A J, Law Officers' Department, Morier House, Halkett Place, St Helier JE1 1DD
Michel, R J, Walkers, PO Box 72, Walker House, 28-34 Hill Street, St Helier JE4 8PN
Michel, J P
Millar, M E
Milner, J F E, Bedell Cristin, PO Box 75, 26 New Street, St Helier JE4 8PP
Milner, V S, Bedell Cristin, PO Box 75, 26 New Street, St Helier JE4 8PP
Milner, R D, Carey Olsen, 47 The Esplanade, St Helier JE1 0BD
Morgan, T M, Mourant Ozannes, PO Box 87, 22 Grenville Street, St Helier JE4 8PX
Morgan, T H, Ogier, PO Box 404, Whiteley Chambers, Don Street, St Helier JE4 9WG
Morley-Kirk, R C L
Morris, R G, Legal Advisers' Office
Mourant, P D C
Mulry, M J, Ogier, PO Box 404, Whiteley Chambers, Don Street, St Helier JE4 9WG
Myerson, V, Appleby, PO Box 207, 13/14 Esplanade, St Helier JE1 1BD
Nicholls, P G, Walkers, PO Box 72, Walker House, 28-34 Hill Street, St Helier JE4 8PN
Nicolle, C L, Crill Canavan, 40 Don Street, St Helier JE1 4XD
Nisbet, M G, Carey Olsen, 47 The Esplanade, St Helier JE1 0BD
Obbard, V J, Judicial Greffe, Royal Court House, Royal Square, St Helier JE1 1JG
O'Connell, M S J, Appleby, PO Box 207, 13/14 Esplanade, St Helier JE1 1BD
O'Connor, D R M, Carey Olsen, 47 The Esplanade, St Helier JE1 0BD
Ohlsson, A A, Carey Olsen, 47 The Esplanade, St Helier JE1 0BD
Olsen, A J, Carey Olsen, 47 The Esplanade, St Helier JE1 0BD
O'Shea, C D, Crill Canavan, 40 Don Street, St Helier JE1 4XD
Ozouf, K S, Bedell Cristin, PO Box 75, 26 New Street, St Helier JE4 8PP
Pallot, M L A, Carey Olsen, 47 The Esplanade, St Helier JE1 0BD
Pallot, S C K, Law Officers' Department, Morier House, Halkett Place, St Helier JE1 1DD
Parslow, C G, Bedell Cristin, PO Box 75, 26 New Street, St Helier JE4 8PP
Paul, M, Bedell Cristin, PO Box 75, 26 New Street, St Helier JE4 8PP
Pearmain, S A, Appleby, PO Box 207, 13/14 Esplanade, St Helier JE1 1BD
Pearmain, N G A, Voisin, Templar House, Don Road, St Helier JE1 1AW
Pedley, R C P, Law Officers' Department, Morier House, Halkett Place, St Helier JE1 1DD
Petit, D J
Philpott, C D, Carey Olsen, 47 The Esplanade, St Helier JE1 0BD
Pinel, A C M, Crill Canavan, 40 Don Street, St Helier JE1 4XD
Pirie, R J F, Crill Canavan, 40 Don Street, St Helier JE1 4XD
Powell, N M, Ogier, PO Box 404, Whiteley Chambers, Don Street, St Helier JE4 9WG
Preston, M L, Voisin, Templar House, Don Road, St Helier JE1 1AW
Purkis, K M, Crill Canavan, 40 Don Street, St Helier JE1 4XD
Regal, A S, Bedell Cristin, PO Box 75, 26 New Street, St Helier JE4 8PP
Renouf, M P, Hanson Renouf, Regency House, Regent Road, Hill Street, St Helier JE2 4UZ
Renouf, R J, Lempriere Whittaker Renouf, PO Box 581, Rutland House, Pitt Street, St Helier JE4 0YL
Renouf, C R De J, Ogier, PO Box 404, Whiteley Chambers, Don Street, St Helier JE4 9WG
Richards, D P, Ogier, PO Box 404, Whiteley Chambers, Don Street, St Helier JE4 9WG
Richardson, L K A, Appleby, PO Box 207, 13/14 Esplanade, St Helier JE1 1BD
Richardson, M H, Bedell Cristin, PO Box 75, 26 New Street, St Helier JE4 8PP
Rigby, G A, Mourant Ozannes, PO Box 87, 22 Grenville Street, St Helier JE4 8PX
Riley, S F A, Carey Olsen, 47 The Esplanade, St Helier JE1 0BD
Rive, N J, Appleby, PO Box 207, 13/14 Esplanade, St Helier JE1 1BD
Robertson, F B, Appleby, PO Box 207, 13/14 Esplanade, St Helier JE1 1BD
Robinson, G S, Appleby, PO Box 207, 13/14 Esplanade, St Helier JE1 1BD
Robinson, A D, Bedell Cristin, PO Box 75, 26 New Street, St Helier JE4 8PP
Roscouet, A P, Jenners, PO Box 260, Broad Street Chambers, 4 & 6 Broad Street, St Helier JE4 8TS
Ruelle, H E, Mourant Ozannes, PO Box 87, 22 Grenville Street, St Helier JE4 8PX
Sandercombe, C E M
Sanders, N M, Ogier, PO Box 404, Whiteley Chambers, Don Street, St Helier JE4 9WG
Santos-Costa, N M, Crill Canavan, 40 Don Street, St Helier JE1 4XD
Saunders, A M, Ogier, PO Box 404, Whiteley Chambers, Don Street, St Helier JE4 9WG
Scholefield, C J, Viberts, PO Box 737, Pirouet House, Union Street, St Helier JE4 8ZQ
Scott, E L
Sharp, H, Law Officers' Department, Morier House, Halkett Place, St Helier JE1 1DD
Sharpe, S, Law Officers' Department, Morier House, Halkett Place, St Helier JE1 1DD
Simpson, E D
Sinel, M L, Ogier, PO Box 404, Whiteley Chambers, Don Street, St Helier JE4 9WG
Sinel, P C, Sinels, PO Box 595, 79 Bath Street, St Helier JE4 9XE
Slater, S, Steven Slater Legal Services, Lincoln Chambers, 31 Broad Street, St Helier JE2 3RR
Smith, R J, Carey Olsen, 47 The Esplanade, St Helier JE1 0BD
Sowden, P F C, Crill Canavan, 40 Don Street, St Helier JE1 4XD
Speck, J P, Mourant Ozannes, PO Box 87, 22 Grenville Street, St Helier JE4 8PX
Springate, L J, Bedell Cristin, PO Box 75, 26 New Street, St Helier JE4 8PP
Steel, A L, Mourant Ozannes, PO Box 87, 22 Grenville Street, St Helier JE4 8PX
Steenson, D S, Walkers, PO Box 72, Walker House, 28-34 Hill Street, St Helier JE4 8PN
Stone, M K, Mourant Ozannes, PO Box 87, 22 Grenville Street, St Helier JE4 8PX
Stone, V
Stott, R A, Carey Olsen, 47 The Esplanade, St Helier JE1 0BD
Strang, I W S, Voisin, Templar House, Don Road, St Helier JE1 1AW
Sturrock, S E, Ogier, PO Box 404, Whiteley Chambers, Don Street, St Helier JE4 9WG
Sugden, P B, Carey Olsen, 47 The Esplanade, St Helier JE1 0BD
Sullivan, N S E, Noirmont Consulting, La Fontaine, Le Mont Suzanne, St Lawrence JE3 1HH
Sullivan, J R
Swan, M J, Ogier, PO Box 404, Whiteley Chambers, Don Street, St Helier JE4 9WG
Swart, C J, Mourant Ozannes, PO Box 87, 22 Grenville Street, St Helier JE4 8PX
Taylor, M H D, Bedell Cristin, PO Box 75, 26 New Street, St Helier JE4 8PP
Temple, M H, Mourant Ozannes, PO Box 87, 22 Grenville Street, St Helier JE4 8PX
Thacker, C M B, Viberts, PO Box 737, Pirouet House, Union Street, St Helier JE4 8ZQ
Thomas, R W, Ogier, PO Box 404, Whiteley Chambers, Don Street, St Helier JE4 9WG
Thompson, M J, Ogier, PO Box 404, Whiteley Chambers, Don Street, St Helier JE4 9WG
Tibbo, H D, Ogier, PO Box 404, Whiteley Chambers, Don Street, St Helier JE4 9WG
Tracey, P M T, Sinels, PO Box 595, 79 Bath Street, St Helier JE4 9XE
Tremoceiro, R D S
Troy, B E, Viberts, PO Box 737, Pirouet House, Union Street, St Helier JE4 8ZQ
Voisin, M M G, Voisin, Templar House, Don Road, St Helier JE1 1AW

Wakeham, R J C, Sinels, PO Box 595, 79 Bath Street, St Helier JE4 9XE
Ward, N J, Ogier, PO Box 404, Whiteley Chambers, Don Street, St Helier JE4 9WG
Weaver, A J, Appleby, PO Box 207, 13/14 Esplanade, St Helier JE1 1BD
Weaver, S L, Mourant Ozannes, PO Box 87, 22 Grenville Street, St Helier JE4 8PX
Welton, R J
Weston, N J, Walkers, PO Box 72, Walker House, 28-34 Hill Street, St Helier JE4 8PN
Wheeler, J G P, Judicial Greffe, Royal Court House, Royal Square, St Helier JE1 1JG
Whelan, C E, Bakerplatt, PO Box 842, 2 Mulcaster Street, St Helier JE4 0US
White, G G P, Mourant Ozannes, PO Box 87, 22 Grenville Street, St Helier JE4 8PX
White, J G, Ogier, PO Box 404, Whiteley Chambers, Don Street, St Helier JE4 9WG
Whittaker, M E, Lempriere Whittaker Renouf, PO Box 581, Rutland House, Pitt Street, St Helier JE4 0YL
Willing, S J, Ogier, PO Box 404, Whiteley Chambers, Don Street, St Helier JE4 9WG
Wilson, D R, Bakerplatt, PO Box 842, 2 Mulcaster Street, St Helier JE4 0US
Wilson, P, Crill Canavan, 40 Don Street, St Helier JE1 4XD
Winchester, A J D
Wycherley, J L, Ogier, PO Box 404, Whiteley Chambers, Don Street, St Helier JE4 9WG
Yates, C M M, Law Officers' Department, Morier House, Halkett Place, St Helier JE1 1DD
Yates, M S D, Ogier, PO Box 404, Whiteley Chambers, Don Street, St Helier JE4 9WG
Yates, V J, Ogier, PO Box 404, Whiteley Chambers, Don Street, St Helier JE4 9WG
Young, S J, Bois & Bois, PO Box 429, 4 Bond Street, St Helier JE4 5QR

Solicitors

Ballands, F A, Appleby, PO Box 207, 13/14 Esplanade, St Helier JE1 1BD
Barnes, C M, Ogier, PO Box 404, Whiteley Chambers, Don Street, St Helier JE4 9WG
Bisson, J L C, Appleby, PO Box 207, 13/14 Esplanade, St Helier JE1 1BD
Breen, E A
Canavan, C E
Chaplin, C A C, Ogier, PO Box 404, Whiteley Chambers, Don Street, St Helier JE4 9WG
Chapman, J A J, Mourant Ozannes, PO Box 87, 22 Grenville Street, St Helier JE4 8PX
Cope, S A J, Mourant Ozannes, PO Box 87, 22 Grenville Street, St Helier JE4 8PX
Corner, A L J
Coutanche, C E, Mourant Ozannes, PO Box 87, 22 Grenville Street, St Helier JE4 8PX
Crill, G G, Crill Canavan, 40 Don Street, St Helier JE1 4XD
Crill, J D P, Mourant Ozannes, PO Box 87, 22 Grenville Street, St Helier JE4 8PX
Crill, M J D, Mourant Ozannes, PO Box 87, 22 Grenville Street, St Helier JE4 8PX
Crocker, N H, Carey Olsen, 47 The Esplanade, St Helier JE1 0BD
Davenport, E C, Mourant Ozannes, PO Box 87, 22 Grenville Street, St Helier JE4 8PX
Del Amo, A P, Le Gallais & Luce, PO Box 696, 6 Hill Street, St Helier JE4 8YX
Felton, S J V, Mourant Ozannes, PO Box 87, 22 Grenville Street, St Helier JE4 8PX
Hamel, N M, Mourant Ozannes, PO Box 87, 22 Grenville Street, St Helier JE4 8PX
Harben, P R, Crill Canavan, 40 Don Street, St Helier JE1 4XD
Harris, J A, Le Gallais & Luce, PO Box 696, 6 Hill Street, St Helier JE4 8YX
Harrison, A M, Appleby, PO Box 207, 13/14 Esplanade, St Helier JE1 1BD
Hart, T G, Appleby, PO Box 207, 13/14 Esplanade, St Helier JE1 1BD
Hickling, R A, Mourant Ozannes, PO Box 87, 22 Grenville Street, St Helier JE4 8PX
Hillier, C G, Appleby, PO Box 207, 13/14 Esplanade, St Helier JE1 1BD
Huelin, D P, Le Gallais & Luce, PO Box 696, 6 Hill Street, St Helier JE4 8YX
Ingram, L A, Voisin, Templar House, Don Road, St Helier JE1 1AW
James, I C, Mourant Ozannes, PO Box 87, 22 Grenville Street, St Helier JE4 8PX
Jenner, N A
Jeune, R R
Kendall, J P, Voisin, Templar House, Don Road, St Helier JE1 1AW
Lambert, W, Mourant Ozannes, PO Box 87, 22 Grenville Street, St Helier JE4 8PX
Langan, S, Ogier, PO Box 404, Whiteley Chambers, Don Street, St Helier JE4 9WG
Le Boutillier, M J, Le Gallais & Luce, PO Box 696, 6 Hill Street, St Helier JE4 8YX
Le Boutillier, M J, Ogier, PO Box 404, Whiteley Chambers, Don Street, St Helier JE4 9WG
Le Gresley, N P E
Le Liard, R P, Bedell Cristin, PO Box 75, 26 New Street, St Helier JE4 8PP
Le Marquand, M M, Carey Olsen, 47 The Esplanade, St Helier JE1 0BD
Lombardi, M F, Ogier, PO Box 404, Whiteley Chambers, Don Street, St Helier JE4 9WG
Luce, P W, Le Gallais & Luce, PO Box 696, 6 Hill Street, St Helier JE4 8YX
Manning, K R, K R Manning & Co, PO Box 407, Lincoln Chambers, 31 Broad Street, St Helier JE4 5QB
Pickersgill, B K, Pickersgill & Co, Channel House, Green Street, St Helier JE2 4UH
Pim, H A, Appleby, PO Box 207, 13/14 Esplanade, St Helier JE1 1BD
Pipon, D K
Pitter, C M, Investec
Pollano, G A, Mourant Ozannes, PO Box 87, 22 Grenville Street, St Helier JE4 8PX
Quinn, E R, Carey Olsen, 47 The Esplanade, St Helier JE1 0BD
Rainer, J H, Mourant Ozannes, PO Box 87, 22 Grenville Street, St Helier JE4 8PX
Richomme, J A, Mourant Ozannes, PO Box 87, 22 Grenville Street, St Helier JE4 8PX
Robins, B C, Mourant Ozannes, PO Box 87, 22 Grenville Street, St Helier JE4 8PX
Ruane, J F, Mourant Ozannes, PO Box 87, 22 Grenville Street, St Helier JE4 8PX
Scally, P C P, Le Gallais & Luce, PO Box 696, 6 Hill Street, St Helier JE4 8YX
Scott, M R
Skulski, K N, Mourant Ozannes, PO Box 87, 22 Grenville Street, St Helier JE4 8PX
Syvret, K W, Benest & Syvret, Royal Court Chambers, 10 Hill Street, St Helier JE1 1BS
Syvret, P W, Benest & Syvret, Royal Court Chambers, 10 Hill Street, St Helier JE1 1BS
Syvret, A J R, Mourant Ozannes, PO Box 87, 22 Grenville Street, St Helier JE4 8PX
Travis, S A, Mourant Ozannes, PO Box 87, 22 Grenville Street, St Helier JE4 8PX
Tricot, E F
Troy, R E
Walker, J C, Mourant Ozannes, PO Box 87, 22 Grenville Street, St Helier JE4 8PX
Williams, L M
Young, D, Bois & Bois, PO Box 429, 4 Bond Street, St Helier JE4 5QR

GUERNSEY JUDICIARY & COURTS

THE ROYAL COURT OF GUERNSEY

The Bailiff of Guernsey
Rowland, Sir Geoffrey R

The Deputy Bailiff of Guernsey
Collas, Richard

Office
Bailiff's Chambers, The Royal Court House, St Peter Port, Guernsey GY1 2PB Tel: 01481 726161 Fax: 01481 713861

Jurats of the Royal Court
Bartie, Mrs B
Bichard, K, OBE
Bisson, A C
Ferguson, J
Girard, P S T
Helyar-Wilkinson, Mrs C A E
Hodgetts, D P L
Le Conte, D O
Le Pelley, Miss C
Le Poidevin, S E F
Lowe, D C
McCathie, N D
Mowbray, Dr E I S M
Snell, T G
Spaargaren, Mrs M A

THE MAGISTRATES' COURT & JUVENILE COURT

Judge of the Royal Court
Finch, J R

Judge of the Magistrates Court
McMillen, C A
Robey, P

The Greffier (Courts Secretariat)
Tough, K H
The Royal Court House, St Peter Port, Guernsey GY1 2PB Tel: 01481 725277 Fax: 01481 715097

THE LAW OFFICERS OF THE CROWN

Office
PO Box 96, St James Chambers, St Peter Port, Guernsey GY1 4BY Tel: 01481 723355 Fax: 01481 725439

ADVOCATES

Advocate L Strappini & Co, 8 Lefebvre Street, Guernsey GY1 2PE Tel: 01481 724029 Fax: 01481 713934
Strappini, Lloyd Le R

Albany Chambers, 18 New Street, St Peter Port, Guernsey GY1 2PF Tel: 01481 715105 Fax: 01481 715205
Allen, Pauline A

A O Hall, Le Marchant House, Le Marchant Street, St Peter Port, Guernsey GY1 2JJ Tel: 01481 723723 Fax: 01481 723023
Hall, Louise C
Ozanne, Alison M
Barclay, Jonathan J
Gray, Elaine R

Appleby, PO Box 56, HSBC House, Lefebvre Street, St Peter Port, Guernsey GY1 3BN Tel: 01481 755600 Fax: 01481 728992
Ferguson, Gavin
Le Tissier, Jeremy

Ashton Barnes Tee, Old Crown Office, Ann's Place, St Peter Port, Guernsey GY1 2NU Tel: 01481 724124 Fax: 01481 724164
Ashton, Dr Raymond K
Barnes, Nicholas J
Crawford, Thomas
Tee, Clare A

Atkinson Ferbrache Richardson, PO Box 688, Court Place, Rue de Manoir, St Peter Port, Guernsey GY1 3XZ Tel: 01481 743999 Fax: 01481 743990
Atkinson, Peter J G
Ferbrache, Peter T R
Geall, Simon
Mallett, Sara
Richardson, Paul
Wallis, Sarah

Babbe, 18-20 Smith Street, St Peter Port, Guernsey GY1 4BL Tel: 01481 713371 Fax: 01481 712245
Allez, Geoffrey W
Baudains, Martyn
Davidson, A
Dereham, Piers
Fullman, Robert F
Harris, Iain
Howitt, Simon W F
Laws, Andrew D
Pratt, Victoria
Riddiford, Michael J
Swan, Ian
Tostevin, Nicholas J M
Tyler, Stuart

Bailiwick Chambers, 5 The Grange, St Peter Port, Guernsey GY1 2PX Tel: 01481 728666 Fax: 01481 728636
Domaille, David
Morgan, Sarah
Fletcher, Candy

Bedell Cristin, 3rd Floor, La Plaiderie House, La Praiderie, St Peter Port, Guernsey GY1 1WD Tel: 01481 812812 Fax: 01481 812813
Anderson, Christopher
Helyar, Mark
Ovenden, Katherine

Carey Olsen, 7 New Street, St Peter Port, Guernsey GY1 4BZ Tel: 01481 727272 Fax: 01481 711052
Alexander, Annette
Beattie, Ian H
Boyce, Andrew E
Carey, Nigel T
Carey, Tom
Cariou, Marcel
Clark, Russell
Corfield, Tim
Dunster, Mark G A
Eades, Michael J S
Fleming, Fiona (London office)
Friedlaender, Konrad
Greenfield, John P
Hall, Graham A
Le Cras, Karen M
Le Marquand, Davey G
Lewis, Wendy A
Lister, Andrew
Montgomery, Patricia L
Morgan, Ben
Morgan, Jason J L
Sarchet, Adrian
Skirrow, Allan
Ward-Marshall, Geoff
White, Julia A S
Whitmore, Chloe

Collas Day, Manor Place, St Peter Port, Guernsey GY1 4EW Tel: 01481 723191 Fax: 01481 711880
Bell, Gareth
Bound, Chris J
Cheong, Sean S
Green, Jason
Hopkins, Nicola
Kirk, Ian M
Nettleship, Paul
Ogier, Richard
Palmer, Patrick M A
Romer, Jason
Upham, Lisa M M

F Haskins, College Chambers, 3-4 St James Street, St Peter Port, Guernsey GY1 2NZ Tel: 01481 721316 Fax: 01481 721317
Brehaut, Sarah L
Haskins, Felicity J
Merriem, Alan M
Maindonald, Samantha

Mourant Ozannes, 1 Le Marchant Street, St Peter Port, Guernsey GY1 4HP Tel: 01481 723466 Fax: 01481 727935
Bacon, Darren
Bainbridge, Garth T A
Barrett, Chantal
Brown, Adrian
Christie, Kathryn
Christopher, Paul R P
Dawes, Gordon S K
Edwards, Christopher
Evans, Rupert A R
Farrell, Gavin J
Ferbrache, Peter T R
Ferguson, Gavin
Grainge, Penny
Harwood, Peter A
Le Tissier, Jeremy
Lewis, John H
Moore, David C
Prentice, Edward A G
Robilliard, St John A
Roland, Jessica E
Rouse, Val
Shepherd, Robert G
Torode, Mark A
Walters, Andrew
Wessels, Jeremy M
Wood, Alison
Wyatt, Helen

Ogier, St Julian's Avenue, St Peter Port, Guernsey GY1 1WA Tel: 01481 721672 Fax: 01481 721575
Chan, Caroline J
Davies, Simon
Le Tissier, Roger A
Leese, Marcus
Simpson, William P

Randell & Loveridge, 6 Court Row, St Peter Port, Guernsey GY1 2PD Tel: 01481 720225 Fax: 01481 713644
Fooks, Catherine M
Loveridge, John D

Trinity Chambers, 7 Berthelot Street, St Peter Port, Guernsey GY1 1JF Tel: 01481 700072 Fax: 01481 700039
Ayres, Andrew J
Bailey, Samantha
Green, Chris
Lockwood, Paul

ADVOCATES - ALDERNEY

J Kay-Mouat, Esq, The Old Presbytery, Alderney Tel: 01481 822828 Fax: 01481 822065

P J Beer, Esq, 10 Val de Mer, Newton, Alderney Tel: 01481 823365 Fax: 01481 823355

ADVOCATES - SARK

SG Law, SG House, De La Moinerie GY9 0SF Tel: 01481 832801 Fax: 01481 832802
Gomoll, Stefan

THE COURT OF ALDERNEY

Jurats of the Court

Chairman
Partridge, C W

Scott, G W D
Collins, S
Ireland, G H
Boardman, J Q
McLernon, T M
Bohan, R
Blodin, R

Greffier
Kelly, Sarah
Court of Alderney, Queen Elizabeth II Street, St Anne, Alderney GY9 3TB Tel: 01481 822817 Fax: 01481 823709

THE COURT OF THE SENESCHAL OF SARK

Seneschal
Guille, Lt. Col. R J, MBE

Greffier
Hamon, Mr T,

Office
The Greffier, La Chasse Marette, Sark GY9 0SB Tel: 01481 832993 Fax: 01481 832994

16

COURT OF JUSTICE OF THE EUROPEAN UNION

The Court of Justice of the European Union is based in Luxembourg. It comprises three courts: The Court of Justice, the General Court and the Civil Service Tribunal, whose essential tasks are to examine the legality of Union acts and the ensure the uniform interpretation and application of European Union law.

The Court of Justice is composed of 27 Judges (one per Member State) and 8 Advocates General. They are appointed by common accord of the governments of the Member States for a renewable term of 6 years.

The Court of Justice has jurisdiction to hear:

References for preliminary rulings from national courts. A national court which is faced with a question of European Union law to which the answer is not evident, may refer questions to the Court of Justice for a preliminary ruling. These questions concern the interpretation of the Treaties and the interpretation and validity of acts adopted by the European Institution.

Actions on the failure of a Member State to fulfil its obligations under the Treaties. These cases can be brought by the Commission or another Member State. If the Court rules against the Member State, that country must comply with the Court's ruling. Failure to comply can lead to a second court case where the Court has the possibility to fine the Member State.

Actions for annulment and declaration of failure to act. Institutions or Member States may bring an action requesting the annulment of an act of the Parliament and/or Council (with the exception of some Council acts dealt with by the General Court) or a declaration that an Institution has failed to take action following a request to do so.

Appeals against decisions of the General Court.

The **General Court** is composed of 27 Judges, appointed in the same manner as for the Court of Justice. The General Court has no Advocates General.

The General Court has jurisdiction to hear:

Actions for annulment and declaration of failure to act brought by natural or legal persons against acts of the Union institutions.

Actions brought by the Member States against the Commission and certain acts of the Council (notably in the field of State aid and anti-dumping)

Actions for damages for loss caused by the European Union.

Actions relating to the Community Trade Mark.

Appeals against decisions of the Civil Service Tribunal.

The **Civil Service Tribunal** of the European Union is composed of seven judges, appointed for a renewable six-year term by the Council. This Tribunal hears disputes between the institutions of the European Communities and their employees.

In 2009, 561 cases were brought before the Court of Justice including 302 references for a preliminary ruling, 143 direct actions, 104 appeals from judgments of the Court of First Instance and 9 special procedures. 588 cases were closed by means of 377 judgments and 165 orders.

Between 1953 and the end of 2009, 16,204 cases had been brought. There were 741 cases pending at the end of 2009.

In 2009, 568 cases were brought before the General Court, including 246 direct actions (i.e. competition cases etc.), 207 intellectual property cases (appeals against decisions of the Office for Harmonisation in the Internal Market) and 31 appeals against decisions of the Civil Service Tribunal. 555 cases were closed. There were 1191 cases pending at the end of 2009.

In 2009 the Civil Service Tribunal received 113 cases, closed 155 and had 175 cases still outstanding.

ORDER OF PRECEDENCE OF THE COURT OF JUSTICE (AS FROM 12/10/10)

President
Skouris, V

President of the First Chamber
Tizzano, A

President of the Second Chamber
Cunha Rodrigues, J N

President of the Third Chamber
Lenaerts, K

President of the Fourth Chamber
Bonichot, J-C

First Advocate General
Bot, Y

President of the Eighth Chamber
Schiemann, K

President of the Sixth Chamber
Arabadjiev, A

President of the Fifth Chamber
Kasel, J-J

President of the Seventh Chamber
Šváby, D

Judge Rosas, A
Judge Silva de Lapuerta, R
Advocate General Kokott, J
Judge Juhász, E
Judge Arestis, G
Judge Borg Barthet, A
Judge Ilešič, M
Judge Malenovský, J
Judge Lõhmus, U
Judge Levits, E
Judge Caoimh, A Ó
Judge Bay Larsen, L
Advocate General Sharpston, E
Advocate General Mengozzi, P
Judge Lindh, P
Advocate General Mazák, J
Judge von Danwitz, T
Advocate General Trstenjak, V
Judge Toader, C
Judge Safjan, M
Judge Berger, M
Advocate General Jääskinen, N
Advocate General Cruz Villalón, P
Judge Prechal, A
Judge Jarašiūnas, E
Registrar Calot Escobar, A

COMPOSITION OF THE CHAMBERS OF THE COURT OF JUSTICE (AS FROM 12/10/10)

First Chamber
President Tizzano, A
Judge Kasel, J-J
Judge Borg Barthet, A
Judge Ilešič, M
Judge Levits, E
Judge Safjan, M
Judge Berger, M

Second Chamber
President Cunha Rodrigues, J N
Judge Arabadjiev, A
Judge Rosas, A
Judge Lõhmus, U
Judge Caoimh, A Ó
Judge Lindh, P

Third Chamber
President Lenaerts, K
Judge Šváby, D
Judge Silva de Lapuerta, R
Judge Juhász, E
Judge Arestis, G
Judge Malenovský, J
Judge von Danwitz, T

Fourth Chamber
President Bonichot, J C
Judge Schiemann, K
Judge Bay Larsen, L
Judge Toader, C
Judge Prechal, A
Judge Jarašiūnas, E

Fifth Chamber
President Kasel, J-J
Judge Borg Barthet, A
Judge Ilešič, M
Judge Levits, E
Judge Safjan, M
Judge Berger, M

Sixth Chamber
President Arabadjiev, A
Judge Rosas, A
Judge Lõhmus, U
Judge Caoimh, A Ó
Judge Lindh, P

Seventh Chamber
President Šváby, D
Judge Silva de Lapuerta, R
Judge Juhász, E
Judge Arestis, G
Judge Malenovský, J
Judge von Danwitz, T

Eighth Chamber
President Schiemann, K
Judge Bay Larsen, L
Judge Toader, C
Judge Prechal, A
Judge Jarašiūnas, E

ORDER OF PRECEDENCE OF THE GENERAT COURT (AS FROM 26/11/10)

President of the General Court
Jaeger, M

Presidents of Chamber
Azizi, J
Forwood, N J

Czúcz, O
Pelikánová, I
Papasavvas, S
Moavero Milanesi, E
Dittrich, A
Truchot, L

Judges
Martins Ribeiro, M E
Dehousse, F
Cremona, E
Wiszniewska-Bialecka, I
Vadapalas, V
Jürimäe, K
Labucka, I
Wahl, N
Prek, M
Soldevila Fragoso, S
Frimodt Nielsen, S
O'Higgins, K
Kanninen, H
Schwarcz, J
van der Woude, M
Gratsias, D
Popescu, A

Registrar
Coulon, E

COMPOSITION OF THE CHAMBERS OF THE GENERAL COURT (FROM 29/11/10)

First Chamber
Azizi, J
Cremona, E
Frimodt Nielsen, S

First Chamber, Extended Composition
Azizi, J
Cremona, E
Labucka, I
Frimodt Nielsen, S
Gratsias, D

Second Chamber
Forwood, N J
a) Dehousse, F
Popescu, A
b) Dehousse, F
Schwarcz, J
c) Schwarcz, J
Popescu, A

Second Chamber, Extended Composition
Forwood, N J
Dehousse, F
Wiszniewska-Bialecka, I
Prek, M
Schwarcz, J
Popescu, A

Third Chamber
Czúcz, O
Labucka, I
Gratsias, D

Third Chamber, Extended Composition
Czúcz, O
Cremona, E
Labucka, I
Frimodt Nielsen, S
Gratsias, D

Fourth Chamber
Pelikánová, I
Jürimäe, K
van der Woude, M

Fourth Chamber, Extended Composition
Pelikánová, I
Vadapalas, V
Jürimäe, K
O'Higgins, K
van der Woude, M

Fifth Chamber
Papasavvas, S
Vadapalas, V
O'Higgins, K

Fifth Chamber, Extended Composition
Papasavvas, S
Vadapalas, V
Jürimäe, K
O'Higgins, K
van der Woude, M

Sixth Chamber
Moavero Milanesi, E
Wahl, N
Soldevila Fragoso, S

Sixth Chamber, Extended Composition
Moavero Milanesi, E
Martins Ribeiro, M E
Wahl, N
Soldevila Fragoso, S
Kanninen, H

Seventh Chamber
Dittrich, A
Wiszniewska-Bialecka, I
Prek, M

Seventh Chamber, Extended Composition
Dittrich, A
Dehousse , F
Wiszniewska-Bialecka, I
Prek, M
Schwarcz, J
Popescu, A

Eighth Chamber
Truchot, L
Martins Ribeiro, M E
Kanninen, H

Eighth Chamber, Extended Composition
Truchot, L
Martins Ribeiro, M E
Wahl, N
Soldevila Fragoso, S
Kanninen, H

ORDER OF PRECEDENCE OF THE CIVIL SERVICE TRIBUNAL (AS FROM 7/10/09)

President Mahoney, P
President of Chamber Tagaras, H
President of Chamber Gervasoni, S
Judge Kreppel, H
Judge Boruta, I
Judge Van Raepenbusch, S
Judge Rofes i Pujol, M I
Judge Hakenberg, W

COMPOSITION OF THE CIVIL SERVICE TRIBUNAL (FROM 7/10/09)

First Chamber
Gervasoni, S
Kreppel, H
Rofes i Pujol, M I

Second Chamber
Tagaras, H
Boruta, I
Van Raepenbusch, S

Third Chamber
Mahoney, P
a) Kreppel, H
Van Raepenbusch, S
b) Boruta, I
Rofes i Pujol, M I

GOVERNMENT LEGAL SERVICES

CONTENTS

16

GOVERNMENT LEGAL SERVICE

A LIST OF ADDRESSES AND PRINCIPALS

ASSOCIATION OF POLICE AUTHORITIES

Office
15 Greycoat Place, London SW1P 1BN Tel: 020 7664 3096 Fax: 020 7664 3191 Web: www.apa.police.uk

The Association of Police Authorities (APA) is the national body representing all police authorities in England and Wales, the Northern Ireland Policing Board and the British Transport Police Authority. The Civil Nuclear Police Authority, the Ministry of Defence Police Committee, the Scottish Police Authorities Convenor's Forum and the National Policing Improvement Agency are associate members.

Police authority members include local councillors and independent members of the community who set the strategic direction for the Force. They also hold the Chief Constable to account, on behalf of the local community, for the provision of an effective and efficient service.

THE ATTORNEY GENERAL'S OFFICE

Office
The Attorney General's Office, 20 Victoria Street, London SW1H 0NF Tel: 020 7271 2400

Attorney General
Grieve, The Rt. Hon. Dominic, Q.C., M.P.

Solicitor General
Garnier , Edward, Q.C., M.P.

Director General
Fish, Peter

Director of Criminal Law
Patten, Sue

Principal Private Secretary to the Attorney General
Parish, Duncan

Private Secretary to the Attorney General
Parmar, Lena

Private Secretary to the Solicitor General
Peck, John

Diary Secretary to the Law Officers
Lucy, Katie

Head of Communications
Givens, Susan

Legal Advisers
Brown, Richard
Butler, Judith
Deutz, Stephen
Fernandes, Rosemary
Guess, John
Kumar, Vivek
McGinty, Kevin
Watson, Gavin
Weerasinghe, Suresh
Woodings, David
Chaytor, Helen
Grealis, John
Jones, Kristin

Office
Attorney General's Chambers (Northern Ireland), Royal Courts of Justice, Belfast BT1 3JF Tel: 028 9054 6082

Legal Adviser
McGinty, Kevin (NI 1998, G 1982)

CABINET OFFICE

Office
Cabinet Office, 70 Whitehall, London SW1A 2AS Tel: 020 7276 1234 Web: www.cabinetoffice.gov.uk

CHARITY COMMISSION

Non-Executive Commissioners
Woodcraft, Tess
Williams, John

Executive Director of Legal Services & Compliance
Dibble, Kenneth M (L Jul 1977)

Executive Director of Charity Services
Locke, David (1990)

Head of Compliance & Support
Russell, Michelle (May 1998)

LONDON

Head of Legal (Status & Advice)
Holt, Alice (1987)

Senior Legal Policy Adviser
Roberts, Stephen (1978)

Senior Legal Adviser (Compliance)
Baxter, Rachel (1998)

Senior Legal Adviser (Large Charities Division)
Boyd, David (Sep 2001)

Knuckey, Emma (Mar 2002)
Thakor, Aarti (called to the Bar in 2004)
Hannah Lily (Jan 2003)
Kirby, David (Mar 2007)
Gardner-Swift, Helen (Dec 1992)

LIVERPOOL

Head of Liverpool Legal Team
Millington, Elise (Sep 2002)

McGarry, Jane (July 2007)
Lake, Jane (Jan 1991)
Platt, Louise (Oct 2006)

TAUNTON

Head of Legal (Compliance)
Kilby, James (I 1979)

George, Anthony (Nov 1986)
Shanley, Marion (Sep 1997)
Shaw, Gillian (Nov 1990)
Wherrett, Andrew (Sep 2002)

CHILD SUPPORT AGENCY

Office
National Helpline, PO Box 55, Brierly Hill DY5 1YL Tel: 0845 713 3133 Web: www.csa.gov.uk

COMMONWEALTH WAR GRAVES COMMISSION

Office
2 Marlow Road, Maidenhead, Berkshire SL6 7DX Tel: 01628 507138 Fax: 01628 507134 Email: legal@cwgc.org

Direct Legal Services
Stedman, Gillian Susan, LLB (Oct 1978)

CRIMINAL INJURIES COMPENSATION AUTHORITY (CICA)

Office
Tay House, 300 Bath Street, Glasgow G2 4LN Tel: 0800 358 3601 Fax: 0141 331 2287 Web: www.cica.gov.uk

Chief Executive
Oatway, Carole A

Legal Advisor
Kelly, Lynsay

Press Officer
Cairns, Garry
Tel: 0141 331 5944

CROWN ESTATE COMMISSIONERS

Office
16 New Burlington Place, London W1S 2HX Tel: 020 7851 5120 Fax: 020 7851 5125 General Enquiries: 020 7851 5000

Legal Director
King, Miss V I (Mar 1988)

Deputy Head of Legal
Harris, D K N (Jun 1973)

Solicitor
Dagnall, Miss J (Nov 1994)
Peeke, A J (Oct 2002)

DEPARTMENT FOR BUSINESS, INNOVATION AND SKILLS

Office
Ministerial Correspondence Unit, 1 Victoria Street, London SW1H 0ET Tel: 020 7215 5000 Web: www.bis.gov.uk

DEPARTMENT FOR BUSINESS, ENTERPRISE AND REGULATORY REFORM

Office
1 Victoria Street, London SW1H 0ET Tel: 020 7215 5000 Fax: 020 7215 3141

Barristers
Bradley, Alison
Braviner-Roman, Stephen (G 1992)
Carnegie, Jane (M 1998)
Carney, Julie (M 1990)
Churaman, Debbie (M 1984)

Collins, Nadia (M 1994)
Edwards, Susan (G 1972)
Evans, Peter (M 1994)
Fernandes, Nicholas
Frost, Malcolm
Ghobadian, Rameen (M 2005)
Grayson, Stephen (I 1990)
Kilgannon, Jane (I 2006)
Kong, Ming (G 1997)
Lloyd, Catherine
Lyons, Ruth (M 1981)
Mortimore, Claudia
Mustafa, Lara
Norris, Charles
O'Neil, Elizabeth (M 1996)
Onwuazor, Ify (G 1998)
Rae, Helen
Richards, Steven (G 2001)
Reid, Sophie
Reveley, Tom
Shrimplin, Katy (M 1984)
Smith, Mark (Rev) (M 1982)
Welch, Bryan (I 1994)
Whittaker, Ian (I 1994)
Willerton, Katherine (L 2005)

Solicitors
Agar, Jonathan (Legal Trainee)
Allen, Louisa (Mar 2004)
Amodeo, Giovanna (Oct 1992)
Amos, Stephen (Nov 1994)
Arora, Nisha (1993)
Atkins, Richard (Oct 1981)
Bagga, Sonia
Baker, Paul (Feb 1999)
Bell, Alissa (Oct 1998)
Brandon, Simon (Legal Trainee)
Bowring, Mark
Bucknill, Mark (Aug 1980)
Busk, Christopher (Nov 1988)
Capp, Neil (Oct 1999)
Chandrasekhar, Sushuma (May 2004)
Coop, Andrew
Coult, Alison
Cromarty, Isabel (Nov 1990)
Evans, Rachel (Oct 1997)
Farnsworth, Geraldine
Farrington, Lucy (Mar 2002)
Fletcher, Mark (Oct 1985)
Fuller, Jennifer (Sep 2002)
Goh, Binnie
Gordon, Stephanie
Hanrahan, Jane (Nov 1995)
Hare, Bhavna (Sep 2002)
Harris, John (Mar 1991)
Jenkins, Daniel
Juttner, Kate
Kamat, Anita
Keighley, Diane (Sep 2002)
Kennedy, Judy (Oct 1997)
Kitson, Frances
Le Motte, Helen (Oct 2005)
Leslie, Caroline (April 1978)
Lewis, Richard (Nov 1989)
Magrill, Rachel
Martinez-Soto, Jose (July 1994)
McMenemy, Clare (Oct 2004)
Meringo, Nicole (Oct 1999)
Morgan, Richard (Nov 1990)
Morris, James
O'Sullivan, Cinead (Apr 2003)
Palmer, Bridget (Oct 1991)
Penlington, Faye (Sep 2005)
Pragnell, Charlotte
Quinn, Paula (Sep 1999)
Rafferty, Michelle
Ruda, Fleur (Sep 2003)
Sandby-Thomas, Rachel
Skinner, Lindsay (Sep 2000)
Smith, Susan (Oct 1986)
Southern, Alistair
Studzinski, Kristina
Supple, Paul (Nov 1993)
Somaia, Rakesh (Sep 1996)
Susman, Tony (Apr 1975)
Talbot, Michael (Jan 1989)
Walsh, Helen (Apr 2002)
Watson, Richard (Oct 1992)
Wiseman, Lucy (Apr 2003)
Wiskin, Hannah

DEPARTMENT FOR COMMUNITIES AND LOCAL GOVERNMENT

Office
Eland House, Bressenden Place, London SW1E 5DU Tel: 030 3444 0000

Solicitor & Legal Adviser
McGibbon, Susanna

Deputy Legal Adviser
Croft, Frederick (M Jul 1975)

Deputy Directors
Conlon, Pamela (Aug 1976)
Cooper, Cathy
Neilson, James
Stubbs, Matthew (I Jul 1989)
Wilson, Bernard (Oct 1985)

Grade 6s Lawyers
Atkinson, Stephen (Feb 1982)
Briody, Stephen (Nov 1992)
Clarke, Sally (Dec 1991)
Creasy, Richard
Draper, Philippa
Eyeington, Louise (I Oct 1993)
Goulburn, Vivienne
Hands, Jon (Sep 1996)
Hedley-Dent, Gloria (I Jul 1970)
Hodgett, Gavin (Nov 1992)
Jackson, Louise (Jan 1996)
Mackley, Richard (Oct 1979)
Miller, Jacqueline (Nov 1990)
Morley, Alistair (M Nov 1991)
Noor, Nadia
Nuttall, Nicola
Oliver, Judy
Passman, Naomi (Nov 1984)
Philipps, Elizabeth (Dec 1978)
Reay, Catherine
Reed, Jane (M Oct 1987)
Rowles, Linda (Jul 1975)
Sanders, Nicolette
Symes, David
Symons, Louise
Tait, Achara
Viersen-Corser, Sarah
Whittaker, Jill
Wilkinson, Gloria
Wong, May

Grade 7s Lawyers
Bailey, Vicki
Brasnett, Eme
Boon, Mike
Chisholm, Lucy
Kennedy, Katharine
Latty-Dennison, Samantha
Martin, Katharine
Miles, David
Millington, Sarah (Mar 1984)
Noor, Nadia (Oct 1998)
Parr, Victoria
Rakkar, Kerenpaul
Roe, Rachel
Sabapathy, Kate
Senior, Kate
Short, Amanda
Smith, Kellie
Thatcher, Jennifer
Winstanley, Anna

Legal Officers
Brannagan, Michael
Waller, Sarah

DEPARTMENT FOR CULTURE, MEDIA AND SPORT

Office
2-4 Cockspur Street, London SW1Y 5DH Tel: 020 7211 6000 Email: enquiries@culture.gov.uk Web: www.culture.gov.uk

DEPARTMENT FOR EDUCATION

Office
Castle View House, East Lane, Runcorn, Cheshire WA7 2GJ Tel: 0870 000 2288 Fax: 01928 794248 Web: www.education.gov.uk

DEPARTMENT OF ENERGY AND CLIMATE CHANGE

Office
3 Whitehall Place, London SW1A 2AW Tel: 0300 060 4000 Email: correspondence@decc.gsi.gov.uk Web: www.decc.gov.uk

DEPARTMENT FOR ENVIRONMENT FOOD & RURAL AFFAIRS (DEFRA)

Office
3rd Floor, Ergon House, Horseferry Road, London SW1P 2AL Tel: 020 7238 0503

Solicitor and Director General
McGaughrin, Anne

Directors
Mallick, Naomi

Heads of Team
Allen, Charles
Burke, Chris
Cooper, James
Davis, Gisela
Hattan, Elizabeth & Carter, Susan (job share)
McGlone, Alistair
Sachs, Anne
Sylvester, Clare
Truran, Martin
Turnill, James

Grade 6
Anderson, Jillian
Bachoo, Prakash
Brown, Christopher W
Connell, Caroline
Crockford, Pete
Croft, Simon
Durkin, Anthony
Edwards, Sheila
Gill, Eleni
Glen, Judith

Gordon-Lee, Helen
Hamilton, Clare
Harrison, Chris
Harrison, Lisa
Hawker, Gail
Heron, Sarah
Heydon, Matthew
Hill, Alex
Hodgson, Vicki
Irving, Jane
Jacobs, Sue
Kohl, Sarah
Lavery, John
Leow, Abigail
Lloyd, Fiona
Mautner, Michele
Milroy, David
Milton, Laura
Mosedale, Tom
Mundy, Simon
Parker, Simon
Robinson, James
Schultz, Andrew
Smith, Amy
Stockwell, Philippa
Thomson, Jolyon
Vidal, Richard
White, Maria
Wood, Tom
Yri, Emily

Grade 7
Allan, Juliet
Aquilina, Diana
Arinze, Lillian
Austin, Amanda
Bennett, Ann
Blenkinsop, Jacqueline
Bream, Jude
Cameron, Michael
Catherall, Simon
Chaudhry, Safina
Clark, David
Clarke, Georgina
Coffey, Juliette
Coffey, Ruth
Collins, Paul
Dark, Gina
Davies, Jeni
Davies, Rachel
Devani, Juliette
Dove, Elaine
Ferns, Jennifer
Finlay, John
Franklin, Kalyani
Grundy, Madeleine
Halfhead, James
Hamilton, Clare
Hamoda, Susan
Hynes, Sue
Labor, Nchike
Lattuca, Paolo
Leow, Abigail
Mackay, Donna
Mackie, Jo
McConnell, Alix
Nash, Chloe
Pike, Carla
Rhone, Shirley
Roland, Linda
Ruddie, Brian
Ryan, Rebecca
Sabel, Judith
Sargent, Diana
Saunders, Elizabeth
Sheridan, Liam
Stratford, Gilly
Walker, Mags
Wayland, Emma

Legal Officer
Fletcher, Eleanor
Richardson, Ellen
Risbin, Sarah

DEPARTMENT FOR TRANSPORT LEGAL SERVICES DIRECTORATE

Office
Great Minster House, 76 Marsham Street, London SW1P 4DR Tel: 020 7944 8300

The Legal Adviser & Legal Services Director
Muttukumaru, Christopher Peter Jayantha, CB (G 1974)

The Deputy Legal Adviser and Head of Road and Vehicles Unit
Dickinson, Brian (1987)

Divisional Managers
Stewart, Andrew William (M Jul 1983)
Kaya, Hussein Ahmet (G Jul 1977)
Scott, Cathryn Linton (Feb 1993)
MacKenzie, Judith-Anne (L Jul 1987)
Caune, Rob (1995)
Short, Claire Helen (Sep 1991)
Bedford, Martin (1992)
Booth, Karen Heather (Jan 1986)
Goring, Julia (L Oct 1991)
Buckenham, Giles (L Feb 1995)
Gregory, Colin Jan (Apr 1980)
Cave, Stephen (1999)

Grade 6 Lawyers
Keith, Sally Ann (Sept 1994)
Woodrow, Cameron (1986)
Gladysz, Jan Paul (Dec 1978)
Pryce, Sarah (Sep 1995)
Marks, Stuart (G Jul 1982)
Holland, Elizabeth Sophia Mary (Apr 1981)
Viner, Andrew John (Dec 1980)
Browitt, David (I Nov 1998)
McDonald, Robin (Oct 1980)
Serlin, Richard Anthony (L Nov 1987)
Lancaster, Ann (Oct 1982)
Livesey, Nicholas Ralph (L Nov 1991)
Shindler, Winifred, OBE (Jul 2002)
Golding, Alison F (Mar 1985)
Lonergan, Paul (L Oct 1991)
Jones, Roderick John Rothwell (Jul 1979)
Galliford, Gavin William Michael (Dec 1975)
Japanwalla, Farah Abid (Apr 1993)
Moses, Alun (Jul 1987)
Solomon, Daniel (G Oct 1996)
Boone, Caroline Anne (M Feb 1980)
Steer, Anne Marion (Sept 1985)
Prosser, Anthony Michael Holmes (Dec 1978)
Greenhill, Elizabeth Margaret (Oct 1984)
O'Sullivan, Kevin Feolan (Sept 1998)
Clark, Lisa (Sep 2001)
MacMillen, Claire Frances (Mar 2005)
Goodall, Katharine (Mar 2004)
Fox, Jamie Richard (Oct 2005)
Andre, Jean-Francois Charles (I Jul 2001)
Peyton, Stefan (1995)
Donne, Bronwyn (Sep 2001)
Jones, Daniel Hugh (May 1998)
Edwards, Angus (L Oct 1999)
Hudson, Andrew (2002)
Vincent, Tricia (Sep 1997)
Calcutt, Roy (Sep 1993)
Le Marquand, Piers Frank Bruce (Nov 1993)

Grade 7 Lawyers
Biswas, Sujata (Apr 2005)
Clarke, Andrea (Sep 2006)
Enterkin, Paul (Mar 2007)
Carpenter, Hannah Jenny (Sep 2007)
Magill, Margaret Maureen Delve (Sep 2004)
Walters, Scott Trevelyan (Mar 2002)
Watson, Colette (Aug 2005)
Archer, Errol (Nov 1996)
Batstone, Natalie Faye (Sep 2003)
Malhotra, Andrea Claire (Jul 2004)
Wilkinson, Mark (Aug 2007)
Longney, Carolyn (Oct 2004)
Latham, Lesley (Jan 1990)
Tyrrell-Cho, Geraldine (Aug 2001)
Usher, Tara (Nov 1992)
Huehne, Eva Yim Hong (I Jul 2006)
Robinson, Ellen (Sep 2008)
Woodward, Simon (Jun 2008)

Legal Officer
Underwood, Stephen (Nov 2008)

DEPARTMENT FOR WORK & PENSIONS / DEPARTMENT OF HEALTH

Office (Central London)
5th Floor, The Adelphi, 1-11 John Adam Street, London WC2N 6HT Tel: 020 7962 8000

Solicitor - Grade SCS3
Gill Aitken

Directors of Legal Services – Grade SCS2
Isabel Letwin
Logan, Frances
De Blaquiere, Amanda

Assistant Directors of Legal Services - Grade 5
Adutt, James
Antill, Justine
Bowman, Caroline
Bridges, Paul
Cohen, Paula
Cowell, Jane
Crane, John
Davidson, Catherine
Downey, Sally-Ann
Fowler, Denise
Gidden, Mark
Morley, Claire
Pedler, Margaret
Rogers, Simon
Shellard, Julian
Trudinger, Bronwen
Wilson, Mark
Wright, Paul

Senior Principal Legal Officers - Grade 6
Absalom, Esther
Adam, Michael
Barham, Adrian
Bell, Elizabeth Jane
Bergman, Vicky
Brown, Mandy
Brown, Stephen
Burke, Simon
Burke, Vanessa
Butler, Annone
Campbell, Sara Elspeth
Campbell, Rosaleen
Cantrell, Martin John
Chubb, Alison
Cornwell, David

Corrigan, Anne
Coutinho, Melissa
Curtis, Derek James
De, Zoe
Del Monte, Richard Arron
Dhami, Mandeep
Draper, Jane
Edmonds, Tamlyn
Eisa, Sheila
Elvy, Philip
Ferguson, Alexander
Ferrari, Cesare
Foster, Katie
Freedman, Clive Phillip
Glover, Justine
Golden, Connor
Griffiths, Leah
Harris, Sally
Harrison, Emma
Heath, Jeremy
Hodges, Jeremy
Humberstone, Nigel
Ince, Sandra
Jenking-Rees, Mark
Jones, Bethan
Kennedy, Phillippa
Kent, Graham Edward
Kerr, Clare
Leadbetter, Elaine
Lutterodt, Rodger
Majekodunmi, Annette
Mash, Richard
Massey, Sean
Martin, Claire
Matthews, Wendy Ann
McDonagh, Margaret
McEwen, Ruth
McNamara, Teresa
Morgan, Richard
Munday, Jenny
Nelson, Kevin
Onwuchekwa, Joseph
O'Reilly, Siobhan
Paskin, Anne
Pickering, Susan Margaret Leonara
Potter, Caroline
Powell, Linda
Ramzan-Asghar, Zahida
Rees, Anne
Richardson, Nicola
Riggs, Ruth Helen
Robinson, Francoise
Roberts, Carl
Roberts, Howard Vincent
Scoon, Leo Rennie
Scott, John
Smith, Sarah-Louise
Smyth, Julia
Stacy, Kate
Stockwell, Hillary
Swainson, St John
Todhunter, Ian
Trevelyan, Sasha
Venables, Lisa
Vinnikka, Simmy
Warncke, Christiane
Willmer, Elizabeth
Williams, Rhian
Wilson, Sean
Winnifrith, Charlotte
Yeomans, Elizabeth

Principal Legal Officers – Grade 7

Arnold, Karen
Aycliffe, James
Barker, Sally
Barnes, Nerina
Barrett, Joanna
Beamer, Stephane
Beddow, Claire
Boocock, Verity
Bull, Jenny
Busby, Claire
Carey, Frances
Chan-Sui-Hing, Melissa
Da Costa, Marcus
Davidson, Philip
Davies, Richard
Dean, Benjamin
Dean, Bryony
Dianda, Lee
Durham, Julia
Eaton-Makay, Julie
Faruk, Omar
Flynn, Bernadette
Gee, Susanne
Grindey, Philipa
Harding, Anna
Haywood, Deborah
Hedley, Christopher
Heywood, Sarah
Henley, Ken
Higginbotham, Simon
Holliday, Zelda
Hughes, Margaret
Ioannides, Natalie
Jain, Pamela
Jones, Elizabeth
Joachin Jaqueline
Khan, Arslan
King, Ruth
Kirk, Renae
Kumar, Nirupama
Letizia, Leonie
Lobo, Gillian
Lloyd, Rachel
Lindquest, Ragani
Manton, Emily
Mccarroll, Ruth
McMahon, Kate
Melia, Linda
Montalbano, Nina
Moody, Sean
Mulrennan, Brian
Musgrove, Joanna
Naffissi, Sanam
Patel, Rasila
Patrick, Mike
Pendered, Stephane
Phillips, Sara
Potts, Ian
Powick, Anna
Price, Carl
Prior-Steabler, Lyndsey
Rahulan, Shibani
Raithatha, Prakash
Rajani, Preeya
Reddy, Anu
Reid, Fiona
Reid, Simon
Richardson, Nicola
Ricketts, Caroline
Sabey, Matthew
Sarrafi-Gohar, Mitra
Sangghera, Gurminder
Seale, Maria
Shah, Deepa
Sheppard, Nick
Shore, David
Singh, Dalbir
Slough, Philip
Thomas, Melanie
Tomecki, Natalie
Topping, Rose Marie
Tunnicliffe, Simon
Vaja, Prity
Vickery, Rachael
Ward, George
Ward, Robert
Warham-Smith, Ruth
Welsh, Noreen
Wheeler, Nicola
Wise, Sarah
Young, Christian

DRIVER AND VEHICLE LICENSING AGENCY

Legal Adviser
Cleal, Mrs Rosamund S

Office
Legal Group, D16, Longview Road, Morriston, Swansea SA6 7JL Tel: 01792 788074 Email: legal@dvla.gsi.gov.uk

ENVIRONMENT AGENCY

Head Office
Block One/Two, Government Buildings, Burghill Road, Westbury on Trym, Bristol BS10 6BF Tel: 0870 850 6506

Director of Legal Services
Robinson, J

Regional Offices

ANGLIAN
Kingfisher House, Goldhay Way, Orton Goldhay, Peterborough PE2 5ZR

MIDLANDS
Sapphire Street, 550 Streetsbrook Road, Solihull, West Midlands B91 1QT

NORTH EAST
River House, 21 Park Square South, Leeds LS1 2QG

NORTH WEST
Richard Fairclough House, Knutsford Road, Latchford, Warrington WA4 1HT

SOUTHERN
Guildbourne House, Chatsworth Road, Worthing, West Sussex BN11 1LD

SOUTH WEST
Manley House, Kestrel Way, Exeter EX2 7LQ

THAMES
Kings Meadow House, Kings Meadow Road, Reading RG1 8DQ

WALES
Cambria House, 29 Newport Road, Cardiff CF24 0TP

EQUALITY AND HUMAN RIGHTS COMMISSION

Office
3 More London Riverside, Tooley Street, London SE1 2RG Tel: 0845 604 6610 (helpline) / 020 3117 0235 Fax: 020 3117 0237 Email: info@equalityhumanrights.com Web: www.equalityhumanrights.com

16

EXPORT CREDITS GUARANTEE DEPARTMENT

Office
PO Box 2200, 2 Exchange Tower, Harbour Exchange Square, London E14 9GS Tel: 020 7512 7000 Fax: 020 7512 7052 TELEX: 290350 ECGDHQ G

Grade 5: General Counsel
Ridley, David Nicholas (Jan 1980)

Grade 6: Deputy General Counsel
Redfearn, Charles (L 1986)

Grade 6: Senior Principal (Legal)
O'Loan, Arthur James (Apr 2002)
Allen, Michael Guy Tothill (Aug 1981)
Reed, Caroline Denise (Aug 2005)
Cooper, William Anthony Marcus Carmody (Sep 2003)
Murray, Morag Anna Stuart (Sep 2004)
Mann, Davinder Kaur (Sep 2003)
Jankowitz, Reinet Heleen (Dec 2008)
Eshun, Esi Addae (Sep 2008)

FINANCIAL OMBUDSMAN SERVICE

Office
South Quay Plaza, 183 Marsh Wall, London E14 9SR Tel: 020 7964 1000 Fax: 020 7964 1001 Email: complaint.info@financial-ombudsman.org.uk Web: www.financial-ombudsman.org.uk

FINANCIAL SERVICES AUTHORITY

Office
25 The North Colonnade, Canary Wharf, London E14 5HS Tel: 020 7066 1000 Web: www.fsa.gov.uk

FOREIGN & COMMONWEALTH OFFICE

Office
Legal Advisors, K G 124, Main Building, King Charles Street, London SW1A 2AH Tel: 020 7008 1586

HM PROCURATOR GENERAL AND TREASURY SOLICITOR

The Treasury Solicitor's Department
One Kemble Street, London WC2B 4TS Tel: 020 7210 3000 DX: 123242 KINGSWAY

Senior Civil Service

HM Procurator-General and Treasury Solicitor
Jenkins, Paul

Deputy Treasury Solicitor
Jones, Jonathan

Senior Civil Servant (Litigation)
Giles, Hugh

Senior Civil Servant (Advisory)
Berman, Paul

HM REVENUE & CUSTOMS

Office
Solicitor's Office, Bush House, Strand, London WC2B 4RD Tel: 020 7438 7414 Fax: 020 7438 7134

Solicitor's Office, 100 Parliament Street, London SW1A 2BQ Tel: 020 7147 0771 Fax: 020 7147 0666

General Counsel and Solicitor
Inglese, Anthony (Nov 1976)

Director, Sols A (Litigation)
Humm, Robert

Director, Sols B (Business Tax and Corporate Governance)
Evans, Anthony

Director, Sols C: (Personal Tax, Benefits & Credits and Corporate Services)
Hardy, Serena

HEALTH & SAFETY COMMISSION AND HEALTH & SAFETY EXECUTIVE

Office
Redgrave Court, Merton Road, Bootle, Merseyside L20 7HS Tel: 0151 951 4000

Legal Adviser
McNaught, Peter (Sep 2008)

Grade 6 Litigation
Fox, Alan (May 2009)
Skinner, Katherine (Mar 2008)

Grade 7 Litigation
Tiger, Sam (Mar 2008)
McMahon, Jenny (Jan 2009)
Dunn, Darren (Jan 2009)
Hughes, Alan (Apr 2009)
Conway, Richard (Aug 2010)

HOME OFFICE

Office HQ
2 Marsham Street, Seacole Ground, London SW1P 4DF Switchboard: 020 7035 1000

Legal Adviser
Seymour, David (G 1975)

Deputy Legal Advisers
Bramley, Steven Michael Stuart
Carter, Harry

SCS Lawyers
Fussell, Nick
Herberg, Lucan
Hopkins, Emma
Messenger, Robert
Miller, Andrew
Morris, Anne
Smith, Matthew
Weston, Sally

IDENTITY AND PASSPORT SERVICE

Passports
Tel: 0300 222 0000

General Register Office
Tel: 0845 603 7788

Web:www.ips.gov.uk

The Identity and Passport Service (IPS) is an Executive Agency of the Home Office and was established on 1 April 2006. Building on the strong foundations of the UK Passport Service, IPS is a customer focused organisation, providing passports for British citizens and passport verification services. The General Register Office (GRO) also became part of IPS on 1 April 2008. GRO oversees the system of civil registration, including births, stillbirths, adoptions, civil partnerships, marriages and deaths, in England and Wales. It does this in partnership with a range of government departments and the 174 local authorities who provide the service directly to their local community.

LAND REGISTRY AND OFFICES

Head Office
Trafalgar House, 1 Bedford Park, Croydon CR0 2AQ Tel: 020 8781 9100 Fax: 020 8781 9110

Chief Land Registrar
Pierleoni, M

Acting Director of Legal Services and Deputy Chief Land Registrar
Lewis, A M (Oct 1982)

Head of Corporate Legal Services
Westcott Rudd, M P (Sep 1984)

Land Registrar (Head of Guarantee and Litigation Group)
Donaldson, J R (Oct 1985)

Land Registrar (Registration Legal Services)
Twambley, F M (Apr 1980)

Assistant Land Registrars
Acharya, Miss S (Apr 1988)
Allen, Miss J E (Oct 1991)
Floyd, T E (May 1976)
Wilbourn, Miss K P (Sep 1984)
Milne, P J (Jan 1989)
Shah, Mrs B (Jan 1997)
Bailey, Ms J (Nov 1988)
Maroo, A (Sep 1999)

Head of Learning and Development
Chamberlain, Ms L (Nov 1982)

Land Registry, Birkenhead Office
Rosebrae Court, Woodside Ferry Approach, Birkenhead, Merseyside CH41 6DU Tel: 0151 472 6666 Fax: 0151 472 6789

Land Registrar
Mulliner, Ms K M R (Nov 1982)

Assistant Land Registrars
Bickley, J (Oct 1979)
Tanner, K (Mar 1999)
Inge, Miss V J (May 1986)
Salter, Mrs N P (Oct 1984)
Wright, N K (Jun 1978)
Booth, Mrs L F (Aug 1996)

Land Registry, Coventry Office
Leigh Court, Torrington Avenue, Tile Hill, Coventry CV4 9XZ Tel: 024 7686 0860 Fax: 024 7686 0021

Land Registrar
Weaver, Mrs D M (Oct 1984)

Kelway, S P - Land Registrar (E-Services) (Apr 1977)

Assistant Land Registrars
West, Miss N C (Aug 1998)
Whiteside, Mrs H G (Sep 1998)
Hodges, P J (Oct 1995)
Gill, Mrs H K (Dec 1997)
Moore, Miss E A (Sep 1997)

Land Registry, Croydon Office
Trafalgar House, 1 Bedford Park, Croydon CR0 2AQ Tel: 020 8781 9100 Fax: 020 8781 9110

Land Registrar
Sanders, Miss H R (Dec 1973)

Assistant Land Registrars
Dosaj, Miss A K (Mar 1992)
Shaw, Miss A M (Nov 2000)
Reich, L J (Jul 2001)

Land Registry, Durham Office
Southfield House, Southfield Way, Durham DH1 5TR Tel: 0191 301 3500 Fax: 0191 301 0020

Land Registrar
Timothy, P J (Apr 1970)

Assistant Land Registrars
Probee, T M (Jun 1988)
Soulsby, A (Mar 1980)
Barker, Mrs A M (Oct 1993)
Smith, A H (Dec 1969)
Jones, Mrs J (Jul 1999)
Heslop, J R (Oct 1995)
Bulmer, Mrs A S (Jun 1979)
Simpson, Miss C H (Jul 1985)
Clough, Miss F V (Nov 1993)
Campbell, C J G (Nov 1988)
Gorst, Mrs S J (Oct 1987)

Land Registry, Fylde Office
Wrea Brook Court, Lytham Road, Warton PR4 1TE Tel:01772 836700 Fax: 01772 836970

Land Registrar
Kay, Mrs C A (Apr 1980)

Assistant Land Registrars
Abbott, Mrs A L (Oct 1996)
Barr, Mrs A L (Nov 1989)
Barrie, G A (Mar 2002
Cook, Mrs S J (Oct 1996)
Hodgson, Miss S M (Dec 1977)
Morrell, T V (Oct 1996)
Morrison, Ms L (Feb 2002)
Withnell, M H (Nov 1991)

Land Registry, Gloucester Office
Twyver House, Bruton Way, Gloucester GL1 1DQ Tel: 01452 511111 Fax: 01452 510050

Land Registrar
Jenkins, Mrs J E (Dec 1986)

Senior Assistant Land Registrar
Lewis, T H O (Jul 1975)

Assistant Land Registrars
Powell, Mrs P J (Jun 1978)
Barton, Mrs J (Apr 1981)
Brothers, Mrs K (Oct 1986)
Curtis, A R (Oct 1995)
Fullerton, J A (Nov 1982)
Whiteside, J D (Sep 1997)

Land Registry, Kingston Upon Hull Office
Earle House, Colonial Street, Hull HU2 8JN Tel: 01482 223244 Fax: 01482 224278

Land Registrar
Coveney, S R (Dec 1975)

Assistant Land Registrars
Watt, Mrs A M (Nov 1980)
Littlefair, Mrs S J (Jul 1976)
Cavill, D M (Oct 1995)
Duxbury, P B (Oct 1991)
Edon, J A (Dec 1978)
Hargreave, Mrs A M (Jun 1979)
Johnson, A P (Nov 1984)

Land Registry, Leicester Office
Westbridge Place, Leicester LE3 5DR Tel: 0116 265 4000 Fax: 0116 265 4008

Land Registrar
Goodfellow, Mrs J A (Apr 1981)

Assistant Land Registrars
Brown, Mrs F M (Nov 1981)
Goodfellow, N C (Oct 1981)
Khan, R A (Dec 1990)
Owen, Mrs L (Dec 1993)
Parker, J V (Oct 1986)
Hopkins, I J (Jun 1980)
Abed, Ms N (Sep 2003)

Land Registry, Nottingham Office
Chalfont Drive, Nottingham NG8 3RN Tel: 0115 935 1166 Fax: 0116 935 0038

Land Registrar
Brown, P A (Apr 1976)

Assistant Land Registrars
Barclay, J W (Oct 2002)
Betteridge, A (Dec 1983)
Gibson, Mrs A M (Feb 1983)
Harvey, Miss C (Mar 2000)
Keene, Ms A (Oct 1983)
Law, J W H (Jun 1981)
Lall, A K (Jan 1990)
Naylor, S H (Nov 1991)
Mills, C J (Dec 1987)
Noonan, J O P (Oct 1990)
Thomas, R W (Jun 1979)

Land Registry, Peterborough Office
Touthill Close, City Road, Peterborough PE1 1XN Tel: 01733 288288 Fax: 01733 280022

Land Registrar
Post currently not filled.

Senior Assistant Land Registrar
Hardman, I E (Feb 1974)

Assistant Land Registrars
Papworth, Miss S R (Mar 1980)
Brown, Mrs M A E (Oct 1991)
Heaney, R J (Nov 1999)
Purslow, Ms A L (Sep 2003)

Land Registry, Plymouth Office
Plumer House, Tailyour Road, Crownhill, Plymouth PL6 5HY Tel: 01752 636000 Fax: 01752 636161

Land Registrar
Post currently not filled.

Senior Assistant Land Registrar
Parham, H G (Apr 1974)

Assistant Land Registrars
Berry, A G (Jun 1979)
Ellis, D B (Feb 1987)
Smart, Mrs C F (Apr 1985)
Hattersley, Mrs R J (Dec 1987)
Bedford, Mrs C A (Jun 1976)
Turner, Mrs R M (Mar 1991)

Land Registry, Portsmouth Office
St Andrew's Court, St Michael's Road, Portsmouth, Hampshire PO1 2JH Tel: 023 9276 8888 Fax: 023 9276 8768

Land Registrar
Post currently not filled.

Senior Assistant Land Registrar
Mills, J (Oct 1985)

Assistant Land Registrars
Evans, A A (Jan 1978)
Hill, Mr R (Sep 1998)
White, Mrs P I (Oct 1998)

Land Registry, Stevenage Office
Brickdale House, Swingate Stevenage, Hertfordshire SG1 1XG Tel: 01438 788888 Fax: 01438 780107

Land Registrar
Post currently not filled

Assistant Land Registrars
Monk, G A (Jun 1976)
Millinger, Mrs G M (Oct 1982)
Wilkinson, A J (Oct 1984)
Stuart, Ms C (Oct 1985)
Mobbs, J K (Sep 2000)

Land Registry, Telford Office
Parkside Court, Hall Park Way, Telford, Shropshire TF3 4LR Tel: 01952 290355 Fax: 01952 290356

Land Registrar
Fearnley, R J (Jun 1976)

Assistant Land Registrars
Creevey, J (Jul 1978)
Pitt Lewis, C J (Jun 1978)
Rees, D W (Feb 1987)
Wood, Mrs R A (Oct 1984)
Telfer, J L (Jan 1974)

Land Registry, Tunbridge Wells Office
Forest Court, Forest Road, Tunbridge Wells, Kent TN2 5AQ Tel: 01892 510015 Fax: 01892 510032

Land Registrar
Sanders, Miss H R (Dec 1973)

Assistant Land Registrars
Hookway, K A (Aug 1998)
Rabas, Mrs J S (Jun 1982)
Dove, T S (Sep 2002)
Brophy, Miss M L (Aug 1997)
Matheson, Mrs A F (May 1996)

Land Registry, Wales Office
Ty Cwm Tawe, Phoenix Way, Llansamlet, Swansea SA7 9FQ Tel: 01792 355000

Land Registrar
Lewis, T M (May 1980)

Assistant Land Registrars
Cater, Mrs S J (Oct 1985)
Davies, T D L (Mar 1983)
Hinds, C D (Dec 1975)
Stephens, Mrs M D (Jan 1980)
Williams, K (Mar 1974)
Evans, Mrs J (Oct 1991)
Rogers, Miss S L (Jan 1993)
Williams, Mr J H (Nov 1996)
Bateman, N H (Jul 1979)
Moorhouse, Ms A L (1980)
James, Mrs S M (Jun 1973)
Norman, Mrs B A (Feb 1984)
Malpas, R W (Apr 1989)
Lloyd-Parry, D I (Sep 1984)

Land Registry, Weymouth Office
Melcombe Court, 1 Cumberland Drive, Weymouth, Dorset DT4 9TT Tel: 01305 363636 Fax: 01305 363646

Land Registrar
Pownall, J P (Sep 1992)

Assistant Land Registrars
Ellison, D H (Feb 1986)
Conlan, Mrs A J (Jan 1990)
Colvin, J F (Dec 1973)
Knowlden, Mrs A M (Oct 1979)
Moran, T H (Aug 1979)
Briginshaw, R R (Aug 1976)
Williams, Ms L A (Jan 1989)

THE LAW COMMISSION

The Law Commission was set up by Section 1 of the Law Commissions Act 1965 for the purpose of promoting the reform of the law.

The Commissioners are:
Munby, The Hon Mr Justice (Chairman)
Cooke, Prof Elizabeth
Ormerod, Prof David
Patterson, Francis
Hertzell, David

Office
Steel House, 11 Tothill Street, London SW1H 9LJ Tel: 020 3334 0200 Email: chief.executive@lawcommission.gsi.gov.uk

Chief Executive (Senior Civil Service)
Ormerod, M

Head of Statute Law Revision (Senior Civil Service)
Saunders, J D S

Grade 6
Goriely, Ms T
Brown, Ms C
Jolley, M
Percival, R

Grade 7
Birthwright, Ms D
Drummond, Ms E
Emson, R
Hack, Ms S
Hughes, Christina
Jamieson, Ms L
Jarzabkowski, Ms J
Oakley, C
Sparks, Christina
Spencer-Lane, T
Tabbush, S
Teasdale, J
Uggucioni, Jessica
Vincent, K
Vine, Catherine
Wade, Ms C
Waller, Ms S
Wolchover, J
Young, Sarah

Parliamentary Draftsmen*
*On Secondment from Office of Parliamentary Counsel
Caldwell, Ms H
Dormer, R
Hall, D

Economic Adviser
Vindelyn Smith-Hillman

LEGAL SERVICES COMMISSION

Office
4 Abbey Orchard Street, London SW1P 2BS Tel: 0300 200 2020 Web: www.legalservices.gov.uk

The Legal Services Commission runs the legal aid scheme in England and Wales. They work in partnership with solicitors and not-for-profit organisations to provide information, advice and legal representation to people in need.

METROPOLITAN POLICE - DIRECTORATE OF LEGAL SERVICES

Office
First Floor, Victoria Block, New Scotland Yard, 8-10 Broadway, London SW1H 0BG Tel: 020 7230 6999 Fax: 020 7230 7209

Director
Solomons, E B BA (Apr 1979)

Assistant Directors
Morgan, G, LLB (Oct 1983)
Saleh, N F, LLB (May 1987)
Burrows, S D M, BA (Jun 1979)

Team Leaders
Bird, S, BA (Apr 1997)
Carey-Yard, G, LLB (Barrister, Nov 1982)
Cunningham, A, BA(Hons) (Sep 1992)
Hickman, J, BA (Barrister, Nov 1983)
Jones, M, LLB(Hons) (Mar 1996)
Leonard, J M, BSc(Hons) (Nov 1990)
Pierce, N, BA(Keele) (Dec 1981)
Skipper, R J, LLB (Jun 1986)
Spanton, M A, LLB(Hons) (Oct 1993)
Winfield, S, LLB(Hons) (Barrister, Oct 1990)

Lawyers
Baker, R W, LLB(Hons) (Sep 1997)
Barnes, R A, BA(Hons) (Apr 1997)
Bergin, J C, BSc(Hons) (Jun 1994)
Blay, D, BA(Hons) (Sep 2008)
Boahen, C A, LLB(Hons) (Sep 1995)
Brannigan, N W, LLB(Hons) (Dec 1994)
Castiglione, S A, LLB(Hons) (Sep 1997)
Catcheside, S E, BA(Hons) (Oct 1995)
Cooper, V, LLB(Special Hons) (Aug 2002)
Coultas, A E, BA(Hons) (Sep 2006)
Cunningham, A, BA, CPE, LSF (Sep 1992)
Darr, H, LLB(Hons) (May 2003)
Davis, M F, BA(Hons) (Feb 1993)
Fairbrother, A J, LLB(Hons) (Nov 1997)
Fowler, T, LLB(Hons) (Barrister, Feb 1994)
Gale, S B, BA (Jul 1975)
Gluck, L M, LLB (Nov 1978)
Harroway, E L, LLB(Hons) (Oct 1998)
Heron, S, LLB(Hons) (Nov 1990)
Knowles, M T, BA(Hons) (Mar 2010)
Lloyd, J
Loose, P D, BA (Oct 1984)
Mandair, P, BA (Sep 2000)
McCafferty, E, LLB(Hons), ACIB (Barrister, Jul 1979)
McCahon, D, BA (Apr 1994)
Morris, J R, BA(Hons) (Nov 1987)
Moxom, S I (Dec 2000)
O'Dwyer, J M, LLB(Hons) (Mar 1998)
Peacock, A E, BA(Hons) (Feb 2010)
Rai, G, BA(Hons) (Oct 1988)
Roberts, Z, LLB (Oct 2007)
Royan, S M, BA(Hons) (Nov 1995)
Scott, E, LLB(Hons) (Mar 2006)
Templeman, L, LLB(Hons) (Feb 2009)
Tuffuor, T A, LLB(Hons) (Mar 2004)
Wisbey, T, LLB(Hons) (Sep 2000)
Wright, J M, BA (Nov 2005)

METROPOLITAN POLICE SERVICE

Office
New Scotland Yard, Broadway, London SW1H 0BG

Commissioner
Stephenson, Sir Paul

Deputy Commissioner
Godwin, Tim

Assistant Commissioners
Allison, Chris
Dick, Cressida
Fitzpatrick, Rose
Yates, John

Solicitor
Solomons, Edward

MINISTRY OF DEFENCE (CENTRAL LEGAL SERVICES)

Central Office
MOD Main Building, Whitehall, London SW1A 2HB Tel: 020 7218 4691 Fax: 020 7218 9451

MOD Director General Legal Services Grade 3
Nash, Frances

Grade 5
Dann, Linda
Evans, John
Edminson, Bridget
Morrison, Humphrey

Grade 6
Diamond, Che
Todd, Alison
Holder, Edward
Ryb, Samantha
Lane-Watkins, Nyree
Valchero, Michelle
Lee, Daniel
Ziegel, Jonathan
Miller, Caroline
Amir, Shamim
Cole, Vanessa

Huey, Peter
McDonald, Adrian
Cull, Peter
Kitt, Jeremy
Addison, Michael
Padwell, Martine
Isaacs, Esther
Clark, Tamsyn
Brooks, Fenella
Amir, Shamim

Grade 7
Mawby, Hugh
Durston, Polly
McLeod, Anna
Eleyae, Adeola
Hinton, Rebecca
Costelloe, St John
Dempsey, Dawn

Commercial Law (Bristol Office)
Poplar 2b, Mail Point 2216, MOD Abbey Wood, Bristol BS34 8JH

Grade 5
Miller, Robert

Grade 6
Jones, Chris
Park, Andrew
Fox, Andrew
Thompson, Peter
Arakistain, Maitena
Gregory, Catherine
Vickers, Cathryn

Grade 7
Eastwood, Hazel
Chesterman, Robert
Heczko, Asia
Goddard, Phillip
Pestell, Charles
Wildgoose, Emma
Wardell, Nicola
Sellers, Rachel
Kunz, Traci
Murray, Judith
Miles, Catrin
Betty, Claire
Kraehling, Julia
Jessica Robinson
Janette Stewart
Daniel Fitzgerald

Property Law (Foxhill Office)
Foxhill, Bradford Road, Combe Down, Bath BA1 5AB Tel: 01225 883651

Grade 6
Wardell, Robert
Hinch, Alison

Legal Services Germany

Grade 5
Howard, Stuart

Grade 6
Nick Crossley

Legal Advisors Cyprus

Grade 5
Hudson, John

Grade 6
Curwen, Emma
Leahy, Finbarr
Barry, Roisin
Ravi, Sampanthar

OFFICE OF FAIR TRADING

Office
Fleetbank House, 2-6 Salisbury Square, London EC4Y 8JX Tel: 0845 722 4499 Fax: 020 7211 8877

Chairman
Colins, Philip

General Counsel
Barr, Frances

General Counsel's Office: Directors
Gurowich, Paul
Bennett, Peter
Berwick, Sarah

Markets & Projects
Branch, Sonya
Telford, Nerilee
Christofides, Louis
Freeman, Jason
Berg, Claudia
Mordaunt , Alastair
Williams , Simon

Policy
Holland, Jackie

Mergers
Mills, Sheldon

Cartels
Nikpay, Ali
Blake, Stephen

Credit
Brindley, Simon

OFFICE OF TELECOMMUNICATIONS (OFCOM)

Office
2A Southwark Bridge Road, London SE1 9HA Tel: 020 7981 3000 Fax: 020 7981 3159

General Counsel
Weitzman, Polly (Oct 1988)

Legal Directors
Hogg, Philip (Sep 1997)
Smith, Caroline (Nov 1987)
Turnbull, Sarah (Mar 1999)
Hobday, Natasha (Jul 2003)

Legal Advisers
Ball, Steven (Mar 2000)
Ballantyne, Martin (Sep 2001)
Beresford, Nick (Sep 1999)
Bruce, Jennifer (Jun 2007, NZ 1996)
Carter, Hannah (Oct 2008)
Chard, James (Sep 2003)
Christie, David (Sep 1996)
Collini, Mark (Mar 2000)
Cosgrove, Nuala (Sep 1996)
Dadley, Amanda (Sep 1997)
Galloway, Alexander (Sept 2008)
Gouliou, Eleni (June 2006, Greece Dec 2002)
Gordon, Deirdre (Mar 2003)
Gowda, Sukina (Sep 2001)
Hess, Martin (Nov 2002, Germany)
Hinings,Jessica (Oct 2006)
Leathley, Simon (Sep 1999)
McKay, Val (Aug 2008, Australia 1999)
Morgan, Gwen (Sep 1999)
Philips, Paul (Sep 2001)
Richardson, Dr Russell (Mar 1999)
Roberts, Kate (Jan 2007, NZ Jun 2003)
Roy, Dilip (Sep 2001)
Rosso, Selene (Aug 2010, March 2006, Italy)
Wells, Rachel (Sep 2007)
Meier, Stefanie (Mar 2004)
Morrissey, Grainne (Sept 2009)
Spence, Mylene (Sep 2007)
Stewart, Megan (Aug 2008, 2005 Canada)
Vermang, Kira (Sep 2004, Belgium)
Wifalk, Anders (Sep 1999, Sweden 1995)

OFFICE OF THE PUBLIC GUARDIAN

Office
PO Box 15118, Birmingham B16 6GX

Archway Tower, 2 Junction Road, London N19 5SZ DX: 744240 BIRMINGHAM 79 Tel: 0300 456 0300 Fax: 0870 739 5780 Email: customerservices@publicguardian.gsi.gov.uk Website: www.publicguardian.gov.uk

Public Guardian
John, Martin

Senior Judge
Lush, Denzil

OFFICE OF THE SCOTTISH CHARITY REGULATOR (OSCR)

Office
2nd Floor, Quadrant House, 9 Riverside Drive, Dundee DD1 4NY Tel: 01382 220446 Email: info@oscr.org.uk

Chief Executive
Ryder, Jane

OFFICE OF THE PARLIAMENTARY COUNSEL

Office
36 Whitehall, London SW1A 2AY Tel: 020 7210 2588

First Parliamentary Counsel
Laws, Stephen, CB (M Feb 1973)

Parliamentary Counsel
Cook, D J (May 1990)
Davies, P J, CB (M Feb 1981)
Dormer, R J (Jan 1980)
Gardiner, Mrs E A F (Oct 1990)
Hogarth, A J (I July 1983)
Johnston, Miss C E, CB (Dec 1978)
McLaughlin, Mrs L A (Nov 1988)
Ramsay, D J (Nov 1984)
Richardson, Mrs B A (Nov 1990)
Rogers, H (Sep 1991)
Sellers, J M, CB (Jun 1980)
Sprackling, D M (Oct 1988)
Stell, E J (Oct 1990)

Deputy Parliamentary Counsel
Baines, Miss L R (Dec 1993)
Bertlin, Mrs A M (Dec 1987)
Coleman, F T
Crawford, Miss J (L Jan 1991)
de Mounteney, J C
Hall, D P (Oct 1996)
Hudson, M J (Oct 1991)
Lyne, G J (1988)

Moore, Miss H E (Nov 1996)
O'Riordan, Miss C N (Nov 1989)
Packer, C J (Sep 1996)
Rendell, N W (Nov 1995)
Scott, A C (Nov 1995)
Sewell, D J (Nov 1986)
Stephens, J R (M Oct 1992)
Walsh, Miss B (Oct 1995)

Senior Assistant Parliamentary Counsel
Bailey, D G
Bedding, P A
Boileau, H R
Carney, Mrs Kirsty
Carter, J R
Davies, Miss S L (I Oct 1995)
Ember, P G
Holt, Miss N R
Macnamara, Miss C A
Marlin, R G
Morgan, Mrs I L
Norbury, L E
Salimi, S A
Spitz, R A

Assistant Parliamentary Counsel
Cartwright, Mrs J M
Chessum, P A
Clapinska, Ms L A
Daruwala, Ms A-S
Furniss, E L
Martin, N W R
Reynolds-Lewis, Miss C L
Sansom, Mrs C S
Somjee, Mrs K A
Strachan, Miss H M
Wharam, A D
Wicks, Mrs P E

PROBATE REGISTRIES AND LOCAL OFFICES

Please write to the Personal Application Section at the appropriate Probate Registry and state which Probate Registry or local office you wish to be interviewed at:

BIRMINGHAM

Office
The Priory Courts, 33 Bull Street, Birmingham B4 6DU Tel: 0121 681 3400/14

Registrar
Walbeoff, Mrs Pam

Local Offices
Coventry, Kidderminster, Northampton, Wolverhampton

BODMIN

Office
Probate Sub-Registry, Bodmin's Magistrates Court, Launceston Road, Bodmin PL31 2AL Tel: 01208 261581

Local Offices
Truro, Plymouth

BRIGHTON

Office
William Street, Brighton BN2 2LG Tel: 01273 573510

Local Offices
Horsham, Hastings, Chichester

BRISTOL

Office
The Crescent Centre, Temple Back, Bristol BS1 6EP Tel: 0117 927 3915/926 4619

Local Offices
Bath, Weston-Super-Mare

CAERNARFON

Office
Probate Sub-Registry, Criminal Justice Centre, Llanberis Road, Caernarfon, Gwynedd LL55 2DF Tel: 01286 669755

Local Offices
Rhyl, Wrexham

CARDIFF

Office
Probate Registry of Wales, Cardiff Magistrates' Court, 3rd Floor, Fitzalan Place, Cardiff CF24 0RZ Tel: 029 2047 4373

Local Offices
Bridgend, Newport, Pontypridd

CARLISLE

Office
Courts of Justice, Earl Street, Carlisle CA1 1DJ Tel: 01228 521751

CARMARTHEN

Office
14 King Street, Dyfed SA31 1BL Tel: 01267 242560

Local Offices
Aberystwyth, Haverfordwest, Swansea

CHESTER

Office
2nd Floor, Chester Civil Justice Centre, Trident House, Little St John Street, Chester CH1 1RE Tel: 01244 345082

EXETER

Office
2nd Floor, Exeter Crown & County Courts, Southernhay Gardens, Exeter EX1 1UH Tel: 01392 415370

Local Offices
Taunton, Barnstaple, Torquay/Newton Abbot, Yeovil

GLOUCESTER

Office
2nd Floor, Combined Court Building, Kimbrose Way, Gloucester GL1 2DG Tel: 01452 834966

Local Offices
Cheltenham, Hereford, Worcester

IPSWICH

Office
Ground Floor, 8 Arcade Street, Ipswich IP1 1EJ Tel: 01473 284260

Registrar
Whitby, Miss Helen

Local Offices
Chelmsford, Colchester

LANCASTER

Office
Room 111, Mitre House, Church Street, Lancaster LA1 1HE Tel: 01524 36625

Local Offices
Barrow-in-Furness, Blackpool, Preston

LEEDS

Office
3rd Floor, Coronet House, Queen Street, Leeds LS1 2BA Tel: 0113 386 3540

Registrar
Parry, Mrs Angela

LEICESTER

Office
Crown Court Building, 90 Wellington Street, Leicester LE1 6HG Tel: 0116 285 3380

Local Offices
Bedford

LINCOLN

Office
360 High Street, Lincoln LN5 7PS Tel: 01522 523648

LIVERPOOL

Office
Queen Elizabeth II Law Courts, Derby Square, Liverpool L2 1XA Tel: 0151 236 8264

Registrar
Clark-Rimmer, Mrs Karen

Local Offices
Southport, St Helens

LONDON

Office
Probate Department, Principal Registry, Family Division, First Avenue House, 42-49 High Holborn, London WC1V 6NP Tel: 020 7947 6939. Personal Enquiries - Room 83, Opening Hours 10.00am - 4.30pm, Mon - Fri.

Local Offices
Croydon, Edmonton, Harlow, Kingston, Luton, Southend-on-Sea, Woolwich

MAIDSTONE

Office
The Law Courts, Baker Road, Maidstone ME16 8EW Tel: 01622 202048/47

Local Offices
Canterbury, Tunbridge Wells

MANCHESTER

Office
Manchester Civil Justice Centre, Ground Floor, 1 Bridge Street West, PO Box 4240, Manchester M60 1WJ Tel: 0161 240 5700

Registrar
Murphy, K P

Local Offices
Bolton, Nelson, Oldham, Warrington, Wigan

MIDDLESBROUGH

Office
Combined Court Centre, Russell Street, Middlesbrough, Cleveland TS1 2AE Tel: 01642 340001

NEWCASTLE UPON TYNE

Office
No1 Waterloo Square, Newcastle Upon Tyne NE1 4DR Tel: 0191 211 2170

Registrar
Riley, Mrs Christine

Local Offices
Darlington

NORWICH

Office
Combined Court Building, The Law Courts, Bishopsgate, Norwich NR3 1UR Tel: 01603 761776

Local Office
Lowestoft, Kings Lynn

NOTTINGHAM

Office
Butt Dyke House, 33 Park Row, Nottingham NG1 6GR Tel: 0115 941 4288

OXFORD

Office
Combined Court Centre, St Aldates, Oxford OX1 1LY Tel: 01865 793055

Registrar
D'Costa, R

Local Offices
Aylesbury, High Wycombe, Reading, Slough, Swindon

PETERBOROUGH

Office
Crown Buildings, Rivergate, Peterborough PE1 1EJ Tel: 01733 62802

Local Offices
Cambridge

SHEFFIELD

Office
PO Box 832, The Law Courts, 50 West Bar, Sheffield S3 8YR Tel: 0114 281 2599

STOKE-ON-TRENT

Office
Combined Court Centre, Bethesda Street, Hanley, Stoke-on-Trent ST1 3BP Tel: 01782 854065

Local Offices
Crewe, Shrewsbury, Stafford

WINCHESTER

Office
4th Floor, Cromwell House, Andover Road , Winchester SO23 7EW Tel: 01962 897029

Registrar
Butler, Alan

Local offices
Basingstoke, Bournemouth, Dorchester, Guildford, Newport (IOW), Portsmouth, Salisbury, Southampton

YORK

Office
1st Floor, Castle Chambers, Clifford Street, York YO1 9RG Tel: 01904 666777

Local Offices
Hull, Scarborough

SERIOUS FRAUD OFFICE

Office
Elm House, 10-16 Elm Street, London WC1X OBJ Web: www.sfo.gov.uk

TREASURY COUNSEL TO THE CROWN

Senior Treasury Counsel

Laidlaw, Jonathan, Q.C. (1982)
2 Hare Court
Tel: 020 7353 5324

Jafferjee, Aftab, Q.C. (1980)
Atkinson Bevan Chambers
Tel: 020 7353 2112

Altman, Brian, Q.C. (1981)
2 Bedford Row
Tel: 020 7440 8888

Wright, Peter, Q.C. (1981)
2 Hare Court
Tel: 020 7353 5324

Whittam, Richard, Q.C. (1983)
2 Bedford Row
Tel: 020 7440 8888

Brown, Edward, Q.C. (1983)
QEB Hollis Whiteman
Tel: 020 7583 5766

Aylett, Crispin, Q.C. (1985)
3 Raymond Buildings
Tel: 020 7400 6400

Edis, Andrew, Q.C. (1980)
2 Hare Court
Tel: 020 7353 5324

Denison, Simon, Q.C. (1984)
6 Kings Bench Walk
Tel: 020 7583 0410

Heywood, Mark, Q.C. (1985)
5 Kings Bench Walk
Tel: 020 7353 5638

Rees, Jonathan, Q.C. (1987)
2 Hare Court
Tel: 020 7353 5324

Junior Treasury Counsel

Johnson, Zoe (1984)
QEB Hollis Whiteman
Tel: 020 7583 5766

Cheema, Bobbie (1989)
2 Hare Court
Tel: 020 7353 5324

Perry, Duncan (1992)
6 Kings Bench Walk
Tel: 020 7583 0410

Darbishire, Adrian (1993)
QEB Hollis Whiteman
Tel: 020 7583 5766

Whitehouse, Sarah (1993)
6 Kings Bench Walk
Tel: 020 7583 5766

Atkinson, Duncan (1995)
6 Kings Bench Walk
Tel: 020 7583 5766

Glasgow, Oliver (1995)
2 Hare Court
Tel: 020 7353 5324

Nelson, Michelle (1994)
18 Red Lion Court
Tel: 020 7520 6000

Evans, Julian (1997)
QEB Hollis Whiteman
Tel: 020 7583 5766

Mabley, Louis (1997)
6 Kings Bench Walk
Tel: 020 7583 0410

TRIBUNALS SERVICE - CRIMINAL INJURIES COMPENSATION

Office
Wellington House, 134-136 Wellington Street, Glasgow, G2 2XL Tel: 0141 354 8555 Fax: 0141 354 8556

Chairman
Summers, Mr Anthony

THE WATER SERVICES REGULATION AUTHORITY (OFWAT)

Office
Centre City Tower, 7 Hill Street, Birmingham B5 4UA Tel: 0121 644 7500 Fax: 0121 644 7582

Director of Legal Services and Board Secretary
Brooker, Huw (Sep 1996)
Tel: 0121 644 7662

Deputy Director of Legal Services Maternity Leave
Shaw, Sophie (Sep 1999)
Tel: 0121 644 7535

Deputy Director of Legal Services
Beale, Noel
Tel: 0121 644 7663
Called to the bar (Oct 1997)
Qualified as a Solicitor (Sep 2000)

Principal Legal Adviser
Ilett, Bethan (Oct 2003)
Tel: 0121 644 7675

Interim Deputy Director of Legal Services
Yeo, Adrian
Tel: 0121 644 7818
Called to the bar (1999)
Qualified as a Solicitor (Sep 2003)

Principal Legal Adviser
Marsal, Jill (Apr 1999)
Tel: 0121 644 7639

Principal Legal Adviser
Lewis, Sally (Sep 1997)
Tel: 0121 644 7805

Principal Legal Adviser
Taylor, Mandy (Jul 2008)
Tel: 0121 644 7817

Legal Adviser
Baker, Zoe (Oct 2008)
Tel: 0121 644 7700

Principal Legal Adviser
Clayton, Anne (Oct 2001)
Tel: 0121 644 7706

THE WELSH ASSEMBLY GOVERNMENT/ LLYWODRAETH CYNULLIAD CYMRU

Office
Crown Buildings, Cathays Park, Cardiff CF10 3NQ
Bilingual Greeting Tel: 0845 010 3300
Welsh Language Greeting Tel: 0845 010 4400

Director of Legal Services
Godfrey, Jeffrey Charles (Oct 1984)

Deputy Director
Partridge, Mark (Jun 1981)
Lentle, Helen Anne (Oct 1991)
Jones, Elisabeth Velina (Sep 1986)
Clarke, Michael Charles (Aug 1997)

First Welsh Legislative Counsel
Vacant

Senior Lawyer
Buffin, Neil
Roberts, Iwan
Dunning, Diane
Arch, Nerys (Sep 1994)
Davies, Huw Geoffrey (Nov 1997)
Elkin, Phillip Jeffery (Apr 1999)
Davies, Manon
Bradley, Sean John Joseph
Clarke, Patricia
Jones, Amanda
Lubienski, Michael
James, Nia
Davies, Victoria

Senior Commercial Property Lawyer
John, Justin
Jaquelyn, Rees

Lawyers
Davies, Dafydd Huw
Dow, John
Perkins, Adrian
Pike, Ian
Rowlands, Huw
Seculer, Joy Rosing (Mar 1984)
Stephens, Rachel Ann
Williams, Sarah Louise
Charles, Nicola
Hull, Tracy Lynne (Nov 1989)
Jones, Tracey
Williams, Rhian Elizabeth
Wakeling, Sarah
James, Christopher (Jul 2009)
Davis, Jessica
Dawson, Sarah
Huws, Catrin Mererid (Sep 1993)
Moss, Simon David
Sullivan, Rosalind
Richards, Marcus (Jul 2009)
Morea, Simon
Planchant, Ceri J
Rix, Amina
Barry, Sharon
Frith, Margaret
Locke, Emma
Kellaway, Helen
Koppel, Anne
Raynor, Andy
Richards, Deborah
Tobias, Sioned
Hill, Louise (Sep 2009)
Evans, Nia
Humphreys, Christopher
Lancey, Natalie
Morgan, Lucy
Clancy, Rachael (Jan 1999)
Dunstan, Matthew
Flack, John
Osborne, (Sharon) Elaine
Yates, Neil
Brunt, Dorian
Butterworth, Claire
Hill, Julia
Kamalan, Chrishan
Matthews, Caroline
Davies, John
Edwards, Lynsey
Humphries, Claire
Jones, John Tunstal
Evans, Stephanie
Morton, Sarah Ceinwen
Richards, Matthew
Roberts, Mair
Eyre, Peter
Griffiths, Huw
Hopkins, Gillian
John, Geraint
Palmer, Thomas
Williams, Mair
Williams, Nick
Turbervill, Adam (Sep 2009)
Davies, Fiona
Madoc-Jones, David
Elizabeth Harris
Vaughan Lewis – Secondment (Jan 2011)
Robin Lewis (Dec 2009)
Eifiona Williams (Feb 2009)
Catrin Rees (July 2009)
Emily Tuttiet (Sept 2010)
Phillips, Bethan
Lewis, Richard
Hampson, David
Daniel, Siwan
Gammon, Emma

Trainee Legal Executive
Hawkins, Ria
Edwards, Alexandra (Sep 2009)
Gwynne, Catrin (Sep 2009)
Evans, Zoe
Davies, Rhys
Cooper, Lee

WELSH HEALTH LEGAL SERVICES

Office
Bevan House, PO Box 185, 25-30 Lambourne Crescent, Llanishen, Cardiff CF14 5BG Tel: 029 20315500 Fax: 029 20315555

Managing Solicitor
Ferguson, Anne-Louise (Mar 1981)

Solicitors
Jackson, Tracey Ann (Nov 1996)
Llewellyn, Vanessa Nemone (Aug 1996)
Stallard, Elizabeth (Jun 1984)
Walcot, Alison (Sep 1997)
Hynes, Andrew (Nov 1991)
Webber, Fiona (Nov 1998)
Rees, Rhiannon (Jul 1997)
Sparkes, Anne (Nov 1998)
Griffith, Rhian (1984)
Harris, Mark (1996)
Dawson, Elizabeth (Jul 2001)
Symonds, Lorna (Oct 1995)
Mansel, Elizabeth (Oct 1988)
Watt, Sarah (May 1995)
Kaged, David (Sep 2001)
Spencer, Debbie (May 1990)
Victoria Driscoll (Sep 1997)
Braithwaite, Emma (Sep 2009)
Anthony, Helen (Mar 2008)
Osborne, Mari (Sep 2009)
Gwynne, Jessica (Sep 2010)

Practice Manager
Baillie, Ruth

SPECIALISED SERVICES

SECTIONS 17–20

CONTENTS

SPECIALISED SERVICES

SECTION 17

CHARITIES

CONTENTS

Contact details of charitable organisations

17

AGED

AGE concern
Hampshire

AGE CONCERN HAMPSHIRE

putting the WOW into retirement
by engaging the Wealth Of Wisdom to be found amongst older people

0800 328 71 54

- awareness raising and campaigning
- research, training, courses, conferences
- FREE newspaper – "there's more to LIFE"
- promoting active retirement
  i) Pre-retirement Seminars
  ii) annual Golf Challenge
  iii) writers' competition
  iv) activity centres and days
  v) holidays
  vi) home of the OPAL project
  vii) UK online Computer Centres
- INFORMATION AND ADVICE – FREE phone 0800 328 71 54
- DAY CARE – Fifteen day care centres across the County
- FOOT HEALTH SERVICE – PHONE 01329 842895
- Home Alarms, Home Insurance, Motor Insurance and Breakdown Cover, Travel Insurance, Funeral Plan, Stair Lifts, Phone 0800 328 71 54

Listen to Chris Perry every Sunday at 9 am on EXPRESS FM

Customer research has shown that the classified sections within Waterlow's Solicitors' & Barristers' Directory are referred to by thousands of solicitors every week

For more information about advertising opportunities in Waterlow's Legal Range

Contact our Sales Department
+44 (0)20 7566 8227
or email
gdeantonis@waterlow.com

Wilmington Business Intelligence
6-14 Underwood Street
London
N1 7JQ

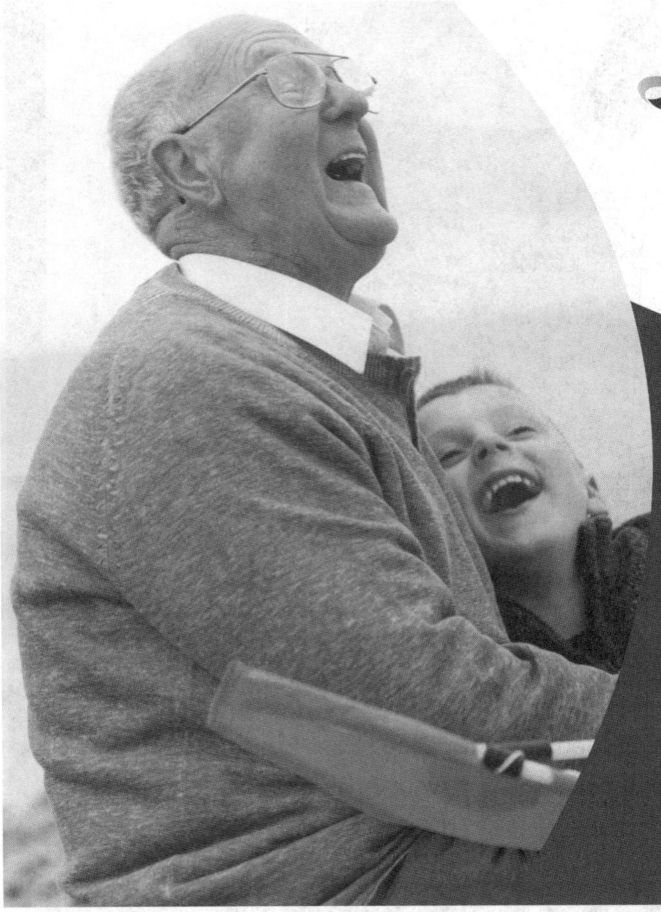

age Scotland

I'm going to live forever

When we are young we don't worry about getting old. When we are old we shouldn't have to fear the future. Age Scotland works hard to take the worry out of growing old.

We work for a better later life, today and tomorrow. We challenge disadvantage and unfairness. We understand what's needed to transform older people's lives for the better.

You can help us transform lives by leaving a legacy in your will. Even a small legacy can make a huge difference to our important work. Speak to your solicitor and remember Age Scotland in your will today.

With your help we can ensure a worry-free future for older people in Scotland.

Age Scotland
Causewayside House
160 Causewayside, Edinburgh EH9 1PR
Tel: 0845 833 0200 Charity number: SC010100

FRSB FundRaising Standards Board

17

ANIMALS

17

KEEP THE FUTURE WILD

"Your gift will help prevent animal suffering and protect rare species. What a wonderful, lasting legacy!" **Virginia McKenna OBE, Born Free Founder & Trustee**

Menelik was found, sicky and starving, tied up by string in an Ethiopian restaurant. Born Free was able to rescue the tiny cheetah cub thanks to the kindness of our supporters, some of whom had left us a gift in their Will. Today Menelik has grown into a beautiful strong adult, and shares a massive enclosure at our rescue centre with another rescued cheetah called Sheba. But lots more work is needed to be done to finish building the Centre.

Your legacy could help us save other animals like Menelik and Sheba. Born Free works to save lives, stop suffering, rescue individuals and protect rare species. Our wildlife charity helps lions, elephants, tigers, gorillas, wolves, bears, dolphins, marine turtles and much more.

Our *Peace of Mind* legacy pack is an easy to understand guide to making and updating your Will.

For your free pack, or to find out how your Will could help Born Free, call 01403 240170 or visit www.bornfree.org.uk

Birmingham Dogs Home New Bartholomew Street, Digbeth, Birmingham, West Midlands, B5 5QS. Tel: 0121 643 5018.
Email: fundraising@birminghamdogshome.org.uk.
Website: www.birminghamdogshome.org.uk.

Bristol Dogs and Cats Home

Registered charity no 205858
50 Albert Road, St Philips
Bristol BS2 0XW
Tel: 0117 977 6043
Website:
www.rspca-bristoldogsandcatshome.org.uk

Bristol Home for Lost & Starving Dogs and Cats was founded in 1887. Every year the Home takes in several thousand cats, dogs, birds and other small pets. Many are in need of veterinary treatment which we provide. Each animal is given all our care and attention with the ultimate aim of finding a new caring owner.

The enormous costs of running the Home are met solely from donated funds and in particular legacies, ranging from £100 to £100,000 that we so gratefully receive from the major part of our income. Every legacy we receive enables us to continue our long history of Animal Welfare in Bristol and the surrounding areas.

For more details contact:
Eddie Grinham
0117 3003 961
egrinham@rspca-bristol.org.uk

Keep us informed of the changes to your firm's details

By post to:
Waterlow Legal Editorial
6-14 Underwood Street
London
N1 7JQ

By phone on:
+44 (0)20 7549 8649

By fax on:
+44 (0)20 7324 2366

By email:
jsmith@waterlow.com

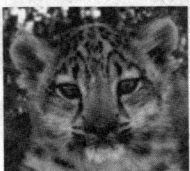

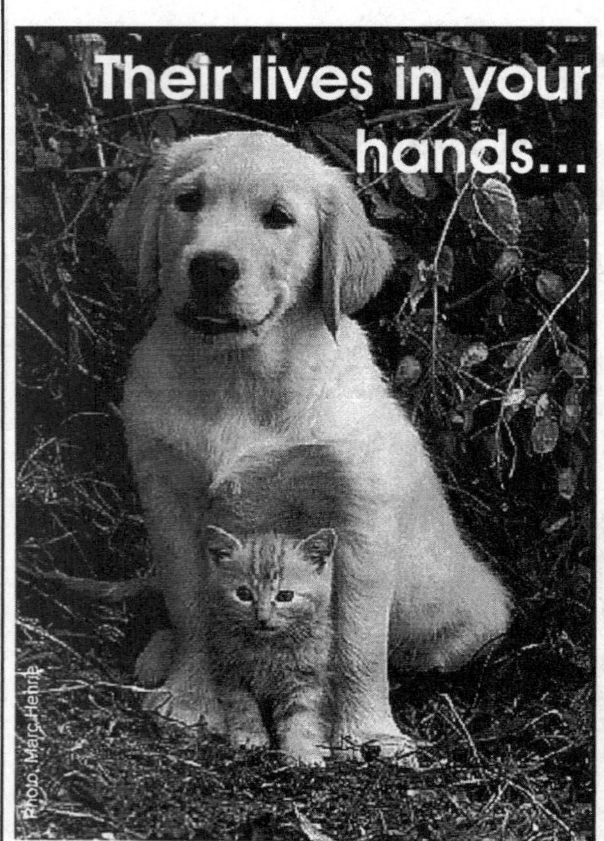

Fund for the Replacement of Animals in Medical Experiments

It's shocking

Every year in Britain, over 3,000,000 experiments are carried out on living animals

FRAME aims to eliminate the use of animals in scientific experiments by developing relevant alternative tests that do not involve the use of animals.

To do this we undertake scientific research in universities, and work closely with industry and government

FRAME

FRAME
Russell & Burch House
96–98 North Sherwood Street
Nottingham, NG1 4EE
Tel: 0115 958 4740
Fax: 0115 950 3570

e-mail:frame@frame.org.uk Web: www.frame.org.uk Registered charity No 259464

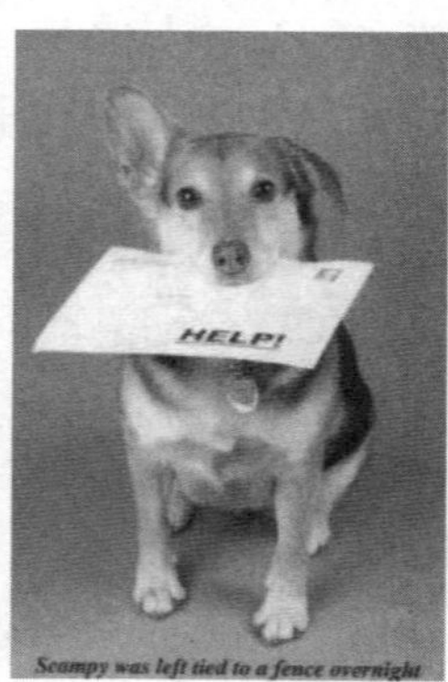

Scampy was left tied to a fence overnight

"FRIENDS OF THE ANIMALS"

**408 Bearwood Road
Bearwood, Warley
West Midlands
B66.4EX.**

FundRaising Standards Board

Telephone 0121-420-4201 and 01983-522-511
www.friendsoftheanimals.co.uk
Reg. Charity No. 1000249

21 YEARS OF CARING

OUR ACHIEVEMENTS INCLUDE:

23,000 plus animals spayed / neutered. **6,300** plus animals re-homed.

17,700 engraved discs supplied. **1,000,000+** items of pet food distributed.

464 Farm animals currently being financed.

THOUSANDS of animals helped with veterinary treatment.

All help gratefully received.

17

Don't leave it to chance... Leave it to LAST CHANCE

As animals can't speak for themselves it falls to me to ask you to consider leaving a legacy to Last Chance Animal Rescue. Any money that we may receive will be spent entirely on the running and improvement at the Centre, which is dedicated to the rescuing, rehabilitation and re-homing of dogs and cats etc.
Many of the number we receive have found their way to our door through circumstances such as their beloved owner passing away, may that door always be open. Many are elderly, in their twilight years, and would just love to find a caring retirement home, something we have great success and pleasure in finding for them, and we continue to care for them, young and old, long after they are settled in their new loving homes, by offering all kinds of support, including financial if needed, for their continued welfare and well being.

As you can imagine this level of commitment doesn't come cheaply, which is why I am appealing to you to remember Last Chance if possible, when you make your will. They do say where there's a Will there's a way!

Last Chance Animal Rescue
Hartfield Road, Edenbridge, Kent TN8 5NH. Tel: 01732 865530
Fax: 01732 865838 Web: www.lastchanceanimalrescue.co.uk
Open: 10am - 3pm every day except Tuesday.
Situated 2 miles south of Edenbridge on B2026
Registered Charity No: 1002349

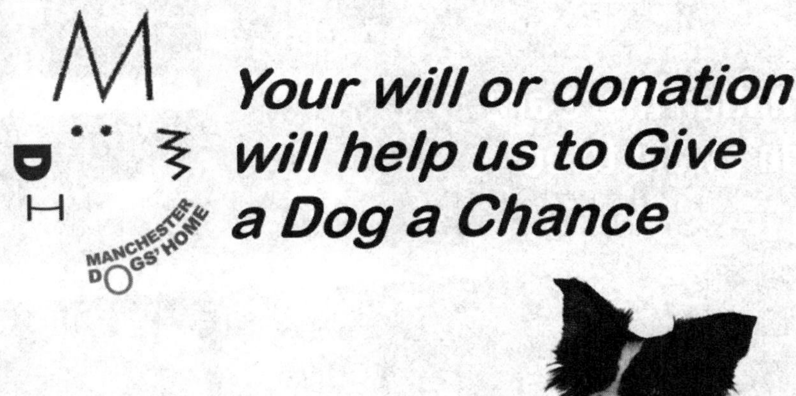

Manchester Dogs' Home
Crofter's House, Moss Brook Road,
Harpurhey, Manchester M9 5PG
Telephone: 0844 504 1212

~~~~~~~~~~~~~~~~~~~~~~

Cheshire Dogs' Home
225 Knutsford Road, Grappenhall,
Warrington WA4 3JZ
Telephone: 0844 504 1212

Registered Charity Number: 1001346

17
~~~~~~~~~~~~~~~~~~~~~~

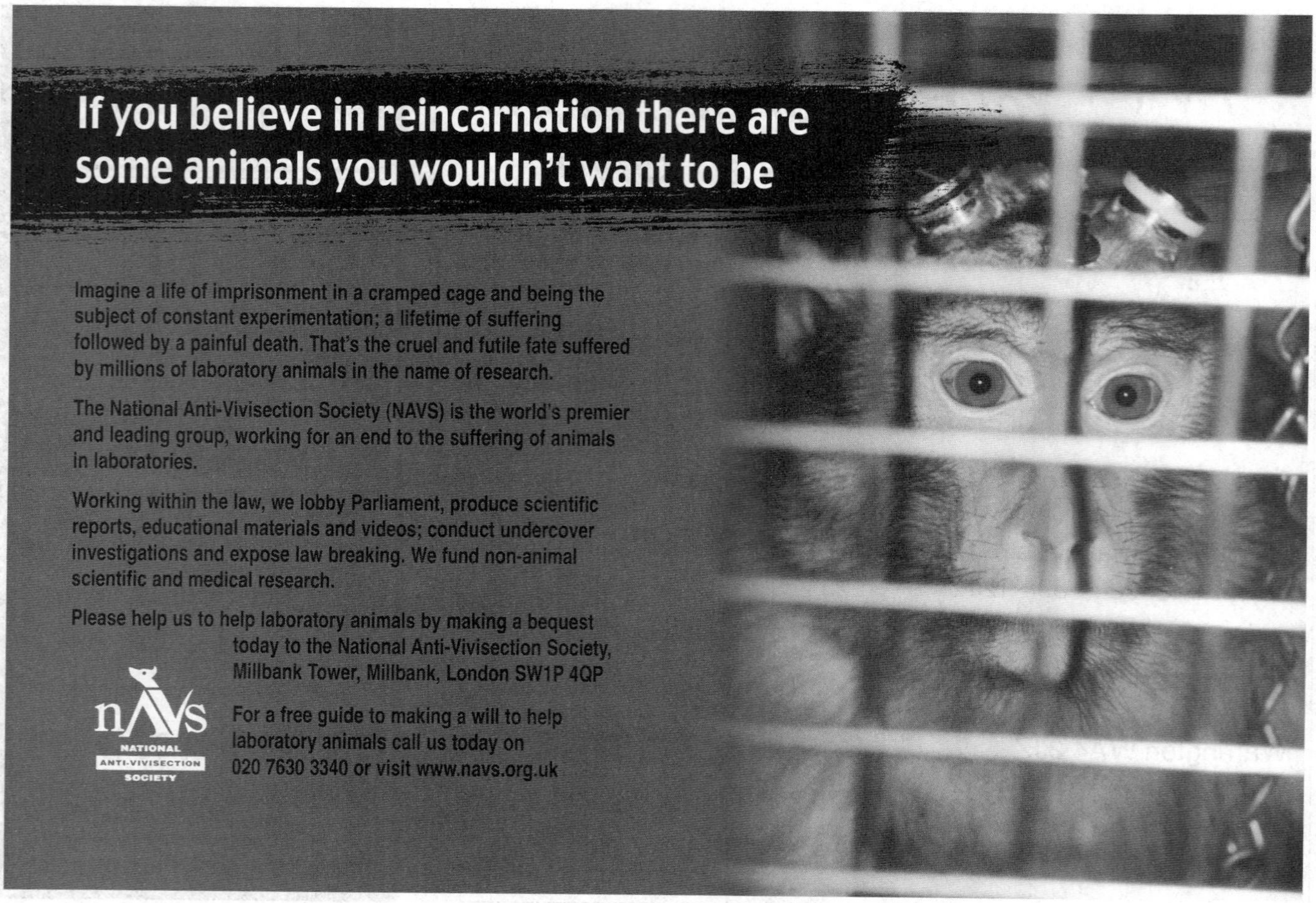

Petsavers

A Division of the British Small Animal Veterinary Association

Reg charity no. 1024811

Improving the health of the nation's pets

Relieving the distress and pain caused by diseases for which we have no effective treatment by:

- Finding cures for diseases that affect our pets.
- Helping your vet to give your pet the best treatment.

Petsavers do not involve the use of experimental animals

Please contact for more information about leaving a legacy to Petsavers

Petsavers, Woodrow House, 1 Telford Way, Waterwells Business Park, Quedgeley, Gloucester GL2 2AB

Tel: 01452 726723 Fax: 01452 726701
Email: info@petsavers.org.uk
Web: www.petsavers.org.uk

DONCASTER, ROTHERHAM & DISTRICT BRANCH

Make a donation to make a difference locally at the

SOUTH YORKSHIRE
ANIMAL CENTRE,
BLACK FIRS FARM,
GREAT NORTH ROAD
BAWTRY,
DONCASTER.
DN10 6DE

Reg Charity No. 506259
email syac@btconnect.com
web www.rspca-doncaster rotherham.org.uk
Tel 01302 714109

- **190 Scudamore Road, Leicester LE3 1UQ**
- **Tel: 0116 2336677**
- **Registered Charity No: 222621**
- **www.rspcaleicester.org.uk**

Our mission is to promote animal welfare and alleviate unnecessary suffering through education, direct intervention and support.

Woodside provides licensed facilities in which to care for animals brought to the centre, be they strays, unwanted pets or victims of cruelty. We rehabilitate and re-home (or return to the wild) where possible all animals brought to the centre. We also educate the public regarding responsible pet ownership.

Approximately 3,500 animals are cared for each year at a cost of £14,000 per week; over £3,000 of this is for veterinary fees.

Woodside Animal Centre is completely self financing. We receive no money from the government, lottery or national society.

If you would like to leave a bequest to the Branch to enable it to continue its work within Leicestershire, please ensure that the correct information is given. Bequests made to the RSPCA will be used by the Society's headquarters: only bequests made to the 'RSPCA Leicestershire Branch' or 'Woodside Animal Centre' will reach us.

"As the spokesman for my brothers and sisters may I say thank you to Pine Ridge for taking us in, to avoid our destruction. We know we shall be found good homes".

Illustrated literature (totally rational) available on request.

One of Great Britain's leading and largest non-destruction sanctuaries for abandoned and unwanted dogs.

Pine Ridge Dog Sanctuary

Priory Road, Ascot,
Berkshire SL5 8RJ.

Telephone: 01344 882689

Registered Charity No 256728
EST. 1958
HELP US PLEASE!

17

A fight for Survival

Thanks to Redwings, Dean not only survived but is thriving

Dean was one of 36 emaciated young ponies rescued from Wales. Exhausted and desperately ill, he needed our help to survive. Despite the odds and with Redwings' care and expertise, Dean gradually overcame his ailments and survived - sadly, four of the ponies did not as they were simply too ill.

Redwings provides permanent sanctuary care for over 1200 horses, ponies and donkeys, rescuing around a further 200 from abuse or neglect every year. **Please consider leaving a legacy to give ponies like Dean a second chance, thank you.**

For more information please contact;
The Legacy Officer Redwings Horse Sanctuary, Hapton, Norwich, NR15 1SP
01508 481030 • legacies@redwings.co.uk • www.redwings.co.uk • Charity Number 1068911

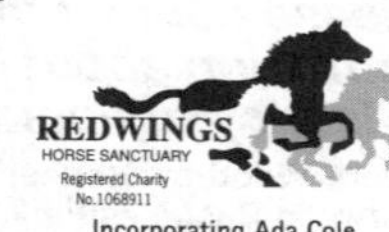

Incorporating Ada Cole Memorial Stables

We believe **every horse** deserves a second chance

Royal College of Veterinary Surgeons Trust

Registered Charity No: 230886 (England and Wales)

62-64 Horseferry Road, London SW1P 2AF
E fundraising@rcvstrust.org.uk

Modern veterinary surgeons face the challenges of a rapidly changing world, where animal and human health needs are interlinked as never before. We encourage and help the veterinary profession to aim for the highest standards of knowledge, treatment and care for all animals.

Just since 2005 we have invested over £2.6 million to fund vital veterinary research and education which has a direct impact on animal health and welfare, our public health, and the environment around us. The research we fund is published so that the lessons learned can be available to all, and we subsidise an extensive and well-resourced veterinary library.

Legacies play a crucial role in enabling more veterinary surgeons to achieving new heights and innovations in clinical practice and scientific understanding of animals. Please help to make a better future for all animals in veterinary care.

For advice on how to make a legacy gift in your Will, do call us on 020 7202 0743, contact us by email or letter, or visit our website www.rcvstrust.org.uk.

SOUTH WEST EQUINE PROTECTION

Charity No. 1087579

Molly
Molly was found by walkers on Dartmoor, nearly drowned in a stream. She was pulled out near death and brought to SWEP. Nursed back to life

Billy
Found by walkers. Billy was stuck in a bog on Dartmoor. Walkers pulled him out- no mare or herd to be seen. Foal followed the walkers to their checkpoint and SWEP were informed and took him in.

Specialising in helping and rescuing wild moorland ponies on Dartmoor and Bodmin Moor

Ponies that are in an emaciated condition, mares having trouble giving birth and injured ponies hit by cars

All ponies receive vetinary treatment

Please help SWEP continue
Helping ponies like Molly and Billy by making a donation and Gift Aid or leaving SWEP a legacy

You can ensure their future is safe in SWEP's care
2 Tor Royal Bungalows,
Princetown,Yelverton,Devon,PL20 6SL
Tel/Fax: 01822 890668 - email: mail@swep.org.uk
website: www.swep.org.uk

Give an old athlete the will to live.

There's a hopeful, trusting look in the eyes of most retired greyhounds. They're hoping for a comfortable retirement home, and they trust us to provide it for them!

How can you help? With the best will in the world, you may not be able to either adopt or sponsor a greyhound right now.

But a legacy could be the answer; for example, a tax effective way of donating is to remember us in your will.

For more information on how to leave a legacy to The Retired Greyhound Trust, email or phone us on

0844 826 8424

You'll be doing us all a big favour.

Retired Greyhound Trust
2nd Floor, Park House,
1-4 Park Terrace, Worcester Park
Surrey KT4 7JZ
www.retiredgreyhounds.co.uk
email:greyhounds@retiredgreyhounds.co.uk

Charity no. 269668

17

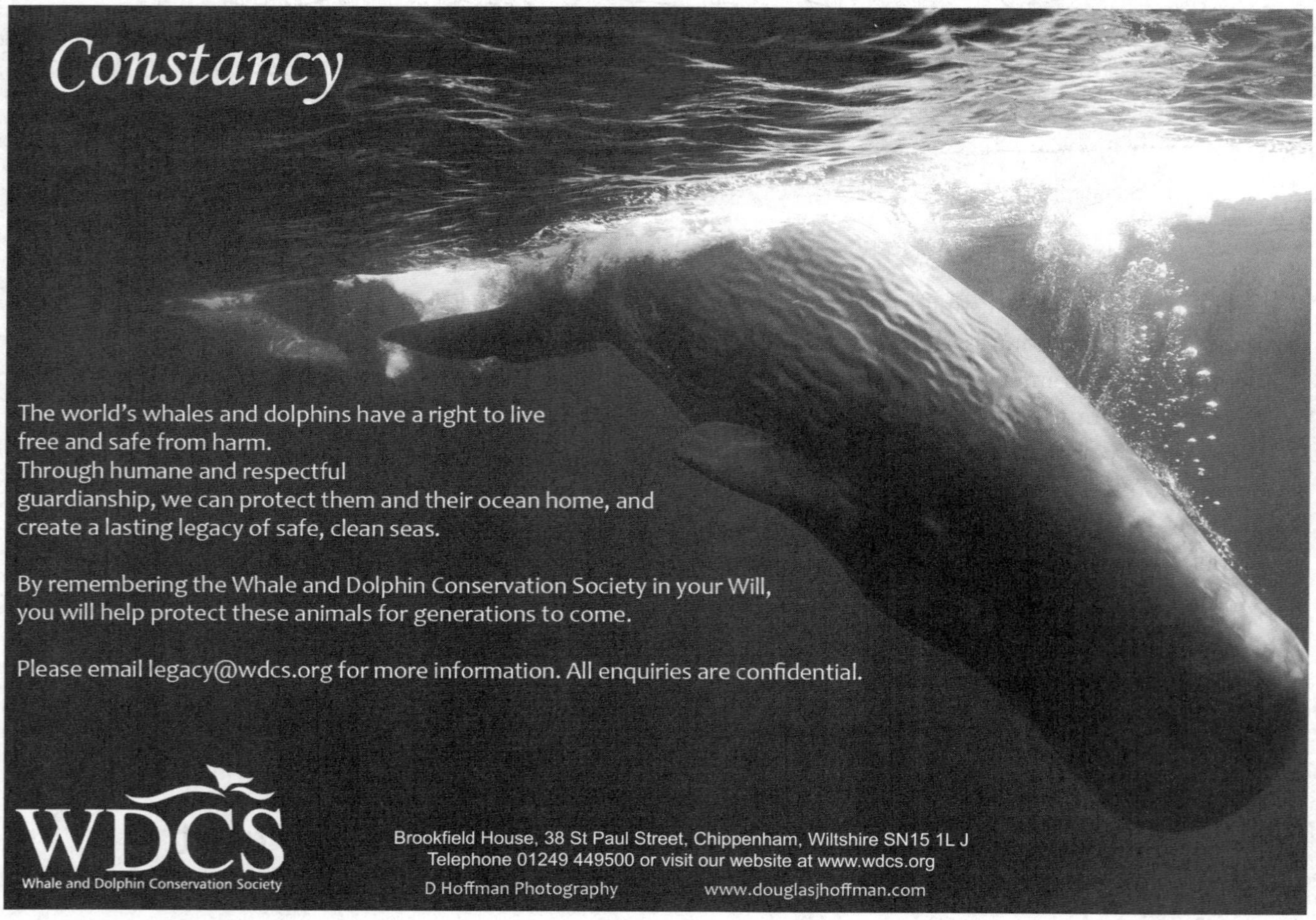

BLIND

17

CANCER

17

CHILDREN

LOST FOR WORDS

Imagine what it would be like to be unable to speak, or to struggle to understand what people are saying to you, or not get a joke. Now imagine that you are a school child and that you have to face that every day. Imagine how hard it would be to make friends, to understand lessons, to get a job.

Over one million children and young people across the UK are affected by the hidden disability of speech, language and communication impairments. Afasic is the UK charity that provides vital help and support for them and their families.

Afasic helps to ensure that those affected have the opportunity to reach their true potential and take an active role in society. Please help us by making a donation or leaving a legacy.

Afasic, unlocking speech and language
20, Bowling Green Lane, London EC1R 0BD
Helpline: 08453 555577 Phone: 020 7490 9410
www.afasic.org.uk registered charity no. 1045617

Birmingham Children's Hospital
making small miracles happen every day

The generous support we receive from **legacies, gifts and donations** allows us to fund research into childhood illnesses, provide state of the art equipment and improve facilities for sick children.
Please help us to give children the best care and the very best lives that we can. For more information or to make a donation, please get in touch.

Thank you

0121 333 8598
www.bch.org.uk

Registered charity 1074850

Make an investment in their future.

Childhood poverty scars children for life. Your donation or gift of a legacy gives children living in poverty the tools to transform their lives.

Contact the Catholtic Children's Society (Westminster) for more information:
Call: 020 8969 5305
Email: info@cathchild.org.uk
www.cathchild.org.uk

Catholic Children's Society (Westminster)
Crusade of Rescue

Give children back their childhood

75,000 children witness domestic violence each year in the UK. They suffer devastating physical and emotional injuries. Hestia helps over 600 families each year to stay safe and build a better future. We provide community outreach, safe housing for homeless families, and direct support for women and children.

It costs just £100 to support 1 child with a programme of holiday activities over the course of a year.

Help us give children back their childhood.
Please support our work.

Please contact: Hestia Housing and Support,
Sovereign Court, 15-21 Staines Road,
Hounslow TW3 3HR
Tel: 0207 8538 2961
Email: fundraising@hestia.org
Website: www.hestia.org

Helping kids to be kids

The freedom to join in, to play, to have fun, to live life to the full – to be kids. That's what Whizz-Kidz gives to disabled children by providing them with the right wheelchair.

And that's only the start. We support them throughout their childhood, providing training and support to help them develop the skills

We've helped over 10,000 children in the UK to get more out of life. But – because disabled children have virtually no chance of getting a powered wheelchair on the NHS – another 70,000 are missing out on childhood.

By remembering Whizz-Kidz in your Will you can help us to improve the lives of disabled children for years to come. To leave a legacy, speak to your solicitor or contact us direct.

Email: legacies@whizz-kidz.org.uk
Phone: 020 7233 6600
www.whizz-kidz.org.uk
registered charity number: 802872

Helping children with renal disease and their families all over Scotland

Kidney Kids Scotland

Merrow House
Church Street, Stenhousemuir
Larbert, FK5 4BU
Tel: 01324 555843
Fax: 01324 555835
e.mail: kidneykids@aol.com
http: www.kidneykids.org.uk

One child in every 600 develops cancer. The types of cancer found are quite different from those in adults and treatment must take account of the patient's future growth and development.

CCLG is a national organisation devoted to the study and treatment of children with cancer.

Help us to continue this vital work.

Children's Cancer and Leukaemia Group
University of Leicester
3rd Floor, Hearts of Oak House
9 Princess Road West
Leicester LE1 6TH

Tel: + 44 (0) 116 249 4460
Fax: + 44 (0) 116 249 4470

Website: www.cclg.org.uk
Email: info@cclg.org.uk

Registered charity number: 286669

NEW PREMISES?

NEW PARTNERS?

Keep us informed of the changes to your firm's details

By post to:
WATERLOW
Legal Editorial
6-14 Underwood Street
London
N1 7JQ

Tel: +44 (0)20 7549 8649
Fax: +44 (0)20 7324 2366

17

DISABLED

EDUCATION

Support the education of young musicians with donations to bursary funds at

The Yehudi Menuhin School

Stoke d'Abernon,
Cobham, Surrey KT11 3QQ

Tel: 01932 864739

Web: www.yehudimenuhinschool.co.uk

Registered as a charity No. 312010

ELDERLY PERSONS WELFARE

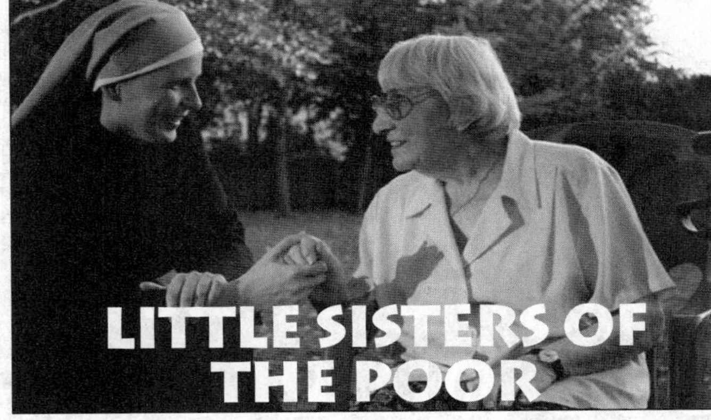

The Little Sisters of the Poor is a Congregation of religious sisters dedicated to the service of the elderly of modest means, regardless of nationality or creed. Founded in France in 1839 by Jeanne Jugan, established in Britain in 1851, our work is today carried out among the elderly in thirty-one countries on five continents, with 17 Homes throughout England, Ireland and Scotland. In providing total care we believe in enabling Residents to fulfil their physical, social, emotional and spiritual needs. We have at heart to recognise their dignity, desire of being respected, esteemed and loved and their longing to feel themselves useful. With your help we wish to respond to their need for companionship, security in health as in sickness, until death, in a family atmosphere.

We really do count on you for support to enable us to continueour care of the elderly.

We greatly appreciate DONATIONS – GIFT AID – LEGACIES

Thank you

LITTLE SISTERS OF THE POOR

Sr. Stephen, Provincial House, 2a Meadow Road, London SW8 1QH
Tel: 020 7735 0788 Fax: 020 7582 0973 Email: mplond@aol.com
www.littlesistersofthepoorenglishprovince.org.uk

Registered Charity No. 234434

17

ENVIRONMENTAL

Leave a gift that
will keep on growing

Plantlife

Wildfowl & Wetlands Trust Slimbridge, Gloucester, Gloucestershire, GL2 7BT. Tel: 01453 891150. Fax: 01453 890827. Email: david.salmon@wwt.org.uk. Saving wetlands for wildlife and people.

17

HEALTH

At the time he said he'd never forget it.
Now he can't remember it.

In the UK, 250 people a day develop dementia. By 2025 there will be one million people with this condition and many more thousands of families affected by it. Legacies are crucial in helping us to continue to provide vital information and support to people affected by dementia, now and in the future.

Our free legacy booklet will tell you more about leaving a gift in your Will; please call 0870 011 0290 to speak to someone or email legacies@alzheimers.org.uk. (please quote SB11)

Alzheimer's Society is the UK's leading care and research charity for people with dementia, their families and carers.
Alzheimer's Society, Devon House, 58 St Katharine's Way, London E1W 1JX

Part of REMEMBER A CHARITY

Leading the fight against dementia
Alzheimer's Society

Registered charity no. 296645

Cancer Research Wales Velindre Cancer Centre, Whitchurch, Cardiff, CF14 2TL. Tel: 029 2031 6976. Fax: 029 2052 1609. Email: crw@wales.nhs.uk. Website: www.crw.org.uk. All funds raised are spent on pioneering research in Wales. For legacies, donations etc please ring 02920 316976.
Est: 1966

Please help us bring better health to the world's poorest people.

Contact us on: 020 7840 3777
general@healthpovertyaction.org
www.healthpovertyaction.org
Charity No. 290535

all money raised is spent in Wales

Cancer Research Wales Ymchwil Canser Cymru

Guaranteeing all money raised is spent in Wales

Cancer Research Wales supports pioneering cancer research projects in Wales which have the potential to benefit millions of lives, as well as those in our local communities.

Please support Cancer Research Wales and help to make a vital difference in the fight against cancer.

Cancer Research Wales
Velindre Hospital, Whitchurch, Cardiff CF14 2TL
Tel: 029 2031 6976
www.cancerresearchwales.co.uk

Registered Charity Number: 248767

"CARE IN THE AIR"

The Lincolnshire and Nottinghamshire Air Ambulance

Needs you.... We must find £1.7 million a year and we are almost entirely dependant on voluntary contributions. The helicopter covers a total of 3000 sq miles. It is airborne within a few minutes and flying at 150mph, can reach the furthest points in either county in under 20 minutes. On board paramedics are trained to give immediate trauma treatment and the average journey time from an incident to the nearest hospital is 8 minutes.

For more information go to: www.ambucopter.org.uk

Or to make a donation please contact our Head office on 01522 548469

With serious trauma time is critical... We need your help to help others.

HORTICULTURAL

HOSPICES

Martin House

Hospice for Children and Young People
Grove Road, Clifford, Wetherby LS23 6TX
Tel: 01937 844569 Fax: 01937 843801
e-mail: appeal@martinhouse.org.uk
website: www.martinhouse.org.uk

Martin House, Yorkshire's first hospice for children and young people, was opened in 1987 and is currently caring for over 300 children and young people with life-limiting, terminal illness, and providing support for their families. We also offer bereavement counselling for parents, siblings and grandparents.

All our services are free of charge to the families who need them but providing the very best of care for so many comes at a cost of over £4m, only 12% of which comes from statutory sources.

We need your support. Please help. Thank you.

St Raphael's HOSPICE

St Raphael's Hospice in North Cheam, Sutton - SW London, serves 900 terminally ill patients each year from the local Boroughs of Sutton and Merton. The Hospice relies on charitable contributions for three-quarters of the £4 million a year needed to run the hospice, and legacies are vitally important.

For more information visit **www.straphaels.org.uk** or telephone the fundraising office on **020 8335 4576**.

Registered Charity 1068661 (Daughters of the Cross, St Raphael's Hospice).

MEDICAL RESEARCH & WELFARE

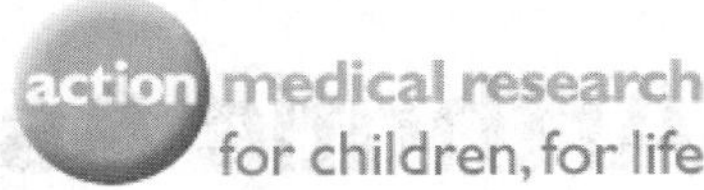

Action Medical Research Vincent House, Horsham, West Sussex, RH12 2DP. Tel: 01403 210406. Fax: 01403 249332. Email: jtarrant@action.org.uk. Website: www.action.org.uk. We are a UK charity funding vital research to help sick babies, children with disabilities and those suffering from a rare disease.

all money raised is spent in Wales

Cancer Research Wales Ymchwil Canser Cymru

Guaranteeing all money raised is spent in Wales

Cancer Research Wales supports pioneering cancer research projects in Wales which have the potential to benefit millions of lives, as well as those in our local communities.

Please support Cancer Research Wales and help to make a vital difference in the fight against cancer.

Cancer Research Wales
Velindre Hospital, Whitchurch, Cardiff CF14 2TL
Tel: 029 2031 6976
www.cancerresearchwales.co.uk

Registered Charity Number: 248767

17

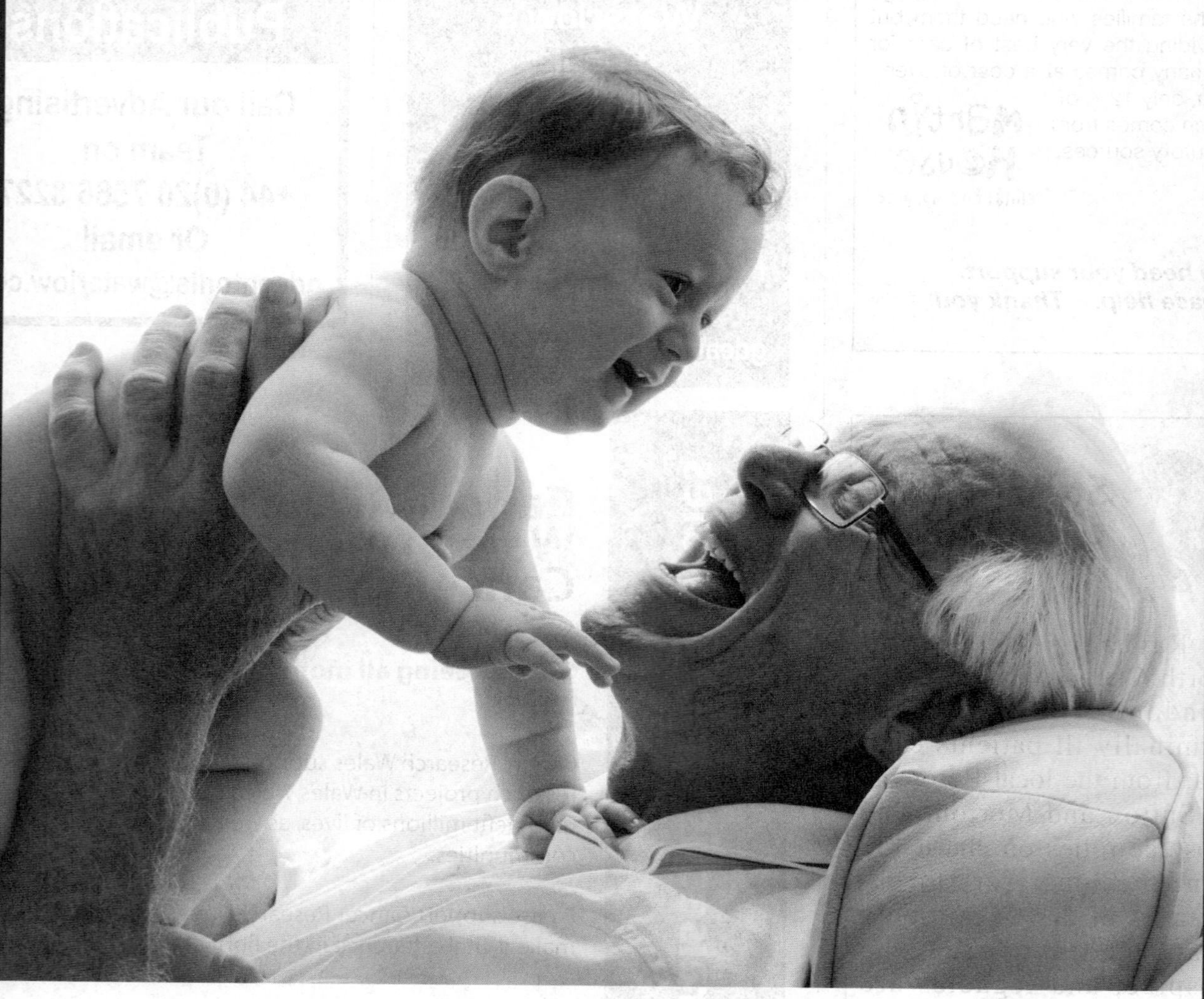

Join us in finding the cure for type 1 diabetes

Call 020 7713 2030

Email - kpickering@jdrf.org.uk

Online - www.jdrf.org.uk/legacy

By post - JDRF,
19 Angel Gate,
City Road,
London
EC1V 2PT

Registered charity numbers
England and Wales (No. 295716)
Scotland (No. SC040123)

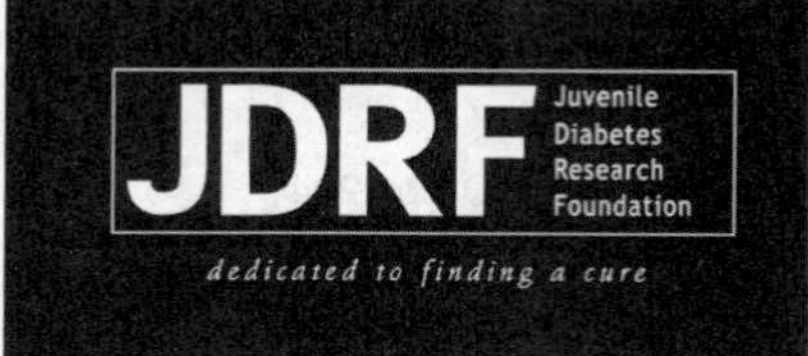

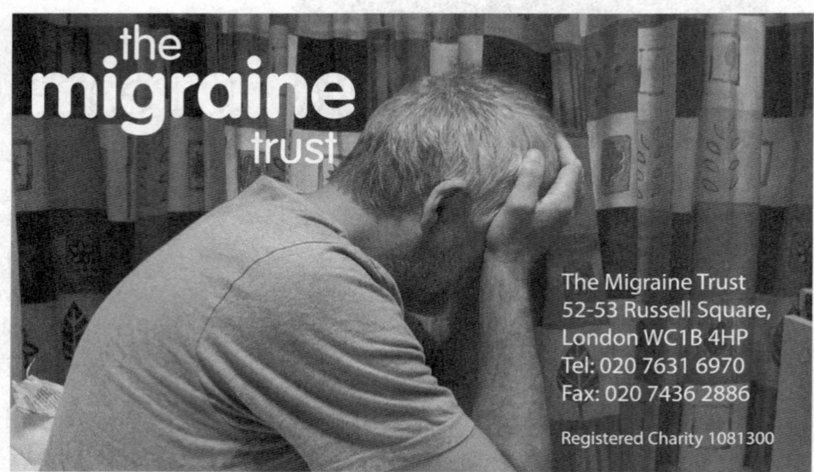

Eight million people in the UK suffer from migraine. It is the most prevalent neurological condition in the country.

The Migraine Trust is the UK's leading health and medical research charity for migraine.

We are committed to supporting people living with migraine by providing them with research based information. We seek to raise awareness of migraine as a significant public health problem.

The Migraine Trust funds and promotes research into migraine in order to better understand it, to improve diagnosis and treatment and ultimately to find a cure.

North Staffs Heart Committee

Founded 1979
(www.northstaffsheart.org.uk/charity)
Reg. Charity 508743

We have raised over £5 MILLION

Caring for cardiac patients supporting research, diagnosis, treatment and welfare.

Donations & bequests welcomed and acknowledged

HELP US TO FIGHT HEART DISEASE IN NORTH STAFFORDSHIRE

**Chairman: A. J. G. (Tony) Berry MBE,
Sneyd Cottage (SBD), 5 Herm Close, Seabridge,
Newcastle, Staffs. ST5 3LL
Tel/Fax (01782) 622463**

The North Staffs Heart Committee is an independent charity serving the interests of cardiac patients residing or receiving treatment in North Staffordshire IT IS NOT ASSOCIATED WITH ANY OTHER NATIONAL OR LOCAL CHARITY OF SIMILAR NAME

NWCRF has been funding groundbreaking research into the causes of all forms of cancer for over 60 years.

We rely on your kind support to generate the bequests and donations needed to fund our experts' vital work. Because almost 90p in every pound donated is spent on actual research you can help us find the causes of so many peoples pain.

North West Cancer Research Fund
22 Oxford Street
Liverpool
L7 7BL
Tel: 0151 709 2919
Fax: 0151 708 7997
www.nwcrf.co.uk
info@nwcrf.co.uk

Registered Charity No. 223598

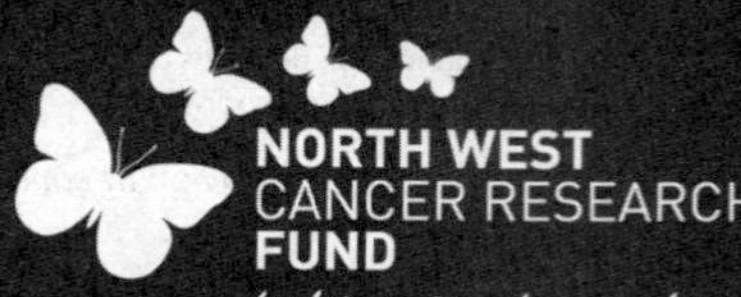

17

Since its inception in 1913, the MRC has been continuously at the forefront of medical research. MRC scientists have won twenty eight Nobel prizes.

The MRC supports specialised research units throughout the UK and gives grants for research and training to scientists in hospitals, GP practices and Universities. It funds both fundamental and clinical research. In the past few years alone the MRC has made many important discoveries. These include simple and affordable treatment for pre-eclampsia - a potentially fatal pregnancy complication, and the finding that tens of thousands of people worldwide could be saved from strokes and heart attacks by taking 'statin' drugs to lower their cholesterol level.

Most MRC funds come from central government but private donations donations to our charity have always been an important addition.

www.mrc.ac.uk

OVERSEAS AID

17

SERVICES & EX-SERVICES

They fight our wars. We fight their battles.

Combat Stress is the leading charity specialising in the care of Veterans' mental ill health. We offer ex-Service men and women a number of services to help rebuild their lives:

- The Combat Stress 24-hour Helpline, **0800 138 1619**
- Community Outreach service
- Dedicated, residential clinical treatment
- A Well-being and rehabilitation programme

Last year alone, we received over 1,400 new referrals, and are under constant pressure to meet an ever growing need for our unique help.

Your gift, however small, will make a real difference to our life-saving work – and help us plan for tomorrow.

COMBAT STRESS
Tyrwhitt House | Oaklawn Road | Leatherhead
Surrey KT22 0BX
www.combatstress.org.uk
tel: 01372 587 140
email: fundraising@combatstress.org.uk
Registered Charity No; 206002 | Charity No Scotland; SC038828

War on Want's mission is to fight the root causes of poverty and bring an end to human rights violations.

In rural communities, in factories and sweatshops, in conflict zones and on the margins of society, we fight to make a lasting difference to people's lives.

Join our fight against poverty.

War on Want
44-48 Shepherdess Walk
London N1 7JP

web waronwant.org
email legacies@waronwant.org
tel 020 7324 5048

Registered Charity No. 208724

RELIGIOUS ORGANISATIONS

GRACE & COMPASSION BENEDICTINES

Grace & Compassion Convent
57 Surrenden Road, Brighton BN1 6PQ
Tel: 01273 502129 Fax: 01273 552540

Our Charity began in 1954 when the late Mother Mary Garson opened a home for the elderly in Brighton. Over the years it has grown into an international organisation which continues to run care homes in the south of England and wide ranging services in India, Sri Lanka, Kenya and Uganda. These include care of the elderly and sick, vocational training, school of nursing, hospital, nursery and primary schools. Our Sisters work with lay staff and volunteers in caring for the elderly, sick and poor of all denominations.

YOUR DONATION COULD HELP US DO SO MUCH MORE!

Web site: graceandcompassionbenedictines.org.uk
Email: osb@graceandcompassion.co.uk
Reg.Charity No. 1056064

17

TRADES & PROFESSIONS

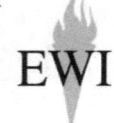

SPECIALISED SERVICES

SECTION 18

EXPERT WITNESS

CONTENTS

ACCIDENT INVESTIGATION

Road Accident Investigation and Reconstruction in the **UK and Ireland**

Barry Seward is an experienced expert witness at all levels.

Retired Police Accident Investigator with 27 years experience dealing with serious and fatal road accidents.

FREE INITIAL ADVICE on any case to allow assessment as to whether expert evidence will assist.

CV together with our services can be found at our website **www.accidentanalysis.co.uk**

Accident Analysis Limited
10 Reedley Road
Westbury-on-Trym
Bristol BS9 3ST
Tel: 0117 3305162
Fax: 0117 9811345
Mob: 07 985 985 300
Email:
barry.seward@accidentanalysis.co.uk

Formedecon Unit 41, Enterprise City, Spennymoor, Durham, Co Durham, DL16 6JF. Tel: 01388 811003. Fax: 01388 811918. DX: 60185 FERRYHILL. Email: formedecon@aol.com.

Need Expert Witness Advice ?

- **Consulting Engineers**
- **Transport Engineering**
- **Lifting and Handling**
- **Machinery Failure**

contact Frazer-Nash
email: k.cleminson@fnc.co.uk

or visit www.fnc.co.uk

HANCE CONSULTING

Accident investigation and associated services, to the highest standards.

33 Felhampton Road,
New Eltham,
LONDON, SE9 3NT
t: 020 8851 6859
f: 07092 045 959
m: 07973 533 820
e: derek@hance.co.uk
w: www.hance.co.uk

Derek HANCE

MA (Dist.), MITAI, MIRTE, MSOE, RFP

Derek Hance is a consultant forensic accident investigator with over 15 years experience (full CV available on request). He specialises in the scientific examination of road accident scenes, the investigation and reconstruction of road accident events based on analysis of available evidence, and the examination of vehicles involved. He will provide detailed reports, photographs, plans, etc., for both civil and criminal cases. Initial advice and an evaluation of the likely strengths of the evidence will be provided free of charge.

e-mail: info@dandhb.com
www.dandhb.com
Phone/Fax: +44 (0)1538 722544
Mobile: +44 (0) 7973 289162

- Expert in Accident Investigation and Reconstruction in both Criminal and Civil cases for over 20 years involving Cars, LGVs and Buses, but specialising in Motorcycle Accidents in particular.
- Full Accident Reconstruction files prepared for Court.
- Locus Reports, photographs, scale drawings and witness statements.

(Also experts in Criminal Road Traffic matters from Speeding to Causing Death by Dangerous and Careless Driving)

Please contact for a full CV and list of services provided.

Names of QCs, Barristers and Solicitors can be provided as reference on request.

Hawkins

Leaders in forensic investigation

Hawkins is a well-established and respected firm of forensic scientists that investigates a wide range of losses including:

- **personal injury**
- **road traffic accidents**
- **engineering problems**
- **fires**
- **explosions**

All our investigations are conducted with potential litigation in mind and we are experienced in the preparation of reports, liaison with solicitors and barristers and presenting at Court.

Hawkins was established in 1980, with our head office being based in Cambridge. We currently have seven regional offices, located in Bristol, Manchester, London, Reigate, Leeds, Birmingham and Glasgow.

Call us for Advice
+44 (0) 1223 420 400

Hawkins Cambridge 25 Cambridge Science Park, Milton Road, Cambridge, Cambridgeshire, CB4 0FW. Tel: 01223 420400. Fax: 01223 420181. Email: cmail@hawkins.biz. Experts in Accident Investigation.

Personal Injury Accident Services Ltd "Pine Tops", 36 Castlewood Close, Clevedon, North Somerset, BS21 7HS. Tel: 01275 878381 / 07970 441563. Fax: 01275 878381. Email: enquiries@pias-ai.co.uk.

ACCOUNTANCY & TAX

Wright Vigar & Co 15 Newland, Lincoln, Lincolnshire, LN1 1XG. Tel: 01522 531341. Fax: 01522 546286. Email: richard.vigar@wrightvigar.co.uk. Offering Litigation Support & Forensic Accountancy

ACTUARIES & MATHEMATICIANS

OAC Actuaries and Consultants Portsoken House, Minories, London, EC3N 1LJ. Tel: 020 7278 9500. Fax: 020 7278 9400. Email: expertwitness@oacplc.com. Website: www.oacplc.com/expertwitness. Financial services and personal finance.

AGRICULTURE

Animal Nutrition And Agricultural Consultants 20 Young Street, Lisburn, Co Antrim, BT27 5EB. Tel: 028 9266 1766. Fax: 028 9266 1128. Email: info@mcilmoyleassociates.co.uk. Expert Witness with over 20 years experience

ALCOHOL & NARCOTICS

Wickham Laboratories Ltd Winchester Road, Wickham, Fareham, Hampshire, PO17 5EU. Tel: 01329 832511. Fax: 01329 834262. Email: mail@wickhamlabs.co.uk.

ANIMALS & VETERINARY

ARBORICULTURE (TREES)

AUDIO VIDEO

Keep us informed of the changes to your firm's details

By post:
WATERLOW LEGAL EDITORIAL
6-14 Underwood Street
London
N1 7JQ

By email:
jsmith@waterlow.com

By fax:
+44 (0)20 7324 2366

By phone:
+44 (0)20 7549 8649

ARCHITECTURE

AVIATION

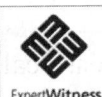

BUILDING & CONSTRUCTION

18

Michael Kilbey Associates PO Box 749, Amersham, Buckinghamshire, HP6 9EB. Tel: 01494 723365. Fax: 01494 721194. Email: info@mkaconsultants.co.uk. Roofing & Cladding. Expert Witnesses. Nationwide Service.

Mr Gordon Charles Lockhart Scott White and Hookins, Harman House, Andover Road, Winchester, Hampshire, SO23 7BS. Tel: 01962 844855. Fax: 01962 841328. Email: glockhart@swh.co.uk.

Thomasons Ltd 86 Epsom Road, Guildford, Surrey, GU1 2BX. Tel: 01483 565886. Fax: 01483 506822. Email: nrussell@thomasons.co.uk. Contact: Nick Russell

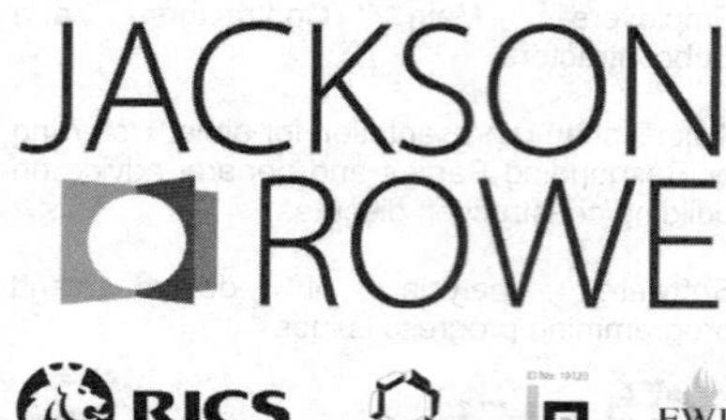

COMPUTING

CHILD PROTECTION

18

Computer and Mobile Phone Forensics

Expert Witness Service

Jargon-free, plain English reports guaranteed

- Computer forensics
- Mobile phone & SatNav Forensics
- Cell site analysis
- IT investigation
- Child pornography specialists

T 0845 644 3652
M 07967 737041

24hr Nationwide Service

www.evidence-matters.com

Griffin Forensics

eForensics and Data Recovery

where every BIT matters

- Digital Investigations
- Computer Forensics
- Mobile Phone Analysis
- Sat Nav Analysis
- CCTV Analysis
- Data Collection
- Audio & Video Transcription
- Digital Forensics Readiness Policy
- Secure Data Destruction
- Data Recovery

2012 EXPERT WITNESS

SWEET & MAXWELL CHECKED 2012 EXPERT WITNESS

UK REGISTER OF EXPERT WITNESSES REGISTERED

Single Joint Expert

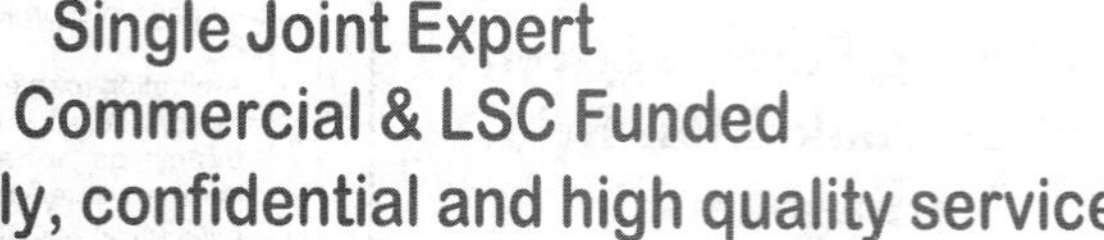

Tel: 01280 707190
Web: www.griffinforensics.com
DX: 16982 Brackley

5 Oxford Court
St James Road
Brackley
Northants NN13 7XY

CONSUMER SAFETY

consumer safety expert network

expertise on any consumer safety issue

DIY / vehicle maintenance equipment • Toys • Nursery / childcare / play equipment Pushchairs • Choking hazards • Child-resistant features • Domestic glazing, doors, other construction products • Ladders • Garden tools • Furniture • Cookware Kitchen equipment • Packaging • Heating • Lighting • Hairdryers • Cycles • Electrical / gas / oil /sold fuel appliances • Barbecues • Cigarette lighters • Clothing Protective equipment • Mobility aids • Exercise / sports / leisure equipment • Rented / holiday accommodation • Hotels • Public leisure facilities • Warnings / instructions Product safety regulations / standards / risk assessments / test methods

Contact us (giving technical details of the safety matter at issue or the expertise sought) in product liability claims, personal injuries to customers, trading standards actions, criminal prosecutions, child care proceedings, etc

phone or fax **020 8343 1754**

e-mail ***experts@consumersafety.co.uk***

post **csen 83 Station Road London N3 2SH**

or search for the technical expertise you need on our web site
www.consumersafetyexpert.net

DENTAL

Philip R. Greene

BDS, FDSRCPS, CUEW, JP.

Specialist in Periodontics

Founder Member Expert Witness Institute
Cardiff University Expert Witness Certificate

Over 35 years of experience in general and specialist dental practice

The Malt House
Specialist Dental Treatment Centre
Deva Centre
Manchester M3 7BD
Tel: 0161 835 1777
Fax: 0161 838 5353
Email:
perioexpert@malthousedental.net
prgreene@sky.com
www.effectiveperio.co.uk

XPC services

- Adverse Drug Reactions
- Drug & Alcohol Related Driving Offences
- Specialist in Toxicology
- Expert Reports

XPC services provides expert witness advice and written reports to both prosecuting and defence counsels in drug related criminal and similar cases. Our clients include the Crown Prosecution Service (CPS), Police Authorities and many private solicitors.

Dr Mould has an extensive and broad knowledge in the action of drugs on the body and the way in which the body deals with drugs once they are taken. He is therefore qualified to answer queries regarding clinical pharmacy, clinical pharmacology and toxicology.

Dr Graham Mould
Surrey Technology Centre
Surrey Research Park, Occam Road
Guildford, Surrey GU2 7YG
d +44 (0) 1483 685785 f +44 (0) 1483 573704
m +44 (0) 7770 820147 e gmould@xpertwitness.co.uk

SOLICITORS JOURNAL

The independent weekly with breaking news, reporting and analysis for the legal professional.

DON'T MISS OUT

For details on subscriptions, contact the Solicitors Journal team on +44 (0)20 7549 2597 or email clientservices@solicitorsjournal.co.uk

DRUGS

Independent Drug Monitoring Unit

®

Expert Witness for Drug Cases

Cannabis, Powders & Pills

Yields, Valuations, Consumption

01942 522946

www.idmu.co.uk

To find out more about promotional opportunities available in

Waterlow's Legal Publications

Call The Advertising Team on +44 (0)20 7566 8227 or email gdeantonis@waterlow.com

ELECTRICAL ENGINEERING

Hawkins Cambridge 25 Cambridge Science Park, Milton Road, Cambridge, Cambridgeshire, CB4 0FW.
Tel: 01223 420400. Fax: 01223 420181.
Email: cmail@hawkins.biz. Experts in Electrical Engineering.

EMPLOYMENT

Peter Davies Employment & Rehabilitation Consultants
27 East King Street, Helensburgh, Argyll & Bute, G84 7QQ.
Tel: 01436 677767. Fax: 01436 678938.
Email: info@employconsult.com.

Langman HRD Ltd
Vocational Rehabilitation and Employment Consultants

We provide Employment Reports and give evidence on earnings, career and labour market issues in the UK, Eire, Europe, USA, Canada, Hong Kong, South Africa and other countries.

We are often instructed as Joint Experts. We prepare reports in personal injury, clinical negligence, matrimonial, employment tribunal, occupational stress, educational negligence, criminal injury, discrimination (race, gender, disability), child abuse, wrongful arrest and other claims. Our reports can include a detailed vocational assessment.

We can report on any type of disability, but many are serious injury claims including spinal cord, cerebral palsy, head injury etc. As practitioners, we also provide vocational rehabilitation services to clients with disabilities and employers.

We operate throughout the UK. Our fees are competitive.

Unit 5A, The South West Centre,
4 Archer Road, Sheffield S8 0JR
Tel: 0114 2581435
Fax: 0114 2555774
DX: 15093 WOODSEATS
Email: info@langmanhrd.co.uk
Web: www.langmanhrd.co.uk

18

ENGINEERING

Cadogans 24 Blythswood Square, 39 Cadogan Street, Glasgow, G2 4BG. Tel: 0141 270 7060. Fax: 0141 270 7061. DX: GW35 GLASGOW. Multi-disciplinary engineers operating worldwide

Frazer-Nash Consultancy Ltd Stonebridge House, Dorking Business Park, Dorking, Surrey, RH4 1HJ. Tel: 01306 885050. Fax: 01306 886464. Email: k.cleminson@fnc.co.uk.

Hawkins Cambridge 25 Cambridge Science Park, Milton Road, Cambridge, Cambridgeshire, CB4 0FW. Tel: 01223 420400. Fax: 01223 420181. Email: cmail@hawkins.biz. Experts in Engineering.

Hoare Lea & Partners 140 Aztec West Business Park, Almondsbury, Bristol, BS32 4TX. Tel: 01454 201020. Fax: 01454 201704. Email: davidsworder@hoarelea.com.

ENGINEERING - POWDERS & BULK SOLIDS

ENVIRONMENT

STRI (The Sports Turf Research Institute) St Ives Estate, Bingley, West Yorkshire, BD16 1AU. Tel: 01274 565131. Fax: 01274 561891. Email: info@stri.co.uk.

FAILURE INVESTIGATION

Hawkins Cambridge 25 Cambridge Science Park, Milton Road, Cambridge, Cambridgeshire, CB4 0FW. Tel: 01223 420400. Fax: 01223 420181. Email: cmail@hawkins.biz. Experts in Failure Investigation

FINANCIAL SERVICES

FINGERPRINT ANALYSIS

Formedecon Unit 41, Enterprise City, Spennymoor, Durham, Co Durham, DL16 6JF. Tel: 01388 811003. Fax: 01388 811918. DX: 60185 FERRYHILL. Email: formedecon@aol.com.

FIRE & EXPLOSION INVESTIGATION

Hawkins Cambridge 25 Cambridge Science Park, Milton Road, Cambridge, Cambridgeshire, CB4 0FW. Tel: 01223 420400. Fax: 01223 420181. Email: cmail@hawkins.biz. Experts in Fire & Explosion Investigation.

FOOD & NUTRITION

D W Everington

C.Eng. F.I.Mech.E. M.Ist.R M.CIBSE

Freezing and chilling of foodstuffs and cold storage. Refrigeration plant. Chilled water, ice banks and flake ice. Vegetable cooling. Expert witness. Experience in frozen foods, fish, meat, poultry, dairy and ice cream industries.

The Grange
Church Street
Kenninghall
Norfolk
NR16 2EP

Tel: 01953 887 456
Fax: 01953 888 581

FORENSIC ACCOUNTANTS

Forensic Accounting Solutions 

With over 20 years experience in quantifying special damages, we offer a partner led service doing expert witness work in the following areas:

- Personal injury
- Fatal accident claims
- Business Interruption
- Contractual or other commercial disputes
- Company, business and shareholder valuations/disputes
- Mediation

Contact: Gail Rifkind:
020 8349 3776
David Rabinowitz:
0161 832 9990
Fax:
020 349 3778
Email:
gail@fas-partnership.co.uk
Website:
www.fas-partnership.co.uk

Forensic Accountants
Local Matters, National Strength.

Insurance/Loss Quantum Issues Advice and Reports

Business Disruptions Business Valuations

Fraud – Particularly Insurance Related

Civil & Criminal Court Experience

Contact: David S Black
BSc CA FCII FCILA MEWI

The Wergs
Keepers Lane
Wolverhampton
WV6 8UA
Tel: 01902 793333
Fax: 01902 793330
E-mail: dsblack@hwca.com
www.hwforensic.com

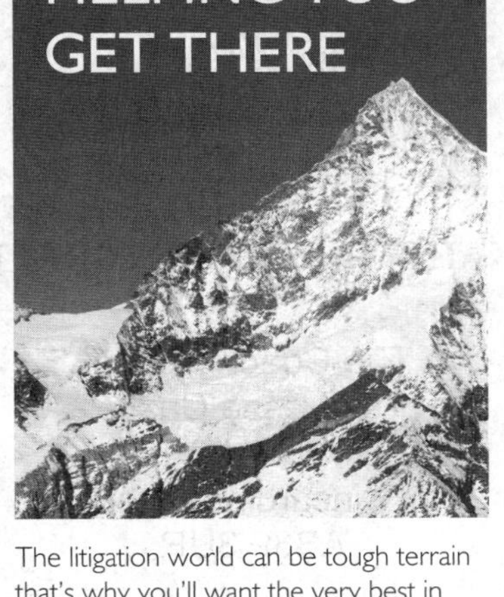

The litigation world can be tough terrain that's why you'll want the very best in forensic accountancy support.
Call John Green or Jeremy Rowe on 01254 688100 or email enquiries@pierce.co.uk for a free consultation.

PIERCE FORENSIC LTD

Headquarters: Mentor House, Ainsworth Street, Blackburn BB1 6AY.
Pierce is a trading name of Pierce Group and its associated companies.

WILDER COE LLP
BUSINESS RECOVERY

Mr Norman Cowan
FCA, FABRP, MCIArb, MEWI
Chartered Accountant

Cardiff University of Expert Witness Accreditation
Professional Negligence Lawyers Association
Network of Independent Forensic Accountants

Our Specialist experience in Forensic and Insolvency Accounting makes us ideally suited to provide single and joint Expert Evidence, in respect of the following:

- Business Valuation
- Loss of Profits
- Loss of Earnings for Personal Accident & Medical Negligence
- Commercial Disputes
- Ancillary Relief
- Expert Determination
- Claims for Business Interruption
- Insolvency Related Offences
- Proceeds of Crime Confiscation Orders

233 - 237 Old Marylebone Road,
London, NW1 5QT
Tel: 020 7724 6060 Fax: 020 7724 6070
DX 38756 Paddington
Email:norman.cowan@wildercore.co.uk
Web: www.wildercore.co.uk

18

FORENSIC HANDWRITING & EXAMINATION

Forensic Document Services Ltd 186 Temple Chambers, 3-7 Temple Avenue, London, EC4Y 0DB. Tel: 020 7583 9962. Fax: 020 7583 9963. DX: 271 LONDON/CHANCERY LN. Email: fds.limited@btconnect.com.

Robert Radley The Forensic Document Laboratory, Macartneys, Kings Road, Silchester, Reading, RG7 2NS. Tel: 0118 970 2394. Fax: 0118 970 2395. Email: info@docexam.co.uk. 35 years of examination of signatures/handwriting, inks etc

FORENSIC SCIENCE

FORENSIC SERVICES

Formedecon Unit 41, Enterprise City, Spennymoor, Durham, Co Durham, DL16 6JF. Tel: 01388 811003. Fax: 01388 811918. DX: 60185 FERRYHILL. Email: formedecon@aol.com.

Hawkins Cambridge 25 Cambridge Science Park, Milton Road, Cambridge, Cambridgeshire, CB4 0FW. Tel: 01223 420400. Fax: 01223 420181. Email: cmail@hawkins.biz. Experts in Forensic Investigation.

HONEST, OBJECTIVE, CLEAR AND HELPFUL

Independent specialist expert witness service to lawyers

We review and give expert opinion on Crown reports, re-examine exhibits and conduct further laboratory testing as required.

With extensive experience in casework and court, our in-house work is quality driven by ISO 9001:2008 registration with scientists that are chartered, Bond Solon CUBS trained, years experience in Crown and defence roles, university lecturers, regulated, published, and cited.

STR DNA profiling - DNA Mixtures - Bloodstain patterns
Scene of crime - Serology (body fluids) - Paternity
Hairs/Fibres - LCN/Y-STR/mtDNA - Botany/Entomology

1, Harley Place, Clifton Down, Bristol BS8 3JT DX 130678 CLIFTON 4
T 0117 370 2727 F 0117 911 8583 E info@dna-defence.co.uk W dna-defence.co.uk
Offices to open in NW and SE in New Year

GLAZING & FENESTRATION

Glass & Glazing Federation 54 Ayres Street, London, SE1 1EU. Tel: 020 7939 9101. Fax: 0870 042 4266. Email: info@ggf.org.uk. Website: www.ggf.org.uk.

HANDWRITING

ROBERT RADLEY
M.Sc., C.Chem., F.R.S.C., F.S.Soc.Dip., F.A.E., R.F.P.

HANDWRITING EXPERT & DOCUMENT EXAMINER

A Registered Forensic Practitioner.
35 years experience in the scientific examination of disputed signatures, handwriting, ESDA, inks etc.
Evidence given worldwide

THE FORENSIC DOCUMENT LABORATORY
MACARTNEYS, KINGS ROAD
SILCHESTER, READING RG7 2NS
TELEPHONE: 0118 970 2394
FAX: 0118 970 2395
EMAIL: info@docexam.co.uk
WEB: www.docexam.co.uk

HANDWRITING & GRAPHOLOGY

Formedecon Unit 41, Enterprise City, Spennymoor, Durham, Co Durham, DL16 6JF. Tel: 01388 811003. Fax: 01388 811918. DX: 60185 FERRYHILL. Email: formedecon@aol.com.

HEALTH & SAFETY

DR JOHN ANDERSON
BSc,MBA,PhD,CEng,FICE,FIMMM,FGS

Consulting Civil Engineer & Expert Witness in occupational health and safety issues in the construction industry

- An engineering specialist in this field since 1970;
- Author of 100 published papers, articles and book chapters;
- Invited lecturer and presenter in many parts of the world including Singapore, Dubai, Hong Kong, Spain, St Petersburg, Stockholm, Washington.
- Retained by construction clients, contractors, designers, insurance companies and legal practices within the UK;

john@safeconstruction.net
www.safeconstruction.net

INSOLVENCY PRACTITIONERS

Richard J Smith & Co 53 Fore Street, Ivybridge, Devon, PL21 9AE. Tel: 01752 690101. Fax: 01752 690808. Email: giles@richardjsmith.com. Contact: Giles Frampton FCA, MAE.

LITIGATION SUPPORT

MATERIALS ANALYSIS & PRODUCT TESTING

MARINE

R&J Maritime Ltd 89 Durnford Street, Stonehouse, Plymouth, PL1 3QW. Tel: 01752 671586. Fax: 01752 265744. Email: rjmedler@supanet.com.

MEDICAL

Dr Howell W Clague Southfields Farm, Houghton le Side, Darlington, DL2 2XH. Tel: 01388 776996 / 07768 132126. Email: howellclague@aol.com. Expert reports in Respiratory Medicine

18

Paul Durdey Litfield House, Litfield Place, Bristol, BS8 3LS. Tel: 0117 317 1406. Fax: 0117 973 3303.

Professor Ian O Ellis Dept Histopathology, City Hospital Campus, Nottingham University Hospitals, Hucknall Road, Nottingham, NG5 1PB. Tel: 0115 969 1169 ext 56875. Fax: 0115 962 7768.

Email: ian.ellis@nottingham.ac.uk. Expertise in breast disease and breast cancer pathology including diagnosis, prognosis, tumour growth and life expectancy assessment.

Dr John B Frazer The Grange, 92 Whitcliffe Road, Cleckheaton, West Yorkshire, BD19 3DR. Tel: 01274 878600. Fax: 01274 869898. Email: alma@the-grange.org.uk.

Mr Bernard Garston F.R.C.Ophth
consulting, ophthalmic surgeon

For over 25 years I was a consultant ophthalmic surgeon attached to the north
west regional health authority. I am still in private practice. I am a member of the United Kingdom and Ireland society of cataract and refractive surgeon.

In the last 20 years I have prepared over 3,000 reports in relation to head and eye injuries and medical negligence. 45% of my instructions have been from solicitors acting for claimants. 45% from solicitors, insurance companies and barristers acting for defendants and 10% have been joint instructions. I have been approved by the Association of personal injury lawyers and the UK register of Expert Witnesses as an expert witness in my speciality.

I have attended several medical legal symposia's and an instruction course on report writing.

I can see claimants in Manchester, Oldham and London.

14 St John Street, Deansgate,
Manchester M34 DZ
Manchester Phone No. 0161 832 9954
Secretary Mrs E Marshall
Phone No.: 0161 652 1227
On Tuesday And Thursday p.m.
E-mail: bernardgarston@aol.com

Consultant Ophthalmic Surgeon and Expert Witness

Mr Kim Hakin has been providing medico-legal reports for over 20 years, completing around 10-20 per year. He can guarantee to produce a report within 6 weeks of receiving instruction, although in practice it is usually 3-4 weeks.

He is happy to work as a single joint expert and to date would estimate his ratio to be around 30% claimant to 70% defendant.
He is happy to take on work from wherever it may arise although travelling afar would need particular consideration.

Mr Hakin has the Expert Witness Certificate from Bond Solon/Cardiff University and has produced many reports for Welsh Health Legal Services, the Medical Protection Society and Medical Defence Union.

BOND SOLON
the experts in expert witness training

Expert Witness Certificate Accreditation - Cardiff University/Bond Solon

Tel: 01823 342122 Mobile: 07887 651551
Email: kimhakin@aol.com
kim.hakin@tst.nhs.uk

Taunton and Somerset NHS Trust
Musgrove Park Hospital,
Taunton
Somerset TA1 5DA

www.kimhakin.com

Mr Kim N Hakin FRCS FRCOphth Consultant Ophthalmic Surgeon Taunton & Somerset Hospital, Musgrove Park, Taunton, Somerset, TA1 5DA. Tel: 01823 342122. Fax: 01823 342943. Email: kim.hakin@tst.nhs.uk. Ophthalmology, cataract and eyelid surgery, ocular trauma.

Gerald J Jarvis Obstetrician & Gynaecologist Yewtree Cottage, Hambledon, Henley-on-Thames, Oxfordshire, RG9 6LT. Tel: 01491 412111. Fax: 01491 412121. Email: gerryjarvis@hotmail.com.

Professor Christopher Kennard Department of Clinical Neurology, Level 6, West Wing, John Radcliffe Hospital, Headington, Oxfordshire, OX3 9DU. Tel: 01865 234637. Email: chris.kennard@clneuro.ox.ac.uk. Expertise: Clinical Neurology, Neuro-ophthalmology

Dr M A Mansell Consultant Nephrologist 13 Ashbourne Avenue, London, NW11 0DP. Tel: 020 8731 8299 / 07836 234258. Fax: 020 8455 3679. Email: m.mansell@kidneylaw.co.uk. Website: www.kidneylaw.co.uk.

Dr Iain M Murray-Lyon 116 Harley Street, Westminster, London, W1G 7JL. Tel: 020 7935 6747. Fax: 020 7935 7017. Email: i.m-lyon@lonclin.co.uk. Medical gastroenterology/liver.

Dr P N Plowman Department of Radiotherapy/Clinical Oncology, St Bartholomews Hospital, West Smithfield, London, EC1A 7BE. Tel: 020 7631 1632. Fax: 020 7323 3487. Email: postmaster@pnplowman.demon.co.uk. Senior Clinical Oncologist to St. Bartholomew's Hospital and The Hospital for Sick Children London. Specialising: Delay to diagnosis, Complications of therapy, Adults and Children.

Dr Michael Sambrook Southbarn, Whitebarn Road, Alderley Edge, Cheshire, SK9 7AN. Tel: 01625 590197. Fax: 01625 584539. Consulting in Manchester and Birmingham.

Maggie Sargent Darlingscott Farm, Darlingscott, Shipston-on-Stour, Warwickshire, CV36 4PN. Tel: 01608 682500. Fax: 01608 682372.

Dr David Gill

MA, MSc, BM,BCh, MRCGP, MR-CPsych

Consultant Psychiatrist

Address:
Dr David Gill
Consultant Psychiatrist
Psychiatry for Lawyers Ltd
10 Harley Street
London
W1G 9PF

Telephone: 07983 318843
Fax: 0207 467 8312

Email:
office@drdavidgill.com

DR. MARTIN MANSELL

- Expert Witness Reports
- All areas of Kidney Medicine
- Acute and Chronic Renal Failure
- Dialysis, Hypertension, Urinary Infection
- Urological Renal Problems
- 3 - 4 Week Preparation Time

DR MARTIN MANSELL MD FRCP
Consultant Nephrologist
(Renal Physician)

Royal Free and UCL Hospitals,
13 Ashbourne Avenue
London
NW11 0DP
Tel (Sec.): 020 8731 8299
(Mobile): 07836 234258
Fax: 020 8455 3679
Email: m.mansell@kidneylaw.co.uk
Web site: www.kidneylaw.co.uk

18

John Sinar 36 Abbey Road, Darlington, DL3 8LR. Tel: 01325 359221. Fax: 01325 464050. Email: sinarej@aol.com. Whiplash/Spinal Injury/Head Injury/Epilepsy

Brian C Sommerlad The Old Vicarage, 17 Lodge Road, Writtle, Chelmsford, Essex, CM1 3HY. Tel: 01245 422477. Fax: 01245 421901. Email: brian@sommerlad.co.uk.

Mr Sanjay K Varma Leicester Nuffield Hospital, Scraptoft Lane, Leicester, LE5 1HY. Tel: 0116 274 3743. Fax: 0800 389 2315. Email: plasticsurgeon@consultant.com. Plastic surgery.

Carol Walker - Birmingham Trichology Centre 57 The Ridgeway, Chasetown, Staffordshire, WS7 4SP.
Tel: 01543 670717.
Email: cpw@birminghamtrichology.co.uk.

Irene Waters

RGN, RSCPHN, LLM, Master of Nursing, MSc Public Health.

Nursing Consultant
Health Visitor
Health Service Manager
Care Assessment

Expert Witness Certificate (CUBS)
Trained in Civil Procedure Rules and a single joint expert.
Experience in Criminal cases for both Prosecution and Defence and at Coroners Court
Recent member for due regard for Fitness to Practice at NMC.

26 Garford Crescent
Newbury, Berkshire
RG14 6EX

Tel: 01635 482 57
Fax: 01635 552 653
E-mail: iwaters@lineone.net

GASTROENTEROLOGY EXPERT WITNESS

Professor Watson has over 26 years experience in his field and written over 2000 legal-medical reports on gastroenterology, endoscopy, hepatology and food poisoning cases.

Contact details:
Simona Flavia Florescu (secretary)
s.florescu@uea.ac.uk
01603 593959

Professor Alastair Watson
alastair.watson@uea.ac.uk
01603 597266

MEDICO LEGAL REPORTS

DR. DEREK EASTWOOD
CONSULTANT IN PAIN MANAGEMENT
MB., ChB., FFARCS., FFPMRCS

- DIRECTOR OF WIRRAL UNIVERSITY TEACHING HOSPITAL PAIN RELIEF SERVICES (CHRONIC);
- INVOLVED IN ALL ASPECTS OF PAIN MANAGEMENT, INJECTION & PAIN MANAGEMENT PROGRAMMES;
- SPECIAL INTEREST: ALL ASPECTS OF SPINAL PAIN, CRPS & NEUROPATHIC PAIN.
- MEDICOLEGAL INSTRUCTIONS 40–50 PER YEAR ; 60% PLAINTIFF 40% DEFENCE

MEMBERSHIPS
- BRITISH MEDICAL ASSOCIATION
- PAIN SOCIETY G.B.
- INTERNATIONAL ASSOCIATION FOR THE STUDY OF PAIN
- ASSOCIATION OF ANAESTHETISTS
- ROYAL COLLEGE OF ANAESTHESTIS.

(Correspondence: Wirral University Hospital NHS Foundation Trust, Upton, Wirral CH49 5PE)
Telephone/Fax: 0151 604 7331
Secretary: Margaret Trowler

Equip2Speak
The specialists in brain & spinal Injury

Long established with many leading law firms and case management companies we offer an integrated solution to speech and language therapy (SLT) and assistive technology (AT) needs. Recognised for our experience in delivering and predicting long term rehabilitation programmes and specialist technology.

Services:

- ☑ Medico Legal Reports
- ☑ Interdisciplinary Assessment
- ☑ Therapy and Training
- ☑ Environmental Control
- ☑ Switch and Device Mounting
- ☑ Equipment Procurement
- ☑ Ongoing Support

Lisa Humberstone (SLT)
M: 07966 143738
E : slt@equip2speak.co.uk
David Humberstone (AT)
M: 07960 753248
E: at@equip2speak.co.uk

W: www.equip2speak.co.uk
Based: NW Coverage: UK

18

METEOROLOGY

WeatherNet Ltd Kingsland House, 21 Hinton Road, Bournemouth, BH1 2DE. Tel: 01202 411122. Fax: 01202 314064. Email: rick@weathernet.co.uk. Website: www.weathernet.co.uk. Road Traffic Accidents (RTAs) Personal Injury Claims (Falling, Tripping and Slipping Accidents)

NOISE, VIBRATION & ACOUSTICS

The Association of Noise Consultants The Old Pump House, 1a Stonecross, St Albans, Hertfordshire, AL1 4AA. Tel: 020 8253 4518. Email: info@theanc.co.uk.

Alan Saunders Associates Westgate House, 39/41 Romsey Road, Winchester, Hampshire, SO22 5BE. Tel: 01962 872130. Fax: 01962 872131. Email: alan@alansaunders.com. Website: www.alansaunders.com.

NURSING

18

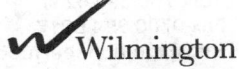

Sheelagh Ward 1 Peckforton Close, Gatley, Cheadle, Greater Manchester, SK8 4JA. Tel: 0161 491 4930. Fax: 0161 491 4930. Email: sheelaghward@yahoo.co.uk. Website: www.sheelaghward.com.

OCCUPATIONAL HEALTH

ORTHOPAEDIC & TRAUMA

PERSONAL INJURY

E J Allen & Associates Suite F6, Addington Business Centre, Vulcan Way, New Addington, Croydon, Surrey, CR0 9UG. Tel: 01689 848570. Fax: 01689 846295. Email: expert@ejallen.co.uk.

Peter Davies Employment & Rehabilitation Consultants 27 East King Street, Helensburgh, Argyll & Bute, G84 7QQ. Tel: 01436 677767. Fax: 01436 678938. Email: info@employconsult.com.

Hawkins Cambridge 25 Cambridge Science Park, Milton Road, Cambridge, Cambridgeshire, CB4 0FW. Tel: 01223 420400. Fax: 01223 420181. Email: cmail@hawkins.biz. Experts in Personal Injury Investigation.

PSYCHIATRY

Allen Associates Suffolk House, 54-55 The Green, Wooburn Green, High Wycombe, Buckinghamshire, HP10 0EU. Tel: 0870 162 0671. Fax: 0870 162 0672. DX: 123618 WOOBURN GREEN. Email: enquiries@allen-associates.com. Website: www.allen-associates. com.

Dr M F Hussain F.R.C. Psych, F.E.W.I. 6 Cadnam Close, Canterbury, Kent, CT2 7SD. Tel: 01227 762267 / 07831 574321. Fax: 01227 455799. Email: drmfhussain@hotmail.com.

PLUMBING, HEATING & DRAINAGE

Mr Gordon Charles Lockhart Scott White and Hookins, Harman House, Andover Road, Winchester, Hampshire, SO23 7BS. Tel: 01962 844855. Fax: 01962 841328. Email: glockhart@swh.co.uk.

PROPERTY SERVICES

Airphoto Interpretation 26 Cross Street, Moretonhampstead, Devon, TQ13 8NL. Tel: 01647 440904. Email: young@airphotointerpretation.com.

PSYCHOLOGY

Charles Burdett PO Box 134, Northallerton, North Yorkshire, DL7 8WZ. Tel: 01609 779433. Fax: 01609 771528. Email: charlesburdett@yahoo.co.uk. Rooms at Leeds, York, Darlington, Middlesbrough

Carstairs Psychological Associates Ltd 7 Mayfield Road, Bromley, Kent, BR1 2HB. Tel: 020 8325 1697. Fax: 020 8325 1697. Website: www.carstairspsych.co.uk. Psychological evaluations in civil, criminal and family cases. Assessments of children & adults for intellectual functioning, emotional and behavioural difficulties, personality disorders, PTSD, anxiety & depression, family dynamics and malingering.
Est: 1993

Irene Martin-Alam 38 Beechwood Avenue, Kew, Richmond upon Thames, Surrey, TW9 4DE. Tel: 020 8948 5414. Fax: 020 8948 5414.

Dr Christopher R Plowman
BSc MSc Clin Psych D CPsychol AFBPsS
Consultant Neuropsychologist

I specialise in the neuropsychological assessment of the cognitive, emotional and behavioural consequences of Acquired Brain Injury in adults following road-traffic accidents, assaults, anoxia, or exposure to toxic substances. I have experience in the assessment of disorders of mood, neurotoxicology, epilepsy, drug and alcohol misuse, tumours, HIV, PTSD, and in the areas of Personal Injury, Occupational Health and the Criminal Justice system.

I am a recognised Expert by Cardiff University Law School and Bond Solon, and I am trained in the legal aspects of report working, giving evidence in Court and the responsibilities of a Single Joint Expert. I have provided medico-legal reports in Criminal, Family and Personal Injury cases for over ten years, and in the past three years have provided around 100 reports for Defence and Claimant solicitors as well as Joint instructions.

Correspondence address: PO Box 15858, Solihull B91 9RN
Tel: 0121 7070482 Fax: 0121 7062822
Email: DrPlowman@inbox.com or DrPlowmanSecretary@mail.com

Consulting rooms: BMI Meriden Hospital, Coventry
The Spire Parkway Hospital, Solihull
Portman Square, London

Domicillary visits throughout England and Wales are also available by request.

ignition

Expert Witness for the Family Court

Domestic violence and abuse risk assessment

- **Consultant Forensic Psychologist**
- **15 years experience in domestic violence and abuse**
- **Credibility of a report from a real specialist**
- **Clear and accurate time and cost structure**
- **In disputed contact, residency cases or care proceedings**

Dr. Mark C. Farrall
BA.,BSc.,MSc.,PhD,CUEW

Suite 155, R&R Consulting Centre, 41 St. Isan Road, Heath, Cardiff, CF14 4LW
Tel 0700 394 6217
Fax 0700 394 6217
Email info@ignition-learn.com

Chartered Psychologist

CLINICAL PSYCHOLOGY PRACTICES
PSYCHOLOGICAL/ NEURO PSYCHOLOGICAL REPORTS

Prepared by
Dr. Don Rowan, Chartered Clinical Psychologist consulting in Birmingham, Wolverhampton and Exeter

- Assessment of psychological problems
- Effects of personal injury/RTAs
- Post Traumatic Stress Disorder
- Cognitive behaviour therapy

8 Summerfield Road, West Park, Wolverhampton WV1 4PR
Tel: 01902 429044
Fax: 01902 773920
E-mail: doncrowan@googlemail.com

PUBLIC ANALYST

SCIENTISTS

Professor Michael J Griffin Institute of Sound & Vibration Research, University of Southampton, Southampton, SO17 1BJ. Tel: 023 8059 2277. Fax: 023 8059 2927. Email: m.j.griffin@soton.ac.uk. Hand-arm vibration syndrome; HAVS; VWF

SPEECH & LANGUAGE THERAPY

Independent Speech and Language Therapy Services Ltd 155 Unthank Road, Norwich, Norfolk, NR2 2PG. Tel: 01603 664433. Fax: 01603 515733. Email: cathy@islts.co.uk. Website: www.islts.co.uk. Cathy MacLennan MSc MRCSLT ASLTIP HPC Nikki Crossman MRCSLT ASLTIP HPC

SPORT

STRI (The Sports Turf Research Institute) St Ives Estate, Bingley, West Yorkshire, BD16 1AU. Tel: 01274 565131. Fax: 01274 561891. Email: info@stri.co.uk.

SURVEYORS

Clifford Dann Albion House, Albion Street, Lewes, East Sussex, BN7 2NF. Tel: 01273 477022. Fax: 01273 480345. Email: msquire@clifforddann.co.uk. Res/Com Valuations, Planning, Surveys.

Hockenhulls - Chartered Valuation Surveyors The Bond, Godstall Lane, Chester, Cheshire, CH1 1LN. Tel: 01244 345147. Fax: 01244 318804. Email: enquiries@hockenhulls.co.uk. Please see our advert under Expert Witness Surveyors.

Edward Watson BSc FRICS MCIArb 2 Osborne Road, Jesmond, Newcastle upon Tyne, Tyne & Wear, NE2 2AA. Tel: 0191 281 2444. Fax: 0191 281 9595. Email: edward@edwardwatson-assoc.com. Residential & commercial valuations. Professional Negligence. Boundary Disputes.

DEREK MONNERY FRICS MCIArb

A housing renovation specialist with over 40 years' experience in the building industry. A quantity surveyor specialising in work on Victorian and Edwardian house types. Expert Witness reports prepared concerning building works, defects and defective works and the associated costs of repairs and rectification. Based in Essex, but working throughout the London Area and East Anglia. Very competitive rates.

Contact: -
Web: - www.derekmonneryqs.com
Email: - derek@monnery.net
Phone: - 01255 870469

JOHN D WOOD & CO.

Chartered Surveyors experienced in residential property valuations for all litigation and matrimonial purposes in London and the South of England.

Contact
James Wyatt FRICS
Member of the Society of Expert Witnesses
Member of the Expert Witness Institute

020 7908 1102
jwyatt@johndwood.co.uk
140 Kensington Church Street,
London W8 4BN

www.johndwood.co.uk

Paul S Withey Limited

PAUL S WITHEY

Paul Withey is a Fellow of the Royal Institute of Chartered Surveyors and a Member of the Expert Witness Institute. He is experienced in the production of accommodation reports dealing with personal injury and accommodation costs having completed in excess of 5000 during his 30 years as a Chartered Surveyor. Reports produced to enable Roberts -v- Johnstone calculations to be made.

Tel: 01274 739216
Fax: 01274 739201

e-mail:
info@paulswithey.co.uk

David Price Associates

CHARTERED SURVEYORS • VALUERS • PROPERTY CONSULTANTS

www.davidpriceassociates.co.uk

Residential, Agricultural & Commercial Valuations

RICS Homebuyer Reports • Building Surveys
Rating, Rent Reviews
Compulsory Purchase & Compensation Claims
Expert Witness Reports • Boundary Disputes

01785 282112

Mobile: 07980 281037

Email: jdmprice100@btinternet.com

The Limes, Eccleshall Road, Great Bridgeford, Stafford ST18 9SQ

GRANT WRIGHT ASSOCIATES LLP

PARTY WALL, CHARTERED SURVEYORS, CONSTRUCTION, COST AND CLAIM CONSULTANTS

Grant Wright Associates LLP (GWA) are Chartered Surveyors/Construction cost and claims consultants. GWA offers Quantity and Building surveying services and specialise in claims related works. These include: arbitration, Party Wall & Boundary Disputes, litigation, insurance and expert witness related works resulting from the construction industry and its associated professions.

GWA approach appointments on the basis that clients may have differing priorities, however they all require a service which encompasses high professional standards and commercial management.

Telephone: 0208 440 8808
Facsimile: 0208 440 7880
Email: enquiries@grantwrightassociates.com

TELECOMMUNICATIONS

Clues & Co

Expert Witness & Forensic Services
Criminal, Civil & Legally Aided Cases

Telecommunications
Cell Site Analysis
GSM & UMTS (3G) Radio Surveys,
Call Pattern & Attribution Analysis,
Call Record & Short Message (SMS) Analysis,
TETRA & Radio Systems
Mobile Phone & SIM Examinations
Radio Free Examination Suite

GPS/SAT NAV/Home Curfew
Analysis of Vehicle Satellite Navigation,
Home Curfew & PID Data

Computer/Cyber Crime
Computer & Disk Capture, Examination and Analysis. Image, Document & Usage Analysis.
Server, Software, LINUX, DOS, Windows

Office Equipment
Fax, Photocopiers & Office Products
Examination, Use, Maintenance & Suitability

Audio/Video Analysis
Capture, Enhancement, Analysis and Transcription of Audio/Video media.
Audio/Noise Analysis

T: 01206 763301
F: 01206 763302
E-mail: info@clues.co.uk
DX 3645 Colchester

Please contact us to request a copy of our brochure

www.clues.co.uk

Computer and Mobile Phone Forensics

Expert Witness Service

Jargon-free, plain English reports guaranteed

- Computer forensics
- Mobile phone & SatNav Forensics
- Cell site analysis
- IT investigation
- Child pornography specialists

T 0845 644 3652
M 07967 737041

24hr Nationwide Service

www.evidence-matters.com

TIMBER & WOOD PRODUCTS

GOT A TIMBER PROBLEM?

Then you need a Woodexpert from TFT.

TFT Woodexperts are all you need when it comes to finding an independent expert in Timber and Wood-based materials.

Our consultants are highly experienced in all aspects of problem investigation, report preparation and Expert Witness work (including legal aid) and we comply with Civil Procedure Rules in respect of Single Joint Expert instructions.

Find us at woodexperts.com

TFT Woodexperts.
Low Mills Unit 1. Phoenix Business Centre
Low Mill Road, Ripon. N Yorks. HG4 1NS
Tel: +44(0)1765 601010
Fax: +44(0)1765 608081

TRANSPORT, VEHICLE & AUTOMOTIVE

Mr Gordon Charles Lockhart Scott White and Hookins, Harman House, Andover Road, Winchester, Hampshire, SO23 7BS. Tel: 01962 844855. Fax: 01962 841328. Email: glockhart@swh.co.uk.

VALUERS & AUCTIONEERS

Adam H Pickervance MRICS
Rural Practice Chartered Surveyor, Land Agent
Director of SHP VALUERS Ltd,
Practising throughout the North West

_Rural Property, Agricultural Land, Farms, Equestrian
_ Commercial Property
_ Residential Property
_ Valuations for all purposes
_ Expert Witness Reports - Part 35
_ Specialist Sales & Letting Services
_ Asset & Dispersal Auctions
_ Landlord & Tenant Matters
_ Compulsory Purchase & Compensation
_ Rural Land Management
_ Auctioneers

Tel: 01772 555403 Fax: 01772 885333
Email: adamp@shpvaluers.co.uk
Website: www.shpvaluers.co.uk

Keep us informed of the changes to your firm's details

By post to:
Waterlow Legal Editorial
6-14 Underwood Street
London
N1 7JQ

By phone on:
+44 (0)20 7549 8649

By fax on:
+44 (0)20 7324 2366

By email:
jsmith@waterlow.com

SPECIALISED SERVICES

SECTION 19

INTERNATIONAL

CONTENTS

19

AUSTRIA

Innsbruck

Greiter Pegger Kofler & Partners Maria-Theresien-Strasse 24, Innsbruck, A-6020. Tel: 00 43 5 125 718 11. Fax: 00 43 5 125 711 52. Email: greiter@lawfirm.at. Corporate Law, Foreign Investment, International Contracts. Members of Firm: Dr Ivo Greiter, Dr Franz Pegger, Dr Stefan Kofler, Dr Christian Zangerle, Dr. Norbert Rinderer, Dr. Herwig Frei, Dr. Georg Huber LL.M, Dr Edwin Grubert LL.M, Dr. Alexandra Eder, Mag. Melanie Gassler-Tischlinger LL.M, Mag. Barbara Egger-Russe. Counsel: Ute Greiter-Knoop, Languages: English, French, German and Italian.

BELGIUM

Antwerp

Flieger Law Office BVBA Mechelsesteenweg 82, B-2018, Antwerp. Tel: 00 32 3 238 7766. Fax: 00 32 3 216 1844. Email: flieger@fliegerlaw.com. Website: www.fliegerlaw.com. Other offices in Brazil - Sào Paulo, Germany - Wiesbaden, Turkey - Mersin & Istanbul, France - Paris, USA - Nashville (TN), Atlanta (FL), Netherlands - Tilburg

BRITISH VIRGIN ISLANDS

Tortola

Farara Kerins 125 Main Street, Road Town, Tortola. Tel: 00 1 284 494 2717. Fax: 00 1 284 494 4834. Email: mail@fararakerins.com. Website: www.fararakerins.com. List of Partners: Gerard St. C. Farara Q.C., Charles Kerins LL.M, Tana'ania Small LL.B. Barristers-at-Law & Solicitors, Trade Marks & Patent Agents and Notaries Public. Specialist Areas of Work: Litigation, Company Law, Banking, Trust, Probate, Insurance, Admiralty and Intellectual Property.
Est: 1984

CROATIA

Zagreb

Eugen Zadravec

Phone:
+385-1-4810643, 4810574

Fax:
+385-1-4810642

E-mail:
eugen.zadravec@zg.t-com.hr

Contact:
Mr Eugen Zadravec

Address:
Petrinjska 2
10000 Zagreb
Croatia

FRANCE

Cannes

Robert Floyd 22-24 Boulevard Alexandre III, Cannes, 06400. Tel: 00 33 4 93 43 93 55. Fax: 00 33 4 93 43 40 26. Email: robert.floyd@wanadoo.fr. LL.M.(Lond), Barrister, Admitted to French Bar. Specialist Areas of Work: General and international law practice.

GIBRALTAR

Gibraltar

ISOLAS PO Box 204, 23 Portland House, Glacis Road, Gibraltar. Tel: 00 350 200 01892. Fax: 00 350 200 78990. Email: info@isolas.gi. Website: www.gibraltarlawyers.com.

Massias & Partners PO Box 213, 279 Main Street, Gibraltar. Tel: 00 350 200 40888. Fax: 00 350 200 40999. Email: massias@massias.gi. Website: www.massiaslaw.com. Barristers-at-law, Acting Solicitors, Commissioners for Oaths. Corporate, Commercial, Banking, Conveyancing, Probate, Trusts, Tax Law, Litigation, General Practice. Languages: English, Spanish and French. Associate offices in Iberian Peninsula.

ICELAND

Reykjavik

Fjeldsted Blondal & Fjeldsted Austurstraeti 10a, PO Box 395, Reykjavik, 121. Tel: 00 354 552 2144. Fax: 00 354 562 1823. Email: fjeldco@fjeldco.is. Website: www.fjeldco.is.

IRELAND (REPUBLIC OF)

Dublin

John Glynn & Co Law Chambers, Village Square, Tallaght, Dublin, Co. Dublin. Tel: 00 353 1 451 5642. Fax: 00 353 1 451 5120. Email: john@solicitor.net. Website: www.solicitor.net. Specialist areas include personal injuries in Republic of Ireland, Probate and Administration of Estates

Duncan Grehan & Partners Gainsboro House, 24 Suffolk Street, Dublin, Co. Dublin, 2. Tel: 00 353 1 677 9078. Fax: 00 353 1 677 9076. DX: 212001 SUFFOLK STREET. Email: dgrehan@duncangrehan.com.

ISRAEL

Jerusalem

Becker Sacofsky Kahn & Co 11 Ramban Street, Jerusalem, 92422. Tel: 00 972 2 623 2603. Fax: 00 972 2 625 9407. Email: shmuel@beckersl.com. Becker, Samuel Laurence, LL.B.(Hons) (1966)

ITALY

Rome

JAMAICA

Mandeville

LIECHTENSTEIN

Vaduz

Norbert Seeger PO Box 1618, Am Schragen Weg 14, Vaduz, FL-9490. Tel: 00 423 232 0808. Fax: 00 423 232 0630. Email: admin@seeger.li. Website: www.seeger.li. Dr. iur. et lic. oec., Attorney-at-Law.

Wolff Gstoehl & Partner Mitteldorf 1, PO Box 343, Vaduz, FL-9490. Tel: 00 423 238 1030. Fax: 00 423 238 1031. Email: info@wgp-law.li.

NORTHERN IRELAND

Belfast

SCOTLAND

Edinburgh

Shepherd + Wedderburn LLP 1 Exchange Crescent, Conference Square, Edinburgh, EH3 8UL. Tel: 0131 228 9900. Fax: 0131 228 1222. DX: ED551970 EDINBURGH 53. Email: info@shepwedd.co.uk. Also in London, Glasgow and Aberdeen.

SERBIA

Belgrade

Mikijelj Jankovic & Bogdanovic Vlajkoviceva 28, Belgrade, 11101. Tel: 00 381 11 323 1970. Fax: 00 381 11 324 5065. Email: office@mjb.rs.

UNITED STATES OF AMERICA

Boston

O'Connell & O'Connell 31 Milk Street, Boston, Massachusetts, 02109. Tel: 00 1 617 426 1224. Email: joseph.oconnell@counselor.com. Website: www.counselor.com. Attorneys at Law since 1897.

COUNSEL PRACTISING IN LONDON

La Puente

Loughran & Co 38 Hertford Street, London, W1J 7SG. Tel: 020 7355 2051. Fax: 020 7355 4975. Email: jloughran@loughranandco.com. International & US practice, commercial, corporate, tax, trusts & estates, off-shore funds. NY, CONN Bars.

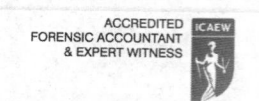

SPECIALISED SERVICES

SECTION 20

LEGAL SERVICES

CONTENTS

ARBITRATION & MEDIATION

Hockenhulls - Chartered Valuation Surveyors The Bond, Godstall Lane, Chester, Cheshire, CH1 1LN. Tel: 01244 345147. Fax: 01244 318804. Email: enquiries@hockenhulls.co.uk. Please see our advert under Expert Witness-Surveyors.

BAILIFFS

Finlay's Bureau of Investigation Ltd FBI House, 54 Church Road, Crystal Palace, London, SE19 2EU. Tel: 020 8771 9511. Fax: 020 8771 7142. Email: info@fbi.ltd.uk. Process Servers, Enquiry Agents, Certificated Bailiffs throughout England and Wales.

COMPANY SERVICES

Oyez Company Services Oyez House, PO Box 55, 7 Spa Road, Bermondsey, London, SE16 3QQ. Tel: 020 7394 9311. Fax: 020 7394 9009. DX: 80700 BERMONDSEY. Email: lynn.hughes@oyez.co.uk.

FINANCIAL SERVICES

Sheralee Ellis

Robin Bailey

INFORMATION TECHNOLOGY SERVICES

Oyez Company Services Oyez House, PO Box 55, 7 Spa Road, Bermondsey, London, SE16 3QQ. Tel: 020 7394 9311. Fax: 020 7394 9009. DX: 80700 BERMONDSEY. Email: lynn.hughes@oyez.co.uk.

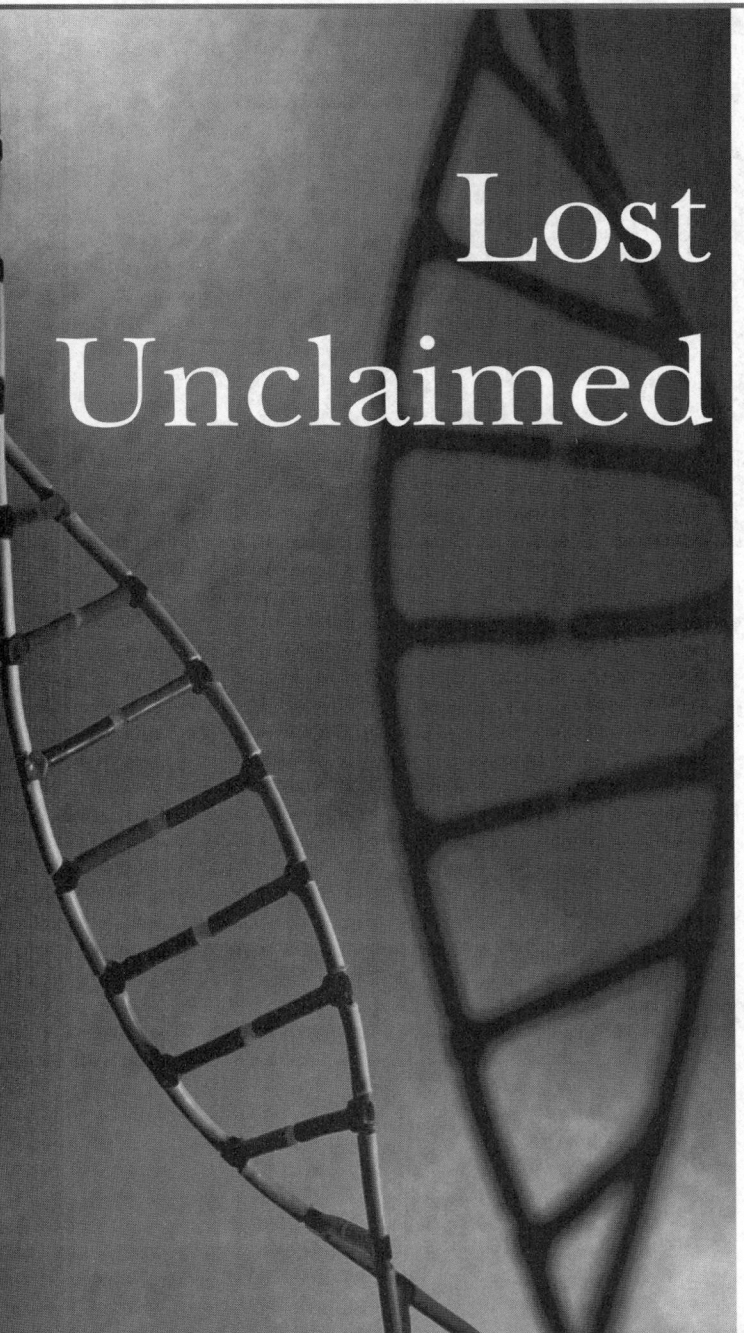

INSURANCE

Countrywide Legal Indemnities Ltd St Crispins, Duke Street, Norwich, Norfolk, NR3 1PD. Tel: 01603 617617. Fax: 01603 622933. DX: 5261 NORWICH. Email: enquiries@cli.co.uk. Website: www.cli.co.uk.

ISIS Conveyancing Insurance Specialists The Royal, 25 Bank Plain, Norwich, Norfolk, NR2 4SF. Tel: 01603 761515. Fax: 01603 616222. DX: 5200 NORWICH. Email: enquiries@isisconveyancing.co.uk. Website: www.isisconveyancing.co.uk.

INTERPRETERS & TRANSLATORS

National Register of Public Service Interpreters (NRPSI Ltd) Saxon House, 48 Southwark Street, London, SE1 1UN. Tel: 020 7940 3166. Fax: 020 7940 3123. Email: nrpsi@iol.org.uk. Website: www.nrpsi.co.uk. Over 2,300 qualified interpreters in 99 languages.

INVESTIGATIVE SERVICES

Finlay's Bureau of Investigation Ltd FBI House, 54 Church Road, Crystal Palace, London, SE19 2EU. Tel: 020 8771 9511. Fax: 020 8771 7142. Email: info@fbi.ltd.uk.

Liddles Detective Agency 50 Albert Road, Middlesbrough, TS1 1QD. Tel: 01642 243866. Fax: 01642 246546. Email: julian-petch@hotmail.co.uk. Mobile: 07768 406063. Process Servers, Enquiry Agent, Certificated Bailiffs. Established 1960, covering Teeside and Durham. A member of the Association of British Investigators.

Inform us of any changes

Legal Editorial 6-14
Underwood Street London
N1 7JQ

By phone:
+44 (0)20 7549 8649
By fax:
+44 (0)20 7324 2366
By email:
jsmith@waterlow.com

LAW COSTS DRAFTSMEN

Masters Legal Costs Services LLP 3-4 New Street, Bishopsgate, London, EC2M 4HD. Tel: 020 7929 4344. Fax: 020 7929 4066. DX: 156795 BISHOPSGATE 5. Email: info@masters-legal.co.uk. Website: www.masters-legal.co.uk. The city's leading firm of specialist law costs draftsmen.

Ashley Rose Ltd 17 The Landway, Kemsing, Sevenoaks, Kent, TN15 6TG. Tel: 01732 760152. Fax: 01732 760152. Email: alanp@ashley-rose.co.uk.

LEGAL REPRESENTATIVES

Russell-Cooke LLP 8 Bedford Row, London, WC1R 4BX. Tel: 020 7405 6566. Fax: 020 7831 2565. DX: 112 LONDON/CHANCERY LN. Email: helpdesk@russell-cooke.co.uk.

MEDIATION

PATENTS & TRADEMARKS SERVICES

Alexander Ramage Associates LLP Griffin House, West Street, Woking, Surrey, GU21 6BS. Tel: 01483 750701. Fax: 01483 740560.
Email: ara@ramage.co.uk. Trade Mark - Design Right - Advocacy and Litigation. Domain Name Management and Dispute Resolution.

PROPERTY SERVICES

Harding Surveyors LLP Suite 4, 27 Ackmar Road, Fulham, London, SW6 4UR. Tel: 020 7736 2383. Fax: 020 7900 2322.
Email: dtoogood@hardingsurveyors.co.uk. Surveyors, Party Wall & Leasehold Reform Matters.

PSYCHOLOGY

British Psychological Society Directory of Expert Witnesses, 48 Princess Road East, Leicester, LE1 7DR. Tel: 0116 254 9568. Fax: 0116 247 0787.
Email: enquiry@bps.org.uk.

SEARCHES - PROPERTY & ENVIRONMENT

The Property Search Group 6 Great Cliffe Court, Great Cliffe Road, Barnsley, South Yorkshire, S75 3SP. Tel: 01226 241010.
Email: customerservices@propertysearchgroup.co.uk. Website: www.psgconnect.co.uk.

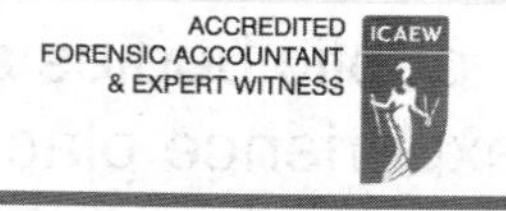

SHORTHAND & TRANSCRIPTION SERVICES

SURVEYORS

TRAINING - UNIVERSITY UNDERGRADUATE

20

ADVERTISER INDEX

AGENCY

CHARITIES

EXPERT WITNESS

INTERNATIONAL

LEGAL SERVICES

SPECIAL POSITION ADVERTISING